FOUNDATION CENTER

Knowledge to build on.

THE FOUNDATION DIRECTORY PART 2

25th Edition

D1227810

FOUNDATION
CENTER

THE
FOUNDATION
DIRECTORY
PART 2

25th Edition

FOUNDATION CENTER
Knowledge to build on.

THE FOUNDATION DIRECTORY PART 2

25th Edition
2016

CONTRIBUTING STAFF

Vice President for Data and Technology Strategy _____Jake Garcia
Vice President for Data Architecture_____ Jeffrey A. Falkenstein
Director, Foundation Information Management _____David G. Jacobs
Director, Grants Information Management _____ Jeannine Corey
Coordinator, Grant Analysis and Collection _____ Denise McLeod
Data Integration Liaison_____Chuck Bartelt
Coordinator, Foundation Directory _____ Elia S. Glenn
Coordinator, Large Foundations _____ Cindy B. Martinez
Senior Editorial Associates_____Regina Judith Faighes
William Giles
Joseph W. Guastella
Cynthia Y. Manick
Editorial Associate_____ Lakesha Spiegel-Reneau
Editorial Assistants _____ Michele Kragalott
Casey Robbins
Data Entry Clerk _____ Willean Baldwin
Manager, Corporate Philanthropy _____ Andrew N. Grabois
Community Foundations Liaison _____David Rosado
Application Developer_____ Kathye Giesler
System Administrator _____ Emmy So
Production Manager _____ Christine Innamorato
Graphic Designer_____ Betty Saronson
Senior Programmer/Analyst _____ Mirek Drozdzowski

The editor gratefully acknowledges the many other Foundation Center staff who contributed
support, encouragement, and information that was indispensable to the preparation of
this volume. Special mention should also be made of the staff members of the New York,
Washington, DC, Cleveland, San Francisco, and Atlanta libraries who assisted in tracking
changes in foundation information. We would like to express our appreciation as well to the
many foundations that cooperated fully in updating information prior to the compilation of
The Foundation Directory Part 2.

CONTENTS

Introduction _____ v

The 2016 Edition   v

Foundations New to the Edition   v

What Is a Foundation?   v

Types of Foundations   v

Sources of Information   vi

   Figure A. General Characteristics of Four Types of Foundations   vi

   Table 1. Aggregate Fiscal Data by Foundation Type   vii

   Table 2. Aggregate Fiscal Data for Foundations New to
              The Foundation Directory Part 2 by Foundation Type   vii

   Table 3. Fiscal Data of Foundations by Region and State   vii

   Table 4. 100 Largest Foundations by Assets   ix

   Table 5. 100 Largest Foundations by Total Giving   x

How to Use *The Foundation Directory Part 2* _____ xi

Glossary _____ xv

Abbreviations _____ xix

Resources of the Foundation Center _____ xxi

DESCRIPTIVE DIRECTORY _____ 1

Appendix _____ 1409

A. Edition 24 Foundations not Included in Edition 25   1409

Indexes _____ 1411

Index to Donors, Officers, Trustees   1411

Geographic Index   1573

International Giving Index   1597

Types of Support Index   1601

Subject Index   1629

Foundations New to the Edition   1709

Foundation Name Index   1715

INTRODUCTION

The *Foundation Directory Part 2* provides complete descriptive information on the second tier of private and community foundations in the U.S. It is designed as a companion volume to *The Foundation Directory*, which reports on those foundations that were among the top 10,000 in terms of awards made in the latest fiscal year of record. Together, *The Foundation Directory* and *The Foundation Directory Part 2* constitute the standard reference work for information on the country's largest 20,000 active grantmaking foundations.

THE 2016 EDITION

The 2016 Edition is the twenty-fifth complete revision of *The Foundation Directory Part 2*. While *The Foundation Directory* contains entries for the top 10,000 largest grantmaking foundations, *The Foundation Directory Part 2* contains entries for the next 10,000 largest foundations by total giving in the most recent fiscal year of record. These foundations held combined assets of over $49.9 billion and awarded more than $2.5 billion in disbursements (Table 1).

FOUNDATIONS NEW TO THE FOUNDATION DIRECTORY PART 2

The 2016 edition of *The Foundation Directory Part 2* includes entries for 1,143 foundations that were not listed in the 2015 Edition. Of these, 1,052 (92.0 percent) are independent foundations, 37 (3.2 percent) are company-sponsored foundations, 17 (1.5 percent) are community foundations, and 37 (3.2 percent) are grantmaking operating foundations. The 1,143 newly qualifying foundations held combined assets of over $6.1 billion, and contributed more than $317.9 million in the most recent year of record (Table 2). Users with a particular interest in these newly qualifying foundations will find them listed separately in the index of Foundations New to the Edition.

WHAT IS A FOUNDATION?

The Center defines a foundation as a nongovernmental, nonprofit organization with its own funds (usually from a single source, either an individual, family, or corporation) and program managed by its own trustees and directors that was established to maintain or aid educational, social, charitable, religious, or other activities serving the common welfare, primarily by making grants to other nonprofit organizations.

The *Foundation Directory Part 2* includes those organizations meeting the Foundation Center's definition of a private or community foundation and are included in the second tier of the largest foundations by total giving in the U.S.

The *Foundation Directory Part 2* does not include organizations whose giving is restricted by charter to one or more specified organizations; foundations that function as endowments for special purposes within and under the governance of a parent institution, such as a college or church; operating foundations that do not maintain active grantmaking programs; organizations that act as associations for industrial or other special groups; or organizations that make general appeals to the public for funds.

TYPES OF FOUNDATIONS

Foundations included in this volume fall into one of four categories:

Independent Foundation: A fund or endowment designated by the Internal Revenue Service (IRS) as a private foundation under the law, the primary function of which is the making of grants. The assets of most independent foundations are derived from the gift of an individual or family. Some function under the direction of family members and are known as "family foundations." Depending on their range of giving, independent foundations may also be known as "general purpose" or "special purpose" foundations.

Company-Sponsored Foundation: A private foundation under the tax law deriving its funds from a profit-making company or corporation but independently constituted, the purpose of which is to make grants, usually on a broad basis although not without regard for the business interests of the corporation. Company-sponsored foundations are legally distinct from contributions programs administered within the corporation directly from corporate funds. Direct corporate giving programs are not listed in *The Foundation Directory* or *The Foundation Directory Part 2*. The Foundation Center's *National Directory of Corporate Giving*, Nineteenth Edition, published in 2013, includes complete corporate giving profiles on nearly 4,200 companies.

Operating Foundation: A fund or endowment designated under the tax law by the Internal Revenue Service as a private operating foundation, the primary purpose of which is to operate research, social welfare, or other programs determined by its governing body or charter. Most operating foundations award few or no grants to outside organizations, and therefore do not appear in *The Foundation Directory Part 2*.

Community Foundation: In its general charitable purposes, a community foundation is much like a private foundation; its funds, however, are derived from many donors rather than a single source, as is usually the case with private foundations. Further, community foundations are usually classified under the tax law as public charities and are therefore subject to different rules and regulations than those which govern private foundations. Public charities other than community foundations are not included in *The Foundation Directory Part 2*.

SOURCES OF INFORMATION

The entries in *The Foundation Directory Part 2* are revised and updated on an ongoing basis, using the newest and most complete information available. This information is either provided by the foundation itself, or it comes from available public records. The main source of information are the foundations' tax returns, the form 990-PF. Other public

sources of information used in this edition include updates from foundation web sites, annual reports, press releases and newspaper articles.

The Internet is an important and effective research tool, enabling staff to learn more about foundations and their most current grantmaking activities. This edition contains 1,056 entries with a URL (Internet web site address), and an additional 1,281 that report having an e-mail address.

A breakdown of the 10,000 foundations by fiscal year end date reveals the following: 111 foundations (1.1 percent) with 2015 fiscal data, 2,598 (26 percent) with 2014 fiscal data, 6,866 (68.7 percent) with 2013 fiscal data, and 424 (4.2 percent) with 2012 fiscal data. Thus, 2015 and 2014 fiscal information is reported for 27.1 percent of the foundations listed. Even when more recent financial information was not available, foundation addresses, contacts, program information, and application procedures reflect the latest updates received by the Center through January 2016.

FIGURE A. General Characteristics of Four Types of Foundations

Foundation Type	Description	Source of Funds	Decision-Making Activity	Grantmaking Requirements	Reporting
Independent Foundation	An independent grant-making organization established to aid social, educational, religious, or other charitable activities.	Endowment generally derived from a single source such as an individual, a family, or a group of individuals. Contributions to endowment limited as to tax deductibility.	Decisions may be made by donor or members of the donor's family; by an independent board of directors or trustees; or by a bank or trust officer acting on the donor's behalf.	Broad discretionary giving allowed but may have specific guidelines and give only in a few specific fields. About 70% limit their giving to local area.	Annual information returns (990-PF) filed with IRS must be made available to public. A small percentage issue separately printed annual reports.
Company-Sponsored Foundation	Legally an independent grantmaking organization with close ties to the corporation providing funds.	Endowment and annual contributions from a profit-making corporation. May maintain small endowment and pay out most of contributions received annually in grants, or may maintain endowment to cover contributions in years when corporate profits are down.	Decisions made by board of directors often composed of corporate officials, but which may include individuals with no corporate affiliation. Decisions may also be made by local company officials.	Giving tends to be in fields related to corporate activities or in communities where corporation operates. Usually give more grants but in smaller dollar amounts than independent foundations.	Same as above.
Operating Foundation	An organization that uses its resources to conduct research or provide a direct service.	Endowment usually provided from a single source, but eligible for maximum deductible contributions from public.	Decisions generally made by independent board of directors.	Makes few, if any grants. Grants generally related directly to the foundation's program.	Same as above.
Community Foundation	A publicly sponsored organization that makes grants for social, educational, religious, or other charitable purposes in a specific community or region.	Contributions received from many donors. Usually eligible for maximum tax deductible contributions from public.	Decisions made by board of directors representing the diversity of the community.	Grants generally limited to charitable organizations in local community.	IRS 990 return available to public. Many publish full guidelines or annual reports.

TABLE 1. Aggregate Fiscal Data by Foundation Type (All dollar figures expressed in thousands)

Foundation Type	Number of Foundations	%	Assets	%	Gifts Received	%	Total Giving*	%	Qualifying Distributions	%	Loans
Independent	9,144	91.4	$43,720,478	87.59	$2,176,346	82.9	$2,308,076	91.1	$2,541,599	84.1	$6,944
Company-Sponsored	449	4.5	1,406,664	2.82	99,618	3.8	115,402	4.6	120,446	4.0	104
Community	127	1.3	1,110,813	2.23	129,566	4.9	35,869	1.4	82,236	2.7	6,624
Operating	280	2.8	3,679,377	7.37	221,413	8.4	73,434	2.9	360,577	11.9	219
Total	10,000	100.0	$49,917,332	100.0	$2,626,942	100.0	$2,532,781	100.0	$3,022,622	100.0	$13,892

Note: Figures may not add up due to rounding.
*Throughout this introduction, "Total Giving" figures include grants, scholarships, employee matching gifts, and other amounts reported as "Grants and Contributions Paid During the Year" on the 990-PF reporting form. Loan amounts including program-related investments (PRIs) are indicated separately. Total giving does not include all qualifying distributions under the tax law, e.g., loans, PRIs, and program or other administrative expenses.

TABLE 2. Aggregate Fiscal Data for Foundations New to *The Foundation Directory Part 2* by Foundation Type
(All dollar figures expressed in thousands)

Foundation Type	Number of Foundations	%	Assets	%	Gifts Received	%	Total Giving*	%	Qualifying Distributions	%	Loans
Independent	1,052	92.0	$5,335,566	87.0	$405,787	91.1	$288,244	90.7	$349,736	90.2	$2,398
Company-Sponsored	37	3.2	163,932	2.7	14,880	3.3	11,508	3.6	12,129	3.1	0
Community	17	1.5	160,087	2.6	10,329	2.3	5,800	1.8	7,342	1.9	6,624
Operating	37	3.2	472,118	7.7	14,420	3.2	12,358	3.9	25,724	6.6	0
Total	1,143	100.0	$6,131,703	100.0	$445,416	100.0	$317,909	100.0	$387,589	100.0	$9,022

Note: Figures may not add up due to rounding.
*Throughout this introduction, "Total Giving" figures include grants, scholarships, employee matching gifts, and other amounts reported as "Grants and Contributions Paid During the Year" on the 990-PF reporting form. Loan amounts including program-related investments (PRIs) are indicated separately. Total giving does not include all qualifying distributions under the tax law, e.g., loans, PRIs, and program or other administrative expenses.

TABLE 3. Fiscal Data of Foundations by Region and State (All dollar figures expressed in thousands)

Region	Number of Foundations	%	Assets	%	Gifts Received	%	Expenditures	%	Total Giving	%
NORTHEAST	3,147	31.5	$14,574,768	29.2	$753,624	28.7	$991,530	28.4	$797,698	31.5
New England	830	8.3	4004711	8.0	216,969	8.3	260,317	7.4	210,314	8.3
Connecticut	220	2.2	971378	2.0	59,220	2.3	67,773	1.9	56,624	2.2
Maine	44	0.4	315179	0.6	6,196	0.2	14,580	0.4	9,928	0.4
Massachusetts	377	3.8	1711979	3.4	74,920	2.9	119,518	3.4	97,346	3.8
New Hampshire	36	0.4	215164	0.4	34,027	1.3	11,976	0.3	9,479	0.4
Rhode Island	131	1.3	691049	1.4	34,091	1.3	39,846	1.1	32,124	1.3
Vermont	22	0.2	99960	0.2	8,515	0.3	6,624	0.2	4,813	0.2
Middle Atlantic	2,317	23.2	10570058	21.2	536,654	20.4	731,213	20.9	587,383	23.2
New Jersey	364	3.6	1506313	3.0	79,250	3.0	113,192	3.2	92,251	3.6
New York	1,408	14.1	6151528	12.3	369,869	14.1	445,348	12.7	357,039	14.1
Pennsylvania	545	5.5	2912216	5.8	87,536	3.3	172,673	4.9	138,093	5.5
MIDWEST	2,232	22.3	10808161	21.7	547,118	20.8	768,121	22.0	567,276	22.4
East North Central	1,578	15.8	7589808	15.2	371,133	14.1	515,225	14.7	400,522	15.8
Illinois	648	6.5	2897972	5.8	152,601	5.8	205,462	5.9	162,577	6.4
Indiana	131	1.3	694790	1.4	45,898	1.8	46,395	1.3	33,899	1.3
Michigan	253	2.5	1238371	2.5	68,184	2.6	87,585	2.5	65,342	2.6
Ohio	355	3.6	1778861	3.6	51,646	2.0	112,823	3.2	88,596	3.5
Wisconsin	191	1.9	979813	2.0	52,804	2.0	62,960	1.8	50,107	2.0
West North Central	654	6.5	3218353	6.5	175,984	6.7	252,895	7.2	166,755	6.6
Iowa	83	0.8	383453	0.8	34,657	1.3	32,381	0.9	20,347	0.8
Kansas	92	0.9	499647	1.0	15,368	0.6	31,378	0.9	25,129	1.0
Minnesota	199	2.0	856878	1.7	28,468	1.1	59,202	1.7	47,842	1.9
Missouri	185	1.9	841927	1.7	35,810	1.4	59,100	1.7	48,665	1.9
Nebraska	65	0.7	429114	0.9	54,550	2.1	58,473	1.7	16,956	0.7
North Dakota	5	0.1	30397	0.1	1,361	0.1	2,032	0.1	1,472	0.1
South Dakota	25	0.3	176938	0.4	5,771	0.2	10,329	0.3	6,343	0.3

Note: Figures may not add up due to rounding.

TABLE 3. Fiscal Data of Foundations by Region and State (All dollar figures expressed in thousands), continued

SOUTH	2,798	28.0	14875208	29.8	861,759	32.8	956,600	27.4	702,086	27.7
South Atlantic	1,718	17.2	9508225	19.1	581,368	22.1	601,627	17.2	425,978	16.8
Delaware	181	1.8	748592	1.5	41,191	1.6	55,902	1.6	45,897	1.8
District of Columbia	55	0.6	1119346	2.2	164,228	6.3	28,705	0.8	13,559	0.5
Florida	589	5.9	2813400	5.6	134,215	5.1	183,076	5.2	144,493	5.7
Georgia	195	2.0	1446278	2.9	79,604	3.0	105,434	3.0	49,734	2.0
Maryland	185	1.9	844919	1.7	61,267	2.3	56,896	1.6	47,647	1.9
North Carolina	257	2.6	1308257	2.6	38,191	1.5	93,315	2.7	61,509	2.4
South Carolina	45	0.5	196279	0.4	9,680	0.4	12,923	0.4	10,060	0.4
Virginia	172	1.7	798656	1.6	51,292	2.0	53,205	1.5	43,265	1.7
West Virginia	39	0.4	232500	0.5	1,700	0.1	12,171	0.4	9,813	0.4
East South Central	293	2.9	1303192	2.6	53,852	2.1	93,847	2.7	73,578	2.9
Alabama	79	0.8	326900	0.7	8,132	0.3	24,336	0.7	19,458	0.8
Kentucky	66	0.7	328423	0.7	20,665	0.8	21,513	0.6	17,169	0.7
Mississippi	38	0.4	153465	0.3	4,533	0.2	12,295	0.4	9,447	0.4
Tennessee	110	1.1	494404	1.0	20,522	0.8	35,702	1.0	27,504	1.1
West South Central	787	7.9	4063791	8.1	226,539	8.6	261,126	7.5	202,529	8.0
Arkansas	37	0.4	199274	0.4	28,497	1.1	12,291	0.4	10,638	0.4
Louisiana	52	0.5	275683	0.6	13,981	0.5	16,807	0.5	12,387	0.5
Oklahoma	86	0.9	502985	1.0	11,487	0.4	29,349	0.8	21,187	0.8
Texas	612	6.1	3085850	6.2	172,574	6.6	202,679	5.8	158,318	6.3
WEST	1,823	18.2	9659194	19.4	464,442	17.7	781,287	22.3	465,721	18.4
Mountain	506	5.1	3772858	7.6	119,293	4.5	342,827	9.8	128,375	5.1
Arizona	93	0.9	1342055	2.7	20,277	0.8	185,567	5.3	24,389	1.0
Colorado	165	1.7	1125680	2.3	39,225	1.5	72,440	2.1	41,378	1.6
Idaho	28	0.3	330562	0.7	10,463	0.4	10,288	0.3	7,646	0.3
Montana	22	0.2	113972	0.2	6,636	0.3	6,663	0.2	5,460	0.2
Nevada	73	0.7	273114	0.6	13,537	0.5	22,396	0.6	17,998	0.7
New Mexico	25	0.3	136434	0.3	7,022	0.3	12,634	0.4	6,140	0.2
Utah	63	0.6	250189	0.5	15,417	0.6	19,703	0.6	16,080	0.6
Wyoming	37	0.4	200853	0.4	6,716	0.3	13,137	0.4	9,284	0.4
Pacific	1,317	13.2	5886336	11.8	345,150	13.1	438,461	12.5	337,346	13.3
Alaska	13	0.1	61920	0.1	10,038	0.4	6,239	0.2	3,445	0.1
California	996	10.0	4447628	8.9	268,982	10.2	332,963	9.5	255,281	10.1
Hawaii	39	0.4	191470	0.4	11,581	0.4	12,613	0.4	9,819	0.4
Oregon	93	0.9	437530	0.9	8,847	0.3	30,215	0.9	23,350	0.9
Washington	176	1.8	747787	1.5	45,701	1.7	56,431	1.6	45,451	1.8
TOTAL	10,000	100.0	$49,917,332	100.0	$2,626,942	100.0	$3,497,538	100.0	$2,532,781	100.0

Note: Figures may not add up due to rounding.

TABLE 4. 100 Largest Foundations by Assets

Name	Assets	Total Giving	Fiscal Date	Name	Assets	Total Giving	Fiscal Date
1. Community Finance Corporation	$904,943,212	$290,000	9/30/14	52. Avery-Tsui Foundation	31,134,963	335,048	12/31/14
2. Glenstone Foundation	849,902,315	121,000	12/31/13	53. Stuttering Foundation of America, Inc.	31,029,694	255,000	12/31/13
3. The University Financing Foundation, Inc.	425,765,970	204,265	12/31/14	54. The Maronda Foundation	30,948,862	177,252	12/31/13
4. Greentree Foundation	282,801,977	374,000	12/31/14	55. The Mel and Grace McLean Foundation	30,894,478	346,174	12/31/13
5. Arison Arts Foundation	273,497,655	333,333	12/31/13	56. The Robert A. Waidner Foundation	30,506,343	169,272	12/31/14
6. J. R. Simplot Foundation, Inc.	204,554,385	400,000	9/30/13	57. Raymond & Ruth Perelman Judaica Foundation	30,217,308	250,550	4/30/13
7. The Myron Stratton Home	179,484,884	277,000	12/31/14	58. Kurt Weill Foundation for Music, Inc.	30,187,500	272,175	12/31/14
8. National Endowment for Financial Education	166,169,812	440,907	12/31/13	59. Joel F. Gemunder Foundation	30,162,272	441,995	12/31/12
9. Elliotsville Plantation Inc	136,877,460	299,950	12/31/14	60. Wayne Duddlesten Foundation	29,792,905	243,500	12/31/13
10. Thompson Educational Foundation	103,540,409	431,165	12/31/14	61. Ferguson Family Baptist Missionary & Educational Foundation, Ltd.	29,589,370	188,550	12/31/12
11. Nebraska Community Foundation	98,799,218	216,707	6/30/14	62. The Harper Family Foundation	29,585,292	405,522	12/31/13
12. New Tamarind Foundation, Inc.	87,002,616	157,658	6/30/14	63. The Shumway Foundation	28,467,915	373,750	12/31/13
13. Milbank Memorial Fund	85,827,207	289,500	12/31/13	64. The Avanessians Foundation	28,070,629	231,000	12/31/13
14. The Elizabeth R. and William J. Patterson Foundation	81,770,201	270,250	12/31/13	65. Robert C. Dart Foundation	27,915,794	252,358	10/31/13
15. Fannie E. Rippel Foundation	81,335,353	317,519	4/30/13	66. Ohio County Community Foundation, Inc.	27,697,842	270,324	12/31/13
16. Chipstone Foundation	76,752,605	248,278	12/31/13	67. Schlessman Family Foundation, Inc.	27,630,361	200,316	3/31/13
17. Daniel P. and Grace I. Tully Charitable Trust	71,025,456	327,250	11/30/13	68. Belz Foundation	27,610,196	345,873	12/31/13
18. Sequoia Farm Foundation	67,655,956	208,593	12/31/13	69. Kaufman Americana Foundation	27,554,472	290,724	11/30/13
19. The Tang Fund	67,417,275	169,175	11/30/13	70. Connolly Family Foundation, Inc.	27,159,022	407,350	6/30/13
20. Boeing Company Charitable Trust	65,294,977	400,000	12/31/13	71. Donnell-Kay Foundation, Inc.	27,040,533	415,000	1/31/13
21. Milton and Sally Avery Arts Foundation	62,950,583	415,750	12/31/13	72. Con Alma Health Foundation, Inc.	26,999,029	366,600	12/31/13
22. The Weill Family Foundation	61,162,769	442,500	12/31/12	73. Charles & Lois Marie Bright Foundation	26,975,055	213,681	9/30/14
23. The Grundy Foundation	60,918,312	143,500	12/31/13	74. The Deason Foundation	26,937,295	425,650	12/31/14
24. Pearl M. & Julia J. Harmon Foundation	60,561,534	173,779	5/31/13	75. Touradji Family Foundation	26,590,452	300,000	12/31/12
25. Arlene & Joseph Meraux Charitable Foundation, Inc.	58,996,797	161,213	12/31/12	76. The Kerr Foundation Inc.	26,266,152	354,146	12/31/13
26. The Tobin Theatre Arts Fund	54,040,829	362,410	12/31/13	77. The Pincus Family Fund	26,248,371	300,000	12/31/13
27. World Food Prize Foundation	51,834,480	250,000	12/31/13	78. McCune Family Foundation	26,178,155	328,500	12/31/13
28. Harvey W. Peters Research Foundation	49,282,036	271,000	6/30/14	79. The Orfalea Family Foundation	25,879,567	435,158	12/31/13
29. Beacon Foundation Inc.	46,287,856	395,494	6/30/13	80. Sonnentag Foundation Ltd.	25,597,471	232,917	9/30/14
30. Newton & Rochelle Becker Charitable Trust	46,056,058	322,499	12/31/13	81. Carlsbad Foundation, Inc.	25,561,218	361,716	6/30/14
31. Building Healthy Lives Foundation	43,945,859	430,425	12/31/12	82. Dubois County Community Foundation, Inc.	25,493,192	383,373	12/31/13
32. Trojan Real Properties Inc.	43,918,809	210,000	7/31/13	83. Meta Alice Keith Bratten Foundation	25,373,396	184,107	12/31/14
33. Kessler Family Foundation	41,549,264	279,484	12/31/13	84. Bauer Family Foundation Inc	25,314,536	283,780	12/31/13
34. Iris & B. Gerald Cantor Foundation	41,485,147	383,825	4/30/13	85. Newell B. Sargent Foundation	24,547,927	188,323	10/31/13
35. Peter & Paula Fasseas Foundation	41,208,241	238,045	12/31/13	86. Marna M. Kuehne Foundation	24,531,351	334,323	10/31/14
36. The Gilbert J. Martin Foundation	40,633,298	439,000	12/31/12	87. Brentwood Foundation	24,111,962	409,648	12/31/13
37. The Greenwich Collection, Ltd.	39,814,516	187,000	12/31/14	88. Max McGraw Wildlife Foundation	24,024,822	161,976	4/30/13
38. The Dr. P. Phillips Foundation	39,351,518	382,816	5/31/13	89. The William F. O'Connor Foundation	23,860,924	350,000	6/30/13
39. The Frederic C. Hamilton Family Foundation	39,002,847	270,362	12/31/13	90. Kiersznowski Family Charitable Trust	23,740,854	344,500	12/31/13
40. The Couch Family Foundation	38,200,101	212,925	12/31/13	91. The Carl H. and Edyth B. Lindner Foundation	23,611,030	379,783	12/31/13
41. Legacy Heritage Fund Limited	37,968,081	213,187	6/30/13	92. The Maks & Lea Rothstein Charitable Youth Trust	23,589,759	395,952	12/31/13
42. Harold S. Geneen Charitable Trust	36,045,388	277,335	12/31/13	93. Ruth Carol Fund, Inc.	23,502,257	180,000	12/31/12
43. Blue Dot Foundation	35,566,860	195,912	12/31/13	94. Orris C. Hirtzel and Beatrice Dewey Hirtzel Memorial Foundation	23,499,548	159,000	12/31/13
44. Doll Family Foundation	35,276,953	246,950	12/31/13	95. The Robert D. Goldfarb Foundation	23,438,278	378,944	12/31/14
45. Pyewacket Foundation	35,011,075	275,000	12/31/13	96. Grotto Foundation Inc.	23,436,072	398,000	4/30/13
46. Winifred L. Stevens Foundation	34,998,829	252,785	12/31/13	97. Raygar Foundation	23,359,069	219,000	8/31/13
47. Marriott Daughters Foundation	34,132,484	322,000	10/31/14	98. John S. and Amy S. Weinberg Foundation	23,187,944	377,750	7/31/13
48. Adolph and Esther Gottlieb Foundation, Inc.	32,839,287	442,150	6/30/14	99. The Webb Foundation	23,175,283	285,590	12/31/13
49. The Laura & Isaac Perlmutter Foundation Inc.	32,712,924	370,250	12/31/13	100. Starvaggi Charities, Inc.	23,109,154	159,619	1/31/13
50. Lukis Foundation	32,151,804	230,150	12/31/13				
51. Stephen M. Seay Foundation, Inc.	31,483,629	401,787	12/31/12				

TABLE 5. 100 Largest Foundations by Total Giving

	Name	Total Giving	Assets	Fiscal Date		Name	Total Giving	Assets	Fiscal Date
1.	McLeod Blue Skye Charitable Foundation, Inc.	$442,950	$8,054,598	12/31/14	51.	Jasam Foundation Fund B	$440,000	$8,097,404	12/31/13
2.	The Greater Everett Community Foundation	442,919	10,525,375	12/31/12	52.	Barbara F. Wheeler Foundation	440,000	9,267,689	12/31/13
3.	United Plankton Charitable Trust	442,618	7,398,942	12/31/14	53.	Jack H. & William M. Light Charitable Trust	440,000	10,875,582	12/31/13
4.	The Rimora Foundation	442,500	9,459,307	12/31/13	54.	James and Ada Horwich Family Foundation	439,950	5,601,276	11/30/13
5.	The Weill Family Foundation	442,500	61,162,769	12/31/12	55.	The Rockdale Foundation Inc.	439,865	5,551,866	12/31/13
6.	Bet Lev Foundation	442,431	10,617,670	12/31/13	56.	The Good Works Institute, Inc.	439,839	57,957	9/30/14
7.	Bob White Memorial Foundation	442,411	8,927,585	12/31/14	57.	Satya and Rao Remala Foundation	439,834	11,692,021	12/31/13
8.	Mortenson Family Foundation	442,330		12/31/12	58.	The Betsy Gordon Foundation	439,815	127,024	10/31/13
9.	The Harry and Estelle Soicher Foundation	442,311	8,095,751	12/31/13	59.	Hollowell Foundation, Inc.	439,750	8,423,427	6/30/14
10.	The Turock Family Foundation	442,244	3,737,528	12/31/13	60.	The Sutton Trust Foundation	439,732	446,246	12/31/13
11.	Adolph and Esther Gottlieb Foundation, Inc.	442,150	32,839,287	6/30/14	61.	Henry W. Bull Foundation	439,700	9,587,786	12/31/13
12.	The Lachman Family Foundation Inc.	442,000	11,119,593	12/31/12	62.	The Borch Foundation	439,620	2,804,324	12/31/14
13.	Joel F. Gemunder Foundation	441,995	30,162,272	12/31/12	63.	Whaley Foundation	439,500	6,549,970	12/31/13
14.	Anschel Eilian Family Charitable Foundation	441,985	797,512	12/31/14	64.	The Sparkplug Foundation	439,480	5,846,258	12/31/13
15.	Hagan Foundation	441,918	8,818,074	12/31/13	65.	Crawford Heritage Community Foundation	439,184	12,741,847	12/31/12
16.	Chiles Foundation	441,800	2,222,009	12/31/14	66.	The Gilbert J. Martin Foundation	439,000	40,633,298	12/31/12
17.	York Community Foundation	441,743	7,050,617	9/30/13	67.	Farnham Foundation	439,000	4,580,937	12/31/13
18.	Oster Family Foundation, Inc.	441,740	6,452,165	4/30/14	68.	Paul Lauzier Scholarship Foundation	438,983	9,060	12/31/13
19.	The Butler Family Fund	441,680	11,543,504	12/31/14	69.	The Stare Fund	438,967	9,673,557	11/30/13
20.	Chizen Family Foundation	441,636	9,912,546	12/31/14	70.	James W. & Betty Dye Foundation, Inc.	438,859	15,540,849	12/31/14
21.	Dinesh and Kalpana Patel Foundation	441,606	239,304	12/31/13	71.	The Chirag Foundation	438,831	4,936,747	12/31/13
22.	Burt Foundation	441,500	13,287,244	12/31/13	72.	Hickrill Foundation, Inc.	438,750	7,087,948	12/31/13
23.	Community Foundation of Madison and Jefferson County, Inc.	441,429	18,126,846	12/31/12	73.	Dan C. Ferguson Charitable Trust	438,700	2,931,969	12/31/13
24.	Leo V. Berger Fund	441,418	8,299,382	12/31/12	74.	Panoram Foundation Inc.	438,636	5,379,257	12/31/13
25.	J. Philip & Jennifer DiNapoli Foundation	441,265	2,489,223	12/31/13	75.	Charles S. Keene Foundation	438,598	9,828,547	12/31/14
26.	Margaret Briggs Foundation	441,250	12,277,014	12/31/13	76.	The S. Leigh Pierson & Douglas R. Conant Family Cookie Jar Foundation, Inc.	438,500	5,456,811	12/31/14
27.	Michael Baker Corporation Foundation	441,242	322,015	12/31/13	77.	The Arthur B. Schultz Foundation	438,348	5,677,962	11/30/13
28.	The Sato Family Foundation, Inc	441,200	6,041,896	12/31/13	78.	Ridgecliff Foundation Inc.	438,313	8,862,511	12/31/13
29.	Chada Foundation, Inc.	441,110	1,449,965	11/30/13	79.	ESL Charitable Foundation	438,250		12/31/13
30.	James and Pauline Hackbarth Foundation, Inc.	441,110	5,421,386	6/30/14	80.	The Frank & Fred Friedman Family Foundation	438,234	10,778,068	3/31/13
31.	Community Foundation of Randolph County, Inc.	441,029	8,262,514	12/31/13	81.	M. M. and P. A. Day Memorial Fund	438,233	7,532,699	12/31/14
32.	Louis Foundation, Inc.	441,000	827,271	12/31/13	82.	Harry Chow & Nee-Chang Chock Wong Foundation	438,220	12,427,762	12/31/14
33.	Sumitomo Corporation of America Foundation	441,000	9,172,979	3/31/14	83.	The Pruet Foundation	438,012	8,208,720	12/31/13
34.	The David and Heidi Welch Foundation	441,000	1,533,326	12/31/13	84.	Verla Nesbitt Joscelyn Foundation	438,004	7,397,120	12/31/13
35.	Robert & Helen Remick Charitable Foundation	440,985	11,554,065	12/31/14	85.	Diermeier Family Foundation	438,000	9,416,371	12/31/13
36.	National Endowment for Financial Education	440,907	166,169,812	12/31/13	86.	New England Biolabs Foundation	437,900	8,711,658	12/31/13
37.	Harold E. & Phyllis S. Thomas Foundation	440,823		12/31/13	87.	The Kronhill Pletka Foundation	437,898	5,920,886	12/31/14
38.	Cafaro-Livingston Charitable Trust	440,700	386,432	12/31/13	88.	The Oppenheimer Family Foundation	437,625	4,590,326	12/31/13
39.	Linked Foundation	440,610	7,340,510	12/31/13	89.	Schoenleber Foundation, Inc.	437,500	8,707,098	12/31/13
40.	R. E. French Family Educational Foundation	440,602	11,483,027	6/30/14	90.	Dreyfus Foundation	437,375	6,193,980	12/31/13
41.	William and Martha Ford Fund	440,540	4,528,687	12/31/13	91.	Community Foundation of Orange County, Inc.	437,324	12,318,758	6/30/14
42.	Bendon Family Foundation	440,400	10,487,153	6/30/14	92.	The Castleman Family Foundation	437,305	9,495,470	12/31/13
43.	Grateful Foundation Inc.	440,250	9,658,089	10/31/13	93.	Richard H. Lewis Family Foundation	437,179	7,963,806	12/31/13
44.	The Klapper Family Foundation, Inc.	440,024	9,949,933	12/31/14	94.	Milano Foundation, Inc.	437,025	2,196,383	12/31/13
45.	Frank N. Andersen Foundation	440,018	7,421,491	12/31/14	95.	Irvin F. & Alice S. Etscorn Charitable Foundation	437,000	8,283,430	6/30/14
46.	The 1994 Christopher W. Johnson Charitable Trust No. 33	440,000	11,912,684	12/31/13	96.	James C. and Teresa K. Day Foundation	436,900	7,208,477	11/30/13
47.	Walter J. and Lille A. Berbecker Scholarship Fund	440,000	77,913	2/28/13	97.	Weathertop Foundation	436,880	11,272,721	7/31/13
48.	Stuart George and Jeanette Charitable Trust	440,000	9,364,578	12/31/14	98.	The Whitwell-Meyer Foundation	436,785	127,469	12/31/13
49.	Alice G. Hanson Family Foundation	440,000	9,152,974	12/31/13	99.	Richard Davoud Donchian Foundation, Inc.	436,725	9,822,850	12/31/14
50.	Geisler Penquite Corporation	440,000	10,659,499	12/31/13	100.	Samuel P. Hunt Foundation	436,695	11,661,021	12/31/14

HOW TO USE
THE FOUNDATION DIRECTORY PART 2

The Foundation Directory Part 2 is designed to help grantseekers identify foundations that might be interested in funding their project or organization. It provides basic descriptions and current fiscal data for the nation's second-tier of foundations by total giving. In addition, indexes help to identify foundations that may have giving interests in particular subject fields or geographic areas, or that provide specific types of support.

Researchers, journalists, grantmakers, and others interested in the philanthropic field should use The Foundation Directory Part 2 in conjunction with The Foundation Directory to get a broad overview of current foundation activities nationally or within a particular geographic region, or to gather facts about one or more specific foundations.

When using The Foundation Directory Part 2 to identify potential funding sources, grantseekers are urged to read each foundation description carefully to determine the nature of the grantmaker's interests and to note any restrictions on giving that would prevent the foundation from considering their proposal. Many foundations limit their giving to a particular subject field or geographic area; others are unable to provide certain types of support, such as funds for buildings and equipment or for general operating budgets. Even when a foundation has not provided an explicit limitations statement, restrictions on giving may exist. This is often the case with entries updated from public records. Further research into the giving patterns of these foundations is necessary before applying for funds. Also, please note that many foundations do not accept applications, or contribute only to pre-selected organizations.

ARRANGEMENT

The Foundation Directory Part 2 is arranged alphabetically by state and, within states, by foundation name. Each descriptive entry is assigned a sequence number; references in the indexes are to these entry numbers.

WHAT'S IN AN ENTRY?

There are 33 basic data elements that could be included in a Foundation Directory Part 2 entry. The content of entries varies widely due to differences in the size and nature of foundation programs and the availability of information from foundations.

Specific data elements that could be included are:

1. The full legal **name of the foundation**.

2. The **former name** of the foundation.

3. The **street address, city,** and **zip code** of the foundation's principal office.

4. The **telephone number** of the foundation.

5. The name and title of the **contact person** of the foundation.

6. Any **additional address** (such as a separate application address) supplied by the foundation. Additional telephone or fax numbers as well as e-mail and/or URL addresses also may be listed here.

7. **Establishment data**, including the legal form (usually a trust or corporation) and the year and state in which the foundation was established.

8. The **donor(s)** or principal contributor(s) to the foundation, including individuals, families, and corporations. If a donor is deceased, the symbol † follows the name.

9. **Foundation type:** community, company-sponsored, independent, or operating.

10. The **year-end date** of the foundation's accounting period for which financial data is supplied.

11. **Assets:** the total value of the foundation's investments at the end of the accounting period. In a few instances, foundations that act as "pass-throughs" for annual corporate or individual gifts report zero assets.

12. **Asset type:** generally, assets are reported at market value (M) or ledger value (L).

13. **Gifts received:** the total amount of new capital received by the foundation in the year of record.

14. **Expenditures:** total disbursements of the foundation, including overhead expenses (salaries; investment, legal, and other professional fees; interest; rent; etc.) and federal excise taxes, as well as the total amount paid for grants, scholarships, and matching gifts.

15. The total amount of **qualifying distributions** made by the foundation in the year of record. This figure includes all grants paid, qualifying administrative expenses, loans and program-related investments, set-asides, and amounts paid to acquire assets used directly in carrying out charitable purposes.

16. The dollar value and number of **grants paid** during the year, with the largest grant paid **(high)** and smallest grant paid **(low)**. When supplied by the foundation, the average range

of grant payments is also indicated. Grant figures generally do not include commitments for future payment or amounts spent for grants to individuals, employee matching gifts, loans, or foundation-administered programs.

17. The total dollar value of **set-asides** made by the foundation during the year. Although set-asides count as qualifying distributions toward the foundation's annual payout requirement, they are distinct from any amounts listed as grants paid.

18. The total amount and number of **grants made directly to or on behalf of individuals,** including scholarships, fellowships, awards, and medical payments. When supplied by the foundation, high, low, and average range are also indicated.

19. The dollar amount and number of **employee matching gifts** awarded, generally by company-sponsored foundations.

20. The total dollars expended for **programs administered by the foundation** and the number of foundation-administered programs. These programs can include museums or other institutions supported exclusively by the foundation, research programs administered by the foundation, etc.

21. The dollar amount and number of **loans** made to nonprofit organizations by the foundation. These can include program-related investments, emergency loans to help nonprofits that are waiting for grants or other income payments, etc. When supplied by the foundation, high, low, and average range are also indicated.

22. The number of **loans to individuals** and the total amount loaned. When supplied by the foundation, high, low, and average range are also indicated.

23. The monetary value and number of **in-kind gifts**.

24. The **purpose and activities**, in general terms, of the foundation. This statement reflects funding interests as expressed by the foundation or, if no foundation statement is available, an analysis of the actual grants awarded by the foundation during the most recent two-year period for which public records exist. Many foundations leave statements of purpose intentionally broad, indicating only the major program areas within which they fund. More specific areas of interest can often be found in the "Fields of Interest" section of the entry.

25. The **fields of interest** reflected in the foundation's giving program. The terminology used in this section conforms to Foundation Center's Philanthropy Classification System (PCS). The terms also provide access to foundation entries through the Subject Index at the back of the volume.

26. The **international giving interests** of the foundation.

27. The **type of support** (such as endowment funds, building/renovation, equipment, fellowships, etc.) offered by the foundation. Definitions of the terms used to describe the forms of support available are provided at the beginning of the Types of Support Index at the back of this volume.

28. Any stated **limitations** on the foundation's giving program, including geographic preferences, restrictions by subject focus or type of recipient, or specific types of support the foundation cannot provide. It is noted here if a foundation does not accept unsolicited applications.

29. **Publications** or other printed materials distributed by the foundation that describe its activities and giving program. These can include annual or multi-year reports, newsletters, corporate giving reports, informational brochures, grant lists, etc.

30. **Application information**, including the preferred form of application, the number of copies of proposals requested, application deadlines, frequency and dates of board meetings, and the general amount of time the foundation requires to notify applicants of the board's decision. Some foundations have indicated that their funds are currently committed to ongoing projects.

31. The names and titles of **officers, principal administrators, trustees,** or **directors,** and members of other governing bodies.

32. The number of professional and support **staff** employed by the foundation, and an indication of part-time or full-time status of these employees, as reported by the foundation.

33. **EIN:** the Employer Identification Number assigned to the foundation by the IRS for tax purposes. This number can be useful when ordering or searching for the foundation's annual information return, Form 990-PF.

INDEXES

Seven indexes to the descriptive entries are provided at the back of the book to assist grantseekers and other users of *The Foundation Directory Part 2:*

1. The **Index to Donors, Officers, Trustees** is an alphabetical list of individual and corporate donors, officers, and members of governing boards whose names appear in *The Foundation Directory Part 2* entries. Many grantseekers find this index helpful in determining whether current or prospective members of their own governing boards, alumni of their schools, or current contributors are affiliated with any foundations.

2. The **Geographic Index** references foundation entries by the state and city in which the foundation maintains its principal office. The index includes "see also" references at the end of each state section to indicate foundations that have made substantial grants in that state but are located elsewhere. Foundations that award grants on a national, regional, or international basis are indicated in bold type. The remaining foundations generally limit their giving to the state or city in which they are located.

3. The **International Giving Index** provides access to foundations whose giving interests extend beyond the United States. A complete alphabetical list of countries, continents, and regions is provided at the beginning of the index. Under each country, continent, or region, entry numbers are listed by the state location and abbreviated name of the foundation. Organizations whose programs benefit foreign countries should use this index to identify funders with similar geographic interests.

4. The **Type of Support Index** provides access to foundation entries by the specific types of support the foundation awards. A glossary of the forms of support listed appears

at the beginning of the index. Under each type of support term, entry numbers are listed by the state location and abbreviated name of the foundation. Foundations that award grants on a national, regional, or international basis are indicated in bold type. When using this index, grantseekers should focus on foundations located in their own state that offer the specific type of support needed, or on foundations listed in bold type if their program has national impact.

5. The **Subject Index** provides access to the giving interests of foundations based on the "Fields of Interest" sections of their entries. The terminology in the index conforms to Foundation Center's Philanthropy Classification System (PCS). A complete alphabetical list of the subject headings in the current edition is provided at the beginning of the index as well as "see also" references to related subject areas included in this volume. Under each subject term, entry numbers are listed by the state location and abbreviated name of the foundation. As in the Types of Support Index, foundations that award grants on a national, regional, or international basis are indicated in bold type. Again, grantseekers should focus on foundations located in their own state that have shown an interest in their subject area, or on foundations listed in bold type if their program is national in scope.

6. The index of **Foundations New to the Edition** is a listing of foundations that appear in the current edition of *The Foundation Directory Part 2* but had not met criteria for inclusion in the previous edition.

7. The **Foundation Name Index** is an alphabetical list of all foundations appearing in *The Foundation Directory Part 2*. Former names of foundations appear with "see" references to the appropriate entry numbers. This index also provides references to Appendix A, which lists foundations that appeared in the previous edition but have since terminated or otherwise become ineligible for inclusion.

APPENDIX

In addition to the descriptive entries and indexes, *The Foundation Directory Part 2* includes an appendix. Appendix A lists foundations described in the previous edition of *The Foundation Directory Part 2* that do not have entries in the current edition because they have terminated operations, merged with another foundation, ceased grantmaking, or changed their legal status.

RESEARCHING FOUNDATIONS

Foundations receive many thousands of requests each year. Most of these requests are declined because there are never enough funds to go around or because the application clearly falls outside the foundation's fields of interest. Sometimes the qualifications of the staff are not well established; the budget or the means of evaluating the project may not be presented convincingly; or the organization may not have asked itself whether it is especially suited to make a contribution to the solution of the problem, whether it can provide the service proposed, or whether others are not already effectively engaged in the same activity.

The first step in researching foundation funding support, then, is to analyze your own program and organization to determine the need you plan to address, the audience you will serve, and the amount and type of support you need. Become familiar with the basic facts about foundations in general as well as how they operate. Consider other sources of funding, such as individual contributors, government grants, earned income possibilities, and so on. Although foundations are an important source of support for nonprofit organizations, their giving represents a relatively small percentage of the total philanthropic dollars contributed annually, and an even smaller percentage of the total when government grants and earned income are included.

Once you have determined the amount and type of support you need and the reasons why you are seeking foundation support, *The Foundation Directory Part 2* can help you to develop an initial list of foundations that might be interested in funding your project. In determining whether or not it is appropriate to approach a particular foundation with a grant request, keep in mind the following questions:

1. Has the foundation demonstrated a real commitment to funding in your subject area?

2. Does it seem likely that the foundation will make a grant in your geographic area?

3. Does the amount of money you are requesting fit within the foundation's grant range?

4. Does the foundation have any policy prohibiting grants for the type of support you are requesting?

5. Does the foundation prefer to make grants that cover the full cost of a project or does it favor projects where other foundations or funding sources share the cost?

6. What types of organizations does the foundation tend to support?

7. Does the foundation have specific application deadlines and procedures or does it review proposals continuously?

Some of these questions can be answered from the information provided in *The Foundation Directory* and *The Foundation Directory Part 2*, but grantseekers will almost always want to consult a few additional resources before submitting a request for funding. If the foundation issues an annual report, application guidelines, or other printed materials describing its program, it is advisable to obtain copies and study them carefully before preparing your proposal. If the foundation has a web site, studying it is essential. The foundation's annual information return (Form 990-PF) includes a list of all grants paid by the foundation, as well as basic data about its finances, officers, and giving policies.

THE FOUNDATION DIRECTORY

The Foundation Directory provides information on the first tier of U.S. grantmaking foundations. Together, *The Foundation Directory* and *The Foundation Directory Part 2* constitute the standard reference work for information on 20,000 of the largest active grantmaking foundations in the United States.

GLOSSARY

The following list includes important terms used by grantmakers and grantseekers. A number of sources have been consulted in compiling this glossary, including *The Handbook on Private Foundations*, 3rd Edition, by David F. Freeman, John A. Edie, Jane C. Nober, and the Council on Foundations (Washington, DC, 2005); *The Law of Tax-Exempt Organizations*, 9th Edition, by Bruce R. Hopkins (Hoboken, NJ: John Wiley & Sons, 2007); and the *AFP Fund-Raising Dictionary*, (2003).

Annual Report: A *voluntary* report issued by a foundation or corporation that provides financial data and descriptions of grantmaking activities. Annual reports vary in format from simple typewritten documents listing the year's grants to detailed publications that provide substantial information about the grantmaking program.

Assets: The amount of capital or principal—money, stocks, bonds, real estate, or other resources—controlled by the foundation or corporate giving program. Generally, assets are invested and the income is used to make grants.

Beneficiary: In philanthropic terms, the donee or grantee receiving funds from a foundation or corporate giving program is the beneficiary, although society benefits as well. Foundations whose legal terms of establishment restrict their giving to one or more named beneficiaries are not included in this publication.

Bricks and Mortar: An informal term for grants for buildings or construction projects.

Capital Support: Funds provided for endowment purposes, buildings, construction, or equipment, and including, for example, grants for "bricks and mortar."

Challenge Grant: A grant awarded that will be paid only if the donee organization is able to raise additional funds from another source(s). Challenge grants are often used to stimulate giving from other donors. (*See also* **Matching Grant**)

Community Foundation: A 501(c)(3) organization that makes grants for charitable purposes in a specific community or region. Funds are usually derived from many donors and held in an endowment independently administered; income earned by the endowment is then used to make grants. Although a few community foundations may be classified by the IRS as private foundations, most are classified as public charities eligible for maximum income tax-deductible contributions from the general public. (*See also* **501(c)(3)**; **Public Charity**)

Community Fund: An organized community program which makes annual appeals to the general public for funds that are usually not retained in an endowment but are used for the ongoing operational support of local social and health service agencies. (*See also* **Federated Giving Program**)

Company-Sponsored Foundation (also referred to as Corporate Foundation): A private foundation whose grant funds are derived primarily from the contributions of a profit-making business organization. The company-sponsored foundation may maintain close ties with the donor company, but it is an independent organization with its own endowment and is subject to the same rules and regulations as other private foundations. (*See also* **Private Foundation**)

Cooperative Venture: A joint effort between or among two or more grantmakers (including foundations, corporations, and government agencies). Partners may share in funding responsibilities or contribute information and technical resources.

Corporate Giving Program: A grantmaking program established and administered within a profit-making company. Corporate giving programs do not have a separate endowment and their annual grant totals are generally more directly related to current profits. They are not subject to the same reporting requirements as private foundations. Some companies make charitable contributions through both a corporate giving program and a company-sponsored foundation.

Distribution Committee: The board responsible for making grant decisions. For community foundations, it is intended to be broadly representative of the community served by the foundation.

Donee: The recipient of a grant. (Also known as the grantee or the beneficiary.)

Donor: The individual or organization that makes a grant or contribution. (Also known as the grantor.)

Employee Matching Gift: A contribution to a charitable organization by a company employee that is matched by a similar contribution from the employer. Many corporations have employee matching gift programs in higher education that stimulate their employees to give to the college or university of their choice.

Endowment: Funds intended to be kept permanently and invested to provide income for continued support of an organization.

Expenditure Responsibility: In general, when a private foundation makes a grant to an organization that is not classified by the IRS as a "public charity," the foundation is required by law to provide some assurance that the funds will be used for the intended charitable purposes. Special reports on such grants must be filed with the IRS. Most grantee organizations are public charities and many foundations do not make "expenditure responsibility" grants.

Family Foundation: An independent private foundation whose funds are derived from members of a single family. Family members often serve as officers or board members of the foundation and have a significant role in grantmaking decisions. (*See also* **Operating Foundation**; **Private Foundation**; **Public Charity**)

Federated Giving Program: A joint fundraising effort usually administered by a nonprofit "umbrella" organization which in turn distributes contributed funds to several nonprofit agencies. United Way and community chests or funds, the United Jewish Appeal and other religious appeals, the United Negro College Fund, and joint arts councils are examples of federated giving programs. (*See also* **Community Fund**)

501(c)(3): The section of the Internal Revenue code that defines nonprofit, charitable (as broadly defined), tax-exempt organizations; 501(c)(3) organizations are further defined as public charities, private operating foundations, and private non-operating foundations. (*See also* **Operating Foundation**; **Private Foundation**; **Public Charity**)

Form 990-PF: The annual information return that all private foundations must submit to the IRS each year and which is also filed with appropriate state officials. The form requires information on the foundation's assets, income, operating expenses, contributions and grants, paid staff and salaries, program funding areas, grantmaking guidelines and restrictions, and grant application procedures.

General Purpose Foundation: An independent private foundation that awards grants in many different fields of interest. (*See also* **Special Purpose Foundation**)

General Purpose Grant: A grant made to further the general purpose or work of an organization, rather than for a specific purpose or project. (*See also* **Operating Support Grant**)

Grantee Financial Report: A report detailing how grant funds were used by an organization. Many corporations require this kind of report from grantees. A financial report generally includes a listing of all expenditures from grant funds as well as an overall organizational financial report covering revenue and expenses, assets and liabilities.

Grassroots Fundraising: Efforts to raise money from individuals or groups from the local community on a broad basis. Usually an organization's own constituents— people who live in the neighborhood served or clients of the agency's services—are the sources of these funds. Grassroots fundraising activities include membership drives, raffles, auctions, benefits, and a range of other activities.

Independent Foundation: A grantmaking organization usually classified by the IRS as a private foundation. Independent foundations may also be known as family foundations, general purpose foundations, special purpose foundations, or private non-operating foundations. The Foundation Center defines independent foundations and company-sponsored foundations separately; however, federal law normally classifies both as private, non-operating foundations subject to the same rules and requirements. (*See also* **Private Foundation**)

In-Kind Contributions: Contributions of equipment, supplies, or other property as distinguished from monetary grants. Some organizations may also donate space or staff time as an in-kind contribution.

Matching Grant: A grant that is made to match funds provided by another donor. (*See also* **Challenge Grant**; **Employee Matching Gift**)

Operating Foundation: A 501(c)(3) organization classified by the IRS as a private foundation whose primary purpose is to conduct research, social welfare, or other programs determined by its governing body or establishment charter. Some grants may be made, but the sum is generally small relative to the funds used for the foundation's own programs. (*See also* **501(c)(3)**)

Operating Support Grant: A grant to cover the regular personnel, administrative, and other expenses of an existing program or project. (*See also* **General Purpose Grant**)

Payout Requirement: The minimum amount that private foundations are required to expend for charitable purposes (includes grants and, within certain limits, the administrative cost of making grants). In general, a private foundation must meet or exceed an annual payout requirement of five percent of the average market value of the foundation's assets.

Private Foundation: A nongovernmental, nonprofit organization with funds (usually from a single source, such as an individual, family, or corporation) and program managed by its own trustees or directors that was established to maintain or aid social, educational, religious or other charitable activities serving the common welfare, primarily through the making of grants. "Private foundation" also means an organization that is tax-exempt under code section 501(c)(3) and is classified by the IRS as a private foundation as defined in the code. The code definition usually, but not always, identifies a foundation with the characteristics first described. (*See also* **501(c)(3)**; **Public Charity**)

Program Amount: Funds that are expended to support a particular program administered internally by the foundation or corporate giving program.

Program Officer: A staff member of a foundation who reviews grant proposals and processes applications for the board of trustees. Only a small percentage of foundations have program officers.

Program-Related Investment (PRI): A loan or other investment (as distinguished from a grant) made by a foundation or corporate giving program to another organization for a project related to the grantmaker's stated charitable purpose and interests. Program-related investments are often made from a revolving fund; the foundation generally expects to receive its money back with interest or some other form of return at less than current market rates, and it then becomes available for further program-related investments.

Proposal: A written application, often with supporting documents, submitted to a foundation or corporate giving program in requesting a grant. Preferred procedures and formats vary. Consult published guidelines.

Public Charity: In general, an organization that is tax-exempt under code section 501(c)(3) and is classified by the IRS as a public charity and not a private foundation. Public charities generally derive their funding or support primarily from the general public in carrying out their social, educational, religious, or other charitable activities serving the common welfare. Some public charities engage in grantmaking activities, although most engage in direct service or other tax-exempt activities. Public charities are eligible for maximum income tax-deductible contributions from the public and are not subject to the same rules and restrictions as private foundations. Some are also referred to as "public foundations" or "publicly supported organizations" and may use the term "foundation" in their names. (See also **501(c)(3)**; **Private Foundation**)

Qualifying Distributions: Expenditures of private foundations used to satisfy the annual payout requirement. These can include grants, reasonable administrative expenses, set-asides, loans and program-related investments, and amounts paid to acquire assets used directly in carrying out exempt purposes.

Query Letter: A brief letter outlining an organization's activities and its request for funding sent to a foundation or corporation to determine whether it would be appropriate to submit a full grant proposal. Many grantmakers prefer to be contacted in this way before receiving a full proposal.

RFP: Request For Proposal. When the government issues a new contract or grant program, it sends out RFPs to agencies that might be qualified to participate. The RFP lists project specifications and application procedures. A few foundations occasionally use RFPs in specific fields, but most prefer to consider proposals that are initiated by applicants.

Seed Money: A grant or contribution used to start a new project or organization. Seed grants may cover salaries and other operating expenses of a new project.

Set-Asides: Funds set aside by a foundation for a specific purpose or project that are counted as qualifying distributions toward the foundation's annual payout requirement. Amounts for the project must be paid within five years of the first set-aside.

Special Purpose Foundation: A private foundation that focuses its grantmaking activities in one or a few special areas of interest. For example, a foundation may only award grants in the area of cancer research or child development. (See also **General Purpose Foundation**)

Technical Assistance: Operational or management assistance given to nonprofit organizations. It can include fundraising assistance, budgeting and financial planning, program planning, legal advice, marketing, and other aids to management. Assistance may be offered directly by a foundation or corporate staff member, or be offered in the form of a grant to pay for the services of an outside consultant. (See also **In-Kind Contributions**)

Trustee: A member of a governing board. A foundation's board of trustees meets to review grant proposals and make decisions. Often also referred to as a "director" or "board member."

ABBREVIATIONS

The following lists contain standard abbreviations frequently used by the Foundation Center's editorial staff. These abbreviations are used most frequently in the addresses of grantmakers and the titles of corporate and grantmaker officers.

STREET ABBREVIATIONS

1st	First*	N.E.	Northeast
2nd	Second*	N.W.	Northwest
3rd	Third*	No.	Number
Apt.	Apartment	Pkwy.	Parkway
Ave.	Avenue	Pl.	Place
Bldg.	Building	Plz.	Plaza
Blvd.	Boulevard	R.R.	Rural Route
Cir.	Circle	Rd.	Road
Ct.	Court	Rm.	Room
Ctr.	Center	Rte.	Route
Dept.	Department	S.	South
Dr.	Drive	S.E.	Southeast
E.	East	S.W.	Southwest
Expwy.	Expressway	Sq.	Square
Fl.	Floor	St.	Saint
Ft.	Fort	St.	Street
Hwy.	Highway	Sta.	Station
Ln.	Lane	Ste.	Suite
M.C.	Mail Code	Terr.	Terrace
M.S.	Mail Stop	Tpke.	Turnpike
Mt.	Mount	Univ.	University
N.	North	W.	West

*Numerics used always

TWO LETTER STATE AND TERRITORY ABBREVIATIONS

AK	Alaska	NC	North Carolina
AL	Alabama	ND	North Dakota
AR	Arkansas	NE	Nebraska
AZ	Arizona	NH	New Hampshire
CA	California	NJ	New Jersey
CO	Colorado	NM	New Mexico
CT	Connecticut	NV	Nevada
DC	District of Columbia	NY	New York
DE	Delaware	OH	Ohio
FL	Florida	OK	Oklahoma
GA	Georgia	OR	Oregon
HI	Hawaii	PA	Pennsylvania
IA	Iowa	PR	Puerto Rico
ID	Idaho	RI	Rhode Island
IL	Illinois	SC	South Carolina
IN	Indiana	SD	South Dakota
KS	Kansas	TN	Tennessee
KY	Kentucky	TX	Texas
LA	Louisiana	UT	Utah
MA	Massachusetts	VA	Virginia
MD	Maryland	VI	Virgin Islands
ME	Maine	VT	Vermont
MI	Michigan	WA	Washington
MN	Minnesota	WI	Wisconsin
MO	Missouri	WV	West Virginia
MS	Mississippi	WY	Wyoming
MT	Montana		

ABBREVIATIONS USED FOR OFFICER TITLES

Acctg.	Accounting	Govt.	Government
ADM.	Admiral	Hon.	Judge
Admin.	Administration	Inf.	Information
Admin.	Administrative	Int.	Internal
Admin.	Administrator	Intl.	International
Adv.	Advertising	Jr.	Junior
Amb.	Ambassador	Lt.	Lieutenant
Assn.	Association	Ltd.	Limited
Assoc(s).	Associate(s)	Maj.	Major
Asst.	Assistant	Mfg.	Manufacturing
Bro.	Brother	Mgmt.	Management
C.A.O.	Chief Accounting Officer	Mgr.	Manager
C.A.O.	Chief Administration Officer	Mktg.	Marketing
		Msgr.	Monsignor
C.E.O.	Chief Executive Officer	Mt.	Mount
C.F.O.	Chief Financial Officer	Natl.	National
C.I.O.	Chief Information Officer	Off.	Officer
		Opers.	Operations
C.I.O.	Chief Investment Officer	Org.	Organization
		Plan.	Planning
C.O.O.	Chief Operating Officer	Pres.	President
Capt.	Captain	Prog(s).	Program(s)
Chair.	Chairperson	RADM.	Rear Admiral
Col.	Colonel	Rels.	Relations
Comm.	Committee	Rep.	Representative
Comms.	Communications	Rev.	Reverend
Commo.	Commodore	Rt. Rev.	Right Reverend
Compt.	Comptroller	Secy.	Secretary
Cont.	Controller	Secy.-Treas.	Secretary-Treasurer
Contrib(s).	Contribution(s)		
Coord.	Coordinator	Sen.	Senator
Corp.	Corporate, Corporation	Soc.	Society
Co(s).	Company(s)	Sr.	Senior
Dep.	Deputy	Sr.	Sister
Devel.	Development	Supt.	Superintendent
Dir.	Director	Supvr.	Supervisor
Distrib(s).	Distribution(s)	Svc(s).	Service(s)
Div.	Division	Tech.	Technology
Exec.	Executive	Tr.	Trustee
Ext.	External	Treas.	Treasurer
Fdn.	Foundation	Univ.	University
Fr.	Father	V.P	Vice President
Genl.	General	VADM.	Vice Admiral
Gov.	Governor	Vice-Chair.	Vice Chairperson

ADDITIONAL ABBREVIATIONS

E-mail	Electronic mail
FAX	Facsimile
LOI	Letter of Inquiry
RFP	Request for Proposals
SASE	Self-Addressed Stamped Envelope
TDD, TTY	Telecommunication Device for the Deaf
Tel.	Telephone
URL	Uniform Resource Locator (web site)

Jan.	January
Feb.	February
Mar.	March
Apr.	April
Aug.	August
Sept.	September
Oct.	October
Nov.	November
Dec.	December

RESOURCES OF THE FOUNDATION CENTER

Established in 1956 and today supported by close to 550 foundations, Foundation Center is the leading source of information about philanthropy worldwide. Through data, analysis, and training, it connects people who want to change the world to the resources they need to succeed. Foundation Center maintains the most comprehensive database on U.S. and, increasingly, global grantmakers and their grants — a robust, accessible knowledge bank for the sector. It also operates research, education, and training programs designed to advance knowledge of philanthropy at every level. Thousands of people visit Foundation Center's website each day and are served in its five library/learning centers and at more than 450 Funding Information Network locations nationwide and around the world.

ONLINE DATABASES

Foundation Directory Online
Which grantmaker is most likely to fund your organization? *Foundation Directory Online* (FDO) will help you answer this question, making it an essential tool for any grantseeker.

With detailed profiles on 140,000+ grantmakers — including U.S. and international foundations, corporations, and grantmaking public charities — FDO eliminates the guesswork from finding the right funder.

Foundation Directory Online includes:
◆ **Grantmaker profiles:** Get application information and deadlines, grant limitations, fields of interest, and geographic focus to help narrow your search.
◆ **Grants information:** Discover grants awarded to organizations similar to yours, with in-depth descriptions.
◆ **Visualization tools:** Easily map and chart a grantmaker's funding patterns by location and subject area.
◆ **Workspace:** Get the tools you need to quickly evaluate foundations, manage projects, track deadlines, and streamline your workflow.

Monthly and annual plans are available to fit your research needs.

LEARN MORE: foundationcenter.org/fdo

Foundation Grants to Individuals Online
Need a scholarship, fellowship or award? Visit the new *Foundation Grants to Individuals Online* built specifically for students, artists, researchers, and individuals like you!

$19.95: ONE MONTH
$36.95: THREE MONTHS
$59.95: SIX MONTHS
$99.95: ONE YEAR

TO SUBSCRIBE, VISIT gtionline.foundationcenter.org

TRASI (Tools and Resources for Assessing Social Impact)
Browse or search the TRASI database for proven approaches to social impact assessment, guidelines for creating and conducting an assessment, and ready-to-use tools for measuring social change. TRASI also features a community page where individuals can connect with peers and experts.
FREE

PLEASE VISIT trasi.foundationcenter.org

Foundation Maps
Foundation Maps brings to life data about U.S. and global philanthropy through extensive mapping, charting, and analytic capabilities. This interactive tool for funders is designed to facilitate more transparent, effective, and collaborative philanthropy.

LEARN MORE: maps@foundationcenter.org

Nonprofit Collaboration Database
This database provides hundreds of real-life examples of how nonprofits are working together.

PLEASE VISIT foundationcenter.org/gainknowledge/collaboration

GRANTMAKER DIRECTORIES

The Foundation Directory, 2016 Edition
Key facts include fields of interest, contact information, financials, and names of decision makers. Convenient indexes are provided for all *Foundation Directories*.
MARCH 2016 / ISBN 978-1-59542-511-9 / $215 / PUBLISHED ANNUALLY

The Foundation Directory Part 2, 2016 Edition
Thorough coverage for the next 10,000 largest foundations.
MARCH 2016 / ISBN 978-1-59542-521-8 / $185 / PUBLISHED ANNUALLY

Guide to Funding for International & Foreign Programs, 11th Edition
Profiles of more than 2,200 grantmakers that provide international relief, disaster assistance, human rights, civil liberties, community development, and education.
MAY 2012 / ISBN 978-1-59542-408-2 / $125

The Celebrity Foundation Directory
5th Digital Edition
This downloadable directory (PDF) includes detailed descriptions of more than 1,880 foundations started by VIPs in the fields of business, entertainment, politics, and sports.
NOVEMBER 2013 / ISBN 978-1-59542-456-3 / $59.95

Foundation Grants to Individuals, 24th Edition

The only publication devoted entirely to foundation grant opportunities for qualified individual applicants, this directory features more than 10,000 entries with current information including foundation name, address, program description, and application guidelines.

JULY 2015 / ISBN 978-1-59542-506-5 / $75 / PUBLISHED ANNUALLY

The PRI Directory, 3rd Edition
Charitable Loans and Other Program-Related Investments by Foundations

This *Directory* lists leading funders, recipients, project descriptions, and includes tips on how to secure and manage PRIs. Foundation listings include funder name and state; recipient name, city, and state (or country); and a description of the project funded.

PUBLISHED IN PARTERNSHIP WITH PRI MAKERS NETWORK.

JULY 2010 / ISBN 978-1-59542-214-9 / $95

Grant Guides

Designed for fundraisers who work within specific areas, 15 digital edition *Grant Guides* list actual foundation grants of $10,000 or more. *Guides* include a keyword search tool and indexes to pinpoint grants of interest to you. As a special bonus, each grantmaker entry contains a link to its *Foundation Directory Online Free* profile for even more details, all in a convenient PDF format.

2015 EDITIONS / $39.95 EACH

TO ORDER, VISIT foundationcenter.org/grantguides

FUNDRAISING GUIDES

After the Grant
The Nonprofit's Guide to Good Stewardship

An invaluable and practical resource for anyone seeking funding from foundations, this *Guide* will help you manage your grant to ensure you get the next one.

MARCH 2010 / ISBN 978-1-59542-301-6 / $39.95

Foundation Fundamentals, 8th Edition
Expert advice on fundraising research and proposal development.

A go-to resource in academic programs on the nonprofit sector. *Foundation Fundamentals* describes foundation funding provides advice on research strategies, including how to best use *Foundation Directory Online*.

MARCH 2008 / ISBN 978-1-59542-156-2 / $39.95

Foundation Center's Guide to Proposal Writing, 6th Edition

Author Jane Geever provides detailed instructions on preparing successful grant proposals, incorporating the results of interviews with 40 U.S. grantmakers.

MAY 2012 / ISBN 978-1-59542-404-4 / $39.95

Guía Para Escribir Propuestas

The Spanish-language translation of *Foundation Center's Guide to Proposal Writing*, 5th edition.

MARCH 2008 / ISBN 978-1-595423-158-6 / $39.95

The Grantseeker's Guide to Winning Proposals

A collection of 35 actual proposals submitted to international, regional, corporate, and local foundations. Each includes remarks by the program officer who approved the grant.

AUGUST 2008 / ISBN 978-1-59542-195-1 / $39.95

Securing Your Organization's Future
A Complete Guide to Fundraising Strategies, Revised Edition

Author Michael Seltzer explains how to strengthen your nonprofit's capacity to raise funds and achieve long-term financial stability.

FEBRUARY 2001 / ISBN 0-87954-900-9 / $39.95

NONPROFIT MANAGEMENT GUIDES

America's Nonprofit Sector
A Primer

The third edition of this publication, by Lester Salamon, is ideal for people who want a thorough, accessible introduction to the nonprofit sector—as well as the nation's social welfare system.

MARCH 2012 / ISBN 978-1-59542-360-3 / $24.95

The 21st Century Nonprofit
Managing in the Age of Governance

This book details the significant improvements in nonprofit management practice that have taken place in recent years.

SEPTEMBER 2009 / ISBN 978-1-59542-249-1 / $39.95

Foundations and Public Policy

This book presents a valuable framework for foundations as they plan or implement their engagement with public policy.

Published in partnership with The Center on Philanthropy & Public Policy.

MARCH 2009 / ISBN 978-1-59542-218-7 / $34.95

Local Mission-Global Vision
Community Foundations in the 21st Century

This book examines the new role of community foundations, exploring the potential impact of transnational evolution on organized philanthropy.

Published in partnership with Transatlantic Community Foundations Network.

AUGUST 2008 / ISBN 978-1-59542-204-0 / $34.95

Wise Decision-Making in Uncertain Times
Using Nonprofit Resources Effectively

This book highlights the critical challenges of fiscal sustainability for nonprofits, and encourages organizations to take a more expansive approach to funding outreach.

AUGUST 2006 / ISBN 1-59542-099-1 / $34.95

Effective Economic Decision-Making
by Nonprofit Organizations

Editor Dennis R. Young offers practical guidelines to help nonprofit managers advance their mission while balancing the interests of trustees, funders, government, and staff.

DECEMBER 2003 / ISBN 1-931923-69-8 / $34.95

The Board Member's Book
Making a Difference in Voluntary Organizations, 3rd Edition

Written by former Independent Sector President Brian O'Connell, this is the perfect guide to the issues, challenges, and possibilities facing a nonprofit organization and its board.

MAY 2003 / ISBN 1-931923-17-5 / $29.95

Philanthropy's Challenge
Building Nonprofit Capacity Through Venture Grantmaking
Author Paul Firstenberg explores the roles of grantmaker and grantee within various models of venture grantmaking. He outlines the characteristics that qualify an organization for a venture grant, and outlines the steps a grantmaker can take to build the grantees' organizational capacity.
FEBRUARY 2003 / SOFTBOUND: ISBN 1-931923-15-9 / $29.95
HARDBOUND: ISBN 1-931923-53-1 / $39.95

Investing in Capacity Building
A Guide to High-Impact Approaches
Author Barbara Blumenthal helps grantmakers and consultants design better methods to help nonprofits, while showing nonprofit managers how to get more effective support.
NOVEMBER 2003 / ISBN 1-931923-65-5 / $34.95

ASSOCIATES PROGRAM

For just $3,000 a year or $2,500 for six months, the Associates Program experts will answer all of your questions about foundation giving, corporate philanthropy, and individual donors.

You will receive online access to several lists that are updated monthly, including new grantmakers and grantmaker application deadlines. In addition, you will receive most results within the next business day.

JOIN NOW AT foundationcenter.org/associates

ADDITIONAL ONLINE RESOURCES

foundationcenter.org

◆ *Philanthropy News Digest* is a daily digest of philanthropy-related articles. Read interviews with leaders, look for RFPs, learn from the experts, and share ideas with others in the field.

◆ Foundation Stats is a web-based tool that provides free and open access to a wealth of data on the U.S. foundation community. The intuitive platform can be used by anyone to generate thousands of custom tables and charts on the size, scope, and giving priorities of the U.S. foundation community.

◆ Access research studies to track trends in foundation growth and giving in grantmaker policies and practices.

◆ To stay current on the latest research trends visit foundationcenter.org/gainknowledge.

grantspace.org

GrantSpace, Foundation Center's learning community for the social sector, features resources organized under the 13 most common subject areas of funding research — including health, education, and the arts.

◆ Dig into the GrantSpace knowledge base for answers to more than 150 questions asked about grantseeking and nonprofits.

◆ Stay up-to-date on classes and events happening in person and online with the GrantSpace training calendar.

◆ Add your voice and help build a community-driven knowledge base: share your expertise, rate content, ask questions, and add comments.

glasspockets.org

Glasspockets provides the data, resources, examples, and action steps foundations need to understand the value of transparency, be more open in their own communications, and help shed more light on how private organizations are serving the public good.

◆ Learn about the online transparency and accountability practices of the largest foundations, and see who has "glass pockets."

◆ Transparency Talk, the Glasspockets blog and podcast series, highlights strategies, findings, and best practices related to foundation transparency.

◆ The Giving Pledge is an effort that encourages the world's wealthiest individuals and families to commit the majority of their assets to philanthropic causes. Eye on the Giving Pledge offers an in-depth picture of Giving Pledge participants, their charitable activities, and the potential impact of the Giving Pledge.

◆ Learn more about the Reporting Commitment, an initiative aimed at developing more timely, accurate, and precise reporting on the flow of philanthropic dollars.

grantcraft.org

GrantCraft combines the practical wisdom of funders worldwide with the expertise of Foundation Center to improve the practice of philanthropy. Since 2001, GrantCraft has delivered the knowledge funders need to be strategic and effective in their work, addressing questions funders face across various strategies and issue areas.

◆ Search the 13 content types including guides, takeaways, discussions, infographics, and videos to find real-life examples from funders.

◆ Register for free access to the monthly newsletter, personal dashboard, and to share content and comment.

◆ All content is free to use and share.

issuelab.org

IssueLab provides free access to resources that analyze the world's most pressing social, economic, and environmental challenges and their potential solutions. The platform contains thousands of case studies, evaluations, white papers, and issue briefs, and represents one the largest collections of social sector knowledge.

◆ Search and browse the database by social issue area, author, publishing organization, or geography.

◆ Learn how to add resources to the IssueLab collection.

DESCRIPTIVE DIRECTORY

ALABAMA

1

Abahac Inc.
3850 River Run Trail
Birmingham, AL   35243-4702

Established in 1988 in Alabama.
Donor: Eugene Britt Butler.
Foundation type: Independent foundation.
Financial data (yr. ended 12/31/13): Assets, $4,295,599 (M); gifts received, $121,052; expenditures, $212,382; qualifying distributions, $200,832; giving activities include $198,000 for 17 grants (high: $36,000; low: $1,000).
Purpose and activities: Giving primarily for the environment, including streams and rivers.
Fields of interest: Environment; Human services.
Type of support: Convening; General support; Land acquisitions; Seed money.
Limitations: Applications not accepted. Giving primarily in the southeastern U.S., with an emphasis on AL. No support for religious programs except when they serve children or the needy. No grants to individuals.
Application information: Unsolicited requests for funds not accepted.
    Board meeting date(s): June and July
Officers: Eugene Britt Butler, Pres.; Janice Butler Tucker, Sr. V.P.; Judy W. Butler, V.P. and Secy.-Treas.; Ellen Kate B. Brackin, V.P.
EIN: 570884084

2

Abroms Charitable Foundation, Inc.
474 Botanical Pl.
Birmingham, AL   35223-1168

Established in 1970 in Alabama.
Donors: Harold L. Abroms; Judith E. Abroms.
Foundation type: Independent foundation.
Financial data (yr. ended 11/30/13): Assets, $5,209,206 (M); gifts received, $75,000; expenditures, $303,216; qualifying distributions, $269,734; giving activities include $267,250 for 29 grants (high: $55,000; low: $1,000).
Fields of interest: Arts and culture; Education; Nonprofits; Judaism; Antidiscrimination; Human services.
Type of support: Regranting.
Limitations: Applications not accepted. Giving primarily in AL. No grants to individuals.
Application information: Contributes only to pre-selected organizations.
Officers: Harold L. Abroms, Pres. and Treas.; James M. Abroms, V.P.; Judith E. Abroms, Secy.
EIN: 237058629

3

Adams Foundation
P.O. Box 4562
Montgomery, AL   36103-4562   (334) 301-0597
Contact: Samuel Adams, Secy.-Treas. and Tr.

Established in 1992 in Alabama.
Donor: Ralph W. Adams, Jr.
Foundation type: Independent foundation.
Financial data (yr. ended 12/31/13): Assets, $1,048,453 (M); expenditures, $148,618; qualifying distributions, $134,000; giving activities include $134,000 for 12 grants (high: $30,000; low: $1,000).
Purpose and activities: Giving primarily for education, health and the arts.
Fields of interest: Theater; Education; Higher education; Diabetes; Human services; Scouting programs.
Type of support: Scholarships.
Limitations: Applications accepted. Giving limited to Montgomery, AL.
Application information: Application form required.
    Initial approach: Proposal
    Deadline(s): None
Officer and Trustee: Samuel Adams, Secy.-Treas. and Trustee.
EIN: 631059010

4

The Mabel Amos Memorial Fund
c/o Regions Bank, Trust Dept.
P.O. Box 2450
Montgomery, AL   36102-2450   (334) 230-6100
Contact: John Bell

Established in 2002 in Alabama.
Donor: Mable Amos.
Foundation type: Independent foundation.
Financial data (yr. ended 12/31/13): Assets, $6,928,536 (M); expenditures, $503,617; qualifying distributions, $214,179; giving activities include $47,527 for 2 grants (high: $36,264; low: $11,263), and $166,652 for 17 grants to individuals (high: $15,000; low: $1,625).
Purpose and activities: Support for education, including scholarship awards to individuals.
Fields of interest: Higher education.
Type of support: Scholarships; Student aid.
Limitations: Applications accepted. Giving primarily in AL.
Application information: Application form required.
    Initial approach: Letter
    Deadline(s): Typically a date in Apr.
Trustee: Regions Bank.
Board Members: Tom Albritton; John Bell; Rick Clifton.
EIN: 527245836

5

Harold and Kayrita Anderson Family Foundation
201 S. Court St., Ste. 610
Florence, AL   35630-5632

Established in 2002 in Alabama.
Donors: Charles C. Anderson; Kayrita Anderson; Hilda Anderson; Harold M. Anderson; Kevin Carroll; Terry and Susan Anderson Foundation; Charlie and Moll Anderson Foundation.
Foundation type: Independent foundation.
Financial data (yr. ended 12/31/13): Assets, $60,331 (M); gifts received, $196,995; expenditures, $245,170; qualifying distributions, $245,099; giving activities include $208,156 for 14 grants (high: $60,000; low: $50).
Purpose and activities: Giving primarily for higher education, medical research, and social services.

Fields of interest: Higher education; Diseases and conditions; Parkinson's disease; Human services; Women's services.
Type of support: Research; Research and evaluation.
Limitations: Applications not accepted. Giving on a national basis, with emphasis on Atlanta, GA. No grants to individuals.
Application information: Contributes only to pre-selected organizations.
Directors: Charles C. Anderson; Harold M. Anderson; Kayrita Anderson.
EIN: 470867588

6

The Clyde and Summer Anderson Foundation
P.O. Box 19768
Birmingham, AL   35219-9768

Established in 1996 in Alabama.
Donors: Clyde B. Anderson; Charles C. Anderson.
Foundation type: Independent foundation.
Financial data (yr. ended 12/31/13): Assets, $1,087,814 (M); expenditures, $241,480; qualifying distributions, $222,997; giving activities include $222,997 for 22 grants (high: $75,000; low: $500).
Fields of interest: Arts and culture; Arts education; Design; Education; Elementary and secondary education; Higher education; Zoos; Philanthropy; Nonprofits; Health; Diseases and conditions; Public libraries; Christianity; Human services; Child welfare.
Type of support: Regranting.
Limitations: Applications not accepted. Giving primarily in AL. No grants to individuals.
Application information: Contributes only to pre-selected organizations.
Directors: Clyde B. Anderson; Summer Anderson; Terry C. Anderson.
EIN: 721368331

7

The Jake Aronov Charitable Foundation
3500 Eastern Blvd.
Montgomery, AL   36116-1781

Donors: Jake F. Aronov; Teri Aronov.
Foundation type: Operating foundation.
Financial data (yr. ended 11/30/13): Assets, $268,125 (M); gifts received, $635,017; expenditures, $370,953; qualifying distributions, $370,116; giving activities include $370,116 for 20 grants (high: $200,000; low: $36).
Fields of interest: Theater; Nonprofits; Judaism.
Type of support: Regranting.
Limitations: Applications not accepted. Giving primarily in AL, GA, NJ, and NY. No grants to individuals.
Application information: Contributes only to pre-selected organizations.
Officer and Director: Jake F. Aronov, Chair. and Director.
EIN: 631215344

8

Atlantis Educational Foundation

c/o Eric Auyang
2101 Dorchester Dr.
Mobile, AL 36695-2920
E-mail: contact@aefinc.org; Main URL: http://
aefinc.org

Donors: Eric Auyang; Sunny Auyang.
Foundation type: Independent foundation.
Financial data (yr. ended 12/31/14): Assets,
$268,721 (M); gifts received, $226,587;
expenditures, $178,195; qualifying distributions,
$178,195; giving activities include $175,500 for 3
grants (high: $105,000; low: $18,000).
Purpose and activities: Provide children from the
poorest parts of China with an opportunity to
complete a minimum of high school and possibly a
college education.
Fields of interest: Education.
International interests: China.
Limitations: Applications not accepted. Giving
primarily in China.
Application information: Unsolicited requests for
funds not accepted.
Directors: Angela Auyang; Eric Auyang; Sunny
Auyang.
EIN: 450889464

9

The Charles Barkley Foundation, Inc.

2 N. 20th St., Ste. 1400
Birmingham, AL 35203-4051
Application address: c/o Glenn Guthrie, 407
Woodward Rd., Trussville, AL 35173-3216,
tel.: (205) 251-8000

Established in 1995 in Alabama.
Donors: Stewart St Production; Mobile AL Bowl;
Brunos Memorial Classic; Barkley Enterprises, Inc.;
Celebrity Golf Championship; Alabama Sports
Foundation; Valley of the Sun YMCA.
Foundation type: Independent foundation.
Financial data (yr. ended 12/31/13): Assets,
$1,593,079 (M); gifts received, $1,504;
expenditures, $211,823; qualifying distributions,
$197,734; giving activities include $197,734 for 26
grants (high: $36,000; low: $1,000).
Purpose and activities: Support for education,
primarily through scholarship funds.
Fields of interest: Education; Higher education;
Human services; Youth development.
Type of support: Equipment; Scholarships; Student
aid.
Limitations: Applications accepted. Giving primarily
in AL.
Application information: Application form required.
Initial approach: Completed application form
Deadline(s): None
Officer: Glenn Guthrie, Fdn. Mgr.
Directors: Charles Barkley; H.B. Lee, Jr.
EIN: 631159820

10

The Battle Family Foundation

6552 Waterfront Dr.
Tuscaloosa, AL 35406-3266

Established in 1997 in Georgia.
Donors: William R. Battle III; Alice Ann Battle;
William P. Battle.

Foundation type: Independent foundation.
Financial data (yr. ended 12/31/13): Assets,
$3,425,184 (M); gifts received, $20,000;
expenditures, $162,640; qualifying distributions,
$129,861; giving activities include $129,861 for 7
grants (high: $50,000; low: $1,000).
Fields of interest: Education; Diseases and
conditions.
Type of support: Research.
Limitations: Applications not accepted. Giving
primarily in Tuscaloosa, AL. No grants to individuals.
Application information: Contributes only to
pre-selected organizations.
Trustee: William R. Battle III.
EIN: 586343708

11

Birmingham Hide & Tallow Charitable Foundation Inc.

P.O. Box 1596
Birmingham, AL 35201-1596
Main URL: http://bhtonline.com/
bht-charitable-foundation

Established in 2005 in Alabama.
Donor: Birmingham Hide & Tallow, Inc.
Foundation type: Company-sponsored foundation.
Financial data (yr. ended 12/31/13): Assets,
$52,595 (M); gifts received, $25,000;
expenditures, $164,464; qualifying distributions,
$163,600; giving activities include $163,600 for 48
grants (high: $50,600; low: $100).
Purpose and activities: The foundation supports
camps and organizations involved with education,
health, cancer, human services, and Christianity.
Fields of interest: Education; Health; Human
services.
Type of support: General support; Program
development.
Limitations: Applications not accepted. Giving
primarily in Birmingham, AL. No grants to
individuals.
Application information: Unsolicited requests for
funds not accepted.
Officers: Marsha Vickers, Pres.; Julia V. Wright, V.P.;
Michael S. Glenn, Secy.-Treas.
EIN: 202077546

12

The Black Belt Community Foundation, Inc.

609 Lauderdale St.
P.O. Box 2020
Selma, AL 36702-2020 (334) 874-1126
Contact: Felecia L. Jones, Pres. and Exec. Dir.
FAX: (334) 874-1131;
E-mail: info@blackbeltfound.org; Toll-free tel.: (866)
874-1126; Main URL: http://blackbeltfound.org
Facebook: https://www.facebook.com/BBCF2004
Twitter: https://twitter.com/BlackBeltFound

Established in 2003 in Alabama.
Foundation type: Community foundation.
Financial data (yr. ended 12/31/13): Assets,
$1,894,454 (M); gifts received, $353,537;
expenditures, $753,871; giving activities include
$226,411 for 7+ grants (high: $24,611).
Purpose and activities: The foundation promotes
community development in the Black Belt region of
Alabama.

Fields of interest: Arts and culture; Education;
Environment; Health; Public affairs; Community and
economic development; Economic development;
Human services; Youth development; Children and
youth; Children; Adolescents; Adults; Young adults;
Seniors; Females; Female children and youth;
Female adults; Males; Male children and youth;
Male adults; Male young adults; LGBTQ people;
Lesbians; Gay men; Transgender people; Single
parents; Ethnic and racial groups; People of African
descent; People of Latin American descent;
Indigenous peoples; American Indians; Homeless
people; Low-income and poor people; Incarcerated
people; Victims of crime and abuse; People with
physical disabilities; People with vision
impairments; People with psychosocial disabilities;
People with HIV/AIDS; Terminally ill people;
Substance abusers; Military personnel.
Type of support: Annual campaigns; Pro bono
consulting services; In-kind gifts; Capital
campaigns; Program development; Scholarships;
Research; Technical assistance.
Limitations: Applications accepted. Giving primarily
to Bullock, Choctaw, Dallas, Greene, Hale,
Lowndes, Macon, Marengo, Perry, Pickens, Sumter,
and Wilcox counties, AL. No support for religious
organizations for religious purposes, political
organizations or candidates for public office, or
school systems. No grants to individuals, or for
national fundraising drives, tickets for benefits,
lobbying activities, or scholarship or endowment
funds.
Publications: Application guidelines; Annual report;
Informational brochure; Newsletter.
Application information: Attendance at one of the
Community Awareness Grant Seekers Workshops is
mandatory for all applicant, including new and
returning organizations; visit web site for application
information. Grants range from $500 to $3,000.
Application form required.
Initial approach: Contact foundation
Deadline(s): Apr. 15
Board meeting date(s): Jan., Mar., May, July, Sept.
and Nov.
Final notification: June
Officers and Directors: Felecia L. Jones, Pres. and
Exec. Dir.; RaSheda Workman, Secy. and Director;
Dr. Richard Holland, Treas. and Director; Dr.
Royrickers Cook; Calvin Harkness; Walter Hill;
Thelma L. Hogue; Barbara Howard; Jerria Martin;
George McMillan; Cathy McVay; Virginia Norman;
Erica Robinson; Sheryl Smedley; Saint Thomas;
Kenneth Webb; Lillian Wideman; Dr. Carol Zippert.
EIN: 631270745

13

The Mildred W. Blount Educational & Charitable Foundation

P.O. Box 607
Tallassee, AL 36078-0007 (334) 283-4931
Contact: Arnold B. Dopson, Chair.

Established in 1981 in Alabama.
Donor: Mildred W. Blount‡.
Foundation type: Independent foundation.
Financial data (yr. ended 06/30/13): Assets,
$2,989,256 (M); gifts received, $25; expenditures,
$181,357; qualifying distributions, $171,939;
giving activities include $170,000 for 28 grants
(high: $54,000; low: $1,000).
Fields of interest: Elementary education; Secondary
education; Higher education; Hospital care;

Community and economic development; Catholicism.

Type of support: General support; Scholarships; Student aid.

Limitations: Applications accepted. Giving limited to Elmore County, AL.

Application information: Application form required.

Initial approach: Proposal

Deadline(s): Early May

Officers: Arnold Dopson, Chair.; Daniel P. Wilbanks, Vice-Chair.; Jimmy R. Norrell, Secy.

Trustees: Ben Atkinson; Lloyd F. Emfinger, Jr.; Gary Fuller; Charles Funderburk; Hollis Mann; Jennie Rinehart; Teddy Taylor; Josephine M. Venable.

EIN: 630817472

14

Bradley Arant Boult Cummings Charitable Foundation

1 Federal Pl.

1819 5th Ave. N.

Birmingham, AL 35203

Main URL: http://www.babc.com/babc_foundation

Donor: Bradley Arant Boult Cummings, LLP.

Foundation type: Company-sponsored foundation.

Financial data (yr. ended 12/31/12): Assets, $100 (M); gifts received, $142,850; expenditures, $142,850; qualifying distributions, $142,850; giving activities include $142,850 for 42 grants (high: $26,000; low: $100).

Fields of interest: Higher education; Law education; Human services.

Limitations: Applications not accepted.

Application information: Unsolicited requests for funds not accepted.

Officers and Directors: K. Wood Herren, Pres. and Director; Paul P. Bolus, V.P. and Director; Andy Murray, V.P. and Director; Glenn Glover, Secy. and Director.

EIN: 271665189

15

Brinkley Foundation

2340 Woodcrest Pl.

Birmingham, AL 35209

Established in 1968 in Tennessee.

Donor: Hugh M. Brinkley†.

Foundation type: Independent foundation.

Financial data (yr. ended 12/31/14): Assets, $4,027,638; expenditures, $229,068; qualifying distributions, $202,978.

Fields of interest: Arts and culture; Education; Environment; Animal welfare; Health; Hospital care; Christianity; Child welfare.

Limitations: Applications not accepted. Giving limited to the Memphis, TN.

Application information: Unsolicited requests for funds not accepted.

Trustees: Iberia Bank; Argent Trust Company of Tennessee.

EIN: 626079631

16

Stokes and Sarah Brown Charitable Foundation

c/o Regions Bank Trust Department

P.O. Box 2886

Mobile, AL 36652-2886 (615) 748-2922

Established in 2005 in Tennessee.

Donor: J. Stokes Brown.

Foundation type: Independent foundation.

Financial data (yr. ended 01/31/14): Assets, $4,937,404 (M); expenditures, $223,095; qualifying distributions, $186,110; giving activities include $177,300 for 7 grants (high: $56,000; low: $5,000).

Fields of interest: Higher education; Health; Public libraries; Christianity; Human services.

Limitations: Applications accepted. Giving primarily in Robertson County, TN, and surrounding communities. No grants to individuals.

Application information: Application form required.

Initial approach: Contact foundation for application form

Deadline(s): Oct. 1

Trustee: Regions Bank.

Advisory Committee Members: Virginia Sory Brown; Joe Gaston; William R. Goodman III; Evelyn A. Smith.

EIN: 260110679

17

Angelo and Ann Bruno Family Foundation

(formerly Ann and Angelo Bruno Foundation)

100 Grandview Pl., Ste. 500

Birmingham, AL 35243-1963

Contact: Suzanne Bruno Bowness, V.P.

Established in 1980 in Alabama.

Donors: Angelo J. Bruno; Suzanne Bruno Bowness; Alan Bruno†; David Bruno; Kenneth Bruno; Ronald Bruno.

Foundation type: Independent foundation.

Financial data (yr. ended 12/31/13): Assets, $3,178,132 (M); expenditures, $342,404; qualifying distributions, $307,933; giving activities include $307,933 for 24 grants (high: $75,000; low: $500).

Purpose and activities: Giving primarily to Roman Catholic organizations, including health and human services outreach.

Fields of interest: Elementary and secondary education; Higher education; Nonprofits; Diseases and conditions; Catholicism; Human services; Homeless people; People with disabilities.

Type of support: General support; Scholarships; Research; Research and evaluation; Regranting.

Limitations: Applications not accepted. Giving primarily in the Birmingham, AL, area. No grants to individuals.

Application information: Unsolicited requests for funds not accepted.

Officers: Ronald Bruno, Chair.; Ann Bruno, Pres. and Secy.-Treas.; Suzanne Bruno Bowness, V.P.

EIN: 630819540

18

Bynum Foundation

c/o Regions Bank, Trust Dept.

P.O. Box 2886

Mobile, AL 36652-2886

Established in 2007 in Alabama.

Donor: Jessie Sue Bynum†.

Foundation type: Independent foundation.

Financial data (yr. ended 12/31/14): Assets, $3,006,137 (M); expenditures, $186,411; qualifying distributions, $162,129; giving activities include $152,090 for 10 grants (high: $31,640; low: $5,040).

Fields of interest: Arts and culture; Education; Religion.

Limitations: Applications not accepted. Giving primarily in AL. No grants to individuals.

Application information: Unsolicited requests for funds not accepted.

Officer: Andrew Skelton, Chair.

Board Members: Graham Skelton; Mark Skelton, Jr.; Mark Skelton, Sr.; William Tally.

Trustee: Regions Bank.

EIN: 203859323

19

The Caddell Foundation

2700 Lagoon Park Dr.

Montgomery, AL 36109-1110 (334) 272-7723

Contact: Earl Jones

Donor: Caddell Construction Co., Inc.

Foundation type: Company-sponsored foundation.

Financial data (yr. ended 12/31/13): Assets, $7,651,422 (M); expenditures, $322,828; qualifying distributions, $313,459; giving activities include $313,459 for 15 grants (high: $100,000; low: $2,936).

Purpose and activities: The foundation supports fairs and festivals and organizations involved with performing arts, higher education, and cancer.

Fields of interest: Performing arts; Theater; Music; Orchestral music; Higher education; Nonprofits; Cancers; Festivals.

Type of support: General support; Regranting.

Limitations: Applications accepted. Giving primarily in Montgomery, AL. No grants to individuals.

Application information: Application form required.

Initial approach: Letter

Deadline(s): None

Officers and Directors: John A. Caddell, Pres. and Director; Joyce K. Caddell, Secy.-Treas. and Director; Cathy L. Caddell; Christopher P. Caddell; Jeffrey P. Caddell; John K. Caddell; Michael A. Caddell.

EIN: 631133304

20

The Chester Foundation

2000 Morris Ave., Ste. 1200

Birmingham, AL 35203

Donors: Stephen F. Snyder; Jamie S. Snyder.

Foundation type: Independent foundation.

Financial data (yr. ended 12/31/13): Assets, $3,966,120 (M); expenditures, $212,113; qualifying distributions, $179,000; giving activities include $179,000 for 8 grants (high: $70,000; low: $2,000).

Fields of interest: Education.

Limitations: Applications not accepted. Giving primarily in Boca Raton and Delray Beach, FL.

Application information: Unsolicited requests for funds not accepted.

Officers and Directors: Stephen F. Snyder, Pres. and Director; Barron F. Snyder, V.P. and Secy. and Director; Jamie S. Snyder, V.P. and Director; Therese Snyder.

EIN: 263899958

21
Christian Workers Foundation of Alabama Inc
5181 Desoto Caverns Pkwy.
Childersburg, AL 35044-9713

Established in 2001 in Alabama.
Donor: Allen W. Mathis, Jr.
Foundation type: Independent foundation.
Financial data (yr. ended 06/30/13): Assets, $7,095,507 (M); expenditures, $397,683; qualifying distributions, $330,000; giving activities include $330,000 for 1 grant.
Purpose and activities: The foundation supports evangelical para-church organizations with which board members have a relationship.
Fields of interest: Christianity.
Limitations: Applications not accepted. Giving on a national basis. No grants to individuals.
Application information: Unsolicited requests for funds not accepted.
Trustee: Allen W. Mathis III.
EIN: 311745056

22
The David J. Cooper Charitable Foundation, Inc.
P.O. Box 1566
Mobile, AL 36633-1566

Donors: David J. Cooper, Sr.; Cooper T. Smith Stevedoring Co., Inc.; Crimson Shipping Company, Inc.
Foundation type: Independent foundation.
Financial data (yr. ended 12/31/13): Assets, $6,701,737 (M); expenditures, $303,567; qualifying distributions, $264,300; giving activities include $258,300 for 35 grants (high: $42,000; low: $500).
Fields of interest: Arts and culture; Education; Religion.
Limitations: Applications not accepted. Giving primarily in AL.
Application information: Unsolicited requests for funds not accepted.
Directors: Margaret Cooper Biggs; David J. Cooper, Jr.; David J. Cooper, Sr.; Joanne K. Cooper; Ashleigh Cooper Leland.
EIN: 263868978

23
Angus R. Cooper II Family Foundation, Inc.
P.O. Box 1566
Mobile, AL 36633-1566

Donors: Cooper T. Smith Stevedoring Co., Inc.; Angus R. Cooper III.
Foundation type: Independent foundation.
Financial data (yr. ended 12/31/13): Assets, $185,251 (M); gifts received, $200,000; expenditures, $162,005; qualifying distributions, $162,000; giving activities include $162,000 for 5 grants (high: $100,000; low: $1,000).
Fields of interest: Education; University education; Domesticated animals; Health.
Limitations: Applications not accepted. Giving primarily in AL and LA.
Application information: Unsolicited requests for funds not accepted.

Directors: Angus R. Cooper II; Angus R. Cooper III; Scott H. Cooper; Claire Ellen Cooper Stephens.
EIN: 263869196

24
Ione C. Davis Trust
c/o Regions Bank
P.O. Box 2886
Mobile, AL 36652-2886 2516901024

Established in 1985 in Indiana.
Foundation type: Independent foundation.
Financial data (yr. ended 12/31/14): Assets, $3,265,382; expenditures, $247,145; qualifying distributions, $199,149.
Fields of interest: University education; Medical education; Sororities and fraternities; Human services.
Limitations: Applications not accepted. Giving primarily in IN. No grants to individuals.
Application information: Contributes only to pre-selected organizations.
Trustee: Regions Bank.
EIN: 356413272

25
Day Family Foundation
2001 Park Pl. Twr., Ste. 320
Birmingham, AL 35203-4800

Established in 1979 in New York.
Donor: H. Corbin Day.
Foundation type: Independent foundation.
Financial data (yr. ended 07/31/13): Assets, $305,124 (M); expenditures, $159,249; qualifying distributions, $153,200; giving activities include $150,200 for 40 grants (high: $30,000; low: $100).
Purpose and activities: Giving primarily for the arts, education, and health and human services.
Fields of interest: Arts and culture; Education; Human services.
Limitations: Applications not accepted. Giving primarily in AL, NJ, and NY. No grants to individuals.
Application information: Contributes only to pre-selected organizations.
Trustees: James D. Davis; H. Corbin Day.
EIN: 133025969

26
The Dixon Foundation
1 Chase Corporate Ctr., Ste 400
Birmingham, AL 35244-7001 (205) 313-6501

Established in 1986 in Alabama.
Donor: Edwin W. Dixon.
Foundation type: Operating foundation.
Financial data (yr. ended 12/31/13): Assets, $8,994,786 (M); expenditures, $953,907; qualifying distributions, $617,938.
Purpose and activities: The foundation primarily awards grants to ministers of the North Alabama Conference of the United Methodist Church for continuing study and programs; support also for health organizations, medical research, and children's services.
Fields of interest: Adult education; Pediatrics; Diseases and conditions; Presbyterianism; Child welfare.

Type of support: Continuing support; Grants to individuals; Program development; Fellowships; Research.
Limitations: Applications accepted. Giving primarily to residents of, and organizations in Birmingham, AL and central AL.
Application information:
Initial approach: Letter
Deadline(s): Sept. 30
Board meeting date(s): Usually 3 times per year
Officers: Alice D. Grotnes, Pres.; Christi C. Dixon, V.P. and Secy.; Joy Levio, V.P. and Treas.; David E. Dixon, V.P.
Director: Lovie K. Montgomery.
Number of staff: 2 part-time professional.
EIN: 630944809

27
The Frank & Fred Friedman Family Foundation
(formerly The Frank and Fred Friedman Foundation)
P.O. Box 430229
Birmingham, AL 35243-1229
E-mail: fredf3443@aol.com

Established in 1990 in Alabama.
Donor: Frank Friedman.
Foundation type: Independent foundation.
Financial data (yr. ended 03/31/13): Assets, $10,778,068 (M); expenditures, $763,528; qualifying distributions, $438,234; giving activities include $438,234 for 97 grants (high: $105,000; low: $100).
Fields of interest: Education; Nonprofits; Health; Diseases and conditions; Judaism; Human services.
Type of support: Annual campaigns; Matching grants; Capital campaigns; Capital and infrastructure; Curriculum development; Regranting.
Limitations: Applications not accepted. Giving limited to Birmingham, AL, and the surrounding counties. No grants to individuals.
Application information: Contributes only to pre-selected organizations.
Board meeting date(s): Biannually
Officers: Fred H. Friedman, Pres. and Treas.; Brenda Friedman, Secy.
Directors: Jeremy Cohen; Leah Cohen; Jordan Friedman.
EIN: 630921651

28
C. D. Helen and Jeff Glaze Foundation
P.O. Box 160427
Mobile, AL 36616-1427
Application address: c/o Stova McFadden, V.P., 718 Downtowner Blvd., Mobile, AL 36609, tel.: (251) 342-9172

Established in 1992 in Alabama.
Donor: Helen M. Glaze†.
Foundation type: Independent foundation.
Financial data (yr. ended 06/30/13): Assets, $5,679,035 (M); expenditures, $299,103; qualifying distributions, $287,962; giving activities include $240,000 for 34 grants (high: $20,000; low: $2,500).
Fields of interest: Arts and culture; Education; Human services.
Limitations: Applications accepted. Giving primarily in Mobile, AL. No grants to individuals.
Application information:

Initial approach: Letter
Deadline(s): None
Officers and Directors: Stova F. McFadden, V.P. and Director; Jeffery A. Head, Secy. and Director; John M. Sirmon, Treas. and Director.
EIN: 636174358

29
The Goodrich Foundation
(formerly Henry C. & Billie G. Goodrich Foundation)
c/o Synovus Trust Co.
800 Shades Creek Pkwy., Ste. 225
Birmingham, AL 35209-4526

Donors: Billie G. Goodrich; Henry C. Goodrich.
Foundation type: Independent foundation.
Financial data (yr. ended 12/31/13): Assets, $1,624,407 (M); expenditures, $327,538; qualifying distributions, $313,844; giving activities include $305,000 for 17 grants (high: $100,000; low: $500).
Purpose and activities: Giving primarily for education, the environment, and human services, including youth and family services.
Fields of interest: Arts and culture; Education; Secondary education; Natural resources; Nonprofits; Hospital care; Diseases and conditions; Human services; Family services; Child welfare.
Type of support: Regranting.
Limitations: Giving primarily in AL, with emphasis on Birmingham. No grants to individuals.
Officers and Trustees: William Goodrich, Chair. and Trustee; Frances Goodrich, Secy.; Sydney Goodrich Green; Synovus Trust Co.
EIN: 630907896

30
Joe Lee Griffin Foundation
P.O. Box 55765
Birmingham, AL 35255-5765

Established in 1989 in Alabama.
Donors: Nasco North Central, Inc.; Joe Lee Griffin†.
Foundation type: Independent foundation.
Financial data (yr. ended 11/30/13): Assets, $4,083,786 (L); expenditures, $209,849; qualifying distributions, $186,800; giving activities include $184,300 for 32 grants (high: $40,500; low: $500).
Fields of interest: Arts and culture; Education; Religion.
Type of support: General support.
Limitations: Applications not accepted. Giving primarily in Birmingham and Vestavia Hills, AL. No grants to individuals.
Application information: Contributes only to pre-selected organizations.
Officers and Directors: Ginger Griffin Burkett, Pres. and Director; Gari Griffin Rogers, V.P. and Director; Gana Griffin Barrentine, Secy. and Director.
EIN: 630995615

31
Harry E. Griswold Scholarships Fund
(formerly Harry E. Griswold Trust)
c/o Regions Bank, N.A.
P.O. Box 2886
Mobile, AL 36652-2886

Established in 1978 in Illinois.

Foundation type: Independent foundation.
Financial data (yr. ended 03/31/14): Assets, $3,759,915 (M); expenditures, $238,675; qualifying distributions, $195,881; giving activities include $188,576 for 7 grants (high: $45,394; low: $1,000).
Purpose and activities: Scholarship awards paid directly to the college or university for graduates of Blue Mound and Taylorville high schools, Illinois.
Fields of interest: Arts and culture; Education; Human services.
Type of support: General support; Continuing support; Endowments; Scholarships.
Limitations: Applications not accepted. Giving primarily in IL.
Application information: Unsolicited requests for funds not accepted.
Trustee: Regions Bank, N.A.
EIN: 376182916

32
Merrill I. & Grace Hanks Charitable Trust
c/o Regions Bank
P. O. Box 1628
Mobile, AL 36633-1628
Application Address: c/o Financial Aid Office, Samford University, 800 Lakeshore Dr., Birmingham, AL, 35229, Application Address: c/o Office of Financial Aid University, University of Mobile, 5735 College Pkwy., Mobile, AL, 36616, Application Phone: (205) 442-2222, Application Phone: (205) 726-2905

Donor: Merrill I. Hanks†.
Foundation type: Independent foundation.
Financial data (yr. ended 03/01/15): Assets, $4,550,613 (M); expenditures, $225,665; qualifying distributions, $206,386; giving activities include $173,511 for 2 grants (high: $135,000; low: $38,511).
Fields of interest: Education; Religion.
Limitations: Applications accepted. Giving primarily in AL.
Application information: Application form required.
Initial approach: Application form available from University of Mobile and from Samford University
Deadline(s): Dec. 15
Trustee: Regions Bank.
EIN: 616394207

33
Verlie P. & John L. Harper Charitable Trust
c/o Regions Bank Trust Dept.
P.O. Box 2886
Mobile, AL 36652-2886

Foundation type: Independent foundation.
Financial data (yr. ended 12/31/13): Assets, $4,287,435 (M); expenditures, $219,489; qualifying distributions, $185,684; giving activities include $177,161 for 4 grants (high: $68,107; low: $19,054).
Fields of interest: Religion; Children and youth.
Limitations: Applications not accepted. Giving primarily in AL.
Application information: Unsolicited requests for funds not accepted.
Trustee: Regions Bank Trust Dept.
EIN: 306046872

34
Harris Foundation Inc.
110 Vincent Ave.
Troy, AL 36079-3007 (334) 566-4844
Contact: Kenneth L. Harris, Pres.

Established in 1986 in Alabama.
Donors: Gary B. Berry; Kenneth L. Harris, Sr.; Kenneth L. Harris, Jr.; Gary Wheeler; Margaret B. Harris.
Foundation type: Independent foundation.
Financial data (yr. ended 10/31/13): Assets, $1,558,905 (M); gifts received, $370,000; expenditures, $298,175; qualifying distributions, $297,200; giving activities include $297,200 for 2 grants (high: $297,000; low: $200).
Purpose and activities: Giving primarily in support of Christian broadcasting, as well as for education.
Fields of interest: Elementary and secondary education; Higher education; Communication media; Christianity.
Limitations: Applications accepted. Giving primarily in AL.
Application information: Application form required.
Initial approach: Proposal
Deadline(s): None
Officers: Kenneth L. Harris, Pres.; Gary Berry, V.P.; Ken Harris, Jr., Secy.; Lisa Wheeler, Treas.
Directors: Deborah Berry; Vonda Harris; Gary Wheeler.
EIN: 630958653

35
Ben F. Harrison Foundation, Inc.
P.O. Box 250
Greenville, AL 36037-0250

Established in 1979 in Florida.
Donors: Harrison Industries, Inc.; Carol M. Harrison.
Foundation type: Independent foundation.
Financial data (yr. ended 08/31/13): Assets, $2,521,636 (M); expenditures, $355,099; qualifying distributions, $340,267; giving activities include $340,215 for 20 grants (high: $100,000; low: $100).
Fields of interest: Arts and culture; Education; Diseases and conditions.
Type of support: Research.
Limitations: Applications not accepted. Giving primarily in Birmingham, AL, FL, and KY. No grants to individuals.
Application information: Unsolicited requests for funds not accepted.
Officers: Carol M. Harrison, Pres.; Tommy Counts, Secy.-Treas.
Director: Wayne Lee.
EIN: 630781485

36
Hartselle Scholarship Foundation
c/o WHSQ&L
1323 Stratford Rd., S.E.
Decatur, AL 35601-6017
Application address: c/o Wells Fargo Wealth Mgmt., 1 W. 4th St., 2nd Fl., Winston Salem, NC 27101, tel.: (336) 747-8179

Established in 1994 in Alabama.
Foundation type: Independent foundation.
Financial data (yr. ended 12/31/12): Assets, $1,268,986 (M); expenditures, $153,453;

qualifying distributions, $140,216; giving activities include $140,216 for grants.

Purpose and activities: Scholarship awards paid directly to the college or university for graduates of Hartselle High School, Alabama.

Fields of interest: Education.

Type of support: Student aid.

Limitations: Applications accepted. Giving primarily to residents of Hartselle, AL.

Application information: Application form required.
  Initial approach: Contact Foundation
  Deadline(s): Apr. 1

Officers: Glenn E. Thompson, Chair.; Larry W. Madison, Vice-Chair.; Jeffrey M. Gray, Secy.; William H. Puckett, Treas.

EIN: 631045867

37

Hawkins Educational Foundation
c/o Compass Bank, WMG- Tax Dept.
P. O. Box 10566
Birmingham, AL 35296-0002 (205) 297-6713
Contact: Patsy Alford, Grants Mgr.
E-mail: info@HawkinsScholarship.com; Application Address: c/o Hawkins Educational Foundation, P.O. Box 10164, Birmingham, AL, 35202; Main URL: http://www.hawkinsscholarship.com
Facebook: http://www.facebook.com/pages/Hawkins-Educational-Foundation/112841992133738

Established in 2005 in Alabama.

Foundation type: Independent foundation.

Financial data (yr. ended 07/31/14): Assets, $4,073,335 (M); expenditures, $289,788; qualifying distributions, $188,173; giving activities include $167,000 for 53 grants to individuals (high: $8,000; low: $1,000).

Purpose and activities: Scholarship awards to residents of Baldwin County, Alabama, who have a minimum of 2.0 GPA from high school and who are pursuing a higher education.

Fields of interest: Higher education.

Type of support: Student aid.

Limitations: Giving primarily to residents of Baldwin County, AL.

Application information: See foundation web site for full application guidelines and requirements, including downloadable application form. Transcripts should be mailed to the BBVA Compass address. Application form required.

Officer: Joyce Woodburn, Chair.

Trustee: Compass Bank.

EIN: 616320623

38

Jeanette E. & Benjamin F. Hunter Scholarship Trust
c/o Regions Bank Trust Dept.
P.O. Box 2886
Mobile, AL 36652-2886

Foundation type: Independent foundation.

Financial data (yr. ended 12/31/13): Assets, $4,804,919 (M); expenditures, $315,761; qualifying distributions, $199,878; giving activities include $189,544 for 1 grant.

Fields of interest: University education.

Limitations: Applications not accepted. Giving primarily in IL.

Application information: Unsolicited requests for funds not accepted.

Trustee: Regions Bank.

EIN: 376022836

39

The C. Eugene Ireland Foundation
c/o Regions Bank
P.O. Box 11426
Birmingham, AL 35202-1426
Contact: Daniel Morris, Secy.
Application address: 3155 Highfield Dr., Montgomery, AL 36111, tel.: (334) 272-8020

Established in 1978 in Alabama.

Donors: Patricia Hall; Robert Hall†; Cecelia Mathews; Alan Matthews; C. Eugene Ireland†.

Foundation type: Independent foundation.

Financial data (yr. ended 12/31/13): Assets, $3,409,451 (M); expenditures, $191,521; qualifying distributions, $161,525; giving activities include $154,500 for 49 grants (high: $12,000; low: $500).

Fields of interest: Arts and culture; Education; Protestantism; Human services; Children and youth; Infants and toddlers; Children; Adolescents; Adults; Young adults; Seniors; Females; Female children and youth; Female infants and toddlers; Female adults; Female young adults; Males; Male children and youth; Male infants and toddlers; Male adults; Male young adults; LGBTQ people; Single parents; Ethnic and racial groups; People of Asian descent; People of African descent; People of Latin American descent; Indigenous peoples; American Indians; Immigrants and migrants; Migrant workers; Homeless people; Low-income and poor people; Incarcerated people; Victims of crime and abuse; People with disabilities; People with physical disabilities; People with vision impairments; People with hearing impairments; People with psychosocial disabilities; People with HIV/AIDS; Terminally ill people; Substance abusers; Military personnel.

Type of support: General support; Employee matching gifts; Matching grants; Continuing support; Capacity-building and technical assistance; Capital and infrastructure; Equipment; Endowments; Debt reduction; Emergency funds; Program development; Recordings; Curriculum development; Scholarships; Research; Technical assistance; Program evaluations.

Limitations: Applications accepted. Giving primarily in AL, with emphasis on Birmingham and Montgomery. No grants to individuals.

Application information:
  Initial approach: Letter
  Copies of proposal: 1
  Deadline(s): None
  Board meeting date(s): Nov.

Officers and Trustees: Richard I. Pigford, Chair. and Trustee; L. Daniel Morris, Secy. and Trustee; Jean H. Sulzby; Regions Bank.

Number of staff: None.

EIN: 630745195

40

JADO Fund
c/o Regions Bank
P.O. Box 2450
Montgomery, AL 36102-2450

Established in 1983 in Alabama.

Donors: Adolph Weil, Jr.; Mrs. Adolph Weil, Jr.; Laurie J. Weil; Adolph Weil III; Jean K. Weil†; Jan K. Weil.

Foundation type: Independent foundation.

Financial data (yr. ended 12/31/13): Assets, $6,216,675 (L); gifts received, $630,678; expenditures, $311,572; qualifying distributions, $287,853; giving activities include $286,278 for 38 grants (high: $44,855; low: $250).

Fields of interest: Arts and culture; Museums; Higher education; Nonprofits; Hospital care; Christianity; Judaism; Human services; Child welfare.

Type of support: Regranting.

Limitations: Applications not accepted. Giving primarily in the Montgomery, AL area. No grants to individuals.

Application information: Unsolicited requests for funds not accepted.

Trustee: Regions Bank Trust Dept.

EIN: 630835562

41

The Kairos Foundation Trust of 2004
61 White Ave.
Fairhope, AL 36532-1317
Application address: Thomas Yearwood, 51 White Ave., Fairhope, AL 36532, tel.: (251) 929-1266

Established in 2004 in Alabama.

Donors: Thomas L. Yearwood; Lisa W. Yearwood; Anna Yearwood.

Foundation type: Independent foundation.

Financial data (yr. ended 12/31/13): Assets, $764,006 (M); gifts received, $243,375; expenditures, $206,017; qualifying distributions, $197,880; giving activities include $197,880 for 13 grants (high: $124,600; low: $100).

Fields of interest: Nonprofits; Religion; Christianity; International development.

Type of support: General support; Regranting.

Limitations: Applications accepted. Giving in the U.S., with some emphasis on AL and GA. No grants to individuals.

Application information:
  Initial approach: Proposal
  Deadline(s): None

Trustees: Lisa W. Yearwood; Thomas L. Yearwood.

EIN: 206214789

42

The Nelson and Charleen Kemp Foundation
P.O. Box 236
Winfield, AL 35594-0236 (205) 487-1903
Contact: Mary Frank Hyche, Pres.

Established in 1987 in Alabama.

Donor: Charleen M. Kemp†.

Foundation type: Independent foundation.

Financial data (yr. ended 12/31/14): Assets, $4,099,145 (M); expenditures, $313,642; qualifying distributions, $246,913; giving activities include $161,000 for 41 grants (high: $17,500; low: $1,000).

Purpose and activities: Giving primarily for education, health, the arts, human services, religion and for the public benefit.

Fields of interest: Arts and culture; Elementary and secondary education; Higher education; Hospital care; Diseases and conditions; Religion; Human services.

Type of support: General support; Matching grants; Annual campaigns; Capital campaigns; Capital and infrastructure; Equipment; Scholarships; Research; Research and evaluation.

Limitations: Applications accepted. Giving primarily in northwestern AL. No support for political organizations. No grants to individuals.

Application information:
  Initial approach: Proposal
  Copies of proposal: 1
  Deadline(s): None

Officers: C.E. Bryant, Jr., Chair. and Secy.; Mary Frank Hyche, Pres. and C.E.O.

Trustees: Kevin L. Bradford; Greg Chaffin; Brian Henley.

Number of staff: 1 full-time professional.

EIN: 630981693

43

The Olin B. King Foundation
c/o Rosemary K. Lee
659 Gallatin St., Ste. 200
Huntsville, AL   35801-4914

Established in 1997 in Alabama.

Donors: Olin B. King; Shelbie Jean King.

Foundation type: Independent foundation.

Financial data (yr. ended 12/31/13): Assets, $2,925,311 (M); expenditures, $152,100; qualifying distributions, $121,300; giving activities include $121,300 for 13 grants (high: $15,000; low: $1,300).

Purpose and activities: Grant for general purpose.

Fields of interest: Arts and culture; Education; Higher education; Health; Hospital care; Christianity.

Limitations: Applications not accepted. Giving primarily in AL; giving also in GA. No grants to individuals.

Application information: Unsolicited requests for funds not accepted.

Officer and Trustee: Rosemary K. Lee, Exec. Dir. and Trustee.

Committee Members: Shelbie A. King; Rosemary K. Lee.

EIN: 586343485

44

Annie Graham King Trust
P.O. Box 2450
Montgomery, AL   36102-2450

Established in 2009 in Alabama.

Foundation type: Independent foundation.

Financial data (yr. ended 12/31/13): Assets, $6,808,614 (M); expenditures, $501,289; qualifying distributions, $429,281; giving activities include $420,000 for 13 grants (high: $84,000; low: $3,360).

Fields of interest: Education; Health; Protestantism; Human services.

Limitations: Applications not accepted. Giving primarily in Selma, AL. No grants to individuals.

Application information: Contributes only to pre-selected organizations.

Trustee: Regions Bank Trust Dept.

EIN: 636102496

45

W. W. Kirkland Charitable Foundation
P.O. Box 356
Chatom, AL   36518
Application address: c/o Edward Henson, 10764 Hawthorn Rd., Wagerville, AL 36585, tel.: (251) 847-2144

Foundation type: Independent foundation.

Financial data (yr. ended 12/31/14): Assets, $4,014,360 (M); expenditures, $338,259; qualifying distributions, $306,825; giving activities include $305,900 for 21 grants (high: $50,000; low: $900).

Fields of interest: Education; Health; Human services.

Trustee: Robert Edward Henson.

EIN: 456382709

46

The Ernestine L. Lenoir Charitable Trust
P.O. Box 32
Butler, AL   36904-0032   (205) 459-2152
Contact: Michael E. Williams, Tr.

Donor: Ernestine Lenoir†.

Foundation type: Independent foundation.

Financial data (yr. ended 12/31/12): Assets, $3,518,843 (M); gifts received, $41,687; expenditures, $524,419; qualifying distributions, $377,000; giving activities include $377,000 for grants.

Fields of interest: Education.

Application information: Application form required.
  Initial approach: Request application form
  Deadline(s): None

Trustees: Jennifer W. Clark; Patricia W. Harris; Michael E. Williams.

EIN: 316632596

47

Loeb Family Foundation Inc.
c/o Regions Morgan Keegan Trust
P.O. Box 2450
Montgomery, AL   36102-2450

Established in 1987 in Alabama.

Donors: James L. Loeb; Mrs. James L. Loeb; Joan B. Loeb.

Foundation type: Independent foundation.

Financial data (yr. ended 03/31/15): Assets, $6,222,901 (M); expenditures, $370,211; qualifying distributions, $298,641; giving activities include $298,641 for 131 grants (high: $28,000; low: $100).

Fields of interest: Arts and culture; Historical activities; Education; Nonprofits; Community and economic development; Religion; Judaism; Human services.

Type of support: Regranting.

Limitations: Applications not accepted. Giving primarily in AL. No grants to individuals.

Application information: Contributes only to pre-selected organizations.

Trustee: Regions Bank Trust Dept.

Directors: Elizabeth L. Friedman; Helen R. Loeb; James L. Loeb, Jr.; Joan B. Loeb; Patricia L. Rosenbaum.

EIN: 630960783

48

Malone Family Foundation
P.O. Box 531085
Birmingham, AL   35253-1085   (205) 423-0901
Contact: Alyson M. Bagby, Pres.
E-mail: info@themalonefamilyfoundation.org; Main URL: http://www.themalonefamilyfoundation.org
Grants List: http://www.themalonefamilyfoundation.org/initiatives.html

Established in 2007 in Alabama.

Donor: Wallace D. Malone, Jr.

Foundation type: Independent foundation.

Financial data (yr. ended 02/28/13): Assets, $6,570,801 (M); expenditures, $366,067; qualifying distributions, $353,213; giving activities include $352,008 for 5 grants (high: $179,000; low: $4,533).

Purpose and activities: The foundation primarily, but not solely, focuses on programs and projects that expand the horizons of and opportunities for children and young adults. Those programs and projects with objectives of providing better education, promoting self-esteem and instilling in its beneficiaries a desire to improve oneself are of great interest to the foundation. The foundation concentrates on 501(c)(3), non-profit organizations that provide programs and projects designed to prevent or solve problems and create opportunities, rather than meet basic needs. Preference will be given to creative programs that directly and positively impact the future of children and young adults in the area of education. The foundation feels that a well-educated and motivated population promotes an economically strong community and, thereby, improves everyones standard of living while simultaneously expanding opportunities for everyone.

Fields of interest: Education; Children; Young adults.

Limitations: Applications accepted. Giving primarily in AL; limited giving in FL and GA.

Application information: Application form required.
  Initial approach: Letter
  Deadline(s): May 15 for June decisions; Oct. 15 for Dec. decisions
  Board meeting date(s): June and Dec.

Officers: Wallace D. Malone, Jr., Chair.; Alyson M. Bagby, Pres. and Treas.; Catherine M. Wilson, V.P. and Secy.

Directors: Ocllo S. Malone; Wallace Davis Malone.

EIN: 204596031

49

Mayer and Arlene Mitchell Charitable Foundation
P.O. Box 16006
Mobile, AL   36616-0006   2513443800

Established in 1986 in Alabama.

Donor: Mayer Mitchell†.

Foundation type: Independent foundation.

Financial data (yr. ended 12/31/14): Assets, $1,105,696; expenditures, $244,179; qualifying distributions, $238,815.

Fields of interest: Arts and culture; Education; Catholicism.

Limitations: Applications not accepted. Giving primarily in AL, Washington, DC, and Atlanta, GA. No grants to individuals.

Application information: Unsolicited requests for funds not accepted.
Officers: Arlene F. Mitchell, Pres.; James M. Grodnick, V.P.; Joy Mitchell Grodnick, Secy.
Director: Melinda M. Wertherim.
EIN: 630935456

50

Mitchell Industries Foundation
200 Kilsby Cir.
Bessemer, AL   35022

Established in 1998 in Alabama.
Donors: Mitchell Industries; Guy K. Mitchell, Jr.
Foundation type: Company-sponsored foundation.
Financial data (yr. ended 12/31/13): Assets, $44,017 (M); gifts received, $275,000; expenditures, $237,803; qualifying distributions, $236,900; giving activities include $236,900 for 31 grants (high: $93,500; low: $350).
Purpose and activities: The foundation supports organizations involved with arts and culture, education, human services, and Christianity.
Fields of interest: Arts and culture; Health; Religion.
Type of support: General support.
Limitations: Applications not accepted. Giving primarily in AL. No grants to individuals.
Application information: Contributes only to pre-selected organizations.
Officers: Guy K. Mitchell, Jr., Pres.; Katherine J. Mitchell, V.P.
Directors: Dorothy L. Mitchell; Guy K. Mitchell III; Malvina M. Whatley.
EIN: 631190038

51

The Laura Lee Pattillo Norquist Charitable Foundation
800 Shades Creek Pkwy., Ste. 125
Birmingham, AL   35209-4526   (205) 414-3300
Contact: Frances A. Danley

Established in 1994 in Alabama.
Donor: Laura Lee Pattillo Norquist.
Foundation type: Independent foundation.
Financial data (yr. ended 12/31/13): Assets, $9,848,976 (M); expenditures, $551,369; qualifying distributions, $482,687; giving activities include $422,422 for 23 grants (high: $150,000; low: $2,500).
Fields of interest: Diseases and conditions; Religion; Human services.
Limitations: Applications accepted. Giving primarily in AL. No grants to individuals.
Application information:
   Initial approach: Letter
   Deadline(s): None
Trustee: Sternee Agee Trust.
Distribution Committee: Frances A. Danley; Franklin Danley; Blair Schoevogel.
EIN: 636189797

52

Pei-Ling Charitable Trust
3015 Barcody Rd.
Huntsville, AL   35802-1110

Established in 1989 in Alabama.
Donors: Pei Ling Chan†; Mrs. Pei Ling Chan†.
Foundation type: Independent foundation.

Financial data (yr. ended 12/31/14): Assets, $6,150,860 (M); expenditures, $314,800; qualifying distributions, $314,800; giving activities include for 13 grants (high: $195,000; low: $2,000).
Fields of interest: Arts and culture; Art museums; Higher education; Nonprofits; Human services.
Type of support: Scholarships; Endowments; Continuing support; Capital campaigns; Annual campaigns; Regranting.
Limitations: Applications not accepted. Giving primarily in Huntsville, AL and New York, NY. No grants to individuals.
Application information: Contributes only to pre-selected organizations.
Trustees: Chia Hwa Chan; Dennis C.C. Chan.
Number of staff: None.
EIN: 570887822

53

The Petra Foundation
2906 Surrey Rd.
Birmingham, AL   35223-1215

Established in 2002 in Alabama.
Donor: Robert Stephen Briggs, Sr.
Foundation type: Independent foundation.
Financial data (yr. ended 12/31/14): Assets, $495,956; expenditures, $168,370; qualifying distributions, $165,000.
Fields of interest: Christianity; Family services; Homeless shelters.
Type of support: Capital campaigns; General support.
Limitations: Applications not accepted. Giving primarily in Bessemer and Birmingham, AL. No grants to individuals.
Application information: Contributes only to pre-selected organizations.
Officers: Robert Stephen Briggs, Sr., Pres.; Robert Stephen Briggs, Jr., V.P.; Lynn Bryan Briggs, Secy.
EIN: 043674511

54

Reese Phifer, Jr. Memorial Foundation
P.O. Box 1700
Tuscaloosa, AL   35403
Application address: c/o Susan Phifer Cork, Phifer, Inc., 4400 Kauloosa Ave., Tuscaloosa AL 35401

Established in 1967 in Alabama.
Donors: Phifer Wire Products; J. Reese Phifer; Phifer, Inc.
Foundation type: Independent foundation.
Financial data (yr. ended 12/31/14): Assets, $440,866 (M); gifts received, $300,256; expenditures, $337,667; qualifying distributions, $333,325; giving activities include $330,200 for 81 grants (high: $84,300; low: $100).
Purpose and activities: Giving primarily for higher education, health associations, children, youth, and social services, federated giving programs, and to an Episcopal church.
Fields of interest: Arts and culture; Education; Higher education; Environment; Nonprofits; Health; Diseases and conditions; Community and economic development; Episcopalianism and Anglicanism; Lutheranism; Human services; Child welfare.
Type of support: Capital campaigns; Annual campaigns; Financial sustainability; General support; Regranting.

Limitations: Applications accepted. Giving primarily in AL. No grants to individuals.
Application information:
   Initial approach: Proposal
   Deadline(s): None
Trustees: Karen Phifer Brooks; Susan Phifer Cork; Beverly C. Phifer.
EIN: 636061552

55

Piassick Family Foundation
3321 Cherokee Rd.
Birmingham, AL   35223-1313   (205) 987-5683
Contact: Joel B. Piassick, Dir.

Donor: Joel B. Piassick.
Foundation type: Independent foundation.
Financial data (yr. ended 12/31/13): Assets, $2,857,895 (M); gifts received, $42,481; expenditures, $265,995; qualifying distributions, $250,594; giving activities include $248,669 for 38 grants (high: $54,000; low: $250).
Fields of interest: Education; Religion; Human services.
Application information: Application form required.
   Initial approach: Letter
   Deadline(s): None
Directors: Joel B. Piassick; Karen Piassick; Louis N. Piassick; Joan P. Swartz.
EIN: 263908886

56

The Propst Foundation
305 Church St. S.W., Ste. 715
Huntsville, AL   35801-4907

Donor: William S. Propost.
Foundation type: Independent foundation.
Financial data (yr. ended 12/31/13): Assets, $5,304,475 (M); expenditures, $234,385; qualifying distributions, $206,359; giving activities include $203,500 for 16 grants (high: $50,000; low: $2,500).
Fields of interest: Education; Community and economic development; Religion.
Limitations: Applications not accepted. Giving primarily in AL.
Application information: Unsolicited requests for funds not accepted.
Officers and Directors: William S. Propost, Pres. and Director; William S. Propst, Jr., Secy.-Treas. and Director; Charles Vincent Propost; Michael K. Propst; Emily P. Reiney.
EIN: 274341346

57

The Ratliff Charitable Foundation
1900 Crestwood Blvd., Ste. 300
Birmingham, AL   35210

Established in 1998 in Alabama.
Donor: William T. Ratliff, Jr.
Foundation type: Independent foundation.
Financial data (yr. ended 12/31/13): Assets, $9,113,877 (M); expenditures, $289,456; qualifying distributions, $276,450; giving activities include $275,000 for 9 grants (high: $75,000; low: $10,000).
Fields of interest: Science museums; Protestantism; Sports.

Type of support: General support.
Limitations: Applications not accepted. Giving primarily in Birmingham, AL; some giving also in Bonita Springs, FL. No grants to individuals.
Application information: Unsolicited requests for funds not accepted.
Officers and Directors: William T. Ratliff, Jr., Pres. and Treas. and Director; William T. Ratliff III, V.P. and Secy. and Director; Carl A. Lessman.
EIN: 631198327

58
Regions/AmSouth Foundation
(formerly AmSouth/First American Foundation)
c/o Regions Bank, Trust Dept.
P.O. Box 2886
Mobile, AL 36652-2886

Donors: First American National Bank; AmSouth Bank.
Foundation type: Company-sponsored foundation.
Financial data (yr. ended 12/31/13): Assets, $5,733,633 (M); expenditures, $401,178; qualifying distributions, $356,000; giving activities include $355,000 for 22 grants (high: $50,000; low: $5,000).
Purpose and activities: The foundation supports organizations involved with arts and culture, education, health, substance abuse treatment, cancer, and youth development.
Fields of interest: Education; Diseases and conditions; Youth development.
Type of support: General support.
Limitations: Applications not accepted. Giving limited to TN. No grants to individuals.
Application information: Contributes only to pre-selected organizations.
Officers and Directors: Ronald G. Smith, Chair.; Jim Schmitz, Pres. and Director; Pamela R. Welch, Secy.; Douglas J. Jackson, Treas.; Donna Cheek; William Cochran; David May; Michael W. McNamee; Renata Soto; Joseph Walker III; Bernard Werthan, Jr.
EIN: 582071018

59
M.A. Rikard Charitable Trust
c/o Synovus Trust Company, N.A.
800 Shades Creek Pkwy., Ste. 225
Birmingham, AL 35209-4526
Application address: c/o Frank A. Rikard, Tr., 9340 Clubhouse Rd., Foley, AL 36535-9322

Established in 2001 in Alabama.
Donor: M.A. Rikard†.
Foundation type: Independent foundation.
Financial data (yr. ended 09/30/14): Assets, $4,421,937; gifts received, $126,825; expenditures, $308,630; qualifying distributions, $264,409.
Fields of interest: Education; Health; Human services.
Limitations: Applications accepted. Giving primarily in GA and HI.
Application information: Application form required.
Initial approach: Letter
Deadline(s): None
Trustees: Frank A. Rikard; Glenn A. Rikard; Elizabeth R. Von Krusenstiern; John Von Krusenstiern; Synovus Trust Company, N.A.
EIN: 636231842

60
Harold W. Ripps Charitable Foundation
100 Village St.
Birmingham, AL 35242-6452

Donor: Harold W. Ripps.
Foundation type: Independent foundation.
Financial data (yr. ended 12/31/14): Assets, $2,147,996; gifts received, $867,745; expenditures, $359,026; qualifying distributions, $359,000.
Fields of interest: Nonprofits; Diseases and conditions; Human services.
Type of support: Regranting.
Limitations: Applications not accepted. Giving primarily in AL. No grants to individuals.
Application information: Unsolicited requests for funds not accepted.
Directors: Michael J. Hallman; Herbert A. Meisler; Larry S. Nickles; Harold W. Ripps.
EIN: 630943463

61
Carol W. & Myron J. Rothschild Fund
c/o Regions Bank
P.O. Box 2450
Montgomery, AL 36102-2450

Established in 1964 in Alabama.
Donor: Carol W. Rothschild.
Foundation type: Independent foundation.
Financial data (yr. ended 12/31/14): Assets, $5,815,176; expenditures, $385,465; qualifying distributions, $327,343.
Purpose and activities: Giving primarily for human services, particularly to a family violence program, and for children and youth services; funding also for health associations, especially organizations researching eyesight restoration, and for the arts and to Jewish organizations.
Fields of interest: Arts and culture; Education; Nonprofits; Diseases and conditions; Domestic violence; Judaism; Camps; Human services; Child welfare; Youth services.
Type of support: Regranting.
Limitations: Applications not accepted. Giving primarily in Montgomery, AL. No grants to individuals.
Application information: Unsolicited requests for funds not accepted.
Trustee: Regions Bank Trust Dept.
EIN: 636050756

62
The W. James Samford, Jr. Foundation
c/o Lucinda Samford Cannon
P.O. Box 3080
Opelika, AL 36803-3080

Established in 2004 in Unspecified.
Donors: William James Samford, Jr.†; W. James Samford Irrevocable Trust, Jr.
Foundation type: Independent foundation.
Financial data (yr. ended 12/31/14): Assets, $10,480,228 (M); gifts received, $1,407,326; expenditures, $575,703; qualifying distributions, $426,518; giving activities include $390,787 for 27 grants (high: $100,000; low: $400).
Fields of interest: Education; Higher education; Sports and recreation; Child welfare.

Limitations: Applications not accepted. Giving primarily in AL. No grants to individuals.
Application information: Contributes only to pre-selected organizations.
Officers and Directors: Lucinda Samford Cannon, Pres. and Director; E. Rasha Cannon, Secy. and Director; Preston B. Barnett, Treas. and Director.
EIN: 200246688

63
Sexton Family Charitable Foundation
P.O. Box 369
Decatur, AL 35602-0369   (256) 355-8110
Contact: William E. Sexton, Chair.

Established in 1994 in Alabama.
Donors: William W. Sexton; William E. Sexton.
Foundation type: Independent foundation.
Financial data (yr. ended 12/31/13): Assets, $1,143,242 (M); gifts received, $33,715; expenditures, $178,912; qualifying distributions, $154,683; giving activities include $154,683 for 43 grants (high: $14,038; low: $200).
Fields of interest: Education; Higher education; Mental health care; Heart and circulatory system diseases; Cancers; Leukemia; Christianity; Food delivery; Scouting programs.
Type of support: General support; Capital campaigns; Endowments; Program development; Fellowships; Scholarships; Research; Student aid.
Limitations: Applications accepted. Giving primarily in AL.
Application information: Application form required.
Initial approach: Letter
Deadline(s): None
Officers: William E. Sexton, Chair.; William B. Sexton, Pres. and Treas.
Number of staff: 1 part-time professional.
EIN: 631117593

64
Barbara Ingalls Shook Foundation
1919 Oxmoor Rd., Ste. 234
Birmingham, AL 35209-3502

Established in 1980 in Alabama.
Donor: Robert I. Ingalls Testamentary Trust II.
Foundation type: Independent foundation.
Financial data (yr. ended 08/31/13): Assets, $5,443,168 (M); expenditures, $450,760; qualifying distributions, $341,110; giving activities include $328,643 for 5 grants (high: $223,542; low: $1).
Fields of interest: Arts and culture; Education; Zoos; Domesticated animals; Science.
Type of support: Research.
Limitations: Applications not accepted. Giving primarily in AL, CO and Washington, DC. No grants to individuals.
Application information: Unsolicited requests for funds not accepted.
Officers: Elesabeth R. Shook, Pres.; Nancy C. Hughes, Secy.
EIN: 630792812

65
Siloam Foundation
P.O. Box 10127
Birmingham, AL 35202-0127

Donors: Jennifer C. McDonald; Jennifer M. Jonas.
Foundation type: Independent foundation.
Financial data (yr. ended 12/31/13): Assets, $3,999,632 (M); expenditures, $123,214; qualifying distributions, $120,800; giving activities include $120,000 for 1 grant.
Fields of interest: Christianity; Human services.
Type of support: Program development; General support.
Limitations: Applications not accepted. Giving primarily in AL, GA, IL and NC. No grants to individuals.
Application information: Contributes only to pre-selected organizations.
Officers and Directors: Jennifer Jonas, Pres. and Director; A. Jefferson McDonald, Jr., V.P. and Director; John L. McDonald, Secy. and Director; Gerald B. Jonas, Treas. and Director.
EIN: 205588217

66
The Simpson Foundation
P.O. Box 240548
Montgomery, AL 36124-0548   (334) 386-2516
FAX: (334) 386-2521; Main URL: http://thesimpsonfoundation.org

Established in 1985 in Alabama.
Foundation type: Independent foundation.
Financial data (yr. ended 04/30/13): Assets, $6,439,713 (M); expenditures, $356,406; qualifying distributions, $279,435; giving activities include $199,200 for 28 grants (high: $28,800; low: $400).
Purpose and activities: Giving primarily for educational scholarships.
Fields of interest: Education.
Type of support: Scholarships.
Limitations: Applications accepted. Giving limited to residents of Wilcox County, AL. No grants to individuals directly.
Application information: Scholarship payments made to the individual's educational institution. Applicants must submit transcripts and letters of recommendation. Application form required.
    Initial approach: Proposal
    Deadline(s): Jan. 1- Mar. 31
Trustees: Mary Hogen; Chris Stone; AlaTrust, Inc.
EIN: 630925496

67
SSAB Foundation for Education
(formerly IPSCO Foundation for Education)
12400 Hwy. 43 N.
Axis, AL 36505-4308

Established in 2004 in Alabama.
Donors: IPSCO Foundation, Ltd.; SSAB Alabama, Inc.
Foundation type: Independent foundation.
Financial data (yr. ended 12/31/13): Assets, $208,046 (M); gifts received, $208,901; expenditures, $197,544; qualifying distributions, $197,544; giving activities include $189,701 for 9 grants (high: $37,235; low: $7,339).
Purpose and activities: Support only for public educational institutions in Alabama.
Fields of interest: Education.
Type of support: General support.

Limitations: Applications not accepted. Giving limited to AL, with emphasis on Mobile County. No grants to individuals.
Application information: Unsolicited requests for funds not accepted.
Officers: Paul Wilson, Chair.; Jon Howley, Pres.; Woody Burke, V.P.; Carleen Varga, Secy.; George Chapman, Treas.
EIN: 201173879

68
Strain Foundation
303 Williams Ave. S.W., Ste. 129
Huntsville, AL 35801-6001
Application address: c/o Juanelle D. Strain, Dir., 4412 Corinth Dr., Birmingham, AL 35213-1816, tel.: (205) 951-2868

Established in 1994 in Alabama.
Donors: John T. Strain; Juanelle D. Strain; Janet Strain.
Foundation type: Independent foundation.
Financial data (yr. ended 10/31/13): Assets, $6,813,652 (M); expenditures, $472,289; qualifying distributions, $407,455; giving activities include $407,455 for 21 grants (high: $50,000; low: $30).
Fields of interest: Agriculture; Protestantism; Human services.
Limitations: Applications accepted. Giving primarily in AL. No grants to individuals.
Application information: Application form required.
    Initial approach: Letter
    Deadline(s): None
Directors: Julia Strain Maloy; Janet Strain McDonald; Mike Segars; Juanelle Strain.
EIN: 631108283

69
Sumners/Nelson/Thompson Foundation
c/o Michael A. Mouron
402 Office Park Dr., Ste. 150
Birmingham, AL 35223-2435

Established in 1999 in Alabama.
Foundation type: Independent foundation.
Financial data (yr. ended 12/31/13): Assets, $940,799 (M); expenditures, $200,583; qualifying distributions, $188,199; giving activities include $188,199 for 14 grants (high: $35,000; low: $800).
Fields of interest: Higher education; Protestantism.
Limitations: Applications not accepted. Giving primarily in AL. No grants to individuals.
Application information: Contributes only to pre-selected organizations.
Trustees: Lynn W. Jinks; John T. Main; Michael A. Mouron.
EIN: 636215560

70
Thompson Family Foundation
2811 Crescent Ave., Ste. 201
Homewood, AL 35209

Donors: Jean C. Thompson; James A. Thompson.
Foundation type: Independent foundation.
Financial data (yr. ended 06/30/13): Assets, $4,725,169 (M); expenditures, $315,767; qualifying distributions, $220,000; giving activities

include $220,000 for 10 grants (high: $50,000; low: $5,000).
Fields of interest: Orchestral music; Religion; Human services; Youth development.
Limitations: Applications not accepted. Giving primarily in AL; with some giving in VA.
Application information: Unsolicited requests for funds not accepted.
Trustee: Jean C. Thompson.
EIN: 271522154

71
William D. Trippe Trust, Inc.
c/o Regions Bank, Trust Dept.
P.O. Box 2886
Mobile, AL 36652-2886
Application address: c/o George E. Mundy P.C., 50 Cherokee Pl., Cedartown, GA 30125, tel.: (770) 748-3870

Established in 1996 in Georgia.
Foundation type: Independent foundation.
Financial data (yr. ended 12/31/13): Assets, $9,493,256 (M); expenditures, $477,730; qualifying distributions, $417,210; giving activities include $400,206 for 1 grant.
Purpose and activities: The trust primarily supports the Polk County, Georgia, school district, and community projects in the city of Cedartown.
Fields of interest: Elementary and secondary education; Foundations; Community and economic development.
Limitations: Applications accepted. Giving limited to Polk County, GA. No grants to individuals.
Application information: Application form required.
    Initial approach: Proposal
    Deadline(s): None
Officers: George E. Mundy, Pres.; Jane C. Wyatt, Secy.-Treas.
Directors: Tobin Ayers; James J. Carter, Jr.; Sandra Galloway; Lloyd H. Gray, Jr.; Michael H. York, Sr.
EIN: 586301950

72
Samuel E. Upchurch, Jr. Charitable
Foundation
2100A Southbridge Pkwy., Ste. 445
Birmingham, AL 35209-1370

Established in 1992 in Alabama.
Donors: Samuel E. Upchurch, Jr.; Cheryl V. Upchurch.
Foundation type: Independent foundation.
Financial data (yr. ended 12/31/13): Assets, $1,242,346 (M); gifts received, $316,710; expenditures, $206,299; qualifying distributions, $201,500; giving activities include $201,500 for 25 grants (high: $75,500; low: $200).
Fields of interest: Higher education; Nonprofits; Protestantism; Human services.
Type of support: General support; Regranting.
Limitations: Applications not accepted. Giving primarily in AL. No grants to individuals.
Application information: Contributes only to pre-selected organizations.
Directors: John S. P. Samford; Cheryl V. Upchurch; Samuel E. Upchurch, Jr.
EIN: 631083893

73
Viro Fund
c/o Regions Bank, N.A.
P.O. Box 2450
Montgomery, AL 36102-2450

Established in 1983 in Alabama.
Donor: Robert S. Weil.
Foundation type: Independent foundation.
Financial data (yr. ended 12/31/13): Assets,
$6,465,745 (M); expenditures, $301,822;
qualifying distributions, $281,400; giving activities
include $280,500 for 40 grants (high: $28,000;
low: $500).
Purpose and activities: Giving primarily for health
and education.
Fields of interest: Performing arts; Historic
preservation; Higher education; Voluntarism;
Health; Hospital care; Judaism; Human services;
Youth development.
Type of support: Program development; General
support.
Limitations: Applications not accepted. Giving
primarily in AL. No grants to individuals.
Application information: Contributes only to
pre-selected organizations.
Trustee: Regions Bank Trust Dept.
Advisory Committee: Robert S. Weil.
EIN: 630835563

74
Allyrae Wallace Educational Trust
P.O. Box 433
Camden, AL 36726-0433 (334) 682-4155
Contact: Haas Strother, Tr.

Established in 1996 in Alabama.
Foundation type: Independent foundation.
Financial data (yr. ended 12/31/13): Assets,
$5,749,938 (M); expenditures, $519,089;
qualifying distributions, $452,447; giving activities
include $395,000 for 47 grants (high: $46,750;
low: $450).
Purpose and activities: Giving primarily for higher
education, including college or vocational school.
Fields of interest: Higher education.
Type of support: Student aid.
Limitations: Applications accepted. Giving limited to
residents of Wilcox County, AL.
Application information: Grade transcripts are
required with application. Application form required.
  Initial approach: Proposal
  Deadline(s): Feb. 1
Trustees: R.J. Browder; Haas Strother.
EIN: 636192432

75
The Warren Family Foundation
5206 Mountain Ridge Pkwy.
Birmingham, AL 35222-4143

Established in 2000 in Alabama.
Donors: Anne McLeod Warren; William Michael
Warren, Jr.
Foundation type: Independent foundation.
Financial data (yr. ended 12/31/13): Assets,
$14,016,234 (M); gifts received, $28,494;
expenditures, $201,403; qualifying distributions,
$192,500; giving activities include $192,500 for 12
grants (high: $100,000; low: $5,000).
Fields of interest: Higher education; Children's
hospital care; Protestantism; Children.
Type of support: Program development.
Limitations: Applications not accepted. Giving
primarily in AL, with emphasis on Birmingham. No
grants to individuals.
Application information: Contributes only to
pre-selected organizations.
Officers and Directors: William Michael Warren, Jr.,
Pres. and Director; Anne McLeod Warren, V.P. and
Director; Amy Warren Neiman.
EIN: 562230240

76
John H. Watson Charitable Foundation
P.O. Box 1207
Dothan, AL 36302-1207

Established in 1997 in Alabama.
Donors: John H. Watson; Gail Watson.
Foundation type: Independent foundation.
Financial data (yr. ended 12/31/13): Assets,
$6,630,213 (M); gifts received, $1,000,055;
expenditures, $285,778; qualifying distributions,
$245,985; giving activities include $245,985 for 15
grants (high: $113,500; low: $1,100).
Fields of interest: Elementary and secondary
education; Higher education; Protestantism; Human
services.
Limitations: Applications not accepted. No grants to
individuals.
Application information: Contributes only to
pre-selected organizations.
Directors: Abby W. Downs; Gail P. Watson; John H.
Watson; John R. Watson.
EIN: 721372393

77
Williams Charitable Foundation
7970 Yorkhaven Rd.
Mobile, AL 36695-4901 (251) 675-5282
Contact: Donna H. Williams, Tr.

Donors: Donald Williams; Donna Williams; Andrew
Williams.
Foundation type: Independent foundation.
Financial data (yr. ended 12/31/13): Assets,
$514,746 (M); gifts received, $241,600;
expenditures, $177,650; qualifying distributions,
$171,420; giving activities include $171,420 for 24
grants (high: $27,750; low: $605).

Fields of interest: Christianity; Protestantism.
Limitations: Applications not accepted.
Application information: Unsolicited requests for
funds not accepted.
Trustees: Andrew J. Williams; Donald F. Williams;
Donna H. Williams.
EIN: 266428722

78
Arthur E. Yates Charitable Trust
P.O. Box 2886
Mobile, AL 36652-2886

Foundation type: Independent foundation.
Financial data (yr. ended 12/31/13): Assets,
$6,563,941 (M); expenditures, $375,777;
qualifying distributions, $335,933; giving activities
include $326,312 for 4 grants (high: $81,578; low:
$81,578).
Fields of interest: Education; Religion.
Limitations: Applications not accepted. Giving
primarily in GA and TN.
Application information: Unsolicited requests for
funds not accepted.
Trustees: Joseph Dana; Regions Bank.
EIN: 586350586

79
The H. Evan, Jr. & Margaret Zeiger
  Charitable Foundation
(formerly Zeiger Charitable Foundation)
2100 3rd Ave. N. Ste. 600
Birmingham, AL 35203

Established in 1990 in Alabama.
Donors: H. Evan Zeiger, Jr., MD; Margaret Shook
Zeiger.
Foundation type: Independent foundation.
Financial data (yr. ended 12/31/13): Assets,
$6,571,187 (M); expenditures, $290,098;
qualifying distributions, $250,000; giving activities
include $250,000 for 62 grants (high: $38,750;
low: $500).
Fields of interest: Christianity.
Limitations: Applications not accepted. Giving
primarily in AL.
Application information: Unsolicited requests for
funds not accepted.
Directors: William W. Brooke; Hugh B. Jacks;
Douglas W. Shook.
EIN: 631018104

ALASKA

80

Alaska Airlines Foundation

4750 International Airport Blvd.
Anchorage, AK 99502   (907) 266-7230
Contact: Tim Thompson, Exec. Dir.

Donor: Alaska Airlines, Inc.
Foundation type: Company-sponsored foundation.
Financial data (yr. ended 12/31/13): Assets, $5,588,287 (M); gifts received, $500,000; expenditures, $143,677; qualifying distributions, $141,500; giving activities include $141,500 for grants.
Purpose and activities: The foundation supports organizations involved with education and aviation.
Fields of interest: Arts and culture; Museums; Education; Aerospace engineering.
Type of support: Program development.
Limitations: Applications accepted. Giving primarily in AK and WA.
Application information: Focus is on education efforts that address a unique need or value of a community. Application form required.
Initial approach: Letter
Copies of proposal: 1
Deadline(s): Sept. 30
Officers: William S. Ayer, Chair. and Pres.; Keith Loveless, V.P.; Brandon S. Pedersen, V.P.; Marilyn F. Romano, V.P.; Jeanne Gammon, Secy.-Treas.; Timothy Thompson, Exec. Dir.
EIN: 920166198

81

Alaska Principals Foundation

P.O. Box 83530
Fairbanks, AK 99708-3530   (907) 458-8880
Contact: Andre Layral

Donor: BP Foundation.
Foundation type: Independent foundation.
Financial data (yr. ended 12/31/12): Assets, $345,633 (M); gifts received, $243,500; expenditures, $206,177; qualifying distributions, $184,000; giving activities include $184,000 for grants.
Fields of interest: Education; Higher education.
Limitations: Applications accepted. Giving primarily in AK.
Application information: Application form required.
Initial approach: Contact foundation for application form
Deadline(s): Oct.
Officers: Adam Mokelke, Pres.; Philip A. Layral, Exec. Dir.
EIN: 651176741

82

Bristol Bay Native Corp., Education Foundation

111 W. 16th Ave., Ste. 400
Anchorage, AK 99501-6299   (907) 278-3602
Contact: Greta L. Goto, Exec. Dir.
FAX: (907) 276-3924; Toll-free tel.: (800) 426-3602; Main URL: http://www.bbnc.net/index.php?

option=com_content&view=category&layout=blog&id=19&Itemid=40

Established in 1992 in Alaska.
Donor: Bristol Bay Native Corp.
Foundation type: Company-sponsored foundation.
Financial data (yr. ended 12/31/13): Assets, $9,352,630 (M); gifts received, $2,090,086; expenditures, $410,413; qualifying distributions, $343,137; giving activities include $332,423 for 196 grants to individuals (high: $5,500; low: $119).
Purpose and activities: The foundation awards college and vocational scholarships to Alaska Native shareholders of Bristol Bay Native Corporation.
Fields of interest: Vocational education; Higher education; Alaskan Natives.
Type of support: Student aid.
Limitations: Applications accepted. Giving primarily in AK.
Publications: Application guidelines; Newsletter (including application guidelines).
Application information: Applicants for Short-Term Vocational Education Program Scholarships must also submit a letter of request that includes employment goals, how the training will relate to your employment goals, and employment opportunities after completion of the training. Application form required.
Initial approach: Download application form and mail to foundation
Deadline(s): Apr. 4 for Higher Education and Vocational Education Scholarships; None for Short-Term Vocational Education Program Scholarships
Board meeting date(s): Quarterly
Officers and Directors: Marie Paul, Pres.; Katrina Johnson, V.P.; Andria Agli, Secy.; Gregory French, Treas.; Greta L. Goto, Exec. Dir.; Jerry Liboff; Evelyn Mujica-Larson; Patrick Patterson III.
Number of staff: 1 full-time professional.
EIN: 920141709

83

Chenega Future, Inc.

3000 C St., Ste. 200 S. Wing
Anchorage, AK 99503-3975   (907) 751-6901
Contact: Patti Andrews, Secy.
FAX: (907) 569-6939;
E-mail: pandrews@chenegacorp.com.; Additional contact: Molly Merrit-Duren, tel.: (907) 677-4987, e-mail: shareholderdevelopment@chenega.com; Additional tel.: (888) 442-5388; Main URL: http://www.chenegafuture.com
Application address: Chenega Future Inc., Shareholder Development Manager, P.O. Box 240988, Anchorage, AK 99524

Donor: Chenega Corp.
Foundation type: Operating foundation.
Financial data (yr. ended 12/31/13): Assets, $15,367 (M); gifts received, $1,323,037; expenditures, $1,359,696; qualifying distributions, $401,325; giving activities include $401,325 for 98 grants to individuals (high: $10,214; low: $15).
Purpose and activities: The foundation awards scholarships for education and training to shareholders and their spouses and descendants of shareholders of Chenega Corp.
Fields of interest: Vocational education; Higher education; American Indians.
Type of support: Internships; Student aid.
Limitations: Applications accepted. Giving limited to AK.

Publications: Application guidelines.
Application information: Application form required.
Initial approach: Download application form and mail to foundation
Deadline(s): May 1 for summer semester, Dec. 1 for spring semester, Aug. 1 for fall semester, 10 days prior to need for short-term vocational or technical training, and Sept. 30 for Chugach School District
Officers and Directors: Patrick C. Selanof, Pres.; Phyllis Pipkin, V.P.; Patricia Totemoff Andrews, Secy.; Joyce L. Kompkoff, Treas.; Lloyd Kompkoff, Exec. Dir.; LaVon Johnson.
EIN: 943111730

84

The Doyon Foundation

615 Bidwell, Ste. 101
Fairbanks, AK 99701-7580   (907) 459-2048
Contact: Doris Miller, Exec. Dir.
FAX: (905) 459-2065;
E-mail: foundation@doyon.com; E-mail for Doris Miller: millerd@doyon.com; Additional tel.: (888) 478-4755; Main URL: http://www.doyonfoundation.com
Doyon Foundation Blog: http://doyonfoundation.wordpress.com
Facebook: http://www.facebook.com/doyonfoundation
Tel. for Tonya. Garnett; (907) 459-2049, e-mail: garnett@doyon.com

Established in 1988 in Alaska.
Donor: Doyon Ltd. and Affiliates.
Foundation type: Company-sponsored foundation.
Financial data (yr. ended 06/30/14): Assets, $19,969,098 (M); gifts received, $1,421,563; expenditures, $1,225,684; qualifying distributions, $705,773; giving activities include $408,945 for 523 grants to individuals (high: $2,500; low: $50).
Purpose and activities: The foundation supports programs designed to improve educational, career, and cultural opportunities for Dayan shareholders. Special emphasis is directed toward programs designed to strengthen Native culture and heritage through education.
Fields of interest: Cultural awareness; Education; Elementary and secondary education; Vocational education; Higher education; American Indians.
Type of support: General support; Internships; Student aid.
Limitations: Applications accepted. Giving primarily in AK.
Publications: Application guidelines; Annual report; Informational brochure; Newsletter.
Application information: Application form required.
Initial approach: Complete online application or download application and mail
Deadline(s): Apr. 15 for Competitive Scholarships; Mar. 15, Apr. 15, and Nov. 15 for Basic Scholarships; Mar. 15, Apr. 15, Sept. 15, and Nov. 15 for Vocational Scholarships
Board meeting date(s): Quarterly
Officers and Board Members: Lanien Livingston, Pres.; Allan Hayton, V.P.; Julie Anderson, Secy.-Treas.; Doris Miller, Exec. Dir.; Paul Mountain; Victor Nicholas; Joshua Peter; Teisha Simmons.
Number of staff: 2 full-time professional.
EIN: 943089624

85
Gillam Foundation
3301 C St., Ste. 500
Anchorage, AK   99503-3956
E-mail: info@gillamfoundation.org
YouTube: http://www.youtube.com/watch?
v=_FtGukRscP4

Established in 2004 in Alaska.
Donors: Robert B. Gillam; McKinley Capital
Management LLC; Robert A. Gillam.
Foundation type: Independent foundation.
Financial data (yr. ended 12/31/13): Assets,
$4,180 (M); gifts received, $132,197;
expenditures, $132,628; qualifying distributions,
$132,628; giving activities include $115,072 for 7
grants (high: $50,000; low: $500).
Purpose and activities: Giving primarily for
scholarship awards to Alaskan graduating seniors to
attend a four-year college or university with intent to
pursue course work in a global commerce field.
Fields of interest: Higher education.
Type of support: General support; Student aid.
Limitations: Applications not accepted. Giving
primarily in Anchorage, AK.
Application information: The foundation's
scholarship program is currently suspended.
Officers and Directors: Robert B. Gillam, Pres. and
Director; Robert Arthur Gillam, V.P. and Treas. and
Director; Diane Wilke, Secy. and Director; J.L.
McCarrey III.
EIN: 300244064

86
Gottstein Family Foundation
935 W. 3rd Ave.
Anchorage, AK   99501-2003

Donor: Barnard J. Gottstein.
Foundation type: Independent foundation.
Financial data (yr. ended 12/31/13): Assets,
$5,326,209 (M); gifts received, $1,748,678;
expenditures, $298,961; qualifying distributions,
$268,335; giving activities include $265,460 for 76
grants (high: $26,000; low: $100).
Purpose and activities: Giving primarily for Jewish
organizations; funding also for the arts and human
services.
Fields of interest: Arts and culture; Museums;
Higher education; Nonprofits; Diseases and
conditions; Judaism; Human services.
Type of support: Research; Regranting.
Limitations: Applications not accepted. Giving
primarily in AK, with emphasis on Anchorage; giving
also in NY. No grants to individuals.
Application information: Contributes only to
pre-selected organizations.
Officers: Barnard J. Gottstein, Pres.; Robert W.
Gottstein, V.P.; James B. Gottstein, Secy.; David R.
Gottstein, Treas.
Directors: Rachel L. Gottstein; Sandra L. Gottstein;
Eytan Jacobsen.
EIN: 943152524

87
Floyd Hooker Foundation
P.O. Box 3865
Soldotna, AK   99669-3865

Foundation type: Independent foundation.

Financial data (yr. ended 12/31/13): Assets,
$791,590 (M); gifts received, $410,618;
expenditures, $349,573; qualifying distributions,
$328,748; giving activities include $328,748 for 23
grants (high: $87,750; low: $710).
Fields of interest: Arts and culture; Education;
Human services.
Limitations: Applications not accepted.
Application information: Unsolicited requests for
funds not accepted.
Trustee: Mark A. Dixson.
EIN: 456524165

88
Juneau Community Foundation
350 N. Franklin St., Ste. 2
Juneau, AK   99801   (907) 463-3223
Contact: Amy Skilbred, Exec. Dir.
FAX: (907) 463-4841; *E-mail:* info@juneaucf.org;
E-Mail for Amy Skilbred: amy@juneaucf.org; Main
URL: http://www.juneaucf.org
Facebook: https://www.facebook.com/pages/
Juneau-Community-Foundation/
281257305264649?ref=br_tf

Established in 2000 in Alaska.
Foundation type: Community foundation.
Financial data (yr. ended 12/31/12): Assets,
$2,298,885 (M); gifts received, $702,233;
expenditures, $314,138; giving activities include
$262,380 for 12 grants (high: $50,000; low: $65).
Purpose and activities: The foundation promotes
philanthropy and effectively responds to the needs
of the community to create a healthy, safe, and
culturally rich environment.
Fields of interest: Performing arts; Natural
resources; Domesticated animals.
Limitations: Giving primarily in the Juneau, AK, area.
No grants to individuals.
Publications: Annual report; Grants list;
Informational brochure.
Application information:
  Deadline(s): Apr. 30 for Scholarships.
  Board meeting date(s): Jan., Apr., June and Oct.
Officers and Directors: Eric Kueffner, Pres. and
Director; Clark Gruening, V.P. and Director; Mike
McKrill, Secy. and Director; Bob Rehfeld, Treas. and
Director; Amy Skilbred, Exec. Dir.; Laraine Derr;
Sioux Douglas; Linda Egan; Sandro Lane; Geoff
Larson; Amanda Mallott; Rick Shattuck; Bob Storer;
Reed Stoops.
Number of staff: 1 part-time professional.
EIN: 522395867

89
Koniag Education Foundation
4241 B. St., Ste. 303B
Anchorage, AK   99503-5920   (907) 562-9093
Contact: Tyan Hayes, Exec. Dir.
FAX: (907) 562-9023;
E-mail: kef@koniageducation.org; Toll-free tel.:
(888) 562-9093; e-mail for Tyan Hayes:
director@koniageducation.org; e-mail for Christina
Fisch: scholarships@koniageducation.org; Main
URL: http://www.koniageducation.org
E Newsletter: http://www.koniageducation.org/
sign-up-for-our-newsletter
Facebook: http://www.facebook.com/pages/
Alaska-Native-Student-Network/59290820727
Grants List: http://www.koniageducation.org/
scholarship-awards

Koniag Education Student Blog: http://
www.koniageducation.org/category/student-blog
Radio Interview with Exective Director Tyan
Hayes: http://www.koniageducation.org/
wp-content/uploads/2012/03/
KEF-on-KMXT-Radio-3-1-2012.mp3
RSS feed: http://www.koniageducation.org/feed

Established in 1993 in Alaska.
Donors: Koniag, Inc.; Gary Sampson; Alyeska
Pipeline Co.; Exxon Mobile.
Foundation type: Company-sponsored foundation.
Financial data (yr. ended 03/31/14): Assets,
$6,498,061 (M); gifts received, $379,366;
expenditures, $534,567; qualifying distributions,
$420,906; giving activities include $259,057 for
grants.
Purpose and activities: The foundation awards
college scholarships and career development grants
to Alaska Native shareholders and descendants of
shareholders of Koniag, Inc.
Fields of interest: Education; Vocational
post-secondary education; Higher education;
Alaskan Natives; American Indians.
Type of support: Internships; Grants to individuals;
Student aid.
Limitations: Applications accepted. Giving primarily
in AK and the Pacific Northwest, with emphasis on
Kodiak Island, AK.
Publications: Application guidelines; Financial
statement; Grants list; Informational brochure;
Newsletter.
Application information: Multi-year funding is not
automatic. Application form required.
  Initial approach: Complete online application or
    download application form and mail to
    foundation
  Deadline(s): Jan. 15 for Angayuk Scholarship &
    Internship; Mar. 15 for KEF General summer
    term; June 1 for KEF General fall term; Aug. 10
    for Alyeksa, Drabek, ExxonMobil, Godfrey, and
    Matfay; None for Career Development Grants
  Board meeting date(s): Quarterly
Officers and Directors: Edward Ward, Pres.; Jon
Panamaroff, V.P.; James Carmichael, Secy.-Treas.;
Tyan Hayes, Exec. Dir.; Loren Anderson; Peter
Boskofsky; Laurie Fagnani; Janissa Johnson;
Jacqueline Madsen; Stephen Parsons; Lorena
Skonberg; Thomas Swensen.
Number of staff: 1 full-time professional; 1 part-time
professional; 1 part-time support.
EIN: 920145017

90
Steve Nash Foundation
9400 Sugar Cir.
Anchorage, AK   99507-6033   (907) 274-0629
Contact: Jenny L. Miller, Exec. Dir.
E-mail: jenny@stevenash.org; Main URL: https://
stevenash.org
Facebook: https://m.facebook.com/stevenash
Instagram: https://instagram.com/stevenashfdn
Twitter: https://twitter.com/SteveNashFdn

Established in 2001 in Texas.
Donors: Stephen Nash; Icap; Natasha Ahuja; Walton
Family Foundation; Steve Nash Sports Club; Phoenix
Suns Charities; Major League Soccer; Glaceau;
Calle; Phebe's Tavern/East Pub; Indochino;
Neurosurgery and Endovascular Associates; St.
Boniface Hospital; United Way of Greater
Milwaukee; Namrata Ahuja; Anne Penn.
Foundation type: Independent foundation.

Financial data (yr. ended 12/31/12): Assets, $163,275 (M); gifts received, $307,406; expenditures, $445,414; qualifying distributions, $156,240; giving activities include $156,240 for grants.

Purpose and activities: The foundation is dedicated to assisting underserved children in their health, personal development, education and enjoyment of life. The foundation awards grants to youth-focused organizations that foster childrens development by addressing underlying conditions of poverty, medical need, and restricted access to those resources that contribute to their well-being. The foundation looks for organizations that work directly with children, or those that work to benefit children through social change and policy reform.

Fields of interest: Health; Youth development; Children; Low-income and poor people.

International interests: Canada; Paraguay; Uganda.

Type of support: General support.

Limitations: Applications accepted. Giving primarily in AZ; some giving also other regions of the U.S. and in British Columbia, Canada, Paraguay, and Uganda. No support for governmental agencies, or for religious programs or programs based within a religious institution, schools, colleges or university administrations or for sports teams or sporting events. No grants to individuals, or for salaries, general operating expenses or travel.

Application information: Application form required.
Initial approach: See website for application form
Deadline(s): See website for deadline
Board meeting date(s): Mar. and Sept.

Officers: Stephen Nash, Pres.; Joann Nash, Secy.-Treas.; Jenny Miller, Exec. Dir.

EIN: 311753206

91
Harvey Samuelsen Scholarship Trust
P.O. Box 1464
Dillingham, AK 99576-1464 (907) 842-4370

Donors: Bristol Bay Econ. Devel. Corp.; American Seafoods Co.; Arctic Fjord, Inc.; Artic Storm, Inc.

Foundation type: Independent foundation.

Financial data (yr. ended 12/31/13): Assets, $11,328,074 (M); gifts received, $421,935; expenditures, $639,797; qualifying distributions, $531,964; giving activities include $412,003 for 86 grants to individuals (high: $8,386; low: $2,280).

Purpose and activities: Scholarships to residents of Bristol Bay CDQ communities: Alcknagik, Clarks Point, Dillingham, Egegik, Ekuk, King Salmon, Levelock, Manokotak, Naknek, Pilot Point, Port Heiden, Portage Creek, South Naknek, Togiak, Twin Hills and Ugashik, AK, who are enrolled in an accredited college or university, are able to demonstrate financial need, are registered as a full-time student and are pursuing an Associates degree or higher. Freshman and sophomores must have a minimum of a 2.0 current and cumulative GPA, juniors and seniors must have a minimum of 2.5, and graduate students must have a minimum of 3.0.

Fields of interest: Higher education.

Type of support: Student aid.

Limitations: Applications accepted. Giving primarily to residents of AK.

Application information: All scholarship applications will be scored according to the application form's attached scoring sheet. The top 20 applicants will receive an additional $500.00. Faxed applications will not be accepted. Application form required.
Initial approach: Completed application form

Officers: Mary Ann K. Johnson, Pres.; Fritz Sharp, V.P.; Patrick Patterson, Jr., Secy.; Gerda Kosbruk, Treas.

Board Members: Cindy Gabel; Kenneth Jensen.

EIN: 300065137

92
UIC Foundation, Inc.
3201 C St., Ste. 801
Anchorage, AK 99503 (907) 852-4460
Contact: Rebecca Brower
FAX: (907) 852-4459;
E-mail: uicfoundation@uicalaska.com; Application Address: P.O. Box 890, Barrow, AK-99723; Main URL: http://www.uicalaska.com/shareholders/uic-foundation

Established in 1994 in Alaska.

Donors: Ukpeagvik Inupiat Corp.; National Park Svc.; UIC Construction LLC.

Foundation type: Company-sponsored foundation.

Financial data (yr. ended 12/31/13): Assets, $238,920 (M); gifts received, $357,774; expenditures, $178,370; qualifying distributions, $178,780; giving activities include $177,718 for 140 grants to individuals (high: $5,000; low: $100).

Purpose and activities: The foundation awards college scholarships to shareholders and descendants of shareholders of Ukpeagvik Inupiat Corporation.

Fields of interest: Education; Higher education.

Type of support: Student aid.

Limitations: Applications accepted. Giving primarily in AK, with emphasis on Barrow. No support for organizations that do not benefit shareholders and descendents of shareholders of Ukpeagvik Inupiat Corporation.

Publications: Application guidelines; Financial statement.

Application information: Grants generally do not exceed $5,000. Application form required.
Initial approach: Download application form and mail to foundation for scholarships
Copies of proposal: 1
Deadline(s): Mar. 1, May 1, Aug. 1, and Dec. 1 for scholarships
Final notification: 2 weeks following deadlines

Officer and Directors: Justin Thomas, Pres. and Director; David Klopp; Tom Martelle; Steve Cronic.

Number of staff: 1 full-time support.

EIN: 920157584

ARIZONA

93
Adelante Foundation Inc.
P.O. Box 488
Chandler, AZ 85244-0488 (480) 895-9350
Contact: Barbara Jefferson

Established in 1999 in Arizona.
Donors: Edward N. Basha, Jr.; Bashas', Inc.; Western American Prints; Tralside Gallery, LLC; William Romley; Bashas Benefit Golf Classic; Don Ulrich; Nadine K. Mathis Basha; Esma Basha Memorial.
Foundation type: Independent foundation.
Financial data (yr. ended 12/31/12): Assets, $4,392,077 (M); gifts received, $144,606; expenditures, $272,781; qualifying distributions, $208,601; giving activities include $168,585 for 89 grants (high: $28,650; low: $25), $20,016 for 13 grants to individuals (high: $4,000; low: $303), and $20,000 for 3 employee matching gifts.
Fields of interest: Higher education; Health; Human services.
Type of support: General support.
Limitations: Applications accepted. Giving primarily in AZ.
Application information: Application form required.
  Initial approach: Request application
  Deadline(s): For scholarships: 90 days before needed
Directors: Edward N. Basha, Jr.; Nadine K. Mathis Basha.
EIN: 860966575

94
Richard C. Adkerson Family Foundation
333 N. Central Ave., 26th Fl.
Phoenix, AZ 85004-4414

Established in 1996 in Louisiana.
Donors: Freeport McMoran Copper & Gold; Richard C. Adkerson.
Foundation type: Independent foundation.
Financial data (yr. ended 12/31/13): Assets, $15,360,571 (M); gifts received, $80,000; expenditures, $369,437; qualifying distributions, $320,000; giving activities include $320,000 for 5 grants (high: $225,000; low: $10,000).
Fields of interest: Education; Basketball; Human services.
Limitations: Applications not accepted. Giving primarily in MS. No grants to individuals.
Application information: Unsolicited requests for funds not accepted.
Trustees: Richard C. Adkerson; Richard Clark Adkerson; William Tyler Adkerson.
EIN: 721353058

95
Ahearn Family Foundation
c/o Eizabeth Anderson
2390 E. Camelback Rd., Ste. 203
Phoenix, AZ 85016-3450

Established in 2007 in Arizona.
Donor: Michael J. Ahearn.
Foundation type: Independent foundation.

Financial data (yr. ended 12/31/13): Assets, $8,849,325 (M); expenditures, $249,875; qualifying distributions, $239,223; giving activities include $237,223 for 18 grants (high: $80,000; low: $50).
Purpose and activities: Giving primarily to a college scholarship foundation; some funding also for human services.
Fields of interest: Education; Human services.
Type of support: Individual development.
Limitations: Applications not accepted. Giving primarily in AZ. No grants to individuals.
Application information: Contributes only to pre-selected organizations.
Trustees: Gayle S. Ahearn; Michael J. Ahearn.
EIN: 137582929

96
Arizona Eastern Star Retirement Center
4600 N. 24th St.
Phoenix, AZ 85016-5204

Donor: Catherine J. Martin†.
Foundation type: Independent foundation.
Financial data (yr. ended 12/31/13): Assets, $520,979 (M); expenditures, $368,778; qualifying distributions, $201,571; giving activities include $195,017 for 1 grant.
Fields of interest: Convalescent care.
Limitations: Applications not accepted. Giving primarily in Phoenix, AZ.
Application information: Unsolicited requests for funds not accepted.
Officers: Terry Loll, Pres.; Barbara Wunder, V.P.; Ruth Brannan, Secy.; Ken Du Bois, Treas.
Director: Charlotte Guild.
EIN: 860131598

97
Fred & Christine Armstrong Foundation
335 N. Wilmot Rd., Ste. 300
Tucson, AZ 85711-2688
Application address: c/o Karen K. Frey, Pres., P.O. Box 12867, Tucson, AZ 85732-2867, tel.: (520) 760-2981

Established in 1994 in Arizona.
Donor: Fred E. Armstrong, Sr.†.
Foundation type: Independent foundation.
Financial data (yr. ended 06/30/14): Assets, $5,629,099 (M); expenditures, $328,794; qualifying distributions, $263,676; giving activities include $250,000 for 34 grants (high: $20,000; low: $2,000).
Fields of interest: Arts and culture; Music; Historic preservation; Education; Health; Pediatrics; Diseases and conditions; Arthritis; Christianity; Human services; Food aid; Children and youth; Low-income and poor people; Victims of crime and abuse.
Type of support: Research.
Limitations: Applications accepted. Giving primarily in AZ and TX. No grants to individuals.
Application information:
  Initial approach: Letter
  Deadline(s): None
Officers and Directors: Karen K. Frey, Pres. and Treas. and Director; Fred E. Armstrong, Jr., V.P. and Director; William W. Lynch, Jr., Secy. and Director; Samuel T. Armstrong, Jr.
EIN: 860779817

98
Madeline Hunter Babbitt Trust
c/o Arizona Bank and Trust Co.
2036 E. Camelback Rd.
Phoenix, AZ 85016-4711

Donor: George Babbitt†.
Foundation type: Independent foundation.
Financial data (yr. ended 09/30/13): Assets, $7,045,952 (M); expenditures, $356,226; qualifying distributions, $342,588; giving activities include $328,100 for 1 grant.
Fields of interest: Catholicism; Human services.
Limitations: Applications not accepted. Giving primarily in Phoenix, AZ.
Application information: Contributes only to pre-selected organizations.
Trustee: Arizona Bank and Trust.
EIN: 866213247

99
Lon D. and Lucille Barton Charitable Foundation
38093 South Samaniego Dr.
Tucson, AZ 85739-1019

Established in 1984 in Illinois.
Donor: Florence Lucille Barton.
Foundation type: Independent foundation.
Financial data (yr. ended 12/31/12): Assets, $6,332,153 (M); expenditures, $339,650; qualifying distributions, $328,000; giving activities include $328,000 for grants.
Fields of interest: Education; Higher education; Diseases and conditions; Protestantism; Human services; Low-income and poor people.
Type of support: Research.
Limitations: Applications not accepted. Giving primarily in AZ and IL. No grants to individuals.
Application information: Contributes only to pre-selected organizations.
Officers: John F. Schmidt, Pres. and Treas.; Margaret Schmidt, Secy.
Director: Tom Schmidt.
EIN: 371161757

100
Vaughn L. & Eleanore M. Beals Charitable Foundation
23005 N. 74th St., Villa 1409
Scottsdale, AZ 85255-7500

Established in 1989 in Wisconsin.
Donors: Vaughn L. Beals; Eleanore M. Beals.
Foundation type: Independent foundation.
Financial data (yr. ended 12/31/14): Assets, $4,371,447 (M); expenditures, $270,957; qualifying distributions, $238,312; giving activities include $235,000 for 12 grants (high: $200,000; low: $250).
Purpose and activities: Giving primarily for education, health care, and community services.
Fields of interest: Arts and culture; Museums; Education; Higher education; Hospital care; Diseases and conditions; Multiple sclerosis; Human services.
International interests: Canada.
Type of support: General support.
Limitations: Applications not accepted. Giving primarily in AZ, MA, OH and OR. No grants to individuals.

Application information: Contributes only to pre-selected organizations.
Trustees: Eleanore M. Beals; Vaughn L. Beals, Jr.
EIN: 391653407

101
Howard R. & Joy M. Berlin Foundation
2007 Smoketree Dr.
P.O. Box 3731
Carefree, AZ 85377-3731

Established in 1994 in Delaware.
Donors: Howard R. Berlin; Joy M. Berlin.
Foundation type: Independent foundation.
Financial data (yr. ended 09/30/14): Assets, $4,397,076 (M); expenditures, $342,637; qualifying distributions, $332,650; giving activities include $332,650 for 24 grants (high: $255,000; low: $150).
Purpose and activities: Giving primarily to museums for Native American culture, as well as to a public charity, a Jewish organization, other to arts and federated giving programs.
Fields of interest: Arts and culture; Ethnic museums; Higher education; Foundations; Nonprofits; Judaism; Human services.
Type of support: Regranting.
Limitations: Applications not accepted. Giving primarily in AZ and NM. No grants to individuals.
Application information: Unsolicited requests for funds not accepted.
Officers and Directors: Howard R. Berlin, Sr., Pres. and Director; Joy M. Berlin, V.P. and Director; Carter F. Berlin; Howard R. Berlin, Jr.
EIN: 223330579

102
Burns Family Foundation
4228 E. Claremont Ave.
Paradise Valley, AZ 85253-3950
E-mail: BoydGentry@aol.com

Established in 1953 in Illinois.
Donors: Arthur E. Keating†; Edward Keating.
Foundation type: Independent foundation.
Financial data (yr. ended 12/31/13): Assets, $3,734,050 (L); expenditures, $208,021; qualifying distributions, $176,690; giving activities include $150,885 for 21 grants (high: $25,000; low: $100).
Purpose and activities: Giving primarily for education, the environment, and children services.
Fields of interest: Elementary and secondary education; Higher education; Natural resources; Hospital care; Christianity; Sports and recreation; Family services; Child welfare.
Type of support: General support.
Limitations: Applications not accepted. Giving primarily in AZ and CA. No grants to individuals.
Application information: Contributes only to pre-selected organizations.
Board meeting date(s): Annually
Officers: Patricia Boyd Gentry, Pres.; Wendy B. Collins, V.P.
Directors: Robin B. Alden; Julie A. Wrigley.
Number of staff: 1
EIN: 366051686

103
C & J Foundation
(formerly C & J Charitable Trust Foundation)
1665 Maguire Dr.
Wickenburg, AZ 85390-3139

Established in 1989 in Indiana.
Donors: James C. Quayle†; Corinne P. Quayle.
Foundation type: Independent foundation.
Financial data (yr. ended 06/30/15): Assets, $4,638,576 (M); expenditures, $341,402; qualifying distributions, $326,500; giving activities include $310,000 for 18 grants (high: $50,000; low: $5,000).
Fields of interest: Museums; Undergraduate education; Cancers; Prostate cancer; Religion.
Type of support: Research.
Limitations: Applications not accepted. Giving primarily in AZ, IN, MD and TX. No grants to individuals.
Application information: Contributes only to pre-selected organizations.
Officers: Corinne P. Quayle, Chair.; Christopher Quayle, Pres.
Directors: James Danforth "Dan" Quayle; Michael Quayle; Martha Thomas.
EIN: 861026568

104
Cadeau Foundation
c/o Vicki J. Rutter
134 Wood Canyon Rd.
Patagonia, AZ 85624-6103

Established in 1990 in Washington.
Donors: Natalie Bryant; Sam Henry Trust.
Foundation type: Independent foundation.
Financial data (yr. ended 12/31/13): Assets, $6,736,334 (M); gifts received, $144,000; expenditures, $290,631; qualifying distributions, $225,750; giving activities include $225,750 for 52 grants (high: $22,100; low: $1,500).
Purpose and activities: Giving primarily for education, environmental conservation, and animal welfare.
Fields of interest: Arts and culture; Performing arts; Education; Higher education; Natural resources; Domesticated animals; Animal welfare; Health; Hospital care; Family planning; Community and economic development; Human services; Food aid.
Type of support: General support.
Limitations: Applications not accepted. No grants to individuals.
Application information: Contributes only to pre-selected organizations.
Officer: Vicki J. Rutter, Admin.
Advisory Committee: Philip Crissman; Lawrence D. Johnson; Chris D. Mikkelsen; Wendy Ninteman; Patrick J. West.
Trustee: Gail H. Goheen.
EIN: 911484455

105
Frances Chapin Foundation
2346 E. Placita de la Victoria
Tucson, AZ 85718-1212

Established in 1966 in Virginia.
Donor: Frances C. Crook†.
Foundation type: Independent foundation.

Financial data (yr. ended 03/31/15): Assets, $5,086,356 (M); expenditures, $445,592; qualifying distributions, $367,505; giving activities include $350,000 for 1 grant.
Fields of interest: Nonprofits; Human services.
Type of support: Regranting.
Limitations: Applications not accepted. Giving primarily in AZ. No grants to individuals.
Application information: Unsolicited requests for funds not accepted.
Officer and Director: Robert Maxfield, Pres. and Director.
EIN: 226087456

106
R. & M. Clark Family Foundation
c/o Marcella S. Clark
7501 E. Thompson Peak Pkwy., Ste. 123
Scottsdale, AZ 85255-4517

Established in 1994 in Arizona.
Donor: Marcella S. Clark.
Foundation type: Independent foundation.
Financial data (yr. ended 12/31/14): Assets, $4,733,488; expenditures, $254,081; qualifying distributions, $221,855.
Fields of interest: Higher education; Alzheimer's disease; Human services; Youth services; Adult and child mentoring.
Limitations: Applications not accepted. No grants to individuals.
Application information: Unsolicited requests for funds not accepted.
Officers and Directors: Marcella S. Clark, Pres. and Director; Carole Lee Randall, V.P.; Thomas E. Clark, Secy.-Treas.; James W. Clark.
EIN: 860778653

107
David and Ruth Coleman Charitable Foundation, Inc.
4431 E. Sunset Dr.
Phoenix, AZ 85028-6112 (480) 367-7367
Contact: Mark Sklar, Pres. and Dir.

Established in 1993 in Wisconsin.
Donors: Ruth Coleman; Ida Soref.
Foundation type: Independent foundation.
Financial data (yr. ended 12/31/13): Assets, $6,941,070 (M); expenditures, $251,583; qualifying distributions, $195,000; giving activities include $195,000 for 6 grants (high: $120,000; low: $5,000).
Fields of interest: Orchestral music; Elementary and secondary education; Judaism; Senior assisted living.
Type of support: General support.
Limitations: Applications accepted. Giving primarily in Milwaukee, WI. No grants to individuals.
Application information:
Initial approach: Proposal
Deadline(s): None
Officers and Directors: Mark Sklar, Pres. and Director; Michael Sklar, V.P. and Director; Roberta Gorenstein Caraway, Secy. and Director; Maggie Glezer, Treas. and Director.
EIN: 391772862

108
Community Finance Corporation
335 N. Wilmot Rd., Ste. 420
Tucson, AZ   85711-3325

Established in 2000 in Arizona.
Foundation type: Independent foundation.
Financial data (yr. ended 09/30/14): Assets, $904,943,212 (M); expenditures, $156,883,485; qualifying distributions, $290,000; giving activities include $290,000 for 10 grants (high: $50,000; low: $5,000).
Fields of interest: University education; Foundations; Nonprofits.
Type of support: Regranting.
Limitations: Applications not accepted. Giving primarily in AZ. No grants to individuals.
Application information: Contributes only to pre-selected organizations.
Officers: Michael Hammond, Pres.; Kendall Bert, Secy.; Michael Arnold, Treas.
Trustees: Kenneth Abrahams; Kathleen Perkins.
EIN: 860683138

109
Cooper Family Foundation
8912 E. Pinnacle Peak Rd., Ste. F9-663
Scottsdale, AZ   85255-3615   (602) 909-4173
Contact: Mary I. Cooper, Dir.

Established in 1998 in Arizona.
Donors: John and Mary Logser Charitable Lead Trust; John Cooper; Mary Cooper; John and Mary Cooper Charitable Lead Annuity Trust.
Foundation type: Independent foundation.
Financial data (yr. ended 12/31/13): Assets, $1,703,432 (M); expenditures, $361,882; qualifying distributions, $349,817; giving activities include $349,700 for 19 grants (high: $70,000; low: $1,500).
Purpose and activities: Giving primarily for children, youth, and social services and to Christian organizations.
Fields of interest: Christianity; Human services; Child welfare; Youth development.
Limitations: Applications accepted. Giving primarily in NY.
Application information: Application form required.
   Initial approach: Letter
   Deadline(s): None
Directors: Christine Cooper; Gary Cooper; John Cooper; Mary Cooper.
EIN: 860905824

110
Robert Kemper Corrigan Foundation
P.O. Box 10392
Phoenix, AZ   85064-0392

Donor: Robert K. Corrigan Family RevocTrust.
Foundation type: Independent foundation.
Financial data (yr. ended 12/31/12): Assets, $641,343 (M); expenditures, $277,955; qualifying distributions, $233,048; giving activities include $227,828 for 5 grants (high: $135,000; low: $8,000).
Fields of interest: Human services.
Limitations: Applications not accepted. Giving primarily in AZ.
Application information: Unsolicited requests for funds not accepted.

Officers: Nancy E. Ball, Pres.; Carol Callahan, V.P.
EIN: 263652876

111
Declaration of Trust of the Joseph and Mary Cacioppo Foundation
4769 E. Camp Lowell Dr.
Tucson, AZ   85712-1256   (520) 326-0703
Contact: Michael-Anne Young, C.E.O. and Tr.

Foundation type: Independent foundation.
Financial data (yr. ended 06/30/14): Assets, $9,932,125 (M); expenditures, $526,819; qualifying distributions, $467,152; giving activities include $199,750 for 24 grants (high: $25,000; low: $750).
Fields of interest: Arts and culture; Museums; Education; Housing development.
Limitations: Applications accepted. Giving primarily in AZ.
Application information: Application form required.
   Initial approach: Contact foundation for application
   Deadline(s): Contact foundation for deadline
Officer and Trustees: Michael-Anne Young, C.E.O. and Trustee; Craig Wills.
EIN: 455596626

112
Dove Foundation
13123 E. Speedway Blvd.
Tucson, AZ   85748-7125

Established in 1986 in Arizona.
Foundation type: Independent foundation.
Financial data (yr. ended 12/31/12): Assets, $3,485,854 (M); expenditures, $283,875; qualifying distributions, $283,875; giving activities include $282,120 for 12 grants (high: $125,000; low: $1,000).
Purpose and activities: Funding primarily for human services.
Fields of interest: Ear, nose and throat diseases; Christianity; Human services.
Type of support: General support.
Limitations: Applications not accepted. Giving primarily in Tucson, AZ and MD. No grants to individuals.
Application information: Contributes only to pre-selected organizations.
Officers: D. Elaine Welp, Pres.; Theodore M. Welp, Secy.-Treas.
Trustee: Katherine M. Nesci.
EIN: 860570382

113
The John and Kathleen Drexler Foundation
c/o Ronald Blue & Co., LLC
60 E. Rio Salado Pkwy.
Tempe, AZ   85281-9124

Established in 2004 in Arizona.
Donors: Kathleen Drexler; John Drexler; Drexler Enterprises, Inc.; Tim Drexler; Pam Drexler.
Foundation type: Independent foundation.
Financial data (yr. ended 12/31/12): Assets, $127,251 (M); gifts received, $120,808; expenditures, $153,140; qualifying distributions, $142,465; giving activities include $142,465 for grants.

Fields of interest: Protestantism; Human services; Child welfare.
Limitations: Applications not accepted. Giving primarily in Scottsdale and Temple, AZ, Hillsborough, CA, and Greenwood Village, CO. No grants to individuals.
Application information: Contributes only to pre-selected organizations.
Officers: John Drexler, Pres.; Michael L. Searcy, Secy.; Kathleen Drexler, Treas.
EIN: 201064161

114
E. Blois du Bois Foundation Inc.
3370 N. Hayden Rd., Ste. 123
P.O. Box 319
Scottsdale, AZ   85251-6632   (480) 874-2226

Established in 1960 in Arizona.
Donor: E. Blois du Bois†.
Foundation type: Independent foundation.
Financial data (yr. ended 05/31/13): Assets, $4,585,230 (M); expenditures, $449,748; qualifying distributions, $427,832; giving activities include $407,500 for 3 grants (high: $400,000; low: $2,500).
Fields of interest: Education; Human services.
Limitations: Applications accepted. Giving limited to AZ. No grants to individuals directly, or for endowment funds.
Application information: Application form required.
   Initial approach: Contact foundation for application form
   Deadline(s): None
Officers: Gail Horne, Pres. and Treas.; Karen Mandell, Secy.
Director: Robert Horne.
EIN: 866052886

115
The Eaton Family Foundation
2400 E. Arizona Biltmore Cir., Bldg. 2, Ste. 1270
Phoenix, AZ   85016-2107

Established in 1998 in Arizona.
Donor: David H. Eaton.
Foundation type: Independent foundation.
Financial data (yr. ended 12/31/13): Assets, $0 (M); expenditures, $286,025; qualifying distributions, $283,347; giving activities include $283,284 for 12 grants (high: $151,024; low: $500).
Fields of interest: Education; Higher education; Christianity; Human services.
Limitations: Applications not accepted. Giving primarily in AZ, CA, and CO. No grants to individuals.
Application information: Contributes only to pre-selected organizations.
   Board meeting date(s): Jan.
Officers: Carol E. Eaton, Pres.; David H. Eaton, V.P. and Secy.-Treas.
Director: Leslie Eaton Vance.
EIN: 860917731

116
Empire Charitable Foundation
1725 S. Country Club Dr.
Mesa, AZ   85210-6003

Established in 2007 in Arizona.

Donor: Empire Southwest LLC.
Foundation type: Independent foundation.
Financial data (yr. ended 12/31/13): Assets, $0 (M); gifts received, $150,000; expenditures, $237,916; qualifying distributions, $237,916; giving activities include $232,025 for 41 grants (high: $100,000; low: $15), and $5,000 for 1 grant to an individual.
Fields of interest: Religion; Human services.
Limitations: Applications not accepted. Giving primarily in AZ. No grants to individuals.
Application information: Unsolicited requests for funds not accepted.
Officers: Jeffrey S. Whiteman, Pres. and Secy.-Treas.; Christopher W. Zahans, V.P.
EIN: 208116534

117
The F2 Family Foundation, Inc.
4469 Moonlight Way
Paradise Valley, AZ 85253
E-mail for Juanita Francis: nitafrancis@msn.com

Established in 2003 in Delaware.
Donors: Philip L. Francis; Juanita F. Francis.
Foundation type: Independent foundation.
Financial data (yr. ended 12/31/14): Assets, $3,019,309; gifts received, $0; expenditures, $344,759; qualifying distributions, $306,403 and $0 for set-asides.
Purpose and activities: Giving primarily for health care and education, with a focus on philanthropy for the next generation.
Fields of interest: Education; Health; Human services; Family services; Child welfare; Children and youth; Adults.
Type of support: Curriculum development; Endowments; Program development; Capital campaigns; General support.
Limitations: Applications not accepted. Giving primarily in AZ, IL and TX.
Application information: Unsolicited requests for funds not accepted.
  Board meeting date(s): July and Dec.
Officers and Directors: Juanita F. Francis, Pres. and Director; Philip Francis, V.P. and Director.
Number of staff: None.
EIN: 320046917

118
P. and T. Feenstra Family Foundation
18521 E. Queen Creek Rd.
Queen Creek, AZ 85142-5866

Established in 2005 in Arizona.
Donors: Tami Feenstra; Patrick W. Feenstra; Feenstra Investment, LLC.
Foundation type: Independent foundation.
Financial data (yr. ended 12/31/13): Assets, $720,106 (M); expenditures, $226,109; qualifying distributions, $207,500; giving activities include $207,500 for 10 grants (high: $100,000; low: $1,500).
Fields of interest: Christianity.
Limitations: Applications not accepted. Giving primarily in AZ.
Application information: Unsolicited requests for funds not accepted.
Trustees: Patrick W. Feenstra; Tami Feenstra.
EIN: 206648534

119
The Forsberg Charitable Foundation Inc.
14550 N. Frank Lloyd Wright Blvd., Ste. 200
Scottsdale, AZ 85260-6158

Foundation type: Independent foundation.
Financial data (yr. ended 12/31/13): Assets, $6,080,466 (M); expenditures, $311,194; qualifying distributions, $300,000; giving activities include $300,000 for 14 grants (high: $75,000; low: $7,500).
Fields of interest: Education; Christianity; Protestantism.
Type of support: General support.
Limitations: Applications not accepted. Giving primarily in AZ, CO, and MN.
Application information: Contributes only to pre-selected organizations.
Officer: Sherman M. Rorvig, Pres.
EIN: 204653999

120
Freedom Wireless Foundation
18801 N. Thompson Peak, Ste. 240
Scottsdale, AZ 85255-6348 (480) 584-5354
E-mail: MTD@freedomwirelessfoundation.org; *Main URL:* http://www.freedomwirelessfoundation.org

Donor: Freedom Wireless Inc.
Foundation type: Independent foundation.
Financial data (yr. ended 12/31/13): Assets, $30,766 (M); gifts received, $350,000; expenditures, $327,135; qualifying distributions, $326,153; giving activities include $320,000 for 3 grants (high: $230,000; low: $15,000).
Fields of interest: Basketball.
Limitations: Applications accepted. Giving primarily in AZ.
Application information: Application form required.
  Initial approach: Completed grant application form
  Deadline(s): None
Directors: Douglas V. Fougnies; Larry L. Day; Kenneth Widner.
EIN: 262692248

121
Teaumen & Grace Fuite Foundation
4314 E. Fairmount Ave.
Phoenix, AZ 85018-5431

Donors: Grace A. Fuite†; Teaumen A. Fuite.
Foundation type: Independent foundation.
Financial data (yr. ended 12/31/14): Assets, $5,952,389 (M); expenditures, $306,285; qualifying distributions, $300,500; giving activities include $300,500 for 13 grants (high: $41,000; low: $3,500).
Fields of interest: Health.
Type of support: General support.
Limitations: Applications not accepted. Giving primarily in AZ. No grants to individuals.
Application information: Unsolicited requests for funds not accepted.
Officers: Dolores G. de Werd, Pres.; Cynthia McGregor, V.P.; Susan L. de Werd, Secy.; Sandra Morse, Treas.
EIN: 860744807

122
Garcia Family Foundation
4020 E. Indian School Rd., Ste. A
Phoenix, AZ 85018-5220 (602) 778-5011
Contact: Nancy V. Young, V.P. and Treas.

Established in 1996 in Arizona.
Donors: Ernest C. Garcia II; Verde Investments, Inc.; Joanne Garcia.
Foundation type: Independent foundation.
Financial data (yr. ended 11/30/13): Assets, $8,296,061 (M); gifts received, $3,690,806; expenditures, $376,846; qualifying distributions, $352,351; giving activities include $348,500 for 9 grants (high: $250,000; low: $1,000).
Fields of interest: Higher education; Human services; Family services; Child welfare; Homeless services; Low-income and poor people.
Limitations: Applications accepted. Giving primarily in AZ.
Application information: Application form required.
  Initial approach: Proposal
  Deadline(s): None
Officers: Ernest C. Garcia II, Pres.; Nancy V. Young, V.P. and Treas.; Steven P. Johnson, Secy.
EIN: 311490067

123
The Ted and Lorraine Glasrud Family Foundation, Inc.
5032 E. Cochise Rd.
Paradise Valley, AZ 85253-1068
Contact: Deborah Lentsch, C.E.O.

Established in 2006 in Minnesota.
Donors: Theodore G. Glasrud; Deborah G. Lentsch; Sharon E. Glasrud.
Foundation type: Independent foundation.
Financial data (yr. ended 12/31/13): Assets, $4,673,018 (M); expenditures, $235,943; qualifying distributions, $224,025; giving activities include $224,000 for 21 grants (high: $20,000; low: $4,000).
Fields of interest: Diseases and conditions; Human services.
Limitations: Applications accepted. Giving primarily in FL and MN.
Application information:
  Initial approach: Letter
  Deadline(s): None
Officers: Deborah Lentsch, C.E.O.; Sharon E. Glasrud, Secy.
EIN: 300094715

124
Goldberg Family Foundation
(formerly Mother Tried Foundation)
10115 E. Bell Rd., Ste. 107
P.O. Box 481
Scottsdale, AZ 85260

Donor: Rita Goldberg†.
Foundation type: Independent foundation.
Financial data (yr. ended 12/31/13): Assets, $4,078,025 (M); expenditures, $279,585; qualifying distributions, $247,699; giving activities include $168,800 for 25 grants (high: $20,000; low: $500).
Fields of interest: Diseases and conditions; Human services; Children.

Limitations: Applications not accepted. Giving primarily in AZ and FL. No grants to individuals.
Application information: Unsolicited requests for funds not accepted.
Directors: Barry Goldberg; Gene Goldberg; Mark Goldberg.
EIN: 261805497

125
William M. & Ann K. Grace Foundation
c/o William Matt Grace Development Co.
7575 N. 16th St., Ste. 1
Phoenix, AZ 85020-4625   (602) 956-8254
FAX: (602) 943-3548;
E-mail: ronrichards@wmgracefoundation.com; Main URL: http://www.wmgracefoundation.com
Facebook: https://www.facebook.com/ron.richards.583

Established in 2005 in Arizona.
Donor: Ann K. Grace Charitable Lea Ann Trust.
Foundation type: Independent foundation.
Financial data (yr. ended 12/31/14): Assets, $13,301,375; gifts received, $1,884,100; expenditures, $435,285; qualifying distributions, $428,744.
Purpose and activities: The foundation provides individual scholarships directly to students (for all levels of school, including private grade schools, high schools, colleges, universities) with scholarships given for merit or need. Individuals must maintain a 2.0 GPA or greater with 12 or more credit hours/semester. The foundation also makes grants for existing scholarship funds, as well as grants directly to schools for facilities, scholarships or general support. The foundation strongly encourages and gives preference to matching funds where it concerns grants to organizations.
Fields of interest: Higher education.
Type of support: General support; Matching grants; Scholarships; Student aid.
Limitations: Applications accepted. Giving primarily in AZ and northwest MO.
Application information: The foundation strongly encourages and gives preference to matching funds. Application form required.
  Initial approach: Submit application form (which can be downloaded from foundation web site) via U.S. mail, fax or e-mail
  Deadline(s): Nov. 15
Officers and Board Members: Howard T. Grace, Pres. and Director; Barb Grace; Matt Grace; Heather G. Kaiser.
Directors: Kate Kaiser; Ron Richards.
EIN: 562529760

126
Harold and Jean Grossman Family Foundation
7301 E. 3rd Ave., Ste. 214
Scottsdale, AZ 85251   (480) 941-2855
Contact: Ryna Jean Grossman, Pres.

Established in 1990 in Arizona.
Donors: Harold I. Grossman†; Ryan Jean Grossman.
Foundation type: Independent foundation.
Financial data (yr. ended 12/31/13): Assets, $5,993,054 (M); expenditures, $374,767; qualifying distributions, $279,695; giving activities include $279,695 for 86 grants (high: $25,000; low: $20).

Purpose and activities: Primary areas of interest include child welfare, family services, cancer treatment and research, museums, and Jewish organizations.
Fields of interest: Performing arts; Museums; Education; Elementary and secondary education; Early childhood education; Nonprofits; Health; Family planning; Diseases and conditions; Cancers; Science; Judaism; Human services; Family services; Child welfare.
Type of support: Continuing support; Matching grants; Annual campaigns; Capital campaigns; Capital and infrastructure; Equipment; Program development; Curriculum development; Research; Regranting.
Limitations: Applications accepted. Giving primarily in Phoenix, AZ. No grants to individuals.
Application information: Application form required.
  Initial approach: Letter
  Deadline(s): None
Officers: Ryna Jean Grossman, Pres.; Judy Johnson, Secy.; David Schuman, Treas.
EIN: 860649389

127
The Robert & Marie Hansen Foundation
10645 N. Oracle Rd., Ste. , 121, No. 338
Oro Valley, AZ   85737   (520) 219-5407

Established in 2002 in Arizona.
Donors: Paul T. Clifton; John P. Hansen; Karen A. Clifton; Mark W. Hansen; Marie E. Hansen; Susan Lea Clifton.
Foundation type: Independent foundation.
Financial data (yr. ended 06/30/14): Assets, $9,569,987 (M); expenditures, $518,730; qualifying distributions, $346,693; giving activities include $280,000 for 5 grants (high: $200,000; low: $5,000).
Fields of interest: Education; Public affairs; Catholicism; Human services.
Type of support: Research; Program development; Curriculum development; Annual campaigns.
Publications: Informational brochure (including application guidelines).
Application information:
  Initial approach: Proposal
  Copies of proposal: 1
  Deadline(s): None
Trustees: Paul T. Clifton; Susan Lea Clifton; Tiara Zarcone, V.P.; Marie E. Hansen.
EIN: 866309859

128
Dorothy and Bill Harmsen, Sr. Charitable Foundation
P.O. Box 40339
Tucson, AZ   85717-0339

Established in 2007 in Colorado.
Donor: Dorothy C. Harmsen†.
Foundation type: Operating foundation.
Financial data (yr. ended 12/31/13): Assets, $8,901,630 (M); expenditures, $557,827; qualifying distributions, $337,119; giving activities include $207,100 for 25 grants (high: $25,000; low: $500).
Fields of interest: Education; Environment; Diseases and conditions; Housing development; Human services.
Type of support: Research.

Limitations: Applications not accepted. Giving primarily in AZ.
Application information: Unsolicited request for funds not accepted.
Officers: Ziad Meziab, Pres.; J. Dennis Bartlett, Treas.
EIN: 202210574

129
Helms Family Foundation
20875 N. 90th Pl.
Scottsdale, AZ   85255

Donor: Helmsbriscoe Performance Group Inc.
Foundation type: Independent foundation.
Financial data (yr. ended 12/31/13): Assets, $0 (M); gifts received, $300,000; expenditures, $181,980; qualifying distributions, $181,000; giving activities include $181,000 for 8 grants (high: $100,000; low: $1,000).
Fields of interest: Education; Religion; Human services.
Limitations: Applications not accepted. Giving primarily in CO. No grants to individuals.
Application information: Unsolicited requests for funds not accepted.
EIN: 203794532

130
Mabel Y. Hughes Charitable Trust
c/o Wells Fargo Bank, N.A.
P.O. Box 53456, MAC S4101, Ste. 22G
Phoenix, AZ   85072-3456
Application address: c/o Wells Fargo Bank, Attn.: Ian Dreifaldt, Private Client Svcs., Denver, CO 80274, tel.: (720) 947-6630; Main URL: https://www.wellsfargo.com/privatefoundationgrants/hughes

Established in 1969 in Colorado.
Donor: Mabel Y. Hughes†.
Foundation type: Independent foundation.
Financial data (yr. ended 08/31/13): Assets, $11,140,630 (M); expenditures, $457,825; qualifying distributions, $366,719; giving activities include $337,513 for 42 grants (high: $22,513; low: $5,000).
Purpose and activities: Support primarily for the arts, health care and education.
Fields of interest: Performing arts; Opera; Museums; Art museums; Children's museums; Education; Higher education; Health; Family planning; Human services; Family services; Child welfare.
Type of support: General support; Continuing support; Annual campaigns; Equipment; Endowments; Emergency funds; Program development; Seed money; Research.
Limitations: Applications accepted. Giving limited to CO, with emphasis on the Denver area. No grants to individuals, or for deficit financing, scholarships, or fellowships; no loans.
Application information: Application form required.
  Initial approach: Letter
  Copies of proposal: 1
  Deadline(s): None
Trustees: W. Robert Alexander; Wells Fargo Bank, N.A.
EIN: 846070398

131
Immanuel Charitable Foundation
1015 E. Caroline Ln.
Tempe, AZ 85284-3202

Established in 1997 in Arizona.
Donors: Charles B. Duff; Dorie J. Duff.
Foundation type: Independent foundation.
Financial data (yr. ended 09/30/14): Assets, $5,346,481; expenditures, $315,777; qualifying distributions, $265,676.
Fields of interest: Education; Religion; Christianity; Human services.
Limitations: Applications not accepted. Giving primarily in AZ. No grants to individuals.
Application information: Unsolicited request for funds not accepted.
Officers: Charles B. Duff, Pres.; Dorie J. Duff, Secy.
Directors: Charles E. Duff; John B. Duff.
EIN: 860894096

132
The Harold James Family Trust
8400 N. U.S. Hwy. 89
Prescott, AZ 86301-6138 (928) 776-9727
Contact: Ronald E. James, Pres.

Established in 1986 in Arizona.
Donor: Jean Butz James.
Foundation type: Independent foundation.
Financial data (yr. ended 12/31/13): Assets, $8,398,767 (M); expenditures, $341,593; qualifying distributions, $240,299; giving activities include $240,299 for 18 grants (high: $50,000; low: $500).
Fields of interest: Community and economic development; Human services; Youth services.
Type of support: General support; Annual campaigns; Capital campaigns; Capital and infrastructure; Emergency funds; Scholarships.
Limitations: Applications accepted. Giving primarily in AZ. No grants to individuals.
Application information: Application form required.
   Initial approach: Letter
   Deadline(s): None
   Board meeting date(s): Fall
Officers: Ronald E. James, Pres.; Laura James, V.P.; Robert B. James, Secy.
Number of staff: None.
EIN: 866158195

133
Jasam Foundation Fund B
286 N. Fenceline Dr.
Tucson, AZ 85748-3726

Established in 2002 in Arkansas.
Foundation type: Independent foundation.
Financial data (yr. ended 12/31/13): Assets, $8,097,404 (M); expenditures, $527,447; qualifying distributions, $461,218; giving activities include $440,000 for 24 grants (high: $75,000; low: $5,000).
Purpose and activities: Giving primarily for education, hospitals and health organizations, Christian organizations, human services and U.S. troop support.
Fields of interest: Education; Hospital care; Diseases and conditions; Christianity; Human services; Child welfare.

Limitations: Applications not accepted. Giving limited to western MI, and the greater Tucson, AZ, area. No grants to individuals.
Application information: Contributes only to pre-selected organizations.
   Board meeting date(s): Varies
Officer: Joan D. Guylas, Pres.
Number of staff: 1 part-time support.
EIN: 383637370

134
J.W. Johnson Family Charitable Trust
10813 E. Windgate Pass Dr.
Scottsdale, AZ 85255-7144

Established in 2006 in Arizona.
Donor: Joel W. Johnson.
Foundation type: Independent foundation.
Financial data (yr. ended 12/31/13): Assets, $9,626,208 (M); gifts received, $506,530; expenditures, $454,584; qualifying distributions, $431,750; giving activities include $429,350 for 44 grants (high: $177,500; low: $100).
Fields of interest: Undergraduate education; Health; Religion.
Type of support: Research and evaluation.
Limitations: Applications not accepted. Giving primarily in AZ, MN and NY. No grants to individuals.
Application information: Contributes only to pre-selected organizations.
Trustees: Elizabeth B. Johnson; Geoffrey B. Johnson; Joel W. Johnson; Peter J. Johnson; Katherine E. Johnson Potter.
EIN: 207203295

135
R. L. "Roz" Johnson Family Foundation of Arizona
9820 E. Thompson Peak Pkwy., Lot 719
Scottsdale, AZ 85255-6657

Established in 2002 in Arizona.
Donors: Mary A. Johnson; Robert L. Johnson.
Foundation type: Independent foundation.
Financial data (yr. ended 12/31/13): Assets, $5,825,540 (M); expenditures, $314,859; qualifying distributions, $256,325; giving activities include $254,000 for 1 grant.
Fields of interest: Education; Graduate and professional education; Christianity; Theology.
Type of support: General support; Scholarships.
Limitations: Applications not accepted. Giving primarily in AZ; some giving in MO. No grants to individuals.
Application information: Unsolicited requests for funds not accepted.
Directors: Mary A. Johnson; Robert L. Johnson.
EIN: 593761693

136
Gary Dean and Christine Newman Jones Foundation
6631 N. 31st St.
Phoenix, AZ 85016-8909

Donors: Gary Dean Jones; Christine Newman Jones.
Foundation type: Independent foundation.
Financial data (yr. ended 12/31/13): Assets, $2,162,179 (M); gifts received, $40,000; expenditures, $378,129; qualifying distributions,

$360,000; giving activities include $360,000 for 14 grants (high: $69,500; low: $2,500).
Fields of interest: Protestantism.
Limitations: Applications not accepted. Giving primarily in AZ.
Application information: Unsolicited requests for funds not accepted.
Trustees: Christine Newman Jones; Gary Dean Jones.
EIN: 456667464

137
Kearny Alliance, Inc.
14901 N. Scottsdale Rd., Rm. 20
Scottsdale, AZ 85254-2718

Established in 2001 in Arizona.
Donor: The Kearny Foundation.
Foundation type: Independent foundation.
Financial data (yr. ended 12/31/13): Assets, $52,421 (M); gifts received, $458,609; expenditures, $418,980; qualifying distributions, $418,980; giving activities include $302,000 for 3 grants (high: $270,000; low: $12,000), and $405,082 for 4 foundation-administered programs.
Purpose and activities: Giving for innovative business education and training, applied research, and other initiatives to promote increased participation in fair and reciprocal international trade.
Fields of interest: Education; International relations.
International interests: Asia.
Limitations: Applications not accepted. Giving primarily in AZ; some funding also in Washington, DC. No grants to individuals.
Application information: Unsolicited requests for funds not accepted.
Officer and Directors: Dr. John E. Walsh, Pres. and Director; Terrence Ray Collins; William Roger Seitz.
EIN: 861041247

138
Knisely Family Foundation, Inc.
8360 E. Brookwood Dr.
Tucson, AZ 85750-2466

Established in 1999 in Arizona.
Foundation type: Independent foundation.
Financial data (yr. ended 12/31/12): Assets, $4,525,763 (M); gifts received, $96,574; expenditures, $193,088; qualifying distributions, $172,320; giving activities include $170,000 for 25 grants (high: $15,000; low: $1,500).
Fields of interest: Foundations.
Type of support: Continuing support.
Limitations: Applications not accepted. Giving primarily in AZ.
Application information: Contributes only to pre-selected organizations.
Officers and Directors: Jil K. Feldhausen, Pres. and Director; John Morton, Secy. and Director; Frank Auletta, Treas. and Director; Jay Knisely; Margy Marton; Sarah Monroe; Joe R. Pennington; Fred A. Rauch.
EIN: 860952581

139
Kuhle Family Foundation
2425 E. Camelback Rd., Ste. 750
Phoenix, AZ 85016-4261

Established in 2005 in Arizona.
Donors: Shelley Kuhle; Richard Kuhle; Kuhle Investments LP.
Foundation type: Independent foundation.
Financial data (yr. ended 12/31/13): Assets, $4,000,122 (M); gifts received, $846,223; expenditures, $170,988; qualifying distributions, $149,600; giving activities include $147,250 for 11 grants (high: $76,000; low: $250).
Fields of interest: Education; Children's hospital care; Diseases and conditions; Human services; Child welfare; Children.
Limitations: Applications not accepted. Giving primarily in AZ.
Application information: Unsolicited requests for funds not accepted.
Officers: Richard Kuhle, Pres.; Shelley Louise Inch Kuhle, Treas.
EIN: 203995755

140
Lapan Memorial Sunshine Foundation, Inc.
(formerly Lapan Educational Loan Foundation, Inc.)
4320 E. Pinnacle Ridge Pl.
Tucson, AZ 85718-3541 5205771311
Application address: c/o Lucy Kin, 1121 N. Camino de Juan, Tucson, AZ 85745 tel.: (520) 360-9881

Donors: Patricia Lapan; Joseph Lapan; June Rosemary Woodman; Lowes Charitable Foundation; David Lapan.
Foundation type: Operating foundation.
Financial data (yr. ended 12/31/14): Assets, $2,224,905; gifts received, $1,237,993; expenditures, $333,003; qualifying distributions, $318,682.
Purpose and activities: Student loans paid directly to the college or university for tuition, preference given to graduates of Alameda County and Pima County, California.
Fields of interest: Education; Medical education.
Type of support: Scholarships.
Limitations: Applications accepted. Giving primarily in the Alameda and Pima counties, CA, area.
Application information: Resume, proof of academic standing and financial need. Application form required.
Initial approach: Proposal
Deadline(s): May 1
Officers: David Lapan, Chair.; Mary Musgrove, Secy.-Treas.; Lucy Kin, Exec. Dir.
EIN: 880192311

141
John F. Long Foundation, Inc.
5035 W. Camelback Rd.
Phoenix, AZ 85031-1331 (602) 272-0421
Contact: Jacob F. Long, Pres. and Dir.
FAX: (623) 846-7208;
E-mail: foundation@jflong.com; Main URL: http://www.jflong.com/foundation.htm

Donor: John F. Long†.
Foundation type: Independent foundation.
Financial data (yr. ended 04/30/14): Assets, $8,570,898 (M); expenditures, $429,667;

qualifying distributions, $361,958; giving activities include $350,717 for 124 grants (high: $30,162; low: $200).
Purpose and activities: Giving primarily for groups who are working to help themselves, their own communities, and help others like themselves through self-empowering, community organizing efforts. The foundation's approach to grant requests focuses on fostering local neighborhood vitality and excellence.
Fields of interest: Arts and culture; Elementary and secondary education; Community and economic development; Christianity; Protestantism; Human services; Family services; Child welfare.
Limitations: Applications accepted. Giving primarily in Phoenix, AZ. No grants to individuals.
Application information: Application guidelines and questionnaire available on foundation web site. Grant requests exceeding $1,000 must be accompanied by financial reports for the past and current fiscal year, and a list of past donors going back no more than 2 years. Application form required.
Initial approach: Letter
Deadline(s): None
Officer and Directors: Jacob F. Long, Pres. and Director; Shirley Long Lewis; James J. Miller.
EIN: 866052431

142
Louis Foundation, Inc.
c/o Herbert J. Louis, M.D.
5110 N. 40th St., Ste. 236
Phoenix, AZ 85018-2193
E-mail: herbst09@aol.com

Established in 1970 in Arizona.
Donors: Henrietta J. Louis Charitable Trust; Julie D. Louis; Julie D. Louis Revocable Trust; Herbert J. Louis Revocable Trust; Herbert J. Louis.
Foundation type: Independent foundation.
Financial data (yr. ended 12/31/13): Assets, $827,271 (M); gifts received, $610,000; expenditures, $454,583; qualifying distributions, $441,659; giving activities include $441,000 for 31 grants (high: $100,000; low: $1,000).
Purpose and activities: Giving primarily for education, medical centers and treatment, and community service organizations.
Fields of interest: Arts and culture; Education; Health; Orthopedics; Community and economic development; Human services.
Type of support: General support; Annual campaigns; Capital campaigns; Endowments; Convening; Research.
Limitations: Applications not accepted. Giving primarily in Phoenix, AZ. No grants to individuals.
Application information: Contributes only to pre-selected organizations.
Board meeting date(s): May and Nov.
Officers: Herbert J. Louis, MD, Pres.; Carrie L. Hulburd, V.P.; Julie D. Louis, Secy.-Treas.
Directors: Philip A. Edlund; Timothy C. Louis.
Number of staff: None.
EIN: 860211888

143
Victoria Lund Foundation
6632 N. 66th Pl.
Paradise Valley, AZ 85253-4332

Established in 2002 in Arizona.
Donors: Bradford Lund; Michelle Lund; The Mary A. Hench Charitable Lead Trust.
Foundation type: Independent foundation.
Financial data (yr. ended 12/31/13): Assets, $7,364,211 (M); expenditures, $552,465; qualifying distributions, $386,600; giving activities include $386,600 for 9 grants (high: $200,000; low: $2,500).
Fields of interest: Education; Diseases and conditions.
Type of support: Research.
Limitations: Applications not accepted. Giving primarily in AZ. No grants to individuals.
Application information: Unsolicited requests for funds not accepted.
Trustees: Bradford D. Lund; Sherry L. Lund; William S. Lund.
EIN: 866316902

144
Ben B. and Iris M. Margolis Foundation
(formerly Ben B. and Iris M. Margolis Foundation for Medical Research)
c/o Wells Fargo Bank, N.A., Trust Tax Dept.
P.O. Box 53456, MAC S4101-22G
Phoenix, AZ 85072-3456
Application address: c/o Wells Fargo Bank, N.A., P.O. Box 30007, Salt Lake City, UT 84111; tel.: (801) 246-1438

Established in 1979 in Utah.
Donors: Iris M. Margolis†; Ben B. Margolis†.
Foundation type: Independent foundation.
Financial data (yr. ended 03/31/14): Assets, $8,871,808 (M); expenditures, $407,874; qualifying distributions, $362,031; giving activities include $352,000 for 4 grants (high: $100,000; low: $52,000).
Purpose and activities: Giving to institutions to conduct and support medical research.
Fields of interest: Graduate and professional education; Medical education; Nursing care; Diseases and conditions.
Type of support: Research; Research and evaluation.
Limitations: Applications accepted. Giving limited to Salt Lake City, UT. No grants to individuals, or for scholarships, fellowships, or endowments; no loans.
Application information:
Initial approach: Proposal
Copies of proposal: 1
Deadline(s): None
Board meeting date(s): Semiannually
Final notification: Varies
Trustees: Wells Fargo Bank, N.A.
EIN: 876180864

145
The Marketplace One Foundation
(formerly The Edson Foundation)
1 N. 1st St., Ste. 700
Phoenix, AZ 85004-2364

Established in 2006 in Arizona.
Donors: Brad Edson; Patricia Edson; Bret Edson.
Foundation type: Independent foundation.
Financial data (yr. ended 12/31/13): Assets, $1,005,023 (M); gifts received, $1,000; expenditures, $310,295; qualifying distributions,

$305,500; giving activities include $305,500 for 3 grants (high: $300,000; low: $500).
Fields of interest: Christianity.
Limitations: Applications not accepted. Giving primarily in GA; some funding nationally. No grants to individuals.
Application information: Contributes only to pre-selected organizations.
Officers and Directors: Bret Edson, Pres. and Director; Brad Edson, V.P. and Director; Brad Routh, Secy.-Treas. and Director.
EIN: 208066031

146
Perry and Sandy Massie Foundation
2004 Promontory
Prescott, AZ   86305-2520   (800) 551-9707
Contact: Perry Massie, Dir.

Donors: Perry Massie; Sandy Massie.
Foundation type: Independent foundation.
Financial data (yr. ended 12/31/13): Assets, $7,070,187 (M); gifts received, $4,369,580; expenditures, $287,377; qualifying distributions, $225,000; giving activities include $225,000 for 4 grants (high: $100,000; low: $5,000).
Fields of interest: Education; Human services; Youth development; Adult and child mentoring.
Limitations: Applications accepted. Giving primarily in AZ.
Application information: Application form required.
Initial approach: Proposal
Deadline(s): None
Directors: Perry Massie; Sandy Massie.
EIN: 200491239

147
Maxinmotion
c/o Jonah Shacknai
4747 N. Scottsdale Rd., Ste. 1009
Scottsdale, AZ   85251-7668
Main URL: http://www.maxinmotion.org

Donors: Jonah Shacknai; Andrew Karen Hirsched; Sam Garvin; Burke Family Foundation; Spencer Davidson; James Habets; Peter Knight; Howrd Lisa Luber; Terry Muffy.
Foundation type: Independent foundation.
Financial data (yr. ended 12/31/13): Assets, $629,346 (M); gifts received, $228,900; expenditures, $384,822; qualifying distributions, $384,495; giving activities include $382,500 for 7 grants (high: $246,000; low: $3,500).
Purpose and activities: Provides financial support to help underwrite the costs associated with inclusion of financially challenged boys and girls who would not otherwise be able to participate in sports programs.
Fields of interest: Sports and recreation; European football; Youth development.
Limitations: Applications accepted. Giving primarily in AZ.
Publications: Application guidelines.
Application information: See foundation web site for application information. Only a limited number of organizations will be selected for funding.
Officer and Directors: Jonah Shacknai, Pres. and Director; R. Taylor Burke, Jr.; Sam Garvin; E.G. Ken Kendrick, Jr.; Tim Riester; Ethan Shacknai; Gabriele Shacknai.
EIN: 453760957

148
Robert H. McKee & M. E. McKee Charitable Family Foundation
24 Biltmore Estates
Phoenix, AZ   85016-2822

Donor: Robert H. McKee.
Foundation type: Independent foundation.
Financial data (yr. ended 06/30/13): Assets, $23,385 (M); gifts received, $224,010; expenditures, $244,780; qualifying distributions, $241,359; giving activities include $239,325 for 27 grants (high: $106,505; low: $100).
Fields of interest: Orchestral music; Museums; Art museums; Higher education; Animal welfare; Nonprofits; Neurology; National defense; Religion; Christianity; Olympics; Human services; Food delivery; Youth services; Females.
Type of support: Research; Regranting.
Limitations: Applications not accepted. Giving primarily in AZ. No grants to individuals.
Application information: Unsolicited requests for funds not accepted.
Officer: Robert H. McKee, Pres.
Directors: Mary Ellen McKee; James P. Tierney.
EIN: 431799994

149
MCS Charitable Foundation
c/o Southern Wealth Management
6927 E. Caballo Dr.
Paradise Valley, AZ   85253-2710

Donor: Mary Carol Gregory.
Foundation type: Independent foundation.
Financial data (yr. ended 12/31/13): Assets, $19,950,811 (M); expenditures, $475,342; qualifying distributions, $288,000; giving activities include $288,000 for 16 grants (high: $114,000; low: $500).
Fields of interest: Education; Animal welfare; Diseases and conditions; Human services.
Limitations: Applications not accepted. Giving primarily in AZ; some funding also in TX. No grants to individuals.
Application information: Unsolicited requests for funds not accepted.
Trustee: Mary Carol Gregory.
EIN: 263016128

150
Joe and Mary Moeller Foundation
27437 N. 97th Pl.
Scottsdale, AZ   85262-8432

Established in 2004 in Kansas.
Donors: Joseph W. Moeller; Mary Moeller.
Foundation type: Independent foundation.
Financial data (yr. ended 12/31/14): Assets, $8,496,672 (M); gifts received, $835; expenditures, $425,577; qualifying distributions, $398,900; giving activities include $398,900 for 42 grants (high: $120,000; low: $250).
Fields of interest: Higher education; Diseases and conditions; Catholicism; Human services; Youth development.
Type of support: General support.
Limitations: Applications not accepted. Giving primarily in AZ, CO, FL, GA, KS, OK and VA. No grants to individuals.

Application information: Contributes only to pre-selected organizations.
Officers: Joseph W. Moeller, Pres.; Mary F. Moeller, Secy.
Director: Margaret Sharon Walker.
EIN: 830411709

151
John and Helen Murphey Foundation, Inc.
4729 E. Sunrise Dr., PMB 424
Tucson, AZ   85718-4534

Established in 1958 in Arizona.
Foundation type: Independent foundation.
Financial data (yr. ended 06/30/13): Assets, $6,098,899 (M); expenditures, $277,127; qualifying distributions, $203,125; giving activities include $200,500 for 18 grants (high: $128,000; low: $1,000).
Fields of interest: Arts and culture; Art museums; Education; University education; Environment; Reproductive rights; Human services; Youth development.
Limitations: Applications not accepted. Giving primarily in Tucson, AZ. No grants to individuals.
Application information: Unsolicited requests for funds not accepted.
Officers: Jay S. Kittle, Chair.; Ana M. Nygren, Pres.; Floyd Sedlmayr, V.P.; Gordon Waterfall, Secy.
Number of staff: 1 part-time professional.
EIN: 860802319

152
The James H. Napier Foundation
(formerly The Napier Foundation)
c/o Wells Fargo Bank N.A.
P.O. Box 53456, MAC S4101-22G
Phoenix, AZ   85072-3456

Established in 1953 in New York.
Donor: James H. Napier†.
Foundation type: Independent foundation.
Financial data (yr. ended 07/31/13): Assets, $3,381,279 (M); expenditures, $227,162; qualifying distributions, $192,478; giving activities include $185,560 for 25 grants (high: $30,000; low: $250).
Fields of interest: Education; Health; Human services.
Type of support: Annual campaigns; Employee matching gifts; Capital campaigns; Capital and infrastructure; Endowments; Scholarships; Research.
Limitations: Applications not accepted. Giving primarily in the Meriden, CT, area. No grants to individuals, or for loans or program-related investments.
Application information: Contributes only to pre-selected organizations.
Board meeting date(s): Quarterly
Trustee: Wells Fargo Bank.
EIN: 136029883

153
National Black McDonalds Franchisee Foundation
15430 E. Crested Butte Trail
Fountain Hills, AZ   85268-5984

Donors: Goodrum Enterprises Inc.; Sims F-1 Management Co.; Susdewitt Enterprises Partnership; Phelps Chancelor Enterprises Inc.; Texden Inc.; The Brewester Co.; Welburn Management Consulting Co.; Johnny Hurt; BCDG LP; Henry J. Thomas; Jones Management; Ababa Co.; F. Ronald Smith; Adair Family Foundation Inc.; KL Ventures LLC; Anthony Grissett; Wayne and Dorthy Stingley Family Trust; Ambrose LLC; McSween Enterprises Inc.; Emerald Management Corp.; Rosmik Inc.; Ice Age Management; Mary Navies; My Blessings Inc.; Arminda Grissett; A. and R. Enterprises LP; Indian Hill Management; Nicker Management 1 Inc.; Chelace Brand Inc.; Cynthia Brown; Yvonne Thomas; C-CK's Inc.; Moreco IV; CA Unlimited LLC; Coaxium Enterprise; Tanway Enterprises LP; Martin I. Washington; National Black McDonalds Operators; DBK Vision Inc.; FWL Sons Inc.; MacKing, V; Tyve Limited Partnership; Jerome Navies; Eva Martin; Tripplett Management Corp.; Golden Partners LLC.
Foundation type: Independent foundation.
Financial data (yr. ended 12/31/13): Assets, $120,037 (M); gifts received, $295,208; expenditures, $175,171; qualifying distributions, $175,000; giving activities include $175,000 for 1 grant.
Fields of interest: Human rights.
Limitations: Applications not accepted. Giving primarily in GA.
Application information: Unsolicited requests for funds not accepted.
Officer: Earnest L. Adair, Pres.
Director: Roland Parrish.
EIN: 461106819

154
O'Rielly Family Foundation
P.O. Box 31000
Tucson, AZ 85751-1000

Foundation type: Independent foundation.
Financial data (yr. ended 12/31/13): Assets, $3,578,447 (M); expenditures, $203,661; qualifying distributions, $167,800; giving activities include $167,800 for 16 grants (high: $25,000; low: $1,300).
Fields of interest: Education; Animal welfare; Catholicism; Human services; Youth services.
Limitations: Applications not accepted. Giving primarily in AZ. No grants to individuals.
Application information: Contributes only to pre-selected organizations.
Officers and Directors: R.B. O'Rielly, Pres. and Director; Amy Draper, V.P. and Director; Veronica Bartz, Secy.-Treas.; Katie Draper; Barbara C. O'Rielly; Patricia Pettis.
EIN: 481265468

155
The Picerne Family Charitable Foundation
(formerly The Picerne Charitable Trust)
1420 E. Missouri Ave., Ste. 100
Phoenix, AZ 85014-2470

Established in 1994 in Arizona.
Donor: Ronald R.S. Picerne.
Foundation type: Independent foundation.
Financial data (yr. ended 11/30/13): Assets, $5,243,539 (M); gifts received, $1,848,750; expenditures, $208,177; qualifying distributions,

$202,750; giving activities include $202,750 for 18 grants (high: $70,000; low: $100).
Purpose and activities: Giving primarily for higher education and for health and medical issues.
Fields of interest: Health; Christianity; Catholicism; Human services.
Limitations: Applications not accepted. Giving primarily in RI. No grants to individuals.
Application information: Unsolicited requests for funds not accepted.
Officer: David R. Picerne, Treas.
Trustee: Ronald R.S. Picerne.
EIN: 050487100

156
Richard H. and Scottie Pierce Family Foundation
10202 E. Journey Ln.
Scottsdale, AZ 85255-3352

Established in 2006 in Arizona.
Foundation type: Independent foundation.
Financial data (yr. ended 12/31/13): Assets, $472,772 (M); expenditures, $282,776; qualifying distributions, $276,276; giving activities include $275,000 for 4 grants (high: $250,000; low: $250).
Fields of interest: Arts and culture; Education; Graduate and professional education; Health; Nursing care.
Limitations: Applications not accepted. Giving primarily in AZ and ME. No grants to individuals.
Application information: Unsolicited requests for funds not accepted.
Trustee: Scottie Pierce.
EIN: 207201885

157
Samuel C. & Myra G. Powell Foundation
c/o Wells Fargo Bank, N.A., Trust Tax Dept.
P.O. Box 53456, MAC S4101-22G
Phoenix, AZ 85072-3456

Established in 1974 in Utah.
Foundation type: Independent foundation.
Financial data (yr. ended 12/31/14): Assets, $5,276,041 (M); expenditures, $335,412; qualifying distributions, $311,795; giving activities include $235,000 for 7 grants (high: $100,000; low: $1,000).
Fields of interest: Education; Environment; Health.
Type of support: General support.
Limitations: Applications not accepted. Giving primarily in UT.
Application information: Unsolicited requests for funds not accepted.
Trustee: Wells Fargo Bank, N.A.
Directors: Anne E. Barker; Charles H. Barker; Mary L. Barker; Orille Rex Chilo; Nathan Felix.
EIN: 876163275

158
Prayer Child Foundation
3903 E. Huber St.
Mesa, AZ 85205-3903 (480) 634-6086
Contact: Laura Washington, Admin.
E-mail: info@prayerchild.org; *Main URL:* http://www.prayerchild.org

Established in 2006 in Arizona.

Donors: Curt Waisath; Karen Waisath; Melanie Bastian; Nona Persons; Gold Canyon Candle.
Foundation type: Operating foundation.
Financial data (yr. ended 06/30/13): Assets, $58,804 (M); gifts received, $242,752; expenditures, $226,886; qualifying distributions, $226,700; giving activities include $400 for 3 grants (high: $150; low: $100), and $226,300 for 333 grants to individuals (high: $1,000; low: $200).
Purpose and activities: Giving for children (18 years of age and younger) with physical and emotional challenges.
Fields of interest: Child welfare.
Limitations: Giving primarily in Mesa, AZ.
Application information: Application form required.
  Initial approach: Use grant request form on foundation web site
  Final notification: Within 4-6 weeks
Officers: Karen Waisath, Pres.; Curt Waisath, V.P.; John Makoff, Secy.; Joe Phillips, Treas.
Advisory Board: Brew Crosby; Troy Crosland; Rick Dutriac; Greg Goeser; David Hejl; Brooks Merrill; Nona Persons; Burke Plummer; Bernie Zimmer.
EIN: 030558277

159
James Arthur Rae Charitable Trust
14602 N. Tatum Blvd.
Phoenix, AZ 85032-4816

Established in 1998 in Arizona.
Donor: Maryland Investments, Inc.
Foundation type: Independent foundation.
Financial data (yr. ended 12/31/13): Assets, $8,550,285 (M); expenditures, $463,139; qualifying distributions, $286,616; giving activities include $255,297 for grants.
Fields of interest: Christianity; Child welfare.
Limitations: Applications not accepted. Giving primarily in AZ and IL. No grants to individuals.
Application information: Contributes only to pre-selected organizations.
Trustees: Joel Kramer; Maryland, LLC.
EIN: 860937247

160
Edward J. and Lanelle B. Robson Foundation
(formerly LaNelle Robson Foundation)
9532 E. Riggs Rd.
Sun Lakes, AZ 85248-7463 (480) 895-9200
Contact: Edward J. Robson, Pres.

Established in 1987 in Arizona.
Donors: Sun Lakes Marketing LP; Robson Communities, Inc.; Saddlebrooke Development Co.; Pebblecreek Properties LP; Scott Management Co.
Foundation type: Independent foundation.
Financial data (yr. ended 01/31/13): Assets, $3,063,994 (M); gifts received, $195,000; expenditures, $196,329; qualifying distributions, $177,359; giving activities include $177,359 for 25 grants (high: $50,000; low: $200).
Purpose and activities: Giving primarily for education, health associations, and children, youth and social services.
Fields of interest: Orchestral music; Education; Philanthropy; Nonprofits; Hospital care; Diseases and conditions; Disasters and emergency management; Human services; Child welfare; Youth development.

Type of support: Regranting.
Limitations: Applications accepted. Giving primarily in AZ, with some emphasis on Phoenix. No grants to individuals.
Application information:
  Initial approach: Proposal
  Copies of proposal: 1
  Deadline(s): None
Officers: Edward J. Robson, Pres.; Mark E. Robson, V.P.; Kimberly A. Robson, V.P.; Lynda Robson Weiser, Secy.; Steven S. Robson, Treas.
Director: Robert D. Robson.
EIN: 742461052

161
Rosztoczy Foundation
c/o Wendy Cooper
11111 W. McDowell Rd.
Avondale, AZ 85392-5000
E-mail: ferenc@rosztoczyfoundation.org; Main URL: http://www.rosztoczyfoundation.com

Established in 2005 in Arizona.
Donors: Ferenc E. Rosztoczy; Thomas F. Rosztoczy.
Foundation type: Independent foundation.
Financial data (yr. ended 01/31/13): Assets, $658,477 (M); gifts received, $514,939; expenditures, $367,427; qualifying distributions, $363,100; giving activities include $363,100 for 70 grants to individuals (high: $30,000; low: $2,000).
Purpose and activities: Giving for students and scientists from Hungary to come to the United States for a period of one year to study at a university or research institute.
Fields of interest: Education; Religion.
International interests: Hungary.
Type of support: Scholarships; Student aid.
Application information: See web site for complete application policies and guidelines and for downloadable application form. Application form required.
  Initial approach: See grantmaker web site
  Deadline(s): None
Trustees: Diane E. Rosztoczy; Ferenc E. Rosztoczy; Robert A. Rosztoczy; Thomas F. Rosztoczy.
EIN: 721583507

162
Rothschild Family Foundation
6432 N. Desert Wind Cir.
Tucson, AZ 85750-0978

Foundation type: Independent foundation.
Financial data (yr. ended 12/31/12): Assets, $0 (M); expenditures, $283,626; qualifying distributions, $279,568; giving activities include $279,568 for 1 grant.
Fields of interest: Education; Health; Human services.
Limitations: Applications not accepted. Giving primarily in AZ, MA, and MO. No grants to individuals.
Application information: Contributes only to pre-selected organizations.
Officers and Directors: James G. Rothschild, Pres. and Director; Andrew G. Rothschild, V.P.; Jeffrey G. Rothschild, Secy.-Treas. and Director; Marci Diane Rothschild.
EIN: 431303640

163
Maureen and Paul Rubeli Foundation Inc.
7181 E. Camelback Rd., Unit 1202
Scottsdale, AZ 85251

Established in 2006 in Arizona.
Donors: Paul E. Rubeli; Maureen E. Rubeli.
Foundation type: Independent foundation.
Financial data (yr. ended 12/31/13): Assets, $5,781,808 (M); expenditures, $265,121; qualifying distributions, $236,061; giving activities include $235,000 for 32 grants (high: $45,000; low: $2,000).
Fields of interest: Education; Nonprofits; Health; Catholicism; Youth services.
Type of support: Regranting.
Limitations: Applications not accepted. Giving primarily in AZ. No grants to individuals.
Application information: Unsolicited requests for funds not accepted.
Officers: Maureen M. Rubeli, Pres.; Paul E. Rubeli, V.P. and Treas.
EIN: 205935203

164
Rudge Foundation
c/o Trust Bank
1525 S. Greenfield Rd.
Mesa, AZ 85206-3301

Established in 2000 in Delaware.
Donor: Howard J. Rudge.
Foundation type: Independent foundation.
Financial data (yr. ended 08/31/14): Assets, $1,522,047; gifts received, $107,847; expenditures, $241,183; qualifying distributions, $224,600.
Fields of interest: Education; Housing development; Religion.
Limitations: Applications not accepted. No grants to individuals.
Application information: Unsolicited requests for funds not accepted.
Directors: Howard J. Rudge; Lois I. Rudge.
EIN: 510403419

165
Schlein Foundation Inc.
c/o Jeffrey G. Schlein
8321 E. Joshua Tree Ln.
Scottsdale, AZ 85250-4809

Established in 2003 in Arizona.
Donor: Jeffrey G. Schlein.
Foundation type: Independent foundation.
Financial data (yr. ended 12/31/13): Assets, $4,226,321 (M); gifts received, $10,000; expenditures, $191,691; qualifying distributions, $185,350; giving activities include $185,350 for 54 grants (high: $85,000; low: $100).
Fields of interest: Arts and culture; Museums; Higher education; Medical education; Health; Hospital care; Community and economic development; Judaism; Human services.
Limitations: Applications not accepted. Giving primarily in AZ and NY. No grants to individuals.
Application information: Contributes only to pre-selected organizations.
Officers: Barbara S. Schlein, Pres.; Jennifer Podhajsky, V.P.; Jeffrey G. Schlein, Secy.-Treas.
EIN: 810554696

166
William E. Schmidt Charitable Foundation
38093 South Samaniego Dr.
Tucson, AZ 85739-1019

Established in 1981 in Illinois.
Donors: William E. Schmidt; John F. Schmidt.
Foundation type: Independent foundation.
Financial data (yr. ended 04/30/13): Assets, $8,013,240 (M); expenditures, $375,138; qualifying distributions, $366,000; giving activities include $366,000 for 48 grants (high: $33,000; low: $500).
Fields of interest: Education; Health.
Limitations: Applications not accepted. Giving primarily in AZ and IL. No grants to individuals.
Application information: Contributes only to pre-selected organizations.
Officers: John Schmidt, Pres.; Margaret C. Schmidt, Secy.
Director: Thomas Schmidt.
EIN: 371098426

167
Max A. Shacknai Foundation
(formerly Noah's Family Foundation)
4747 N. Scottsdale Rd., No. 1009
Scottsdale, AZ 85251-7669
Contact: Jonah Shacknai

Established in 1997 in Arizona.
Donors: Jonah Shacknai; Paterna Enterprises, LLP.
Foundation type: Independent foundation.
Financial data (yr. ended 12/31/13): Assets, $2,412,851 (M); gifts received, $100,000; expenditures, $285,432; qualifying distributions, $270,229; giving activities include $270,000 for 5 grants (high: $200,000; low: $5,000).
Fields of interest: Education; Higher education; Diseases and conditions; Sports and recreation; People with disabilities.
Limitations: Applications not accepted. Giving primarily in AZ. No grants to individuals.
Application information: Contributes only to pre-selected organizations.
Officers and Directors: Jonah Shacknai, Pres. and Director; Howard J. Luber, MD, Secy.-Treas.
EIN: 860887816

168
The Shultz Family Foundation
P.O. Box 10129
Phoenix, AZ 85064-0129

Established in 2006 in Arizona.
Donors: Beth J. Shultz; Mel L. Shultz.
Foundation type: Independent foundation.
Financial data (yr. ended 12/31/13): Assets, $248,783 (M); gifts received, $250,000; expenditures, $201,212; qualifying distributions, $200,972; giving activities include $198,800 for 16 grants (high: $50,000; low: $1,000).
Fields of interest: Education; Philanthropy; Protestantism.
Limitations: Applications not accepted. Giving primarily in AZ, FL, and OR. No grants to individuals.
Application information: Unsolicited requests for funds not accepted.
Officers: Mel L. Shultz, Pres. and Treas.; Beth J. Shultz, V.P. and Secy.
EIN: 205158436

169
Milton & Harriet Sioles Family Foundation
6021 E. Naumann Dr.
Paradise Valley, AZ 85253

Foundation type: Independent foundation.
Financial data (yr. ended 06/30/14): Assets, $3,802,997; expenditures, $207,441; qualifying distributions, $183,026.
Fields of interest: Education; Health care clinics; Catholicism.
Limitations: Applications not accepted. Giving primarily in AZ.
Application information: Unsolicited requests for funds not accepted.
Officers and Directors: Harriet Z. Sioles, Pres. and Director; Elyse C. Sioles, Secy. and Director; Robert M. Sioles, Treas. and Director.
EIN: 272546709

170
Smith Family Foundation, Inc.
701 W. 16th St., Ste. 101
Yuma, AZ 85364-4586

Donors: Victor P. Smith; JV Farms, Inc.
Foundation type: Independent foundation.
Financial data (yr. ended 12/31/13): Assets, $1,364 (M); gifts received, $165,000; expenditures, $170,555; qualifying distributions, $168,915; giving activities include $106,800 for 9 grants (high: $50,000; low: $300), and $62,115 for 19 grants to individuals (high: $6,615; low: $1,500).
Fields of interest: Environment; Human services.
Type of support: General support; Student aid.
Limitations: Applications not accepted. Giving primarily in AZ.
Application information: Unsolicited requests for funds not accepted.
Officers: Victor P. Smith, Pres.; Karen Smith, V.P.; Terre R. Catanzaro, Secy.-Treas.
EIN: 383832261

171
Snell & Wilmer Charitable Foundation
c/o Thomas R. Hoecker
1 Arizona Ctr.
Phoenix, AZ 85004-2202
E-mail: thoecker@swlaw.com

Established in 2002 in Arizona.
Donors: Snell & Wilmer L.L.P.; Warren E. Platt; Thomas R. Hoecker; John J. Bouma; Jon S. Cohen; Matthew Feeney.
Foundation type: Company-sponsored foundation.
Financial data (yr. ended 12/31/14): Assets, $1,256,028; expenditures, $90,000; qualifying distributions, $203,333.
Purpose and activities: The foundation supports museums and organizations involved with education and human services.
Fields of interest: Museums; Education; Early childhood education; Nonprofits; Human services.
Type of support: General support; Program development; Regranting.
Limitations: Applications not accepted. Giving primarily in areas of company operations in AZ, CA, and CO. No grants to individuals.
Application information: Contributes only to pre-selected organizations.

Officers: John J. Bouma, Pres.; Matthew Feeney, V.P.; Thomas R. Hoecker, V.P.; Warren E. Platt, V.P.; Alan L. Sullivan, V.P.; Jon S. Cohen, Secy.
EIN: 470901535

172
The Eliot Spalding Foundation
4801 E. Broadway Blvd., Ste. 301
Tucson, AZ 85711-3635 (520) 624-6691
Contact: James M. Sakrison, Secy.

Established in 1954 in Arizona.
Donors: Clayton N. Niles; Clayton E. Niles.
Foundation type: Independent foundation.
Financial data (yr. ended 12/31/14): Assets, $3,525,305 (M); expenditures, $197,605; qualifying distributions, $167,816; giving activities include $167,000 for 31 grants (high: $10,000; low: $1,000).
Fields of interest: Elementary and secondary education; Botanical gardens; Nonprofits; Community and economic development; Human services.
Type of support: Regranting.
Limitations: Applications accepted. Giving primarily in Tucson, AZ. No grants to individuals.
Application information: Application form required.
Initial approach: Letter
Deadline(s): Nov. 1
Officers: Clayton N. Niles, Pres.; Terry Goddard, V.P.; James M. Sakrison, Secy.; Clayton E. Niles, Treas.
Directors: Holly Clark; Robert Harbour.
EIN: 866050507

173
The William D. Squires Educational Foundation, Inc.
2338 W. Royal Palm Rd., Rm. J
Phoenix, AZ 85021-9339
E-mail: info@wmdsquiresfoundation.org; Application address: c/o Cynthia Squires Gross, P.O. 2940, Jupiter, FL 33468-2940, tel.: (561) 741-7751; Main URL: http://www.wmdsquiresfoundation.org
Grants List: http://wmdsquiresfoundation.org/recipients

Established in 1999 in Arizona.
Donor: William D. Squires.
Foundation type: Independent foundation.
Financial data (yr. ended 12/31/13): Assets, $2,547,208 (M); expenditures, $246,153; qualifying distributions, $230,675; giving activities include $150,000 for 27 grants to individuals (high: $46,500; low: $1,500).
Purpose and activities: Scholarship awards to financially needy graduating seniors in Ohio, who are graduating from high school in the current year.
Fields of interest: Education; Higher education.
Limitations: Applications accepted. Giving limited to residents of OH.
Application information: Applicants must provide a minimum of 2 letters of recommendation, an official high school transcript, a short essay, and a FAFSA. Application form required.
Initial approach: Letter
Deadline(s): Apr. 5
Officers: Pamela A. Bolen, Pres.; Cynthia Squires Gross, V.P. and Exec. Dir.; Deborah A. Squires, V.P.; Judy K. Perry, Secy.; Lena B. Squires, Treas.
EIN: 860946058

174
The Haddock Stanton Foundation
6730 N. Scottsdale Rd., Ste. 233
Scottsdale, AZ 85253

Established in 2007 in Arizona.
Donors: Robert M. Haddock; Ann M. Haddock.
Foundation type: Independent foundation.
Financial data (yr. ended 12/31/14): Assets, $3,689,678 (M); expenditures, $168,000; qualifying distributions, $168,000; giving activities include $160,500 for 12 grants (high: $125,000; low: $1,000).
Fields of interest: University education; Law education.
Limitations: Applications not accepted. Giving primarily in AZ and CA. No grants to individuals.
Application information: Unsolicited requests for funds not accepted.
Officers: Robert Haddock, Pres. and Treas.; Ann M. Stanton, V.P. and Secy.
EIN: 208018615

175
Winifred L. Stevens Foundation
c/o Linda Spady
849 N. 3rd Ave.
Phoenix, AZ 85003

Established in 1996 in California.
Donors: Linda S. Spady; Falcon's Flight, Inc.; John V. Stevens, Sr.; McKee Foods Corp.
Foundation type: Independent foundation.
Financial data (yr. ended 12/31/13): Assets, $34,998,829 (M); gifts received, $10,000; expenditures, $453,179; qualifying distributions, $360,760; giving activities include $252,785 for 5 grants (high: $180,000; low: $5,000).
Purpose and activities: Funding primarily for a Seventh-day Adventist Church and other religious organizations.
Fields of interest: Wildlife biodiversity; Christianity; Protestantism; Human services.
Limitations: Applications not accepted. Giving primarily in AZ and CA. No grants to individuals.
Application information: Contributes only to pre-selected organizations.
Officers and Directors: John V. Stevens, Sr., Pres. and Director; Linda S. Spady, V.P. and Director; John V. Stevens, Jr., Secy. and Director; Jeff Spady.
EIN: 954505998

176
The Stephen H. Sturges & Rose P. Sturges Charitable Trust
P.O. Box 4997
Yuma, AZ 85366-4997
Application address: c/o Amy Gill, 833 Plz. Cir., Yuma, AZ 85364, tel.: 783-8321

Established in 1983 in Arizona.
Donors: Rose Sturges; The Stephen H. Sturges & Rose P. Sturges Trust; Harold W. Sturges; Theresa L. Sturges.
Foundation type: Independent foundation.
Financial data (yr. ended 11/30/13): Assets, $4,850,292 (M); expenditures, $280,188; qualifying distributions, $220,442; giving activities include $60,000 for 1 grant, and $140,310 for 73 grants to individuals (high: $3,750; low: $1,250).

Purpose and activities: Giving primarily for education and youth development.
Fields of interest: University education; Foundations; Human services; Youth development.
Type of support: Student aid; Scholarships.
Limitations: Giving primarily in AZ and CA.
Application information: Individual must apply through high school using school's application form. Application form required.
  Initial approach: Letter
  Deadline(s): Within 45 days of awards
Trustees: Kathleen Bench; Gary Black; Valarie Donnelly; George Gallaher; Linda Rundell; Jane E. Schoenherr.
EIN: 860427923

177
The Virginia M. Ullman Foundation
2201 E. Camelback Rd., Ste. 227B
Phoenix, AZ 85016-9028 (602) 956-0980

Established in 1986 in Arizona.
Foundation type: Independent foundation.
Financial data (yr. ended 12/31/14): Assets, $7,276,082; expenditures, $385,277; qualifying distributions, $362,300.
Fields of interest: Arts and culture; Museums; University education; Zoos; Botanical gardens; Foundations; Nonprofits.
Type of support: Regranting.
Limitations: Applications accepted. Giving primarily in AZ. No grants to individuals.
Application information: Application form required.
  Initial approach: Letter
  Deadline(s): Oct. 1
Officers and Directors: Harry Papp, V.P. and Treas. and Director; Louis Comus, Jr., Secy. and Director; Susan Levine.
Trustees: Kim Sterling-Heflin; Gay Firestone Wray.
EIN: 860550097

178
Valley Anesthesiology Foundation
1850 N. Central Ave., Ste. 1600
Phoenix, AZ 85004-4633
Contact: Michelle Stuehling, Secy.

Established in 2007 in Arizona.
Foundation type: Independent foundation.
Financial data (yr. ended 12/31/12): Assets, $234,613 (M); gifts received, $212,929; expenditures, $190,411; qualifying distributions, $188,195; giving activities include $188,195 for grants.
Fields of interest: Education; Foundations; Hospital care; Health care clinics; Diabetes.
Type of support: Research.
Limitations: Applications accepted. Giving primarily in AZ. No grants to individuals. No grants to organizations lacking 501(c)(3) and 509(a).
Application information: Application form required.
  Initial approach: Letter
  Deadline(s): None
Officers: James Fleck, Chair. and Pres.; Steve Yee, MD, V.P.; Michelle Stuehling, Secy.; Lawrence Serrano, MD, Treas.
Directors: Patricia Durlam; Michele Harrison, MD; Dave Katz, MD; Aubrey Maze, MD; Melissa Rosenfeld, MD; Stephen Smith, MD.
EIN: 204408428

179
Van Horn Foundation
1110 E. Missouri Ave., Ste. 200
Phoenix, AZ 85014-2754 (602) 861-1080
Contact: Daniel Haworth, Pres.

Established in 1985 in Arizona.
Donor: Daniel Haworth.
Foundation type: Independent foundation.
Financial data (yr. ended 06/30/13): Assets, $1,364,114 (M); gifts received, $80,000; expenditures, $308,575; qualifying distributions, $301,678; giving activities include $301,558 for 6 grants (high: $156,032; low: $726).
Fields of interest: Education; Protestantism; Child development.
Limitations: Applications accepted. Giving primarily in AZ and CO.
Application information: Application form required.
  Initial approach: Proposal
  Deadline(s): None
Officers: Daniel Haworth, Pres.; William Barr Haworth, V.P. and Treas.; Donna Haworth, Secy.
EIN: 742451341

180
Warmer Research Foundation, Inc.
4425 W. Flying Diamond Rd.
Tucson, AZ 85742-9650 (520) 629-4624
Contact: Steven Goldman MD, Secy.-Treas.

Established in 1992 in Arizona.
Donors: Steven Goldman, MD; Wallace A. Reed, MD; Kathryn L. Reed, MD; Belle Goldman‡; Dee Maloof; Maurice Storck; Keith McKennon.
Foundation type: Independent foundation.
Financial data (yr. ended 12/31/14): Assets, $543,721 (M); gifts received, $107,150; expenditures, $382,744; qualifying distributions, $380,215; giving activities include $375,000 for 2 grants (high: $325,000; low: $50,000).
Fields of interest: Education; Diseases and conditions.
Type of support: Research.
Limitations: Applications accepted. Giving primarily in AZ.
Application information: Application form required.
  Initial approach: Letter
  Deadline(s): None
Officers: Kathryn L. Reed, MD, Pres.; Steven Goldman, MD, Secy.-Treas.
Director: Marc Fleischman.
EIN: 860707135

181
The Weil Foundation
(formerly Polaris Foundation)
P.O. Box 13006
Tucson, AZ 85732-3006
Contact: Nancy Olmstead, Recording Secy.
E-mail: info@weilfoundation.org; Proposal e-mails: James Dalen: jdalenmd@gmail.com, and Nancy Olmstead: nancy@x9ranch.com; Express package address: c/o Nancy Olmstead, The Weil Foundation, 1670 N. Kolb Rd., Ste. 240, Tucson, AZ 85715; Main URL: http://www.weilfoundation.org
Facebook: http://www.facebook.com/WeilFoundation
Twitter: https://twitter.com/WeilFoundation
Vimeo: http://vimeo.com/weilfoundation

Established in 2002 in Arizona.
Donors: Custom Nutrition Services, LLC; drugstore.com, Inc.; Andrew Weil.
Foundation type: Independent foundation.
Financial data (yr. ended 12/31/13): Assets, $714,188 (M); gifts received, $652,687; expenditures, $350,909; qualifying distributions, $291,000; giving activities include $291,000 for 18 grants (high: $50,000; low: $1,000).
Purpose and activities: Support for the advancement of integrative medicine. The foundation's current strategic focus is the training and education of medical students, physicians and other health care professionals in integrative medicine.
Fields of interest: Higher education; Medical education; Holistic medicine.
Limitations: Applications accepted. Giving on a national basis.
Publications: Application guidelines; Grants list.
Application information: Grants are funded from July 1 until June 30. If any material that is to be submitted does not exist in electronic form, indicate in e-mail that such material is being sent by regular mail. Specific instructions available on foundation web site. Application form required.
  Initial approach: Proposal (5-10 pages, to be e-mailed to both James Dalen and Nancy Olmstead), along with cover page which is located on foundation web site
  Deadline(s): Jan. 31
  Final notification: Mar.
Officers: Andrew Weil, Chair.; Richard Baxter, Secy.-Treas.; Nancy Olmstead, Recording Secy.; James Dalen, MD, Exec. Dir.
Directors: Donald Abrams, MD; Janet Lang; Humberto S. Lopez; Daria Myers; Robert G. Sarver; Adele Simmons.
EIN: 861049023

182
Woody and Kim Williams Foundation
60 E. Rio Salado Pkwy., Ste. 1012
Tempe, AZ 85281-9501

Established in 2006 in Arizona.
Donors: Gregory Williams; Kim Williams.
Foundation type: Independent foundation.
Financial data (yr. ended 12/31/13): Assets, $65,103 (M); expenditures, $178,335; qualifying distributions, $178,335; giving activities include $177,700 for 12 grants (high: $120,000; low: $1,000).
Fields of interest: Education; Health; Religion; Christianity.
Limitations: Applications not accepted. Giving primarily in TX. No grants to individuals.
Application information: Unsolicited requests for funds not accepted.
Officers: Gregory Williams, Pres.; Kim Williams, V.P.
EIN: 205337562

183
Williams-Malone Foundation, Inc.
18721 E. Buckskin Dr.
Rio Verde, AZ 85263

Donor: Robert E. Malone.
Foundation type: Independent foundation.
Financial data (yr. ended 12/31/14): Assets, $4,351,236 (M); expenditures, $200,460;

qualifying distributions, $183,846; giving activities include $182,000 for 19 grants (high: $25,000; low: $5,000).
Fields of interest: Arts and culture; Agriculture.
Limitations: Applications not accepted. No grants to individuals.
Application information: Contributes only to pre-selected organizations.
Officers and Directors: Margaret M. Hopkins, Pres.; Thomas E. Malone, Secy.; Eileen M. Pflug, Treas.; Robert E. Malone.
EIN: 263876112

184
Withycombe Foundation
6237 N. 59th Pl.
Paradise Valley, AZ   85253-8011

Established in 1997 in Arizona.
Donors: F. Keith Withycombe; Patricia A. Withycombe.

Foundation type: Independent foundation.
Financial data (yr. ended 12/31/13): Assets, $554,323 (M); expenditures, $171,018; qualifying distributions, $167,755; giving activities include $167,755 for 7 grants (high: $75,505; low: $250).
Fields of interest: Secondary education; Higher education; Nonprofits; Health care administration and financing; National defense; Religion.
Type of support: Regranting.
Limitations: Applications not accepted. Giving primarily in AZ and CO. No grants to individuals.
Application information: Contributes only to pre-selected organizations.
Trustees: F. Keith Withycombe; Patricia A. Withycombe.
EIN: 860818957

185
Zicarelli Foundation
4555 E. Mayo Blvd., Ste. 3426
Phoenix, AZ   85050-6992

Established in 1986 in Arizona.
Donor: Robert F. Zicarelli†.
Foundation type: Independent foundation.
Financial data (yr. ended 12/31/13): Assets, $4,558,923 (M); expenditures, $272,452; qualifying distributions, $247,039; giving activities include $242,000 for 24 grants (high: $100,000; low: $1,000).
Fields of interest: Arts and culture; Museums; Education; Environment; Cancers; Human services.
Type of support: General support; Annual campaigns; Capital campaigns; Research.
Limitations: Applications not accepted. Giving primarily in AZ. No grants to individuals.
Application information: Contributes only to pre-selected organizations.
Officer: John D. Zicarelli, Treas.
Directors: David Zicarelli; James R. Zicarelli; Thomas Zicarelli.
Trustee: Mary L. Zicarelli.
EIN: 860569257

ARKANSAS

186
Bailey Family Foundation
1400 W. Markham St., Ste. 202
Little Rock, AR 72201-1843

Established in 2006 in Arkansas.
Donors: John Bailey; Patricia Bailey.
Foundation type: Independent foundation.
Financial data (yr. ended 12/31/14): Assets, $249; gifts received, $355,000; expenditures, $383,622; qualifying distributions, $383,622; giving activities include $383,622 for 39 grants (high: $250,000; low: $50).
Fields of interest: Education; Higher education; Human services; Youth development; Youth services.
Limitations: Applications not accepted. Giving primarily in AR. No grants to individuals.
Application information: Unsolicited requests for funds not accepted.
Officers: John Bailey, Pres.; Patricia Bailey, V.P.; Rachel Oberste, Secy.
EIN: 208350641

187
Bailey Foundation
(formerly Virginia and Ted Bailey Family Foundation)
1400 W. Markham St., Ste. 202
Little Rock, AR 72201-1822

Established in 1985 in Arkansas.
Donors: H.A. Ted Bailey; Unity Trust; Unity Timberlands, LLC.
Foundation type: Independent foundation.
Financial data (yr. ended 12/31/13): Assets, $0 (M); gifts received, $50,000; expenditures, $294,342; qualifying distributions, $267,700; giving activities include $267,700 for 69 grants (high: $50,000; low: $100).
Fields of interest: Arts and culture; Higher education; Diseases and conditions; Cancers; Christianity; Human services; Family services.
Limitations: Applications not accepted. Giving primarily in Little Rock, AR. No grants to individuals.
Application information: Contributes only to pre-selected organizations.
Officer and Director: H.A. Ted Bailey, Jr., MD, Pres. and Director.
EIN: 710356802

188
Baldor Electric Company Foundation, Inc.
P.O. Box 2400
Fort Smith, AR 72902-2400

Donor: Baldor Electric Co.
Foundation type: Company-sponsored foundation.
Financial data (yr. ended 12/31/13): Assets, $583,696 (M); gifts received, $605,520; expenditures, $339,254; qualifying distributions, $394,900; giving activities include $229,600 for 23 grants (high: $159,300; low: $1,000), and $150,000 for 60 grants to individuals (high: $2,500; low: $2,500).
Fields of interest: Education; Nonprofits; Human services.

International interests: Canada.
Type of support: Individual development; Regranting.
Limitations: Applications not accepted. Giving in the U.S., with some emphasis on AR, OK and SC; some giving also in Canada.
Application information: Unsolicited requests for funds not accepted.
Officers: Tracy Long, Chair.; Merlin Augustine, Vice-Chair.; Jason Green, Secy.-Treas.
Trustees: John Martini; John McFarland; John Taylor.
EIN: 263738996

189
Blue Ridge Charitable Trust
920 South St.
Mountain Home, AR 72653-4714 (870) 424-0130
Contact: Don Brandsgaard, Tr.

Established in 1997 in Arkansas.
Donor: Dennis Stattman.
Foundation type: Independent foundation.
Financial data (yr. ended 12/31/13): Assets, $2,478,309 (M); expenditures, $158,756; qualifying distributions, $150,000; giving activities include $150,000 for 5 grants (high: $100,000; low: $10,000).
Fields of interest: Family planning; Maternal and perinatal health; Agriculture; Human services; Food aid.
Limitations: Applications accepted. Giving primarily in NJ. No grants to individuals.
Application information: Application form required.
   Initial approach: Letter
   Deadline(s): None
Trustee: Don Brandsgaard.
EIN: 626323908

190
Bodenhamer Foundation
P.O. Box 7588
Little Rock, AR 72217-7588

Established in 1986 in Arkansas.
Donors: Lee Bodenhamer; Centennial Consulting Corp.
Foundation type: Independent foundation.
Financial data (yr. ended 11/30/13): Assets, $6,588,622 (M); gifts received, $2,004,300; expenditures, $346,320; qualifying distributions, $329,000; giving activities include $329,000 for 18 grants (high: $120,000; low: $500).
Fields of interest: Education; Higher education; Health; Eye diseases.
Type of support: Research.
Limitations: Applications not accepted. Giving primarily in AR. No grants to individuals.
Application information: Unsolicited requests for funds not accepted.
Trustee: Lee Bodenhamer.
EIN: 752070352

191
Bogle Family Foundation
P.O. Box 2389
Bentonville, AR 72712-2389

Donors: Robert Bogle; Marilyn Bogle.

Foundation type: Independent foundation.
Financial data (yr. ended 06/30/13): Assets, $6,721,005 (M); gifts received, $7,001,500; expenditures, $179,941; qualifying distributions, $177,753; giving activities include $169,000 for 11 grants (high: $30,000; low: $5,000).
Fields of interest: Arts and culture; Sports and recreation; Human services.
Limitations: Applications not accepted. Giving primarily in AR.
Application information: Unsolicited requests for funds not accepted.
Officers: Robert Bogle, Pres.; Marilyn Bogle, V.P.; Rebecca Bogle Alexander, Secy.
Directors: David Bogle; Leslie Ann Bogle McKenzie.
EIN: 461620316

192
The Buck Foundation
15249 Dutchman's Dr.
Rogers, AR 72756-7868 (479) 925-2597
Contact: Jan Buck, Exec. Dir.
E-mail: info@buckforscholarships.com; Main URL: http://buckforscholarships.com
Facebook: http://www.facebook.com/pages/Buck-Foundation/105830369465112
Twitter: https://twitter.com/#!/buckfoundation

Established in 1999 in Arkansas.
Foundation type: Independent foundation.
Financial data (yr. ended 04/30/13): Assets, $6,160,358 (M); expenditures, $242,538; qualifying distributions, $235,717; giving activities include $38,000 for 7 grants (high: $10,000; low: $500), and $190,500 for grants to individuals.
Purpose and activities: Giving primarily to help meet financial needs of college students by awarding scholarships to students from Rogers Heritage High School and Rogers High School in Rogers, Arkansas.
Fields of interest: Education; Human services.
Type of support: General support; Student aid.
Limitations: Applications accepted. Giving limited to residents of Rogers, AR who are students from Rogers Heritage High School or Rogers High School.
Application information: Complete application guidelines available on foundation web site. Application form required.
Officers and Directors: Richard E. Buck, Pres. and Director; Jan G. Buck, Exec. Dir.; John Garner Buck.
EIN: 710824287

193
Fred Darragh Foundation
P.O. Box 250746
Little Rock, AR 72225-0746 (501) 663-7180
Contact: Ernie Dumas, Dir.

Established in 1968 in Arkansas.
Donor: Fred K. Darragh, Jr.†.
Foundation type: Independent foundation.
Financial data (yr. ended 12/31/13): Assets, $3,609,639 (M); expenditures, $382,049; qualifying distributions, $353,200; giving activities include $353,200 for 18 grants (high: $80,000; low: $5,000).
Fields of interest: Higher education; Environment; Human rights; Individual liberties; International peace and security; Children; LGBTQ people; Single parents; Ethnic and racial groups; Low-income and poor people.

Type of support: General support; Endowments; Program development; Convening; Recordings; Scholarships; Research.
Limitations: Applications accepted. Giving limited to AR. No support for non-ecumenical religious organizations or for political organizations. No grants to individuals.
Publications: Financial statement.
Application information: Application form required.
Initial approach: Letter
Copies of proposal: 5
Deadline(s): None
Officer: Charles B. Cliett, Jr., Secy.
Directors: Max Brantley; Ernie Dumas; Freddie Nixon; Kathy Wells.
Number of staff: None.
EIN: 710406242

194
George H. Dunklin, Jr. Charitable Foundation

620 E. 22nd St., Ste. 206
Stuttgart, AR 72160-9009

Established in 2002 in Arkansas.
Donors: L.A. Black & J.H. Boone Foundation; George H. Dunklin, Jr.; M.E. Black Dunklin Trust; GHD Jr. Descendants Charitable Lead Annuity Trust; George H. Dunklin Association.
Foundation type: Independent foundation.
Financial data (yr. ended 12/31/14): Assets, $9,001,955 (M); gifts received, $1,161,445; expenditures, $395,467; qualifying distributions, $339,155; giving activities include $339,155 for 26 grants (high: $132,306; low: $100).
Fields of interest: Cancers; Religion; Protestantism.
Limitations: Applications not accepted. Giving primarily in AR and TN. No grants to individuals.
Application information: Unsolicited requests for funds not accepted.
Trustee: George H. Dunklin, Jr.
EIN: 686213253

195
Ben M. and Betty Lou Elrod Foundation

c/o OBU
Box 3790
Arkadelphia, AR 71998-3790

Donor: Ben M. Elrod.
Foundation type: Independent foundation.
Financial data (yr. ended 12/31/13): Assets, $0 (M); gifts received, $510,000; expenditures, $250,000; qualifying distributions, $250,000; giving activities include $250,000 for 1 grant.
Fields of interest: Education.
Limitations: Applications not accepted. Giving primarily in AR.
Application information: Unsolicited requests for funds not accepted.
Trustees: Ben M. Elrod; Betty Lou Elrod.
Board of Directors: Ian R. Cosh; William Searcy Elrod; Cynthia Lou Elrod Stroud.
EIN: 383892886

196
Families Outreach Inc.

1815 Pleasant Grove Rd.
Jonesboro, AR 72401-7870   (870) 897-4285
FAX: (870) 336-1339; Main URL: http://familiesoutreach.org
Facebook: https://www.facebook.com/pages/Families-Outreach/177853285581874
Twitter: https://twitter.com/Fam_Outreach

Donors: Families Inc. of Arkansas; Joy Davis.
Foundation type: Independent foundation.
Financial data (yr. ended 06/30/13): Assets, $257,199 (M); gifts received, $459,958; expenditures, $435,523; qualifying distributions, $269,195; giving activities include $92,195 for 5 grants (high: $62,694; low: $1,250), and $177,000 for 108 grants to individuals (high: $3,000; low: $1,000).
Fields of interest: Religion; Human rights; Human services; Adoption.
Limitations: Applications accepted. Giving primarily in CO.
Application information: See foundation web site for complete application guidelines. Application form required.
Deadline(s): None
Officers: Cassie Morgan, Pres.; Mark Thurman, V.P.; Jason Turner, Secy.
Board Members: Bryce Blackman; Joy Davis; Stacy Medley.
Director: Jonathan Morgan.
EIN: 201444391

197
Heflin Family Foundation Trust

P.O. Box 8910
Little Rock, AR 72219-8910

Established in 1996 in Arkansas.
Donors: John L. Heflin, Jr.; Sharon Heflin; Jay M. Heflin; Marc W. Heflin; Lynn Heflin.
Foundation type: Independent foundation.
Financial data (yr. ended 12/31/13): Assets, $2,401,661 (M); expenditures, $232,465; qualifying distributions, $225,000; giving activities include $225,000 for 18 grants (high: $50,000; low: $1,000).
Fields of interest: Education; Higher education; Diseases and conditions; Human services; Child welfare.
Limitations: Applications not accepted. Giving primarily in AR. No grants to individuals.
Application information: Unsolicited requests for funds not accepted.
Trustees: J.N. Boo Heflin; Jay M. Heflin; Marc W. Heflin; Sharon K. Heflin.
EIN: 716168230

198
William Thomas & May Pitman Hennessy Foundation

P.O. Box 7
Fort Smith, AR 72902-0007   (479) 782-2041

Established in 1962 in Arkansas.
Donors: May P. Hennessy Trust; W.T. Hennessy Testamentary Trust.
Foundation type: Independent foundation.
Financial data (yr. ended 12/31/13): Assets, $5,648,728 (M); expenditures, $295,972;

qualifying distributions, $260,000; giving activities include $260,000 for 38 grants (high: $104,000; low: $1,000).
Fields of interest: Arts and culture; Early childhood education; Nonprofits; Health; Cancers; Housing development; Human services; Child welfare.
Type of support: Regranting.
Limitations: Applications accepted. Giving limited to Fort Smith, AR. No grants to individuals.
Application information:
Initial approach: Proposal
Deadline(s): Dec. 1
Trustee: First National Bank of Fort Smith.
EIN: 716058272

199
Frank D. Hickingbotham Charitable Foundation Trust

11300 Rodney Parham Rd.
Little Rock, AR 72212-4105   (501) 223-1000

Established in 1984 in Arkansas.
Donors: Frank D. Hickingbotham; VIP Motorcars Ltd.; Par's Custom Cycle Inc.; FDH Enterprises Inc.; Riverbike of Tennessee Inc.; Hickingbotham Family Ltd Ptnr.
Foundation type: Independent foundation.
Financial data (yr. ended 11/30/14): Assets, $348,723; gifts received, $135,500; expenditures, $121,167; qualifying distributions, $121,167.
Purpose and activities: Giving primarily for education, health associations, and Christian organizations.
Fields of interest: Education; Health; Protestantism.
Type of support: General support; Program-related investments; Continuing support; Annual campaigns; Capital campaigns; Capital and infrastructure; Equipment; Land acquisitions; Endowments; Debt reduction; Emergency funds; Program development; Curriculum development; Research.
Limitations: Applications accepted. Giving primarily in AR, with emphasis on Little Rock. No grants to individuals.
Application information: Application form required.
Initial approach: Letter
Copies of proposal: 1
Deadline(s): None
Trustee: Frank D. Hickingbotham.
EIN: 716124938

200
John and Robyn Horn Foundation, Inc.

24300 Chenal Pkwy.
P.O. Box 71
Little Rock, AR 72223-9168
Contact: Pat Forgy, Exec. Dir.
E-mail: jrhornfoundation @gmail.com

Donors: John Horn; Robyn Horn.
Foundation type: Independent foundation.
Financial data (yr. ended 12/31/13): Assets, $6,791,897 (M); gifts received, $6,147,805; expenditures, $460,927; qualifying distributions, $410,707; giving activities include $358,100 for 20 grants (high: $26,250; low: $7,350).
Fields of interest: Arts and culture; Education; Religion.
Application information: Application form required.
Initial approach: Proposal
Deadline(s): None

Officer: Pat Forgy, Exec. Dir.
Directors: Gayle Corley; Mia Hall; John Horn; Robyn Horn; Stoney Lamar.
EIN: 461908869

201
The Hussman Foundation
P.O. Box 2221
Little Rock, AR 72203-2221 (501) 378-3402
Contact: Walter Hussman Jr., Tr.

Established in 1984 in Arkansas.
Donors: Wehco Video, Inc.; Walter Hussman, Jr.; Arkansas Democrat-Gazette, Inc.
Foundation type: Independent foundation.
Financial data (yr. ended 12/31/13): Assets, $8,379,604 (M); expenditures, $394,335; qualifying distributions, $349,970; giving activities include $349,970 for 34 grants (high: $57,200; low: $500).
Purpose and activities: Giving primarily to educational organizations.
Fields of interest: Education; Publishing; Human rights; Child welfare.
Limitations: Applications accepted. Giving primarily in Little Rock, AR.
Application information: Application form required.
Initial approach: Letter
Deadline(s): None
Trustees: Robena Hussman; Walter Hussman, Jr.; Robert Tucker.
EIN: 581605071

202
Carl & Alleen McKinney Charitable Trust
c/o Arvest Trust Co., N.A.
P.O. Box 2389
Bentonville, AR 72712-2389 (479) 273-3111
Contact: Diana Smith, Trust Specialist

Established in 1997 in Arkansas.
Foundation type: Independent foundation.
Financial data (yr. ended 12/31/13): Assets, $3,725,399 (M); expenditures, $211,230; qualifying distributions, $194,751; giving activities include $180,277 for 15 grants (high: $20,000; low: $2,000).
Purpose and activities: The trust awards scholarships to Northwest Arkansas Community College for students in the Bentonville, AR, area. Students to receive these scholarships are chosen by the trustees' scholarship board. Students apply to the community college's financial aid office. One-year scholarships are also allocated for vocational technical training to graduates of Bentonville High School; these students are also selected by the trustees' board. Some funding is also given to projects benefiting children, youth, the elderly, and the poor and disadvantaged of Benton County, AR.
Fields of interest: Vocational education; Higher education; Child welfare; Special population support.
Type of support: Scholarships; General support; Student aid.
Limitations: Applications accepted. Giving primarily in Benton County, AR.
Application information: Application form required for scholarships. Scholarship applications are through the financial aid office of Northwest Arkansas Community College; recipients are chosen

by the trustees' scholarship board. Application form required.
Initial approach: Completed application form for scholarships, with 3 letters of reference and grade transcripts
Copies of proposal: 1
Deadline(s): June 30
Trustees: Dana Davis; Blaine Jackson; Tabita Lipscomb; Arvest Trust Co., N.A.
EIN: 716167536

203
The Merkle Family Foundation
2205 W. Oak St.
El Dorado, AR 71730-5281 (870) 863-3896
Contact: Robert J. Merkle, Tr.

Established in 1997 in Arkansas.
Foundation type: Independent foundation.
Financial data (yr. ended 06/30/15): Assets, $7,519,098 (M); expenditures, $401,058; qualifying distributions, $349,174; giving activities include $349,174 for 12 grants (high: $42,314; low: $18,691).
Fields of interest: Arts and culture; Education; Health; Hospital care; Protestantism; Human services; Youth services.
Limitations: Applications accepted. Giving primarily in AR, TN, and TX. No grants to individuals.
Application information: Application form required.
Initial approach: Letter
Deadline(s): None
Trustees: Robert J. Merkle; Sarah E. Merkle.
EIN: 710794808

204
Jewel Minnis Trust
P.O. Box 552
Brinkley, AR 72021-0552

Foundation type: Independent foundation.
Financial data (yr. ended 04/30/13): Assets, $530,009 (M); expenditures, $192,566; qualifying distributions, $185,000; giving activities include $185,000 for 1 grant.
Purpose and activities: The trust provides scholarships to freshmen entering the University of Arkansas system.
Fields of interest: Education.
Type of support: Scholarships.
Limitations: Applications not accepted. Giving limited to AR.
Application information: Unsolicited requests for funds not accepted.
Trustees: Carl Frein; Dave Lee; J. Baxter Sharp III.
EIN: 716059838

205
Morris Foundation, Inc.
(formerly Vera & Walter Morris Foundation, Inc.)
358 Palos Verdes Dr.
Hot Springs, AR 71913-7359

Established in 1983 in Arkansas.
Donors: Walter S. Morris; Dorothy Morris.
Foundation type: Independent foundation.
Financial data (yr. ended 12/31/13): Assets, $2,146,006 (M); gifts received, $10,000; expenditures, $246,257; qualifying distributions,

$225,083; giving activities include $225,083 for 136 grants (high: $10,000; low: $150).
Purpose and activities: Giving primarily for health and human services.
Fields of interest: Arts and culture; Education; Health; Human services.
Limitations: Applications not accepted. Giving primarily in AR, with emphasis on Hot Springs and Little Rock. No grants to individuals.
Application information: Unsolicited requests for funds not accepted.
Officers: Dorothy Morris, Pres. and Secy.; Jerry Bedford, V.P.; Gordon Morris, Treas.
EIN: 710597938

206
Murphy Education Program, Inc.
200 Peach St.
P.O. Box 7000
El Dorado, AR 71730
Main URL: http://www.murphyoilcorp.com/responsibility/community.aspx

Established in 1998 in Arkansas.
Donor: Murphy Oil Corp.
Foundation type: Company-sponsored foundation.
Financial data (yr. ended 12/31/14): Assets, $266,044; gifts received, $237,878; expenditures, $220,165; qualifying distributions, $218,100.
Purpose and activities: The foundation awards grants to El Dorado, Arkansas, public school students in grades 1 through 12 who score high on standardized tests, and to teachers.
Fields of interest: Elementary and secondary education.
Type of support: Grants to individuals.
Limitations: Applications not accepted. Giving limited to El Dorado, AR.
Application information: Contributes only to pre-selected individuals.
Officers and Directors: David Wood, Pres. and Director; Walter K. Compton, V.P.; J. A. Moore, Secy.; Mindy K. West, Treas.
EIN: 710814094

207
M. W. Murphy Foundation
200 N. Jefferson Ave., Ste. 400
El Dorado, AR 71730-5854 (870) 862-4961
Contact: Martha W. Murphy, Pres., Treas. and Dir.

Established in 1998 in Louisiana.
Donor: Martha W. Murphy.
Foundation type: Independent foundation.
Financial data (yr. ended 12/31/13): Assets, $4,554,830 (M); gifts received, $150,000; expenditures, $194,099; qualifying distributions, $191,590; giving activities include $191,590 for 5 grants (high: $150,000; low: $2,000).
Fields of interest: Higher education; Human services.
Type of support: General support; Student aid.
Limitations: Applications accepted. Giving primarily in AR and MS.
Application information: Application form required.
Initial approach: Letter
Deadline(s): None
Officers and Directors: Martha W. Murphy, Pres. and Treas. and Director; Charles A. Snyder, Secy.; Robert Madison Murphy; Suzanne Nodini Murphy.
EIN: 710802701

208
Nabholz Charitable Foundation
P.O. Box 2090
Conway, AR 72033-2090   (501) 327-7781
Contact: Charles Nabholz, Dir.

Established in 1987 in Arkansas.
Donors: Robert D. Nabholz; Nabholz Construction Corp.; Nabhloz Mechanical & Electrical, Inc.; Nabholz, Inc.; Charles Nabholz; Nabholz Propoerties Inc.
Foundation type: Independent foundation.
Financial data (yr. ended 03/31/14): Assets, $1,440,198 (M); gifts received, $654,481; expenditures, $420,825; qualifying distributions, $418,700; giving activities include $418,700 for 87 grants (high: $25,000; low: $100).
Fields of interest: Higher education; Health; Hospital care; Specialty hospital care; Health care clinics; Catholicism; Human services; Youth services.
Limitations: Applications accepted. Giving primarily in AR.
Application information:
  Initial approach: Proposal
  Deadline(s): None
Directors: Bill Hannah; Charles Nabholz; Greg Williams.
EIN: 581748037

209
Robert D. & Barbara Nabholz Charitable Trust
c/o Regions Bank, Trust Dept.
P.O. Box 100
Russellville, AR   72811

Established in 2003 in Arkansas.
Donors: Robert D. Nabholz†; Robert D. Nabholz Revocable Trust.
Foundation type: Independent foundation.
Financial data (yr. ended 12/31/13): Assets, $6,783,156 (M); gifts received, $15,984; expenditures, $387,648; qualifying distributions, $330,000; giving activities include $330,000 for 9 grants (high: $110,000; low: $5,000).
Fields of interest: Elementary and secondary education; Community and economic development; Catholicism; Human services.
Limitations: Applications not accepted. Giving primarily in AR, KY, and MS. No grants to individuals.
Application information: Contributes only to pre-selected organizations.
Trustee: Regions Bank Trust Dept.
EIN: 736337547

210
Olds Foundation
P.O. Box 114
Amity, AR   71921-0114   (870) 342-5191
Contact: Millard Aud, Chair. and Genl. Mgr.
E-mail: oldsxaud@windstream.net

Established in 1993 in Arkansas.
Donors: W. Cleda Olds†; Eutha Olds†; Hazel Richardson†.
Foundation type: Independent foundation.
Financial data (yr. ended 11/30/14): Assets, $16,213,407 (M); expenditures, $419,087; qualifying distributions, $319,514; giving activities

include $270,774 for 17 grants (high: $100,000; low: $3).
Purpose and activities: Giving primarily for programs and activities that benefit the residents of Amity, Arkansas and the immediately surrounding area; giving also for scholarships to graduating seniors of Centerpoint High School and Kirby High School who are residents of Pike and Clark counties, Arkansas.
Fields of interest: Elementary education; Higher education; Youth development; Children; Adults; Young adults; Seniors; Females; Female children and youth; Female infants and toddlers; Female adults; Males; Male children and youth; Male infants and toddlers; Male adults; People with disabilities; People with psychosocial disabilities.
Type of support: Equipment; Endowments; Curriculum development; Scholarships; Student aid.
Limitations: Applications accepted. Giving primarily in Amity, AR and the immediately surrounding area. No support for political organizations.
Application information: Application form required.
  Initial approach: Letter requesting application form
  Copies of proposal: 5
  Deadline(s): At least 1 month prior to start of college term
  Board meeting date(s): Varies
  Final notification: Normally within 90 days
Officers and Trustees: Millard Aud, Chair. and Gen. Mgr. and Trustee; Theda Aud, Secy.; Michael Aud; Harry C. Erwin; Robert Erwin.
Number of staff: 1 part-time professional.
EIN: 710747091

211
Oliver Charitable Corporation
P.O. Box 3417
Little Rock, AR   72203-3417

Donors: Bess Chisum Stephens; Elizabeth Stephens Campbell; Craig Dobbs Campbell.
Foundation type: Independent foundation.
Financial data (yr. ended 12/31/14): Assets, $6,438,607; expenditures, $342,000; qualifying distributions, $342,000.
Purpose and activities: Giving primarily for education and the arts.
Fields of interest: Orchestral music; Secondary education; Foundations.
Limitations: Applications not accepted. Giving primarily in Little Rock, AR.
Application information: Contributes only to pre-selected organizations.
Directors: Rebecca Carr; Kathy Conley; Robert L. Schulte.
EIN: 204399824

212
M. N. Osborne Charitable Foundation Trust
3417 U of A Way
Texarkana, AR   71854-1419   (870) 774-2222
Contact: M.N. Osborne, Tr.

Established in 1986 in Arkansas.
Donors: M.N. Osborne; Edith M. Osborne.
Foundation type: Independent foundation.
Financial data (yr. ended 11/30/13): Assets, $3,685,215 (M); gifts received, $340,000; expenditures, $315,308; qualifying distributions,

$302,283; giving activities include $297,926 for 8 grants (high: $211,778; low: $748).
Fields of interest: Religion; Human services.
Limitations: Applications accepted. Giving primarily in AR and TX. No grants to individuals.
Application information: Application form required.
  Initial approach: Letter
  Deadline(s): None
Trustees: Edith M. Osborne; M.N. Osborne.
EIN: 716128871

213
Ottenheimer Brothers Foundation
425 W. Capitol Ave., Ste. 1516
Little Rock, AR   72201-3486
Contact: Gus Blass III, Dir.

Established in 1965 in Arkansas.
Donors: Gus Ottenheimer†; Leonard J. Ottenheimer†; Gladys Ottenheimer Hirsch†; Joseph B. Hirsch†.
Foundation type: Independent foundation.
Financial data (yr. ended 04/30/13): Assets, $6,289,235 (M); expenditures, $343,179; qualifying distributions, $305,939; giving activities include $287,200 for 16 grants (high: $100,000; low: $500).
Purpose and activities: Giving primarily in the health and higher education fields in Little Rock, Arkansas, and surrounding areas.
Fields of interest: Higher education; Community and economic development; Judaism; Senior services; Seniors.
Limitations: Applications accepted. Giving primarily in the Little Rock, AR, area. No grants to individuals or for scholarships.
Application information: Application form required.
  Initial approach: Letter
  Copies of proposal: 1
  Deadline(s): None
Officers: Julianne D. Grundfest, Chair.; Steve Bauman, Secy.; Gus Blass III, Project Chair.; Larry Alman, C.F.O.
Board Members: Edward M. Penick, Sr.; Joe Selz; E. Grainger Williams.
Number of staff: 1 part-time support.
EIN: 716059988

214
Riggs Benevolent Fund
P.O. Box 1399
Little Rock, AR   72203   (501) 570-3100

Established in 1959 in Arkansas.
Donors: Robert G. Cress; J.A. Riggs Tractor Co.; Lamar W. Riggs Trust; Jack Riggs III; Lamar W. Riggs.
Foundation type: Company-sponsored foundation.
Financial data (yr. ended 12/31/13): Assets, $8,235,158 (M); gifts received, $279,388; expenditures, $507,110; qualifying distributions, $460,721; giving activities include $433,350 for 48 grants (high: $85,000; low: $1,000).
Purpose and activities: The fund supports museums and hospitals and organizations involved with education, cancer, youth development, children services, and Christianity.
Fields of interest: Museums; Education; Elementary and secondary education; Higher education; Nonprofits; Hospital care; Cancers; Christianity;

Child welfare; Youth development; Agriculture for youth.

Type of support: General support; Scholarships; Regranting.

Limitations: Applications accepted. Giving primarily in Little Rock, AR. No grants to individuals.

Application information: Application form required.

Initial approach: Proposal

Deadline(s): None

Trustees: Robert G. Cress; Edwin Keith Riggs; John A. Riggs III; Bank of America Private Client Group.

EIN: 716050130

215
Southland Greyhound Park Community Foundation, Inc.

1550 N. Ingram Blvd.
West Memphis, AR 72301-2234 (870) 735-3670
Contact: Troy Keeping, Pres.

Established in 2007 in Arkansas.

Donors: Southland Racing Corporation; Delaware North Companies, Inc.; Autozone; Walmart; Crittenden County-Crime Stoppers; Fidelity National Bank.

Foundation type: Independent foundation.

Financial data (yr. ended 12/31/13): Assets, $66,925 (M); gifts received, $230,175; expenditures, $163,380; qualifying distributions, $163,380; giving activities include $163,380 for 6 grants (high: $145,880; low: $500).

Fields of interest: Education; Human services; Youth development.

Limitations: Applications accepted. Giving primarily in AR.

Application information:

Initial approach: Letter

Deadline(s): None

Officers: Troy Keeping, Pres.; Terry C. Burton, Secy.

Directors: William J. Bissett; Noah S. Sechrest.

EIN: 204249277

216
Harriet and Warren Stephens Family Foundation

P.O. Box 3507
Little Rock, AR 72203-3507

Established in 2007 in Arkansas.

Donors: Warren A. Stephens; Harriet Stephens.

Foundation type: Independent foundation.

Financial data (yr. ended 12/31/13): Assets, $17,738,108 (M); gifts received, $7,769,223; expenditures, $462,275; qualifying distributions, $433,000; giving activities include $433,000 for 2 grants (high: $383,000; low: $50,000).

Fields of interest: Historic preservation.

Limitations: Applications not accepted. Giving primarily in Stratford, VA. No grants to individuals.

Application information: Contributes only to pre-selected organizations.

Trustees: Harriet C. Stephens; Warren A. Stephens.

EIN: 261634531

217
W. P. Sturgis Foundation

P.O. Box 394
Arkadelphia, AR 71923-0394 8702466514

Established in 1958 in Arkansas.

Foundation type: Independent foundation.

Financial data (yr. ended 12/31/14): Assets, $3,704,147; gifts received, $162,997; expenditures, $271,417; qualifying distributions, $212,079.

Fields of interest: Higher education; Hospital care; Child welfare.

Type of support: General support; Student aid.

Limitations: Applications accepted. Giving primarily in Little Rock, AR.

Application information: Application form required.

Initial approach: Completed Application form

Deadline(s): May 1.

Officer: June Anthony, Secy.-Treas.

EIN: 716057063

218
Trinity Foundation

P.O. Box 7008
Pine Bluff, AR 71611-7008 (870) 534-7120
Contact: Drew Atkinson

Established in 1952 in Arkansas.

Donors: Pine Bluff Sand & Gravel Co.; McGeorge Contracting Co.; Cornerstone Farm & Gin Co.; Standard Investment Co.; Harvey W. McGeorge†.

Foundation type: Independent foundation.

Financial data (yr. ended 09/30/13): Assets, $16,414,600 (M); expenditures, $469,997; qualifying distributions, $363,000; giving activities include $363,000 for grants (high: $50,000; low: $1,000).

Purpose and activities: Giving primarily for education, youth services, and student scholarships.

Fields of interest: Arts and culture; Education; Higher education; Environment; Child welfare; Youth services.

Type of support: General support; Student aid; Individual development.

Limitations: Applications accepted. Giving primarily in central AR. No grants to individuals directly.

Application information:

Initial approach: Proposal

Deadline(s): None

Board meeting date(s): Varies

Officers: Scott McGeorge, Pres.; Haskell Dickinson, V.P.; Wallace P. McGeorge III, V.P.

Number of staff: None.

EIN: 716050288

219
Union County Community Foundation, Inc.

P.O. Box 148
El Dorado, AR 71731-0148 (870) 862-8223
Contact: Rodney Landes, Chair.
FAX: 8708628254; E-mail: elise@uccfar.org

Established in 1996 in Arkansas.

Foundation type: Community foundation.

Financial data (yr. ended 09/30/13): Assets, $16,626,464 (M); gifts received, $215,584; expenditures, $761,705; giving activities include $336,571 for 40+ grants (high: $93,000; low: $500), and $94,530 for 56 grants to individuals.

Purpose and activities: The foundation provides a charitable vehicle that accepts, invests and distributes resources according to the donors' wishes. Giving also to individuals for scholarships.

Fields of interest: Historic preservation; Education; Community and economic development; Protestantism; Human services.

Type of support: Student aid; Employee matching gifts; In-kind gifts; Individual development.

Limitations: Applications not accepted. Giving limited to the El Dorado, AR, area.

Publications: Financial statement; Grants list; Newsletter.

Officers and Board Members: Rodney Landes, Chair. and Director; Gill Colvin, Vice-Chair. and Director; Ginger Bullard, Secy. and Director; Mike Murphy, Treas. and Director; Scott Enzor; Lynn Landers; Lois Meekins; Tandy Menefee; Bob Risor; Mary Jo Scott; Stacy Scroggins; Matthew Shepherd; Pete Sims; Scott Simpson; Kenna Williams.

Number of staff: 1 full-time professional; 1 full-time support.

EIN: 311500805

220
Bob White Memorial Foundation

(also known as BWMF Farm)
P.O. Box 537
Eudora, AR 71640-9419

Established in 1982 in Arkansas.

Donor: J. Austin White.

Foundation type: Independent foundation.

Financial data (yr. ended 12/31/14): Assets, $8,927,585 (M); expenditures, $563,322; qualifying distributions, $442,411; giving activities include $442,411 for 17 grants (high: $132,000; low: $3,511).

Purpose and activities: Giving to improve the standard of living in Eudora and Chicot County, Arkansas.

Fields of interest: Community and economic development; Human services.

Type of support: General support; Capital and infrastructure; Endowments; Scholarships.

Limitations: Applications not accepted. Giving primarily in Chicot County, AR and the immediate area of the southeast AR geographical region. No grants to individuals.

Application information: Contributes only to pre-selected organizations.

Trustees: Alvin Reynold Meyer.

Number of staff: 1 full-time support.

EIN: 311041899

221
Robert E and Catherine Woodson Sampley Educational Foundation, Inc.

P.O. Box 1147
Mount Ida, AR 71957-1147
Contact: Robert E. Samply

Established in 1994 in Arkansas.

Foundation type: Independent foundation.

Financial data (yr. ended 12/31/13): Assets, $4,678,178 (M); expenditures, $179,120; qualifying distributions, $221,590; giving activities include $216,000 for 38 grants.

Purpose and activities: Scholarship awards to graduates of high schools wholly or partly situated in Montgomery County, Arkansas, for undergraduate or graduate study at an Arkansas college or university.

Fields of interest: Higher education.

Type of support: Student aid.

Limitations: Applications accepted. Giving limited to residents of the Montgomery County, AR, area.
Application information: Application form required.
Initial approach: Proposal
Deadline(s): Apr.
Officers: Jeff Black, Pres.; William Edwards, V.P.; Frances Dobbs, Secy.
Directors: Jason Enderman; Teena Forthman; Barbara Fryar; Tammy McCarter.
EIN: 716156225

222
Wrape Family Charitable Trust
P.O. Box 193455
Little Rock, AR 72219-3455 (501) 224-6164
Contact: W.R. Wrape II, Tr.

Established in 1953 in Arkansas.
Donors: Regina Sellmeyer†; A.M. Wrape†.
Foundation type: Independent foundation.
Financial data (yr. ended 12/31/13): Assets, $4,319,580 (M); expenditures, $306,303; qualifying distributions, $235,579; giving activities include $159,000 for 37 grants (high: $40,000; low: $1,000).
Purpose and activities: Support primarily for Roman Catholic educational and religious organizations.
Fields of interest: Elementary and secondary education; Religion; Catholicism.
Limitations: Applications accepted. Giving primarily in AR. No grants to individuals.
Application information: Application form required.
Initial approach: Letter

Deadline(s): None
Board meeting date(s): Dec.
Officer: Jarrell V. Wrape, Mgr.
Trustees: Tom K. Wrape; W.R. Wrape II.
Number of staff: 1 part-time professional; 1 full-time support.
EIN: 716050323

CALIFORNIA

223
2005 Tomchin Family Charitable Trust
727 Lilac Dr.
Santa Barbara, CA 93108-1436

Established in 2005 in California.
Foundation type: Independent foundation.
Financial data (yr. ended 12/31/13): Assets, $6,707,621 (M); expenditures, $458,311; qualifying distributions, $388,055; giving activities include $388,055 for 40 grants (high: $25,000; low: $55).
Fields of interest: Arts and culture; Education; Environment; Human services.
Limitations: Applications not accepted. Giving primarily in CA. No grants to individuals.
Application information: Contributes only to pre-selected organizations.
Trustees: Rose Delles; Deborah Naish; Cheryl Tomchin; Emily Tomchin.
EIN: 206708205

224
Nina Abrams Fund
c/o Jonathan Brooks
3056 Earlmar Dr.
Los Angeles, CA 90064-4632

Established in 2002 in New York.
Donors: Nina Abrams; Nina Abrams Revocable Trust; The Nina Abrams Charitable Remainder Unitrust.
Foundation type: Independent foundation.
Financial data (yr. ended 12/31/13): Assets, $2,937,323 (M); expenditures, $186,646; qualifying distributions, $183,822; giving activities include $181,000 for 38 grants (high: $37,500; low: $1,000).
Fields of interest: Land resources.
Limitations: Applications not accepted. Giving primarily in CA and NY. No grants to individuals.
Application information: Unsolicited requests for funds not accepted.
Officers: Jonathan Brooks, Pres. and Treas.; Jonathan Self, V.P.; Celia Berk, Secy.
EIN: 550818279

225
Acacia Foundation
300 Drakes Landing Rd., Ste. 280
Greenbrae, CA 94904-3109

Established in 1996 in California.
Donors: Judy Chandler Webb; Scott Haskins; Eliza Koeppel; John C. Haskins.
Foundation type: Independent foundation.
Financial data (yr. ended 05/31/13): Assets, $812,995 (M); gifts received, $192,500; expenditures, $194,871; qualifying distributions, $182,538; giving activities include $180,000 for 5 grants (high: $150,000; low: $5,000).
Fields of interest: Orchestral music; Botanical gardens.
Type of support: Capital and infrastructure; Research.

Limitations: Applications not accepted. Giving primarily in CA and HI. No grants to individuals.
Application information: Unsolicited requests for funds not accepted.
Trustees: Eliza Haskins Koeppel; John C. Haskins; Scott Haskins; John T. Lewis; Judy Chandler Webb.
EIN: 954585686

226
Rosenberg Ach Foundation
c/o Linda Ach
P.O. Box 590155
San Francisco, CA 94159-0155

Donor: Linda Rosenberg Ach.
Foundation type: Independent foundation.
Financial data (yr. ended 08/31/13): Assets, $7,488,838 (M); expenditures, $253,483; qualifying distributions, $186,000; giving activities include $186,000 for 31 grants (high: $50,000; low: $100).
Fields of interest: Education; Environment; Health; Sports and recreation; Human services.
Limitations: Applications not accepted. Giving primarily in San Francisco, CA. No grants to individuals.
Application information: Contributes only to pre-selected organizations.
Officers and Directors: Linda Rosenberg Ach, Pres. and Secy. and Director; Andrew Ach, Treas. and Director; Elizabeth Atcheson.
EIN: 270965935

227
The Thomas C. Ackerman Foundation
3755 Avocado Blvd., Ste. 518
La Mesa, CA 91941-7301   (619) 741-0113
Main URL: http://www.ackermanfoundation.org

Established in 1991 in California.
Donor: Thomas C. Ackerman, Jr.†.
Foundation type: Independent foundation.
Financial data (yr. ended 12/31/14): Assets, $6,170,600; expenditures, $322,696; qualifying distributions, $242,100.
Purpose and activities: The Thomas C. Ackerman Foundation is committed to helping youth achieve success in their early education, whether they are college-bound or entering the work force directly after high school. The foundation believes that a well-rounded kindergarten through twelfth-grade education including music, arts, culture, math and science is essential to helping students fulfill their future roles as parents/professionals and citizens. Support for organizations involved with arts and culture, education, health and human services, and community development. The foundation also supports well-rounded kindergarten through twelfth-grade educational programs that include music, arts, culture, math and science.
Fields of interest: Arts and culture; Education; Elementary and secondary education; Secondary education; Health; Community and economic development; Special population support.
Type of support: General support; Matching grants; Capacity-building and technical assistance; Equipment; Program development; Seed money; Curriculum development; Scholarships; Program evaluations.
Limitations: Applications accepted. Giving primarily in San Diego County, CA. No support for religious

organizations for religious purposes, or for international organizations, or medical/biological research organizations. No grants to individuals, or for continuing support, conferences or symposia.
Publications: Application guidelines; Annual report; Grants list.
Application information: Guidelines for completing Letter of Intent are available on foundation web site. Full proposals accepted only after approval of Letter of Intent. Application form required.
  Initial approach: Letter of Intent not exceeding 3 pages, which can also be submitted via the foundation web site, as well as complete online grant application questionnaire
  Copies of proposal: 3
  Deadline(s): Application deadlines available on foundation web site
  Board meeting date(s): Quarterly
  Final notification: Within 30 days of board meeting
Officers: Robert G. Copeland, Pres.; JoAnne M. Pastula, V.P.; Kenneth G. Coveney, Secy.; H. Michael Collins, Treas.
Directors: Christopher C. Calkins; Gail K. Naughton; John G. Rebelo.
Number of staff: 1 full-time professional.
EIN: 330477490

228
Adams Fund
915 Wilshire Blvd., Ste. 1760
Los Angeles, CA 90017-3486

Established in 1959 in California.
Donors: Morgan Adams, Jr.; Suzanne V. Parry; Adams Plaza; Nash Mariposa, Ltd.; John King Adams; David V. Adams; Mary Adams O'Connell; Richard E. Beth.
Foundation type: Independent foundation.
Financial data (yr. ended 12/31/13): Assets, $4,406,499 (M); gifts received, $52,500; expenditures, $323,304; qualifying distributions, $265,928; giving activities include $265,928 for 45 grants (high: $54,612; low: $500).
Purpose and activities: Giving primarily for the arts, education, health care, including a children's hospital, children, youth, and social services; some funding for Roman Catholic organizations, missions, and education.
Fields of interest: Arts and culture; Museums; Education; Higher education; Foundations; Hospital care; Specialty hospital care; Diseases and conditions; Catholicism; Human services; Child welfare.
Type of support: General support; Publications.
Limitations: Applications not accepted. Giving primarily in CA. No grants to individuals.
Application information: Unsolicited requests for funds not accepted.
Trustees: David V. Adams; John King Adams; Richard E. Beth; Mary Adams O'Connell.
Number of staff: 2 part-time support.
EIN: 956015986

229
Adams Legacy Foundation
P.O. Box 1957
Los Alamitos, CA 90720-1957   (562) 431-0011
Contact: Blair Carty, Exec. Dir.

E-mail: bcarty@adamslegacyfoundation.org; Main URL: http://www.adamslegacyfoundation.org Grants List: http://www.adamslegacyfoundation.org/untitled.html

Donor: Peter D. Adams.
Foundation type: Independent foundation.
Financial data (yr. ended 12/31/13): Assets, $4,931,778 (M); expenditures, $249,853; qualifying distributions, $207,355; giving activities include $148,000 for 23 grants (high: $20,000; low: $500).
Purpose and activities: Giving primarily for education and land conservation.
Fields of interest: Education; Land resources.
Limitations: Applications accepted. Giving primarily in CA, OH and Washington, DC.
Application information: See foundation web site for complete application guidelines. Application form required.
Officers: Peter D. Adams, Pres.; Rebecca B. Adams, V.P.; Blair Carty, Exec. Dir.
EIN: 263373791

230
Adelaide Christian Home For Children Inc.
(formerly Adelaide Christian Home for Children)
122 Avenida Del Mar
San Clemente, CA 92672
Contact: Sheri Parsons, Dir.

Foundation type: Independent foundation.
Financial data (yr. ended 12/31/13): Assets, $4,945,017 (M); expenditures, $454,040; qualifying distributions, $434,146; giving activities include $374,460 for 25 grants (high: $52,000; low: $1,000).
Purpose and activities: Giving primarily to evangelical Christian organizations serving children and youth. Priority is given to local California ministries.
Fields of interest: Education; Religion; Christianity; Human services; Youth development; Children; Single parents; Low-income and poor people.
Limitations: Applications accepted. Giving primarily in southern CA. No support for churches.
Application information: Application form required.
  Initial approach: Letter
  Deadline(s): None
  Board meeting date(s): Jan. and Sept.
Directors: Norma J. Broudy; Lawrence A. Bush; Mary Lou Bush; Lydia Hocking; Fred Kaiser; Sheri Parsons; Paul Rosa; James Simpson.
Number of staff: 1 full-time professional.
EIN: 951855642

231
Lucy & Isadore B. Adelman Foundation
10880 Wilshire Blvd., Ste. 800
Los Angeles, CA 90024-4124

Established in 1981 in Texas.
Donors: Lucy Adelman; Susan Adelman; Claudio Llanos.
Foundation type: Independent foundation.
Financial data (yr. ended 06/30/14): Assets, $1,387,944 (M); expenditures, $217,076; qualifying distributions, $205,598; giving activities include $199,191 for 46 grants (high: $50,000; low: $60).

Fields of interest: Education; Philanthropy; Human services.
Limitations: Applications not accepted. Giving primarily in CA. No grants to individuals.
Application information: Unsolicited requests for funds not accepted.
Officers: Susan Adelman, Pres. and Treas.; Aron Adelman Llanos, V.P.; Lisa Adelman Llanos, V.P.; Claudio Llanos, Secy.
EIN: 751806018

232
Adonai Foundation Inc.
877 Independence Ave.
Mountain View, CA 94043-2331

Donors: Yuet-Ming Chu; Miriam Chu.
Foundation type: Independent foundation.
Financial data (yr. ended 12/31/13): Assets, $2,975,373 (M); gifts received, $300,000; expenditures, $217,442; qualifying distributions, $213,414; giving activities include $213,414 for 51 grants (high: $40,000; low: $100).
Fields of interest: Education; Religion; Human services.
Type of support: General support.
Limitations: Applications not accepted. Giving primarily in CA.
Application information: Unsolicited requests for funds not accepted.
Officers and Directors: Yuet-Ming Chu, Pres. and Director; Miriam Chu, Secy.-Treas. and Director; Terry Parker.
EIN: 582592055

233
Ady Gil World Conservation
7635 Airport Business Pkwy.
Van Nuys, CA 91406-1725   (818) 222-0022

Donor: Ady Gil.
Foundation type: Operating foundation.
Financial data (yr. ended 12/31/13): Assets, $5,746,084 (M); gifts received, $8,986; expenditures, $529,313; qualifying distributions, $456,756; giving activities include $293,397 for 14 grants (high: $80,000; low: $1,200).
Fields of interest: Animal welfare.
Limitations: Applications accepted. Giving primarily in CA.
Application information: Application form required.
  Initial approach: Letter
  Deadline(s): None
Officers: Ady Gil, C.E.O. and Pres.; Rod Summers, Secy.
EIN: 300611901

234
Akian Foundation
26235 Technology Dr.
Valencia, CA 91355-1147

Established in 2009 in California.
Donors: Zaven P. Akian; Sonia Akian.
Foundation type: Independent foundation.
Financial data (yr. ended 11/30/13): Assets, $4,970,174 (M); gifts received, $40,000; expenditures, $286,122; qualifying distributions, $271,554; giving activities include $270,050 for 7 grants (high: $119,050; low: $10,000).

Fields of interest: Higher education.
International interests: Armenia.
Limitations: Applications not accepted. Giving primarily in CA.
Application information: Unsolicited requests for funds not accepted.
Officers: Haig P. Akian, Pres.; Lori J. Stephan, V.P. and Secy.; Lena G. Akian, V.P. and C.F.O.
Directors: Sonia Akian; Zaven P. Akien.
EIN: 263913336

235
Alafi Family Foundation
P.O. Box 7338
Berkeley, CA 94707-0338
Contact: Moshe Alafi, C.F.O.

Established in 1999 in California.
Donors: Alafi Capital Company, LLC; Moshe Alafi.
Foundation type: Independent foundation.
Financial data (yr. ended 12/31/13): Assets, $2,796,936 (M); expenditures, $403,993; qualifying distributions, $347,600; giving activities include $347,600 for 10 grants (high: $125,000; low: $1,000).
Purpose and activities: Giving primarily for the performing arts, learning disorders, child abuse prevention, women who are homeless, and biological research on mental disorders.
Fields of interest: Performing arts; Mental health care; Neurology; Learning disorders; Child abuse; Women's services; Homeless people.
Type of support: Convening; Matching grants; Grants to individuals; Equipment; Research; Internships; Scholarships; Student aid.
Limitations: Applications accepted. Giving primarily in northern CA. No support for religious or political organizations.
Application information: Application form required.
  Initial approach: Letter
  Copies of proposal: 1
  Deadline(s): None
  Board meeting date(s): Jan. 5, Mar. 6, and Sept. 28
Officers: Margaret Alafi, Pres.; Moshe Alafi, C.F.O.; Christopher Alafi, V.P.; Shireen Alafi, Secy.
Number of staff: 4 part-time professional; 1 part-time support.
EIN: 943343568

236
Alalusi Foundation
1975 National Ave.
Hayward, CA 94545-1709   (510) 887-2374
E-mail: info@alalusifoundation.org; Main URL: http://www.alalusifoundation.org
Facebook: https://www.facebook.com/pages/Alalusi-Foundation/497928536916586?ref=br_tf

Established in 2001 in California.
Donors: Hesham Al-Alusi; Ayam Alshar; Mirza Baig; Patricia Baig; Husam Shuayb; Ahd Shuayb; Mohammed Raheemuddin Ahmed; Syed K. Raza; Nabeela Sajjad.
Foundation type: Independent foundation.
Financial data (yr. ended 03/31/14): Assets, $0 (M); gifts received, $435,535; expenditures, $450,353; qualifying distributions, $449,135; giving activities include $408,361 for 11 grants (high: $55,650; low: $1,300).

Purpose and activities: Giving primarily for Muslim and Islamic relief and affairs, as well as for humanitarian assistance in other regions.
Fields of interest: Religion; Islam; Human rights; Basic and emergency aid; International development.
International interests: Africa; Asia; China; Middle East.
Type of support: General support; Grants to individuals.
Limitations: Applications accepted. Giving on an international basis with emphasis on China; some giving also in CA.
Application information:
  Initial approach: Letter
  Deadline(s): None
Director: Hesham Al-Alusi.
EIN: 912158518

237
Altos Foundation, Inc.
171 Main St., No. 292
Los Altos, CA 94022-2912

Established in 1982 in California.
Donors: David Jackson; Susan Jackson.
Foundation type: Independent foundation.
Financial data (yr. ended 09/30/12): Assets, $17,228 (M); gifts received, $6,099; expenditures, $383,508; qualifying distributions, $376,174; giving activities include $373,000 for 30 grants (high: $30,000; low: $3,500).
Purpose and activities: Giving primarily for human services.
Fields of interest: Hospital care; Abuse prevention; Housing development; Human services; Family services; Child welfare; Homeless people.
Type of support: General support.
Limitations: Applications not accepted. Giving primarily in CA. No grants to individuals.
Application information: Contributes only to pre-selected organizations.
Officers: Susan Jackson, Pres.; Robert N. Grant, Secy.; Mark Jackson, Treas.
Directors: Judi Fowler; Caroline A. Trowbridge.
EIN: 942853627

238
Amador Community Foundation, Inc.
148 Main St.
P.O. Box 1154
Jackson, CA 95642   (209) 223-2148
Contact: Kathleen Harmon, Exec. Dir.
FAX: (209) 223-4569;
E-mail: acf@amadorcommunityfoundation.org; Main URL: http://www.amadorcommunityfoundation.org
Facebook: http://www.facebook.com/pages/
Amador-Community-Foundation/
356786497672627?sk=wall

Established in 2000 in California.
Donors: Janet Aberley†; Helen Fallis†.
Foundation type: Community foundation.
Financial data (yr. ended 12/31/12): Assets, $1,597,727 (M); gifts received, $806,661; expenditures, $730,667; giving activities include $193,076 for 9+ grants (high: $20,000).
Purpose and activities: The foundation supports organizations that enhance the quality of life for the people of Amador County by: 1) encouraging private giving for the public good by providing a flexible,

cost-effective and tax-exempt vehicle for donors with varied charitable interests and abilities to give; 2) building and maintaining a permanent endowment fund in order to provide a continuing source of income for grants; 3) making grants that are innovative, strategic and relevant in the support of nonprofit sectors; 4) and serving as a catalyst to address changing and challenging community issues.
Fields of interest: Arts and culture; Education; Environment; Diseases and conditions; Community and economic development; Sports and recreation; Human services.
Type of support: Building and renovations; Matching grants; Capital campaigns; Convening; Continuing support; Curriculum development; Equipment; General support; Capacity-building and technical assistance; Program development; Scholarships; Student aid; Technical assistance.
Limitations: Applications accepted. Giving limited to the Amador County, CA, area. No support for private foundations or religious purposes. No grants for long-term debt retirement.
Publications: Application guidelines; Grants list; Informational brochure.
Application information: Visit foundation web site for online grant application and guidelines.
Application form required.
  Initial approach: Contact foundation
  Copies of proposal: 1
  Deadline(s): None
  Board meeting date(s): Every month
  Final notification: Within 30 to 60 days
Officers and Directors: Pat Crew, Pres. and Director; Karl Knobelauch, V.P. and Director; Wayne Garibaldi, Secy.-Treas. and Director; Kathleen Harmon, Exec. Dir.; Gretchen Kingsbury; Stan Lukowicz; Melody Mauck; Eric Rouen; Charlie Spinetta; Meg Verardi.
Number of staff: 1 full-time professional; 1 part-time support.
EIN: 680447992

239
Amerman Family Foundation
P.O. Box 894030
Temecula, CA 92589-4030

Established in 1997 in California.
Donors: Jerome T. Amerman; John W. Amerman.
Foundation type: Independent foundation.
Financial data (yr. ended 12/31/14): Assets, $676,958; expenditures, $295,131; qualifying distributions, $250,000.
Purpose and activities: Giving primarily for children's health programs, including a children's hospital.
Fields of interest: Specialty hospital care; Child welfare.
Limitations: Applications not accepted. Giving primarily in CA. No grants to individuals.
Application information: Contributes only to pre-selected organizations.
Officers: John W. Amerman, Pres.; Anne H. Thompson, Secy.; Jerome T. Amerman, Treas.
Directors: Anne J. Amerman; Garrett J. Amerman; Glenn Bozarth; John Conners.
EIN: 330757355

240
Amin Foundation
3166 Shandwick Cir.
Corona, CA 92882-7583   (909) 208-5655
Contact: Chirag Amin MD, Tr.

Foundation type: Independent foundation.
Financial data (yr. ended 12/31/12): Assets, $2,855,167 (M); expenditures, $238,395; qualifying distributions, $145,000; giving activities include $145,000 for grants.
Fields of interest: Health; Religion; Tribal and indigenous religions; Human services; Indigenous peoples.
Limitations: Applications accepted. Giving primarily in CA and IL.
Application information: Application form required.
  Initial approach: Proposal
  Deadline(s): None
Trustees: Chirag Amin; Kelly Amin; David Evans; Joseph Hammond; Derek Muro.
EIN: 800075857

241
Bijan and Soraya Amin Foundation Trust
10203 Santa Monica Blvd., 3rd Fl.
Los Angeles, CA 90067-6440   (310) 225-5112
Contact: Mohammed Mark Amin, Mgr.

Established in 2000 in California.
Donors: Mohammed Mark Amin; Reza Amin.
Foundation type: Independent foundation.
Financial data (yr. ended 12/31/12): Assets, $1,353,698 (M); expenditures, $129,195; qualifying distributions, $127,725; giving activities include $127,725 for 14 grants (high: $25,000; low: $1,000).
Fields of interest: Health; Diseases and conditions; Housing development.
Application information: Application form required.
  Initial approach: Letter
  Deadline(s): None
Officers: Mohammed Mark Amin, Mgr.; Reza Amin, Mgr.
EIN: 957110956

242
Anatman Foundation
(formerly John D. & Betty R. Howard Family Foundation, Inc.)
127 W. Ortega St.
Santa Barbara, CA 93101-3340

Established in 1996 in California.
Donors: Betty R. Howard†; John D. Howard; Industrial Centers Corp.; Cynthia D. Howard.
Foundation type: Independent foundation.
Financial data (yr. ended 12/31/13): Assets, $1,095,757 (M); gifts received, $15,000; expenditures, $145,733; qualifying distributions, $137,136; giving activities include $137,111 for 8 grants (high: $53,500; low: $1,600).
Fields of interest: Arts and culture; Education; Human services.
Limitations: Applications not accepted. Giving primarily in CA. No grants to individuals.
Application information: Unsolicited requests for funds not accepted.
Officers: Cynthia D. Howard, Pres.; Teha Colleen Eliassen Drew, Secy.; John Todd Eliassen, Treas.
EIN: 954580181

243
Joseph R. and Katherine Anderson Foundation
669 Starbush Dr.
Sunnyvale, CA 94086-8245

Established in 2004 in California.
Donors: Devin Mathews Trust; Elaine Mathews Trust; Jane Harvill Trust.
Foundation type: Independent foundation.
Financial data (yr. ended 12/31/14): Assets, $4,125,013 (M); gifts received, $195,722; expenditures, $207,664; qualifying distributions, $140,000; giving activities include $140,000 for 5 grants (high: $60,000; low: $10,000).
Fields of interest: Education; Agriculture; Human services.
Limitations: Applications not accepted. Giving primarily in CA.
Application information: Unsolicited requests for funds not accepted.
Officer: Elaine Mathews, Exec. Dir.
EIN: 352182745

244
Martin & Illie Anderson Foundation
5688 Columbia Dr., S.
Fresno, CA 93727-6113

Established in 1996 in California.
Donors: E. Martin Anderson; Illie Anderson.
Foundation type: Independent foundation.
Financial data (yr. ended 12/31/14): Assets, $2,626,382 (M); expenditures, $295,912; qualifying distributions, $280,000; giving activities include $280,000 for grants.
Fields of interest: Museums; Higher education; University education; Public policy.
Type of support: Policy, advocacy and systems reform.
Limitations: Applications not accepted. Giving primarily in Stanford, CA and Honolulu, HI. No grants to individuals.
Application information: Unsolicited requests for funds not accepted.
Officers: E. Martin Anderson, Pres.; Christine Docker, Secy.; W.F. Docker, Treas.
EIN: 770440292

245
Alberta S. Kimball-Mary L. Anhaltzer Foundation, Inc.
(formerly Alberta S. Kimball Foundation, Inc.)
601 California St., 17th Fl.
San Francisco, CA 94108-2702 (415) 675-1090

Established in 1986 in Wisconsin.
Donor: Alberta S. Kimball†.
Foundation type: Independent foundation.
Financial data (yr. ended 12/31/14): Assets, $5,743,779; expenditures, $401,492; qualifying distributions, $349,253.
Purpose and activities: Giving primarily for the arts, medicine, and education.
Fields of interest: Arts and culture; Education; Diseases and conditions; Human services.
Type of support: General support; Research; Continuing support; Annual campaigns; Capital campaigns; Capital and infrastructure; Land acquisitions; Emergency funds; Program development.

Limitations: Applications accepted. Giving primarily in Oshkosh, WI; giving also in the western U.S. No support for private foundations or organizations lacking 501(c)(3) status. No grants to individuals.
Application information: Application form required.
Initial approach: Letter
Copies of proposal: 1
Deadline(s): None
Officers: Gregory C. Anhaltzer, Pres.; Jeffrey O. Anhaltzer, V.P.; Kelly D. Sanders, Treas.
Number of staff: 1 part-time professional; 2 part-time support.
EIN: 391848233

246
Animal Guardians, Inc.
(formerly Compassion for Animals Foundation, Inc.)
3962 Landmark St.
Culver City, CA 90232-2315
Contact: Bettina Rosmarino, Prog. Dir.
E-mail: info@compassionforanimals.com; Additional address: P.O. Box 1925, Culver City, CA 90232-1925, tel.: (310) 204-6600

Established in 1986 in California.
Donor: Gilbert N. Michaels.
Foundation type: Operating foundation.
Financial data (yr. ended 12/31/13): Assets, $2,682,596 (M); gifts received, $325,000; expenditures, $562,859; qualifying distributions, $504,071; giving activities include $181,740 for 22 grants (high: $50,000; low: $500).
Purpose and activities: Giving strictly for the protection and advancement of animal rights and the prevention of cruelty to animals, through scientific research, literary and educational efforts, and charitable activities.
Fields of interest: Research on animals.
International interests: China.
Type of support: General support.
Limitations: Applications not accepted. Giving primarily in China.
Application information: Unsolicited requests for funds not accepted.
Officers: Gilbert N. Michaels, C.E.O. and Pres.; Pam Tucker, Secy.-Treas. and C.F.O.
Directors: Judy Fisher; Crystal Zarpas.
Number of staff: 2 full-time professional; 2 part-time professional.
EIN: 954082225

247
Carmelo Anthony Foundation, Inc.
1880 Century Park E., Ste. 1600
Los Angeles, CA 90067-1661
E-mail: carmelocares@gmail.com; Main URL: http://www.thisismelo.com/foundation/about
Facebook: https://www.facebook.com/CarmeloAnthony
Twitter: https://twitter.com/carmeloanthony
YouTube: https://www.youtube.com/user/ThisIsMeloTV

Established in 2005 in California.
Donors: Melo Enterprises, Inc.; Carmelo K. Anthony; Perennial Sports & Entertainment, LLC; Time Warner Cable; Hyde Park.
Foundation type: Independent foundation.
Financial data (yr. ended 12/31/13): Assets, $80,530 (M); gifts received, $505,322; expenditures, $451,380; qualifying distributions,

$397,233; giving activities include $127,054 for 3 + grants (high: $100,000), and $245,434 for 2 foundation-administered programs.
Purpose and activities: The foundation's mission is to invest in programs, leaders and community organizations that empower and provide opportunity for underserved children and families.
Fields of interest: Basketball; Youth services.
Limitations: Applications not accepted. Giving primarily in Baltimore, MD; some giving nationally.
Application information: Contributes only to pre-selected organizations.
Officers and Directors: Carmelo K. Anthony, Pres. and Director; Robert Frazier; Alani Vazquez.
EIN: 203293195

248
Arata Brothers Trust
P.O. Box 1028
Dixon, CA 95620-1028
E-mail: info@aratabrotherstrust.org; Main URL: http://aratabrotherstrust.org

Established in 1976 in California.
Foundation type: Independent foundation.
Financial data (yr. ended 12/31/14): Assets, $6,702,811; expenditures, $454,489; qualifying distributions, $335,000.
Purpose and activities: Giving primarily for the arts, health, education, and youth and social services.
Fields of interest: Arts and culture; Education; Elementary and secondary education; Law education; Foundations; Health; Diseases and conditions; Human services; Child welfare.
Type of support: General support; Research; Research and evaluation.
Limitations: Applications accepted. Giving primarily in CA, with emphasis on Sacramento. No grants to individuals.
Application information: Application form required.
Initial approach: See website
Deadline(s): None
Trustees: Elfrena Foord; Lisa Malvini; Mark Sewell.
EIN: 237204615

249
Arbor Foundation
P.O. Box 459
San Carlos, CA 94070-0459

Established in 2000 in Nevada.
Donors: D. James Guzy; Marcia O. Guzy.
Foundation type: Independent foundation.
Financial data (yr. ended 11/30/12): Assets, $4,215,266 (M); expenditures, $291,088; qualifying distributions, $250,000; giving activities include $250,000 for grants.
Fields of interest: Historic preservation; Health care clinics; Diseases and conditions; Orthodox Christianity.
Type of support: Research.
Limitations: Applications not accepted. Giving primarily in MN. No grants to individuals.
Application information: Contributes only to pre-selected organizations.
Officers: D. James Guzy, Chair.; Marcia O. Guzy, Secy. and C.F.O.
EIN: 880480379

250
The Archer Family Foundation

P.O. Box 757
San Jose, CA 95106-0757 (408) 453-5510
Contact: Robert A. Archer, Pres.

Established in 2001 in California.
Donor: Robert A. Archer.
Foundation type: Independent foundation.
Financial data (yr. ended 12/31/14): Assets, $976,180 (M); gifts received, $159,478; qualifying distributions, $150,831; giving activities include $150,125 for 29 grants (high: $50,500; low: $250).
Purpose and activities: Giving to organizations that improve the quality of life for residents of CA.
Fields of interest: Higher education; Diseases and conditions; Agriculture; Human services.
Type of support: General support.
Limitations: Applications accepted. Giving primarily in CA.
Application information:
 Initial approach: Proposal
 Deadline(s): None
Officer: Robert A. Archer, C.E.O. and Pres.
EIN: 300010211

251
The Ark Watch Foundation

106 E. Portola Ave.
Los Altos, CA 94022
Main URL: http://www.knightsbridgefarm.org

Donor: The Roberts Foundation.
Foundation type: Independent foundation.
Financial data (yr. ended 09/30/13): Assets, $45,141 (M); gifts received, $597,745; expenditures, $592,370; qualifying distributions, $579,493; giving activities include $428,142 for 12 grants (high: $200,000; low: $2,500).
Purpose and activities: Giving primarily for animal welfare, particularly causes dealing with horses.
Fields of interest: Animal welfare.
Limitations: Applications not accepted.
Application information: Unsolicited requests for funds not accepted.
Officers and Directors: Celine Myers, Pres. and Exec. Dir.; Vicki Kerr, Secy.-Treas. and Director; Allison Argo; Anna Twinney.
EIN: 203618680

252
Arlene Foundation

100 Wilshire Blvd., Ste. 1755
Santa Monica, CA 90401-1142

Established in 2005 in California.
Donors: Steven D. Levine; Loren L. Levine.
Foundation type: Independent foundation.
Financial data (yr. ended 12/31/13): Assets, $1,441,606 (M); gifts received, $7,775; expenditures, $224,942; qualifying distributions, $220,822; giving activities include $216,516 for 15 grants (high: $86,000; low: $500).
Fields of interest: Diseases and conditions; Human rights; Human services; Foster care.
Limitations: Applications not accepted. Giving primarily in CA and NY. No grants to individuals.
Application information: Unsolicited requests for funds not accepted.
Trustees: Loren L. Levine; Steven D. Levine.
EIN: 320158768

253
Armrod Charitable Foundation

4020 Sierra College Blvd., Ste. 200
Rocklin, CA 95677-3906 (916) 624-6200
Contact: Martin A. Harmon, Pres.

Established in 1996 in California.
Donors: Martin A. Harmon; AllPro, Inc.; Sierra Medical Enterprises, Inc.; Plum Healthcare Group LLC.
Foundation type: Independent foundation.
Financial data (yr. ended 12/31/13): Assets, $946,111 (M); gifts received, $43,900; expenditures, $277,460; qualifying distributions, $277,460; giving activities include $270,300 for 37 grants (high: $50,000; low: $500).
Fields of interest: Human services.
Type of support: Research.
Limitations: Applications accepted. Giving primarily in CA. No grants to individuals.
Application information: Application form required.
 Initial approach: Letter
 Deadline(s): None
Officers: Martin A. Harmon, Pres.; Robert Meaglia, C.F.O.; Donald T. Trowbridge, Secy.
EIN: 680370503

254
The Beverly and Frank Arnstein Foundation

1017 Laurel Way
Beverly Hills, CA 90210-2304

Established in 2005 in California.
Donors: Beverly J. Arnstein; Frank G. Arnstein.
Foundation type: Independent foundation.
Financial data (yr. ended 12/31/13): Assets, $2,702,598 (M); gifts received, $400,000; expenditures, $208,575; qualifying distributions, $165,000; giving activities include $165,000 for 6 grants (high: $50,000; low: $10,000).
Fields of interest: Ear, nose and throat diseases.
Type of support: Research.
Limitations: Applications not accepted. Giving primarily in CA. No grants to individuals.
Application information: Unsolicited requests for funds not accepted.
Officers and Directors: Frank G. Arnstein, Pres. and Director; Beverly J. Arnstein, C.F.O. and Director; Tom Nau, Jr., V.P. and Director; Daniel C. Arnstein, Secy. and Director.
EIN: 203246394

255
Aroma Foundation

6469 Flanders Dr.
San Diego, CA 92121-4104

Established in 2003 in California.
Donors: Chung Yuan Chang; Wenbo Zhuang; Yen Shiu-Run Chang.
Foundation type: Operating foundation.
Financial data (yr. ended 12/31/13): Assets, $2,169,231 (M); gifts received, $253,699; expenditures, $239,466; qualifying distributions, $228,985; giving activities include $210,685 for 15 grants (high: $80,000; low: $1,000).
Fields of interest: Christianity.
Limitations: Applications not accepted. Giving primarily in CA. No grants to individuals.

Application information: Unsolicited requests for funds not accepted.
Officers: Chung Yuan Chang, Pres.; Shiu Run Shirley Chang, Secy.; Wenbo Zhuang, Treas.
EIN: 330937914

256
David S. Ascher, M.D. Charitable Foundation

P.O. Box 57
Santa Ana, CA 92702 (951) 256-8630
Contact: Pamela Ascher, Dir.

Established in 1986 in California.
Donors: David S. Ascher, MD; Deloris Ascher.
Foundation type: Independent foundation.
Financial data (yr. ended 11/30/13): Assets, $2,109,252 (M); expenditures, $295,750; qualifying distributions, $295,750; giving activities include $267,124 for 26 grants (high: $88,824; low: $500).
Purpose and activities: Giving to organizations in the areas of health, education and welfare.
Fields of interest: Education; Higher education; Diseases and conditions; Cancers; Human services.
Limitations: Applications accepted. Giving primarily in CA and MA. No grants to individuals.
Application information: Application form required.
 Initial approach: Letter
 Deadline(s): None
Officers and Directors: Renetta Ascher Caya, C.E.O. and Director; David S. Ascher II, C.F.O. and Director; Pamela Ascher; Shane Ascher; Aaron Brent; Vivian Tabb.
EIN: 330243114

257
Asia Connection, Inc.

18400 Overlook Rd., Ste. 43
Los Gatos, CA 95030-5849
Main URL: http://www.asiaconnectioninc.org

Donors: George Christian; Kerry Heubeck; Hilary Smith; E.K. Rose f/b/o Asia Connection Trust.
Foundation type: Independent foundation.
Financial data (yr. ended 12/31/13): Assets, $485,966 (M); gifts received, $208,870; expenditures, $142,820; qualifying distributions, $135,250; giving activities include $135,250 for 5 grants (high: $46,975; low: $15,000).
Fields of interest: Health; Religion; Human services.
International interests: Asia.
Limitations: Applications not accepted. Giving on a worldwide basis, with emphasis on Asia. No grants to individuals.
Application information: Unsolicited requests for funds not accepted.
Officers: John Havican, Chair.; Mary Held, Vice-Chair.; Lily Ackerman, Secy.; Ted Rose, Treas.
Directors: Kerry Heubeck; Hilary Smith.
EIN: 593619790

258
A-T Medical Research Foundation

(also known as A-T Medical Research Foundation)
16224 Elisa Pl.
Encino, CA 91436-3320
Contact: Pamela J. Smith, Pres. and C.F.O.

FAX: (818) 906-2870; E-mail: ATMRF@aol.com; Main URL: http://www.ninds.nih.gov/find_people/voluntary_orgs/volorg17.htm

Established in 1983 in California.
Donors: George A. Smith†; Pamela J. Smith.
Foundation type: Operating foundation.
Financial data (yr. ended 09/30/13): Assets, $17,111 (M); gifts received, $202,035; expenditures, $202,106; qualifying distributions, $200,000; giving activities include $200,000 for 1 grant.
Purpose and activities: Awards are granted for medical research projects related to ataxia-telangiectasia.
Fields of interest: Diseases and conditions.
Type of support: Research; Seed money; Research and evaluation.
Limitations: Applications not accepted. Giving on a national and international basis. No support for religious or political organizations. No grants to individuals directly, or for scholarships; no student loans.
Publications: Annual report; Informational brochure; Newsletter.
Application information: Unsolicited requests for funds not accepted.
Officers: Pamela J. Smith, Pres. and C.F.O.; Lois Rosen, V.P.
Directors: Jill Omen; James Smith; Matthew Smith.
EIN: 953882022

259
Myrtle L. Atkinson Foundation
c/o William N. Harris, Pres.
5 Pembroke Pl.
Menlo Park, CA 94025-5859
E-mail: pembrokepl@mindspring.com

Donor: E.A. Whitsett†.
Foundation type: Independent foundation.
Financial data (yr. ended 12/31/13): Assets, $8,679,302 (M); expenditures, $455,789; qualifying distributions, $378,000; giving activities include $378,000 for 56 grants (high: $25,000; low: $2,000).
Purpose and activities: Giving to teach, promulgate and disseminate the Gospel of Jesus Christ throughout the world and also to unite in Christian Fellowship the large number of consecrated Christians in the various evangelical churches; to encourage and promote religious, scientific, technical and all other kinds of education, enlightenment and research. Giving mainly for capital funds for Christian churches and evangelism; support also for local and international relief and welfare agencies, literacy, hospices, and hunger.
Fields of interest: Education; Graduate and professional education; Adult literacy; Reading promotion; Health; Hospice care; Christianity; Protestantism; Theology; Human services; Food aid; Females; Ethnic and racial groups; Christians; Victims of crime and abuse; People with physical disabilities; Terminally ill people.
Type of support: Capital campaigns; Capital and infrastructure; Endowments; Research.
Limitations: Applications not accepted. Giving primarily in CA and on the West Coast. No support for political organizations. No grants to individuals.
Application information: Unsolicited requests for funds not accepted.
Board meeting date(s): Summer

Officers: William N. Harris, Pres.; Robert N. Harris, V.P.; William W. Harris, Secy.-Treas.
Directors: J. Harris; J. Whitsett.
Number of staff: None.
EIN: 956047161

260
Avery-Fuller-Welch Children's Foundation
(formerly Avery-Fuller Children's Center)
c/o Pacific Foundation Services, LLC
1660 Bush St., Ste. 300
San Francisco, CA 94109-5308 (415) 561-6540
Contact: Hector Melendez, Exec. Dir.
FAX: (415) 561-5477;
E-mail: hmelendez@pfs-llc.net; Main URL: http://www.pfs-llc.net/afw/index.html

Established in 1914 in California.
Donor: Jean A. McCallum†.
Foundation type: Independent foundation.
Financial data (yr. ended 06/30/15): Assets, $6,140,640 (M); expenditures, $209,918; qualifying distributions, $196,700; giving activities include $150,580 for 14 grants (high: $40,690; low: $3,610).
Purpose and activities: Giving for early intervention and professional guidance to children with physical, behavioral, emotional, and learning challenges. All applications must be submitted by the service provider on behalf of a single child and all grants are paid directly to said provider.
Fields of interest: Human services; Child welfare; Ethnic and racial groups; Low-income and poor people; People with disabilities.
Type of support: Grants to individuals.
Limitations: Applications accepted. Giving limited to residents of Alameda, Contra Costa, Marin, San Francisco, and San Mateo counties, CA. No support for preliminary evaluations, orthodontia, eye glasses or routine eye care, or for groups of children.
Publications: Application guidelines; Informational brochure (including application guidelines); Program policy statement.
Application information: See foundation web site for additional application policies and guidelines, as well as for downloadable application forms. Application form required.
Initial approach: Letter
Copies of proposal: 1
Deadline(s): See foundation web site for current submission deadlines and application review dates
Board meeting date(s): Jan., Apr. and Oct.
Final notification: Within 4 weeks of deadline
Officers: David Wisnom, Jr., Pres.; David B. Flinn, Secy.; Nicholas Raggio, Treas.; Hector Melendez, Exec. Dir.
Directors: J.R. Aboud; Arlene Auerbach; Martha M. Brigham; Alice Jackson; Sherry Madding; Richard L. Oken, MD; Benson Roe, MD; Ruth Wisnom.
Number of staff: 1 part-time support.
EIN: 941243657

261
Avery-Tsui Foundation
5075 Ruffin Rd., Ste. A
San Diego, CA 92123-4684

Established in 2004 in California.
Donor: The R. Stanton Avery Foundation.
Foundation type: Independent foundation.

Financial data (yr. ended 12/31/14): Assets, $31,134,963 (M); expenditures, $918,022; qualifying distributions, $601,895; giving activities include $335,048 for grants.
Fields of interest: Higher education; Foundations; Human services.
Limitations: Applications not accepted. Giving primarily in CA; some funding also in OH. No grants to individuals.
Application information: Contributes only to pre-selected organizations.
Officers and Directors: Sally Tsui Wong-Avery, C.E.O. and Pres. and Director; Tom Hom, V.P. and C.F.O. and Director; Natasha Wong, Secy. and Director.
EIN: 656431837

262
Ayz Family Foundation
4168 Solana Dr.
Palo Alto, CA 94306-3168

Established in 2005 in California.
Donors: Gordon Yan; Gloria Guohong Zhang; Guochen Yan.
Foundation type: Independent foundation.
Financial data (yr. ended 11/30/13): Assets, $5,095,398 (M); gifts received, $750,000; expenditures, $228,492; qualifying distributions, $210,510; giving activities include $176,691 for 6 grants (high: $125,000; low: $191).
Fields of interest: Education; Domesticated animals; Religion.
International interests: China.
Limitations: Applications not accepted. Giving primarily in CA, with some giving in China. No grants to individuals.
Application information: Unsolicited requests for funds not accepted.
Officers: Guochen Yan, C.E.O.; Gloria Guohong Zhang, Secy.
EIN: 201973760

263
Peter H. And Marietta K. Bach Charitable Trust Conservatorship
248 Ashdale Pl.
Los Angeles, CA 90049-2431

Foundation type: Independent foundation.
Financial data (yr. ended 12/31/13): Assets, $7,290,573 (M); expenditures, $463,139; qualifying distributions, $288,182; giving activities include $258,925 for 34 grants (high: $70,650; low: $200).
Fields of interest: Arts and culture; Education; Undergraduate education; Graduate and professional education; Mental health care; News and public information.
Limitations: Applications not accepted. Giving primarily in CA and Washington, DC.
Application information: Unsolicited requests for funds not accepted.
Trustees: Deborah B. Kallick; Ivan L. Kallick.
EIN: 906148666

264
Bob Baker Family Foundation
(formerly Bob Baker Foundation, Inc.)
591 Camino de la Reina, Ste. 1100
San Diego, CA   92108-3113   (619) 297-1001
Contact: Cindy Parga; Robet H. Baker, Dir.

Established in 1987 in California.
Donors: Bob Baker Enterprises, Inc.; Robert H. Baker; Rekab Properties.
Foundation type: Independent foundation.
Financial data (yr. ended 06/30/13): Assets, $1,222,918 (M); gifts received, $400,000; expenditures, $383,797; qualifying distributions, $391,710; giving activities include $382,700 for 17 grants (high: $50,000; low: $1,000).
Purpose and activities: Giving primarily for Roman Catholic organizations and education.
Fields of interest: Education; Health; Community and economic development.
Type of support: Annual campaigns; Capital and infrastructure; Scholarships.
Limitations: Applications accepted. Giving primarily in San Diego County, CA; the foundation will consider from outside of this geographic region depending on the situation and greatness of need.
Application information: Application form required.
  Initial approach: Letter
  Deadline(s): None
  Board meeting date(s): Annually
Officer: Jeffrey D. Maxwell, C.F.O. and Secy.
Directors: Christopher R. Baker; Robert H. Baker; Wade W. Poulson.
EIN: 330265135

265
The Edward and Rosemary Baker Family Foundation
395 Hampton Rd.
Piedmont, CA   94611-3525   (510) 428-0955
Contact: Edward D. Baker III, C.F.O.

Established in 2004 in California.
Donor: Edward D. Baker III.
Foundation type: Independent foundation.
Financial data (yr. ended 12/31/12): Assets, $1,240,555 (M); expenditures, $238,669; qualifying distributions, $223,240; giving activities include $223,240 for 11 grants (high: $100,000; low: $2,000).
Purpose and activities: Giving to organizations that enhance the education and welfare of children, support or perform research in the mathematical sciences, provide medical care, support or perform medical research, promote the fine and performing arts, promote the welfare of animals, or fund other projects that are consistent with the foundation's general charitable purposes.
Fields of interest: Ballet; Opera; Child educational development; Animal welfare; Diseases and conditions; Mathematics; Children.
Type of support: Research.
Limitations: Applications accepted. Giving primarily in San Francisco Bay Area, CA.
Application information:
  Initial approach: Letter
  Deadline(s): None
Officers: Rosemary Boccio Baker, Pres.; Edward D. Baker III, Secy. and C.F.O.
EIN: 201175382

266
The Baker Family Foundation
c/o Douglas Baker
6082 Lido Ln.
Long Beach, CA   90803-4152

Established in 1997 in California.
Donor: Douglas W. Baker.
Foundation type: Independent foundation.
Financial data (yr. ended 12/31/14): Assets, $3,505,621 (M); expenditures, $201,684; qualifying distributions, $167,005; giving activities include $167,005 for 11 grants (high: $55,000; low: $2,005).
Fields of interest: Cancers; Sexual abuse; Human services; Scouting programs.
Limitations: Applications not accepted. No grants to individuals.
Application information: Unsolicited requests for funds not accepted.
Officers and Directors: Douglas W. Baker, Pres. and Director; Carol Jean Baker, V.P. and Director; Carrie Lynn Baker, Treas. and Director.
EIN: 954590881

267
The Solomon R. & Rebecca D. Baker Foundation
(formerly The Baker Fund)
614 N. Alpine Dr.
Beverly Hills, CA   90210-3304
Application address: c/o Malcolm F. Baker, Pres., 9454 Wilshire Blvd., Penthouse, Beverly Hills, CA 90210, tel.: (310) 276-1070

Established in 1996 in California.
Donors: Malcolm F. Baker; Solomon R. Baker.
Foundation type: Independent foundation.
Financial data (yr. ended 04/30/13): Assets, $547,044 (M); expenditures, $242,236; qualifying distributions, $236,395; giving activities include $233,000 for 11 grants (high: $80,000; low: $3,000).
Purpose and activities: Giving primarily for medical research in autism, the care and therapy of autistic individuals, and related fields.
Fields of interest: Higher education; Mental health care; Autism; Depression; Cancers.
Type of support: Research; Research and evaluation.
Limitations: Applications accepted. Giving primarily in CA and NJ. No grants to individuals.
Application information: Application form required.
  Initial approach: Brief proposal
  Deadline(s): None
Officers: Malcolm F. Baker, Pres.; Eric H. Baker, V.P.; Norma Baker, Secy.-Treas.
EIN: 954591581

268
Paul & Betty Baldacci Family Foundation
12885 Alcosta Blvd., Ste. A
San Ramon, CA   94583-1355

Established in 2003 in California.
Donors: Elizabeth Baldacci; Paul Baldacci; Paul R. Baldacci, Jr.
Foundation type: Independent foundation.
Financial data (yr. ended 12/31/12): Assets, $806,269 (M); expenditures, $112,849; qualifying distributions, $112,511; giving activities include $112,511 for 42 grants (high: $33,225; low: $100).
Fields of interest: Arts and culture; Education; Religion; Sports and recreation.
Limitations: Applications not accepted. Giving primarily in CA. No grants to individuals.
Application information: Unsolicited requests for funds not accepted.
Officers and Trustees: Elizabeth Baldacci, Co-Chair. and Trustee; Paul R. Baldacci, Jr., Co-Chair. and Trustee; James Baldacci, Secy.-Treas.; Elizabeth Martino, Secy. and Trustee; Marilyn Burchard, Treas. and Trustee; Loretta Glesener.
EIN: 880516865

269
Banchik Family Foundation
11440 San Vicente Blvd., No. 200
Los Angeles, CA   90049-6216

Established in 1997 in California.
Donor: Howard Banchik.
Foundation type: Independent foundation.
Financial data (yr. ended 12/31/13): Assets, $229,033 (M); gifts received, $318,582; expenditures, $299,801; qualifying distributions, $299,801; giving activities include $299,801 for 106 grants (high: $65,125; low: $15).
Fields of interest: Arts and culture; Nonprofits; Diseases and conditions; Judaism; Human services.
Type of support: Regranting.
Limitations: Applications not accepted. Giving primarily in CA. No grants to individuals.
Application information: Contributes only to pre-selected organizations.
Officers: Howard Banchik, Pres.; Jacqueline Banchik, Secy.
Directors: Randall Banchik; Anissa Siegel.
EIN: 954653371

270
Bancroft-Clair Foundation
c/o Texas Saratoga Management, LLC
2600 10th St., Ste. 402
Berkeley, CA   94710-2597   (415) 537-8383
Contact: James R. Bancroft, Tr.

Established in 1997 in California.
Donors: James R. Bancroft; James M. Bancroft Unitrust.
Foundation type: Independent foundation.
Financial data (yr. ended 03/31/14): Assets, $10,323,689 (M); expenditures, $763,981; qualifying distributions, $472,313; giving activities include $430,000 for 66 grants (high: $180,000; low: $500).
Purpose and activities: Giving primarily for education, the environment, and vascular research.
Fields of interest: Arts and culture; Art museums; Elementary and secondary education; Higher education; Environment; Heart and circulatory system diseases; Human services; Food aid; Child welfare; People with vision impairments.
Type of support: General support; Research.
Limitations: Applications accepted. Giving primarily in CA and WA. No grants to individuals.
Application information: Application form required.
  Initial approach: Proposal
  Deadline(s): None
  Board meeting date(s): Varies

Trustees: James R. Bancroft; John R. Bancroft; Paul M. Bancroft; Sara B. Clair.
EIN: 943269107

271

The Bandai Foundation
5551 Katella Ave.
Cypress, CA 90630-5002

Established in 1995 in California.
Foundation type: Operating foundation.
Financial data (yr. ended 12/31/13): Assets, $8,014,838 (M); expenditures, $473,887; qualifying distributions, $428,507; giving activities include $424,005 for 55 grants (high: $62,500; low: $200).
Purpose and activities: The foundation is focusing their resources on children's issues, particularly for the benefit of children with AIDS.
Fields of interest: HIV/AIDS; Child welfare.
Limitations: Applications not accepted. Giving primarily in CA, Washington, DC and NY. No grants to individuals.
Application information: Contributes only to pre-selected organizations.
Officers and Directors: Akihiro Sato, Co-Chair.; Masayuki Matsuo, Co-Chair. and Director; Cynthia Nishimoto, Secy. and Director; Paul Hausback, Treas. and Director.
EIN: 330655933

272

Bank of the West Charitable Foundation
(formerly Commercial Federal Charitable Foundation)
P.O. Box 5155
San Ramon, CA 94583-5155
Contact: Rebeca Rangel, Tr.
Application address: Community Affairs Dept., 180 Montgomery St., 14th Fl., San Francisco, CA 94104; Main URL: https://www.bankofthewest.com

Established in 2001 in Nebraska.
Donor: Commercial Federal Bank, FSB.
Foundation type: Company-sponsored foundation.
Financial data (yr. ended 12/31/13): Assets, $3,045,006 (M); expenditures, $222,779; qualifying distributions, $200,000; giving activities include $200,000 for 4 grants (high: $100,000; low: $5,000).
Purpose and activities: The foundation supports programs designed to promote education and job training; and community and economic development. Special emphasis is directed toward programs designed to serve low-to-moderate income individuals.
Fields of interest: Education; Higher education; Reading promotion; Community and economic development; Employment; Job training; Housing development; Home ownership; Microfinance; Financial counseling; Business and industry; Business promotion; Entrepreneurship; Human services; Homeless services; Low-income and poor people.
Type of support: General support; Annual campaigns; Capital campaigns; Capital and infrastructure; Program development; Scholarships.
Limitations: Applications accepted. Giving in areas of company operations in AZ, CA, CO, IA, ID, KS, MN, MO, ND, NE, NM, NV, OK, OR, SD, UT, WA, WI and WY. No support for fraternal or alumni organizations,

political action committees, political candidates, or lobbying organizations. No grants to individuals, or for capital campaigns, trips or tours, or talent or beauty contests.
Publications: Application guidelines.
Application information: A full on-line application may be requested at a later date. Support is limited to 1 contribution per organization during any given year. Application form required.
Initial approach: Complete online letter of inquiry
Deadline(s): None
Trustees: Michael Bracco; Duke Dayal; Jenny Flores; Vanessa L. Washington.
EIN: 396765096

273

Banky La Rocque Foundation
P.O. Box 5596
Santa Monica, CA 90409-5596
Contact: Donna Deitch

Established in 1981 in California.
Donor: Vilma Banky La Rocque†.
Foundation type: Independent foundation.
Financial data (yr. ended 12/31/13): Assets, $2,157,500 (M); expenditures, $272,785; qualifying distributions, $258,500; giving activities include $246,500 for 20 grants (high: $50,000; low: $200).
Fields of interest: Health; Human services; Child welfare; Females.
Limitations: Applications accepted. Giving primarily in CA and NY. No grants to individuals.
Application information:
Initial approach: Letter
Deadline(s): None
Directors: Donna Deitch; Phyllis P. Wolf.
EIN: 953637348

274

The William C. Bannerman Foundation
9255 Sunset Blvd., Ste. 400
West Hollywood, CA 90069-3302 (310) 273-9933
Contact: Elliot Ponchick, Pres.

Established in 1958 in California.
Foundation type: Independent foundation.
Financial data (yr. ended 04/30/14): Assets, $7,973,733 (M); expenditures, $581,364; qualifying distributions, $396,333; giving activities include $300,000 for 45 grants (high: $100,000; low: $500).
Purpose and activities: Giving for education, women and children, and the environment.
Fields of interest: Education; Secondary education; Environment; Child welfare; Females.
Type of support: General support; Matching grants; Annual campaigns; Capital campaigns; Capital and infrastructure; Equipment; Program development; Seed money.
Limitations: Applications accepted. Giving limited to the Los Angeles, CA, area. No support for political organizations, religious or medical/health organizations, or universities. No grants to individuals.
Publications: Application guidelines.
Application information: Application form required.
Initial approach: Letter no more than 2 pages
Deadline(s): Oct. 31

Board meeting date(s): July and Mar.
Final notification: Mar. 15
Officers: Elliot Ponchick, Pres.; Elizabeth T. Ponchick, V.P.; Gail Matthews, Treas.
Directors: Mark Eiduson; Will Frost; William D. Frost.
Number of staff: 1 part-time professional.
EIN: 956061353

275

Barbera Foundation, Inc.
610 W. Foothill Blvd., Apt. A.
Monrovia, CA 91016-2046

Foundation type: Independent foundation.
Financial data (yr. ended 12/31/12): Assets, $1,610,143 (M); expenditures, $164,508; qualifying distributions, $164,508; giving activities include $164,508 for 3 grants (high: $89,508; low: $25,000).
Fields of interest: Education.
Limitations: Applications not accepted. Giving primarily in CA.
Application information: Unsolicited requests for funds not accepted.
Directors: Josephine Barbera; Robert Barbera; Patricia Johnson; Beartriz Loera; Vito Roberti.
EIN: 954474896

276

Joseph L. Barbonchielli and Marie and Manuel B. Perez Foundation
44 Montgomery St., Ste. 3585
San Francisco, CA 94104-4829 (415) 433-5446
Contact: Clifton W. Ohman, Pres. and C.E.O.

Donor: Joseph L. Barbonchielli Trust.
Foundation type: Independent foundation.
Financial data (yr. ended 09/30/13): Assets, $6,397,442 (M); expenditures, $375,911; qualifying distributions, $317,000; giving activities include $317,000 for 13 grants (high: $60,000; low: $5,000).
Purpose and activities: Giving limited to helping the elderly and needy to live in their own residences, by assisting them to meet expenses related to food, health care, and transportation.
Fields of interest: Home health care; Human services; Seniors; Low-income and poor people.
Limitations: Applications accepted. Giving limited to San Francisco, CA.
Application information:
Initial approach: Proposal
Deadline(s): Aug. 31
Officers and Trustees: Clifton W. Ohman, Pres. and C.E.O.; Mary K. Lopez, C.F.O. and Trustee; Patricia Olcomendy, Esq., Secy.-Treas. and Trustee; Joanna Robertson; James Watts.
EIN: 943343590

277

Barco's Nightingales Foundation
350 W. Rosecrans Ave.
Gardena, CA 90248-1728
E-mail: info@barcosnightingales.org; Main URL: http://barcosnightingales.org
Blog: http://barcosnightingales.org/blog

Donors: Michael Donner; Frida Donner; Barco Uniforms, Inc.
Foundation type: Independent foundation.

Financial data (yr. ended 12/31/13): Assets, $466,259 (M); gifts received, $466,869; expenditures, $394,381; qualifying distributions, $345,100; giving activities include $345,100 for 16 grants (high: $112,500; low: $100).

Purpose and activities: The mission of the foundation is to elevate and promote nursing, while also honoring the spirit of the profession by focusing our funding on helping children.

Fields of interest: Nursing care; Children.

Limitations: Applications not accepted. Giving primarily in CA and NY.

Application information: Unsolicited requests for funds not accepted.

Officer: Michael Donner, Pres.

Director: Frida Donner.

EIN: 264274148

278
The Glen and Opal Barnett Foundation
P.O. Box 5470
Palm Springs, CA 92263-5470

Established in 2006 in California.

Donor: Glen C. Barnett.

Foundation type: Independent foundation.

Financial data (yr. ended 12/31/13): Assets, $369,541 (M); gifts received, $150,000; expenditures, $157,364; qualifying distributions, $154,100; giving activities include $153,000 for 15 grants (high: $15,000; low: $3,000).

Fields of interest: Agriculture; Religion; Human services; Youth services.

Limitations: Applications not accepted. Giving primarily in CA.

Application information: Unsolicited requests for funds not accepted.

Officers: Glen C. Barnett, Pres.; Wesley A. Witt, V.P.; Estelle M. Layton, Secy.

EIN: 204330852

279
The Barth Foundation
5 Dos Pasos
Orinda, CA 94563-1849

Established in 1986 in California.

Donors: Worldwide Educational Svcs. of California; Eugene F. Barth; Aneila Barth.

Foundation type: Independent foundation.

Financial data (yr. ended 09/30/13): Assets, $3,700,620 (M); expenditures, $254,950; qualifying distributions, $213,143; giving activities include $213,143 for 52 grants (high: $27,000; low: $250).

Fields of interest: Arts and culture; Theater; Higher education; Natural resources; Land resources.

Type of support: Annual campaigns; Scholarships.

Limitations: Applications not accepted. Giving primarily in CA. No grants to individuals.

Application information: Unsolicited requests for funds not accepted.

Trustee: Eugene F. Barth.

EIN: 943025710

280
The Jeanne and William Barulich Family Foundation
451 El Arroyo Rd.
Hillsborough, CA 94010-6670 6506216909

Donors: William Barulich; Jeanne Barulich.

Foundation type: Independent foundation.

Financial data (yr. ended 12/31/14): Assets, $3,889,920; expenditures, $240,839; qualifying distributions, $212,085.

Fields of interest: Education; Nonprofits; National defense; Catholicism; Youth development.

Type of support: Regranting.

Limitations: Applications not accepted. Giving primarily in CA.

Application information: Unsolicited requests for funds not accepted.

Trustees: Aaron Barulich; Jeanne Barulich; Lauren Barulich; Nathan Barulich; William Barulich; Zachary Barulich.

EIN: 208086003

281
The Peggy and Jack Baskin Foundation
5214F Diamond Heights Blvd., Ste. 808
San Francisco, CA 94131-2175
E-mail: support@baskinfoundation.org; Main URL: http://baskinfoundation.org

Established in 2007 in California.

Donor: Jack Baskin.

Foundation type: Independent foundation.

Financial data (yr. ended 12/31/13): Assets, $3,286,067 (M); expenditures, $570,474; qualifying distributions, $415,565; giving activities include $415,565 for 16 grants (high: $105,000; low: $400).

Purpose and activities: Giving primarily for education and women's issues. The foundation is currently funding programs in the areas of: girls in engineering, gender/ women's studies, women in public policy, media and digital literacy, women re-entering the workforce, and transitional housing and legal services programs for survivors of domestic violence. Scholarships also to exceptional, highly motivated, underprivileged women attending Cabrillo, Hartnell or Monterey Peninsula College with a strong potential for making a difference in their community. Each year, the program provides 3 students from the participating community colleges a $20,000 scholarship, to be distributed over 2 years. Students must be enrolled in one of these three community colleges and dedicated to enrolling in and completing their junior and senior years of their college education as full-time students at a University of California campus. Scholarship candidates must be nominated by the president of their respective community college.

Fields of interest: Education; Women's studies; Human services; Women's services; Females.

Type of support: Scholarships.

Limitations: Giving limited to the Monterey Bay Peninsula, Santa Cruz, and the Greater San Francisco Bay Area of CA. No support for scientific or medical research, or for programs that promote religious doctrine. No grants to individuals directly, or for endowments, special events or conferences.

Publications: Application guidelines.

Application information: Unsolicited proposals are not accepted, only Letters of Inquiry. Applicants should e-mail a version of the coversheet, Letter of Inquiry, and required attachments, and send 1 hard copy of the same material via U.S. mail. Faxed applications are not accepted at this time.

Initial approach: Use Letter of Inquiry form on foundation web site

Deadline(s): None for Letters of Inquiry

Final notification: Within 2 months for Letters of Inquiry

Officers and Board Members: Peggy Downes Baskin, Pres. and C.E.O. and Director; Nicole Baran, V.P. and C.F.O. and Director; Cammy Torgenrud, Secy. and Director; Jack Baskin; Robert Ridino.

EIN: 260677825

282
Battle Family Foundation
35 Vicente Rd.
Berkeley, CA 94705-1603
Contact: A. George Battle

Established in 1999 in California.

Donor: A. George Battle.

Foundation type: Independent foundation.

Financial data (yr. ended 12/31/13): Assets, $9,519,791 (M); gifts received, $1,585,600; expenditures, $352,756; qualifying distributions, $292,841; giving activities include $249,621 for 11 grants (high: $50,000; low: $1).

Purpose and activities: Giving primarily for higher education.

Fields of interest: Arts and culture; Higher education.

International interests: Africa.

Type of support: General support.

Limitations: Applications not accepted. Giving primarily in CA and NH. No grants to individuals.

Application information: Contributes only to pre-selected organizations.

Officers: A. George Battle, Pres.; Emily T. Battle, V.P. and Treas.; Daniel K. Battle, Secy.

EIN: 943350554

283
The Baumann Foundation
(formerly Baumann Institute)
1770 Post St., Ste. 185
San Francisco, CA 94115-3606 (415) 723-9718
Contact: Peter Baumann, Chair.
E-mail: info@thebaumannfoundation.org; Main URL: http://www.thebaumannfoundation.org

Donors: Alison Baumann; Alistar Corp.; Peter Baumann.

Foundation type: Independent foundation.

Financial data (yr. ended 12/31/13): Assets, $2,058,333 (M); gifts received, $10,000; expenditures, $1,111,003; qualifying distributions, $1,055,362; giving activities include $246,100 for 29 grants (high: $20,000; low: $700).

Purpose and activities: Giving to advance understanding of how human experience is informed by how we relate to our internal and external environment by: 1) Facilitating dialogue and research among the scientific community, contemplatives and the general public; 2) Outreach and education through media, conferences, workshops, and other events; and 3) Developing, publishing and disseminating information related to the mission of the foundation .

Fields of interest: Science; Spirituality.

Limitations: Applications accepted. Giving primarily in CA and CO.

Application information: Application form required.

Initial approach: Letter

Deadline(s): None

Officers and Directors: Peter Baumann, Chair. and Pres. and Director.
Advisory Board: Richard Davidson; Sona Dimidjian; Elissa S. Epel; Richard Miller; Clifford Saron; Philip Zelazo.
EIN: 264542081

284
K. & F. Baxter Family Foundation Inc.
1563 Solano Ave., No. 404
Berkeley, CA 94707-2116 (510) 524-8145
FAX: (510) 524-4101;
E-mail: staceybell@kfbaxterfoundation.com; Main URL: http://www.kfbaxterfoundation.com

Established in 1997 in California.
Donors: Frank E. Baxter; Stacey K. Bell.
Foundation type: Independent foundation.
Financial data (yr. ended 12/31/14): Assets, $45,549; gifts received, $185,000; expenditures, $224,900; qualifying distributions, $185,000.
Purpose and activities: The foundation supports creating successful schools for low income children and acknowledging, supporting and celebrating biracial children, including support for charter schools.
Fields of interest: Education; Elementary and secondary education.
Type of support: Curriculum development; Research and evaluation; General support; Equipment; Public engagement and education; Program development; Program evaluations; Publications; Research.
Limitations: Applications accepted. Giving limited to schools located within the geographic areas of the following school districts: Berkeley, Oakland, West Contra Costa, and Los Angeles, CA. Grants for Celebrating Biracial Children are made nationwide. No support for early childhood programs or for biracial research.
Application information: See foundation website for complete application guidelines. Application form required.
Initial approach: Proposal
Officers and Directors: Stacey K. Bell, Pres.; Matthew Baxter, Secy. and Director; Anthony Kline, C.F.O.; Pamela A. Riley.
Number of staff: 1 part-time professional.
EIN: 954633505

285
Baye Foundation, Inc.
469 18th St.
Santa Monica, CA 90402-2429 (310) 612-9114
Contact: Joan Eisenberg, Pres.

Donors: Sam Stahl†; Nathan L. Berkowitz; Pearl S. Berkowitz; Muriel Stahl; Jonathan Schnur; Susan Silverstein; Daniel Schnur; Joan Eisenberg.
Foundation type: Independent foundation.
Financial data (yr. ended 12/31/13): Assets, $1,288,297 (M); expenditures, $225,628; qualifying distributions, $210,000; giving activities include $210,000 for 5 grants (high: $100,000; low: $10,000).
Fields of interest: Education; Nonprofits; Judaism.
Type of support: Continuing support; Emergency funds; Regranting; Seed money; Curriculum development; Scholarships.
Limitations: Applications not accepted. Giving primarily in Milwaukee, WI. No grants to individuals.

Application information: Unsolicited requests for funds not accepted.
Officers: Joan Eisenberg, Pres.; Daniel Schnur, V.P.; Susan B. Silverstein, Secy.; Jonathan Schnur, Treas.
EIN: 396040573

286
Beagle Charitable Foundation
c/o Brian Kuehnis, CPA
P.O. Box 6978
Redwood City, CA 94063

Established in 1999 in Washington.
Donor: Joy D. Covey.
Foundation type: Independent foundation.
Financial data (yr. ended 12/31/13): Assets, $7,314,109 (M); expenditures, $532,616; qualifying distributions, $422,749; giving activities include $420,999 for 4+ grants (high: $415,000).
Purpose and activities: Giving primarily for wildlife and environmental conservation.
Fields of interest: Education; Environment; Natural resources; Domesticated animals; Foundations; Judaism.
Limitations: Applications not accepted. Giving on a national basis. No grants to individuals.
Application information: Contributes only to pre-selected organizations.
Officer: Lisa Berglund, Pres.
EIN: 770529181

287
The Beam Foundation
c/o Jennings, Steine & Co.
12100 Wilshire Blvd., Ste. 200
Los Angeles, CA 90025-7127

Established in 1986 in New Jersey.
Donor: Bernard Myerson.
Foundation type: Independent foundation.
Financial data (yr. ended 09/30/14): Assets, $5,804,976 (M); expenditures, $298,294; qualifying distributions, $259,675; giving activities include $259,675 for 23 grants (high: $60,000; low: $500).
Fields of interest: Arts and culture; Performing arts; Museums; Education; Hospital care; Diseases and conditions; Judaism; Human services; Youth services.
Limitations: Applications not accepted. Giving primarily in New York, NY. No grants to individuals.
Application information: Contributes only to pre-selected organizations.
Trustees: Alan Myerson; Edward Myerson; Muriel Myerson.
EIN: 222786271

288
Bear Gulch Foundation
c/o Robert B. Flint, Jr.
185 Bear Gulch Rd.
Woodside, CA 94062-4417

Established in 1994 in Delaware.
Donors: Lucile E. Dupont Flint†; Robert B. Flint, Jr.; Alexis S. Flint.
Foundation type: Independent foundation.
Financial data (yr. ended 12/31/13): Assets, $9,353,091 (M); expenditures, $429,338;

qualifying distributions, $394,645; giving activities include $379,495 for 48 grants (high: $91,391; low: $1,000).
Purpose and activities: Giving primarily for education and the environment.
Fields of interest: Arts and culture; Education; Secondary education; Environment; Land resources; Population studies; Adolescent parenting.
Type of support: General support; Continuing support; Annual campaigns; Capital campaigns; Capital and infrastructure; Land acquisitions; Seed money; Program evaluations.
Limitations: Applications not accepted. Giving primarily in northern CA. No grants to individuals.
Application information: Contributes only to pre-selected organizations.
Board meeting date(s): Varies
Officers and Directors: Robert B. Flint, Jr., Pres. and Treas. and Director; William G. Roe, V.P. and Director; Susan J. Flint, Secy. and Director; Alexis S. Flint; Katie L. Flint.
Number of staff: None.
EIN: 510355031

289
The Frances & William H. Beattie Foundation
(formerly The Beattie Foundation)
333 S. Hope St., 34th Fl.
Los Angeles, CA 90071

Donor: William H. Beattie†.
Foundation type: Independent foundation.
Financial data (yr. ended 12/31/12): Assets, $5,487,580 (M); expenditures, $322,962; qualifying distributions, $281,824; giving activities include $271,000 for 46 grants (high: $20,000; low: $1,500).
Purpose and activities: Giving primarily for higher education; also giving for the performing arts, conservation, and YWCAs.
Fields of interest: Performing arts; Education; Higher education; Natural resources; Housing development.
Limitations: Applications not accepted. Giving primarily in Asheville, NC and the Greenville, SC, area. No grants to individuals.
Application information: Contributes only to pre-selected organizations.
Board meeting date(s): Varies
Trustee: Capital Guardian Trust Co.
EIN: 576113645

290
Beauregard Family Foundation
3417 St. Helena Hwy.
Saint Helena, CA 94574-9710

Established in 2005 in California.
Donors: Valerie M. Johnson Fish; Robert H. Fish.
Foundation type: Independent foundation.
Financial data (yr. ended 12/31/13): Assets, $188,934 (M); gifts received, $150,000; expenditures, $310,454; qualifying distributions, $307,135; giving activities include $304,020 for 14 grants (high: $150,000; low: $300).
Fields of interest: Education; Catholicism; Equestrianism; Human services.
Limitations: Applications not accepted. Giving primarily in CA. No grants to individuals.

Application information: Unsolicited requests for funds not accepted.
Officers and Directors: Valerie M. Johnson Fish, Pres. and Director; Robert H. Fish, Secy. and C.F.O. and Director.
EIN: 203541584

291
Newton & Rochelle Becker Charitable Trust

700 Larkspur Landing Cir., Ste. 199
Larkspur, CA 94939-0199

Established in 2006 in California.
Donors: Newton D. Becker; Rochelle Becker; Newton & Rochelle Becker Family Foundation; David Becker.
Foundation type: Independent foundation.
Financial data (yr. ended 12/31/13): Assets, $46,056,058 (M); gifts received, $14,027,903; expenditures, $1,426,655; qualifying distributions, $567,986; giving activities include $322,499 for 12 grants (high: $185,000; low: $500).
Purpose and activities: Giving primarily to Jewish organizations, as well as for human services.
Fields of interest: Foundations; Nonprofits; Judaism; Human services.
Type of support: Regranting.
Limitations: Applications not accepted. Giving primarily in CA, Washington, DC, New York, NY and OH. No grants to individuals.
Application information: Contributes only to pre-selected organizations.
Officer and Trustees: David Becker, Exec. Dir. and Trustee; Rochelle Becker.
EIN: 203822168

292
Becker Family Foundation

1106 Coast Village Rd., Ste. E
Santa Barbara, CA 93108 (805) 564-7352

Established in 2001 in Kentucky.
Donors: Gary Becker; Mary Becker; Gary E. Becker Unitrust.
Foundation type: Independent foundation.
Financial data (yr. ended 12/31/13): Assets, $2,187,572 (M); gifts received, $100; expenditures, $186,951; qualifying distributions, $169,630; giving activities include $169,300 for 31 grants (high: $50,000; low: $100).
Fields of interest: Education; Foundations; Christianity; Human services; International development.
Limitations: Applications accepted. Giving primarily in Louisville, KY and NY.
Application information: Application form required.
Initial approach: Letter
Deadline(s): None
Trustees: Montecito Bank & Trust.
EIN: 306006912

293
The Sanford and Phyllis Beim Family Foundation

17337 Palora St.
Encino, CA 91316

Established in 2000 in California.
Donors: Phyllis Beim; Sanford Beim.

Foundation type: Independent foundation.
Financial data (yr. ended 12/31/13): Assets, $1,063,279 (M); gifts received, $496,874; expenditures, $327,427; qualifying distributions, $315,300; giving activities include $315,300 for 30 grants (high: $102,500; low: $200).
Purpose and activities: Giving primarily for Jewish organizations.
Fields of interest: Arts and culture; Performing arts; Education; Nonprofits; Judaism.
Type of support: Regranting.
Limitations: Applications not accepted. Giving primarily in CA. No grants to individuals.
Application information: Unsolicited requests for funds not accepted.
Trustees: Phyllis Beim; Sanford Beim.
EIN: 954829935

294
Milo W. Bekins Foundation

15332 Antioch St., No. 871
Los Angeles, CA 90272-3628

Established in 1953 in California.
Donors: Milo W. Bekins†; The Bekins Co.
Foundation type: Independent foundation.
Financial data (yr. ended 12/31/12): Assets, $5,723,592 (M); expenditures, $407,995; qualifying distributions, $301,077; giving activities include $290,000 for 20 grants (high: $30,000; low: $3,000).
Purpose and activities: Giving primarily for education and to health organizations, including children's hospitals; funding also for social services.
Fields of interest: Arts and culture; Education; Higher education; Foundations; Hospital care; Specialty hospital care; Human services; Child welfare.
Type of support: General support; Scholarships.
Limitations: Applications not accepted. Giving primarily in CA, with emphasis on Los Angeles. No grants to individuals.
Application information: Contributes only to pre-selected organizations.
Trustees: Jacqueline Bekins; Michael D. Bekins; Richard Bekins; Wells Fargo Bank, N.A.
EIN: 956039745

295
Bell Charitable Foundation

P.O. Box 642
Rancho Santa Fe, CA 92067-0642

Established in 1994 in California.
Donor: Bell Family Trust.
Foundation type: Independent foundation.
Financial data (yr. ended 10/31/13): Assets, $8,153,446 (M); expenditures, $447,708; qualifying distributions, $408,473; giving activities include $402,600 for 44 grants (high: $80,000; low: $500).
Fields of interest: Education; Diseases and conditions; Human services; Child welfare; Scouting programs.
Type of support: Research; Research and evaluation.
Limitations: Applications not accepted. Giving primarily in CA and Washington, DC; some funding also in VA. No grants to individuals.

Application information: Contributes only to pre-selected organizations.
Officers and Directors: Kathleen Bell-Flynn, Pres. and Director; Martha A. Bell, V.P. and Director; Steve Flynn, Secy. and Director.
EIN: 330640946

296
The Belle Jar Foundation

c/o Rockefeller Philanthropy Advisors
575 Market St., Ste. 3625
San Francisco, CA 94105-4725
Contact: Christpher Payne, Pres. and Dir.

Donor: Christopher Payne.
Foundation type: Independent foundation.
Financial data (yr. ended 12/31/13): Assets, $7,731,635 (M); gifts received, $160,000; expenditures, $545,373; qualifying distributions, $454,157; giving activities include $380,419 for 33 grants (high: $60,000; low: $1,000).
Fields of interest: Education; Health; Human services.
Limitations: Applications not accepted. Giving primarily in CA.
Application information: Unsolicited requests for funds not accepted.
Officers and Directors: Christopher Payne, Pres. and Director; Gregory Payne, Secy.-Treas. and Director; Douglas Payne.
EIN: 900432743

297
Ron Beller & Jennifer Moses Family Foundation, Inc.

139 24th Ave.
San Francisco, CA 94121-1220

Established in 1990 in California.
Donors: Ron Beller; Jennifer Moses.
Foundation type: Independent foundation.
Financial data (yr. ended 12/31/13): Assets, $3,006,975 (M); gifts received, $210,000; expenditures, $336,939; qualifying distributions, $331,250; giving activities include $331,250 for 12 grants (high: $180,000; low: $500).
Purpose and activities: Giving for youth programs and education.
Fields of interest: Higher education; Foundations; Child welfare; Youth development.
Limitations: Applications not accepted. No grants to individuals.
Application information: Unsolicited requests for funds not accepted.
Officers: Ron Beller, Pres.; Jennifer Moses, V.P.
EIN: 223077176

298
Bellini Foundation

80 Cabrillo Hwy. N., Ste. Q
P.O. Box 329
Half Moon Bay, CA 94019-1650

Established in 1981 in California.
Donor: J. Bellini†.
Foundation type: Independent foundation.
Financial data (yr. ended 06/30/13): Assets, $6,843,566 (M); gifts received, $1,450; expenditures, $385,024; qualifying distributions,

$338,100; giving activities include $338,100 for 41 grants (high: $33,500; low: $500).

Purpose and activities: Giving primarily to health organizations and for medical research; funding also for education.

Fields of interest: Secondary education; Hospital care; Diseases and conditions; Human services; Youth services.

Type of support: General support; Continuing support; Research; Research and evaluation.

Limitations: Applications not accepted. Giving primarily in CA. No grants to individuals.

Application information: Contributes only to pre-selected organizations.

Officers: Patrick W. Bellini, Pres.; Michael J. Bellini, V.P.; B.K. Jayswal, Secy.-Treas.

EIN: 942768903

299
The Bellwether Foundation Ii
16255 Ventura Blvd., Ste. 625
Encino, CA   91436-2307

Foundation type: Independent foundation.

Financial data (yr. ended 09/30/13): Assets, $10,990,336 (M); expenditures, $518,958; qualifying distributions, $467,955; giving activities include $410,000 for 13 grants (high: $45,000; low: $15,000).

Fields of interest: Education; Environment; Cancers; Agriculture; Housing development; Family services.

Type of support: General support.

Limitations: Applications not accepted. Giving primarily in CA, Washington, DC, New York, NY and VA.

Application information: Unsolicited requests for funds not accepted.

Officers: Jaimee Lisa Davis, Pres.; Paul Oliver Davis, Secy.

EIN: 364665428

300
The Benedek Family Foundation
c/o Gelfand, Rennert & Feldman, LLP
1880 Century Park E., Ste. 1600
Los Angeles, CA   90067-1600

Established in 2002 in California.

Donors: Barbara Benedek; Peter Benedek.

Foundation type: Independent foundation.

Financial data (yr. ended 12/31/13): Assets, $686,579 (M); gifts received, $163,476; expenditures, $185,762; qualifying distributions, $183,050; giving activities include $183,050 for 2 grants (high: $180,050; low: $3,000).

Purpose and activities: Giving primarily for education.

Fields of interest: Charter school education; Higher education; School-based health care.

Limitations: Applications not accepted. Giving primarily in Ann Arbor, MI; giving also in Los Angeles, CA, and New York, NY. No grants to individuals.

Application information: Contributes only to pre-selected organizations.

Officers: Barbara Benedek, Co-C.E.O.; Peter Benedek, Co-C.E.O.

EIN: 710914469

301
Beneto Foundation
4080 Seaport Blvd.
West Sacramento, CA   95691-3417   (916) 677-0817
Contact: Amy Monroe, Board Member
E-mail: amy@benetoinc.com

Established in 1997 in California.

Donors: Stephen T. Beneto; Oates Family Foundation; KWD Video; Riverview Intl.; Michelin North America; Fuel Delivery Services; NU West Petroleum; Tesoro Petroleum Co.; Chuck Matthewson; ConocoPhillips Co.; Freightliner Corp.; Heil Trailer Intl. Inc.; John R. Lawson Rock and Oil Co.; Keenan Advantage Group.

Foundation type: Independent foundation.

Financial data (yr. ended 12/31/13): Assets, $2,416,874 (M); gifts received, $207,575; expenditures, $523,617; qualifying distributions, $418,311; giving activities include $418,311 for 35 grants (high: $100,000; low: $250).

Fields of interest: Education; Higher education; Hospital care; Neurology; Human services; Child welfare.

Type of support: Research.

Limitations: Applications accepted. Giving primarily in CA. No grants to individuals.

Application information:
Initial approach: Proposal
Deadline(s): Nov. 1

Officer: Stephen T. Beneto, Pres.

Board Members: Darlene J. Beneto; Lucille R. Friday; Gene Hume; Paul Marchi; Nina Pucci.

EIN: 680397473

302
Berakah Foundation, Inc.
P.O. Box 1279
Santa Maria, CA   93456-1279   (805) 925-9533

Established in 1998 in California.

Donors: Robert P. Diani; James A. Diani; Michael J. Diani; Donald L. Ward.

Foundation type: Operating foundation.

Financial data (yr. ended 12/31/13): Assets, $480,362 (M); gifts received, $100; expenditures, $196,659; qualifying distributions, $192,916; giving activities include $192,916 for 25 grants (high: $30,000; low: $250).

Purpose and activities: Giving for the promotion and enhancement of Christianity through the support of Christian activities and education.

Fields of interest: Christianity; Human services; Child welfare.

Limitations: Applications accepted. Giving primarily in Santa Maria, CA. No grants to individuals.

Application information: Application form required.
Initial approach: Completed application form
Copies of proposal: 1
Deadline(s): None
Final notification: 4-6 weeks

Officers: Michael J. Diani, C.E.O.; Donald L. Ward, Secy.; James A. Diani, C.F.O.

EIN: 770489106

303
The Berglund Family Foundation
P.O. Box 35552
Monte Sereno, CA   95030-0552

Established in 2007 in California.

Donors: Steven Berglund; Sandra Berglund.

Foundation type: Independent foundation.

Financial data (yr. ended 12/31/14): Assets, $3,505,855 (M); gifts received, $222,985; expenditures, $193,853; qualifying distributions, $184,000; giving activities include $184,000 for 5 grants (high: $60,000; low: $20,000).

Fields of interest: Education; Environment; Human services; Children.

Limitations: Applications not accepted. Giving primarily in CA, CT and TX. No grants to individuals.

Application information: Unsolicited requests for funds not accepted.

Officers and Directors: Sandra Berglund, Pres. and Director; Steven Berglund, Secy. and C.F.O. and Director; Eric W. Berglund; Kari D. Berguland.

EIN: 261350411

304
Bergman Family Foundation
1217 Emerald Bay
Laguna Beach, CA   92651-1262   (949) 494-6046

Established in 1997 in California.

Donors: James R. Bergman; Judy G. Bergman.

Foundation type: Independent foundation.

Financial data (yr. ended 12/31/14): Assets, $1,729,715; expenditures, $179,493; qualifying distributions, $163,000.

Fields of interest: Education; Religion; International relations.

Type of support: General support.

Limitations: Applications accepted. Giving primarily in CA. No grants to individuals.

Application information:
Initial approach: Proposal
Deadline(s): None

Officers: James R. Bergman, Pres. and C.F.O.; Judy G. Bergman, Secy.

EIN: 330743999

305
Berkshire Foundation
P.O. Box 221432
Carmel, CA   93922-1432

Established in 1996 in California.

Donors: Hilton Bialek†; Roberta Buffett Bialek; Berkshire Hathaway Inc.

Foundation type: Independent foundation.

Financial data (yr. ended 12/31/13): Assets, $6,463,978 (M); expenditures, $398,224; qualifying distributions, $389,078; giving activities include $385,000 for 6 grants (high: $175,000; low: $30,000).

Purpose and activities: Giving primarily for education and human services.

Fields of interest: Education; Reproductive rights; Human services.

Limitations: Applications not accepted. Giving primarily in CA. No grants to individuals.

Application information: Contributes only to pre-selected organizations.

Officers: Susan S. Lansbury, Pres. and Treas.; Cynthia Roberts Snorf, Secy.

Director: Carolyn Snorf Akcan.

EIN: 770438710

306
Jack and Florence Berlin Foundation
c/o A Delaware Non Profit Corp.
29853 Westlink Dr.
Menifee, CA 92584-8840

Established in 2003 in Delaware.
Donor: Jack Berlin.
Foundation type: Independent foundation.
Financial data (yr. ended 12/31/14): Assets,
$7,369,832 (M); expenditures, $413,524;
qualifying distributions, $286,407; giving activities
include $283,500 for 13 grants (high: $40,000;
low: $4,000).
Fields of interest: Nonprofits; Judaism.
Type of support: Regranting.
Limitations: Applications not accepted. Giving
primarily in CA. No grants to individuals.
Application information: Unsolicited requests for
funds not accepted.
Officers and Directors: Patrice E. Berry, Pres. and
Director; Mary E. Berlin, Secy. and Director; Jeffrey
H. Berlin, Treas. and Director; Marci Allen; Mark
Allen; Mimi Allen; Sheila Berlin; Mark S. Berry.
EIN: 721551106

307
Bernstein Family Foundation, Inc.
8 Oxford Ave.
Mill Valley, CA 94941-2912

Established in 1997 in Maryland.
Donors: David Bernstein; Patricia Bernstein; Jeffrey
Bernstein; Carolyn Bernstein; Laurel Bernstein.
Foundation type: Independent foundation.
Financial data (yr. ended 12/31/12): Assets,
$1,748,651 (M); expenditures, $352,845;
qualifying distributions, $338,100; giving activities
include $338,100 for grants.
Fields of interest: Theater; Higher education;
Health; Hospital care; Out-patient medical care;
Medical support services; Judaism.
Limitations: Applications not accepted. Giving
primarily in MD. No grants to individuals.
Application information: Contributes only to
pre-selected organizations.
Officers: David Bernstein, Pres.; Carolyn Bernstein,
V.P.; Jeffrey Bernstein, V.P.; Laurel Bernstein, V.P.;
Patricia Bernstein, Secy.-Treas.
EIN: 522068202

308
Bernstein Family Fund
P.O. Box 50740
Santa Barbara, CA 93150-0740
Contact: Philip L. Bernstein

Donors: Philip L. Bernstein; Leslie S. Bernstein;
Jacob Stern & Sons, Inc.
Foundation type: Independent foundation.
Financial data (yr. ended 08/31/13): Assets,
$987,899 (M); gifts received, $95,577;
expenditures, $194,988; qualifying distributions,
$189,134; giving activities include $186,250 for 16
grants (high: $51,000; low: $500).
Purpose and activities: Giving primarily for the arts,
cancer institutes, and human services.
Fields of interest: Theater; Diseases and
conditions; Cancers; Housing development.
Type of support: Research.

Limitations: Applications not accepted. Giving
primarily in CA.
Application information: Contributes only to
pre-selected organizations.
Officer: Leslie S. Bernstein, Treas.
Trustee: Philip L. Bernstein.
EIN: 236420229

309
C. J. Berry Foundation
1484 Pollard Rd., Ste. 406
Los Gatos, CA 95032-1031
FAX: (408) 374-9258; E-mail: info@cjberry.org; Main
URL: http://www.cjberry.org

Donors: Nella F. Berry; William F. Berry.
Foundation type: Independent foundation.
Financial data (yr. ended 12/31/14): Assets,
$5,167,190; expenditures, $226,503; qualifying
distributions, $185,763.
Fields of interest: Philanthropy; Human services;
Youth development.
Limitations: Applications not accepted. Giving
primarily in CA.
Application information: Unsolicited requests for
funds not accepted.
Officers and Directors: Derek W. Berry, Pres. and
C.E.O. and Director; Koryne Smith, V.P. and Director;
Joanne Berry, Secy. and Director; Taylor Smith,
Treas. and Director; Bill Berry; Nella F. Berry.
EIN: 273496864

310
The Burton G. Bettingen Corporation
9663 Santa Monica Blvd., Ste. 943
Beverly Hills, CA 90210-4303 (310) 490-8436
Contact: Patricia A. Brown, Exec. Dir.
E-mail: burtonbet@aol.com

Established in 1984 in California.
Donor: Burton G. Bettingen†.
Foundation type: Independent foundation.
Financial data (yr. ended 09/30/13): Assets,
$11,247,363 (M); expenditures, $774,232;
qualifying distributions, $548,810; giving activities
include $273,650 for 9 grants (high: $60,000; low:
$650).
Fields of interest: Human services; Family services;
Child welfare.
Type of support: General support; Capital
campaigns.
Limitations: Applications accepted. Giving primarily
in CA. No grants to individuals or for general
fundraising events, conferences, seminars, dinners,
or mass mailings.
Application information: Application form required.
Initial approach: Letter
Deadline(s): None
Board meeting date(s): Mar.
Officers: George D. O'Neill, Jr., Chair. and Pres.;
W.M. Lyles IV, V.P.; Patricia A. Brown, Secy.-Treas.
and Exec. Dir.
Number of staff: 1 full-time professional; 1 part-time
support.
EIN: 953942826

311
The Beulah Fund
c/o Shapiro & Co.
9229 W. Sunset Blvd., Ste. 607
Los Angeles, CA 90069-3402

Donor: Drew A. Carey.
Foundation type: Independent foundation.
Financial data (yr. ended 12/31/13): Assets, $0
(M); gifts received, $500,000; expenditures,
$223,555; qualifying distributions, $217,363;
giving activities include $217,363 for 16 grants
(high: $100,000; low: $601).
Fields of interest: Catholicism; Human services;
Child welfare.
Limitations: Applications not accepted. Giving
primarily in CA and HI.
Application information: Contributes only to
pre-selected organizations.
Officers: Drew A. Carey, Pres.; Bradford S. Cohen,
Esq., C.F.O. and Secy.
EIN: 271517611

312
The Kathryne Beynon Foundation
P.O. Box 90815
Pasadena, CA 91109-0815 (626) 731-1185
Contact: Alexandra Laboutin Bannon, Tr.
E-mail: beynonfoundation@gmail.com

Established in 1967 in California.
Donor: Kathryne Beynon†.
Foundation type: Independent foundation.
Financial data (yr. ended 10/31/14): Assets,
$10,106,506 (M); expenditures, $635,232;
qualifying distributions, $490,709; giving activities
include $376,560 for 21 grants (high: $50,000;
low: $5,000).
Purpose and activities: Giving primarily for
hospitals, youth agencies, child welfare, Roman
Catholic church support, and higher education.
Fields of interest: Higher education; Hospital care;
Asthma; Catholicism; Child welfare; Youth services.
Type of support: General support; Capital and
infrastructure; Endowments; Scholarships.
Limitations: Applications accepted. Giving primarily
in southern CA. No grants to individuals.
Application information:
Initial approach: Proposal
Deadline(s): None
Trustees: Alexandra Laboutin Bannon; Mel B.
Bannon; Mary Ellen Stambaugh.
EIN: 956197328

313
Bialis Family Foundation
10880 Wilshire Blvd., Ste. 800
Los Angeles, CA 90024
*Application address for Award for Nursing
Excellence:* Attn.: Selection Committee, P.O. Box
30570, Santa Barbara, CA 93130

Established in 1981 in California.
Donors: Gary C. Bialis; Bialis Trading; Ellen G. Bialis.
Foundation type: Independent foundation.
Financial data (yr. ended 06/30/14): Assets,
$4,434,126 (M); gifts received, $112;
expenditures, $213,932; qualifying distributions,
$212,417; giving activities include $147,527 for 12
grants (high: $100,000; low: $1,000), and $18,000

for 6 grants to individuals (high: $3,000; low: $3,000).

Purpose and activities: Giving primarily for education, health associations, human services, and Jewish agencies. Giving also to nurses for excellence in nursing and to individuals who lack resources to meet their basic human needs.

Fields of interest: Arts and culture; Education; University education; Diseases and conditions; Judaism; American football; Human services; Homeless people.

Type of support: General support; Grants to individuals.

Limitations: Applications accepted. Giving primarily in CA, with emphasis on Santa Barbara and Los Angeles.

Application information: Applicants for the Nursing Excellence Awards Program must complete the nomination form; each applicant must be a nurse with at least 5 years continuous experience working as a nurse in Santa Barbara County, CA. Proposed recipients of grants for food, shelter, and medical care must provide documentation of need. Application form required.

> *Initial approach:* Completed application form
> *Deadline(s):* None

Officers and Directors: Ellen G. Bialis, Pres. and Director; Hellen Wu, Secy.-Treas. and Director; Jonathan G. Bialis.

EIN: 953646277

314
Lynn & Les Bider Family Foundation
23622 Calabasas Rd., Ste. 107
Calabasas, CA 91302

Established in 1997 in California.
Donors: Leslie E. Bider; Lynn Bider.
Foundation type: Independent foundation.
Financial data (yr. ended 12/31/13): Assets, $2,607,488 (M); expenditures, $179,825; qualifying distributions, $170,703; giving activities include $167,500 for 10 grants (high: $30,000; low: $2,500).
Fields of interest: Arts and culture; Secondary education; Higher education; Nonprofits.
Type of support: Regranting.
Limitations: Applications not accepted. Giving primarily in CA. No grants to individuals.
Application information: Unsolicited requests for funds not accepted.
Officers: Albert Praw, Pres.; Fred Elkins, C.F.O.; Jonathan A. Karp, Secy.
EIN: 954621358

315
The Big D Foundation
1700 Sonoma Ave.
Albany, CA 94706-2550

Established in 2007 in Unspecified.
Donor: Donald M. Kendall.
Foundation type: Independent foundation.
Financial data (yr. ended 12/31/13): Assets, $4,331,447 (M); expenditures, $216,725; qualifying distributions, $189,450; giving activities include $185,000 for 5 grants (high: $50,000; low: $10,000).
Fields of interest: Environment; Water resources.

Limitations: Applications not accepted. Giving primarily in CA, Washington, DC, and VA. No grants to individuals.
Application information: Unsolicited requests for funds not accepted.
Trustees: Donald M. Kendall; Kent C. Kendall.
EIN: 260726380

316
Bigglesworth Family Foundation, Inc.
1012 Torney Ave.
San Francisco, CA 94129

Donor: The Marcled Foundation.
Foundation type: Independent foundation.
Financial data (yr. ended 12/31/13): Assets, $11,517,314 (M); expenditures, $447,685; qualifying distributions, $392,634; giving activities include $260,000 for 1 grant.
Fields of interest: Education; Nonprofits; Religion.
Type of support: Regranting.
Limitations: Applications not accepted. Giving primarily in OH.
Application information: Unsolicited requests for funds not accepted.
Officers and Directors: Claire Solot, Pres. and Director; St. John Bain, Secy. and Director.
EIN: 273854526

317
The Milton Bilak Family Foundation
433 N. Camden Dr., Ste. 500
Beverly Hills, CA 90210-4406

Established in 2004 in California.
Donors: Milton Bilak; Dorian Frances Bilak.
Foundation type: Independent foundation.
Financial data (yr. ended 09/30/13): Assets, $1,307 (M); gifts received, $145,065; expenditures, $144,960; qualifying distributions, $141,825; giving activities include $141,825 for 14 grants (high: $63,960; low: $500).
Fields of interest: Education; Religion; Judaism; Human services.
Limitations: Applications not accepted. Giving primarily in CA. No grants to individuals.
Application information: Unsolicited requests for funds not accepted.
Officers: Dorian Bilak, Pres.; Frances Bilak, V.P.; James A. Ginsburg, Secy. and C.F.O.
EIN: 202100967

318
Blachford-Cooper Foundation Inc.
(formerly NB Foundation, Inc.)
P.O. Box 8249
La Jolla, CA 92038

Established in 2000 in California.
Donor: Norman Blachford.
Foundation type: Independent foundation.
Financial data (yr. ended 12/31/13): Assets, $4,369,405 (M); expenditures, $412,547; qualifying distributions, $400,110; giving activities include $400,110 for 12 grants (high: $189,410; low: $1,000).
Fields of interest: Arts and culture; Education; University education; HIV/AIDS; LGBTQ people.
Type of support: Research.

Limitations: Applications not accepted. Giving primarily in CA. No grants to individuals.
Application information: Contributes only to pre-selected organizations.
Officers: Norman Blachford, Pres.; Peter Cooper, Treas.
EIN: 330911609

319
Blackie Foundation
P.O. Box 575
Nicasio, CA 94946 4156629136

Established in 1995 in California.
Donor: Florence M. Blackie.
Foundation type: Independent foundation.
Financial data (yr. ended 12/31/14): Assets, $7,506,971; expenditures, $497,822; qualifying distributions, $470,556.
Purpose and activities: Giving primarily for education and human services to benefit inner city youth.
Fields of interest: Education; Diseases and conditions; Human services; Youth services.
Type of support: Research.
Limitations: Applications accepted. Giving in the U.S., with emphasis on CA.
Application information:

> *Initial approach:* Proposal
> *Deadline(s):* None

Officers: Heather Blackie, Pres.; Heidi Blackie, C.F.O.
EIN: 943236876

320
The Aaron and Marie Blackman Foundation, Inc.
423 Broadway, Rm. 706
Millbrae, CA 94030-1905 (650) 589-5111

Established in 1989 in California.
Donor: Marie Blackman.
Foundation type: Independent foundation.
Financial data (yr. ended 12/31/14): Assets, $7,856,493; expenditures, $423,844; qualifying distributions, $466,438.
Purpose and activities: Giving primarily to Jewish organizations, temples, and schools.
Fields of interest: Education; Judaism; Human services; Senior services.
International interests: Israel.
Limitations: Applications accepted. Giving primarily in CA and NY. No grants to individuals.
Application information:

> *Initial approach:* Proposal
> *Deadline(s):* None

Officers: Milton Jacobs, Pres.; Elizabeth Landers, Secy.
Directors: Peter Samuels; Ron Solomon; Stuart Weinstein.
EIN: 943105905

321
The Blanchard Foundation
c/o Marjorie M. Blanchard
125 State Pl.
Escondido, CA 92029-1323

Established in 1990 in California.

Donors: Kenneth H. Blanchard; Marjorie M. Blanchard; Blanchard Training & Development.
Foundation type: Operating foundation.
Financial data (yr. ended 12/31/13): Assets, $464,582 (M); gifts received, $434,134; expenditures, $400,625; qualifying distributions, $354,056; giving activities include $270,308 for 235 grants (high: $26,375; low: $20), and $164,114 for 1 foundation-administered program.
Fields of interest: Higher education; Hospital care; Diseases and conditions; Christianity; Youth development.
Limitations: Applications not accepted. Giving primarily in CA and NY. No grants to individuals.
Application information: Unsolicited requests for funds not accepted.
Officers: Kenneth H. Blanchard, C.E.O.; Marjorie M. Blanchard, C.F.O.; Lynette Grunenberg, Secy.
EIN: 956003017

322
Blatteis Family Foundation
1940 Century Park E., Ste. 200
Los Angeles, CA 90067-1728
Contact: Daniel Blatteis, Pres.

Established in 2006 in California.
Donors: Daniel Blatteis; Angela Blatteis.
Foundation type: Independent foundation.
Financial data (yr. ended 12/31/12): Assets, $28,324 (M); gifts received, $256,000; expenditures, $231,073; qualifying distributions, $229,000; giving activities include $227,750 for 6 grants (high: $203,500; low: $250).
Fields of interest: Education; Judaism; Human services.
Limitations: Applications accepted. Giving primarily in CA.
Application information:
   Initial approach: Proposal
   Deadline(s): None
Officers: Daniel Blatteis, Pres. and C.F.O.; Angela Blatteis, Secy.
EIN: 204331652

323
Board Family Foundation
13440 Paramount Blvd., No. G
South Gate, CA 90280-8250

Established in 1990 in California.
Donors: Harry Boand, Jr.; Catherine Jane Boand; Boand Marital Trust.
Foundation type: Independent foundation.
Financial data (yr. ended 12/31/13): Assets, $3,254,971 (M); expenditures, $178,576; qualifying distributions, $163,850; giving activities include $163,850 for 13 grants (high: $30,000; low: $100).
Fields of interest: Education; Human services; Youth development.
Limitations: Applications not accepted. Giving primarily in CA.
Application information: Unsolicited requests for funds not accepted.
Directors: Nicole Boand; Teresa Evans; Lucinda McDermott; Derrick Mercurio.
EIN: 954262373

324
The Wanda Bobowski Fund
566 Oak St.
Mountain View, CA 94041-1921

Established in 1996 in California.
Donors: Debra Simons Trust; Stephen Simons; Debra W. Simons.
Foundation type: Independent foundation.
Financial data (yr. ended 12/31/13): Assets, $3,804,592 (M); expenditures, $300,615; qualifying distributions, $257,395; giving activities include $252,930 for 15 grants (high: $100,000; low: $5,000).
Fields of interest: Wildlife biodiversity; Human services; Child welfare; Females.
Type of support: General support.
Limitations: Applications not accepted. Giving primarily in CA and VA. No grants to individuals.
Application information: Unsolicited requests for funds not accepted.
Officers: Debra Simons, Pres.; Daniel R. Corbet, C.F.O.; Erica J. Simons, Secy.
EIN: 770443629

325
Bochnowski Family Foundation
28 Camino Por Los Arboles
Atherton, CA 94027-5941

Established in 2000 in California.
Donors: James J. Bochnowski; Janet A. Bochnowski.
Foundation type: Independent foundation.
Financial data (yr. ended 12/31/13): Assets, $6,868,527 (M); gifts received, $29,923; expenditures, $428,855; qualifying distributions, $389,340; giving activities include $376,000 for 21 grants (high: $82,500; low: $1,000).
Fields of interest: University education; Public affairs; Human rights; Human services.
Limitations: Applications not accepted. Giving primarily in CA. No grants to individuals.
Application information: Unsolicited requests for funds not accepted.
Officers: James J. Bochnowski, Pres.; Janet A. Bochnowski, C.F.O. and Secy.; Stasia M. Bochnowski, V.P.; Thomas J. Bochnowski, V.P.
EIN: 943383095

326
Bonner Family Foundation
P.O. Box 26327
Fresno, CA 93729-6327
Application address: c/o Kaye B. Cummings, Exec. Dir., 565 E. Mallard Cir., Fresno, CA 93720, tel.: (559) 434-5061

Established in 1984 in California.
Donors: Charles W. Bonner†; Elizabeth B. Bonner.
Foundation type: Independent foundation.
Financial data (yr. ended 09/30/13): Assets, $1,620,318 (M); expenditures, $211,162; qualifying distributions, $150,500; giving activities include $150,000 for 35 grants (high: $20,000; low: $500).
Purpose and activities: Support primarily for a philharmonic orchestra and public radio and television stations; support also for other musical organizations and museums. On-going initiative to bring visual and performing arts into designated

elementary schools in low socio-economic neighborhoods.
Fields of interest: Arts and culture; Education; Human services.
Type of support: General support; Matching grants; Continuing support; Endowments; Program development; Seed money; Curriculum development.
Limitations: Applications accepted. Giving limited to the Fresno, CA, area. No grants to individuals.
Application information:
   Initial approach: Request application form
   Deadline(s): None
Officers: Gus Bonner, Pres.; Susan B. Martin, Secy.; Annette Leifer, Treas.; Kaye B. Cummings, Exec. Dir.
Directors: Christina Bonner-Cline; Jerry Palladino; Larry Wayte.
Number of staff: 1 part-time professional.
EIN: 770046990

327
Clark and Nancy Bonner Foundation
(formerly Pinetops Foundation)
18552 MacArthur Blvd., Ste. 495
Irvine, CA 92612-1271
Contact: Marlys Pianin

Established in 2002 in California.
Donor: Clark J. Bonner.
Foundation type: Independent foundation.
Financial data (yr. ended 01/31/13): Assets, $5,085,783 (M); expenditures, $270,099; qualifying distributions, $235,965; giving activities include $235,965 for 24 grants (high: $107,155; low: $40).
Fields of interest: Nonprofits; Hospital care; Christianity.
Type of support: Regranting.
Limitations: Applications accepted. Giving primarily in CA and OR. No grants to individuals.
Application information: Application form required.
   Initial approach: Completed application form
   Deadline(s): None
Officers and Directors: Clark J. Bonner, Pres. and Director; Nancy S. Bonner, C.F.O.
EIN: 460477322

328
Pat Boone Foundation, Inc.
4450 W. Lakeside Dr., Ste. 320
Burbank, CA 91505-4082

Established in 1959 in California.
Donor: Charles E. Boone.
Foundation type: Independent foundation.
Financial data (yr. ended 12/31/13): Assets, $6,586 (M); gifts received, $167,000; expenditures, $170,611; qualifying distributions, $154,285; giving activities include $154,285 for 78 grants (high: $20,000; low: $50).
Fields of interest: Arts and culture; Education; Elementary and secondary education; Nonprofits; Christianity; Human services.
Type of support: Regranting.
Limitations: Applications not accepted. Giving in the U.S., with some emphasis on CA. No grants to individuals.
Application information: Contributes only to pre-selected organizations.
Officer: Charles E. Boone, Mgr.
EIN: 237013815

329
The Boone Foundation
602 E. Huntington Dr., Ste. D
Monrovia, CA 91016-3600 (626) 305-5530
Contact: Mary Lou Boone, Chair.

Established in 1983 in California.
Donors: George N. Boone†; Mary Lou Boone.
Foundation type: Independent foundation.
Financial data (yr. ended 12/31/13): Assets,
$711,981 (M); gifts received, $200,000;
expenditures, $431,434; qualifying distributions,
$405,645; giving activities include $399,495 for 8
grants (high: $200,000; low: $15,000).
Purpose and activities: To provide the foundation's
local and national community with economic support
and to support philanthropic endeavors in
education, social welfare, historical preservation,
research, and cultural pursuits.
Fields of interest: Arts and culture; Education; Child
welfare; Youth development; Youth services.
Type of support: Continuing support; Program
development.
Limitations: Applications accepted. Giving primarily
in southern CA. No grants to individuals.
Publications: Biennial report.
Application information: Application form required.
 Initial approach: Proposal
 Deadline(s): None
Officers: Mary Lou Boone, Chair.; George N. Boone,
Jr., Pres.; Lynda Boone Fetter, Secy.-Treas.
Number of staff: 1 full-time professional.
EIN: 953883757

330
The Borch Foundation
14315 Taos Dr.
Saratoga, CA 95070-5567 (408) 395-5585
Contact: Andrea W. Borch, C.E.O.

Established in 2007 in California.
Donors: Sacardia, LLC; Christopher R. Borch;
Andrea W. Borch.
Foundation type: Independent foundation.
Financial data (yr. ended 12/31/14): Assets,
$2,804,324 (M); gifts received, $300,000;
expenditures, $446,612; qualifying distributions,
$441,338; giving activities include $439,620 for 28
grants (high: $282,010; low: $500).
Fields of interest: University education; Water
resources; Marine science; Housing development.
Limitations: Applications accepted. Giving primarily
in CA and SC. No grants to individuals.
Application information:
 Initial approach: Letter
 Deadline(s): None
Officers: Andrea W. Borch, C.E.O.; Christopher R.
Borch, C.F.O.
EIN: 208777443

331
L. & L. Borok Foundation
1237 Rembrandt Dr.
Sunnyvale, CA 94087-2851

Established in 2004 in California.
Donors: Leonard Borok; Lois Borok.
Foundation type: Independent foundation.
Financial data (yr. ended 12/31/13): Assets,
$3,854,758 (M); expenditures, $196,485;
qualifying distributions, $196,485; giving activities

include $193,676 for 56 grants (high: $25,000;
low: $150).
Fields of interest: Specialty hospital care; Diseases
and conditions; Public libraries; Judaism; Human
services.
Type of support: General support.
Limitations: Applications not accepted. Giving
primarily in CA. No grants to individuals.
Application information: Contributes only to
pre-selected organizations.
Officers: Jack Borok, Pres. and C.F.O.; Ronald
Borok, V.P.; Robert Borok, Secy.
EIN: 200936535

332
Jay and Carol Borzi Family Foundation
10 Johns Canyon Rd.
Rolling Hills, CA 90274-5082

Established in 2005 in California.
Donors: Jay Borzi; William J. Borzi.
Foundation type: Independent foundation.
Financial data (yr. ended 12/31/13): Assets,
$772,557 (M); expenditures, $185,925; qualifying
distributions, $174,750; giving activities include
$174,750 for 16 grants (high: $50,000; low: $500).
Fields of interest: Education; Diseases and
conditions.
Type of support: Research.
Limitations: Applications not accepted. No grants to
individuals.
Application information: Unsolicited requests for
funds not accepted.
Officer and Trustees: William Jay Borzi, Pres. and
Trustee; Carol Borzi.
EIN: 203977239

333
Allan and Patricia Boscacci Family Foundation
P.O. Box 1637
Lafayette, CA 94549-1637

Established in 2005 in California.
Donors: Allan J. Boscacci; Patricia A. Boscacci.
Foundation type: Independent foundation.
Financial data (yr. ended 06/30/14): Assets,
$1,083,577 (M); expenditures, $270,116;
qualifying distributions, $267,294; giving activities
include $264,800 for 5 grants (high: $200,000;
low: $4,800).
Fields of interest: Education; Housing development;
Catholicism.
Limitations: Applications not accepted. Giving
primarily in CA. No grants to individuals.
Application information: Unsolicited requests for
funds not accepted.
Officers: Allan J. Boscacci, Chair.; Patricia A.
Boscacci, Pres.; Allison Mein, C.F.O.
EIN: 202407119

334
Boukai Family Foundation
32 Edelman
Irvine, CA 92618

Established in 2003 in California.
Donors: Continental Food Mgmt.; Global Link
Solutions, Inc.; Amer Boukai; Amer Boukai; Ziad
Boukai; Issam Boukai; General Procurment Inc.

Foundation type: Company-sponsored foundation.
Financial data (yr. ended 12/31/13): Assets, $0
(M); gifts received, $253,400; expenditures,
$220,221; qualifying distributions, $219,350;
giving activities include $219,350 for 15 grants
(high: $60,000; low: $980).
Purpose and activities: The foundation supports
organizations involved with education, adoption,
Muslim rights, and Islam.
Fields of interest: Education; Health; Religion.
Type of support: General support.
Limitations: Applications not accepted. Giving
primarily in CA. No grants to individuals.
Application information: Contributes only to
pre-selected organizations.
Officers: Ziad Boukai, Pres.; Amer A. Boukai, Treas.
Director: Akhram Boukai.
EIN: 010788855

335
The Herbert & Marigrace Boyer Foundation
101 Larkspur Landing Cir., Ste. 221
Larkspur, CA 94939-1750

Established in 1986 in California.
Donors: Herbert W. Boyer; Marigrace Boyer.
Foundation type: Independent foundation.
Financial data (yr. ended 12/31/13): Assets,
$658,921 (M); gifts received, $250,000;
expenditures, $328,055; qualifying distributions,
$320,000; giving activities include $320,000 for 3
grants (high: $200,000; low: $50,000).
Purpose and activities: Giving primarily to
universities for medical education.
Fields of interest: University education; Medical
education.
Type of support: Capital and infrastructure;
Scholarships.
Limitations: Applications not accepted. Giving
primarily in New Haven, CT; some giving also in San
Francisco, CA and Latrobe, PA. No grants to
individuals.
Application information: Contributes only to
pre-selected organizations.
Officers: Herbert W. Boyer, Pres.; Douglas M. Boyer,
C.F.O.; Ethan T. Boyer, V.P.; Marigrace Boyer, Secy.
EIN: 680118055

336
Robert C. & Lois C. Braddock Charitable Foundation
1999 Harrison, 25th Fl.
Oakland, CA 94612
Main URL: http://www.braddockfoundation.org
Grants List: http://www.braddockfoundation.org/
grants.html

Established in 1990 in California.
Donors: Robert C. Braddock; Lois C. Braddock.
Foundation type: Operating foundation.
Financial data (yr. ended 06/30/13): Assets,
$5,598,907 (M); expenditures, $327,701;
qualifying distributions, $283,363; giving activities
include $237,800 for 25 grants (high: $50,000;
low: $1,000).
Purpose and activities: The foundation directs
funding efforts toward projects that enhance the well
being of children, youth, the elderly, the disabled
and veterans. The foundation is dedicated to
assisting these groups in the areas of basic life

necessities, education, job training, rehabilitation, and environmental issues that have an impact upon people's lives.

Fields of interest: Higher education; Business education; Environment; Natural resources; Diseases and conditions; Arthritis; Cancers; Aerospace engineering; Public libraries; Christianity; Human services; Food aid; Domestic violence shelters.

Limitations: Giving primarily in San Leandro and Oakland, CA, and in Central FL.

Publications: Grants list.

Application information: Complete application information available on foundation web site. Check foundation web site whether foundation is accepting applications from new applicants.

   Initial approach: Letter
   Deadline(s): Mar. 14

Trustees: Lois C. Braddock; Robert C. Braddock, Jr.; Cheryl Lee Keemar.

EIN: 680234966

337
George and Ruth Bradford Foundation

P.O. Box 720
Ukiah, CA 95482-0720 (707) 462-6694
Contact: Myrna L. Oglesby, Dir.

Established in 1985 in California.
Donor: Ruth Bradford.
Foundation type: Independent foundation.
Financial data (yr. ended 06/30/14): Assets, $3,608,599 (M); expenditures, $183,840; qualifying distributions, $173,700; giving activities include $173,700 for 36 grants (high: $13,000; low: $1,000).
Fields of interest: Museums; Education; Higher education; Natural resources; Health; Camps; Human services; Family services; Child welfare; Youth development; Temporary accommodations.
Type of support: General support; Scholarships.
Limitations: Applications accepted. Giving limited to Mendocino County, CA. No grants to individuals.
Application information: Application form required.

   Initial approach: Letter
   Copies of proposal: 1
   Deadline(s): None
   Board meeting date(s): Monthly

Directors: Peter R. Bradford; Bruce S. Cameron; Myrna L. Oglesby.
EIN: 943015722

338
The Bravo Foundation

(formerly Everhealth Foundation)
1042 N. El Camino Real, B409
Encinitas, CA 92024-1322 (619) 889-1244
Main URL: http://www.bravofdn.org
Grants List: http://www.bravofdn.org/grants_prior.html

Established in 1997 in California.
Foundation type: Independent foundation.
Financial data (yr. ended 12/31/13): Assets, $12,106,104 (M); expenditures, $528,434; qualifying distributions, $380,438; giving activities include $256,000 for 27 grants (high: $20,000; low: $2,500).
Purpose and activities: The foundation awards grants only to human service organizations which

serve the poor and disadvantaged, with special focus on the Hispanic community.
Fields of interest: Education; Elementary and secondary education; Diseases and conditions; Catholicism; Human services; Child welfare.
Limitations: Applications not accepted. Giving limited to San Diego, Imperial, and Riverside counties, CA, and CO. No support for religious or political purposes. No grants to individuals, or for capital campaigns, endowment funds, research, deficit budgets, conferences, transportation and lodging, testimonial dinners, ceremonies, or for publications or media projects.
Publications: Grants list.
Application information: Unsolicited requests for funds not accepted. See foundation web site for letter of inquiry guidelines.
Officers and Directors: E. Zeke Lopez, Chair.; Michael J. Lopez, C.E.O. and Pres. and Director; Beatriz Ramirez, Secy.; Wind W. Ralston, Treas.; Jesus Varela.
Number of staff: 1 full-time professional; 1 full-time support.
EIN: 952160081

339
Mara W. Breech Foundation

c/o DOCS
2120 Wilshire Blvd., Ste. 400
Santa Monica, CA 90403-5708 (310) 828-4748
Contact: Michelle Doherty

Established in 1994 in California.
Donors: Mara W. Breech; Mara Breech Trust; Mara Breech Charitable Lead Annuity Trust.
Foundation type: Independent foundation.
Financial data (yr. ended 12/31/13): Assets, $6,721,751 (M); gifts received, $419,616; expenditures, $351,775; qualifying distributions, $305,167; giving activities include $305,167 for 26 grants (high: $26,000; low: $1,000).
Fields of interest: Teacher education.
Limitations: Applications accepted. Giving limited to CA. No grants to individuals.
Application information: Application form required.

   Initial approach: Proposal
   Deadline(s): Oct. 31

Officers: Andrew L. Breech, Pres.; Debra N. Breech, Secy.-Treas.
Number of staff: 1 part-time professional.
EIN: 954474892

340
Warren and Elaine Breslow Family Foundation

9454 Wilshire Blvd., 4th Fl.
Beverly Hills, CA 90212

Established in 2002 in California.
Donors: Elaine R. Breslow; Warren L. Breslow.
Foundation type: Independent foundation.
Financial data (yr. ended 12/31/13): Assets, $7,466,616 (M); gifts received, $198,782; expenditures, $456,653; qualifying distributions, $394,391; giving activities include $392,155 for 40 grants (high: $100,000; low: $100).
Fields of interest: Education; Health; Judaism; Human services.
Limitations: Applications not accepted. Giving primarily in CA and VA. No grants to individuals.

Application information: Unsolicited requests for funds not accepted.
Officer and Director: Warren L. Breslow, Pres. and Director.
EIN: 134210209

341
Brewster West Foundation

57 Post St., Ste. 503
San Francisco, CA 94104-5020

Established in 1994 in California.
Donors: Eric Johnson; Barbara B. Johnson.
Foundation type: Independent foundation.
Financial data (yr. ended 12/31/12): Assets, $4,346,848 (M); expenditures, $480,715; qualifying distributions, $458,125; giving activities include $433,000 for 34 grants (high: $30,000; low: $1,000).
Purpose and activities: Giving primarily for Episcopal churches, education, and human services.
Fields of interest: Museums; Education; Episcopalianism and Anglicanism; Lutheranism; Human services; Food banks.
Type of support: General support.
Limitations: Applications not accepted. Giving primarily in CA. No grants to individuals.
Application information: Contributes only to pre-selected organizations.
Trustees: Barbara B. Johnson; Eric L. Johnson; Martine B. Larsen; Barbara Loveless; Richard G. Malone.
EIN: 680343603

342
Robert & Alice Bridges Foundation

P.O. Box 1228
Lafayette, CA 94549-1228

Established in 1957 in California.
Donors: Robert L. Bridges; Alice M. Bridges†.
Foundation type: Independent foundation.
Financial data (yr. ended 12/31/13): Assets, $4,168,647 (M); expenditures, $180,328; qualifying distributions, $165,613; giving activities include $157,000 for 39 grants (high: $10,000; low: $1,000).
Fields of interest: Education; Agriculture; Human services.
Type of support: General support; Continuing support; Capital campaigns; Professorships.
Limitations: Applications not accepted. Giving primarily in the San Francisco Bay Area, CA. No grants to individuals.
Publications: Annual report.
Application information: Unsolicited requests for funds not accepted.
Officers: Linda B. Ingham, Pres.; James R. Bridges, Secy.-Treas.
EIN: 946066355

343
The Bridges/Larson Foundation

P.O. Box 3365
Beverly Hills, CA 90212-0365
Contact: R. Koblin

Established in 1993 in California.
Donor: James Bridges†.

Foundation type: Independent foundation.
Financial data (yr. ended 12/31/14): Assets, $4,086,229 (M); gifts received, $1,473,158; expenditures, $201,069; qualifying distributions, $156,300; giving activities include $156,300 for grants.
Purpose and activities: Giving primarily for higher education, arts and culture, and federated giving programs.
Fields of interest: Arts and culture; Higher education; Domesticated animals; Nonprofits; HIV/AIDS; Film and video; Television.
Type of support: Research; Regranting.
Limitations: Giving primarily in CA. No grants to individuals.
Trustee: Ronald R. Koblin, CPA.
EIN: 954422320

344
Bright China Social Fund
777 Silver Spur Rd., Ste. 230
Rolling Hills Estates, CA 90274-3644

Donor: Light Year Holdings, Ltd.
Foundation type: Independent foundation.
Financial data (yr. ended 03/31/13): Assets, $50,105 (M); gifts received, $270,000; expenditures, $272,433; qualifying distributions, $170,000; giving activities include $170,000 for 2 grants (high: $95,000; low: $75,000), and $102,453 for 1 foundation-administered program.
Fields of interest: Higher education; Employment.
Limitations: Applications not accepted. Giving primarily in Claremont, CA and New York, NY.
Application information: Unsolicited requests for funds not accepted.
Officers: Ming Lo Shao, Pres.; Robert La, Secy.; Yeh Wah Chong, Treas.
Directors: Frances Hesselbein; Stephen Lee; Joseph Maciariello; William C. Pollard; Henry To.
EIN: 262487075

345
The Bright Family Foundation
1620 N. Carpenter Rd., Bldg. B
Modesto, CA 95351-1155   (209) 526-8242
Contact: Calvin E. Bright, Pres.

Established in 1986 in California.
Donor: Calvin E. Bright.
Foundation type: Independent foundation.
Financial data (yr. ended 12/31/13): Assets, $10,253,547 (M); expenditures, $405,586; qualifying distributions, $390,487; giving activities include $389,000 for 36 grants (high: $57,000; low: $500).
Purpose and activities: Giving primarily for education, including scholarship grants, and for medical services and internships.
Fields of interest: Arts and culture; Higher education; Medical education; Human services; Child welfare.
Limitations: Applications accepted. Giving primarily in Stanislaus County, CA, within a 20-mile radius of Modesto.
Application information: Application form required.
   Initial approach: Application form or Letter
   Copies of proposal: 1
   Deadline(s): None
Officers: Calvin E. Bright, Pres.; Carol Bright Tougas, V.P. and Secy.-Treas.

Directors: John Dunn; Susan Hunter; Cathee Vaughn.
EIN: 770126942

346
Judy and Bernard Briskin Foundation
9595 Wilshire Blvd., Ste. 411
Beverly Hills, CA 90212-2504

Established in 1981 in California.
Donors: Bernard Briskin; Judy Briskin.
Foundation type: Operating foundation.
Financial data (yr. ended 04/30/13): Assets, $3,824,482 (M); expenditures, $372,571; qualifying distributions, $368,726; giving activities include $364,931 for 6 grants (high: $341,696; low: $150).
Fields of interest: Foundations; Diseases and conditions; Judaism.
Limitations: Applications not accepted. Giving primarily in CA. No grants to individuals.
Application information: Contributes only to pre-selected organizations.
Trustees: Bernard Briskin; Judy Briskin; Kenneth Goldman; Julie Harelson.
EIN: 953625640

347
Gary Broad Foundation
(formerly Gary and Sheri Broad Foundation)
10900 Wilshire Blvd., 12th Fl.
Los Angeles, CA 90024-6532

Established in 1997 in California.
Donor: Gary Broad.
Foundation type: Independent foundation.
Financial data (yr. ended 12/31/14): Assets, $7,296,026; gifts received, $988,934; expenditures, $325,660; qualifying distributions, $325,660.
Fields of interest: Arts and culture; Higher education; Natural resources; Animal welfare; Hospital care; Human services; Child welfare; Senior services.
Limitations: Applications not accepted. Giving primarily in CA and Washington, DC. No grants to individuals.
Application information: Contributes only to pre-selected organizations.
Trustees: Gary Broad; Cindy S. Quane.
EIN: 330757689

348
The Broder Foundation
6345 Balboa Blvd., Ste. 375
Encino, CA 91316-5238
Contact: Singer Burke

Established in 2006 in California.
Donors: Robert Broder; Cynthia Broder.
Foundation type: Independent foundation.
Financial data (yr. ended 12/31/12): Assets, $1,643,957 (M); expenditures, $361,799; qualifying distributions, $359,650; giving activities include $359,650 for grants.
Fields of interest: Education; Early childhood education; Nonprofits; Health; Mental health care.
Type of support: Regranting.
Limitations: Applications not accepted. Giving primarily in CA and CO. No grants to individuals.

Application information: Unsolicited requests for funds not accepted.
Officers and Directors: Robert Broder, Pres. and Director; Cynthia Broder, Secy. and C.F.O. and Director.
EIN: 711018166

349
Sunshine Brooks Foundation
P.O. Box 34627
San Diego, CA 92163-4627
Contact: Michael Kearney, Dir.
E-mail: mkearney@costco.com; Main URL: http://www.sunshinebrooks.com

Established in 1985 in California.
Donors: Hattie H. Brooks; Sol Price; Sunshine Brooks†; Costco Wholesale Corp.
Foundation type: Company-sponsored foundation.
Financial data (yr. ended 06/30/13): Assets, $1,576,571 (M); gifts received, $78,000; expenditures, $166,081; qualifying distributions, $156,000; giving activities include $156,000 for 104 grants to individuals.
Purpose and activities: Scholarship awards to employees and children of employees of Costco Wholesale.
Fields of interest: Education.
Type of support: Scholarships; Student aid.
Limitations: Applications accepted. Giving primarily in CA.
Application information: See foundation web site for application information. Application form required.
   Deadline(s): May 1
Officer: John Matthews, Secy.-Treas.
Directors: Michael Kearney; Julius Pearl; Henry Wolff, Jr.
EIN: 330190411

350
Brooks-Mathews Foundation
4725 Thornton Ave.
Fremont, CA 94536-6408   (510) 797-7980
Contact: John Brooks, Pres.

Donors: John Brooks; John and Barbara Brooks Trust; Barbara Brooks; Susan Jane Moldow; William Mathews Brooks.
Foundation type: Independent foundation.
Financial data (yr. ended 12/31/13): Assets, $1,147,585 (M); gifts received, $500,000; expenditures, $419,172; qualifying distributions, $415,250; giving activities include $415,250 for 20 grants (high: $64,000; low: $1,000).
Fields of interest: Art museums; Alumni relations; Sports and recreation; Human services.
Type of support: General support.
Limitations: Applications accepted. Giving primarily in CA; funding also in CO and Kings Point, NY.
Application information: Application form required.
   Initial approach: Letter
   Deadline(s): None
Officers: John Brooks, Pres.; William Mathews Brooks, V.P.; Gail Fishley, Secy.
EIN: 946098103

351

Brotman Foundation of California
11845 W. Olympic Blvd., Ste. 845
Los Angeles, CA 90064-1149
Contact: Michael B. Sherman, Pres.

Foundation type: Independent foundation.
Financial data (yr. ended 12/31/13): Assets, $6,360,004 (M); expenditures, $457,994; qualifying distributions, $412,621; giving activities include $346,000 for 44 grants (high: $78,000; low: $2,000).
Purpose and activities: Giving mainly for children, health and medical research; some support for arts, education, and environmental organizations.
Fields of interest: Arts and culture; Education; Environment; Health; Diseases and conditions; HIV/AIDS; Child welfare.
Type of support: General support; Continuing support; Convening; Research; Research and evaluation.
Limitations: Applications accepted. Giving primarily in southern CA. No grants to individuals.
Application information:
 Initial approach: Letter
 Copies of proposal: 1
 Deadline(s): None
 Board meeting date(s): 3rd Wed. of each month
 Final notification: 3-4 weeks
Officers and Directors: Michael B. Sherman, Pres. and Director; Craig Tessler, Secy. and Director; Toni Brotman, Treas. and Director.
Number of staff: None.
EIN: 956094639

352

Harold and Colene Brown Family Foundation
1640 S. Sepulveda Blvd., Ste. 515
Los Angeles, CA 90025-7538

Established in 1997 in California.
Donors: Colene Brown; Harold Brown.
Foundation type: Independent foundation.
Financial data (yr. ended 12/31/13): Assets, $8,176,579 (M); expenditures, $410,553; qualifying distributions, $331,751; giving activities include $331,751 for 22 grants (high: $75,000; low: $1).
Fields of interest: Education; Higher education; Technology; International relations.
Type of support: General support; Research and evaluation.
Limitations: Applications not accepted. Giving primarily in CA, Washington, DC, and New York, NY. No grants to individuals.
Application information: Unsolicited requests for funds not accepted.
Trustees: Colene Brown; Harold Brown; Ellen Brown Merewether; Deborah Brown Ploumis.
EIN: 336203761

353

Patricia Crail Brown Foundation
6405 River Grove St.
Bakersfield, CA 93308-9694

Established in 1998 in California.
Donor: Patricia A. Brown Trust.
Foundation type: Independent foundation.

Financial data (yr. ended 12/31/12): Assets, $3,131,182 (M); gifts received, $73,333; expenditures, $228,497; qualifying distributions, $218,646; giving activities include $201,350 for 22 grants (high: $50,000; low: $2,500).
Fields of interest: Museums; Education; Animal welfare; Alzheimer's disease; Cancers; Child welfare.
Limitations: Applications not accepted. Giving primarily to organizations located in Kern County, CA. No grants to individuals.
Application information: Unsolicited requests for funds not accepted.
Officers and Directors: Lynn A. Brown, Pres. and Director; Patricia M. Soldano, C.F.O. and Secy.
EIN: 330379373

354

Lewis Brunswick and Rebecca Matoff Foundation, Inc.
1015 Calle Amanecer
San Clemente, CA 92673-6260

Established in 2000 in California.
Donors: Lewis Brunswick†; The Rebecca Matoff Admin Trust.
Foundation type: Operating foundation.
Financial data (yr. ended 12/31/13): Assets, $8,402,723 (M); gifts received, $141,000; expenditures, $400,927; qualifying distributions, $317,500; giving activities include $317,500 for 21 grants (high: $50,000; low: $3,000).
Fields of interest: Graduate and professional education; Nonprofits; Cystic fibrosis; Judaism; Theology.
Type of support: General support; Research; Regranting.
Limitations: Applications not accepted. Giving primarily in CA. No grants to individuals.
Application information: Contributes only to pre-selected organizations.
Officers and Trustees: Brad Shapiro, C.F.O. and Trustee; Leslie Raven, V.P.
EIN: 954748693

355

The John M. Bryan Family Fund
c/o Bryan Partners
475 Sansome St., Ste. 840
San Francisco, CA 94111-2810

Donors: John M. Bryan; Florence E. Bryan†; Kathryn B. Bryan; Suzanne E. Bryan; Amanda A. Bryan; Anne L. Bryan; Kathryn B. Hampton.
Foundation type: Independent foundation.
Financial data (yr. ended 12/31/14): Assets, $13,921,612 (M); expenditures, $423,112; qualifying distributions, $410,463; giving activities include $410,378 for 50 grants (high: $251,200; low: $100).
Purpose and activities: Giving primarily for arts and culture, health, education, and human services.
Fields of interest: Arts and culture; Performing arts; Opera; Education; Health; Diseases and conditions; Human services.
Type of support: General support.
Limitations: Applications not accepted. Giving primarily in CA. No grants to individuals.
Application information: Contributes only to pre-selected organizations.

Trustees: Alan R. Brudos; Amanda A. Bryan; Anne E. Bryan; Florence E. Bryan; Suzanne E. Bryan; Kathryn B. Hampton.
EIN: 941657247

356

Giovanni Bucolo Family Foundation
5190 Governor Dr., Ste. 207
San Diego, CA 92122-2849 (858) 554-1830

Donor: GB Living Trust.
Foundation type: Independent foundation.
Financial data (yr. ended 12/31/14): Assets, $0 (M); gifts received, $240,000; expenditures, $240,048; qualifying distributions, $239,742; giving activities include $239,742 for 2 grants (high: $119,871; low: $119,871).
Fields of interest: Education; Animal welfare; Health; Hospice care; Human services.
Limitations: Applications accepted. Giving primarily in CA.
Application information:
 Initial approach: Letter
 Deadline(s): 3/1
Officer and Directors: Michael Wright, Pres. and C.E.O. and Director; Patricia Clavell.
EIN: 010840176

357

Susie Tompkins Buell Foundation
(formerly Esprit Foundation)
P.O. Box 29921
San Francisco, CA 94129-9921 (415) 248-7825
Contact: Belinda Viray-Munoz, Exec. Dir.
FAX: (415) 441-6381;
E-mail: info@buellofficesf.com; Additional e-mail: belindavm@earthlink.net; Main URL: http://www.susietompkinsbuell.org
Grants List: http://susietompkinsbuell.org/grantees

Established in 1990 in California.
Donor: Susie R. Tompkins Buell.
Foundation type: Independent foundation.
Financial data (yr. ended 11/30/13): Assets, $7,251,305 (M); expenditures, $384,370; qualifying distributions, $283,082; giving activities include $278,250 for 9 grants (high: $100,000; low: $5,000), and $2,740 for 16 employee matching gifts.
Purpose and activities: Primarily funds programs that improve the lives of women and girls, with emphasis on programs aimed at 1) creating an awareness of social responsibility, 2) promoting civic participation, 3) leadership development, and 4) activism training.
Fields of interest: Science; Community service; Youth development; Women's services; Females.
Type of support: General support; Pro bono consulting services; Matching grants; Continuing support; Program development; Equal access; Technical assistance.
Limitations: Applications not accepted. Giving limited to San Francisco, CA. No support for international programs, drug and alcohol rehabilitation programs, or for health service organizations. No grants to individuals or for capital campaigns or film and video projects.
Publications: Grants list.
Application information: Unsolicited requests for funds not accepted. However, a 2-page letter of

inquiry describing the program's objectives and funding needs is accepted. Formal proposals are to be submitted upon invitation only.

Board meeting date(s): Jan.

Officers and Directors: Susie R. Tompkins Buell, Pres. and Director; Mark Buell, V.P.; Joan Steckler, Secy.; Belinda Viray-Munoz, Exec. Dir.

EIN: 770266801

358
Henry W. Bull Foundation

P.O. Box 45174
San Francisco, CA 94145-0174 8055646211
Application address: c/o Janice Gibbons, Union Bank, 1021 Anacapa St., Santa Barbara, CA 93101
Tel: (805) 564-6211

Established in 1960 in California.

Donor: Maud L. Bull†.

Foundation type: Independent foundation.

Financial data (yr. ended 12/31/14): Assets, $9,587,786; expenditures, $485,141; qualifying distributions, $460,452.

Purpose and activities: Giving primarily for the arts, education and health and human services.

Fields of interest: Arts and culture; Music; Education; Health; Diseases and conditions; Christianity.

Type of support: General support; Matching grants; Continuing support; Annual campaigns; Capital campaigns; Capital and infrastructure; Equipment; Program development; Research.

Limitations: Applications accepted. Giving on a national basis. No grants to individuals or private foundations.

Publications: Application guidelines.

Application information: Application form required.

Initial approach: Letter
Copies of proposal: 1
Deadline(s): Apr. 1 and Sept. 1
Board meeting date(s): 2 times per year

Trustees: Roy Gaskin; Union Bank, N.A.

Number of staff: None.

EIN: 956062058

359
Bundy Family Foundation

601 California St., Ste. 1151
San Francisco, CA 94108-2711

Established in 1994 in California.

Donors: Frederick L. Carroll; Mrs. Frederick L. Carroll.

Foundation type: Independent foundation.

Financial data (yr. ended 12/31/13): Assets, $3,845,678 (M); gifts received, $22,139; expenditures, $187,005; qualifying distributions, $178,500; giving activities include $173,000 for 12 grants (high: $56,000; low: $2,000).

Fields of interest: Museums; Higher education; Zoos; Youth services.

Limitations: Applications not accepted. Giving primarily in CA, ID, NJ and NY. No grants to individuals.

Application information: Contributes only to pre-selected organizations.

Officers: Timothy D. Orr, Pres.; Katherine O. Traina, C.F.O. and Secy.

Director: Kristin Orr.

EIN: 943215971

360
Bruce and Anne Bundy Foundation

P.O. Box 45174
San Francisco, CA 94145-0174

Established in 1993 in California.

Donors: Anne S. Bundy†; Bruce Bundy†.

Foundation type: Independent foundation.

Financial data (yr. ended 08/31/13): Assets, $8,635,075 (M); expenditures, $492,065; qualifying distributions, $408,764; giving activities include $381,038 for 8 grants (high: $100,000; low: $6,000).

Purpose and activities: Giving primarily for medical research, including biomedical institutes, as well as for services for people who are blind, including a center for blind children; funding also for and ear institute and human services.

Fields of interest: Speech and hearing rehabilitation; Diseases and conditions; Eye diseases; Biology; Human services; People with vision impairments.

Type of support: Research; Research and evaluation.

Limitations: Applications not accepted. Giving limited to southern CA. No grants to individuals.

Application information: Contributes only to pre-selected organizations.

Board meeting date(s): July

Trustees: Douglas Nosworthy; Union Bank of California, N.A.

EIN: 946659802

361
Burbank Health Care Foundation

(formerly Burbank Community Hospital Foundation)
200 W. Magnolia Blvd.
Burbank, CA 91502-1724 (818) 559-2423
FAX: (818) 559-2427; E-mail: info@burbankhcf.org;
Main URL: http://burbankhcf.org

Established in 1996 in California.

Foundation type: Independent foundation.

Financial data (yr. ended 12/31/12): Assets, $4,888,490 (M); expenditures, $232,887; qualifying distributions, $211,703; giving activities include $132,748 for 13 grants (high: $68,248; low: $2,000).

Purpose and activities: Grants are made to organizations that promote and provide for better health care in the city of Burbank.

Fields of interest: Medical education; Health care administration and financing.

Limitations: Applications accepted. Giving primarily in Burbank, CA. No grants to individuals.

Application information: Application guidelines available on foundation web site. Application form required.

Initial approach: Request application
Copies of proposal: 1
Deadline(s): Nov. 1 and 30

Officers: Dr. Keith Emmons, Chair.; Sundewr Ramani, Vice-Chair.; Marsha Jackson, Secy.; Randy Stevenson, Treas.

Board Members: T.J. Baptie; Dr. James P. Feloney; Dr. Boyd Flinders; Sue Georgino; Connie Lackey; Tomme Lenz; Gary Olson.

EIN: 951643337

362
Anton B. Burg Foundation

4829 Falcon Ave.
Long Beach, CA 90807-1205

Established in 2003 in California.

Donor: Anton Burg†.

Foundation type: Independent foundation.

Financial data (yr. ended 12/31/13): Assets, $3,962,792 (M); expenditures, $177,837; qualifying distributions, $153,360; giving activities include $153,360 for 4 grants (high: $92,000; low: $18,760).

Fields of interest: Higher education; Cancers; Science; Chemistry.

Type of support: Scholarships.

Limitations: Applications not accepted. Giving primarily in CA. No grants to individuals (directly).

Application information: Unsolicited requests for funds not accepted.

Officers: David R. Dauer, Pres.; Sara Walker, Secy.; David A. Dows, Treas.

Board Member: Jason Dauer.

EIN: 651210987

363
James And Deborah Burrows Foundation

c/o Flekman, Baren & Co.
9171 Wilshire Blvd., Ste. 400
Beverly Hills, CA 90210-5516 (310) 274-5847
Contact: James Burrows, Tr.

Donors: James Burrows; Deborah Burrows.

Foundation type: Independent foundation.

Financial data (yr. ended 12/31/13): Assets, $6,418,226 (M); expenditures, $300,937; qualifying distributions, $258,763; giving activities include $258,603 for 141 grants (high: $47,000; low: $30).

Fields of interest: Education; Health; Religion.

Limitations: Applications accepted. Giving primarily in CA, Washington, DC, IL and NY.

Application information:

Initial approach: Proposal
Deadline(s): None

Trustees: Charles Baren; Deborah Burrows; James Burrows; Manny Flekman.

EIN: 456196471

364
Lee & Dorene Butler Family Charitable Foundation

19 Valley View Rd.
Orinda, CA 94563 (435) 658-0333
FAX: (435) 604-6536;
E-mail: butlerfcf@hotmail.com

Established in 1998 in Nebraska.

Donors: Dorene Nunley Butler; George Lee Butler.

Foundation type: Independent foundation.

Financial data (yr. ended 12/31/14): Assets, $4,096,808; expenditures, $251,376; qualifying distributions, $229,800.

Fields of interest: Arts and culture; Museums; Education; Zoos; Diseases and conditions; Human services; Youth services.

Limitations: Applications accepted. Giving primarily in southern CA, KY, NE, and UT.

Publications: Application guidelines.

Application information: Application form required.

Initial approach: Completed application form

Copies of proposal: 1
Deadline(s): None
Board meeting date(s): Dec.
Officers and Directors: Dorene Nunley Butler, Pres. and Director; George Lee Butler, Secy.-Treas. and Director; Lisa Butler Herring, Exec. Dir.; Brett Lee Butler; Patti Dawn Butler; Michael Herring.
Number of staff: 1 part-time professional.
EIN: 470816345

365
Marilyn and Marshall Butler Foundation
11990 San Vicente Blvd., Ste. 350
Los Angeles, CA 90049-4775

Established in 1990 in New York.
Donors: Marshall D. Butler; The Butler Charitable Lead Annuity Trust 9/30/97; The Butler Charitable Lead Annuity Trust 6/30/99.
Foundation type: Independent foundation.
Financial data (yr. ended 12/31/13): Assets, $2,717,488 (M); gifts received, $377,000; expenditures, $184,165; qualifying distributions, $155,525; giving activities include $155,275 for 45 grants (high: $25,300; low: $15).
Purpose and activities: Giving primarily for Jewish organizations.
Fields of interest: Arts and culture; Education; Nonprofits; Hospital care; Diseases and conditions; Judaism; Human services.
International interests: Israel.
Type of support: Curriculum development; Scholarships; Fellowships; Capital and infrastructure; Capital campaigns; Continuing support; Regranting; Annual campaigns; General support.
Limitations: Applications not accepted. Giving primarily in CA and NY. No grants to individuals.
Application information: Unsolicited requests for funds not accepted.
Trustees: Eliot Butler; Hillary Butler; Lawrence Butler; Marilyn Butler; Michael Butler.
EIN: 133591664

366
Butte Creek Foundation
14916 Eagle Ridge Dr.
Forest Ranch, CA 95942-9707
Contact: John L. Burghardt, Dir.

Donors: Barbara Boyle; John Boyle; Shipley Trust; Portland Cement; Vulcan Materials; Cemex; Teichert Materials; Conco Companies; Central Concrete Supply Co.; Lehigh Southwest Cement Co.
Foundation type: Independent foundation.
Financial data (yr. ended 12/31/13): Assets, $3,534,875 (M); gifts received, $101,056; expenditures, $202,475; qualifying distributions, $202,475; giving activities include $192,975 for 26 grants (high: $79,700; low: $50), and $9,500 for 9 grants to individuals (high: $1,500; low: $1,000).
Fields of interest: Education; Foundations; Hospital care; Maternal and perinatal health; Human services; Child welfare.
Type of support: General support; Student aid.
Application information: Application form required.
Initial approach: Letter
Deadline(s): None
Directors: Barbara Boyle; John L. Burghardt.
EIN: 680111634

367
Buttonwillow Community Foundation
P.O. Box 874
Buttonwillow, CA 93206-0874 (661) 589-0900
Contact: Regina Houchin

Established in 1994 in California.
Donor: Clean Harbors Inc.
Foundation type: Independent foundation.
Financial data (yr. ended 03/31/14): Assets, $736,663 (M); gifts received, $244,418; expenditures, $171,320; qualifying distributions, $166,693; giving activities include $166,693 for 13 grants (high: $37,996; low: $2,200).
Fields of interest: Education; Sports and recreation; Human services; Food aid.
Limitations: Applications accepted. Giving limited to Buttonwillow, CA.
Application information: Application form required.
Initial approach: Letter
Deadline(s): None
Officers: Chon Hernandez, Pres.; Barbara Copeland, Secy.; Regina Houchin, Treas.
Director: Bill McGarrah.
EIN: 770377965

368
Patricia Duque Byrne Charitable Foundation
P.O. Box 50030
Pasadena, CA 91115-0030 (213) 489-1015
Contact: Richard A. Grant, Tr.

Established in 2004 in California.
Donor: Richard A. Grant.
Foundation type: Independent foundation.
Financial data (yr. ended 12/31/13): Assets, $2,825,322 (M); expenditures, $383,255; qualifying distributions, $355,112; giving activities include $354,500 for 19 grants (high: $75,000; low: $5,000).
Fields of interest: Education; Catholicism; Human services.
Type of support: General support.
Limitations: Applications accepted. Giving primarily in CA. No grants to individuals.
Application information:
Initial approach: Proposal
Deadline(s): None
Trustee: Richard A. Grant.
EIN: 206253698

369
Calaveras Community Foundation
1241 S. Main St.
P. O. Box 1436
Angels Camp, CA 95222 (209) 736-1845
E-mail: info@calaverascommunityfoundation.org;
Main URL: http://
www.calaverascommunityfoundation.org

Established in 2001 in California.
Foundation type: Community foundation.
Financial data (yr. ended 12/31/13): Assets, $948,433 (M); gifts received, $217,171; expenditures, $179,483; giving activities include $129,556 for 7 grants (high: $15,525), and $14,100 for grants to individuals.
Purpose and activities: The foundation's mission is to raise and receive funds from individuals, families, businesses, and community organizations who want to help support Calaveras County charitable causes, and disburse those funds to worthy charitable organizations, helping the residents of Calaveras County.
Fields of interest: Arts and culture; Youth development; Senior services; Children and youth.
Type of support: Program development; Scholarships; General support.
Limitations: Applications accepted. Giving primarily in Calaveras County, CA. No support for private foundations or other grantmaking organizations, or to promote a specific religion. No grants for endowment funds, annual campaigns, or personnel expenses.
Publications: Grants list.
Application information: Competitive grants are announced to the local media and through the foundation's website; see web site for more information. Application form required.
Initial approach: Contact foundation
Deadline(s): Jan. 31
Board meeting date(s): Monthly
Officers and Directors: Linda McCall Kangeter, Pres. and Director; Paul Stein, V.P., Admin. and Director; Denise Ebbett, Secy. and Director; Brent Harrington, Treas. and Director; Allen Breed, Dir. Emeritus; Genna Hurst, Dir. Emeritus; Terry Beaudoin; Chyrl Hillis; Christy Maynard; Lynette Norfolk; Pam Taylor; Gilbert Valtierra; Barbara Boyd White.
EIN: 680472056

370
California Institute of Contemporary Art
4545 Park Blvd., Ste. 206
San Diego, CA 92116-2669

Donors: Regina Klein; Fritz Klein; Ed L. Anderson; Fritz Klein Foundation.
Foundation type: Independent foundation.
Financial data (yr. ended 06/30/14): Assets, $2,825,181 (M); expenditures, $383,878; qualifying distributions, $377,195; giving activities include $323,450 for 16 grants (high: $50,000; low: $4,150), and $25,178 for 4 grants to individuals (high: $13,200; low: $750).
Purpose and activities: Grants to individuals who have the support of an organization for projects in the arts, including theater, music, visual arts, and cultural education.
Fields of interest: Arts and culture; Health; Human services.
Type of support: General support; Grants to individuals.
Limitations: Applications not accepted. Giving primarily in CA and MN.
Application information: Unsolicited requests for funds not accepted.
Officers: Tom Reise, Pres.; Mike Szynanski, Secy.; Jason Dean, Treas.
EIN: 330094053

371
The Callison Foundation
969G Edgewater Blvd., PMB 148
Foster City, CA 94404-3775 (650) 340-1800

Established in 1965 in California.
Donor: Fred W. Callison†.
Foundation type: Independent foundation.

Financial data (yr. ended 12/31/14): Assets, $10,014,805; expenditures, $368,861; qualifying distributions, $344,648.
Purpose and activities: Giving primarily for the arts and education, and senior support.
Fields of interest: Arts and culture; Education; Community and economic development; Religion; Seniors.
Type of support: General support; Scholarships.
Limitations: Giving primarily in the San Francisco Bay Area, CA. No grants to individuals.
Application information: Application form required.
  Initial approach: Letter
  Copies of proposal: 4
  Deadline(s): All Year-Round
  Board meeting date(s): Varies
Officers: Mort Pactor, Pres.; Peter O'Hara, C.F.O.; Gerald Hing, Secy.
EIN: 946127962

372
Candelaria Fund
P.O. Box 398
Littleriver, CA 95456-0398
Contact: Richard L. Tower, Pres.; Caroline Tower, Secy.-Treas.
E-mail: candelaria_fund@sbcglobal.net

Established in 1997 in California.
Donors: Richard L. Tower, Sr.‡; Richard L. Tower; Caroline Tower.
Foundation type: Independent foundation.
Financial data (yr. ended 12/31/13): Assets, $1,820,507 (M); expenditures, $206,926; qualifying distributions, $199,694; giving activities include $191,434 for 13 grants (high: $80,434; low: $1,000).
Fields of interest: Historical activities; Community and economic development; Economic development.
International interests: Mexico.
Type of support: General support; Program development.
Limitations: Applications accepted. Giving primarily in northern CA, CO, Albuquerque, NM and OR.
Publications: Application guidelines; Grants list.
Application information:
  Initial approach: Letter
  Copies of proposal: 1
  Deadline(s): None
  Board meeting date(s): As needed
Officers: Richard L. Tower, Pres.; Caroline Tower, Secy.Treas.
Number of staff: None.
EIN: 943246086

373
Candor Foundation, Inc.
6 Middleridge Ln. S.
Rolling Hills, CA 90274-4055

Donors: Irene W. Keng; Donald Lam; Riking (USA) Inc.; Sam Lam; Civic Riking Inc.; RFA International Inc.; Susan Lam.
Foundation type: Independent foundation.
Financial data (yr. ended 12/31/13): Assets, $4,974,583 (M); gifts received, $767,900; expenditures, $394,975; qualifying distributions, $388,824; giving activities include $388,824 for 13 grants (high: $162,320; low: $6,757).

Purpose and activities: Giving primarily to schools and educational programs in China.
Fields of interest: Education; Human services; Child welfare; Youth development.
Limitations: Applications not accepted. No grants to individuals.
Application information: Contributes only to pre-selected organizations.
Officers: Irene W. Keng, Pres.; Su-chu Wang, Secy.
Directors: James Keng; Donald Lam.
EIN: 311794327

374
Cannon Family Foundation
c/o Robert Cannon
P.O. Box 1306
Santa Monica, CA 90406-1306

Donor: Francis Cannon.
Foundation type: Independent foundation.
Financial data (yr. ended 12/31/14): Assets, $5,037,993; expenditures, $233,810; qualifying distributions, $225,000.
Fields of interest: Nonprofits; Diseases and conditions; Judaism; Human services; Females.
Type of support: Regranting.
Limitations: Applications not accepted. Giving primarily in CA. No grants to individuals.
Application information: Contributes only to pre-selected organizations.
Officers: Sara Cannon, Pres.; Robert Cannon, Secy.-Treas.
EIN: 954405467

375
Iris & B. Gerald Cantor Foundation
(formerly The B. G. Cantor Art Foundation)
1180 S. Beverly Dr., Ste. 321
Los Angeles, CA 90035-1154
Contact: Judith Sobol, Exec. Dir.
E-mail: jsobol@ibgcf.org; Additional contact: Annie Allen, Off. Mgr., e-mail: aallen@ibgcf.org; Main URL: http://www.cantorfoundation.org

Established in 1978 in California.
Donors: Iris Cantor; B. Gerald Cantor‡; Cantor Fitzgerald Inc.; Cantor Fitzgerald, LP; Amethyst, Inc.
Foundation type: Independent foundation.
Financial data (yr. ended 04/30/13): Assets, $41,485,147 (M); gifts received, $249,896; expenditures, $910,216; qualifying distributions, $910,216; giving activities include $383,825 for grants.
Purpose and activities: Giving primarily for medical research and clinical care, as well as for art museums and educational institutions.
Fields of interest: Arts and culture; Museums; Health; Hospital care; Diseases and conditions; Adults; Female adults.
International interests: France.
Type of support: General support; Grants to individuals; Matching grants; Continuing support; Annual campaigns; Capital campaigns; Capital and infrastructure; Endowments; Research; Convening; Research and evaluation; Professorships; Publications; Fellowships; Scholarships.
Limitations: Applications accepted. Giving primarily in CA and NY, or for Rodin studies at Musee Rodin in Paris, France. No support for arts projects or studio artists.

Application information: Applicants are required to have a preliminary discussion with foundation staff prior to submitting a proposal.
  Initial approach: E-mail inquiry
  Copies of proposal: 10
  Board meeting date(s): Quarterly
  Final notification: 6 months
Officers and Directors: Iris Cantor, Chair. and Pres. and Director; Ryan Fisher, V.P. and Director; Kimberly Fetridge, Secy. and Director; Joel Rothstein, Treas. and Director; Judith Sobol, Exec. Dir.; Randi Ross Aitken; Suzanne Fisher; Michele Geller; Monica Ross Muhart.
Number of staff: 1 full-time professional; 1 full-time support.
EIN: 136227347

376
Cardinal Collection Educational Foundation
P.O. Box 2867
Sunnyvale, CA 94087-5227

Established in 1999 in California.
Donors: Martin A. Logies; John E. Skirtich; Rossana H. Ho; S.L. Contursi Rare Coin Gallery; Century Coin and Collectibles; Terry L. Root; Z. Victor Paparigian‡; S.L. Contursi Inc.
Foundation type: Operating foundation.
Financial data (yr. ended 12/31/13): Assets, $21,550,701 (M); gifts received, $3,046,000; expenditures, $981,832; qualifying distributions, $7,884,103; giving activities include $300,000 for 1 grant, and $7,584,103 for foundation-administered programs.
Fields of interest: Education; Diseases and conditions; Human services.
Limitations: Applications not accepted. Giving primarily in CA. No grants to individuals.
Application information: Unsolicited requests for funds not accepted.
Officers and Directors: Martin A. Logies, Pres. and Director; John E. Skirtich, Secy.-Treas. and Director.
EIN: 770529783

377
Carlston Family Foundation
(formerly Broderbund Foundation)
2933 Quedada
Newport Beach, CA 92660 (949) 640-7840
Contact: Timothy J. Allen, Exec. Dir.
FAX: (949) 640-7841;
E-mail: tima@carlstonfamilyfoundation.com;
Northern California tel.: (415) 388-4763; Main URL: http://www.carlstonfamilyfoundation.org
Facebook: https://www.facebook.com/pages/Carlston-Family-Foundation/104985366209091

Established in 1987 in California.
Donor: Alice Carlston.
Foundation type: Independent foundation.
Financial data (yr. ended 12/31/13): Assets, $3,376,812 (M); expenditures, $323,429; qualifying distributions, $323,429; giving activities include $148,865 for grants, and $323,429 for 4 foundation-administered programs.
Purpose and activities: The mission of the foundation is to recognize and reward outstanding teachers in California public schools. To be considered for the award, a teacher must be nominated by former students who are either

currently enrolled in or who have graduated from four year colleges or universities.
Fields of interest: Secondary education.
Type of support: Program development; Grants to individuals.
Limitations: Applications accepted. Giving primarily in CA.
Publications: Annual report; Grants list; Program policy statement.
Application information: Nomination guidelines and nominating form available on foundation web site. Application form required.
Officers and Directors: Douglas G. Carlston, Chair. and Director; Timothy J. Allen, Exec. Dir.; Don Carlston; Gary Carlston; Jude Cooks; Arun Ramanathan; Jan M. Rizzuti; Kathy Williams.
Number of staff: 1 full-time professional; 1 part-time professional.
EIN: 680154752

378
CAS Foundation, Inc.
404 21st St.
Santa Monica, CA 90402-2436

Established in 2002 in California.
Donors: Carole J. Meltzner; Sidney J. Meltzner; Aron Meltzner.
Foundation type: Independent foundation.
Financial data (yr. ended 12/31/13): Assets, $11,781,616 (M); expenditures, $293,582; qualifying distributions, $293,486; giving activities include $284,200 for 71 grants (high: $116,500; low: $500).
Fields of interest: Education; Nonprofits; Judaism.
Type of support: Regranting.
Limitations: Applications not accepted. Giving primarily in CA. No grants to individuals.
Application information: Unsolicited requests for funds not accepted.
Officers and Directors: Sidney J. Meltzner, C.E.O. and Director; Carole J. Meltzner, Secy. and Director; Aron Meltzner, Treas. and Director.
EIN: 481292269

379
Casillas Foundation
7946 Ivanhoe Ave., Ste. 302
La Jolla, CA 92037-4518

Established in 1989 in California.
Donors: Frederic H. Clark; Margaret Nolan.
Foundation type: Independent foundation.
Financial data (yr. ended 12/31/13): Assets, $3,428,337 (M); gifts received, $42,395; expenditures, $263,547; qualifying distributions, $185,112; giving activities include $183,500 for 25 grants (high: $25,000; low: $1,000).
Fields of interest: Education; Religion; Human services.
Limitations: Applications not accepted. Giving primarily in the San Francisco Bay Area, CA. No grants to individuals.
Application information: Contributes only to pre-selected organizations.
Officers: Frederic H. Clark, Pres.; Margaret Nolan Clark, V.P. and Secy.
Directors: Sean Fieler; Greg Pfundstein; Anthony J. Saroki.
EIN: 943107207

380
Castellano Family Foundation
1922 the Alameda., Ste. 210-A
San Jose, CA 95126 (408) 868-1655
FAX: (408) 645-5659; E-mail: info@castellano-ff.org;
Main URL: http://www.castellano-ff.org

Established in 2001 in California.
Donors: Alcario Castellano; Carmen Castellano; Carmela Castelano-Garcia.
Foundation type: Independent foundation.
Financial data (yr. ended 06/30/14): Assets, $3,537,226 (M); gifts received, $500,000; expenditures, $504,635; qualifying distributions, $461,612; giving activities include $363,867 for 60 grants (high: $25,000; low: $1,000).
Purpose and activities: Giving primarily for education and Latino organizations.
Fields of interest: Arts and culture; Education; Human services; Child welfare; People of Latin American descent.
Limitations: Applications accepted. Giving primarily in CA, with emphasis on San Jose.
Application information: Application guidelines available on foundation web site. Application form required.
Officers: Carmen Castellano, Pres.; Carmela Castellano-Garcia, V.P.; Armando Castellano, Secy.; Maria C. West, Treas.
Trustee: Alcario Castellano.
EIN: 912164439

381
Cavaricci Foundation
23161 Mill Creek Dr., Ste. 320
Laguna Hills, CA 92653-7907 (949) 597-9900
Contact: Marty Sturgeon

Established in 2005 in California.
Donors: James A. Cavaricci; Diane L. Cavaricci; Deloitte Touche.
Foundation type: Independent foundation.
Financial data (yr. ended 09/30/13): Assets, $130,720 (M); gifts received, $225,000; expenditures, $340,706; qualifying distributions, $335,801; giving activities include $335,801 for 11 grants (high: $261,000; low: $265).
Fields of interest: Health; Christianity; Human services.
Limitations: Applications accepted. Giving primarily in CA. No grants to individuals.
Application information: Application form required.
  Initial approach: Letter
  Deadline(s): None
Officers: James A. Cavaricci, Pres.; Caesar A. Cavaricci, V.P.; Marcello Cavaricci, C.F.O.; Diane L. Cavaricci, Secy.
EIN: 203920121

382
The CEC Foundation
c/o John R. Fuqua
P.O. Box 1324
Los Alamitos, CA 90720-2420

Established in 1999 in California.
Donor: Carol Electric Company Inc.
Foundation type: Operating foundation.
Financial data (yr. ended 12/31/13): Assets, $3,586,485 (M); gifts received, $195,000; expenditures, $453,929; qualifying distributions,

$427,630; giving activities include $427,630 for 12 grants (high: $125,000; low: $1,500).
Fields of interest: Christianity; Human services; Homeless services.
Type of support: General support; Grants to individuals.
Limitations: Applications not accepted. Giving primarily in CA.
Application information: Unsolicited requests for funds not accepted.
Officers: John R. Fuqua, C.E.O.; Allen W. Moffitt, C.F.O. and Secy.
EIN: 330859870

383
Celebrate Foundation, Inc.
2 6th Ave.
San Francisco, CA 94118-1324

Donor: Robert P. McGrath.
Foundation type: Independent foundation.
Financial data (yr. ended 07/31/13): Assets, $6,706,604 (M); expenditures, $358,370; qualifying distributions, $358,369; giving activities include $351,500 for 43 grants (high: $37,500; low: $250).
Purpose and activities: Giving primarily for Roman Catholic churches, agencies, schools, and federated giving programs.
Fields of interest: Education; Higher education; Nonprofits; Catholicism; Human services.
Type of support: Capital campaigns; Regranting.
Limitations: Applications not accepted. No grants to individuals.
Application information: Contributes only to pre-selected organizations.
Officers: R. McGrath, Pres.; J. McGrath, Secy.
EIN: 942449535

384
Rosi Cerri Foundation, Inc.
P. O. Box 1607
Stockton, CA 95201-1607

Established in 2006 in California.
Donor: Rossi Cerri 2002 Trust.
Foundation type: Independent foundation.
Financial data (yr. ended 12/31/13): Assets, $5,478,374 (M); expenditures, $294,642; qualifying distributions, $275,010; giving activities include $275,000 for 16 grants (high: $30,000; low: $2,500).
Fields of interest: Philanthropy; Hospice care; Catholicism; Human services.
Limitations: Applications not accepted. Giving primarily in Stockton, CA. No grants to individuals.
Application information: Unsolicited requests for funds not accepted.
Officers: Rudy G. Croce, Pres. and C.F.O.; Joseph N. Filipelli, V.P.; Dennis Donald Geiger, Secy.
Directors: Rosemary M. Katicich; Robert Kavanaugh.
EIN: 205272991

385
The Irma Ceunis and Simone C. Wynant Foundation
433 2nd St., Ste. 106
Woodland, CA 95695-4065
Application address: c/o Eric Wais, Pres., 446 3rd
St., Woodland, CA 95695, tel.: (530) 668-6650

Established in 2001 in California.
Donors: Simone C. Wynant; Irma Ceunis†.
Foundation type: Independent foundation.
Financial data (yr. ended 12/31/12): Assets,
$3,828,859 (M); expenditures, $285,564;
qualifying distributions, $198,500; giving activities
include $198,500 for grants.
Purpose and activities: Giving primarily to
organizations focused on children or animals.
Fields of interest: Animal welfare; Christianity;
Human services; Child welfare.
Limitations: Applications accepted. Giving primarily
in CA. No grants to individuals.
Application information: Application form required.
  Initial approach: Letter
  Deadline(s): None
Officers: Eric Wais, Pres.; Anthony Delevati, Treas.
EIN: 680441999

386
The Champions Volunteer Foundation
78-200 Miles Ave.
Indian Wells, CA 92210-6803

Donors: Desert Champions, LLC; War Caualty Family
Assistance Fund.
Foundation type: Independent foundation.
Financial data (yr. ended 12/31/13): Assets,
$9,816 (M); gifts received, $180,071;
expenditures, $170,794; qualifying distributions,
$170,794; giving activities include $166,100 for 45
grants (high: $10,700; low: $1,200).
Fields of interest: Education; Sports and recreation;
Human services.
Limitations: Applications not accepted. Giving
primarily in CA.
Application information: Unsolicited requests for
funds not accepted.
Officer: Celia M. Pauls, Treas.
Directors: Georgia D. Felich; Steven R. Simon.
EIN: 330952475

387
The Chan Family Foundation
19620 Stevens Creek Blvd., Ste. 200
Cupertino, CA 95014-2488

Established in 2007 in California.
Donors: Annie M.H. Chan; David Y.W. Chan; Edward
Y.C. Chan; Shiu Leung Chan.
Foundation type: Independent foundation.
Financial data (yr. ended 12/31/14): Assets,
$3,962,103; expenditures, $350,435; qualifying
distributions, $350,435.
Fields of interest: University education;
Foundations.
Limitations: Applications not accepted. Giving
primarily in CA.
Application information: Contributes only to
pre-selected organizations.

Officers and Directors: Shiu Leung Chan, Pres. and
Director; Edward Y.C. Chan, C.F.O. and Director;
David Y.W. Chan, Secy. and Director.
EIN: 260597765

388
The Chan Foundation
1388 Sutter St., Ste. 730
San Francisco, CA 94109-5437

Established in 1983 in California.
Donors: CRO America Charitable Trust; Great Pacific
Land Corporation.
Foundation type: Independent foundation.
Financial data (yr. ended 10/31/14): Assets,
$5,147,520 (M); expenditures, $450,895;
qualifying distributions, $256,115; giving activities
include $256,115 for 10 grants (high: $80,000;
low: $1,000).
Fields of interest: Higher education; Hospital care;
Alzheimer's disease; Cancers; Christianity; Human
services; Youth services; People of Asian descent.
International interests: Canada.
Limitations: Applications not accepted. Giving
primarily in CA, HI and NY; with some giving in
Vancouver, BC. No grants to individuals.
Application information: Contributes only to
pre-selected organizations.
Trustees: Caleb Chan; Christian Chan; Tom Chan.
EIN: 942922923

389
The Charitable Foundation, Inc.
(doing business as The Charitable Foundation/
Agent Community Outreach of Prudential California
Realty)
(formerly Aaroe Associates Charitable Foundation,
Inc.)
12544 High Bluff Dr., Ste. 420
San Diego, CA 92130-3052
Contact: Natalie M. Hill, Mgr.
FAX: (818) 784-8609;
E-mail: foundation@prusocal.com

Established in 1995 in California.
Donors: David Offer; Prudential California Realty;
Andrew Manning; Laurence M. Young; Rosalie Klein.
Foundation type: Independent foundation.
Financial data (yr. ended 04/30/14): Assets,
$52,494 (M); gifts received, $198,381;
expenditures, $203,158; qualifying distributions,
$203,158; giving activities include $197,100 for
101 grants (high: $10,000; low: $250).
Purpose and activities: Giving primarily for
education, the arts, children, youth, and family and
social services, including a center for blind children.
Fields of interest: Community and economic
development; Human services.
Type of support: General support; Continuing
support; Program development; Research.
Limitations: Giving limited to Los Angeles County,
CA. No support for religious or political
organizations. No grants to individuals.
Application information:
  Board meeting date(s): Monthly
Officers: Kathy King, C.E.O.; Martha Mosier, Secy.;
Candace Brown, Treas.
EIN: 954528536

390
Cheeryble Foundation
9171 Wilshire Blvd., Ste. 400
Beverly Hills, CA 90210-5516   (310) 274-5847
Contact: Zora Charles, Pres.

Established in 1987 in California.
Donors: Les Charles; Zora Charles.
Foundation type: Independent foundation.
Financial data (yr. ended 12/31/12): Assets,
$1,552,844 (M); expenditures, $200,534;
qualifying distributions, $199,128; giving activities
include $199,128 for grants.
Fields of interest: Ballet; Art museums; Higher
education; Wildlife biodiversity; Nonprofits; Family
planning; Human services; Food aid; Youth services.
Type of support: General support; Regranting.
Limitations: Applications accepted. Giving primarily
in CA.
Application information:
  Initial approach: Proposal
  Deadline(s): None
Officers: Zora Charles, Pres. and Secy.; Les Charles,
C.F.O.
EIN: 954121906

391
SJV and EJ Chelvanayakam Charitable Foundation, Inc.
88 Ontare Rd.
Arcadia, CA 91006—1839

Donors: James C. Ravindran; Savithri P. Ravindran.
Foundation type: Independent foundation.
Financial data (yr. ended 10/31/13): Assets,
$5,098,607 (M); expenditures, $287,624;
qualifying distributions, $287,624; giving activities
include $265,000 for 3 grants (high: $130,000;
low: $5,000).
Fields of interest: Community and economic
development.
Limitations: Applications not accepted.
Application information: Unsolicited requests for
funds not accepted.
Officers: James C. Ravindran, Pres.; Savithri P.
Ravindran, Secy.; Navaratnam M. Jesudason, Treas.
Director: Sugirthamalar Buell.
EIN: 263522062

392
The Chestnut Foundation
5150 Overland Ave.
Culver City, CA 90230-4914

Established in 2000 in California.
Donors: Sol Kest; Clara Kest.
Foundation type: Operating foundation.
Financial data (yr. ended 12/31/12): Assets,
$11,098,358 (M); gifts received, $356,397;
expenditures, $510,348; qualifying distributions,
$410,572; giving activities include $397,150 for 31
grants (high: $152,500; low: $50).
Fields of interest: Education; Judaism.
Limitations: Applications not accepted. Giving
primarily in NJ and New York, NY. No grants to
individuals.
Application information: Contributes only to
pre-selected organizations.
Officers: Benjamin Kest, Pres.; Anna Kest,
Secy.-Treas.
EIN: 954793268

393

The Jay Chiat Foundation Inc.
c/o Nathan & Soroko C.P.A's
16133 Ventura Blvd., Ste. 620
Encino, CA   91436-2404   (818) 906-1690

Established in 1985 in New York.
Donor: Jay Chiat.
Foundation type: Independent foundation.
Financial data (yr. ended 12/31/13): Assets, $3,197,102; expenditures, $216,350; qualifying distributions, $200,000.
Purpose and activities: Funding primarily for arts and culture and early childhood centers and education.
Fields of interest: Education; Human services.
Limitations: Applications accepted. Giving primarily in CA. No grants to individuals.
Application information:
   Initial approach: Proposal
   Deadline(s): None
Officers and Directors: Marc Chiat, Pres. and Secy. and Director; Debra Chiat D'Angelo, V.P. and Treas. and Director; Elyse Chiat-Rosales, V.P.
EIN: 133310453

394

Julia Child Foundation for Gastronomy and the Culinary Arts
1187 Coast Village Rd., Ste. 556
Santa Barbara, CA   93108
Contact: Jennifer Krauss, Admin.
E-mail: contact@juliachildfoundation.org; Main URL: http://www.juliachildfoundation.org
Facebook: https://www.facebook.com/JuliaChild

Established in 1996 in Massachusetts.
Donor: Julia Child†.
Foundation type: Independent foundation.
Financial data (yr. ended 12/31/13): Assets, $5,778,426 (M); expenditures, $485,349; qualifying distributions, $347,355; giving activities include $249,500 for 19 grants (high: $60,000; low: $5,000).
Fields of interest: Arts and culture; Education; Agriculture.
Limitations: Applications not accepted. Giving primarily in Washington, DC, MA and NY. No grants to individuals.
Application information: Unsolicited requests for funds not accepted.
Officers: Eric W. Spivey, Chair.; Todd Schulkin, Exec. Dir.
Trustees: Philadelphia Cousins; Alex Prud'homme; William A. Truslow.
EIN: 043294783

395

Chisick Family Foundation
8018 E. Santa Ana Canyon Rd., Ste. 100-183
Anaheim, CA   92808

Established in 2003 in California.
Donors: Sarah Chisick; Brian Chisick.
Foundation type: Independent foundation.
Financial data (yr. ended 12/31/13): Assets, $4,905,963 (M); gifts received, $86,935; expenditures, $199,814; qualifying distributions, $190,880; giving activities include $190,800 for 21 grants (high: $55,000; low: $1,000).
Fields of interest: Health; Diseases and conditions; Religion; Human services.
Limitations: Applications not accepted. Giving primarily in CA. No grants to individuals.
Application information: Unsolicited requests for funds not accepted.
Officers: Mark D. Chisick, Pres.; Brad Chisick, Secy.
Trustees: Jamie P. Chisick; Sarah Chisick.
EIN: 200632546

396

Harry and Ovsanna Chitjian Family Foundation
344 N. Vista St.
Los Angeles, CA   90036-5739

Established in 2002 in California.
Donor: Zaruhy Sara Chitjian.
Foundation type: Independent foundation.
Financial data (yr. ended 12/31/13): Assets, $371,853 (M); gifts received, $550,500; expenditures, $339,702; qualifying distributions, $336,294; giving activities include $242,985 for 31 grants (high: $125,000; low: $100), and $90,785 for 2 foundation-administered programs.
Fields of interest: Education; Higher education; Health; Human services.
Limitations: Applications not accepted. Giving primarily in CA and MA. No grants to individuals.
Application information: Unsolicited requests for funds not accepted.
Officers: Zaruhy Sara Chitjian, Pres. and Treas.; George R. Phillips, Secy.
EIN: 954840313

397

Chizen Family Foundation
11100 Santa Monica Blvd., Ste. 600
Los Angeles, CA   90025-3328   3108064000

Donors: Bruce R. Chizen; Gail B. Chizen.
Foundation type: Independent foundation.
Financial data (yr. ended 12/31/14): Assets, $9,912,546; expenditures, $485,591; qualifying distributions, $451,073.
Fields of interest: Education; Health; Sports and recreation; Camps; Food banks.
Limitations: Applications not accepted. Giving primarily in CA and NY.
Application information: Unsolicited requests for funds not accepted.
Officers and Directors: Bruce R. Chizen, Pres. and Director; Gail B. Chizen, Secy.-Treas.; Jessica H. Chizen; Steven M. Chizen.
EIN: 262450509

398

Subir and Malini Chowdhury Foundation
32040 Cape Point Dr.
Rancho Palos Verdes, CA   90275-4556   (734) 306-0550

Established in 2006 in Michigan.
Donors: Subir Chowdhury; Malini Chowdhury.
Foundation type: Operating foundation.
Financial data (yr. ended 12/31/14): Assets, $3,546,336; expenditures, $234,607; qualifying distributions, $228,997.
Fields of interest: Higher education.
Limitations: Applications accepted. Giving primarily in MI.
Application information: Application form required.
   Initial approach: Proposal
   Deadline(s): None
Directors: Malini Chowdhury; Subir Chowdhury.
EIN: 205991853

399

Chrissie's Fund
111 E. Victoria St., 2nd Fl.
Santa Barbara, CA   93101-2018
Main URL: http://www.chrissiesfund.org

Established in 2007 in California.
Donors: Kimberly Lowell; Dwight E. Lowell.
Foundation type: Independent foundation.
Financial data (yr. ended 12/31/13): Assets, $923 (M); gifts received, $216,100; expenditures, $228,815; qualifying distributions, $226,255; giving activities include $226,255 for 19 grants (high: $101,485; low: $200).
Purpose and activities: Giving for the well-being of dogs who have been abandoned, injured, mistreated, neglected, exploited, or are otherwise in need. The foundation seeks to promote an appreciation of dogs and humane values through education and advocacy.
Fields of interest: Animal welfare; Human services.
Limitations: Applications not accepted. Giving primarily in CA.
Application information: Unsolicited requests for funds not accepted.
Officers: Kimberly Lowell, Pres.; Dwight E. Lowell, C.F.O.
Directors: Francis Battista; Christine Devries; Eric Fingleson.
EIN: 208989443

400

The Christensen Family Foundation
801 American St.
San Carlos, CA   94070-4101

Established in 2003 in California.
Donors: Herman Christensen, Jr.; Isobel Christensen.
Foundation type: Independent foundation.
Financial data (yr. ended 12/31/13): Assets, $5,012,239 (M); gifts received, $300,000; expenditures, $261,069; qualifying distributions, $248,938; giving activities include $246,959 for 34 grants (high: $42,000; low: $1,000).
Fields of interest: Historic preservation; Education.
Type of support: General support.
Limitations: Applications not accepted. Giving primarily in CA. No grants to individuals.
Application information: Unsolicited requests for funds not accepted.
Officers and Directors: Isobel Christensen, Pres.; Amy Christensen; Andrew Christensen; Gavin Christensen; Herman Christensen, Jr.; Maren Christensen.
EIN: 710929445

401
Christian Community Development Corporation

130 Dartmouth Pl.
Benicia, CA   94510-2019   (707) 745-3300
Contact: Margo Mccarty

Donors: Raleys Stores, Inc.; Safeway Stores, Inc.
Foundation type: Independent foundation.
Financial data (yr. ended 12/31/13): Assets, $839,991 (M); gifts received, $268,671; expenditures, $302,234; qualifying distributions, $268,671; giving activities include $268,671 for grants.
Fields of interest: Housing development; Food aid.
Type of support: General support; Program-related investments.
Limitations: Applications accepted. Giving primarily in CA.
Application information: Application form required.
 Initial approach: Proposal
 Deadline(s): None
Officers: Arlene Jones, C.E.O.; Ronald DeMello, Secy.; Clifford Olson, C.F.O.
EIN: 237248584

402
Christian Development Foundation, Inc.

1825 Gillespie Way, Ste. 102
El Cajon, CA   92020-0501

Donors: Robert Tschantz; Mike McFarland; Suzanne Suzanne DeBerry Trust; Mike Moser; Edmund Banning; Hanson Scott.
Foundation type: Independent foundation.
Financial data (yr. ended 03/31/13): Assets, $252,768 (M); gifts received, $156,794; expenditures, $203,363; qualifying distributions, $198,424; giving activities include $198,424 for 15 grants (high: $94,630; low: $294).
Fields of interest: Christianity; Human services.
Type of support: General support.
Limitations: Applications not accepted. Giving primarily in CA.
Application information: Unsolicited requests for funds not accepted.
Directors: Janet A. Tschantz; William P. Tschantz.
EIN: 953169724

403
Sally Hughes Church Foundation

295 Main St., Ste. 600
Salinas, CA   93901-3414
FAX: (831) 758-2028; Application address: c/o Anne Leach, 17 E. Gabilan St., Salinas, CA 93901, tel.: (831) 758-2401
Grants List: http://www.sallychurchfoundation.org/grants

Donors: Sally Hughes Church†; Kathy McNamara; Pat McNamara; Tom McNamara.
Foundation type: Independent foundation.
Financial data (yr. ended 12/31/13): Assets, $7,023,617 (M); expenditures, $426,856; qualifying distributions, $321,278; giving activities include $312,083 for 18 grants (high: $45,000; low: $5,000).
Purpose and activities: The foundation assists non-profit organizations related to youth, arts and culture, and agriculture.

Fields of interest: Arts and culture; Health; Hospital care; Public libraries; Agriculture; Community recreation; Child welfare.
Type of support: General support; Continuing support; Annual campaigns; Capital campaigns; Capital and infrastructure; Program development.
Limitations: Applications accepted. Giving primarily in Salinas, CA. No grants to individuals.
Application information:
 Initial approach: Proposal
 Deadline(s): None
Officers and Directors: Anne C. Leach, Pres.; W.B. Lindley, V.P. and Director; Harry Wardwell, Secy. and Director; Ross Merrill, Treas. and Director.
Number of staff: None.
EIN: 770344378

404
Chino Cienega Foundation

901 N. Palm Canyon Dr., Ste. 200
Palm Springs, CA   92262-4451
E-mail: info@chinofound.org; Main URL: http://www.chinofound.org

Established in 1985 in California.
Donor: Frank Culver Nichols Revocable Trust.
Foundation type: Independent foundation.
Financial data (yr. ended 12/31/14): Assets, $7,113,962 (M); expenditures, $416,747; qualifying distributions, $731,104.
Purpose and activities: Giving to engage in and support educational and charitable activities that foster crosscultural and international understanding and cooperation, that encourage the viability of local communities and that promote sustainable natural ecosystems.
Fields of interest: University education; Economic development; Goodwill promotion; International development.
International interests: Southeastern Asia.
Type of support: General support; Mission-related investments.
Limitations: Applications not accepted. No grants to individuals.
Application information: Contributes only to pre-selected organizations; unsolicited grant requests or applications not accepted.
Officers and Directors: Steven C. Nichols, Pres. and Director; Robert Wolcott, V.P. and Director; Sarah J. Benson, Secy.-Treas. and Director; Lauren A.B. Nichols; June Taylor; Chet Tchozewski.
EIN: 412075864

405
The Cirila Fund

(formerly The Albert and Tricia Nichols Foundation)
c/o M. Blank & Company
23705 Birtcher Dr.
Lake Forest, CA   92630-1772   (949) 830-5231
Contact: Marilyn M. Blank

Established in 1994 in California.
Donors: Albert Nichols; Mrs. Albert Nichols; Tricia Nichols; Patricia Nicholas.
Foundation type: Independent foundation.
Financial data (yr. ended 06/30/13): Assets, $6,387 (M); gifts received, $196,500; expenditures, $199,068; qualifying distributions, $194,047; giving activities include $194,047 for 57 grants (high: $55,000; low: $150).

Fields of interest: Performing arts; Higher education; Natural resources; Maternal and perinatal health; Human services.
Limitations: Applications accepted. Giving primarily in CA.
Application information: Application form required.
 Initial approach: Proposal
 Deadline(s): None
Officers: Patricia Nichols, Pres.; Lisa Jenkins, Treas.
EIN: 330638574

406
The Clara Fund

101 1st St., No. 235
Los Altos, CA   94022-2778

Established in 2003 in California.
Donors: Lorene Arey; Rothschild Trust.
Foundation type: Independent foundation.
Financial data (yr. ended 12/31/13): Assets, $4,740,278 (M); expenditures, $450,096; qualifying distributions, $228,133; giving activities include $221,600 for 9 grants (high: $100,000; low: $600).
Fields of interest: Education; Philanthropy; Women's services; International development; Children and youth; Females; Low-income and poor people.
Limitations: Applications not accepted. Giving primarily in CA. No grants to individuals.
Application information: Unsolicited requests for funds not accepted.
Officers: Lorene Arey, Pres.; Paris Arey, V.P.; Haley Perkins, Secy.
Director: Hansen Perkins.
EIN: 582672863

407
The Cleo Foundation

1660 Bush St., Ste. 300
San Francisco, CA   94109-5308
Contact: Mary Gregory, Exec. Dir.
E-mail: mgregory@pfs-llc.net; Main URL: http://pfs-llc.net/cleo/cleo.html

Established in 1997 in California.
Foundation type: Independent foundation.
Financial data (yr. ended 12/31/12): Assets, $2,848,323 (M); expenditures, $177,324; qualifying distributions, $143,362; giving activities include $123,500 for 13 grants (high: $15,000; low: $500).
Purpose and activities: Giving primarily to support programs for the economically disadvantaged.
Fields of interest: Education; Environmental education; Hospice care; Child welfare; Youth development; Low-income and poor people.
Type of support: General support; Continuing support; Capital campaigns; Capital and infrastructure; Program development.
Limitations: Applications accepted. Giving primarily in San Francisco and Mendocino counties, CA. No support for religious entities. No grants to individuals or for medical research, endowments or annual appeals.
Publications: Grants list.
Application information: Prospective applicants strongly advised to speak to Exec. Dir. prior to submitting proposal.
 Initial approach: Telephone

Deadline(s): June 20 (for organizations that have been asked to apply)
Board meeting date(s): Sept.
Officer: Mary Gregory, Exec. Dir.
Number of staff: None.
EIN: 943269201

408
Cloud Nine Foundation
4504 Redwood Rd.
Napa, CA 94558
Application address: c/o Patricia M. McDowell, 7 Park Pl., Tiburon, CA 94920, tel.: (415) 789-0178

Established in 2000 in California.
Donor: Patricia M. McDowell.
Foundation type: Independent foundation.
Financial data (yr. ended 12/31/13): Assets, $1,328,414 (M); expenditures, $427,741; qualifying distributions, $416,725; giving activities include $415,000 for 3 grants (high: $400,000; low: $5,000).
Fields of interest: Education; Basic and remedial instruction; Human services.
Type of support: General support; Continuing support; Program development.
Limitations: Applications accepted. Giving primarily in CA.
Application information: Application form required.
Initial approach: Proposal
Deadline(s): None
Officers and Directors: Patricia M. McDowell, Pres. and Director; Scott McDowell, V.P.; Steve Blake, Secy. and Director; Laura Moran, Treas. and Director; Clare Christofferson; Lester Kaufman.
Number of staff: 1 part-time support.
EIN: 943371225

409
Francis H. Clougherty Charitable Trust
500 Newport Center Dr., Ste. 910
Newport Beach, CA 92660-7009

Established in 1984 in California.
Donors: Bernard J. Clougherty; Joseph D. Clougherty.
Foundation type: Independent foundation.
Financial data (yr. ended 12/31/13): Assets, $4,430,057 (M); expenditures, $218,453; qualifying distributions, $172,160; giving activities include $167,600 for 9 grants (high: $52,600; low: $5,000).
Purpose and activities: Giving primarily for Roman Catholic high schools, higher education, and churches; some giving also to a Roman Catholic archdiocese.
Fields of interest: Secondary education; Higher education; Catholicism.
Type of support: General support.
Limitations: Applications not accepted. Giving primarily in southern CA. No grants to individuals.
Application information: Contributes only to pre-selected organizations.
Officers: Anthony P. Clougherty, Fdn. Mgr.; Kathleen C. Regan, Fdn. Mgr.
Trustees: Bernard J. Clougherty; Joseph D. Clougherty.
EIN: 956818523

410
CNC Foundation
1423 Hamilton Ave.
Palo Alto, CA 94301-3150

Established in 1998 in California.
Donors: Charles T. Munger, Jr.; Charlotte Lowell.
Foundation type: Independent foundation.
Financial data (yr. ended 12/31/14): Assets, $2,320,478 (M); gifts received, $1,894,325; expenditures, $216,542; qualifying distributions, $191,535; giving activities include $191,535 for 16 grants (high: $60,000; low: $25).
Purpose and activities: Giving primarily to Christian organizations and Presbyterian churches; funding also for social services and health organizations.
Fields of interest: Education; Diseases and conditions; Christianity; Protestantism; Human services.
Limitations: Applications not accepted. No grants to individuals.
Application information: Contributes only to pre-selected organizations.
Trustees: Charlotte Lowell; Charles T. Munger, Jr.
EIN: 776160567

411
The James and Paula Coburn Foundation
3550 Wilshire Blvd., Ste. 840
Los Angeles, CA 90010-2433
E-mail: lynda@jamesandpaulacoburnfoundation.org;
Main URL: http://jamesandpaulacoburnfoundation.org
Facebook: https://www.facebook.com/JamesandPaulaCoburnFoundation
Grants List: http://jamesandpaulacoburnfoundation.org/beneficiaries
Twitter: https://twitter.com/jpcoburnfdtn

Donors: Coburn Survivor's Trust; Julius Gianninni; Soleyman John Nobatian.
Foundation type: Independent foundation.
Financial data (yr. ended 06/30/13): Assets, $3,348,455 (M); expenditures, $594,295; qualifying distributions, $530,345; giving activities include $206,000 for 8 grants (high: $100,000; low: $1,000).
Purpose and activities: Giving to support the arts and sciences, and to charities involved in the treatments or cures for cancer and the care of indigent cancer patients.
Fields of interest: Arts and culture; Health care administration and financing; Cancers; Communication media; Human services.
Limitations: Applications not accepted. Giving primarily in CA and VA. No grants to individuals.
Application information: Contributes only to pre-selected organizations.
Officer: Lynda Erkiletian, Exec. Dir.
Director: Aaron Lager.
Trustees: Robert Harabedian; Cynthia Webb.
EIN: 201512237

412
Codding Foundation
P.O. Box 3550
Rohnert Park, CA 94928 (707) 795-3550
Contact: Constance L. Codding, Pres.

Established in 1960 in California.

Donors: Constance L. Codding; Hugh B. Codding; Codding Enterprises; Petaluma Wildlife Museum.
Foundation type: Independent foundation.
Financial data (yr. ended 12/31/13): Assets, $1,414,717 (M); gifts received, $145,000; expenditures, $427,331; qualifying distributions, $408,868; giving activities include $408,868 for 80 grants (high: $100,000; low: $10).
Purpose and activities: Giving primarily to organizations that assist children (up to age 18), including the prevention of substance abuse, physical abuse, and teenage pregnancy; support also for family strengthening, education, health, physical fitness, and programs that help young people help themselves.
Fields of interest: Education; Child educational development; Nonprofits; Family planning; Youth pregnancy prevention; Addiction services; Family services; Child development; Youth services.
Type of support: General support; Employee matching gifts; Matching grants; Regranting; Continuing support; Seed money.
Limitations: Applications accepted. Giving limited to Sonoma County, CA. No grants to individuals, or for building funds, annual campaigns, or endowment funds.
Publications: Application guidelines.
Application information: Application form required.
Initial approach: Letter
Copies of proposal: 1
Deadline(s): Last working days of Mar., June, Sept., and Dec.
Board meeting date(s): May
Officers: Constance L. Codding, Pres.; Reginald E. Bayley, C.F.O. and Secy.; Eric J. Reid, Treas.
Number of staff: 1 part-time support.
EIN: 946089419

413
Kleiner Cohen Foundation
14156 Magnolia Blvd., Ste. 102
Sherman Oaks, CA 91423-6411

Established in 2000 in California.
Donors: Aaron C. Clark; Laurel K. Clark.
Foundation type: Independent foundation.
Financial data (yr. ended 12/31/13): Assets, $3,856,104 (M); expenditures, $216,705; qualifying distributions, $215,025; giving activities include $215,025 for 74 grants (high: $20,000; low: $500).
Fields of interest: Human services; Youth services.
Limitations: Applications not accepted. Giving primarily in CA.
Application information: Contributes only to pre-selected organizations.
Officers: Aaron C. Clark, Chair.; David L. Clark, Pres.; Jay Grodin, C.F.O.; Jody A. Clark, V.P.; Laurel K. Clark, Secy.
EIN: 954817618

414
Said Cohen Foundation
P.O. Box 15234
Irvine, CA 92623
Application address: c/o Said Cohen, 1862 Park Skyline Drive, Santa Ana, CA 92705, tel.: (714) 544-6946

Established in 2007 in California.
Foundation type: Independent foundation.

Financial data (yr. ended 12/31/13): Assets, $6,184,824 (M); gifts received, $3,601; expenditures, $339,178; qualifying distributions, $301,010; giving activities include $300,000 for 2 grants (high: $250,000; low: $50,000).
Fields of interest: Education.
Limitations: Applications accepted. Giving primarily in New York and Syracuse, NY.
Application information:
  Initial approach: Proposal
  Deadline(s): None
Officers and Directors: Said Cohen, Pres. and Director; Peter J. Cohen, C.F.O. and Director; Natalie Cohen, Secy. and Director.
EIN: 208686587

415

Teddy Cole Foundation for Horses Inc
4976 Sunline Ave.
San Diego, CA 92117-1613

Established in 2002 in California.
Donor: Theora Ruth Cole.
Foundation type: Independent foundation.
Financial data (yr. ended 12/31/13): Assets, $0 (M); expenditures, $224,145; qualifying distributions, $154,393; giving activities include $151,400 for 8 grants (high: $53,000; low: $2,000).
Fields of interest: Animal welfare; Equestrianism.
Limitations: Applications not accepted. Giving primarily in CA. No grants to individuals.
Application information: Contributes only to pre-selected organizations.
Officers: Jill Eshenbaugh, Pres.; Kris Kudas, Secy.-Treas.
Director: Brian Maryott.
EIN: 431957535

416

The Clarence B. Coleman and Joan F. Coleman Charitable Foundation
(formerly Coleman Charitable Foundation)
5530 Fernhoff Rd.
Oakland, CA 94619-3113

Established in 1986 in Unspecified.
Donors: Clarence B. Coleman†; Joan F. Coleman.
Foundation type: Independent foundation.
Financial data (yr. ended 12/31/13): Assets, $3,426,683 (M); expenditures, $167,916; qualifying distributions, $156,865; giving activities include $156,865 for 54 grants (high: $15,000; low: $25).
Purpose and activities: Giving primarily for youth organizations, higher education, museums, and health.
Fields of interest: Arts and culture; Museums; Higher education; In-patient medical care; School libraries and media centers; Judaism; Food delivery; Youth services.
Type of support: General support; Continuing support; Capital campaigns; Capital and infrastructure; Endowments; Debt reduction; Emergency funds; Program development; Curriculum development; Scholarships; Research.
Limitations: Applications not accepted. Giving primarily in CA. No grants to individuals (directly).
Application information: Contributions only to pre-selected organizations.
  Board meeting date(s): Aug. or Sept.

Officers: Joan F. Coleman, Pres. and C.F.O.; Elinor Coleman, Co-Secy.; Allison Frey, Co-Secy.
EIN: 942973572

417

The Angela D. Collier Foundation
16530 Ventura Blvd., Ste. 306
Encino, CA 91436-4595

Foundation type: Independent foundation.
Financial data (yr. ended 12/31/13): Assets, $6,032,394 (M); expenditures, $464,971; qualifying distributions, $413,382; giving activities include $336,000 for 5 grants (high: $280,000; low: $1,000).
Fields of interest: Domesticated animals; Health; Human services.
Type of support: Research.
Limitations: Applications not accepted. Giving primarily in Los Angeles, Santa Clarita, and Sylmar, CA. No grants to individuals.
Application information: Unsolicited requests for funds not accepted.
Trustee: Mohammad J. Virani.
EIN: 954564475

418

Collingwood Foundation
8882 Collingwood Dr.
Los Angeles, CA 90069-1244

Established in 1994 in California.
Donors: Daniel Renberg; Eugene Kapaloski.
Foundation type: Independent foundation.
Financial data (yr. ended 11/30/13): Assets, $0 (M); gifts received, $325,700; expenditures, $346,222; qualifying distributions, $320,500; giving activities include $320,500 for 25 grants (high: $56,000; low: $1,000).
Purpose and activities: Giving primarily for gay and lesbian services, medical and health services and research, and for legal services.
Fields of interest: Higher education; Nonprofits; HIV/AIDS; Legal services; LGBTQ people.
Type of support: General support; Regranting.
Limitations: Applications not accepted. Giving primarily in CA, NY, VA and Washington, DC. No grants to individuals.
Application information: Contributes only to pre-selected organizations.
Officer: Eugene Kapaloski, Pres.
EIN: 954509731

419

Combs-Hughes Charitable Trust
c/o Charlotte F. Hughes
11601 Wilshire Blvd., Ste. 1925
Los Angeles, CA 90025-1757

Donor: Charlotte F. Hughes.
Foundation type: Independent foundation.
Financial data (yr. ended 12/31/14): Assets, $915,510; expenditures, $252,942; qualifying distributions, $250,835.
Fields of interest: Arts and culture; Philanthropy; Food banks; Child welfare.
Limitations: Applications not accepted. Giving primarily in Los Angeles, CA.
Application information: Contributes only to pre-selected organizations.

Trustees: Christopher W. Combs; Charlotte F. Hughes.
EIN: 356802348

420

Community Foundation of Merced County
P.O. Box 3846
Merced, CA 95344-3846   (209) 201-4113
FAX: (209) 381-5979;
E-mail: info@mercedfoundation.org; Main URL: http://www.mercedfoundation.org
Facebook: https://www.facebook.com/pages/Community-Foundation-of-Merced-County/1453799058189507?sk=likes
Twitter: https://twitter.com/mercedfound

Established in 2006 in California.
Foundation type: Community foundation.
Financial data (yr. ended 12/31/12): Assets, $375,068 (M); gifts received, $220,828; expenditures, $256,650; giving activities include $146,992 for 4+ grants (high: $18,716), and $1,120 for grants to individuals.
Purpose and activities: The foundation partners with donors to ensure a permanent source of charitable funds to meet the changing needs and dreams of the Merced County communities.
Fields of interest: Arts and culture; Education; Environment; Domesticated animals; Health; Human services.
Type of support: Capacity-building and technical assistance; Seed money; Program development.
Limitations: Applications accepted. Giving primarily in Merced County, CA. No support for sectarian purposes or private foundations. No grants for annual fundraising campaigns, or debt reduction.
Publications: Application guidelines.
Application information: Visit foundation web site for proposal guidelines.
  Initial approach: Telephone
  Deadline(s): Feb. 15, May 15, Aug. 15 and Nov. 15
  Board meeting date(s): Mar., June, Sept., Dec.
Officers and Directors: Dennis Haines, Pres. and Director; Maria Giampaoli, V.P. and Director; Bill Crivelli, C.F.O. and Director; Nellie McGarry, Secy. and Director; Crystal Andersen; Stephanie Perez; Mark Seivert; Alfred Souza; Linda Tatum.
EIN: 861151358

421

Community Foundation of the Verdugos
(formerly Glendale Community Foundation)
111 E. Broadway, Ste. 200
Glendale, CA 91205   (818) 241-8040
Contact: Edna Karinski, C.E.O.
FAX: (818) 241-8045; E-mail: info@cfverdugos.org; Main URL: http://www.cfverdugos.org
Facebook: https://www.facebook.com/pages/Community-Foundation-of-the-Verdugos/132731506768493?sk=wall
YouTube: https://www.youtube.com/user/cfverdugos

Established in 1956 in California.
Donors: Albert Dunford†; Pearl Gray†; Maryon Greaves†; Don Packer†; Juanita Duncan†; Bernie Larson†; Dorothy Larson†.
Foundation type: Community foundation.
Financial data (yr. ended 12/31/12): Assets, $9,238,660 (M); gifts received, $247,344;

expenditures, $697,756; giving activities include $218,535 for 12+ grants (high: $42,883), and $89,750 for 62 grants to individuals.

Purpose and activities: The mission of the foundation is to provide financial support to a broad range of charitable and educational endeavors within the geographic area served by the foundation.

Fields of interest: Arts and culture; Performing arts; Education; Higher education; Basic and remedial instruction; Environment; Health; Hospital care; School-based health care; Hospice care; Public libraries; Disasters and emergency management; Sports and recreation; Human services; Family services; Child welfare; Youth development; Senior services; Children; Seniors; Homeless people; Low-income and poor people; People with disabilities.

Type of support: General support; Loans to individuals; Matching grants; Equipment; Program development; Seed money; Scholarships; Technical assistance; Student aid.

Limitations: Applications accepted. Giving limited to the Glendale, CA, area, including La Canada-Flintridge, La Crescenta, Montrose, and Verdugo City. No support for religious purposes, or athletic groups. No grants to individuals (except for scholarships and student loans), budget deficits, salaries, maintenance, or repairs, annual campaigns, building campaigns, conferences, multi-year funding for new programs, or endowments.

Publications: Application guidelines; Annual report; Financial statement; Grants list; Informational brochure; Newsletter; Program policy statement (including application guidelines).

Application information: Visit foundation web site for application form and guidelines. Application form must be mailed and e-mailed to the foundation (attachments accepted via mail only). Application form required.

   Initial approach: Letter, telephone, or e-mail
   Copies of proposal: 1
   Deadline(s): May 15
   Board meeting date(s): 6 times a year
   Final notification: Within 8 weeks

Officers and Directors: Ernest P. Burger, Esq., Pres. and Director; Edna Karinski, C.E.O. and Director; Mary Ann Plumley, Secy. and Director; Michael W. Deaktor, C.F.O. and Director; Charles Alleman, Jr.; Eric A. Ashton, Jr.; Michael Cusumano; Toni Beck Espinoza; Norman H. Green; Arye Gross; Robert J. Knauf; Charles L. LeCroy III; David S. Levy; Lawrence F. Meyer; Sunder Ramani; Jose L. Sierra; Lee Wochner.

Number of staff: 2 full-time professional.

EIN: 956068137

422
Confetti Consortium Foundation
1660 Monrovia Ave., Unit. D
Costa Mesa, CA   92627-4466   (949) 852-1600
Contact: Kenneth Roath, Tr.; Dayle, Roath

Foundation type: Independent foundation.

Financial data (yr. ended 12/31/13): Assets, $789,904 (M); expenditures, $153,010; qualifying distributions, $149,000; giving activities include $149,000 for 7 grants (high: $125,000; low: $500).

Fields of interest: Arts and culture; Health; Children's hospital care; Community and economic development; Children.

Limitations: Applications accepted. Giving primarily in CA.

Application information: Application form required.
   Initial approach: Proposal
   Deadline(s): None

Trustees: Claire D. Cesta; Jennifer L. Fox; Dayle I. Roath; Gregory T. Roath; Kenneth B. Roath.

EIN: 206770315

423
Congregation Joseph Jacob Abraham
344 S. Almont Dr.
Beverly Hills, CA   90211-3548

Foundation type: Independent foundation.

Financial data (yr. ended 12/31/13): Assets, $3,878,930 (M); expenditures, $380,092; qualifying distributions, $241,187; giving activities include $149,862 for 9 grants (high: $50,000; low: $72).

Fields of interest: Judaism.

Limitations: Applications not accepted. Giving primarily in CA and NJ.

Application information: Contributes only to pre-selected organizations.

Officers: Daniel M. Arnall, Pres.; Judith A. Arnall, Secy. and C.F.O.

Trustee: Tzepah Freedland.

EIN: 954746504

424
Charles M. & Linda J. Corbalis Family Foundation
P.O. Box 2426
Saratoga, CA   95070-0426

Established in 1997 in California.

Donors: Charles M. Corbalis; Linda J. Corbalis.

Foundation type: Independent foundation.

Financial data (yr. ended 12/31/13): Assets, $6,204,332 (M); expenditures, $384,657; qualifying distributions, $295,234; giving activities include $194,000 for 17 grants (high: $30,000; low: $1,000).

Fields of interest: Education; Nonprofits; Religion; Catholicism.

Type of support: Regranting.

Limitations: Applications not accepted. Giving primarily in CA. No grants to individuals.

Application information: Unsolicited requests for funds not accepted.

Officers: Charles M. Corbalis, Chair.; Linda J. Corbalis, Secy.

EIN: 770456278

425
The Corcoran Community Foundation
1321 Whitley Ave.
Corcoran, CA   93212-2329   (559) 992-5107

Established in 1965 in California.

Donors: W.W. Boswell; Mrs. W.W. Boswell.

Foundation type: Community foundation.

Financial data (yr. ended 12/31/13): Assets, $6,298,999 (M); gifts received, $574,543; expenditures, $452,312; giving activities include $276,323 for grants.

Purpose and activities: The purpose of the foundation is to receive contributions, gifts and bequests, and to distribute these funds for charitable, educational, religious and scientific purposes to improve the community of Corcoran, CA.

Fields of interest: Arts and culture; Education; Community and economic development; Human services.

Limitations: Giving limited to the Corcoran, CA, area.

Officers and Trustees: Mary Wadsworth, Pres. and Trustee; Terry Kwast, V.P. and Trustee; Jon Rachford, Treas. and Trustee; Debbie Bello; Michael Boyett; David Deiter; Kirk Gilkey; Barbara Gomez; Phillip Hansen; Jim Razor; Jeanette Todd; Troy Van Velson; Carlo Wilcox.

Number of staff: 1 full-time professional.

EIN: 941608857

426
Corday Family Foundation
(formerly Eliot Corday Foundation)
c/o Joanne C. Kozberg
721 N. Linden Dr.
Beverly Hills, CA   90210-3225

Established in 1996 in California.

Donors: Marian Corday; Eliot Corday†.

Foundation type: Independent foundation.

Financial data (yr. ended 04/30/14): Assets, $5,013,059 (M); expenditures, $206,146; qualifying distributions, $203,286; giving activities include $192,050 for 37 grants (high: $55,000; low: $100).

Fields of interest: Arts and culture; Arts education; Higher education; Foundations; Hospital care; Family planning; Diseases and conditions.

Type of support: General support; Continuing support; Annual campaigns; Capital campaigns; Capital and infrastructure; Endowments; Professorships; Research; Fellowships.

Limitations: Applications not accepted. Giving primarily in CA. No grants to individuals.

Application information: Unsolicited requests for funds not accepted.

   Board meeting date(s): Semiannually

Directors: Marian Corday; Stephen Corday; Anthony Kozberg; Joanne Kozberg.

EIN: 956118908

427
Corde Valle Youth Golf Foundation, Inc.
1 CordeValle Club Dr.
San Martin, CA   95046-9472   (408) 695-4550
Contact: Alan Campey, Secy.
Main URL: http://www.cygf.org

Established in 2004 in California.

Donors: Frys.com Open; Cordevalle Golf Club.

Foundation type: Operating foundation.

Financial data (yr. ended 12/31/13): Assets, $2,765 (M); gifts received, $201,081; expenditures, $300,241; qualifying distributions, $155,600; giving activities include $155,600 for 34 grants (high: $6,000; low: $2,300).

Purpose and activities: Giving primarily to expand opportunities for youth of all income levels to have access to the sport of golf. To be eligible for funding, the applicant must spend no more than 15 percent of the total budget on administrative and overhead costs, and no more than 15 percent of funds received from the foundation can be spent on administrative and overhead costs combined.

Fields of interest: Golf; Child welfare.

Limitations: Applications accepted. Giving primarily in CA.

Application information: See foundation website for complete application guidelines. Application form required.

 Initial approach: See website

 Deadline(s): Nov. 1

Officers: Janet Strangis, Chair.; Laurie Barke, Vice-Chair; Alan Campey, Secy.; Steve Ormsby, Treas.

Directors: James Bariteau; Jack Bohan; Georgie Huff; Julie Inkster.

EIN: 200956422

428
Corwin Family Foundation
(formerly The Bruce and Toni Corwin Foundation)
708 N. Sierra Dr.
Beverly Hills, CA 90210-3524

Established in 1986 in California.

Donors: Bruce C. Corwin; Toni Corwin.

Foundation type: Independent foundation.

Financial data (yr. ended 12/31/13): Assets, $1,622,160 (M); gifts received, $23,307; expenditures, $233,401; qualifying distributions, $224,996; giving activities include $224,996 for 46 grants (high: $100,000; low: $200).

Purpose and activities: Giving primarily for Jewish organizations.

Fields of interest: Children's museums; Education; Elementary and secondary education; Animal welfare; Nonprofits; Health; Hospital care; Diseases and conditions; HIV/AIDS; Film and video; Public affairs; Leadership development; Community and economic development; Religion; Judaism; Human rights; Human services; Food aid; Youth organizing; Homeless services; Homeless people; People with disabilities.

Type of support: General support; Continuing support; Annual campaigns; Capital campaigns; Capital and infrastructure; Endowments; Research; Regranting.

Limitations: Applications not accepted. Giving primarily in CA. No grants to individuals.

Application information: Contributes only to pre-selected organizations.

Directors: Bruce C. Corwin; Daniel Corwin; David Corwin; Toni Corwin.

Number of staff: 1 part-time support.

EIN: 954076122

429
Costa Family Foundation
4285 Spyres Way
Modesto, CA 95356-9270
Application address: c/o Denise L. Costa, Secy., 1204 Country View Dr., Modesto, CA 95356, tel.: (209) 577-1280

Donors: Dan J. Costa; Denise L. Costa.

Foundation type: Operating foundation.

Financial data (yr. ended 12/31/13): Assets, $0 (M); gifts received, $300,000; expenditures, $302,159; qualifying distributions, $295,858; giving activities include $295,858 for 21 grants (high: $150,000; low: $100).

Fields of interest: Arts and culture.

Limitations: Applications accepted. Giving primarily in Modesto, CA.

Application information: Application form required.

 Initial approach: Letter

 Deadline(s): None

Officers and Directors: Dan J. Costa, Pres. and Director; Jeffrey R. Hamilton, C.F.O. and Director; Denise L. Costa, Secy. and Director; Daniel S. Costa; Kelsie L. Costa.

EIN: 270989324

430
Cotsen Foundation for Academic Research
12100 Wilshire Blvd., Ste. 905
Los Angeles, CA 90025-7128

Established in 2007 in California.

Donor: Lloyd E. Cotsen.

Foundation type: Independent foundation.

Financial data (yr. ended 12/31/13): Assets, $344,429 (M); gifts received, $800,000; expenditures, $745,210; qualifying distributions, $745,210; giving activities include $217,500 for 2 grants (high: $200,000; low: $17,500).

Fields of interest: Arts and culture.

Limitations: Applications not accepted. Giving primarily in Washington, DC.

Application information: Unsolicited requests for funds not accepted.

Officers and Directors: Lloyd Cotsen, Chair.; Barry Munitz, Pres. and Director; Marilyn Payne, C.F.O.; David Hardacre, Secy.; Margit Cotsen.

EIN: 020794202

431
Anthony Crabb and Barbara Grasseschi Foundation
1083 Vine St.
P.O. Box 249
Healdsburg, CA 95448-3459

Established in 1999 in California.

Donors: Barbara Grasseschi; Anthony Crabb.

Foundation type: Independent foundation.

Financial data (yr. ended 12/31/14): Assets, $6,585,425; expenditures, $298,210; qualifying distributions, $298,150.

Fields of interest: Arts and culture; Education; Land resources; Human services.

Type of support: General support.

Limitations: Applications not accepted. Giving primarily in San Jose, CA; with some giving in MA.

Application information: Unsolicited requests for funds not accepted.

Officers: Barbara Grasseschi, Pres.; Anthony Crabb, V.P.

EIN: 770517537

432
The Cramblit Family Foundation
300 Hot Springs Rd., Ste. A29
Santa Barbara, CA 93108-2037
Contact: Lue D. Cramblit, Tr.

Donors: Geraldine Cramblit; Lue D. Cramblit.

Foundation type: Independent foundation.

Financial data (yr. ended 12/31/13): Assets, $711,529 (M); gifts received, $16,240; expenditures, $195,463; qualifying distributions, $175,330; giving activities include $173,100 for 19 grants (high: $110,000; low: $100).

Fields of interest: Education; Philanthropy; Human services.

Type of support: General support.

Limitations: Applications accepted. Giving primarily in CA. No grants to individuals.

Application information:

 Initial approach: Letter

 Deadline(s): None

Trustees: Geraldine Cramblit; Lue D. Cramblit; Amy Magnuson; Ann Olson.

EIN: 770389565

433
Elizabeth N. Crane Foundation
8270 La Mesa Blvd., Ste. 201
La Mesa, CA 91942-8256

Established in 2007 in California.

Foundation type: Independent foundation.

Financial data (yr. ended 12/31/13): Assets, $5,591,368 (M); expenditures, $279,061; qualifying distributions, $251,028; giving activities include $220,831 for 2 grants (high: $120,000; low: $100,831).

Fields of interest: Mental health care.

Limitations: Applications not accepted. Giving primarily in CA and IL.

Application information: Unsolicited requests for funds not accepted.

Officers and Trustees: Jill Underwood, Pres. and Trustee; Lincoln H. Banks, Treas. and Trustee.

EIN: 266234431

434
The Craves Family Foundation
7 Scott Pl.
Greenbrae, CA 94904-3026

Established in 2005 in California.

Donors: Frederick B. Craves; Vickie Soulier.

Foundation type: Independent foundation.

Financial data (yr. ended 12/31/13): Assets, $6,581,191 (M); expenditures, $357,283; qualifying distributions, $357,000; giving activities include $357,000 for 29 grants (high: $50,000; low: $2,000).

Fields of interest: University education; Bioethics.

Limitations: Applications not accepted. Giving primarily in CA. No grants to individuals.

Application information: Contributes only to pre-selected organizations.

Directors: Frederick B. Craves; Ryan Soulier Craves; Sara Soulier Craves; Vickie Soulier.

EIN: 510562419

435
Crawford Family Foundation
520 Georgian Rd.
La Canada, CA 91011-3546

Established in 1999 in California.

Donors: Gordon Crawford; Dona Crawford.

Foundation type: Independent foundation.

Financial data (yr. ended 12/31/13): Assets, $4,607,622 (M); expenditures, $369,086; qualifying distributions, $348,330; giving activities include $347,000 for 11 grants (high: $100,000; low: $2,000).

Fields of interest: Education; Hospital care; Specialty hospital care; Christianity; Human services; Youth development.

Limitations: Applications not accepted. Giving primarily in CA. No grants to individuals.

Application information: Contributes only to pre-selected organizations.
Officers: Gordon Crawford, Pres.; Dona Crawford, V.P.; Orsi Z. Crawford, Secy.; Jeffrey G. Crawford, Treas.
EIN: 954737866

436
Roy E. Crummer Foundation
567 San Nicolas Dr., Ste. 410B
Newport Beach, CA   92660-6923   (949) 644-4702
Contact: Marge Brown

Established in 1964 in Nevada.
Donor: Jean Crummer Coburn.
Foundation type: Independent foundation.
Financial data (yr. ended 12/31/13): Assets, $5,958,832 (M); expenditures, $519,058; qualifying distributions, $300,000; giving activities include $300,000 for 119 grants (high: $15,000; low: $500).
Fields of interest: Arts and culture; Secondary education; Higher education; Animal welfare; Health; Diseases and conditions; National defense; Human services; Food banks.
Limitations: Applications accepted. Giving primarily in CA. No grants to individuals.
Application information: Application form required.
   Initial approach: Letter
   Deadline(s): Oct. 31
Officers and Trustees: Roy E. Crummer III, Pres. and Trustee; Donn J. Crummer, V.P. and Trustee; Margarite Brown, Secy.-Treas. and Trustee; Keith R. Crummer; Ian F. Gow.
EIN: 886004422

437
The Cush Family Foundation
(formerly Cush Automotive Charitable Foundation)
10620 Treena St., Ste. 110
San Diego, CA   92131-1140   (858) 549-2874
Contact: Johnna Ridenour, Admin.
FAX: (866) 707-5843;
E-mail: jridenour@cushnet.net; Main URL: http://www.cushenterprises.com

Established in 1994 in California.
Donors: Stephen P. Cushman; Noyce Foundation.
Foundation type: Independent foundation.
Financial data (yr. ended 06/30/14): Assets, $19,178,798; gifts received, $1,908,800; expenditures, $450,400; qualifying distributions, $450,400.
Fields of interest: Education; Foundations; Diseases and conditions; Human services; Child welfare.
Limitations: Applications accepted. Giving primarily in San Diego, CA. No grants to individuals.
Application information: Application form available on foundation web site. Application form required.
   Deadline(s): None
Officers: Marjorie L. Cushman, Pres.; Lori A. Moore, V.P.; Debra L. Parrish, Secy.
Director: Stephen P. Cushman.
EIN: 330643458

438
The Burt and Diana Cutler Family Foundation
10 Middle Ridge Ln. S.
Rolling Hills, CA   90274-4055   (310) 541-8973

Established in 1997 in California.
Donors: Burt Cutler; Diana Cutler.
Foundation type: Independent foundation.
Financial data (yr. ended 12/31/14): Assets, $2,057,428 (M); expenditures, $250,926; qualifying distributions, $244,659; giving activities include $244,659 for 7 grants (high: $80,000; low: $5,000).
Fields of interest: Nonprofits; Law; Human rights.
Type of support: General support; Regranting.
Limitations: Applications not accepted. No grants to individuals.
Application information: Unsolicited requests for funds not accepted.
Officers and Directors: Burt Cutler, C.E.O. and Director; Diana Cutler, C.F.O. and Director; Jay Cutler, Secy. and Director.
EIN: 954664800

439
Robert & Patricia Dahl Foundation
c/o Robert Dahl, Keith Dahl
7195 Oakport St.
Oakland, CA   94621-1947

Established in 1999 in California.
Donors: Robert Dahl; Patricia Dahl.
Foundation type: Independent foundation.
Financial data (yr. ended 12/31/14): Assets, $2,396,080 (M); expenditures, $178,895; qualifying distributions, $168,085; giving activities include $160,750 for 12 grants (high: $50,000; low: $500).
Fields of interest: Animal welfare; Disasters and emergency management; Human services.
Limitations: Applications not accepted. Giving primarily in CA. No grants to individuals.
Application information: Unsolicited requests for funds not accepted.
Officers: Keith Dahl, Pres.; Kenneth Dahl, V.P. and C.F.O.; Karen Bradley, V.P. and Secy.
Directors: Patricia Dahl; Robert Dahl.
EIN: 680442961

440
Edward J. Daly Foundation
c/o Michael Helms
111 Pine St., 18th Fl.
San Francisco, CA   94111-5620

Donor: Edward J. Daly†.
Foundation type: Independent foundation.
Financial data (yr. ended 12/31/12): Assets, $5,797,394 (M); expenditures, $319,053; qualifying distributions, $251,000; giving activities include $251,000 for grants.
Purpose and activities: Giving primarily for glaucoma research, as well as for the arts, and human services.
Fields of interest: Arts and culture; Education; Eye diseases; Protestantism; Child welfare.
Type of support: Research.
Limitations: Applications not accepted. Giving primarily in CA, with emphasis on San Francisco. No grants to individuals.

Application information: Unsolicited requests for funds not accepted.
Officers and Directors: June Berhendt, Pres. and Director; Sean Otto, V.P.; Michael Helms, Secy.
EIN: 946109262

441
Danem Foundation
c/o Thomas Hahn
1236 Ashmount Ave.
Piedmont, CA   94610-1211

Established in 1999 in California.
Foundation type: Independent foundation.
Financial data (yr. ended 12/31/13): Assets, $6,724,444 (M); expenditures, $296,075; qualifying distributions, $260,000; giving activities include $260,000 for 31 grants (high: $25,000; low: $1,000).
Fields of interest: Education; Domesticated animals; Human services.
Limitations: Applications not accepted. Giving primarily in CA. No grants to individuals.
Application information: Unsolicited requests for funds not accepted.
Trustee: Thomas A. Hahn.
EIN: 943304594

442
Danvera Foundation
1340 Treat Blvd., Ste. 525
Walnut Creek, CA   94597-7984

Established in 2001 in California.
Donor: Patrick J. Morrin.
Foundation type: Independent foundation.
Financial data (yr. ended 12/31/13): Assets, $7,112,150 (M); expenditures, $393,325; qualifying distributions, $278,795; giving activities include $276,035 for 10 grants (high: $88,600; low: $200).
Purpose and activities: Giving primarily for education, particularly a high school.
Fields of interest: Education; Elementary and secondary education; Higher education; Environment; Youth services.
Limitations: Applications not accepted. Giving primarily in CA. No grants to individuals.
Application information: Unsolicited requests for funds not accepted.
Officers: Patrick J. Morrin, Pres.; Janice Jagelski, Secy.-Treas.
EIN: 752979435

443
The Gordhan Dass Foundation
1400 Easton Dr., No. 106
Bakersfield, CA   93309-9403
Application address: c/o Dr. Ramesh C. Gupta, P.O. Box 2738 Bakersfield, CA 93303-2738; tel.: (661) 631-4312

Established in 2003 in Texas.
Donors: RSG Charitbale Trust; Vinod K. Gupta; Kiran B. Gupta; Ramesh C. Gupta; Santosh Gupta.
Foundation type: Independent foundation.
Financial data (yr. ended 12/31/12): Assets, $14,385,062 (M); gifts received, $1,114,999; expenditures, $469,441; qualifying distributions,

$319,828; giving activities include $319,828 for grants.

Purpose and activities: Giving primarily to a donor-advised fund, as well as for human services and mind/body enrichment programs.

Fields of interest: Philanthropy; Spirituality; Human services.

Limitations: Giving primarily in CA. No grants to individuals.

Application information:

Initial approach: Letter

Deadline(s): None

Officers: Ramesh C. Gupta, Pres.; Vinod Kumar Gupta, V.P.; Santosh Gupta, Secy.

EIN: 830380508

444

R. K. Davies Charitable Trust

c/o Whittier Trust Co.
1600 Huntington Dr.
S. Pasadena, CA 91030-4709

Established in 1974 in California.

Donor: Ralph K. Davies†.

Foundation type: Independent foundation.

Financial data (yr. ended 09/30/13): Assets, $6,995,945 (M); expenditures, $257,307; qualifying distributions, $218,880; giving activities include $215,100 for 24 grants (high: $35,000; low: $500).

Purpose and activities: Giving primarily for arts and culture, education, wildlife conservation, and social services.

Fields of interest: Arts and culture; Performing arts; Opera; Orchestral music; Art museums; Education; Natural resources; Biodiversity; Wildlife biodiversity; Health; Diseases and conditions; Cancers; Human services.

Type of support: General support; Research.

Limitations: Applications not accepted. Giving primarily in CA, with emphasis on San Francisco. No grants to individuals.

Application information: Contributes only to pre-selected organizations.

Trustees: Lucy Lewis Dreyer; Maryon Davies Lewis; Whittier Trust Co.

EIN: 237417287

445

The John & Jordan Davis Foundation

11601 Wilshire Blvd., No. 1840
Los Angeles, CA 90025-1754

Established in 1990 in California.

Donors: John Davis; Jordan Davis.

Foundation type: Independent foundation.

Financial data (yr. ended 11/30/13): Assets, $124,241 (M); gifts received, $400,695; expenditures, $324,320; qualifying distributions, $322,500; giving activities include $322,500 for 15 grants (high: $50,000; low: $500).

Fields of interest: Arts and culture; Education; University education; Health.

Type of support: General support.

Limitations: Applications not accepted. Giving primarily in CA; some funding also in Cambridge, MA, NC and OR.

Application information: Unsolicited requests for funds not accepted.

Officers: John Davis, Pres. and Secy.; Jordan Davis, V.P.

EIN: 954303419

446

De Miranda Foundation, Inc.

P.O. Box 2127
Palos Verdes Peninsula, CA 90274-8127

Established in 2001 in California.

Donors: Jay R. De Miranda; Shirley Y. De Miranda.

Foundation type: Operating foundation.

Financial data (yr. ended 03/31/13): Assets, $4,445,214 (M); gifts received, $231,700; expenditures, $191,382; qualifying distributions, $191,382; giving activities include $182,054 for 12 grants (high: $72,000; low: $250).

Fields of interest: HIV/AIDS; Christianity.

Limitations: Applications not accepted. Giving primarily in CA.

Application information: Unsolicited requests for funds not accepted.

Officers: Jay R. De Miranda, Pres.; Mary Harris, Secy.

EIN: 954855401

447

Deacon Charitable Foundation

7745 Greenback Ln., Ste. 250
Citrus Heights, CA 95610 (503) 764-1810
Contact: Susan Bender Phelps, Exec. Dir.
Application address: 901 N.E. Glisan St., Ste. 100, Portland, OR 97232; Main URL: http://www.deaconcharitablefoundation.org

Established in 2006 in California.

Donors: S.D. Deacon of California; Richard Smith.

Foundation type: Company-sponsored foundation.

Financial data (yr. ended 09/30/13): Assets, $218,068 (M); gifts received, $457,500; expenditures, $364,142; qualifying distributions, $364,142; giving activities include $314,050 for 164 grants (high: $11,054; low: $50).

Purpose and activities: The foundation supports organizations involved with the environment, animal welfare, and human services.

Fields of interest: Environment; Animal welfare; Human services; Child welfare.

Type of support: General support; Employee matching gifts.

Limitations: Applications accepted. Giving primarily in areas of company operations Irvine and Sacramento, CA, Portland, OR and Seattle, WA.

Publications: Application guidelines.

Application information: Application form required.

Initial approach: Completed online application form

Deadline(s): None

Officers: Steven D. Deacon, Pres.; Richard Smith, V.P. and Secy.; Susan Bender Phelps, Exec. Dir.

Directors: Paul Cunha; Jarrod Fogle; Kendra Howell; Anke Rind.

EIN: 205702192

448

Dearborn Family Foundation

P.O. Box 475580
San Francisco, CA 94147-5580

Donor: Gill Cogan.

Foundation type: Independent foundation.

Financial data (yr. ended 12/31/13): Assets, $276,182 (M); gifts received, $323,661; expenditures, $150,655; qualifying distributions, $150,655; giving activities include $150,000 for 1 grant.

Fields of interest: Arts and culture.

Type of support: General support.

Limitations: Applications not accepted. Giving primarily in CA.

Application information: Unsolicited requests for funds not accepted.

Trustees: Gill Cogan; Laura Cogan; Ann Goldsmith.

EIN: 900944589

449

Del Corazon

9252 Chesapeake Dr., No. 100
San Diego, CA 92123-1025

Donors: Amar Infinity Foundation; H&A Partners.

Foundation type: Independent foundation.

Financial data (yr. ended 08/31/14): Assets, $2,456 (M); gifts received, $297,500; expenditures, $299,099; qualifying distributions, $297,532; giving activities include $297,532 for 15 grants (high: $105,334; low: $500).

Fields of interest: Education; Health; Cancers; Human services.

Limitations: Applications not accepted. Giving primarily in CA and TN.

Application information: Unsolicited request for funds not accepted.

Officers: William G. Ayyad, Pres.; Daniel Ayyad, Secy.-Treas.

EIN: 205553069

450

Delzell Foundation, Inc.

200 E. Carrillo St., Ste. 303
Santa Barbara, CA 93101-1200

Established in 1996 in California.

Donors: Robert M. Delzell; Charles L. Delzell Trust.

Foundation type: Independent foundation.

Financial data (yr. ended 12/31/13): Assets, $371,723 (M); gifts received, $390,000; expenditures, $325,796; qualifying distributions, $324,783; giving activities include $242,223 for 17 grants (high: $35,484; low: $1,235).

Fields of interest: Arts and culture; Education; Health.

International interests: Russia.

Limitations: Applications not accepted. No grants to individuals.

Application information: Unsolicited requests for funds not accepted.

Officer: Robert M. Delzell, Chair.

Directors: Eugene Polzik; Tatiana Polzik; Ekaterina Sirakanian.

EIN: 330725441

451

The Dermalogica Foundation

1535 Beachey Pl.
Carson, CA 90746-4005
Main URL: http://www.dermalogica.com/us/about/dermalogica_foundation.html

Established in 1998 in California.

Donors: International Dermal Institute; Dermalogica, Inc.
Foundation type: Independent foundation.
Financial data (yr. ended 12/31/13): Assets, $13,160,353 (M); gifts received, $5,350,000; expenditures, $485,590; qualifying distributions, $444,036; giving activities include $432,100 for 40 grants (high: $125,000; low: $175).
Fields of interest: Education; Nonprofits; Human services; Food banks; Youth development; Females.
Type of support: General support; Regranting.
Limitations: Applications not accepted. Giving primarily in CA. No grants to individuals.
Application information: Contributes only to pre-selected organizations.
Officers: Raymond L. Wurwand, Pres.; Jane Drake Wurwand, Secy. and C.F.O.
EIN: 330814409

452
Diamantine Family Foundation Inc.
(formerly Eva and Frank Diamantine Foundation, Inc.)
P.O. Box 21242
Oakland, CA   94620-1242

Established in 1991 in California.
Donor: Frank A. Diamantine.
Foundation type: Independent foundation.
Financial data (yr. ended 12/31/13): Assets, $2,276,191 (M); expenditures, $169,344; qualifying distributions, $163,500; giving activities include $163,500 for 33 grants (high: $16,500; low: $1,000).
Purpose and activities: Giving for education, Roman Catholic organizations, and health associations.
Fields of interest: Education; Diseases and conditions; Catholicism; Human services.
Limitations: Applications not accepted. Giving primarily in CA. No grants to individuals.
Application information: Contributes only to pre-selected organizations.
Officers: James A. Diamantine, Pres.; George Diamantine, V.P.; Richard Diamantine, C.F.O. and Treas.
EIN: 943142993

453
Sanders Dickinson Foundation
7 Crockett Dr.
Moraga, CA   94556-2829

Established in 2000 in California.
Donor: Robert W. Sanders.
Foundation type: Independent foundation.
Financial data (yr. ended 12/31/13): Assets, $6,585,117 (M); gifts received, $200,000; expenditures, $270,210; qualifying distributions, $265,105; giving activities include $260,000 for 7 grants (high: $75,000; low: $20,000).
Fields of interest: University education; Human services; Food banks; Scouting programs.
Limitations: Applications not accepted. Giving primarily in CA and LA. No grants to individuals.
Application information: Contributes only to pre-selected organizations.
Officers and Directors: Robert W. Sanders, Pres. and Director; Derek A. Sanders, V.P. and Secy. and Director; Kevin R. Sanders, V.P. and Director; John R. Henkel, Treas.
EIN: 330940501

454
J. Philip & Jennifer DiNapoli Foundation
99 Almaden Blvd., Ste. 565
San Jose, CA   95113-1600

Established in 1984 in California.
Donors: J. Philip DiNapoli; Jennifer DiNapoli.
Foundation type: Independent foundation.
Financial data (yr. ended 12/31/13): Assets, $2,489,223 (M); gifts received, $266,000; expenditures, $470,238; qualifying distributions, $441,270; giving activities include $441,126 for 29 grants (high: $150,000; low: $250).
Purpose and activities: Giving primarily for the arts, education, and human services.
Fields of interest: Arts and culture; Education; Higher education; Nonprofits; Human services.
Type of support: Regranting.
Limitations: Applications not accepted. Giving primarily in Santa Clara County, CA.
Application information: Unsolicited requests for funds not accepted.
Officers and Directors: J. Philip DiNapoli, Pres.; John B. DiNapoli, V.P. and Director; Jennifer G. DiNapoli, Secy. and C.F.O. and Director.
Number of staff: 2 part-time support.
EIN: 770053451

455
Dmarlou Foundation
35 Mountain Ln.
Mill Valley, CA   94941-5008

Established in 1994 in California.
Donor: M.J. Kaliski.
Foundation type: Independent foundation.
Financial data (yr. ended 12/31/13): Assets, $5,340,760 (M); expenditures, $314,953; qualifying distributions, $245,000; giving activities include $245,000 for 6 grants (high: $90,000; low: $10,000).
Fields of interest: Wildlife biodiversity; Bird preservation; Zoos; Animal welfare.
Limitations: Applications not accepted. Giving primarily in CA. No grants to individuals.
Application information: Unsolicited requests for funds not accepted.
Officers: Barry T. Joseph, Pres.; Susan E. Rahl, V.P.; Richard H. Rahl, Secy.; Felipe R. Santiago, Treas.
EIN: 680320399

456
The Julia Stearns Dockweiler Charitable Foundation
P.O. Box 7597
Dockweiler Station
Los Angeles, CA   90007-0597

Established in 2000 in California.
Foundation type: Independent foundation.
Financial data (yr. ended 12/31/13): Assets, $7,848,054 (M); expenditures, $495,057; qualifying distributions, $357,362; giving activities include $337,500 for 40 grants (high: $25,000; low: $1,000).
Fields of interest: Higher education; University education.
Type of support: Scholarships.
Limitations: Applications not accepted. Giving primarily in CA. No grants to individuals.

Application information: Contributes only to pre-selected organizations. Unsolicited requests for funds not accepted.
Trustees: Betty Brady; C. Quinn Brady, Jr.; Caryl Crahan; Michelle Crahan; Sean Crahan.
EIN: 954803299

457
Thelma Doelger Trust for Animals
1611 Telegraph Ave., Ste. 803
Oakland, CA   94612-2128   (510) 465-0900
Contact: Paul M. Gordon, Tr.
E-mail: questions@thelmadoelgertrustforanimals.or g; Main URL: http:// www.thelmadoelgertrustforanimals.org

Foundation type: Independent foundation.
Financial data (yr. ended 06/30/13): Assets, $8,124,406 (M); expenditures, $376,651; qualifying distributions, $190,500; giving activities include $190,500 for grants.
Purpose and activities: Giving for the care and maintenance of animals and the prevention of cruelty to animals.
Fields of interest: Domesticated animals; Human services.
Type of support: General support.
Limitations: Applications accepted. Giving limited to CA. No grants to individuals.
Application information: Application guidelines available on Trust web site. Application form required.
  Copies of proposal: 3
  Deadline(s): None
Trustees: Margaret K. Burks; Susan Doelger; Paul M. Gordon.
EIN: 943318485

458
Donegan Burns Foundation
(formerly Helen M. Donegan Foundation)
5967 Redondo Dr.
Bonsall, CA   92003-1543
Contact: Bettye Geurin-Burns
E-mail: info@doneganburnsfoundation.com

Established in 2005 in California.
Foundation type: Operating foundation.
Financial data (yr. ended 12/31/13): Assets, $7,314,483 (M); expenditures, $545,340; qualifying distributions, $328,062; giving activities include $328,062 for 24 grants (high: $25,000; low: $800).
Fields of interest: Education; HIV/AIDS; Youth services.
Limitations: Applications not accepted. Giving primarily in CA and MA.
Application information: Contributes only to pre-selected organizations.
Officers: Bettye Lou Geurin Burns, C.E.O. and Pres.; Denis O. Hettinger, C.F.O.
Directors: Deborah Humphries; Calvin Nelson; Byron Samaras; Jennifer Woodard.
EIN: 201760871

459
Dorskind Family Foundation, Inc.
10112 Empyrean Way, Unit 103
Los Angeles, CA   90067-3809

Donors: Albert Dorskind†; Sue M. Dorskind.
Foundation type: Independent foundation.
Financial data (yr. ended 06/30/14): Assets, $657,060 (M); expenditures, $235,631; qualifying distributions, $226,463; giving activities include $226,463 for 24 grants (high: $57,124; low: $150).
Purpose and activities: Giving to Jewish organizations, health and medical services, and for art and cultural organizations.
Fields of interest: Arts and culture; Education; Nonprofits; Hospital care; Health care clinics; Diseases and conditions; Heart and circulatory system diseases; Film and video; Television; Judaism; Human services.
Type of support: Research; Regranting.
Limitations: Applications not accepted. Giving primarily in CA. No grants to individuals.
Application information: Unsolicited requests for funds not accepted.
Officers: Sue M. Dorskind, Pres.; Dorothy D. Dorskind, C.F.O.; James A. Dorskind, V.P.
EIN: 953954650

460
The James E. Downey Foundation
23 Brookline
Aliso Viejo, CA 92656-1461 (949) 474-0900
Contact: Karl Jonson, Secy. and C.F.O.

Established in 2005 in California.
Donor: James E. Downey.
Foundation type: Independent foundation.
Financial data (yr. ended 06/30/14): Assets, $4,058,161 (M); gifts received, $53,699; expenditures, $497,611; qualifying distributions, $401,700; giving activities include $401,700 for 258 grants to individuals (high: $3,000; low: $700).
Purpose and activities: Giving for scholarship awards to single parents.
Fields of interest: Higher education; Single parents.
Type of support: Student aid.
Limitations: Applications accepted. Giving primarily in CA and IL.
Application information: Application form required.
  Initial approach: Request application form
  Deadline(s): Apr. 30 preceding the applicable school year
Officers and Directors: James E. Downey, Pres. and Director; Keith M. Downey, V.P. and Director; Karl Jonson, C.F.O. and Director.
EIN: 203510627

461
Downey-Short Foundation
23 Brookline
Aliso Viejo, CA 92656-1461 (949) 474-0900

Donors: James E. Downey; C&D Zodiac; The Wave Equity Parners, LLC; Jamie Short; Tom McFarland; John Hargreaves; Mike McCarthy; Tracy Short; Valentine Clark; Access All Directory Placement; Gus Osterkamp.
Foundation type: Independent foundation.
Financial data (yr. ended 06/30/14): Assets, $4,526,174; gifts received, $49,318; expenditures, $275,224; qualifying distributions, $195,000.
Purpose and activities: Giving to organizations and individuals dedicated to the field of Oncology.
Fields of interest: Oncology.
Type of support: Grants to individuals.

Limitations: Applications accepted. Giving primarily in CA, NE and WA.
Application information: Application form required.
  Initial approach: Proposal
  Deadline(s): None
Officers and Directors: James E. Downey, Pres. and Director; Karl Johnson, V.P. and Director; Virginia Blades-Rodriguez, Secy. and Director.
EIN: 020759145

462
Downing Family Foundation
(formerly The J. C. Downing Foundation)
2052 Galveston St.
San Diego, CA 92110-1303

Established in 1990 in California.
Donor: John C. Downing.
Foundation type: Independent foundation.
Financial data (yr. ended 12/31/13): Assets, $3,201,889 (M); expenditures, $214,666; qualifying distributions, $155,500; giving activities include $155,500 for 10 grants (high: $65,000; low: $5,000).
Fields of interest: Arts and culture; Museums; Education; Environment; Health; Communication media; Water sports.
Type of support: General support; Matching grants; Equipment; Program development; Convening; Seed money; Research and evaluation; Fellowships; Research.
Limitations: Applications not accepted. Giving primarily in southern CA. No support for religious organizations, or for public schools. No grants to individuals, or for scholarships.
Application information: Contributes only to pre-selected organizations.
Officers: John C. Downing, Pres.; Tracy Downing, Secy.; Toni M. Leadingham, Treas.
Number of staff: 1 full-time professional; 1 full-time support; 1 part-time support.
EIN: 330445623

463
The Drexler Foundation
25440 Becky Ln.
Los Altos Hills, CA 94022-4520

Donors: Jerome Drexler; Sylvia Drexler.
Foundation type: Independent foundation.
Financial data (yr. ended 10/31/14): Assets, $142,282 (M); expenditures, $351,035; qualifying distributions, $350,040; giving activities include $349,000 for 8 grants (high: $300,000; low: $2,000).
Fields of interest: Education; Environment; Religion.
Type of support: Scholarships.
Limitations: Applications not accepted. Giving primarily in CA. No grants to individuals.
Application information: Unsolicited requests for funds not accepted.
Officers: Jerome Drexler, Pres.; Jerald E. Rosenblum, Secy.; Sylvia B. Drexler, C.F.O.
EIN: 237006177

464
The Drum Foundation
180 Montgomery St., Ste. 1616
San Francisco, CA 94104-4235

Established in 1956 in California.
Donor: Frank G. Drum†.
Foundation type: Independent foundation.
Financial data (yr. ended 12/31/13): Assets, $4,718,918 (M); expenditures, $304,774; qualifying distributions, $245,683; giving activities include $177,000 for 23 grants (high: $30,000; low: $1,000).
Purpose and activities: Giving to aid Roman Catholic Church-related educational and charitable organizations, usually limited to the Archdiocese of San Francisco, including those supported by Mr. Drum during his lifetime.
Fields of interest: Elementary and secondary education; Higher education; Nonprofits; Catholicism; Human services.
Type of support: General support; Continuing support; Annual campaigns; Capital and infrastructure; Regranting; Equipment; Land acquisitions; Debt reduction; Emergency funds; Program development; Convening; Professorships; Publications; Seed money; Fellowships; Internships; Scholarships; Research; Individual development.
Limitations: Applications not accepted. Giving primarily in CA. No grants to individuals or for endowment funds or matching gifts.
Application information: Unsolicited requests for funds not accepted.
  Board meeting date(s): As required
Officers and Directors: Janet Abbott, Pres. and Director; Philip Hudner, Secy.-Treas. and Director.
EIN: 946067469

465
Ducommun & Gross Foundation
P.O. Box 2172
Healdsburg, CA 95448-2172

Established in 1968 in California.
Foundation type: Independent foundation.
Financial data (yr. ended 12/31/13): Assets, $7,826,707 (M); expenditures, $459,247; qualifying distributions, $426,493; giving activities include $422,500 for 26 grants (high: $175,000; low: $2,500).
Fields of interest: Arts and culture; Education; Secondary education; Higher education; University education; Land resources; Hospital care; Diseases and conditions; Communication media.
Type of support: Research.
Limitations: Applications not accepted. No grants to individuals.
Application information: Unsolicited requests for funds not accepted.
  Board meeting date(s): Dec.
Officers: Robert E. Ducommun, Pres.; Electra Ducommun de Peyster, V.P.; Frederick A. Richmand, Secy.
Advisory Directors: Anthony C. Ward; Courtlandt D. Gross.
EIN: 956210834

466
Warren and Zoann Little Dusenbury
  ### Charitable Trust
5938 Almond Ave.
Orangevale, CA 95662 (916) 989-5472
Contact: Warren Dusenbury, Tr.

Established in 1986 in Ohio.

Donors: Warren Dusenbury†; Zoann L. Dusenbury; Warren Dusenbury Marital Trust.
Foundation type: Independent foundation.
Financial data (yr. ended 12/31/13): Assets, $8,413,693 (M); expenditures, $441,858; qualifying distributions, $378,141; giving activities include $376,521 for 16 grants (high: $80,000; low: $5,000).
Fields of interest: Arts and culture; Education.
Type of support: General support.
Limitations: Applications accepted. Giving primarily in Cleveland, OH. No grants to individuals.
Application information:
  Initial approach: Proposal
  Deadline(s): None
Trustees: Warren Dusenbury; Wynne Odell.
EIN: 346847641

467
Dwelle Family Foundation Inc.
9301 Airport Dr.
Visalia, CA 93277-9500

Established in 1998 in Unspecified.
Donor: Thomas Dwelle.
Foundation type: Independent foundation.
Financial data (yr. ended 12/31/14): Assets, $4,134,021; expenditures, $241,807; qualifying distributions, $198,950.
Fields of interest: Arts and culture; Education; Health; Storms; Human services; Youth services.
Limitations: Applications not accepted. Giving primarily in CA. No grants to individuals.
Application information: Unsolicited requests for funds not accepted.
Directors: David Dwelle; Stephen Dwelle; Thomas Dwelle; Walter Dwelle.
EIN: 770472647

468
The Richard F. and Eleanor W. Dwyer Fund
for Excellence
(formerly American Foundation for Oceanography)
321 N. Las Casas Ave.
Pacific Palisades, CA 90272-3307

Established in 1953 in California.
Donors: Darlene Lasher; Allan Lasher; Richard F. Dwyer.
Foundation type: Independent foundation.
Financial data (yr. ended 06/30/13): Assets, $7,036,749 (M); expenditures, $349,240; qualifying distributions, $309,750; giving activities include $309,750 for 13 grants (high: $229,000; low: $100).
Fields of interest: Education; Foundations; Diseases and conditions; Human services.
Limitations: Applications not accepted. Giving primarily in Los Angeles and Santa Monica, CA. No grants to individuals.
Application information: Contributes only to pre-selected organizations.
Officers: Darlene Lasher, Pres. and Secy.; Allan Lasher, V.P. and Director; Susan Lasher, C.F.O. and Treas.
EIN: 956027788

469
Dyer Family Foundation
1099 E. Champlain Dr., Ste. A
P.O. Box 103
Fresno, CA 93720-5033

Established in 2003 in California.
Donor: Dyer Charitable Trust.
Foundation type: Independent foundation.
Financial data (yr. ended 12/31/13): Assets, $3,627,238 (M); expenditures, $198,641; qualifying distributions, $175,000; giving activities include $175,000 for 15 grants (high: $30,000; low: $1,500).
Fields of interest: Education; Animal welfare; Autism; Human services.
Limitations: Applications not accepted. Giving primarily in CA. No grants to individuals.
Application information: Unsolicited requests for funds not accepted.
Officers: Darleen R. Dyer, Pres.; Cristi Y. Dyer, C.F.O.; Deloris W. Kinghorn, V.P.; Walden O'Neill, Secy.
Board Member: Debora Y. Odzinski.
EIN: 336338010

470
The Eagle Globerman & Kodama
Foundation
14111 Freeway Dr., Ste. 208
Santa Fe Springs, CA 90670-5834

Established in 2000 in California.
Donor: The Bravo Foundation.
Foundation type: Independent foundation.
Financial data (yr. ended 11/30/13): Assets, $4,218,078 (M); expenditures, $235,966; qualifying distributions, $198,975; giving activities include $191,500 for 21 grants (high: $40,000; low: $500).
Fields of interest: Education; Judaism; Human services; Child welfare; Youth services; Senior assisted living; Homeless people.
Limitations: Applications not accepted. No grants to individuals.
Application information: Unsolicited requests for funds not accepted.
Trustees: Michael Globerman; Mitchell M. Kodama.
EIN: 954776398

471
Ebell of Los Angeles Rest Cottage
Association
743 S. Lucerne Blvd.
Los Angeles, CA 90005-3707 (323) 931-1277
FAX: (323) 937-0272; E-mail: inquiry@ebellla.com;
Main URL: http://www.ebellla.com

Established in 1894 in California.
Foundation type: Independent foundation.
Financial data (yr. ended 06/30/14): Assets, $3,337,166 (M); gifts received, $2,128; expenditures, $207,857; qualifying distributions, $158,424; giving activities include for 15 grants (high: $12,500; low: $5,000).
Purpose and activities: Giving primarily to medical care institutions that service needy persons in the Los Angeles, CA, area.
Fields of interest: Health; Housing development; Human services.

Type of support: General support; Continuing support; Program development.
Limitations: Applications accepted. Giving limited to Los Angeles County, CA. No grants to individuals.
Application information:
  Initial approach: Letter
  Deadline(s): None
Officers: Loyce Braun, V.P.; Patty Hill, Pres.; Ginger Bernard, Secy.; Nan Williams, Treas.; Patricia Lombard, Chair.
Board Members: Janna Harris; Kelly Nelson; Evelyn Toliver; Angelique Campen; Joyce Davidson; Amy Vuckovich; Portia Lee; Cassie Nelson; Donna Russell.
EIN: 956102928

472
Ebell of Los Angeles Scholarship
Endowment Fund
743 S. Lucerne Blvd.
Los Angeles, CA 90005-3707 (323) 931-1277; 184
Contact: Harriette Williams, Chair.
E-mail: scholarship@ebelloflosangeles.com; Main URL: http://www.ebellofla.wordpress.com/scholarship

Established in 1921 in California.
Donors: Lottie Clinton†; Thelma Pickett Family Trust.
Foundation type: Independent foundation.
Financial data (yr. ended 06/30/13): Assets, $4,122,552 (M); gifts received, $1,330; expenditures, $243,753; qualifying distributions, $182,538; giving activities include $170,000 for 42 grants to individuals (high: $5,000; low: $1,500).
Purpose and activities: Scholarships for qualifying undergraduate college students who are U.S. citizens, residents of Los Angeles County for one year or more, and in attendance at an accredited Los Angeles County educational institution.
Fields of interest: Higher education.
Type of support: Student aid.
Limitations: Applications accepted. Giving limited to Los Angeles County, CA, residents attending Los Angeles County, CA, colleges. No loans or program-related investments.
Publications: Application guidelines.
Application information: Complete application guidelines and procedures available on fund web site. Application form required.
  Initial approach: Application available on fund web site
  Deadline(s): See fund web site for current deadline
Officers: Harriette Williams, Chair; Patty Hill, Pres.; Loyce Braun, V.P.; Marjorie Fierstadt, Secy.; Jane Martin, Chair of Fin.
Members: Laura Cohen; Janna Harris; Caroline Moser; Kelley Nelson; Paddy Schapiro; Dia Schuldenfrei; Shan Sutherland; Evelyn Toliver; Amy Vuckovich; Nan Williams.
Number of staff: None.
EIN: 237049580

473
Ray Thomas Edwards Foundation
c/o Donald G. Yeckel
1616 Nautilus St.
La Jolla, CA 92037-6411
E-mail: info@edwardsfoundation.org; Main
URL: http://edwardsfoundation.org
Grants List: http://edwardsfoundation.org/current/
index.html

Established in 1997 in California.
Donor: Ray Thomas Edwards†.
Foundation type: Independent foundation.
Financial data (yr. ended 12/31/13): Assets,
$4,093,885 (M); expenditures, $227,155;
qualifying distributions, $199,000; giving activities
include $199,000 for 3 grants (high: $76,000; low:
$60,000).
Purpose and activities: Giving primarily to support
basic research in the biomedical sciences. The
foundation believes that discovery and innovation in
the biomedical sciences for the public's good
depends on the training and support of the highest
quality for young scientists in the very best research
environments. In pursuit of this goal, the foundation
offers a Career Award in the Biomedical Sciences for
researchers working in San Diego County. The
purpose of the award is to foster the development
of biomedical researchers who are early in their
careers, during the critical transition to becoming
independent investigators. The foundation supports
research across the spectrum of the biomedical
sciences, including: biochemistry; cell,
developmental, molecular, and structural biology;
endocrinology; immunology; microbiology;
neurobiology; physiology; virology.
Fields of interest: University education;
Biomedicine.
Type of support: Convening; Research.
Limitations: Applications not accepted. Giving
primarily in La Jolla, CA. No grants to individuals.
Application information: Contributes only to
pre-selected organizations.
Officer: Donald G. Yeckel, Chair.
Trustees: Andrew J. Yeckel; Mark F. Yeckel.
EIN: 330778248

474
**The Eichenberg-Larson Charitable
    Foundation**
(formerly Robert & LaDorna Eichenberg Charitable
Foundation)
1 Collins Island
Newport Beach, CA 92662-1003

Established in 1990 in California.
Donors: Robert Eichenberg; LaDorna Eichenberg.
Foundation type: Independent foundation.
Financial data (yr. ended 09/30/13): Assets,
$6,547,004 (M); gifts received, $1,068,782;
expenditures, $321,713; qualifying distributions,
$300,000; giving activities include $300,000 for 23
grants (high: $20,000; low: $10,000).
Fields of interest: Arts and culture; Orchestral
music; Higher education; University education;
Patient social services; Diseases and conditions;
Alzheimer's disease; Cancers; Mormonism; Human
services.
Limitations: Applications not accepted. Giving
primarily in CA. No grants to individuals.
Application information: Contributes only to
pre-selected organizations.

Directors: Ladorna Eichenberg; Robert Eichenberg;
Jorli Perine.
EIN: 330431855

475
Elder Family Foundation
3028 Hillegass Ave.
Berkeley, CA 94705-2514

Established in 2002 in Massachusetts.
Donors: Robert C. Elder; Ralph K. Elder.
Foundation type: Independent foundation.
Financial data (yr. ended 12/31/14): Assets,
$4,511,709; gifts received, $0; expenditures,
$364,818; qualifying distributions, $364,818.
Fields of interest: Education; In-patient medical
care; Hospital care; Housing development;
Catholicism.
Limitations: Applications not accepted. Giving
primarily where trustees reside: CA, MA, PA, and TX.
No grants to individuals.
Application information: Contributes only to
pre-selected organizations.
Trustees: Coley K. Elder; Ralph K. Elder; Robert C.
Elder; Elizabeth Mentzinger.
EIN: 510426160

476
Eleven Twenty Seven Foundation
301 E. Colorado Blvd., Ste. 426
Pasadena, CA 91101-1920

Established in 2001 in California.
Donor: Henry C. Yuen.
Foundation type: Independent foundation.
Financial data (yr. ended 12/31/13): Assets,
$3,947,926 (M); expenditures, $268,423;
qualifying distributions, $215,298; giving activities
include $208,573 for 36 grants (high: $30,000;
low: $73).
Fields of interest: Arts and culture; Museums;
Education; Foundations; Human services; Youth
mentoring.
Limitations: Applications not accepted. No grants to
individuals.
Application information: Unsolicited requests for
funds not accepted.
Trustee: Temo A. Arjani.
Number of staff: None.
EIN: 916549814

477
The Elfenworks Foundation
20 Park Rd., Ste. D
Burlingame, CA 94011-0431 (650) 347-9700
FAX: (650) 347-9702;
E-mail: admin@elfenworks.org; Main URL: http://
www.elfenworksfoundation.org
Facebook: https://www.facebook.com/elfenworks
Twitter: http://twitter.com/elfenworks
YouTube: http://www.youtube.com/elfenworks

Established in 2006 in California.
Donor: Maples Burlingame, LLC.
Foundation type: Operating foundation.
Financial data (yr. ended 12/31/13): Assets,
$2,250,035 (M); gifts received, $422,831;
expenditures, $1,231,214; qualifying distributions,
$1,212,373; giving activities include $381,790 for
17 grants (high: $200,000; low: $100).

Purpose and activities: The mission of the
foundation is to foster a world in harmony with hope.
The foundation seeks to use expertise in
communications, computers, film music, the law,
finance and business administration to advance
their goals of measurable and sustainable
transformative change, with emphasis on fighting
domestic poverty.
Fields of interest: Human services; Low-income and
poor people.
Limitations: Applications not accepted. Giving in the
U.S., with some emphasis on CA.
Application information: Unsolicited requests for
funds not accepted. See foundation web site for list
of current initiatives.
Officer: Kenneth C. Tam, Exec. Dir.
Trustees: Vivian Kane; Kim Schoknecht; Lauren
Speeth; Mark Vorsatz; Elizabeth Wied.
EIN: 205522254

478
**Mary Ellen and Michael E. Fox Family
    Foundation**
14751 Quito Rd.
Saratoga, CA 95070-6291

Established in 2001 in California.
Donors: M.E. Fox and Company, Inc.; Dennis P. Fox;
Lori Fox; Michael E. Fox, Jr.; Michael Fox; Monica
Fox; Terence Fox; Michele Fox; Michael E. Fox, Sr.;
Mary Ellen Fox.
Foundation type: Independent foundation.
Financial data (yr. ended 12/31/13): Assets,
$141,115 (M); gifts received, $322,600;
expenditures, $247,770; qualifying distributions,
$247,000; giving activities include $247,000 for
202 grants (high: $35,250; low: $15).
Fields of interest: Theater; Education; Elementary
and secondary education; Higher education;
Nonprofits; Hospital care; Catholicism; Human
services.
Type of support: Regranting.
Limitations: Applications not accepted. Giving
primarily in CA. No grants to individuals.
Application information: Unsolicited requests for
funds not accepted.
Officers and Directors: Mary Ellen Fox, Pres. and
Secy.; Michael E. Fox, Sr., C.F.O. and Director;
Catherine Fox Bloyd; Dennis P. Fox; Michael E. Fox,
Jr.
EIN: 912151673

479
**Harry C. and Deborah L. Elliott Family
    Foundation**
340 Palladio Pkwy., Ste. 521
Folsom, CA 95630-8574

Established in 2003 in California.
Donors: Harry C. Elliott; Elliott Homes, Inc.
Foundation type: Independent foundation.
Financial data (yr. ended 12/31/13): Assets,
$8,066,638 (M); expenditures, $431,112;
qualifying distributions, $382,250; giving activities
include $382,250 for 13 grants (high: $235,000;
low: $1,250).
Fields of interest: Education; Diseases and
conditions; Human services.
Type of support: Research.
Limitations: Applications not accepted. Giving
primarily in CA. No grants to individuals.

Application Information: Contributes only to pre-selected organizations.
Officers and Directors: Harry C. Elliott III, Pres. and Director; Chelsea Elliott, V.P.; Deborah Elliott, V.P. and Director; Harry C. Elliott IV, V.P.; Roxanne Elliott, V.P.; Stephen Hemington, Secy.-Treas.
EIN: 200521937

480
Quinn Emanuel Foundation
865 S. Figueroa St., 10th Fl.
Los Angeles, CA 90017-5003

Established in 2003 in California.
Donors: Patrick Selendy; John B. Quinn; Steve Neuwirth; A. Urquhart; Harry Oliver; Dan Bromberg; Kenneth Chiate; Rick Werder; Claude Stern; Carey Ramos; William Price; Christopher Tayback; Quinn Emanuel Urquhart & Sullivan, LLP; Kathleen Sullivan; Phillippe Selendy; Ray Nimrod; Michael Carlinski; Daniel Brockett; Albert Bedecccare; Peter Calamari; Faith Gay; Patrick Shields; Eric Winston; A. William Urquhart; Michael Zeller; Jonathan Pickhardt; David Elsberg; Michael Williams.
Foundation type: Company-sponsored foundation.
Financial data (yr. ended 12/31/13): Assets, $94,657 (M); gifts received, $394,947; expenditures, $386,319; qualifying distributions, $386,319; giving activities include $386,319 for 33 grants (high: $50,000; low: $1,000).
Fields of interest: Higher education; Law; Human rights; Human services; People with HIV/AIDS.
Type of support: Research.
Limitations: Applications not accepted. Giving primarily in CA. No grants to individuals.
Application information: Unsolicited requests for funds not accepted.
Officers and Directors: John B. Quinn, Pres. and Director; Jacqueline Toth, Secy.; David Henri, Treas.; Robert Juman; Steven Madison.
EIN: 200423348

481
Emmett Foundation
c/o Norm Tamkin
2400 Broadway, Ste. D590
Santa Monica, CA 90404

Established in 2003 in California.
Donor: Dan A. Emmett.
Foundation type: Independent foundation.
Financial data (yr. ended 11/30/13): Assets, $8,926,323 (M); gifts received, $108,657; expenditures, $237,708; qualifying distributions, $237,708; giving activities include $229,250 for 16 grants (high: $51,000; low: $1,000).
Fields of interest: Higher education; Law education; Environment.
Limitations: Applications not accepted. Giving primarily in CA; some funding also in Cambridge, MA. No grants to individuals.
Application information: Contributes only to pre-selected organizations.
Officers and Directors: Dan A. Emmett, Pres. and Director; Daniel W. Emmett, V.P., C.F.O., and Treas. and Director; Rae M. Emmett, V.P. and Secy. and Director; Morgan W. Emmett, V.P. and Director; Rosalind Emmett Nieman, V.P. and Director; Tyler A. Emmett.
EIN: 200429029

482
The Endurance Fund
4749 Nicasio Valley Rd.
Nicasio, CA 94946-9743
Application address: c/o Robert G. Schiro, Tr., 1749 Nicasio Valley Rd., Nicasio, CA 94946, tel.: (415) 488-4311

Established in 1993 in California.
Foundation type: Independent foundation.
Financial data (yr. ended 12/31/13): Assets, $5,896,629 (M); expenditures, $276,226; qualifying distributions, $256,855; giving activities include $192,139 for 55 grants (high: $60,000; low: $100).
Fields of interest: Environment; Health; Human services.
Limitations: Applications accepted. Giving primarily in West Marin, CA.
Application information:
   Initial approach: Proposal
   Deadline(s): None
Trustees: Dorene C. Schiro; Robert G. Schiro.
Number of staff: 1 part-time support.
EIN: 943170349

483
Epstein/Roth Foundation
618 Santa Barbara Rd.
Berkeley, CA 94707-1718

Established in 2000 in California.
Donors: Amy Roth; Robert Epstein.
Foundation type: Independent foundation.
Financial data (yr. ended 12/31/13): Assets, $3,830,471 (M); expenditures, $243,280; qualifying distributions, $226,300; giving activities include $222,700 for 9 grants (high: $40,000; low: $5,100).
Fields of interest: Education; Higher education; Environment; Foundations; Human services.
Limitations: Applications not accepted. Giving primarily in CA. No grants to individuals.
Application information: Unsolicited requests for funds not accepted.
Officers: Amy Roth, Pres.; Robert Epstein, Treas.
Directors: Abbie Coburn; Colin Epstein; Harris Epstein.
EIN: 943357645

484
T. R. Eriksen Trust Fund
P.O. Box 806
Ukiah, CA 95482-0806
Contact: Joanne Lacasse, Tr.

Established in 2000 in California.
Foundation type: Independent foundation.
Financial data (yr. ended 12/31/13): Assets, $5,663,891 (M); expenditures, $458,795; qualifying distributions, $250,750; giving activities include $201,750 for 22 grants (high: $27,500; low: $250).
Purpose and activities: Giving primarily for human services.
Fields of interest: Natural resources; Human services; Food banks; Youth services; Adult and child mentoring; Senior services.
Type of support: General support.
Limitations: Applications accepted. Giving primarily in Mendocino County, CA. No grants to individuals.

Application information: Applicant must be a 501(c)(3) organization. Application form required.
   Initial approach: Letter
   Final notification: 6 weeks
Trustee: Joanne Lacasse.
Grant Committee: Sandra Hendrickx; Larry McLeitch.
EIN: 916513400

485
The Ray and Wyn Ritchie Evans Foundation
8563 Higuera St.
Culver City, CA 90232-2539

Established in 2008 in California.
Foundation type: Independent foundation.
Financial data (yr. ended 12/31/14): Assets, $9,081,166 (M); expenditures, $744,376; qualifying distributions, $671,315; giving activities include $218,500 for 13 grants (high: $85,000; low: $5,000), and $173,953 for foundation-administered programs.
Purpose and activities: Giving primarily for the arts, and civil liberties and policies.
Fields of interest: Arts services; Art museums; Higher education; Judaism; Individual liberties.
Limitations: Applications not accepted. Giving primarily in CA, with some emphasis on Culver City and Los Angeles, and PA.
Application information: Unsolicited requests for funds not accepted.
Officers: Frederick M. Nicholas, Pres.; Anthony E. Nicholas, Secy.; Lisa F. Duckett, C.F.O.
EIN: 263147090

486
The Ryan Evans Foundation
P.O. Box 2738
Visalia, CA 93279-2738

Established in 2004 in California.
Donors: Sara G. Evans; Norman K. Evans.
Foundation type: Independent foundation.
Financial data (yr. ended 06/30/13): Assets, $7,383,068 (M); gifts received, $750,000; expenditures, $193,478; qualifying distributions, $180,978; giving activities include $180,978 for 9 grants (high: $100,000; low: $500).
Fields of interest: Education; Antidiscrimination; Human services; Child welfare; Youth services; Adult and child mentoring.
Limitations: Applications not accepted. Giving primarily in CA. No grants to individuals.
Application information: Contributes only to pre-selected organizations.
Officers and Directors: Norman K. Evans, Pres. and Director; Sara G. Evans, Secy. and C.F.O. and Director.
EIN: 202060209

487
Evening Star Foundation
(formerly Clement and Lynn Hirsch Charitable Foundation)
10431 Bellagio Rd.
Los Angeles, CA 90077-3818

Established in 1998 in California.
Donor: Clement L. Hirsch†.

Foundation type: Independent foundation.
Financial data (yr. ended 09/30/13): Assets, $7,303,241 (M); expenditures, $375,739; qualifying distributions, $340,758; giving activities include $333,243 for 23 grants (high: $45,000; low: $500).
Fields of interest: Performing arts; Higher education; Diseases and conditions; Ear, nose and throat diseases; Archives and special collections; Christianity.
Type of support: General support; Research; Research and evaluation.
Limitations: Applications not accepted. Giving primarily in CA. No grants to individuals.
Application information: Unsolicited requests for funds not accepted.
Officers and Directors: Lynn A. Booth, Pres. and Director; Greg Hirsch, C.F.O. and Director; Michelle Read, V.P. and Director.
EIN: 330833895

488
Everest Edwin Foundation
11766 Wilshire Blvd., Ste. 1450
Los Angeles, CA   90025-6538

Donor: Residents Medical Group, Inc.
Foundation type: Independent foundation.
Financial data (yr. ended 12/31/13): Assets, $7,841 (M); gifts received, $251,558; expenditures, $244,031; qualifying distributions, $150,700; giving activities include $150,700 for 6 grants (high: $102,500; low: $200).
Fields of interest: Education; Health; Diseases and conditions.
Type of support: Research.
Officers: Bimla Everest, C.E.O.; Gregory Heffernan, C.F.O.; Craig Meier, Secy.
EIN: 451274059

489
Frederico and Elvia Faggin Foundation Inc.
1940 Broadway St., Ste. 1W
San Francisco, CA   94109-2216   (650) 941-4079
Contact: Federico Faggin, C.E.O.

Donor: Federico Faggin.
Foundation type: Independent foundation.
Financial data (yr. ended 12/31/13): Assets, $11,115,734 (M); expenditures, $386,536; qualifying distributions, $352,100; giving activities include $352,100 for 5 grants (high: $200,000; low: $100).
Fields of interest: Education; Science.
Limitations: Applications accepted. Giving primarily in Petaluma, CA.
Application information: Application form required.
Initial approach: Letter
Deadline(s): None
Officers: Federico Faggin, C.E.O.; Elvia Faggin, Secy.
EIN: 451027778

490
Fairview Foundation
c/o Whittier Trust Co.
505 Montgomery St., Ste. 620
San Francisco, CA   94111-6545

Donors: Wendy E. Jordan; Wendy E. Jordan Charitable Lead Anuity Trust.

Foundation type: Independent foundation.
Financial data (yr. ended 12/31/14): Assets, $9,450,529 (M); gifts received, $123,910; expenditures, $513,663; qualifying distributions, $424,649; giving activities include $395,000 for 10 grants (high: $100,000; low: $5,000).
Fields of interest: Education; Environment.
Limitations: Applications not accepted. Giving primarily in CA.
Application information: Unsolicited requests for funds not accepted.
Officers: Wendy E. Jordan, C.E.O. and Pres.; M. Jordan Gudebski, Secy.; Jay A. Gudebski, C.F.O.
EIN: 364684604

491
Zalec Familian and Lilian Levinson Foundation
(formerly Zalec Familian Foundation)
c/o Loma Verde Properties, LLC
2200 Powell St., Ste. 970
Emeryville, CA   94608-1834

Established in 1958 in California.
Donors: Zalec Familian†; Lilian Levinson†; Rio Lindo, LLC.
Foundation type: Independent foundation.
Financial data (yr. ended 03/31/13): Assets, $4,218,204 (M); gifts received, $300,000; expenditures, $329,441; qualifying distributions, $329,000; giving activities include $329,000 for 54 grants (high: $30,000; low: $500).
Purpose and activities: Giving primarily for higher education and human services, including organizations benefiting the disabled.
Fields of interest: Arts education; Orchestral music; Museums; Higher education; Diseases and conditions; Human services; Child welfare; People with disabilities.
Type of support: General support; Fellowships; Scholarships; Research; Research and evaluation.
Limitations: Applications not accepted. Giving primarily in CA. No grants to individuals.
Application information: Contributes only to pre-selected organizations.
Officers: Ann Levinson Parker, Pres.; Jessica L. Parker, V.P.; Michael L. Parker, Secy.-Treas.
EIN: 956099164

492
The Friesen Family Foundation
(formerly Gilbert B. Friesen Foundation)
770 Bonhill Rd.
Los Angeles, CA   90049-2304

Established in 1997 in California.
Donors: Gilbert B. Friesen; David Suzanne Johnson; Moss Foundation.
Foundation type: Independent foundation.
Financial data (yr. ended 12/31/12): Assets, $24,043 (M); gifts received, $225,000; expenditures, $289,919; qualifying distributions, $289,782; giving activities include $289,782 for grants.
Purpose and activities: Giving primarily for arts and culture; some funding for health associations and human services.
Fields of interest: Arts and culture; Art museums; Education; Natural resources; Diseases and conditions; Human services; Child welfare.

Limitations: Applications not accepted. Giving primarily in Los Angeles, CA; some giving also in New York, NY. No grants to individuals.
Application information: Contributes only to pre-selected organizations.
Trustees: Joel S. Ehrenkranz; Gilbert B. Friesen.
EIN: 954632580

493
The Jim Hicks Family Foundation
565 Mercury Ln.
Brea, CA   92821

Donors: Jim Hicks; Jim Hicks & Company, Inc.; Neta Hicks.
Foundation type: Independent foundation.
Financial data (yr. ended 10/31/14): Assets, $11,098,781; gifts received, $492,944; expenditures, $336,103; qualifying distributions, $335,929.
Fields of interest: Education; Philanthropy; Youth development.
Limitations: Applications not accepted. Giving primarily in CA.
Application information: Unsolicited requests for funds not accepted.
Officers: Jim Hicks, Pres.; Gary H. Edelstone, Secy.
Board Members: Jennifer E. Hicks; Wayland R. Hicks; Gary Milhous.
EIN: 271357705

494
Faraway Foundation
P.O. Box 189
San Anselmo, CA   94979-0189

Foundation type: Independent foundation.
Financial data (yr. ended 10/31/13): Assets, $9,630,401 (M); expenditures, $539,096; qualifying distributions, $501,133; giving activities include $160,949 for 19 grants (high: $25,000; low: $500).
Purpose and activities: The organization supports education and the preservation of the environment.
Fields of interest: Education; Environment; Communication media.
Limitations: Applications not accepted. Giving primarily in Telluride, CO.
Application information: Unsolicited requests for funds not accepted.
Officers: Betsy Hall McKinney, Pres. and Treas.; Ulli Sir Jesse, Secy.
Director: John McKinney.
EIN: 841194394

495
Anne & Jason Farber Foundation
c/o PMB Helin Donovan
1340 Treat Blvd., Ste. 525
Walnut Creek, CA   94597-7984

Established in 1981 in California.
Donor: James A. Farber.
Foundation type: Independent foundation.
Financial data (yr. ended 11/30/13): Assets, $3,009,262 (M); expenditures, $267,856; qualifying distributions, $245,354; giving activities include $200,000 for 1 grant.
Purpose and activities: Giving for brain tumor research.

Fields of interest: Neurology; Diseases and conditions; Brain and nervous system disorders.
Type of support: Research; Grants to individuals.
Limitations: Applications not accepted. Giving primarily in CA.
Application information: Unsolicited requests for funds not accepted.
Officers: James A. Farber, Pres.; Randall E. Kessler, Secy.-Treas.
Director: Ward Pynn.
EIN: 942778778

496
Farmers Insurance Group Safety Foundation
4680 Wilshire Blvd.
Los Angeles, CA 90010-3863
Contact: Doren E. Hohl, Secy.

Donor: Farmers Group, Inc.
Foundation type: Company-sponsored foundation.
Financial data (yr. ended 12/31/13): Assets, $280,288 (M); expenditures, $231,500; qualifying distributions, $231,500; giving activities include $231,500 for 9 grants (high: $50,000; low: $2,500).
Purpose and activities: The foundation supports police agencies and organizations involved with disaster relief and fire safety.
Fields of interest: Education; Disasters and emergency management; Human services.
Type of support: General support; Equipment; Emergency funds; Program development; Sponsorships.
Limitations: Applications accepted. Giving limited to areas of company operations in CA and OR. No support for religious, political, or international organizations. No grants to individuals, or for construction projects.
Application information: Application form required.
  Initial approach: Proposal
  Deadline(s): 2 months prior to need
Officers and Directors: Dons L. Dunn, Chair. and Pres. and Director; Anthony J. Morris, V.P. and Treas. and Director; Scott R. Lindquist, V.P. and Director; Ronald G. Myhan, V.P.; Peter Teuscher, V.P.; Karyn Williams, V.P.; Doren E. Hohl, Secy.; Deborah L. Aldredge; Bryan F. Murphy; David A. Travers.
EIN: 956016633

497
Faro Foundation
1801 Century Park E., Ste. 2160
Los Angeles, CA 90067-2343

Established in 2004 in California.
Donor: K. Reeves.
Foundation type: Independent foundation.
Financial data (yr. ended 12/31/14): Assets, $4,259,952; expenditures, $346,481; qualifying distributions, $265,000.
Fields of interest: Education; Diseases and conditions; Human services; Child welfare.
Limitations: Applications not accepted. Giving primarily in Los Angeles and Santa Monica, CA; some funding also in New York, NY.
Application information: Contributes only to pre-selected organizations.
Trustee: Paul Knell.
EIN: 276020872

498
The Fast Forward Foundation
16530 Ventura Blvd., Ste. 400
Encino, CA 91436-4551

Foundation type: Independent foundation.
Financial data (yr. ended 12/31/13): Assets, $0 (M); expenditures, $151,133; qualifying distributions, $151,133; giving activities include $141,147 for 2 grants (high: $70,574; low: $70,573).
Fields of interest: Agriculture; Human services; Food banks.
Limitations: Applications not accepted. Giving primarily in CA and MN.
Application information: Unsolicited requests for funds not accepted.
Officers: Mark Fisher, Co-Chair; David Bishop, Co-Chair; Mark Horak, Secy.
Directors: Scott Burns; Jeff Bridges; Dwight Krizman; Don Rosenberg; Gary Ross; Mark Vrieling.
EIN: 931196153

499
The Fat Tire Foundation
50 Paso del Arroyo
Portola Valley, CA 94028-7900 (650) 529-0345
Contact: Jeff Jordan, Dir.; Karen Shishino Jordan, Dir.

Established in 2006 in California.
Donors: Jeff Jordan; Karen Shishino Jordan.
Foundation type: Independent foundation.
Financial data (yr. ended 12/31/13): Assets, $11,623,502 (M); gifts received, $1,231,461; expenditures, $361,994; qualifying distributions, $346,400; giving activities include $346,400 for 34 grants (high: $100,000; low: $100).
Fields of interest: Foundations; Diabetes; Child welfare.
Type of support: General support; Research.
Limitations: Applications accepted. Giving primarily in CA.
Application information:
  Initial approach: Proposal
  Deadline(s): None
Directors: Jeff Jordan; Karen Shishino Jordan.
EIN: 208066058

500
The Farrah Fawcett Foundation
P.O. Box 6478
Beverly Hills, CA 90212-1478 3102777351
E-mail: info@thefarrahfawcettfoundation.org; Main URL: http://www.thefarrahfawcettfoundation.org
E Newsletter: http://www.thefarrahfawcettfoundation.org/documents/FFFNewsletter2013.pdf
Facebook: https://www.facebook.com/pages/The-Farrah-Fawcett-Foundation/175709109105967?ref=hl

Donor: Farrah Fawcett†.
Foundation type: Independent foundation.
Financial data (yr. ended 12/31/13): Assets, $8,996,467 (M); gifts received, $1,884,186; expenditures, $643,824; qualifying distributions, $347,000; giving activities include $347,000 for 8 grants (high: $250,000; low: $5,000).
Purpose and activities: The organization aims to provide funding for alternative methods of cancer research, clinical trials, prevention, and awareness with an emphasis on anal and pediatric cancers.
Fields of interest: Cancers.
Type of support: Research.
Officers and Board Members: Alana Stewart, Pres. and C.E.O. and Director; Shira Nachshon, Secy.-Treas. and Director; Dr. Brad Allen; David Kessler; Kim Swartz.
EIN: 208076177

501
Paul E. and Margaret Feder Family Foundation
9601 Wilshire Blvd., Ste. 560
Beverly Hills, CA 90210-5208 3102471988

Established in 1986 in California.
Donors: Paul E. Feder; Margaret Feder; Donald L. Feder; Steven H. Feder.
Foundation type: Independent foundation.
Financial data (yr. ended 06/30/14): Assets, $2,850,541; gifts received, $50,652; expenditures, $192,257; qualifying distributions, $181,406.
Fields of interest: Education; Health; Religion.
Limitations: Applications not accepted. Giving primarily in CA. No grants to individuals.
Application information: Unsolicited requests for funds not accepted.
Officer: Paul E. Feder, Secy. and C.F.O.
Directors: Donald L. Feder; Helene T. Feder; Margaret Feder; Steven H. Feder.
EIN: 954012416

502
Evelyn M. & Norman Feintech Family Foundation
c/o Evelyn M. Feintech
321 S. Beverly Dr., Ste. K
Beverly Hills, CA 90212-4303

Established in 1990 in California.
Donors: Irving Feintech†; Evelyn M. Feintech; Norman Feintech; Lynn Diane Feintech; Shapell Industries.
Foundation type: Independent foundation.
Financial data (yr. ended 12/31/13): Assets, $2,307,434 (M); gifts received, $1,000,000; expenditures, $299,739; qualifying distributions, $297,228; giving activities include $295,214 for 12 grants (high: $150,000; low: $250).
Purpose and activities: Giving for art and cultural programs, health and human services, and for Jewish organizations.
Fields of interest: Arts and culture; Performing arts; Higher education; Health; Judaism; Human services.
Limitations: Applications not accepted. Giving primarily in CA. No grants to individuals.
Application information: Contributes only to pre-selected organizations.
Officers and Directors: Evelyn M. Feintech, Pres. and Director; Vivian A. Feintech, V.P.; Lynn Diane Feintech, Secy.-Treas. and Director.
EIN: 954268945

503
The Ferguson Foundation
3600 Dragonfly Dr., W 108
Thousand Oaks, CA 91360-8453

Donor: Nancy L. Ferguson.
Foundation type: Independent foundation.
Financial data (yr. ended 07/31/14): Assets, $2,011,608 (M); gifts received, $250,000; expenditures, $183,934; qualifying distributions, $163,500; giving activities include $163,500 for 19 grants (high: $25,000; low: $1,000).
Fields of interest: Arts and culture.
Limitations: Applications not accepted. No grants to individuals.
Application information: Unsolicited requests for funds not accepted.
Officers: Nancy L. Ferguson, Pres.; Kenneth Golden, C.F.O.; Dina F. Killen, Secy.
Directors: Allan F. Hershfield, Ph.D; James E. Killen; Tommy Slater.
EIN: 953930655

504
The Richard M. and Maude M. Ferry Charitable Foundation
c/o John Di Carlo
P.O. Box 87
Long Beach, CA 90801-0087

Established in 1994 in California.
Donors: Richard M. Ferry; Maude M. Ferry.
Foundation type: Independent foundation.
Financial data (yr. ended 06/30/13): Assets, $3,131,710 (M); gifts received, $575,420; expenditures, $366,082; qualifying distributions, $356,760; giving activities include $356,760 for 41 grants (high: $52,500; low: $500).
Fields of interest: Education; Nonprofits; Catholicism.
Type of support: Regranting.
Limitations: Applications not accepted. Giving primarily in CA and WA. No grants to individuals.
Application information: Unsolicited requests for funds not accepted.
Officers: Richard M. Ferry, Pres. and C.F.O.; Maude M. Ferry, Secy.
EIN: 954456601

505
The Finestra Foundation
23202 Oxnard St.
Woodland Hills, CA 91367-3121

Established in 2007 in California.
Donor: Carmen J. Finestra.
Foundation type: Independent foundation.
Financial data (yr. ended 12/31/12): Assets, $1 (M); gifts received, $375,000; expenditures, $319,712; qualifying distributions, $317,100; giving activities include $317,100 for grants.
Fields of interest: Elementary and secondary education; Catholicism.
Limitations: Applications not accepted. No grants to individuals.
Application information: Unsolicited requests for funds not accepted.
Officers: Carmen J. Finestra, Pres.; Tonia Stivale Finestra, V.P.
EIN: 261485201

506
First American Financial Foundation
c/o Parker S. Kennedy
1 First American Way
Santa Ana, CA 92707-5913
Main URL: http://www.firstam.com/about/caring-for-our-community/index.html

Established in 1985 in California.
Donors: The First American Corp.; Parker S. Kennedy.
Foundation type: Company-sponsored foundation.
Financial data (yr. ended 10/31/14): Assets, $8,765 (M); gifts received, $115,000; expenditures, $194,435; qualifying distributions, $191,850; giving activities include $191,850 for 17 grants (high: $75,000; low: $100).
Purpose and activities: The foundation supports hospitals and organizations involved with higher education, rodeo's, and youth development.
Fields of interest: Arts and culture; Museums; Higher education; Hospital care; Equestrianism; Youth development.
Type of support: General support; Cash grants; Annual campaigns; Program development; Scholarships; Sponsorships.
Limitations: Applications not accepted. Giving primarily in areas of company operations in Costa Mesa, Irvine, Los Angeles, Newport Beach, Orange, and Santa Ana, CA. No grants to individuals.
Application information: Contributes only to pre-selected organizations.
Directors: Dennis Gilmore; Parker S. Kennedy.
EIN: 330148572

507
First Harvest Foundation
30937 Steeplechase Dr.
San Juan Capistrano, CA 92675-5402

Established in 2000 in California.
Donors: Dennis Sweeney; Judith Sweeney.
Foundation type: Independent foundation.
Financial data (yr. ended 07/31/14): Assets, $2,069,326 (M); gifts received, $99,222; expenditures, $327,090; qualifying distributions, $326,356; giving activities include $322,024 for 36 grants (high: $81,290; low: $85).
Fields of interest: Ballet; Education; Nonprofits; Christianity; Child welfare.
Type of support: General support; Regranting.
Limitations: Applications not accepted. Giving primarily in CA and CO. No grants to individuals.
Application information: Unsolicited requests for funds not accepted.
Trustees: Dennis J. Sweeney; Judith L. Sweeney; Kim Post Watson.
EIN: 330938198

508
Fitzpatrick Foundation
345 Lorton Ave., Ste. 401
Burlingame, CA 94010-4133   (650) 373-1040
FAX: (650) 373-1037;
E-mail: info@fitzpatrickfoundation.org

Established in 1999 in California.
Donors: Patricia W. Fitzpatrick; Michael J. Fitzpatrick.
Foundation type: Independent foundation.

Financial data (yr. ended 12/31/13): Assets, $7,155,601 (M); expenditures, $420,187; qualifying distributions, $416,482; giving activities include $408,524 for 12 grants (high: $125,000; low: $500).
Purpose and activities: The primary interest of the foundation is to support elementary and secondary school programs for students and educators, with emphasis on programs serving economically disadvantaged youth in the San Francisco Bay Area. The foundation also supports a variety of initiatives including in-school and after-school programs for students which enhance academic achievement, arts education, and technology skills. Additionally, the foundation supports professional staff development programs for teachers with emphasis on the provision and application of technology to improve instruction and learning.
Fields of interest: Arts and culture; Education; Elementary education; Secondary education; Youth services.
Limitations: Giving primarily in the San Francisco Bay Area, CA. No support for political or religious organizations. No grants to individuals, or for endowments or for annual fund drives.
Publications: Grants list.
Application information: The foundation is not accepting letters of inquiry or new grant requests at this time. However, the foundation will fulfill all of its current grant commitments.
  Copies of proposal: 1
  Board meeting date(s): Quarterly
Officer: Michael J. Fitzpatrick, Pres.
Directors: Christopher Fitzpatrick; Kimberly Fitzpatrick; Michael J. Fitzpatrick, Jr.
EIN: 943347336

509
Five Bridges Foundation
P.O. Box 194405
San Francisco, CA 94119-4405
E-mail: contact@fivebridges.org; *Main URL:* http://fivebridges.org

Established in 1998 in California.
Foundation type: Independent foundation.
Financial data (yr. ended 09/30/14): Assets, $12,180,339 (M); expenditures, $625,490; qualifying distributions, $538,838; giving activities include $400,000 for 10 grants (high: $60,000; low: $15,000).
Purpose and activities: The foundation is committed to effecting positive change for at-risk and transition-age youth, ages 14-24, in five Bay Area counties: Alameda, Contra Costa, Marin, San Francisco, and San Mateo. The foundation will fund organizations providing shelter and basic services, employment supports, family reunification, and alternatives to the juvenile justice system. Through the efforts of its grantees, the foundation hopes to generate immediate and measurable positive changes, and to work towards long term solutions that mitigate the need for more costly or punitive interventions in the future. The foundation will make grants to organizations working on: family reunification and supportive adult relationships for youth; food, housing, and other essential services for youth; job skills and employment opportunities for unemployed youth and young adults; and alternatives to judicial system involvement.
Fields of interest: Youth development; Youth services; Adolescents; Young adults; Homeless people; Low-income and poor people.

Type of support: General support; Program development.
Limitations: Giving limited to five Bay Area counties: Alameda, Contra Costa, Marin, San Francisco, and San Mateo, CA. No support for organizations that mainly distribute grants to other organizations. No grants to artistic and aesthetic programs, or for receptions, banquets, displays, shows, or other similar programs.
Publications: Application guidelines; Grants list.
Application information: Unsolicited applications are no longer accepted. The foundation uses an online system for all stages of grantmaking including grant applications, grant agreements, and grant reports. Proposals attached to e-mail messages or paper copies of any of these documents are no longer accepted. Please e-mail all inquiries.
 Initial approach: Refer to online application process on foundation web site
 Deadline(s): Refer to foundation web site for deadline dates
 Board meeting date(s): Varies
 Final notification: Sept.
Officers and Directors: Charles Kallgren, Pres. and Secy. and Director; Amy Matthew, V.P. and Treas.; Allan Casalou, V.P.
Number of staff: 3 part-time professional; 1 part-time support.
EIN: 940732210

510
The Flanagan Family Foundation
6 Evergreen Dr.
Kentfield, CA 94904-2826

Established in 1999 in California.
Donors: Darla Flanagan; Patrick Flanagan.
Foundation type: Independent foundation.
Financial data (yr. ended 09/30/14): Assets, $4,822,412; expenditures, $272,470; qualifying distributions, $231,540.
Fields of interest: Education; University education.
Type of support: Scholarships; Individual development.
Limitations: Applications not accepted. Giving limited to residents of San Anselmo, CA. No grants to individuals.
Application information: Contributes only to pre-selected organizations.
Officers: Darla Flanagan, Pres.; Patrick Flanagan, Secy.-Treas. and C.F.O.
EIN: 680430582

511
The Louise M. and Perry G. Flicker Foundation
1531 Ramona Ave.
South Pasadena, CA 91030-3734

Donors: Louise M. Flicker†; Perry G. Flicker.
Foundation type: Independent foundation.
Financial data (yr. ended 12/31/13): Assets, $485,850 (M); gifts received, $150,000; expenditures, $167,624; qualifying distributions, $156,140; giving activities include $156,140 for 12 grants (high: $50,000; low: $1,000).
Fields of interest: Human services; Senior services; Adolescents.
Limitations: Applications not accepted. Giving primarily in CA. No grants to individuals.

Application information: Unsolicited requests for funds not accepted.
Trustees: Joanne M. Nuckols; Perry G. Flicker; Roger Powers.
EIN: 770458155

512
G.A. Fliesbach Foundation
3952 D Clairemont Mesa Blvd., Ste. 154
San Diego, CA 92117-2714

Donor: Gail Fliesbach.
Foundation type: Independent foundation.
Financial data (yr. ended 11/30/13): Assets, $3,760,654 (M); gifts received, $3,635,989; expenditures, $205,283; qualifying distributions, $179,665; giving activities include $168,800 for 24 grants (high: $19,000; low: $1,000).
Fields of interest: Environment; Domesticated animals; Foundations; Community and economic development.
Limitations: Applications not accepted. Giving primarily in CA and NE.
Application information: Unsolicited requests for funds not accepted.
Officers and Directors: Gail Fliesbach, Pres. and Director; Gloria Koch, Secy.-Treas.
EIN: 900808859

513
Floyd Family Foundation
620 Sand Hill Rd., Apt. 127D
Palo Alto, CA 94304-2096

Established in 1989 in California.
Donors: William S. Floyd; Mary Bell Floyd†.
Foundation type: Independent foundation.
Financial data (yr. ended 06/30/13): Assets, $8,379,162 (M); gifts received, $187,576; expenditures, $357,536; qualifying distributions, $312,000; giving activities include $312,000 for 49 grants (high: $128,500; low: $250).
Purpose and activities: Giving primarily for education and human services.
Fields of interest: Education; Philanthropy; Human services.
Limitations: Applications not accepted. Giving on a national basis. No grants to individuals.
Application information: Contributes only to pre-selected organizations. Unsolicited requests for funds not considered.
Officers: William S. Floyd, Pres.; Jeanne Floyd Downs, V.P. and Secy.-Treas.
EIN: 943106119

514
Kay Richard and Elizabeth Bates Flynt Foundation
13350 Country Way
Los Altos Hills, CA 94022-2437

Donor: Christine F. Hemrick.
Foundation type: Independent foundation.
Financial data (yr. ended 12/31/13): Assets, $1,477,502 (M); expenditures, $412,954; qualifying distributions, $670,476; giving activities include $400,001 for 6 grants (high: $264,001; low: $1,000).
Fields of interest: Wildlife biodiversity.
International interests: Africa.

Limitations: Applications not accepted. Giving primarily in CA and Washington, DC. No grants to individuals.
Application information: Contributes only to pre-selected organizations.
Officer: Peggy Flynt Reavis, C.F.O. and Secy.
Trustee: Christine F. Hemrick.
EIN: 770498527

515
Beverly M. Folger Foundation
(formerly Well Foundation)
180 Montgomery St., Ste. 1616
San Francisco, CA 94104-3552

Donor: Beverly M. Folger.
Foundation type: Independent foundation.
Financial data (yr. ended 12/31/13): Assets, $4,461,648 (M); expenditures, $289,520; qualifying distributions, $236,505; giving activities include $198,500 for 22 grants (high: $75,000; low: $1,500).
Fields of interest: Orchestral music; Nonprofits; Health care clinics; Rehabilitation; Diseases and conditions; HIV/AIDS; Cancers; Leukemia; Community and economic development; Christianity; Human services.
Type of support: Research; Regranting; Research and evaluation.
Limitations: Applications not accepted. Giving primarily in CA. No grants to individuals.
Application information: Unsolicited requests for funds not accepted.
Officers and Directors: Elizabeth J. Folger, Pres. and Director; Gary E. Botto, Secy. and Director; Michael L. Helms, Treas. and Director.
EIN: 942790167

516
The Foor Foundation
P.O. Box 6190
Chico, CA 95927-6190

Established in 1999 in California.
Foundation type: Independent foundation.
Financial data (yr. ended 12/31/13): Assets, $4,344,903 (M); gifts received, $300; expenditures, $262,680; qualifying distributions, $253,833; giving activities include $227,297 for 41 grants (high: $35,000; low: $200).
Fields of interest: Museums; Education; Elementary and secondary education; Higher education; Natural resources; Hospital care; Family planning; Christianity; Human services.
Type of support: Program development; Seed money.
Limitations: Applications not accepted. Giving primarily in CA.
Application information: Contributes only to pre-selected organizations.
Officers: Dan Hunt, Pres.; Kent Ahlswede, V.P.; Joe Drakulic, Secy.
Directors: Peter Wells; Wally Marshall.
EIN: 680422822

517
Forgatch Family Foundation
301 N. Lake Ave., Ste. 900
Pasadena, CA 91101

Established in 2007 in California.
Donors: Lorraine E. Forgatch; Gregory T. Forgatch.
Foundation type: Independent foundation.
Financial data (yr. ended 12/31/14): Assets, $489,801; expenditures, $319,729; qualifying distributions, $307,109.
Fields of interest: Education; Christianity; Human services.
Type of support: General support.
Limitations: Applications not accepted. Giving primarily in CA. No grants to individuals.
Application information: Contributes only to pre-selected organizations.
Officers: Gregory T. Forgatch, Pres.; Lorraine E. Forgatch, Secy.-Treas.
EIN: 261547063

518
Fortisure Foundation
1900 S. Norfolk St., Ste. 270
San Mateo, CA   94403-1183

Donors: Srinivasan Subramanian; Nita Subramanian.
Foundation type: Independent foundation.
Financial data (yr. ended 12/31/13): Assets, $1,749,528 (M); expenditures, $260,225; qualifying distributions, $255,145; giving activities include $250,000 for 1 grant.
Fields of interest: Higher education; Eye diseases.
Type of support: Research.
Limitations: Applications not accepted. Giving primarily in San Francisco, CA.
Application information: Unsolicited requests for funds not accepted.
Trustees: Meghna Subramanian; Nita Subramanian; Priyal Subramanian; Srinivasan Subramanian.
EIN: 456169952

519
Foster Charitable Trust
6100 Via Subida
Rancho Palos Verdes, CA   90275-6444

Established in 1997 in California.
Foundation type: Independent foundation.
Financial data (yr. ended 12/31/13): Assets, $4,319,150 (M); expenditures, $342,809; qualifying distributions, $322,080; giving activities include $322,080 for 30 grants (high: $89,465; low: $640).
Purpose and activities: Giving primarily to Roman Catholic schools and churches.
Fields of interest: Education; Secondary education; University education; Catholicism; Youth services.
Limitations: Applications not accepted. Giving primarily in CA.
Application information: Unsolicited requests for funds not accepted.
Trustees: Gina Dominique Foster; Robert D. Foster.
EIN: 336195828

520
Foundation for Enterprise Development
1241 Cave St.
La Jolla, CA   92037-3602   (866) 936-4333
Contact: Grants Admin.
E-mail: inquire@fed.org
Facebook: https://www.facebook.com/Foundation.for.Enterprise.Development?ref=mf

RSS feed: http://www.fed.org/feed
Twitter: https://twitter.com/fedfellows
YouTube: http://www.youtube.com/user/fedvideos

Established in 1986 in California.
Donors: John Robert Beyster; Jim Russel; Barbara Schmidt; Mary Ann Beyster; Employee Ownership Foundation.
Foundation type: Operating foundation.
Financial data (yr. ended 06/30/13): Assets, $3,142,519 (M); gifts received, $761,706; expenditures, $1,403,087; qualifying distributions, $891,049; giving activities include $163,261 for 9 grants (high: $81,434; low: $2,500), and $995,824 for foundation-administered programs.
Purpose and activities: Giving primarily for the development of entrepreneurialism and employee ownership.
Fields of interest: University education; Business and industry.
Type of support: Grants to individuals.
Limitations: Giving primarily in CA and NJ. No support for political, social or fraternal organizations, or for medical research or international programs. No grants for endowments, the arts, start-up expenses, seed capital, or scholarships; no loans.
Application information: Formal proposals are by invitation only, upon review of the letter of inquiry. Large volumes of material are not accepted. If the foundation deems it fit, it will contact the applicant with a request for more information.
  Initial approach: Letter of inquiry (no more than 3 pages)
  Deadline(s): None
  Final notification: Within 2 weeks if the foundation is willing to consider a formal proposal.
Officers and Trustees: Dr. John Robert Beyster, Chair.; Mary Ann Beyster, Pres.; David Binns, Secy.; Thomas E. Darcy; Steven P. Fischer.
EIN: 330207662

521
The Mortar Foundation, Inc.
3880 Sacramento St.
San Francisco, CA   94118-1626

Donor: Rydex NV, Inc.
Foundation type: Independent foundation.
Financial data (yr. ended 12/31/14): Assets, $4,972,475; expenditures, $347,400; qualifying distributions, $320,798.
Fields of interest: Education; Youth services; Adolescents; Females; Homeless people.
Limitations: Applications not accepted. Giving primarily in CA.
Application information: Contributes only to pre-selected organizations.
Officers: Paula Viragh-Williams, Pres.; Mark Williams, Secy.-Treas.
EIN: 300510976

522
Four Friends Foundation
2405 Briarcrest Rd.
Beverly Hills, CA   90210-1819

Donors: Robert Shaye; Eva Shaye.
Foundation type: Independent foundation.
Financial data (yr. ended 12/31/13): Assets, $4,737,843 (M); gifts received, $596,792;

expenditures, $390,730; qualifying distributions, $389,202; giving activities include $384,000 for 23 grants (high: $50,000; low: $1,000).
Fields of interest: Arts and culture; Museums; Human services.
Limitations: Applications not accepted. Giving primarily in New York, NY. No grants to individuals.
Application information: Contributes only to pre-selected organizations.
Trustees: Eva Shaye; Katja Shaye; Robert Shaye.
EIN: 954292739

523
Frieda C. Fox Family Foundation
12411 Ventura Blvd.
Studio City, CA   91604-2407   (818) 308-4369
Contact: Annie Hernandez, Exec. Dir.
E-mail: info@fcfox.org; Main URL: http://www.fcfox.org
LinkedIn: http://www.linkedin.com/company/the-frieda-c-fox-family-foundation
Twitter: http://twitter.com/fcfoxfamfound
YouTube: http://www.youtube.com/user/fcfoxorg#p/u/6/nwqRVYS-BMQ

Established in 1999 in California.
Foundation type: Independent foundation.
Financial data (yr. ended 12/31/13): Assets, $6,074,634 (M); gifts received, $19,350; expenditures, $590,400; qualifying distributions, $554,771; giving activities include $233,500 for 20 grants (high: $101,650; low: $200), and $321,271 for 1 foundation-administered program.
Purpose and activities: The foundation seeks inquiries from programs that improve and expand learning environments of children, especially for those from economically- and socially-disadvantaged families; provides needed financial support for existing, highly-successful, results-oriented programs; and actively promotes positive interactions between children, youth, and adults, through programs that actively involve parents and/or staff and embrace professional development and training for those that deal directly with children or create their learning environments.
Fields of interest: Child welfare; Youth development; Youth mentoring; Civics for youth; Parents; Low-income and poor people.
Type of support: Leadership and professional development; Pro bono consulting services; In-kind gifts; Institutional evaluations; Program development; Matching grants; Technical assistance.
Limitations: Giving limited to Los Angeles and Santa Clara counties, CA. No support for schools; religious institutions; organizations that unfairly discriminate against people because of age, race, creed, gender, national origin, handicap, sexual orientation, or ethnicity; or organizations that do not have at least one full year's operational and financial history to share with the foundation. No grants to individuals, or for capital improvement projects, support for past operating deficits, or fundraising events; no loans.
Publications: Application guidelines; Grants list; Program policy statement (including application guidelines).
Application information: See foundation web site for complete application guidelines.
  Initial approach: Online Letter of Introduction through foundation web site
  Board meeting date(s): Summer and winter
Officers and Directors: Alan C. Fox, Pres. and Director; Daveen Fox, V.P. and Director; Alexis

Marion, Secy. and Director; Cathy Reynolds, Treas. and Director; Annie Hernandez, Exec. Dir.; Carolyn Fox; Nancy Miller; Katie Marcus Reker; Scott Semel.
Number of staff: 1 full-time professional; 1 part-time professional.
EIN: 954775770

524
Keith and Pamela Fox Family Trust
c/o Pamela and Keith Fox
21793 Congress Springs Ln.
Saratoga, CA   95070-9725

Established in 2000 in California.
Donors: Keith Fox; Pamela Fox.
Foundation type: Operating foundation.
Financial data (yr. ended 12/31/13): Assets, $7,843,695 (M); gifts received, $400,000; expenditures, $482,930; qualifying distributions, $420,275; giving activities include $327,500 for 6 grants (high: $100,000; low: $10,000).
Purpose and activities: Giving primarily for health care, particularly to children's hospitals; some funding for education.
Fields of interest: Education; Specialty hospital care; Diseases and conditions; Child welfare.
Limitations: Applications not accepted. Giving primarily in CA; some funding in Boston, MA. No grants to individuals.
Application information: Unsolicited requests for funds not accepted.
Officers: Keith Fox, C.E.O. and Pres.; Christine Ratcliffe, Secy.; Kenneth Ratcliffe, C.F.O.
EIN: 770560716

525
Samuel I. & John Henry Fox Foundation
(formerly John H. Fox Foundation)
P.O. Box 45174
San Francisco, CA   94145-0174

Established in 1955 in California.
Foundation type: Independent foundation.
Financial data (yr. ended 03/31/15): Assets, $6,070,595 (M); expenditures, $370,170; qualifying distributions, $314,355; giving activities include $300,250 for 83 grants (high: $4,000; low: $1,250).
Purpose and activities: Giving to charitable institutions in San Diego County, CA.
Fields of interest: Arts and culture; Performing arts; Museums; Education; Animal welfare; Health; Hospice care; Diseases and conditions; Human services; Child welfare; Scouting programs; Senior services.
Type of support: General support; Continuing support; Capacity-building and technical assistance; Equipment; Program development; Curriculum development; Scholarships; Research; Technical assistance.
Limitations: Applications not accepted. Giving limited to San Diego County, CA.
Application information: Unsolicited requests for funds not accepted.
Trustee: Union Bank, N.A.
Number of staff: None.
EIN: 956010288

526
The Frankel Foundation
c/o Law Offices of Marc C. Rosenberg
18321 Ventura Blvd., Ste. 900
Tarzana, CA   91356-4238

Established in 1988 in New York.
Donor: Raymond Frankel.
Foundation type: Independent foundation.
Financial data (yr. ended 12/31/12): Assets, $11,108,237 (M); gifts received, $303,967; expenditures, $541,381; qualifying distributions, $541,381; giving activities include $417,992 for 26 grants (high: $100,000; low: $400).
Purpose and activities: Giving for education, the environment, and Jewish organizations.
Fields of interest: Higher education; Environment; Academic libraries; Judaism; Human services.
Limitations: Applications not accepted. Giving primarily in CA. No grants to individuals.
Application information: Contributes only to pre-selected organizations.
Trustees: Belinda Frankel; Maxine Frankel; Raymond Frankel.
EIN: 133187074

527
The Fremont Group Foundation
P.O. Box 193809
San Francisco, CA   94119-3809

Established in 1996 in California.
Donor: Fremont Sequoia Holding, L.P.
Foundation type: Company-sponsored foundation.
Financial data (yr. ended 12/31/14): Assets, $11,749,691; expenditures, $478,047; qualifying distributions, $443,512.
Purpose and activities: The foundation supports food banks and organizations involved with education, the environment, animal welfare, child welfare, human services, and international affairs and matches contributions made by its employees.
Fields of interest: Education; Agriculture; Human services.
Type of support: General support; Employee volunteer services; Employee matching gifts; Annual campaigns; Program development; Scholarships.
Limitations: Applications not accepted. Giving primarily in CA. No support for political or religious organizations or organizations involved with reproductive issues. No grants to individuals.
Application information: Contributes only to pre-selected organizations.
  Board meeting date(s): Twice per year
Officers and Directors: Brenda A. Levine, Pres. and Director; Richard S. Kopf, V.P. and Secy. and Director; Deborah L. Duncan, V.P. and Treas. and Director; Shu C. Huang, V.P. and Director; Alan M. Dachs.
Number of staff: 1 part-time support.
EIN: 333255428

528
Freshwind Foundation
44238 Fremont Blvd.
Fremont, CA   94538-6000

Donors: Charles K. Chang; Grace T. Wu; Eagletech International, Inc.
Foundation type: Company-sponsored foundation.

Financial data (yr. ended 12/31/13): Assets, $2,152,396 (M); expenditures, $240,432; qualifying distributions, $210,000; giving activities include $210,000 for 9 grants (high: $100,000; low: $500).
Purpose and activities: The foundation supports organizations involved with historic preservation, education, and religion.
Fields of interest: Historic preservation; Education; Religion; Christianity.
Type of support: General support.
Limitations: Applications not accepted. Giving primarily in CA.
Application information: Contributes only to pre-selected organizations.
Officers: Charles K. Chang, Pres.; Grace T. Wu, Secy.
EIN: 202031040

529
Virginia Friedhofer Charitable Trust
8730 Wilshire Blvd., Ste. 530
Beverly Hills, CA   90211-2708
Contact: Arnold Seidel, Tr.

Established in 1995 in California.
Foundation type: Independent foundation.
Financial data (yr. ended 12/31/13): Assets, $9,783,425 (M); expenditures, $378,590; qualifying distributions, $349,090; giving activities include $244,500 for 21 grants (high: $50,000; low: $1,000).
Purpose and activities: Giving primarily for the benefit of scientific and educational nonprofit agencies.
Fields of interest: Arts and culture; Opera; Education; Diseases and conditions.
Type of support: Research.
Limitations: Applications not accepted. Giving primarily in Los Angeles, CA. No grants to individuals.
Application information: Unsolicited requests for funds not accepted.
Trustee: Arnold Seidel.
EIN: 956995937

530
Lisa and Maury Friedman Foundation
29480 Bertrand Dr.
Agoura Hills, CA   91301-4126
E-mail: lisa@friedmanfoundation.net; Application address: 5737 Kanan Rd., Ste. 529, Agoura Hills, CA 91301, tel.: (818) 991-7914

Established in 2004 in California.
Foundation type: Independent foundation.
Financial data (yr. ended 12/31/13): Assets, $1,820,790 (M); gifts received, $4,948; expenditures, $161,015; qualifying distributions, $140,901; giving activities include $127,360 for 32 grants (high: $36,000; low: $36).
Purpose and activities: Giving primarily to support classroom and outdoor educators that enable students to develop environmental values of peaceful cooperation, moderation and conservation. Particular interest is taken in environmental education programs in Jewish and Israeli education.
Fields of interest: Education; Natural resources; Diseases and conditions; Judaism; Human services; Family services.
Type of support: Research.

Limitations: Applications accepted. Giving primarily in CA and NY.
Application information:
Initial approach: E-mail
Deadline(s): Apr. 1 or Oct. 1
Final notification: June 1 or Dec. 1
Officer: Lisa Friedman, Pres.
Director: Maury Friedman.
EIN: 201380310

531

Morton and Marcine Friedman Foundation
1530 J. St., Ste. 200
Sacramento, CA 95814-2053 (916) 383-3333
Contact: Marcy Friedman, Pres.

Established in 1997 in California.
Donors: Marcine Friedman; Morton L. Friedman.
Foundation type: Independent foundation.
Financial data (yr. ended 12/31/13): Assets,
$5,674,777 (M); expenditures, $306,906;
qualifying distributions, $300,990; giving activities
include $300,990 for 19 grants (high: $100,000;
low: $500).
Fields of interest: Arts and culture; Performing arts;
Education; Higher education; Diseases and
conditions; Judaism; Human services.
Type of support: General support.
Limitations: Applications accepted. Giving primarily
in Sacramento, CA. No grants to individuals.
Application information:
Initial approach: Proposal
Deadline(s): None
Officer: Marcine Friedman, Pres.
EIN: 680282444

532

**The Michelle and Robert Friend
Foundation**
355 Hayes St.
San Francisco, CA 94102-4420 (415) 546-0696
Contact: Michelle Friend, Pres.

Established in 2004 in California.
Donors: Robert Friend; Michelle Friend.
Foundation type: Independent foundation.
Financial data (yr. ended 06/30/13): Assets,
$3,193,368 (M); gifts received, $1,000,000;
expenditures, $214,668; qualifying distributions,
$211,830; giving activities include $210,250 for 37
grants (high: $50,000; low: $100).
Fields of interest: Animal welfare; Community
service for youth.
Limitations: Applications accepted. Giving primarily
in CA and MO. No grants to organizations lacking
501(c)(3); no grants to individuals.
Application information:
Initial approach: Proposal
Deadline(s): None
Officers: Michelle Friend, Pres.; Nicole Friend, V.P.
and Secy.-Treas.
EIN: 201893124

533

Friends of Soochow University
1766 N. Orange Grove Ave.
Los Angeles, CA 90046-2149

Donor: J.T. Tai & Co Foundation Inc.
Foundation type: Independent foundation.

Financial data (yr. ended 12/31/13): Assets,
$607,465 (M); gifts received, $313,100;
expenditures, $331,057; qualifying distributions,
$330,019; giving activities include $323,610 for 1
grant.
Purpose and activities: Giving primarily to Soochow
University in Shihlin, Taipei, Taiwan.
Fields of interest: University education.
International interests: Taiwan.
Limitations: Applications not accepted. Giving
primarily in Shihlin, Taipei, Taiwan.
Application information: Unsolicited requests for
funds not accepted.
Officers: Edward Rada, Jr., Pres.; Robert Oehler,
V.P.; Gilbert Tsao, Secy.; Edward Y.H. Lee, Treas.
Directors: Luanne Chang; Andrew H. Chen; Sue
Chen; Dennis Lin; Helene Lin; Yee-Horn Shuai;
Kenny Tang.
EIN: 956100332

534

The Barbara and Jay Fritz Foundation
2006 Washington St., Ste. 8
San Francisco, CA 94109-2844

Established in 1988 in California.
Donors: Arthur J. Fritz, Jr.; Barbara Fritz.
Foundation type: Independent foundation.
Financial data (yr. ended 12/31/13): Assets,
$5,476,776 (M); expenditures, $491,046;
qualifying distributions, $252,000; giving activities
include $252,000 for 17 grants (high: $76,800;
low: $500).
Fields of interest: Opera; Education; Foundations;
Nonprofits; Catholicism.
Type of support: General support; Regranting.
Limitations: Applications not accepted. Giving
limited to CA. No grants to individuals.
Application information: Contributes only to
pre-selected organizations.
Officers: Arthur J. Fritz, Jr., Pres.; Barbara Fritz,
C.F.O.
EIN: 943083753

535

Walter and Mary Frome Family Foundation
151 Kalmus Dr., Ste. F-2
Costa Mesa, CA 92626-5965

Established in 2003 in California.
Donors: Walter Frome; Mary Frome.
Foundation type: Independent foundation.
Financial data (yr. ended 12/31/13): Assets,
$6,116,664 (M); gifts received, $547,792;
expenditures, $273,590; qualifying distributions,
$255,552; giving activities include $255,552 for 55
grants (high: $15,000; low: $1,000).
Fields of interest: Education; Environment;
Nonprofits; Health; Maternal and perinatal health;
Youth organizing; Special population support;
Adolescents; Females; American Indians; People
with disabilities.
Type of support: Regranting; Research and
evaluation.
Limitations: Applications not accepted. Giving
primarily in CA. No grants to individuals.
Application information: Contributes only to
pre-selected organizations.
Officers: Stan Frome, Pres.; Mary Frome, C.F.O. and
Secy.
EIN: 200396894

536

The Fry Foundation
P.O. Box 20670
Oakland, CA 94620

Donors: Charles L. Fry; Alice J. Fry.
Foundation type: Independent foundation.
Financial data (yr. ended 12/31/13): Assets,
$3,313,318 (M); gifts received, $167,540;
expenditures, $171,777; qualifying distributions,
$150,000; giving activities include $150,000 for 1
grant.
Purpose and activities: Giving primarily to the
American Institute of Mathematics in Morgan Hill,
CA.
Fields of interest: Mathematics.
Limitations: Applications not accepted. Giving
primarily in Morgan Hill, Palo Alto, CA. No grants to
individuals.
Application information: Unsolicited requests for
funds not accepted.
Officers: Charles L. Fry, Pres.; Alice J. Fry, V.P.; John
C. Fry, Secy.
EIN: 010570536

537

Fudge Family Foundation
711 W. 17th St., D-12
Costa Mesa, CA 92627-4350 (919) 642-6659
Contact: Gary A. Fudge, Pres.

Established in 1997 in California.
Donor: Gary A. Fudge.
Foundation type: Independent foundation.
Financial data (yr. ended 12/31/13): Assets,
$3,052,028 (M); expenditures, $247,453;
qualifying distributions, $245,399; giving activities
include $244,500 for 17 grants (high: $112,100;
low: $150).
Fields of interest: Education; University education;
Human services.
Limitations: Applications accepted. Giving primarily
in CA, with some giving in WA.
Application information:
Initial approach: Letter
Deadline(s): None
Officers: Gary A. Fudge, Pres.; Austyn R. Fudge, V.P.
EIN: 330757057

538

The Gillian S. Fuller Foundation, Inc.
(formerly The Fuller Foundation, Inc.)
9200 Sunset Blvd., PH 22
Los Angeles, CA 90069-3306

Established in 1951 in Texas.
Donors: Andrew P. Fuller‡; William M. Fuller.
Foundation type: Independent foundation.
Financial data (yr. ended 12/31/13): Assets,
$6,489,973 (M); gifts received, $1,000,000;
expenditures, $299,780; qualifying distributions,
$273,513; giving activities include $255,000 for 13
grants (high: $80,000; low: $5,000).
Fields of interest: Arts and culture; Higher
education; Law education; Reading promotion;
Nonprofits; Health; Diseases and conditions;
Multiple sclerosis; Community and economic
development; Human services; Child welfare.
Type of support: Regranting; Research.
Limitations: Applications not accepted. Giving
primarily in CA and New York, NY.

Application information: Contributes only to pre-selected organizations.
Officers and Directors: Gillian Fuller, Pres. and Director; William Fuller French, V.P. and Treas. and Director; Mark Tinglof, Secy. and Director.
EIN: 756015942

539
Marilyn and Robert Funari Family Foundation
2100 Huntington Dr., Ste. 1
San Marino, CA   91108-2000

Established in 2001 in California.
Donor: Robert Funari.
Foundation type: Independent foundation.
Financial data (yr. ended 12/31/13): Assets, $3,254,999 (M); expenditures, $204,910; qualifying distributions, $161,700; giving activities include $161,700 for 17 grants (high: $26,000; low: $250).
Fields of interest: Education; Christianity; Human services.
Limitations: Applications not accepted. Giving primarily in CA. No grants to individuals.
Application information: Contributes only to pre-selected organizations.
Officers and Directors: Robert Funari, Pres. and Director; Russell Breeden III; Dan B. Floyd.
EIN: 954835367

540
Furth Family Foundation
2347 Becker Blvd.
Santa Rosa, CA   95403   (707) 526-1389
Contact: Frederick P. Furth, Mgr. and Tr.

Established in 1969 in California.
Donor: Frederick P. Furth.
Foundation type: Independent foundation.
Financial data (yr. ended 12/31/13): Assets, $995,215 (M); expenditures, $703,955; qualifying distributions, $417,700; giving activities include $417,700 for 28 grants (high: $170,000; low: $100).
Purpose and activities: Giving primarily for education and human services.
Fields of interest: Arts and culture; Education; Public affairs.
Limitations: Applications accepted. Giving primarily in CA. No grants to individuals.
Application information:
   Initial approach: Proposal
   Deadline(s): None
Officers and Trustees: Peggy J. Furth, Pres. and Trustee; Donna W. Furth, Secy.-Treas. and Trustee; Frederick P. Furth, Mgr. and Trustee; Darby Furth Bonomi.
EIN: 237062014

541
Georges and Germaine Fusenot Charity Foundation, Inc.
12711 Ventura Blvd., Ste. 390
Studio City, CA   91604-2491

Established in 1967 in California.
Donors: Germaine Fusenot†; Andre Blanchard†; Marcelle Blanchard†; Virginia W. Markel†.
Foundation type: Independent foundation.

Financial data (yr. ended 07/31/14): Assets, $5,864,802 (M); expenditures, $337,969; qualifying distributions, $291,944; giving activities include $262,000 for 39 grants (high: $20,000; low: $1,000).
Purpose and activities: Giving primarily for education, youth services and the arts.
Fields of interest: Arts and culture; Education; Environment; Health; Hospital care; Diseases and conditions; Religion; Human services; Food delivery; Child welfare; Child development; Youth development; People with vision impairments.
Type of support: General support; Matching grants; Continuing support; Capital campaigns; Capital and infrastructure; Equipment.
Limitations: Applications not accepted. Giving limited to CA. No support for religious organizations for religious purposes, or for political organizations. No grants to individuals, or for emergency or endowment funds, deficit financing, demonstration projects, publications, conferences, scholarships, or fellowships; no loans.
Application information: Unsolicited requests for funds not accepted.
Officers: Guy Arnold Stone, Chair.; Richard G. Herlihy, Mgr.
Trustees: Viveca Ann S. Berry; Charles F. Gorder; Janet W. Kernon; Patricia H. Stone; Richard H. Stone; Norman C. Walker; Scott L. Whitman.
Number of staff: 1 full-time professional.
EIN: 956207831

542
The Sanford & Linda Gallanter Foundation
525 El Camino del Mar
San Francisco, CA   94121-1041

Established in 2007 in California.
Donors: Sanford Gallanter; TAG, Inc.
Foundation type: Independent foundation.
Financial data (yr. ended 12/31/12): Assets, $2,466,277 (M); gifts received, $296,969; expenditures, $310,961; qualifying distributions, $294,935; giving activities include $294,935 for grants.
Fields of interest: Judaism; Human services.
Limitations: Applications not accepted. Giving primarily in CA and NY. No grants to individuals.
Application information: Contributes only to pre-selected organizations.
Officers: Sanford Gallanter, Pres.; Linda Gallanter, Secy.-Treas.
EIN: 261506996

543
Bob & Marie Gallo Foundation
P.O. Box 1130
Modesto, CA   95353-1130

Established in 2000 in California.
Donors: Marie D. Gallo; Robert J. Gallo; Aileen Gallo Survivor's Trust.
Foundation type: Independent foundation.
Financial data (yr. ended 12/31/13): Assets, $9,831,402 (M); expenditures, $600,849; qualifying distributions, $504,507; giving activities include $214,250 for 65 grants (high: $21,000; low: $100).
Purpose and activities: Giving primarily for the arts, education, human services, and Roman Catholic churches; funding also for the restoration and

development of a wildlife habitat in a portion of the San Joaquin Valley, CA.
Fields of interest: Education; Environment; Catholicism.
Limitations: Applications not accepted. Giving primarily in CA. No grants to individuals.
Application information: Unsolicited requests for funds not accepted.
Officers: Robert J. Gallo, C.E.O.; Matthew I. Friedrich, Secy.; John R. Gallo, C.F.O.
Directors: Amy M. Gallo-Ballatore; Gina M. Gallo; Marie D. Gallo; Mary E. Gallo; Matthew J. Gallo; Thomas J. Gallo; Julie G. Vander Wall.
EIN: 912048972

544
The Shelby and Frederick Gans Foundation
2288 Broadway St., Ste. 7
San Francisco, CA   94115-1240

Donors: Shelby M. Gans; Frederick M. Gans.
Foundation type: Independent foundation.
Financial data (yr. ended 12/31/13): Assets, $0 (M); gifts received, $212,549; expenditures, $297,942; qualifying distributions, $282,003; giving activities include $278,415 for 22 grants (high: $72,000; low: $150).
Fields of interest: Human services.
Limitations: Applications not accepted.
Application information: Unsolicited requests for funds not accepted.
Trustees: Frederick M. Gans; Shelby M. Gans.
EIN: 263209213

545
The Bertha and John Garabedian Charitable Foundation
P.O. Box 26270
Fresno, CA   93729-6270   (559) 970-7994
Contact: Nancy Steitz, Grants Asst.
FAX: (559) 432-1025;
E-mail: nsaslaw@sbcglobal.net

Established in 1993 in California.
Donor: John Garabedian†.
Foundation type: Independent foundation.
Financial data (yr. ended 07/31/13): Assets, $4,910,618 (M); expenditures, $549,963; qualifying distributions, $486,544; giving activities include $350,700 for 89 grants (high: $45,000; low: $1,000).
Purpose and activities: The private foundation serves charitable organizations primarily located in central California, which benefit arts, culture, and humanities, community activities and improvements, education, ethics, religion, and health and human services.
Fields of interest: Arts and culture; Education; Higher education; Health; Public policy; Religion; Human services.
Type of support: Policy, advocacy and systems reform.
Limitations: Giving primarily in central CA.
Publications: Informational brochure (including application guidelines).
Application information: Application form required.
   Initial approach: Letter of inquiry
   Copies of proposal: 1
   Deadline(s): Aug. 1 for letter of inquiry; Sept. 1 for completed application

Board meeting date(s): Monthly
Final notification: Dec.
Trustees: Silvestre Arias; Malcolm H. Stewart; H. Tookoian, MD; Bank of America, N.A.
Number of staff: 1 part-time professional.
EIN: 943188321

546
Silvio and Mary Garaventa Family Foundation
4080 Mallard Dr.
Concord, CA 94520-1245   (925) 689-8350
Contact: Mary Garaventa, Mgr.

Established in 1986 in California.
Donors: Silvio Garaventa; Mary Garaventa; SEG Trucking; Contra Costa Waste, Inc.; Garaventa Enterprises, Inc.; Mallard Financial Group.
Foundation type: Independent foundation.
Financial data (yr. ended 03/31/14): Assets, $1,102,972 (M); gifts received, $314,156; expenditures, $316,674; qualifying distributions, $297,000; giving activities include $297,000 for 5 grants (high: $100,000; low: $47,000).
Fields of interest: Education; Health; Catholicism.
Type of support: Capital campaigns.
Limitations: Applications accepted. Giving primarily in CA. No grants to individuals.
Application information: Application form required.
   Initial approach: Letter
   Deadline(s): None
Officer: Mary Garaventa, Mgr.
Trustees: Marie Adler; Louisa Binswanger; Linda Colvis.
EIN: 680100302

547
Gareatis Foundation
P.O. Box 14436
Fremont, CA 94539-1136

Donor: Gust Perlegos.
Foundation type: Independent foundation.
Financial data (yr. ended 12/31/13): Assets, $4,325,372 (M); expenditures, $219,182; qualifying distributions, $215,000; giving activities include $215,000 for 5 grants (high: $50,000; low: $35,000).
Fields of interest: Higher education.
Type of support: Scholarships.
Limitations: Applications not accepted. Giving primarily in CA and PA.
Application information: Unsolicited requests for funds not accepted.
Officers: Pete C. Perlegos, Pres.; Archie G. Perlegos, C.F.O.; Gust Perlegos, V.P.; Mary Perlegos, V.P.; Nick J. Perlegos, Secy.
EIN: 273001288

548
The Gareeb Family Foundation
1200 Newport Center Dr., Ste. 230
Newport Beach, CA 92660-0933

Established in 2005 in Missouri.
Donor: Nabeel K. Gareeb.
Foundation type: Independent foundation.
Financial data (yr. ended 12/31/13): Assets, $6,487,516 (M); gifts received, $960,500; expenditures, $303,359; qualifying distributions,

$246,000; giving activities include $246,000 for 11 grants (high: $130,000; low: $1,000).
Fields of interest: Diseases and conditions; Islam; Human services.
Type of support: Research; Research and evaluation.
Limitations: Applications not accepted. Giving in the U.S., with some emphasis on CA. No grants to individuals.
Application information: Unsolicited requests for funds not accepted.
Trustee: Nabeel K. Gareeb.
EIN: 436925988

549
GAT Family Foundation
P.O. Box 1558
Rancho Santa Fe, CA 92067-1558

Established in 2004 in California.
Donors: Gillian M. Thornley; Anthony S. Thornley.
Foundation type: Independent foundation.
Financial data (yr. ended 12/31/13): Assets, $7,175,687 (M); expenditures, $398,883; qualifying distributions, $325,740; giving activities include $322,000 for 18 grants (high: $117,000; low: $500).
Fields of interest: Arts and culture; Animal welfare; Diseases and conditions; Human services; Child welfare.
Limitations: Applications not accepted. Giving primarily in CA. No grants to individuals.
Application information: Contributes only to pre-selected organizations.
Officers and Directors: Gillian M. Thornley, Pres. and Director; Anthony S. Thornley, C.F.O. and Secy. and Director; Claire M. Thornley Smith; Alexander N. Thornley; Christian A. Thornley; Warren T. Thornley.
EIN: 562490647

550
The Fred Gellert Family Foundation
1038 Redwood Hwy., Bldg. B, Ste. 2
Mill Valley, CA 94941-1620   (415) 381-7575
E-mail: FGFamilyfoundation@gmail.com; Main URL: http://www.fgfamilyfoundation.com
Grants List: http://www.fgfamilyfoundation.com/grant-awards

Established in 1958 in California.
Donor: Fred Gellert, Sr.✝.
Foundation type: Independent foundation.
Financial data (yr. ended 12/31/13): Assets, $8,972,850 (M); expenditures, $614,631; qualifying distributions, $454,012; giving activities include $346,000 for 138 grants (high: $25,000; low: $1,000).
Purpose and activities: Giving primarily in the areas of long-term sustainability planning, community support and social services, advanced and specialized education, and reproductive health.
Fields of interest: Arts and culture; Education; Environment; Natural resources; Health; Hospital care; Family planning; Youth pregnancy prevention; Mental health care; Community and economic development; Human services; Family services; Child welfare; Senior services; Children and youth; Adolescents; Adults; Young adults; Females; People of African descent; Immigrants and migrants; Low-income and poor people; Victims of crime and

abuse; People with disabilities; People with physical disabilities.
Type of support: General support; Matching grants; Continuing support; Capital campaigns; Equipment; Program development; Convening; Recordings; Publications; Seed money; Curriculum development; Scholarships; Research; Technical assistance.
Limitations: Applications not accepted. Giving on a national and international basis, but primary focus is San Francisco and Marin counties, CA. No grants to individuals or for annual campaigns, land acquisition or K-12 school reform; no loans.
Publications: Annual report; Grants list.
Application information: The foundation is currently not accepting any unsolicited letters of inquiry or grant proposals.
   Board meeting date(s): Apr. and Nov.
Officers and Trustees: Annette Gellert, Co-Chair. and Trustee; Fred Gellert, Co-Chair. and Trustee.
Number of staff: 1 full-time professional; 2 part-time professional; 1 part-time support.
EIN: 946062859

551
Joanne and Marcel George Foundation
630 Tigertail Rd.
Los Angeles, CA 90049-2333   (310) 472-3552
Contact: Joanne M. George, V.P.

Established in 2000 in California.
Donors: Marcel George; Joanne M. George.
Foundation type: Independent foundation.
Financial data (yr. ended 12/31/13): Assets, $2,914,718 (M); gifts received, $200,000; expenditures, $179,248; qualifying distributions, $148,035; giving activities include $148,035 for 24 grants (high: $34,000; low: $5,000).
Fields of interest: Education; Higher education; Health; Human services.
Type of support: General support.
Limitations: Applications accepted. Giving primarily in Los Angeles, CA.
Application information: Application form required.
   Initial approach: Letter
   Deadline(s): None
Officers: Marcel George, Pres.; Carol George, C.F.O.; Joanne M. George, V.P.; Elyse Kaiser, Secy.
Directors: Jim Childs; Bob Phillipich.
EIN: 954831881

552
The Georgina-Frederick Children's Foundation
1214 E. Green St., Ste. 104
Pasadena, CA 91106-3955

Established in 2001 in California.
Donors: Fred L. Astman; Jean Astman.
Foundation type: Operating foundation.
Financial data (yr. ended 12/31/13): Assets, $5,876,709 (M); expenditures, $348,177; qualifying distributions, $340,000; giving activities include $340,000 for 30 grants (high: $45,000; low: $3,000).
Fields of interest: Higher education; Zoos; Health care clinics; Community and economic development; Catholicism; Human services.
Limitations: Applications not accepted. Giving primarily in CA. No grants to individuals.
Application information: Contributes only to pre-selected organizations.

Officers: Scott Hood, Pres.; Heidi Hood, Secy.
Director: Denise Cook.
EIN: 522364243

553
The Gifts of the Magi Foundation
16885 Via Del Campo Ct., Ste. 300
San Diego, CA   92127-1753

Established in 2004 in Unspecified.
Donors: Thomas Liguori; Susan Liguori.
Foundation type: Independent foundation.
Financial data (yr. ended 12/31/13): Assets,
$2,771,292 (M); gifts received, $15,000;
expenditures, $188,489; qualifying distributions,
$180,000; giving activities include $180,000 for 3
grants (high: $173,000; low: $2,000).
Fields of interest: Education; Foundations;
Diseases and conditions; Judaism; People with
vision impairments.
Limitations: Applications not accepted. Giving
primarily in CA. No grants to individuals.
Application information: Contributes only to
pre-selected organizations.
Officers and Directors: Thomas A. Liguori, Chair.
and Director; Susan K. Liguori, C.E.O. and Director;
Catherine E. Liguori, V.P.; Daniel T. Liguori, V.P.;
Lisa A. Liguori, Secy. and C.F.O.
EIN: 202029251

554
Giles O'Malley Foundation
(formerly The Terry M. Giles Foundation)
2020 Main St., Ste. 600
Irvine, CA   92614-8226

Donor: Terry M. Giles.
Foundation type: Independent foundation.
Financial data (yr. ended 12/31/13): Assets,
$101,155 (M); gifts received, $254,014;
expenditures, $153,345; qualifying distributions,
$152,610; giving activities include $152,610 for 16
grants (high: $75,029; low: $100).
Purpose and activities: Giving primarily for higher
education, federated giving programs, and children,
youth, and social services.
Fields of interest: Arts education; Education; Law
education; Nonprofits; Specialty hospital care;
Human services; Child welfare; Youth organizing;
Female children and youth.
Type of support: Regranting.
Limitations: Applications not accepted. Giving
primarily in TX and VA, with some giving in CA. No
grants to individuals.
Application information: Contributes only to
pre-selected organizations.
Directors: Kristen Blackford; Terry M. Giles; Kalli
O'Malley.
EIN: 481295831

555
Stephen & Margaret Gill Family
Foundation
32 Flood Cir.
Atherton, CA   94027-2151

Donors: Margaret G. Gill; Stephen P. Gill.
Foundation type: Independent foundation.
Financial data (yr. ended 12/31/12): Assets,
$4,585,913 (M); expenditures, $275,999;

qualifying distributions, $228,700; giving activities
include $228,700 for grants.
Fields of interest: Ballet; Higher education; Natural
resources; Protestantism.
Type of support: Program development; General
support; Capital campaigns; Annual campaigns.
Limitations: Applications not accepted. Giving in the
U.S., primarily in CA. No grants to individuals.
Application information: Unsolicited requests for
funds not accepted.
Officers: Margaret G. Gill, Pres.; Stephen P. Gill,
C.F.O.
Directors: Elizabeth O. Gill; Richard P. Gill.
EIN: 943335952

556
The Richard and Ellen Gilleland
Foundation
(formerly The Richard Gilleland Foundation)
4994 Summit View Dr.
Westlake Village, CA   91362-5610

Established in 1995 in Texas.
Donors: Carrie Jo Gilleland; Ellen Gilleland; Richard
Gilleland.
Foundation type: Independent foundation.
Financial data (yr. ended 12/31/12): Assets,
$2,480,774 (M); expenditures, $140,804;
qualifying distributions, $140,200; giving activities
include $140,200 for 15 grants (high: $39,300;
low: $200).
Purpose and activities: Giving primarily for religious
organizations.
Fields of interest: Religion; Human services.
Limitations: Applications not accepted. Giving
primarily in CA. No grants to individuals.
Application information: Unsolicited requests for
funds not accepted.
Officers: Richard Gilleland, Pres. and Treas.; Ellen
Gilleland, V.P. and Secy.
Director: Joyce Strazulla.
EIN: 770418822

557
Earl B. Gilmore Foundation
P.O. Box 480314
Los Angeles, CA   90048-1314

Established in 1958 in California.
Donors: A.F. Gilmore Co.; Marie Dent Gilmore†.
Foundation type: Independent foundation.
Financial data (yr. ended 12/31/13): Assets,
$2,935,458 (M); expenditures, $136,540;
qualifying distributions, $132,485; giving activities
include $131,860 for 76 grants (high: $12,500;
low: $185).
Purpose and activities: Emphasis on social
services; grants also for higher and secondary
education, health agencies, and youth agencies.
Fields of interest: Arts and culture; Education;
Human services.
Limitations: Applications not accepted. Giving
primarily in CA. No grants to individuals.
Application information: Unsolicited requests for
funds not accepted.
Officers and Directors: Henry L. Hilty, Jr., Pres. and
Director; Andrew G. Hilen, V.P. and Director; Frances
Gilmore Hilen, V.P. and Director; Karl M. Samuelian,
V.P. and Director; M.B. Hartman, Secy.-Treas.
EIN: 956029602

558
The Ginder Family Foundation
31597 Table Rock Dr.
Laguna Beach, CA   92651-8328

Established in 2003 in California.
Donor: Ginder Charitable Lead Trust.
Foundation type: Operating foundation.
Financial data (yr. ended 11/30/13): Assets,
$1,108,051 (M); gifts received, $202,405;
expenditures, $226,205; qualifying distributions,
$212,597; giving activities include $212,597 for 5
grants (high: $100,597; low: $2,000).
Fields of interest: Health; Human services; Youth
development.
Limitations: Applications not accepted. No grants to
individuals.
Application information: Unsolicited requests for
funds not accepted.
Officers and Directors: Stephen P. Ginder, Pres. and
Director; Deborah A. Ginder, Secy.-Treas; Brad
Ginder; Grant S. Ginder; Reid G. Ginder.
EIN: 200495435

559
Girls Rights Project
(formerly Keare/Hodge Family Foundation)
155 Mountain Wood Ln.
Woodside, CA   94062-2563
Contact: Stacey Keare, Pres.
E-mail: stacey@girlsrightsproject.com

Established in 2001 in California.
Donors: John Hodge; Stacey Keare.
Foundation type: Independent foundation.
Financial data (yr. ended 12/31/13): Assets,
$4,801,368 (M); expenditures, $283,150;
qualifying distributions, $249,533; giving activities
include $237,833 for 47 grants (high: $25,000;
low: $1,000).
Purpose and activities: Giving in areas that will
improve girls rights and achieve girls empowerment
worldwide. Primary issues of importance are girls
education, antitrafficking, ending child marriage,
etc.
Fields of interest: Education; Health; Child abuse;
Human services; Child welfare; Children; Female
children and youth; Low-income and poor people.
Type of support: Equal access.
Limitations: Applications accepted. Giving on a
national and international basis, with some
emphasis on the San Francisco Bay Area, CA. No
support for religious organizations that discriminate
or require statements of faith in hiring.
Publications: Grants list.
Application information:
   Initial approach: Letter
   Copies of proposal: 1
   Deadline(s): None
Officers: Stacey Keare, Pres.; John Hodge, V.P. and
Treas.
Number of staff: 1 full-time support.
EIN: 522364195

560
GirlSMART Literacy Program
(formerly National Literacy Program Fund)
21 Orinda Way, Ste. C, #358
Orinda, CA   94563-2534   (925) 254-6358
Contact: Barclay Simpson, Pres.

Donor: Barclay Simpson.
Foundation type: Independent foundation.
Financial data (yr. ended 12/31/13): Assets, $121,044 (M); gifts received, $390,000; expenditures, $328,170; qualifying distributions, $171,033; giving activities include $171,033 for 5 grants (high: $68,750; low: $5,000).
Purpose and activities: Giving for the improvement of children's literacy.
Fields of interest: Early childhood education.
Limitations: Applications accepted. Giving primarily in Omaha, NE, NH, Buffalo, NY, Rapid City, SD.
Application information:
  Initial approach: Letter
  Deadline(s): None
Officers: Barclay Simpson, Pres.; Sharon Simpson, Secy.
EIN: 263542627

561
The Erika Glazer Family Foundation
P.O. Box 2489
Beverly Hills, CA   90213-2489

Donor: Erika J. Glazer.
Foundation type: Independent foundation.
Financial data (yr. ended 12/31/13): Assets, $7,193,173 (M); expenditures, $221,618; qualifying distributions, $210,000; giving activities include $210,000 for 2 grants (high: $200,000; low: $10,000).
Purpose and activities:
Fields of interest: Health; Human services.
Limitations: Applications not accepted. Giving primarily in CA.
Application information: Unsolicited requests for funds not accepted.
Officers and Directors: Erika J. Glazer, Pres. and Director; Zachary Shabtai, C.F.O. and Director; Alexandra Shabtai, Secy. and Director; Richard D. Jacobs.
EIN: 461519428

562
The Diane & Guilford Glazer Foundation
c/o James L. Krasne APC
9440 Santa Monica Blvd., Ste. 610
Beverly Hills, CA   90210-4619

Established in 1997 in California.
Donors: Guilford Glazer; Inst. Advancement of Ed in Jaffa.
Foundation type: Independent foundation.
Financial data (yr. ended 12/31/13): Assets, $10,869,046 (M); gifts received, $4,000,000; expenditures, $134,222; qualifying distributions, $131,516; giving activities include $131,516 for 9 grants (high: $100,000; low: $100).
Purpose and activities: Funding primarily for Jewish agencies and temples, education, and human services.
Fields of interest: Education; Voluntarism; Nonprofits; Catholicism; Judaism; Human services.
Type of support: Regranting.
Limitations: Applications not accepted. Giving primarily in CA and NY. No grants to individuals.
Application information: Contributes only to pre-selected organizations.
Officers: Guilford Glazer, Pres.; Diane Glazer, C.F.O. and Secy.
EIN: 954657165

563
Peter Glenville Foundation
c/o Dennis F. Rose & Assocs.
4312 Woodman Ave.
Sherman Oaks, CA   91423
Application address: 32 Golden Glen Dr., Simi Valley, CA 93065, tel.: (818) 882-3125

Established in 2003 in New York.
Donor: Hardy William Smith†.
Foundation type: Independent foundation.
Financial data (yr. ended 12/31/13): Assets, $4,220,294 (M); expenditures, $685,713; qualifying distributions, $376,148; giving activities include $177,159 for 8 grants (high: $57,159; low: $5,000).
Purpose and activities: Giving primarily to organizations that benefit the arts, specifically the performing arts, theater, film, actors and directors.
Fields of interest: Arts and culture.
Limitations: Applications accepted. Giving primarily in CA; funding also in GA, NY and UT.
Application information: Application form required.
  Initial approach: Letter
  Deadline(s): None
Officer: Holly Book, Exec. Dir.
Directors: Hollyann Book; Leilani Downer.
EIN: 141889271

564
William and Charlene Glikbarg Foundation
(formerly The Glikbarg Foundation, Inc.)
200 W. Victoria St.
Santa Barbara, CA   93101-3627
E-mail: susanh@glikbarg.com

Donor: William K. Glikbarg.
Foundation type: Independent foundation.
Financial data (yr. ended 12/31/13): Assets, $9,034,349 (M); gifts received, $412,036; expenditures, $360,921; qualifying distributions, $317,829; giving activities include $317,829 for 68 grants (high: $100,000; low: $100).
Purpose and activities: Giving to help low-income people help themselves.
Fields of interest: Education; Nonprofits; Judaism; Human services.
Type of support: Continuing support; Annual campaigns; Convening; Regranting; Scholarships.
Limitations: Applications not accepted. Giving primarily in CA.
Application information: Contributes only to pre-selected organizations.
Officers: Susan Hanson, Pres.; Steven Glikbarg, V.P. and Treas.; Charlene Glikbarg, Secy.
Number of staff: 1 part-time support.
EIN: 522302532

565
Global Catalyst Foundation
530 Lytton Ave., 2nd Fl.
Palo Alto, CA   94301-1541   (650) 486-2430
FAX: (650) 560-6218;
E-mail: info@global-catalyst.org; *Main URL:* http://www.global-catalyst.org

Established in 2000 in California.
Donors: Kamran Elahian; Global Catalyst Partners; Art Schneiderman.
Foundation type: Independent foundation.

Financial data (yr. ended 12/31/13): Assets, $58,493 (M); gifts received, $415,000; expenditures, $362,679; qualifying distributions, $311,000; giving activities include $311,000 for 2 grants (high: $301,000; low: $10,000).
Purpose and activities: The foundation's mission is to improve people's lives through the effective application of information technologies. It initiates and supports innovative projects worldwide to improve education, alleviate poverty, promote social tolerance and celebrate diversity.
Fields of interest: Education; Computer science; Economic development; Immigrants and migrants.
International interests: Africa; Asia; Middle East; United Kingdom of Great Britain and Northern Ireland.
Type of support: Equipment; Program development; Technical assistance.
Limitations: Applications not accepted. Giving primarily for U.S.-based NGO's delivering services to developing countries. No grants to individuals, or for capital campaigns.
Application information: Contributes only to pre-selected organizations.
Officer and Directors: Kamran Elahian, Chair. and Director; Arthur Schneiderman, Secy.; Zohre Elahian, Treas.; Koji Osawa; Vijay Parikh.
EIN: 770555801

566
Godric Foundation
625 S. Fair Oaks Ave., Ste. 360
South Pasadena, CA   91030-5813
Contact: Nancy Davis

Donor: Marcia W. Constance.
Foundation type: Independent foundation.
Financial data (yr. ended 12/31/13): Assets, $6,054,784 (M); expenditures, $265,789; qualifying distributions, $243,998; giving activities include $208,750 for 14 grants (high: $100,000; low: $2,500).
Fields of interest: Education; Environment; Youth development.
Type of support: General support; Curriculum development; Capital and infrastructure; Program development.
Limitations: Applications not accepted. Giving primarily in Santa Barbara, CA. No grants to individuals; no loans.
Application information: Unsolicited requests for funds not accepted.
  Board meeting date(s): Twice per year and as necessary
Officers and Directors: Marcia W. Constance, Pres. and Director; Jamie Constance, V.P. and Director; Julie Lytle Nesbit, Secy. and Director; Richard E. Llewellyn II, C.F.O. and Director; Sharon Bradford; Brett Hodges; Brian Hodges.
Number of staff: None.
EIN: 953500486

567
Joseph and Dorothy Goldberg Charitable Trust
14004 Mercado Dr.
Del Mar, CA   92014
Contact: Earl N. Feldman, Tr.

Established in 1996 in California.
Donors: Dorothy Goldberg†; Goldberg Interim Trust.

Foundation type: Independent foundation.
Financial data (yr. ended 12/31/13): Assets,
$7,059,901 (M); expenditures, $499,690;
qualifying distributions, $465,573; giving activities
include $329,100 for 21 grants (high: $80,000;
low: $2,000).
Purpose and activities: Giving primarily for Jewish
organizations.
Fields of interest: Nonprofits; Judaism; Human
services.
Type of support: Scholarships; Regranting.
Limitations: Applications accepted. Giving primarily
in CA and NY.
Application information:
Initial approach: Proposal
Deadline(s): None
Trustees: Edward A. Applbaum; Earl N. Feldman;
Robert S. Goldberg.
EIN: 336195814

568
The Frank M. & Lee Goldberg Foundation
1333 Camino Del Rio S., Ste. 310
San Diego, CA 92108-3520

Established in 1981 in California.
Foundation type: Independent foundation.
Financial data (yr. ended 11/30/13): Assets,
$1,365,769 (M); expenditures, $364,301;
qualifying distributions, $349,489; giving activities
include $346,700 for 18 grants (high: $200,000;
low: $500).
Fields of interest: Nonprofits.
Type of support: Regranting.
Limitations: Applications not accepted. Giving
primarily in San Diego, CA. No grants to individuals.
Application information: Unsolicited requests for
funds not accepted.
Officers: Frank M. Goldberg, Chair.; Anne Nagorner,
Pres.; Lee Goldberg, Secy.
Director: Edward Goldberg.
EIN: 953678549

569
Ruth & Sheldon Goldstein Foundation
1035 19th St., Unit 2
Santa Monica, CA 90403-4498

Established in 1995 in New York.
Donors: Sheldon Goldstein; Ruth Goldstein; Rita
Goldstein Ashton.
Foundation type: Independent foundation.
Financial data (yr. ended 12/31/13): Assets,
$648,222 (M); gifts received, $44,250;
expenditures, $177,693; qualifying distributions,
$165,931; giving activities include $153,000 for 4
grants (high: $150,000; low: $1,000).
Fields of interest: Education; Domesticated
animals; Health.
Type of support: General support.
Limitations: Applications not accepted. Giving
primarily in NY. No grants to individuals.
Application information: Unsolicited requests for
funds not accepted.
Trustees: Rita Goldstein Ashton; Sarah Nargiso.
EIN: 161478693

570
Goodall Family Foundation
(formerly Jack W. Goodall Family Foundation)
401 W. A Street, Ste. 2300
San Diego, CA 92101-7915

Established in 2000 in California.
Donor: Jackson W. Goodall, Jr.
Foundation type: Independent foundation.
Financial data (yr. ended 12/31/13): Assets,
$1,077,566 (M); gifts received, $30,000;
expenditures, $199,700; qualifying distributions,
$171,600; giving activities include $171,600 for 7
grants (high: $110,000; low: $600).
Fields of interest: Education; Religion; Human
services.
Limitations: Applications not accepted. Giving
primarily in San Diego, CA.
Application information: Unsolicited requests for
funds not accepted.
Officers: Jackson W. Goodall, Jr., Pres.; Jeff Goodall,
V.P.
Directors: Kathleen M. Hart; Minnette M. Rundlett.
EIN: 330929117

571
The Gooding Family Foundation
4954 Rancho del Mar Trail
San Diego, CA 92130-5214
Contact: Terence J. Gooding, Tr.

Established in 1997 in California.
Donors: Terence J. Gooding; Scripps Foundation.
Foundation type: Independent foundation.
Financial data (yr. ended 12/31/13): Assets,
$1,149,240 (M); expenditures, $284,897;
qualifying distributions, $278,687; giving activities
include $265,500 for 6 grants (high: $100,000;
low: $500).
Purpose and activities: Giving primarily for medical
research, human services, and children and youth
services.
Fields of interest: Elementary education; Higher
education; Zoos; Hospital care; Heart and
circulatory system diseases; Community and
economic development; Human services; Child
welfare.
Type of support: Research.
Limitations: Applications accepted. Giving primarily
in CA.
Application information: Application form required.
Initial approach: Letter
Deadline(s): None
Trustee: Terence J. Gooding.
EIN: 336203973

572
Donald G. Goodwin Family Foundation Inc.
16492 Somerset Ln.
Huntington Beach, CA 92649-2835

Established in 1996 in California.
Donor: Donald G. Goodwin.
Foundation type: Independent foundation.
Financial data (yr. ended 12/31/13): Assets,
$7,209,239 (M); gifts received, $100,000;
expenditures, $416,539; qualifying distributions,
$378,855; giving activities include $375,000 for 25
grants (high: $20,000; low: $10,000).
Fields of interest: Cancers; People with disabilities.
Type of support: General support.

Limitations: Applications not accepted. Giving
primarily in CA. No grants to individuals.
Application information: Unsolicited requests for
funds not accepted.
Officer: Donald G. Goodwin, Pres.
EIN: 954609975

573
Ellen F. Gordon Charitable Trust
201 Kings Pl.
Newport Beach, CA 92663-5704

Foundation type: Independent foundation.
Financial data (yr. ended 12/31/12): Assets,
$4,404,824 (M); expenditures, $250,890;
qualifying distributions, $250,390; giving activities
include $250,390 for grants.
Fields of interest: Higher education; Foundations;
Public health.
Limitations: Applications not accepted.
Application information: Unsolicited requests for
funds not accepted.
Trustee: Ellen Gordon.
EIN: 066519553

574
The Betsy Gordon Foundation
c/o Elizabeth Gordon
1537 4th St.
P.O. Box 15
San Rafael, CA 94901-2737

Donor: Elizabeth Gordon.
Foundation type: Independent foundation.
Financial data (yr. ended 10/31/13): Assets,
$127,024 (M); gifts received, $481,454;
expenditures, $446,950; qualifying distributions,
$446,950; giving activities include $439,815 for 28
grants (high: $138,134; low: $1,000).
Purpose and activities: Giving primarily for
education and spiritual enrichment.
Fields of interest: Education; Foundations; Human
services.
Limitations: Applications not accepted. No grants to
individuals.
Application information: Contributes only to
pre-selected organizations.
Officers: Elizabeth Gordon, Pres.; Jean Merlin,
Secy.; Louis Leeburg, Treas.
Trustees: Angeles Arrien; Ricci Coddington; Frances
Vaughan, Ph.D.
EIN: 113634807

575
The Berry Gordy Family Foundation
933 Cecina Way
Los Angeles, CA 90077-2630

Established in 1996 in California.
Donor: Berry Gordy.
Foundation type: Independent foundation.
Financial data (yr. ended 12/31/13): Assets,
$1,636,225 (M); expenditures, $259,741;
qualifying distributions, $252,950; giving activities
include $252,950 for 20 grants (high: $50,000;
low: $1,000).
Fields of interest: Arts and culture; Dance;
Education; Diseases and conditions; Heart and
circulatory system diseases; Employment; Diversity
and intergroup relations.

Limitations: Applications not accepted. Giving primarily in CA. No grants to individuals.
Application information: Contributes only to pre-selected organizations.
Officers: Berry Gordy, Chair.; Edna V. Anderson-Owens, Secy.; Gary Iskowitz, CPA, Treas.
Directors: Bernard Donnenfeld, Esq.; Berry Gordy IV, Esq.; Yakub Hazzard, Esq.; Sherrlyn Jackson.
Number of staff: 2 full-time professional.
EIN: 954605488

576
Lee Graff Foundation
1515 E. 15th St.
Los Angeles, CA 90021-2711

Established in 1989 in California.
Donor: Lee Graff.
Foundation type: Independent foundation.
Financial data (yr. ended 12/31/14): Assets, $2,873,902 (M); expenditures, $286,545; qualifying distributions, $194,243; giving activities include $194,243 for 7 grants (high: $101,000; low: $1,000).
Purpose and activities: Giving primarily for education, the arts, health, and social services.
Fields of interest: Arts and culture; Music; Higher education; Nonprofits; Human services; Family services.
Type of support: Regranting.
Limitations: Applications not accepted. Giving primarily in CA. No grants to individuals.
Application information: Contributes only to pre-selected organizations.
Trustees: Scott Morielli; Victoria Schaffer.
EIN: 954252561

577
The Grass Foundation
P.O. Box 241458
Los Angeles, CA 90024-9258 (424) 832-4188
FAX: (310) 986-2252;
E-mail: info@grassfoundation.org; Main URL: http://www.grassfoundation.org
Blog: http://grasslab11.blogspot.com
Twitter: https://twitter.com/#!/grassfoundation

Established in 1957 in Massachusetts.
Donors: Grass Instrument Co.; Albert M. Grass†; Ellen R. Grass†; Cannon Manufacturing Co.; The Ellen R. Grass Trust.
Foundation type: Independent foundation.
Financial data (yr. ended 12/31/13): Assets, $22,423,891 (M); expenditures, $1,207,949; qualifying distributions, $1,047,398; giving activities include $363,464 for 8 grants (high: $110,566; low: $10,000).
Purpose and activities: Giving to encourage research in neurophysiology and the neurosciences; grants primarily for fellowships for summer study at a marine biological laboratory, lectureships, and for higher education.
Fields of interest: Biomedicine; Neurology; Diseases and conditions; Marine science; Biology.
International interests: Africa; Latin America.
Type of support: Fellowships; Research.
Limitations: Applications accepted. Giving primarily in Washington, DC and Woods Hole, MA; with some giving internationally.

Publications: Application guidelines; Informational brochure (including application guidelines); Program policy statement.
Application information: Application formats and deadlines depend upon type of grant; specific information will be sent upon request. Application guidelines and form are available on foundation web site. Application form required.
    Initial approach: Refer to foundation web site
    Board meeting date(s): Jan. and July
Officers and Trustees: Felix E. Schweizer, Ph.D, Pres. and Trustee; Bernice Grafstein, Ph.D, V.P. and Trustee; Catherine E. Carr, Ph.D, Secy. and Trustee; Richard Larkin, CPA, Treas. and Trustee; Graeme W. Davis, Ph.D; Henry J. Grass, MD; Gregory Holmes, MD; Ronald R. Hoy, Ph.D; George Langford, Ph.D; Jeff Lichtman, MD; Edwin McCleskey, Ph.D; Amy R. Segal, Esq.; Janis C. Weeks, Ph.D; Steven J. Zottoli, Ph.D.
Number of staff: 2 part-time support.
EIN: 046049529

578
Green Earth Charitable Organization
2906 Belmont Terr.
Fremont, CA 94539-8340

Donors: Charles Liang; Chiu-Chu Liu; Sara Liang.
Foundation type: Independent foundation.
Financial data (yr. ended 12/31/13): Assets, $5,586,978 (M); expenditures, $146,750; qualifying distributions, $145,090; giving activities include $143,560 for 5 grants (high: $110,000; low: $2,993).
Fields of interest: Education; Domesticated animals; Human services.
Limitations: Applications not accepted. Giving primarily in CA.
Application information: Unsolicited requests for funds not accepted.
Officer: Carly Kao, Treas.
Director: Sara Liu.
EIN: 261701023

579
Lenore S. & Bernard A. Greenberg Fund
1009 N. Roxbury Dr.
Beverly Hills, CA 90210-3021

Established in 1990 in California.
Donors: Bernard A. Greenberg; Lenore S. Greenberg.
Foundation type: Independent foundation.
Financial data (yr. ended 04/30/13): Assets, $2,253,791 (M); expenditures, $238,548; qualifying distributions, $231,000; giving activities include $231,000 for 8 grants (high: $207,000; low: $1,000).
Fields of interest: Arts and culture; Composition; Opera; Philanthropy; Community and economic development.
Limitations: Applications not accepted. Giving primarily in Los Angeles, CA, and New York, NY. No grants to individuals.
Application information: Contributes only to pre-selected organizations.
Directors: Bernard A. Greenberg; Lenore S. Greenberg.
EIN: 954300830

580
Greenwood Foundation
1500 Park Pl.
San Marino, CA 91108-1039

Established in 1994 in California.
Donors: Guilford C. Babcock; Gwendolyn Garland Babcock.
Foundation type: Independent foundation.
Financial data (yr. ended 11/30/14): Assets, $3,564,973 (M); gifts received, $300,000; expenditures, $169,070; qualifying distributions, $167,873; giving activities include $165,000 for 1 grant.
Fields of interest: Education.
Limitations: Applications not accepted. Giving primarily in CA. No grants to individuals.
Application information: Contributes only to pre-selected organizations.
Trustees: Guilford C. Babcock; Gwendolyn Garland Babcock.
EIN: 956980924

581
The Lewis Greenwood Foundation
34816 Staccato St.
Palm Desert, CA 92211-3079

Established in 1999 in California.
Donor: Lewis Greenwood.
Foundation type: Independent foundation.
Financial data (yr. ended 12/31/13): Assets, $5,466,845 (M); expenditures, $219,780; qualifying distributions, $219,780; giving activities include $212,000 for 46 grants (high: $25,000; low: $500).
Fields of interest: Arts and culture; Nonprofits; Religion; Judaism; Youth development.
Type of support: Regranting.
Limitations: Applications not accepted. Giving primarily in CA. No grants to individuals.
Application information: Unsolicited requests for funds not accepted.
Officers: Rita Greenwood, Pres.; Mel Aballe, C.F.O.
EIN: 770527064

582
Grey Family Charitable Foundation
c/o Grey Management Inc.
1990 S. Bundy Dr., Ste. 420
Los Angeles, CA 90025-1578 (310) 237-1700

Donor: Brad A. Grey.
Foundation type: Independent foundation.
Financial data (yr. ended 12/31/13): Assets, $2,808 (M); gifts received, $380,000; expenditures, $390,289; qualifying distributions, $381,071; giving activities include $378,000 for 7 grants (high: $143,000; low: $15,000).
Fields of interest: Education; University education; Human services.
Limitations: Applications not accepted. Giving primarily in CA.
Application information: Contributes only to pre-selected organizations.
Officers and Directors: Brad A. Grey, Pres. and Director; Cassandra H. Grey, V.P. and Director; Samuel I. Grey, V.P. and Director; Bonnie R. Grey, Secy.-Treas.
EIN: 454241188

583
Grey Family Foundation
c/o Mowat Mackie & Anderson, LLP
1999 Harrison St., Ste. 1500
Oakland, CA 94612-4547

Foundation type: Independent foundation.
Financial data (yr. ended 12/31/13): Assets,
$5,531,050 (M); gifts received, $394,850;
expenditures, $186,372; qualifying distributions,
$182,940; giving activities include $178,590 for 82
grants (high: $100,000; low: $20).
Fields of interest: Education; University education;
Health; Human services.
Limitations: Applications not accepted. No grants to
individuals.
Application information: Contributes only to
pre-selected organizations.
Officers: Margaret Grey, Pres.; Carolyn K. Grey,
Secy.; Richard S. Grey, C.F.O.
EIN: 680323540

584
G.H. and O.J. Griffiths Charitable Foundation
P.O. Box 45174
San Francisco, CA 94145-0174

Foundation type: Independent foundation.
Financial data (yr. ended 12/31/13): Assets,
$5,406,274 (M); expenditures, $285,883;
qualifying distributions, $234,850; giving activities
include $174,000 for 11 grants (high: $40,000;
low: $10,000).
Fields of interest: Arts and culture; Museums;
Education.
Limitations: Applications not accepted. Giving
primarily in Santa Barbara, CA.
Application information: Unsolicited requests for
funds not accepted.
Trustees: John A. Berryhill; Union Bank, N.A.
EIN: 306265990

585
The Grimm Family Education Foundation
11001 River Run Blvd., Ste. 101
Bakersfield, CA 93311-8981

Donors: The Rodney Grimm Family Foundation; Keith
Gardiner; S.A. Camp Company.
Foundation type: Independent foundation.
Financial data (yr. ended 06/30/13): Assets,
$1,950,399 (M); gifts received, $1,150,000;
expenditures, $963,418; qualifying distributions,
$877,815; giving activities include $176,736 for 4
grants, and $1,163,418 for 3
foundation-administered programs.
Fields of interest: Education.
Limitations: Applications not accepted. Giving
primarily in CA.
Application information: Unsolicited requests for
funds not accepted.
Officers: Barbara Grimm-Marshall, Pres.; Steve
Barnes, C.F.O. and Secy.
Director: Sean McNally.
EIN: 273194151

586
The Lillian Sherwood Griswold Foundation
2803 Barranca Pkwy.
Irvine, CA 92606-5114

Established in 1995 in California.
Donor: Griswold Industries.
Foundation type: Independent foundation.
Financial data (yr. ended 12/31/13): Assets,
$138,137 (M); gifts received, $195,833;
expenditures, $206,536; qualifying distributions,
$206,160; giving activities include $205,000 for 2
grants (high: $105,000; low: $100,000).
Fields of interest: Education; Agriculture; Religion.
Type of support: General support.
Limitations: Applications not accepted. Giving
primarily in CA and Washington, DC. No grants to
individuals.
Application information: Unsolicited requests for
funds not accepted.
Officers: David E. Griswold, Pres.; Doris Meyers,
Secy.; Kris Olsen, Treas.
EIN: 330668667

587
Stella B. Gross Charitable Trust
P.O. Box 60078, SC-MPK-03-M
Los Angeles, CA 90060-0078
Application Address: c/o Bank of the West, 50 W.
Fernando St., Ste. 425, San Jose, CA, 95113

Established in 1966 in California.
Donor: Stella B. Gross‡.
Foundation type: Independent foundation.
Financial data (yr. ended 06/30/14): Assets,
$7,171,968 (M); expenditures, $315,199;
qualifying distributions, $251,623; giving activities
include $199,999 for 20 grants (high: $55,000;
low: $1,666).
Fields of interest: Arts and culture; Visual arts;
Performing arts; Museums; Education; Elementary
education; Child educational development; Higher
education; Nonprofits; Health; Hospital care;
Hospice care; Diseases and conditions; Heart and
circulatory system diseases; Cancers; Public
administration; Human services; Child welfare; Child
development; Senior services; Seniors; People with
disabilities.
Type of support: General support; Continuing
support; Program development; Seed money;
Research; Regranting.
Limitations: Applications accepted. Giving limited to
Santa Clara County, CA. No grants to individuals.
Publications: Annual report; Grants list.
Application information:
 Copies of proposal: 1
 Deadline(s): None
 Board meeting date(s): June and Dec.
 Final notification: 6 months
Trustee: Bank of the West.
Directors: Thomas P. Hansen; Arthur K. Lund;
Jeffrey O'Neal.
EIN: 237142181

588
Grossberg Abrams Foundation
P.O. Box 2067
Saratoga, CA 95070-0067

Established in 1997 in New York.
Donors: Georgia Abrams; Nat Abrams.

Foundation type: Independent foundation.
Financial data (yr. ended 08/31/14): Assets,
$7,825,843 (M); expenditures, $390,192;
qualifying distributions, $389,645; giving activities
include $237,500 for 23 grants (high: $46,000;
low: $2,000).
Fields of interest: Religion; Judaism.
Type of support: General support.
Limitations: Applications not accepted. Giving
primarily in CA. No grants to individuals.
Application information: Unsolicited requests for
funds not accepted.
Trustees: Georgia Abrams; Isaac N. Abrams.
EIN: 776148976

589
Guerin Foundation
355 S. Grand Ave., Ste. 1710
Los Angeles, CA 90071-1560

Established in 1967 in California.
Donor: J.P. Guerin.
Foundation type: Independent foundation.
Financial data (yr. ended 11/30/14): Assets,
$6,122,116; expenditures, $333,857; qualifying
distributions, $284,400.
Purpose and activities: Giving primarily for
education.
Fields of interest: Arts and culture; Education;
Domesticated animals.
Limitations: Applications not accepted. Giving
primarily in CA. No grants to individuals.
Application information: Unsolicited requests for
funds not accepted.
Officers: J.P. Guerin, Chair. and Pres.; Fabienne
Guerin, V.P. and Treas.; Charles E. Rickershauser,
Secy.
Trustee: Kelly G. Day.
EIN: 952504545

590
The H. & S. Foundation
P.O. Box 6526
Malibu, CA 90264-6526

Established in 2004 in Delaware.
Donors: Harriet Nichols; Steven Nichols.
Foundation type: Independent foundation.
Financial data (yr. ended 12/31/14): Assets,
$1,878,520; expenditures, $159,362; qualifying
distributions, $155,800.
Fields of interest: Education; Hospital care;
Judaism; Human services.
Limitations: Applications not accepted. Giving
primarily in CA. No grants to individuals.
Application information: Unsolicited requests for
funds not accepted.
Officers: Harriet Nichols, Pres.; Sharyn Nichols
Levey, V.P.; Steven Nichols, Secy.-Treas.
EIN: 651237583

591
Hagar Family Foundation
P.O. Box 5395
Novato, CA 94948-5395   3107776555

Donors: Sam R. Hagar; Red Head Inc.; IP Mississippi
Charities, LLC.
Foundation type: Independent foundation.

Financial data (yr. ended 12/31/13): Assets, $3,299 (M); gifts received, $287,450; expenditures, $292,684; qualifying distributions, $290,645; giving activities include $287,000 for 40 grants (high: $75,000; low: $1,500).

Fields of interest: Cancers; Food banks; Child welfare.

Limitations: Applications accepted. Giving primarily in HI, KY and NV.

Application information: Application form required.
Initial approach: Proposal
Deadline(s): None

Officers: Sam R. Hagar, Chair.; Renata Ravina, Secy.; Dan Frattalli, Treas.

Directors: Hugh V. Stan Curtis; Kari Hagar; Velma Hagar-Otterman; Bobbi Harrell; Jane Hightower; Marco Monroy; Benjamin R. Winslow.

EIN: 263052507

592
Hagopian Family Foundation
11150 Santa Monica Blvd., Ste. 1200
Los Angeles, CA 90025-3386

Established in 1989 in California.

Donors: B. Kipling Hagopian; Mary Ann Hagopian.

Foundation type: Independent foundation.

Financial data (yr. ended 12/31/13): Assets, $2,213,851 (M); expenditures, $213,627; qualifying distributions, $172,091; giving activities include $169,000 for 33 grants (high: $25,000; low: $3).

Fields of interest: Education; Health; Religion; Human services.

Type of support: General support.

Limitations: Applications not accepted. Giving primarily in CA and Washington, DC. No grants to individuals.

Application information: Unsolicited requests for funds not accepted.

Officers: B. Kipling Hagopian, Chair. and Pres.; Mary Ann Hagopian, V.P. and Secy.; Gina Lauren Hagopian, V.P.; Todd Kipling Hagopian, V.P.

EIN: 954247008

593
Hakka Foundation
P.O. Box 662124
Arcadia, CA 91066-2124
E-mail: fsw-884@yahoo.com

Foundation type: Independent foundation.

Financial data (yr. ended 12/31/13): Assets, $5,770,503 (M); expenditures, $372,748; qualifying distributions, $322,783; giving activities include $198,780 for 29 grants (high: $100,000; low: $200).

Fields of interest: Arts and culture; Education; Health.

Limitations: Applications accepted. Giving primarily in CA.

Application information: Application form required.
Initial approach: Letter
Deadline(s): None

Officers: Kwei Kuang Hsu; Chiyun Ho; Frank S. Wu.

EIN: 810553705

594
The Armen and Gloria Hampar Family Foundation
10247 Valley Spring Ln.
Toluca Lake, CA 91602-2931

Established in 1998 in California.

Donor: Armen Hampar.

Foundation type: Independent foundation.

Financial data (yr. ended 12/31/13): Assets, $3,974,995 (M); gifts received, $34,079; expenditures, $181,934; qualifying distributions, $181,934; giving activities include $159,000 for 20 grants (high: $122,000; low: $250).

Purpose and activities: Giving primarily to Armenian organizations and churches.

Fields of interest: Education; Christianity; Human services.

International interests: Armenia.

Limitations: Applications not accepted. Giving primarily in CA. No grants to individuals.

Application information: Contributes only to pre-selected organizations.

Officers: Armen Hampar, Pres.; Steven Hampar, C.F.O.; Audrey L. Matoesian, Secy.

EIN: 954714147

595
The Hand Foundation
P.O. Box 5655
Redwood City, CA 94063-0655
Contact: Radha Blackman, Exec. Dir.
FAX: (650) 599-9025;
E-mail: info@thehandfoundation.org; *Main URL:* http://www.thehandfoundation.org
E Newsletter: http://thehandfoundation.org/newsletter
Facebook: https://www.facebook.com/pages/The-HAND-Foundation/397390166996630
LinkedIn: http://www.linkedin.com/company/3286976?trk=prof-exp-company-name
Twitter: https://twitter.com/HandFound

Established in 2003 in California.

Donors: Farzad Nazem; Noosheen Hashemi.

Foundation type: Independent foundation.

Financial data (yr. ended 06/30/13): Assets, $12,812,622 (M); gifts received, $721,799; expenditures, $452,490; qualifying distributions, $354,609; giving activities include $202,191 for 49 grants (high: $50,000; low: $250).

Purpose and activities: The foundation's mission is to advance the philanthropic sector, prevent child sexual abuse, build a global middle class, and prepare and engage the Next Generation.

Fields of interest: Education; Philanthropy; Sexual abuse; Community and economic development.

Type of support: Annual campaigns; Fellowships; Research; Student aid.

Limitations: Applications accepted. Giving primarily in CA and Washington, DC. No support for political and religious organizations. No grants for travel expenses.

Publications: Grants list.

Application information: The foundation will accept unsolicited proposals, but for the most part will only fund organizations it knows well. See web site for application and for guidelines. Application form required.
Initial approach: Letter of inquiry
Copies of proposal: 1

Deadline(s): Mar. 1, June 1, Sept. 1, and Dec. 1 (for letters of inquiry)
Board meeting date(s): Varies

Officers and Board Members: Noosheen Hashemi, Pres. and Director; Farzad Nazem, Secy. and Director; Nasrin Hashemi, Treas. and Director; Radha Blackman, Exec. Dir.

Number of staff: 1 full-time professional; 2 part-time professional.

EIN: 562403164

596
The Handlery Foundation
180 Geary St., Ste. 700
San Francisco, CA 94108-5604   (415) 781-4550
Contact: Margaret Handlery, Chair.

Established in 1998 in California.

Donors: Ardyce A. Handlery; Paul R. Handlery.

Foundation type: Independent foundation.

Financial data (yr. ended 12/31/13): Assets, $5,649,052 (M); gifts received, $240,562; expenditures, $271,314; qualifying distributions, $242,541; giving activities include $227,122 for 34 grants (high: $20,230; low: $100).

Purpose and activities: Giving primarily for higher education, with a particular focus on hotel and hospitality management, and human services.

Fields of interest: Art museums; University education; Hospital care; Diseases and conditions; Leukemia; Disasters and emergency management; Wildfires; Protestantism; Judaism; Human services; International development.

Type of support: General support; Program development; Research.

Limitations: Applications not accepted. Giving for human services primarily in the San Francisco Bay Area, CA.

Application information: Unsolicited requests for funds not accepted.

Officers: Margaret Handlery, Chair.; Michael K. Handlery, Secy.-Treas.

Trustee: A. John Pekrul.

EIN: 943302912

597
Harbison Scholarship Trust
215 North D St.
San Bernardino, CA 92401
Contact: Doreen Thornes, Tr.

Established in 1994 in California.

Foundation type: Operating foundation.

Financial data (yr. ended 10/31/13): Assets, $3,374,161 (M); expenditures, $261,041; qualifying distributions, $210,652; giving activities include $188,457 for 9 grants to individuals (high: $42,224; low: $9,635).

Purpose and activities: Awards 4-year scholarships to San Bernardino County high school students for college tuition and books. Scholarship awards are based on previous record of scholarship, character, motivation, interests, skills, extracurricular activities, and financial need.

Fields of interest: Undergraduate education.

Type of support: Student aid.

Limitations: Applications not accepted. Giving limited to high school students of San Bernardino County, CA.

Application information: Unsolicited requests for funds not accepted.

Trustee: Doreen Thornes.
EIN: 330621341

598

The Reed L. & Nan M. Harman Foundation
608 Silver Spur Rd., Ste. 315
Rolling Hills Estates, CA 90274-3662

Established in 1987 in California.
Donors: Nan M. Harman; Reed L. Harman; Hayden K. Harman; Southwest Investment Partners.
Foundation type: Independent foundation.
Financial data (yr. ended 12/31/13): Assets, $3,862,764 (M); expenditures, $343,263; qualifying distributions, $211,862; giving activities include $186,167 for 49 grants (high: $20,000; low: $22).
Fields of interest: Museums; Historic preservation; Education; Higher education; Nonprofits; Hospital care; Hospice care; Family planning; Human services.
Type of support: Regranting.
Limitations: Applications not accepted. Giving primarily in CA, with some giving in CT. No grants to individuals.
Application information: Contributes only to pre-selected organizations.
Officers: Reed L. Harman, Pres.; Nan M. Harman, V.P.
Number of staff: 1 part-time professional.
EIN: 330271109

599

The Harqua Foundation
700 Lombard St.
San Francisco, CA 94133-2317

Donors: Don Ed Hardy; Douglas Hardy; Francesca Passalacqua.
Foundation type: Independent foundation.
Financial data (yr. ended 12/31/12): Assets, $391,521 (M); gifts received, $120,000; expenditures, $156,664; qualifying distributions, $155,615; giving activities include $55,615 for 20 grants (high: $30,000; low: $600).
Fields of interest: Arts and culture; Domesticated animals; Human services.
Limitations: Applications not accepted. Giving primarily in CA and HI.
Application information: Unsolicited requests for funds not accepted.
Officers: Dave Rosenberg, Pres.; Francesca Passalacqua, C.F.O.; Douglas Hardy, V.P. and Secy.
EIN: 270884823

600

Harris Family Foundation
8 Via Capistrano
Tiburon, CA 94920
Contact: Andrew L. Harris, Mgr.

Established in 1999 in Illinois.
Donor: Charles U. Harris.
Foundation type: Independent foundation.
Financial data (yr. ended 12/31/14): Assets, $4,268,474 (M); expenditures, $234,009; qualifying distributions, $210,500; giving activities include $210,500 for 26 grants (high: $52,000; low: $1,000).

Fields of interest: Arts and culture; Education; Natural resources; Domesticated animals; Nonprofits; Human services.
Type of support: Regranting.
Limitations: Applications not accepted. Giving primarily in DC. No grants to individuals.
Application information: Unsolicited requests for funds not accepted.
Officer: Andrew L. Harris, Fdn. Mgr.
Trustee: John C. Harris.
EIN: 364333755

601

Robert & Shirley Harris Family Foundation
P.O. Box 1439
Santa Rosa, CA 95402-1439

Established in 1987 in California.
Donors: Robert W. Harris; Shirley M. Harris.
Foundation type: Independent foundation.
Financial data (yr. ended 12/31/14): Assets, $17,668,250 (M); gifts received, $3,320,667; expenditures, $723,907; qualifying distributions, $582,794; giving activities include $335,289 for 38 + grants (high: $35,000).
Fields of interest: Education; University education; Health; Geriatrics; Protestantism; Human services; Child welfare; Domestic violence shelters; Women's services; International development.
Type of support: General support; Capital and infrastructure; Equipment; Scholarships; Student aid.
Limitations: Applications not accepted. Giving primarily in CA and NJ.
Application information: Contributes only to pre-selected organizations.
Officers: Judith Harris Frisk, V.P.; Kathy Kumpula, Secy.; Michael Nelligan, Pres.
Directors: Robert W. Harris; James I. Harris.
EIN: 680121965

602

Brian and Phyllis Harvey Foundation
c/o Brian L. Harvey
10940 Wilshire Blvd., Ste. 1900
Los Angeles, CA 90024-3930

Established in 2000 in California.
Donor: Brian L. Harvey.
Foundation type: Independent foundation.
Financial data (yr. ended 12/31/13): Assets, $7,211,103 (M); gifts received, $1,950,000; expenditures, $19,970; qualifying distributions, $245,000; giving activities include $245,000 for 4 grants (high: $100,000; low: $20,000).
Purpose and activities: Giving primarily for medical research; funding also for human services.
Fields of interest: Nonprofits; Neurology; Diseases and conditions; Human services; Family services.
Type of support: Research; Regranting.
Limitations: Applications not accepted. Giving primarily in CA, IL and MN. No grants to individuals.
Application information: Contributes only to pre-selected organizations.
Directors: Brian L. Harvey; Darin Harvey.
EIN: 954833595

603

Hausman Family Foundation
2500 Michelson Dr., Ste. 200
Irvine, CA 92612-1568

Established in 2003 in California.
Donors: Marilyn E. Hausman; Hausman Felicidad LLC.
Foundation type: Independent foundation.
Financial data (yr. ended 12/31/13): Assets, $5,685,207 (M); expenditures, $382,174; qualifying distributions, $327,312; giving activities include $327,250 for 33 grants (high: $50,500; low: $500).
Fields of interest: Education; Diseases and conditions; Multiple sclerosis; Human services.
Limitations: Applications not accepted. Giving primarily in CA. No grants to individuals.
Application information: Contributes only to pre-selected organizations.
Trustees: William J. Cox; Richard P. Hausman; Richard P. Hausman, Jr.
EIN: 766685165

604

The Havner Family Foundation
2275 Chaucer Rd.
San Marino, CA 91108-1315

Donors: Ronald L. Havner, Jr.; LeeAnn R. Havner; Union Bank of California.
Foundation type: Independent foundation.
Financial data (yr. ended 12/31/13): Assets, $747,009 (M); gifts received, $200,000; expenditures, $275,237; qualifying distributions, $265,115; giving activities include $261,474 for 28 grants (high: $66,000; low: $250).
Fields of interest: Arts and culture; Education; Human services; Child welfare.
Limitations: Applications not accepted. Giving primarily in CA. No grants to individuals.
Application information: Unsolicited requests for funds not accepted.
Trustees: LeeAnn R. Havner; Ronald L. Havner.
EIN: 043762697

605

Hawley Family Charitable Foundation
(formerly Hawley Lexus Charitable Foundation)
195 Austin Ave.
Atherton, CA 94027-3949

Established in 1992 in California.
Donors: Wallace H. Hawley; Alexandra W. Hawley; Wallace R. Hawley.
Foundation type: Independent foundation.
Financial data (yr. ended 11/30/13): Assets, $80,104 (M); gifts received, $100,000; expenditures, $223,085; qualifying distributions, $223,000; giving activities include $223,000 for 9 grants (high: $75,000; low: $2,000).
Fields of interest: Higher education; Foundations; Christianity; Protestantism; Child welfare.
Limitations: Applications not accepted. Giving primarily in CO and CA. No grants to individuals.
Application information: Contributes only to pre-selected organizations.
Officers: Wallace R. Hawley, Pres.; Alexandra W. Hawley, Secy.
EIN: 943166561

606
Fred Hayman Family Foundation
190 N. Canon Dr., Ste. 310
Beverly Hills, CA 90210-5327

Established in 1985 in California.
Donor: Fred J. Hayman.
Foundation type: Independent foundation.
Financial data (yr. ended 12/31/13): Assets, $311,797 (M); expenditures, $217,184; qualifying distributions, $212,585; giving activities include $211,750 for 26 grants (high: $105,000; low: $200).
Fields of interest: Performing arts; Higher education; Nonprofits; Health; Hospital care; Diseases and conditions; HIV/AIDS.
Type of support: General support; Regranting; Research.
Limitations: Applications not accepted. Giving primarily in CA. No grants to individuals.
Application information: Contributes only to pre-selected organizations.
Officers and Board Members: Robert Hayman, Pres. and Director; Betty C. Hayman, V.P. and Secy.-Treas.; Fred J. Hayman.
EIN: 953996817

607
HCSC Foundation, Inc.
15220 Green Valley Dr.
Chino Hills, CA 91709-4267

Foundation type: Independent foundation.
Financial data (yr. ended 06/30/14): Assets, $5,742,434 (M); gifts received, $14,600; expenditures, $274,176; qualifying distributions, $167,330; giving activities include $167,330 for 2 grants (high: $157,330; low: $10,000).
Fields of interest: Youth development.
Limitations: Applications not accepted. Giving primarily in CA.
Application information: Unsolicited requests for funds not accepted.
Officers: Paul Simons, Chair.; Ron Salzetti, Vice-Chair.; Larry Noble, Secy.-Treas.
Board Members: Frank Fitzpatrick; Wayne Harmon; Mirth Meyer; Stan Newton; Jeff Paige; Ron Rhoads; Alan Rogers; Bill Shaver; Virginia Stoops; Tony Zarifis.
EIN: 956090571

608
Health Net Foundation, Inc.
21650 Oxnard St., 22nd Fl.
Woodland Hills, CA 91367-7824

Established in 2007 in California.
Donors: Health Net, Inc.; Health Net of California.
Foundation type: Company-sponsored foundation.
Financial data (yr. ended 12/31/13): Assets, $193,138 (M); gifts received, $269,939; expenditures, $350,672; qualifying distributions, $350,672; giving activities include $322,107 for 15 grants (high: $150,000; low: $500).
Purpose and activities: The foundation programs designed to improve healthcare in communities.
Fields of interest: Health; Human services; Youth development.
Type of support: General support.

Limitations: Applications not accepted. Giving primarily in CA, FL, TX, and WA. No grants to individuals.
Application information: Contributes only to pre-selected organizations.
Officers and Directors: Patricia Clarey, Pres. and Director; Capezza C. Joseph, C.F.O.; Angelee F. Bouchard, Secy. and Director; Marie Montgomery, Treas.; Jay M. Gellert; Juanell Hefner; Karin D. Mayhew; Steven J. Sell; John P. Sivori; Steven D. Tough; James E. Woys.
EIN: 412241862

609
The Heck Foundation
13250 River Rd.
Guerneville, CA 95446-9593 (707) 824-7225
Contact: David C. Faris, C.F.O.

Established in 2006 in California.
Donor: Gary B. Heck.
Foundation type: Independent foundation.
Financial data (yr. ended 06/30/14): Assets, $3,437,824 (M); expenditures, $161,905; qualifying distributions, $161,570; giving activities include $161,570 for 81 grants (high: $30,220; low: $250).
Fields of interest: Education; Domesticated animals; Agriculture.
Limitations: Applications accepted. Giving primarily in CA. No grants to individuals.
Application information: Application form required.
  Initial approach: Letter
  Deadline(s): None
Officers and Directors: Gary B. Heck, C.E.O. and Director; David C. Faris, C.F.O. and Director.
EIN: 205570213

610
Dr. John and Marian Hefferlin Foundation
(formerly Dr. John Hefferlin Foundation)
6035 Jumilla Ave.
Woodland Hills, CA 91367-5609
Main URL: http://www.hefferlin.org

Established in 1993 in California.
Donor: Marian W. Hefferlin†.
Foundation type: Independent foundation.
Financial data (yr. ended 12/31/13): Assets, $5,304,560 (M); expenditures, $261,244; qualifying distributions, $204,188; giving activities include $204,188 for 38 grants (high: $50,000; low: $850).
Purpose and activities: Giving to promote the teaching of the Science of Mind philosophy and to advance the growth and expansion of Religious Science churches.
Fields of interest: Education; Religion; Children; Adults; Young adults.
Type of support: Capital and infrastructure; Equipment; Program development; Convening; Publications; Curriculum development; Scholarships; Student aid.
Limitations: Applications not accepted. Giving on a national and international basis.
Application information: Unsolicited requests for funds not accepted.
  Board meeting date(s): 3 to 4 times yearly

Directors: George St. Johns; Roger Juline; Marilyn Leo; Kenneth Lind; Dorianne Cotter Lockard; Dore J. Patlian; Jean Parcher.
EIN: 330550728

611
Lenore B. & Frank M. Heffernan Family Foundation, Inc.
P.O. Box 1742
Ross, CA 94957-1742 (415) 453-2073
Contact: Lenore Heffernan, Co-Pres.; Frank Heffernan, Co-Pres.
Main URL: http://thinkdynamic.com/fandl.html

Donors: Lenore Heffernan; Frank Heffernan.
Foundation type: Independent foundation.
Financial data (yr. ended 12/31/13): Assets, $262,890 (M); gifts received, $275,000; expenditures, $259,278; qualifying distributions, $257,500; giving activities include $257,500 for 7 grants (high: $150,000; low: $1,000).
Fields of interest: Education; Youth development.
Limitations: Applications accepted. Giving primarily in CA.
Application information:
  Initial approach: Proposal
  Deadline(s): None
Officers: Lenore Heffernan, Co-Pres.; Frank Heffernan, Jr., Co-Pres.; Ann Marie Heffernan, Secy.
Directors: F. Michael Heffernan III; John Warren Heffernan.
EIN: 273960915

612
Kenneth Heinz Family Foundation
742 Spring Dr.
Walnut Creek, CA 94598-4249

Established in 1997 in California.
Donor: Kenneth G. Heinz.
Foundation type: Independent foundation.
Financial data (yr. ended 12/31/13): Assets, $3,055,735 (M); gifts received, $49,326; expenditures, $210,088; qualifying distributions, $210,088; giving activities include $207,206 for 33 grants (high: $40,000; low: $15).
Fields of interest: Education; Christianity; Human services.
Limitations: Applications not accepted. Giving primarily in CA. No grants to individuals.
Application information: Unsolicited requests for funds not accepted.
Officers and Directors: Kenneth G. Heinz, Pres. and Director; Patricia B. Heinz, V.P. and Director; Scott K. Heinz, Treas. and Director; Wendy Davis; Cheri Heinz.
EIN: 911803001

613
Heller Foundation of San Diego
P.O. Box 45174
San Francisco, CA 94104-0174

Established in 1960 in California.
Donors: Elwyn Heller†; Hattie Heller Marsh†.
Foundation type: Independent foundation.
Financial data (yr. ended 12/31/13): Assets, $5,293,861 (M); expenditures, $286,161; qualifying distributions, $242,456; giving activities

include $229,280 for 35 grants (high: $40,000; low: $780).

Purpose and activities: Giving primarily for environmental and conservation issues.

Fields of interest: Education; Natural resources; Health; Human services; Child welfare.

Type of support: General support; Program-related investments; Matching grants; Continuing support; Capacity-building and technical assistance; Equipment; Land acquisitions; Program development; Curriculum development; Fellowships; Scholarships; Research; Technical assistance; Program evaluations.

Limitations: Applications not accepted. Giving primarily in CA for conservation and the environment; giving for all other areas is limited to San Diego County. No support for locally-based programs outside San Diego County, CA. No grants to individuals.

Application information: Unsolicited request for funds not accepted.

Trustee: Union Bank of California, N.A.

Number of staff: None.

EIN: 956010314

614
Bud and Barbara Hellman Foundation
10490 Wilshire Blvd., Ste. 2704
Los Angeles, CA 90024-4621

Established in 1986 in California.

Donors: Bud Hellman; Barbara Hellman.

Foundation type: Independent foundation.

Financial data (yr. ended 06/30/13): Assets, $1,155,175 (M); expenditures, $200,647; qualifying distributions, $185,985; giving activities include $185,985 for 50 grants (high: $105,000; low: $25).

Fields of interest: Arts and culture; Orchestral music; Higher education; Foundations; Nonprofits; Health; Hospital care; Diseases and conditions; Religion; Human services.

Type of support: Regranting.

Limitations: Applications not accepted. Giving primarily in CA. No grants to individuals.

Application information: Unsolicited requests for funds not accepted.

Officers: Bud Hellman, Pres.; Barbara Hellman, Secy.

EIN: 954079313

615
Helms Foundation, Inc.
c/o Saddington Shusko LLP
18201 Von Karman Ave., Ste. 150
Irvine, CA 92612-1014

Established in 1946 in California.

Donor: Helms Bakeries.

Foundation type: Independent foundation.

Financial data (yr. ended 06/30/13): Assets, $3,977,981 (M); expenditures, $246,766; qualifying distributions, $237,645; giving activities include $214,003 for 39 grants (high: $30,000; low: $3).

Purpose and activities: Giving primarily for education and to Christian agencies and churches.

Fields of interest: Arts and culture; Education; Higher education; Diseases and conditions; Christianity; Human services; Child welfare.

Limitations: Applications not accepted. No support for private foundations. No grants to individuals.

Application information: Unsolicited requests for funds not accepted.

Officers: Stephen Helms Bell, Pres.; Fonza Bell Lawther, Treas.

Trustees: Elizabeth Helms Adams; Elizabeth Bennett; Michael F. Kane.

EIN: 956091335

616
Helmstetter Family Foundation
2211 Encinitas Blvd., Ste. 223
Encinitas, CA 92024-4361

Established in 1994 in California.

Donors: Jeaninne Helmstetter†; Richard C. Helmstetter.

Foundation type: Independent foundation.

Financial data (yr. ended 12/31/13): Assets, $2,834,718 (M); expenditures, $168,805; qualifying distributions, $168,100; giving activities include $168,100 for 29 grants (high: $25,000; low: $500).

Fields of interest: Performing arts; Education; Elementary and secondary education; Child welfare; Senior services.

Limitations: Applications not accepted. No grants to individuals.

Application information: Unsolicited requests for funds not accepted.

Officer: Richard C. Helmstetter, V.P.

Directors: Deidre Helmstetter; Erik M. Helmstetter.

EIN: 330673581

617
The Ernest G. Herman Foundation
(formerly The Herman Brothers Foundation)
1900 Ave. of the Stars, Ste. 2100
Los Angeles, CA 90067-4502

Established in 2005 in California.

Foundation type: Independent foundation.

Financial data (yr. ended 12/31/13): Assets, $2,838,709 (M); expenditures, $172,655; qualifying distributions, $147,934; giving activities include $145,000 for 20 grants (high: $15,000; low: $2,500).

Fields of interest: Health; Diseases and conditions; Religion.

Limitations: Applications not accepted. Giving primarily in CA. No grants to individuals.

Application information: Unsolicited requests for funds not accepted.

Officers: Patrick Barber, Pres.; Betty Hollingsworth, Secy.; Sidney J. Machtinger, Treas.

EIN: 202120521

618
Carl and Henrietta Herrmann Family Foundation
899 El Centro St., Ste. 101
South Pasadena, CA 91030-3101

Established in 2001 in Illinois.

Donors: Carl L. Herrmann III; Carron M. Herrmann; Christopher M. Herrmann; Catherine L. Herrmann Kerley; Christopher Herrmann Trust; Carron M. Herrmann Trust; Catherine L. Hermann Trust; Carl Herrmann III Trust.

Foundation type: Independent foundation.

Financial data (yr. ended 12/31/14): Assets, $4,198,839; gifts received, $200,000; expenditures, $295,613; qualifying distributions, $161,500.

Fields of interest: Elementary and secondary education; Nonprofits; Diseases and conditions; Christianity.

Type of support: Regranting; Research.

Limitations: Applications not accepted. Giving primarily in CA. No grants to individuals.

Application information: Unsolicited requests for funds not accepted.

Officers: Catherine L. Herrmann Kerley, Pres.; Carron M. Herrmann, V.P.; Carl L. Herrmann III, Secy.; Christopher M. Herrmann, Treas.

EIN: 311815521

619
Chavi F. Hertz Foundation Inc.
525 N. Hillcrest Rd.
Beverly Hills, CA 90210-3513   (310) 435-4655
Contact: Chavi F. Hertz, Pres.

Established in 2001 in California.

Donor: Chavi F. Hertz.

Foundation type: Independent foundation.

Financial data (yr. ended 12/31/13): Assets, $243,617 (M); gifts received, $2,412; expenditures, $161,909; qualifying distributions, $154,712; giving activities include $154,712 for 34 grants (high: $49,500; low: $180).

Fields of interest: Judaism.

Limitations: Applications accepted. Giving primarily in CA. No grants to individuals.

Application information: Application form required.

Initial approach: Proposal
Deadline(s): None

Officers: Chavi F. Hertz, Pres.; Zev Hertz, C.F.O.; Sandy Gordon, V.P.; Yisrael Gordon, V.P.; Isaac Hertz, Secy.

EIN: 912152284

620
Hidden Leaf Foundation
P.O. Box 865
Occidental, CA 95465-0865
E-mail: info@hiddenleaf.org; Main URL: http://hiddenleaf.org

Donor: David A. Brown.

Foundation type: Independent foundation.

Financial data (yr. ended 12/31/13): Assets, $653,002 (M); gifts received, $650,000; expenditures, $531,704; qualifying distributions, $525,156; giving activities include $402,000 for 20 grants (high: $50,000; low: $3,000).

Purpose and activities: Giving primarily for social justice.

Fields of interest: Human rights.

Limitations: Giving primarily in CA.

Publications: Application guidelines; Grants list.

Application information: Grant applicants are required to first submit a Letter of Inquiry rather than a proposal to allow the foundation to determine if there is an appropriate match. Unsolicited proposals are not accepted.

Initial approach: Letter of Inquiry, no more than 2 pages, via e-mail
Deadline(s): None, for Letters of Inquiry; Sept. 1 for proposals

Officers: David A. Brown, Pres.; Tara Brown, V.P.; Karen Brown, Secy.-Treas.
Board Member: Kristen Stinnett-Brown.
EIN: 352338463

621

Hilltop Foundation
P.O. Box 1027
Tiburon, CA   94920-4027

Established in 2004 in California.
Donor: C. Price.
Foundation type: Independent foundation.
Financial data (yr. ended 12/31/13): Assets, $5,284,086 (M); expenditures, $281,548; qualifying distributions, $241,688; giving activities include $235,850 for 58 grants (high: $13,000; low: $250).
Fields of interest: Nonprofits; Community and economic development; Human services; Child welfare.
Type of support: Regranting.
Limitations: Applications not accepted. Giving primarily in CA. No grants to individuals.
Application information: Contributes only to pre-selected organizations.
Officers: C. Price, Pres.; A. Price, V.P.; J. Price, Treas.
EIN: 200499862

622

Hinman Charitable Foundation
14 Glen Ridge Ave.
Los Gatos, CA   95030-5820

Established in 1998 in California.
Donors: Brian L. Hinman; Suzanne R. Skees.
Foundation type: Independent foundation.
Financial data (yr. ended 12/31/13): Assets, $4,421,870 (M); expenditures, $260,298; qualifying distributions, $225,748; giving activities include $217,250 for 4 grants (high: $200,000; low: $1,500).
Fields of interest: Higher education.
Limitations: Applications not accepted. Giving primarily in MD. No grants to individuals.
Application information: Contributes only to pre-selected organizations.
Officers and Directors: Brian L. Hinman, Pres. and Director; George R. Kaplan, Treas.
EIN: 770496541

623

His Glory Ministries
(formerly The Kvandal Family Foundation)
13663 Etude Rd.
San Diego, CA   92128-4719

Established in 2003 in California.
Donors: Scott Kvandal; Michelle Kvandal.
Foundation type: Independent foundation.
Financial data (yr. ended 10/31/13): Assets, $9,973 (M); gifts received, $285,584; expenditures, $286,150; qualifying distributions, $287,374; giving activities include $217,878 for 6 grants (high: $191,053; low: $1,000).
Fields of interest: Religion; Protestantism.
International interests: Paraguay.
Type of support: General support.

Limitations: Applications not accepted. Giving primarily in CA. No grants to individuals.
Application information: Contributes only to pre-selected organizations.
Officers: Scott Kvandal, Pres. and C.E.O.; Michelle Kvandal, Secy.
EIN: 300218431

624

Hitter Family Foundation
10755 Palms Blvd.
Los Angeles, CA   90034

Established in 2000 in California.
Donor: Anna Hitter.
Foundation type: Independent foundation.
Financial data (yr. ended 12/31/13): Assets, $4,200,955 (M); gifts received, $300,000; expenditures, $196,574; qualifying distributions, $192,155; giving activities include $192,155 for 12 grants (high: $3,000; low: $2,000).
Fields of interest: Museums; University education; Diseases and conditions; Judaism.
Type of support: Research.
Limitations: Applications not accepted. Giving primarily in Los Angeles, CA. No grants to individuals.
Application information: Unsolicited requests for funds not accepted.
Officers and Directors: Steve Hitter, Pres. and Director; Sabrina Hitter, Secy. and Director.
EIN: 954790803

625

Hoag Foundation
7730 4th Pl.
Downey, CA   90241-3230

Established in 1991 in California.
Donors: C. Larry Hoag; Helen Hoag.
Foundation type: Independent foundation.
Financial data (yr. ended 12/31/13): Assets, $9,333,092 (M); gifts received, $1,160,000; expenditures, $422,287; qualifying distributions, $378,250; giving activities include $378,250 for 7 grants (high: $129,500; low: $17,000).
Purpose and activities: Giving primarily for the arts, education, and to a children's hospital.
Fields of interest: Arts and culture; Opera; University education; Medical education; Specialty hospital care.
Limitations: Applications not accepted. Giving primarily in Orange and Downey, CA; some giving also in Houston, TX. No grants to individuals.
Application information: Contributes only to pre-selected organizations.
Directors: Helen Hoag; Robert W. Latimer.
EIN: 954315096

626

Philip & Rebecca Hochman Foundation
P.O. Box 1936
Los Altos, CA   94023-1936

Established in 2005 in California.
Donors: Dennis Troper; Susan Wojcicki.
Foundation type: Independent foundation.
Financial data (yr. ended 12/31/12): Assets, $5,996,743 (M); expenditures, $328,142;

qualifying distributions, $300,000; giving activities include $300,000 for grants.
Fields of interest: Education; Health; Judaism.
Limitations: Applications not accepted. Giving in the U.S., with emphasis on CA. No grants to individuals.
Application information: Unsolicited requests for funds not accepted.
Officers: Susan Wojcicki, Pres.; Dennis Troper, C.F.O. and Secy.-Treas.; Anne Wojcicki, V.P.; Janet Wojcicki, V.P.
EIN: 202777268

627

Bess J. Hodges Foundation
5100 E. Anaheim Rd.
Long Beach, CA   90815-4215   (562) 961-4115

Established in 1984 in California.
Donor: Bess J. Hodges†.
Foundation type: Independent foundation.
Financial data (yr. ended 12/31/14): Assets, $7,177,094; expenditures, $724,156; qualifying distributions, $215,019.
Purpose and activities: Giving primarily for education, health, human services, public affairs and community development, religion, and the arts. The trustees are more likely to look with favor toward projects which improve the quality of life, increase responsiveness of agencies to community needs, develop self-reliance, direct themselves to prevention as well as treatment, and eliminate duplication of services and encourage cooperation.
Fields of interest: Arts and culture; Education; Higher education; Health; Community and economic development; Religion; Human services; Child welfare.
Limitations: Applications accepted. Giving primarily in Long Beach, CA. No support for private foundations. No grants to individuals, or for endowments, intermediary funding agencies, continuing support, or debts.
Application information:
  Initial approach: Proposal
  Copies of proposal: 2
  Deadline(s): Mar. 31
Officer: Joyce Murchison, Exec. Dir.
Trustees: George Murchison; Michael Murchison.
Number of staff: 1
EIN: 330046140

628

Hoefer Family Foundation
c/o Alan Hoefer
P.O. Box 7487
Burlingame, CA   94010-7487

Foundation type: Independent foundation.
Financial data (yr. ended 12/31/14): Assets, $6,659,783; expenditures, $293,381; qualifying distributions, $280,209.
Purpose and activities: Giving primarily for health care and higher education.
Fields of interest: Arts and culture; Education; Higher education; Health; Hospital care; Science; Human services.
Type of support: Individual development.
Limitations: Applications not accepted. Giving primarily in CA. No grants to individuals.
Application information: Contributes only to pre-selected organizations.

Officers: Alan Hoefer, Pres.; Gladys Hoefer, Secy.; Kurt Hoefer, Treas.
Directors: Alan Hoefer, Jr.; Craig Hoefer.
EIN: 366065404

629
The Philip Hohnstein Family Foundation
c/o Principe & Associates, CPAS
30423 Canwood St.
Agoura Hills, CA 91301-4366

Established in 1999 in California.
Donor: Philip Hohnstein.
Foundation type: Independent foundation.
Financial data (yr. ended 11/30/13): Assets, $3,585,039 (M); expenditures, $194,577; qualifying distributions, $179,500; giving activities include $179,500 for 22 grants (high: $35,000; low: $1,000).
Fields of interest: Protestantism; Human services; Child welfare; People with vision impairments.
Limitations: Applications not accepted. Giving primarily in CA. No grants to individuals.
Application information: Contributes only to pre-selected organizations.
Officers: Belinda Sue Chrysiliou, Pres.; Chrysilios Chrysiliou, V.P.; Anthony M. Principe, Secy.-Treas.
EIN: 330884088

630
Hollywood Canteen Foundation
P.O. Box 45174
San Francisco, CA 94145-0174
Application address: P. O. Box 30, Beverly Hills, CA 90210

Established in 1946 in California.
Foundation type: Independent foundation.
Financial data (yr. ended 02/28/14): Assets, $2,404,557; expenditures, $173,292; qualifying distributions, $167,560.
Purpose and activities: Giving to hospitals, colleges, social service agencies, and other similar institutions to promote the well-being of military personnel, veterans, and their families.
Fields of interest: Health; National defense; Housing development; Sports and recreation.
Limitations: Applications accepted. Giving primarily to CA. No grants to individuals.
Application information:
  Initial approach: Proposal
  Deadline(s): Oct. 1
Trustee: Union Bank, N.A.
Board Members: Tracey Boldemann-Tatkin; Donald E. Karl, Esq.; Lorraine McIntire; Gerald Oppenheimer; Karen Randall; Kevin Rogers.
EIN: 956023639

631
Hong Family Foundation
25252 Prado Del Grandioso
Calabasas, CA 91302-3108

Donors: Peter Hong; Catherine Hong.
Foundation type: Independent foundation.
Financial data (yr. ended 12/31/13): Assets, $45,041 (M); gifts received, $400,000; expenditures, $388,766; qualifying distributions, $388,766; giving activities include $388,706 for 6 grants (high: $314,000; low: $200).

Fields of interest: Religion; Human services.
Limitations: Applications not accepted. Giving primarily in CA.
Application information: Unsolicited requests for funds not accepted.
Officers: Peter Hong, Pres.; Catherine Hong, V.P.; Anthony Kim, Treas.
EIN: 274213318

632
James and Ada Horwich Family Foundation
630 N. Maple Dr.
Beverly Hills, CA 90210-3410

Established in 1986 in California.
Donors: Atlas Carpet Mills, Inc.; Ada R. Horwich; James Horwich.
Foundation type: Independent foundation.
Financial data (yr. ended 11/30/13): Assets, $5,601,276 (M); gifts received, $975,567; expenditures, $439,985; qualifying distributions, $439,950; giving activities include $439,950 for 142 grants (high: $250,000; low: $35).
Purpose and activities: Giving primarily for education and Jewish organizations.
Fields of interest: Arts and culture; Elementary and secondary education; Higher education; Nonprofits; Judaism; Human services.
Type of support: Regranting.
Limitations: Applications not accepted. Giving primarily in CA. No grants to individuals.
Application information: Contributes only to pre-selected organizations.
Officers: James Horwich, Pres.; Ada Horwich, Secy.-Treas.
EIN: 954074377

633
The Horwitz Family Memorial Foundation
(formerly The Diane M. Horwitz Memorial Foundation)
3332 E. Romelle Ave.
Orange, CA 92869-5218
Contact: Louis B. Horwitz, Pres.
E-mail for Louis B. Horwitz: lbhorwitz@sbcglobal.net

Established in 2000 in California.
Donors: Louis B. Horwitz; Bradley J. Horwitz.
Foundation type: Independent foundation.
Financial data (yr. ended 12/31/13): Assets, $1,062,423 (M); expenditures, $352,486; qualifying distributions, $340,150; giving activities include $328,004 for 34 grants (high: $100,000; low: $500).
Fields of interest: Nonprofits; Hospital care; Judaism; Human services; Children and youth; Homeless people; Low-income and poor people; People with physical disabilities; People with vision impairments; People with psychosocial disabilities.
Type of support: General support; Matching grants; Annual campaigns; Capital campaigns; Capital and infrastructure; Endowments; Emergency funds; Program development; Regranting.
Limitations: Applications not accepted. Giving primarily in CA, TX and WA. No support for non-501(c)(3) organizations. No grants to individuals.
Application information: Contributes only to pre-selected organizations.
  Board meeting date(s): Spring and winter

Officers: Louis B. Horwitz, C.E.O. and Pres.; Bradley J. Horwitz, V.P. and C.F.O.
Number of staff: None.
EIN: 330912754

634
Preston B. & Maurine M. Hotchkis Family Foundation
125 E. Victoria St., Ste. L
Santa Barbara, CA 93101-2050

Established in 2002 in California.
Donors: Maurine M. Hotchkis; Preston B. Hotchkis.
Foundation type: Independent foundation.
Financial data (yr. ended 06/30/14): Assets, $17,251; gifts received, $138,941; expenditures, $133,726; qualifying distributions, $132,497.
Fields of interest: Arts and culture; Environment; Domesticated animals.
Limitations: Applications not accepted. Giving primarily in CA. No grants to individuals.
Application information: Contributes only to pre-selected organizations.
Officers and Directors: Preston B. Hotchkis, Pres. and Director; Maurine M. Hotchkis, C.F.O. and Director; Jeannette L. Christensen, Secy. and Director.
EIN: 954766131

635
Hotchkis Foundation
c/o Johnson & Grover Accountancy Corp.
11150 W. Olympic Blvd., Ste. 920
Los Angeles, CA 90064-1839

Established in 1963 in California.
Donors: John F. Hotchkis; Joan Hotchkis.
Foundation type: Independent foundation.
Financial data (yr. ended 01/31/15): Assets, $2,679,182 (M); expenditures, $296,253; qualifying distributions, $284,063; giving activities include $279,000 for 29 grants (high: $45,000; low: $1,000).
Fields of interest: Arts and culture; Music; Education; Higher education; Community and economic development; Youth services.
Limitations: Applications not accepted. Giving primarily in CA. No grants to individuals.
Application information: Contributes only to pre-selected organizations.
Officers: John F. Hotchkis, Pres.; Sarah H. Ketterer, V.P. and Secy.-Treas.; Carolyn R. Hotchkis, V.P.; John F. Hotchkis, Jr., V.P.; Mark B. Hotchkis, V.P.
EIN: 956058775

636
The Hsieh Christian Foundation
c/o Wen-Jai Hsieh
2546 Webster St.
Palo Alto, CA 94301-4249

Donors: Wen-Jai Hsieh; Pai-Her Hsieh.
Foundation type: Independent foundation.
Financial data (yr. ended 12/31/14): Assets, $3,117,137; expenditures, $254,452; qualifying distributions, $220,100.
Purpose and activities: Giving primarily to Christian missions and organizations.
Fields of interest: Christianity; Human services.
International interests: Taiwan.

Type of support: General support.
Limitations: Applications not accepted. Giving primarily in CA. No grants to individuals.
Application information: Contributes only to pre-selected organizations.
Officers: Wen-Jai Hsieh, Chair.; Pai-Her Hsieh, Secy.; Shirley Chen, Treas.
Director: Stephen Chen.
EIN: 770257267

637
Hong-Yen & Lin-Run Hsu Charitable Foundation
6380 E. Sheri Ln.
Long Beach, CA   90815-4741

Established in 1990 in California.
Donors: Hsu Family Trust; Lingkogin, Inc.
Foundation type: Independent foundation.
Financial data (yr. ended 12/31/13): Assets, $9,209,916 (M); expenditures, $479,079; qualifying distributions, $417,629; giving activities include $413,000 for 7 grants (high: $150,000; low: $3,000).
Fields of interest: Arts and culture; Diseases and conditions; Religion; Human services.
International interests: Taiwan.
Type of support: Research.
Limitations: Applications not accepted. Giving primarily in CA and Taipei, Taiwan. No grants to individuals.
Application information: Contributes only to pre-selected organizations.
Officers: Chau Hsu, Pres.; Melissa See, Treas.
Director: David Lu.
EIN: 330419283

638
Bernice Peltier Huber Charitable Trust
231 E. Alessandro Blvd., Ste. 110
Riverside, CA   92508-5084
Contact: Carol Rector, Tr.

Established in 1993 in California.
Foundation type: Independent foundation.
Financial data (yr. ended 07/31/14): Assets, $931,488 (M); expenditures, $151,947; qualifying distributions, $150,000; giving activities include $150,000 for 2 grants (high: $100,000; low: $50,000).
Fields of interest: Museums; Education; Health.
Type of support: General support.
Limitations: Applications not accepted. Giving primarily in CA and OR. No grants to individuals.
Application information: Contributes only to pre-selected organizations.
Trustee: Carol Rector.
EIN: 336135510

639
Paul Hughes Family Foundation
10591 Bloomfield St.
Los Alamitos, CA   90720-2501

Donor: The Marital Trust.
Foundation type: Independent foundation.
Financial data (yr. ended 12/31/13): Assets, $6,172,680 (M); expenditures, $330,705; qualifying distributions, $330,705; giving activities

include $252,319 for 37 grants (high: $57,941; low: $200).
Fields of interest: Education; Diseases and conditions; Community and economic development; Human services; Child welfare.
Type of support: Research.
Limitations: Applications not accepted. Giving primarily in CA. No grants to individuals.
Application information: Contributes only to pre-selected organizations.
Officers and Directors: Teresa L. Hughes, Pres.; Steve Strickler, Secy. and C.F.O. and Director; Paul J. Hughes.
EIN: 954806982

640
Hunsaker Foundation
17761 Mitchell N.
Irvine, CA   92614-6028

Foundation type: Independent foundation.
Financial data (yr. ended 09/30/13): Assets, $0 (M); expenditures, $217,624; qualifying distributions, $215,393; giving activities include $215,393 for 1 grant.
Fields of interest: Education.
Limitations: Applications not accepted. Giving primarily in CA. No grants to individuals.
Application information: Unsolicited requests for funds not accepted.
Officers and Directors: Richard C. Hunsaker, Co-Pres. and Director; Virginia A. Hunsaker, Co-Pres. and Director.
EIN: 330007589

641
HunterWard Foundation
c/o W & R
15910 Ventura Blvd., Ste. 1100
Encino, CA   91436-2812
Application address: c/o Ross Winn, 11400 W. Olympic Blvd., 9th Fl., Los Angeles, CA 90064, tel.: (310) 478-4100

Established in 1992 in California.
Donor: Blake C. Hunter.
Foundation type: Independent foundation.
Financial data (yr. ended 12/31/13): Assets, $5,576,498 (M); gifts received, $1,057,438; expenditures, $283,188; qualifying distributions, $258,000; giving activities include $258,000 for 26 grants (high: $20,000; low: $2,500).
Fields of interest: Arts and culture; Theater; Orchestral music; Historical activities; Education; Animal welfare; HIV/AIDS; Human services.
Type of support: Research.
Application information: Application form required.
   Initial approach: Proposal
   Deadline(s): Aug. 31
Officer: Blake C. Hunter, Pres. and Secy.
Trustees: Diane Shelby; Kerry Shelby.
EIN: 954399227

642
John Brockway Huntington Foundation
c/o Peter K. Maier
80 E. Sir Francis Drake Blvd., 2nd Fl.
Larkspur, CA   94939-1709   (415) 925-1375
FAX: (415) 461-7537; E-mail: pkm@prii.net

Established in 1997 in California.
Donor: John B. Huntington Charitable Trust.
Foundation type: Independent foundation.
Financial data (yr. ended 12/31/13): Assets, $7,044,982 (M); expenditures, $502,302; qualifying distributions, $360,000; giving activities include $360,000 for 42 grants (high: $40,000; low: $2,000).
Fields of interest: Arts and culture; Education; Higher education; Nonprofits; Health; Cancers; Libraries; Spirituality; Family services; Child welfare.
Type of support: Endowments; Matching grants; Capital campaigns; Capital and infrastructure; Annual campaigns; Research and evaluation; Regranting.
Limitations: Applications not accepted. Giving primarily in CA and OR. No grants to individuals.
Application information: Contributes only to pre-selected organizations.
   Board meeting date(s): Oct.
Officer: Peter K. Maier, Pres.
Directors: Julie Huntington De Polo; Elizabeth Huntington; Marian Huntington Schinske.
EIN: 943252483

643
The Hurliman Scholarship Foundation
5150 Fair Oaks Blvd., No. 101-306
Carmichael, CA   95608-5758
E-mail: hurlimansf@comcast.net; Main URL: http://www.hurlimanscholarshipfoundation.com
Grants List: http://www.hurlimanscholarshipfoundation.com/about.html#winners

Donor: Edith E. Hurliman†.
Foundation type: Operating foundation.
Financial data (yr. ended 12/31/13): Assets, $6,932,514 (M); expenditures, $386,682; qualifying distributions, $311,986; giving activities include $269,525 for 21 grants to individuals (high: $25,866; low: $1,195).
Purpose and activities: Scholarship awards to students in Custer, Fremont, and Pueblo counties, Colorado.
Fields of interest: Higher education.
Type of support: Student aid.
Limitations: Applications accepted. Giving limited to residents of Custer, Fremont, and Pueblo counties, CO.
Publications: Application guidelines.
Application information: Complete application guidelines available on foundation web site. Application form required.
   Initial approach: Download application on foundation web site
   Deadline(s): See foundation web site for current deadlines
Officers: Lila L. Anastas, Pres. and Treas.; Deanne Nocetti, V.P. and Secy.
EIN: 205993001

644
I Have a Dream Foundation - Clio, SC
P.O. Box 8
Paicines, CA   95043-0008

Established in 2000 in South Carolina.
Donors: Sallie Calhoun; Community Foundation of San Benito; Rainwater Charitable Foundation.
Foundation type: Operating foundation.

Financial data (yr. ended 12/31/13): Assets, $13,627 (M); gifts received, $170,000; expenditures, $209,693; qualifying distributions, $209,693; giving activities include $152,776 for 17 grants to individuals (high: $14,754; low: $3,200).
Fields of interest: Higher education.
Limitations: Applications not accepted.
Application information: Unsolicited requests for funds not accepted.
Officer: Sallie Calhoun, Pres., V.P. and Secy.
EIN: 571111271

645
i.am.angel Foundation
10960 Wilshire Blvd., 5th Fl.
Los Angeles, CA   90024-3702
Toll-free tel.: (800) 839-1754; Main URL: http://iamangelfoundation.org
Causes.com URL: http://www.causes.com/causes/434950-i-am-angel
Facebook: http://www.facebook.com/iamangelfoundation
Google Plus: https://plus.google.com/118314738112858440523/posts
Twitter: https://twitter.com/iamangelfdn
Vimeo: http://vimeo.com/34679422
YouTube: http://www.youtube.com/user/iamangelfnd

Donors: William James "will.i.am" Adams, Jr.; Sean Parker; Jennifer M. Van Natta; Misael Vasquez; Entertainment Industry Foundation; Jeanne and Sanford Roberston Fund; Michael Murphy; Quantum Realtors Inc.; Silicon Valley Community Foundation; Wells Fargo bank.
Foundation type: Independent foundation.
Financial data (yr. ended 12/31/13): Assets, $95,131 (M); gifts received, $1,598,334; expenditures, $1,619,516; qualifying distributions, $1,619,516; giving activities include $140,000 for 3 grants (high: $100,000; low: $15,000), and $1,064,438 for 2 foundation-administered programs.
Purpose and activities: The foundation works to make a difference in the lives of individuals and families through education, opportunity, and inspiration.
Fields of interest: Education; Housing development; Low-income and poor people.
Limitations: Applications not accepted. Giving primarily in CA.
Application information: Unsolicited requests for funds not accepted.
Officers: William James "will.i.am" Adams, Jr., Pres. and Secy.; Justin Paschal, Exec. Dir.
Directors: Ron Conway; Polo Molina.
EIN: 273419857

646
Nina and S. A. Ibrahim Foundation
c/o Edward A. Robinson, CPA
44808 S. Grimmer Blvd.
Fremont, CA   94538-6328

Established in 2004 in California.
Donors: S.A. Ibrahim; Nina Ibrahim.
Foundation type: Independent foundation.
Financial data (yr. ended 12/31/14): Assets, $1,018,712; expenditures, $287,651; qualifying distributions, $282,500.
Fields of interest: Education; Higher education.

Limitations: Applications not accepted. Giving primarily in Philadelphia, PA; some funding also in New York, NY. No grants to individuals.
Application information: Contributes only to pre-selected organizations.
Officers: S.A. Ibrahim, C.E.O.; Nina Ibrahim, Secy.-Treas.
EIN: 202026571

647
Tsutayo Ichioka & Satsuki Nakao Charitable Foundation
1792 Windsor Rd.
San Marino, CA   91108-2528

Established in 2001 in California.
Donor: Satsuki Nakao Trust.
Foundation type: Operating foundation.
Financial data (yr. ended 06/30/13): Assets, $8,544,125 (M); expenditures, $504,873; qualifying distributions, $453,201; giving activities include $355,000 for 11 grants (high: $174,000; low: $3,000).
Purpose and activities: Giving primarily for social services and to Protestant churches.
Fields of interest: Education; Religion; Human services.
Limitations: Applications not accepted. Giving primarily in CA. No grants to individuals.
Application information: Unsolicited requests for funds not accepted.
Officer: George T. Hori, Pres.
Trustees: Helen Hori; Douglas Krech; Jane Krech.
EIN: 954845625

648
George Ignatius Foundation
800 Wilshire Blvd., 15th Fl.
Los Angeles, CA   90017-2619   (213) 680-9212
Contact: George R. Phillips Sr., Chair.

Foundation type: Independent foundation.
Financial data (yr. ended 12/31/13): Assets, $3,741,704 (M); expenditures, $226,893; qualifying distributions, $195,824; giving activities include $175,250 for 49 grants (high: $25,000; low: $60).
Purpose and activities: The foundation gives primarily to organizations promoting Armenian history, culture, and religion.
Fields of interest: Arts and culture; Education; Law education; Philanthropy.
Limitations: Applications accepted. Giving primarily in Los Angeles, CA. No grants to individuals.
Application information: Application form required.
  Initial approach: Letter
  Deadline(s): None
Officer: George R. Phillips, Sr., Chair.
Trustees: Michael Amerian; Walter J. Karabian.
EIN: 510198566

649
IM Wintercreek Foundation
c/o Patricia Higgins
5093 Dogtown Rd.
San Andreas, CA   95249-9573

Established in 2005 in California.
Donors: Betty Higgins; Sam Higgins.
Foundation type: Independent foundation.

Financial data (yr. ended 06/30/13): Assets, $9,632,245 (M); gifts received, $1,000,000; expenditures, $436,884; qualifying distributions, $362,713; giving activities include $343,500 for 12 grants (high: $78,000; low: $5,000).
Fields of interest: Education; Secondary education.
Limitations: Applications not accepted. Giving primarily in CA. No grants to individuals.
Application information: Contributes only to pre-selected organizations.
Trustee: Patricia Higgins.
Agent: Wells Fargo Bank, N.A.
EIN: 203929259

650
In Christo Vera Educatio
P.O. Box 661525
Arcadia, CA   91066-1525

Foundation type: Independent foundation.
Financial data (yr. ended 06/30/14): Assets, $6,142,612 (M); expenditures, $378,600; qualifying distributions, $301,960; giving activities include $257,914 for 4 grants (high: $108,570; low: $23,526).
Purpose and activities: Giving primarily for Christian high school scholarship funds.
Fields of interest: Education.
Type of support: Scholarships.
Limitations: Applications not accepted. Giving primarily in CA.
Application information: Contributes only to pre-selected organizations.
Officers and Directors: Tippi Manske, Chair. and Director; Timothy Fenderson, Secy. and Director; Craig Takata, Treas. and Director; Richard Riesen, Mgr. and Director; Ken Horton; Jordan Morton.
EIN: 952394638

651
Indo-American Foundation Inc.
8254 E. Lorain Rd.
San Gabriel, CA   91775-1028   (626) 286-4162

Established in 1988 in California.
Donors: D.C. Dellinger†; Ramadas Abboy; S. Jagannathan; Naina Mohamed Rahman; V. Venkatesh; Grace Jones Richardson Trust; Rajamannar Abboy; Sridevi Abboy; S. Arjunan; Chandar Abboy.
Foundation type: Operating foundation.
Financial data (yr. ended 12/31/14): Assets, $211,967; gifts received, $220,272; expenditures, $182,206; qualifying distributions, $181,841.
Fields of interest: Education; Higher education; Goodwill promotion.
International interests: India.
Type of support: Scholarships.
Limitations: Applications accepted. Giving primarily in India.
Application information: Application form required.
  Initial approach: Letter
  Deadline(s): None
Officers: Ramadas Abboy, Pres.; Rajamannar Abboy, Secy.
EIN: 954156556

652
International Christian Scholarship Foundation

P.O. Box 392
La Verne, CA   91750-0392

Foundation type: Independent foundation.
Financial data (yr. ended 06/30/14): Assets, $3,940,714 (M); gifts received, $70,882; expenditures, $217,933; qualifying distributions, $201,600; giving activities include $201,600 for 33 grants (high: $15,000; low: $2,800).
Fields of interest: Education; Undergraduate education; Health.
International interests: Philippines.
Type of support: Scholarships.
Limitations: Applications not accepted. Giving primarily in IA; with some giving in the Philippines.
Application information: Unsolicited requests for funds not accepted.
Officers: Marie Durfinger, Pres.; Rosemary Gonzales, V.P.; Diomy Alexander, Secy.; Lynnae Herandez, Treas.
EIN: 956048302

653
J. & M. Foundation

18900 Portola Dr., Ste. 200
Salinas, CA   93908-1296

Established in 2007 in California.
Donor: Jane B. Dunaway.
Foundation type: Independent foundation.
Financial data (yr. ended 12/31/13): Assets, $4,009,312 (M); expenditures, $216,572; qualifying distributions, $190,000; giving activities include $190,000 for 15 grants (high: $50,000; low: $2,500).
Fields of interest: Education; Environment; Foundations; Health care clinics.
Limitations: Applications not accepted. Giving primarily in CA.
Application information: Unsolicited requests for funds not accepted.
Officers: Jane B. Dunaway, Pres.; Tena D. Farr, Treas.
EIN: 261392022

654
Norman and Lela Beren Jacoby Family Foundation

13801 Ventura Blvd.
Sherman Oaks, CA   91423-3603

Established in 1988 in California.
Donors: The Robert M. Beren Foundation, Inc.; Lela Jacoby; Norman Jacoby.
Foundation type: Independent foundation.
Financial data (yr. ended 12/31/13): Assets, $4,359,811 (M); expenditures, $242,146; qualifying distributions, $215,875; giving activities include $212,955 for 23 grants (high: $54,000; low: $200).
Purpose and activities: Giving primarily for educational programs.
Fields of interest: Education; Elementary and secondary education; Higher education; Nonprofits; Judaism.
Type of support: Regranting.
Limitations: Applications not accepted. Giving on a national basis. No grants to individuals.

Application information: Contributes only to pre-selected organizations.
Officers: Lela Beren Jacoby, Pres.; Norman Jacoby, Secy.-Treas.
Directors: Judith Jacoby Chiel; Taren Jacoby Metson; Susan Jacoby Stern.
EIN: 954197993

655
Jade and Coral Foundation

P.O. Box 712
San Gabriel, CA   91778-0712

Donors: Kenneth Lam; Samantha Lam.
Foundation type: Independent foundation.
Financial data (yr. ended 12/31/14): Assets, $2,650,150 (M); expenditures, $180,817; qualifying distributions, $150,942; giving activities include $150,000 for 2 grants (high: $110,000; low: $40,000).
Fields of interest: Religion.
Type of support: General support.
Limitations: Applications not accepted. Giving primarily in CA.
Application information: Unsolicited requests for funds not accepted.
Officers: Kenneth Lam, Pres.; Samantha Lam, Secy.
EIN: 263901161

656
The Parveen and Neeraj Jain Endowment Fund

2636 Gayley Pl.
San Jose, CA   95135-1268

Established in 2004 in California.
Donors: Parveen Jain; Neeraj Jain.
Foundation type: Independent foundation.
Financial data (yr. ended 12/31/13): Assets, $226,436 (M); gifts received, $50,000; expenditures, $189,124; qualifying distributions, $180,310; giving activities include $180,310 for 3 grants (high: $106,000; low: $2,500).
Fields of interest: Science; Religion.
International interests: India.
Type of support: General support.
Limitations: Applications not accepted. Giving on an international basis, with emphasis on India. No grants to individuals.
Application information: Unsolicited requests for funds not accepted.
Officers: Neeraj Jain, Pres.; Parveen Jain, Secy. and C.F.O.
EIN: 470934264

657
Jain Foundation

1005 Brisa Del Mar
Santa Cruz, CA   95060   (831) 621-7953

Established in 1990 in California.
Donors: Navindra K. Jain; Madhu Jain.
Foundation type: Independent foundation.
Financial data (yr. ended 12/31/13): Assets, $0 (M); expenditures, $310,360; qualifying distributions, $310,360; giving activities include $309,200 for 5 grants (high: $190,000; low: $10,000).
Fields of interest: Education; Hospital care; Religion.

Limitations: Applications accepted. Giving primarily in C.
Application information: Application form required.
Initial approach: Proposal
Deadline(s): None
Officers: Navindra Jain, Pres.; David Heintz, V.P.; Madhu Jain, Secy.-Treas.
EIN: 770261398

658
Jamieson Foundation

959 Natoma St.
San Francisco, CA   94103-2514

Established in 1986 in California.
Donor: G.W. Jamieson†.
Foundation type: Independent foundation.
Financial data (yr. ended 11/30/13): Assets, $2,312,223 (M); expenditures, $128,816; qualifying distributions, $122,130; giving activities include $118,500 for 15 grants (high: $20,000; low: $250).
Fields of interest: Higher education; Environment; Hospital care; Community and economic development; Christianity; Sports and recreation; Human services.
Type of support: General support; Program-related investments; In-kind gifts; Continuing support; Equipment; Emergency funds; Program development; Research; Technical assistance.
Limitations: Applications not accepted. Giving primarily in the San Francisco Bay Area, CA. No grants to individuals.
Application information: Contributes only to pre-selected organizations.
Board meeting date(s): Feb.
Officers: Doug Jamieson, Pres.; Aileen Jamieson, V.P.; Jennifer Jamieson, Secy.-Treas.
EIN: 943025704

659
Jatain Charitable Foundation

58 Archipelago Dr.
Newport Coast, CA   92657-2106   (714) 825-0140
Contact: Bob Cheng, Tr.

Established in 2000 in New Jersey.
Donor: Fema Electronics Corp.
Foundation type: Company-sponsored foundation.
Financial data (yr. ended 12/31/13): Assets, $7,516,310 (M); gifts received, $558,110; expenditures, $410,800; qualifying distributions, $312,000; giving activities include $312,000 for 2 grants (high: $310,000; low: $2,000).
Purpose and activities: The foundation supports organizations involved with cultural and ethnic awareness, higher education, and Taiwanese heritage.
Fields of interest: Education; Religion; Human services.
Type of support: General support.
Limitations: Applications accepted. Giving primarily CA, NJ, and PA.
Application information:
Initial approach: Proposal
Deadline(s): None
Trustees: Bob Cheng; Clifford Cheng; George Cheng; Jean Cheng.
EIN: 226824275

660
JDH Family Foundation
c/o J. Dale Harvey
1415 Lomita Dr.
Pasadena, CA 91106-4340

Established in 2005 in California.
Donors: Stephanie F. Harvey; J. Dale Harvey.
Foundation type: Independent foundation.
Financial data (yr. ended 12/31/14): Assets,
$1,077,201; expenditures, $188,585; qualifying
distributions, $188,585.
Fields of interest: Education; Environment;
Protestantism.
Limitations: Applications not accepted. No grants to
individuals.
Application information: Unsolicited requests for
funds not accepted.
Officers: J. Dale Harvey, Pres.; Stephanie F. Harvey,
Secy. and C.F.O.
Director: Eddie Newman.
EIN: 203168194

661
Jeangerard Foundation
37596 Avenue 12 1/4
Madera, CA 93636-8682

Established in 1992 in California.
Donor: Ralph W. Jeangerard†.
Foundation type: Independent foundation.
Financial data (yr. ended 06/30/13): Assets,
$2,254,159 (M); expenditures, $192,448;
qualifying distributions, $180,336; giving activities
include $180,336 for 5 grants (high: $155,000;
low: $336).
Fields of interest: Natural resources; Forest
preservation.
Limitations: Applications not accepted. Giving
primarily in CA. No grants to individuals.
Application information: Unsolicited requests for
funds not accepted.
Officers: Jack J. Jeangerard, Pres.; Michael R.
Sutherland, V.P.; Kelli A. Sutherland, Secy.
EIN: 770299812

662
William Sloane Jelin Charitable Foundation
c/o Holthouse, Carlin and Van Trigt, LLP
11444 W., Olympic Blvd., 11th Fl.
Los Angeles, CA 90064-1500 (310) 566-1900
Contact: Deborah Newmyer, Tr.

Established in 1996 in Maine.
Donor: William S. Jelin.
Foundation type: Independent foundation.
Financial data (yr. ended 12/31/13): Assets,
$1,748,002 (M); expenditures, $160,287;
qualifying distributions, $139,143; giving activities
include $135,292 for 36 grants (high: $16,000;
low: $1,000).
Purpose and activities: Giving primarily to Jewish
agencies and children's services.
Fields of interest: Arts and culture; Cancers;
Judaism; Human services; Child welfare; Youth
organizing.
Limitations: Applications accepted. Giving primarily
in CA, ME and NJ. No grants to individuals.
Application information: Application form required.

Initial approach: Letter
Deadline(s): Annualy prior to the first day of Aug.
Trustees: Brian Meyhew; Deborah Newmyer; Harold
C. Pachios.
EIN: 223436131

663
Jennings Family Foundation
11661 San Vincente Blvd., Ste. 910
Los Angeles, CA 90049 (310) 472-6150

Established in 2006 in California.
Donors: Paul Jennings; Adrienne Jennings.
Foundation type: Independent foundation.
Financial data (yr. ended 12/31/14): Assets,
$6,203; expenditures, $223,173; qualifying
distributions, $220,663.
Fields of interest: Elementary and secondary
education; Higher education; Youth development.
Limitations: Applications accepted. Giving primarily
in CA.
Application information: Application form required.
Initial approach: Letter
Deadline(s): None
Officers: Adrienne Grant, Pres.; Paul Jennings,
Secy.-Treas.
Director: Joshua S. Jennings.
EIN: 204780703

664
Jesy Foundation
372 Piercy Rd.
San Jose, CA 95138-1401

Donors: Ning Lee; Tu-Lien Lee.
Foundation type: Independent foundation.
Financial data (yr. ended 08/31/14): Assets,
$3,067,109 (M); expenditures, $166,466;
qualifying distributions, $151,668; giving activities
include $136,750 for 32 grants (high: $7,000; low:
$750).
Fields of interest: Education; Health; Human
services.
Type of support: General support.
Limitations: Applications not accepted. No grants to
individuals.
Application information: Unsolicited requests for
funds not accepted.
Officers: Ning Lee, Pres.; Tu-Lien Lee, Secy.
EIN: 912156243

665
Joerger Family Charitable Foundation
1708 Via Violeta
San Clemente, CA 92673

Established in 2004 in California.
Donor: Dolores Joerger.
Foundation type: Independent foundation.
Financial data (yr. ended 12/31/13): Assets,
$1,043,691 (M); expenditures, $186,446;
qualifying distributions, $182,175; giving activities
include $182,175 for 14 grants (high: $30,000;
low: $5,000).
Fields of interest: Christianity; Human services;
Shelter and residential care.
Type of support: General support.
Limitations: Applications not accepted. Giving
primarily in CA, with some giving in AZ. No grants to
individuals.

Application information: Contributes only to
pre-selected organizations.
Officers and Directors: Jean Griffin, Pres. and
Director; Janet Moore, Secy. and Director; Michael
Joerger, Treas. and Director.
EIN: 202046432

666
James Hervey Johnson Charitable Educational Trust
P.O. Box 16160
San Diego, CA 92176-6160
Contact: Kevin V. Munnelly, Tr.

Established in 1989 in California.
Foundation type: Independent foundation.
Financial data (yr. ended 07/31/13): Assets,
$8,928,001 (M); expenditures, $692,873;
qualifying distributions, $517,532; giving activities
include $385,140 for 24 grants (high: $140,000;
low: $2,000).
Purpose and activities: Giving primarily to
organizations involved in free thinking, humanism,
the separation of church and state, and freedom
from religion; support also for natural hygiene and
promotion and advocacy of vegetarianism.
Fields of interest: Philosophy; University education.
Limitations: Applications accepted. Giving primarily
in CA. No grants to individuals.
Publications: Application guidelines; Financial
statement.
Application information: Application form required.
Initial approach: Request application form
Deadline(s): July 31
Trustee: Kevin V. Munnelly.
Number of staff: 1 part-time professional.
EIN: 336081439

667
The Bernard J. & Mary T. Johnson Family Foundation
225 S. Lake Ave., Ste. 300
Pasadena, CA 91101-3009
Contact: Bernard J. Johnson, Pres.

Established in 1998 in California.
Donors: Bernard J. Johnson; Mary T. Johnson.
Foundation type: Independent foundation.
Financial data (yr. ended 06/30/14): Assets,
$895,587 (M); gifts received, $513,511;
expenditures, $365,074; qualifying distributions,
$289,144; giving activities include $280,000 for 27
grants (high: $26,000; low: $4,000).
Fields of interest: Theater; Elementary and
secondary education; Nonprofits; Health;
Alzheimer's disease; Diabetes; Christianity; Human
services; Senior services.
Type of support: Regranting; Research.
Limitations: Applications accepted. Giving primarily
in CA. No grants to individuals.
Application information: Application form required.
Initial approach: Letter
Deadline(s): None
Officers and Directors: Bernard J. Johnson, Pres.
and Director; Mark C. Johnson, V.P. and Director;
Elizabeth A. Wray, V.P.; Mary T. Johnson, Secy. and
Director; Philip B. Johnson, Treas.
EIN: 954712836

668

J. Stanley and Mary W. Johnson Family Foundation
2280 University Dr.
Newport Beach, CA 92660-3327

Established in 1998 in California.
Donor: Mary W. Johnson‡.
Foundation type: Independent foundation.
Financial data (yr. ended 12/31/14): Assets, $10,240,587; expenditures, $510,914; qualifying distributions, $430,402.
Fields of interest: Education.
Limitations: Applications not accepted. Giving primarily in Orange County, CA. No grants to individuals.
Application information: Contributes only to pre-selected organizations.
Officers: Donald P. Johnson, Pres.; Robert W. Johnson, Treas.
EIN: 330809657

669

Carl W. Johnson Foundation
5900 Wilshire Blvd., Ste. 2300
Los Angeles, CA 90036-3697 (323) 634-2400
Contact: Susan J. Ollweiler

Established in 1993 in California.
Donor: Carl W. Johnson.
Foundation type: Independent foundation.
Financial data (yr. ended 12/31/13): Assets, $5,909,596 (M); gifts received, $505; expenditures, $422,529; qualifying distributions, $295,000; giving activities include $295,000 for 21 grants (high: $45,000; low: $3,000).
Purpose and activities: Giving primarily for education, health care, and aid to individuals with developmental needs.
Fields of interest: Higher education; Health; Human services; People with disabilities.
Limitations: Applications accepted. Giving primarily in southern CA. No grants to individuals.
Application information: Application form required.
  Initial approach: Letter
  Deadline(s): Aug. 1
Officers: Wallace D. Franson, Pres.; David D. Watts, Secy.; Tim Bodner, Treas.
Directors: Christopher D. Montan; Kathleen Nelson; Gene Torncello.
EIN: 954438839

670

Mark Chapin Johnson Foundation
P.O. Box 3088
Mission Viejo, CA 92690-1088

Established in 1990 in California.
Donor: Mark Chapin Johnson.
Foundation type: Independent foundation.
Financial data (yr. ended 12/31/13): Assets, $6,421,411 (M); expenditures, $440,731; qualifying distributions, $386,118; giving activities include $309,127 for 22 grants (high: $85,987; low: $500).
Fields of interest: Performing arts; Higher education; Public libraries; Christianity; Human services; Youth services.
Type of support: Scholarships.
Limitations: Applications not accepted. Giving primarily in CA. No grants to individuals.

Application information: Contributes only to pre-selected organizations.
Officers and Directors: Mark Chapin Johnson, Pres. and C.E.O. and Director; Barbara Hiller Johnson, Secy.
EIN: 330441985

671

The Dorothy L. Johnston Foundation
301 E. Colorado Blvd., 9th Fl.
Pasadena, CA 91101-1915

Established in 2010 in California.
Donor: Harry E. Johnston Separate Party Trust.
Foundation type: Independent foundation.
Financial data (yr. ended 12/31/13): Assets, $8,277,179 (M); expenditures, $371,955; qualifying distributions, $391,109; giving activities include $346,009 for 26 grants (high: $50,000; low: $500).
Fields of interest: Arts and culture; Education.
Limitations: Applications not accepted. Giving primarily in CA. No grants to individuals.
Application information: Contributes only to pre-selected organizations.
Trustee: Karl Swaidan.
EIN: 276390335

672

The Jolson Family Foundation
600 Montgomery St., Ste. 1100
San Francisco, CA 94111-2713

Established in 2003 in California.
Donor: Joseph A. Jolson.
Foundation type: Independent foundation.
Financial data (yr. ended 12/31/13): Assets, $7,041,358 (M); expenditures, $400,125; qualifying distributions, $342,270; giving activities include $342,270 for 46 grants (high: $40,000; low: $120).
Purpose and activities: Giving for education as well as for children, youth, families, and social services, including community programs for the needy and homeless.
Fields of interest: Arts and culture; Education; Elementary and secondary education; Higher education; Human services; Family services; Child welfare; Homeless people; Low-income and poor people.
Limitations: Applications not accepted. Giving primarily in CA, with emphasis on Marin County. No grants to individuals.
Application information: Contributes only to pre-selected organizations.
Officers: Joseph A. Jolson, Pres. and Treas.; Kathleen Jolson, Secy.
EIN: 200391079

673

E. Richard Jones Family Foundation
(formerly The Jones Foundation)
c/o E. Richard Jones
P.O. Box 352
Calistoga, CA 94515 (707) 942-0467
E-mail: erjfoundation@joneswine.com

Donors: Jones Living Trust; Marilyn Jones; ERJ Living Trust.
Foundation type: Independent foundation.

Financial data (yr. ended 12/31/14): Assets, $5,947,735; gifts received, $0; expenditures, $469,633; qualifying distributions, $395,986.
Purpose and activities: Giving to organizations that assist individuals in changing their lives and becoming self-sufficient.
Fields of interest: Education; Elementary and secondary education; Higher education; Foundations; Health; Human services; Family services.
Type of support: Annual campaigns; Seed money.
Limitations: Applications accepted. Giving primarily in the San Francisco Bay Area, CA.
Application information: Application form required.
  Initial approach: Letter, no more than 2 pages
  Copies of proposal: 1
  Deadline(s): None
Officers: Stephanie Bailey, V.P.; Heather Melvin, V.P.
Director: E. Richard Jones.
Number of staff: 1 part-time professional.
EIN: 943288860

674

Louis and Donna Jones Family Foundation
500 E. Olive Ave., Ste. 670
Burbank, CA 91501-2197 (818) 260-0544
Contact: Louis E. Jones, Dir.

Established in 1998 in California.
Donors: LJA Insurance Co.; Donna D. Jones; Louis E. Jones.
Foundation type: Company-sponsored foundation.
Financial data (yr. ended 12/31/13): Assets, $2,246,550 (M); gifts received, $194,000; expenditures, $138,215; qualifying distributions, $136,000; giving activities include $136,000 for 13 grants (high: $25,000; low: $1,000).
Purpose and activities: The foundation supports organizations involved with education, health, and human services.
Fields of interest: Arts and culture; Education; Human services.
Type of support: General support.
Limitations: Applications accepted. Giving primarily in CA. No grants to individuals.
Application information:
  Initial approach: Proposal
  Deadline(s): None
Directors: Daniel E. Jones; Donna D. Jones; Louis E. Jones; Judi E. Shupper.
EIN: 954716272

675

Steaven K. and Judith G. Jones Foundation
1048 Amalfi Dr.
Pacific Palisades, CA 90272-4028

Established in 2007 in California.
Donors: Steaven K. Jones; Judith G. Jones; Steven Jones Development Co. Inc.
Foundation type: Independent foundation.
Financial data (yr. ended 12/31/13): Assets, $6,810 (M); gifts received, $165,035; expenditures, $198,793; qualifying distributions, $196,796; giving activities include $196,796 for 47 grants (high: $50,000; low: $45).
Fields of interest: Elementary and secondary education; Higher education; Family planning; Catholicism.

Type of support: General support.
Limitations: Applications not accepted. Giving primarily in CA. No grants to individuals.
Application information: Unsolicited requests for funds not accepted.
Officers: Judith G. Jones, Pres.; Steaven K. Jones, Secy.
EIN: 261323339

676
David and Annette Jorgensen Foundation
20 Zapata Way
Portola Valley, CA   94028-7918

Established in 1988 in California.
Donors: Annette Jorgensen; David G. Jorgensen.
Foundation type: Independent foundation.
Financial data (yr. ended 12/31/13): Assets, $8,006,639 (M); expenditures, $434,105; qualifying distributions, $391,451; giving activities include $351,255 for 30 grants (high: $100,000; low: $100).
Fields of interest: Cultural awareness; Museums; Higher education; Foundations; Public affairs; Human rights.
Limitations: Applications not accepted. No grants to individuals.
Application information: Unsolicited requests for funds not accepted.
Officers: David G. Jorgensen, Pres.; Annette Jorgensen, V.P. and Secy.; Jennifer A. Jorgensen, V.P.; Thomas D. Jorgensen, V.P.
EIN: 943058478

677
The Ken and Judith Joy Family Foundation
171 Main St., Ste. 263
Los Altos, CA   94022-2912

Established in 1997 in California.
Donors: Judith C. Joy; Ken E. Joy.
Foundation type: Independent foundation.
Financial data (yr. ended 12/31/13): Assets, $3,763,844 (M); expenditures, $267,401; qualifying distributions, $263,658; giving activities include $263,000 for 33 grants (high: $50,000; low: $2,000).
Purpose and activities: Giving primarily for education and Christian agencies and churches.
Fields of interest: Arts and culture; Architecture; Museums; Art museums; Education; Higher education; Graduate and professional education; Hospice care; Storms; Christianity; Theology; Human services.
Limitations: Applications not accepted. Giving primarily in CA, MA, and NY. No grants to individuals.
Application information: Contributes only to pre-selected organizations.
Officers and Directors: Jessica M. Joy, Pres. and Director; Ken E. Joy, C.F.O. and Director; Hilary Joy Harmssen, Secy. and Director; Joshua A. Harmssen; Jennifer L. Joy; Judith C. Joy; Matthew T. Joy.
EIN: 770442117

678
JP Foundation Trust
960 W. Hedding St.
San Jose, CA   95126

Established in 2008 in California.

Donor: Joan and John Vatterott Family Foundation.
Foundation type: Independent foundation.
Financial data (yr. ended 12/31/13): Assets, $152,216 (M); gifts received, $100,000; expenditures, $130,729; qualifying distributions, $130,729; giving activities include $130,729 for 10 grants (high: $34,229; low: $500).
Fields of interest: Education.
Limitations: Applications not accepted. Giving primarily in CA.
Application information: Unsolicited requests for funds not accepted.
Trustees: Paul G. Sheridan; John Vatterott; Jerry Wade.
EIN: 266088124

679
JTB Cultural Exchange Corp.
19700 Mariner Ave., 2nd Fl.
Torrance, CA   90503-1648

Established in 1988 in New York.
Donor: JTB Americas, Ltd.
Foundation type: Company-sponsored foundation.
Financial data (yr. ended 12/31/13): Assets, $1,699,530 (M); expenditures, $181,862; qualifying distributions, $181,862; giving activities include $177,881 for 29 grants (high: $100,000; low: $1,000).
Purpose and activities: The foundation supports hospitals and festivals and organizations involved with arts and culture, education, business, and Japanese culture.
Fields of interest: Arts and culture; Education; Agriculture.
Type of support: General support.
Limitations: Applications not accepted. No grants to individuals.
Application information: Unsolicited requests for funds not accepted.
Officers: Yoshinori Himeno, Pres.; Francis W. Costello, Secy.; Keiichiro Otofuji, Treas.
Director: Kazuharu Abe.
Number of staff: 1 part-time support.
EIN: 133456886

680
The Jubas Family Foundation
951 Ocean Ave., Ste. 401
Santa Monica, CA   90403-2461

Established in 1998 in California.
Donor: Marvin Jubas.
Foundation type: Independent foundation.
Financial data (yr. ended 12/31/13): Assets, $896,929 (M); expenditures, $235,075; qualifying distributions, $233,710; giving activities include $233,250 for 16 grants (high: $40,000; low: $2,000).
Fields of interest: Arts and culture; Education; Philanthropy; Judaism.
Type of support: General support.
Limitations: Applications not accepted. Giving primarily in CA. No grants to individuals.
Application information: Unsolicited requests for funds not accepted.
Officers and Directors: Marvin Jubas, Pres. and Director; Andrea Heisser, Secy.-Treas. and Director.
EIN: 954717499

681
Felix And Helen Juda Foundation
20201 SW Birch St.
Newport Beach, CA   92660

Established in 1951 in California.
Donors: Felix M. Juda; Helen Juda.
Foundation type: Independent foundation.
Financial data (yr. ended 11/30/14): Assets, $488,989 (M); expenditures, $159,235; qualifying distributions, $152,000; giving activities include $152,000 for 2 grants.
Fields of interest: Arts and culture; Foundations.
Type of support: General support.
Limitations: Applications not accepted. No grants to individuals.
Application information: Unsolicited requests for funds not accepted.
Trustees: Tom Juda; Patsy Juda Palmer.
EIN: 956048035

682
The Don & Maxine Judkins Family Foundation
6851 McDivitt Dr., Ste. B
Bakersfield, CA   93313-2004

Established in 2002 in California.
Donors: Don Judkins; Donavan Judkins; Jufa Capital LLC; Maxine Judkins.
Foundation type: Independent foundation.
Financial data (yr. ended 12/31/13): Assets, $7,157,069 (M); gifts received, $485,500; expenditures, $356,450; qualifying distributions, $296,187; giving activities include $296,187 for 2 grants (high: $222,087; low: $74,100).
Purpose and activities: Giving primarily to Christian organizations and for higher education.
Fields of interest: Higher education; Christianity; Human services.
Limitations: Applications not accepted. Giving primarily in CA and MO. No grants to individuals.
Application information: Contributes only to pre-selected organizations.
Officers: Don Judkins, Mgr.; Maxine Judkins, Mgr.
Directors: Donavan Judkins; Greg Judkins.
EIN: 460476311

683
The Donavan and Randie Judkins Family Foundation
P.O. Box 20582
Bakersfield, CA   93390

Donors: Randie Judkins; Donavan Judkins.
Foundation type: Independent foundation.
Financial data (yr. ended 12/31/13): Assets, $4,941,043 (M); expenditures, $246,894; qualifying distributions, $209,425; giving activities include $209,425 for 8 grants (high: $83,325; low: $500).
Fields of interest: Christianity.
Type of support: General support.
Limitations: Applications not accepted. Giving primarily in CA and TX. No grants to individuals.
Application information: Contributes only to pre-selected organizations.
Officers: Donavan Judkins, Fdn. Mgr.; Randie Judkins, Fdn. Mgr.
EIN: 200761150

684

Just Keep Livin Foundation

(also known as j.k. livin Foundation)
1107 Glendon Ave.
Los Angeles, CA   90024-3501   (310) 857-1555
FAX: (310) 388-1084;
E-mail: jklfoundation@jklivin.net; Main URL: http://www.jklivinfoundation.org
E Newsletter: http://www.jklivinfoundation.org/contact/join-our-email-list
Facebook: https://www.facebook.com/jklivin?ref=ts
RSS feed: http://jklivinfoundation.org/rss
Twitter: https://twitter.com/jklivinFNDN
YouTube: http://www.youtube.com/user/justkeeplivin

Established in 2006 in California.
Donors: Matthew McConaughey; Entertainment Industry Foundation; JK Living Foundation; JP Morgan Chase; Best Buy; Texas Rangers Baseball Foundation; Active Network; Competitor Group Inc.; Chime on Inc.
Foundation type: Independent foundation.
Financial data (yr. ended 12/31/13): Assets, $1,847,149 (M); gifts received, $912,803; expenditures, $904,914; qualifying distributions, $804,684; giving activities include $353,678 for 23 grants (high: $58,292; low: $500).
Purpose and activities: The foundation is dedicated to helping teenage kids lead active lives and make healthy choices to become great men and women. The foundation is partnered with Communities in Schools (CIS), the nations largest, non-profit, dropout prevention organization in the nation, to implement fitness and wellness programs in large inner-city high schools in the community. Through after school programs, students are encouraged to improve their physical and mental health through exercise, teamwork, gratitude, and positive life choices.
Fields of interest: Student retention; Exercise; Nutrition; Youth development; Children and youth; Dropouts; Slum youth.
Limitations: Applications not accepted. Giving primarily in CA; some giving also in TX. No grants to individuals.
Application information: Contributes only to pre-selected organizations.
Officers and Directors: Matthew McConaughey, C.E.O. and Pres. and Director; P. Kevin Morris, Secy.; Shannon Mabrey Rotenberg, Exec. Dir.; Rick George; Blaine Lourd; Camila McConaughey; Jim Toth.
EIN: 203921057

685

Kabcenell Family Foundation

4900 Alpine Rd.
Portola Valley, CA   94028-8036

Donors: Charlene C. Kabcenell; Dirk A. Kabcenell.
Foundation type: Independent foundation.
Financial data (yr. ended 12/31/13): Assets, $19,440,895 (M); expenditures, $439,506; qualifying distributions, $206,225; giving activities include $200,000 for 1 grant.
Fields of interest: Foundations.
Limitations: Applications not accepted. Giving primarily in CA. No grants to individuals.
Application information: Contributes only to pre-selected organizations.

Officers: Charlene C. Kabcenell, Pres.; Dirk A. Kabcenell, C.F.O. and Secy.
EIN: 912198779

686

Kadima Foundation

38 Miller Ave., Ste. 220
Mill Valley, CA   94941-1939   (415) 295-7423
Contact: Rhonda Anderson

Established in 1997 in California.
Donors: MCR Foundation; The Max Webb Lead Unitrust; Cara Schreyer.
Foundation type: Independent foundation.
Financial data (yr. ended 12/31/12): Assets, $1,278,807 (M); gifts received, $363,148; expenditures, $439,405; qualifying distributions, $412,836; giving activities include $406,000 for 14 grants (high: $110,000; low: $1,000).
Purpose and activities: The mission of the foundation focuses primarily on creating opportunities for promising young adults to access education and training that will help them realize their potential. In addition, the foundation also supports institutions and programs dedicated to the cure, prevention, and management of insulin-dependent diabetes whose goals are to cure diabetes, to delay and/or prevent complications, and to improve the quality of life through disease management to ultimately prevent the disease. Also giving for the understanding and encouragement of contemporary art, as well as the encouragement and support of emerging young artists, and causes that promote the people of Israel, with a special interest in women's rights.
Fields of interest: Arts and culture; Museums; Elementary and secondary education; Higher education; Nonprofits; Diabetes; Judaism; Youth organizing; International relations.
Type of support: Research; Regranting; Fundraising.
Limitations: Applications accepted. Giving primarily in CA.
Application information:
  Deadline(s): None
Officers: Chara Schreyer, Pres.; Justine Schreyer, Secy.-Treas.
Director: Natalie Schreyer.
EIN: 943254834

687

James and Virginia Kallins Foundation

3720 S. Susan St., Ste. 100
Santa Ana, CA   92704-6957

Established in 1999 in California.
Donors: James G. Kallins; Virginia Kallins; George Kallins; Barbara Kallins.
Foundation type: Independent foundation.
Financial data (yr. ended 12/31/13): Assets, $4,410,929 (M); expenditures, $263,729; qualifying distributions, $254,463; giving activities include $252,825 for 37 grants (high: $150,000; low: $50).
Purpose and activities: Giving primarily to Greek Orthodox agencies.
Fields of interest: Orthodox Christianity.
Limitations: Applications not accepted. Giving primarily in CA and NY. No grants to individuals.
Application information: Contributes only to pre-selected organizations.

Officers: James G. Kallins, Pres.; Virginia Kallins, V.P. and Secy.-Treas.
EIN: 330850189

688

John and Ursula Kanel Charitable Foundation

c/o Alan T. Yoshitake
333 S. Hope St., Ste. 3900
Los Angeles, CA   90071-3043

Established in 1992 in California.
Donor: Ursula Kanel.
Foundation type: Independent foundation.
Financial data (yr. ended 12/31/13): Assets, $7,087,753 (M); expenditures, $399,063; qualifying distributions, $325,310; giving activities include $244,075 for 12 grants (high: $112,000; low: $1,000).
Fields of interest: Education; Higher education; Graduate and professional education; Nonprofits; Specialty hospital care; Engineering; Protestantism; Child welfare; People with vision impairments.
Type of support: General support; Regranting.
Limitations: Applications not accepted. Giving primarily in Los Angeles and Pasadena, CA. No grants to individuals.
Application information: Unsolicited requests for funds not accepted.
Directors: Victor Andeson; Tetsu Taimoto; Alan T. Yoshitake.
EIN: 954400580

689

Kanoff Family Foundation

c/o Jefferies & Co.
11100 Santa Monica Blvd.
Los Angeles, CA   90025-3384

Established in 1997 in California.
Donors: Chris M. Kanoff; Mary Ellen Kanoff.
Foundation type: Independent foundation.
Financial data (yr. ended 12/31/13): Assets, $1,377,890 (M); gifts received, $54,990; expenditures, $136,434; qualifying distributions, $125,394; giving activities include $125,394 for 28 grants (high: $25,299; low: $70).
Fields of interest: Education; Catholicism; Human services.
Limitations: Applications not accepted. Giving primarily in CA. No grants to individuals.
Application information: Contributes only to pre-selected organizations.
Officers and Directors: Chris M. Kanoff, Pres. and Director; Daniel O. Conwill, Secy.; Mary Ellen Kanoff, Treas. and Director.
EIN: 954662947

690

The Kao Family Foundation

c/o Favor & Favor, CPAS
24422 Avenida de la Carlota, Ste.275
Laguna Hills, CA   92653-4615

Donors: John E. Kao; Susan S. Kao.
Foundation type: Independent foundation.
Financial data (yr. ended 12/31/13): Assets, $1,914,201 (M); expenditures, $320,295; qualifying distributions, $281,970; giving activities

include $281,970 for 9 grants (high: $132,000; low: $50).
Fields of interest: Christianity; Human services.
Limitations: Applications not accepted. Giving primarily in CA.
Application information: Unsolicited requests for funds not accepted.
Officers: John E. Kao, Pres.; Susan S. Kao, Secy.
EIN: 453859531

691
Richard A. Karp Charitable Foundation
849-B Independence Ave.
Mountain View, CA 94043-2301

Established in 2004 in California.
Donor: Richard A. Karp.
Foundation type: Independent foundation.
Financial data (yr. ended 12/31/14): Assets, $7,615,235; gifts received, $0; expenditures, $409,049; qualifying distributions, $409,049 and $0 for set-asides.
Fields of interest: Arts and culture; Education; Vocational education.
Limitations: Applications not accepted. Giving primarily in CA. No grants to individuals.
Application information: Unsolicited requests for funds not accepted.
Directors: Richard A. Karp; Sarah J. Roberts.
EIN: 201866106

692
Katz Family Foundation
(formerly Springhouse Foundation)
409 Summit Ave.
Mill Valley, CA 94941-1029
Contact: Bruce Katz, Tr.

Established in 1986 in Massachusetts.
Donor: Bruce R. Katz.
Foundation type: Independent foundation.
Financial data (yr. ended 11/30/14): Assets, $2,121,481 (M); expenditures, $181,804; qualifying distributions, $166,405; giving activities include $155,310 for 45 grants (high: $25,000; low: $100).
Fields of interest: Arts and culture; Environment; Human services.
Type of support: Program development.
Limitations: Applications not accepted. Giving primarily on the West Coast, with emphasis on northern CA. No grants to individuals.
Application information: Contributes only to pre-selected organizations.
Trustees: Bruce Katz; Roger Katz.
Number of staff: 1 part-time professional.
EIN: 042947276

693
The Charles and Roberta Katz Family Foundation
P.O. Box 411
Palo Alto, CA 94302-0411

Established in 1999 in Washington.
Donors: Charles J. Katz, Jr.; Roberta B. Katz; Roberta R. Katz.
Foundation type: Independent foundation.

Financial data (yr. ended 12/31/14): Assets, $4,584,761; expenditures, $238,958; qualifying distributions, $213,500.
Fields of interest: Arts education; Music; Higher education; Wildlife biodiversity; Philanthropy.
Limitations: Applications not accepted. Giving primarily in CA. No grants to individuals.
Application information: Contributes only to pre-selected organizations.
Officers: Charles J. Katz, Jr., Pres.; Roberta B. Katz, 1st V.P. and Secy.-Treas.; Sarah B. Katz, V.P.; Sydney M. Katz, V.P.
EIN: 912001806

694
KC Family Foundation
203 Redwood Shores Pkwy., Ste. 145
Redwood City, CA 94065 (415) 362-5990
Contact: Karen K. Christensen, Pres., C.F.O. and Dir.

Established in 2005 in California.
Donor: Karen K. Christensen.
Foundation type: Independent foundation.
Financial data (yr. ended 12/31/13): Assets, $4,444,474 (M); expenditures, $195,998; qualifying distributions, $159,425; giving activities include $156,000 for 3 grants (high: $100,000; low: $6,000).
Fields of interest: Education; Secondary education.
Limitations: Applications accepted. Giving primarily in VT.
Application information: Application form required.
Initial approach: Letter
Deadline(s): None
Officers and Directors: Karen K. Christensen, Pres. and C.F.O. and Director; Selena Y. Wong, Secy.
EIN: 203947601

695
Kevin and Masha Keating Family Foundation
1564 Cantera Ave.
Santa Barbara, CA 93110-2446 (805) 687-6525
Contact: Kevin B. Keating, Pres., C.E.O and Dir.

Donors: James B. Ax Family Foundation; Kevin Keating.
Foundation type: Independent foundation.
Financial data (yr. ended 12/31/13): Assets, $4,860,345 (M); gifts received, $30,260; expenditures, $237,966; qualifying distributions, $189,267; giving activities include $189,267 for 12 grants (high: $100,000; low: $300).
Fields of interest: Hospital care; Judaism.
Limitations: Applications accepted. Giving primarily in CA and New York, NY.
Application information:
Initial approach: Proposal
Deadline(s): None
Officers and Directors: Kevin B. Keating, Pres. and C.E.O. and Director; Masha Keating, Secy. and Director.
EIN: 271527514

696
The Aram and Margie Keith Family Foundation
420 Monarch Bay Dr.
Irvine, CA 92629

Established in 2005 in California.
Donor: Aram & Margie Keith Trust.
Foundation type: Independent foundation.
Financial data (yr. ended 12/31/13): Assets, $5,760,599 (M); expenditures, $188,437; qualifying distributions, $177,569; giving activities include $169,140 for 11 grants (high: $80,000; low: $250).
Purpose and activities: Giving primarily to Christian churches and organizations, as well as for education and social services.
Fields of interest: Elementary and secondary education; Higher education; Christianity; Human services.
Limitations: Applications not accepted. Giving primarily in CA. No grants to individuals.
Application information: Unsolicited requests forr funds not accepted.
Officers: Aram H. Keith, Pres.; Ryan Derrick Keith, V.P.; Kimberly Dawn Kihm, V.P.; Erica Joy Norton, V.P.; Margie R. Keith, Secy. and C.F.O.
EIN: 593824853

697
Kelly Foundation
3610 American River Dr., Ste. 190
Sacramento, CA 95864-5922
Application address: P.O. Box 255868, Sacramento, CA 95865-5868; Main URL: http://kellyfoundationsacramento.org

Established in 1988 in California.
Donors: Kelly Television Co.; Kelly Broadcasting Co.; Jon S. Kelly; Gregory G. Kelly; J.S. Kelly, LLC; River City Bank, N.A.; G.G. Kelly, LLC.
Foundation type: Independent foundation.
Financial data (yr. ended 09/30/14): Assets, $9,352,382; gifts received, $125,000; expenditures, $416,734; qualifying distributions, $409,206.
Purpose and activities: Giving for health and human services, education, and civic improvement.
Fields of interest: Cultural awareness; Museums; Education; Environment; Veterinary medicine; Health; Diseases and conditions; Public libraries; Community and economic development; Special Olympics; Human services; Food aid; Family services; People with vision impairments.
Type of support: General support; Capital campaigns; Capital and infrastructure; Equipment; Program development; Fellowships; Scholarships.
Limitations: Applications accepted. Giving primarily in Sacramento, CA. No grants to individuals; no support for religious organizations for explicit religious activities, political organizations or campaigns, fraternal organizations or societies, telephone solicitations, national fundraising efforts, or for labor organizations.
Application information: Organizations may apply only once per year. Application form required.
Initial approach: Completed application form
Copies of proposal: 2
Deadline(s): Jan. 15, Apr. 15, July 15 and Oct. 15
Officers and Directors: Gregory G. Kelly, Pres. and Director; Shawn L. Devlin, Secy. and Director; Scott G. Nichols, Treas. and Director; Kelly Brothers; Anker Christensen; Wendy Duer; Stephen Fleming; Stephen H. Johanson; Jon S. Kelly; Mike Newell; Bob Woods.
EIN: 680175739

698
Kelton Fund, Inc.
2716 Ocean Park Blvd., Ste. 3006
Santa Monica, CA 90405-5299

Donors: Richard Kelton; Louis L. Kelton; Allied Farms, Inc.; Educational Contractors of America, Inc.; David Kelton.
Foundation type: Independent foundation.
Financial data (yr. ended 12/31/12): Assets, $2,837,400 (M); expenditures, $125,266; qualifying distributions, $123,741; giving activities include $122,137 for 30 grants (high: $20,000; low: $200).
Fields of interest: Arts and culture; Education; Nonprofits; Religion.
Type of support: Regranting.
Limitations: Applications not accepted. Giving primarily in CA. No grants to individuals.
Application information: Unsolicited requests for funds not accepted.
Officers and Directors: David Kelton, Pres. and Director; Richard Kelton, V.P. and Secy. and Director.
EIN: 956092356

699
The Kelvin Foundation
12008 Emerald Hill Ln.
Los Altos Hills, CA 94022-4546

Established in 1999 in California.
Donors: Mary Bechmann; Albert Yu; Larry Yu.
Foundation type: Independent foundation.
Financial data (yr. ended 12/31/13): Assets, $3,904,641 (M); gifts received, $17,477; expenditures, $248,570; qualifying distributions, $249,830; giving activities include $248,420 for 8 grants (high: $75,000; low: $920).
Fields of interest: Arts and culture; Museums; Education; University education; Medical education; Immunology; Diseases and conditions.
Type of support: Research.
Limitations: Applications not accepted. Giving primarily in CA. No grants to individuals.
Application information: Contributes only to pre-selected organizations.
Officers: Albert Yu, Chair.; Mary Bechmann, Pres.
EIN: 770528782

700
The Herbert & Elaine Kendall Charitable Foundation
1185 Fife Ln.
Santa Barbara, CA 93108-2254

Established in 1987 in California.
Donors: Elaine Kendall; Herbert J. Kendall; Alexander Kendall; Christopher Kendall; William McCabe; Katherine McCabe; Alexander and Christopher Kendall Charitable Lead Unitrust; William and Katherine McCabe Charitable Lead Unitrust.
Foundation type: Independent foundation.
Financial data (yr. ended 12/31/13): Assets, $9,684,287 (M); gifts received, $290,003; expenditures, $202,882; qualifying distributions, $177,448; giving activities include $177,448 for 39 grants (high: $20,000; low: $100).
Purpose and activities: Giving primarily for the arts, education, and community development.
Fields of interest: Arts and culture; Theater; Music; Art museums; Education; University education; Nonprofits; Cancers; Community and economic development; Family services.
Type of support: Regranting.
Limitations: Applications not accepted. Giving primarily in CA. No grants to individuals.
Application information: Contributes only to pre-selected organizations.
Officers: Herbert J. Kendall, Pres.; Elaine Kendall, Secy.-Treas.
Directors: Nancy Kendall McCabe; Richard Kendall.
EIN: 954077657

701
The Donna L. Kendall Foundation
3334 E. Coast Hwy.
Box 244
Corona Del Mar, CA 92625-2328

Established in 2007 in Unspecified.
Donor: Donald M. Kendall.
Foundation type: Independent foundation.
Financial data (yr. ended 12/31/14): Assets, $5,623,385; expenditures, $279,519; qualifying distributions, $272,424.
Fields of interest: Arts and culture; Music; Opera; Education; Human services.
Limitations: Applications not accepted. Giving primarily in CA. No grants to individuals.
Application information: Unsolicited requests for funds not accepted.
Trustees: Donald M. Kendall; Donna L. Kendall; Clifton A. Leonhardt.
EIN: 260725984

702
Tawfiq and Richel Khoury Family Foundation
2505 Congress St., Ste. 100
San Diego, CA 92110-2847 (619) 299-5112
Contact: Tammy Miller

Established in 1999 in California.
Donors: Jason B. Khoury; Brian N. Khoury; Noelle K. Ludwig; Sundance Financial, Inc.; Tawfiq Khoury; K Enterprises; Tnkrgk Family Trust.
Foundation type: Independent foundation.
Financial data (yr. ended 12/31/14): Assets, $40,822 (M); gifts received, $38,900; expenditures, $173,706; qualifying distributions, $171,000; giving activities include $171,000 for 6 grants (high: $115,000; low: $1,000).
Purpose and activities: Grant contribution to promote civil liberties and cultural awareness.
Fields of interest: Education; Religion.
Limitations: Applications accepted. Giving primarily in CA, Washington DC, and New York, NY. No grants to individuals.
Application information: Application form required.
Initial approach: Proposal
Deadline(s): None
Officers and Directors: Tawfiq N. Khoury, Chair. and Director; Richel G. Khoury, Vice Chair. and Director; Jason B. Khoury, Pres. and Director; Brian N. Khoury, V.P. and Director; Noelle K. Ludwig, Secy.-Treas. and Director.
EIN: 330820439

703
Kieve Foundation
2359 Mt. Davidson Dr.
San Jose, CA 95124-2513 (408) 293-8030
Contact: Robert S. Kieve, Pres. and Dir.

Established in 2002 in California.
Donor: Robert S. Kieve.
Foundation type: Independent foundation.
Financial data (yr. ended 12/31/13): Assets, $4,723,721 (M); expenditures, $283,040; qualifying distributions, $226,000; giving activities include $226,000 for 62 grants (high: $50,000; low: $500).
Fields of interest: Arts and culture; Music; Education; Animal welfare; Nonprofits; Diseases and conditions; Human services; Food banks; Youth services; Scouting programs.
Type of support: Regranting.
Limitations: Applications accepted. Giving primarily in CA.
Application information:
Initial approach: Proposal
Deadline(s): None
Officers and Directors: Robert S. Kieve, Pres. and Director; Lenoir Kieve, V.P. and Director; Vita Nevis, C.F.O. and Secy. and Director.
EIN: 010664998

704
D. K. Kim Foundation, Inc.
5300 E. Concours St.
Ontario, CA 91764-5399 (909) 481-0227
FAX: (909) 987-9875; Main URL: http://www.dkkimfoundation.org
Facebook: https://www.facebook.com/dkkimfoundation
YouTube: http://www.youtube.com/user/dkkimfoundation

Donors: Dong Koo Kim; Kim Family Revocable Trust.
Foundation type: Independent foundation.
Financial data (yr. ended 12/31/12): Assets, $3,828,915 (M); gifts received, $100,000; expenditures, $183,880; qualifying distributions, $161,239; giving activities include $153,318 for 4 grants (high: $100,000; low: $5,500).
Purpose and activities: The foundation's mission is to construct a global community that fights poverty and promotes innovation through entrepreneurship, scholarship, and service. The foundation will focus on raising the future leaders of society by supporting an educational institution that meets its vision; create a learning environment where the next generation is taught valuable skills and Christian values; and give tools to those in need to become financially self-sufficient and self-reliant.
Fields of interest: Arts and culture; Education; Human services.
Limitations: Applications not accepted. Giving primarily in CA. No grants to individuals.
Application information: Contributes only to pre-selected organizations.
Directors: Maria Hon; Brent Jeon; Dong Koo Kim.
EIN: 331059702

705
The Kimbo Foundation
72 Santa Ana Ave.
San Francisco, CA   94127-1508
E-mail: info@kimbofoundation.org; Main
URL: http://www.kimbofoundation.org
Grants List: http://www.kimbofoundation.org/
history.html
Application addresses: Northern CA: c/o The SF
Korea Daily, Attn.: Business Planning Dept., 33288
Central Ave., Union City, CA 94587-2010, tel.: (510)
429-3230, fax: (510) 429-3260,
e-mail: kwang@koreadaily.com; Southern CA and
other states: c/o The LA Korean Central Daily,
Attn.: Business Planning Dept., 690 Wilshire Pl., Los
Angeles, CA 90005-3930, tel.: (213) 368-2607,
fax: (213) 389-6196, e-mail: info@jkoreadaily.com

Established in 1987 in California.
Donors: Geon Y. Kim‡; Sunny S. Hwang; Sunrise
Foundation.
Foundation type: Independent foundation.
Financial data (yr. ended 12/31/13): Assets, $0
(M); gifts received, $227,000; expenditures,
$366,558; qualifying distributions, $355,200;
giving activities include $55,200 for 11 grants (high:
$37,000; low: $2,000), and $300,000 for 7 grants
to individuals (high: $105,000; low: $22,500).
Purpose and activities: Scholarship awards to
Korean-American students; some giving for
missions assistance.
Fields of interest: Christianity; Protestantism;
People of East Asian descent.
Type of support: Student aid.
Limitations: Applications accepted. Giving in the
U.S., with an emphasis on CA.
Application information: See web site for complete
application policies, guidelines and forms.
Application form required.
  Initial approach: Complete application form
  Deadline(s): May 20 to July 15
  Board meeting date(s): July through Aug.
  Final notification: Aug. 27
Officer: Jeanne M. Kim, Pres.
EIN: 943047547

706
Kinnoull Foundation
c/o Ryan & McDonald, LLP
913 Blanco Cir.
Salinas, CA   93901

Foundation type: Independent foundation.
Financial data (yr. ended 12/31/14): Assets,
$8,255,182 (M); expenditures, $435,295;
qualifying distributions, $357,482; giving activities
include $272,121 for 22 grants (high: $70,000;
low: $2,000).
Fields of interest: Wildlife biodiversity; Animal
welfare; Catholicism.
International interests: Belize; Mauritius.
Limitations: Applications not accepted. Giving
primarily in CA; some giving internationally. No
grants to individuals.
Application information: Contributes only to
pre-selected organizations.
Officer: J.C. Vernor-Miles, Chair.
Trustees: Gloria Taviner; Paul Williams; Wilfred
Vernor-Miles.
EIN: 946186982

707
The Norman and Joan Kinsey Foundation
11481 San Pablo Ave.
El Cerrito, CA   94530-1916

Donors: Joan Kinsey; Norman E. Kinsey.
Foundation type: Independent foundation.
Financial data (yr. ended 12/31/13): Assets,
$4,713,572 (M); gifts received, $1,300,000;
expenditures, $199,852; qualifying distributions,
$170,000; giving activities include $170,000 for 13
grants (high: $20,000; low: $5,000).
Fields of interest: Education; Agriculture; Human
services.
Limitations: Applications not accepted. Giving
primarily in CA.
Application information: Unsolicited requests for
funds not accepted.
Trustees: Anthony P. Carion; Joan Kinsey; Norman
E. Kinsey; Jennifer M. Sylvestri.
EIN: 271509393

708
The Kirby-Jones Foundation
32133 W. Lindero Canyon Rd., Ste. 208
Westlake Village, CA   91361-4226

Donors: Marvel B. Kirby; The Kirby Family Trust.
Foundation type: Independent foundation.
Financial data (yr. ended 12/31/13): Assets,
$11,094,636 (M); gifts received, $5,380,000;
expenditures, $378,864; qualifying distributions,
$362,985; giving activities include $353,500 for 30
grants (high: $35,000; low: $1,000).
Fields of interest: Theater; Elementary and
secondary education; Child welfare.
Limitations: Applications not accepted. Giving
primarily in CA; some giving in NJ. No grants to
individuals.
Application information: Contributes only to
pre-selected organizations.
Officers: Brynn Crowe, Pres.; Clarence E. Francis,
Secy.; Emily Jones, Treas.
Directors: Charles Crowe; Blake W. Jones; William
K. Jones; Tyrena Jones; Marvel B. Kirby.
EIN: 208067676

709
The Kirkorian Family Foundation
1630 W. Campbell Ave.
Campbell, CA   95008-1500

Established in 2004 in California.
Donor: Marguerite Kirkorian.
Foundation type: Independent foundation.
Financial data (yr. ended 12/31/12): Assets,
$12,400 (M); gifts received, $200,110;
expenditures, $204,603; qualifying distributions,
$204,493; giving activities include $204,493 for
grants.
Fields of interest: Education; Health; Human
services; Child welfare.
Limitations: Applications not accepted. Giving
primarily in CA. No grants to individuals.
Application information: Unsolicited requests for
funds not accepted.
Officers: Marleen Kirkorian, Pres.; Kim Brodnik,
Secy.; John Kirkorian, Treas.
EIN: 201968695

710
Kisco Cares Foundation
c/o Kisco Senior Living
5790 Fleet St., Ste. 300
Carlsbad, CA   92008-4703

Donor: Andrew S. Kohlberg.
Foundation type: Independent foundation.
Financial data (yr. ended 12/31/13): Assets,
$410,798 (M); expenditures, $317,464; qualifying
distributions, $313,000; giving activities include
$298,000 for 7 grants (high: $100,000; low:
$13,000).
Fields of interest: Education; Domesticated
animals; Biology; Human services.
Limitations: Applications not accepted. Giving
primarily in AZ and CA.
Application information: Unsolicited requests for
funds not accepted.
Officer and Directors: Andrew S. Kohlberg, Pres.
and Secy. and Director; Larry Gilbert; Jason K.
Howerton; David P. King; Annica Kreuter.
EIN: 272239057

711
The Kite Key Foundation
c/o Dreyer, Edmonds & Robbins
355 S. Grand Ave., Ste. 1710
Los Angeles, CA   90071-3103

Established in 1998 in California.
Donors: Charles T. Munger; Barry A. Munger; Sarah
Q. O'Neill.
Foundation type: Independent foundation.
Financial data (yr. ended 12/31/13): Assets,
$1,030,835 (M); gifts received, $5,085;
expenditures, $203,608; qualifying distributions,
$201,700; giving activities include $201,700 for 41
grants (high: $100,000; low: $100).
Fields of interest: Education; Community and
economic development; Human services.
Type of support: General support.
Limitations: Applications not accepted. Giving
primarily in New York, NY. No grants to individuals.
Application information: Contributes only to
pre-selected organizations.
Trustees: Barry A. Munger; Sarah Q. O'Neill.
EIN: 061518993

712
Harvey and Ellen Knell Foundation
117 E. Colorado Blvd., Ste. 400
Pasadena, CA   91105-1938

Donors: Harvey Knell; HGK 2009 Trust.
Foundation type: Independent foundation.
Financial data (yr. ended 12/31/13): Assets,
$622,373 (M); gifts received, $133,667;
expenditures, $219,806; qualifying distributions,
$211,417; giving activities include $210,650 for 21
grants (high: $100,000; low: $1,000).
Fields of interest: Arts and culture; Education; Youth
development.
Limitations: Applications not accepted.
Application information: Unsolicited requests for
funds not accepted.
Directors: Ellen R. Knell; Harvey G. Knell.
EIN: 276163510

713
KNU Foundation, Inc.
5450 Trabuco Rd.
Irvine, CA 92620-5704
E-mail: gkehle@aol.com

Established in 1986 in California.
Foundation type: Independent foundation.
Financial data (yr. ended 12/31/14): Assets, $5,200,134 (M); gifts received, $0; expenditures, $339,115; qualifying distributions, $318,748; giving activities include $309,000 for 15 grants (high: $36,500; low: $500).
Purpose and activities: Giving for children and youth services, and higher education.
Fields of interest: Performing arts; Education; Human services; Child welfare; Children and youth; Children; People with physical disabilities.
Type of support: Continuing support.
Limitations: Applications not accepted. Giving primarily in southern CA, including Los Angeles and Orange County; giving also in Pitkin County, CO. No grants to individuals.
Application information: Contributes only to pre-selected organizations.
   Board meeting date(s): As required
Officers and Directors: Gerald Kehle, Pres. and Director; Jacqueline Kehle, Secy. and Director; Ashley Nelson; Kristen Nelson; Karen Ulman.
Number of staff: None.
EIN: 330204705

714
The James and Barbara Knuppe Family Foundation
4545 Crow Canyon Pl.
Castro Valley, CA 94552-4803

Established in 2007 in California.
Donors: H. James Knuppe; Barbara Knuppe.
Foundation type: Independent foundation.
Financial data (yr. ended 12/31/13): Assets, $136,567 (M); gifts received, $50,000; expenditures, $224,892; qualifying distributions, $224,150; giving activities include $224,150 for 7 grants (high: $150,000; low: $200).
Fields of interest: Religion; Water sports.
Limitations: Applications not accepted. No grants to individuals.
Application information: Contributes only to pre-selected organizations.
Officers: H. James Knuppe, Pres.; Barbara Knuppe, C.F.O. and Secy.
EIN: 261614488

715
The Shannon & Amy Ko Foundation
(formerly The Ko Family Foundation)
25622 Rapid Falls Rd.
Laguna Hills, CA 92653-7816

Donor: Amy F.M. Ko.
Foundation type: Operating foundation.
Financial data (yr. ended 12/31/13): Assets, $12,840,380 (M); expenditures, $822,694; qualifying distributions, $448,131; giving activities include $289,300 for 4 grants (high: $200,000; low: $1,300).
Fields of interest: University education.
Limitations: Applications not accepted. Giving primarily in CA. No grants to individuals.

Application information: Contributes only to pre-selected organizations.
Trustees: Amy F.M. Ko; Shannon J.S. Ko.
EIN: 330955371

716
Kobor Family Foundation
250 N. Robertson Blvd., Ste. 421
Beverly Hills, CA 90211-1788

Established in 2000 in California.
Donors: George Kobor; Kathy Javor; Erika Kobor.
Foundation type: Independent foundation.
Financial data (yr. ended 12/31/13): Assets, $2,634,465 (M); expenditures, $217,142; qualifying distributions, $173,931; giving activities include $173,846 for 33 grants (high: $52,624; low: $12).
Fields of interest: Judaism.
Type of support: General support.
Limitations: Applications not accepted. Giving primarily in CA. No grants to individuals.
Application information: Unsolicited requests for funds not accepted.
Officers: Erika Kobor, Pres. and C.E.O.; Kathy Javor, Secy. and C.F.O.
Director: Carmen Kobor.
EIN: 954831786

717
The Bradford & Lauren Koenig Foundation
c/o Seiler, LLP
3 Lagoon Dr., Ste. 400
Redwood City, CA 94065-1565

Established in 1997 in California.
Donors: Bradford Koenig; Lauren Koenig.
Foundation type: Independent foundation.
Financial data (yr. ended 12/31/12): Assets, $1,998,833 (M); gifts received, $518,565; expenditures, $200,000; qualifying distributions, $200,000; giving activities include $200,000 for grants.
Fields of interest: Elementary and secondary education; Higher education.
Limitations: Applications not accepted. Giving primarily in CA. No grants to individuals; no loans or scholarships.
Application information: Contributes only to pre-selected organizations.
Trustees: Bradford Koenig; Lauren Koenig; Mark R. Tercek.
EIN: 133993307

718
Kornwasser Charitable Foundation
5670 Wilshire Blvd., Ste. 1250
Los Angeles, CA 90036-2166

Established in 1960 in California.
Donors: Mark Kornwasser; Sonia Kornwasser; Kornland Building Co.; Joseph Kornwasser; Sonia Kornwasser; Kram Construction.
Foundation type: Independent foundation.
Financial data (yr. ended 05/31/14): Assets, $4,867,760 (M); gifts received, $5,790; expenditures, $445,751; qualifying distributions, $445,751; giving activities include $413,050 for 44 grants (high: $56,000; low: $180).

Purpose and activities: Giving primarily to Jewish agencies and temples, and for Jewish education.
Fields of interest: Elementary and secondary education; Higher education; Judaism; Jewish people.
Limitations: Applications not accepted. Giving primarily in CA and NY. No grants to individuals.
Application information: Contributes only to pre-selected organizations.
Officers: Joseph Kornwasser, Pres.; Judy Moskovits, Secy.
EIN: 956091565

719
Barbara and Fred Kort Foundation
P.O. Box 642987
Los Angeles, CA 90064-8353

Donors: Barbara Kort; Fred Kort Marital Trust.
Foundation type: Independent foundation.
Financial data (yr. ended 11/30/13): Assets, $6,543,917 (M); gifts received, $6,000,000; expenditures, $413,739; qualifying distributions, $413,590; giving activities include $407,000 for 3 grants (high: $330,000; low: $35,000).
Fields of interest: Nonprofits; Breast cancer.
Type of support: Research; Regranting.
Limitations: Applications not accepted. Giving primarily in Los Angeles, CA and New York, NY. No grants to individuals.
Application information: Contributes only to pre-selected organizations.
Officer: Lan Fong Lee, Pres.; Steven M. Frankiel, C.F.O.; Martin Cheung, Secy.
EIN: 261609012

720
Michael Koss Charitable Foundation
12410 Santa Monica Blvd.
Los Angeles, CA 90025-2522

Donor: Michael A. Koss.
Foundation type: Independent foundation.
Financial data (yr. ended 12/31/13): Assets, $20,653 (M); gifts received, $2,000; expenditures, $125,622; qualifying distributions, $122,500; giving activities include $122,500 for 9 grants (high: $100,000; low: $100).
Fields of interest: Education; Nonprofits; Community and economic development; Human services.
Type of support: Regranting.
Limitations: Applications not accepted. Giving primarily in CA.
Application information: Unsolicited requests for funds not accepted.
Officers: Michael A. Koss, Pres.; Zane Koss, C.F.O.; Cornelia Koss, Secy.
EIN: 263766034

721
Kreitzberg Family Foundation
1283 Coast Village Cir.
Santa Barbara, CA 93108-3753

Donor: Fred Kreitzberg.
Foundation type: Independent foundation.
Financial data (yr. ended 12/31/14): Assets, $1,352,673; expenditures, $191,201; qualifying distributions, $180,677.

Fields of interest: Education; Health; Human services.
Limitations: Applications not accepted.
Application information: Unsolicited requests for funds not accepted.
Officers: Fred Kreitzberg, Pres.; Allison Ross, Secy.; Bruce Kreitzberg, Treas.; Lois Mitchell, Exec. Dir.
Directors: Caroline Kreitzberg; Catherine Yona.
EIN: 201802917

722
Krishnan-Shah Family Foundation, Inc.
27241 Altamont Rd.
Los Altos Hills, CA 94022-4278
Contact: Lata Krishnan-Shah, Pres.

Established in 1997 in California.
Donors: Ajay B. Shah; Lata Krishnan-Shah.
Foundation type: Independent foundation.
Financial data (yr. ended 12/31/13): Assets, $18,114,947 (M); gifts received, $5,630,483; expenditures, $491,922; qualifying distributions, $395,717; giving activities include $315,611 for 16 grants (high: $167,611; low: $1,000).
Purpose and activities: Giving to organizations for the health, education and cultural development of youth and families.
Fields of interest: Arts and culture; Education; Community service; Human services; Family services; Youth services.
Type of support: General support.
Limitations: Applications not accepted. Giving primarily in CA.
Application information: Contributes only to pre-selected organizations.
Officers: Lata Krishnan-Shah, Pres.; Ajay B. Shah, Secy.
Director: Raj Krishnan.
EIN: 943288599

723
KT Charitable Organization, Inc.
4350 La Jolla Village Dr., No. 150
San Diego, CA 92122-1243

Established in 2007 in California.
Donors: Thomas G. Blake; Kathleen B. Blake.
Foundation type: Independent foundation.
Financial data (yr. ended 12/31/13): Assets, $76,002 (M); gifts received, $215,000; expenditures, $199,515; qualifying distributions, $197,900; giving activities include $197,900 for 9 grants (high: $70,000; low: $400).
Fields of interest: Elementary and secondary education; Higher education.
Limitations: Applications not accepted. Giving primarily in San Diego, CA.
Application information: Contributes only to pre-selected organizations.
Directors: Daniel Curran; Derek Hanson; Erinn Hanson; Jennifer Curran; Kathleen B. Blake; Thomas G. Blake.
EIN: 204872891

724
Kwoh and Pong Foundation
5029 Fox Point Ln.
Rolling Hills Estates, CA 90274-2410

Established in 1998 in California.

Donor: Cassandra Kwoh.
Foundation type: Independent foundation.
Financial data (yr. ended 12/31/13): Assets, $4,296,838 (M); gifts received, $120,000; expenditures, $117,052; qualifying distributions, $113,200; giving activities include $113,200 for 5 grants (high: $100,000; low: $200).
Purpose and activities: Giving for organizations that assist in improving the quality of life for Chinese people in America.
Fields of interest: Education; Human services.
Type of support: General support.
Limitations: Applications not accepted. Giving primarily in CA and MA. No grants to individuals.
Application information: Unsolicited requests for funds not accepted.
Officer: Cassandra Kwoh, Pres.
EIN: 954694115

725
The L.B. Research and Education Foundation
5950 Canoga Ave., Ste. 200
Woodland Hills, CA 91367-5036

Established in 1997 in California.
Donors: Gerald D. Buckberg, MD; C.L. Athanasuleas; Correstore LLC; Somanetics Corp.
Foundation type: Independent foundation.
Financial data (yr. ended 11/30/13): Assets, $1,680,887 (M); expenditures, $262,419; qualifying distributions, $240,047; giving activities include $233,000 for 2 grants (high: $144,000; low: $89,000).
Fields of interest: Education; Higher education.
Limitations: Applications not accepted. Giving primarily in OH. No grants to individuals.
Application information: Unsolicited requests for funds not accepted.
Officers and Directors: Constantine Athanasuleas, C.E.O. and Director; Gerald D. Buckberg, Pres. and Director; Saleh Saleh, Secy.; Art Podell, C.F.O.
EIN: 954664361

726
Laguna Beach Community Foundation
303 Broadway Ave., Ste. 212
Laguna Beach, CA 92651 (949) 715-8223
Contact: Dan Pingaro, Exec. Dir.
FAX: (949) 661-1475;
E-mail: info@lagunabeachcf.org; Mailing address: P.O. Box 1628, Laguna Beach, CA 92652; Main URL: http://www.lagunabeachcf.org
E Newsletter: http://visitor.r20.constantcontact.com/d.jsp?llr=qtbcjidab&p=oi&m=1103010793072&sit=wlmk5x9eb&f=0a83dee5-e9f8-47ac-9982-ee5ccf5f0617
Facebook: http://www.facebook.com/lagunabeachcf

Established in 2004 in California.
Foundation type: Community foundation.
Financial data (yr. ended 12/31/13): Assets, $2,368,139 (M); gifts received, $539,838; expenditures, $642,206; giving activities include $396,522 for 22+ grants (high: $71,430).
Purpose and activities: The foundation strengthens the community by encouraging philanthropy. The foundation provides expertise and resources to assist local charities, connect donor passions with

nonprofit needs, and work with local professional advisors in assisting their clients in giving now and beyond their lifetimes with a legacy gift.
Fields of interest: Arts and culture; Education; Environment; Domesticated animals; Human services.
Type of support: General support; Capacity-building and technical assistance; Program development.
Limitations: Giving primarily in Laguna Beach, CA. No support for labor organizations, fraternal organizations, athletic clubs or social clubs. No grants for annual fund drives, endowments, or for underwriting or sponsoring special events.
Application information: The foundation has shifted its grant making, concentrating its resources on established partnerships and collaborating on strategic initiatives that support our funding strategies through donor directed granting. Visit foundation web site for application, guidelines and specific deadline.
Initial approach: Contact foundation
Officers and Trustees: Rick Balzar, Chair. and Trustee; Thomas P. Davis, Vice-Chair. and Trustee; Robert J. Harryman, Treas. and Trustee; Dan Pingaro, Exec. Dir. and Trustee; Printer Friendly, Emeritus; Nicole Anderson; Jerry Bieser; Dennis Boyer; Donnie Crevier; Mandi Dossin; James P. Fletcher; Lynee M. Kniss, Esq.; John G. Mansour; Lisa Mansour; Angie Miller; Laura Tarbox.
EIN: 206390272

727
Lake Family Foundation
c/o Cynthia G. Lake
P.O. Box 20896
Bakersfield, CA 93390-0896
Main URL: http://www.lakefamilyfoundation.org

Established in 1998 in California.
Donor: Western Oilfield Supply Co.
Foundation type: Independent foundation.
Financial data (yr. ended 12/31/13): Assets, $4,418,096 (M); gifts received, $650,000; expenditures, $306,139; qualifying distributions, $302,910; giving activities include $287,133 for 13 grants (high: $233,333; low: $1,000).
Fields of interest: Health; Religion; Human services.
Limitations: Applications not accepted. Giving primarily in Bakersfield, CA. No grants to individuals.
Application information: Contributes only to pre-selected organizations.
Officers: Cynthia G. Lake, Pres.; Sheila Lake, Secy.; John Paul Lake, Treas.
EIN: 770499114

728
The Darlene & Harry Lambert Foundation
P.O. Box 45174
San Francisco, CA 94145-0174

Established in 1999 in California.
Donor: Darlene Lambert†.
Foundation type: Independent foundation.
Financial data (yr. ended 12/31/13): Assets, $4,956,792 (M); expenditures, $224,947; qualifying distributions, $183,153; giving activities include $179,000 for 13 grants (high: $33,000; low: $5,000).
Fields of interest: Animal welfare; Animal training; Hospice care; Human services.

Limitations: Applications not accepted. Giving primarily in CA. No grants to individuals.
Application information: Contributes only to pre-selected organizations.
Trustee: Union Bank, N.A.
EIN: 954788330

729
Lamond Family Foundation
167 Isabella Ave.
Atherton, CA 94027-4044 (650) 845-8100
Contact: Pierre Lamond, Pres.; Christine Lamond, V.P. and Treas.

Established in 1994 in California.
Donors: Pierre Lamond; Christine Lamond.
Foundation type: Independent foundation.
Financial data (yr. ended 12/31/14): Assets, $351,891 (M); expenditures, $279,900; qualifying distributions, $266,000; giving activities include $266,000 for 8 grants (high: $125,000; low: $1,000).
Purpose and activities: Giving primarily for the arts and human services.
Fields of interest: Arts and culture; Orchestral music; Art museums; Higher education; Human services.
Application information:
Initial approach: Proposal
Deadline(s): None
Officers: Pierre Lamond, Pres.; Christine Lamond, V.P. and Treas.
EIN: 943204401

730
Lash Foundation
P.O. Box 22916
San Diego, CA 92192-2916

Established in 2004 in California.
Foundation type: Independent foundation.
Financial data (yr. ended 12/31/12): Assets, $7,838,077 (M); expenditures, $584,263; qualifying distributions, $150,742; giving activities include $150,742 for grants.
Fields of interest: Education; Diseases and conditions; Judaism; Human services.
Limitations: Applications not accepted. Giving primarily in CA. No grants to individuals.
Application information: Contributes only to pre-selected organizations.
Officers: Lawrence E. Kline, Pres. and Exec. Dir.; Sherry M. Kline, Secy.-Treas.
EIN: 336338008

731
Latkin Charitable Foundation
P.O. Box 45174
San Francisco, CA 94145-0174
Application address: c/o Janice Gibbons, Union Bank, N.A., 1021 Anacapa St., Santa Barbara, CA 93101, tel: (805) 564-6211

Established in 1992 in California.
Donor: Herbert and Gertrude Latkin Trust.
Foundation type: Independent foundation.
Financial data (yr. ended 12/31/13): Assets, $6,777,429 (M); gifts received, $1,171; expenditures, $332,203; qualifying distributions,

$285,949; giving activities include $213,880 for 55 grants (high: $6,000; low: $2,500).
Purpose and activities: Giving primarily to provide assistance to and promote the welfare and health of the aged, prevent cruelty to animals, provide educational scholarships for deserving students enrolled in institutions of higher learning, provide medical assistance, supplies, and equipment for persons suffering as a result of calamity or disaster, prevent child abuse, and provide assistance to the needy.
Fields of interest: Health; Agriculture; Human services.
Type of support: General support; Equipment; Emergency funds; Scholarships.
Limitations: Applications accepted. Giving limited to Santa Barbara County, CA. No grants to individuals.
Application information: Application form required.
Initial approach: Letter
Copies of proposal: 1
Deadline(s): Apr. 1 and Oct. 1
Trustees: John A. Berryhill; Union Bank, N.A.
EIN: 776070540

732
Laurance Family Foundation
(formerly LFT Pacific Trust Foundation)
11100 Santa Monica Blvd., Ste. 600
Los Angeles, CA 90025-3392

Established in 2001 in California.
Donors: Dale R. Laurance; Lynda E. Laurance.
Foundation type: Independent foundation.
Financial data (yr. ended 12/31/13): Assets, $1,927,540 (M); gifts received, $1,700; expenditures, $342,258; qualifying distributions, $326,383; giving activities include $326,318 for 25 grants to individuals (high: $40,800; low: $720).
Fields of interest: Education; Health; Christianity.
Limitations: Applications not accepted. Giving primarily in CA.
Application information: Unsolicited requests for funds not accepted.
Trustees: Dale R. Laurance; Lynda E. Laurance.
EIN: 266005102

733
Richard and Ruth Lavine Family Foundation
11075 Santa Monica Blvd., Ste. 150
Los Angeles, CA 90025-7541 3104464820
Application address: 315 Conway Ave., Los Angeles, CA 90024

Established in 1990 in California.
Donors: Richard A. Lavine; Ruth J. Lavine.
Foundation type: Independent foundation.
Financial data (yr. ended 06/30/14): Assets, $4,720,319; expenditures, $240,950; qualifying distributions, $161,090.
Purpose and activities: Giving primarily for education and Jewish organizations.
Fields of interest: Education; Health; Religion.
Limitations: Applications accepted. Giving primarily in Los Angeles, CA. No grants to individuals.
Application information: Application form required.
Initial approach: Proposal
Deadline(s): None
Officers and Directors: Ruth J. Lavine, Chair. and Pres.; Catherine L. Unger, V.P. and Director; Leonard

Unger, Secy.-Treas. and Director; Laura Dudley; Daniel Unger.
EIN: 954300271

734
The Lawrence Foundation
530 Wilshire Blvd., Ste. 207
Santa Monica, CA 90401-1461
Contact: Lori Mitchell, Exec. Dir.
FAX: (310) 451-7580;
E-mail: info@thelawrencefoundation.org; Direct tel.: (970) 870-9456; Main URL: http://www.thelawrencefoundation.org
Grant Database: http://www.commongrantapplication.com/grantmaker_statistics.php?orgId=20

Established in 2000 in California.
Donors: Jeff Lawrence; Diane Troth.
Foundation type: Independent foundation.
Financial data (yr. ended 12/31/13): Assets, $4,242,166 (M); expenditures, $295,862; qualifying distributions, $276,818; giving activities include $205,542 for 40 grants (high: $20,000; low: $542).
Purpose and activities: The mission of the foundation is to make a difference in the world by providing contributions and grants to organizations that are working to solve pressing educational, environmental, health and other issues.
Fields of interest: Education; Environment; Natural resources; Human services.
Type of support: General support; In-kind gifts; Emergency funds; Program development; Convening; Program evaluations.
Limitations: Applications accepted. Giving limited to the U.S., including international organizations that have a U.S.-based office. No support for voter registration, music, gardening, recreational, religious programs, or theater or performance arts programs, hospices or home programs for the elderly, or for international organizations that do not have a qualified domestic 501(c)(3) representative. No grants to individuals or for program related investments, computers or software, audio or video equipment or designing and producing videos, kiosks or promotional material, or dinners, balls or other ticketed events.
Publications: Application guidelines; Grants list.
Application information: Applicants must use Common Grant Application at www.commongrantapplication.com. Full proposal upon invitation, per review of letter. The most efficient way to currently contact the foundation is via e-mail. Application form required.
Deadline(s): Apr. 30 and Oct. 31
Board meeting date(s): May and Nov.
Final notification: June and Nov.
Officer: Lori Read Mitchell, Exec. Dir.
Trustees: Jeff Lawrence; Diane Troth.
Number of staff: 1 part-time professional.
EIN: 954804431

735
The Lebherz Family Foundation
1600 W. Hillsdale Blvd.
San Mateo, CA 94402-3768

Donors: Phillip Lebherz; Sharon Lebherz.
Foundation type: Independent foundation.

Financial data (yr. ended 12/31/13): Assets, $6,026,492 (M); gifts received, $1,750,000; expenditures, $465,096; qualifying distributions, $438,830; giving activities include $430,625 for 20 grants (high: $312,265; low: $100).
Fields of interest: Education; Health; Human services.
Limitations: Applications not accepted.
Application information: Unsolicited requests for funds not accepted.
Officers: Phil Lebherz, Pres.; Regan Musgrave, C.F.O.; Dean Westly, Secy.
Director: Sharon Lebherz.
EIN: 273048346

736
The Steven and Deborah Lebowitz Foundation
439 N. Bedford Dr.
Beverly Hills, CA 90210-4302

Donors: Steve Lebowitz; Deborah Lebowitz.
Foundation type: Independent foundation.
Financial data (yr. ended 12/31/13): Assets, $199,973 (M); expenditures, $260,018; qualifying distributions, $260,000; giving activities include $260,000 for 1 grant.
Fields of interest: Education.
Limitations: Applications not accepted. Giving primarily in CA.
Application information: Unsolicited requests for funds not accepted.
Trustees: Deborah Lebowitz; Steven D. Lebowitz.
EIN: 463125936

737
Lee Foundation
c/o Clarity Partners
100 N. Crescent Dr., Ste. 300
Beverly Hills, CA 90210-5408

Established in 2007 in California.
Foundation type: Independent foundation.
Financial data (yr. ended 12/31/12): Assets, $4,332,311 (M); expenditures, $203,818; qualifying distributions, $179,554; giving activities include $179,554 for grants.
Fields of interest: Arts and culture; Music; Hospital care; Human services.
Limitations: Applications not accepted. Giving primarily in CA. No grants to individuals.
Application information: Contributes only to pre-selected organizations.
Officers and Directors: Ellen W. Lee, Pres. and Director; Benjamin K. Lee, Secy. and Director; David L. Lee, Treas. and Director; Bonnie A. Lee; Rachel R. Lee.
EIN: 743235054

738
Joseph Stanley Leeds Charitable Foundation
6345 Balboa Blvd., Ste. 200
Encino, CA 91316-1517
Contact: Marilyn Le Rud, Pres.
Application address: 1833 N. Evelyn Ave., Tucson, AZ 85715-5560

Established in 1996 in California.
Donor: Stanley Leeds Trust.

Foundation type: Independent foundation.
Financial data (yr. ended 12/31/13): Assets, $5,367,490 (M); expenditures, $241,015; qualifying distributions, $219,000; giving activities include $165,000 for 13 grants (high: $20,000; low: $10,000).
Purpose and activities: Giving to programs of any type which benefit children.
Fields of interest: Education; Children and youth.
Limitations: Applications accepted. Giving primarily in AZ and CA. No support for organizations receiving any type of government funding. No grants to individuals.
Application information: Application form required.
  Initial approach: Letter requesting application form
  Copies of proposal: 1
  Deadline(s): None
  Board meeting date(s): As required
  Final notification: Varies, but usually during the 1st quarter of each year
Officers: Marilyn Le Rud, Pres.; Ellis Stern, Secy.; Paul Litz, Treas.
EIN: 954564229

739
LEF Foundation
c/o MLB Assocs.
2422 Debbie Way
Calistoga, CA 94515-1202 (707) 486-6806
Contact: Marina Drummer, Grants Advisor (CA); Lyda Kuth, Dir. (New England)
E-mail: marina@lef-foundation.org; New England and Moving Image Fund address: P.O. Box 382066, Cambridge, MA 02238-2866, tel.: (617) 492-5333, fax: (617) 868-5603; e-mail: lyda@lef-foundation.org; Main URL: http://www.lef-foundation.org
Facebook: http://www.facebook.com/pages/LEF-Foundation/175887364326
New England blog: http://www.lef-foundation.org/NewEngland/Blog/tabid/193/Default.aspx

Established in 1985 in California.
Donor: Lyda Ebert†.
Foundation type: Independent foundation.
Financial data (yr. ended 06/30/13): Assets, $6,411,646 (M); expenditures, $829,114; qualifying distributions, $757,094; giving activities include $417,635 for 48 grants (high: $50,000; low: $1,000).
Purpose and activities: The foundation supports contemporary work in the areas of film, architecture, design, and the visual and performing arts.
Fields of interest: Arts and culture; Architecture; Spoken word; Communication media; Film and video; Adults; American Indians; Artists and performers.
Type of support: Grantee relations; Recordings; Publications; Seed money.
Limitations: Applications accepted. Giving primarily in CA and New England; giving in other regions of the U.S. with relevant interests, including the Southwest and Hawaii. No grants to individuals, or for general/operating support, capital campaigns, building/renovation, land acquisition, endowments, emergency funds, fellowships, research, or matching/challenge support; no program-related investments or loans.
Publications: Application guidelines; Grants list; Occasional report; Program policy statement.
Application information: Applicants based in New England should contact Cambridge, MA, office. LEF

California is no longer accepting unsolicited proposals. See foundation web site for application procedures and guidelines.
  Initial approach: Refer to foundation web site
  Copies of proposal: 1
  Deadline(s): Varies; refer to web site
  Board meeting date(s): Varies
  Final notification: 2-3 months
Officers: Marion E. Greene, Pres.; Byron Kuth, V.P.; Lyda Kuth, Exec. Dir.
Directors: Laurey Finneran; Byron Kuth; Sarah Treeson.
Number of staff: 1 full-time professional; 2 part-time professional.
EIN: 680070194

740
Legacy - San Jose Alviso Youth Foundation
(formerly Alviso/San Jose Foundation)
507 Valley Way
Milpitas, CA 95035-4105
Contact: Jennifer Loving
E-mail: contactus@legacyalvisoyouth.org

Established in 2002 in California.
Donors: Legacy Partners Commercial, LP; WCSJ, LLC.
Foundation type: Operating foundation.
Financial data (yr. ended 12/31/13): Assets, $3,889,383 (M); expenditures, $213,500; qualifying distributions, $186,270; giving activities include $186,270 for 6 grants (high: $93,000; low: $7,500).
Purpose and activities: The foundation is dedicated to the well-being of children and youth through financial support of programs and services provided by nonprofit organizations, including support of education, social services, the arts, physical and mental health, and capital development. Current areas of major interest for youth ages 18 or younger include education, services for children and youth in Alviso, California and in George Mayne Elementary School, early intervention programs for children and youth, and recreational and enrichment activities for youth.
Fields of interest: Education; Child welfare; Youth development; Children; Adolescents.
Type of support: General support; Scholarships.
Limitations: Applications accepted. Giving limited to benefit youth of Alviso/San Jose, CA, the attendance area of George Mayne Elementary School. No grants to individuals.
Application information: Application form required.
  Deadline(s): May 1 and Dec. 1
  Board meeting date(s): Spring and Winter
Officers and Board Members: Edgar M. Thrift, Chair. and Director; Jennifer C. Niklaus, Secy.; Michael J. Kelly, C.F.P., Jr., Treas.; Barry Del Buono; Ragan Henninger; Rita Rothstein; Tony A. Santos.
EIN: 943345365

741
The John & Sandra Leland Foundation
2252 Encinal Ave.
Alameda, CA 94501-4413

Established in 1997 in California.
Donors: John D. Leland, Jr.; Sandra S. Leland.
Foundation type: Independent foundation.
Financial data (yr. ended 12/31/13): Assets, $1,207,279 (M); gifts received, $882;

expenditures, $173,702; qualifying distributions, $164,287; giving activities include $157,950 for 50 grants (high: $20,000; low: $100).

Purpose and activities: Giving primarily for arts and culture, education, and human services.

Fields of interest: Arts and culture; Orchestral music; Art museums; Education; Higher education; Human services.

Limitations: Applications accepted. Giving primarily in San Francisco, CA. No grants to individuals.

Application information: Application form required.

　Initial approach: Letter

　Deadline(s): None

Officers: John D. Leland, Jr., C.E.O.; Sandra S. Leland, V.P.; Carolyn Seid, Secy.

EIN: 943266226

742

The Robert Lemelson Foundation

725 El Medio Dr.

Pacific Palisades, CA　90272-3452

Donors: Robert Lemelson, Ph.D; Beate Ritz; Irene Sukwandi.

Foundation type: Independent foundation.

Financial data (yr. ended 12/31/13): Assets, $5,483,518 (M); expenditures, $279,559; qualifying distributions, $262,136; giving activities include $261,232 for 10 grants (high: $158,621; low: $150).

Fields of interest: Education; University education; Diseases and conditions; Anthropology; Community and economic development; Human services.

Limitations: Applications not accepted. Giving primarily in CA.

Application information: Unsolicited requests for funds not accepted.

Officers: Robert Lemelson, Ph.D, Pres.; Irene Sukwandi, Secy.; Beate Ritz, C.F.O.

EIN: 273423670

743

Brad Lemons Foundation

(formerly W. B. Lemons Foundation)

1880 Century Park E., Ste. 613

Los Angeles, CA　90067-1622　(310) 271-4272

Established in 1999 in California.

Donors: Brad Lemons; Brad Lemons Charitable Lead Ann Trust; Brad Lemons Charitable Lead Unitrust.

Foundation type: Independent foundation.

Financial data (yr. ended 12/31/13): Assets, $7,427,455 (M); gifts received, $403,839; expenditures, $456,019; qualifying distributions, $405,500; giving activities include $405,500 for 32 grants (high: $25,000; low: $5,000).

Fields of interest: Higher education; Developmental disability services.

Limitations: Applications accepted. Giving primarily in CA. No grants to individuals.

Application information: Application form required.

　Initial approach: Proposal

　Deadline(s): None

Trustee: William B. Lemons.

EIN: 954718603

744

Mark C. Lemons Foundation

3029 Wilshire Blvd., Ste. 200

Santa Monica, CA　90403-2364

Established in 1997 in California.

Donor: Mark C. Lemons Charitable Trust.

Foundation type: Independent foundation.

Financial data (yr. ended 12/31/13): Assets, $6,327,472 (M); gifts received, $248,000; expenditures, $311,414; qualifying distributions, $244,927; giving activities include $201,600 for 16 grants (high: $60,000; low: $500).

Fields of interest: Education; University education; Autism; Christianity; Human services; Food aid.

Limitations: Applications not accepted. Giving primarily in CA. No grants to individuals.

Application information: Contributes only to pre-selected organizations.

Trustee: Mark C. Lemons.

EIN: 954712282

745

Lennox Family Foundation

11100 Santa Monica Blvd., Ste. 600

Los Angeles, CA　90025-3328

Established in 2004 in California.

Donors: Lillian Lennox; Gregory P. Lennox.

Foundation type: Independent foundation.

Financial data (yr. ended 12/31/13): Assets, $2,389,136 (M); gifts received, $943,100; expenditures, $171,999; qualifying distributions, $170,152; giving activities include $168,000 for 6 grants (high: $100,000; low: $1,000).

Fields of interest: Housing development; Religion; Human services.

Limitations: Applications not accepted. Giving primarily in CA, ID and TX. No grants to individuals.

Application information: Unsolicited requests for funds not accepted.

Officers: Gregory P. Lennox, C.E.O.; Lillian Lennox, Secy.

EIN: 201886915

746

The Frederick P. Lenz Foundation for American Buddhism

1901 Avenue of the Stars, Ste. 1100

Los Angeles, CA　90067-6002

E-mail: info@fredericklenzfoundation.org; Main URL: http://www.fredericklenzfoundation.org

Blog: http://lenzcommunity.wordpress.com

Foundation type: Independent foundation.

Financial data (yr. ended 12/31/13): Assets, $13,301,248 (M); gifts received, $33,045; expenditures, $670,743; qualifying distributions, $544,067; giving activities include $235,333 for 17 grants (high: $50,000; low: $2,500).

Purpose and activities: The foundation is dedicated to promoting the benefits of Zen Buddhism, meditation, yoga and related Buddhist practices as a pathway to self-realization and the harmonious blending of the material and spiritual in contemporary American society.

Fields of interest: Education; Buddhism.

Limitations: Giving on a national basis. No grants to individuals.

Application information: See foundation web site for guidelines and form of letter of interest.

Officers and Directors: Norman Marcus, Pres. and Director; Norman S. Oberstein, V.P. and Director; Lisa Lewinson.

EIN: 134014022

747

The Kenneth A. Lester Family Foundation

c/o First Foundation Advisors

18101 Von Karman Ave., Ste. 700

Irvine, CA　92612-0145　(877) 968-6328

FAX: (949) 833-9584; Main URL: http://www.lesterfoundation.org

Donors: Kenneth A. Lester; Lana Christine Lester.

Foundation type: Independent foundation.

Financial data (yr. ended 12/31/14): Assets, $4,115,761 (M); gifts received, $114,500; expenditures, $208,610; qualifying distributions, $184,539; giving activities include $163,500 for 14 grants (high: $17,000; low: $2,150).

Purpose and activities: Giving to conserve and enhance the environment, create educational opportunities for disadvantaged children and young people, and support the health, cultural, and civic life of the residents of Orange and Marin counties, California.

Fields of interest: Education; Human services; Youth development.

Application information: See foundation web site for application guidelines. Application form required.

　Initial approach: Use online application system on foundation web site

Officers and Directors: Kenneth A. Lester, Pres. and Director; Lana Christine Lester, Secy.-Treas. and Director; Norman Lester; Karen Ulshafer; Karen Lester.

EIN: 200191517

748

The Lester Family Foundation

c/o Kirk Lester

1140 Wall St., Ste. 2089

La Jolla, CA　92038

Established in 1994 in California.

Donors: W. Howard Lester; Friends of Torrey Pines, LLC; Mary Lester.

Foundation type: Independent foundation.

Financial data (yr. ended 12/31/13): Assets, $5,610,517 (M); gifts received, $1,103,227; expenditures, $226,146; qualifying distributions, $206,760; giving activities include $206,000 for 16 grants (high: $40,000; low: $500).

Purpose and activities: Giving primarily for education and human services.

Fields of interest: Performing arts; Education; Higher education; Diseases and conditions; Human services.

Limitations: Applications not accepted. No grants to individuals.

Application information: Unsolicited requests for funds not accepted.

Officers: Mary Lester, Pres.; Kirk Lester, Treas.

EIN: 943205279

749

Richard and Emily Levin Foundation

718 University Ave., Ste. 215

Los Gatos, CA　95032-7608

Established in 1989 in California.
Donors: Richard Levin†; Elsie George; Emily Levin.
Foundation type: Independent foundation.
Financial data (yr. ended 12/31/14): Assets, $5,445,663 (M); expenditures, $265,725; qualifying distributions, $265,725; giving activities include $257,500 for 60 grants (high: $12,500; low: $500).
Fields of interest: Orchestral music; Nonprofits; Hospital care; Hospice care; Alzheimer's disease; Fire prevention and control; Judaism; Human services; Child welfare; Youth services.
Type of support: Regranting; Research; Equal access.
Limitations: Applications not accepted. Giving primarily in CA. No grants to individuals.
Application information: Unsolicited requests for funds not accepted.
Trustees: Elsie George; Sydney Levin.
EIN: 770263490

750
Hyman Levine Family Foundation L'Dor V'Dor
9460 Wilshire Blvd., Ste. 300
Beverly Hills, CA 90212-2710

Donors: Dena Schechter; Meldon Levine; Sid B. Levine Trust; Irv Schechter; Max A. Levine Trust.
Foundation type: Independent foundation.
Financial data (yr. ended 12/31/13): Assets, $7,037,042 (M); gifts received, $326,046; expenditures, $375,569; qualifying distributions, $348,547; giving activities include $347,962 for 85 grants (high: $71,417; low: $250).
Fields of interest: Education; University education; Religion; Judaism.
Limitations: Applications not accepted. Giving primarily in CA.
Application information: Unsolicited requests for funds not accepted.
Officers: Dena Schechter, Pres.; Nancy Clavin, Secy.; Meldon Levine, Treas.
Directors: Andrew Clavin; Daniel Clavin; Elizabeth Cohn; Adam Paul Levine; Cara E. Levine; Jacob C. Levine; Robert Levine; Mieke Neumann; Asher Lev Schechter; Joshua Schechter; Noah Blum Schechter.
EIN: 201917833

751
The Gloria & Ken Levy Foundation
51 University Ave., Ste. G
Los Gatos, CA 95030-6037

Established in 1994 in California.
Donors: Gloria Levy; Kenneth Levy.
Foundation type: Independent foundation.
Financial data (yr. ended 10/31/13): Assets, $255,955 (M); expenditures, $177,178; qualifying distributions, $175,334; giving activities include $171,980 for 11 grants (high: $75,000; low: $150).
Purpose and activities: Giving primarily for Jewish agencies and federated giving programs; funding also for higher education and social services.
Fields of interest: Higher education; Nonprofits; Judaism; Human services.
Type of support: Regranting.
Limitations: Applications not accepted. Giving primarily in CA and Washington, DC. No grants to individuals.

Application information: Contributes only to pre-selected organizations.
Officers: Gloria Levy, Pres.; Kenneth Levy, Secy. and C.F.O.
EIN: 770388772

752
Hyman Jebb Levy Foundation
6634 Valjean Ave.
Van Nuys, CA 91406-5816 (818) 781-4552
Contact: Hyman Levy, Pres.

Established in 1974 in California.
Donors: Hyman Levy; Raymond Mallel; Aaron Cohen.
Foundation type: Independent foundation.
Financial data (yr. ended 12/31/13): Assets, $5,123,179 (M); gifts received, $125; expenditures, $445,476; qualifying distributions, $421,600; giving activities include $421,600 for 40 grants (high: $200,000; low: $500).
Purpose and activities: Grants primarily for Jewish education and temple support, including support for institutions in Israel.
Fields of interest: Education; Elementary and secondary education; Nonprofits; Judaism; Human services.
International interests: Israel.
Type of support: Regranting.
Limitations: Applications accepted. Giving primarily in CA and NY. No support for private foundations. No grants to individuals.
Application information:
  Initial approach: Proposal
  Deadline(s): None
Officers: Hyman Levy, Pres.; Donna Levy, Secy.
EIN: 237422872

753
Robert and Beverly Lewis Family Foundation
626 Via Lido Nord
Newport Beach, CA 92663-5521

Established in 1987 in California.
Donor: Beverly J. Lewis.
Foundation type: Independent foundation.
Financial data (yr. ended 06/30/15): Assets, $1,211 (M); expenditures, $188,000; qualifying distributions, $179,000; giving activities include $179,000 for 5 grants (high: $80,000; low: $10,000).
Fields of interest: Animal welfare; Hospital care; Diseases and conditions; Equestrianism; Human services.
Type of support: Research; Research and evaluation.
Limitations: Applications not accepted. Giving primarily in CA. No grants to individuals.
Application information: Contributes only to pre-selected organizations.
Officers: Margery Lewis, V.P. and Treas.; Jeffrey Lewis, Treas. and C.F.O.; Beverly J. Lewis, Pres.; Robert Lewis, V.P.
EIN: 330210203

754
Mildred Luck Lewis Foundation
3247 W. March Ln.
Stockton, CA 95219

Foundation type: Independent foundation.
Financial data (yr. ended 12/31/14): Assets, $1,341,445; gifts received, $250,000; expenditures, $190,402; qualifying distributions, $175,000.
Fields of interest: Health; Community and economic development; Human services.
Limitations: Applications not accepted. Giving primarily in CA.
Application information: Unsolicited requests for funds not accepted.
Officers: Mildred Luck Lewis, Chair.; Barbara Greene, Pres.; Lynette Cleland, V.P.; Karren Peterson, Secy.; Louise Barbagelata, Treas.
EIN: 208655653

755
The Susan Liautaud Foundation
(formerly The Liautaud Family Foundation)
c/o PricewaterhouseCoopers, LLP
3 Embarcadero Ctr., Fl. 20
San Francisco, CA 94111-4003

Established in 1999 in California.
Donors: Susan Liautaud; Bernard Liautaud.
Foundation type: Independent foundation.
Financial data (yr. ended 11/30/13): Assets, $1,623,652 (M); gifts received, $5,000; expenditures, $169,109; qualifying distributions, $156,259; giving activities include $151,259 for 9 grants (high: $42,754; low: $1,000).
Fields of interest: Arts and culture; Education; Higher education; Health; Child welfare.
Limitations: Applications not accepted. Giving primarily in CA. No grants to individuals.
Application information: Unsolicited requests for funds not accepted.
Officers: Susan Liautaud, C.E.O. and Secy.; Bernard Liautaud, C.F.O.
EIN: 770511717

756
Lighthouse - A Christian Effort
4016 Atlas Peak Rd.
Napa, CA 94558-9668

Established in 1979 in California.
Donors: Garrett Brown; Stucco Stone Products; Richard Brown; Beverly Brown.
Foundation type: Independent foundation.
Financial data (yr. ended 09/30/13): Assets, $0 (M); gifts received, $3,440; expenditures, $326,919; qualifying distributions, $311,936; giving activities include $310,870 for 19 grants (high: $73,000; low: $150).
Fields of interest: Housing development; Religion; Human services; Homeless people.
Limitations: Applications not accepted. Giving primarily in CA. No grants to individuals.
Application information: Unsolicited requests for funds not accepted.
Officers: Garrett Brown, Pres.; Beverly Brown, V.P.; Mark Petersen, Secy.
EIN: 942623602

757
Raymond and Joanne Lin Foundation
25 Brandon Ct.
Hillsborough, CA 94010-7469 6505229987

Established in 1995 in California.
Donors: Joanne Lin; Raymond Lin.
Foundation type: Independent foundation.
Financial data (yr. ended 10/31/14): Assets, $998,902; expenditures, $145,943; qualifying distributions, $138,519.
Fields of interest: Education; Human services; Youth development.
Limitations: Applications not accepted. Giving primarily in CA. No grants to individuals.
Application information: Unsolicited requests for funds not accepted.
Officers: Joanne Lin, Pres.; Raymond Lin, Secy.
Director: Vincent Lin.
EIN: 943228498

758
Linked Foundation

3749 Santa Claus Ln., Ste. B
Carpinteria, CA 93013-1104 (805) 880-1990
Contact: Nancy Swanson, Exec. Dir.
FAX: (805) 684-5530; Main URL: http://www.linkedfoundation.org/
Blog: http://www.linkedfoundation.org/blog

Established in 2006 in California.
Donors: Dorothy F. Largay; Wayne E. Rosing; Tabasgo Foundation.
Foundation type: Independent foundation.
Financial data (yr. ended 12/31/13): Assets, $7,340,510 (M); expenditures, $772,045; qualifying distributions, $575,788; giving activities include $440,610 for 9 grants (high: $200,000; low: $3,000), and $135,178 for 1 foundation-administered program.
Purpose and activities: Giving primarily to U.S.-based organizations to advance the development of holistic approaches which combine microfinance with health targeted to very poor women in Latin America. .
Fields of interest: Economic development; Women's rights; Human services; International development; Females.
International interests: Caribbean; Latin America.
Limitations: Applications not accepted. Giving primarily in CA; funding also in Washington, DC. No grants to individuals.
Application information: Contributes only to pre-selected organizations.
Officers: Dorothy F. Largay, C.E.O.; Wayne E. Rossing, Secy.; Nancy Swanson, Exec. Dir.
EIN: 203880761

759
The Lipp Family Foundation

1001 B Ave., Ste. 211
Coronado, CA 92118-3424

Established in 2005 in California.
Donors: David W. Lipp; David W. Lipp Revocable Trust.
Foundation type: Independent foundation.
Financial data (yr. ended 06/30/13): Assets, $4,100,782 (M); expenditures, $389,016; qualifying distributions, $352,892; giving activities include $310,500 for 15 grants (high: $60,000; low: $5,000).
Purpose and activities: Giving primarily for higher education.
Fields of interest: Education; Higher education; Hospital care; Science.

Limitations: Applications not accepted. Giving primarily in Coronado and San Diego, CA, and Amherst, MA. No grants to individuals.
Application information: Unsolicited requests for funds not accepted.
Directors: William J. Barkhurst; Charles W. Hayes; Sydney J. Stanley.
EIN: 201985794

760
Lorance Lisle Foundation

c/o Cheadle
1000 Quail St., Ste. 100
Newport Beach, CA 92660-2764

Donor: Sally Lisle.
Foundation type: Independent foundation.
Financial data (yr. ended 12/31/13): Assets, $3,070,274 (M); expenditures, $430,185; qualifying distributions, $430,000; giving activities include $430,000 for 20 grants (high: $100,000; low: $1,000).
Fields of interest: Theater; Christianity; Human services.
Limitations: Applications not accepted. No grants to individuals.
Application information: Unsolicited requests for funds not accepted.
Officer: Lora Jane Harv Lisle, C.F.O. and Secy.
EIN: 263026425

761
Livingston Memorial Foundation

c/o Musick, Peeler & Garrett, LLP
2801 Townsgate Rd., No. 200
Westlake Village, CA 91361-5842 (805) 418-3115
Contact: Laura K. McAvoy, Asst. Secy. and C.F.O.
FAX: (805) 418-3101;
E-mail: l.mcavoy@mpglaw.com; Main URL: http://livingstonmemorialfoundation.org

Established in 1974 in California.
Donor: Ruth Daily Livingston†.
Foundation type: Independent foundation.
Financial data (yr. ended 04/30/13): Assets, $9,750,770 (M); expenditures, $610,079; qualifying distributions, $457,653; giving activities include $352,000 for 26 grants (high: $151,000; low: $1,000).
Purpose and activities: Support for health and health-related agencies serving citizens of Ventura County, California.
Fields of interest: Health; Community health care; Hospital care; Health care clinics; Dental care; Vision care; Home health care; Hospice care; Infant care; Rehabilitation; Mental health care; Sexual assault victim services; Bereavement counseling.
Type of support: General support; Matching grants; Continuing support; Equipment; Public engagement and education.
Limitations: Giving limited to organizations benefiting the health of residents of Ventura County, CA. No grants to individuals.
Publications: Application guidelines; Informational brochure (including application guidelines); Program policy statement.
Application information: Application form required.
Initial approach: Letter not exceeding 3 pages
Copies of proposal: 9

Deadline(s): Varies; contact foundation for information
Board meeting date(s): As required
Officers and Directors: Charles M. Hair, MD, Chair. and Pres. and Director; W.C. Huff, MD, Vice-Chair. and V.P. and Director; Richard Loft, MD, Vice-Chair. and V.P. and Director; Marcia Donlon, Secy. and Director; Laura K. McAvoy, C.F.O. and Director; Thomas F. McGrath III; John R. Walters, MD.
Number of staff: None.
EIN: 237364623

762
Llagas Foundation

3697 Mt. Diablo Blvd., Ste. 205
Lafayette, CA 94549-7113

Established in 1980 in California.
Donors: Paul L. Davies III; Paul L. Davies, Jr.
Foundation type: Independent foundation.
Financial data (yr. ended 06/30/13): Assets, $3,995,350 (M); expenditures, $204,891; qualifying distributions, $193,000; giving activities include $193,000 for 55 grants (high: $25,000; low: $500).
Purpose and activities: Supports the charitable interests of the directors.
Fields of interest: Education; Higher education; Human services.
Limitations: Applications not accepted. Giving primarily in CA. No grants to individuals; no loans.
Application information: Contributes only to pre-selected organizations. Unsolicited requests for funds are not considered.
Board meeting date(s): Varies
Officers and Directors: Paul L. Davies III, Pres. and Director; Pilar H. Davies, V.P. and Secy. and Director; Paul L. Davies, Jr., V.P. and Director; Andrew E. Zeisler, Treas.; Natalie L. Davies; Robert H. Davies; Tyler S. Davies.
EIN: 942678807

763
John M. Lloyd Foundation

11777 San Vicente Blvd., Ste. 745
Los Angeles, CA 90049-5052 (310) 622-1050
FAX: (310) 622-1070; E-mail: info@johnmlloyd.org;
Main URL: http://www.johnmlloyd.org
Grants List: http://www.johnmlloyd.org/grant_awards.html
John M. Lloyd Foundation's Philanthropy Promise: http://www.ncrp.org/philanthropys-promise/who

Established in 1991 in California.
Foundation type: Independent foundation.
Financial data (yr. ended 12/31/13): Assets, $8,295,472 (M); gifts received, $803; expenditures, $349,142; qualifying distributions, $268,354; giving activities include $210,000 for 7 grants (high: $37,500; low: $20,000).
Purpose and activities: Support for innovative programs throughout the world in public policy, education/awareness, and prevention for HIV/AIDS.
Fields of interest: HIV/AIDS.
Type of support: Convening; Continuing support; Curriculum development; General support; Capacity-building and technical assistance; Program development; Publications; Seed money; Technical assistance.

Limitations: Giving on a worldwide basis. No grants to individuals, or for annual campaigns; generally no grants for operating budgets of established organizations, capital expenditures, health care or service provision, or for indirect costs.

Publications: Application guidelines; Financial statement; Grants list.

Application information: Applicants whose concept letters are reviewed favorably by the Board will be asked to submit a formal proposal. Unsolicited formal proposals will not be considered. Application guidelines available on foundation web site.

  Initial approach: Concept letter (no more than 4 pages) via e-mail (preferred) or fax
  Copies of proposal: 1
  Deadline(s): Varies; refer to foundation web site
  Board meeting date(s): Oct. and Mar.

Officers and Directors: Zoe Lloyd Foxley, Chair. and Director; Mary Lloyd Estrin, Vice-Chair. and Director; Robert L. Estrin, Pres. and Director; Jesse Estrin, Secy. and Director; Trish Devine Karlin, Treas. and Director; Heather Chandler, Cont.; Griff Foxley; Mark Isaac; Linda Dorn Klein; Heidi Mage Lloyd.

Number of staff: None.

EIN: 363766003

764

Owen Locke Memorial Foundation
3879-B Brockton Ave.
Riverside, CA 92501-3263 (951) 781-7545
Contact: Brenda Johnson, Scholarship Coord.
E-mail: bami_joe@hotmail.com; Main URL: http://www.owenlocke.org

Established in 2007 in California.

Donor: Gwendolyn Locke‡.

Foundation type: Independent foundation.

Financial data (yr. ended 02/29/12): Assets, $4,987,978 (M); expenditures, $474,295; qualifying distributions, $461,697; giving activities include $50,000 for 2 grants (high: $25,000; low: $25,000), and $385,866 for grants to individuals.

Purpose and activities: The purpose of the fund is to provide educational scholarships to fund tuition, school fees and books for applicants in California. Preference will be given to persons who have limited financial resources available for school, but who are not eligible to be awarded funds from public or government sources.

Fields of interest: Education.

Limitations: Applications accepted. Giving limited to residents of CA.

Application information: Application and recommendation forms may be downloaded from foundation web site. Applicants must be high school graduates of CA schools who are attending an accredited college, university or vocational school. Application form required.

  Initial approach: Download applications
  Deadline(s): May 30

Trustee: Carol Bartels.

EIN: 208561536

765

The Lockridge Charitable Foundation Trust
1475 Padre Ln.
Pebble Beach, CA 93953

Established in 2000 in California.

Donors: Erika H. Lockridge; John P. Lockridge; The Lockridge Trust.

Foundation type: Independent foundation.

Financial data (yr. ended 12/31/14): Assets, $462 (M); gifts received, $265,000; expenditures, $278,985; qualifying distributions, $278,000; giving activities include $278,000 for 4 grants (high: $200,000; low: $12,000).

Fields of interest: Higher education; Basketball.

Limitations: Applications not accepted. Giving primarily in CO, OH, and WY. No grants to individuals.

Application information: Unsolicited requests for funds not accepted.

Trustee: Erika H. Lockridge.

EIN: 776198547

766

The Looker Foundation
1591 E. El Segundo Blvd.
El Segundo, CA 90245 (310) 414-9117
Contact: Robert L. Looker, Pres.
FAX: (310) 322-1480; E-mail for Robert L. Looker: rlooker1@aol.com

Established in 1995 in California.

Donors: Robert Looker; Satco., Inc.; Mary M. Looker.

Foundation type: Independent foundation.

Financial data (yr. ended 12/31/13): Assets, $5,484,051 (M); expenditures, $275,300; qualifying distributions, $231,219; giving activities include $231,219 for 29 grants (high: $30,000; low: $550).

Purpose and activities: Giving primarily to support: 1) Children and families to encourage and enhance individual and family independence among complex issues such as health, food, shelter, counseling and responsible care of children and adolescents; 2) Educational experiences for children, adolescents and adults through arts and music, tutoring, literacy, technical skills and parenting skills; 3) Conservation, protection and enhancement of the environment; and 4) Cultural and arts programs encouraging cultural awareness and restoration and conservation of arts and literature.

Fields of interest: Arts and culture; Education; Natural resources; Human services; Family services; Child welfare.

Type of support: General support; Matching grants; Continuing support; Capital campaigns; Capital and infrastructure; Equipment; Land acquisitions; Endowments; Emergency funds; Program development; Seed money; Scholarships.

Limitations: Applications not accepted. Giving primarily in CA and NY. No support for political or religious organizations. No grants to individuals.

Publications: Grants list; Occasional report; Program policy statement.

Application information: Unsolicited requests for funds not accepted. The foundation does not solicit requests.

  Board meeting date(s): First Mon. in Mar., June, Sept, and Nov.

Officers and Directors: Mary Looker, Chair. and Director; Robert L. Looker, Pres. and Director; Blair Ridenour, Secy.; Tonia Looker, Treas.; Gina Liberotti; Amy Looker; Erin Looker; Monica Looker.

Number of staff: 1 part-time professional.

EIN: 770397495

767

Virginia Lopez Foundation
(formerly Lopez Low Foundation)
135 Jordan Ave.
San Francisco, CA 94118-2565

Established in 1998 in California.

Donors: Roger Low; Virginia Lopez.

Foundation type: Independent foundation.

Financial data (yr. ended 12/31/13): Assets, $1,755,051 (M); expenditures, $150,006; qualifying distributions, $146,421; giving activities include $145,300 for 15 grants (high: $98,000; low: $200).

Purpose and activities: Giving to further educational opportunities for people between the ages of 5 and 18, through grants to specific non-discriminatory tax qualified independent and public schools and programs.

Fields of interest: Education; Children.

Type of support: Capital and infrastructure; Program development; Curriculum development; Scholarships.

Limitations: Applications not accepted. Giving primarily in San Francisco, CA and New York, NY. No grants to individuals.

Publications: Annual report; Grants list.

Application information: Unsolicited requests for funds not accepted.

Officers and Directors: Virginia Lopez, Pres. and Director; Jesse Lopez Low, C.F.O.; Gabriel Lopez Low, Secy.

Number of staff: 1 part-time professional.

EIN: 943313228

768

The Los Angeles Jewish Fund
c/o Fenigstein & Kaufman
1900 Ave. of the Stars, Ste. 2300
Los Angeles, CA 90067-4314

Established in 1996 in California.

Foundation type: Independent foundation.

Financial data (yr. ended 12/31/13): Assets, $4,427,857 (M); expenditures, $261,078; qualifying distributions, $260,171; giving activities include $260,000 for 35 grants (high: $23,000; low: $500).

Purpose and activities: Giving primarily to Jewish agencies and temples and for Jewish education.

Fields of interest: Education; Secondary education; Judaism.

Limitations: Applications not accepted. Giving primarily in CA. No grants to individuals.

Application information: Unsolicited requests for funds not accepted.

Officers: Rudolph Lowy, Chair.; Leslie Mendelsohn, Pres.; David Frank, C.F.O.; Jack Fenigstein, V.P. and Secy.

EIN: 954519638

769

Los Feliz Foundation
70-750 Sunny Ln.
Rancho Mirage, CA 92270-2302

Established in 1998 in California.

Donor: Quadara Charitable Lead Annuity Trust.

Foundation type: Independent foundation.

Financial data (yr. ended 10/31/13): Assets, $1,789,463 (M); expenditures, $207,327;

qualifying distributions, $192,500; giving activities include $192,500 for 4 grants (high: $107,000; low: $5,500).
Fields of interest: Education; Catholicism; Human services.
Limitations: Applications not accepted. Giving primarily in CA. No grants to individuals.
Application information: Unsolicited requests for funds not accepted.
Officer: Scott Roberts, Pres.
EIN: 954660704

770
Kim and Harold Louie Family Foundation
445 Pullman Rd.
Hillsborough, CA 94010-6749   (650) 491-3434
Contact: Stanley Sze, C.F.O., Secy.-Treas., and Dir.

Established in 2005 in California.
Donor: Betty B. Louie.
Foundation type: Independent trust foundation.
Financial data (yr. ended 12/31/13): Assets, $9,128,419 (M); expenditures, $452,256; qualifying distributions, $389,618; giving activities include $342,511 for 53 grants (high: $122,991; low: $1,500).
Fields of interest: Education; University education; Health; Diseases and conditions; National defense; People with disabilities.
Type of support: Public engagement and education; Research.
Limitations: Applications accepted. Giving primarily in CA, CO, Washington, DC, OH, and VA.
Application information: Application form required.
  Initial approach: Letter
  Deadline(s): None
Officers and Directors: Betty B. Louie, Pres. and Director; Stanley Sze, C.F.O. and Secy.-Treas. and Director; David Louie.
EIN: 870757807

771
Lui Foundation
433 California St., 7th Fl.
San Francisco, CA 94104

Established in 2005 in California.
Donors: Lawrence Lui; Harbor View Holdings Inc.
Foundation type: Independent foundation.
Financial data (yr. ended 12/31/13): Assets, $1,714,323 (M); gifts received, $700,000; expenditures, $208,766; qualifying distributions, $208,000; giving activities include $208,000 for 5 grants (high: $100,000; low: $3,000).
Fields of interest: Cultural awareness; Education; Higher education.
International interests: China.
Limitations: Applications not accepted. Giving primarily in CA and Beijing, China. No grants to individuals.
Application information: Contributes only to pre-selected organizations.
Directors: Gorretti Lui; Lawrence Lui.
EIN: 203813205

772
Carolyn C. Lundgren Trust
P.O. Box 45174
San Francisco, CA 94145-0174

Donor: Carolyn Lundgren†.
Foundation type: Independent foundation.
Financial data (yr. ended 12/31/14): Assets, $6,069,538; expenditures, $462,947; qualifying distributions, $318,516.
Fields of interest: Human services.
Limitations: Applications not accepted.
Application information: Unsolicited requests for funds not accepted.
Trustee: Union Bank, N.A.
EIN: 306330655

773
Miranda Lux Foundation
57 Post St., Ste. 510
San Francisco, CA 94104-5020   (415) 981-2966
Contact: Kenneth J. Blum, Exec. Dir.
E-mail: admin@mirandalux.org; Main URL: http://www.mirandalux.org
Grants List: http://www.mirandalux.org/grant-recipients.php

Established in 1908 in California.
Donor: Miranda W. Lux†.
Foundation type: Independent foundation.
Financial data (yr. ended 06/30/14): Assets, $10,661,457 (M); expenditures, $557,496; qualifying distributions, $505,235; giving activities include $403,500 for 39 grants (high: $20,000; low: $2,500).
Purpose and activities: Support to promising proposals for preschool through junior college programs in the fields of pre-vocational and vocational education. Also supports innovative academic enrichment, technology training, and performing and visual arts programs to help participants develop core job skills. The foundation limits its grantmaking to organizations and programs within the San Francisco Bay area that serve people under the age of 18.
Fields of interest: Vocational education; Basic and remedial instruction; Reading promotion; Employment; Job training; Child welfare.
Type of support: General support; Matching grants; Continuing support; Equipment; Program development; Seed money; Fellowships; Internships; Scholarships.
Limitations: Applications accepted. Giving limited to San Francisco, CA. No support for sectarian religious facilities. No grants to individuals, or for annual campaigns, emergency funds, deficit financing, building or endowment funds, land acquisition, renovations, research, publications, or conferences; no loans.
Publications: Application guidelines; Annual report; Grants list; Informational brochure; Program policy statement.
Application information: Application form required.
  Initial approach: Letter
  Copies of proposal: 1
  Deadline(s): None
  Board meeting date(s): Quarterly
Officers: Robert J. Cappelloni, Pres.; Roland E. Tognazzini, Jr., V.P.; Beatrice Bowles, Secy.-Treas.
Trustees: Bert Damner; Nina Gladish; Betsy Keller; Philip F. Spalding.
EIN: 941170404

774
The Lyman Family Foundation
P.O. Box 676046
Rancho Santa Fe, CA 92067-6046

Established in 2004 in California.
Donors: Steven A. Lyman; Vicki Jo Lyman.
Foundation type: Independent foundation.
Financial data (yr. ended 12/31/14): Assets, $2,460,157 (M); expenditures, $248,774; qualifying distributions, $145,529; giving activities include $143,345 for 25 grants (high: $25,125; low: $300).
Fields of interest: Health; Christianity; Human services; Child welfare.
Limitations: Applications not accepted. Giving primarily in CA. No grants to individuals.
Application information: Contributes only to pre-selected organizations.
Officers: Steven A. Lyman, Pres.; Vicki Jo Lyman, Secy. and C.F.O.
EIN: 202019997

775
The Lynch Family Foundation
1040 Main St., Ste. 103
Napa, CA 94559

Established in 1999 in California.
Donors: Daniel C. Lynch; Karen D. Lynch; Julie E. Lynch.
Foundation type: Independent foundation.
Financial data (yr. ended 12/31/13): Assets, $1,200,909 (M); expenditures, $326,574; qualifying distributions, $313,784; giving activities include $283,200 for 39 grants (high: $75,000; low: $100).
Fields of interest: Arts and culture; Education; Human services.
Limitations: Applications not accepted. Giving primarily in CA. No grants to individuals.
Application information: Contributes only to pre-selected organizations.
Officers: Daniel C. Lynch, C.E.O. and Exec. Dir.; Julie E. Lynch-Sasson, C.F.O. and Secy.
EIN: 770513616

776
Lyons Family Foundation, Inc.
3015 State St., Ste. D
Santa Barbara, CA 93105-3330

Established in 1990 in California.
Donors: Evelyn Lyons; Steven Lyons.
Foundation type: Independent foundation.
Financial data (yr. ended 06/30/13): Assets, $536,972 (M); gifts received, $642,616; expenditures, $400,927; qualifying distributions, $398,780; giving activities include $398,780 for 42 grants (high: $200,000; low: $100).
Fields of interest: Education; Nonprofits; Hospital care; Diseases and conditions; Child abuse; Judaism; Human rights.
Type of support: Regranting.
Limitations: Applications not accepted. Giving primarily in Los Angeles and Santa Barbara, CA. No grants to individuals.
Application information: Contributes only to pre-selected organizations.

Officers and Directors: Steven Lyons, Pres. and Director; Cynthia Willis Lyons, C.F.O. and Secy. and Director; Robert Egenolf.
Number of staff: None.
EIN: 770260636

777

Chuan Lyu Foundation
(formerly The Lee Foundation)
P.O. Box 1294
Menlo Park, CA 94026-1294

Established in 1986 in California.
Donors: Dr. Hwalin Lee; Taiwanese American Center of Northern California.
Foundation type: Independent foundation.
Financial data (yr. ended 11/30/13): Assets, $4,136,587 (M); expenditures, $216,302; qualifying distributions, $209,228; giving activities include $200,000 for 1 grant.
Purpose and activities: Giving primarily for the study of topics related to Taiwan.
Fields of interest: Cultural awareness; Education.
International interests: Taiwan.
Limitations: Applications not accepted. Giving primarily in CA for Taiwan-related projects. No grants to individuals.
Application information: Contributes only to pre-selected organizations.
Officer: Dr. Hwalin Lee, Mgr. and Director.
EIN: 586203563

778

The MacCready Family Foundation
P.O Box 1501, NJ2-130-03-31
South Pasadena, CA 91031-1501

Donor: Judith MacCready.
Foundation type: Independent foundation.
Financial data (yr. ended 12/31/13): Assets, $7,855,975 (M); expenditures, $438,792; qualifying distributions, $387,339; giving activities include $355,000 for 4 grants (high: $125,000; low: $40,000).
Fields of interest: Foundations; Human services.
Limitations: Applications not accepted. Giving primarily in CA.
Application information: Unsolicited requests for funds not accepted.
Officers: Molly Knox, Pres.; Marshall MacCready, V.P.; Parker MacCready, V.P.; Jillian Knox, Secy.; Tyler MacCready, Treas.
EIN: 271241337

779

MacDonald Family Charitable Trust
c/o Mark and Donna MacDonald
1561 Gates Ave.
Manhattan Beach, CA 90266-7026

Established in 2000 in California.
Donors: Donna Marie MacDonald; Mark MacDonald.
Foundation type: Independent foundation.
Financial data (yr. ended 12/31/13): Assets, $10,609,360 (M); gifts received, $2,045,680; expenditures, $363,254; qualifying distributions, $310,521; giving activities include $310,521 for 38 grants (high: $56,100; low: $100).

Purpose and activities: Giving primarily for education, health, and social services; funding also to a Roman Catholic church.
Fields of interest: Education; Diseases and conditions; Human services.
Limitations: Applications not accepted. Giving primarily in CA. No grants to individuals.
Application information: Contributes only to pre-selected organizations.
Trustees: Donna Marie MacDonald; Mark MacDonald.
EIN: 336269762

780

Mary Mae Foundation
c/o Frank, Rimerman & Co., LLP
1801 Page Mill Rd.
Palo Alto, CA 94304

Established in 2000 in California.
Donor: Patricia A. House.
Foundation type: Independent foundation.
Financial data (yr. ended 12/31/13): Assets, $934,977 (M); expenditures, $297,405; qualifying distributions, $297,405; giving activities include $220,000 for 3 grants (high: $160,000; low: $21,000).
Fields of interest: Arts and culture; Education; Natural resources; Health; Housing development; Human services.
Type of support: General support.
Limitations: Applications not accepted. Giving primarily in MI and VA. No grants to individuals.
Application information: Contributes only to pre-selected organizations.
Officers: Jeanne Jessup, Pres.; Patricia A. House, C.F.O.
Director: Marilyn Aberlich.
EIN: 943352982

781

The Magali Foundation
8454 El Paseo Grande
La Jolla, CA 92037-3013

Donors: Maria G. Sulpizio; Richard Sulpizio.
Foundation type: Independent foundation.
Financial data (yr. ended 12/31/13): Assets, $2,386,784 (M); expenditures, $424,388; qualifying distributions, $399,767; giving activities include $395,601 for 10 grants (high: $297,500; low: $446).
Fields of interest: Children's museums; Education; Higher education; Human services; Child welfare.
Limitations: Applications not accepted. Giving primarily in CA.
Application information: Unsolicited requests for funds not accepted.
Officers: Maria G. Sulpizio, Pres.; Richard Sulpizio, Secy.
EIN: 912169989

782

Deborah J. & Peter A. Magowan Family Foundation
c/o Pam J. Royer
111 Pine St.
San Francisco, CA 94111

Established in 2005 in California.

Donor: Magowan Family Trust.
Foundation type: Independent foundation.
Financial data (yr. ended 12/31/13): Assets, $3,466,667 (M); expenditures, $178,628; qualifying distributions, $176,294; giving activities include $169,350 for 50 grants (high: $27,750; low: $500).
Fields of interest: Elementary and secondary education; Higher education; Community college education; Foundations; Human services.
Limitations: Applications not accepted. Giving primarily in CA; funding also in MA and OR. No grants to individuals.
Application information: Unsolicited requests for funds not accepted.
Trustee: Pam J. Royer.
Directors: Deborah Magowan; Peter Magowan.
EIN: 201511142

783

Maher Foundation
248 Pearl St.
Monterey, CA 93940-3119
Contact: Thomas C. Maher, Pres.

Donor: Thomas C. Maher.
Foundation type: Independent foundation.
Financial data (yr. ended 12/31/13): Assets, $0 (M); gifts received, $395,000; expenditures, $287,166; qualifying distributions, $239,626; giving activities include $239,626 for 13 grants (high: $122,500; low: $2,000).
Fields of interest: Religion; Human services.
Application information:
Initial approach: Proposal
Deadline(s): None
Officers: Tomas C. Maher, Pres.; Joan K. Maher, Secy.
Director: Steve Barone.
EIN: 271791842

784

Majestic Realty Foundation
13191 Crossroads Pkwy. N., 6th Fl.
City of Industry, CA 91746-3497 (562) 654-2725
Contact: Frances L. Inman, Pres.
E-mail: majesticfoundation@majesticrealty.com; Additional tel.: (562) 948-4375; Main URL: http://www.majesticfoundation.org

Established in 2002 in California.
Donors: Majestic Realty Co.; Commerce Construction; David A. Wheeler; Edward P. Roski, Jr.; Curci-Turner Company LLC.
Foundation type: Company-sponsored foundation.
Financial data (yr. ended 12/31/13): Assets, $283,543 (M); gifts received, $392,819; expenditures, $387,142; qualifying distributions, $381,432; giving activities include $378,592 for 96 grants (high: $35,107; low: $50).
Purpose and activities: The foundation supports organizations involved with education, health, violence prevention, youth, and families.
Fields of interest: Education; Higher education; Health; Crime prevention; Leadership development; Human services; Family services; Youth development; Youth services; Young adults; Families.
Type of support: General support; Employee matching gifts; Cash grants; Continuing support;

Capital campaigns; Matching grants; Employee volunteer services; Program development.
Limitations: Applications accepted. Giving primarily in areas of company operations in Phoenix, AZ, Inland Empire, San Gabriel Valley, and Greater Los Angeles, CA, Aurora and Denver, CO, Jacksonville, FL, Atlanta, GA, Las Vegas, NV, Bethlehem, PA, Dallas and Fort Worth, TX, Salt Lake City, UT, and WI. No support for federated funds or pass-through organizations, religious or other organizations not of direct benefit to the entire community, or lobbying organizations. No grants to individuals, or for start-up needs.
Publications: Application guidelines; Annual report (including application guidelines).
Application information: Additional information may be requested at a later date. A site visit may be requested. Application form required.
   Initial approach: Letter
   Copies of proposal: 1
   Deadline(s): None
Officers and Directors: Frances L. Inman, Pres. and Director; Gail Kiralla, Secy. and Director; Kevin McCarthy.
EIN: 043722125

785
Malachi 3 Foundation
(formerly The Circle Family Foundation, Inc.)
1006 Segovia Cir.
Placentia, CA 92870-7100

Established in 2003 in Delaware.
Donors: Douglas Circle; Jan Circle.
Foundation type: Independent foundation.
Financial data (yr. ended 12/31/13): Assets, $2,677,623 (M); gifts received, $225,000; expenditures, $252,577; qualifying distributions, $246,586; giving activities include $206,546 for 17 grants (high: $52,524; low: $1,000).
Fields of interest: Education; Higher education; Christianity; Human services; Family services; Child welfare.
Limitations: Applications not accepted. Giving primarily in CA, with emphasis on Orange and Yorba Linda. No grants to individuals.
Application information: Contributes only to pre-selected organizations.
Officers and Directors: Douglas Circle, Pres. and Director; Jan Circle, Secy. and Director; Brendan Circle; Kyle Circle; Leah Circle; Tom Curtis.
EIN: 200500539

786
The Chris and Melody Malachowsky Family Foundation
635 Campbell Technology Pkwy., Ste. 100
Campbell, CA 95008-5075

Established in 2001 in Delaware.
Donors: Chris Malachowsky; Melody Malachowsky.
Foundation type: Independent foundation.
Financial data (yr. ended 12/31/13): Assets, $6,591,895 (M); expenditures, $372,618; qualifying distributions, $307,537; giving activities include $299,493 for 55 grants (high: $50,000; low: $18).
Fields of interest: Natural resources; Nonprofits; Diseases and conditions; Alzheimer's disease; Food banks.
Type of support: Regranting.

Limitations: Applications not accepted. Giving primarily in CA, IL and OR. No grants to individuals.
Application information: Contributes only to pre-selected organizations.
Officers and Directors: Chris Malachowsky, Pres. and Director; Melody Malachowsky, Secy.-Treas. and Director.
EIN: 010555028

787
The Maley-Thawley Family Foundation
931 W. Woodbridge Rd.
Lodi, CA 95242-9616 (209) 369-7434
Contact: Richard Thawley, Pres. and Dir.

Established in 1999 in California.
Donors: Richard Thawley; Cynthia Thawley; N. L. Maley; David K. Holland.
Foundation type: Independent foundation.
Financial data (yr. ended 12/31/13): Assets, $320,611 (M); gifts received, $473,500; expenditures, $164,567; qualifying distributions, $163,852; giving activities include $162,237 for 9 grants to individuals (high: $100,000; low: $100).
Fields of interest: Education; Diseases and conditions.
Type of support: Student aid.
Limitations: Applications accepted. Giving primarily in UT.
Application information: Application form required.
   Initial approach: Proposal
   Deadline(s): None for grants; Mar. 31st for scholarships
Officers and Directors: Richard Thawley, Pres. and Director; Cynthia Thawley, V.P. and Secy.-Treas. and Director; Norman Maley.
EIN: 680442684

788
Manchester Family Life Foundation
(formerly The Douglas F. Manchester Life Foundation)
350 Camino De La Reina
San Diego, CA 92108-3003

Established in 1990 in California.
Donors: Pacific Landmark Hotel, Ltd.; Douglas F. Manchester; Bill Simon; Brian Sweeney; Manchester Resorts.
Foundation type: Independent foundation.
Financial data (yr. ended 03/31/14): Assets, $1,730,829 (M); gifts received, $750; expenditures, $291,731; qualifying distributions, $264,000; giving activities include $264,000 for 5 grants (high: $150,000; low: $12,000).
Fields of interest: Museums; Education; Philanthropy; Nonprofits; Community and economic development.
Type of support: Regranting.
Limitations: Applications not accepted. Giving limited to CA and VA. No grants to individuals.
Application information: Contributes only to pre-selected organizations.
Officers: Douglas F. Manchester, Chair. and Pres.; Richard V. Gibbons, C.F.O.
EIN: 330416002

789
Mangold Family Foundation, Inc.
P.O. Box 10035
Pleasanton, CA 94588-0035

Established in 1993 in California.
Donors: Karl G. Mangold; Janet L. Mangold.
Foundation type: Independent foundation.
Financial data (yr. ended 12/31/14): Assets, $3,544,698 (M); expenditures, $163,217; qualifying distributions, $158,515; giving activities include $158,515 for 18 grants (high: $50,000; low: $750).
Fields of interest: Health; Diseases and conditions.
Type of support: General support; Scholarships.
Limitations: Applications not accepted. Giving primarily in CA. No grants to individuals.
Application information: Unsolicited requests for funds not accepted.
Officer: Janet L. Mangold, Secy. and C.F.O.
EIN: 680290468

790
Mann Center for Education & Family Development
c/o Dionne Nastasi
9320 Wilshire Blvd., No. 300
Beverly Hills, CA 90212-3218

Established in 1992 in California.
Donor: Ted Mann Foundation.
Foundation type: Operating foundation.
Financial data (yr. ended 12/31/13): Assets, $3,215,093 (M); expenditures, $307,589; qualifying distributions, $148,239; giving activities include $145,000 for 2 grants (high: $125,000; low: $20,000).
Fields of interest: Art museums; Philanthropy; Nonprofits; Hospital care; Family services.
Type of support: Regranting.
Limitations: Applications not accepted. Giving primarily in CA, Washington, DC, NJ, NY and VA. No grants to individuals.
Application information: Unsolicited requests for funds not accepted.
Officers and Directors: Victoria Mann Simms, Pres. and Director; Ronald A. Simms, C.F.O. and Secy.-Treas. and Director; Josh Simms, V.P. and Director.
EIN: 954369610

791
March Family Foundation
c/o Takata & Marzalek Inc.
20300 Ventura Blvd., Ste. 160
Woodland Hills, CA 91364-0944

Established in 2005 in California.
Donors: Roy Hilton March; Barbara Baldieri March.
Foundation type: Independent foundation.
Financial data (yr. ended 12/31/13): Assets, $64,995 (M); gifts received, $170,201; expenditures, $276,269; giving activities include $269,946 for 34 grants (high: $70,000; low: $100).
Fields of interest: Health; Catholicism; Human services.
Limitations: Applications not accepted. Giving primarily in CA. No grants to individuals.
Application information: Unsolicited requests for funds not accepted.

Trustees: Barbara Baldieri March; Roy Hilton March.
EIN: 206627496

792

Marchese Family Foundation

270 E. Main St.
Los Gatos, CA 95030-6107

Established in 2006 in California.
Donor: Mary Marchese.
Foundation type: Independent foundation.
Financial data (yr. ended 12/31/13): Assets,
$4,878,667 (M); expenditures, $567,657;
qualifying distributions, $294,009; giving activities
include $294,009 for 31 grants (high: $50,591;
low: $100).
Fields of interest: Education; Religion; International
relations.
Limitations: Applications not accepted. Giving
primarily in CA.
Application information: Unsolicited requests for
funds not accepted.
Officers: Chris Marchese, Pres.; Helen Owen, Secy.
EIN: 205187898

793

Marcil Family Foundation

43 Malaga Cove Plz., Ste. D
Palos Verdes Estates, CA 90274-1360

Established in 2003 in California.
Donor: Gerald J. Marcil.
Foundation type: Independent foundation.
Financial data (yr. ended 12/31/13): Assets,
$2,797 (M); gifts received, $163,100;
expenditures, $186,125; qualifying distributions,
$184,673; giving activities include $184,673 for 72
grants (high: $70,000; low: $50).
Fields of interest: Health; Christianity; Catholicism;
Human services.
Type of support: General support.
Limitations: Applications not accepted. Giving
primarily in CA. No grants to individuals.
Application information: Unsolicited requests for
funds not accepted.
Officers: Gerald J. Marcil, Pres.; Carol L. Marcil, V.P.;
Esther Brunner, Secy.
EIN: 710937069

794

The Marcus & Millichap Company Foundation

777 California Ave.
Palo Alto, CA 94304-1102

Established in 1998 in California.
Donor: The Marcus & Millichap Co.
Foundation type: Company-sponsored foundation.
Financial data (yr. ended 12/31/14): Assets,
$7,697,643; expenditures, $328,440; qualifying
distributions, $320,500.
Purpose and activities: The foundation supports
food banks and organizations involved with ballet,
higher and business education, land conservation,
heart disease, human services, community
development, and Judaism.
Fields of interest: Education; Sports and recreation;
Human services.
Limitations: Applications not accepted. Giving
primarily in CA. No grants to individuals.

Application information: Unsolicited requests for
funds not accepted.
Officers and Directors: George M. Marcus, C.E.O.
and Pres. and Director; Marianne Empedocles,
Secy. and Director; Alex Yarmolinsky, Treas.; Robert
H. Kennis.
EIN: 770480868

795

Margoes Foundation

c/o Pacific Foundation Services, LLC
1660 Bush St., Ste. 300
San Francisco, CA 94109 (415) 561-6540
Contact: Hector Melendez, Mng. Dir.; Emily
Schroeder, Grants Mgr.
E-mail for Hector Melendez: hmelendez@pfs-llc.net;
E-mail for Emily Schroeder: eschroeder@pfs-llc.net;
Main URL: http://www.margoesfoundation.org

Established in 1984 in California.
Donor: John A. Margoes†.
Foundation type: Independent foundation.
Financial data (yr. ended 02/28/13): Assets,
$4,703,770 (M); expenditures, $301,090;
qualifying distributions, $264,197; giving activities
include $213,500 for 9 grants (high: $50,000; low:
$20,000).
Purpose and activities: Giving primarily to support
low-income and disadvantaged students accessing
and completing a post-secondary education as well
as programs providing services to people living with
mental illness.
Fields of interest: Higher education; Mental health
care; Ethnic and racial groups; People with
psychosocial disabilities.
Type of support: Program development; Matching
grants; Seed money.
Limitations: Applications accepted. Giving primarily
in the San Francisco Bay Area, CA. No support for
federated campaigns, or for sectarian religious
activities or sectarian religious facilities. No grants
to individuals, or for operating budgets of
established agencies, recurring expenses for direct
services or administrative costs.
Publications: Annual report (including application
guidelines); Grants list.
Application information: Application form required.
   Initial approach: Proposal
   Copies of proposal: 1
   Deadline(s): None
   Board meeting date(s): June and Dec.
Officers and Directors: Cal C. Harling, Chair. and
Director; Neal L. Peterson, Secy. and Director;
Douglas W. Johnson, C.F.O. and Director; Barbara
McClung; Mary Anne Schuett.
Number of staff: None.
EIN: 942955164

796

Margolis Family Foundation

3334 E. Coast Hwy.
Corona Del Mar, CA 92625-2328

Donors: Jeffrey H. Margolis; Deborah H. Margolis.
Foundation type: Independent foundation.
Financial data (yr. ended 12/31/13): Assets,
$6,313,670 (M); expenditures, $385,486;
qualifying distributions, $358,456; giving activities
include $315,664 for 20 grants (high: $100,200;
low: $500).

Fields of interest: Arts and culture; Health; Religion;
Judaism.
Limitations: Applications not accepted. Giving
primarily in CA.
Application information: Unsolicited requests for
funds not accepted.
Officers: Jeffrey H. Margolis, Pres. and C.F.O.;
Deborah H. Margolis, V.P.; Alexandria A. Margolis,
Secy.
Director: Allegra H. Margolis.
EIN: 260558342

797

The Robert Margolis Foundation, Inc.

14701 MulHolland Dr.
Los Angeles, CA 90077-1730

Established in 1997 in California.
Donor: Robert Margolis.
Foundation type: Independent foundation.
Financial data (yr. ended 12/31/13): Assets,
$3,678,735 (M); expenditures, $330,832;
qualifying distributions, $325,000; giving activities
include $325,000 for 21 grants (high: $175,000;
low: $400).
Purpose and activities: Giving primarily to Jewish
organizations.
Fields of interest: Nonprofits; Pediatrics; Judaism;
Human services.
Type of support: Regranting.
Limitations: Applications not accepted. Giving
primarily in CA. No grants to individuals.
Application information: Contributes only to
pre-selected organizations.
Officers: Robert Margolis, Pres.; Valentina Stoianof,
C.F.O.; Barbara Weiser, Secy.
EIN: 954662710

798

Marineau Family Foundation

3464 Clay St., Ste. 2
San Francisco, CA 94118-2009
E-mail: info@marineaufamilyfoundation.org; Main
URL: http://www.marineaufamilyfoundation.org

Established in 2006 in California.
Donors: Susan G. Marineau; Philip A. Marineau.
Foundation type: Independent foundation.
Financial data (yr. ended 12/31/13): Assets,
$3,715,837 (M); expenditures, $354,060;
qualifying distributions, $326,000; giving activities
include $326,000 for 6 grants (high: $146,000;
low: $10,000).
Purpose and activities: Giving primarily for women
and children, through education, violence
prevention, and opportunities to further economic
self sufficiency.
Fields of interest: Opera; Education; Undergraduate
education; Human services; Youth development;
Women's services.
Type of support: Public engagement and education.
Limitations: Applications not accepted. Giving
primarily in CA and NM. No grants to individuals.
Application information: Contributes only to
pre-selected organizations.
Officers: Susan G. Marineau, Pres.; Philip A.
Marineau, Secy.-Treas.
EIN: 208043517

799
The Marshburn Foundation
529 Mercury Ln.
Brea, CA 92821-4831

Foundation type: Independent foundation.
Financial data (yr. ended 10/31/13): Assets,
$2,882,727 (M); expenditures, $196,549;
qualifying distributions, $172,040; giving activities
include $172,040 for 19 grants (high: $44,400;
low: $600).
Fields of interest: Christianity; Human services;
Youth development.
Limitations: Applications not accepted. Giving
primarily in CA.
Application information: Unsolicited requests for
funds not accepted.
Trustees: James Kuhn; Daniel Marshburn; D.C.
Marshburn; Mark Marshburn; Leon Petikas.
EIN: 956049100

800
Steve Martin Charitable Foundation
(formerly Roger's & Betty's Charitable Foundation)
10960 Wilshire Blvd., No. 1900
Los Angeles, CA 90024-3702

Established in 1997 in California.
Donor: Stephen G. Martin.
Foundation type: Independent foundation.
Financial data (yr. ended 12/31/13): Assets,
$319,032 (M); gifts received, $290,000;
expenditures, $232,548; qualifying distributions,
$232,310; giving activities include $182,310 for 13
grants (high: $100,000; low: $100), and $50,000
for 1 grant to an individual.
Purpose and activities: Giving primarily for the arts;
some funding also for research in hearing.
Fields of interest: Arts and culture; Theater;
Museums; Ear, nose and throat diseases; Archives
and special collections.
Type of support: Research.
Limitations: Applications not accepted. Giving
primarily in CA and NY. No grants to individuals.
Application information: Contributes only to
pre-selected organizations.
Trustee: Stephen G. Martin.
EIN: 954656545

801
Della Martin Foundation
c/o Sheppard, Mullin, Richter & Hampton LLP
333 S. Hope St., 43rd Fl.
Los Angeles, CA 90071-1406 (213) 617-4143
Contact: Laurence K. Gould Jr., Tr.

Donor: Della Martin†.
Foundation type: Independent foundation.
Financial data (yr. ended 12/31/14): Assets,
$8,087,934 (M); expenditures, $475,120;
qualifying distributions, $377,347; giving activities
include $300,000 for 1 grant.
Purpose and activities: Giving to advance the study
and discovery of causes and cures for mental illness
through grants for research to publicly-supported
charitable organizations.
Fields of interest: Mental health care.
Type of support: Endowments; Research and
evaluation; Professorships; Research.

Limitations: Applications accepted. Giving primarily
in CA. No grants to individuals, for general support,
or for films.
Application information: Application form required.
Initial approach: Letter
Copies of proposal: 7
Deadline(s): None
Board meeting date(s): Quarterly
Trustees: Laurence K. Gould, Jr.; James A.
Lonergan; Allen W. Mathies, Jr., MD; Nancy B.
Reimann; Jane H. Roney; Eileen D. Sheppard; Philip
A. Swan.
Number of staff: None.
EIN: 237444954

802
The Gilbert J. Martin Foundation
685 Turquoise St.
La Jolla, CA 92037-8131
Contact: Roger Anderson, Tr.

Established in 1983 in California.
Donor: Gilbert J. Martin.
Foundation type: Independent foundation.
Financial data (yr. ended 12/31/12): Assets,
$40,633,298 (M); gifts received, $3,078,091;
expenditures, $3,592,309; qualifying distributions,
$439,000; giving activities include $439,000 for
grants.
Purpose and activities: Giving primarily for
education and Christian churches.
Fields of interest: Ballet; Elementary education;
Secondary education; Higher education;
Christianity; Human services; Scouting programs.
Limitations: Applications not accepted. Giving
primarily in San Diego County, CA.
Application information: Contributes only to
pre-selected organizations.
Trustees: Judy Anderson; Roger Anderson; Paul
Berning; Marc Lanci; Susan Lanci.
EIN: 330002513

803
Florence MacFarlane Martin Memorial Foundation
P.O. Box 12060
San Luis Obispo, CA 93406-2060

Donors: Ann Martin Bowler; Mary Martin Weyrich;
Noreen Martin; John Bowler; Tom Martin; Laura
Martin Sherlock; Bowler Charitable Lead Trust;
Francis Bowler.
Foundation type: Independent foundation.
Financial data (yr. ended 12/31/13): Assets,
$2,388,360 (M); gifts received, $82,048;
expenditures, $210,358; qualifying distributions,
$181,950; giving activities include $181,950 for 18
grants (high: $20,000; low: $2,400).
Purpose and activities: Giving primarily for
children's services and support for pregnant women.
Fields of interest: Children's museums; Education;
Reproductive health care; Child abuse; Child
welfare; Low-income and poor people.
Type of support: General support; Scholarships.
Limitations: Applications not accepted. Giving
primarily in CA and VA. No grants to individuals.
Application information: Unsolicited requests for
funds not accepted.
Officers: Ann Martin Bowler, Pres.; Laura Martin
Sherlock, V.P.; Julie Martin, Secy.; Francis Bowler,
Treas.

Board Members: Nicole Bowler; Meghan Martin;
Mary Martin Weyrich.
EIN: 770299925

804
Mashhoon Family Foundation
4525 District Blvd.
Vernon, CA 90058-2711

Established in 2007 in California.
Donors: Bon Appetit Danish, Inc.; Arlington, LLC;
Hillsboro, Ltd.
Foundation type: Independent foundation.
Financial data (yr. ended 12/31/14): Expenditures,
$252,553; qualifying distributions, $233,550.
Fields of interest: Education; Health; Human
services.
Type of support: General support.
Limitations: Applications not accepted. Giving
primarily in Los Angeles, CA, Washington, DC, New
York, NY, Memphis, TN, and Arlington, VA.
Application information: Unsolicited requests for
funds not accepted.
Directors: Hamid R. Mashhoon; Mahasti Mashhoon.
EIN: 260663435

805
Jack & Adele Mason Family Foundation Inc
2785 Pacific Coast Hwy., Ste. E-807
Torrance, CA 90505-7066

Established in 2003 in California.
Foundation type: Independent foundation.
Financial data (yr. ended 12/31/13): Assets,
$1,515,855 (M); expenditures, $428,111;
qualifying distributions, $400,000; giving activities
include $400,000 for 16 grants (high: $50,000;
low: $10,000).
Fields of interest: Education; Higher education;
Diseases and conditions; Human services.
Type of support: Individual development; Research;
Research and evaluation.
Limitations: Applications not accepted. Giving
primarily in CA, with some giving also in MI, VA, and
Washington, DC. No grants to individuals.
Application information: Contributes only to
pre-selected organizations.
Officers and Directors: Richard J. Mason, Pres. and
Director; Danna B. Mason, Secy. and Director;
Melvin T. Matsukane, Treas. and Director.
EIN: 330732436

806
The Massie Family Foundation
1801 Tribute Rd.
Sacramento, CA 95815-4301

Established in 1997 in California.
Donors: Clara K. Massie; Debbie Massie; Rick
Massie.
Foundation type: Independent foundation.
Financial data (yr. ended 12/31/13): Assets,
$5,432,854 (M); gifts received, $200,000;
expenditures, $373,529; qualifying distributions,
$285,763; giving activities include $285,763 for 16
grants (high: $87,410; low: $3,000).
Fields of interest: Education; Christianity; Human
services; Family services; Adoption.

Limitations: Applications not accepted. Giving primarily in Sacramento, CA. No grants to individuals.
Application information: Contributes only to pre-selected organizations.
Officers: Rick W. Massie, Pres.; Clara K. Massie, C.F.O. and Secy.
EIN: 911823177

807

The Masson Foundation

c/o Melinda Masson
1200 S. Coast Hwy., Ste. 205A
Laguna Beach, CA   92651-3184

Established in 1997 in California.
Donors: Melinda Masson; Merit Property Management, Inc.; Maurice Masson.
Foundation type: Independent foundation.
Financial data (yr. ended 12/31/13): Assets, $3,460,854 (M); expenditures, $224,631; qualifying distributions, $179,322; giving activities include $173,231 for 16+ grants (high: $62,500).
Fields of interest: Arts and culture; Human services.
Type of support: General support.
Limitations: Applications not accepted. Giving primarily in CA.
Application information: Unsolicited requests for funds not accepted.
Officers: Benjamin Shaffer, Pres.; Pierre Masson, V.P.; Melinda Masson, Secy.; Melena Masson, Treas.
Trustee: Maurice Masson.
EIN: 330758342

808

The Maxfield Foundation

171 Main St., No. 256
Los Altos, CA   94022-2912   (650) 559-1560
Contact: Robert R. Maxfield, Pres. and C.F.O.

Established in 1985 in California.
Donor: Robert R. Maxfield.
Foundation type: Independent foundation.
Financial data (yr. ended 12/31/14): Assets, $5,805,463 (M); expenditures, $316,478; qualifying distributions, $299,677; giving activities include $295,000 for 6 grants (high: $125,000; low: $1,000).
Purpose and activities: Giving primarily to institutions and individuals doing research in fields related to understanding and treating cancer, with special emphasis on leukemia. Occasionally grants are made to other fields. Grants are generally limited to operational research rather than capital funds, with preference given to short-term (3 years or less) projects rather than general research funds.
Fields of interest: Cancers; Leukemia; Science.
Type of support: Annual campaigns; Research and evaluation; Research.
Limitations: Applications accepted. Giving in the U.S., with some emphasis on CA.
Publications: Annual report; Annual report (including application guidelines).
Application information: Application form required.
  Initial approach: Letter
  Deadline(s): None
Officers: Robert R. Maxfield, Pres.; Melinda C. Maxfield, V.P.; Katherine Maxfield, V.P.; Michael P. Groom, Secy.; Valerie Gillen, C.F.O.
EIN: 770099366

809

The Michael and Sally Mayer Family Foundation

880 Culebra Rd.
Hillsborough, CA   94010-6964

Established in 2005 in Unspecified.
Donors: Michael Mayer; Sally Mayer.
Foundation type: Independent foundation.
Financial data (yr. ended 12/31/13): Assets, $4,805,388 (M); expenditures, $298,952; qualifying distributions, $235,059; giving activities include $220,205 for 15 grants (high: $120,500; low: $100).
Fields of interest: Education; Diseases and conditions; Christianity.
Limitations: Applications not accepted. Giving primarily in CA, MA, and MD. No grants to individuals.
Application information: Unsolicited requests for funds not accepted.
Officers: Sally Mayer, Pres.; Rosemary-Mayer Hintz, Secy.; Michael Mayer, Treas.
Directors: Greg Hintz; David Mayer; Olivia Mayer; Stephen Mayer.
EIN: 203874924

810

The Mazda Foundation (USA), Inc.

7755 Irvine Ctr. Dr.
Irvine, CA   92618-2906   (202) 467-5097
Contact: Tamara Mlynasczyk, Prog. Dir.
FAX: (202) 223-6490;
E-mail: MazdaFoundationApplications@gmail.com;
Application address: Grant Applications, Mazda Foundation, 1025 Connecticut Ave. N.W., Ste. 910, Washington, DC 20036; Main URL: http://www.mazdafoundation.org

Established in 1990 in Michigan.
Donors: Mazda Research & Development of North America; Mazda Motor of America; Mazda North American Opers.
Foundation type: Company-sponsored foundation.
Financial data (yr. ended 09/30/13): Assets, $8,190,525 (M); expenditures, $491,841; qualifying distributions, $415,672; giving activities include $387,314 for 18 grants (high: $59,670; low: $10,000).
Purpose and activities: The foundation supports programs designed to promote education and literacy; environmental conservation; cross-cultural understanding; social welfare; and scientific research.
Fields of interest: Cultural awareness; Historic preservation; Education; Reading promotion; Natural resources; Hospital care; Diseases and conditions; Science; Diversity and intergroup relations; Human services; Food banks; Adolescents; Ethnic and racial groups.
Type of support: Individual development; Fellowships; General support; Program development; Curriculum development; Scholarships; Research; Research and evaluation.
Limitations: Applications accepted. Giving to national organizations located in CA, Washington, DC, LA, NH, NC, and TX. No support for political or religious organizations. No grants to individuals, or for fundraising dinners or events, capital campaigns, endowments, or debt reduction.
Publications: Application guidelines; Annual report.
Application information: A full proposal may be requested at a later date. Organizations receiving

support are asked to submit progress reports. Application form required.
  Initial approach: Download application form and mail or fax to foundation
  Copies of proposal: 1
  Deadline(s): Between May 1 and July 1
  Board meeting date(s): Oct.
  Final notification: Early Nov.
Officers and Trustees: James J. O'Sullivan, Chair. and Trustee; Jay Amestoy, Pres. and Trustee; Renee Lewis, Secy.; Robert T. Davis, Treas. and Trustee.
EIN: 382952236

811

McClatchy Company Foundation

(formerly Star Tribune Foundation)
2100 Q St.
Sacramento, CA   95816-6816   (916) 321-1891
Contact: Karole Morgan-Prager, Dir.

Established in 1945 in Minnesota.
Donors: Cowles Media Co.; The Star Tribune Co.; The McClatchy Co.
Foundation type: Company-sponsored foundation.
Financial data (yr. ended 12/31/13): Assets, $7,939,916 (M); expenditures, $379,466; qualifying distributions, $360,945; giving activities include $360,945 for 45 grants (high: $35,000; low: $1,000).
Purpose and activities: The foundation supports hospitals and organizations involved with arts and culture, education, mental health, children's services, the first amendment, and Judaism.
Fields of interest: Arts and culture; Agriculture; Human services.
Type of support: General support; Employee volunteer services; Employee matching gifts; Continuing support; Annual campaigns; Matching grants; Capital campaigns; Endowments; Program development; Convening; Scholarships.
Limitations: Applications accepted. Giving primarily in CA; giving also to national organizations.
Application information: Application form required.
  Initial approach: Contact foundation for application form
  Deadline(s): None
  Board meeting date(s): Quarterly
Officer: Patrick J. Talamantes, Chair.
Directors: Heather L. Fagundes; Anders Gyllenhaal; Elaine Lintecum; Karole Morgan-Prager; Mark Zieman.
Number of staff: 1 full-time professional; 1 part-time support.
EIN: 416031373

812

Neil & Amelia McDaniel Charitable Trust

505 Montgomery St., Ste. 620
San Francisco, CA   94111

Established in 1977 in California.
Donors: Neil McDaniel; Neil McDaniel Administrative Trust.
Foundation type: Independent foundation.
Financial data (yr. ended 12/31/13): Assets, $8,057,676 (M); expenditures, $375,279; qualifying distributions, $337,234; giving activities include $230,000 for 83 grants (high: $20,000; low: $500).
Purpose and activities: Giving primarily for education.

Fields of interest: Arts and culture; Education; Health; Diseases and conditions; Christianity; Human services.
Type of support: General support; Capital campaigns; Scholarships.
Limitations: Applications not accepted. Giving primarily in CA. No grants to individuals.
Application information: Unsolicited requests for funds not accepted.
   Board meeting date(s): Varies
Officers: Joanne Dale, Pres.; Marianne Gagen, V.P; Lisa Parker, Secy.; William Gagen, Jr., Treas.
EIN: 942450149

813
The McDaniel Family Foundation
c/o J. White, C.P.A.
18241 Fieldbury Ln.
Huntington Beach, CA   92648-1053

Established in 2001 in California.
Donors: Thomas R. McDaniel; McDaniel Family Trust.
Foundation type: Independent foundation.
Financial data (yr. ended 12/31/13): Assets, $1,495,196 (M); gifts received, $402,350; expenditures, $150,955; qualifying distributions, $143,158; giving activities include $143,158 for 1 + grant.
Fields of interest: Health; Youth services.
Limitations: Applications not accepted. Giving primarily in CA. No grants to individuals.
Application information: Contributes only to pre-selected organizations.
Officers: Thomas R. McDaniel, Pres.; James A. White, C.F.O.; Carol Barbarow, Secy.
Director: Nancy Newman.
EIN: 912168116

814
McGraw Family Foundation
3 Evening Star Dr.
Rancho Mirage, CA   92270-3463

Established in 1999 in California.
Donors: John M. McGraw; Ann McGraw Morrical; John V. McGraw, Jr.; Joan D. McGraw; The McGraw Co.; Jack McGraw.
Foundation type: Independent foundation.
Financial data (yr. ended 12/31/13): Assets, $709,576 (M); gifts received, $500,000; expenditures, $187,720; qualifying distributions, $183,780; giving activities include $183,780 for 12 grants (high: $39,280; low: $1,000).
Fields of interest: Education; Catholicism; Human services.
Limitations: Applications not accepted. No grants to individuals.
Application information: Unsolicited requests for funds not accepted.
Officers: John V. McGraw, Jr., Pres.; John M. McGraw, V.P.; Ann McGraw Morrical, V.P.; Michael J. McGraw, C.F.O.; Joan D. McGraw, Secy.
EIN: 943348872

815
The McKay Foundation
177 Post St., No. 550
San Francisco, CA   94108-4731
The McKay Foundation's Philanthropy Promise: http://www.ncrp.org/philanthropys-promise/who

Established in 1992 in California.
Donors: Robert L. McKay, Sr.; Elaine McKay.
Foundation type: Independent foundation.
Financial data (yr. ended 12/31/13): Assets, $61,895 (M); gifts received, $565,485; expenditures, $874,779; qualifying distributions, $208,630; giving activities include $208,630 for 6 grants (high: $75,700; low: $10,000).
Purpose and activities: To strengthen our democracy and promote a more just and equitable American culture, the foundation funds activities that build civil society's energy, leadership, and resources, and utilizes these in the political and policy spheres of civil society. Through grants, capacity building assistance, and other support to allied organizations, the foundation partners with diverse communities in working for long term social, political, and economic progress.
Fields of interest: Environment; Public policy; Community and economic development; Human services; Homeless services.
Type of support: General support; Policy, advocacy and systems reform; Fundraising; Leadership and professional development; Technical assistance.
Limitations: Applications not accepted. Giving primarily in CA.
Publications: Grants list; Occasional report.
Application information: Contributes only to pre-selected organizations. The majority of funding goes to a core set of community organizing groups, located mostly in CA.
Officers: Elaine McKay, Secy.; John P. McKay, Treas.; Robert L. McKay, Sr., C.F.O.; Robert McKay, Exec. Dir.
Number of staff: 3 full-time professional; 1 part-time support.
EIN: 363946926

816
The McKenzie Foundation
1160 Battery St., Ste. 118
San Francisco, CA   94111-1215

Established in 2006 in California.
Donors: Joseph M. Wessinger; Ashley Wessinger.
Foundation type: Independent foundation.
Financial data (yr. ended 12/31/13): Assets, $4,361,894 (M); gifts received, $457; expenditures, $518,374; qualifying distributions, $421,338; giving activities include $380,470 for 26 grants (high: $128,850; low: $75).
Fields of interest: Education; Diseases and conditions; Youth services.
Type of support: Research; Individual development.
Limitations: Applications not accepted. Giving primarily in CA. No grants to individuals.
Application information: Contributes only to pre-selected organizations.
Officers: Joseph M. Wessinger, Pres.; Ashley Wessinger, Secy.
EIN: 205634109

817
The Mel and Grace McLean Foundation
1336 Main St.
Fortuna, CA   95540-2128   (707) 725-1722
Contact: Leigh Pierre-Oetker
E-mail: leigh@mcleanfoundation.org; Additional e-mail addresses: denise@mcleanfoundation.org, mclean@mcleanfoundation.org; Main URL: http://mcleanfoundation.org
Facebook: https://www.facebook.com/mcleanfoundation.org

Established in 1998 in California.
Donor: Melvin F. McLean†.
Foundation type: Independent foundation.
Financial data (yr. ended 12/31/13): Assets, $30,894,478 (M); gifts received, $750; expenditures, $692,921; qualifying distributions, $548,330; giving activities include $346,174 for 76 grants (high: $50,000; low: $139).
Purpose and activities: Mission: The foundation honors the memory of Mel and Grace McLean through proactive grantmaking to maintain and improve the quality of life for the people of Humboldt County. Vision: Humboldt County will be a better place to live as a result of the foundation's work. Belief: Quality of life in Humboldt County will be enhanced by funding projects and organizations that benefit children, youth, families, seniors and those in need while having a sustained, vibrant economy that provides opportunities to live and work. Strategy: The foundation will provide funding, leadership and support to actively engage our local communities through partnerships, collaborations and involvement with our nonprofit sector.
Type of support: General support; Matching grants; Continuing support; Leadership and professional development; Capital campaigns; Capital and infrastructure; Equipment; Program development; Seed money; Technical assistance.
Limitations: Applications accepted. Giving limited to Humboldt County, CA. No support for deferred maintenance or annual operating costs of public institutions, churches, special tax districts, or government except for a single, one-time special project. No grants to individuals, or for scholarships, travel expenses or conferences.
Publications: Application guidelines.
Application information:
   Initial approach: Use Preliminary Request Form on foundation web site
   Deadline(s): None
   Board meeting date(s): Monthly
Officers and Directors: Jennifer Budwig, Chair. and Director; Dennis Scott, Pres. and Director; Jon Sapper, Secy. and Director; Tiara Brown; Erin Dunn.
Number of staff: 1 full-time professional; 1 part-time support.
EIN: 680400603

818
Steven and Kelly McLeod Family Foundation
4223 Country Club Dr.
Long Beach, CA   90807-1907

Donor: Steve McLeod.
Foundation type: Independent foundation.
Financial data (yr. ended 12/31/13): Assets, $3,930,244 (M); expenditures, $294,674; qualifying distributions, $267,995; giving activities include $261,000 for 9 grants (high: $85,000; low: $5,000).

Fields of interest: Arts and culture; Museums; Human services.
Type of support: General support.
Limitations: Applications not accepted. Giving primarily in CA. No grants to individuals.
Application information: Unsolicited requests for funds not accepted.
Trustees: Kelly S. McLeod; Steven B. McLeod.
EIN: 266161887

819
McMahon Family Foundation
26 Harbor Island
Newport Beach, CA 92660-7201 9496756984

Established in 2000 in California.
Donor: John A. McMahon.
Foundation type: Independent foundation.
Financial data (yr. ended 01/31/14): Assets, $26,857; gifts received, $120,000; expenditures, $119,250; qualifying distributions, $117,585.
Fields of interest: Education; Religion; Christianity; Human services.
Limitations: Applications not accepted. Giving primarily in CA. No grants to individuals.
Application information: Unsolicited requests for funds not accepted.
Trustees: Joanne McMahon; John McMahon.
EIN: 336275988

820
Margaret L. McQuinn Scholarship Foundation
3263 San Jose Ave.
Alameda, CA 94501-4863 (510) 522-8749
Contact: Linda Larkin, Pres.

Established in 2005 in California.
Foundation type: Independent foundation.
Financial data (yr. ended 12/31/13): Assets, $3,811,965 (M); gifts received, $200,000; expenditures, $199,317; qualifying distributions, $183,000; giving activities include $183,000 for 41 grants (high: $5,000; low: $1,500).
Fields of interest: Education.
Type of support: Scholarships; Student aid.
Limitations: Giving primarily in CA.
Application information:
 Initial approach: Letter
 Deadline(s): None
Officers: Linda Larkin, Pres.; Ron Goldman, V.P.
EIN: 450499860

821
Meister Family Foundation
1369 Beachmont St.
Ventura, CA 93001-4225
Contact: Barbara Meister, Pres.

Donors: Barbara Meister; Larry Meister.
Foundation type: Independent foundation.
Financial data (yr. ended 12/31/13): Assets, $490,016 (M); gifts received, $280,000; expenditures, $257,641; qualifying distributions, $221,013; giving activities include $221,013 for 36 grants (high: $92,090; low: $250).
Purpose and activities: Giving primarily for the arts, health, and Jewish organizations.
Fields of interest: Arts and culture; Theater; Nonprofits; Health; Judaism; Human services.

Type of support: Regranting.
Limitations: Applications accepted. Giving primarily in CA.
Application information: Application form required.
 Initial approach: Letter
 Deadline(s): None
Officers: Barbara Meister, Pres. and Treas.; Auna Simon, Secy.
EIN: 770386251

822
The Louise Merage Family Foundation
660 Newport Center Dr.
Newport Beach, CA 92660-2007

Donors: Louise Merage; Paul Merage; Katherine Merage.
Foundation type: Independent foundation.
Financial data (yr. ended 12/31/13): Assets, $3,910,745 (M); expenditures, $175,678; qualifying distributions, $166,763; giving activities include $160,170 for 11 grants (high: $90,000; low: $1,000).
Fields of interest: Orchestral music; Art museums; Judaism; Youth services.
Type of support: General support.
Limitations: Applications not accepted. Giving primarily in CA, Washington, DC and NY. No grants to individuals.
Application information: Contributes only to pre-selected organizations.
Officers and Directors: Louise Merage, Pres. and Director; Paul Merage, Secy.-Treas. and Director; Gregory Merage; Jeff Merage.
EIN: 020657537

823
Russell A. Meyer Charitable Trust
3121 Arrowhead Dr.
Hollywood, CA 90068-1661

Foundation type: Independent foundation.
Financial data (yr. ended 12/31/14): Assets, $2,601,826 (M); expenditures, $415,620; qualifying distributions, $143,864; giving activities include $143,864 for 2 grants (high: $71,932; low: $71,932).
Fields of interest: Medical education.
Type of support: Research.
Limitations: Applications not accepted. Giving primarily in CA. No grants to individuals.
Application information: Unsolicited requests for funds not accepted.
Trustee: Janice Cowart.
EIN: 900238637

824
The Dorothy Phillips Michaud Charitable Trust
6310 San Vicente Blvd., Ste. 250
Los Angeles, CA 90048-5447

Established in 2008 in California.
Donor: Dorothy P. Michaud Administrative Trust.
Foundation type: Independent foundation.
Financial data (yr. ended 06/30/13): Assets, $4,702,506 (M); expenditures, $274,003; qualifying distributions, $245,035; giving activities include $220,000 for 24 grants (high: $25,000; low: $2,500).

Fields of interest: Education; Health; Hospital care; Diseases and conditions; Human services.
Type of support: Research.
Limitations: Applications not accepted. No grants to individuals.
Application information: Contributes only to pre-selected organizations.
Trustees: Frank Lee; Joel A. Levine.
EIN: 870778040

825
Phil and Amy Mickelson Charitable Trust
21731 Ventura Blvd., Ste. 300
Woodland Hills, CA 91364-1845

Donors: Grafil Inc.; Philip A. Mickelson; Amy McBride Mickelson; Garry Geis; John C. Williams; M. Kost; James V. Gage; Amy Mickelson; Anna Moody; The Thunder Birds; PGA Tour Charities, Inc.; Leo G. Murphy; M. Susan McConnell; Phil Mickelson; Christina Maune; Jeffrey P. Brogan; Tara Golem; Cheryl J. Johnson; PGA Tour Inc.; Amgen USA Inc.
Foundation type: Independent foundation.
Financial data (yr. ended 12/31/13): Assets, $0 (M); gifts received, $100,923; expenditures, $220,157; qualifying distributions, $215,000; giving activities include $215,000 for 5 grants (high: $80,000; low: $7,500).
Fields of interest: Education; Golf; Child welfare.
Limitations: Applications not accepted. Giving primarily in CA. No grants to individuals.
Application information: Unsolicited requests for funds not accepted.
Officers: Gary McBride, Pres.; Amy McBride Mickelson, V.P.; Phillip A. Mickelson, V.P.; Renee McBride, Secy.; Stephen L. Taylor, Treas.
Directors: R. Steve Loy; Mary Santos Mickelson; Phil Mickelson, Sr.
EIN: 203565192

826
Military Women In Need Foundation
(formerly California Soldiers' Widows Home Association)
10767 National Pl., Unit B
Los Angeles, CA 90034 (310) 684-3854
FAX: (866) 425-8096;
E-mail: info@militarywomeninneed.org; Mailing address: c/o Mariana Sosa, Opers. Mgr., 2355 Westwood Blvd., No. 350, Los Angeles, CA 90064; Main URL: http://www.militarywomeninneed.org
Facebook: https://www.facebook.com/MWINCA
Twitter: https://twitter.com/MWIN_CA

Established in 1921 in California.
Foundation type: Independent foundation.
Financial data (yr. ended 06/30/13): Assets, $1,701,554 (M); expenditures, $461,142; qualifying distributions, $360,607; giving activities include $319,000 for 1 grant.
Purpose and activities: Giving to provide emergency subsidies, housing subsidies, advocacy and referral services, and home visits to female veterans and widows of veterans, who have an annual income of less than $24,000 per year, assets of $20,000 or less (not including 1 automobile), who are able to live independently, and who are living alone.
Fields of interest: Human services; Rent and mortgage assistance; Seniors; Females; Veterans.
Type of support: Emergency funds.

Limitations: Applications not accepted. Giving limited to southern CA.
Application information: Unsolicited requests for funds not accepted.
   Board meeting date(s): Quarterly
Officers: Meredith Brenalvirez, Pres.; Ranlyn Tilley Hill, Exec. Dir.
Number of staff: 1 full-time professional; 1 part-time professional.
EIN: 953533990

827
The Mill Foundation
250 Ebbtide Ave.
Sausalito, CA   94965-1309   (415) 729-9404

Foundation type: Independent foundation.
Financial data (yr. ended 03/31/14): Assets, $50,000 (M); gifts received, $497,064; expenditures, $144,864; qualifying distributions, $139,537; giving activities include $136,766 for 8 grants (high: $50,000; low: $300).
Fields of interest: Arts and culture; Education.
Limitations: Applications not accepted. Giving primarily in NM.
Application information: Unsolicited requests for funds not accepted.
Trustee: Mary Mill.
EIN: 262485950

828
The Barbara and Fred Miller Family Foundation
10580 Wilshire Blvd., Ste. 25N.W.
Los Angeles, CA   90024-4500

Established in 2001 in California.
Donors: Barbara Miller; Fred Miller.
Foundation type: Independent foundation.
Financial data (yr. ended 12/31/13): Assets, $443,076 (M); gifts received, $300,000; expenditures, $140,205; qualifying distributions, $140,120; giving activities include $140,120 for 20 grants (high: $57,000; low: $50).
Fields of interest: Higher education; Nonprofits; Diseases and conditions; Cystic fibrosis; Cancers; Judaism.
Type of support: Research; Regranting.
Limitations: Applications not accepted. Giving primarily in CA and also some giving in NY. No grants to individuals.
Application information: Contributes only to pre-selected organizations.
Officers: Barbara Miller, C.E.O. and Secy.-Treas.; Fred Miller, Pres.
EIN: 954846488

829
J. & T. Miller Family Foundation
c/o Miller Mayer Sullivan & Stev
215 Carnation Ave.
Corona Del Mar, CA   92625-2806

Established in 2007 in California.
Donors: John Miller; Tammy Miller.
Foundation type: Independent foundation.
Financial data (yr. ended 06/30/14): Assets, $2,513,947; expenditures, $160,246; qualifying distributions, $112,535.
Fields of interest: Christianity.

Limitations: Applications not accepted. Giving primarily in CA.
Application information: Unsolicited requests for funds not accepted.
Officers: John Miller, C.E.O. and C.F.O.; Tammy Miller, Secy.
EIN: 205780175

830
The Miller Family Foundation
11100 Santa Monica Blvd., No. 600
Los Angeles, CA   90025-3392

Established in 2004 in California.
Donors: Jeffrey Miller; Karen Miller.
Foundation type: Independent foundation.
Financial data (yr. ended 12/31/12): Assets, $5,483,008 (M); expenditures, $213,359; qualifying distributions, $165,800; giving activities include $165,800 for grants.
Fields of interest: Science museums; Elementary and secondary education; Higher education; Wildlife biodiversity.
Limitations: Applications not accepted. Giving primarily in CA and MT.
Application information: Contributes only to pre-selected organizations.
Officers: Jeffrey Miller, Pres.; Karen Miller, Secy.-Treas.
EIN: 201979637

831
Arjay R. & Frances F. Miller Foundation
225 Mountain Home Rd.
Woodside, CA   94062-2511

Established in 1955 in Michigan.
Donors: Arjay Miller; Frances Miller.
Foundation type: Independent foundation.
Financial data (yr. ended 12/31/13): Assets, $7,799,102 (M); expenditures, $227,495; qualifying distributions, $185,371; giving activities include $154,900 for 18 grants (high: $25,000; low: $100).
Fields of interest: Education; Religion; Human rights.
Limitations: Applications not accepted.
Application information: Contributes only to pre-selected organizations.
Officers: Kenneth F. Miller, Pres. and Secy.; Sarah O. Kingsbury, V.P. and Treas.; Arjay R. Miller, V.P.; Ann M. Olstad, V.P.
EIN: 386082895

832
The Carole and Mike Miller Foundation
10380 Wilshire Blvd., Ste. 2002
Los Angeles, CA   90024-4761

Established in 2001 in California.
Donors: Michael E. Miller; Carole R. Miller.
Foundation type: Independent foundation.
Financial data (yr. ended 12/31/13): Assets, $756,719 (M); expenditures, $198,736; qualifying distributions, $194,300; giving activities include $194,300 for 22 grants (high: $50,000; low: $375).
Fields of interest: Theater; Nonprofits; In-patient medical care; Cancers; Judaism.
Type of support: Regranting.

Limitations: Applications not accepted. Giving primarily in CA. No grants to individuals.
Application information: Contributes only to pre-selected organizations.
Officers and Directors: Michael E. Miller, Pres.; Carole R. Miller, Secy.-Treas. and C.F.O.; Randy Gold; David E. Miller; Gayle T. Miller.
EIN: 912166204

833
G. Willard Miller Foundation
4300 Long Beach Blvd., Ste. 350
Long Beach, CA   90807-2017

Established in 1998 in California.
Donor: G. Willard Miller.
Foundation type: Independent foundation.
Financial data (yr. ended 12/31/13): Assets, $5,591,333 (M); expenditures, $291,610; qualifying distributions, $289,455; giving activities include $287,300 for 34 grants (high: $80,000; low: $500).
Fields of interest: Education; University education; Animal training; Multiple sclerosis; Cancers; Human services; People with physical disabilities.
Limitations: Applications not accepted. Giving primarily in CA. No grants to individuals.
Application information: Contributes only to pre-selected organizations.
Officers: Stephen R. Miller, Chair.; Stephen R. Miller, Jr., C.F.O.; Courtney Dettlinger, Secy.
Directors: Nancy S. Miller; Sandra Rowe.
EIN: 943315964

834
The David W. Mills Foundation
1205 Pacific Ave., Ste. 203
Santa Cruz, CA   95060-3936

Donor: David W. Mills.
Foundation type: Independent foundation.
Financial data (yr. ended 12/31/13): Assets, $1,400,230 (M); expenditures, $630,566; qualifying distributions, $250,000; giving activities include $250,000 for 2 grants (high: $200,000; low: $50,000).
Fields of interest: Arts and culture; Philanthropy; Human rights.
Limitations: Applications not accepted.
Application information: Unsolicited requests for funds not accepted.
Trustee: David W. Mills.
EIN: 352408752

835
The Millstreet Foundation, Inc.
1100 Alma St., Ste. 210
Menlo Park, CA   94025-3344

Established in 2004 in California.
Donor: Paul Hegarty.
Foundation type: Independent foundation.
Financial data (yr. ended 12/31/14): Assets, $3,787,955; gifts received, $12,090; expenditures, $212,853; qualifying distributions, $174,400.
Purpose and activities: Giving primarily for education.
Fields of interest: Education; Elementary education; Higher education; Foundations.

Limitations: Applications not accepted. Giving primarily in CA. No grants to individuals.
Application information: Unsolicited requests for funds not accepted.
Officers: Paul Hegarty, C.E.O.; William L. McClure, Secy.
EIN: 201826618

836
Neil And Anna Mintz Foundation
P. O. Box 236073
Encinitas, CA 92023-6073

Donors: Neil Mintz; Anna Mintz.
Foundation type: Independent foundation.
Financial data (yr. ended 12/31/12): Assets, $1 (M); expenditures, $303,221; qualifying distributions, $276,250; giving activities include $276,250 for grants.
Fields of interest: Spirituality.
Limitations: Applications not accepted. Giving primarily in CA.
Application information: Unsolicited requests for funds not accepted.
Directors: Anna Mintz; Neil Mintz.
EIN: 274315469

837
Yvonne H. Mitchell Charitable Trust
14004 Mercado Dr.
Del Mar, CA 92014-2950
Contact: Earl N. Feldman, Tr.

Donor: Yvonnett Mitchell‡.
Foundation type: Independent foundation.
Financial data (yr. ended 12/31/13): Assets, $105,243 (M); expenditures, $251,932; qualifying distributions, $220,588; giving activities include $194,700 for 45 grants (high: $30,100; low: $500).
Fields of interest: Arts and culture; Diseases and conditions; Human services.
Limitations: Applications accepted. Giving primarily in CA.
Application information:
Initial approach: Proposal
Deadline(s): None
Trustee: Earl N. Feldman.
EIN: 776228895

838
Edward D. and Anna Mitchell Family Foundation
13801 Ventura Blvd.
Sherman Oaks, CA 91423-3603

Donors: Anna Mitchell‡; Edward D. Mitchell‡.
Foundation type: Independent foundation.
Financial data (yr. ended 12/31/13): Assets, $13,048,391 (M); expenditures, $504,275; qualifying distributions, $306,289; giving activities include $119,205 for 18 grants (high: $23,500; low: $250).
Purpose and activities: Giving primarily for Jewish welfare funds, higher education, and social services.
Fields of interest: Higher education; Nonprofits; Hospital care; Human services.
Type of support: Regranting.
Limitations: Applications not accepted. Giving primarily in CA, with emphasis on Los Angeles; some

funding also in Washington, DC. No grants to individuals.
Application information: Contributes only to pre-selected organizations.
Officers: Jonathan E. Mitchell, Pres.; Jason H. Mitchell, Secy.-Treas.
Number of staff: 1 part-time professional.
EIN: 954715236

839
Mitchell, Silberberg & Knupp Foundation
11377 W. Olympic Blvd., No. 200
Los Angeles, CA 90064-1625   (310) 312-3100

Established in 1979 in California.
Donors: Thomas P. Lambert; Allan Cutrow; Russell Frackman; William L. Cole; Adam Levin; James Guerra; Andrew Katz; Robert Rotstein; Frida Glucoft; Paul Licalsi; Jeffrey Richardson; Hayward Kaiser; Evan Kent; David Newman.
Foundation type: Independent foundation.
Financial data (yr. ended 09/30/14): Assets, $190,450; gifts received, $237,236; expenditures, $176,670; qualifying distributions, $176,610.
Fields of interest: Higher education; Nonprofits; Diseases and conditions; Legal services; Judaism; Human services.
Type of support: General support; Regranting.
Limitations: Applications accepted. Giving primarily in CA. No grants to individuals.
Application information:
Initial approach: Proposal
Deadline(s): None
Trustees: William L. Cole; Kevin E. Gaut; Thomas P. Lambert.
EIN: 953426615

840
The Modglin Family Foundation
3100 Airway Ave., Ste. 124
Costa Mesa, CA 92626-4604

Established in 1987 in California.
Donors: Donald L. Modglin; Judy Eastman; Grace Baptist Church; THC Business Services; Manzanita Baptist Church; Grace Modglin; Pat Cottrell; Calvary Baptist Church; Dennis Davies.
Foundation type: Independent foundation.
Financial data (yr. ended 12/31/14): Assets, $4,170,250; gifts received, $10,690; expenditures, $469,863; qualifying distributions, $436,179.
Fields of interest: Christianity; Human services.
International interests: South Africa; Thailand.
Type of support: Program development; Pro bono consulting services; Convening; Matching grants; Scholarships.
Limitations: Applications not accepted. Giving primarily in the U.S.; some giving in South Africa and Thailand.
Application information: Unsolicited requests for funds not accepted.
Officers: Donald L. Modglin, Pres.; Sharon Marino, V.P.; Steven Modglin, V.P.; Grace M. Modglin, Secy.
Number of staff: 2 full-time professional; 1 part-time professional.
EIN: 330266405

841
The Moley Family Foundation
P.O. Box 4316
Carmel, CA 93921-4316

Established in 1999 in California.
Donors: Elizabeth Moley; Richard Moley.
Foundation type: Independent foundation.
Financial data (yr. ended 10/31/13): Assets, $630,392 (M); gifts received, $489,657; expenditures, $379,658; qualifying distributions, $363,500; giving activities include $357,500 for 3 grants (high: $300,000; low: $2,500).
Purpose and activities: Giving primarily for education and to Christian organizations.
Fields of interest: Education; Nonprofits.
International interests: Israel.
Type of support: Regranting.
Limitations: Applications not accepted. Giving primarily in the U.S., funding also in Jerusalem, Israel. No grants to individuals.
Application information: Contributes only to pre-selected organizations.
Officers: Elizabeth Moley, Pres.; Richard Moley, V.P. and Treas.
EIN: 770528059

842
Louise Mollath Charitable Trust 3
P.O. Box 910
Lompoc, CA 93436-0910

Established in 2006 in California.
Donor: Louise Mollath‡.
Foundation type: Independent foundation.
Financial data (yr. ended 05/31/14): Assets, $2,302,098 (M); expenditures, $161,748; qualifying distributions, $138,000; giving activities include $138,000 for 4 grants (high: $46,000; low: $23,000).
Fields of interest: Arts and culture; Orchestral music; Education; Domesticated animals; Search and rescue; Religion.
Type of support: Public engagement and education.
Limitations: Applications not accepted. Giving primarily in CA.
Application information: Unsolicited requests for funds not accepted.
Trustee: Ronald W. Sabo, Esq.
EIN: 776147618

843
The Isabel and Michael Mondavi Foundation
P.O. Box 2350
Napa, CA 94558-0235   7072249418

Donors: Isabel Mondavi; Michael Mondavi.
Foundation type: Independent foundation.
Financial data (yr. ended 12/31/14): Assets, $3,597,890; expenditures, $269,612; qualifying distributions, $241,833.
Fields of interest: Foundations; Human services; Child welfare.
Limitations: Applications accepted. Giving primarily in CA. No grants to individuals.
Application information: Application form required.
Initial approach: Letter
Deadline(s): None

Officers: Michael Mondavi, Chair.; Isabel Mondavi, Secy.
EIN: 202002457

844

Money-Arenz Foundation, Inc.
3525 Del Mar Heights Rd.
San Diego, CA 92130-2199

Established in 1993 in Georgia.
Donors: John Marshall Money; Betty Arenz.
Foundation type: Independent foundation.
Financial data (yr. ended 12/31/13): Assets, $898,298 (M); gifts received, $185,000; expenditures, $254,290; qualifying distributions, $245,100; giving activities include $245,100 for 71 grants (high: $16,000; low: $300).
Fields of interest: Education; Plant biodiversity; Environmental education; Human services; Child welfare.
Limitations: Applications not accepted. Giving primarily in CA. No grants to individuals.
Application information: Contributes only to pre-selected organizations.
Officers: John Marshall Arenz, Pres.; Robert F. Arenz, Jr., V.P.; Betty Money Arenz, Secy.; Julie Arenz Tifft, C.F.O. and Treas.
EIN: 582049998

845

Silva Watson Moonwalk Fund
c/o Vivian L. Schneider
62 Rose Ln.
Larkspur, CA 94939

Established in 1997 in California.
Donor: Douglas Watson 1995 Trust.
Foundation type: Independent foundation.
Financial data (yr. ended 09/30/14): Assets, $2,801,945 (M); expenditures, $551,298; qualifying distributions, $480,221; giving activities include $410,500 for 52 grants (high: $44,000; low: $1,000).
Fields of interest: HIV/AIDS; Human services; Women's services; LGBTQ people; People with HIV/AIDS.
Limitations: Applications not accepted. Giving primarily in CA, with emphasis on Los Angeles and San Francisco. No grants to individuals.
Application information: Contributes only to pre-selected organizations.
Officer: Vivian L. Schneider, Pres.
EIN: 943286835

846

The James and Rebecca Morgan Charitable Foundation
P.O. Box 1742
Los Altos, CA 94023-1742

Established in 2004 in California.
Donors: Rebecca Q. Morgan; James C. Morgan.
Foundation type: Independent foundation.
Financial data (yr. ended 05/31/14): Assets, $3,079,667 (M); expenditures, $180,891; qualifying distributions, $180,800; giving activities include $180,800 for 13 grants (high: $50,000; low: $500).
Fields of interest: Theater; Education; Environment; Foundations; Diseases and conditions.

Type of support: Scholarships; Research.
Limitations: Applications not accepted. Giving primarily in CA and NY. No grants to individuals.
Application information: Unsolicited requests for funds not accepted.
Officers: James Morgan, Chair. and C.F.O.; Rebecca Morgan, C.E.O. and Pres.; Linda Verhulp, Secy.
EIN: 202029688

847

Morgan Family Foundation, Inc.
6130 Stoneridge Mall Rd., Ste. 185
Pleasanton, CA 94588-3290

Established in 2000 in California.
Donors: Kile Morgan, Jr.; Judy L. Morgan.
Foundation type: Independent foundation.
Financial data (yr. ended 12/31/13): Assets, $3,910 (M); gifts received, $115,050; expenditures, $235,155; qualifying distributions, $233,095; giving activities include $89,900 for 26 grants (high: $25,000; low: $250); and $141,300 for 66 grants to individuals (high: $12,855; low: $300).
Purpose and activities: Giving primarily for higher education, and children and social services.
Fields of interest: Higher education; Human services; Child welfare; Youth services.
Type of support: General support; Scholarships; Student aid.
Limitations: Applications not accepted. Giving primarily in CA, with emphasis on National City; some funding also in Boulder, CO.
Application information: Unsolicited requests for funds not accepted.
Officers: Linda F. Morasch, C.E.O. and Secy.; Kile Morgan, Jr., Pres.; Judy L. Morgan, V.P.
EIN: 912081052

848

Morris Morgenstern Foundation
c/o Paul Goodnough, C.P.A.
543 Country Club Dr., Ste. B-116
Simi Valley, CA 93065

Established in 1949 in New York.
Donors: Morris Morgenstern†; Frank N. Morgenstern.
Foundation type: Independent foundation.
Financial data (yr. ended 12/31/13): Assets, $11,169,472 (M); expenditures, $135,308; qualifying distributions, $119,453; giving activities include $119,453 for 58 grants (high: $10,150; low: $50).
Purpose and activities: Support for Jewish organizations, including welfare funds, synagogues and other religious institutions, and yeshivas; funding also for hospitals and medical research.
Fields of interest: Education; Nonprofits; Hospital care; Diseases and conditions; Judaism; Human services.
Type of support: General support; Research; Research and evaluation; Regranting.
Limitations: Applications not accepted. Giving primarily in FL and the metropolitan New York, NY, area. No grants to individuals.
Application information: Contributes only to pre-selected organizations.
Trustee: Richard Morgenstern.
EIN: 131635719

849

Moskowitz Family Foundation
2444 Wilshire Blvd., Ste. 410
Santa Monica, CA 90403-5811

Donors: Jeffrey Moskowitz; Madeleine Moskowitz.
Foundation type: Independent foundation.
Financial data (yr. ended 11/30/14): Assets, $1,455,419 (M); gifts received, $1,401,415; expenditures, $174,972; qualifying distributions, $173,000; giving activities include $173,000 for 9 grants (high: $60,000; low: $1,000).
Fields of interest: Education; Health; Housing development.
Limitations: Applications not accepted. Giving primarily in CA.
Application information: Unsolicited requests for funds not accepted.
Officers: Jeffrey Moskowitz, Pres.; Madeleine Moskowitz, Secy. and C.F.O.
EIN: 465160772

850

John and Linda Muckel Foundation
6024 Ocean Terr. Dr.
Rancho Palos Verdes, CA 90275-5755

Established in 1999 in California.
Donors: Indiana Plumbing Supply Co., Inc.; John Muckel; Linda Muckel.
Foundation type: Company-sponsored foundation.
Financial data (yr. ended 12/31/13): Assets, $83,218 (M); gifts received, $46,391; expenditures, $155,348; qualifying distributions, $155,114; giving activities include $155,114 for 41 grants (high: $60,200; low: $134).
Purpose and activities: The foundation supports organizations involved with historical activities, higher education, animal welfare, human services, and Christianity.
Fields of interest: Historical activities; Higher education; Animal welfare; Christianity; Human services; Homeless services.
Type of support: General support.
Limitations: Applications not accepted. Giving primarily in CA, Washington, DC, and VA. No grants to individuals.
Application information: Contributes only to pre-selected organizations.
Officers: John Muckel, Pres.; Linda Muckel, Secy. and C.F.O.
EIN: 330882395

851

Dennis and Pamela Mudd Charitable Foundation
c/o Kuhn & Koviak CPA's, Inc.
7676 Hazard Center Dr., Ste. 700
San Diego, CA 92108-4510
Contact: Pamela Mudd, V.P.

Established in 2004 in California.
Donors: Pamela Mudd; Dennis Mudd; Mudd Charitable Remainder Uni-Trust.
Foundation type: Independent foundation.
Financial data (yr. ended 12/31/13): Assets, $3,687,095 (M); expenditures, $270,492; qualifying distributions, $263,765; giving activities include $259,651 for 8 grants (high: $254,750; low: $100).

Fields of interest: Education; Agriculture; Human services; Food aid.
Limitations: Applications accepted. Giving primarily in CA, with some giving in MD. No grants to individuals.
Application information:
  Initial approach: Letter
  Deadline(s): None
Officers: Dennis Mudd, Pres.; Pamela Mudd, V.P.
EIN: 870721248

852
The Munson Family Foundation
5753G Santa Ana Canyon Rd., Ste. 199
Anaheim, CA 92807-3229

Established in 1989 in California.
Donors: Ward Munson†; Alice Munson†.
Foundation type: Independent foundation.
Financial data (yr. ended 12/31/12): Assets, $1,821,967 (M); expenditures, $205,770; qualifying distributions, $185,000; giving activities include $185,000 for grants.
Purpose and activities: Emphasis on health care, higher education, and Christian organizations.
Fields of interest: Higher education; Hospital care; Mental health care; Christianity; Human services.
Type of support: General support.
Limitations: Applications not accepted. Giving on a national basis, primarily on the West Coast. No grants to individuals.
Publications: Annual report; Grants list.
Application information: Contributes only to pre-selected organizations.
  Board meeting date(s): July 10 and as needed
Officers: Kenneth R. Munson, C.E.O. and Pres.; Candace Leasure, Secy. and C.F.O.
Directors: Colleen Monson Kelly; Rosemary Tracy.
Number of staff: None.
EIN: 330375101

853
Jack Munushian Charitable Trust
800 Wilshire Blvd., Ste. 1500
Los Angeles, CA 90017-2619

Established in 2006 in California.
Donor: Jack Munushian Revocable Trust of 1997.
Foundation type: Independent foundation.
Financial data (yr. ended 12/31/13): Assets, $7,592,846 (M); expenditures, $397,978; qualifying distributions, $293,619; giving activities include $285,000 for 2 grants (high: $150,000; low: $135,000).
Purpose and activities: Giving for the promotion of Armenian identity.
Fields of interest: Education.
Limitations: Applications not accepted. Giving primarily in CA and NY. No grants to individuals.
Application information: Contributes only to pre-selected organizations.
Trustees: Zouhrab Bassmajian; George R. Phillips, Sr.
EIN: 206601987

854
Murad Family Foundation
2121 Rosecrans Ave.,5th Fl.
El Segundo, CA 90245-4744

Donors: Murad Family; Murad Inc.
Foundation type: Independent foundation.
Financial data (yr. ended 12/31/13): Assets, $0 (M); gifts received, $257,000; expenditures, $341,112; qualifying distributions, $338,800; giving activities include $338,800 for 28 grants (high: $90,000; low: $200).
Fields of interest: Education; Nonprofits; Community and economic development; Human services.
Type of support: Regranting.
Limitations: Applications not accepted. Giving primarily in CA.
Application information: Unsolicited requests for funds not accepted.
Officers: Hilarie Murad, Pres. and C.E.O.; Richard Murad, C.F.O.; Jeff Murad, Secy.
EIN: 451585141

855
Muskin Family Foundation
16530 Ventura Blvd., Ste. 305
Encino, CA 91436-4594

Foundation type: Independent foundation.
Financial data (yr. ended 06/30/13): Assets, $2,872,034 (M); expenditures, $238,600; qualifying distributions, $186,500; giving activities include $186,500 for 27 grants (high: $30,000; low: $1,000).
Fields of interest: Education; Human services.
Limitations: Applications not accepted. Giving primarily in Los Angeles, CA.
Application information: Unsolicited requests for funds not accepted.
Officers and Directors: John E. Saunders, Pres., V.P. and Secy. and Director; Richard Corleto.
EIN: 261139075

856
Nachtsheim Family Foundation
420 Walsh Rd.
Atherton, CA 94027-6439

Established in 2002 in California.
Donors: Stephen Nachtsheim; Jami Nachtsheim.
Foundation type: Independent foundation.
Financial data (yr. ended 11/30/13): Assets, $734,285 (M); gifts received, $296,267; expenditures, $366,827; qualifying distributions, $353,000; giving activities include $353,000 for 9 grants (high: $255,000; low: $250).
Fields of interest: Arts and culture; Museums; Education; Youth development.
Limitations: Applications not accepted. Giving primarily in CA.
Application information: Unsolicited requests for funds not accepted.
Officers: Jami Nachtsheim, Pres.; Stephen Nachtsheim, C.F.O.
EIN: 550544553

857
Edward M. Nagel Foundation
c/o Melvyn Mark
201 Mission St., No. 2270
San Francisco, CA 94105-1831

Established in 1992 in California.
Donors: Edward M. Nagel; Edward M. Nagel Trust.

Foundation type: Independent foundation.
Financial data (yr. ended 09/30/14): Assets, $2,596,493 (M); expenditures, $395,411; qualifying distributions, $350,000; giving activities include $350,000 for 10 grants (high: $35,000; low: $35,000).
Fields of interest: Education; Higher education.
Type of support: Scholarships; Individual development.
Limitations: Applications not accepted. Giving primarily in CA, with emphasis on San Francisco. No grants to individuals.
Application information: Contributes only to pre-selected organizations.
Directors: Frank Brucia; Michael Dotson; Melvyn I. Mark; Daniel Sober.
EIN: 943171093

858
Nasaw Family Foundation
700 Larkspur Landing Cir., Ste. 200
Larkspur, CA 94939-1741

Established in 2005 in California.
Donors: Carla J. Roth; David G. Nasaw.
Foundation type: Independent foundation.
Financial data (yr. ended 12/31/13): Assets, $100,078 (M); gifts received, $200,000; expenditures, $159,572; qualifying distributions, $158,101; giving activities include $156,600 for 42 grants (high: $25,000; low: $75).
Fields of interest: Education; Higher education; Natural resources; Foundations; Hospital care; Diseases and conditions; National defense; Human services.
Limitations: Applications not accepted. Giving primarily in CA, IL and MO. No grants to individuals.
Application information: Unsolicited requests for funds not accepted.
Trustees: David G. Nasaw; James David Nasaw; Carla J. Roth.
EIN: 206681645

859
The Nell Newman Foundation Inc.
P.O. Box 3263
Santa Cruz, CA 95063-3263
Main URL: http://nellnewmanfoundation.org
Grants List: http://nellnewmanfoundation.org/recipients

Foundation type: Independent foundation.
Financial data (yr. ended 12/31/14): Assets, $88,688; gifts received, $307,000; expenditures, $262,025; qualifying distributions, $261,525.
Fields of interest: Environment; Agriculture; Human services.
Limitations: Applications not accepted.
Application information: Unsolicited requests for funds not accepted.
Officers: Nell Newman, Pres.; Bob Scowcroft, Secy.; James Cox, Treas.
EIN: 271972605

860
C. and M. Nelson Family Foundation
1804 Garnet Ave., Ste. 420
San Diego, CA 92109-3352

Established in 2004 in California.

Donors: Margaret A. Nelson; Stephen D. Nelson; Terri J. Nelson; Margaret A. Nelson Charitable Lead Trust.
Foundation type: Independent foundation.
Financial data (yr. ended 12/31/13): Assets, $3,224,470 (M); gifts received, $519,557; expenditures, $347,499; qualifying distributions, $335,500; giving activities include $335,500 for 10 grants (high: $250,000; low: $2,000).
Purpose and activities: Giving primarily to an elementary school, as well as for human services and Protestant churches.
Fields of interest: Education; Elementary education; Protestantism; Human services.
Limitations: Applications not accepted. Giving primarily in CA and MT. No grants to individuals.
Application information: Contributes only to pre-selected organizations.
Directors: Stephen D. Nelson; Terri J. Nelson.
EIN: 731694029

861
Vivien A. Nelson Foundation
P.O. Box 180734
Coronado, CA 92178-0734 (619) 435-9056
Contact: Robert T. Plumb, Tr.

Foundation type: Operating foundation.
Financial data (yr. ended 06/30/13): Assets, $6,687,313 (M); expenditures, $436,960; qualifying distributions, $328,875; giving activities include $291,850 for 12 grants (high: $84,000; low: $1,000).
Fields of interest: Education; Protestantism; Human services.
Limitations: Applications accepted. Giving primarily in Coronado and San Diego, CA.
Application information: Application form required.
  Initial approach: Letter
  Deadline(s): None
Trustee: Robert T. Plumb.
EIN: 806173862

862
The Neu Foundation of California Inc.
250 N. Canon Dr., 3rd Fl.
Beverly Hills, CA 90210-5322

Established in 1994 in California.
Donor: Neu Holdings Corp.
Foundation type: Independent foundation.
Financial data (yr. ended 12/31/12): Assets, $3,048,647 (M); expenditures, $181,185; qualifying distributions, $160,650; giving activities include $160,650 for grants.
Purpose and activities: Giving primarily for Jewish agencies and human services.
Fields of interest: Arts and culture; Education; Nonprofits; Diseases and conditions; Judaism; Human services.
Type of support: Regranting.
Limitations: Applications not accepted. Giving primarily in CA. No grants to individuals.
Application information: Contributes only to pre-selected organizations.
Officers: Richard W. Neu, Pres.; Amy P. Neu, V.P.; Steven W. Neu, Secy.-Treas.
EIN: 954446793

863
The New Jerusalem Foundation
4691 Rancho Laguna
San Diego, CA 92130-5220

Established in 2007 in California.
Donors: Zhi-Qiang Jacob Zhou; Nan Zou.
Foundation type: Independent foundation.
Financial data (yr. ended 12/31/13): Assets, $8,640,406 (M); expenditures, $405,874; qualifying distributions, $340,000; giving activities include $340,000 for 1 grant.
Purpose and activities: Giving for Christian missionary work in China.
Fields of interest: Undergraduate education; Christianity.
International interests: China.
Limitations: Applications not accepted. Giving primarily in CA.
Application information: Contributes only to pre-selected organizations.
Officer and Trustees: Nan Zou, Pres. and Trustee; Jordan Wilson; Zhi Qiang Jacob Zhou.
EIN: 207370119

864
New Opportunities Foundation, Inc.
200 N. Maryland Ave., No. 201
Glendale, CA 91206-4274

Established in 2002 in California.
Donors: Andrew T. Skipper; Laurie Skipper.
Foundation type: Independent foundation.
Financial data (yr. ended 12/31/14): Assets, $3,043,797 (M); expenditures, $208,159; qualifying distributions, $177,500; giving activities include $177,500 for 5 grants (high: $103,000; low: $4,500).
Fields of interest: Education; Community and economic development; Housing development; Youth development.
Type of support: Advocacy.
Limitations: Applications not accepted. No grants to individuals.
Application information: Contributes only to pre-selected organizations.
Officers: Andrew T. Skipper, Pres.; Laurie Skipper, Secy.-Treas.
Directors: Katherine Skipper; Peter Skipper.
EIN: 820577111

865
New Priorities Foundation
127 University Ave.
Berkeley, CA 94710-1616

Established in 1996 in Washington.
Donor: Nancy G. Schaub.
Foundation type: Independent foundation.
Financial data (yr. ended 12/31/13): Assets, $3,937,725 (M); gifts received, $1,014,556; expenditures, $387,408; qualifying distributions, $963,484; giving activities include $301,648 for 13 grants (high: $38,548; low: $1,500), and $600,000 for 2 loans/program-related investments.
Purpose and activities: The foundation is committed to supporting citizen-initiated efforts to create a more vibrant, diverse and beautiful environment through hands-on experience, democracy-building, and preservation of natural areas.

Fields of interest: Environmental justice; Natural resources; Environmental studies.
Type of support: General support; Equal access; Continuing support; Land acquisitions; Program development; Curriculum development.
Limitations: Applications not accepted. Giving primarily in CA. No support for religious activities or institutes. No grants to individuals.
Application information: Unsolicited requests for funds not accepted.
Officers and Directors: Nancy G. Schaub, Pres. and Director; Anne Schaub Watson, Secy. and Director; Harald Leventhal, C.F.O.; David Schaub, Treas. and Director; Tim Schaub.
Number of staff: 1 full-time professional.
EIN: 911805939

866
The Nicholson Family Foundation
335 Spreckels Dr., Ste. G
Aptos, CA 95003-3952 (831) 662-2550
Contact: Bruce Nicholson, Pres.; Kelsey Nicholson, Exec. Dir.
FAX: (831) 662-1955; E-mail for Kelsey Nicholson: kelsey@tnff.org

Established in 1996 in California.
Donors: Bruce Nicholson; W. John Nicholson; Kathleen Nicholson Hull; Martha Nicholson McAllister; W.J. Nicholson†.
Foundation type: Independent foundation.
Financial data (yr. ended 05/31/13): Assets, $5,457,792 (M); expenditures, $281,299; qualifying distributions, $230,815; giving activities include $210,150 for 45 grants (high: $60,000; low: $500).
Purpose and activities: Giving for the arts, health care, education, and human services focusing on youth.
Fields of interest: Arts and culture; Education services; Human services; Child welfare; Children and youth; Infants and toddlers; Children; Adolescents; Low-income and poor people.
Type of support: General support; Matching grants; Program development; Seed money.
Limitations: Applications accepted. Giving limited to the southern San Francisco Bay and the northern Monterey Bay, CA areas.
Application information: Preliminary inquiries only; application guidelines provided after approval of preliminary inquiry.
  Initial approach: Letter
  Copies of proposal: 1
  Deadline(s): Feb. 28 and Aug. 31
  Board meeting date(s): Apr. and Oct.
Officers and Directors: Bruce Nicholson, Pres. and Director; Martha Nicholson McAllister, V.P. and Secy. and Director; Kathleen Nicholson Hull; W. John Nicholson.
EIN: 770444787

867
Nickoll Family Foundation, Inc.
10800 Wilshire Blvd., No. 1503
Los Angeles, CA 90024-4220

Established in 1997 in California.
Donor: John F. Nickoll.
Foundation type: Independent foundation.
Financial data (yr. ended 12/31/13): Assets, $2,297,526 (M); gifts received, $1,525,650;

expenditures, $232,468; qualifying distributions, $229,200; giving activities include $229,200 for 22 grants (high: $103,700; low: $1,000).
Fields of interest: Education; Health; Human rights.
Type of support: Annual campaigns.
Limitations: Applications not accepted. Giving primarily in CA and RI. No grants to individuals.
Application information: Unsolicited requests for funds not accepted.
  Board meeting date(s): Dec.
Officers: John F. Nickoll, Pres.; Patricia Nickoll, V.P.; David Ari Nickoll, Secy. and C.F.O.
EIN: 954630520

868
The Nima Taghavi Foundation
(formerly The Taghavi and Ghazi Foundation)
111 Theory, Ste. 250
Irvine, CA 92617

Donor: Nima Taghavi.
Foundation type: Independent foundation.
Financial data (yr. ended 11/30/13): Assets, $230,790 (M); expenditures, $220,683; qualifying distributions, $220,683; giving activities include $217,500 for 3 grants (high: $200,000; low: $7,500).
Fields of interest: Health; Human services.
Limitations: Applications not accepted.
Application information: Unsolicited requests for funds not accepted.
Officers: Nima Taghavi, Pres.; Jennifer Schilling, Secy.-Treas.
EIN: 203959759

869
The North Ridge Foundation
P.O. Box 2233
Mill Valley, CA 94942-2233

Established in 1997 in California.
Donors: Douglas H. Ogden; Emilie M. Ogden.
Foundation type: Independent foundation.
Financial data (yr. ended 12/31/13): Assets, $347,425 (M); expenditures, $208,555; qualifying distributions, $204,000; giving activities include $204,000 for 42 grants (high: $40,000; low: $500).
Fields of interest: Education; Environment.
Type of support: General support.
Limitations: Applications not accepted. No grants to individuals.
Application information: Unsolicited requests for funds not accepted.
Trustees: Douglas H. Ogden; Emilie M. Ogden.
EIN: 946710591

870
The Northern California DX Foundation
P.O. Box 2012
Cupertino, CA 95015-2012
Main URL: http://www.ncdxf.org

Established in 1972 in California.
Donors: Robert Allphin; Donald Dubon; Charles Epps; Arecio Hernandez; Michael Mraz; Eric Scace; Wayne Starnes; Gary Stouder; YASME Foundation; Parten Trust; International DX Association.
Foundation type: Operating foundation.
Financial data (yr. ended 12/31/13): Assets, $924,400 (M); gifts received, $338,703;

expenditures, $278,173; qualifying distributions, $292,005; giving activities include $258,300 for 12 grants (high: $112,200; low: $225).
Purpose and activities: The foundation makes grants to projects it believes will benefit amateur radio in general and DXing in particular. The foundation provides financial support to individuals and groups who use radio communications to advance and promote education, science and international goodwill. Well-designed amateur radio DXpeditions to rare and unusual locations usually meet this criterion. Major support is normally restricted to expeditions that generate world-wide interest. A smaller amount of support is sometimes awarded to other expeditions and projects which in the judgment of the NCDXF directors are unusually strong in supporting the goals of the foundation. Participants themselves should have a significant financial stake in their expedition and the expedition should be likely to proceed even without financial support from the foundation. The foundation also provides scholarships to students attending a junior college, or 4-year college, university or trade school in the U.S., who demonstrate interest and activity in DXing.
Fields of interest: Diseases and conditions; Human services.
Type of support: Research; Grants to individuals.
Limitations: Applications accepted. Giving on a national and international basis. No support for operations restricted to unusual communications such as RTTY, satellite, EME, VHF and UHF, although HF CW and SSB operations that the foundation does support may use these modes as an enhancement.
Application information: Complete application guidelines available on foundation web site. Application form required.
Officers: Tom Berson, Pres.; Glenn Johnson, V.P.; Kip Edwards, Secy.; Don Greenbaum, Treas.
Directors: Steve Merchant; John Miller; Glenn Rattmann; Ned Stearns; Craig Thompson; Glenn Vinson.
EIN: 942853576

871
Maury and Lillian Novak Charitable Trust
14004 Mercado Dr.
Del Mar, CA 92014-2950
Contact: Earl N. Feldman, Tr.

Established in 1997 in California.
Foundation type: Independent foundation.
Financial data (yr. ended 12/31/13): Assets, $1,222,070 (M); expenditures, $450,560; qualifying distributions, $392,594; giving activities include $350,384 for 64 grants (high: $50,514; low: $500).
Fields of interest: Arts and culture; Diseases and conditions; Judaism.
Type of support: Research.
Limitations: Applications accepted. Giving primarily in CA and NY. No grants to individuals.
Application information: Application form required.
  Initial approach: Proposal
  Deadline(s): None
Trustee: Earl N. Feldman.
EIN: 336201249

872
The Oak Tree Philanthropic Foundation
330 Oxford St., Ste. 212
Chula Vista, CA 91911-3119

Established in 1992 in California.
Foundation type: Independent foundation.
Financial data (yr. ended 12/31/13): Assets, $6,954,633 (M); expenditures, $500,151; qualifying distributions, $374,600; giving activities include $335,000 for 36 grants (high: $75,000; low: $1,500).
Purpose and activities: Giving primarily for children and social services, including hurricane and international relief, as well as for education, including support of U.S.-based Lithuanian education.
Fields of interest: Education; Higher education; Hospital care; Disasters and emergency management; Storms; Catholicism; Human services; Child welfare; International development.
Limitations: Applications not accepted. No grants to individuals.
Application information: Contributes only to pre-selected organizations.
Officers: Dr. Dana Maciunas-Mockus, C.E.O. and Pres.; Dr. Robert Maciunas, V.P.; Dr. Vytautas Mockus, Secy.-Treas.
Board Member: Ann L. Failinger.
EIN: 363779795

873
October Saints Foundation
1182 Market St., Ste. 400
San Francisco, CA 94102-4922

Established in 2002 in California.
Donors: Isobel Murphy Charitable Trust; John D. Murphy.
Foundation type: Independent foundation.
Financial data (yr. ended 06/30/14): Assets, $7,859,705 (M); gifts received, $22,500; expenditures, $446,083; qualifying distributions, $335,500; giving activities include $295,000 for 21 grants (high: $50,000; low: $5,000).
Fields of interest: Education; Catholicism; Human services.
Limitations: Applications not accepted. Giving primarily in CA, Washington, DC, and IL. No grants to individuals.
Application information: Contributes only to pre-selected organizations.
Trustee: Wade Hughan.
EIN: 686224342

874
The O'Donnell Foundation
1050 Chestnut St., Ste. 207
Menlo Park, CA 94025-5428

Established in 2007 in California.
Donors: Sue D. O'Donnell; Robert G. O'Donnell.
Foundation type: Independent foundation.
Financial data (yr. ended 12/31/13): Assets, $7,433,651 (M); gifts received, $733,140; expenditures, $296,626; qualifying distributions, $262,353; giving activities include $260,000 for 8 grants (high: $55,000; low: $10,000).
Fields of interest: Education; Employment; Youth development.

Limitations: Applications not accepted. Giving primarily in CA. No grants to individuals.
Application information: Unsolicited requests for funds not accepted.
Officers and Directors: Robert G. O'Donnell, Pres. and Director; Sue D. O'Donnell, Secy.-Treas. and Director; Darrell W. Baggs; Ann M. Dolan.
EIN: 208766740

875
The Offield Center for Billfish Studies
P.O. Box 2080
Avalon, CA 90704

Donor: Paxson H. Offield.
Foundation type: Independent foundation.
Financial data (yr. ended 12/31/13): Assets, $354,084 (M); gifts received, $517,500; expenditures, $413,324; qualifying distributions, $407,574; giving activities include $235,000 for 1 grant.
Fields of interest: Domesticated animals.
Limitations: Applications not accepted. Giving primarily in FL.
Application information: Unsolicited requests for funds not accepted.
Officers: Paxon H. Offield, C.E.O.; Gail Hodge, Secy. and C.F.O.; Chase P. Offield, V.P.
EIN: 461309989

876
Thomas Ohana Foundation
515 Amphitheatre Dr.
Del Mar, CA 92014-2611

Donors: Frank Thomas; Joan C. Thomas.
Foundation type: Independent foundation.
Financial data (yr. ended 12/31/13): Assets, $3,310,468 (M); gifts received, $750,000; expenditures, $427,343; qualifying distributions, $424,657; giving activities include $197,110 for 4 grants (high: $131,200; low: $15,000), and $227,547 for 7 grants to individuals (high: $65,618; low: $1,380).
Fields of interest: Education.
Type of support: Student aid.
Limitations: Applications not accepted.
Application information: Unsolicited requests for funds not accepted.
Officers: Joan C. Thomas, Pres.; Jillian G. Thomas, Secy.; Jeffrey K. Thomas, Treas.
Director: Megan A. Thomas.
EIN: 271538278

877
Steven Ohren Foundation
1010 Sycamore Ave., Ste. 308
South Pasadena, CA 91030-6139

Donor: The Steven Ohren Living Trust.
Foundation type: Independent foundation.
Financial data (yr. ended 07/31/13): Assets, $3,134,659 (M); expenditures, $179,187; qualifying distributions, $170,631; giving activities include $170,631 for 5 grants (high: $93,333; low: $2,800).
Fields of interest: Religion; Judaism.
Limitations: Applications not accepted. Giving primarily in AZ and CA.

Application information: Unsolicited requests for funds not accepted.
Officers: Ellen Pansky, Pres.; Marilyn Sullivan, Secy.; Julie Rice-Davis, Treas.
EIN: 263305763

878
Olander Family Foundation, Inc.
10 Almaden Blvd., 11th Fl.
San Jose, CA 95113-2226

Established in 2002 in California.
Donor: Minola Olander‡.
Foundation type: Independent foundation.
Financial data (yr. ended 12/31/13): Assets, $5,408,252 (M); expenditures, $223,275; qualifying distributions, $219,000; giving activities include $219,000 for 103 grants (high: $10,000; low: $250).
Fields of interest: Arts and culture; Education; Elementary and secondary education; Higher education; Nonprofits; Health; Christianity; Sports and recreation; Human services; Child welfare.
Type of support: General support; Regranting.
Limitations: Applications not accepted. Giving primarily in CA. No grants to individuals.
Application information: Contributes only to pre-selected organizations.
Officer: Steven L. Hallgrimson, C.F.O. and Secy.
Director: Ronald Olander.
EIN: 943400451

879
Olson Family Foundation Trust
22632 Golden Springs Dr., Ste. 315
Diamond Bar, CA 91765-4170

Established in 1995 in California.
Donors: Craig Olson; Jane Olson.
Foundation type: Independent foundation.
Financial data (yr. ended 12/31/13): Assets, $5,672,106 (M); expenditures, $373,902; qualifying distributions, $341,200; giving activities include $341,200 for 16 grants (high: $100,000; low: $2,000).
Purpose and activities: Giving primarily for Lutheran churches, schools, and organizations; funding also for social services.
Fields of interest: Secondary education; Higher education; Graduate and professional education; Methodism; Theology; Human services.
Limitations: Applications not accepted. Giving primarily in CA and MO. No grants to individuals.
Application information: Contributes only to pre-selected organizations.
Trustees: Craig Olson; Jane Olson.
EIN: 336156479

880
On Shore Foundation
(formerly Luster Family Foundation, Inc.)
23768 Malibu Rd.
Malibu, CA 90265-4603
E-mail: nanadogs@verizon.net; *Main URL:* http://www.onshorefoundation.org

Established in 1987 in California.
Donors: Elizabeth Luster; Freda Friedman‡.
Foundation type: Independent foundation.

Financial data (yr. ended 12/31/13): Assets, $6,559,945 (M); gifts received, $2,000; expenditures, $378,025; qualifying distributions, $289,717; giving activities include $210,855 for 339 grants (high: $5,500; low: $50).
Purpose and activities: Giving primarily for animal welfare, wildlife preservation and environmental protection, and animal and human population control.
Fields of interest: Environment; Natural resources; Biodiversity; Wildlife biodiversity; Animal welfare; Family planning.
Type of support: General support.
Limitations: Applications not accepted. Giving primarily in the U.S., with some emphasis on CA, Washington, DC, MT and TX; some giving internationally. No support for religious, media or political organizations, or for advocacy and advisory groups. No grants to individuals.
Application information: Unsolicited requests for funds not accepted.
Board meeting date(s): Fall
Officers: Elizabeth S. Luster, Pres. and Fdn. Mgr.; Amy Luster Mueller, Secy. and C.F.O.
Number of staff: None.
EIN: 954100318

881
Onehope Foundation
17981 Sky Park Cir., Ste. F
Irvine, CA 92614-6345

Foundation type: Independent foundation.
Financial data (yr. ended 12/31/13): Assets, $6,835 (M); gifts received, $305,872; expenditures, $310,327; qualifying distributions, $307,943; giving activities include $209,633 for 9 grants (high: $87,675; low: $1,682).
Fields of interest: Health; Diseases and conditions; Human services.
Limitations: Applications not accepted. Giving primarily in Washington, DC, New York, NY and TX.
Application information: Unsolicited requests for funds not accepted.
Officer: Melissa Lake, Exec. Dir.
EIN: 271530711

882
Ontario Community Foundation
154-A W. Foothill Blvd., Ste. 314
Upland, CA 91786-3847   (909) 985-7338

Established in 1977 in California.
Donor: Ontario Community Hospital, Inc.
Foundation type: Independent foundation.
Financial data (yr. ended 12/31/13): Assets, $3,000,263 (M); expenditures, $189,786; qualifying distributions, $177,747; giving activities include $150,000 for 22 grants (high: $15,000; low: $1,000).
Purpose and activities: Giving primarily for local health-related services in the Ontario, CA, area.
Fields of interest: Education; Health; Human services.
Type of support: General support; Matching grants; Continuing support; Equipment; Emergency funds; Program development; Seed money; Curriculum development.
Limitations: Applications accepted. Giving limited to the Ontario, CA, area, including Pomona Valley and

western San Bernardino County. No grants to individuals.

Publications: Application guidelines; Grants list; Informational brochure (including application guidelines); Program policy statement (including application guidelines).

Application information: Application form required.
   Initial approach: Letter
   Copies of proposal: 2
   Deadline(s): None
   Board meeting date(s): Quarterly
   Final notification: 3 months from receipt

Officers: Rene Biane, Pres.; Bob Eldridge, V.P.; Don E. Wight, Secy.; J. Glenn Robson, Treas.

Trustees: Bill Dingle; Linda Gladson; Leon Lott; Bill Rugg; Lowell Stark; Maggie Vinnedge.

Number of staff: 1 part-time support.

EIN: 951811238

883
Open Stewardship Foundation

c/o Jackie Shin
1000 Wilshire Blvd., Ste. 500
Los Angeles, CA   90017-2462

Donor: Open Bank.

Foundation type: Independent foundation.

Financial data (yr. ended 12/31/13): Assets, $665 (M); gifts received, $229,000; expenditures, $229,525; qualifying distributions, $229,525; giving activities include $194,000 for 53 grants (high: $10,000; low: $2,000).

Fields of interest: Diseases and conditions; Religion; Human services.

Limitations: Applications not accepted.

Application information: Unsolicited requests for funds not accepted.

Officers: Christine Oh, Pres.; Kathi Duncan, C.F.O.; Jackie Shin, Secy.

Board Members: Min Kim; Ock Hee Kim; Susan Park; Yong Sin Shin.

EIN: 453682002

884
Optivest Foundation

(formerly The Mark Van Mourick Foundation)
24901 Dana Point Harbor Dr., Ste. 230
Dana Point, CA   92629-2930   (949) 363-8686
Contact: Mark Van Mourick, C.E.O.
E-mail: info@optivestfoundation.org; Main URL: http://www.optivestfoundation.org
Facebook: https://www.facebook.com/TheOptivestFoundation
Grants List: http://www.optivestfoundation.org/impact

Donors: Mark Van Mourick; Tricia Van Mourick; Optivest Properties, LLC; Judith Sweeney; Charles Rosenberge; Optivest Inc; Charles Fry; Dennis Sweeney; Kristen Verdieck; Russell Wertz; John Harzan; Patrick Jones; David Nix; Optivest Properties Protection; Greg Buckingham; Judy Gaede; Stan Gaede; John Gossett; Lyn Gossett; Nancy Hunsaker; Brain Hunsaker; Virginia Nix; Lisa Jones; Annette Harzan; Frank Childers; Donna Wertz; Lisa Wahlberg; Doug Grant; Laura Staph; Bryan Flynn; John Burke; Jodie Lynn Wollman; Mary Skjonsby; Joanne Sanders; Gregory Skjonsby; The John L. Cashion Family Foundation; Monica Younger; Christine Burke; Nancy Flynn; Sandy Grant; Kirk Wahlberg; Brenda Wilkinson; Gerald Wilkinson.

Foundation type: Independent foundation.

Financial data (yr. ended 12/31/13): Assets, $87,370 (M); gifts received, $467,555; expenditures, $389,906; qualifying distributions, $389,906; giving activities include $358,778 for 44 grants (high: $61,049; low: $400).

Purpose and activities: Giving primarily for Christian causes.

Fields of interest: Education; Christianity.

Type of support: General support; Grants to individuals; Student aid.

Limitations: Applications accepted. Giving primarily in CA.

Application information: Application form required.
   Initial approach: E-mail
   Deadline(s): None

Officers: Mark Van Mourick, C.E.O.; Tricia Van Mourick, Secy.

EIN: 260011296

885
Opus Foundation

c/o CBIZ MHM LLC
10474 Santa Monica Blvd., Ste. 200
Los Angeles, CA   90025-6930

Established in 2006 in California.

Donor: Stacey Nicholas.

Foundation type: Independent foundation.

Financial data (yr. ended 12/31/13): Assets, $14,319,445; gifts received, $26,141; expenditures, $321,250; qualifying distributions, $279,000.

Fields of interest: Education.

Limitations: Applications not accepted. Giving primarily in CA. No grants to individuals.

Application information: Contributes only to pre-selected organizations.

Officers and Directors: Stacey Nicholas, Pres. and Director; Robert D. Feller, Secy.-Treas. and Director; James R. Parks.

EIN: 204927621

886
Oreggia Family Foundation

951 Blanco Cir., Ste. A
Salinas, CA   93901-4451

Established in 2006 in California.

Donors: Arden Oreggia Living Trust; Sabina Oreggia Living Trust.

Foundation type: Independent foundation.

Financial data (yr. ended 12/31/14): Assets, $8,674,515 (M); expenditures, $702,538; qualifying distributions, $445,000; giving activities include $405,000 for 3 grants (high: $350,000; low: $25,000).

Fields of interest: Education; University education.

Limitations: Applications not accepted. Giving primarily in CA. No grants to individuals.

Application information: Unsolicited requests for funds not accepted.

Trustees: Arlene Bertelsman; Robert C. Taylor, Jr.

EIN: 010854918

887
The Orfalea Family Foundation

1283 Coast Village Cir., Ste. A
Santa Barbara, CA   93108-3753   (805) 565-7550
Contact: Camille Kurreck, Foundation Coord. and Grants Admin.
FAX: (805) 565-7554; E-mail: Dean@Orfalea.org; E-mail for Camille Kurreck: Camille@Orfalea.org; Main URL: http://www.orfaleafoundation.org
Giving pledge: http://www.glasspockets.org/philanthropy-in-focus/eye-on-the-giving-pledge/profiles/orfalea

Established in 2000 in California.

Donors: Paul J. Orfalea; Kinko's Corporation; Paul Vit.

Foundation type: Independent foundation.

Financial data (yr. ended 12/31/13): Assets, $25,879,567 (M); expenditures, $1,445,869; qualifying distributions, $4,934,342; giving activities include $435,158 for 30 grants (high: $195,000; low: $70).

Purpose and activities: Giving for the improvement of life for children and families through learning opportunities, and to support sustainable systemic change in the community, and around the world.

Fields of interest: Early childhood education; Higher education; Human services; Youth development.

Type of support: General support; Employee matching gifts; In-kind gifts; Program development; Scholarships; Matching grants.

Limitations: Applications accepted. Giving primarily in San Luis Obispo, Santa Barbara, and Ventura County, CA. No grants to individuals.

Application information: See foundation web site for application guidelines and procedures. If letter of inquiry is approved, then the foundation will request the submission of a detailed proposal and other documented materials. A detailed proposal is by invitation only.
   Initial approach: Letter of inquiry (1-2 pages) via e-mail

Officers and Directors: Natalie Fleet Orfalea, Chair. and Director; Lois Mitchell, Pres.; Catherine Brozowski, V.P.; Judy Frost; Peter MacDougall; Paul J. Orfalea; Ken Saxon.

Number of staff: 2 full-time professional; 1 part-time professional.

EIN: 770541226

888
Ornest Family Foundation

15 Latimer Rd.
Santa Monica, CA   90402-1011

Established in 1994 in California.

Foundation type: Independent foundation.

Financial data (yr. ended 02/28/13): Assets, $7,751,736 (M); expenditures, $434,874; qualifying distributions, $348,212; giving activities include $308,878 for 51 grants (high: $60,000; low: $100).

Purpose and activities: Giving primarily to Jewish organizations and Jewish federated giving programs; some giving also to health organizations and for social services.

Fields of interest: Education; Higher education; Nonprofits; Diseases and conditions; Judaism; Human services; Child development.

Type of support: Regranting.

Limitations: Applications not accepted. Giving primarily in CA. No grants to individuals.

Application information: Contributes only to pre-selected organizations.
Officers and Directors: Ruth Ornest, Pres. and Director; Laura Ornest, C.F.O. and Director; Cindy Ornest; Maury Ornest; Michael Ornest.
EIN: 954436139

889
Orphan and Cancer Care for India Foundation
1860 S. Watson St.
La Habra, CA 90631-9511

Foundation type: Independent foundation.
Financial data (yr. ended 12/31/13): Assets, $62,196 (M); expenditures, $256,958; qualifying distributions, $255,736; giving activities include $255,736 for 4 grants (high: $200,000; low: $14,601).
Fields of interest: Education; Religion.
International interests: India.
Type of support: Research.
Limitations: Applications not accepted. Giving primarily in Mumbai, India.
Application information: Unsolicited requests for funds not accepted.
Officers: Manan Mehta, Pres.; Devangi Mehta, Secy.-Treas.
Directors: Rita Mehta; Samir Mehta.
EIN: 271562043

890
Orthodox Vision Foundation
4412 Oakwood Ave.
La Canada-Flintridge, CA 91011-3414

Established in 2000 in California.
Donors: Charles R. Ajalat; Marilee N. Ajalat.
Foundation type: Independent foundation.
Financial data (yr. ended 01/31/15): Assets, $9,970,758 (M); gifts received, $82,257; expenditures, $445,227; qualifying distributions, $413,929; giving activities include $413,929 for 13 grants (high: $180,165; low: $50).
Fields of interest: Education; Christianity; Orthodox Christianity.
Limitations: Applications not accepted. Giving primarily in CA; funding also in NJ. No grants to individuals.
Application information: Contributes only to pre-selected organizations.
Trustees: Charles R. Ajalat; Marilee N. Ajalat.
EIN: 954834517

891
Ralph and Hazel Osborn and Lois J. Roork Charitable Trust
3010 Old Ranch Pkwy., Ste. 100
Seal Beach, CA 90740-2750

Established in 2009 in California.
Donor: Hazel R. Osborn†.
Foundation type: Independent foundation.
Financial data (yr. ended 12/31/13): Assets, $5,365,225 (M); expenditures, $296,937; qualifying distributions, $260,000; giving activities include $260,000 for 6 grants (high: $65,000; low: $25,000).
Fields of interest: Domesticated animals; Christianity; Human services.

Limitations: Applications not accepted.
Application information: Unsolicited requests for funds not accepted.
Trustee: Stephen E. Olson.
EIN: 276188697

892
The O'Shea Foundation
P.O. Box 31321
San Francisco, CA 94131-0321
E-mail: info@osheafoundation.org; Main
URL: http://www.osheafoundation.org
Grants List: http://www.osheafoundation.org/grants

Donors: Carole O'Shea†; John P. O'Shea†.
Foundation type: Independent foundation.
Financial data (yr. ended 10/31/14): Assets, $6,550,700 (M); expenditures, $337,463; qualifying distributions, $298,550; giving activities include $295,175 for 24 grants (high: $77,500; low: $1,000).
Fields of interest: Education; Human services.
Limitations: Applications not accepted. Giving primarily in CA. No grants to individuals.
Application information: Contributes only to pre-selected organizations.
Officers and Directors: Dolores Donahue, Pres. and Director; Alicia Donahue Silva, V.P. and Director; Shealagh Meehan, Secy. and Director; Eddie Niiya, Treas. and Director; Joseph D. Hurley, Jr.
EIN: 946084555

893
Otto Family Foundation
17764 Creciente Way
San Diego, CA 92127-1059

Established in 2000 in California.
Donors: Neil Otto; Margaret Otto.
Foundation type: Independent foundation.
Financial data (yr. ended 06/30/13): Assets, $4,365,335 (M); expenditures, $226,617; qualifying distributions, $189,395; giving activities include $176,296 for 4 grants (high: $162,071; low: $700).
Purpose and activities: Giving to protect the lives of children in our communities and around the world.
Fields of interest: Arts and culture; Education; International relations.
Limitations: Applications not accepted. Giving primarily in San Diego, CA and New York, NY. No grants to individuals.
Application information: Unsolicited requests for funds not accepted.
Officers: Margaret Otto, Pres.; Neil Otto, Secy.-Treas.
Directors: Ian Grant; Madeline Grant; Christopher Otto; Daniel Otto; Michel Otto.
Number of staff: None.
EIN: 330916411

894
The Outrageous Foundation, Inc.
2 6th Ave.
San Francisco, CA 94118-1324

Donor: Robert P. McGrath.
Foundation type: Independent foundation.

Financial data (yr. ended 09/30/13): Assets, $7,523,660 (M); expenditures, $337,700; qualifying distributions, $330,500; giving activities include $330,500 for 49 grants (high: $25,000; low: $1,500).
Fields of interest: Arts and culture; Education; Catholicism; Human services; Child welfare.
Type of support: Capital campaigns; Scholarships.
Limitations: Applications not accepted. Giving primarily in CA. No grants to individuals.
Application information: Contributes only to pre-selected organizations.
Officers: R. McGrath, Pres.; J. McGrath, Secy.
EIN: 942474423

895
Overall Family Foundation
1362 Oak Creek Canton Rd.
Santa Barbara, CA 93108-1247

Established in 1998 in California.
Donors: John B. Overall IV; Sheryl V. Overall; Jack B. Overall.
Foundation type: Independent foundation.
Financial data (yr. ended 12/31/13): Assets, $5,442,145 (M); gifts received, $1,442; expenditures, $365,670; qualifying distributions, $352,819; giving activities include $351,590 for 32 grants (high: $153,250; low: $100).
Fields of interest: Natural resources; Biodiversity; Wildlife biodiversity.
Limitations: Applications not accepted. Giving primarily in Santa Barbara, CA. No grants to individuals.
Application information: Unsolicited requests for funds not accepted.
Officers and Directors: Sheryl V. Overall, Pres. and Secy.; Jack B. Overall, C.F.O. and Director.
EIN: 770500005

896
OZ Foundation
1804 Garnet Ave., Ste. 389
San Diego, CA 92109-3352

Established in 2000 in California.
Donors: David D. Osborne; Georgia Osborne.
Foundation type: Independent foundation.
Financial data (yr. ended 12/31/13): Assets, $4,418,209 (M); expenditures, $232,864; qualifying distributions, $217,078; giving activities include $29,500 for 4 grants (high: $12,500; low: $4,500), and $158,453 for 19 grants to individuals (high: $17,061; low: $3,717).
Fields of interest: Education; Public housing; Human services.
Limitations: Applications not accepted. Giving primarily in Oakland, CA.
Application information: Unsolicited requests for funds not accepted.
Officers and Directors: Mike Smith, Pres. and Treas. and Director; Georgia Osborne, V.P. and Director; Don Welter, Secy. and Director; David D. Osborne; Jeremy Osborne; Kelly Osborne; Colby Smith; Kristin Welter.
EIN: 770556210

897
Pacific Western Foundation

P.O. Box 3350
South Pasadena, CA 91031 (626) 441-0330
Contact: Patrick L. Nally, Pres. and Treas.

Established in 1953 in California.
Donor: Western Gear Corp.
Foundation type: Independent foundation.
Financial data (yr. ended 11/30/13): Assets,
$2,922,087 (M); expenditures, $241,146;
qualifying distributions, $164,664; giving activities
include $157,000 for grants.
Purpose and activities: Giving primarily for
education and to Roman Catholic agencies and
churches.
Fields of interest: Education; Catholicism; Human
services.
Type of support: Scholarships; General support;
Emergency funds; Continuing support.
Limitations: Applications accepted. Giving primarily
in CA. No support for political organizations.
Application information: Application form required.
  Initial approach: Request application form
  Deadline(s): None
Officers: Patrick L. Nally, Pres. and Treas.; C. Forrest
Bannan, V.P.; John Cruden, Secy.
Trustees: Peter Moore; Joseph T. Nally.
Number of staff: 1 part-time support.
EIN: 956097360

898
PADI Foundation

(also known as Professional Association of Diving
Instructors Foundation)
9150 Wilshire Blvd., Ste. 300
Beverly Hills, CA 90212-3430 (310) 859-1430
Contact: Charles Rettig, Pres.
FAX: (310) 859-1430;
E-mail: grants@padifoundation.org; Main
URL: http://www.padifoundation.org
Grants List: http://www.padifoundation.org/
Recipients/Recipient11.htm

Established in 1991 in California.
Donors: Department of Justice, State of California;
Capital Investments & Ventures Corp.
Foundation type: Operating foundation.
Financial data (yr. ended 05/31/15): Assets,
$4,084,905 (M); gifts received, $100,000;
expenditures, $365,356; qualifying distributions,
$315,864; giving activities include $266,371 for
grants.
Purpose and activities: The foundation supports
programs designed to enrich mankind's
understanding of the aquatic environment;
encourage the protection of the delicate ecological
balance of underwater life; and increase the
understanding of sports diving physics and
physiology.
Fields of interest: Education; Environment; Natural
resources; Water resources; Water pollution;
Aquatic wildlife protection; Marine science; Water
sports.
International interests: Asia; Australia; Brazil;
Europe; South Africa.
Type of support: Research; Grants to individuals.
Limitations: Applications accepted. Giving on a
national and international basis. No grants for diving
equipment, standard photographic equipment,
personal computers, overhead costs, or indirect
expenses.

Publications: Application guidelines; Financial
statement; Grants list.
Application information: The foundation utilizes the
Common Grant Application, a web-based
management program to receive and administer
grant proposals. Grants range from $2,000 to
$10,000. Application form required.
  Initial approach: Complete online application
  Copies of proposal: 1
  Deadline(s): Nov. 1 to Feb. 1
  Board meeting date(s): Apr.
  Final notification: May 10
Officer and Directors: Charles Rettig, Esq., Pres.
and Dir.; Paul K. Dayton, Ph.D; Daniel M. Hanes,
Ph.D; Jeff Nadler; Andrew Saxon, MD.
EIN: 954326850

899
George B. Page Foundation

P.O. Box 1299
Santa Barbara, CA 93102-1299 (805)
730-3634
Contact: Denise Meza, Exec. Dir.

Established in 1961 in California.
Donors: Mission Linen Cos.; Montecto
Manufacturing Co.; George B. Page Foundation.
Foundation type: Independent foundation.
Financial data (yr. ended 12/31/13): Assets,
$4,457,685 (M); expenditures, $229,733;
qualifying distributions, $209,915; giving activities
include $191,000 for 13 grants (high: $30,000;
low: $2,500).
Fields of interest: Education; Community and
economic development; Special Olympics; Human
services; Child welfare; Youth development;
Scouting programs; People with disabilities.
Type of support: General support; Continuing
support; Annual campaigns; Debt reduction;
Emergency funds; Program development; Seed
money.
Limitations: Applications accepted. Giving primarily
in Santa Barbara County, CA and Amarillo, TX. No
grants to individuals, or for endowment funds or
matching gifts.
Application information: Application form required.
  Initial approach: Contact foundation for
    application form
  Deadline(s): Oct. 1
Officers: Richard Nightingale, Pres.; Denise Meza,
Exec. Dir.
Trustees: Tony Guntermann; Nick Katzenstein;
Linda Page McGaughey; Joe Plowman; Kathy Stuva;
Karl Willig.
EIN: 956121985

900
The Palo Alto Community Fund

(formerly Palo Alto Endowment Fund)
P.O. Box 50634
Palo Alto, CA 94303-0634 (650) 690-0370
Contact: Cammie Vail, Exec. Dir.
FAX: (650) 324-1215;
E-mail: info@paloaltocommfund.org; Grant
application e-mail: grants@paloaltocommfund.org;
Main URL: http://www.paloaltocommfund.org
Facebook: https://www.facebook.com/
paloaltocommunityfund
LinkedIn: https://www.linkedin.com/groups/
Palo-Alto-Community-Fund-6631213?

home=&gid=6631213&trk=groups_members-h-log
o
YouTube: http://www.youtube.com/view_play_list?
p=2108F4140610812B

Established in 1998 in California.
Foundation type: Community foundation.
Financial data (yr. ended 12/31/13): Assets,
$5,857,063 (M); gifts received, $470,788;
expenditures, $427,135; giving activities include
$311,000 for 38+ grants (high: $10,000).
Purpose and activities: The fund builds and
sustains a philanthropic endowment that responds
to the goals and needs of the Palo Alto, CA,
community by supporting new or existing programs
sponsored by a broad spectrum of Palo Alto area
nonprofit organizations.
Fields of interest: Arts and culture; Music;
Education; Environment; Health; Mental health care;
Nutrition; Community and economic development;
Economic development; Housing development;
Human services; Family services; Child welfare;
Domestic violence shelters; Developmental
disability services; Senior services; Adolescents;
Seniors; People with disabilities.
Limitations: Applications accepted. Giving limited to
Palo Alto, CA and neighboring communities. No
support for religious activities, or for-profit schools.
No grants to individuals, or for fundraising events,
endowment funds, capital or endowment
campaigns, deficit funding or cash reserves, or
basic research projects.
Publications: Application guidelines; Grants list;
Informational brochure; Newsletter.
Application information: Visit foundation web site
for application form and guidelines. One copy of your
complete grant application and attachments must
be mailed or hand-delivered, and a second copy of
just your grant application must be emailed to the
foundation. Faxed applications are not accepted.
Application form required.
  Initial approach: Submit application form and
    attachments
  Copies of proposal: 1
  Deadline(s): Feb. 6
  Final notification: May.
Officers and Directors: Anne Dauer, Co-Pres. and
Director; Mandy Lowell, Co-Pres. and Director;
Cammie Vail, Exec. Dir.; Cynthia Brinkmann; Brian
Chancellor; Enoch Choi, MD; Sarah Clark; Karen
Douglas; Nitesh Dullabh; Lenoard Ely III; Catherine
Crystal Foster; Bruce Gee; Peter B. Gifford; Mary
Haverstock; Scott Joachim; Jean K. McCown; Cindy
Miller; Javad Mostofizadeh; Karen Nierenberg;
Missy Reller; Karen Ross; Joel Spolin; Michael Trigg;
Lanie Wheeler.
EIN: 770483215

901
Palo Hills Foundation

10413 Torre Ave., Ste. 500
Cupertino, CA 95014-3240

Established in 1999 in California.
Donors: Don R. Scifres; Carol Scifres.
Foundation type: Independent foundation.
Financial data (yr. ended 12/31/12): Assets,
$4,962,228 (M); gifts received, $701,823;
expenditures, $338,858; qualifying distributions,
$302,300; giving activities include $302,300 for
grants.
Fields of interest: Education; Diseases and
conditions; Protestantism; Human services.

Type of support: Research; Research and evaluation.
Limitations: Applications not accepted. Giving in the U.S., with emphasis on CA and MO. No grants to individuals.
Application information: Unsolicited requests for funds not accepted.
Officer: Don R. Scifres, Pres.
EIN: 770529206

902
The J. Douglas and Marian R. Pardee Foundation
6310 San Vicente Blvd., Ste. 255
Los Angeles, CA 90048-5447

Established in 1986 in California.
Donors: J. Douglas Pardee; Marian R. Pardee.
Foundation type: Independent foundation.
Financial data (yr. ended 11/30/14): Assets, $2,732,357 (M); expenditures, $465,541; qualifying distributions, $463,641; giving activities include $428,230 for 31 grants (high: $118,000; low: $250).
Purpose and activities: Giving primarily for education, health associations, human services, and to an Episcopal church.
Fields of interest: Arts and culture; Education; Health; Diseases and conditions; Episcopalianism and Anglicanism; Lutheranism; Human services; Youth services; Scouting programs.
Limitations: Applications not accepted. Giving primarily in CA. No grants to individuals.
Application information: Contributes only to pre-selected organizations.
Officers: J. Douglas Pardee, Pres.; Marian R. Pardee, V.P.; Craig C. Birker, Secy.; Julian M. Bieber, Treas.
Trustees: Mary-Alice Benson; James D. Pardee; Julie Pardee; Jeanne Pursell.
EIN: 954070020

903
Eleanor Hutchinson Parker Foundation Inc.
5836 Brittany Forrest Ln.
San Diego, CA 92130

Established in 2008 in California.
Donor: Eleanor Hutchinson Parker Charitable Lead Trust.
Foundation type: Independent foundation.
Financial data (yr. ended 12/31/13): Assets, $6,668,270 (M); gifts received, $213,010; expenditures, $353,114; qualifying distributions, $342,006; giving activities include $342,006 for 21 grants (high: $100,000; low: $6).
Fields of interest: Opera; Higher education.
Limitations: Applications not accepted.
Application information: Unsolicited requests for funds not accepted.
Officers and Directors: Suzanne Parker Sutton, Pres. and Director; Robert M. Parker, Secy.-Treas. and Director.
EIN: 743246967

904
Parsemus Foundation
P.O. Box 2246
Berkeley, CA 94702-0246
Main URL: http://www.parsemusfoundation.org
Facebook: https://www.facebook.com/ParsemusFoundation
Vimeo: http://vimeo.com/parsemus

Established in 2005 in Unspecified.
Donor: Elaine Lissner.
Foundation type: Independent foundation.
Financial data (yr. ended 12/31/13): Assets, $486,933 (M); gifts received, $346,854; expenditures, $505,763; qualifying distributions, $550,719; giving activities include $126,781 for 7 grants (high: $52,498; low: $2,000), and $292,899 for foundation-administered programs.
Purpose and activities: Giving primarily for pharmaceutical and contraceptive development and research, treating breast cancer, and perimenopausal and menopausal rosacea.
Fields of interest: Pharmacology; Diseases and conditions; Breast cancer.
International interests: Australia; Italy; United Kingdom of Great Britain and Northern Ireland.
Type of support: Research.
Limitations: Applications not accepted. Giving primarily in NC, OR and TX; some giving in Australia, Italy and the United Kingdom. No grants to individuals.
Application information: Applications for support are by invitation only.
Officer: Elaine Lissner, Pres. and Secy.
EIN: 203968895

905
The Albert Parvin Foundation
c/o Posivak & Joffe, LLP
11150 W. Olympic Blvd., Ste. 860
Los Angeles, CA 90064-1839 (310) 473-7317

Established in 1960 in California.
Donor: Albert B. Parvin†.
Foundation type: Independent foundation.
Financial data (yr. ended 12/31/13): Assets, $8,017,763 (M); expenditures, $460,750; qualifying distributions, $423,259; giving activities include $407,646 for 53 grants (high: $100,000; low: $200).
Purpose and activities: Giving primarily for higher education and human services.
Fields of interest: Arts and culture; Higher education; Health; Judaism; Human services; Seniors.
Type of support: General support; Fellowships.
Limitations: Applications accepted. Giving primarily in CA. No grants to individuals.
Application information: Application form required.
Initial approach: Proposal
Deadline(s): None
Officer: Phyllis Parvin, Pres.
Directors: Harvey G. Joffe; Mary C. Rudin; Stanley Parvin; Stephen Silbert.
EIN: 952158989

906
Robert J. & Claire Pasarow Foundation
3029 Wilshire Blvd., Ste. 200
Santa Monica, CA 90403-2364 (310) 828-7547
Contact: Anthony Pasarow, Treas.

Established in 1986 in California.
Donors: Claire Pasarow; Robert J. Pasarow.
Foundation type: Independent foundation.
Financial data (yr. ended 10/31/13): Assets, $2,313,069 (M); expenditures, $257,628; qualifying distributions, $207,127; giving activities include $180,000 for 9 grants to individuals (high: $20,000; low: $20,000).
Purpose and activities: Awards grants to individuals for medical and scientific research.
Fields of interest: Diseases and conditions; Science.
Type of support: Research; Grants to individuals; Research and evaluation.
Limitations: Applications accepted. Giving primarily in CA, NY and TX.
Application information: Application form required.
Initial approach: Proposal
Deadline(s): None
Officers: Jack David Barchas, Chair.; Michael R. Pasarow, Pres.; Susan Adele Pasarow, Secy.; Anthony H. Pasarow, Treas.
Directors: Shaun R. Coughlin, M.D., Ph.D; Christopher J. Evans, Ph. D; Ronald Evans, Ph. D; Brian E. Henderson, MD; Alexander Varshavsky, Ph. D.
EIN: 954079676

907
The Elizabeth R. and William J. Patterson Foundation
P.O. Box 580
San Anselmo, CA 94979

Established in 2002 in California.
Donors: Elizabeth R. Patterson; William J. Patterson; William J. Patterson Trust; William J. Patterson 2002 Family Trust; Elizabeth R. Patterson 2002 Descendants Trust.
Foundation type: Independent foundation.
Financial data (yr. ended 12/31/13): Assets, $81,770,201 (M); gifts received, $32,298,628; expenditures, $552,875; qualifying distributions, $336,624; giving activities include $270,250 for 10 grants (high: $210,000; low: $250).
Fields of interest: Human services.
Limitations: Applications not accepted. Giving primarily in CA. No grants to individuals.
Application information: Contributes only to pre-selected organizations.
Officers and Directors: Elizabeth R. Patterson, Pres. and Treas. and Director; Lori Kulvin Crawford, Secy.
EIN: 383667071

908
Peter T. Paul Foundation, Inc.
1401 Los Gamos Dr.
San Rafael, CA 94903-1840

Donors: Peter T. Paul; Peter T. Paul Living Trust.
Foundation type: Independent foundation.
Financial data (yr. ended 12/31/13): Assets, $62,314 (M); expenditures, $427,754; qualifying distributions, $407,500; giving activities include $407,500 for 5 grants (high: $250,000; low: $10,000).
Fields of interest: Higher education.
Limitations: Applications not accepted. Giving primarily in CA and MA.
Application information: Contributes only to pre-selected organizations.

Officers: Peter T. Paul, Chair.; Kristen Decker, C.F.O.
EIN: 262621431

909
The Edwin W. Pauley Foundation
1801 Century Park E., Ste. 2230
Los Angeles, CA 90067 (323) 954-3131
Contact: Stephen M. Pauley MD, Chair. and Pres.

Established in 1993 in California.
Donor: Barbara Pauley Pagen†.
Foundation type: Independent foundation.
Financial data (yr. ended 12/31/13): Assets, $4,170,746 (M); expenditures, $503,537; qualifying distributions, $439,540; giving activities include $411,120 for 22 grants (high: $100,120; low: $500).
Purpose and activities: Grants primarily for higher education (in support of marine biology).
Fields of interest: Higher education; Youth development.
Type of support: General support; Continuing support; Annual campaigns; Capital and infrastructure.
Limitations: Applications accepted. Giving primarily in CA. No grants to individuals.
Application information: Application form required.
Initial approach: Letter
Copies of proposal: 1
Deadline(s): None
Officers: Stephen M. Pauley, Chair. and Pres.; Kevin Pauley Hillyer, V.P.; Tanya Hendrix, Secy.; Matthew V. Pauley, Treas.
EIN: 954332470

910
Payne Family Foundation
3490 California St., Ste. 209
San Francisco, CA 94118-1892
Contact: Lisle W. Payne, Secy.-Treas.; Roslyn B. Payne, Pres.

Established in 1994 in California.
Donors: Roslyn B. Payne; Lisle W. Payne.
Foundation type: Independent foundation.
Financial data (yr. ended 12/31/13): Assets, $0 (M); gifts received, $650,000; expenditures, $248,150; qualifying distributions, $245,879; giving activities include $245,879 for 23 grants (high: $71,429; low: $100).
Purpose and activities: Giving primarily for higher education, the arts, and children, youth, and social services.
Fields of interest: Education; Health; Sports and recreation.
Type of support: Continuing support; In-kind gifts; Capital campaigns; Scholarships.
Limitations: Applications accepted. Giving primarily in AZ and CA. No grants to individuals.
Application information:
Initial approach: Proposal
Deadline(s): None
Board meeting date(s): Dec.
Officers: Roslyn B. Payne, Pres.; Lisle W. Payne, Secy.-Treas.
EIN: 943207544

911
Pearlstein Family Foundation
P.O. Box 620505
Woodside, CA 94062
Contact: Jack Pearlstein, Tr.

Established in 1997 in California.
Donors: Carl Pearlstein; Virginia Pearlstein.
Foundation type: Independent foundation.
Financial data (yr. ended 12/31/13): Assets, $6,566,339 (M); expenditures, $366,347; qualifying distributions, $316,333; giving activities include $313,305 for 26 grants (high: $50,000; low: $1,000).
Purpose and activities: Giving to Jewish organizations, to higher education, to agricultural research and education, and to organizations in Half Moon Bay, California.
Fields of interest: Education; Higher education; Health; Agricultural education; Judaism.
Type of support: Individual development.
Limitations: Applications accepted. Giving primarily in CA. No grants to individuals.
Application information: Application form required.
Initial approach: Letter
Deadline(s): None
Trustees: Gail Hollingsworth; Jack Pearlstein; Kitty Shiotani; Jimmy L. Simon, MD.
EIN: 943254888

912
Mario Pedrozzi Scholarship Foundation
1040 Florence Rd., No. 21
Livermore, CA 94550-5543 (925) 456-3700
FAX: (925) 456-3701;
E-mail: info@pedrozzifoundation.org; Main URL: http://www.pedrozzifoundation.org
Facebook: https://www.facebook.com/pages/Pedrozzi-Scholarship-Foundation/123721531934
YouTube: http://www.youtube.com/user/PedrozziFoundation

Established in 2007 in California.
Donor: Mario Pedrozzi†.
Foundation type: Operating foundation.
Financial data (yr. ended 09/30/13): Assets, $8,578,083 (M); gifts received, $5,200; expenditures, $507,635; qualifying distributions, $461,443; giving activities include $286,000 for grants.
Purpose and activities: Scholarship awards to graduates of Livermore high schools in pursuit of higher education and to graduates of Alameda County high schools who will be attending St. Patricks Seminary and University in Menlo Park, California.
Fields of interest: Higher education.
Type of support: Scholarships; Student aid.
Limitations: Applications accepted. Giving primarily to residents of CA.
Application information: Contact by e-mail preferred. Complete application guidelines available on foundation web site. Application form required.
Initial approach: E-mail
Deadline(s): Mar. 1
Officers and Directors: Bryan Balazs, Pres. and Director; Kathye Coyle, Secy. and Director; John W. Houghton, Jr., Treas. and Director; Sean Batchelor; Tom Felter; Richard Gumbs; Lisa Lagorio; Bob Mendonca; Mark Shawver.
EIN: 201025764

913
Penney Family Fund
c/o Common Counsel Foundation
405 14th St., Ste. 809
Oakland, CA 94612-2706 (510) 834-2995
FAX: (510) 834-2998;
E-mail: info@commoncounsel.org; Main URL: http://www.commoncounsel.org/Penney%20Family%20Fund
Grants List: http://www.commoncounsel.org/Penney+Family+Fund/2014-grants-list
Grants List: http://www.commoncounsel.org/Penney+Family+Fund/2013-grants-list
Grants List: http://www.commoncounsel.org/Penney+Family+Fund/2012-grants-list
Penney Family Fund's Philanthropy Promise: http://www.ncrp.org/philanthropys-promise/who

Established in 1998 in California.
Foundation type: Independent foundation.
Financial data (yr. ended 12/31/12): Assets, $6,847,234 (M); expenditures, $457,605; qualifying distributions, $378,508; giving activities include $300,000 for 23 grants (high: $18,000; low: $10,000).
Purpose and activities: Giving primarily to organizations that work to advance human rights, community social, political and economic empowerment, government accountability and environmental sustainability.
Fields of interest: Education; Economics; Public affairs; Human services; Child welfare.
Type of support: General support; Program development.
Limitations: Applications not accepted. Giving primarily in CA, OR and WA.
Publications: Grants list.
Application information: Contributes only to pre-selected organizations. Unsolicited requests for funds not accepted.
Officers: Alissa Keny-Guyer, Pres.; Sarah Malachowsky, Secy.; Diana Trump, Treas.
Trustees: Leigh Guyer; Tom Huntington; Jeff Malachowsky.
EIN: 943314431

914
Rose Perenin Foundation
P.O. Box 441
Fortuna, CA 95540-1916

Donor: Rose Perenin.
Foundation type: Independent foundation.
Financial data (yr. ended 12/31/13): Assets, $7,326,765 (M); expenditures, $336,288; qualifying distributions, $317,266; giving activities include $305,186 for 6 grants (high: $145,000; low: $10,000).
Fields of interest: Performing arts; Basic and remedial instruction; Hospital care; Senior services.
Type of support: General support.
Limitations: Applications not accepted. Giving primarily in CA and HI. No grants to individuals.
Application information: Contributes only to pre-selected organizations.
Officers: John A. Gromala, Pres.; Kim Gans, Secy.; Keith Borges, Treas.
EIN: 680004983

915
The Pergo Foundation
(formerly The Andrew and Denise Goldfarb Family Foundation)
14170 Chandler Blvd.
Sherman Oaks, CA   91401-5714

Established in 1997 in California.
Donors: Andrew Goldfarb; Denise Goldfarb; Smith Family Foundation.
Foundation type: Independent foundation.
Financial data (yr. ended 06/30/14): Assets, $4,031,770; expenditures, $264,235; qualifying distributions, $245,848.
Purpose and activities: Giving primarily for education, the arts, and human services.
Fields of interest: Arts and culture; Higher education; University education; Diseases and conditions; Human services.
Type of support: General support; Student aid.
Limitations: Giving primarily in CA.
Application information:
  Initial approach: Letter
  Deadline(s): None
Officers and Directors: Andrew Goldfarb, Pres. and Director; Denise Goldfarb, C.F.O. and Secy. and Director; Jessica Goldfarb; Rebecca Goldfarb.
EIN: 954610805

916
Perricone Family Foundation
P.O. Box 21845
Los Angeles, CA   90021-0845

Established in 1999 in California.
Donor: Sam Perricone.
Foundation type: Independent foundation.
Financial data (yr. ended 12/31/13): Assets, $774,430 (M); expenditures, $224,938; qualifying distributions, $224,938; giving activities include $216,362 for 6+ grants (high: $181,752).
Purpose and activities: Giving primarily to Roman Catholic churches and institutions.
Fields of interest: Education; Catholicism.
Type of support: Individual development.
Application information: Application form required.
  Initial approach: Letter
  Deadline(s): Dec. 1
Officers and Directors: Joseph Perricone, Pres. and Director; Sam G. Perricone, V.P. and Director; Lucy P. Klumok, Secy. and Director.
EIN: 954752894

917
The Peszynski Foundation
1069 Wilhaggin Park Ln.
Sacramento, CA   95864

Established in 2007 in California.
Donors: Davison Iron Works, Inc.; Andrew F. Peszynski; Loretto High School.
Foundation type: Company-sponsored foundation.
Financial data (yr. ended 12/31/13): Assets, $3,200,498 (M); expenditures, $176,010; qualifying distributions, $176,000; giving activities include $176,000 for 11 grants (high: $35,000; low: $2,000).
Purpose and activities: The foundation supports organizations involved with K-12 and higher education, human services, and Catholicism.

Fields of interest: Education; Health; Human services.
International interests: Poland; United Kingdom of Great Britain and Northern Ireland.
Type of support: General support; Capital and infrastructure.
Limitations: Applications not accepted. Giving primarily in CA; limited giving in Poland and the United Kingdom. No grants to individuals.
Application information: Contributes only to pre-selected organizations.
Officers and Directors: Andrew F. Peszynski, Pres. and Director; I.G. Peszynski, C.F.O. and Director; Helena Szmit, V.P. and Director; Elizabeth Perschevitch, Secy. and Director.
EIN: 261349949

918
Peterson Charitable Foundation
7979 Ivanhoe Ave., Ste. 520
La Jolla, CA   92037-7127

Established in 2000 in California.
Donors: Paul A. Peterson; Peterson Brothers LLC.
Foundation type: Independent foundation.
Financial data (yr. ended 12/31/13): Assets, $113,064 (M); gifts received, $182,628; expenditures, $171,223; qualifying distributions, $171,211; giving activities include $169,531 for 36 grants (high: $68,500; low: $10).
Fields of interest: Higher education; Specialty hospital care; Christianity; Human services; Child welfare.
Limitations: Applications not accepted. Giving primarily in CA. No grants to individuals.
Application information: Contributes only to pre-selected organizations.
Officers: Paul A. Peterson, Pres.; Andrew G. Peterson, V.P.; James F. Peterson, V.P.; Matthew A. Peterson, V.P.; Daniel C. Peterson, C.F.O. and Secy.
EIN: 522255789

919
The Arnold and Margaret Peterson Family Foundation
534 S. Bayfront
Balboa Island, CA   92660

Foundation type: Independent foundation.
Financial data (yr. ended 12/31/12): Assets, $3,394,434 (M); expenditures, $273,711; qualifying distributions, $205,900; giving activities include $205,900 for grants.
Fields of interest: Religion; Human services; Youth development.
Limitations: Applications not accepted.
Application information: Unsolicited requests for funds not accepted.
Officers and Directors: Judith G. Tucker, Pres. and Director; Ronald E. Peterson, Secy.-Treas. and Director.
EIN: 262919688

920
M. & I. Pfister Foundation
5580 La Jolla Blvd., No. 527
La Jolla, CA   92037-7651   (858) 551-8785
Contact: Maryanne Pfister, Pres.

Established in 2006 in California.

Donors: Irwin Pfister; Maryanne Pfister.
Foundation type: Independent foundation.
Financial data (yr. ended 12/31/13): Assets, $1,160,070 (M); gifts received, $303,926; expenditures, $398,249; qualifying distributions, $395,914; giving activities include $395,914 for 7 grants (high: $168,000; low: $2,500).
Fields of interest: Arts and culture; Domesticated animals.
Limitations: Applications accepted. Giving primarily in CA.
Application information: Application form required.
  Initial approach: Proposal
  Deadline(s): None
Officers: Maryanne Pfister, Pres.; Irwin Pfister, Secy.-Treas.
EIN: 205994513

921
PG & E/PSEA Emergency Assistance Fund
1390 Willow Pass Rd., Ste. 240
Concord, CA   94520-7904   (925) 246-6224
Contact: Doug Chadbourne, Dir.
Main URL: http://www.psea.info/emergency_assistance.html

Donor: Pacific Gas and Electric Co.
Foundation type: Independent foundation.
Financial data (yr. ended 12/31/13): Assets, $985,824 (M); gifts received, $151,092; expenditures, $125,807; qualifying distributions, $118,434; giving activities include $83,121 for 3 grants (high: $78,365; low: $2,045), and $35,313 for 93 grants to individuals (high: $10,006; low: $250).
Fields of interest: Human services.
Limitations: Applications accepted. Giving primarily in CA.
Application information: Application form required.
  Initial approach: Letter
  Deadline(s): None
Directors: Charlie Bailon; Doug Chadbourne; Mary Contaxis; Robert Grimm; Al Janz; Deni Lee; Da'Chon Pace.
EIN: 680234757

922
Phelps Family Foundation
16720 Huerta Rd.
Encino, CA   91436-3544

Established in 2005 in California.
Donors: Michael E. Phelps; Patricia E. Phelps.
Foundation type: Independent foundation.
Financial data (yr. ended 03/31/15): Assets, $3,548,142 (M); gifts received, $405,638; expenditures, $896,049; qualifying distributions, $301,666; giving activities include $301,666 for 3 grants (high: $261,666; low: $20,000).
Fields of interest: Higher education.
Limitations: Applications not accepted. Giving primarily in CA. No grants to organizations lacking 501(c)(3) which are not private foundations and/or governmental entities.
Application information: Contributes only to pre-selected organizations.
Officers: Michael E. Phelps, Pres.; Patricia E. Phelps, V.P. and Secy.; Randy Rich, Treas.
EIN: 201974643

923
Wilson W. Phelps Foundation
P.O. Box 10127
Fullerton, CA   92838-9127

Established in 1997 in California.
Donors: James S. Phelps; Michael Herring; Ann Herring.
Foundation type: Independent foundation.
Financial data (yr. ended 12/31/14): Assets, $8,514,386; expenditures, $435,578; qualifying distributions, $417,564.
Purpose and activities: Giving primarily for education and human services.
Fields of interest: Education; Elementary and secondary education; Human services; Child welfare.
Limitations: Applications not accepted. Giving primarily in Fullerton, CA. No grants to individuals.
Application information: Contributes only to pre-selected organizations.
Officers: John W. Phelps, Pres.; Louise Shamblen, V.P.; Carol B. Phelps, Secy.; James S. Phelps, Treas.
Directors: James F. Atkinson III; Marlene McGlensey; Sheryl Phelps-Fisher.
EIN: 330743687

924
Amy Phillips Charitable Foundation
2716 Bagley Ave.
Los Angeles, CA   90034-1804

Established in 1995 in California.
Donor: Amy D. Phillips†.
Foundation type: Independent foundation.
Financial data (yr. ended 12/31/13): Assets, $6,788,911 (M); expenditures, $315,226; qualifying distributions, $293,520; giving activities include $249,693 for 5 grants (high: $116,693; low: $25,000).
Fields of interest: Nonprofits; HIV/AIDS; Cancers; Judaism; Human services; Youth development; Adult and child mentoring.
Type of support: Regranting.
Limitations: Applications not accepted. Giving primarily in Los Angeles, CA. No grants to individuals.
Application information: Unsolicited requests for funds not accepted.
Officer and Trustee: Robert C. Zapel, Fdn. Mgr. and Trustee.
EIN: 954525435

925
Physicians Aid Association
(also known as Aleck Sandler and Co.)
7985 Santa Monica Blvd., Ste. 109-90
Los Angeles, CA   90046-5186   (310) 427-7892

Established in 1940 in California.
Donor: Barbara Lewin†.
Foundation type: Independent foundation.
Financial data (yr. ended 12/31/13): Assets, $4,564,786 (M); gifts received, $16,149; expenditures, $284,461; qualifying distributions, $247,791; giving activities include $30,000 for 2 grants (high: $15,000; low: $15,000), and $166,140 for 9 grants to individuals (high: $52,800; low: $3,000).
Purpose and activities: Provides financial and medical assistance to current, disabled or retired

physicians or people in related occupations, and their immediate families.
Fields of interest: Human services.
Type of support: Grants to individuals.
Limitations: Applications accepted. Giving limited to Los Angeles County, CA.
Application information:
  Initial approach: Letter
  Board meeting date(s): First week of Feb., May, Aug., and Nov.
Officers: Rama E. Chandran, MD, Pres.; Patrick A. Mauer, MD, V.P.; Sidney Gold, MD, Secy.; George B. Stoneman, MD, Treas.
Number of staff: 1 full-time professional.
EIN: 951660852

926
Kenneth A. Picerne Foundation
30950 Rancho Viejo Rd., No. 200
San Juan Capistrano, CA   92675-1766   (949) 267-1517
FAX: (949) 487-6263; Main URL: http://www.picernefoundation.org
Facebook: https://www.facebook.com/KAPFoundation
Google Plus: https://plus.google.com/106549244621362618329
LinkedIn: http://www.linkedin.com/company/2968469
YouTube: http://www.youtube.com/user/KAPFoundation

Established in 2004 in California.
Donor: Kenneth A. Picerne.
Foundation type: Operating foundation.
Financial data (yr. ended 11/30/13): Assets, $18,440,565 (M); expenditures, $655,204; qualifying distributions, $658,900; giving activities include $2,519 for 1 grant, and $118,845 for 20 grants to individuals (high: $10,000; low: $1,000).
Purpose and activities: Giving to support healthy and adaptive human development throughout the life cycle by creating, developing and evaluating innovative and creative programs that are sustainable and provide significant value to the lives of individuals and a healthy society.
Fields of interest: Artist's services; Youth development.
Type of support: General support; Grants to individuals.
Limitations: Applications not accepted. Giving primarily in CA.
Application information: Contributes only to preselected organizations.
Officers: Kenneth A. Picerne, Chair. and Pres.; Jon D. Demorest, Secy.; Victor D. Nelson, Exec. Dir.
Directors: Kenneth M. Golden; Michael Whalen.
Number of staff: 1
EIN: 432070561

927
Mary Pickford Foundation
40836 Calle Bandido
Murrieta, CA   92562-8700   (951) 461-6637
Contact: Henry Stotsenberg, Pres.

Donor: Mary Pickford Rogers†.
Foundation type: Independent foundation.
Financial data (yr. ended 05/31/14): Assets, $16,167,312 (M); expenditures, $1,098,571; qualifying distributions, $1,081,061; giving

activities include $398,250 for 7 grants (high: $200,000; low: $1,500), and $420,517 for foundation-administered programs.
Purpose and activities: Giving primarily for education, particularly to an institute for film education, as well as for the arts, health organizations and human services.
Fields of interest: Arts and culture; Education; Diseases and conditions; Film and video; Human services.
Type of support: General support; Endowments; Scholarships.
Limitations: Applications accepted. Giving primarily in Los Angeles, CA. No support for drug rehabilitation programs. No grants to individuals, or for building funds, land acquisition, or medical research.
Application information:
  Initial approach: Letter or telephone
  Copies of proposal: 1
  Deadline(s): None
  Board meeting date(s): Varies
Officers and Directors: Henry Stotsenberg, Pres. and Director; Gary E. Shoffner, Secy. and Director; Keith Lawrence.
EIN: 956093487

928
M. Piuze Foundation
11755 Wilshire Blvd., No. 2370
Los Angeles, CA   90025-1539

Donor: Michael J. Piuze.
Foundation type: Independent foundation.
Financial data (yr. ended 11/30/13): Assets, $13,175,040 (M); gifts received, $3,787,002; expenditures, $426,459; qualifying distributions, $360,500; giving activities include $360,500 for 27 grants (high: $50,000; low: $1,500).
Fields of interest: Arts and culture; Environment; Domesticated animals; Human services; Family services.
Limitations: Applications not accepted. Giving primarily in Washington, DC. No grants to individuals.
Application information: Contributes only to pre-selected organizations.
Officers: Michael J. Piuze, Pres.; Marion Piuze, C.F.O. and Secy.
EIN: 611460815

929
Plum Foundation
4182 Beck Ave.
Studio City, CA   91604
Application address: c/o Pamela Phillips Kaizer, P.O. Box 1613, Studio City, CA 91604

Established in 1991 in California.
Donors: Dorothy Gail Secrest; John Montford; Debbie Montford.
Foundation type: Independent foundation.
Financial data (yr. ended 08/31/13): Assets, $2,900,553 (M); expenditures, $427,734; qualifying distributions, $383,172; giving activities include $332,600 for 17 grants (high: $50,000; low: $2,500).
Fields of interest: Arts and culture; Performing arts; Dance; Theater; Music; Education; Elementary and secondary education; Environment; Wildlife biodiversity.

Type of support: Research; General support; Continuing support; Program development; Scholarships.
Limitations: Applications accepted. Giving primarily in southern CA and TX for the arts; giving on a national basis for the environment and wildlife preservation and protection. No support for religious organizations for religious purposes, or for local animal shelters. No grants to individuals, or for land acquisition, building or endowment funds, annual fund drives of unified campaigns or capital campaigns, deficit financing, brochures, or public relations campaigns.
Publications: Informational brochure.
Application information: Application form required.
　Initial approach: Letter
　Deadline(s): Apr. 1 - Aug. 31
　Board meeting date(s): Mar.
Officers: John Montford, Pres.; Emily Maupin, V.P.; Bill Baldridge, Secy.-Treas.
Number of staff: 1 part-time professional.
EIN: 752406666

930
Michael and Catherine Podell Fund
1201 Howard Ave., 3rd Fl.
Burlingame, CA　94010-4242　(650) 579-7900
Contact: Michael H. Podell, Pres.

Established in 2005 in California.
Donors: Michael H. Podell; Catherine H. Podell.
Foundation type: Independent foundation.
Financial data (yr. ended 12/31/13): Assets, $6,769,135 (M); gifts received, $2,157,610; expenditures, $225,470; qualifying distributions, $218,475; giving activities include $214,500 for 10 grants (high: $100,000; low: $1,000).
Fields of interest: Arts and culture; Higher education; Nonprofits; Diseases and conditions; Community beautification; Human services.
Type of support: Research; Regranting.
Limitations: Applications accepted. Giving primarily in CA.
Application information:
　Initial approach: Proposal
　Deadline(s): None
Officer: Michael H. Podell, Pres.
Director: Catherine H. Podell.
EIN: 203483888

931
The Muriel Pollia Foundation
6255 W. Sunset Blvd., Ste. 1520
Los Angeles, CA　90028-7409

Donors: CIMA Pollia Trust; Muriel Pollia†.
Foundation type: Independent foundation.
Financial data (yr. ended 03/31/15): Assets, $9,627,027 (M); expenditures, $559,789; qualifying distributions, $342,837; giving activities include $249,250 for 24 grants (high: $80,000; low: $500).
Fields of interest: Education; Nonprofits; Community and economic development.
Type of support: Regranting.
Limitations: Applications not accepted. Giving primarily in CA. No grants to individuals.
Application information: Contributes only to pre-selected organizations.

Officers: Jay Rodriquez, Chair.; Jerry D. Luedders, Pres.; Michael Keegan, V.P.; Atsuko Kikuchi, Secy.
EIN: 954111302

932
Hughes and Sheila Potiker Family Foundation
(formerly Potiker Family Foundation)
875 Prospect St., Ste. 220
La Jolla, CA　92037-4264　(858) 657-9400
Contact: Lowell Potiker, Pres.

Established in 1992 in Michigan.
Donors: Sheila Potiker; Lowell Potiker.
Foundation type: Independent foundation.
Financial data (yr. ended 12/31/13): Assets, $3,208,862 (M); expenditures, $470,658; qualifying distributions, $447,428; giving activities include $422,025 for 2 grants (high: $372,025; low: $50,000).
Purpose and activities: Giving primarily for a Jewish community foundation; funding also for the arts.
Fields of interest: Arts and culture; Performing arts; Theater; Nonprofits; Diseases and conditions.
Type of support: Regranting.
Application information:
　Initial approach: Proposal
　Deadline(s): None
Officers: Lowell Potiker, Pres.; Brian Potiker, Secy.; Jori Potiker, Treas.
EIN: 383066992

933
The Robert R. and Helga Pralle Family Foundation
1249A E. Imperial Hwy.
Placentia, CA　92870-1745
Contact: Robert R. Case, Exec. Dir.
E-mail: grantproposals@prallefamilyfoundation.org;
Main URL: http://www.prallefamilyfoundation.org

Established in 2002 in California.
Donors: Robert R. and Helga Pralle Family Foundation; Robert R. Pralle†.
Foundation type: Independent foundation.
Financial data (yr. ended 06/30/13): Assets, $7,715,136 (M); expenditures, $424,799; qualifying distributions, $331,777; giving activities include $331,777 for 27 grants (high: $105,000; low: $500).
Fields of interest: Higher education; University education; Animal welfare; Child welfare; Youth development; Youth services.
Limitations: Applications not accepted. Giving primarily in Orange County, CA. No grants to individuals.
Application information: Contributes only to pre-selected organizations.
Officers: Helga Pralle, Pres.; Phil Case, Secy.; Kim Pralle Krotts, Treas.; Robert R. Case, Exec. Dir.
EIN: 710888527

934
Ernest Prete, Jr. Foundation
16530 Ventura Blvd., Ste. 306
Encino, CA　91436-4595

Donor: Ernest Prete, Jr.†.
Foundation type: Independent foundation.

Financial data (yr. ended 05/31/13): Assets, $6,703,893 (M); expenditures, $351,060; qualifying distributions, $259,932; giving activities include $171,000 for 8 grants (high: $100,000; low: $500).
Fields of interest: University education; Natural resources; Biodiversity; Wildlife biodiversity; Human services; People with disabilities.
Limitations: Applications not accepted. Giving primarily in CA. No grants to individuals.
Application information: Contributes only to pre-selected organizations.
Directors: Rebecca Natalia; Leon Small; Mohammad J. Virani.
EIN: 954333283

935
The Preuss Family Foundation
2223 Avenida De La Playa, Ste. 220
La Jolla, CA　92037-3218

Donors: Peter G. Preuss; Peggy Preuss.
Foundation type: Independent foundation.
Financial data (yr. ended 12/31/14): Assets, $423,388 (M); gifts received, $13,730; expenditures, $386,015; qualifying distributions, $379,190; giving activities include $378,110 for 21 grants (high: $115,000; low: $14,610).
Purpose and activities: Giving for the opera and to support scientific research, especially related to brain tumors.
Fields of interest: Opera; Education; Foundations; Brain and nervous system disorders; Diabetes; Mathematics; Human services.
International interests: Germany.
Type of support: General support; Scholarships; Research.
Limitations: Applications not accepted. Giving primarily in La Jolla, CA. No grants to individuals.
Application information: Contributes only to pre-selected organizations.
Officers: Peter G. Preuss, Pres.; Peter J. Preuss, V.P.; Peggy Preuss, Secy.
EIN: 330229180

936
Prevent Cruelty To Animals (PVCA)
101 Mission St., No. 1105
San Francisco, CA　94105-1733

Donors: Cairo Gregor; Richard Parasol; Morris Foundation.
Foundation type: Independent foundation.
Financial data (yr. ended 12/31/13): Assets, $74,489 (M); gifts received, $275,338; expenditures, $345,585; qualifying distributions, $311,900; giving activities include $311,900 for 1 grant.
Fields of interest: Domesticated animals.
Limitations: Applications not accepted.
Application information: Unsolicited requests for funds not accepted.
Officer: Cairo Gregor, Pres.
EIN: 263656362

937
John P. Previti Memorial Foundation
(formerly Led By Love Foundation)
8300 Utica Ave., Ste. 300
Rancho Cucamonga, CA 91730-3852
Main URL: http://previtimemorialfoundation.org
Facebook: https://www.facebook.com/
PrevitiMemorialFoundation
Google Plus: https://plus.google.com/
115516234793995330324/posts
Twitter: https://twitter.com/JPPFoundation
YouTube: http://www.youtube.com/channel/
UCmJLgToyVgzTvbeMjxuU_kQ

Donor: James L. Previti.
Foundation type: Independent foundation.
Financial data (yr. ended 06/30/14): Assets,
$1,416,883 (M); expenditures, $196,552;
qualifying distributions, $193,467; giving activities
include $190,804 for 21 grants (high: $50,000;
low: $500).
Fields of interest: Community and economic
development; Religion; Human services; Children.
Limitations: Applications accepted. Giving primarily
in CA.
Application information: In a typical year, less than
1 percent of unsolicited inquiries result in a grant.
Initial approach: Submit the foundation's grant
inquiry form from its web site.
Directors: Richard Munkvold; James L. Previti;
Katelyn Marie Previti.
EIN: 274256513

938
The Arthur & Patricia Price Foundation
(formerly Arthur L. Price Foundation)
c/o Gettleson, Witzer & O'Connor
16000 Ventura Blvd., Ste. 900
Encino, CA 91436-2760

Established in 1990 in California.
Donors: Arthur L. Price; Patricia A. Price; Arthur
Patricia Price Family Trust.
Foundation type: Independent foundation.
Financial data (yr. ended 02/28/14): Assets,
$3,133,952 (M); expenditures, $182,455;
qualifying distributions, $162,195; giving activities
include $158,325 for 58 grants (high: $68,500;
low: $50).
Fields of interest: Arts and culture; Music; Health;
Diseases and conditions; Communication media;
Human services; Child welfare.
Type of support: General support.
Limitations: Applications not accepted. Giving
primarily in Santa Monica, CA. No grants to
individuals.
Application information: Contributes only to
pre-selected organizations.
Officers: Arthur L. Price, Pres. and C.E.O.; Patricia A.
Price, V.P., Secy., and C.F.O.
Director: David A. Weinstein.
EIN: 954303203

939
The William L. Price Foundation
570 El Camino Real, Box 150-505
Redwood City, CA 94063-1200

Established in 2004 in Unspecified.
Donor: William L. Price.
Foundation type: Independent foundation.

Financial data (yr. ended 12/31/13): Assets,
$4,367,849 (M); gifts received, $9,100;
expenditures, $252,825; qualifying distributions,
$235,840; giving activities include $235,350 for 73
grants (high: $15,000; low: $250).
Fields of interest: Education; Health; Diseases and
conditions; Human services; Child welfare.
Limitations: Applications not accepted. Giving
primarily in CA; funding also in NY and OR. No grants
to individuals.
Application information: Contributes only to
pre-selected organizations.
Officer: W.L. Price, Pres.
Directors: J. Frost; A. Price; J. Price.
EIN: 200140310

940
Priory Fund
1482 E. Valley Rd., No. 678
Montecito, CA 93108-1200

Donors: Edward J. McKinley; Kathleen A. Lavidge.
Foundation type: Independent foundation.
Financial data (yr. ended 12/31/13): Assets,
$7,372,680 (M); gifts received, $1,340,060;
expenditures, $190,676; qualifying distributions,
$127,917; giving activities include $120,000 for 2
grants (high: $60,000; low: $60,000).
Fields of interest: Education; Higher education;
Mental health care.
Limitations: Applications not accepted. Giving
primarily in CA; some funding also in CT.
Application information: Unsolicited requests for
funds not accepted.
Officers: Kathleen A. Lavidge, Pres.; Edward J.
McKinley, Treas.
EIN: 274014193

941
The Private Foundation
c/o Gelfand, Rennert and Feldman
1880 Century Park E., Ste. 1600
Los Angeles, CA 90067-1661

Established in 1998 in California.
Donors: Marc J. Turtletaub; The Turtletaub
Foundation, Inc.
Foundation type: Independent foundation.
Financial data (yr. ended 12/31/13): Assets,
$1,788,069 (M); expenditures, $215,637;
qualifying distributions, $174,750; giving activities
include $174,750 for 10 grants (high: $40,000;
low: $1,000).
Fields of interest: Arts and culture; Education;
Diseases and conditions.
Limitations: Applications not accepted. Giving
primarily in CA. No grants to individuals.
Application information: Unsolicited requests for
funds not accepted.
Officers: Marc J. Turtletaub, Pres.; Alex E.
Turtletaub, V.P.; Jesse Sprecher, Secy.-Tres.
EIN: 943303674

942
Project Paradigm
11377 W. Olympic Blvd.
Los Angeles, CA 90064-1625

Donor: Stefanyshyn Settlement.
Foundation type: Independent foundation.

Financial data (yr. ended 07/31/13): Assets,
$10,639,314 (M); gifts received, $21,605;
expenditures, $646,486; qualifying distributions,
$547,802; giving activities include $402,000 for 25
grants (high: $60,000; low: $2,000).
Fields of interest: Fire prevention and control.
Limitations: Applications not accepted. Giving
primarily in IL, MA and VA.
Application information: Unsolicited requests for
funds not accepted.
Officers and Directors: Jeffrey L. Richardson, Chair.
and Pres.; Jennifer Dulay, Secy. and Director; John
G. Crabtree, C.F.O. and Director; David Krahulik;
Mark Morrison; Matt J. Railo.
EIN: 271444039

943
PTSRK Foundation
18 Crow Canyon Ct., Ste. 250
San Ramon, CA 94583-1669

Established in 2005 in California.
Donors: Patrisia Spezzaferro; Ross Koningstein.
Foundation type: Independent foundation.
Financial data (yr. ended 12/31/13): Assets,
$4,088,443 (M); gifts received, $139,524;
expenditures, $310,898; qualifying distributions,
$290,000; giving activities include $290,000 for 19
grants (high: $50,000; low: $1,000).
Fields of interest: University education; Human
rights; Human services.
Limitations: Applications not accepted. Giving
primarily in CA. No grants to individuals.
Application information: Unsolicited requests for
funds not accepted.
Officers: Ross Koningstein, C.E.O.; Patrisia
Spezzaferro, C.F.O. and Secy.
EIN: 203960774

944
The Pulido Walker Foundation
P.O. Box 1334
Rancho Santa Fe, CA 92067-1334 (858)
756-6150
Contact: Donna J. Walker, Pres.

Established in 1996 in California.
Donors: Mark A. Pulido; Donna J. Walker.
Foundation type: Independent foundation.
Financial data (yr. ended 12/31/13): Assets,
$1,926,999 (M); expenditures, $214,719;
qualifying distributions, $189,494; giving activities
include $186,100 for 8 grants (high: $125,000;
low: $100).
Fields of interest: Education; University education;
Diseases and conditions; Human services.
Type of support: General support.
Limitations: Applications accepted. Giving primarily
in CA and SC.
Application information: Application form required.
Initial approach: Letter
Deadline(s): None
Officers: Donna J. Walker, Pres.; Mark A. Pulido, V.P.
EIN: 943249877

945
Quiksilver Foundation
15202 Graham St.
Huntington Beach, CA 92649-1109 (714) 889-7132
Contact: Ryan Ashton, Dir.
E-mail: ryan.ashton@quiksilver.com; Additional contact: Kathie Armstrong, Dir., kathie.armstrong@quicksilver.com; E-mail for U.S., Canada, and Latin America inquiries: foundation@quicksilver.com; E-mail for South Pacific and Australia inquiries: quicksilver.foundation@quicksilver.com.au; Main URL: http://www.quiksilverfoundation.org
Facebook: http://www.facebook.com/quikfoundation
RSS feed: http://www.quiksilverfoundation.org/feed
Twitter: http://twitter.com/QuikFoundation

Established in 2004 in California.
Donor: Quiksilver, Inc.
Foundation type: Company-sponsored foundation.
Financial data (yr. ended 10/31/13): Assets, $109,653 (M); gifts received, $60,503; expenditures, $275,948; qualifying distributions, $219,714; giving activities include $219,714 for 16 grants (high: $100,000; low: $1,010).
Purpose and activities: The foundation supports programs that benefit and enhance the quality of life for communities of boardriders across the world. Special emphasis is directed towards community-based organizations involved with education, oceans, the environment, health, science, children, and youth.
Fields of interest: Education; Environment; Oceans and coastal waters; Environmental education; Health; Science; Community and economic development; Children; Adolescents.
International interests: Asia; Australia; Europe.
Type of support: Research; Donated products; In-kind gifts; General support; Continuing support; Program development; Scholarships.
Limitations: Applications not accepted. Giving primarily in areas of company operations, with emphasis on CA, Asia, Australia, and Europe. No grants to individuals or for fundraising activities.
Publications: Grants list.
Application information: Unsolicited applications are currently not accepted. The foundation utilizes an invitation only process for giving at this time.
Officers and Directors: Ryan Ashton, Mgr.; Fernando Aguerre; Kathie Armstrong; Maritxu Darrigrand; Scott Fullerton; Richard A. Gadbois III; Jeffrey Ishmael; Julia Ladgrove; Sean Pence; Jeff Wilson.
Number of staff: 1 full-time professional; 1 part-time professional.
EIN: 200986472

946
RA5 Foundation
4640 Admiralty Way., Ste. 1200
Marina del Rey, CA 90292-6642

Foundation type: Independent foundation.
Financial data (yr. ended 12/31/13): Assets, $8,798,609 (M); gifts received, $4,860,605; expenditures, $286,756; qualifying distributions, $282,127; giving activities include $277,500 for 2 grants (high: $257,500; low: $20,000).
Fields of interest: Education; Foundations; Community and economic development.

Limitations: Applications not accepted. Giving primarily in CA.
Application information: Unsolicited requests for funds not accepted.
Trustees: Alecia Seidler; Robert Seidler.
EIN: 456627637

947
The Rabinovitch Foundation
8888 W. Olympic Blvd., Ste. 100
Beverly Hills, CA 90211-3616

Established in 1997 in California.
Donor: Anita Rabinovitch.
Foundation type: Independent foundation.
Financial data (yr. ended 12/31/13): Assets, $3,253,924 (M); expenditures, $181,362; qualifying distributions, $160,300; giving activities include $160,250 for 8 grants (high: $125,000; low: $2,000).
Purpose and activities: Emphasis is on providing support to recreational camps for disadvantaged or ill children.
Fields of interest: Arts and culture; Museums; Religion; Human services.
Limitations: Applications not accepted. Giving primarily in Los Angeles, CA. No grants to individuals.
Application information: Contributes only to pre-selected organizations.
Officers: Arnold Nelson, Chair.; Gregory Nelson, Pres.; Brian Nelson, V.P.; Matthew Nelson, V.P.; Andrea Nelson Kopald, Secy.-Treas.
EIN: 954619032

948
Radin Foundation
3142 Willow Ave., Ste. 101
Clovis, CA 93612-4745

Donor: Leta H. Radin†.
Foundation type: Independent foundation.
Financial data (yr. ended 12/31/13): Assets, $4,179,047 (M); expenditures, $407,268; qualifying distributions, $407,268; giving activities include $369,000 for 8 grants (high: $200,000; low: $3,000).
Purpose and activities: Funding primarily for hospitals; some funding for the arts and education.
Fields of interest: Arts and culture; Higher education; Hospital care; Specialty hospital care.
Limitations: Applications not accepted. Giving primarily in Fresno, CA. No grants to individuals.
Application information: Unsolicited requests for funds not accepted.
Officers and Directors: Leslie E. Findley, Pres. and Director; Jason S. Liao, C.F.O. and Director.
EIN: 237155525

949
Rady Family Foundation
11455 El Camino Real, Ste. 200
San Diego, CA 92130-2047

Established in 2002 in California.
Donors: Ernest S. Rady; Evelyn Rady; Margo S. Alon.
Foundation type: Independent foundation.
Financial data (yr. ended 12/31/13): Assets, $11,314,739 (M); gifts received, $3,400,000; expenditures, $518,467; qualifying distributions,

$349,499; giving activities include $312,049 for 21 grants (high: $250,000; low: $200).
Purpose and activities: Giving primarily for education, human services, Jewish organizations, and a children's hospital.
Fields of interest: Education; Health; Human services.
Limitations: Applications not accepted. Giving primarily in San Diego, CA and Chicago, IL. No grants to individuals.
Application information: Contributes only to pre-selected organizations.
Trustee: Ernest S. Rady.
EIN: 760708193

950
Meyer J. and Norma L. Ragir Foundation
c/o Marshall Ragir/Blooma Stark
3220 Federal Ave.
Los Angeles, CA 90066-1227

Established in 1991 in Illinois.
Foundation type: Independent foundation.
Financial data (yr. ended 12/31/14): Assets, $6,867,137; expenditures, $518,526; qualifying distributions, $333,972.
Fields of interest: Arts and culture; Education; Religion; Judaism.
Type of support: Annual campaigns; Program-related investments; Matching grants; Capital campaigns; Capital and infrastructure; Internships; Scholarships.
Limitations: Applications not accepted. Giving primarily in CA, MN and WI. No grants to individuals.
Application information: Unsolicited requests for funds not accepted.
Officers and Directors: Judith Ragir, Pres. and Director; Robert Ragir, V.P. and Director; Marshall Ragir, Secy.-Treas. and Director; Lydia H. Madrigal; Alexander V. Ragir.
Number of staff: 3 part-time professional.
EIN: 363797780

951
The Rallis Foundation
P.O. Box 1219
Newport Beach, CA 92659-0019

Established in 1993 in California.
Donors: John Rallis; Mary Lynn Bergman-Rallis.
Foundation type: Independent foundation.
Financial data (yr. ended 11/30/13): Assets, $3,422,616 (M); gifts received, $2,000,000; expenditures, $187,022; qualifying distributions, $170,000; giving activities include $170,000 for 10 grants (high: $50,000; low: $5,000).
Purpose and activities: Giving primarily for human services.
Fields of interest: Education; Health; Diseases and conditions.
Limitations: Applications not accepted. No grants to individuals.
Application information: Unsolicited requests for funds not accepted.
Officers and Directors: John Rallis, Pres. and Director; Mary Lynn Bergman-Rallis, V.P. and Director.
EIN: 330590516

952
Ramsay Family Foundation
(formerly ABC Foundation)
P.O. Box 193809
San Francisco, CA 94119-3809

Established in 1977 in California.
Donors: Nonie B. Ramsay; Stephen D. Bechtel, Jr.
Foundation type: Independent foundation.
Financial data (yr. ended 12/31/13): Assets, $13,049,868 (M); gifts received, $2,000,000; expenditures, $426,901; qualifying distributions, $403,435; giving activities include $369,500 for 33 grants (high: $200,000; low: $500).
Purpose and activities: Giving primarily for education; some funding also for arts and culture and human services.
Fields of interest: Arts and culture; Elementary and secondary education; Wildlife biodiversity; Philanthropy; Human services.
Limitations: Applications not accepted. Giving primarily in CA and CT. No grants to individuals.
Application information: Contributes only to pre-selected organizations.
Officers and Directors: Nonie B. Ramsay, Pres. and Director; Andrew C. Ramsay, V.P. and Director; Stephen A. Ramsay, V.P. and Director; George T. Argyris, Secy.; Shu Huang, Treas.; Stephen D. Bechtel, Jr.; Nancy S. Hair; Lindsay G. Ramsay; Sheldon C. Ramsay.
EIN: 942415607

953
Rappaport Family Foundation
1748 Union St.
San Francisco, CA 94123-4407 (415) 593-7111
Contact: Catalina Ruiz-Healy, V.P.
E-mail: info@rappaportfamilyfoundation.org; Main URL: http://www.rappaportfamilyfoundation.org
Facebook: https://www.facebook.com/pages/RFF-Spark/463115230384712
Grants List: http://rappaportfamilyfoundation.org/grants
Rappaport Family Foundation's Philanthropy Promise: http://www.ncrp.org/philanthropys-promise/who
Twitter: https://twitter.com/RffSpark

Established in 2003 in California.
Donors: Andrew Rappaport; Deborah Rappaport.
Foundation type: Independent foundation.
Financial data (yr. ended 10/31/13): Assets, $8,111,203 (M); gifts received, $820,950; expenditures, $518,043; qualifying distributions, $437,961; giving activities include $249,500 for 9 grants (high: $40,000; low: $2,000).
Purpose and activities: The foundation's interests are: 1) Finding innovative and promising ideas for engaging community college students in California, especially those focused on pocketbook issues; 2) Identifying and supporting promising institutional or third-party programs, or faculty members who have unique solutions to ignite and maintain civic participation and community engagement among community college students; 3) Solutions that address specific challenges to successful program implementation faced by students, faculty, and administration; 4) Using new tools, technologies and organizing methods to support distributed models of engagement and activism on a community college or among community college students; and 5) Taking a risk on unconventional or untried approaches.

Fields of interest: Education; Philanthropy; Public affairs; Public policy.
Type of support: Research and evaluation; Policy, advocacy and systems reform.
Limitations: Giving in the U.S., with some emphasis on CA and Washington, DC. No support for religious organizations, international or foreign-based programs, or social service programs. No grants to individuals, or for scholarships, or capital campaigns.
Application information: The foundation is currently not accepting unsolicited proposals. Check foundation web site for updates.
Officers: Deborah Rappaport, C.E.O.; Catalina Ruiz-Healy, V.P.; Andrew Rappaport, Treas.
EIN: 200433083

954
Jerome and Toby Rapport Foundation
516 Moreno Ave.
Los Angeles, CA 90049-4811

Established in 1996 in California.
Donors: Jerome Rapport; Toby Rapport.
Foundation type: Independent foundation.
Financial data (yr. ended 12/31/13): Assets, $4,410,736 (M); expenditures, $326,022; qualifying distributions, $235,000; giving activities include $235,000 for 20 grants (high: $50,000; low: $1,000).
Fields of interest: Education; Health; International relations.
Limitations: Applications not accepted. Giving primarily in CA. No grants to individuals.
Application information: Unsolicited requests for funds not accepted.
Officers: Lauren G. Rapport, Pres.; Jerome Rapport, Secy. and C.F.O.; Toby Rapport, V.P.
EIN: 954573578

955
Rar Family Foundation
c/o Savitsky, Satin & Bacon
10880 Wilshire Blvd., Ste. 2100
Los Angeles, CA 90024-4121

Donors: Raymond Romano; Anna Romano.
Foundation type: Independent foundation.
Financial data (yr. ended 12/31/13): Assets, $5,741,318 (M); gifts received, $2,089,548; expenditures, $222,245; qualifying distributions, $196,974; giving activities include $170,000 for 4 grants (high: $152,000; low: $1,000).
Fields of interest: Health; Diseases and conditions; Sports and recreation.
Type of support: General support.
Limitations: Applications not accepted. Giving primarily in CA.
Application information: Unsolicited requests for funds not accepted.
Officers: Anna Ramano, Pres.; Raymond Romano, V.P. and Secy.
Directors: Alexandra Romano; Gary Satin.
EIN: 274347026

956
The Raymond Foundation
2000 Wellington Dr.
Milpitas, CA 95035

Established in 2003 in California.
Donor: Raymond Wu.
Foundation type: Independent foundation.
Financial data (yr. ended 12/31/13): Assets, $2,348,571 (M); expenditures, $213,785; qualifying distributions, $210,000; giving activities include $210,000 for 3 grants (high: $100,000; low: $10,000).
Fields of interest: Buddhism; Human services; People of Asian descent; Immigrants and migrants.
International interests: China.
Limitations: Applications not accepted. Giving primarily in CA and NY; giving also in China. No grants to individuals.
Application information: Contributes only to pre-selected organizations.
Officers: Jeffrey Wu, Pres.; Raymond Wu, C.F.O. and Secy.
EIN: 432003792

957
The Razi Family Foundation
2201 Dupont Dr., Ste. 300
Irvine, CA 92612-7509 9498331554

Established in 2001 in California.
Donors: Ali Cyrus Razi; Anousheh Razi.
Foundation type: Independent foundation.
Financial data (yr. ended 12/31/14): Assets, $3,668,759; gifts received, $1,096,970; expenditures, $246,550; qualifying distributions, $215,457.
Purpose and activities: Giving primarily for education and human services, particularly to Iranian causes.
Fields of interest: Cultural awareness; Art museums; University education; Child welfare; Homeless shelters.
Limitations: Applications accepted. Giving primarily in CA. No grants to individuals.
Application information: Application form required.
   Initial approach: Letter
   Deadline(s): None
Officers: Ali Cyrus Razi, Pres.; Anousheh Razi, Secy.-Treas.
Directors: Niloofar Razi Howe; Babak Cyrus Razi; Keyvan Cyrus Razi.
EIN: 912169259

958
L. B. Reddy Family Foundation
2278 Shattuck Ave.
Berkeley, CA 94704-1431

Established in 2000 in California.
Donor: Lakireddy B. Reddy.
Foundation type: Independent foundation.
Financial data (yr. ended 06/30/13): Assets, $928,319 (M); gifts received, $370,000; expenditures, $266,169; qualifying distributions, $200,000; giving activities include $200,000 for 1 grant.
Fields of interest: Architecture; Education; Graduate and professional education; Engineering.
International interests: India.
Limitations: Applications not accepted. Giving primarily in IL; with some giving India. No grants to individuals.
Application information: Unsolicited requests for funds not accepted.

Officers: L.B. Reddy, Pres. and Treas.; P. Lakireddy, Secy.
EIN: 943368453

959
Reddy's Heart to Heart Foundation
12934 Galewood Dr.
Apple Valley, CA 92308
Application address: c/o Naidu Reddy, 20022 Rancherias Rd., Apple Valley, CA 92307 tel.: (760) 242-6500

Donors: Anuradha Reddy; Naidu Reddy.
Foundation type: Independent foundation.
Financial data (yr. ended 12/31/13): Assets, $1,869,328 (M); expenditures, $237,376; qualifying distributions, $231,701; giving activities include $231,701 for 7 grants (high: $145,000; low: $51).
Fields of interest: Education; Diseases and conditions.
Limitations: Applications not accepted.
Application information: Unsolicited requests for funds not accepted.
Officers: Naidu Reddy, Pres.; Kaavya Reddy, Secy.; Anuradha Reddy, Treas.
EIN: 208966784

960
The Rediger Family Foundation
500 E. Olive Ave., Ste. 840
Burbank, CA 91501

Donors: Daren Rediger; Denis K. Rediger; Donald E. Rediger; Duane E. Rediger.
Foundation type: Independent foundation.
Financial data (yr. ended 12/31/13): Assets, $8,655,466 (M); gifts received, $545,405; expenditures, $391,530; qualifying distributions, $381,850; giving activities include $381,850 for 29 grants (high: $76,500; low: $100).
Fields of interest: University education; Foundations; Christianity; Camps; Human services; Child welfare.
Limitations: Applications not accepted. Giving primarily in CA, with some giving in MA. No grants to individuals.
Application information: Contributes only to pre-selected organizations.
Officers: Donald E. Rediger, Chair.; Daren R. Rediger, Pres. and Treas.; Duane E. Rediger, V.P.; Denis K. Rediger, Secy.
EIN: 954700641

961
Nancy E. Barry & Letitia P. Rees Foundation
1056 Amalfi Dr.
Pacific Palisades, CA 90272-4028
Contact: William H. Borthwick

Donor: Charles Munger.
Foundation type: Independent foundation.
Financial data (yr. ended 12/31/13): Assets, $2,822,535 (M); expenditures, $251,898; qualifying distributions, $242,035; giving activities include $242,035 for 19 grants (high: $71,000; low: $100).
Fields of interest: Education; Health; Hospital care; Housing development.

Type of support: General support.
Limitations: Applications not accepted. Giving primarily in CT and VA. No grants to individuals.
Application information: Unsolicited requests for funds not accepted.
Directors: Maribeth A. Borthwick; William H. Borthwick.
EIN: 957026070

962
Janet and Clint Reilly Family Foundation
465 California St.
San Francisco, CA 94104-1804

Donors: Clint Reilly; Janet Reilly.
Foundation type: Independent foundation.
Financial data (yr. ended 12/31/13): Assets, $4,171 (M); gifts received, $206,700; expenditures, $193,500; qualifying distributions, $193,500; giving activities include $193,500 for 83 grants (high: $2,500; low: $1,500).
Fields of interest: Secondary education.
Limitations: Applications not accepted. Giving primarily in San Francisco, CA.
Application information: Unsolicited requests for funds not accepted.
Officers and Directors: Clint Reilly, Pres.; Janet Reilly, Secy. and C.F.O. and Director.
EIN: 262835658

963
The Reinhold Foundation
c/o B. Terry Reinhold
624 Harbor Island Dr.
Newport Beach, CA 92660-7226

Established in 1997 in California.
Donors: Baldwin Reinhold, Jr.; Mary E. Reinhold.
Foundation type: Independent foundation.
Financial data (yr. ended 12/31/14): Assets, $5,072,388; expenditures, $403,381; qualifying distributions, $375,585.
Fields of interest: Higher education; Hospital care; Cancers; Human services; Child welfare; Youth services.
Type of support: General support.
Limitations: Applications not accepted. Giving primarily in CA and CT. No grants to individuals.
Application information: Contributes only to pre-selected organizations.
Officers: B. Terry Reinhold, Pres.; Carol A. Reinhold, C.F.O.
EIN: 330756400

964
The Reitman Foundation
10960 Wilshire Blvd., Ste. 700
Los Angeles, CA 90024-3710

Established in 1986 in California.
Donors: Genevieve Reitman; Ivan Reitman.
Foundation type: Independent foundation.
Financial data (yr. ended 06/30/13): Assets, $894,069 (M); gifts received, $150,000; expenditures, $234,160; qualifying distributions, $230,503; giving activities include $228,500 for 7 grants (high: $200,000; low: $1,000).
Fields of interest: Arts and culture; Art museums; Education; Elementary and secondary education;

Health; Hospital care; Film and video; Religion; Judaism; Youth services.
Limitations: Applications not accepted. Giving primarily in CA and IL. No grants to individuals.
Application information: Contributes generally to pre-selected organizations.
Trustees: Genevieve Reitman; Ivan Reitman.
EIN: 954081980

965
Resource Partners Foundation
4757 Old Cliffs Rd.
San Diego, CA 92120-1134

Established in 2006 in California.
Donor: Jean Shea.
Foundation type: Independent foundation.
Financial data (yr. ended 12/31/14): Assets, $9,457,789 (M); gifts received, $1,700,000; expenditures, $364,344; qualifying distributions, $360,000; giving activities include $360,000 for 3 grants (high: $255,000; low: $5,000).
Fields of interest: Animal welfare; Cancers.
Limitations: Applications not accepted. Giving primarily in CA. No grants to individuals.
Application information: Unsolicited requests for funds not accepted.
Officer: Jean Shea, Pres. and C.F.O.
EIN: 205885806

966
Rest Haven Preventorium for Children, Inc.
(also known as Children's Health Fund)
P.O. Box 420369
San Diego, CA 92142-0369 (858) 576-0590
Contact: Peggy McNamara, Exec. Secy.
FAX: (858) 576-0029;
E-mail: resthavenchfund@sbcglobal.net; *Main URL:* http://resthavenchf.org

Established in 1963 in California.
Donors: Anna M. Spring Trust; Jessie Castle Roberts Trust.
Foundation type: Operating foundation.
Financial data (yr. ended 12/31/13): Assets, $11,018,415 (M); expenditures, $350,196; qualifying distributions, $268,134; giving activities include $228,075 for 15 grants (high: $50,000; low: $1,000), and $303,642 for 1 foundation-administered program.
Purpose and activities: Provides monetary assistance for the benefit of needy children in the San Diego, CA, area for medical, dental, therapy, hearing, child care, and nutrition expenses. No giving to those outside the target area.
Fields of interest: Health; Human services; Youth organizing; Low-income and poor people.
Type of support: General support; Grants to individuals.
Limitations: Applications not accepted. Giving exclusively for the benefit of residents of San Diego and Imperial County, CA.
Application information: Unsolicited requests for funds will not be accepted from families outside San Diego or Imperial County, CA.
Officers: Raymond M. Peterson, MD, Pres.; David N. Allsbrook III, V.P.; Alison F. Gildred, Secy.; Christine Bryant, Treas.; Peggy McNamara, Exec. Dir.

Directors: Paul S. Condon; Richard B. Hancock, D.D.S.; Beatrice W. Kemp; Patricia Tisdale; W. Harold Tuck; Paul Wozniak, MD.
EIN: 952128344

967
The Reveas Foundation
P.O. Box 1733
Pebble Beach, CA 93953

Donors: Charles Scott Hulme; Elizabeth R. Hulme; Elizabeth W. Reeves; Samuel T. Reeves; Sandra R. Spears; Pinnacle Trading, LLC; Drake Capital LLC; Virginia Reeves Apple.
Foundation type: Independent foundation.
Financial data (yr. ended 12/31/13): Assets, $523,512 (M); gifts received, $499,508; expenditures, $270,310; qualifying distributions, $268,500; giving activities include $268,500 for 10 grants (high: $110,000; low: $2,500).
Purpose and activities: Giving primarily for education, human services, and to Presbyterian and Congregational churches.
Fields of interest: Education; Higher education; Medical education; Foundations; Protestantism; Human services.
Limitations: Applications not accepted. Giving in the U.S., with emphasis on CA. No grants to individuals.
Application information: Contributes only to pre-selected organizations.
Officers: Samuel T. Reeves, Pres. and Treas.; Charles Scott Hulme, Secy.
Directors: Virginia Reeves Apple; Elizabeth R. Hulme; Elizabeth W. Reeves; Sandra R. Spears.
EIN: 223621474

968
Rhe Charitable Foundation
51 Sussex St.
San Francisco, CA 94131-3011
Contact: Jennifer Heyneman

Foundation type: Independent foundation.
Financial data (yr. ended 12/31/13): Assets, $4,310,575 (M); expenditures, $437,520; qualifying distributions, $393,884; giving activities include $226,297 for 35 grants (high: $35,000; low: $50).
Fields of interest: Domesticated animals; Human services.
Type of support: General support.
Limitations: Applications not accepted. Giving primarily in CA.
Application information: Unsolicited requests for funds not accepted.
Officers and Directors: Jennifer Heyneman, Pres. and Director; William Sousae, V.P.; Patricia Hamilton, Secy. and Director; Michael Arnold, Treas. and Director.
EIN: 262469224

969
Rice Family Foundation
4471 Jutland Dr.
San Diego, CA 92117

Established in 1993 in California.
Donor: Morgan S. Rice†.
Foundation type: Independent foundation.

Financial data (yr. ended 12/31/14): Assets, $7,190,319; expenditures, $471,796; qualifying distributions, $358,696.
Purpose and activities: Giving primarily for education.
Fields of interest: Museums; Education.
Type of support: Continuing support; Matching grants; Publications; Curriculum development; Fellowships; Internships; Scholarships.
Limitations: Applications not accepted. Giving limited to San Diego County, CA. No grants to individuals.
Application information: Contributes only to pre-selected organizations.
Board meeting date(s): Sept.
Officers and Directors: Lisa Wilson, C.F.O. and Treas. and Director; Shar Salter, V.P. and Director; Michelle Brookman, Secy. and Director.
Number of staff: None.
EIN: 330592384

970
The Georgia B. Ridder Foundation
531 S. Marengo Ave.
Pasadena, CA 91101-3114

Established in 2000 in California.
Donors: Georgia B. Ridder; Georgia B. Ridder Charitable Trust.
Foundation type: Independent foundation.
Financial data (yr. ended 12/31/13): Assets, $6,161,222 (M); gifts received, $145,649; expenditures, $274,666; qualifying distributions, $213,504; giving activities include $197,000 for 5 grants (high: $105,000; low: $10,000).
Fields of interest: Environment; Animal welfare; Hospital care; Family planning; Human services.
Limitations: Applications not accepted. Giving primarily in southern CA and NY. No grants to individuals.
Application information: Contributes only to pre-selected organizations.
Officer and Director: Michael S. Whalen, Pres. and Director.
EIN: 954813547

971
Rieger Foundation
P.O. Box 45174
San Francisco, CA 94145-0174

Established in 1987 in California.
Donors: Norbert Rieger†; Charlotte Rieger†.
Foundation type: Independent foundation.
Financial data (yr. ended 12/31/14): Assets, $4,431,003; expenditures, $460,385; qualifying distributions, $356,202.
Fields of interest: Higher education; Nonprofits; Health; Diseases and conditions; Judaism; Human services.
International interests: Israel.
Type of support: Regranting.
Limitations: Applications not accepted. Giving primarily in CA, Washington, DC, and NY; also giving in Israel. No grants to individuals.
Publications: Informational brochure.
Application information: Contributes only to pre-selected organizations.
Trustee: Union Bank, N.A.
EIN: 770159141

972
Robert Gore Rifkind Foundation
P.O. Box 662147
Los Angeles, CA 90066-8547 (818) 990-1125
Contact: Max Rifkind-Barron, Dir.

Established in 1979 in California.
Donors: Robert Gore Rifkind; Max Rifkind-Barron.
Foundation type: Operating foundation.
Financial data (yr. ended 03/31/13): Assets, $8,051,608 (M); expenditures, $532,966; qualifying distributions, $435,186; giving activities include $413,285 for 38 grants (high: $135,000; low: $250).
Purpose and activities: Giving primarily for the arts, especially art museums; in addition, grant awards enable scholars to come to Los Angeles to study at the Rifkind Center for German Expressionist Studies.
Fields of interest: Arts and culture; Arts education; Orchestral music; Museums; Domesticated animals; Diseases and conditions; Libraries; Judaism.
International interests: Israel.
Type of support: General support; Continuing support; Research.
Limitations: Applications accepted. Giving primarily in southern CA.
Application information: Application form required.
Initial approach: Letter
Deadline(s): None
Officers: Max Rifkind-Barron, Pres.; Jane Levikow, Secy.; Jonathan Davidson, Treas.
EIN: 953397350

973
Susan E. Riley Foundation
13949 Ventura Blvd., Ste. 215
Sherman Oaks, CA 91423-5735

Established in 2001 in California.
Donor: Susan Riley†.
Foundation type: Independent foundation.
Financial data (yr. ended 12/31/13): Assets, $8,971,372 (M); expenditures, $439,760; qualifying distributions, $356,018; giving activities include $314,784 for 6 grants (high: $100,000; low: $10,500).
Purpose and activities: Giving primarily for pancreatic cancer research.
Fields of interest: Education; Pancreatic cancer; Human services.
Type of support: General support; Research.
Limitations: Applications not accepted. Giving primarily in CA and New York, NY. No grants to individuals.
Application information: Contributes only to pre-selected organizations.
Trustees: Douglas L. Johnson, Emeritus; Harry L. Hathaway; Robert M. Newell.
EIN: 954819693

974
Robert & Karen Rishwain Family Foundation
2800 W. March Ln., Ste. 360
Stockton, CA 95219-8208

Donors: Robert J. Rishwain; Karen S. Rishwain; Richard Paulsen.
Foundation type: Independent foundation.

Financial data (yr. ended 12/31/13): Assets, $196,971 (M); gifts received, $312,980; expenditures, $333,036; qualifying distributions, $333,036; giving activities include $332,450 for 18 grants (high: $105,000; low: $750).
Fields of interest: Theater; Music; Education; Elementary and secondary education; University education; Foundations; Hospital care.
Limitations: Applications not accepted. Giving primarily in CA; some giving also in VA. No grants to individuals.
Application information: Contributes only to pre-selected organizations.
Officers and Directors: Robert J. Rishwain, Pres. and Director; Mark B. Rishwain, V.P. and Director; Karen S. Rishwain, Secy. and Director.
EIN: 942860997

975
Sally and Dick Roberts Coyote Foundation
c/o Foundation Source
7222 Cirrus Way
West Hills, CA 91307-1415
LinkedIn: http://www.linkedin.com/pub/the-sally-and-dick-roberts-coyote-foundation/5/a08/924

Established in 2006 in California.
Donors: Dick Roberts; Sally Roberts; Richard F. Roberts.
Foundation type: Independent foundation.
Financial data (yr. ended 12/31/13): Assets, $6,596,689 (M); expenditures, $513,450; qualifying distributions, $464,379; giving activities include $297,842 for 16 grants (high: $40,800; low: $5,000).
Fields of interest: Arts and culture; Orchestral music; Education; University education; Diseases and conditions; Social sciences; Family services.
Type of support: Policy, advocacy and systems reform.
Limitations: Applications not accepted. Giving primarily in CA, IL, MO and NY.
Application information: Contributes only to pre-selected organizations.
Officers and Directors: Sally Roberts, Co-Chair. and Director; Richard F. Roberts, Co-Chair. and Pres. and Director; Jon-Paul Cowen, Vice-Chair. and Director; Terry Lloyd, Secy.-Treas. and Director.
EIN: 205970941

976
The Courtney Roberts Foundation
c/o KKRAS
2755 Campus Dr., Ste. 240
San Mateo, CA 94403

Established in 2007 in California.
Donors: George Roberts; Glem Co.; Courtney A. Roberts; Roberts Children 1987 Trust f/b/o Courtney.
Foundation type: Independent foundation.
Financial data (yr. ended 12/31/13): Assets, $3,350,403 (M); gifts received, $3,205,548; expenditures, $240,910; qualifying distributions, $240,899; giving activities include $240,899 for 4 grants (high: $130,000; low: $10,000).
Fields of interest: Art museums; Environment; Domesticated animals.
Type of support: General support.

Limitations: Applications not accepted. Giving primarily in CA. No grants to individuals.
Application information: Contributes only to pre-selected organizations.
Trustee: Courtney Roberts.
EIN: 260271526

977
The Robinson Foundation
700 S. Flower St., Ste. 1222
Los Angeles, CA 90017-4110 (213) 626-4481
Contact: Henry H. Dearing, Tr.

Established in 1981 in California.
Donor: Laura A. Robinson.
Foundation type: Independent foundation.
Financial data (yr. ended 06/30/13): Assets, $2,602,634 (M); expenditures, $203,246; qualifying distributions, $169,460; giving activities include $147,500 for 32 grants (high: $25,000; low: $500).
Purpose and activities: Grants primarily to the First Church of Christ, Scientist, in Boston, MA, and organizations that directly or indirectly promote and extend religion of Christian Science; support also for organizations that promote man's recognition of his highest selfhood, including education and artistic expression.
Fields of interest: Arts and culture; Orchestral music; Education; Christian Science; Human services.
Type of support: General support.
Limitations: Applications accepted. Giving primarily in CA, with emphasis on Los Angeles. No support for any entity engaging in the manufacture, production, distribution, or promotion of alcohol, tobacco, medicines, or drugs.
Publications: Annual report.
Application information: Application form required.
  Initial approach: Contact foundation for application form
  Copies of proposal: 1
  Deadline(s): None
  Board meeting date(s): Jan. and July
Trustees: Henry H. Dearing; Anne Gifford.
EIN: 953681443

978
B. T. Rocca, Jr. Foundation
3053 Fillmore St., No. 344
San Francisco, CA 94123-4009

Established in 1986 in California.
Donors: B.T. Rocca, Jr.†; K. Rocca.
Foundation type: Independent foundation.
Financial data (yr. ended 12/31/13): Assets, $6,652,209 (M); expenditures, $314,906; qualifying distributions, $310,463; giving activities include $310,100 for 42 grants (high: $22,000; low: $1,000).
Purpose and activities: Giving for emergency relief services, cultural institutes, health and medical services, youth services, and secondary and higher education; giving also for family services and nature conservation.
Fields of interest: Arts and culture; Education; Higher education; Environment; Wildlife biodiversity; Nonprofits; Family planning; Diseases and conditions; Human services; Family services; Scouting programs.

Type of support: General support; Continuing support; Annual campaigns; Endowments; Research; Regranting.
Limitations: Applications not accepted. Giving primarily in CA, IL and NY. No grants to individuals.
Application information: Contributes only to pre-selected organizations.
Trustees: M.R. Johnson; B.T. Rocca III; L. H. Rocca.
Number of staff: 1 part-time professional.
EIN: 943028203

979
The Roche Foundation
(formerly The Hoffmann-La Roche Foundation)
1 DNA Way, MS #24
South San Francisco, CA 94080-4918
Application address: P.O. Box 278, Nutley, NJ 07110-0278; Main URL: http://www.rocheusa.com/portal/usa/the_roche_foundation

Established in 1945 in New Jersey.
Donors: Hoffmann-La Roche Inc.; Roche Laboratories Inc.
Foundation type: Company-sponsored foundation.
Financial data (yr. ended 12/31/14): Assets, $3,604,604; expenditures, $667,202; qualifying distributions, $225,202.
Purpose and activities: The foundation supports organizations involved with arts and culture, education, health, the environment, human services, and science.
Fields of interest: Arts and culture; Museums; Education; Elementary and secondary education; Higher education; Teacher education; Environment; Health; Diseases and conditions; Science; Human services; Food banks.
Type of support: General support; Program development; Curriculum development.
Limitations: Applications accepted. Giving primarily in areas of company operations, with emphasis on NJ. No support for political organizations, candidates, or office holders, sectarian groups (except for education or health programs which serve the general public), or labor or veterans' organizations not of direct benefit to the entire community. No grants to individuals, or for endowments, scholarship funds, purchasing or renovating facilities, equipment, capital campaigns, sponsorships of athletic teams or events, or goodwill advertising.
Publications: Application guidelines.
Application information: Application form required.
  Initial approach: Complete online application
  Copies of proposal: 1
  Deadline(s): 60 days prior to need
  Board meeting date(s): As required
Officers and Trustees: Frederick C. Kentz III, Secy. and Trustee; Patricia Hughes, Exec. Dir.; Jean-Jacques Garaud; David P. McDede.
EIN: 226063790

980
Rogers Family Charitable Trust
c/o Tim and Twanna Rogers
1983 W. 190th St.
Torrance, CA 90504-6234

Established in 2008 in California.
Donors: Tim Rogers; Twanna Rogers.
Foundation type: Independent foundation.

Financial data (yr. ended 09/30/13): Assets, $2,810,430 (M); expenditures, $227,370; qualifying distributions, $210,762; giving activities include $207,000 for 3 grants (high: $100,000; low: $7,000).
Fields of interest: Education; Housing development.
Limitations: Applications not accepted.
Application information: Unsolicited requests for funds not accepted.
Trustees: Tim Rogers; Twanna Rogers.
EIN: 266160756

981
The Roke Foundation, Inc.
1570 San Leandro Ln.
Santa Barbara, CA 93108-2655

Established in 1999 in Florida.
Donors: Brian J. Smith; Janet Smith.
Foundation type: Independent foundation.
Financial data (yr. ended 12/31/13): Assets, $1,132,052 (M); gifts received, $542,635; expenditures, $178,796; qualifying distributions, $177,710; giving activities include $177,710 for 7 grants (high: $125,000; low: $100).
Fields of interest: Arts and culture; Diseases and conditions.
Type of support: Research.
Limitations: Applications not accepted. Giving primarily in Santa Barbara, CA. No grants to individuals.
Application information: Unsolicited requests for funds not accepted.
Officers and Directors: Brian J. Smith, Pres. and Treas. and Director; Janet Smith, V.P. and Secy. and Director; Margaret M. Vanden Heuvel.
EIN: 650967897

982
Murphy and Ed Romano Family Foundation
10960 Wilshire Blvd., 5th Fl.
Los Angeles, CA 90024-3708 3102774657

Donors: Murphy Romano; Ed Romano.
Foundation type: Independent foundation.
Financial data (yr. ended 12/31/14): Assets, $531,296; gifts received, $325,000; expenditures, $170,740; qualifying distributions, $170,600.
Fields of interest: Education; University education; Philanthropy.
Type of support: General support.
Limitations: Applications not accepted. Giving primarily in CA and NY.
Application information: Unsolicited requests for funds not accepted.
Officers: Murphy Romano, Pres.; Ed Romano, Secy. and C.F.O.
EIN: 263792101

983
The Roney Family Foundation
560 Meadow Wood Ln.
Santa Barbara, CA 93108-2274

Established in 2000 in California.
Donor: Richard Roney.
Foundation type: Independent foundation.
Financial data (yr. ended 12/31/13): Assets, $1,589,103 (M); expenditures, $183,233; qualifying distributions, $183,208; giving activities

include $171,178 for 41 grants (high: $31,583; low: $75).
Fields of interest: Arts and culture; Music; Education; Nonprofits; Community and economic development; Human services; Child welfare; Youth organizing.
Type of support: Regranting.
Limitations: Applications not accepted. Giving primarily in CA. No grants to individuals.
Application information: Contributes only to pre-selected organizations.
Officers and Directors: Regina Roney, Pres. and Director; Richard Roney, Treas. and Director; Jessica Roney.
EIN: 680451062

984
Ernest & Irma Rose Foundation
c/o First Foundation Advisors
18101 Von Karman Ave., Ste. 700
Irvine, CA 92612-0145

Established in 2004 in Unspecified.
Donor: Irma Rose.
Foundation type: Independent foundation.
Financial data (yr. ended 12/31/13): Assets, $5,233,384 (M); expenditures, $308,168; qualifying distributions, $244,013; giving activities include $216,478 for 10 grants (high: $50,000; low: $1,478).
Fields of interest: Artist's services; Education; Judaism.
Limitations: Applications not accepted. Giving primarily in CA. No grants to individuals.
Application information: Unsolicited requests for funds not accepted.
Officers: Douglas K. Freeman, Pres.; Lynn Freeman, Secy.-Treas.
EIN: 200677267

985
The Meta and George Rosenberg Foundation
5900 Wilshire Blvd., Ste. 2300
Los Angeles, CA 90036-5050 (323) 634-2400
Contact: Susan J. Ollweiler; Jess S. Morgan

Established in 1991 in California.
Donor: Meta Reis Rosenberg.
Foundation type: Independent foundation.
Financial data (yr. ended 12/31/13): Assets, $3,751,447 (M); expenditures, $252,874; qualifying distributions, $180,900; giving activities include $180,900 for 10 grants (high: $87,500; low: $2,500).
Fields of interest: Arts and culture; Education; Diseases and conditions; HIV/AIDS; Human services; Unknown or not classified.
Type of support: Research.
Limitations: Applications accepted. Giving primarily in southern CA; some giving in IA.
Application information: Application form required.
  Initial approach: Letter
  Deadline(s): Aug. 31
Officers and Directors: Wallace D. Franson, Pres. and Director; David D. Watts, Secy. and Director; Tim Bodner, Treas.; Susan Whittaker Mullins; Bill Robinson; Gene Torncello.
EIN: 954332344

986
The Gene and Maxine Rosenfeld Family Foundation
1100 Glendon Ave., Ste. 1140
Los Angeles, CA 90024-3515

Established in 2004 in California.
Donors: Eugene S. Rosenfeld; Maxine Rosenfeld.
Foundation type: Independent foundation.
Financial data (yr. ended 12/31/13): Assets, $3,610,893 (M); gifts received, $1,050,000; expenditures, $412,429; qualifying distributions, $391,039; giving activities include $391,039 for 26 grants (high: $175,000; low: $75).
Purpose and activities: Giving primarily for children, youth and social services, as well as for higher education, the arts, including a public television station, and to Jewish organizations.
Fields of interest: Arts and culture; Human services; Youth development.
Limitations: Applications not accepted. Giving primarily in Los Angeles, CA. No grants to individuals.
Application information: Contributes only to pre-selected organizations.
Officers and Directors: Eugene S. Rosenfeld, C.E.O. and Pres. and Director; Maxine Rosenfeld, C.F.O. and Secy. and Director.
EIN: 383710097

987
Robert and Nina Rosenthal Foundation, Inc.
4444 Riverside Dr., St. 303
Burbank, CA 91505-4077 8185592480
Main URL: http://spiritofamericatour.org

Established in 1983 in California.
Donors: Robert M. Rosenthal; Nina Rosenthal.
Foundation type: Independent foundation.
Financial data (yr. ended 12/31/14): Assets, $328,284; gifts received, $100,000; expenditures, $218,110; qualifying distributions, $216,568.
Fields of interest: Education; Diseases and conditions; Human services.
Type of support: Research.
Limitations: Applications not accepted. Giving primarily in MI. No grants to individuals.
Application information: Unsolicited requests for funds not accepted.
Officers and Directors: Robert M. Rosenthal, Pres. and Director; Nina Rosenthal, Secy. and C.F.O. and Director.
EIN: 953875854

988
Gordon Ross Medical Foundation
150 S. Los Robles Ave.
Pasadena, CA 91101

Established in 1962 in California.
Foundation type: Independent foundation.
Financial data (yr. ended 12/31/13): Assets, $3,862,955 (M); expenditures, $176,990; qualifying distributions, $156,342; giving activities include $155,000 for 18 grants (high: $23,750; low: $1,000).
Purpose and activities: Giving primarily in the field of health, with a focus on medical research, hospitals, and nursing scholarships.

Fields of Interest: Education; Higher education; Hospital care; Out-patient medical care; Diseases and conditions; Human services.
Type of support: General support; Continuing support; Individual development; Capital and infrastructure; Equipment; Endowments; Program development; Research; Research and evaluation; Curriculum development; Scholarships.
Limitations: Applications not accepted. Giving primarily in CA and ID. No grants to individuals.
Application information: Unsolicited requests for funds not accepted.
Officers: Stephen Malkmus, Pres.; Jeffrey Cook, V.P.; Jeffrey Cook, Secy.-Treas.
EIN: 956044011

989
Rossi Family Foundation
c/o Janeen Tuitupou
1100 Sharon Park Dr., No. 2
Menlo Park, CA 94025-7001

Established in 1989 in California.
Donors: L. Jay Rossi; Mrs. L. Jay Rossi; Marjorie Rossi.
Foundation type: Independent foundation.
Financial data (yr. ended 06/30/14): Assets, $2,658,015; expenditures, $235,716; qualifying distributions, $199,300.
Fields of interest: Higher education; Health; Diseases and conditions; Human services.
Type of support: Capital and infrastructure; Equipment; Seed money; Research.
Limitations: Applications not accepted. Giving primarily in CA. No support for religious or political organizations. No grants to individuals.
Application information: Unsolicited requests for funds not accepted.
Officers: Marjorie Rossi, Pres.; Safford J. Rossi, Secy.; Craig Hall Rossi, Treas.; Janeen Rossi Tuitupou, Exec. Dir.
Directors: Merilee Rossi; Lizabeth Rossi Schuetz.
EIN: 943106122

990
The Rosso Family Foundation
P.O. Box 9917
Rancho Santa Fe, CA 92067-4917 (949) 600-7550

Donors: Louise P. Rosso; Maura T. Rosso; Louis T. Rosso.
Foundation type: Independent foundation.
Financial data (yr. ended 05/31/13): Assets, $4,362,257 (M); gifts received, $16,300; expenditures, $161,919; qualifying distributions, $161,919; giving activities include $145,619 for 13 grants (high: $126,000; low: $250).
Fields of interest: Arts and culture; Diseases and conditions; Human services.
Limitations: Applications accepted. Giving primarily in CA.
Application information: Application form required.
   Initial approach: Letter
   Deadline(s): None
Officers: Maura P. Rosso, Pres.; Louis T. Rosso, Chair.
Directors: Nancy Kalamaris; Thomas Rosso; Kim Sherman.
EIN: 275364190

991
Rotasa Foundation
(formerly Webb Roven Foundation)
775 E. Blithedale Ave., Ste. 309
Mill Valley, CA 94941-1554

Established in 2001 in California.
Donors: Max Webb; Max Webb Charitable Lead Trust; Rose Webb Roven.
Foundation type: Independent foundation.
Financial data (yr. ended 06/30/13): Assets, $233,430 (M); gifts received, $552,319; expenditures, $445,448; qualifying distributions, $440,048; giving activities include $436,348 for 38 grants (high: $100,000; low: $250).
Purpose and activities: Giving primarily to increase the knowledge of art jewelry and related metalsmithing.
Fields of interest: Visual arts; Theater; Early childhood education; Natural resources; Health; Diabetes; Communication media; Housing development.
Limitations: Applications not accepted. Giving on a national basis, with an emphasis on CA. No grants to individuals.
Application information: Contributes only to pre-selected organizations.
Officers: Rose Webb Roven, Pres.; Susan Cummins, Secy.
EIN: 943412390

992
Barbara N. Rubin Foundation
215 E. Mission St.
Santa Barbara, CA 93117-1044
Contact: Barbara N. Rubin, Pres.

Established in 2000 in California.
Donor: Gerrold R. Rubin.
Foundation type: Independent foundation.
Financial data (yr. ended 07/31/13): Assets, $2,542,203 (M); expenditures, $236,376; qualifying distributions, $236,200; giving activities include $236,200 for 31 grants (high: $100,000; low: $200).
Fields of interest: Education; Health; Human services.
Limitations: Applications accepted. Giving on a national basis, with emphasis on CA.
Application information: Application form required.
   Initial approach: Letter
   Deadline(s): None
Officers: Barbara N. Rubin, Pres.; Marcia N. Smith, C.F.O.; Gerrold R. Rubin, Secy.
EIN: 770551902

993
Sol R. and Neddy Rubin Foundation
6129 Bluebell Ave.
Valley Glen, CA 91606-4414

Established in 1991 in Unspecified.
Donor: Sol R. Rubin.
Foundation type: Independent foundation.
Financial data (yr. ended 12/31/14): Assets, $219,512; expenditures, $240,083; qualifying distributions, $195,000.
Fields of interest: Higher education; Environment; Diseases and conditions.
Type of support: Research.

Limitations: Applications not accepted. Giving primarily in CA. No grants to individuals.
Application information: Contributes only to pre-selected organizations.
Officers: Donald Rubin, Pres.; Howard M. Rubin, V.P.; Judith E. Rubin, V.P.; Stephen M. Rubin, C.F.O.
EIN: 954303079

994
Loni and Jeff Rush Family Foundation
12348 High Bluff Dr., Ste. 100
San Diego, CA 92130-3545 (858) 794-1900
Contact: Linda R. Rush, Secy. and Dir.

Established in 2001 in California.
Donors: Jeffrey L. Rush, MD; Linda R. Rush.
Foundation type: Independent foundation.
Financial data (yr. ended 12/31/13): Assets, $994,917 (M); gifts received, $250,000; expenditures, $165,491; qualifying distributions, $160,460; giving activities include $155,848 for 32 grants (high: $72,549; low: $50).
Fields of interest: Education; Diseases and conditions; Religion.
Limitations: Applications accepted. Giving primarily in CA.
Application information:
   Initial approach: Proposal
   Deadline(s): None
Officers and Directors: Jeffrey L. Rush, MD, Pres. and C.F.O. and Director; Linda R. Rush, Secy. and Director; Jennifer L. Morton; Elisa Beth Port; Daniel E. Rush.
EIN: 330938416

995
William Knight Russell Family Foundation
8 Canyon Fairway Dr.
Newport Beach, CA 92660-5916

Established in 1996 in California.
Donor: William Knight Russell.
Foundation type: Independent foundation.
Financial data (yr. ended 12/31/13): Assets, $2,475,227 (M); gifts received, $197,865; expenditures, $158,894; qualifying distributions, $148,700; giving activities include $148,700 for 62 grants (high: $50,000; low: $100).
Fields of interest: Education; Health; Catholicism.
Type of support: General support.
Limitations: Applications not accepted. Giving primarily in CA. No grants to individuals.
Application information: Unsolicited requests for funds not accepted.
Officers: William Knight Russell, Pres.; Carol M. Russell, C.F.O.; Carolyn A. Russell, Secy.
Directors: Robert A. Russell; Steven M. Russell.
EIN: 330708284

996
Sammut Family Foundation
659 Huntington Ave.
San Bruno, CA 94066-3608

Established in 1990 in California.
Donor: Artichoke Joe's Casino.
Foundation type: Company-sponsored foundation.
Financial data (yr. ended 11/30/13): Assets, $477,043 (M); gifts received, $282,300; expenditures, $141,950; qualifying distributions,

$140,695; giving activities include $139,500 for 30 grants (high: $25,000; low: $500).
Purpose and activities: The foundation supports organizations involved with education, human services, and community development.
Fields of interest: Education; Public libraries; Community and economic development; Community service; Human services.
Type of support: Program development; Scholarships; General support.
Limitations: Applications not accepted. Giving limited to San Mateo County, CA, with emphasis on San Bruno. No grants to individuals.
Application information: Unsolicited requests for funds not accepted.
Officers: Dennis J. Sammut, Pres.; Helen Sammut, C.F.O.; Sally S. Johnson, V.P.
EIN: 943113076

997
San Diego Scottish Rite Community Foundation
1895 Camino del Rio S.
San Diego, CA   92108-3601   (619) 293-4888
Contact: Randy Brill

Foundation type: Independent foundation.
Financial data (yr. ended 12/31/13): Assets, $3,694,084 (M); gifts received, $79,263; expenditures, $188,638; qualifying distributions, $185,000; giving activities include $62,500 for 15 grants (high: $37,500; low: $200), and $122,500 for 22 grants to individuals (high: $6,000; low: $1,000).
Fields of interest: Theater; Higher education; Disasters and emergency management.
Type of support: General support; Student aid; Volunteer development.
Limitations: Applications accepted. Giving for scholarships limited to residents of San Diego and Imperial counties, CA.
Application information:
Initial approach: Letter or brochure request for organizations; application with letters of recommendation for scholarships
Deadline(s): None for organizations; May 15th for scholarships
Officers: John A. Schneidmiller, Chair.; Randall Brill, Secy.
Trustees: Ralph Bryan; Philip Johnson; F.I. Quimpo.
EIN: 330718473

998
San Francisco Challenge
(doing business as AmericaOne)
127 University Ave.
Berkeley, CA   94710-1616
Main URL: http://www.americaone.org

Foundation type: Independent foundation.
Financial data (yr. ended 12/31/13): Assets, $6,264,414 (M); expenditures, $480,015; qualifying distributions, $408,103; giving activities include $321,320 for 5 grants (high: $142,987; low: $10,000).
Fields of interest: Sports and recreation; Water sports; Youth development.
Limitations: Applications not accepted. Giving primarily in CA and RI.
Application information: Unsolicited requests for funds not accepted.

Officers and Directors: Lawrence Finch, Chair. and Director; Robert I.C. Billingham, Pres. and C.E.O.; Harald J. Leventhal, C.F.O.; Douglas D. Smith, Secy.-Treas. and Director; Paul Cayard; Tom Seip.
EIN: 943242538

999
Tawny and Jerry Sanders Charitable Foundation
360 N. Bedford Dr., Ste. 204
Beverly Hills, CA   90210-5124

Established in 1997 in California.
Donor: Walter J. Sanders III.
Foundation type: Independent foundation.
Financial data (yr. ended 12/31/13): Assets, $1,043,394 (M); expenditures, $227,908; qualifying distributions, $220,835; giving activities include $220,835 for 36 grants (high: $50,000; low: $100).
Fields of interest: Education; Philanthropy; Diseases and conditions; Child welfare.
Limitations: Applications not accepted. Giving primarily in CA. No grants to individuals.
Application information: Unsolicited requests for funds not accepted.
Officers: Tawny Sanders, Pres.; W.J. Sanders III, Secy. and C.F.O.
EIN: 954632383

1000
Sandnes Family Foundation
15810 Mill Meadow Rd.
Santa Clarita, CA   91387-3940

Established in 2006 in California.
Donor: Richard Sandnes.
Foundation type: Independent foundation.
Financial data (yr. ended 10/31/13): Assets, $208,243 (M); gifts received, $200,000; expenditures, $139,028; qualifying distributions, $137,750; giving activities include $137,750 for 8 grants (high: $75,000; low: $250).
Fields of interest: Arts and culture; Education; Youth development.
Limitations: Applications not accepted. No grants to.
Application information: Unsolicited requests for funds not accepted.
Officers: Richard Sandnes, Pres.; Marian Sandnes, Secy.
EIN: 205994239

1001
Corrine and Lenny Sands Foundation
c/o Leonard and Corrine Sands
321 St. Pierre Rd.
Los Angeles, CA   90077-3432

Established in 2001 in California.
Donor: Leonard Sands.
Foundation type: Independent foundation.
Financial data (yr. ended 12/31/13): Assets, $620,367 (M); gifts received, $500,000; expenditures, $324,053; qualifying distributions, $321,341; giving activities include $319,000 for 13 grants (high: $100,000; low: $1,000).
Fields of interest: Higher education; Nonprofits; Hospital care; Judaism.
Type of support: Regranting.

Limitations: Applications not accepted. Giving primarily in CA and Washington, DC. No grants to individuals.
Application information: Contributes only to pre-selected organizations.
Directors: Corrine Sands; Leonard Sands.
EIN: 954891834

1002
Martha E. Sanfilippo Foundation
c/o Shannon & Snyder
650 N. Winchester Blvd., Ste. 6
San Jose, CA   95128-1511

Established in 2003 in California.
Donor: Martha E. Sanfilippo.
Foundation type: Independent foundation.
Financial data (yr. ended 06/30/13): Assets, $6,563,800 (M); gifts received, $500; expenditures, $507,675; qualifying distributions, $320,565; giving activities include $320,565 for 10 grants (high: $154,900; low: $5,000).
Fields of interest: Education; Secondary education; Human services; Family services; Child welfare; Low-income and poor people.
Limitations: Applications not accepted. Giving primarily in CA; some funding also in HI. No grants to individuals.
Application information: Contributes only to pre-selected organizations.
Officer: William J. Snyder, C.F.O., Secy. and Mgr.
Directors: Pearl N. Hind; Garrett Rajkovich.
EIN: 820578141

1003
The Santa Rita Foundation
(doing business as The Ludwick Family Foundation)
491 Santa Rita Ave.
Palo Alto, CA   94301-3944

Established in 1997 in California.
Donors: Andrew Ludwick; Worth Z. Ludwick; Jocelyn Ludwick.
Foundation type: Independent foundation.
Financial data (yr. ended 12/31/13): Assets, $7,470,136 (M); expenditures, $311,248; qualifying distributions, $305,488; giving activities include $297,355 for 28 grants (high: $70,000; low: $55).
Purpose and activities: Support primarily for education and human services.
Fields of interest: Secondary education; Higher education; Foundations; Health; Human services.
Type of support: General support; Matching grants; Capital campaigns; Endowments.
Limitations: Applications not accepted. Giving primarily in CA and MA. No grants to individuals.
Application information: Contributes only to pre-selected organizations.
Board meeting date(s): Quarterly
Officers: Worth Z. Ludwick, Pres. and C.E.O.; Andrew Ludwick, C.F.O.; Theodore Ludwick, Secy.
Directors: Christopher Ludwick; Jocelyn Ludwick.
EIN: 770472486

1004
The Susan Sarandon Charitable Foundation
501 S. Beverly Dr., 3rd Fl.
Beverly Hills, CA   90212-4514

Established in 2002 in California.
Donor: Susan Sarandon.
Foundation type: Independent foundation.
Financial data (yr. ended 12/31/13): Assets, $3,719,451 (M); expenditures, $254,580; qualifying distributions, $210,632; giving activities include $210,632 for 118 grants (high: $50,000; low: $15).
Fields of interest: Education; Natural resources; Human services; Family services.
Limitations: Applications not accepted. Giving primarily in NY. No grants to individuals.
Application information: Contributes only to pre-selected organizations.
Officers and Directors: Susan Sarandon, Pres. and Secy.-Treas. and Director; Eva Amuri Martino, V.P.; Jack Henry Robbins, V.P.; Miles Robbins, V.P.
EIN: 611437696

1005
The Gladys W. Sargent Foundation
P.O. Box 557
Alamo, CA 94507-0557 (925) 9524686
Contact: Lynda Lyon, Pres.

Established in 1998 in California.
Donor: Gladys W. Sargent Trust.
Foundation type: Independent foundation.
Financial data (yr. ended 12/31/13): Assets, $5,639,823 (M); expenditures, $295,075; qualifying distributions, $235,900; giving activities include $228,000 for 1 grant.
Purpose and activities: The foundation supports 4 major areas of activity: 1) Animal population control through spaying and neutering; 2) Operating an animal shelter for domestic pets; 3) Acquiring unwanted domestic pets and placing them in suitable homes; 4) Education to promote kindness towards animals.
Fields of interest: Domesticated animals; Animal welfare.
Type of support: General support; Continuing support.
Limitations: Applications accepted. Giving on a national basis. No support for religious or political organizations. No grants to individuals, or for endowments, debt reduction, scholarships, fundraising, advertising or medical/scientific research; no loans.
Application information:
  Initial approach: Letter
  Board meeting date(s): Nov.
Officers and Directors: Lynda Lyon, Pres. and Director; James C. Page, V.P.; Astrid Varteressian, Secy.; Sue Molen, Treas. and Director; Denise Cornwell-Bruce; Virginia Handley; Betty Denny Smith.
EIN: 911843277

1006
The Sassoon Family Foundation
1945 S. La Cienega Blvd.
Los Angeles, CA 90034-1601

Donor: Sunny Sassoon.
Foundation type: Independent foundation.
Financial data (yr. ended 12/31/13): Assets, $3,463,412 (M); gifts received, $3,600,000; expenditures, $167,866; qualifying distributions, $164,335; giving activities include $164,335 for 15 grants (high: $25,000; low: $150).

Fields of interest: Education; Religion; Human services.
Limitations: Applications not accepted. Giving primarily in CA.
Application information: Unsolicited requests for funds not accepted.
Officers: Sunny Sassoon, Pres.; Victor Sassoon, V.P.; Debbie Sassoon, Secy.; Michelle Sassoon, Treas.
EIN: 463872022

1007
The Sato Foundation
264 Mountain View Ave.
San Rafael, CA 94901-1501

Established in 2000 in California.
Donors: Kozo Sato; Nieves Sato; Sato Lead Trust 80C-74C03; Sato Lead Trust 80C-7C04.
Foundation type: Independent foundation.
Financial data (yr. ended 12/31/13): Assets, $7,934,370 (M); expenditures, $436,889; qualifying distributions, $393,078; giving activities include $384,180 for 20 grants (high: $51,530; low: $5,000).
Fields of interest: Arts and culture; Education.
Limitations: Applications not accepted. Giving primarily in CA. No grants to individuals.
Application information: Contributes only to pre-selected organizations.
Officers: Kozo Sato, Pres.; Nieves Sato, Secy.-Treas.
Directors: Kate Sato Burton; Sonia Sato.
EIN: 943356933

1008
Saturno Brothers Italian Orphan Foundation
c/o Wells Fargo Bank, N.A.
P.O. Box 63954, MAC A0348-012
San Francisco, CA 94163-0001

Foundation type: Independent foundation.
Financial data (yr. ended 06/30/14): Assets, $8,910,880; expenditures, $519,221; qualifying distributions, $420,515.
Fields of interest: Human services; Shelter and residential care.
Limitations: Applications not accepted. Giving primarily in New York, NY. No grants to individuals.
Application information: Contributes only to pre-selected organizations.
Trustee: Wells Fargo Bank, N.A.
EIN: 946128681

1009
Savage Charitable Foundation
c/o Bruno Skorheim, LLP
9665 Chesapeake Dr., Ste. 470
San Diego, CA 92123-1378
Application address: c/o Ronald J. Savage, 632 Regency Hills Dr., Collegeville, PA 19426, tel.: (703) 987-5407

Established in 2006 in California.
Donors: Savage Administrative Trust; Visual Communications Co., Inc.
Foundation type: Independent foundation.
Financial data (yr. ended 12/31/13): Assets, $415,388 (M); expenditures, $181,592; qualifying

distributions, $169,765; giving activities include $157,939 for 10 grants (high: $63,425; low: $1,000).
Fields of interest: Catholicism.
Limitations: Applications accepted. Giving primarily in CA, IL, PA and VA.
Application information: Application form required.
  Initial approach: Letter
  Deadline(s): None
Officers: Ronald J. Savage, Chair. and Pres.; Samuel Roberts, Secy.-Treas.
EIN: 204589164

1010
Sawchuk Family Foundation
P.O. Box 24831
Los Angeles, CA 90024-0831

Established in 2000 in California.
Donors: Mariette T. Sawchuk; Alexander A. Sawchuk.
Foundation type: Independent foundation.
Financial data (yr. ended 06/30/14): Assets, $3,876,501 (M); expenditures, $197,284; qualifying distributions, $180,416; giving activities include $168,000 for 11 grants (high: $20,000; low: $10,000).
Fields of interest: Reading promotion; Health; Eye diseases; LGBTQ rights; Human services; Food banks; Youth services; Homeless services; Women's services.
Type of support: General support; Research.
Limitations: Applications not accepted. Giving primarily in CA and Washington, DC. No grants to individuals.
Application information: Contributes only to pre-selected organizations.
Officers: Mariette T. Sawchuk, Pres.; Alexander A. Sawchuk, Secy.
EIN: 954831929

1011
Saya Foundation
515 S. Figueroa St., No. 1600
Los Angeles, CA 90071-3301

Established in 2005 in California.
Donors: Murad & Kristi Siam Living Trust; Saya Trust.
Foundation type: Independent foundation.
Financial data (yr. ended 12/31/12): Assets, $2,224,495 (M); gifts received, $350,000; expenditures, $429,169; qualifying distributions, $415,585; giving activities include $415,585 for grants.
Fields of interest: Education; Health; Islam; Human services.
International interests: Pakistan.
Limitations: Applications not accepted. Giving primarily in CA and IL; with some giving in Pakistan. No grants to individuals.
Application information: Contributes only to pre-selected organizations.
Officers: Salim Adaya, C.E.O. and Pres.; Yasmin Adaya, V.P.; Halima Mohammed, V.P.; Muhammad Adaya, Secy.
EIN: 203343622

1012
Scandling Family Foundation
P.O. Box 2056
Saratoga, CA 95070-0056

Established in 2000 in California.
Donor: William Scandling‡.
Foundation type: Independent foundation.
Financial data (yr. ended 12/31/13): Assets, $4,311,630 (M); expenditures, $236,573; qualifying distributions, $196,500; giving activities include $196,500 for 1 grant.
Fields of interest: Human services; Child welfare.
Limitations: Applications not accepted. Giving primarily in CA. No grants to individuals.
Application information: Contributes only to pre-selected organizations.
Officers: Michael Scandling, Pres.; John D. Scandling, MD, Treas.
Number of staff: None.
EIN: 943381080

1013
Schaeffer Family Foundation
903 N. Roxbury Dr.
Beverly Hills, CA 91210

Established in 2000 in California.
Donors: OPI Products, Inc.; Miriam Schaeffer.
Foundation type: Independent foundation.
Financial data (yr. ended 12/31/13): Assets, $673,974 (M); gifts received, $300,000; expenditures, $367,869; qualifying distributions, $367,869; giving activities include $365,525 for 11 grants (high: $180,000; low: $500).
Fields of interest: Education; Higher education; Diseases and conditions; Judaism.
Type of support: Research.
Limitations: Applications not accepted. Giving primarily in CA and NY.
Application information: Unsolicited requests for funds not accepted.
Officers: Miriam Schaeffer, Pres.; Susan Weiss-Fischmann, Secy.; Miriam Schaeffer, Treas.
Director: Robert Schaeffer.
EIN: 954785084

1014
Ray & Janet Scherr Foundation
2630 Townsgate Rd., Ste. B
Westlake Village, CA 91361-2785

Established in 1997 in California.
Donors: Janet Scherr; Raymond Scherr.
Foundation type: Independent foundation.
Financial data (yr. ended 12/31/14): Assets, $1,996,300 (M); expenditures, $186,139; qualifying distributions, $160,160; giving activities include $152,500 for 9 grants (high: $70,000; low: $1,000).
Fields of interest: Education; Health; Judaism.
Limitations: Applications not accepted. Giving primarily in CA. No grants to individuals.
Application information: Unsolicited requests for funds not accepted.
Officers: Janet Scherr, C.E.O.; Lauren Scherr, C.F.O.; Raymond Scherr, Secy.
EIN: 770457757

1015
The Stephen Harold Schimmel Foundation, Inc.
8 Archipelago Dr.
Newport Coast, CA 92657-2106

Established in 1995 in Delaware.
Donors: Stephen Harold Schimmel; Rosalba Schimmel.
Foundation type: Independent foundation.
Financial data (yr. ended 09/30/14): Assets, $6,204,111 (M); expenditures, $307,515; qualifying distributions, $246,302; giving activities include $225,000 for 1 grant.
Purpose and activities: Giving primarily for Christian organizations.
Fields of interest: Christianity.
Type of support: General support.
Limitations: Applications not accepted. Giving primarily in VA. No grants to individuals.
Application information: Unsolicited requests for funds not accepted.
Officers: Stephen Harold Schimmel, Pres. and Secy.; Rosalba Schimmel, V.P. and Treas.
EIN: 223386066

1016
Schlinger Chrisman Foundation
426 Ennisbrook Dr.
Santa Barbara, CA 93108-2678

Donors: Katharine Schlinger; Warren Schlinger.
Foundation type: Independent foundation.
Financial data (yr. ended 12/31/13): Assets, $500,751 (M); gifts received, $605,000; expenditures, $354,757; qualifying distributions, $354,757; giving activities include $353,000 for 23 grants (high: $155,000; low: $1,000).
Fields of interest: Arts and culture; Education; Environment; Cancers.
Limitations: Applications not accepted. Giving primarily in CA. No grants to individuals.
Application information: Contributes only to pre-selected organizations.
Trustees: Roger Packard Chrisman; Sarah Schlinger Chrisman.
EIN: 270096038

1017
The Schoen Family Foundation
10618 Pico Blvd.
Los Angeles, CA 90064-2214

Established in 1997 in California.
Donors: Louis B. Schoen; David Schoen.
Foundation type: Independent foundation.
Financial data (yr. ended 12/31/13): Assets, $22,631 (M); gifts received, $50,000; expenditures, $219,867; qualifying distributions, $219,867; giving activities include $217,304 for 4 + grants (high: $214,200).
Fields of interest: Judaism.
Limitations: Applications not accepted. Giving primarily in CA and NY; some funding also in Israel.
Application information: Unsolicited requests for funds not accepted.
Trustee: Louis B. Schoen.
EIN: 954564412

1018
Rudi Schulte Family Foundation
P.O. Box 60921
Santa Barbara, CA 93160-0921

Established in 1997 in California.
Donor: Rudolf R. Schulte.
Foundation type: Independent foundation.
Financial data (yr. ended 12/31/13): Assets, $11,317,027 (M); expenditures, $575,074; qualifying distributions, $424,274; giving activities include $412,850 for 97 grants (high: $42,500; low: $25).
Purpose and activities: Giving primarily for social services.
Fields of interest: Arts and culture; Education; Home health care; Rehabilitation; Human services; Food banks; Youth services.
Limitations: Applications not accepted. Giving primarily in CA. No grants to individuals.
Application information: Contributes only to pre-selected organizations.
Officers: Paul S. Schulte, Pres.; Peter R. Schulte, V.P.; Henry G. Schulte, Secy.-Treas.
Director: Mark M. Aijian.
EIN: 770452600

1019
Schultz Foundation
1095 State Ln.
Yountville, CA 94599-9473

Donors: Craig M. Schultz; Norman C. Schultz.
Foundation type: Independent foundation.
Financial data (yr. ended 12/31/14): Assets, $2,305,629 (M); expenditures, $271,235; qualifying distributions, $230,960; giving activities include $217,700 for 18 grants (high: $100,000; low: $450).
Purpose and activities: Giving primarily for arts and education.
Fields of interest: Arts and culture; Secondary education; Higher education; Diseases and conditions; Human services.
Type of support: General support.
Limitations: Applications not accepted. Giving in the U.S., primarily in CA. No grants to individuals.
Application information: Contributes only to pre-selected organizations.
Trustee: Norman C. Schultz.
EIN: 431310425

1020
Geiser Schweers Family Foundation
307 N. Bristol Ave.
Los Angeles, CA 90049-2605

Established in 2005 in California.
Foundation type: Independent foundation.
Financial data (yr. ended 11/30/13): Assets, $1,888,130 (M); expenditures, $293,370; qualifying distributions, $270,000; giving activities include $270,000 for 4 grants (high: $220,000; low: $10,000).
Fields of interest: Higher education.
Limitations: Applications not accepted. Giving primarily in CA. No grants to individuals.
Application information: Contributes only to pre-selected organizations.
Officers: Donna Schweers, Chair.; Thomas C. Geiser, Pres. and Secy.-Treas.

Director: Kelsey Schweers Geiser.
EIN: 721589761

1021
Red Scott Family Foundation
7158 Fairway Rd.
La Jolla, CA 92037

Established in 1987 in California.
Donors: Charles R. Scott; Red Scott; Kathy Scott.
Foundation type: Independent foundation.
Financial data (yr. ended 12/31/12): Assets, $470,467 (M); gifts received, $89,366; expenditures, $171,996; qualifying distributions, $170,411; giving activities include $165,590 for 21 grants (high: $60,740; low: $500).
Fields of interest: Arts and culture; Diseases and conditions; Religion.
Type of support: Research.
Limitations: Applications not accepted. Giving primarily in CA. No grants to individuals.
Application information: Unsolicited reques for funds not accepted.
Officers: Charles R. Scott, Pres.; Katherine A. Scott, V.P.; Patrick W. Scott, Secy.; Kelly D. Scott, C.F.O.
EIN: 330278900

1022
The R. & E. Scott Foundation
1723 Karameos Dr.
Sunnyvale, CA 94087-5227

Established in 1998 in California.
Donors: Randal W. Scott; Eileen M. Scott.
Foundation type: Independent foundation.
Financial data (yr. ended 12/31/14): Assets, $486,265 (M); expenditures, $234,198; qualifying distributions, $226,680; giving activities include $223,000 for 6 grants (high: $100,000; low: $3,000).
Fields of interest: Secondary education; Community and economic development; Human services.
Limitations: Applications not accepted. Giving primarily in CA, CO and MI. No grants to individuals.
Application information: Unsolicited requests for funds not accepted.
Officers and Directors: Randal W. Scott, Pres. and Director; Eileen M. Scott, Secy.-Treas. and Director.
EIN: 770486556

1023
Susan Scott Foundation
15 Old Ranch Rd.
Laguna Niguel, CA 92677-9221

Established in 1994 in California.
Donors: John T. Scott; Florence H. Scott; Richard Schneider; Richard J. Muscio; Dorothy Heitman; Scott Family Char Remainder Trust.
Foundation type: Independent foundation.
Financial data (yr. ended 12/31/13): Assets, $6,117,265 (M); expenditures, $357,223; qualifying distributions, $306,933; giving activities include $305,000 for 18 grants (high: $105,000; low: $5,000).
Fields of interest: Arts and culture; Education; Hospital care; Infant care; Pediatrics; Diseases and conditions; Human services.
Type of support: Research.

Limitations: Applications not accepted. Giving primarily in CA. No grants to individuals.
Application information: Contributes only to pre-selected organizations.
Officers and Directors: George McFarlin, Pres. and Director; Tina McFarlin, Secy. and Director; Sarah McFarlin; Tim McFarlin; Claudia Schneider; Frederic Schneider.
EIN: 330622262

1024
The Scottsdale Foundation
1592 Virginia Rd.
San Marino, CA 91108-1934

Established in 2000 in California.
Donors: Stephen Chandler; Sue W. Chandler.
Foundation type: Independent foundation.
Financial data (yr. ended 12/31/13): Assets, $1,060,070 (M); gifts received, $1,378; expenditures, $381,307; qualifying distributions, $360,750; giving activities include $360,750 for 18 grants (high: $105,000; low: $250).
Fields of interest: Art museums; Libraries.
Type of support: General support.
Limitations: Applications not accepted. No grants to individuals.
Application information: Contributes only to pre-selected organizations.
Officers: Stephen Chandler, Pres.; Sue W. Chandler, Secy. and C.F.O.
EIN: 954799859

1025
Drs. Janene and Tom Scovel Foundation, Inc.
391 S. Rosemead Blvd.
Pasadena, CA 91107-4955

Established in 2001 in California.
Donors: Bing Yang; Out of the Shell, LLC.
Foundation type: Independent foundation.
Financial data (yr. ended 12/31/13): Assets, $7,320,617 (M); gifts received, $26,456; expenditures, $425,928; qualifying distributions, $400,576; giving activities include $352,525 for 14 grants (high: $270,000; low: $100).
Fields of interest: Education; Community and economic development; Human services.
International interests: China.
Limitations: Applications not accepted. Giving primarily in CA and China. No grants to individuals.
Application information: Unsolicited requests for funds not accepted.
Officer: Bing Yang, Pres.
Director: Katherine B. Purgason.
EIN: 100002893

1026
The Seaver Endowment
(formerly The Seaver Charitable Fund)
P.O. Box 1210
Sierra Madre, CA 91025-4210

Established in 2005 in California.
Donor: Richard Seaver.
Foundation type: Independent foundation.
Financial data (yr. ended 12/31/13): Assets, $5,386,235 (M); expenditures, $229,805; qualifying distributions, $200,793; giving activities

include $198,824 for 25 grants (high: $30,000; low: $1,000).
Fields of interest: Opera; Higher education; Public libraries.
Type of support: General support.
Limitations: Applications not accepted. Giving primarily in CA. No grants to individuals.
Application information: Unsolicited requests for funds not accepted.
Trustee: R. Carlton Seaver.
EIN: 206595504

1027
August Sebastiani Charitable Trust
35 Maple St.
Sonoma, CA 95476-7014
Contact: Don Sebastiani, Tr.

Established in 1996 in California.
Donors: Sebastiani Vineyards, Inc.; Don Sebastiani; Nancy Sebastiani; August D. Sebastiani; Allison Sebastiani; The Other Guys, Inc.; Don Sebastiani & Sons Int'l Wine.
Foundation type: Independent foundation.
Financial data (yr. ended 12/31/12): Assets, $253,542 (M); gifts received, $518,700; expenditures, $267,131; qualifying distributions, $250,516; giving activities include $250,516 for 36 grants (high: $50,345; low: $200).
Fields of interest: Education; Higher education; Catholicism; Right to life; Human services.
Limitations: Applications accepted. Giving primarily in CA. No grants to individuals.
Application information: Application form required.
   Initial approach: Contact foundation for application form
   Deadline(s): None
Trustees: August D. Sebastiani; Don A. Sebastiani, Jr.; Emilia Sebastiani.
EIN: 680386154

1028
The Seip Family Foundation
c/o Myron G. Sugarman & Co.
101 California St., 5th Fl.
San Francisco, CA 94111-5800 (415) 693-2040
Contact: Alexa C. Seip, Pres.

Established in 1997 in California.
Donors: Alexa C. Seip; Tom D. Seip.
Foundation type: Independent foundation.
Financial data (yr. ended 12/31/13): Assets, $1,715,628 (M); gifts received, $149,955; expenditures, $330,207; qualifying distributions, $305,577; giving activities include $302,000 for 10 grants (high: $100,000; low: $5,000).
Fields of interest: Maritime museums; Education; Higher education; Environment; Hospital care; Human services.
Type of support: General support; Capital campaigns; Capital and infrastructure.
Limitations: Applications accepted. Giving primarily in MD and NY. No grants to individuals.
Application information: Application form required.
   Initial approach: Proposal
   Deadline(s): None
Officers: Alexa C. Seip, Pres.; Tom D. Seip, Secy. and C.F.O.
EIN: 680401790

1029
The Setzer Foundation
2555 3rd St., Ste. 200
Sacramento, CA 95818-1100 (916) 442-2555
Contact: Scott H. Setzer, Tr.
E-mail: scott@setzerforest.com

Established in 1965 in California.
Foundation type: Independent foundation.
Financial data (yr. ended 12/31/13): Assets, $2,677,359 (M); gifts received, $1; expenditures, $273,587; qualifying distributions, $187,328; giving activities include $187,328 for 167 grants (high: $20,000; low: $30).
Purpose and activities: Giving primarily for education, health, children, youth, social services, and the arts.
Fields of interest: Arts and culture; Art museums; Education; Hospital care; Diseases and conditions; Cancers; Christianity; Human services; Child welfare.
Limitations: Applications accepted. Giving primarily in CA. No grants to individuals.
Application information:
Initial approach: Proposal
Deadline(s): None
Trustees: G. Cal Setzer; Mark D. Setzer; Scott H. Setzer.
EIN: 946115578

1030
The E. L. and Ruth B. Shannon Family Foundation
c/o Ruth B. Shannon
14081 Summit Dr.
Whittier, CA 90602-1955

Established in 1991 in California.
Donors: E.L. Shannon, Jr.; Ruth B. Shannon.
Foundation type: Independent foundation.
Financial data (yr. ended 12/31/13): Assets, $208,946 (M); gifts received, $77,185; expenditures, $191,050; qualifying distributions, $166,342; giving activities include $166,342 for 54 + grants (high: $63,044).
Fields of interest: Arts and culture; Higher education; Hospital care; Addiction services; Libraries; Christianity; Human services; Youth development.
Limitations: Applications not accepted. Giving primarily in southern CA and KY. No grants to individuals.
Application information: Contributes only to pre-selected organizations.
Officers and Directors: Ruth B. Shannon, Pres. and Director; Kathryn Shannon Johnson, Secy. and Director; Michael L. Shannon, Treas. and Director; Bruce L. Shannon.
EIN: 954348050

1031
Benjamin and Susan Shapell Foundation, Inc.
9401 Wilshire Blvd., Ste. 1200
Beverly Hills, CA 90212-2926

Established in 1997 in California.
Donors: The David and Fela Shapell Lead Unitrust; Susan Shapell; Benjamin Shapell.
Foundation type: Independent foundation.

Financial data (yr. ended 12/31/13): Assets, $1,887,343 (M); expenditures, $170,435; qualifying distributions, $161,930; giving activities include $161,930 for 29 grants (high: $26,300; low: $180).
Purpose and activities: Giving primarily for Jewish organizations.
Fields of interest: Public libraries; Judaism.
International interests: Israel.
Limitations: Applications not accepted. Giving primarily in NY; some giving also in Israel. No grants to individuals.
Application information: Unsolicited requests for funds not accepted.
Officers: Benjamin Shapell, Pres.; Susan Shapell, Secy.-Treas.
EIN: 954653430

1032
Shayne Foundation
c/o David Shayne
3201 Fernwood Ave.
Los Angeles, CA 90039-3510

Established in 1993 in Tennessee.
Donors: Herbert M. Shayne†; May W. Shayne†; May W. Shayne Charitable Lead Trust; Herbert M. Shayne Charitable Lead Trust.
Foundation type: Independent foundation.
Financial data (yr. ended 12/31/13): Assets, $10,067,101 (M); gifts received, $493,615; expenditures, $458,869; qualifying distributions, $388,200; giving activities include $388,200 for 53 grants (high: $89,800; low: $150).
Purpose and activities: Giving primarily for education.
Fields of interest: Higher education; Philanthropy; Job training; Human services; Females.
Limitations: Applications not accepted. Giving primarily in MA, TN and VT. No grants to individuals.
Application information: Unsolicited requests for funds not accepted.
Trustees: David R. Shayne; Elizabeth S. Shayne; Joan Blum Shayne; Jonathan A. Shayne.
EIN: 621540372

1033
Shenandoah Foundation
c/o Frank, Rimerman & Co., LLP
1 Embarcadero Ctr., Ste. 2410
San Francisco, CA 94111-3737

Established in 1968 in California.
Donors: Shana B. Johnstone; R. Clinton Johnstone, Jr.; Stephen Bechtel, Jr.; Elizabeth Hogan-Bechtel.
Foundation type: Independent foundation.
Financial data (yr. ended 12/31/13): Assets, $9,498,027 (M); gifts received, $2,000,000; expenditures, $860,901; qualifying distributions, $415,660; giving activities include $387,500 for 50 grants (high: $100,000; low: $500).
Purpose and activities: Giving primarily for medical, educational, environmental and cultural causes.
Fields of interest: Health; Disasters and emergency management; Human services.
Type of support: General support; Annual campaigns.
Limitations: Applications not accepted. Giving primarily in CA and NY. No grants to individuals.
Application information: Unsolicited requests for funds not accepted.

Officers and Directors: Shana B. Johnstone, Pres. and Director; Kyle Johnstone, V.P. and Director; George T. Argyris, Secy. and Director; Nancy S. Hair, Treas.; R.C. Johnstone, Jr.
EIN: 941675019

1034
David and Judy Shore Foundation, Inc.
9100 Wilshire Blvd., Ste. 400W
Beverly Hills, CA 90212

Donors: Judith Shore; David Shore.
Foundation type: Independent foundation.
Financial data (yr. ended 12/31/12): Assets, $160,355 (M); gifts received, $345,000; expenditures, $199,494; qualifying distributions, $196,066; giving activities include $196,066 for 49 grants (high: $25,000; low: $100).
Fields of interest: Education; Domesticated animals; Diseases and conditions; Judaism; Human services.
Type of support: Research.
Limitations: Applications not accepted. Giving primarily in CA and MI.
Application information: Unsolicited requests for funds not accepted.
Directors: David Shore; Judith Shore.
EIN: 263575222

1035
SHP Foundation
2882 Sand Hill Rd., No. 241
Menlo Park, CA 94025 (650) 344-1500
Contact: Susanna Pau, Secy.

Established in 1999 in California.
Donors: Susanna Pau; Peter Pau; Sandhill Properties.
Foundation type: Independent foundation.
Financial data (yr. ended 12/31/13): Assets, $2,327,654 (M); expenditures, $411,232; qualifying distributions, $408,264; giving activities include $408,264 for 24 grants (high: $109,000; low: $250).
Purpose and activities: Giving primarily for Christian organizations and evangelistic ministries.
Fields of interest: Christianity; Human services; Child welfare; Children.
Limitations: Applications accepted. Giving primarily in CA. No grants to individuals.
Application information: Application form required.
Initial approach: Proposal
Deadline(s): Dec. 31
Officers and Directors: Peter Pau, C.E.O. and Director; Susanna Pau, Secy. and Director.
EIN: 912017312

1036
The Blossom Siegel Family Foundation
1924 Santiago Dr.
Newport Beach, CA 92660

Established in 1998 in California.
Donor: Blossom Siegel.
Foundation type: Independent foundation.
Financial data (yr. ended 10/31/14): Assets, $3,817,209 (M); expenditures, $153,369; qualifying distributions, $149,795; giving activities include $149,795 for 29 grants (high: $56,872; low: $500).

Fields of interest: Arts and culture; Religion; Human services.
Limitations: Applications not accepted. Giving primarily in CA. No grants to individuals.
Application information: Unsolicited requests for funds not accepted.
Officers and Directors: Blossom Siegel, Chair. and Pres. and Director; Helene S. Kassover, V.P. and Director; Seth A. Siegel, C.F.O. and Director; David W. Siegel, Secy. and Director.
EIN: 330782965

1037
The Sikand Foundation, Inc.
15230 Burbank Blvd.
Van Nuys, CA 91411-3534

Established in 1986 in California.
Donor: Gunjit S. Sikand.
Foundation type: Operating foundation.
Financial data (yr. ended 11/30/13): Assets, $6,271,857 (M); gifts received, $731,672; expenditures, $826,628; qualifying distributions, $323,255; giving activities include $323,255 for 137 grants (high: $20,000; low: $75).
Purpose and activities: Giving primarily for education and health.
Fields of interest: Education; Medical education; Nonprofits; Diseases and conditions.
International interests: India.
Type of support: General support; Regranting.
Limitations: Applications not accepted. Giving primarily in CA. No grants to individuals.
Application information: Contributes only to pre-selected organizations.
Officers: Gunjit S. Sikand, Pres.; Annette C. Sikand, C.F.O.; Renee Sikand, Secy.
EIN: 954109267

1038
The Silicon Valley Bank Foundation
3003 Tasman Dr.
Santa Clara, CA 95054-1191 (405) 987-9147
E-mail: craactivities@svb.com.; Main URL: http://www.svb.com/Company/Corporate-Social-Responsibility/Social-Responsibility

Established in 1995 in California.
Donor: Silicon Valley Bank.
Foundation type: Company-sponsored foundation.
Financial data (yr. ended 12/31/13): Assets, $1,383,331 (M); expenditures, $200,110; qualifying distributions, $198,250; giving activities include $198,250 for 81 grants (high: $25,000; low: $500).
Purpose and activities: The foundation supports organizations with which employees of Silicon Valley Bank volunteer or serve in leadership positions; and programs designed to serve low-and-moderate income communities.
Fields of interest: Arts and culture; Education; Nonprofits; Health; Community and economic development; Employment; Housing development; Human services; Homeless services; Low-income and poor people.
Type of support: General support; Employee volunteer services; Capital campaigns; Equipment; Program development; Regranting.
Limitations: Applications accepted. Giving primarily in areas of company operations in northern CA. No

support for religious organizations, discriminatory organizations, or parent teacher associations. No grants to individuals, or for memorial campaigns, fundraising, political activities, research, sponsorship of athletic events or programs, endowments, or advertising.
Publications: Application guidelines.
Application information: Preference is given to organizations sponsored by a Silicon Valley Bank employee. Grants range from $500 to $2,500. Application form required.
  Initial approach: Email
  Deadline(s): None
  Board meeting date(s): Quarterly
Officers: Jim Hori, Chair. and Pres.; Scott Bergquist, V.P.; Ann Fong, Secy.; Alice Koht-Phipps, Treas.
Directors: Pamela Aldsworth; Dan Allred; Scott Case; Don Chandler; Sue Plotnik; Katie Knepley; Carrie Merritt; Craig Robinson; Brenda Santoro; Jeff Strawn; Marc Verissimo.
EIN: 770414630

1039
Silton Family Foundation
972 Hilgard Ave.
Los Angeles, CA 90024-3060

Donor: Fred Silton.
Foundation type: Independent foundation.
Financial data (yr. ended 12/31/12): Assets, $119,784 (M); gifts received, $57,908; expenditures, $162,378; qualifying distributions, $160,000; giving activities include $160,000 for 27 grants (high: $65,000; low: $100).
Fields of interest: Arts and culture; Housing development; Judaism.
Limitations: Applications not accepted. Giving primarily in Los Angeles, CA.
Application information: Unsolicited requests for funds not accepted.
Officer: Karen Balin, Chair.; Fred Silton, Pres.
Board Members: Debra Cowan; James Silton; Lee Silton; Susan Silton.
EIN: 263605273

1040
Lucille Ellis Simon Foundation
c/o Avery & Greig, LLP
2811 Wilshire Blvd., Ste. 700
Santa Monica, CA 90403-4804

Established in 1960 in California.
Donors: Donald Ellis Simon; Lucille Ellis Simon; Douglas Simon Charitable Trust; Pamela Simon-Jensen Charitable Trust; Eric Simon Charitable Trust.
Foundation type: Independent foundation.
Financial data (yr. ended 12/31/14): Assets, $10,160,571 (M); expenditures, $544,303; qualifying distributions, $450,026; giving activities include $421,000 for 56 grants (high: $50,000; low: $1,000).
Purpose and activities: Giving for Jewish organizations, education, health services, the environment, and art organizations.
Fields of interest: Arts and culture; Education; Diseases and conditions; Community and economic development.
Type of support: Research.
Limitations: Applications not accepted. No grants to individuals.

Application information: Contributes only to pre-selected organizations.
Officers: Donald Simon, Pres.; Pamela Simon Jensen, V.P.; Douglas Simon, V.P.; Eric Simon, V.P.; Jerome H. Craig, Esq., Secy.-Treas.
EIN: 956035906

1041
Robert Ellis Simon Foundation
312 S. Canyon View Dr.
Los Angeles, CA 90049-3812

Established in 1961 in California.
Donor: Robert Ellis Simon†.
Foundation type: Independent foundation.
Financial data (yr. ended 12/31/13): Assets, $4,448,387 (M); expenditures, $408,313; qualifying distributions, $335,000; giving activities include $335,000 for 7 grants (high: $50,000; low: $40,000).
Purpose and activities: Grants for preventive or educational approaches to any of a variety of mental health issues; support for new, short-term, and innovative programs or demonstration projects and not for long-term funding.
Fields of interest: Mental health care.
Type of support: Pilot programs; Matching grants; Seed money; Research.
Limitations: Applications not accepted. Giving limited to Los Angeles County, CA. No grants to individuals.
Publications: Informational brochure.
Application information: Unsolicited requests for funds not accepted.
  Board meeting date(s): Fall
Officer: Ralph Williams, Exec. Dir.
Trustees: Harold M. Williams; Joan G. Willens.
Number of staff: 1 part-time professional; 1 part-time support.
EIN: 956035905

1042
Simon-Strauss Foundation
c/o William Simon
1433 Allenford Ave.
Los Angeles, CA 90049-3613

Established in 2007 in California.
Foundation type: Independent foundation.
Financial data (yr. ended 12/31/14): Assets, $9,973,964 (M); expenditures, $503,498; qualifying distributions, $484,445; giving activities include $413,500 for 76 grants (high: $30,000; low: $1,000).
Fields of interest: Arts and culture; Education; Diseases and conditions.
Type of support: Research; Research and evaluation.
Limitations: Applications not accepted. Giving primarily in CA.
Application information: Contributes only to pre-selected organizations.
Officers and Directors: Paul Simon, Pres. and Director; Michelle Simon Fromme, V.P. and Director; John Simon, V.P. and Director; Michael Simon, V.P. and Director; Ralph Simon, V.P. and Director; Steven Simon, V.P. and Director; William Simon, Secy.-Treas. and Director.
EIN: 260604831

1043
SJL Foundation
1482 E. Valley Rd., Ste. 712
Montecito, CA 93108

Established in 1988 in Montana.
Donors: George D. Lilly; WICU-TV; Brian Lilly; Kevin Lilly.
Foundation type: Independent foundation.
Financial data (yr. ended 12/31/13): Assets, $57,568 (M); gifts received, $55,417; expenditures, $181,133; qualifying distributions, $170,446; giving activities include $152,151 for 18 grants (high: $100,000; low: $100).
Fields of interest: Arts and culture; Education; University education; Religion.
Limitations: Applications not accepted. Giving primarily in CA. No grants to individuals.
Application information: Contributes only to pre-selected organizations.
Trustees: Brian M. Lilly; Denise L. Lilly; George D. Lilly; Kevin T. Lilly; Parker Lilly.
EIN: 363584276

1044
SKB Foundation
1247 Elko Dr.
Sunnyvale, CA 94089-2211   (408) 747-1769
Contact: Ho-Tzu Yen, Pres.

Established in 1986 in California.
Donors: Yung-Tsai Yen; Ho-Tzu Yen.
Foundation type: Independent foundation.
Financial data (yr. ended 11/30/13): Assets, $5,240,672 (M); gifts received, $335,300; expenditures, $263,662; qualifying distributions, $250,449; giving activities include $248,500 for 22 grants (high: $60,000; low: $1,000).
Purpose and activities: Provides student loans to those of Taiwanese or Chinese origin residing in the San Francisco Bay Area for post-secondary education; funding also for health associations, family services, and federated giving programs.
Fields of interest: Arts and culture; Higher education; Nonprofits; Family planning; Diseases and conditions; Family services.
Type of support: General support; Loans to individuals; Student aid; Regranting.
Limitations: Applications accepted. Giving primarily in CA, IL, NY and VA.
Application information:
    Initial approach: Proposal
    Deadline(s): None
Officers: Ho-Tzu Yen, Pres.; Yung-Tsai Yen, Secy.; Sophia Yen, Treas.
EIN: 943024121

1045
The Skowronski Family Foundation
1325 Este Vista Ct.
Encinitas, CA 92024-5251
Contact: F. Stanley Skowronski, Pres.

Established in 2004 in California.
Donors: F. Stanley Skowronski; Christine Skowronski.
Foundation type: Independent foundation.
Financial data (yr. ended 12/31/14): Assets, $3,538,826 (M); gifts received, $324,720; expenditures, $173,628; qualifying distributions,

$146,065; giving activities include $143,000 for 10 grants (high: $43,000; low: $5,000).
Fields of interest: Arts and culture; Health; Diseases and conditions.
Limitations: Applications accepted. Giving primarily in CA and NY.
Application information: Application form required.
    Initial approach: Proposal
    Deadline(s): None
Officers: F. Stanley Skowronski, Pres.; Christine Skowronski, Secy.-Treas.
EIN: 202032901

1046
Skynyrd Foundation
c/o Haber Corp.
16830 Ventura Blvd., Ste. 501
Encino, CA 91436-1717

Donors: Live Nation; Still Unbroken, Inc.; DCF Enterprises, Inc.; The Bethel Performing Arts Ctr.; Waterfront Concerts, LLC; Bell Country Expo., Inc.; Project 324; Blue Deuce Ent., LLC; Red Mountain Entertainment; Champlain Valley Expo.
Foundation type: Independent foundation.
Financial data (yr. ended 12/31/12): Assets, $72,777 (M); gifts received, $72,221; expenditures, $164,038; qualifying distributions, $161,865; giving activities include $161,865 for 11 grants (high: $66,865; low: $2,000).
Fields of interest: University education; Diseases and conditions; Human services.
Type of support: Research.
Limitations: Applications not accepted. Giving primarily in CA.
Application information: Unsolicited requests for funds not accepted.
Officers and Directors: Ken Levitan, Pres.; Larkin Collins, V.P. and Director; Judy Van Zant, V.P. and Director; Gary Haber, Secy.-Treas.; Gary Rossington.
EIN: 272761116

1047
The Skyscrape Foundation
(formerly The Marie D. Jeffrey Foundation)
1823 Vineyard Ave.
Saint Helena, CA 94574-1747

Established in 1986 in California.
Donors: Marie D. Jeffrey; Lynda J. Martin.
Foundation type: Independent foundation.
Financial data (yr. ended 11/30/13): Assets, $6,122,064 (M); gifts received, $45,482; expenditures, $381,194; qualifying distributions, $292,068; giving activities include $216,861 for 33 grants (high: $77,475; low: $200).
Fields of interest: Theater; Museums; University education; Environment; Animal welfare; Hospital care; Family services.
International interests: France.
Limitations: Applications not accepted. Giving primarily in CA; some giving in France. No grants to individuals.
Application information: Contributes only to pre-selected organizations.
Officer: Richard L. Martin, Pres.
Directors: Mark Capellano; Anne Marie Martin; Jeffrey S. Martin; Lynda J. Martin.
EIN: 943037301

1048
Margaret K. Sloss Foundation
818 Cherry St.
Santa Rosa, CA 95404-4207

Established in 1958 in California.
Donors: Louis Sloss, Jr.; Anthony Sloss; Karen Sloss; Elizabeth Sloss; Jeffrey Sloss; Jean Sloss.
Foundation type: Independent foundation.
Financial data (yr. ended 12/31/13): Assets, $13,665 (M); gifts received, $161,568; expenditures, $157,069; qualifying distributions, $156,304; giving activities include $155,597 for 173 grants (high: $21,000; low: $30).
Fields of interest: Education; Religion; Human services.
Limitations: Applications not accepted. No grants to individuals.
Application information: Unsolicited applications not accepted.
    Board meeting date(s): Annually
Trustees: Anthony Sloss; Karen Sloss; Louis Sloss, Jr.
Number of staff: None.
EIN: 946065985

1049
The Small Change Foundation
19 Sutter St.
San Francisco, CA 94104-4901
Contact: Raymond L. Mulliner, V.P. and Secy.

Established in 1996 in California.
Donor: James C. Hormel.
Foundation type: Independent foundation.
Financial data (yr. ended 10/31/14): Assets, $5,801,290 (M); expenditures, $408,756; qualifying distributions, $347,000; giving activities include $347,000 for 20 grants (high: $50,000; low: $1,000).
Purpose and activities: Giving primarily for gay and lesbian issues, as well as for human services.
Fields of interest: Performing arts; Art museums; Education; Environmental education; Communication media; LGBTQ rights; Human services; LGBTQ people; People of Asian descent; People with HIV/AIDS; Military personnel.
Type of support: Advocacy.
Limitations: Applications accepted. Giving primarily in San Francisco, CA; funding also in Washington, DC, and New York, NY.
Application information: Application form required.
    Initial approach: Letter
    Deadline(s): None
Officers: James C. Hormel, Pres.; Raymond L. Mulliner, V.P. and Secy.; Paul Grippardi, Treas.
EIN: 943271247

1050
Marvin & Sondra Smalley Family Foundation
963 Stone Canyon Rd.
Los Angeles, CA 90077-2913

Donors: Marvin Smalley; Sondra Smalley; Arnold & Edith Familian Foundation; Isadore Familian Intervivos Trust.
Foundation type: Independent foundation.
Financial data (yr. ended 12/31/13): Assets, $3,371,281 (M); expenditures, $207,230; qualifying distributions, $187,206; giving activities

include $186,626 for 25 grants (high: $50,000; low: $50).

Fields of interest: Arts and culture; Education; Nonprofits; Diseases and conditions; Human services; Child welfare.

Type of support: Regranting; Research.

Limitations: Applications not accepted. Giving primarily in CA. No grants to individuals.

Application information: Contributes only to pre-selected organizations.

Officers: Marvin Smalley, Pres.; Sondra Smalley, Secy.

Trustees: Lori Smalley Schwartz; Debra Smalley; Jeffrey Smalley; Scott Smalley.

EIN: 952535589

1051

The Roy W. Smith Charitable Foundation Inc.

17602 17th St., Ste 102-281
Tustin, CA   92780-1961

Donor: Roy W. Smith†.

Foundation type: Independent foundation.

Financial data (yr. ended 12/31/13): Assets, $3,114,079 (M); expenditures, $332,319; qualifying distributions, $164,650; giving activities include $164,650 for 16 grants (high: $54,985; low: $200).

Fields of interest: Mental health care; Human services.

Limitations: Applications not accepted. Giving primarily in CA and VA. No grants to individuals.

Application information: Contributes only to pre-selected organizations.

Officers: Carla Jacobs, Pres.; Randall Hagar, V.P.; Brian Jacobs, Treas.

EIN: 202071882

1052

The Ted and Joyce Smith Family Foundation

P.O. Box 8799
Fresno, CA   93747-8799

Donors: Galene J. Demars; Lori Lum; Steve Lum; Amanda Smith; Greg Smith; Joyce Smith; Ted Smith; Brian L. Demars.

Foundation type: Independent foundation.

Financial data (yr. ended 12/31/13): Assets, $2,917,325 (M); expenditures, $173,300; qualifying distributions, $136,150; giving activities include $136,000 for 4 grants (high: $88,000; low: $8,000).

Fields of interest: Education; Religion; Human services.

Limitations: Applications not accepted. Giving primarily in GA. No grants to individuals.

Application information: Unsolicited requests for funds not accepted.

Officers: Gregory T. Smith, C.E.O. and Pres.; Joyce Smith, Secy.; Steven D. Lum, C.F.O.

Directors: Brian L. DeMars; Gaylene J. DeMars; Lori R. Lum; Amanda B. Smith; Ted Smith.

EIN: 262870689

1053

Will and Jada Smith Family Foundation

(formerly Will Smith Foundation)
c/o Gelfand Rennert & Feldman
1880 Century Park E., Ste. 1600
Los Angeles, CA   90067-1661

Established in 1996 in California.

Donors: Willard Smith II; WJS Trust; Howard J. Saks; Treyball, Inc.; Sony Pictures Entertainment.

Foundation type: Independent foundation.

Financial data (yr. ended 12/31/13): Assets, $17,878 (M); gifts received, $560,000; expenditures, $564,027; qualifying distributions, $435,160; giving activities include $435,160 for 48 grants (high: $50,000; low: $340).

Purpose and activities: Giving primarily for social services, health organizations, including an organization determined to end malaria deaths, as well as for arts education, and to Christian and Baptist churches and organizations.

Fields of interest: Arts education; Foundations; Diseases and conditions; Malaria; Christianity; Baptist; Human services; Child welfare.

Limitations: Applications not accepted. Giving primarily in Los Angeles, CA, Baltimore, MD, New York, NY, and Philadelphia, PA. No grants to individuals.

Application information: Contributes only to pre-selected organizations.

Officers: Willard Smith II, Pres.; Harry Smith, C.F.O.; Jada P. Smith, V.P.

Directors: Karen Evans; James Lassiter.

EIN: 954607014

1054

Grace Pepper Smith Foundation

P.O. Box 93
Balboa Island, CA   92662-0093

Established in 1959 in California.

Donors: Clarinda C. Smith; Markle C. Smith; Mary C. Hamilton; June MacAdam.

Foundation type: Independent foundation.

Financial data (yr. ended 12/31/13): Assets, $891,003 (M); gifts received, $25,038; expenditures, $305,383; qualifying distributions, $276,516; giving activities include $226,235 for 18 grants (high: $209,000; low: $180), and $30,692 for 4 grants to individuals (high: $10,825; low: $811).

Fields of interest: Christianity.

Limitations: Applications not accepted. Giving primarily in CA and FL.

Application information: Unsolicited requests for funds not accepted.

Officer: Markle C. Smith, Pres.

EIN: 956052292

1055

Linda I. Smith Foundation

3197-A Airport Loop Dr.
Costa Mesa, CA   92626-3424

Established in 1998 in California.

Donor: Linda I. Smith.

Foundation type: Independent foundation.

Financial data (yr. ended 12/31/14): Assets, $3,753,935; expenditures, $242,523; qualifying distributions, $173,000.

Fields of interest: Arts education; Theater; Higher education; Hospital care; Child welfare; Youth services.

Limitations: Applications not accepted. Giving primarily in CA. No grants to individuals.

Application information: Unsolicited requests for funds not accepted.

Officers and Directors: Linda I. Smith, Pres. and Director; Diana Gaede Blatz, Secy.-Treas. and Director; Tracey L. Gaede.

EIN: 330804049

1056

Mark and Dorothy Smith Foundation

2011 S. Broadway, Ste. J
Santa Maria, CA   93454-7886   (805) 928-6628

Established in 2007 in Unspecified.

Donors: Mark Smith; Dorothy Smith; Cameron Smith; Craig Smith.

Foundation type: Independent foundation.

Financial data (yr. ended 12/31/13): Assets, $2,671,347 (M); expenditures, $187,984; qualifying distributions, $145,550; giving activities include $145,550 for 11 grants (high: $25,000; low: $1,500).

Fields of interest: Higher education; Animal welfare; Hospital care; Public libraries; Human services; Youth services.

Limitations: Applications accepted. Giving primarily in Santa Maria, CA.

Application information: Application form required.

Initial approach: Letter

Deadline(s): None

Directors: Cameron Smith; Craig Smith.

EIN: 208775647

1057

Smith-Walker Foundation

1260 Coast Village Cir.
Santa Barbara, CA   93108-2790

Established in 1989 in California.

Foundation type: Independent foundation.

Financial data (yr. ended 09/30/13): Assets, $3,538,576 (M); expenditures, $236,415; qualifying distributions, $210,420; giving activities include $210,000 for 29 grants (high: $30,000; low: $1,500).

Purpose and activities: Giving primarily to Protestant organizations, for youth services, and for health care.

Fields of interest: Arts and culture; Historic preservation; Education; Health; Hospital care; Diseases and conditions; Protestantism; Camps; Child welfare.

Type of support: General support.

Limitations: Applications not accepted. Giving limited to CA. No grants to individuals.

Application information: Contributes only to pre-selected organizations.

Board meeting date(s): Dec.

Officers: Clarke A. Smith, Pres.; Janet G. Gates, Secy.; Kim S. Smith, Treas.

Trustees: Nathan C. Gates; Matthew McCall; Shelly S. Royalty; Walker Smith III.

EIN: 330327308

1058
Smith-Welsh Foundation
28925 Pacific Coast Hwy., 2nd Fl.
Malibu, CA 90265-3922
Contact: Karl Reinecker

Established in 1985 in California.
Donor: Omer Smith Marital Trust.
Foundation type: Independent foundation.
Financial data (yr. ended 12/31/13): Assets,
$3,858,842 (M); expenditures, $260,826;
qualifying distributions, $208,700; giving
activities include $208,700 for 34 grants (high: $35,000;
low: $350).
Purpose and activities: Giving primarily for the arts
and for human services.
Fields of interest: Arts and culture; Natural history
museums; Education; Environment; Nonprofits;
Human services.
Type of support: Regranting.
Limitations: Applications not accepted. Giving
primarily in CA. No grants to individuals.
Application information: Contributes only to
pre-selected organizations.
Officers: James E. Welsh, Co-C.E.O.; Nancy S.
Welsh, Co-C.E.O.
EIN: 953958030

1059
The Smittcamp Family Foundation
1265 N. Minnewawa Ave.
Clovis, CA 93619-8738

Established in 1996 in California.
Donors: William Smittcamp; Muriel Smittcamp;
Robert Smittcamp; Earl Smittcamp; Summer Prize
Fruit Co.; Wawona Frozen Foods; Lyons Magnus,
Inc.; Brent Smittcamp.
Foundation type: Independent foundation.
Financial data (yr. ended 12/31/13): Assets,
$6,733,263 (M); gifts received, $85,000;
expenditures, $411,111; qualifying distributions,
$323,120; giving activities include $323,120 for 29
grants (high: $120,000; low: $750).
Purpose and activities: Giving primarily for higher
education, and human services.
Fields of interest: Education; Higher education;
Health; Human services; Child welfare.
Limitations: Applications not accepted. Giving
limited to CA. No grants to individuals, no loans.
Application information: Contributes only to
pre-selected organizations.
Officers: Elizabeth Kimball, Pres.; Herb Liles, C.F.O.;
William Smittcamp, V.P.; Carol Copeland, Secy.;
Robert Smittcamp, Treas.
Directors: James M. Bell; Albert Peterson; Marie
Riggs; Charles Shillito.
EIN: 770343026

1060
Patricia D. and William B. Smullin Foundation
2930 Domingo Ave., No. 163
Berkeley, CA 94705-2454 (510) 704-0194
Contact: Carol Anne Smullin Brown, Pres.
FAX: (510) 704-0295;
E-mail: smullin.foundation@gmail.com; Main
URL: http://foundationcenter.org/grantmaker/
smullin

Established in 1990 in Oregon.

Donors: Patricia D. Smullin†; William B. Smullin†.
Foundation type: Independent foundation.
Financial data (yr. ended 12/31/13): Assets,
$14,378,548 (M); expenditures, $644,618;
qualifying distributions, $435,030; giving activities
include $435,030 for 28 grants (high: $80,000;
low: $530).
Purpose and activities: The mission of the
foundation is to help educate the citizens of
Northern California and Oregon through gifts to
higher education, health education, and the
Episcopal Church.
Fields of interest: Higher education; Foundations;
Health; Hospice care; Maternal and perinatal health;
Alzheimer's disease; Episcopalianism and
Anglicanism; Lutheranism.
Type of support: General support; Capital
campaigns; Endowments; Program development;
Scholarships.
Limitations: Applications not accepted. Giving
limited to northern CA and OR.
Publications: Financial statement; Program policy
statement.
Application information: Unsolicited requests for
funds not accepted.
    Board meeting date(s): Nov.
Officers and Directors: Carol Anne Smullin Brown,
Pres. and Exec. Dir.; Meredith A. Brown, V.P. and
Director; Nikki C. Hatton, Secy. and Director; Kevin
Smullin Brown; Susan Dawson.
Number of staff: 1 full-time professional.
EIN: 931055546

1061
William D. Smythe Family Foundation
142 S. Santa Cruz Ave.
Los Gatos, CA 95030-6712 (408) 399-5551
Contact: Michael D. Smythe

Established in 2000 in California.
Donors: William D. Smythe; Michael D. Smythe;
Linda Smythe; Karen Smythe Cocumelli; William D.
Smythe, Jr.; Catherine Smythe Grasso; James J.
Smythe; Sally Smythe Godwin; Stephen Godwin.
Foundation type: Independent foundation.
Financial data (yr. ended 12/31/14): Assets,
$800,568 (M); expenditures, $176,325; qualifying
distributions, $135,000; giving activities include
$135,000 for 8 grants (high: $50,000; low:
$10,000).
Fields of interest: Agriculture; Human services;
Youth development.
Limitations: Applications accepted. Giving primarily
in San Jose, CA.
Application information: Application form required.
    Initial approach: Letter
    Deadline(s): Dec. 31
Officers: William D. Smythe, Jr., C.F.O.; Karen
Smythe Cocumelli, Secy.
Directors: Sally Smythe Godwin; Catherine Smythe
Grasso; James J. Smythe.
EIN: 770535273

1062
The Harry and Estelle Soicher Foundation
1925 Century Park E., No. 620
Los Angeles, CA 90067-2730

Established in 2007 in California.
Donor: The Estelle Soicher Trust.

Foundation type: Independent foundation.
Financial data (yr. ended 12/31/13): Assets,
$8,095,751 (M); gifts received, $7,910;
expenditures, $460,467; qualifying distributions,
$442,311; giving activities include $442,311 for 9
grants (high: $70,000; low: $1,000).
Fields of interest: Specialty hospital care.
Limitations: Applications not accepted. Giving
primarily in CA. No grants to individuals.
Application information: Contributes only to
pre-selected organizations.
Officers: Stanley B. Gitlin, Pres.; Joni Gitlin, Secy.;
Sheri Rosen, Treas.
EIN: 208477430

1063
Solano Community Foundation
470 Chadbourne Rd., Ste. D
Fairfield, CA 94534 (707) 399-3846
Contact: Constance Harris, C.E.O. and C.O.O.
FAX: (707) 399-3849; E-mail: ceo@solanocf.org;
Main URL: http://www.solanocf.org
Facebook: https://www.facebook.com/pages/
Solano-Community-Foundation/
170743039679397

Established in 2000 in California.
Foundation type: Community foundation.
Financial data (yr. ended 12/31/13): Assets,
$9,174,264 (M); gifts received, $526,513;
expenditures, $659,430; giving activities include
$366,685 for 31+ grants (high: $28,000).
Purpose and activities: The Solano Community
Foundation is dedicated to strengthening the local
community both now and for future generations. The
foundation is a vehicle for private donors to make a
lasting contribution to the community. The Solano
Community Foundation fulfills its mission by: 1)
encouraging private giving for public good; 2)
building and maintaining permanent endowments to
respond to changing community needs; 3) providing
flexible tax-exempt vehicles for donors with varied
charitable interests and abilities to give; 4) serving
as a catalyst and resource to effectively respond to
community problems; and 5) strengthening the
nonprofit sector through capacity-building trainings,
workshops, and research tools for donor
identification.
Fields of interest: Arts and culture; Elementary and
secondary education; Higher education;
Environment; Domesticated animals; Medical
support services; Community and economic
development; Human services; Child welfare; Foster
care; Youth mentoring; Intergenerational mentoring;
Temporary accommodations; Children and youth;
Adolescents; Seniors; Foster and adoptive children;
Low-income and poor people; Military personnel.
Type of support: General support; Continuing
support; Capacity-building and technical assistance;
Program development; Scholarships.
Limitations: Applications accepted. Giving primarily
in Solano County, CA. No grants to individuals
(except for scholarships), or for capital campaigns,
seed money or start up money for organizations
applying for tax exempt status.
Publications: Application guidelines; Financial
statement; Grants list; Informational brochure.
Application information: The foundation is not
currently accepting unsolicited grant proposals.
However, grant funds are available from certain
program funds held on a recurring basis. For more
information about programs and grant schedules,
visit website. Application form required.

Initial approach: Letters of Inquiry (LOI) no longer than one page
Copies of proposal: 1
Deadline(s): No deadlines for general requests. Deadlines for RFP's from SCF Programs are listed on foundation website
Board meeting date(s): Each month, except July and Dec.
Officers and Directors: Teresa Fitzgerald, Chair. and Director; Becky Gardiner, Vice-Chair. and Director; Constance Harris, C.E.O. and C.O.O. and Director; Tim Kubli, Treas. and Director; Matt Lucas; Gary Passama.
Number of staff: 1 full-time professional; 2 part-time support.
EIN: 680354961

1064
The Somekh Family Foundation
25625 Moody Rd.
Los Altos Hills, CA   94022-4405

Established in 1997 in California.
Donors: Sasson Somekh; Eta Somekh.
Foundation type: Independent foundation.
Financial data (yr. ended 12/31/13): Assets, $3,093,892 (M); expenditures, $261,671; qualifying distributions, $233,573; giving activities include $232,473 for 58 grants (high: $90,000; low: $100).
Fields of interest: Arts and culture; Museums; Higher education; Nonprofits; Non-natural disasters; Judaism; Human services.
Type of support: Regranting.
Limitations: Applications not accepted. Giving primarily in CA. No grants to individuals.
Application information: Contributes only to pre-selected organizations.
Trustees: Eta Somekh; Sasson Somekh.
EIN: 770471511

1065
The Sondheimer Foundation
2346 Westwood Blvd., Ste. 8
Los Angeles, CA   90064

Donor: Ida N. Sondheimer.
Foundation type: Independent foundation.
Financial data (yr. ended 12/31/14): Assets, $7,165,052; expenditures, $384,636; qualifying distributions, $325,679.
Fields of interest: Nonprofits; Health; Human services.
Type of support: Regranting.
Limitations: Applications not accepted.
Application information: Unsolicited requests for funds not accepted.
Officers: Ida N. Sondheimer, 1st V.P.; Jane Rissman, 2nd V.P. and Secy.; Richard J. Sondheimer, Treas. and Exec. Dir.
EIN: 263060699

1066
Martin & Dorothy Spatz Foundation
966 Ferguson Rd.
Sebastopol, CA   95472

Donor: Spatz Revocable Trust.
Foundation type: Independent foundation.

Financial data (yr. ended 12/31/13): Assets, $9,507,524 (M); gifts received, $39,945; expenditures, $424,635; qualifying distributions, $370,653; giving activities include $246,292 for 5 grants (high: $100,000; low: $15,000).
Fields of interest: Education; Health.
Limitations: Applications not accepted.
Application information: Unsolicited requests for funds not accepted.
Trustees: Kathleen Price; Joseph Greensher, MD; Leon Berg, CPA.
EIN: 306221033

1067
Spielman Family Foundation
2517 Ruette Nicole
La Jolla, CA   92037-2009

Donors: Thomas & Lonnie Schwartz Foundation; Alvin Schwartz Charitable Lead Trust.
Foundation type: Independent foundation.
Financial data (yr. ended 12/31/13): Assets, $2,696,359 (M); gifts received, $527,169; expenditures, $290,139; qualifying distributions, $269,535; giving activities include $269,535 for 34 grants (high: $70,000; low: $200).
Fields of interest: Arts and culture; Disasters and emergency management; Religion; Judaism.
Limitations: Applications not accepted. Giving primarily in CA.
Application information: Unsolicited requests for funds not accepted.
Officers: Charles Spielman, Pres.; Amy Spielman, V.P.
EIN: 452957019

1068
Stephan & Barbara Spiva Foundation
742 Marsolan Ave.
Solana Beach, CA   92075-1949

Foundation type: Independent foundation.
Financial data (yr. ended 12/31/13): Assets, $2,460,851 (L); expenditures, $305,916; qualifying distributions, $265,700; giving activities include $265,700 for 12 grants (high: $100,000; low: $100).
Fields of interest: Human services.
Limitations: Applications not accepted. Giving primarily in CA.
Application information: Unsolicited requests for funds not accepted.
Trustees: Barbara Spiva; Stephan Spiva; Jacob M. Wallace.
EIN: 770529631

1069
Robert R. Sprague Foundation
c/o William Stinehart, Jr.
2029 Century Park E., Ste. 4000
Los Angeles, CA   90067-3026

Established in 1998 in California.
Donors: Robert R. Sprague; Margaret L. Sprague.
Foundation type: Independent foundation.
Financial data (yr. ended 05/31/13): Assets, $12,967,366 (M); expenditures, $450,138; qualifying distributions, $402,088; giving activities include $361,800 for 11 grants (high: $150,000; low: $1,000).

Purpose and activities: Giving primarily for higher education.
Fields of interest: Arts and culture; Education; Human services.
Limitations: Applications not accepted. Giving primarily in CA.
Application information: Unsolicited requests for funds not accepted.
Officers: Margaret L. Sprague; William Stinehart, Jr.
EIN: 957052355

1070
Caryll M. & Norman F. Sprague, Jr. Foundation
11726 San Vincente Blvd., Ste. 625
Los Angeles, CA   90049

Established in 1957 in California.
Donors: Caryll M. Sprague; Norman F. Sprague, Jr., MD; Norman F. Sprague III.
Foundation type: Independent foundation.
Financial data (yr. ended 12/31/13): Assets, $4,953,718 (M); expenditures, $267,488; qualifying distributions, $196,050; giving activities include $196,050 for 78 grants (high: $12,500; low: $60).
Fields of interest: Museums; Art museums; Education; Higher education; Natural resources; Hospital care; Human services.
Limitations: Applications not accepted. Giving primarily in CA. No grants to individuals.
Application information: Unsolicited requests for funds not accepted.
Board meeting date(s): Annually and as required
Trustees: Cynthia Sprague Connolly; Caryll S. Mingst; Charles T. Munger; Norman F. Sprague III, MD.
EIN: 956021187

1071
Florence and Laurence Spungen Family Foundation
P.O. Box 5262
Santa Barbara, CA   93150-5262
Contact: David Hafft
E-mail: info@spungenfoundation.org; Main URL: http://www.spungenfoundation.org
Grants List: http://www.spungenfoundation.org/grants.html

Established in 2006 in Illinois.
Donors: Florence Spungen†; Heidi Leventhal; Paul Leventhal.
Foundation type: Independent foundation.
Financial data (yr. ended 12/31/13): Assets, $4,615,399 (M); gifts received, $44,217; expenditures, $212,908; qualifying distributions, $206,597; giving activities include $137,670 for 51 grants (high: $21,900; low: $100).
Purpose and activities: The foundation focuses its grantmaking on health related issues, especially cancer research, care and treatment, and Jewish causes. The geographic focus is in the northern suburbs of Chicago, Illinois and Santa Barbara, California, as well as nationally and internationally, when appropriate to the mission of the foundation.
Fields of interest: Arts and culture; Education; Philanthropy.
Limitations: Applications not accepted. Giving primarily in Santa Barbara, CA and northern Chicago, IL.

Application information: Unsolicited requests for funds not accepted.
Officers and Trustees: Carol Spungen, Pres. and Treas. and Trustee; Debra Spungen, V.P. and Trustee; Daniel Spungen, Secy. and Trustee; Glenn Spungen.
EIN: 207155204

1072
Srivastava Foundation
13901 W. Edith Ave.
Los Altos, CA 94022-2684

Established in 2010 in California.
Donor: Sanjay Srivastava.
Foundation type: Independent foundation.
Financial data (yr. ended 12/31/13): Assets, $236,434 (M); expenditures, $264,910; qualifying distributions, $261,750; giving activities include $261,750 for 5 grants (high: $200,000; low: $10,000).
Fields of interest: Higher education; Foundations.
Type of support: General support.
Limitations: Applications not accepted. Giving primarily in CA and IL.
Application information: Unsolicited requests for funds not accepted.
Officer: Freda Charlene, Secy. and C.F.O.
Trustee: Sanjay Srivastava.
EIN: 273679145

1073
Nancy and Geoffrey Stack Family Foundation
18802 Bardeen Ave.
Irvine, CA 92612-1521
Contact: Geoffrey L. Stack, Dir.; Marylyn Milburn; Nancy Stack, Dir.
E-mail: jstack@sares-regis.com

Donors: Geoffrey Stack; Nancy Stack.
Foundation type: Independent foundation.
Financial data (yr. ended 12/31/13): Assets, $1,220,966 (M); gifts received, $305,000; expenditures, $308,110; qualifying distributions, $308,110; giving activities include $307,500 for 40 grants (high: $30,000; low: $500).
Fields of interest: Performing arts; Education; Nonprofits.
Type of support: Regranting.
Limitations: Applications not accepted. Giving primarily in CA.
Application information: Contributes only to pre-selected organizations.
Directors: Geoffrey L. Stack; Nancy Stack.
EIN: 711019812

1074
James M. Stafford Foundation
c/o Majestic Realty
13191 Crossroads Pkwy. N., 6th Fl.
City of Industry, CA 91746-3421

Donor: James M. Stafford Trust.
Foundation type: Independent foundation.
Financial data (yr. ended 12/31/13): Assets, $71,146 (M); expenditures, $345,902; qualifying distributions, $344,574; giving activities include $344,574 for 3 grants (high: $239,574; low: $5,000).

Fields of interest: Education; Foundations; Human services.
Limitations: Applications not accepted. Giving primarily in CA.
Application information: Unsolicited requests for funds not accepted.
Trustee: Edward P. Roski, Jr.
EIN: 206298209

1075
David T. and Dorris E. Staples Foundation
950 Boardwalk, Ste. 201
San Marcos, CA 92078-2600

Established in 1996 in California.
Donor: Dorris E. Staples.
Foundation type: Independent foundation.
Financial data (yr. ended 07/31/13): Assets, $5,520,162 (M); expenditures, $427,488; qualifying distributions, $364,955; giving activities include $345,056 for 30 grants (high: $75,000; low: $500).
Fields of interest: Arts and culture; Education; Higher education; Food aid; Youth services.
Type of support: General support.
Limitations: Applications not accepted. Giving primarily in CA. No grants to individuals.
Application information: Unsolicited requests for funds not accepted.
Officers and Directors: M. Joseph Bowe, Pres. and Director; Colleen Hueblein, Secy.; Barbara Fischer, Treas. and Director; Karen Jobe.
EIN: 330723110

1076
John and Beverly Stauffer Foundation
333 S. Hope St., 43rd Fl.
Los Angeles, CA 90071-1406

Established in 1954 in California.
Donors: Beverly Stauffer†; John Stauffer†.
Foundation type: Independent foundation.
Financial data (yr. ended 12/31/13): Assets, $5,059,822 (M); expenditures, $329,238; qualifying distributions, $280,466; giving activities include $252,500 for 34 grants (high: $20,000; low: $1,500).
Fields of interest: Arts and culture; Theater; Secondary education; Higher education; Addiction services; Diseases and conditions; Cancers; Child welfare.
Type of support: General support; Continuing support; Annual campaigns; Capital and infrastructure; Equipment; Scholarships; Research; Research and evaluation.
Limitations: Applications not accepted. Giving primarily in southern CA. No support for political organizations. No grants to individuals.
Application information: Contributes only to pre-selected organizations.
Officers: Brooke B. Tinney, Pres.; Leslie S. Bartleson, V.P.; Ben A. Schuck III, V.P.; Winifred H. Rutter, Secy.; Laurence K. Gould, Jr., Treas.
Director: Caroline Bartleson.
Number of staff: None.
EIN: 952241406

1077
Mary R. Stauffer Foundation
P.O. Box 4688
Downey, CA 90241-1688   (562) 861-7378
Contact: Mary Stauffer, C.E.O.
E-mail: DRMRS10@aol.com

Established in 1993 in California.
Donors: Mary R. Owens; Judith A. Saunders; Masa Suzuki; Mary Suzuki; Katherine Suzuki; Janet Suzuki; Susan Stauffer; Jim Stauffer; Robert Saunders; Dorothy Blowers; Dawn Martens; John Stauffer; Jordan Stauffer; Kim Stauffer; Jessica Stauffer.
Foundation type: Operating foundation.
Financial data (yr. ended 04/30/13): Assets, $6,571,191 (M); gifts received, $285,485; expenditures, $376,386; qualifying distributions, $365,543.
Purpose and activities: Giving primarily for education. The foundation also awards grants to students of the Downey High schools who have applied through their school counselors. The foundation does not consider these grants to be scholarships, as this means of giving has evolved into a need program. Grants are awarded to students who want to make something of themselves and contribute to society. Selected students are given a check for $500 (per semester for 4 times) by the high school bookkeeper after they register at a junior college of their choice. This process can be repeated for 3 more times if a 2.5 GPA is maintained, for a total of $2,000.
Fields of interest: Opera; Art museums; Elementary and secondary education; Higher education; Human services; Children and youth; Adolescents.
Type of support: Equipment; Matching grants; Program development; Seed money; Internships.
Limitations: Applications not accepted. Giving limited to Downey, CA. No support for political organizations.
Publications: Grants list; Informational brochure; Program policy statement.
Application information: Unsolicited requests for funds not accepted.
   Board meeting date(s): Apr. 9
Officers: Mary R. Stauffer, C.E.O. and Pres.; Alison Blowers, Secy.
Number of staff: None.
EIN: 954433269

1078
The Stearns Foundation
6902 The Preserve Terr.
San Diego, CA 92130-6858

Established in 2005 in California.
Donor: Esther M. Stearns.
Foundation type: Independent foundation.
Financial data (yr. ended 12/31/12): Assets, $1,424,193 (M); expenditures, $194,003; qualifying distributions, $189,380; giving activities include $185,800 for 5 grants (high: $76,000; low: $1,000).
Fields of interest: Elementary and secondary education; Higher education; Protestantism.
Limitations: Applications not accepted. Giving primarily in CA. No grants to individuals.
Application information: Contributes only to pre-selected organizations.

Officers and Directors: Esther M. Stearns, Pres. and Director; Jan Cohn Stearns, Secy. and C.F.O. and Director.
EIN: 203936786

1079
The Stein Family Foundation
P.O. Box 8650
Rancho Santa Fe, CA   92067-8650   (858) 756-5753

Established in 2008 in California.
Foundation type: Independent foundation.
Financial data (yr. ended 12/31/13): Assets, $4,099,674 (M); expenditures, $232,247; qualifying distributions, $188,042; giving activities include $175,730 for 19 grants (high: $65,500; low: $1,000).
Fields of interest: Mental health care; Housing development; Religion.
Limitations: Applications accepted. Giving primarily in CA.
Application information:
  Initial approach: Proposal
  Deadline(s): None
Officers: Jerome Stein, Pres.; Sharon Stein, V.P.
Trustee: Gregory Stein.
EIN: 261173132

1080
Stellar Solutions Foundation
250 Cambridge Ave., Ste. 204
Palo Alto, CA   94306-1555

Established in 1998 in California.
Donors: Celeste V. Ford; Kevin E. Ford; Douglas Ross Construction, Inc.; Currie Family Foundation; Stellar Solutions, Inc.
Foundation type: Independent foundation.
Financial data (yr. ended 12/31/13): Assets, $699,720 (M); gifts received, $200,000; expenditures, $261,522; qualifying distributions, $256,730; giving activities include $251,946 for 208 grants (high: $25,100; low: $100).
Fields of interest: Theater; Music; Historic preservation; University education; Diseases and conditions; Christianity; Baseball and softball; Reproductive rights; Human services; Food banks; Youth organizing.
Limitations: Applications not accepted. Giving primarily in CA and CO. No grants to individuals.
Application information: Contributes only to pre-selected organizations.
Officers: Celeste V. Ford, Pres.; Kevin E. Ford, Secy.-Treas.
Director: Ann C. Pert.
EIN: 770485705

1081
Sterling Foundation
1112 Montana Ave., No. 246
Santa Monica, CA   90403-1652   (310) 230-3883
Contact: Leslie A. Dorman, Pres.

Established in 1997 in California.
Donors: John C. Dorman; Leslie A. Dorman.
Foundation type: Independent foundation.
Financial data (yr. ended 12/31/13): Assets, $1,667,944 (M); expenditures, $249,666; qualifying distributions, $233,615; giving activities

include $227,063 for 19 grants (high: $50,000; low: $500).
Purpose and activities: Giving for teen services, with an emphasis on education, and college access for low-income minority students.
Fields of interest: Education; Adolescents.
Type of support: Continuing support; Program development.
Limitations: Giving limited to Los Angeles, CA. No grants to individuals, or for capital support.
Application information:
  Initial approach: Letter of introduction, not request
  Copies of proposal: 1
Officers and Directors: Leslie A. Dorman, Pres. and Director; John C. Dorman, Secy.-Treas. and Director.
Number of staff: 1 full-time professional; 1 part-time professional.
EIN: 954656864

1082
Stewart Foundation
9169 W. Sunset Blvd.
West Hollywood, CA   90069-3857
Contact: Gregory M. Paul

Established in 1997 in California.
Donor: Stewart Living Trust.
Foundation type: Independent foundation.
Financial data (yr. ended 06/30/13): Assets, $4,179,239 (M); expenditures, $270,927; qualifying distributions, $170,000; giving activities include $170,000 for grants.
Fields of interest: Arts and culture; Museums; Health; Specialty hospital care; Film and video; Human services.
Limitations: Applications not accepted. Giving primarily in CA and IN. No grants to individuals.
Application information: Unsolicited requests for funds not accepted.
Trustees: Kelly Stewart Harcourt; Michael H. McLean; Judy Stewart Merrill; Gregory M. Paul.
EIN: 954646884

1083
Sarah A. Stewart Foundation
212 Yale Ave.
Claremont, CA   91711-4724

Established in 1980 in California.
Foundation type: Independent foundation.
Financial data (yr. ended 09/30/14): Assets, $7,335,792 (M); expenditures, $394,806; qualifying distributions, $369,902; giving activities include $345,000 for 18 grants (high: $70,000; low: $5,000).
Fields of interest: Education; Undergraduate education; Forest preservation; Health; Exercise; Diseases and conditions; Christianity; Protestantism; Spirituality; Human services.
Type of support: Research; Research and evaluation.
Limitations: Applications not accepted. Giving primarily in CA. No grants to individuals.
Application information: Unsolicited requests for funds not accepted.
Officers: Daniel M. Gibbs, MD, Pres.; Mollie Malone, Secy.; Nancy Richard, Treas.
Number of staff: 1 part-time professional.
EIN: 953705192

1084
The Mike and Corky Hale Stoller Foundation
P.O. Box 1760
Santa Monica, CA   90406-1760

Established in 1997 in California.
Donors: Corky Hale Stoller; Mike Stoller.
Foundation type: Independent foundation.
Financial data (yr. ended 12/31/14): Assets, $263,339; gifts received, $100,000; expenditures, $274,645; qualifying distributions, $274,585.
Fields of interest: Arts and culture; Diseases and conditions; Human services.
Limitations: Applications not accepted. Giving primarily in CA; giving also in AL and NY. No grants to individuals.
Application information: Unsolicited requests for funds not accepted.
Officers: Corky Hale Stoller, Pres. and C.E.O.; Mike Stoller, Secy.-Treas.
EIN: 954625956

1085
J. Ralph and Lois Stone Family Foundation
P.O. Box 3027
Santa Rosa, CA   95402-3027

Established in 1986 in California.
Donors: J. Ralph Stone†; Lois Stone.
Foundation type: Independent foundation.
Financial data (yr. ended 12/31/13): Assets, $4,291,320 (M); expenditures, $199,801; qualifying distributions, $186,318; giving activities include $182,000 for 23 grants (high: $20,000; low: $1,000).
Purpose and activities: Giving primarily for the arts, and for health and human services.
Fields of interest: Agriculture; Human rights; Human services.
Type of support: General support.
Limitations: Applications not accepted. Giving primarily in CA. No grants to individuals.
Application information: Unsolicited requests for funds not accepted.
Officers: Robert G. Stone, Pres.; Gregory R. Stone, Secy.
EIN: 680105540

1086
Joseph and Fiora Stone Foundation
c/o Oster and Wolf C.P.A.'s
21031 Ventura Blvd., Ste. 1105
Woodland Hills, CA   91364-2256

Established in 1996 in California.
Donor: Fiora Stone†.
Foundation type: Independent foundation.
Financial data (yr. ended 12/31/14): Assets, $5,640,904; expenditures, $296,686; qualifying distributions, $200,000.
Purpose and activities: Giving primarily to a cancer research hospital.
Fields of interest: Specialty hospital care.
Type of support: Research.
Limitations: Applications not accepted. Giving primarily in Duarte, CA.
Application information: Unsolicited requests for funds not accepted.

Officers: Harris D. Bass, Pres.; Lara L. Ladd, Secy.; Steven J. Wolf, Treas.
EIN: 954509664

1087
Storm Castle Foundation
2775 Sand Hill Rd., Ste. 100
Menlo Park, CA   94025-7085   (650) 233-8120
Contact: Julia Loewy Davidson, Pres.

Donors: James A. Davidson; Julia Loewy Davidson.
Foundation type: Independent foundation.
Financial data (yr. ended 12/31/13): Assets, $5,474,398 (M); gifts received, $721,312; expenditures, $240,969; qualifying distributions, $227,712; giving activities include $227,712 for 49 grants (high: $20,000; low: $500).
Fields of interest: Arts and culture; Education; Diseases and conditions; Human services.
Limitations: Applications accepted. Giving primarily in CA.
Application information: Application form required.
Initial approach: Letter
Deadline(s): None
Officers: Julia Loewy Davidson, Pres.; James A. Davidson, Secy. and C.F.O.
EIN: 208681172

1088
Robert K. and Barbara J. Straus Family Foundation, Inc.
(formerly Penelope Straus More Family Foundation)
c/o DBNTM
200 E. Carrillo St., Ste. 303
Santa Barbara, CA   93101-2145

Established in 1987 in New York.
Donor: Robert K. Straus†.
Foundation type: Independent foundation.
Financial data (yr. ended 12/31/14): Assets, $3,122,223; expenditures, $169,734; qualifying distributions, $149,538.
Fields of interest: Arts and culture; Historic preservation; Education; Higher education; Nonprofits; Libraries; Christianity; Human services; Child welfare.
Type of support: Regranting.
Limitations: Applications not accepted. Giving primarily in CA. No grants to individuals.
Application information: Contributes only to pre-selected organizations.
Officers and Directors: Penelope Straus More, Pres. and Director; Christopher Straus, V.P. and Director; Marshall H. Turner, Jr., Secy.; Braden More, Treas. and Director; Alexandra More.
EIN: 133377987

1089
Strome Family Foundation
100 Wilshire Blvd., Ste. 1750
Santa Monica, CA   90401-3604

Donor: Mark E. Strome.
Foundation type: Independent foundation.
Financial data (yr. ended 12/31/13): Assets, $2,009,739 (M); expenditures, $435,704; qualifying distributions, $435,430; giving activities include $435,430 for 13 grants (high: $200,000; low: $500).

Fields of interest: Arts and culture; Education; Higher education; Health; Diseases and conditions.
Type of support: Research.
Limitations: Applications not accepted. Giving primarily in CA and MD.
Application information: Unsolicited requests for funds not accepted.
Officers and Directors: Mark E. Strome, Pres. and Director; Tammy Strome, Secy. and Director.
EIN: 510646108

1090
The Sudikoff Family Foundation
1398 Breckford Ct.
Westlake Village, CA   91361-1701
Contact: Joyce Sudikoff, C.E.O.
Application addresses: P.O. Box 491669, Los Angeles, CA 90049-8669, or V.P., 23 Karen Rd., Waban, MA 02468-1123

Established in 1992 in California.
Donors: Jeffrey Sudikoff; Joan Sudikoff; Joyce Sudikoff; Kilhillet Israel; New Moon Trust; Chris Edgecomb; James Lippman; J.N. Rubin; Santa Barbara Land and Cattle; Peter Zimble; Bruce Newberg.
Foundation type: Independent foundation.
Financial data (yr. ended 05/31/13): Assets, $11,450 (M); gifts received, $335,000; expenditures, $333,854; qualifying distributions, $320,000; giving activities include $320,000 for grants.
Fields of interest: History museums; Higher education; Judaism.
Type of support: Capital and infrastructure; Program development.
Limitations: Applications accepted. Giving primarily in CA, Washington, DC, NH, and NY. No grants to individuals.
Application information: Application form required.
Initial approach: Letter
Deadline(s): None
Officers: Joyce Sudikoff, C.E.O.; Joan Sudikoff, V.P.; Jeffrey Sudikoff, Treas.
Number of staff: 1 part-time support.
EIN: 956941160

1091
The Suggs Family Foundation
754 Calle Laredo
Thousand Oaks, CA   91360
E-mail: sidsuggs@hotmail.com

Established in 2007 in California.
Donor: Sidney V. Suggs.
Foundation type: Independent foundation.
Financial data (yr. ended 12/31/13): Assets, $9,495,789 (M); gifts received, $1,090,600; expenditures, $355,316; qualifying distributions, $254,874; giving activities include $254,874 for 39 grants (high: $25,000; low: $40).
Fields of interest: Education.
Limitations: Applications not accepted. Giving primarily in CA. No grants to individuals.
Application information: Contributes only to pre-selected organizations.
Trustees: Pamela J. Suggs; Sidney V. Suggs.
EIN: 261592436

1092
Sun Shine on You Foundation
(formerly The Emerson Glazer Foundation)
9440 Santa Monica Blvd., Ste. 705
Beverly Hills, CA   90210-4609

Established in 1997 in California.
Donor: Emerson Glazer.
Foundation type: Independent foundation.
Financial data (yr. ended 12/31/13): Assets, $9,319,973 (M); gifts received, $96,802; expenditures, $422,638; qualifying distributions, $255,700; giving activities include $255,700 for 26 grants (high: $72,000; low: $200).
Fields of interest: Education; Diseases and conditions; Religion.
Type of support: Research.
Limitations: Applications not accepted. Giving primarily in CA. No grants to individuals.
Application information: Contributes only to pre-selected organizations.
Officers: Emerson Glazer, C.E.O.; Arthur Malmgren, C.F.O. and Secy.
EIN: 954634200

1093
Sunrise Foundation
8949 Buffalo Ave.
Rancho Cucamonga, CA   91730-5534

Established in 2006 in California.
Donors: Sunny Whang; Sunny Designs, Inc.
Foundation type: Independent foundation.
Financial data (yr. ended 12/31/13): Assets, $1,524,889 (M); gifts received, $800,000; expenditures, $313,938; qualifying distributions, $313,138; giving activities include $313,130 for 5 grants (high: $227,000; low: $10,000).
Fields of interest: Higher education.
Limitations: Applications not accepted. Giving primarily in CA. No grants to individuals.
Application information: Contributes only to pre-selected organizations.
Officers: Sunny S. Hwang, Pres.; Chin Hee Hwang, Secy.
Director: Willy Hwang.
EIN: 651288276

1094
The Sunwest Bank Charitable Foundation
2050 Main St., Ste. 300
Irvine, CA   92614-8279   (714) 881-3039
Contact: Jeffrey Boyd, Exec. Dir.
E-mail: jboyd@sunwestbank.com; *Main URL:* http://www.sunwestbankfoundation.org
Grants List: http://www.sunwestbankfoundation.org/grants.htm

Established in 2009 in California.
Donor: Sunwest Bank.
Foundation type: Company-sponsored foundation.
Financial data (yr. ended 12/31/13): Assets, $2,013,827 (M); gifts received, $500,000; expenditures, $441,332; qualifying distributions, $377,962; giving activities include $377,962 for 23 grants (high: $132,462; low: $1,000).
Purpose and activities: The foundation supports programs designed to assist poor, needy, and vulnerable populations, and children. Special emphasis is directed toward programs that provide

food, shelter, housing, healthcare, and other primary needs.

Fields of interest: Health; Housing development; Human services; Food aid; Food banks; Homeless services; Children; Low-income and poor people.

International interests: Ghana.

Type of support: General support; Continuing support; Capital and infrastructure.

Limitations: Applications accepted. Giving primarily in Flagstaff and Phoenix, AZ and Orange County and San Diego County, CA; limited giving in Ghana. No support for political candidates. No grants to individuals, or for political campaigns, scholarships, or sponsorships.

Publications: Application guidelines; Grants list.

Application information: Extra consideration is given to organizations with which Sunwest Bank employees serve as volunteers. Application form required.

Initial approach: Download application form and mail to foundation

Deadline(s): None

Board meeting date(s): Quarterly

Officers: Eric D. Hovde, Chair.; Jeffrey Boyd, Exec. Dir.

Trustees: Glenn Gray; Jason Raefski.

EIN: 271607730

1095
Support Of Partners For Sustainable Development

255 Shoreline Dr., Ste.520
Redwood City, CA 94065-1432 6504862430
Main URL: http://www.supportofpartners forsustainabledevelopment.or

Donors: CCC Wood Group; Plug and Play; Zan Foundation; Skoll Foundation; Hamid Moghadam; Saeed Amidhozour.

Foundation type: Independent foundation.

Financial data (yr. ended 12/31/12): Assets, $12,090 (M); gifts received, $279,640; expenditures, $281,183; qualifying distributions, $253,000; giving activities include $253,000 for 1 grant.

Fields of interest: Community and economic development.

International interests: Israel.

Limitations: Applications not accepted. Giving primarily in Israel.

Application information: Unsolicited request for funds not accepted.

Officers: Zohre Elahaian, Chair. and Pres.; Ellie Clelland, Vice Chair. and C.F.O.; Marilynn Ahern, Secy.

Director: Tara Derak.

EIN: 800609323

1096
Sustainable Arts Foundation

1032 Irving St., Ste. 609
San Francisco, CA 94122-2200
Main URL: http://www.sustainableartsfoundation.org
Grants List: http://www.sustainableartsfoundation.org/residencygrantees

Donors: Grant Anthony; Caroline Grant.

Foundation type: Independent foundation.

Financial data (yr. ended 12/31/13): Assets, $1,737,798 (M); gifts received, $6,028; expenditures, $171,526; qualifying distributions, $152,300; giving activities include $73,300 for 14 grants (high: $10,000; low: $1,000), and $79,000 for 23 grants to individuals (high: $6,000; low: $1,000).

Fields of interest: Arts and culture.

Type of support: Student aid.

Limitations: Applications accepted. Giving primarily in CA and NM.

Application information: See foundation web site for complete application guidelines. Application form required.

Initial approach: Online application

Officers and Directors: Anthony Grant, Pres. and Secy. and Director; Caroline Grant, V.P.

EIN: 263373919

1097
The Keith and Judy Swayne Family Foundation

668 N. Coast Hwy., PMB #251
Laguna Beach, CA 92651-1513
Main URL: http://swaynefoundation.org
Grants List: http://swaynefoundation.org/?page_id=70
Keith and Judy Swayne Family Foundation's Philanthropy Promise: http://www.ncrp.org/philanthropys-promise/who

Established in 2005 in California.

Donors: Judy K. Swayne; Keith D. Swayne.

Foundation type: Independent foundation.

Financial data (yr. ended 12/31/13): Assets, $6,603,530 (M); gifts received, $1,501,657; expenditures, $367,272; qualifying distributions, $314,190; giving activities include $245,000 for 13 grants (high: $20,000; low: $5,000).

Purpose and activities: Giving primarily for social justice, youth development, education, environmental practices, and also support the health and well-being of women in need.

Fields of interest: Arts and culture; Education; Environmental education; Youth services; Females.

Limitations: Applications accepted. Giving primarily in CA and HI. No grants to individuals.

Application information: See foundation web site for complete application guidelines.

Initial approach: Letter of inquiry

Deadline(s): Deadline for letter of inquiry is May 25

Officers and Directors: Anne Swayne Keir, Pres. and Director; Keith D. Swayne, Secy.-Treas. and Director; Gretchen Weisenburger Carillo; Janis Reischmann; Robert W. Wright.

EIN: 201577885

1098
The Swinerton Foundation

P.O. Box 77048
San Francisco, CA 94107-0048 (415) 984-1372
FAX: (415) 984-1384;
E-mail: swinertonfoundation@swinerton.com; Main URL: http://www.swinerton.com/web/do/content/about/swinertonFoundation

Established in 2002 in California.

Donors: Swinerton Inc.; Swinerton Builders.

Foundation type: Company-sponsored foundation.

Financial data (yr. ended 12/31/13): Assets, $905,153 (M); gifts received, $623,774; expenditures, $564,523; qualifying distributions, $416,087; giving activities include $328,052 for 56 grants (high: $15,483), and $85,000 for 20 grants to individuals (high: $5,000; low: -$3,500).

Purpose and activities: The foundation supports organizations involved with arts and culture, construction education, the environment, health, human services, and community development.

Fields of interest: Arts and culture; Education; Environment; Health; Community and economic development; Business and industry; Construction; Human services; Youth services.

Type of support: Equipment; Employee volunteer services; Program development; Sponsorships.

Limitations: Applications not accepted. Giving primarily in areas of company operations in CA. No grants to individuals.

Application information: Contributes only to pre-selected organizations and individuals.

Officers and Directors: Linda Schowalter, Chair.; Eric Foster, Pres.; Meggie Hollywood, Secy.; Brad Brad Peterson, Treas.; George S. Ehara; Frank Foellmer; Charles Rick Moore; Mark Payne; Gary J. Rafferty; Myrna Wagner; David K. White.

EIN: 030490864

1099
Syar Foundation

c/o Susan L. Syar
2301 Napa Vallejo Hwy.
Napa, CA 94558-6242

Foundation type: Independent foundation.

Financial data (yr. ended 09/30/13): Assets, $8,085,675 (M); expenditures, $398,431; qualifying distributions, $389,100; giving activities include $389,100 for 25 grants (high: $100,000; low: $500).

Purpose and activities: Giving primarily for animal welfare, health associations, and for human services, including for the purchase of life saving equipment for emergency services.

Fields of interest: Education; Health; Human services.

Type of support: Equipment.

Limitations: Applications not accepted. Giving primarily in CA, with emphasis on Fairfield, Vallejo, and Woodland. No grants to individuals.

Application information: Contributes only to pre-selected organizations.

Director: Susan L. Syar.

EIN: 943315815

1100
Synopsys Silicon Valley Science and Technology Outreach Foundation

(also known as Synopsys Outreach Foundation)
700 E. Middlefield Rd.
Mountain View, CA 94043 (415) 306-1764
Contact: Gary Robinson, Pres.
Main URL: http://www.outreach-foundation.org

Established in 1999 in California.

Donors: Synopsys Technology Education Opportunity Foundation; Industry Initiatives; Synopsys Community Fund; Kaiser Permanente; Synopsys Foundation.

Foundation type: Operating foundation.

Financial data (yr. ended 12/31/13): Assets, $465,363 (M); gifts received, $927,250; expenditures, $814,021; qualifying distributions, $729,711; giving activities include $161,930 for 7 grants (high: $70,618; low: $2,250).

Purpose and activities: The foundation awards grants to teachers and students developing science projects at K-12 schools; and sponsors programs, competitions, fairs, and seminars involved with science.

Fields of interest: Education.

Type of support: Equipment; Program development; Convening; Sponsorships.

Limitations: Applications accepted. Giving limited to Santa Clara County, CA, and areas of field office operations. No grants for technical papers.

Publications: Application guidelines.

Application information: Application form required.
Initial approach: See website for application form
Deadline(s): Oct. 1

Officers: Erin Brennock, Chair.; Gary Robinson, Pres.; Erika Varga McEnroe, Secy.; Anna Garcia, Treas.

Directors: Dana Ditmore; Carol Evans; Tom Ferry; Richard Goldman; Zahra Karami; Michael Keating; Murlin Marks; Roy Okuda; Venkata Ravella; Larke Reeber; Lynn Shannon; Jaci Spross.

EIN: 770520414

1101
SYZYGY Foundation
c/o Edward T. Hanley Jr.
505 Montgomery St., 5th Fl.
San Francisco, CA   94111-6529   (415) 397-4444
Application address: c/o Linda Dodwell Dehennis, Pres., 2443 Fillmore St., Ste. 375, San Francisco, CA 94115, tel.: (425) 397-4444

Established in 2000 in California.

Donor: Linda Dodwell.

Foundation type: Independent foundation.

Financial data (yr. ended 06/30/14): Assets, $3,679,911 (M); expenditures, $188,369; qualifying distributions, $172,773; giving activities include $170,000 for 7 grants (high: $65,000; low: $5,000).

Fields of interest: Arts and culture; Education; Human services.

Limitations: Applications accepted. Giving primarily in CA; some funding also in Washington, DC. No grants to individuals.

Application information:
Initial approach: Proposal

Officers and Directors: Linda Dodwell Dehennis, Pres.; Maida Lynn Brankman, Secy. and Director; Ed Hanley, Treas.; John David Brankman.

EIN: 770559202

1102
Szekely Family Foundation
(formerly Szekely Foundation for American Volunteers)
3232 Dove St.
San Diego, CA   92103-5548   (619) 295-3144

Established in 1986 in California.

Donors: Deborah Szekely; Sarah Livia Brightwood; Flores de la Montana; Alex Szekely†.

Foundation type: Independent foundation.

Financial data (yr. ended 12/31/13): Assets, $6,195,644 (M); expenditures, $285,876;

qualifying distributions, $253,869; giving activities include $244,044 for 91 grants (high: $57,000; low: $100).

Purpose and activities: The foundation's primary interests include: 1) addressing environmental concerns for the area along the border between California and Baja California, Mexico to protect the land for future generations of Americans and Mexicans; and 2) support for the newly established Immigration Museum of New Americans, honoring those who have chosen to make new lives for themselves and their families in the United States.

Fields of interest: Environment; Immigrants.

Type of support: General support; Pro bono consulting services; Capital and infrastructure; Program development; Convening; Curriculum development.

Limitations: Applications accepted. Giving primarily in the area along the border between CA and Baja California, Mexico. No grants to individuals.

Application information:
Initial approach: Letter
Deadline(s): None
Board meeting date(s): As needed

Officers: Sarah Livia Brightwood, Pres.; Deborah Szekely, V.P. and C.F.O.; Mary Walshok, Secy.

Director: Ned Chambers.

Number of staff: None.

EIN: 953655645

1103
The Tanimura Family Foundation
P.O. Box 4070
Salinas, CA   93912-4070

Established in 1997 in California.

Donors: Tom T. Tanimura; Robert T. Tanimura; George T. Tanimura; George M. Tanimura.

Foundation type: Independent foundation.

Financial data (yr. ended 09/30/14): Assets, $10,988,965 (M); gifts received, $200,000; expenditures, $473,294; qualifying distributions, $371,134; giving activities include $360,000 for 24 grants (high: $140,000; low: $1,500).

Fields of interest: Education; Diseases and conditions; Public libraries; Buddhism; Human services; Scouting programs.

Limitations: Applications not accepted. Giving primarily in CA. No grants to individuals.

Application information: Contributes only to pre-selected organizations.

Officers and Directors: Gary K. Tanimura; Ken Morishita, C.F.O. and Treas.; George M. Tanimura; Sheila C. Tanimura, V.P.; Tom T. Tanimura; Ronald Yokota, Pres.; Bonita A.T. Yokota, Secy.; Kerry Varney, Exec. Dir.; Kelly Tanimura, V.P. and Director; Cathy Yuki; Susan Tanimura.

EIN: 770456779

1104
Teachers Housing Cooperative
1717 Powell St., Ste. 300
San Francisco, CA   94133-2843

Established in 2000 in California.

Donor: Russell B. Flynn.

Foundation type: Operating foundation.

Financial data (yr. ended 05/31/13): Assets, $5,773 (M); gifts received, $150,975; expenditures, $147,064; qualifying distributions, $145,900; giving activities include $25,000 for 1

grant, and $120,900 for 41 grants to individuals (high: $3,900; low: $975).

Purpose and activities: Grant awards to teachers in the San Francisco Unified School District for housing.

Fields of interest: Arts and culture; Education.

Type of support: Grants to individuals.

Limitations: Applications not accepted. Giving primarily in the San Francisco Bay Area, CA.

Application information: Unsolicited requests for funds not accepted.

Officers: Russell B. Flynn, Pres.; R. Michael Delagnes, Secy.

Directors: Natalie J. Delagnes; Sara Flynn; Denise Lieberman.

EIN: 943370330

1105
Tecumseh Foundation
1711 Tainter St.
Saint Helena, CA   94574-1935

Established in 1993 in Nevada.

Donors: Gerald Wing; Caroline S. Wing.

Foundation type: Independent foundation.

Financial data (yr. ended 10/31/13): Assets, $4,306,640 (M); expenditures, $146,308; qualifying distributions, $124,850; giving activities include $124,850 for 31 grants (high: $59,700; low: $100).

Fields of interest: Health; Protestantism; Human services; Child welfare.

Limitations: Applications not accepted. Giving primarily in CA. No grants to individuals.

Application information: Unsolicited requests for funds not accepted.

Officers and Directors: Caroline S. Wing, Pres. and Director; Jil Wing Armijo, V.P. and Secy.-Treas.; Will Holmes, V.P. and Secy.-Treas. and Director; Allison Wing, V.P. and Director; Holly Wing, V.P.

EIN: 880299804

1106
The Teichman Family Charitable Foundation
6100 Bandini Blvd.
Los Angeles, CA   90040-3112

Established in 1982 in California.

Donors: Sol Teichman; Ruth Teichman; Teichman Enterprises, Inc.; Sidney Teichman; Marcia Teichman; Bernard Teichman; Alan Teichman; Samuel Teichman.

Foundation type: Independent foundation.

Financial data (yr. ended 03/31/13): Assets, $2,746,676 (M); gifts received, $101,000; expenditures, $283,161; qualifying distributions, $251,200; giving activities include $251,200 for grants.

Purpose and activities: Giving primarily for education and for Jewish organizations.

Fields of interest: Museums; Education; Judaism; Human services.

International interests: Israel.

Type of support: General support; Continuing support; Annual campaigns; Capital and infrastructure; Emergency funds; Convening; Publications; Curriculum development; Scholarships; Research.

Limitations: Applications not accepted. Giving primarily in NY. No grants to individuals.

Publications: Annual report.
Application information: Contributes only to pre-selected organizations.
Officers: Sol Teichman, Pres.; Ruth Teichman, V.P.; Sidney Teichman, Secy.-Treas.
Number of staff: None.
EIN: 953710911

1107
Terra Family Foundation
144 Tomlinson Dr.
Folsom, CA 95630-7401

Established in 2007 in California.
Donor: Konda Charitable Lead Annuity Trust.
Foundation type: Independent foundation.
Financial data (yr. ended 12/31/13): Assets, $3,732,855 (M); gifts received, $685,268; expenditures, $235,578; qualifying distributions, $205,136; giving activities include $200,000 for 11 grants (high: $50,000; low: $8,000).
Fields of interest: Education; Catholicism; Child welfare.
Limitations: Applications not accepted. Giving primarily in CA. No grants to individuals.
Application information: Contributes only to pre-selected organizations.
Directors: Tom Baber; Marie Henao; Christine Weske.
EIN: 208360832

1108
Teshinsky Family Foundation
c/o Fred & Lucy Teshinsky
24442 Santa Clara Ave.
Dana Point, CA 92629-3022
Contact: Adam Teshinsky

Established in 2006 in California.
Donors: Robert D. Teshinsky; Lucy Teshinsky; Fred Teshinsky; Adam J. Teshinsky; Neil Bersch.
Foundation type: Independent foundation.
Financial data (yr. ended 12/31/13): Assets, $6,820,068 (M); expenditures, $269,613; qualifying distributions, $244,500; giving activities include $244,500 for 26 grants (high: $30,000; low: $2,000).
Fields of interest: Education; Public affairs; Religion.
Limitations: Applications not accepted. Giving primarily in CA. No grants to individuals.
Application information: Unsolicited requests for funds not accepted.
Trustees: Fred Teshinsky; Lucy Teshinsky.
EIN: 207165016

1109
Thagard Foundation
215 E. Commonwealth Ave., Ste. A
Fullerton, CA 92832-1957 (714) 738-7349
Contact: Richard L. O'Connor, Tr.

Established in 1968 in California.
Foundation type: Independent foundation.
Financial data (yr. ended 04/30/13): Assets, $3,939,536 (M); expenditures, $253,560; qualifying distributions, $165,000; giving activities include $165,000 for grants.

Purpose and activities: Giving primarily to hospitals and to Protestant churches; some giving also for higher education.
Fields of interest: Elementary and secondary education; Higher education; Foundations; Hospital care; Neurology; Diseases and conditions; Protestantism; Human services; Youth services.
Type of support: General support; Scholarships; Research; Research and evaluation.
Limitations: Applications accepted. Giving primarily in CA, IN and TX. No grants to individuals.
Application information:
Initial approach: Proposal
Deadline(s): None
Trustees: John C. Bagwell; Belle L. Ellis; Richard L. O'Connor; Edward Olivarez; William N. Ratkovic; George F. Thagard III; Ray G. Thagard; Raymond G. Thagard, Jr.; Kirk A. Vanmatre.
Number of staff: 1 part-time support.
EIN: 956225425

1110
David J. & Mary L. G. Theroux Foundation
c/o Mary L.G. Theroux
100 Swan Way, Ste. 200
Oakland, CA 94621-1459

Established in 1993 in California.
Donor: Garvey International, Inc.
Foundation type: Independent foundation.
Financial data (yr. ended 12/31/14): Assets, $6,918,205; gifts received, $939,628; expenditures, $314,235; qualifying distributions, $292,930.
Fields of interest: Public policy; Human services.
Type of support: General support; Annual campaigns; Policy, advocacy and systems reform; Endowments; Research.
Limitations: Applications not accepted. Giving primarily in the San Francisco Bay Area, CA. No grants to individuals.
Application information: Contributes only to pre-selected organizations.
Trustees: David J. Theroux; Mary L.G. Theroux.
EIN: 943180069

1111
The Evan C. Thompson Foundation
47 Beverly Park Cir.
Beverly Hills, CA 90210-1534

Established in 1997 in California.
Donor: Evan C. Thompson.
Foundation type: Independent foundation.
Financial data (yr. ended 12/31/13): Assets, $5,333,813 (M); gifts received, $433,648; expenditures, $436,006; qualifying distributions, $431,915; giving activities include $431,915 for 1 grant.
Purpose and activities: Giving primarily for higher education.
Fields of interest: Arts and culture; Higher education.
Limitations: Applications not accepted. Giving primarily in CA. No grants to individuals.
Application information: Unsolicited requests for funds not accepted.
Officers: Evan C. Thompson, Chair. and Pres.; Constance Frank, C.F.O. and Secy.-Treas.
EIN: 954633501

1112
Porter E. & Helenmae Thompson Foundation
P.O. Box 417
Lafayette, CA 94549-0417

Donors: Porter E. Thompson; Helenmae Thompson.
Foundation type: Independent foundation.
Financial data (yr. ended 12/31/13): Assets, $2,851,864 (M); expenditures, $190,760; qualifying distributions, $176,305; giving activities include $176,001 for 34 grants (high: $15,000; low: $1).
Purpose and activities: Giving for education, health, human services, and Catholic organizations.
Fields of interest: Higher education; Health; Catholicism; Human services; Seniors; Low-income and poor people.
Limitations: Applications not accepted. Giving primarily in CA. No grants to individuals.
Application information: Contributes only to pre-selected organizations. Unsolicited applications not accepted.
Officers: Barbara J. Cadle, Pres.; Suzanne Cadle Glaubitz, Secy.; Carolyn Cadle, Treas.
EIN: 942831112

1113
The Thomson Family Foundation
P.O. Box 26150
San Francisco, CA 94126-6150 (415) 684-1903
E-mail: megan@tffhome.org; Main URL: http://www.tffhome.org
Facebook: https://www.facebook.com/pages/Thomson-Family-Foundation/113479115335566

Established in 2007 in Unspecified.
Donors: Clifford L. Thomson; Bonnie M. Thomson.
Foundation type: Independent foundation.
Financial data (yr. ended 12/31/13): Assets, $4,045,488 (M); expenditures, $365,678; qualifying distributions, $365,136; giving activities include $240,895 for 12 grants (high: $50,000; low: $5,000).
Purpose and activities: Giving to foster opportunities for families to increase their economic success and security by supporting community-based initiatives that improve access to education and asset-building resources and services.
Fields of interest: Community and economic development; Human services; Family services.
Type of support: General support.
Limitations: Applications not accepted. Giving primarily in CA and TX. No grants to individuals.
Application information: Unsolicited requests for funds not accepted.
Officers: Clifford L. Thomson, Pres.; C. Jay Thomson, V.P.; Megan McTiernan, Exec. Dir.
Directors: Bonnie M. Thomson; Shannon M. Thomson.
EIN: 208132099

1114
Stephen & Pamela Thorne Foundation
17000 Red Hill Ave.
Irvine, CA 92614-5626 (714) 845-8680
E-mail: blaisdellk@pacden.com

Established in 2007 in California.
Donors: Stephen E. Thorne IV; Pamela Thorne.

Foundation type: Independent foundation.
Financial data (yr. ended 12/31/12): Assets, $202,208 (M); gifts received, $200,000; expenditures, $150,110; qualifying distributions, $150,025; giving activities include $150,000 for 1 grant.
Fields of interest: Christianity.
Limitations: Applications accepted. Giving primarily in Little Rock, AR.
Application information:
  Initial approach: Letter or e-mail
  Deadline(s): 6 months prior to requested grant
Officers: Stephen E. Thorne IV, Exec. Dir.; Pamela A. Thorne, Secy.-Treas.
EIN: 260276194

1115
John M. & Sally B. Thornton Foundation
2125 Evergreen St.
San Diego, CA 92106-1618

Established in 1982 in California.
Donors: John M. Thornton; Sally B. Thornton; Steven B. Thornton.
Foundation type: Independent foundation.
Financial data (yr. ended 09/30/14): Assets, $243,239 (M); gifts received, $260,350; expenditures, $218,590; qualifying distributions, $217,577; giving activities include $216,565 for 51 grants (high: $22,550; low: $80).
Fields of interest: Arts and culture; Performing arts; Museums; Diseases and conditions; Crime prevention; Human services.
Type of support: General support.
Limitations: Applications not accepted. Giving primarily in CA. No grants to individuals.
Application information: Unsolicited requests for funds not accepted.
Officers: Sally B. Thornton, Pres.; John M. Thornton, Secy.
Director: Steven B. Thornton.
EIN: 953800986

1116
Three Guineas Fund
153 Upper Terr.
San Francisco, CA 94117-4513
E-mail: info@3gf.org; Main URL: http://www.3gf.org

Established in 1994 in California.
Foundation type: Independent foundation.
Financial data (yr. ended 12/31/13): Assets, $3,771,591 (M); gifts received, $24,500; expenditures, $202,609; qualifying distributions, $228,302; giving activities include $117,300 for 11 grants (high: $50,000; low: $300), and $64,997 for 1 loan/program-related investment.
Purpose and activities: The foundation seeks to promote social justice for women and girls by expanding access to economic opportunity.
Fields of interest: Human services; Females; Female children and youth.
Type of support: General support.
Limitations: Applications not accepted. Giving in the U.S., with emphasis on CA, MA and NY. No grants to individuals.
Application information: Unsolicited requests for funds not accepted.
Officers: Catherine S. Muther, Pres.; Margaret Leahy, Secy.

Number of staff: 2 part-time professional.
EIN: 943215954

1117
Thrill Hill Foundation
c/o Chapman Bird & Grey
1990 Bundy Dr., Ste. 200
Los Angeles, CA 90025-5249

Established in 1987 in California.
Donor: Bruce Springsteen.
Foundation type: Independent foundation.
Financial data (yr. ended 12/31/13): Assets, $4,850,842 (M); expenditures, $357,736; qualifying distributions, $356,600; giving activities include $356,600 for 31 grants (high: $100,000; low: $1,000).
Purpose and activities: Giving for AIDS and medical research, food services, and youth programs.
Fields of interest: Mental health care; Diseases and conditions; HIV/AIDS; Sports and recreation; Human rights; Food aid; Child welfare; Homeless shelters; Military personnel.
Type of support: General support; Annual campaigns; Research; Research and evaluation.
Limitations: Applications not accepted. Giving primarily in AL, CA, MA, NJ and NY. No grants to individuals.
Application information: Contributes only to pre-selected organizations.
Officers: Nancy Chapman, Pres. and Secy.; Jon Landau, V.P.; Terry Bird, Treas.
EIN: 954150461

1118
Tilley Family Foundation
c/o Rose, Snyder & Jacobs
15821 Ventura Blvd., Ste. 490
Encino, CA 91436-4778

Established in 1997 in California.
Donors: William H. Tilley; The William Tilley Trust.
Foundation type: Independent foundation.
Financial data (yr. ended 12/31/13): Assets, $9,690,803 (M); expenditures, $238,790; qualifying distributions, $157,768; giving activities include $150,300 for 16 grants (high: $50,000; low: $1,450).
Fields of interest: Museums; Education; Health; Diseases and conditions; Eye diseases; Human services.
Type of support: Research.
Limitations: Applications not accepted. Giving primarily in CA. No grants to individuals.
Application information: Contributes only to pre-selected organizations.
Officer: James A. Dal Pozzo, Secy.-Treas.
Directors: Gregory D. Snyder; John Tilley; Nadine B. Tilley; Nicole Tilley.
Trustee: The William Tilley Trust.
EIN: 954659623

1119
The William Hall and Ruth Rathell Tippett Foundation
2604 B El Camino Real, Ste. 356
Carlsbad, CA 92008 (760) 310-3105
Contact: Robbin C. Powell, Chief Administrative Officer

E-mail: info@tippettfoundation.org; Main URL: http://www.tippettfoundation.org

Established in 2000 in California.
Foundation type: Independent foundation.
Financial data (yr. ended 12/31/14): Assets, $4,852,843 (M); expenditures, $283,853; qualifying distributions, $250,000; giving activities include $250,000 for 20 grants (high: $100,000; low: $5,000).
Purpose and activities: Giving primarily for health care and research into the cause and cure of illnesses affecting older people; education, particularly musical arts, for younger people; and animal welfare.
Fields of interest: Arts and culture; Theater; Education; Animal welfare; Human services; Youth services.
Limitations: Applications accepted. Giving primarily in San Diego, CA. No support for athletic organizations, political organizations or to national organizations and/or their local chapters. No grants to individuals, directly; no loans.
Application information: See foundation website for complete grant procedures and online grant submission information.
  Initial approach: Proposal
  Deadline(s): Mar. 15 and Oct. 15
  Board meeting date(s): Twice per year
Officers and Trustees: Barbara Zobell, Pres. and Trustee; Karen Zobell, V.P. and Trustee; Mildred V. Basden, Secy. and C.F.O. and Trustee; Robbin C. Powell, Chief Administrative Officer.
EIN: 330903811

1120
Jamie Tisch Foundation
10960 Wilshire Blvd., 5th Fl.
Los Angeles, CA 90024-3708

Foundation type: Independent foundation.
Financial data (yr. ended 12/31/13): Assets, $8,231,474 (M); expenditures, $282,840; qualifying distributions, $240,740; giving activities include $236,592 for 44 grants (high: $50,200; low: $150).
Fields of interest: Diseases and conditions; Community and economic development; Sports and recreation.
Type of support: Research.
Limitations: Applications not accepted.
Application information: Unsolicited requests for funds not accepted.
Officers: Jamie A. Tisch, Pres.; Ethel Dolores Alexander, Secy.-Treas.
EIN: 263992742

1121
The Susanne and Gary Tobey Family Foundation
16030 Ventura Blvd., Ste. 380
Encino, CA 91436-2778

Established in 2007 in California.
Donors: Gary Tobey; Suzanne Tobey.
Foundation type: Independent foundation.
Financial data (yr. ended 12/31/13): Assets, $2,695,091 (M); expenditures, $148,642; qualifying distributions, $144,759; giving activities include $140,600 for 23 grants (high: $25,000; low: $250).

Fields of interest: Arts and culture; Museums; Animal welfare; Human services.
Limitations: Applications not accepted. Giving primarily in AZ and CA. No grants to individuals.
Application information: Contributes only to pre-selected organizations.
Officers: Suzanne Tobey, Pres.; Gary Tobey, V.P.; Robert Philpott, Treas.
EIN: 261600807

1122
Tomkins Family Foundation
240 Del Casa Dr.
Mill Valley, CA 94941

Donor: Trevor Tomkins.
Foundation type: Independent foundation.
Financial data (yr. ended 12/31/13): Assets, $3,075,234 (M); gifts received, $29; expenditures, $187,386; qualifying distributions, $160,810; giving activities include $160,200 for 46 grants (high: $30,000; low: $250).
Fields of interest: Environment; Community and economic development; Human services.
Limitations: Applications not accepted.
Application information: Unsolicited requests for funds not accepted.
Officers: Trevor Tomkins, Pres.; Nicholas Tomkins, V.P.; Jennifer Tomkins, Secy.; Claire Tomkins, Treas.
EIN: 453998558

1123
Tomlinson Foundation
3652 Monte Real
Escondido, CA 92029-7911

Established in 1989 in California.
Donors: Thomas W. Tomlinson; Mary A. Tomlinson; Loren Tomlinson†; Gary Gallerstein.
Foundation type: Independent foundation.
Financial data (yr. ended 12/31/13): Assets, $88,357 (M); gifts received, $74,292; expenditures, $304,987; qualifying distributions, $302,256; giving activities include $300,075 for 19 grants (high: $56,000; low: $275).
Fields of interest: Higher education; Diseases and conditions; Protestantism; Human services; Youth services; Scouting programs.
Limitations: Applications not accepted. Giving primarily in CA. No grants to individuals.
Application information: Unsolicited requests for funds not accepted.
Officers: Thomas W. Tomlinson, Pres.; Lynora S. Brown, V.P.; Mary A. Tomlinson, Secy.
EIN: 330383793

1124
The Toole Charitable Foundation
c/o Esther Levandoski
100 Bay Hgts.
Soquel, CA 95073-3204

Established in 1994 in California.
Donors: Monte Toole; Ruthellen Toole.
Foundation type: Independent foundation.
Financial data (yr. ended 12/31/13): Assets, $3,816,042 (M); expenditures, $241,039; qualifying distributions, $198,535; giving activities

include $198,500 for 14 grants (high: $50,000; low: $2,500).
Fields of interest: Arts and culture; Judaism; Human services.
Limitations: Applications not accepted. No grants to individuals.
Application information: Unsolicited requests for funds not accepted.
Officers: Ruthellen Toole, Pres.; David Toole, V.P.; Esther Levandoski, Secy.
EIN: 770384189

1125
Francis P. Torino Foundation
2450 Madison St., Ste. 101
Torrance, CA 90505

Established in 1986 in California.
Donors: Francis P. Torino; Torino Residual Trust.
Foundation type: Independent foundation.
Financial data (yr. ended 05/31/13): Assets, $5,702,077 (M); expenditures, $264,967; qualifying distributions, $219,000; giving activities include $219,000 for grants.
Purpose and activities: Giving primarily for medical research and education.
Fields of interest: Arts and culture; Cultural awareness; Education; Special needs education; Undergraduate education; Medical education; Diseases and conditions; Human services; Youth development; Youth services.
Type of support: Research; Research and evaluation.
Limitations: Applications not accepted. Giving primarily in Torrance, CA and NV. No grants to individuals.
Application information: Unsolicited requests for funds not accepted.
Officer: Victor M. Crisostomo, C.F.O.
Directors: Francesca Deaver; Brett Torino; Courtney Torino.
EIN: 330219408

1126
The Nick Traina Foundation
P.O. Box 470427
San Francisco, CA 94147-0427 4157715335
E-mail: info@nicktrainafoundation.com; Main URL: http://nicktrainafoundation.com

Established in 1998 in California.
Donors: Alexander Mehran; The San Francisco Foundation; William M. Haber; Danielle Steel.
Foundation type: Independent foundation.
Financial data (yr. ended 12/31/14): Assets, $2,851,145; gifts received, $56,425; expenditures, $193,996; qualifying distributions, $192,293.
Purpose and activities: Support to organizations involved in the diagnosis, research, treatment, and/or family support of manic-depression, suicide prevention, child abuse and children in jeopardy, and provides assistance to struggling musicians in the areas of health and mental illness.
Fields of interest: HIV/AIDS; Mental and behavioral disorders; Depression; Psychology and behavioral science; Human services; Child welfare.
Limitations: Applications accepted. Giving primarily in San Francisco, CA. No support for organizations lacking 501(c)(3) status. No grants to individuals.

Application information: Non-profit organizations can apply for one grant each calendar year.
Initial approach: Proposal, not more than 3 pages
Copies of proposal: 2
Deadline(s): None
Board meeting date(s): Quarterly
Officers and Directors: Danielle Steel, Pres. and Director; Heather Ponts, Secy.; Cecily Waterman, C.F.O. and Director.
EIN: 943296757

1127
Traub-Brittan Family Foundation
9949 Santa Monica Blvd.
Beverly Hills, CA 90212-1647
Contact: Maynard M. Brittan, Chair.

Donors: Vera Traub; Maynard Brittan; Alexandra Brittan.
Foundation type: Independent foundation.
Financial data (yr. ended 11/30/14): Assets, $1,467,033 (M); gifts received, $172,000; expenditures, $279,843; qualifying distributions, $260,832; giving activities include $260,832 for 41 grants (high: $46,000; low: $150).
Fields of interest: Arts and culture; Performing arts; Opera; Nonprofits; Judaism.
Type of support: Regranting.
Limitations: Applications accepted. Giving primarily in Los Angeles, CA.
Application information:
Initial approach: Proposal
Deadline(s): None
Officers: Maynard M. Brittan, Chair.; Graydon Brittan, C.F.O. and V.P.; Linda Brittan, Secy.
EIN: 953870520

1128
S. D. Trombetta Foundation
23428 Summit Rd.
Los Gatos, CA 95033-9203 4083533931

Established in 1993 in California.
Donors: SDT Trust; Diane Trombetta Davis.
Foundation type: Independent foundation.
Financial data (yr. ended 12/31/14): Assets, $3,912,423; expenditures, $222,972; qualifying distributions, $217,000.
Fields of interest: Education; Environment; Human services.
Limitations: Applications not accepted. Giving primarily in CA. No grants to individuals.
Application information: Unsolicited requests for funds not accepted.
Officers: Marvin G. Dole, Pres.; Diane Trombetta Davis, V.P.
Directors: Liza Reynolds; Loren Reynolds.
EIN: 770342667

1129
The Troob Family Foundation
c/o David H. Troob
12 Trafalgar
Newport Beach, CA 92660-6830

Established in 1999 in New York.
Donor: David H. Troob.
Foundation type: Operating foundation.
Financial data (yr. ended 11/30/12): Assets, $4,196,179 (M); expenditures, $255,022;

qualifying distributions, $413,273; giving activities include $252,500 for 2 grants (high: $250,000; low: $2,500).
Fields of interest: Arts and culture.
Limitations: Applications not accepted. No grants to individuals.
Application information: Contributes only to pre-selected organizations.
Trustee: David H. Troob.
Directors: Douglas M. Troob; Marjorie D. Troob; Peter J. Troob; Robyn W. Troob; Tara K. Troob.
EIN: 367252941

1130
Gary Troy Foundation
c/o Garrard & Davis, LLP
1448 15th St., Ste. 200
Santa Monica, CA 90404-2756

Established in 1998 in California.
Foundation type: Independent foundation.
Financial data (yr. ended 12/31/14): Assets, $4,219,550; expenditures, $372,144; qualifying distributions, $245,000.
Purpose and activities: Giving primarily for youth and transitional housing.
Fields of interest: Education; Housing rehabilitation; Human services; Family services; Youth organizing.
Limitations: Applications not accepted. Giving primarily in CA. No grants to individuals.
Application information: Unsolicited requests for funds not accepted.
Officers: Steven D. Davis, C.E.O. and Secy.; Brian Catalde, Pres.; Michelle Catalde, V.P.; Jane Cudworth, V.P.
EIN: 954701751

1131
Trust Funds Incorporated
100 Broadway, 3rd Fl.
San Francisco, CA 94111-1404 (415) 434-3323

Established in 1934 in California.
Donors: Bartley P. Oliver†; Alfreda S. Cullinan†; Rev. James J. Wynne.
Foundation type: Independent foundation.
Financial data (yr. ended 12/31/14): Assets, $8,770,883; expenditures, $602,480; qualifying distributions, $443,597.
Purpose and activities: Grants primarily for Roman Catholic educational, religious, and social service charitable organizations.
Fields of interest: Elementary and secondary education; Religion; Catholicism; Human services.
Type of support: General support; Equipment; Emergency funds; Program development; Convening; Publications; Seed money; Curriculum development; Scholarships.
Limitations: Applications accepted. Giving primarily in the San Francisco Bay Area, CA. No support for organizations that draw substantial public support. No grants to individuals directly, or for capital or endowment funds, or annual campaigns; no loans.
Publications: Application guidelines; Informational brochure.
Application information: Application form required.
Initial approach: Letter or telephone
Copies of proposal: 5
Deadline(s): Quarterly
Board meeting date(s): Quarterly
Final notification: Within 3 months

Officers and Directors: James T. Healy, Pres. and Director; John Strain, Secy. and Director; Thomas F. Kubasak, C.F.O. and Director; Thomas J. Kelley; Joan C. O'Rourke.
Number of staff: 1 part-time professional.
EIN: 946062952

1132
Trustees of Ivan V. Koulaieff Educational Fund
c/o Rothstein Kass
101 Montgomery St., Ste. 22
San Francisco, CA 94104-4104

Established in 1930 in California.
Donor: Ivan V. Koulaieff.
Foundation type: Independent foundation.
Financial data (yr. ended 12/31/13): Assets, $8,313,543 (M); expenditures, $462,079; qualifying distributions, $367,300; giving activities include $367,300 for 35 grants (high: $48,800; low: $500).
Purpose and activities: The fund awards aid to Russian immigrants throughout the world through grants, scholarships, and loans; support also for Russian publications and Russian Orthodox education and churches in the U.S.
Fields of interest: Orthodox Christianity; Immigrants.
International interests: Russia.
Type of support: Publications; Program-related investments; Student aid; Grants to individuals.
Limitations: Applications not accepted. Giving on a national and international basis.
Application information: Unsolicited requests for funds not accepted.
Officers and Trustees: Michel Mirkovitch, Pres. and Trustee; Peter A. Yakoubovsky-Lerke, V.P. and Trustee; Alex D. Psiol, Treas. and Trustee; Anatol Shmelev; Natalia Tkachov.
EIN: 946088762

1133
Tsao Family Foundation
P.O. Box 1115
Corona del Mar, CA 92625-6115 (949) 706-3355
Contact: Michael Liyoung Tsao, Pres.

Established in 2004 in California.
Donors: Janie Chien Tsao; Victor Ying-Wei Tsao; Tsao Family Trust.
Foundation type: Independent foundation.
Financial data (yr. ended 12/31/13): Assets, $8,006,385 (M); gifts received, $506,087; expenditures, $419,440; qualifying distributions, $299,440; giving activities include $299,440 for 8 grants (high: $142,010; low: $100).
Fields of interest: Education; Religion; Human services.
Limitations: Applications accepted. Giving primarily in CA.
Application information: Application form required.
Initial approach: Request application form
Deadline(s): None
Officers: Michael Liyoung Tsao, Pres.; Steven Lidah Tsao, Secy.
EIN: 202043022

1134
The Tuffli Family Foundation
1412 Lower Paseo La Cresta
Palos Verdes Estates, CA 90274-2075

Established in 1996 in California.
Donor: Don L. Tuffli.
Foundation type: Independent foundation.
Financial data (yr. ended 12/31/14): Assets, $14,659,910; gifts received, $303,099; expenditures, $655,651; qualifying distributions, $403,550.
Fields of interest: Higher education; University education; Business education; Land resources; Foundations; Diseases and conditions; Multiple sclerosis; Community and economic development; Human services.
Limitations: Applications not accepted. Giving primarily in CA. No grants to individuals.
Application information: Unsolicited requests for funds not accepted.
Officers: Don L. Tuffli, Pres.; Martha T. Tuffli, V.P.; Laura T. Carruth, Secy.; Carol T. Cutting, Treas.
EIN: 330658864

1135
Twanda Foundation
(formerly Lisa and Sidne Long Foundation)
P.O. Box 986
Alamo, CA 94507-0986

Established in 2005 in California.
Donors: Lisa K. Laird; Sidne J. Long; Sidne J. Long Trust; Lisa K. Laird Trust.
Foundation type: Independent foundation.
Financial data (yr. ended 12/31/13): Assets, $34,825 (M); gifts received, $325,000; expenditures, $339,003; qualifying distributions, $268,600; giving activities include $268,600 for 53 grants (high: $25,000; low: $700).
Fields of interest: Education; Human services; Family services; Women's services.
Limitations: Applications not accepted. Giving primarily in CA.
Application information: Contributes only to pre-selected organizations.
Officers and Directors: Sidne J. Long, Pres. and Director; Lisa K. Larid, V.P. and Director; William Henry Delevati, C.F.O. and Secy. and Director; Mardi Beck; Robnett Beck; Rosemary Beck.
EIN: 203508036

1136
United Plankton Charitable Trust
11400 W. Olympic Blvd., Ste. 590
Los Angeles, CA 90064-1574

Established in 2005 in California.
Donors: Hillenburg Family Trust; Karen Hillenburg; Stephen Hillenburg.
Foundation type: Independent foundation.
Financial data (yr. ended 12/31/14): Assets, $7,398,942 (M); gifts received, $1,000,000; expenditures, $505,214; qualifying distributions, $442,618; giving activities include $442,618 for 17 grants (high: $125,000; low: $500).
Fields of interest: Arts education; Elementary and secondary education; University education; Hospital care; Females.
Limitations: Applications not accepted. Giving primarily in CA. No grants to individuals.

Application information: Contributes only to pre-selected organizations.
Trustees: Karen Hillenburg; Stephen Hillenburg.
EIN: 206582607

1137
The Unz Foundation
555 Bryant St., No. 371
Palo Alto, CA   94301-1704

Established in 2006 in California.
Donor: Ron Unz.
Foundation type: Independent foundation.
Financial data (yr. ended 12/31/13): Assets, $16,202 (M); gifts received, $1,000; expenditures, $212,136; qualifying distributions, $206,000; giving activities include $117,000 for 4 grants (high: $50,000; low: $15,000), and $89,000 for 4 grants to individuals (high: $32,000; low: $11,000).
Fields of interest: Education.
Type of support: Grants to individuals.
Limitations: Applications not accepted. Giving primarily in CA, NM and OR.
Application information: Unsolicited requests for funds not accepted.
Officer: Ron Unz, Pres.
EIN: 207181582

1138
The Uplands Family Foundation
(formerly Rosengarten Horowitz Fund)
134 The Uplands
Berkeley, CA   94705-2817

Established in 1996 in California.
Donors: Jeffrey Horowitz; Lynn Horowitz.
Foundation type: Independent foundation.
Financial data (yr. ended 12/31/13): Assets, $7,874,228 (M); expenditures, $538,144; qualifying distributions, $416,295; giving activities include $360,050 for 57 grants (high: $115,000; low: $500).
Fields of interest: Education; Environment; Domesticated animals; Human services; International relations.
Limitations: Applications not accepted. Giving primarily in CA, Washington, DC, and MA. No grants to individuals.
Application information: Contributes only to pre-selected organizations.
Officers and Directors: Lynn Horowitz, Pres. and Director; Jeffrey Horowitz, Secy. and Director.
EIN: 943257271

1139
The Uplands Foundation
321 S. Beverly Dr., Ste. K
Beverly Hills, CA   90212-4303

Established in 1994 in California.
Donors: Lynn Feintech; Anthony F. Bernhardt.
Foundation type: Independent foundation.
Financial data (yr. ended 12/31/13): Assets, $2,876,130 (M); expenditures, $277,830; qualifying distributions, $269,750; giving activities include $269,750 for 25 grants (high: $50,000; low: $250).
Fields of interest: Arts and culture; Dance; Education; Education services; Natural resources;

Health; Hospital care; Human services; Low-income and poor people.
Limitations: Applications not accepted. Giving primarily in CA. No grants to individuals.
Application information: Contributes only to pre-selected organizations.
Officers and Directors: Anthony F. Bernhardt, Pres. and Director; Evelyn Feintech, V.P. and Director; Lynn Feintech, Secy.-Treas. and Director.
EIN: 954442329

1140
Upside Down Foundation
399 Flintridge Oaks Dr.
La Canada, CA   91011-3515   (818) 952-4120
Contact: Jerry Wada, Pres.

Established in 2005 in California.
Donors: Jane Wada; Jerry Wada; Matthew Wada; Wada Family Trust; Jerry and Jane Wada Irrevocable Trust.
Foundation type: Independent foundation.
Financial data (yr. ended 12/31/13): Assets, $752,447 (M); gifts received, $22,685; expenditures, $118,860; qualifying distributions, $118,750; giving activities include $118,750 for 25 grants (high: $20,200; low: $100).
Fields of interest: Christianity.
International interests: India.
Limitations: Applications not accepted. Giving primarily in CA and FL; with some giving in India.
Application information: Unsolicited requests for funds not accepted.
Officers and Directors: Jerry Wada, Pres. and Director; Jane Wada, Secy. and Director.
EIN: 203701540

1141
Urbanek-Levy Education Fund
180 Harbor Dr., Ste. 205
Sausalito, CA   94965

Established in 2000 in California.
Donors: Gloria Levy; Kenneth Levy; Lida Urbanek.
Foundation type: Independent foundation.
Financial data (yr. ended 12/31/13): Assets, $534,411 (M); gifts received, $407,610; expenditures, $196,974; qualifying distributions, $194,986; giving activities include $190,500 for grants to individuals.
Fields of interest: Higher education.
Type of support: Student aid.
Limitations: Applications not accepted. Giving primarily to residents of CA.
Application information: Unsolicited requests for funds not accepted.
Officers: Lida Urbanek, Pres.; Karl-Heinz Lachnit, Secy.; Maureen Mackowski, Treas.
EIN: 943372793

1142
Uvas Foundation
3697 Mount Diablo Blvd., Ste. 205
Lafayette, CA   94549-7113

Established in 1980 in California.
Donor: Paul L. Davies, Jr.
Foundation type: Independent foundation.
Financial data (yr. ended 06/30/13): Assets, $3,124,828 (M); expenditures, $182,015;

qualifying distributions, $163,000; giving activities include $163,000 for grants.
Purpose and activities: Supports charitable interests of its directors.
Fields of interest: Education; Human services.
Type of support: General support.
Limitations: Applications not accepted. Giving primarily in CA and SC. No grants to individuals; no loans.
Application information: Contributes only to pre-selected organizations. Unsolicited requests for funds not considered.
   Board meeting date(s): Varies
Officers and Directors: Kenneth P. Mateo, Pres. and Director; Laura D. Mateo, Secy. and Director; Andrew E. Zeisler, Treas.; Paul L. Davies, Jr.; Gregory W. Mateo; Wesley D. Mateo.
EIN: 942678808

1143
Pablo Valenzuela & Bernardita Mendez Foundation
2919 Avalon Ave.
Berkeley, CA   94705-1401

Donors: Pablo Valenzuela; Bernardita Mendez.
Foundation type: Operating foundation.
Financial data (yr. ended 11/30/13): Assets, $2,997,802 (M); expenditures, $313,714; qualifying distributions, $308,000; giving activities include $300,000 for 1 grant.
Purpose and activities: Giving for medical care.
Fields of interest: Education; Health.
International interests: Chile.
Type of support: Research and evaluation.
Limitations: Applications not accepted. Giving primarily in CA; some giving also in Chile. No grants to individuals.
Application information: Contributes only to pre-selected organizations.
Officers and Directors: Pablo Valenzuela, Pres. and Director; Bernardita Mendez, V.P. and Director.
EIN: 943215323

1144
The Van Cleve Foundation Trust
c/o First Foundation Advisors
18101 Von Karman Ave., Ste. 700
Irvine, CA   92612-0145

Established in 2002 in California.
Donors: Russell G. Van Cleve; Kathy M. Van Cleve.
Foundation type: Independent foundation.
Financial data (yr. ended 12/31/13): Assets, $8,298,190 (M); expenditures, $414,656; qualifying distributions, $335,361; giving activities include $326,000 for 12 grants (high: $200,000; low: $1,000).
Fields of interest: Arts education; Diseases and conditions; Human services.
Type of support: Individual development.
Limitations: Applications not accepted. Giving primarily in Rochester, MN; support also in CA. No grants to individuals.
Application information: Unsolicited requests for funds not accepted.
Officer: Russell G. Van Cleve, Pres.
Director: Kathleen M. Van Cleve.
EIN: 816108712

1145
James Rush Varner Family Foundation
5900 E. Lerdo Hwy.
Shafter, CA 93263-4023

Donors: James Varner; JD Rush Company, Inc.
Foundation type: Independent foundation.
Financial data (yr. ended 11/30/13): Assets, $0 (M); gifts received, $200,000; expenditures, $155,910; qualifying distributions, $155,000; giving activities include $155,000 for 3 grants (high: $100,000; low: $5,000).
Fields of interest: Education; Religion.
Limitations: Applications not accepted. Giving primarily in Bakersfield, CA and KS.
Application information: Unsolicited requests for funds not accepted.
Officers: James Varner, Pres.; Joanne D. Varner, V.P.
EIN: 432069053

1146
Mary Beth Vogelzang Foundation
(formerly Mary Beth and James C. Vogelzang Foundation)
1129 State St., Ste. 3E
Santa Barbara, CA 93101-6746

Established in 1995 in Colorado.
Donors: James C. Vogelzang; Mary Beth Vogelzang.
Foundation type: Independent foundation.
Financial data (yr. ended 12/31/12): Assets, $1,960,493 (M); expenditures, $538,363; qualifying distributions, $370,253; giving activities include $370,253 for grants.
Fields of interest: Arts and culture; Education; Corrections and penology; Christianity.
Type of support: General support; Student aid.
Limitations: Applications not accepted. Giving on a national basis.
Application information: Unsolicited requests for funds not accepted.
Officer: Mary Beth Vogelzang, Pres.
EIN: 841314262

1147
Von Der Ahe Foundation
4605 Lankershim Blvd., Ste. 707
North Hollywood, CA 91602-1878

Established in 1951 in California.
Donor: Von's Grocery Co.
Foundation type: Independent foundation.
Financial data (yr. ended 12/31/13): Assets, $7,723,516 (M); expenditures, $420,940; qualifying distributions, $343,609; giving activities include $335,000 for 25 grants (high: $50,000; low: $2,000).
Purpose and activities: Giving to promote scientific and charitable causes; emphasis on Roman Catholic religious institutions and health and welfare services; support also for higher and secondary education and a community foundation.
Fields of interest: Arts and culture; Education; Secondary education; Higher education; Health; Alcoholism; Public administration; Catholicism; Human services.
Type of support: Capital campaigns; Capital and infrastructure; Emergency funds.
Limitations: Applications not accepted. Giving primarily in CA. No grants to individuals.

Application information: Contributes only to pre-selected organizations.
Board meeting date(s): July and Dec.
Officers: Thomas R. von der Ahe, Pres.; Clyde V. von der Ahe, MD, V.P.; Vincent M. von der Ahe, Secy.; Frederick T. von der Ahe, Treas.
Board Member: Chris von der Ahe.
Number of staff: 1 part-time professional.
EIN: 956051857

1148
Theodore A. Von Der Ahe, Jr. Trust
177 Sierra View Rd.
Pasadena, CA 91105-1447

Established in 1978 in California.
Donor: Theodore A. Von der Ahe, Jr.
Foundation type: Independent foundation.
Financial data (yr. ended 01/31/14): Assets, $3,610,014 (M); expenditures, $199,872; qualifying distributions, $158,501; giving activities include $158,000 for 52 grants (high: $10,000; low: $1,000).
Purpose and activities: Grants primarily for religious giving, with emphasis on Catholic welfare; support also for international affairs programs and social services.
Fields of interest: Foundations; Religion; Christianity; Catholicism; Human rights; Diversity and intergroup relations; Human services; International relations; International development.
Limitations: Applications not accepted. Giving primarily in CA, Washington, DC, and NY. No grants to individuals.
Application information: Unsolicited requests for funds not accepted.
Trustee: Ted Von Der Ahe, Jr.
Number of staff: 1 part-time support.
EIN: 953371127

1149
H.A.M.K. Wagner Family Foundation
4031 Savannah Trail
Santa Rosa, CA 95404-8897 (707) 545-5483
Contact: Harold A. Wagner, Tr.

Established in 1997 in Pennsylvania.
Donors: Harold A. Wagner; Marcia K. Wagner.
Foundation type: Independent foundation.
Financial data (yr. ended 12/31/13): Assets, $1,735,318 (M); expenditures, $274,575; qualifying distributions, $259,575; giving activities include $259,575 for 17 grants (high: $50,000; low: $500).
Fields of interest: Natural history museums; Higher education; Foundations; Nonprofits; Hospital care.
Type of support: Regranting.
Limitations: Applications accepted. Giving primarily in CA and PA.
Application information: Application form required.
Initial approach: Proposal
Deadline(s): None
Trustees: Sandra Boyce; Harold A. Wagner; Harold E. Wagner; Kristi Wagner; Marcia K. Wagner; Tracey Wagner.
EIN: 237886100

1150
Wakerly Family Foundation
373 Foxborough Dr.
Mountain View, CA 94041-1667
Contact: John F. Wakerly, Chair. and Pres.
E-mail: john@wakerly.com; *Main URL:* http://www.wakerly.org/WFF

Established in 1996 in California.
Donors: John F. Wakerly; Katherine S. Wakerly†.
Foundation type: Independent foundation.
Financial data (yr. ended 06/30/13): Assets, $6,891,257 (M); gifts received, $180,000; expenditures, $185,624; qualifying distributions, $185,500; giving activities include $185,500 for 18 grants (high: $20,000; low: $500), and $300,000 for loans/program-related investments.
Purpose and activities: The foundation provides financial assistance to qualified public charitable organizations, with a focus on the areas of social services, education and economic development. The foundation has interest in programs that: 1) Benefit Catholic education; 2) Support at-risk children and economically disadvantaged households; 3) Provide low income housing; 4) Foster job skills training; 5) Create new areas of employment through entrepreneurship; 6) Assist immigrants; 7) Assist low-income populations; 8) Provide emergency aid to the disadvantaged; and 9) Promote individual responsibility and economic freedom.
Fields of interest: Secondary education; University education; Economic development; Employment; Housing development; Catholicism; Human services; Children and youth; Adolescents; Females; People of Latin American descent; Immigrants; Low-income and poor people.
Type of support: General support; Program-related investments; Matching grants; Continuing support; Annual campaigns; Capital campaigns; Endowments; Program development; Seed money; Scholarships.
Limitations: Applications not accepted. Giving on a national basis, primarily in areas outside of CA. No support for non-501(c)(3) public charities, or for government agencies or entities receiving the majority of their support from government sources (including public schools). No grants to individuals.
Application information: The foundation no longer accepts unsolicited proposals.
Officers: John F. Wakerly, Chair. and Pres.; Regina Rich, V.P. and Secy.; Ralph T. Wakerly, Treas.
Board Members: Marie Wakerly; Michael Wakerly; Susanne Wakerly.
Number of staff: None.
EIN: 770441943

1151
C. A. Wall Family Foundation
290 Santa Clara Ave.
San Francisco, CA 94127-1522

Donors: C. Allen Wall; Catherine Brooks; Elizabeth Hanson; David R. Wall.
Foundation type: Operating foundation.
Financial data (yr. ended 12/31/13): Assets, $3,574,528 (M); gifts received, $1,157,342; expenditures, $283,567; qualifying distributions, $263,000; giving activities include $263,000 for 6 grants (high: $200,000; low: $3,000).
Fields of interest: Higher education.

Limitations: Applications not accepted. Giving primarily in San Francisco, CA. No grants to individuals.
Application information: Unsolicited requests for funds not accepted.
Officers: C. Allen Wall, Pres.; Elizabeth Hanson, Secy.-Treas.
Director: Catherine Brooks.
EIN: 943081338

1152
Robert A. Waller Foundation
15821 Ventura Blvd., Ste. 490
Encino, CA 91436

Established in 1994 in California.
Donors: Robert A. Waller; Judy T. Waller.
Foundation type: Independent foundation.
Financial data (yr. ended 12/31/13): Assets, $9,130,723 (M); gifts received, $5,820,567; expenditures, $156,306; qualifying distributions, $141,000; giving activities include $140,550 for 47 grants (high: $18,000; low: $500).
Purpose and activities: Giving primarily for education and health.
Fields of interest: Arts and culture; Museums; Education; Higher education; Zoos; Hospital care; Diseases and conditions; Public libraries; Human services.
Type of support: Research; Research and evaluation.
Limitations: Applications not accepted. No grants to individuals.
Application information: Unsolicited requests for funds not accepted.
Officers: Robert A. Waller, Pres.; Judy T. Waller, Secy.-Treas.
EIN: 954509776

1153
Walters Family Foundation
735 E. Carnegie Dr., Ste. 100
San Bernardino, CA 92408-3569 (909) 889-0871
Contact: Clifford Walters, Pres.; Leena Shanbhag CPA

Established in 2000 in Oregon.
Donors: Glenn Walters; Viola Walters.
Foundation type: Independent foundation.
Financial data (yr. ended 09/30/13): Assets, $4,320,382 (M); expenditures, $375,675; qualifying distributions, $209,126; giving activities include $209,126 for 15 grants (high: $104,244; low: $1,442).
Purpose and activities: Giving primarily for programs which enable at-risk individuals and at-risk families to become productive and self-sufficient members of society.
Fields of interest: Christianity; Human services; Family services; Low-income and poor people.
Limitations: Applications accepted. Giving primarily in the metropolitan Portland, OR, area with emphasis on the Hillsboro area.
Application information: Application form required.
Initial approach: Letter
Deadline(s): None
Board meeting date(s): Aug. and Jan.
Final notification: 2-6 months
Officers: Clifford Walters, Pres.; Mindy Youngs, Secy.; Chad Walters, Treas.

Board Members: Steve Kerr; Jim Roufener; Phil Waller; Viola Walters; Randy Unterseher.
Number of staff: 1 part-time support.
EIN: 931280994

1154
Walther Foundation
3636 Buchanan St.
San Francisco, CA 94123-1709

Established in 2004 in California.
Donor: Roger O. Walther.
Foundation type: Independent foundation.
Financial data (yr. ended 03/31/13): Assets, $213,647 (M); gifts received, $550,800; expenditures, $463,065; qualifying distributions, $368,745; giving activities include $368,745 for grants.
Fields of interest: Orchestral music; Education; Foundations.
Type of support: General support.
Limitations: Applications not accepted. Giving primarily in CA. No grants to individuals.
Application information: Unsolicited requests for funds not accepted.
Officers: Roger O. Walther, Pres.; Anne N. Walther, V.P. and Treas.; Christine W. Tripp, Secy. and Exec. Dir.
EIN: 721580927

1155
Waltmar Foundation
c/o Larry Beltramo
20 Corporate Park, Ste. 160
Irvine, CA 92606-5183

Established in 1980 in California.
Donors: Don W. Schmid; Richard R. Schmid; Walter R. Schmid†.
Foundation type: Independent foundation.
Financial data (yr. ended 12/31/13): Assets, $8,880,510 (M); expenditures, $536,526; qualifying distributions, $423,644; giving activities include $400,000 for 18 grants (high: $60,000; low: $5,000).
Purpose and activities: Giving primarily for higher education, and youth and social services.
Fields of interest: Education; Human services; Youth development.
Type of support: Capital campaigns; Capital and infrastructure; Program development; Scholarships; Research.
Limitations: Applications not accepted. Giving primarily in CA. No grants to individuals.
Application information: Unsolicited requests for funds not accepted.
Officers: Richard R. Schmid, Pres.; David W. Schmid, V.P.; Laura Cook, Secy.; Larry Beltramo, Treas.; Shauna Farley, Exec. Dir.
Directors: Lisa Beltramo; Bonnie McCormack.
EIN: 952371506

1156
Walton Avenue Foundation
5075 Shoreham Pl., No. 250
San Diego, CA 92122-3966

Established in 1958 in California.
Donor: Harvey Furgatch.
Foundation type: Independent foundation.

Financial data (yr. ended 11/30/13): Assets, $475,097 (M); gifts received, $255,000; expenditures, $310,571; qualifying distributions, $307,709; giving activities include $304,510 for 15 grants (high: $145,000; low: $100).
Fields of interest: Museums; Natural resources; Biodiversity; Wildlife biodiversity; Nonprofits; Cancers; Human services.
Type of support: General support; Regranting.
Limitations: Applications not accepted. Giving primarily in CA, Washington, DC, NM, NY, and VA. No grants to individuals.
Application information: Unsolicited requests for funds not accepted.
Officers: Harvey Furgatch, Pres.; Harvey Amster, C.F.O.; Kimberly Britton, Secy.
EIN: 956039853

1157
Wang Family Foundation
3268 Villa Ln.
Napa, CA 94558

Established in 1994 in California.
Donor: Francis S.L. Wang.
Foundation type: Operating foundation.
Financial data (yr. ended 12/31/13): Assets, $2,664,962 (M); gifts received, $50,000; expenditures, $269,835; qualifying distributions, $252,945; giving activities include $252,945 for 7 grants (high: $136,316; low: $500).
Fields of interest: Education; Human services.
Limitations: Applications not accepted. Giving primarily in CA and NY.
Application information: Contributes only to pre-selected organizations.
Directors: Elizabeth Wang; Francis S.L. Wang; Mary Wang; Laura W.Y. Young.
EIN: 680338738

1158
Ward Family Foundation
P.O. Box 917
Sunset Beach, CA 90742-0917

Established in 1998 in California.
Donors: Catherine Ward; George Ward.
Foundation type: Independent foundation.
Financial data (yr. ended 12/31/13): Assets, $1,346,062 (M); gifts received, $40,000; expenditures, $440,429; qualifying distributions, $435,000; giving activities include $435,000 for 2 grants (high: $335,000; low: $100,000).
Fields of interest: Secondary education; Water resources; Radio; Human services.
Limitations: Applications not accepted. Giving primarily in CA; some funding also in Glenside, PA. No grants to individuals.
Application information: Contributes only to pre-selected organizations.
Officers: Catherine Ward, Pres.; George Ward, V.P.; Katherine Watt, Secy.; Brenna Oberlin, Treas.
EIN: 954659533

1159
Warren Family Foundation
P.O. Box 915
Rancho Santa Fe, CA 92067-0915 (858) 756-3711
Contact: Tracy W. St. Amour, Exec. V.P.

Established in 1977 in California.
Donors: Frank R. Warren; Joanne C. Warren.
Foundation type: Independent foundation.
Financial data (yr. ended 06/30/13): Assets, $1,082,024 (M); gifts received, $300,000; expenditures, $361,323; qualifying distributions, $361,285; giving activities include $361,200 for 16 grants (high: $100,000; low: $500).
Fields of interest: Art museums; Education; Zoos; Human services; Child welfare.
Type of support: General support; Capital and infrastructure; Research.
Limitations: Applications accepted. Giving primarily in CA, with emphasis on San Diego. No grants to individuals.
Application information: Application form required.
  Initial approach: Letter
  Deadline(s): None
Officers: Joanne C. Warren, Pres.; Tracy W. St. Amour, Exec. V.P.
Directors: Lisa W. Campbell; Bruce L. Warren; Carol L. Warren.
EIN: 953201177

1160
The Wasserman Foundation
740 Elk Clover Cir.
Palm Desert, CA 92211-3400

Foundation type: Independent foundation.
Financial data (yr. ended 12/31/13): Assets, $2,939,602 (M); expenditures, $166,707; qualifying distributions, $166,707; giving activities include $155,400 for 50 grants (high: $28,000; low: $100).
Fields of interest: Arts and culture; Higher education; Cancers.
Limitations: Applications not accepted. Giving primarily in NY. No grants to individuals.
Application information: Contributes only to pre-selected organizations.
Officers: Peter J. Wasserman, Pres.; Judi Wasserman, V.P.
EIN: 010722408

1161
Phyllis C. Wattis Foundation
720 York St., Ste. 103
San Francisco, CA 94110-2148   (415) 986-1571
FAX: (415) 986-1547;
E-mail: info@wattisfoundation.org; Main URL: http://www.wattisfoundation.org
Facebook: https://www.facebook.com/PCWFoundation?ref=tn_tnmn
Twitter: https://twitter.com/pcwfoundation

Donors: Carol Casey; Paul L. Wattis Foundation.
Foundation type: Independent foundation.
Financial data (yr. ended 12/31/14): Assets, $10,678,484; expenditures, $450,879; qualifying distributions, $423,696.
Purpose and activities: Giving for the support of the fine arts, including the exhibition of painting and sculpture, and the performing arts, including opera, symphony, and dance.
Fields of interest: Arts and culture; Visual arts; Performing arts.
Limitations: Giving primarily in San Francisco, Berkeley, and Oakland, as well as in Marin County, California. No grants for general support, operating expenses, capital expansion, endowment funds,

seed grants, scholarships, awards, or research and planning.
Publications: Application guidelines.
Application information:
  Initial approach: Letter of inquiry of no more than 2 pages
  Deadline(s): See foundation web site for current deadlines
  Board meeting date(s): Spring and fall
Directors: Carol Casey; Carlie Wilmans.
EIN: 900653262

1162
The Webb Foundation
(formerly The Webb-Berger Foundation)
P.O. Box 13390
Palm Desert, CA 92255-3390

Established in 1992 in California.
Donor: H.N. and Frances C. Berger Foundation.
Foundation type: Independent foundation.
Financial data (yr. ended 12/31/13): Assets, $23,175,283 (M); expenditures, $1,079,410; qualifying distributions, $963,208; giving activities include $285,590 for 47 grants (high: $65,000; low: $540).
Fields of interest: Arts and culture; Museums; Education; Higher education; Hospital care; Protestantism; Human services; Child welfare; Youth services; Youth organizing.
Type of support: Equipment; Research.
Limitations: Applications not accepted. Giving primarily in CA, with emphasis on southern CA. No grants to individuals.
Application information: Unsolicited requests for funds not accepted.
Trustee: Lewis Webb, Jr.
EIN: 954320582

1163
The Patricia and Christopher Weil Family Foundation
c/o Patricia Weil
12555 High Bluff Dr., Ste. 180
San Diego, CA 92130-3005
FAX: (858) 704-1456; Main URL: http://www.weilfamilyfoundation.org

Donors: Christopher Weil; Patricia Weil; Christopher and Patricia Weil Family Trust.
Foundation type: Independent foundation.
Financial data (yr. ended 12/31/13): Assets, $3,487,364 (M); gifts received, $372,936; expenditures, $420,249; qualifying distributions, $403,570; giving activities include $403,570 for 50 grants (high: $209,500; low: $50).
Purpose and activities: Giving to provide support to arts organizations, and to provide scholarship support for students with financial need. Scholarships are available to selected graduates of the Preuss School, UCSD, and to students at San Diego City College.
Fields of interest: Arts and culture; Education.
Type of support: General support; Matching grants; Continuing support; Capacity-building and technical assistance; Annual campaigns; Student aid.
Limitations: Applications not accepted. Giving primarily in the greater San Diego, CA, area.
Publications: Financial statement.

Application information: Unsolicited requests for funds not accepted.
  Board meeting date(s): Varies
Officers and Directors: Christopher Weil, Pres.; Patricia Weil, Secy.-Treas.; Caitlin Weil; Matthew Weil; Kit-Victoria Wells.
Number of staff: None.
EIN: 330833801

1164
Adolph and Etta Weinberg Foundation
15510 Olive Branch Dr.
La Mirada, CA 90638-2429   (560) 947-7143
Contact: Rhona Weinberg Gewelber, Pres. and C.E.O.

Established in 1952 in California.
Donor: Coast Grain Co.
Foundation type: Independent foundation.
Financial data (yr. ended 09/30/14): Assets, $1,706,705 (M); expenditures, $155,551; qualifying distributions, $138,795; giving activities include $138,795 for 41 grants (high: $20,000; low: $100).
Fields of interest: Education; Health; Disasters and emergency management.
Type of support: General support.
Limitations: Applications accepted. Giving primarily in CA. No grants to individuals.
Application information: Application form required.
  Initial approach: Letter
  Deadline(s): June 30
Officers and Directors: Rhona Weinberg Gewelber, Pres. and C.E.O.; Hali Gewelber, Secy. and Director; Robert A. Weinberg, MD, C.F.O. and Director; Roxann Weinberg.
Number of staff: 1 part-time support.
EIN: 956075855

1165
William E. and Aenid R. Weisgerber Foundation
180 Montgomery St., Ste. 1616
San Francisco, CA 94104-4235

Established in 1998 in California.
Donor: Aenid R. Weisgerber Trust.
Foundation type: Independent foundation.
Financial data (yr. ended 12/31/13): Assets, $5,951,504 (M); expenditures, $350,038; qualifying distributions, $311,463; giving activities include $290,000 for 7 grants (high: $150,000; low: $5,000).
Fields of interest: Health; Child welfare.
Limitations: Applications not accepted. Giving primarily in CA. No grants to individuals.
Application information: Contributes only to pre-selected organizations.
Officers and Directors: Gary E. Botto, Pres. and Director; Dorothy J. Oliphant, V.P.; Ann C. Matthews, Secy.-Treas.
Number of staff: None.
EIN: 943306221

1166
Mandell Weiss Charitable Trust
P.O. Box 221071
San Diego, CA 92192-1071   (858) 454-2933

Established in 1994 in California.

Foundation type: Independent foundation.
Financial data (yr. ended 12/31/13): Assets, $10,573,095 (M); expenditures, $482,956; qualifying distributions, $454,589; giving activities include $378,300 for 39 grants (high: $50,000; low: $1,000).
Purpose and activities: Giving primarily for the arts.
Fields of interest: Arts and culture; Education; Health.
Limitations: Applications accepted. Giving primarily in CA. No grants to individuals.
Application information: Application form required.
  Initial approach: Letter
  Deadline(s): None
Trustees: Joseph Satz; Linda Satz.
EIN: 336145298

1167
David and Sylvia Weisz Family Philanthropic Fund
1901 Ave. of the Stars, Ste. 610
Los Angeles, CA   90067-6001   (310) 284-8856
Contact: Syliva Weisz, Chair. and Pres.

Established in 2001 in California.
Donor: Sylvia Weisz.
Foundation type: Independent foundation.
Financial data (yr. ended 12/31/12): Assets, $14,895,627 (M); expenditures, $911,070; qualifying distributions, $380,200; giving activities include $380,200 for grants.
Fields of interest: Arts and culture; Education; Animal welfare; Nonprofits; Human services.
Type of support: Regranting.
Limitations: Giving primarily in CA.
Application information:
  Initial approach: Letter
  Deadline(s): None
Officers: Sylvia Weisz, Chair. and Pres.; Jay H. Grodin, V.P. and Treas.; Judith Carroll, V.P.; Katherine Ireland, V.P.; Carey Pearlman, Secy.
Directors: Jennifer Caroll; John Caroll.
EIN: 912172529

1168
The David and Heidi Welch Foundation
217 Camino Al Lago
Atherton, CA   94027-5424

Established in 1999 in California.
Donors: David F. Welch; Heidi A. Welch; Mindy Rogers; LRFA LLC; Gary Morgenthaler; Jesse Rogers.
Foundation type: Independent foundation.
Financial data (yr. ended 12/31/13): Assets, $1,533,326 (M); gifts received, $1,152,972; expenditures, $460,924; qualifying distributions, $457,100; giving activities include $441,000 for 8 grants (high: $250,000; low: $1,000).
Fields of interest: Education; Higher education; Environment.
Type of support: General support.
Limitations: Applications not accepted. Giving primarily in CA. No grants to individuals.
Application information: Unsolicited requests for funds not accepted.
Officers and Directors: David F. Welch, Pres. and Director; Heidi A. Welch, V.P., C.F.O. and Secy. and Director.
EIN: 943332166

1169
Welfund Inc.
152 N. Almont Dr.
West Hollywood, CA   90048-2909

Established in 1963 in California.
Foundation type: Independent foundation.
Financial data (yr. ended 12/31/13): Assets, $3,138,076 (M); expenditures, $201,234; qualifying distributions, $141,284; giving activities include $136,500 for 35 grants (high: $15,000; low: $500).
Fields of interest: Arts and culture; Education; Diseases and conditions; Religion; Judaism; Human services.
Limitations: Applications not accepted. Giving primarily in WA.
Application information: Contributes only to pre-selected organizations.
Officers: Wylie G. Burke, Pres. and Director; M. Anthony Keyser, V.P.; Bertha H. Briley, Secy.-Treas.
Directors: Frank J. Baron; Mary Anne Keyser.
EIN: 956091887

1170
The Lawrence Welk Family Foundation
(formerly The 1988 L.W. Foundation)
11400 W. Olympic Blvd.
Los Angeles, CA   90064-1550

Established in 1995 in California.
Donors: The Lawrence Welk Foundation; The Welk Group.
Foundation type: Independent foundation.
Financial data (yr. ended 12/31/13): Assets, $1,554,053 (M); gifts received, $128,300; expenditures, $211,672; qualifying distributions, $146,218; giving activities include $140,000 for 6 grants (high: $25,000; low: $15,000).
Fields of interest: Family services; Youth organizing; Children; Low-income and poor people.
Type of support: General support; Continuing support; Program development; Seed money; Program evaluations.
Limitations: Applications not accepted. Giving primarily in Escondido, Santa Monica, Venice, and South Central Los Angeles, CA. No grants to individuals.
Application information: Contributes only to pre-selected organizations.
Officers: Lisa Parker, Pres.; David Mack, Treas.
Directors: Robert Fredricks; Ronald Gother; James Mack; Jennifer Mack; Lindy Welk; Tracey Welk.
Number of staff: 1 part-time professional.
EIN: 954705477

1171
Wells Family Charitable Foundation
450 Newport Ctr. Dr., Ste. 450
Newport Beach, CA   92660-7620

Established in 1985 in California.
Donors: Frank G. Wells†; Luanne C. Wells; W. Kevin Wells.
Foundation type: Independent foundation.
Financial data (yr. ended 12/31/13): Assets, $7,983,676 (M); gifts received, $2,199,482; expenditures, $366,701; qualifying distributions, $304,415; giving activities include $304,415 for 19 grants (high: $100,000; low: $520).

Purpose and activities: Giving primarily for the arts and education.
Fields of interest: Arts and culture; Visual arts; Early childhood education; Elementary education; Higher education; Natural resources.
Limitations: Applications not accepted. Giving primarily in CA. No grants to individuals.
Application information: Contributes only to pre-selected organizations.
Officers: Luanne C. Wells, Pres.; Paul C. Heeschen, Secy.
EIN: 953982216

1172
Wendell Family Foundation
1400 Fashion Blvd.
San Mateo, CA   94404

Established in 2001 in California.
Donors: Peter Wendell; Schmidt Family Living Trust.
Foundation type: Independent foundation.
Financial data (yr. ended 12/31/13): Assets, $623,674 (M); gifts received, $496,930; expenditures, $403,507; qualifying distributions, $386,203; giving activities include $386,203 for 87 grants (high: $168,045; low: $75).
Fields of interest: Education; Diseases and conditions; Human services.
Type of support: Research; Advocacy.
Limitations: Applications not accepted. Giving primarily in CA; some giving in MA and NJ. No grants to individuals.
Application information: Contributes only to pre-selected organizations.
Officer and Directors: Peter Wendell, Pres. and Secy. and Director; Brian Wendell; Christopher Wendell; Lynn Wendell.
EIN: 943374830

1173
The Wertheimer Foundation
14191 Alisal Ln.
Santa Monica, CA   90402-1311   (310) 454-0573
Contact: Susan Wertheimer, Secy.

Established in 1986 in California.
Donors: Thomas Wertheimer; Ira T. Wertheimer.
Foundation type: Independent foundation.
Financial data (yr. ended 12/31/13): Assets, $1,173,913 (M); gifts received, $300,000; expenditures, $255,653; qualifying distributions, $251,463; giving activities include $249,320 for 44 grants (high: $50,000; low: $45).
Purpose and activities: Giving primarily for higher education, human services, Jewish agencies, and eye diseases and blindness research.
Fields of interest: Arts and culture; Education; Higher education; Diseases and conditions; Eye diseases; Judaism; Human services; People with vision impairments.
Limitations: Applications accepted. Giving primarily in the Los Angeles, CA, area. No grants to individuals.
Application information:
  Initial approach: Proposal
  Deadline(s): None
Officers: Thomas Wertheimer, Pres.; Douglas Wertheimer, C.F.O.; Elinor Wertheimer, Co-Secy.; Susan Wertheimer, Co-Secy.
EIN: 954090231

1174
West Davis & Bergard Foundation
303 Hegenberger Rd., Ste. 305
Oakland, CA 94621-1419

Established in 1996 in California.
Donor: Carl A. Bergard.
Foundation type: Independent foundation.
Financial data (yr. ended 06/30/14): Assets, $3,013,284 (M); gifts received, $240,000; expenditures, $208,945; qualifying distributions, $202,018; giving activities include $150,000 for 27 grants (high: $20,750; low: $750).
Purpose and activities: Giving for education, and for human and children's services.
Fields of interest: Arts and culture; Environment; Human services.
Limitations: Applications not accepted. Giving limited to Alameda and Contra Costa counties, CA. No grants to individuals.
Application information: Unsolicited requests for funds not accepted.
Officers: Carl A. Bergard, Pres.; Lillian R. Harding, Secy.-Treas.; Patrick F. Feeney, Treas.
Board Members: Eleanor M. Manual; Jeanne M. Richards; Robert F. Wright.
EIN: 943255381

1175
Harry & Ethel West Foundation
P.O. Box 1825
Bakersfield, CA 93303-1825 (661) 873-0360
Contact: Richard G. McBurnie, Mgr.

Foundation type: Operating foundation.
Financial data (yr. ended 12/31/13): Assets, $6,423,299 (M); expenditures, $343,984; qualifying distributions, $177,550; giving activities include $177,500 for 42 grants (high: $35,000; low: $50).
Purpose and activities: Giving primarily for education, human services, and children and youth services.
Fields of interest: Arts and culture; Secondary education; Higher education; Diseases and conditions; Christianity; Human services; Child welfare.
Limitations: Applications accepted. Giving primarily in Kern County, CA.
Application information: Application form required.
Initial approach: Letter
Deadline(s): None
Officers: Mary C. Means, Secy.; Richard G. McBurnie, Mgr.
Director: Silver D. Sack.
EIN: 237168492

1176
Western Cardiac Foundation
15060 Ventura Blvd., Ste. 300
Sherman Oaks, CA 91403-2426 (818) 783-6028
Contact: Seaborn Kennamer, Secy.

Donors: Katherine R. Vance‡; Wilbur May Foundation; Broccoli Foundation; The Schuman Foundation.
Foundation type: Independent foundation.
Financial data (yr. ended 12/31/13): Assets, $5,346,974 (M); gifts received, $75; expenditures, $319,872; qualifying distributions, $271,125; giving activities include $270,000 for 4 grants (high: $210,000; low: $5,000).
Purpose and activities: Giving primarily for medical education and medical research, and to hospitals.
Fields of interest: Higher education; Medical education; Hospital care; Diseases and conditions; Eye diseases.
Type of support: Fellowships; Research; Capacity-building and technical assistance.
Limitations: Applications accepted. Giving primarily in Birmingham, AL, and Los Angeles, CA. No grants to individuals.
Application information:
Initial approach: Letter
Copies of proposal: 1
Deadline(s): None
Officers and Directors: Richard Kennamer, Pres. and Director; Mary Ann Flinn, V.P. and Director; Seaborn Kennamer, Secy. and Director.
Number of staff: 1 part-time professional.
EIN: 956116853

1177
The Westphal Family Foundation
60 Berry Dr.
Pacheco, CA 94553-5601

Established in 1999 in California.
Donors: Bay Alarm Co.; Balco Holdings, Inc.
Foundation type: Company-sponsored foundation.
Financial data (yr. ended 12/31/13): Assets, $18,246 (M); gifts received, $195,694; expenditures, $198,402; qualifying distributions, $198,342; giving activities include $148,342 for 26 grants (high: $32,000; low: $500), and $50,000 for 16 grants to individuals (high: $4,500; low: $500).
Purpose and activities: The foundation supports organizations involved with education, health, ALS, child welfare, and children and youth.
Fields of interest: Health; Diseases and conditions; Human services.
Type of support: General support; Annual campaigns; Research; Program development; Scholarships.
Limitations: Applications not accepted. Giving limited to CA. No grants to individuals (except for employee-related scholarships).
Application information: Contributes only through employee-related scholarships and pre-selected organizations.
Trustees: Bruce A. Westphal; Patricia A. Westphal; Penny L. Westphal; Roger L. Westphal.
EIN: 916491365

1178
The Wharton Foundation, Inc.
1001 Arbolado Rd.
Santa Barbara, CA 93103-2037 (805) 845-8861
Contact: Jean W. Pettitt, Pres.

Established in 1954 in Maryland.
Foundation type: Independent foundation.
Financial data (yr. ended 06/30/14): Assets, $3,460,714 (M); expenditures, $270,042; qualifying distributions, $224,491; giving activities include $167,178 for 29 grants (high: $42,000; low: $500).
Purpose and activities: Giving for programs that focus on education. Priority given to programs benefiting grades 1 through 12 students with limited access to educational resources.
Fields of interest: Arts and culture; Education; Religion.
Type of support: General support; Pro bono consulting services; Continuing support; Capital and infrastructure; Emergency funds; Program development; Convening; Seed money; Curriculum development; Scholarships; Research; Technical assistance; Program evaluations.
Limitations: Applications accepted. Giving primarily in Coconino County, AZ and Santa Barbara and Ventura counties, CA. No grants to individuals or for multi-year commitments; no loans.
Publications: Application guidelines; Annual report (including application guidelines); Grants list.
Application information: Application form required.
Initial approach: Letter, Email, or Fax
Deadline(s): Jan.
Officers: J.W. Pettitt, Pres.; W. Pettitt, V.P.; J. Meisel, Secy.; J. Edwards, Treas.
Directors: E.W. Peterson; S.D. Pettitt; K. Schafer.
EIN: 366130748

1179
William A. Wheeler & Florence R. Wheeler Foundation
2012 E. St.
Bakersfield, CA 93301 (661) 836-2184
Contact: Nancy L. Wheeler Smith, Tr.

Established in 1987 in Nevada.
Donors: William A. Wheeler; Florence R. Wheeler.
Foundation type: Independent foundation.
Financial data (yr. ended 05/31/14): Assets, $6,264,936 (M); expenditures, $448,361; qualifying distributions, $308,663; giving activities include $308,663 for 22 grants (high: $115,000; low: $400).
Purpose and activities: Giving primarily for human services and education.
Fields of interest: Education; Hospital care; Agriculture; Human services; Youth services; Children and youth.
Limitations: Applications accepted. Giving primarily in Bakersfield, CA. No grants to individuals.
Application information: Application form required.
Initial approach: Letter
Deadline(s): None
Trustee: Nancy L. Wheeler Smith.
EIN: 880233486

1180
White Mountain Institute
(formerly Ambulatory Anesthesia Research Foundation)
144 Ashby Ln.
Los Altos, CA 94022-1615 (650) 559-1754
Contact: Paul F. White, Pres.

Donors: Roche Laboratories; Baxter Healthcare Corp.
Foundation type: Independent foundation.
Financial data (yr. ended 09/30/13): Assets, $2,138,020 (M); gifts received, $14,500; expenditures, $310,665; qualifying distributions, $290,475; giving activities include $280,500 for 4 grants (high: $251,000; low: $500).
Fields of interest: Education; University education; Sports and recreation.

Type of support: General support; Capital and infrastructure; Scholarships.
Limitations: Applications accepted. Giving primarily in CA. No grants to individuals.
Application information: Application form required.
 Initial approach: Letter
 Deadline(s): None
Officers: Paul F. White, M.D., Ph.D., Pres.; Giovanni Pittoni, MD, V.P.; Linda D. White, Secy.; Charles E. White, Treas.
Directors: Battista Borghi; Franco Carli, MD; Michael B. Howie, MD; Kristine N. Lopes; Pablo MacClure, Ph.D; Larry R. Mayne; John Raeder, M.D., Ph.D.; Ed A. White; Lisa M. White.
EIN: 770094396

1181
The Ronald Whittier Family Foundation
3130 Alpine Rd., Ste. 288, P.M.B. 602
Portola Valley, CA 94028-7521
Contact: Jacqueline Whittier Kubicka
E-mail: familiescanprogram@sbcglobal.net; Main URL: http://www.familiescan.org
Facebook: http://www.facebook.com/pages/
FamiliesCAN/116926001669240?http%3A%2F%2Fwww.facebook.com%2Fpages%2FFamiliesCAN%2F116926001669240

Established in 1999 in California.
Donor: Ronald J. Whittier.
Foundation type: Independent foundation.
Financial data (yr. ended 12/31/13): Assets, $1,427,778 (M); expenditures, $164,819; qualifying distributions, $157,477; giving activities include $27,040 for 16 grants (high: $6,000; low: $50), and $96,733 for grants to individuals.
Purpose and activities: Giving to U.S. citizens between the ages of 18 and 65 who are currently receiving, or will be receiving within 3 months, cancer treatment in Santa Clara County, CA. The patient's family must have 1 or more dependents under the age of 18 who are immediate family members.
Fields of interest: Cancers; Human services; Low-income and poor people.
Type of support: General support; Grants to individuals.
Limitations: Applications accepted. Giving limited to Santa Clara County, CA.
Publications: Informational brochure.
Application information: Applicant must submit tax returns and medical records to support qualifications. See web site for additional application policies and guidelines. Application form required.
 Initial approach: Contact Program Dir. to schedule an appointment for an application
 Final notification: Qualified applicants are processed once a month
Officers: Ronald J. Whittier, Chair.; Jacqueline Whittier Kubicka, C.O.O. and Secy.; Jennifer L. Miller, V.P.
Number of staff: 1 part-time professional.
EIN: 770525013

1182
Brayton Wilbur Foundation
345 California St., 27th Fl.
San Francisco, CA 94104-2644

Established in 1947 in California.

Donors: Wilbur-Ellis Co.; Brayton Wilbur, Jr.†; Judy Wilbur.
Foundation type: Company-sponsored foundation.
Financial data (yr. ended 12/31/13): Assets, $4,268,179 (M); expenditures, $237,372; qualifying distributions, $218,335; giving activities include $216,050 for 14 grants (high: $105,000; low: $50).
Purpose and activities: The foundation supports aquariums and organizations involved with arts and culture, secondary education, and civic affairs.
Fields of interest: Arts and culture; Health; Human services.
Limitations: Applications not accepted. Giving primarily in San Francisco, CA. No grants to individuals.
Application information: Contributes only to pre-selected organizations.
Officers: Judy Wilbur, Pres.; Claire W. Pollini, V.P.; Michael D. Wilbur, V.P.; Jaye G. Stedman, Secy.; Susan W. Harrington, Treas.
EIN: 946088667

1183
Wilkinson Foundation
3435 Pacific Ave.
San Francisco, CA 94118-2029

Established in 1986 in Michigan.
Donor: Warren S. Wilkinson.
Foundation type: Independent foundation.
Financial data (yr. ended 01/31/14): Assets, $6,063,864 (M); expenditures, $274,871; qualifying distributions, $253,663; giving activities include $250,250 for 90 grants (high: $14,000; low: $250).
Fields of interest: Arts and culture; Historical activities; Education; Higher education; Environment; Health; Human services.
Type of support: Continuing support; Annual campaigns; Capital campaigns; Endowments; Program development; Seed money.
Limitations: Applications not accepted. Giving on a national basis, with an emphasis on MI.
Application information: Contributes only to pre-selected organizations.
Trustees: Bary Wilkinson; Bruce Wilkinson; Guerin S. Wilkinson; Dr. Stephen Wilkinson; Tom S. Wilkinson; Warren S. Wilkinson.
EIN: 386497639

1184
Williamson Foundation for Music
P.O. Box 524
Pebble Beach, CA 93953-0524
Main URL: http://wfmusic.org

Established in 2005 in California.
Donor: Kate Williamson.
Foundation type: Independent foundation.
Financial data (yr. ended 12/31/12): Assets, $2,931,915 (M); expenditures, $174,842; qualifying distributions, $146,437; giving activities include $53,119 for 16 grants (high: $4,605; low: $3,000), and $86,905 for 42 grants to individuals (high: $19,472; low: $302).
Fields of interest: Music; Education.
International interests: France.
Type of support: Student aid.
Limitations: Applications not accepted. Giving primarily in CA and France. No grants to.

Application information: Unsolicited requests for funds not accepted.
Officers: Julie Hansen, Pres.; Wendy Burnham, Secy.; Maeve Murphy, Treas.
EIN: 202468781

1185
Amos and Ruth Wilnai Foundation
885 Northampton Dr.
Palo Alto, CA 94303-3434

Established in 2006 in California.
Donors: Amos Wilnai; Ruth Wilnai; Nitzan Wilnai; Sigal Wilnai-Tzoore.
Foundation type: Independent foundation.
Financial data (yr. ended 12/31/13): Assets, $10,084,055 (M); gifts received, $1,504,155; expenditures, $367,687; qualifying distributions, $352,791; giving activities include $350,750 for 22 grants (high: $85,000; low: $500).
Fields of interest: Judaism; Human services.
Limitations: Applications not accepted. Giving primarily in CA and NY. No grants to individuals.
Application information: Contributes only to pre-selected organizations.
Officers: Amos Wilnai, Pres.; Ruth Wilnai, V.P. and Secy.-Treas.; Nitzan Wilnai, V.P.; Sigal Wilnai-Tzoore, V.P.; Yael Wilnai-Ziskind, V.P.
EIN: 204839728

1186
The Wilson Family Foundation Inc.
11150 Santa Monica Blvd., Ste. 760
Los Angeles, CA 90025-3392

Established in 2006 in California.
Donors: Margaret Bloomfield; Robert S. Wilson.
Foundation type: Independent foundation.
Financial data (yr. ended 12/31/13): Assets, $282,645 (M); expenditures, $162,260; qualifying distributions, $161,000; giving activities include $161,000 for 4 grants (high: $100,000; low: $15,000).
Fields of interest: Education; Higher education.
Limitations: Applications not accepted. Giving primarily in Los Angeles, CA. No grants to individuals.
Application information: Contributes only to pre-selected organizations.
Officers: Robert S. Wilson, Pres.; Marion L. Wilson, Secy.; Dennis C. Wilson, Treas.
Trustees: David S. Wilson; Gregory S. Wilson; Richard A. Wilson; Thomas B. Wilson.
EIN: 205982816

1187
Winiarski Family Foundation
P.O. Box 3327
Yountville, CA 94599-3327

Established in 2007 in California.
Donors: Warren Winiarski; Barbara Winiarski.
Foundation type: Independent foundation.
Financial data (yr. ended 12/31/13): Assets, $20,030,855 (M); expenditures, $525,503; qualifying distributions, $347,238; giving activities include $338,300 for 21 grants (high: $100,000; low: $500).
Fields of interest: Land resources.

Limitations: Applications not accepted. Giving primarily in CA. No grants to individuals.
Application information: Contributes only to pre-selected organizations.
Officers: Warren Winiarski, Pres.; Barbara Winiarski, Secy.-Treas.
EIN: 260474242

1188
Margo and Irwin Winkler Charitable Foundation
11812 San Vicente Blvd., No. 200
Los Angeles, CA   90049-6622

Established in 1998 in California.
Donors: Margo Winkler; Irwin Winkler.
Foundation type: Independent foundation.
Financial data (yr. ended 12/31/13): Assets, $1,095,561 (M); expenditures, $302,832; qualifying distributions, $301,367; giving activities include $301,367 for 49 grants (high: $67,500; low: $50).
Fields of interest: Ballet; Orchestral music; Education; Out-patient medical care; Family planning; Diseases and conditions; Film and video; Judaism; Child welfare; Women's services.
Type of support: Research; Research and evaluation.
Limitations: Applications not accepted. No grants to individuals.
Application information: Contributes only to pre-selected organizations.
Officers: Margo Winkler, Pres. and Treas.; Irwin Winkler, V.P.
EIN: 954688928

1189
Thomas P. Winn Foundation
3001 I St., Ste. 300
Sacramento, CA   95816-8308

Established in 1991 in California.
Donors: Thomas P. Winn; W.M. Corp.
Foundation type: Independent foundation.
Financial data (yr. ended 12/31/14): Assets, $7,495,047; expenditures, $412,092; qualifying distributions, $356,636.
Fields of interest: Education; Environment; Catholicism; Human services; Child welfare; International relations.
Limitations: Applications not accepted. Giving primarily in CA. No grants to individuals.
Application information: Contributes only to pre-selected organizations.
Officer: Thomas P. Winn, Pres.
EIN: 680244296

1190
The Withim Foundation
17801 Cartwright Rd.
Irvine, CA   92614-6216

Donors: Phillip Chang; Michelle Chang.
Foundation type: Independent foundation.
Financial data (yr. ended 12/31/12): Assets, $112,149 (M); gifts received, $7,580; expenditures, $127,596; qualifying distributions, $127,596; giving activities include $122,100 for 18 grants (high: $19,400; low: $1,000).
Fields of interest: Religion.

Limitations: Applications not accepted. Giving primarily in CA.
Application information: Unsolicited requests for funds not acceped.
Officers: Phillip Chang, Pres.; Michelle Chang, Secy.
EIN: 271491723

1191
Bernard E. & Alba Witkin Charitable Foundation
P.O. Box 7190
Berkeley, CA   94707-0190
Contact: Kenneth Kuchman, Secy.

Established in 2003 in California.
Donor: Alba Witkin†.
Foundation type: Independent foundation.
Financial data (yr. ended 12/31/13): Assets, $505 (M); gifts received, $400,000; expenditures, $402,340; qualifying distributions, $400,215; giving activities include $396,000 for 42 grants (high: $40,000; low: $2,000).
Purpose and activities: Giving primarily for children, youth and social services.
Fields of interest: Education; Human services; Family services; Child welfare; Youth organizing.
Limitations: Applications not accepted. Giving primarily in CA. No grants to individuals.
Application information: Contributes only to pre-selected organizations.
Officers: Kenneth Kuchman, Secy.; Laurence E. Lange, Treas.
Board Members: Lisa Karplus; Hon. Lawrence O'Neill; Sue Supple.
EIN: 731661679

1192
The Robert W. Witter Family Foundation
501 Crocker Rd.
Sacramento, CA   95864-5607

Established in 1997 in California.
Foundation type: Independent foundation.
Financial data (yr. ended 12/31/13): Assets, $6,267,472 (M); expenditures, $351,864; qualifying distributions, $300,000; giving activities include $300,000 for 4 grants (high: $200,000; low: $25,000).
Fields of interest: Higher education; Business education; American football.
Limitations: Applications not accepted. Giving primarily in CA. No grants to individuals.
Application information: Unsolicited requests for funds not accepted.
Officers: Robert Witter, Jr., C.E.O.; Richard Witter, C.F.O.
Directors: David Witter; Margot Witter.
EIN: 911801754

1193
The Barbara A. and Thomas F. Wolfe Foundation Inc.
c/o Calegari & Morris
123 Mission St., 18th Fl.
San Francisco, CA   94105-1551

Established in 1994 in California.
Donors: Barbara A. Wolfe; Thomas F. Wolfe.
Foundation type: Independent foundation.

Financial data (yr. ended 07/31/14): Assets, $6,652,115 (M); gifts received, $10,446; expenditures, $250,476; qualifying distributions, $233,203; giving activities include $225,000 for 3 grants (high: $150,000; low: $25,000).
Fields of interest: Higher education; Youth organizing.
Type of support: General support.
Limitations: Applications accepted. Giving primarily in CA, NY, and VA. No grants to individuals.
Application information: Application form required.
Initial approach: Letter
Deadline(s): None
Officer and Directors: Barbara A. Wolfe, Secy. and Director; Thomas F. Wolfe.
EIN: 943215896

1194
Wong & Cheng Family Foundation
14594 Sobey Oaks Ct.
Saratoga, CA   95070-6143

Established in 2006 in California.
Donors: Jimmy Shingfai Wong; Angela Kamling Cheng.
Foundation type: Independent foundation.
Financial data (yr. ended 11/30/13): Assets, $0 (M); gifts received, $100,000; expenditures, $361,467; qualifying distributions, $365,865; giving activities include $265,842 for 7 grants (high: $113,256; low: $325).
Fields of interest: Education; University education; Human services.
International interests: China.
Limitations: Applications not accepted. Giving primarily in CA, NY and PA; with some giving in China. No grants to individuals.
Application information: Unsolicited requests for funds not accepted.
Officers: Jimmy Shingfai Wong, Pres.; Angela Kamling Cheng, Secy.
EIN: 208034621

1195
Woo Education Foundation
767 N. Hill St., Ste. 402
Los Angeles, CA   90012-2894

Established in 2007 in California.
Donor: Helen Woo.
Foundation type: Independent foundation.
Financial data (yr. ended 12/31/13): Assets, $766 (M); gifts received, $239,500; expenditures, $243,379; qualifying distributions, $241,400; giving activities include $241,400 for 10 grants (high: $36,500; low: $10,000).
Fields of interest: Education; University education.
International interests: China.
Type of support: Individual development.
Limitations: Applications not accepted. Giving primarily in Lanzhou, Gansu, China.
Application information: Unsolicited requests for funds not accepted.
Officers: Helen Woo, Pres.; Daniel Chu, C.F.O.; Zheng Li, V.P.; Yanling Ma, Secy.
EIN: 260549410

1196
World Impact Foundation
20418 Seaboard Rd.
Malibu, CA   90265-5350

Foundation type: Independent foundation.
Financial data (yr. ended 12/31/14): Assets, $3,572,797; expenditures, $146,992; qualifying distributions, $136,884.
Fields of interest: International development.
Limitations: Applications not accepted.
Application information: Unsolicited Requests for funds not accepted.
Officers: Sara Agha, Pres.; Jaffar H. Agha, C.F.O; Hassnain Agha, V.P.; Adnan Merchant, Secy.
EIN: 453265116

1197
Susan & Bruce Worster Foundation
11271 Magdalena Rd.
Los Altos Hills, CA   94024

Established in 2000 in California.
Donors: Bruce Worster; Susan Worster.
Foundation type: Independent foundation.
Financial data (yr. ended 12/31/13): Assets, $6,183,177 (M); expenditures, $490,639; qualifying distributions, $429,993; giving activities include $425,000 for 4 grants (high: $275,000; low: $25,000).
Fields of interest: Higher education; Nonprofits.
Type of support: Regranting.
Limitations: Applications not accepted. Giving primarily in CA. No grants to individuals.
Application information: Contributes only to pre-selected organizations.
Officers: Bruce Worster, Pres.; Susan Worster, Secy.
EIN: 770549392

1198
Wrather Family Foundation
(formerly J. D. & Mazie Wrather Foundation)
c/o Ellis, Bristol, Harmon & Marsh
14310 Ventura Blvd., 2nd Fl.
Sherman Oaks, CA   91423-2738

Foundation type: Independent foundation.
Financial data (yr. ended 12/31/13): Assets, $4,788,084 (M); expenditures, $195,053; qualifying distributions, $174,341; giving activities include $168,500 for 23 grants (high: $20,000; low: $500).
Purpose and activities: Giving primarily for health care, including a substance abuse treatment center, as well as for education, medical research, and human services.
Fields of interest: Arts and culture; Education; Higher education; Nonprofits; Health; Hospital care; Substance abuse treatment; Cancers; Human services; Family services; Child welfare.
Type of support: Regranting.
Limitations: Applications not accepted. Giving primarily in CA and PA. No grants to individuals.
Application information: Unsolicited requests for funds not accepted.
Officers and Directors: Christopher C. Wrather, Pres.; Linda W. Finocchiaro, V.P. and Director; Gerald L. Weisberger, Secy.; Molly W. Dolle, Treas. and Director.
EIN: 956100110

1199
The Lilian Wren Foundation
c/o Seiler LLP
220 Montgomery St., Ste. 300
San Francisco, CA   94104-3436

Established in 2005 in California.
Donor: John P. Barabino.
Foundation type: Independent foundation.
Financial data (yr. ended 12/31/13): Assets, $5,596,134; gifts received, $0; expenditures, $387,772; qualifying distributions, $350,000 and $0 for set-asides.
Fields of interest: Foundations; HIV/AIDS; LGBTQ people.
Type of support: Equal access.
Limitations: Applications not accepted. Giving primarily in Los Angeles, CA, New York, NY and Holladay, UT. No grants to individuals.
Application information: Contributes only to pre-selected organizations.
Directors: John P. Barabino; David Huebner.
EIN: 203355798

1200
Writer Family Foundation
1510 Monte Vista Rd.
Santa Barbara, CA   93108-1015   (805) 565-3936
Contact: George S. Writer, Pres. and Treas.
E-mail: writergeo@gmail.com

Established in 2003 in Colorado.
Donor: George S. Writer.
Foundation type: Independent foundation.
Financial data (yr. ended 12/31/13): Assets, $147,261 (M); gifts received, $99,045; expenditures, $172,198; qualifying distributions, $169,500; giving activities include $169,500 for 21 grants (high: $50,000; low: $1,000).
Fields of interest: Arts and culture; Maritime museums; Education; Environment.
Type of support: General support.
Limitations: Applications accepted. Giving primarily in CA and CO.
Application information: Application form required.
   Initial approach: Proposal
   Deadline(s): None
Officers: George S. Writer, Pres. and Treas.; Jeffrey H. Writer, V.P.; Judith H. Writer, Secy.
Number of staff: None.
EIN: 200275156

1201
Yen Chuang Foundation
(formerly Yen Chuang Charitable Corporation)
1247 Elko Dr.
Sunnyvale, CA   94089-2211   (408) 474-1769
Contact: Yung Tsai Yen, Pres.

Established in 1984 in California.
Donors: Yung-Tsai Yen; Ho-Tzu Yen.
Foundation type: Independent foundation.
Financial data (yr. ended 11/30/13): Assets, $4,356,390 (M); gifts received, $531,938; expenditures, $187,929; qualifying distributions, $182,899; giving activities include $180,187 for 34 grants (high: $50,000; low: $42).
Purpose and activities: Giving primarily for cultural, scientific and educational endeavors.

Fields of interest: Arts and culture; Education; Higher education; Health; Reproductive health care; Family planning; Sexual education; Sexually transmitted disease control; Radio; Crime prevention; Domestic violence; Leadership development; Human rights; Parent education; Children; People of Asian descent.
Type of support: General support; Loans to individuals; Student aid; Public engagement and education; Policy, advocacy and systems reform.
Limitations: Applications accepted. Giving primarily in San Francisco, CA, CO, Washington, DC, and Chicago, IL and NY.
Application information:
   Initial approach: Proposal
   Deadline(s): None
Officers: Yung Tsai Yen, Pres.; Ho Tzu Yen, Secy.; Sophia Yen, Treas.
EIN: 770071175

1202
The Don Yoder Foundation
1340 Riebli Rd.
Santa Rosa, CA   95404-1034

Established in 1998 in California.
Donor: Patricia R. Yoder.
Foundation type: Independent foundation.
Financial data (yr. ended 08/31/14): Assets, $5,482,773 (M); gifts received, $20; qualifying distributions, $219,000; giving activities include $219,000 for 20 grants (high: $80,000; low: $150).
Fields of interest: Ballet; Education; Hospital care; Cancers; Christianity; Human services.
Limitations: Applications not accepted. Giving primarily in CA. No grants to individuals.
Application information: Unsolicited requests for funds not accepted.
Officers: Judy Yoder Badgley, Pres.; Coleman Badgley, V.P.; Debora Lee, Secy.; Allison Badgley, Corr. Secy.; Pamela Yoder, C.F.O.; Megan Lee, Treas.
EIN: 330771627

1203
Takeo Yuki Charitable Trust
P.O. Box 567
Los Gatos, CA   95031-0567

Donors: Miyoko Yuki; Miyoko Yuki 2008 Non Grantor Charitable Trust; Miyoko Yuki Charitable Lead Trust.
Foundation type: Independent foundation.
Financial data (yr. ended 03/31/13): Assets, $4,496,473 (M); gifts received, $588,356; expenditures, $216,744; qualifying distributions, $175,000; giving activities include $175,000 for 2 grants (high: $100,000; low: $75,000).
Fields of interest: Museums; Higher education; Buddhism.
Type of support: General support; Capital and infrastructure; Endowments; Scholarships.
Limitations: Applications not accepted. Giving primarily in CA. No grants to individuals.
Application information: Unsolicited requests for funds not accepted.
Trustees: Herbert T. Yuki; Thomas M. Yuki.
EIN: 942558692

1204
Zabala Family Foundation
c/o Kearley Green
University of San Francisco, Bus. and Fin., LM 142
2130 Fulton St.
San Francisco, CA 94117-1080 (415) 422-6602

Donor: Luis Zabala, Sr.
Foundation type: Independent foundation.
Financial data (yr. ended 12/31/13): Assets, $4,589,578 (M); expenditures, $204,367; qualifying distributions, $200,000; giving activities include $200,000 for 1 grant.
Fields of interest: University education.
Type of support: Scholarships.
Limitations: Applications accepted. Giving primarily in San Francisco, CA. No grants to individuals.
Application information: Application form required.
  Initial approach: Proposal
  Deadline(s): Jun. 15
Trustees: Charles E. Cross; Donna Davis; Fr. Daniell Kendall; John Koeplin; Tom Lucas.
EIN: 946079348

1205
Zacky Family Foundation
11900 W. Olympic Blvd., Ste. 650
Los Angeles, CA 90064-1046

Foundation type: Independent foundation.
Financial data (yr. ended 12/31/12): Assets, $2,268,819 (M); expenditures, $433,169; qualifying distributions, $407,715; giving activities include $407,715 for 7 grants (high: $132,115; low: $100).
Fields of interest: Health; Judaism; Youth development.
Limitations: Applications not accepted. Giving primarily in CA.
Application information: Unsolicited requests for funds not accepted.
Officers: Lillian Zacky, Pres.; Patricia Jaffee, Secy.
Trustees: Joe Ruby; Marshall Sachs.
EIN: 954812261

1206
Zacky Family Foundation Inc.
11900 W. Olympic Blvd.
Los Angeles, CA 90064

Foundation type: Independent foundation.
Financial data (yr. ended 12/31/13): Assets, $2,145,216 (M); expenditures, $217,715; qualifying distributions, $188,175; giving activities include $188,175 for 9 grants (high: $112,175; low: $2,500).
Fields of interest: Education; Health; Religion.
Type of support: Building and renovations.
Limitations: Applications not accepted. Giving primarily in CA.
Application information: Unsolicited requests for funds not accepted.
Officers: Lillian Zacky, Pres.; Patricia Jaffee, Secy.
Trustees: Joe Ruby; Marshall Sachs.
EIN: 460550263

1207
Zafiropoulo Family Foundation
c/o Blanding, Boyer & Rockwell
1340 Treat Blvd., Ste. 525
Walnut Creek, CA 94597-7984
Contact: Arthur Zafiropoulo

Established in 1994 in California.
Donors: Arthur Zafiropoulo; Lisa Cooper.
Foundation type: Independent foundation.
Financial data (yr. ended 12/31/13): Assets, $3,490,633 (M); expenditures, $230,390; qualifying distributions, $230,350; giving activities include $230,000 for 3 grants (high: $150,000; low: $30,000).
Fields of interest: Orchestral music; Undergraduate education; Pediatrics; Cancers; Human services; Child welfare.
Type of support: General support.
Limitations: Applications not accepted. Giving primarily in CA. No grants to individuals.
Application information: Unsolicited requests for funds not accepted.
Officers: Arthur Zafiropoulo, Pres.; Lisa Cooper, Secy.-Treas.
EIN: 680344787

1208
The Kenneth Zankel Foundation
333 Grant Ave., Ste. 704
San Francisco, CA 94108-3657

Established in 2005 in California.
Donor: Arthur Zankel†.
Foundation type: Independent foundation.
Financial data (yr. ended 12/31/13): Assets, $12,078,692 (M); expenditures, $625,810; qualifying distributions, $461,816; giving activities include $391,000 for 27 grants (high: $40,000; low: $1,000).
Fields of interest: Diseases and conditions; Human services; Child welfare.
Limitations: Applications not accepted. Giving primarily in CA, NJ, and New York, NY. No grants to individuals.
Application information: Contributes only to pre-selected organizations.
Trustee: Kenneth Zankel.
EIN: 206667302

1209
The Christine Zecca Foundation
c/o Christine Zecca
5 Marion Ave.
Sausalito, CA 94965-2521

Established in 1997 in California.
Foundation type: Independent foundation.
Financial data (yr. ended 12/31/13): Assets, $2,149,542 (M); expenditures, $324,100; qualifying distributions, $300,500; giving activities include $212,500 for 10 grants (high: $10,000; low: $2,500), and $88,000 for 2 grants to individuals (high: $85,000; low: $3,000).
Purpose and activities: Giving primarily for human services and the arts; funding also for education and health.
Fields of interest: Arts and culture; Education; Health; Film and video; Human services.
Type of support: General support; Student aid.

Limitations: Applications not accepted. Giving primarily in CA.
Application information: Unsolicited requests for funds not accepted.
Officers: Christine Zecca, Pres.; Judith Arago, Secy.
EIN: 943265224

1210
Ruth/Allen Ziegler Foundation
c/o Gumbiner Savett
1723 Cloverfield Blvd.
Santa Monica, CA 90404-4007

Established in 1986 in California.
Donors: Allen S. Ziegler; Ruth B. Ziegler.
Foundation type: Independent foundation.
Financial data (yr. ended 11/30/14): Assets, $7,057,995 (M); expenditures, $331,880; qualifying distributions, $325,500; giving activities include $325,500 for 43 grants (high: $20,000; low: $1,000).
Purpose and activities: Funding primarily for Jewish organizations, as well as children, youth, and social services, including services for people who are blind.
Fields of interest: Nonprofits; Judaism; Human services; Child welfare.
Type of support: Regranting.
Limitations: Applications not accepted. Giving primarily in CA. No grants to individuals.
Application information: Contributes only to pre-selected organizations.
Trustees: Richard Corleto, Esq.; David Rose; Ronald Ziegler; Ruth B. Ziegler.
EIN: 954113690

1211
Harold & Libby Ziff Foundation
c/o Rina Accountancy Corp.
475 14th St., Ste. 1200
Oakland, CA 94612

Established in 1991 in California.
Donors: Harold Ziff; Libby Ziff.
Foundation type: Independent foundation.
Financial data (yr. ended 12/31/13): Assets, $3,154,241 (M); expenditures, $316,837; qualifying distributions, $289,184; giving activities include $287,000 for 6 grants (high: $191,000; low: $1,000).
Fields of interest: Judaism; Human services; Child welfare.
Limitations: Applications not accepted. Giving limited to CA and NY. No grants to individuals.
Application information: Contributes only to pre-selected organizations.
Directors: Emma Sarnet; Lela Z. Sarnat.
EIN: 952383366

1212
Max & Pauline Zimmer Family Foundation
1880 Century Park E., Ste. 613
Los Angeles, CA 90067-1622

Established in 1951 in California.
Donor: Max Zimmer.
Foundation type: Independent foundation.
Financial data (yr. ended 05/31/14): Assets, $4,909,460 (M); expenditures, $566,733; qualifying distributions, $434,000; giving activities

include $431,000 for 25 grants (high: $109,000; low: $500).

Purpose and activities: Giving primarily for higher education and Jewish agencies and temples.

Fields of interest: Orchestral music; Museums; Higher education; Judaism.

Limitations: Applications not accepted. Giving primarily in CA and NY. No grants to individuals.

Application information: Contributes only to pre-selected organizations.

Officers: Jonathan Flier, Pres.; Edith Flier, Secy.; Ruth Lieberman, Treas.

Directors: David Z. Krems; Charles Lieberman.

EIN: 956097374

1213
Joan Zimmerman, Jason and Jordan Sills Foundation
1929 Van Ness Ave.
San Francisco, CA 94109-3007

Established in 2007 in California.

Donors: Edward & Marion Goodman Foundation; Joan Goodman Davis.

Foundation type: Independent foundation.

Financial data (yr. ended 12/31/13): Assets, $1,053,709 (M); gifts received, $96,807; expenditures, $187,148; qualifying distributions, $179,123; giving activities include $179,123 for 13 + grants (high: $68,313).

Fields of interest: Arts and culture; Religion; Judaism; Human services.

Limitations: Applications not accepted. Giving primarily in CA. No grants to individuals.

Application information: Unsolicited requests for funds not accepted.

Directors: Jason Sills; Jordan Sills; Joan Goodman Zimmerman.

EIN: 205812630

1214
Arthur & Charlotte Zitrin Foundation
333 Green St.
San Francisco, CA 94133-4103

Donors: Arthur Zitrin; Charlotte Zitrin.

Foundation type: Independent foundation.

Financial data (yr. ended 10/31/13): Assets, $5,380,214 (M); expenditures, $327,210; qualifying distributions, $324,934; giving activities include $309,614 for 72 grants (high: $155,000; low: $100).

Fields of interest: Higher education; Medical education; Law.

Limitations: Applications not accepted. Giving primarily in CA and NY.

Application information: Unsolicited requests for funds not accepted.

Officer: Richard Zitrin, Pres.

EIN: 264299156

1215
Zitrustin Foundation
c/o WDJ & Co., CPAs, LLP
595 Market St., Ste. 1450
San Francisco, CA 94105-2830 (415) 824-5974
Contact: Elizabeth Zitrin, Pres.

Donor: Charlotte Zitrin.

Foundation type: Independent foundation.

Financial data (yr. ended 12/31/13): Assets, $6,669,653 (M); gifts received, $1,082,853; expenditures, $278,936; qualifying distributions, $239,292; giving activities include $239,292 for 28 + grants (high: $112,500).

Fields of interest: Arts and culture; Education; Higher education; Judaism.

Limitations: Applications accepted. Giving primarily in CA and New York, NY.

Application information:
Initial approach: Letter
Deadline(s): None

Officer: Elizabeth Zitrin, Pres.

EIN: 264650967

1216
Zolla Family Foundation
2525 Ocean Park Blvd., Ste. 216
Santa Monica, CA 90405-5216 (310) 399-7333
Contact: Susan Zolla, Pres.

Established in 2001 in California.

Donors: Edward M. Zolla†; Susan Zolla; Charles Larsen; Nancy Updegrave; Patrick Bezdek; Lynda Bezdek.

Foundation type: Independent foundation.

Financial data (yr. ended 12/31/13): Assets, $6,139,637 (M); gifts received, $58,906; expenditures, $374,990; qualifying distributions, $289,428; giving activities include $267,543 for 31 grants (high: $25,000; low: $500).

Purpose and activities: Giving primarily for education and the arts. Also grants scholarship awards to students from Los Angeles, California, pursuing a higher education; some scholarships set aside for employees and dependents of employees of Packaging Advantage Corp. under the "PAC Team Scholarship Program".

Fields of interest: Arts and culture; Opera; Education.

Type of support: General support; Scholarships; Student aid.

Limitations: Applications accepted. Giving primarily in Los Angeles, CA.

Application information: Application form required.
Initial approach: Completed application form

Deadline(s): Nov. 15
Board meeting date(s): Quarterly

Officers and Directors: Susan Zolla, Pres. and Director; Allissa Zolla Bartle, V.P. and Director; Erik Neandross, Secy. and Director; Joseph Hurwich, C.F.O. and Director; Peter Bartle; Miriam Zolla Neandross; Anne Zolla.

Number of staff: None.

EIN: 522365200

1217
The Gwladys and John Zurlo Charitable Foundation
c/o Given Co.
3029 Wilshire Blvd., No. 200
Santa Monica, CA 90403-2364

Established in 2001 in California.

Donor: Gwladys Zurlo†.

Foundation type: Independent foundation.

Financial data (yr. ended 05/31/13): Assets, $6,154,678 (M); expenditures, $296,997; qualifying distributions, $247,983; giving activities include $240,000 for 18 grants (high: $30,000; low: $1,200).

Fields of interest: Education; Environment; Health; Hospital care; Fire prevention and control; Christianity; Child welfare.

Limitations: Applications not accepted. Giving primarily in CA and OR. No grants to individuals.

Application information: Contributes only to pre-selected organizations.

Officers: Robert H. Given, Pres.; Suzi Given, Secy.

EIN: 957120701

1218
The Zwick Foundation Inc
1933 Cliff Dr., Ste. 26
Santa Barbara, CA 93109-1520

Established in 1994 in New Jersey.

Donor: Nicholas Zwick.

Foundation type: Independent foundation.

Financial data (yr. ended 12/31/13): Assets, $559,714 (M); expenditures, $284,582; qualifying distributions, $273,680; giving activities include $270,590 for 9 grants (high: $83,940; low: $200).

Fields of interest: Undergraduate education; Diseases and conditions; Basketball; Golf; Human services.

Limitations: Applications not accepted. Giving primarily in CA. No grants to individuals.

Application information: Contributes only to pre-selected organizations.

Officers: Nicholas Zwick, Pres.; Kathryn Gibler-Zwick, V.P.; Melanie Zwick, Secy.-Treas.

EIN: 223349583

COLORADO

1219
6/S Foundation
1755 Shy Cir.
Westcliffe, CO 81252-1348

Established in 1998 in Nebraska.
Donors: Audrey M. Stermer; Richard A. Stermer.
Foundation type: Independent foundation.
Financial data (yr. ended 06/30/14): Assets, $2,339,411 (M); expenditures, $156,148; qualifying distributions, $139,569; giving activities include $135,000 for 4 grants (high: $40,000; low: $5,000).
Fields of interest: Natural resources; Human services; Family services; Child welfare.
Limitations: Applications not accepted. Giving primarily in CO and Baltimore, MD. No grants to individuals.
Application information: Unsolicited requests for funds not accepted.
Officers and Directors: Richard A. Stermer, Pres. and Director; Audrey M. Stermer, V.P. and Director; Patricia M. Dunn, Secy.-Treas. and Director; Lisa A. Freeseman; Katherine E. Schulze; Richard C. Stermer.
EIN: 841457491

1220
James C. Allen Charitable Foundation
P.O. Box 1619
Edwards, CO 81632-1619

Established in 1995 in Colorado.
Donor: James C. Allen.
Foundation type: Independent foundation.
Financial data (yr. ended 12/31/14): Assets, $3,260,685 (M); expenditures, $210,406; qualifying distributions, $191,652; giving activities include $167,781 for 84 grants (high: $8,000; low: $100).
Purpose and activities: Giving primarily for education, human services, and religion.
Fields of interest: Arts and culture; Education; Nonprofits; Health care clinics; Community and economic development; Religion; Christianity; Human services.
Type of support: General support; Regranting.
Limitations: Applications not accepted. Giving primarily in CA and CO. No grants to individuals.
Application information: Contributes only to pre-selected organizations.
Officers: Matthew Allen, Pres. and Treas.; Barbara Allen, V.P. and Secy.
EIN: 841331519

1221
Andrews Family Foundation
P.O. Box 6637
Snowmass Village, CO 81615-6637

Established in 2004 in Colorado.
Donors: Karen E. Andrews; Harry C. Andrews.
Foundation type: Independent foundation.
Financial data (yr. ended 06/30/13): Assets, $3,952,895 (M); gifts received, $150,000; expenditures, $215,537; qualifying distributions, $185,300; giving activities include $185,300 for 19 grants (high: $86,000; low: $250).
Fields of interest: Education.
Limitations: Applications not accepted. No grants to individuals.
Application information: Unsolicited requests for funds not accepted.
Directors: Harry C. Andrews; Karen E. Andrews.
EIN: 200368768

1222
The Arches Foundation
1150 River Dr.
Aspen, CO 81611-3008

Established in 2003 in Colorado.
Donor: Sara Ransford.
Foundation type: Independent foundation.
Financial data (yr. ended 12/31/13): Assets, $4,470,799 (M); gifts received, $11,599; expenditures, $252,230; qualifying distributions, $212,850; giving activities include $212,850 for 68 grants (high: $50,000; low: $200).
Purpose and activities: Giving to organizations dedicated to preserving natural resources and promoting arts, education, and civil rights.
Fields of interest: Arts and culture; Education; Environment; Domesticated animals; Human rights; Human services.
Type of support: General support.
Limitations: Applications not accepted. Giving primarily in CO.
Application information: Unsolicited requests for funds not accepted.
Officer: Sara Ransford, Pres.
EIN: 460468960

1223
Arrowhead Foundation, Inc.
P.O. Box 6431
Snowmass Village, CO 81615-6431

Established in 1988 in Connecticut.
Donors: Thomas E. O'Connor; Janet O'Conor.
Foundation type: Independent foundation.
Financial data (yr. ended 12/31/14): Assets, $4,616,488; expenditures, $267,844; qualifying distributions, $188,782.
Fields of interest: Arts and culture; Education.
Limitations: Applications not accepted. No grants to individuals.
Application information: Unsolicited requests for funds not accepted.
Officers and Directors: Thomas E. O'Connor, Pres. and Director; Janet M. O'Connor, Secy. and Director; Christopher E. O'Connor.
EIN: 223118157

1224
The Arsenault Family Foundation, Inc.
371 Centennial Pkwy., Ste. 200
Louisville, CO 80027-9440

Established in 2000 in Colorado.
Donors: Marcel J.C. Arsenault; Cynda Arsenault; John Arsenault.
Foundation type: Independent foundation.
Financial data (yr. ended 12/31/13): Assets, $10,930,430 (M); gifts received, $500; expenditures, $929,279; qualifying distributions, $511,476; giving activities include $295,000 for 18 grants (high: $75,000; low: $1,000), and $131,000 for 3 loans/program-related investments.
Fields of interest: Higher education; Human services; International peace and security.
Limitations: Applications not accepted. Giving primarily in NY; funding also in CO, Washington, DC, and Portland, OR. No grants to individuals.
Application information: Unsolicited requests for funds not accepted.
Officers: Marcel J.C. Arsenault, Pres.; Sharon K. Eshima, V.P. and Secy.; Cynda Collins Arsenault, V.P.; John F.C. Arsenault, Treas.
EIN: 841569419

1225
Lev Avoth Foundation
1888 Sherman St., Ste. 600
Denver, CO 80203-1160

Established in 2006 in New York.
Donors: Isaac Grossman; Dena Grossman.
Foundation type: Independent foundation.
Financial data (yr. ended 04/30/13): Assets, $2,851,979 (M); gifts received, $361,027; expenditures, $242,076; qualifying distributions, $239,500; giving activities include $239,500 for 14 grants (high: $94,000; low: $500).
Fields of interest: Judaism.
Limitations: Applications not accepted. Giving primarily in NY. No grants to individuals.
Application information: Unsolicited requests for funds not accepted.
Officer: Isaac Grossman, Pres.
Trustee: Dena Grossman.
EIN: 204819340

1226
Ballantine Family Fund
(formerly Ballantine Family Charitable Fund)
162 Stewart St.
Durango, CO 81303-7999 (970) 385-2440
Contact: Nancy Whitson, Exec. Dir.
FAX: (970) 797-6376;
E-mail: grant@ballantinefamilyfund.com; Main
URL: http://www.ballantinefamilyfund.com

Established in 1957 in Colorado.
Donor: Morley C. Ballantine.
Foundation type: Independent foundation.
Financial data (yr. ended 12/31/13): Assets, $4,541,333 (M); expenditures, $281,183; qualifying distributions, $276,507; giving activities include $242,510 for 103 grants (high: $10,000; low: $500).
Fields of interest: Arts and culture; Education; Foundations; Human services.
Type of support: General support; Continuing support; Capital and infrastructure; Land acquisitions; Research.
Limitations: Applications accepted. Giving primarily in CO. No grants to individuals.
Publications: Application guidelines; Annual report.
Application information: Application guidelines available on Fund web site. Application form required.
> *Copies of proposal: 1*
> *Deadline(s): July 1*
> *Board meeting date(s): Feb., May, Aug., and Nov.*

Officers: Richard G. Ballantine, Pres.; Elizabeth Ballantine, V.P.; Mary Jane Clark, Secy.; Helen B. Healy, Treas.; Nancy Whitson, Exec. Dir.
Directors: Christopher Ballantine; David Ballantine; Morley Healy; Joe Keck; Sarah Leavitt; William Leavitt.
EIN: 846026270

1227
Bardsley Foundation
(formerly The Peter & Betsy Luce Family Fund)
2400 E. Cherry Creek S. Dr.
Denver, CO 80209

Established in 2000 in Colorado.
Donors: Peter Paul Luce; Elizabeth Bardsley Luce.
Foundation type: Independent foundation.
Financial data (yr. ended 12/31/13): Assets, $8,068,792 (M); expenditures, $479,252; qualifying distributions, $399,050; giving activities include $399,050 for 31 grants (high: $100,000; low: $200).
Fields of interest: Arts and culture; Education; University education; Zoos; Botanical gardens; Community and economic development; Human services.
Limitations: Applications not accepted. Giving primarily in Denver, CO and IA. No grants to individuals.
Application information: Contributes only to pre-selected organizations.
Officers: Peter Paul Luce, Pres.; Elizabeth Luce, Secy.-Treas.
EIN: 841521212

1228
The Thomas W. Bean Foundation
2608 Welton St.
Denver, CO 80205-2912 (303) 296-1340
Contact: Elvin Caldwell Jr., Pres.

Established in 1990 in Colorado.
Foundation type: Independent foundation.
Financial data (yr. ended 12/31/13): Assets, $6,804,676 (M); expenditures, $677,044; qualifying distributions, $225,128; giving activities include $160,000 for 80 grants (high: $5,000; low: $1,000).
Purpose and activities: Giving primarily for sororities and fraternities, human services, civil rights, and churches.
Fields of interest: Sororities and fraternities; Christianity; Minority rights; Human services.
Type of support: General support; Scholarships; Program evaluations.
Limitations: Applications accepted. Giving primarily in Denver, CO. No grants to individuals.
Application information: Application form required.
Initial approach: Letter
Deadline(s): None
Officers: Elvin Caldwell, Jr., Pres.; Fran Fuller, V.P.; Gaylene V. Harris, Secy.
EIN: 742552296

1229
Benson Family Foundation
c/o The Foundation Manager
1436 Shavano Ct.
Evergreen, CO 80439-9752

Established in 2002 in Colorado.
Donor: Robert S. Benson.
Foundation type: Independent foundation.
Financial data (yr. ended 12/31/13): Assets, $2,225,618 (M); gifts received, $200,000; expenditures, $302,420; qualifying distributions, $289,492; giving activities include $289,000 for 16 grants (high: $30,000; low: $10,000).
Fields of interest: Arts and culture; Higher education; Human services.
Limitations: Applications not accepted. Giving primarily in CO. No grants to individuals.
Application information: Unsolicited requests for funds not accepted.
Officers: Cynthia C. Benson, Pres.; Robert S. Benson, Treas.
Directors: Erik B. Benson; Kiersa J. Benson.
EIN: 431969687

1230
P. Bruce and Virginia C. Benson Foundation
1422 Alamo St.
Colorado Springs, CO 80907-7302

Established in 1988 in Colorado.
Donor: P. Bruce Benson†.
Foundation type: Independent foundation.
Financial data (yr. ended 06/30/13): Assets, $3,921,084 (M); expenditures, $237,803; qualifying distributions, $194,500; giving activities include $194,500 for 29 grants (high: $20,000; low: $500).
Fields of interest: Education; Elementary and secondary education; Higher education; Environment; Diseases and conditions; Human services.
Limitations: Applications not accepted. Giving primarily in CA, CO, and IL. No grants to individuals.
Application information: Contributes only to pre-selected organizations.
Officers: Lucia Dhaens, Pres.; Polly Benson-Brown, V.P.; Dave Benson, Secy.-Treas.
EIN: 841090517

1231
Sheldon K. Beren Charitable Trust
c/o Zev Beren
1888 Sherman St., Ste. 600
Denver, CO 80203-1120

Donor: Sheldon K. Beren†.
Foundation type: Independent foundation.
Financial data (yr. ended 06/30/13): Assets, $8,463,363 (M); expenditures, $342,194; qualifying distributions, $304,512; giving activities include $304,512 for 18 grants (high: $54,924; low: $1,000).
Fields of interest: Judaism.
Limitations: Applications not accepted. Giving primarily in CO, NJ and NY. No grants to individuals.
Application information: Contributes only to pre-selected organizations.
Trustees: David Beren; Zev Beren; Yechezkel Feldberger; Dena Beren Grossman.
EIN: 470862874

1232
Harry H. Beren Foundation Z.B.
c/o Zev Beren
1888 Sherman St., Ste. 600
Denver, CO 80203-1160

Foundation type: Independent foundation.
Financial data (yr. ended 12/31/13): Assets, $6,484,166 (M); expenditures, $299,202; qualifying distributions, $263,000; giving activities include $263,000 for 29 grants (high: $33,000; low: $1,000).
Fields of interest: Education; Judaism.
Limitations: Applications not accepted. Giving primarily in Denver, CO, and New York, NY. No grants to individuals.
Application information: Unsolicited requests for funds not accepted.
Officer: Zev Beren, Pres.
EIN: 201203311

1233
Harry H. Beren Foundation
c/o David Beren
1888 Sherman St., Ste. 600
Denver, CO 80203-1160

Foundation type: Independent foundation.
Financial data (yr. ended 12/31/13): Assets, $3,220,078 (M); expenditures, $188,797; qualifying distributions, $171,500; giving activities include $171,500 for 34 grants (high: $23,000; low: $500).
Fields of interest: Graduate and professional education; Judaism; Theology.
Limitations: Applications not accepted. Giving primarily in CO, NJ, NY, and OH.
Application information: Contributes only to pre-selected organizations.
Officer: David Beren, Pres.
EIN: 201203410

1234
The Ross R. and Candy L. Bhappu Family Foundation
4927 S. Fillmore Ct.
Englewood, CO 80113-7146

Donors: Candy L. Bhappu; Ross R. Bhappu.
Foundation type: Independent foundation.
Financial data (yr. ended 11/30/13): Assets, $804,131 (M); gifts received, $200,000; expenditures, $264,125; qualifying distributions, $253,400; giving activities include $253,400 for 19 grants (high: $200,000; low: $100).
Fields of interest: Education; Health; Religion.
Limitations: Applications not accepted. Giving primarily in CO.
Application information: Unsolicited requests for funds not accepted.
Officers and Directors: Ross R. Bhappu, Pres. and Director; Candy L. Bhappu, V.P. and Director; Elizabeth M. Bhappu; Katherine L. Bhappu.
EIN: 453988249

1235
Big Blue Sky Foundation
109 Shavano Dr.
Aspen, CO 81611-3358

Established in 2001 in California.
Donors: Adam Z. Cherry; Mary Catherine Cherry.
Foundation type: Independent foundation.
Financial data (yr. ended 12/31/13): Assets, $4,553,680 (M); gifts received, $99; expenditures, $352,791; qualifying distributions, $324,565; giving activities include $300,280 for 27 grants (high: $100,000; low: $250).
Fields of interest: Elementary and secondary education; Human services.
Limitations: Applications not accepted. Giving primarily in CA. No grants to individuals.
Application information: Contributes only to pre-selected organizations.
Officers and Directors: Adam Z. Cherry, Pres. and Director; Mary Catherine Cherry, C.F.O. and Secy.
EIN: 912157163

1236
The Carl George Bjorkman Foundation
c/o Philip Thomas Griffith
P.O.Box 38043
Colorado Springs, CO 80937-8043

Established in 1993 in Colorado.
Foundation type: Independent foundation.
Financial data (yr. ended 12/31/13): Assets, $3,523,656 (M); gifts received, $1,931; expenditures, $228,765; qualifying distributions, $199,305; giving activities include $181,000 for 25 grants (high: $20,000; low: $1,000).
Fields of interest: Environment; Health; Human services.
Type of support: General support; Program development.
Limitations: Applications not accepted. Giving primarily in CO.
Application information: Unsolicited requests for funds not accepted.
Officers: Drake Ewing Taylor, Pres.; Clay Dudley Taylor, V.P. and Treas.; Keith B. Stockman, Secy.
Directors: Philip Thomas Griffith; George Shepard; William Ewing Taylor.
EIN: 841236138

1237
Blair Family Foundation Inc.
12900 Stroh Ranch Way
Parker, CO 80134-7401

Established in 1998 in California.
Donors: James R. Blair; Donna R. Blair.
Foundation type: Independent foundation.
Financial data (yr. ended 12/31/13): Assets, $5,579,957 (M); gifts received, $289,307; expenditures, $280,146; qualifying distributions, $223,261; giving activities include $220,000 for 16 grants (high: $43,000; low: $1,000).
Fields of interest: Education; University education; Health; Winter sports; Human services; Youth development.
Limitations: Applications not accepted. Giving primarily in CA, CO and IL. No grants to individuals.
Application information: Contributes only to pre-selected organizations.
Officers: James R. Blair, Pres.; Steven R. Blair, C.F.O.; Ronald J. Blair, V.P.; Donna R. Blair, Secy.
EIN: 943301545

1238
Bloedorn Foundation
P.O. Box 1385
Fort Morgan, CO 80701-1385 (970) 867-2768
Contact: Jerry K. Jones, Tr.

Donors: H.B. Bloedorn†; J.H. Bloedorn†; C.F.W. Bloedorn†; A.O. Bloedorn†; W.A. Bloedorn†.
Foundation type: Independent foundation.
Financial data (yr. ended 12/31/13): Assets, $3,379,515 (M); expenditures, $196,467; qualifying distributions, $158,019; giving activities include $147,395 for 36 grants (high: $30,000; low: $200).
Purpose and activities: Giving primarily for higher education and community development.
Fields of interest: Elementary and secondary education; Higher education; Hospital care; Community and economic development; Christianity.
Type of support: General support; Scholarships.
Limitations: Applications accepted. Giving primarily in Morgan County, CO. No grants to individuals.
Application information: Application form required.
  Initial approach: Letter
  Copies of proposal: 1
  Deadline(s): None
Trustees: Jerry K. Jones; Corliss Bloedorn Littlefield; Andrew F. McClary; Donald A. Ostwald; Anna Segura.
EIN: 846025296

1239
The Sam S. Bloom Foundation
P.O. Box 2413
Littleton, CO 80161-2413 (303) 771-2266
Contact: Connie L. Crowley, Mgr.

Established in 1983 in Colorado.
Donor: Sam S. Bloom†.
Foundation type: Independent foundation.
Financial data (yr. ended 11/30/14): Assets, $10,186,438 (M); expenditures, $537,947; qualifying distributions, $444,072; giving activities include $411,000 for 66 grants (high: $30,000; low: $1,000).
Purpose and activities: Support to organizations that serve financially disadvantaged residents of Colorado. The foundation wishes to support programs designed to bring self-sufficiency to members of highly motivated at-risk populations, particularly family units with infants and young children.
Fields of interest: Early childhood education; Child educational development; Job training; Human services; Parent education.
Type of support: General support; Program development.
Limitations: Applications accepted. Giving primarily in CO. No support for religious organizations, or for healthcare programs, violence prevention programs, food distribution programs, animal rights organizations, recreational programs (including wilderness adventures or camps) residential treatment facilities for at-risk populations or substance abusers, or for care for the elderly. No grants to individuals, or for endowments, or for reserve funds, debt reduction, medical, scientific or academic research, or for multi-year funding.
Publications: Application guidelines; Annual report.
Application information: Colorado Common Grant Application form accepted. Contact foundation for complete application guidelines. Application form required.

Initial approach: Proposal
Deadline(s): May 1
Board meeting date(s): May and Oct.
Final notification: Nov.
Officers: Donald R. Jacobs, Pres.; L. Jay Labe, V.P.; Edward N. Kesselman, Secy.; A. Marvin Strait, Treas.; C. Crowley, Mgr.
Directors: Cheryl L. Caldwell; Tonie L. Gatch; Debbie Strait Gonzales; Rodger A. Hara; Sasha Jacobs-Lowry; Jon Ludwigson; JoAnn Radetsky.
Number of staff: 1 part-time professional.
EIN: 840929690

1240
The Brent Family Foundation
3105 Lafayette Dr.
Boulder, CO 80305-7112

Established in 1999 in Delaware.
Donor: Douglas B. Brent.
Foundation type: Independent foundation.
Financial data (yr. ended 12/31/13): Assets, $5,020,318 (M); expenditures, $412,489; qualifying distributions, $389,290; giving activities include $389,290 for 20 grants (high: $100,000; low: $750).
Fields of interest: Education; Hospital care; Human services.
Type of support: General support.
Limitations: Applications not accepted. Giving primarily in NY. No grants to individuals.
Application information: Contributes only to pre-selected organizations.
Officers: Douglas B. Brent, Pres.; Averil R. Brent, V.P.
EIN: 510395364

1241
Bright Mountain Foundation
(formerly The Wessell Family Foundation)
1800 Broadway, Ste. 100
Boulder, CO 80302-5234 (303) 381-2255
Contact: Irene Lopez-Wessell, Exec. Dir

Established in 1999 in Colorado.
Donors: Leonard P. Wessell III; Lee Sands; TINA.
Foundation type: Independent foundation.
Financial data (yr. ended 06/30/13): Assets, $1,673,567 (M); expenditures, $380,065; qualifying distributions, $343,855; giving activities include $161,700 for 22 grants (high: $25,000; low: $200).
Purpose and activities: The foundation is committed to programs that assist children and youth, seniors, and persons living with HIV/AIDS.
Fields of interest: Child welfare; Seniors; People with HIV/AIDS.
Type of support: Program development; Matching grants.
Limitations: Giving limited to CO. No support for religious organizations or their affiliates. No grants to individuals, or for existing scholarships, general endowments, fundraising events, annual fund drives, debt reduction, or administrative costs.
Officers: Cathy Lopez-Wessell, Exec. Dir.; Irene Lopez-Wessell, Exec. Dir.
Directors: Amy P. Wessell; Leonard P. Wessell.
Trustees: Deborah Foy; Gabriel Guillaume; Tony Tapia.
Number of staff: 2 full-time professional.
EIN: 841524099

1242
The Broomfield Community Foundation
26 Garden Ctr., Ste. 4D
P.O. Box 2040
Broomfield, CO   80038   (303) 469-7208
Contact: Karen Smith, Exec. Dir.
FAX: (303) 410-1733;
E-mail: info@broomfieldfoundation.org; Main
URL: http://www.broomfieldfoundation.org
Facebook: http://www.facebook.com/pages/
Broomfield-CO/Broomfield-Community-Foundation/
112914033437
LinkedIn: https://www.linkedin.com/company/
broomfield-community-foundation
Twitter: http://www.twitter.com/BroomfieldCF
YouTube: https://www.youtube.com/user/
BroomfieldCF

Established in 1993 in Colorado.
Foundation type: Community foundation.
Financial data (yr. ended 12/31/13): Assets,
$2,605,213 (M); gifts received, $346,331;
expenditures, $285,540; giving activities include
$165,377 for grants, and $24,500 for 14 grants to
individuals.
Purpose and activities: The Broomfield Community
Foundation's purpose is to accept contributions and
provide support through grants in the areas of civic
projects, human services, arts, humanities, seniors
and education which benefit Broomfield citizens; to
manage an endowment whose income provides
support for the grant making process; and to
educate the public and encourage community
leadership in the areas of philanthropy and
community service.
Fields of interest: Arts and culture; Humanities;
Education; Public affairs; Human services; Senior
services; Seniors.
Type of support: General support; In-kind gifts;
Matching grants; Annual campaigns; Emergency
funds; Public engagement and education;
Scholarships.
Limitations: Applications accepted. Giving limited to
Broomfield, CO. No support for sectarian religious
purposes. No grants to individuals (except for
scholarships), or for general overhead, capital
campaigns, or for trip or event sponsorship.
Publications: Application guidelines; Annual report;
Grants list; Informational brochure; Newsletter.
Application information: Visit foundation web site
for application form and guidelines. Application form
required.
   Initial approach: Letter, telephone, or e-mail
   Copies of proposal: 11
   Deadline(s): June 1
   Board meeting date(s): 3rd Thurs. of each month
   Final notification: Aug. 21
Officers and Directors: Ben Vagher, Pres. and
Director; Paula Reynolds, V.P. and Director; Bruce
Erley, Secy. and Director; Brandon Kane, Treas. and
Director; Karen Smith, Exec. Dir.; Greg Blanchard,
Emeritus; Leslee Balten; Larry Beck; Lisa Gouran;
Lisa Herman; Kevin Jacobs; Bruce Johnson; Geoff
Leopold; Dave Manley; Veralex Roda; Charlotte
Santoro; Tom Silvers.
Number of staff: 1 part-time professional; 1
part-time support.
EIN: 841246756

1243
Tim & Libby Brown Family Foundation
(formerly Tim and Libby Brown Family Foundation)
1727 Tremont Pl.
Denver, CO   80202-4006

Established in 2002 in Colorado.
Donor: The Anschutz Foundation.
Foundation type: Independent foundation.
Financial data (yr. ended 11/30/13): Assets,
$10,594 (M); gifts received, $340,000;
expenditures, $367,333; qualifying distributions,
$367,333; giving activities include $367,333 for 30
grants (high: $63,333; low: $1,500).
Fields of interest: Education; Zoos; Archives and
special collections; Child abuse.
Limitations: Applications not accepted. Giving
primarily in CO. No grants to individuals.
Application information: Contributes only to
pre-selected organizations.
Officers: Elizabeth A. Brown, Chair. and Pres.; M.
Lavoy Robison, Exec. Dir.
EIN: 460732753

1244
Nathan B. & Florence R. Burt Foundation, Inc.
1660 Lincoln St., No. 2830
Denver, CO   80264-3100   (303) 863-8980
Contact: Harry L. Arkin, Pres.
FAX: (303) 832-4703; Main URL: http://
www.burtfoundation.org

Donors: N.B. Burt†; F.R. Burt†.
Foundation type: Independent foundation.
Financial data (yr. ended 09/30/14): Assets,
$3,813,698 (M); expenditures, $283,514;
qualifying distributions, $238,578; giving activities
include $216,850 for 104 grants (high: $5,000;
low: $1,000).
Purpose and activities: Supports organizations
dealing with and affecting the needs of children and
senior citizens.
Fields of interest: Health; Geriatrics; Child welfare;
Seniors.
Type of support: General support; Matching grants;
Continuing support; Equipment; Emergency funds.
Limitations: Applications accepted. Giving primarily
in the Denver, CO metropolitan area. No support for
political organizations or for religious organizations,
except those that provide non-denominational
assistance within the foundation's fields of interest.
No grants for overhead or capital campaigns, or for
construction.
Publications: Application guidelines.
Application information: See foundation web site
for complete application guidelines. Application
form required.
   Initial approach: Use online application system on
   foundation web site
   Deadline(s): See foundation web site for current
   deadlines
   Board meeting date(s): Spring and fall
Officers and Directors: Harry L. Arkin, Chair. and
Pres. and Director; John C. Baker, V.P. and Director;
Natalie Meyer, Secy. and Director; Greg Dickson,
Treas. and Director; Margaret Fomer, MD; Harrison
F. Hayes, MD; Bruce W. Jafek, MD.
Number of staff: 1 part-time professional; 2
part-time support.
EIN: 840972203

1245
Caulkins Family Foundation
250 Steele St., Ste. 375
Denver, CO   80206-5200

Established in 1993 in Colorado.
Donors: George P. Caulkins, Jr.†; John N. Caulkins;
Mary I. Caulkins; Eleanor N. Caulkins.
Foundation type: Independent foundation.
Financial data (yr. ended 12/31/13): Assets,
$5,931,568 (M); expenditures, $341,508;
qualifying distributions, $301,500; giving activities
include $301,500 for 59 grants (high: $32,000;
low: $500).
Fields of interest: Arts and culture; Elementary and
secondary education; Natural resources; Human
services; Food aid; Child welfare; Youth services.
Limitations: Applications not accepted. Giving
primarily in CO. No grants to individuals.
Application information: Contributes only to
pre-selected organizations.
Officers: Eleanor N. Caulkins, Pres.; David I.
Caulkins, V.P.; George P. Caulkins III, V.P.; John N.
Caulkins, V.P.; Maxwell O.B. Caulkins, Secy.; Mary
I. Caulkins, Secy.
EIN: 841251441

1246
The Chotin Foundation
5675 DTC Blvd., Ste. 200
Greenwood Village, CO   80111   (303) 741-0100
Contact: Jennifer M. Land, Exec. Dir.
FAX: (303) 741-6944; E-mail: jland@chotin.com;
Additional tel.: (800) 943-008; Main URL: http://
www.chotinfoundation.org

Established in 2004 in Colorado.
Donors: Steven B. Chotin; The Chotin Group Corp.;
Cayrac Corp.
Foundation type: Company-sponsored foundation.
Financial data (yr. ended 12/31/13): Assets,
$3,052 (M); gifts received, $190,535;
expenditures, $194,469; qualifying distributions,
$190,850; giving activities include $190,850 for 99
grants (high: $20,780; low: $30).
Purpose and activities: The foundation supports
organizations involved with arts and culture,
education, health, human services, and leadership
development. Special emphasis is directed toward
Judaism and economically disadvantaged people.
Fields of interest: Education; Religion; Human
services.
Type of support: General support; Program
development; Research.
Limitations: Applications not accepted. Giving
primarily in Denver, CO. No grants to individuals.
Application information: Contributes only to
pre-selected organizations.
Officers: Nicole Brown, Secy.; Jennifer Land, Exec.
Dir.
Directors: Robin Chotin; Steven Chotin; Helen
Dickens.
EIN: 710950446

1247
The Cliffline Foundation
(formerly The Hayes Foundation)
191 University Blvd., No. 237
Denver, CO   80206-4613

Established in 1995 in Colorado.

Donors: Helen Young Hayes; Matthew S. Hayes.
Foundation type: Independent foundation.
Financial data (yr. ended 12/31/13): Assets, $6,333,780 (M); gifts received, $45,000; expenditures, $281,003; qualifying distributions, $250,000; giving activities include $250,000 for 7 grants (high: $60,000; low: $20,000).
Fields of interest: Higher education; Christianity; Human services.
Limitations: Applications not accepted. Giving primarily in CO, FL, and TX. No grants to individuals.
Application information: Contributes only to pre-selected organizations.
Officers and Board Member: Helen Young Hayes, Chair. and Treas.; Matthew S. Hayes, Pres.; Jim Tinsley, Secy. and Director.
EIN: 841343061

1248
Clough Family Foundation
c/o Ted V. Clark, C.P.A., PC
P.O. Box 930
Palisade, CO   81526-0930
Application address: c/o Stuver & Lemoine, PC, P.O. Box 907, Rifle, CO 81650, tel.: (970) 625-1887

Foundation type: Independent foundation.
Financial data (yr. ended 12/31/13): Assets, $5,667,958 (M); expenditures, $214,511; qualifying distributions, $203,950; giving activities include $203,950 for 21 grants (high: $40,000; low: $500).
Fields of interest: Undergraduate education; Animal welfare; Religion; Christianity; Human services.
Limitations: Applications accepted. Giving primarily in CO.
Application information: Application form required.
  Initial approach: Letter
  Deadline(s): None
Officers: Bonnie McKenzie, Pres.; Sharon Bistline, Secy.; S. Stormy Anderson, Treas.
Director: David Ryan McKenzie.
EIN: 264098267

1249
Comprecare Foundation
P.O. Box 740610
Arvada, CO   80006   (303) 432-2808
Contact: James R. Gilsdorf, Exec. Dir.
Main URL: http://www.comprecarefoundation.org
Grants List: http://www.comprecarefoundation.org/Grantees.html

Established in 1986 in Colorado.
Foundation type: Independent foundation.
Financial data (yr. ended 12/31/13): Assets, $4,523,948 (M); gifts received, $126,579; expenditures, $376,933; qualifying distributions, $295,453; giving activities include $236,182 for 12 grants (high: $35,000; low: $17,532).
Purpose and activities: To encourage, aid or assist specific health related programs and to support the activities of organizations and individuals who advance and promote healthcare education, the delivery of healthcare services, and the improvement of community health and welfare.
Fields of interest: Health; Mental health care; Diseases and conditions; Alcoholism; Child welfare; Senior services; Seniors.

Type of support: General support; Continuing support; Equipment; Program development; Seed money; Research.
Limitations: Giving limited to CO. No grants to individuals, or for fellowships, scholarships, operating expenses, debt reduction, land acquisition, fundraising events, or testimonial dinners or promotions.
Application information: The foundation is not considering unsolicited requests for funding until further notice. See foundation web site for current information.
  Board meeting date(s): Monthly
Officers and Directors: Dennis E. Baldwin, Chair. and Director; Milford H. Schulhof II, Vice-Chair. and Director; Frederick G. Ihrig, Secy.-Treas. and Director; James R. Gilsdorf, Exec. Dir.; Milton W. Bollman; Bradford L. Darling; Raymond C. Delisle; Ellen J. Mangione, MD; M. Eugene Sherman, MD.
Number of staff: 1 part-time professional; 1 part-time support.
EIN: 840641406

1250
John J. Connor & Irene A. Connor Family Foundation
1206 Forest St.
Denver, CO   80220

Established in 2004 in Colorado.
Donor: Robert F. Connor, Sr.
Foundation type: Independent foundation.
Financial data (yr. ended 12/31/14): Assets, $5,660,398; expenditures, $251,960; qualifying distributions, $245,070.
Fields of interest: Children's hospital care; Cancers; Catholicism; Food banks; Family services; Children.
Type of support: General support.
Limitations: Applications not accepted. Giving primarily in CO and MO. No grants to individuals.
Application information: Contributes only to pre-selected organizations.
Trustees: Christopher Connor; Claire E. Connor; John J. Connor II; Patricia A. Connor; Robert F. Connor, Jr.
EIN: 766197905

1251
The Cornerstone Foundation
8475 S. Wildcat St.
Highlands Ranch, CO   80126-2019   (303) 854-4145
Contact: Michael Littlefield, Chair.

Established in 1986 in Massachusetts.
Donors: Joseph H. Moore III; J. Christy Wilson, Jr.†; Moore Family Trust.
Foundation type: Operating foundation.
Financial data (yr. ended 10/31/13): Assets, $41 (M); gifts received, $160,766; expenditures, $171,912; qualifying distributions, $171,899; giving activities include $171,899 for 3 grants (high: $57,313; low: $57,273).
Purpose and activities: Giving to organizations that are involved in the missionary outreach of Christian churches, in the discipleship and nurturing of a local church or churches, or in the teaching, training or discipleship of Christian leaders or laity.
Fields of interest: Education; Christianity.
Limitations: Applications accepted. Giving primarily in MA and CA. No grants to individuals.

Application information: Application form required.
  Initial approach: Proposal
  Deadline(s): Varies
Officer: Michael E. Littlefield, Chair. and Director.
Trustee: Timothy C. Tennent.
EIN: 042940520

1252
Craig-Scheckman Family Foundation
P.O. Box 776429
Steamboat Springs, CO   80477-6429   (970) 879-0148
Contact: Sara Craig-Scheckman, Pres.
E-mail: admindirector@yap4rc.org; Main
URL: http://yap4rc.org
Grants List: http://yap4rc.org/wp-content/uploads/downloads/2014/12/CurrentGrantRecipientsNov14May14.pdf

Established in 2005 in Colorado.
Donors: Sara Craig-Scheckman; Michael Craig-Scheckman; Deer Park Road Corp.; STSM.
Foundation type: Independent foundation.
Financial data (yr. ended 12/31/13): Assets, $6,842,947 (M); gifts received, $1,411,701; expenditures, $586,740; qualifying distributions, $349,550; giving activities include $349,550 for 41 grants (high: $51,000; low: $250).
Fields of interest: Education; Youth development.
Limitations: Applications accepted. Giving limited to Routt County, CO. No grants to individuals.
Application information: Application form required.
  Initial approach: Letter
  Deadline(s): May 1 and Nov. 1
Officers: Sara Craig-Scheckman, Pres.; Michael Craig-Scheckman, Treas.
EIN: 202835678

1253
Creative Providers Foundation
P. O. Box 729
Divide, CO   80814-0729

Established in 2003 in Colorado.
Donor: Peter C. Kuyper.
Foundation type: Independent foundation.
Financial data (yr. ended 12/31/12): Assets, $168,057 (M); gifts received, $440,000; expenditures, $356,086; qualifying distributions, $354,497; giving activities include $354,497 for grants.
Fields of interest: Education; Religion; Human services.
Limitations: Applications not accepted. Giving primarily in CO.
Application information: Contributes only to pre-selected organizations.
Officer: Peter C. Kuyper, Pres. and Secy.-Treas.
EIN: 920192597

1254
Dea Family Foundation
1520 W. Canal Ct., Ste. 220
Littleton, CO   80120-5651

Established in 2006 in Colorado.
Donors: Peter A. Dea; Cathy Carpenter Dea.
Foundation type: Independent foundation.
Financial data (yr. ended 11/30/13): Assets, $4,502,794 (M); gifts received, $12,712;

expenditures, $302,121; qualifying distributions, $265,916; giving activities include $259,560 for 25 grants (high: $75,000; low: $200).
Fields of interest: Science museums; Animal welfare; Youth organizing.
Limitations: Applications not accepted. Giving primarily in Denver, CO. No grants to individuals.
Application information: Unsolicited requests for funds not accepted.
Officers: Peter A. Dea, Chair. and Pres.; Cathy Carpenter Dea, Secy.-Treas.
EIN: 208005948

1255
Denver Public Schools Retired Employees Association Foundation
2408 S. Utica St.
Denver, CO   80219-6402   (303) 279-0590
Contact: Bernadette Seick
E-mail: brseick@yahoo.com; Main URL: http://www.dpsrea.org

Foundation type: Independent foundation.
Financial data (yr. ended 12/31/13): Assets, $8,218,262 (M); gifts received, $17,774; expenditures, $415,615; qualifying distributions, $391,667; giving activities include $391,667 for 39 grants to individuals (high: $15,000; low: $6,667).
Fields of interest: Undergraduate education.
Type of support: Student aid.
Limitations: Applications accepted. Giving primarily in CO.
Application information: Application form required.
  Initial approach: Letter
  Deadline(s): None
Officers: Lynne Williams, Pres.; Leslie Moore, 1st V.P.; Marge Tepper, 2nd V.P.; Jane Rodish, Secy.; Pam Woods, Treas.
EIN: 841331121

1256
Nick Dewolf Foundation
P.O. Box 4540
Aspen, CO   81612-4540

Established in 2007 in Colorado.
Donor: Nicholas Dewolf†.
Foundation type: Independent foundation.
Financial data (yr. ended 12/31/12): Assets, $4,159,710 (M); expenditures, $582,687; qualifying distributions, $353,496; giving activities include $353,496 for grants.
Fields of interest: Historic preservation; Science; Television.
Type of support: Research and evaluation.
Limitations: Applications not accepted. Giving primarily in Aspen, CO. No grants to individuals.
Application information: Contributes only to pre-selected organizations.
Officers: Margaret Lee Dewolf, Pres.; Nicole Dewolf, Secy.
EIN: 201829265

1257
Donahue Foundation
P.O. Box 2554
Littleton, CO   80161-2254
Contact: Lisa A. Donahue-Goodwin, Exec. Dir.

E-mail: info@donahuefoundation.org; Main URL: http://www.donahuefoundation.org
Grants List: http://www.donahuefoundation.org/grants.html

Established in 1990 in Colorado.
Donors: William L. Donahue†; Leonice M. Donahue†.
Foundation type: Independent foundation.
Financial data (yr. ended 12/31/13): Assets, $4,608,028 (M); gifts received, $1,000; expenditures, $338,419; qualifying distributions, $309,881; giving activities include $273,985 for 13 grants (high: $109,000; low: $500).
Purpose and activities: Giving primarily for non-public and parochial school education for low-income families.
Fields of interest: Education.
Type of support: General support; Continuing support; Emergency funds; Curriculum development; Scholarships.
Limitations: Applications accepted. Giving limited to CO. No grants for capital funding, financial aid for college-level education, or for other foundations.
Publications: Application guidelines; Informational brochure.
Application information: CGA Colorado Common Grant Application accepted. See web site for application policies and guidelines. Application form required.
  Initial approach: Preliminary letter
  Copies of proposal: 1
  Deadline(s): Mar. 1
  Board meeting date(s): June
  Final notification: 10 days after meeting
Officers: Teri Goddard, Pres.; Lisa Donahue-Goodwin, Secy. and Exec. Dir.; Mark Donahue, Treas.
Directors: Greg Donahue; William P. Donahue; Rita Ochs.
Number of staff: 1 part-time professional.
EIN: 841151637

1258
Donnell-Kay Foundation, Inc.
730 17th St., No. 950
Denver, CO   80202-3599   (720) 932-1544
Contact: Carmelita Galicia-Munoz, Dir., Admin.
FAX: (303) 534-5785;
E-mail: cgaliciamunoz@dkfoundation.org; Main URL: http://www.dkfoundation.org
Facebook: https://www.facebook.com/pages/Donnell-Kay-Foundation/134013736616454?ref=search
LinkedIn: http://www.linkedin.com/company/2234127
Twitter: http://twitter.com/donnellkay

Established in 1965 in Florida.
Donor: Elizabeth D. Kay†.
Foundation type: Independent foundation.
Financial data (yr. ended 01/31/13): Assets, $27,040,533 (M); expenditures, $1,793,404; qualifying distributions, $1,622,610; giving activities include $415,000 for 30 grants (high: $35,000; low: $1,000), and $48,142 for 4 foundation-administered programs.
Purpose and activities: The foundation improves public education and drives systemic school reform in Colorado through solid research, creative dialogue, and critical thinking. Giving primarily for public school reform, higher education, and early childhood education.

Fields of interest: Education; Elementary and secondary education; Secondary education; Higher education; Education services; Child welfare; Children and youth; Children; Adolescents.
Type of support: Technical assistance; Pro bono consulting services; Fellowships; Matching grants; General support; Continuing support; Annual campaigns; Capital campaigns; Public engagement and education; Convening; Publications; Research.
Limitations: Applications not accepted. Giving primarily in CO. No support for religious or political organizations. No grants to individuals.
Publications: Newsletter; Occasional report.
Application information: Contributes only to pre-selected organizations; unsolicited applications not considered; however the foundation does accept one-page concept papers that address statewide educational policy issues.
  Board meeting date(s): Varies
Officers and Directors: Sidney A. Dines, Pres. and Treas. and Director; Allen Dines, V.P. and Director; Connie Dines, Secy. and Director; Tony Lewis, Exec. Dir.
Advisory Board: Bryan C. Hassel; Rick Hess; Michael B. Horn; Chris Sturgis.
Number of staff: 5 full-time professional; 3 part-time professional.
EIN: 596169704

1259
Dorset Foundation Inc.
34 Tanglewood Dr.
Durango, CO   81301-5849
Application address: c/o Jane Quentan Piper, 4816 Fast Fox Trl., Austin, TX 78746, tel.: (512) 328-5626

Established in 1957 in Texas.
Donor: W.S. Dorset†.
Foundation type: Independent foundation.
Financial data (yr. ended 12/31/13): Assets, $2,603,914 (M); expenditures, $226,226; qualifying distributions, $226,226; giving activities include $194,000 for 24 grants (high: $21,000; low: $500).
Purpose and activities: Giving primarily for youth and human services.
Fields of interest: Higher education; Health; Christianity; Human services; Child welfare.
Type of support: Scholarships; General support.
Limitations: Applications accepted. Giving primarily in TX. No grants to individuals, or for program-related investments.
Application information: Application form required.
  Initial approach: Letter
  Deadline(s): None
Officers: Martha Q. Sanderson, Pres.; Jane Quentan Piper, V.P.; Kay Ellen Kirby, Secy.
Board Member: Judge Jim Fallon.
EIN: 756013384

1260
DWB Family Foundation
c/o Northern Trust, Carol B. Lay
1573 Market St.
Denver, CO   80202-1607

Donor: Louann Benbow.
Foundation type: Independent foundation.
Financial data (yr. ended 12/31/13): Assets, $5,330,096 (M); expenditures, $299,117;

qualifying distributions, $270,200; giving activities include $270,200 for 22 grants (high: $33,000; low: $3,400).
Fields of interest: Education; Disasters and emergency management; Human services.
Limitations: Applications not accepted. Giving primarily in CO.
Application information: Unsolicited requests for funds not accepted.
Officers: Louann Benbow, Pres.; Brian Benbow, V.P.; Natalie Baker, Secy.-Treas.
EIN: 453942962

1261
Walter and Ursula Eberspacher Foundation
c/o Walter Eberspacher
14233 U.S. Hwy., Ste.287
Longmont, CO 80504

Donors: Walter Eberspacher; Ursula Eberspacher.
Foundation type: Independent foundation.
Financial data (yr. ended 12/31/13): Assets, $1,961,467 (M); gifts received, $220,000; expenditures, $198,544; qualifying distributions, $198,544; giving activities include $187,000 for 23 grants (high: $50,000; low: $2,000).
Fields of interest: Community and economic development.
Limitations: Applications not accepted. Giving primarily in Evergreen, CO. No grants to individuals.
Application information: Contributes only to pre-selected organizations.
Officers: Ursula Eberspacher, Mgr.; Walter Eberspacher, Mgr.
EIN: 203864263

1262
The Elf Foundation
702 W. Drake Rd., Unit D
Fort Collins, CO 80526-5563

Established in 2000 in Colorado.
Donor: Lusia D. Preston.
Foundation type: Independent foundation.
Financial data (yr. ended 04/30/14): Assets, $4,204,412 (M); expenditures, $443,824; qualifying distributions, $363,441; giving activities include $138,500 for 6 grants (high: $100,000; low: $1,000).
Fields of interest: Museums; Natural resources; Foundations; Nonprofits; Human services; Homeless people.
Type of support: Regranting.
Limitations: Applications not accepted. Giving primarily in Fort Collins, CO. No grants to individuals.
Application information: Unsolicited requests for funds not accepted.
Trustee: Sean Shelley.
EIN: 841548560

1263
The Elizabeth Foundation
215 Monarch St., Ste. 102
Aspen, CO 81611-2915

Established in 1999 in California.
Donor: Karen E. Lemons Charitable Lead Unitrust.
Foundation type: Independent foundation.

Financial data (yr. ended 12/31/13): Assets, $5,456,032 (M); gifts received, $227,200; expenditures, $267,486; qualifying distributions, $236,158; giving activities include $228,292 for 29 grants (high: $26,000; low: $100).
Fields of interest: Arts and culture; Education; Film and video; Human services; Food aid.
Limitations: Applications not accepted. Giving primarily in CO. No grants to individuals.
Application information: Unsolicited requests for funds not accepted.
Trustee: Karen E. Lemons Hollins.
EIN: 770497261

1264
The Energy Cup
8450 E. Crescent Pkwy., Ste. 400
Greenwood Village, CO 80111-2856
3032900990
Contact: George Solich

Foundation type: Independent foundation.
Financial data (yr. ended 12/31/12): Assets, $0 (M); expenditures, $372,095; qualifying distributions, $371,076; giving activities include $371,076 for 10 grants (high: $80,000; low: $1,000).
Purpose and activities: Giving primarily for higher education.
Fields of interest: Education; Sports and recreation.
Limitations: Applications not accepted. Giving primarily in CO, OK and TX. No grants to individuals.
Application information: Unsolicited requests for funds not accepted.
Director: George H. Solich.
EIN: 311750923

1265
Erion Foundation
114 E. 5th St.
Loveland, CO 80537-5504 (970) 667-4549
FAX: (970) 663-6187;
E-mail: contact@erionfoundation.org; Mailing Address: P.O. Box 732, Loveland, CO 80539; General inquiries should be directed to Summer Scott, Admin., Comms. at the foundation's main e-mail address; E-mail for applications: GrantRequest@erionfoundation.org; Applications sent via U.S. mail should be to the attention of the Board of Directors; Main URL: http://www.erionfoundation.org

Established in 1997 in Colorado.
Donors: Ken Erion†; Helen Erion†.
Foundation type: Independent foundation.
Financial data (yr. ended 12/31/13): Assets, $10,710,840 (M); gifts received, $850; expenditures, $510,369; qualifying distributions, $363,552; giving activities include $299,910 for 35 grants (high: $57,000; low: $87).
Purpose and activities: The foundation balances its grantmaking between 5 general areas of interest: 1) Major Project Advocacy; 2) Health and Welfare; 3) Basic Needs; 4) Education; and 5) Culture and Community. The foundation prefers grants for capital projects, specific programs, and joint ventures with other funder.
Fields of interest: Arts and culture; Education; Health; Human services.
Limitations: Applications accepted. Giving primarily in Northern CO, particularly in the Loveland Planning

Area, the Thomson and Poudre School Districts, and in Larimer County. No support for private foundations, organizations that dont have fiscal responsibility for the proposed project, private schools, or religious or political programs. No grants to individuals, or for debt reduction.
Application information: The foundation prefers that grant requests be sent via e-mail. Complete application guidelines available on foundation web site. Application form required.
  Initial approach: Letter requesting application form or download form from foundation web site
  Copies of proposal: 1
  Deadline(s): Last day of Jan., Apr., July, and Oct.
  Board meeting date(s): Quarterly
  Final notification: Last day of Mar., June, Sept., and Dec.
Officers and Directors: Douglas J. Erion, Pres. and Director; Roger E. Clark, V.P. and Director; Eli Scott, Treas. and Director; Janice Erion Pierce Atnip; Justin Erion; Travis Erion; Christine Erion Klein.
Trustee: First National Bank.
EIN: 841358074

1266
F Cubed Foundation
c/o Finkel
P.O. Box 7175
Breckenridge, CO 80424-7175
Application address: Diana J. Finkel, 359 Ridge Trail, South Fork, CO 81154-9597, tel.:(719) 849-1866

Donors: Eileen Finkel; Paul Finkel.
Foundation type: Independent foundation.
Financial data (yr. ended 12/31/13): Assets, $2,165,378 (M); gifts received, $67,000; expenditures, $153,819; qualifying distributions, $146,750; giving activities include $146,750 for 10 grants (high: $50,000; low: $200).
Fields of interest: Education; Environment; Human services.
Limitations: Applications accepted. Giving primarily in CO; some funding also in MT.
Application information: Application form required.
  Initial approach: Colorado Common Grant Application
  Deadline(s): None
Officers and Directors: Diana J. Finkel, Pres. and Director; Bemjamin C. Woodbeck, Secy. and Director; Paul A. Finkel, Treas. and Director; Jill B. Finkel; Michael J. Finkel.
EIN: 274155850

1267
Madden Family Charitable Foundation
6501 S. Fiddler's Green Cir., Ste. 110
Greenwood Village, CO 80111-4932

Established in 2010 in Colorado.
Donor: John W. Madden, Jr.
Foundation type: Independent foundation.
Financial data (yr. ended 12/31/13): Assets, $44,073 (M); gifts received, $290,180; expenditures, $258,976; qualifying distributions, $258,976; giving activities include $258,976 for 11 grants (high: $177,500; low: $500).
Fields of interest: Arts and culture; Health; Youth development.
Limitations: Applications not accepted.

Application information: Unsolicited requests for funds not accepted.
Officers and Directors: John W. Madden, Jr., Pres. and Director; David Windfeldt, Treas. and Director; David Steiner.
EIN: 272147837

1268
Gooding Family Foundation
6400 S. Fiddlers Green Cir.
Greenwood Village, CO   80111

Established in 1992 in Colorado.
Donor: Paragon Ranch Inc.
Foundation type: Independent foundation.
Financial data (yr. ended 12/31/13): Assets, $360,610 (M); gifts received, $87,568; expenditures, $137,669; qualifying distributions, $133,000; giving activities include $133,000 for 13 grants (high: $15,000; low: $1,000).
Fields of interest: Art museums; University education; Community and economic development; Camps; Human services; Child welfare; Scouting programs.
Type of support: General support.
Limitations: Applications not accepted. Giving primarily in Denver, CO. No grants to individuals.
Application information: Contributes only to pre-selected organizations.
Directors: Nancy A. Gooding; Richard L. Gooding.
EIN: 841187150

1269
First Data Employee Hardship Fund
6200 S. Quebec St.
Greenwood Village, CO   80111-4729

Donor: First Data Corp.
Foundation type: Company-sponsored foundation.
Financial data (yr. ended 12/31/13): Assets, $32,107 (M); gifts received, $186,294; expenditures, $165,130; qualifying distributions, $165,130; giving activities include $164,798 for grants.
Limitations: Applications not accepted.
Application information: Unsolicited requests for funds not accepted.
Officer: Ronald M. Pierce, Treas.
EIN: 261641296

1270
Harmes C. Fishback Foundation Trust
8 Village Rd.
Englewood, CO   80110-4908   (303) 789-1753
Contact: Katharine H. Stapleton, Tr.
E-mail: kties@aol.com

Established in 1972 in Colorado.
Donor: Harmes C. Fishback†.
Foundation type: Independent foundation.
Financial data (yr. ended 12/31/13): Assets, $12,471,320 (M); expenditures, $512,174; qualifying distributions, $476,300; giving activities include $421,300 for 83 grants (high: $29,000; low: $100).
Purpose and activities: Giving primarily for education, health and human services, and the arts.
Fields of interest: Arts and culture; Museums; Historical activities; Higher education; Hospital care; Diseases and conditions; Child welfare;

Adults; Young adults; People with physical disabilities.
International interests: France.
Type of support: Continuing support; General support; Scholarships; Research; Research and evaluation.
Limitations: Applications accepted. Giving primarily in the metropolitan Denver, CO, area. No support for health organizations or hospitals, with few exceptions. No grants to individuals.
Application information:
   Initial approach: Proposal
   Copies of proposal: 1
   Deadline(s): None
Trustees: Benjamin F. Stepleton III; Craig R. Stapleton; Jenna Stapleton; Katharine H. Stapleton.
Number of staff: None.
EIN: 846094542

1271
Jeremy and Angie Flug Foundation
370 17th St., Ste. 5150
Denver, CO   80202-5649

Donors: Jeremy Flug; Angela Flug.
Foundation type: Independent foundation.
Financial data (yr. ended 12/31/13): Assets, $7,736 (M); gifts received, $309,236; expenditures, $301,710; qualifying distributions, $301,110; giving activities include $301,110 for 23 grants (high: $65,000; low: $1,000).
Fields of interest: Arts and culture; Education; Human services.
Limitations: Applications not accepted.
Application information: Unsolicited requests for funds not accepted.
Officers: Jeremy Flug, Pres.; Angie Flug, Secy.-Treas.
EIN: 273867289

1272
Flying J Foundation
1427 W. Mountain Ave.
Fort Collins, CO   80521-2305

Donors: Kimberley Jordan; Zachary Danielson; Nickolas Lebesch.
Foundation type: Independent foundation.
Financial data (yr. ended 11/30/13): Assets, $6,477,676 (M); gifts received, $6,600,000; expenditures, $207,696; qualifying distributions, $175,697; giving activities include $152,500 for 12 grants (high: $40,000; low: $1,500).
Fields of interest: Arts and culture; Health; Human services.
Limitations: Applications not accepted. Giving primarily in CA and CO.
Application information: Unsolicited requests for funds not accepted.
Officers: Kimberley Jordan, Pres.; Lucy Cantwell, Secy.; Christine Perich, Treas.
Board Members: Dick Cantwell; Zachary Danielson; Paul Hudnut; Nickolas Lebesch.
EIN: 461557560

1273
Sheila Fortune Foundation, Inc.
2135 4th St.
Boulder, CO   80302-4901   (303) 443-5348
Contact: Sheila Fortune, Pres.

FAX: (303) 443-5365;
E-mail: sheilafortunefnd@gmail.com; Main URL: http://www.sheilafortunefoundation.com
Grants List: http://www.sheilafortunefoundation.com/glsf.htm

Donors: Sheila M. Fortune; Martha Murray Fortune Foundation.
Foundation type: Independent foundation.
Financial data (yr. ended 12/31/13): Assets, $7,212,691 (M); gifts received, $68,427; expenditures, $394,873; qualifying distributions, $302,914; giving activities include $301,500 for 57 grants (high: $12,500; low: $2,500).
Purpose and activities: The foundation is dedicated to helping at-risk youth gain access to, and expression through, the performing arts.
Fields of interest: Performing arts; Child welfare.
Type of support: Program development.
Limitations: Applications accepted. Giving primarily in CO, IN, NM and PA.
Publications: Newsletter.
Application information: Complete application guidelines available on foundation web site.
   Initial approach: Concise request by letter preferred
   Deadline(s): May 7
   Board meeting date(s): June
Officers and Directors: Sheila M. Fortune, Pres.; Sophia Gold, V.P. and Director; Michelle Winebrenner-Nizam, Secy.-Treas.; Michelle Guyton, Exec. Dir.; Douglas M. Cain; Marc A. Hetzner; William C. Metzger.
EIN: 841467131

1274
T. & R. Fund
(formerly T. & R. Birdsong Fund)
4949 S. Syracuse St., Ste. 300
Denver, CO   80237-2714

Established in 1997 in Colorado.
Donors: Robert T. Birdsong; Teresa A. Birdsong; The Pioneer Fund.
Foundation type: Independent foundation.
Financial data (yr. ended 03/31/14): Assets, $1,199,871 (M); expenditures, $154,050; qualifying distributions, $148,049; giving activities include $141,707 for 6 grants (high: $128,407; low: $300).
Fields of interest: Education; Philanthropy; Human services.
Limitations: Applications not accepted. Giving primarily in CO. No grants to individuals.
Application information: Unsolicited requests for funds not accepted.
Officers and Directors: Robert T. Birdsong, Pres. and Director; Teresa A. Birdsong, V.P. and Secy. and Director; David C. Irvine, Treas. and Director.
EIN: 841405753

1275
The Jerry Gart Family Foundation
(also known as TGFF)
299 Milwaukee St., Ste. 500
Denver, CO   80206-5045

Established in 1994 in Colorado.
Donors: Paul Gerald Gart; Sally S. Gart; Thomas A. Gart; Ken Gart.
Foundation type: Independent foundation.

Financial data (yr. ended 11/30/13): Assets, $4,480,987 (M); gifts received, $100,000; expenditures, $320,759; qualifying distributions, $294,412; giving activities include $294,412 for 19 grants (high: $48,742; low: $500).
Fields of interest: Education; Diseases and conditions; Judaism.
Type of support: General support.
Limitations: Applications not accepted. Giving primarily in CO. No grants to individuals.
Application information: Contributes only to pre-selected organizations.
Officers: Thomas A. Gart, Pres. and Treas.; Ken Gart, V.P. and Secy.
Directors: John Gart; Sally Gart.
EIN: 841289883

1276
The Samuel Gary Jr. Family Foundation
1515 Wynkoop St., Ste. 700
Denver, CO   80202-2062

Donor: Samuel Gary, Jr.
Foundation type: Independent foundation.
Financial data (yr. ended 12/31/13): Assets, $14,351 (M); gifts received, $186,500; expenditures, $187,010; qualifying distributions, $185,500; giving activities include $185,500 for 15 grants (high: $75,000; low: $500).
Fields of interest: Land resources.
Limitations: Applications not accepted. Giving primarily in CO, ID and VA.
Application information: Unsolicited requests for funds not accepted.
Officers: Samuel Gary, Jr., Pres.; Kathryn W. Gary, V.P.
EIN: 262307528

1277
Gerrish Foundation
c/o A. Gerrish
1032 Timber Ln.
Boulder, CO   80304-0485
Contact: A. Gerrish

Established in 2000 in Colorado.
Donors: Allan M. Gerrish; Gail S. Gerrish.
Foundation type: Independent foundation.
Financial data (yr. ended 12/31/13): Assets, $297,268 (M); gifts received, $134,731; expenditures, $153,998; qualifying distributions, $144,500; giving activities include $144,500 for 13 grants (high: $70,000; low: $1,000).
Fields of interest: Education; Environment; Land resources; Christianity; Basic and emergency aid; Senior services; International development.
Limitations: Applications not accepted. Giving primarily in CO, with some giving in ME and TX. No grants to individuals.
Application information: Unsolicited requests for funds not accepted.
Directors: Allan M. Gerrish; Allison D. Gerrish; Gail S. Gerrish.
EIN: 841564881

1278
The Getz Foundation
(formerly Emma & Oscar Getz Foundation)
c/o Richard Getz
17450 W. 167th St.
Arvada, CO   80007

Established in 1966 in Illinois.
Donors: Oscar Getz†; Emma Getz; William M. Getz.
Foundation type: Independent foundation.
Financial data (yr. ended 12/31/13): Assets, $3,786,418 (M); expenditures, $347,743; qualifying distributions, $277,969; giving activities include $227,500 for 30 grants (high: $25,000; low: $500).
Purpose and activities: Giving primarily for the arts, particularly a jazz festival; funding also for education, health, and social services.
Fields of interest: Arts and culture; Music; Museums; Education; University education; Diseases and conditions; Human services.
Limitations: Applications not accepted. Giving in the U.S., with emphasis on CO, particularly Aspen, and KY. No grants to individuals.
Application information: Contributes only to pre-selected organizations.
Officers and Directors: William M. Getz, Pres. and Director; Richard Getz, V.P.; H. Debra Levin, Treas. and Director.
EIN: 366150787

1279
The Goodwin Foundation
P.O. Box 2106
Grand Junction, CO   81502-4010   (970) 243-1003

Established in 1951 in Colorado.
Donor: Harry B. Goodwin†.
Foundation type: Independent foundation.
Financial data (yr. ended 10/31/14): Assets, $3,616,809; expenditures, $212,437; qualifying distributions, $189,842.
Fields of interest: Arts and culture; Music; Museums; Environment; Health; Hospital care; Biomedicine; Diseases and conditions; Public administration; Community and economic development; Human services.
Type of support: General support; Continuing support; Annual campaigns; Capital campaigns; Capital and infrastructure; Land acquisitions; Scholarships; Research; Research and evaluation.
Limitations: Applications accepted. Giving primarily in Mesa County and Grand Junction, CO. No grants to individuals.
Publications: Annual report.
Application information: Application form required.
    Initial approach: Letter
    Copies of proposal: 1
    Deadline(s): None
Officers: John Gormley, Chair.; Dan Ela, Secy.; Linda Bacon Reid, Treas.
EIN: 846036758

1280
William H. Graves Family Foundation
1750 Green Oaks Dr.
Greenwood Village, CO   80121-1535   (303) 794-6998
Contact: Martha Reese Graves, Tr.

Established in 1994 in Kansas.
Donors: William H. Graves; Helen M. Graves; William P. Graves.
Foundation type: Independent foundation.
Financial data (yr. ended 06/30/13): Assets, $1,920,936 (M); expenditures, $175,272; qualifying distributions, $165,000; giving activities include $165,000 for 2 grants (high: $160,000; low: $5,000).
Purpose and activities: Scholarship awards paid directly to the college or university for Salina County High School students; Also, some giving to organizations within the Greater Salina communities.
Fields of interest: Education; Housing development.
Type of support: General support; Scholarships.
Limitations: Applications accepted. Giving primarily in Salina County, KS.
Application information: Application form required.
    Initial approach: Letter
    Deadline(s): None
Trustees: William P. Graves; Martha Reese Graves.
EIN: 481157162

1281
Sanford J. Grossman Charitable Trust
c/o Quantitative Financial Strategies
350 Market St., No. 301
Basalt, CO   81621-7402

Established in 2002 in Connecticut.
Donor: Sanford J. Grossman.
Foundation type: Independent foundation.
Financial data (yr. ended 12/31/14): Assets, $2,286,195; expenditures, $307,140; qualifying distributions, $306,376.
Purpose and activities: Giving primarily for education, the arts, and health associations.
Fields of interest: Arts and culture; Higher education; Diseases and conditions; Counterterrorism; Human services.
Type of support: Research; Research and evaluation.
Limitations: Applications not accepted. Giving primarily in CA, Washington, DC, IL, and New York, NY. No grants to individuals.
Application information: Contributes only to pre-selected organizations.
Trustee: Sanford J. Grossman.
EIN: 336316059

1282
The Grosvenor Family Foundation
c/o Grosvenor Industries
6355 Ward Rd., Ste. 301
Arvada, CO   80004-8323
Contact: Craig Crosvenor

Established in 2007 in Wyoming.
Donor: Grosvenor Foundation.
Foundation type: Independent foundation.
Financial data (yr. ended 12/31/13): Assets, $3,508,277 (M); expenditures, $282,131; qualifying distributions, $187,983; giving activities include $181,500 for 4 grants (high: $91,000; low: $500).
Fields of interest: Foundations; Nonprofits.
Type of support: Regranting.
Limitations: Applications not accepted. Giving primarily in CA and CO. No grants to individuals.

Application information: Contributes only to pre-selected organizations.
Officers and Directors: Craig Lusk Grosvenor, Pres. and Treas. and Director; Alexander Lusk Grosvenor, V.P. and Director; Nicholas Craig Grosvenor, Secy. and Director.
EIN: 260741640

1283
The J. Mark Grosvenor Foundation
6355 Ward Rd., Ste. 301
Arvada, CO   80004-3823

Established in 2007 in Wyoming.
Donor: Grosvenor Foundation.
Foundation type: Independent foundation.
Financial data (yr. ended 12/31/13): Assets, $2,804,155 (M); expenditures, $165,788; qualifying distributions, $115,140; giving activities include $114,818 for 13 grants (high: $50,000; low: $18).
Fields of interest: Environment; Philanthropy; Nonprofits.
Type of support: Regranting.
Limitations: Applications not accepted. Giving primarily in CA and CO. No grants to individuals.
Application information: Contributes only to pre-selected organizations.
Officers: J. Mark Grosvenor, Pres.; Stephen O. James, V.P.; David Yeager, Secy.
EIN: 260741701

1284
Growing the Vision of Light Foundation
P.O. Box 609
Lamar, CO   81052-0069   (719) 336-2251
Contact: Jane A. Weber, Pres.

Established in 2004 in Colorado.
Donors: J.J. Schneider Farms, LLP; Jane A. Weber; Agnes E. Weber; McConnaughey and Young, LLC; Thomas Hanlon, LLC.
Foundation type: Independent foundation.
Financial data (yr. ended 12/31/13): Assets, $3,059,672 (M); gifts received, $297,404; expenditures, $202,208; qualifying distributions, $181,000; giving activities include $181,000 for 8 grants (high: $56,000; low: $5,000).
Fields of interest: Health; Catholicism; Human services.
Limitations: Applications accepted. Giving primarily in Pueblo, CO.
Application information: Application form required.
   Initial approach: Letter
   Deadline(s): Nov. 15
Officer: Jane A. Weber, Pres. and Secy.
EIN: 470923385

1285
The Frederic C. Hamilton Family Foundation
1560 Broadway, Ste. 2200
Denver, CO   80202-5100

Donors: Frederic C. Hamilton; Jane M. Hamilton.
Foundation type: Independent foundation.
Financial data (yr. ended 12/31/13): Assets, $39,002,847 (M); expenditures, $321,613; qualifying distributions, $270,362; giving activities

include $270,362 for 20 grants (high: $100,000; low: $200).
Purpose and activities: Giving primarily for the arts, particularly art museums, education, health care, including a children's hospital, and human services.
Fields of interest: Arts and culture; Art museums; Elementary and secondary education; Higher education; Health; Specialty hospital care; Human services; Child welfare; Scouting programs.
Limitations: Applications not accepted. Giving primarily in CO; with emphasis on Aurora and Denver. No grants to individuals.
Application information: Contributes only to pre-selected organizations.
Trustees: Crawford M. Hamilton; Frederic C. Hamilton; Frederic C. Hamilton, Jr.; Jane M. Hamilton; Christy Hamilton McGraw.
EIN: 542099318

1286
Hanson Family Foundation
P.O. Box 9295
Avon, CO   81620-9203

Established in 2007 in Colorado.
Donors: John Nils Hanson; Stephanie M. Hanson.
Foundation type: Independent foundation.
Financial data (yr. ended 12/31/13): Assets, $4,787,272 (M); expenditures, $243,830; qualifying distributions, $238,325; giving activities include $232,250 for 14 grants (high: $102,250; low: $5,000).
Fields of interest: Education; Public policy; Leadership development.
Type of support: Policy, advocacy and systems reform.
Limitations: Applications not accepted. Giving primarily in Washington, DC and VA.
Application information: Unsolicited requests for funds not accepted.
Trustees: John Nils Hanson; Stephanie M. Hanson.
EIN: 256912093

1287
Cannon Y. & Lyndia K. Harvey Family Foundation
236 Dexter St.
Denver, CO   80220-5656

Established in 2000 in Colorado.
Donors: Cannon Y. Harvey; Lyndia K. Harvey.
Foundation type: Independent foundation.
Financial data (yr. ended 12/31/14): Assets, $150,541 (M); gifts received, $1,913; expenditures, $119,434; qualifying distributions, $117,500; giving activities include $117,500 for 10 grants (high: $35,000; low: $3,000).
Fields of interest: Education; Health; Mental health care.
Limitations: Applications not accepted. Giving primarily in Denver, CO. No grants to individuals.
Application information: Unsolicited requests for funds not accepted.
Officers and Directors: Cannon Y. Harvey, Chair. and Director; Lyndia K. Harvey, Pres. and Secy. and Director; Tyler Y. Harvey; Amy B. Zajkowski.
EIN: 841563033

1288
The HAVRK8 Ranch
(formerly Castle Oaks Foundation)
c/o The Shafer Group, P.C.
13710 Struthers Rd., No. 220
Colorado Springs, CO   80921-2469

Established in 2007 in Colorado.
Donor: Mark Haverkate.
Foundation type: Independent foundation.
Financial data (yr. ended 02/28/13): Assets, $1,490,523 (M); expenditures, $369,445; qualifying distributions, $365,000; giving activities include $365,000 for 9 grants (high: $251,500; low: $2,000).
Fields of interest: Christianity; Human services.
Limitations: Applications not accepted. Giving primarily in CO. No grants to individuals.
Application information: Unsolicited requests for funds not accepted.
Officers: Mary Ann Haverkate, Pres.; Mark Haverkate, Treas.
Directors: Ernest Berkas; Andrea H. Fells; Jeffrey M. Haverkate; Caroline M. Vivian.
EIN: 204798631

1289
Will Heginbotham Trust
P.O. Box 245
Holyoke, CO   80734-0245   (970) 854-2497
Contact: David O. Colver, Tr.

Established in 1968 in Colorado.
Donor: Will E. Heginbotham†.
Foundation type: Independent foundation.
Financial data (yr. ended 12/31/13): Assets, $3,106,196 (M); expenditures, $208,479; qualifying distributions, $201,235; giving activities include $89,655 for 14 grants (high: $20,000; low: $15).
Fields of interest: Elementary and secondary education; Hospital care; Public administration; Community and economic development; Housing development.
Type of support: General support; Capital and infrastructure; Equipment.
Application information:
   Initial approach: Proposal
   Deadline(s): None
Trustees: David O. Colver; Mary Louise Evans; John Schneider.
EIN: 846053496

1290
Heider Family Foundation
2225 Island Pt.
Evergreen, CO   80439-9422
Contact: Susan H. Coleman

Established in 2001 in Colorado.
Foundation type: Independent foundation.
Financial data (yr. ended 12/31/13): Assets, $4,595,748 (M); expenditures, $199,554; qualifying distributions, $194,808; giving activities include $189,500 for 18 grants (high: $40,000; low: $500).
Fields of interest: Higher education; Graduate and professional education; Land resources; Theology; Youth organizing; Females.
Type of support: General support; Scholarships.

Limitations: Applications not accepted. Giving primarily in the Denver, CO, metro area. No grants to individuals.
Application information: Unsolicited requests for funds not accepted.
Officers and Directors: Elizabeth A. Scannell, V.P. and Director; Susan H. Coleman, Secy.-Treas. and Exec. Dir.
EIN: 841601007

1291
Helmar Skating Fund
1228 15th St., Ste. 309
Denver, CO 80202-1642

Established in 1986 in Colorado.
Donors: Helen M. McLoraine; The Pioneer Fund.
Foundation type: Independent foundation.
Financial data (yr. ended 06/30/14): Assets, $801,238 (M); gifts received, $100,000; expenditures, $195,610; qualifying distributions, $194,841; giving activities include $194,841 for 13 grants (high: $39,985; low: $3,468).
Purpose and activities: Awards grants to amateur U.S.F.S.A. recognized figure-skating participants at novice, junior, and senior levels.
Fields of interest: Sports and recreation.
Type of support: Grants to individuals.
Limitations: Applications not accepted. Giving primarily in CA, MI and PA.
Application information: Unsolicited requests for funds not accepted.
Officers: Scott Hamilton, Pres.; Kathy Casey, V.P.; Robert Anderson, Secy.-Treas.
EIN: 841032757

1292
Hewit Family Foundation
191 University Blvd., Ste. 832
Denver, CO 80206-4613 (303) 955-4983
Contact: Richard J. Andrews, Pres.
E-mail: hewitfamilyfoundation@gmail.com

Established in 1985 in Colorado.
Foundation type: Independent foundation.
Financial data (yr. ended 11/30/13): Assets, $17,642,655 (M); expenditures, $253,444; qualifying distributions, $215,000; giving activities include $215,000 for 5 grants (high: $125,000; low: $20,000).
Fields of interest: Elementary and secondary education; Higher education; Health; Human services.
Limitations: Applications accepted. Giving primarily in CO. No support for private foundations or religious organizations. No grants to individuals.
Application information: Application form required.
 Initial approach: Letter
 Deadline(s): None
Officers: Richard J. Andrews, Pres.; Christie F. Andrews, V.P.; Renee Elise Andrews, Secy.; Candace J. Johnson, Treas.
EIN: 742397040

1293
LeVert W. Hoag Foundation
115 E. Riverwalk, Ste. 400
Pueblo, CO 81003-3124

Established in 1995 in Colorado.

Donor: LeVert W. Hoag.
Foundation type: Independent foundation.
Financial data (yr. ended 03/31/13): Assets, $4,307,849 (M); expenditures, $221,313; qualifying distributions, $216,000; giving activities include $216,000 for 3 grants (high: $195,000; low: $1,000).
Fields of interest: Animal welfare; Foundations.
Type of support: Capital and infrastructure; Equipment.
Limitations: Applications not accepted. Giving limited to southern CO.
Application information: Unsolicited requests for funds not accepted.
 Board meeting date(s): Varies
Officers and Directors: Bob D. Wertz, Pres. and Director; Adrian Comer, V.P. and Director; David B. Shaw, Secy.-Treas. and Director.
Number of staff: None.
EIN: 841310564

1294
Hope's Enduring Flame Foundation
4711 Xenia St. S.
Denver, CO 80237

Foundation type: Independent foundation.
Financial data (yr. ended 12/31/13): Assets, $3,141,584 (M); expenditures, $164,246; qualifying distributions, $131,000; giving activities include $131,000 for 4 grants (high: $56,000; low: $5,000).
Fields of interest: Higher education.
Limitations: Applications not accepted. Giving primarily in CO.
Application information: Unsolicited requests for funds not accepted.
Officers: Paul E. Dorr, Pres.; Terri L. Dorr, V.P.; Jamie C. Dorr, Secy.; Jeffry B. Dorr, Treas.
EIN: 274176031

1295
The Gary and Leslie Howard Family Foundation
9 Waterside Terr.
Cherry Hills Village, CO 80113-4141

Established in 2001 in Unspecified.
Donors: Gary D. Howard; Leslie D. Howard; Aspen Industries; USA Hockey; University of Denver; Starz Entertainment LLC; Liberty Global, Inc.; Honest Teas; National Cine Media; Charles T. Beaird; Sentinent Flight Group; Heidi MacIntyre; Dottie Dibble; Peggy Morris; Marilyn Carroll; Pat Nelson; Kristin Celusniak; Bernie Dvorak; Neal Dermer; Tom Alley; Starbucks; University of Denver Athletics &Recreation; Sprouts Farmers Market; Pasquinis Pizza; Teresa Alley; Discovery Communications; University of Denver; Colorado State University; Education Measures; J&A Corporation; Starz Entertainment, LLC; Directv, Inc.; Laura Baldi; Kelly King; Fran Hamlin; Mike Crawford; Ross Posner; Sherri York; Daniel York; Elizabeth Posner; Lou Gobis; Marty Flessner; Mark Richards; Peggy Knight; Charles Welch; Keri Dermer; Mark Celusniak; Clint Nelson; John Muraglia; Ken Carroll; Dave Dibble; C.A. Ryan; Liberty Gives Foundation; Carolyn W. Beaird; Arapahoe and Holly Self Storage; Dish Network; Liberty Global, Inc.; Wells Fargo; Aspen Industries; Elements Therapeutic Massage; Rocky Mountain Popcorn; Crocs Cares; Altitude Sports &

Entertainment; Tom Alley; Larkburger; Illegal Pete's; Subway; Sodexo; Kroenke Sports Charities; Vubiquity; Teletech.
Foundation type: Independent foundation.
Financial data (yr. ended 12/31/13): Assets, $4,438,648 (M); gifts received, $63,246; expenditures, $503,481; qualifying distributions, $364,782; giving activities include $364,782 for 18 grants (high: $101,665; low: $200).
Fields of interest: Higher education; Winter sports; Human services; Child welfare.
Limitations: Applications not accepted. Giving primarily in Denver, CO. No grants to individuals.
Application information: Contributes only to pre-selected organizations.
Officers: Leslie D. Howard, Pres.; Gary S. Howard, V.P.
EIN: 841612399

1296
The Hunt Family Foundation
1727 Tremont Pl.
Denver, CO 80202-4006

Established in 2000 in Colorado.
Donor: The Anschutz Foundation.
Foundation type: Independent foundation.
Financial data (yr. ended 12/31/13): Assets, $412,589 (M); gifts received, $580,000; expenditures, $204,392; qualifying distributions, $204,402; giving activities include $204,392 for 10 grants (high: $100,000; low: $500).
Fields of interest: Education; Higher education; Community and economic development; Human services.
Limitations: Applications not accepted. Giving primarily in Denver, CO and Princeton, NJ. No grants to individuals.
Application information: Unsolicited requests for funds not accepted.
Officers and Directors: Sarah A. Hunt, Pres. and Director; M. Lavoy Robison, V.P. and Secy.-Treas.; Christopher W. Hunt, V.P. and Director; Donald J. Hopkins.
EIN: 841537664

1297
Hunter-White Foundation
1520 S. University Blvd.
Denver, CO 80210-2813

Established in 1998 in Colorado.
Donor: Catherine P. Cole.
Foundation type: Independent foundation.
Financial data (yr. ended 12/31/13): Assets, $2,879,332 (M); expenditures, $256,895; qualifying distributions, $224,451; giving activities include $221,000 for 17 grants (high: $40,000; low: $2,500).
Purpose and activities: Giving primarily for human services, employment programs, and the environment.
Fields of interest: Natural resources; Storms; Employment; Human services; International peace and security.
Limitations: Applications not accepted. Giving primarily in CO, MA and NY. No support for religious and political programs. No grants to individuals.
Application information: Unsolicited requests for funds not accepted.

Directors: Amy C. Berkley; Linda C. Call; Catherine P. Cole; Lisa A. Cole.
EIN: 841443958

1298
The Jim Jacobs Charitable Foundation
c/o Wall Group, LLC
P.O. Box 59
Denver, CO 80201-0059

Established in 1998 in New York.
Donor: Loraine Jacobs.
Foundation type: Independent foundation.
Financial data (yr. ended 12/31/13): Assets, $1,473,125 (M); expenditures, $188,641; qualifying distributions, $183,667; giving activities include $175,000 for 10 grants (high: $40,000; low: $5,000).
Fields of interest: Education; Leukemia; Housing development; Human services; Food aid; Food delivery; Child welfare.
Type of support: Scholarships; General support.
Limitations: Applications not accepted. Giving primarily in New York, NY. No grants to individuals.
Application information: Contributes only to pre-selected organizations.
Officers: Loraine Jacobs, Pres.; Timothy M. Costello, Secy.-Treas.
Directors: Michael Atter; James Brady; Gregg Fisher; Martin H. Lager.
EIN: 134008195

1299
JJP Family Foundation Inc.
c/o Harding and Hittesdorf, P.C.
650 S. Cherry St., Ste. 1050
Denver, CO 80246-1811

Established in 1999 in Colorado.
Donors: Jack T. Pottle; Judith E. Pottle.
Foundation type: Independent foundation.
Financial data (yr. ended 12/31/13): Assets, $6,605,900 (M); expenditures, $328,873; qualifying distributions, $288,500; giving activities include $288,500 for 11 grants (high: $100,000; low: $500).
Fields of interest: Elementary and secondary education; Undergraduate education; Family planning; Catholicism; Right to life; Human services.
Limitations: Applications not accepted. Giving primarily in Denver, CO and NY. No grants to individuals.
Application information: Unsolicited requests for funds not accepted.
Officers: Jack T. Pottle, Pres. and Treas.; Judith E. Pottle, V.P.; Elizabeth K. Poell, Secy.
EIN: 841517947

1300
Joslin-Needham Family Foundation
c/o Farmers State Bank
200 Clayton St.
Brush, CO 80723-2104
Application address: c/o Judith A. Gunnon, P.O. Box 324, Brush, CO 80723, tel.: (970) 842-5101

Donor: Gladys Joslin†.
Foundation type: Independent foundation.
Financial data (yr. ended 12/31/13): Assets, $6,670,156 (M); expenditures, $395,337;

qualifying distributions, $369,987; giving activities include $356,217 for 7 grants (high: $269,350; low: $500).
Fields of interest: Education; Hospital care; Diseases and conditions; Libraries; Public administration; Christianity; Human services.
Type of support: General support; Equipment; Scholarships.
Limitations: Applications accepted. Giving limited to the Brush, CO, area.
Application information: Application form required.
  Initial approach: Letter
  Deadline(s): Dec. 1
Trustee: The Farmers State Bank.
Director: Robert Hansen.
EIN: 846038670

1301
Joy Family Foundation, Inc
627 W. Smuggler St.
Aspen, CO 81611-1262

Established in 1996 in Colorado.
Donors: Sara R. Joy; William N. Joy.
Foundation type: Independent foundation.
Financial data (yr. ended 12/31/13): Assets, $8,159,945 (M); expenditures, $587,213; qualifying distributions, $459,221; giving activities include $343,552 for 12 grants (high: $100,778; low: $1,000).
Purpose and activities: Giving primarily for projects and foundations engaged in ocean and global conservation of species and habitats. The foundation's focus is education, innovative technologies and the visual arts as tools to spotlight critical issues and showcase solutions for a sustainable future.
Fields of interest: Natural resources; Land resources; Domesticated animals; Health; Human services.
Limitations: Applications not accepted. Giving primarily in CO and CA. No grants to individuals.
Application information: Contributes only to pre-selected organizations.
Officer: William N. Joy, Pres.; Shannon O'Leary-Joy, Exec. Dir.
Directors: Hayden N. Joy; Madison C. Joy.
EIN: 841361004

1302
The Kenney Brothers Foundation
(formerly Jay P.K. Kenney Private Foundation)
910 Gaylord St.
Denver, CO 80206-3754

Established in 1993 in Colorado.
Donors: Jay P.K. Kenney; Chad Kenney.
Foundation type: Independent foundation.
Financial data (yr. ended 12/31/13): Assets, $1,172,466 (M); gifts received, $10,000; expenditures, $200,487; qualifying distributions, $195,850; giving activities include $195,850 for 33 grants (high: $15,250; low: $100).
Fields of interest: Arts and culture; Elementary and secondary education; Environment; Wildlife biodiversity; HIV/AIDS; Legal services; Sports and recreation.
International interests: China.
Limitations: Applications not accepted. Giving primarily in CO. No grants to individuals.

Application information: Contributes only to pre-selected organizations.
Officers: Jay P.K. Kenney, Pres.; Thomas J. Barrett, Jr., Secy.
Trustees: Clayton Kendall Kenney; Duncan Stross Kenney.
EIN: 841249377

1303
Kern Family Foundation
1133 14th St., Ste. 4300
Denver, CO 80202-2282

Established in 1999 in Colorado.
Donors: Jerome Kern; Mary Kern.
Foundation type: Independent foundation.
Financial data (yr. ended 12/31/14): Assets, $381,882 (M); expenditures, $120,370; qualifying distributions, $119,000; giving activities include $119,000 for 6 grants (high: $100,000; low: $2,500).
Fields of interest: Arts and culture; Human services.
Limitations: Applications not accepted. Giving primarily in Denver, CO.
Application information: Unsolicited requests for funds not accepted.
Officer: Jerome Kern, Pres.
EIN: 841522247

1304
Kesher Foundation
950 S. Cherry St., Ste. 1100
Denver, CO 80246-2667

Donors: Diana Anderson; Zeff Anderson.
Foundation type: Independent foundation.
Financial data (yr. ended 12/31/12): Assets, $3,852,000 (M); gifts received, $4,000,000; expenditures, $148,000; qualifying distributions, $148,000; giving activities include $148,000 for 2 grants (high: $133,000; low: $15,000).
Fields of interest: Education; Judaism.
Limitations: Applications not accepted. Giving primarily in Denver, CO.
Application information: Unsolicited requests for funds not accepted.
Officers and Directors: Diana Anderson, Pres. and Secy.-Treas. and Director; Adam Yehoshua Wolfson, V.P. and Director; Elan Hadar Wolfson, V.P. and Director.
EIN: 461444858

1305
The Lloyd L. and Eleanor R. King Foundation
26 W. Dry Creek Cir., Ste. 450
Littleton, CO 80120-8064

Donor: Eleanor Eleanor King†.
Foundation type: Independent foundation.
Financial data (yr. ended 12/31/13): Assets, $9,653,864 (M); gifts received, $12,176; expenditures, $654,061; qualifying distributions, $563,767; giving activities include $333,387 for 43 grants (high: $25,000; low: $300).
Fields of interest: Human services.
Type of support: General support.
Limitations: Applications not accepted. Giving primarily in CO.

Application information: Unsolicited requests for funds not accepted.
Officers: Robert L. Eckelberry, C.E.O. and Pres.; Dave Evans, V.P.; Joyce Stockley, Secy.; David H. Ezra, Treas.
Directors: Carol Walters.
EIN: 263000472

1306
Koelbel Family Foundation
5291 E. Yale Ave.
Denver, CO 80222-6911

Established in 1996 in Colorado.
Donor: Walter A. Koelbel.
Foundation type: Independent foundation.
Financial data (yr. ended 12/31/13): Assets, $3,021,294 (M); expenditures, $464,456; qualifying distributions, $429,150; giving activities include $427,650 for 40 grants (high: $250,000; low: $500).
Fields of interest: Education; Domesticated animals; Human services.
Limitations: Applications not accepted. Giving primarily in Denver, CO. No grants to individuals.
Application information: Contributes only to pre-selected organizations.
Officers: Walter A. Koelbel, Jr., Pres.; Gene N. Koelbel, V.P.; Vanda N. Werner, V.P.; Thomas E. Whyte, Secy.-Treas.
EIN: 841369773

1307
Jess, Rose Kortz & Pearl Rae Foundation
7600 E. Eastman Ave., Ste. 410
Denver, CO 80231-4374

Donors: Jess Kortz; Pearle Rae Kortz Levey.
Foundation type: Independent foundation.
Financial data (yr. ended 11/30/13): Assets, $3,647,544 (M); gifts received, $100,000; expenditures, $189,601; qualifying distributions, $188,886; giving activities include $187,485 for 62 grants (high: $50,000; low: $100).
Purpose and activities: Giving primarily for Jewish organizations.
Fields of interest: Arts and culture; Education; Nonprofits; Hospital care; Diseases and conditions; Christianity; Judaism; Human services.
Type of support: Regranting.
Limitations: Applications not accepted. Giving primarily in CA and CO. No grants to individuals.
Application information: Contributes only to pre-selected organizations.
Officers: Pearle Rae Kortz Levey, Pres.; Kenneth M. Laff, V.P.
EIN: 846021153

1308
The Vernon K. Krieble Foundation, Inc.
1777 S. Harrison St., Ste. 807
Denver, CO 80210-3933 (303) 758-3956
Contact: Helen E. Krieble, Pres.
FAX: (303) 488-0068; E-mail: info@krieble.org; Main URL: http://www.krieble.org

Established in 1985 in Connecticut.
Donor: Gladys V.K. Delmas†.
Foundation type: Independent foundation.

Financial data (yr. ended 12/31/13): Assets, $19,118,727 (M); expenditures, $1,272,792; qualifying distributions, $1,131,040; giving activities include $327,400 for 27 grants (high: $45,000; low: $1,000).
Purpose and activities: Giving only to organizations and projects which involve public policy research and education on issues supporting the preservation, and in some cases the restoration, or freedom and democracy in the United States, according to the principles of the Founding Fathers.
Fields of interest: Education; Archives and special collections; Public affairs; Public policy; Public administration.
Type of support: Policy, advocacy and systems reform.
Limitations: Applications accepted. Giving in the U.S., with emphasis on the Washington, DC area, including VA. No grants to individuals.
Publications: Annual report (including application guidelines).
Application information:
  Initial approach: Letter
  Copies of proposal: 1
  Deadline(s): None
  Board meeting date(s): June and Dec.
Officers: Helen E. Krieble, Pres. and Director; Frederick Krieble, V.P.; Amanda C. Fusscas, Secy. and Director; Christopher P. Fusscas, Treas. and Director; Shari Williams, Exec. Dir.
Director: Frederick B. Krieble.
Number of staff: 1 part-time support.
EIN: 222538914

1309
Kroh Charitable Trust
c/o Home State Bank
300 E. 29th St.
Loveland, CO 80538-2762 9706227412
E-mail: lahlawyer@aol.com; Application address: c/o Lynn A. Hammond, 200 E. 7th St., Ste. 418, Loveland, CO 80537-4871, tel.: (970) 667-1023

Donor: Lois L. Kroh Marital Trust.
Foundation type: Independent foundation.
Financial data (yr. ended 12/31/14): Assets, $118,152; expenditures, $128,523; qualifying distributions, $126,862.
Fields of interest: Arts and culture; Education; Health.
Limitations: Applications accepted. Giving primarily in the Loveland, CO, area.
Application information: Application form required.
  Initial approach: Letter
  Deadline(s): None
Trustee: Home State Bank.
EIN: 846214217

1310
The Ladd Foundation
1520 W. Canal Ct., Ste. 220
Littleton, CO 80120-5651

Established in 1993 in Colorado.
Donor: J.B. Ladd.
Foundation type: Independent foundation.
Financial data (yr. ended 11/30/13): Assets, $6,211,375 (M); expenditures, $294,134; qualifying distributions, $252,500; giving activities include $252,500 for 18 grants (high: $125,000; low: $1,000).

Fields of interest: Botanical gardens; Foundations; Nonprofits; Health; Hospital care; Diseases and conditions; Cancers.
Type of support: Regranting; Research; Research and evaluation.
Limitations: Applications not accepted. Giving primarily in Los Angeles, CA and Denver, CO. No grants to individuals.
Application information: Contributes only to pre-selected organizations.
Officers and Directors: J.B. Ladd, Pres. and Director; Jerry D. Ladd, V.P. and Treas. and Director; Jack M. Stern, Secy.; Stan Sprinkle.
EIN: 841250646

1311
The Leighty Foundation
c/o Jane Leighty Justis
P.O. Box 37
Cascade, CO 80809-0037
E-mail: jane@leightyfoundation.org; Main URL: http://www.leightyfoundation.org
Grants List: http://leightyfoundation.org/grantees

Donors: H.D. Leighty; William C. Leighty.
Foundation type: Independent foundation.
Financial data (yr. ended 08/31/13): Assets, $6,050,737 (M); gifts received, $30,000; expenditures, $490,925; qualifying distributions, $455,702; giving activities include $320,150 for 117 grants (high: $18,000; low: $200), and $54,107 for 2 foundation-administered programs.
Purpose and activities: Support for organizations which seek to deal with today's problems and opportunities in ways that meet current needs without compromising the ability of future generations to meet their needs. The foundation concentrates its efforts in areas of special concern to its board members. Priorities include: earth protection, education, promotion of philanthropy and volunteerism.
Fields of interest: Education; Environment; Philanthropy; Voluntarism.
Type of support: General support; Pro bono consulting services; Matching grants; Capacity-building and technical assistance; Program development; Convening; Curriculum development; Internships; Technical assistance.
Limitations: Applications not accepted. Giving primarily in AK, CO, and IA. No grants to individuals.
Publications: Annual report.
Application information: Unsolicited requests for funds not accepted.
  Board meeting date(s): Mar., May, Aug., Sept., and Dec.
Officers and Directors: H.D. Leighty, Pres. and Director; Robert F. Justis, V.P.; William Clyde Leighty, V.P.; Nancy J. Waterman, Secy.-Treas.; Jane Leighty Justis, Exec. Dir.
Number of staff: 1 full-time professional; 1 part-time support.
EIN: 421264476

1312
The Leininger Family Foundation
c/o Kathy Leininger
1 Penrose Blvd.
Colorado Springs, CO 80906-4213

Donors: B. Joseph Leininger; Kathryn L. Leininger.
Foundation type: Independent foundation.

Financial data (yr. ended 12/31/13): Assets, $592,483 (M); gifts received, $640,000; expenditures, $392,359; qualifying distributions, $387,985; giving activities include $386,000 for 26 grants (high: $100,000; low: $500).
Fields of interest: Christianity; Family services.
Limitations: Applications not accepted. Giving primarily in CO, PA and WA.
Application information: Unsolicited requests for funds not accepted.
Officers: B. Joseph Leininger, Pres.; Kathryn L. Leininger, Secy.
EIN: 271535407

1313
The Mike Leprino Family Foundation
1830 W. 38th Ave.
Denver, CO   80211-2200   (303) 480-7612
Contact: Nancy Leprino, Secy.

Established in 1997 in Colorado.
Donor: Mike Leprino.
Foundation type: Independent foundation.
Financial data (yr. ended 12/31/13): Assets, $5,221,411 (M); expenditures, $230,120; qualifying distributions, $188,456; giving activities include $185,000 for 6 grants (high: $110,000; low: $5,000).
Fields of interest: Art museums; Higher education; Hospital care; Human services.
Limitations: Applications accepted. Giving primarily in CO. No grants to individuals, or for lobbying activities.
Application information:
  Initial approach: Proposal
  Deadline(s): None
Officers: Mike Leprino, Pres.; Laura Leprino, V.P.; Mary Leprino, V.P.; Nancy Leprino, Secy.
EIN: 311510265

1314
Lewan Family Foundation
1400 S. Colorado Blvd., Ste. 400
Denver, CO   80222-3651

Donors: Paul & Marjorie Lewan Charitable Remainder Trust; Marjorie Lewan; Paul R. Lewan.
Foundation type: Independent foundation.
Financial data (yr. ended 12/31/14): Assets, $1,164,257; gifts received, $200,000; expenditures, $374,557; qualifying distributions, $368,026.
Fields of interest: Christianity; Community service for youth.
Type of support: General support.
Limitations: Applications not accepted. No grants to individuals.
Application information: Unsolicited requests for funds not accepted.
Officers: Paul R. Lewan, Pres.; Lloyd S. Lewan, V.P.; Marjorie A. Lewan, Secy.; Kimberly Lewan Laydon, Treas.
Directors: Jennifer E. Lewan; Matthew R. Lewan.
EIN: 841251741

1315
Richard H. Lewis Family Foundation
7117 S. Locust Cir.
Englewood, CO   80112-1576

Established in 2000 in Colorado.
Donor: Richard H. Lewis.
Foundation type: Independent foundation.
Financial data (yr. ended 12/31/13): Assets, $7,963,806 (M); gifts received, $410,789; expenditures, $544,090; qualifying distributions, $462,109; giving activities include $437,179 for 57 grants (high: $123,300; low: $79).
Purpose and activities: Giving primarily for education, youth and social services, and Christian churches and organizations.
Fields of interest: Higher education; Nonprofits; Christianity; Human services; Child welfare.
Type of support: General support; Regranting.
Limitations: Applications not accepted. Giving primarily in CO. No grants to individuals.
Application information: Contributes only to pre-selected organizations.
Directors: Bradford H. Lewis; Carol A. Lewis; Richard H. Lewis.
EIN: 841568116

1316
The Living Legacy Foundation
2000 Little Raven St., Ste. 6A
Denver, CO   80202-6101

Donors: Jacque Abadie; Craig Manning; Eric Lies; Kevin Kalamar; Bill Gourger; Deb Gorman; Terry L. Leprino; Bryan ND Suzanne Chrisman; Cameron Services; James Baum; Jeff Berget; Alexander-Cameron Services; Instar Service; Marc Espinosa; Thomas Gorman; Tim Hodges; Scott and Debbie; Life Rescue; FirstBank Holding Company; James Whyte; Eric Protzman; David Meloy; Christopher McBee; Nancy Protzman; Universal Stylz; Sandi Zimmerman; Lauren Reitsman; Meadows Consulting; Josh Reitsman; Simple Heart Charitable Trust.
Foundation type: Independent foundation.
Financial data (yr. ended 12/31/13): Assets, $1,490 (M); gifts received, $334,305; expenditures, $407,317; qualifying distributions, $363,571; giving activities include $363,571 for 30 grants (high: $80,196; low: $270).
Fields of interest: Higher education.
Type of support: Grants to individuals.
Limitations: Applications not accepted. Giving primarily in CO.
Application information: Unsolicited requests for funds not accepted.
Officers: Bill Maston, Pres.; Terry L. Leprino, Secy.; Frank Dipentino, Treas.
EIN: 201239533

1317
Living Rock Foundation
1544 Oxbow Dr., Ste. 200
Montrose, CO   81401-5190
E-mail: info@livingrockfoundation.org; Main
URL: http://livingrockfoundation.org

Donors: Kenneth A. Eldred; Robert E. Eldred.
Foundation type: Independent foundation.
Financial data (yr. ended 11/30/14): Assets, $6,309,904 (M); expenditures, $923,459; qualifying distributions, $762,391; giving activities include $242,843 for 13 grants (high: $30,000; low: $4,843).
Fields of interest: Community and economic development; Religion; Human services.

Limitations: Applications not accepted. Giving in the U.S., with emphasis on CA and GA.
Application information: Unsolicited requests for funds not accepted.
Officers and Trustees: Kenneth A. Eldred, Chair. and Trustee; Roberta E. Eldred, Pres. and Trustee; Alex Brubaker, V.P. and Trustee; Justin Eldred, Treas. and Trustee; Kary Eldred; Monica Eldred; Rachel Eldred.
EIN: 451656663

1318
Lustig Family Foundation
410 17th St., Ste. 1705
Denver, CO   80202-4430
Contact: Debra Lustig, Secy.-Treas. and Dir.

Established in 2000 in Colorado.
Donor: James A. Lustig.
Foundation type: Independent foundation.
Financial data (yr. ended 12/31/13): Assets, $6,652,149 (M); expenditures, $261,665; qualifying distributions, $245,000; giving activities include $245,000 for 5 grants (high: $100,000; low: $25,000).
Fields of interest: Museums; Hospital care; Judaism.
Limitations: Applications accepted. Giving primarily in Los Angeles, CA and CO.
Application information: Application form required.
  Initial approach: Letter
  Deadline(s): None
  Final notification: Within 2 months
Officers and Directors: James A. Lustig, Pres. and Director; Debra Lustig, Secy.-Treas. and Director; Jennifer Ann Gardner; Brooke Dana Lande.
EIN: 841225026

1319
Maki Foundation
421D Aspen Airport Business Ctr.
Aspen, CO   81611-3551   (970) 925-3272
Contact: Patricia A. Humphry
E-mail: makifoundation@gmail.com; Main
URL: http://www.makifoundation.org
Grants List: http://www.makifoundation.org/grantmaking-overview.html

Established in 1981 in Colorado.
Foundation type: Independent foundation.
Financial data (yr. ended 12/31/14): Assets, $3,874,367; gifts received, $0; expenditures, $233,766; qualifying distributions, $241,853 and $0 for set-asides.
Purpose and activities: Giving primarily for wilderness and wildlands protection, river and wetlands conservation, biological diversity conservation, and public lands management.
Fields of interest: Environment; Natural resources.
Type of support: General support; Program development.
Limitations: Applications accepted. Giving primarily in the western U.S., including NM, CO, UT, ID, WY, and MT. No support for recycling programs, tree planting projects, toxic waste cleanup, or wildlife rehabilitation centers. No grants for acquisition or construction of community recreation facilities, buildings, municipal parks, reservoirs, film production, fellowships or private land trusts.
Publications: Application guidelines.

Application information: Complete application guidelines available on foundation web site. Application form required.

    Initial approach: Letter or telephone

    Deadline(s): May 1

    Final notification: Sept. 15

Directors: Ann Harvey; Constance Harvey; Mark Harvey; Nelson Harvey; Kim Springer.

Number of staff: 1 full-time professional.

EIN: 840836242

1320

Margulf Foundation

(formerly Martin & Deborah Flug Foundation)
616 E. Hyman Ave., No. 2D
Aspen, CO 81611-2391

Donors: Martin Flug; James Flug; Robert Flug; Barbara Colin; Gulftech International, Inc.; Jeremy Flug; Gulfco, Ltd.

Foundation type: Independent foundation.

Financial data (yr. ended 11/30/13): Assets, $14,436,500 (M); gifts received, $254,848; expenditures, $502,658; qualifying distributions, $486,124; giving activities include $326,500 for 16 grants (high: $100,000; low: $500).

Purpose and activities: Support given to organizations that provide scholarships, support the arts, or provide community services.

Fields of interest: Arts and culture; Music; Elementary and secondary education; Higher education; Law education; Nonprofits; Diseases and conditions; Human services.

Type of support: General support; Regranting; Capital campaigns; Scholarships.

Limitations: Applications not accepted. Giving primarily in CO; some giving also in MA and OH. No grants to individuals.

Application information: Contributes only to pre-selected organizations.

Officers: Martin Flug, Pres.; Jeremy Flug, V.P.; Richard Boerner, Treas.

EIN: 132927245

1321

Martischang Foundation

1777 S. Harrison St., Ste. 1000
Denver, CO 80210

Donor: Alphonse Martischang†.

Foundation type: Independent foundation.

Financial data (yr. ended 12/31/13): Assets, $14,498,194 (M); expenditures, $1,410,009; qualifying distributions, $162,387; giving activities include $162,387 for 18 grants (high: $25,935; low: $5,000).

Fields of interest: Education.

Limitations: Applications not accepted. Giving primarily in CO.

Application information: Unsolicited requests for funds not accepted.

Trustees: Kevin McDonald; Lynn McDonald.

EIN: 840762733

1322

McGrath Family Foundation

(formerly McGrath Investment Foundation)
c/o Ann Pena
P.O. Box 1284
Englewood, CO 80150-1284

Established in 1995 in Colorado.

Foundation type: Independent foundation.

Financial data (yr. ended 12/31/13): Assets, $3,362,941 (M); expenditures, $184,370; qualifying distributions, $167,043; giving activities include $166,793 for 13 grants (high: $40,000; low: $1,500).

Purpose and activities: Giving to protect the environment and promote conservation; giving also to strengthen and expand the growth and education of children.

Fields of interest: Natural resources; Catholicism; Human services; Child welfare.

Limitations: Applications not accepted. Giving on a national basis. No support for political organizations.

Application information: Unsolicited requests for funds not accepted.

    Board meeting date(s): Quarterly

Officer: Ann Pena, Pres.

Directors: Barbara L. McGrath; Bruce K. McGrath; Tracey F. McGrath.

EIN: 841307861

1323

McPherson Family Foundation

4531 Silver Gate Dr.
Castle Pines, CO 80108-8472

Established in 2005 in Colorado.

Donor: J. Mark McPherson.

Foundation type: Independent foundation.

Financial data (yr. ended 12/31/13): Assets, -$49,833 (M); gifts received, $284,000; expenditures, $411,729; qualifying distributions, $409,500; giving activities include $409,500 for 6 grants (high: $346,000; low: $1,000).

Fields of interest: Basic and emergency aid; International development.

Limitations: Applications not accepted. Giving primarily in CO. No grants to individuals.

Application information: Unsolicited requests for funds not accepted.

Officers: J. Mark McPherson, Pres.; Kim L. McPherson, Secy.-Treas.

Director: Brad Brady.

EIN: 202378383

1324

Medical Education Collaborative

(doing business as Foundation for Greater Good)
33-A Gamble St.
P.O. Box 4085
Eagle, CO 81631
Main URL: http://www.f2g2.org

Foundation type: Independent foundation.

Financial data (yr. ended 06/30/14): Assets, $5,160,345 (M); expenditures, $486,784; qualifying distributions, $295,226; giving activities include $235,260 for 3 grants (high: $200,000; low: $5,000).

Fields of interest: Education; Youth development.

Limitations: Applications not accepted. Giving primarily in CO.

Application information: Unsolicited requests for funds not accepted.

Officers: Brian McCartney, Chair.; Judith Over, Secy.; Barry Johnson, Treas.

EIN: 742498948

1325

Randy and Michele Mehrberg Schara Family Foundation

390 Interlocken Crescent
Broomfield, CO 80021

Donor: Randy Mehrberg.

Foundation type: Independent foundation.

Financial data (yr. ended 12/31/13): Assets, $402,055 (M); gifts received, $108,052; expenditures, $208,755; qualifying distributions, $208,755; giving activities include $203,190 for 14 grants (high: $102,500; low: $100).

Fields of interest: Education; Domesticated animals; Diseases and conditions.

Type of support: Research.

Limitations: Applications not accepted. Giving primarily in PA.

Application information: Unsolicited requests for funds not accepted.

Officers: Randall E. Mehrberg, Pres.; Dillon Mehrberg, V.P.; Michele Schara, Secy.-Treas.

EIN: 262026540

1326

Frances A. Melrose Foundation

c/o Michael J Kleinman, Esq.
9490 S. Aspen Hill Way
Lone Tree, CO 80124-5489

Established in 2005 in Colorado.

Donor: Frances A. Melrose†.

Foundation type: Independent foundation.

Financial data (yr. ended 12/31/13): Assets, $3,421,859 (M); gifts received, $249; expenditures, $210,476; qualifying distributions, $159,149; giving activities include $156,247 for 4 grants (high: $66,247; low: $30,000).

Fields of interest: Environment.

Limitations: Applications not accepted. Giving primarily in CO.

Application information: Unsolicited requests for funds not accepted.

Officers and Directors: Michael J. Kleinman, Chair. and Director; Larry D. Harvey, Esq., Secy. and Director; Dean J. Boosalis, CPA, Treas. and Director; Victoria Philpott Jones; Doron L. Kleinman.

EIN: 202955518

1327

The Moniker Foundation

1308 W. Colorado Ave.
Colorado Springs, CO 80904-4023

Established in 1998 in Colorado.

Donors: Blanche W. Sinton; Laura K. Sinton; Mari Sinton-Martinez; Laura Sinton-Emery; Linda S. Hammond; Margie Sinton; Frank J. Sinton.

Foundation type: Independent foundation.

Financial data (yr. ended 04/30/13): Assets, $4,245,018 (M); gifts received, $429,844; expenditures, $234,862; qualifying distributions, $234,862; giving activities include $213,000 for 32 grants (high: $20,000; low: $2,000).

Fields of interest: Arts and culture; Higher education; Zoos; Human services; Victim aid.

Type of support: General support; Scholarships.

Limitations: Applications not accepted. Giving primarily in CO. No grants to individuals.

Application information: Contributes only to pre-selected organizations.

Officer: Linda S. Hammond, Pres.
EIN: 841461847

1328
Morse Family Foundation
410 17th St., No. 1150
Denver, CO 80202-4414

Established in 2004 in Colorado.
Donors: Julie Morse; Brent J. Morse.
Foundation type: Independent foundation.
Financial data (yr. ended 12/31/12): Assets,
$3,971,879 (M); expenditures, $259,755;
qualifying distributions, $224,380; giving activities
include $224,380 for grants.
Purpose and activities: Giving primarily to Jewish
organizations.
Fields of interest: Nonprofits; Judaism.
Type of support: Regranting.
Limitations: Applications not accepted. Giving
primarily in CO. No grants to individuals.
Application information: Unsolicited requests for
funds not accepted.
Officers: Brent J. Morse, Pres.; Julie A. Morse,
Secy.-Treas.
Number of staff: None.
EIN: 721586887

1329
J. K. Mullen Foundation
5310 DTC Pkwy., Ste. C
Greenwood Village, CO 80111-3010 (303)
722-3557

Established in 1924 in Colorado.
Donors: John K. Mullen†; Catherine S. Mullen†; The
J.K. Mullen Foundation.
Foundation type: Independent foundation.
Financial data (yr. ended 07/31/13): Assets,
$5,638,173 (M); expenditures, $367,480;
qualifying distributions, $298,699; giving activities
include $279,020 for 65 grants (high: $47,450;
low: $500).
Purpose and activities: Focus is on the poor and
disadvantaged members of our society, victims of
family and substance abuse, the mentally
challenged, physically impaired, and others whose
lives are outside the mainstream. Education is also
of interest.
Fields of interest: Elementary and secondary
education; Secondary education; Diseases and
conditions; Human services; Youth services; People
with disabilities.
Type of support: General support; Annual
campaigns; Capital and infrastructure; Equipment.
Limitations: Applications accepted. Giving limited to
the Denver, CO, metropolitan area. No support for
taxpayer-supported organizations. No grants to
individuals.
Publications: Application guidelines; Financial
statement.
Application information: Application form required.
Initial approach: Letter
Copies of proposal: 1
Deadline(s): June 1
Officers and Trustees: Timothy M. O'Connor, Pres.
and Trustee; John K. Weckbaugh, V.P. and Trustee;
Sheila Sevier, Secy. and Trustee; Walter S.
Weckbaugh, Treas. and Trustee; J. Kenneth Malo,
Jr.; John F. Malo; Kathleen M. Malo; Marcus Sevier;
Heather Weckbaugh.

Number of staff: 1 part-time support.
EIN: 846002475

1330
National Endowment for Financial
Education
(also known as NEFE)
1331 17th St., Ste. 1200
Denver, CO 80202-1595
Contact: Londell Jackson, Asst. Dir., Grants &
Research
FAX: (303) 220-0838; E-mail: ldj@nefe.org; Main
URL: http://www.nefe.org
E Newsletter: http://www.nefe.org/NEFENews/
PressRoom/Subscribe/tabid/230/Default.aspx
Twitter: http://twitter.com/NEFE_ORG
YouTube: http://www.youtube.com/user/
NonprofitNEFE

Established in 1972 in Colorado.
Foundation type: Operating foundation.
Financial data (yr. ended 12/31/13): Assets,
$166,169,812 (M); gifts received, $443,833;
expenditures, $6,789,404; qualifying distributions,
$5,603,497; giving activities include $440,907 for
8 grants (high: $131,997; low: $27,571), and
$4,485,947 for 4 foundation-administered
programs.
Purpose and activities: The National Endowment for
Financial Education (NEFE) is the only private,
nonprofit, national foundation wholly dedicated to
improving the financial well-being of all Americans.
The mission of the National Endowment for Financial
Education is to help individual Americans acquire
the knowledge and skills necessary to take control
of their financial destiny. NEFEs mission is grounded
in the belief that regardless of background or income
level, financially informed individuals are better able
to 1) take control of their circumstances, 2) improve
their quality of life, and 3) ensure a stable future for
themselves and their families. NEFEs guiding
principles are stated in eight initiatives. These
initiatives describe how NEFE achieves its mission,
and outlines the goals and standards that guide the
foundations activities. Every project or program
undertaken by NEFE must fit within the scope of at
least one initiative. NEFE accomplishes its mission
primarily by partnering with other organizations to:
1) provide practical, reliable, and unbiased financial
education to members of the public, 2) accomplish
research in the field of financial literacy education,
and 3) create demand for financial education. NEFEs
activities place special emphasis on those who face
financial challenges that are not being addressed by
others. Among the target audiences are: youth,
low-income individuals and families, and people in
difficult or unusual life circumstances. NEFEs
partnerships and the foundations own efforts result
in a wide range of free and low-cost activities and
materials, including: resources for consumers,
materials for educators and facilitators, the NEFE
High School Financial Planning Program, which
includes joint efforts with numerous nonprofit,
for-profit, and government entities to develop
financial literacy resources for specific audiences,
research, conferences, and think tanks on a variety
of financial literacy topics, and grant awards to
organizations and academic institutions whose work
can contribute to the field of financial literacy.
Fields of interest: Education; Foundations.
Type of support: Program development; Research;
Program evaluations; Research and evaluation;
Public engagement and education.

Limitations: Applications accepted. Giving on a
national basis. No support for organizations lacking
501(c)(3) IRS status, or foreign organizations. No
grants to individuals, or for general operating
support, deficits, salaries, capital costs, computer
equipment, pass-through funding, conferences,
seminars, fundraisers, sponsorships, endowments,
challenge grants, matching funds, scholarships, or
for registration fees.
Publications: Application guidelines; Informational
brochure; Newsletter.
Application information: Full proposals will be
accepted by invitation only following submission of
inquiry. See foundation web site for application
information. Application form required.
Initial approach: Complete the Concept Inquiry
form after checking guidelines and eligibility
Copies of proposal: 1
Deadline(s): June and Dec.
Board meeting date(s): Apr. and Nov.
Final notification: 5 business days following board
meetings
Officers and Directors: Karen Vahouny, Chair. and
Director; Michael A. Bedke, Vice-Chair. and Director;
Ted Beck, C.E.O. and Pres. and Director; Alexander
Gonzalez, Ph.D, Tr. Emeritus and Director; Patrick
Bannigan; Dorothy J. Bridges; Denise V. Crawford.
Number of staff: 10 full-time professional; 5 full-time
support; 2 part-time support.
EIN: 840632115

1331
Neuman Family Foundation
819 10th St.
Boulder, CO 80302-7551

Established in 1998 in Illinois.
Donor: Werner Neuman.
Foundation type: Independent foundation.
Financial data (yr. ended 12/31/14): Assets,
$2,456,406 (M); expenditures, $433,282;
qualifying distributions, $431,574; giving activities
include $431,000 for 4 grants (high: $300,000;
low: $1,000).
Purpose and activities: Giving primarily for
education, the arts, the environment, and human
services.
Fields of interest: Arts and culture; Education;
Environment; Human services.
Limitations: Applications not accepted. Giving
primarily in Chicago, IL; some giving also in CA, CO,
MN and NY. No grants to individuals.
Application information: Unsolicited requests for
funds not accepted.
Trustees: Judith Neuman; Suzanne Neuman;
Werner Neuman; William Neuman.
EIN: 367234939

1332
The Nord Foundation
9226 Teddy Ln., Ste. 125
Lone Tree, CO 80124-6725

Established in 1997 in Colorado.
Donors: Nord Capital Group, Inc.; Arlen D.
Nordhagen; Wendy P. Nordhagen.
Foundation type: Company-sponsored foundation.
Financial data (yr. ended 11/30/13): Assets,
$6,403,629 (M); expenditures, $385,034;
qualifying distributions, $367,676; giving activities

include $280,563 for 25 grants (high: $50,909; low: $961).
Purpose and activities: The foundation supports organizations involved with Christianity.
Fields of interest: Christianity.
Type of support: General support; Loans to individuals; Continuing support; Emergency funds; Seed money.
Limitations: Applications not accepted. Giving on a national and international basis, with some emphasis on Denver and Littleton, CO. No support for secular organizations. No grants to individuals.
Application information: Unsolicited requests for funds not accepted.
Officers and Directors: Arlen D. Nordhagen, Pres. and Treas. and Director; Wendy P. Nordhagen, V.P. and Secy. and Director; Fred V. Lian; Ken J. Timboe.
Number of staff: None.
EIN: 841409115

1333
Oak Lodge Foundation
P.O. Box 7951
Aspen, CO 81612-7951
Contact: William O. Hunt Jr.

Donor: William O. & Jeannette P. Hunt Foundation.
Foundation type: Independent foundation.
Financial data (yr. ended 12/31/13): Assets, $2,495,643 (M); expenditures, $148,151; qualifying distributions, $130,000; giving activities include $130,000 for 23 grants (high: $20,000; low: $2,000).
Fields of interest: Arts and culture; Education; Human services.
Limitations: Applications not accepted. Giving primarily in CO, IL, MI, and NY. No grants to individuals.
Application information: Unsolicited requests for funds not accepted.
Officers and Directors: William O. Hunt, Jr., Pres. and Treas. and Director; Christopher Hunt, Secy.; Ian C. Hunt; Hilary H. McCutcheon.
EIN: 311604793

1334
The Okinaga Foundation
3001 S. Federal Blvd.
Denver, CO 80236-2711

Foundation type: Independent foundation.
Financial data (yr. ended 06/30/13): Assets, $2,471,831 (M); expenditures, $178,210; qualifying distributions, $176,617; giving activities include $165,000 for 2 grants (high: $115,000; low: $50,000).
Purpose and activities: Giving primarily for research in the medical science field.
Fields of interest: Education.
International interests: Germany.
Type of support: General support; Research.
Limitations: Applications not accepted. Giving primarily in Cambridge, MA and in Germany. No grants to individuals.
Application information: Unsolicited requests for funds not accepted.
Officers and Trustees: Yoshihito Okinaga, Chair. and Trustee; Etsuko Okinaga, Co-Pres. and Co-Treas. and Trustee; Shohachi Okinaga, Co-Pres.

and Co-Treas. and Trustee; Barbara Haley, Secy.; Tomoatsu Inoue.
EIN: 421354468

1335
Oreg Foundation
(formerly Weaver Family Foundation)
P.O. Box 20587
Boulder, CO 80308-0587 (720) 565-4064
Contact: Julie Shaffer, Exec.Dir. and Treas.

Established in 1999 in Colorado.
Donors: Lindsey A. Weaver, Jr.; Francine Lavin Weaver.
Foundation type: Independent foundation.
Financial data (yr. ended 12/31/13): Assets, $8,810,818 (M); expenditures, $575,668; qualifying distributions, $471,898; giving activities include $319,518 for 55 grants (high: $59,000; low: $50).
Purpose and activities: The foundation funds Colorado based, non-sectarian charitable programs that focus on education, community service, and the preservation of our natural environment. The foundation also supports programs that enhance Jewish life and spiritual renewal in the United States, Israel, and other countries around the world.
Fields of interest: Education; Environment; Housing development; Judaism; Human services.
International interests: Israel.
Type of support: General support; Pro bono consulting services; Program-related investments; Continuing support; Program development; Matching grants; Convening; Curriculum development; Fellowships.
Limitations: Applications accepted. Giving primarily in Boulder, CO, and Israel. No grants to individuals.
Application information: Application form required.
 Initial approach: Proposal
 Deadline(s): None
Officer: Julie Shaffer, Exec.Dir. and Treas.
Director: Lindsay A. Weaver, Jr.
Number of staff: 1 full-time professional.
EIN: 841513850

1336
The Petunia Foundation
400 Cook St.
Denver, CO 80206-4425

Established in 2000 in Colorado.
Donors: Patricia A. Zecchi; Paul J. Zecchi; Central Argentina Corp.
Foundation type: Independent foundation.
Financial data (yr. ended 12/31/12): Assets, $1 (M); gifts received, $200,000; expenditures, $189,972; qualifying distributions, $186,825; giving activities include $186,825 for grants.
Fields of interest: Education; Higher education; Human services; Low-income and poor people.
Limitations: Applications not accepted. Giving primarily in CO, MD, and OH. No grants to individuals.
Application information: Contributes only to pre-selected organizations.
Officers: Paul J. Zecchi, Pres.; Patricia J. Zecchi, Secy.
EIN: 841577696

1337
The Pluss Family Foundation
3033 E. 1st Ave., Ste. 502
Denver, CO 80206-3673

Established in 1985 in Colorado.
Donors: James Pluss; Sam Pluss; Pluss Poultry; Strear Farms Co., Inc.
Foundation type: Independent foundation.
Financial data (yr. ended 11/30/14): Assets, $2,336,637; expenditures, $287,393; qualifying distributions, $242,565.
Purpose and activities: Giving for health and Jewish organizations.
Fields of interest: Nonprofits; Health; Diseases and conditions; Judaism; Human services.
Type of support: General support; Regranting.
Limitations: Applications not accepted. Giving primarily in CO. No grants to individuals.
Application information: Contributes only to pre-selected organizations.
Officers: Sam Pluss, Pres.; Douglas Pluss, V.P. and Secy.; James Pluss, V.P. and Treas.
EIN: 841011699

1338
The Porphyry Road Foundation
(formerly The Jordanna Foundation)
2525 Arapahoe Ave., Ste. E-4
Boulder, CO 80302-6746

Established in 2001 in Colorado.
Donor: Jordanna Schutz.
Foundation type: Independent foundation.
Financial data (yr. ended 06/30/14): Assets, $3,812,735 (M); gifts received, $225,000; expenditures, $173,297; qualifying distributions, $173,000; giving activities include $172,000 for 11 grants (high: $62,000; low: $5,000).
Fields of interest: Environment; Human services; Youth development.
Limitations: Applications not accepted. No grants to individuals.
Application information: Unsolicited requests for funds not accepted.
Officer: Jordanna Schutz, Pres. and Secy.-Treas.
EIN: 841605637

1339
Praise Him Ministries, Inc.
120 Redcliff Dr.
Ridgway, CO 81432-9228 (970) 626-5243
Contact: Victoria Hearst, Dir.
Main URL: http://www.praisehimministries.org
E Newsletter: http://praisehimministries.org/events

Established in 2003 in Colorado.
Donor: Victoria Hearst.
Foundation type: Operating foundation.
Financial data (yr. ended 06/30/13): Assets, $2,447,122 (M); gifts received, $2,094,049; expenditures, $2,154,473; qualifying distributions, $1,781,475; giving activities include $213,170 for 6 grants (high: $70,408; low: $80), and $1,594,854 for 3 foundation-administered programs.
Purpose and activities: Giving to spread the Gospel of Jesus Christ by serving the people of Colorado.
Fields of interest: Christianity; Human services.

Limitations: Applications accepted. Giving primarily in CO, IL, MO, and VA.
Application information:
Deadline(s): None
Directors: Dean Freed; Victoria Hearst; John Peyton.
EIN: 030410199

1340
Priester Foundation
135 Silver Fox Ct.
Greenwood Village, CO 80121-2123

Established in 1997 in Colorado.
Donors: John Priester; Rosemary Priester.
Foundation type: Independent foundation.
Financial data (yr. ended 12/31/14): Assets, $2,758,624; expenditures, $256,070; qualifying distributions, $241,133.
Purpose and activities: Giving to local cultural organizations and for at-risk youth.
Fields of interest: Arts and culture; Education; Catholicism; Youth services; Low-income and poor people.
Limitations: Applications not accepted. Giving primarily in CO. No grants to individuals.
Application information: Unsolicited requests for funds not accepted.
Board meeting date(s): Jan.
Officers: Rosemary Priester, Chair. and Pres.; John D. Priester, Secy.-Treas.
Number of staff: None.
EIN: 841384487

1341
Harry L. and Eva J. Puksta Foundation
2221 W. 30th Ave.
Denver, CO 80211-3808 (303) 595-2031
Contact: John Mulstay, Pres.
Main URL: http://www.pukstafoundation.org
Facebook: https://www.facebook.com/pages/The-Puksta-Foundation/54697291984
Tumblr: http://pukstafoundation.tumblr.com
Twitter: https://twitter.com/PukstaFdn

Established in 2001 in Colorado.
Foundation type: Independent foundation.
Financial data (yr. ended 12/31/14): Assets, $4,397,372; gifts received, $12,816; expenditures, $306,043; qualifying distributions, $258,276.
Purpose and activities: The mission of the foundation is to provide the opportunity for underprivileged Colorado students to pursue a college education and to develop a commitment to citizenship, leadership and community engagement.
Fields of interest: Education; Higher education.
Type of support: Individual development.
Limitations: Applications accepted. Giving primarily in CO. No grants to individuals.
Application information: See grantmaker web site for application policies, contacts and guidelines.
Initial approach: Letter
Deadline(s): None
Officer: John Mulstay, Pres.
EIN: 841555566

1342
QEP Resources Education Foundation
1050 17th St., Ste. 500
Denver, CO 80265-1050

Donor: QEP Resources, Inc.
Foundation type: Independent foundation.
Financial data (yr. ended 12/31/14): Assets, $3,935,450; gifts received, $984,500; expenditures, $230,189; qualifying distributions, $229,623 and $0 for set-asides.
Fields of interest: Education; Higher education.
Type of support: Scholarships.
Limitations: Applications not accepted. Giving primarily in OK and TX.
Application information: Unsolicited requests for funds not accepted.
Officers: Charles B. Stanley, Chair. and Pres.; Jay B. Neese, V.P.; Richard J. Doleshek, V.P. and Treas.; Abigail L. Jones, Secy.
EIN: 273608211

1343
Rakowich Family Foundation
1700 N. Lincoln St., MAC C7300-498
Denver, CO 80203-4500

Donor: Rakowich Living Trust.
Foundation type: Independent foundation.
Financial data (yr. ended 12/31/13): Assets, $2,799,629 (M); gifts received, $306,999; expenditures, $284,183; qualifying distributions, $266,500; giving activities include $266,500 for 11 grants (high: $70,000; low: $2,000).
Fields of interest: Education; Human services; International relations.
Limitations: Applications not accepted. Giving primarily in CO.
Application information: Unsolicited requests for funds not accepted.
Officer: Walter C. Rakowich, Pres.
EIN: 460933919

1344
RBG, Inc.
P.O. Box 1799
Denver, CO 80201-1799

Established in 2006 in Unspecified.
Donor: WGS, Ltd.
Foundation type: Independent foundation.
Financial data (yr. ended 06/30/13): Assets, $404,570 (M); gifts received, $470,250; expenditures, $390,742; qualifying distributions, $397,303; giving activities include $397,303 for 28 grants (high: $299,395; low: $200).
Fields of interest: Education; Human services; Homeless people.
Limitations: Applications not accepted. Giving primarily in CO. No grants to individuals.
Application information: Contributes only to pre-selected organizations.
Officers and Directors: T. Andrew Roberts, Pres. and V.P. and Director; Janet Dimarco, Secy.- Treas.; J. Phillip Roberts; Richard D. Roberts.
EIN: 205662470

1345
Reel Family Foundation, Inc.
5600 S. Quebec St., Ste. 148B
Englewood, CO 80111-2209

Foundation type: Independent foundation.
Financial data (yr. ended 12/31/13): Assets, $4,203,540 (M); expenditures, $84,083; qualifying

distributions, $203,550; giving activities include $203,550 for 37 grants (high: $11,000; low: $1,000).
Fields of interest: Education; Christianity; Judaism; Youth development.
Limitations: Applications not accepted. Giving primarily in Denver, CO.
Application information: Unsolicited requests for funds not accepted.
Officer: Louis J. Davis, Pres.
EIN: 263442960

1346
Relationship Enrichment Collaborative
817 Pearl St.
Boulder, CO 80302

Donor: National Christian Foundation.
Foundation type: Operating foundation.
Financial data (yr. ended 06/30/14): Assets, $269,617 (M); gifts received, $3,412,500; expenditures, $3,367,399; qualifying distributions, $3,367,399; giving activities include $192,500 for 6 grants (high: $130,000; low: $2,500).
Fields of interest: Education; Diseases and conditions; Human services.
Limitations: Applications not accepted. Giving primarily in IL and WI.
Application information: Unsolicited requests for funds not accepted.
Officers: Timothy Popadic, Pres.; Stuart Fullenwider, Secy.
Directors: Ryan Findley; William B. Novak.
EIN: 452532380

1347
Rockwise Foundation
11525 Howells Rd.
Colorado Springs, CO 80908-3735 (719) 331-1915
Contact: Randall Welsch, Pres.

Donors: Randall Welsch; Harry J. Lloyd Charitable Trust.
Foundation type: Independent foundation.
Financial data (yr. ended 12/31/13): Assets, $58,233 (M); expenditures, $172,432; qualifying distributions, $170,019; giving activities include $169,522 for 1 grant.
Fields of interest: Community and economic development; Human services.
Application information: Application form required.
Initial approach: Proposal
Deadline(s): None
Officers: Randall Welsch, Pres.; Louellen Welsch, Secy.-Treas.
Board Member: Jolynn Welsch.
EIN: 260208987

1348
Routzon Family Foundation, Inc.
5425 W. Princeton Dr.
Denver, CO 80235-3128 (303) 988-3493

Established in 2004 in Colorado.
Donors: Edward P. Routzon; Marsha J. Routzon; Sarah Routzon-Landry.
Foundation type: Independent foundation.
Financial data (yr. ended 12/31/13): Assets, $3,853,673 (M); gifts received, $72,570;

expenditures, $245,867; qualifying distributions, $221,216; giving activities include $144,436 for 11 + grants (high: $25,000; low: $2,500), and $76,780 for 1 grant to an individual.
Fields of interest: Education; Catholicism; Human services.
Type of support: General support.
Limitations: Applications accepted. Giving primarily in Denver, CO.
Application information: Application form required.
  Initial approach: Proposal
  Deadline(s): Nov. 1
  Final notification: Dec. 31
Officers: Sarah Routzon-Landry, Pres.; Matthew E. Routzon, Treas.
EIN: 201945666

1349

Schlessman Family Foundation, Inc.

(formerly Schlessman Foundation, Inc.)
c/o Patricia Middendorf
1555 Blake St., Ste. 400
Denver, CO 80202-1866 (303) 831-5683
Contact: Lee E. Schlessman, Pres.
FAX: (303) 831-5676;
E-mail: contact@schlessmanfoundation.org; Main URL: http://www.schlessmanfoundation.org

Established in 1957 in Colorado.
Donors: Florence M. Schlessman†; Gerald L. Schlessman†; Lee E. Schlessman.
Foundation type: Independent foundation.
Financial data (yr. ended 03/31/13): Assets, $27,630,361 (M); expenditures, $463,941; qualifying distributions, $200,416; giving activities include $200,316 for 17 grants (high: $119,370; low: $100).
Purpose and activities: Giving primarily for: 1) education, 2) disadvantaged youth programs and services, particularly those that foster initiative and a positive work ethic, 3) elderly/senior programs that assist in providing the necessities of life, 4) special needs groups, such as people who are handicapped, homeless families and people who are mentally ill, and 5) established cultural institutions such as museums, libraries and zoos. .
Fields of interest: Education; Human services; Child welfare; People with disabilities.
Type of support: General support; Matching grants; Continuing support; Annual campaigns; Equipment; Endowments; Program development; Curriculum development; Scholarships.
Limitations: Applications accepted. Giving limited to CO, primarily the greater Denver area. No support for charter, private or public school programs. No grants to individuals, or for benefits, conferences or start-up grants.
Publications: Application guidelines.
Application information: Colorado Common Grant Application form accepted, but not required.
  Initial approach: Proposal
  Copies of proposal: 1
  Deadline(s): Dec. 31
  Board meeting date(s): Mar.
  Final notification: Mar. 31
Officers and Board Members: Lee E. Schlessman, Pres. and Director; Susan M. Duncan, V.P. and Director; Dolores J. Schlessman, V.P. and Director; Gary L. Schlessman, Secy. and Director; Patricia A. Middendorf, Treas. and Exec. Dir.; Sandra Garnett.
EIN: 846030309

1350

The Schramm Foundation

800 Grant St., Ste. 330
Denver, CO 80203-2944 (303) 861-8291
Contact: Gary S. Kring, Pres.

Foundation type: Independent foundation.
Financial data (yr. ended 06/30/13): Assets, $5,163,804 (M); expenditures, $448,068; qualifying distributions, $393,600; giving activities include $393,600 for grants.
Fields of interest: Arts and culture; Education; Higher education; Hospital care; Diseases and conditions; Human services; Family services; Child welfare.
Type of support: General support; Matching grants; Continuing support; Annual campaigns; Capital and infrastructure; Research; Equipment; Research and evaluation; Debt reduction; Program development.
Limitations: Applications accepted. Giving in CO, with emphasis on the Denver area. No support for political, religious organizations or animal welfare rights organizations. No grants to individuals.
Publications: Annual report (including application guidelines).
Application information: Application form required.
  Initial approach: Letter
  Copies of proposal: 1
  Deadline(s): Submissions must be postmarked between July 1 and Aug. 31
Officers: Gary S. Kring, Pres.; Mark H. Carson, V.P.; Matthew Kring, Secy.; Mara Marks, Treas.
Number of staff: 1 part-time professional.
EIN: 846032196

1351

SEAKR Foundation

6221 S. Racine Cir.
Centennial, CO 80111-6427 (303) 708-5210
Contact: Raymond E. Anderson, Chair.
E-mail: info@seakrfoundation.com; Additional contact: Melissa Coen, Fdn. Rep., tel.: (303) 858-4559; Main URL: http://www.seakrfoundation.com
Facebook: https://www.facebook.com/seakrfoundation
YouTube: https://www.youtube.com/watch?v=mrYQVKPYYOA

Established in 2004 in Colorado.
Donors: SEAKR Engineering, Inc.; Raymond E. Anderson.
Foundation type: Company-sponsored foundation.
Financial data (yr. ended 12/31/13): Assets, $195,498 (M); gifts received, $219,000; expenditures, $275,095; qualifying distributions, $251,725; giving activities include $225 for 1 grant, and $251,500 for 16 grants to individuals (high: $24,000; low: $2,000).
Purpose and activities: The foundation awards grants to the families of soldiers killed or wounded in the line of duty.
Fields of interest: Family services; Military personnel.
Type of support: Grants to individuals.
Limitations: Applications not accepted. Giving primarily in CO.
Application information: Contributes only to pre-selected individuals.
Officer and Director: Raymond E. Anderson, Chair. and Director; Lorraine W. Anderson.
EIN: 200979291

1352

The Servant Leadership Foundation

950 E. Westglow Ln.
Littleton, CO 80121-1375

Donors: TYL Foundation; McVaney Family Foundation; Larry LaKamp; Martha LaKamp; Lepitas Foundation; Pete Morgan Foundation; Valencia Foundation; Jon Sittko; Kitsy Gregory; Peggy Wolfe; Leverage Discovery LLC; Mark Wolfe.
Foundation type: Independent foundation.
Financial data (yr. ended 12/31/13): Assets, $13,844 (M); gifts received, $421,700; expenditures, $432,554; qualifying distributions, $430,850; giving activities include $21,500 for 2 grants (high: $11,500; low: $10,000), and $409,350 for 21 grants to individuals (high: $28,000; low: $500).
Purpose and activities: Provides scholarships for people in full-time ministry who must raise their own financial support to do so. Funding also to grant men and women who have been in full-time ministry for ten consecutive years or more, and who, due to salary limitations of their ministry, have acquired financial debt. The scholarships will be used strictly for the purpose of paying off, or down, their debt.
Fields of interest: Education; Human services.
Limitations: Applications not accepted. Giving primarily in CO.
Application information: Unsolicited requests for funds not accepted.
Directors: Dan Jessup; Jeff Newman; Steven G. Sittko.
EIN: 841400820

1353

Shamrock Foundation

15555 Hwy. 83
Colorado Springs, CO 80921-1514

Established in 2000 in Colorado.
Donors: David A. Wismer; Mary Anne Wismer.
Foundation type: Independent foundation.
Financial data (yr. ended 06/30/14): Assets, $7,739,636; gifts received, $0; expenditures, $442,938; qualifying distributions, $383,574 and $0 for set-asides.
Fields of interest: Higher education; Religion; Human services.
Type of support: Research and evaluation.
Limitations: Applications accepted. Giving primarily in Sun Valley, CA, Colorado Springs, CO and Atlanta, GA.
Application information: Application form required.
  Initial approach: Letter
  Deadline(s): None
Officers: David A. Wismer, Pres. and Treas.; Mary Anne Wismer, Secy.
Directors: Jennifer A. Leach; David A. Wismer III.
EIN: 311715049

1354

Someone Cares Charitable Trust

P.O. Box 669
Kittredge, CO 80457-0669

Established in 1986 in Illinois.
Donor: Philip Yancey.
Foundation type: Independent foundation.
Financial data (yr. ended 05/31/13): Assets, $679,664 (M); gifts received, $68,322;

expenditures, $178,169; qualifying distributions, $176,339; giving activities include $166,750 for 30 grants (high: $109,000; low: $100).
Purpose and activities: Giving primarily for education, health centers, human services, and community service organizations.
Fields of interest: Education; Health; Human services.
Type of support: General support; Capital and infrastructure.
Limitations: Applications not accepted. Giving on a national and international basis.
Application information: Unsolicited requests for funds not accepted.
Board meeting date(s): Varies
Officers: Philip Yancey, Pres.; Janet Yancey, V.P.; Diane Davis, Secy.; Bruce Otto, Treas.
Director: Tim Odgen.
EIN: 363415880

1355
Southwestern Foundation for Education and Historical Preservation
2596 S. Milwaukee St.
Denver, CO 80210-6215   (303) 715-9056
Contact: Timothy N. Gardner, Tr.

Established in 1992 in Arizona.
Donor: Jane Harrison Ivancovich†.
Foundation type: Independent foundation.
Financial data (yr. ended 12/31/13): Assets, $6,851,859 (M); expenditures, $413,033; qualifying distributions, $353,071; giving activities include $315,977 for 18 grants (high: $71,000; low: $3,500).
Fields of interest: Museums; Historic preservation; Elementary and secondary education; Higher education; Libraries.
Type of support: Capital and infrastructure; Matching grants; Equipment; Endowments; Publications; Scholarships; Research.
Limitations: Applications accepted. Giving primarily in Tucson, AZ. No grants to individuals.
Publications: Informational brochure.
Application information: Application form required.
Initial approach: Contact foundation for application form
Copies of proposal: 1
Deadline(s): None
Board meeting date(s): Mar. and Oct.
Trustees: Timothy N. Gardner; Jessica Harrison.
Number of staff: 1 part-time professional; 1 part-time support.
EIN: 860701832

1356
Galen & Ada Belle Spencer Foundation
600 S. Cherry St., Ste. 715
Denver, CO 80246-1709

Established in 1982 in Colorado.
Foundation type: Independent foundation.
Financial data (yr. ended 06/30/13): Assets, $1,046,482 (M); expenditures, $157,899; qualifying distributions, $146,500; giving activities include $146,500 for grants.
Purpose and activities: Giving for cultural programs, including opera companies and museums; support also for hospitals, higher education, and social services.

Fields of interest: Arts and culture; Performing arts; Opera; Science museums; Higher education; Hospital care; Human services; Food aid; Youth services.
Type of support: Continuing support; Seed money.
Limitations: Applications not accepted. Giving primarily in Denver, CO. No grants to individuals.
Application information: Unsolicited requests for funds not accepted.
Officers and Directors: Thomas P. Kearns, Pres. and Director; John K. Weckbaugh, 1st V.P. and Treas. and Director; John J. Silver, 2nd V.P. and Secy. and Director.
EIN: 742259763

1357
The Richard Seth Staley Educational Foundation
(formerly Richard Seth Staley Foundation for Psychological Development)
P.O. Box 4129
Aspen, CO 81612-4129   (970) 920-9003
Contact: Donald H. Keltner, Pres.

Donor: James Gillett.
Foundation type: Operating foundation.
Financial data (yr. ended 09/30/13): Assets, $12,984,719 (M); expenditures, $713,349; qualifying distributions, $627,860; giving activities include $368,606 for 52 grants (high: $240,924; low: $32).
Purpose and activities: Giving primarily for education; also giving for social issues, human services, with emphasis on children, the arts, and health organizations.
Fields of interest: Arts and culture; Music; Education; Higher education; Diseases and conditions; Social sciences; Economics; Public affairs.
Limitations: Applications accepted. Giving primarily in CA and CO; some giving also in NY.
Application information: Application form required for educational grants only. Application form required.
Initial approach: Letter
Deadline(s): None
Officers and Directors: Donald H. Keltner, Pres. and Treas. and Director; James F. Beley, V.P. and Director; Kathleen Keltner, Secy. and Director.
EIN: 953532336

1358
Steffens Foundation
P.O. Box 271170
Louisville, CO 80027-5021

Established in 2005 in Colorado.
Donors: Mary S. Schweitzer; Mary S. Schweitzer Charitable Lead Annuity Trust.
Foundation type: Independent foundation.
Financial data (yr. ended 12/31/13): Assets, $7,114,649 (M); gifts received, $183,830; expenditures, $311,251; qualifying distributions, $262,750; giving activities include $262,750 for 47 grants (high: $30,000; low: $250).
Fields of interest: Education; Higher education; Science; Economic development; Catholicism; Human services; Women's services; International development; Immigrants and migrants.

Limitations: Applications not accepted. Giving primarily in IL, KS, MD, and WA. No grants to individuals.
Application information: Contributes only to pre-selected organizations.
Officers: Mary S. Schweitzer, Pres.; Stephanie L. Schweitzer, V.P.; Edmund A. Schweitzer, Secy.; Paul A. Schweitzer, Treas.
EIN: 202420941

1359
The Myron Stratton Home
555 Gold Pass Heights
Colorado Springs, CO 80906   (719) 579-0930
Contact: Mark Turk, Exec. Dir.
FAX: (719) 579-0447;
E-mail: myronstratton@myron.org; Main URL: http://www.myronstratton.org

Foundation type: Operating foundation.
Financial data (yr. ended 12/31/14): Assets, $179,484,884 (M); gifts received, $608; expenditures, $5,480,310; qualifying distributions, $4,545,380; giving activities include $277,000 for 26 grants (high: $23,000; low: $5,000), and $3,779,516 for foundation-administered programs.
Purpose and activities: Giving primarily to maintain and operate residential facilities and services for the elderly poor of El Paso County, Colorado.
Fields of interest: Community and economic development; Family services; Child welfare; Senior services; Low-income and poor people.
Type of support: General support; Continuing support; Capital campaigns; Capital and infrastructure; Equipment; Emergency funds; Program development; Seed money; Curriculum development.
Limitations: Applications accepted. Giving primarily in Colorado Springs and El Paso County, CO. No grants to individuals, or for fundraising or conferences.
Publications: Informational brochure (including application guidelines); Multi-year report.
Application information: See foundation web site for grants program information. Application form required.
Initial approach: Letter of intent
Copies of proposal: 2
Deadline(s): For letter of intent: May 1 for Sept. cycle and Nov. 1 for Mar. cycle
Final notification: Apr. and Oct.
Officers: Robert G. Baker, Jr., Pres.; Jon J. Medved, V.P.; Nechie Hall, Secy.-Treas.; Mark Turk, Exec. Dir.
Trustees: Leonard Farr; C. David McDermott.
Number of staff: 50
EIN: 840404260

1360
William Stretesky Foundation
104 W. 1st St.
Julesburg, CO 80737-1502

Foundation type: Independent foundation.
Financial data (yr. ended 06/30/13): Assets, $22,235,593 (M); expenditures, $803,014; qualifying distributions, $487,011; giving activities include $350,352 for 25 grants (high: $92,651; low: $500).
Fields of interest: Health; Community and economic development; Human services.
Type of support: General support; Scholarships.

Limitations: Applications not accepted. Giving primarily in Julesburg, CO. No grants to individuals.
Application information: Unsolicited requests for funds not accepted.
Officers: Donald A. Stretesky, Pres.; Leon K. Stoppel, V.P.; Max E. Carlson, Secy.
EIN: 721529410

1361

The Strohm Link Family Foundation

1420 W. Canal Ct., No. 250
Littleton, CO 80120-4529 (303) 794-6655
Contact: John D. Strohm, Pres.
E-mail: johnstrohm@farrell-roeh.com

Established in 2001 in Colorado.
Donors: John D. Strohm; Mary Pat Link.
Foundation type: Independent foundation.
Financial data (yr. ended 11/30/14): Assets, $826,845 (M); expenditures, $170,286; qualifying distributions, $154,742; giving activities include $149,183 for 10 grants (high: $50,000; low: $183).
Fields of interest: Arts and culture; Education; Diseases and conditions.
Type of support: Research.
Limitations: Applications accepted. Giving primarily in CO. No grants to individuals.
Application information:
  Initial approach: Proposal
  Deadline(s): None
Officers: John D. Strohm, Pres.; Mary Pat Link, V.P.
Directors: Kelly R. Strohm; Kristin E. Strohm; Matthew R. Strohm.
EIN: 841601838

1362

Taddonio Family Foundation, Inc.

(formerly Mile Hi Foods Foundation, Inc.)
4770 E. 51st Ave.
Denver, CO 80216-3112

Donors: Mile Hi Investments; Mile Hi Bakery, Inc.; Canteen; Mile Hi Foods Co.; Pamela Taddonio; UMB Bank; Mile Hi Shared Service; Wells Fargo Bank; New PST; Bundy Baking Solutions; GHP Horwath P.C.; SmallwoodFinancial Services; Colorado Business Bank; Einstein Noah Restaurant; Specialized Loan Services; John Bandimere Foundation.
Foundation type: Operating foundation.
Financial data (yr. ended 12/31/13): Assets, $85,053 (M); gifts received, $18,449; expenditures, $212,299; qualifying distributions, $149,994; giving activities include $149,994 for 15 grants (high: $106,808; low: $70).
Fields of interest: Education; Human services; Youth development.
Limitations: Applications not accepted. Giving primarily in Denver, CO.
Application information: Unsolicited requests for funds not accepted.
Officers: Toni M. Taddonio, Pres.; Tony Marie Taddonio, V.P.; Pamela S. Taddonio, Secy.; Kristy A. Taddonio, Treas.
EIN: 272178679

1363

The Tappan Foundation

4086 26th St.
Boulder, CO 80304-0905
Contact: Constance T. Clancy, Pres.

Established in 1995 in California.
Donors: David S. Tappan, Jr.; Jeanne B. Tappan.
Foundation type: Independent foundation.
Financial data (yr. ended 12/31/13): Assets, $8,209,548 (M); expenditures, $387,273; qualifying distributions, $363,813; giving activities include $341,847 for 37 grants (high: $30,000; low: $1,000).
Purpose and activities: Giving primarily for education, the arts, and federated giving programs.
Fields of interest: Education; Health; Human services.
Type of support: Fellowships; Scholarships.
Limitations: Applications accepted. Giving primarily in CA.
Application information: Application form required.
  Initial approach: Letter
  Deadline(s): None
Officers: Constance T. Clancy, Pres.; Janet T. Dryren, Secy.; Diane T. Easton, Treas.
Directors: David S. Tappan IV; Jeanne B. Tappan; Steven G. Tappan.
EIN: 330673727

1364

The Ruth and Vernon Taylor Foundation

518 17th St., Ste. 1450
Denver, CO 80202-4151

Established in 1950 in Pennsylvania.
Foundation type: Independent foundation.
Financial data (yr. ended 06/30/13): Assets, $7,840,381 (M); expenditures, $414,260; qualifying distributions, $381,397; giving activities include $300,006 for 49 grants (high: $50,000; low: $6).
Fields of interest: Arts and culture; Secondary education; Higher education; University education; Environment; Natural resources; Hospital care; Diseases and conditions; Human services; Youth services.
Type of support: General support; Capital and infrastructure; Endowments; Research; Research and evaluation.
Limitations: Applications not accepted. Giving primarily in CO. No grants to individuals.
Application information: Unsolicited requests for funds not accepted.
  Board meeting date(s): May and Sept.
Trustees: Friday A. Green; Douglas Taylor; Vernon F. Taylor, Jr.; Vernon F. Taylor III.
Number of staff: 1 full-time professional.
EIN: 846021788

1365

The Ervil A. and Ronald E. Thiel Charitable Trust

13540 Meadowgrass Dr.
Colorado Springs, CO 80921

Established in 2000 in Kansas.
Donors: Ervil A. Thiel; Ronald E. Thiel.
Foundation type: Independent foundation.
Financial data (yr. ended 08/31/14): Assets, $6,793,993 (M); expenditures, $352,297;

qualifying distributions, $289,584; giving activities include $278,517 for 8 grants (high: $75,000; low: $10,000).
Fields of interest: University education; Cancers; Christianity.
Limitations: Applications not accepted. Giving primarily in FL, KS, PA and TX. No grants to individuals.
Application information: Contributes only to pre-selected organizations.
Trustee: Integrity Bank and Trust.
EIN: 486373749

1366

Tigertree Foundation

4643 S. Ulster St., Ste. 325
Denver, CO 80237
Application address: c/o Robert Rhue, P.O. Box 371437, Aurora, CO 80237, tel.: (303) 671-0650

Donor: Robert Rhue.
Foundation type: Independent foundation.
Financial data (yr. ended 12/31/13): Assets, $48,072 (M); gifts received, $150,000; expenditures, $119,739; qualifying distributions, $119,725; giving activities include $119,725 for 33 grants (high: $33,400; low: $300).
Fields of interest: Education; Domesticated animals; Human services.
Limitations: Applications accepted. Giving primarily in CO.
Application information:
  Initial approach: Proposal
  Deadline(s): None
Officers and Directors: Robert Rhue, Pres. and Director; Mary Wilson Daugherty, Secy.-Treas.
EIN: 263865843

1367

The Titus Foundation

c/o Starkschenkein, LLP
3600 S. Yosemite St., Ste. 600
Denver, CO 80237-1829

Established in 2005 in Colorado.
Donor: Canton Investment Holdings LLC.
Foundation type: Independent foundation.
Financial data (yr. ended 12/31/13): Assets, $5,426,881 (M); gifts received, $797,690; expenditures, $277,506; qualifying distributions, $253,450; giving activities include $253,450 for 8 grants (high: $100,000; low: $5,000).
Fields of interest: Elementary and secondary education; Community and economic development; Child welfare.
Limitations: Applications not accepted. Giving primarily in CO. No grants to individuals.
Application information: Contributes only to pre-selected organizations.
Officers: Tami J. Paumier, Pres.; Glen C. Warren, Jr., Secy.-Treas.
EIN: 203466900

1368

Tomkins Gates Foundation

(formerly Philips Industries Foundation)
1551 Wewatta St., MS 9N A4
Denver, CO 80202

Established in 1986 in Ohio.

Donors: Tomkins Industries, Inc.; David Newlands.
Foundation type: Company-sponsored foundation.
Financial data (yr. ended 12/31/14): Assets,
$7,279,860 (M); expenditures, $443,069;
qualifying distributions, $427,782; giving activities
include $427,782 for 177 grants (high: $106,500;
low: $20).
Purpose and activities: The foundation supports
organizations involved with education, cancer,
human services, and Christianity.
Fields of interest: Education; Higher education;
Cancers; Christianity; Human services.
Type of support: General support; Employee
matching gifts; Scholarships; Cash grants;
Individual development.
Limitations: Applications not accepted. Giving
primarily in Denver, CO, Chicago, IL, KS, MI, and OH;
giving also to national organizations. No grants to
individuals.
Application information: Contributes only to
pre-selected organizations.
Officers: John Barker, V.P. and Secy.; David Carroll,
Pres.; David Naemura, Treas. and C.F.O.; Rasmani
Bhattacharya, V.P.; Gregory Kirchhoff, V.P.
EIN: 311207183

1369
The Morris & Sylvia Trachten Family Foundation, Inc.
4950 S. Yosemite St., F2-184
Greenwood Village, CO 80111-1349 (303)
488-2057
Contact: Vicki Trachten Schwartz

Established in 1984 in Connecticut.
Donor: Morris Trachten.
Foundation type: Independent foundation.
Financial data (yr. ended 06/30/13): Assets,
$6,402,821 (M); gifts received, $6,003,722;
expenditures, $353,806; qualifying distributions,
$316,974; giving activities include $316,974 for 55
grants (high: $76,500; low: $25).
Fields of interest: Higher education; University
education; Nonprofits; Judaism.
Type of support: General support; Regranting.
Limitations: Applications accepted. Giving primarily
in CO, CT, FL, and NY.
Application information:
Initial approach: Letter
Deadline(s): None
Officers: David Trachten, Chair.; Vicki Trachten
Schwartz, Pres. and Treas.; Roberta Zeve, V.P.; Gary
Trachten, Secy.
Board Member: Sylvia Trachten.
EIN: 222518063

1370
Triune Foundation, Ltd.
3926 S. Magnolia Way
Denver, CO 80237-2014

Established in 1986 in Arizona.
Donors: Brenda L. Baller; M.L. Baller; Baller Living
Trust.
Foundation type: Independent foundation.
Financial data (yr. ended 12/31/13): Assets,
$2,203,294 (M); gifts received, $57,312;
expenditures, $257,666; qualifying distributions,
$257,666; giving activities include $252,100 for 10
grants (high: $54,250; low: $3,000).
Fields of interest: Christianity; Human services.

Limitations: Applications not accepted. Giving in the
U.S., with emphasis on CO. No grants to individuals.
Application information: Contributes only to
pre-selected organizations.
Officers: M.L. Baller, Pres.; Brenda L. Baller, Secy.
EIN: 841039939

1371
The Harry Trueblood Foundation
1720 S. Bellaire, Ste. 912
Denver, CO 80222-4334 (303) 300-6792
Contact: Harry A. Trueblood Jr., V.P. and Treas.
FAX: (303) 300-6794;
E-mail: hajtrueblood@yahoo.com

Established in 1969 in Colorado.
Donor: Harry A. Trueblood, Jr.
Foundation type: Independent foundation.
Financial data (yr. ended 04/30/13): Assets,
$5,855,826 (M); expenditures, $354,865;
qualifying distributions, $300,000; giving activities
include $300,000 for grants.
Fields of interest: Secondary education; Higher
education; Graduate and professional education;
Business education; Nursing care; Technology.
Type of support: Fellowships; Scholarships.
Limitations: Applications accepted. Giving primarily
in CO; limited giving also in TX. Scholarships are
awarded only for institutions in CO. No direct grants
to individuals for partial scholarships.
Application information:
Initial approach: Letter
Copies of proposal: 1
Deadline(s): None
Board meeting date(s): Biannually
Final notification: Up to one month
Officers and Directors: John B. Trueblood, Pres. and
Director; Harry A. Trueblood, Jr., V.P. and Treas. and
Director; Lucile B. Trueblood, Secy. and Director;
Katherine T. Astin.
Number of staff: None.
EIN: 840593623

1372
The Verdoorn Foundation
10463 Park Meadows Dr., Ste. 207
Littleton, CO 80124-5318
Contact: Denise M. Overhardt, Secy.

Established in 2000 in Colorado.
Donors: Daniel C. Verdoorn; Denise M. Overhardt;
Donald W. Verdoorn.
Foundation type: Independent foundation.
Financial data (yr. ended 06/30/13): Assets,
$4,022,562 (M); expenditures, $240,573;
qualifying distributions, $201,000; giving activities
include $201,000 for grants.
Fields of interest: Undergraduate education;
Nonprofits; Health; Specialty hospital care; Child
welfare.
Type of support: Regranting.
Limitations: Applications accepted. Giving primarily
in CO, FL and IA. No grants to individuals.
Application information:
Initial approach: Letter
Deadline(s): None
Officers and Directors: Daniel C. Verdoorn, Pres.
and Treas. and Director; Denise M. Overhardt, Secy.
and Director; Carla A. Verdoorn.
EIN: 841568378

1373
The Vision Charitable Trust
9422 Pikes Peak Way
Parker, CO 80138-5251

Established in 2005 in Colorado.
Donors: John G. Emig; Sealy Yates; Michael S.
Yates; Land Services, Inc.
Foundation type: Independent foundation.
Financial data (yr. ended 12/31/14): Assets,
$23,639 (M); gifts received, $152,433;
expenditures, $134,043; qualifying distributions,
$134,043; giving activities include $130,383 for 2
grants (high: $113,583; low: $16,800).
Purpose and activities: The organization supports
Christian ministry initiatives.
Fields of interest: Religion.
International interests: Costa Rica.
Limitations: Applications not accepted. Giving
primarily in WA and Costa Rica.
Application information: Unsolicited requests for
funds not accepted.
Trustee: Michael S. Yates.
EIN: 486393123

1374
Bee Vradenburg Foundation
730 N. Nevada Ave.
Colorado Springs, CO 80903-1008 (719)
477-0185
Contact: David Siegel, Exec. Dir.
FAX: (719) 389-1252;
E-mail: david@beevradenburgfoundation.org; Main
URL: http://www.beevradenburgfoundation.org
Facebook: https://www.facebook.com/
BeeVradenburgFoundation
Grants List: http://
www.beevradenburgfoundation.org/grantees/
grant-recipients/2012-2

Established in 2001 in Colorado.
Donors: George A. Vradenburg, Jr.†; George A.
Vradenburg III; Beatrice W. Vradenburg; Philip A.
Kendall.
Foundation type: Independent foundation.
Financial data (yr. ended 12/31/13): Assets,
$4,496,044 (M); expenditures, $279,355;
qualifying distributions, $268,852; giving activities
include $191,121 for 31 grants (high: $57,704;
low: $1,000).
Purpose and activities: The foundation supports a
thriving and diverse cultural community by investing
in the excellence, innovation, and sustainability of
the arts.
Fields of interest: Arts and culture.
Type of support: General support; Pro bono
consulting services; Matching grants; Continuing
support; Capacity-building and technical assistance;
Capital campaigns; Capital and infrastructure;
Equipment; Emergency funds; Program
development; Convening; Scholarships; Technical
assistance; Program evaluations.
Limitations: Applications accepted. Giving limited to
organizations based in and serving the Pikes Peak
region, defined as El Paso County and the Ute Pass
corridor of Teller County, CO, to include Woodland
Park but not beyond. No support for religious or
political organizations. No grants to individuals or for
fund-raisers for non-arts organizations or to advance
causes unrelated to the arts.
Publications: Application guidelines; Annual report;
Grants list.

Application information: See web site for complete application policies, guidelines and forms. Application form required.

Initial approach: First time applicants should call or e-mail in advance of applying

Copies of proposal: 1

Deadline(s): Quarterly

Board meeting date(s): Jan., Apr., July, Oct.

Final notification: 45 days after submission

Officers: George A. Vradenburg III, Chair.; Philip A. Kendall, Pres.; Kathleen Fox Collins, Secy.; Libby Rittenberg, Treas.; David Siegel, Exec. Dir.

Trustees: Noel Black; Susan J. Edmondson; Susan Pattee; Alissa Vradenburg; Tyler Vradenburg.

Number of staff: 1

EIN: 841579108

1375
W.J.D. Foundation

1 Littleridge Ln.
Englewood, CO   80113-4036

Established in 1985 in Colorado.

Donor: Brian M. Deevy.

Foundation type: Independent foundation.

Financial data (yr. ended 12/31/13): Assets, $7,495,837 (M); gifts received, $150,000; expenditures, $339,581; qualifying distributions, $266,250; giving activities include $266,250 for 32 grants (high: $55,000; low: $1,000).

Purpose and activities: Giving primarily for education, and health and human services.

Fields of interest: Higher education; Nonprofits; Hospital care; Human services.

Type of support: Regranting.

Limitations: Applications not accepted. Giving primarily in Denver, CO. No grants to individuals.

Application information: Contributes only to pre-selected organizations.

Officers and Directors: Brian M. Deevy, Pres. and Director; Caryn Ostergard, V.P. and Secy.

EIN: 742398199

1376
Albert & Bessie Warner Fund

P.O. Box 2784
Telluride, CO   81435-2784
Contact: John Steel, Tr.

Established in 1955 in New York.

Foundation type: Independent foundation.

Financial data (yr. ended 12/31/13): Assets, $4,554,488 (M); expenditures, $309,751; qualifying distributions, $197,450; giving activities include $197,450 for 45 grants (high: $31,000; low: $100).

Fields of interest: Environment; Nonprofits; Health; Hospital care; Legal services; Organized labor; Human rights; Diversity and intergroup relations; Child welfare; International peace and security; Arms control; American Indians; Immigrants and migrants.

Type of support: General support; Land acquisitions; Program development; Seed money; Technical assistance; Regranting.

Limitations: Applications accepted. Giving primarily in CO, Washington, DC, and NY. No grants to individuals, or for building or endowment funds.

Application information: Application form required.

Initial approach: Letter

Deadline(s): None

Trustees: Bernice Freidus; John Steel; Sabrina Steel.

Number of staff: 1 part-time support.

EIN: 136095213

1377
Mark and Muriel Wexler Foundation

P.O. Box 5470
Avon, CO   81620-5470   (763) 834-1533
Contact: Steven Wexler, Secy.

Established in 1985 in Minnesota.

Donors: Mark Wexler; Muriel Wexler; Medical Arts Press, Inc.

Foundation type: Independent foundation.

Financial data (yr. ended 06/30/13): Assets, $2,495,995 (M); expenditures, $211,559; qualifying distributions, $182,349; giving activities include $182,349 for 78 grants (high: $100,000; low: $200).

Purpose and activities: Giving primarily for health associations, human services, and Jewish agencies and temples.

Fields of interest: Education; Diseases and conditions; Human services.

Limitations: Applications accepted. Giving primarily in MN.

Application information: Application form required.

Initial approach: Letter

Deadline(s): None

Officers: Muriel Wexler, V.P.; Steven Wexler, Secy.

Directors: Paul Schmeck; Dan Wexler; Elizabeth Wexler; Ed Winthrop.

EIN: 411543321

1378
The Connie Burwell and William W. White Foundation

c/o Beth Holcombe
P.O. Box 621428
Littleton, CO   80162   (303) 475-3570

Donors: William B. White; Connie Burwell White.

Foundation type: Independent foundation.

Financial data (yr. ended 12/31/13): Assets, $7,795,163 (M); expenditures, $511,712; qualifying distributions, $363,500; giving activities include $363,500 for 31 grants (high: $36,000; low: $2,500).

Fields of interest: Art museums; Higher education; Graduate and professional education; Health care clinics; Mental health care; News and public information; Christianity; Human services.

Type of support: General support.

Limitations: Applications accepted. Giving limited to CO, NC, and VA. No grants to individuals.

Application information:

Initial approach: Proposal

Deadline(s): None

Officers: Heather Lurie, Pres.; Beth E. Holcombe, Secy.; Sarah Marks, Treas.

Trustee: Ollie Hickel.

EIN: 742346047

1379
The Don and May Wilkins Charitable Trust

110 E. Oak, Ste. 200
Fort Collins, CO   80524-7127   (970) 482-4322
Contact: J. Brad March, Tr.

Established in 1999 in Colorado.

Foundation type: Independent foundation.

Financial data (yr. ended 12/31/12): Assets, $7,540,212 (M); expenditures, $819,648; qualifying distributions, $313,127; giving activities include $313,127 for grants.

Purpose and activities: Giving primarily to benefit the city of Fort Collins, Colorado, and the surrounding area.

Fields of interest: Community and economic development.

Type of support: Capital campaigns; In-kind gifts; Capital and infrastructure; Endowments; Program development; Seed money.

Limitations: Applications accepted. Giving limited to CO.

Publications: Annual report; Financial statement; Grants list.

Application information:

Initial approach: Letter

Deadline(s): None

Final notification: Varies

Trustee: J. Brad March.

EIN: 846336318

1380
Wilson Family Foundation

101 S. 3rd. St., Ste. 101
Grand Junction, CO   81501-2455

Established in 1995 in Colorado.

Donors: William L. Wilson; Joan B. Wilson; Hollis C. Wilson.

Foundation type: Independent foundation.

Financial data (yr. ended 12/31/14): Assets, $1,298,605; gifts received, $755,000; expenditures, $333,816; qualifying distributions, $331,900.

Fields of interest: Education; Health; Catholicism; Human services.

Type of support: General support.

Limitations: Applications not accepted. Giving primarily in CO. No grants to individuals.

Application information: Unsolicited requests for funds not accepted.

Officers: William L. Wilson, Pres.; William B. Wilson, Secy.-Treas.

EIN: 841318359

1381
Wolcott Family Foundation

3651 S. Pontiac Way
Denver, CO   80237-1326

Donors: Kerri Wolcott; MadAnt Energy, LLC; Joshua Wolcott.

Foundation type: Independent foundation.

Financial data (yr. ended 11/30/13): Assets, $700,138 (M); gifts received, $967,580; expenditures, $267,609; qualifying distributions, $267,429; giving activities include $267,375 for 5 grants (high: $200,000; low: $75).

Fields of interest: Education; Religion; Human services.

Limitations: Applications not accepted. Giving primarily in IN.

Application information: Unsolicited requests for funds not accepted.

Officers: Kerri Wolcott, Pres. and Secy.; Joshua Wolcott, Treas.

EIN: 900924095

1382
Woodford Foundation
205 E. Cheyenne Mountain Blvd.
Colorado Springs, CO 80906-3704

Established in 1995 in Colorado.
Donors: Joseph C. Woodford; Daniel J. Woodford; Steve Kristin Woodford.
Foundation type: Independent foundation.
Financial data (yr. ended 12/31/12): Assets, $127,976 (M); gifts received, $415,600; expenditures, $313,343; qualifying distributions, $278,000; giving activities include $278,000 for grants.
Purpose and activities: Giving primarily for higher education.
Fields of interest: Higher education; Public affairs.
Type of support: General support.

Limitations: Applications not accepted. Giving primarily in CO; some giving also in Washington, DC. No grants to individuals.
Application information: Contributes only to pre-selected organizations.
Trustees: Daniel J. Woodford; John M. Woodford; Joseph C. Woodford; Kristin M. Woodford; Linda M. Woodford; Stephen D. Woodford.
EIN: 846282092

1383
The Kal Zeff Family Foundation
950 S. Cherry St., Ste. 1100
Denver, CO 80246-2667

Established in 2006 in Delaware.

Donors: Kal Zeff†; Joyce Zeff.
Foundation type: Independent foundation.
Financial data (yr. ended 12/31/13): Assets, $6,192,345 (M); expenditures, $358,400; qualifying distributions, $300,589; giving activities include $300,000 for 4 grants.
Fields of interest: Nonprofits; Diseases and conditions; Judaism.
Type of support: Research; Regranting.
Limitations: Applications not accepted. Giving primarily in Denver, CO, and New York, NY. No grants to individuals.
Application information: Contributes only to pre-selected organizations.
Officers and Directors: R. Joyce Zeff, Pres. and Treas.; Diana Zeff Anderson, V.P. and Secy. and Director.
EIN: 204429026

CONNECTICUT

1384
Kenneth and Nira Abramowitz Foundation
(formerly Abramowitz Family Foundation)
P.O. Box 958
Southport, CT 06890-0958

Established in 2002 in New York.
Donors: Kenneth Abramowitz; Nira Abramowitz.
Foundation type: Independent foundation.
Financial data (yr. ended 12/31/12): Assets,
$325,079 (M); gifts received, $325,000;
expenditures, $340,026; qualifying distributions,
$337,140; giving activities include $337,140 for
grants.
Purpose and activities: Giving primarily to Jewish
organizations.
Fields of interest: Education; Nonprofits; Hospital
care; Judaism; Human services.
Type of support: Regranting.
Limitations: Applications not accepted. Giving
primarily in NY. No grants to individuals.
Application information: Contributes only to
pre-selected organizations.
Trustees: Kenneth Abramowitz; Nira Abramowitz.
EIN: 331017742

1385
Acorn Alcinda Foundation Inc.
c/o Jan Kennedy
25 Palmer Dr.
South Windsor, CT 06074-2816

Established in 1984 in Virginia.
Donor: Robert J. Kennedy†.
Foundation type: Independent foundation.
Financial data (yr. ended 05/31/14): Assets,
$5,181,315; expenditures, $332,706; qualifying
distributions, $226,834.
Purpose and activities: Giving primarily to
organizations that promote scientific research,
advancement, and knowledge in wood chemistry,
forestry, and tree farming; giving also to assist in
developing means and procedures for the recovery,
training, and education of the elderly who have
become disabled as the result of strokes, heart
attacks, or disease.
Fields of interest: Performing arts; Higher
education; University education; Environment;
Natural resources; Aquatic wildlife protection;
Hospital care; Rehabilitation; Diseases and
conditions; Christianity; Protestantism; Human
services; Senior services; Seniors; People with
vision impairments.
Type of support: General support.
Limitations: Applications not accepted. No grants to
individuals.
Application information: Unsolicited requests for
funds not accepted.
Officers and Directors: Kit C. Kennedy, Pres. and
Secy. and Director; Jan B. Kennedy, V.P. and
Director.
EIN: 541303250

1386
Ellen H. Adams Foundation, Inc.
16 Old Mill Rd.
Greenwich, CT 06830-3345
Contact: Ellen H. Adams, Pres.

Donor: Ellen H. Adams.
Foundation type: Independent foundation.
Financial data (yr. ended 12/31/13): Assets,
$278,186 (M); gifts received, $235; expenditures,
$386,235; qualifying distributions, $386,235;
giving activities include $386,235 for 6 grants (high:
$120,000; low: $36,000).
Fields of interest: Education; Religion.
Limitations: Applications not accepted. Giving
primarily in CT, IL and PA.
Application information: Contributes only to
pre-selected organizations.
Officers: Ellen H. Adams, Pres.; James W. Adams,
V.P.; Karen Adams, Secy.-Treas.
EIN: 271495276

1387
The Agape Foundation, Inc.
87 Laurel Brook Ln.
Fairfield, CT 06824-2079

Donors: Sherry Thorne; Steven Thorne.
Foundation type: Independent foundation.
Financial data (yr. ended 12/31/13): Assets,
$324,505 (M); gifts received, $159,577;
expenditures, $167,164; qualifying distributions,
$167,164; giving activities include $162,164 for 21
grants (high: $73,315; low: $250), and $5,000 for
1 grant to an individual.
Fields of interest: Christianity.
Limitations: Applications not accepted. Giving
primarily in CO, CT and GA.
Application information: Contributes only to
pre-selected organizations.
Officers and Directors: Sherry A. Thorne, Pres. and
Director; Steven D. Thorne, Secy. and Director;
Reginald Corinaldi.
EIN: 203677167

1388
Howard & Katherine Aibel Foundation
183 Steep Hill Rd.
Weston, CT 06883-1924

Established in 1969 in Connecticut.
Donor: Howard J. Aibel.
Foundation type: Independent foundation.
Financial data (yr. ended 12/31/13): Assets,
$1,395,942 (M); gifts received, $410,963;
expenditures, $256,929; qualifying distributions,
$237,385; giving activities include $237,385 for
110 grants (high: $50,000; low: $20).
Purpose and activities: Giving primarily for the arts
and also for the improvement of justice
administration, legal education, and equal access to
legal remedies.
Fields of interest: Arts and culture; Education;
Judaism.
Limitations: Applications not accepted. Giving
primarily in Westport, CT, New York, NY and MA. No
grants to individuals.
Application information: Unsolicited requests for
funds not accepted.

Officer and Directors: Howard J. Aibel, Pres. and
Director; Daniel Aibel; David Aibel; Jonathan Aibel.
EIN: 237046798

1389
J.R. Albert Charitable Trust
120 1st St.
Suffield, CT 06078-1808

Established in 2000 in Texas.
Donor: John R. Albert†.
Foundation type: Independent foundation.
Financial data (yr. ended 12/31/13): Assets,
$7,998,010 (M); expenditures, $397,158;
qualifying distributions, $349,828; giving activities
include $300,000 for 12 grants (high: $55,000;
low: $2,000).
Fields of interest: Health; Specialty hospital care;
Housing development; Human services; Homeless
people.
Limitations: Applications not accepted. Giving
primarily in CT, MA and TX. No grants to individuals.
Application information: Contributes only to
pre-selected organizations.
Trustee: Karen Lima.
EIN: 766163079

1390
The Allwin Family Foundation
c/o Maria Allwin
116 Clapboard Ridge Rd.
Greenwich, CT 06830-3433

Established in 1997 in New York.
Donors: James M. Allwin†; Maria Allwin.
Foundation type: Independent foundation.
Financial data (yr. ended 12/31/13): Assets,
$289,052 (M); gifts received, $10,225;
expenditures, $445,127; qualifying distributions,
$442,125; giving activities include $432,000 for 8
grants (high: $250,000; low: $500).
Purpose and activities: Giving primarily for
education and the arts.
Fields of interest: Museums; Education; Higher
education; Hospital care; Child welfare.
Limitations: Applications not accepted. Giving
primarily in CT, NH, and NY.
Application information: Contributes only to
pre-selected organizations.
Trustee: Maria Allwin.
EIN: 137088461

1391
Alpha/Omega Charitable Foundation
c/o Frank J. Gilbride II
31 Brookside Dr.
Greenwich, CT 06836

Established in 1994 in Florida.
Donors: Tauni De Lesseps; DeLesseps Charitable
Reminder Unitrust.
Foundation type: Independent foundation.
Financial data (yr. ended 12/31/14): Assets,
$5,927,208 (M); expenditures, $383,451;
qualifying distributions, $319,126; giving activities
include $299,000 for 39 grants (high: $25,000;
low: $500).
Fields of interest: University education; Land
resources; Wildlife biodiversity; Animal welfare;
Human services.

Limitations: Applications not accepted. Giving primarily in CT and FL.
Application information: Unsolicited requests for funds not accepted.
Officers: Geoffrey de Lesseps, Pres.; Anita L. Keefe, V.P.; Thomas Verderber, V.P.; Frank J. Gilbride II, Secy.-Treas.
EIN: 650510147

1392
Elizabeth Raymond Ambler Trust
44 Old Ridgefield Rd., Ste. 215
P.O. Box 7266
Wilton, CT 06897-7266 (203) 761-1150
FAX: (203) 555-5555;
E-mail: amblertrust@sbcglobal.net; Main
URL: http://www.amblertrust.org

Established in 2000 in Connecticut.
Foundation type: Independent foundation.
Financial data (yr. ended 12/31/13): Assets, $7,800,731 (M); gifts received, $7,800,731; expenditures, $458,688; qualifying distributions, $355,429; giving activities include $99,000 for 17 grants (high: $15,000; low: $2,000), and $153,000 for 50 grants to individuals (high: $8,000; low: $1,000).
Purpose and activities: Scholarships are awarded to high school graduates who are, in the opinion of the foundation's trustees, deserving and in need of financial assistance in obtaining a college education or specialized education of the kind furnished by technical schools. Funding also for children, youth and social services. .
Fields of interest: Higher education; Human services; Child welfare.
Type of support: Student aid.
Limitations: Applications accepted. Giving primarily in the town of Wilton, CT, and surrounding towns.
Application information: Preference for scholarships is given to students who reside in the Town of Wilton, CT and surrounding towns; for charitable distributions preference is given to entities servicing the Town of Wilton and its surrounding communities. Application form required.
   Initial approach: Use application form on foundation web site
   Deadline(s): Mar. 1
Trustees: Thomas T. Adams; Dr. David F. Clune; Rev. William L. Sachs.
EIN: 066473263

1393
Harlan E. Anderson Foundation
c/o The Maples Ph
179 Oenoke Ridge Rd.
New Canaan, CT 06840 (203) 544-8488
Contact: Harlan E. Anderson, Tr.

Established in 1969 in Connecticut.
Donor: Harlan E. Anderson.
Foundation type: Independent foundation.
Financial data (yr. ended 12/31/13): Assets, $3,772,826 (M); expenditures, $208,190; qualifying distributions, $175,000; giving activities include $175,000 for 27 grants (high: $25,000; low: $2,000).
Purpose and activities: Giving primarily for the elderly and educational programs.

Fields of interest: Arts and culture; Education; Human services.
Type of support: Capital campaigns; Capital and infrastructure; Endowments.
Limitations: Applications accepted. Giving primarily in CT.
Application information:
   Initial approach: Proposal
   Deadline(s): None
Trustees: Susan L. Abbott; Brian A. Anderson; Gregory S. Anderson; Harlan E. Anderson; Lois J. Anderson; Susan E. Anderson.
EIN: 237011480

1394
Anderson-Paffard Foundation, Inc.
P.O. Box 88
New London, CT 06320-0088

Established in 1981 in Connecticut.
Foundation type: Independent foundation.
Financial data (yr. ended 09/30/13): Assets, $0 (M); expenditures, $174,235; qualifying distributions, $170,000; giving activities include $170,000 for 28 grants (high: $20,000; low: $1,000).
Fields of interest: Arts and culture; Education; Diseases and conditions; Community beautification; Human services.
Limitations: Applications not accepted. Giving primarily in southeastern CT. No support for amateur sports competitions. No grants to individuals.
Application information: Unsolicited requests for funds not accepted.
Officers: Frederick P. Anderson, MD, Pres.; Willa T. Schuster, V.P.; Robert P. Anderson, Jr., Secy.-Treas.
Number of staff: 1 part-time support.
EIN: 061047468

1395
The Antonacci Foundation for Charitable Giving, Inc.
15 Mullen Rd.
Enfield, CT 06082-6033

Established in 1994 in Connecticut.
Donors: Gaetano Antonacci; Frank Antonacci; Gerald Antonacci; F&G Realty Recycling, LLC; USA Hauling & Recycling, Inc.
Foundation type: Independent foundation.
Financial data (yr. ended 12/31/13): Assets, $3,155,339 (M); gifts received, $1,050,000; expenditures, $286,442; qualifying distributions, $286,442; giving activities include $286,340 for 51 grants (high: $50,000; low: $250).
Fields of interest: Museums; Education; Undergraduate education; Fire prevention and control; Religion; Human services; Child welfare.
Type of support: General support.
Limitations: Applications not accepted. No grants to individuals.
Application information: Unsolicited requests for funds not accepted.
Officers: Frank Antonacci, V.P.; Gerald Antonacci, V.P.
EIN: 061414354

1396
John E. & Caron G. Avery Foundation Inc.
59 Merrimac Dr.
Trumbull, CT 06611-1725

Established in 1996 in New Jersey.
Donor: John E. Avery.
Foundation type: Independent foundation.
Financial data (yr. ended 09/30/14): Assets, $1,478,570 (M); expenditures, $189,736; qualifying distributions, $171,975; giving activities include $168,600 for 38 grants (high: $30,000; low: $700).
Purpose and activities: Giving for education, health and human services.
Fields of interest: Arts and culture; Museums; Education; Elementary and secondary education; Higher education; Health; Hospital care; Religion; Human services.
Limitations: Applications not accepted. Giving primarily in CT and NY; some giving also in FL. No grants to individuals.
Application information: Unsolicited requests for funds not accepted.
Officers and Trustees: John E. Avery, Pres. and Trustee; Alicia Avery, V.P.; Christopher J. Koehm, Treas.
EIN: 311481506

1397
Axe-Houghton Foundation
c/o Foundation Source
55 Walls Dr., 3rd. Fl.
Fairfield, CT 06824-5163

Established in 1965 in New York.
Donor: Emerson W. Axe†.
Foundation type: Independent foundation.
Financial data (yr. ended 02/28/14): Assets, $7,720,460 (M); expenditures, $386,798; qualifying distributions, $345,217; giving activities include $302,000 for 73 grants (high: $8,500; low: $2,000).
Purpose and activities: Giving to foster and encourage an appreciation of the English language, with major emphasis on the spoken language. Priority is given to projects for the improvement of speech and its uses in the areas of public affairs, education, theater, poetry, debate, and the oral interpretation of literature. A portion of available funds may be devoted to speech remediation.
Fields of interest: Theater; Opera; Performing arts education; Linguistics; Higher education; Public libraries; Television.
Type of support: Program development.
Limitations: Applications not accepted. Giving primarily in the metropolitan New York, NY, area. No support for private foundations or organizations outside the U.S. No grants to individuals, or for operating budgets, general purposes, continuing support, annual campaigns, emergency funds, deficit financing, capital funds, endowment funds, matching gifts, scholarships, fellowships, or publications; no loans.
Application information: Unsolicited requests for funds not accepted.
Officers and Directors: Jeffrey Steinman, Pres. and Director; Lynn F. Angelson, V.P. and Director; Suzanne Schwartz Davidson, Secy. and Director; Bruce D. Haims, Treas. and Director; Charles Forster; Carolyn Weber.
Number of staff: None.
EIN: 136200200

1398
The Arnold F. Baggins Foundation Inc.
2061 Ponus Ridge Rd.
New Canaan, CT 06840-2527

Established in 1993 in Connecticut.
Donors: Robert D. Kennedy; Sally D. Kennedy.
Foundation type: Independent foundation.
Financial data (yr. ended 12/31/14): Assets, $4,088,887; expenditures, $212,476; qualifying distributions, $192,492.
Fields of interest: Arts and culture; Education; Animal welfare; Nonprofits; Health; Diseases and conditions; Religion; Human services.
Type of support: Regranting.
Limitations: Applications not accepted. Giving primarily in CT. No grants to individuals.
Application information: Unsolicited requests for funds not accepted.
Officer: Robert D. Kennedy, Pres.
EIN: 061385734

1399
The Baldwin Foundation
c/o D. Brandrup
57 Old Post Rd., No. 2
Greenwich, CT 06830-6241

Donor: Winifred B. Baldwin†.
Foundation type: Independent foundation.
Financial data (yr. ended 12/31/14): Assets, $11,569,057; gifts received, $0; expenditures, $555,872; qualifying distributions, $524,462.
Purpose and activities: Giving primarily for health care and education; some support also for environmental conservation and animal welfare.
Fields of interest: Elementary and secondary education; Natural resources; Biodiversity; Wildlife biodiversity; Health; Hospital care.
Type of support: General support; Matching grants; Annual campaigns; Capital campaigns; Capital and infrastructure; Land acquisitions; Emergency funds.
Limitations: Applications not accepted. Giving primarily in southern ME. No grants to individuals, or for scholarships.
Publications: Annual report.
Application information: Contributes only to pre-selected organizations.
Board meeting date(s): July and Aug.
Officers and Directors: Diana B. Dunnan, Pres. and Director; Rev. D. Stuart Dunnan, V.P. and Director; Douglas M. Dunnan, V.P. and Director; Winifred D. Faust, V.P. and Director; Joan W. Trimble, V.P. and Director; Douglas W. Brandrup, Secy.-Treas.; Bruce B. Dunnan; John M. Dunnan; Brian W. Gregg.
Number of staff: None.
EIN: 133039728

1400
The Bannow-Larson Foundation, Inc.
54 Harvest Moon Rd.
Easton, CT 06612-1723

Established in 1966 in Connecticut.
Donor: Dorothy Larson.
Foundation type: Independent foundation.
Financial data (yr. ended 07/31/13): Assets, $3,581,228 (M); expenditures, $275,137; qualifying distributions, $226,750; giving activities include $226,750 for 14 grants (high: $100,000; low: $250).

Fields of interest: Arts and culture; Education; Health care clinics; Human services.
Limitations: Applications not accepted. Giving primarily in CT. No grants to individuals.
Application information: Unsolicited requests for funds not accepted.
Officers: Dorothy B. Larson, Pres.; Denise Larson-Fenton, Secy.
Directors: David Gombos; Joanne Spalla.
EIN: 066084233

1401
Louis F. & Virginia C. Bantle Charitable Foundation, Inc.
1 Centre St.
Darien, CT 06820-4503

Established in 1992 in Connecticut.
Donors: Louis F. Bantle; Virginia C. Bantle.
Foundation type: Independent foundation.
Financial data (yr. ended 12/31/13): Assets, $6,607,526 (M); expenditures, $428,087; qualifying distributions, $241,500; giving activities include $237,900 for 18 grants (high: $50,000; low: $500).
Fields of interest: Diseases and conditions; Spinal cord injuries and diseases; Diabetes; Alcoholism; Human services; Family services.
Type of support: Research.
Limitations: Applications not accepted. Giving primarily in CT and NY. No grants to individuals.
Application information: Contributes only to pre-selected organizations.
Officers: Robert C. Bantle, Pres.; Terri Ann Walker, Secy.
Director: Virginia C. Bantle.
EIN: 223199626

1402
The Barden Foundation, Inc.
1146 Barnum Ave.
Bridgeport, CT 06610-2705
Contact: Robin Bergman, Secy.-Treas. and Tr.
Scholarship application address: c/o The Scholarship Committee, 200 Park Ave., Danbury, CT 06810

Established in 1959 in Delaware.
Donor: The Barden Corp.
Foundation type: Independent foundation.
Financial data (yr. ended 10/31/14): Assets, $6,064,112 (M); expenditures, $299,581; qualifying distributions, $281,153; giving activities include $202,500 for 35 grants (high: $25,000; low: $500), and $70,000 for 43 grants to individuals (high: $2,000; low: $500).
Purpose and activities: The foundation supports hospitals and organizations involved with education, health, human services, and children and youth services.
Fields of interest: Education; Higher education; Nonprofits; Hospital care; Diseases and conditions; Human services; Child welfare; Scouting programs.
Type of support: General support; Scholarships; Regranting.
Limitations: Applications accepted. Giving primarily in CT.
Publications: Informational brochure.
Application information: Application form required.

Initial approach: Letter; Complete application form
Deadline(s): Jan. 1 for other requests and Mar. 31 for Scholarships
Officers and Trustees: Thomas F. Loughman, Pres. and Trustee; Robin Bergman, Secy.-Treas. and Trustee; Robert Davis; Jeannine Frink; Robert P. More; Stanley Noss.
EIN: 066054855

1403
Harry F. & Carol H. Barnes Family Foundation
1900 Perkins St.
Bristol, CT 06010-8924

Established in 2007 in Connecticut.
Donor: The Harry Fuller Barnes.
Foundation type: Independent foundation.
Financial data (yr. ended 12/31/13): Assets, $5,140,815 (M); gifts received, $524,917; expenditures, $188,726; qualifying distributions, $180,000; giving activities include $180,000 for 43 grants (high: $20,000; low: $1,000).
Fields of interest: Arts and culture; Education; Community and economic development.
Limitations: Applications not accepted. Giving primarily in CA, CT and WA. No grants to individuals.
Application information: Unsolicited requests for funds not accepted.
Officers: Nancy Dey, Chair.; Thomas O. Barnes, Pres.; Jarre Barnes Betts, Secy.; Michael Wray, Treas.
EIN: 208718203

1404
The Barnes Foundation Inc
P.O. Box 288
East Hartland, CT 06027-0288 (860) 653-0462

Established in 1945 in Connecticut.
Donors: Carlyle F. Barnes; Aurelia B. Bristow†; Louise B. Adams; Myrtle I. Barnes†; Fuller F. Barnes†.
Foundation type: Independent foundation.
Financial data (yr. ended 12/31/14): Assets, $9,358,843; expenditures, $465,490; qualifying distributions, $398,295.
Purpose and activities: Giving to promote excellence in education with an emphasis on programs that benefit students in grades kindergarten through high school.
Fields of interest: Education; Elementary education; Secondary education.
Type of support: Equipment; Program development; Curriculum development.
Limitations: Applications accepted. Giving primarily in CT. No support for programs outside the focus area. No grants to individuals, or for endowment funds, capital campaigns, buildings, renovations, scholarships, or debt reduction.
Application information: Application form required.
Initial approach: Letter
Copies of proposal: 1
Deadline(s): Submission should be made six to twelve months in advance
Officers: Joan W. Barnes, Pres.; Sally A. O'Connor, V.P. and Exec. Dir.; Brenna K. Flynn, Secy.; Elliott B. Bristow, Treas.
Directors: Edward Thomas Adams; Heather B. Adams; Louise B. Adams; Wendy E. Adams; Gail I.

Bristow; Corey W. Flynn; Patricia Hamon; Lynne B. Leahy; Brooke L. O'Connor; Timothy J. O'Connor.
Number of staff: 1 full-time professional.
EIN: 066037160

1405
The Morris S. & Florence H. Bender Foundation, Inc.
c/o J. D. Port
170 Mason St.
Greenwich, CT   06830-6644

Established in 1978 in New York.
Donors: Florence H. Bender†; Morris Bender†.
Foundation type: Independent foundation.
Financial data (yr. ended 06/30/14): Assets, $3,810,064; expenditures, $219,558; qualifying distributions, $180,267.
Purpose and activities: Giving primarily for the arts, hospitals, and medical research, particularly to an institute for otolaryngology, as well as to organizations for terminally ill children.
Fields of interest: Arts and culture; Performing arts; Ballet; Hospital care; Diseases and conditions; Child welfare.
Type of support: General support; Program development; Research; Research and evaluation.
Limitations: Applications not accepted. Giving primarily in CT, NJ and New York, NY. No grants to individuals.
Application information: Unsolicited requests for funds not accepted.
Officers: Jane Laffend, Pres.; Jennifer D. Port, Secy.; Ralph M. Engel, Treas.
EIN: 132951469

1406
Walter J. and Lille A. Berbecker Scholarship Fund
(formerly Walter J. Berbecker and Lille A. Webb Scholarship Fund)
30 Maltbie Rd.
Newtown, CT   06470-2508
Contact: Robert A. Beer, Tr.

Established in 1988 in New York.
Foundation type: Independent foundation.
Financial data (yr. ended 02/28/13): Assets, $77,913 (M); expenditures, $443,196; qualifying distributions, $440,597; giving activities include $440,000 for 4 grants (high: $150,000; low: $95,000).
Fields of interest: Higher education; Diseases and conditions; Autism.
Type of support: Research; Research and evaluation.
Limitations: Applications accepted. Giving in the U.S., with some emphasis on CT and NC. No grants to individuals.
Application information: Application form required.
  Initial approach: Letter
  Deadline(s): None
Trustees: Robert A. Beer; F. Brower Moffitt.
EIN: 222801843

1407
Cornelia and Michael Bessie Foundation
296 Joshuatown Rd.
Lyme, CT   06371-3035

Established in 2008 in Connecticut.
Foundation type: Independent foundation.
Financial data (yr. ended 12/31/13): Assets, $3,578,814 (M); expenditures, $173,126; qualifying distributions, $165,831; giving activities include $165,831 for 13 grants (high: $30,000; low: $831).
Fields of interest: Education; Domesticated animals; Catholicism.
Limitations: Applications not accepted.
Application information: Unsolicited requests for funds not accepted.
Trustees: Cornelia Bessie; George Black; Anne Nelson-Black; James Ottaway, Jr.
EIN: 262341663

1408
David and Eunice Bigelow Foundation
134 East Ave.
Norwalk, CT   06851

Established in 1998 in Connecticut.
Donors: David C. Bigelow; Eunice J. Bigelow; Lori Bigelow; Cynthia R. Bigelow; 16W Marketing LLC; International Marketing Systems; R.C. Bigelow Inc.; AmGraph; Joe Torre; Wausau Container Corporation.
Foundation type: Independent foundation.
Financial data (yr. ended 12/31/13): Assets, $4,691,284 (M); gifts received, $173,618; expenditures, $312,110; qualifying distributions, $288,520; giving activities include $288,500 for 44 grants (high: $15,000; low: $500).
Fields of interest: Higher education; Catholicism; Human services; Domestic violence shelters.
Type of support: General support.
Limitations: Applications not accepted. Giving primarily in CT. No grants to individuals.
Application information: Contributes only to pre-selected organizations.
Officers: David C. Bigelow, Pres.; Eunice J. Bigelow, V.P. and Treas.; David L. Godfrey, Secy.
Directors: Cynthia R. Bigelow; Lori Bigelow.
EIN: 061535327

1409
UD, JC & AJ Bowling Foundation
(formerly The JC & AJ Bowling Foundation)
c/o Blair & Potts
P.O. Box 1214
Stamford, CT   06904-1214

Established in 1997 in Unspecified.
Donor: Ann J. Bowling.
Foundation type: Independent foundation.
Financial data (yr. ended 12/31/13): Assets, $2,507,415 (M); expenditures, $156,051; qualifying distributions, $143,000; giving activities include $143,000 for 6+ grants.
Purpose and activities: Giving primarily for education and human services.
Fields of interest: Museums; Elementary and secondary education; Higher education; Health; Human services.
Limitations: Applications not accepted. Giving primarily in CT and KY. No grants to individuals.
Application information: Contributes only to pre-selected organizations.
Directors: Ann J. Bowling; Nancy Bowling Gramps; Belinda Bewkes Metzger; Stephanie B. Ziegler.
EIN: 311522458

1410
Donald C. Brace Foundation
c/o Robert A. Beer
30 Maltbie Rd.
Newtown, CT   06470-2508   (203) 426-3093

Established in 1987 in Connecticut.
Donor: Donna Brace Ogilvie.
Foundation type: Independent foundation.
Financial data (yr. ended 12/31/14): Assets, $4,979,282 (M); expenditures, $302,490; qualifying distributions, $210,500; giving activities include $188,000 for grants.
Fields of interest: Arts and culture; Education; Foundations.
Type of support: Scholarships.
Limitations: Applications accepted. Giving in the U.S., with some emphasis on HI, ID and NH.
Application information: Application form required.
  Initial approach: Letter
  Deadline(s): None
Trustees: Robert A. Beer, Esq.; Katharine Butler; Donna Brace Ogilvie; Karen Scheid.
EIN: 133442680

1411
Eleanor and Raymond Bradley Foundation
c/o Kearns & Kearns
1121 New Britain Ave.
West Hartford, CT   06110-2412

Donors: Eleanor R. Bradley Trust; Eleanor R. Bradley.
Foundation type: Independent foundation.
Financial data (yr. ended 12/31/14): Assets, $5,528,246 (M); expenditures, $305,273; qualifying distributions, $242,490; giving activities include $227,500 for 10 grants (high: $100,000; low: $2,500).
Fields of interest: Education; Philanthropy; Health; Catholicism.
Type of support: General support.
Limitations: Applications not accepted. Giving primarily in CT. No grants to individuals.
Application information: Unsolicited requests for funds not accepted.
Trustee: John F. Kearns III.
EIN: 066516193

1412
Bridgemill Foundation
c/o Foundation Source
55 Walls Dr., 3rd Fl.
Fairfield, CT   06824-5173

Donor: John H.T. Wilson†.
Foundation type: Independent foundation.
Financial data (yr. ended 12/31/12): Assets, $18,361,391 (M); expenditures, $572,207; qualifying distributions, $351,597; giving activities include $337,375 for 17 grants (high: $50,122; low: $5,000).
Purpose and activities: Giving primarily for higher education, health associations, and children and social services.
Fields of interest: Higher education; Diseases and conditions; Human services; Child welfare.
Type of support: Research.
Limitations: Applications not accepted. Giving primarily in CT and NY. No grants to individuals.

Application information: Contributes only to pre-selected organizations.
Officers: Sandra W. Wilson, V.P.; Emily Wilson Burns, Secy.
Members: David Wilson; William Wilson.
EIN: 133671059

1413
The Ruth W. Brown Foundation

170 Mason St.
Greenwich, CT 06830-6644
Contact: Wilmot L. Harris Jr., Tr.

Established in 1995 in Connecticut.
Foundation type: Independent foundation.
Financial data (yr. ended 12/31/14): Assets, $3,477,686 (M); expenditures, $263,636; qualifying distributions, $190,282; giving activities include $159,500 for 31 grants (high: $27,000; low: $1,000).
Fields of interest: Arts and culture; Diseases and conditions; Human services; Family services; Child welfare; Females.
Type of support: General support.
Limitations: Applications not accepted. Giving primarily in CT. No grants to individuals.
Application information: Unsolicited requests for funds not accepted.
Trustees: Stuart D. Adelberg; Sally C. Harris; Wilmot L. Harris, Jr.
EIN: 061409590

1414
The Calarco Family Foundation Inc.

27 Forest Glen Dr.
Woodbridge, CT 06525-1420

Established in 2004 in Connecticut.
Donors: Linda Calarco; Vincent Calarco.
Foundation type: Independent foundation.
Financial data (yr. ended 12/31/13): Assets, $735,945 (M); expenditures, $231,600; qualifying distributions, $231,600; giving activities include $226,400 for 2 grants (high: $200,000; low: $26,400).
Fields of interest: Education; Diseases and conditions; Human services.
Type of support: Research.
Limitations: Applications not accepted. No grants to individuals.
Application information: Unsolicited requests for funds not accepted.
Officers: Vincent Calarco, Pres. and Treas.; Linda Calarco, V.P. and Secy.; Christopher Calarco, V.P.; David Calarco, V.P.
EIN: 201976848

1415
Philip & Betsey C. Caldwell Foundation

167 Deep Valley Rd.
New Canaan, CT 06840-2804

Donors: Betsey C. Caldwell; Philip Caldwell.
Foundation type: Independent foundation.
Financial data (yr. ended 12/31/13): Assets, $5,170,221 (M); expenditures, $230,949; qualifying distributions, $183,000; giving activities include $183,000 for 20 grants (high: $42,000; low: $500).

Purpose and activities: Giving for higher education, religion, museums and historic preservation, and relief services.
Fields of interest: Arts and culture; Education; Public libraries; Human services.
Limitations: Applications not accepted. Giving primarily in CT, MA, and NY. No grants to individuals.
Application information: Unsolicited requests for funds not accepted.
Officers: Philip Caldwell, Pres.; Betsey C. Caldwell, Secy.
Directors: Desiree C. Armitage; Lawrence C. Caldwell; Lucy Caldwell Stair.
EIN: 061164130

1416
Cenveo Scholarship Fund, Inc.

200 1st Samford Pl.
Stamford, CT 06902
Scholarship application address: c/o Scholarship Management Services, 1 Scholarship Way, St. Peter, MN 56082; Main URL: http://www.cenveo.com/cenveo-scholarship-fund

Donors: Robert G. Burton, Sr.; Balakian Family Foundation; Robert G. Burton Charitable Foundation; Karla Feltes; Timothy Feltes; Gerald S. Armstrong; Leonard C. Green; Paula Burton; Leonard C. and Lois S. Charitable Foundation.
Foundation type: Company-sponsored foundation.
Financial data (yr. ended 12/31/13): Assets, $12,915 (M); gifts received, $259,200; expenditures, $253,825; qualifying distributions, $240,000; giving activities include $240,000 for 49 grants to individuals (high: $10,000; low: $1,000).
Purpose and activities: The Fund provides scholarships to children of Cenveo employees who plan to continue their education in college or vocational school programs.
Fields of interest: Education.
Type of support: Student aid.
Application information: Application form required.
Initial approach: Proposal
Deadline(s): Apr. 30
Officers: Robert G. Burton, C.E.O.; Scott J. Goodwin, C.F.O.; Linda J. Austin, Secy.
EIN: 262808338

1417
Chaikin-Wile Foundation Inc.

c/o Friedberg, Smith
855 Main St., 6th Fl.
Bridgeport, CT 06604-4915

Established in 1994 in Connecticut.
Donor: Ruth C. Wile.
Foundation type: Independent foundation.
Financial data (yr. ended 12/31/14): Assets, $1,486,767; expenditures, $145,856; qualifying distributions, $135,490.
Fields of interest: Higher education; Medical education; Nonprofits; Judaism; Food banks.
Type of support: General support; Regranting.
Limitations: Applications not accepted. No grants to individuals.
Application information: Unsolicited requests for funds not accepted.
Officers: Ruth C. Wile, Pres. and Treas.; David M. Zieff, V.P. and Secy.
Director: Lawrence C. Wile.
EIN: 061413203

1418
Chelsea Groton Foundation, Inc.

1 Franklin Sq.
Norwich, CT 06360-5825 (860) 823-4800
Grants List: http://www.chelseagroton.com/foundation.php

Established in 1998 in Connecticut.
Donor: Chelsea Groton Bank.
Foundation type: Company-sponsored foundation.
Financial data (yr. ended 12/31/13): Assets, $3,312,582 (M); gifts received, $114,509; expenditures, $168,225; qualifying distributions, $152,130; giving activities include $150,405 for 64 grants (high: $20,000; low: $500).
Purpose and activities: The foundation supports organizations involved with arts and culture, education, health, and human services.
Fields of interest: Arts and culture; Education; Higher education; Reading promotion; Nonprofits; Health; Hospital care; Human services; Child welfare.
Type of support: General support; Regranting; Continuing support; Capital and infrastructure; Equipment; Program development; Scholarships.
Limitations: Applications accepted. Giving primarily in areas of company operations in southeastern CT. No support for municipal, public, political, or religious entities. No grants to individuals.
Application information: Application form required.
Initial approach: Letter
Deadline(s): Mar. for Spring and Sept. for Fall
Trustees: D. Ben Benoit; Harry Colonis; Jeffrey Godley; Eric Janney; Mary Ellen Jukoski; Anne L. Ogden; Zuzanna Olszewski; Michael Rauh; Denise Stapienski; Lori-Ellen Wesolowski; Anne Wilkinson; Laureen Tracey-Dufficy.
EIN: 061520330

1419
Rona and Jeffrey Citrin Charitable Foundation

7 Dewart Rd.
Greenwich, CT 06830-3418

Donor: Jeffrey Citrin.
Foundation type: Independent foundation.
Financial data (yr. ended 06/30/14): Assets, $3,128,870 (M); gifts received, $520,589; expenditures, $324,091; qualifying distributions, $307,500; giving activities include $307,500 for 5 grants (high: $150,000; low: $7,500).
Fields of interest: Higher education.
Limitations: Giving primarily in Hanover, NH; some funding also in MA and NY.
Trustees: Jeffrey Citrin; Rona Hollander Citrin.
EIN: 203144815

1420
Andrew R. & Dorothy L. Cochrane Foundation

P.O. Box 47
Guilford, CT 06437-0047
Contact: Dorothy L. Cochrane, Tr.

Donors: Andrew R. Cochrane†; Dorothy Lott Cochrane†; Lucile Cochrane Augustine†.
Foundation type: Independent foundation.
Financial data (yr. ended 12/31/13): Assets, $4,980,827 (M); expenditures, $247,565; qualifying distributions, $228,308; giving activities

include $226,115 for 43 grants (high: $37,365; low: $500).

Purpose and activities: Giving for human services.

Fields of interest: Christianity; Camps; Human services; Youth services; Senior services; Children; Seniors; Low-income and poor people.

Type of support: General support; Matching grants; Continuing support; Annual campaigns; Emergency funds.

Limitations: Giving primarily in Pittsburgh, PA. No grants to individuals.

Application information:
Initial approach: Letter
Copies of proposal: 3
Deadline(s): None
Board meeting date(s): Apr. 10, Aug. 10 and Dec. 10
Final notification: Within 3 or 4 months

Trustees: Eleanor Cochrane Clark; Dorothy Louise Cochrane; Christine Cochrane Yukevich.

Number of staff: None.

EIN: 256093648

1421
Colburn-Keenan Foundation, Inc.

P.O. Box 811
Enfield, CT 06083-0811 (860) 749-7522
FAX: (860) 763-6494; E-mail: admin@colkeen.org;
Toll free tel.: (800) 966-2431; Main URL: http://www.colkeen.org

Established in 2006 in Connecticut.

Donors: Donald Colburn Trust; Donald Colburn; Kathy Ann Keenan Trust; American Homecare Federation, Inc.; Real State Company.

Foundation type: Independent foundation.

Financial data (yr. ended 12/31/13): Assets, $11,187,746 (M); gifts received, $65,310; expenditures, $543,816; qualifying distributions, $455,425; giving activities include $97,050 for 16 grants (high: $10,000; low: $2,000), and $310,349 for 93 grants to individuals.

Purpose and activities: Giving primarily to provide assistance and support to individuals and families impacted by chronic inherited bleeding disorders or other chronic illnesses. The foundation also supports students with bleeding disorders through a designated scholarship program to ten undergraduate students per year for higher education.

Fields of interest: Higher education; Hemophilia; Family services.

Type of support: Research; Grants to individuals.

Limitations: Applications accepted. Giving in the U.S., with emphasis on Enfield, CT.

Publications: Application guidelines.

Application information: Application form and guidelines for all programs available on foundation web site. Application form required.
Initial approach: Letter or telephone
Deadline(s): Oct. 1 (for organizations); none for emergency grants

Officers and Directors: Sasha Zatyrka, Chair. and Director; Christine Pineo, Secy. and Director; Dawn Bryant, Treas. and Director; Jane Cavanaugh Smith, Exec. Dir.; Hilary Keenan; Richard Steingart, MD.

EIN: 204634920

1422
Carle C. Conway Scholarship Foundation, Inc.

c/o Marsha L. Colten
95 Alexandra Dr.
Stamford, CT 06903-1731

Donors: Continental Can Co., Inc.; Franklin Holdings, Inc.

Foundation type: Company-sponsored foundation.

Financial data (yr. ended 06/30/14): Assets, $4,664,765 (M); expenditures, $328,055; qualifying distributions, $291,637; giving activities include $50,000 for 1 grant, and $222,050 for 24 grants to individuals (high: $10,000; low: $5,800).

Purpose and activities: The foundation supports organizations involved with higher education.

Fields of interest: Higher education.

Type of support: Scholarships; General support.

Limitations: Applications not accepted. Giving primarily in areas of company operations in FL, IL, NY, KS, and PA.

Application information: Contributes only through employee-related scholarships and to pre-selected organizations.
Board meeting date(s): Usually May

Officers: Marsha L. Colten, Pres. and Treas.; Patricia DelTorro Heck, V.P. and Secy.

Trustees: Stephen Bermas; Robert S. Cohen.

EIN: 136088936

1423
C. S. Craig Family Foundation, Inc.

c/o Craig Capital Corp.
127 Pecksland Rd.
Greenwich, CT 06831-3651 (203) 869-7700
Contact: Charles S. Craig, Dir.

Established in 1997 in Delaware.

Donor: Charles S. Craig.

Foundation type: Independent foundation.

Financial data (yr. ended 04/30/15): Assets, $2,096,024 (M); expenditures, $366,765; qualifying distributions, $366,450; giving activities include $366,450 for 30 grants (high: $200,000; low: $600).

Fields of interest: Education; Higher education; Diseases and conditions.

Type of support: General support.

Limitations: Applications accepted. Giving primarily in New York, NY and RI.

Application information:
Initial approach: Proposal
Deadline(s): None

Directors: Charles S. Craig; Amy W. Harwood; Paul L. Maddock, Jr.

EIN: 061502485

1424
The Crew Family Foundation Inc

100 E. Main St.
Plainville, CT 06062-1954 (860) 793-6955

Established in 1986 in Connecticut.

Donors: Ted J. Crew; Peggy Lynn Crew.

Foundation type: Independent foundation.

Financial data (yr. ended 10/31/13): Assets, $2,707,709 (M); gifts received, $822,164; expenditures, $386,011; qualifying distributions, $374,980; giving activities include $374,980 for 28 grants (high: $100,000; low: $250).

Fields of interest: Christianity; Human services; Basic and emergency aid; International development.

Type of support: General support.

Limitations: Applications accepted. Giving primarily in GA. No grants to individuals.

Application information:
Initial approach: Proposal
Deadline(s): None

Officers and Directors: Ted J. Crew, Pres. and Director; Peggy Lynn Crew, Secy. and Director; Pamela Baker; Kimberly Crew.

EIN: 061191170

1425
Crosswicks Foundation, Ltd.

93 West St.
Goshen, CT 06756-1520
Contact: Josephine F. Jones, Exec. V.P.
Application address: C/o Josephine Jones,73 W. St., Goshen,CT 06756, tel.: (860) 496-8119

Established in 1972 in New York.

Donors: Hugh Franklin; Madeleine Franklin.

Foundation type: Independent foundation.

Financial data (yr. ended 11/30/14): Assets, $3,078,723 (M); expenditures, $222,472; qualifying distributions, $177,000; giving activities include $177,000 for 38 grants (high: $10,000; low: $1,000).

Fields of interest: Arts and culture; Education; Hospital care; Public libraries; Religion; Human services.

Type of support: General support; Continuing support; Scholarships.

Limitations: Applications accepted. Giving primarily in CT and NY. No grants to individuals.

Application information: Application form required.
Initial approach: Letter
Deadline(s): Nov. 1

Officers: Josephine F. Jones, Exec. V.P.; Maria R. Rooney, V.P.; Morton L. Price, Secy.; Madeleine J. Roy, Treas.

Directors: Charlotte Jones; Edward A. Jones.

EIN: 132732197

1426
Crow Hill Foundation

c/o Thomas E. Finn PC, Marcum LLP
35 Mason St.
Greenwich, CT 06830-5433

Established in 1997 in Connecticut.

Donor: Douglas Campbell, Jr.

Foundation type: Independent foundation.

Financial data (yr. ended 12/31/13): Assets, $6,116,537 (M); expenditures, $352,049; qualifying distributions, $265,774; giving activities include $257,000 for 4 grants (high: $100,000; low: $1,000).

Fields of interest: Natural resources; Family planning.

Limitations: Applications not accepted. Giving primarily in CT. No grants to individuals.

Application information: Unsolicited requests for funds not accepted.

Trustee: Douglas Campbell, Jr.

EIN: 061475924

1427
The Curran Foundation
(formerly The Jane and William Curran Foundation)
401 Temple St.
New Haven, CT 06511-6801

Established in 1986 in Connecticut.
Donors: Jane F. Curran†; William E. Curran; James Andreassi; Margaret Andreassi; Jean Sosnaud; Jeffrey Sosnaud.
Foundation type: Independent foundation.
Financial data (yr. ended 12/31/13): Assets, $5,533,220 (M); expenditures, $248,094; qualifying distributions, $218,700; giving activities include $218,700 for 65 grants (high: $50,000; low: $500).
Fields of interest: Arts and culture; Elementary education; Higher education; Hospital care; Religion; Females; Female children and youth; Military personnel.
Type of support: General support; Continuing support; Annual campaigns; Scholarships.
Limitations: Applications not accepted. Giving primarily in CT. No grants to individuals.
Publications: Annual report.
Application information: Unsolicited requests for funds not accepted.
Officers: Margaret C. Andreassi, Pres.; William E. Curran, V.P. and Treas.; John W. Barnett, Secy.
Directors: Janet S. Maley; Jean C. Sosnaud; James S. Zoldy, Jr.
Number of staff: 1 part-time professional.
EIN: 222668435

1428
The Dr. R. Lee and Adeline J. Damuth Foundation
1121 New Britain Ave.
West Hartford, CT 06110-2412
Contact: John F. Kearns, Tr.

Donor: Adeline J. Damuth Trust.
Foundation type: Independent foundation.
Financial data (yr. ended 12/31/13): Assets, $1,505,711 (M); gifts received, $6,246; expenditures, $243,394; qualifying distributions, $153,449; giving activities include $153,449 for 1 grant.
Fields of interest: Education.
Limitations: Applications accepted. Giving primarily in West Hartford, CT.
Application information: Application form required.
   Initial approach: Letter
   Deadline(s): None
Trustee: John Kearns.
EIN: 456763207

1429
Davis-McCullough Foundation Inc.
c/o Wikstrom Group
30 Buxton Farms Rd., No. 325
Stamford, CT 06905-1223
Application address: 500 W. Putnam Ave., Greenwich, CT 06830, tel.: (203) 862-2470

Established in 2006 in Connecticut.
Donor: Victoria McCullough.
Foundation type: Independent foundation.
Financial data (yr. ended 12/31/13): Assets, $3,948,781 (M); expenditures, $363,406; qualifying distributions, $319,760; giving activities

include $307,260 for 7 grants (high: $200,000; low: $5,000).
Fields of interest: Nonprofits; Human services.
International interests: Netherlands.
Type of support: Regranting.
Limitations: Applications accepted. Giving primarily in FL; giving also in MA, and VA; some giving also in the Netherlands.
Application information: Application form required.
   Initial approach: Letter
   Deadline(s): None
Officers and Trustees: Victoria Davis McCullough, Pres. and Trustee; Eric A. Peterson, Secy. and Trustee; Harry E. Peden III, Treas. and Trustee.
EIN: 205589596

1430
The Juan Jacobo & Jonne Low De Lara Foundation, Inc.
c/o Day Pitney, LLP
1 Canterbury Green
Stamford, CT 06901-2032

Donor: Jonne Low De Lara.
Foundation type: Independent foundation.
Financial data (yr. ended 04/30/13): Assets, $5,925,730 (M); expenditures, $434,373; qualifying distributions, $333,568; giving activities include $315,000 for 4 grants (high: $160,000; low: $5,000).
Fields of interest: Higher education; Community college education; Television; Child welfare.
Limitations: Applications not accepted. Giving primarily in CT, New York, NY, NC and PA. No grants to individuals.
Application information: Contributes only to pre-selected organizations.
Officers and Directors: Angela D. De Lara, Pres. and Director; Robert J. Miller, Secy. and Director; Dilia Carmela De Jacobo.
EIN: 061004121

1431
The Frederick A. DeLuca Foundation, Inc.
300 Bic Dr.
Milford, CT 06461-3055 (203) 877-4281
Contact: Janice Szabo
E-mail: delucafoundation@subway.com

Established in 1997 in Unspecified.
Donor: Frederick A. DeLuca.
Foundation type: Independent foundation.
Financial data (yr. ended 12/31/14): Assets, $2,467,066 (M); gifts received, $860,421; expenditures, $295,995; qualifying distributions, $288,826; giving activities include $274,075 for 2 grants (high: $264,075; low: $10,000).
Fields of interest: Arts and culture; Elementary and secondary education; Foundations; School athletics; Adolescents.
Type of support: General support.
Limitations: Applications accepted. Giving primarily in CT and OH.
Application information: For an application form email: delucafoundation@subway.com. Application form required.
   Initial approach: Letter and Email
   Deadline(s): Oct. 8

Officers and Directors: Elizabeth DeLuca, Pres. and Director; Jonathan DeLuca, Secy.-Treas. and Director; Frederick A. DeLuca.
EIN: 650755554

1432
Marie G. Dennett Foundation
c/o Fogarty Cohen Selby & Nemiroff LLC
1700 E. Putnam Ave., No. 406
Old Greenwich, CT 06870-1366

Established in 1956 in Illinois.
Donors: Marie G. Dennett†; Priscilla D. Ramsey†.
Foundation type: Independent foundation.
Financial data (yr. ended 08/31/14): Assets, $6,955,955 (M); expenditures, $343,638; qualifying distributions, $327,500; giving activities include $325,000 for 72 grants (high: $25,000; low: $500).
Fields of interest: Arts and culture; Education; Hospital care; Diseases and conditions; Christianity; Human services; Child welfare; Youth services; People with vision impairments.
Limitations: Applications not accepted. No grants to individuals.
Application information: Contributes only to pre-selected organizations.
Officers and Trustees: Dennett W. Goodrich, Pres. and Trustee; John A. Goodrich, V.P. and Trustee; Everett Fisher, Secy.-Treas. and Trustee; Langdon P. Cook; Ramsey W. Goodrich; Anne M. Piedade; Richard H. Ramsey; Richard L. Ramsey.
EIN: 061060970

1433
The DeNunzio Foundation
c/o Crown Horwath, LLP
3 Bridle Path Ln.
Riverside, CT 06878-2601

Established in 1990 in Connecticut.
Donor: Ralph DeNunzio.
Foundation type: Independent foundation.
Financial data (yr. ended 12/31/13): Assets, $4,246,840 (M); expenditures, $221,931; qualifying distributions, $178,244; giving activities include $177,000 for 14 grants (high: $70,000; low: $500).
Fields of interest: Education; Philanthropy.
Limitations: Applications not accepted. Giving primarily in CT, MA, NJ, and NY. No grants to individuals.
Application information: Unsolicited requests for funds not accepted.
Trustees: Jean Ames DeNunzio; Ralph DeNunzio.
EIN: 222738275

1434
The Herman & Henrietta Denzler Charitable Trust
P.O. Box 291
Monroe, CT 06468-0291

Established in 1985 in Connecticut.
Donors: Herman Denzler†; Henrietta Denzler†.
Foundation type: Independent foundation.
Financial data (yr. ended 12/31/13): Assets, $8,274,946 (M); expenditures, $403,847; qualifying distributions, $403,278; giving activities

include $281,745 for 74 grants (high: $18,700; low: $200).

Purpose and activities: Support for education, Roman Catholic organizations, and aid to the elderly, the sick, the infirm, and other people in need.

Fields of interest: Education; Higher education; Nonprofits; Hospital care; Diseases and conditions; Catholicism; Human services.

Type of support: Regranting.

Limitations: Applications not accepted. No grants to individuals.

Application information: Unsolicited requests for funds not accepted.

Trustees: Dennis G. Boyd; Kevin M. Boyd; Michael J. Boyd; Eileen Hornor; Kathleen McGannon; Patricia B. Severson; Maryann B. Shafter.

EIN: 222600755

1435
Robert G. & Marguerite M. Derx Foundation Inc.

c/o USB Valerie Ernst & Eugene McRedmond Cotrus
P.O. Box 578
Litchfield, CT 06759-0578

Established in 2003 in Connecticut.

Donor: Marguerite M. Derx Trust.

Foundation type: Independent foundation.

Financial data (yr. ended 12/31/14): Assets, $5,257,273; expenditures, $317,346.

Fields of interest: Television; Special Olympics; Youth development.

Limitations: Applications not accepted. No grants to individuals.

Application information: Unsolicited requests for funds not accepted.

Trustees: Valerie M. Ernst; Eugene McRedmond; Union Savings Bank, N.A.

EIN: 066449960

1436
The William J. and Frances E. Deutsch Charitable Foundation

113 Round Hill Rd.
Greenwich, CT 06831-3722

Established in 2004 in Unspecified.

Donors: Frances E. Deutsch; William J. Deutsch.

Foundation type: Independent foundation.

Financial data (yr. ended 12/31/13): Assets, $4,968,208 (M); expenditures, $239,485; qualifying distributions, $208,599; giving activities include $208,599 for 37 grants (high: $54,636; low: $305).

Fields of interest: Higher education; Judaism; Human services.

Limitations: Applications not accepted. No grants to individuals.

Application information: Unsolicited requests for funds not accepted.

Officers: William J. Deutsch, Pres.; Frances E. Deutsch, Secy.

EIN: 201163727

1437
Diageo North America Foundation, Inc.

(formerly UDV North America Foundation, Inc.)
c/o Tax Dept.
801 Main Ave., 4th Fl.
Norwalk, CT 06851-1127

Established in 1960 in Delaware.

Donors: Heublein, Inc.; United Distillers & Vintners North America, Inc.; Guinness UDV North America, Inc.; Diageo North America, Inc.

Foundation type: Company-sponsored foundation.

Financial data (yr. ended 12/31/13): Assets, $178,253 (M); gifts received, $314,942; expenditures, $297,408; qualifying distributions, $297,408; giving activities include $293,714 for 285 grants (high: $25,000; low: $25).

Purpose and activities: The foundation supports organizations involved with education, health, cancer, human services, religion, and economically disadvantaged people.

Fields of interest: Education; Secondary education; Higher education; Business education; Nonprofits; Health; Patient social services; Cancers; Leukemia; Religion; Christianity; Human services; Child welfare; Senior services; Low-income and poor people.

Type of support: General support; Employee matching gifts; Scholarships; Regranting.

Limitations: Applications accepted. Giving limited to areas of company operations, with emphasis CO, CT, MA, MD, and NY. No grants to individuals (except for employee-related scholarships), or for endowments.

Application information: Application form required.
Initial approach: Completed Application form
Deadline(s): None

Officers: Ivan M. Menezes, Chair.; Guy Smith, Pres.; Gabriel Bisio, Secy.

EIN: 066051280

1438
Dime Bank Foundation, Inc.

(formerly The Dime Savings Bank Foundation, Inc.)
290 Salem Tpke.
Norwich, CT 06360-6456   (860) 859-4300
Contact: Deirdre Sullivan, Secy.
E-mail: foundation@dime-bank.com; E-mail for Deirdre Sullivan: dsullivan@dime-bank.com; Main URL: https://dime-bank.com/dime-foundation.php
Grants List: https://dime-bank.com/dime-foundation-awards.php

Established in 1998 in Connecticut.

Donors: Dime Savings Bank of Norwich; Dime Bank.

Foundation type: Company-sponsored foundation.

Financial data (yr. ended 12/31/14): Assets, $3,885,113; expenditures, $169,295; qualifying distributions, $163,071.

Purpose and activities: The foundation supports programs designed to promote affordable housing; basic human services for those at-risk; cultural enrichment with emphasis on disadvantaged populations; education, job training, and literacy; opportunities for collaborative efforts; and services for under-served children, families, or the elderly with emphasis on those with low-to-moderate income levels.

Fields of interest: Arts and culture; Cultural awareness; Education; Reading promotion; Nonprofits; Public libraries; Employment; Job training; Housing development; Human services;

Family services; Child welfare; Senior services; Low-income and poor people.

Type of support: General support; Matching grants; Capital campaigns; Capital and infrastructure; Equipment; Program development; Scholarships; Regranting.

Limitations: Applications accepted. Giving primarily in areas of company operations in Baltic, Bozrah, East Lyme, Franklin, Gales Ferry, Griswold, Groton, Jewett City, Ledyard, Lisbon, Mystic, Montville, New London, Niantic, North Stonington, Norwich, Oakdale, Pawcatuck, Preston, Sprague, Stonington, Taftville, Uncasville, Voluntown, Waterford, West Mystic, and Yantic, CT, and Hopkinton, Richmond, and Westerly, RI. No support for pass-through organizations, political or fraternal organizations, religious institutions, parent-run organizations, or organizations that do not demonstrate fiscal stability or administrative responsibility. No grants to individuals (except for catastrophic situations) or for fundraising.

Publications: Application guidelines; Grants list; Informational brochure.

Application information: Organizations receiving support are asked to submit a post-grant report. Application form required.
Initial approach: Download application form and mail to foundation
Deadline(s): Year-round but are reviewed three times per year

Officers: Nicholas Caplanson, Pres.; David Standland, V.P. and Treas.; Deirdre Sullivan, Secy.

Directors: Steven L. Bokoff; Lee-Ann Gomes; Roland J. Harris; James M. Kirker, Esq.; Linda L. Mariani, Esq.; Robert A. Stanley; Mark Tramontozzi.

EIN: 061507800

1439
Alma Gibbs Donchian Charitable Foundation, Inc.

(formerly Alma Gibbs Donchian Foundation)
c/o Fogarty Cohen Selby & Nemiroff, LLC
88 Field Point Rd.
Greenwich, CT 06836-2508
Contact: Geoffrey M. Parkinson, Dir.
FAX: (203) 629-0806; E-mail: agd@fsllc.net; Mailing address: c/o Foundation Services, LLC, 640 W. Putnam Ave., 3rd Fl., Greenwich, CT 06830-6008; Additional e-mail: info@fsllc.net; Main URL: http://www.agdonchian.org

Established in 1991 in Connecticut.

Donor: Alma G. Donchian†.

Foundation type: Independent foundation.

Financial data (yr. ended 12/31/14): Assets, $6,150,252 (M); expenditures, $384,932; qualifying distributions, $389,351; giving activities include $241,690 for 16 grants (high: $25,000; low: $2,000).

Purpose and activities: Giving primarily to provide assistance to various specified institutions in Castleton, VT and the immediate environs. Beyond that, to address the following areas of concern: issues affecting the elderly, education (especially as pertaining to those with disabilities) and programs that further fundamental values (such as self-reliance and respect for tradition).

Fields of interest: Education; Special needs education; Environment; Human services; Seniors.

Limitations: Giving primarily in VT. No grants to individuals.

Application information: Application form available on foundation web site. Online application form is preferred. Application form required.

　　Initial approach: Complete application form online
　　Deadline(s): None

Directors: Holly Hitchcock; Geoffrey M. Parkinson; Leland C. Selby.

EIN: 061514400

1440
Richard Davoud Donchian Foundation, Inc.

(formerly Richard D. Donchian Charitable Foundation, Inc.)
c/o Foundation Services, LLP
640 W. Putnam Ave., 3rd Fl.
Greenwich, CT　06830-6008
E-mail: rdd@fsllc.net; *Main URL:* http://www.rddonchian.org

Established in 1991 in Connecticut.
Donor: Richard D. Donchian†.
Foundation type: Independent foundation.
Financial data (yr. ended 12/31/14): Assets, $9,822,850 (M); expenditures, $624,851; qualifying distributions, $531,584; giving activities include $436,725 for 65 grants (high: $40,000; low: $500).
Purpose and activities: The foundation focuses its grantmaking in four key areas: 1) Literacy & Education; 2) Humanitarian Efforts; 3) Health; and 4) Ethics and Personal Development.
Fields of interest: Education; Adult education; Health; Search and rescue; Leadership development; Economic development; Employment; Housing development; Business and industry; Human services; Youth development; Homeless shelters; Homeless services; International development.
Type of support: Ethics and accountability.
Publications: Application guidelines.
Application information: Application form available on foundation web site. Application form required.
　　Initial approach: See foundation web site for guidelines
　　Deadline(s): None
　　Board meeting date(s): Quarterly
Officers and Directors: Geoffrey M. Parkinson, Pres. and Director; Leland C. Selby, Secy.-Treas. and Director; Geoffrey M. Parkinson, Jr.
EIN: 061514402

1441
Eder Family Foundation Inc.

(formerly The Andrew J. Eder Family Foundation, Inc.)
11 Eder Rd.
West Haven, CT　06516-4128

Established in 1998 in Connecticut.
Donors: Andrew J. Eder; Eileen F. Eder; Eder Brothers, Inc.; Andrew Eder Annuity Trust.
Foundation type: Independent foundation.
Financial data (yr. ended 09/30/14): Assets, $6,635,488 (M); gifts received, $483,760; expenditures, $293,119; qualifying distributions, $273,450; giving activities include $273,450 for 54 grants (high: $50,000; low: $250).
Fields of interest: Education; Higher education; Nonprofits; Judaism; Camps; Human services.
Type of support: Student aid; Regranting.

Limitations: Applications not accepted. Giving primarily in PA.
Application information: Unsolicited requests for funds not accepted.
Officers and Directors: Andrew J. Eder, Pres. and Director; Eileen F. Eder, Secy.
EIN: 061465369

1442
The Ensign-Bickford Foundation, Inc.

125 Powder Forest Dr.
P.O. Box 7
Simsbury, CT　06070-9658　(860) 843-2334
Contact: Richard Roberts

Donor: Ensign-Bickford Industries, Inc.
Foundation type: Company-sponsored foundation.
Financial data (yr. ended 12/31/13): Assets, $30,149 (M); gifts received, $280,406; expenditures, $253,256; qualifying distributions, $252,316; giving activities include $248,375 for 126 grants (high: $25,000; low: $16).
Purpose and activities: The foundation supports zoos and organizations involved with arts and culture, education, animal welfare, housing, youth development, business promotion, and military and veterans.
Fields of interest: Education; Housing development; Human services.
Type of support: General support; Program development; Scholarships; Research.
Limitations: Applications accepted. Giving primarily in areas of company operations in CT, with emphasis on the Avon and Simsbury areas. No grants to individuals (except for employee-related scholarships), or for endowments, general operating support, emergency needs, or debt reduction; no loans.
Application information: Application form required.
　　Initial approach: Letter
　　Deadline(s): None
　　Board meeting date(s): Approximately every 2 months
　　Final notification: 3 months
Officers: Joan D. Lovejoy, Chair.; Caleb E. White, Pres.; Scott M. Deakin, Treas.
Directors: Paul Bacon; Jacquelyn A. Levin; Joseph E. Lovejoy, Jr.; John Markin; Brendan M. Walsh.
Number of staff: 1 part-time professional.
EIN: 066041097

1443
Holloway Family Foundation

707 West Rd.
New Canaan, CT　06840-2518

Established in 2000 in Connecticut.
Donor: Gary F. Holloway.
Foundation type: Independent foundation.
Financial data (yr. ended 06/30/14): Assets, $1,917,758 (M); expenditures, $211,369; qualifying distributions, $210,814; giving activities include $210,014 for 29 grants (high: $90,909; low: $100).
Fields of interest: Education; Human services.
Type of support: General support.
Limitations: Applications not accepted. Giving primarily in CT and VA. No grants to individuals.
Application information: Unsolicited requests for funds not accepted.

Trustees: Gary F. Holloway; Julie D. Holloway.
EIN: 061604276

1444
Farid Foundation

95 Barnes Rd.
Wallingford, CT　06492-1800　(203) 774-8000
Contact: Tariq Farid, Tr.

Established in 2005 in Connecticut.
Donors: Edible Arrangements Franchise Group, Inc.; Edible Brands, LLC; Tariq Farid; Netsolace, Inc.; Kamran Farid.
Foundation type: Company-sponsored foundation.
Financial data (yr. ended 12/31/13): Assets, $583,432 (M); gifts received, $246,650; expenditures, $353,952; qualifying distributions, $337,150; giving activities include $307,971 for 11 grants (high: $139,000; low: $500).
Purpose and activities: The foundation supports organizations involved with education and Islam.
Fields of interest: Education; Community and economic development; Human services.
Type of support: General support.
Limitations: Applications accepted. Giving primarily in CT.
Application information:
　　Initial approach: Proposal
　　Deadline(s): None
Trustees: Kamran Farid; Tariq Farid.
EIN: 203096696

1445
Marie Fauth Charitable Trust

c/o Cummings & Lockwood
2 Greenwich Plz.
Greenwich, CT　06830-6353

Established in 2005 in Connecticut.
Foundation type: Independent foundation.
Financial data (yr. ended 09/30/14): Assets, $6,908,189 (M); expenditures, $380,074; qualifying distributions, $321,485; giving activities include $302,333 for 2 grants (high: $287,333; low: $15,000).
Fields of interest: Philanthropy.
Type of support: Capacity-building and technical assistance.
Limitations: Applications not accepted. Giving primarily in MA. No grants to individuals.
Application information: Contributes only to pre-selected organizations.
Trustee: B. Cort Delany.
EIN: 202576232

1446
Ferguson Family Foundation, Inc.

c/o Weinshel, Wynnick & Assoc., LLC
457 Castle Ave., Ste. 101
Fairfield, CT　06825

Established in 1999 in Connecticut.
Donors: Carol J. Ferguson; Ronald E. Ferguson.
Foundation type: Independent foundation.
Financial data (yr. ended 12/31/13): Assets, $4,518,287 (M); gifts received, $157,395; expenditures, $187,038; qualifying distributions, $182,664; giving activities include $180,014 for 17 grants (high: $40,000; low: $14).

Fields of interest: Education; Higher education; Hospital care; Cystic fibrosis; Cancers; Religion; Homeless services.
Type of support: General support.
Limitations: Applications not accepted. No grants to individuals.
Application information: Unsolicited requests for funds not accepted.
Officers and Directors: Carol J. Ferguson, Pres. and Director; Cathy Ferguson, V.P. and Director; Ronald E. Ferguson, V.P. and Director; James A. Wackerman, V.P. and Director; Kristin A. Ferguson Wackerman, Secy. and Director; Brian C. Ferguson, Treas. and Director.
EIN: 061549937

1447
Gaetano Filingieri Philosophical Society of America, Inc.
14 Paddock Dr.
Greenwich, CT 06831-3044 (203) 861-9229
Contact: Lawrence Auriana, Pres.

Established in 2004 in Connecticut.
Donor: Lawrence Auriana.
Foundation type: Operating foundation.
Financial data (yr. ended 12/31/13): Assets, $45,591 (M); gifts received, $525,000; expenditures, $503,901; qualifying distributions, $318,164; giving activities include $318,164 for 11 grants (high: $130,000; low: $200), and $297,064 for 4 foundation-administered programs.
Purpose and activities: Giving primarily for education, children and social services, and to Italian-American organizations.
Fields of interest: Linguistics; Education; Higher education; Diseases and conditions; Human services; Child welfare.
Type of support: Scholarships; General support; Research; Research and evaluation.
Limitations: Giving primarily in NY. No grants to individuals.
Application information: Personal interview required. Application form required.
  Initial approach: Letter
  Deadline(s): None
Officers: Lawrence Auriana, Pres.; Mark Auriana, Secy.
Director: Ira S. Nordlicht.
EIN: 201547673

1448
The Finkelstein Foundation, Inc.
c/o Michael Finkelstein
373 Stamford Ave.
Stamford, CT 06902-8204

Established in 1997 in New York.
Donor: Michael Finkelstein.
Foundation type: Independent foundation.
Financial data (yr. ended 12/31/13): Assets, $1,780,082 (M); expenditures, $224,984; qualifying distributions, $208,875; giving activities include $208,875 for 16 grants (high: $100,000; low: $100).
Fields of interest: Education; Health; Religion.
Limitations: Applications not accepted. Giving primarily in CT and NY. No grants to individuals.
Application information: Contributes only to pre-selected organizations.

Officers: Michael Finkelstein, Pres.; Sue-Ann Friedman, V.P.; Alix Finkelstein, Secy.; David Finkelstein, Treas.
EIN: 223477816

1449
The Finn Family Foundation, Inc.
c/o Maarcum LLP
35 Mason St.
Greenwich, CT 06830-5433

Established in 1994 in Connecticut.
Donors: Daniel R. Finn; Daniel R. Finn, Jr.; David Finn; Christopher Finn.
Foundation type: Independent foundation.
Financial data (yr. ended 12/31/13): Assets, $5,376,698 (M); expenditures, $268,179; qualifying distributions, $256,685; giving activities include $254,649 for 38 grants (high: $51,000; low: $100).
Fields of interest: Education; Higher education; Nonprofits; Diseases and conditions; Breast cancer; Prostate cancer; Public libraries; Christianity; Human services; Food delivery; Child welfare; Homeless services.
Type of support: Research; Regranting.
Limitations: Applications not accepted. No grants to individuals.
Application information: Unsolicited requests for funds not accepted.
Officers: Phyllis Finn, Pres.; Daniel R. Finn, Jr., Secy.
EIN: 061405387

1450
Grace J. Fippinger Foundation, Inc.
c/o Hynes, Himmelreich, Glennon & Co.
P.O. Box 4004
Darien, CT 06820-1404

Established in 1989 in Connecticut.
Donor: Grace J. Fippinger†.
Foundation type: Independent foundation.
Financial data (yr. ended 12/31/13): Assets, $5,861,688 (M); gifts received, $12,000; expenditures, $344,420; qualifying distributions, $323,564; giving activities include $245,575 for 11 grants (high: $50,000; low: $375).
Purpose and activities: The foundation is committed to education, medical research, human development, and entrepreneurship.
Fields of interest: Education; Higher education; Cancers; Children and youth; Adolescents; Young adults; Females; Female adults; American Indians; Homeless people; Incarcerated people; People with psychosocial disabilities.
Type of support: Endowments; Employee matching gifts; Matching grants; Fellowships; General support; Research; Scholarships; Seed money.
Limitations: Applications not accepted. Giving primarily in CT, NY and SD. No support for religious or political organizations. No grants to individuals.
Application information: Contributes only to pre-selected organizations.
  Board meeting date(s): Quarterly
Officer: Eileen G. Hynes, Exec. Dir.
Directors: David B. Himmelreich; Liz Hynes; Thomas L. Hynes; Thomas W. Hynes; Marian McCaffrey; Michael Patrona; Lorraine Pennoyer; Chris Petrona; Johanna Sweet.
Number of staff: 1 full-time professional.
EIN: 223019876

1451
The Floren Family Foundation
210 Round Hill Rd.
Greenwich, CT 06831-3357 (203) 622-5850
Contact: Douglas C. Floren, Pres.

Established in 2000 in Connecticut.
Donor: Douglas C. Floren.
Foundation type: Independent foundation.
Financial data (yr. ended 10/31/13): Assets, $5,716,224 (M); expenditures, $424,078; qualifying distributions, $358,800; giving activities include $358,800 for 18 grants (high: $75,000; low: $2,000).
Fields of interest: Education; Higher education; University education; Nonprofits; Health; Hospital care; Christianity; Human services.
Type of support: Regranting.
Limitations: Applications accepted. Giving primarily in CA, CO, and NH.
Application information: Application form required.
  Initial approach: Proposal
  Deadline(s): None
Officer: Douglas C. Floren, Pres.
EIN: 066503521

1452
Lawrence & Megan Foley Family Foundation Inc.
P.O. Box 824
Southport, CT 06890-0824

Established in 2001 in Connecticut.
Donors: Lawrence G. Foley; Megan M. Foley; Andrew Schwartz.
Foundation type: Independent foundation.
Financial data (yr. ended 11/30/14): Assets, $3,675,942 (M); gifts received, $1,008,210; expenditures, $458,033; qualifying distributions, $427,489; giving activities include $427,489 for 29 grants (high: $117,975; low: $200).
Fields of interest: Elementary and secondary education; Higher education; Diseases and conditions; Catholicism; Human services; Child welfare; Catholics.
Limitations: Applications not accepted. No grants to individuals.
Application information: Contributes only to pre-selected organizations.
Directors: Lawrence G. Foley; Megan M. Foley; David J. McCabe.
EIN: 421528874

1453
Jacob L. and Lewis Fox Foundation
280 Trumbull St., 24th Fl.
Hartford, CT 06103-3599
Application address: c/o Arthur Querido, Pres., 45 Lake St., South Windsor, CT 06074, tel.: (860) 644-1995

Established in 1951 in Connecticut.
Donors: Lewis Fox†; Betty Stevens.
Foundation type: Independent foundation.
Financial data (yr. ended 12/31/13): Assets, $5,142,035 (M); expenditures, $253,789; qualifying distributions, $218,232; giving activities include $159,910 for 71 grants to individuals (high: $9,500; low: $14).

Purpose and activities: Scholarship awards limited to students graduating from and chosen by Hartford, Connecticut, public high schools.
Fields of interest: Education.
Type of support: Student aid.
Limitations: Applications accepted. Giving limited to graduates of Hartford, CT, public high schools.
Application information: Application form required.
   Initial approach: Proposal
   Deadline(s): Usually in late Jan. or early Feb.
Officers: Arthur J. Querido, Pres.; David J. Cocola, Treas.
Trustees: Nichelle Brooks-Mullins; Jerry Clapis; Robert Coykendall; Claudia Cruz-Reis; Israel Flores; Elizabeth Noel; David Parmelee; Gary Rhule; Carol Terry-Hewitt.
EIN: 066067700

1454
Evelyn Fraites Foundation
41 Hemlock Ridge
Weston, CT   06883-2000

Established in 1984 in New Jersey.
Donor: Joseph Lawrence Fraites, Sr.
Foundation type: Independent foundation.
Financial data (yr. ended 11/30/12): Assets, $0 (M); expenditures, $237,151; qualifying distributions, $236,651.
Purpose and activities: Scholarship awards to graduates of Cranford High School, New Jersey.
Fields of interest: Education.
Type of support: Student aid.
Limitations: Applications not accepted. Giving limited to residents of Cranford, NJ.
Application information: Unsolicited requests for funds not accepted.
Officers and Directors: Joseph L. Fraites, Pres. and Director; Lisa Fraites Dworkin, V.P. and Director; Christopher G. Fraites, V.P. and Director.
EIN: 113241845

1455
Friends of Kang Yun Foundation
192 Armory St.
Hamden, CT   06517
Main URL: http://kangyunfriends.org

Donors: Accademia Charitable Foundation; Berkeley Philatropies Ltd.
Foundation type: Independent foundation.
Financial data (yr. ended 12/31/14): Assets, $81,415 (M); gifts received, $193,500; expenditures, $207,557; qualifying distributions, $188,722; giving activities include $136,700 for 2 grants (high: $70,200; low: $66,500).
Fields of interest: Education; Philanthropy.
International interests: China.
Limitations: Applications not accepted. Giving primarily in Hong Kong, China.
Application information: Unsolicited requests for funds not accepted.
Officers: Thomas Hsu, Pres.; Brian D. Starer, Esq., V.P. and Treas.; Christopher Hsu, Secy. and Exec. Dir.
EIN: 510579003

1456
The Friends of the Center for American Studies Society
157 Church St., 19th Fl.
New Haven, CT   06510-2100

Foundation type: Independent foundation.
Financial data (yr. ended 12/31/13): Assets, $20,062 (M); expenditures, $185,450; qualifying distributions, $185,000; giving activities include $185,000 for 1 grant.
Fields of interest: Human services.
International interests: Italy.
Limitations: Applications not accepted. Giving primarily in Italy.
Application information: Unsolicited requests for funds not accepted.
Officers and Directors: Peter Alegi, Pres. and Director; James M. Carolan, Secy. and Director; Joseph Lapalombara, Treas.
EIN: 262048114

1457
The Friezo Family Foundation
495 Post Rd. E.
Westport, CT   06880   2035711309

Donors: David Friezo; Joan Friezo; Charles Friezo.
Foundation type: Independent foundation.
Financial data (yr. ended 12/31/14): Assets, $1,306,906; gifts received, $196,781; expenditures, $200,640; qualifying distributions, $179,948.
Fields of interest: Education; Higher education; Religion; Human services.
Type of support: General support.
Limitations: Applications not accepted. Giving primarily in LA.
Application information: Unsolicited requests for funds not accepted.
Officers: David Friezo, Pres.; Jorgelina Friezo, V.P.; Richard Li, Secy.
EIN: 274256760

1458
Lily Palmer Fry Memorial Trust
(formerly L. P. Fry Memorial Trust)
c/o U.S. Trust
200 Glastonbury Blvd., Ste. 200, CT2-545-02-05
Glastonbury, CT   06033-4056
Contact: Kate Kerchaert
E-mail: kate.kerchaert@ustrust.com; Main URL: https://www.bankofamerica.com/philanthropic/grantmaking.go

Established in 1953 in Connecticut.
Donor: William Henry Fry†.
Foundation type: Independent foundation.
Financial data (yr. ended 12/31/14): Assets, $5,891,092; expenditures, $330,696; qualifying distributions, $271,150.
Purpose and activities: The Lily Palmer Fry Memorial Trust was established in 1954 to support and promote summer camp opportunities for underserved children. Special consideration is given to traditional camp programs that take urban children out of the city to experience the natural environment.
Fields of interest: Sports and recreation; Child welfare; Children and youth; Adolescents; Ethnic

and racial groups; Low-income and poor people; People with disabilities.
Type of support: General support; Continuing support; Program development.
Limitations: Giving primarily in Fairfield and Hartford counties, CT, and New York City and Westchester County, NY. No grants to individuals.
Publications: Application guidelines.
Application information: Complete application guidelines available on Trust web site.
   Initial approach: Online through Trust web site
   Deadline(s): Feb. 1
   Final notification: 2 to 3 months following deadline
Trustees: Virginia Fry Odell; William Fry Peterson; Bank of America, N.A.
Number of staff: None.
EIN: 066033612

1459
The Fuchs Family Foundation, Inc.
975 Banks N. Rd.
Fairfield, CT   06430-1704   2033395027

Established in 2001 in Connecticut.
Donor: Russell Fuchs.
Foundation type: Independent foundation.
Financial data (yr. ended 12/31/14): Assets, $2,794,076; gifts received, $1,440; expenditures, $275,998; qualifying distributions, $271,320.
Fields of interest: Hospital care; Cancers; Breast cancer; Judaism.
Limitations: Applications not accepted. Giving primarily in CT.
Application information: Unsolicited requests for funds not accepted.
Officer: Russell Fuchs, Pres. and Secy.
EIN: 311803252

1460
Frank R. Fuller Trust
c/o Bank of America, N.A.
777 Main St.
Hartford, CT   06115-2303
Contact: Carmen Britt
Application address: c/o Fuller Scholarship Committee, 300 Summit St., Hartford, CT 06106, tel.: (203) 527-3157, ext. 365

Established in 1986 in Connecticut.
Foundation type: Independent foundation.
Financial data (yr. ended 12/31/14): Assets, $5,026,109 (M); expenditures, $274,589; qualifying distributions, $242,864; giving activities include $207,500 for grants to individuals.
Purpose and activities: Scholarship awards to Hartford County, Connecticut, high school seniors who are members of the Congregational Church and plan to obtain a B.A. degree at a four-year institution.
Fields of interest: Education; Protestantism; Protestants.
Type of support: Student aid; Undergraduate support; Aid to graduates or students of specific schools; Individual development.
Limitations: Giving limited to residents of Hartford County, CT.
Application information: Application form required.
   Initial approach: Letter requesting application form
   Deadline(s): 4/15

Trustee: Bank of America, N.A.
EIN: 066028136

1461
E. Clayton and Edith P. Gengras, Jr. Foundation, Inc.
300 Connecticut Blvd.
East Hartford, CT 06108-3065 (860) 289-3461

Established in 1986 in Connecticut.
Donors: Edith P. Gengras; E. Clayton Gengras, Jr.; Gengras Motor Cars, Inc.
Foundation type: Independent foundation.
Financial data (yr. ended 09/30/14): Assets, $370,636; gifts received, $180,595; expenditures, $273,649; qualifying distributions, $268,150.
Fields of interest: Arts and culture; Education; Nonprofits; Christianity.
Type of support: General support; Regranting.
Application information: Application form required.
Initial approach: Completed application form
Deadline(s): None
Officers and Directors: Edith P. Gengras, Pres. and Director; E. Clayton Gengras, Jr., Secy. and Director; Merrily Moynihan.
EIN: 061188156

1462
Gerald and Claire Gerath Foundation
24 Arapahoe Rd.
West Hartford, CT 06107-2701 (860) 232-7200
Contact: Owen Eagan, Tr.

Donor: Clair Gerath†.
Foundation type: Operating foundation.
Financial data (yr. ended 12/31/13): Assets, $2,078,604 (M); expenditures, $199,943; qualifying distributions, $175,000; giving activities include $175,000 for 3 grants (high: $75,000; low: $50,000).
Fields of interest: Domesticated animals.
Limitations: Applications not accepted. Giving primarily in CT.
Application information: Unsolicited requests for funds not accepted.
Trustee: Owen Egan.
EIN: 266648184

1463
Edward & Verna Gerbic Family Foundation
c/o Cummings & Lockwood LLC
P.O. Box 271820
West Hartford, CT 06127-1820 (860) 313-4930
Contact: Paul L. Bourdeau Esq., Tr.

Established in 1997 in Connecticut.
Donor: Verna A. Gerbic.
Foundation type: Independent foundation.
Financial data (yr. ended 04/30/13): Assets, $9,133,422 (M); gifts received, $151,429; expenditures, $223,408; qualifying distributions, $202,500; giving activities include $202,500 for 52 grants (high: $10,000; low: $500).
Purpose and activities: Giving for higher education, services for indigenous peoples, spinal cord research and human services.
Fields of interest: Higher education; Diseases and conditions; Spinal cord injuries and diseases; Human services.

Type of support: Research; Research and evaluation.
Limitations: Applications accepted. Giving primarily in Washington, DC, IL, MN and NY.
Application information:
Initial approach: Letter
Deadline(s): None
Trustees: Paul L. Bourdeau; Joseph Caruso; Celina Gerbic; Peter E. Gerbic.
EIN: 223457387

1464
Herbert and Sarah M. Gibor Charitable Foundation
c/o Wofsey
600 Summer St., 7th Fl.
Stamford, CT 06901-1490

Established in 2003 in Connecticut.
Donor: Herbert and Sarah M. Gibor Revocable Trust.
Foundation type: Independent foundation.
Financial data (yr. ended 12/31/13): Assets, $4,276,858 (M); expenditures, $318,547; qualifying distributions, $278,898; giving activities include $241,000 for 31 grants (high: $68,000; low: $500).
Fields of interest: Secondary education; University education; Nonprofits; Judaism; Food aid.
Type of support: Regranting.
Limitations: Applications not accepted. Giving primarily in CT. No grants to individuals.
Application information: Unsolicited requests for funds not accepted.
Trustees: Steven D. Grushkin; Edward A. Smith.
EIN: 066505200

1465
Marsha Lilien Gladstein Foundation
c/o Gary S. Gladstein
15 Wyckham Hill Ln.
Greenwich, CT 06831-3049

Donor: Gary S. Gladstein.
Foundation type: Independent foundation.
Financial data (yr. ended 12/31/14): Assets, $10,306,127 (M); expenditures, $521,281; qualifying distributions, $411,780.
Fields of interest: Education; Higher education; Nonprofits; Diseases and conditions; Judaism; Human services; Low-income and poor people.
Type of support: Regranting.
Limitations: Applications not accepted. Giving primarily in CT and NY.
Application information: Unsolicited requests for funds not accepted.
Trustees: Gary S. Gladstein; Jeff Gladstein; Mindy A. Grafstein.
EIN: 061581875

1466
The Harry E. Goldfarb Family Foundation, Inc.
P.O. Box 945
Farmington, CT 06034-0945

Established in 1980 in Connecticut.
Donors: Harry E. Goldfarb†; Robert B. Goldfarb; William H. Goldfarb†; Harry E. Goldfarb Revocable Living Trust.
Foundation type: Independent foundation.

Financial data (yr. ended 05/31/13): Assets, $4,976,053 (M); expenditures, $422,673; qualifying distributions, $418,550; giving activities include $417,500 for grants.
Purpose and activities: Giving primarily for Jewish federated giving programs and agencies, and education; support also for human services.
Fields of interest: Health; Religion; Human services.
Type of support: Annual campaigns; Endowments.
Limitations: Applications not accepted. Giving primarily in Hartford, CT. No grants to individuals.
Application information: Contributes only to pre-selected organizations.
Officers and Directors: Robert B. Goldfarb, Pres. and Director; William H. Goldfarb, V.P. and Secy. and Director; Mary D. Elder, Treas.; David Marks.
EIN: 061025623

1467
The Ellen Jeanne Goldfarb Memorial Charitable Trust
P.O. Box 945
Farmington, CT 06034-0945

Established in 1992 in Connecticut.
Donors: Harry E. Goldfarb; Robert B. Goldfarb; Francine L. Goldfarb; William H. Goldfarb; Pam Cronin; Rod Reynolds; Jan Reynolds; Tuck Miller; Ki Miller; Maureen Goldfarb; Boston Foundation.
Foundation type: Independent foundation.
Financial data (yr. ended 03/31/13): Assets, $1,255,063 (M); gifts received, $126,014; expenditures, $183,975; qualifying distributions, $183,027; giving activities include $182,300 for 49 grants (high: $15,000; low: $600).
Purpose and activities: Giving primarily for education.
Fields of interest: Arts and culture; Performing arts education; Education; Secondary education; University education; Libraries; Judaism.
Type of support: Scholarships; General support; Individual development.
Limitations: Applications not accepted. No grants to individuals.
Application information: Unsolicited requests for funds not accepted.
Trustees: Mary D. Elder; Francine L. Goldfarb; Robert B. Goldfarb; William H. Goldfarb; Lucy K. Miller.
EIN: 066371228

1468
Eugene A. & Suzanne H. Gorab Foundation
c/o Greenfield Partners LLC
2 Post Rd. W.
Westport, CT 06880-4203

Established in 2000 in Connecticut.
Donors: Eugene A. Gorab; Suzanne H. Gorab.
Foundation type: Independent foundation.
Financial data (yr. ended 12/31/13): Assets, $71,043 (L); gifts received, $475,000; expenditures, $440,361; qualifying distributions, $440,361; giving activities include $435,350 for 15 grants (high: $200,000; low: $200).
Fields of interest: University education; Water resources; Hospice care; Cancers.
Limitations: Applications not accepted. Giving primarily in CT and PA. No grants to individuals.

Application information: Contributes only to pre-selected organizations.
Trustees: Eugene A. Gorab; Suzanne H. Gorab.
EIN: 061603317

1469
Grampy's Charities

(formerly Callahan Foundation, Inc.)
c/o Apache Oil Co.
261 Ledyard St.
New London, CT 06320-5337 8604376200
Contact: Fran Walenta; Jim Castle
Main URL: http://grampys.com

Established in 2003 in Connecticut.
Donors: James H. Castle; Energy North, Inc.
Foundation type: Independent foundation.
Financial data (yr. ended 10/31/14): Assets, $1,345,603; gifts received, $60,814; expenditures, $310,398; qualifying distributions, $220,064.
Fields of interest: Arts and culture; Education; Human services.
Type of support: Student aid.
Limitations: Applications not accepted.
Application information: Unsolicited requests for funds not accepted.
Trustees: Courtney A. Castle; James H. Castle; Jennie Y. Castle; Jonatha Y. Castle; William H. Castle.
EIN: 200523402

1470
Mabel Burchard Fischer Grant Foundation

30 Maltbie Rd.
Newtown, CT 06470-2508
Contact: Robert A. Beer, Tr.
Application address: c/o Adele P. Edgerton, 40 Marvel Rd., New Haven, CT 06515

Established in 1990 in Connecticut.
Donor: Mabel B. Grant‡.
Foundation type: Independent foundation.
Financial data (yr. ended 04/30/14): Assets, $6,599,367 (M); expenditures, $481,444; qualifying distributions, $361,153; giving activities include $330,700 for 68 grants (high: $7,500; low: $1,750).
Fields of interest: Arts and culture; Law education; Natural resources; Protestantism; Catholicism; Human services; Child welfare.
Limitations: Applications accepted. Giving primarily in CT. No grants to individuals.
Application information:
  Initial approach: Letter
  Deadline(s): None
Trustees: Robert A. Beer; Adele P. Edgerton.
EIN: 066351343

1471
Stewart & Constance Greenfield
Foundation

279 Sturges Hwy.
Westport, CT 06880-1722

Established in 1987 in Connecticut.
Donor: Stewart H. Greenfield.
Foundation type: Independent foundation.
Financial data (yr. ended 12/31/12): Assets, $3,933,145 (M); expenditures, $249,294;

qualifying distributions, $227,750; giving activities include $227,750 for grants.
Fields of interest: Arts and culture; Museums; Undergraduate education; Natural resources; Biodiversity; Wildlife biodiversity; Science; Judaism; Human services.
Type of support: Research and evaluation.
Limitations: Applications not accepted. Giving primarily in CT and NY. No grants to individuals.
Application information: Contributes only to pre-selected organizations.
Officer: Stewart H. Greenfield, Mgr.
EIN: 066301506

1472
Greenhill Family Foundation

c/o Robert Greenhill
433 Riversville Rd.
Greenwich, CT 06831-3231

Established in 1997 in Connecticut.
Donor: Robert F. Greenhill.
Foundation type: Independent foundation.
Financial data (yr. ended 12/31/13): Assets, $46,439 (M); gifts received, $150,000; expenditures, $150,981; qualifying distributions, $148,740; giving activities include $146,500 for 21 grants (high: $48,000; low: $1,000).
Purpose and activities: Giving primarily for education, public policy research, hospitals, human services, and to a photography center.
Fields of interest: Photography; Historic preservation; Education; Higher education; Hospital care; Public policy; Human services.
Type of support: Policy, advocacy and systems reform.
Limitations: Applications not accepted. Giving primarily in CT, MA, and NY. No grants to individuals.
Application information: Contributes only to pre-selected organizations.
Trustees: Gayle G. Greenhill; Robert F. Greenhill.
EIN: 061488779

1473
Harold & Rebecca H. Gross Foundation

c/o U.S. Trust, Philanthropic Solutions
200 Glastonbury Blvd., Ste. 200, CT2-545-02-05
Glastonbury, CT 06033 (860) 657-7016
Contact: Kate Kerchaert, V.P.
E-mail: kate.kerchaert@ustrust.com; *Main URL:* https://www.bankofamerica.com/philanthropic/grantmaking.go

Established in 2006 in Connecticut.
Donors: Rosalind Gross Trust; Rosalind Gross Unitrust.
Foundation type: Independent foundation.
Financial data (yr. ended 05/31/13): Assets, $8,513,909 (M); expenditures, $426,578; qualifying distributions, $359,008; giving activities include $307,870 for 6 grants (high: $70,000; low: $15,000).
Purpose and activities: To support and promote charitable organizations that assist persons with physical disabilities to become better adjusted to their environments.
Fields of interest: Health; Human services; People with physical disabilities.
Limitations: Applications accepted. Giving primarily in CT. No grants to individuals.

Application information: Full applications will be accepted by invitation only following submission of a concept paper. Application form required.
  Initial approach: Submit 1-page concept paper
  Deadline(s): Apr. 1 for concept papers
  Final notification: 4-6 weeks following concept paper deadline
Trustee: Bank of America, N.A.
EIN: 597266000

1474
The Gryphon Fund

36 Drumlin Rd.
West Simsbury, CT 06092-2906 (860) 658-5433

Established in 1993 in Connecticut.
Donor: Schiro Fund, Inc.
Foundation type: Independent foundation.
Financial data (yr. ended 12/31/14): Assets, $5,009,035; expenditures, $230,146; qualifying distributions, $210,000.
Fields of interest: Arts and culture; Education; Environment; Health; Human services.
Limitations: Applications accepted. Giving primarily in CT.
Application information:
  Initial approach: Proposal
  Deadline(s): None
Trustees: David H. Kaplan; Helen B. Kaplan.
EIN: 223199039

1475
Charles H. Hall Foundation

c/o U.S. Trust, Bank of America, N.A.
200 Glastonbury Blvd., Ste. 200, CT2-545-02-03
Glastonbury, CT 06033-4056 (860) 657-7015
Contact: Amy Lynch, Market Director
E-mail: amy.r.lynch@ustrust.com; *Main URL:* https://www.bankofamerica.com/philanthropic/grantmaking.go

Established in 2007 in Rhode Island.
Foundation type: Independent foundation.
Financial data (yr. ended 04/30/13): Assets, $4,881,480 (M); expenditures, $246,434; qualifying distributions, $217,404; giving activities include $195,319 for 29 grants (high: $15,000; low: $2,500).
Purpose and activities: The foundation supports and promotes educational, health & human services, religious, and arts & cultural programming for underserved populations. Special consideration is given to programs whose purpose is the prevention of cruelty to children or animals.
Fields of interest: Theater; Education; Health; Youth services.
Limitations: Giving to organizations based in Berkshire, Hampden, Hampshire, and Franklin counties, Massachusetts.
Application information:
  Initial approach: Online via foundation web site
  Deadline(s): Dec. 1
Trustee: Bank of America, N.A.
EIN: 261227617

1476
Hamm Family Foundation Inc.

6 Cove Hill Rd.
Mystic, CT 06355-3219

Established in 2005 in Connecticut.
Donor: Charles J. Hamm.
Foundation type: Independent foundation.
Financial data (yr. ended 12/31/14): Assets, $2,796,418; gifts received, $340; expenditures, $354,995; qualifying distributions, $320,000.
Purpose and activities: Giving primarily for the arts and education.
Fields of interest: Arts and culture; Arts education; Education; Higher education.
Limitations: Applications not accepted. Giving primarily in CT. No grants to individuals.
Application information: Contributes only to pre-selected organizations.
Officers and Directors: Charles J. Hamm, Pres. and Treas. and Director; Irene F. Hamm, V.P. and Secy. and Director; Liza H. Hamm.
EIN: 203963109

1477
Harold Webster Smith Foundation, Inc.
(formerly Webster Bank Foundation, Inc.)
145 Bank St. (WBK-100)
Waterbury, CT   06702-2211   (203) 578 - 2396
Contact: Kathryn T Luria, V.P.

Established in 1988 in Connecticut.
Donors: Bristol County Savings Bank; Webster Bank, N.A.; Webster Financial Corp.
Foundation type: Company-sponsored foundation.
Financial data (yr. ended 12/31/13): Assets, $3,803,184 (M); gifts received, $133,000; expenditures, $249,107; qualifying distributions, $244,721; giving activities include $225,000 for 2 grants (high: $125,000; low: $100,000).
Purpose and activities: The foundation supports organizations involved with theater, housing, and community development.
Fields of interest: Arts and culture; Community and economic development.
Type of support: General support.
Publications: Annual report.
Application information: Application form required.
Initial approach: Proposal
Deadline(s): None
Officers and Directors: James C. Smith, Chair. and Pres. and Director; Gregory S. Madar, Sr. V.P. and Treas.; Kathryn T. Luna, V.P. and Director; Mark S. Lyon, Secy.; Robert L. Guenther; Nitin J. Mhatre; William E. Wrang.
Board Members: Peter Mosbacher; Bruce E. Wandelmaier.
EIN: 222947047

1478
George J. and Jessica Harris Foundation
1100 Summer St., 4th Fl.
Stamford, CT   06905-5534   (203) 323-1191
Contact: Robert P. Masotti, Tr.

Established in 1994 in Connecticut.
Donor: Jessica Harris.
Foundation type: Independent foundation.
Financial data (yr. ended 06/30/14): Assets, $6,160,054 (M); expenditures, $379,039; qualifying distributions, $312,959; giving activities include $275,000 for 20 grants (high: $50,000; low: $5,000).
Purpose and activities: Giving primarily for the arts, health care, including children's hospitals and

medical research, and human services, particularly a homeless shelter and food for the needy.
Fields of interest: Arts and culture; Performing arts; Museums; Health; Specialty hospital care; Housing development; Human services; Child welfare; Retirement housing; Low-income and poor people.
Type of support: Research.
Limitations: Applications accepted. Giving primarily in CT. No grants to individuals.
Application information: Application form required.
Initial approach: Letter
Deadline(s): None
Trustees: Laura A. Masotti; Robert P. Masotti; Charlotte Wise; Robert B. Wise, Esq.
EIN: 061393429

1479
Jane Hope Hastings Philanthropic Trust
c/o BMBL
530 Old Post Rd., No. 3
Greenwich, CT   06836-0788
Contact: David F. Babson, Tr.

Established in 2007 in Connecticut.
Donor: Jane Hope Hastings Trust.
Foundation type: Independent foundation.
Financial data (yr. ended 12/31/13): Assets, $1,306,869 (M); expenditures, $210,826; qualifying distributions, $210,826; giving activities include $181,500 for 10 grants (high: $100,000; low: $500).
Fields of interest: Arts and culture; Historic preservation; Education; Health.
Limitations: Applications accepted. Giving primarily in CT and KY.
Application information:
Initial approach: Contact Foundation
Deadline(s): None
Trustee: David F. Babson.
EIN: 207142550

1480
The Helping Hand Foundation
58 Dawn Harbor Ln.
Riverside, CT   06878-2609

Established in 2004 in Connecticut.
Donor: Jonathan B. Weiner.
Foundation type: Independent foundation.
Financial data (yr. ended 12/31/13): Assets, $301,764; gifts received, $552,500; expenditures, $266,387; qualifying distributions, $266,327 and $0 for set-asides.
Fields of interest: Health; Judaism; Human services.
Limitations: Applications not accepted. Giving primarily in CT and NY. No grants to individuals.
Application information: Contributes only to pre-selected organizations.
Trustees: Jill Weiner; Jonathan B. Weiner.
EIN: 137409533

1481
Joyce Hergenhan Private Foundation
715 Sasco Hill Rd.
Fairfield, CT   06824-6376

Established in 1998 in Connecticut.
Donor: Joyce Hergenhan.
Foundation type: Independent foundation.

Financial data (yr. ended 12/31/13): Assets, $4,959,754 (M); gifts received, $297,886; expenditures, $210,981; qualifying distributions, $200,500; giving activities include $200,500 for 16 grants (high: $50,000; low: $1,000).
Fields of interest: Higher education.
Type of support: General support.
Limitations: Applications not accepted. Giving primarily in NY. No grants to individuals.
Application information: Unsolicited requests for funds not accepted.
Officer: Joyce Hergenhan, Pres.
EIN: 061519008

1482
Hewitt Foundation, Inc.
P.O. Box 386
Shelton, CT   06484-0386   (203) 387-1427
Contact: Patrick M. Carey, Pres.; Harry Diadamo, Treas.

Foundation type: Independent foundation.
Financial data (yr. ended 09/30/14): Assets, $8,115,593 (M); gifts received, $30,386; expenditures, $404,651; qualifying distributions, $335,000; giving activities include $335,000 for 2 grants (high: $265,000; low: $70,000).
Purpose and activities: Giving primarily for healthcare and for services for the elderly.
Fields of interest: Hospital care; Cancers; Human services; Child welfare; Senior services.
Type of support: General support; Student aid.
Limitations: Applications accepted. Giving primarily in the lower Naugatuck Valley, CT.
Application information:
Deadline(s): None
Officers: Patrick M. Carey, Pres.; Achille A. Apicella, V.P.; Elsie S. Scott, Secy.; Harry P. Diadamo, Treas.
Directors: Virginia Costigan; Laura J. Donahue; Janet Girardat; Janice Sheehy.
EIN: 061064288

1483
Hildes-Heim Foundation Inc.
7 Meadow Brook Rd.
Newtown, CT   06470-2630

Foundation type: Independent foundation.
Financial data (yr. ended 06/30/14): Assets, $25,961 (M); gifts received, $50,000; expenditures, $238,025; qualifying distributions, $229,862; giving activities include $229,862 for 1 grant.
Fields of interest: Education; Higher education.
Limitations: Applications not accepted.
Application information: Unsolicited requests for funds not accepted.
Officers and Directors: Robert Giusti, Pres. and Director; David D. Kardos, Secy.-Treas. and Director.
EIN: 461614488

1484
Ron & Cheryl Howard Family Foundation
c/o WTAS, LLC
1700 E. Putnam Ave., Ste. 206
Old Greenwich, CT   06870-1370

Established in 1998 in California.
Donors: Ron Howard; Cheryl Howard.
Foundation type: Independent foundation.

Financial data (yr. ended 12/31/13): Assets, $202,787 (M); gifts received, $350,000; expenditures, $324,597; qualifying distributions, $324,597; giving activities include $323,087 for 154 grants (high: $25,000; low: $25).
Fields of interest: Arts and culture; Education; Higher education; Wildlife biodiversity; Foundations; Nonprofits; Hospital care; Diseases and conditions; Public libraries; Disasters and emergency management; Human services; Child welfare.
Type of support: Research; Research and evaluation; Regranting.
Limitations: Applications not accepted. Giving primarily in CA, CT, Washington, DC and NY. No grants to individuals.
Application information: Contributes only to pre-selected organizations.
Officers: Ron Howard, Pres.; Cheryl Howard, Secy.
EIN: 954715638

1485
The Warren and Augusta Hume Foundation Inc.
c/o McGladrey LLP
850 Canal St.
Stamford, CT 06902-6943

Established in 1993 in New York.
Donor: Warren C. Hume†.
Foundation type: Independent foundation.
Financial data (yr. ended 12/31/13): Assets, $7,321,345 (M); gifts received, $526,965; expenditures, $349,550; qualifying distributions, $257,058; giving activities include $230,000 for 23 grants (high: $50,000; low: $5,000).
Fields of interest: Ballet; Elementary and secondary education; Higher education; Public libraries; Christianity; Child welfare.
Limitations: Applications not accepted. No grants to individuals.
Application information: Contributes only to pre-selected organizations.
Officers and Directors: Warren C. Hume, Chair.; Augusta Hume, Vice-Chair. and Director; Christina Hume, V.P. and Director; Harold A. Ward III, Secy. and Director; G. Russell Creighton, Treas. and Director; Elizabeth Brothers.
EIN: 133675579

1486
The Huntington Foundation, Inc.
104 Point Lookout
Milford, CT 06460

Established in 2006 in Connecticut.
Donors: Daniel L. Leary; Linda Leary.
Foundation type: Independent foundation.
Financial data (yr. ended 12/31/12): Assets, $2,435,955 (M); gifts received, $946,997; expenditures, $120,988; qualifying distributions, $119,548; giving activities include $118,500 for 15 grants (high: $37,500; low: $3,000).
Fields of interest: Education; Health; Religion.
Limitations: Applications not accepted. Giving primarily in CT, with some giving in NY. No grants to individuals.
Application information: Unsolicited requests for funds not accepted.

Officers and Directors: Daniel L. Leary, Pres.; Linda K. Leary, V.P. and Treas.; Jennifer Duerr, V.P. and Director; Katherine L. Staffey, V.P. and Director.
EIN: 205478746

1487
The Inglesea Charitable Trust
301 Merritt 7
Norwalk, CT 06851-1070

Foundation type: Independent foundation.
Financial data (yr. ended 12/31/13): Assets, $5,657,367 (M); expenditures, $447,730; qualifying distributions, $389,253; giving activities include $389,253 for 67 grants (high: $100,000; low: $100).
Fields of interest: Arts and culture; Education; Protestantism.
Limitations: Applications not accepted. Giving primarily in CT.
Application information: Unsolicited requests for funds not accepted.
Trustees: Gaier Palmisano; Samuel Palmisano.
EIN: 357011350

1488
The Jaffe Foundation
P.O. Box 429
Guilford, CT 06437-0429

Established in 1997 in Unspecified.
Donor: David Jaffe.
Foundation type: Independent foundation.
Financial data (yr. ended 12/31/13): Assets, $3,753,077 (M); gifts received, $298,826; expenditures, $346,979; qualifying distributions, $332,685; giving activities include $332,685 for 10 grants (high: $149,858; low: $142).
Fields of interest: Higher education.
Limitations: Applications not accepted. Giving primarily in MA and NY. No grants to individuals.
Application information: Unsolicited requests for funds not accepted.
Directors: Amy D. Jaffe; David Jaffe; Douglas Jaffe.
EIN: 061469004

1489
Cyrus W. & Amy F. Jones & Bessie D. Phelps Foundation, Inc.
2 Corporate Dr., Ste. 212
Trumbull, CT 06611

Established in 1976 in Connecticut.
Donor: Amy F. Jones†.
Foundation type: Independent foundation.
Financial data (yr. ended 09/30/14): Assets, $4,924,389 (M); expenditures, $293,237; qualifying distributions, $246,375; giving activities include $154,000 for 32 grants (high: $10,000; low: $1,000).
Fields of interest: Arts and culture; Health; Religion.
Type of support: General support; Capital campaigns.
Limitations: Applications not accepted. No grants to individuals.
Application information: Contributes only to pre-selected organizations.
Officers and Trustees: Robert S. Tellalian, Jr., Pres. and Treas. and Trustee; Alexander R. Nestor, V.P.

and Secy. and Trustee; Aram H. Tellalian III, V.P. and Trustee.
EIN: 060943204

1490
Janet Stone Jones Foundation
c/o Chilton Trust Company LLC
1290 E. Main St., 3rd Fl.
Stamford, CT 06902-3556

Established in 1978 in New York.
Donors: Janet Stone Jones Charitable Lead Trust; Benjamin Brewster; Whitney B. Armstrong; Janet B. York.
Foundation type: Independent foundation.
Financial data (yr. ended 12/21/14): Assets, $8,288 (M); gifts received, $232,389; expenditures, $253,621; qualifying distributions, $246,367; giving activities include $245,087 for 78 grants (high: $40,500; low: $100).
Fields of interest: Education; Elementary and secondary education; Domesticated animals; Nonprofits; Health; Human services; Youth services.
Type of support: General support; Regranting.
Limitations: Applications not accepted. Giving primarily in VA. No grants to individuals.
Application information: Unsolicited requests for funds not accepted.
Officers and Directors: Benjamin Brewster, Pres. and Director; Whitney Brewster Armstrong, V.P. and Director; Janet B. York, Secy. and Director; Antoinette B. Brewster, Treas.
EIN: 132988287

1491
Paul L. Jones Fund
c/o Webster Bank, N.A.
123 Bank St.
Waterbury, CT 06702-2205

Established in 1979 in Connecticut.
Foundation type: Independent foundation.
Financial data (yr. ended 10/31/13): Assets, $6,699,782 (M); expenditures, $414,229; qualifying distributions, $367,195; giving activities include $365,000 for 12 grants (high: $50,000; low: $5,000).
Purpose and activities: Giving only for scholarship programs to assist students in medical and health-related fields.
Fields of interest: Higher education.
Type of support: Scholarships.
Limitations: Applications not accepted. Giving limited to CT. No grants to individuals.
Application information: Contributes only to pre-selected organizations.
Trustee: Webster Bank, N.A.
EIN: 066222118

1492
Charles & Mabel P. Jost Foundation, Inc.
1140 Fairfield Ave.
Bridgeport, CT 06605-1118
Contact: Alexander R. Nestor

Established in 1969 in Connecticut.
Foundation type: Independent foundation.
Financial data (yr. ended 04/30/13): Assets, $4,154,846 (M); expenditures, $244,641;

qualifying distributions, $194,561; giving activities include $135,200 for 27 grants (high: $25,000; low: $1,000).
Purpose and activities: Giving primarily for education, rehabilitation centers, and hospitals.
Fields of interest: Education; Health; Human services.
Type of support: General support; Capital and infrastructure.
Limitations: Applications not accepted. Giving primarily in CT. No grants to individuals, or for scholarships, fellowships, or prizes; no loans.
Application information: Contributes only to pre-selected organizations.
Officers and Trustees: Alexander R. Nestor, Chair. and Pres. and Trustee; Sally D. Nestor, V.P. and Trustee.
EIN: 237070398

1493
Charles H. Kaman Charitable Foundation, Inc.
c/o C.H. Kaman
43 Prattling Pond Rd.
Farmington, CT 06032

Established in 1993 in Connecticut.
Donors: Charles H. Kaman; Murtha Cullina LLP; Kaman Corporation.
Foundation type: Independent foundation.
Financial data (yr. ended 11/30/13): Assets, $11,087,329 (M); expenditures, $515,734; qualifying distributions, $460,513; giving activities include $382,129 for 7 grants (high: $200,000; low: $2,029).
Fields of interest: Education; Animal welfare; Specialty hospital care; Human services.
Limitations: Applications not accepted. Giving primarily in CT; some funding also in IN. No grants to individuals.
Application information: Contributes only to pre-selected organizations.
Officers and Trustees: C. William Kaman II, Pres. and Treas. and Trustee; Cathleen H. Kaman, V.P. and Trustee; Glenn M. Messemer, Secy. and Trustee.
EIN: 061386119

1494
The Karen Katen Foundation
P.O. Box 2630
Westport, CT 06880-0630

Donor: Karen L. Katen.
Foundation type: Independent foundation.
Financial data (yr. ended 12/31/13): Assets, $209,179 (M); gifts received, $312,080; expenditures, $230,177; qualifying distributions, $222,975; giving activities include $222,975 for 34 grants (high: $25,000; low: $100).
Fields of interest: Arts and culture; Higher education; Natural resources; Botanical gardens; Hospital care.
Limitations: Applications not accepted. Giving primarily in the Bronx and New York, NY.
Application information: Contributes only to pre-selected organizations.
Trustees: Elwood Davis; Donna Katen-Bahensky; Karen L. Katen.
EIN: 207103490

1495
Kaufmann Foundation, Inc.
c/o McGladrey LLP
850 Canal St., 4th Fl.
Stamford, CT 06902-6943

Established in 1990 in New York.
Donors: Peter Kaufmann; Jacqueline K. Tooter; Ruth Kaufmann; Andrew Kaufmann; Howard Tooter; Ronald Kaufmann.
Foundation type: Independent foundation.
Financial data (yr. ended 12/31/13): Assets, $563,196 (M); expenditures, $196,660; qualifying distributions, $188,130; giving activities include $184,000 for 25 grants (high: $27,500; low: $500).
Fields of interest: Arts and culture; Education; Health; Human services; Food aid; Child welfare; Females; Homeless people; Low-income and poor people.
Limitations: Applications not accepted. Giving primarily in CT and NY. No grants to individuals.
Application information: Contributes only to pre-selected organizations.
Officers: Andrew Kaufmann, Pres.; Ronald Kaufmann, V.P.; Ruth Kaufmann, V.P.; Jacqueline K. Tooter, Secy.; Howard Tooter, Treas.
EIN: 133603247

1496
Louis J. and June E. Kay Foundation
c/o Salomon
85 Old Long Ridge Rd., No. A4
Stamford, CT 06903

Established in 2008 in Delaware.
Donors: Louis J. Kay; June E. Kay.
Foundation type: Operating foundation.
Financial data (yr. ended 12/31/13): Assets, $4,820,739 (M); gifts received, $550,000; expenditures, $371,387; qualifying distributions, $341,750; giving activities include $262,500 for 7 grants (high: $75,000; low: $10,000).
Fields of interest: Hospital care; Alzheimer's disease; Digestive system diseases; Genetic conditions and birth defects.
Type of support: General support.
Limitations: Applications not accepted. Giving primarily in IL and NY. No grants to individuals.
Application information: Contributes only to pre-selected organizations.
Officers: Louis J. Kay, Pres.; Jack Salomon, V.P. and Secy.; June E. Kay, Treas.
EIN: 262145377

1497
Keefe Family Foundation
21 Aiken Rd.
Greenwich, CT 06831-2707

Established in 1989 in New York.
Donor: Harry V. Keefe, Jr.
Foundation type: Independent foundation.
Financial data (yr. ended 12/31/13): Assets, $8,667,411 (M); expenditures, $454,555; qualifying distributions, $434,151; giving activities include $428,450 for 14 grants (high: $100,000; low: $6,280).
Purpose and activities: Giving primarily for education and children and family services.

Fields of interest: Education; Higher education; Domesticated animals; Human services; Family services; Child welfare.
Type of support: General support; Capital campaigns; Program development.
Limitations: Applications not accepted. Giving primarily in MA. No support for private foundations. No grants to individuals.
Application information: Contributes only to pre-selected organizations.
Officers and Directors: Anita L. Keefe, Pres. and Director; Harry V. Keefe III, V.P. and Director; Kathleen Keefe Raffel, Secy.-Treas. and Director; Carol A. Keefe; Corey Raffel.
EIN: 133520397

1498
The Kendall Family Foundation
c/o UBS Financial Services, Inc.
10 Old Easton Tpke.
Weston, CT 06883-2426

Established in 2007 in California.
Donor: Donald M. Jendall, Sr.
Foundation type: Independent foundation.
Financial data (yr. ended 06/30/13): Assets, $4,743,458 (M); expenditures, $462,755; qualifying distributions, $419,546; giving activities include $382,880 for 18 grants (high: $250,000; low: $1,000).
Fields of interest: Foundations.
Type of support: General support.
Limitations: Applications not accepted. Giving primarily in CA, CT and NY. No grants to individuals.
Application information: Contributes only to pre-selected organizations.
Trustees: Donald M. Kendall, Jr.; Donald M. Kendall, Sr.; Kendall Ann Webb.
EIN: 260726065

1499
Klein Family Foundation Inc.
42 Tuckahoe Rd.
Easton, CT 06612-5210

Donor: Carla S. Kelin.
Foundation type: Independent foundation.
Financial data (yr. ended 12/31/13): Assets, $6,206,194 (M); expenditures, $412,766; qualifying distributions, $363,000; giving activities include $359,000 for 27 grants (high: $80,000; low: $500).
Fields of interest: Hospital care; Human services.
Limitations: Applications not accepted. Giving primarily in CT.
Application information: Unsolicited requests for funds not accepted.
Officers: Carla S. Klein, Pres.; Kristen Chiodo, Secy.; Eric Klein, Treas.
EIN: 263134339

1500
Robert and Jeanne Knox Foundation
c/o Cornerstone Equities
281 Tresser Blvd.
Stamford, CT 06901-3284

Donor: Robert A. Knox.
Foundation type: Independent foundation.

Financial data (yr. ended 12/31/13): Assets, $1,153,945 (M); gifts received, $827,851; expenditures, $120,409; qualifying distributions, $116,000; giving activities include $116,000 for 3 grants (high: $105,000; low: $1,000).
Fields of interest: Education; Diseases and conditions.
Type of support: Research.
Limitations: Applications not accepted. Giving in the U.S., with emphasis on MA.
Application information: Unsolicited requests for funds not accepted.
Trustees: Jeanne M. Knox; Robert A. Knox.
EIN: 611661551

1501
Doris & Simon Konover Family Foundation
342 N. Main St., Ste. 200
West Hartford, CT 06117-2507

Established in 2002 in Connecticut.
Donors: Doris Konover; Simon Konover; Konover Coppa Family LLC.
Foundation type: Independent foundation.
Financial data (yr. ended 12/31/13): Assets, $2,580,413 (M); expenditures, $281,368; qualifying distributions, $266,041; giving activities include $266,041 for 26 grants (high: $191,621; low: $180).
Fields of interest: Theater; Museums; University education; Libraries; Judaism; Child welfare.
Limitations: Applications not accepted. Giving primarily in CT and FL. No grants to individuals.
Application information: Unsolicited requests for funds not accepted.
Trustees: Doris Konover; Simon Konover.
EIN: 300104501

1502
Kreitler Foundation, Inc.
792 Hulls Farm Rd.
Southport, CT 06890-1032 (203) 216-4802
Contact: Hobart C. Kreitler, Pres.

Established in 1991 in Connecticut.
Donors: Hobart C. Kreitler; Sally S. Kreitler.
Foundation type: Independent foundation.
Financial data (yr. ended 12/31/13): Assets, $3,991,084 (M); expenditures, $269,530; qualifying distributions, $217,947; giving activities include $217,947 for 63 grants (high: $36,967; low: $25).
Fields of interest: Education; Higher education; Christianity; Human services; Child welfare.
Type of support: General support; Capital campaigns; Capital and infrastructure; Scholarships.
Limitations: Applications accepted. Giving primarily in the Bridgeport, CT, area. No grants to individuals.
Application information: Application form required.
Initial approach: Letter
Deadline(s): None
Board meeting date(s): May 15
Officers: Hobart C. Kreitler, Pres.; Thomas S. Kreitler, V.P.; Sally S. Kreitler, Secy.; Katherine K. Hodge, Treas.
Directors: James S. Kreitler; John M. Kreitler; Karen R. Kreitler.
EIN: 061311676

1503
Louis J. Kuriansky Foundation Inc.
c/o Edward Backer
855 Main St., 6th Fl.
Bridgeport, CT 06604-4915

Established in 1956 in Connecticut.
Foundation type: Independent foundation.
Financial data (yr. ended 12/31/14): Assets, $2,315,743; expenditures, $197,702; qualifying distributions, $183,166.
Purpose and activities: Giving for Jewish organizations, the arts, and human services.
Fields of interest: Arts and culture; Nonprofits; Judaism; Human services.
Type of support: Regranting.
Limitations: Applications not accepted. Giving primarily in CT, FL and NY. No grants to individuals.
Application information: Unsolicited requests for funds not accepted.
Officers: Edward Backer, Pres.; Joan Kuriansky, V.P.; Joyce B. Shapiro, Secy.-Treas.
Director: Sary Backer.
EIN: 066035305

1504
Lamando Family Foundation
P.O. Box 2630
Westport, CT 06880

Established in 2004 in Connecticut.
Donor: BNS Family Trust.
Foundation type: Independent foundation.
Financial data (yr. ended 12/31/13): Assets, $5,300,164 (M); expenditures, $221,278; qualifying distributions, $206,270; giving activities include $206,270 for 12 grants (high: $190,000; low: $250).
Fields of interest: Arts and culture; Historic preservation; Education; Domesticated animals; Nonprofits; Human services.
Type of support: Regranting.
Limitations: Applications not accepted. Giving primarily in CT, MA, and NY. No grants to individuals.
Application information: Contributes only to pre-selected organizations.
Trustee: Stephen M. Lamando.
EIN: 206388980

1505
Raymond P. Lavietes Foundation, Inc.
c/o Achille A. Apicella
680 Bridgeport Ave.
Shelton, CT 06484-4705

Established in 1989 in Connecticut.
Donor: Raymond P. Lavietes.
Foundation type: Independent foundation.
Financial data (yr. ended 12/31/13): Assets, $3,186,095 (M); expenditures, $410,973; qualifying distributions, $346,750; giving activities include $346,750 for 6 grants (high: $110,000; low: $36,750).
Fields of interest: Graduate and professional education; Nonprofits; Specialty hospital care; Public health; Human services; Child welfare; Youth services; Youth organizing.
Type of support: Regranting.
Limitations: Applications not accepted. Giving primarily in CT and MA. No grants to individuals.

Application information: Contributes only to pre-selected organizations.
Officers and Directors: Achille A. Apicella, Pres. and Director; Donald Anderson, V.P. and Director; Estelle Lavietes.
EIN: 061276735

1506
The Lebovitz Fund
218 Ferris Hill Rd.
New Canaan, CT 06840-3830 (203) 219-3667
Contact: Peter M. Lebovitz, Pres., Treas., and Dir.

Established in 1944 in Pennsylvania.
Donor: Beth Ann Segal Trust.
Foundation type: Independent foundation.
Financial data (yr. ended 07/31/13): Assets, $4,737,685 (M); gifts received, $70,000; expenditures, $263,888; qualifying distributions, $259,250; giving activities include $259,250 for 43 grants (high: $50,000; low: $150).
Fields of interest: Art museums; Natural resources; Biodiversity; Wildlife biodiversity; Bird preservation; Nonprofits; Hospice care; Public libraries; Human services; Child welfare; People with vision impairments.
Type of support: General support; Regranting; Scholarships.
Limitations: Applications accepted. Giving primarily in CT, FL, and MN.
Application information:
Initial approach: Letter
Deadline(s): None
Officers and Directors: Peter M. Lebovitz, Pres. and Treas. and Director; Beth Ann Segal, V.P. and Secy. and Director; Jonathan Javitch; James Lebovitz.
EIN: 236270079

1507
The Lee Family Foundation, Inc.
c/o Day Pitney LLP
1 Canterbury Green
Stamford, CT 06901-2032

Established in 1999 in Connecticut.
Donor: Charles R. Lee.
Foundation type: Independent foundation.
Financial data (yr. ended 10/31/13): Assets, $5,043,930 (M); expenditures, $441,823; qualifying distributions, $435,000; giving activities include $435,000 for 22 grants (high: $100,000; low: $1,000).
Purpose and activities: Giving primarily for education, health and medical research, and to a Congregational and Unitarian-Universalist church.
Fields of interest: Dance; Education; Higher education; Medical education; Health; Diseases and conditions; Breast cancer; Protestantism.
Type of support: Research; Research and evaluation.
Limitations: Applications not accepted. Giving primarily in CT, NY, and TX. No grants to individuals.
Application information: Contributes only to pre-selected organizations.
Officers and Directors: Charles R. Lee, Pres. and Director; Ilda G. Lee, V.P. and Director; Robert J. Miller, Secy. and Director; Bruce Carswell, Treas. and Director.
EIN: 061563501

1508
Gordon F. and Jocelyn B. Linke Foundation
c/o Scott Linke
116 Eleven Levels Rd.
Ridgefield, CT 06877-3009

Established in 1997 in Maryland.
Foundation type: Independent foundation.
Financial data (yr. ended 12/31/14): Assets, $2,912,773; expenditures, $184,839; qualifying distributions, $160,375.
Purpose and activities: Giving primarily for animals, education, health and human services, and to Catholic churches.
Fields of interest: Arts and culture; Museums; Elementary and secondary education; Higher education; Environment; Domesticated animals; Catholicism; Human services.
Limitations: Applications not accepted. Giving primarily in CA, CT, Washington, DC, MD, and NY. No grants to individuals.
Application information: Contributes only to pre-selected organizations.
Officers and Directors: Gordon F. Linke, Pres. and Mgr. and Director; Jocelyn B. Linke, V.P. and Mgr. and Director; Jocelyn S. Witt, Treas. and Mgr. and Director.
EIN: 521985801

1509
Lippincott Foundation, Inc.
2399 Ridge Rd.
North Haven, CT 06473-1273

Foundation type: Independent foundation.
Financial data (yr. ended 08/31/14): Assets, $1,408,314; expenditures, $114,673; qualifying distributions, $112,400.
Fields of interest: Education; Environment; Human services.
Limitations: Applications not accepted.
Application information: Unsolicited requests for funds not accepted.
Officers and Trustees: Donald B. Lippincott, Pres. and Trustee; Alfred Lippincott, V.P. and Trustee; Diane Lippincott, Treas.
EIN: 222760718

1510
LLL Foundation
67 Mason St.
Greenwich, CT 06830-3104
Contact: Daniel M. Rosen

Established in 2003 in Illinois.
Foundation type: Independent foundation.
Financial data (yr. ended 12/31/13): Assets, $2,399,946 (M); gifts received, $233,292; expenditures, $331,830; qualifying distributions, $300,906; giving activities include $295,033 for 28 grants (high: $55,000; low: $20).
Fields of interest: Arts and culture; Education; Higher education; University education.
Limitations: Applications not accepted. Giving primarily in New York, NY. No grants to individuals.
Application information: Unsolicited requests for funds not accepted.
Officers and Directors: Leila Shakkour, Pres. and Treas. and Director; Michael Thorne, V.P. and Director; Daniel M. Rosen.
EIN: 571147978

1511
David H. Lodbell Irreving Charitable Trust
850 Main St., RC 13-505
Bridgeport, CT 06604-4913

Foundation type: Independent foundation.
Financial data (yr. ended 12/31/13): Assets, $5,039,770 (M); expenditures, $245,373; qualifying distributions, $209,096; giving activities include $205,821 for 1 grant.
Fields of interest: Human services.
Limitations: Applications not accepted. Giving limited to West Nyack, NY.
Application information: Unsolicited requests for funds not accepted.
Trustee: People's United Bank.
EIN: 277096784

1512
Philip H. and Christine Lodewick Foundation, Inc.
201 Spring Valley Rd.
Ridgefield, CT 06877-1229

Established in 1994 in Connecticut.
Donors: Philip H. Lodewick; Christine Lodewick; The Tradewell Corp.
Foundation type: Independent foundation.
Financial data (yr. ended 12/31/13): Assets, $160,003 (M); gifts received, $76,289; expenditures, $162,825; qualifying distributions, $160,150; giving activities include $160,150 for 24 grants (high: $55,000; low: $100).
Fields of interest: Education; Environment; Protestantism.
Limitations: Applications not accepted. Giving primarily in CT. No grants to individuals.
Application information: Unsolicited requests for funds not accepted.
Officers: Philip H. Lodewick, Pres.; Christine Lodewick, V.P.
Directors: Sharon Dornfeld; Roy Lloyd.
EIN: 061386836

1513
Low Road Foundation
c/o Lynn Kearcher
P.O. Box 642
Sharon, CT 06069-0642

Established in 2004 in Connecticut.
Donor: Jasper Johns.
Foundation type: Independent foundation.
Financial data (yr. ended 12/31/13): Assets, $3,260,411 (M); gifts received, $150,000; expenditures, $275,418; qualifying distributions, $268,840; giving activities include $265,850 for 39 grants (high: $200,000; low: $50).
Purpose and activities: Giving primarily in support of the contemporary arts.
Fields of interest: Arts and culture; Performing arts; Dance; Human services.
Limitations: Applications not accepted. Giving primarily in CT and NY. No grants to individuals.
Application information: Unsolicited requests for funds not accepted.
Trustee: Jasper Johns.
EIN: 201737242

1514
The Macauley Foundation, Inc.
131 Hazel Plain Rd.
Woodbury, CT 06798-1919
E-mail: info@themacauleyfoundation.org; Main URL: http://www.themacauleyfoundation.com

Established in 1995 in Connecticut.
Donors: Robert C. Macauley; Alma Jane Macauley.
Foundation type: Independent foundation.
Financial data (yr. ended 06/30/14): Assets, $1,517,676 (M); gifts received, $475; expenditures, $409,240; qualifying distributions, $308,000; giving activities include $308,000 for 17 grants (high: $100,000; low: $4,000).
Fields of interest: Foundations; Human services; Basic and emergency aid; Child welfare; International development.
Limitations: Applications not accepted. Giving primarily in CT; some funding also in NY. No grants to individuals.
Application information: Unsolicited requests for funds not accepted.
Officers and Directors: Annie Yates, Exec. Dir.; Alma Jane Macauley, Exec. V.P. and Director; Anne Marie Weirether, Secy.; Melinda Rice Macauley; Robert C. Macauley, Jr., MD.
Number of staff: 1 part-time professional.
EIN: 061439255

1515
The MacInnis Family Foundation
7 Sturges Hollow
Westport, CT 06880-2851

Established in 2005 in Connecticut.
Donors: Frank T. MacInnis; Williams Companies Inc.
Foundation type: Independent foundation.
Financial data (yr. ended 12/31/13): Assets, $1,250,298 (M); gifts received, $308,285; expenditures, $158,947; qualifying distributions, $158,947; giving activities include $158,947 for 32 grants (high: $48,847; low: $500).
Fields of interest: Arts and culture; Philanthropy; Human services.
International interests: Canada.
Type of support: General support.
Limitations: Applications not accepted. Giving primarily in CA, CT, IL, and NY; some funding also in Alberta, Canada.
Application information: Unsolicited requests for funds not accepted.
Officers: Lauren MacInnis, Pres.; Frank T. MacInnis, V.P. and Secy.; Beverly J. MacInnis, V.P. and Treas.
EIN: 203825167

1516
Magaro Family Foundation, Inc.
1248 Oenoke Ridge
New Canaan, CT 06840-2612

Donors: Diviya Magaro; Alex Magaro.
Foundation type: Independent foundation.
Financial data (yr. ended 12/31/13): Assets, $2,403,867 (M); gifts received, $2,171,000; expenditures, $170,355; qualifying distributions, $170,250; giving activities include $170,250 for 5 grants (high: $125,000; low: $250).
Fields of interest: Arts and culture; Education.
Limitations: Applications not accepted.

Application information: Unsolicited requests for funds not accepted.
Officers: Diviya Magaro, Pres. and Treas.; Al P. Trebing, Secy.
Director: Alex Magaro.
EIN: 461558048

1517
Mahadeva Family Foundation
15 E. Putnam Ave., No. 407
Greenwich, CT 06830-5424

Established in 2004 in New Jersey.
Donor: Wijeyaraj A. Mahadeva.
Foundation type: Independent foundation.
Financial data (yr. ended 12/31/13): Assets, $5,319,595 (M); expenditures, $277,158; qualifying distributions, $262,910; giving activities include $262,910 for 16 grants (high: $100,160; low: $250).
Fields of interest: Cultural awareness; Education; Nonprofits; Human rights; Human services.
Type of support: Regranting.
Limitations: Applications not accepted. Giving primarily in MA, NY and OH. No grants to individuals.
Application information: Contributes only to pre-selected organizations.
Trustee: Wijeyaraj A. Mahadeva.
EIN: 137437490

1518
B. L. Manger Foundation
c/o Zone & Bernstein
123 Prospect St.
Stamford, CT 06901-1200 (203) 324-4131
Contact: Harold Bernstein, Secy.-Treas.

Established in 1974 in Connecticut.
Foundation type: Independent foundation.
Financial data (yr. ended 04/30/13): Assets, $8,935,116 (M); expenditures, $469,024; qualifying distributions, $361,350; giving activities include $361,350 for 51 grants (high: $55,000; low: $150).
Purpose and activities: Giving primarily for Jewish organizations.
Fields of interest: Education; Nonprofits; Judaism; Human services.
Type of support: Regranting.
Limitations: Applications accepted. Giving primarily in CT. No grants to individuals.
Application information: Application form required.
  Initial approach: Letter
  Deadline(s): None
Officers: Joseph Lieberman, Pres.; Harold Bernstein, Secy.-Treas.
EIN: 237405994

1519
The Mann Family Foundation
777 Summer St., Ste. 503
Stamford, CT 06901-1022

Established in 1986 in Connecticut.
Donors: Milton Mann; Norma Mann.
Foundation type: Independent foundation.
Financial data (yr. ended 12/31/13): Assets, $19,392 (M); gifts received, $100,000; expenditures, $142,699; qualifying distributions,

$142,699; giving activities include $142,649 for 53 grants (high: $32,996; low: $75).
Purpose and activities: Giving for Jewish organizations, education, and the arts.
Fields of interest: Education; Health; Judaism.
Limitations: Applications not accepted. No grants to individuals.
Application information: Unsolicited requests for funds not accepted.
Officers: Milton Mann, Pres.; Madeline B. Mann, V.P.; Pamela G. Mann, Treas.
EIN: 222776320

1520
The John G. Martin Foundation
433 S. Main St., Ste. 200
West Hartford, CT 06110-2815 (860) 561-1245
Contact: Frank M. Loehmann Jr., Pres.

Donor: John G. Martin†.
Foundation type: Independent foundation.
Financial data (yr. ended 12/31/13): Assets, $9,086,710 (M); expenditures, $437,040; qualifying distributions, $370,730; giving activities include $310,955 for 47 grants (high: $50,000; low: $50).
Purpose and activities: Giving primarily for higher and other education, including a law school foundation; funding also for human services.
Fields of interest: Education; Secondary education; Higher education; Law education; Nonprofits; Public libraries; Human services.
Type of support: Capital campaigns; Matching grants; Capital and infrastructure; Regranting.
Limitations: Applications accepted. Giving primarily in the Hartford, CT, area.
Application information: Application form required.
  Initial approach: Letter
  Copies of proposal: 1
  Deadline(s): None
Officers and Directors: Frank M. Loehmann, Jr., Pres. and Treas. and Director; Donna Flamio, V.P. and Director; Barbara L. Flynn, V.P. and Director; Sandra Johnson, V.P. and Director; Mary C. Henzy, Secy.; Linda R. Owsianik, Cont. and Director; Laura F. Baldini; Garrett S. Flynn; Gregory M. Loehmann.
EIN: 066042495

1521
The Patricia M. and Robert H. Martinsen Foundation
761 Ridgebury Rd.
Ridgefield, CT 06877-1014

Donors: Robert H. Martinsen; Patricia M. Martinsen.
Foundation type: Independent foundation.
Financial data (yr. ended 12/31/13): Assets, $290,821 (M); gifts received, $45,047; expenditures, $173,842; qualifying distributions, $170,800; giving activities include $170,800 for 10 grants (high: $160,000; low: $100).
Fields of interest: Arts and culture; Education; Diseases and conditions.
Type of support: Research.
Limitations: Applications not accepted.
Application information: Unsolicited request for funds not accepted.
Trustees: Patricia M. Martinsen; Robert H. Martinsen.
EIN: 276961238

1522
Katharine K. and Henry R. McLane Charitable Trust
c/o Shipman & Goodwin LLP
1 Constitution Plz.
Hartford, CT 06103-1919 (860) 251-5000

Established in 2004 in Connecticut.
Donors: K.K. McLane Unitrust; Henry McLane.
Foundation type: Independent foundation.
Financial data (yr. ended 12/31/14): Assets, $6,266,272; expenditures, $319,180; qualifying distributions, $301,356.
Fields of interest: Arts and culture; Historic preservation; Education; Environment; Domesticated animals; Human services.
Limitations: Applications accepted. Giving primarily in CT. No grants to individuals.
Application information: Application form required.
  Initial approach: Letter
  Deadline(s): Applications considered on a rolling basis in the order received
Trustees: James T. Betts; Henry R. McLane III.
EIN: 066537915

1523
James P. & Genevieve M. McLaughlin Family Foundation, Inc.
232 Mill Rd.
Stamford, CT 06903-1613
Contact: Paul B. McLaughlin, Pres.

Donors: James P. McLaughlin†; Genevieve M. McLaughlin†.
Foundation type: Independent foundation.
Financial data (yr. ended 06/30/13): Assets, $6,708,883 (M); expenditures, $370,169; qualifying distributions, $305,000; giving activities include $305,000 for 10 grants (high: $75,000; low: $15,000).
Purpose and activities: Giving primarily to Roman Catholic organizations.
Fields of interest: Music; Education; Specialty hospital care; Community and economic development; Catholicism.
Limitations: Applications accepted. Giving primarily in NY. No grants to individuals.
Application information:
  Initial approach: Letter
  Deadline(s): None
Officers: Paul B. McLaughlin, Pres.; Jean M. McLaughlin, Secy.-Treas.
Director: Frank A. Suchomel.
EIN: 133335298

1524
McLeod Blue Skye Charitable Foundation, Inc.
86 Seaview Ave.
Branford, CT 06405-5444

Established in 1992 in Connecticut.
Donor: Christopher K. McLeod.
Foundation type: Independent foundation.
Financial data (yr. ended 12/31/14): Assets, $8,054,598 (M); expenditures, $518,901; qualifying distributions, $442,974; giving activities include $442,950 for 7 grants (high: $125,000; low: $5,000).
Purpose and activities: Giving primarily for educational purposes.

Fields of interest: Secondary education; Higher education; Nonprofits.

Type of support: Scholarships; Regranting; Capital campaigns.

Limitations: Applications not accepted. Giving primarily in CT and MA. No grants to individuals.

Application information: Contributes only to pre-selected organizations.

Officers and Directors: Christopher K. McLeod, Pres. and Treas. and Director; Elaine M. McLeod, Secy. and Director; Scott McLeod.

EIN: 223216389

1525
The Mellen Foundation, Inc.
460 Coe Ave.
East Haven, CT 06512

Foundation type: Independent foundation.

Financial data (yr. ended 12/31/13): Assets, $1,882,883 (M); expenditures, $250,505; qualifying distributions, $243,135; giving activities include $243,135 for 61 grants (high: $45,000; low: $250).

Fields of interest: Higher education; Hospital care; Judaism; Human services.

Limitations: Applications not accepted. Giving primarily in CT and NY. No grants to individuals.

Application information: Unsolicited requests for funds not accepted.

Officers: Diane Mellen, Pres.; Neil Mellen, Secy.-Treas.

EIN: 222778847

1526
MLE Foundation Inc.
c/o Marie Creaturo, Emily B. Nissley, Thomas W. Niss
P.O. Box 147
New Canaan, CT 06840-0147

Donor: Emily B. Nissley.

Foundation type: Independent foundation.

Financial data (yr. ended 12/31/14): Assets, $12,029,101; gifts received, $1,000,000; expenditures, $498,378; qualifying distributions, $389,052 and $0 for set-asides.

Fields of interest: Arts and culture; Domesticated animals; Protestantism.

Limitations: Applications not accepted.

Application information: Unsolicited requests for funds not accepted.

Directors: Marie Creaturo; Emily B. Nissley; Thomas W. Nissley.

EIN: 300517812

1527
Joseph J. and Claire Morrow Charitable Foundation
7 Close Rd.
Greenwich, CT 06831-2721

Established in 1994 in Connecticut.

Donors: Joseph J. Morrow; Claire Morrow.

Foundation type: Independent foundation.

Financial data (yr. ended 06/30/13): Assets, $4,615,332 (M); gifts received, $500,000; expenditures, $429,994; qualifying distributions, $365,000; giving activities include $365,000 for grants.

Fields of interest: Opera; Orchestral music; Secondary education; Higher education; Specialty hospital care; Cancers; Breast cancer; National defense; Protestantism; Catholicism.

Type of support: General support; Annual campaigns.

Limitations: Applications not accepted. Giving primarily in CT. No grants to individuals.

Application information: Contributes only to pre-selected organizations.

Trustees: Tracy M. Bundy; Claire Morrow; Donna M. Morrow; Joseph J. Morrow; Kim A. Morrow.

EIN: 223326900

1528
Alex G. Nason Foundation, Inc.
1177 High Ridge Rd., Ste. 111
Stamford, CT 06905-1221   2038565299

Established in 1992 in Ohio.

Donors: Alexander G. Nason; The Nason Foundation.

Foundation type: Independent foundation.

Financial data (yr. ended 12/31/14): Assets, $4,343,986; expenditures, $494,213; qualifying distributions, $342,394.

Purpose and activities: Giving primarily for the arts, education and human services.

Fields of interest: Arts and culture; Elementary and secondary education; Higher education; Marine science.

Limitations: Applications not accepted. Giving primarily in CT, FL, and NY. No grants to individuals.

Application information: Contributes only to pre-selected organizations.

Officers and Directors: Sofia Blanchard, Chair. and Director; Alexander G. Nason, Pres. and Treas. and Director; Lucie Burke, Secy. and Director; Vincent Burke; Alexandra Nason.

EIN: 341757149

1529
The Irwin and Dorothy Nessel Foundation Inc.
(formerly Irwin and Dorothy Nessel Foundation, Inc.)
134 East Ave.
Norwalk, CT 06851

Established in 2000 in Connecticut.

Donor: Dorothy M. Nessel.

Foundation type: Independent foundation.

Financial data (yr. ended 12/31/13): Assets, $4,772,566 (M); expenditures, $231,908; qualifying distributions, $203,839; giving activities include $199,000 for 19 grants (high: $40,000; low: $1,000).

Fields of interest: Human services; Family services.

Limitations: Applications not accepted. Giving primarily in CT. No grants to individuals.

Application information: Contributes only to pre-selected organizations.

Officers: Dorothy M. Nessel, Pres.; David L. Nessel, V.P.; David L. Godfrey, Secy.

Director: Judy Nessel.

EIN: 061596433

1530
Leo Nevas Family Foundation, Inc.
(formerly Leo & Libby Nevas Family Foundation, Inc.)
P.O. Box 299
Chester, CT 06412-0299
Contact: Jo-Ann Price, Pres.

Established in 1961 in Connecticut.

Donor: Leo Nevas†.

Foundation type: Independent foundation.

Financial data (yr. ended 11/30/13): Assets, $12,385,246 (M); gifts received, $5,000,000; expenditures, $263,672; qualifying distributions, $226,820; giving activities include $201,600 for 9 grants (high: $40,000; low: $100).

Fields of interest: Education; Student services; Judaism.

Type of support: General support.

Limitations: Applications accepted. Giving primarily in CT and New York, NY. No grants to individuals.

Application information:
  Deadline(s): None

Officers: Jo-Ann Price, Pres.; Bernard Nevas, Treas.

EIN: 066068842

1531
Newpol Foundation, Inc.
2 Rainbow Ct.
P.O. Box 839
New Milford, CT 06776-2053   (203) 775-9766

Established in 1981 in Connecticut.

Donors: Stanley Newman; Marlowe Cole†.

Foundation type: Independent foundation.

Financial data (yr. ended 12/31/14): Assets, $3,647,975; expenditures, $240,126; qualifying distributions, $223,850.

Fields of interest: Arts and culture; Law education; Diseases and conditions; HIV/AIDS; LGBTQ people.

Type of support: Research.

Application information: Application form required.
  Initial approach: Letter
  Deadline(s): None

Officers and Directors: Stanley Newman, Pres. and Treas. and Director; Nancy Polikoff, Secy. and Director; George Robertson; Brian Rosenthal, MD.

EIN: 510259621

1532
Newtown Savings Bank Foundation Inc.
c/o Newtown Savings Bank
39 Main St.
Newtown, CT 06470   (203) 426-4440
Contact: John F. Trentacosta, Pres. and C.E.O.

Established in 1997 in Connecticut.

Donor: Newtown Savings Bank.

Foundation type: Company-sponsored foundation.

Financial data (yr. ended 09/30/13): Assets, $1,228,453 (M); gifts received, $184,675; expenditures, $164,829; qualifying distributions, $155,000; giving activities include $155,000 for 26 grants (high: $100,000; low: $1,000).

Purpose and activities: The foundation supports organizations involved with education, health, and housing.

Fields of interest: Education; Higher education; Health; Hospital care; Social sciences; Housing development.

Type of support: General support; Scholarships; Individual development.

Limitations: Applications accepted. Giving limited to the Newtown, CT, area. No grants to individuals.
Application information: Application form required.
Initial approach: Letter
Deadline(s): None
Officers: John J. Martocci, Chair.; John F. Trentacosta, Pres. and C.E.O.; Duane Giannini, Sr. V.P.; Tanya Wulff Traux, Secy.
Trustees: William A. Brimmer; Alan C. Clavette; James A. Kennedy; Paul S. Lux; John S. Madzula; Carol L. Mahoney; James T. Morley, Jr.; Brian C. White.
EIN: 061514980

1533
The Niblack Foundation
c/o Day Pitney LLP
1 Canterbury Green
Stamford, CT   06901-2032

Established in 2003 in Connecticut.
Donors: Heidi G. Niblack; John F. Niblack.
Foundation type: Independent foundation.
Financial data (yr. ended 12/31/14): Assets, $754,543 (M); expenditures, $164,368; qualifying distributions, $162,405; giving activities include $162,405 for 14 grants (high: $30,000; low: $1,000).
Fields of interest: Museums; Education; Higher education; Science; Human services.
Limitations: Applications not accepted. Giving primarily in CT, FL, NH and NY. No grants to individuals.
Application information: Contributes only to pre-selected organizations.
Trustees: Elwood B. Davis; Robert J. Miller; Heidi G. Niblack; John F. Niblack.
EIN: 527323778

1534
Nirenberg Foundation, Inc.
(formerly Nirenberg Family Charitable Foundation, Inc.)
1 Hartfield Blvd., Ste. 102
East Windsor, CT   06088-9582
Contact: Charles Nirenberg, Pres. and Dir.
Application address: 24 Deep Brook Harbor, Suffield, CT 06078, tel.: (860) 623-5252

Established in 1989 in Connecticut.
Donors: Charles Nirenberg; Janet Nirenberg.
Foundation type: Independent foundation.
Financial data (yr. ended 04/30/13): Assets, $1,324,121 (M); expenditures, $290,543; qualifying distributions, $225,750; giving activities include $225,750 for grants.
Purpose and activities: Giving primarily for Jewish organizations and schools.
Fields of interest: Education; Elementary and secondary education; Higher education; Graduate and professional education; Nonprofits; Hospital care; Judaism; Theology; Human services.
Type of support: Regranting.
Limitations: Applications accepted. Giving primarily in MA. No grants to individuals.
Application information: Application information available upon request. Application form required.
Initial approach: Letter
Deadline(s): None

Officers and Directors: Charles Nirenberg, Pres. and Director; Jonathan K. Bernstein, Secy. and Director; Janet Nirenberg, Treas. and Director.
EIN: 223059287

1535
Penn Oberlander Family Foundation Inc.
c/o Laurence Penn, Ellington Mgmt. Group
53 Forest Ave.
Old Greenwich, CT   06870-1526

Established in 2005 in Unspecified.
Donors: Jill Oberlander; Larry Penn.
Foundation type: Independent foundation.
Financial data (yr. ended 12/31/13): Assets, $2,261,190 (M); gifts received, $1,000,000; expenditures, $241,235; qualifying distributions, $238,235; giving activities include $235,485 for 39 grants (high: $60,000; low: $85).
Fields of interest: Education; Health; Human services.
Limitations: Applications not accepted. Giving primarily in NY. No grants to individuals.
Application information: Contributes only to pre-selected organizations.
Officers: Laurence Penn, Pres.; Jill Oberlander, Secy.
EIN: 203858920

1536
The O'Herron Family Foundation
(formerly Jonathan & Shirley O'Herron Foundation)
P.O. Box 4816
Stamford, CT   06907-0816
Contact: Anne O'Herron Burleigh, Pres.

Established in 1984 in New York.
Donor: Shirley O'Herron†.
Foundation type: Independent foundation.
Financial data (yr. ended 06/30/14): Assets, $7,853,515 (M); gifts received, $7,290,140; expenditures, $430,167; qualifying distributions, $411,860; giving activities include $411,860 for 64 grants (high: $25,000; low: $250).
Fields of interest: Elementary and secondary education; Higher education; Business education; Medical education; Nonprofits; Diseases and conditions; Catholicism; Human services.
Type of support: General support; Regranting; Capital campaigns.
Limitations: Giving primarily in CT, MA, NH, NY, and VT. No grants to individuals.
Application information:
Initial approach: Letter
Deadline(s): None
Officers and Directors: Anne O'Herron Burleigh, Pres. and Exec. Dir.; Sarah O'Herron Casey; Jonathan O'Herron, Jr.
EIN: 133244207

1537
The O'Meara Foundation, Inc.
P.O. Box 290157
Wethersfield, CT   06109-0157   (860) 563-2918
Contact: Claude-Evelyne O'Diata
E-mail: BPINCMAX@aol.com; Application address: 1900 Berlin Tpke., Wethersfield, CT 06109

Established in 1944 in Connecticut.
Foundation type: Independent foundation.

Financial data (yr. ended 06/30/13): Assets, $335,267 (M); gifts received, $2,200; expenditures, $340,158; qualifying distributions, $314,863; giving activities include $297,500 for 125 grants to individuals.
Purpose and activities: Support for scholarships to residents of Hartford County, CT, attending institutions of higher education.
Fields of interest: Education.
Type of support: Scholarships; Student aid.
Limitations: Applications accepted. Giving limited to residents of Hartford County, CT.
Publications: Annual report.
Application information: Application form required.
Initial approach: Request application form
Deadline(s): June 1
Board meeting date(s): Late July
Officers and Directors: Martin J. O'Meara, Jr., Pres. and Director; William F. O'Meara, Secy. and Director; Edward L. Storrs, Treas. and Director.
Number of staff: 1 full-time professional.
EIN: 066034580

1538
Panoram Foundation Inc.
(formerly The Copp Foundation, Inc.)
19 Smith Neck Rd.
Old Lyme, CT   06371-2618

Established in 1984 in Connecticut.
Donor: Joseph A. Copp†.
Foundation type: Independent foundation.
Financial data (yr. ended 12/31/13): Assets, $5,379,257 (M); gifts received, $5,000; expenditures, $471,286; qualifying distributions, $441,431; giving activities include $438,636 for 7 grants (high: $200,000; low: $4,000).
Fields of interest: Museums; Historic preservation.
Type of support: General support.
Limitations: Applications not accepted. Giving primarily in CT. No grants to individuals.
Application information: Unsolicited requests for funds not accepted.
Officers: B. Allyn Copp, Pres.; Betsey A. Copp, Secy.; Eugenie C.T. Copp, Treas.
Director: Lucy A. Copp.
EIN: 222647132

1539
Panwy Foundation, Inc.
15 E. Putnam Ave., No. 3100
Greenwich, CT   06830-5424   2036616616

Donors: Olga Resseguier†; Henry W. Wyman†; Maria Wyman†; Ralph M. Wyman; Ruth L. Russell; Carla Benka; Alexis Dorf; Matthew Dorf; Leslie Cooper.
Foundation type: Independent foundation.
Financial data (yr. ended 12/31/14): Assets, $4,145,188; gifts received, $32,500; expenditures, $363,526; qualifying distributions, $293,895.
Fields of interest: Arts and culture; Diseases and conditions; Christianity; Protestantism; Human services.
Type of support: Program development; Seed money.
Limitations: Applications not accepted. Giving primarily in southern CT, and the Boston, MA, area. No grants to individuals, or for matching gifts,

scholarship funds, capital campaigns, or operating deficit funding.

Application information: Unsolicited requests for funds not accepted. Foundation initiates contact.

Board meeting date(s): As required

Officers and Trustees: Ralph M. Wyman, Pres. and Trustee; Carla Benka, V.P.; Ruth L. Russell, V.P. and Trustee; Leslie A.W. Cooper, Secy.-Treas.; Virginia A.W. Meyer; Alexandra N.P. Dorf; Peggy R. Rosenblum; Cristina Wyman.

EIN: 136130759

1540
Paoloian Family Foundation Inc.
265 Longmeadow Rd.
Fairfield, CT 06824-1734

Donors: Karen Paloian; John Paloian.
Foundation type: Independent foundation.
Financial data (yr. ended 12/31/14): Assets, $2,830; gifts received, $250,000; expenditures, $263,021; qualifying distributions, $250,650.
Fields of interest: Education; Diseases and conditions; Youth development.
Limitations: Applications not accepted.
Application information: Unsolicited requests for funds not accepted.
Officer: Karen Paloian, Pres.
EIN: 274539210

1541
The Robert & Margaret Patricelli Family Foundation
77 Hartford Rd.
Simsbury, CT 06070-2506
Contact: Robert E. Patricelli, Chair.

Established in 1996 in Connecticut.
Donors: Robert E. Patricelli; Margaret S. Patricelli.
Foundation type: Independent foundation.
Financial data (yr. ended 06/30/15): Assets, $3,667,449 (M); gifts received, $250,837; expenditures, $389,151; qualifying distributions, $377,288; giving activities include $375,188 for grants.
Fields of interest: Arts and culture; Education; Higher education; Graduate and professional education; Natural resources; Nonprofits; Health; Science; Human services.
Type of support: General support; Annual campaigns; Program development; Research; Regranting.
Publications: Application guidelines.
Application information:
Initial approach: Proposal
Deadline(s): None
Officers: Robert E. Patricelli, Chair.; Margaret S. Patricelli, Pres.
Directors: Alison J. Patricelli; Thomas R. Patricelli.
Number of staff: 1 part-time professional.
EIN: 061487230

1542
The Perna-Rose Foundation for Hope, Inc.
(formerly The Perna Foundation for Hope, Inc.)
50 Knobloch Ln.
Stamford, CT 06902-1702
Main URL: http://www.pernafoundationforhope.org

Donor: Janet Perna.

Foundation type: Independent foundation.
Financial data (yr. ended 06/30/14): Assets, $6,335,684 (M); gifts received, $300,000; expenditures, $219,256; qualifying distributions, $200,091; giving activities include $195,000 for 15 grants (high: $100,000; low: $1,000).
Purpose and activities: The purpose of the foundation is to provide funding to domestic and international organizations which: Help people attain or regain self-sufficiency by providing education, food/clothing/shelter and supporting micro-businesses. Supports initiatives in animal welfare ..
Fields of interest: Education; Undergraduate education; Domesticated animals; Human services.
Limitations: Applications not accepted. Giving primarily in CT and NY.
Application information: Unsolicited requests for funds not accepted.
Officers and Board Members: Melanie Rose, Pres.; Tina Woodward, V.P.; Janet Perna, Treas.; Ginger Parrish, Secy.; Daniella Engan.
EIN: 352357099

1543
Post College Foundation, Inc.
43 Field St.
Waterbury, CT 06702-1906

Established in 2005 in Connecticut.
Foundation type: Independent foundation.
Financial data (yr. ended 06/30/13): Assets, $5,973,394 (M); gifts received, $500; expenditures, $392,241; qualifying distributions, $339,481; giving activities include $325,000 for 122 grants to individuals (high: $8,000; low: $1,500).
Fields of interest: Education.
Limitations: Applications not accepted. Giving primarily in CT.
Application information: Unsolicited requests for funds not accepted.
Officers: Edmund White, Chair.; Gary Post, Pres.; Peter Meriman, Secy.-Treas.
EIN: 061298333

1544
Lucien B. and Katherine E. Price Foundation
P.O. Box 790
Manchester, CT 06040-0790 (860) 643-2688
Contact: Edward P. Flanagan, Secy.

Established in 1922 in Connecticut.
Foundation type: Independent foundation.
Financial data (yr. ended 12/31/12): Assets, $4,637,879 (M); expenditures, $303,377; qualifying distributions, $230,000; giving activities include $230,000 for grants.
Purpose and activities: Emphasis on Roman Catholic church support, religious associations, and church-related schools, colleges, and hospitals.
Fields of interest: Elementary and secondary education; Nonprofits; Religion; Catholicism; Human services.
Type of support: General support; Regranting.
Limitations: Applications accepted. Giving primarily in CT and UT.
Application information: Application form required.
Initial approach: Letter
Deadline(s): None

Officers: Rev. Msgr. J. Terrence Fitzgerald, Pres.; Rev. Colin Bircumshaw, V.P.; Edward P. Flanagan, Secy.; Sheila B. Flanagan, Treas.
Director: Timothy Devanney.
EIN: 066068868

1545
Mortimer R. Proctor Foundation
c/o Chittenden Bank
P.O. Box 820
Bridgeport, CT 06604-4913

Foundation type: Independent foundation.
Financial data (yr. ended 12/31/13): Assets, $4,151,960 (M); expenditures, $231,525; qualifying distributions, $190,358; giving activities include $186,406 for 8 grants (high: $98,502; low: $2,350).
Fields of interest: Elementary and secondary education; Public administration; Community and economic development; Christianity; Youth services.
Type of support: General support; Continuing support; Capital campaigns; Capital and infrastructure; Equipment; Emergency funds; Program development; Curriculum development; Technical assistance.
Limitations: Applications not accepted. Giving primarily in Proctor, VT. No grants to individuals.
Application information: Unsolicited requests for funds not accepted.
Trustee: People's United Bank, N.A.
EIN: 036020099

1546
The Pryor Foundation
29 Fernbrook
West Hartford, CT 06107-1613
Contact: Esther A. Pryor, Tr.

Established in 1947 in Michigan.
Donors: Mary S. Pryor; Corey Kienholz; Daniel A. Pryor; Millard H. Pryor, Jr.
Foundation type: Independent foundation.
Financial data (yr. ended 12/31/13): Assets, $3,465,893 (M); expenditures, $320,566; qualifying distributions, $288,350; giving activities include $279,500 for 20 grants (high: $85,000; low: $1,000).
Purpose and activities: Giving to the arts, culture and education.
Fields of interest: Arts and culture; Higher education; Nonprofits; Human services.
Type of support: Annual campaigns; Pro bono consulting services; Capital campaigns; Emergency funds; Regranting.
Limitations: Applications accepted. No support for religious or political organizations . No grants for building funds or land acquisition.
Application information: Application form required.
Initial approach: Letter
Deadline(s): None
Board meeting date(s): Nov.
Officer and Trustees: F. Loyal Bemiller, Secy. and Trustee; Elizabeth P. Bradley; Daniel A. Pryor; Esther A. Pryor.
Number of staff: None.
EIN: 386056108

1547
Pulvermann Charitable Trust
c/o James A. Fulton
6 Nolan La
Darien, CT 06820

Donor: Arcade Trust.
Foundation type: Independent foundation.
Financial data (yr. ended 12/31/14): Assets, $3,447,129 (M); expenditures, $212,234; qualifying distributions, $151,000; giving activities include $151,000 for 3 grants (high: $100,000; low: $5,000).
Fields of interest: Arts and culture; Education; Human services.
Limitations: Applications not accepted.
Application information: Unsolicited requests for funds not accepted.
Trustee: James A. Fulton.
EIN: 276762467

1548
Theodore A. Rapp Foundation
c/o Omar R. Adame
514 Indian Field Rd.
Greenwich, CT 06830-7239 (203) 661-2474

Established in 2002 in Connecticut.
Donors: Omar R. Adame; Theodore A. Rapp†.
Foundation type: Independent foundation.
Financial data (yr. ended 06/30/14): Assets, $4,366,486; gifts received, $285,000; expenditures, $260,620; qualifying distributions, $260,620.
Fields of interest: Education; Health; Diseases and conditions.
Limitations: Applications accepted. Giving primarily in New York, NY. No grants to individuals.
Application information: Application form required.
  Initial approach: Proposal
  Deadline(s): None
Trustees: Margaret Hayes Adame; Omar R. Adame; Brian E. Skinner.
EIN: 331013781

1549
RBS Foundation, Inc.
(formerly Greenwich Capital Foundation)
600 Washington Blvd.
Stamford, CT 06901-3726

Donors: Greenwich Capital Markets, Inc.; Benjamin Carpenter; Jay Levine; Jeffrey Mullins.
Foundation type: Company-sponsored foundation.
Financial data (yr. ended 08/31/13): Assets, $183,568 (M); gifts received, $2,319; expenditures, $152,320; qualifying distributions, $152,170; giving activities include $151,870 for 2 grants (high: $150,655; low: $1,215).
Purpose and activities: The foundation supports camps and organizations involved with health, legal aid, human services, and small businesses.
Fields of interest: Health; Community and economic development; Human services.
Type of support: General support; Program development.
Limitations: Applications not accepted. Giving primarily in CT and NY. No grants to individuals.
Application information: Contributes only to pre-selected organizations.

Officers and Directors: Robert McKillip, Chair. and Pres. and Director; Carol P. Mathis, C.F.O. and Director; Jennifer Fitzgibbon, Treas. and Director; James Esposito, Genl. Counsel and Director; Andreas Papadatos.
EIN: 061630962

1550
Faye and Michael Richardson Charitable Trust
c/o Richardson J. Michael
33 Joshuatown Rd.
Lyme, CT 06371-3119 (860) 434-3349
Contact: Faye Richardson, Tr.

Established in 1994 in Connecticut.
Donor: Michael Richardson.
Foundation type: Independent foundation.
Financial data (yr. ended 06/30/13): Assets, $2,548,301 (M); expenditures, $217,694; qualifying distributions, $212,511; giving activities include $211,171 for 7 grants (high: $100,000; low: $1,000).
Fields of interest: Environment; Christianity.
International interests: Guatemala; Myanmar.
Limitations: Applications accepted. Giving primarily in CA, CT, NJ and NY. No grants to individuals.
Application information: Application form required.
  Initial approach: Letter
  Deadline(s): None
Trustees: Faye Richardson; J. Michael Richardson; Peter Richardson; Thomas Richardson.
EIN: 137044993

1551
Clinton S. Roberts Foundation, Inc.
201 West St.
P.O. Box 1399
Bristol, CT 06010-5745

Foundation type: Independent foundation.
Financial data (yr. ended 12/31/13): Assets, $7,627,567 (M); expenditures, $413,529; qualifying distributions, $345,250; giving activities include $345,250 for 32 grants (high: $50,000; low: $650).
Purpose and activities: Giving primarily to museums, as well as for human services.
Fields of interest: Museums; Historic preservation; Education; Community improvement; Christianity; Protestantism; Human services; Family services.
Limitations: Applications not accepted. Giving primarily in the greater Bristol, CT, area.
Application information: Contributes only to pre-selected organizations.
Officer: Christopher Ziogas, Exec. Dir.
Trustees: Linda Roberts Arbesman; Ellen Roberts Ferrier; Gail Roberts; Leonard Roberts.
EIN: 222867088

1552
Edward C. & Ann T. Roberts Foundation, Inc.
P.O. Box 271588
West Hartford, CT 06127-1588
E-mail: edwannroberts@att.net; *Main URL:* http://fdnweb.org/roberts/

Established in 1964 in Connecticut.
Donors: Edward C. Roberts†; Ann T. Roberts†.

Foundation type: Independent foundation.
Financial data (yr. ended 12/31/14): Assets, $7,321,242 (M); expenditures, $442,491; qualifying distributions, $365,067; giving activities include $319,750 for 34 grants (high: $25,000; low: $2,000).
Purpose and activities: Funding for Excellence in the Arts grants to support and encourage excellence in the arts in the Hartford, Connecticut, area.
Fields of interest: Arts and culture; Visual arts; Performing arts; Dance.
Type of support: Capital campaigns; Capital and infrastructure; Equipment; Program development.
Limitations: Applications accepted. Giving limited to Hartford, CT, and the immediately surrounding area. No grants to individuals or for scholarship aid, endowment funds, projects that have already occurred or are underway at the time the Board considers the application, proposals that use a fiscal agent or a pass-through organization, or for general operating expenses.
Publications: Application guidelines; Annual report; Grants list.
Application information: When mailing an application, use P.O. Box only. There is no mail delivery to the street address, however proposals may be hand-delivered to the street address. The Connecticut Council for Philanthropy Common Grant Application Form will be accepted. Application guidelines are available on foundation web site.
  Initial approach: See foundation web site
  Deadline(s): Feb. 1, May 1, Aug. 1, and Nov. 1
  Board meeting date(s): Mar., June, Sept., and Dec.
  Final notification: Mar. 31, June 30, Sept. 30, and Dec. 31
Officers and Trustees: Kelley R. Bonn, Chair.; Jack Kennedy, Pres. and Trustee; Terry Gellin, Secy. and Trustee; Douglas Boains, Treas. and Trustee; Lisa M. Curran, Exec. Dir.; John Alves; Thea Montanez; Elizabeth Normen; Carol Terry.
Number of staff: 1 part-time professional.
EIN: 066067995

1553
Charles Nelson Robinson Fund
(formerly Carse Robinson Foundation)
c/o US Trust, Philanthropic Solutions
200 Glastonbury Blvd., Ste. 200, CT2-545-02-05
Glastonbury, CT 06033 (860) 657-7019
Contact: Carmen Britt, V.P.
E-mail: kim.m.igoe-kasper@ustrust.comcarmen.britt@ustrust.com; *Main URL:* https://www.bankofamerica.com/philanthropic/grantmaking.go

Established in 1970 in Connecticut.
Donors: Charles Nelson Robinson†; Elizabeth Carse†; Joseph Stackpole†; Mabel Hoffman†; Henry Hall†.
Foundation type: Independent foundation.
Financial data (yr. ended 06/30/13): Assets, $4,338,250 (M); expenditures, $229,229; qualifying distributions, $197,660; giving activities include $170,500 for 46 grants (high: $8,000; low: $1,500).
Purpose and activities: To support and promote quality educational, human services, and health care programming for underserved populations in Hartford, CT.
Fields of interest: Arts and culture; Education; Health; Human services; Low-income and poor people.

Type of support: Program development; Regulation and administration.

Limitations: Applications accepted. Giving primarily in the Hartford, CT, area. No grants to individuals, or for capital campaigns.

Application information: Forms and guidelines available on foundation web site. Preference is given to organizations that provide human services programming to underserved adults. Application form required.

  Initial approach: Letter
  Copies of proposal: 5
  Deadline(s): Feb. 15 and Aug. 15
  Board meeting date(s): Apr. and Oct.
  Final notification: Within 2-3 months following deadlines

Trustee: Bank of America, N.A.

EIN: 066029468

1554
The Rock Foundation
70 Zaccheus Mead Ln.
Greenwich, CT 06831-3752

Established in 2000 in Connecticut.

Donors: Peter O. Scannell; Jean G. Scannell.

Foundation type: Independent foundation.

Financial data (yr. ended 12/31/13): Assets, $6,891,444 (M); expenditures, $381,429; qualifying distributions, $379,829; giving activities include $379,829 for 10 grants (high: $200,329; low: $1,000).

Fields of interest: Education; Undergraduate education; Sports and recreation.

Limitations: Applications not accepted. Giving primarily in CT and NH. No grants to individuals.

Application information: Contributes only to pre-selected organizations.

Trustees: Jean G. Scannell; Peter O. Scannell.

EIN: 061603870

1555
Lil & Julie Rosenberg Foundation Inc.
100 Browning St.
Stratford, CT 06615-7130 (203) 375-5671
Contact: Jerry Rosenberg, Pres.

Established in 1963 in Connecticut.

Donor: Julius Rosenberg.

Foundation type: Independent foundation.

Financial data (yr. ended 12/31/13): Assets, $2,614,384 (M); expenditures, $156,371; qualifying distributions, $150,000; giving activities include $150,000 for 20 grants (high: $62,200; low: $90).

Purpose and activities: Giving primarily to Jewish organizations and charities.

Fields of interest: Nonprofits; Judaism; Human services.

Type of support: Regranting.

Limitations: Applications accepted. Giving primarily in CT. No grants to individuals.

Application information: Application form required.
  Initial approach: Letter
  Deadline(s): None

Officer: Jerry Rosenberg, Pres.

EIN: 066064351

1556
The Rubin-Ladd Foundation
P.O. Box 63
Georgetown, CT 06829-0063 (203) 938-0903
Contact: Robert S. Walzer, Pres.

Foundation type: Independent foundation.

Financial data (yr. ended 06/30/14): Assets, $7,859,269 (M); expenditures, $636,396; qualifying distributions, $559,760; giving activities include $398,555 for 24 grants (high: $265,000; low: $95).

Purpose and activities: The foundation supports fine arts, education, cultural events and health facilities.

Fields of interest: Arts and culture; Education; Higher education.

Type of support: General support.

Limitations: Applications accepted. Giving primarily in CT, Miami, FL, and NY. No grants to individuals.

Application information: Application form required.
  Initial approach: Letter
  Deadline(s): None

Officers: Robert S. Walzer, Pres.; Ann Walzer, V.P.; Eric Walzer, V.P.

Directors: Ivy Engel; Steven Walzer; Shelley Weiner.

EIN: 061556098

1557
James A. Salatto and Family Charitable Foundation Inc.
129 Church St.
New Haven, CT 06510

Donor: James A. Salatto.

Foundation type: Independent foundation.

Financial data (yr. ended 12/31/14): Assets, $481,032 (M); gifts received, $400,000; expenditures, $319,979; qualifying distributions, $315,764; giving activities include $314,864 for 19 grants (high: $245,000; low: $50).

Fields of interest: Education; Health; Human services.

Limitations: Applications not accepted.

Application information: Unsolicited requests for funds not accepted.

Officers and Trustees: James A. Salatto, Chair. and Trustee; Albert Yavarone, Vice-Chair. and Trustee; Beverley Simeone, Secy.-Treas. and Trustee; Robert Bartolommeo.

EIN: 271970901

1558
The Santoro Family Charitable Foundation
3 Alden Terr.
Greenwich, CT 06831-4422

Established in 2006 in Connecticut.

Donor: Charles W. Santoro.

Foundation type: Independent foundation.

Financial data (yr. ended 12/31/14): Assets, $421,386 (M); gifts received, $350,000; expenditures, $198,176; qualifying distributions, $198,001; giving activities include $198,001 for 9 grants (high: $112,500; low: $250).

Fields of interest: Education; Human services.

Limitations: Applications not accepted. No grants to individuals.

Application information: Contributes only to pre-selected organizations.

Trustee: Charles W. Santoro.

EIN: 205676915

1559
Savings Bank of Danbury Foundation, Inc.
220 Main St.
Danbury, CT 06810-6635 (203) 743-3849
Contact: David H. Woessner, Dir.
E-mail: web-email@sbdanbury.com; Main
URL: https://www.sbdanbury.com/about/explore/sbd-foundation
Grants List: https://www.sbdanbury.com/docs/default-source/default-document-library/2015-foundation-grants.pdf?sfvrsn=0

Established in 2003 in Connecticut.

Donor: Savings Bank of Danbury.

Foundation type: Company-sponsored foundation.

Financial data (yr. ended 12/31/14): Assets, $1,483,672 (M); gifts received, $125,000; expenditures, $150,861; qualifying distributions, $150,111; giving activities include $146,610 for grants.

Purpose and activities: The foundation supports organizations involved with arts and culture, education, health, affordable housing, human services, economic development, and community development.

Fields of interest: Arts and culture; Education; Health; Community and economic development; Economic development; Housing development; Human services.

Limitations: Applications accepted. Giving primarily in areas of company operations in CT.

Application information: Application form required.
  Initial approach: Request application form
  Deadline(s): Sept. 30

Officers and Directors: Harold C. Wibling, Chair. and Director; Kathleen Romangano, Pres. and Director; Steven Cacchio, Exec. V.P. and Director; David H. Woessner, Secy.-Treas. and Director; Philip Cammarano; Karl H. Epple; Gary W. Hawley; Donald D. Mitchell; James W. Schmotter; June Renzulli.

EIN: 113709335

1560
Lewis G. Schaeneman, Jr. Foundation, Inc.
1 Hamden Ctr.
2319 Whitney Ave. Ste. 1D
Hamden, CT 06518-3509

Established in 1998 in Connecticut.

Donors: Lewis G. Schaeneman, Jr.†; Priscilla Schaeneman.

Foundation type: Independent foundation.

Financial data (yr. ended 12/31/13): Assets, $7,760,120 (L); expenditures, $407,298; qualifying distributions, $370,307; giving activities include $229,693 for 44 grants (high: $35,900; low: $10).

Fields of interest: Education; Secondary education; Domesticated animals; Nonprofits; Human services; Food aid; Child welfare.

Type of support: Individual development; Regranting.

Limitations: Applications not accepted. No grants to individuals.

Application information: Unsolicited requests for funds not accepted.

Officers and Directors: Lewis G. Schaeneman III, Pres. and Director; William S. Colwell, Secy. and Director; Laura Burrows.
EIN: 061390923

1561
The Walter G. Schendel III Family Foundation
c/o Walter G. Schendel
649 Merwins Ln.
Fairfield, CT 06824-1973

Established in 1999 in Connecticut.
Donor: Walter G. Schendel III.
Foundation type: Independent foundation.
Financial data (yr. ended 11/30/13): Assets, $583,699 (M); expenditures, $172,392; qualifying distributions, $170,275; giving activities include $170,275 for 10 grants (high: $50,000; low: $200).
Fields of interest: Education; Christianity; Human services.
Type of support: General support.
Limitations: Applications not accepted. Giving primarily in CT and NJ. No grants to individuals.
Application information: Contributes only to pre-selected organizations.
Trustees: Sharon M. Schendel; Walter G. Schendel III.
EIN: 061566679

1562
The Schloss Family Foundation Inc.
c/o Edwin Schloss, TweedyBrowne Co.
1 Station Pl.
Stamford, CT 06902

Established in 1997 in New York.
Donors: Walter J. Schloss; Edwin W. Schloss; Walter J. Schloss Irrevocable Trust.
Foundation type: Independent foundation.
Financial data (yr. ended 12/31/13): Assets, $6,692,898 (M); gifts received, $2,003,990; expenditures, $228,716; qualifying distributions, $225,000; giving activities include $225,000 for 9 grants (high: $50,000; low: $5,000).
Purpose and activities: Giving primarily for art and cultural programs, and for education.
Fields of interest: Art museums; Natural history museums; Education; Natural resources; Biodiversity; Wildlife biodiversity; Family planning; Communication media; Television; Human rights; Human services; Adult day care.
Type of support: General support.
Limitations: Applications not accepted. Giving primarily in NY and Washington, DC. No grants to individuals.
Application information: Unsolicited requests for funds not accepted.
Officers: Edwin W. Schloss, Pres. and Treas.; Stephanie Cassel Scott, Secy.
EIN: 133935646

1563
The Virginia & Warren Schwerin Family Foundation, Inc.
1700 E. Putnam Ave.
Old Greenwich, CT 06870-1366

Established in 1997 in Delaware.
Donor: Warren Schwerin.

Foundation type: Independent foundation.
Financial data (yr. ended 12/31/13): Assets, $1,630,522 (M); expenditures, $159,934; qualifying distributions, $156,275; giving activities include $154,000 for 5 grants (high: $50,000; low: $4,000).
Fields of interest: Education; Wildlife biodiversity; Animal welfare; People with hearing impairments.
Type of support: General support.
Limitations: Applications not accepted. Giving primarily in FL, MD, and NY. No grants to individuals.
Application information: Unsolicited requests for funds not accepted.
Officers: Warren Schwerin, Pres.; Virginia Schwerin, V.P.; Sherri D. Wilson, Treas.
EIN: 133620145

1564
Arthur Sekerak Charitable Trust
190 Brinsmayd Ave.
Stratford, CT 06614-1351
Contact: George Ferrio

Established in 1999 in Connecticut.
Foundation type: Independent foundation.
Financial data (yr. ended 12/31/12): Assets, $0 (M); expenditures, $316,259; qualifying distributions, $299,998; giving activities include $285,000 for 7 grants (high: $70,000; low: $25,000).
Fields of interest: Museums; Medical education; Hospital care; Communication media; Catholicism.
Limitations: Applications not accepted. Giving primarily in CT and NY. No grants to individuals.
Application information: Unsolicited requests for funds not accepted.
Trustees: George Ferrio; Clayton A. Friedberg.
EIN: 066466916

1565
Selkowitz Family Foundation
262 Ocean Dr. E.
Stamford, CT 06902-8238

Established in 2000 in Connecticut.
Donors: Arthur Selkowitz; Betsey Selkowitz.
Foundation type: Independent foundation.
Financial data (yr. ended 12/31/14): Assets, $1,454,562 (M); gifts received, $472,802; expenditures, $332,499; qualifying distributions, $304,246; giving activities include $298,183 for 49 grants (high: $84,500; low: $500).
Fields of interest: Diseases and conditions; Judaism; Child welfare.
Limitations: Applications not accepted. Giving primarily in CA, CT, and NY. No grants to individuals.
Application information: Contributes only to pre-selected organizations.
Trustees: Adam Selkowitz; Arthur Selkowitz; Betsey Selkowitz; Jed Selkowitz.
EIN: 061599301

1566
Senior Services of Stamford, Inc.
2009 Summer St., Ste. 301
Stamford, CT 06905-5023 (203) 324-6584
Contact: Michael G. Mezzapelle, Treas.

Established in 1908 in Connecticut.

Donors: Katherine D. Uehling†; Katharine J. Adamson; St. John's Community Foundation; Friendship House, Inc.; Wachovia Bank, N.A.; The Advocate and Greenwich Times Holiday Fund; First County Bank; Interfaith Council; Saugatuck Capital; Stamford Hospital; Barry Coutant.
Foundation type: Independent foundation.
Financial data (yr. ended 02/28/13): Assets, $13,354,203 (M); gifts received, $97,492; expenditures, $928,284; qualifying distributions, $840,166; giving activities include $319,334 for 545 grants to individuals.
Purpose and activities: Support for: 1) social service organizations serving the elderly; 2) organizations that provide information, referral, counseling, advocacy, and emergency financial assistance to needy elderly; and 3) operation of a senior center. Focus on programs offering innovative solutions to problems of older persons, particularly in access to health care, housing, transportation, and isolation.
Fields of interest: Home health care; Senior services; Seniors.
Type of support: Annual campaigns; Grants to individuals; Endowments.
Limitations: Applications accepted. Giving limited to Stamford, CT.
Publications: Annual report; Informational brochure.
Application information: Application form required.
  Initial approach: Letter requesting application form
  Copies of proposal: 1
  Deadline(s): None
Officers: Carmen Domonkos, Chair.; Barry Coutant, Vice-Chair.; Jevera Hennessey, Vice-Chair.; Kate Mulvany, Secy.; Michael G. Mezzapelle, Treas.; Marie Johnson, Exec. Dir.
Trustees: Donald Case; Kathleen Ego; Alejandro Knopoff; Fern Pessin; Karen Kelly.
Number of staff: 1 full-time professional; 2 part-time professional; 1 full-time support; 1 part-time support.
EIN: 060646916

1567
The Shanley Family Foundation
c/o Cummings & Lockwood LLC
P.O. Box 2505
Greenwich, CT 06836 (203) 869-1200
Contact: Edward F. Rodenbach, Secy.-Treas.

Established in 1999 in Connecticut.
Donor: William C. Shanley III.
Foundation type: Independent foundation.
Financial data (yr. ended 09/30/13): Assets, $4,390,989 (M); gifts received, $404,776; expenditures, $186,669; qualifying distributions, $180,000; giving activities include $180,000 for 3 grants (high: $60,000; low: $60,000).
Fields of interest: Education; Communication media; Human services.
Type of support: General support.
Limitations: Applications accepted. Giving primarily in CT. No grants to individuals.
Application information: Application form required.
  Initial approach: Letter
  Deadline(s): None
Officers: William C. Shanley III, Chair. and Pres.; Grace R. Shanley, V.P.; William C. Shanley IV, V.P.; Sharon S. Sniffen, V.P.; Edward F. Rodenbach, Secy.-Treas.
EIN: 061548816

1568
Shenandoah Foundation
c/o Walter, Berlingo & Co.
P.O. Box 4080
Darien, CT 06820-1480

Established in 1992 in Connecticut.
Donor: Winifred Read Wilson.
Foundation type: Independent foundation.
Financial data (yr. ended 11/30/14): Assets,
$4,291,774 (M); expenditures, $346,067;
qualifying distributions, $310,000; giving activities
include $310,000 for 15 grants (high: $60,000;
low: $6,000).
Purpose and activities: Giving primarily for family
planning and population studies.
Fields of interest: Family planning; Population
studies; International relations.
Limitations: Applications not accepted. Giving
primarily in Washington, DC. No grants to
individuals.
Application information: Contributes only to
pre-selected organizations.
Trustees: Robert S. Anderson; Susan Brown;
Douglas Wilson.
EIN: 223259552

1569
Shoemate Foundation
c/o Cummings & Lockwood, LLC
P.O. Box 271820
West Hartford, CT 06127-1820 (860) 313-4930
Contact: Paul L. Bourdeau

Established in 2001 in Florida.
Donors: Charles Shoemate; Nancy Shoemate;
Charles R. Shoemate Charitable Lead Annuity Trust.
Foundation type: Independent foundation.
Financial data (yr. ended 05/31/14): Assets,
$4,076,789 (M); gifts received, $511,334;
expenditures, $257,372; qualifying distributions,
$257,355; giving activities include $257,355 for 34
grants (high: $100,000; low: $255).
Fields of interest: Arts and culture; Health; Human
services.
Limitations: Applications accepted. Giving on a
national basis. No grants to individuals.
Application information: Application form required.
Initial approach: Letter
Deadline(s): None
Trustees: Charles Shoemate; Jeffrey D. Shoemate;
Nancy Shoemate; Scott C. Shoemate; Steven R.
Shoemate.
EIN: 266000834

1570
The Shumway Foundation
(formerly The Shumway Capital Foundation)
c/o Shumway Capital
100 W. Putnam Ave.
Greenwich, CT 06830-5342
E-mail: grants@shumwayfoundation.org

Established in 2007 in Connecticut.
Donors: SCP Holding Co., LP; Shumway Capital
Partners; Chris Shumway.
Foundation type: Independent foundation.
Financial data (yr. ended 12/31/13): Assets,
$28,467,915 (M); gifts received, $8,254,444;
expenditures, $412,988; qualifying distributions,

$398,650; giving activities include $373,750 for 16
grants (high: $245,000; low: $250).
Purpose and activities: The foundation targets
poverty in Connecticut by investing in high-impact
non-profits that tackle local communitys most
pressing challenges.
Fields of interest: Children and youth.
Type of support: Program development.
Limitations: Applications not accepted. Giving
primarily in CT. No grants to individuals.
Application information: Contributes only to
pre-selected organizations.
Trustees: Kenneth Palumbo; Chris Shumway.
EIN: 066556405

1571
The Margaret Dunn Smith Family Foundation, Inc.
155-A Alain White Rd.
Morris, CT 06763-1426

Established in 2005 in Delaware.
Donor: Winthrop H. and Margaret D. Smith Family
Foundation.
Foundation type: Independent foundation.
Financial data (yr. ended 12/31/13): Assets,
$1,186,772 (M); expenditures, $149,551;
qualifying distributions, $129,770; giving activities
include $129,770 for 11 grants (high: $60,000;
low: $250).
Fields of interest: Education; Diseases and
conditions; Libraries; Youth services.
Limitations: Applications not accepted. Giving
primarily in CT and IL.
Application information: Unsolicited requests for
funds not accepted.
Officers: Margaret Dunn Smith, Pres.; Winthrop H.
Smith III, Secy.; Christina S. DiSabato, Treas.
EIN: 202642871

1572
The Grant and Jacqui Smith Foundation
42 Lillis Rd.
New Milford, CT 06776-3126

Donor: Grant Smith.
Foundation type: Independent foundation.
Financial data (yr. ended 12/31/13): Assets,
$3,083,267 (M); gifts received, $295;
expenditures, $157,589; qualifying distributions,
$156,500; giving activities include $156,500 for 19
grants (high: $35,000; low: $500).
Fields of interest: Opera; Philanthropy.
Limitations: Applications not accepted. Giving
primarily in NY. No grants to individuals.
Application information: Unsolicited requests for
funds not accepted.
Officers: Grant Smith, Pres.; Jacqui Smith, Secy.
Director: Anthony Smith.
EIN: 061454098

1573
The Sonja Foundation
c/o John Ferguson
25 Field Pt Rd.
Greenwich, CT 06830-6473

Established in 2003 in New York.
Donor: Sonja Dezorillo†.
Foundation type: Independent foundation.

Financial data (yr. ended 12/31/13): Assets,
$1,123,735 (M); expenditures, $425,246;
qualifying distributions, $424,087; giving activities
include $389,750 for 127 grants (high: $30,000;
low: $100).
Fields of interest: Education; Higher education;
Diseases and conditions; Catholicism; Human
services.
International interests: Iceland.
Type of support: General support.
Limitations: Applications not accepted. Giving
primarily in the U.S., with some emphasis on NY;
funding also in Reykjavik, Iceland.
Application information: Unsolicited requests for
funds not accepted.
Trustees: Gundmundur A. Brigission; John J.
Ferguson.
EIN: 137371356

1574
Sorenson-Pearson Family Foundation, Inc.
51 West Rd.
Canton, CT 06019-3739 (860) 693-6441

Foundation type: Independent foundation.
Financial data (yr. ended 12/31/13): Assets,
$4,463,209 (M); expenditures, $222,762;
qualifying distributions, $220,000; giving activities
include $220,000 for 55 grants (high: $40,000;
low: $1,000).
Fields of interest: Arts and culture; Elementary and
secondary education; Health; Protestantism;
Human services.
Type of support: Endowments.
Limitations: Applications accepted. Giving primarily
in CT. No grants to individuals.
Application information: Application form required.
Initial approach: Letter
Deadline(s): None
Officers: Wendy S. Pearson, Pres.; Edward F.
Rosenthal, Esq., V.P.; Richard W. Sorenson, Secy.
EIN: 066099725

1575
The Storr Family Foundation
c/o Blair & Potts
P.O. Box 1214
Stamford, CT 06904-1214

Established in 1997 in Connecticut.
Donor: Hans G. Storr.
Foundation type: Independent foundation.
Financial data (yr. ended 04/30/13): Assets,
$5,565,050 (M); expenditures, $230,606;
qualifying distributions, $205,609; giving activities
include $205,609 for grants.
Fields of interest: Opera; University education;
Nonprofits; Health care administration and
financing; Hospital care; Protestantism.
Type of support: Regranting.
Limitations: Applications not accepted. Giving
primarily in WI. No grants to individuals.
Application information: Unsolicited requests for
funds not accepted.
Trustees: Carol F. Storr; Christina L. Storr; Hans G.
Storr; John C. Storr; Suzanne M. Storr.
EIN: 061489906

1576
Stratfield Fund
10 Middle St.
Bridgeport, CT 06604-4223

Established in 1955 in Connecticut.
Donors: Burton Hoffman; Hyacinthe K. Hoffman; Stephen J. Hoffman.
Foundation type: Independent foundation.
Financial data (yr. ended 03/31/13): Assets, $1,346,643 (M); gifts received, $12; expenditures, $165,809; qualifying distributions, $147,016; giving activities include $147,016 for 31 grants (high: $25,300; low: $20).
Purpose and activities: Giving primarily for Jewish welfare, temple support, and schools.
Fields of interest: Arts and culture; Education; Secondary education; Higher education; Nonprofits; Judaism.
Type of support: Regranting.
Limitations: Applications not accepted. Giving primarily in CT and NY. No grants to individuals.
Application information: Contributes only to pre-selected organizations.
Officer: Laurence K. Hoffman, Mgr.
Trustees: Burton Hoffman; Edna R. Hoffman; Hyacinthe K. Hoffman; Stephen J. Hoffman.
EIN: 066046672

1577
The Sullivan Family Foundation
c/o Blair & Potts
107 Elm St., Stamford Plz.
Stamford, CT 06902
Application address: c/o William & Susan Sullivan, 10 Tokeneke Trail, Darien, CT 06820-6125, tel.: (203) 656-0418

Established in 1997 in Connecticut.
Donors: William M. Sullivan; Susan B. Sullivan.
Foundation type: Independent foundation.
Financial data (yr. ended 12/31/13): Assets, $9,237 (M); gifts received, $165,500; expenditures, $163,925; qualifying distributions, $162,025; giving activities include $162,025 for 5 + grants (high: $100,500).
Fields of interest: Education; Diseases and conditions; Human services.
Type of support: General support.
Limitations: Applications accepted. Giving primarily in CT, MA and MN. No grants to individuals.
Application information:
Initial approach: Proposal
Deadline(s): None
Trustees: Susan B. Sullivan; William M. Sullivan.
EIN: 061484566

1578
William Matheus Sullivan Musical Foundation
P.O. Box 189
Kent, CT 06757-0189 (860) 927-1320
FAX: (860) 927-1680;
E-mail: info@sullivanfoundation.org; Application address: c/o Margaret Stearns, P.O. Box 222, Kent, CT 06757; Main URL: http://www.sullivanfoundation.org
Facebook: https://www.facebook.com/pages/The-Sullivan-Foundation/229867510415331
Grants List: http://www.sullivanfoundation.org/pastWinners.html

Established in 1956 in New York.
Donors: William Matheus Sullivan†; Arcie Lubetkin†.
Foundation type: Independent foundation.
Financial data (yr. ended 12/31/13): Assets, $4,274,187 (M); expenditures, $321,034; qualifying distributions, $219,000; giving activities include $5,000 for 1 grant, and $214,000 for 45 grants to individuals (high: $15,800; low: $600).
Purpose and activities: The foundation helps talented young singers develop their careers by offering continuing financial support over a period of five years.
Fields of interest: Human services.
Type of support: Continuing support; Grants to individuals; Emergency funds.
Limitations: Applications accepted. Giving on a national and international basis. No support for general fields of music education and vocal or instrument training. No grants for building or endowment funds or operating budgets.
Publications: Application guidelines; Informational brochure.
Application information: See foundation website for complete application guidelines. Application form required.
Initial approach: Letter detailing musical experience
Copies of proposal: 1
Deadline(s): Aug. 13
Board meeting date(s): 2 times per year as required
Officers: Barbara Bliss, Pres.; Peter Merrill, Treas.; Margaret Stearns, Exec. Dir.
Number of staff: 1 full-time professional; 3 part-time professional.
EIN: 136069096

1579
The Bennington Taylor Foundation
c/o Mark Broach
1465 Post Rd. E.
Westport, CT 06880-5528

Established in 2000 in Connecticut.
Donor: Mark A. Broach.
Foundation type: Independent foundation.
Financial data (yr. ended 02/28/13): Assets, $1,130,931 (M); expenditures, $180,911; qualifying distributions, $180,895; giving activities include $180,000 for 3 grants (high: $150,000; low: $10,000).
Fields of interest: Education; Environment; Human services; Youth development.
Limitations: Applications not accepted. Giving primarily in CT, NY and PA.
Application information: Unsolicited requests for funds not accepted.
Trustee: Mark A. Broach.
EIN: 061577282

1580
William & Karen Tell Foundation
235 Whipstick Rd.
Wilton, CT 06897-1315

Established in 1986 in Connecticut.
Donors: William Tell; Karen N. Tell.
Foundation type: Independent foundation.
Financial data (yr. ended 12/31/13): Assets, $6,592,337 (M); expenditures, $485,522; qualifying distributions, $405,718; giving activities include $374,413 for 72 grants (high: $41,400; low: $100).
Purpose and activities: Giving for public policy institutes, education, and for federated giving programs.
Fields of interest: Arts and culture; Education; Nonprofits; Hospital care; Social sciences; Human services.
Type of support: Regranting; Policy, advocacy and systems reform.
Limitations: Applications not accepted. Giving primarily in CT. No grants to individuals.
Application information: Contributes only to pre-selected organizations.
Officers: Karen N. Tell, Pres.; Catherine K. Tell, Secy.-Treas.
Directors: Caroline Tell Falk; William F. Tell.
EIN: 222777617

1581
Thomaston Savings Bank Foundation, Inc.
P.O. Box 907
Thomaston, CT 06787-0907 (860) 283-4373
Contact: James Nichol, Secy.
Application address: 203 Main St., Thomaston, CT 06787 Tel.: (860) 283-4373; Main URL: https://www.thomastonsavingsbank.com/about-thomaston-savings-bank/foundation.aspx

Established in 1997 in Connecticut.
Donor: Thomaston Savings Bank.
Foundation type: Company-sponsored foundation.
Financial data (yr. ended 12/31/13): Assets, $5,332,652 (M); gifts received, $346,439; expenditures, $353,592; qualifying distributions, $346,314; giving activities include $341,222 for 186 grants (high: $15,000; low: $300).
Purpose and activities: The foundation supports fire departments and organizations involved with arts and culture, education, health, safety, human services, and religion.
Fields of interest: Education; Health; Youth development.
Type of support: General support; Capital and infrastructure; Equipment; Program development.
Publications: Application guidelines.
Application information: Application form required.
Initial approach: Letter
Deadline(s): June 30
Officers and Trustees: George Seabourne, Chair. and Trustee; Stephen Lewis, Pres. and Trustee; James Nichol, Secy.; Mark Blum, Treas.; Paul Broomhead; David Carlson; Bradford Erickson; James Kaniewski; David Merchant; Thomas Parisot; Carrie Zimyeski.
EIN: 061483909

1582
Arthur E. Thornton Trust
c/o Bank of America, N.A.
777 Main St.
Hartford, CT 06115-2303

Established in 2001 in Connecticut.
Foundation type: Independent foundation.
Financial data (yr. ended 12/31/14): Assets, $5,194,086 (M); expenditures, $297,260; qualifying distributions, $265,241.

Purpose and activities: Giving primarily for cardio-pulmonary research; some giving also to family services.
Fields of interest: Nonprofits; Hospital care; Heart and circulatory system diseases; Human services; Family services; Child welfare.
Type of support: Research; Regranting.
Limitations: Applications not accepted. Giving primarily in CT. No grants to individuals.
Application information: Contributes only to pre-selected organizations.
Trustee: Bank of America, N.A.
EIN: 066445132

1583
F. Curtis and Susan B. Thrall Foundation Trust
102 Wolcott Rd.
Wolcott, CT 06716-2618
Application address: c/o Margaret Ransom, 5 DiNatale Dr., Wallingford, CT 06492, tel.: (203) 879-4329

Established in 2005 in Connecticut.
Donor: Susan Thrall‡.
Foundation type: Independent foundation.
Financial data (yr. ended 12/31/13): Assets, $5,864,376 (M); expenditures, $268,388; qualifying distributions, $268,388; giving activities include $108,500 for 8 grants (high: $25,000; low: $2,000), and $75,500 for 37 grants to individuals (high: $2,500; low: $2,000).
Fields of interest: Arts and culture; Education; University education; Health care administration and financing; Human services.
Type of support: General support; Student aid.
Application information:
  Initial approach: Proposal
  Deadline(s): None
Trustees: Stephen Landow, MD; Margaret Ransom.
EIN: 066520730

1584
The Tierney Family Foundation, Inc.
17 Butlers Island Rd.
Darien, CT 06820-6203

Donor: Paul E. Tierney, Jr.
Foundation type: Independent foundation.
Financial data (yr. ended 12/31/13): Assets, $6,858,229 (M); expenditures, $427,214; qualifying distributions, $395,132; giving activities include $390,521 for 53 grants (high: $100,000; low: $100).
Purpose and activities: Giving primarily for higher education and social issues.
Fields of interest: Higher education; Economic development; Human rights; Child welfare; International development.
Limitations: Applications not accepted. Giving primarily in MA and NY.
Application information: Unsolicited requests for funds not accepted.
Officers: Susan E. Tierney, Pres.; Michael P. Tierney, V.P.; Patricia E. Tierney, V.P.; Paul E. Tierney, Jr., Secy.
EIN: 133541596

1585
The Titus Foundation Inc.
c/o Anna M. Boronow
1 Maple St.
New Canaan, CT 06840-5731

Established in 2000 in Connecticut.
Donors: Anna M. Boronow; Gordon Boronow.
Foundation type: Independent foundation.
Financial data (yr. ended 12/31/13): Assets, $3,420,679 (M); gifts received, $61,855; expenditures, $278,452; qualifying distributions, $272,500; giving activities include $272,500 for 23 grants (high: $42,000; low: $2,000).
Fields of interest: Education; Christianity; Human services.
Limitations: Applications not accepted. Giving primarily in CT and NH. No grants to individuals.
Application information: Contributes only to pre-selected organizations.
Officers: Anna M. Boronow, Chair. and Treas.; Gordon Boronow, Secy.
Trustee: Russell C. Gocht.
EIN: 061587986

1586
Town Fair Tire Foundation Inc.
460 Coe Ave.
East Haven, CT 06512-3836

Established in 2001 in Connecticut.
Donors: Neil Mellen; Robert Lakin; Deborah Wegeleben; Nancy Mellen.
Foundation type: Independent foundation.
Financial data (yr. ended 12/31/13): Assets, $5,802,744 (M); gifts received, $1,900,600; expenditures, $436,584; qualifying distributions, $406,291; giving activities include $406,291 for 33 grants (high: $60,000; low: $250).
Fields of interest: Diseases and conditions.
Type of support: General support; Research.
Limitations: Applications not accepted. Giving primarily in CT. No grants to individuals.
Application information: Contributes only to pre-selected organizations.
Officers: Neil Mellen, Pres. and Treas.; Michael Mellen, V.P. and Secy.
Directors: Michael Barbaro; Kathryn Tutino.
EIN: 061592259

1587
The Mary Ann and Lawrence C. Tucker Foundation
593 Riversville Rd.
Greenwich, CT 06831-2529

Established in 2004 in Connecticut.
Donors: Mary Ann Cody Tucker; Lawrence C. Tucker.
Foundation type: Independent foundation.
Financial data (yr. ended 12/31/13): Assets, $87,604 (M); gifts received, $210,000; expenditures, $147,631; qualifying distributions, $147,000; giving activities include $147,000 for 14 grants (high: $50,000; low: $1,000).
Fields of interest: Arts and culture; Education; International relations.
Limitations: Applications not accepted. Giving primarily in NY. No grants to individuals.
Application information: Unsolicited requests for funds not accepted.

Trustees: Katherine Cody Tucker; Lawrence C. Tucker; Mary Ann Cody Tucker.
EIN: 542140479

1588
Daniel P. and Grace I. Tully Charitable Trust
P.O. Box 4080
Darien, CT 06820-4824
Contact: Eileen Ceglarski, Dir.

Established in 1986 in Connecticut.
Donor: Daniel P. Tully.
Foundation type: Independent foundation.
Financial data (yr. ended 11/30/13): Assets, $71,025,456 (M); gifts received, $609,918; expenditures, $447,477; qualifying distributions, $363,250; giving activities include $327,250 for 26 grants (high: $100,000; low: $100).
Purpose and activities: Giving primarily to hospitals, schools, and educational facilities.
Fields of interest: Education; University education; Nonprofits; Hospital care; Diseases and conditions; Cancers; Human services; Youth services.
Type of support: General support; Program development; Curriculum development; Research; Research and evaluation; Regranting.
Limitations: Applications accepted. Giving primarily in CT, MA and NY. No grants to individuals.
Application information: Application form required.
  Initial approach: Letter
  Deadline(s): None
Trustees: Daniel P. Tully; Grace I. Tully.
Directors: Elizabeth Berry; Eileen Ceglarski; Mark Ricca; Daniel G. Tully.
EIN: 222804896

1589
The UIL Holdings Corporation Foundation
P.O. Box 1564, Tax Section 1-15F
New Haven, CT 06506-0901

Donor: UIL Holdings Corp.
Foundation type: Company-sponsored foundation.
Financial data (yr. ended 12/31/14): Assets, $1,726,737; expenditures, $279,012; qualifying distributions, $279,012.
Purpose and activities: The foundation supports hospitals and organizations involved with arts and culture, human services, children and youth services, and community development.
Fields of interest: Health; Human services; Youth development.
Type of support: General support; Capital campaigns.
Limitations: Applications not accepted. Giving limited to CT. No grants to individuals.
Application information: Contributes only to pre-selected organizations.
Trustees: Richard J. Nicholas; John Prete; James Torgerson.
EIN: 061310455

1590
Union Savings Bank Foundation, Inc.
226 Main St.
Danbury, CT 06810-6635 (203) 830-4200
Contact: Marie O'Neil, Sr. V.P., Mktg.

Additional tel.: (203) 803-4202
Grants List: http://www.unionsavings.com/
page.cfm?p=621

Established in 1998 in Connecticut.
Donor: Union Savings Bank.
Foundation type: Company-sponsored foundation.
Financial data (yr. ended 12/31/13): Assets,
$2,849,914 (M); gifts received, $10,650;
expenditures, $233,148; qualifying distributions,
$211,558; giving activities include $200,808 for 46
grants (high: $10,000; low: $500).
Purpose and activities: The foundation supports
organizations involved with health, hunger, and
human services. Special emphasis is directed
toward programs designed to promote education
and youth development.
Fields of interest: Education; Reading promotion;
Health; Health care clinics; Home health care;
Financial counseling; Human services; Food aid;
Food banks; Food delivery; Family services; Child
welfare; Youth development; Developmental
disability services.
Type of support: Annual campaigns; General
support; Capital and infrastructure; Equipment;
Program development; Convening.
Limitations: Applications accepted. Giving primarily
in areas of company operations in CT. No support
for public entities, municipalities, or sectarian
organizations. No grants to individuals, or for capital
expenses, multi-year funding, endowments, or
start-up or first-year programs.
Publications: Application guidelines; Grants list.
Application information: Grants range from $2,500
to $10,000. Mailed applications are not accepted.
Applications are reviewed by The Grants Committee.
Additional information may be requested at a later
date. Application form required.
Initial approach: Download application form and
e-mail to foundation
Copies of proposal: 1
Deadline(s): June 1 to Aug. 31
Board meeting date(s): Oct.
Final notification: Oct.
Officers and Trustees: Jack T. Tyransky, Chair. and
Trustee; John C. Kline, Pres. and Trustee; Elizabeth
B. Durkin, Secy.; David A. Birkins, Treas.; Thomas A.
Frizzell; Lynne A. Beardsley; Ray P. Boa; Abner
Burgos-Rodriquez; Arnold E. Finaldi, Jr.; Mary Ann
Frede; Thomas R. Green; David S. Hawley; Maryann
S. Kiely; Jay C. Lent; Jeffrey M. Levine; John M.
Murphy; Stephen G. Rosentel; Cynthia Stevens;
Donald T. Studley; Lucie H. Voves.
EIN: 061508286

1591
H. A. Vance Foundation Inc
c/o Conifer Investments Ltd
100 Pearl St.
Hartford, CT 06103-4506

Established in 1992 in Connecticut.
Donors: H. Alex Vance, Jr.; Dorothy J. Vance.
Foundation type: Independent foundation.
Financial data (yr. ended 12/31/13): Assets,
$8,996,828 (M); gifts received, $140,254;
expenditures, $455,893; qualifying distributions,
$416,018; giving activities include $350,000 for 10
grants (high: $60,000; low: $15,000).
Purpose and activities: Giving primarily for
education, youth services, and religion.

Fields of interest: Art museums; Education; Higher
education; Nonprofits; Academic libraries; Religion;
Human services; Youth services.
Type of support: General support; Capital
campaigns; Regranting.
Limitations: Applications not accepted. Giving
primarily in CT. No grants to individuals.
Application information: Contributes only to
pre-selected organizations.
Officers: H. Alex Vance, Jr., Pres.; William C. Vance,
V.P.; Coleman H. Casey, Esq., Secy.; David W.
Parmelee, Treas.
Director: Alison V. Scherer.
EIN: 061355463

1592
The Velaj Foundation
P.O. Box 110306
Stamford, CT 06911-0306
Contact: Alexander Velaj

Established in 2007 in Connecticut.
Donor: Congressional Youth Leadership Council.
Foundation type: Independent foundation.
Financial data (yr. ended 12/31/13): Assets,
$5,846,071 (M); expenditures, $534,361;
qualifying distributions, $464,726; giving activities
include $311,100 for 26 grants (high: $70,000;
low: $100).
Fields of interest: Elementary and secondary
education; Higher education; Health; Hospital care.
Limitations: Applications not accepted. Giving
primarily in CT, Washington, DC and NY. No grants
to individuals.
Application information: Unsolicited requests for
funds not accepted.
Officers and Directors: Alexander Velaj, Pres. and
Director; Patricia Wells Velaj, V.P. and Secy.-Treas.
and Director; Nicole R. Velaj.
EIN: 261102664

1593
Westbrook Foundation
P.O. Box 528
Westbrook, CT 06498-0528
E-mail: KGarrity@westbrookfoundation.org; *Main
URL:* http://www.westbrookfoundation.org
Facebook: https://www.facebook.com/pages/
The-Westbrook-Foundation/143539869081715?
sk=wall&filter=2

Established in 1984 in Connecticut.
Foundation type: Community foundation.
Financial data (yr. ended 12/31/13): Assets,
$4,255,827 (M); gifts received, $46,511;
expenditures, $211,825; giving activities include
$52,505 for 4+ grants (high: $10,700), and
$80,900 for 69 grants to individuals.
Purpose and activities: The foundation seeks to
receive and administer funds and other property to
help meet the medical and educational, social,
welfare, cultural, recreational, and civic needs of the
citizens of the town of Westbrook, Connecticut.
Fields of interest: Community and economic
development.
Limitations: Applications accepted. Giving limited to
Westbrook, CT.
Publications: Application guidelines; Annual report.

Application information: Visit foundation website
for grant information and guidelines. Application
form required.
Deadline(s): Apr. 1 and Oct. 1
Officers and Board Members: James Crawford,
Chair. and Director; David Russell, Chair., Grants
Committee and Director; Constance Vogell, Chair.,
Scholarship Committee and Director; Bernadette
Jones, Vice-Chair. and Director; Harry Ruppenicker,
Jr., Treas. and Director; Eve Barakas; Paul Polo.
EIN: 222549826

1594
Wilmot Wheeler Foundation, Inc.
P.O. Box 429
Southport, CT 06890—0429

Established in 1941 in Delaware.
Donors: Wilmot F. Wheeler†; Hulda C. Wheeler.
Foundation type: Independent foundation.
Financial data (yr. ended 12/31/14): Assets,
$5,078,327; gifts received, $0; expenditures,
$359,329; qualifying distributions, $320,500 and
$0 for set-asides.
Fields of interest: Arts and culture; Secondary
education; Higher education; Environment;
Domesticated animals; Health; Protestantism;
Catholicism; Human services.
Limitations: Applications not accepted. Giving
primarily in CT. No grants to individuals.
Application information: Contributes only to
pre-selected organizations.
Officers: Alexandra Wheeler, Pres.; Wilmot Wheeler
III, V.P.; Alexa M. Wheeler, Secy.; Halsted W.
Wheeler, Treas.
EIN: 066039119

1595
Widows Society
c/o Bank of America
200 Glastonbury Blvd., Ste. 2
Glastonbury, CT 06033 (860) 952-7380
Contact: Pat Staffaroni

Established in 1847 in Connecticut.
Donors: City of Hartford; Sarah W. Pardee Fund;
Sarah N. Pardee Fund.
Foundation type: Independent foundation.
Financial data (yr. ended 08/31/13): Assets,
$4,998,211 (M); gifts received, $14,579;
expenditures, $223,208; qualifying distributions,
$223,208; giving activities include $12,000 for 1
grant, and $183,511 for 144 grants to individuals.
Purpose and activities: Primarily provides aid to
needy, single women of Hartford, Connecticut.
Fields of interest: Family services; Females.
Type of support: Grants to individuals.
Limitations: Applications accepted. Giving limited to
Hartford, CT, and surrounding towns.
Application information:
Initial approach: Proposal
Deadline(s): None
Officers: Joan Harris Thomas, Pres.; Mary Luciano,
V.P.
Board Members: Joyce Falkin; Elizabeth Fitzpatrick;
Jeanne Goldbach; Janet Henderson; Carol Mumford.
Trustee: Bank of America, N.A.
EIN: 066026060

1596
The Gabe Wiener Foundation, Inc.
35 Raven Rock Rd.
Roxbury, CT 06783-1023

Established in 1997 in Connecticut.
Donors: Michael A. Wiener; Zena Wiener.
Foundation type: Independent foundation.
Financial data (yr. ended 12/31/13): Assets, $840,083 (M); expenditures, $334,981; qualifying distributions, $332,435; giving activities include $275,000 for 1 grant.
Fields of interest: Health; Cancers.
Limitations: Applications not accepted. Giving primarily in New York, NY. No grants to individuals.
Application information: Contributes only to pre-selected organizations.
Officers and Directors: Jennifer Steingart, Pres.; Zena Wiener, V.P. and Director; Jonathan Steingart, Secy.
EIN: 061484239

1597
Winokur Family Foundation, Inc.
30 E. Elm St.
Greenwich, CT 06830-6529 (203) 661-4518
Contact: Deanne Howard Winokur, Dir.

Established in 1987 in Connecticut.
Donors: Herbert S. Winokur, Jr.; Deanne Howard Winokur.
Foundation type: Independent foundation.
Financial data (yr. ended 06/30/13): Assets, $4,024 (M); gifts received, $360,000; expenditures, $361,089; qualifying distributions, $359,617; giving activities include $359,617 for grants.
Purpose and activities: Giving to foundations, health and medical services, and the arts.
Fields of interest: Arts and culture; Performing arts; Humanities; Higher education; Health; Diseases and conditions; Human services; Child welfare.
Type of support: Capital and infrastructure; Program-related investments; Equipment; Seed money; Fellowships; Internships; Research; Research and evaluation.
Limitations: Applications accepted. Giving primarily in CA, CT, and NY. No grants to individuals.
Application information: Application form required.
Initial approach: Letter
Deadline(s): None
Directors: Andra Winokur Newman; Annick M. Winokur; Deanne Howard Winokur; Herbert Winokur.
EIN: 943065806

1598
WMP Family Foundation Trust
c/o Tina Marshall, US Trust
29 S. Main St.
West Hartford, CT 06107
Application address: c/o William M. Pastore, 1600 4th St. S., Naples, FL 34102, tel.: (239) 300-0816

Established in 2007 in Massachusetts.
Donor: William M. Pastore.
Foundation type: Independent foundation.
Financial data (yr. ended 12/31/13): Assets, $1,353,235 (M); expenditures, $387,162; qualifying distributions, $380,000; giving activities include $380,000 for 4 grants (high: $200,000; low: $5,000).

Fields of interest: Botanical gardens; Hospital care.
Limitations: Applications accepted. Giving primarily in CT and FL.
Application information: Application form required.
Initial approach: Request application form
Deadline(s): None
Trustees: Dana Pastore; Marie Pastore; William M. Pastore; Stacey Safryn.
EIN: 266163411

1599
Woodland Anesthesiology Associates Foundation, Inc
114 Woodland St.
Hartford, CT 06105-1208 (860) 714-6654
Contact: Franklin Rosenberg MD, Pres.

Donors: Jonathan Abrams, MD; Qassem Kishawi, MD; Kenneth Gutierrez, MD; Craig Dennen, MD; Leo Contois, MD; Victor Camacho, MD; Sivasenthil Arumugam, MD; John Barnett, MD; Alison Considine, MD; John D'Allessio, MD; David Freitas, MD; Robert Herreria, MD; Raymond Squier, MD; Sanjay Sinha, MD; Franklin Rosenberg, MD; Gwendolyn Moraski, MD; Frank Setter, MD; Mark Spencer, MD; Goolcher Wadia, MD; Philip Stark, MD; Roxanne Zarmsky, MD; Gary Wilson, MD; Saadia Zafar, MD; Inna Marantes, MD; Shu-Ming Wang, MD.
Foundation type: Independent foundation.
Financial data (yr. ended 12/31/13): Assets, $7,742 (M); gifts received, $149,500; expenditures, $152,459; qualifying distributions, $152,459; giving activities include $150,533 for 18 grants (high: $133,333; low: $250).
Fields of interest: Health; Diseases and conditions; Human services.
Limitations: Applications accepted. Giving primarily in CT.
Application information: Application form required.
Initial approach: Request application form
Deadline(s): None
Officers: Franklin Rosenberg, MD, Pres.; Gwendolyn Moraski, MD, V.P.; Raymond Squier, MD, V.P.; Goolcher Wadia, MD, Secy.; Sivasenthil Arumugam, MD, Treas.
EIN: 275271871

1600
WorldQuant Foundation Corp.
1700 E. Putnam Ave.
Old Greenwich, CT 06870-1366
E-mail: info@worldquant.org; Main URL: http://worldquant.org

Donor: Igor Tulchinsky.
Foundation type: Independent foundation.
Financial data (yr. ended 12/31/12): Assets, $3,841,944 (M); gifts received, $100; expenditures, $495,978; qualifying distributions, $432,000; giving activities include $432,000 for grants.
Purpose and activities: Offers scholarships to benefit outstanding students who are highly motivated, committed to pursuing higher education in the fields of science and quantitative studies and have a demonstrated financial need.
Fields of interest: Education; Human services.
Limitations: Applications not accepted.
Application information: Unsolicited requests for funds not accepted.

Officers: Mina Joy Tulchinsky, Chair. and Secy.; Igor Tulchinsky, Pres.
EIN: 263576736

1601
Isaac Herman Zacharia Foundation, Inc.
P.O. Box 4512
Greenwich, CT 06831

Donor: Isaac Herman Zacharia.
Foundation type: Independent foundation.
Financial data (yr. ended 12/31/13): Assets, $4,785,036 (M); expenditures, $286,932; qualifying distributions, $234,942; giving activities include $234,000 for 3 grants (high: $78,000; low: $78,000).
Fields of interest: Elementary and secondary education; Nonprofits; Judaism; Human services.
Type of support: Regranting.
Limitations: Applications not accepted.
Application information: Contributes only to pre-selected organizations.
Directors: Mona Zacharia Beerman; Rachel Zacharia Brier; Estelle Zacharia Ross.
EIN: 510108212

1602
The Zelnick/Belzberg Charitable Trust
c/o Vogel & Co.
685 Post Rd.
Darien, CT 06820-4718

Established in 1999 in New York.
Donors: H. Strauss Zelnick; Wendy Belzberg; Zelnick Belzberg Living Trust.
Foundation type: Independent foundation.
Financial data (yr. ended 06/30/13): Assets, $250,772 (M); gifts received, $550,000; expenditures, $383,896; qualifying distributions, $377,846; giving activities include $377,846 for 42 grants (high: $169,250; low: $100).
Fields of interest: Education; Higher education; Diseases and conditions; Religion; Human services.
Type of support: Research.
Limitations: Applications not accepted. Giving primarily in CT and NY. No grants to individuals.
Application information: Unsolicited requests for funds not accepted.
Officers and Trustees: Strauss Zelnick, Chair. and Trustee; Wendy Belzberg, Pres. and Secy. and Trustee.
EIN: 137187853

1603
The Lynn and Robert Zimmer Family Foundation
75 Byram Shore Rd.
Greenwich, CT 06830-6906 (203) 532-0044
Contact: Robert Zimmer

Donors: Lynn Zimmer; Robert Zimmer.
Foundation type: Independent foundation.
Financial data (yr. ended 12/31/13): Assets, $1,455,158 (M); expenditures, $155,300; qualifying distributions, $137,300; giving activities include $137,284 for 11 grants (high: $48,334; low: $200).
Purpose and activities: Giving to organizations that promote education and health within the Jewish community of Connecticut.

Fields of interest: Ballet; Museums; Judaism; Youth development.
Type of support: General support.
Limitations: Applications accepted. Giving primarily in CA and CT. No grants to individuals.

Application information: Application form required.
Initial approach: Letter
Deadline(s): None

DELAWARE

1604
18 Pomegranates Inc.
c/o Foundation Source
501 Silverside Rd., Ste. 123
Wilmington, DE 19809-1377

Established in 2008 in Colorado.
Donors: Weaver Family Foundation; Francine Lavin Weaver.
Foundation type: Independent foundation.
Financial data (yr. ended 12/31/13): Assets, $1,395,241 (M); expenditures, $504,066; qualifying distributions, $498,630; giving activities include $380,615 for 42 grants (high: $72,000; low: $180).
Fields of interest: Education; Judaism; Human services.
Type of support: General support; Program development.
Limitations: Applications not accepted. Giving primarily in Boulder, CO. No grants to individuals.
Application information: Unsolicited requests for funds not accepted.
Officer and Director: Francine Lavin Weaver, Pres. and Secy. and Director.
EIN: 262000133

1605
The 1916 Foundation
P.O. Box 115
Montchanin, DE 19710-0115

Donors: Nathan Hayward III; Marilyn Rushworth Hayward.
Foundation type: Independent foundation.
Financial data (yr. ended 12/31/14): Assets, $4,835,320 (M); expenditures, $339,944; qualifying distributions, $335,058; giving activities include $331,250 for 5 grants (high: $210,000; low: $6,250).
Fields of interest: Arts and culture; Theater; Animal welfare; Foundations.
Limitations: Applications not accepted. Giving primarily in DE.
Application information: Unsolicited requests for funds not accepted.
Officers: Nathan Hayward III, Pres.; Marilyn Rushworth Hayward, V.P.; Nathan Hayward IV, Secy.; George Stewart Marshall Hayward, Treas.
Trustee: David Ley Hamilton, Esq.
EIN: 273330508

1606
The 613 Foundation
c/o Foundation Source
501 Silverside Rd., Ste. 123
Wilmington, DE 19809-1377

Established in 2007 in Delaware.
Donor: Donna L. Fried-Calcaterra.
Foundation type: Independent foundation.
Financial data (yr. ended 12/31/13): Assets, $37,650 (M); gifts received, $200,000; expenditures, $318,776; qualifying distributions, $318,776; giving activities include $313,600 for 11 grants (high: $100,000; low: $3,100).

Fields of interest: Blood banks; Hematology.
Type of support: Research.
Limitations: Applications not accepted. Giving primarily in New York, NY. No grants to individuals.
Application information: Unsolicited requests for funds not accepted.
Officers and Directors: Donna L. Fried-Calcaterra, Pres. and Secy. and Director; Jenna Calcaterra, V.P.; Raphael Rosenblatt, V.P.; Bennett Wasserman, V.P.
EIN: 260639147

1607
The ABE Charitable Foundation, Inc.
c/o Foundation Source
501 Silverside Rd., Ste. 123
Wilmington, DE 19809-1377

Established in 2004 in Delaware.
Donors: Deanna L. Serra; Jeffrey R. Serra.
Foundation type: Independent foundation.
Financial data (yr. ended 12/31/13): Assets, $925,252 (M); expenditures, $386,216; qualifying distributions, $357,567; giving activities include $347,700 for 31 grants (high: $106,500; low: $200).
Purpose and activities: Giving primarily for Roman Catholic education, Christian churches, and social services.
Fields of interest: Theater; Education; Elementary and secondary education; Housing development; Christianity; Catholicism; Human services; Child welfare; Children.
Limitations: Applications not accepted. Giving primarily in TX. No grants to individuals.
Application information: Contributes only to pre-selected organizations.
Officers and Directors: Deanna L. Serra, Pres. and Secy. and Director; Amanda Serra, V.P.; Benjamin Serra, V.P.; Jeffrey R. Serra, V.P. and Director; Gunnar Teltow, V.P.; Michael Worden.
EIN: 201650254

1608
Alcyon Foundation
1205 N. Orange St.
Wilmington, DE 19801-1120

Established in 1994 in Delaware.
Donors: Lucile E. Dupont Flint; Frederick H. West; Mrs. Frederick H. West; Constance F. West.
Foundation type: Independent foundation.
Financial data (yr. ended 12/31/13): Assets, $6,497,139 (M); gifts received, $150,168; expenditures, $189,128; qualifying distributions, $158,772; giving activities include $141,860 for 23 grants (high: $35,656; low: $1,000).
Fields of interest: Arts and culture; Education; Environment.
Type of support: General support; Annual campaigns; Capital campaigns; Capital and infrastructure.
Limitations: Applications not accepted. Giving primarily in VA and VT. No grants to individuals.
Application information: Unsolicited requests for funds not accepted.
Officers: Frederick H. West, Pres. and Treas.; Constance F. West, V.P. and Secy.
EIN: 510355030

1609
Kohorst Allen Family Foundation
c/o Foundation Source
501 Silverside Rd., Ste. 123
Wilmington, DE 19809-1377

Established in 2007 in Delaware.
Donors: Shelley Anne Allen; W. Robert Kohorst.
Foundation type: Independent foundation.
Financial data (yr. ended 12/31/13): Assets, $204,399 (M); gifts received, $300,000; expenditures, $186,674; qualifying distributions, $186,660; giving activities include $180,750 for 15 grants (high: $50,000; low: $250).
Fields of interest: Education.
Limitations: Applications not accepted. Giving primarily in CA. No grants to individuals.
Application information: Contributes only to pre-selected organizations.
Officers and Directors: W. Robert Kohorst, Pres. and C.F.O. and Director; Shelley Anne Allen, V.P. and Secy. and Director; Kevin A. Kohorst, V.P. and Director; Matthew A. Kohorst, V.P. and Director.
EIN: 261385295

1610
The Anne Anastasi Charitable Foundation
c/o Foundation Source
501 Silverside Rd., Ste. 123
Wilmington, DE 19809-1377

Foundation type: Independent foundation.
Financial data (yr. ended 12/31/13): Assets, $5,887,354 (M); expenditures, $326,887; qualifying distributions, $282,026; giving activities include $216,700 for 43 grants (high: $15,000; low: $500).
Fields of interest: Education; Hospital care; Human services.
Limitations: Applications not accepted. Giving primarily in New York, NY. No grants to individuals.
Application information: Contributes only to pre-selected organizations.
Officers and Directors: Jonathan Nicolas Galente, Chair.; Vincent P. Gianatasio, Secy. and Director; Kevin Kitson, Treas.; De Anna Galente; Phil Greco.
EIN: 134013290

1611
The Anbinder Family Foundation
c/o Foundation Source
501 Silverside Rd., Ste. 123
Wilmington, DE 19809-1377

Established in 2003 in New York.
Donors: Madeline Anbinder; Stephen Anbinder.
Foundation type: Operating foundation.
Financial data (yr. ended 10/31/13): Assets, $3,580,060 (M); expenditures, $470,611; qualifying distributions, $407,892; giving activities include $324,000 for 50 grants (high: $50,000; low: $1,000).
Fields of interest: Education; Foundations; Health; Human services; Family services; Child welfare.
Limitations: Applications not accepted. Giving primarily in NY. No grants to individuals.
Application information: Contributes only to pre-selected organizations.
Officers and Directors: Stephen Anbinder, Pres. and Director; Tyler Anbinder, V.P. and Director; Tracy Baron, V.P. and Director; Vivian Malloy, V.P.;

Marshal Bernstein, Secy.; Madeline Anbinder, Treas. and Director.
EIN: 200482457

1612
Babcock Charitable Trust
1105 N. Market St., Ste.1300
Wilmington, DE 19801 (302) 428-6099

Established in 1957 in Pennsylvania.
Donors: Fred C. Babcock; Mary A. Babcock.
Foundation type: Independent foundation.
Financial data (yr. ended 12/31/14): Assets, $5,122,247; expenditures, $260,450; qualifying distributions, $246,077.
Purpose and activities: Giving primarily for education and health care.
Fields of interest: Education; University education; Health; Religion; Child welfare.
Type of support: Annual campaigns; Capital and infrastructure; Equipment; Program development.
Limitations: Applications accepted. Giving primarily in PA. No support for political organizations. No grants to individuals.
Application information:
  Initial approach: Proposal
  Copies of proposal: 1
  Deadline(s): None
  Board meeting date(s): Spring/ end of year
  Final notification: 6 months
Trustees: Courtney B. Borntraeger; Richard S. Cuda.
EIN: 256035161

1613
Bailey-Stanford Family Foundation, Inc.
c/o Foundation Source
501 Silverside Rd., Ste. 123
Wilmington, DE 19809-1377

Established in 2006 in Delaware.
Donors: Don V. Bailey; Leslie Stanford.
Foundation type: Independent foundation.
Financial data (yr. ended 12/31/13): Assets, $1,363,513 (M); expenditures, $296,172; qualifying distributions, $295,772; giving activities include $285,000 for 9 grants (high: $200,000; low: $1,000).
Fields of interest: Education; Health; Community and economic development.
Limitations: Applications not accepted. Giving primarily in CO and UT. No grants to individuals.
Application information: Unsolicited requests for funds not accepted.
Officers and Directors: Don V. Bailey, Pres. and Secy. and Director; Leslie Stanford, V.P. and Director.
EIN: 204973345

1614
Barnabas Foundation
c/o Foundation Source
501 Silverside Rd., Ste. 123
Wilmington, DE 19809-1377

Established in 1998 in Texas.
Donors: Dale P. Jones; Anita C. Jones; Anita C. Jones Charitable Trust; Anita R. Jones Charitable Trust.
Foundation type: Independent foundation.

Financial data (yr. ended 12/31/13): Assets, $1,267,897 (M); gifts received, $120,981; expenditures, $174,738; qualifying distributions, $170,621; giving activities include $161,200 for 21 grants (high: $36,000; low: $200).
Fields of interest: Christianity; Family services.
Limitations: Applications not accepted. Giving in TX, with emphasis on Houston and Missouri City. No grants to individuals.
Application information: Unsolicited requests for funds not accepted.
Officers and Directors: R. Brandon Lackey, Pres. and Director; Lee Anna Jones Lackey, V.P. and Secy. and Director; Leisa Raye Jones Winters, V.P. and Director; Anita R. Collier Jones; James Winters.
EIN: 752708264

1615
Jim and Dede Bartlett Foundation
c/o Foundation Source
501 Silverside Rd., Ste. 123
Wilmington, DE 19809-1377

Donors: Jim W. Bartlett; Dede Bartlett.
Foundation type: Independent foundation.
Financial data (yr. ended 12/31/13): Assets, $2,583,256 (M); gifts received, $2,539,065; expenditures, $312,082; qualifying distributions, $297,812; giving activities include $288,000 for 28 grants (high: $45,000; low: $1,000).
Fields of interest: Education; Foundations; Health; Community and economic development.
Type of support: General support.
Limitations: Applications not accepted. Giving primarily in CT.
Application information: Unsolicited requests for funds not accepted.
Officers and Directors: Jim W. Bartlett, Co-Pres. and Secy.-Treas. and Director; Dede Bartlett, Co-Pres. and Director.
EIN: 462331849

1616
Bauer Family Foundation Inc
c/o Foundation Source
501 Silverside Rd., Ste. 123
Wilmington, DE 19809-1377

Established in 2005 in Delaware.
Donors: Nancy A Bauer; Jon Bauer.
Foundation type: Independent foundation.
Financial data (yr. ended 12/31/13): Assets, $25,314,536 (M); gifts received, $12,500,000; expenditures, $428,781; qualifying distributions, $328,849; giving activities include $283,780 for 30 grants (high: $109,780; low: $500).
Fields of interest: University education; Food delivery.
Limitations: Applications not accepted. Giving primarily in New York, NY and RI. No grants to individuals.
Application information: Contributes only to pre-selected organizations.
Officers and Directors: Jon R. Bauer, Pres. and Secy. and Director; Jeff Bauer, V.P.; Laura Bauer, V.P.; Nancy A. Bauer, V.P. and Director.
EIN: 203448306

1617
The Beiser Charitable Foundation
1309 Ponderosa Dr.
Magnolia, DE 19962-1165

Established in 2007 in Delaware.
Donors: Janis W. Beiser; John T. Beiser.
Foundation type: Operating foundation.
Financial data (yr. ended 12/31/13): Assets, $3,090,888 (M); expenditures, $415,107; qualifying distributions, $400,000; giving activities include $400,000 for 1 grant.
Limitations: Applications not accepted. No grants to individuals.
Application information: Contributes only pre-selected organizations.
Directors: Janis W. Beiser; John T. Beiser.
EIN: 256820790

1618
C. E. Bennett Foundation
Little Falls Two
2751 Centerville Rd., Ste. 300
Wilmington, DE 19808-1632

Established in 1964 in Delaware.
Donor: C. Eugene Bennett‡.
Foundation type: Independent foundation.
Financial data (yr. ended 12/31/13): Assets, $9,036,002 (M); expenditures, $473,940; qualifying distributions, $436,875; giving activities include $435,000 for 6 grants (high: $100,000; low: $10,000).
Fields of interest: Performing arts; Education; Christianity; Human services.
Type of support: Annual campaigns; Professorships; Scholarships.
Limitations: Applications not accepted. Giving primarily in DE and NY. No grants to individuals.
Application information: Contributes only to pre-selected organizations. Telephone calls will not be accepted.
  Board meeting date(s): Nov.
Officers: Edna B. Pierce, Pres.; Karl E. Bennett, V.P.
Number of staff: None.
EIN: 510102289

1619
The Berghorst Foundation, Inc.
c/o Foundation Source
501 Silverside Rd., Ste. 123
Wilmington, DE 19809-1377
E-mail: kforeman@foundationsource.com

Established in 2003 in Delaware.
Donors: David T. Berghorst; Deborah H. Berghorst.
Foundation type: Independent foundation.
Financial data (yr. ended 12/31/13): Assets, $1,791,159 (M); expenditures, $282,805; qualifying distributions, $282,105; giving activities include $275,750 for 45 grants (high: $45,000; low: $200).
Fields of interest: Higher education; Hospice care.
Limitations: Applications not accepted. Giving primarily in FL and IL. No grants to individuals.
Application information: Contributes only to pre-selected organizations.
Officers and Directors: David T. Berghorst, Pres. and Secy. and Director; Alexander Berghorst, V.P.; Deborah H. Berghorst, V.P. and Director; Lisa

Hinckley Berghorst, V.P.; Sarah Berghorst, V.P.; Thomas C. Dorn, V.P. and Director.
EIN: 412116698

1620
Dr. Donald N. and Jane L. Berning Private Foundation
c/o Foundation Source
501 Silverside Rd., Ste. 123
Wilmington, DE 19809-1377

Donor: Jane L. Berning†.
Foundation type: Independent foundation.
Financial data (yr. ended 12/31/13): Assets, $9,442,725 (M); gifts received, $300,000; expenditures, $280,481; qualifying distributions, $214,660; giving activities include $181,000 for 2 grants (high: $175,000; low: $6,000).
Fields of interest: Education; Public affairs; Food delivery.
Limitations: Applications not accepted. Giving primarily in KY.
Application information: Unsolicited requests for funds not accepted.
Officers and Directors: Jack Benson, Pres. and Director; Brooks D. Benson, Secy.
EIN: 452457323

1621
Bharat Family Foundation
c/o Foundation Source
501 Silverside Rd., Ste. 123
Wilmington, DE 19809-1377

Established in 2006 in Delaware.
Donor: Krishna Bharat.
Foundation type: Independent foundation.
Financial data (yr. ended 12/31/13): Assets, $10,232,678 (M); expenditures, $374,786; qualifying distributions, $374,436; giving activities include $366,911 for 1 grant.
Fields of interest: Foundations.
Limitations: Applications not accepted. Giving primarily in CA. No grants to individuals.
Application information: Contributes only to pre-selected organizations.
Officer and Director: Krishna Bharat, Pres. and Secy. and Director.
EIN: 208037904

1622
The Black Dog Private Foundation Inc.
c/o Foundation Source
501 Silverside Rd., Ste. 123
Wilmington, DE 19809-1377

Established in 2004 in Delaware.
Donors: David L. Mahoney; Winnifred C. Ellis.
Foundation type: Independent foundation.
Financial data (yr. ended 12/31/13): Assets, $1,654,024 (M); gifts received, $332,846; expenditures, $400,727; qualifying distributions, $395,806; giving activities include $385,834 for 20 grants (high: $100,000; low: $1,000).
Fields of interest: Education; Higher education; Environment; Human services.
Limitations: Applications not accepted. Giving primarily in CA. No grants to individuals.
Application information: Unsolicited requests for funds not accepted.

Officers and Directors: David L. Mahoney, Pres. and Secy. and Director; Winnifred Ellis, V.P. and Director.
EIN: 201266221

1623
Florence Blau Charitable Annuity Trust
200 Bellevue Pkwy., Ste. 220
Wilmington, DE 19809

Foundation type: Independent foundation.
Financial data (yr. ended 12/31/14): Assets, $901,901; expenditures, $210,469; qualifying distributions, $203,626.
Fields of interest: Arts and culture; Education; Human services.
Limitations: Applications not accepted.
Application information: Unsolicited Requests for funds not accepted.
Trustees: Pervez Patel; CitiBank, N.A.; Reliance Trust Co. of Delaware.
EIN: 300212054

1624
Richard L. and Diane M. Block Foundation
c/o Foundation Source
501 Silverside Rd., Ste. 123
Wilmington, DE 19809-1377 (907) 563-5121
Contact: Richard L. Block, Dir.
E-mail: blockfoundation@arctic.net; Email for Richard L. Block: rlblock@arctic.net; Main URL: https://online.foundationsource.com/public/home/blockfoundation

Established in 2007 in Alaska.
Donors: Richard L. Block; Diane M. Block.
Foundation type: Independent foundation.
Financial data (yr. ended 12/31/13): Assets, $9,824,419 (M); expenditures, $370,529; qualifying distributions, $353,815; giving activities include $312,989 for 24 grants (high: $95,000; low: $100).
Purpose and activities: Giving to support those resources in Alaska which can most effectively enhance the quality of life of Alaska's people; the young who will lead and power the state's future, the cultural organizations that inspire the community intellectually and artistically and the social service organizations that lift up the poor so they may permanently and independently share in Alaska's bounty. .
Limitations: Applications accepted. Giving primarily in AK and MA. No grants for See part xv, line 2a.
Publications: Application guidelines.
Application information: See foundation web site for complete application guidelines. Application form required.
    Initial approach: Use online application system on foundation web site
Directors: Debbie Bellange; Warren Berckmann; David R. Block; Diane M. Block; Patrick Block; Richard L. Block; Jennifer D. Green; Ned McCarty.
EIN: 306136901

1625
The Bowman Family Foundation
c/o Brandywine Trust Company
7234 Lancaster Pike, Ste. 300A
Hockessin, DE 19707-8743

Donors: Matthias B. Bowman; Penny M. Bowman.

Foundation type: Independent foundation.
Financial data (yr. ended 12/31/13): Assets, $5,323,079 (M); expenditures, $265,772; qualifying distributions, $184,784; giving activities include $147,629 for 14 grants (high: $40,000; low: $120).
Purpose and activities: Giving primarily for education, health, and human services.
Fields of interest: Higher education; Nonprofits; Diseases and conditions; Human services; Child welfare.
Type of support: Regranting.
Limitations: Applications not accepted. Giving primarily in NY. No grants to individuals.
Application information: Unsolicited requests for funds not accepted.
Officers and Directors: Matthias B. Bowman, Pres. and Secy.-Treas. and Director; Penny M. Bowman, V.P. and Director.
EIN: 133801244

1626
Kerry and Laura Bradley Foundation
c/o Foundation Source
501 Silverside Rd., Ste. 123
Wilmington, DE 19809-1377

Donors: Kerry Bradley; Laura Bradley.
Foundation type: Independent foundation.
Financial data (yr. ended 12/31/13): Assets, $1,336,676 (M); gifts received, $299,739; expenditures, $197,129; qualifying distributions, $184,978; giving activities include $175,000 for 6 grants (high: $100,000; low: $10,000).
Fields of interest: Education; Christianity; Human services.
Limitations: Applications not accepted.
Application information: Unsolicited requests for funds not accepted.
Officers and Directors: Kerry Bradley, Pres. and Secy. and Director; Laura Bradley, V.P. and Director.
EIN: 461511607

1627
The Brandsma Family Foundation
c/o Foundation Source
501 Silverside Rd., Ste. 123
Wilmington, DE 19809-1377

Established in 1997 in Illinois.
Donors: Lee Brandsma; Pamela Brandsma.
Foundation type: Independent foundation.
Financial data (yr. ended 12/31/14): Assets, $472,744 (M); gifts received, $103,577; expenditures, $213,141; qualifying distributions, $208,763; giving activities include $201,588 for 104 grants (high: $25,000; low: $100).
Fields of interest: Christianity; Human services.
Type of support: General support; Program-related investments.
Limitations: Applications not accepted. Giving primarily in IL and MI. No grants to individuals.
Application information: Unsolicited requests for funds not accepted.
Officers and Directors: Pamela Brandsma, Pres. and Director; Lee Brandsma, Secy.-Treas. and Director; Joshua Brandsma; Ryan Brandsma; Tessa Brandsma; Kristen L. Hagstrom.
EIN: 364137431

1628
Bill and Ann Bresnan Foundation Inc.
(formerly Bresnan Family Foundation, Inc.)
c/o Foundation Source
501 Silverside Rd., Ste. 123
Wilmington, DE   19809-1377

Established in 2004 in Connecticut.
Donors: William J. Bresnan†; Bresnan Family
Foundation Trust; Ann Bresnan.
Foundation type: Independent foundation.
Financial data (yr. ended 12/31/14): Assets,
$1,854,815; gifts received, $0; expenditures,
$244,847; qualifying distributions, $224,541 and
$0 for set-asides.
Fields of interest: Education; Prostate cancer;
Catholicism; Human services; Child welfare.
Type of support: General support.
Limitations: Applications not accepted. Giving
primarily in CA, CT, and NY; some funding also in
MN. No grants to individuals.
Application information: Contributes only to
pre-selected organizations.
Officers and Directors: Ann L. Bresnan, Pres. and
Director; Jennifer Benedict, Secy.-Treas. and
Director.
EIN: 200765497

1629
The Broder Family Foundation Inc.
c/o Foundation Source
501 Silverside Rd., Ste. 123
Wilmington, DE   19809-1377

Established in 2005 in Delaware.
Donors: Paul G. Broder; Kimberly J. Griffiths.
Foundation type: Independent foundation.
Financial data (yr. ended 12/31/13): Assets,
$20,863,520 (M); expenditures, $324,558;
qualifying distributions, $306,346; giving activities
include $241,000 for 17 grants (high: $70,000;
low: $1,000).
Fields of interest: Elementary and secondary
education; Health.
Limitations: Applications not accepted. Giving
primarily in NY. No grants to individuals.
Application information: Unsolicited requests for
funds not accepted.
Officers and Directors: Paul G. Broder, Pres. and
Secy. and Director; Kimberly J. Griffiths, V.P.
EIN: 203979691

1630
The Bruce Ford Brown Charitable Trust
c/o Foundation Source
501 Silverside Rd., Ste. 123
Wilmington, DE   19809-1377

Established in 1965 in Maryland.
Donor: Donnaldson Kathryn Brown†.
Foundation type: Independent foundation.
Financial data (yr. ended 12/31/13): Assets,
$1,684,932 (M); expenditures, $174,449;
qualifying distributions, $168,856; giving activities
include $157,750 for 106 grants (high: $21,100;
low: $250).
Purpose and activities: Giving primarily for
education.
Fields of interest: Arts and culture; Education;
Higher education; Health; Christianity; Human
services.

Limitations: Applications not accepted. Giving
primarily in CA and IL. No grants to individuals.
Application information: Unsolicited requests for
funds not accepted.
Trustees: Bruce F. Brown, Jr.; Donnaldson Kathryn
Brown; Lorraine Eddy Brown; Sally Brown; Stephen
D. Brown; Thomas M. Brown; Cherry Peters; Kelly L.
Popovec.
EIN: 526063085

1631
**Mary Alice and Bennett Brown
 Foundation, Inc.**
(formerly Bennett A. Brown Family Charitable Fund,
Inc.)
c/o Foundation Source
501 Silverside Rd., Ste. 123
Wilmington, DE   19809-1377
Main URL: http://www.mabbf.org

Established in 1998 in Georgia.
Foundation type: Independent foundation.
Financial data (yr. ended 12/31/13): Assets,
$8,574,391 (M); expenditures, $353,442;
qualifying distributions, $300,181; giving activities
include $255,000 for 19 grants (high: $60,000;
low: $5,000).
Purpose and activities: Giving for the support of
nonprofits working with underserved children, with
an emphasis on education.
Fields of interest: Elementary and secondary
education; Child welfare; Youth services.
Type of support: General support; Matching grants;
Equipment; Program development; Scholarships.
Limitations: Applications not accepted. Giving
primarily in Atlanta, GA. No grants to individuals; no
annual funds; no building funds.
Publications: Informational brochure; Program
policy statement.
Application information: Proposals are accepted by
invitation only.
  Board meeting date(s): Fall and spring
Officers: Bennett A. Brown III, Co-Chair. and Secy.;
Charlotte B. Dixon, Co-Chair.
Trustees: Leila B. Armknecht; Katherine B.
Ohlhausen.
Number of staff: 1 part-time support.
EIN: 586332776

1632
Brown-Whitworth Foundation
c/o Wilmington Trust Co.
1100 N. Market St.
Wilmington, DE   19890-0001

Established in 1988 in Georgia.
Donors: James E. Brown; Maxine Brown†.
Foundation type: Independent foundation.
Financial data (yr. ended 12/31/14): Assets,
$6,935,356; expenditures, $389,652; qualifying
distributions, $350,000.
Fields of interest: Arts and culture; Higher
education; Foundations; Nonprofits; Health;
Protestantism; Human services.
Type of support: General support; Capital
campaigns; Regranting.
Limitations: Applications not accepted. Giving
primarily in Dalton, GA. No grants to individuals.
Application information: Contributes only to
pre-selected organizations.

Trustee: Wilmington Trust Co.
EIN: 581813095

1633
The Bulova Stetson Fund
(formerly Louise and Arde Bulova Fund, Inc.)
c/o Foundation Source
501 Silverside Rd., Ste. 123
Wilmington, DE   19809-1377

Established in 1987 in New York.
Donors: Louise B. Guilden†; Paul B. Guilden.
Foundation type: Independent foundation.
Financial data (yr. ended 09/30/13): Assets,
$8,946,482 (M); expenditures, $413,304;
qualifying distributions, $347,722; giving activities
include $309,250 for 39 grants (high: $25,000;
low: $250).
Fields of interest: Performing arts; Education;
Human services.
Type of support: General support.
Limitations: Applications not accepted. Giving
primarily in New York, NY. No grants to individuals.
Application information: Contributes only to
pre-selected organizations.
Officers and Directors: Paul B. Guilden, Pres. and
Director; Wendy Sager, Secy.; Philip Li, Treas. and
Director; Linda Ardigo; Dr. Stephen Becker; Dr.
Sonja J.M. Cooper; Alisa Feinstein Swidler; Xiao Li
Tan.
EIN: 133470502

1634
David G. Burton Trust
1104 Philadelphia Pike
Wilmington, DE   19809-2031
Contact: David G. Burton
Application Address: c/o David G. Burton, 411 N.
Rehoboth Blvd., Milford, DE 19963, tel.: (302)
422-3041

Established in 1986 in Delaware.
Donor: David G. Burton.
Foundation type: Independent foundation.
Financial data (yr. ended 12/31/14): Assets,
$3,736,727 (M); expenditures, $191,032;
qualifying distributions, $164,850; giving activities
include $158,000 for 27 grants (high: $78,000;
low: $500).
Purpose and activities: Giving primarily to support
Catholic churches and charities.
Fields of interest: Education; Nonprofits;
Christianity; Catholicism; Human services; Family
services.
Type of support: Regranting.
Limitations: Applications accepted. Giving primarily
in DE, MD, and VA; giving also in Washington, DC,
and MO. No grants to individuals.
Application information: Application form required.
  Initial approach: Letter
  Deadline(s): None
Trustee: David G. Burton.
EIN: 526072646

1635
The Burt's Bees Greater Good Foundation
c/o Foundation Source
501 Sliverside Rd., Ste. 123
Wilmington, DE   19809-1377   (919) 433-4533
Contact: Paula Alexander, Pres. and Exec. Dir.

Application address: C/o. Burts Bees, 210 W. Pettigrew St., Durham, NC 27701, tel.: (919) 433-4533; Main URL: http://www.burtsbees.com/Community-Partnerships/sustain-community,default,pg.html

Established in 2007 in Delaware.
Donor: Burt's Bees.
Foundation type: Company-sponsored foundation.
Financial data (yr. ended 12/31/13): Assets, $63,364 (M); gifts received, $363,134; expenditures, $343,861; qualifying distributions, $343,853; giving activities include $331,760 for 43 grants (high: $31,200; low: $100).
Purpose and activities: The foundation supports programs designed to protect honeybees, support sustainable agriculture, and promote community development in Durham.
Fields of interest: Natural resources; Domesticated animals; Agriculture; Sustainable agriculture; Community and economic development; Human services.
Type of support: Program development; Employee volunteer services; General support.
Application information: Application form required.
Initial approach: Letter or E-mail.
Deadline(s): None
Officers and Directors: Paula Alexander, Co-Pres., Co-Secy. and Exec. Dir.; Beth Ritter, Co-Pres. and Co-Secy. and Director; Matt Kopac, V.P. and Director; Manah Kulp Eckhardt.
EIN: 260143643

1636
Bushong Family Foundation
c/o Foundation Source
501 Silverside Rd., Ste. 123
Wilmington, DE   19809-1377   (800) 839-1754

Donor: Sarah Bushong-Weeks.
Foundation type: Independent foundation.
Financial data (yr. ended 12/31/14): Assets, $5,492,724; gifts received, $0; expenditures, $353,598; qualifying distributions, $304,165 and $0 for set-asides.
Fields of interest: Education; Domesticated animals; Human services.
Limitations: Applications accepted. Giving primarily in CO.
Application information: Application form required.
Initial approach: Proposal
Deadline(s): None
Officer and Director: Sarah Bushong-Weeks, Pres. and Secy. and Director.
EIN: 453589756

1637
The Edward D. Cammarota Foundation Inc.
c/o Foundation Source
501 Silverside Rd., Ste. 123
Wilmington, DE   19809-1377

Established in 2004 in Delaware.
Donor: Edward D. Cammarota†.
Foundation type: Independent foundation.
Financial data (yr. ended 12/31/13): Assets, $4,869,045 (M); expenditures, $230,144; qualifying distributions, $214,539; giving activities include $191,000 for 3 grants (high: $77,000; low: $37,000).

Fields of interest: Health; Community improvement; Community recreation; Human services.
Type of support: Volunteer development.
Limitations: Applications not accepted. No grants to individuals.
Application information: Unsolicited requests for funds not accepted.
Officers and Directors: Sandra L. Hutchinson, Pres. and Secy. and Director; Christopher Hutchinson, V.P. and Director; John Tabner.
EIN: 201262503

1638
Edwin Caplin Foundation
1100 N. Market St., DE3-C070
Wilmington, DE   19809

Donor: Edwin Caplin.
Foundation type: Independent foundation.
Financial data (yr. ended 12/31/13): Assets, $6,562,884 (M); expenditures, $301,231; qualifying distributions, $267,954; giving activities include $173,400 for 6 grants (high: $50,000; low: $7,500).
Fields of interest: Arts and culture; Religion.
Limitations: Applications not accepted. Giving primarily in NY.
Application information: Unsolicited requests for funds not accepted.
Officer: Cretien Risley, Mgr.
Trustee: Wilmington Trust Co.
EIN: 276815227

1639
The Cedarcrest Charitable Foundation
c/o Foundation source
501 Silverside Rd., Ste. 123
Wilmington, DE   19809-1377

Donors: Elizabeth K. Burke; Franklin A. Burke.
Foundation type: Independent foundation.
Financial data (yr. ended 12/31/13): Assets, $744,897 (M); expenditures, $158,276; qualifying distributions, $157,781; giving activities include $151,480 for 19 grants (high: $75,225; low: $100).
Fields of interest: Education; Religion; Human services.
Limitations: Applications not accepted. Giving primarily in PA.
Application information: Unsolicited Requests for funds not accepted.
Officers and Directors: Franklin A. Burke, Pres. and Director; Robert Burke, V.P.; Elizabeth K. Burke, V.P.; Sally J. Badali, V.P.; Clifford Haugen, Secy. and Director; Laura W. Brewer; W. Dean Karrash; John T. Lawton.
EIN: 273420282

1640
Chaney Foundation Ltd.
(formerly Eugene Chaney Foundation, Ltd.)
c/o Foundation Source
501 Silverside Rd.
Wilmington, DE   19809-1377
Main URL: http://www.chaneyenterprises.com/index.cfm/go/WhoWeAre.Chaney-Foundation

Established in 1987 in Maryland.

Donors: B.P.O.E.; Chaney Enterprises, L.P.; Southstar, LP; Renditions Washington DC LLC; Places Inc.
Foundation type: Company-sponsored foundation.
Financial data (yr. ended 12/31/12): Assets, $427,418 (M); gifts received, $5,123; expenditures, $246,786; qualifying distributions, $246,569; giving activities include $235,350 for 53 grants (high: $25,000; low: $100).
Purpose and activities: The foundation supports programs designed to promote children advocacy and services; cultural arts; education; the environment; health care and health education; and historical education and preservation.
Fields of interest: Arts and culture; Historical activities; Historic preservation; Education; Environment; Health; Community and economic development; Child welfare.
Type of support: General support; Matching grants; Annual campaigns; Capital campaigns; Building and renovations; Equipment; Program development; Scholarships; Student aid.
Limitations: Applications not accepted. Giving primarily in Waldorf, MD, with emphasis on Anne Arundel, Calvert, Caroline, Charles, Prince George, and St. Mary's County. No support for religious organizations. No grants for endowments.
Application information: Unsolicited requests for funds not accepted. The grant application process is currently under construction.
Officers and Directors: Francis H. Chaney II, Pres. and Director; William F. Childs IV, V.P. and Director; Carol M. Jackson, Secy. and Director; Mike Middleton, Treas. and Director; Robert D. Agee; Rebekah Lare; Barbara Lawson.
EIN: 521525001

1641
The Choptank Foundation
c/o Thomas R. Pusifer, Esq.
P.O. Box 1347
Wilmington, DE   19899-1347
Contact: Thomas R. Pulsifer Esq., Secy.-Treas. and Tr.

Established in 1965 in Delaware.
Donors: Sewell C. Biggs†; Franklin B. Biggs†.
Foundation type: Independent foundation.
Financial data (yr. ended 12/31/13): Assets, $9,576,238 (M); expenditures, $474,295; qualifying distributions, $401,240; giving activities include $401,240 for 2 grants (high: $330,000; low: $51,240).
Purpose and activities: Giving primarily for the arts.
Fields of interest: Art museums.
Limitations: Applications accepted. Giving primarily in DE. No grants to individuals.
Application information:
Initial approach: Proposal
Deadline(s): None
Officers and Trustees: Pierre duPont Hayward, Pres. and Trustee; Glenn C. Kenton, V.P. and Trustee; Thomas R. Pulsifer, Secy.-Treas. and Trustee; Johannes R. Krahmer, Esq.
EIN: 516019601

1642
City Hill Foundation
c/o Foundation Source
501 Silverside Rd., Ste. 123
Wilmington, DE   19809-1377

Donor: Jonathan Conyee Lim Family Trust.
Foundation type: Independent foundation.
Financial data (yr. ended 12/31/14): Assets,
$2,089,053; gifts received, $0; expenditures,
$284,169; qualifying distributions, $256,650 and
$0 for set-asides.
Fields of interest: Higher education; Protestantism;
Human services.
Limitations: Applications not accepted. Giving
primarily in CA.
Application information: Unsolicited requests for
funds not accepted.
Officers and Directors: Jonathan Lim, Co-Pres. and
Secy. and Director; Conyee Lim, Co-Pres. and
Director.
EIN: 453824368

1643
Melvin S. Cohen Foundation, Inc.
1011 Centre Rd., Ste. 310
Wilmington, DE   19805-1266
Application address: c/o Maryjo Cohen, 3925 N.
Hastings Way, Eau Claire, WI 54703, tel.: (715)
839-2139

Established in 1963 in Wisconsin.
Donors: Melvin S. Cohen; Eileen F. Cohen.
Foundation type: Independent foundation.
Financial data (yr. ended 12/31/14): Assets,
$4,566,923 (M); expenditures, $272,297;
qualifying distributions, $266,284; giving activities
include $265,300 for 5 grants (high: $234,000;
low: $300).
Fields of interest: Education; Nonprofits; Health;
Diseases and conditions.
Type of support: General support; Regranting;
Scholarships.
Limitations: Applications accepted. Giving primarily
in MN and northwestern WI, preferably Chippewa
and Eau Claire counties. No grants to individuals.
Application information: Application form required.
  Initial approach: Letter
  Deadline(s): None
Officers: Maryjo Cohen, Pres.; Randy F. Liebe, V.P.;
Eileen F. Cohen, Secy.-Treas.
EIN: 396075009

1644
Coleman Family Charitable Foundation
121 Continental Dr., No. 107
Newark, DE   19713-4326

Established in 2007 in Delaware.
Donors: William R. Coleman; Marjorie T. Coleman.
Foundation type: Independent foundation.
Financial data (yr. ended 12/31/13): Assets,
$493,032 (M); gifts received, $122,002;
expenditures, $285,759; qualifying distributions,
$285,000; giving activities include $285,000 for 30
grants (high: $75,000; low: $1,000).
Fields of interest: Historic preservation; Education;
Higher education; Hospital care.
Limitations: Applications not accepted. Giving
primarily in New York, NY. No grants to individuals.
Application information: Contributes only to
pre-selected organizations.
Officers: Marjorie T. Coleman, Pres.; William R.
Coleman, Secy.-Treas.
EIN: 261373618

1645
Russell Colgate Fund, Inc.
c/o The Corporation Trust Co.
1209 Orange St.
Wilmington, DE   19801-1120

Foundation type: Independent foundation.
Financial data (yr. ended 12/31/13): Assets,
$8,649,669 (M); expenditures, $440,778;
qualifying distributions, $396,590; giving activities
include $396,590 for grants.
Fields of interest: Arts and culture; Higher
education; Nonprofits; Hospital care; Diseases and
conditions; Human services; International relations.
International interests: France.
Type of support: General support; Annual
campaigns; Endowments; Regranting.
Limitations: Applications not accepted. Giving
primarily in Greenwich, CT, Boston, MA, and New
York, NY. No grants to individuals.
Application information: Contributes only to
pre-selected organizations.
Officers: Russell C. Wilkinson, Pres.; John C.
Colgate, Jr., V.P.; Mary C. Kirk, Secy.
EIN: 221713065

1646
Gladys & Irving Coopersmith Charitable Trust
P.O. Box 396
Wilmington, DE   19899-0396

Established in 2007 in New York.
Donor: Gladys Coopersmith†.
Foundation type: Independent foundation.
Financial data (yr. ended 12/31/14): Assets,
$6,565,781; expenditures, $509,414; qualifying
distributions, $438,006.
Fields of interest: Nonprofits.
Type of support: Regranting.
Limitations: Applications not accepted. Giving
primarily in NY. No grants to individuals.
Application information: Contributes only to
pre-selected organizations.
Trustee: Neuberger Berman Trust Co., N.A.
EIN: 326052002

1647
The Phyllis M. Coors Foundation
c/o Foundation Source
501 Silverside Rd., Ste. 123
Wilmington, DE   19809-1377

Established in 1999 in Colorado.
Donor: Phyllis M. Coors.
Foundation type: Independent foundation.
Financial data (yr. ended 12/31/13): Assets,
$974,651 (M); expenditures, $229,025; qualifying
distributions, $223,457; giving activities include
$214,500 for 33 grants (high: $50,000; low:
$1,000).
Fields of interest: Higher education; Human
services; Child welfare.
Limitations: Applications not accepted. Giving
primarily in CO. No grants to individuals.
Application information: Contributes only to
pre-selected organizations.
Officers and Directors: Phyllis M. Coors, Pres. and
Director; William Scott Coors, V.P. and Secy.; Anita
Russell, V.P.; David Hurt, Treas.

Board Members: Carin Bremer; Holly Coors.
EIN: 841502623

1648
Corkins Family Foundation
c/o Foundation Source
501 Silverside Rd., Ste. 123
Wilmington, DE   19809-1377

Donor: David Corkins.
Foundation type: Independent foundation.
Financial data (yr. ended 12/31/13): Assets,
$6,426,229 (M); gifts received, $500; qualifying
expenditures, $336,785; qualifying distributions,
$315,277; giving activities include $285,000 for 3
grants (high: $250,000; low: $10,000).
Fields of interest: Education; Camps.
Limitations: Applications not accepted. No grants to
individuals.
Application information: Unsolicited requests for
funds not accepted.
Officer and Director: David Corkins, Pres. and Secy.
and Director.
EIN: 270858631

1649
The Corrigan-Walla Foundation
501 Silverside Rd.
Wilmington, DE   19809-1377

Established in 1993 in California.
Donors: Sigrun Corrigan; Wilfred J. Corrigan.
Foundation type: Independent foundation.
Financial data (yr. ended 10/31/13): Assets,
$5,810,753 (M); expenditures, $258,157;
qualifying distributions, $254,386; giving activities
include $219,000 for 8 grants (high: $100,000;
low: $2,500).
Purpose and activities: Funding primarily for the
arts.
Fields of interest: Arts and culture; Education;
Human services.
Limitations: Applications not accepted. Giving
primarily in CA. No grants to individuals.
Application information: Unsolicited requests for
funds not accepted.
  Board meeting date(s): Variable
Officers and Directors: Wilfred James Corrigan,
Pres. and Director; Eric Corrigan, Secy. and
Director; Sean Corrigan, Treas. and Director; Elsa
Corrigan.
Number of staff: None.
EIN: 770359520

1650
Irma L. & Abram S. Croll Charitable Trust
c/o Neuberger Berman Trust Co., N.A.
P.O. Box 396
Wilmington, DE   19899-0396

Established in 2001 in New York.
Foundation type: Independent foundation.
Financial data (yr. ended 09/30/14): Assets,
$7,024,646 (M); expenditures, $253,882;
qualifying distributions, $174,184; giving activities
include $166,667 for 1 grant.
Fields of interest: Higher education; Nonprofits;
Hospital care; Specialty hospital care; Judaism;
Human services.
Type of support: Regranting.

Limitations: Applications not accepted. Giving primarily in New York, NY. No grants to individuals.
Application information: Contributes only to pre-selected organizations.
Trustees: Sarah J. Schlesinger; Neuberger Berman Trust Co., N.A.
EIN: 137312974

1651
Cross H Foundation
c/o Foundation Source
501 Silverside Rd., Ste. 123
Wilmington, DE 19809-1377

Established in 2004 in Colorado.
Donors: Michele L. Bergner; William S. Bergner.
Foundation type: Independent foundation.
Financial data (yr. ended 12/31/13): Assets, $2,676,315 (M); expenditures, $393,629; qualifying distributions, $392,493; giving activities include $376,690 for 26 grants (high: $250,000; low: $1,000).
Fields of interest: Education; Nonprofits; Human services; Child welfare; Cemeteries and burial services.
Type of support: Regranting.
Limitations: Applications not accepted. Giving primarily in CO. No grants to individuals.
Application information: Unsolicited requests for funds not accepted.
Trustees: Michele L. Bergner; William S. Bergner.
EIN: 470948591

1652
Cultures of Resistance Network Foundation
(formerly Caipirinha Foundation)
c/o Foundation Source
501 Silverside Rd., Ste. 123
Wilmington, DE 19809-1377

Established in 2006 in Delaware.
Donors: George Gund III; Iara Lee; Riverbank Technologies, Inc.
Foundation type: Operating foundation.
Financial data (yr. ended 12/31/13): Assets, $38,578 (M); gifts received, $200,000; expenditures, $465,059; qualifying distributions, $458,989; giving activities include $413,380 for 56 grants (high: $46,800; low: $100).
Purpose and activities: Support for human rights, international law, United States foreign policy, independent media, and arts and culture.
Fields of interest: Arts and culture; Law; Film and video; National security; Human rights; Human services; Basic and emergency aid; Democracy and civil society development; Foreign policy; International development.
Limitations: Applications not accepted. Giving primarily in CA, DE, Washington, DC, and NY.
Application information: Unsolicited requests for funds not accepted.
Officers and Directors: Iara Lee, Pres. and Director; Thomas Suniville, Secy.-Treas.; George Gund III.
EIN: 203587464

1653
CVW Family Foundation
c/o Foundation Source
501 Silverside Rd., Ste. 123
Wilmington, DE 19809-1377

Established in 2007 in Delaware.
Donor: Rancho La Mesa.
Foundation type: Independent foundation.
Financial data (yr. ended 12/31/13): Assets, $4,599,437 (M); expenditures, $337,411; qualifying distributions, $317,045; giving activities include $299,000 for 11 grants (high: $60,000; low: $5,000).
Fields of interest: Health; Christianity.
Limitations: Applications not accepted. Giving primarily in CA, CO and GA. No grants to individuals.
Application information: Contributes only to pre-selected organizations.
Trustees: Darlene Van Wagner; Roger K. Van Wagner.
EIN: 208711343

1654
M. M. and P. A. Day Memorial Fund
c/o Wilmington Trust Co.
1100 N. Market St.
Wilmington, DE 19890-0900 (302) 855-2257
Contact: Susan Nickel

Donor: Margaret Day Interim Trust.
Foundation type: Independent foundation.
Financial data (yr. ended 12/31/14): Assets, $7,532,699 (M); expenditures, $560,996; qualifying distributions, $492,089; giving activities include $438,233 for 6 grants (high: $249,793; low: $17,529).
Purpose and activities: Giving primarily for Episcopal and United Methodist churches and organizations.
Fields of interest: Episcopalianism and Anglicanism; Lutheranism; Presbyterianism; Human services.
Limitations: Applications not accepted. Giving primarily in DE. No grants to individuals.
Application information: Generally contributes to pre-selected organizations.
Trustees: Patricia G. Zaharko; Wilmington Trust Co.
EIN: 207053268

1655
Josephine De Karman Scholarship Trust
1100 N. Market St., DE3-C070
Wilmington, DE 19891-0001

Foundation type: Independent foundation.
Financial data (yr. ended 12/31/13): Assets, $3,412,188 (M); expenditures, $204,453; qualifying distributions, $166,128; giving activities include $140,250 for 12 grants to individuals (high: $22,000; low: $6,250).
Purpose and activities: Scholarship awards for higher education; funds are provided directly to the college or university.
Fields of interest: Education.
Type of support: Student aid; Scholarships.
Limitations: Applications not accepted. Giving primarily in CA, MA, and NJ.
Application information: Unsolicited requests for funds not accepted.

Trustees: Advisory Trust Co. of Delaware; Reliance Trust Co. of Delaware.
EIN: 956019527

1656
Dion Family Foundation
c/o Foundation Source
501 Silverside Rd., Ste. 123
Wilmington, DE 19809-1377

Established in 2007 in Delaware.
Donors: Donald R. Dion; Bay Cedar Charitable Trust.
Foundation type: Independent foundation.
Financial data (yr. ended 12/31/13): Assets, $141,325 (M); gifts received, $17,775; expenditures, $414,124; qualifying distributions, $405,913; giving activities include $398,219 for 4 grants (high: $273,219; low: $35,000).
Fields of interest: Elementary and secondary education; Higher education; Catholicism.
Limitations: Applications not accepted. Giving primarily in ME and VT. No grants to individuals.
Application information: Unsolicited requests for funds not accepted.
Officer and Director: Donald R. Dion, Pres. and Secy. and Director.
EIN: 260144020

1657
Dixon and Carol Doll Family Foundation
c/o Foundation Source
501 Silverside Rd., Ste. 123
Wilmington, DE 19809—1377

Established in 2000 in California.
Donors: Carol Ann Doll; Dixon R. Doll.
Foundation type: Independent foundation.
Financial data (yr. ended 12/31/13): Assets, $203,517 (M); gifts received, $717,118; expenditures, $298,088; qualifying distributions, $293,661; giving activities include $275,975 for 28 grants (high: $62,500; low: $250).
Purpose and activities: Giving primarily for higher education and the arts.
Fields of interest: Arts and culture; Higher education; Human services; Child welfare.
Limitations: Applications not accepted. Giving primarily in San Francisco, CA.
Application information: Unsolicited requests for funds not accepted.
Officers: Carol Ann Doll, Pres.; Dixon R. Doll, V.P. and Secy.-Treas.
EIN: 943346287

1658
Nancy C. and Dale Dougherty Foundation
c/o Foundation Source
501 Silverside Rd., Ste. 123
Wilmington, DE 19809-1377

Established in 1999 in California.
Donors: Nancy C. Dougherty; Dale Dougherty.
Foundation type: Independent foundation.
Financial data (yr. ended 12/31/13): Assets, $2,542,236 (M); expenditures, $388,473; qualifying distributions, $374,956; giving activities include $360,000 for 5 grants (high: $200,000; low: $25,000).
Fields of interest: Theater; Venture philanthropy; Equestrianism; Child welfare.

Limitations: Applications not accepted. Giving primarily in CA; some giving in MA. No grants to individuals.
Application information: Contributes only to pre-selected organizations.
Officers: Nancy C. Dougherty, Pres.; Dale Dougherty, Secy.-Treas.
EIN: 943347140

1659
Mary B. Dunn Charitable Trust
c/o Wilmington Trust Co.
1100 N. Market St,. DE3-C070
Wilmington, DE   19890-0900
Application address: c/o Bingham McCutchen, LLP, Attn.: Barbara F. Wand, Esq., 1 Federal St., Boston, MA 02109

Established in 1992 in Massachusetts.
Donor: Mary B. Dunn.
Foundation type: Independent foundation.
Financial data (yr. ended 12/31/13): Assets, $1,922,708 (M); gifts received, $150,329; expenditures, $340,910; qualifying distributions, $312,084; giving activities include $309,200 for 56 grants (high: $25,000; low: $1,000).
Purpose and activities: Giving for educational and medical purposes.
Fields of interest: Arts and culture; Health; Human services.
Limitations: Applications accepted. Giving primarily in MA.
Application information: Application form required.
   Initial approach: Letter
   Copies of proposal: 1
   Deadline(s): None
Trustees: Mary B. Dunn; Barbara Freedman Wand.
EIN: 226573797

1660
The Claud E. Easterly Foundation Inc.
c/o Foundation Source
501 Silverside Rd., Ste. 123
Wilmington, DE   19809-1377

Established in 1999 in Georgia.
Donors: David E. Easterly; Judy B. Easterly.
Foundation type: Independent foundation.
Financial data (yr. ended 12/31/13): Assets, $4,105,099 (M); expenditures, $190,787; qualifying distributions, $168,166; giving activities include $148,100 for 21 grants (high: $20,000; low: $1,000).
Fields of interest: Education; Cancers; Youth development.
Limitations: Applications not accepted. No grants to individuals.
Application information: Unsolicited requests for funds not accepted.
Officers and Directors: David E. Easterly, Pres. and Director; Jennifer R. Dorian, Secy. and Director; Gregory C. Easterly, Treas. and Director; Anne H. Easterly Duguid; Judy B. Easterly.
EIN: 582486146

1661
EON Charitable Foundation
c/o Foundation Source
501 Silverside Rd., Ste. 123
Wilmington, DE   19809-1377

Donor: Brian K. Bess.
Foundation type: Independent foundation.
Financial data (yr. ended 12/31/13): Assets, $2,774,704 (M); expenditures, $200,156; qualifying distributions, $165,134; giving activities include $147,600 for 7 grants (high: $50,000; low: $2,500).
Fields of interest: Health; Religion; Human services.
Limitations: Applications not accepted. Giving primarily in CO. No grants to individuals.
Application information: Unsolicited requests for funds not accepted.
Officer and Director: Brian K. Bess, Pres. and Secy. and Director.
EIN: 274094169

1662
Farr Family Foundation Inc.
16192 Coastal Hwy.
Lewes, DE   19958-3608

Foundation type: Independent foundation.
Financial data (yr. ended 12/31/14): Assets, $4,563,546; expenditures, $305,486; qualifying distributions, $228,055.
Fields of interest: Education; Higher education; Health; Religion; Christianity.
Limitations: Applications not accepted. Giving primarily in the Washington, DC, area.
Application information: Unsolicited requests for funds not accepted.
Officers: Joseph G. Farr, Pres.; Patrick M. Farr, Exec. V.P.; Catherine E. Farr, Secy.; Michael J. Farr, Treas.
Directors: Caroline M. Farr; Rebecca C. Farr.
EIN: 455419103

1663
Fernandina Foundation
c/o Charles Schwab Bank
500 Delaware Ave., Ste. 730
Wilmington, DE   19801-7407   (800) 745-7721

Donor: Burns Family Charitable Trust.
Foundation type: Independent foundation.
Financial data (yr. ended 12/31/13): Assets, $944,499 (M); expenditures, $158,543; qualifying distributions, $152,775; giving activities include $148,050 for 10 grants (high: $75,900; low: $150).
Fields of interest: Education; Archives and special collections; Community and economic development; Sports and recreation; Human services.
Limitations: Applications accepted. Giving primarily in Fernandina, FL.
Application information: Application form required.
   Initial approach: Letter
   Deadline(s): None
Trustee: Charles Schwab Bank.
EIN: 263804793

1664
Soran Foundation
c/o Foundation Source
501 Silverside Rd., Ste. 123
Wilmington, DE   19809-1377

Donors: Philip E. Soran; Christine Soran; Alysa Soran Gardino; Margaret Soran.
Foundation type: Independent foundation.
Financial data (yr. ended 01/31/14): Assets, $2,847,613 (M); gifts received, $464,390;

expenditures, $356,226; qualifying distributions, $335,686; giving activities include $310,000 for 15 grants (high: $76,500; low: $500).
Fields of interest: Education; Protestantism; Human services.
Limitations: Applications not accepted. Giving primarily in MN.
Application information: Unsolicited requests for funds not accepted.
Officers and Directors: Philip E. Soran, Pres. and Secy. and Director; Margaret Soran, V.P. and Director.
EIN: 274449723

1665
Freedman Family Fund
(formerly The Eisner Family Fund)
c/o Tiedemann Trust Co.
200 Bellevue Pkwy., Ste. 525
Wilmington, DE   19809

Established in 1988 in New York.
Donors: Michael D. Eisner; Margot E. Freedman.
Foundation type: Independent foundation.
Financial data (yr. ended 12/31/13): Assets, $1,811,188 (M); expenditures, $248,317; qualifying distributions, $233,507; giving activities include $233,507 for 53 grants (high: $30,000; low: $100).
Fields of interest: Arts and culture; Museums; Education; Higher education; Nonprofits; Health; Hospital care; Diseases and conditions; Communication media; Judaism; Human services.
Type of support: General support; Regranting; Continuing support; Research; Research and evaluation.
Limitations: Applications not accepted. Giving primarily in NY. No grants to individuals.
Application information: Unsolicited requests for funds not accepted.
Trustees: Douglas M. Freedman; Margot E. Freedman; Amy F. Lieberman.
EIN: 133486425

1666
Geltzer Family Foundation
c/o Foundation Source
501 Silverside Rd., Ste. 123
Wilmington, DE   19809-1377

Established in 2005 in New Jersey.
Donors: David R. Geltzer; Leslee Geltzer.
Foundation type: Independent foundation.
Financial data (yr. ended 12/31/13): Assets, $1,070,569 (M); expenditures, $205,433; qualifying distributions, $205,133; giving activities include $189,000 for 12 grants (high: $100,000; low: $1,000).
Fields of interest: Theater; Higher education.
Limitations: Applications not accepted. Giving primarily in NJ and PA. No grants to individuals.
Application information: Unsolicited requests for funds not accepted.
Trustees: David R. Geltzer; Ethan M. Geltzer; Isaac S. Geltzer; Leslee V. Geltzer.
EIN: 432075972

1667
The George Family Charitable Foundation
c/o Foundation Source
501 Silverside Rd.
Wilmington, DE 19809-1377

Established in 2007 in Delaware.
Donor: Timothy M. George.
Foundation type: Independent foundation.
Financial data (yr. ended 12/31/13): Assets, $64,539 (M); gifts received, $49,340; expenditures, $234,174; qualifying distributions, $234,174; giving activities include $228,500 for 13 grants (high: $50,000; low: $1,500).
Fields of interest: Elementary and secondary education.
Limitations: Applications not accepted. Giving primarily in CT and New York, NY. No grants to individuals.
Application information: Unsolicited requests for funds not accepted.
Officer and Director: Timothy M. George, Pres. and Secy. and Director.
EIN: 261596005

1668
The Giving Back Foundation
c/o Foundation Source
501 Silverside Rd., Ste. 123
Wilmington, DE 19809-1377

Donor: Meera T. Gandhi.
Foundation type: Independent foundation.
Financial data (yr. ended 12/31/13): Assets, $398,075 (M); gifts received, $100; expenditures, $660,878; qualifying distributions, $651,453; giving activities include $274,552 for 15 grants (high: $100,000; low: $1,000), $2,000 for 4 grants to individuals (high: $500; low: $500), and $17,277 for 3 foundation-administered programs.
Fields of interest: Arts and culture; Education; Higher education; Human services.
Limitations: Applications not accepted. Giving primarily in RI.
Application information: Unsolicited requests for funds not accepted.
Officer and Director: Meera T. Gandhi, Pres. and Secy. and Director.
EIN: 273143272

1669
Glencoe Foundation, Inc.
3801 Kennett Pike, Ste. 101
Wilmington, DE 19807-2377
Contact: John T. Fay, Secy.-Treas.
E-mail: Jfav289491@aol.com

Established in 1975 in Delaware.
Donors: Ellice McDonald, Jr.†; Rosa H. McDonald.
Foundation type: Independent foundation.
Financial data (yr. ended 12/31/13): Assets, $6,167,186 (M); expenditures, $451,349; qualifying distributions, $370,400; giving activities include $370,400 for 1 grant.
Purpose and activities: Gives exclusively to Scottish and American charitable organizations, such as museums, hospitals, educational institutions, and other publicly-oriented organizations that promote and preserve Scottish-American traditions and culture located in the Highlands and the islands of Scotland.

Fields of interest: Environment.
International interests: Scotland.
Type of support: General support; Continuing support; Capital and infrastructure; Equipment; Emergency funds.
Limitations: Applications not accepted. Giving limited to the Highlands and islands of Scotland. No grants to individuals, or for scholarships, fellowships, or matching gifts; no loans.
Application information: Unsolicited requests for funds not accepted.
Board meeting date(s): Annually and as required
Officers: Gregory Inskip, Esq., Chair.; John T. Fay, CPA, Secy.-Treas.
Board Member: Robert MacDonald.
EIN: 510164761

1670
Gloria Dei Foundation
c/o Foundation Source
501 Silverside Rd., Ste. 123
Wilmington, DE 19809-1377
Main URL: http://www.gloriadeifoundation.org/

Established in 2005 in Florida.
Donor: Mary Cade.
Foundation type: Independent foundation.
Financial data (yr. ended 12/31/13): Assets, $3,377,704 (M); expenditures, $345,630; qualifying distributions, $339,930; giving activities include $307,970 for 10 grants (high: $48,000; low: $5,000).
Purpose and activities: Giving primarily for causes dealing with the arts, the community, education, evangelism, discipleship and outreach, justice and public policy, and the sanctity of life.
Fields of interest: Arts and culture; Education; Public health; Public affairs; Christianity; Right to life; Low-income and poor people.
Limitations: Giving on a worldwide basis. No grants to individuals.
Officers and Directors: Emily Cade Morrison, Pres. and Director; Phoebe C. Miles, V.P. and Director; Robert L. Morrison, Secy.-Treas. and Director; Martha Cade; Mary Cade.
EIN: 203723933

1671
Gorny Foundation
c/o Foundation Source
501 Silverside Rd., Ste. 123
Wilmington, DE 19809-1377

Donor: Thomas Gorny.
Foundation type: Independent foundation.
Financial data (yr. ended 12/31/13): Assets, $1,274,146 (M); expenditures, $151,579; qualifying distributions, $145,551; giving activities include $130,500 for 7 grants (high: $75,000; low: $1,000).
Fields of interest: Education; Religion; Judaism.
Limitations: Applications not accepted. Giving primarily in Washington, DC and NY.
Application information: Unsolicited requests for funds not accepted.
Officer and Director: Thomas Gorny, Pres. and Secy. and Director.
EIN: 453947729

1672
Gromet Foundation
(formerly The Janice & Ben Gromet Fund for Disadvantaged Children)
40 E. Main St., Ste. 754
Newark, DE 19711-4639 (808) 384-1456
Contact: Sung Stubenberg
E-mail: info@gromet.org; Main URL: http://www.grometfoundation.org
Facebook: http://www.facebook.com/pages/The-Gromet-Foundation-Hawaii/110736534085?
Twitter: http://twitter.com/GrometFDN_HI

Established in 1990 in Hawaii.
Donor: Ben Gromet†.
Foundation type: Independent foundation.
Financial data (yr. ended 12/31/13): Assets, $10,286,835 (M); expenditures, $750,840; qualifying distributions, $552,290; giving activities include $156,350 for 48 grants to individuals (high: $5,770; low: $182).
Purpose and activities: Giving to financially disadvantaged students from Hawaii who are enrolled in a 4-year college.
Fields of interest: Education.
Type of support: Student aid.
Limitations: Applications accepted. Giving limited to residents of HI.
Application information: See foundation web site for complete application guidelines.
Initial approach: Letter
Deadline(s): Nov. 15
Board meeting date(s): Monthly
Officers and Directors: Charles Rolles, Pres. and Director; Sung Stubenberg, C.F.O.; James A. Stubenberg, Exec. Dir.
Number of staff: 4 part-time professional.
EIN: 990281966

1673
The John and Phyllis Groot Foundation
c/o Foundation Source
501 Silverside Rd., Ste. 123
Wilmington, DE 19809-1377

Established in 1993 in Illinois.
Donor: Phyllis Christine Groot†.
Foundation type: Independent foundation.
Financial data (yr. ended 12/31/12): Assets, $2,654,202 (M); expenditures, $389,226; qualifying distributions, $340,000; giving activities include $340,000 for grants.
Purpose and activities: Giving primarily to Christian organizations, including Christian schools.
Fields of interest: Education; Christianity.
Limitations: Applications not accepted. Giving primarily in IL and MI. No grants to individuals.
Application information: Contributes only to pre-selected organizations.
Officer and Directors: Robin J. Ipema, Pres. and Director; Valerie Van Woerkom, V.P. and Secy. and Director; Pamela Brandsma; Larry Groot; Gayle Ellen Vryhof.
EIN: 363924778

1674
Hagan Foundation
c/o Foundation Source
501 Silverside Rd., Ste. 123
Wilmington, DE 19809-1377

Established in 2005 in Delaware.
Donor: Mike Hagan.
Foundation type: Independent foundation.
Financial data (yr. ended 12/31/13): Assets, $412,303 (M); expenditures, $317,543; qualifying distributions, $312,639; giving activities include $305,050 for 19 grants (high: $70,800; low: $1,000).
Fields of interest: Elementary and secondary education; Higher education; Diseases and conditions; Catholicism.
Type of support: Research; Research and evaluation.
Limitations: Applications not accepted. Giving primarily in PA, with emphasis on Philadelphia. No grants to individuals.
Application information: Contributes only to pre-selected organizations.
Officers and Directors: John J. Hagan, Pres. and Secy. and Director; John Hagan, Jr., V.P. and Director.
EIN: 203757753

1675
James Stuart Haldan Charitable Foundation
c/o Wilmington Trust
1100 Market St. DE3-C070
Wilmington, DE 19890-0001

Established in 2002 in Nevada.
Donors: Ethelmae S. Haldan; Haldan Family Charitable Foundation.
Foundation type: Independent foundation.
Financial data (yr. ended 12/31/14): Assets, $2,315,060; expenditures, $129,060; qualifying distributions, $115,000.
Fields of interest: Health; Community and economic development; Human services.
Type of support: General support.
Limitations: Applications not accepted. Giving primarily in CA and NV. No grants to individuals.
Application information: Unsolicited requests for funds not accepted.
Trustee: James Stuart Haldan.
EIN: 710865534

1676
Dwight S. Haldan Family Charitable Foundation
c/o Wilmington Trust
1100 Market St., DE3-C070
Wilmington, DE 19890-0900

Established in 2002 in Arizona.
Donor: Haldan Family Foundation.
Foundation type: Independent foundation.
Financial data (yr. ended 12/31/14): Assets, $1,636,092; expenditures, $131,256; qualifying distributions, $119,580.
Fields of interest: Education; Foundations; Cancers; Human services.
Limitations: Applications not accepted. Giving primarily in AZ and CA. No grants to individuals.
Application information: Contributes only to pre-selected organizations.
Trustee: Dwight S. Haldan.
EIN: 710865524

1677
The Harkness Trust
c/o Theodore H. Ashford
One Walkers Mill Rd.
Wilmington, DE 19807-2134

Established in 1994 in Delaware.
Donor: Theodore H. Ashford.
Foundation type: Independent foundation.
Financial data (yr. ended 12/31/14): Assets, $5,420,739 (M); expenditures, $222,777; qualifying distributions, $213,000; giving activities include $213,000 for 6 grants (high: $152,000; low: $1,000).
Fields of interest: Higher education; Christianity; Human services.
Limitations: Applications not accepted. Giving primarily in DE and MA. No grants to individuals.
Application information: Contributes only to pre-selected organizations.
Trustee: Theodore H. Ashford.
EIN: 516498255

1678
The Kurt and Julie Hauser Foundation
c/o Foundation Source
501 Silverside Rd., Ste. 123
Wilmington, DE 19809-1377

Established in 2006 in Delaware.
Donors: W. Kurt Hauser; Hauser Family Revocable Living Trust; Julianne Hauser.
Foundation type: Independent foundation.
Financial data (yr. ended 12/31/13): Assets, $4,943,917 (M); gifts received, $600,000; expenditures, $218,773; qualifying distributions, $202,792; giving activities include $180,000 for 7 grants (high: $50,000; low: $10,000).
Fields of interest: Education; Human services; Youth development.
Limitations: Applications not accepted. Giving primarily in CA and PA. No grants to individuals.
Application information: Unsolicited requests for funds not accepted.
Officers and Directors: W. Kurt Hauser, Pres. and Secy. and Director; Julianne Hauser, V.P. and Director.
EIN: 205174415

1679
Catherine Hawkins Foundation
c/o John I. & Elizabeth Taylor, Wilmington Trust Co.
1100 N. Market St.
Wilmington, DE 19890-0900

Established in 1998 in Massachusetts.
Donor: John I. Taylor.
Foundation type: Independent foundation.
Financial data (yr. ended 04/30/14): Assets, $6,624,287 (M); expenditures, $340,045; qualifying distributions, $298,570; giving activities include $297,500 for 43 grants (high: $20,000; low: $1,000).
Fields of interest: Education; Environment; Human services.
Limitations: Applications not accepted. Giving primarily in CO. No grants to individuals.
Application information: Contributes only to pre-selected organizations.
Trustees: Elizabeth C. Taylor; John I. Taylor.
EIN: 046864140

1680
The Russell P. & Elizabeth Crimian Heuer Foundation
(formerly The Heuer Foundation)
c/o Wilmington Trust Co.
1100 N. Market St.
Wilmington, DE 19890-0900

Donors: Charlotte H. de Serio; Russell P. Heuer, Jr.†.
Foundation type: Independent foundation.
Financial data (yr. ended 11/30/13): Assets, $2,531,793 (M); expenditures, $345,335; qualifying distributions, $314,244; giving activities include $285,350 for 46 grants (high: $100,000; low: $500).
Fields of interest: Opera; Orchestral music; Undergraduate education; University education; Hospital care.
Type of support: General support.
Limitations: Applications not accepted. Giving primarily in PA. No grants to individuals.
Application information: Unsolicited requests for funds not accepted.
Trustees: Gabrielle Crouchly; Charlotte Deserio; James Johnston; Michael Scarborough; Robert Watts; Jennifer Watty; W. Steven Woodward; Wilmington Trust Co.
EIN: 510255378

1681
The Hill Family Charitable Foundation
c/o Foundation Source
501 Silverside Rd., Ste. 123
Wilmington, DE 19809-1377

Established in 2007 in Delaware.
Donors: Eugene D. Hill III; Joan L. Hill.
Foundation type: Independent foundation.
Financial data (yr. ended 12/31/13): Assets, $851,900 (M); gifts received, $318,000; expenditures, $404,743; qualifying distributions, $387,626; giving activities include $379,500 for 26 grants (high: $100,000; low: $1,000).
Fields of interest: Education.
Limitations: Applications not accepted. Giving primarily in MA. No grants to individuals.
Application information: Unsolicited requests for funds not accepted.
Officers and Directors: Eugene D. Hill III, Pres. and Secy. and Director; Alyssa Anne Hill, V.P.; Eugene Hill, V.P.; Gregory Alexander Hill, V.P.; Joan L. Hill, V.P. and Director.
EIN: 261385083

1682
The Hoops Family Foundation Inc.
c/o Foundation Source
501 Silverside Rd., Ste. 123
Wilmington, DE 19809-1377

Established in 2003 in Delaware.
Donors: Patricia Hoops; Jeffrey A. Hoops.
Foundation type: Independent foundation.
Financial data (yr. ended 12/31/13): Assets, $1,380,863 (M); expenditures, $198,233; qualifying distributions, $182,802; giving activities include $171,400 for 11 grants (high: $120,000; low: $1,000).
Fields of interest: Health; Children's hospital care; Religion; Basketball; Human services; Children.

Limitations: Applications not accepted. Giving primarily in WV. No grants to individuals.
Application information: Unsolicited requests for funds not accepted.
Officers and Directors: Jeffrey A. Hoops, Pres. and Secy. and Director; Patricia Hoops, V.P. and Director.
EIN: 810636348

1683
The Jackman Family Foundation
c/o Foundation Source
501 Silverside Rd., Ste. 123
Wilmington, DE   19809-1377

Established in 2006 in Delaware.
Donors: Hugh Jackman; Deborra-Lee Furness.
Foundation type: Independent foundation.
Financial data (yr. ended 12/31/13): Assets, $3,951,396 (M); gifts received, $500,000; expenditures, $232,987; qualifying distributions, $206,792; giving activities include $186,481 for 42 grants (high: $15,000; low: $60).
Fields of interest: Education; Philanthropy; Human services.
International interests: Global Programs; Zimbabwe.
Type of support: General support; Financial sustainability; Program development; Curriculum development.
Limitations: Applications not accepted. No grants to individuals.
Application information: Unsolicited requests for funds not accepted.
Officers and Directors: Hugh Jackman, Pres. and Secy. and Director; Deborra-Lee Furness, V.P. and Director.
EIN: 204702478

1684
Jade Tree Foundation
c/o Wilmington Trust Co.
1100 N. Market St., DE3-C070, Ste. 330960
Wilmington, DE   19890

Established in 1994 in Delaware.
Donors: Alice F. Roe; Mrs. Robert B. Flint.
Foundation type: Independent foundation.
Financial data (yr. ended 12/31/14): Assets, $3,975,476; gifts received, $25; expenditures, $173,682; qualifying distributions, $167,000.
Fields of interest: Education; Sports and recreation; Human services.
Type of support: General support.
Limitations: Applications not accepted. No grants to individuals.
Application information: Unsolicited requests for funds not accepted.
Board meeting date(s): Spring and fall
Officers: Alice F. Roe, Pres. and Treas.; Barbara A. Madley, V.P.; Henry G. Roe, V.P.; William G. Roe, Secy.
EIN: 510355035

1685
Motwani Jadeja Family Foundation
c/o Foundation Source
501 Silverside Rd., Ste. 123
Wilmington, DE   19809-1377

Donor: Asha Jadeja.
Foundation type: Independent foundation.
Financial data (yr. ended 12/31/13): Assets, $244,428 (M); gifts received, $435,665; expenditures, $245,747; qualifying distributions, $236,627; giving activities include $223,920 for 7 grants (high: $100,000; low: $5,000).
Fields of interest: Education; Human services.
Limitations: Applications not accepted.
Application information: Unsolicited requests for funds not accepted.
Officer and Director: Asha Jadeja, Pres. and Secy.-Treas. and Director.
EIN: 462186408

1686
JBL Scholarship Trust
P.O. Box 4248
Wilmington, DE   19807-0248

Established in 1963 in Delaware.
Foundation type: Independent foundation.
Financial data (yr. ended 12/31/13): Assets, $6,885,155 (M); gifts received, $5,232; expenditures, $419,728; qualifying distributions, $267,984; giving activities include $38,000 for 3 grants (high: $20,000; low: $3,000), and $165,450 for 85 grants to individuals (high: $3,000; low: $1,500).
Purpose and activities: Scholarship awards to Delaware graduating high school seniors and college students or students residing in the immediate area of adjoining states: Maryland, New Jersey and Pennsylvania.
Fields of interest: Higher education.
Type of support: Student aid.
Limitations: Applications not accepted. Giving primarily to residents of DE, MD, NJ and PA. No grants for graduate study.
Application information: Unsolicited requests for funds not accepted.
Trustees: Michael G. Duffy; Dana P. Robinson; Kathleen D. Smith.
EIN: 516016533

1687
Jockers Family Foundation
c/o Goldman Sachs Trust Co., N.A.
601 Delaware Ave., 2nd Fl.
Wilmington, DE   19801-1489

Established in 1994 in Delaware.
Donor: Helen Jockers.
Foundation type: Independent foundation.
Financial data (yr. ended 12/31/13): Assets, $7,083,890 (M); expenditures, $374,366; qualifying distributions, $314,664; giving activities include $297,500 for 33 grants (high: $34,000; low: $2,000).
Fields of interest: Education; Elementary and secondary education; Higher education; Health; Human services.
Limitations: Applications not accepted. Giving primarily in Washington, DC, MA and NH and NY. No grants to individuals.
Application information: Contributes only to pre-selected organizations.
Trustee: Goldman Sachs Trust Co.
EIN: 516497412

1688
Just Us for All Foundation
c/o Foundation source
501 Silverside Rd.
Wilmington, DE   19809-1377

Donors: Scott Weiss; Pamela Weiss.
Foundation type: Independent foundation.
Financial data (yr. ended 12/31/13): Assets, $1,795,561 (M); expenditures, $218,356; qualifying distributions, $198,987; giving activities include $187,250 for 13 grants (high: $75,000; low: $200).
Fields of interest: Education; Public affairs; Housing development; Religion.
Limitations: Applications not accepted. Giving primarily in CA and FL. No grants to individuals.
Application information: Unsolicited requests for funds not accepted.
Officers and Directors: Pamela Weiss, Pres. and Secy. and Director; Scott Weiss, V.P.; Zach Weiss, V.P.; Zeta Weiss, V.P.; Zoe Weiss, V.P.
EIN: 260143833

1689
Don & Susan Kang Charitable Foundation Inc.
c/o Foundation Source
501 Silverside Rd., Ste. 123
Wilmington, DE   19809-1377

Established in 2005 in Delaware.
Donors: Susan Kang; Don Kang.
Foundation type: Independent foundation.
Financial data (yr. ended 12/31/13): Assets, $846,038 (M); expenditures, $216,485; qualifying distributions, $211,336; giving activities include $202,850 for 22 grants (high: $30,000; low: $500).
Fields of interest: Education; Nonprofits; Legal services; Child welfare.
Type of support: Regranting.
Limitations: Applications not accepted. Giving primarily in CA. No grants to individuals.
Application information: Unsolicited requests for funds not accepted.
Officers and Directors: Don Kang, Pres. and Secy. and Director; Susan Kang, V.P.
EIN: 203757896

1690
The Herman H. Kaye Charitable Foundation
c/o Foundation Source
501 Silverside Rd., Ste. 123
Wilmington, DE   19809-1377

Donor: Herman H. Kaye Trust.
Foundation type: Independent foundation.
Financial data (yr. ended 12/31/13): Assets, $1,175,345 (M); gifts received, $320,000; expenditures, $212,508; qualifying distributions, $212,448; giving activities include $150,000 for 9 grants (high: $100,000; low: $3,000).
Fields of interest: Arts and culture; Public affairs; Human services.
Limitations: Applications not accepted. Giving primarily in CA.
Application information: Unsolicited requests for funds not accepted.

Officer and Director: Cary W. Spencer, Pres. and Secy. and Director.
EIN: 274449593

1691
Kent-Lucas Foundation, Inc.
101 Springer Bldg.
3411 Silverside Rd.
Wilmington, DE 19810-4811 (302) 478-4383
Contact: James L. Van Alen II, Pres. and Treas.

Donor: Atwater Kent Foundation, Inc.
Foundation type: Independent foundation.
Financial data (yr. ended 12/31/14): Assets, $3,544,952 (M); expenditures, $156,471; qualifying distributions, $143,451; giving activities include $140,000 for 91 grants (high: $22,000; low: $50).
Purpose and activities: Giving primarily to hospitals, community organizations, children's services, and education.
Fields of interest: Education; Environment; Sports and recreation.
Limitations: Applications accepted. Giving primarily in FL, ME, and the metropolitan Philadelphia, PA, area. No grants to individuals, or for endowment funds.
Publications: Application guidelines.
Application information: Application form required.
Initial approach: Letter
Copies of proposal: 1
Deadline(s): None
Officers and Trustees: James L. Van Alen II, Pres. and Treas. and Trustee; Elizabeth K. Van Alen, V.P. and Trustee; Cassandra V.A. Ludington II, V.P. and Trustee; James R. Weaver, Secy.
Number of staff: 4
EIN: 237010084

1692
Kerr Family Foundation
c/o Foundation Source
501 Silverside Rd., Ste. 123
Wilmington, DE 19809-1377

Foundation type: Independent foundation.
Financial data (yr. ended 12/31/13): Assets, $1,816,836 (M); expenditures, $230,017; qualifying distributions, $212,551; giving activities include $199,810 for 37 grants (high: $30,000; low: $400).
Fields of interest: Arts and culture; Health; Diseases and conditions.
Limitations: Applications not accepted. Giving primarily in San Diego, CA.
Application information: Unsolicited requests for funds not accepted.
Officers and Directors: Richard Kerr, Pres. and Director; Lynda Kerr, Secy. and Director.
EIN: 330940583

1693
Kingsley Foundation
c/o Wilmington Trust Co.
1100 N. Market St., DE3-C070
Wilmington, DE 19890-0900

Established in 1961 in Connecticut.
Donors: F.G. Kingsley; Ora K. Smith.
Foundation type: Independent foundation.

Financial data (yr. ended 12/31/13): Assets, $8,970,382 (M); expenditures, $396,595; qualifying distributions, $391,604; giving activities include $390,216 for 32 grants (high: $91,000; low: $1,000).
Fields of interest: Arts and culture; Opera; Education; Undergraduate education; Environment.
Limitations: Applications not accepted. Giving primarily in CT, NH and NY. No grants to individuals.
Application information: Contributes only to pre-selected organizations.
Trustee: Wilmington Trust Co.
Advisors: Catherine S. Cuthell; Elizabeth S. Reed; Margaret J. Smith; Ora K. Smith; Roger K. Smith.
EIN: 516163698

1694
David L. Klein, Jr. Foundation
(formerly David L. Klein, Jr. Memorial Foundation, Inc.)
c/o Foundation Source
501 Silverside Rd., Ste. 123
Wilmington, DE 19809-1377
E-mail: kleinjr@blueprintrd.com

Established in 1959 in New York.
Donors: David L. Klein†; Miriam Klein†; Endo Laboratories, Inc.; Barry Traub; Marjorie Traub; Saretta Barnet.
Foundation type: Independent foundation.
Financial data (yr. ended 12/31/13): Assets, $6,973,028 (M); expenditures, $446,327; qualifying distributions, $414,719; giving activities include $381,251 for 38 grants (high: $35,000; low: $1,000).
Purpose and activities: Giving primarily for education and human services.
Fields of interest: Arts and culture; Education; Foundations; Diseases and conditions; Judaism; Human services.
Limitations: Applications not accepted. Giving primarily in the San Francisco Bay Area, CA, and New York, NY. No grants to individuals.
Application information: Contributes only to pre-selected organizations. Grants initiated by trustees.
Board meeting date(s): Annually in Nov.
Officers and Trustees: Jane Barnet, Pres. and Trustee; Peter Barnet, Secy. and Trustee; Howard Barnet, Jr., Treas.; Geoff Barnet; Saretta Barnet.
Number of staff: 1 part-time professional.
EIN: 136085432

1695
Paul and Patricia Kuehner Family Foundation
c/o Foundation Source
501 Silverside Rd., Ste. 123
Wilmington, DE 19809-1377

Established in 2007 in Delaware.
Donors: Patricia Kuehner; Paul J. Kuehner.
Foundation type: Independent foundation.
Financial data (yr. ended 12/31/13): Assets, $599,739 (M); gifts received, $900,000; expenditures, $325,275; qualifying distributions, $325,275; giving activities include $271,500 for 9 grants (high: $50,000; low: $10,500).
Fields of interest: Human services; Basic and emergency aid; International development.

Limitations: Applications not accepted. Giving in the U.S., with emphasis on CT. No grants to individuals.
Application information: Contributes only to pre-selected organizations.
Officers and Directors: Paul J. Kuehner, Pres. and Secy. and Director; Patricia Kuehner, V.P. and Director.
EIN: 260849308

1696
Milton and Hattie Kutz Foundation
101 Garden of Eden Rd.
Wilmington, DE 19803-1511 (302) 427-2100
Contact: Leslie Newman, Pres.

Established in 1955 in Delaware.
Donors: Milton Kutz†; Hattie Kutz†.
Foundation type: Independent foundation.
Financial data (yr. ended 06/30/14): Assets, $2,722,321 (M); gifts received, $31; expenditures, $184,569; qualifying distributions, $173,154; giving activities include $160,752 for 27 grants (high: $20,000; low: $1,800).
Purpose and activities: Giving largely for social service organizations; grants also for children and youth programs, scholarships to organizations (not individuals), and capital campaigns. Preference for capital rather than program.
Fields of interest: Education; Human services; Child welfare; Seniors.
Type of support: General support; Capital campaigns; Capital and infrastructure; Program development; Seed money.
Limitations: Applications accepted. Giving limited to DE. No grants to individuals.
Publications: Grants list.
Application information: Application form required.
Initial approach: Proposal
Copies of proposal: 1
Deadline(s): Mar. 15
Board meeting date(s): June and Dec.
Officers: Leslie Newman, Pres.; Suzanne B. Grant, V.P.; Jerome K. Grossman, Secy.; Rolf F. Erikson, Treas.; Seth J. Katzen, Exec. Secy.
Directors: Jack Blumenfeld; Donald F. Parsons; Susan Kirk Ryan, Esq.; Barbara H. Schoenberg; Connie J. Sugarman; Craig Sternberg; William W. Wagner.
Number of staff: None.
EIN: 510187055

1697
Ellen and Alan Levin Family Foundation
P.O. Box 320
Montchanin, DE 19710-0320

Established in 2006 in Delaware.
Donors: Alan B. Levin; Ellen K. Levin.
Foundation type: Independent foundation.
Financial data (yr. ended 12/31/14): Assets, $4,434,372; expenditures, $280,747; qualifying distributions, $229,850.
Fields of interest: Education; Health; Human services.
Type of support: General support.
Limitations: Applications not accepted. Giving primarily in DE. No grants to individuals.
Application information: Unsolicited requests for funds not accepted.
Officers and Directors: Ellen K. Levin, Pres. and Treas. and Director; Alan B. Levin, V.P. and Secy.

and Director; Andrew G. Levin; Daniel B. Levin; Jason S. Levin.
EIN: 205679477

1698
Lighten Family Foundation
c/o Foundation Source
501 Silverside Rd., Ste. 123
Wilmington, DE 19809-1377

Donors: William E. Lighten; Janifer Lynn Lighten.
Foundation type: Independent foundation.
Financial data (yr. ended 12/31/13): Assets, $5,869,004 (M); expenditures, $442,432; qualifying distributions, $391,591; giving activities include $376,056 for 23 grants (high: $250,000; low: $400).
Fields of interest: Higher education; Protestantism; Human services.
Limitations: Applications not accepted. Giving primarily in CT and NY. No grants to individuals.
Application information: Unsolicited requests for funds not accepted.
Officers and Directors: William E. Lighten, Pres. and Secy. and Director; Adrienne J. Lighten, V.P.; Alexis N. Lighten, V.P.; Christopher W. Lightpen, V.P.; Janifer Lynn Lighten, V.P.
EIN: 208069108

1699
Larry Lightner Sams Foundation, Inc.
c/o Foundation Source
501 Silverside Rd., Ste. 123
Wilmington, DE 19809-1377
Contact: Larry Lightner, Tr.

Established in 1994 in Texas.
Foundation type: Independent foundation.
Financial data (yr. ended 12/31/13): Assets, $13,661,509 (M); expenditures, $743,749; qualifying distributions, $628,758; giving activities include $429,000 for 45 grants (high: $30,000; low: $500).
Fields of interest: Education; Diseases and conditions; Community and economic development; Human services; Child welfare; Children and youth; Seniors; Females.
Type of support: General support; Matching grants; Annual campaigns; Capital campaigns; Capital and infrastructure; Equipment; Research; Debt reduction; Research and evaluation; Program development.
Limitations: Applications not accepted. Giving primarily in Dallas, TX. No support for political organizations. No grants to individuals, or for fundraisers.
Application information: Unsolicited requests for funds not accepted; applications are by trustee invitation only.
> *Board meeting date(s):* Late Mar., late July, and late Nov.

Officers and Trustees: Larry Lightner, Pres. and Treas. and Trustee; Sue B. Lightner, V.P. and Secy. and Trustee; Charles Derek Adleta; Earl Sams Lightner; Robin H. Lightner; Kamala A. Lightner-Scammahorn.
Number of staff: 1 full-time professional; 1 part-time professional; 1 full-time support.
EIN: 752555622

1700
The Loftus Family Foundation
c/o Foundation Source
501 Silverside Rd., Ste. 123
Wilmington, DE 19809-1377

Established in 2006 in Delaware.
Donor: John Loftus.
Foundation type: Independent foundation.
Financial data (yr. ended 12/31/14): Assets, $6,006,309 (M); expenditures, $324,586; qualifying distributions, $321,126; giving activities include $290,999 for 17 grants (high: $96,000; low: $1,000).
Fields of interest: Vocal music; Christianity; Human services.
Limitations: Applications not accepted. Giving primarily in CA and FL. No grants to individuals.
Application information: Contributes only to pre-selected organizations.
Officer and Director: John Loftus, Pres. and Secy. and Director.
EIN: 208067422

1701
The Caroline M. Lowndes Foundation Inc.
c/o Foundation Source
501 Silverside Rd., Ste. 123
Wilmington, DE 19809-1377

Established in 2007 in Delaware.
Donor: Caroline M. Lowndes.
Foundation type: Independent foundation.
Financial data (yr. ended 12/31/13): Assets, $5,191,352 (M); expenditures, $238,176; qualifying distributions, $218,396; giving activities include $180,100 for 26 grants (high: $50,000; low: $500).
Fields of interest: Arts and culture; Environment; Religion.
Limitations: Applications not accepted. Giving primarily in MA and NY. No grants to individuals.
Application information: Unsolicited requests for funds not accepted.
Officer and Director: Caroline M. Lowndes, Pres. and Secy. and Director.
EIN: 260379209

1702
The Martyn Foundation
c/o Foundation Source
501 Silverside Rd., Ste. 123
Wilmington, DE 19809-1377

Donors: Ignacio Rodriguez; Joan Stiefel Rodriguez.
Foundation type: Independent foundation.
Financial data (yr. ended 12/31/13): Assets, $612,990 (M); expenditures, $167,285; qualifying distributions, $165,624; giving activities include $158,000 for 13 grants (high: $35,000; low: $5,000).
Fields of interest: Education; Domesticated animals; Health.
Limitations: Applications not accepted. Giving primarily in Washington, DC, GA and NC.
Application information: Unsolicited requests for funds not accepted.
Officers and Directors: Joan Stiefel Rodriguez, Pres. and Secy. and Director; Andrew Rodriguez, V.P.;

Ignacio Rodriguez, V.P.; Marilyn Rodriguez, V.P.; Melanie Rodriguez, V.P.
EIN: 274462223

1703
Mary's Fund Foundation
c/o Foundation Source
501 Silverside Rd., Ste. 123
Wilmington, DE 19809-1377

Donors: Margaret Hartshorn; Michael Hartshorn.
Foundation type: Independent foundation.
Financial data (yr. ended 12/31/13): Assets, $1,326,690 (M); expenditures, $144,120; qualifying distributions, $131,781; giving activities include $62,000 for 8 grants (high: $40,000; low: $2,000), and $58,500 for 11 grants to individuals (high: $5,000; low: $500).
Fields of interest: Health; Human services.
Type of support: Grants to individuals.
Limitations: Applications not accepted. Giving primarily in OH.
Application information: Unsolicited requests for funds not accepted.
Officers and Directors: Michael Hartshorn, Pres. and Secy. and Director; Margaret Hartshorn, V.P. and Director; Jason Dwyer, V.P.; Kathleen Dwyer, V.P.; Kelly Hartshorn, V.P.; Timothy Hartshorn, V.P.
EIN: 271424474

1704
Elizabeth and Joseph Massoud Family Foundation
c/o Foundation Source
501 Silverside Rd., Ste. 123
Wilmington, DE 19809-1377

Donors: Elizabeth Allman Massoud; Ihab Joseph Massoud.
Foundation type: Independent foundation.
Financial data (yr. ended 12/31/13): Assets, $2,766,238 (M); gifts received, $2,993,986; expenditures, $416,469; qualifying distributions, $399,740; giving activities include $390,700 for 15 grants (high: $150,000; low: $100).
Fields of interest: Catholicism; Human services; Youth development.
Limitations: Applications not accepted. Giving primarily in CT.
Application information: Unsolicited requests for funds not accepted.
Officers and Directors: Ihab Joseph Massoud, Pres. and Secy.-Treas. and Director; Elizabeth Allman Massoud, V.P. and Director.
EIN: 462495320

1705
McIntosh Family Foundation
c/o Foundation Source
501 Silverside Rd.
Wilmington, DE 19809-1377

Foundation type: Independent foundation.
Financial data (yr. ended 12/31/12): Assets, $4,357,580 (M); expenditures, $180,692; qualifying distributions, $133,310; giving activities include $133,310 for grants.
Fields of interest: Foundations; Human services.
Limitations: Applications not accepted. Giving primarily in Phoenix, AZ; funding also in CO.

Application information: Unsolicited requests for funds not accepted.
Officers and Directors: Carolyn McIntosh, Pres. and Secy. and Director; Scott McIntosh, V.P. and Director.
EIN: 262199799

1706
McKiernan Family Foundation
c/o Foundation Source
501 Silverside Rd.
Wilmington, DE 19809-1377

Donor: William S. McKiernan.
Foundation type: Independent foundation.
Financial data (yr. ended 05/31/14): Assets, $266,918; gifts received, $0; expenditures, $149,603; qualifying distributions, $146,453 and $0 for set-asides.
Fields of interest: Education; University education; Human services; Youth development.
Limitations: Applications not accepted. Giving primarily in CA and MA.
Application information: Unsolicited requests for funds not accepted.
Officer and Director: William S. McKiernan, Pres. and Secy. and Director.
EIN: 272216128

1707
Merrion Family Foundation
c/o Foundation Source
501 Silverside Rd., Ste. 123
Wilmington, DE 19809-1377

Donor: Merrion Oil & Gas.
Foundation type: Independent foundation.
Financial data (yr. ended 12/31/13): Assets, $6,049,629 (M); expenditures, $250,107; qualifying distributions, $226,800; giving activities include $201,754 for 34 grants (high: $100,000; low: $150).
Fields of interest: Education; Religion; Human services.
Limitations: Applications not accepted. Giving primarily in NM.
Application information: Unsolicited requests for funds not accepted.
Officers and Directors: T. Greg Merrion, Pres. and Secy.; Anne M. Merrion, V.P.; Brittany K.M. Merrion, V.P.; Hannah J. Merrion, V.P.; Molly J. Merrion, V.P.; Ryan G. Merrion, V.P.; Samantha C. Merrion, V.P.; Sara L. Merrion, V.P.; Tori G. Merrion, V.P.
EIN: 263374889

1708
Messing Family Charitable Foundation
(formerly Roswell Messing, Jr. Charitable Foundation)
c/o Foundation Source
501 Silverside Rd., Ste 123
Wilmington, DE 19809-1377

Established in 1961 in Missouri.
Donors: Roswell Messing, Jr.; Mrs. Roswell Messing, Jr.; Wilma E. Messing; Noel Hefty; Roswell Messing III; Tara Hefty Hume; Bart Partners, LP; Jeanne Walsh; Jake Messing; Ali Messing; Niya's Nest; Jeanne Elise Messing Walsh.
Foundation type: Independent foundation.

Financial data (yr. ended 12/31/13): Assets, $5,385,916 (M); gifts received, $50,333; expenditures, $344,104; qualifying distributions, $322,166; giving activities include $295,365 for 62 grants (high: $50,000; low: $250).
Purpose and activities: Giving for dance programs, Jewish agencies, higher education, and to health and medical issues.
Fields of interest: Dance; Education; University education; Environment; Hospital care; Diseases and conditions; Judaism; Family services.
Type of support: Research.
Limitations: Applications not accepted. Giving primarily in CA and CO.
Application information: Contributes only to pre-selected organizations.
Officers and Directors: Roswell Messing III, Pres. and Director; Terrance Hefty, V.P. and Director; Arlene Naschke, Secy. and Director; Noel Messing Hefty, Treas. and Director.
EIN: 436034863

1709
The Midvale Foundation
c/o Foundation Source
501 Silverside Rd., Ste. 123
Wilmington, DE 19809-1377

Established in 2007 in Delaware.
Donor: Sheila Hearne.
Foundation type: Independent foundation.
Financial data (yr. ended 12/31/13): Assets, $4,645,775 (M); expenditures, $223,260; qualifying distributions, $192,981; giving activities include $171,250 for 30 grants (high: $50,500; low: $500).
Fields of interest: Education.
Type of support: General support.
Limitations: Applications not accepted. Giving primarily in CT. No grants to individuals.
Application information: Contributes only to pre-selected organizations.
Officers and Directors: Moira Hintsa, Pres. and Secy. and Director; Matthew Hintsa, V.P. and Director; Michael Hintsa, V.P. and Director.
EIN: 208678873

1710
Mark and Jessie Milano Foundation
c/o Foundation Source
501 Silverside Rd., Ste. 123
Wilmington, DE 19809-1377

Established in 2006 in Delaware.
Foundation type: Independent foundation.
Financial data (yr. ended 12/31/13): Assets, $5,633,157 (M); expenditures, $295,958; qualifying distributions, $250,209; giving activities include $223,000 for 17 grants (high: $80,000; low: $1,000).
Fields of interest: Undergraduate education; Foundations; Multiple sclerosis; Scouting programs.
Type of support: Equipment.
Limitations: Applications not accepted. Giving primarily in CA, with some giving DC, MT and NY. No grants to individuals.
Application information: Contributes only to pre-selected organizations.
Officers and Directors: Mark R. Milano, Pres. and Secy. and Director; Jessie Milano, V.P. and Director.
EIN: 208004580

1711
Gerrish H. Milliken Foundation
c/o Wilmington Trust Co.
1100 N. Market St., DE3-C070
Wilmington, DE 19890-0001

Donors: Gerrish H. Milliken, Jr.; Phoebe G. Milliken.
Foundation type: Independent foundation.
Financial data (yr. ended 12/31/14): Assets, $6,451,414; expenditures, $267,851; qualifying distributions, $250,980.
Purpose and activities: Giving for education, environmental conservation, art and cultural programs, historical preservation and research, and health and human services.
Fields of interest: Historic preservation; Education; Higher education; Environment; Health; Hospital care; Public administration; Human services.
Type of support: General support.
Limitations: Applications not accepted. Giving in the U.S., with emphasis on CT, MA, and ME. No grants to individuals.
Application information: Contributes only to pre-selected organizations.
Officers and Trustees: Thomas Hamilton, Co-Treas. and Trustee; James F. Zahrn, Co-Treas. and Trustee; John W. Milliken; Peter Milliken; Phoebe Milliken; Stephen G. Milliken.
EIN: 066037106

1712
MMK Foundation
c/o Foundation Source
501 Silverside Rd.
Wilmington, DE 19809-1377

Established in 2007 in Texas.
Donors: Marcia King; Mark A. King.
Foundation type: Independent foundation.
Financial data (yr. ended 12/31/13): Assets, $2,527,330 (M); expenditures, $274,719; qualifying distributions, $243,650; giving activities include $212,000 for 19 grants (high: $30,000; low: $500).
Fields of interest: Education; Health; Human services.
Type of support: General support.
Limitations: Applications not accepted. Giving primarily in Dallas, TX. No grants to individuals.
Application information: Contributes only to pre-selected organizations.
Officers: Mark A. King, Pres.; Warren Edwards, Secy.; Marcia King, Treas.
EIN: 260372739

1713
John L. Mulvaney Foundation
919 N. Market St., Ste. 420
Wilmington, DE 19801-3014

Established in 2001 in Pennsylvania.
Donors: Brian Mulvaney; Kay Mulvaney.
Foundation type: Independent foundation.
Financial data (yr. ended 11/30/13): Assets, $2,481,701 (M); gifts received, $1,000; expenditures, $243,626; qualifying distributions, $219,138; giving activities include $201,000 for 9 grants (high: $50,000; low: $5,000).
Fields of interest: Hospital care; Christianity; Youth development.

Limitations: Applications not accepted. Giving primarily in CA, NY, PA and SC. No grants to individuals.
Application Information: Contributes only to pre-selected organizations.
Trustees: Brian Mulvaney; Kay Mulvaney; Brown Brothers Harriman Trust Co.
EIN: 256796673

1714
Donna and Dave Nelson Family Foundation

c/o Foundation Source
501 Silverside Rd., Ste. 123
Wilmington, DE   19809-1377

Established in 2007 in Tennessee.
Donors: David E. Nelson; Ned E.J. Nelson; C. Lynn Nelson; Donna K. Nelson.
Foundation type: Independent foundation.
Financial data (yr. ended 12/31/13): Assets, $2,229,506 (M); expenditures, $167,921; qualifying distributions, $148,446; giving activities include $134,450 for 23 grants (high: $25,000; low: $200).
Fields of interest: Foundations; Human services.
Limitations: Applications not accepted. Giving primarily in TN. No grants to individuals.
Application Information: Contributes only to pre-selected organizations.
Officers and Directors: David E. Nelson, Pres. and Director; Donna K. Nelson, Secy. and Director.
EIN: 261600828

1715
New City Foundation

c/o Foundation Source
501 Silverside Rd., Ste. 123
Wilmington, DE   19809-1377

Established in 1997 in Connecticut.
Donor: Richard Ferguson.
Foundation type: Independent foundation.
Financial data (yr. ended 12/31/13): Assets, $2,322,889 (M); expenditures, $250,882; qualifying distributions, $234,514; giving activities include $220,475 for 60 grants (high: $50,000; low: $300).
Purpose and activities: Giving primarily for the arts, education, and human services.
Fields of interest: Arts and culture; Education; Nonprofits; Human services.
Type of support: Continuing support; Matching grants; Seed money; Scholarships; Regranting; Emergency funds; Debt reduction; Capital and infrastructure; Capital campaigns; Annual campaigns; Capacity-building and technical assistance; Financial sustainability; General support.
Limitations: Applications not accepted. Giving primarily in CT. No grants to individuals.
Application Information: Contributes only to pre-selected organizations.
Trustees: Marissa V.G. Ferguson; Richard A. Ferguson.
Number of staff: None.
EIN: 061475198

1716
New Covenant Foundation, Inc.

c/o Foundation Source
501 Silverside Rd., Ste. 123
Wilmington, DE   19809-1377

Established in 2004 in Massachusetts.
Donors: Patricia M. Morell; Allen N. Morell.
Foundation type: Independent foundation.
Financial data (yr. ended 12/31/13): Assets, $2,919,341 (M); expenditures, $294,159; qualifying distributions, $264,111; giving activities include $166,423 for 21 grants (high: $30,000; low: $400).
Fields of interest: Christianity; Child welfare.
Limitations: Applications not accepted. Giving primarily in ME, TX and VA. No grants to individuals.
Application Information: Contributes only to pre-selected organizations.
Officers and Directors: Allen N. Morell, Pres. and Director; Patricia M. Morell, Clerk and Treas. and Director.
EIN: 201986617

1717
Night Heron Foundation

c/o Foundation Source
501 Silverside Rd., Ste. 123
Wilmington, DE   19809-1377

Donors: Nancy Goroff Whitney; Mathenaeum Foundation.
Foundation type: Independent foundation.
Financial data (yr. ended 12/31/13): Assets, $10,319,332 (M); gifts received, $350,000; expenditures, $424,471; qualifying distributions, $378,759; giving activities include $337,498 for 2 grants (high: $200,000; low: $137,498).
Fields of interest: Museums.
Limitations: Applications not accepted. Giving primarily in New York, NY.
Application Information: Unsolicited requests for funds not accepted.
Officer and Director: Nancy Goroff Whitney, Pres. and Secy. and Director.
EIN: 273785123

1718
Palmer Home, Inc.

P.O. Box 1751
Dover, DE   19903-1751
Contact: Jean T. Deleo, Pres.

Foundation type: Operating foundation.
Financial data (yr. ended 02/28/13): Assets, $4,782,061 (M); gifts received, $18,447; expenditures, $321,082; qualifying distributions, $278,292; giving activities include $275,650 for 15 grants (high: $45,000; low: $3,500).
Purpose and activities: Giving to organizations that benefit the elderly (over 65).
Fields of interest: Hospital care; Hospice care; Catholicism; Human services; Food aid; Senior services; Seniors.
Limitations: Applications accepted. Giving primarily in DE. No grants to individuals.
Application Information:
Initial approach: Letter
Deadline(s): Sept. 1
Board meeting date(s): Quarterly

Officers: Jean T. DeLeo, Pres.; Carol Braverman, V.P.; Ellen Harbeson, Secy.
EIN: 510066737

1719
Patterson Family Foundation Inc.

c/o Foundation Source
501 Silverside Rd., Ste. 123
Wilmington, DE   19809-1377

Established in 1995 in Georgia.
Donors: Solon P. Patterson; Marianna R. Patterson; Joseph Peter Patterson; John Solon Patterson.
Foundation type: Independent foundation.
Financial data (yr. ended 12/31/13): Assets, $6,131,673 (M); gifts received, $227,484; expenditures, $256,487; qualifying distributions, $236,292; giving activities include $207,373 for 65 grants (high: $30,000; low: $100).
Fields of interest: Elementary and secondary education; University education; Catholicism; Orthodox Christianity; Youth services; Low-income and poor people.
Type of support: Continuing support; Annual campaigns; Capital campaigns; Capital and infrastructure.
Limitations: Applications not accepted. Giving primarily in GA, with an emphasis on the metropolitan Atlanta, GA, area and north GA. No support for political causes. No grants to individuals or for independent schools, except where trustees or other family members have a special relationship or interest.
Application Information: Unsolicited requests for funds not accepted.
Officers: Solon P. Patterson, Pres.; Marianna R. Patterson, Secy.-Treas.
Trustees: John Solon Patterson; Joseph Peter Patterson.
Number of staff: None.
EIN: 582145618

1720
Hugh E. & Marjorie S. Petersen Foundation Inc.

c/o Foundation Source
501 Silverside Rd., Ste. 123
Wilmington, DE   19809-1377

Established in 2005 in Delaware.
Donors: La Arcada Investments Corp.; Marjorie S. Petersen.
Foundation type: Independent foundation.
Financial data (yr. ended 12/31/14): Assets, $277,704 (M); gifts received, $637,794; expenditures, $373,000; qualifying distributions, $369,775; giving activities include $364,750 for 31 grants (high: $65,000; low: $1,000).
Fields of interest: Christianity; Youth services.
Limitations: Applications not accepted. Giving primarily in CA, Colorado Springs, CO, and IL. No grants to individuals.
Application Information: Contributes only to pre-selected organizations.
Officers and Directors: Lynne Tahmisian, Pres. and Director; Ruth Kovacs, V.P. and Secy. and Director; Sharon Peck, V.P.
EIN: 203757530

1721
Pinkerton Foundation
c/o Foundation Source
501 Silverside Rd., Ste. 123
Wilmington, DE 19809-1377

Established in 1994 in Washington.
Donors: Guy C. Pinkerton; Nancy J. Pinkerton.
Foundation type: Independent foundation.
Financial data (yr. ended 04/30/13): Assets, $4,048,640 (M); gifts received, $332,400; expenditures, $258,485; qualifying distributions, $213,710; giving activities include $194,400 for 52 grants (high: $40,000; low: $500).
Purpose and activities: Giving for federated giving programs, Christian churches, youth services, higher education and music organizations.
Fields of interest: Education; Nonprofits; Hospital care; Christianity; Human services; Youth development.
Type of support: General support; Regranting.
Limitations: Applications not accepted. Giving primarily in WA. No grants to individuals.
Application information: Contributes only to pre-selected organizations.
Officers and Directors: Guy C. Pinkerton, Pres. and Treas. and Director; Nancy J. Pinkerton, V.P. and Secy. and Director.
EIN: 911665004

1722
The Mark E. Pollack Foundation
c/o Foundation Source
501 Silverside Rd., Ste. 123
Wilmington, DE 19809-1377

Established in 2007 in Delaware.
Donor: Mark E. Pollack.
Foundation type: Independent foundation.
Financial data (yr. ended 12/31/13): Assets, $989,333 (M); expenditures, $403,693; qualifying distributions, $402,693; giving activities include $392,500 for 25 grants (high: $150,000; low: $1,000).
Fields of interest: University education; Cancers; Individual liberties.
Limitations: Applications not accepted. Giving primarily in Washington, DC. No grants to individuals.
Application information: Contributes only to pre-selected organizations.
Officer and Director: Mark E. Pollack, Pres. and Secy. and Director.
EIN: 261532753

1723
Praxis Foundation
(formerly The Spilka Family Foundation, Inc.)
c/o Foundation Source
501 Silverside Rd., Ste. 123
Wilmington, DE 19809-1377

Established in 2003 in Delaware.
Donor: Robert Edward Spilka.
Foundation type: Independent foundation.
Financial data (yr. ended 12/31/13): Assets, $2,378,093 (M); expenditures, $173,566; qualifying distributions, $170,124; giving activities include $158,430 for 11 grants (high: $60,000; low: $500).

Fields of interest: Education; Philanthropy; Human services.
Limitations: Applications not accepted. Giving primarily in CT and NY. No grants to individuals.
Application information: Unsolicited requests for funds not accepted.
Officer and Director: Robert Edward Spilka, Pres. and Secy. and Director.
EIN: 542133110

1724
The Horowitz Ratner Family Foundation
c/o Foundation Source
501 Silverside Rd., Ste. 123
Wilmington, DE 19809-1377

Established in 2006 in Delaware.
Donors: Chuck Ratner; Ilana Horowitz Ratner; Charles A. Ratner.
Foundation type: Independent foundation.
Financial data (yr. ended 12/31/14): Assets, $528,002 (M); expenditures, $175,956; qualifying distributions, $172,156; giving activities include $166,766 for 11 grants (high: $50,000; low: $500).
Fields of interest: Music; Education; Nonprofits; Judaism.
Type of support: Regranting.
Limitations: Applications not accepted. Giving primarily in OH.
Application information: Unsolicited requests for funds not accepted.
Officers and Directors: Ilana Horowitz Ratner, Pres. and Secy. and Director; Robert Gephart, V.P.; Charles A. Ratner, V.P. and Director.
EIN: 208004682

1725
Relgalf Charitable Foundation
c/o Wilmington Trust Co.
1100 N. Market St.
Wilmington, DE 19890-0900
Application address: c/o George G. Matthews, 1925 Flagler Dr., West Palm Beach, FL 33407

Established in 1986 in Florida.
Donor: George G. Matthews.
Foundation type: Independent foundation.
Financial data (yr. ended 11/30/13): Assets, $8,308,019 (M); expenditures, $399,707; qualifying distributions, $388,791; giving activities include $388,791 for 23 grants (high: $108,291; low: $2,000).
Fields of interest: Education; Higher education; Health; Human services.
Limitations: Applications accepted. Giving primarily in FL and NC. No grants to individuals.
Application information: Application form required.
Initial approach: Proposal
Deadline(s): None
Trustees: Kelly Hopkins; Elizabeth E. Matthews; George G. Matthews; George G. Matthews, Jr.; William Matthews.
EIN: 596874133

1726
Remmer Family Foundation
c/o Foundation Source
501 Silverside Rd., Ste. 123
Wilmington, DE 19809-1377

Established in 1990 in Connecticut.
Donor: The Patricia C. Remmer 1995 Charitable Lead Trust.
Foundation type: Independent foundation.
Financial data (yr. ended 12/31/13): Assets, $4,566,040 (M); gifts received, $20,000; expenditures, $248,672; qualifying distributions, $209,014; giving activities include $183,500 for 14 grants (high: $30,000; low: $5,000).
Fields of interest: Child welfare; Female children and youth.
Type of support: Program development; Convening; Seed money; Research.
Limitations: Applications not accepted. Giving primarily in CT, FL, and MA. No grants to individuals.
Application information: Contributes only to pre-selected organizations.
Board meeting date(s): June
Officers and Directors: Ellen E. Remmer, Pres. and Director; Anne R. Cole, Secy. and Director; Susan R. Ryzewic, Treas. and Director.
EIN: 061313986

1727
The Repass-Rodgers Family Foundation, Inc.
c/o Foundation Source
501 Silverside Rd., Ste. 123
Wilmington, DE 19809-1377

Established in 2002 in Delaware.
Donors: Randy Repass; Sally-Christine Rodgers.
Foundation type: Independent foundation.
Financial data (yr. ended 12/31/13): Assets, $7,255,088 (M); expenditures, $293,308; qualifying distributions, $276,654; giving activities include $246,850 for 26 grants (high: $100,000; low: $100).
Fields of interest: Education; Environment; Human services.
Limitations: Applications not accepted. Giving primarily in CA. No grants to individuals.
Application information: Contributes only to pre-selected organizations.
Officers and Directors: Randy Repass, Pres. and Secy. and Director; Elizabeth Peck Repass Holmes, V.P.; Kent-Harns Repass, V.P.; Randolph Kent Repass, Jr., V.P.; Sally-Christine Rodgers, V.P. and Director.
EIN: 050545292

1728
Replogle Family Foundation
c/o Foundation Source
501 Silverside Rd., Ste. 123
Wilmington, DE 19809-1377

Established in 2007 in Delaware.
Donors: John B. Replogle; Kristin G. Replogle.
Foundation type: Independent foundation.
Financial data (yr. ended 12/31/13): Assets, $3,911,269 (M); expenditures, $336,699; qualifying distributions, $290,779; giving activities include $271,124 for 33 grants (high: $100,000; low: $67).
Fields of interest: Education; Higher education; Land resources; Foundations; Child welfare; Shelter and residential care.
Limitations: Applications not accepted. Giving primarily in MA and NC. No grants to individuals.

Application information: Contributes only to pre-selected organizations.
Officers and Directors: John B. Replogle, Pres. and Secy. and Director; Kristin G. Replogle, V.P.
EIN: 261385486

1729
The Riecker Charitable Foundation
c/o Foundation Source
501 Silverside Rd., Ste. 123
Wilmington, DE 19809-1377

Established in 2007 in Delaware.
Donor: William Riecker†.
Foundation type: Independent foundation.
Financial data (yr. ended 12/31/13): Assets, $5,020,662 (M); expenditures, $282,042; qualifying distributions, $231,387; giving activities include $190,000 for 25 grants (high: $35,000; low: $1,000).
Fields of interest: Nonprofits; Christianity.
Type of support: Scholarships; Regranting.
Limitations: Applications not accepted. Giving primarily in NY and VA. No grants to individuals.
Application information: Unsolicited requests for funds not accepted.
Officers and Directors: Ted Lillestolen, Co-Pres. and Secy. and Director; Robert Eliason, Co-Pres. and Director.
EIN: 208607750

1730
Mariano Rivera Foundation
321 Chattahoochee Dr.
Bear, DE 19701-4809 (847) 291-0603
Main URL: http://www.marianoriverafoundation.org

Donors: Mariano Rivera; Steiner Sports; Charity Buzz; Neuro Rays Imaging; VF Services; BTIG, LLC; Topps Us; Wish You Were Here Productions; Major League Baseball; Yes Network; Ridgefield High School Student Activity Account; Frozen Ropes of Morris County NJ, LLC; Curmark; Mariners Care; Colorado Rockies Baseball Club Foundation; OLILVY; Chardan Capital; David R. Tarella; Joseph Nicolla; Racing Rest of America II Inc.; Minnesota Twins; Royals Charities Inc.; Michael Weinberger; Arianne Weinberger; KCH Group.
Foundation type: Independent foundation.
Financial data (yr. ended 06/30/14): Assets, $5,085,683; gifts received, $844,863; expenditures, $348,611; qualifying distributions, $324,134.
Fields of interest: Christianity.
Limitations: Applications accepted. Giving in the U.S., with some emphasis on NY and TN.
Application information: Application form required.
Initial approach: Letter
Deadline(s): None
Officers: Mariano Rivera, Pres.; Clara Rivera, V.P.; Naomi Gandia, Secy.-Treas.
EIN: 134076067

1731
The Rivers Foundation
c/o Foundation Source
501 Silverside Rd., Ste. 123
Wilmington, DE 19809-1377

Established in 2009 in Delaware.

Donors: Philip M. Rivers; Tiffany Rivers.
Foundation type: Independent foundation.
Financial data (yr. ended 12/31/13): Assets, $2,373,655 (M); gifts received, $721,500; expenditures, $452,464; qualifying distributions, $439,259; giving activities include $424,000 for 13 grants (high: $125,000; low: $1,000).
Fields of interest: Education; Catholicism; Human services.
Limitations: Applications not accepted.
Application information: Unsolicited requests for funds not accepted.
Officers and Directors: Philip M. Rivers, Pres. and Secy. and Director; Tiffany Rivers, V.P. and Director.
EIN: 270167279

1732
Mary & Emmanuel Rosenfeld Foundation
c/o Advisory Trust Company of Delaware
1100 N. Market St., DE3-C070
Wilmington, DE 19890-0900

Foundation type: Independent foundation.
Financial data (yr. ended 12/31/13): Assets, $0 (M); expenditures, $355,060; qualifying distributions, $300,525; giving activities include $293,432 for 2 grants (high: $146,716; low: $146,716).
Fields of interest: Arts and culture; Performing arts; Higher education; Nonprofits; Hospital care; Hospice care; Diseases and conditions; Biology; Judaism; Human services; Food aid.
Type of support: Regranting.
Limitations: Applications accepted. Giving primarily in FL, PA and VA. No grants to individuals.
Application information: Application form required.
Initial approach: Letter
Deadline(s): None
Trustees: Lowell H. Dubrow, Esq.; Lester Rosenfeld; Rita Stein; Advisory Trust Company of Delaware.
EIN: 236220061

1733
Seymore and Sylvia Rothchild Family 2004 Charitable Foundation
c/o Foundation Source
501 Silverside Rd., Ste. 123
Wilmington, DE 19809-1377

Donor: Seymour Rothchild Family Trust.
Foundation type: Independent foundation.
Financial data (yr. ended 08/31/14): Assets, $4,211,165 (M); expenditures, $203,085; qualifying distributions, $171,564; giving activities include $150,000 for 41 grants (high: $12,500; low: $1,000).
Fields of interest: Diseases and conditions; Judaism; Human services.
Type of support: Research.
Limitations: Applications not accepted. Giving primarily in MA.
Application information: Unsolicited requests for funds not accepted.
Trustees: Alice Rothchild; Joseph Rothchild; Judith Rothchild.
EIN: 206307347

1734
The Douglas and Gloria Rumberger Foundation
c/o Foundation Source
501 Silverside Rd., Ste. 123
Wilmington, DE 19809-1377

Donor: Douglas Phares Rumberger†.
Foundation type: Independent foundation.
Financial data (yr. ended 12/31/13): Assets, $6,410,611 (M); expenditures, $316,911; qualifying distributions, $311,566; giving activities include $283,500 for 31 grants (high: $50,000; low: $500).
Fields of interest: Education; Nonprofits; Scouting programs.
Type of support: Capital campaigns; Regranting.
Limitations: Applications not accepted. Giving primarily in CA, NV, OH and OR. No grants to individuals.
Application information: Contributes only to pre-selected organizations.
Trustees: Kelly S. Gutierrez; Gloria D. Rumberger; Kiersten Jane Shaw.
EIN: 204049757

1735
Tom Russell Charitable Foundation, Inc.
c/o Foundation Source
501 Silverside Rd., Ste. 123
Wilmington, DE 19809-1377

Established in 1960 in Illinois.
Donors: Thomas C. Russell†; Wrap-On Co., Inc.; Huron & Orleans Building Corp.; F.D. Russell Trust f/b/o Mary J. Dickie.
Foundation type: Independent foundation.
Financial data (yr. ended 08/31/13): Assets, $15,861,684 (M); expenditures, $628,682; qualifying distributions, $561,637; giving activities include $375,000 for 35 grants (high: $45,000; low: $2,500).
Purpose and activities: The mission of the foundation is to "help people to help themselves." The foundation fulfills this mission by distributing charitable funds through charitable agencies that are most effective in yielding a positive social benefit.
Fields of interest: Education; Nonprofits; Health; Diseases and conditions; Community and economic development; Religion; Human services; Family services; Child welfare; Youth services; Adult and child mentoring.
Type of support: Regranting.
Limitations: Applications not accepted. Giving primarily in the metropolitan Chicago, IL area; funding also in NC, and OK. No support for governmental agencies, or for political or fraternal organizations. No grants to individuals, or for advertising, benefits, conferences, workshops or luncheons.
Application information: Contributes only to pre-selected organizations.
Officers and Directors: David S. Lindquist, Pres. and Director; J. Kirby Aiken, V.P. and Director; Crawford Cranshaw, Secy. and Director; John L. Bishop, Treas. and Director; Dan A. Felson.
EIN: 366082517

1736
John B. & Jane M. Ryerson Charitable Trust

c/o Wilmington Trust Co.
1100 N. Market St.
Wilmington, DE 19890-1100

Established in 1992 in New York.
Foundation type: Independent foundation.
Financial data (yr. ended 02/28/13): Assets, $5,502,098 (M); expenditures, $487,225; qualifying distributions, $315,990; giving activities include $228,331 for 11 grants (high: $34,250; low: $11,418).
Fields of interest: Animal welfare; Diseases and conditions; Arthritis; Alzheimer's disease; Cancers; Protestantism; Human services; Cemeteries and burial services.
Limitations: Applications not accepted. Giving limited to Palm Beach and West Palm Beach FL, and Cooperstown, NY. No grants to individuals.
Application information: Contributes only to pre-selected organizations.
Trustees: Uriel W. Carlton; Bernard Allen Heeke; Wilmington Trust Co.
EIN: 166349529

1737
The Sanders Family Foundation

c/o Wilmington Trust Co.
Rodney Square N.
1100 N. Market St.
Wilmington, DE 19890-0001

Established in 2007 in Texas.
Donors: Daniel S. Sanders; Emilyn C. Sanders.
Foundation type: Independent foundation.
Financial data (yr. ended 12/31/13): Assets, $8,244,727 (M); gifts received, $431,836; expenditures, $313,945; qualifying distributions, $310,426; giving activities include $286,950 for 7 grants (high: $111,950; low: $5,000).
Fields of interest: History museums; Higher education; Christianity; Human services.
Limitations: Applications not accepted. Giving primarily in Greenville, SC.
Application information: Unsolicited requests for funds not accepted.
Trustees: Daniel S. Sanders; Daniel Sanders, Jr.; Emilyn C. Sanders; John Sanders.
EIN: 766227833

1738
Robert M. Schiffman Foundation Inc.

c/o Foundation Source
501 Silverside Rd., Ste. 123
Wilmington, DE 19809-1377

Established in 1989 in Connecticut.
Donor: Richard Schiffman.
Foundation type: Independent foundation.
Financial data (yr. ended 12/31/13): Assets, $4,143,517 (M); expenditures, $161,164; qualifying distributions, $157,250; giving activities include $153,000 for 19 grants (high: $20,000; low: $2,000).
Fields of interest: Environment; Nonprofits; Health; Diseases and conditions; Human services.
Type of support: Regranting.
Limitations: Applications accepted. Giving primarily in CA, CT, MA, and NY.

Application information:
Initial approach: Proposal
Deadline(s): None
Officers: Ellen Schiffman, Pres.; Richard Lee Schiffman, V.P.; Tyler David Philpott, Secy.-Treas.
EIN: 061261222

1739
The Gerald and Susan Schwalbach Family Foundation

c/o Foundation Source
501 Silverside Rd., Ste. 123
Wilmington, DE 19809-1377

Established in 2006 in Arizona.
Donors: Gerald A. Schwalbach; Susan Jostrom Schwalbach.
Foundation type: Independent foundation.
Financial data (yr. ended 12/31/13): Assets, $5,044,515 (M); expenditures, $506,916; qualifying distributions, $457,468; giving activities include $432,000 for 12 grants (high: $200,000; low: $1,000).
Fields of interest: Education; Nonprofits; Diseases and conditions; Food banks.
Type of support: General support; Regranting.
Limitations: Applications not accepted. Giving primarily in MN, NH, OR and WA. No grants to individuals.
Application information: Contributes only to pre-selected organizations.
Officers and Directors: Susan Jostrom Schwalbach, Pres. and Director; Mari M. Schwalbach, V.P. and Director; Winsome Y. Schwalbach, V.P. and Director; Brian Anthony Schwalbach, Secy. and Director; Nathan Paul Schwalbach, Treas. and Director; Gerald Anthony Schwalbach.
EIN: 204822291

1740
Joyce and V.D. Scott Foundation Inc.

c/o Foundation Source
501 Silverside Rd., Ste. 123
Wilmington, DE 19809-1377

Donor: Joyce Scott†.
Foundation type: Independent foundation.
Financial data (yr. ended 12/31/13): Assets, $5,019,791 (M); expenditures, $237,627; qualifying distributions, $214,000; giving activities include $214,000 for 35 grants (high: $25,000; low: $1,000).
Fields of interest: Education; Community and economic development; Religion.
Limitations: Applications not accepted. Giving primarily in KY.
Application information: Unsolicited requests for funds not accepted.
Officers and Directors: Tommy Joe Fridy, Chair. and Pres. and Director; Meredith Fridy Helm, Secy. and Director; George Emery Warren II, Treas. and Director; Allison Fridy Arbuckle; Tommie Ann Fridy McCormack.
EIN: 263403693

1741
The William and Kathryn Scripps Family Foundation

c/o Foundation Source
501 Silverside Rd., Ste. 123
Wilmington, DE 19809-1377

Established in 2004 in Delaware.
Donors: William Hawkins Scripps; Kathryn Ann Scripps.
Foundation type: Independent foundation.
Financial data (yr. ended 12/31/13): Assets, $124,849 (M); gifts received, $350,000; expenditures, $370,843; qualifying distributions, $370,843; giving activities include $363,000 for 15 grants (high: $50,000; low: $1,000).
Fields of interest: Education; Cancers; Human services.
Limitations: Applications not accepted. Giving primarily in CA. No grants to individuals.
Application information: Contributes only to pre-selected organizations.
Officer and Directors: William Hawkins Scripps, Pres. and Secy. and Director; Kathryn Ann Scripps.
EIN: 200514611

1742
The Nina & Ivan Selin Family Foundation Inc

P.O. Box 396
Wilmington, DE 19899-0396

Established in 1994 in Maryland.
Donors: Nina E. Selin; Ivan Selin.
Foundation type: Independent foundation.
Financial data (yr. ended 12/31/13): Assets, $210,827 (M); expenditures, $405,917; qualifying distributions, $404,968; giving activities include $399,000 for 25 grants (high: $225,000; low: $1,000).
Fields of interest: Arts and culture; Museums; Education; Aquariums; Hospital care; Orthopedics; Cancers.
Limitations: Applications not accepted. Giving primarily in Washington, DC. No grants to individuals.
Application information: Unsolicited requests for funds not accepted.
Officers: Nina Evvie Selin, Chair. and Pres.; Ivan Selin, V.P. and Secy.
EIN: 521891582

1743
Signal Foundation for Wireless Innovation, Inc.

200 Bellevue Pkwy., Ste. 300
Wilmington, DE 19809-3727

Donor: Interdigital, Inc.
Foundation type: Independent foundation.
Financial data (yr. ended 12/31/13): Assets, $0 (M); gifts received, $150,000; expenditures, $150,000; qualifying distributions, $150,000; giving activities include $150,000 for 1 grant.
Fields of interest: Education.
Limitations: Applications not accepted. Giving primarily in VA.
Application information: Unsolicited requests for funds not accepted.

Officers and Directors: Lawrence F. Shay, Pres. and Director; Ranae S. McElvaine, Secy.; Richard J. Brezski, Treas.; Jannie K. Lau; William J. Merritt.
EIN: 463948126

1744

The Gordon and Jenny Singer Foundation

1105 N. Market St., Ste. 1300
Wilmington, DE   19801-1241

Donors: The Paul Singer Family Foundation; Paul E. Singer.
Foundation type: Independent foundation.
Financial data (yr. ended 11/30/13): Assets, $3,559,172 (M); gifts received, $1,000,000; expenditures, $275,443; qualifying distributions, $264,243; giving activities include $261,682 for 5 grants (high: $100,000; low: $10,000).
Fields of interest: Arts and culture; Sports and recreation; Human services.
International interests: United Kingdom of Great Britain and Northern Ireland.
Limitations: Applications not accepted. Giving primarily in MA, NH, and NY; funding also in the U.K.
Application information: Unsolicited requests for funds not accepted.
Officers and Directors: Gordon Singer, Pres. and Treas. and Director; Jenny Singer, V.P. and Director; Myron Kaplan, Secy.
EIN: 272010156

1745

Singhal Family Charitable Foundation

c/o Foundation Source
501 Silverside Rd., Ste. 123
Wilmington, DE   19809-1377

Established in 2006 in Delaware.
Donors: Amit Singhal; Shilpa Singhal.
Foundation type: Independent foundation.
Financial data (yr. ended 12/31/13): Assets, $4,554,921 (M); expenditures, $222,554; qualifying distributions, $195,000; giving activities include $189,975 for 1 grant.
Type of support: Endowments.
Limitations: Applications not accepted. Giving primarily in PA. No grants to individuals.
Application information: Contributes only to pre-selected organizations.
Officers and Directors: Amit Singhal, Pres. and Secy. and Director; Shilpa Singhal, V.P.
EIN: 208037921

1746

The Carl and Toby Sloane Family Foundation

c/o Foundation Source
501 Silverside Rd., Ste. 123
Wilmington, DE   19809-1377

Established in 2006 in Delaware.
Donors: Carl Sloane; Toby Sloane.
Foundation type: Independent foundation.
Financial data (yr. ended 12/31/13): Assets, $1,095,409 (M); expenditures, $374,764; qualifying distributions, $369,663; giving activities include $360,050 for 27 grants (high: $100,000; low: $250).
Fields of interest: Education; Nonprofits; Health; Judaism.

Type of support: Regranting.
Limitations: Applications not accepted. Giving primarily in MA. No grants to individuals.
Application information: Contributes only to pre-selected organizations.
Officers and Directors: Carl Sloane, Co-Pres. and Secy. and Director; Toby Sloane, Co-Pres. and Director; Lisa Sloane, V.P. and Director; Amy Sloane-Pinel, V.P. and Director; Todd C. Sloane, V.P. and Director.
EIN: 205632178

1747

SNAVE Foundation

c/o Foundation Source
501 Silverside Rd., Ste. 123
Wilmington, DE   19809-1377
E-mail: wceassoc@comcast.net

Established in 1988 in Pennsylvania.
Donors: J. Morris Evans; Anne T. Evans.
Foundation type: Independent foundation.
Financial data (yr. ended 12/31/13): Assets, $8,465,429 (M); expenditures, $489,097; qualifying distributions, $459,821; giving activities include $411,417 for 13 grants (high: $50,000; low: $250).
Purpose and activities: Giving primarily for education and human services.
Fields of interest: Education; Elementary and secondary education; Higher education; Human services.
Type of support: Land acquisitions; Matching grants; Capital campaigns; Capital and infrastructure; Equipment; Endowments; Program development; Curriculum development.
Limitations: Applications not accepted. Giving primarily in CT, DC, DE, MA, MD, ME, NH, NJ, NY, PA, RI, VA, and VT. No grants to individuals.
Publications: Financial statement; Grants list.
Application information: Unsolicited requests for funds not accepted.
Officers and Trustees: Walter C. Evans, Secy. and Trustee; Jason C. Rylander, Treas. and Trustee; Peter A. Evans; Megan E. Kafer; Jennifer E. Kravitz.
EIN: 236928009

1748

Solot Family Foundation

c/o Foundation Source
501 Silverside Rd., Ste. 123
Wilmington, DE   19809-1377

Established in 1998 in Pennsylvania.
Donors: Howard L. Solot; Howard L. and Janet N. Solot Charitable Lead Annuity Trust.
Foundation type: Independent foundation.
Financial data (yr. ended 12/31/13): Assets, $5,055,402 (M); gifts received, $508,055; expenditures, $238,504; qualifying distributions, $210,444; giving activities include $188,500 for 68 grants (high: $30,000; low: $500).
Fields of interest: Arts and culture; Education; Judaism.
Limitations: Applications not accepted. No grants to individuals.
Application information: Unsolicited requests for funds not accepted.

Trustees: Marsha B. Karp; Robert N. Karp; Howard L. Solot; Janet F. Solot; Julie E. Solot; Michael J. Solot.
EIN: 237933630

1749

Don and Roy Splawn Charitable Foundation West, Inc.

(formerly Roy L. Splawn Charitable Foundation)
c/o Foundation Source
501 Silverside Rd., Ste. 123
Wilmington, DE   19809-1377

Established in 1997 in California.
Donor: Roy Splawn Trust.
Foundation type: Independent foundation.
Financial data (yr. ended 12/31/13): Assets, $5,281,415 (M); expenditures, $263,817; qualifying distributions, $216,800; giving activities include $8,075 for 7 grants (high: $1,500; low: $566); and $145,000 for 107 grants to individuals (high: $2,500; low: $250).
Fields of interest: Education; Secondary education; Higher education; Nonprofits; Christianity; People with vision impairments.
Type of support: Student aid; Regranting.
Limitations: Applications not accepted. Giving primarily in CA.
Application information: Unsolicited requests for funds not accepted.
Officers and Directors: Phillips Yee, Pres. and Director; Natalie Yee, Exec. Dir.
EIN: 943276752

1750

The Stein Family Charitable Foundation

c/o Foundation Source
501 Silverside Rd., Ste. 123
Wilmington, DE   19809-1377

Donors: Sharon Stein; William J. Stein.
Foundation type: Independent foundation.
Financial data (yr. ended 12/31/13): Assets, $872,538 (M); gifts received, $500,000; expenditures, $324,047; qualifying distributions, $316,734; giving activities include $307,336 for 24 grants (high: $120,340; low: $250).
Fields of interest: Education; Diseases and conditions; Judaism; Human services.
Limitations: Applications not accepted. Giving primarily in MI and NY.
Application information: Unsolicited requests for funds not accepted.
Officers and Directors: William J. Stein, Pres. and Secy. and Director; Matthew Stein, V.P.; Sara Stein, V.P.; Sharon Stein, V.P.
EIN: 452732010

1751

Stiefel Freethought Foundation

c/o Foundation Source
501 Silverside Rd.
Wilmington, DE   19809-1377

Donor: Todd Stiefel.
Foundation type: Independent foundation.
Financial data (yr. ended 12/31/13): Assets, $1,556,929 (M); expenditures, $265,911; qualifying distributions, $261,851; giving activities

include $249,700 for 30 grants (high: $100,000; low: $200).

Fields of interest: Education; Religion; Human services.

Limitations: Applications not accepted.

Application information: Unsolicited requests for funds not accepted.

Officer and Director: Todd Stiefel, Pres. and Secy. and Director.

EIN: 270858715

1752
Sulentic Family Foundation
c/o Foundation Source
501 Silverside Rd., Ste. 123
Wilmington, DE 19809-1377

Established in 2006 in Texas.

Donors: Susan L. Sulentic; Robert E. Sulentic.

Foundation type: Independent foundation.

Financial data (yr. ended 12/31/13): Assets, $4,750,634 (M); gifts received, $149,025; expenditures, $340,376; qualifying distributions, $265,484; giving activities include $241,358 for 33 grants (high: $85,000; low: $100).

Fields of interest: Education; Elementary and secondary education; Nonprofits; Health.

Type of support: Regranting.

Limitations: Applications not accepted. Giving primarily in CA and TX. No grants to individuals.

Application information: Unsolicited requests for funds not accepted.

Officers: Robert E. Sulentic, Pres.; Judy Robertson, Secy.

Directors: Bob James; Susan L. Sulentic.

EIN: 208025263

1753
The Bernard M. and Caryl H. Susman Foundation
c/o Foundation Source
501 Silverside Rd., Ste. 123
Wilmington, DE 19809-1377

Established in 2006 in Delaware.

Donor: Bernard M. Susman Revocable Trust.

Foundation type: Independent foundation.

Financial data (yr. ended 12/31/13): Assets, $1,338,456 (M); expenditures, $167,822; qualifying distributions, $167,023; giving activities include $157,075 for 46 grants (high: $128,000; low: $100).

Fields of interest: Nonprofits; Judaism; Human services.

Type of support: Regranting.

Limitations: Applications not accepted. Giving primarily in IL. No grants to individuals.

Application information: Unsolicited requests for funds not accepted.

Officers and Directors: Bernard Susman, Pres. and Secy. and Director; Caryl Susman, V.P. and Director.

EIN: 208068788

1754
George P. Swift, Jr. Family Foundation
c/o NY Private Trust Co.
200 Bellevue Pkwy., Ste. 150
Wilmington, DE 19809-3725

Established in 1998 in Georgia.

Donors: Ann W. Swift; George P. Swift, Jr.

Foundation type: Independent foundation.

Financial data (yr. ended 12/31/14): Assets, $3,142,184; expenditures, $183,030; qualifying distributions, $155,000.

Fields of interest: Museums; Higher education; Animal welfare; Hospital care; Protestantism; Human services; Youth development.

Type of support: General support.

Limitations: Applications not accepted. Giving primarily in Columbus, GA. No grants to individuals.

Application information: Unsolicited requests for funds not accepted.

Distribution Committee: Virginia Swift.

EIN: 586379564

1755
Swinmurn Family Foundation
c/o Foundation Sourcce
501 Silverside Rd., Ste. 123
Wilmington, DE 19809-1377

Established in 2009 in Oregon.

Donors: Gabriela Swinmurn; C. John Swinmurn; Sandra C. Swinmurn; Nick Swinmurn.

Foundation type: Independent foundation.

Financial data (yr. ended 12/31/13): Assets, $6,800,565 (M); gifts received, $3,702,775; expenditures, $243,109; qualifying distributions, $214,041; giving activities include $197,360 for 11 grants (high: $50,000; low: $160).

Fields of interest: Child welfare.

Limitations: Applications not accepted.

Application information: Unsolicited requests for funds not accepted.

Trustees: C. John Swinmurn; Sandra C. Swinmurn.

EIN: 270690223

1756
The Synthesis Foundation, Inc.
c/o Foundation Source
501 Silverside Rd., Ste. 123
Wilmington, DE 19809-1377

Established in 2005 in Delaware.

Donor: Olivia B. Hansen.

Foundation type: Independent foundation.

Financial data (yr. ended 12/31/13): Assets, $162,209 (M); expenditures, $303,560; qualifying distributions, $303,560; giving activities include $298,000 for 7 grants (high: $100,000; low: $1,000).

Fields of interest: Education; University education; Spirituality.

Limitations: Applications not accepted. Giving primarily in AZ, CA and NY. No grants to individuals.

Application information: Contributes only to pre-selected organizations.

Officer and Director: Olivia B. Hansen, Pres. and Secy. and Director.

EIN: 203559799

1757
The Robert and Audrey Talbott Foundation
(formerly Audrey S. Talbott Foundation)
c/o Foundation Source
501 Silverside Rd., Ste. 123
Wilmington, DE 19809

Established in 1994 in California.

Donor: Audrey S. Talbott†.

Foundation type: Independent foundation.

Financial data (yr. ended 11/30/13): Assets, $6,163,933 (M); expenditures, $342,119; qualifying distributions, $260,164; giving activities include $232,000 for 21 grants (high: $25,000; low: $5,000).

Fields of interest: Education; University education; Public libraries; Human services; Youth development.

Limitations: Applications not accepted. Giving primarily in CA. No grants to individuals.

Application information: Unsolicited requests for funds not accepted.

Officers: Robert S. Talbott, Chair. and Pres.; Sarah Case Hawthome, Secy.-Treas.

EIN: 770389983

1758
Jeffrey Tarrant Family Foundation
P.O. Box 158
St. Georges, DE 19733-0158

Donor: Jeffrey Tarrant.

Foundation type: Independent foundation.

Financial data (yr. ended 06/30/14): Assets, $382,803 (M); gifts received, $230,000; expenditures, $156,893; qualifying distributions, $331,893; giving activities include $154,100 for 1 grant, and $175,000 for 3 loans/program-related investments (high: $100,000; low: $25,000).

Purpose and activities: Giving primarily to a film company that seeks to finance the development of films intended to raise public awareness of important social issues.

Fields of interest: Film and video.

Limitations: Applications not accepted. Giving primarily in New York, NY.

Application information: Unsolicited requests for funds not accepted.

Officers and Directors: Jeffrey Tarrant, C.E.O. and Pres. and Director; Terri Meeks, Secy.-Treas. and Director.

EIN: 271311573

1759
Ben & Kate Taylor Charitable Foundation
1100 N. Market DE3-C070
Wilmington, DE 19890-0900

Donor: Benjamin B. Taylor.

Foundation type: Independent foundation.

Financial data (yr. ended 10/31/13): Assets, $2,963,892 (M); expenditures, $268,836; qualifying distributions, $247,124; giving activities include $246,089 for 123 grants (high: $50,000; low: $100).

Fields of interest: Arts and culture; Education; Nonprofits; Human services.

Type of support: Regranting.

Limitations: Applications not accepted. Giving primarily in MA. No grants to individuals.

Application information: Contributes only to pre-selected organizations.

Trustees: Benjamin B. Taylor; Katherine S. Taylor.

EIN: 043536784

1760

The Teddy Foundation

(formerly Evelyn Donaldson Charitable Foundation)
c/o Wilmington Trust Co.
1100 N. Market St., DE3-C070
Wilmington, DE   19890-0001

Established in 1999 in Delaware.
Donor: Evelyn Donaldson†.
Foundation type: Independent foundation.
Financial data (yr. ended 12/31/13): Assets,
$5,838,964 (M); expenditures, $299,343;
qualifying distributions, $259,528; giving activities
include $222,012 for 9 grants (high: $90,012; low:
$3,000).
Purpose and activities: Giving primarily for human
services, including a Boys and Girls Club; support
also for a wildlife sanctuary.
Fields of interest: Wildlife sanctuaries; Human
services; Youth services.
Limitations: Applications not accepted. Giving in the
U.S., with emphasis on CA. No grants to individuals.
Application information: Contributes only to
pre-selected organizations.
Trustee: Elise Donaldson Bulger.
EIN: 516511786

1761

TeleTech Community Foundation

(formerly TeleTech Foundation)
c/o Foundation Source
501 Silverside Rd., No. 123
Wilmington, DE   19809-1374
Contact: Emily Eikelberner, Exec. Dir.
E-mail: TeleTechFoundation@TeleTech.com; E-mail
for Emily Eikelberner:
emilyeikelberner@teletech.com; Main URL: http://
www.teletech.com/corporate-responsibility/
foundation

Established in 2007 in Delaware.
Donor: TeleTech Holdings, Inc.
Foundation type: Company-sponsored foundation.
Financial data (yr. ended 12/31/13): Assets,
$6,149 (M); gifts received, $287,955;
expenditures, $284,745; qualifying distributions,
$282,241; giving activities include $253,332 for 51
grants (high: $50,000; low: $500).
Purpose and activities: The foundation supports
orchestras and organizations involved with health,
heart disease, Multiple sclerosis, breast cancer,
hunger, and human services. Special emphasis is
directed toward programs designed to maximize the
educational experience for students who
demonstrate the greatest need.
Fields of interest: Orchestral music; Education;
Educational management; Elementary and
secondary education; Reading promotion; Multiple
sclerosis; Heart and circulatory system diseases;
Breast cancer; Human services; Food aid; Food
banks; Adult and child mentoring; Domestic violence
shelters; Adolescents.
International interests: Europe; Latin America;
Switzerland.
Type of support: General support; Employee
volunteer services; Donated products; Program
development; Capacity-building and technical
assistance; Sponsorships.
Limitations: Applications not accepted. Giving
primarily in areas of company operations in CO, MT,
NJ, WA, WV, Europe, Latin America, and Switzerland.
No support for discriminatory organizations,
grantmaking foundations, religious organizations

not of direct benefit to the entire community,
lobbying, political, or fraternal organizations, or
sports teams. No grants to individuals, or for debt
financing, endowments, memorials, advertising,
sporting events, festivals, or parades.
Application information: Contributes only to
organizations pre-selected by employees. All
organizations seeking grants must have
sponsorship from a minimum of 25 TeleTech
employees.
Board meeting date(s): Quarterly
Officer and Directors: Emily Eikelberner, Pres.,
Secy., and Exec. Dir.; Mike Jossi; Kenneth D.
Tuchman; John Troka.
EIN: 208954966

1762

The Telluray Foundation

(formerly Ergen Family Foundation)
c/o Foundation Source
501 Silverside Rd., Ste. 123
Wilmington, DE   19809-1377

Established in 2003 in Colorado.
Donors: Cantey M. Ergen; Charles W. Ergen.
Foundation type: Independent foundation.
Financial data (yr. ended 12/31/13): Assets,
$4,041,219 (M); expenditures, $196,219;
qualifying distributions, $191,171; giving activities
include $166,550 for 9 grants (high: $125,000;
low: $100).
Fields of interest: Education; Natural resources;
Diseases and conditions; Christianity; Human
services; Youth organizing.
Type of support: Research.
Limitations: Applications not accepted. Giving
primarily in CO. No grants to individuals.
Application information: Contributes only to
pre-selected organizations.
Officers and Directors: William R. Gouger,
Secy.-Treas.; Cantey M. Ergen, Co-Exec. Dir.;
Charles W. Ergen, Co-Exec. Dir.; Christopher Ergen;
Courtney Ergen; Katherine Ergen; Kerry Ergen.
EIN: 201090247

1763

Third Avenue Management Private Foundation

c/o Foundation Source
501 Silverside Rd., Ste.123
Wilmington, DE   19809-1377   8008391754

Donor: Third Avenue Management, LLC.
Foundation type: Independent foundation.
Financial data (yr. ended 12/31/14): Assets,
$601,372; gifts received, $0; expenditures,
$240,604; qualifying distributions, $240,604 and
$0 for set-asides.
Fields of interest: Arts and culture; Education;
Human services.
Limitations: Applications not accepted. Giving
primarily in NY.
Application information: Unsolicited requests for
funds not accepted.
Officers and Directors: David M. Barse, Pres. and
Secy. and Director; Vincent J. Dugan, V.P. and
Director; Curtis Jensen; Michael Winer.
EIN: 261865570

1764

The John Edgar Thomson Foundation

c/o Wilmington Trust Co.
1100 N. Market St., DE-3-C070
Wilmington, DE   19890-0001

Established in 1882 in Pennsylvania.
Donor: John Edgar Thomson†.
Foundation type: Operating foundation.
Financial data (yr. ended 12/31/13): Assets,
$17,927,033 (M); expenditures, $566,421;
qualifying distributions, $533,253; giving activities
include $376,348 for grants to individuals.
Purpose and activities: The foundation provides
limited financial assistance to orphans under age
18, whose parents were active employees of a
United States railroad at the time of their death,
although the cause of death need not be
work-related.
Fields of interest: Education; Child welfare;
Low-income and poor people.
Type of support: Grants to individuals.
Limitations: Applications not accepted.
Application information: Unsolicited requests for
funds not accepted.
Officer and Trustees: Wayne E. Bogardus, Secy. and
Trustee; John J. Haslett II; Carl L. Rugart.
Number of staff: 1 full-time professional; 1 part-time
professional.
EIN: 231382746

1765

The Three Sisters Foundation

(formerly The Deutsch Foundation)
c/o Foundation Source
501 Silverside Rd., Ste. 123
Wilmington, DE   19809-1377

Established in 1947 in California.
Donors: The Deutsch Co.; Carl Deutsch; Eleanor
Deutsch; Lester Deutsch; Dworman Foundation,
Inc.; Alexis Deutsch-Adler; Gina Deutsch-Zakarin;
Victoria D. Sutherland.
Foundation type: Company-sponsored foundation.
Financial data (yr. ended 12/31/14): Assets,
$5,618,701; gifts received, $0; expenditures,
$254,514; qualifying distributions, $220,180 and
$0 for set-asides.
Purpose and activities: The foundation supports
organizations involved with elementary education,
health, human services, and international relief.
Fields of interest: Health; Religion; Human services.
Type of support: General support.
Limitations: Applications not accepted. Giving
primarily in CA. No grants to individuals.
Application information: Contributes only to
pre-selected organizations.
Officers and Directors: Gina Deutsche-Zakarin,
Pres. and Director; Victoria D. Sutherland, C.F.O.
and Director; Alexis Deutsch-Adler, Secy. and
Director; Leslie Lichtenstein.
EIN: 956027369

1766

Edgar A. Thronson Foundation

P.O. Box 3707, Ste. B-200
Greenville, DE   19807-0707

Established in 1993 in Delaware.
Donor: Edgar A. Thronson†.
Foundation type: Independent foundation.

Financial data (yr. ended 12/31/13): Assets, $3,518,559 (M); expenditures, $234,678; qualifying distributions, $171,894; giving activities include $165,625 for 18 grants (high: $50,000; low: $100).
Fields of interest: Art museums; Undergraduate education; Leukemia; Housing development; Christianity; Youth services.
Type of support: General support; Continuing support; Capital campaigns; Capital and infrastructure; Equipment; Emergency funds; Program development; Convening; Research; Technical assistance.
Limitations: Applications not accepted. Giving primarily in DE and surrounding areas. No grants to individuals.
Application information: Unsolicited requests for funds not accepted.
Trustees: Donald C. DeWees; Cecelia L. Dugan.
EIN: 510348055

1767
Robert and Martha Trussell Family Foundation
c/o Foundation Source
501 Silverside Rd., Ste. 123
Wilmington, DE   19809-1377

Established in 2005 in Delaware.
Foundation type: Independent foundation.
Financial data (yr. ended 12/31/12): Assets, $2,224,726 (M); expenditures, $372,682; qualifying distributions, $355,058; giving activities include $338,200 for 54 grants (high: $75,000; low: $200).
Fields of interest: Higher education; Catholicism; Human services; Food aid; Child welfare.
Limitations: Applications not accepted. Giving primarily in KY.
Application information: Contributes only to pre-selected organizations.
Officers and Directors: Robert B. Trussell, Pres. and Treas. and Director; Martha O. Trussell, Secy. and Director.
EIN: 203992488

1768
The Uberoi Foundation for Religious Studies
c/o Foundation Source
501 Silverside Rd., Ste. 123
Wilmington, DE   19809-1377

Established in 2007 in Colorado.
Donors: Manohar Shinde; Aarwal Family Foundation.
Foundation type: Independent foundation.
Financial data (yr. ended 12/31/13): Assets, $7,937,201 (M); expenditures, $443,794; qualifying distributions, $330,488; giving activities include $197,500 for 12 grants (high: $65,000; low: $2,500).
Fields of interest: University education.
Limitations: Applications not accepted. Giving primarily in CA and MA.
Application information: Unsolicited requests for funds not accepted.
Officers: Ved P. Nanda, Chair.; Praveen K. Setia, Vice-Chair.; Katharine Nanda, Secy.; James Polsfut, Treas. and Exec. Dir.
Trustees: Anu Bhatia; Jyothi Bhatia; Sneha Harjai.
EIN: 266101307

1769
The Van der Stricht Foundation
c/o Fiduciary Trust Co.
1220 N. Market St.
Wilmington, DE   19801

Established in 2005 in New York.
Donor: Nora van der Stricht†.
Foundation type: Independent foundation.
Financial data (yr. ended 12/31/14): Assets, $8,416,124; expenditures, $264,238; qualifying distributions, $327,375.
Fields of interest: Arts and culture; Environment; Religion.
Limitations: Applications not accepted. Giving primarily in VA.
Application information: Unsolicited requests for funds not accepted.
Trustees: John Paul van der Stricht; Susan R. van der Stricht; Fiduciary Trust International - Delaware.
EIN: 202717846

1770
Viridiun Christian Foundation
c/o Foundation Source
501 Silverside Rd.
Wilmington, DE   19809-1377

Donor: Viridiun LLC.
Foundation type: Independent foundation.
Financial data (yr. ended 12/31/13): Assets, $49,703; gifts received, $141,478; expenditures, $135,971; qualifying distributions, $135,803 and $0 for set-asides.
Fields of interest: Education; Health; Human services.
Limitations: Applications not accepted. Giving primarily in AL and GA.
Application information: Unsolicited requests for funds not accepted.
Officers and Directors: Charles Glenn, Pres. and Secy. and Director; Eric Hickman, V.P.; William A. House, V.P.; Rhett Marlow, V.P.; Ed Rice, V.P.
EIN: 273633724

1771
The Vitale Family Foundation Inc.
c/o Foundation Source
501 Silverside Rd., Ste. 123
Wilmington, DE   19809-1377

Established in 2002 in Delaware.
Donors: David Vitale; Marilyn Vitale; David J. Vitale Trust.
Foundation type: Independent foundation.
Financial data (yr. ended 12/31/13): Assets, $3,103,830 (M); gifts received, $400,000; expenditures, $321,565; qualifying distributions, $305,438; giving activities include $288,500 for 19 grants (high: $50,000; low: $1,000).
Fields of interest: Arts and culture; Education; Higher education; Human services.
Limitations: Applications not accepted. Giving primarily in Chicago, IL. No grants to individuals.
Application information: Contributes only to pre-selected organizations.
Officers and Directors: David Vitale, Pres. and Secy. and Director; Marilyn Vitale, V.P. and Director.
EIN: 510414438

1772
VWR Charitable Foundation
c/o Foundation Source
501 Silverside Rd., Ste. 123
Wilmington, DE   19809-1377

Donor: VWR International, LLC.
Foundation type: Independent foundation.
Financial data (yr. ended 12/31/13): Assets, $1,896,882 (M); gifts received, $488,572; expenditures, $398,795; qualifying distributions, $398,346; giving activities include $363,125 for 41 grants (high: $50,000; low: $1,000).
Fields of interest: Education; Health; Religion.
Limitations: Applications not accepted.
Application information: Unsolicited requests for funds not accepted.
Officers and Directors: Jim Bramwell, Pres. and Director; Valerie Collado, V.P. and Secy.; Paul Dumas, V.P.; Kathleen Pankanin, V.P. and Director; Peter Trow, V.P.; John Michael Colyer; Greg Cowan; Stan Haas; Matt Lope.
EIN: 262934953

1773
Wei Wei Wang Fund
P.O. Box 15627
Wilmington, DE   19850-5627

Established in 2007 in Rhode Island.
Donors: Wang Ji; PEM-America Inc.
Foundation type: Independent foundation.
Financial data (yr. ended 12/31/13): Assets, $3,872,563 (M); gifts received, $306,661; expenditures, $270,435; qualifying distributions, $262,011; giving activities include $261,164 for 2 grants (high: $251,164; low: $10,000).
Fields of interest: Education; University education; Graduate and professional education; Theology; Youth development.
Limitations: Applications not accepted. No grants to individuals.
Application information: Unsolicited requests for funds not accepted.
Officers and Directors: Wang Ji, Pres. and Director; Mary Brannon, Secy. and Director; Edward Greenberg, Treas. and Director; Wei Na.
EIN: 260238100

1774
Washakie Foundation
c/o Foundation Source
501 Silverside Rd., Ste. 123
Wilmington, DE   19809-1377

Established in 2007 in Delaware.
Foundation type: Independent foundation.
Financial data (yr. ended 12/31/14): Assets, $7,330,344; gifts received, $0; expenditures, $432,696; qualifying distributions, $363,529 and $0 for set-asides.
Fields of interest: Human services.
Limitations: Applications not accepted. Giving primarily in CA and NY. No grants to individuals.
Application information: Contributes only to pre-selected organizations.
Officers and Directors: Tracy Weeks Hahn, Co-Pres. and Secy. and Director; Stephen Weeks, Co-Pres. and Director.
EIN: 261459358

1775
The Adam J. Weissman Foundation
(formerly The Joby Foundation, Inc.)
c/o Foundation Source
501 Silverside Rd., Ste. 123
Wilmington, DE   19809-1377

Established in 2005 in Delaware.
Donors: Adam J. Weissman; Google Inc.
Foundation type: Independent foundation.
Financial data (yr. ended 12/31/12): Assets,
$9,479,930 (M); gifts received, $2,117,798;
expenditures, $421,670; qualifying distributions,
$360,500; giving activities include $360,500 for
grants.
Fields of interest: Catholicism; Human services;
Basic and emergency aid; International
development.
Limitations: Applications not accepted. Giving
primarily in AR, CA, NY and WA. No grants to
individuals.
Application information: Contributes only to
pre-selected organizations.
Officers and Directors: Adam J. Weissman, Pres.
and Secy. and Director; Tabitha Jordan, V.P.
EIN: 202624778

1776
Welton Foundation
c/o Foundation Source
501 Silverside Rd., Ste. 123
Wilmington, DE   19809-1377

Established in 2008 in Delaware.
Donors: Annette L. Welton; Patrick L. Welton.
Foundation type: Independent foundation.
Financial data (yr. ended 12/31/13): Assets,
$867,968 (M); expenditures, $237,131; qualifying
distributions, $226,802; giving activities include
$216,750 for 12 grants (high: $112,250; low:
$500).
Fields of interest: Education; Environment; Human
services.
Limitations: Applications not accepted. Giving
primarily in CA.
Application information: Unsolicited requests for
funds not accepted.
Officers and Directors: Patrick L. Welton, Pres. and
Secy. and Director; Annette L. Welton, V.P. and
Director.
EIN: 263843649

1777
Ruth Winkelman Wender Foundation
c/o Oppenheimer Trust
405 Silverside Rd., 2nd Fl.
Wilmington, DE   19809

Established in 2000 in New York.
Donors: Ruth Wender; Theodore A. Wender; The
Ruth Wender Trust; Wender Clat; Irene Winkelman;
Irene Winkelman.
Foundation type: Independent foundation.
Financial data (yr. ended 12/31/13): Assets,
$4,857,218 (M); gifts received, $500,000;
expenditures, $428,364; qualifying distributions,
$374,670; giving activities include $252,380 for 62
grants (high: $130,000; low: $225).
Fields of interest: Education; Health; Judaism.
Limitations: Applications not accepted. Giving
primarily in NJ and NY. No grants to individuals.

Application information: Unsolicited requests for
funds not accepted.
Trustees: Jill Wender Spitz; Theodore A. Wender.
EIN: 113465667

1778
W. F. Whitman Family Foundation Inc.
c/o Foundation Source
501 Silverside Rd., Ste. 123
Wilmington, DE   19809-1377

Established in 2003 in Florida.
Donors: William F. Whitman, Jr.; Whitman Charitable
Lead Unitrust; William F. Whitman, Jr. Declararion of
Trust; Barbara K. Whitman Declaration of Trust;
Barbara K. Whitman.
Foundation type: Independent foundation.
Financial data (yr. ended 12/31/13): Assets,
$5,230,354 (M); gifts received, $161,543;
expenditures, $237,388; qualifying distributions,
$201,197; giving activities include $178,000 for 29
grants (high: $20,000; low: $500).
Fields of interest: Arts and culture; Opera;
Education; Higher education; Hospital care; Human
services; Youth services.
Type of support: Capital and infrastructure.
Limitations: Applications not accepted. Giving
primarily in FL, MA, ME, NY and SC. No grants to
individuals.
Application information: Contributes only to
pre-selected organizations.
Officers and Directors: William F. Whitman, Jr.,
Pres. and Treas. and Director; Laura B. Whitman,
1st V.P. and Director; William Fifield Whitman, 2nd
V.P. and Director; Thomas C. Danziger, Secy.;
Barbara K. Whitman.
EIN: 200413209

1779
Penelope Wong and Tim Kochis Charitable Foundation
c/o Foundation Source
501 Silverside Rd., Ste. 123
Wilmington, DE   19809-1377

Donor: S. Timothy Kochis.
Foundation type: Independent foundation.
Financial data (yr. ended 12/31/14): Assets,
$877; gifts received, $186,301; expenditures,
$205,354; qualifying distributions, $202,985 and
$0 for set-asides.
Fields of interest: Arts and culture; Education;
Diseases and conditions.
Limitations: Applications not accepted. Giving
primarily in CA.
Application information: Unsolicited requests for
funds not accepted.
Officer and Director: S. Timothy Kochis, Pres. and
Secy. and Director.
EIN: 262702458

1780
William H. Wood Family Foundation
c/o Foundation Source
501 Silverside Rd., Ste. 123
Wilmington, DE   19809-1377

Donor: William H. Wood.
Foundation type: Independent foundation.

Financial data (yr. ended 12/31/13): Assets,
$1,664,291 (M); gifts received, $474,000;
expenditures, $268,319; qualifying distributions,
$228,296; giving activities include $178,250 for 3
grants (high: $147,500; low: $14,750).
Fields of interest: Education.
Limitations: Applications not accepted. Giving
primarily in OH.
Application information: Unsolicited requests for
funds not accepted.
Officer and Director: William H. Wood, Pres. and
Secy. and Director.
EIN: 461599491

1781
Wyeth Foundation for American Art
1020 N. Bancroft Pkwy., Ste. 100
Wilmington, DE   19805-2666   (302) 888-2502
Contact: William J. Martin, Secy.-Treas.
FAX: (302) 888-2505; Main URL: http://
www.wyethfoundationforamericanart.com

Established in 2002 in Delaware.
Donors: Betsy James Wyeth; MBNA Foundation;
Andrew Wyeth.
Foundation type: Independent foundation.
Financial data (yr. ended 12/31/13): Assets,
$1,985,860 (M); expenditures, $401,890;
qualifying distributions, $365,001; giving activities
include $331,040 for 11 grants (high: $64,500;
low: $5,000).
Purpose and activities: Giving primarily to
encourage the study, appreciation, and recognition
of excellence in American art.
Fields of interest: Arts and culture; Art museums.
Limitations: Applications accepted. Giving in the
U.S., with some emphasis on Washington, DC, NY
and PA.
Application information: Complete application
guidelines available on Foundation web site.
   Deadline(s): June 15. and Dec 15.
   Board meeting date(s): 1; 7
Officers and Trustees: J. Robinson West, Pres. and
Trustee; John Wilmerding, V.P. and Trustee; William
J. Martin, Esq., Secy.-Treas. and Trustee; Charles M.
Cawley; Wanda M. Corn; Chris Crosman; Kathleen
A. Foster; Joyce Hill Stoner; Betsy James Wyeth;
James Browning Wyeth.
EIN: 061662503

1782
The Yablon Family Foundation Inc.
c/o Foundation Source
501 Silverside Rd., Ste. 123
Wilmington, DE   19809-1377

Established in 2005 in Delaware.
Donors: Paul Yablon; Jill Yablon.
Foundation type: Independent foundation.
Financial data (yr. ended 11/30/13): Assets,
$463,158 (L); gifts received, $611,325;
expenditures, $373,123; qualifying distributions,
$370,765; giving activities include $366,990 for 49
grants (high: $80,000; low: $250).
Fields of interest: Nonprofits; Judaism; Human
services; Child welfare.
Type of support: Regranting.
Limitations: Applications not accepted. Giving
primarily in CT, NJ and NY. No grants to individuals.
Application information: Unsolicited requests for
funds not accepted.

Officers and Directors: Jill Yablon, Co-Pres. and Director; Paul Yablon, Co-Pres. and Director.
EIN: 202031127

1783
Yaverland Foundation Inc.

P. O. Box 314
Montchanin, DE 19710

Established in 2005 in Delaware.
Donors: Heather Evans; Castelnau Foundation; Heather Evans Charitable Lead Trust.
Foundation type: Independent foundation.
Financial data (yr. ended 12/31/12): Assets, $5,185,557 (M); gifts received, $281,135; expenditures, $259,079; qualifying distributions, $237,900; giving activities include $237,900 for grants.

Fields of interest: Arts and culture; Education; Environment; Diseases and conditions.
Type of support: General support.
Limitations: Applications not accepted. Giving primarily in DE, NJ and PA. No grants to individuals.
Application information: Contributes only to pre-selected organizations.
Officer: Heather Evans, Pres. and Secy.-Treas.
EIN: 202417830

1784
Yokota Foundation

c/o Foundation Source
501 Silverside Rd., Ste. 123
Wilmington, DE 19809-1377

Donors: Brenna L. Winiecki; Tina L. Warren; John R. Warren; Robert C. Winiecki.
Foundation type: Independent foundation.
Financial data (yr. ended 12/31/13): Assets, $7,274,685 (M); expenditures, $365,691; qualifying distributions, $282,380; giving activities include $253,928 for 66 grants (high: $83,400; low: $10,000).
Fields of interest: Diseases and conditions; Cancers; Religion.
Type of support: Research.
Limitations: Applications not accepted. Giving primarily in CA, DE and TN.
Application information: Unsolicited requests for funds not accepted.
Officers and Directors: Tina L. Warren, Chair. and Director; Robert C. Winiecki, Pres. and Director; John R. Warren, V.P. and Treas. and Director; Brenna L. Winiecki.
EIN: 270602001

DISTRICT OF COLUMBIA

1785
American Clean Skies Foundation
1875 Connecticut Ave. N.W., Suite 405
Washington, DC 20009-5728 (202) 682-6294
FAX: (202) 682-3050; Main URL: http://
www.cleanskies.org

Donor: Chesapeake Energy Corporation.
Foundation type: Independent foundation.
Financial data (yr. ended 12/31/13): Assets,
$5,684,765 (M); gifts received, $2,890,000;
expenditures, $4,564,775; qualifying distributions,
$1,359,395; giving activities include $240,500 for
8 grants (high: $50,000; low: $3,500).
Purpose and activities: The foundation is working
for cleaner energy in the U.S. transportation and
power sectors.
Fields of interest: Education; Environment; Energy
resources; Human services.
Limitations: Applications not accepted. Giving
primarily in CO, Washington, DC, and VA.
Application information: Unsolicited requests for
funds not accepted.
Officer and Directors: Gregory C. Staple, C.E.O. and
Director; James A. Roth; David M. Lubitz.
EIN: 208837141

1786
Arcana Foundation, Inc.
1156 15th St. N.W., Ste. 605
Washington, DC 20005-1767

Established in 1986 in Delaware.
Donors: Ladislaus von Hoffmann†; Beatrix von
Hoffmann.
Foundation type: Independent foundation.
Financial data (yr. ended 09/30/14): Assets,
$3,956,121 (M); expenditures, $212,148;
qualifying distributions, $201,360; giving activities
include $200,000 for 3 grants (high: $150,000;
low: $20,000).
Fields of interest: Arts and culture; Philanthropy.
Type of support: General support.
Limitations: Applications not accepted. Giving
primarily in MD. No grants to individuals.
Application information: Unsolicited requests for
funds not accepted.
Officers and Directors: Beatrix von Hoffmann, V.P.
and Director; Holly Kennedy Passantino, Secy.; Paul
Hansen, Treas. and Director; Alexandra von
Hoffman.
Number of staff: 1 part-time professional.
EIN: 521515952

1787
Arnold & Porter Foundation
c/o Arnold & Porter
555 12th St., N.W.
Washington, DC 20004-1206

Established in 1989 in District of Columbia.
Donors: Arnold & Porter; Washington Lawyer's
Committee; American Civil Liberties Union.
Foundation type: Company-sponsored foundation.

Financial data (yr. ended 12/31/13): Assets,
$15,504,411 (M); gifts received, $536,345;
expenditures, $125,794; qualifying distributions,
$125,500; giving activities include $118,000 for 1
grant.
Purpose and activities: The foundation supports the
LSUHSC Foundation in New Orleans, Louisiana.
Fields of interest: Medical education; Health.
Type of support: General support; Fellowships.
Limitations: Applications not accepted. Giving
primarily in New Orleans, LA. No grants to
individuals.
Application information: Unsolicited requests for
funds not accepted.
Officers and Directors: Richard M. Alexander, Pres.
and Director; Elizabeth C. Respess, Secy.-Treas.
and Director; James P. Joseph.
EIN: 521656501

1788
Bench Trail Fund
901 New York Ave. N.W., No. 823E
Washington, DC 20001-4432
Contact: Stephen J. Pollak, Secy.

Donors: Ruth S. Pollak; Stephen J. Pollak.
Foundation type: Independent foundation.
Financial data (yr. ended 12/31/13): Assets,
$916,802 (M); gifts received, $50,319;
expenditures, $171,188; qualifying distributions,
$168,894; giving activities include $167,300 for 90
grants (high: $25,000; low: $40).
Purpose and activities: Giving primarily for
education and human services.
Fields of interest: Arts and culture; Education;
Higher education; Law education; Legal services;
Judaism; Human services; Ethnic and racial groups.
Type of support: General support; Annual
campaigns; Capital campaigns; Seed money;
Curriculum development.
Limitations: Applications accepted. Giving primarily
in the greater metropolitan Washington, DC, area.
No grants to individuals.
Application information: Application form required.
   Initial approach: Letter
   Deadline(s): None
Officers: Ruth S. Pollak, Pres.; Stephen J. Pollak,
Secy.
Directors: Eve J. Pollak; Linda J. Pollak; Roger L.
Pollak.
EIN: 526080785

1789
The Dorothy G. Bender Foundation, Inc.
1025 Connecticut Ave. N.W., Ste. 1104
Washington, DC 20036-5437
Contact: Morton A. Bender, Pres.

Established in 1985 in District of Columbia.
Donors: Dorothy G. Bender†; Morton A. Bender.
Foundation type: Independent foundation.
Financial data (yr. ended 12/31/12): Assets,
$5,993,295 (M); expenditures, $328,936;
qualifying distributions, $301,604; giving activities
include $301,604 for grants.
Purpose and activities: Giving primarily for the arts,
health associations, social services, and education.
Fields of interest: Arts and culture; Education;
Diseases and conditions; Human services; Child
welfare.

Type of support: General support; Annual
campaigns; Capital campaigns; Endowments;
Scholarships.
Limitations: Applications accepted. Giving limited to
the greater metropolitan Washington, DC, area.
Application information: Application form required.
   Initial approach: Letter
   Copies of proposal: 1
   Deadline(s): None
   Board meeting date(s): As needed
Officers and Directors: Morton A. Bender, Pres. and
Director; Grace M. Bender, Secy. and Director; Jay
S. Bender, Treas. and Director.
EIN: 521406566

1790
Walter A. Bloedorn Foundation
888 17th St. N.W., Ste. 210
Washington, DC 20006-3319

Established in 1966 in District of Columbia.
Donor: Walter A. Bloedorn†.
Foundation type: Independent foundation.
Financial data (yr. ended 12/31/14): Assets,
$7,293,073; expenditures, $452,154; qualifying
distributions, $365,412.
Fields of interest: Arts and culture; Education;
Health; Community service; Children and youth.
Limitations: Applications accepted. Giving primarily
in the metropolitan Washington, DC, area. No grants
to individuals.
Application information:
   Initial approach: Letter
   Copies of proposal: 1
   Deadline(s): Submit proposal preferably by Dec.
      31 for consideration at Apr. meeting
   Board meeting date(s): Apr.
Officers and Directors: Robert E. Davis, Pres. and
Treas. and Director; Anne D. Spratt, Secy. and
Director; H. Gregory Platts; John A. Sargent.
Number of staff: None.
EIN: 520846147

1791
Kenneth D. Brody Family Foundation, Inc.
c/o Winslow Partners, LLC
2401 Kalorama Rd.
Washington, DC 20008-1626

Established in 1999 in District of Columbia.
Donors: Carolyn Brody; Kenneth D. Brody.
Foundation type: Independent foundation.
Financial data (yr. ended 09/30/13): Assets,
$31,579 (M); gifts received, $175,000;
expenditures, $153,268; qualifying distributions,
$153,268; giving activities include $152,700 for 3
grants (high: $100,000; low: $2,700).
Fields of interest: Historic preservation; Education;
Higher education; Business education; International
relations.
Limitations: Applications not accepted. Giving
primarily in Washington, DC, MA, MD, and New York,
NY. No grants to individuals.
Application information: Contributes only to
pre-selected organizations.
Officers: Kenneth D. Brody, Chair. and Pres.; Frank
Brosens, V.P.; Christopher DeLong, Secy.-Treas.
Directors: Caroline W. Brody; Charles W. Brody.
EIN: 522140128

1792
The Butler Family Fund

1634 I St. N.W., Ste. 1000
Washington, DC 20006-4015 (202) 463-8288
Contact: Martha A. Toll, Exec. Dir.; Anne H. Morin, Prog. Assoc.
FAX: (202) 783-8499;
E-mail: info@butlerfamilyfund.org; Main URL: http://www.butlerfamilyfund.org
Grant Database: http://www.butlerfamilyfund.org/grantees.php

Established in 1992 in District of Columbia.
Donor: J.E. and Z.B. Butler Foundation.
Foundation type: Independent foundation.
Financial data (yr. ended 12/31/13): Assets, $11,543,504 (M); gifts received, $67,000; expenditures, $750,173; qualifying distributions, $666,938; giving activities include $441,680 for 32 grants (high: $40,000; low: $500).
Purpose and activities: Support for homeless families and criminal justice reform (death penalty and juvenile justice).
Fields of interest: Climate change; Housing development; Capital punishment; Homeless people.
International interests: England; United Kingdom of Great Britain and Northern Ireland.
Type of support: General support; Public engagement and education; Systems reform; Seed money.
Limitations: Applications not accepted. Giving primarily in Los Angeles, San Diego and the San Francisco Bay Area, CA, Washington, DC, Chicago, IL, NY, Philadelphia, PA, WI, and London, England. No grants to individuals.
Publications: Grants list; Multi-year report; Program policy statement.
Application information: Unsolicited proposals or letters of inquiry are not accepted. No grants for more than 3 consecutive years.
Board meeting date(s): Biannually
Officers and Directors: Eve B. Wildrick, Pres. and Director; Martha A. Toll, Exec. Dir.; Jennifer Gravin; Phineas Hirsch; Nina Morrison; Lisa Siegel; Jody Snider.
Number of staff: 1 part-time professional; 1 part-time support.
EIN: 521786778

1793
Carter and Melissa Cafritz Charitable Trust

1660 L St. N.W., Ste. 300
Washington, DC 20036-5641 (703) 742-9859
Contact: Mary Hallisy
E-mail: mthallisy@aol.com

Donor: Carter Cafritz.
Foundation type: Independent foundation.
Financial data (yr. ended 12/31/13): Assets, $3,592,747 (M); gifts received, $100,000; expenditures, $272,297; qualifying distributions, $270,996; giving activities include $210,000 for 16 grants (high: $25,000; low: $5,000).
Purpose and activities: To support efforts that improve the lives of at-risk children, youth and families in the District of Columbia. Areas of interest include at-risk children, youth and families, out-of-school time programs. elementary and secondary education, early childhood and parent education, with special focus on older and/or disconnected youth.
Fields of interest: Elementary and secondary education; Family services; Child welfare; Youth services; Low-income and poor people.
Type of support: General support; Continuing support; Capital campaigns; Capital and infrastructure; Program development.
Limitations: Applications accepted. Giving limited to Washington, DC.
Publications: Annual report.
Application information:
Initial approach: Proposal
Deadline(s): None
Trustees: Teresa D. Bertholf; Carter Cafritz; Melissa Cafritz; Thomas B. Wilner.
Number of staff: 1 part-time professional.
EIN: 137049874

1794
E. Eugene Carter Foundation

3075 Ordway St. N.W.
Washington, DC 20008-3255

Established in 1993 in District of Columbia.
Donor: E. Eugene Carter.
Foundation type: Independent foundation.
Financial data (yr. ended 12/31/13): Assets, $6,328,357 (M); expenditures, $249,050; qualifying distributions, $249,050; giving activities include $238,619 for 8 grants (high: $99,793; low: $250).
Fields of interest: Higher education; Engineering; Females; Ethnic and racial groups; People of Latin American descent; Immigrants and migrants.
Type of support: Scholarships.
Limitations: Applications not accepted. Giving on a national basis. No grants to individuals.
Application information: Contributes only to pre-selected organizations.
Officers: E. Eugene Carter, Chair.; Jane R. O'Neil, Secy.
Trustee: John Aldridge.
Number of staff: None.
EIN: 521829253

1795
Choksi Family Charitable Trust

c/o Mary C. Choksi
2340 Kalorama Rd. N.W.
Washington, DC 20008-1623

Donors: Mary C. Choksi; Armeane M. Choksi.
Foundation type: Independent foundation.
Financial data (yr. ended 12/31/13): Assets, $708,674 (M); gifts received, $5,922; expenditures, $280,453; qualifying distributions, $278,859; giving activities include $277,600 for 14 grants (high: $70,000; low: $5,000).
Fields of interest: Arts and culture; Education; Human services.
Limitations: Applications not accepted. Giving primarily in Washington, DC.
Application information: Unsolicited requests for funds not accepted.
Officers and Directors: Armeane M. Choksi, Pres. and Director; Mary C. Choksi, Secy.-Treas.; Maaren A. Choksi.
EIN: 271546647

1796
George E. Coleman, Jr. Foundation

c/o Alan Dye, Webster
1747 Pennsylvania Ave.
Washington, DC 20006-4604
E-mail: doliver@verizon.net; Application address: c/o Daniel Oliver, 3105 Woodley Rd., Washington, DC 20008, tel.: (202) 986-2888

Foundation type: Independent foundation.
Financial data (yr. ended 12/31/13): Assets, $6,694,698 (M); expenditures, $433,605; qualifying distributions, $379,718; giving activities include $379,718 for 68 grants (high: $64,000; low: $150).
Fields of interest: Arts and culture; Higher education; Public policy; International relations.
Type of support: General support; Policy, advocacy and systems reform.
Limitations: Applications accepted. Giving primarily in Washington, DC. No grants to individuals.
Application information: Application form required.
Initial approach: Letter
Deadline(s): None
Trustees: Andrew Oliver, Jr.; Daniel Oliver.
EIN: 527044220

1797
Gayle and Bill Cook Foundation

c/o Kozusko Harris Duncan LLP, Donald D. Kozusko
1666 K St. N.W., Ste. 400
Washington, DC 20006-1219
Application address: c/o George N. Harris, Jr., Asst. Secy., 750 Daniels Way, Bloomington, IN 47404;
E-Mail: gharris@kozlaw.com

Donor: Gayle T. Cook.
Foundation type: Independent foundation.
Financial data (yr. ended 12/31/13): Assets, $1,868,674 (M); gifts received, $2,000,000; expenditures, $151,645; qualifying distributions, $150,000; giving activities include $150,000 for 3 grants (high: $50,000; low: $50,000).
Fields of interest: Education; Catholicism; Human services.
Limitations: Applications accepted. Giving primarily in IN.
Application information: Application form required.
Initial approach: Letter
Deadline(s): None
Officers: Gayle T. Cook, Pres.; Carl A. Cook, V.P.; Donald D. Kozusko, Secy.
EIN: 463061919

1798
Cornerstone Foundation, Inc.

5212 Partridge Ln., N.W.
Washington, DC 20016-5338

Established in 2004 in Maryland.
Donor: Bradley G. Vogt.
Foundation type: Independent foundation.
Financial data (yr. ended 12/31/13): Assets, $12,259,955 (M); expenditures, $440,000; qualifying distributions, $415,000; giving activities include $415,000 for 4 grants (high: $140,000; low: $75,000).
Fields of interest: Community and economic development; Human services; Family services; Child welfare; Females.

Limitations: Applications not accepted. Giving primarily in Washington, DC; funding also in Rockland, ME, and New York, NY. No grants to individuals.
Application information: Unsolicited requests for funds not accepted.
Officers: Bradley J. Vogt, Pres.; Katherine M. Vogt, Treas.
EIN: 113737220

1799
Crowell & Moring Foundation
1001 Pennsylvania Ave. N.W.
Washington, DC 20004-2543

Donors: David Naseman; Wm. Randolph Smith; Crowell & Moring LLP; Elizabeth Hilder.
Foundation type: Company-sponsored foundation.
Financial data (yr. ended 12/31/13): Assets, $381,265 (M); gifts received, $341,786; expenditures, $210,540; qualifying distributions, $210,535; giving activities include $210,500 for 22 grants (high: $45,000; low: $2,000).
Purpose and activities: The foundation supports organizations involved with education, legal aid, youth development, human services, and leadership development.
Fields of interest: Education; Middle school education; Child educational development; Legal aid; Leadership development; Human services; Youth development; Youth services; Homeless services.
Type of support: General support; Program development; Convening.
Limitations: Applications not accepted. Giving primarily in Washington, DC. No grants to individuals.
Application information: Contributes only to pre-selected organizations.
Officers and Directors: Susan Hoffman, Pres. and Director; George Ruttinger, Secy. and Director; Kent Morrison, Treas. and Director; Deborah E. Arbabi; John T. Brennan, Jr.; Gary R. Edwards; Trina Fairley-Barlow; Clifford Hendler; Andy Liu; Michael L. Martinez; Monica G. Parham; Nicole Quigley; Luther Ziegler.
EIN: 522207644

1800
Dart Group II Foundation, Inc.
(formerly Crown Books Foundation, Inc.)
1025 Thomas Jefferson St., N.W., Ste. 700 E.
Washington, DC 20007

Established in 1988 in Maryland.
Donor: Crown Books Corp.
Foundation type: Company-sponsored foundation.
Financial data (yr. ended 12/31/13): Assets, $2,038,472 (M); expenditures, $196,747; qualifying distributions, $185,200; giving activities include $185,200 for 34 grants (high: $17,000; low: $500).
Purpose and activities: The foundation supports organizations involved with arts and culture, education, health, and human services.
Fields of interest: Education; Health; Religion.
Type of support: General support.
Limitations: Applications accepted. Giving primarily in CA, Washington, DC, MD, and VA. No support for political organizations. No grants to individuals.
Application information: Application form required.

Initial approach: Proposal
Deadline(s): None
Directors: Elliot Arditti; Ronald S. Haft.
Number of staff: None.
EIN: 521590726

1801
The Davies Foundation
c/o Kassie Rempel
2412 Tracy Pl. N.W.
Washington, DC 20008-2633

Donor: John L. Davies.
Foundation type: Independent foundation.
Financial data (yr. ended 12/31/13): Assets, $690,699 (M); expenditures, $148,552; qualifying distributions, $145,834; giving activities include $145,834 for 6 grants (high: $83,334; low: $2,000).
Fields of interest: Education; Undergraduate education; Health; Housing development.
Limitations: Applications not accepted. Giving primarily in Washington, DC and Meadville, PA.
Application information: Unsolicited requests for funds not accepted.
Trustee: John L. Davies.
EIN: 263867274

1802
The John Dickson Home
c/o Terence Collins
2722 N St. N.W.
Washington, DC 20007-3323

Donor: John A. Johnston Trust.
Foundation type: Operating foundation.
Financial data (yr. ended 06/30/13): Assets, $10,529,216 (M); gifts received, $93,711; expenditures, $674,228; qualifying distributions, $603,045; giving activities include $172,500 for 7 grants (high: $75,000; low: $10,000), and $430,545 for 1 foundation-administered program.
Fields of interest: Agriculture; Religion; Human services.
Limitations: Applications not accepted. Giving primarily in Washington, DC. No grants to individuals.
Application information: Unsolicited requests for funds not accepted.
Officers: Terence W. Collins, Pres.; Barbara L.F. Ingraham, Secy.
Trustees: Judith Bair; Arthur Elgin; Jean Hartman; Pat Johnson.
EIN: 530204688

1803
The Dimick Foundation
3000 K St. N.W., Ste. 600
Washington, DC 20007-5143 (202) 672-5511
Contact: John M. Lynham Jr., Tr.
E-mail: cbelinky@foley.com

Established in 1957 in Unspecified.
Donors: John Dimick†; Marion T. Dimick†.
Foundation type: Independent foundation.
Financial data (yr. ended 12/31/13): Assets, $6,910,850 (M); expenditures, $424,568; qualifying distributions, $286,500; giving activities include $286,500 for 103 grants (high: $20,000; low: $500).

Purpose and activities: Emphasis on cultural programs, especially music and other performing arts groups; social services; and youth education/development.
Fields of interest: Performing arts; Human services; Child welfare; Youth development.
Type of support: General support; Continuing support; Annual campaigns.
Limitations: Applications accepted. Giving primarily in the Washington, DC, metropolitan area. No support for political or lobbying organizations. No grants to individuals.
Publications: Application guidelines; Financial statement; Grants list.
Application information: The grantmaker accepts the Washington Regional Association of Grantmakers form.
Initial approach: Letter
Copies of proposal: 1
Deadline(s): About 8 weeks prior to meetings
Board meeting date(s): Generally in May or June, and Nov. or Dec.
Final notification: Shortly after board meetings
Trustees: Nancy Johnson; Michelle Riley Levenson; John M. Lynham, Jr.
EIN: 526038149

1804
William Orr Dingwall Foundation, Inc.
2201 N St. N.W., Ste. 117
Washington, DC 20037-1113
Contact: John D. Ward Esq., Pres.
E-mail: apply@dingwallfoundation.org; Main
URL: http://www.dingwallfoundation.org

Established in 1994 in Missouri.
Donors: Dingwall Family, LP; Marion Orr Dingwall Trust.
Foundation type: Independent foundation.
Financial data (yr. ended 12/31/13): Assets, $6,525,036 (M); expenditures, $296,835; qualifying distributions, $260,850; giving activities include $260,850 for 93 grants to individuals (high: $15,000; low: $500).
Purpose and activities: Scholarship awards to individuals of Asian ancestry to pursue undergraduate or graduate studies in any subject offered by well-established universities throughout the world and to individuals of any national origin to pursue graduate studies devoted to the neural bases of language.
Fields of interest: Linguistics; Higher education; Graduate and professional education.
International interests: Asia; South Korea.
Type of support: Student aid.
Limitations: Applications accepted. Giving primarily in VA.
Application information: See foundation web site for complete application guidelines. Application form required.
Initial approach: Letter
Final notification: Varies
Officers and Directors: John D. Ward, Pres. and Director; Sheldon Steinbach, Treas. and Director; Mimi Ghim; William Hodos, Ph.D; Chin-Wu Kim, Ph.D; Young-Key-Renaud Kim, Ph.D; Brenda Rapp.
Number of staff: 1 full-time professional.
EIN: 521877552

1805
The Samuel R. Dweck Foundation
1730 M St. N.W., Ste. 408
Washington, DC   20036-4569

Established in 1971 in District of Columbia.
Donors: Samuel R. Dweck; Morris Dweck; Ralph Dweck; Rena Dweck; Aboud Dweck; Susan Dweck.
Foundation type: Independent foundation.
Financial data (yr. ended 12/31/14): Assets, $1,293,036 (M); expenditures, $194,809; qualifying distributions, $190,760; giving activities include $187,360 for 13 grants (high: $60,000; low: $250).
Fields of interest: Secondary education; Higher education; Nonprofits; Diseases and conditions; Judaism; Human services; Child welfare.
Type of support: Regranting.
Application information:
 Initial approach: Proposal
 Deadline(s): None
Directors: Aboud Dweck; Morris Dweck; Ralph Dweck; Rena Dweck; Susan Dweck.
EIN: 526060826

1806
Farvue Foundation Inc.
c/o The Organization
4910 Massachusetts Ave., Ste. 221
Washington, DC   20016-4368

Donors: Jean Wallace Douglas; Leslie Douglas†; Joan Murray.
Foundation type: Independent foundation.
Financial data (yr. ended 12/31/13): Assets, $3,527,595 (M); gifts received, $5,000; expenditures, $179,427; qualifying distributions, $177,176; giving activities include $175,000 for 15 grants (high: $25,000; low: $5,000).
Fields of interest: Environment; Domesticated animals.
Limitations: Applications not accepted. Giving primarily in MD.
Application information: Unsolicited requests for funds not accepted.
Officer: Joan Douglas Murray, Pres.
Directors: David Murray; Sara Murray.
EIN: 271938940

1807
Foundation for Middle East Peace
1761 N St. N.W.
Washington, DC   20036-2801   (202) 835-3650
Contact: Philip C. Wilcox Jr., Pres.
FAX: (202) 835-3651; E-mail: info@fmep.org; Main URL: http://www.fmep.org
Blog: http://fmep.org/blog

Established in 1979 in District of Columbia.
Donors: Merle Thorpe, Jr.†; Stephen Hartwell; Nelson B. Delavan Foundation; W.H. Rosenwald Family Fund.
Foundation type: Independent foundation.
Financial data (yr. ended 09/30/13): Assets, $8,993,360 (M); gifts received, $10,893; expenditures, $872,544; qualifying distributions, $545,197; giving activities include $281,000 for 27 grants (high: $37,500; low: $2,500).
Purpose and activities: To promote an understanding of the Israeli-Palestinian conflict, including the identification of U.S. interests, and to contribute to a just and peaceful resolution of the conflict with security for both peoples. Support directed to elements within the Arab and Jewish communities working for a peaceful resolution of the conflict.
Fields of interest: International peace and security.
International interests: Israel; Middle East; West Bank/Gaza (Palestinian Territories).
Type of support: General support; Matching grants; Convening; Publications; Research.
Limitations: Applications accepted. Giving primarily in Washington, DC, Israel, and Palestine.
Application information: Application form required.
 Initial approach: Request application form
 Deadline(s): None
Officers: Amb. Nicholas A. Veliotes, Chair.; Philip C. Wilcox, Jr., Pres.; Calvin Hayes Cobb, Jr., Co-Secy.; Richard S.T. Marsh, Co-Secy.; Jean Newsom, Treas.
Directors: Landrum R. Bolling; Edison Dick; Joseph Englehardt; Arthur H. Hughes; Richard Murphy; Gail Pressberg; William B. Quandt.
Number of staff: 2 full-time professional; 1 full-time support.
EIN: 526055574

1808
Freeman Foundation
1700 Pennsylvania Ave. N.W., Ste. 600
Washington, DC   20006-4704

Established in 1990 in Delaware.
Donor: Weston F. Milliken.
Foundation type: Independent foundation.
Financial data (yr. ended 12/31/14): Assets, $6,459,681 (M); gifts received, $750,000; expenditures, $313,754; qualifying distributions, $305,545; giving activities include $263,800 for 15 grants (high: $75,000; low: $500).
Fields of interest: LGBTQ rights; Adolescents.
Type of support: General support.
Limitations: Applications not accepted. Giving primarily in CA, NC and SC. No grants to individuals.
Application information: Unsolicited requests for funds not accepted.
Trustees: Michael A. Dively; Weston F. Milliken; Anand Pandya.
EIN: 521667228

1809
Glenstone Foundation
(formerly Glenstone Museum Foundation)
2200 Pennsylvania Ave. N.W., Ste. 800W
Washington, DC   20037
E-mail: info@glenstone.org; Main URL: http://www.glenstone.org

Established in 2006 in Delaware.
Donors: Mitchell P. Rales; MPR Family Foundation.
Foundation type: Operating foundation.
Financial data (yr. ended 12/31/13): Assets, $849,902,315 (M); gifts received, $149,307,322; expenditures, $6,615,107; qualifying distributions, $204,768,997; giving activities include $121,000 for 8 grants (high: $35,000; low: $1,000).
Purpose and activities: The foundation was created to promote the study, improvement, and advancement of the arts, to foster academic and professional research of art, and to support public and educational exhibitions of art. The foundation's primary activities include promoting the study and appreciation of the visual arts, primarily through 1) the operation of its Glenstone Museum in Potomac, Maryland and 2) lending works of art to other public charities for study and exhibition.
Fields of interest: Arts and culture; Art museums.
Limitations: Applications not accepted. No grants to individuals.
Application information: Unsolicited requests for funds not accepted.
Officers and Directors: Mitchell P. Rales, Chair. and Director; Emily W. Rales, Pres.; Teresa L.C. Baldwin, Secy.; Michael G. Ryan, Treas. and Director; Joseph O. Bunting III.
EIN: 205938416

1810
The Aaron and Cecile Goldman Foundation
4201 Connecticut Ave. N.W., Ste. 600
Washington, DC   20008-1128

Established in 1962 in District of Columbia.
Donors: Aaron Goldman†; Cecile Goldman†.
Foundation type: Independent foundation.
Financial data (yr. ended 12/31/13): Assets, $3,827,735 (M); expenditures, $223,990; qualifying distributions, $196,850; giving activities include $163,631 for 33 grants (high: $18,000; low: $1,711).
Purpose and activities: Giving primarily to Jewish and local agencies, including education and human services, and to local children's programs and camps.
Fields of interest: Arts and culture; Education; Nonprofits; Judaism; Camps; Human services; Child welfare.
Type of support: Scholarships; Matching grants; Program development; Professorships; Fellowships; Equipment; Regranting; Endowments; Emergency funds; Capital campaigns; Capital and infrastructure.
Limitations: Applications not accepted. Giving primarily in the greater Washington, DC, area, and for the benefit of Israel. No grants to individuals.
Application information: Unsolicited requests for funds not accepted.
Trustee: Michael D. Goldman.
Number of staff: 1 part-time professional.
EIN: 526037949

1811
Gorlitz Foundation, Ltd.
(formerly Samuel J. Gorlitz Foundation)
3935 Morrison St. N.W.
Washington, DC   20015-2944   (301) 229-0761

Established in 1986 in Maryland.
Foundation type: Independent foundation.
Financial data (yr. ended 12/31/13): Assets, $4,712,450 (M); expenditures, $413,545; qualifying distributions, $279,252; giving activities include $265,500 for 176 grants (high: $20,000; low: $25).
Purpose and activities: Giving primarily for the arts and Jewish organizations.
Fields of interest: Arts and culture; Education; Nonprofits; Judaism; Human services; Women's services.
Type of support: Regranting.
Limitations: Applications accepted. Giving on a national basis. No grants to individuals.
Application information: Application form required.

Initial approach: Letter
Deadline(s): None
Officers: Grace K. Gorlitz, Pres.; Paula Gorlitz, V.P. and Secy.; Gail Gorlitz, V.P. and Treas.
Number of staff: 1 part-time professional; 1 part-time support.
EIN: 521439097

1812
The Harold & Sylvia Greenberg Family Foundation, Inc.
4200 Massachusetts Ave. N.W., Ste. 514
Washington, DC 20016-4752

Established in 2002 in Maryland.
Foundation type: Independent foundation.
Financial data (yr. ended 12/31/13): Assets, $314,995 (M); expenditures, $198,670; qualifying distributions, $195,000; giving activities include $195,000 for 4 grants (high: $100,000; low: $20,000).
Purpose and activities: Giving primarily for higher education and Jewish federated giving programs.
Fields of interest: Higher education; Nonprofits; Judaism; Human services.
Type of support: Regranting.
Limitations: Applications not accepted. Giving primarily in the greater metropolitan Washington, DC, area, including MD and VA; also giving in FL. No grants to individuals.
Application information: Contributes only to pre-selected organizations.
Officers and Directors: Sylvia Greenberg, Pres., V.P. and Treas. and Director; Paul Greenberg, V.P. and Secy. and Director; Kenneth Greenberg, V.P. and Director; Beverly Halpert; Stuart Halpert.
EIN: 030422800

1813
Ronald S. Haft Foundation
1025 Thomas Jefferson St., N.W., Ste. 700 E.
Washington, DC 20007 (202) 293-4500
Contact: Michael Sanders, Dir.; Kathreine Roberson, Dir.; Ronald Haft, Dir.

Established in 2006 in District of Columbia.
Donor: Ronald S. Haft.
Foundation type: Independent foundation.
Financial data (yr. ended 12/31/13): Assets, $423,646 (M); expenditures, $179,279; qualifying distributions, $176,085; giving activities include $176,085 for 30 grants (high: $30,000; low: $250).
Fields of interest: Nonprofits; Human services.
Type of support: Regranting.
Limitations: Applications accepted. Giving primarily in CA.
Application information: Application form required.
Initial approach: Request application form
Deadline(s): None
Directors: Ronald Haft; Katherine Roberson; Michael Sanders.
EIN: 204667032

1814
The Hanley Foundation
1101 30th St. N.W., Ste. 500
Washington, DC 20007-3772

Established in 1999 in District of Columbia.
Donor: Michael J. Hanley.

Foundation type: Independent foundation.
Financial data (yr. ended 12/31/13): Assets, $6,891,404 (M); expenditures, $374,403; qualifying distributions, $304,000; giving activities include $304,000 for 18 grants (high: $50,000; low: $500).
Purpose and activities: Giving primarily for health and human services.
Fields of interest: Education; Water resources; Health; Hospital care; Human services; Child welfare; Youth services; Homeless services.
Limitations: Applications not accepted. Giving in the U.S., primarily in the greater metropolitan Washington, DC, area, including portions of MD and VA; giving also in MN. No grants to individuals.
Application information: Contributes only to pre-selected organizations.
Officers: Michael J. Hanley, Pres.; Kathryn J. Hanley, V.P.; Ellen McMackin, Secy.
EIN: 522204367

1815
Paul & Annetta Himmelfarb Foundation Inc.
1240-A Upshur St. N.W.
Washington, DC 20011-5626

Established in 1947 in Delaware.
Foundation type: Independent foundation.
Financial data (yr. ended 12/31/13): Assets, $5,726,559 (M); expenditures, $294,504; qualifying distributions, $211,988; giving activities include $203,000 for 7 grants (high: $110,000; low: $5,000).
Purpose and activities: Support primarily to organizations that combat homelessness and/or addiction in Washington, D.C.; giving also to organizations that provide summer camp services to Washington, D.C. youth.
Fields of interest: Addiction services; Camps; Child welfare; Homeless services; Children and youth; Homeless people.
Limitations: Applications not accepted. Giving primarily in the Washington, DC, area. No support for political organizations. No grants to individuals.
Publications: Annual report.
Application information: Contributes only to pre-selected organizations.
Officers and Directors: Paul Himmelfarb, Pres. and Director; Norma Lee Naiman, V.P. and Director; Lauren K. Hester, Secy. and Director; Michael E. Preston, Treas. and Exec. Dir.; Lisa Ulanow.
Number of staff: 1 full-time professional; 1 part-time professional.
EIN: 520784206

1816
Institute of Current World Affairs, Inc.
(also known as Crane-Rogers Foundation)
1779 Massachusetts Ave., NW, Ste. 615
Washington, DC 20036-2109 (202) 364-4068
Contact: Edward P. Joseph, Exec. Dir.
FAX: (202) 364-0498; E-mail: icwa@icwa.org; Main URL: http://www.icwa.org
Facebook: https://www.facebook.com/InstituteOfCurrentWorldAffairs
Twitter: https://twitter.com/ICWAnews
Application e-mail: apply@icwa.org

Established in 1925 in New York.

Donors: Charles R. Crane; Robert McColl; Suzanne McColl; The Beinecke Foundation; Friendship Fund, Inc.
Foundation type: Operating foundation.
Financial data (yr. ended 12/31/13): Assets, $6,719,703 (M); gifts received, $571,138; expenditures, $884,830; qualifying distributions, $602,522; giving activities include $184,257 for 8 grants to individuals (high: $37,893; low: $715).
Purpose and activities: Support for a limited number of long-term fellowships to persons 35 years or younger of exceptional ability to enable them to work in and write about foreign areas of significance to the U.S.
Fields of interest: International relations.
Type of support: Fellowships.
Limitations: Applications accepted. No support for formal education. No grants for research projects.
Publications: Application guidelines; Informational brochure.
Application information: Complete application information available on Institute web site.
Initial approach: Letter of interest and resume (by email preferred)
Copies of proposal: 1
Deadline(s): See Institute web site for deadlines for letter of interest and resume. If appropriate, candidates will be invited to submit a more detailed written application
Board meeting date(s): June and Dec.
Officers and Trustees: Dirk Vandewalle, Chair. and Trustee; Cynthia Caron, Vice-Chair. and Trustee; Neri Zilber, Secy. and Trustee; Camila Gonzalez, Treas. and Trustee; Edward P. Joseph, Exec. Dir. and Trustee; Julie Barlow; Mary Lynne Bird; Robert Levinson; Cheng Li; Edmund Sutton.
Number of staff: 1 full-time professional; 2 full-time support.
EIN: 131621044

1817
Jovid Foundation
5335 Wisconsin Ave. N.W., Ste. 440
Washington, DC 20015-2003 (202) 686-2616
Contact: Bob Wittig, Exec. Dir.
FAX: (202) 686-2621;
E-mail: jovidfoundation@gmail.com; Main URL: http://fdnweb.org/jovid
Grants List: http://fdnweb.org/jovid/grants-awarded

Established in 1990 in District of Columbia.
Donors: David O. Maxwell; Joan P. Maxwell.
Foundation type: Independent foundation.
Financial data (yr. ended 12/31/13): Assets, $3,932,820 (M); gifts received, $250,000; expenditures, $527,576; qualifying distributions, $518,851; giving activities include $371,500 for 34 grants (high: $30,000; low: $1,500).
Purpose and activities: The foundation's primary interest is in supporting nonprofit organizations in the District of Columbia whose work is aimed at helping people in or at risk of long-term poverty to become more self-sufficient. Because the foundation is small and seeks to make a real difference to the projects it funds, it is particularly interested in neighborhood-based efforts that provide programs and services to adults, including its funding for vocational education and job counseling. The foundation also has a modest budget for support of the arts.
Fields of interest: Vocational education; Job counseling; Adolescents; Adults; Young adults;

Females; Female adults; Female young adults; Males; Male adults; Male young adults; Single parents; Ethnic and racial groups; People of Asian descent; People of African descent; People of Latin American descent; American Indians; Immigrants and migrants; Homeless people; Low-income and poor people; Incarcerated people; Substance abusers.

Type of support: Technical assistance; General support; Continuing support; Capacity-building and technical assistance; Program development; Seed money; Research; Program evaluations.

Limitations: Applications accepted. Giving primarily in Washington, DC. No support for sectarian projects. No grants to individuals.

Publications: Annual report (including application guidelines); Grants list.

Application information: Jovid will consider letters of inquiry from organizations which have not received previous funding from the foundation. Please note that the foundations funding remains very limited. Therefore the letter of inquiry must clearly address the proposals anticipated effectiveness and impact in helping DC adults obtain and retain employment. Full proposals are by invitation only, upon consideration of letter of inquiry. See Foundation web site for application guidelines.

Initial approach: Letter of inquiry (not exceeding 3 pages) by fax or e-mail; or telephone Exec. Dir. prior to submission
Copies of proposal: 1
Deadline(s): See foundation web site for current deadlines
Board meeting date(s): Mar., June, and Nov.
Final notification: After board meeting

Officers and Directors: Joan P. Maxwell, Pres. and Director; David O. Maxwell, V.P. and Treas. and Director; Doris D. Blazek-White, Secy. and Director; Bob Wittig, Exec. Dir.

Number of staff: 1 full-time professional.

EIN: 521694387

1818
Kolar Charitable Foundation of Buckley Sandler

c/o Buckley Sandler LLP
1250 24th St. NW., Ste. 700
Washington, DC   20037-1222

Donor: Buckley Sandler, LLP.
Foundation type: Independent foundation.
Financial data (yr. ended 12/31/13): Assets, $331,672 (M); gifts received, $307,856; expenditures, $267,089; qualifying distributions, $267,089; giving activities include $263,055 for 77 grants (high: $12,500; low: $100).
Fields of interest: Education; Health; Community and economic development.
Limitations: Applications not accepted.
Application information: Unsolicited requests for funds not accepted.
Officers and Directors: Joseph M. Kolar, Pres. and Director; Jeremiah S. Buckley, V.P. and Director; Andrew L. Sandler, V.P. and Director; Benjamin B. Klubes, Secy. and Director; John P. Kromer, Treas. and Director; Margo H.K. Tank; Jonice Gray Tucker.
EIN: 272748046

1819
The Lemon Foundation
(formerly The James H. & Martha McG. Lemon Foundation)
1101 Vermont Ave. N.W., Ste. 800
Washington, DC   20005-3521
Contact: James H. Lemon Jr., Pres.

Donors: Martha McG. Lemon; James H. Lemon, Jr.
Foundation type: Independent foundation.
Financial data (yr. ended 12/31/14): Assets, $8,464,868 (M); expenditures, $197,923; qualifying distributions, $186,949; giving activities include $180,170 for 68 grants (high: $25,000; low: $50).
Purpose and activities: Giving primarily for health care and educational organizations.
Fields of interest: Education; Health; Hospital care; Diseases and conditions; Human services; Child welfare.
Limitations: Applications not accepted. Giving primarily in the metropolitan Washington, DC area, including MD and VA. No grants to individuals.
Application information: Contributes only to pre-selected organizations.
Officers: James H. Lemon, Jr., Pres.; John A. Beck, V.P. and Secy.; Ashley Lemon Shaw, V.P.
EIN: 521176430

1820
Merriman Foundation
c/o Linda Sonnenmoser
1747 Pennsylvania Ave.
Washington, DC   20006-4604

Donors: Joe Jack Merriman†; Trading Partners I; Trading Partners II.
Foundation type: Independent foundation.
Financial data (yr. ended 12/31/13): Assets, $9,744,892 (M); expenditures, $365,406; qualifying distributions, $332,685; giving activities include $332,685 for 27 grants (high: $100,000; low: $400).
Fields of interest: Arts and culture; Education; Higher education; Nonprofits; Diseases and conditions; Religion; Human services; Youth services; Scouting programs.
International interests: Bahamas.
Type of support: Research; Research and evaluation; Regranting.
Limitations: Applications not accepted. Giving primarily in FL, MO and TX. No grants to individuals.
Application information: Unsolicited requests for funds not accepted.
Officers: Michael A. Merriman, Pres. and Treas.; Elaine A. Merriman, V.P.; Marybeth M. Sotos, Secy.
EIN: 237113720

1821
The Miller-Wehrle Family Foundation
5448 33rd St. N.W.
Washington, DC   20015-1627
E-mail: millerwehrlefoundation@gmail.com

Established in 2006 in District of Columbia.
Donors: Elizabeth M. Wehrle; Matthew B. Miller.
Foundation type: Independent foundation.
Financial data (yr. ended 12/31/12): Assets, $4,519,132 (M); expenditures, $290,243; qualifying distributions, $240,000; giving activities include $240,000 for grants.

Fields of interest: Health; Human services.
Limitations: Applications not accepted. Giving primarily in Washington, DC, and Hagerstown, MD. No grants to individuals.
Application information: Contributes only to pre-selected organizations.
Officers: Elizabeth M. Wehrle, Pres. and Treas.; Matthew B. Miller, V.P. and Secy.
Directors: Colin A. Miller; E. Lynne Miller.
EIN: 208091563

1822
Mimi Fund Inc.
1010 Wisconsin Ave. N.W., Ste. 550
Washington, DC   20007-3678

Established in 2003 in District of Columbia.
Donors: CMC Trust; Catherine M. Conover; CMC Charitable Lead Annuity Trust.
Foundation type: Independent foundation.
Financial data (yr. ended 12/31/14): Assets, $1,142,082; gifts received, $196,750; expenditures, $265,910; qualifying distributions, $264,345.
Fields of interest: Education; Community and economic development; Human services.
Type of support: General support.
Limitations: Applications not accepted. No grants to individuals.
Application information: Unsolicited requests for funds not accepted.
Officers: Cecily Kihn, Secy.; Bonita Tindley, Treas.
Directors: Nina Cicero; R.J. Cicero; Mary Conover; John W. Warner IV.
EIN: 680568404

1823
Monarch Fund
c/o Alison Olsen
1901 Pennsylvania Ave. N.W., Ste. 40
Washington, DC   20006-3447

Established in 2007 in District of Columbia.
Donor: Donald E. Graham.
Foundation type: Independent foundation.
Financial data (yr. ended 12/31/13): Assets, $2,228,008 (M); expenditures, $171,545; qualifying distributions, $142,000; giving activities include $142,000 for 2 grants (high: $92,000; low: $50,000).
Fields of interest: Foundations; Diseases and conditions.
Type of support: Research; Research and evaluation.
Limitations: Applications not accepted. Giving primarily in Washington, DC, and MA. No grants to individuals.
Application information: Contributes only to pre-selected organizations.
Trustee: Mary Graham.
EIN: 266049750

1824
Jack H. & Lovell R. Olender Foundation
888 17th St. N.W., 4th Fl.
Washington, DC   20006-3939
Application address: c/o, Jack Olender or Lovell Olender, 4312-J Evergreen Ln., Annandale, VA 22003, tel.: (703) 354-1800

Donors: Jack H. Olender; Lovell R. Olender.
Foundation type: Independent foundation.
Financial data (yr. ended 12/31/13): Assets, $268,800 (M); gifts received, $289,840; expenditures, $361,388; qualifying distributions, $359,071; giving activities include $343,171 for 160 grants (high: $40,000; low: $100), and $12,000 for 12 grants to individuals (high: $1,000; low: $1,000).
Purpose and activities: Giving for higher education, consumer protection, legal services, health care, and Jewish organizations. Scholarships only to students from low income families in Washington, DC.
Fields of interest: Education; Higher education; Nonprofits; Hospital care; Diseases and conditions; Legal services; Consumer protection; Judaism; Human services; Child welfare; People of African descent.
Type of support: General support; Student aid; Regranting.
Limitations: Applications accepted. Giving primarily to organizations in the greater metropolitan Washington, DC, area; giving to individuals limited to residents of the greater metropolitan Washington, DC, area, including MD and VA.
Application information: Application form required.
Initial approach: Letter
Deadline(s): Before fall term
Officers: Jack H. Olender, Pres.; James Case Reed, Secy.
EIN: 521622462

1825

O. L. Pathy Family Foundation, Inc.

3000 Connecticut Ave., N.W., Ste. 406
Washington, DC 20008-2552

Foundation type: Independent foundation.
Financial data (yr. ended 12/31/13): Assets, $11,475,914 (M); expenditures, $478,721; qualifying distributions, $387,126; giving activities include $342,862 for 24 grants (high: $100,000; low: $2,000).
Limitations: Applications not accepted. Giving primarily in Washington, DC and New York, NY.
Application information: Unsolicited requests for funds not accepted.
Officers: Elizabeth Pathy Salett, Pres.; Peter Salett, V.P. and Secy.; Stephen Salett, V.P. and Treas.
Director: Stanley Salett.
EIN: 452617992

1826

Alicia Patterson Foundation

1090 Vermont Ave. NW, Ste. 1000
Washington, DC 20005-4965 (202) 393-5995
Contact: Margaret Engel, Exec. Dir.
FAX: (301) 951-8512;
E-mail: info@aliciapatterson.org; Main URL: http://aliciapatterson.org
Blog: http://aliciapatterson.org/blog
Facebook: https://www.facebook.com/pages/Alicia-Patterson-Foundation/38469057147
RSS feed: http://aliciapatterson.org/rss

Established in 1960 in New York.
Donors: Alicia Patterson†; Aria Foundation; Cissy Patterson Foundation.
Foundation type: Operating foundation.

Financial data (yr. ended 12/31/13): Assets, $5,537,766 (M); gifts received, $60,000; expenditures, $432,635; qualifying distributions, $420,201; giving activities include $40,000 for 1 grant, and $234,775 for 10 grants to individuals (high: $40,000; low: $3,333).
Purpose and activities: Grants one-year fellowships for a small number of print journalists and photojournalists to examine and write about areas or problems of special interest; candidates must be U.S. citizens who have been working professionally as print journalists for five years or longer.
Fields of interest: Publishing; Adults.
Type of support: Fellowships.
Publications: Application guidelines; Annual report; Grants list; Informational brochure; Newsletter.
Application information: Application guidelines available on foundation web site. Application form required.
Initial approach: Typewritten statement not exceeding 3 single-spaced pages. Contact foundation for full submission details
Copies of proposal: 3
Deadline(s): Submit proposal between June and Sept.; deadline Oct. 1
Board meeting date(s): Annually in Dec.
Final notification: Early Dec.
Officers and Directors: Alice Arlen, Chair. and Director; Robert Lee Hotz, Pres. and Director; Margaret Engel, Exec. Dir.; Joseph M.P. Albright, Chair. Emeritus; Anne K. Albright; Maud Beelman; Frances Fitzgerald; Louis Freedburg; Patrick Hoge; Michael Massing; Kristal Brent Zook.
Number of staff: 1 part-time professional.
EIN: 136092124

1827

H.O. Peet Foundation

P.O. Box 320
Washington, DC 20044-0320 (202) 965-3951
Contact: Adam Foster, Treas.

Established in 1947 in Missouri.
Foundation type: Independent foundation.
Financial data (yr. ended 12/31/13): Assets, $10,406,223 (M); gifts received, $4,818,824; expenditures, $307,227; qualifying distributions, $257,000; giving activities include $257,000 for 22 grants (high: $35,000; low: $1,000).
Fields of interest: Arts and culture; Museums; Higher education; Natural resources; Domesticated animals; Protestantism; Human services.
Limitations: Applications accepted. Giving primarily in Washington, DC. No grants to individuals.
Application information: Application form required.
Initial approach: Letter
Deadline(s): Oct. 1
Officers: Marguerite Peet Foster, Pres; Leslie K. Smith, Secy.; Adam Rockwood Foster, Treas.
EIN: 446005945

1828

Pettus-Crowe Foundation Inc.

1200 18th St. N.W., Ste. 900
Washington, DC 20036-2573

Established in 1968 in New York.
Donors: Irene Pettus-Crowe†; Mary Crowe.
Foundation type: Independent foundation.
Financial data (yr. ended 12/31/13): Assets, $2,408,723 (M); expenditures, $198,698;

qualifying distributions, $149,560; giving activities include $149,560 for 12 grants (high: $45,000; low: $500).
Purpose and activities: Support for bioethical issues and AIDS.
Fields of interest: Bioethics; HIV/AIDS.
Type of support: General support; Continuing support; Program development; Convening; Seed money.
Limitations: Applications not accepted. Giving limited to the U.S. No grants to individuals.
Application information: Contributes only to pre-selected organizations.
Board meeting date(s): Annually
Officers: Irene Crowe, Pres. and Treas.; Mary Crowe, V.P.
EIN: 237025310

1829

Porter Family Charitable Foundation, Inc.

1250 24th St. N.W., Ste. 300
Washington, DC 20037-1186
E-mail: jdmackenzie@mac.com

Established in 1989 in District of Columbia.
Donors: John R. Porter, Jr.; Margaret Nicholson Porter†; Amelie W. Porter.
Foundation type: Independent foundation.
Financial data (yr. ended 12/31/13): Assets, $5,558,193 (M); expenditures, $357,234; qualifying distributions, $278,840; giving activities include $265,499 for 43 grants (high: $101,000; low: $100).
Purpose and activities: Giving primarily for education, particularly charter schools, medical research, autism, and social services, particularly organizations where board members are currently involved.
Fields of interest: Education; Catholicism; Human services.
Type of support: General support; Matching grants; Annual campaigns; Capital campaigns; Seed money.
Limitations: Applications not accepted. Giving primarily in Hartford, CT, Washington, DC, and New York, NY. No grants to individuals.
Publications: Grants list.
Application information: Unsolicited requests for funds not accepted.
Officers: Amelie Porter Stroh, Pres.; Jennifer P. MacKenzie, Secy.-Treas.
Director: Walter C. Wilson.
Number of staff: None.
EIN: 521811780

1830

The Ptarmigan Foundation Inc.

2900 N St. N.W.
Washington, DC 20007-3341

Established in 2007 in Unspecified.
Donors: Constance B. Hanson Trust; Margaret P. Hanson.
Foundation type: Independent foundation.
Financial data (yr. ended 12/31/13): Assets, $3,948,488 (M); gifts received, $67,663; expenditures, $195,790; qualifying distributions, $194,017; giving activities include $191,200 for 1 grant.
Fields of interest: Bird preservation; Catholicism.

Limitations: Applications not accepted. Giving primarily in New York, NY, and Washington, DC. No grants to individuals.
Application information: Unsolicited requests for funds not accepted.
Directors: Margaret P. Hanson; Frederic Kellogg; Cristy West.
EIN: 208152230

1831
Luther I. Replogle Foundation
1720 N. Street N.W.
Washington, DC 20036-2907 (202) 679-0677
Contact: Gwenn Gebhard, Exec. Dir.
FAX: (202) 580-6579; E-mail: info@lirf.org; Main URL: http://www.lirf.org

Foundation type: Independent foundation.
Financial data (yr. ended 12/31/13): Assets, $11,273,438 (M); expenditures, $620,615; qualifying distributions, $462,434; giving activities include $413,154 for 57 grants (high: $28,774; low: $500).
Purpose and activities: The foundation funds programs addressing the needs of youth and children, and women with children living in, or at risk of, long-term poverty (especially children of inner-city residents). Of particular interest are: 1) Programs designed to address immediate crisis situations and the provision of stabilization services; 2) Programs designed to assist individuals in developing skills for self-sufficiency and to be able to participate constructively in society and the workforce; 3) Programs designed to provide supplementary services to improve educational opportunities for inner city children, including enrichment programs in the arts and sciences, alternative schools, after-school tutoring and mentoring, and scholarship programs. Programs for affordable and supportive housing with a focus on single mothers and families with children, and youth on their own.
Fields of interest: Arts and culture; Education; Elementary and secondary education; Human services; Family services; Child welfare; Children and youth; Children; Adolescents; Females; Single parents; Homeless people; Low-income and poor people; Slum youth.
Type of support: General support; Matching grants; Continuing support; Program development; Fellowships; Scholarships.
Limitations: Applications accepted. Giving primarily in the inner city neighborhoods of Minneapolis, MN, Chicago, IL, and Washington, DC. Generally no support for nationally-affiliated organizations. No grants to individuals (except for the Luther I. Replogle Award for Management Improvement as selected by the U.S. Dept. of State).
Publications: Annual report; Grants list; Program policy statement.
Application information: Letters of inquiry must be submitted on-line, using the "request form" link on the foundation web site. Application guidelines available on the foundation web site. Application form required.
Initial approach: Letter of inquiry via online form. Paper documents not accepted.
Deadline(s): Feb. 15 and Aug. 15
Board meeting date(s): Apr. and Oct.
Final notification: Between 1-week and 1-month
Officers and Directors: Paul R.S. Gebhard, Pres. and Director; William McClintic, Secy. and Director; Elizabeth R. Dickie, Treas.; Gwenn H.S. Gebhard,

Exec. Dir.; Sophia Gebhard Anema; David Replogle; Anne Witkowsky.
Number of staff: 1 part-time professional.
EIN: 366141697

1832
The Rossotti Foundation
3314 N. St. N.W.
Washington, DC 20037-2807

Established in 1992 in Delaware.
Donors: Charles O. Rossotti; Barbara M. Rossotti.
Foundation type: Independent foundation.
Financial data (yr. ended 06/30/14): Assets, $275,689 (M); gifts received, $497,150; expenditures, $423,640; qualifying distributions, $416,550; giving activities include $416,550 for 28 grants (high: $156,000; low: $250).
Fields of interest: Music; Education; Water resources; Health.
Limitations: Applications not accepted. Giving primarily in Washington, DC. No grants to individuals.
Application information: Unsolicited requests for funds not accepted.
Officers and Directors: Charles O. Rossotti, Pres. and Treas.; Barbara M. Rossotti, Secy. and Director.
EIN: 521793989

1833
Harold Rubenstein Family Charitable Foundation
1824 Phelps Pl. N.W., Ste. 1810
Washington, DC 20008-1850

Established in 1952 in Massachusetts.
Donors: Brockton Wholesale Beverage Co., Inc.; Harold Rubenstein†.
Foundation type: Independent foundation.
Financial data (yr. ended 12/31/14): Assets, $4,695,022 (M); expenditures, $320,352; qualifying distributions, $262,650; giving activities include $251,050 for 53 grants (high: $20,000; low: $500).
Purpose and activities: Giving primarily for the arts, education, health, and children, youth, and social services.
Fields of interest: Arts and culture; Opera; Museums; Historic preservation; Education; Higher education; Business education; Foundations; Health; Human services; Child welfare.
Type of support: General support.
Limitations: Applications not accepted. Giving primarily in Washington, D. No grants to individuals.
Application information: Unsolicited requests for funds not accepted.
Trustee: Bonnie Cohen.
EIN: 046041597

1834
Curt C. & Else Silberman Foundation
c/o Peter Friedmann
1120 G St. N.W., Ste. 1020
Washington, DC 20005-3828

Donors: Curt C. Silberman; Else Silberman†.
Foundation type: Independent foundation.
Financial data (yr. ended 06/30/14): Assets, $7,047,197 (M); expenditures, $350,415;

qualifying distributions, $300,000; giving activities include $300,000 for 1 grant.
Fields of interest: Arts and culture; Education; Nonprofits; Religion.
Type of support: General support; Regranting.
Limitations: Applications not accepted. Giving primarily in MD. No grants to individuals.
Application information: Unsolicited requests for funds not requested.
Officers and Trustees: Peter Friedmann, Pres. and Trustee; Evi Meinhardt, Secy. and Trustee; Joseph W. Friedmann, Treas. and Trustee; Debbie Friedmann; Edward Meinhardt.
EIN: 226065494

1835
Leonard & Elaine Silverstein Family Foundation
(formerly Silverstein Family Foundation)
1700 K St. N.W., Ste. 300
Washington, DC 20006-3807

Established in 1965 in District of Columbia.
Donor: Leonard L. Silverstein.
Foundation type: Independent foundation.
Financial data (yr. ended 11/30/13): Assets, $4,256,776 (M); gifts received, $385,000; expenditures, $157,400; qualifying distributions, $140,125; giving activities include $136,100 for 30 grants (high: $25,000; low: $500).
Purpose and activities: Giving primarily for the fine and performing arts.
Fields of interest: Arts and culture.
Limitations: Applications not accepted. Giving primarily in Washington, DC. No grants to individuals.
Application information: Unsolicited requests for funds not accepted.
Officers: Elaine W. Silverstein, Pres.; Leonard L. Silverstein, V.P.; Susan Silverstein Scott, Secy.-Treas.
EIN: 520845731

1836
Albert L. & Elizabeth T. Tucker Foundation
c/o Jackson & Campbell
1120 20th St. N.W., Ste. 300
Washington, DC 20036-3406 (202) 457-1600
Contact: Nicholas S. McConnell

Established in 1995 in District of Columbia.
Foundation type: Independent foundation.
Financial data (yr. ended 12/31/13): Assets, $2,787,758 (M); expenditures, $399,318; qualifying distributions, $348,057; giving activities include $341,000 for 10 grants (high: $200,000; low: $1,000).
Purpose and activities: Giving primarily to hospitals and medical centers; support also for other organizations providing health services, including hospices and nursing homes.
Fields of interest: Convalescent care; Hospital care; Specialty hospital care; Hospice care; Cancers.
Type of support: General support; Equipment; Program development; Fellowships; Research.
Limitations: Applications accepted. Giving primarily in Washington, DC. No grants to individuals.
Application information: Application form required.
Initial approach: Letter
Deadline(s): None

Officers and Directors: Nicholas C. McConnell, Pres. and Director; Nancy McConnell, V.P. and Director; James R. Michael, Secy.-Treas. and Director.
EIN: 521866940

1837
Union Privilege Relief Fund Trust
(also known as Union Plus Disaster Relief Fund)
1100 1st St., N.E., Ste. 850
Washington, DC 20002-4894
E-mail: info@unionprivilege.org; Main URL: http://www.unionplus.org/disaster-relief/sandy-october-2012

Established in 2005 in District of Columbia.
Donors: Union Privilege; Household Bank; Capital One.
Foundation type: Independent foundation.
Financial data (yr. ended 12/31/13): Assets, $426,004 (M); gifts received, $350,000; expenditures, $144,690; qualifying distributions, $143,000; giving activities include $143,000 for grants to individuals.
Purpose and activities: Giving primarily for financial assistance to union members harmed by events beyond their control, such as natural disasters, terrorist acts, accidents, and disease.
Fields of interest: Disasters and emergency management.
Type of support: Grants to individuals.
Limitations: Applications not accepted. Giving on a national basis.
Application information: Unsolicited requests for funds not accepted.
Trustees: Stephen Goldsmith; Leslie Tolf.
EIN: 841678738

1838
Westport Fund
4225 Lenore Ln., N.W.
Washington, DC 20008

Donors: Milton McGreevy†; Jean McGreevy Green.
Foundation type: Independent foundation.
Financial data (yr. ended 12/31/13): Assets, $7,487,439 (M); expenditures, $414,800; qualifying distributions, $398,954; giving activities include $358,734 for 231 grants (high: $40,000; low: $250).
Fields of interest: Arts and culture; Ballet; Theater; Musical ensembles and groups; Opera; Orchestral music; Vocal music; Museums; Children's museums; Historic preservation; Elementary and secondary education; Vocational education; Higher education; Undergraduate education; Nonprofits; Hospital care; Hospice care; Family planning; Cancers; Public libraries; Television; Crime prevention; Community and economic development; Christianity; Human services; Food banks; Youth services; Females.
Type of support: General support; Continuing support; Annual campaigns; Capital campaigns; Capital and infrastructure; Equipment; Endowments; Publications; Curriculum development; Scholarships; Research; Regranting.
Limitations: Applications not accepted. Giving primarily in Washington, DC, NY, MA and MO. No grants to individuals, or for consulting services, deficit financing, exchange programs, internships, matching funds, land acquisition, seed money, or technical assistance; no loans.
Application information: Unsolicited requests for funds not accepted.
Officers and Directors: Gail McGreevy Harmon, Pres. and Director; Pam McGreevy, Secy. and

Director; Stuart Green, Treas. and Director; Eve H. Bould; Jean McGreevy Green; Annie James McGreevy; Colin McNay.
EIN: 446007971

1839
Woodward Walsh Foundation
3027 Que St. N.W.
Washington, DC 20007-3081

Established in 1994 in District of Columbia.
Donors: Elsa Walsh; Robert U. Woodward.
Foundation type: Independent foundation.
Financial data (yr. ended 06/30/13): Assets, $2,884,352 (M); gifts received, $100,000; expenditures, $174,225; qualifying distributions, $170,225; giving activities include $170,225 for grants.
Fields of interest: Arts and culture; Education; Animal welfare; Diseases and conditions; Catholicism; Child welfare.
Type of support: General support.
Limitations: Applications not accepted. Giving primarily in Washington, DC. No grants to individuals.
Application information: Unsolicited requests for funds not accepted.
Officers and Directors: Robert U. Woodward, Pres. and Treas. and Director; Elsa Walsh, V.P. and Secy. and Director; Redmond Walsh.
EIN: 521907452

FLORIDA

1840
4 Girls Foundation Inc.
565 E. Hillsboro Blvd.
Deerfield Beach, FL 33441-3543
Main URL: http://www.4girlsfoundation.org

Donors: Randal Perkins; Saily Perkins; Ron Book P.A.; Ashbritt Inc.
Foundation type: Independent foundation.
Financial data (yr. ended 12/31/13): Assets, $5,513,720 (M); gifts received, $1,102,840; expenditures, $304,902; qualifying distributions, $211,105; giving activities include $211,105 for 21 grants (high: $25,000; low: $80).
Fields of interest: Health; Mental health care; Human services.
Limitations: Applications not accepted. Giving primarily in FL.
Application information: Unsolicited requests for funds not accepted.
Officers: Randal Perkins, Chair.; Saily Perkins, Pres.; Brittany Perkins, V.P. and Secy.; Ashley Perkins, Treas.
EIN: 261739189

1841
A. & R. Charitable Foundation, Inc.
c/o Robert D. Falese, Jr.
10661 Copper Lake Dr.
Bonita Springs, FL 34135-8438

Established in 2005 in New Jersey.
Donors: Robert D. Falese; Robert D. Falese, Jr.
Foundation type: Independent foundation.
Financial data (yr. ended 06/30/13): Assets, $43,719 (M); gifts received, $153,939; expenditures, $175,228; qualifying distributions, $170,000; giving activities include $170,000 for 4 grants (high: $105,000; low: $10,000).
Fields of interest: Education; University education; Christianity; Human services.
Limitations: Applications not accepted. Giving primarily in NJ and PA. No grants to individuals.
Application information: Contributes only to pre-selected organizations.
Officer: Robert D. Falese, Jr., Pres.
EIN: 201647309

1842
Rita & Jeffrey Adler Foundation
1301 Alberta Dr.
Winter Park, FL 32789-3900

Donors: Jeffrey A. Adler; Rita N. Adler.
Foundation type: Independent foundation.
Financial data (yr. ended 12/31/13): Assets, $4,373,696 (M); expenditures, $283,916; qualifying distributions, $255,448; giving activities include $255,448 for 29 grants (high: $75,000; low: $100).
Fields of interest: Arts and culture; Education; Nonprofits; Hospital care; Judaism.
Type of support: Regranting.
Limitations: Applications not accepted. Giving primarily in Aspen, CO and the greater Orlando, FL, area. No grants to individuals.

Application information: Contributes only to pre-selected organizations.
Trustees: Jeffrey A. Adler; Rita N. Adler.
EIN: 597177100

1843
Ael Family Foundation
1417 Sadler Rd., No. 378
Fernandina Beach, FL 32034-4466

Established in 2007 in Georgia.
Donor: Roderick D. Odom.
Foundation type: Independent foundation.
Financial data (yr. ended 12/31/13): Assets, $4,892,139 (M); expenditures, $348,055; qualifying distributions, $294,200; giving activities include $294,200 for 22 grants (high: $100,000; low: $500).
Fields of interest: University education; Hospital care; Christianity; Camps; Human services.
Limitations: Applications not accepted. Giving primarily in FL and GA. No grants to individuals.
Application information: Contributes only to pre-selected organizations.
Officers: Elizabeth C. Odom, Pres.; Roderick D. Odom, Secy.-Treas.
Directors: Catherine O. Hawkins; Dorothy E. Odom; Patricia A. Odom.
EIN: 260445549

1844
Ahavas Yisroel Charitable Foundation
3190 Pine Tree Dr.
Miami Beach, FL 33140-3929 (305) 864-9191
Contact: Abraham Shaulson, Tr.

Donors: The Emunah Trust; Institutional Leasing Trust.
Foundation type: Independent foundation.
Financial data (yr. ended 06/30/13): Assets, $11,710,660 (M); expenditures, $325,661; qualifying distributions, $311,198; giving activities include $246,900 for 15 grants (high: $150,000; low: $500).
Purpose and activities: Giving primarily to Jewish agencies, temples, and schools.
Fields of interest: Education; Judaism.
Limitations: Applications accepted. Giving primarily in Doral and Miami Beach, FL, and Brooklyn, NY.
Application information: Application form required.
　Initial approach: Letter
　Deadline(s): None
Trustee: Abraham Shaulson.
EIN: 203848253

1845
John & Linda Anderson Charitable Foundation
4151 Gulf Shore Blvd. N., Ste. 404
Naples, FL 34103-2294

Established in 2000 in Illinois.
Donor: John R. Anderson.
Foundation type: Independent foundation.
Financial data (yr. ended 12/31/13): Assets, $6,774,470 (M); gifts received, $665,610; expenditures, $274,524; qualifying distributions, $219,346; giving activities include $219,346 for 74 grants (high: $24,640; low: $100).

Fields of interest: Natural history museums; Education; University education; Environment; Nonprofits; Health; Protestantism; Human services.
Type of support: Regranting.
Limitations: Applications not accepted. Giving primarily in IL. No grants to individuals.
Application information: Contributes only to pre-selected organizations.
Officers and Directors: Linda Anderson, Pres. and Director; John R. Anderson, V.P. and Secy. and Director; Duane R. Bach, Treas. and Director.
EIN: 364332910

1846
Anderson Family Charitable Foundation, Inc.
P.O. Box 38
Old Town, FL 32680-0038

Donors: Anderson Columbia Co., Inc.; Cynthia Anderson Childers; Bruce Rogow; Joe H. Anderson, Jr.; M. Douglas Anderson; The Taylor Foundation.
Foundation type: Independent foundation.
Financial data (yr. ended 12/31/13): Assets, $10,531 (M); gifts received, $468,065; expenditures, $472,812; qualifying distributions, $472,812; giving activities include $421,041 for grants.
Fields of interest: Christianity; Human services.
Limitations: Applications not accepted. Giving primarily in FL.
Application information: Unsolicited requests for funds not accepted.
Officers: Joe H. Anderson, Jr., Pres.; Cynthia T. Anderson, V.P.; Cynthia Anderson Childers, Secy.-Treas.
Directors: Joe H. Anderson III; Marion Douglas Anderson; Skipper K. Jones; Harriet Anderson Wall.
EIN: 262409879

1847
Robert C. & Sadie G. Anderson Foundation
P.O. Box 40200, FL9-100-10-19
Jacksonville, FL 32203-0200

Established in 1952 in North Carolina.
Donors: Robert C. Anderson†; Sadie Gaither Anderson†.
Foundation type: Independent foundation.
Financial data (yr. ended 12/31/14): Assets, $3,270,570 (M); expenditures, $191,219; qualifying distributions, $162,034; giving activities include $146,000 for 6 grants (high: $66,500; low: $5,000).
Purpose and activities: Support primarily for Presbyterian causes and institutions.
Fields of interest: Education; Protestantism.
Type of support: Continuing support; Program development; Scholarships.
Limitations: Applications not accepted. Giving limited to NC. No grants to individuals, or for matching gifts; no loans.
Application information: Unsolicited requests for funds not accepted.
Trustee: Bank of America, N.A.
EIN: 566065233

1848
W. T. Anderson Trust
P.O. Box 40200, FL9-100-10-19
Jacksonville, FL 32203-0200 (877) 461-7287

Established in 1996 in Georgia.
Donor: W.T. Anderson†.
Foundation type: Independent foundation.
Financial data (yr. ended 10/31/14): Assets,
$3,250,485 (M); expenditures, $180,699;
qualifying distributions, $155,496; giving activities
include $144,000 for 3 grants (high: $64,000; low:
$40,000).
Purpose and activities: Giving primarily to
organizations that provide medical care to indigent
individuals. Any income not used for this purpose
will be used by the trustee to provide aid to indigent
unwed mothers.
Fields of interest: Health; Human services.
Application information: Application form required.
  Initial approach: Letter
  Deadline(s): Submit applications between Aug. 1
  and Aug. 31
Trustee: Bank of America, N.A.
EIN: 586331063

1849
The Andre Family Foundation, Inc.
341 4th Ave.
Indialantic, FL 32903-4213 (321) 725-2232
Contact: Jeanne M. Andre, Pres.

Donors: Edward A. Andre; Jeanne M. Andre.
Foundation type: Independent foundation.
Financial data (yr. ended 06/30/13): Assets,
$1,123,348 (M); gifts received, $15,420;
expenditures, $192,455; qualifying distributions,
$188,850; giving activities include $188,850 for 22
grants (high: $43,000; low: $500).
Fields of interest: Hospice care; Cancers;
Christianity.
Limitations: Applications accepted. Giving primarily
in FL; some giving in MO and VA. No grants to
individuals.
Application information: Application form required.
  Initial approach: Obtain and complete application
  form
  Deadline(s): None
Officers: Jeanne M. Andre, Pres.; Edward A. Andre,
V.P.
Director: Jessica L. Andre.
EIN: 203966428

1850
Andreeff Foundation
140 E. St. Lucia Ln.
Santa Rosa Beach, FL 32459-7609

Donor: Dane Andreeff.
Foundation type: Independent foundation.
Financial data (yr. ended 12/31/13): Assets,
$2,711,574 (M); expenditures, $362,808;
qualifying distributions, $209,524; giving activities
include $207,379 for 11 grants (high: $55,000;
low: $500).
Fields of interest: Health; Religion; Youth
development.
Limitations: Applications not accepted. Giving
primarily in LA.
Application information: Unsolicited requests for
funds not accepted.

Trustee: Carla Andreef; Dane Andreeff; Starr
Andreef; Richard Rhoads; Peter Stewart.
EIN: 263455674

1851
B. Anton Memorial Foundation
P.O. Box 1908
Orlando, FL 32802-1908

Donor: Barbara Anton Trust.
Foundation type: Independent foundation.
Financial data (yr. ended 12/31/13): Assets,
$4,276,636 (M); gifts received, $7,445;
expenditures, $215,062; qualifying distributions,
$201,638; giving activities include $187,159 for 1
grant.
Fields of interest: Religion; Children.
Limitations: Applications not accepted. Giving
primarily in Richmond, VA.
Application information: Unsolicited requests for
funds not accepted.
Trustee: Suntrust Bank, N.A.
EIN: 656473083

1852
Archibald Foundation, Inc.
7100 Roberts Rd.
Tallahassee, FL 32309-9278
Contact: Kathy Archibald, Pres.

Established in 1996 in Florida.
Donors: Delbert M. Archibald†; Kathy Archibald.
Foundation type: Independent foundation.
Financial data (yr. ended 12/31/13): Assets,
$5,555,552 (M); expenditures, $289,798;
qualifying distributions, $246,678; giving activities
include $240,500 for 21 grants (high: $30,000;
low: $2,000).
Fields of interest: Education; Environment; Health;
Diseases and conditions; Housing development;
Child welfare.
Type of support: Program evaluations;
Program-related investments; Internships; Matching
grants; General support; Curriculum development;
Continuing support; Capital campaigns; Capital and
infrastructure; Equipment; Endowments; Program
development; Scholarships; Research.
Limitations: Giving primarily in the Big Bend region
of north FL. No support for organizations lacking 501
(c)(3) status. No grants to individuals.
Application information:
  Initial approach: Letter
  Deadline(s): Jan. 1 to July 31
  Board meeting date(s): Semiannually
  Final notification: 4th quarter of calendar year
Officer and Directors: Kathy Archibald, Pres. and
Director; Daniel Isaac Archibald; Kenneth Cole
Archibald.
EIN: 593414615

1853
Arison Arts Foundation
c/o Richard Kohan, Afo, LLC
2 Alhambra Plz., Ste. 1040
Coral Gables, FL 33134-5249 (786) 270-3701

Established in 2005 in Florida.
Foundation type: Independent foundation.
Financial data (yr. ended 12/31/13): Assets,
$273,497,655 (M); gifts received, $32,820,062;

expenditures, $2,623,132; qualifying distributions,
$333,333; giving activities include $333,333 for 1
grant.
Fields of interest: Art museums.
Limitations: Applications not accepted. Giving
primarily in New York, NY. No grants to individuals.
Application information: Contributes only to
pre-selected organizations.
Officers: Marilyn B. Arison, Chair.; Sarah Arison,
Pres.; Harry Hersh, Exec. V.P.; Richard L. Kohan,
Secy.-Treas.
EIN: 137450689

1854
The Around Foundation
748 Windsor Ln.
Key West, FL 33040-6441
Contact: J. Gleick

Established in 1997 in New York.
Donor: James Gleick.
Foundation type: Independent foundation.
Financial data (yr. ended 04/30/14): Assets,
$5,082,459 (M); expenditures, $345,881;
qualifying distributions, $305,950; giving activities
include $305,750 for 35 grants (high: $25,000;
low: $250).
Fields of interest: Arts and culture; Education;
Radio; Human rights; Human services.
Limitations: Applications not accepted. Giving
primarily in NY. No grants to individuals.
Application information: Contributes only to
pre-selected organizations.
Trustees: Cynthia Crossen; James Gleick.
EIN: 113377271

1855
ATAP Universe Learning Centers, Inc.
555 S. Highland St.
Mount Dora, FL 32757-6156

Donors: Robert E. Hewell; Joyce S. Hewell, Ph.D.
Foundation type: Operating foundation.
Financial data (yr. ended 12/31/13): Assets,
$3,662,875 (M); expenditures, $355,872;
qualifying distributions, $355,801; giving activities
include $355,801 for 51 grants (high: $256,006;
low: $3,295).
Fields of interest: Health; National defense.
Type of support: Equipment.
Limitations: Applications not accepted.
Application information: Unsolicited requests for
funds not accepted.
Officers and Directors: Joyce S. Hewell, Ph.D, Pres.
and Director; Robert E. Hewell, V.P. and Director;
Gregory A. Stelly, V.P. and Director; Larry Phalin.
EIN: 592142480

1856
The Atkins Foundation, Inc.
(formerly The PBSJ Foundation, Inc.)
4030 W. Boy Scout Blvd., Ste. 700
Tampa, FL 33607-1757
Main URL: http://www.atkinsglobal.com

Donors: Atkins North America, Inc.; The Atkins North
America Holdings Corp.
Foundation type: Operating foundation.
Financial data (yr. ended 12/31/13): Assets,
$584,480 (M); gifts received, $237,206;

expenditures, $191,475; qualifying distributions, $189,867; giving activities include $188,000 for 37 grants (high: $15,000; low: $2,000).

Fields of interest: Education; University education.

Type of support: Individual development.

Limitations: Applications not accepted. Giving in the U.S., with emphasis on FL. No grants to individuals.

Application information: Contributes only to pre-selected organizations.

Officers: C. Ernest Edgar, Secy.; Judith Aldrovandi, Cont.; Carol L. Craft, Admin.

Directors: John Buckley; Richard W. Galloway; Eric McLaurin; Maureen Nayowith; Victor P. Poteat.

EIN: 204235058

1857
Eugene and Carol Atkinson Family Foundation

212 Island Creek Dr.
Vero Beach, FL 32963-3364

Established in 1985 in New Jersey.

Donors: Eugene D. Atkinson; Carol A. Atkinson.

Foundation type: Independent foundation.

Financial data (yr. ended 06/30/14): Assets, $1,692,795 (M); gifts received, $308,716; expenditures, $347,202; qualifying distributions, $324,412; giving activities include $316,736 for 26 grants (high: $217,561; low: $100).

Fields of interest: Arts and culture; Education; Religion.

Type of support: General support.

Limitations: Applications not accepted. Giving primarily in NJ and NY. No grants to individuals; no loans or scholarships.

Application information: Unsolicited requests for funds not accepted.

Trustees: Carol A. Atkinson; Eugene D. Atkinson.

EIN: 133318157

1858
Atlantis Blue Project Foundation, Inc.

(formerly Kerzner Marine Foundation, Inc.)
1000 S. Pine Island Rd., Ste. 800
Plantation, FL 33324-3909
Contact: Debra Erickson, Exec. Dir.
E-mail: info@kerznermarinefoundation.org; E-mail for Debra Erickson: debra.erickson@kerzner.com; Main URL: http://www.atlantisthepalm.com/marineandwaterpark/kerznermarinefoundation.aspx

Established in 2005 in Florida.

Donor: Kerzner International Bahamas.

Foundation type: Company-sponsored foundation.

Financial data (yr. ended 12/31/13): Assets, $418,843 (M); gifts received, $250,182; expenditures, $301,109; qualifying distributions, $301,109; giving activities include $209,963 for 6 grants (high: $100,011; low: $5,200).

Purpose and activities: The foundation supports programs designed to preserve and enhance global marine ecosystems through scientific research, education, and community outreach. Special emphasis is directed toward marine protected areas, coral reef conservation, cetacean conservation, and research in the Caribbean, Middle East, and Southeast Asia.

Fields of interest: Environment; Natural resources; Coral reefs; Oceans and coastal waters; Wildlife

biodiversity; Endangered species protection; Domesticated animals.

International interests: Asia; Caribbean; Middle East.

Type of support: Capital and infrastructure; Research and evaluation; Continuing support; System and operational improvements; Program development; Research.

Limitations: Applications accepted. Giving primarily in CA, FL, NY and in the Caribbean, Middle East, and Southeast Asia. No support for political activism. No grants for litigation, or for fundraising, scholarships, endowments or overhead costs for universities.

Publications: Informational brochure.

Application information: Proposals should include a cover page; 2 page abstract; a program or research description of up to 20 pages; an intuitional capacity description of up to 3 pages; a project team description with resumes; and past performance references.

Initial approach: Proposal
Copies of proposal: 5
Deadline(s): Apr. 15 and Sept. 15

Officers and Directors: George Markantonis, Pres. and Managing Dir.; Paul K. Dayton, V.P. and Director; Tim Wise, Treas. and Director; Debra Erickson, Exec. Dir.; Steve Kaiser.

EIN: 342045752

1859
Isaac and Carol Auerbach Family Foundation

(formerly Auerbach Family Foundation)
130 S. Village Way
Jupiter, FL 33458-7828 (610) 581-7788
Contact: Carol B. Auerbach, Tr.

Established in 1981 in Pennsylvania.

Donors: Isaac L. Auerbach✝; Carol B. Auerbach.

Foundation type: Independent foundation.

Financial data (yr. ended 03/31/13): Assets, $3,657,733 (M); gifts received, $125,000; expenditures, $338,766; qualifying distributions, $293,001; giving activities include $282,534 for 28 grants (high: $156,000; low: $54).

Fields of interest: Theater; Education; Nonprofits; Judaism; Human services; Family services; Child welfare.

Type of support: Annual campaigns; Program development; Curriculum development; Research; Regranting.

Limitations: Applications accepted. Giving primarily in NY, MA and PA. No grants to individuals.

Application information: Accepts Delaware Valley Grantmakers Common Grant Application and Common Report Form.

Initial approach: Letter
Deadline(s): None

Trustee: Carol B. Auerbach.

Number of staff: None.

EIN: 232169951

1860
The Aurora Foundation

(also known as The Aurora Ministries)
P.O. Box 1848
Bradenton, FL 34206-1848
Contact: Joseph A. Aleppo, Exec. Dir.
FAX: (941) 748-2625;
E-mail: aurora@auroraministries.org; Main URL: http://www.auroraministries.org

Donor: Anthony T. Rossi.

Foundation type: Independent foundation.

Financial data (yr. ended 12/31/13): Assets, $599,829 (M); expenditures, $459,225; qualifying distributions, $207,115; giving activities include $160,963 for 2 grants (high: $157,263; low: $3,700).

Purpose and activities: Support largely for missionary work; grants also for Christian church support, religious associations, education, and social services; also administers and operates the Bradenton Missionary Village, a rent-free housing complex for retired missionaries.

Fields of interest: Christianity.

Type of support: General support; Continuing support.

Limitations: Applications not accepted. Giving primarily in FL. No grants for professorships or building funds of schools and colleges.

Application information: Unsolicited requests for funds not considered.

Board meeting date(s): Usually mid-Oct.

Officers: Joseph A. Aleppo, Chair.; Nicholas J. Trofemuk, Jr., Vice-Chair. and Treas.

Trustee: Georgia Aleppo.

Number of staff: 38 full-time support; 2 part-time support.

EIN: 237044641

1861
Aviation Education Foundation

100 Aviation Dr. S., Ste. 203
Naples, FL 34104-3583 (239) 649-5733
Contact: James C. Ray, Pres.

Established in 2005 in Unspecified.

Donors: Ray Foundation; James C. Ray.

Foundation type: Independent foundation.

Financial data (yr. ended 12/31/13): Assets, $0 (M); gifts received, $373,900; expenditures, $409,268; qualifying distributions, $377,000; giving activities include $377,000 for 7 grants (high: $250,000; low: $10,000).

Purpose and activities: Giving to organizations that place emphasis on programs involving the education and introduction of children and young adults to aviation.

Fields of interest: Museums; Education; Aerospace engineering; Safety education.

Type of support: Capital and infrastructure; General support.

Limitations: Applications accepted. Giving primarily in FL, MD and WI. No grants to individuals.

Application information: Application form required.

Initial approach: Letter, not to exceed 2 pages
Deadline(s): None

Officers and Directors: James C. Ray, Pres. and Director; Charles J. Ahearn, Secy. and Director; Jeffrey J. Tempas, Treas. and Director; Theodore Brousseau, Jr.

EIN: 201647297

1862
Bailey Family Foundation, Inc.

7839 Vizcaya Way
Naples, FL 34108-7534

Established in 2000 in Connecticut.

Donor: James L. Bailey.

Foundation type: Independent foundation.

Financial data (yr. ended 12/31/14): Assets, $695,308; expenditures, $167,878; qualifying distributions, $152,610.
Fields of interest: Education; Higher education; Religion; Human services.
Limitations: Applications not accepted. No grants to individuals.
Application information: Unsolicited requests for funds not accepted.
Officers and Directors: James L. Bailey, Pres. and Director; Judith A. Bailey, V.P. and Director; Sara F. Bailey, Secy. and Director; Elizabeth Bailey Rogers, Treas. and Director.
EIN: 223768811

1863
Bailey Family Foundation, Inc.
c/o Stephen M. Bailey
P.O. Box 643486
Vero Beach, FL 32964-3486

Established in 1992 in Florida.
Donors: Stephen M. Bailey; Lucia H. Bailey; B.B. Berge.
Foundation type: Independent foundation.
Financial data (yr. ended 12/31/13): Assets, $11,501,892 (M); gifts received, $5,851; expenditures, $444,833; qualifying distributions, $438,950; giving activities include $397,878 for 182 grants (high: $40,550; low: $30).
Purpose and activities: Giving primarily for education and religion.
Fields of interest: Arts and culture; Education; Natural resources; Hospital care; Religion; Christianity; Human services.
Limitations: Applications not accepted. Giving primarily in FL. No grants to individuals.
Application information: Contributes only to pre-selected organizations.
Board meeting date(s): Quarterly
Officers: Stephen M. Bailey, Pres.; Lucia H. Bailey, V.P. and Secy.; B.B. Berge, V.P. and Treas.
EIN: 593154364

1864
Baldwin Family Foundation Trust
312 E. Key Palm Rd.
Boca Raton, FL 33432

Donor: Eleanor R. Baldwin.
Foundation type: Independent foundation.
Financial data (yr. ended 12/31/13): Assets, $6,175,557 (M); gifts received, $400,000; expenditures, $449,094; qualifying distributions, $259,881; giving activities include $206,000 for 5 grants (high: $130,000; low: $500).
Fields of interest: Education.
Limitations: Applications not accepted. No grants to individuals.
Application information: Contributes only to pre-selected organizations.
Trustees: Walter F. Adams III; Eleanor R. Baldwin.
EIN: 026169513

1865
The Bernard and Pamela Barbash Family Foundation
12241 Tillinghast Cir.
Palm Beach Gardens, FL 33418-6202

Established in 2005 in Ohio.
Donor: Bernard Barbash.
Foundation type: Independent foundation.
Financial data (yr. ended 12/31/13): Assets, $4,523,350 (M); expenditures, $259,000; qualifying distributions, $201,625; giving activities include $197,741 for 26 grants (high: $100,000; low: $20).
Fields of interest: Diseases and conditions; Judaism; Human services.
Limitations: Applications not accepted. Giving primarily in OH. No grants to individuals.
Application information: Unsolicited requests for funds not accepted.
Officers: Bernard Barbash, Pres. and Treas.; Pamela Barbash, V.P.; Michael G. Schwartz, Secy.
EIN: 161743055

1866
E. H. Barnard Charitable Trust
P.O. Box 1908
Orlando, FL 32802-1908

Established in 1988 in North Carolina.
Donor: E.H. Barnard†.
Foundation type: Independent foundation.
Financial data (yr. ended 05/31/13): Assets, $4,829,066 (M); expenditures, $253,932; qualifying distributions, $222,628; giving activities include $194,301 for 5 grants (high: $105,000; low: $5,500).
Fields of interest: Arts and culture; Arts councils; Education; Nonprofits; Breast cancer; Libraries; Christianity; European football.
Type of support: Regranting.
Limitations: Applications not accepted. Giving primarily in Yadkin County, NC. No grants to individuals.
Application information: Unsolicited requests for funds not accepted.
Trustee: Suntrust Bank.
EIN: 566299574

1867
J. H. Baroco Foundation, Inc.
P.O. Box 9727
Pensacola, FL 32513-2441
Application address: c/o Vicki Ann Baroco, Pres., 1182 E. Lakeview Ave., Pensacola, FL 32503, tel.: (850) 380-2530

Established in 1988 in Florida.
Donor: James H. Baroco, Sr.†.
Foundation type: Independent foundation.
Financial data (yr. ended 12/31/13): Assets, $854,930 (M); expenditures, $439,488; qualifying distributions, $435,245; giving activities include $435,245 for 53 grants (high: $25,000; low: $1,000).
Fields of interest: Health; Catholicism; Human services; Food aid; Homeless services.
Type of support: General support; Capital campaigns; Capital and infrastructure.
Limitations: Applications accepted. Giving primarily in Pensacola, FL. No grants to individuals.
Application information: Application form required.
Initial approach: Proposal
Deadline(s): None
Officers and Directors: Vicki Ann Baroco, Pres. and Director; Ronald Anthony Baroco, V.P. and Director;

Mary Antonia Noonan, Secy.- Treas.; J. H. Baroco III; Julie M. Baroco.
EIN: 592912852

1868
The Barrington Foundation Inc.
3780 N.E. 31st Ave.
Lighthouse Point, FL 33064-8431

Established in 2003 in Florida.
Donors: Bruce D. Barrington; Gayle M. Barrington.
Foundation type: Independent foundation.
Financial data (yr. ended 12/31/13): Assets, $2,938,824 (M); gifts received, $61; expenditures, $163,723; qualifying distributions, $160,000; giving activities include $160,000 for 6 grants (high: $40,000; low: $5,000).
Fields of interest: Education; Human services.
Limitations: Applications not accepted. Giving primarily in FL. No grants to individuals.
Application information: Unsolicited requests for funds not accepted.
Officers: Gayle M. Barrington, Pres.; Arthur Barrington, V.P.; Paige Dunne, Secy.; Kenneth Barrington, Treas.
Director: Bruce D. Barrington.
EIN: 200497546

1869
Bartner Family Foundation Trust
601 Heritage Dr., Ste. 484
Jupiter, FL 33458-2777

Established in 2000 in Connecticut.
Donors: Robert G. Bartner; Beverly D.N. Bartner; Jennifer Indeck; Arabella Higgins; Nicole Bartner.
Foundation type: Independent foundation.
Financial data (yr. ended 12/31/13): Assets, $359,454 (M); gifts received, $85,000; expenditures, $175,821; qualifying distributions, $174,210; giving activities include $174,210 for 5 grants (high: $59,210; low: $5,000).
Purpose and activities: Giving primarily for the arts; funding also for education and human services.
Fields of interest: Arts and culture; Performing arts; Opera; Orchestral music; Education; Human services.
Limitations: Applications not accepted. Giving primarily in FL and NY; some funding also in CT. No grants to individuals.
Application information: Unsolicited requests for funds not accepted.
Trustees: Beverly D.N. Bartner; Robert G. Bartner; Nicole Bartner Graff; Arabella Bartner Higgins; Jennifer Bartner Indeck.
EIN: 137235081

1870
Danker Basham Foundation, Inc.
c/o Robert Basham
4343 Anchor Plz. Pkwy., Ste. 1
Tampa, FL 33634

Established in 1994 in Florida.
Donor: Robert D. Basham.
Foundation type: Independent foundation.
Financial data (yr. ended 12/31/13): Assets, $9,728,045 (M); expenditures, $470,938; qualifying distributions, $433,058; giving activities

include $433,058 for 23 grants (high: $71,358; low: $100).

Purpose and activities: Giving primarily for Christian ministries, and children, youth, and human services.
Fields of interest: Education; Nonprofits; Wildfires; Christianity; Human services; Child welfare; Youth development; Youth services; International development.
Type of support: Regranting.
Limitations: Applications not accepted. Giving primarily in FL. No grants to individuals.
Application information: Contributes only to pre-selected organizations.
Officer: Robert D. Basham, Pres.
Director: Richard Danker.
EIN: 593284079

1871
Basser Arts Foundation
251 Royal Palm Way, Ste. 400
Palm Beach, FL 33480-4337

Donor: Wendy Orange.
Foundation type: Independent foundation.
Financial data (yr. ended 12/31/13): Assets, $507,170 (M); gifts received, $7,046; expenditures, $230,164; qualifying distributions, $230,164; giving activities include $225,000 for 9 grants (high: $90,000; low: $5,000).
Fields of interest: Arts and culture; Health; Judaism; International relations.
International interests: Israel.
Type of support: Research; Grants to individuals.
Limitations: Applications not accepted. Giving primarily in Washington, DC, FL and NY; some giving also in Israel.
Application information: Unsolicited requests for funds not accepted.
Officer: Wendy Orange, Pres.
EIN: 133193560

1872
John E. and Nellie J. Bastien Memorial Foundation
440 E. Sample Rd., Ste. 209
Pompano Beach, FL 33064-4440

Established in 1965 in Florida.
Donor: Nellie J. Bastien†.
Foundation type: Independent foundation.
Financial data (yr. ended 12/31/14): Assets, $10,621,679 (M); expenditures, $568,365; qualifying distributions, $495,214; giving activities include $360,000 for 97 grants (high: $20,000; low: $1,000).
Fields of interest: Performing arts; Child educational development; Higher education; Environment; Animal welfare; Nonprofits; Health; Hospital care; Hospice care; Addiction services; Biomedicine; Diseases and conditions; Heart and circulatory system diseases; HIV/AIDS; Alcoholism; Cancers; Marine science; Religion; Human services; Family services; Child development; Youth services; Senior services; Seniors; Low-income and poor people.
Type of support: General support; Scholarships; Research; Research and evaluation; Regranting.
Limitations: Applications accepted. Giving primarily in FL.
Application information: Application form required.
 Initial approach: Letter
 Copies of proposal: 1

Deadline(s): None
Final notification: 3 weeks
Trustees: Jill T. Lawson; Scott L. Porter; Carolyn E. Schneider.
EIN: 596160694

1873
TCH Baulch Family Foundation
P.O. Box 1908
Orlando, FL 32802-1908

Established in 1990 in Tennessee.
Donors: Viola S. Baulch Trusts; R.E. Baulch, Jr.; Mrs. R.E. Baulch, Jr.; Robert Baulch, Jr.
Foundation type: Independent foundation.
Financial data (yr. ended 12/31/14): Assets, $3,688,030 (M); expenditures, $216,254; qualifying distributions, $189,002; giving activities include $171,000 for 38 grants (high: $15,000; low: $1,000).
Purpose and activities: Giving primarily for education, health and religion.
Fields of interest: Performing arts; Education; Hospital care; Religion; Christianity; Human services.
Type of support: General support.
Limitations: Applications not accepted.
Application information: Contributes only to pre-selected organizations.
Trustee: SunTrust Bank, Inc.
EIN: 626233587

1874
Baxter Family Foundation
156 Sunset Ave.
Palm Beach, FL 33480-3913

Established in 2000 in Pennsylvania.
Donor: Harold J. Baxter.
Foundation type: Independent foundation.
Financial data (yr. ended 12/31/13): Assets, $2,791,624 (M); expenditures, $272,308; qualifying distributions, $272,308; giving activities include $272,308 for 20 grants (high: $75,000; low: $100).
Fields of interest: Education; Higher education; Diseases and conditions; Autism; Cancers; Community and economic development; Christianity; Human services; Youth services.
Type of support: Research.
Limitations: Applications not accepted. Giving primarily in CA, NJ, FL, MA and PA. No grants to individuals.
Application information: Unsolicited requests for funds not accepted.
Officer: Harold J. Baxter, Pres.
EIN: 311739566

1875
Florence Bayuk Educational Trust
c/o SunTrust Bank-Endowment Services
200 S. Orange Ave., 10th Fl.
Orlando, FL 32801

Established in 1998 in Florida.
Donor: Florence Bayuk†.
Foundation type: Independent foundation.
Financial data (yr. ended 03/31/14): Assets, $4,992,573 (M); expenditures, $362,081; qualifying distributions, $279,200; giving activities

include $279,200 for 3 grants (high: $159,400; low: $50,000).
Fields of interest: Higher education.
Type of support: Scholarships.
Limitations: Applications not accepted. Giving primarily in FL. No grants to individuals.
Application information: Contributes only to pre-selected organizations.
Trustees: Eugene W. Sulzberger, Sr.; SunTrust Bank.
EIN: 656281463

1876
R. M. Beall, Sr. Charitable Foundation
1806 38th Ave. E.
Bradenton, FL 34208-4708
Contact: Patricia Johnson

Established in 1987 in Florida.
Donors: Beall's Department Stores, Inc.; Beall's, Inc.
Foundation type: Company-sponsored foundation.
Financial data (yr. ended 12/31/13): Assets, $5,843,212 (M); gifts received, $1,791; expenditures, $328,112; qualifying distributions, $291,288; giving activities include $241,402 for 83 grants to individuals (high: $8,500).
Purpose and activities: The foundation supports organizations involved with education and youth development and awards college scholarships to student members of the Palmetto Youth Center in Palmetto, Florida.
Fields of interest: Education; Higher education; Sororities and fraternities; Reading promotion; Youth development; Youth services.
Type of support: General support; Scholarships; Student aid.
Limitations: Applications accepted. Giving primarily in Bradenton, FL.
Application information: Application form required.
 Initial approach: Completed application form
 Deadline(s): None
Board Members: Beverly Beall; Robert M. Beall II; Betty B. Szymanski; Clifford L. Walters.
EIN: 592851924

1877
Jane Beasley Foundation
1001 W. Indiantown Rd.
Jupiter, FL 33458

Established in 2005 in Florida.
Donor: Jane Beasley.
Foundation type: Independent foundation.
Financial data (yr. ended 12/31/13): Assets, $2,760,911 (M); expenditures, $183,821; qualifying distributions, $174,401; giving activities include $170,045 for 29 grants (high: $50,000; low: $100).
Fields of interest: Arts and culture; Opera; Education; Nonprofits; Hospital care; Catholicism; Human services.
Type of support: Individual development; Regranting.
Limitations: Applications not accepted. Giving primarily in AL, CT, FL, MA, and NY. No grants to individuals.
Application information: Contributes only to pre-selected organizations.
Officer: Jane Beasley, Pres.
EIN: 656440150

1878
The Beauregard Foundation Inc.
P.O. Box 3242
Palm Beach, FL 33480-1442

Established in 1999 in Florida.
Donor: Irving W. Bailey II.
Foundation type: Independent foundation.
Financial data (yr. ended 12/31/13): Assets, $6,635,889 (M); gifts received, $3,450; expenditures, $295,384; qualifying distributions, $287,000; giving activities include $287,000 for 3 grants (high: $173,500; low: $1,000).
Fields of interest: Foundations; Foster care.
Limitations: Applications not accepted. Giving primarily in KY. No grants to individuals.
Application information: Contributes only to pre-selected organizations.
Officers: Irving W. Bailey II, Pres. and Treas.; Catherine T. Bailey, V.P. and Secy.
Director: William John Receveur.
EIN: 650929642

1879
Richard E. & Lillian M. Becker Family Foundation, Inc.
501 Swim Club Dr., Ph-A
Vero Beach, FL 32963

Established in 2007 in Florida.
Donors: Lillian M. Becker; Richard E. Becker; Richard E. & Lillian M. Becker Charitable Lead Annuity Trust.
Foundation type: Independent foundation.
Financial data (yr. ended 12/31/13): Assets, $744,902 (M); gifts received, $450,369; expenditures, $346,427; qualifying distributions, $341,340; giving activities include $341,340 for 33 grants (high: $50,000; low: $500).
Fields of interest: Arts and culture; Animal welfare; Nonprofits; Diseases and conditions; Human services; Child welfare.
Type of support: Regranting.
Limitations: Applications not accepted. Giving primarily in FL. No grants to individuals.
Application information: Unsolicited requests for funds not accepted.
Officers: Barbara B. Hurley, Pres.; Jo Ann Becker, Secy.
Director: Bruce R. Abernethy, Esq.
EIN: 204371982

1880
Becton Family Foundation
c/o Justin W. Heatter
930 Caxambas Dr.
Marco Island, FL 34145

Foundation type: Independent foundation.
Financial data (yr. ended 12/31/13): Assets, $5,670,118 (M); expenditures, $217,560; qualifying distributions, $200,000; giving activities include $200,000 for 41 grants (high: $22,000; low: $500).
Purpose and activities: Giving primarily to the arts and medical organizations.
Fields of interest: Arts and culture; Museums; Higher education; Health; Hospital care; Diseases and conditions; Community and economic development.

Limitations: Applications not accepted. No grants to individuals.
Application information: Unsolicited requests for funds not accepted.
Trustees: Henry P. Becton, Jr.; Justin W. Heatter.
EIN: 046834092

1881
The Alberto & Olga Maria Beeck Family Foundation, Inc.
6 Harbor Pt.
Key Biscayne, FL 33149
Application address: c/o Carl Munana, 701 Brickell Ave., Miami, FL 33131, tel.: (305) 361-0234

Established in 2009 in Florida.
Donor: The Cranley Trust.
Foundation type: Independent foundation.
Financial data (yr. ended 12/31/13): Assets, $4,836,006 (M); expenditures, $474,130; qualifying distributions, $411,840; giving activities include $368,357 for 5 grants (high: $252,107; low: $250).
Fields of interest: Education; Human services.
Limitations: Applications accepted. Giving primarily in Washington, DC, and FL.
Application information:
  Initial approach: Proposal
  Deadline(s): None
Officer: Olga Maria Beeck, Pres.
Directors: Alberto Beeck; Alberto Miguel Beeck; Carl Munana.
EIN: 271394499

1882
Bell Family Foundation for Hope, Inc.
1500 Beville Rd., Ste. 606, PMB 220
Daytona Beach, FL 32114-5644
Contact: Kelli Bell Ritter, Dir.

Established in 1993 in Florida.
Donor: Ron H. Bell.
Foundation type: Independent foundation.
Financial data (yr. ended 12/31/12): Assets, $7,638,498 (M); expenditures, $363,846; qualifying distributions, $296,000; giving activities include $296,000 for grants.
Fields of interest: Education; Environment; In-patient medical care; Religion; Christianity; Human services; Child welfare; Female children and youth.
Type of support: General support.
Limitations: Applications accepted. Giving primarily in GA.
Application information:
  Initial approach: Letter
  Deadline(s): Sept. 30
Directors: Patricia S. Bell; Curtis H. Ritter; Kelli Bell Ritter.
EIN: 593166060

1883
The James E. and Constance L. Bell Foundation, Inc.
(formerly Bell Foundation, Inc.)
11450 Southeast Dixie Hwy., Ste. 208
Hobe Sound, FL 33455-5235

Established in 1984 in Florida.
Donors: James E. Bell; Constance L. Bell.

Foundation type: Independent foundation.
Financial data (yr. ended 06/30/14): Assets, $0 (M); expenditures, $355,896; qualifying distributions, $355,896; giving activities include $295,425 for 52 grants (high: $156,000; low: $100).
Purpose and activities: Giving primarily for education, social services, federated giving programs, and Episcopal and Presbyterian churches and organizations.
Fields of interest: Education; Higher education; Foundations; Nonprofits; Health; Community and economic development; Episcopalianism and Anglicanism; Lutheranism; Human services; Youth services.
Type of support: General support; Regranting.
Limitations: Applications not accepted. Giving primarily in CT, FL, NC, and PA. No grants to individuals.
Application information: Contributes only to pre-selected organizations.
Officers and Directors: Constance B. Moser, Pres. and Director; Constance L. Bell, V.P. and Director; Stuart M. Bell, Secy.-Treas. and Director.
EIN: 592473417

1884
The Benedict Foundation for Independent Schools
3970 Duncan Dr.
Boca Raton, FL 33434-4431
Contact: Peter B. Benedict II, Pres.
Main URL: http://thebenedictfoundation.org
Grants List: http://www.thebenedictfoundation.org/previous-grantees

Established in 1983 in Delaware.
Donor: Peter B. Benedict.
Foundation type: Independent foundation.
Financial data (yr. ended 12/31/13): Assets, $5,557,667 (M); gifts received, $326,188; expenditures, $364,281; qualifying distributions, $325,000; giving activities include $325,000 for 15 grants (high: $30,000; low: $15,000).
Purpose and activities: Giving for independent secondary schools that have been members of the National Association of Independent Schools for ten consecutive years. Challenge grants are preferred for purposes of improving academic programs, scholarship aid, building programs, faculty salaries, faculty summer workshops, or other programs to improve the quality of the school's educational activities.
Fields of interest: Education; Secondary education.
Type of support: Building and renovations; Matching grants; Scholarships.
Limitations: Applications accepted. Giving on a national basis. No grants to individuals, or for endowment funds or operating costs; or multi-year grants; no loans.
Publications: Informational brochure (including application guidelines).
Application information: After receipt of letter, BFIS sends a brochure and cover letter specifying requirements. Complete application guidelines available on foundation web site. Application form required.
  Initial approach: Letter
  Copies of proposal: 6
  Deadline(s): Applications should be received between Jan. 1 and Mar. 31

Board meeting date(s): June
Final notification: July
Officers and Directors: Peter B. Benedict II, Pres. and Director; Davis M. Benedict, V.P. and Treas. and Director; Randall D. Corwin, Secy. and Director; Nancy H. Benedict; Peter B. Benedict.
Number of staff: None.
EIN: 592383209

1885
The David & Lyn Berelsman Family Charitable Foundation Trust

238 Acadia Terr.
Celebration, FL 34747-5004

Established in 1996 in Unspecified.
Donors: David W. Berelsman; Lynell D. Cameron.
Foundation type: Independent foundation.
Financial data (yr. ended 12/31/13): Assets, $2,477,712 (M); expenditures, $170,333; qualifying distributions, $147,173; giving activities include $142,000 for 35 grants (high: $35,000; low: $100).
Fields of interest: Arts and culture; Community and economic development; Human services.
Limitations: Applications not accepted. Giving primarily in FL; some giving in OH. No grants to individuals.
Application information: Unsolicited requests for funds not accepted.
Trustees: David W. Berelsman; Lynell D. Cameron.
EIN: 522003023

1886
Jeff and Yolanda Berkowitz Family Charitable Foundation Inc.

c/o Berkowitz Pollack Brant
2665 S. Bayshore Dr., Ste. 1200
Coconut Grove, FL 33133-5468

Donor: Jeffrey Berkowitz.
Foundation type: Independent foundation.
Financial data (yr. ended 12/31/13): Assets, $793,434 (M); expenditures, $246,411; qualifying distributions, $230,800; giving activities include $230,800 for 17 grants (high: $51,000; low: $300).
Fields of interest: Arts and culture; Health; Human services.
Limitations: Applications not accepted. Giving primarily in FL.
Application information: Unsolicited requests for funds not accepted.
Officers: Jeffrey Berkowitz, Pres.; Richard Berkowitz, Secy.; Yolanda Berkowitz, Treas.
EIN: 275215409

1887
Biddinger Family Foundation

P.O. Box 68
Safety Harbor, FL 34695-0068 (727) 216-4000
Contact: Clay M. Biddinger, Tr.

Established in 2005 in Florida.
Donor: Clay M. Biddinger.
Foundation type: Independent foundation.
Financial data (yr. ended 12/31/13): Assets, $3,563,254 (M); expenditures, $270,000; qualifying distributions, $270,000; giving activities include $270,000 for 6 grants (high: $100,000; low: $10,000).

Fields of interest: Human services.
Limitations: Applications accepted. Giving primarily in FL.
Application information: Application form required.
Initial approach: Letter
Deadline(s): None
Trustee: Clay M. Biddinger.
Number of staff: None.
EIN: 206764756

1888
Margaret R. Binz Foundation Inc.

175 E. Nasa Blvd., Ste. 300
Melbourne, FL 32901-1998 (321) 725-3425
Contact: Jack L. Platt Esq., Secy.

Established in 1981 in Florida.
Donor: Margaret R. Binz†.
Foundation type: Independent foundation.
Financial data (yr. ended 12/31/13): Assets, $23,296 (M); expenditures, $165,816; qualifying distributions, $135,000; giving activities include $135,000 for 34 grants (high: $25,000; low: $500).
Purpose and activities: Giving for underprivileged children and the prevention of cruelty to animals.
Fields of interest: Arts and culture; Domesticated animals; Human services.
Limitations: Applications accepted. Giving limited to FL. No grants to individuals or for scholarships.
Application information: Application form required.
Initial approach: Letter
Deadline(s): None
Officers: Henry Carnegie, Pres.; Jack Platt, Secy.
Directors: Helen Carnegie; Jeffery C. Locke; David S. Shapiro.
EIN: 591367134

1889
The Blake Family Charitable Foundation

356 Seabreeze Dr.
Marco Island, FL 34145-1827 (239) 642-7372

Established in 2001 in Indiana.
Donors: Norman P. Blake, Jr.; Karen S. Blake.
Foundation type: Independent foundation.
Financial data (yr. ended 12/31/14): Assets, $2,616,410; gifts received, $305,569; expenditures, $128,514; qualifying distributions, $118,005.
Fields of interest: Education; Religion; Human services.
Type of support: General support.
Limitations: Applications accepted. Giving primarily in IN.
Application information: Application form required.
Initial approach: Letter
Deadline(s): None
Officer: Norman P. Blake, Jr., Pres.
Director: Karen Blake.
EIN: 352128225

1890
Blank Charitable Foundation

1172 S. Dixie Hwy., Ste. 497
Coral Gables, FL 33146-2918 (305) 670-2323
Contact: Mark Blank, Pres. and Dir.

Established in 2002 in Florida.
Donor: Blank Family Foundation, Inc.
Foundation type: Independent foundation.

Financial data (yr. ended 12/31/13): Assets, $3,425,411 (M); expenditures, $195,449; qualifying distributions, $185,949; giving activities include $185,949 for 42 grants (high: $50,000; low: $100).
Fields of interest: Higher education; Nonprofits; Health; Hospital care; Human services.
Type of support: Regranting.
Limitations: Applications accepted. Giving primarily in FL. No grants to individuals.
Application information: Application form required.
Initial approach: Letter
Deadline(s): None
Officers and Directors: Tony Blank, Chair. and Director; Mark Blank, Pres. and Director; Karen Neuman.
EIN: 431953412

1891
Goldie & David Blanksteen Foundation

P.O. Box 43250
Jacksonville, FL 32203-3250
Application address: c/o David Blanksteen, 866 United Nations Plz., New York, NY 10017

Established in 1995 in New York.
Donors: David Blanksteen; Goldie Blanksteen.
Foundation type: Independent foundation.
Financial data (yr. ended 06/30/13): Assets, $1,752,696 (M); expenditures, $158,372; qualifying distributions, $155,295; giving activities include $154,795 for 23 grants (high: $75,000; low: $50).
Fields of interest: Arts and culture; Museums; Education; Higher education; Graduate and professional education; Judaism; Human services.
Type of support: General support.
Limitations: Applications accepted. Giving primarily in New York, NY. No grants to individuals.
Application information: Application form required.
Initial approach: Letter
Deadline(s): None
Trustees: David Blanksteen; Goldie Blanksteen.
EIN: 137072675

1892
Hilda Sutton & William D. Blanton Charitable Foundation, Inc.

200 Lake Morton Dr.
Lakeland, FL 33801-5318 (863) 688-7611
Contact: E. Snow Martin Jr., V.P.

Established in 1993 in Florida.
Donor: Hilda Sutton Blanton†.
Foundation type: Independent foundation.
Financial data (yr. ended 12/31/14): Assets, $5,124,063 (M); expenditures, $201,044; qualifying distributions, $150,100; giving activities include $150,100 for 22 grants (high: $52,500; low: $1,000).
Purpose and activities: Giving primarily for scholarships for the study of organ and church music, and for humanitarian causes.
Fields of interest: Music; Orchestral music; Higher education; Golf.
Type of support: General support; Scholarships; Student aid.
Limitations: Applications accepted. Giving primarily in FL.
Application information: Contact foundation for application guidelines. Application form required.

Initial approach: Letter
Deadline(s): None
Officers and Directors: E. Snow Martin, Jr., V.P. and Director; Mettie Withers, Secy.-Treas. and Director; Beth Mason.
EIN: 593162785

1893
Blatt Family Foundation
c/o Sydell Blatt
471 N. Arrowhead Trail
Vero Beach, FL 32963-3933   (772) 234-3822
Contact: Lee Blatt, Tr.

Established in 2006 in Florida.
Donor: Lee Blatt.
Foundation type: Independent foundation.
Financial data (yr. ended 12/31/13): Assets, $391,720 (M); expenditures, $252,643; qualifying distributions, $252,500; giving activities include $252,500 for 2 grants (high: $250,000; low: $2,500).
Fields of interest: Arts and culture; Education; Human rights; Human services.
Limitations: Applications accepted. Giving primarily in New York, NY; funding also in Pittsfield, MA.
Application information: Application form required.
Initial approach: Letter
Deadline(s): None
Trustees: Lee Blatt; Sydell Blatt; Randi Rossignol; Kathi Thonet.
EIN: 137529459

1894
Jean and David Blechman Foundation
401 E. Linton Blvd., Ste. 505
Delray Beach, FL 33483-5041

Established in 1996 in Florida.
Donors: Jean Blechman; David Blechman†; Jean Blechman Revocable Trust.
Foundation type: Independent foundation.
Financial data (yr. ended 12/31/13): Assets, $2,962,914 (M); gifts received, $1,998,970; expenditures, $231,728; qualifying distributions, $224,600; giving activities include $224,600 for 14 grants (high: $201,000; low: $100).
Purpose and activities: Giving primarily for Jewish temples and agencies.
Fields of interest: Hospital care; Judaism.
Limitations: Applications not accepted. Giving primarily in FL and NY. No grants to individuals.
Application information: Unsolicited requests for funds not accepted.
Officer: Jean Blechman, Pres.
EIN: 656218624

1895
Bohnert Foundation, Inc.
24 Dockside Ln., Ste. 209
Key Largo, FL 33037-5267

Established in 2002 in New Jersey.
Donor: Robert Manzo.
Foundation type: Independent foundation.
Financial data (yr. ended 12/31/13): Assets, $4,240,599 (M); expenditures, $339,804; qualifying distributions, $309,470; giving activities include $309,470 for 15 grants (high: $200,000; low: $50).

Fields of interest: Education; Higher education.
Limitations: Applications not accepted. Giving primarily in NJ and NY.
Application information: Contributes only to pre-selected organizations.
Officers: Robert Manzo, Pres.; Cynthia Manzo, V.P.
Trustee: Ellen Jacob Wraith.
EIN: 542072845

1896
Paul S. Bomberger Jr. Foundation Inc.
6003 S. Honore Ave.
Sarasota, FL 34238-5717

Foundation type: Independent foundation.
Financial data (yr. ended 07/31/14): Assets, $5,308,404 (M); expenditures, $245,639; qualifying distributions, $202,570; giving activities include $198,523 for 33 grants (high: $20,000; low: $2,500).
Fields of interest: Education; Diseases and conditions; Human services.
Limitations: Applications not accepted.
Application information: Unsolicited requests for funds not accepted.
Directors: Frances N. Bomberger; Brent Richter; Gregory S. Roper.
EIN: 205349740

1897
The Bond Foundation, Inc.
800 S. Dillard St.
Winter Garden, FL 34787-3910

Established in 1997 in Florida.
Donor: Walter Bond†.
Foundation type: Independent foundation.
Financial data (yr. ended 06/30/13): Assets, $7,085,784 (M); expenditures, $493,632; qualifying distributions, $303,962; giving activities include $280,556 for 50 grants (high: $25,000; low: $1,000).
Fields of interest: Arts and culture; Education; Higher education; Diseases and conditions; Community and economic development; Christianity; Human services; Child welfare; Homeless people; Low-income and poor people; People with disabilities.
Limitations: Applications not accepted. Giving primarily in FL. No grants to individuals.
Application information: Contributes only to pre-selected organizations.
Officers: Derek J. Blakeslee, Pres.; Ann G. Blakeslee, Secy.-Treas.
Directors: Arden Griffith; Mark Griffith; Ginnie Stanford; Carole Wingate; Don Wingate.
EIN: 593468830

1898
Boston Center for Blind Children, Inc.
859 N.W. Sorrento Ln.
Port Saint Lucie, FL 34986-2199   (617) 296-4232
Contact: Donald E. Boucher, Grants Coordinator
E-mail: info@bostoncenterforblindchildren.org; Main URL: http://www.bostoncenterforblindchildren.org
Grants List: http://www.bostoncenterforblindchildren.org/#!recipients/cfvg

Established in 1901 in Massachusetts.
Donor: Evelyn L. Kendall Charitable Remainder.
Foundation type: Independent foundation.
Financial data (yr. ended 06/30/13): Assets, $4,491,362 (M); gifts received, $1,063; expenditures, $232,511; qualifying distributions, $212,780; giving activities include $212,780 for 14 grants (high: $40,000; low: $5,000).
Purpose and activities: Giving primarily to organizations that provide care, treatment, and services to blind, visually impaired, or otherwise disabled children as well as other children and families in need.
Fields of interest: Education; Sports and recreation; Child welfare; People with vision impairments.
Limitations: Applications accepted. Giving primarily in MA. No grants to individuals.
Publications: Application guidelines.
Application information: Application guidelines available on foundation web site.
Deadline(s): Apr. 15 and Oct. 15
Board meeting date(s): May and Nov.
Officers: William G. McDevitt III, Pres.; Carol C. Cleven, Treas.
Directors: John T. Bennett, Jr.; Caroline B. Grady; Anne V. McBride.
EIN: 042103910

1899
Brighton Foundation Trust
c/o Robert D. Markley
150 Brightwaters Blvd. N.E.
Saint Petersburg, FL 33704-3608

Established in 1997 in Indiana.
Donors: Robert D. Markley; Jean Markley.
Foundation type: Independent foundation.
Financial data (yr. ended 12/31/14): Assets, $3,848,402; expenditures, $202,260; qualifying distributions, $198,950.
Purpose and activities: Giving primarily for the arts, education, human services, and Christian organizations.
Fields of interest: Arts and culture; Higher education; Christianity; Human services; Child welfare; Children and youth; Children; Ethnic and racial groups; Homeless people; Low-income and poor people; People with physical disabilities; People with psychosocial disabilities; Terminally ill people.
Type of support: General support.
Limitations: Applications not accepted. Giving primarily in St. Petersburg, FL, Indianapolis, IN, and Cashiers, NC. No grants to individuals.
Application information: Contributes only to pre-selected organizations.
Trustees: Jean Markley; Jeffrey D. Markley; Robert D. Markley; Robert J. Markley.
Number of staff: None.
EIN: 352032393

1900
Brinckerhoff Family Foundation
291 Sabal Palm Ln.
Vero Beach, FL 32963-3309
Contact: Peter R. Brinckerhoff, Tr.
E-mail: prbrinck@yahoo.com

Established in 1998 in Connecticut.
Donor: Peter R. Brinckerhoff.
Foundation type: Independent foundation.

Financial data (yr. ended 05/31/13): Assets, $5,921,564 (M); expenditures, $272,251; qualifying distributions, $267,820; giving activities include $188,316 for 20 grants (high: $100,000; low: $500).
Fields of interest: Education; Public libraries; Christianity.
Type of support: General support.
Limitations: Applications not accepted. Giving primarily in CT, NJ, and NY.
Publications: Annual report.
Application information: Unsolicited requests for funds not accepted.
   Board meeting date(s): Annually in the fall
Trustees: Ashley M. Brinckerhoff; Coleman M. Brinckerhoff; Peter R. Brinckerhoff; Susan C. Brinckerhoff.
Number of staff: 3 part-time support.
EIN: 061484248

1901
William and Joan Brodsky Foundation
2800 Ponce De Leon Blvd., Ste. 1125
Coral Gables, FL   33134-1125

Established in 1997 in Florida.
Donors: William Brodsky; Joan Brodsky.
Foundation type: Independent foundation.
Financial data (yr. ended 12/31/14): Assets, $4,898,415; gifts received, $1,133,170; expenditures, $255,873; qualifying distributions, $255,873.
Fields of interest: Higher education; Nonprofits; Judaism; Human services.
Type of support: Regranting.
Limitations: Applications not accepted. Giving primarily in IL. No grants to individuals.
Application information: Unsolicited requests for funds not accepted.
Officers and Directors: William J. Brodsky, Pres. and Director; Joan B. Brodsky, Secy. and Director; Jonathan P. Brodsky; Michael B. Brodsky; Stephen A. Brodsky.
EIN: 650724452

1902
The Edwin and Sara Brody Family Charitable Foundation
231 Bay Colony Dr., Ste. 2001
Naples, FL   34108-2849

Established in 1998 in Massachusetts.
Donors: The Sara Strouss Brody 1998 Charitable Lead Unitrust #2; The Sara Strouss Brody 1998 Charitable Lead Unitrust; Sara S. Brody; Paula J. Brody; Merrill I. Hassenfeld.
Foundation type: Independent foundation.
Financial data (yr. ended 12/31/13): Assets, $0 (M); expenditures, $244,708; qualifying distributions, $238,195; giving activities include $238,195 for 27 grants (high: $100,000; low: $65).
Fields of interest: Elementary and secondary education; Higher education; Nonprofits; Judaism; Human services.
Type of support: Regranting.
Limitations: Applications not accepted. Giving primarily in FL and MA. No grants to individuals.
Application information: Contributes only to pre-selected organizations.
Trustees: Paula J. Brody; Merrill I. Hassenfeld.
EIN: 043428896

1903
Louis S. Brooke Trust
P.O. Box 1908
Orlando, FL   32802-1908

Foundation type: Independent foundation.
Financial data (yr. ended 12/31/14): Assets, $3,991,823; expenditures, $213,142; qualifying distributions, $192,535.
Fields of interest: Education; Health; Human services.
Type of support: General support.
Limitations: Applications not accepted. Giving primarily in GA.
Application information: Unsolicited requests for funds not accepted.
Trustee: SunTrust Bank.
EIN: 586040006

1904
The Craig & Vicki Brown Foundation Inc.
1240 Gordon River Trail
Naples, FL   34105-2773

Donors: Vicki Brown; Craig Brown.
Foundation type: Independent foundation.
Financial data (yr. ended 12/31/13): Assets, $4,338,873 (M); gifts received, $250,907; expenditures, $240,046; qualifying distributions, $185,985; giving activities include $185,000 for 2 grants (high: $100,000; low: $85,000).
Fields of interest: Animal welfare; Environmental education; Brain and nervous system disorders; Human services.
Type of support: Research.
Limitations: Applications not accepted. Giving primarily in CA and NY. No grants to individuals.
Application information: Contributes only to pre-selected organizations.
Officers: Vicki Brown, Pres.; Christina Brown, Secy.; Craig Brown, Treas.
Directors: Robert Beardslee; Jeffrey Brown; Jennifer Brown.
EIN: 161689348

1905
Richard F. and Pearl P. Brown Foundation
P.O. Box 1908
Orlando, FL   32802-1908

Donor: Richard F Brown.
Foundation type: Independent foundation.
Financial data (yr. ended 12/31/14): Assets, $2,752,260; expenditures, $366,196; qualifying distributions, $135,775.
Fields of interest: Higher education; Animal welfare; Health care administration and financing; Diseases and conditions; Protestantism.
Type of support: Research.
Limitations: Applications not accepted. Giving primarily in GA.
Application information: Unsolicited requests for funds not accepted.
Trustees: Landy New; SunTrust Bank.
EIN: 356822289

1906
Harry J. Brown Jr. Foundation Inc.
c/o Reichel Realty
8845 N. Miltary Trail, Ste. 100
Palm Beach Gardens, FL   33410-6290

Established in 2005 in Florida.
Donor: Harry J. Brown, Jr.†.
Foundation type: Independent foundation.
Financial data (yr. ended 12/31/13): Assets, $2,399,293 (M); expenditures, $281,095; qualifying distributions, $260,000; giving activities include $260,000 for 11 grants (high: $75,000; low: $5,000).
Fields of interest: Education; Health; Human services.
Limitations: Applications not accepted. No grants to individuals.
Application information: Contributes only to pre-selected organizations.
Directors: Catherine Brown; Morgan Brown; Annabel Goff-Davis.
EIN: 522451464

1907
Walter Brownley Trust
c/o Bank of America, N.A.
P.O. Box 40200, FL9-100-10-19
Jacksonville, FL   32203-0200   2403801739
Application address: c/o Uday Shah, 5550 Friendship Blvd., MD4-924-01-02, Chevy Chase, MD 20815, tel.: (301) 986-6716

Foundation type: Independent foundation.
Financial data (yr. ended 12/31/14): Assets, $5,439,192; expenditures, $278,773; qualifying distributions, $252,402.
Purpose and activities: Giving restricted to public hospitals, orphanages, and asylums in Washington, DC.
Fields of interest: Hospital care; Hospice care; Child welfare.
Limitations: Applications accepted. Giving limited to the Washington, DC, area. No grants to individuals.
Application information:
   Initial approach: Letter
   Deadline(s): Nov. 15
Trustee: Bank of America, N.A.
EIN: 526028605

1908
The Burgoon Family Foundation, Inc.
11 Dove Plum Rd.
Vero Beach, FL   32963-3719   3525081945

Established in 2001 in Florida.
Donors: Richard R. Burgoon; Patricia B. Burgoon.
Foundation type: Independent foundation.
Financial data (yr. ended 12/31/14): Assets, $554,520; expenditures, $141,041; qualifying distributions, $135,700.
Fields of interest: Philanthropy; Community and economic development; Human services.
Limitations: Applications not accepted. Giving primarily in FL. No grants to individuals.
Application information: Unsolicited requests for funds not accepted.
Directors: Patricia B. Burgoon; Richard R. Burgoon; Paul T. Vogel.
EIN: 260000764

1909
Burks Family Foundation Inc.
c/o Keith W. Burks
300 Neptunes Bight
Naples, FL 34103-3535

Established in 2001 in Indiana.
Donors: Keith W. Burks; Tina L. Burks Charitable Lead Annuity Trust.
Foundation type: Independent foundation.
Financial data (yr. ended 12/31/12): Assets, $1,511,471 (M); gifts received, $95,597; expenditures, $139,673; qualifying distributions, $135,525; giving activities include $133,100 for 7 grants (high: $105,000; low: $1,000).
Fields of interest: Education; Nonprofits; Child welfare.
Type of support: Regranting.
Limitations: Applications not accepted. Giving primarily in Indianapolis, IN. No grants to individuals.
Application information: Unsolicited requests for funds not accepted.
Directors: Keith W. Burks; Tina L. Burks; James G. Sinclair.
EIN: 311809715

1910
Al and Nancy Burnett Charitable Foundation, Inc.
(formerly Al Burnett Charitable Foundation, Inc.)
2465 Snook Trail
Palm Beach Gardens, FL 33410-1270
Contact: Amy Gravina

Established in 1985 in Florida.
Donors: J. Albert Burnett†; Nancy L. Burnett.
Foundation type: Independent foundation.
Financial data (yr. ended 11/30/13): Assets, $7,192,805 (M); gifts received, $2,923,000; expenditures, $316,687; qualifying distributions, $313,462; giving activities include $304,175 for 16 grants (high: $50,000; low: $500).
Fields of interest: Higher education; Health; Protestantism.
Limitations: Applications not accepted. Giving primarily in FL and ME. No grants to individuals.
Application information: Unsolicited requests for funds not accepted.
Officers and Directors: Amy Gravina, Pres. and Director; Becky B. Moore, Treas. and Director; Bruce K. Burnett; Melinda Steele.
EIN: 592620060

1911
A. H. Burnett Foundation
205 Waterwood Dr.
Yalaha, FL 34797-3118

Established in 2007 in Florida.
Donor: Alexander H. Burnett†.
Foundation type: Independent foundation.
Financial data (yr. ended 06/30/14): Assets, $9,479,451 (M); gifts received, $655,000; expenditures, $534,888; qualifying distributions, $473,000; giving activities include $427,000 for 18 grants (high: $145,000; low: $2,000).
Fields of interest: Education; Christianity; Protestantism; Catholicism.
Limitations: Applications not accepted. Giving primarily in FL.

Application information: Unsolicited requests for funds not accepted.
Trustees: Mary Ellen Burnett; H. John Feldman; Janet Louise Jones.
EIN: 203624633

1912
Burnetti Childrens Foundation Inc.
211 S. Florida Ave.
Lakeland, FL 33801-4621

Donor: Patricia A. Burnetti.
Foundation type: Independent foundation.
Financial data (yr. ended 12/31/13): Assets, $21,164 (M); gifts received, $148,500; expenditures, $159,052; qualifying distributions, $159,052; giving activities include $151,808 for 20 grants (high: $65,000; low: $100).
Fields of interest: Higher education; Protestantism.
Type of support: General support.
Limitations: Applications not accepted. Giving primarily in FL. No grants to individuals.
Application information: Contributes only to pre-selected organizations.
Officers: Douglas K. Burnetti, Pres.; Dean Burnetti, V.P.; Denise L. Burnetti, Secy.; Patricia A. Burnetti, Treas.
EIN: 593760786

1913
Michael G. Callas Charitable Trust
309 E. Dilido Dr.
Miami Beach, FL 33139-1231 (410) 537-5491
Contact: Douglas G. Moul, Tr.

Established in 1997 in Maryland.
Donor: Michael G. Callas.
Foundation type: Independent foundation.
Financial data (yr. ended 12/31/13): Assets, $6,287,401 (M); expenditures, $232,091; qualifying distributions, $158,186; giving activities include $158,186 for 14 grants (high: $50,000; low: $100).
Fields of interest: Education; Human services; Youth development; Youth services; Scouting programs.
Limitations: Applications accepted. Giving primarily in Hagerstown, MD. No support for political endorsements. No grants to individuals.
Application information: Application form required.
Initial approach: Letter
Deadline(s): None
Trustees: Catherine G. Bushey; Douglas G. Moul.
EIN: 521764391

1914
Campbell Foundation
5975 N. Federal Hwy., Ste. 126
Fort Lauderdale, FL 33308-2685 (954) 493-8822
Contact: William Venuti, Tr. and Exec. Dir.
FAX: (954) 493-8801; E-mail: campfound@aol.com;
Additional e-mail: ken@campbellfoundation.net;
Main URL: http://www.campbellfoundation.net
Facebook: https://www.facebook.com/CampbellFoundation
Google Plus: https://plus.google.com/101791887848110694616#101791887848110694616/posts

Grants List: http://www.campbellfoundation.net/Resources/Campbell%20Foundation%20Funding%201995-Present.pdf
Twitter: https://twitter.com/campfoundftl

Established in 1986 in Florida.
Donors: Richard Campbell Zahn†; Thomas Todd†.
Foundation type: Independent foundation.
Financial data (yr. ended 12/31/13): Assets, $8,079,231 (M); gifts received, $23,600; expenditures, $676,318; qualifying distributions, $573,942; giving activities include $374,531 for 25 grants (high: $100,000; low: $100).
Purpose and activities: The foundation supports other nonprofit organizations conducting clinical research into the prevention and treatment of HIV/AIDS, and related conditions and illnesses. The focus of the Campbell Foundation's funding lies in alternative, nontraditional avenues of research.
Fields of interest: HIV/AIDS.
Type of support: Research.
Limitations: Applications accepted. Giving primarily on a national basis; some consideration also for foreign nonprofit entities. No support for educational effects or behavioral research (only for clinical research). No grants to individuals, or for discretionary grants, equipment or travel expenses.
Publications: Application guidelines; Grants list.
Application information: Full grant proposals are by invitation only, upon review of initial Letter of Inquiry. See foundation web site for complete application procedures and guidelines.
Initial approach: Letter of Inquiry (no more than 2 pages)
Deadline(s): Letters of Inquiry are accepted during Jan., Apr., July, and Oct.
Officer and Trustee: William Venuti, Exec. Dir. and Trustee.
Directors: David Ferebee, Jr.; Jeanne R. Kos, MSN, RN; Sandy Kristoff; Gerald Nicklas; Robert H. Samuels; Corklin R. Steinhart, MD; Patricia M. Whetstone-Foltz.
Number of staff: 2 full-time professional.
EIN: 586205065

1915
Michael G. Cantonis Foundation Inc.
P.O. Box 338
Tarpon Springs, FL 34688-0338

Established in 1982 in Florida.
Donors: Michael G. Cantonis; Anastasia H. Cantonis; George H. Cantonis; Acme Sponge and Chamois Co.
Foundation type: Independent foundation.
Financial data (yr. ended 12/31/13): Assets, $2,639,721 (M); expenditures, $171,010; qualifying distributions, $142,970; giving activities include $142,970 for 21 grants (high: $63,500; low: $120).
Purpose and activities: Giving primarily for the Greek Orthodox Church, medicine and nursing, and medical-related fields on the island of Symi, Greece. Scholarships will be granted to students who have made the commitment to become a priest in the Greek Orthodox Church. The directors will also grant scholarship loans to students selected by a special committee who will study medicine or nursing and will serve in the medical-related field on the island of Symi, Greece.
Fields of interest: Education; Orthodox Christianity.
International interests: Greece.
Type of support: General support.

Limitations: Applications not accepted. Giving primarily in FL; some giving also in NY and in Greece. No grants to individuals.
Application information: Unsolicited requests for funds not accepted.
Officers and Directors: George M. Cantonis, Pres. and Director; Cynthia Heller, V.P. and Secy. and Director; James M. Cantonis, V.P. and Treas. and Director; Anastasia H. Cantonis, V.P. and Director.
EIN: 592214565

1916
Samuel C. Cantor Charitable Trust
7203 Francisco Bend Dr.
Delray Beach, FL   33466-5613

Established in 1996 in Florida.
Foundation type: Independent foundation.
Financial data (yr. ended 12/31/13): Assets, $3,920,405 (M); expenditures, $236,512; qualifying distributions, $179,744; giving activities include $173,226 for 36 grants (high: $17,590; low: $1,000).
Purpose and activities: Giving primarily to hospitals and health associations.
Fields of interest: Specialty hospital care; Diseases and conditions; Cancers; Judaism; Child welfare.
Limitations: Applications not accepted. Giving primarily in FL. No grants to individuals.
Application information: Unsolicited requests for funds not accepted.
Trustee: Eddy Cantor.
EIN: 656184678

1917
Cape Coral Community Foundation
(formerly Philanthropic Foundation of Cape Coral, Inc.)
1405 S.E. 47th St., Unit 2
Cape Coral, FL   33904   (239) 542-5594
Contact: Beth T. Sanger, Exec. Dir.
FAX: (239) 549-8307; E-mail: cccf@capecoralcf.org;
Main URL: http://www.capecoralcf.org
Facebook: https://www.facebook.com/pages/
Cape-Coral-Community-Foundation/
235740559776341
LinkedIn: https://www.linkedin.com/groups/
Cape-Coral-Community-Foundation-40th-3948929.
S.5799589107113930756
Twitter: https://twitter.com/Capecoralcf

Established in 1973 in Florida.
Foundation type: Community foundation.
Financial data (yr. ended 06/30/13): Assets, $8,408,362 (M); gifts received, $222,026; expenditures, $475,422; giving activities include $178,919 for 102+ grants (high: $97,784), and $58,750 for 57 grants to individuals.
Purpose and activities: The mission of the foundation is to support the public well being and to improve the quality of life in the greater Cape Coral community through the stewardship of permanently endowed and gifted funds.
Fields of interest: Arts and culture; Education; Environment; Domesticated animals; Health; Human services; Youth development; Adolescents; Seniors; People with disabilities.
Type of support: Equipment; Matching grants; Program development; Scholarships.
Limitations: Applications accepted. Giving primarily in Cape Coral, FL. No grants for general operating

expenses, travel, training seminars, or staff salaries.
Publications: Application guidelines; Annual report; Informational brochure; Newsletter.
Application information: Visit foundation web site for application form and guidelines. Applications must be mailed or hand delivered. Application form required.
   Initial approach: Letter or telephone
   Copies of proposal: 3
   Deadline(s): July 10
   Board meeting date(s): 3rd Thurs. monthly
   Final notification: Oct.
Officers and Directors: Brian D. Gomer, Chair. and Director; ToniRae Hurley, Vice-Chair. and Director; Steve Riggs, Secy. and Director; Keith A. Veres, Treas. and Director; Beth T. Sanger, Exec. Dir.; John G. Bobb; Donna Caruso; MerriBeth Farnham; Pastor Dennis Gingerich; Alison Hussey; Sally Jackson; Wayne R. Kirkwood; Robert D. Knight; Joe Padgett; Steve Pohlman; Tyra Read; Rebecca Ross; Marty Warchol.
Number of staff: 1 full-time professional; 2 part-time support.
EIN: 237410312

1918
Capital City Bank Group Foundation, Inc.
217 N. Monroe St.
Tallahassee, FL   32301-7619   (850) 402-8521
Additional address: P.O. Box 11248, Tallahassee, FL 32302; Main URL: http://www.ccbgfoundation.org
Grants List: http://www.ccbgfoundation.org/
list.php

Donors: Capital City First National Bank; Capital City Bank.
Foundation type: Company-sponsored foundation.
Financial data (yr. ended 12/31/14): Assets, $2,727,998; gifts received, $4,448; expenditures, $240,027; qualifying distributions, $238,210.
Purpose and activities: The foundation supports organizations involved with arts and culture, education, health, heart disease, Alzheimer's, housing development, school athletics, human services, and community development.
Fields of interest: Arts and culture; Theater; Education; Higher education; Nonprofits; Health; Hospital care; Hospice care; Alzheimer's disease; Heart and circulatory system diseases; Community and economic development; Housing development; School athletics; Human services; Child welfare; Youth services; Developmental disability services.
Type of support: Program development; General support; Scholarships; Regranting.
Limitations: Applications accepted. Giving primarily in areas of company operations in FL. No support for athletic teams. No grants for advertising, association memberships, athletic or fundraising event sponsorships, professional telephone sale solicitations, tickets to attend community functions or fundraisers, or activities with religious or political affiliation.
Publications: Application guidelines; Grants list.
Application information: Application form required.
   Initial approach: Complete online application
   Deadline(s): Apr. 1; Nov. 1 for Tipping Points grants
   Board meeting date(s): Annually
   Final notification: 30 days of the Grant Committee meeting

Officers and Directors: William G. Smith, Jr., Chair.; Robert H. Smith, Pres.; Brooke Hallock, Secy.; Ray A. Johnson, Treas.; Jeff Wahlen; Alma Littles.
EIN: 592276367

1919
Carbonari Family Foundation
c/o Bruce A. Carbonari
4541 Shore Ln.
P.O. Box 1384
Boca Grande, FL   33921-1384

Donors: Bruce A. Carbonari; Kathy Carbonari.
Foundation type: Independent foundation.
Financial data (yr. ended 12/31/13): Assets, $2,470,015 (M); gifts received, $892,058; expenditures, $218,427; qualifying distributions, $209,260; giving activities include $209,250 for 15 grants (high: $100,000; low: $100).
Fields of interest: Education; Human services; Youth development.
Limitations: Applications not accepted. Giving primarily in MA and OH. No grants to individuals.
Application information: Unsolicited requests for funds not accepted.
Officers: Bruce A. Carbonari, Pres. and Treas.; Kathryn E. Carbonari, V.P. and Secy.
Directors: Danielle M. Carbonari; Nicole K. Carbonari.
EIN: 341787787

1920
Caring Friends Foundation
P.O. Box 40200, FL9-100-10-19
Jacksonville, FL   32203-0200

Established in 2004 in Florida.
Donor: Edmund J. Wassell Trust.
Foundation type: Independent foundation.
Financial data (yr. ended 12/31/13): Assets, $4,026,328 (M); expenditures, $234,127; qualifying distributions, $193,604; giving activities include $167,354 for 4 grants (high: $50,206; low: $25,103).
Fields of interest: Performing arts; Specialty hospital care; Diseases and conditions; Diabetes; Food aid; People with HIV/AIDS.
Type of support: Research.
Limitations: Applications not accepted. No grants for individuals.
Application information: Unsolicited requests for funds not accepted.
Trustees: Robert Bernacki; Bank of America, N.A.
EIN: 656301156

1921
Audre and Donald Carlin Foundation, Inc.
(formerly The Carlin Charitable Foundation, Inc.)
5500 Collins Ave.
Miami, FL   33140

Established in 2001 in Florida.
Donor: Donald Carlin.
Foundation type: Independent foundation.
Financial data (yr. ended 12/31/12): Assets, $34,478 (M); expenditures, $113,816; qualifying distributions, $113,787; giving activities include $113,787 for grants.
Fields of interest: Ballet; Opera.

Limitations: Applications not accepted. Giving primarily in Miami, FL and New York, NY. No grants to individuals.
Application information: Contributes only to pre-selected organizations.
Officers and Directors: Audre Carlin, Pres. and Director; Robert Breier, V.P. and Director; Michael S. Mermelstein, Secy.-Treas. and Director.
EIN: 650925372

1922
Hazel Crosby Carlton Foundation Inc.
3500 Reynolds Rd.
Lakeland, FL 33803-7327
E-mail: info@hcc-foundation.org; Main URL: http://www.hcc-foundation.com

Established in 2005 in Florida.
Donors: Charles Funk; James D. Bunch; Cynthia L. Bunch; Lief Goodson; Bunch and Assocs., Inc.; Kathy Sergi.
Foundation type: Independent foundation.
Financial data (yr. ended 12/31/13): Assets, $1,412,567 (M); gifts received, $8,369; expenditures, $405,561; qualifying distributions, $387,491; giving activities include $386,136 for 8 grants (high: $150,000; low: $50).
Fields of interest: Education; Maternal and perinatal health; Diseases and conditions; Right to life; Human services; Family services; Children; Females.
Limitations: Applications not accepted. Giving primarily in FL and OH.
Application information: Unsolicited requests for funds not accepted.
Officers: Cynthia L. Bunch, Pres. and Treas.; James D. Bunch, V.P. and Secy.
Directors: Charles A. Funk; Lief G. Goodson; Kathy J. Sergi; Nila C. Watkins.
EIN: 203163711

1923
Janet A. Carrington Foundation
251 Royal Palm Way, Ste. 400
Palm Beach, FL 33480-4337

Established in 1998 in Florida.
Donor: Janet A. Carrington.
Foundation type: Independent foundation.
Financial data (yr. ended 12/31/13): Assets, $3,538,301 (M); expenditures, $250,183; qualifying distributions, $202,043; giving activities include $200,250 for 9 grants (high: $60,000; low: $250).
Fields of interest: Education; Vocational education; Animal welfare; Health; Cancers; Human services.
Type of support: General support.
Limitations: Applications not accepted. Giving primarily in FL and MI. No grants to individuals.
Application information: Contributes only to pre-selected organizations.
Trustees: Robert L. Andrews; Janet A. Carrington; Robert G. Simses.
EIN: 061519819

1924
The Jean Keller and Robert Carros Foundation
400 Royal Palm Way, Ste. 304
Palm Beach, FL 33480

Donors: Jean Carros Revocable Trust; Jean Carros†.
Foundation type: Independent foundation.
Financial data (yr. ended 12/31/12): Assets, $4,065,842; expenditures, $1,118,797; qualifying distributions, $243,484.
Fields of interest: Sports and recreation; Youth organizing.
Limitations: Applications not accepted.
Application information: Unsolicited requests for funds not accepted.
Trustee: Robert G. Simses.
EIN: 260902413

1925
The Leo S. & Emogene Burton Case Foundation
32 Country Club Dr. E.
Destin, FL 32541-4404

Established in 2007 in Texas.
Foundation type: Independent foundation.
Financial data (yr. ended 01/31/15): Assets, $5,838,024 (M); gifts received, $3,000; expenditures, $292,330; qualifying distributions, $288,000; giving activities include $288,000 for 26 grants (high: $50,000; low: $1,000).
Fields of interest: Animal welfare; Hospice care; Christianity; Human services; Food aid; Children.
Limitations: Applications not accepted. Giving primarily in LA and TX. No grants to individuals.
Application information: Contributes only to pre-selected organizations.
Trustees: Pamela Jean Case; Robert B. Case; Samuel L. Case.
EIN: 208115212

1926
The Cassill Foundation, Inc.
2740 N.E. 44th St.
Lighthouse Point, FL 33064-7275

Donor: John Shaw.
Foundation type: Independent foundation.
Financial data (yr. ended 12/31/13): Assets, $2,079,419 (M); expenditures, $225,620; qualifying distributions, $166,085; giving activities include $166,085 for 35 grants (high: $25,000; low: $100).
Fields of interest: Education; Religion; Human services.
Limitations: Applications not accepted. Giving primarily in FL.
Application information: Unsolicited requests for funds not accepted.
Directors: Robin Selbach; Christopher Shaw; John F. Shaw.
EIN: 271972621

1927
Lawrence P. Castellani Family Foundation
667 Mourning Dove Dr.
Sarasota, FL 34236-1903

Established in 1993 in New York.
Donors: Lawrence P. Castellani; Joan J. Castellani.
Foundation type: Independent foundation.
Financial data (yr. ended 12/31/13): Assets, $3,577,125 (M); expenditures, $357,619; qualifying distributions, $329,245; giving activities

include $329,245 for 17 grants (high: $147,800; low: $600).
Fields of interest: Arts and culture; Education; Nonprofits; Cancers; Christianity; Human services.
Type of support: General support; Regranting.
Limitations: Applications not accepted. Giving primarily in CA, FL, NY, and VA. No grants to individuals.
Application information: Contributes only to pre-selected organizations.
Trustees: Joan J. Castellani; Lawrence P. Castellani; Lawrence P. Castellani, Jr.; Julianne N. Vardan.
EIN: 166399132

1928
Catalina Marketing Charitable Foundation
200 Carillon Pkwy.
Saint Petersburg, FL 33716-1242
Contact: Bill Protz, Pres.

Established in 1991 in California.
Donors: Catalina Marketing Corp.; Trademark Metals Recycling LLC.
Foundation type: Company-sponsored foundation.
Financial data (yr. ended 07/31/14): Assets, $2,833,305 (M); gifts received, $3,932; expenditures, $271,397; qualifying distributions, $231,547; giving activities include $231,547 for 147 grants (high: $30,000; low: $25).
Purpose and activities: The foundation supports organizations involved with education, water conservation, health, hunger, housing development, athletics, youth business development, and children services.
Fields of interest: Education; Health; Human services.
Type of support: General support; Continuing support; Annual campaigns; Program development; Scholarships.
Limitations: Applications accepted. Giving primarily in FL.
Application information:
  Initial approach: Proposal
  Deadline(s): None
Officers: Debbie Booth, Chair.; Bill Protz, Pres.; James Flanigan, Treas.
Directors: Joni Elmore; Chad Keller; Tricia Stelges.
EIN: 330489905

1929
CCJ Foundation
11941 Turtle Beach Rd.
North Palm Beach, FL 33408-2936

Donor: Michael A. Ruane.
Foundation type: Independent foundation.
Financial data (yr. ended 12/31/13): Assets, $9,513,135 (M); gifts received, $2,098,809; expenditures, $293,584; qualifying distributions, $250,000; giving activities include $250,000 for 1 grant.
Fields of interest: Education.
Limitations: Applications not accepted. Giving primarily in RI.
Application information: Unsolicited requests for funds not accepted.
Trustees: Michael A. Bass; John Curtis; Elizabeth J. Ruane; Michael A. Ruane.
EIN: 461612574

1930
Cedar Branch Foundation
c/o Keith C. Wold Jr., Esq.
1515 S. Fereral Hwy. Ste. 201
Boca Raton, FL 33432-7404

Donor: Elaine J. Wold.
Foundation type: Independent foundation.
Financial data (yr. ended 10/31/14): Assets,
$6,133,347 (M); gifts received, $5,276;
expenditures, $230,351; qualifying distributions,
$227,525; giving activities include $225,000 for 6
grants (high: $50,000; low: $30,000).
Fields of interest: Arts and culture; Health;
Diseases and conditions.
Limitations: Applications not accepted. Giving
primarily in VA. No grants to individuals.
Application information: Unsolicited requests for
funds not accepted.
Trustee: Keith C. Wold, Jr.
EIN: 263601096

1931
The Celebrity Foundation Inc.
19667 Turnberry Way, Ste. 26D
Aventura, FL 33180-2514

Established in 2002 in Florida.
Donors: Vitamins Playwear, Ltd.; Celebrity
International, Inc.; Amar Industries, Inc.; Michael
Matalon; Samuel Matalon; Morris D. Matalon; Eli
Matalon; Luna Investments, Inc.; Morris Matalon;
Sharon Matalon.
Foundation type: Company-sponsored foundation.
Financial data (yr. ended 09/30/13): Assets,
$2,714,525 (M); gifts received, $830,000;
expenditures, $215,485; qualifying distributions,
$205,608; giving activities include $205,608 for 38
grants (high: $96,000; low: $100).
Fields of interest: Cancers; Judaism.
Limitations: Applications not accepted. Giving
primarily in NY. No grants to individuals.
Application information: Unsolicited requests for
funds not accepted.
Officer and Directors: Morris D. Matalon, Chair. and
Director; Eli Matalon; Michael Matalon; Samuel
Matalon.
EIN: 810587000

1932
The Chadbourne Foundation, Inc.
(formerly The Chadbourne Family Foundation, Inc.)
192 Hewitt St.
Pensacola, FL 32503-2265 (850) 434-2244
Contact: Edward M. Chadbourne Jr., Pres.

Established in 1980 in Florida.
Donors: Edward M. Chadbourne III; Edward M.
Chadbourne, Jr.; Caroline C. DeMaria; Mrs. Edward
M. Chadbourne, Jr.; Ruth Chabrourne.
Foundation type: Independent foundation.
Financial data (yr. ended 12/31/13): Assets,
$10,752,288 (M); gifts received, $1,010,516;
expenditures, $450,741; qualifying distributions,
$380,285; giving activities include $376,244 for 33
grants (high: $50,000; low: $500).
Fields of interest: Education; Higher education;
Catholicism; Human services; Low-income and poor
people.

Type of support: General support; Matching grants;
Capital campaigns; Endowments; Emergency funds;
Scholarships.
Limitations: Applications accepted. Giving primarily
in Pensacola, FL. No grants to individuals.
Application information:
   Initial approach: Proposal
   Deadline(s): None
Officers: Edward M. Chadbourne, Jr., Pres.; Edward
M. Chadbourne III, V.P.; Caroline C. DeMaria, Secy.
Directors: Ruth J. Chadbourne; Brian F. DeMaria.
EIN: 592126313

1933
The Chaffiot Family Foundation, Inc.
1802 S. Fiske Blvd.
Rockledge, FL 32955-3029

Established in 1998 in Florida.
Donors: Mark K. Chaffiot; Robert R. Chaffiot, Jr.;
Robeana Chaffiot; Victor Chaffiot.
Foundation type: Independent foundation.
Financial data (yr. ended 08/31/14): Assets,
$1,651,772 (M); gifts received, $212,000;
expenditures, $395,369; qualifying distributions,
$391,486; giving activities include $391,486 for 20
grants (high: $301,231; low: $20).
Fields of interest: Education; Agriculture; Religion;
Christianity.
Limitations: Applications not accepted. Giving
primarily in FL.
Application information: Unsolicited requests for
funds not accepted.
Directors: Mark K. Chaffiot; Robeana Chaffiot;
Robert R. Chaffiot; Robert R. Chaffiot, Jr.; Victor A.
Chaffiot.
EIN: 593547226

1934
Marcy and Leona Chanin Foundation, Inc.
130 Sunrise Ave.
Palm Beach, FL 33480-3961

Foundation type: Independent foundation.
Financial data (yr. ended 12/31/13): Assets,
$6,936,994 (M); expenditures, $403,430;
qualifying distributions, $361,756; giving activities
include $353,121 for 77 grants (high: $100,000;
low: $25).
Purpose and activities: Giving primarily for Jewish
religious, educational, and welfare organizations;
support also for health associations, the arts, and
higher education.
Fields of interest: Arts and culture; Performing arts;
Museums; Education; Higher education; Medical
education; Neurology; Diseases and conditions;
Judaism; Human services.
Type of support: General support; Research.
Limitations: Applications not accepted. Giving
primarily in New York, NY. No grants to individuals.
Application information: Contributes only to
pre-selected organizations.
Officer: Leona F. Chanin, Pres.
EIN: 237156719

1935
Alvah H. & Wyline P. Chapman Foundation, Inc.
P.O. Box 55398
Saint Petersburg, FL 33732-5398
E-mail: vsayler@saylerfamily.com; Additional e-mail:
cfsecretary@aol.com; Main URL: http://
www.chapmanfoundation.org

Established in 1967 in Florida.
Donors: Wyline Chapman Sayler; Chris Chapman
Hilton; Alvah H. Chapman; Betty Bateman Chapman;
Dale Chapman Webb; Van C. Sayler; Wyline Page
Chapman†.
Foundation type: Independent foundation.
Financial data (yr. ended 12/31/13): Assets,
$4,294,353 (M); expenditures, $202,178;
qualifying distributions, $169,740; giving activities
include $165,000 for 23 grants (high: $18,000;
low: $1,000).
Fields of interest: Arts and culture; Orchestral
music; Literature and writing; Education;
Rehabilitation; Substance abuse prevention;
Science; Christianity; Diversity and intergroup
relations; Human services; Family services; Child
welfare; Homeless services.
Type of support: General support; Continuing
support; Capital campaigns; Capital and
infrastructure; Endowments; Emergency funds.
Limitations: Giving primarily in FL. No grants to
individuals, and no endowments or loans to
organizations engaged in partisan political
activities.
Publications: Application guidelines; Informational
brochure (including application guidelines).
Application information: Letter of inquiry should
include requested amount and description of
project. After letter of inquiry, if endorsed by a
foundation director, submit application.
   Initial approach: Email brief letter of inquiry
   Copies of proposal: 1
   Board meeting date(s): Early summer and late fall
   Final notification: After board meeting
Officers and Trustees: Van C. Sayler, Chair. and
Trustee; Chris Hilton, Pres. and Trustee; Bob Hilton,
V.P. and Trustee; Lee B. Sayler, Secy.-Treas. and
Trustee; Page Beckwith; Alan P. Sayler; Brey Webb;
Kristy Webb.
Number of staff: 1 part-time support.
EIN: 586069146

1936
Chardonnay Foundation
1641 Scott Rd.
Amelia Island, FL 32034-5642 9042771597

Donors: David R. Smith; Patricia R. Smith.
Foundation type: Independent foundation.
Financial data (yr. ended 12/31/14): Assets,
$3,046,418; gifts received, $3,850; expenditures,
$203,732; qualifying distributions, $144,630.
Fields of interest: Agriculture; Religion; Human
services.
Type of support: General support.
Limitations: Applications not accepted. Giving
primarily in FL, IA, and VA. No grants to individuals.
Application information: Unsolicited requests for
funds not accepted.
Officers: David R. Smith, Pres.; Patricia R. Smith,
V.P.
EIN: 743055189

1937
Charles Woodson Foundation

10010 Tavistock Rd.
Orlando , FL 32827-7053

Donors: Charles Woodson; Green Bay Converting, Inc.
Foundation type: Independent foundation.
Financial data (yr. ended 12/31/13): Assets, $8,707 (M); gifts received, $11,397; expenditures, $255,773; qualifying distributions, $200,000; giving activities include $200,000 for 1 grant.
Purpose and activities: Giving primarily for higher education, and to a children's hospital.
Fields of interest: Higher education; Specialty hospital care.
Limitations: Applications not accepted. Giving primarily in Ann Arbor, MI.
Application information: Unsolicited requests for funds not accepted.
Officers: Charles Woodson, Pres.; Georgia Woodson, V.P.; Teron Carter, Secy.-Treas.
Director: Kevin Poston.
EIN: 261234522

1938
Charlotte Community Foundation, Inc.

(formerly Charlotte County Foundation, Inc.)
227 Sullivan St.
P. O. Box 512047
Punta Gorda, FL 33950-5244 (941) 637-0077
Contact: Connie Kantor, C.E.O.
FAX: (941) 637-6202;
E-mail: ccf@charlottecommunityfoundation.org;
Additional e-mail:
gbobonich@charlottecommunityfoundation.org;
Main URL: http://
www.charlottecommunityfoundation.org

Established in 1993 in Florida.
Foundation type: Community foundation.
Financial data (yr. ended 12/31/13): Assets, $5,808,834 (M); gifts received, $1,067,311; expenditures, $685,170; giving activities include $273,421 for 14+ grants (high: $128,103).
Purpose and activities: The foundation seeks to enhance the quality of life in Charlotte County, FL. The foundation's mission is to advance the common good by nurturing a giving community and connecting people who care with causes that matter.
Fields of interest: Arts and culture; Historic preservation; Education; Environment; Animal welfare; Nonprofits; Health; Community and economic development; Human services; Seniors.
Type of support: Capacity-building and technical assistance; Matching grants; Equipment; Program development; Recordings; Publications; Program evaluations; Student aid.
Limitations: Applications accepted. Giving limited to Charlotte County, FL. No support for religious organization for sectarian purposes, or fraternal organizations, societies or orders. No grants for general operating support, building or capital campaigns, deficit financing or debt reduction, endowment funds, fundraising events, basic scientific research, start-up funding, or travel expenses; no loans.
Publications: Application guidelines; Annual report; Grants list; Informational brochure; Multi-year report; Occasional report; Occasional report (including application guidelines); Program policy statement.

Application information: Visit foundation web site for letter of intent, application form, and guidelines. The foundation will invite applicants to submit a full application based on letter of intent. Application form required.
Initial approach: Complete online letter of intent
Copies of proposal: 1
Deadline(s): Apr. 11 for letter of intent; July 1 for full grant application
Board meeting date(s): 2nd Thurs. of each 2nd month
Final notification: Within 3 weeks for letter of intent determination; Sept. 26 for award notification
Officers and Directors: Ronald Olsen, Chair. and Director; Mary Byrski, Vice-Chair. and Director; Julia Steele, C.E.O. and Director; Ronald R. Monck, Secy. and Director; Douglas L. Young, Treas. and Director; Laura Amendola; Jimmy Dean; Connie Kantor.
Number of staff: 1 full-time professional; 1 part-time professional; 1 full-time support.
EIN: 650455319

1939
The Chenzyme Foundation Inc.

121 Lansing Island Dr.
Indian Harbour Beach, FL 32937-4875

Donors: Yuan-Tsong Chen; Alice Der Shan Chen.
Foundation type: Independent foundation.
Financial data (yr. ended 12/31/13): Assets, $5,411,476 (M); gifts received, $30; expenditures, $334,971; qualifying distributions, $304,000; giving activities include $304,000 for 4 grants (high: $250,000; low: $5,000).
Fields of interest: Education; Health; Science.
International interests: France; Taiwan.
Type of support: Research and evaluation.
Limitations: Applications not accepted. Giving primarily in FL, NC, France and Taiwan.
Application information: Unsolicited requests for funds not accepted.
Officers: Yuan-Tsong Chen, Pres.; Alice Der-Shan Chen, Secy.-Treas.
Directors: Gerald G. Chen; Jerome G. Chen.
EIN: 271649534

1940
Cherry Family Foundation

1207 Spyglass Ln.
Naples, FL 34102-7738

Established in 2003 in Pennsylvania.
Donor: Arthur L. Cherry.
Foundation type: Independent foundation.
Financial data (yr. ended 12/31/13): Assets, $2,935,810 (M); gifts received, $701,585; expenditures, $254,384; qualifying distributions, $236,317; giving activities include $232,124 for 32 grants (high: $50,935; low: $50).
Fields of interest: Education; Higher education; Diseases and conditions; Children.
Limitations: Applications not accepted. Giving primarily in FL, MA and NY. No grants to individuals.
Application information: Contributes only to pre-selected organizations.
Officers: Arthur L. Cherry, Pres.; Alison L. Cherry, V.P. and Secy.; Carolyn N. Cherry, V.P.; Christopher R. Cherry, V.P.; John Scott Cherry, V.P.; Beverly M. Cherry, Treas.
EIN: 161675283

1941
Chicone Family Foundation

(formerly Jerry J. Chicone Foundation)
P.O. Box 547636
Orlando, FL 32854-7636

Established in 1966 in Florida.
Donor: Jerry J. Chicone, Jr.
Foundation type: Independent foundation.
Financial data (yr. ended 12/31/13): Assets, $904,606 (M); expenditures, $245,631; qualifying distributions, $238,500; giving activities include $238,500 for 9 grants (high: $85,000; low: $5,000).
Fields of interest: Historic preservation; Education; Nonprofits; Learning disorders; Child welfare.
Type of support: Regranting.
Limitations: Applications not accepted. Giving primarily in FL. No grants to individuals.
Application information: Unsolicited requests for funds not accepted.
Trustee: Jerry J. Chicone, Jr.
EIN: 596194416

1942
The Francis and Miranda Childress Foundation

c/o George C. Lee
865 Lane Ave. S.
Jacksonville, FL 32205-4704

Established in 1963 in Florida.
Donors: Francis B. Childress†; Miranda Y. Childress.
Foundation type: Independent foundation.
Financial data (yr. ended 12/31/13): Assets, $7,138,893 (M); expenditures, $438,669; qualifying distributions, $312,000; giving activities include $312,000 for 16 grants (high: $50,000; low: $6,000).
Purpose and activities: Giving primarily for education and medical research, including sports medicine, and a cultural council.
Fields of interest: Arts and culture; Education; Higher education; Nonprofits; Health; Diseases and conditions; Christianity; Child welfare.
Type of support: Research; Regranting.
Limitations: Applications not accepted. Giving primarily in FL and NY. No grants to individuals.
Application information: Contributes only to pre-selected organizations.
Officers: Francis Childress Lee, Pres.; Lewis S. Lee, V.P.; George C. Lee, Secy.; Lewis S. Lee, Jr., Treas.
EIN: 591051733

1943
Chowdhury Family Foundation Inc.

2851 N.W. 107th Ave.
Doral, FL 33172-2130

Donor: Miami Perfume Junction Inc.
Foundation type: Independent foundation.
Financial data (yr. ended 12/31/13): Assets, $535 (M); gifts received, $280,202; expenditures, $364,705; qualifying distributions, $360,900; giving activities include $360,900 for 4 grants (high: $310,000; low: $8,000).
Fields of interest: Health; Hospital care; Specialty hospital care; Child welfare.
Limitations: Applications not accepted. Giving primarily in FL.

Application information: Unsolicited requests for funds not accepted.
Directors: Anand Preet Singh Chowdhury; Ravneet Chowdhury, Esq.; Andrew Trumbach.
EIN: 453996134

1944
The Chris Foundation, Inc.
259 Buttonwood Dr.
Key Biscayne, FL   33149-1202
Main URL: http://www.ipadsforsoldiers.org

Donors: Wesley V. Pritchett; Untied Capital Markets; Winnie Pritchett; Tom Shadyac.
Foundation type: Independent foundation.
Financial data (yr. ended 12/31/13): Assets, $10,664 (M); gifts received, $139,262; expenditures, $141,704; qualifying distributions, $134,375; giving activities include $134,375 for 2 + grants (high: $73,906).
Fields of interest: National defense; Human services.
Limitations: Applications not accepted.
Application information: Unsolicited requests for funds not accepted.
Officers and Directors: Winnie Pritchett, Pres. and Director; Wesley V. Pritchett, Secy. and Director; Nicole Grace Pritchett; Wesley John Pritchett.
EIN: 274012385

1945
The Clements Family Charitable Trust
c/o Thomas Clements III
1025 Fleming St.
Key West, FL   33040-6962

Established in 1993 in Florida.
Donor: Helen T. Clements†.
Foundation type: Independent foundation.
Financial data (yr. ended 12/31/14): Assets, $2,967,465; expenditures, $194,784; qualifying distributions, $180,810.
Fields of interest: Arts and culture; Education; Religion.
Limitations: Applications not accepted. Giving primarily in FL, ME, and NY. No grants to individuals.
Application information: Unsolicited requests for funds not accepted.
Trustees: Alice B. Clements; John B. Clements; Robert M. Clements; Thomas Clements III; Tyler M. Clements; KeyBank, N.A.
Number of staff: None.
EIN: 341748724

1946
Cody Foundation
16787 Crown Bridge Dr.
Delray Beach, FL   33446-2410

Donors: Stuart Steckler; Sue-Ann Steckler.
Foundation type: Independent foundation.
Financial data (yr. ended 12/31/13): Assets, $4,210,591 (M); gifts received, $150,000; expenditures, $132,502; qualifying distributions, $130,000; giving activities include $130,000 for 6 grants (high: $50,000; low: $5,000).
Fields of interest: Education; Human services.
Limitations: Applications not accepted. Giving primarily in NJ and New York, NY.

Application information: Unsolicited requests for funds not accepted.
Trustees: Stuart Steckler; Sue-Ann Steckler.
EIN: 276362131

1947
Eleanor and Menachem Cohen Family Foundation, Inc.
25 S.E. 2nd St., Ste. 1120
Miami, FL   33131-1605
Contact: Eleanor Cohen

Established in 1999 in Florida.
Donors: Recovery Management Systems Corp.; Eleanor Cohen.
Foundation type: Independent foundation.
Financial data (yr. ended 12/31/13): Assets, $534,483 (M); expenditures, $414,223; qualifying distributions, $413,338; giving activities include $411,552 for 30 grants (high: $125,000; low: $72).
Fields of interest: Judaism.
Limitations: Applications not accepted. Giving primarily in FL. No grants to individuals.
Application information: Contributes only to pre-selected organizations.
Officers and Directors: Eleanor Cohen, Pres. and Director; Candice N. Cohen, Secy.-Treas. and Director.
EIN: 650883308

1948
George M. Cohen Foundation, Inc.
8265 Bayberry Rd.
Jacksonville, FL   32256-7432

Established in 1984 in Florida.
Donors: George M. Cohen†; Lawrence J. DuBow; Carolyn Cohen; Carolyn Munro Wilson.
Foundation type: Independent foundation.
Financial data (yr. ended 11/30/13): Assets, $2,564,374 (M); expenditures, $243,760; qualifying distributions, $212,216; giving activities include $210,000 for 17 grants (high: $85,000; low: $600).
Purpose and activities: Giving primarily for education and Christian Scientist churches.
Fields of interest: Education; University education; Religion.
Limitations: Applications not accepted. Giving primarily in Jacksonville, FL. No grants to individuals.
Application information: Unsolicited requests for funds not accepted.
Officers and Directors: Carolyn Munro Wilson, Pres. and Treas.; David J. Hull, Secy. and Director; Travis Lunsford; Jessica Noel West.
EIN: 592469069

1949
William L. & Lesley H. Collins Family Foundation, Inc.
6825 Grenadier Blvd., Ste. 1701
Naples, FL   34108-7218

Established in 1993 in New Jersey.
Donors: William Collins; Lesley Collins.
Foundation type: Independent foundation.
Financial data (yr. ended 12/31/13): Assets, $8,640,394 (M); expenditures, $265,130; qualifying distributions, $231,100; giving activities

include $231,100 for 48 grants (high: $50,000; low: $150).
Fields of interest: Arts and culture; Education; Higher education; Health; Catholicism; Human services; Child welfare.
Type of support: General support; Student aid.
Limitations: Applications not accepted. Giving primarily in New York, NY.
Application information: Unsolicited requests for funds not accepted.
Officers: William Collins, Pres.; Lesley Collins, Secy.
Trustees: Brian Collins; Courtney Collins; Jennifer Collins; Andre Montero, CPA.
EIN: 521872190

1950
The Concourse Council, Inc.
11905 Oak Trail Way
Port Richey, FL   34668-1064
Main URL: http://floridaconcourse.com

Foundation type: Independent foundation.
Financial data (yr. ended 06/30/13): Assets, $3,001,450 (M); expenditures, $187,701; qualifying distributions, $170,572; giving activities include $150,175 for 2 grants (high: $150,000; low: $175).
Fields of interest: Education; Agriculture; Housing development.
Limitations: Applications not accepted. Giving primarily in FL.
Application information: Unsolicited requests for funds not accepted.
Officers: Mark Deeb, Pres.; Kurt Conover, V.P.; Thad Lowrey, Secy.; James S. Luikart, Treas.
Directors: Steve Henry; Al Messina; Jeff Montgomery; James Wilcox.
EIN: 237313687

1951
Consolidated Anti-Aging Foundation
2390 Tamiami Trail N., Ste. 204
Naples, FL   34103-4484

Established in 1996 in Florida.
Donors: R. Ross†; F. Ross†.
Foundation type: Independent foundation.
Financial data (yr. ended 12/31/13): Assets, $8,572,985 (M); expenditures, $641,760; qualifying distributions, $480,000; giving activities include $360,000 for 6 grants (high: $160,000; low: $10,000).
Fields of interest: Diseases and conditions.
Type of support: Research; Research and evaluation.
Limitations: Applications not accepted. Giving primarily in GA, IL, MA and NY. No grants to individuals.
Application information: Contributes only to pre-selected organizations.
Trustees: Cheryl L. Ross; Robin S. Ross.
EIN: 656222748

1952
Coral Gables Community Foundation
(formerly The Coral Gables Foundation)
3001 Ponce de Leon Blvd., Ste. 203
Coral Gables, FL   33134-6824   (305) 446-9670
Contact: Mary Snow, Exec. Dir.

FAX: (305) 446-3773;
E-mail: info@gablesfoundation.org; Grant inquiry
e-mail: mary@gablesfoundation.org, Mailing
Address: 1825 Ponce De Leon Blvd., PMB #447
Coral Gables, FL 33134-4418; Main URL: http://
www.gablesfoundation.org
E Newsletter: http://www.gablesfoundation.org/
subscribe.php
Facebook: http://www.facebook.com/
GablesHomePage
Twitter: http://twitter.com/CGCF
YouTube: http://www.youtube.com/
gableshomepage

Established in 1991 in Florida.
Donors: Suzanna P. Tweed; Jose Calvo; Ralph
Moore; Shelly Roberts; Kerdyle Liljedahl†.
Foundation type: Community foundation.
Financial data (yr. ended 12/31/13): Assets,
$1,252,892 (M); gifts received, $641,631;
expenditures, $419,837; giving activities include
$185,865 for 1+ grant (high: $7,000).
Purpose and activities: The foundation seeks to
promote programs and initiatives that enhance the
quality of life for people living and working in Coral
Gables, FL.
Fields of interest: Arts and culture; Museums;
Historic preservation; Education; Health;
Community and economic development; Parks;
Youth organizing; Children and youth; Seniors;
People with disabilities.
Type of support: General support; Grants to
individuals; In-kind gifts; Annual campaigns; Capital
and infrastructure; Matching grants; Land
acquisitions; Emergency funds; Convening;
Scholarships.
Limitations: Applications accepted. Giving limited to
Coral Gables, FL. No support for religious or
sectarian purposes. No grants to individuals (except
for scholarships), or for tickets for charitable
functions.
Publications: Annual report; Newsletter.
Application information: Grants are reviewed on a
bi-annual basis; visit foundation web site for
application information.
    Initial approach: Letter
    Copies of proposal: 5
    Deadline(s): Apr. 17 and Sept. 14
    Board meeting date(s): Mar., June, Sept., and
    Dec.
    Final notification: 45 following the bi-annual
    review period
Officers and Directors: Carlos F. Garcia, CPA, Chair.
and Director; Anthony L. Rogers, Chair.-Elect. and
Director; John ORourke III, Chair., Community Giving
Committee; Matthew Meehan, Secy. and Director; F.
David Olazabal, Treas. and Director; Mary Snow,
Exec. Dir.; Pat H. Clarke, Dir., Emeritus; Albert H.
Friedman, Dir., Emeritus; Marian Cline Krutulis, Dir.,
Emeritus; Verneka Silva, Dir., Emeritus; John R.
Allen, Jr.; Pat Blanco; William A. Bonn, Esq.; William
Colas; Sissy DeMaria; Sasha Dolgicer; Wayne
Cameron Eldred; Zeke Guilford, Esq.; Andria Hanley;
Jack Lowell; Paul Lowenthal; Lee J. Osiason, Esq.;
Scott Poulin; Aurelia A. Reinhardt; Ari Rollnick; Venny
Torre; Marielena Villamil.
Number of staff: 2 full-time professional.
EIN: 650208290

1953
Couch Family Foundation, Inc.
1717 E. Fowler Ave.
Tampa, FL 33612-5523
Contact: Theodore J. Couch Sr., V.P.
FAX: (813) 971-0148;
E-mail: info@couchfamilyfoundation.org; Main
URL: http://www.couchfamilyfoundation.org

Established in 1989 in Florida.
Donor: Theodore J. Couch, Sr.
Foundation type: Independent foundation.
Financial data (yr. ended 12/31/13): Assets,
$6,137,622 (M); gifts received, $350,000;
expenditures, $277,531; qualifying distributions,
$245,576; giving activities include $235,333 for 19
grants (high: $58,333; low: $2,000).
Purpose and activities: The mission of the Couch
Family Foundation is to support the following needs
in the Hillsborough County community: 1) Religious
Organizations The Couch Family Foundation is
committed to supporting religious based programs
whose purpose is to serve and provide for societys
underserved; 2) Education The Couch Family
Foundation is committed to stimulating creativity
and productivity among young disadvantaged people
and adults through programs that encourage
learning as a lifelong process; 3) Medical
Advancement The Couch Family Foundation is
committed to advancing and supporting basic and
applied medical research in the areas of curing
cancer.
Fields of interest: Arts education; Performing arts;
Theater; Museums; Education; Elementary and
secondary education; Secondary education; Child
educational development; Higher education;
Community college education; Undergraduate
education; Business education; Teacher education;
Adult education; Basic and remedial instruction;
Continuing education; Health; Hospital care;
Hospice care; Community mental health care;
Diseases and conditions; Cancers; Abuse
prevention; Child abuse; Community and economic
development; Housing development; Human
services; Food banks; Food delivery; Child welfare;
Child development; Youth services; Senior services;
Children and youth; Children; Homeless people;
Low-income and poor people.
Type of support: General support; Employee
matching gifts; Capital and infrastructure; Matching
grants; Equipment; Emergency funds; Program
development; Scholarships; Research; Systems
reform.
Limitations: Applications accepted. Giving primarily
in Tampa, FL and Blowing Rock, NC. No grants to
individuals.
Application information: Application guidelines and
form available on foundation web site. Application
form required.
    Initial approach: Letter, e-mail or fax
    Copies of proposal: 1
    Deadline(s): Oct. 1
    Board meeting date(s): Dec.
    Final notification: 30-180 days
Officers and Directors: Theodore J. Couch, Sr.,
Chair. and V.P. and Director; Martha K. Couch, Pres.
and Director; William C. Crowder, Secy.- Treas. and
Director; Theodore J. Couch, Jr.
Number of staff: None.
EIN: 592926563

1954
Laura Gene Coulter-Jones Foundation
(also known as Laura Gene Colter-Jones Foundation)
65 Leucadendra Dr.
Coral Gables, FL 33156-2371

Established in 1997 in Florida.
Donor: Laura Gene Coulter-Jones.
Foundation type: Independent foundation.
Financial data (yr. ended 12/31/14): Assets,
$840,694; expenditures, $352,530; qualifying
distributions, $350,000.
Purpose and activities: Giving primarily for health
organizations, particularly a university medical
school's department of pediatrics; funding also for
federated giving programs.
Fields of interest: University education; Medical
education; Foundations; Nonprofits; Pediatrics;
Diseases and conditions; Alzheimer's disease.
Type of support: Regranting.
Limitations: Applications not accepted. Giving
primarily in Coral Gables, FL. No grants to
individuals.
Application information: Unsolicited requests for
funds not accepted.
Director: Laura Gene Coulter-Jones.
EIN: 656245657

1955
Raymond E. and Ellen F. Crane Foundation
P.O. Box 2097
Alachua, FL 32615

Established in 1949 in Pennsylvania.
Donors: Raymond E. Crane†; Ellen F. Crane†.
Foundation type: Independent foundation.
Financial data (yr. ended 12/31/13): Assets,
$4,232,864 (M); expenditures, $199,200;
qualifying distributions, $193,997; giving activities
include $160,000 for 58 grants (high: $10,000;
low: $500).
Fields of interest: Arts and culture; Education;
Higher education; Animal welfare; Nonprofits;
Health; Hospice care; Diseases and conditions;
Christianity; Human services; Food banks; Family
services.
Type of support: Regranting.
Limitations: Applications not accepted. Giving
primarily in FL, HI, and NC. No grants to individuals.
Application information: Contributes only to
pre-selected organizations.
Officer: John D. Zuidema, Jr., Exec. Secy.
Trustees: Aldrich Boss; David Radford Crane; Arlette
Crane Dumke; Elizabeth Crane Swent.
EIN: 596139265

1956
Julia W. Croft Charitable Trust
P.O. Box 40200, FL9-100-10-19
Jacksonville, FL 32203-0200

Foundation type: Independent foundation.
Financial data (yr. ended 12/31/13): Assets,
$6,120,916 (M); expenditures, $331,966;
qualifying distributions, $289,342; giving activities
include $265,950 for 2 grants (high: $132,975;
low: $132,975).
Fields of interest: Education; University education.
Limitations: Applications not accepted. Giving
primarily in GA and SC.

Application information: Unsolicited requests for funds not accepted.
Trustee: Bank of America, N.A.
EIN: 576029071

1957
Crutchfield Family Foundation
(formerly Edward E. Crutchfield Family Foundation)
219 Island Creek Dr.
Vero Beach, FL   32963-3304

Established in 2000 in North Carolina.
Donor: Edward E. Crutchfield.
Foundation type: Independent foundation.
Financial data (yr. ended 12/31/13): Assets, $92,775 (M); gifts received, $136,602; expenditures, $221,856; qualifying distributions, $216,602; giving activities include $216,602 for 17 grants (high: $40,000; low: $5,000).
Fields of interest: Education; Higher education; Health; Diseases and conditions; Human services; Child welfare.
Limitations: Applications not accepted. No grants to individuals.
Application information: Contributes only to pre-selected organizations.
Officers: Edward E. Crutchfield, Chair. and Pres.; Sarah Crutchfield Davis, V.P.; Edward E. Crutchfield, Jr., Secy.-Treas.
EIN: 562220389

1958
CSX Foundation, Inc.
500 Water St., Ste. C-115
Jacksonville, FL   32202-4423

Donors: CSX Corp.; CSX Transportation, Inc.
Foundation type: Independent foundation.
Financial data (yr. ended 12/31/13): Assets, $254,555 (M); gifts received, $90,456; expenditures, $212,923; qualifying distributions, $212,923; giving activities include $207,550 for 217 grants (high: $10,000; low: $150).
Fields of interest: Diseases and conditions; Human services; Youth development.
Limitations: Applications not accepted. Giving primarily in FL.
Application information: Unsolicited requests for funds not accepted.
Officers and Directors: Tori Kaplan, Pres. and Director; Joel W. Pangbom, V.P. and Director; Mark D. Austin, Corp. Secy.; Angela C. Williams, V.P. and Treas.; John L. Kitchens, V.P.; David J. Bowling; Steve E. Crable; Ellen M. Fitzsimmons; Jim M. Marks, Jr.; Peter K. Mills; Michelle Ross; Derrick W. Smith.
EIN: 262248439

1959
The Cunnane Foundation
60 Seagate Dr., Unit P106
Naples, FL   34103-2402

Established in 1993 in Virginia.
Donor: James J. Cunnane, Sr.
Foundation type: Independent foundation.
Financial data (yr. ended 12/31/13): Assets, $3,525,277 (M); gifts received, $300,387; expenditures, $155,996; qualifying distributions,

$145,000; giving activities include $145,000 for 9 grants (high: $100,000; low: $1,000).
Purpose and activities: Giving primarily to St. Louis-based Roman Catholic churches and charities.
Fields of interest: Arts and culture; Education; Christianity.
Limitations: Applications not accepted. Giving primarily in St. Louis, MO.
Application information: Unsolicited requests for funds not accepted.
Officers and Directors: Cornelia B. Stebelman, Pres. and Director; Edith C. Cunnane, V.P. and Secy.; James J. Cunnane, Jr., V.P. and Treas.; James J. Cunnane, Sr.
EIN: 541691517

1960
The Dalton Family Foundation
3739 Woodlake Dr.
Bonita Springs, FL   34134-2616   (330) 715-0914
Contact: Arthur R. Dalton, Tr.

Established in 2008 in Ohio.
Donor: Arthur R. Dalton.
Foundation type: Independent foundation.
Financial data (yr. ended 12/31/12): Assets, $2,429,110 (M); gifts received, $2,184; expenditures, $295,442; qualifying distributions, $280,480; giving activities include $280,480 for grants.
Fields of interest: Housing development; Christianity; Human services.
Application information: Application form required.
  Initial approach: Letter
  Deadline(s): None
Trustees: Arthur R. Dalton; Janet B. Dalton; Breanne C. Huguenard; Lindsay R. Sines.
EIN: 263432969

1961
Meredyth Anne Dasburg Foundation
791 Crandon Blvd., No. 408
Key Biscayne, FL   33149-2200

Established in 1989 in Minnesota.
Donors: John H. Dasburg; Mary L. Dasburg.
Foundation type: Independent foundation.
Financial data (yr. ended 12/31/12): Assets, $443,008 (M); gifts received, $4,347; expenditures, $237,127; qualifying distributions, $232,457; giving activities include $232,457 for 19 grants (high: $125,000; low: $500).
Purpose and activities: Giving primarily for education, and for children and social services; funding also for a children's theater.
Fields of interest: Education; Higher education; Law education; Human services; Child welfare.
Type of support: General support; Annual campaigns; Capital campaigns; Convening; Scholarships.
Limitations: Applications not accepted. Giving primarily in MN, with emphasis on the greater metropolitan Twin Cities area; some funding also in FL and VA.
Application information: Contributes only to pre-selected organizations.
Trustees: John H. Dasburg; Mary Lou Dasburg.
EIN: 521608565

1962
James E. Davis Family Charities, Inc.
(formerly James E. Davis Family - W.D. Charities, Inc.)
4310 Pablo Oaks Ct.
Jacksonville, FL   32224-9631

Established in 1949 in Florida.
Donor: James E. Davis.
Foundation type: Independent foundation.
Financial data (yr. ended 12/31/14): Assets, $7,853,467; expenditures, $214,357; qualifying distributions, $186,695.
Purpose and activities: Giving primarily for medical research; some giving for education and human services.
Fields of interest: Education; Diseases and conditions; International relations.
Limitations: Applications not accepted. Giving primarily in FL, with emphasis on Jacksonville. No grants to individuals.
Application information: Unsolicited requests for funds not accepted.
Officers and Directors: A. Dano Davis, Pres. and Director; E. Ellis Zahra, Jr., V.P. and Director; Harry D. Francis, V.P.; Scott A. Oko, V.P.; Judy B. Morgan, Secy.; Dorothy D. Smith.
EIN: 596128733

1963
Davis Family Charitable Trust
300 5th Ave. S., Ste. 101/446
Naples, FL   34102-6504   (239) 649-4755
Contact: Susan Davis, Tr.; Richard Davis, Tr.

Donors: Richard P. Davis; Susan P. Davis.
Foundation type: Independent foundation.
Financial data (yr. ended 12/31/13): Assets, $3,112,667 (M); expenditures, $174,628; qualifying distributions, $172,000; giving activities include $172,000 for 7 grants (high: $75,000; low: $1,000).
Fields of interest: Education; Catholicism.
Application information: Application form required.
  Initial approach: Letter
  Deadline(s): None
Trustees: Richard P. Davis; Susan P. Davis.
EIN: 271501472

1964
The Davis Family Foundation, Inc.
c/o Seaside Community Development Corp.
P.O. Box 4730
Santa Rosa Beach, FL   32459-4730

Established in 2004 in Florida.
Donors: Daryl Rose Davis; Robert S. Davis.
Foundation type: Independent foundation.
Financial data (yr. ended 12/31/13): Assets, $1,295,329 (M); expenditures, $365,768; qualifying distributions, $355,625; giving activities include $355,625 for 29 grants (high: $168,000; low: $100).
Fields of interest: Education; Secondary education; Community and economic development; Human services.
Limitations: Applications not accepted. Giving primarily in CA and FL. No grants to individuals.
Application information: Contributes only to pre-selected organizations.

Officers: Robert S. Davis, Pres.; Daryl Rose Davis, Secy.
Director: Jacky Barker.
EIN: 200705023

1965
Dr. Harry M. Day Charitable Foundation
129 Wisteria Dr.
Longwood, FL   32779-4950   (321) 422-0575
Contact: Pete Lapp

Established in 1987 in Florida.
Donor: Harry M. Day†.
Foundation type: Independent foundation.
Financial data (yr. ended 12/31/13): Assets, $10,529,233 (M); expenditures, $513,705; qualifying distributions, $423,771; giving activities include $227,000 for 11 grants (high: $100,000; low: $1,000).
Purpose and activities: Giving primarily to universities; some support also for health and performing arts.
Fields of interest: Performing arts; University education; Health; Youth services.
Type of support: General support; Capital and infrastructure.
Limitations: Applications accepted. Giving primarily in CT, FL, and NY.
Application information: Application form required.
   Initial approach: Request application form
   Deadline(s): None
Trustees: Jack Crider; Harry M. Day; Jerry Day; Setsuko Day.
EIN: 592845883

1966
Henrietta Countess de Hoernle Foundation
c/o Marjorie A. Horwin, C.P.A.
225 N.E. Mizner Blvd., Ste. 685
Boca Raton, FL   33432-4080

Donor: Countess Henrietta de Hoernle.
Foundation type: Independent foundation.
Financial data (yr. ended 12/31/14): Assets, $1,852,821 (M); expenditures, $157,077; qualifying distributions, $141,761; giving activities include $141,761 for 6 grants (high: $125,000; low: $100).
Fields of interest: Arts and culture; University education; Hospital care; Community and economic development; Youth development.
Type of support: General support.
Limitations: Applications not accepted. Giving primarily in Boca Raton, FL. No grants to individuals.
Application information: Unsolicited requests for funds not accepted.
Officer: Countess Henrietta de Hoernle, Pres.
Board Member: Carolina Wagman.
EIN: 030475225

1967
The De Vink Foundation, Inc.
123 S. Beach Rd.
Hobe Sound, FL   33455-2437
Application address: Lodewink J.R. De Vink, Untracht Early LLC, 325 Columbia Tpke., Ste. 202, Florham Park, NJ 07932, tel.: (973) 408-6700

Established in 1998 in New Jersey.
Donor: Lodewijk J.R. De Vink.

Foundation type: Independent foundation.
Financial data (yr. ended 12/31/13): Assets, $2,152,303 (M); gifts received, $2,680; expenditures, $384,430; qualifying distributions, $384,415; giving activities include $381,750 for 21 grants (high: $155,000; low: $250).
Fields of interest: Arts and culture; Performing arts; Education; Secondary education; Nursing care; Religion.
Limitations: Applications accepted. Giving primarily in CO, NJ and NY. No grants to individuals or private foundations.
Application information: Application form required.
   Initial approach: Letter
   Deadline(s): None
Directors: Lodewijk J.R. De Vink; L. Rupert A. De Vink; Marijke B.E. De Vink; Rutger J.L. De Vink.
EIN: 223587250

1968
Neil & Sandra Defeo Family Foundation
4067 Shell Rd.
Sarasota, FL   34242

Donor: Neil Defeo.
Foundation type: Independent foundation.
Financial data (yr. ended 12/31/13): Assets, $4,130,138 (M); gifts received, $298; expenditures, $220,575; qualifying distributions, $162,000; giving activities include $162,000 for 17 grants (high: $50,000; low: $500).
Fields of interest: Education; Health; Human services.
Limitations: Applications not accepted. Giving primarily in NY.
Application information: Unsolicited requests for funds not accepted.
Directors: Elizabeth Defeo; Julia Defeo; Lauren Defeo; Neil Defeo; Sandra Defeo.
EIN: 266141110

1969
Overton and Katherine Dennis Fund
P.O. Box 1908
Orlando, FL   32802-1908
Application address: c/o Manager, P.O. Box 26548, Richmond, VA 23261, tel.: (804) 782-5230

Established in 1987 in Virginia.
Foundation type: Independent foundation.
Financial data (yr. ended 05/31/13): Assets, $6,775,398 (M); expenditures, $346,267; qualifying distributions, $328,989; giving activities include $318,800 for grants.
Purpose and activities: Giving primarily for education, children and social services, Episcopal churches, and federated giving programs.
Fields of interest: Education; Higher education; Environment; Nonprofits; Episcopalianism and Anglicanism; Lutheranism; Human services; Child welfare.
Type of support: Scholarships; Regranting.
Limitations: Applications accepted. Giving primarily in VA, with emphasis on Richmond. No grants to individuals.
Application information: Application form required.
   Initial approach: Letter
   Deadline(s): None
   Board meeting date(s): Apr.
Officers: Janet J. Dennis, Pres.; Janet D. Branch, Secy.-Treas.

Director: Elizabeth O. Dennis.
Trustee: SunTrust Bank.
EIN: 541418161

1970
Wayne M. Densch Charities, Inc.
P.O. Box 536845
Orlando, FL   32853-6845

Established in 1992 in Michigan.
Donor: Wayne Densch Charitable Trust.
Foundation type: Operating foundation.
Financial data (yr. ended 12/31/13): Assets, $17,004,518 (M); gifts received, $328,000; expenditures, $1,116,351; qualifying distributions, $947,073; giving activities include $367,163 for 42 grants (high: $80,000; low: $25).
Fields of interest: Health; Human services; Food aid; Retirement housing.
Type of support: Emergency funds; Grants to individuals.
Limitations: Applications accepted. Giving primarily in FL.
Application information: Application form required.
   Initial approach: Proposal
   Deadline(s): None
Officers and Directors: Leonard E. Williams, Pres. and Director; John A. Williams, V.P.
EIN: 582013696

1971
Detter Family Foundation Inc.
c/o Iris F. Detter
11519 Aerie Ln.
Naples, FL   34120-4334

Established in 2005 in Florida.
Donor: Gerald Detter.
Foundation type: Independent foundation.
Financial data (yr. ended 12/31/13): Assets, $4,544,003 (M); expenditures, $236,027; qualifying distributions, $206,445; giving activities include $177,648 for 40 grants (high: $20,000; low: $148).
Fields of interest: Education; Diseases and conditions; Human services.
Type of support: Scholarships; General support.
Limitations: Applications not accepted. Giving primarily in MI, with emphasis on Ann Arbor, Saline, and Grand Rapids; giving also in Naples, FL, and New York, NY.
Application information: Unsolicited requests for funds not accepted.
Officers: Iris F. Detter, Pres.; Jodi M. Koerner, V.P.; Jason M. Detter, Secy.; Jill M. Wiedmeyer, Treas.
EIN: 203696924

1972
Deus Spes Mea Foundation Inc.
P.O. Box 15456
Clearwater, FL   33766-5456

Established in 1998 in Florida.
Donors: Charles I. Babcock, Jr.; Mary H. Babcock.
Foundation type: Independent foundation.
Financial data (yr. ended 12/31/13): Assets, $3,436,963 (M); expenditures, $182,220; qualifying distributions, $152,061; giving activities include $150,000 for 19 grants (high: $30,000; low: $1,500).

Purpose and activities: Giving primarily for Christian organizations.

Fields of interest: Nonprofits; Christianity; Human services; Child welfare.

Type of support: Regranting.

Limitations: Applications not accepted. No grants to individuals.

Application information: Unsolicited requests for funds not accepted.

  Board meeting date(s): Apr. 15

Directors: Calvin H. Babcock; Charles I. Babcock III; Evelyn E. Babcock; Mary H. Babcock; Mary B. Taylor.

EIN: 650841971

1973
Ruby Diamond Foundation
P.O. Box 1549
Tallahassee, FL   32302-1549

Established in 1984 in Florida.

Donor: Ruby Diamond Charitable Remainder Trust.

Foundation type: Independent foundation.

Financial data (yr. ended 12/31/13): Assets, $5,677,435 (M); gifts received, $40,600; expenditures, $299,885; qualifying distributions, $276,133; giving activities include $254,245 for 24 grants (high: $73,280; low: $1,450).

Purpose and activities: Giving primarily for social services and Jewish organizations.

Fields of interest: Arts and culture; Nonprofits; Judaism; Human services.

Type of support: Regranting.

Limitations: Applications not accepted. Giving primarily in FL. No grants to individuals.

Application information: Unsolicited requests for funds not accepted.

Trustees: Stephan Fregger; Jacqueline Gilberg; Capital City Trust Co.

EIN: 596781684

1974
Diane Lynn Family Foundation Inc.
7050 W. Palmeto Park Rd., No. 15-646
Boca Raton, FL   33433-3407
Contact: Angela Fisher, Dir.

Established in 2001 in Florida.

Donors: Diane Lynn DaSilva; DLD Family, Ltd.

Foundation type: Independent foundation.

Financial data (yr. ended 11/30/13): Assets, $5,681,280 (M); expenditures, $277,275; qualifying distributions, $242,846; giving activities include $224,500 for 8 grants (high: $60,000; low: $1,000).

Fields of interest: Education; University education; Hospital care; Health care clinics; Arthritis; Muscular dystrophy; Multiple sclerosis; Immune system diseases; Cystic fibrosis; Cancers; Human services; Child welfare.

Type of support: Research.

Limitations: Applications accepted. Giving primarily in FL, GA and HI.

Application information: Application form required.

  Initial approach: Letter

  Deadline(s): Aug. 31

Directors: Diane Lynn DaSilva; Krista Mary DaSilva; Angela Fisher; Joel Reinstein.

EIN: 651156490

1975
The Dickinson Foundation, Inc.
c/o Robert H. Dickinson
29 Tahiti Beach Island Rd.
Coral Gables, FL   33143-6540

Established in 2004 in Florida.

Donors: Robert H. Dickinson; Camillus House.

Foundation type: Independent foundation.

Financial data (yr. ended 12/31/13): Assets, $1,008,720 (M); gifts received, $175,546; expenditures, $287,279; qualifying distributions, $279,450; giving activities include $279,450 for 17 grants (high: $65,000; low: $300).

Purpose and activities: Giving primarily to a federated giving program, as well as to Roman Catholic agencies and churches.

Fields of interest: Nonprofits; Catholicism; Human services; Child welfare.

Type of support: Regranting.

Limitations: Applications not accepted. Giving primarily in Miami, FL.

Application information: Unsolicited requests for funds not accepted.

Officers: Robert H. Dickinson, Pres.; Jolynn Dickinson, V.P.; Kristin M. Hogue, Treas.

EIN: 223901478

1976
Diermeier Family Foundation
2113 Canna Way
Naples, FL   34105-3069   (630) 655-8845
Contact: Julie Diermeier, Tr.
FAX: (630) 789-6249;
E-mail: diermeier1@comcast.net; Main URL: http://www.diermeierff.org
Grants List: http://www.diermeierff.org/past-grants.html

Established in 2003 in Illinois.

Donors: Jeffrey J. Diermeier; Julia M. Diermeier.

Foundation type: Independent foundation.

Financial data (yr. ended 12/31/13): Assets, $9,416,371 (M); expenditures, $506,781; qualifying distributions, $443,615; giving activities include $438,000 for 15 grants (high: $100,000; low: $1,000).

Fields of interest: Elementary and secondary education; Higher education; Health; Mental health care; Human services.

Type of support: General support.

Limitations: Giving primarily in FL, GA, IL, and WI. No grants to individuals.

Application information: Application form available on foundation web site. Application form required.

  Initial approach: Download application form from foundation web site. Applications may be submitted via fax or e-mail.

Trustees: Jeffrey J. Diermeier; Julie M. Diermeier.

EIN: 364545339

1977
Lloyd L. and Helen R. Dilworth Foundation
7901 S.W. 6th Ct., Ste. 140
Plantation, FL   33324-3248   9549617940

Established in 1988 in Florida.

Donor: Helen R. Dilworth Trust.

Foundation type: Independent foundation.

Financial data (yr. ended 12/31/14): Assets, $3,002,082; expenditures, $204,985; qualifying distributions, $145,000.

Fields of interest: Higher education; Nonprofits; Diseases and conditions.

Type of support: Regranting.

Limitations: Applications not accepted. Giving primarily in FL. No grants to individuals.

Application information: Unsolicited requests for funds not accepted.

Trustees: Alfred J. Katzin; Wells Fargo Bank, N.A.

EIN: 650022652

1978
Doctors Hospital, Inc.
6700 E. Tropical Way
Plantation, FL   33317-3315   (954) 791-9999
Contact: Donald L. Gross, Pres.

Established in 1987 in Florida.

Foundation type: Independent foundation.

Financial data (yr. ended 12/31/13): Assets, $4,569,950 (M); expenditures, $445,711; qualifying distributions, $217,100; giving activities include $217,100 for 2 grants (high: $216,550; low: $550).

Purpose and activities:

Fields of interest: University education; Diseases and conditions.

Limitations: Applications accepted. Giving limited to Broward and West Palm Beach counties, FL. No grants to individuals.

Publications: Application guidelines.

Application information:

  Initial approach: Letter

  Copies of proposal: 1

  Deadline(s): Oct. 1

Officers: Howard L. Neer, DO, Chair.; Donald L. Gross, Pres.

Director: Anthony Krayer.

EIN: 590906961

1979
Dorset Charitable Trust
(formerly Byron H. Somers Foundation)
P.O. Box 2165
Naples, FL   34106-2165

Established in 1977 in Indiana.

Donors: Jeanette D. Schouweiler; Jane D. Eberly; Druscilla Doehrman.

Foundation type: Independent foundation.

Financial data (yr. ended 11/30/13): Assets, $4,303,532 (M); gifts received, $80,000; expenditures, $320,688; qualifying distributions, $307,263; giving activities include $305,500 for 49 grants (high: $60,000; low: $1,000).

Fields of interest: Elementary and secondary education.

Type of support: General support; Matching grants; Capital campaigns; Capital and infrastructure.

Limitations: Applications not accepted. Giving primarily in AZ and IN. No grants to individuals.

Application information: Contributes only to pre-selected organizations.

Trustees: Druscilla S. Doehrman; Jane D. Eberly; Elizabeth D. Haenel; Jeanette D. Schoweiler.

EIN: 351410969

1980
The Doyle Foundation, Inc.
11201 Corporate Cir. N., Ste. 120
Saint Petersburg, FL   33716-3701   (727)
942-7003
Contact: Frederick E. Fisher, Secy.
Application address: 1166 Lindenwood Dr., Tarpon
Springs, FL 34689

Established in 1995 in Florida.
Foundation type: Independent foundation.
Financial data (yr. ended 12/31/12): Assets,
$19,318 (M); gifts received, $1,811; expenditures,
$127,181; qualifying distributions, $125,000;
giving activities include $125,000 for 3 grants (high:
$75,000; low: $25,000).
Purpose and activities: Giving primarily for youth
services.
Fields of interest: Religion.
Limitations: Applications accepted. Giving limited to
Tampa, FL.
Application information:
   Initial approach: Proposal
   Deadline(s): None
Officers: Daniel M. Doyle, Sr., Pres.; Rosaleen J.
Doyle, V.P.; Frederick E. Fisher, Secy.
Director: Daniel M. Doyle, Jr.
EIN: 593311469

1981
Melvin C. Draft Family Foundation
2513 Seven Springs Blvd.
Trinity, FL   34655-3628

Foundation type: Independent foundation.
Financial data (yr. ended 12/31/13): Assets,
$3,187,931 (M); expenditures, $223,070;
qualifying distributions, $150,000; giving activities
include $150,000 for 20 grants (high: $15,000;
low: $2,000).
Fields of interest: Education; Domesticated
animals; Protestantism.
Limitations: Applications not accepted. Giving
primarily in FL.
Application information: Unsolicited requests for
funds not accepted.
Trustees: David R. Draft; Robert Draft; Leslie Thiel;
Janice E. Thompson.
EIN: 306321344

1982
Frank E. Duckwall Foundation
P.O. Box 3351
Tampa, FL   33601-3351   (813) 634-4172

Established in 1983 in Florida.
Donor: Frank E. Duckwall†.
Foundation type: Independent foundation.
Financial data (yr. ended 12/31/14): Assets,
$8,623,019; gifts received, $4,500; expenditures,
$517,978; qualifying distributions, $441,410.
Purpose and activities: Giving primarily for
scientific, educational and charitable purposes, with
primary focus on the Tampa Bay, FL, area.
Fields of interest: Arts and culture; Education;
Higher education; Foundations; Health; Cancers;
Human services.
Type of support: Capital campaigns; Matching
grants; Capital and infrastructure; Equipment;
Endowments; Professorships; Scholarships;
Research.

Limitations: Applications accepted. Giving limited to
the Tampa Bay, FL, area.
Publications: Application guidelines; Financial
statement; Informational brochure (including
application guidelines); Occasional report.
Application information: Application form required.
   Initial approach: Proposal
   Copies of proposal: 3
   Deadline(s): None
Trustees: G. Lowe Morrison; Frank J. Rief III.
EIN: 596773462

1983
The John & Katherine Duda Foundation, Inc.
(formerly The John Duda Foundation, Inc.)
P.O. Box 620257
Oviedo, FL   32762-0257

Established in 1991 in Florida.
Donors: A. Duda & Sons, Inc.; A. Duda & Sons, Inc.
Foundation type: Company-sponsored foundation.
Financial data (yr. ended 12/31/13): Assets,
$3,023,366 (M); gifts received, $366,925;
expenditures, $178,846; qualifying distributions,
$154,437; giving activities include $149,000 for 30
grants (high: $26,000; low: $500).
Purpose and activities: The foundation supports
organizations involved with education, human
services, and Christianity.
Fields of interest: Education; Religion; Human
services.
Type of support: General support; Capital and
infrastructure.
Limitations: Applications not accepted. No grants to
individuals.
Application information: Contributes only to
pre-selected organizations.
Officers: Linda Duda Nichols, Pres.; Diane Duda
Miller, V.P.; Audrey Stinson, Secy.; Lisa Duda
Bocchino, Treas.
Director: Mark Edward Dingwell.
EIN: 593041359

1984
The Durden Foundation, Inc.
2605 Thomas Dr.
Panama City Beach, FL   32408-6240   (850)
230-8331
Contact: Scott Helms, Dir.

Established in 1998 in Florida.
Donors: K. Earl Durden; Durden Enterprises II Inc.
Foundation type: Independent foundation.
Financial data (yr. ended 12/31/13): Assets,
$135,137 (M); gifts received, $300,000;
expenditures, $227,826; qualifying distributions,
$224,750; giving activities include $224,750 for 16
grants (high: $150,000; low: $250).
Fields of interest: Museums; Education; Cancers;
School athletics; Low-income and poor people;
Military personnel.
Limitations: Applications accepted. Giving primarily
in CA and FL.
Application information: Application form required.
   Initial approach: Letter
   Deadline(s): None
Directors: Karen L. Durden; Michael E. Durden; D.
Scott Helms.
EIN: 593546150

1985
David and Harriet Dyer Family Foundation
300 Beach Dr. N.E., Ste. 2801
Saint Petersburg, FL   33701-3468

Established in 2002 in Wisconsin.
Donors: David F. Dyer; Harriet Dyer.
Foundation type: Independent foundation.
Financial data (yr. ended 12/31/13): Assets,
$1,659,456 (M); expenditures, $356,854;
qualifying distributions, $331,600; giving activities
include $331,600 for 21 grants (high: $74,000;
low: $1,000).
Purpose and activities: Giving primarily for higher
education, health care, and to art museums.
Fields of interest: Art museums; Higher education;
Medical education; Foundations; Hospital care;
Substance abuse treatment; Alcoholism.
Limitations: Applications not accepted. Giving
primarily in CA, FL, NY, OH, and PA. No grants to
individuals.
Application information: Contributes only to
pre-selected organizations.
Trustees: David F. Dyer; Harriet Dyer.
EIN: 716193877

1986
Dysimmune Neuromuscular Diseases Foundation
7940 Front Beach Rd., PMB 159
Panama City Beach, FL   32407-4817

Donors: Sohail Masood; Mona Masood.
Foundation type: Independent foundation.
Financial data (yr. ended 12/31/13): Assets,
$12,666 (M); gifts received, $237,500;
expenditures, $256,765; qualifying distributions,
$249,000; giving activities include $75,000 for 1
grant, and $174,000 for 2 grants to individuals
(high: $96,000; low: $78,000).
Fields of interest: Education; Health; Specialty
hospital care; Diseases and conditions.
Type of support: Research.
Limitations: Applications not accepted. Giving
primarily in CA, MD and TX.
Application information: Unsolicited requests for
funds not accepted.
Officers: Sohail Masood, Pres.; Mona Masood,
Secy.; Aslam Masood, C.F.O.
EIN: 451477924

1987
Echevarria Family Foundation, Inc.
c/o Adam Prida
4002 W. State St., Ste. 200
Tampa, FL   33609-1223

Donor: Michael J. Echevarria.
Foundation type: Independent foundation.
Financial data (yr. ended 12/31/12): Assets,
$258,319 (M); expenditures, $144,342; qualifying
distributions, $141,243; giving activities include
$141,000 for 4 grants (high: $100,000; low:
$1,000).
Fields of interest: Education; Domesticated
animals; Foundations.
Limitations: Applications not accepted. Giving
primarily in Tampa, FL; funding also in Houston, TX.
Application information: Unsolicited requests for
funds not accepted.

Officers: Michael J. Echevarria, Pres.; Laurie B. Echevarria, V.P.
Directors: Christina M. Echevarria; Emily C. Echevarria.
EIN: 270774490

1988
EGW Foundation, Inc.
P.O. Box 1288
Tampa, FL 33601-1288

Established in 2006 in Florida.
Donors: Dennis McNicholas; Lisa McNicholas; Thomas R. Thompson Charitable Lead Annuity Trust II; Eleanor S. Thompson Charitable Lead Annuity Trust II; Elenor S. Thompson Charitable Lead Annuity Trust II; James R. Thompson Charitable Lead Annuity Trust II.
Foundation type: Independent foundation.
Financial data (yr. ended 12/31/13): Assets, $7,522,847 (M); expenditures, $423,879; qualifying distributions, $330,000; giving activities include $330,000 for 3 grants (high: $225,000; low: $30,000).
Fields of interest: University education; Christianity.
Limitations: Applications not accepted. Giving primarily in FL.
Application information: Unsolicited requests for funds not accepted.
Officers: Lisa M. McNicholas, Pres. and Secy.; Dennis T. McNicholas, V.P. and Treas.
Director: Nylah J. Thompson.
EIN: 204662760

1989
The Robert M. Ellis Foundation
10 North Dr.
Key Largo, FL 33037-2917
Contact: Don Ellis

Donors: Madelon L. Ellis; Donald Ellis.
Foundation type: Independent foundation.
Financial data (yr. ended 12/31/13): Assets, $3,786,494 (M); gifts received, $536,425; expenditures, $290,076; qualifying distributions, $256,000; giving activities include $256,000 for grants.
Purpose and activities: Giving for youth and family services, education and for women.
Fields of interest: Elementary and secondary education; Higher education; Health; Catholicism; Human services; Family services; Women's services.
Type of support: General support.
Limitations: Applications not accepted. No grants to individuals.
Application information: Unsolicited requests for funds not accepted.
Trustees: Donald Ellis; Janice B. Ellis; Muriel E. Lanciault; Stephen D. Mortenson.
Number of staff: None.
EIN: 222871852

1990
Elster Foundation
35 Watergate Dr., Apt. 1504
Sarasota, FL 34236-4501

Established in 1964 in New York.
Donor: Robert S. Elster‡.

Foundation type: Independent foundation.
Financial data (yr. ended 12/31/13): Assets, $5,870,229 (M); expenditures, $396,091; qualifying distributions, $343,826; giving activities include $307,920 for 45 grants (high: $130,000; low: $500).
Purpose and activities: Giving for the arts, education, the environment, health, and Jewish organizations.
Fields of interest: Arts and culture; Education; Higher education; Nonprofits; Housing development; Judaism.
Type of support: Continuing support; Annual campaigns; Capital campaigns; Capital and infrastructure; Regranting.
Limitations: Applications not accepted. Giving primarily in FL, Atlanta, GA, Buffalo, NY, and Martinsville, VA. No support for political organizations or religious education. No grants to individuals.
Application information: Contributes only to pre-selected organizations.
Trustees: Amy Gerome-Acuff; Douglas R. Goldstein; Elizabeth Geer Goldstein; Jerome E. Goldstein; Sydney E. Goldstein.
EIN: 166054742

1991
The Enlightenment Foundation
4800 N. Federal Hwy., Ste. 108D
Boca Raton, FL 33431-5178 (561) 393-5623
Contact: Thomas C. Walser, Tr.

Established in 2007 in Florida.
Foundation type: Independent foundation.
Financial data (yr. ended 12/31/13): Assets, $1,062,847 (M); expenditures, $481,824; qualifying distributions, $350,253; giving activities include $333,786 for 3 grants (high: $236,786; low: $5,000).
Purpose and activities: Giving primarily for education.
Fields of interest: Education; Human services.
Limitations: Applications accepted. Giving primarily in Boca Raton, FL. No support for Education k-12.
Application information: Application form required.
Initial approach: Letter
Deadline(s): None
Officer and Trustees: Barbara M. Walser, Mgr. and Trustee; Thomas C. Walser; Thomas R. Walser.
EIN: 207178452

1992
David and Geri Epstein Private Foundation
3140 Burgundy Dr., N.
Palm Beach Gardens, FL 33410-1485
Contact: Geri Epstein
Application address: c/o Mellon Corp., 830 Post Rd., Ste. 105, Westport, CT 06880, tel.: (203) 454-3001

Established in 2005 in Florida.
Donor: David Epstein.
Foundation type: Independent foundation.
Financial data (yr. ended 12/31/13): Assets, $5,141,177 (M); expenditures, $308,084; qualifying distributions, $289,568; giving activities include $260,000 for 17 grants (high: $50,000; low: $5,000).
Fields of interest: Education; Domesticated animals; Diseases and conditions.

Type of support: General support; Student aid.
Limitations: Applications accepted. Giving primarily in CT, FL and NY.
Application information:
Initial approach: Proposal
Deadline(s): None
Trustees: Michael Connell; Geraldine Epstein; Robert Hess.
EIN: 201069019

1993
Erdie Foundation
3720 S. Ocean Blvd.
Highland Beach, FL 33487

Established in 1964 in New York.
Donors: Jack A. Erdle; Norma Erdle; Harvey B. Erdle; Brenda E. Moss.
Foundation type: Independent foundation.
Financial data (yr. ended 12/31/13): Assets, $0 (M); gifts received, $155,868; expenditures, $187,916; qualifying distributions, $187,916; giving activities include $179,839 for 101 grants (high: $50,000; low: $25).
Purpose and activities: Giving primarily for education and human services.
Fields of interest: Higher education; Nonprofits; Judaism; Human services.
Type of support: Program development; Grants to individuals; Capital campaigns; Regranting; General support; Continuing support; Annual campaigns; Emergency funds; Scholarships; Student aid.
Limitations: Applications not accepted. Giving primarily in FL and NY.
Application information: Unsolicited requests for funds not accepted.
Officers: Jack A. Erdle, Pres. and C.E.O.; Harvey B. Erdle, V.P.; Lee C. Moss, V.P.; Norma Erdle, Secy.
Number of staff: None.
EIN: 237002682

1994
The John D. Evans Foundation
P.O. Box 40200, FL9-100-10-19
Jacksonville, FL 32203-0200
Application address: c/o John D. Evans, 2716 Barcelona Dr., Ft. Lauderdale, FL 33301

Established in 1993 in Virginia.
Donors: John D. Evans; Evans Telecommunication, Inc.
Foundation type: Independent foundation.
Financial data (yr. ended 09/30/13): Assets, $10,371,627 (M); expenditures, $513,325; qualifying distributions, $472,095; giving activities include $374,000 for 26 grants (high: $30,000; low: $500).
Fields of interest: Arts and culture; Higher education; Immunology; HIV/AIDS.
Type of support: Equipment; Program-related investments; Program development; Research.
Limitations: Applications accepted. Giving primarily in FL, MI, NY, OR and VA. No grants to individuals.
Application information: Application form required.
Initial approach: Proposal
Deadline(s): None
Officers: John D. Evans, Pres.; Edward J. Beckwith, Esq., Secy.; Jack Porter, Treas.
EIN: 541685616

1995
Paul and Carol Evanson Family Foundation
11696 Lost Tree Way
North Palm Beach, FL 33408-2911

Established in 2007 in Florida.
Donor: Paul J. Evanson.
Foundation type: Independent foundation.
Financial data (yr. ended 12/31/14): Assets,
$7,812,515; gifts received, $391,250;
expenditures, $178,162; qualifying distributions,
$165,600.
Fields of interest: University education; Business
education.
Limitations: Applications not accepted. Giving
primarily in Jamaica, NY. No grants to individuals.
Application information: Contributes only to
pre-selected organizations.
Officers: Paul J. Evanson, Pres.; Carol L. Evanson,
V.P. and Secy.; Lisa J. Washburn, Treas.
EIN: 260891008

1996
Michael & Annie Falk Foundation
(formerly Falk Family Foundation)
P.O. Box 2616
Palm Beach, FL 33480-2616
E-mail: grantrequest@thefalkfoundation.org

Established in 1997 in New York.
Donors: Annie Falk; Michael Falk.
Foundation type: Independent foundation.
Financial data (yr. ended 12/31/13): Assets,
$4,475,332 (M); expenditures, $285,565;
qualifying distributions, $219,579; giving activities
include $208,679 for 35 grants (high: $50,000;
low: $100).
Fields of interest: Arts and culture; Education;
Human services.
International interests: Chile.
Limitations: Applications accepted. Giving primarily
in FL, NY and in Chile.
Application information: Application form required.
Initial approach: Proposal
Deadline(s): None
Directors: Annie Falk; Michael Falk.
EIN: 133949135

1997
Chupp Family Foundation
c/o Charles O. Chupp
P.O. Box 40606
Jacksonville, FL 32203-0606

Established in 2005 in Florida.
Donor: Load King Manufacturing Co.
Foundation type: Independent foundation.
Financial data (yr. ended 12/31/13): Assets,
$1,147,206 (M); gifts received, $7,461;
expenditures, $146,288; qualifying distributions,
$145,430; giving activities include $145,430 for 13
grants (high: $39,300; low: $50).
Fields of interest: Christianity; Human services;
Child welfare; Women's services.
Limitations: Applications not accepted. Giving
primarily in FL. No grants to individuals.
Application information: Unsolicited requests for
funds not accepted.

Trustees: Carrie N. Chupp; Charles O. Chupp;
Charles O. Chupp, Jr.; L. Gayle Chupp; Todd M.
Chupp.
EIN: 203999121

1998
The Farrell Foundation
10611 Glen Lakes Dr.
Bonita Springs, FL 34135

Established in 1996 in Illinois.
Donors: Maxine P. Farrell; W. James Farrell.
Foundation type: Independent foundation.
Financial data (yr. ended 12/31/14): Assets,
$753,785; gifts received, $1,515; expenditures,
$266,188; qualifying distributions, $263,957.
Fields of interest: Theater; Opera; Orchestral music;
Science museums; Education; Nonprofits; Cancers;
Youth services.
Type of support: Regranting.
Limitations: Applications not accepted. Giving
primarily in IL, with some emphasis on Chicago. No
grants to individuals.
Application information: Contributes only to
pre-selected organizations.
Officers: Maxine P. Farrell, Pres.; W. James Farrell,
Secy.
Directors: Kathleen Esposito; David J. Farrell;
James M. Farrell; Andrew L. Powell; Julie Simak.
EIN: 364120660

1999
Dan C. Ferguson Charitable Trust
3033 Riviera Dr., No. 202
Naples, FL 34103-2750
Application address: Daniel C. Ferguson, 1300 3rd
St. S., Ste. 300, Naples, FL 34102, tel.: (239)
262-0203

Established in 1986 in Florida.
Donor: Daniel C. Ferguson.
Foundation type: Independent foundation.
Financial data (yr. ended 12/31/13): Assets,
$2,931,969 (M); expenditures, $464,408;
qualifying distributions, $438,700; giving activities
include $438,700 for 9 grants (high: $100,000;
low: $2,000).
Fields of interest: Education; Health; Human
services.
Type of support: General support.
Application information: Application form required.
Initial approach: Letter
Deadline(s): None
Trustee: Daniel C. Ferguson.
EIN: 366848627

2000
The Doak Finch Foundation
c/o Bank of America, N.A.
P.O. Box 40200, FL9-100-10-19
Jacksonville, FL 32203-0200
Application address: c/o David R. Williams, M.D.,
705 Salem St., Thomasville, NC 27360-2810,
tel.: (336) 475-2348

Established in 1961 in North Carolina.
Donor: Doak Finch†.
Foundation type: Independent foundation.
Financial data (yr. ended 10/31/13): Assets,
$3,170,898 (M); expenditures, $234,914;

qualifying distributions, $213,746; giving activities
include $200,000 for 12 grants (high: $60,000;
low: $2,000).
Purpose and activities: Giving primarily for human
services.
Fields of interest: Arts and culture; Secondary
education; Protestantism; Human services.
Limitations: Giving limited to the Thomasville, NC,
area.
Application information:
Initial approach: Letter
Deadline(s): None
Board meeting date(s): Nov.
Trustee Bank: Bank of America, N.A.
EIN: 566042823

2001
The Bert Fish Foundation, Inc.
(formerly Bert Fish Testamentary Trust)
P.O. Box 46
DeLand, FL 32721-0046

Foundation type: Independent foundation.
Financial data (yr. ended 09/30/14): Assets,
$7,630,812 (M); expenditures, $528,648;
qualifying distributions, $347,973; giving activities
include $273,395 for 4 grants (high: $123,395;
low: $25,000).
Purpose and activities: Giving primarily for a
hospital and health services; support also for higher
education and social services.
Fields of interest: Higher education; Health;
Hospital care; Nursing care; Diseases and
conditions; Human services.
Type of support: Equipment; Seed money;
Scholarships.
Limitations: Applications not accepted. Giving
primarily in Volusia County, FL. No grants to
individuals.
Application information: Contributes only to
pre-selected organizations.
Officers and Trustees: Noah C. McKinnon, Jr., Chair.
and Pres.; William C. Keebler, Treas.; Pamela
Carbiener, MD; Luckey M. Dunn, MD; Frank Ford;
Thomas C. Kelley; William W. Schildecker; Edward F.
Simpson.
Number of staff: 1 full-time professional.
EIN: 593020772

2002
Five Millers Family Foundation Inc.
c/o Paul Steinberg & Neil Mangot
767 Arthur Godfrey Rd.
Miami Beach, FL 33140-3413

Established in 1997 in Florida.
Donors: Dora Miller Irrevocable Trust; Sadye Miller
Irrevocable Trust.
Foundation type: Independent foundation.
Financial data (yr. ended 12/31/13): Assets,
$3,971,997 (M); expenditures, $565,149;
qualifying distributions, $462,220; giving activities
include $416,100 for 38 grants (high: $210,000;
low: $250).
Purpose and activities: Giving primarily to hospitals,
and Jewish agencies and temples. Organizations to
which Sadye or Dora Miller or members of their
families contributed during their lifetimes will be
given greater consideration.
Fields of interest: Performing arts; Nonprofits;
Hospital care; Specialty hospital care; Diseases and

conditions; Diabetes; Judaism; Human services; Child welfare; Adult and child mentoring.
Type of support: Research; Regranting.
Limitations: Applications not accepted. Giving primarily in FL, with emphasis on Miami and Miami Beach, and in NY, with emphasis on the metropolitan New York area, including Long Island. No grants to individuals.
Application information: Contributes only to pre-selected organizations.
Officers and Directors: Paul Steinberg, Pres. and Director; Neil Mangot, V.P. and Secy. and Director.
EIN: 650715711

2003
The Aaron I. Fleischman Foundation Inc.
(formerly The Art Institute of Miami Beach, Inc.)
c/o Kaufman, Rossin
2699 S. Bayshore Dr., Ste. 300
Miami, FL 33133-5408

Established in 2004 in Florida.
Donors: Aaron I. Fleischman; The Aaron I. Fleischman Foundation.
Foundation type: Independent foundation.
Financial data (yr. ended 05/31/14): Assets, $2,861,301 (M); expenditures, $168,845; qualifying distributions, $166,000; giving activities include $166,000 for 4 grants (high: $100,000; low: $1,000).
Fields of interest: Arts and culture; Art museums; Education; Undergraduate education; Health.
Type of support: General support.
Limitations: Applications not accepted. Giving primarily in CT, FL and NY. No grants to individuals.
Application information: Contributes only to pre-selected organizations.
Directors: Aaron I. Fleischman; Linford L. Lougheed; Robert A. Stone.
EIN: 300265819

2004
Focus Foundation
2419 Laguna Dr.
Fort Lauderdale, FL 33316-2311 (440) 892-5022
Contact: Keith A. Brown, Pres.

Established in 1997 in Ohio.
Donor: Keith A. Brown.
Foundation type: Independent foundation.
Financial data (yr. ended 12/31/13): Assets, $1,467,175 (M); expenditures, $168,414; qualifying distributions, $146,113; giving activities include $139,363 for 3 grants (high: $100,000; low: $750).
Fields of interest: Higher education; Leukemia; Marine science; Agriculture.
Type of support: Research.
Limitations: Applications accepted. Giving primarily in FL and OH.
Application information: Application form required.
Initial approach: Letter
Deadline(s): None
Officer: Keith A. Brown, Pres.
Trustees: Andrea C. Brown; Christopher R. Brown; Ian D. Brown; Dale Kucaj.
EIN: 311526199

2005
Focus on Excellence Inc.
7035 Philips Hwy. 36
Jacksonville, FL 32216
Main URL: http://www.foejax.org

Donors: Chartered Foundation; The Henriksen Trust; John Baker; Everbank; Preston Haskell; Carol Beth Grilliland Living Trust; Florida Blue; The Community Foundation; Mary Virginia Terry.
Foundation type: Independent foundation.
Financial data (yr. ended 12/31/13): Assets, $76,307 (M); gifts received, $533,699; expenditures, $516,174; qualifying distributions, $512,662; giving activities include $279,962 for 5 grants (high: $161,642; low: $4,854).
Fields of interest: Education.
Limitations: Applications not accepted. Giving primarily in FL.
Application information: Unsolicited requests for funds not accepted.
Directors: Gerald M. Baxter; Marcus Broadnax; Joel Settembrini; James R. Swanson.
EIN: 262483759

2006
Denis L. Fontaine Foundations, Inc.
c/o Merritt Gardner
5415 Mariner St., Ste. 200
Watermark 5
Tampa, FL 33609-3438 8132889600

Established in 1992 in Florida.
Donor: Denis L. Fontaine.
Foundation type: Independent foundation.
Financial data (yr. ended 12/31/14): Assets, $3,311,070; expenditures, $350,520; qualifying distributions, $323,740.
Fields of interest: Children's museums; Secondary education; Higher education; Hospital care; Autism; Cystic fibrosis; Christianity; Human services.
Type of support: Research.
Limitations: Applications accepted. Giving primarily in Lakeland, FL. No grants to individuals.
Application information: Application form required.
Initial approach: Request application form
Deadline(s): None
Officers: Glenda C. Fontaine, Pres.; Merritt A. Gardner, Secy.-Treas.
Directors: Gregory J. Fontaine; Warren Shatzer.
EIN: 593157129

2007
For Giving Foundation, Inc.
(formerly Rick & Nancy Bosserman Charitable Foundation)
125 A E. Marks St.
Orlando, FL 32803-3816

Donors: Richard E. Bosserman; C.E. Bosserman Revocable Trust; Gladys Bosserman Revocable Trust.
Foundation type: Independent foundation.
Financial data (yr. ended 12/31/13): Assets, $2,862,804 (M); gifts received, $870,800; expenditures, $185,934; qualifying distributions, $165,260; giving activities include $165,260 for 23 grants (high: $54,760; low: $100).
Purpose and activities: Giving primarily to Christian organizations.

Fields of interest: Health; Christianity; Human services.
Limitations: Applications not accepted. Giving primarily in FL. No grants to individuals.
Application information: Unsolicited requests for funds not accepted.
Directors: Nancy H. Bosserman; Richard E. Bosserman; Sean Cuda.
EIN: 593703693

2008
Mary C. Forbes Charitable Foundation
c/o D'Arcy R. Clarie
1101 Pasadena Ave. S., Ste. 3
South Pasadena, FL 33707-2891

Donor: Mary C. Forbes.
Foundation type: Independent foundation.
Financial data (yr. ended 06/30/13): Assets, $3,120,278 (M); expenditures, $514,951; qualifying distributions, $379,672; giving activities include $290,225 for 60 grants (high: $31,625; low: $188), and $17,950 for 68 grants to individuals (high: $575; low: $250).
Purpose and activities: Giving to schools on behalf of students who reside within the Diocese of St. Petersburg, FL and who are in pursuit of a Catholic education at college, graduate, seminary or other schools of religious studies based on the teaching of the Roman Catholic faith.
Fields of interest: Education; Elementary and secondary education; Higher education; Graduate and professional education; Theology.
Limitations: Applications not accepted. Giving primarily in FL.
Application information: Unsolicited requests for funds not accepted.
Trustee: D'Arcy R. Clarie.
EIN: 597112797

2009
Mary Force Stead Trust
c/o Bank of America, N.A.
P.O. Box 40200, FL9-100-10-19
Jacksonville, FL 32203-0200

Foundation type: Independent foundation.
Financial data (yr. ended 12/31/14): Assets, $6,537,233; expenditures, $310,976; qualifying distributions, $207,898.
Fields of interest: Sports and recreation.
Limitations: Applications not accepted. Giving primarily in Washington, DC.
Application information: Unsolicited requests for funds not accepted.
Trustee: Bank of America, N.A.
EIN: 526030034

2010
Kathleen DuRoss Ford Fund, Inc.
c/o L. Frank Chopin PLC
P.O. Box 4297
West Palm Beach, FL 33402-4297
Contact: L. Frank Chopin, Dir.

Established in 1988 in Florida.
Donor: Kathleen DuRoss Ford.
Foundation type: Independent foundation.
Financial data (yr. ended 12/31/13): Assets, $6,748,677 (M); gifts received, $3,500,000;

expenditures, $199,199; qualifying distributions, $176,725; giving activities include $176,725 for 17 grants (high: $100,000; low: $25).
Purpose and activities: Giving primarily for medical research and human services.
Fields of interest: Health; Diseases and conditions; Housing development.
Limitations: Applications accepted. Giving in the U.S., with emphasis on FL. No grants to individuals.
Application information: Application form required.
   Initial approach: Letter
   Deadline(s): None
Officer: Kathleen DuRoss Ford, Pres.
Directors: L. Frank Chopin; John L. Shaw.
EIN: 650088771

2011
Hamilton M. & Blanche C. Forman Christian Foundation
P.O. Box 292037
Davie, FL 33329-2037

Established in 1955 in Florida.
Foundation type: Independent foundation.
Financial data (yr. ended 10/31/13): Assets, $0 (M); gifts received, $574,529; expenditures, $249,231; qualifying distributions, $236,050; giving activities include $228,550 for 15+ grants (high: $112,500), and $7,500 for 2 grants to individuals.
Fields of interest: Arts and culture; Religion; Youth development.
Type of support: General support; Grants to individuals.
Limitations: Applications not accepted. Giving primarily in FL.
Application information: Unsolicited requests for funds not accepted.
Officers: Hamilton Collins Forman, Pres.; M. Austin Forman, Secy.-Treas.
Director: Walter Collins Forman.
EIN: 596131560

2012
Mary Alice Fortin Child Care Foundation
c/o L. Frank Chopin PLC
P.O. Box 4297
West Palm Beach, FL 33402-4297 (561) 655-9500
Contact: L. Frank Chopin, Secy.

Established in 1991 in Florida.
Donors: Mary Alice Fortin; Danielle Hickox; Lesly S. Smith; Fortin Foundation of Florida; Mary Alice Fortin Foundation; William H. Pitt Foundation.
Foundation type: Independent foundation.
Financial data (yr. ended 12/31/13): Assets, $7,502,589 (M); gifts received, $602,750; expenditures, $440,469; qualifying distributions, $389,176; giving activities include $389,176 for 1 grant.
Fields of interest: Family services.
Limitations: Applications accepted. Giving primarily in Belle Glade, FL.
Application information: Application form required.
   Initial approach: Letter
   Deadline(s): None
Officers: Lesly S. Smith, Pres.; David Robb, V.P.; L. Frank Chopin, Secy.
Director: Danielle Moore.
EIN: 650244281

2013
The John H. Foster Foundation
c/o Barbara Cording
3947 Clark Rd.
Sarasota, FL 34233-2364

Established in 1984 in Pennsylvania.
Donor: John H. Foster.
Foundation type: Independent foundation.
Financial data (yr. ended 12/31/13): Assets, $3,232,047 (M); expenditures, $190,800; qualifying distributions, $169,737; giving activities include $164,478 for 20 grants (high: $47,750; low: $250).
Purpose and activities: Giving primarily to Asian cultural organizations; funding also for social services.
Fields of interest: Cultural awareness; Christianity; Human services; People of Asian descent.
Limitations: Applications not accepted. Giving in the U.S., with emphasis on NY. No grants to individuals.
Application information: Contributes only to pre-selected organizations.
Officers and Directors: John H. Foster, Pres. and Director; Stephen C. Curley, Esq., Treas. and Director.
EIN: 133249353

2014
Claiborne F. Foulds Foundation Trust
(formerly Claiborne and Ned Foulds Foundation)
P.O. Box 40200, MC FL9-100-10-19
Jacksonville, FL 32203-0200
Application address: c/o Bank of America, MC, FL4-060-02-01, 13099 US Hwy. 44 S.E., Fort Myers, FL 33907

Established in 1981 in Florida.
Foundation type: Independent foundation.
Financial data (yr. ended 07/31/14): Assets, $4,089,808 (M); expenditures, $222,000; qualifying distributions, $174,358; giving activities include $154,412 for 12 grants (high: $37,675; low: $1,616).
Purpose and activities: Giving primarily for education and human services.
Fields of interest: Orchestral music; Historic preservation; Education; Higher education; Animal welfare; Addiction services; Human services; Child welfare.
Type of support: Capital and infrastructure; Equipment.
Limitations: Applications accepted. Giving primarily in Fort Meyers, FL. No support for churches or religious organizations. No grants to individuals, or for administrative or operational expenses.
Application information: Application form required.
   Initial approach: Request application form
   Copies of proposal: 1
   Deadline(s): July 1
Trustee: Bank of America, N.A.
EIN: 596705105

2015
Foundation 3311
(formerly Elizabeth Foundation)
1295 Little Harbour Ln.
Vero Beach, FL 32960-2180

Established in 2001 in Ohio.
Donor: Marcia Ross Blackburn.

Foundation type: Independent foundation.
Financial data (yr. ended 12/31/14): Assets, $5,995,319; gifts received, $987,397; expenditures, $395,345; qualifying distributions, $371,032.
Fields of interest: Protestantism; Human services; International relations.
Limitations: Applications not accepted. No grants to individuals.
Application information: Unsolicited requests for funds not accepted.
Officers: Marcia Ross Blackburn, Pres.; Katherine Blackburn Reay, Secy.; William W. Blackburn II, Treas.
Directors: William Ross Blackburn; Elizabeth Blackburn Lane.
EIN: 311796184

2016
Bill and Katherine Fox Foundation
6955 Carlisle Ct., Ste. 237
Naples, FL 34109

Established in 1999 in Minnesota.
Donors: Bill C. Fox; Katherine M. Fox.
Foundation type: Independent foundation.
Financial data (yr. ended 12/31/13): Assets, $214,368 (M); gifts received, $200,000; expenditures, $201,025; qualifying distributions, $201,000; giving activities include $201,000 for 20 grants (high: $100,000; low: $1,000).
Fields of interest: Higher education; Protestantism.
Type of support: Scholarships; Student aid.
Limitations: Applications not accepted. Giving primarily in CA, IA, and MN.
Application information: Contributes only to pre-selected organizations.
Officer: Bill C. Fox, Pres.
Directors: David K. Fox; Gerald C. Fox; Margene B. Fox.
EIN: 411954162

2017
The Frangakis Family Charitable Foundation
285 Grande Way, No. 1601
Naples, FL 34110-2230

Established in 1999 in Pennsylvania.
Donors: F. John Frangakis; Reynolds Services, Inc.
Foundation type: Independent foundation.
Financial data (yr. ended 12/31/13): Assets, $28,552 (M); gifts received, $150,465; expenditures, $130,591; qualifying distributions, $130,591; giving activities include $129,350 for 19 grants (high: $100,000; low: $100).
Fields of interest: Arts and culture; Education; Higher education; Religion.
Limitations: Applications not accepted. Giving primarily in PA.
Application information: Unsolicited requests for funds not accepted.
Trustees: F. John Frangakis; Joyce Frangakis.
EIN: 251849784

2018
Herman and Sharon Frankel Foundation
535 Sanctury Dr., No. 808C
Longboat Key, FL 34228-3852

Established in 1993 in Michigan.
Donors: Herman Frankel; Simwood Co.; Suburban Communities, LLC.
Foundation type: Company-sponsored foundation.
Financial data (yr. ended 12/31/13): Assets, $1,689,296 (M); expenditures, $250,238; qualifying distributions, $248,786; giving activities include $248,136 for 25 grants (high: $200,000; low: $100).
Purpose and activities: The foundation supports organizations involved with performing arts, education, health, children and youth, family services, and Judaism.
Fields of interest: Arts and culture; Health; Human services.
Type of support: General support.
Limitations: Applications not accepted. Giving primarily in FL and MI. No grants to individuals.
Application information: Contributes only to pre-selected organizations.
Trustee: Herman Frankel.
EIN: 383149105

2019
Frankle Family Foundation, Inc.
201 N. Franklin St., Ste. 2000
Tampa, FL 33602-5627

Established in 2008 in Florida.
Donors: Mary A. Frankle; Mary D. Frankle.
Foundation type: Independent foundation.
Financial data (yr. ended 12/31/13): Assets, $2,211,600; gifts received, $300,000; expenditures, $144,869; qualifying distributions, $115,200.
Fields of interest: Arts and culture; Diseases and conditions; Agriculture.
Limitations: Applications not accepted.
Application information: Unsolicited requests for funds not accepted.
Officers: Mark A. Frankle, Pres.; Mary D. Frankle, V.P.
Director: Nicholas A. Frankle.
EIN: 263861579

2020
Wilson P. & Anne W. Franklin Foundation
7395 Acorn Way
Naples, FL 34119-9611 (404) 312-8951
Contact: W. Stevens Franklin, Tr.

Established in 1996 in Georgia.
Donors: Wilson P. Franklin†; Richard R. Franklin†.
Foundation type: Independent foundation.
Financial data (yr. ended 09/30/14): Assets, $2,902,993 (M); expenditures, $275,781; qualifying distributions, $252,000; giving activities include $252,000 for 3 grants (high: $150,000; low: $2,000).
Fields of interest: Education; University education; Health.
Limitations: Applications accepted. Giving primarily in GA. No grants to individuals.
Application information: Application form required.
  Initial approach: Proposal
  Deadline(s): None
Trustees: James D. Bryce; Tammy G. Franklin; W. Stevens Franklin.
EIN: 586329924

2021
Freewill Charitable Trust
657 N.W. Hooten Hollow Rd.
Greenville, FL 32331-4800

Established in 2005 in Florida.
Donor: E. Peter H. Wilkens.
Foundation type: Independent foundation.
Financial data (yr. ended 12/31/14): Assets, $1,481,615; expenditures, $118,492; qualifying distributions, $118,485 and $0 for set-asides.
Purpose and activities: Giving primarily for the support of Christian evangelism, training, and aid.
Fields of interest: Christianity.
International interests: Bangladesh; Benin; China; India; Nigeria; Paraguay; Philippines; Poland; Senegal; South Africa; Sudan; Vietnam.
Type of support: General support; Matching grants; Continuing support; Financial sustainability; Capital and infrastructure; Equipment; Land acquisitions; Emergency funds; Convening; Publications; Curriculum development; Scholarships; Research; Program evaluations.
Limitations: Giving primarily in CA and VA. No grants to individuals.
Trustees: Laura Holland; Peter Wilkens; Dena Woodburn.
EIN: 202911795

2022
The Mark & Mary Freitas Foundation Inc.
(formerly Mark Edward Freitas Foundation, Inc.)
201 EL Vedado Rd.
Palm Beach, FL 33480-4733

Established in 2005 in New York.
Donors: Brian Sullivan; Mark E. Freitas.
Foundation type: Independent foundation.
Financial data (yr. ended 12/31/13): Assets, $1,022,984 (M); gifts received, $101,625; expenditures, $273,136; qualifying distributions, $270,777; giving activities include $267,677 for 25 grants (high: $37,000; low: $1,000).
Fields of interest: Theater; Higher education; Catholicism; School athletics; Human services.
Limitations: Applications not accepted. Giving primarily in CT and FL. No grants to individuals.
Application information: Contributes only to pre-selected organizations.
Officers: Mark E. Freitas, Pres.; Mary Fairbanks Freitas, Secy.
Directors: Anthony J. Cernera; Paul J. Pisano.
EIN: 203920000

2023
The Fricks Private Foundation Trust
2641 Bulrush Ln.
Naples, FL 34105-3049

Established in 2001 in Florida.
Donor: William P. Fricks.
Foundation type: Independent foundation.
Financial data (yr. ended 12/31/14): Assets, $4,836,316; gifts received, $50,000; expenditures, $312,506; qualifying distributions, $269,547.
Fields of interest: Higher education; Christianity.
Limitations: Applications not accepted. Giving primarily in VA. No grants to individuals.
Application information: Contributes only to pre-selected organizations.

Officer: William P. Fricks, Pres.
Trustee: Deanie D. Fricks.
EIN: 656387910

2024
Eric Friedheim Foundation, Inc.
P.O. Box 551260
Jacksonville, FL 32255-1260

Established in 2002 in Florida.
Donor: Eric Friedheim†.
Foundation type: Independent foundation.
Financial data (yr. ended 12/31/13): Assets, $4,610,713 (M); expenditures, $276,554; qualifying distributions, $223,500; giving activities include $221,000 for 15 grants (high: $50,000; low: $5,000).
Fields of interest: Education; University education; Health; Religion.
Limitations: Applications not accepted. Giving primarily in FL.
Application information: Unsolicited requests for funds not accepted.
Officers and Directors: Sidney Gefen, Pres. and Director; Edith H. Friedheim, V.P. and Director.
EIN: 592313058

2025
The Annette & Jack Friedland Charitable Foundation Inc.
186 Spyglass Ln.
Jupiter, FL 33477-4037

Established in 1994 in Florida.
Donors: Jack Friedland; Annette Friedland.
Foundation type: Independent foundation.
Financial data (yr. ended 12/31/13): Assets, $644,495 (M); expenditures, $193,409; qualifying distributions, $187,439; giving activities include $187,439 for 24 grants (high: $81,300; low: $100).
Fields of interest: Arts and culture; Museums; Art museums; Education; University education; Nonprofits; Hospital care; Judaism; Human services.
Type of support: Regranting.
Limitations: Applications not accepted. Giving primarily in FL, IL and PA. No grants to individuals.
Application information: Contributes only to pre-selected organizations.
Directors: Annette Friedland; Rodger Friedland.
EIN: 650288541

2026
Friend of the Fatherless Foundation
2033 Main St., Ste. 300
Sarasota, FL 34237-6062

Donors: James O. McCarver; Patsy E. McCarver.
Foundation type: Independent foundation.
Financial data (yr. ended 12/31/13): Assets, $2,716,078 (M); gifts received, $500,872; expenditures, $202,139; qualifying distributions, $179,710; giving activities include $174,000 for 7 grants (high: $54,000; low: $1,000).
Fields of interest: Protestantism; Human services.
Limitations: Applications not accepted.
Application information: Unsolicited requests for funds not accepted.
Trustee: Patsy E. McCarver.
EIN: 276888664

2027
The Fry Family Foundation
The Oaks Preserve, 385 N. Point Rd., Ste. 901
Osprey, FL 34229

Established in 1997 in New Jersey.
Donors: Darryl D. Fry; Marlene D. Fry.
Foundation type: Independent foundation.
Financial data (yr. ended 12/31/13): Assets,
$8,580,807 (M); expenditures, $426,244;
qualifying distributions, $399,974; giving activities
include $399,974 for 31 grants (high: $115,000;
low: $363).
Purpose and activities: Giving primarily for
education and human services.
Fields of interest: University education; Crime
prevention; Community and economic development;
Religion; Human services.
Limitations: Applications not accepted. No grants to
individuals.
Application information: Contributes only to
pre-selected organizations.
Officers and Trustees: Darryl D. Fry, Chair. and
Trustee; Marlene D. Fry, Pres. and Trustee; Paul J.
Burt; Cheryl E. Fry; J. April Lee; Gerry Repple; Judy
Repple.
EIN: 223515940

2028
Victor & Sandra Fuller Family Foundation, Inc.
2 Alhambra Plz., Ste. 1280
Coral Gables, FL 33134-5237

Established in 2006 in Florida.
Donors: Sandra Fuller; Stephen M. Fuller; Victor
Fuller; Fuller Family Irrevocable Trust.
Foundation type: Independent foundation.
Financial data (yr. ended 12/31/13): Assets,
$1,687,565 (M); gifts received, $7,788;
expenditures, $201,654; qualifying distributions,
$182,500; giving activities include $182,500 for 5
grants (high: $100,000; low: $7,500).
Fields of interest: Arts and culture; Education;
Speech and hearing rehabilitation; National
defense; Christianity; Baseball and softball;
International relations.
Type of support: Research and evaluation.
Limitations: Applications not accepted. Giving
primarily in FL, MA, SC, and TX. No grants to
individuals.
Application information: Unsolicited requests for
funds not accepted.
Officers: Victor Fuller, Pres.; Sandra Fuller, V.P. and
Treas.; Michael Katz, Secy.
EIN: 203736887

2029
Gagnon Foundation Inc.
124 Harbor View Dr.
Largo, FL 33770-2605

Established in 2005 in Florida.
Donors: Christine L. Gagnon; Christie V. Gagnon.
Foundation type: Independent foundation.
Financial data (yr. ended 12/31/13): Assets,
$1,140,718 (M); gifts received, $152,530;
expenditures, $190,911; qualifying distributions,
$180,500; giving activities include $180,500 for 11
grants (high: $104,000; low: $1,000).

Fields of interest: Down syndrome; Community and
economic development; Religion; Special Olympics.
Limitations: Applications not accepted. Giving
primarily in IL. No grants to individuals.
Application information: Unsolicited requests for
funds not accepted.
Officers: Christine L. Gagnon, Pres. and Secy.;
Christy V. Gagnon, V.P. and Treas.
Director: Eric E. Gagnon.
EIN: 202302405

2030
Elizabeth K. Galeana Charitable Foundation, Inc.
12955 Pond Apple Dr., E.
Naples, FL 34119-8595

Established in 2006 in Florida.
Donors: Jerry L. Galeana; Mrs. Greg Hila; Mrs. R.P.
Magrann; Instant Combo Savings; R.P. Magrann;
Joan Baker; Tina Dennis; Pat Dennis; Mr. Greg Hila;
Allison Yore; Joseph Marin; Carol Rhodes; Tom
Tibbles.
Foundation type: Independent foundation.
Financial data (yr. ended 12/31/13): Assets,
$5,352,036 (M); gifts received, $1,832,010;
expenditures, $298,735; qualifying distributions,
$248,000; giving activities include $248,000 for 13
grants (high: $64,000; low: $2,500).
Fields of interest: Education; Housing development;
Human services; Youth development.
Limitations: Applications not accepted. Giving
primarily in FL and VA. No grants to individuals.
Application information: Unsolicited requests for
funds not accepted.
Officer and Directors: Jerry L. Galeana, Pres. and
Treas. and Director; Andrew J. Krause.
EIN: 510611645

2031
The Olivia R. Gardner Foundation Inc.
402 Indies Dr.
Vero Beach, FL 32963 (404) 355-4747
Contact: Olivia R. Gardner, Pres.

Established in 2003 in Georgia.
Donors: Olivia R. Gardner; J. Alston Gardner.
Foundation type: Independent foundation.
Financial data (yr. ended 12/31/13): Assets,
$3,050,835 (M); expenditures, $193,246;
qualifying distributions, $172,050; giving activities
include $168,000 for 24 grants (high: $65,000;
low: $1,000).
Fields of interest: Elementary and secondary
education; Higher education; Human services.
Limitations: Applications accepted. Giving primarily
in FL and GA; some giving also in NC.
Application information: Application form required.
Initial approach: Proposal
Deadline(s): None
Officer: Olivia R. Gardner, Pres.
EIN: 582659095

2032
The Garner Foundation, Inc.
333 N.E. 23rd St.
Miami, FL 33137-4926
Contact: John M. Garner; Gerald W. Moore

Established in 1987 in Florida.

Foundation type: Independent foundation.
Financial data (yr. ended 03/31/13): Assets,
$9,866,466 (M); expenditures, $411,142;
qualifying distributions, $390,659; giving activities
include $374,100 for 48 grants (high: $60,000;
low: $500).
Purpose and activities: Giving primarily for
educational, religious, and medical organizations;
support also for community and cultural
organizations in FL and NC.
Fields of interest: Education; Diseases and
conditions; Community and economic development;
Human services.
Limitations: Applications not accepted. Giving
primarily in FL and NC. No support for political
organizations. No grants to individuals.
Application information: Unsolicited requests for
funds not accepted.
Board meeting date(s): Apr. and Dec.
Officers and Directors: Beverly Garner Graves, Pres.
and Director; John Michael Garner, V.P. and
Director; James W. Moore, Secy. and Director;
Kathryn Anne Paulk, Treas. and Director; Gerald W.
Moore; Janice Gayle Topping; Mary Garner Wright.
Number of staff: 1 part-time professional.
EIN: 311471961

2033
Garvy Family Foundation, Inc.
200 Esplanade Way
Palm Beach, FL 33480-3018

Established in 2002 in Florida.
Donors: Robert A. Garvy; Carol K. Garvy.
Foundation type: Independent foundation.
Financial data (yr. ended 12/31/13): Assets,
$642,408 (M); gifts received, $211,950;
expenditures, $357,950; qualifying distributions,
$353,070; giving activities include $350,595 for 14
grants (high: $250,000; low: $1,000).
Fields of interest: Education; Higher education;
Health; Human services.
Type of support: General support.
Limitations: Applications not accepted. Giving
primarily in FL; some funding also in Cleveland, OH.
No grants to individuals.
Application information: Contributes only to
pre-selected organizations.
Directors: Carol K. Garvy; Robert A. Garvy; Thomas
Kelly.
EIN: 030498860

2034
The Gate Foundation, Inc.
9540 San Jose Blvd.
P.O. Box 23627
Jacksonville, FL 32241-3627 (904) 448-2979
Contact: Kathy J. Brady
Main URL: http://www.gatepetro.com

Donor: Gate Petroleum Company.
Foundation type: Company-sponsored foundation.
Financial data (yr. ended 06/30/14): Assets,
$8,609 (M); gifts received, $374,511;
expenditures, $374,539; qualifying distributions,
$289,615; giving activities include $289,615 for 31
grants (high: $77,000; low: $275).
Purpose and activities: The foundation supports
programs designed to create affordable housing for
low-to-moderate income families; provide shelter for
those in crisis; provide youth activity initiatives to

reduce crime in communities; offer food, nourishment, and clothing to those in need; protect the communities; provide assisted or independent living for the disabled or elderly; and promote access to quality health care and health education.

Fields of interest: Health; Nutrition; Cancers; Crime prevention; Housing development; Human services; Food aid; Family services; Youth services; Adult and child mentoring; Homeless shelters; Temporary accommodations; Independent living for people with disabilities; Seniors; Low-income and poor people; People with disabilities.

Type of support: General support.

Limitations: Applications accepted. Giving primarily in Jacksonville, FL. No support for discriminatory organizations, international organizations, political committees or candidates, fraternal or alumni organizations, religious-based organizations, private foundations, individual pre-college schools or individual public school systems, or athletic teams. No grants to individuals, or for travel or conferences for employees of nonprofit organizations, political causes, books, research papers, or articles in professional journals, general operating expenses for organizations supported by the United Way, sponsorships, events, or projects for which the GATE Petroleum Company receive tangible benefits.

Publications: Application guidelines.

Application information: Application form required.

Initial approach: Download application form and mail to foundation
Deadline(s): None

Officers and Directors: Hill Peyton, Chair. and Pres. and Director; Frank Gwaltney, V.P. and Secy.-Treas. and Director; David Dill; Drew Frick; Dean Gwin; Dale Haney; Sammy Patten.

EIN: 262990671

2035
June Baumgardner Gelbart Foundation

c/o Suntrust Bank
P.O. Box 1908
Orlando, FL 32802-1908
Application address: c/o Norman Lipoff, Esq., Greenberg Traurig, P.A., 1221 Brickell Ave., Miami, FL 33131, tel.: (305) 579-0500

Established in 2002 in Florida.

Donor: June Baumgardner Gelbart†.

Foundation type: Independent foundation.

Financial data (yr. ended 12/31/14): Assets, $5,349,810 (M); expenditures, $418,101; qualifying distributions, $351,325; giving activities include $279,800 for 66 grants (high: $31,000; low: $1,000).

Purpose and activities: Giving limited to programs providing financial support, education, medical services, and shelter to needy children in Israel and to those providing for the health, education, care, and welfare of Jewish children in the United States.

Fields of interest: Museums; Education; Nonprofits; Health; Housing development; Judaism; Human services.

Type of support: Regranting.

Limitations: Applications not accepted. No grants to individuals.

Application information: Contributes only to pre-selected organizations.

Trustees: Norman Lipoff; Marc A.B. Silverman; Greenberg Traurig, Mgr.

EIN: 656390197

2036
Joel F. Gemunder Foundation

35 Canvasback Dr.
Amelia Island, FL 32034-6623 (513) 579-5310
Contact: Joel F. Gemunder, Tr.

Established in 1997 in Ohio.

Foundation type: Independent foundation.

Financial data (yr. ended 12/31/12): Assets, $30,162,272 (M); expenditures, $503,234; qualifying distributions, $458,415; giving activities include $441,995 for 6 grants (high: $377,895; low: $2,500).

Fields of interest: Education; Judaism.

Limitations: Applications accepted. Giving primarily in Washington, DC, IL, NY, and OH. No grants to individuals.

Application information: Application form required.

Initial approach: Letter
Deadline(s): None

Trustee: Joel F. Gemunder.

EIN: 311534042

2037
The Gerry-Corbett Foundation, Inc.

c/o Cornelia G. Corbett
509 Guisando De Avila, Ste. 201
Tampa, FL 33613-5235

Established in 1995 in Florida.

Donor: Gerry Charitable Lead Trust.

Foundation type: Independent foundation.

Financial data (yr. ended 12/31/12): Assets, $6,392,540 (M); expenditures, $371,902; qualifying distributions, $323,250; giving activities include $323,250 for grants.

Fields of interest: Education; Elementary and secondary education; Human services; Child welfare.

Limitations: Applications not accepted. No grants to individuals.

Application information: Contributes only to pre-selected organizations.

Trustees: Cornelia Gerry Corbett; Libbie F. Gerry; William F. Gerry.

EIN: 593287385

2038
Givens Charitable Trust

P.O. Box 40200, FL9-100-10-19
Jacksonville, FL 32203-0200

Foundation type: Independent foundation.

Financial data (yr. ended 10/31/13): Assets, $2,880,069 (M); expenditures, $238,928; qualifying distributions, $222,830; giving activities include $211,023 for 11 grants (high: $49,024; low: $6,395).

Fields of interest: Education; Graduate and professional education; Nursing care; Religion.

Limitations: Applications not accepted. Giving primarily in CT and MD.

Application information: Unsolicited requests for funds not accepted.

Trustee: Bank of America, N.A.

EIN: 596134557

2039
The Leslie Glass Foundation, Inc.

(formerly The Forty-Five Foundation)
990 Blvd. of the Arts, Apt. 1202D
Sarasota, FL 34236-4878

Established in 1991 in Florida.

Donor: Leslie Gordon Glass.

Foundation type: Independent foundation.

Financial data (yr. ended 12/31/13): Assets, $1,448,956 (M); expenditures, $298,954; qualifying distributions, $274,067; giving activities include $262,212 for 9 grants (high: $135,000; low: $350).

Purpose and activities: Giving primarily for fellowships in psychoanalytic research; also some giving for theater development and for education.

Fields of interest: Education; Community and economic development; Human services.

Type of support: Convening; Seed money; Research.

Limitations: Applications not accepted. Giving primarily in NY. No grants to individuals.

Application information: Unsolicited requests for funds not accepted.

Trustee: Leslie Gordon Glass.

EIN: 133586150

2040
The Glaubinger Foundation

c/o Sterling House
6307 S. Hwy. A1A, Ste. 253
Melbourne Beach, FL 32951-3716

Established in 1988 in Florida.

Donor: Lawrence D. Glaubinger.

Foundation type: Independent foundation.

Financial data (yr. ended 12/31/13): Assets, $2,985,093 (M); gifts received, $6,501; expenditures, $318,704; qualifying distributions, $278,151; giving activities include $273,409 for 5 grants (high: $84,428; low: $2,500).

Fields of interest: University education; Medical education.

Type of support: Scholarships.

Limitations: Applications not accepted. Giving primarily in CT, IN, NJ, New York, NY, PA and VT. No grants to individuals.

Application information: Contributes only to pre-selected organizations.

Trustees: Jane Glaubinger; Lawrence D. Glaubinger; Lucienne M. Glaubinger.

EIN: 592862615

2041
Godbold Foundation Inc.

1625 Oceanview Dr.
Tierra Verde, FL 33715-2501

Established in 1997 in Florida.

Donor: Francis Godbold.

Foundation type: Independent foundation.

Financial data (yr. ended 12/31/13): Assets, $3,497,030 (M); gifts received, $201,840; expenditures, $252,704; qualifying distributions, $242,463; giving activities include $242,463 for 40 grants (high: $119,111; low: $50).

Fields of interest: Education; Nonprofits; Publishing; Christianity; Human services.

Type of support: General support; Scholarships; Regranting.

Limitations: Applications not accepted. Giving primarily in FL and GA. No grants to individuals.
Application information: Contributes only to pre-selected organizations.
Officers: Francis Godbold, Pres. and Treas.; Laura Blair, V.P.; John Godbold, V.P.; Elizabeth Godbold, Secy.
EIN: 593455170

2042
The Frederick J. Goddard Charitable Trust
P.O. Box 1908
Orlando, FL 32802-1908

Foundation type: Independent foundation.
Financial data (yr. ended 12/31/14): Assets, $5,775,578; expenditures, $330,478; qualifying distributions, $277,859.
Fields of interest: Health; Human services.
Limitations: Applications not accepted.
Application information: Unsolicited requests for funds not accepted.
Trustee: Suntrust Banks, Inc.
EIN: 264216754

2043
Godsey Foundation, Inc.
15208 Gulf Blvd., No. 304
Madeira Beach, FL 33708-1861

Established in 2008 in Tennessee.
Donors: Donald W. Godsey; Joyce W. Godsey.
Foundation type: Independent foundation.
Financial data (yr. ended 12/31/13): Assets, $1,171,026 (M); expenditures, $163,125; qualifying distributions, $146,750; giving activities include $146,750 for 5 grants (high: $102,250; low: $500).
Fields of interest: Health; Protestantism; Human services.
Limitations: Applications not accepted. Giving primarily in TN.
Application information: Unsolicited requests for funds not accepted.
Officers: Donald W. Godsey, Pres.; Geoffrey G. Young, Secy.; Joyce W. Godsey, Treas.
EIN: 263915186

2044
Goetz Family Foundation
2367 S. Ocean Blvd.
Highland Beach, FL 33487-1834

Established in 2007 in Pennsylvania.
Donor: 2007 David R. Goetz Delaware Gift Trust.
Foundation type: Independent foundation.
Financial data (yr. ended 12/31/13): Assets, $5,594,204 (M); expenditures, $308,086; qualifying distributions, $237,156; giving activities include $212,500 for 15 grants (high: $57,500; low: $2,000).
Fields of interest: Diseases and conditions; Religion; Human services.
Limitations: Applications not accepted. Giving primarily in OH and PA. No grants to individuals.
Application information: Unsolicited requests for funds not accepted.
Officers and Directors: David R. Goetz, Pres. and Treas. and Director; Mary Sue Goetz, V.P.; Kathryn

Meehan, Secy. and Director; David R. Goetz, Jr.; Gregory E. Goetz.
EIN: 770707624

2045
Goldberg Foundation, Inc.
3140 Miro Dr. S.
Palm Beach Gardens, FL 33410-1284

Donor: J. Arthur Goldberg.
Foundation type: Independent foundation.
Financial data (yr. ended 12/31/13): Assets, $3,367,238 (M); gifts received, $100,000; expenditures, $255,201; qualifying distributions, $243,000; giving activities include $243,000 for 8 grants (high: $105,000; low: $3,000).
Fields of interest: Arts and culture; Education; Diseases and conditions.
Limitations: Applications not accepted. Giving primarily in Jupiter, FL.
Application information: Contributes only to pre-selected organizations.
Trustee: J. Arthur Goldberg.
EIN: 592471635

2046
The Raymond L. Golden Family Foundation, Inc.
11609 Charisma Way
Palm Beach Gardens, FL 33418-1535

Donor: Raymond L. Golden.
Foundation type: Independent foundation.
Financial data (yr. ended 11/30/14): Assets, $2,345,314 (M); gifts received, $119,181; expenditures, $200,920; qualifying distributions, $193,049; giving activities include $190,299 for 21 grants (high: $100,000; low: $100).
Purpose and activities: Giving primarily for health care and Jewish federated giving programs.
Fields of interest: Arts and culture; Nonprofits; Health; Cancers; Judaism; Human services.
Type of support: Emergency funds; Annual campaigns; Capital and infrastructure; Research; Regranting.
Limitations: Applications not accepted. Giving primarily in FL and TX. No grants to individuals.
Application information: Contributes only to pre-selected organizations.
Officers: Raymond L. Golden, Pres.; Linda H. Golden, Secy.-Treas.; Layton F. Smith, V.P.
Directors: Nathan Golden; Neal Golden; Stephanie Golden.
EIN: 133072940

2047
Sally Goldman Foundation, Inc.
706 Verona Ct.
Weston, FL 33326-3543

Established in 2007 in Florida.
Donor: Sally Goldman†.
Foundation type: Independent foundation.
Financial data (yr. ended 12/31/14): Assets, $2,978,457 (M); expenditures, $248,855; qualifying distributions, $154,182; giving activities include $154,182 for 51 grants (high: $16,000; low: $100).
Fields of interest: Education; Housing development; Judaism.

Limitations: Applications not accepted. Giving primarily in FL. No grants to individuals.
Application information: Unsolicited requests for funds not accepted.
Officer and Trustees: George R. Levie, Pres. and Trustee; Elliot P. Borkson; Sam Greenfeder.
EIN: 208558523

2048
Jacqueline & Todd Goodwin Charitable Trust
857 Lake House Dr.
North Palm Beach, FL 33408-3309
5616262390

Established in 1986 in New York.
Donor: Todd Goodwin.
Foundation type: Independent foundation.
Financial data (yr. ended 10/31/14): Assets, $2,956,339; expenditures, $231,380; qualifying distributions, $167,655.
Purpose and activities: Giving primarily for health and youth services.
Fields of interest: Health; Human services; Youth development; Youth services.
Limitations: Applications not accepted. Giving primarily in NY. No grants to individuals.
Application information: Unsolicited requests for funds not accepted.
Officer: Todd Goodwin, V.P.
Trustees: Elizabeth Frost; Alexandra Olavarria; Amanda Ricciarini; Leslie Stonestreet.
EIN: 133389802

2049
Goody Two Shoes Inc.
6345 N.W. 23rd Ct.
Boca Raton, FL 33496-3612 5612419248

Donors: Barry Schnittman; Jackie Koo; Fred Loeb; Adelaide Schnittman; Norman Schnittman; Steve Schnittman; Leon Hariton; Henry Weitz; Mrs. Steve Schnittman; Mrs. Leon Hariton; Mrs. Barry Schnittman; Merle Schnittman; Hsiu Chun Weitz; Richard Kaiser; Tina Schnittman.
Foundation type: Independent foundation.
Financial data (yr. ended 12/31/14): Assets, $4,077,159; gifts received, $147,500; expenditures, $285,110; qualifying distributions, $280,487.
Fields of interest: Arts and culture; Education; Human services; Food banks.
Type of support: Capital and infrastructure.
Limitations: Applications accepted. Giving primarily in FL.
Application information: Application form required.
Initial approach: Letter
Deadline(s): None
Directors: Leon Hariton; Barry Schnittman; Cari Schnittman; Steve Schnittman; William Shofstall.
EIN: 650685709

2050
Gordon Family Foundation Inc.
c/o Stacy Studnik
1835 E. Hallandale Beach Blvd., Ste. 483
Hallandale, FL 33009-4619
Main URL: http://www.gordonfamilyfoundation.org

Foundation type: Independent foundation.

Financial data (yr. ended 12/31/13): Assets, $4,385,975 (M); expenditures, $381,550; qualifying distributions, $287,100; giving activities include $287,100 for 20 grants (high: $50,000; low: $1,000).
Fields of interest: Hospital care; Diseases and conditions; Judaism; Human services.
Type of support: Research; Research and evaluation.
Limitations: Applications not accepted. Giving primarily in FL and NY. No grants to individuals.
Application information: Contributes only to pre-selected organizations.
Officer: Gail Gordon, Chair. and Pres.
Directors: Wayne Carson; Jason Gordon; Alec Studnik; Amanda Studnik; Ashley Studnick; Shani Studnik; Stacy Studnik.
EIN: 650708527

2051
Mark J. Gordon Foundation
(formerly Gail and Mark Gordon Foundation)
2875 N.E. 191st St., Ste. 400
Aventura, FL 33180-2831
Main URL: http://www.markjgordonfoundation.org

Donor: Mark J. Gordon.
Foundation type: Independent foundation.
Financial data (yr. ended 12/31/13): Assets, $234,279 (M); expenditures, $508,199; qualifying distributions, $434,914; giving activities include $252,800 for 16 grants (high: $160,000; low: $250), and $5,000 for 1 grant to an individual.
Purpose and activities: Giving primarily for children, youth and social services, as well as for health organizations.
Fields of interest: Health; Leadership development; Human services; Child welfare.
International interests: Kenya.
Limitations: Applications not accepted. Giving primarily in FL.
Application information: Unsolicited requests for funds not accepted.
Officer: Mark J. Gordon, Pres.
EIN: 650995291

2052
Michael S. Gordon, M.D. Charitable Foundation
3225 Aviation Ave., Ste. 500
Miami, FL 33133-4741

Established in 2010 in Florida.
Donor: Michael S. Gordon, MD.
Foundation type: Independent foundation.
Financial data (yr. ended 12/31/14): Assets, $22,587; gifts received, $269,716; expenditures, $282,855; qualifying distributions, $282,500.
Fields of interest: Education.
Limitations: Applications not accepted.
Application information: Unsolicited requests for funds not accepted.
Trustees: Cathy Anne Gordon; Kevin Edward Gordon; Lynda S. Gordon; Michael S. Gordon; Mitchell A. Yelen.
EIN: 273521461

2053
Grabe Family Foundation
c/o Foundation Source
5099 Joewood Dr.
Sanibel, FL 33957-7512

Established in 1998 in Connecticut.
Donors: William O. Grabe; Mercadolibre,Inc.; Bottomline Technologies,Inc.
Foundation type: Operating foundation.
Financial data (yr. ended 12/31/13): Assets, $1,991,967 (M); gifts received, $163,124; expenditures, $182,272; qualifying distributions, $167,520; giving activities include $154,225 for 45 grants (high: $18,500; low: $500).
Fields of interest: Education; Higher education; Nonprofits; Health; Diseases and conditions; Christianity.
Type of support: Individual development; Regranting.
Limitations: Applications not accepted. Giving primarily in CT and New York, NY. No grants to individuals.
Application information: Unsolicited requests for funds not accepted.
Officers and Directors: William O. Grabe, Pres. and Director; Caryn Grabe Robinson, V.P. and Director; Joan H. Grabe, Secy. and Director; Douglas Grabe, Treas. and Director; Laura Grabe; Lisa Grabe-Taffe.
EIN: 061532628

2054
K. W. Grader Foundation, Inc.
P.O. Box 431
Bartow, FL 33831-0431

Established in 1976 in Florida.
Donors: K.W. Grader†; Evelyn L. Grader†.
Foundation type: Independent foundation.
Financial data (yr. ended 12/31/14): Assets, $562,254 (M); expenditures, $176,860; qualifying distributions, $173,500; giving activities include $173,500 for 42 grants (high: $20,000; low: $500).
Purpose and activities: Giving primarily for education, Christian agencies and churches, health associations and children's hospitals, and human services.
Fields of interest: Education; Higher education; Graduate and professional education; Hospital care; Diseases and conditions; Christianity; Interfaith; Theology; Human services; Child welfare.
Type of support: General support; Capital and infrastructure; Scholarships.
Limitations: Applications not accepted. Giving primarily in FL. No grants to individuals.
Application information: Contributes only to pre-selected organizations.
Officers: Lee G. Kleppel, Pres.; Lynn G. Johnson, V.P. and Secy.-Treas.
Trustees: Thomas E. Jennings; R. Randall Johnson; Cathy Parker; Gregory Thompson; Michael Westberry.
EIN: 591708165

2055
Clifford and LaVonne Graese Foundation
5193 Fairway Oaks Dr.
Windermere, FL 34786-8934

Established in 1986 in Delaware.
Donors: Clifford E. Graese†; LaVonne B. Graese.

Foundation type: Independent foundation.
Financial data (yr. ended 12/31/14): Assets, $5,024,240; expenditures, $195,694; qualifying distributions, $195,694.
Fields of interest: Nonprofits; Health; Specialty hospital care; Child welfare.
Type of support: Annual campaigns; Capital and infrastructure; Information and Referral; Public engagement and education; Continuing support; Capital campaigns; Endowments; Regranting.
Limitations: Applications not accepted. Giving primarily in Orlando, FL, Chicago, IL, Charlotte, NC, and Rapid City, SD. No support for religious or political organizations. No grants to individuals.
Application information: Contributes only to pre-selected organizations.
Board meeting date(s): Nov./Dec.
Officers and Directors: LaVonne B. Graese, Chair. and Treas. and Director; Diane M. Graese, V.P. and Pres. and Director; Susan Alfirevic, V.P. and Secy. and Director; Sally Daugherty, V.P. and Director; Larry Graese, V.P. and Director.
Number of staff: None.
EIN: 133388411

2056
The Marvin and Helene Gralnick Foundation, Inc.
2340 Perwinkle Way, Ste. M-1
Sanibel Island, FL 33957

Established in 1993 in Florida.
Donors: Marvin J. Gralnick; Helene B. Gralnick.
Foundation type: Independent foundation.
Financial data (yr. ended 09/30/13): Assets, $4,461,426 (M); expenditures, $373,992; qualifying distributions, $287,190; giving activities include $246,800 for 4 grants (high: $196,800; low: $1,000).
Fields of interest: Historic preservation; Early childhood education; Wildlife biodiversity.
Type of support: General support.
Limitations: Applications not accepted. Giving primarily in Sanibel, FL, Clayton, MO and Asheville, NC. No grants to individuals.
Application information: Contributes only to pre-selected organizations.
Officers and Directors: Roseanne Giordani, Pres.; Marvin J. Gralnick, Secy. and Director; Helene B. Gralnick, Treas. and Director; Leslie C. Giordani.
EIN: 650445458

2057
Grassy Creek Foundation
c/o Richard W. Howthorne
221 N. Hogan St., Ste. 403
Jacksonville, FL 32202-4201

Donor: Fillmore West Investment Trust.
Foundation type: Independent foundation.
Financial data (yr. ended 12/31/13): Assets, $1,055,607 (M); expenditures, $208,372; qualifying distributions, $175,000; giving activities include $175,000 for 2 grants (high: $150,000; low: $25,000).
Fields of interest: Education; Domesticated animals.
Limitations: Applications not accepted.
Application information: Unsolicited requests for funds not accepted.

Trustees: Richard W. Hawthorne; Austin Lowery; Wesley Lipner.
EIN: 456614724

2058
The Graymer Foundation
c/o C. Graydon Rogers
30 Beachside Dr., Ste. 301
Vero Beach, FL 32963-9587

Established in 2000 in New Jersey.
Donor: C. Graydon Rogers.
Foundation type: Independent foundation.
Financial data (yr. ended 12/31/13): Assets, $8,530,576 (M); expenditures, $339,537; qualifying distributions, $317,240; giving activities include $309,001 for grants.
Fields of interest: Human services.
Limitations: Applications not accepted. No grants to individuals.
Application information: Contributes only to pre-selected organizations.
Officers: C. Graydon Rogers, Pres.; Mary Elizabeth Rogers, V.P.; Stacy Rogers Golding, Secy.-Treas.
Trustees: Ann Bronwyn Rogers Parlette; David S. Rogers; Stuart G. Rogers.
EIN: 226798520

2059
Greater Lake Wales Health Care Foundation Inc.
410 S. 11th St.
Lake Wales, FL 33853-4203

Foundation type: Independent foundation.
Financial data (yr. ended 06/30/13): Assets, $3,538,358 (M); expenditures, $224,515; qualifying distributions, $198,937; giving activities include $198,937 for 1 grant.
Fields of interest: Religion.
Limitations: Applications not accepted. Giving primarily in FL.
Application information: Contributes only to pre-selected organizations.
Officers: G. Ellis Hunt, Chair.; Norman White, Pres.; Scott Smith, Secy.; Lee Wheeler, Treas.
Directors: Colette Braunstein; James D. Nelson, MD.
EIN: 141849586

2060
Greaton Family Foundation, Inc.
P.O. Box 39238
Fort Lauderdale, FL 33339-9238

Established in 1987 in Florida.
Donors: Wilson B. Greaton, Jr.; Evelyn S. Greaton.
Foundation type: Independent foundation.
Financial data (yr. ended 09/30/13): Assets, $0 (M); gifts received, $18,020; expenditures, $270,952; qualifying distributions, $270,952; giving activities include $270,620 for 6 grants (high: $235,620; low: $1,000).
Fields of interest: Arts and culture; Education; Human services.
Limitations: Applications not accepted. Giving primarily in MA. No grants to individuals.
Application information: Contributes only to pre-selected organizations.

Officers and Directors: Wilson B. Greaton, Jr., Pres. and Treas. and Director; Susan Greaton, V.P. and Director; Elizabeth Stephany, Secy. and Director.
EIN: 650018498

2061
Louis & Anne Green Family Foundation
(formerly Green Family Foundation)
2700 Date Palm Rd.
Boca Raton, FL 33432-7976
Contact: Louis B. Green, Tr.

Established in 1969 in Ohio.
Donors: Louis B. Green; First Financial Partners of Texas.
Foundation type: Independent foundation.
Financial data (yr. ended 12/31/14): Assets, $76,336 (M); gifts received, $185,172; expenditures, $161,603; qualifying distributions, $154,556; giving activities include $154,556 for 26 grants (high: $51,282; low: $100).
Fields of interest: Education; Health; Human services.
Limitations: Applications accepted. Giving primarily in FL and TX. No grants to individuals.
Application information:
    Initial approach: Letter
    Deadline(s): None
Trustees: Andrew Green; Anne W. Green; Louis B. Green; Oliver H. Green.
EIN: 316087315

2062
The Martin F. & Jane F. Greenberg Foundation Inc.
c/o Linda Blank
17951 Lake Estates Dr.
Boca Raton, FL 33496-1429

Established in 2006 in Florida.
Donors: Martin F. Greenberg; Jane F. Greenberg; Brett Greenberg.
Foundation type: Independent foundation.
Financial data (yr. ended 12/31/13): Assets, $1,468,383 (M); gifts received, $49,881; expenditures, $269,125; qualifying distributions, $255,519; giving activities include $255,519 for 19 grants (high: $75,000; low: $20).
Fields of interest: Arts and culture; Nonprofits; Diseases and conditions; Judaism.
Type of support: Regranting; Research; Research and evaluation.
Limitations: Applications not accepted.
Application information: Unsolicited requests for funds not accepted.
Officers and Directors: Martin F. Greenberg, Pres. and Director; Jane F. Greenberg, V.P. and Director; Brett A. Greenberg, Secy. and Director.
EIN: 205894228

2063
Allan & Muriel Greenblatt Charitable Foundation, Inc.
2000 S. Ocean Blvd.
Palm Beach, FL 33480-5205

Established in 1994 in New Jersey.
Donor: Allan Greenblatt.
Foundation type: Independent foundation.

Financial data (yr. ended 11/30/14): Assets, $2,245,270 (M); expenditures, $241,024; qualifying distributions, $239,449; giving activities include $239,449 for 45 grants (high: $100,000; low: $25).
Purpose and activities: Giving primarily for the arts, education, health, youth, and Jewish organizations.
Fields of interest: Arts and culture; Art museums; Education; Higher education; Graduate and professional education; Nonprofits; Hospital care; Diseases and conditions; Judaism; Theology; Youth development.
Type of support: Regranting.
Limitations: Applications not accepted. Giving primarily in FL and NY. No grants to individuals.
Application information: Contributes only to pre-selected organizations.
Officers: Allan Greenblatt, Pres.; Muriel Greenblatt, V.P.; Joel Greenblatt, Secy.; Richard Greenblatt, Treas.
EIN: 223339812

2064
Greene Family Foundation Inc.
1417 Sadler Rd., Ste. 378
Fernandina, FL 32034-0301

Donor: Carolyn A. Greene.
Foundation type: Independent foundation.
Financial data (yr. ended 12/31/13): Assets, $482,726 (M); expenditures, $122,455; qualifying distributions, $122,107; giving activities include $118,000 for 8 grants (high: $50,000; low: $1,500).
Fields of interest: Education; Judaism.
Limitations: Applications not accepted. Giving primarily in MD and NC.
Application information: Unsolicited requests for funds not accepted.
Officers: Carolyn A. Greene, Pres. and Secy.; Douglas H.S. Greene, V.P. and Treas.
EIN: 273982208

2065
The Greene-Sawtell Foundation
P.O. Box 1908
Orlando, FL 32802-1908
Contact: Raymond King, Sr. V.P., SunTrust Bank
Main URL: http://www.suntrust.com/Microsites/foundation/funds.htm

Established in 1963 in Georgia.
Donor: Alice Greene-Sawtell†.
Foundation type: Independent foundation.
Financial data (yr. ended 12/31/14): Assets, $9,764,220 (M); expenditures, $253,580; qualifying distributions, $223,525; giving activities include $200,000 for 8 grants (high: $55,000; low: $5,000).
Purpose and activities: Giving primarily to support worthwhile educational, cultural, and human service programs in the metropolitan Atlanta, GA, community.
Fields of interest: Higher education; Hospital care; Diseases and conditions; Human services; Children.
Type of support: Capital campaigns; Capital and infrastructure; Equipment; Research.
Limitations: Applications not accepted. Giving primarily in Atlanta, GA. No grants to individuals.

Application information: Contributes only to pre-selected organizations.

Board meeting date(s): Jan., May, and Oct.

Officers: Jennifer Wood, Chair.; Kirby Thompson, Secy.

Trustee: SunTrust Bank.

EIN: 586037828

2066
Richard and Peggy Greenfield Foundation
(formerly The Whitehat Foundation)
525 S. Flagler Dr., Ste. 16G/H
West Palm Beach, FL 33401

Donor: Richard D. Greenfield.

Foundation type: Independent foundation.

Financial data (yr. ended 11/30/13): Assets, $2,737,791 (M); expenditures, $203,290; qualifying distributions, $196,225; giving activities include $196,225 for 27 grants (high: $55,000; low: $55).

Purpose and activities: Giving primarily for federated giving programs and art and cultural programs.

Fields of interest: Arts and culture; Art museums; Education; Nonprofits; Diseases and conditions; Human services.

Type of support: Regranting.

Limitations: Applications not accepted. Giving primarily in FL. No grants to individuals.

Application information: Unsolicited requests for funds not accepted.

Officers: Richard D. Greenfield, Pres.; Marguerite G. Greenfield, Treas.

EIN: 650627104

2067
William A. Gregory Jr. Foundation Inc.
3225 S. Macdill Ave., Ste. 129
Tampa, FL 33629-8171 (813) 760-2792
Contact: Christopher H. Taylor, Dir.

Established in 2001 in Florida.

Donor: William A. Gregory, Jr.†.

Foundation type: Independent foundation.

Financial data (yr. ended 12/31/13): Assets, $3,912,561 (M); gifts received, $38,546; expenditures, $291,947; qualifying distributions, $246,000; giving activities include $246,000 for 5 grants (high: $96,000; low: $25,000).

Purpose and activities: Giving primarily for education, including scholarship funds, and community development.

Fields of interest: Education; Hospital care; Diseases and conditions; Community and economic development; Human services.

Type of support: General support; Scholarships; Individual development.

Limitations: Applications accepted. Giving primarily in Tampa, FL.

Application information: Application form required.

Initial approach: Letter

Deadline(s): July 1 and Feb. 1

Directors: Heidi B. McCree; Karen F. Mills; Christopher H. Taylor.

EIN: 593607455

2068
The Robert and Lynne Grossman Foundation, Inc.
509 Bald Eagle Dr.
Jupiter, FL 33477-4205

Established in 1996 in Florida.

Donors: Louis Grossman†; Marion Grossman; Lynne Grossman; Robert Grossman.

Foundation type: Independent foundation.

Financial data (yr. ended 12/31/13): Assets, $52,317 (M); gifts received, $65,000; expenditures, $392,314; qualifying distributions, $387,900; giving activities include $387,900 for 55 grants (high: $100,000; low: $250).

Fields of interest: Hospital care; Diseases and conditions; Cancers; Human services; Food aid; Child welfare.

Limitations: Applications not accepted. Giving primarily in CT, FL, and NY.

Application information: Unsolicited requests for funds not accepted.

Directors: Alison Grossman; Lynne Grossman; Robert Grossman.

EIN: 650630576

2069
Gulf Power Foundation Inc.
500 Bayfront Pkwy.
Pensacola, FL 32501 (850) 444-6057
Contact: Sandy Sims
Application address: 1 Energy Pl., Pensacola, FL 32520-0786, tel.: (850) 444-6057

Established in 1987 in Florida.

Donor: Gulf Power Co.

Foundation type: Company-sponsored foundation.

Financial data (yr. ended 12/31/13): Assets, $4,307,767 (M); gifts received, $300,000; expenditures, $365,057; qualifying distributions, $360,369; giving activities include $351,589 for 76 grants (high: $62,898; low: $200), and $8,780 for 1 employee matching gift.

Purpose and activities: The foundation supports organizations involved with arts and culture, education, health, human services, community development, and civic affairs.

Fields of interest: Education; Community and economic development; Human services.

Type of support: General support; Employee matching gifts; Continuing support; Annual campaigns; Capital campaigns; Capital and infrastructure; Equipment; Emergency funds; Program development; Scholarships.

Limitations: Applications accepted. Giving limited to areas of company operations in northwestern FL. No support for political or lobbying organizations or arts councils (except for capital campaigns). No grants to individuals.

Publications: Annual report; Informational brochure (including application guidelines).

Application information: Requests should include a copy of the organization's Florida Solicitation Letter. Application form required.

Initial approach: Contact foundation for application form

Copies of proposal: 1

Deadline(s): Feb. 15, May 15, Aug. 15, and Nov. 15

Board meeting date(s): Quarterly

Final notification: 1 month

Officers: P. Bernard Jacob, Chair.; Susan D. Ritenour, Secy.-Treas.

Trustees: Michael L. Burroughs; Constance Erickson; Scott Teel; Bentina C. Terry.

EIN: 592817740

2070
The John R. and Ruth W. Gurtler Foundation, Inc.
P.O. Box 880
Winter Park, FL 32790-0880 (407) 645-5469
Contact: Mary W. Christian, Pres. and Secy.-Treas.

Established in 1999 in Florida.

Foundation type: Independent foundation.

Financial data (yr. ended 12/31/13): Assets, $7,409,652 (M); expenditures, $416,182; qualifying distributions, $341,544; giving activities include $302,540 for 13 grants (high: $62,933; low: $1,500).

Purpose and activities: Giving to support youth programs in the Orlando, FL, area.

Fields of interest: Youth development.

Limitations: Applications accepted. Giving primarily in central FL. No grants to individuals.

Application information: Application form required.

Initial approach: Letter

Copies of proposal: 3

Deadline(s): None

Officers: Mary W. Christian, Pres. and Secy.-Treas.; Harold A. Ward III, V.P.; W. Graham White, V.P.

Number of staff: 1 part-time professional.

EIN: 593437461

2071
Annette J. Hagens Memorial Foundation
800 S. Osprey Ave.
Sarasota, FL 34236
Application address: Annette J. Hagens Memorial Foundation Trust, 1515 Ringling Blvd., Sarasota, FL 34236, tel.: (941) 329-2627

Donor: Annette J. Hagens†.

Foundation type: Independent foundation.

Financial data (yr. ended 12/31/13): Assets, $3,687,241 (M); expenditures, $264,642; qualifying distributions, $190,040; giving activities include $183,500 for 34 grants (high: $35,000; low: $1,000).

Purpose and activities: Giving primarily for children's services.

Fields of interest: Education; Nonprofits; Human services; Family services; Child welfare; Youth development; Youth services.

Type of support: Regranting.

Limitations: Applications accepted. Giving primarily in Manatee and Sarasota counties, FL.

Application information: Application form required.

Initial approach: Proposal

Deadline(s): None

Trustees: Norman J. Shea III, CPA; Matt A. Sperling; The Northern Trust Co.

EIN: 656248208

2072
The Hahn Family Foundation
9204 Sloane St.
Orlando, FL 32827-7026

Established in 2006 in Nevada.

Donors: Paul Hahn; David J. Hahn; Sang Hoon Hahn; Hai Joung Hahn; Hahn Waianae Land, LLC; Mauna Kea Villages, LLC.
Foundation type: Independent foundation.
Financial data (yr. ended 12/31/14): Assets, $13,485,620 (M); expenditures, $515,561; qualifying distributions, $392,000; giving activities include $392,000 for 27 grants (high: $100,000; low: $500).
Fields of interest: Christianity; Protestantism.
Type of support: General support.
Limitations: Applications not accepted. Giving primarily in NJ; some funding also in CA, HI and MA. No grants to individuals.
Application information: Unsolicited requests for funds not accepted.
Trustees: Hai Joung Yoon Hahn; Sang Hoon Hahn.
EIN: 207055857

2073
Halbrook Family Foundation
728 Promenade Pointe Dr.
Saint Augustine, FL 32095-6854

Established in 2006 in Illinois.
Donors: John A. Halbrook; Benita K. Halbrook.
Foundation type: Independent foundation.
Financial data (yr. ended 06/30/13): Assets, $8,582,427 (M); gifts received, $997,192; expenditures, $366,999; qualifying distributions, $362,040; giving activities include $362,040 for 14 grants (high: $152,870; low: $350).
Fields of interest: Higher education; Graduate and professional education; Diseases and conditions; Theology.
Type of support: Research.
Limitations: Applications not accepted. Giving primarily in FL and KY. No grants to individuals.
Application information: Contributes only to pre-selected organizations.
Trustees: Benita K. Halbrook; John A. Halbrook; Nathan Halbrook; Jennifer Stevenson.
EIN: 203898148

2074
Hall-Halliburton Foundation, Inc.
(formerly William M. Hall, Jr. Foundation, Inc.)
P.O. Box 141746
Gainesville, FL 32614-1746 (904) 677-9000
Contact: Randolph B. Mahoney, Pres.

Donor: William M. Hall†.
Foundation type: Independent foundation.
Financial data (yr. ended 11/30/13): Assets, $11,897,048 (M); expenditures, $288,209; qualifying distributions, $210,140; giving activities include $210,140 for 4 grants (high: $125,000; low: $5,000).
Fields of interest: Education.
Limitations: Applications accepted. Giving primarily in AL, CA, FL, NC, and NY. No grants to individuals.
Application information: Application form required.
Initial approach: Letter
Deadline(s): None
Officers: Randolph B. Mahoney, Pres.; R. Bruce Shealy, V.P.; Frances L. Moulder, Secy.-Treas.
EIN: 591731934

2075
Steven J. Halmos Family Foundation, Inc.
17 W. Las Olas Blvd.
Fort Lauderdale, FL 33301-1823

Established in 1993 in Florida.
Donor: Steven J. Halmos.
Foundation type: Independent foundation.
Financial data (yr. ended 12/31/13): Assets, $5,232,937 (M); expenditures, $245,428; qualifying distributions, $230,000; giving activities include $230,000 for 13 grants (high: $60,000; low: $2,500).
Fields of interest: Arts and culture; Education; Human services.
Limitations: Applications not accepted. Giving primarily in Fort Lauderdale, FL. No grants to individuals.
Application information: Unsolicited requests for funds not accepted.
Officers: Steven J. Halmos, Pres.; Madeline G. Halmos, V.P.; Stephanie Halmos, Secy.; Jeffry Halmos, Treas.
EIN: 830305837

2076
Halperin Foundation Inc.
(formerly Empire Foundation)
2494 S. Ocean Blvd., Apt. PH C-9
Boca Raton, FL 33432 (407) 989-0382
Contact: Barry S. Halperin, Tr.

Established in 1977 in Connecticut.
Foundation type: Independent foundation.
Financial data (yr. ended 12/31/13): Assets, $4,158,037 (M); expenditures, $270,566; qualifying distributions, $202,849; giving activities include $188,820 for 57 grants (high: $25,000; low: $15).
Fields of interest: Nonprofits; Health; Diseases and conditions; Judaism.
Type of support: Regranting.
Limitations: Applications accepted. Giving primarily in FL.
Application information: Application form required.
Initial approach: Proposal
Deadline(s): Oct. 31
Board meeting date(s): May and Nov.
Trustees: Barry S. Halperin; Carol Minkin.
EIN: 060972125

2077
The Hand Foundation, Inc.
1499 Forest Hill Blvd., Ste. 116
West Palm Beach, FL 33406-6050 (561) 439-0171
Contact: Ruben Ledesma Jr., Dir.

Established in 1989 in Florida.
Donors: Homer J. Hand; Frances R. Hand.
Foundation type: Independent foundation.
Financial data (yr. ended 12/31/13): Assets, $4,376 (M); gifts received, $250,000; expenditures, $250,117; qualifying distributions, $250,117; giving activities include $250,000 for 64 grants (high: $24,000; low: $1,000).
Fields of interest: Education; Higher education.
Type of support: Student aid; Individual development.

Limitations: Applications accepted. Giving primarily in FL.
Application information: Application form required.
Initial approach: Letter
Deadline(s): None
Directors: Thomas L. Altman; Francis R. Hand; Homer J. Hand; Ruben Ledesma, Jr.; Paul R. Orsemigo.
EIN: 650118848

2078
Joseph Handleman Trust Foundation
(formerly Joseph & Sally Handleman Charitable Foundation Trust C)
c/o Fiduciary Trust
200 S. Biscayne Blvd., Ste. 3050
Miami, FL 33131-3101 (305) 349-2350

Foundation type: Independent foundation.
Financial data (yr. ended 12/31/14): Assets, $6,760,035; expenditures, $335,108; qualifying distributions, $294,572.
Fields of interest: Diseases and conditions; Judaism; Human services.
International interests: Israel.
Type of support: Research; General support; Research and evaluation.
Limitations: Applications accepted. Giving primarily in FL, NY, and RI; some giving also in Israel. No grants to individuals.
Application information: Application form required.
Initial approach: Proposal
Deadline(s): None
Trustees: Joyce Ann Muller; Marisa Muller.
EIN: 656263328

2079
Hansen Family Foundation
15413 Milan Way
Naples, FL 34110

Established in 1994 in Minnesota.
Donor: Helen M. Hansen.
Foundation type: Independent foundation.
Financial data (yr. ended 12/31/13): Assets, $4,366,518 (M); expenditures, $244,790; qualifying distributions, $182,125; giving activities include $171,500 for 12 grants (high: $50,000; low: $1,000).
Fields of interest: Undergraduate education; Diseases and conditions; Cancers; Human services; Child welfare.
Type of support: Research; Research and evaluation.
Limitations: Applications not accepted. Giving primarily in MN.
Application information: Unsolicited requests for funds not accepted.
Trustees: Carl M. Hansen; Harvey C. Hansen; Kelsey L. Piquette.
EIN: 411740710

2080
Ann Hardeman and Combs Lawson Fort Trust
(formerly TCH Fort Foundation)
P.O. Box 1908
Orlando, FL 32802-1908

Established in 1999 in Tennessee.

Donor: Combs Lawson Fort†.
Foundation type: Independent foundation.
Financial data (yr. ended 09/30/14): Assets, $6,354,013 (M); expenditures, $348,904; qualifying distributions, $318,858; giving activities include $299,300 for 16 grants (high: $29,930; low: $11,972).
Fields of interest: Education; Health; Human services.
Type of support: General support.
Limitations: Applications not accepted. Giving primarily in TN.
Application information: Unsolicited requests for funds not accepted.
Trustee: SunTrust Bank, Inc.
EIN: 626356582

2081
The Hardison Family Foundation
1682 Edith Esplanade
Cape Coral, FL 33904-5614

Established in 1996 in Florida.
Donor: Leslie C. Hardison.
Foundation type: Independent foundation.
Financial data (yr. ended 12/31/13): Assets, $8,167,327 (M); expenditures, $353,540; qualifying distributions, $345,550; giving activities include $345,000 for 13 grants (high: $50,000; low: $10,000).
Purpose and activities: Giving primarily for social services.
Fields of interest: Higher education; Graduate and professional education; Nonprofits; Children's hospital care; Engineering; Human services; Food banks; Child welfare; Children.
Type of support: Regranting.
Limitations: Applications not accepted. Giving primarily in FL, IL and TN. No grants to individuals.
Application information: Unsolicited requests for funds not accepted.
Trustees: Susan Black; James Hardison; Janet Hardison; Jill Hardison; John Hardison; Leslie C. Hardison; Paul Hardison; Patricia Jackson.
EIN: 650700303

2082
Harper Family Charitable Foundation, Inc.
6917 S. Round Lake Rd.
Mount Dora, FL 32757-9646   (407) 886-4613
Contact: Robert W. Harper, Treas.

Established in 2003 in Florida.
Donor: George Harper†.
Foundation type: Independent foundation.
Financial data (yr. ended 06/30/14): Assets, $8,997,251 (M); gifts received, $250; expenditures, $536,257; qualifying distributions, $455,794; giving activities include $432,611 for 63 grants (high: $27,000; low: $500).
Purpose and activities: Giving primarily for health, education, and maintenance and well being of disabled children and adults in central Florida.
Fields of interest: Education; Specialty hospital care; Human services; Child welfare; People with disabilities.
Type of support: General support.
Limitations: Giving primarily in FL. No grants to individuals.
Application information:
Initial approach: Letter

Deadline(s): Within 10 days of board meeting
Board meeting date(s): Monthly
Officers and Directors: Freida H. Martin, Pres. and Director; Patrick J. Dougherty, V.P. and Secy. and Director; Robert W. Harper, Treas. and Director.
EIN: 020685568

2083
The Haskell Foundation
111 Riverside Ave.
Jacksonville, FL 32202-4905

Established in 2001 in Florida.
Donors: Preston H. Haskell III; Joan S. Haskell; Preston H. Haskell.
Foundation type: Independent foundation.
Financial data (yr. ended 12/31/13): Assets, $8,324,774 (M); gifts received, $2,070,464; expenditures, $373,253; qualifying distributions, $320,500; giving activities include $320,500 for 47 grants (high: $80,000; low: $150).
Fields of interest: Education; Environment; Christianity; Human services.
Limitations: Applications not accepted. Giving primarily in Jacksonville, FL. No grants to individuals.
Application information: Unsolicited requests for funds not accepted.
Trustees: Elizabeth H. Callaghan; Joan Haskell; Preston H. Haskell IV; Sally H. Singletary.
EIN: 597216309

2084
The Haugland Family Foundation, Inc.
60 Edgewater Dr., Apt. TSA
Coral Gables, FL 33133-6970

Established in 1998 in New York.
Donors: William J. Haugland; Hogwild Associates, Inc.; Linda Haugland; Haugland Group, LLC.
Foundation type: Independent foundation.
Financial data (yr. ended 12/31/13): Assets, $265,411 (M); gifts received, $322,907; expenditures, $221,180; qualifying distributions, $213,953; giving activities include $211,348 for 64 grants (high: $50,000; low: $45).
Fields of interest: Elementary and secondary education; Higher education; Hospital care; Human services.
Limitations: Applications not accepted. Giving primarily in CT, FL and NY. No grants to individuals.
Application information: Contributes only to pre-selected organizations.
Officers: William J. Haugland, Pres.; Linda Haugland, V.P.; Myron S. Bloom, Secy.-Treas.
EIN: 113440392

2085
Nina Haven Scholarships, Inc.
(formerly Nina Haven Charitable Foundation)
P.O. Box 1978
Stuart, FL 34995-1978   (772) 287-7645
Contact: Judith Weber, Pres.
FAX: (772) 221-1970; E-mail: info@ninahaven.org;
Main URL: http://www.ninahaven.org
Facebook: https://www.facebook.com/pages/Nina-Haven-Scholarships-Inc/326352364155936

Donor: Clyde Fair†.
Foundation type: Independent foundation.

Financial data (yr. ended 01/01/15): Assets, $6,048,233 (M); gifts received, $45,669; expenditures, $355,452; qualifying distributions, $331,993; giving activities include $307,000 for 37 grants (high: $36,500; low: $1,250).
Purpose and activities: Giving for scholarships for higher education, benefiting graduates of the Martin County, Florida, school system and local community colleges.
Fields of interest: Education.
Type of support: Scholarships; Student aid.
Limitations: Applications accepted. Giving primarily in FL, especially to Martin County residents.
Application information: Application guidelines available on foundation web site. Application form required.
Officers: Judith Weber, Pres.; Lawrence E. Crary III, V.P.; Theresa Gallant, Secy.-Treas.
Board Members: Charles L. Anderson, Sr.; Gordon Gaster; Karen Ripper.
EIN: 136099012

2086
The Warren J. and Marylou Hayford Family Foundation
7341 S.E. Golfhouse Dr.
Hobe Sound, FL 33455-8008

Established in 1994 in Illinois.
Donors: Warren J. Hayford; James Meyer; Marylou Hayford†.
Foundation type: Independent foundation.
Financial data (yr. ended 06/30/13): Assets, $1,506,445 (M); expenditures, $275,649; qualifying distributions, $268,953; giving activities include $265,188 for grants.
Fields of interest: Education; Elementary and secondary education; Higher education; Catholicism; Human services.
Limitations: Applications not accepted. Giving primarily in CA, CT, Washington, DC, FL, GA, IL, IN, TX, and VA. No grants to individuals.
Application information: Unsolicited requests for funds not accepted.
Officers and Directors: Warren John Hayford, Pres. and Director; June Hayford, Treas. and Director; Laura A. Blatchford; Carolyn E. Goodmaster; David Patrick Hayford; Michael Edward Hayford; Warren John Hayford, V; Susan Marie Luciu; Mary Beth Phillip.
EIN: 363992941

2087
William H. and Leonora K. Hegamyer Family Foundation Inc.
P.O. Box 565910
Miami, FL 33256-5910

Foundation type: Independent foundation.
Financial data (yr. ended 12/31/13): Assets, $9,764,122 (M); expenditures, $475,456; qualifying distributions, $354,822; giving activities include $350,255 for 14 grants (high: $55,000; low: $3,125).
Fields of interest: Health; Agriculture; Human services; Veterans.
Limitations: Applications not accepted. Giving primarily in FL.
Application information: Unsolicited requests for funds not accepted.

Officers and Directors: Katharine Hegamyer, Pres. and Director; Jacquelyn Hegamyer Hinckley, V.P. and Treas. and Director; Harry Hinckley.
EIN: 201593749

2088
James Held & Kenn Karakul Charitable Foundation Inc.
241 Jungle Rd.
Palm Beach, FL   33480-4811
Contact: James Held

Established in 2000 in Florida.
Donors: Kenn Karakul; James Held.
Foundation type: Independent foundation.
Financial data (yr. ended 10/31/14): Assets, $9,447 (M); gifts received, $100,000; expenditures, $137,625; giving activities include $137,625 for 14 grants (high: $75,000; low: $100).
Fields of interest: Education; Health; Human services.
Limitations: Applications not accepted. Giving primarily in FL, MA and NY. No grants to individuals.
Application information: Unsolicited requests for funds not accepted.
Officers and Directors: Kenn Karakul, Pres. and Director; James Held, Secy.-Treas. and Director.
EIN: 522280075

2089
Margaret & George Helow Family Foundation Inc.
(formerly George A. Helow Family Foundation, Inc.)
7545 Centurion Pkwy., Ste. 102
Jacksonville, FL   32256-7149

Established in 1988 in Florida.
Foundation type: Independent foundation.
Financial data (yr. ended 12/31/14): Assets, $6,315,956; expenditures, $325,038; qualifying distributions, $320,000.
Purpose and activities: Giving primarily to Roman Catholic organizations.
Fields of interest: Education; Hospice care; Catholicism; Human services; Women's services.
Limitations: Applications not accepted. Giving primarily in Jacksonville, FL. No grants to individuals.
Application information: Contributes only to pre-selected organizations.
Officers and Directors: Joseph P. Helow, Pres. and Director; Margaret O. Helow, Secy.-Treas. and Director; Anne Helow Darling; Katherine Helow Gilligan; Diane Helow Parker; Mary Helow Pritchard; Theresa Helow Ryan.
EIN: 592904267

2090
Willard & Frances Hendrix Foundation
P.O. Box 1908
Orlando, FL   32802-1908
Application address: c/o Charlotte Csabi, P.O. Box 305110, Nashville, TN 37230-5510

Established in 1981 in Tennessee.
Donors: Frances Hendrix; Hendrix Charitable Lead Annuity Trust.
Foundation type: Independent foundation.
Financial data (yr. ended 04/30/14): Assets, $5,193,270 (M); expenditures, $409,794; qualifying distributions, $391,271; giving activities

include $353,112 for 41 grants (high: $97,112; low: $500).
Purpose and activities: Giving primarily for education and human services.
Fields of interest: Education; Higher education; Hospice care; Human services.
Limitations: Applications accepted. Giving primarily in Nashville, TN.
Application information:
    Deadline(s): None
    Board meeting date(s): Nov.
Trustees: John Anderson; James Gooch, Esq.; James Hendrix; Jane Star; SunTrust Banks, Inc.
EIN: 626158855

2091
Melvin & Melva Herrin Charitable Foundation
1111 Ritz Carlton Dr., Unit 1001
Sarasota, FL   34236-4500

Established in 1998 in Pennsylvania.
Donors: Melvin B. Herrin; Melva J. Herrin.
Foundation type: Independent foundation.
Financial data (yr. ended 12/31/13): Assets, $1,287,865 (M); gifts received, $100,000; expenditures, $186,797; qualifying distributions, $184,240; giving activities include $184,240 for 23 grants (high: $75,740; low: $50).
Fields of interest: Nonprofits; Geriatrics; Judaism.
Type of support: Regranting.
Limitations: Applications not accepted. Giving primarily in OK and PA. No grants to individuals.
Application information: Contributes only to pre-selected organizations.
Trustee: Melva J. Herrin.
EIN: 232954135

2092
HFRX Foundation
(formerly Joseph G. Nicholas Foundation)
17001 Collins Ave., Ste. 4304
Sunny Isles Beach, FL   33160-4317

Established in 2006 in Illinois.
Donor: Joseph G. Nicholas.
Foundation type: Independent foundation.
Financial data (yr. ended 12/31/14): Assets, $2,265,972 (M); expenditures, $154,051; qualifying distributions, $154,051; giving activities include $151,660 for 12 grants (high: $45,000; low: $1,000).
Fields of interest: Dance; Art museums; Brain and nervous system disorders; Human services; Military personnel.
Type of support: General support; Research.
Limitations: Applications not accepted. Giving primarily in IL, VA and Washington, DC. No grants to individuals.
Application information: Contributes only to pre-selected organizations.
Officer and Directors: Joseph G. Nicholas, Pres. and Director; John Klimek; George Nicholas.
EIN: 208018497

2093
HI Foundation Inc.
2848 E. Oakland Park Blvd.
Fort Lauderdale, FL   33306-1814   (954) 566-7559
Contact: Lucie Smith

Established in 1998 in Florida.
Donors: Helen Ann Hubbell Ingham; Richard S. Ingham.
Foundation type: Independent foundation.
Financial data (yr. ended 12/31/13): Assets, $7,524,713 (M); gifts received, $80,000; expenditures, $294,068; qualifying distributions, $262,632; giving activities include $260,000 for 49 grants (high: $15,000; low: $500).
Fields of interest: Historical activities; Protestantism; Human services; Family services; Youth development; Youth services.
Limitations: Applications accepted. Giving primarily in FL. No grants to individuals.
Application information: Application form required.
    Initial approach: Letter
    Deadline(s): None
Directors: Annelle I. Carney; Hilary I. Hickman; Sharon I. Horal; Frederick H. Ingham; Richard S. Ingham; Richard S. Ingham, Jr.; Timothy C. Ingham.
EIN: 650848161

2094
The Hicks Charitable Foundation
1725 Memorial Park Dr.
Jacksonville, FL   32204-4117

Donors: David M. Hicks; Wendell C. Webster; Jacksonville Housing Authority; United Way of Northeast Florida; Ann C. Hicks.
Foundation type: Independent foundation.
Financial data (yr. ended 03/31/13): Assets, $860,977 (M); gifts received, $1,037,696; expenditures, $191,212; qualifying distributions, $188,787; giving activities include $188,787 for grants.
Fields of interest: Art museums; Education; Higher education; Nonprofits; Diseases and conditions; Community and economic development; Protestantism; Human services.
Type of support: Regranting.
Limitations: Applications not accepted. Giving primarily in FL. No grants to individuals (except for scholarships).
Application information: Unsolicited requests for funds not accepted.
Trustees: W. Robinson Frazier; Ann C. Hicks; David M. Hicks.
EIN: 591947616

2095
Hieronymus Charities Inc
100 S. Ashley Dr., Ste. 1650
Tampa, FL   33602-5310

Donors: Michael Connelly; Linda Connelly.
Foundation type: Independent foundation.
Financial data (yr. ended 12/31/13): Assets, $466,394 (M); gifts received, $100,061; expenditures, $357,715; qualifying distributions, $350,621; giving activities include $350,621 for 27 grants (high: $72,000; low: $500).
Fields of interest: Education; Religion; Human services.

Limitations: Applications not accepted.
Application information: Unsolicited requests for funds not accepted.
Officers and Directors: Michael J. Connelly, Pres. and Director; Linda M. Connelly, V.P. and Director; Jane C. Davis, Secy.-Treas. and Director.
EIN: 453478876

2096
Higgs Family Foundation
350 Shores Dr.
Vero Beach, FL   32963-3904
Contact: George Higgs, Pres.

Established in 1996 in New Jersey.
Donor: George Higgs.
Foundation type: Independent foundation.
Financial data (yr. ended 05/31/13): Assets, $2,320,978 (M); expenditures, $198,575; qualifying distributions, $177,986; giving activities include $176,496 for 25 grants (high: $70,500; low: $200).
Purpose and activities: Giving primarily for the arts and youth programs.
Fields of interest: Theater; Undergraduate education; Business education; Environment; Health; Housing development; Human services; Youth development; Youth services.
Limitations: Applications accepted. Giving on a national basis, with emphasis on FL. No grants to individuals.
Application information: Application form required.
   Initial approach: Letter
   Deadline(s): None
Officer: George Higgs, Pres.
EIN: 223306407

2097
Walter Clay Hill and Family Foundation Trust
P.O. Box 1908
Orlando, FL   32802-1908
Application address: c/o SunTrust Bank, Jacqueline Tucker, P.O. Box 4655, Atlanta, GA 30302-4655

Established in 1967 in Georgia.
Donor: Rebecca Travers Hill†.
Foundation type: Independent foundation.
Financial data (yr. ended 12/31/14): Assets, $3,741,883; expenditures, $192,878; qualifying distributions, $177,699.
Purpose and activities: Giving primarily for the arts.
Fields of interest: Arts and culture; Performing arts; Art museums; Wildlife biodiversity; Zoos; Botanical gardens; Foundations.
Type of support: General support; Continuing support; Annual campaigns; Capital and infrastructure; Equipment; Endowments; Emergency funds; Program development; Seed money.
Limitations: Applications accepted. Giving primarily in FL. No grants to individuals, or for research, publications, conferences, scholarships, fellowships, or matching gifts; no loans.
Application information: Application form required.
   Initial approach: Letter
   Deadline(s): None
Trustees: Joseph L. Boland; Travers Hill Polak; SunTrust Bank.
EIN: 586065956

2098
Hill Family Foundation, Inc.
373 Royal Tern Rd. S.
Ponte Vedra, FL   32082-6209   9042964281

Donors: Margaret Hill; Robert Hill.
Foundation type: Independent foundation.
Financial data (yr. ended 12/31/14): Assets, $3,313,281; expenditures, $183,864; qualifying distributions, $156,000.
Fields of interest: University education; Foundations.
Limitations: Applications not accepted. Giving primarily in FL.
Application information: Unsolicited requests for funds not accepted.
Officers: Robert Hill, Pres. and Treas.; Margaret Hill, V.P. and Secy.
EIN: 453981095

2099
The Hinman Foundation
(formerly The Hinman Family Foundation)
3560 Creekview Dr.
Bonita Springs, FL   34134-2624

Established in 1997 in Pennsylvania.
Donors: Beverly J. Hinman; Larry J. Hinman.
Foundation type: Independent foundation.
Financial data (yr. ended 12/31/14): Assets, $8,617,840 (M); gifts received, $963,650; expenditures, $446,448; qualifying distributions, $399,696; giving activities include $392,000 for 25 grants (high: $80,000; low: $5,000).
Fields of interest: Higher education; Diseases and conditions; Human services.
Limitations: Applications not accepted. Giving primarily in FL, MN and NY.
Application information: Unsolicited requests for funds not accepted.
Trustees: Christina G. Alt; Joseph Argenziano; Susan E. Argenziano; Beverly J. Hinman; Larry J. Hinman.
EIN: 237845383

2100
Muna and Basem Hishmeh Foundation Inc.
1850 S. Ocean Dr., Ste. 3104
Hallandale Beach, FL   33009-7685

Established in 2006 in New Jersey.
Donors: Basem L. Hishmeh; Muna Hishmeh.
Foundation type: Independent foundation.
Financial data (yr. ended 12/31/13): Assets, $4,619,683 (M); gifts received, $25,000; expenditures, $345,141; qualifying distributions, $256,080; giving activities include $230,000 for 14 grants (high: $35,000; low: $2,500).
Purpose and activities: Giving to programs for children between the ages of one and eighteen that focus on the fields of art and music.
Fields of interest: Arts and culture; Education.
International interests: Israel.
Limitations: Applications not accepted. Giving primarily in NY and Israel. No grants to individuals.
Application information: Contributes only to pre-selected organizations.
Officers and Directors: Basem L. Hishmeh, Pres. and Director; Amal Ibrahimaj, V.P. and Director;

Muna Hishmeh, Secy. and Director; Robert Hishmeh, Treas. and Director.
EIN: 651270242

2101
W. Paul Hoenle Foundation, Inc.
7887 Midnight Pass Rd.
Sarasota, FL   34242-2717   (941) 747-5566
Contact: W. Paul Hoenle, Chair.

Donor: W. Paul Hoenle.
Foundation type: Independent foundation.
Financial data (yr. ended 11/30/13): Assets, $3,648,449 (M); gifts received, $160,000; expenditures, $194,218; qualifying distributions, $191,675; giving activities include $190,348 for 19 grants (high: $50,000; low: $1,000).
Fields of interest: Museums; Wildlife biodiversity; Cancers; Religion; Human services.
Limitations: Applications accepted. Giving primarily in FL. No grants to individuals.
Application information:
   Initial approach: Letter
   Deadline(s): None
Officer: W. Paul Hoenle, Chair.
EIN: 383385672

2102
Marie R. Hoerner Foundation
c/o William Dishong
2270 S.E. 27th Dr.
Homestead, FL   33035-1335

Established in 2007 in Mississippi.
Donor: Marie Hoerner†.
Foundation type: Independent foundation.
Financial data (yr. ended 12/31/14): Assets, $5,380,880; expenditures, $343,961; qualifying distributions, $255,000.
Fields of interest: Planetariums; Animal welfare; Christianity.
Limitations: Applications not accepted. Giving primarily in MS. No grants to individuals.
Application information: Contributes only to pre-selected organizations.
Officers: William Dishong, Pres.; Claudia Dishong, Secy.-Treas.
Trustee: Jack G. Admire.
EIN: 260217942

2103
MK Hoffman Family Foundation
3104 S. Emerson St.
Tampa, FL   33629-6524

Established in 2003 in Florida.
Donors: Matthew Payne Hoffman; Kimberly Swain-Hoffman.
Foundation type: Independent foundation.
Financial data (yr. ended 12/31/12): Assets, $2,041,016 (M); expenditures, $253,382; qualifying distributions, $156,350; giving activities include $156,350 for grants.
Fields of interest: Arts and culture; Education; Religion.
Limitations: Applications not accepted. Giving primarily in FL. No grants to individuals.
Application information: Unsolicited requests for funds not accepted.

Officers: Kimberly Swain-Hoffman, Pres.; Blair Anderson, V.P.; Cindy Tipton, Secy.; Matthew Payne Hoffman, Treas.
EIN: 510448896

2104
Hollinger Charitable Trust
125 W. Romana St., Ste. 224
Pensacola, FL 32502-5849

Established in 1994 in Florida.
Foundation type: Independent foundation.
Financial data (yr. ended 05/31/14): Assets, $5,550,868 (M); expenditures, $375,326; qualifying distributions, $308,056; giving activities include $308,056 for 5 grants (high: $124,302; low: $29,596).
Purpose and activities: Giving primarily to Baptist organizations and churches.
Fields of interest: Baptist.
Limitations: Applications not accepted. Giving primarily in FL. No grants to individuals.
Application information: Unsolicited requests for funds not accepted.
Board meeting date(s): July
Trustee: Synovus Trust Company.
EIN: 597045666

2105
Tibor and Sheila Hollo Charitable Foundation, Inc.
100 S. Biscayne Blvd., Ste. 900
Miami, FL 33131-2031

Donors: Tibor Hollo; Sheila Hollo.
Foundation type: Independent foundation.
Financial data (yr. ended 12/31/13): Assets, $72 (M); gifts received, $157,825; expenditures, $161,058; qualifying distributions, $160,331; giving activities include $160,331 for 81 grants (high: $75,000; low: $10).
Fields of interest: Education; Public affairs; Human services.
Limitations: Applications not accepted. Giving primarily in FL.
Application information: Unsolicited requests for funds not accepted.
Officers: Tibor Hollo, Pres.; Sheila Hollo, V.P.; Jerome Hollo, Secy.-Treas.
EIN: 263805116

2106
Caswell F. Holloway, Jr. and Marie B. Holloway Foundation
18465 S.E. Village Cir.
Tequesta, FL 33469-1786

Established in 1996 in Florida.
Donors: Caswell F. Holloway, Jr.; Marie B. Holloway.
Foundation type: Independent foundation.
Financial data (yr. ended 12/31/14): Assets, $1,171,140; expenditures, $212,446; qualifying distributions, $207,083.
Fields of interest: Education; Diseases and conditions; Christianity.
Limitations: Applications not accepted. Giving primarily in FL and NJ. No grants to individuals.
Application information: Unsolicited requests for funds not accepted.

Trustees: B. Scott Holloway; Marie B. Holloway.
EIN: 650717395

2107
Jack Holloway Foundation
390 N. Orange Ave., MC FLO-800-07-08
Orlando, FL 32801-1640
Application address: John W. Holloway, P.O. Box 593688, Orlando, FL 32859-3688

Donor: John D. Holloway Revocable Trust.
Foundation type: Independent foundation.
Financial data (yr. ended 05/31/13): Assets, $4,941,417 (M); expenditures, $269,539; qualifying distributions, $234,991; giving activities include $233,500 for 15 grants (high: $80,000; low: $3,500).
Fields of interest: Specialty hospital care; Diseases and conditions; Cerebral palsy; Protestantism; Catholicism; Human services; Child welfare.
Limitations: Applications accepted. Giving limited to FL. No grants to individuals.
Application information: Application form required.
Initial approach: Letter
Deadline(s): None
Trustees: Jacqueline H. Bailes; John W. Holloway.
EIN: 596076468

2108
Holopaw Homeowners, Inc.
8801 Community Center Rd.
Saint Cloud, FL 34773-9188 (407) 498-8053

Donor: Omni Waste of Osceola, LLC.
Foundation type: Independent foundation.
Financial data (yr. ended 12/31/12): Assets, $0 (M); gifts received, $410,463; expenditures, $352,731; qualifying distributions, $218,413; giving activities include $115,496 for 16 grants (high: $53,996; low: $250).
Purpose and activities: Scholarship awards to residents of Holopaw, Florida, for at least 6 months and must maintain a GPA of 2.0.
Fields of interest: Higher education.
Type of support: Student aid.
Limitations: Applications accepted. Giving primarily in FL.
Application information: Application form required.
Initial approach: Contact foundation
Deadline(s): Feb. 5
Officers: John Haystead, Pres.; Harry Booher, V.P.; Amanda Longhini-Halbin, Secy.; Karey Halbin, Treas.
EIN: 202046030

2109
Holtz Charitable Foundation Inc.
9209 Cromwell Park Pl.
Orlando, FL 32827-7005

Donors: Kevin Keyes; John Coban; Jacques Chappuis; Louis L. "Lou" Holtz; Medtronic; Brian Savage; Trinity Health; Comerica Bank; Irish Legends; Louis Beth Holtz; Silverio Basile; Michael Moran; Louis Beth Holtz; J. Russell Perlich; David Butler; Brian Savage; Heisman Trophy Trust; Scott Candrian; Andrew Van Eekeren; Peter M. Evans; Alexander Van Eekeren; Springfield Partners; Arthur Frigo, Sr.; Art Irish; Silverio Basile; Trinity Health; Jeff Q. Irish; Charles Van Eekeren.
Foundation type: Independent foundation.

Financial data (yr. ended 12/31/13): Assets, $4,034,176 (M); gifts received, $432,035; expenditures, $320,290; qualifying distributions, $160,400; giving activities include $160,400 for 14 grants (high: $93,000; low: $100).
Fields of interest: Museums; Education; University education; Diseases and conditions; Diabetes; Christianity; Human services.
Type of support: Research.
Limitations: Applications not accepted. No grants to individuals.
Application information: Unsolicited requests for funds not accepted.
Officers and Directors: Louis L. Holtz, Chair. and Director; Beth B. Holtz, Pres. and Director; Kevin R. Holtz, Secy.-Treas. and Director; Luanne E. Altenbaumer; Louis L. Skip Holtz, Jr.; Elizabeth H. Messaglia.
EIN: 352042978

2110
Jack and Irma Hoornstra Foundation Trust
4518 N.W. 35th St.
Gainesville, FL 32605-5415

Established in 2014 in Florida.
Foundation type: Independent foundation.
Financial data (yr. ended 06/30/14): Assets, $4,837,978 (M); gifts received, $4,260,760; expenditures, $279,043; qualifying distributions, $279,043; giving activities include $225,480 for 21 grants (high: $30,000; low: $1,000).
Fields of interest: Health; Diseases and conditions; Human services.
Limitations: Applications not accepted. Giving primarily in FL.
Application information: Unsolicited requests for funds not accepted.
Trustees: Shirley Gulden; Nancy Stinson.
EIN: 306330584

2111
Hornik Family Foundation
(formerly Joseph & Frieda Ross Foundation, Inc.)
P.O. Box 440606
Miami, FL 33144-0606
Main URL: http://www.hornikfamilyfoundation.org

Established in 2000 in Florida.
Foundation type: Independent foundation.
Financial data (yr. ended 12/31/13): Assets, $3,035,479 (M); expenditures, $350,534; qualifying distributions, $298,153; giving activities include $233,266 for 23 grants (high: $60,021; low: $350).
Purpose and activities: The foundation's major goal is to foster an interest in Jewish and Israeli matters in teenagers and young adults, mostly through educational endeavors, including encouragement in receiving Hebrew and other religious instruction.
Fields of interest: Elementary and secondary education; Higher education; Communication media; Protestantism; Judaism; Human services; Child welfare.
Limitations: Applications not accepted. Giving primarily in FL and NC. No grants to individuals.
Application information: Contributes only to pre-selected organizations.

Officers: Peter F. Hornik, Pres. and Treas.; Robin H. Parritz, V.P.; Steven R. Hornik, V.P.; Todd A. Hornik, V.P.; Ari Parritz, V.P.
EIN: 650919356

2112

Hsu Family Foundation Inc.

4100 E. Lake Estates Dr.
Davie, FL 33328-3074 (305) 503-4200
Contact: Jane H. Hsiao, Pres.

Established in 2006 in Florida.
Donor: Jane H. Hsiao.
Foundation type: Independent foundation.
Financial data (yr. ended 03/31/13): Assets, $13,692,870 (M); expenditures, $376,595; qualifying distributions, $320,000; giving activities include $320,000 for grants.
Fields of interest: Health; Goodwill promotion.
International interests: Taiwan.
Limitations: Applications accepted. Giving primarily in FL and NJ; some giving in Taiwan.
Application information: Application form required.
   Initial approach: Letter
   Deadline(s): None
Officers and Directors: Jane H. Hsiao, Pres. and Treas. and Director; Kristy Hsiao, Secy. and Director; Bernard Hsiao; Michael Hsiao.
EIN: 711017117

2113

Huang Family Foundation, Inc.

1039 Ponte Vedra Blvd.
Ponte Vedra Beach, FL 32082-4016

Established in 1999 in Florida.
Donors: Lawrence P. Huang; Huang Family Foundation, Inc.
Foundation type: Independent foundation.
Financial data (yr. ended 09/30/13): Assets, $1,080,024 (M); expenditures, $184,127; qualifying distributions, $170,000; giving activities include $170,000 for 2 grants (high: $145,000; low: $25,000).
Fields of interest: Higher education; Human services.
Limitations: Applications not accepted. Giving primarily in Atlanta, GA; some giving also in Jacksonville, FL. No grants to individuals.
Application information: Unsolicited requests for funds not accepted.
Officers: Lawrence P. Huang, Pres. and Director; Adam Huang, V.P. and Director; Kristine Impey, Secy. and Director; Nancy J. Huang, Treas. and Director.
EIN: 593613297

2114

Hufty Foundation

520 Village Blvd., Ste. 110
West Palm Beach, FL 33409

Established in 1953 in Florida.
Donor: Frances Archbold Hufty.
Foundation type: Independent foundation.
Financial data (yr. ended 12/31/13): Assets, $2,738,054 (M); expenditures, $154,991; qualifying distributions, $135,000; giving activities include $135,000 for 66 grants (high: $14,000; low: $500).

Purpose and activities: Giving for various public foundations with an emphasis on environmental conservation, Christian and Jewish organizations and churches, public affairs, research institutes, and education.
Fields of interest: Education; Natural resources; Foundations; Urban development; Christianity; Judaism.
Limitations: Applications not accepted. No grants to individuals.
Application information: Unsolicited requests for funds not accepted.
Trustee: John A. Hufty; Mary P. Hufty; Frances H. Leidy.
EIN: 526041681

2115

The Hultquist Foundation

c/o Timothy Hultquist
130 Island Creek Dr.
John's Island
Vero Beach, FL 32963-3301

Established in 1991 in Delaware.
Donor: Timothy Hultquist.
Foundation type: Independent foundation.
Financial data (yr. ended 12/31/13): Assets, $4,200,558 (M); expenditures, $187,723; qualifying distributions, $183,716; giving activities include $180,500 for 21 grants (high: $50,000; low: $2,500).
Purpose and activities: Giving primarily for universities, secondary education, medical research, and human service organizations.
Fields of interest: Elementary and secondary education; University education; Diseases and conditions; Libraries; Human services; Youth services.
Type of support: General support; Capital campaigns; Capital and infrastructure; Research; Emergency funds; Research and evaluation; Scholarships.
Limitations: Applications not accepted. Giving primarily in Fairfield County, CT, and the metropolitan New York, NY, area. No grants to individuals.
Application information: Contributes only to pre-selected organizations.
   Board meeting date(s): Varies
Officers: Timothy A. Hultquist, Pres.; Cynthia M. Hultquist, V.P.
Directors: Andrew Hultquist; Matthew Hultquist; Kirsten Rastrick.
EIN: 980120582

2116

Emily S. and Coleman A. Hunter Trust

P.O. Box 1908
Orlando, FL 32802-1908 8047825703

Established in 1985 in Virginia.
Donors: Emily S. Hunter†; Coleman A. Hunter†.
Foundation type: Independent foundation.
Financial data (yr. ended 02/28/15): Assets, $6,752,161 (M); expenditures, $269,199; qualifying distributions, $223,051.
Purpose and activities: Giving primarily for education and human services.
Fields of interest: Arts and culture; Education; Religion.

Limitations: Applications not accepted. No grants to individuals.
Application information: Contributes only to pre-selected organizations.
Trustee: SunTrust Banks, Inc.
EIN: 546219496

2117

Hutchison Family Foundation Inc.

545 Delaney Ave., Bldg. 8
Orlando, FL 32801-3866 (407) 876-6312
Contact: Deanne Hutchison, Pres.

Established in 2005 in Florida.
Donors: Deanne Hutchison; Thomas Hutchison.
Foundation type: Independent foundation.
Financial data (yr. ended 12/31/12): Assets, $1,413,429 (M); gifts received, $1,180; expenditures, $339,488; qualifying distributions, $280,186; giving activities include $280,186 for grants.
Purpose and activities: The foundation provides support to Christian based organizations.
Fields of interest: Protestantism; Human services.
Type of support: General support.
Limitations: Applications accepted. Giving primarily in FL and VA. No grants to individuals.
Application information:
   Initial approach: Proposal
   Deadline(s): None
Officers: Deanne Hutchison, Pres.; Catherine Hutchison, V.P.; Allison Hendrix, Secy.; Jennifer Krueger, Treas.
EIN: 202690152

2118

The W. Bradford Ingalls Charitable Foundation

840 U.S. Hwy. 1, Ste. 340
Summit Bldg.
North Palm Beach, FL 33408-3834 (561) 627-4448

Established in 2005 in Massachusetts.
Foundation type: Independent foundation.
Financial data (yr. ended 12/31/14): Assets, $11,608,380; gifts received, $713,516; expenditures, $712,882; qualifying distributions, $537,829.
Fields of interest: Education; Hospital care; Diseases and conditions; National defense; Human services.
Type of support: Research and evaluation.
Limitations: Applications accepted. Giving primarily in FL and MA.
Application information:
   Initial approach: Proposal
   Deadline(s): Mar. 1
Trustees: Joan D. Ingalls; Raymond M. Mascerrella II.
EIN: 203294470

2119

The Insetta Family Foundation, Inc.

3600 Darnall Pl.
Jacksonville, FL 32217-4252

Established in 2007 in Florida.
Foundation type: Independent foundation.

Financial data (yr. ended 09/30/13): Assets, $3,711,045 (M); expenditures, $204,164; qualifying distributions, $195,000; giving activities include $195,000 for 9 grants (high: $50,000; low: $10,000).

Fields of interest: Education; Diseases and conditions; Catholicism; Human services; Homeless people.

Limitations: Applications not accepted. Giving primarily in FL; some funding also in CT. No grants to individuals.

Application information: Contributes only to pre-selected organizations.

Directors: Diane Insetta; Victor Insetta; Kathy Kelly.

EIN: 261093740

2120
Irwin Saks Charitable Foundation, Inc.
16855 N.E. 2nd Ave., Ste. 303
North Miami Beach, FL 33162-1744

Foundation type: Independent foundation.

Financial data (yr. ended 12/31/14): Assets, $4,280,085; gifts received, $347,029; expenditures, $347,620; qualifying distributions, $297,815.

Fields of interest: Education; Judaism; Human services.

Limitations: Applications not accepted.

Application information: Unsolicited requests for funds not accepted.

Officer: Jack Levine, CPA, Pres. and Secy.-Treas.

EIN: 454230416

2121
The Isenberg Family Charitable Trust
c/o Ceniarth LLC
P.O. Box 351
Palm Beach, FL 33480

Established in 1987 in Florida.

Donors: Eugene M. Isenberg; Salmon Atlas, LP; Diane Isenberg.

Foundation type: Independent foundation.

Financial data (yr. ended 12/31/13): Assets, $6,963,563 (M); expenditures, $392,107; qualifying distributions, $378,360; giving activities include $378,360 for 28 grants (high: $150,000; low: $60).

Purpose and activities: Support primarily for arts and culture, education, health care, and Jewish organizations.

Fields of interest: Arts and culture; Opera; Education; Higher education; Nonprofits; Health; Hospital care; Diseases and conditions; Judaism; Human rights; Human services; Youth services.

Type of support: Regranting.

Limitations: Applications not accepted. Giving primarily in FL, MA, and NY, some giving also in TX. Generally no grants to individuals.

Application information: Generally contributes only to pre-selected organizations.

Trustees: Diane S. Isenberg; Christopher Papouras.

EIN: 596874814

2122
J. C. Foundation
2 Banchory Ct.
Palm Beach Gardens, FL 33418-6811

Established in 2005 in Florida.

Donors: Loretta D. Caudill; Richard W. Caudill.

Foundation type: Independent foundation.

Financial data (yr. ended 12/31/13): Assets, $8,181,582 (M); expenditures, $421,168; qualifying distributions, $351,750; giving activities include $351,750 for 26 grants (high: $35,000; low: $3,000).

Fields of interest: Education; Religion; Christianity; Catholicism; Human services.

Limitations: Applications not accepted. Giving primarily in FL. No grants to individuals.

Application information: Contributes only to pre-selected organizations.

Officers and Directors: Loretta D. Caudill, Pres. and Director; Michael S. Caudill, V.P. and Secy. and Director; Richard J. Caudill, V.P. and Director; Karen A. Dyer, V.P. and Director; Phyllis G. Hadaway, V.P. and Director; Steven G. Dell; Sandra Kutcel; Don Rachon; Basil J. Zaloom.

EIN: 611489700

2123
Hans & Cay Jacobsen Charitable Foundation Inc.
P.O. Box 2149
Winter Park, FL 32790-2149   (407) 810-6672
Contact: Teresa W. Borcheck, Pres.
E-mail: info@hansandcayjacobsenfoundation.org

Established in 1990 in Florida.

Foundation type: Independent foundation.

Financial data (yr. ended 05/31/13): Assets, $5,558,900 (M); expenditures, $343,683; qualifying distributions, $282,427; giving activities include $240,000 for 15 grants (high: $45,000; low: $1,000).

Purpose and activities: Giving primarily for services for children.

Fields of interest: Education; Elementary and secondary education; Diseases and conditions; Human services; Child welfare; Youth services; Children and youth; Low-income and poor people; People with disabilities; People with physical disabilities.

Type of support: General support; Matching grants; Program development; Scholarships; Individual development; Equal access.

Limitations: Applications accepted. Giving primarily in the Lake and Sumpter County, FL, area. No grants to individuals.

Publications: Application guidelines.

Application information: Application form required.
Copies of proposal: 1
Deadline(s): May 1 and Nov. 1
Board meeting date(s): Feb., May, Aug. and Nov.

Officers: Teresa W. Borcheck, Pres.; Tom Brooks, V.P.; Shannon McLin Carlyle, Secy.; Brian Brooks, Treas.

EIN: 593010451

2124
The Robert and Deborah Jacobson Charitable Trust
P.O. Box 3475
West Palm Beach, FL 33402-3475

Donor: Robert Jacobson Family Trust.

Foundation type: Independent foundation.

Financial data (yr. ended 12/31/13): Assets, $6,082,671 (M); expenditures, $462,507;

qualifying distributions, $381,315; giving activities include $329,303 for 21 grants (high: $135,500; low: $2,500).

Fields of interest: Education; Higher education; Community and economic development; Youth development.

Type of support: Student aid.

Limitations: Applications not accepted. Giving primarily in West Palm Beach, FL.

Application information: Unsolicited requests for funds not accepted.

Trustee: Thornton Henry.

EIN: 656466536

2125
Roni and Sam Jacobson Family Foundation Inc.
c/o K & O, C.P.A.
169 E. Flagler St., Ste. 800
Miami, FL 33131-1296

Established in 2001 in Florida.

Donor: Contribution of Securities.

Foundation type: Independent foundation.

Financial data (yr. ended 12/31/13): Assets, $1,582,865 (M); expenditures, $250,655; qualifying distributions, $243,492; giving activities include $241,405 for 20 grants (high: $121,500; low: $100).

Fields of interest: Arts and culture; Health; Health care clinics; Diseases and conditions.

Type of support: Research.

Limitations: Applications not accepted. Giving primarily in FL. No grants to individuals.

Application information: Unsolicited requests for funds not accepted.
Board meeting date(s): Jan. 3

Directors: Roni Jacobson; Sam Jacobson; Margery Robbins.

EIN: 651150439

2126
The Janke Charitable Foundation
2136 N. Porpoise Point Ln.
Vero Beach, FL 32963-2845

Established in 2007 in Florida.

Donor: Walter Janke.

Foundation type: Operating foundation.

Financial data (yr. ended 12/31/13): Assets, $7,113,753 (M); gifts received, $500,000; expenditures, $321,056; qualifying distributions, $286,624; giving activities include $262,550 for 19 grants (high: $80,600; low: $500).

Fields of interest: Addiction services; Christianity; Human services; Food aid; Child welfare.

Limitations: Applications not accepted. Giving primarily in FL. No grants to individuals.

Application information: Contributes only to pre-selected organizations.

Trustees: Lalita Janke; Walter Janke.

EIN: 656467846

2127
Jasam Foundation Fund A
25 Bay Ridge Rd.
Key Largo, FL 33037-3779

Established in 2002 in Ohio.

Foundation type: Independent foundation.

Financial data (yr. ended 12/31/13): Assets, $6,416,233 (M); expenditures, $340,346; qualifying distributions, $291,100; giving activities include $291,100 for 35 grants (high: $30,000; low: $100).

Purpose and activities: Giving primarily to perpetuate the philanthropic philosophy of Samuel S. and Janette A. Davis in order to promote the general good.

Fields of interest: Higher education; Christianity; Human services.

Limitations: Applications not accepted. No grants to individuals.

Application information: Contributes only to pre-selected organizations.

Trustee: Jane D. Ferger.

EIN: 311815983

2128
The Jelks Family Foundation, Inc.
516 McKenzie Ave.
Panama City, FL   32401-3060   (850) 784-0809
Main URL: http://www.jelksfamilyfoundation.org

Established in 1995 in Florida.
Foundation type: Independent foundation.
Financial data (yr. ended 12/31/14): Assets, $4,802,856; expenditures, $230,774; qualifying distributions, $221,511.

Purpose and activities: The foundation seeks to promote cultural, educational, environmental, historical, and humanitarian programs through charitable giving and active participation. The foundation is increasingly focused on conserving natural resources.

Fields of interest: Arts and culture; University education; Natural resources; Animal welfare; Nonprofits; Diseases and conditions; Child welfare.

Type of support: Regranting.

Limitations: Applications not accepted. Giving primarily in FL. No grants to individuals.

Application information: Contributes only to pre-selected organizations.

Directors: Allen N. Jelks, Jr.; Deborah Stephens Jelks; Howard L. Jelks; Lisa Grace Jelks; Dr. Mary Jelks; Benjamin A. King; Bryan King; Dr. Christopher B. King; Dr. Helen J. King; Alice J. Lezcano; Edgar Lezcano.

EIN: 593270436

2129
Jenkins Family Charitable Institute
9611 N. U.S. Hwy. 1
Box 390
Sebastian, FL   32958-6363
Contact: David A. Jenkins, Tr.

Established in 2005 in Louisiana.
Donor: David A. Jenkins.
Foundation type: Independent foundation.
Financial data (yr. ended 12/31/13): Assets, $2,908,720 (M); expenditures, $253,257; qualifying distributions, $208,800; giving activities include $190,800 for 4 grants (high: $100,000; low: $300).

Fields of interest: Health; Diseases and conditions.

International interests: Tanzania.

Type of support: Research.

Limitations: Applications accepted. Giving primarily in KS and NJ. No grants to individuals.

Application information:

Initial approach: Proposal
Deadline(s): None
Trustee: David A. Jenkins.
EIN: 202860540

2130
The Johnson Family Foundation, Inc.
582 Island Dr.
Palm Beach, FL   33480

Established in 1997 in New York.
Donors: Thomas S. Johnson; Margaret A. Johnson.
Foundation type: Independent foundation.
Financial data (yr. ended 12/31/13): Assets, $6,287,399 (M); gifts received, $250; expenditures, $277,785; qualifying distributions, $231,454; giving activities include $224,000 for 16 grants (high: $52,500; low: $1,000).

Purpose and activities: Giving for higher education, and art and cultural programs.

Fields of interest: Arts and culture; Education; Higher education.

Limitations: Applications not accepted. Giving primarily in CT, and New York, NY. No grants to individuals.

Application information: Contributes only to pre-selected organizations.

Officers: Thomas S. Johnson, Chair. and Secy.-Treas.; Margaret Ann Johnson, Pres. and Director.

Director: Thomas P. Johnson.

EIN: 137118242

2131
Clay and Debbie Jones Family Foundation
2059 Isla Vista Ln.
Naples, FL   34105

Donors: Clay Jones; Debbie Jones.
Foundation type: Independent foundation.
Financial data (yr. ended 12/31/13): Assets, $0 (M); gifts received, $400,000; expenditures, $328,950; qualifying distributions, $328,950; giving activities include $328,950 for 7 grants (high: $250,000; low: $1,000).

Fields of interest: Higher education.

Limitations: Applications not accepted.

Application information: Unsolicited requests for funds not accepted.

Officers: Clay Jones, Pres.; Debbie Jones, V.P.

EIN: 263838076

2132
The Joshua Foundation, Inc.
5331 Congo Ct.
Cape Coral, FL   33904-5863

Established in 1991 in Florida.
Donors: Michael Duda; Sandra Duda; Luther Duda; Melanie Duda; William Wise; Dorothy Wise; Eleanor Mikler†; Elizabeth Mikler Duda; Mark Kloha; David Kloha; Elizabeth Kloha; A. Duda & Sons, Inc.
Foundation type: Independent foundation.
Financial data (yr. ended 12/31/13): Assets, $1,175,399 (M); gifts received, $633,925; expenditures, $348,419; qualifying distributions, $339,154; giving activities include $271,198 for 16 grants (high: $60,000; low: $5,000), and $61,000 for 7 grants to individuals (high: $15,000; low: $3,000).

Purpose and activities: Giving primarily to Protestant agencies and churches.

Fields of interest: Diseases and conditions; Christianity; Human services.

International interests: Africa; Estonia.

Type of support: Research.

Limitations: Applications not accepted. Giving primarily in CO, FL, IL, TN, TX, and VA.

Application information: Unsolicited requests for funds not accepted.

Officers and Trustees: Daniel J. Carruthers, Pres.; Andrew Duda, V.P.; William Wise, Secy. and Trustee; Rebecca Duda, Treas.; Andrew Duda, Jr.; David Kloha; Andrea Kruse.

EIN: 593076339

2133
The Gilbert S. & John J. Noffo Kahn Foundation
2650 N. Military Trail, Ste. 240
Boca Raton, FL   33431-6346

Established in 2007 in Florida.
Donors: Gilbert S. Kahn; John J. Noffo Kahn.
Foundation type: Independent foundation.
Financial data (yr. ended 12/31/13): Assets, $53,697 (M); gifts received, $250,000; expenditures, $250,000; qualifying distributions, $250,000; giving activities include $250,000 for 1 grant.

Fields of interest: Opera; Wildlife biodiversity; Hospital care; Youth services.

Limitations: Applications not accepted. Giving primarily in FL, New York, NY and RI.

Application information: Contributes only to pre-selected organizations.

Directors: John J. Noffo Kahn; Daniel D. Mielnicki.

EIN: 260623604

2134
The Jay and Becky Kaiserman Foundation
5104 Windward Ave.
Sarasota, FL   34242-1557

Established in 1986 in Florida.
Donors: J.J. Kaiserman; Rebecca Kaiserman.
Foundation type: Operating foundation.
Financial data (yr. ended 12/31/13): Assets, $3,669,671 (M); expenditures, $406,408; qualifying distributions, $315,200; giving activities include $313,550 for 16 grants (high: $95,000; low: $700).

Fields of interest: Arts and culture; Judaism.

Type of support: General support.

Limitations: Applications not accepted. Giving primarily in FL. No grants to individuals.

Application information: Unsolicited requests for funds not accepted.

Trustees: Judy Sperling; Lisa Sperling.

EIN: 592549476

2135
Kanders Foundation, Inc.
2100 S. Ocean Blvd., Ste. 302N
Palm Beach, FL   33480-5225

Established in 1989 in Florida.
Donors: Alan Kanders; Beatrice Kanders; Emily Kanders; Jeanne Kanders Trust.

Foundation type: Independent foundation.
Financial data (yr. ended 06/30/13): Assets, $4,031,141 (M); gifts received, $70,283; expenditures, $198,803; qualifying distributions, $191,873; giving activities include $191,873 for 37 grants (high: $135,000; low: $100).
Purpose and activities: Giving primarily for higher education and to Jewish agencies and temples.
Fields of interest: Arts and culture; Art museums; Elementary and secondary education; Higher education; Nonprofits; Judaism; Reproductive rights; Human services.
Type of support: General support; Scholarships; Regranting.
Limitations: Applications not accepted. Giving primarily in FL and NY. No grants to individuals.
Application information: Contributes only to pre-selected organizations.
Directors: Alan J. Kanders; Jeanne Kanders; Warren B. Kanders.
EIN: 650124714

2136
Warren B. Kanders Foundation
2100 S. Ocean Blvd., Ste. 302N
Palm Beach, FL 33480-5225

Established in 1994 in Florida.
Donor: Warren B. Kanders.
Foundation type: Independent foundation.
Financial data (yr. ended 12/31/13): Assets, $783,377 (M); expenditures, $207,587; qualifying distributions, $202,750; giving activities include $201,000 for 18 grants (high: $63,050; low: $30).
Fields of interest: Arts and culture; Performing arts; Museums; Art museums; Education; Judaism.
Limitations: Applications not accepted. Giving primarily in CT and NY. No grants to individuals.
Application information: Contributes only to pre-selected organizations.
Trustee: Warren B. Kanders.
EIN: 137048184

2137
Janet and Stanley Kane Foundation
1 S. School Ave., Ste. 401
Sarasota, FL 34237-1029

Established in 1993 in Florida.
Donor: Stanley Kane.
Foundation type: Independent foundation.
Financial data (yr. ended 12/31/13): Assets, $135,610 (M); expenditures, $173,991; qualifying distributions, $173,927; giving activities include $173,927 for 23 grants (high: $25,000; low: $50).
Fields of interest: Performing arts; Theater; Orchestral music; Higher education; Health; Hospital care; Reproductive health care; Multiple sclerosis; Gerontology; Judaism; Human services.
Type of support: General support.
Limitations: Applications not accepted. Giving primarily in Sarasota, FL. No grants to individuals.
Application information: Contributes only to pre-selected organizations.
Officer: Stanley Kane, Pres.
Trustees: Priscilla Kane Hellweg; Betsy Kane-Hartnett; Katherine Kane West.
EIN: 650405758

2138
The Deanne & Arnold Kaplan Foundation
13235 Palmers Creek Terr.
Lakewood Ranch, FL 34202-5006

Established in 1998 in Minnesota.
Donors: Deanne Kaplan; Arnold H. Kaplan.
Foundation type: Independent foundation.
Financial data (yr. ended 12/31/13): Assets, $1,840,247 (M); expenditures, $266,738; qualifying distributions, $262,688; giving activities include $260,693 for 19 grants (high: $119,800; low: $50).
Fields of interest: Arts and culture; Art museums; History museums; Education; Nonprofits; Judaism; Human services.
Type of support: Regranting.
Limitations: Applications not accepted. Giving primarily in PA, with some giving in FL. No grants to individuals.
Application information: Unsolicited requests for funds not accepted.
Trustees: Arnold H. Kaplan; Deanne Kaplan; Pamela Ryba.
EIN: 232961830

2139
The Kaul Foundation
c/o Victor Holcomb
3203 W. Cypress St.
Tampa, FL 33607-5109

Established in 1986 in Florida.
Donor: Ralph Kaul†.
Foundation type: Independent foundation.
Financial data (yr. ended 11/30/13): Assets, $8,575,671 (M); expenditures, $334,114; qualifying distributions, $295,500; giving activities include $287,500 for 16 grants (high: $100,000; low: $5,000).
Purpose and activities: The foundation provides awards for excellence on both a national and local level to individuals. Its board of directors requests nominations from anonymous groups and selects recipients after review.
Fields of interest: Education.
Type of support: Grants to individuals.
Limitations: Applications not accepted. Giving primarily in FL and GA.
Application information: Unsolicited requests for funds not accepted.
Trustees: John Holcomb; Victor Holcomb; William F. Poe, Jr.; William Smalley.
EIN: 546244744

2140
The Ernest W. & Agnes W. Kaulbach Charitable Foundation
c/o Austin S. Felis
P.O. Box 32756
Palm Beach Gardens, FL 33420-0422

Established in 1996 in Connecticut.
Donors: John G. George; Mrs. John G. George.
Foundation type: Independent foundation.
Financial data (yr. ended 08/31/14): Assets, $3,583,255 (M); expenditures, $186,789; qualifying distributions, $148,500; giving activities include $148,500 for 9 grants (high: $65,000; low: $1,000).

Purpose and activities: Giving primarily for hospitals; funding also for Roman Catholic agencies and churches, and youth services.
Fields of interest: Health; Catholicism; Human services.
Limitations: Applications not accepted. Giving primarily in Bridgeport, CT. No grants to individuals.
Application information: Unsolicited requests for funds not accepted.
Trustee: Austin S. Felis.
EIN: 066418644

2141
The Carole and Barry Kaye Foundation, Inc.
5100 Town Center Cir., Ste. 550
Boca Raton, FL 33486-1008 (561) 417-5883
Contact: Carole Kaye, Dir.; Barry Kaye, Dir.

Established in 2006 in Florida.
Donors: Carole Kaye; Barry Kaye; Joseph Criscione; Wealth Creation Foundation; CCF I, Inc.
Foundation type: Independent foundation.
Financial data (yr. ended 05/31/13): Assets, $332,749 (M); expenditures, $378,617; qualifying distributions, $350,300; giving activities include $350,300 for 20 grants (high: $100,000; low: $100).
Purpose and activities: Giving primarily for hospitals, human services, and Jewish organizations.
Fields of interest: Art museums; Nonprofits; Hospital care; Judaism; Human services.
Type of support: Regranting.
Limitations: Applications accepted. Giving primarily in FL and NY.
Application information: Application form required.
  Initial approach: Letter
  Deadline(s): None
Directors: Barry Kaye; Carole Kaye; Howard Kaye.
EIN: 202204909

2142
KBR Foundation
7012 Portmarnock Pl.
Bradenton, FL 34202-2593

Established in 1992 in Virginia.
Donor: Margaret Dole Rust†.
Foundation type: Independent foundation.
Financial data (yr. ended 12/31/13): Assets, $5,456,130 (M); expenditures, $466,861; qualifying distributions, $372,312; giving activities include $265,830 for 41 grants (high: $35,000; low: $650).
Purpose and activities: Giving primarily to health associations and human services.
Fields of interest: Education; Natural resources; Biodiversity; Wildlife biodiversity; Health; Hospital care; Diseases and conditions; Biology; Botany; Special Olympics; Human services; Family services; Child welfare.
Type of support: Individual development.
Limitations: Applications not accepted. Giving primarily in Washington, DC. No grants to individuals.
Application information: Contributes only to pre-selected organizations.
Officers and Directors: Joseph P. Bornstein, Pres. and Director; Herbert S. Rosenblum, V.P. and

Director; Lynn Harris Bornstein, Secy. and Director; Paul M. Vincent, Treas. and Director.
EIN: 521772480

2143
Carole C. & Charles A. Kehrer Charitable Trust
P.O. Box 14407
Saint Petersburg, FL 33733-4407

Foundation type: Independent foundation.
Financial data (yr. ended 12/31/13): Assets, $3,368,252 (M); gifts received, $20,634; expenditures, $220,329; qualifying distributions, $165,289; giving activities include $146,432 for 10 grants (high: $22,528; low: $11,264).
Fields of interest: Arts and culture; Animal welfare; Christianity; Human services.
Limitations: Applications not accepted. Giving primarily in OH.
Application information: Unsolicited requests for funds not accepted.
Trustee: Raymond James Trust, N.A.
EIN: 276699145

2144
Kelly Family Foundation
4845 River Village Dr.
Vero Beach, FL 32967-7452

Established in 2004 in Pennsylvania.
Donor: David M. Kelly.
Foundation type: Independent foundation.
Financial data (yr. ended 12/31/13): Assets, $5,773,479 (M); gifts received, $253,442; expenditures, $228,744; qualifying distributions, $223,753; giving activities include $191,655 for 34 grants (high: $101,643; low: $100).
Fields of interest: Secondary education; Christianity.
Limitations: Applications not accepted. No grants to individuals.
Application information: Unsolicited requests for funds not accepted.
Officer: David M. Kelly, Pres.
Directors: Michelle Kelly; Michelle B. Kelly; Susan B. Kelly.
Trustees: David M. Kelly, Jr.; Robert Kelly.
EIN: 202025122

2145
Kessler Family Foundation
120 Casa Bendita
Palm Beach, FL 33480-3602

Established in 1993 in Massachusetts.
Donors: Howard J. Kessler; Patricia M. Kessler; The Kessler Family Fund f/b/o David; The Kessler Family Fund f/b/o Brian.
Foundation type: Independent foundation.
Financial data (yr. ended 12/31/13): Assets, $41,549,264 (M); expenditures, $579,508; qualifying distributions, $454,921; giving activities include $279,484 for 51 grants (high: $50,000; low: $150).
Purpose and activities: Giving primarily for education, medical research, and human services; funding also for Jewish and other federated giving programs.

Fields of interest: Education; Higher education; Nonprofits; Hospital care; Diseases and conditions; Human services; Youth services.
Type of support: Research; Research and evaluation; Regranting.
Limitations: Applications not accepted. Giving primarily in MA and FL. No grants to individuals.
Application information: Contributes only to pre-selected organizations.
Trustees: Howard J. Kessler; Patricia M. Kessler.
EIN: 043213614

2146
The Edward & Lucille Kimmel Foundation, Inc.
625 N. Flagler Dr.
West Palm Beach, FL 33401-4027

Established in 1983 in Florida.
Donors: Joan K. Eigen; Edward A. Kimmel†; Edward A. Kimmel Trust.
Foundation type: Independent foundation.
Financial data (yr. ended 12/31/13): Assets, $9,424,506 (M); gifts received, $19,995; expenditures, $841,375; qualifying distributions, $448,612; giving activities include $345,174 for 78 grants (high: $43,000; low: $2).
Purpose and activities: Giving primarily for education, health care, and to Jewish federated giving programs.
Fields of interest: Arts and culture; Education; Medical education; Nonprofits; Diseases and conditions; Human services.
Type of support: Research; Research and evaluation; Regranting.
Limitations: Applications not accepted. Giving primarily in FL, with emphasis on West Palm Beach, and in New York, NY. No grants to individuals.
Application information: Contributes only to pre-selected organizations.
Officers and Directors: Joan K. Eigen, Pres. and Director; David L. Eigen, Secy.-Treas. and Director; Deborah Barth; David Kimmel.
EIN: 592380662

2147
The Louise Baxter King Charitable Foundation, Inc.
c/o Osborne & Osborne, PA
P.O. Box 40
Boca Raton, FL 33429-0040

Established in 1999 in Florida.
Foundation type: Independent foundation.
Financial data (yr. ended 08/31/14): Assets, $3,537,046 (M); expenditures, $163,813; qualifying distributions, $162,261; giving activities include $160,500 for 13 grants (high: $50,000; low: $1,000).
Fields of interest: Education; Health; Human services.
Limitations: Applications not accepted. No grants to individuals.
Application information: Unsolicited requests for funds not accepted.
Officers and Directors: Mary Thom Osborne, Pres. and V.P. and Director; Wendy H. Jones, Secy. and Director; Molly P. Osborne, Treas. and Director.
EIN: 650972297

2148
Basil L. King Scholarship Foundation, Inc.
(formerly Fort Pierce Memorial Hospital Scholarship Foundation, Inc.)
c/o Indian River State College Foundation, Inc.
3209 Virginia Ave.
Fort Pierce, FL 34981-5596 (772) 462-7246
E-mail: lthomas@irsc.edu; Main URL: http://www.blksf.org

Established in 1973 in Florida.
Donor: Yearsley Memorial Fund.
Foundation type: Independent foundation.
Financial data (yr. ended 09/30/13): Assets, $6,032,419 (M); gifts received, $21,035; expenditures, $312,490; qualifying distributions, $267,698; giving activities include $247,035 for 2 grants (high: $226,000; low: $21,035).
Purpose and activities: Scholarships to St. Lucie County, Florida, residents, who are pursuing study in health sciences, medicine, dentistry and pharmacy; payments also made for the medical care of indigent children under 14 years of age.
Fields of interest: Medical education; Health; Dental care; Nursing care; Diseases and conditions; Low-income and poor people.
Type of support: Scholarships; Grants to individuals; Student aid.
Limitations: Applications accepted. Giving limited to residents of St. Lucie County, FL.
Application information: Complete guidelines and application available on foundation web site. Application form required.
  Deadline(s): See foundation web site for current deadline
Officers and Directors: Frank H. Fee III, Chair. and Director; Frederick T. Johnston, Secy.-Treas. and Director; Jimmie Anne Haisley, Exec. Dir.; Bruce Abernethy, Jr.; Barbara Allen; Margaret Benton; Ann Decker; Betty King.
EIN: 590651084

2149
Kiwanis Club of Bradenton Foundation, Inc.
P.O. Box 1032
Bradenton, FL 34206-1032
Contact: Teri Roberts, Exec. Dir.
E-mail for Teri Roberts: palmroberts@gmail.com; Main URL: http://www.bradentonkiwanis.org

Established in 1990 in Florida.
Donors: Dozier Hilliard; Kiwanis Club of Bradenton, Inc.; Stanley Nieby Revocable Trust; Revocable Living Trust of Elmer J. Trulaske.
Foundation type: Independent foundation.
Financial data (yr. ended 09/30/14): Assets, $11,461,480 (M); gifts received, $2,702; expenditures, $484,452; qualifying distributions, $329,038; giving activities include $329,038 for 28 grants (high: $50,000; low: $500).
Fields of interest: Education; Higher education; Nonprofits; Christianity; Human services; Child welfare; Economics for youth.
Type of support: General support; Scholarships; Regranting.
Limitations: Applications accepted. Giving primarily in FL.
Publications: Application guidelines.
Application information: Complete application guidelines available on foundation web site. Application form required.

Initial approach: For grants e-mail the Club Admin. to request application; for scholarships download the scholarship application on the foundation web site
Deadline(s): Aug. 1
Officers: Teri Roberts, Exec. Dir.; Steven Tinsworth, Chair.; John Tucker, Vice-Chair.; Mark Nelson, Secy.; Thomas A. Moseley, Treas.
Directors: Robert Bartz; Larry Bustle; Jack Hawkins, Esq.; Lemoyne Johnson; Jerry L. Neff; Bob Turner.
EIN: 650221660

2150
Kiwanis of Little Havana Foundation, Inc.

1400 S.W. 1st St.
Miami, FL 33135-2203
Contact: Enriqueta Fernandez, Exec. Dir.

Donors: Kiwanis Club of Little Havana, Inc.; Philip Morris USA; The BSP Group; Montemayor y Asociados.
Foundation type: Independent foundation.
Financial data (yr. ended 09/30/13): Assets, $760,216 (M); gifts received, $176,982; expenditures, $190,719; qualifying distributions, $201,671; giving activities include $130,075 for 6 + grants (high: $49,490), and $71,596 for 48 grants to individuals (high: $4,363; low: $50).
Purpose and activities: Through various community programs, the Foundation assists the children and youth of the community through educational, sports, and outreach related programs.
Fields of interest: Education; Sports and recreation; People of Latin American descent.
Type of support: General support; Grants to individuals.
Limitations: Applications accepted. Giving primarily in Miami, FL.
Application information: Application information found on foundation's web site. Application form required.
Deadline(s): April 29th
Officers and Trustees: Eugenio Hernandez, Chair. and Trustee; Manuel A. Gonzalez, First Vice-Chair. and Trustee; Pedro L. Gonzalez, Second Vice-Chair.; Orestes Wrves, Secy.; Andres Bolano, Jr., Treas.; Enriqueta Fernandez, Exec. Dir.; Agustin Barrera; Raul A. Camaliche; Manuel A. Cuervo; Ricardo Gonzalez; Peter Isern; Raul Perez, Jr.
EIN: 650093807

2151
KLM Fund

3035 Golfside Dr.
Naples, FL 34110

Established in 1986 in Minnesota.
Donors: Robert S. Moe; Karin L. Moe.
Foundation type: Independent foundation.
Financial data (yr. ended 12/31/13): Assets, $154,104 (M); expenditures, $158,713; qualifying distributions, $155,845; giving activities include $155,820 for 45 grants (high: $35,600; low: $100).
Fields of interest: Arts and culture; Higher education; Health; Diseases and conditions; Alzheimer's disease; Human services.
Type of support: Research.
Limitations: Applications not accepted. Giving primarily in FL and MN. No grants to individuals.
Application information: Contributes only to pre-selected organizations.

Officer: Karin L. Moe, Pres. and Treas.
Trustee: Robert S. Moe.
EIN: 363499979

2152
KML Foundation, Inc.

9800 4th St. N., Ste. 204
Saint Petersburg, FL 33702-2462 (727) 578-8980
Contact: John E. Kearney, Chair.
FAX: (727) 578-8982;
E-mail: info@kmlfoundation.org; Main URL: http://www.kmlfoundation.org

Established in 2005 in Florida.
Donor: Krauss Miller Lutz Charitable Foundation.
Foundation type: Operating foundation.
Financial data (yr. ended 05/31/13): Assets, $6,307,479 (M); gifts received, $400,680; expenditures, $332,463; qualifying distributions, $236,826; giving activities include $236,826 for 72 grants to individuals (high: $8,000; low: $500).
Purpose and activities: Giving financial assistance to individuals who are residents of Hillsborough, Pasco or Pinellas counties, Florida, facing the economic challenges of obtaining a higher education.
Fields of interest: Higher education.
Type of support: Student aid; Loans to individuals.
Limitations: Applications accepted. Giving primarily in Hillsborough, Pasco or Pinellas Counties, FL.
Application information: See foundation web site to download the application. Application form required.
Deadline(s): Oct. 1 and Mar. 31 for Fall term and Apr. 1 through Sept. 30 for Spring term
Officers and Directors: John E. Kearney, Chair. and Pres. and Director; Andrew T. Siriani, V.P. and Director; Kim S. Miller, Secy.-Treas.; Virginia R. Miller; Walter G. Weinlander.
EIN: 203344671

2153
The Jules & Gwen Knapp Charitable Foundation

2948 S.E. Southview Dr.
Stuart, FL 34996
Appication address: Gwen Knapp c/o Knapp Charitable Foundation, Glencoe, IL 60022.
tel: (847) 835-8898.

Established in 1985 in Illinois.
Donors: Jules Knapp; Gwen Knapp.
Foundation type: Independent foundation.
Financial data (yr. ended 12/31/14): Assets, $2,279,941 (M); gifts received, $288,469; expenditures, $288,469; qualifying distributions, $287,970; giving activities include $287,970 for 57 grants (high: $100,000; low: $25).
Purpose and activities: Giving primarily to Jewish organizations.
Fields of interest: Arts and culture; Education; Nonprofits; Diseases and conditions; Judaism.
Type of support: Regranting.
Limitations: Applications accepted. Giving primarily in FL and IL; some giving also in CA and NY. No grants to individuals.
Application information: Application form required.
Initial approach: Letter
Deadline(s): None
Officers: Gwen Knapp, Pres.; Jules Knapp, Secy.

Directors: Susan Knapp Schulman; Elyse Knapp Sollender.
EIN: 363381401

2154
The Charles F. and Ruth J. Knippenberg Foundation Inc.

c/o Richard Aboia
11569 Long Shore Way E.
Naples, FL 34119-8965

Established in 2000 in New Jersey.
Donor: Ruth J. Knippenberg.
Foundation type: Independent foundation.
Financial data (yr. ended 12/31/13): Assets, $4,095,672 (M); expenditures, $231,341; qualifying distributions, $198,500; giving activities include $198,500 for 27 grants (high: $20,000; low: $1,000).
Fields of interest: Education; Diseases and conditions; Religion; Human services.
Type of support: Research.
Limitations: Applications not accepted. Giving primarily in NJ. No grants to individuals.
Application information: Contributes only to pre-selected organizations.
Trustees: Patricia Aboia; Richard Aboia; Regina Aboia-Vall.
EIN: 223746616

2155
Knopf Family Foundation, Inc.

6680 S.E. Harbor Cir.
Stuart, FL 34996-1961 (772) 225-1932
Contact: Charles E. Knopf Jr., Tr.

Established in 2003 in Florida.
Donor: Charles E. Knopf, Jr.
Foundation type: Independent foundation.
Financial data (yr. ended 12/31/13): Assets, $6,428,578 (M); gifts received, $2,900,000; expenditures, $285,197; qualifying distributions, $215,350; giving activities include $215,350 for 30 grants (high: $20,000; low: $200).
Fields of interest: Education; Environment; Domesticated animals; Animal welfare.
Limitations: Applications accepted. Giving primarily in FL, NH, and PA. No grants to individuals.
Application information: Application form required.
Initial approach: Letter
Deadline(s): None
Trustees: Ashley J. Knopf Cappelen; Charles E. Knopf, Jr.; Jeffrey P. Manning.
EIN: 571179990

2156
Max & Rika Knopf Foundation

3535 Indian Creek Dr., Ste. 204
Miami, FL 33140-4037

Established in 1988 in New York.
Donors: Max Knopf; Rika Knopf; Flagstaff Financial Corp.; Knopf Assocs.; Solomon Knopf; Eli Knopf; Gitty Neger; Zev Pollak; Rachel Gutman.
Foundation type: Independent foundation.
Financial data (yr. ended 11/30/13): Assets, $1,934,407 (M); gifts received, $312,000; expenditures, $254,419; qualifying distributions, $245,312; giving activities include $241,712 for 38 + grants (high: $61,000).

Purpose and activities: Giving primarily to Jewish agencies, temples, and schools.
Fields of interest: Education; Judaism.
Limitations: Applications not accepted. Giving primarily in NY. No grants to individuals.
Application information: Contributes only to pre-selected organizations.
Officers: Rika Knopf, Mgr.; Solomon Knopf, Mgr.
EIN: 133523504

2157
The Koski Family Foundation, Inc.
5135 Willow Leaf Dr.
Sarasota, FL 34241-6232

Donors: Robert E. Koski; Beverly L. Koski.
Foundation type: Independent foundation.
Financial data (yr. ended 11/30/13): Assets, $6,621,404 (M); expenditures, $420,271; qualifying distributions, $374,292; giving activities include $364,150 for 27 grants (high: $50,000; low: $1,500).
Fields of interest: Performing arts; Museums; Education; Elementary education.
Type of support: General support.
Limitations: Applications not accepted. Giving primarily in Sarasota, FL. No grants to individuals.
Application information: Contributes only to pre-selected organizations.
Officers: Beverly L. Koski, Pres. and Treas.; Robert C. Koski, V.P.; Christine L. Koski, Secy.
Director: Thomas L. Koski.
EIN: 650764285

2158
The Krause Family Foundation
509 Idlewyld Dr.
Fort Lauderdale, FL 33301-2731

Donors: Roy Krause; Kathryn Krause.
Foundation type: Independent foundation.
Financial data (yr. ended 07/31/13): Assets, $4,173,119 (M); gifts received, $1,004,639; expenditures, $243,443; qualifying distributions, $229,000; giving activities include $229,000 for 25 grants (high: $30,000; low: $500).
Fields of interest: Protestantism; Human services.
Limitations: Applications not accepted. Giving primarily in FL.
Application information: Unsolicited requests for funds not accepted.
Directors: Kathryn Krause; Roy Krause.
EIN: 452872991

2159
David and Susan Kreisman Family Foundation
8370 Del Prado Dr.
Delray Beach, FL 33446-9504

Established in 2009 in Florida.
Donors: David S. Kreisman; Susan A. Kreisman.
Foundation type: Independent foundation.
Financial data (yr. ended 12/31/13): Assets, $2,827,718 (M); expenditures, $375,545; qualifying distributions, $354,750; giving activities include $354,500 for 18 grants (high: $250,000; low: $1,000).

Fields of interest: Arts and culture; Education; University education; Nonprofits; Judaism; Human services.
Type of support: Regranting.
Limitations: Applications not accepted. Giving primarily in IL.
Application information: Unsolicited requests for funds not accepted.
Trustees: David S. Kreisman; Susan A. Kreisman.
EIN: 271527925

2160
KT Family Foundation
986 Seagrape Ln.
Vero Beach, FL 32963-2103

Established in 1992 in Michigan.
Donors: Orville K. Thompson†; OKT Char. Lead Trust.
Foundation type: Independent foundation.
Financial data (yr. ended 12/31/13): Assets, $3,844,294 (M); gifts received, $10,007; expenditures, $203,601; qualifying distributions, $171,000; giving activities include $171,000 for 22 grants (high: $20,000; low: $1,000).
Fields of interest: Education; Agriculture; Housing development; Youth development; Children.
Type of support: General support; Continuing support; Emergency funds.
Limitations: Applications not accepted. Giving primarily in MI. No grants to individuals.
Application information: Unsolicited requests for funds not accepted.
Directors: Lauri A. Palazzolo; Janice L. Thompson; Kristen L. Thompson.
Number of staff: 1 part-time professional.
EIN: 383085402

2161
The Kugelman Foundation Inc
c/o Bloomer Geri CPAs
375 N. 9th Ave.
Pensacola, FL 32502-4905 (850) 432-0440

Established in 1961 in Florida.
Donors: D. Jack Kugelman; Standard Distributing Co., Inc.; United Distributors, Inc.; Richmond Distributors, Inc.; Jane S. Kugelman; Nancy K. McSweeney; Jacklyn K. McMahon.
Foundation type: Independent foundation.
Financial data (yr. ended 12/31/13): Assets, $5,814,308 (M); gifts received, $1,151,614; expenditures, $334,380; qualifying distributions, $315,298; giving activities include $315,298 for 40 grants (high: $30,000; low: $1,000).
Purpose and activities: Support primarily for a cancer center, a public television station, human services, youth organizations, and Jewish temples and federated giving programs.
Fields of interest: Arts and culture; Higher education; Nonprofits; Health; Diseases and conditions; Cancers; Judaism; Human services; Food aid; Child welfare; Youth development.
Type of support: General support; Capital and infrastructure; Regranting.
Limitations: Applications accepted. Giving primarily in Pensacola, FL.
Application information:
Initial approach: Proposal
Copies of proposal: 1
Deadline(s): Oct. 1

Officers and Directors: Jane S. Kugelman, Chair. and Pres.; Jacklyn K. McMahon, Secy. and Director; David Jack Foster, Treas. and Director; Robert C. Cameron; Marsha Cameron Kugelman; Janet K. Livingston; Nancy K. McSweeny.
EIN: 596177695

2162
The Louis J. Kuriansky Foundation, Inc.
1100 E. Las Olas Blvd.
Fort Lauderdale, FL 33301-2387

Established in 1995 in Florida.
Foundation type: Independent foundation.
Financial data (yr. ended 12/31/13): Assets, $5,627,989 (M); expenditures, $383,608; qualifying distributions, $301,384; giving activities include $294,200 for 47 grants (high: $39,000; low: $250).
Fields of interest: Graduate and professional education; Nonprofits; Hospital care; Diseases and conditions; Judaism; Theology.
Type of support: Research; Research and evaluation; Regranting.
Limitations: Applications not accepted. Giving primarily in CT, FL and NY. No grants to individuals.
Application information: Contributes only to pre-selected organizations.
Directors: Joan Kuriansky; Sheldon S. Polish; Northern Bank of Florida.
EIN: 650363659

2163
Constance C. and Linwood A. Lacy, Jr. Foundation
c/o Bank of America, N.A.
P.O. Box 40200, FL9-100-10-19
Jacksonville, FL 32203-0200
Application address: c/o Sarah D. Kay, Bank of America, 1111 E. Main St., 12th Fl., Richmond, VA 23219, tel.: (804) 887-8773

Established in 1998 in Virginia.
Donors: Linwood A. Lacy, Jr.; Constance C. Lacy; The Linwood A. Lacy Charitable Lead Annuity Trust.
Foundation type: Independent foundation.
Financial data (yr. ended 12/31/14): Assets, $4,536,214 (M); gifts received, $623,060; expenditures, $362,193; qualifying distributions, $331,883; giving activities include $315,500 for 31 grants (high: $20,000; low: $2,500).
Fields of interest: Arts and culture; Higher education; Housing development; Christianity; Human services; Child welfare; Youth services.
Limitations: Applications accepted. Giving primarily in Richmond and Charlottesville, VA.
Application information: Application form required.
Initial approach: Letter
Deadline(s): None
Officers: Linwood A. Lacy, Jr., Pres.; Constance C. Lacy, Secy.
Directors: Adam M. Lacy; Christopher L. Lacy.
EIN: 541919627

2164
Lambert Foundation, Inc.
2935 20th St.
Vero Beach, FL 32960-3097

Established in 1997 in Florida.

Donors: Patsy J. Lambert; Roy H. Lambert.
Foundation type: Independent foundation.
Financial data (yr. ended 12/31/13): Assets, $3,913,552 (M); expenditures, $180,414; qualifying distributions, $150,660; giving activities include $148,860 for 27 grants (high: $34,360; low: $500).
Purpose and activities: Giving primarily for education.
Fields of interest: Education; Elementary and secondary education; Higher education; Christianity; Human services; Child welfare.
Limitations: Applications not accepted. Giving primarily in FL, with some giving in IL. No grants to individuals.
Application information: Unsolicited requests for funds not accepted.
Officers and Directors: Roy H. Lambert, Pres. and Director; Patsy J. Lambert, V.P. and Director; Donna G. Davis, Secy. and Director; Neal Lohuis, Treas.; Philip A. Lambert; Ronald S. Lambert; Roy H. Lambert, Jr.
EIN: 650749367

2165
The Lambrecht Family Foundation
1002 S.E. Monterey Commons Blvd., Ste. 102
Stuart, FL   34996-2515

Donor: Patricia Lambrecht.
Foundation type: Independent foundation.
Financial data (yr. ended 12/31/13): Assets, $1,513,404 (M); expenditures, $275,121; qualifying distributions, $338,158; giving activities include $142,033 for 16 grants (high: $50,000; low: $100), and $100,000 for 19 grants to individuals (high: $10,000; low: $5,000).
Fields of interest: Higher education; Nonprofits.
Type of support: Student aid; Regranting.
Limitations: Applications not accepted. Giving primarily in IL.
Application information: Unsolicited requests for funds not accepted.
Directors: Melissa Lambrecht; Michelle Greuling; Patricia Lambrecht.
EIN: 204817215

2166
John F. & Rita Lamoureux Foundation, Inc.
3730 Cadbury Cir. W., Unit 623
Venice, FL   34293-2216

Established in 1986 in Florida.
Donor: John F. Lamoureux.
Foundation type: Independent foundation.
Financial data (yr. ended 12/31/14): Assets, $785,167 (M); gifts received, $1,233; expenditures, $163,807; qualifying distributions, $162,365; giving activities include $162,365 for 13 grants (high: $116,415; low: $100).
Fields of interest: Education; Religion; Human services.
Limitations: Applications accepted. Giving primarily in FL and MN. No grants to individuals.
Application information: Application form required.
   Initial approach: Letter
   Deadline(s): None
Officer: Rita Lamoureux, Pres.; Roberta Swanson, Secy.
Director: Renee Noland.
EIN: 411584725

2167
Fanny Landwirth Foundation, Inc.
830-13 US A1A N., No. 103
Ponte Vedra Beach, FL   32082   (904) 860-4409
E-mail: info@fannylandwirthfoundation.org; Main URL: http://fannylandwirthfoundation.org
Grants List: http://fannylandwirthfoundation.org/Recent_Grants.html

Established in 1980 in Florida.
Donor: Henri Landwirth.
Foundation type: Independent foundation.
Financial data (yr. ended 12/31/13): Assets, $5,661,961 (M); gifts received, $78,015; expenditures, $254,193; qualifying distributions, $219,398; giving activities include $202,835 for 29 grants (high: $20,500; low: $200).
Purpose and activities: Giving primarily for human services, education and Jewish affiliations.
Fields of interest: Arts and culture; Education; Religion; Judaism; Tribal and indigenous religions; Human services; Family services; Youth services; Children and youth; Children; Adults; Young adults; Indigenous peoples; Homeless people; Low-income and poor people; Victims of crime and abuse; Terminally ill people.
Type of support: General support; Matching grants; Continuing support; Program development; Seed money.
Limitations: Applications not accepted. Giving primarily in FL and Asheville, NC. No grants to individuals or for capital campaigns; no loans.
Publications: Financial statement; Program policy statement.
Application information: Unsolicited requests for funds not accepted.
   Board meeting date(s): Oct. and Nov.
Officers and Trustees: Gregory D. Landwirth, Pres. and Trustee; Gary M. Landwirth, V.P. and Trustee; Glenn Ullmann, Secy. and Trustee; Linda Landwirth, Treas.; Henri Landwirth, Chair. Emeritus and Trustee; Margot Glazer; Theresa Landwirth; Lisa Landwirth Ullmann.
Number of staff: 2 part-time support.
EIN: 592080560

2168
The Lastinger Family Foundation, Inc.
8342 A1A S.
Saint Augustine, FL   32080-8401

Established in 1998 in Florida.
Donor: Allen L. Lastinger, Jr.
Foundation type: Independent foundation.
Financial data (yr. ended 05/31/14): Assets, $9,512,161; gifts received, $3,946,828; expenditures, $429,571; qualifying distributions, $338,097.
Fields of interest: Natural history museums; Early childhood education; Secondary education; Higher education; Natural resources; Biodiversity; Wildlife biodiversity.
Limitations: Applications not accepted. Giving primarily in FL. No grants to individuals.
Application information: Unsolicited requests for funds not accepted.
Officers: Allen L. Lastinger, Jr., Pres.; Lindsey Riggs, V.P.; Delores T. Lastinger, Secy.
Directors: Beth Lastinger; Lane Lastinger; Ryan Riggs; Amy Vigilante; Jason Vigilante.
EIN: 593512737

2169
Wayne L. Laufer Charitable Foundation, Inc.
c/o Cummings & Lockwood LLC
8000 Health Center Blvd., Ste. 300
Bonita Springs, FL   34135-8178

Donor: Wayne L. Laufer.
Foundation type: Independent foundation.
Financial data (yr. ended 06/30/13): Assets, $1,764,325 (M); gifts received, $540,358; expenditures, $218,742; qualifying distributions, $211,231; giving activities include $211,000 for 11 grants (high: $87,500; low: $2,000).
Fields of interest: Education; Science.
Limitations: Applications not accepted. Giving primarily in IL and MO.
Application information: Unsolicited requests for funds not accepted.
Officers and Directors: Wayne L. Laufer, Pres. and Director; Bradley W. Laufer, V.P. and Director; Gayle M. Laufer, Secy.-Treas. and Director; Brandie L. Ettinger.
EIN: 263246955

2170
Lawson Family Charitable Foundation
c/o John K. Lawson
263 Ferry Landing Dr.
Sanibel, FL   33957

Established in 1997 in Illinois.
Donor: John K. Lawson.
Foundation type: Independent foundation.
Financial data (yr. ended 12/31/13): Assets, $4,447,776 (M); gifts received, $142,000; expenditures, $195,584; qualifying distributions, $179,200; giving activities include $179,200 for 22 grants (high: $80,000; low: $200).
Fields of interest: University education; Religion; Human services.
Type of support: Scholarships.
Limitations: Applications not accepted. No grants to individuals.
Application information: Unsolicited requests for funds not accepted.
Trustees: Ann L. Reed; Jennifer S. Cavins; John K. Lawson; Robert J. Lawson; Suzanne D. Lawson.
EIN: 364199442

2171
The Layden Family Foundation
4761 W. Bay Blvd., Ste. 2101
Estero, FL   33928-3322

Established in 2000 in Pennsylvania.
Donors: Donald W. Layden Agency; Barbara Layden; Donald W. Layden.
Foundation type: Independent foundation.
Financial data (yr. ended 12/31/13): Assets, $843,527 (M); expenditures, $137,361; qualifying distributions, $130,000; giving activities include $130,000 for 11 grants (high: $35,000; low: $1,000).
Fields of interest: Arts and culture; Education; Religion.
Type of support: General support.
Limitations: Applications not accepted. Giving primarily in NC. No grants to individuals.
Application information: Unsolicited requests for funds not accepted.

Trustees: Barbara Layden; Donald W. Layden.
EIN: 233039715

2172
The Rudi Lazarus Foundation
c/o M.A. Buzzeo
1128 Grand Cay Dr.
Palm Beach Gardens, FL 33418-8400
Contact: Richard Zelisko, Pres.

Established in 1985 in Florida.
Donors: Rudolph G. Lazarus†; Richard Zelisko; Michael A. Buzzeo.
Foundation type: Independent foundation.
Financial data (yr. ended 06/30/14): Assets, $1,613,763 (M); expenditures, $197,741; qualifying distributions, $152,500; giving activities include $132,500 for 3 grants (high: $55,000; low: $22,500).
Purpose and activities: Giving primarily for youth and the arts.
Fields of interest: Arts and culture; Arts education; Historic preservation; Education; Environment; Environmental and resource rights; Human services; Youth development; Youth services.
Type of support: Continuing support; Program-related investments; Endowments; Seed money; Internships; Scholarships; Technical assistance.
Application information:
  Initial approach: Letter
Officers: Richard Zelisko, Pres.; Michael A. Buzzeo, Treas.
EIN: 592621678

2173
The Alice E. and Mischa Lazoff Foundation Inc.
2000 Island Blvd., Ste. 3004
Aventura, FL 33160-4957

Established in 2007 in Florida.
Donor: Alice E. Lazoff Irrevocable Trust.
Foundation type: Independent foundation.
Financial data (yr. ended 06/30/14): Assets, $2,777,376 (M); expenditures, $297,155; qualifying distributions, $148,650; giving activities include $148,550 for 5 grants (high: $50,300; low: $250).
Fields of interest: Health; Religion; Human services.
Limitations: Applications not accepted. Giving primarily in FL and NY. No grants to individuals.
Application information: Contributes only to pre-selected organizations.
Director: Edward Meinstein.
EIN: 510612077

2174
Gasper & Irene Lazzara Charitable Foundation
5000 Sawgrass Village Cir., Ste. 3
Ponte Vedra Beach, FL 32082-5042

Established in 1996 in Florida.
Donors: Gasper Lazzara; Irene Lazzara.
Foundation type: Independent foundation.
Financial data (yr. ended 04/30/13): Assets, $2,830,440 (M); expenditures, $377,427; qualifying distributions, $353,515; giving activities

include $350,665 for 58 grants (high: $150,000; low: $20).
Purpose and activities: Grants are awarded to non-profit institutions that engage in research relevant to developing strategies for the prevention and treatment of cancer. Particular interests of the foundation are ocular melanoma and metastatic liver cancer.
Fields of interest: Nonprofits; Cancers; Community and economic development; Human services.
Type of support: Regranting.
Limitations: Applications accepted. Giving primarily in Jacksonville, FL.
Application information: Application form required.
  Initial approach: Letter
  Deadline(s): None
Officers: Irene Lazzara, Pres.; Gasper Lazzara, V.P.
EIN: 597079426

2175
Iris and Junming Le Foundation
1000 S. Ocean Blvd., Ste. 407
Boca Raton, FL 33432-7733

Established in 2006 in New York.
Donor: Junming Le.
Foundation type: Independent foundation.
Financial data (yr. ended 12/31/13): Assets, $12,699,102 (M); gifts received, $2,286,860; expenditures, $456,682; qualifying distributions, $449,735; giving activities include $414,000 for 3 grants (high: $300,000; low: $5,000).
Fields of interest: Education; Diseases and conditions; Religion; Domestic violence shelters.
Type of support: Research.
Limitations: Applications not accepted. No grants to individuals.
Application information: Contributes only to pre-selected organizations.
Trustees: Junming Le; Daniella Loh; Sai Hong Yan.
EIN: 206861899

2176
Louis Leibowitz Charitable Trust
2121 Ponce de Leon Blvd., Ste. 1100
Coral Gables, FL 33134-5213

Established in 1986 in Florida.
Donor: Marvin Leibowitz.
Foundation type: Independent foundation.
Financial data (yr. ended 12/31/13): Assets, $261,328; expenditures, $377,418; qualifying distributions, $372,523; giving activities include $372,523 for 75 grants (high: $100,000; low: $500).
Fields of interest: Arts and culture; Youth development.
Limitations: Applications not accepted. Giving primarily in FL and IL. No grants to individuals.
Application information: Unsolicited requests for funds not accepted.
Trustees: Michael B. Goldstein; Marvin Leibowitz.
EIN: 596862966

2177
Josephine S. Leiser Foundation, Inc.
c/o Hackleman, Olive & Judd, P.A.
2438 E. Las Olas Blvd.
Fort Lauderdale, FL 33301
Contact: Robert Judd, Pres. and Treas.

Established in 1992 in Florida.
Donor: Josephine S. Leiser†.
Foundation type: Independent foundation.
Financial data (yr. ended 05/31/14): Assets, $7,760,184 (M); expenditures, $536,400; qualifying distributions, $261,342; giving activities include $147,500 for 7 grants (high: $50,000; low: $2,500).
Purpose and activities: Giving primarily for the arts, and children, youth and social services.
Fields of interest: Arts and culture; Performing arts; Opera; Nonprofits; Television; Human services; Child welfare.
Type of support: General support; Regranting.
Limitations: Applications not accepted. Giving primarily in FL. No grants to individuals.
Application information: Contributes only to pre-selected organizations.
Officers: Robert Judd, Pres. and Treas.; Theodore Friedt, V.P.; Ruth Turner Camp, Secy.
EIN: 650347903

2178
Marie Keese Lelash Foundation, Inc.
6919 W. Broward Blvd., Ste. 164
Plantation, FL 33317-2902

Established in 1988 in Florida.
Donor: Marie Keese Lelash†.
Foundation type: Independent foundation.
Financial data (yr. ended 06/30/14): Assets, $4,988,914; expenditures, $328,680; qualifying distributions, $206,630.
Fields of interest: Historic preservation; Education; Animal welfare; Hospital care; Hospice care; Cancers; Libraries; Human services; Food banks; Youth services; Seniors; People with vision impairments.
Type of support: General support; Mission-related investments; Capital campaigns; Capital and infrastructure; Program development.
Limitations: Applications not accepted. Giving primarily in FL; some giving in NY and RI. No grants to individuals.
Application information: Contributes only to pre-selected organizations.
Officers: Richard W. LeLash, Pres.; Gail Anderson, Secy.; Curtis W. LeLash, Treas.
Director: William J. LeLash.
Number of staff: 4 part-time professional; 1 part-time support.
EIN: 650011076

2179
The Thelma and Melvin Lenkin Charitable Foundation, Inc.
1500 S. Ocean Blvd.
Boca Raton, FL 33432-8529

Established in 1997 in Florida.
Donors: Melvin Lenkin; Thelma Lenkin.
Foundation type: Independent foundation.
Financial data (yr. ended 11/30/13): Assets, $6,483,915 (M); expenditures, $296,290; qualifying distributions, $217,010; giving activities include $210,065 for 34 grants (high: $30,815; low: $100).
Fields of interest: Performing arts; Art museums; Elementary and secondary education; Nonprofits; Hospital care; Judaism.
Type of support: Regranting.

Limitations: Applications not accepted. No grants to individuals.
Application information: Unsolicited requests for funds not accepted.
Officers: Thelma Lenkin, Pres.; Melvin Lenkin, Secy.-Treas.
Directors: Edward J. Lenkin; Judy Lenkin Lerner.
EIN: 522071692

2180
Lerner Family Foundation
1545 Hillview Ave.
Sarasota, FL 34239-9735

Established in 2005 in Florida.
Donor: Donald Lerner.
Foundation type: Independent foundation.
Financial data (yr. ended 12/31/13): Assets, $1,339,619 (M); gifts received, $663; expenditures, $222,852; qualifying distributions, $222,852; giving activities include $215,250 for 14 grants (high: $25,000; low: $10,000).
Fields of interest: Christianity; Child welfare; Youth services.
Limitations: Applications not accepted. Giving primarily in FL, IL and NY. No grants to individuals.
Application information: Unsolicited requests for funds not accepted.
Directors: Brittney Bezirgan; Yasir Bezirgan; Julie Jacobs; Donald Lerner; Michael Lerner; Sharon Shoemaker.
EIN: 202550588

2181
Mildred & Abner Levine Family Foundation
16858 River Birch Cir.
Delray Beach, FL 33445-7055 5614981500

Foundation type: Independent foundation.
Financial data (yr. ended 12/31/14): Assets, $2,891,932; gifts received, $1,305,492; expenditures, $866,401; qualifying distributions, $172,507.
Purpose and activities: Giving primarily to Jewish agencies and associations.
Fields of interest: Nonprofits; Judaism; Human services.
Type of support: Regranting.
Limitations: Applications not accepted. Giving on a national basis. No grants to individuals.
Application information: Contributes only to pre-selected organizations.
Officers and Directors: Lawrence I. Levine, Pres. and Director; Mildred Levine, V.P. and Director; Michael F. Levine, Secy. and Director; Ellen K. Miller, Treas. and Director.
EIN: 136172502

2182
Jonathan D. Lewis Foundation Inc.
(formerly POLE Foundation, Inc.)
3595 Anchorage Way
Coconut Grove, FL 33133-5923 (305) 669-8990
Contact: Jonathan D. Lewis, Pres.

Donors: Jonathan D. Lewis; Jonathan D. Lewis Trust.
Foundation type: Independent foundation.
Financial data (yr. ended 12/31/13): Assets, $6,605,655 (M); gifts received, $166,000; expenditures, $336,683; qualifying distributions, $323,677; giving activities include $312,307 for 11 grants (high: $222,000; low: $500).
Fields of interest: Arts and culture; Education; Foundations; Human services; Youth services; LGBTQ people.
Limitations: Applications accepted. Giving primarily in Aspen, CO, Washington, DC, FL, and NY. No grants to individuals.
Application information: Application form required.
   Initial approach: Proposal
   Deadline(s): None
Officers: Jonathan D. Lewis, Pres.; Dania De La Vega, Secy.
Board Member: Paul Yandura.
EIN: 650330579

2183
Liebhaber Family Foundation
1500 S. Ocean Blvd., Apt. 505 S.
Boca Raton, FL 33432
Application address: 4509 Minnetonka Blvd., Minneapolis, MN 55416-5192, tel.: (952) 259-5222

Established in 1983 in Minnesota.
Donors: Henia Liebhaber; Marc Liebhaber; Sharon F. Liebhaber.
Foundation type: Independent foundation.
Financial data (yr. ended 12/31/13): Assets, $812,592 (M); expenditures, $135,382; qualifying distributions, $125,550; giving activities include $125,550 for 17 grants (high: $60,000; low: $500).
Fields of interest: Religion.
Type of support: General support.
Limitations: Applications accepted. Giving primarily in PA.
Application information: Application form required.
   Initial approach: Proposal
   Deadline(s): None
Officers: Marc Liebhaber, Pres. and Treas.; Alan Iser, V.P. and Secy.
Director: Sharon F. Liebhaber.
EIN: 411454333

2184
Life's Requite, Inc.
2201 4th St. N., Ste. 201
Saint Petersburg, FL 33704-4300

Established in 1997 in Florida.
Donor: Thomas A. Sansone.
Foundation type: Independent foundation.
Financial data (yr. ended 12/31/13): Assets, $7,226,855 (M); expenditures, $369,639; qualifying distributions, $355,000; giving activities include $355,000 for 14 grants (high: $100,000; low: $10,000).
Purpose and activities: Giving primarily for the arts, human services, and to charitable foundations.
Fields of interest: Arts and culture; Art museums; Foundations; Cancers; Religion; Human services; Child welfare.
Limitations: Applications not accepted. Giving primarily in St. Petersburg and Tampa, FL; with some giving in Houston, TX. No grants to individuals.
Application information: Contributes only to pre-selected organizations.

Officer and Directors: Thomas A. Sansone, Pres. and Secy.-Treas. and Director; Jeffery T. Sansone; Laura A. Sansone; Cathy L. Unruh.
EIN: 593446719

2185
Lipton Foundation
655 Ocean Blvd.
Golden Beach, FL 33160-2217 (305) 935-3338
FAX: (305) 935-3440; Main URL: http://liptonfoundation.com

Donors: Alan Lipton; Janice Lipton.
Foundation type: Independent foundation.
Financial data (yr. ended 12/31/13): Assets, $6,385,583 (M); gifts received, $200,000; expenditures, $423,788; qualifying distributions, $369,438; giving activities include $315,796 for 22 grants (high: $85,400; low: $100).
Fields of interest: Foundations; Nonprofits; Judaism; Human services.
Type of support: Regranting.
Limitations: Applications not accepted. Giving primarily in FL.
Application information: Unsolicited requests for funds not accepted.
Trustees: Alan Lipton; Janice Lipton.
EIN: 650098730

2186
Michael R. Lissack Foundation
2338 Immokalee Rd., Ste. 113
Naples, FL 34110-1445

Established in 1998 in Massachusetts.
Donors: Michael R. Lissack; Williams College.
Foundation type: Independent foundation.
Financial data (yr. ended 12/31/12): Assets, $1,154,395 (M); expenditures, $361,678; qualifying distributions, $278,000; giving activities include $278,000 for grants.
Fields of interest: Education.
Limitations: Applications not accepted. Giving primarily in FL and MA. No grants to individuals.
Application information: Contributes only to pre-selected organizations.
Officer: Michael R. Lissack, Pres.
EIN: 043304952

2187
Mollie Parnis Livingston Foundation, Inc.
389 Eagle Dr.
Jupiter, FL 33477-4065

Established in 1967 in New York.
Donors: Mollie Parnis Livingston†; Robert L. Livingston†.
Foundation type: Independent foundation.
Financial data (yr. ended 12/31/12): Assets, $2,901,279 (M); expenditures, $211,767; qualifying distributions, $154,635; giving activities include $154,635 for grants.
Purpose and activities: Giving primarily for urban affairs and medical research; support also for a journalism awards program for journalists under 35 who are not students and are working for a U.S.-owned publication or broadcast organization.
Fields of interest: Performing arts; Diseases and conditions; Publishing; Community and economic development.

Type of support: General support; Grants to individuals; Research; Research and evaluation.
Limitations: Applications accepted. Giving primarily in New York, NY for organizations.
Application information: Application form required for journalism awards, along with printed or broadcast concert entries. Application form required.

   Initial approach: Letter
   Deadline(s): Feb. 1
Officers: Neal S. Hochman, Pres. and Treas.; Eugene V. Kokot, Secy.
Directors: Cynthia Hochman; David P. Hochman; Sara B. Hochman; Mike Wallace.
EIN: 136265280

2188
The Loftis Foundation, Inc.
1202 Seminole Circle
Moore Haven, FL 33471-5746

Established in 1994 in Florida.
Foundation type: Independent foundation.
Financial data (yr. ended 12/31/13): Assets, $5,620,957 (M); gifts received, $1,285,607; expenditures, $212,520; qualifying distributions, $182,400; giving activities include $167,323 for 9 grants (high: $140,000; low: $70).
Purpose and activities: Giving primarily to Christian churches for building and operating expenses.
Fields of interest: Education; Christianity.
Limitations: Applications not accepted. Giving primarily in CA, FL, and KY. No grants to individuals.
Application information: Unsolicited requests for funds not accepted.
Officer: Robert W. Loftis, Pres.
EIN: 582110528

2189
D. R. Long Foundation, Inc.
3940 Somerset Dr.
Sarasota, FL 34242-1110

Established in 1983 in Maryland.
Donor: Daniel R. Long III.
Foundation type: Independent foundation.
Financial data (yr. ended 10/31/13): Assets, $2,100,467 (M); expenditures, $194,385; qualifying distributions, $190,027; giving activities include $188,200 for 26 grants (high: $52,000; low: $400).
Fields of interest: Philanthropy; Mental health care; Human services.
Type of support: General support; Continuing support; Emergency funds; Program development.
Limitations: Applications not accepted. Giving primarily in FL. No grants to individuals.
Publications: Annual report.
Application information: Unsolicited requests for funds not accepted.
Officers: Daniel R. Long III, Pres.; Barbara O'Brien, V.P.; Susan E. Kertz, Secy.
Number of staff: 2 part-time professional.
EIN: 521379622

2190
Lookout Foundation, Inc.
934 Flagship Dr.
Summerland Key, FL 33042-4827

Established in 2000 in New Jersey.
Donors: Nancy Z. Noblitt; Niles L. Noblitt.
Foundation type: Independent foundation.
Financial data (yr. ended 12/31/13): Assets, $11,440,562 (M); gifts received, $1,137,591; expenditures, $412,596; qualifying distributions, $408,050; giving activities include $408,050 for 83 grants (high: $69,000; low: $100).
Fields of interest: Natural resources; Nonprofits; Human services; Child welfare.
Type of support: Regranting.
Limitations: Applications not accepted. Giving primarily in DC, IA, IN and NJ. No grants to individuals.
Application information: Contributes only to pre-selected organizations.
Officers and Directors: Nancy Z. Noblitt, Pres. and Director; Niles L. Noblitt, Treas. and Director; Sarah E. Erlandson; Catherine N. Keating; Joseph F Noblitt.
EIN: 223745074

2191
The Lowry Murphey Family Foundation, Inc.
(formerly The Sumter and Ivilyn Lowry Foundation, Inc.)
P.O. Box 18065
Tampa, FL 33679-8065

Established in 1987 in Florida.
Donors: Sumter Lowry†; Ivilyn Lowry†; Anne Murphy†.
Foundation type: Independent foundation.
Financial data (yr. ended 12/31/13): Assets, $5,505,518 (M); expenditures, $291,984; qualifying distributions, $238,709; giving activities include $220,000 for 50 grants (high: $75,000; low: $500).
Purpose and activities: Giving primarily to a YMCA and to Christian organizations and churches.
Fields of interest: Education; Zoos; Health; Protestantism; Catholicism.
Limitations: Applications not accepted. Giving primarily in Tampa, FL. No grants to individuals.
Application information: Unsolicited requests for funds not accepted.
Officers: Helen M. Brown, Pres.; Caroline Snyder, Secy.-Treas.
Directors: Matthew M. Holpsinger; David R. Murphy.
EIN: 592824550

2192
The Lyle Foundation
c/o Thomas Sienicki
1811 N.W. 51st St.
Hangar PMB 1063
Fort Lauderdale, FL 33309-7119

Established in 2003 in New York.
Donor: James R. Lyle.
Foundation type: Independent foundation.
Financial data (yr. ended 12/31/13): Assets, $3,549 (M); gifts received, $79,000; expenditures, $153,079; qualifying distributions, $152,759; giving activities include $147,192 for 13 grants (high: $100,000; low: $1,000).
Fields of interest: Education.
Limitations: Applications not accepted. Giving primarily in New York, NY.
Application information: Unsolicited requests for funds not accepted.

Officer: James R. Lyle, Exec. Dir.
EIN: 200466096

2193
MAH Foundation, Inc.
7121 Fairway Dr., Ste. 400
Palm Beach Gardens, FL 33418-3776 (561) 656-0609
Contact: Mark Albers, C.F.O.
Main URL: http://www.mahfoundation.org
Grants List: http://www.mahfoundation.org/recipients.html

Established in 2002 in Florida.
Donor: Allan E. Hadhazy.
Foundation type: Independent foundation.
Financial data (yr. ended 11/30/12): Assets, $3,695,252 (M); expenditures, $160,500; qualifying distributions, $155,500; giving activities include $155,500 for 35 grants (high: $30,000; low: $1,500).
Fields of interest: Disasters and emergency management; Religion; Human services.
Type of support: General support.
Limitations: Applications accepted. Giving primarily in CA and FL.
Application information: Application form required.
   Initial approach: Letter
   Deadline(s): None
Officer: Mark N. Albers, C.F.O.
Directors: Helen J. Barrionnuevo; Allan E. Hadhazy; Andrew H. Kayton.
EIN: 651165800

2194
Marco Family Foundation, Inc.
(formerly Seymour R. Marco Family Foundation, Inc.)
8265 Bayberry Rd.
Jacksonville, FL 32256-7432

Established in 1982 in Florida.
Donors: Carolyn C. Marco; David A. Marco.
Foundation type: Independent foundation.
Financial data (yr. ended 06/30/14): Assets, $3,994,281 (M); expenditures, $189,347; qualifying distributions, $183,027; giving activities include $181,500 for 14 grants (high: $25,000; low: $1,000).
Purpose and activities: Giving primarily for optometric education.
Fields of interest: Education; Diseases and conditions; Human services.
Type of support: Capital and infrastructure; Research; Scholarships.
Limitations: Applications not accepted. Giving primarily in FL. No grants to individuals.
Application information: Unsolicited requests for funds not accepted.
Officers and Trustees: David A. Marco, Pres. and Trustee; Charon M. Dyer, V.P. and Trustee; Mark Shorstein, Secy. and Trustee; Jack F. Shorstein, Treas. and Trustee; Samuel R. Shorstein.
EIN: 592197357

2195
Harriet McDaniel Marshall Trust in Memory of Sanders McDaniel
P.O. Box 1908
Orlando, FL 32802-1908

Established in 1962 in Georgia.
Donor: Harriet McDaniel Marshall†.
Foundation type: Independent foundation.
Financial data (yr. ended 12/31/14): Assets, $8,866,125; expenditures, $338,755; qualifying distributions, $311,739.
Purpose and activities: Giving primarily for education and building funds for educational institutions, health, and the handicapped; support also for welfare, including organizations assisting the disadvantaged, the homeless, and the elderly, community funds and development, and arts and culture.
Fields of interest: Arts and culture; Education; Elementary and secondary education; Higher education; Community and economic development.
Type of support: Capital campaigns; Building and renovations; Equipment.
Limitations: Applications accepted. Giving primarily in the metropolitan Atlanta, GA, area. No grants to individuals, or for scholarships or fellowships; no loans.
Publications: Application guidelines; Program policy statement.
Application information: Application form required.
  Initial approach: See Website
  Deadline(s): Mar. 31, Aug. 31, Nov. 30
Officers: E. Jenner Wood, Chair.; Kirby Thompson, Secy.
Distribution Committee: John Geraghty; Dave Dierker.
Trustee: SunTrust Bank, Inc.
Number of staff: None.
EIN: 586089937

2196
G. Roxy & Elizabeth C. Martin Charitable Trust
c/o SunTrust Bank, Charitable Services Group
300 S. Orange Ave., Ste. 1600
Orlando, FL 32801-3382
E-mail: fdnsvcs.fl@suntrust.com; Application address: c/o SunTrust Bank, 200 S. Orange Ave., SOAB-10, Orlando, FL 32801; Main URL: http://fdnweb.org/martin

Established in 1988 in Florida.
Donors: G. Roxy Martin; Elizabeth C. Martin; Alfred S. Martin.
Foundation type: Independent foundation.
Financial data (yr. ended 11/30/13): Assets, $4,071,044 (M); expenditures, $249,126; qualifying distributions, $225,905; giving activities include $90,500 for 9 grants (high: $20,000; low: $3,000), and $112,250 for 87 grants to individuals (high: $2,500; low: $750).
Purpose and activities: Giving primarily for education, health and human services, arts and culture, religion, children and youth services, and environment.
Fields of interest: Arts and culture; Secondary education; Higher education; Environment; Christianity; Human services; Child welfare.
Type of support: General support; Capital campaigns; Student aid.
Limitations: Applications accepted. Giving primarily in Lake County, FL.
Application information: Application guidelines available on trust web site. Application form required.
  Initial approach: Telephone for application
  Copies of proposal: 1

Deadline(s): Mar. 31 for scholarships. Oct. 1 for grants
Board meeting date(s): Nov.
Final notification: May for scholarships
Trustee: SunTrust Bank.
Directors: Alfred C. Haliday, Jr.; J. Stephen Pullum; David Weiss.
EIN: 596920693

2197
The Patrick J. Martin Family Foundation
5286 Kensington High St.
Naples, FL 34105 (303) 931-3723
Contact: Patrick J. Martin, Tr.
FAX: (239) 643-3263; E-mail: patmartin@qwest.net

Established in 2005 in Colorado.
Donor: Patrick J. Martin.
Foundation type: Independent foundation.
Financial data (yr. ended 12/31/12): Assets, $4,396,087 (M); expenditures, $300,832; qualifying distributions, $273,844; giving activities include $58,844 for 6 grants (high: $26,400; low: $250), and $215,000 for 43 grants to individuals (high: $5,000; low: $5,000).
Purpose and activities: Giving primarily to encourage the study of math, science, and engineering at the college or undergraduate level. Preference is given to students who wish to study at Iona College in New Rochelle, NY, or The George Washington University in Washington, DC. Applicants must 1) demonstrate financial need, 2) be in the top 10 percent of their graduating class and have a desire to study math, science, or engineering, 3) take a challenging course of study in math and science and have successfully completed available AP Science and Math courses, 4) score in the top ten percentile in the Math, Reading and Writing SATs or equivalent, and 5) have strong character demonstrated in school and/or community. The foundation also supports efforts in the arts, the environment and humanitarian needs.
Fields of interest: Higher education.
Type of support: General support; Student aid.
Limitations: Applications accepted. Giving primarily in NY.
Publications: Application guidelines; Annual report.
Application information: Application form required.
  Initial approach: Proposal
  Deadline(s): None
Trustee: Patrick J. Martin.
EIN: 206758585

2198
Mary Anna Foundation Charitable Trust
7791 N.W. 146th St.
Miami Lakes, FL 33016-1567

Established in 1997 in Florida.
Donor: Mary Anna Fowler.
Foundation type: Independent foundation.
Financial data (yr. ended 02/28/13): Assets, $3,807,124 (M); gifts received, $99,000; expenditures, $272,736; qualifying distributions, $192,708; giving activities include $189,440 for 20 grants (high: $35,000; low: $250).
Fields of interest: Arts and culture; Education; Health; Religion; Christianity; Human services.
Limitations: Applications not accepted. No grants to individuals.

Application information: Unsolicited requests for funds not accepted.
Trustees: Dennis D. Nichols; Gregory A. Nichols.
EIN: 650741939

2199
Mayberg Family Charitable Foundation
10295 Collins Ave., Unit 2208
Bal Harbour, FL 33154-1605

Established in 2004 in Maryland.
Donors: Louis Mayberg; Helene Morton†; Manette Mayberg.
Foundation type: Independent foundation.
Financial data (yr. ended 12/31/13): Assets, $7,612,281 (M); gifts received, $1,325,000; expenditures, $549,646; qualifying distributions, $920,265; giving activities include $252,000 for 11 grants (high: $150,000; low: $1,000).
Purpose and activities: Giving primarily for Jewish education and outreach.
Fields of interest: Education; Judaism.
Type of support: Annual campaigns; Program-related investments; Capital campaigns; Capital and infrastructure.
Limitations: Applications not accepted. Giving primarily in the greater Washington, DC, area. No grants to individuals.
Publications: Annual report.
Application information: Contributes only to pre-selected organizations.
Trustee: Louis Mayberg.
Number of staff: None.
EIN: 546588139

2200
Mb Caddyshack Charity Golf, Inc.
2002 San Marco Blvd., Ste. 201
Jacksonville, FL 32207-3271

Foundation type: Independent foundation.
Financial data (yr. ended 12/31/13): Assets, $778 (M); expenditures, $711,186; qualifying distributions, $140,000; giving activities include $140,000 for 7 grants (high: $111,000; low: $500).
Fields of interest: Education; Health; Safety education.
Limitations: Applications not accepted. Giving primarily in FL.
Application information: Unsolicited requests for funds not accepted.
Officers and Directors: Edward Murray, Pres. and Director; Nancy Seely, Secy.; Penny Logan, Treas.; Bill Clifford; Mikael Kyling; Greg Peters; Judd White.
EIN: 264195961

2201
The Robert F. & Eleonora W. McCabe Foundation, Inc.
(formerly The Wahlstrom Foundation, Inc.)
3055 Cardinal Dr., Ste. 106
Vero Beach, FL 32963-4901 (772) 231-7513
Contact: Lenora A. Ritchie, Exec. Dir.
FAX: (772) 234-1632;
E-mail: mccabefoundation@aol.com; Mailing address: P.O. Box 643276, Vero Beach, FL 32964

Established in 1956 in Unspecified.
Donors: Magnus Wahlstrom†; Agnes S. Wahlstrom†.

Foundation type: Independent foundation.
Financial data (yr. ended 12/31/13): Assets, $3,111,043 (M); expenditures, $435,206; qualifying distributions, $378,797; giving activities include $237,890 for 43 grants (high: $92,750; low: $100).
Purpose and activities: Giving to improve access to mental health services for people in Indian River County, FL. Giving also to support and promote philanthropic activity in Indian River County, FL.
Fields of interest: Philanthropy; Mental health care.
Type of support: Seed money; Matching grants; Program development; Endowments; Capital campaigns; Annual campaigns.
Limitations: Applications not accepted. Giving primarily in Indian River County, FL. No grants to individuals.
Application information: Unsolicited requests for funds not accepted.
  Board meeting date(s): May
Officers and Directors: Eleonora W. McCabe, Pres. and Director; Robert F. McCabe, V.P. and Director; Beverley Mastrinanni, Secy. and Director; Robert R. Harris, Treas. and Director; Lenora A. Ritchie, Exec. Dir.
Number of staff: 1 full-time professional; 1 part-time support.
EIN: 066053378

2202
McClanathan Family Foundation

3100 Rum Row
Naples, FL   34102-7837

Donors: Joseph W. McClanathan; Robin McClanathan.
Foundation type: Independent foundation.
Financial data (yr. ended 12/31/13): Assets, $703,876 (M); gifts received, $1,800; expenditures, $273,949; qualifying distributions, $260,561; giving activities include $260,561 for 29 grants (high: $150,000; low: $100).
Fields of interest: Diseases and conditions; Community and economic development; Religion.
Limitations: Applications not accepted. Giving primarily in MO.
Application information: Unsolicited requests for funds not accepted.
Trustees: Joseph W. McClanathan; Laura D. McClanathan; Robin McClanathan; Susan A. McClanathan.
EIN: 272152799

2203
The Malcolm S. & Sonia R. McDonald Foundation

1124 Dormie Dr.
Naples, FL   34108-1928
Application address: c/o Malcolm S.McDonald, 8002 Discovery Dr., Ste. 420, Richmond, VA 23229

Established in 1986 in Virginia.
Donors: Malcolm S. McDonald; Sonia R. McDonald.
Foundation type: Independent foundation.
Financial data (yr. ended 12/31/13): Assets, $97,344 (M); gifts received, $121,234; expenditures, $210,638; qualifying distributions, $194,676; giving activities include $183,715 for 25 grants (high: $75,415; low: $100).
Fields of interest: Arts and culture; Education; Nonprofits; Health.

Type of support: Regranting.
Limitations: Applications accepted. Giving primarily in Richmond, VA. No grants to individuals.
Application information: Application form required.
  Initial approach: Letter
  Deadline(s): None
Officers: Malcolm S. McDonald, Pres.; Sonia R. McDonald, Secy.
EIN: 541395806

2204
Marjorie & Richard McGahren Foundation

c/o Marjorie & Richard McGahren, Kevin Waterhouse
7117 Peligan Bay Blvd., Ste. PH 21
St. Rafael Bldg.
Naples, FL   34108-5569

Established in 1997 in Connecticut.
Donors: Marjorie McGahren; Richard McGahren.
Foundation type: Independent foundation.
Financial data (yr. ended 12/31/12): Assets, $2,363,537 (M); expenditures, $131,644; qualifying distributions, $118,000; giving activities include $118,000 for 38 grants (high: $30,000; low: $500).
Fields of interest: Education; Diseases and conditions; Community and economic development; Human services.
Limitations: Applications not accepted. Giving primarily in FL and NY. No grants to individuals.
Application information: Contributes only to pre-selected organizations.
Trustees: Marjorie McGahren; Richard McGahren.
EIN: 066447410

2205
McLaughlin Family Foundation

c/o John McLaughlin II
131 Grand Heron Dr.
Panama City Beach, FL   32407-2402

Established in 2005 in Florida.
Donor: John W. McLaughlin.
Foundation type: Independent foundation.
Financial data (yr. ended 12/31/13): Assets, $1,561,348 (M); gifts received, $1,600; expenditures, $276,863; qualifying distributions, $216,721; giving activities include $216,721 for 34 grants (high: $25,000; low: $300).
Purpose and activities: Giving primarily to Baptist churches, organizations, and missions.
Fields of interest: Baptist.
Limitations: Applications not accepted. Giving primarily in FL. No grants to individuals.
Application information: Contributes only to pre-selected organizations.
Officer: John W. McLaughlin, Mgr.
EIN: 201684047

2206
MCM-Munilla Family Foundation Inc.

6201 S.W. 70th St.
Miami, FL   33143-4718

Established in 2007 in Florida.
Donor: Magnum Construction Corp.
Foundation type: Independent foundation.

Financial data (yr. ended 12/31/13): Assets, $278,517 (M); gifts received, $1,700; expenditures, $248,072; qualifying distributions, $248,072; giving activities include $246,505 for 39 grants (high: $75,000; low: $240).
Fields of interest: University education; Nonprofits; Family services.
Type of support: Regranting.
Limitations: Applications not accepted. Giving primarily in FL. No grants to individuals.
Application information: Contributes only to pre-selected organizations.
Officers: Jorge Munilla, Pres.; Fernando Munilla, V.P.; Juan Munilla, V.P.; Raul Munilla, V.P.; Pedro Munilla, Treas.
EIN: 261615611

2207
McNamara Family Foundation Inc.

2000 Ponce de Leon Blvd., Ste. 500
Coral Gables, FL   33134-4422

Established in 2002 in Florida.
Donors: James M. McNamara; Lana McNamara.
Foundation type: Independent foundation.
Financial data (yr. ended 12/31/13): Assets, $1,776,940 (M); expenditures, $332,424; qualifying distributions, $316,700; giving activities include $316,700 for 6 grants (high: $310,000; low: $200).
Purpose and activities: Giving primarily for education, particularly to a scholarship fund for Hispanic-Americans; funding also for medical research, and social services.
Fields of interest: Education; Health; Human services.
Limitations: Applications not accepted. Giving primarily in CA and FL. No grants to individuals.
Application information: Contributes only to pre-selected organizations.
Directors: Christine McNamara; Elizabeth McNamara; James M. McNamara; Lana McNamara.
EIN: 141861856

2208
Victor and Ethel McQuistion Scholarship Trust

1877 S. Federal Hwy., Ste. 304
Boca Raton, FL   33432-7411
*Application address:*C/O Michael H. Schill,

Donor: Ethel K. McQuistion†.
Foundation type: Operating foundation.
Financial data (yr. ended 12/31/13): Assets, $1,960,229 (M); expenditures, $252,848; qualifying distributions, $225,085; giving activities include $225,085 for 3 grants (high: $195,000; low: $10,000).
Purpose and activities: Giving for scholarship funds for law students.
Fields of interest: Law education.
Type of support: Scholarships.
Limitations: Applications accepted. Giving primarily in IL; some giving also in FL, GA, and SC. No grants to individuals directly.
Application information: The availability of the scholarship will be announced in the law school bulletins for the year preceding the year the scholarships will be awarded. Application form required.

Initial approach: Proposal
   Deadline(s): None
Trustee: Thomas L. Newman.
EIN: 592602794

2209
Meerwarth Family Foundation
340 Royal Palm Way, Ste. 100
Palm Beach, FL 33480-4067
Contact: Michael Sterlacci
Application address: c/o Lurenna M. Meerwarth,
Pres., 340 Royal Poinciana Way, Ste. 340, Palm
Beach, FL 33480, tel.: (561) 833-5691

Established in 1993 in Florida.
Donors: Ralph N. Meerwarth; Lurenna M.
Meerwarth.
Foundation type: Independent foundation.
Financial data (yr. ended 12/31/13): Assets,
$4,940,853 (M); expenditures, $269,070;
qualifying distributions, $268,750; giving activities
include $268,750 for 31 grants (high: $133,000;
low: $1,000).
Purpose and activities: Giving to promote
educational facilities, homeless services, medical
facilities, and the performing arts.
Fields of interest: Arts and culture; Ballet; Art
museums; Elementary and secondary education;
Human services.
Limitations: Applications accepted. Giving primarily
in NJ.
Application information:
   Initial approach: Letter
   Deadline(s): None
Officer: Lurenna M. Meerwarth, Pres.
Director: Tracy Meerwarth.
EIN: 137018740

2210
Olga and David Melin Foundation, Inc.
16051 Collins Ave., Ste. 2601
Sunny Isles Beach, FL 33160-4621 (305)
944-9994
Contact: Olga Melin, Dir.

Established in 2000 in Florida.
Donors: David Melin; Olga Melin.
Foundation type: Independent foundation.
Financial data (yr. ended 12/31/13): Assets,
$713,927 (M); gifts received, $496,720;
expenditures, $187,986; qualifying distributions,
$183,904; giving activities include $183,904 for
118 grants (high: $94,500; low: $20).
Fields of interest: Arts and culture; Education;
Catholicism; Judaism.
Limitations: Applications accepted. Giving primarily
in Miami, FL. No grants to individuals.
Application information: Application form required.
   Initial approach: Letter
   Deadline(s): None
Directors: David Melin; Gina Melin; Olga Melin.
EIN: 651036928

2211
Laurans A. & Arlene H. Mendelson
   Charitable Foundation Inc.
825 Brickell Bay Dr., Ste. 1643
Miami, FL 33131-2920 (305) 374-1745
Contact: Laurans A. Mendelson, Dir.

Established in 1996 in Florida.
Foundation type: Independent foundation.
Financial data (yr. ended 06/30/13): Assets,
$3,863,304 (M); expenditures, $190,769;
qualifying distributions, $190,628; giving activities
include $190,628 for grants.
Fields of interest: Arts and culture; Education;
Hospital care; Judaism.
Application information: Application form required.
   Initial approach: Letter
   Deadline(s): None
Directors: Arlene H. Mendelson; Eric Mendelson;
Laurans A. Mendelson; Victor Mendelson.
EIN: 650716316

2212
MIDA Foundation
617 N. 21st Ave.
Hollywood, FL 33020-4049

Established in 1988 in Florida.
Donor: Isaac Arguetty.
Foundation type: Independent foundation.
Financial data (yr. ended 12/31/12): Assets,
$1,336,067 (M); expenditures, $354,808;
qualifying distributions, $270,000; giving activities
include $270,000 for grants.
Fields of interest: Education; Foundations;
Nonprofits; Judaism; Human services.
Type of support: Regranting.
Limitations: Applications not accepted. Giving
primarily in FL; funding also in New York, NY. No
grants to individuals.
Application information: Unsolicited requests for
funds not accepted.
Trustees: Isaac Arguetty; Miriam Arguetty.
Number of staff: 1 part-time professional.
EIN: 650098919

2213
The Miller Family Charitable Trust
(formerly NFM Charitable Trust)
P.O. Box 40200, FL9-100-10-19
Jacksonville, FL 32203-0200

Foundation type: Independent foundation.
Financial data (yr. ended 12/31/13): Assets,
$1,135,248 (M); expenditures, $236,123;
qualifying distributions, $230,950; giving activities
include $229,700 for 24 grants (high: $50,000;
low: $1,000).
Fields of interest: Public policy; Christianity; Human
services; Family services.
Type of support: Policy, advocacy and systems
reform.
Limitations: Applications not accepted. Giving
primarily in CO, CA, GA, KY, and VA. No grants to
individuals.
Application information: Contributes only to
pre-selected organizations.
Trustee: Norman F. Miller.
EIN: 586456369

2214
The Millsaps Charitable Trust
P.O. Box 1908
Orlando, FL 32802-1908

Established in 2000 in Florida.
Donors: Fred Millsaps; Audrey Millsaps.

Foundation type: Independent foundation.
Financial data (yr. ended 12/31/14): Assets,
$4,933,002 (M); expenditures, $382,703;
qualifying distributions, $353,954; giving activities
include $330,500 for 13 grants (high: $200,000;
low: $1,000).
Fields of interest: Education; Higher education;
Graduate and professional education; Nonprofits;
Health; Nursing care.
Type of support: Regranting.
Limitations: Applications not accepted. Giving
primarily in FL. No grants to individuals.
Application information: Unsolicited requests for
funds not accepted.
Trustee: SunTrust Bank, Inc.
EIN: 656347501

2215
The Alfred & Rose Miniaci Foundation, Inc.
1411 S.W. 31st Ave.
Pompano Beach, FL 33069-4834 (954)
978-0500
Contact: Rose Miniaci, Pres.

Established in 1994 in Florida.
Donors: Rose Minaci Charitable Lead Trust; Rose
Miniaci.
Foundation type: Independent foundation.
Financial data (yr. ended 06/30/14): Assets,
$1,315,018 (M); gifts received, $180,000;
expenditures, $256,613; qualifying distributions,
$254,384; giving activities include $198,733 for 12
grants (high: $100,000; low: $1,000), and $55,641
for 22 grants to individuals (low: $1,000).
Purpose and activities: Giving primarily for higher
education.
Fields of interest: Undergraduate education;
University education; Human services.
Limitations: Applications accepted. Giving primarily
in FL.
Application information: Application form required.
   Initial approach: Letter
   Deadline(s): None
Officers and Directors: Rose Miniaci, Pres. and
Director; Dominick F. Miniaci, Secy. and Director;
Albert J. Miniaci, Treas. and Director.
EIN: 651107701

2216
Minto Foundation, Inc.
4400 W. Sample Rd.
Coconut Creek, FL 33073-3473 (954)
973-4490
Contact: Lilliam Costello

Established in 1996 in Florida.
Donors: Minto Communities, Inc.; Kenneth
Greenberg; Michael Greenberg.
Foundation type: Company-sponsored foundation.
Financial data (yr. ended 04/30/13): Assets,
$4,409,150 (M); expenditures, $206,113;
qualifying distributions, $181,392; giving activities
include $180,500 for 21 grants (high: $50,000;
low: $1,000).
Purpose and activities: The foundation supports
public charities and community foundations and
organizations involved with education, heath care,
human services, and the arts.
Fields of interest: Education; Elementary and
secondary education; Foundations; Diseases and
conditions; Multiple sclerosis; Cancers; Judaism;

Human services; Child welfare; Developmental disability services; Senior services.
Type of support: General support; Employee volunteer services.
Limitations: Applications accepted. Giving primarily in FL, MA, and NC. No grants to individuals.
Application information:
Initial approach: Proposal
Deadline(s): None
Directors: Michael Greenberg; Roger Greenberg.
EIN: 650655805

2217
Martha G. Moore Foundation, Inc.
2020 N.E. 55th Ct.
Fort Lauderdale, FL 33308-3110

Established in 1976 in Florida.
Donor: Martha G. Moore†.
Foundation type: Independent foundation.
Financial data (yr. ended 12/31/13): Assets, $6,015,584 (M); expenditures, $408,523; qualifying distributions, $303,936; giving activities include $275,000 for 31 grants (high: $25,000; low: $5,000).
Purpose and activities: Giving primarily for health organizations and human services.
Fields of interest: Health; Diseases and conditions; Human services; Food banks.
Limitations: Applications not accepted. Giving primarily in FL. No grants to individuals.
Application information: Contributes only to pre-selected organizations.
Officers and Trustees: Dean R. Bailey, Chair. and Trustee; Calvin M. Johnson, Vice-Chair. and Treas. and Trustee; Sharon J. Kraby, Secy.; Donald J. O'Malley.
EIN: 510201970

2218
The Morningstar Foundation
c/o Bank of America, N.A.
P.O. Box 40200, FL9-100-10-19
Jacksonville, FL 32203-0200 8774461410
Application address: c/o Bank of America, N.A., Attn.: Sarah D. Kay, P.O. Box 26688 (VA2-300-12-92), Richmond, VA 23261-6688, tel.: (804) 887-8773

Established in 2007 in Virginia.
Donor: Mary Ann Elliott.
Foundation type: Independent foundation.
Financial data (yr. ended 06/30/14): Assets, $4,820,597; gifts received, $350,000; expenditures, $238,089; qualifying distributions, $196,309.
Purpose and activities: The mission of the foundation is twofold: to provide support for the environment and to nurture, serve and minister in the areas of health research, education, children's initiatives and animal welfare.
Fields of interest: Education; Animal welfare; Health.
Type of support: General support; Research and evaluation.
Limitations: Applications accepted. Giving primarily in NC and VA. No grants to individuals.
Application information: Application form required.
Trustees: Daniel Keith Elliott; James Ray Elliott, Jr.; Mary Ann Elliott; Sharon Elliott Hensely.
EIN: 261557579

2219
R. A. Morris Family Foundation Corp.
6039 Collins Ave., Ste. 1429
Miami Beach, FL 33140-2254 (561) 362-8685
Contact: Ronnie Morris, Pres.
E-mail: ehudk@bdo.co.il

Foundation type: Independent foundation.
Financial data (yr. ended 12/31/13): Assets, $4,692,766 (M); expenditures, $289,716; qualifying distributions, $262,000; giving activities include $262,000 for 2 grants (high: $250,000; low: $12,000).
Fields of interest: Judaism; Human services.
Limitations: Applications not accepted.
Application information: Unsolicited requests for funds not accepted.
Officers: Ronnie Morris, Pres.; Bernard Kaminetsky, Secy.; Saul Kaszovitz, Treas.
EIN: 261624430

2220
John & Cherie Morris Family Foundation
621 Ponte Vedra Blvd, Unit A
Ponte Vedra Beach, FL 32082-2982

Established in 2003 in California.
Donor: John and Sharon Morris Family Trust.
Foundation type: Independent foundation.
Financial data (yr. ended 12/31/13): Assets, $3,448 (M); gifts received, $150,809; expenditures, $152,436; qualifying distributions, $150,214; giving activities include $150,214 for 9 grants (high: $90,000; low: $500).
Fields of interest: Domesticated animals; Health; Sports and recreation.
Limitations: Applications not accepted.
Application information: Unsolicited requests for funds not accepted.
Officers: John Morris, Pres.; Cherie Morris, Secy.-Treas.
EIN: 200434698

2221
Cary Jay Morrison Charitable Trust
2065 Constitution Blvd.
Sarasota, FL 34231-4108

Donor: Cary Jay Morrison.
Foundation type: Independent foundation.
Financial data (yr. ended 12/31/13): Assets, $6,393,647 (M); expenditures, $614,824; qualifying distributions, $310,000; giving activities include $310,000 for 1 grant.
Fields of interest: Education; Higher education.
Limitations: Applications not accepted. Giving primarily in Sarasota, FL.
Application information: Unsolicited requests for funds not accepted.
Trustee: K. Judson Boedecker.
EIN: 456968359

2222
Glenn W. & Hazelle Paxson Morrison Foundation, Inc.
P.O. Box 7518
Lakeland, FL 33807-7518 (863) 602-2968

Established in 1982 in Florida.
Donor: Hazelle Paxson Morrison Eduction Fund.

Foundation type: Independent foundation.
Financial data (yr. ended 06/30/14): Assets, $4,488,037; expenditures, $242,426; qualifying distributions, $216,526.
Purpose and activities: Giving primarily for scholarships for students from Polk County, FL who are interested in religion and music, and to help small churches in Polk County, FL.
Fields of interest: Education; Higher education; Foundations; Christianity; Youth services.
Type of support: General support; Continuing support; Scholarships; Individual development; Student aid.
Limitations: Applications accepted. Giving primarily in FL, with emphasis on the Polk County area.
Application information: Applications should be typed or written and should include a copy of the applicant's (if self supporting) or parents' tax return.
Initial approach: Letter
Copies of proposal: 1
Deadline(s): 2 months
Board meeting date(s): May and Dec.
Officers: Ralph C. Allen, Pres.; John Attaway, Secy.
Trustees: Hunt Berryman; Mary E. Jenko; Patricia Ricker.
Number of staff: None.
EIN: 592220612

2223
Mount Dora Community Trust
714 N. Donnelly St.
P.O. Box 1451
Mount Dora, FL 32756 (352) 267-0957
Contact: Kevin Batliner, Exec. Dir.
FAX: (352) 383-1219;
E-mail: info@mountdoracommunitytrust.com; *Main URL:* http://www.mountdoracommunitytrust.com
E Newsletter: http://mountdoracommunitytrust.com/wp-content/uploads/9-25-13-Final.pdf

Established in 1972 in Florida.
Foundation type: Community foundation.
Financial data (yr. ended 08/31/13): Assets, $10,419,891 (M); gifts received, $834,593; expenditures, $578,825; giving activities include $271,215 for grants, and $109,057 for grants to individuals.
Purpose and activities: The foundation supports organizations benefiting the Mount Dora, FL, area community.
Fields of interest: Arts and culture; Education; Community and economic development; Community improvement; Sports and recreation; Human services; Youth development; Children and youth; Adults; Young adults.
Type of support: Student aid.
Limitations: Applications accepted. Giving limited to the Mount Dora, FL, area. No grants to individuals (except for scholarships), or for routine operating expenses, debt retirement, research, travel, or fellowships.
Publications: Application guidelines; Annual report; Informational brochure; Newsletter.
Application information: Visit foundation web site for application form and guidelines. Application form required.
Initial approach: Telephone
Copies of proposal: 1
Deadline(s): 30 days prior to Distribution Committee meetings

Board meeting date(s): Jan., May., and Sept.
Final notification: 30 days after Distribution
   Committee meetings
Officer and Distribution Committee: Kevin Batliner,
Exec. Dir.; Merrell Beebe; Alan Jones; Sam Sadler;
Kim Stewart; Michael Tedder.
Trustee: First National Bank of Mount Dora.
Number of staff: 1 part-time professional.
EIN: 237227875

2224
Thomas Moye Trust
P.O. Box 40200, FL9-100-10-19
Jacksonville, FL   32203-0200

Foundation type: Independent foundation.
Financial data (yr. ended 12/31/14): Assets,
$5,574,954; expenditures, $348,257; qualifying
distributions, $309,487.
Fields of interest: Education; Religion.
Limitations: Applications not accepted. Giving
primarily in FL and GA.
Application information: Unsolicited requests for
funds not accepted.
Trustee: Bank of America, N.A.
EIN: 586129959

2225
The Muccia Family Fund
6529 S.E. Mourning Dove Way
Hobe Sound, FL   33455-8029

Established in 1993 in New York.
Donors: Carrol A. Muccia, Jr.; Margaret D. Muccia.
Foundation type: Independent foundation.
Financial data (yr. ended 12/31/14): Assets,
$2,907,612 (M); expenditures, $204,264;
qualifying distributions, $184,253; giving activities
include $181,500 for 56 grants (high: $25,000;
low: $100).
Fields of interest: Education; Catholicism; Human
services.
Limitations: Applications not accepted. Giving
primarily in MA and NY. No grants to individuals.
Application information: Contributes only to
pre-selected organizations.
Officer: Carrol A. Muccia, Jr., Pres.
Trustee: Margaret D. Muccia.
EIN: 137002560

2226
Mukti Fund
1616 Atlantic Blvd.
Key West, FL   33040-5350
E-mail: madively@aol.com

Established in 1983 in Michigan.
Donors: George S. Dively†; Michael A. Dively.
Foundation type: Independent foundation.
Financial data (yr. ended 12/31/13): Assets,
$1,743,783 (M); expenditures, $361,226;
qualifying distributions, $357,269; giving activities
include $344,240 for 19 grants (high: $102,092;
low: $3,500).
Purpose and activities: Giving to promote individual
awareness and improve the quality of life; giving
primarily for natural and cultural resource
conservation.
Fields of interest: Cultural awareness; Natural
resources.

International interests: Caribbean.
Type of support: Continuing support; Pro bono
consulting services; Matching grants; Capital and
infrastructure; Equipment; Emergency funds;
Program development; Convening; Seed money;
Technical assistance.
Limitations: Applications not accepted. Giving
primarily in FL and IL; some giving also in the
Caribbean. No grants to individuals; research,
endowments, capital campaigns, or operational
phases of established programs.
Application information: Unsolicited requests for
funds not accepted.
Officers: Michael A. Dively, Pres. and Treas.; Weston
Milliken, V.P. and Secy.
Trustee: Martin D. Dupuis.
EIN: 382480731

2227
Pamela and Leslie Muma Family
Foundation, Inc.
(formerly Muma Family Foundation, Inc.)
100 Palmetto Rd.
Belleair, FL   33756-1428

Established in 1998 in Wisconsin.
Donor: Leslie M. Muma.
Foundation type: Independent foundation.
Financial data (yr. ended 12/31/13): Assets,
$2,441,143 (M); expenditures, $308,548;
qualifying distributions, $304,383; giving activities
include $304,383 for 21 grants (high: $103,870;
low: $250).
Fields of interest: Arts and culture; Art museums;
Higher education; Cancers; Child abuse; Religion;
Child welfare.
Limitations: Applications not accepted. Giving
primarily in FL and WI. No grants to individuals.
Application information: Contributes only to
pre-selected organizations.
Officers: Leslie M. Muma, Pres.; Pamela S. Muma,
Secy.-Treas.
Director: Lisa D. Weitz.
EIN: 391933039

2228
Richard C. Munroe Foundation
466 Champion Oaks Cir.
Havana, FL   32333-4804   (404) 351-6976
Contact: Bobbie D. Munroe
FAX: (404) 355-0157;
E-mail: info@rcmfoundation.org; Main URL: http://
www.rcmfoundation.org

Established in 1990 in Georgia.
Donor: Richard C. Munroe†.
Foundation type: Independent foundation.
Financial data (yr. ended 12/31/13): Assets,
$4,155,854 (M); expenditures, $206,752;
qualifying distributions, $187,096; giving activities
include $169,700 for 34 grants (high: $13,000;
low: $2,000).
Purpose and activities: Giving primarily for
technology education for underprivileged and at-risk
youth in the metropolitan Atlanta, GA area.
Fields of interest: Education; Housing development;
Human services; Child welfare.
Type of support: General support; Capital
campaigns; Capital and infrastructure; Equipment;
Program development.

Limitations: Applications accepted. Giving primarily
in the Atlanta, GA area. No grants to individuals.
Publications: Application guidelines.
Application information: Application form required.
   Initial approach: Request application form
   Copies of proposal: 3
   Deadline(s): Aug. 15
   Board meeting date(s): Annually, usually between
      Aug. and Nov.
Officers: Richard G. Munroe, Pres.; Bobbie D.
Munroe, Secy.; Jan H. Munroe, Treas.
EIN: 581925844

2229
Nalith, Inc.
13611 S. Dixie Hwy., Ste. 109-514
Miami, FL   33176-7254

Foundation type: Independent foundation.
Financial data (yr. ended 12/31/14): Assets,
$5,718,713; expenditures, $348,500; qualifying
distributions, $0 and $0 for set-asides.
Purpose and activities: Support for the promotion
of research and development of natural organic
farming methods and promotion of vegetarianism
and vegetarian lifestyles to enhance good health.
Fields of interest: Nutrition; Organic farming.
Limitations: Applications not accepted. Giving
primarily in NY. No grants to individuals.
Application information: Unsolicited requests for
funds not accepted.
Officers and Directors: Michael Tucker, Pres. and
Director; Jeffrey Tucker, V.P. and Director; George
Eisman; David M. Glassberg, Esq.; Haim Karp.
EIN: 592323680

2230
Nelson Family Charitable Foundation
857 Macewen Dr.
Osprey, FL   34229-9244

Established in 1998 in Florida.
Donor: Arnold L. Nelson.
Foundation type: Independent foundation.
Financial data (yr. ended 12/31/13): Assets,
$2,362,596 (M); expenditures, $115,489;
qualifying distributions, $113,600; giving activities
include $113,600 for 22 grants (high: $40,000;
low: $100).
Fields of interest: Graduate and professional
education; Christianity; Theology; Human services.
Type of support: General support.
Limitations: Applications not accepted. Giving
primarily in GA. No grants to individuals.
Application information: Unsolicited requests for
funds not accepted.
Trustees: Arnold L.V. Nelson; Helen Nelson.
EIN: 656285322

2231
Nissim Charitable Trust
18457 Long Lake Dr.
Boca Raton, FL   33496-1934   (561) 470-1181
Contact: Max Abecassis, Pres.

Established in 2002 in Florida.
Donor: Max Abecassis.
Foundation type: Independent foundation.
Financial data (yr. ended 12/31/13): Assets,
$556,627 (M); expenditures, $400,750.

Fields of interest: Human services; Child welfare; Homeless people; Low-income and poor people.
Limitations: Applications accepted. Giving primarily in FL.
Application information: Application form required.
Initial approach: Proposal
Deadline(s): None
Officer: Max Abecassis, Pres.
EIN: 656395716

2232
The Fred I. and Gilda Nobel Foundation, Inc.
3331 Lake Pt. Blvd.
Sarasota, FL 34231-6829 5165702154

Established in 1993 in Nevada.
Donors: Fred I. Nobel; Gilda Nobel.
Foundation type: Independent foundation.
Financial data (yr. ended 11/30/14): Assets, $2,061,624; expenditures, $119,923; qualifying distributions, $119,923.
Fields of interest: Arts and culture.
Limitations: Applications not accepted. Giving primarily in Long Island and New York, NY. No grants to individuals.
Application information: Unsolicited requests for funds not accepted.
Officers: Fred I. Nobel, Pres.; Laurie B. Everitt, V.P.; Judy A. Kakups, V.P.; Barry Nobel, V.P. and Director; Gilda Nobel, V.P. and Director.
EIN: 113187562

2233
Terrance and Bette Noble Foundation
15433 Milan Way
Naples, FL 34110-2727

Donors: Terrence Noble; Bette Noble.
Foundation type: Independent foundation.
Financial data (yr. ended 06/30/14): Assets, $6,298,674 (M); gifts received, $3,000,000; expenditures, $249,611; qualifying distributions, $232,365; giving activities include $232,365 for 5 grants (high: $100,000; low: $300).
Fields of interest: Education; Health; Human services.
Limitations: Applications not accepted. Giving primarily in MN.
Application information: Unsolicited requests for funds not accepted.
Trustees: Bette A. Noble; Terrance O. Noble.
EIN: 453843458

2234
The Nommontu Foundation, Inc.
(formerly Marisa Muller Charitable Foundation, Inc.)
c/o Fiduciary Trust
200 S. Biscayne, Ste. 3050
Miami, FL 33131-5337

Donor: Joyce Ann Mueller‡.
Foundation type: Independent foundation.
Financial data (yr. ended 12/31/14): Assets, $7,114,564 (M); expenditures, $524,501; qualifying distributions, $449,470; giving activities include $425,000 for 18 grants (high: $60,000; low: $5,000).
Fields of interest: Nonprofits; Health; Human services.

Type of support: Regranting.
Limitations: Applications not accepted. Giving primarily in NY.
Application information: Unsolicited requests for funds not accepted.
Directors: Hans Muller; Joyce Muller; Marisa Muller.
EIN: 311787455

2235
The Norjana Charitable Foundation
9001 Daniels Pkwy., Ste. 200
Fort Myers, FL 33912-8200

Established in 2004 in Unspecified.
Donor: Norma Parker.
Foundation type: Independent foundation.
Financial data (yr. ended 12/31/12): Assets, $0 (M); gifts received, $251,131; expenditures, $296,771; qualifying distributions, $296,338; giving activities include $296,338 for grants.
Purpose and activities: Giving primarily for the ballet, higher education, environmental conservation, and human services; some funding also to a juvenile diabetes organization.
Fields of interest: Ballet; Higher education; Natural resources; Diabetes; Human services.
Type of support: General support.
Limitations: Applications not accepted. No grants to individuals.
Application information: Unsolicited requests for funds not accepted.
Officers: Adam P. Glick, Pres.; John Reisman, Secy.-Treas.
Directors: Nancy Magoon; Jane Parker.
EIN: 202028800

2236
The Nuzzo Family Foundation
570 Ocean Dr., Ste. 1101
Juno Beach, FL 33408-1955

Established in 1999 in Florida.
Donor: Salvatore J. Nuzzo.
Foundation type: Independent foundation.
Financial data (yr. ended 12/31/13): Assets, $2,568,634 (M); expenditures, $219,288; qualifying distributions, $204,656; giving activities include $203,095 for 5 grants (high: $93,915; low: $2,500).
Fields of interest: Education; Christianity; Human services.
Type of support: General support.
Limitations: Applications not accepted. No grants to individuals.
Application information: Unsolicited requests for funds not accepted.
Officers and Directors: Salvatore J. Nuzzo, Chair. and Director; Lucille Nuzzo, Pres. and Director; D. Nuzzo, V.P. and Director; J. Nuzzo, V.P. and Director.
EIN: 223700343

2237
Olemberg Family Foundation Inc.
(formerly The Isaac Olemberg and Nieves Olemberg Private Foundation)
800 N.W. 21st St.
Miami, FL 33127-4626 (305) 325-9000
Contact: Isaac Olemberg, Dir.

Established in 1992 in Florida.

Donors: Isaac Olemberg; Nieves Olemberg; Michael A. Kirsh; Michael Furst; Olem Shoe Corp.
Foundation type: Independent foundation.
Financial data (yr. ended 12/31/13): Assets, $4,843,295 (M); expenditures, $298,876; qualifying distributions, $281,395; giving activities include $281,395 for 35 grants (high: $105,000; low: $400).
Purpose and activities: Giving primarily to Jewish organizations.
Fields of interest: Nonprofits; Judaism; Human services.
Type of support: Regranting.
Limitations: Applications accepted. Giving primarily in FL and NY. No grants to individuals.
Application information: Application form required.
Initial approach: Letter
Deadline(s): None
Board Member: Olem Shoe Corporation.
Directors: Isaac Olemberg; Nieves Olemberg; Roberto Olemberg.
EIN: 650375570

2238
The Oliver Foundation, Inc.
1904 Espanola Dr.
Orlando, FL 32804-7020

Foundation type: Independent foundation.
Financial data (yr. ended 12/31/13): Assets, $1,609 (M); gifts received, $175,000; expenditures, $175,360; qualifying distributions, $175,000.
Limitations: Applications not accepted.
Application information: Unsolicited requests for funds not accepted.
Directors: J. Fenimore Cooper, Jr.; Katherine Cooper; Charles H. Stark.
EIN: 030442925

2239
Matred Carlton Olliff Foundation
P.O. Box 995
Wauchula, FL 33873-0995
Application address: c/o Doyle E. Carlton, III, Tr., P.O. Box 144, Wauchula, Florida 33873

Established in 1982 in Florida.
Donor: Matred Carlton Olliff‡.
Foundation type: Independent foundation.
Financial data (yr. ended 08/31/13): Assets, $3,387,061 (M); expenditures, $171,183; qualifying distributions, $158,597; giving activities include $91,150 for 50 grants (high: $15,000; low: $200), and $54,498 for 84 grants to individuals (high: $5,773; low: $250).
Purpose and activities: Giving primarily for human services, higher education, and community support. Scholarships limited to Hardee High School graduates.
Fields of interest: Education; Community and economic development; Religion.
Type of support: General support; Student aid.
Limitations: Applications accepted. Giving primarily in Hardee County, FL.
Application information:
Initial approach: Letter
Copies of proposal: 1
Deadline(s): July 1
Trustees: Doyle E. Carlton III; Walter S. Farr.
EIN: 592241303

2240
C. Olsen 1990 Private Foundation
11891 U.S. Highway 1, Ste. 100
North Palm Beach, FL 33408-2864
Contact: Joshua M. Fleming

Established in 2002 in Florida.
Donor: Christian Olsen Charitable Trust.
Foundation type: Independent foundation.
Financial data (yr. ended 09/30/13): Assets, $9,179,790 (M); expenditures, $683,674; qualifying distributions, $471,629; giving activities include $392,913 for 71 grants (high: $13,000; low: $1,000).
Fields of interest: Education; Diseases and conditions; Cancers; Human services; Food banks; Child welfare; Developmental disability services.
Limitations: Applications accepted. Giving primarily in FL; some emphasis on West Palm Beach. No grants to individuals.
Application information:
Initial approach: Proposal
Deadline(s): Feb. 15, May 15, Aug. 15, and Nov. 15
Trustee: Joseph M. Fleming.
EIN: 656400515

2241
The Oristano Foundation
11614 Lake House Ct.
North Palm Beach, FL 33408

Donor: Victor Oristano.
Foundation type: Independent foundation.
Financial data (yr. ended 12/31/13): Assets, $3,762,674 (M); expenditures, $295,996; qualifying distributions, $270,113; giving activities include $171,235 for 33 grants (high: $27,800; low: $2).
Purpose and activities: Giving primarily to educational institutions; support also for community and family service organizations.
Fields of interest: Education; Child educational development; Vocational education; Family planning; Housing development; Diversity and intergroup relations; Human services; Family services; Child welfare; Child development; Arms control; Ethnic and racial groups; Low-income and poor people; People with disabilities.
Type of support: General support; Continuing support; Annual campaigns; Capital campaigns; Capital and infrastructure; Seed money.
Limitations: Applications not accepted. No grants to individuals.
Application information: Unsolicited requests for funds not accepted.
Board meeting date(s): 3 times annually
Trustees: Christopher J. Citrone; Debra A. Citrone; George B. Stowell; Henry Baer; Philip Guarnieri, Jr.
Directors: Jane Oristano; Victor Oristano.
Number of staff: 1 part-time support.
EIN: 222471915

2242
Overstreet Foundation
c/o Ronald Blue & Co., LLC
1900 Summit Tower Blvd.
Orlando, FL 32810

Established in 1965 in Florida.

Donors: Overstreet Investment Co.; M. Overstreet Charitable Trust.
Foundation type: Independent foundation.
Financial data (yr. ended 12/31/12): Assets, $3,527,691 (M); expenditures, $268,053; qualifying distributions, $175,000; giving activities include $175,000 for grants.
Purpose and activities: The foundation supports Christian agencies and churches and organizations involved with health and human services, particularly the homeless.
Fields of interest: Higher education; Nonprofits; Diseases and conditions; Christianity; Special Olympics; Human services; Homeless people.
Type of support: Regranting.
Limitations: Applications not accepted. Giving primarily in FL. No grants to individuals.
Application information: Unsolicited requests for funds not accepted.
Trustees: Nancy Kann; Daniel Sheldon; Robin O. Sheldon; Stephen Sheldon; Harry J. Weiss, Jr.
EIN: 596164658

2243
Owen Charitable Foundation
96 Lighthouse Dr.
Jupiter, FL 33469-3512

Established in 1986 in Maryland.
Donor: Lee S. Owen.
Foundation type: Independent foundation.
Financial data (yr. ended 12/31/13): Assets, $125,785 (M); gifts received, $276,283; expenditures, $159,364; qualifying distributions, $159,249; giving activities include $157,136 for 33 grants (high: $25,000; low: $250).
Fields of interest: Education; Environment; Health.
Limitations: Applications not accepted. Giving primarily in Baltimore, MD. No grants to individuals.
Application information: Unsolicited requests for funds not accepted.
Trustees: Jenny Owen; Lee S. Owen.
EIN: 526287381

2244
P.M. Foundation, Inc.
4800 N.E. 23rd Ave.
Fort Lauderdale, FL 33308-4723

Established in 1987 in Michigan.
Donors: Paul Marco; Barbara Voorheis; Mack Renaud, Inc.
Foundation type: Independent foundation.
Financial data (yr. ended 12/31/13): Assets, $6,312,512 (M); gifts received, $2,000; expenditures, $201,651; qualifying distributions, $198,280; giving activities include $198,280 for 24 grants (high: $26,988; low: $100).
Purpose and activities: Giving to Christian organizations, including churches, ministries, and affiliated family services.
Fields of interest: Family planning; Christianity; Right to life; Family services.
Limitations: Applications not accepted. Giving primarily in CA, CO, FL and KS. No grants to individuals.
Application information: Unsolicited requests for funds not accepted.
Officers: Barbara Voorheis, Pres. and Secy.-Treas.; Anne-Marie Reid, V.P.

Director: Paul V. Kraus.
EIN: 381802049

2245
The Pagoumian Family Charitable Trust
c/o George Pagoumian
175 S.W. 7th St., Ste. 2409
Miami, FL 33130

Established in 1997 in New Jersey.
Donor: George K. Pagoumian.
Foundation type: Independent foundation.
Financial data (yr. ended 12/31/13): Assets, $4,630,694 (M); expenditures, $156,891; qualifying distributions, $150,500; giving activities include $148,638 for 3+ grants (high: $112,000).
Purpose and activities: Giving for Armenian related organizations.
Fields of interest: Human services; Child welfare.
International interests: Armenia.
Limitations: Applications not accepted. No grants to individuals.
Application information: Unsolicited requests for funds not accepted.
Trustees: Carolyn D. Pagoumian; David P. Pagoumian; George K. Pagoumian; John G. Pagoumian.
EIN: 226747183

2246
Patricia M. & Emanuel M. Papper Foundation Inc.
1 Grove Isle Dr., Apt. 1501
Miami, FL 33133-4107
Application address: Patricia Papper, c/o MBAF, LLC, 1450 Brickell Ave., 18th Fl., Miami, FL 33131, tel.: (305) 373-5500

Established in 1983 in Unspecified.
Donors: Patricia M. Papper; Emanuel M. Papper.
Foundation type: Independent foundation.
Financial data (yr. ended 11/30/13): Assets, $1,872,154 (M); expenditures, $369,071; qualifying distributions, $362,806; giving activities include $361,358 for grants.
Purpose and activities: Giving primarily for the arts and human services.
Fields of interest: Arts and culture; Art museums; University education; Medical education; Nonprofits; Radio; Human services.
Type of support: Regranting.
Limitations: Applications accepted. Giving primarily in Miami, FL.
Application information:
Initial approach: Proposal
Deadline(s): None
Board meeting date(s): As needed
Directors: Richard I. Furman; Patricia M. Papper; Richard N. Papper.
EIN: 592500044

2247
The Richard Laurence Parish Foundation
(formerly Psychists, Inc.)
100 Lakeshore Dr., No. L-7
North Palm Beach, FL 33408-3660

Established in 1943 in New York.
Donors: Richard L. Parish†; American Flange & Manufacturing Co., Inc.

Foundation type: Independent foundation.
Financial data (yr. ended 08/31/13): Assets, $6,975,251 (M); expenditures, $317,922; qualifying distributions, $312,189; giving activities include $304,000 for 62 grants (high: $62,000; low: $250).
Purpose and activities: Support primarily for secondary education; giving also for hospitals, higher education, and health care services.
Fields of interest: Education; Secondary education; Medical education; Health; Human services.
Limitations: Applications not accepted. Giving primarily in CT, FL, NJ, and NY. No grants to individuals.
Application information: Contributes only to pre-selected organizations.
Directors: Richard C. Bondy; David L. McKissock; Richard L. Parish, Jr.; Richard L. Parish III.
EIN: 131869530

2248
Partners in Advertising Education, Inc.
955 Alton Rd.
Miami Beach, FL 33139-5203

Foundation type: Independent foundation.
Financial data (yr. ended 06/30/13): Assets, $543,216 (M); expenditures, $150,000; qualifying distributions, $150,000; giving activities include $150,000 for 1 grant.
Fields of interest: Arts education; Visual arts.
Type of support: Scholarships.
Limitations: Applications not accepted. Giving primarily in FL.
Application information: Unsolicited requests for funds not accepted.
Directors: Adelaind Horton; Bonnie Lunt; Pippa Seichrist.
EIN: 650828721

2249
Pascal International Inc.
222 Royal Palm Way
Palm Beach, FL 33480
Application address: c/o Bessemer Trust, 801 Brickell Ave., Miami, FL 33131 tel: (305) 372-5005.

Foundation type: Independent foundation.
Financial data (yr. ended 12/31/13): Assets, $2,461,333 (M); expenditures, $469,918; qualifying distributions, $456,253; giving activities include $392,500 for 4 grants (high: $330,000; low: $17,500).
Purpose and activities: Giving primarily for children, youth, and social services.
Fields of interest: Christianity; Human services; Child welfare.
Limitations: Applications accepted. Giving primarily in FL. No grants to individuals.
Application information: Application form required.
  Initial approach: Letter
  Deadline(s): None
Officers and Directors: Clara Pascal, Pres. and Treas. and Director; Nancy Wainwright, V.P. and Secy. and Director; Robin Pascal.
EIN: 651066949

2250
The Patterson Foundation
11410 Dickey Ln.
P.O. Box 790
Captiva, FL 33924-0790

Established in 2007 in Missouri.
Donors: Neal Patterson; Jeanne Patterson.
Foundation type: Independent foundation.
Financial data (yr. ended 12/31/14): Assets, $10,674,996 (M); gifts received, $2,010,000; expenditures, $446,967; qualifying distributions, $432,000; giving activities include $432,000 for 2 grants (high: $262,000; low: $170,000).
Fields of interest: Higher education; Human services; Youth services; Children and youth.
Limitations: Applications not accepted. Giving primarily in KS and MO. No grants to individuals.
Application information: Contributes only to pre-selected organizations.
Trustees: Jeanne Patterson; Neal Patterson.
EIN: 207550081

2251
H. S. & C. G. Patterson Jr. Charitable Foundation Trust
P.O. Box 1908
Orlando, FL 32802-1908

Established in 2004 in Virginia.
Donor: Helen S. Patterson Trust.
Foundation type: Independent foundation.
Financial data (yr. ended 12/31/14): Assets, $7,578,431; expenditures, $408,633; qualifying distributions, $352,109.
Purpose and activities: Giving primarily to education, museums and to Episcopal churches.
Fields of interest: Arts and culture; Museums; Undergraduate education; Episcopalianism and Anglicanism; Lutheranism.
Limitations: Applications not accepted. Giving primarily in VA. No grants to individuals.
Application information: Contributes only to pre-selected organizations.
Trustee: SunTrust Bank, Inc.
EIN: 206369229

2252
The Dr. M. Lee Pearce Foundation, Inc.
5601 N. Dixie Hwy., Ste. 411
Fort Lauderdale, FL 33334-4147

Donor: M. Lee Pearce, MD.
Foundation type: Independent foundation.
Financial data (yr. ended 12/31/13): Assets, $12,414,068; gifts received, $0; expenditures, $526,291; qualifying distributions, $260,151 and $0 for set-asides.
Purpose and activities: Giving primarily for the arts, education, health and human services.
Fields of interest: Arts and culture; Performing arts; Education; Higher education; Hospital care; Diseases and conditions; Human services.
Type of support: Research; Research and evaluation.
Limitations: Applications not accepted. Giving in the U.S., with some emphasis on Washington, DC, FL and NY. No grants to individuals.
Application information: Contributes only to pre-selected organizations.

Officers and Directors: M. Lee Pearce, MD, Chair. and C.E.O. and Director; Charles Douglas, Vice-Chair. and Pres.; Robert Potts, Sr. V.P. and Director; Scott Kent, V.P. and Director; Tim Lincoln, Secy.; Jose Valle, Treas. and Director; Robert L. Achor; Jeffrey Bivins; Dale Rusted.
EIN: 592424272

2253
Pearle Foundation Charitable Trust
7791 N.W. 146th St.
Miami Lakes, FL 33016-1567

Established in 2006 in Florida.
Donor: Boyer and Meyrovitz Foundation.
Foundation type: Independent foundation.
Financial data (yr. ended 07/31/13): Assets, $546,705 (M); expenditures, $265,646; qualifying distributions, $251,953; giving activities include $244,740 for 6 grants (high: $208,873; low: $100).
Fields of interest: Animal welfare; Nonprofits; Christianity.
Type of support: Regranting.
Limitations: Applications not accepted. Giving primarily in FL. No grants to individuals.
Application information: Contributes only to pre-selected organizations.
Trustees: Gregory A. Nichols; Maira M. Nichols.
EIN: 204755005

2254
The Laura & Isaac Perlmutter Foundation Inc.
P.O. Box 1028
Lake Worth, FL 33460-1028

Established in 1997 in Florida.
Donors: Isaac Perlmutter; Laura Perlmutter.
Foundation type: Independent foundation.
Financial data (yr. ended 12/31/13): Assets, $32,712,924 (M); expenditures, $885,397; qualifying distributions, $845,397; giving activities include $370,250 for 12 grants (high: $181,500; low: $500).
Fields of interest: University education; Medical education; Nonprofits; Sustainable development; Urban development; Judaism.
Type of support: Regranting.
Limitations: Applications not accepted. Giving primarily in Palm Beach, FL and New York, NY. No grants to individuals.
Application information: Contributes only to pre-selected organizations.
Officers and Directors: Isaac Perlmutter, Pres. and Director; Laura Perlmutter, V.P. and Director; Neal J. Nissel, Treas. and Director.
EIN: 650742318

2255
Perryman Family Foundation
797 N. Beach St.
Ormond Beach, FL 32174-4001

Donor: Betty Perryman.
Foundation type: Independent foundation.
Financial data (yr. ended 12/31/13): Assets, $3,772,968 (M); expenditures, $191,462; qualifying distributions, $115,500; giving activities include $115,500 for 25 grants (high: $30,000; low: $300).

Fields of interest: Arts and culture; Education; Human services.
Limitations: Applications not accepted. Giving primarily in FL.
Application information: Unsolicited requests for funds not accepted.
Directors: Amanda Perryman; Andrew Perryman; Barbara Perryman; David Perryman.
EIN: 261199865

2256
Gary Peters Family Foundation, Inc.
6013 Le Lac Rd.
Boca Raton, FL   33496-2302
Contact: Gary Peters, Dir.
E-mail for Gary Peters: gpii203@gmail.com

Established in 2004 in Florida.
Foundation type: Independent foundation.
Financial data (yr. ended 12/31/13): Assets, $8,643,877 (M); gifts received, $240,000; expenditures, $531,936; qualifying distributions, $330,050; giving activities include $330,050 for 22 grants (high: $100,000; low: $750).
Fields of interest: Arts and culture; Education; Christianity; Human services; Child welfare.
Type of support: General support.
Limitations: Applications not accepted. Giving primarily in FL and TN. No grants to individuals.
Application information: Contributes only to pre-selected organizations.
Board meeting date(s): Annually
Directors: Cecilia Peters; Gary Peters; Steven Mark Peters; William Gregory Peters; Jennifer Simons.
Number of staff: 1
EIN: 201067444

2257
Folke H. Peterson Charitable Foundation
c/o SunTrust Bank Foundations Endowment
200 S. Orange Ave., SOAB-10
Orlando, FL   32801-3410   (407) 237-4354
FAX: (407) 237-5604; Main URL: http://fdnweb.org/peterson

Established in 1988 in Florida.
Donor: Folke H. Peterson†.
Foundation type: Independent foundation.
Financial data (yr. ended 11/30/13): Assets, $10,019,182 (M); expenditures, $307,011; qualifying distributions, $286,286; giving activities include $256,500 for 22 grants (high: $80,000; low: $2,000).
Purpose and activities: Giving primarily for nonprofit organizations involved in the health and well-being of animals, including no-kill animal shelters.
Fields of interest: Animal welfare.
Type of support: Program development; In-kind gifts; Emergency funds; General support.
Limitations: Applications accepted. Giving primarily in FL. No grants to individuals.
Application information: See foundation website for complete application guidelines. Application form required.
Initial approach: Letter
Copies of proposal: 1
Deadline(s): None
Trustees: SunTrust Bank; University of Florida; University of Miami; Wildlife Care Center.
EIN: 656040055

2258
The Peyton Family Foundation
800 S. Point Dr., No. 1603
Miami Beach, FL   33139-7359

Donor: Patrick J. Peyton.
Foundation type: Independent foundation.
Financial data (yr. ended 12/31/13): Assets, $2,769,240 (M); expenditures, $264,697; qualifying distributions, $258,575; giving activities include $257,180 for 7 grants (high: $173,060; low: $2,120).
Fields of interest: Education; Diseases and conditions; Alzheimer's disease; Human rights.
Type of support: Research.
Limitations: Applications not accepted. Giving primarily in IL.
Application information: Unsolicited requests for funds not accepted.
Trustee: Patrick J. Peyton.
EIN: 326195377

2259
A. P. Phillips Foundation, Inc.
P.O. Box 560126
Orlando, FL   32856-0126   (407) 428-5121
Contact: Carla W. Adams, Pres.

Established in 1965 in Florida.
Foundation type: Independent foundation.
Financial data (yr. ended 06/30/14): Assets, $3,245,896 (M); expenditures, $291,842; qualifying distributions, $201,380; giving activities include $164,465 for 20 grants (high: $54,000; low: $3,500).
Fields of interest: Education; Human services; Youth development.
Type of support: General support; Program development.
Limitations: Applications accepted. Giving primarily in FL. No grants to individuals.
Application information: Application form required.
Initial approach: Letter
Copies of proposal: 1
Deadline(s): Mar. 1
Board meeting date(s): Requests considered in May
Final notification: June 30
Officers: Carla W. Adams, Pres.; Harvey H. Harper IV, V.P.; Kimberly M. Harper, Secy.; Thomas L. Adams, Treas.
Number of staff: 1 part-time support.
EIN: 596165157

2260
The Dr. P. Phillips Foundation
P.O. Box 692709
Orlando, FL   32869-2709   (407) 422-6105
Contact: Robert L. Mellen III, Pres.
FAX: (407) 422-4952; E-mail: info@drphillips.org; Main URL: http://www.drphillips.org

Established in 1953 in Florida.
Donors: Della Phillips†; Howard Phillips†; Dr. Phillips, Inc.
Foundation type: Independent foundation.
Financial data (yr. ended 05/31/13): Assets, $39,351,518 (M); expenditures, $534,711; qualifying distributions, $483,545; giving activities include $382,816 for 23 grants (high: $124,404;

low: $750), and $73,954 for 2 foundation-administered programs.
Fields of interest: Arts and culture; Health; Public affairs; Community and economic development; Employment; Human services; Child welfare.
Type of support: Capital campaigns; Loans to individuals; Program-related investments; Capital and infrastructure; Matching grants; Equipment; Program development.
Limitations: Applications accepted. Giving generally limited to Orange and Osceola counties, FL. No support for social, religious, fraternal or veterans' groups that primarily benefit their own members or adherents, or for legislative lobbying. No support to Type III support organizations. No grants to individuals, or for endowment funds, or to retire accumulated debt.
Publications: Application guidelines; Grants list; Newsletter.
Application information: Application guidelines available on foundation web site. Application form required.
Copies of proposal: 1
Officers and Directors: J.A. Hinson, Chair. and Director; Kenneth D. Robinson, Pres. and C.E.O. and Director; H.L. Burnett, Secy. and Director; Eva M. Tukdarian, Treas. and Director; Don Ammerman; James W. Ferber; Margaret G. Miller.
Number of staff: None.
EIN: 596135403

2261
Place of Hope International, Inc.
5343 Northlake Blvd.
Palm Beach Gardens, FL   33418-4554
E-mail: info@placesofhope.com

Established in 2000 in Florida.
Donors: Woerner World Ministries; Boswell House Ministries; Absolute Yacht Refinishing; Doug Twohill; Richard Scott Hearing; John Holly Boswell; Shannon Ramirez.
Foundation type: Operating foundation.
Financial data (yr. ended 12/31/13): Assets, $41,197 (M); gifts received, $185,203; expenditures, $188,206; qualifying distributions, $183,847; giving activities include $183,847 for 5 grants (high: $124,800; low: $500).
Purpose and activities: The foundation supports underprivileged children around the world, and to reach them with the love and message of Jesus Christ.
Fields of interest: Christianity; Human services; Child welfare; Low-income and poor people.
International interests: Bolivia; Brazil; Costa Rica; El Salvador; Honduras; India; Mexico; Peru; Romania.
Type of support: General support; Emergency funds.
Limitations: Applications not accepted. Giving primarily in FL, and in Bolivia, Brazil, Costa Rica, El Salvador, Honduras, India, Mexico, Peru and Romania. No support for for-profit agencies. No grants to individuals.
Publications: Informational brochure; Occasional report.
Application information: Contributes only to pre-selected organizations. The foundation only supports Christian-based charities they already have existing strong partnerships with. Unsolicited requests for funds will not be acknowledged.
Board meeting date(s): Quarterly
Officers: Thomas Mullins, Chair.; Leo Abdella, Pres.; Larry Woerner, V.P.; Todd Mullins, Secy.-Treas.

Number of staff: None.
EIN: 651030972

2262
Posnack Foundation of Hollywood
(formerly Posnack Family Foundation of Hollywood)
P.O. Box 40200, FL9-100-10-19
Jacksonville, FL 32203-0200
Application address: c/o Bank of America, 401 E.
Las Olas Blvd., Fort Lauderdale, FL 33301-2230

Established in 1984 in Florida.
Foundation type: Independent foundation.
Financial data (yr. ended 01/31/15): Assets,
$1,221,493 (M); expenditures, $212,084;
qualifying distributions, $200,893; giving activities
include $192,520 for 9 grants (high: $100,000;
low: $2,500).
Purpose and activities: Support for Jewish
organizations, including welfare funds and
educational institutions.
Fields of interest: Education; Elementary and
secondary education; Higher education; Nonprofits;
Judaism; Human services; Adoption.
International interests: Israel.
Type of support: Regranting.
Limitations: Applications accepted. Giving primarily
in FL and NY. No grants to individuals.
Application information:
  Initial approach: Proposal
  Deadline(s): None
Trustee: Bank of America, N.A.
EIN: 592484512

2263
F and M Potter Memorial Fund
P.O. Box 40200, FL-9-100-10-19
Jacksonville, FL 32203-0200

Foundation type: Independent foundation.
Financial data (yr. ended 07/31/14): Assets,
$9,392,662; expenditures, $525,823; qualifying
distributions, $420,584.
Fields of interest: Protestantism.
Limitations: Applications not accepted. Giving
primarily in FL and WV.
Application information: Contributes only to
pre-selected organizations.
Trustees: Hewitt DuPont; Bank of America, N.A.
EIN: 597238035

2264
Powell Family Foundation
550 S. Dixie Hwy., Ste. 300
Miami, FL 33146-2701

Established in 1999 in Florida.
Foundation type: Independent foundation.
Financial data (yr. ended 12/31/12): Assets,
$2,988,578 (M); expenditures, $131,598;
qualifying distributions, $116,732; giving activities
include $115,685 for 13 grants (high: $20,000;
low: $500).
Fields of interest: Arts and culture; Higher
education; Human services; Child welfare.
Limitations: Applications not accepted. No grants to
individuals.
Application information: Unsolicited requests for
funds not accepted.

Officers and Directors: Earl Powell, Pres. and
Director; Christy Powell, Secy. and Director; Linda
Baker, Treas. and Director.
EIN: 650934241

2265
Bernard F. & Mary Ann Powell Foundation Inc.
12102 Creole Ct.
Parrish, FL 34219-1201

Established in 2000 in Florida.
Donors: B.F. Powell; C & B Foundation.
Foundation type: Independent foundation.
Financial data (yr. ended 12/31/13): Assets, $0
(M); expenditures, $303,863; qualifying
distributions, $269,350; giving activities include
$209,000 for 29 grants (high: $25,000; low:
$1,000).
Fields of interest: Education; Higher education;
Hospice care; Cancers; Catholicism; Human
services; Youth services.
Limitations: Applications not accepted. Giving
primarily in FL and MI. No grants to individuals.
Application information: Contributes only to
pre-selected organizations.
Directors: Elizabeth Archangeli; Matthew
Archangeli; Kathleen Strong.
EIN: 593575091

2266
The Preik Family Foundation, Inc.
7 Sound Point Ct.
Fernandina Beach, FL 32034-6443

Established in 2007 in Florida.
Donors: Reinhold Preik; Jennifer Preik.
Foundation type: Independent foundation.
Financial data (yr. ended 12/31/14): Assets,
$8,544,561 (M); expenditures, $384,737;
qualifying distributions, $326,000; giving activities
include $326,000 for 12 grants (high: $170,000;
low: $1,000).
Fields of interest: Diseases and conditions;
Religion; Human services.
Limitations: Applications not accepted. Giving
primarily in FL, GA and TX. No grants to individuals.
Application information: Unsolicited requests for
funds not accepted.
Officers and Trustees: Reinhold Preik, Pres. and
Trustee; Jennifer Preik, V.P. and Trustee; Diana
Huynen, Secy.-Treas.; Erin Lee; Austin Preik; Curtis
Preik.
EIN: 261590815

2267
The John E. & Aliese Price Foundation, Inc.
1279 Lavin Ln.
Fort Myers, FL 33917-5341
Contact: T. Wainwright Miller Jr., Pres.

Established in 1961 in Florida.
Donors: John E. Price†; Aliese Price†.
Foundation type: Independent foundation.
Financial data (yr. ended 08/31/13): Assets,
$8,742,221 (M); expenditures, $707,684;
qualifying distributions, $532,956; giving activities
include $228,400 for 40 grants (high: $20,000;
low: $300), and $71,856 for 2
foundation-administered programs.

Purpose and activities: Grants primarily for church
support and religious associations; some support
also for youth agencies, health agencies, and
education associations in the Fort Myers, FL, area.
Fields of interest: Performing arts; Education;
Elementary and secondary education; Early
childhood education; Graduate and professional
education; Basic and remedial instruction; Reading
promotion; Health; Nursing care; Hospice care;
Biomedicine; Diseases and conditions; HIV/AIDS;
Engineering; Mathematics; Civic participation;
Religion; Christianity; Youth services; Civics for
youth.
Type of support: Continuing support; Matching
grants; Research; Research and evaluation.
Limitations: Applications accepted. Giving primarily
in southwest FL, with emphasis on the Fort Myers
area. No grants to individuals.
Application information:
  Initial approach: Letter
  Deadline(s): None
  Board meeting date(s): Jan. and Sept.
Officers and Trustees: T. Wainwright Miller, Jr.,
Pres. and Treas. and Trustee; Dennis G. Small, V.P.
and Trustee; Daniel F. Adams, Secy. and Trustee;
Mavis S. Miller; Russell Priddy; Mary Jo Sanders
Walker.
Number of staff: 3 full-time support.
EIN: 591056841

2268
Prime Time Foundation, Inc.
570 Ocean Dr., Ste. 701
Juno Beach, FL 33408-1954

Donors: Robert A. Yanover; Robert A. Yanover Clat.
Foundation type: Independent foundation.
Financial data (yr. ended 12/31/14): Assets,
$1,778,063; gifts received, $149,870;
expenditures, $168,337; qualifying distributions,
$143,814.
Purpose and activities: Scholarship awards
available to worthy students from the Bahamas
attending the University of Michigan, Louisiana
State University or the University of Florida.
Fields of interest: Education.
International interests: Bahamas.
Type of support: Scholarships; Student aid.
Limitations: Applications accepted. Giving limited to
residents of the Bahamas, with special
consideration given to the Abacos and Eleuthera.
Application information: Application form required.
  Initial approach: Proposal
  Deadline(s): None
Officer: Judith P. Yanover, Pres. and Treas.
Directors: Jennifer D. Lariviere; J. Jonathan Yanover.
EIN: 650875903

2269
Marni & Morris Propp II Family Foundation, Inc.
366 Eagle Dr.
Jupiter, FL 33477-4066 (561) 346-7048
Contact: Morris Propp, V.P.
E-mail: morrse@aol.com

Donors: Marni Propp; Morris Propp.
Foundation type: Independent foundation.
Financial data (yr. ended 12/31/13): Assets,
$3,673,055 (M); gifts received, $197,750;
expenditures, $199,687; qualifying distributions,

$196,500; giving activities include $196,500 for grants.
Fields of interest: Education; Higher education; Health; Human services.
Application information: Application form required.
Initial approach: Letter
Deadline(s): None
Officers: Marni Propp, Pres.; Morris Propp, Treas.
Directors: Adrienne Propp; Harold Reed.
EIN: 800057787

2270
Millard & Lillian Prutky Charitable Trust
27424 Sora Blvd.
Wesley Chapel, FL   33544-3469

Foundation type: Independent foundation.
Financial data (yr. ended 12/31/13): Assets, $864,137 (M); expenditures, $291,483; qualifying distributions, $289,600; giving activities include $289,600 for 13 grants (high: $70,000; low: $2,000).
Fields of interest: Education; Specialty hospital care; Medical specialties; Heart and circulatory system diseases; Human services.
Type of support: Research.
Limitations: Applications not accepted. No grants to individuals.
Application information: Unsolicited requests for funds not accepted.
Trustees: Janice Gloneck; Brian Melick; Kimberly Melick; Deborah Timmons; Frank Timmons.
EIN: 412178669

2271
Pulichino Tong Family Foundation, Inc.
3621 Princeton Pl.
Boca Raton, FL   33496-2711

Donors: Joy Tong; John Pulichino.
Foundation type: Independent foundation.
Financial data (yr. ended 12/31/13): Assets, $3,033,646 (M); expenditures, $427,469; qualifying distributions, $427,105; giving activities include $425,000 for 2 grants (high: $400,000; low: $25,000).
Fields of interest: Education.
Limitations: Applications not accepted. Giving primarily in MA.
Application information: Unsolicited request for funds not accepted.
Officers and Directors: John Pulichino, Jr., Pres. and Secy- Treas.; Joy Tong, V.P. and Director; Seth E. Ellis, Esq.
EIN: 204920710

2272
Paul H. Pusey Foundation
P.O. Box 111928
Naples, FL   34108   (239) 591-0562
Contact: Nancy P. Ayres, Pres. and Secy.-Treas.

Established in 1969 in Virginia.
Donors: Paul H. Pusey, Jr.; Vernelle B. Pusey.
Foundation type: Independent foundation.
Financial data (yr. ended 12/31/13): Assets, $3,674,545 (M); expenditures, $194,857; qualifying distributions, $155,460; giving activities include $155,460 for 61 grants (high: $15,015; low: $100).

Fields of interest: Arts and culture; Education; Hospital care; Diseases and conditions; Christianity; Human services; Child welfare.
Type of support: Research.
Limitations: Applications accepted. Giving primarily in CA and VA. No grants to individuals.
Application information: Application form required.
Initial approach: Letter
Deadline(s): None
Officers: Nancy P. Ayres, Pres. and Secy.-Treas.; Patricia P. Clark, V.P.; Patricia P. Pusey, V.P.; William A. Pusey, V.P.
Board Members: Paul W. Ayers; William A. Pusey, Jr.; John B. Reece.
EIN: 237043682

2273
Quinn Family Charitable Foundation, Inc.
P.O. Box 358688
Gainesville, FL   32635-8688

Established in 1993 in Florida.
Donors: John H. Quinn; Hallie H. Quinn.
Foundation type: Independent foundation.
Financial data (yr. ended 12/31/14): Assets, $3,926,673; expenditures, $257,213; qualifying distributions, $249,000.
Fields of interest: Arts and culture; Education; Diseases and conditions.
Limitations: Applications not accepted. Giving primarily in FL and SC. No grants to individuals.
Application information: Unsolicited requests for funds not accepted.
Trustees: Hallie Q. McFetridge; Brooks C. Quinn; John H. Quinn, Jr.
EIN: 593207710

2274
Maria L. Ransburg Charitable Foundation
c/o Urish Popeck & Co., LLC
P.O. Box 111419
Naples, FL   34108-0124
Application address: c/o Richard L. Swope, C.P.A., 8955 Fontana Del Sol Way, Naples, FL 34109, tel.: (239) 262-0170

Donor: Maria L. Ransburg.
Foundation type: Independent foundation.
Financial data (yr. ended 12/31/13): Assets, $6,499,787 (M); expenditures, $470,458; qualifying distributions, $400,000; giving activities include $400,000 for 10 grants (high: $40,000; low: $40,000).
Fields of interest: Education; Zoos; Domesticated animals; Housing development; Human services.
Limitations: Applications accepted. Giving primarily in FL.
Application information:
Deadline(s): None
Directors: Elizabeth Bancroft; Jack Fulop; Kimberly Leach Johnson; Maria L. Ransburg; Richard L. Swope.
EIN: 386870585

2275
Ray Foundation
(formerly EAA Flight Academy, Inc.)
100 Aviation Dr. S., Ste. 203
Naples, FL   34104-3583   (239) 649-5733
Contact: James C. Ray, Pres.

Established in 1962 in Montana.
Donors: James C. Ray; Joan L. Ray†.
Foundation type: Independent foundation.
Financial data (yr. ended 06/30/13): Assets, $18,894,699 (M); gifts received, $132,628; expenditures, $417,884; qualifying distributions, $395,803; giving activities include $395,803 for 6 grants (high: $170,000; low: $2,000).
Purpose and activities: Focus on aviation safety and education; support also for sports and aviation as an alternative to drug use.
Fields of interest: Higher education; Substance abuse prevention; Child welfare.
Type of support: General support; Matching grants; Continuing support; Equipment; Endowments; Program development; Seed money; Research; Technical assistance.
Limitations: Applications accepted. Giving primarily in Grand Forks, ND. No support for religious organizations, unless they are requesting funds for a community project. No grants to individuals or for deficit financing; no loans.
Application information: Application form required.
Initial approach: Letter
Copies of proposal: 1
Deadline(s): None
Board meeting date(s): Oct. or Nov. for annual meeting; as needed throughout the year
Officers and Directors: James C. Ray, Pres. and Director; Charles J. Ahearn, Secy. and Director; Jeffrey J. Tempas, Treas. and Director.
Number of staff: 1 part-time professional.
EIN: 810288819

2276
Raymund Foundation, Inc.
5350 Tech Data Dr.
Clearwater, FL   33760   (727) 599-2630

Donors: Sonia V. Raymund; Steven A. Raymund; Raymund 2003 Charitable Lead Trust.
Foundation type: Independent foundation.
Financial data (yr. ended 12/31/13): Assets, $4,114,075 (M); gifts received, $137,064; expenditures, $278,278; qualifying distributions, $262,575; giving activities include $262,575 for 29 grants (high: $100,000; low: $70).
Purpose and activities: Giving primarily for education, social services, and religious purposes.
Fields of interest: Education; Higher education; Community and economic development; Judaism; Child welfare.
Limitations: Applications accepted. Giving primarily in FL; with some giving also in Washington, DC and OR.
Application information: Application form required.
Initial approach: Letter
Deadline(s): None
Officer: Steven A. Raymund, Pres.
EIN: 593447494

2277
The Ethel and Harry Reckson Foundation
2525 Ponce De Leon Blvd., Ste. 1040
Coral Gables, FL   33134-6037
Contact: Michael Spritzer

Established in 2006 in Florida.
Donors: Harry Reckson Trust; Ethel Reckson Trust.
Foundation type: Independent foundation.

Financial data (yr. ended 12/31/13): Assets, $3,420,214 (M); expenditures, $432,307; qualifying distributions, $339,665; giving activities include $336,500 for 18 grants (high: $100,000; low: $500).
Fields of interest: Elementary and secondary education; Autism; Judaism; Human services.
Limitations: Applications not accepted. Giving primarily in FL and MA. No grants to individuals.
Application information: Unsolicited requests for funds not accepted.
Directors: Marjorie A. Baron; Dennis Ginsburg; Michael Spritzer.
EIN: 205120699

2278
Calvin H. Reed Family Foundation, Inc.
3301 Bayshore Blvd., Ste. 1706
Tampa, FL 33629-8845

Donors: Calvin H. Reed; Wendy Reed; Christopher Allaben Reed; David H. Reed; Neva J. Dell; Katherine Chase Reed.
Foundation type: Independent foundation.
Financial data (yr. ended 12/31/13): Assets, $4,350 (M); gifts received, $126,010; expenditures, $122,655; qualifying distributions, $121,705; giving activities include $121,705 for 39 grants (high: $28,500; low: $100).
Fields of interest: Arts and culture; Education; Diseases and conditions.
Limitations: Applications not accepted.
Application information: Unsolicited requests for funds not accepted.
Officers and Directors: Calvin H. Reed, Pres. and Director; David H. Reed, V.P. and Secy.; Neva J. Dell; Christopher Allaben Reed; Katherine Chase Reed; Wendy Reed.
EIN: 263668924

2279
Eleanor Patterson Reeves Foundation, Inc.
169 Seaview Ave.
Palm Beach, FL 33480-4232

Established in 1998 in Florida.
Foundation type: Operating foundation.
Financial data (yr. ended 12/31/13): Assets, $4,125,609 (M); expenditures, $521,716; qualifying distributions, $397,850; giving activities include $222,264 for 22 grants (high: $51,500; low: $1,000).
Fields of interest: Museums; Cancers; Human services; Family services; Child welfare.
Limitations: Applications not accepted. Giving primarily in TX and FL. No grants to individuals.
Application information: Contributes only to pre-selected organizations.
Officer: Patricia A. Myura, Exec. Dir.
Director: Anthony Myura.
EIN: 656230803

2280
Paul E. & Klare N. Reinhold Foundation, Inc.
(formerly Paul E. & Ida Klare Reinhold Foundation, Inc.)
1845 Town Ctr. Blvd., Ste. 105
Fleming Island, FL 32003-3358 (904) 269-5857; 404
Contact: Amy Parker, Exec. Dir.
FAX: (904) 269-8382; E-mail: aparker@reinhold.net;
Main URL: http://www.reinhold.net
Blog: http://www.reinhold.net/blog
Grants List: http://www.reinhold.net/grant_summary.php
RSS feed: http://reinhold.net/blog/?feed=rss2

Established in 1954 in Florida.
Donor: Paul E. Reinhold†.
Foundation type: Independent foundation.
Financial data (yr. ended 12/31/13): Assets, $8,084,838 (M); gifts received, $362,021; expenditures, $255,985; qualifying distributions, $340,772; giving activities include $173,400 for 85 grants (high: $83,500; low: $300), and $82,585 for 1 employee matching gift.
Purpose and activities: The mission of the foundation is to perpetuate the ethos of cathedral building in doing good in the community, within the context of Christian values and family continuity (unity), and to share in the celebration of family heritage. The foundation also operates a program dedicated to enhancing the leadership skills of senior staff members and volunteers that manage non-profit organizations. This grant program is restricted to organizations that provide meaningful services to the citizens of Clay County, Florida.
Fields of interest: Education; Foundations; Health care administration and financing; Hospital care; Diseases and conditions; Religion; Christianity; Human services; Youth development.
Type of support: Capital campaigns; Matching grants; Building and renovations; Equipment; Land acquisitions; Emergency funds; Seed money.
Limitations: Applications accepted. Giving limited to Clay County, FL. No support for private operating foundations. No grants to individuals.
Publications: Application guidelines; Program policy statement.
Application information: See web site for complete application policies and guidelines. Application form required.
Initial approach: 2-3 page proposal
Copies of proposal: 1
Deadline(s): See web site
Board meeting date(s): Oct.
Final notification: See web site
Officers: J.F. Bryan IV, Chair.; Leah B. Burnette, Secy.-Treas.
Trustees: Megan Baptist; Jeff Bryan; George Egan; Jack Myers; John C. Myers IV; June R. Myers; Paul Myers; Neely D. Towe.
EIN: 596140495

2281
Rembert Family Foundation, Inc.
c/o Charles Muller, Esq.
447 Atlantic Blvd., Ste. 5
Atlantic Beach, FL 32233-4050
Application address: P.O. Box 790, Alachua, FL 32616; tel.: (904) 249-1776

Foundation type: Independent foundation.

Financial data (yr. ended 12/31/13): Assets, $1,333,847 (M); gifts received, $62,537; expenditures, $271,087; qualifying distributions, $235,982; giving activities include $235,982 for 6 grants (high: $100,100; low: $2,500).
Fields of interest: Higher education; Hospice care; Christianity.
Limitations: Applications accepted. Giving primarily in Gainesville, FL.
Application information:
Initial approach: Letter
Deadline(s): None
Officer: Davis M. Rembert, Jr., Pres.
EIN: 593652983

2282
Howard & Helaine Resnick Foundation
16355 Mirasol Way
Delray Beach, FL 33446-2370
Contact: Howard Resnick, Pres.

Established in 1967 in Illinois.
Donors: Howard Resnick; Max Resnick; Helaine Resnick.
Foundation type: Independent foundation.
Financial data (yr. ended 12/31/13): Assets, $5,020,821 (M); gifts received, $200,000; expenditures, $215,437; qualifying distributions, $210,661; giving activities include $210,661 for 28 grants (high: $67,779; low: $50).
Fields of interest: Museums; Education; Nonprofits; Judaism; Human services.
Type of support: General support; Regranting.
Limitations: Applications accepted. Giving primarily in Chicago and Highland Park, IL. No grants to individuals.
Application information:
Initial approach: Proposal
Deadline(s): None
Officers: Howard Resnick, Pres.; Helaine Resnick, Secy.
EIN: 237024808

2283
The Dianne T. & Charles E. Rice Family Foundation
c/o Bessemer Trust Co., N.A.
801 Brickell Ave.
Miami, FL 33131-2951 (305) 372-5005
Contact: Celeste Rice Donovan, C.E.O.

Established in 2001 in Florida.
Donors: Charles E. Rice†; CSX Corporation; Charles E. Rice Charitable Lead UniTrust.
Foundation type: Independent foundation.
Financial data (yr. ended 12/31/13): Assets, $10,539,777 (M); gifts received, $648,550; expenditures, $570,057; qualifying distributions, $451,948; giving activities include $373,911 for 12 grants (high: $62,911; low: $5,000).
Purpose and activities: The foundation's mission is to empower individuals, particularly children, by investing in educational initiatives in Florida.
Fields of interest: Education; Catholicism.
Limitations: Applications accepted. Giving primarily in Jacksonville, FL. No support for political activities, lobbying, or foreign-based organizations. No grants to individuals, or for events, endowments, fund raising, legislative initiatives, or debt/loan relief.
Application information: See foundation web site for application information.

Initial approach: Letter
Copies of proposal: 1
Deadline(s): Feb. 1 for spring board meeting; Aug. 1 for fall board meeting
Board meeting date(s): As necessary
Final notification: Monthly
Officer and Directors: Celeste Rice Donovan, C.E.O. and Director; Michelle Rice Mitchell; Thomas Mitchell; C. Daniel Rice; Dianne T. Rice; Julie F. Rice.
Number of staff: 1 part-time professional.
EIN: 593701678

2284
Walter Rich Memorial Fund
P.O. Box 1908
Orlando, FL 32802-1908 4048139304

Foundation type: Independent foundation.
Financial data (yr. ended 12/31/14): Assets, $7,988,882; expenditures, $288,973; qualifying distributions, $264,807.
Fields of interest: Arts and culture; Education; University education; Health.
Type of support: General support.
Limitations: Applications not accepted. Giving primarily in Atlanta, GA.
Application information: Contributes only to pre-selected organizations.
Officers: Jenner Wood, Chair.; Kirby Thompson, Secy.
Distribution Committee: Dave Dierker; John Geraghty.
Trustee: SunTrust Bank.
EIN: 586026053

2285
The Richard Foundation
181 Oleander Way
Vero Beach, FL 32963-3320

Established in 1948 in New York.
Foundation type: Independent foundation.
Financial data (yr. ended 12/31/13): Assets, $5,680,823 (M); expenditures, $354,365; qualifying distributions, $276,899; giving activities include $270,301 for 258 grants (high: $5,025; low: $16).
Fields of interest: Museums; Education; Secondary education; University education; Nonprofits; Hospital care; Biomedicine; Diseases and conditions; National defense; Human services; Child welfare.
Type of support: Research; Research and evaluation; Regranting.
Limitations: Applications not accepted. Giving primarily in FL, NJ, and NY. No grants to individuals.
Application information: Unsolicited requests for funds not accepted.
Officers and Directors: Jeremy Wood, Pres.; Harold Van B. Richard, V.P. and Treas. and Director; James A. Fritts, V.P. and Director; Phyllis Fritts, V.P. and Director; Cecily Richard, V.P. and Director; Virginia Richard, V.P. and Director; Zachary Richard, V.P. and Director; Roy Stephens, V.P. and Director; Virginia Susi, V.P. and Director; Elizabeth H.W. Fry, Secy.
EIN: 136083721

2286
B. Beall & R. Kemp Riechmann Foundation
P.O. Box 25207
Bradenton, FL 34206-5207 (941) 747-2355
Contact: Beverly Beall, Tr.

Established in 1998 in Florida.
Donors: Beverly Beall; R. Kemp Reichman.
Foundation type: Operating foundation.
Financial data (yr. ended 11/30/13): Assets, $1,750,519 (M); expenditures, $297,342; qualifying distributions, $271,564; giving activities include $15,400 for 15 grants (high: $4,000; low: $200), and $154,338 for 66 grants to individuals (high: $9,650; low: $40).
Purpose and activities: Scholarships for students and grants for teachers at Manatee High School, FL.
Fields of interest: Secondary education.
Type of support: Student aid; Grants to individuals.
Limitations: Applications accepted. Giving primarily in FL.
Application information: Scholarship applicants must be formally accepted to a four year accredited Florida college or university and submit letters of acceptance. Application form required.
Initial approach: Request application form
Deadline(s): June 30 and Apr. 1
Final notification: Aug. 1
Trustees: Beverly Beall; R. Kemp Reichmann; R. kemp Reichmann, Jr.; Rolf C. Reichmann.
EIN: 650808807

2287
David and Leighan Rinker Foundation, Inc.
310 Okeechobee Blvd., Ste. 100
West Palm Beach, FL 33401-6419 (561) 835-9200
Contact: Paul Bremer

Established in 1993 in Florida.
Donors: David B. Rinker; Leighan R. Rinker.
Foundation type: Independent foundation.
Financial data (yr. ended 12/31/13): Assets, $4,187,839 (M); gifts received, $100,000; expenditures, $183,972; qualifying distributions, $177,000; giving activities include $177,000 for 8 grants (high: $43,000; low: $2,500).
Fields of interest: Education; Christianity; Food aid.
Type of support: Capital campaigns.
Limitations: Applications accepted. Giving primarily in FL.
Application information: Application form required.
Initial approach: Letter
Deadline(s): None
Directors: Allison R. St. John; Marc C. St. John; Christopher R. Rinker; Margaret H. Rinker.
EIN: 650454037

2288
River Oaks Foundation, Inc.
(formerly William & Norma Horvitz Family Foundation, Inc.)
401 E. Las Olas Blvd., Ste. 2200
Fort Lauderdale, FL 33301-2244

Established in 1986 in Florida.
Donors: William D. Horvitz; Norma Horvitz.
Foundation type: Independent foundation.
Financial data (yr. ended 12/31/13): Assets, $5,338,855 (M); expenditures, $292,561; qualifying distributions, $231,000; giving activities

include $231,000 for 20 grants (high: $50,000; low: $500).
Purpose and activities: Giving primarily for the arts, education and human services.
Fields of interest: Arts and culture; Art museums; Higher education; Nonprofits; Specialty hospital care; Rehabilitation; Eye diseases; Judaism; Human services.
Type of support: Regranting.
Limitations: Applications not accepted. Giving primarily in FL. No grants to individuals.
Application information: Contributes only to pre-selected organizations.
Directors: Alicia Gregory; Wayne A. Gregory, Jr.; Norma Horvitz.
EIN: 592722308

2289
Thomas E. Rodgers, Jr. Foundation, Inc.
27 N.E. 27th St.
Miami, FL 33137-3952

Donor: Thomas E. Rodgers, Jr.
Foundation type: Independent foundation.
Financial data (yr. ended 12/31/13): Assets, $0 (M); gifts received, $235,937; expenditures, $247,206; qualifying distributions, $246,937; giving activities include $246,937 for 27 grants (high: $75,000; low: $250).
Fields of interest: Domesticated animals; Health; Community and economic development.
Limitations: Applications not accepted. Giving primarily in Miami, FL. No grants to individuals.
Application information: Unsolicited requests for funds not accepted.
EIN: 651068247

2290
Rogers Family Foundation, Inc.
1401 E. Broward Blvd., Ste. 300
Fort Lauderdale, FL 33301-2116 (954) 462-1431
Contact: Romney C. Rogers, Pres. and Treas.

Foundation type: Independent foundation.
Financial data (yr. ended 12/31/13): Assets, $5,506,927 (M); expenditures, $220,733; qualifying distributions, $216,717; giving activities include $215,000 for 10 grants (high: $130,000; low: $5,000).
Fields of interest: Hospice care; Protestantism.
Limitations: Applications accepted. Giving primarily in FL.
Application information:
Initial approach: Proposal
Deadline(s): None
Officers and Board Members: Romney C. Rogers, Pres. and Treas. and Director; Eleanor M. Welch, Secy. and Director; Dwight L. Rogers III; Florence Ann Rogers; Virginia B. Rogers.
EIN: 204934225

2291
Rogers Family Foundation, Inc.
(formerly J. Carlisle Rogers, Ruth G. Rogers & James Carlisle Rogers, Jr. Family Foundation, Inc.)
215 N. Joanna Ave.
Tavares, FL 32778-2317

Established in 1989 in Unspecified.

Donor: Ruth Rogers Trust.
Foundation type: Independent foundation.
Financial data (yr. ended 12/31/14): Assets, $5,505,057; expenditures, $289,497; qualifying distributions, $260,343.
Purpose and activities: Giving primarily for education and Christian agencies and churches.
Fields of interest: Education; Secondary education; Undergraduate education; Domesticated animals; Community health care; Public libraries; Housing development; Christianity; Human services; Food banks; Youth services.
Type of support: General support; Public engagement and education.
Limitations: Applications not accepted. Giving primarily in Leesburg, FL. No grants to individuals.
Application information: Contributes only to pre-selected organizations.
Officers: William Cauthen, Pres.; Phil Braun, V.P.; Howard Hewitt, Secy.-Treas.
EIN: 592969938

2292

The Rogers Family Foundation

381 Indian Harbor Rd.
Vero Beach, FL 32963-3304
Contact: Clarence B. Rogers Jr., Tr.

Established in 1997 in Georgia.
Donor: Clarence B. Rogers, Jr.
Foundation type: Independent foundation.
Financial data (yr. ended 12/31/13): Assets, $2,779,043 (M); expenditures, $297,749; qualifying distributions, $289,390; giving activities include $289,390 for 23 grants (high: $165,194; low: $200).
Purpose and activities: Giving primarily to hospitals, schools, and Presbyterian churches.
Fields of interest: Education; Hospital care; Diseases and conditions; Cancers; Protestantism; Human services.
Application information: Application form required.
 Initial approach: Proposal
 Deadline(s): None
Trustee: Clarence B. Rogers, Jr.
Distribution Committee: Hank Mitchell; Sally R. Mitchell; Chase A. Rogers; John B. Rogers; Nancy E. Rogers.
EIN: 586343705

2293

Rose Family Foundation

1654 Tigertail Ave.
Miami, FL 33133-2543

Donor: Marian H. Rose.
Foundation type: Independent foundation.
Financial data (yr. ended 12/31/14): Assets, $5,240,163 (M); expenditures, $356,295; qualifying distributions, $320,200; giving activities include $313,650 for 7 grants (high: $75,000; low: $20,000).
Fields of interest: Arts and culture; Environment; Sports and recreation.
Limitations: Applications not accepted. Giving primarily in NY and Sante Fe, NM. No grants to individuals.
Application information: Contributes only to pre-selected organizations.
Officers: Simon M. Rose, Pres.; Ann R. Podlipny, V.P. and Secy.; James A. Rose, Treas.

Director: Marian H. Rose.
EIN: 134016964

2294

The Martin and Doris Rosen Foundation

(formerly The Rosen Family Foundation)
5500 Collins Ave., Apt. 1803
Miami Beach, FL 33140-3298 (757) 499-0535
Contact: Martin L. Rosen, Pres.

Established in 1982 in Virginia.
Donors: Martin L. Rosen; Doris B. Rosen; Nancy N. Rosenblatt.
Foundation type: Independent foundation.
Financial data (yr. ended 11/30/13): Assets, $2,123,512 (M); expenditures, $196,141; qualifying distributions, $168,476; giving activities include $167,105 for 5 grants (high: $160,000; low: $50).
Fields of interest: Education; Religion; Human services.
Type of support: Endowments.
Limitations: Applications accepted. Giving primarily in FL, NC, and VA. No grants to individuals.
Application information: Application form required.
 Initial approach: Letter
 Deadline(s): Sept. 30
Officers and Directors: Martin L. Rosen, Pres. and Director; Doris B. Rosen, Secy. and Director; Nancy N. Rosenblatt; Robert Stone.
EIN: 510233937

2295

Jack and Harriet Rosenfeld Foundation

c/o Lynn W. Fromberg
20295 N.E. 29th Pl., Ste. 200
Aventura, FL 33180-4109

Established in 2009 in Florida.
Donor: Harriet Rosenfeld Sahs Revocable Trust.
Foundation type: Independent foundation.
Financial data (yr. ended 12/31/14): Assets, $3,555,129; expenditures, $369,438; qualifying distributions, $278,575.
Fields of interest: Education; Human services.
Limitations: Applications not accepted.
Application information: Unsolicited requests for funds not accepted.
Trustees: Lynn W. Fromberg; Jay Kaufman.
EIN: 656476677

2296

Miriam Rosenthal Foundation for the Arts

6424 Autumn Woods Way
Sarasota, FL 34243-3882 (941) 350-0158
Contact: Richard C. McCauley, Chair.
E-mail: ricmcc@verizon.net; *Main URL:* http://miriamrosenthalfoundation.org/
Grants List: http://miriamrosenthalfoundation.org/grant-recipients/

Foundation type: Independent foundation.
Financial data (yr. ended 06/30/15): Assets, $3,541,610 (M); expenditures, $243,803; qualifying distributions, $193,979; giving activities include $155,710 for 3 grants (high: $100,000; low: $15,710).
Fields of interest: Arts and culture.
Type of support: General support.

Limitations: Applications accepted. Giving limited to FL and OH. No grants to individuals.
Application information: See web site for complete application policies, guidelines and application form. Application form required.
 Initial approach: Letter
 Copies of proposal: 15
 Deadline(s): Apr. 1 for projects beginning no earlier than Nov. of the same year; Oct. 1 for projects beginning no earlier than May of the following year.
 Final notification: 45-60 days following the deadlines
Officers and Board Members: Richard McCauley, Chair. and Director; Gayle B. Price, Vice-Chair. and Director; Richard F. Carlile, Secy. and Director; David M. Berry; William H. Caldwell; Mrs. Franklin Handel; Ray Lane; Steven Petitjean; Cathy Ponitz; Scott A. Spears.
Trustee: PrivateBank.
EIN: 316055183

2297

Roshan Institute of Cultural Heritage

c/o Suntrust Banks
P.O. Box 1908
Orlando, FL 32802-1908
Contact: Stephanie Moana Doi, Exec. Asst.
Main URL: http://www.roshan-institute.org
Grants List: http://www.roshan-institute.org/474563
Pierre and Pam Omidyar's Giving Pledge Profile: http://glasspockets.org/philanthropy-in-focus/eye-on-the-giving-pledge/profiles/omidyar

Established in 2000 in Tennessee.
Donor: Pierre Omidyar.
Foundation type: Independent foundation.
Financial data (yr. ended 06/30/13): Assets, $9,355,492 (M); expenditures, $544,074; qualifying distributions, $521,784; giving activities include $358,500 for 11 grants (high: $250,000; low: $2,000).
Purpose and activities: The institute sponsors activities and programs whose primary focus is the preservation, transmission, and instruction of Persian culture. To execute its mission, the Institute develops initiatives that provide support for partnerships with other nonprofit organizations and institutions such as schools, universities, libraries, museums, and private sector donors. It also offers a limited number of individual fellowships to qualified graduate students engaged in writing their doctoral dissertation in the field of Persian Studies.
Fields of interest: Arts and culture; Education; Science; Human services.
Type of support: Program development; Convening; Professorships; Curriculum development; Fellowships; Scholarships; Research; Program evaluations.
Limitations: Applications not accepted. No support for political organizations.
Application information: Contributes only to pre-selected organizations.
 Board meeting date(s): May
Officers and Directors: Elah'e Mir-Djalali Omidyar, Chair. and Pres. and Director; Dorn McGrath, V.P. and Treas. and Director; Jan Schneider, Esq., Secy. and Director; James J. Bickerton, Esq.; Virginia Hinshaw, Ph.D; Pierre Omidyar.
EIN: 770560800

2298
The Darrell & Susan Ross Charitable Foundation
300 Polmer Park
Palm Beach, FL 33480-3402 4012742000
Application address: c/o Stephen J. Carlotti, 1500 Fleet Ctr., Providence, RI 02903, tel.: (401) 274-2000

Established in 2000 in Rhode Island.
Donors: Darrell S. Ross; Susan S. Ross.
Foundation type: Independent foundation.
Financial data (yr. ended 12/31/14): Assets, $3,488,353; expenditures, $181,901; qualifying distributions, $153,145.
Fields of interest: Education; Higher education; Judaism.
Limitations: Applications accepted. Giving primarily in CT and RI. No grants to individuals.
Application information: Application form required.
  Initial approach: Proposal
  Deadline(s): None
Trustees: Darrell S. Ross; Susan S. Ross.
EIN: 056125455

2299
Maurice A. Rothman and Thelma P. Rothman Family Foundation, Inc.
(formerly Maurice A. and Thelma P. Rothman Foundation, Inc.)
5700 70th Ave. N.
Pinellas Park, FL 33781-4238

Established in 1959 in Florida.
Donors: Maurice A. Rothman†; Thelma P. Rothman; Rothman Trust; Rothman Charitable Lead Trust.
Foundation type: Independent foundation.
Financial data (yr. ended 09/30/13): Assets, $6,204,730 (M); gifts received, $200,000; expenditures, $353,903; qualifying distributions, $318,874; giving activities include $318,874 for 29 grants (high: $112,500; low: $50).
Purpose and activities: Giving primarily for education and Jewish agencies and temples.
Fields of interest: Arts and culture; Education; Hospital care; Diseases and conditions; Cancers; Judaism; Human services.
Type of support: General support; Continuing support; Annual campaigns; Capital campaigns; Endowments.
Limitations: Applications not accepted. Giving primarily in central and southwest FL. No grants to individuals.
Application information: Contributes only to pre-selected organizations.
Officers and Trustees: Margie R. Green, Chair. and Trustee; Kevin A. Lane, V.P. and Trustee; Carol R. Lane, Secy. and Trustee; Jason E. Green.
EIN: 592061386

2300
The Rothschild Family Foundation Inc.
130 Sunrise Ave.
Palm Beach, FL 33480

Donors: Barbara Rothschild; Richard Rothschild; Daniel Floersheimer.
Foundation type: Independent foundation.
Financial data (yr. ended 04/30/13): Assets, $198,882 (M); gifts received, $350,000; expenditures, $220,850; qualifying distributions,

$211,810; giving activities include $211,810 for 38 grants (high: $50,200; low: $100).
Fields of interest: Museums; Education; Health; Religion; Judaism.
Limitations: Applications not accepted. Giving primarily in NY.
Application information: Unsolicited requests for funds not accepted.
Officers: Barbara Rothschild, Pres.; Richard Rothschild, V.P. and Treas.; Robert Michaelson, Secy.
EIN: 352413378

2301
Rubens Family Foundation
6598 Grande Orchid Way
Delray Beach, FL 33446-4333

Established in 1997 in Florida.
Donors: Jack Rubens; Merton Rubens; Monroe Securities.
Foundation type: Independent foundation.
Financial data (yr. ended 12/31/14): Assets, $5,558,583; expenditures, $245,908; qualifying distributions, $222,172.
Fields of interest: Education; Foundations; Health; Judaism.
Limitations: Applications not accepted. Giving primarily in FL, IL, and NY. No grants to individuals.
Application information: Contributes only to pre-selected organizations.
Officers and Trustees: Jack Rubens, Chair. and Trustee; Helen Rubens, Secy. and Trustee; Nicole E. Druckman; Suzanne Rubens Kanter; Nathan Robfogel; Margaret Rubens-Ellis.
EIN: 656235868

2302
The Ruskin Family Trust
P.O. Box 40200, FL9-100-10-19
Jacksonville, FL 32203-0200

Foundation type: Independent foundation.
Financial data (yr. ended 11/30/14): Assets, $5,228,804 (M); expenditures, $402,047; qualifying distributions, $354,539; giving activities include $330,848 for 5 grants (high: $132,339; low: $33,085).
Fields of interest: Health; Health care access; Diseases and conditions; Human services; Children.
Type of support: General support.
Limitations: Applications not accepted. Giving primarily in FL, GA, NE and NY.
Application information: Unsolicited requests for funds not accepted.
Trustee: Bank of America, N.A.
EIN: 586331072

2303
Richard B. Russell Foundation
P.O. Box 1908
Orlando, FL 32802—1908

Donor: The Shepherd Foundation.
Foundation type: Independent foundation.
Financial data (yr. ended 12/31/13): Assets, $5,708,408 (M); gifts received, $2,500; expenditures, $276,190; qualifying distributions, $260,208; giving activities include $224,228 for 1 grant.

Fields of interest: University education.
Type of support: Grants to individuals.
Limitations: Applications not accepted. Giving primarily in GA.
Application information: Contributes only to pre-selected organizations.
Officer: Norman Underwood, Chair.
Trustee: SunTrust Bank.
EIN: 237075206

2304
The Ryan Family Foundation
11027 Old Harbour Rd.
North Palm Beach, FL 33408-3422

Established in 2004 in Rhode Island.
Donors: Cathy H. Ryan; Thomas M. Ryan.
Foundation type: Independent foundation.
Financial data (yr. ended 12/31/13): Assets, $20,177,371 (M); gifts received, $1,506,291; expenditures, $508,889; qualifying distributions, $381,650; giving activities include $381,600 for 6 grants (high: $300,000; low: $10,000).
Fields of interest: Elementary and secondary education; Nonprofits; Hospital care.
Type of support: Regranting.
Limitations: Applications not accepted. Giving primarily in RI. No grants to individuals.
Application information: Contributes only to pre-selected organizations.
Trustees: Cathy H. Ryan; Thomas M. Ryan.
EIN: 201518978

2305
The Ryan Foundation
207 W. State Road 434, Ste. A
Winter Springs, FL 32708-2512
Application address: c/o Sheryl Kisling, Secy., 100 E. Sybelia Ave., Maitland, FL 32751, tel.: (407) 740-7311

Established in 1988 in Florida.
Donor: Sheelah Ryan†.
Foundation type: Independent foundation.
Financial data (yr. ended 10/31/13): Assets, $4,218,754 (M); expenditures, $235,576; qualifying distributions, $232,853; giving activities include $200,600 for 14 grants (high: $20,000; low: $600).
Purpose and activities: Provides emergency assistance to needy local area residents for the basic necessities of life, i.e. food, clothing, shelter, and essential medical care; support also to social service agencies for children and families.
Fields of interest: Crime prevention; Human services; Family services; Homeless services; Homeless people; Low-income and poor people.
Type of support: Emergency funds; Grants to individuals.
Limitations: Applications accepted. Giving primarily in Seminole County, FL.
Application information: Application form required.
  Initial approach: Letter or telephone
  Deadline(s): None
  Final notification: Within 10 days for emergency aid
Officers: Pamela Ohab, Pres. and Treas.; Dennis Ryan, V.P.; Jennifer Ryan, V.P.; Joseph Ryan, V.P.; Sheryl Kisling, Secy.
Director: Rosemary Finnegan.

Number of staff: 1 part-time professional.
EIN: 592950299

2306

Sadler Family Foundation

226 Ridgeview Dr.
Palm Beach, FL 33480

Established in 2006 in New York.
Donor: Robert E. Sadler, Jr.
Foundation type: Independent foundation.
Financial data (yr. ended 12/31/13): Assets, $3,344,611 (M); expenditures, $169,132; qualifying distributions, $164,890; giving activities include $164,890 for 9 grants (high: $50,195; low: $500).
Fields of interest: Education; University education; Human services.
Limitations: Applications not accepted. Giving primarily in VA. No grants to individuals.
Application information: Contributes only to pre-selected organizations.
Trustees: Elizabeth Robinson Coffin; Elizabeth S. Cryan; Robert E. Sadler, Jr.; Trelsie H. Sadler; Catherine T. Seaman.
EIN: 208040696

2307

The Milton and Marilyn Safenowitz Family Foundation Inc.

7124 Queenferry Cir.
Boca Raton, FL 33496-5950   8182228862

Established in 2001 in Florida.
Donor: Marilyn Safenowitz.
Foundation type: Independent foundation.
Financial data (yr. ended 12/31/14): Assets, $2,753,306; expenditures, $151,720; qualifying distributions, $148,200.
Fields of interest: Nonprofits; Health; ALS.
International interests: Israel.
Type of support: Regranting.
Limitations: Applications not accepted. Giving primarily in FL and NY. No grants to individuals.
Application information: Contributes only to pre-selected organizations.
Officers: Marilyn Safenowitz, Pres.; Susan Levine, V.P.; Ellen Silverman, V.P.; Howard Safenowitz, Secy.-Treas.
EIN: 651118908

2308

Stuart Salenger Foundation, Inc.

P.O. Box 8905
Longboat Key, FL 34228-8905

Donors: Stuart Salenger; Slinger Family Charitable Foundation Inc.
Foundation type: Independent foundation.
Financial data (yr. ended 12/31/13): Assets, $347,952 (M); gifts received, $75,000; expenditures, $191,834; qualifying distributions, $191,834; giving activities include $191,278 for 15 grants (high: $97,747; low: $100).
Fields of interest: Arts and culture; Environment; Domesticated animals.
Type of support: General support.
Limitations: Applications not accepted. No grants to individuals.

Application information: Contributes only to pre-selected organizations.
Officer and Directors: Stuart Salenger, Pres. and Secy.-Treas. and Director; George Browning III.
EIN: 205834171

2309

Salizzoni Family Foundation

(formerly Frank & Sarah Salizzoni Family Foundation, Inc.)
288 Locha Dr.
Jupiter, FL 33458-7733

Established in 1997 in Florida.
Donors: Frank Salizzoni; Sarah Salizzoni.
Foundation type: Independent foundation.
Financial data (yr. ended 12/31/14): Assets, $5,442,394; gifts received, $327,049; expenditures, $276,882; qualifying distributions, $250,294.
Purpose and activities: Giving primarily to higher education.
Fields of interest: University education; Nonprofits.
Type of support: Regranting.
Limitations: Applications not accepted. Giving primarily in PA. No grants to individuals.
Application information: Unsolicited requests for funds not accepted.
Officers and Directors: Frank Salizzoni, Pres. and Director; Sarah Salizzoni, V.P. and Secy.-Treas. and Director; Laura Dean; Susan Reverdy; John Salizzoni.
EIN: 650710698

2310

The Elaine Dewey Sammons Foundation

1712 Corporate Dr.
Boynton Beach, FL 33426-6662

Established in 2004 in Texas.
Donor: Elaine D. Sammons.
Foundation type: Independent foundation.
Financial data (yr. ended 12/31/13): Assets, $994,140 (M); expenditures, $223,998; qualifying distributions, $215,500; giving activities include $215,500 for 8 grants (high: $100,000; low: $500).
Fields of interest: Reading promotion; Animal welfare; Human services.
Limitations: Applications not accepted. Giving primarily in FL and NC. No grants to individuals.
Application information: Unsolicited requests for funds not accepted.
Trustees: Vester T. Hughes; Robert W. Korba; J. Craig Madison; Brenda G. Medore; Cuyler P. Medore.
EIN: 746534254

2311

The Samowitz Foundation

(formerly The Stanley C. Samowitz Foundation, Inc.)
3030 Grand Bay Blvd., Unit 3102
Longboat Key, FL 34228-4411

Established in 2003 in Florida.
Donors: Stanley C. Samowitz†; Martin A. Samowitz.
Foundation type: Independent foundation.
Financial data (yr. ended 12/31/13): Assets, $5,303,614 (M); expenditures, $244,602; qualifying distributions, $224,312; giving activities

include $224,312 for 37 grants (high: $30,517; low: $70).
Fields of interest: Historic preservation; Animal welfare; Health; Cancers; Religion; Human services.
Limitations: Applications not accepted. Giving primarily in FL, with some giving in NY. No grants to individuals.
Application information: Contributes only to pre-selected organizations.
Officers: Martin A. Samowitz, Pres. and Treas.; Paulette Samowitz, Secy.
EIN: 200444658

2312

Adrian M. Sample Scholarship Trust

c/o Indian River State College Foundation, Inc.
3209 Virginia Ave.
Fort Pierce, FL 34981-5541   (772) 462-7246
E-mail: lthomas@irsc.edu; Main URL: http://www.adriansamplescholarship.com

Established in 1972 in Florida.
Foundation type: Independent foundation.
Financial data (yr. ended 12/31/14): Assets, $3,950,034; expenditures, $224,371; qualifying distributions, $197,073.
Purpose and activities: Awards scholarship aid to active Protestant church members who are accepted for full-time enrollment at an accredited junior or community college in the State of Florida, an accredited four-year college or university in the State of Florida, or Davidson College in Davidson, North Carolina. Scholarships are also available for students pursuing a degree in veterinary medicine or theology.
Fields of interest: Education.
Type of support: Scholarships; Student aid.
Limitations: Applications accepted. Giving limited to residents of St. Lucie and Okeechobee counties, FL or of a foreign country.
Publications: Application guidelines; Program policy statement.
Application information: See trust web site for complete application guidelines. Application form required.
  Initial approach: Download application form on trust web site
  Deadline(s): See trust web site for current deadlines
  Board meeting date(s): May, and as required
Trustee: SunTrust Bank.
EIN: 596490788

2313

The George And Mary Jo Sanders Foundation Inc.

2026 Wilna St.
Fort Myers, FL 33901-3212   (239) 334-8681
Contact: Mary Jo Walker, Pres.

Established in 1995 in Florida.
Foundation type: Independent foundation.
Financial data (yr. ended 12/31/13): Assets, $8,473,488 (M); expenditures, $449,740; qualifying distributions, $368,897; giving activities include $325,863 for 43 grants (high: $26,900; low: $1,000).
Fields of interest: Education; Religion; Youth development.
Limitations: Applications accepted. Giving primarily in FL. No grants to individuals.

Application information: Application form required.
Initial approach: Letter
Deadline(s): None
Officer and Directors: Mary Jo Walker, Pres. and Director; Michael C. Sanders, V.P. and Director; Richard O. Hilliker; T. Wainwright Miller; Michael A. Sanders.
EIN: 593189770

2314
SBJ Resch Family Foundation Inc.
2900 E. 7th Ave.
Tampa, FL 33605 (813) 636-9808
Contact: James S. Resch, V.P.

Donors: James S. Resch; Jill M. Buhler; Bradley J. Resch; Molly A. Resch; Stephanie A. Rich.
Foundation type: Independent foundation.
Financial data (yr. ended 12/31/13): Assets, $1,825,825 (M); gifts received, $500,000; expenditures, $118,430; qualifying distributions, $118,300; giving activities include $118,300 for 17 grants (high: $33,500; low: $1,000).
Fields of interest: Diseases and conditions; Human services; Adoption.
Limitations: Applications accepted. Giving primarily in FL.
Application information:
Initial approach: Proposal
Deadline(s): None
Officers: Bradley J. Resch, Pres.; James S. Resch, V.P.; Stephanie A. Rich, Secy.; Jill M. Buhler, Treas.
EIN: 453783595

2315
The Scharlin Family Foundation, Inc.
4197 Douglas Rd.
Miami, FL 33133 (305) 661-7515
Contact: Gloria Scharlin, Pres.; Mary Fawkes

Established in 2000 in Unspecified.
Donors: Gloria G. Scharlin; Howard R. Scharlin†; Norman Braman.
Foundation type: Independent foundation.
Financial data (yr. ended 11/30/13): Assets, -$5,583 (M); expenditures, $401,746; qualifying distributions, $399,578; giving activities include $397,410 for 28 grants (high: $100,000; low: $100).
Purpose and activities: Giving primarily for the arts, particularly art museums, and education.
Fields of interest: Arts and culture; Performing arts; Art museums; Education; Judaism; Human services.
Limitations: Applications accepted. Giving primarily in Aspen, CO, and Miami, FL.
Application information: Application form required.
Initial approach: Contact foundation for application form
Deadline(s): Contact foundation for deadline
Officers: Gloria Scharlin, Pres.; Peggy Scharlin, V.P.; David Scharlin, Secy.; Kerri Scharlin, Treas.
EIN: 651063194

2316
Vera and Walter Scherr and Family Foundation, Inc.
100 Central Ave., Ste. 713
Sarasota, FL 34236-5728

Established in 2007 in Florida.

Donors: Laura Scherr Saggese; Robert J. Scherr; Walter J. Scherr.
Foundation type: Independent foundation.
Financial data (yr. ended 12/31/13): Assets, $16,988 (M); gifts received, $150,000; expenditures, $158,355; qualifying distributions, $155,175; giving activities include $155,175 for 4 grants (high: $72,800; low: $4,850).
Fields of interest: Foundations; Human services; Family services; Developmental disability services; People with disabilities.
Limitations: Applications not accepted. Giving primarily in NY. No grants to individuals.
Application information: Unsolicited requests for funds not accepted.
Officer: Walter J. Scherr, Chair.
Directors: Laura Scherr Saggese; Robert J. Scherr.
EIN: 260208043

2317
Schiano Family Foundation Inc.
4814 Culbreath Isles Rd.
Tampa, FL 33629

Donor: Gregory E. Schiano.
Foundation type: Independent foundation.
Financial data (yr. ended 12/31/13): Assets, $94,516 (M); gifts received, $275,000; expenditures, $327,800; qualifying distributions, $327,800; giving activities include $325,851 for 18 grants (high: $52,500; low: $100).
Fields of interest: Arts and culture; Education; Religion.
Limitations: Applications not accepted. Giving primarily in NJ and OH.
Application information: Unsolicited requests for funds not accepted.
Officers: Gregory E. Schiano, Pres.; Chrisina M. Schiano, Secy.
Trustee: Lauren S. Lauderdale.
EIN: 273779179

2318
The Schlanger Family Foundation Inc.
19685 Oakbrook Cir.
Boca Raton, FL 33434-3203

Donor: Norman Schlanger.
Foundation type: Independent foundation.
Financial data (yr. ended 09/30/13): Assets, $5,151,131 (M); gifts received, $300,000; expenditures, $255,282; qualifying distributions, $249,562; giving activities include $248,250 for 28 grants (high: $90,000; low: $500).
Fields of interest: Diseases and conditions; Religion.
Limitations: Applications not accepted. Giving primarily in NY.
Application information: Unsolicited requests for funds not accepted.
Officers: Norman Schlanger, Pres. and Treas.; Craig Schlanger, V.P.; Darren Schlanger, V.P.; Jill Schlanger, V.P.
EIN: 260854652

2319
The Schultz Foundation, Inc.
118 W. Adams St.
Jacksonville, FL 32202

Established in 1964 in Florida.
Donors: Mae W. Schultz†; Genevieve S. Ayers†; Frederick H. Schultz; Nancy R. Schultz.
Foundation type: Independent foundation.
Financial data (yr. ended 12/31/13): Assets, $3,718,576 (M); expenditures, $238,539; qualifying distributions, $145,118; giving activities include $145,118 for 42 grants (high: $26,200; low: $10).
Fields of interest: Education; Health; Religion.
Type of support: General support.
Limitations: Applications not accepted. Giving primarily in Jacksonville, FL. No grants to individuals.
Publications: Annual report.
Application information: Unsolicited requests for funds not accepted.
Officers: Clifford G. Schultz, Pres.; Frederick H. Schultz, Jr., V.P.; John R. Schultz, Secy.-Treas.
Directors: Catherine McFarland; Nancy R. Schultz.
Number of staff: 1 part-time professional.
EIN: 591055869

2320
Douglas and Eleanor Seaman Charitable Foundation
164 Gomez Rd.
Hobe Sound, FL 33455-2513

Established in 1997 in Wisconsin.
Donors: Douglas Seaman; Douglas Securitiies Corp.
Foundation type: Independent foundation.
Financial data (yr. ended 12/31/13): Assets, $1,140,354 (M); expenditures, $152,903; qualifying distributions, $152,500; giving activities include $152,500 for 17 grants (high: $45,000; low: $250).
Purpose and activities: Giving primarily for human services, education, medical centers, arts, and women's associations.
Fields of interest: Education; Higher education; Religion; Youth development.
Limitations: Applications not accepted. Giving primarily in FL, MA and WI. No grants to individuals.
Application information: Unsolicited requests for funds not accepted.
Trustees: Mark Feinberg; Douglas Seaman, Jr.; Eleanor H. Seaman; Eleanor R. Seaman.
EIN: 396636617

2321
Second Chance Foundation
5085 Seahorse Ave.
Naples, FL 34103-2411

Established in 1986 in Florida.
Donors: Lloyd S. Taylor†; Lorraine Huloschman.
Foundation type: Independent foundation.
Financial data (yr. ended 12/31/13): Assets, $8,671,480 (M); gifts received, $61,525; expenditures, $390,946; qualifying distributions, $342,211; giving activities include $181,465 for 2 grants (high: $160,000; low: $21,465).
Fields of interest: History museums; Humanities; Education; Secondary education; Higher education; Cystic fibrosis; Cancers; Leukemia; International development.
Type of support: Program-related investments.
Limitations: Applications not accepted. Giving primarily in Naples, FL. No grants to individuals (except for scholarships).

Application information: Unsolicited requests for funds not accepted.
Trustee: Bruce Conley.
EIN: 592708392

2322

Charles & Rena B. Selders Foundation

(formerly Rena B. Selders Foundation)
P.O. Box 40200, FL9-100-10-19
Jacksonville, FL 32203-0200

Established in 1971 in Florida.
Foundation type: Independent foundation.
Financial data (yr. ended 10/31/14): Assets, $6,865,949 (M); expenditures, $417,426; qualifying distributions, $366,652; giving activities include $338,720 for 8 grants (high: $56,689; low: $18,896).
Fields of interest: Education; Religion; Christianity; Human services.
Limitations: Applications not accepted. Giving primarily in Wallingford, CT, and Jacksonville and Live Oak, FL.
Application information: Unsolicited requests for funds not accepted.
Trustee: Bank of America, N.A.
EIN: 237061597

2323

Sender Charitable Trust

1000 5th St., Ste. 303
Miami Beach, FL 33139-6510

Established in 1999 in New York.
Donor: Adam Sender.
Foundation type: Independent foundation.
Financial data (yr. ended 12/31/12): Assets, $581 (M); gifts received, $375,353; expenditures, $375,207; qualifying distributions, $371,619; giving activities include $371,619 for 19,000 grants (high: $130,000; low: $1,000).
Fields of interest: Art museums; Animal welfare; Foundations; Nonprofits; Judaism; Human services.
Type of support: Regranting.
Limitations: Applications not accepted. Giving primarily in Washington, DC, FL and NY. No grants to individuals.
Application information: Unsolicited requests for funds not accepted.
Trustees: Adam Sender; Lenore Sender.
EIN: 137187854

2324

The Sequoia Foundation for Achievement in the Arts & Education, Inc.

1172 S. Dixie Hwy., Ste. 628
Miami, FL 33146-2918
Main URL: http://www.sqafoundation.org/en.index.php

Established in 1994 in Florida.
Donors: Jeffrey L. Neuman; Sequioa Charitable Trust.
Foundation type: Independent foundation.
Financial data (yr. ended 11/30/13): Assets, $9,947,029 (M); gifts received, $523,144; expenditures, $681,819; qualifying distributions, $476,163; giving activities include $345,242 for 42 grants (high: $62,790; low: $100).
Fields of interest: Arts and culture; Education.

Limitations: Applications not accepted. Giving primarily in MN and NY. No grants to individuals.
Application information: Contributes only to pre-selected organizations.
Directors: H.H. Leonards; Jeffrey L. Neuman; Mark Vineis.
EIN: 650541856

2325

Setzer Family Foundation Inc.

8650-12 Old Kings Rd. S.
Jacksonville, FL 32217

Established in 1986 in Florida.
Donor: Sidney Setzer.
Foundation type: Independent foundation.
Financial data (yr. ended 06/30/14): Assets, $2,071,982 (M); gifts received, $7,754; expenditures, $184,638; qualifying distributions, $155,500; giving activities include $155,500 for 4 grants (high: $100,000; low: $1,000).
Purpose and activities: Giving primarily for Jewish organizations and hospitals.
Fields of interest: Nonprofits; Hospital care; Judaism; Human services.
Type of support: Regranting.
Limitations: Applications not accepted. Giving primarily in Jacksonville, FL. No grants to individuals.
Application information: Contributes only to pre-selected organizations.
Trustees: Debra Setzer; Leonard R. Setzer.
EIN: 592685979

2326

The Sexton Family Foundation

c/o O. Griffith Sexton
410 Coconut Palm Rd.
Vero Beach, FL 32963-3709

Established in 1996 in Connecticut.
Donor: O. Griffith Sexton.
Foundation type: Independent foundation.
Financial data (yr. ended 12/31/13): Assets, $5,104,678 (M); gifts received, $7,235; expenditures, $223,600; qualifying distributions, $218,260; giving activities include $211,025 for 68 grants (high: $25,000; low: $250).
Purpose and activities: Giving primarily for education and social services.
Fields of interest: Education; Higher education; Nonprofits; Cancers; Community and economic development; Human services; Child welfare.
Type of support: Annual campaigns; Regranting; Capital campaigns; Endowments; Emergency funds.
Limitations: Applications not accepted. Giving primarily in Greenwich, CT, FL, NJ and New York, NY.
Application information: Contributes only to pre-selected organizations.
Trustee: O. Griffith Sexton.
EIN: 137106277

2327

Margaret F. Shackelford Charitable Trust

P.O. Box 1908
Orlando, FL 32802-1908
Application address: c/o Paul A. Calame, Jr., 326 S. Goodlett St., Memphis, TN 38117, tel.: (901) 458-6654

Established in 1999 in Tennessee.

Foundation type: Independent foundation.
Financial data (yr. ended 12/31/13): Assets, $8,590,542 (M); expenditures, $426,623; qualifying distributions, $370,870; giving activities include $315,000 for 2 grants (high: $236,250; low: $78,750).
Purpose and activities: Giving primarily for natural resource and wildlife conservation and protection, with particular interest in hardwood trees, (reforestation and management).
Fields of interest: Higher education; Natural resources; Biodiversity; Wildlife biodiversity.
Limitations: Applications accepted. Giving primarily in New York, NY and Knoxville, TN. No grants to individuals.
Application information: Application form required.
 Initial approach: Letter of request
 Copies of proposal: 3
 Deadline(s): None
Trustee: SunTrust Banks, Inc.
Advisory Board: W. Carlyle Blakeney; Paul Calame; Orma R. Smith III.
EIN: 626363101

2328

Tom and Kathy Shannon Family Foundation, Inc.

17635 Tobacco Rd.
Lutz, FL 33558-4850

Donors: Thomas J. Shannon, Jr.; Mary Kathryn Shannon.
Foundation type: Independent foundation.
Financial data (yr. ended 12/31/13): Assets, $3,155,402 (M); gifts received, $70,500; expenditures, $205,209; qualifying distributions, $190,464; giving activities include $190,464 for 38 grants (high: $44,867; low: $100).
Fields of interest: Education; Infant care; Child welfare.
Type of support: Individual development.
Limitations: Applications not accepted. Giving primarily in FL. No grants to individuals.
Application information: Unsolicited requests for funds not accepted.
Officers and Directors: Thomas J. Shannon, Jr., Pres. and Director; Mary Kathryn Shannon, V.P. and Secy.; Crystal S. Deal; April Shannon McDonald; Thomas Joseph Shannon III.
EIN: 208070461

2329

The Sharaby Family Foundation

4001 Hillcrest Dr., Bldg. 26, Ste. 402
Hollywood, FL 33021-7924

Established in 2007 in Florida.
Donors: Elliott J. Sharaby; Joseph Hamiowitz; Susan Stupak; Danny Sharaby; Oshra Raskas.
Foundation type: Independent foundation.
Financial data (yr. ended 11/30/13): Assets, $131,538 (M); gifts received, $82,091; expenditures, $157,217; qualifying distributions, $157,214; giving activities include $157,214 for 81 grants (high: $71,000; low: $18).
Purpose and activities: Giving primarily to Jewish agencies, temples, and schools.
Fields of interest: Elementary and secondary education; Graduate and professional education; Judaism; Theology; Human services.
Limitations: Applications not accepted.

Application information: Contributes only to pre-selected organizations.
Officers: Elliott J. Sharaby, Chair. and Treas.; Emanuel Goldfeiz, Vice-Chair.; Michael Sharaby, Secy.
Trustees: Eddie Blanco; Barry Nabozny; Meir Niknava.
EIN: 208109283

2330
The Sharing Foundation, Inc.
P.O. Box 3688
Fort Pierce, FL 34948-3688

Established in 2007 in Florida.
Donors: Standish Crippen; Audrey Crippen.
Foundation type: Independent foundation.
Financial data (yr. ended 12/31/13): Assets, $1,307,890 (M); gifts received, $45,000; expenditures, $223,572; qualifying distributions, $209,000; giving activities include $209,000 for 9 grants (high: $30,000; low: $5,000).
Fields of interest: Arts and culture; Education; Community and economic development; Christianity; Protestantism; Human services.
Limitations: Applications not accepted. Giving primarily in Fort Pierce, FL.
Application information: Unsolicited requests for funds not accepted.
Officers: Stan Crippen, Pres.; Scott Crippen, V.P.; Audrey Crippen, Secy.-Treas.
EIN: 208997628

2331
Charles E. Shepard Trust
P.O. Box 1908
Orlando, FL 32802-1908 4048131316

Foundation type: Independent foundation.
Financial data (yr. ended 12/31/14): Assets, $5,752,794; expenditures, $318,208; qualifying distributions, $271,854.
Fields of interest: Education; Christianity.
International interests: United Kingdom of Great Britain and Northern Ireland.
Type of support: General support; Scholarships; Student aid.
Limitations: Applications not accepted. Giving primarily in AL, GA and MA; some giving in the United Kingdom.
Application information: Unsolicited requests for funds not accepted.
Trustee: SunTrust Bank.
EIN: 207039436

2332
Shockley Foundation
276 Eagle Estates Dr.
DeBary, FL 32713-2264

Established in 2001 in Wisconsin.
Donors: Terry Shockley; Sandy Shockley.
Foundation type: Independent foundation.
Financial data (yr. ended 12/31/14): Assets, $341,935; expenditures, $154,133; qualifying distributions, $147,900.
Purpose and activities: Giving primarily for education and human services.
Fields of interest: Arts and culture; Education; Environment.

Type of support: General support; Capacity-building and technical assistance; Endowments; Scholarships.
Limitations: Applications not accepted. Giving primarily in IL, KS, MN, and WI. No grants to individuals.
Application information: Unsolicited requests for funds not accepted.
Trustees: Toni K. Peterson; Sandra K. Shockley; Terry K. Shockley; Todd L. Shockley.
Number of staff: None.
EIN: 396764154

2333
H. L. Shuey Orphanage Trust
P.O. Box 40200, FL9-100-10-19
Jacksonville, FL 32203-0200 8774461410

Foundation type: Independent foundation.
Financial data (yr. ended 12/31/14): Assets, $4,235,817; expenditures, $236,170; qualifying distributions, $192,613.
Fields of interest: Housing development; Human services; Family services; Children.
Limitations: Applications not accepted. Giving primarily in NC.
Application information: Unsolicited requests for funds not accepted.
Trustee: Bank of America, N.A.
EIN: 566066544

2334
The Sidhu Family Foundation
10229 Tavistock Rd.
Orlando, FL 32827-7054

Established in 1997 in Florida.
Donors: Rupinder S. Sidhu; Lisa Eaton Sidhu.
Foundation type: Independent foundation.
Financial data (yr. ended 04/30/13): Assets, $6,450,776 (M); gifts received, $654,517; expenditures, $296,848; qualifying distributions, $250,400; giving activities include $241,790 for 21 grants (high: $71,000; low: $100).
Fields of interest: Arts and culture; Education; Human services.
Limitations: Applications not accepted. No grants to individuals.
Application information: Unsolicited requests for funds not accepted.
Officers: Rupinder S. Sidhu, Pres.; Lisa Eaton Sidhu, V.P.
Director: Michele D. Rosenberg.
EIN: 593449183

2335
The Stuart and Jill Siegel Charitable Trust
3785 Coventry Ln.
Boca Raton, FL 33496-4062 (215) 881-8868
Contact: Stuart Siegel, Tr.

Established in 1995 in New York.
Donor: Stuart Siegel.
Foundation type: Independent foundation.
Financial data (yr. ended 12/31/13): Assets, $1,862,414 (M); gifts received, $3,870; expenditures, $214,239; qualifying distributions, $188,792; giving activities include $188,792 for 35 grants (high: $52,120; low: $25).

Fields of interest: Education; Environment; Children's hospital care; Diseases and conditions; Judaism; Human services; Children.
Limitations: Applications accepted. Giving primarily in FL. No grants to individuals.
Application information:
Initial approach: Proposal
Deadline(s): None
Trustees: Jill Siegel; Stuart Siegel.
EIN: 113297021

2336
Sierra Foundation, Inc.
509 Guisando de Avila, Ste. 200
Tampa, FL 33613-5235 (813) 549-7707
Contact: Thomas H. Gray, Secy.-Treas.; John Robert Sierra, Pres.

Established in 1987 in Florida.
Donors: J. Robert Sierra; Mary Sierra.
Foundation type: Independent foundation.
Financial data (yr. ended 06/30/13): Assets, $9,407,614 (M); expenditures, $448,216; qualifying distributions, $447,492; giving activities include $397,361 for 66 grants (high: $200,000; low: $100).
Fields of interest: Education; Foundations; Diseases and conditions; Religion; Human services; Child welfare.
Type of support: Research.
Limitations: Applications accepted. Giving primarily in FL. No grants to individuals.
Application information:
Initial approach: Proposal
Deadline(s): None
Officers: John Robert Sierra, Pres.; Mary Sierra, V.P.; Thomas H. Gray, Secy.-Treas.; James Kilbride, Secy.
EIN: 592846736

2337
Barry & Judy Silverman Foundation, Inc.
(formerly Silverman Family Foundation, Inc.)
2801 N.E. 208th Terr., Ste. 102
Aventura, FL 33180-1428 (305) 705-0026
Contact: Ronni Silverman Bianco, Treas.

Donors: Barry Silverman; Judy Silverman.
Foundation type: Independent foundation.
Financial data (yr. ended 09/30/13): Assets, $4,571,130 (M); expenditures, $289,330; qualifying distributions, $277,615; giving activities include $277,615 for 36 grants (high: $115,000; low: $100).
Purpose and activities: Funding primarily for Jewish agencies and federated giving programs. Some funding also for higher education and human services.
Fields of interest: Higher education; Nonprofits; Judaism; Human services.
Type of support: Continuing support; Matching grants; Annual campaigns; Capital campaigns; Regranting; Capital and infrastructure; Equipment; Emergency funds; Research.
Limitations: Applications accepted. Giving primarily in southern FL.
Application information:
Initial approach: Letter
Deadline(s): None
Board meeting date(s): Varies

Officers: Barry J. Silverman, Chair. and Pres.; Laurie Karen Silverman, V.P.; Judy Silverman, Secy.; Ronni Silverman Bianco, Treas.
Number of staff: 1 full-time professional.
EIN: 650526279

2338
The Mabel & Ellsworth Simmons Charitable Foundation, Inc.
6718 Simmons Loop
Riverview, FL   33569-9420

Foundation type: Operating foundation.
Financial data (yr. ended 12/31/13): Assets, $9,348,911 (M); expenditures, $375,328; qualifying distributions, $201,500; giving activities include $201,500 for 20 grants (high: $35,000; low: $1,000).
Fields of interest: Diseases and conditions; Human services; Family services; Child welfare; Youth services.
Type of support: Research; Research and evaluation.
Limitations: Applications accepted. Giving primarily in FL.
Application information: Application form required.
   Deadline(s): Applications are accepted between May 1 and July 1
Officer: Sandra Simmons, Pres.
Directors: Michelle Henry; Christine Hogan; Jean Simmons Odell; George Simmons.
EIN: 593594418

2339
The Six Pillar Foundation, Inc.
440 S. Babcock St.
Melbourne, FL   32901-1276   (321) 984-1876
Contact: James W. Toy, Pres. and Treas.

Established in 1999 in Florida.
Donor: James W. Toy.
Foundation type: Independent foundation.
Financial data (yr. ended 10/31/13): Assets, $6,864,925 (M); expenditures, $365,561; qualifying distributions, $365,561; giving activities include $365,000 for 17 grants (high: $35,000; low: $5,000).
Purpose and activities: Giving primarily for children and family activities offering Christian spiritual content; funding also for the construction and renovation of educational and human service buildings, and the rehabilitation of teen drug addicts.
Fields of interest: Education; Substance abuse treatment; Youth services.
Limitations: Applications accepted. Giving primarily in central FL, particularly Brevard County.
Application information: Application form required.
   Initial approach: Request foundation for application form
   Copies of proposal: 1
   Deadline(s): None
Officers: James W. Toy, Pres. and Treas.; Clare C. Toy, V.P. and Secy.
Directors: Brian D. Toy; Steven C. Toy.
EIN: 593573979

2340
The David & Vickie Smick Foundation
c/o Johnson Smick Intl.
10670 Eton Way
Vero Beach, FL   32963-9437
Contact: David Smick, Pres.

Established in 1994 in District of Columbia.
Donors: David Smick; Vickie Smick.
Foundation type: Independent foundation.
Financial data (yr. ended 12/31/12): Assets, $11,552,131 (M); gifts received, $500,000; expenditures, $253,500; qualifying distributions, $253,500; giving activities include $253,500 for 15 grants (high: $50,000; low: $1,000).
Fields of interest: Education; Higher education; Hospital care; Human services; Child welfare.
Application information:
   Initial approach: Letter
   Deadline(s): None
Officers: David Smick, Pres.; Vickie Smick, Secy.
EIN: 521905419

2341
Buckingham Smith Benevolent Association
17 Pacific St., Ste. A
Saint Augustine, FL   32084-2753   (904) 819-1799
Contact: Bradley K. Davis, Secy.-Treas. and Tr.

Established in 1873 in Florida.
Foundation type: Independent foundation.
Financial data (yr. ended 12/31/13): Assets, $6,961,192 (M); expenditures, $395,234; qualifying distributions, $326,826; giving activities include $316,456 for 12 grants (high: $70,000; low: $210).
Purpose and activities: Giving limited to organizations aiding indigent African Americans of St. Augustine, FL; aid includes medical care, emergency food, and utilities.
Fields of interest: Education; Christianity; Human services; Child welfare; Domestic violence shelters; Home repairs; People of African descent.
Type of support: Continuing support; Scholarships.
Limitations: Applications accepted. Giving limited to St. Augustine, FL.
Application information: Application form required.
   Initial approach: Proposal
   Deadline(s): Sept. 15th
   Board meeting date(s): Quarterly
Officers and Trustees: Darrell Poli, Pres. and Trustee; Reuben J. Plant, V.P. and Trustee; Bradley K. Davis, Secy.-Treas. and Trustee; John D. Bailey, Jr.; Joseph L. Boles, Jr.; Otis Mason; Michael Sanders.
Number of staff: 1 part-time professional.
EIN: 596137514

2342
Nora and William Smith Foundation
c/o Bank of America, N.A.
P.O. Box 40200, FL9-100-10-19
Jacksonville, FL   32203-0200
Application address: c/o Bank of America, N.A., Attn.: Brenton Thurston, Trust Off., 111 Westminster St., Providence, RI 02903, tel.: (866) 461-7287

Established in 1986 in South Carolina.

Foundation type: Independent foundation.
Financial data (yr. ended 05/31/15): Assets, $3,667,474 (M); expenditures, $211,260; qualifying distributions, $178,667; giving activities include $150,508 for 12 grants (high: $42,836; low: $1,880).
Fields of interest: Higher education; Graduate and professional education; Hospice care; Christianity; Theology; Child welfare.
Limitations: Applications accepted. Giving primarily in GA and SC. No grants to individuals.
Application information: Contributes mostly to pre-selected organizations. Trustees may make discretionary grants.
   Initial approach: Letter
   Copies of proposal: 1
   Deadline(s): 2/15
   Board meeting date(s): Mar.
Trustee: Bank of America, N.A.
EIN: 576110584

2343
Soter Kay Foundation
(formerly Sarah Ross Soter Foundation)
198 Via Marina
Palm Beach, FL   33480-4718

Established in 2003 in Ohio.
Donors: Sarah Ross Soter; Richard M. and Elizabeth M. Ross Foundation.
Foundation type: Independent foundation.
Financial data (yr. ended 12/31/13): Assets, $3,916,329 (M); expenditures, $181,800; qualifying distributions, $177,792; giving activities include $177,500 for 17 grants (high: $25,000; low: $2,500).
Fields of interest: Arts and culture; Education.
Limitations: Applications not accepted. Giving primarily in FL. No grants to individuals.
Application information: Unsolicited requests for funds not accepted.
Directors: Sarah Ziegler Kay; Sarah Ross Soter; William J. Soter.
EIN: 311793690

2344
Speranza Foundation, Inc.
7402 Ox Bow Cir.
Tallahassee, FL   32312-7548

Donor: The Beatitude Foundation Inc.
Foundation type: Independent foundation.
Financial data (yr. ended 12/31/13): Assets, $609,403 (M); gifts received, $240,000; expenditures, $194,485; qualifying distributions, $185,000; giving activities include $185,000 for 4 grants (high: $105,000; low: $5,000).
Fields of interest: Education; University education; Health; Religion; Christianity.
Limitations: Applications not accepted. Giving primarily in FL.
Application information: Unsolicited requests for funds not accepted.
Officers: Mary Bernadette Kearney, Pres.; Scott Kearney, V.P.; Michelle Kearney, Secy.; Erica Kearney, Treas.
EIN: 453716031

2345
Spier Family Foundation
6955 Carlisle Ct., Ste. D148
Naples, FL   34109-8972

Established in 2004 in Florida.
Donors: Sonja R. Spier; Alexander L. Spier.
Foundation type: Independent foundation.
Financial data (yr. ended 12/31/13): Assets,
$9,460,914 (M); gifts received, $3,195,074;
expenditures, $231,092; qualifying distributions,
$214,850; giving activities include $214,850 for 15
grants (high: $78,700; low: $1,000).
Fields of interest: Hospital care; Housing
development; Christianity.
Type of support: General support.
Limitations: Applications not accepted. Giving
primarily in MA. No grants to individuals.
Application information: Unsolicited requests for
funds not accepted.
Trustees: Kathryn Crane-Spier; Jack Mozes;
Alexander L. Spier; Gregory P. Spier; Sonja R. Spier.
EIN: 656423627

2346
The John R. and Inge P. Stafford
Foundation
16682 Captiva Dr.
P.O. Box 355
Captiva, FL   33924-0355
Contact: John R. Stafford, Tr.

Established in 1996 in New Jersey.
Donors: John R. Stafford; Inge P. Stafford.
Foundation type: Independent foundation.
Financial data (yr. ended 06/30/13): Assets,
$1,979,724 (M); expenditures, $201,198;
qualifying distributions, $201,129; giving activities
include $201,031 for 40 grants (high: $50,000;
low: $35).
Purpose and activities: Giving primarily for
education, health, particularly a cancer hospital,
human services, and to a Presbyterian church.
Fields of interest: Education; Health; Specialty
hospital care; Cancers; Protestantism; Human
services; Youth services.
Limitations: Applications accepted. Giving primarily
in NJ and NY. No grants to individuals.
Application information:
   Initial approach: Letter
   Deadline(s): None
Trustees: Christina Stafford Chaplin; Jennifer
Stafford Farrow; Charlotte Stafford; John R. Stafford;
Carolyn Stafford Stein.
EIN: 226710521

2347
Steele Family Foundation
196 Gomez Rd.
Hobe Sound, FL   33455-2513
Application address: c/o Bessemer Trust,
Attn.: Michael C. Steele, 100 Woodbridge Center
Dr., Woodbridge, NJ, 07095, tel.: (212) 708-9216

Established in 1996 in New Jersey.
Donors: Edward C. Steele; Joan M. Steele; Joan M.
Steele Charitable Lead Trust; E.C. and Joan Steele
Charitable Lead Trust.
Foundation type: Independent foundation.
Financial data (yr. ended 12/31/13): Assets,
$3,483,844 (M); gifts received, $156,191;

expenditures, $165,173; qualifying distributions,
$160,500; giving activities include $160,500 for 20
grants (high: $20,000; low: $2,500).
Fields of interest: Education; Health; Community
and economic development.
Type of support: Scholarships.
Limitations: Applications accepted. Giving primarily
in NY.
Application information: Application form required.
   Initial approach: Letter
   Deadline(s): None
Trustees: Susan Jennings; Jenna Scanlon; Brooke
Skinner; Annie L. Steele; Edward C. Steele; Edward
L. Steele; Joan M. Steele; Michael C. Steele.
EIN: 223431692

2348
The Stellar Foundation
2900 Hartley Rd.
Jacksonville, FL   32257-8221   (904) 260-2900
FAX: (904) 260-2959;
E-mail: info@thestellarfoundation.org; Main
URL: http://www.thestellarfoundation.org

Established in 2006 in Florida.
Donors: Structural Components; McGladrey LLP;
Hansen; Rogers Towers, P.A.; The Stellar Group;
Dilling Mechanical; Dryco LLC.; Cooper Steel; Amex
Evapco.; Assurance Dimensions.
Foundation type: Independent foundation.
Financial data (yr. ended 12/31/13): Assets,
$8,243 (M); gifts received, $264,989;
expenditures, $259,604; qualifying distributions,
$187,670; giving activities include $187,670 for 82
grants (high: $21,500; low: $50).
Fields of interest: Secondary education; University
education; Nonprofits; Health care administration
and financing; Hospice care.
Type of support: Regranting.
Limitations: Applications accepted. Giving primarily
in FL. No grants to individuals.
Application information: See foundation website for
complete application guidelines. Application form
required.
Directors: Richard M. Lovelace; Clint E. Pyle;
Michael S. Santarone; Allison Korman Shelton;
Scott V. Witt.
EIN: 203808875

2349
The B. & B. Stern Foundation, Inc.
P.O. Box 948
Lake Worth, FL   33460-0948   (561) 493-2238

Established in 2001 in Florida.
Foundation type: Independent foundation.
Financial data (yr. ended 12/31/13): Assets,
$3,779,346 (M); expenditures, $290,189;
qualifying distributions, $245,563; giving activities
include $201,100 for 11 grants (high: $70,000;
low: $1,000).
Fields of interest: Higher education; Nonprofits;
Judaism; Child welfare.
Type of support: Regranting.
Limitations: Applications accepted. Giving primarily
in FL, GA, and NY. No grants to individuals, or for
scholarships, fellowships, loans, prizes or similar
benefits.
Application information:
   Initial approach: Letter
   Deadline(s): None

Directors: L. Reed Catlett; Steven B. Kaufman; John
M. Stern.
EIN: 651150831

2350
Steve and Bonnie Stern Foundation,
Inc.
(formerly Gustav and Irene Stern Foundation, Inc.)
184 Bradley Pl.
Palm Beach, FL   33480-3705

Donors: Roy Stern; Steven Stern.
Foundation type: Independent foundation.
Financial data (yr. ended 03/31/14): Assets,
$7,016,969 (M); expenditures, $436,756;
qualifying distributions, $436,756; giving activities
include $401,143 for grants.
Purpose and activities: Giving primarily to Jewish
agencies and temples, and for education and the
arts.
Fields of interest: Performing arts; Opera;
Education; Higher education; Nonprofits; Judaism;
Human services.
Type of support: Regranting.
Limitations: Giving primarily in New York, NY. No
grants to individuals.
Officer and Director: Steven E. Stern, Pres.,
Secy.-Treas. and Director.
EIN: 136121155

2351
Douglas E. Stewart and Virginia E. Stewart
Charitable Foundation
P.O. Box 1908
Orlando, FL   32802-1908

Established in 2002 in Florida.
Donors: Douglas E. Stewart; Virginia E. Stewart.
Foundation type: Independent foundation.
Financial data (yr. ended 12/31/14): Assets,
$3,626,456; expenditures, $298,572; qualifying
distributions, $260,195.
Fields of interest: Education; Higher education;
Graduate and professional education; Nursing care.
Limitations: Applications not accepted. Giving
primarily in FL. No grants to individuals.
Application information: Unsolicited requests for
funds not accepted.
Trustees: John M. Farell; Gary A. Luing; Douglas M.
Stewart; SunTrust Banks, Inc.
EIN: 656389167

2352
Barbara A. Stiefel Foundation, Inc.
c/o Berkowitz Dick Pollack & Brant, LLP
200 S. Biscayne Blvd., 6th Fl.
Miami, FL   33131-5351

Donor: Barbara A. Stiefel.
Foundation type: Independent foundation.
Financial data (yr. ended 12/31/13): Assets,
$997,272 (M); gifts received, $340,934;
expenditures, $382,316; qualifying distributions,
$364,861; giving activities include $330,310 for 4
grants (high: $132,000; low: $50,000).
Purpose and activities: Giving primarily for a nature
conservancy, education, and to a foundation for
dermatology.
Fields of interest: Education; Environment;
Diseases and conditions.

International interests: England; Rwanda.
Limitations: Applications not accepted. Giving primarily in Arlington, VA, as well as in London, England, and the District of Kayonza in Rwanda. No grants to individuals.
Application information: Unsolicited requests for funds not accepted.
Officers and Directors: Barbara A. Stiefel, Pres. and Treas. and Director; Christine E. Stiefel, V.P. and Director; Erik Schmollinger, Secy. and Director.
EIN: 270878154

2353
The Strong Family Foundation
c/o William Strong
701 Brickell Ave., Ste. 1620
Miami, FL 33131

Donors: William Walker Strong; Brigitte Vosse.
Foundation type: Independent foundation.
Financial data (yr. ended 12/31/13): Assets, $193,038 (M); gifts received, $200,000; expenditures, $410,277; qualifying distributions, $405,437; giving activities include $400,450 for 19 grants (high: $70,000; low: $50).
Fields of interest: Arts and culture; Higher education; Hospital care; Human services.
Limitations: Applications not accepted. Giving primarily in New York, NY.
Application information: Contributes only to pre-selected organizations.
Officers: William Walker Strong, Co-Pres. and Secy.; Brigitte Vosse, Co-Pres. and Treas.
EIN: 273565029

2354
Don and Joan Strube Family Foundation Inc
3521 All American Blvd.
Orlando, FL 32810

Established in 2008 in Florida.
Donors: Don Strube, Jr.; Joan Strube, Jr.; Richard K. Sandberg; Donald K. Strube, Jr.; Susan K. Sandberg; Don Strube, Sr.; Thomas W. Strube; Timothy A. Strube; Richard K. Strube; Joan Strube, Sr.
Foundation type: Independent foundation.
Financial data (yr. ended 06/30/13): Assets, $19,619 (M); gifts received, $300,000; expenditures, $301,611; qualifying distributions, $301,000; giving activities include $301,000 for 2 grants (high: $300,000; low: $1,000).
Fields of interest: Arts and culture; Diseases and conditions; Religion.
Limitations: Applications not accepted. Giving primarily in FL.
Application information: Unsolicited requests for funds not accepted.
Officer and Directors: Richard K. Strube, Pres. and Treas. and Director; Susan K. Sandberg; Donald K. Strube, Jr.; Donald K. Strube, Sr.; Joan E. Strube; Thomas W. Strube; Timothy A. Strube.
EIN: 260682823

2355
Studer Foundation, Inc.
P.O. Box 2096
Pensacola, FL 32513-2096
Application address: c/o Elizabeth Denny-Abernathy, 41 N. Jefferson St., Ste. 107, Pensacola, FL 32502, tel.: (850) 696-2415

Donors: Quinton D. Studer; Mary P. Studer.
Foundation type: Independent foundation.
Financial data (yr. ended 12/31/13): Assets, $3,652,271 (M); gifts received, $1,900,000; expenditures, $155,563; qualifying distributions, $152,782; giving activities include $150,000 for 3 grants (high: $75,000; low: $25,000).
Fields of interest: Opera; Education; Human services.
Limitations: Applications accepted. Giving primarily in FL.
Application information: Application form required.
   Initial approach: Completed application form
   Deadline(s): None
Board Members: Mallory M. Studer; Mary P. Studer; Michael W. Studer; Quinton D. Studer.
EIN: 611583764

2356
Harry Sudakoff Foundation Inc.
50 Central Ave., Ste. 750
Sarasota, FL 34236-5743
Contact: Janet Lynn Dickens, A.V.P.
E-mail: janet.dickens@ustrust.com; Main URL: http://fdnweb.org/sudakoff
Grants List: http://fdnweb.org/sudakoff/grants/year/grants-for-2012

Established in 1956 in New York.
Donors: Harry Sudakoff; The Harry and Ruth Sudakoff Trust; Ruth Sudakoff†.
Foundation type: Independent foundation.
Financial data (yr. ended 12/31/13): Assets, $6,404,138 (M); expenditures, $400,274; qualifying distributions, $400,274; giving activities include $314,997 for 12 grants (high: $105,000; low: $2,500).
Fields of interest: Arts and culture; Education; Environment; Health; Science; Human services; Family services; Youth services; Senior services; Children and youth; People with disabilities.
Limitations: Applications accepted. Giving primarily in Sarasota County, FL. No grants to individuals, or for endowments, deficit financing, debt reduction, operating expenses, conferences, seminars, workshops, travel, surveys, advertising, fund raising, research, or for annual campaigns.
Application information: Complete application guidelines available on foundation web site.
   Initial approach: Letter
   Deadline(s): Aug. 14
Officers: Gary A. Bucholtz, Pres.; Elizabeth Marshall, V.P. and Treas.; William T. Harrison, Jr., Secy.
EIN: 650439722

2357
Chris T. Sullivan Foundation, Inc.
c/o Chris T. Sullivan
3717 W. North B St.
Tampa, FL 33609-1335

Established in 2003 in Florida.

Donors: Chris T. Sullivan; Tom Fanning; James Burke; CTS Equities LP.
Foundation type: Independent foundation.
Financial data (yr. ended 12/31/13): Assets, $14,193,934 (M); gifts received, $651,270; expenditures, $607,501; qualifying distributions, $358,307; giving activities include $358,307 for 33 grants (high: $120,000; low: $90).
Fields of interest: Philanthropy; Leadership development; Youth organizing.
Limitations: Applications not accepted. No grants to individuals.
Application information: Contributes only to pre-selected organizations.
Officers and Directors: Chris T. Sullivan, Pres. and Director; Alexander L. Sullivan, V.P. and Director; Ashley M. Sullivan, Secy. and Director.
EIN: 593773382

2358
Sun, Moon and Stars Foundation, Inc.
401 E. Las Olas Blvd., Ste. 2000
Fort Lauderdale, FL 33301-4223

Established in 2007 in Florida.
Donor: Peter Wittich.
Foundation type: Independent foundation.
Financial data (yr. ended 12/31/14): Assets, $1,635,176; gifts received, $250,000; expenditures, $126,165; qualifying distributions, $125,000.
Fields of interest: Graduate and professional education; Cancers; Engineering.
Limitations: Applications not accepted. Giving primarily in CA, FL, and MA. No grants to individuals.
Application information: Unsolicited requests for funds not accepted.
Trustee: Peter Wittich.
EIN: 261578697

2359
Sunburst Foundation, Inc.
2285 Potomac Rd.
Boca Raton, FL 33431-5518   (561) 995-7755
Contact: James M. Hankins, Pres.
E-mail: sunfound@bellsouth.net; Main URL: http://www.sunburst-foundation.org

Established in 1986 in Florida.
Foundation type: Independent foundation.
Financial data (yr. ended 06/30/13): Assets, $5,488,714 (M); expenditures, $265,952; qualifying distributions, $254,589; giving activities include $125,000 for 1 grant, and $102,250 for 31 grants to individuals (high: $6,000; low: $1,500).
Purpose and activities: Scholarship awards to minority seniors graduating from participating Florida high schools who are planning to study the physical sciences at a four year college or university; also some community giving.
Fields of interest: Higher education; Foundations; Physical and earth sciences.
Type of support: General support; Student aid.
Application information: Application guidelines available on foundation web site. Application form required.
Officers and Trustees: James M. Hankins, Pres. and Trustee; John M. Wargo, V.P. and Treas. and Trustee; Kenneth A. Wenzel, Secy. and Trustee.
Number of staff: 1 part-time professional.
EIN: 592637289

2360
Jim & Jonnie Swann Corporation
516 Delannoy Ave.
Cocoa, FL 32922-7814

Established in 1989 in Florida.
Donors: Jack Eckerd; Jim Swann; Eckerd Family Foundation.
Foundation type: Independent foundation.
Financial data (yr. ended 04/30/14): Assets, $3,214,035 (M); gifts received, $167,585; expenditures, $202,688; qualifying distributions, $175,412; giving activities include $175,412 for 35 grants (high: $30,000; low: $500).
Fields of interest: Education; Environment; Human services.
Limitations: Applications not accepted. Giving primarily in FL. No grants to individuals.
Application information: Unsolicited requests for funds not accepted.
Officers and Directors: Jim Swann, Pres. and Director; Jonnie Swann, V.P. and Director; M.R. Kirschenbaum.
EIN: 650118651

2361
Carl S. Swisher Foundation, Inc.
Concorde I
3030 Hartley Rd., Ste. 250
Jacksonville, FL 32257-8233 (904) 399-8000
Contact: Kenneth G. Anderson, Pres. and Tr.

Established in 1949 in Florida.
Donor: Carl S. Swisher†.
Foundation type: Independent foundation.
Financial data (yr. ended 12/31/14): Assets, $6,371,407 (M); expenditures, $389,384; qualifying distributions, $296,813; giving activities include $286,500 for 34 grants (high: $30,000; low: $2,000).
Purpose and activities: Support for higher education; grants also for youth agencies, health associations, and social services.
Fields of interest: Arts and culture; Education; Higher education; Adult education; Hospital care; Diseases and conditions; Human services; Food banks; Child welfare.
Type of support: General support; Matching grants; Scholarships.
Limitations: Applications accepted. Giving primarily in the Jacksonville, FL, area. No grants to individuals; no loans.
Application information: Application form required.
Initial approach: Proposal
Copies of proposal: 1
Deadline(s): None
Board meeting date(s): Generally quarterly
Officers and Trustees: Kenneth G. Anderson, Pres. and Trustee; John H. Lindsey, V.P. and Trustee; Carolyn H. Charbonnet, Secy. and Trustee; James P. Stevens, Treas. and Trustee.
Number of staff: 1 part-time professional.
EIN: 590998262

2362
Tampa Bay Times Fund, Inc.
(formerly St. Petersburg Times Fund, Inc.)
P.O. Box 1121
Saint Petersburg, FL 33731-1121
FAX: (727) 892-2257; Application address: Attn.: Jounice Nealy-Brown, Tampa Bay Times, 490 1st Ave. S., St. Petersburg, FL 33701-4204; E-mail for Jounice Nealy-Brown: nealybrown@tampabay.com; Main URL: http://www.tampabay.com/company/times-fund

Established in 1953 in District of Columbia.
Donors: Henrietta M. Poynter†; Nelson Poynter†; Congressional Quarterly; Times Publishing Co.; Godbold Foundation.
Foundation type: Independent foundation.
Financial data (yr. ended 12/31/13): Assets, $12,606,635 (M); gifts received, $13,836; expenditures, $599,782; qualifying distributions, $590,288; giving activities include $275,755 for grants, and $155,825 for grants to individuals.
Purpose and activities: The fund provides grants to non-profit organizations in these general categories: education, arts/culture, social services and journalism. The focus is primarily on helping to improve the quality of life in West Central Florida, specifically the counties of Pinellas, Hillsborough, Pasco, Hernando, and Citrus.
Fields of interest: Arts and culture; Education; Communication media; Publishing; Human services; Ethnic and racial groups.
Type of support: Capital campaigns; Employee matching gifts; Matching grants; Fellowships; Scholarships; Student aid.
Limitations: Applications accepted. Giving limited to west central FL: Pinellas, Hillsborough, Pasco, and Hernando, and Citrus counties. No support for religious or political organizations, or for fraternal groups, athletic teams, bands, school newspapers or yearbooks, veterans organizations, or volunteer firefighter groups. No grants for annual fund drives, golf tournaments or raffles; no loans.
Publications: Application guidelines; Financial statement; Grants list.
Application information: Grant applicants may submit only 1 request per calendar year (Jan. 1 to Dec. 31). Complete grant and scholarship application information available on fund web site. Application form required.
Initial approach: Concept letter for grants (no more than 2 pages) or see fund web site
Copies of proposal: 1
Deadline(s): See fund web site for current deadline dates
Board meeting date(s): Apr. and Nov.
Final notification: Within 30 days
Officers and Trustees: Paul Tash, Pres. and Trustee; Andrew P. Corty, Secy. and Trustee; Jana Jones, Treas. and Trustee; Neil Brown; Sebastian Dortch; Jennifer Orsi.
Number of staff: 1 full-time professional; 1 full-time support.
EIN: 596142547

2363
Sol Taplin Charitable Foundation
7027 W. Broward Blvd., No. 2116
Plantation, FL 33317-2208 (954) 584-0715
Contact: Barbara Ingalls

Established in 1998 in Florida.
Donors: Jack G. Taplin; Martin W. Taplin; Sheila Elias Taplin.
Foundation type: Independent foundation.
Financial data (yr. ended 06/30/13): Assets, $7,515,974 (M); expenditures, $417,889; qualifying distributions, $349,500; giving activities include $349,500 for grants.
Fields of interest: Museums; Education; University education; Medical education; Nonprofits; Judaism; Homeless shelters.
Type of support: Regranting.
Limitations: Applications accepted. Giving primarily in FL. No grants to individuals.
Application information: Application form required.
Initial approach: Letter
Deadline(s): None
Trustees: Aaron S. Podhurst; Jack G. Taplin; Martin W. Taplin; Sheila Elias Taplin.
EIN: 656272903

2364
Mary E. Taylor Charitable Foundation Trust
678 4th St. N.
Saint Petersburg, FL 33701-2320

Established in 2009 in Florida.
Foundation type: Independent foundation.
Financial data (yr. ended 06/30/13): Assets, $3,819,444 (M); expenditures, $369,141; qualifying distributions, $203,000; giving activities include $203,000 for 22 grants (high: $25,000; low: $1,500).
Fields of interest: Domesticated animals; Health; Housing development.
Limitations: Applications not accepted. Giving primarily in St. Petersburg, FL.
Application information: Unsolicited requests for funds not accepted.
Directors: Guy G. Van Middlesworth; Jill M. Van Middlesworth.
EIN: 264714018

2365
Taylor Family Foundation, Inc.
1111 9th Ave. W., Ste. E
Bradenton, FL 34205-7745

Foundation type: Independent foundation.
Financial data (yr. ended 12/31/13): Assets, $13,862,173 (M); expenditures, $719,899; qualifying distributions, $659,768; giving activities include $272,762 for 24 grants (high: $52,700; low: $500).
Purpose and activities: Giving primarily for children, youth and social services, medical research, and Christian organizations.
Fields of interest: Animal welfare; Diseases and conditions; Christianity; Human services; Child welfare; Low-income and poor people.
International interests: Chile; Scotland; United Kingdom of Great Britain and Northern Ireland.
Type of support: Research; Research and evaluation.
Limitations: Applications not accepted. Giving primarily in FL; some giving also in Chile, Aberdeen, Scotland and United Kingdom. No grants to individuals.
Application information: Contributes only to pre-selected organizations.
Officers and Board Member: Katherine Kittsmiller, Pres.; Ritchey Nelson Taylor, V.P. and Treas.; Darlene Westermeyer, Secy. and Director.
EIN: 396058301

2366
Jack Taylor Family Foundation, Inc.
P.O. Box 402309
Miami Beach, FL   33140-0309

Donors: Taylor Development Corp.; Jack Taylor; Mitchell Taylor.
Foundation type: Independent foundation.
Financial data (yr. ended 12/31/14): Assets, $8,215,841 (M); expenditures, $440,024; qualifying distributions, $402,500; giving activities include $402,500 for 10 grants (high: $100,000; low: $2,500).
Purpose and activities: Giving primarily for health organizations, as well as for the arts, education, and human services.
Fields of interest: Arts and culture; Higher education; Foundations; Diseases and conditions; Human services.
Type of support: Research; Research and evaluation.
Limitations: Applications not accepted. No grants to individuals.
Application information: Unsolicited requests for funds not accepted.
Officers and Directors: Elizabeth Taylor, Pres. and Director; Mitchell Taylor, V.P. and Secy.-Treas. and Director; Seth D. Rosen, MD.
EIN: 596205187

2367
TECO Energy Foundation Inc.
P.O. Box 111
Tampa, FL   33601-0111   (813) 228-4111
Contact: Jack Amor, Exec. Dir.
Application address: 702 N. Franklin St., Tampa, FL 33602 Tel.: (813) 228-4111

Donor: TECO Energy, Inc.
Foundation type: Operating foundation.
Financial data (yr. ended 12/31/13): Assets, $475,200 (M); gifts received, $416,677; expenditures, $261,419; qualifying distributions, $260,000; giving activities include $260,000 for 3 grants (high: $160,000; low: $50,000).
Purpose and activities: The foundation supports museums and performing art centers and organizations involved with higher education.
Fields of interest: Arts and culture; Education.
Type of support: Capital campaigns; Matching grants.
Limitations: Applications accepted. Giving primarily in Tampa, FL.
Application information: Application form required.
Initial approach: Proposal
Deadline(s): None
Officers and Directors: Sandra W. Callahan, V.P. and Director; David E. Schwartz, Secy.; Kim M. Caruso, Treas.; Jack Amor, Exec. Dir.; Charles A. Attal; Phil Barringer; Deirdre A. Brown; Gordon L. Gillete; Bruce Narzissenfeld.
EIN: 010598444

2368
C. Herman & Mary Virginia Terry Foundation
(formerly C. Herman Terry Foundation)
4196 Herschel St., Ste. 1
Jacksonville, FL   32210-2245

Established in 1982 in Florida.

Donor: C. Herman Terry.
Foundation type: Independent foundation.
Financial data (yr. ended 12/31/13): Assets, $4,165,055 (M); expenditures, $397,632; qualifying distributions, $383,463; giving activities include $380,000 for 4 grants (high: $250,000; low: $5,000).
Purpose and activities: Giving primarily for higher education, and children and youth services, particularly a children's hospital.
Fields of interest: University education; Specialty hospital care; Human services; Child welfare.
Limitations: Applications not accepted. Giving primarily in Jacksonville, FL. No grants to individuals.
Application information: Contributes only to pre-selected organizations.
Trustees: Kenneth A. Barneby; Kathleen Cold; Sandra M. Corbett; Betsy Cox; Mary Virginia Terry; James H. Winston.
EIN: 592241642

2369
Max B. Tharpe Charitable Foundation, Inc.
2081 N.E. 56th St., Ste. 205
Fort Lauderdale, FL   33308-2533

Donor: Max B. Tharpe Irrevocable Trust.
Foundation type: Independent foundation.
Financial data (yr. ended 12/31/13): Assets, $1,862,515 (M); gifts received, $10,000; expenditures, $249,402; qualifying distributions, $193,558; giving activities include $170,000 for 4 grants (high: $120,000; low: $1,000).
Fields of interest: Protestantism.
Limitations: Applications not accepted. Giving primarily in FL.
Application information: Unsolicited requests for funds not accepted.
Officer: Barbara Morin, Pres.
EIN: 261569652

2370
The Thomas Family Foundation, Inc.
P.O. Box 30580
Fort Lauderdale, FL   33303-0580

Established in 1998 in Illinois.

Donor: Alfred Thomas.
Foundation type: Independent foundation.
Financial data (yr. ended 09/30/14): Assets, $6,983,185 (M); gifts received, $378,679; expenditures, $306,771; qualifying distributions, $291,120; giving activities include $289,825 for 31 grants (high: $74,500; low: $500).
Fields of interest: Arts and culture; Education; Health; Children's hospital care; Domestic violence; Christianity; Child welfare; Children; Females; Homeless people.
Type of support: General support.
Limitations: Applications not accepted. Giving primarily in Chicago, IL and FL. No grants to individuals.
Application information: Contributes only to pre-selected organizations.
Officers: Alfred Thomas, Pres. and Treas.; Phylis Thomas, V.P. and Secy.; Lydia Bart, V.P.
EIN: 364311966

2371
Dorothy Thomas Foundation, Inc.
c/o Michael Thomas
P.O. Box 10070
Tampa, FL   33679-0070

Established in 1960 in Florida.

Donors: Wayne Thomas†; Robert Thomas; Port Sutton, Inc.; Michael Thomas.
Foundation type: Independent foundation.
Financial data (yr. ended 12/31/13): Assets, $4,756,138 (M); expenditures, $256,297; qualifying distributions, $251,148; giving activities include $250,198 for 9 grants (high: $121,198; low: $2,500).
Purpose and activities: Giving to health organizations, and Christian ministries and associations.
Fields of interest: Hospital care; Diseases and conditions; Christianity; Human services.
Type of support: General support; Matching grants; Continuing support; Capital and infrastructure; Emergency funds.
Limitations: Applications not accepted. Giving primarily in FL. No grants to individuals.
Application information: Unsolicited requests for funds not accepted.
Officers: Michael Thomas, Chair. and Treas.; Stephen Thomas, Secy.
Trustee: Robert M. Thomas.
Number of staff: None.
EIN: 596059765

2372
L.V. Thompson Family Foundation, Inc.
5015 E. Hillsborough Ave.
Tampa, FL   33610-4814   (813) 248-3456
Contact: Leslie V. Thompson, Pres.

Established in 2004 in Florida.

Donor: Leslie V. Thompson.
Foundation type: Independent foundation.
Financial data (yr. ended 12/31/13): Assets, $4,342,949 (M); gifts received, $100,000; expenditures, $225,195; qualifying distributions, $194,596; giving activities include $192,140 for 51 grants (high: $25,000; low: $500).
Fields of interest: Education; Graduate and professional education; Wildlife biodiversity; Nursing care; Christianity; Human services; Child welfare.
Limitations: Applications accepted. Giving primarily in FL.
Application information:
Initial approach: Proposal
Deadline(s): None
Officers: Leslie V. Thompson, Pres.; Tami Y. Thompson, Secy.
Directors: David Austin; Michael D. LaBarbera; T. Corey Neil; Thomasena Supan.
EIN: 202015225

2373
Thomsen Foundation, Inc.
701 E. Commercial Blvd., Ste. 300
Fort Lauderdale, FL   33334-3391

Donors: Pipp, Inc.; Carl J. Thomsen; Frances D. Thomsen; Robert J. Thomsen.
Foundation type: Independent foundation.

Financial data (yr. ended 10/31/13): Assets, $6,587,349 (M); expenditures, $353,867; qualifying distributions, $332,972; giving activities include $320,000 for 1 grant.
Fields of interest: Higher education; Health.
Limitations: Applications not accepted. Giving primarily in MI and MN. No grants to individuals.
Application information: Contributes only to pre-selected organizations.
Officers and Directors: Carl J. Thomsen, Secy. and Director; Susan Davis, Treas. and Director; Valerie S. Armagno; Kathleen M. McMillan.
EIN: 592070983

2374
The Thornburgh Family Foundation
14 Golfview Rd.
Palm Beach, FL 33480

Established in 2005 in New York.
Donor: Richard E. Thornburgh.
Foundation type: Independent foundation.
Financial data (yr. ended 12/31/13): Assets, $7,206,133; gifts received, $0; expenditures, $370,497; qualifying distributions, $346,937 and $0 for set-asides.
Fields of interest: Education; Environment; Christianity; Human services.
Limitations: Applications not accepted. Giving primarily in CT and NY. No grants to individuals.
Application information: Contributes only to pre-selected organizations.
Trustees: Cornelia P. Thornburgh; Richard E. Thornburgh.
EIN: 203950886

2375
The Edgar A. Thurman Charitable
Foundation for Children
P.O. Box 1908
Orlando, FL 32802-1908
Application address: c/o SunTrust Bank, Attn.: Jacquetta Simmons, P.O. Box 13888, Roanoke, VA 24038, tel.: (540) 982-3076

Established in 1952 in Virginia.
Donor: Edgar A. Thurman†.
Foundation type: Independent foundation.
Financial data (yr. ended 07/01/14): Assets, $7,186,474 (M); expenditures, $315,197; qualifying distributions, $271,719; giving activities include $237,500 for 35 grants (high: $10,000; low: $2,000).
Purpose and activities: Giving to provide maintenance, care, and education for needy children; support for orphanages, youth agencies, preschool education, and social service agencies.
Fields of interest: Museums; Early childhood education; Christianity; Human services; Food banks; Child welfare; Youth development; Low-income and poor people; People with vision impairments.
Limitations: Applications accepted. Giving limited to VA, with emphasis on the Roanoke area.
Publications: Application guidelines; Program policy statement.
Application information: Application form required.
  Initial approach: Letter
  Copies of proposal: 1
  Deadline(s): Dec. 31

Board meeting date(s): Annually
Final notification: 3 months from receipt
Trustee: SunTrust Bank.
EIN: 546113281

2376
Liz Whitney Tippett Foundation, Inc.
3325 Griffin Rd., Ste. E-186
Fort Lauderdale, FL 33312-5500

Established in 1998 in Florida.
Foundation type: Operating foundation.
Financial data (yr. ended 12/31/13): Assets, $5,403,739 (M); expenditures, $267,331; qualifying distributions, $254,798; giving activities include $183,500 for 26 grants (high: $30,000; low: $500).
Fields of interest: Arts and culture; Higher education; Hospital care; Christianity; Human services; Food delivery.
Type of support: Research.
Limitations: Applications not accepted. Giving primarily in FL, MO, and NC.
Application information: Contributes only to pre-selected organizations.
Officer: Janet Lindsley, Mgr.
Director: William Lindsley.
EIN: 650083442

2377
The Toppel Family Foundation, Inc.
(formerly Harold & Patricia Toppel Foundation)
6267 N.W. 77th Terr.
Parkland, FL 33067-1111
Contact: Patricia Toppel, Pres.

Donors: Harold Toppel; Patricia Toppel.
Foundation type: Independent foundation.
Financial data (yr. ended 12/31/13): Assets, $2,230,042 (M); expenditures, $323,629; qualifying distributions, $319,009; giving activities include $319,009 for 19 grants (high: $200,000; low: $500).
Purpose and activities: The foundation focuses its philanthropy in the areas of youth, education (early childhood and higher education), the arts and community betterment programs.
Fields of interest: Arts and culture; Education; Human services.
Type of support: Annual campaigns; In-kind gifts; Matching grants; Equipment; Endowments; Program development; Curriculum development; Program evaluations.
Limitations: Applications not accepted. Giving primarily in southeastern FL. No grants to individuals.
Application information: Contributes only to pre-selected organizations.
  Board meeting date(s): Quarterly
Officers and Directors: Patricia Toppel, Chair. and Pres. and Director; Jonathan Toppel, V.P. and Treas. and Director; Jeffrey Toppel, V.P. and Director; Jennifer Toppel-Sawyer, V.P. and Director; Sheri Sauer, Secy. and Director.
EIN: 237050394

2378
Toral Family Foundation, Inc.
13131 S.W. 19th St.
Davie, FL 33325-5752

Foundation type: Independent foundation.
Financial data (yr. ended 12/31/13): Assets, $2,241 (M); gifts received, $393,300; expenditures, $406,210; qualifying distributions, $262,258; giving activities include $262,258 for 9 grants (high: $95,630; low: $400).
Fields of interest: Higher education; Health; Diseases and conditions; Human services.
Limitations: Applications not accepted. Giving primarily in FL.
Application information: Unsolicited requests for funds not accepted.
Officer: Frank Toral, Mgr.
EIN: 264094366

2379
Tupperware Brands Foundation
(formerly Tupperware Children's Foundation)
14901 S. Orange Blossom Trail
Orlando, FL 32837-6600

Established in 2003 in Florida.
Donors: Tupperware U.S., Inc.; Tupperware Brands Corp.
Foundation type: Company-sponsored foundation.
Financial data (yr. ended 12/31/13): Assets, $30,521 (M); gifts received, $318,868; expenditures, $425,535; qualifying distributions, $425,535; giving activities include $418,358 for 17 grants (high: $250,000; low: $25,000), and $7,050 for 5 grants to individuals (high: $500; low: $250).
Purpose and activities: The foundation supports programs designed to educate and empower women and girls.
Fields of interest: Youth services; Economics for youth; Females; Female children and youth.
Type of support: General support; Capital campaigns.
Limitations: Applications not accepted. Giving primarily in Lakeland and Orlando, FL. No grants to individuals.
Application information: Contributes only to pre-selected organizations.
Officers and Directors: Lillian D. Garcia, Pres. and Director; Josef Hajek, Secy.; Michael Poteshman, Treas. and Director; Yolanda Londono, Exec. Dir.; Thomas M. Roehlk, Director.
Trustee: Tupperware Brands Corp.
EIN: 550824285

2380
The Darla Dee Turlington Charitable
Foundation
85 Ave. De La Mer, Ste. 806
Palm Coast, FL 32137-1229
Contact: Darla Dee Turlington, Pres.

Established in 1993 in Texas.
Donor: Alroc Real Estate Associates LTD.
Foundation type: Independent foundation.
Financial data (yr. ended 12/31/14): Assets, $2,381,563 (M); expenditures, $143,816; qualifying distributions, $143,816; giving activities include $141,996 for 103 grants (high: $9,300; low: $21).
Purpose and activities: Giving primarily for education, human services, and to Baptist churches and organizations.
Fields of interest: Education; Health; Christianity; Baptist; Baptists.

Limitations: Applications accepted. Giving on a national basis, with some emphasis on NY. No grants to individuals.
Application information:
Initial approach: Proposal
Deadline(s): None
EIN: 760420404

2381
Herman E. & Helen H. Turner Foundation Trust
5004 Riverview Blvd. W.
Bradenton, FL 34209-1940

Donor: Herman E. Turner Trust.
Foundation type: Independent foundation.
Financial data (yr. ended 12/31/13): Assets, $2,144,555 (M); expenditures, $324,618; qualifying distributions, $288,725; giving activities include $270,725 for 17 grants (high: $100,000; low: $5,000).
Purpose and activities: Giving primarily for children, youth, and human services; some funding for the arts.
Fields of interest: Arts and culture; Museums; Nonprofits; Protestantism; Human services; Child welfare; Youth services.
Type of support: Scholarships; Matching grants; Capital campaigns; Capital and infrastructure; Annual campaigns; Regranting.
Limitations: Applications not accepted. Giving primarily in Bradenton, FL. No grants to individuals.
Application information: Contributes only to pre-selected organizations.
Trustees: Richard E. Turner, Sr.; Richard E. Turner, Jr.
Number of staff: None.
EIN: 656260563

2382
The Turock Family Foundation
2501 E. Commercial Blvd.
Fort Lauderdale, FL 33308
Contact: Stuart Wardlaw, CPA

Established in 1998 in New Jersey.
Foundation type: Independent foundation.
Financial data (yr. ended 12/31/13): Assets, $3,737,528 (M); expenditures, $491,222; qualifying distributions, $442,244; giving activities include $442,244 for grants.
Purpose and activities: Giving primarily for education and for children, youth, and social services, including a children's hospital.
Fields of interest: Elementary and secondary education; Higher education; Specialty hospital care; Human services; Child welfare.
Limitations: Applications not accepted. Giving primarily in MD; with some giving in New York, NY.
Application information: Unsolicited requests for funds not accepted.
Trustees: David L. Turock; Nancy G. Turock.
EIN: 223758083

2383
Uncle Larry's Fund
c/o Winterer
P.O. Box 1009
Boca Grande, FL 33921-1009

Established in 2000 in Florida.
Donors: William G. Winterer; Victoria T. Winterer; Theresa S. Thompson.
Foundation type: Independent foundation.
Financial data (yr. ended 12/31/14): Assets, $3,078,587; expenditures, $177,132; qualifying distributions, $161,810.
Purpose and activities: The fund's primary focus is education. But it also supports opportunities that provide for creativity, growth towards self-sufficiency, and leadership. The fund will consider environmental, cultural and spiritual projects that contribute to a community's well-being, as well as projects that develop personal responsibility, initiative, moral standards and leadership.
Fields of interest: Education; Protestantism; Human services.
International interests: Central America; South America.
Type of support: General support; Pro bono consulting services; Matching grants; Leadership and professional development; Annual campaigns; Capital campaigns; Capital and infrastructure; Equipment; Land acquisitions; Endowments; Curriculum development; Internships; Scholarships; Individual development.
Limitations: Applications not accepted. Giving on a national basis, with preference given to organizations in communities with a personal connection to the trustees.
Application information: Unsolicited requests for funds not accepted.
Board meeting date(s): June, Nov. and as needed
Trustees: Theresa S. Thompson; Victoria T. Winterer; William G. Winterer.
Number of staff: 2 part-time professional.
EIN: 316653673

2384
Vanneck-Bailey Foundation
c/o William P. Vanneck
217 West Indies Dr.
Palm Beach, FL 33480-3408

Established in 1949 in New York.
Donors: John Vanneck†; Barbara Bailey Vanneck.
Foundation type: Independent foundation.
Financial data (yr. ended 12/31/14): Assets, $6,814,085; gifts received, $0; expenditures, $378,297; qualifying distributions, $366,643.
Fields of interest: Elementary and secondary education; Higher education; Natural resources; Botanical gardens; Health; Hospital care; Diseases and conditions; Cancers; Community and economic development; Protestantism; Child welfare.
Type of support: Research.
Limitations: Applications not accepted. Giving primarily in the greater metropolitan New York, NY, area and CT; giving also in CA, FL, IL, MA, TX, and VT. No grants to individuals.
Application information: Contributes only to pre-selected organizations.
Officers: Barbara V. May, Pres.; William P. Vanneck, V.P.; Domenick A. Salsa, Secy.-Treas.
EIN: 237165285

2385
The Vasey Foundation
3580 Gin Ln.
Naples, FL 34102-7815 2037819800

Established in 1993 in Connecticut.
Donor: Roger M. Vasey.
Foundation type: Independent foundation.
Financial data (yr. ended 12/31/14): Assets, $591,773; gifts received, $2,843; expenditures, $134,806; qualifying distributions, $129,427.
Fields of interest: Higher education; Nonprofits; Hospital care; Diabetes; Human services; People of Latin American descent.
Type of support: Research; Regranting.
Limitations: Applications not accepted. No grants to individuals.
Application information: Contributes only to pre-selected organizations.
Trustee: Roger M. Vasey.
EIN: 061360683

2386
Verner Foundation, Inc.
P.O. Box 1118
Plant City, FL 33564-1118

Donors: John V. Verner Revocable Living Trust; Sally P. Verner Revocable Living Trust; Ryder Homes & Groves Co.
Foundation type: Operating foundation.
Financial data (yr. ended 12/31/14): Assets, $2,840,958 (M); expenditures, $311,732; qualifying distributions, $297,008; giving activities include $267,030 for 25 grants (high: $90,000; low: $50).
Purpose and activities: Giving primarily for education, religion, and human services.
Fields of interest: Orchestral music; Education; Religion; Protestantism; Human services; Child welfare.
Limitations: Applications not accepted. Giving primarily in FL. No grants to individuals.
Application information: Contributes only to pre-selected organizations.
Trustees: Sally G. Rucker; E.M. Verner; James P. Verner; John V. Verner; S.P. Verner.
EIN: 593155858

2387
Emily Vernon Foundation for Homeless & Abused Animals, Inc.
5315 S. Shore Blvd.
Wellington, FL 33449-6031
Application address: The Emily Vernon Foundation for Homeless and Abused Animals Inc, Att.: Sharon Scanlon, 1515 N. University Dr., Coral Springs, FL 33071, tel.: (954) 752-6329

Established in 2005 in Florida.
Donors: Marmi, Ltd.; Emily Vernon†.
Foundation type: Independent foundation.
Financial data (yr. ended 12/31/13): Assets, $16,062,079 (M); expenditures, $904,278; qualifying distributions, $569,473; giving activities include $180,000 for 8 grants (high: $100,000; low: $5,000).
Purpose and activities: Giving to organizations that work to prevent animal cruelty or provide assistance in the care of homeless and abused animals.
Fields of interest: Domesticated animals; Housing development; Human services.
Limitations: Applications accepted. Giving primarily in FL. No grants to individuals.
Application information: Application form required.

Initial approach: Request application form
    Deadline(s): None
Officers: Sharon Scanlon, Co-Pres. and V.P.;
Timothy Scanlon, Co-Pres. and V.P.
EIN: 203785692

2388
The Michael and Louisa von Clemm Foundation
c/o Ethan Johnson, Stefanie Von Clemm
200 S. Biscayne Blvd., Ste. 5300
Miami, FL 33131-2339 (305) 415-3383
Contact: Stefanie C. von Clemm, Treas.

Donors: Tirtanus Majutana; Louisa von Clemm;
Stefanie C. von Clemm; Robert Miller; Michael von
Clemm Memorial Trust.
Foundation type: Independent foundation.
Financial data (yr. ended 12/31/13): Assets,
$4,361,599 (M); expenditures, $256,492;
qualifying distributions, $189,414; giving activities
include $187,179 for 8 grants (high: $67,563; low:
$2,500).
Purpose and activities: Giving primarily for scientific
education and cultural activities.
Fields of interest: Arts and culture; Education;
University education; Hospital care; Hospice care;
Christianity.
Limitations: Applications accepted. Giving primarily
in MA and NY.
Application information: Application form required.
    Initial approach: Letter
    Deadline(s): None
Officers: Louisa von Clemm, Pres.; Ethan W.
Johnson, Secy.; Stefanie C. von Clemm, Treas.
Directors: Charlotte von Clemm Iselin; Brewster
Mcn Righter; James V. Righter.
EIN: 650541059

2389
Vorsheck Family Foundation, Inc.
(formerly Willspring Foundation, Inc.)
9293 Winfield Ct.
Weeki Wachee, FL 34613-3986

Established in 2001 in Florida.
Donors: Elizabeth A. Vorsheck; William J. Vorsheck,
Jr.; William Vorsheck.
Foundation type: Independent foundation.
Financial data (yr. ended 12/31/13): Assets,
$6,047,732 (M); gifts received, $372,800;
expenditures, $373,686; qualifying distributions,
$284,907; giving activities include $280,157 for 47
grants (high: $50,000; low: $400).
Fields of interest: Spirituality; Dining services.
Limitations: Applications not accepted. Giving
primarily in PA. No grants to individuals.
Application information: Contributes only to
pre-selected organizations.
Officer and Directors: Elizabeth A. Vorsheck, Pres.
and Secy.-Treas. and Director; Michelle Conrad;
Valerie Greene; William J. Vorsheck, Jr.; William J.
Vorsheck III.
EIN: 593686566

2390
Votum Foundation, Inc.
P.O. Box 5252
Lakeland, FL 33807-5252

Established in 1999 in Florida.
Donors: Jonquill LLC; Anchor Mosn, LLC.
Foundation type: Independent foundation.
Financial data (yr. ended 12/31/13): Assets,
$6,925,928 (M); expenditures, $423,583;
qualifying distributions, $423,583; giving activities
include $420,000 for 5 grants (high: $300,000;
low: $10,000).
Fields of interest: Elementary and secondary
education; Higher education; Nonprofits.
Type of support: General support; Regranting;
Capital and infrastructure; Endowments; Curriculum
development; Student aid.
Limitations: Applications accepted. Giving primarily
in FL.
Application information: Application form required.
    Initial approach: Proposal
    Deadline(s): None
Officers: Lawrence W. Maxwell, Pres. and Treas.;
Anita K. Maxwell, V.P. and Secy.
Directors: Amanda R. Drost; Benjamin D.E. Falk.
Number of staff: None.
EIN: 593580800

2391
Wagmore Foundation Inc.
5015 N.W. 24th Dr.
Gainsville, FL 32605-6227 (352) 371-5929
Contact: Jeannette Peters

Donors: Cladys G. Cofrin; AEC Trust.
Foundation type: Independent foundation.
Financial data (yr. ended 12/31/13): Assets,
$2,788,120 (M); expenditures, $254,373;
qualifying distributions, $234,274; giving activities
include $209,545 for 11 grants (high: $80,556;
low: $4,000).
Fields of interest: Education; Domesticated
animals; Health.
Limitations: Applications accepted. Giving primarily
in FL.
Application information: Application form required.
    Initial approach: Contact Foundation
    Deadline(s): None
Directors: Gladys Cofrin; Pegeen Hanrahan; Robert
Hutchinson; Mary Ippoltti-Smith.
EIN: 453660440

2392
The Waugh Family Foundation
11572 Turtle Beach Rd.
North Palm Beach, FL 33408-3345

Established in 2005 in Delaware.
Donors: Sheila C. Waugh; Seth H. Waugh.
Foundation type: Independent foundation.
Financial data (yr. ended 12/31/13): Assets,
$610,592 (M); gifts received, $10,000;
expenditures, $265,568; qualifying distributions,
$256,800; giving activities include $256,800 for 15
grants (high: $100,000; low: $100).
Fields of interest: Education; Health; Sports and
recreation.
Limitations: Applications not accepted. Giving
primarily in FL, MA, NJ and NY. No grants to
individuals.
Application information: Unsolicited requests for
funds not accepted.
Officers: Seth H. Waugh, Pres.; Sheila C. Waugh,
V.P.
EIN: 421687485

2393
Ted and Jean Weiler Foundation, Inc.
663 Mourning Dove Dr.
Sarasota, FL 34236-1903 (941) 954-6978
Contact: Edwin A. Weiller III, Pres.

Established in 1995 in Florida.
Donor: Edwin A. Weiller III.
Foundation type: Independent foundation.
Financial data (yr. ended 12/31/13): Assets,
$811,257 (M); expenditures, $216,522; qualifying
distributions, $205,206; giving activities include
$204,465 for 11 grants (high: $100,000; low: $49).
Purpose and activities: Giving primarily for arts and
culture, and to a community foundation.
Fields of interest: Arts and culture; Theater;
Foundations; Diseases and conditions; Human
services.
Limitations: Applications accepted. Giving limited to
Manatee and Sarasota counties, FL, and Berkshire
County, MA. No grants to individuals.
Application information: Application form required.
    Initial approach: Letter requesting application
    package
    Deadline(s): Jul. 31
Officers: Edwin A. Weiller III, Pres.; Jean A. Weiller,
V.P.; Donna T. Pickup, Exec. Dir.
EIN: 650538553

2394
Weinberger Family Foundation, Inc.
4469 White Cedar Ln.
Delray Beach, FL 33445-7069

Established in 1991 in Florida.
Donor: Saul Weinberger.
Foundation type: Independent foundation.
Financial data (yr. ended 12/31/13): Assets,
$5,149,054 (M); expenditures, $301,044;
qualifying distributions, $297,075; giving activities
include $297,040 for 12 grants (high: $100,000;
low: $110).
Fields of interest: Nonprofits; Judaism.
Type of support: Regranting.
Limitations: Applications not accepted. No grants to
individuals.
Application information: Unsolicited requests for
funds not accepted.
Officer: Ruth Weinberger, Pres.
EIN: 650245748

2395
Joseph Weintraub Family Foundation Inc.
(formerly Weintraub-Landfield Charity Foundation,
Inc.)
801 Brickell Ave., Ste. 2470
Miami, FL 33131-4943 (305) 377-6942
Contact: Michael Weintraub, Pres.

Established in 1949 in Florida.
Donor: Joseph Weintraub.
Foundation type: Independent foundation.
Financial data (yr. ended 10/31/13): Assets,
$7,756,579 (M); expenditures, $435,668;
qualifying distributions, $379,100; giving activities
include $379,100 for 13 grants (high: $222,000;
low: $500).
Purpose and activities: Support primarily for higher
education, social services, and health
organizations.

Fields of interest: Higher education; Law education; Foundations; Nonprofits; Diseases and conditions; Judaism; Human services.

Type of support: Regranting.

Limitations: Applications accepted. Giving primarily in FL. No grants to individuals.

Application information: Application form required.

Initial approach: Proposal

Deadline(s): None

Officers and Trustees: Michael Weintraub, Pres. and Trustee; Sandra S. Spooner, V.P. and Secy.-Treas.; Miles Gauntt; Barbara A. Weintraub.

EIN: 590975815

2396
The Weisman Family Foundation

c/o Robert D. Weisman
1216 N. Atlantic Dr.
Lantana, FL 33462-1936

Established in 2005 in Florida.

Foundation type: Independent foundation.

Financial data (yr. ended 12/31/13): Assets, $6,137,422 (M); expenditures, $349,635; qualifying distributions, $253,150; giving activities include $244,614 for 48 grants (high: $62,480; low: $100).

Fields of interest: Education; Nonprofits; Judaism; Human services.

Type of support: Regranting.

Limitations: Applications not accepted.

Application information: Unsolicited requests for funds not accepted.

Trustees: Fran Weisman; Robert Weisman.

EIN: 562475540

2397
Wells Family Foundation, Inc.

680 Via Lugano
Winter Park, FL 32789-1534

Established in 2005 in Florida.

Donors: Stephen L. Wells; Stephanie Shackelford; John Shackelford.

Foundation type: Independent foundation.

Financial data (yr. ended 06/30/13): Assets, $4,653,592 (M); gifts received, $102,415; expenditures, $210,939; qualifying distributions, $191,430; giving activities include $180,580 for 9 grants (high: $83,000; low: $100).

Fields of interest: Christianity; Child welfare; Children.

Limitations: Applications not accepted. Giving primarily in FL. No grants to individuals.

Application information: Contributes only to pre-selected organizations.

Directors: Stephanie W. Shackelford; Kristi Wells; Stephen L. Wells.

EIN: 204003386

2398
Richard L. & Lois S. Werner Family Foundation

3500 N.W. Clubside Cir.
Boca Raton, FL 33496-4001 (561) 994-8890
Contact: Richard L. Werner, Tr.

Established in 1997 in Pennsylvania.

Donors: Lois S. Werner; Richard L. Werner.

Foundation type: Independent foundation.

Financial data (yr. ended 12/31/14): Assets, $1,889,165 (M); expenditures, $169,905; qualifying distributions, $161,431; giving activities include $158,750 for 85 grants (high: $40,000; low: $250).

Fields of interest: Arts and culture; Education; Medical education; Nonprofits; Health; Judaism; Human services.

Type of support: Regranting.

Limitations: Applications accepted. Giving primarily in FL, OH, PA and NY.

Application information: Application form required.

Initial approach: Letter

Deadline(s): Jan. 1

Trustees: Bruce D. Werner; Daniel M. Alter; Elise W. Frost; Ira M. Frost; Lois S. Werner; Mindy H. Werner; Richard L. Werner; Tammy H. Werner.

EIN: 237911213

2399
Wescustogo Foundation

1644 Lands End Village
Captiva, FL 33924

Established in 2005 in Maine.

Donors: Robert S. Nanovic; Robert S. Nanovic 2009 Charitable Lead Annuity Trust.

Foundation type: Independent foundation.

Financial data (yr. ended 12/31/13): Assets, $10,388,476 (M); gifts received, $666,423; expenditures, $314,865; qualifying distributions, $301,520; giving activities include $301,520 for 16 grants (high: $50,000; low: $5,000).

Fields of interest: Arts and culture; Orchestral music; Art museums; Education; Health.

Type of support: General support.

Limitations: Applications not accepted. Giving primarily in Portland, ME. No grants to individuals.

Application information: Unsolicited requests for funds not accepted.

Board meeting date(s): Dec.

Officers: Robert S. Nanovic, Pres.; Rebecca E. Lin, Secy.; Kathryn M. Nanovic-Morlet, Treas.

EIN: 203848164

2400
Westgate Resorts Foundation, Inc.

(formerly Westgate Foundation, Inc.)
5601 Windhover Dr.
Orlando, FL 32819-7914
E-mail: foundation@wgresorts.com; Main URL: http://www.westgateresortsfoundation.org

Established in 2001 in Florida.

Donors: Central Florida Investments, Inc.; David Siegel; Furniture Design Studios; Moen; Pepsi Bottling Group; Lodging Kit Co.; QTS Logistics; Simmons Hospitality Group; Roger B. Kennedy.

Foundation type: Independent foundation.

Financial data (yr. ended 12/31/13): Assets, $3,034,745 (M); gifts received, $447,997; expenditures, $536,800; qualifying distributions, $334,816; giving activities include $334,816 for 57 grants (high: $50,000; low: $100).

Purpose and activities: The foundation supports charitable activities in areas where Westgate Resorts employees live and work. Emphasis is placed on Westgate employees, children, women, families, seniors and other local programs that improve the quality of life in the foundation's communities.

Fields of interest: Education; Health; Human services; Child welfare; Unknown or not classified.

Type of support: General support; Scholarships.

Limitations: Giving limited to areas of company operations in Mesa, AZ, Miami and central FL, Branson, MO, Tunica, MS, Las Vegas, NV, Myrtle Beach, SC, Gatlinburg and Knoxville, TN, Park City, UT, and Williamsburg, VA. No grants to individuals.

Publications: Newsletter.

Application information: See foundation website for complete application guidelines.

Officers and Directors: David Siegel, Pres.; Mark Waltrip, V.P.; Tom Dugan; Jim Gissy; Barry Siegel; Jacqueline Siegel; Richard Siegel; Steve Siegel; Karen Waltrip.

EIN: 593725617

2401
Westreich Finaly Foundation, Inc.

7808 Palencia Way
Delray Beach, FL 33446-4405

Established in 2008 in Florida.

Donor: Helene Westreich.

Foundation type: Independent foundation.

Financial data (yr. ended 12/31/13): Assets, $4,233,260 (M); expenditures, $215,681; qualifying distributions, $196,750; giving activities include $196,750 for 13 grants (high: $85,000; low: $250).

Fields of interest: Education; Health; Community and economic development.

Limitations: Applications not accepted. No grants to individuals.

Application information: Contributes only to pre-selected organizations.

Directors: William Finaly Cohen; Diane Lynn Harris; Gail Marcy White.

EIN: 262718009

2402
Lawrence E. White Family Foundation

625 Waltham Ave.
Orlando, FL 32809-4205

Established in 2002 in Florida.

Donor: Patrick L. White.

Foundation type: Independent foundation.

Financial data (yr. ended 02/28/14): Assets, $2,366,872 (M); gifts received, $88,000; expenditures, $236,740; qualifying distributions, $236,740; giving activities include $149,729 for 8 grants (high: $45,000; low: $3,654).

Fields of interest: University education; Sports and recreation.

Limitations: Applications not accepted. Giving primarily in FL.

Application information: Unsolicited requests for funds not accepted.

Trustee: J.W. Hoechst.

EIN: 043608094

2403
Macauley & Helen Dow Whiting Foundation

3185 Hammock Way
Vero Beach, FL 32963

Established in 1957 in Michigan.

Foundation type: Independent foundation.

Financial data (yr. ended 12/31/13): Assets, $3,745,302 (M); expenditures, $183,603; qualifying distributions, $155,000; giving activities include $155,000 for 6 grants (high: $80,000; low: $5,000).
Fields of interest: Education; Higher education; Natural resources; Hospital care; Cancers; Public libraries; Sports and recreation.
Limitations: Applications not accepted. Giving primarily in FL, ID and ME. No grants to individuals.
Application information: Contributes only to pre-selected organizations.
Board meeting date(s): At least twice a year
Officers and Trustees: Macauley Whiting, Jr., Pres. and Trustee; Mary M. Whiting, Secy. and Trustee; Macauley Whiting; Sara S. Whiting.
EIN: 237418814

2404
H. Angela Whitman Foundation Inc.
P.O. Box 1908
Orlando, FL 32802-1908

Donors: H. Angela Whitmanred Trust; Marsha Madorsky.
Foundation type: Independent foundation.
Financial data (yr. ended 12/31/13): Assets, $195,894 (M); gifts received, $225,000; expenditures, $184,988; qualifying distributions, $171,530; giving activities include $159,030 for 13 grants (high: $60,000; low: $125).
Fields of interest: Education; Sports and recreation; Human services; People with vision impairments.
Type of support: General support.
Limitations: Applications not accepted. Giving primarily in FL.
Application information: Unsolicited requests for funds not accepted.
Officers and Directors: Raymond Kuhn, Pres. and Director; H. Angela Whitman, Secy.-Treas.; Robert Kuhn.
EIN: 460747528

2405
The Israel, Rose, Henry & Robert Wiener Charitable Foundation Inc.
7401 S.W. 56th Ct.
Miami, FL 33143

Established in 2004 in Florida.
Donor: Robert Wiener†.
Foundation type: Independent foundation.
Financial data (yr. ended 04/30/14): Assets, $5,402,734 (M); expenditures, $359,950; qualifying distributions, $261,750; giving activities include $261,750 for 45 grants (high: $65,000; low: $750).
Fields of interest: Arts and culture; Education; Diseases and conditions; Judaism; Human services; Child welfare.
Limitations: Applications not accepted. Giving primarily in FL. No grants to individuals.
Application information: Contributes only to pre-selected organizations.
Officer: Joan Rozansky, Mgr.
EIN: 201125267

2406
The B.J. and Eve Wilder Family Foundation, Inc.
(formerly Epilepsy Research Foundation of Florida, Inc.)
10530 N.W. 15th Pl.
Gainesville, FL 32606-5400
Contact: B.J. Wilder MD, Pres.

Donors: McNeil Pharmaceuticals; Cybelonics; E.I. du Pont de Nemours and Co.; Abbott/Wendermere; Warner-Lambert Co.; Rose Wichtenstein†; Pfizer Pharmaceutical Co., Inc.; Ortho-McNeil Pharmaceutical, Inc.; Parke, Davis & Co.; Novartis Corp., Inc.
Foundation type: Independent foundation.
Financial data (yr. ended 08/31/13): Assets, $7,167,558 (M); expenditures, $508,648; qualifying distributions, $502,635; giving activities include $364,300 for 6 grants (high: $250,000; low: $300).
Purpose and activities: Giving for the study of the nature and treatment of epileptic disorders.
Fields of interest: Natural history museums; Higher education; Diseases and conditions; Epilepsy.
Type of support: Research; Research and evaluation.
Limitations: Applications accepted. Giving limited to northern FL.
Application information:
Initial approach: Letter
Copies of proposal: 1
Deadline(s): None
Officer: B.J. Wilder, MD, Pres.
Director: B.J. Wilder, Jr.
EIN: 237290166

2407
Wilkes-Desmond Educational Foundation
c/o J. Cole, C.P.A.
2211 S. Flagler Dr.
West Palm Beach, FL 33401-8007

Donor: William C. Desmond†.
Foundation type: Operating foundation.
Financial data (yr. ended 05/31/13): Assets, $7,514,419 (M); expenditures, $547,340; qualifying distributions, $526,213; giving activities include $349,456 for 46 grants (high: $99,978; low: $285).
Fields of interest: Higher education.
Limitations: Applications not accepted. Giving primarily in NY. No grants to individuals.
Application information: Contributes only to pre-selected organizations.
Trustee: David Beuttenmuller.
EIN: 650961676

2408
Wilson-Wood Foundation, Inc.
(formerly Hugh & Mary Wilson Foundation, Inc.)
2283 Harrier Way
Nokomis, FL 34275-5338
Contact: Susan Wood, Treas. and Exec. Dir.

Established in 1983 in Florida.
Donors: Hugh H. Wilson†; Mary P. Wilson†; John R. Wood.
Foundation type: Independent foundation.
Financial data (yr. ended 12/31/13): Assets, $10,380,239 (M); expenditures, $498,634;

qualifying distributions, $426,115; giving activities include $327,000 for 27 grants (high: $20,000; low: $7,000).
Purpose and activities: Giving primarily for the underprivileged and the less fortunate in the local community.
Fields of interest: Education; Basic and remedial instruction; Reading promotion; Health; Nutrition; Housing development; Human services; Child welfare; Housing for the homeless; Senior services; Women's services; Children and youth; Seniors; Females; Ethnic and racial groups; Homeless people; Low-income and poor people; People with psychosocial disabilities.
Type of support: General support; Capital campaigns; Capital and infrastructure; Equipment.
Limitations: Giving limited to the Manatee-Sarasota, FL, area. No support for foreign organizations, supporting organizations, or private foundations. No grants to individuals, or for endowment funds, deficit financing, travel projects, research, fundraising costs, multi-year projects, conferences, emergency funding or start up costs.
Publications: Annual report (including application guidelines).
Application information:
Initial approach: Telephone call prior to letter of inquiry
Copies of proposal: 2
Deadline(s): Initial letter of inquiry must be received by June 1
Board meeting date(s): Mar., June, and Sept.
Final notification: July
Officers and Directors: John R. Wood, Pres. and Director; George Fraley, V.P. and Director; Thomas A. Faessler, Secy. and Director; Susan Wood, Treas. and Exec. Dir.
Number of staff: 1 full-time professional.
EIN: 592243926

2409
Woerner World Ministries, Inc.
525 Okeechobbe Blvd., Ste. 720
West Palm Beach, FL 33401

Established in 1998 in Florida.
Donors: Woerner Management, Inc.; Lester J. Woerner.
Foundation type: Operating foundation.
Financial data (yr. ended 06/30/14): Assets, $168,172 (M); gifts received, $55,000; expenditures, $304,709; qualifying distributions, $301,565; giving activities include $211,300 for 3 grants (high: $207,000; low: $1,000).
Purpose and activities: The foundation supports organizations involved with child welfare, athletics, human services, and Christianity.
Fields of interest: Child abuse; Christianity; Track and field; Human services; Child welfare.
Type of support: General support.
Limitations: Applications not accepted. Giving primarily in FL.
Application information: Unsolicited requests for funds not accepted.
Officers: Lester J. Woerner, Chair.; Kathy Miller, Pres.; Dave Williams, Secy.; Christina Wiemer, Treas.
EIN: 650907241

2410

Clarence, Jr. and Alma B. Wolf Foundation, Inc.

169 E. Flagler St., Ste. 800
Miami, FL 33131-1296

Donor: Clarence Wolf, Jr. Revocable Trust.
Foundation type: Independent foundation.
Financial data (yr. ended 12/31/13): Assets,
$6,089,725 (M); expenditures, $355,190;
qualifying distributions, $278,670; giving activities
include $242,750 for 11 grants (high: $100,000;
low: $1,000).
Fields of interest: University education;
Foundations; Nonprofits; Hospital care; Alzheimer's
disease; Judaism.
Type of support: Regranting.
Limitations: Applications not accepted. Giving
primarily in FL; with some funding in NY. No grants
to individuals.
Application information: Unsolicited requests for
funds not accepted.
Officers and Directors: Richard M. Kwal, Pres. and
Treas. and Director; Gail Rubin, V.P. and Secy. and
Director; Steven H. Hagen; Jaclyn M. Kwal; Rachel
A. Kwal.
EIN: 650920365

2411

Sidney and Jacqueline Wolgin Foundation, Inc.

3226 N.W. 65th St.
Boca Raton, FL 33496-3398

Established in 1994 in Florida.
Foundation type: Independent foundation.
Financial data (yr. ended 12/31/12): Assets,
$4,191,754 (M); gifts received, $238,380;
expenditures, $237,591; qualifying distributions,
$196,620; giving activities include $196,620 for
grants.
Purpose and activities: Giving for Jewish
organizations and higher education.
Fields of interest: Art museums; Elementary and
secondary education; Higher education; Nonprofits;
Cancers; Television; Judaism; Family services.
Type of support: Regranting.
Limitations: Applications not accepted. Giving
primarily in FL and PA. No grants to individuals.
Application information: Unsolicited requests for
funds not accepted.
Officers: Rachelle Wolgin, Pres.; Jacqueline Wolgin,
Secy.
EIN: 650556029

2412

Wollowick Family Foundation

(formerly Rubin and Gladys Wollowick Foundation,
Inc.)
c/o Golomb, Schwartz & Cove, P.A.
2000 N.W. 150th Ave., Ste. 2106
Pembroke Pines, FL 33028-2870 (954)
889-0075

Established in 1984 in Florida.
Donor: Gladys Wollowick†.
Foundation type: Independent foundation.
Financial data (yr. ended 01/31/14): Assets,
$3,895,272 (M); expenditures, $475,941;
qualifying distributions, $400,250; giving activities

include $400,250 for 55 grants (high: $150,000;
low: $1,000).
Purpose and activities: Giving primarily for
education, hospitals and health organizations,
social services, and Jewish organizations.
Fields of interest: Higher education; Nonprofits;
Hospital care; Diseases and conditions; Judaism;
Human services.
International interests: Israel.
Type of support: General support; Matching grants;
Annual campaigns; Equipment; Research;
Emergency funds; Research and evaluation;
Regranting.
Limitations: Applications accepted. Giving primarily
in Boca Raton and Miami, FL. No grants to
individuals.
Application information:
  Initial approach: Letter
  Deadline(s): Sept. 30
  Board meeting date(s): Varies
Trustee: BNY Mellon, N.A.
Directors: Megan Lowe; Richard Lowe; Sandra Lois
Lowe; Jason Stein; Rhoda Stein; Ronnit Stein; Dr.
Robert Tesher; Janet Amy Wollowick.
Number of staff: None.
EIN: 592469452

2413

Woodbery Carlton Foundation

222 S. 6th Ave.
Wauchula, FL 33873-2921
Application address: c/o Doyle E. Carlton III, Rt. 1,
P.O. Box 412, Cloverhill, Wauchula, FL 33873-0412

Established in 1988 in Florida.
Donor: Doyle E. Carlton, Jr.
Foundation type: Independent foundation.
Financial data (yr. ended 08/31/13): Assets,
$2,307,761 (M); expenditures, $203,503;
qualifying distributions, $190,602; giving activities
include $177,500 for 12 grants (high: $95,000;
low: $500), and $11,820 for 4 grants to individuals
(high: $6,820; low: $1,000).
Fields of interest: Education; Christianity.
Type of support: General support; Scholarships.
Limitations: Applications accepted. Giving primarily
in FL.
Application information:
  Initial approach: Letter
  Deadline(s): July 1
Directors: Doyle E. Carlton III; Jane Carlton Durando;
Walter S. Farr; Susan C. Smith.
EIN: 650068703

2414

The Woolard Family Foundation

107 Via Capri
Palm Beach Gardens, FL 33418-6202
Application address: c/o Lynda Woolard, 1233 Fern
St., New Orleans, LA 70118, tel.: (504) 862-5945

Established in 1996 in Florida.
Donor: Edgar S. Woolard, Jr.
Foundation type: Independent foundation.
Financial data (yr. ended 12/31/14): Assets,
$3,149,473 (M); expenditures, $166,711;
qualifying distributions, $162,481; giving activities
include $151,281 for 31 grants (high: $50,000;
low: $500).

Purpose and activities: Giving primarily to arts,
education, animal welfare, and human service
programs, including hurricane recovery programs.
Fields of interest: Arts and culture; Art museums;
Education; Sports and recreation; Human services.
Limitations: Applications accepted. Giving primarily
in DE and LA. No grants to individuals.
Application information:
  Initial approach: Proposal
Directors: Edgar Woolard; Lynda D. Woolard; Peggy
Woolard; Annette Woolard-Provine.
EIN: 650711855

2415

Charles G. Wright Endowment for Humanity Inc.

91750 Overseas Hwy.
Tavernier, FL 33070-2642

Established in 2006 in Florida.
Donors: Jeanette S. Wright; JSW & JCW, LP; Jeffrey
C. Wright.
Foundation type: Independent foundation.
Financial data (yr. ended 12/31/13): Assets, $0
(M); expenditures, $306,275; qualifying
distributions, $267,829; giving activities include
$267,829 for 22 grants (high: $35,000; low: $680).
Fields of interest: Gardening; Christianity.
Limitations: Applications not accepted. Giving
primarily in ME and NJ; some funding also in FL. No
grants to individuals.
Application information: Contributes only to
pre-selected organizations.
Directors: Sarah D'Anto; Kay Wright; Laura Wright.
EIN: 203514304

2416

Wrightson-Ramsing Foundation, Inc.

P.O. Box 3450
Palm Beach, FL 33480-1650 8049741401

Established in 1952 in New York.
Donors: Martha Wrightson Ramsing; Thor H.
Ramsing.
Foundation type: Independent foundation.
Financial data (yr. ended 12/31/14): Assets,
$4,390,233; expenditures, $269,973; qualifying
distributions, $233,099.
Purpose and activities: Funding primarily for
education, human services and Christian churches.
Fields of interest: Museums; Education; Hospital
care; Diseases and conditions; Christianity; Human
services.
Type of support: General support; Research;
Research and evaluation.
Limitations: Applications not accepted. Giving
primarily in FL. No grants to individuals.
Application information: Unsolicited requests for
funds not accepted.
Officers: Martha R. Zoubek, Pres.; Dennis Palmgren,
V.P. and Treas.
Directors: Cynthia R. McGinnes; Elizabeth
Palmgren; Charles Zoubek.
EIN: 131967462

2417

Misdee Wrigley and James Mather Miller Foundation, Inc.

12444 Highfield Cir.
Bradenton, FL 34202-7909

Established in 2004 in Kentucky.
Donor: Misdee Wrigley Miller.
Foundation type: Independent foundation.
Financial data (yr. ended 12/31/13): Assets, $8,259,822 (M); expenditures, $484,895; qualifying distributions, $376,860; giving activities include $373,260 for 28 grants (high: $100,000; low: $500).
Fields of interest: Arts and culture; Environment; Diseases and conditions.
Limitations: Applications not accepted. Giving primarily in FL and KY. No grants to individuals.
Application information: Contributes only to pre-selected organizations.
Officer: Misdee Wrigley Miller, Pres.
Directors: Sloan M. Haney; Brian McNally; James Miller.
EIN: 201456820

2418
Norman E. & Harriet S. Wymbs Foundation
200 N.E. 8th Ave.
Delray Beach, FL 33444-3758

Established in 1993 in Florida.
Donors: Harriet S. Wymbs; Norman E. Wymbs; F.B. Stevens Family Trust.
Foundation type: Independent foundation.
Financial data (yr. ended 12/31/13): Assets, $2,842,616 (M); expenditures, $440,300; qualifying distributions, $417,552; giving activities include $415,152 for 1 grant.
Purpose and activities: Giving primarily to a history center.
Fields of interest: History museums.
Limitations: Applications not accepted. Giving primarily in Dixon, IL. No grants to individuals.
Application information: Contributes only to pre-selected organizations.
Officer: Norman E. Wymbs, Pres.
Directors: William E. Jones; James Ness; Bradley S. Wymbs.
EIN: 650352321

2419
Wynne Charitable Foundation
12804 S.W. 122nd Ave.
Miami, FL 33186-6203

Established in 2007 in Florida.
Donors: Joel F. Wynne; Wynne Building Corporation.
Foundation type: Company-sponsored foundation.
Financial data (yr. ended 09/30/14): Assets, $339,583 (M); gifts received, $253,535; expenditures, $280,865; qualifying distributions, $275,224; giving activities include $275,224 for 55 grants (high: $245,894; low: $50).
Purpose and activities: The foundation supports organizations involved with education and human services.
Fields of interest: Education; Higher education; Education services; Nonprofits; Human services; Child welfare; Senior services.
Type of support: Program development; General support; Regranting.
Limitations: Applications not accepted. Giving primarily in FL. No grants to individuals.
Application information: Unsolicited requests for funds not accepted.

Trustees: Deena L. Wynne; Dorothy Wynne; Eric P. Wynne; Joel F. Wynne; Matthew Lyle Wynne.
EIN: 261583201

2420
The Yerrid Foundation Inc.
101 E. Kennedy Blvd., No. 3910
Tampa, FL 33602-5192

Established in 2000 in Florida.
Donor: C. Steven Yerrid.
Foundation type: Independent foundation.
Financial data (yr. ended 12/31/12): Assets, $2,082,169 (M); gifts received, $991,350; expenditures, $275,052; qualifying distributions, $268,598; giving activities include $268,598 for grants.
Fields of interest: Arts and culture; Performing arts; Education; Higher education; Law education; Hospital care; Pediatrics; Diseases and conditions; Musculoskeletal diseases; Human services; Family services; Child welfare; Homeless services; Low-income and poor people.
Type of support: Research; Research and evaluation.
Limitations: Applications not accepted. Giving primarily in FL, with emphasis on Tampa. No grants to individuals.
Application information: Contributes only to pre-selected organizations.
Officer and Directors: C. Steven Yerrid, C.E.O. and Pres. and Director; Cindy Jameson; Gable Yerrid.
EIN: 593571804

2421
James and Cecilia Tse Ying Foundation
P.O. Box 43250
Jacksonville, FL 32203-3205

Established in 2000 in New York.
Donors: James Ying; Cecilia Ying.
Foundation type: Independent foundation.
Financial data (yr. ended 12/31/14): Assets, $3,388,261; expenditures, $211,295; qualifying distributions, $209,103.
Fields of interest: Higher education.
Limitations: Applications not accepted. Giving primarily in MA, NH and NV. No grants to individuals.
Application information: Unsolicited requests for funds not accepted.
Trustees: Cecilia Tse Ying; Charlene Cecilia Ying; James W. Ying; John J. Ying.
EIN: 134149503

2422
Younger Family Foundation
1011 Bentley Dr.
Naples, FL 34110-8640 (239) 591-3342
Contact: William H. Younger, Pres.

Established in 1985 in Wisconsin.
Donor: William H. Younger.
Foundation type: Independent foundation.
Financial data (yr. ended 12/31/12): Assets, $490,429 (M); expenditures, $142,291; qualifying distributions, $141,300; giving activities include $141,300 for 12 grants (high: $110,000; low: $500).
Fields of interest: Education; Christianity; Human services.

Limitations: Applications accepted. Giving primarily in WI.
Application information:
Deadline(s): None
Officers: William H. Younger, Pres.; Phyllis L. Younger, V.P.
Directors: Sherry Y. Artemenko; William H. Younger, Jr.
EIN: 391097290

2423
James P. and Margaret L. Zehnder Foundation, Inc.
28709 Tanner Dr.
Wesley Chapel, FL 33543-5406

Donors: James P. Zehnder; Margaret L. Zehnder; Trinity Logistics Corp.
Foundation type: Independent foundation.
Financial data (yr. ended 12/31/13): Assets, $344,067 (M); gifts received, $597,624; expenditures, $359,005; qualifying distributions, $334,247; giving activities include $334,247 for 29 grants (high: $222,932; low: $100).
Fields of interest: Archives and special collections; National defense; Housing development; Christianity; Human services.
Limitations: Applications not accepted. No grants to individuals.
Application information: Contributes only to pre-selected organizations.
Officers and Directors: James P. Zehnder, Pres. and Director; Daniel J. Zehnder, V.P. and Director; Barbara J. Zehnder, Secy. and Director; Margaret L. Zehnder, Treas. and Director; Mary J. Cajthaml.
EIN: 562334965

2424
Zichron Foundation for Special Needs, Inc.
10800 Biscayne Blvd., No. 800
North Miami, FL 33161
E-mail: aklein@magnum-mgt.com; Application address: c/o Avi Klein, 5030 Pine Tree Dr., Miami Beach, FL 33140, tel.: (786) 888-3310

Established in 2007 in Florida.
Donors: Continium Healthcare Mgmt., LLC; Millennium Healthcare Mgmt., LLC; Avi Klein; Dennis Feierman, MD.
Foundation type: Independent foundation.
Financial data (yr. ended 12/31/13): Assets, $1,372,984 (M); expenditures, $212,139; qualifying distributions, $173,690; giving activities include $173,690 for 18 grants (high: $41,500; low: $180).
Fields of interest: Nonprofits; Judaism.
International interests: Ukraine.
Type of support: Regranting.
Limitations: Applications accepted. Giving primarily in FL and NY.
Application information: Application form required.
Initial approach: Letter
Deadline(s): None
Trustee: Avi Klein.
EIN: 261231712

2425
The Zimmer Family Foundation, Inc.
P.O. Box 15222
Sarasota, FL 34277-1222
Contact: R. Scott Zimmer, V.P.
E-mail: info@zimmerfamilyfoundation.com; Main
URL: http://www.zimmerfamilyfoundation.com

Established in 1998 in Florida.
Donors: Robert S. Zimmer; Cheryl B. Zimmer.
Foundation type: Independent foundation.
Financial data (yr. ended 12/31/13): Assets, $4,527,866 (M); expenditures, $313,545; qualifying distributions, $254,047; giving activities include $171,000 for 29 grants (high: $20,000; low: $500).
Purpose and activities: Giving primarily for religious, educational and social programs, that bring help and hope to the less fortunate, primarily by seeding short-term pilot projects that have potential of self-support.
Fields of interest: Christianity; Human services.
Type of support: Pilot programs; Matching grants; Seed money.
Limitations: Applications accepted. Giving on a local, national, and international basis. No grants for general operating expenses, or for buildings.
Publications: Application guidelines; Program policy statement.
Application information: Application form required.
  Initial approach: E-mail only, via foundation Web
    site
  Copies of proposal: 1
  Deadline(s): At least 60 days before the board
    meetings
  Board meeting date(s): Jan., Apr., July, and Oct.
  Final notification: Mar. 1 and Sept. 1
Officers and Board Members: Cheryl B. Zimmer, Pres. and Director; R. Scott Zimmer, V.P. and Admin. and Director; Jordan Z. Baesler, Secy. and Director; Jared S. Zimmer, Treas. and Director; Colin Baesler; Collins C. Zimmer; Jacob Zimmer; Joshua Zimmer.
Number of staff: 1 part-time professional.
EIN: 311596973

2426
Raymond Zimmerman Charitable Trust
P.O. Box 810939
Boca Raton, FL 33487-0939

Established in 1982 in Tennessee.
Donor: Raymond Zimmerman Charitable Lead Trust.
Foundation type: Independent foundation.
Financial data (yr. ended 05/31/14): Assets, $3,323,049 (M); expenditures, $184,304; qualifying distributions, $158,761; giving activities include $155,632 for 2 grants (high: $130,000; low: $25,632).
Fields of interest: Nonprofits; Religion.
Type of support: Regranting.
Limitations: Applications not accepted. No grants to individuals.
Application information: Unsolicited requests for funds not accepted.
Trustees: James R. Mills; Robyn Z. Rubinoff; Fred E. Zimmerman.
EIN: 621327356

2427
Zimmerman Family Foundation, Inc.
3644 Philips Hwy.
Jacksonville, FL 32207-5614

Established in 1997 in Florida.
Donors: Morrie Zimmerman; Seeman Zimmerman; Charles Zimmerman.
Foundation type: Independent foundation.
Financial data (yr. ended 06/30/13): Assets, $2,549,891 (M); gifts received, $250,780; expenditures, $319,272; qualifying distributions, $300,606; giving activities include $300,475 for 31 grants (high: $70,000; low: $100).
Purpose and activities: Giving primarily for health care, human services, and Jewish agencies and temples.
Fields of interest: Art museums; Nonprofits; Health; Cancers; Judaism; Human services.

Type of support: General support; Regranting.
Limitations: Applications not accepted. Giving primarily in Jacksonville, FL. No grants to individuals.
Application information: Contributes only to pre-selected organizations.
Officers: Seeman Zimmerman, Pres.; Charles Zimmerman, V.P.; Elyne Zimmerman, V.P.; Morrie Zimmerman, V.P.
EIN: 593503647

2428
The Jordan Zimmerman Family Foundation, Inc.
(formerly The Denise and Jordan Zimmerman Family Foundation, Inc.)
1000 W. MCNAB Rd., Ste. 243
Pompano, FL 33069-4719

Established in 2004 in Florida.
Donors: Jordan Zimmerman; Denise Zimmerman; Z Group Advertising, Inc.
Foundation type: Independent foundation.
Financial data (yr. ended 12/31/13): Assets, $794,373 (M); expenditures, $346,820; qualifying distributions, $341,159; giving activities include $341,159 for 17 grants (high: $109,400; low: $435).
Purpose and activities: Giving primarily for children and youth services, as well as for health organizations and human services.
Fields of interest: Arts and culture; Education; Nonprofits; Diseases and conditions; Judaism; Child welfare; Youth development.
Type of support: Regranting.
Limitations: Applications not accepted. Giving primarily in FL.
Application information: Unsolicited requests for funds not accepted.
Officers and Directors: Jordan Zimmerman, Pres. and Director; David Valdes, Treas. and Director.
EIN: 202016951

GEORGIA

2429
10/1 Foundation, Inc.
P.O. Box 2533
Thomasville, GA 31799-2533
Contact: Michael A. Grimsley, C.E.O.

Established in 2004 in Georgia.
Donors: T. Cole Forsyth; Michael A. Grimsley.
Foundation type: Independent foundation.
Financial data (yr. ended 12/31/13): Assets,
$4,620,013 (M); expenditures, $457,371;
qualifying distributions, $412,222; giving activities
include $412,222 for 30 grants (high: $79,000;
low: $250).
Purpose and activities: Giving primarily for
Presbyterian churches and organizations.
Fields of interest: Protestantism; Human services.
Application information:
Initial approach: Proposal
Deadline(s): None
Officers: Michael A. Grimsley, C.E.O.; T. Cole
Forsyth, C.F.O. and Secy.
EIN: 593789335

2430
The A.E.M. Family Foundation
600 Peachtree St. N.E., Ste. 1900
Atlanta, GA 30308-2217

Established in 2003 in South Carolina.
Donor: Ann E. Middelthon.
Foundation type: Independent foundation.
Financial data (yr. ended 12/31/12): Assets,
$9,321,273 (M); gifts received, $500,010;
expenditures, $457,862; qualifying distributions,
$410,610; giving activities include $385,000 for 14
grants (high: $93,000; low: $5,000).
Fields of interest: Performing arts; Ballet;
Education; Nonprofits; Christianity; Youth services.
Type of support: Regranting.
Limitations: Applications not accepted. Giving
primarily in FL and GA. No grants to individuals.
Application information: Contributes only to
pre-selected organizations.
Trustee: Ann E. Middelthon.
EIN: 201105296

2431
May P. & Francis L. Abreu Charitable Trust
(formerly M & F Abreu Charitable Trust)
c/o SunTrust Bank
P.O. Box 502407
Atlanta, GA 31150-2407 (404) 549-6743
Contact: Katherine M. Abreu, Prog. Dir.
FAX: (404) 549-6752;
E-mail: info@abreufoundation.org; Main
URL: http://www.abreufoundation.org

Established in 2003 in Georgia.
Donor: Francis Abreu Trust.
Foundation type: Independent foundation.
Financial data (yr. ended 12/31/14): Assets,
$9,205,650; gifts received, $2,500; expenditures,
$395,200; qualifying distributions, $367,133.
Purpose and activities: The trust benefits others by
providing grants to arts and cultural programs,

education, health associations, human services,
and children and youth services.
Fields of interest: Cultural awareness; Human
services; Children and youth; Infants and toddlers;
Children; Adults; Young adults; Females; Female
children and youth; Female infants and toddlers;
Female adults; Female young adults; Male children
and youth; Male infants and toddlers; Male adults;
Male young adults; Single parents; Ethnic and racial
groups; Homeless people; Low-income and poor
people; Victims of crime and abuse; People with
disabilities; People with physical disabilities; People
with vision impairments; People with hearing
impairments; People with psychosocial disabilities;
People with HIV/AIDS; Terminally ill people;
Substance abusers.
Type of support: Capital campaigns; Matching
grants; Capital and infrastructure; Equipment;
Program development; Seed money; Curriculum
development; Fellowships.
Limitations: Applications accepted. Giving primarily
in the Atlanta, GA, area. No grants for operating
support.
Publications: Application guidelines.
Application information: Applications must be
submitted through the online application system.
Complete application form and guidelines available
on Trust web site. No international proposals
accepted. Application form required.
Copies of proposal: 1
Deadline(s): Mar. 31 for Apr. consideration or
Sept. 30 for Oct. consideration
Officer: Mike Abreu, Chair.
Committee Members: Claire Abreu; Katherine M.
Abreu; Michael Abreu; Charles D. Menser, Jr.; John
A. Wallace.
Trustee: SunTrust Bank.
Number of staff: 3
EIN: 586455665

2432
Akers Foundation, Inc.
3500 Lenox Rd. N.E., Ste. 1700
Atlanta, GA 30326-4236
Contact: C. Akers

Established in 1955 in North Carolina.
Foundation type: Independent foundation.
Financial data (yr. ended 12/31/14): Assets,
$3,765,561 (M); expenditures, $181,017;
qualifying distributions, $176,725; giving activities
include $160,000 for 28 grants (high: $10,000;
low: $2,500).
Fields of interest: Arts and culture; Education;
Higher education; Protestantism; Human services.
Limitations: Applications not accepted. No grants to
individuals.
Application information: Unsolicited requests for
funds not accepted.
Officers: C. Scott Akers, Jr., Pres.; J. Frederick
Akers, V.P. and Treas.; Mary Kathleen Akers, V.P.;
Mary Catherine Hawes, Secy.
EIN: 566044428

2433
John and Elena Amos Foundation, Inc.
(formerly John and Elena Diaz-Verson Amos
Foundation, Inc.)
4245 Milgen Rd.
Columbus, GA 31907-1208 (706) 653-1802
Contact: Maria T. Fritch, Secy.

Established in 1992 in Georgia.
Donor: Elena Diaz-Verson Amos†.
Foundation type: Independent foundation.
Financial data (yr. ended 12/31/12): Assets,
$4,984,818 (M); expenditures, $459,960;
qualifying distributions, $382,500; giving activities
include $382,500 for grants.
Fields of interest: Diseases and conditions;
Cancers; Human services; Child welfare; People of
Latin American descent.
Limitations: Applications accepted. Giving primarily
in GA, with emphasis on Columbus.
Application information:
Initial approach: Letter
Deadline(s): None
Officers: Salvador Diaz-Verson, Chair.; Maria Teresa
Amos Frith, Secy.; John Shelby Amos II, Treas.
EIN: 582006020

2434
The Jim Andrews Family Foundation Inc.
P.O. Box 159
Chickamauga, GA 30707-0159

Established in 2000 in Georgia.
Donor: Robert S. Andrews.
Foundation type: Independent foundation.
Financial data (yr. ended 12/31/14): Assets,
$1,892,911; expenditures, $179,391; qualifying
distributions, $172,195.
Fields of interest: Education; Health; Religion.
Limitations: Applications not accepted. Giving
primarily in GA. No grants to individuals.
Application information: Unsolicited requests for
funds not accepted.
Officers: Joseph F. Dana, Chair.; Mike Bunn, Secy.;
Michael Wright, Treas.
EIN: 582559643

2435
Arcadia Wildlife Preserve, Inc.
P.O. Box 813218
Smyrna, GA 30081-3218
Contact: Joyce Tapp

Established in 1994 in Georgia.
Foundation type: Independent foundation.
Financial data (yr. ended 06/30/13): Assets, $0
(M); expenditures, $228,615; qualifying
distributions, $215,591; giving activities include
$215,591 for 1 grant.
Fields of interest: Domesticated animals.
Limitations: Applications not accepted. Giving
primarily in SC. No grants to individuals.
Application information: Unsolicited requests for
funds not accepted.
Officer: Wendy B. King, Chair.
Directors: Lonnie C. Baxter; John R. Fisher, Ph.D;
Charles King, Dr.; Ken D. Tapp.
EIN: 581959654

2436
The Arnold Foundation, Inc.
1100 Peachtree St., Ste. 800
Atlanta, GA 30309-4516

Established in 1999 in Georgia.
Foundation type: Independent foundation.
Financial data (yr. ended 09/30/14): Assets,
$4,645,718 (M); expenditures, $310,775;

qualifying distributions, $275,971; giving activities include $275,971 for 37 grants (high: $30,895; low: $100).

Fields of interest: Arts and culture; Orchestral music; Education; Higher education; Nonprofits; Hospital care; Mental health care; Diseases and conditions; Protestantism; Judaism; School athletics; Youth services; Scouting programs.

Type of support: Regranting.

Limitations: Applications not accepted. Giving primarily in GA. No grants to individuals.

Application information: Unsolicited requests for funds not accepted.

Trustees: Bryan H. Flint; David H. Flint; Michael D. Flint.

EIN: 582450328

2437
Athens Area Community Foundation

P.O. Box 1543
Athens, GA 30603-1543 (706) 542-7044
Contact: Delene W. Porter, Pres. and C.E.O.
FAX: (706) 542-1744;
E-mail: info@athensareacf.org; Additional e-mail: dporter@athensareacf.org; Cell: (706)-207-6631; Main URL: http://www.athensareacf.org
Facebook: https://www.facebook.com/
Athens-Area-Community-Foundation-12281524776
5813/timeline/

Established in 2008 in Georgia.
Foundation type: Community foundation.
Financial data (yr. ended 06/30/13): Assets, $1,754,158 (M); gifts received, $259,659; expenditures, $208,845; giving activities include $120,745 for grants.
Purpose and activities: The purpose of the foundation is to promote and facilitate strategic philanthropy by connecting donors with what they care about through charitable giving and by serving as a well-informed and effective grantmaker to meet needs and identify opportunities that improve quality of life and economic well-being of Clarke, Oconee, Oglethorpe, Barrow, Jackson, and Madison counties. The foundation fulfills its mission by encouraging private giving for the public good; providing a flexible and cost effective vehicle for donors with varied charitable interests and abilities to give; helping to enhance the capacity of service delivery providers in the greater Athens area; and serving as a catalyst, convener and partner in shaping effective responses to problems and opportunities of all local communities.
Fields of interest: Arts and culture; Education; Environment; Health; Community and economic development; Economic development; Public transportation; Employment; Housing development; Human services; Low-income and poor people.
Type of support: General support; Pro bono consulting services; Matching grants; Fundraising; Capacity-building and technical assistance; Equipment; Emergency funds; Program development; Convening; Seed money; Curriculum development; Technical assistance; Program evaluations.
Limitations: Applications accepted. Giving primarily to the Athens, GA, area, including Clarke, Oconee, Oglethorpe, Jackson, Barrow, and Madison counties, though there are no geographic limitations on grantmaking. No grants to individuals.
Publications: Application guidelines; Grants list; Informational brochure.

Application information: See foundation web site for specific deadlines and full application requirements, including downloadable grants program packet containing policies and procedures, application, and report form and guidelines.
Initial approach: Submit application and attachments
Copies of proposal: 1
Deadline(s): Spring and Fall grant cycles
Final notification: late Apr. and late Oct.
Officers and Directors: Bill Douglas, Chair. and Director; Buddy Allen, Chair., Devel. Committee and Director; Grant Tribble, Chair., Finance Comm. and Treas. and Director; Alex Patterson, Esq., Vice-Chair. and Director; Delene W. Porter, C.E.O. and Pres. and Director; Kelly Holloway, Esq., Secy. and Director; Dr. David Allen; Phil Bettendorf; Ricky Chastain; Bill Cowsert; Bertis Downs, Esq.; Doc Eldridge; Robert Fezekas; Dexter Fisher; Dr. Jennifer Frum; Webster Hewitt; Tim Johnson; Judge Steve Jones; Kathy Kirbo; Cynthia Lester; Pat Mercardante; Helen Mills; Scot Morrissey; Jinx Patel; Ed Perkins; Dr. Tom Rodgers; Lewis Shropshire; Dr. Regina Smith; Ovita Thornton; Janice Mathis, Esq.; Dr. Carol Winthrop; Dr. Steve Wrigley.
Number of staff: 1 full-time professional.
EIN: 261838979

2438
Jack N. & Addie D. Averitt Foundation, Inc.

P.O. Box 568
Statesboro, GA 30459-0568 (912) 489-9226
Contact: Molly Sisson

Foundation type: Independent foundation.
Financial data (yr. ended 12/31/13): Assets, $3,645,531 (M); expenditures, $200,848; qualifying distributions, $199,424; giving activities include $129,135 for 2 grants (high: $77,500; low: $51,635).
Fields of interest: Historic preservation; Higher education.
Limitations: Applications accepted. Giving primarily in Statesboro, GA. No grants to individuals.
Application information:
Initial approach: Proposal
Deadline(s): None
Trustees: Kathy Bradley; Albert Burke; M.F. DeLoach, Jr.; Aubrey Highsmith; Jane Jackson Highsmith; Bradley W. Holmes; Mimi Averitt Potter; Delma E. Presley.
EIN: 582093653

2439
Clark and Ruby Baker Foundation

c/o US Trust, Bank of America, N.A.
3455 Peachtree Rd. N.E., 16th FL
Atlanta, GA 30326-3254 (404) 264-1377
Contact: Mark S. Drake, V.P., Sr. Philanthropic Relationship Manager
Main URL: https://www.bankofamerica.com/
philanthropic/grantmaking.go

Established in 1974 in Georgia.
Donor: Clark A. Baker‡.
Foundation type: Independent foundation.
Financial data (yr. ended 12/31/14): Assets, $3,459,478 (M); expenditures, $178,881; qualifying distributions, $165,280; giving activities include $157,000 for 26 grants (high: $20,000; low: $2,000).

Purpose and activities: Emphasis on higher education at a college or university operated by or affiliated with the Methodist Church. Support also for Protestant welfare funds and pensions for Methodist ministers.
Fields of interest: Higher education; Presbyterianism.
Type of support: General support; Endowments; Convening; Scholarships.
Application information: Application form required.
Initial approach: Check online
Deadline(s): June 1
Final notification: 1-2 months after deadline
Trustee: Bank of America, N.A.
Number of staff: None.
EIN: 581429097

2440
The Bancker-Williams Foundation Inc.

130 Riverwood Pl.
Atlanta, GA 30327-4280
Contact: Thomas Oastler

Established in 1989 in Georgia.
Foundation type: Independent foundation.
Financial data (yr. ended 06/30/13): Assets, $2,776,326 (M); expenditures, $226,591; qualifying distributions, $226,591; giving activities include $181,000 for 19 grants (high: $26,000; low: $1,000).
Fields of interest: Environment; Natural resources; Biodiversity; Wildlife biodiversity; Human services; Women's services; Females.
International interests: Africa; Latin America.
Type of support: Continuing support; Program development; Seed money; Scholarships.
Limitations: Applications not accepted. Giving in the U.S., with emphasis on GA. No grants to individuals.
Application information: Contributes only to pre-selected organizations.
Officers and Trustees: Elaine O. Blackmon, Chair. and Trustee; Beverly Kelly, Secy.-Treas.; Belitje B. Bull; Elizabeth O. Jackson; Katharine B. Johnson; Sunni Johnson; Dorothy B. Robertson; Charlotte H. Versfeld.
EIN: 581868577

2441
James M. Barnett Jr. Foundation, Inc.

c/o Perry & Walters LLP
P.O. Box 71209
Albany, GA 31708-1209
Contact: James E. Reynolds Jr., Dir.

Established in 2004 in Georgia.
Donor: Albert L. Betz‡.
Foundation type: Independent foundation.
Financial data (yr. ended 12/31/13): Assets, $6,380,777 (M); expenditures, $365,442; qualifying distributions, $211,620; giving activities include $155,350 for 9 grants (high: $35,000; low: $1,750), and $51,950 for 13 grants to individuals (high: $15,000; low: $500).
Purpose and activities: Giving primarily to provide financial aid to deserving music students, with a focus on organ studies.
Fields of interest: Performing arts; Education.
Type of support: General support; Grants to individuals; Scholarships; Individual development; Student aid.

Limitations: Applications accepted. Giving primarily in Albany and southern GA. No grants to non-U.S. citizens.

Application information: Application form required.

Initial approach: Letter

Copies of proposal: 1

Deadline(s): None

Board meeting date(s): As needed

Final notification: Generally within 3 months

Directors: J. Huff Croxton, Jr.; Helen V. Kirbo; James E. Reynolds, Jr.

Number of staff: None.

EIN: 562360848

2442

The Beard-Payne Family Foundation

4130 E. Brookhaven Dr. N.E.

Atlanta, GA 30319-2862

Established in 2007 in Georgia.

Donor: William P. Payne.

Foundation type: Independent foundation.

Financial data (yr. ended 12/31/14): Assets, $79,926 (M); gifts received, $134,873; expenditures, $203,000; qualifying distributions, $200,635; giving activities include $200,635 for 31 grants (high: $125,000; low: $25).

Fields of interest: Higher education; Community and economic development; Protestantism; Human services.

Limitations: Applications not accepted. Giving primarily in GA.

Application information: Unsolicited requests for funds not accepted.

Officers: Martha B. Payne, Pres.; William P. Payne, Secy.

EIN: 261441249

2443

Elizabeth Hurlock Beckman Award Trust

c/o Wells Fargo Bank, N.A.

MAC G0141-041, 100 Terminus Bldg.

3280 Peachtree Rd. N.E., Ste. 400

Atlanta, GA 30305-2449

E-mail: grantadministration@wellsfargo.com; Main URL: https://www.wellsfargo.com/privatefoundationgrants/beckman

Foundation type: Independent foundation.

Financial data (yr. ended 12/31/13): Assets, $6,273,458 (M); expenditures, $390,369; qualifying distributions, $336,201; giving activities include $250,000 for 10 grants to individuals (high: $25,000; low: $25,000).

Purpose and activities: Grant awards to current and former academic teachers who have inspired students to make significant contributions for the benefit of the community.

Fields of interest: Education; Public affairs; Community and economic development.

Type of support: Grants to individuals.

Application information: Recipients must be current or former teachers, professors, or instructors at a college, university, junior college, community college, or technical school located in the United States. Preference will be given to educators who teach or who taught in the fields of psychology, medicine, or law. See foundation website for

complete application policies and guidelines. Application form required.

Deadline(s): July 15

Trustee: Wells Fargo Bank, N.A.

Advisory Committee: Dr. Andrew Davidson; Dr. Nadine Kaslow; Dr. Ruth Lindeborg; Phyllis Silverstein.

EIN: 371564854

2444

S. E. Belcher, Jr. Private Foundation No. 3

P.O. Box 23024

Columbus, GA 31902

Established in 2005 in Alabama.

Foundation type: Independent foundation.

Financial data (yr. ended 12/31/13): Assets, $6,970,652 (M); expenditures, $478,335; qualifying distributions, $353,000; giving activities include $353,000 for 10 grants (high: $75,000; low: $10,000).

Fields of interest: Alzheimer's disease; Christianity.

Limitations: Applications not accepted. Giving primarily in AL, with some emphasis on Tuscaloosa.

Application information: Contributes only to pre-selected organizations.

Trustee: Synovus Trust Company, N.A.

Governors: G. Howard Graham; Robert L. Ingram, Jr.; William T. Watson.

EIN: 203353220

2445

L.O. Benton Banking Foundation

P.O. Box 4450

Eatonton, GA 31024-4450

Established in 2000 in Georgia.

Donors: The Farmers Bank; Putnam-Greene Financial Corp.; Farmers and Merchants Bank & Trust Co.; First Bank of Coastal Georgia; Lurner O. Benton III.

Foundation type: Company-sponsored foundation.

Financial data (yr. ended 12/31/13): Assets, $7,314,929 (M); gifts received, $115,850; expenditures, $306,057; qualifying distributions, $301,690; giving activities include $301,690 for 10 grants (high: $127,050; low: $3,600).

Purpose and activities: The foundation supports fire departments and organizations involved with theater and K-12 education.

Fields of interest: Education; Community and economic development; Religion.

Type of support: General support; Equipment; Scholarships.

Limitations: Applications not accepted. Giving primarily in the Eatontown, Greensboro, Monticello, and Pembroke, GA, areas. No grants to individuals.

Application information: Unsolicited requests for funds not accepted.

Officer: Lurner O. Benton III, Pres.

Trustees: Lurner O. Benton IV; Nancy T. Benton.

EIN: 582568248

2446

Dan and Merrie Boone Foundation, Inc.

2660 Peachtree Rd., Apt. 35H

Atlanta, GA 30305-3682   (404) 876-9411

Contact: Daniel W. Boone III, Dir.

E-mail: dwb@atlcap.com

Established in 2001 in Georgia.

Donors: Daniel W. Boone III; Merrie Boone; Virginia M. Boone.

Foundation type: Independent foundation.

Financial data (yr. ended 12/31/13): Assets, $9,307,204 (M); expenditures, $341,139; qualifying distributions, $326,765; giving activities include $325,765 for 45 grants (high: $120,000; low: $1).

Purpose and activities: Giving primarily for education, folk art, low-income housing, and hunger.

Fields of interest: Folk arts; Art museums; Education; Higher education; Diseases and conditions; Housing development; Food aid; Child welfare.

Type of support: Land acquisitions; Research; Endowments.

Limitations: Applications not accepted. Giving primarily in the Southeast, with emphasis on Atlanta, GA, and Tappahannock, VA. No support for religious organizations.

Application information: Unsolicited requests for funds not accepted.

Board meeting date(s): Dec.

Directors: Daniel W. Boone III; Daniel W. Boone IV; Virginia M. Boone; Meredith B. Tutterow; Susanna B. Ver Eecke.

Number of staff: None.

EIN: 582663615

2447

The R. A. Bowen Trust

P.O. Box 4611

Macon, GA 31208-4611   (478) 345-0317

Contact: R.A. Bowen Jr., Tr.

FAX: (866) 823-9410; E-mail: rabtrust@juno.com;

Main URL: http://www.rabowentrust.org

Established in 1943 in Georgia.

Donor: R. A. Bowen, Jr.

Foundation type: Independent foundation.

Financial data (yr. ended 12/31/14): Assets, $5,446,162; gifts received, $450; expenditures, $230,690; qualifying distributions, $220,912.

Purpose and activities: The trust awards scholarships to undergraduate students for the purpose of attending an accredited college or university full time.

Fields of interest: Education; Higher education.

Type of support: Scholarships.

Limitations: Applications accepted. Giving through scholarships are limited to residents of GA, particularly Bibb County and its surrounding counties of Crawford, Houston, Jones, Monroe, Peach and Twiggs, and to undergraduate students who plan to attend college in Macon, GA, at Wesleyan College or Mercer University.

Publications: Informational brochure (including application guidelines).

Application information: See foundation web site for complete application guidelines. Application form required.

Initial approach: Proposal

Copies of proposal: 1

Deadline(s): Jun. 1

Trustees: R.A. Bowen, Jr.; Robert A. Bowen III; Charles H. Yates.

Number of staff: 1 part-time support.

EIN: 586032145

2448
The Virginia & Charles Brewer Family Foundation
(formerly The McHenry Foundation)
229 The Prado
Atlanta, GA 30309-3335

Established in 1999 in Georgia.
Donor: Charles M. Brewer.
Foundation type: Independent foundation.
Financial data (yr. ended 06/30/13): Assets, $4,931,524 (M); expenditures, $215,858; qualifying distributions, $212,332; giving activities include $210,832 for 61 grants (high: $38,333; low: $250).
Fields of interest: Ballet; Education; Elementary and secondary education; Environment; Environmental justice; Zoos; Human services.
Type of support: Equal access.
Limitations: Applications not accepted. Giving primarily in Atlanta, GA. No grants to individuals.
Application information: Unsolicited requests for funds not accepted.
Trustee: Charles M. Brewer.
Distribution Committee: Virginia F. Brewer.
EIN: 586396904

2449
The Broadfield Foundation
P.O. Box 30351
Sea Island, GA 31561-0351

Established in 2003 in Georgia.
Donor: Alfred W. Jones III.
Foundation type: Independent foundation.
Financial data (yr. ended 12/31/13): Assets, $1,014,316 (M); expenditures, $245,409; qualifying distributions, $226,586; giving activities include $226,586 for 24 grants (high: $40,000; low: $25).
Purpose and activities: Giving primarily for education, historical societies, and environmental conservation.
Fields of interest: Historic preservation; Higher education; Natural resources; Biodiversity; Wildlife biodiversity; Foundations; Nonprofits; Protestantism; Child welfare; Youth services.
Type of support: Regranting.
Limitations: Applications not accepted. Giving primarily in GA. No grants to individuals.
Application information: Contributes only to pre-selected organizations.
Trustee: Alfred W. Jones III.
Distribution Committee: Sarah Hopper Jones; Davis Love III.
EIN: 586462442

2450
Finn Brooks Family Foundation, Inc.
1775 S. Ponce de Leon Ave.
Atlanta, GA 30307-1784

Established in 2007 in New York.
Donors: Martha Finn Brooks; Oliver Brooks, Jr.
Foundation type: Independent foundation.
Financial data (yr. ended 12/31/13): Assets, $2,910,675 (M); expenditures, $231,656; qualifying distributions, $218,000; giving activities include $218,000 for 10 grants (high: $100,000; low: $3,000).
Fields of interest: Education; Nonprofits.
Type of support: Regranting.
Limitations: Applications not accepted. No grants to individuals.
Application information: Unsolicited requests for funds not accepted.
Officers: Oliver Brooks, Jr., Chair. and Pres.; Martha Finn Brooks, C.F.O. and Secy.-Treas.
EIN: 261324841

2451
The Thomas C. Burke Foundation
c/o Bank of America, N.A.
3414 Peachtree Rd. NE, Ste. 1475, GA7-813-14-04
Atlanta, GA 30326-1113
E-mail: ga.grantmaking@ustrust.com; Main
URL: https://www.bankofamerica.com/philanthropic/grantmaking.go

Established in 1965 in Georgia.
Donor: Thomas C. Burke†.
Foundation type: Independent foundation.
Financial data (yr. ended 09/30/14): Assets, $6,592,706 (M); gifts received, $520; expenditures, $330,729; qualifying distributions, $285,461; giving activities include $269,848 for 8 grants (high: $80,000; low: $21,750).
Purpose and activities: The foundation has a strong interest in programs focused on cancer prevention and treatment. The foundation specifically serves Bibb County, Georgia and its surrounding communities.
Fields of interest: Patient social services; Cancers.
Limitations: Applications accepted. Giving in Bibb County, GA and its surrounding communities.
Application information:
  Initial approach: Consult online guidelines on foundation web site
  Deadline(s): July 1
Trustee: Bank of America, N.A.
Advisory Board Members: Mrs. John D. Comer; Cheryl Jones, MD; Donald Rhame, MD.
EIN: 586047627

2452
Walter G. Canipe Foundation
3336 Cochise Dr.
Atlanta, GA 30339-4321
Contact: W. Kent Canipe, Pres.

Established in 1985 in North Carolina.
Foundation type: Independent foundation.
Financial data (yr. ended 06/30/13): Assets, $2,918,212 (M); expenditures, $165,226; qualifying distributions, $138,000; giving activities include $138,000 for 38 grants (high: $17,000; low: $500).
Purpose and activities: Giving primarily for education, religious institutions, and children and youth services.
Fields of interest: Education; Protestantism; Human services.
Limitations: Applications accepted. Giving primarily in GA. No grants to individuals.
Application information: Application form required.
  Initial approach: Letter
  Deadline(s): None
  Board meeting date(s): June
Officers: W. Kent Canipe, Pres. and Treas.; Jane Canipe Rooks, V.P. and Secy.
Directors: Anne Canipe; Virginia Canipe; Dennis Rooks.

Number of staff: None.
EIN: 581712262

2453
John Huland Carmical Foundation, Inc.
c/o John G. Alston, Sr.
87 W. Paces Ferry Rd.
Atlanta, GA 30305-1310 (404) 574-6540
FAX: (404) 574-6545;
E-mail: bupchurch@alstons.com

Foundation type: Independent foundation.
Financial data (yr. ended 12/31/13): Assets, $5,102,253 (M); expenditures, $199,847; qualifying distributions, $182,550; giving activities include $165,000 for 4 grants (high: $70,000; low: $20,000).
Fields of interest: University education.
Type of support: Scholarships.
Limitations: Applications accepted. Giving primarily in Athens, GA and PA. No grants to individuals.
Application information: Unsolicited requests for funds generally not accepted.
  Initial approach: Letter
  Copies of proposal: 2
  Deadline(s): June 30
  Board meeting date(s): July and Dec.
Officer and Trustee: John G. Alston, Pres. and Trustee.
Director: Blain A. Upchurch.
Number of staff: 1 part-time professional.
EIN: 582348810

2454
Carters Charitable Foundation, Inc.
3438 Peachtree Rd.
Atlanta, GA 30326-1554

Donor: William Carter Company.
Foundation type: Independent foundation.
Financial data (yr. ended 12/31/13): Assets, $1,336,212 (M); gifts received, $12,154; expenditures, $205,040; qualifying distributions, $205,000; giving activities include $205,000 for 6 grants (high: $50,000; low: $12,500).
Fields of interest: Nonprofits; Diseases and conditions; Human services.
Type of support: Regranting.
Limitations: Applications not accepted. Giving primarily in GA and NJ.
Application information: Unsolicited requests for funds not accepted.
Officers: Michael D. Casey, Pres.; Michael Wu, Secy.; Richard F. Westenberger, Treas.
EIN: 274165605

2455
The Chandler Foundation, Inc.
750 Park Ave. N.E., Apt. 24N
Atlanta, GA 30326-3268

Established in 1986 in Georgia.
Donor: A. Russell Chandler III.
Foundation type: Independent foundation.
Financial data (yr. ended 06/30/13): Assets, $5,104,901 (M); gifts received, $25,000; expenditures, $366,703; qualifying distributions, $336,902; giving activities include $336,902 for 18 grants (high: $218,700; low: $90).

Purpose and activities: Giving primarily for education, health organizations, human services, children's services, and religion, including a Presbyterian church.
Fields of interest: Education; Diseases and conditions; Protestantism; Human services; Child welfare.
Limitations: Applications not accepted. Giving limited to northern GA, and the metropolitan Atlanta area. No grants to individuals.
Application information: Unsolicited requests for funds not accepted.
Directors: A. Russell Chandler III; Ashley E. Chandler; Maria Planes Chandler; Morgan A. Chandler; Whitney R. Chandler; Gearl Spicer; Patricia Walker.
EIN: 581672017

2456
The Charter Foundation, Inc.
P.O. Box 472
West Point, GA   31833-0472   (706) 645-1391

Established in 1995 in Alabama.
Foundation type: Independent foundation.
Financial data (yr. ended 12/31/14): Assets, $7,710,605; expenditures, $429,005; qualifying distributions, $367,972.
Fields of interest: Arts and culture; Historic preservation; Education; Community and economic development; Human services; Child welfare; Youth development.
Type of support: Scholarships; General support; Student aid.
Limitations: Applications accepted. Giving limited to Chambers and Lee counties, AL, and Troup County, GA.
Application information:
 Initial approach: Letter
 Copies of proposal: 1
 Deadline(s): Aug. 1
 Board meeting date(s): 2nd Tues. of Feb., May, Aug., and Nov.
 Final notification: Within 1 week of May and Nov. board meetings
Officers: Robert L. Johnson, Pres.; William C. Gladden, V.P.; Bonnie F. Bonner, Secy.
Directors: Beverlye Brady; Nancy Durand; Shirley Flora; Pippa Larson; Peggy Tauton Nunn; Edward Smith; Monroe Smith; Trish Strobel.
EIN: 582144961

2457
The Chatham Foundation
(formerly Savannah Foods Foundation)
P.O. Box 1313
Savannah, GA   31402-1313

Established in 1953 in Georgia.
Foundation type: Independent foundation.
Financial data (yr. ended 12/31/13): Assets, $6,167,392 (M); expenditures, $351,787; qualifying distributions, $305,468; giving activities include $275,000 for 88 grants (high: $25,000; low: $100).
Purpose and activities: Giving primarily for education and human services.
Fields of interest: Arts and culture; Education; Nonprofits; Health; Diseases and conditions; Human services; Family services; Child welfare.

Type of support: General support; Annual campaigns; Capital and infrastructure; Endowments; Regranting.
Limitations: Applications not accepted. Giving primarily in Savannah, GA. No grants to individuals.
Application information: Contributes only to pre-selected organizations.
 Board meeting date(s): 1st Tues. in June and Dec.
Officers: Benjamin Oxnard III, Chair.; Odilo Blanco, Secy.
Trustees: Courtney Flexon; Marion McKenna; William W. Sprague, Jr.; William W. Sprague III.
EIN: 586033047

2458
Chesed, Inc.
c/o Marcus Family Office, LLC
1266 W. Paces Ferry Rd., Ste. 615
Atlanta, GA   30327-2306

Established in 1993 in Georgia.
Donor: Frederick R. Marcus.
Foundation type: Independent foundation.
Financial data (yr. ended 12/31/13): Assets, $6,642,962 (M); expenditures, $454,777; qualifying distributions, $377,092; giving activities include $357,632 for 19 grants (high: $140,000; low: $100).
Purpose and activities: Giving primarily for Jewish education and organizations.
Fields of interest: Secondary education; Higher education; Judaism.
Limitations: Applications not accepted. Giving primarily in Atlanta, GA, and Glendale, WI. No grants to individuals.
Application information: Contributes only to pre-selected organizations.
Officers and Directors: Frederick R. Marcus, Pres.; Sara Ognibene Loft, Secy. and Director; Douglas Dinapoli, Treas.; Nancy Dubois Marcus; Frederick Slagle.
EIN: 580231691

2459
J. Donald Childress Foundation, Inc.
300 Galleria Pkwy. N.W., Ste. 200
Atlanta, GA   30339-3149

Established in 1998 in Georgia.
Donor: J. Donald Childress.
Foundation type: Independent foundation.
Financial data (yr. ended 12/31/13): Assets, $6,843,300 (M); expenditures, $346,110; qualifying distributions, $344,850; giving activities include $344,850 for 5 grants (high: $255,000; low: $1,000).
Fields of interest: Education; Human services.
Limitations: Applications not accepted. No grants to individuals.
Application information: Contributes only to pre-selected organizations.
Officer: J. Donald Childress, Pres. and C.E.O.
EIN: 582436179

2460
The John and Therese Church Family
 Foundation, Inc.
1502 N. Thornton Ave.
Dalton, GA   30720-3064

Established in 2007 in Georgia.
Donors: John Clayton Church; Therese Maxwell Church.
Foundation type: Independent foundation.
Financial data (yr. ended 12/31/13): Assets, $6,492,373 (M); gifts received, $1,776,801; expenditures, $258,167; qualifying distributions, $222,538; giving activities include $222,538 for grants.
Fields of interest: Higher education; Religion.
Type of support: Scholarships.
Limitations: Applications not accepted.
Application information: Unsolicited requests for funds not accepted.
Officers: Therese Maxwell Church, Pres.; John Clayton Church, V.P.; William A. Ponder, Secy.-Treas.
EIN: 260599298

2461
Churches Homes Foundation, Inc.
c/o Buckhead Capital Mgmt.
3330 Cumberland Blvd., Ste. 650
Atlanta, GA   30339-8124
Application address: c/o V. Faye White, 3475 Piedmont Rd. N.E., Atlanta, GA 30305, tel.: (404) 995-3052

Established in 1984 in Georgia.
Donor: Keane Corporation.
Foundation type: Independent foundation.
Financial data (yr. ended 03/31/15): Assets, $5,695,774 (M); expenditures, $449,366; qualifying distributions, $372,741; giving activities include $372,741 for 49 grants (high: $76,786; low: $500).
Purpose and activities: Awards scholarships to individuals in financial need with prior satisfactory academic performance; support also for youth and social services.
Fields of interest: Higher education; Graduate and professional education; Medical education; Theology; Scouting programs.
Type of support: General support; Student aid.
Limitations: Applications accepted. Giving primarily to organizations and residents of the metropolitan Atlanta, GA area.
Application information: Individuals should submit a brief resume of previous academic performances and references from previous instructors. A personal interview will then be arranged. Application form required.
 Initial approach: Letter
 Deadline(s): None
Officers: J. Thomas Kilpatrick, Pres.; Winsome Hawkins, V.P.; Robert S. Wiggins, Jr., V.P.; Beverly D. Hanson, Secy.; Claire Lewis Arnold, Treas.
EIN: 580568689

2462
Eugene M. Clary Foundation Inc.
P.O. Box 669065
Marietta, GA   30066-0102

Established in 1997 in Georgia.
Donor: Eugene M. Clary†.
Foundation type: Independent foundation.
Financial data (yr. ended 12/31/13): Assets, $8,697,924 (M); expenditures, $500,672; qualifying distributions, $353,918; giving activities

include $282,448 for 23 grants (high: $65,145; low: $360).
Fields of interest: Nonprofits; Christianity.
Limitations: Applications not accepted. Giving primarily in GA. No grants to individuals.
Application information: Unsolicited requests for funds not accepted.
Officers and Trustees: Kenneth B. Clary, C.E.O. and Trustee; Mary S. Teague, Secy.-Treas.; Jean Clary; Nancy Lee Oxford.
EIN: 582310406

2463
The Cobb Community Foundation
240 Interstate N. Pkwy.
Atlanta, GA   30339   (770) 859-2329
Contact: Tommy Allegood, Exec. Dir.
FAX: (770) 690-4029;
E-mail: info@cobbfoundation.org; Mailing address: PO Box 671868, Marietta, GA 30006-0032; Main URL: http://www.cobbfoundation.com
Facebook: https://www.facebook.com/pages/Cobb-Community-Foundation/186458158156819?ref=stream

Established in 1993 in Georgia.
Foundation type: Community foundation.
Financial data (yr. ended 12/31/12): Assets, $3,827,413 (M); gifts received, $864,830; expenditures, $538,086; giving activities include $336,435 for 11+ grants (high: $90,000).
Purpose and activities: The foundation invests in solutions to solve Cobb County's civic, educational, health, human service, and cultural challenges.
Fields of interest: Arts and culture; Education; Environment; Health; Community and economic development; Human services.
Limitations: Applications accepted. Giving primarily in Cobb County, GA.
Application information: Visit foundation web site for application information.
Officers and Directors: Dale Hughes, Chair. and Director; Shari Martin, Vice-Chair. and Treas. and Director; Tommy Allegood, Exec. Dir.; Tommy Barrow; Bruce Clayton; David S. Fisher; Spencer Gelernter, Ph.D; Kim Gresh; Steve Imler; Johnny Johnson; Leslie Kehoe; Dr. Jack Kennedy; Michael W. Knowles; Charlie Leonard; J. Kevin Moore; Pete Quinones; James L. Rhoden, Jr.; Victor Sanchez; Timothy S. Sheehan; Randy Shrum; Rose Wing.
Advisory Board: Gary T. Bottoms; Douglas H. Chaffins; Ronald H. Francis; Rick Hamilton; Hon. G. Conley Ingram; Robert R. Kiser; Lisa Olens; Thomas H. Rogers III; Calder Sinclair; Jack Wilson.
EIN: 205652970

2464
The Edward Colston Foundation, Inc.
299 Glencastle Dr.
Atlanta, GA   30327-4823

Established in 1988 in Georgia.
Donors: Edward C. Mitchell, Jr.; Virginia C. Mitchell.
Foundation type: Independent foundation.
Financial data (yr. ended 12/31/13): Assets, $6,763,281 (M); expenditures, $278,052; qualifying distributions, $236,000; giving activities include $236,000 for 32 grants (high: $20,000; low: $2,500).
Fields of interest: Elementary and secondary education; Higher education; Nonprofits; Health;

Specialty hospital care; Protestantism; Catholicism; Child welfare; Homeless services.
Type of support: Regranting.
Limitations: Applications not accepted. Giving primarily in Atlanta, GA. No grants to individuals.
Application information: Contributes only to pre-selected organizations.
Officers and Directors: Edward C. Mitchell, Jr., Pres. and Director; Jennifer B. Hovis, Secy.; Dustin Martin; Amanda K. Mitchell; Edward C. Mitchell III; Virginia C. Mitchell.
EIN: 581818739

2465
Community Enterprises, Inc.
P.O. Box 1089
Thomaston, GA   30286-0014   (706) 647-7684
Contact: Neil H. Hightower Sr., Pres.

Established in 1944 in Georgia.
Donors: Julian T. Hightower†; Thomaston Cotton Mills.
Foundation type: Independent foundation.
Financial data (yr. ended 06/30/13): Assets, $7,991,618 (M); expenditures, $370,080; qualifying distributions, $318,440; giving activities include $304,850 for 29 grants (high: $50,000; low: $705).
Purpose and activities: Giving primarily for education, community development, human services, and to Protestant churches.
Fields of interest: Education; Elementary and secondary education; Higher education; Community and economic development; Protestantism; Human services.
Limitations: Applications accepted. Giving primarily in GA, within approximately 100 miles of Thomaston, GA; also some giving to the City of Thomaston and County of Upson, Georgia. No grants to individuals.
Application information:
   Initial approach: Letter
   Deadline(s): Dec. 31
Officers and Trustees: Neil H. Hightower, Sr., Pres. and Trustee; George H. Hightower, Jr., V.P. and Trustee; H. Stewart Davis, Secy.-Treas. and Trustee; John S. Davis; John B. Hightower; Neil H. Hightower, Jr.; William H. Hightower IV.
EIN: 586043415

2466
Community Welfare Association of Colquitt County, GA
P.O. Box 38
Moultrie, GA   31776-0038   (229) 985-5210
Contact: William J. Vereen, Tr.

Established in 1937 in Georgia.
Donors: Lottie T. Vereen†; W.C. Vereen Trust.
Foundation type: Independent foundation.
Financial data (yr. ended 12/31/13): Assets, $4,398,198 (M); expenditures, $282,782; qualifying distributions, $236,675; giving activities include $229,175 for 1 grant, and $7,500 for 6 grants to individuals (high: $2,250; low: $750).
Purpose and activities: Giving primarily for the arts, health care, and human services; scholarships awarded to graduates of Colquitt County High School in Moultrie, GA, who attend an accredited college for higher education.

Fields of interest: Arts and culture; Elementary and secondary education; Higher education; Nonprofits; Health; Diseases and conditions; Community and economic development; Christianity; Human services; Child welfare; Youth services; Low-income and poor people.
Type of support: General support; Student aid; Research and evaluation; Regranting.
Limitations: Applications accepted. Giving limited to GA, with emphasis on Colquitt County.
Application information: Application form available for scholarships. Application form required.
   Initial approach: Proposal
   Deadline(s): None
Trustees: Barbara B. Vereen; Harvey B. Vereen; William J. Vereen.
EIN: 586032259

2467
Connolly Family Foundation, Inc.
3971 Club Dr.
Atlanta, GA   30319-1146

Donors: John L. Connolly; Leigh Z. Connolly.
Foundation type: Independent foundation.
Financial data (yr. ended 06/30/13): Assets, $27,159,022 (M); gifts received, $25,000,000; expenditures, $589,495; qualifying distributions, $482,621; giving activities include $407,350 for 24 grants (high: $64,850; low: $1,000).
Fields of interest: Diseases and conditions; Cancers; Agriculture; Human services.
Type of support: General support; Research.
Limitations: Applications not accepted. Giving primarily in GA.
Application information: Unsolicited requests for funds not accepted.
Officers: John L. Connolly, Pres.; Joe Hall, Secy.; Leigh Z. Connolly, Treas.
EIN: 460809078

2468
Claude P. Cook, Sr. Charitable Trust
c/o Suntrust Bank
P.O. Box 4248
Macon, GA   31208-4248
Application address: c/o Distribution Committee, 541 Burketts Ferry Rd., Hazlehurst, GA 31539, tel.: (912) 375-2712

Established in 2004 in Georgia.
Donor: Claude P. Cook, Sr.†.
Foundation type: Independent foundation.
Financial data (yr. ended 12/31/14): Assets, $4,543,588; expenditures, $291,661; qualifying distributions, $215,000.
Fields of interest: Education; Religion; Sports and recreation.
Type of support: Capital and infrastructure; Equipment.
Limitations: Applications accepted. Giving limited to Jefferson Davis County, GA.
Application information: Application form required.
   Initial approach: Request application form
   Deadline(s): Dec. 1 of each year
Trustee: SunTrust Bank Middle GA.
EIN: 336339018

2469
Frederick E. Cooper and Helen Dykes Cooper Charitable Foundation, Inc.
170 W. Paces Ferry Rd. N.E.
Atlanta, GA 30305-1352 (404) 467-0905

Established in 1998 in Florida.
Donors: Frederick E. Cooper; Helen D. Cooper.
Foundation type: Independent foundation.
Financial data (yr. ended 09/30/14): Assets, $7,258,715 (M); expenditures, $505,217; qualifying distributions, $309,314; giving activities include $307,525 for 10 grants (high: $175,000; low: $325).
Fields of interest: Art museums; Historic preservation; Higher education; Health; Cancers; Christianity; Human services.
Type of support: General support.
Limitations: Applications accepted. Giving primarily in GA, NC and VA.
Application information: Application form required.
  Initial approach: Proposal
  Deadline(s): None
Directors: Beckwith Archer Cooper; Frederick E. Cooper; Frederick E. Cooper, Jr.; Johnson Joseph Cooper; Bernard Lanigan, Jr.
EIN: 582433546

2470
Davison Bruce Foundation
c/o SunTrust Bank
P.O. Box 4655, MC 221
Atlanta, GA 30302-4655 (404) 588-7347
Contact: Emily Butler, Grants Mgr., SunTrust Bank
E-mail: fdnsvcs.ga@suntrust.com; Main URL: http://www.davisonbrucefoundation.org

Established in 2005 in Georgia.
Donor: Elizabeth Davison Bruce.
Foundation type: Independent foundation.
Financial data (yr. ended 12/31/13): Assets, $14,773,448 (M); gifts received, $10,000,011; expenditures, $412,764; qualifying distributions, $355,240; giving activities include $251,121 for 26 grants (high: $30,000; low: $400).
Fields of interest: Education; Foundations; Libraries; Human services.
Limitations: Applications accepted. Giving in GA.
Application information: Connection to the Bruce family is strongly encouraged before sending an application.
  Deadline(s): Feb. 1
Trustee: SunTrust Bank.
EIN: 206565366

2471
Waldo DeLoache Testamentary Charitable Trust
25 2nd Ave., S.W.
Moultrie, GA 31768-4570 (229) 873-3870
Contact: Steve Johnson

Established in 2007 in Georgia.
Donor: Waldo DeLoache†.
Foundation type: Independent foundation.
Financial data (yr. ended 12/31/13): Assets, $2,955,147 (M); gifts received, $63,283; expenditures, $185,979; qualifying distributions, $138,111; giving activities include $138,111 for 9 grants (high: $50,000; low: $2,126).

Fields of interest: Education; Foundations; Human services.
Limitations: Applications accepted. Giving primarily in GA.
Application information: Application form required.
  Initial approach: Proposal
  Deadline(s): None
Trustee: Southwest Georgia Bank.
EIN: 261638674

2472
The Echlin Foundation Inc
8 Priory Rd.
Savannah, GA 31411-1731

Established in 1960 in Connecticut.
Donors: John E. Echlin; Beryl G. Echlin.
Foundation type: Independent foundation.
Financial data (yr. ended 11/30/13): Assets, $8,320,087 (M); expenditures, $354,309; qualifying distributions, $308,000; giving activities include $308,000 for 19 grants (high: $64,000; low: $8,000).
Purpose and activities: Giving primarily for medical research and for health care.
Fields of interest: Higher education; Nonprofits; Health; Hospital care; Hospice care; Diseases and conditions; Human services; Youth development.
Type of support: Research; Regranting.
Limitations: Applications not accepted. No grants to individuals.
Application information: Unsolicited requests for funds not accepted.
Trustees: John E. Echlin, Jr.; Jane Kammerer.
EIN: 066037282

2473
Eden Charitable Foundation, Inc.
9182 Selborne Ln.
Palmetto, GA 30268

Donor: Carl Lynn Eden.
Foundation type: Independent foundation.
Financial data (yr. ended 12/31/13): Assets, $3,770,957 (M); expenditures, $192,601; qualifying distributions, $155,502; giving activities include $152,102 for 5 grants (high: $115,000; low: $1,000).
Fields of interest: Orchestral music.
Limitations: Applications not accepted. Giving primarily in Atlanta, GA.
Application information: Unsolicited requests for funds not accepted.
Officer: Carol Lynn Eden, Mgr.
EIN: 454093034

2474
The Florence C. and Harry L. English Memorial Fund
c/o SunTrust Bank
P.O. Box 4418, MC041
Atlanta, GA 30302-4655 (404) 588-8250
Contact: Kirby A. Thompson, Secy.
FAX: (404) 724-3082; Main URL: http://www.suntrust.com/microsites/foundation/application_info.htm

Established in 1964 in Georgia.
Donor: Florence Cruft English†.
Foundation type: Independent foundation.

Financial data (yr. ended 12/31/14): Assets, $16,883,539 (M); expenditures, $432,367; qualifying distributions, $383,823; giving activities include $345,000 for 8 grants (high: $75,000; low: $25,000).
Purpose and activities: Grants only for education, health, general welfare, and culture, with emphasis on assisting the aged and chronically ill, the blind, and those persons generally designated as being underprivileged.
Fields of interest: Arts and culture; Education; Higher education; Community and economic development.
Type of support: Capital and infrastructure; Capital campaigns; Equipment; Land acquisitions.
Limitations: Applications accepted. Giving limited to the metropolitan Atlanta, GA, area. No support for veterans' organizations or organizations which have not been operating without a deficit for at least a year. No grants to individuals, or for general operating support, maintenance, or for debt service; no loans.
Application information: Application form required.
  Initial approach: See foundation web site for online application. Required attachments can be in Microsoft Word or Excel or Adobe PDF format. Do not include compressed ZIP files
  Copies of proposal: 1
  Deadline(s): Mar. 31, Aug. 31, and Nov. 30
  Board meeting date(s): Jan., May and Oct.
Trustee: SunTrust Bank, Inc.
Number of staff: 1 full-time professional.
EIN: 586045781

2475
The Enterline Foundation
2699 Buford Hwy.
Buford, GA 30518-6051 (770) 271-3032
E-mail: info@enterlinefoundation.org; Main URL: http://www.enterlinefoundation.org

Established in 2001 in Unspecified.
Donors: Larry L. Enterline; Vulcan Holdings, Inc.; Joseph Massoud; Compass Group Management, LLC.
Foundation type: Independent foundation.
Financial data (yr. ended 12/31/13): Assets, $626,260 (M); gifts received, $182,085; expenditures, $224,902; qualifying distributions, $219,512; giving activities include $133,926 for 18 grants (high: $25,000; low: $500).
Purpose and activities: The foundation was established to provide financial resources to improve the lives of individuals with mental retardation and developmental disabilities, historically designating 80 percent of its contributions to such organizations. The foundation also makes contributions to other organizations that serve broad charitable purposes, such as the American Cancer Society, the Humane Society, and the American Heart Association.
Fields of interest: Environment; Diseases and conditions; Human services.
Type of support: General support.
Limitations: Applications accepted. Giving primarily in GA, NC, and OH. No grants to individuals.
Application information: See foundation website for complete application guidelines.
  Initial approach: Contact Foundation
Trustees: Louis S. Baga; Larry L. Enterline; Keith E. Pugh; Kathleen M. Richards; Anthony P. Rivera; Phillip C. Thornberry.
EIN: 036073689

2476
The Exposition Foundation
P.O. Box 421099
Atlanta, GA   30342-8099

Established in 1950 in Georgia.
Donor: Frances F. Cocke.
Foundation type: Independent foundation.
Financial data (yr. ended 08/31/13): Assets, $2,095,854 (M); expenditures, $200,841; qualifying distributions, $182,500; giving activities include $182,500 for 9 grants (high: $80,500; low: $1,000).
Purpose and activities: Giving primarily for historical preservation, higher education, particularly a university for agricultural sciences, and natural resources.
Fields of interest: Historic preservation; Higher education; Botanical gardens; Environmental studies; Nonprofits; Human services.
Type of support: General support; Annual campaigns; Capital campaigns; Capital and infrastructure; Equipment; Endowments; Regranting; Program development; Scholarships.
Limitations: Applications not accepted. Giving primarily in Atlanta, GA.
Publications: Annual report.
Application information: Contributes only to pre-selected organizations.
  Board meeting date(s): Varies
Officers: Jane Cocke Black, Pres.; James Floyd Black, V.P.; Dameron Black III, V.P.; Dameron Black IV, V.P.
EIN: 586043273

2477
Faith Ventures Foundation, Inc.
748 Iron Mountain Rd.
Canton, GA   30115-7300

Established in 2002 in Georgia.
Donors: The William M. and Phyllis B. Johnson Foundation, Inc.; Matthew Johnson; Johnson Supporting Foundation.
Foundation type: Independent foundation.
Financial data (yr. ended 12/31/13): Assets, $6,889,544 (M); gifts received, $2,234,423; expenditures, $408,465; qualifying distributions, $328,449; giving activities include $328,449 for 24 grants (high: $98,000; low: $500).
Purpose and activities: Giving primarily to United Methodist and other Christian organizations and churches; funding also for social services.
Fields of interest: Christianity; Presbyterianism; Human services.
International interests: Kenya.
Limitations: Applications not accepted. Giving primarily in FL and GA; with some giving in Kenya. No grants to individuals.
Application information: Contributes only to pre-selected organizations.
Officers: William M. Johnson, Pres. and Treas.; Phyllis B. Johnson, V.P. and Secy.
Trustees: Matthew S. Johnson; Russell M. Johnson; Ryan W. Johnson.
EIN: 820554456

2478
Fickling Family Foundation Inc.
P.O. Box 1976
Macon, GA   31202-1976   (478) 742-6601
Contact: Tom B. Wight, Secy.-Treas.

Established in 1995 in Georgia.
Donors: William A. Fickling, Jr.; Julia F. Tiller; Roy H. Fickling; Neva L. Fickling; William A. Fickling III; Jane F. Skinner.
Foundation type: Independent foundation.
Financial data (yr. ended 12/31/13): Assets, $5,932,779 (M); gifts received, $1,200,000; expenditures, $350,871; qualifying distributions, $297,859; giving activities include $289,329 for 16 grants (high: $100,000; low: $500).
Fields of interest: Arts and culture; Museums; Education; Community and economic development; Protestantism; Human services.
Type of support: Policy, advocacy and systems reform.
Limitations: Applications accepted. Giving primarily in the Macon and Bibb County, GA, area; with some giving in TX. No grants to individuals or private foundations.
Application information: Application form required.
  Initial approach: Proposal
  Copies of proposal: 8
  Deadline(s): Nov. 1
  Board meeting date(s): Nov. or Dec.
Officers and Directors: William A. Fickling, Jr., Pres. and Director; Neva L. Fickling, V.P. and Director; Roy H. Fickling, V.P. and Director; William A. Fickling III, V.P. and Director; Jane Fickling Skinner, V.P. and Director; Julia C. Fickling Tiller, V.P. and Director; Tom B. Wight, Secy.-Treas. and Director.
EIN: 582142231

2479
The Forehand Family Foundation
1753 Pine Ridge Dr., N.E.
Atlanta, GA   30324-4937   (229) 938-5156
Contact: David A. Forehand Jr., Tr.

Donors: David A. Forehand, Jr.; Elizabeth G. Forehand.
Foundation type: Independent foundation.
Financial data (yr. ended 12/31/13): Assets, $1,263,823 (M); expenditures, $201,767; qualifying distributions, $174,210; giving activities include $172,020 for 4 grants (high: $85,000; low: $4,220).
Fields of interest: Education; Housing development; Religion.
Application information:
  Initial approach: Proposal
  Deadline(s): None
Trustees: David A. Forehand, Jr.; Elizabeth G. Forehand.
EIN: 276368488

2480
TIF Foundation Fnd
(formerly The Iverson Foundation)
P.O. Box 250
Decatur, GA   30031-0250

Established in 2006 in Georgia.
Donor: Michelle A. Iverson Trust.
Foundation type: Independent foundation.

Financial data (yr. ended 12/31/14): Assets, $6,785,337 (M); expenditures, $367,984; qualifying distributions, $313,000; giving activities include $313,000 for 31 grants (high: $36,000; low: $2,000).
Fields of interest: Arts and culture; Diseases and conditions; Human services.
Limitations: Applications not accepted.
Application information: Unsolicited requests for funds not accepted.
Directors: Wendy M. Austin-Keevil; Robert Michael F. Iverson.
EIN: 352275342

2481
The Frank Family Foundation, Inc.
920 Crest Valley Dr., N.W.
Atlanta, GA   30327-4530

Established in 1994 in Georgia.
Donors: Larry Frank; Adam Frank; Isaac Frank; M. Joshua Frank; Aaron Frank; Emet Corp.
Foundation type: Independent foundation.
Financial data (yr. ended 12/31/13): Assets, $8,013,960 (M); expenditures, $362,540; qualifying distributions, $292,022; giving activities include $292,022 for 118 grants (high: $20,602; low: $50).
Purpose and activities: Giving primarily to Jewish agencies and temples.
Fields of interest: Health; Sports and recreation; Human services.
Limitations: Applications not accepted. Giving primarily in CA and GA. No grants to individuals.
Application information: Contributes only to pre-selected organizations.
Officers: Larry Frank, Chair.; Lois Frank, Pres.; Adam Frank, Secy.; M. Joshua Frank, Treas.
Directors: Aaron Frank; Isaac Frank.
EIN: 582082981

2482
Philip and Irene Toll Gage Foundation
3414 Peachtree Rd., Ste. 722
Atlanta, GA   30326-1166

Established in 1985 in Georgia.
Donor: Betty G. Holland†.
Foundation type: Independent foundation.
Financial data (yr. ended 11/30/13): Assets, $8,441,795 (M); expenditures, $425,289; qualifying distributions, $359,976; giving activities include $338,500 for 26 grants (high: $50,000; low: $1,000).
Purpose and activities: Support for education, culture, including the arts and theater, and hospitals and health services; some funding also for Protestant agencies and churches.
Fields of interest: Arts and culture; Theater; Museums; Education; Environment; Animal welfare; Health; Hospital care; Diseases and conditions; Community and economic development; Protestantism; Child welfare.
International interests: England; Italy.
Type of support: General support; Annual campaigns; Capital and infrastructure; Regranting; Fundraising.
Limitations: Applications not accepted. Giving primarily outside of the U.S. No grants to individuals, or for endowment programs.

Application information: Unsolicited requests for funds will not be accepted.

Board meeting date(s): Annually in May or June

Trustee: Larry Hooks.

Number of staff: 1 part-time professional.

EIN: 581727394

2483
Allan C. and Leila J. Garden Foundation

c/o U.S. Trust, Bank of America, N.A.
3414 Peachtree Rd. NE, Ste. 1475, GA7-813-14-04
Atlanta, GA   30326-1113   (404) 264-1377
E-mail: quanda.allen@ustrust.com; Main
URL: https://www.bankofamerica.com/
philanthropic/grantmaking.go

Established in 1972 in Georgia.

Foundation type: Independent foundation.

Financial data (yr. ended 05/31/14): Assets, $5,269,407 (M); expenditures, $252,546; qualifying distributions, $194,849; giving activities include $175,625 for 42 grants (high: $25,000; low: $1,750).

Purpose and activities: The mission of the foundation is to support charitable organizations that maintain, care, and educate orphan or underprivileged children. It is also the foundation's intent to support organizations that provide medical, dental, hospital care, nursing, and treatment of physically handicapped children.

Type of support: Loans to individuals.

Limitations: Applications accepted. Giving primarily in Ben Hill, Irwin, and Wilcox counties in Georgia.

Application information:
Initial approach: Online via foundation web site
Deadline(s): June 1

Trustee: Bank of America, N.A.

EIN: 586103546

2484
Georgia Health Foundation, Inc.

3050 Peachtree Rd., Ste. 270
Atlanta, GA   30305-2283   (404) 658-9066
Contact: John Borek, Treas.
E-mail: info@gahealthfdn.org; Main URL: http://
www.gahealthfdn.org
Grants List: http://gahealthfdn.org/
grants-awarded-in-2013

Established in 1985 in Georgia.

Donor: Georgia Medical Plan, Inc.

Foundation type: Independent foundation.

Financial data (yr. ended 12/31/13): Assets, $10,087,648 (M); expenditures, $466,160; qualifying distributions, $402,360; giving activities include $326,250 for 47 grants (high: $25,000).

Purpose and activities: Giving for public health education, as well as for health-related projects and programs in GA. Consideration is given to proposals that are of local importance, and to opportunities that may address regional and national issues.

Fields of interest: Graduate and professional education; Medical education; Health; Public health; Diseases and conditions.

Type of support: General support; Matching grants; Equipment; Program development; Convening; Publications; Research; Seed money; Research and evaluation.

Limitations: Applications accepted. Giving limited to GA.

Publications: Application guidelines; Grants list; Informational brochure (including application guidelines).

Application information: Between Jan. 1 and May 1, submit a thorough request outlining the project or proposal. Complete application guidelines and procedures are available on foundation web site.
Initial approach: Outline of the project or proposal (3 page limit)
Copies of proposal: 1
Deadline(s): Aug. 1 final deadline
Board meeting date(s): Feb., May, Aug., and Nov.

Officers and Directors: Martha Katz, Chair. and Director; Nancy M. Paris, Vice-Chair. and Director; S. Jarvin Levison, J.D., Secy. and Director; John M. Borek, Jr., Ph.D, Treas. and Director; Jaquelin Gottieb, MD; Robert L. Zwald.

Number of staff: 3 part-time support.

EIN: 581352076

2485
Georgia Pine Level Foundation, Ltd.

c/o SunTrust Bank, Atlanta
P.O. Box 4418, MC 0269
Atlanta, GA   30302-4418
Contact: John P. Schlichting

Established in 1981 in Georgia.

Donors: Coleman Meadows Pate Drug Co.; Robert F. Hatcher.

Foundation type: Independent foundation.

Financial data (yr. ended 12/31/13): Assets, $6,431,603 (M); gifts received, $14,400; expenditures, $440,509; qualifying distributions, $375,168; giving activities include $350,000 for 11 grants (high: $155,000; low: $1,000).

Purpose and activities: Giving primarily for education, museums, human services, health, and children and youth services.

Fields of interest: Museums; Higher education; Foundations; Health; Leadership development; Housing development; Christianity; Human services; Child welfare.

Type of support: General support; Scholarships.

Limitations: Giving primarily in Bibb County, GA, with emphasis on Macon. No grants to individuals, or for program-related investments.

Publications: Application guidelines.

Application information:
Initial approach: Letter or proposal
Copies of proposal: 1
Deadline(s): None

Officer: Robert F. Hatcher, Pres.

Trustee: SunTrust Bank.

EIN: 586176783

2486
J. Knox Gholston Foundation

c/o US Trust, Bank of America, N.A.
3414 Peachtree Rd., NE GA7-813-14-04
Atlanta, GA   30326-1113   (404) 264-1377
Contact: Mark Drake
E-mail: ga.grantmaking@ustrust.com; Main
URL: http://www.bankofamerica.com/grantmaking

Established in 1967 in Georgia.

Donor: J. Knox Gholston†.

Foundation type: Independent foundation.

Financial data (yr. ended 02/28/14): Assets, $7,230,509 (M); expenditures, $368,559; qualifying distributions, $305,787; giving activities

include $288,423 for 58 grants (high: $277,323; low: $100).

Purpose and activities: The mission of the foundation is to support charitable organizations that provide for the education of children within the City of Comer in Madison County, GA.

Fields of interest: Education; Human services.

Limitations: Giving in GA, with emphasis on City of Comer. No grants to individuals directly.

Application information:
Initial approach: See foundation information on web site
Deadline(s): June 1

Trustee: Bank of America, N.A.

EIN: 586056879

2487
J. William Gholston Foundation

(formerly J. William Gholston Trust)
c/o U.S. Trust, Bank of America, N.A.
3414 Peachtree Rd. N.E., Ste. 1475,
GA7-813-14-04
Atlanta, GA   30326-1113   (404) 264-1377
Contact: Quanda Allen, V.P.
E-mail: quanda.allen@ustrust.com; Main
URL: https://www.bankofamerica.com/
philanthropic/grantmaking.go

Foundation type: Independent foundation.

Financial data (yr. ended 12/31/13): Assets, $4,544,973 (M); expenditures, $239,858; qualifying distributions, $192,510; giving activities include $181,426 for 5 grants (high: $145,226; low: $200).

Purpose and activities: Support for charitable organizations that provide for the education of children within the city of Comer in Madison County, Georgia.

Fields of interest: Elementary and secondary education; Protestantism.

Limitations: Giving primarily in the city of Comer in Madison County, GA. No grants to individuals.

Application information:
Initial approach: Consult guidelines online on foundation web site
Deadline(s): June 1
Final notification: 1 to 2 months after the deadline

Trustee: Bank of America, N.A.

EIN: 586027903

2488
Price Gilbert, Jr. Charitable Fund

c/o Wells Fargo Philanthropic Svcs.
3280 Peachtree Rd. N.E., Ste. 400
Atlanta, GA   30305-2449   (888) 234-1999
Contact: Joyce Yamaato
FAX: (877) 746-5889;
E-mail: grantadministration@wellsfargo.com;
Information telephone number for technical assistance regarding the online grant application: 1-888-235-4351; Main URL: https://
www.wellsfargo.com/privatefoundationgrants/
gilbert

Established in 1973 in Georgia.

Foundation type: Independent foundation.

Financial data (yr. ended 05/31/14): Assets, $8,792,377 (M); expenditures, $522,118; qualifying distributions, $421,322; giving activities include $381,000 for 17 grants (high: $75,000; low: $6,000).

Purpose and activities: Giving primarily for arts and culture, education, human services, and federated giving programs.
Fields of interest: Arts and culture; Education; Environment; Nonprofits; Health; Human services.
Type of support: Regranting.
Limitations: Giving limited to the Atlanta, GA, area. No grants to individuals.
Publications: Application guidelines; Grants list.
Application information: Application guidelines and form available on fund web site. Application form required.

Initial approach: 1-page letter
Deadline(s): Feb. 1
Board meeting date(s): Sept.

Trustee: Wells Fargo Bank, N.A.
Number of staff: 4
EIN: 582064640

2489
The Glancy Foundation, Inc.
c/o Benjamin T. White Alston & Bird LLP
1201 W. Peachtree St.
Atlanta, GA 30309-3424 (404) 881-7488
E-mail: ben.white@alston.com

Foundation type: Independent foundation.
Financial data (yr. ended 12/31/14): Assets, $4,389,978; expenditures, $400,665; qualifying distributions, $358,490.
Fields of interest: Orchestral music; Education.
Application information: Application form required.

Initial approach: Letter
Deadline(s): None

Officers and Trustees: Alfred R. Glancy III, Chair. and Treas. and Trustee; Ruth R. Glancy, Vice Chair. and Secy. and Trustee; Alfred R. Glancy IV; Andrew Roby Glancy; Douglas R. Glancy; Joan C. Glancy.
EIN: 582115482

2490
The Go Big Red Foundation
5038 Carol Ln.
Atlanta, GA 30327

Donors: James K. Walton; Sarah J. Walton.
Foundation type: Independent foundation.
Financial data (yr. ended 12/31/13): Assets, $1,725,527 (M); gifts received, $1,805,000; expenditures, $279,771; qualifying distributions, $264,200; giving activities include $264,200 for 14 grants (high: $176,000; low: $50).
Fields of interest: Education; Religion; Human services.
Limitations: Applications not accepted.
Application information: Unsolicited requests for funds not accepted.
Trustees: James K. Walton; Sarah J. Walton.
EIN: 376532744

2491
The Goddard Foundation
3390 Peachtree Rd. N.E., Ste. 1200
Atlanta, GA 30326-2821

Established in 2002 in Georgia.
Donors: Robert C. Goddard III; Kathleen H. Goddard.
Foundation type: Independent foundation.
Financial data (yr. ended 12/31/13): Assets, $1,096,899 (M); gifts received, $400,000;

expenditures, $191,547; qualifying distributions, $188,792; giving activities include $188,792 for 33 grants (high: $100,000; low: $100).
Fields of interest: Arts and culture; Education; Higher education; Land resources; Zoos; Diseases and conditions; Human services.
Type of support: General support; Research.
Limitations: Applications not accepted. Giving primarily in GA. No grants to individuals.
Application information: Unsolicited requests for funds not accepted.
Trustee: Robert C. Goddard III.
EIN: 586457988

2492
I.A. Lanier Goodman Foundation
c/o SunTrust Bank
P.O. Box 4655, MC 221
Atlanta, GA 30302 (404) 588-7347
E-mail: fdnsvcs.ga@suntrust.com

Established in 1995 in Georgia.
Donor: Helen S. Lanier Foundation, Inc.
Foundation type: Independent foundation.
Financial data (yr. ended 12/31/14): Assets, $8,823,818; expenditures, $275,994; qualifying distributions, $233,001.
Purpose and activities: Giving primarily for the arts, particularly museums, and a center for puppetry arts; funding also for education, including an Episcopal high school.
Fields of interest: Arts and culture; Art museums; Natural history museums; Education; Secondary education; Nonprofits; Hospital care; Diseases and conditions; Spinal cord injuries and diseases; Human services; Child welfare.
Type of support: Regranting.
Limitations: Applications accepted. Giving primarily in GA.
Application information: Connection to the Goodman family is strongly encouraged. Application form required.

Initial approach: Proposal
Deadline(s): July 31

Trustees: Carol Doty; Carol Lanier Goodman; Scott Goodman; SunTrust Bank.
EIN: 586396903

2493
The Evelyn and Frank Gordy Foundation
3330 Cumberland Blvd., Ste. T-40
Atlanta, GA 30339-5985
Contact: Steven H. Simms, Tr.
E-mail: stevesimms@thevarsity.com

Established in 1997 in Georgia.
Donor: Evelyn Gordy Rankin†.
Foundation type: Independent foundation.
Financial data (yr. ended 04/30/13): Assets, $10,535,092 (M); gifts received, $13,144; expenditures, $647,617; qualifying distributions, $420,000; giving activities include $420,000 for grants.
Fields of interest: Education; Higher education; Health; Christianity; Human services; Child welfare.
Limitations: Applications accepted. Giving primarily in the Atlanta and Marietta, GA, area. No grants to individuals.
Application information: Application form required.

Initial approach: Letter

Deadline(s): None
Board meeting date(s): Apr. 25

Trustees: Caroline Muir Browne; Douglas Gordon Muir III; Nancy Gordy Simms; Steven H. Simms.
Number of staff: 1 full-time professional; 1 part-time professional.
EIN: 586343707

2494
The Gould Family Foundation, Inc.
c/o David Gould
1880 Durand Mill Dr., N.E.
Atlanta, GA 30307-1170

Established in 2007 in Georgia.
Donors: Carolyn J. Gould; David B. Gould.
Foundation type: Independent foundation.
Financial data (yr. ended 12/31/13): Assets, $3,909,734 (M); gifts received, $299,990; expenditures, $238,699; qualifying distributions, $203,500; giving activities include $200,000 for 14 grants (high: $45,000; low: $500).
Fields of interest: Elementary and secondary education; Human services.
Limitations: Applications not accepted. Giving primarily in Atlanta, GA. No grants to individuals.
Application information: Unsolicited requests for funds not accepted.
Officers: Carolyn Gould, Pres.; David Gould, Secy.
EIN: 261377120

2495
Graham Family Foundation Inc.
c/o Pathstone Family Office
P.O. Box 52047
Atlanta, GA 30355-0047

Established in 2008 in Georgia.
Foundation type: Independent foundation.
Financial data (yr. ended 12/31/12): Assets, $7,827,780 (M); expenditures, $448,285; qualifying distributions, $365,000; giving activities include $365,000 for grants.
Fields of interest: Protestantism.
Limitations: Applications not accepted. Giving primarily in GA, HI and OH. No grants to individuals.
Application information: Contributes only to pre-selected organizations.
Officers: Eva C. Graham, Chair.; Mark E. Graham, Pres. and Treas.; Dianna G. Hellmann, V.P. and Secy.
Director: Stephen B. Graham.
EIN: 263706006

2496
The Graves Foundation, Inc.
P.O. Box 53015
Atlanta, GA 30355-1015

Established in 1989 in Georgia.
Donor: William M. Graves.
Foundation type: Independent foundation.
Financial data (yr. ended 12/31/12): Assets, $3,485,229 (M); expenditures, $196,944; qualifying distributions, $190,351; giving activities include $190,351 for grants.
Purpose and activities: Giving primarily for education, and to Presbyterian churches and agencies; funding also for the performing arts,

juvenile diabetes research, and federated giving programs.
Fields of interest: Arts and culture; Performing arts; Orchestral music; Education; Higher education; Nonprofits; Health; Diabetes; Protestantism.
Type of support: Research; Regranting.
Limitations: Applications not accepted. Giving primarily in the greater Atlanta, GA, area. No grants to individuals.
Application information: Unsolicited requests for funds not accepted.
Officers: William M. Graves, Pres. and Treas.; Frances B. Graves, V.P. and Secy.
Trustees: John Hill Bailey, Jr.; William M. Graves, Jr.; Robert E. Hicks; Martha Graves Marriott.
EIN: 581876906

2497
Gray Matters Capital, Inc.
2200 Century Pkwy., Ste. 100
Atlanta, GA   30345-3103
Main URL: http://www.graymatterscap.com/

Established in 2006 in Georgia.
Donors: Robert A. Pattillo; Robert A. Pattillo Properties, Inc.; Pattillo-Markaz Industrial Partners, LLC.
Foundation type: Operating foundation.
Financial data (yr. ended 12/31/12): Assets, $21,651,059 (M); gifts received, $7,078,897; expenditures, $3,594,372; qualifying distributions, $9,234,153; giving activities include $162,635 for 101 grants to individuals (high: $3,600; low: $435), and $1,770,445 for foundation-administered programs.
Purpose and activities: The foundation researches and co-creates initiatives with local partners to build sustainable, replicable business models for the benefit of underserved populations. Special emphasis is directed toward programs that improve the quality and access to education for poor children in developing countries.
Fields of interest: Entrepreneurship; Children; Low-income and poor people.
Type of support: Seed money; Mission-related investments; Program-related investments.
Limitations: Applications not accepted. No grants to individuals.
Application information: Unsolicited requests for funds not accepted.
Officers and Directors: Robert A. Pattillo, Pres., V.P., and Treas. and Director; Clay Reese, Secy.
EIN: 205176973

2498
Greiner Family Foundation, Inc.
2043 Cripped Oak Trail, Ste. 20807
Jasper, GA   30143-5802

Donors: Lorine Greiner†; Lorine Greiner Trust.
Foundation type: Independent foundation.
Financial data (yr. ended 12/31/13): Assets, $5,708,525 (M); expenditures, $432,323; qualifying distributions, $294,500; giving activities include $294,500 for 11 grants (high: $200,000; low: $2,000).
Purpose and activities: Giving primarily for multiple sclerosis research and educating the marginally disabled.

Fields of interest: Special needs education; Multiple sclerosis; Fire prevention and control; People with disabilities.
Type of support: Continuing support; Research.
Limitations: Applications not accepted. Giving primarily in GA and TN. No grants to individuals.
Application information: Unsolicited requests for funds not accepted.
Officers and Directors: Albert L. Greiner, Pres. and Director; Josephine L. Greiner, V.P. and Secy. and Director; Alexis L. Fankhouser; Kaivan Greiner; Trandy G. Koth; Collin Loesch; Amy E. Sulpazo.
EIN: 592912507

2499
R. A. Griffin Family Foundation, Inc.
3821 Skipper Bridge Rd.
Valdosta, GA   31605-5806

Established in 1991 in Georgia.
Donor: R.A. Griffin, Jr.
Foundation type: Independent foundation.
Financial data (yr. ended 12/31/13): Assets, $3,919,044 (M); expenditures, $219,850; qualifying distributions, $194,216; giving activities include $189,620 for 12 grants (high: $89,000; low: $1,000).
Fields of interest: Education; Nonprofits; Christianity; Human services; Youth services.
Type of support: General support; Regranting.
Limitations: Applications not accepted. Giving primarily in GA. No grants to individuals.
Application information: Unsolicited requests for funds not accepted.
Officer: R.A. Griffin, Jr., C.E.O.
Directors: Amy King; Thomas Reed; Wendy Rogers.
EIN: 581977357

2500
The Guillaume Family Foundation, Inc.
1190 W. Garmon Rd.
Atlanta, GA   30327-4402

Established in 2005 in Georgia.
Donor: Roger N. Guillaume, Jr.
Foundation type: Independent foundation.
Financial data (yr. ended 12/31/13): Assets, $518,424 (M); expenditures, $300,815; qualifying distributions, $291,284; giving activities include $242,500 for 9 grants (high: $184,000; low: $500).
Fields of interest: Education; Catholicism.
Limitations: Applications not accepted. Giving primarily in GA. No grants to individuals.
Application information: Contributes only to pre-selected organizations.
Directors: Mary K. Guillaume; Roger N. Guillaume, Jr.
EIN: 260127651

2501
Hands of Blessing, Inc.
1791 O.G. Skinner Dr., Ste. D
West Point, GA   31833-1900   (877) 276-7783
Contact: M.V. Thomas, Tr.
E-mail: mvthomas@crosstel.com

Donors: M.V. Thomas; Croostelex, Inc.; Crosstel, Inc.
Foundation type: Independent foundation.

Financial data (yr. ended 12/31/13): Assets, $260,162 (M); gifts received, $248,000; expenditures, $164,625; qualifying distributions, $174,825; giving activities include $151,206 for 57 grants (high: $8,500; low: $1,000).
Fields of interest: Arts and culture; Education; Religion.
International interests: India.
Limitations: Applications accepted. Giving primarily in GA; with some giving to India.
Application information: Application form required.
   Initial approach: Letter or E-mail
   Deadline(s): None
Trustees: Frenny Thomas Anthony; Geetha Thomas; Jenny Thomas; M.V. Thomas; Stephanie Thomas.
EIN: 455186076

2502
The Albert E. Harrison Foundation
c/o John M. Harrison
224 Dalton St.
Ellijay, GA   30540-3119

Established in 2000 in Georgia.
Donor: Albert E. Harrison.
Foundation type: Independent foundation.
Financial data (yr. ended 12/31/14): Assets, $5,927,253 (M); expenditures, $171,449; qualifying distributions, $150,500; giving activities include $150,500 for 32 grants (high: $25,000; low: $500).
Purpose and activities: Giving primarily for education, including a Christian academy; support also for human services, the arts, and health care.
Fields of interest: Education; Elementary and secondary education; Health; School-based health care; Public health; Public libraries; Christianity; Human services.
Type of support: General support; Scholarships.
Limitations: Applications not accepted. Giving primarily in Gilmer County, GA. No grants to individuals.
Application information: Contributes only to pre-selected organizations.
Officers and Trustees: John M. Harrison, Pres. and Trustee; Marianne H. Bowman, V.P. and Trustee; Douglas P. Harrison, Secy.-Treas. and Trustee.
EIN: 582501770

2503
The Hawkins Foundation Inc.
4403 Northside Pkwy., Ste. 1103
Atlanta, GA   30327

Established in 1997 in Georgia.
Donors: Susan M. Hawkins; The Hawkins Family Charitable Annuity Trust; Scott D. Hawkins.
Foundation type: Independent foundation.
Financial data (yr. ended 12/31/13): Assets, $828,546 (M); gifts received, $345,000; expenditures, $437,823; qualifying distributions, $412,950; giving activities include $412,950 for 25 grants (high: $175,000; low: $350).
Fields of interest: Higher education.
Limitations: Applications not accepted. Giving primarily in Atlanta and LaGrange, GA. No grants to individuals.
Application information: Contributes only to pre-selected organizations.
Trustees: Scott D. Hawkins; Susan M. Hawkins.
EIN: 582360574

2504
Health 1st Foundation, Inc.
P.O. Box 310390
Atlanta, GA 31131-0390 (404) 344-6768
Contact: DeLutha H. King Jr. MD, Exec. Dir.

Established in 1986 in Georgia.
Foundation type: Independent foundation.
Financial data (yr. ended 06/30/13): Assets,
$4,841,087 (M); expenditures, $280,891;
qualifying distributions, $233,412; giving activities
include $193,000 for 10 grants (high: $35,000;
low: $5,000).
Purpose and activities: Giving limited to education
and health care related activities.
Fields of interest: Higher education; Medical
education; Health; Diseases and conditions;
Genetic conditions and birth defects.
Type of support: Continuing support; Research.
Limitations: Applications accepted. Giving limited to
GA, with emphasis on Atlanta. No grants to
individuals.
Application information: Applicants must use the
foundation's standard application form. Application
form required.
  Initial approach: Write or telephone foundation to
    obtain application form
  Copies of proposal: 4
  Deadline(s): Apr. 1
  Board meeting date(s): Oct.
  Final notification: Oct.
Officer: DeLutha H. King, Jr., MD, Exec. Dir.
Number of staff: 1 part-time professional.
EIN: 581265915

2505
The Higher Foundation
1019 Falling Creek Dr.
Greensboro, GA 30642

Established in 2001 in Georgia.
Donors: Steven J. Heyer; Margaret R. Heyer.
Foundation type: Independent foundation.
Financial data (yr. ended 06/30/14): Assets,
$1,150,811 (M); expenditures, $167,133;
qualifying distributions, $160,000; giving activities
include $160,000 for 1 grant.
Fields of interest: Education.
Limitations: Applications not accepted. Giving
primarily in Atlanta, GA and Millbrook, NY. No grants
to individuals.
Application information: Unsolicited requests for
funds not accepted.
Trustee: Steven J. Heyer.
EIN: 586442623

2506
The Hodge Foundation, Inc.
c/o J. Wiley Ellis
P.O. Box 9946
Savannah, GA 31412-9946 (912) 233-9700
Contact: Kathy Oliphant

Established in 1962 in Georgia.
Donor: Sarah Mills Hodge†.
Foundation type: Independent foundation.
Financial data (yr. ended 07/31/14): Assets,
$4,529,964 (M); expenditures, $224,265;
qualifying distributions, $199,642; giving activities
include $185,889 for 8 grants (high: $75,800; low:
$1,000).

Purpose and activities: Support for charitable
organizations of special interest to the donor,
primarily for youth and family services; some giving
also for scholarship funds at local colleges.
Fields of interest: Education; Foundations; Human
services; Child care; Youth development.
Limitations: Applications accepted. Giving limited to
Savannah, GA; scholarships limited to residents of
Chatham County.
Application information:
  Initial approach: Letter
  Copies of proposal: 2
  Deadline(s): None
Trustees: Christopher W. Cay; J. Wiley Ellis; Walter
O. Evans; Margaret D. Minis; Therese Pindar; Paul
M. Pressly.
EIN: 580909476

2507
The Hodgson Charitable Trust
1135 Peachtree Battle Ave. N.W.
Atlanta, GA 30327-1419

Established in 2001 in Georgia.
Donor: Hodgson Charitable Remainder Trust.
Foundation type: Independent foundation.
Financial data (yr. ended 12/31/13): Assets,
$4,789,407; expenditures, $366,875; qualifying
distributions, $290,000; giving activities include
$290,000 for 20 grants (high: $50,000; low:
$5,000).
Fields of interest: Higher education; Health;
Hospital care.
Limitations: Applications not accepted. Giving
primarily in AL, GA and NC.
Application information: Contributes only to
pre-selected organizations.
Trustees: T. Kevin Clayton; Lydia A. Hodgson;
Morton S. Hodgson III; Patricia S. Hodgson.
EIN: 586437963

2508
Holland-Underwood Foundation, Inc.
P.O. Box 280
Dublin, GA 31040-0280

Established in 2000 in Georgia.
Donor: L.A. Holland†.
Foundation type: Independent foundation.
Financial data (yr. ended 12/31/13): Assets,
$3,803,625 (M); expenditures, $417,002;
qualifying distributions, $382,470; giving activities
include $382,470 for 8 grants (high: $300,000;
low: $200).
Purpose and activities: Giving primarily for
education and to a United Methodist church.
Fields of interest: Higher education; Community and
economic development; Presbyterianism; Human
services.
Type of support: General support; Capital and
infrastructure; Program development; Scholarships.
Limitations: Applications not accepted. Giving
primarily in GA. No grants to individuals.
Application information: Unsolicited requests for
funds not accepted.
Officers: John E. Roller, Pres.; Don R. Christian,
Secy.; Faye O. Dukes, Treas.
EIN: 582590535

2509
Holly Lane Foundation Inc
(formerly The Gatchell Home, Inc.)
P. O. Box 421754
Atlanta, GA 30342-8754

Foundation type: Independent foundation.
Financial data (yr. ended 12/31/12): Assets,
$6,693,618 (M); expenditures, $424,355;
qualifying distributions, $284,047; giving activities
include $284,047 for grants.
Fields of interest: Education; Health; Autism;
Camps; Children and youth; People with disabilities.
Type of support: Equipment.
Limitations: Applications not accepted. Giving
primarily in GA. No grants to individuals.
Application information: Contributes only to
pre-selected organizations.
Officers and Directors: Charles A. Meriwether, **Pres.**
and Director; Harold D. Berger, Secy.-Treas.; **Cathy**
Arnoff, Exec. Dir.; Eliot M. Arnovitz; Douglas J. **Hertz.**
EIN: 580692908

2510
Hooters Community Endowment Fund, Inc.
1815 The Exchange
Atlanta, GA 30339-2027 (770) 951-2040

Donors: Hooters of America, Inc.; McCain Foods;
Tyson; Heineken; RMD Corp.; Marinos Charity; **Miller**
Brewing Co.; Sam Adams; Bacardi; Brown-Forman;
Thompson Elaree; KPMG; ISI International; Lamb
Weston; Pernod Ricard USA; Pace Airlines; US
Foodservice; Rocky Mountain Mktg. and Promo.;
Pepsico; Vienna Beef; Hootwinc 100; Wings
Investors Co.; Texas Wings; IMI; Million Dollars
Media; Hooters, Inc.; Royal Cup; Texas Wings
Holdings; Tom Valentine Inflows Corporate **Stores.**
Foundation type: Company-sponsored foundation.
Financial data (yr. ended 12/29/13): Assets,
$655,276 (M); gifts received, $577,701;
expenditures, $371,683; qualifying distributions,
$328,661; giving activities include $328,661 **for 39**
grants (high: $150,000; low: $25).
Purpose and activities: The foundation supports
organizations involved with health, genetic
diseases, cancer, muscular dystrophy, diabetes,
cancer research, hunger, athletics, human **services,**
military and veterans, and Christianity.
Fields of interest: Health; Diseases and **conditions;**
Human services.
Type of support: General support.
Limitations: Applications accepted. Giving **primarily**
in areas of company operations in FL, GA, NC, **and**
SC. No grants to individuals.
Application information:
  Initial approach: Proposal
  Deadline(s): None
Officers: Terrance Marks, C.E.O.; Matthew
Wickesberg, C.F.O. and Secy.
EIN: 582006561

2511
Barbara N. and Don N. Howell Foundation
1479 Parkview Blvd.
Stone Mountain, GA 30087

Established in 1986 in Georgia.
Donors: Don N. Howell; Barbara N. Howell.
Foundation type: Independent foundation.

Financial data (yr. ended 12/31/13): Assets, $3,313,969 (M); gifts received, $102,000; expenditures, $176,093; qualifying distributions, $174,085; giving activities include $170,450 for 25 grants (high: $22,000; low: $400).
Fields of interest: Christianity.
Limitations: Applications not accepted. Giving primarily in GA. No grants to individuals.
Application information: Unsolicited requests for funds not accepted.
Trustees: Barbara N. Howell; Don N. Howell.
EIN: 586203025

2512
The Howell Fund, Inc.
c/o SunTrust Bank
P.O. Box 4655, Mail Code GA-ATL-0221
Atlanta, GA   30302-4655   (404) 813-2021
Contact: Emily Butler, Grants Mgr., SunTrust Bank
E-mail: fdnsvcs.ga@suntrust.com

Established in 1951 in Georgia.
Donor: Clark Howell†.
Foundation type: Independent foundation.
Financial data (yr. ended 12/31/13): Assets, $9,100,774 (M); gifts received, $200; expenditures, $379,315; qualifying distributions, $352,118; giving activities include $335,000 for 15 grants (high: $100,000; low: $5,000).
Fields of interest: Arts and culture; Education; Community improvement.
Type of support: Capital campaigns; Endowments.
Limitations: Applications not accepted. Giving limited to GA, with emphasis on Atlanta. No grants to individuals.
Application information: Unsolicited requests for funds not accepted.
  Board meeting date(s): Nov.
Officers and Directors: Faye Howell, Chair. and Director; Mark Drake, Secy.; Ron Bobo; Clark Howell III; W. Barrett Howell; W. Barrett Howell II.
Trustee: SunTrust Bank.
EIN: 586026027

2513
Ruth R. Hoyt - Anne H. Jolley Foundation Inc.
(formerly Ruth Rogers Hoyt Foundation, Inc.)
5490 Long Island Dr. N.W.
Atlanta, GA   30327-4838
Application address: P.O. Box 421425, Atlanta, GA 30342-8425, tel.: (404) 847-9719

Established in 1993 in Georgia.
Foundation type: Independent foundation.
Financial data (yr. ended 12/31/13): Assets, $5,413,493 (M); expenditures, $272,507; qualifying distributions, $272,507; giving activities include $220,500 for 41 grants (high: $63,500; low: $500).
Fields of interest: Historic preservation; Education; Higher education; Health; Christianity; Sports and recreation; Child welfare.
Type of support: Scholarships.
Limitations: Applications accepted. Giving primarily in GA.
Application information: Application form required.
  Initial approach: Letter
  Deadline(s): None

Directors: Ruthanna Jolley Bost; F. Lex Jolley, Jr.; William Hoyt Jolley.
EIN: 582034987

2514
The Sara and Fred Hoyt Charitable Trust
P.O. Box 12366
Atlanta, GA   30355-2366

Established in 1996 in Georgia.
Donors: Fred A. Hoyt, Jr.; Sara J. Hoyt.
Foundation type: Independent foundation.
Financial data (yr. ended 12/31/13): Assets, $5,894,679 (M); gifts received, $301,480; expenditures, $409,353; qualifying distributions, $347,887; giving activities include $342,500 for 16 grants (high: $100,000; low: $5,000).
Fields of interest: Art museums; Historic preservation; Environmental education; Health care clinics; Rehabilitation; Child welfare.
Limitations: Applications not accepted. Giving primarily in GA, with some emphasis on Atlanta. No grants to individuals.
Application information: Unsolicited requests for funds not accepted.
Trustee: Sara J. Hoyt.
Distribution Committee: Walter J. Hoyt; William D. Hoyt; Dancy H. Wynne.
EIN: 586331684

2515
The Hunter Foundation Inc.
110 E. President St., 2nd Fl.
Savannah, GA   31401-3763

Established in 2002 in Georgia.
Donor: Edith Minis Charitable Trust.
Foundation type: Independent foundation.
Financial data (yr. ended 12/31/13): Assets, $2,953,285 (M); expenditures, $186,749; qualifying distributions, $168,823; giving activities include $142,000 for 9 grants (high: $50,000; low: $1,000).
Fields of interest: Museums; Education; Christianity.
Type of support: Capital campaigns; General support.
Limitations: Applications not accepted. Giving primarily in GA and TN. No grants to individuals.
Application information: Contributes only to pre-selected organizations.
Directors: James R. Hungerpiller; Susan Hungerpiller.
Number of staff: None.
EIN: 311548114

2516
The Hurlbert Family Foundation
240 Berry Glen Ct.
Alpharetta, GA   30022-1675

Established in 2003 in Pennsylvania.
Donors: Gordon C. Hurlbert; Patricia J. Hurlbert†.
Foundation type: Independent foundation.
Financial data (yr. ended 12/31/14): Assets, $2,812,021 (M); expenditures, $143,797; qualifying distributions, $143,000; giving activities include $143,000 for 18 grants (high: $25,000; low: $1,000).

Fields of interest: University education; Alzheimer's disease; Cancers; Christianity; Human services.
Limitations: Applications not accepted. Giving primarily in CO, IL, NY and OK. No grants to individuals.
Application information: Unsolicited requests for funds not accepted.
Officers: Mary Jean Volpe, Pres.; James G. Hurlbert, Treas.
EIN: 200134216

2517
John P. and Dorothy S. Illges Foundation, Inc.
P.O. Box 1673
Columbus, GA   31902-1673   (706) 576-6625
Contact: John P. Illges III, Pres.

Established in 1947 in Georgia.
Donor: John P. Illges†.
Foundation type: Independent foundation.
Financial data (yr. ended 09/30/13): Assets, $7,431,433 (M); expenditures, $372,436; qualifying distributions, $297,959; giving activities include $285,026 for 26 grants (high: $30,000; low: $2,500).
Purpose and activities: Giving primarily for education, the arts, youth, social services, and local community concerns in the Columbus, GA, area.
Fields of interest: Arts and culture; Museums; Art museums; Education; Community and economic development; Human services; Child welfare; Youth services.
Type of support: Annual campaigns; Capital campaigns; Capital and infrastructure; Equipment; Program development.
Limitations: Applications accepted. Giving primarily in the Columbus, GA, area. No grants to individuals, or for seed money.
Application information:
  Initial approach: Letter
  Copies of proposal: 1
  Deadline(s): None
  Board meeting date(s): 3rd Thurs. of Jan., May, and Sept.
  Final notification: Following board meeting review
Officers: John P. Illges III, Pres.; Philip A. Badcock, V.P.; Mary S. Boyd, Secy.; Richard B. Illges, Treas.
Directors: Mrs. Bruce Lanier; John W. Mayher, Jr.
Number of staff: 1 part-time professional.
EIN: 580691476

2518
The Norman & Emmy Lou Illges Foundation
P.O. Box 23024
Columbus, GA   31902-3024

Established in 1998 in Georgia.
Donor: Emmy Lou Illges†.
Foundation type: Independent foundation.
Financial data (yr. ended 12/31/13): Assets, $6,105,231 (M); expenditures, $292,724; qualifying distributions, $267,892; giving activities include $248,300 for 15 grants (high: $50,000; low: $1,000).
Fields of interest: Performing arts; Museums; University education; Wildlife biodiversity; Animal welfare.
Type of support: General support.
Limitations: Applications not accepted. Giving primarily in GA. No grants to individuals.

Application information: Unsolicited requests for funds not accepted.
Trustee: Synovus Trust Co., N.A.
Distribution Committee: Shannon I. Candler; Judith I. Harding; Susan I. Lanier.
EIN: 586368426

2519
Hugh M. Inman Foundation, Inc.
3715 Northside Pkwy.
400 Northcreek, No. 650
Atlanta, GA 30327-2803

Donor: Hugh M. Inman.
Foundation type: Independent foundation.
Financial data (yr. ended 12/31/13): Assets, $5,334,214 (M); expenditures, $474,570; qualifying distributions, $407,869; giving activities include $407,869 for 39 grants (high: $170,600; low: $100).
Fields of interest: Nonprofits; Hospital care; Protestantism.
Type of support: General support; Regranting.
Limitations: Applications not accepted. Giving primarily in Atlanta, GA. No support for individuals.
Application information: Unsolicited requests for funds not accepted.
Officers and Trustees: Hugh M. Inman, Jr., Chair. and Treas.; John S. Inman, Secy. and Trustee; Betty Ann Inman; William E. Inman; Margaret I. Wilson.
EIN: 582588890

2520
The Invisible Hand Foundation, Inc.
737 Kennesaw Due West Rd.
Kennesaw, GA 30152-4068
Main URL: http://theinvisiblehand.org

Established in 2006 in Georgia.
Donors: Robert E. Matthews; Matthew D. Burton; Christopher Braaksma; Narwhal Capital Management.
Foundation type: Independent foundation.
Financial data (yr. ended 12/31/14): Assets, $409,809 (M); gifts received, $170,000; expenditures, $188,169; qualifying distributions, $186,750; giving activities include $186,750 for 4 grants (high: $105,000; low: $6,000).
Fields of interest: Education; Human services; Children.
International interests: Georgia.
Limitations: Applications not accepted. Giving primarily in GA. No grants to individuals.
Application information: Unsolicited requests for funds not accepted.
Directors: Matthew D. Burton; David Hall.
EIN: 205791133

2521
Irving Foundation Inc.
P.O. Box 1983
Athens, GA 30603-1983

Established in 1991 in Georgia.
Donor: Joe D. Irving.
Foundation type: Independent foundation.
Financial data (yr. ended 12/31/13): Assets, $983 (M); gifts received, $191,859; expenditures, $191,093; qualifying distributions, $190,000;

giving activities include $190,000 for 20 grants (high: $100,000; low: $1,000).
Fields of interest: Education; Health; Agriculture.
Limitations: Applications not accepted. Giving primarily in Athens, GA. No grants to individuals.
Application information: Unsolicited requests for funds not accepted.
Officers and Directors: Joe D. Irving, Pres. and Treas.; Tony G. Mills, Secy. and Director; Michael Irving; James L. Newland; Amy White.
EIN: 581943208

2522
The Franklin D. Jackson Family Foundation
260 Rivermere Way
Sandy Springs, GA 30350

Established in 2000 in Georgia.
Donor: Frank Jackson.
Foundation type: Independent foundation.
Financial data (yr. ended 12/31/13): Assets, $3,051,802 (M); expenditures, $179,884; qualifying distributions, $148,015; giving activities include $148,015 for 4 grants (high: $50,000; low: $8,000).
Fields of interest: Arts and culture; Higher education; Cancers.
Type of support: General support.
Limitations: Applications not accepted. Giving primarily in GA. No grants to individuals.
Application information: Contributes only to pre-selected organizations.
Trustees: Karen Drexinger; Franklin Jackson.
EIN: 586409664

2523
JBS Foundation
(formerly Jocelyn Botterell Staton Foundation)
c/o SunTrust Bank
P.O. Box 4655, Mail Code GA-ATL-0221
Atlanta, GA 30302-4655 (404) 813-2021
Contact: Emily Butler, Grants Mgr., SunTrust Bank
E-mail: fdnsvcs.ga@suntrust.com

Established in 1995 in Georgia.
Foundation type: Independent foundation.
Financial data (yr. ended 12/31/13): Assets, $5,046,038 (M); expenditures, $355,796; qualifying distributions, $334,843; giving activities include $317,500 for 19 grants (high: $30,000; low: $5,000).
Fields of interest: Arts and culture; Education; Botanical gardens; Nonprofits; Spinal cord injuries and diseases; Human services; Scouting programs.
Type of support: Regranting.
Limitations: Applications not accepted. Giving primarily in GA, with emphasis on Atlanta. No grants to individuals.
Application information:
 Board meeting date(s): Dec.
Trustee: SunTrust Bank.
Committee Members: Louise Staton Gunn; John C. Staton, Jr.; Margaret A. Staton; Mary Staton.
EIN: 586301523

2524
The George W. Jeter Foundation Inc.
c/o George W. Jeter
1222 Broadway, Ste. 101
Columbus, GA 31901-4244

Established in 1998 in Georgia.
Donor: George W. Jeter.
Foundation type: Independent foundation.
Financial data (yr. ended 12/31/13): Assets, $236,542 (M); expenditures, $276,218; qualifying distributions, $256,296; giving activities include $256,296 for 12 grants (high: $175,571; low: $500).
Fields of interest: Opera; Higher education; Nonprofits; Health; Protestantism; Human services; Child welfare; Scouting programs.
Type of support: Regranting.
Limitations: Applications not accepted. Giving primarily in Columbus, GA. No grants to individuals.
Application information: Contributes only to pre-selected organizations.
Director: George W. Jeter.
EIN: 582399492

2525
The Tom & Edwina Johnson Family Foundation Inc.
3280 Rilman Rd.
Atlanta, GA 30327-1551

Established in 2000 in Georgia.
Donors: Tom Johnson; Edwina Johnson.
Foundation type: Independent foundation.
Financial data (yr. ended 12/31/13): Assets, $462,145 (M); expenditures, $336,332; qualifying distributions, $332,250; giving activities include $332,250 for 46 grants (high: $100,000; low: $250).
Fields of interest: Arts and culture; Elementary education; Higher education; Environment; Diseases and conditions; Human services; Child welfare.
Limitations: Applications not accepted. Giving primarily in CA, GA and TX. No grants to individuals.
Application information: Unsolicited requests for funds not accepted.
Officers: Tom Johnson, Chair. and Treas.; Edwina Johnson, Vice-Chair. and Secy.
Directors: Wyatt Johnson III; Christa Shaffer.
EIN: 582575540

2526
Leodelle Lassiter Jolley Foundation
P.O. Box 30828
Sea Island, GA 31561-0828

Established in 2002 in Georgia.
Foundation type: Independent foundation.
Financial data (yr. ended 12/31/14): Assets, $2,928,468 (M); expenditures, $264,517; qualifying distributions, $260,000; giving activities include $260,000 for 11 grants (high: $100,000; low: $10,000).
Fields of interest: Elementary and secondary education; Special needs education; Nonprofits; People with disabilities.
Type of support: General support; Regranting; Capital and infrastructure; Capital campaigns.
Limitations: Applications not accepted. Giving in GA. No grants to individuals.
Application information: Contributes only to pre-selected organizations.
Trustees: Ruthanna Jolley Bost; Malinda J. Mortin; Catherine Peters.
EIN: 586454877

2527
Joyce Family Foundation Inc.
250 Pine Valley Rd. S.E.
Marietta, GA 30067-4822

Donor: Jeffery Joyce.
Foundation type: Independent foundation.
Financial data (yr. ended 12/31/13): Assets,
$2,800,365 (M); gifts received, $3,281;
expenditures, $192,737; qualifying distributions,
$166,000; giving activities include $166,000 for 3
grants (high: $110,000; low: $6,000).
Fields of interest: Education; Foundations.
Limitations: Applications not accepted. Giving
primarily in MD and PA. No grants to individuals.
Application information: Unsolicited requests for
funds not accepted.
Directors: Cynthia Joyce; Jeffrey Joyce.
EIN: 452684840

2528
K. Charitable Foundation, Inc.
13560 Morris Rd., 1st Fl., Ste. 1140
Alpharetta, GA 30004

Established in 2006 in Georgia.
Donor: Eric Swartz.
Foundation type: Independent foundation.
Financial data (yr. ended 12/31/13): Assets,
$206,069 (M); gifts received, $200,897;
expenditures, $247,854; qualifying distributions,
$246,100; giving activities include $246,100 for
grants.
Fields of interest: Christianity.
Limitations: Applications not accepted. Giving
primarily in Alpharetta, GA.
Application information: Contributes only to
pre-selected organizations.
Officers: Eric S. Swartz, Pres. and Treas.; Kama D.
Swartz, Secy.
EIN: 204515065

2529
David & Jennifer Kahn Family Foundation,
Inc.
(formerly The David B. Kahn Foundation, Inc.)
3755 Atlanta Industrial Pkwy.
Atlanta, GA 30331-1027

Established in 1999 in Georgia.
Donor: David B. Kahn.
Foundation type: Independent foundation.
Financial data (yr. ended 12/31/13): Assets,
$21,208,389 (M); gifts received, $3,500;
expenditures, $519,882; qualifying distributions,
$428,150; giving activities include $428,150 for 31
grants (high: $325,000; low: $50).
Fields of interest: Arts and culture; Education;
Health; Human services; Child welfare.
Limitations: Applications not accepted. Giving
primarily in Atlanta, GA. No grants to individuals.
Application information: Contributes only to
pre-selected organizations.
Officers: David B. Kahn, Chair.; Jennifer M. Kahn,
Vice-Chair.
EIN: 582472876

2530
Kids II Foundation Inc.
c/o Susan Finn
3333 Piedmont Rd., Ste. 1800
Atlanta, GA 30305

Established in 2005 in Georgia.
Donors: Ryan T. Gunnigle; Kids II Vendors; Kids II
Inc.; Kids II Employees.
Foundation type: Company-sponsored foundation.
Financial data (yr. ended 12/31/13): Assets,
$55,356 (M); gifts received, $233,184;
expenditures, $192,306; qualifying distributions,
$192,306; giving activities include $190,770 for 50
grants (high: $50,000; low: $500).
Purpose and activities: The foundation supports
nonprofit organizations involved with health care,
recreation, and human services.
Fields of interest: Health; Storms; Sports and
recreation; Human services; Child welfare.
Limitations: Applications not accepted. Giving
primarily in NJ. No grants to individuals.
Application information: Contributes only to
pre-selected organizations.
Officers: Ryan T. Gunnigle, Pres.; Jeff Cornelison,
V.P.; Carl J. Watry, V.P.; J. Dwaine Clarke,
Secy.-Treas.
EIN: 203635565

2531
Kingdom School and Ministry Center Inc.
515 N. Broad St.
Thomasville, GA 31792-4424
Contact: Charlie Lewis, Pres.

Foundation type: Independent foundation.
Financial data (yr. ended 12/31/13): Assets,
$469,593 (M); gifts received, $705,229;
expenditures, $712,811; qualifying distributions,
$629,000; giving activities include $183,155 for 25
grants (high: $50,000; low: $500).
Fields of interest: Arts and culture; Education;
Christianity; Human services.
Limitations: Applications not accepted. Giving
primarily in VA.
Application information: Contributes only to
pre-selected organizations.
Officer: Charlie Lewis, Pres.
EIN: 273450229

2532
King-White Family Foundation, Inc.
50 Woodcrest Ave. N.E.
Atlanta, GA 30309-1525

Established in 2006 in Georgia.
Donors: John J. White; Midland Manufacturing
Money Purchase Plan and Trust.
Foundation type: Independent foundation.
Financial data (yr. ended 12/31/13): Assets,
$2,744,387 (M); expenditures, $176,525;
qualifying distributions, $155,938; giving activities
include $155,908 for 21 grants (high: $40,174;
low: $200).
Fields of interest: Arts and culture; Education;
Higher education; Health.
Limitations: Applications not accepted. Giving
primarily in CT and VA.
Application information: Unsolicited requests for
funds not accepted.

Officers and Directors: Jeffrey J. White, V.P. and
Director; Michael J. White, Secy.-Treas. and
Director; J. Douglas White; Kathleen M. White;
Madeleine E. White; Mary Carolyn White.
EIN: 205855797

2533
The Klump Family Foundation, Inc.
1 Buckhead Plz.
3060 Peachtree Rd. N.W., Ste. 400
Atlanta, GA 30305-2256
Contact: Michael Klump, Pres.

Established in 2006 in Georgia.
Donors: Michael Klump; Elizabeth Klump.
Foundation type: Independent foundation.
Financial data (yr. ended 12/31/14): Assets,
$8,539,808 (M); gifts received, $5,914,286;
expenditures, $314,735; qualifying distributions,
$305,580; giving activities include $305,580 for 37
grants (high: $60,500; low: $100).
Fields of interest: Arts and culture; Education;
Protestantism.
Limitations: Applications accepted. Giving primarily
in Atlanta, GA. No grants to individuals.
Application information:
Initial approach: Proposal
Deadline(s): None
Officers and Trustees: Elizabeth Klump, Co-Pres.
and Trustee; Michael Klump, Co-Pres. and Trustee.
EIN: 205756777

2534
Knox Charity Fund, Inc.
P.O. Box 1900
Thomson, GA 30824-5900

Established in 1985 in Georgia.
Donors: Wyckliffe A. Knox, Jr.; Byrnece Swanson
Charitable Remainder Trust; Wyckliffe A. Knox.
Foundation type: Independent foundation.
Financial data (yr. ended 12/31/13): Assets,
$6,358,648 (M); expenditures, $393,258;
qualifying distributions, $350,817; giving activities
include $350,817 for 19 grants (high: $50,000;
low: $100).
Purpose and activities: Giving for the arts,
education, children and youth services, and
historical preservation societies.
Fields of interest: Arts and culture; Historic
preservation; Education; Higher education;
Nonprofits; Health; Protestantism; Human services;
Child welfare.
Type of support: General support; Capital
campaigns; Regranting.
Limitations: Applications not accepted. Giving
primarily in GA. No grants to individuals.
Application information: Contributes only to
pre-selected organizations.
Officers: Wyckliffe A. Knox, Pres.; Shell H. Knox,
Secy.
EIN: 592640739

2535
The L. And C. Wood Family Foundation,
Inc.
3621 Vinings Slope S.E., Ste. 4400
Atlanta, GA 30339-4194

Donors: Carla O' Neill Wood; Leonard W. Wood.

Foundation type: Independent foundation.
Financial data (yr. ended 06/30/13): Assets, $658,842 (M); gifts received, $1,041,252; expenditures, $386,995; qualifying distributions, $386,580; giving activities include $379,550 for 7 grants (high: $250,000; low: $250).
Fields of interest: Education; Religion; Human services; Children.
Limitations: Applications not accepted. Giving primarily in GA and NC.
Application information: Unsolicited requests for funds not accepted.
Officers and Directors: Leonard W. Wood, Pres. and Director; Carla O' Neill Wood, Secy. and Director; Vicki Manus, Treas.; Keving John Wood; Leonard W. Wood, Jr.
EIN: 461605907

2536
Mills Bee Lane Memorial Foundation

c/o South State Bank
25 Bull St., Ste. 501
Savannah, GA 31401 (912) 629-6503

Established in 1947 in Georgia.
Foundation type: Independent foundation.
Financial data (yr. ended 12/31/13): Assets, $7,139,815 (M); expenditures, $424,068; qualifying distributions, $409,958; giving activities include $404,647 for 23 grants (high: $160,000; low: $1,000).
Purpose and activities: Giving primarily for education and conservation.
Fields of interest: Elementary and secondary education; Higher education; Natural resources; Biodiversity; Wildlife biodiversity.
Limitations: Applications accepted. Giving primarily in GA, and Charleston, SC,. No grants to individuals or for operating budgets; no loans.
Application information:
  Initial approach: Proposal
  Copies of proposal: 1
  Deadline(s): None
Officers: Hugh C. Lane, Jr., Pres.; Mills Lane Morrison, Secy.
Trustee: Charles G. Lane.
EIN: 586033043

2537
The Alice and Noah N. Langdale, Jr. Foundation, Inc.

1100 Peachtree St., Ste. S1600
Atlanta, GA 30309-4501

Established in 2005 in Georgia.
Donor: Noah N. Langdale, Jr.†.
Foundation type: Independent foundation.
Financial data (yr. ended 12/31/13): Assets, $7,965,899 (M); gifts received, $17,147; expenditures, $430,580; qualifying distributions, $375,000; giving activities include $375,000 for 22 grants (high: $100,000; low: $1,000).
Fields of interest: Education; Health.
Limitations: Applications not accepted. Giving primarily in GA.
Application information: Unsolicited requests for funds not accepted.
Officers: Harold E. Abrams, Pres.; Ed L. Stelling III, V.P.; Mary Balent Long, Secy.; Margaret M. Smith, Treas.
EIN: 203149328

2538
The Thomas H. Lanier Foundation

c/o Yancey L. McCollum
456 Peachtree Battle Ave. N.W.
Atlanta, GA 30305-4061

Established in 1994 in Georgia.
Donor: Reese J. Lanier.
Foundation type: Independent foundation.
Financial data (yr. ended 03/31/13): Assets, $7,841,639 (M); expenditures, $355,391; qualifying distributions, $331,900; giving activities include $331,900 for 67 grants (high: $25,000; low: $500).
Purpose and activities: Giving primarily for arts and culture, education, health, and social services.
Fields of interest: Arts and culture; Education; Diseases and conditions; Human services; Youth services.
Limitations: Applications not accepted. Giving primarily in Atlanta, GA. No grants to individuals.
Application information: Contributes only to pre-selected organizations.
Trustees: J. Reese Lanier; Yancey L. McCollum.
EIN: 586266735

2539
The Lassiter Family Charitable Foundation

3750 N. Stratford Rd. N.E.
Atlanta, GA 30342-4327

Donors: E.G. Lassiter III; Marianne B. Lassiter.
Foundation type: Independent foundation.
Financial data (yr. ended 06/30/13): Assets, $9,953,425 (M); gifts received, $10,016,909; expenditures, $328,172; qualifying distributions, $302,804; giving activities include $294,200 for 13 grants (high: $145,000; low: $1,000).
Fields of interest: Education; Christianity; Human services.
Limitations: Applications not accepted. Giving primarily in Atlanta, GA.
Application information: Unsolicited requests for funds not accepted.
Officers: E.G. Lassiter III, Pres.; Marianne B. Lassiter, Secy.; Richard G. Lassiter, Treas.
Trustee: Ann Marie Johnston.
EIN: 461402786

2540
The Ray M. and Mary Elizabeth Lee Foundation, Inc.

3414 Peachtree Rd., Ste. 722
Atlanta, GA 30326-1166 (404) 842-1870
Contact: Larry B. Hooks, Admin. Mgr.

Established in 1966 in Georgia.
Donors: Ray M. Lee†; Mary Elizabeth Lee†.
Foundation type: Independent foundation.
Financial data (yr. ended 09/30/13): Assets, $9,643,003 (M); expenditures, $502,874; qualifying distributions, $430,701; giving activities include $365,600 for 70 grants (high: $30,000; low: $1,000).
Fields of interest: Arts and culture; Performing arts; Theater; Education; Elementary and secondary education; Higher education; Health; Hospital care; Diseases and conditions; Religion; Christianity; Human services; Family services; Child welfare.
Type of support: General support; Pro bono consulting services; Matching grants; Continuing

support; Annual campaigns; Capital campaigns; Capital and infrastructure; Equipment; Land acquisitions; Debt reduction; Emergency funds; Program development; Convening; Professorships; Publications; Curriculum development; Fellowships; Internships; Scholarships; Research; Technical assistance; Individual development.
Limitations: Applications accepted. Giving limited to the metropolitan Atlanta, GA, area. No grants to individuals or for endowments.
Publications: Application guidelines.
Application information:
  Initial approach: Letter
  Copies of proposal: 1
  Deadline(s): Jan. 31, Apr. 30, July 31, and Oct. 31
  Board meeting date(s): Feb., May, Aug., and Nov.
  Final notification: Following board meeting
Trustees: Ronald Gann; Donald D. Smith.
Number of staff: 1 part-time professional.
EIN: 586049441

2541
Blanche Lipscomb Foundation, Inc.

c/o Doug Ellis
3350 Riverwood Pkwy., Ste. 1900
Atlanta, GA 30339

Established in 1945 in Georgia.
Donors: William D. Ellis†; Southern Mills.
Foundation type: Independent foundation.
Financial data (yr. ended 12/31/13): Assets, $3,991,825 (M); gifts received, $425,000; expenditures, $201,000; qualifying distributions, $196,000; giving activities include $195,000 for 13 grants (high: $50,000; low: $5,000).
Purpose and activities: Giving primarily for education, the arts and for human services.
Fields of interest: Arts and culture; Higher education; Basic and remedial instruction; Reading promotion; Nonprofits; Hospital care; Community and economic development; Christianity; Human services; Child welfare.
Type of support: Annual campaigns; Capital and infrastructure; Seed money; Regranting.
Limitations: Applications not accepted. Giving limited to the metropolitan Atlanta, GA, area. No grants to individuals.
Application information: Contributes only to pre-selected organizations.
Officers: Richard A. Oglesby, Jr., Pres.; Florida Ellis Huff, V.P.; William D. Ellis, Jr., Secy.
Number of staff: None.
EIN: 586033155

2542
The Martha and Wilton Looney Foundation, Inc.

4470 Sentinel Post Rd. N.W.
Atlanta, GA 30327-3912 (404) 261-0473
Contact: Bruce L. Dick, Secy.-Treas.

Established in 1992 in Georgia.
Donors: Wilton D. Looney; Martha W. Looney.
Foundation type: Independent foundation.
Financial data (yr. ended 12/31/13): Assets, $7,908,760 (M); gifts received, $51,500; expenditures, $316,181; qualifying distributions, $310,498; giving activities include $310,100 for 33 grants (high: $65,000; low: $1,000).

Fields of interest: Education; Higher education; Animal welfare; Health; Diseases and conditions; Protestantism; Human services; Children.
Limitations: Applications accepted. Giving primarily in GA, with some emphasis on Atlanta. No grants to individuals.
Application information:
Initial approach: Proposal
Deadline(s): None
Officers: Sylvia L. Dick, Chair.; Wilton D. Looney, Vice-Chair.; Bruce L. Dick, Secy.-Treas.
Trustee: Martha W. Looney.
EIN: 582022885

2543
James D. and Diane S. Magnus Foundation Inc.
2410 Hilton Way, S.W.
Gainesville, GA 30501-6192

Donor: Conditioned Air Systems, Inc.
Foundation type: Company-sponsored foundation.
Financial data (yr. ended 12/31/13): Assets, $1,636,529 (M); expenditures, $174,256; qualifying distributions, $168,600; giving activities include $168,600 for 12 grants (high: $10,000; low: $500).
Purpose and activities: The foundation supports organizations involved with K-12 education, health, children services, residential care, and Christianity.
Fields of interest: Education; Elementary and secondary education; Health; Christianity; Human services; Child welfare; Shelter and residential care.
Type of support: General support; Continuing support; Annual campaigns; Program development; Scholarships; Student aid.
Limitations: Applications not accepted. Giving primarily in Gainesville, GA.
Application information: Unsolicited requests for funds not accepted.
Trustees: Brooke Kalinauskas; Diane S. Magnus; James D. Magnus; Matthew Magnus; Baya M. Pruitt.
EIN: 600000489

2544
The Billi Marcus Foundation, Inc.
1266 W. Paces Ferry Rd., Ste. 615
Atlanta, GA 30327-2306
Bernie and Billi Marcus's Giving Pledge
Profile: http://glasspockets.org/
philanthropy-in-focus/eye-on-the-giving-pledge/
profiles/marcus
Givesmart: http://www.givesmart.org/Stories/
Donors/Bernie-Marcus

Established in 1998 in Georgia.
Donor: Bernard Marcus.
Foundation type: Independent foundation.
Financial data (yr. ended 12/31/13): Assets, $10,537,064 (M); expenditures, $427,256; qualifying distributions, $377,292; giving activities include $375,292 for 144 grants (high: $30,000; low: $100).
Purpose and activities: Giving primarily for Jewish organizations, including through an affiliated family foundation.
Fields of interest: Education; Nonprofits; Hospice care; Judaism; Human services.
Type of support: Scholarships; Program development; General support; Regranting.

Limitations: Applications not accepted. Giving primarily in GA. No grants to individuals.
Application information: Contributes only to pre-selected organizations.
Officers: Billi Marcus, Chair.; Frederick S. Slagle, Secy.-Treas.
Directors: Carolyn Paller; Jason Smith.
EIN: 582396542

2545
Mattie H. Marshall Foundation
c/o SunTrust Bank
P.O. Box 4655, MC221
Atlanta, GA 30302-4655 (404) 813-2021
Contact: Emily Butler, Grants Mgr., SunTrust Bank
E-mail: fdnsvcs.ga@suntrust.com; Main URL: http://
fdnweb.org/marshall

Established in 1963 in Georgia.
Donors: Thomas O. Marshall; Mrs. Thomas O. Marshall.
Foundation type: Independent foundation.
Financial data (yr. ended 12/31/13): Assets, $8,861,127 (M); expenditures, $410,426; qualifying distributions, $388,680; giving activities include $363,669 for 21 grants (high: $40,000; low: $7,262).
Purpose and activities: Giving to organizations that provide support to orphans, hospitals, nursing for the aged, and Methodist churches that assist retired ministers.
Fields of interest: Higher education; Animal welfare; Hospital care; Presbyterianism; Human services; Senior services; Seniors; Retired people.
Type of support: General support; Annual campaigns; Capital campaigns; Capital and infrastructure; Endowments; Program development.
Limitations: Applications accepted. Giving limited to GA, with emphasis on Americus and southern GA. No grants to individuals.
Publications: Application guidelines.
Application information:
Initial approach: Letter
Copies of proposal: 1
Deadline(s): Feb. 15 and Aug. 15
Board meeting date(s): Spring and fall
Final notification: Dec. 31
Trustee: SunTrust Bank.
Director: Martha Marshall Dykes.
EIN: 586042019

2546
The Devereaux F. and Dorothy McClatchey Foundation, Inc.
66 Avery Dr., N.E.
Atlanta, GA 30309-2702
Contact: Eve McCLatchey Saunders, Pres.

Established in 1990 in Georgia.
Donors: Devereaux F. McClatchey; Dorothy M. McClatchey†.
Foundation type: Independent foundation.
Financial data (yr. ended 12/31/13): Assets, $4,726,108 (M); expenditures, $440,414; qualifying distributions, $307,894; giving activities include $289,000 for 18 grants (high: $118,500; low: $1,000).
Purpose and activities: Giving primarily for the arts, environmental conservation and protection, animal/wildlife welfare and protection, and social services; some funding for research projects.

Fields of interest: Arts and culture; Natural history museums; Education; Community college education; Environment; Natural resources; Biodiversity; Wildlife biodiversity; Domesticated animals; Nonprofits; Human services.
Type of support: General support; Scholarships; Research; Regranting.
Limitations: Applications accepted. Giving primarily in Atlanta, GA. No grants to individuals directly.
Application information: Application form required.
Initial approach: Required application form
Deadline(s): None
Officers: John M. Saunders, Pres.; Eve McClatchey Saunders, V.P.; Elaine Knight, Secy.; Patricia J. Klein, Treas.
EIN: 586250115

2547
McKinney-Geib Foundation, Inc.
3758 Kasey Ln.
Buford, GA 30519-7857

Established in 2004 in Georgia.
Donor: Barkley M. Geib.
Foundation type: Independent foundation.
Financial data (yr. ended 12/31/14): Assets, $3,904,103; expenditures, $430,673; qualifying distributions, $244,275.
Fields of interest: Environmental education; Diabetes; Christianity; Human services; Child welfare.
Type of support: General support; Research.
Limitations: Applications not accepted. Giving primarily in GA; giving also in DE, FL, MA, NY, and TN. No grants to individuals.
Application information: Contributes only to pre-selected organizations.
Officers and Directors: Barkley M. Geib, Pres. and Treas. and Director; Denise N. Geib, Secy. and Director; David Groom.
EIN: 202017121

2548
Loretta Haley McKnight Charitable Trust Fund
c/o Regions Bank, Trust Dept.
333 W. Broad Ave.
Albany, GA 31701-2568 (229) 438-2450
Contact: G. Edmund Nobles

Established in 1975 in Georgia.
Donor: Loretta Haley McKnight†.
Foundation type: Independent foundation.
Financial data (yr. ended 04/30/13): Assets, $4,118,647 (M); expenditures, $230,665; qualifying distributions, $192,760; giving activities include $192,760 for 28 grants (high: $61,710; low: $250).
Fields of interest: Theater; Historical activities; Higher education; Environment; Human services; Youth services.
Type of support: General support; Continuing support; Capital campaigns; Capital and infrastructure.
Limitations: Applications accepted. Giving primarily in GA.
Application information:
Initial approach: Proposal
Deadline(s): None

Trustees: Emily Jean H. McAfee; Regions Bank Trust Dept.
EIN: 586222875

2549
The Miracle Makers Foundation, Inc.
1273 Manor Oaks Ct.
Dunwoody, GA   30338-2756

Established in 2006 in Georgia.
Donor: Penni A. Alper.
Foundation type: Independent foundation.
Financial data (yr. ended 06/30/13): Assets, $4,102,456 (M); expenditures, $231,721; qualifying distributions, $207,750; giving activities include $205,000 for 7 grants (high: $80,000; low: $15,000).
Fields of interest: Education.
Limitations: Applications not accepted. Giving primarily in GA, MO and TN. No grants to individuals.
Application information: Unsolicited requests for funds not accepted.
Officers and Directors: Penni A. Alper, Chair. and Treas. and Director; Wendi Alper Pressman, Vice-Chair. and Director; Dale E. Reid.
EIN: 208063764

2550
Charles L. Mix Memorial Fund, Inc.
P.O. Box 704
Americus, GA   31709-0704   2299284008

Established in 1957 in Georgia.
Donor: Jeannette C. Mix†.
Foundation type: Independent foundation.
Financial data (yr. ended 12/31/14): Assets, $8,928,077; expenditures, $502,694; qualifying distributions, $417,458.
Purpose and activities: Giving primarily for higher and other education, as well as for the arts and human services.
Fields of interest: Arts and culture; Theater; Historical activities; Education; Higher education; Hospital care; Human services.
Limitations: Applications not accepted. Giving primarily in Americus, GA. No grants to individuals.
Application information: Unsolicited requests for funds not accepted.
Officers: Russell Thomas, Jr., Chair.; Charles R. Crisp, Vice-Chair.; James C. Gatewood, Secy.-Treas.
Directors: Gatewood Dudley; Wade Halstead; George Hooks; Rick Whaley.
EIN: 580699008

2551
Montgomery Foundation II Inc.
1230 Peachtree St. N.E., Ste. 3100
Atlanta, GA   30309-3550

Donor: The Montgomery Foundation.
Foundation type: Independent foundation.
Financial data (yr. ended 12/31/13): Assets, $7,237,420 (M); expenditures, $367,901; qualifying distributions, $345,135; giving activities include $330,000 for 7 grants (high: $100,000; low: $5,000).
Fields of interest: Education; Health; Speech and hearing rehabilitation; Diseases and conditions.
Type of support: Research.

Limitations: Applications not accepted. Giving primarily in GA and TN.
Application information: Unsolicited requests for funds not accepted.
Officers: Nancy T. Montgomery, Pres.; Laura L. Wartner, Secy.; Harry Morgan, Treas.
EIN: 274036345

2552
W. Newton Morris Charitable Foundation
c/o The Forum
3290 Northside Pkwy. N.W., Ste. 950
Atlanta, GA   30327   (678) 538-2000
Contact: Melissa B. White

Established in 1998 in Georgia.
Donor: W. Newton Morris.
Foundation type: Independent foundation.
Financial data (yr. ended 06/30/13): Assets, $4,119,946 (M); expenditures, $281,902; qualifying distributions, $240,101; giving activities include $193,459 for 1 grant.
Purpose and activities: Support for programs that further public awareness of American, European, and Asian (including those cultures defined as Oriental and Islamic) decorative art, paintings, drawings and prints representative of these cultures for use solely within the U.S. or its possessions.
Fields of interest: Arts and culture; Art museums.
Type of support: General support.
Limitations: Applications accepted. Giving primarily in GA.
Application information:
   Initial approach: Proposal
   Deadline(s): None
Officers: Edward S. Hallman, Fdn. Mgr.; D. Jack Sawyer, Jr., Fdn. Mgr.; William E. Torres, Fdn. Mgr.
Trustee: BNY Mellon, N.A.
EIN: 586335613

2553
The Morris Family Foundation, Inc.
(formerly The Michael A. Morris Foundation, Inc.)
1266 W. Paces Ferry Rd., Ste. 615
Atlanta, GA   30327-2306
Bernie and Billi Marcus's Giving Pledge
Profile: http://glasspockets.org/philanthropy-in-focus/eye-on-the-giving-pledge/profiles/marcus
Givesmart: http://www.givesmart.org/Stories/Donors/Bernie-Marcus

Established in 1998 in Georgia.
Donor: Bernard Marcus.
Foundation type: Independent foundation.
Financial data (yr. ended 12/31/12): Assets, $1,891,988 (M); expenditures, $336,632; qualifying distributions, $325,611; giving activities include $225,897 for 68 grants (high: $18,000; low: $100).
Fields of interest: Museums; Secondary education; Higher education; Nonprofits; Judaism.
Type of support: Regranting.
Limitations: Applications not accepted. Giving primarily in the greater Atlanta, GA, area. No grants to individuals.
Application information: Contributes only to pre-selected organizations.
Officers: Michael Morris, Chair.; Frederick Slagle, Secy.-Treas.
Director: Belinda Morris.

Trustee: Andrew Suss.
EIN: 582396544

2554
Myfifident Foundation
555 Sun Valley Dr., Ste. K-4
Roswell, GA   30076-5629   (770) 709-5010
Contact: Derek V. Smith, Tr.

Established in 2004 in Georgia.
Donor: Derek V. Smith.
Foundation type: Independent foundation.
Financial data (yr. ended 12/31/13): Assets, $11,165,750 (M); expenditures, $727,161; qualifying distributions, $588,129; giving activities include $354,164 for 4 grants (high: $278,075; low: $2,500).
Fields of interest: Literature and writing; Education; University education; Science; Religion.
Type of support: General support.
Limitations: Applications accepted. Giving primarily in GA. No grants to individuals.
Application information: Application form required.
   Initial approach: Letter
   Deadline(s): None
Trustee: Derek V. Smith.
EIN: 206363957

2555
The Nabors to Neighbors Foundation Inc.
P.O. Box 1405
Dalton, GA   30722-1405   (706) 226-5507
FAX: (706) 275-6691;
E-mail: naborstoneighbors@gmail.com; Main URL: http://www.naborstoneighbors.org

Foundation type: Independent foundation.
Financial data (yr. ended 12/31/13): Assets, $5,529,305 (M); expenditures, $271,992; qualifying distributions, $243,063; giving activities include $243,063 for 17 grants (high: $50,000; low: $2,000).
Fields of interest: Education; Health; Protestantism.
Limitations: Applications accepted. Giving primarily in GA and TN.
Application information: See foundation web site for complete application guidelines. Application form required.
   Deadline(s): Feb. 1, July 1, or Oct. 1
Officer: Eddie Nabors, Mgr.
Trustee: Caleb J. Carnes, C.P.A.
EIN: 260763254

2556
Marjorie A. Neuhoff Private Foundation Inc.
c/o Oliver C. Murray Jr.
964 Racetrack Rd.
McDonough, GA   30252-6847

Donor: Majorie A. Neuhoff Recovable Trust.
Foundation type: Independent foundation.
Financial data (yr. ended 12/31/14): Assets, $7,717,116; expenditures, $415,229; qualifying distributions, $337,000.
Fields of interest: Animal welfare.
Limitations: Applications not accepted.
Application information: Unsolicited requests for funds not accepted.

Officers: Robert L. Dozier, Pres.; Matthew B. Dozier, Exec. V.P.; Oliver C. Murray, Jr., Secy.
EIN: 264520756

2557
The Nonami Foundation, Inc.
3445 Peachtree Rd., Ste. 175
Atlanta, GA 30326-1234

Established in 2006 in Georgia.
Donors: Thomas G. Cousins; Lillian C. Giornelli; Gregory J. Giornelli.
Foundation type: Independent foundation.
Financial data (yr. ended 12/31/13): Assets, $6,742,252 (M); expenditures, $329,392; qualifying distributions, $318,238; giving activities include $315,208 for 19 grants (high: $100,000; low: $1,500).
Fields of interest: Higher education; Nonprofits.
Type of support: Regranting.
Limitations: Applications not accepted. Giving primarily in GA and NH. No grants to individuals.
Application information: Unsolicited requests for funds not accepted.
Officers and Directors: Lillian C. Giornelli, Pres. and Director; Gregory J. Giornelli, V.P. and Director; Laura Whitaker, Secy.-Treas.
EIN: 208083384

2558
The Thomas E. Noonan Family Foundation
3500 Riverly Rd. N.W.
Atlanta, GA 30327-2526

Established in 2006 in Georgia.
Donor: Thomas E. Noonan.
Foundation type: Independent foundation.
Financial data (yr. ended 09/30/14): Assets, $7,085,769; expenditures, $394,942; qualifying distributions, $336,110.
Fields of interest: Arts and culture; Elementary and secondary education; Higher education; Environment; Health; Christianity; Camps; Children; People with disabilities.
Limitations: Applications not accepted. Giving primarily in GA. No grants to individuals.
Application information: Contributes only to pre-selected organizations.
Trustee: Thomas E. Noonan.
Distribution Committee: Christopher B. Noonan; Kimbrough P. Noonan.
EIN: 205508805

2559
Barbara and Sanford H. Orkin Foundation
(formerly Sanford H. Orkin Foundation)
3050 Peachtree Rd. N.W., Ste. 530
Atlanta, GA 30305

Donor: Sanford H. Orkin.
Foundation type: Independent foundation.
Financial data (yr. ended 12/31/13): Assets, $15,843,240 (M); expenditures, $569,546; qualifying distributions, $385,862; giving activities include $385,862 for 21 grants (high: $131,500; low: $50).
Purpose and activities: Giving primarily for higher education and Jewish organizations.
Fields of interest: Arts and culture; Art museums; Higher education; Nonprofits; Judaism.

Type of support: Regranting.
Limitations: Applications not accepted. Giving primarily in GA. No grants to individuals.
Application information: Contributes only to pre-selected organizations.
Officers: Sanford Orkin, Pres.; Barbara Orkin, V.P. and Secy.
EIN: 581451650

2560
William B. Orkin Foundation, Inc.
12600 Deerfield Pkwy., Ste. 150
Milton, GA 30004-5099
Main URL: http://www.orkinandassociates.com/about/community-involvement

Established in 2004 in Georgia.
Donor: William B. Orkin.
Foundation type: Independent foundation.
Financial data (yr. ended 12/31/13): Assets, $5,609,275 (M); expenditures, $315,345; qualifying distributions, $258,936; giving activities include $255,825 for 26 grants (high: $95,000; low: $500).
Purpose and activities: The foundation's mission is to support a variety of causes, with a focus on helping children and animals.
Fields of interest: Elementary and secondary education; Higher education; Animal welfare; Health; Diseases and conditions; Christianity; Judaism; Child welfare.
Type of support: General support.
Limitations: Applications not accepted. Giving primarily in GA. No grants to individuals.
Application information: Contributes only to pre-selected organizations.
Officer: Adam Orkin, Pres.
EIN: 202011970

2561
Oxford Industries Foundation, Inc.
999 Peachtree St., NEm Ste. 688
Atlanta, GA 30309 (404) 653-1419
Contact: Ginger Moff
E-mail: gmoff@oxfordinc.com; Main URL: http://investor.oxfordinc.com/community.cfm

Established in 1975 in Georgia.
Donor: Oxford Industries, Inc.
Foundation type: Company-sponsored foundation.
Financial data (yr. ended 12/31/14): Assets, $463,433 (M); expenditures, $196,815; qualifying distributions, $186,776; giving activities include $186,776 for 26 grants (high: $30,000; low: $100).
Purpose and activities: The foundation supports organizations involved with arts and humanities, health, and public affairs. Special emphasis is directed toward education and human and community services.
Fields of interest: Arts and culture; Humanities; Education; Health; Public affairs; Human services.
Type of support: General support; Employee matching gifts; Cash grants; Regranting; Continuing support; Annual campaigns; Capital campaigns.
Limitations: Applications accepted. Giving limited to Pasadena, CA, Atlanta, Lyons, Toccoa, and Vidalia, GA, New York, NY, and Seattle, WA. No support for lobbying organizations. No grants to individuals, or for goodwill or journal advertisements, political campaigns, conferences, or surveys.
Publications: Application guidelines.

Application information: Support is limited to 1 contribution per organization during any given year.
Initial approach: Proposal
Deadline(s): None
Trustees: Thomas C. Chubb III; K. Scott Grassmyer; J. Hicks Lanier.
EIN: 581209452

2562
Patrick Family Foundation, Inc.
P.O. Box 1048
Decatur, GA 30031-1048 (404) 687-8999
Contact: Hilda B. Patrick, Secy.-Treas.

Established in 1988 in Georgia.
Donors: Joseph E. Patrick, Sr.†; Geraldine A. Patrick.
Foundation type: Independent foundation.
Financial data (yr. ended 09/30/14): Assets, $5,544,619 (M); expenditures, $314,952; qualifying distributions, $266,845; giving activities include $260,000 for 41 grants (high: $35,000; low: $1,000).
Purpose and activities: The primary emphasis of the foundation is support of institutions of the Presbyterian Church (USA), and a secondary focus is on the capital expenditures of local charities in the communities of the directors.
Fields of interest: Higher education; Protestantism; Human services.
Type of support: Capital campaigns.
Limitations: Applications accepted. Giving primarily in GA and OH, and nationally for institutions of the Presbyterian Church. No support for private, primary, or secondary schools or national organizations. No grants to individuals.
Application information: Application form required.
Initial approach: Proposal
Deadline(s): Nov. 1 for Winter meeting and May 1 for Summer meeting
Board meeting date(s): Summer
Officers: Dorothea P. Smith, Pres.; Joseph E. Patrick, Jr., 1st V.P.; William L. Smith IV, 2nd V.P.; Hilda B. Patrick, Secy.-Treas.
EIN: 581820403

2563
The Pattillo Family Foundation
(formerly The Dan and Anne Pattillo Family Foundation, Inc.)
10 Old Vermont Pl. N.W.
Atlanta, GA 30328-4760

Established in 1988 in Georgia.
Donor: Daniel B. Pattillo, Sr.
Foundation type: Independent foundation.
Financial data (yr. ended 12/31/13): Assets, $5,259,575 (M); expenditures, $293,806; qualifying distributions, $204,401; giving activities include $204,401 for 15 grants (high: $60,000; low: $1,000).
Fields of interest: Elementary and secondary education; Higher education; Health; Christianity; Protestantism; Human services.
Limitations: Applications not accepted. Giving primarily in GA. No grants to individuals.
Application information: Unsolicited requests for funds not accepted.
Officers: David A. Pattillo, Pres.; Daniel B. Pattillo, Jr., V.P. and Secy.-Treas.

Director: Daniel B. Pattillo, Sr.
EIN: 581774097

2564

The Pechter Foundation

1266 Bellaire Ln.
Atlanta, GA 30319-3391

Donor: Richard S. Pechter.
Foundation type: Independent foundation.
Financial data (yr. ended 12/31/13): Assets,
$1,970,033 (M); expenditures, $442,209;
qualifying distributions, $434,375; giving activities
include $434,375 for 40 grants (high: $194,500;
low: $100).
Fields of interest: Arts and culture; Education;
Higher education; Diseases and conditions; Human
services.
Limitations: Applications not accepted. Giving
primarily in NJ and NY. No grants to individuals.
Application information: Contributes only to
pre-selected organizations.
Officer: Richard S. Pechter, Pres. and Secy.-Treas.
EIN: 133711334

2565

Pennies From Heaven Foundation, Inc.

1373 Hwy. 85 Connector
Brooks, GA 30205-2230

Established in 1998 in Georgia.
Donors: Carol F. McClain; Randolph S. McClain.
Foundation type: Operating foundation.
Financial data (yr. ended 12/31/14): Assets,
$5,106,994; expenditures, $320,281; qualifying
distributions, $300,760.
Fields of interest: Elementary and secondary
education; Residential mental health care;
Christianity; Human services; Substance abusers.
Type of support: General support.
Limitations: Applications not accepted. Giving
primarily in GA. No grants to individuals.
Application information: Contributes only to
pre-selected organizations.
Officers: Randy McClain, Chair.; Charles B. Pyke, Jr.,
Secy.; Carol F. McClain, Treas.
EIN: 582419565

2566

Piedmont Charitable Foundation, Inc.

Piedmont 14, 3535 Piedmont Rd., Ste. P88
Atlanta, GA 30305-1530
Contact: Margaret R. Buker, Pres.

Established in 1957 in Georgia.
Donor: Elizabeth S. Robinson.
Foundation type: Independent foundation.
Financial data (yr. ended 12/31/13): Assets,
$5,757,843 (M); expenditures, $282,062;
qualifying distributions, $237,779; giving activities
include $214,500 for 38 grants (high: $20,000;
low: $500).
Fields of interest: Arts and culture; Performing arts;
Museums; Elementary and secondary education;
Higher education; Hospital care; Youth
development; Youth services.
Limitations: Applications accepted. Giving primarily
in VA and GA. No grants to individuals.
Application information: Application form required.

Initial approach: Letter
Deadline(s): None
Officers: Margaret R. Buker, Pres.; Elizabeth S.
Robinson, V.P.; R. Lee Robinson, Secy.-Treas.
EIN: 586035073

2567

The Frances Pilling and John B. Cross, Jr. Foundation

P. O. Box 4655 Mail Code 221
Atlanta, GA 30302-4655

Established in 2005 in Georgia.
Donor: Frances Pilling Cross†.
Foundation type: Independent foundation.
Financial data (yr. ended 12/31/14): Assets,
$2,839,708 (M); expenditures, $171,937;
qualifying distributions, $136,000; giving activities
include $136,000 for 13 grants (high: $85,000;
low: $2,000).
Fields of interest: Elementary and secondary
education; Health; Child welfare.
Limitations: Applications not accepted. Giving
primarily in GA. No grants to individuals.
Application information: Unsolicited requests for
funds not accepted.
Trustees: Alton H. Hopkins; Carolyn F. Hopkins; T.
Downing Hopkins; Virginia C. Hopkins; SunTrust
Bank.
EIN: 206340099

2568

The Mark C. Pope III Foundation

120 Ottley Dr. N.E.
Atlanta, GA 30324-3925

Established in 1997 in Georgia.
Donor: Mark C. Pope III.
Foundation type: Independent foundation.
Financial data (yr. ended 12/31/13): Assets,
$5,001,574 (M); gifts received, $50,000;
expenditures, $230,566; qualifying distributions,
$228,089; giving activities include $228,089 for
145 grants (high: $30,000; low: $25).
Fields of interest: Historic preservation; Elementary
and secondary education; Diseases and conditions;
Protestantism.
Type of support: General support.
Limitations: Applications not accepted. Giving
primarily in Atlanta, GA. No grants to individuals.
Application information: Contributes only to
pre-selected organizations.
Trustee: Mark C. Pope III.
EIN: 586353574

2569

The Price Family Foundation, Inc.

4418 Club Dr.
Atlanta, GA 30319-1122

Established in 2003 in Georgia.
Donor: James K. Price.
Foundation type: Independent foundation.
Financial data (yr. ended 12/31/14): Assets,
$14,355; expenditures, $115,723; qualifying
distributions, $115,000.
Fields of interest: Education; Nonprofits;
Protestantism; Human services.
Type of support: Regranting.

Limitations: Applications not accepted. Giving
primarily in Atlanta, GA. No grants to individuals.
Application information: Contributes only to
pre-selected organizations.
Officers: James K. Price, Pres. and Treas.; Christina
M. Price, V.P. and Secy.
EIN: 200253270

2570

The Price-Campbell Foundation

900 Pineridge Dr.
Valdosta, GA 31602-2333

Donor: Mildred M. Price†.
Foundation type: Independent foundation.
Financial data (yr. ended 04/30/14): Assets,
$2,514,960 (M); expenditures, $196,602;
qualifying distributions, $175,205; giving activities
include $150,000 for 10 grants (high: $57,500;
low: $3,000).
Fields of interest: Arts and culture; Education;
Environment; Natural resources; Public libraries;
Human services; Food banks.
Type of support: General support.
Limitations: Applications not accepted. Giving
primarily in Valdosta, GA.
Application information: Unsolicited requests for
funds not accepted.
Trustees: Lucy Acree; John R. Bennett; Barbara K.
Passmore.
EIN: 581530873

2571

Tripp & Blair Rackley Family Foundation, Inc.

c/o Patricia Martin
P.O. Box 966
Commerce, GA 30529-0018

Established in 2007 in Georgia.
Donors: Tripp Rackley; Blair Rackley.
Foundation type: Independent foundation.
Financial data (yr. ended 12/31/13): Assets,
$7,221,335 (M); expenditures, $361,359;
qualifying distributions, $304,500; giving activities
include $304,500 for 5 grants (high: $250,000;
low: $500).
Fields of interest: Education; Protestantism.
Limitations: Applications not accepted. Giving
primarily in Atlanta, GA. No grants to individuals.
Application information: Unsolicited requests for
funds not accepted.
Officer: Brady Rackley III, Pres.; Blair Rackley,
Secy.- Treas.
EIN: 261586843

2572

Carolyn King Ragan Charitable Foundation

(formerly Ragan and King Charitable Foundation)
c/o Wells Fargo Bank, N.A.
3280 Peachtree Rd. N.W., Ste. 300
Atlanta, GA 30305-2449 (404) 238-0444
Contact: Joyce Yamaato
E-mail: grantinquiries8@wachovia.com; Main
URL: https://www.wellsfargo.com/
privatefoundationgrants/ragan-king

Established in 1972 in Georgia.
Donor: Carolyn King Ragan†.
Foundation type: Independent foundation.

Financial data (yr. ended 09/30/13): Assets, $4,842,511 (M); expenditures, $296,046; qualifying distributions, $232,981; giving activities include $215,000 for 5 grants (high: $75,750; low: $9,500).
Purpose and activities: Giving primarily for Baptist organizations and churches; funding also for higher education and human services.
Fields of interest: Higher education; Baptist; Human services.
Limitations: Applications accepted. Giving limited to GA (except for two specific out-of-state beneficiaries). No grants to individuals.
Publications: Application guidelines.
Application information: See foundation web site for complete application guidelines and procedures.
  Initial approach: Use online application system on foundation web site
  Copies of proposal: 1
  Deadline(s): Aug. 1
  Board meeting date(s): Fall
Trustee: Wells Fargo Bank, N.A.
EIN: 586138950

2573
W. G. Raoul Foundation
c/o SunTrust Bank
P.O. Box 4655, MC GA-ATL-0221
Atlanta, GA 30302-4655 (404) 813-2021
Contact: Emily Butler, Grants Mgr., SunTrust Bank
E-mail: fdnsvcs.ga@suntrust.com; Main URL: http://fdnweb.org/raoul

Established in 1913 in Georgia.
Foundation type: Independent foundation.
Financial data (yr. ended 12/31/13): Assets, $4,593,324 (M); expenditures, $208,938; qualifying distributions, $198,135; giving activities include $188,000 for 3 grants (high: $93,100; low: $25,000).
Purpose and activities: The foundation was established to address lung-related diseases in the State of Georgia. The foundation is particularly interested in pediatric asthma programs.
Fields of interest: Respiratory system diseases; Asthma.
Type of support: General support; Research; Capital campaigns; Program development.
Limitations: Applications accepted. Giving limited to GA. No grants to individuals.
Application information: Online application on foundation web site. Application form required.
  Board meeting date(s): Spring and fall
Officers: Frederick VanWinkle, Chair.; Brenda Rambeau, Pres.; Charles Stokes, V.P.; Greg Gerhard, Secy.-Treas.
Trustee: Linda Laird.
EIN: 586026051

2574
Thomas B. and Patricia R. Reynolds Family Foundation, Inc.
P.O. Box 808
Norcross, GA 30091-0808

Established in 1997 in Georgia.
Donors: Thomas B. Reynolds; Patricia R. Renolds; Peach State Truck Center.
Foundation type: Independent foundation.
Financial data (yr. ended 11/30/13): Assets, $1,692,780 (M); gifts received, $200,000;

expenditures, $188,584; qualifying distributions, $187,400; giving activities include $186,525 for 9 grants (high: $75,000; low: $1,000).
Fields of interest: Education; Health; Cancers; Religion.
Type of support: General support.
Limitations: Applications not accepted. Giving limited to Atlanta and Duluth, GA. No grants to individuals.
Application information: Unsolicited requests for funds not accepted.
Officers: Thomas B. Reynolds, Pres.; Ann Reynolds Crouse, Secy.
EIN: 582362169

2575
Charles & Catherine B. Rice Foundation
c/o Pathstone Family Office
P.O. Box 52047
Atlanta, GA 30355-0047

Established in 2004 in Georgia.
Donors: Charles B. Rice, Sr.; Catherine B. Rice.
Foundation type: Independent foundation.
Financial data (yr. ended 12/31/13): Assets, $5,960,577 (M); expenditures, $292,843; qualifying distributions, $214,506; giving activities include $184,472 for 23 grants (high: $55,071; low: $401).
Purpose and activities: Giving primarily for the revitalization of communities, preservation of historical landmarks, the safeguarding of natural resources, promotion of cultural and spiritual heritage, and to serve as a catalyst for collaboration with others for positive and sustainable change.
Fields of interest: Higher education; Environment; Protestantism; Camps; Human services.
Limitations: Applications not accepted. Giving primarily in GA, with some emphasis on Atlanta. No grants to individuals.
Application information: Unsolicited requests for funds not accepted.
Officer: Allan J. Zachariah, Secy.
Trustees: Catherine B. Rice; Charles B. Rice, Sr.
EIN: 201957591

2576
The Rockdale Foundation Inc.
(formerly Rockdale Fund for Social Investment, Inc.)
916 Joseph E. Lowery Blvd. N.W., Ste. 4
Atlanta, GA 30318-5280

Donor: Kathleen M. Barksdale.
Foundation type: Independent foundation.
Financial data (yr. ended 12/31/13): Assets, $5,551,866 (M); expenditures, $660,498; qualifying distributions, $521,263; giving activities include $439,865 for 44 grants (high: $89,590; low: $100).
Fields of interest: Education; Foundations; Right to free movement and asylum; Human services; Child welfare; Low-income and poor people.
Limitations: Applications not accepted. Giving primarily in Atlanta, GA. No grants to individuals.
Application information: Contributes only to pre-selected organizations.
Officers: Kathleen M. Barksdale, Pres.; Winsome Hawkins, Secy.; Jody Stephenson, C.F.O.
Board Members: Joanna Adams; Beverly Hall.
EIN: 582668065

2577
Jonathan D. Rosen Family Foundation, Inc.
1200 Ashwood Pkwy., Ste. 150
Atlanta, GA 30338-4725 (678) 218-1299
Contact: Tracy Tanner, Exec. Dir.

Established in 2009 in Georgia.
Donors: Jonathan D. Rosen; Entaire Global Companies, Inc.; Michelle Spiro; Andy Trotti.
Foundation type: Operating foundation.
Financial data (yr. ended 10/31/13): Assets, $2,666,546 (M); gifts received, $3,238; expenditures, $237,133; qualifying distributions, $222,270; giving activities include $167,895 for 1 grant, and $222,270 for 1 foundation-administered program.
Fields of interest: Economic development; Financial counseling.
Limitations: Applications accepted. Giving primarily in Atlanta, GA.
Application information: Application form required.
  Initial approach: Letter
  Deadline(s): None
Officer: Tracy Tanner, Exec. Dir.
Trustees: Jonathan D. Rosen; Michelle S. Spiro; Andy Trotti.
EIN: 271263846

2578
The Frank Samford Jr. Chess Foundation
3406 Wembley Walk
Tucker, GA 30084-2202

Foundation type: Independent foundation.
Financial data (yr. ended 12/31/14): Assets, $2,161,098 (M); expenditures, $274,419; qualifying distributions, $274,418; giving activities include $211,000 for 3 grants (high: $111,000; low: $10,000).
Purpose and activities: Giving primarily to provide opportunities to promote chess competition for youth.
Fields of interest: Education; Sports and recreation; Human rights; Human services.
Limitations: Applications not accepted. Giving primarily in Wallkill, NY; giving also in AL. No grants to individuals.
Application information: Contributes only to pre-selected organizations.
Trustee: Frank Samford III.
EIN: 586412804

2579
Helen and Harry Saul Foundation, Inc.
2100 Fiber Park Dr.
Dalton, GA 30720-3739

Established in 1993 in Georgia.
Donor: Harry I. Saul†.
Foundation type: Independent foundation.
Financial data (yr. ended 12/31/12): Assets, $3,373,668 (M); expenditures, $438,688; qualifying distributions, $436,440; giving activities include $436,440 for grants.
Fields of interest: Arts and culture; Education; Elementary and secondary education; Higher education; Nonprofits; Judaism.
Type of support: General support; Regranting.
Limitations: Applications not accepted. Giving primarily in GA and TN. No grants to individuals.

Application information: Contributes only to pre-selected organizations.
Trustees: Julian D. Saul; Linda S. Schejola.
EIN: 582063931

2580
Raymond F. Schinazi and Family Foundation, Inc.
1860 Montreal Rd.
Tucker, GA   30084

Established in 2005 in Georgia.
Donors: Raymond F. Schinazi; William H. Prusoff.
Foundation type: Independent foundation.
Financial data (yr. ended 03/31/14): Assets, $17,309,557 (M); gifts received, $849,460; expenditures, $661,178; qualifying distributions, $388,365; giving activities include $380,089 for 30 grants (high: $100,000; low: $100).
Fields of interest: Education; Diseases and conditions; Christianity; Judaism.
Type of support: Research.
Limitations: Applications not accepted. Giving primarily in Atlanta, GA. No grants to individuals.
Application information: Unsolicited requests for funds not accepted.
Officers: Raymond F. Schinazi, Pres.; Nicholas Guttridge, V.P; Charlene Mcnabb, Secy.-Treas.
EIN: 203693012

2581
Schwob Family Foundation, Inc.
(formerly Simon Schwob Foundation)
750 Park Ave., Ste. 41 S.W.
Atlanta, GA   30326-3278

Established in 1949 in Georgia.
Donors: Schwob Manufacturing Co.; Schwob Realty Co.; Schwob Co. of Florida; Henry Schwob.
Foundation type: Independent foundation.
Financial data (yr. ended 12/31/13): Assets, $1,842,531 (M); expenditures, $303,614; qualifying distributions, $273,687; giving activities include $229,600 for 16 grants (high: $100,000; low: $1,000).
Purpose and activities: Giving primarily to Jewish federated giving programs and temples, and for the arts and education.
Fields of interest: Orchestral music; Museums; Higher education; Nonprofits; Judaism.
Type of support: General support; Regranting.
Limitations: Applications not accepted. Giving primarily in Atlanta, GA. No grants to individuals.
Application information: Unsolicited requests for funds not accepted.
Officers: Henry Schwob, Pres.; Joyce Schwob, V.P.; Simone Nehman, Secy.-Treas.
Trustee: Jan Heiman.
EIN: 586038932

2582
SCS Foundation, Inc.
4500 Hugh Howell Rd., Ste. 190
Tucker, GA   30084

Established in 1999 in Georgia.
Donor: Kay S. Swanson.
Foundation type: Independent foundation.
Financial data (yr. ended 11/30/13): Assets, $37,079 (M); gifts received, $150,000;

expenditures, $181,349; qualifying distributions, $181,349; giving activities include $177,465 for 20 grants (high: $31,400; low: $150).
Purpose and activities: Giving primarily to a Methodist church.
Fields of interest: Presbyterianism.
Limitations: Applications not accepted. Giving primarily in GA. No grants to individuals.
Application information: Contributes only to pre-selected organizations.
Officers: Kay S. Swanson, Pres. and Treas.; Dean C. Swanson, V.P. and Secy.
EIN: 582508877

2583
Emily and Bill Searcy Charitable Trust
c/o Thomas H. Vann, Jr. and Richard Mooney
411 Gordon Ave.
Thomasville, GA   31792-6643

Foundation type: Independent foundation.
Financial data (yr. ended 12/31/13): Assets, $7,368,131 (M); expenditures, $343,239; qualifying distributions, $330,000; giving activities include $330,000 for 7 grants (high: $82,500; low: $16,500).
Fields of interest: Cultural awareness; Performing arts; Historic preservation.
Limitations: Applications not accepted. Giving primarily in GA. No grants to individuals.
Application information: Contributes only to pre-selected organizations.
Trustees: Richard G. Mooney III; Thomas H. Vann, Jr.
EIN: 266185511

2584
Warren P. & Ava F. Sewell Foundation, Inc.
217 Davis Blvd.
Bremen, GA   30110-2569
Application address: c/o The Meigs Group, PC, Attn.: Richard Meigs, 411 Alabama Ave., Bremen, GA, tel.: (770) 537-2326

Established in 1989 in Georgia.
Foundation type: Independent foundation.
Financial data (yr. ended 06/30/13): Assets, $4,865,328 (M); expenditures, $297,112; qualifying distributions, $237,243; giving activities include $215,002 for 47 grants (high: $30,000; low: $50).
Purpose and activities: Giving primarily to Baptist churches and for education.
Fields of interest: Elementary education; Secondary education; Baptist; Sports and recreation; Human services.
Type of support: Capital campaigns; Capital and infrastructure.
Limitations: Applications accepted. Giving primarily in eastern AL and Haralson and Carroll counties, GA. No grants to individuals.
Publications: Annual report.
Application information:
Initial approach: Letter
Copies of proposal: 1
Deadline(s): None
Board meeting date(s): Every 60 days
Trustees: L. Richard Plunkett; Warren P. Sewell, Jr.; Robin S. Worley.
EIN: 581791240

2585
The SF Foundation II
c/o Dorothy C. Sadler
P.O. Box 88482
Atlanta, GA   30356

Established in 1996 in Georgia.
Donors: Dorothy C. Sadler; Phillip E. Sadler.
Foundation type: Independent foundation.
Financial data (yr. ended 12/31/13): Assets, $4,930,068 (M); gifts received, $2,784; expenditures, $256,699; qualifying distributions, $206,060; giving activities include $206,060 for 12 grants (high: $100,000; low: $3,500).
Purpose and activities: Giving primarily for education, health associations, children and social services, and to Protestant churches.
Fields of interest: Education; Higher education; Medical education; Diseases and conditions; Alzheimer's disease; Protestantism; Human services; Child welfare.
Limitations: Applications not accepted. Giving primarily in GA. No grants to individuals.
Application information: Contributes only to pre-selected organizations.
Trustee: Dorothy C. Sadler.
EIN: 582277136

2586
William R. and Sara Babb Smith Foundation
P.O. Box 2000
McDonough, GA   30253-1720   (770) 288-7367
Contact: James T. Chafin III, Treas.

Established in 1995 in Georgia.
Donors: Sara Babb Smith; William R. Smith; William R. and Sara Babb Smith Charitable Lead Trust.
Foundation type: Independent foundation.
Financial data (yr. ended 12/31/14): Assets, $3,773,384 (M); expenditures, $274,457; qualifying distributions, $215,256; giving activities include $196,000 for 13 grants (high: $56,000; low: $1,000).
Purpose and activities: Giving primarily for education and social services.
Fields of interest: Education; Higher education; Hospice care; Community and economic development; Christianity; Human services; Food banks.
Type of support: General support; Emergency funds; Scholarships.
Limitations: Applications accepted. Giving primarily in Henry County, GA.
Application information: Application form required.
Initial approach: Letter
Deadline(s): None
Board meeting date(s): Quarterly
Officers: Hans Broder, Pres.; Nancy R. Smith, V.P.; Nancy B. Taylor, Secy.; James T. Chafin III, Treas.
Trustees: Allison Ausband; Kathy H. Engeman; Candace Hoover; Mary Lynn Lambert; Jack Parish, Ph.D.
Number of staff: 1 part-time professional; 1 part-time support.
EIN: 586306403

2587

The Solstice Foundation Inc.
(formerly The Lindenbaum Foundation, Inc.)
6300 Powers Ferry Rd. N.W., Ste. 600
P.O. Box 354
Atlanta, GA 30339-2961

Established in 1996 in Georgia.
Donor: David S. Lindenbaum.
Foundation type: Independent foundation.
Financial data (yr. ended 12/31/13): Assets,
$2,922,632 (M); expenditures, $253,066;
qualifying distributions, $220,280; giving activities
include $220,280 for 22 grants (high: $25,000;
low: $2,500).
Fields of interest: Natural resources; Health;
Nutrition; Diseases and conditions; Christianity;
Special Olympics; Child welfare.
Type of support: General support; Emergency funds;
Program development; Research.
Limitations: Applications not accepted. Giving
primarily in GA. No grants to individuals.
Application information: Contributes only to
pre-selected organizations.
  Board meeting date(s): June 21 and Dec. 21
Directors: Carol S. Lindenbaum; David S.
Lindenbaum.
EIN: 582117440

2588

The Stahl Family Foundation, Inc.
271 17th St. N.W., Ste. 1600
Atlanta, GA 30363-1072

Established in 2001 in Georgia.
Donors: Jack Stahl; Lynn Stahl.
Foundation type: Independent foundation.
Financial data (yr. ended 12/31/14): Assets,
$4,570,972; gifts received, $2,500; expenditures,
$285,112; qualifying distributions, $240,000 and
$0 for set-asides.
Fields of interest: Elementary and secondary
education; Graduate and professional education;
Animal welfare; Nursing care; Holistic medicine;
Human services; Child welfare; Youth services;
People with disabilities.
Type of support: General support; Program
development; Scholarships.
Limitations: Applications not accepted. Giving
primarily in GA, with emphasis on Atlanta.
Application information: Unsolicited requests for
funds not accepted.
Officer: Lynn Stahl, Pres. and Secy.-Treas.
Directors: Katharine Stahl; Samuel Stahl.
EIN: 300017007

2589

Storey Foundation, Inc.
(formerly The Mallie Bert Storey Foundation, Inc.)
3531 Walton Way Ext.
Augusta, GA 30909-1821

Established in 1997 in Georgia.
Donor: Mallie Bert Storey.
Foundation type: Independent foundation.
Financial data (yr. ended 12/31/13): Assets,
$6,225,127 (M); gifts received, $350,000;
expenditures, $246,520; qualifying distributions,
$223,689; giving activities include $222,595 for 85
grants (high: $50,000; low: $10).

Fields of interest: Arts and culture; Education;
Graduate and professional education; Nonprofits;
Engineering; Human services.
Type of support: Regranting.
Limitations: Applications not accepted. Giving
primarily in Augusta, GA. No grants to individuals.
Application information: Unsolicited requests for
funds not accepted.
Officers: Mallie Bert Storey, Chair.; Barry L. Storey,
Secy.; Nan S. Easterlin, Treas.
EIN: 582305034

2590

Strong Tower, Inc.
P.O. Box 56
Hinesville, GA 31310-0056
Application address: c/o C. Joel Osteen, 100 Fraser
St., Hinesville, GA 31313, tel.: (912) 877-2211

Established in 1998 in Georgia.
Donors: Clay Sikes; Justin Osteen; J. Noel Osteen;
Osteen and Osteen; Youman's Trust; United Way.
Foundation type: Independent foundation.
Financial data (yr. ended 12/31/13): Assets,
$15,410 (M); gifts received, $48,211;
expenditures, $131,833; qualifying distributions,
$130,635; giving activities include $130,635 for 4
grants (high: $120,516; low: $750).
Fields of interest: Housing development; Religion;
Youth development.
Limitations: Applications accepted. Giving primarily
in GA. No grants to individuals.
Application information:
  Initial approach: Contact foundation
  Deadline(s): None
Officers: C. Joel Osteen, Pres.; L. Kelly Davis, V.P.
EIN: 582360794

2591

The Sweetgrass Foundation, Inc.
c/o The Forum
3290 Northside Pkwy., N.W., Ste. 950
Atlanta, GA 30327-2273 (678) 538-2029
Contact: Thomas Fuller IV, Chair.
E-mail: contact@thesweetgrassfoundation.org; Main
URL: http://www.thesweetgrassfoundation.org

Established in 1992 in Georgia.
Foundation type: Independent foundation.
Financial data (yr. ended 09/30/14): Assets,
$3,368,953 (M); expenditures, $216,418;
qualifying distributions, $173,646; giving activities
include $167,500 for 18 grants (high: $35,000;
low: $1,500).
Purpose and activities: Giving primarily to
individuals and organizations working directly for
ecological health, and cultural diversity and
preservation. The foundation has a special interest
in the protection of pristine wilderness areas and in
work that supports young people in gaining respect
for the earth.
Fields of interest: Education; Environment; Natural
resources; Human services.
Type of support: General support.
Publications: Application guidelines.
Application information: See foundation web site
for complete application guidelines and procedures.
  Initial approach: Review foundation web site and
    submit an Executive Summary and Proposal via
    foundation web site
Officer: Thomas Fuller IV, Chair.

Directors: Sarah Graham Candler; Cynthia F.
Drisaldi; Aulbrey G. Fuller; Samuel P. Fuller; Kenneth
R. Margolis.
EIN: 582011000

2592

TALX Charitable Foundation
c/o John Elwood
1550 Peachtree St. N.E.
Atlanta, GA 30309-2402
Main URL: http://www.talx.com/aboutus/
foundation.asp

Established in 2004 in Missouri.
Donor: TALX Corporation.
Foundation type: Company-sponsored foundation.
Financial data (yr. ended 03/31/12): Assets,
$2,448,853 (M); gifts received, $2,116;
expenditures, $166,440; qualifying distributions,
$145,013; giving activities include $145,000 for 9
grants (high: $40,000; low: $2,500).
Purpose and activities: The foundation supports
programs designed to enhance the education of
disadvantaged youth in the St. Louis area.
Fields of interest: Education; Charter school
education; Higher education; Economics for youth;
Homeless services; Adolescents; Low-income and
poor people.
Type of support: General support.
Limitations: Applications not accepted. Giving
primarily in St. Louis, MO. No grants to individuals.
Application information: Contributes only to
pre-selected organizations.
Officers and Directors: J. Dann Adams, Pres. and
Director; Ellen A. Stanko, V.P. and Director; William
F. Barge, Secy.-Treas.; Robert Kamerschen;
Kenneth Marshall.
EIN: 202021573

2593

**Terwilliger Family Foundation Charitable
Trust**
6020 Winterthur Dr.
Atlanta, GA 30328-4623

Established in 1990 in Georgia.
Donor: J. Ronald Terwilliger.
Foundation type: Independent foundation.
Financial data (yr. ended 12/31/13): Assets,
$12,149,755 (M); expenditures, $513,482;
qualifying distributions, $408,576; giving activities
include $405,200 for 32 grants (high: $158,500;
low: $200).
Purpose and activities: Giving primarily for
education, health associations, including an
Epilepsy foundation, and children and youth
services, including a children's healthcare
foundation.
Fields of interest: Education; Health; Diseases and
conditions; Epilepsy; Protestantism; Human
services; Child welfare.
Limitations: Applications not accepted. No grants to
individuals.
Application information: Contributes only to
pre-selected organizations.
Trustees: Tracy T. Dean; Bonnie T. Leadbetter;
Patricia B. Terwilliger.
EIN: 586218070

2594

Thames Family Foundation Inc.
c/o Gerald W. Thames
275 Scientific Dr., Ste. 2500
Norcross, GA   30092

Established in 1998 in Georgia.
Donors: Gerald W. Thames; Judy Kaye J. Thames.
Foundation type: Independent foundation.
Financial data (yr. ended 12/31/14): Assets, $2,674,574; expenditures, $219,314; qualifying distributions, $184,688.
Fields of interest: Christianity; Human services.
Type of support: General support.
Limitations: Applications not accepted. Giving primarily in GA.
Application information: Unsolicited requests for funds not accepted.
Officers: Gerald W. Thames, Chair.; Judy Kaye J. Thames, Secy.; David Walker Thames, Treas.
EIN: 582433066

2595

Mark & Evelyn Trammell Foundation, Inc.
1201 W. Peachtree St., Ste. 4200
Atlanta, GA   30309-3424

Donor: Evelyn Trammell†.
Foundation type: Independent foundation.
Financial data (yr. ended 12/31/13): Assets, $5,905,204 (M); expenditures, $296,951; qualifying distributions, $268,000; giving activities include $241,000 for 10 grants (high: $66,000; low: $5,000).
Fields of interest: Arts and culture; Theater; Education; Environment; Human services.
Limitations: Applications not accepted. Giving limited to Atlanta, GA.
Application information: Contributes only to pre-selected organizations.
Officers and Trustees: Philip C. Cook, Chair. and Treas. and Trustee; Benjamin T. White, Pres. and Secy. and Trustee; James S. Hutchinson.
EIN: 581304676

2596

Ramie A. Tritt Family Foundation Inc.
5362 Hallford Dr.
Dunwoody, GA   30338-3610

Established in 1999 in Georgia.
Donors: Ramie A. Tritt; Joyce Tritt; Erica Tritt; Jordan Tritt.
Foundation type: Independent foundation.
Financial data (yr. ended 12/31/13): Assets, $5,175,600 (M); gifts received, $276,509; expenditures, $275,822; qualifying distributions, $238,486; giving activities include $235,631 for 30 grants (high: $120,505; low: $250).
Fields of interest: Elementary and secondary education; Nonprofits; Judaism.
Type of support: General support; Capital campaigns; Regranting.
Limitations: Applications not accepted. Giving primarily in Atlanta and Marietta, GA. No grants to individuals.
Application information: Unsolicited requests for funds not accepted.
Officer and Directors: Ramie A. Tritt, C.E.O. and Director; Joyce Tritt; Lorne Tritt.
EIN: 582500822

2597

The University Financing Foundation, Inc.
(formerly Georgia Scientific and Technical Research Foundation)
3333 Busbee Dr., Ste. 150
Kennesaw, GA   30144-3089   (404) 214-9440
Contact: Thomas H. Hall III, Pres.
FAX: (404) 214-9441; E-mail: tuff@tuff.org; Main URL: http://www.tuff.org
Blog: http://www.tuff.org/news
E Newsletter: http://www.tuff.org/newsletter

Donor: Florida Institute of Technology.
Foundation type: Operating foundation.
Financial data (yr. ended 12/31/14): Assets, $425,765,970 (M); gifts received, $15,600; expenditures, $38,930,414; qualifying distributions, $6,203,953; giving activities include $204,265 for grants, and $36,903,577 for foundation-administered programs.
Purpose and activities: Giving primarily to institutions of education and research, and assists such institutions in the planning, development, and financing of facilities and equipment.
Fields of interest: Higher education; Public policy.
Type of support: Capital and infrastructure; Program-related investments; Equipment; Policy, advocacy and systems reform.
Limitations: Giving primarily in Atlanta, GA.
Application information: Very limited outright grants or gifts awarded.
  Initial approach: Letter, telephone or fax
  Deadline(s): None
Officers and Directors: Thomas Ventulett, Chair. and Director; Thomas H. Hall III, C.E.O. and Pres. and Director; Kevin Byrne, C.O.O. and V.P.; John E. Aderhold, Dir. Emeritus; James M. Sibley, Dir. Emeritus; Lisa A. Beall, Cont.; David M. McKenney; A.J. Robinson.
EIN: 581505902

2598

The Vaughan Foundation
366 Powder Springs St.
Marietta, GA   30064-3424
Contact: C. Frank Moore, Secy.-Treas.

Established in 1996 in Georgia.
Donor: Maud P. Vaughan.
Foundation type: Independent foundation.
Financial data (yr. ended 12/31/13): Assets, $6,616,085 (M); expenditures, $358,570; qualifying distributions, $235,735; giving activities include $235,735 for 28 grants (high: $31,500; low: $500).
Fields of interest: Ballet; Museums; Children's museums; Family services; Youth services; Youth organizing.
Limitations: Applications accepted. Giving primarily in GA. No grants to individuals.
Application information: Application form required.
  Initial approach: Letter
  Deadline(s): None
Officers: Bill Rohner, Pres.; C. Frank Moore, Secy.-Treas.
Trustee: Jean K. Hawkins.
EIN: 581900965

2599

S.Julian Vaughter Charitable Trust
3448 Aberron Pl.
Buford, GA   30519-7982

Foundation type: Independent foundation.
Financial data (yr. ended 12/31/12): Assets, $4,693,907 (M); expenditures, $294,587; qualifying distributions, $163,000; giving activities include $163,000 for 5 grants (high: $32,600; low: $32,600).
Fields of interest: Protestantism; Human services; Youth development.
Limitations: Applications not accepted. Giving primarily in GA.
Application information: Unsolicited requests for funds not accepted.
Trustees: Clyde T. Adams; Harry Hardaway.
EIN: 586404800

2600

Vogel Family Foundation, Inc.
2410 Spalding Dr.
Atlanta, GA   30350   (770) 698-9257
Contact: William A. Vogel, Dir.

Established in 2004 in Georgia.
Foundation type: Independent foundation.
Financial data (yr. ended 12/31/13): Assets, $7,578,782 (M); expenditures, $396,200; qualifying distributions, $384,779; giving activities include $384,779 for 82 grants (high: $60,000; low: $100).
Fields of interest: Music; Higher education; Nonprofits; Housing development; Protestantism; Human services.
Type of support: Regranting.
Limitations: Applications accepted. Giving primarily in Atlanta, GA.
Application information:
  Initial approach: Proposal
  Deadline(s): None
Directors: Judith M. Vogel; William A. Vogel.
EIN: 202015587

2601

Andrew and Cleo Voight Charitable Trust
P.O. Box 23024
Columbus, GA   31902-3024

Established in 2009 in Georgia.
Foundation type: Independent foundation.
Financial data (yr. ended 12/31/13): Assets, $4,380,347 (M); expenditures, $216,874; qualifying distributions, $195,609; giving activities include $177,100 for 1 grant.
Fields of interest: Protestantism.
Limitations: Applications not accepted.
Application information: Unsolicited requests for funds not accepted.
Trustee: Synovus Trust Company, N.A.
EIN: 266760339

2602

Waffle House Foundation, Inc.
(formerly GFF Educational Foundation, Inc.)
5986 Financial Dr.
Norcross, GA   30071-2949   (770) 729-5780
Contact: Tracy Bradshaw, V.P.

Donor: Waffle House, Inc.
Foundation type: Company-sponsored foundation.
Financial data (yr. ended 05/31/13): Assets, $419,789 (M); gifts received, $256,909; expenditures, $248,168; qualifying distributions, $248,168; giving activities include $244,668 for 38 grants (high: $27,842; low: $500), and $3,500 for 1 grant to an individual.
Purpose and activities: The foundation supports organizations involved with education, health, human services, civic affairs, youth, and economically disadvantaged people and awards college scholarships to students in financial need.
Fields of interest: Education; Secondary education; Health; Public affairs; Human services; Developmental disability services; Independent living for people with disabilities; Adolescents; Low-income and poor people.
Type of support: Equipment; Program development; Scholarships; Student aid.
Limitations: Applications accepted. Giving primarily in the metropolitan Atlanta, GA, area, including Butts, Cherokee, Clayton, Cobb, Coweta, DeKalb, Douglas, Fayette, Forsyth, Fulton, Gwinnett, Henry, Paulding, and Rockdale counties. No support for religious organizations not of direct benefit to the entire community or political candidates. No grants for capital campaigns, endowments, debt reduction, general operating support, or sponsorships of charity balls, dinner, golf outings, etc.
Publications: Application guidelines.
Application information: Application form required.
   Initial approach: Letter
   Deadline(s): None
Officers: Andy Bomberger, Pres.; Tracy Bradshaw, V.P.; Mike Howard, Treas.
EIN: 581477023

2603
Alex C. Walker Educational and Charitable Foundation
1729 Coventry Pl.
Decatur, GA 30030-1006   (404) 378-2752
Contact: Barrett Walker, Tr.
FAX: (404) 378-2751;
E-mail: barrettwalker@mac.com; Main URL: http://walker-foundation.org
Grant Database: http://walker-foundation.org/net/content/projects.aspx?s=0.0.69.5316&siteid=5316&wrapid=69

Established in 1967 in Pennsylvania.
Donor: Alex C. Walker†.
Foundation type: Independent foundation.
Financial data (yr. ended 12/31/14): Assets, $9,927,241; expenditures, $519,977; qualifying distributions, $465,315 and $0 for set-asides.
Purpose and activities: The foundation awards grants to: (1) investigate the causes of economic imbalances, particularly in relation to ecosystem services, climate change, energy security, food production, and other environmental matters; (2) investigate the effects of the global financial system and monetary policy in fostering a sustainable economy; (3) investigate causes tending to destroy or impair the free-market system; (4) explore and develop market-based solutions; and (5) disseminate information on the results and findings.
Fields of interest: Environment; Economics.
Type of support: Program development; Convening; Publications; Seed money; Research; Program evaluations.

Limitations: Applications accepted. No support for religious or political organizations. No grants to individuals, or for building or endowment funds.
Publications: Application guidelines; Financial statement; Grants list; Multi-year report; Program policy statement.
Application information: Check foundation web site for application information. Application form required.
   Initial approach: Pre-proposal or application accepted only via foundation web site
   Copies of proposal: 1
   Deadline(s): Apr. 1 and Oct. 1
   Board meeting date(s): Biannually
Trustees: Barrett P. Walker; Thomas U. Walker; PNC Bank, N.A.
Number of staff: 1 full-time professional.
EIN: 256109746

2604
Walton County Foundation, Inc.
P.O. Box 232
Monroe, GA 30655-0232   (770) 466-2266
Contact: Jean Gallman, Secy.-Treas.

Established in 1958 in Georgia.
Donor: Emily B. Tichenor†.
Foundation type: Independent foundation.
Financial data (yr. ended 09/30/13): Assets, $4,695,394 (M); expenditures, $270,032; qualifying distributions, $222,177; giving activities include $222,177 for 25 grants (high: $90,000; low: $750).
Purpose and activities: Giving primarily for youth services and Christian organizations.
Fields of interest: Arts and culture; Secondary education; Christianity; Youth services.
Type of support: General support.
Limitations: Applications accepted. Giving limited to Walton County, GA. No grants to individuals.
Application information: Application form required.
   Initial approach: Letter
   Deadline(s): None
Officers: Donald Lee Garrett, Chair.; Charles F. Sanders, Vice-Chair.; Jean Gallman, Secy.-Treas.
Trustees: Rebecca P. Dally; Benjamin E. Garrett; Shirley W. Johnson; Eugene Kelly, Jr.; Mickey D. Lankford; Virginia Metcalf.
EIN: 586034766

2605
The Ward Foundation
(formerly The Ward Family Charitable Trust)
100 Galleria Pkwy. S.E., Ste. 1540
Atlanta, GA 30339-5948

Established in 2001 in Georgia.
Donors: John F. Ward; Jean G. Ward; Suntrust Bank Inc., Foundation Svcs.
Foundation type: Independent foundation.
Financial data (yr. ended 12/31/13): Assets, $3,713,759 (M); expenditures, $203,876; qualifying distributions, $171,412; giving activities include $156,500 for 16 grants (high: $60,000; low: $1,500).
Fields of interest: Education; Philanthropy; Health.
Limitations: Applications not accepted. Giving primarily in GA.
Application information: Unsolicited requests for funds not accepted.

Trustee: John F. Ward.
EIN: 586440277

2606
Catherine C. Warren Charitable Trust
3621 Vinings Slope., Ste. 4420
Atlanta, GA 30339-4194

Established in 2001 in Georgia.
Donors: Catherine C. Warren; The Catherine Candler Warren NonGrantor Charitable Lead Annu; Howard Warren Trust.
Foundation type: Independent foundation.
Financial data (yr. ended 12/31/13): Assets, $9,602,469 (M); gifts received, $1,812,890; expenditures, $306,331; qualifying distributions, $262,500; giving activities include $262,500 for 16 grants (high: $40,000; low: $5,000).
Fields of interest: Arts and culture; Education; Health.
Limitations: Applications not accepted. Giving primarily in GA and IL. No grants to individuals.
Application information: Unsolicited request for funds no accepted.
Trustees: Lamar Q. Ball III; Howard C. Warren; William C. Warren III.
EIN: 586433255

2607
Harold Warren Charitable Trust
969 Coldwater Creek Rd.
Dewy Rose, GA 30634-2509   (706) 376-9773
Contact: Wade A. Gaines, Tr.

Donor: Harold Warren†.
Foundation type: Independent foundation.
Financial data (yr. ended 12/31/14): Assets, $6,796,845 (M); expenditures, $478,865; qualifying distributions, $362,456; giving activities include $261,700 for 27 grants (high: $75,000; low: $1,000), and $59,000 for 54 grants to individuals (high: $2,000; low: $1,000).
Purpose and activities: Scholarships awarded to graduating senior of Hart County High School in an approved University, College and Technical school.
Fields of interest: Health; Religion.
Type of support: Student aid.
Limitations: Applications accepted. Giving primarily in GA.
Application information: Application form required.
   Initial approach: Completed application form
   Deadline(s): Mar. 15
Trustees: Kevin T. Gaines; Wade A. Gaines.
EIN: 273033642

2608
The Edus H. and Harriet H. Warren Foundation, Inc.
2660 Peachtree Rd. N.W., Ste. 11C
Atlanta, GA 30305-3675

Established in 1997 in Georgia.
Donors: Edus H. Warren; Harriet H. Warren.
Foundation type: Independent foundation.
Financial data (yr. ended 12/31/14): Assets, $3,723,331 (M); expenditures, $196,888; qualifying distributions, $159,373; giving activities include $158,500 for 5 grants (high: $102,000; low: $5,000).

Fields of interest: Education; Community and economic development.
Limitations: Applications not accepted. Giving primarily in GA. No grants to individuals.
Application information: Unsolicited requests for funds not accepted.
Officers: Edus H. Warren, Chair. and Treas.; Harriet H. Warren, Vice-Chair.; Marge N. Jackson, Secy.
EIN: 311486911

2609
White Family Foundation, Inc.
P.O. Box 1943
Dalton, GA 30722-1943

Established in 1999 in Georgia.
Donors: C. Kenneth White; White Capital Group, LLC.
Foundation type: Independent foundation.
Financial data (yr. ended 12/31/13): Assets, $10,018,695 (M); gifts received, $62,000; expenditures, $701,222; qualifying distributions, $384,085; giving activities include $380,322 for 14 grants (high: $250,000; low: $232).
Fields of interest: Undergraduate education.
Type of support: General support.
Limitations: Applications not accepted. Giving primarily in GA. No grants to individuals.
Application information: Contributes only to pre-selected organizations.
Officers: C.K. White, Chair.; M.L. White, Secy.
Director: K.T. White.
EIN: 582510056

2610
The Whitehead Charitable Foundation
c/o Crosspoint Advisory LLC
3330 Cumberland Blvd., Ste. 400
Atlanta, GA 30339

Established in 1976 in Delaware.
Donor: Edwin C. Whitehead†.
Foundation type: Independent foundation.
Financial data (yr. ended 11/30/13): Assets, $4,866,651 (M); expenditures, $274,010; qualifying distributions, $231,000; giving activities include $231,000 for 5 grants (high: $100,000; low: $15,000).
Fields of interest: Education; Higher education; Foundations; Diseases and conditions; Biology; Child welfare; Homeless people.
Type of support: General support; Endowments; Research; Research and evaluation.
Limitations: Applications not accepted. Giving primarily in Washington, DC, GA, MA, NY, and VA.
Application information: Unsolicited requests for funds not accepted.
Officers and Directors: John J. Whitehead, Pres. and Director; Peter J. Whitehead, V.P.; Susan E. Whitehead.
EIN: 060956618

2611
Whitepath Fabtech Foundation, Inc.
P.O. Box 1154
Ellijay, GA 30540-0015

Established in 2004 in Georgia.
Donors: Janice H. Durden; Randall E. Durden; Randy Durden.

Foundation type: Independent foundation.
Financial data (yr. ended 12/31/14): Assets, $12,681; gifts received, $100,000; expenditures, $125,570; qualifying distributions, $125,570.
Purpose and activities: Giving for Christian education.
Fields of interest: Education; Health; Religion.
Type of support: General support.
Limitations: Applications not accepted. Giving primarily in GA. No grants to individuals.
Application information: Unsolicited requests for funds not accepted.
Officers and Trustees: Randall E. Durden, Pres. and Trustee; Janice H. Durden, Secy. and Trustee.
EIN: 200304560

2612
Betty A. and James B. Williams Foundation, Inc.
c/o SunTrust Bank
P.O. Box 4655, MC 221
Atlanta, GA 30302-4655 (404) 813-9105
Contact: Allen Mast

Established in 1996 in Georgia.
Donor: James B. Williams.
Foundation type: Independent foundation.
Financial data (yr. ended 12/31/13): Assets, $4,161,164 (M); expenditures, $186,955; qualifying distributions, $173,128; giving activities include $170,000 for 5 grants (high: $100,000; low: $5,000).
Purpose and activities: Giving primarily for education, and to a Presbyterian church.
Fields of interest: Arts and culture; Education; Elementary and secondary education; Natural resources; Nonprofits; Diseases and conditions; Protestantism; Youth services; Scouting programs.
Type of support: Regranting.
Limitations: Applications not accepted. Giving primarily in GA and TN. No grants to individuals.
Application information: Contributes only to pre-selected organizations.
Officers: Betty A. Williams, Chair.; James B. Williams, Secy.
EIN: 582302288

2613
Warren and Sallie Williamson Charitable Trust
(formerly Jimmy & Hazel Sanders Charitable Trust II)
2100 Riveredge Pkwy.
Atlanta, GA 30328

Established in 1997 in Mississippi.
Donor: James M. Sanders.
Foundation type: Independent foundation.
Financial data (yr. ended 12/31/13): Assets, $3,148,716 (M); expenditures, $208,940; qualifying distributions, $170,000; giving activities include $170,000 for 20 grants (high: $40,000; low: $1,000).
Fields of interest: Arts and culture; Higher education; Christianity.
Type of support: General support.
Limitations: Applications not accepted. Giving primarily in AL. No grants to individuals.
Application information: Unsolicited requests for funds not accepted.
Trustee: Sallie S. Williamson.
EIN: 311570620

2614
Windolf Family Foundation, Inc.
404 Pikes Bluff Dr.
Saint Simons Island, GA 31522-5690 (973) 993-9767
Contact: John A. Windolf, Pres.

Donors: Muriel B. Windolf; John A. Windolf.
Foundation type: Independent foundation.
Financial data (yr. ended 12/31/13): Assets, $720,731 (M); gifts received, $7,140; expenditures, $278,100; qualifying distributions, $278,100; giving activities include $278,100 for 27 grants (high: $150,000; low: $500).
Fields of interest: Education; Religion; Human services.
Limitations: Applications accepted. Giving primarily in VA.
Application information:
Initial approach: Letter
Deadline(s): None
Officers: John A. Windolf, Pres.; Muriel B. Windolf, V.P.; Lori Windolf Crispo, Secy.; Paul S. Archbold, Treas.
EIN: 463892649

2615
The Wish Foundation, Inc.
(formerly The Lauren Amos Foundation, Inc.)
c/o Gleneagles Group, LLC
Northcreek Bldg. 200
3715 Northside Pkwy., Ste. 600
Atlanta, GA 30327-2807

Established in 2003 in Georgia.
Donor: Lauren A. Amos.
Foundation type: Independent foundation.
Financial data (yr. ended 12/31/12): Assets, $5,039,111 (M); gifts received, $174,145; expenditures, $223,492; qualifying distributions, $152,500; giving activities include $152,500 for grants.
Fields of interest: Arts and culture; Human services; Youth development.
Type of support: General support.
Limitations: Applications not accepted. Giving primarily in Atlanta, GA. No grants to individuals.
Application information: Unsolicited requests for funds not accepted.
Officers: Lauren A. Amos, Pres.; Daniel P. Amos, Treas.
Trustees: Courtney G. Amos; Paul Amos II.
EIN: 200483100

2616
The Woodcrest Foundation
3595 Hiram-Douglasville Hwy.
Hiram, GA 30141-4961

Established in 1998 in Georgia.
Donors: Catherine N. Fisher; Louise Fisher†; Robert W. Fisher.
Foundation type: Independent foundation.
Financial data (yr. ended 12/31/13): Assets, $2,525,873 (M); expenditures, $168,686; qualifying distributions, $167,100; giving activities include $167,100 for 18 grants (high: $67,000; low: $300).
Fields of interest: Arts and culture; Education; Foundations; Religion; Human services; Child welfare; Child development.

Limitations: Applications not accepted. Giving primarily in Atlanta, GA and Highlands, NC. No grants to individuals.
Application Information: Contributes only to pre-selected organizations.
Officer and Trustee: Robert W. Fisher, Mgr. and Trustee.
EIN: 586368034

2617
The Woodruff Family Foundation
(formerly The George and Kathleen Woodruff Foundation)
2900 Warm Springs Rd.
Columbus, GA 31904-5269

Established in 1996 in Georgia.
Donor: George C. Woodruff, Jr.
Foundation type: Independent foundation.
Financial data (yr. ended 12/31/13): Assets, $5,117,788 (M); expenditures, $284,963; qualifying distributions, $244,750; giving activities include $244,750 for 12 grants (high: $105,250; low: $5,000).
Purpose and activities: Giving primarily for higher education and human services.
Fields of interest: Education; Higher education; Nonprofits; Hospice care; Diseases and conditions; Christianity; Human services; Family services; Youth development.
Type of support: General support; Regranting.
Limitations: Applications not accepted. Giving primarily in Columbus, GA. No grants to individuals.
Application Information: Contributes only to pre-selected organizations.
Directors: Patty Kilgore; Otis Scarborough; Laurie Waldrop; Julie Woodruff; George C. Woodruff III.
EIN: 582275952

2618
J. A. & H. G. Woodruff, Jr. Charitable Trust
P.O. Box 709
Athens, GA 30603

Established in 1998 in Florida.
Donor: Merrill Lynch Trust Co.
Foundation type: Independent foundation.
Financial data (yr. ended 05/31/13): Assets, $5,427,970 (M); expenditures, $276,660; qualifying distributions, $235,000; giving activities include $235,000 for 27 grants (high: $40,000; low: $1,500).
Fields of interest: Arts and culture; Education; Higher education; Botanical gardens; Domesticated animals; Camps; Reproductive rights; Human services; Child welfare; Youth services.
Limitations: Applications not accepted. Giving primarily in NC, NY and UT. No grants to individuals.
Application Information: Unsolicited requests for funds not accepted.
Trustees: James Woodruff III; Thomas Woodruff.
EIN: 656246750

2619
Wormsloe Foundation, Inc.
22 W. Bryan St.
P.O. Box 300
Savannah, GA 31401-2604
Contact: Craig Barrow III, Treas.

Application address: P.O. Box 8346, Savannah, GA 31412

Established in 1951 in Georgia.
Donor: Elfrida Derenne Barrow†.
Foundation type: Independent foundation.
Financial data (yr. ended 12/31/13): Assets, $3,944,847 (M); gifts received, $3,500; expenditures, $206,931; qualifying distributions, $187,941; giving activities include $162,980 for 7 grants (high: $60,000; low: $2,600).
Purpose and activities: Giving primarily for the study of agriculture, horticulture, and forestry, and for the preservation of historical sites and documents.
Fields of interest: Education; Environment.
Type of support: General support; Scholarships.
Limitations: Applications accepted. Giving primarily in GA.
Application Information: Application form required.
  Initial approach: Letter
  Deadline(s): None
Officers: Diana D. Barrow, Chair.; Sarah Ross, Pres.; Juliet Chisolm, Secy.; Craig Barrow III, Treas.
Trustees: Thornton D. Barrow; Malcolm Bell III; Dorinda Dallmeyer; J. Wiley Ellis; Charles Knapp; Elfrida B. Moore.
EIN: 586034319

2620
Ray M. and Jane R. Wright Foundation, Inc.
6400 Bradley Park Dr.
Columbus, GA 31904-3615

Established in 1994 in Georgia.
Foundation type: Independent foundation.
Financial data (yr. ended 12/31/13): Assets, $7,574,803 (M); expenditures, $266,550; qualifying distributions, $264,587; giving activities include $264,500 for 19 grants (high: $86,000; low: $1,000).
Fields of interest: Arts and culture; Higher education; Community college education; Diseases and conditions; Christianity; Children and youth; Children; Homeless people; Low-income and poor people.
Type of support: Annual campaigns; Matching grants; Capital and infrastructure; Research.
Limitations: Applications not accepted. Giving primarily in AL and GA. No grants to individuals.
Application Information: Contributes only to pre-selected organizations.
Officers: Ernest S. Wright, Pres. and Treas.; John M. Wright, V.P. and Secy.
Trustees: Anne S. Wright; Kimberly O. Wright.
Number of staff: 2 part-time support.
EIN: 582135480

2621
Andrew J. Young Foundation Inc.
260 14th St. NW
Atlanta, GA 30318-5360
Contact: Andrea Young

Established in 2000 in Georgia.
Donors: Carolyn Young; Andrew J. Young; Coca Cola East Africa; Burrell; Delta Air Lines; Aaron's; Wells Fargo Bank; Georgia-Pacific; Atlanta Public Schools; Natas; Lockheed Martin; ING America; Chic-Fil-A;

H.E. Butt Foundation; Mary Rose Taylor; PRM Consulting Inc.; Cox Enterprises.
Foundation type: Independent foundation.
Financial data (yr. ended 12/31/13): Assets, $1,363,101 (M); gifts received, $2,213,786; expenditures, $1,688,289; qualifying distributions, $262,971; giving activities include $262,971 for 27 grants (high: $50,000; low: $800).
Fields of interest: Museums; Elementary and secondary education; Higher education; Christianity; People of African descent.
Limitations: Applications not accepted. Giving primarily in GA.
Application Information: Contributes only to pre-selected organizations.
Officers: Andrew J. Young, Pres.; Carolyn Young, Secy.
EIN: 582591049

2622
Zawadi Africa Educational Fund Inc.
1820 Peachtree Ave., No. 1902
Atlanta, GA 30309-8406 (020) 230-5655
Application address: c/o Rose Nyaondo, P.O. Box 59949-00200, Nairobi, Kenya, tel.: (020) 230-5655

Donors: Susan Mboya; Coca Cola Foundation; Google UK Ltd.; National Media Group Limited; US State Department; KML Royal Dutch Airlines; Commercial Bank of Africa; Safaricom; Baloo Patel; Lunchpad Communication; Kenya Embassy; Red Dot Printers.
Foundation type: Independent foundation.
Financial data (yr. ended 12/31/13): Assets, $239,515 (M); gifts received, $438,862; expenditures, $381,473; qualifying distributions, $381,473; giving activities include $234,928 for grants to individuals, and $381,473 for foundation-administered programs.
Purpose and activities: Giving assistance to women from Africa to attend U.S. or other institutions of higher education.
Fields of interest: Higher education; Females.
Officers and Trustees: Eva Muraya, Chair. and Trustee; Susan Mboya, Pres.; Isaac Awuondo; Tom Okuku; Carol Sterling.
EIN: 205744658

2623
Zvolensky Family Foundation Inc.
1101 Swift Creek
Greensboro, GA 30642-6835 (706) 999-1689
Contact: John Zvolensky, Dir.

Donors: John Zvolensky; Rachael Zvolensky, Jr.
Foundation type: Independent foundation.
Financial data (yr. ended 12/31/13): Assets, $217,749 (M); gifts received, $51,750; expenditures, $172,628; qualifying distributions, $170,000; giving activities include $170,000 for 20 grants (high: $50,000; low: $500).
Fields of interest: Arts and culture; Human services.
Limitations: Applications accepted. Giving primarily in VA.
Application Information:
  Initial approach: Proposal
  Deadline(s): None
Directors: John Zvolensky, Jr.; Matthew S. Zvolensky; Rachael Zvolensky.
EIN: 263635379

HAWAII

2624

Armstrong Foundation

80 Sand Island Access Rd., Ste. 209
Honolulu, HI 96819 (808) 848-2484
Contact: Robert H. Armstrong, Pres., Treas., and Dir.

Established in 1993 in Hawaii.
Donors: Kelly R. Armstrong; Robert H. Armstrong.
Foundation type: Independent foundation.
Financial data (yr. ended 12/31/13): Assets,
$12,647 (M); expenditures, $248,432; qualifying
distributions, $246,750; giving activities include
$246,750 for 40 grants (high: $52,500; low: $100).
Fields of interest: Business and industry; Human
services; Food banks; Unknown or not classified.
Limitations: Applications accepted. Giving primarily
in HI. No grants to individuals.
Application information: Application form required.
Initial approach: Letter
Deadline(s): None
Officers and Directors: Robert H. Armstrong, Pres.
and Treas. and Director; Kelly R. Armstrong, V.P. and
Secy. and Director; Dean I. Sugimoto.
EIN: 990308992

2625

Fred Baldwin Memorial Foundation

827 Fort Street Mall
Honolulu, HI 96813-4317 (808) 566-5524
Contact: Amy Luersen
E-mail: foundations@hcf-hawaii.org; Application
address: c/o The Hawaii Community Foundation,
1164 Bishop St., Ste. 800, Honolulu, HI 96813,
tel.: (808) 537-6333 or toll-free (888) 731-3863
from neighbor islands; e-mail for Amy Luersen:
aluersen@hcf-hawaii.org; URL: http://
www.hawaiicommunityfoundation.org; Main
URL: http://www.fredbaldwinfoundation.org
Grants List: http://
www.hawaiicommunityfoundation.org/index.php?
id=338

Established in 1910 in Hawaii.
Donor: Fred Baldwin†.
Foundation type: Independent foundation.
Financial data (yr. ended 12/31/13): Assets,
$5,638,595 (M); expenditures, $256,504;
qualifying distributions, $197,082; giving activities
include $159,735 for 28 grants (high: $12,000;
low: $2,000).
Purpose and activities: The foundation is interested
in supporting projects that will benefit the people of
Maui County, HI. The foundation is most interested
in health and human services projects. However, the
foundation also supports arts and cultural
organizations, as well as education and the
environment.
Fields of interest: Arts and culture; Education;
Environment; Health; Diseases and conditions;
Human services; Child welfare.
Type of support: Capital and infrastructure; Program
development; Seed money.
Limitations: Applications accepted. Giving limited to
Maui County, HI. No grants to individuals; no loans
or debt service, endowments, funds for re-granting,
scholarships, grants to units of government, or
activities that have already occurred.

Publications: Application guidelines.
Application information: See Hawaii Community
Foundation web site (http://
www.hawaiicommunityfoundation.org/
privatefoundations) for complete application
policies, guidelines and forms. Completed
coversheet required with proposal.
Initial approach: Complete 2-page cover sheet. No
cover letters, executive summaries, business
cards, videos or CDs accepted
Copies of proposal: 1
Deadline(s): Jan. 2 for Apr. meeting and July 2 for
Oct. meeting
Board meeting date(s): Apr. and Oct.
Final notification: One month following board
meetings
Officers and Trustees: Kristina E. Lyons, Pres. and
Trustee; Shaun B. Lyons, V.P. and Trustee; Mary
Sanford, Secy. and Trustee; Elizabeth Norcross,
Treas. and Trustee; Edward Baldwin; Jeremy C.
Baldwin; Frances Ort; Wendy Rice Peterson; Claire
C. Sanford.
Number of staff: None.
EIN: 990075264

2626

George P. & Ida Tenney Castle Trust

P.O. Box 3170, Dept. 715
Honolulu, HI 96802-3170

Established in 1919 in Hawaii.
Donors: George P. Castle†; Ida Tenney Castle†.
Foundation type: Independent foundation.
Financial data (yr. ended 09/30/14): Assets,
$3,986,140; expenditures, $191,956; qualifying
distributions, $185,605.
Fields of interest: Arts and culture; Child
educational development; Animal welfare; Human
services; Child welfare; Child development.
Type of support: Program development.
Limitations: Giving primarily in HI. No grants to
individuals, or for capital projects, endowment
funds, or general operating costs.
Trustee: Bank of Hawaii, N.A.
Number of staff: None.
EIN: 996003320

2627

Central Pacific Bank Foundation

c/o Scott Hino
220 S. King St.
Honolulu, HI 96813-4526 (808) 544-3673
E-mail: CPBFoundation@centralpacificbank.com;
Alternate Phone: (808) 544-3609; Main
URL: https://www.centralpacificbank.com/
About-CPB/Works-For-You/In-Our-Community.aspx

Established in 2007 in Hawaii.
Donors: John Dean; Central Pacific Bank.
Foundation type: Company-sponsored foundation.
Financial data (yr. ended 12/31/13): Assets,
$11,380,396 (M); gifts received, $1,117,361;
expenditures, $502,822; qualifying distributions,
$397,374; giving activities include $396,182 for 31
grants (high: $50,000; low: $3,300).
Purpose and activities: The foundation supports
programs designed to create opportunities for youth
and foster social progress in Hawaii.
Fields of interest: Education; Education services;
Leadership development; Community and economic

development; Human services; Youth services;
Children and youth.
Type of support: General support; Cash grants;
Program development; Building and renovations.
Limitations: Applications accepted. Giving primarily
in areas of company operations Honolulu, HI. No
support for political action committees or
candidates, fraternal or alumni organizations,
private non-operating foundations, athletic teams,
social groups, or discriminatory organizations. No
grants to individuals, or for conferences, festivals,
or other one-time events, or activities that have
already occurred; no lobbying loans.
Application information: Support it limited to 1
contribution per organization during any given year.
Applying organizations must be in existence for at
least two years and be in stable financial condition.
Application form required.
Initial approach: Complete online application form
Deadline(s): Mar. 31, June 30, and Sept. 30
Officers: Denis K. Isono, Chair. and Pres.; Glenn
Ching, V.P. and Secy.; Reid A. Gushiken, V.P. and
Treas.; Wayne H. Kirihara, V.P.; Catherine Ngo, V.P.;
Donna Takeda, V.P.
EIN: 392068708

2628

Hung Wo & Elizabeth Lau Ching Foundation

841 Bishop St., Ste. 940
Honolulu, HI 96813-3910 (808) 521-4961
Contact: Han Hsin Ching, V.P.; Han P. Ching, V.P.

Donors: Hung Wo Ching; Elizabeth Lau Ching; Chui
Ying Soo Rev Trust Dtd.
Foundation type: Independent foundation.
Financial data (yr. ended 01/31/13): Assets,
$5,642,679 (M); gifts received, $1,500;
expenditures, $462,545; qualifying distributions,
$379,900; giving activities include $364,900 for 40
grants (high: $125,000; low: $200), and $15,000
for 12 grants to individuals (high: $2,500; low:
$625).
Fields of interest: Education; Diseases and
conditions; Human services.
Type of support: Grants to individuals.
Limitations: Giving primarily in HI.
Application information:
Initial approach: Proposal
Deadline(s): None
Officers and Directors: Han Hsin Ching, V.P. and
Director; Han Ping Ching, V.P. and Director; Edric M.
Ching, Secy. and Director; Marie Sakamoto, Treas.;
Shelli Mei Li Ching.
EIN: 996008990

2629

Gertrude M. Damon Trust

c/o FHB, Robin Midkiff
P.O. Box 3708
Honolulu, HI 96811-3708

Established in 1957 in Hawaii.
Donor: Harriet D. Baldwin.
Foundation type: Independent foundation.
Financial data (yr. ended 12/31/13): Assets,
$2,072,742 (M); expenditures, $230,705;
qualifying distributions, $197,514; giving activities
include $185,000 for 2 grants (high: $92,500; low:
$92,500).
Fields of interest: Health; Youth development.

Limitations: Applications not accepted. Giving primarily in HI. No grants to individuals.
Application information: Unsolicited requests for funds not accepted.
Trustees: Brendan Damon Ethington; Heide Snow; Pia Damon Spee; First Hawaiian Bank.
EIN: 996002637

2630
Jean Estes Epstein Charitable Foundation
P.O. Box 3170, Dept. 715
Honolulu, HI 96802-3170

Donor: Jean Desmarais†.
Foundation type: Independent foundation.
Financial data (yr. ended 12/31/14): Assets, $5,261,354 (M); gifts received, $466,237; expenditures, $311,080; qualifying distributions, $258,313; giving activities include $4,000 for 1 grant, and $201,081 for 4 grants to individuals (high: $63,550; low: $13,700).
Fields of interest: Education; University education; Domesticated animals; Diseases and conditions.
Type of support: Scholarships; Research; Student aid.
Limitations: Applications accepted. Giving primarily in CA, HI and MA.
Application information: Application form required.
  Deadline(s): None
Trustees: Harmon A. Brown; Bank of Hawaii.
EIN: 263478306

2631
First Insurance Company of Hawaii Charitable Foundation
1100 Ward Ave.
Honolulu, HI 96814-1600   (808) 527-7616
Contact: Allen B. Uyeda, Tr.

Established in 1998 in Hawaii.
Donor: First Insurance Co. of Hawaii, Ltd.
Foundation type: Company-sponsored foundation.
Financial data (yr. ended 12/31/13): Assets, $7,996,425 (M); expenditures, $435,304; qualifying distributions, $400,440; giving activities include $400,440 for 99 grants (high: $50,000; low: $25).
Purpose and activities: The foundation supports organizations involved with arts and culture, education, human services, goodwill promotion, and community economic development.
Fields of interest: Arts and culture; Education; Human services.
Type of support: General support.
Limitations: Applications accepted. Giving limited to HI. No grants to individuals.
Application information: Application form required.
  Initial approach: Letter
  Deadline(s): None
Trustees: Faye W. Kurren; Jeffrey A. Shonka; Stephen J. Tabussi; Allen B. Uyeda; Jeffrey N. Watanabe.
EIN: 990339536

2632
Frost Family Foundation
c/o Horizon Financial
353 Hanamau St., Ste. 21
Kahului, HI 96732-2474   (808) 524-8099
Contact: Karin A. Frost, Tr.

Donor: Karin A. Frost.
Foundation type: Independent foundation.
Financial data (yr. ended 08/31/14): Assets, $11,302,453 (M); expenditures, $490,187; qualifying distributions, $434,855; giving activities include $423,284 for 7 grants (high: $245,084; low: $10,000).
Fields of interest: Foundations.
Limitations: Applications accepted. Giving primarily in HI.
Application information: Application form required.
  Initial approach: Proposal
  Deadline(s): None
Trustee: Karin A. Frost.
EIN: 273374284

2633
Fukunaga Scholarship Foundation
2850 Pukoloa St., Ste. 300
Honolulu, HI 96819-4475   (808) 564-1386
FAX: (808) 523-3937; E-mail: sandyw@servco.com

Established in 1950 in Hawaii.
Donors: George J. Fukunaga†; George J. Fukunaga Memorial Fund.
Foundation type: Independent foundation.
Financial data (yr. ended 12/31/12): Assets, $3,611,035 (M); gifts received, $5,495; expenditures, $193,762; qualifying distributions, $176,033; giving activities include $160,499 for 45 grants to individuals (high: $5,333; low: $500).
Purpose and activities: Scholarship awards to high school students in Hawaii to pursue a higher education in business administration, or other business-related course of study, at any accredited four-year college or university. Students who are already attending college will also be considered.
Fields of interest: Business education.
Type of support: Student aid.
Limitations: Applications accepted. Giving limited to residents of HI.
Publications: Application guidelines.
Application information: Application form required.
  Initial approach: Completed application
  Deadline(s): Mar. 1
  Board meeting date(s): Varies
Trustees: Eric S. Fukunaga; Grace M. Fukunaga; Mark H. Fukunaga; Joyce S. Tsunoda.
Number of staff: None.
EIN: 990600370

2634
Gear Up Hawaii Scholarship Trust
P.O. Box 3170, Dept. 715
Honolulu, HI 96802-3170
E-mail: notify@nawebsolutions.com

Established in 2005 in Hawaii.
Donor: University of Hawaii.
Foundation type: Independent foundation.
Financial data (yr. ended 06/30/13): Assets, $1,104,839 (M); expenditures, $253,542; qualifying distributions, $243,059; giving activities include $213,675 for 40 grants to individuals (high: $5,550; low: $2,775).
Fields of interest: Higher education.
Type of support: Student aid.
Limitations: Applications accepted. Giving primarily to residents of HI.

Application information: Applicants should use the Hawai'i Community Foundation's Application form. Application form required.
  Initial approach: Letter or E-mail
  Deadline(s): Feb. 22
Trustee: Bank of Hawaii.
EIN: 266026352

2635
Ron and Sanne Higgins Family Foundation
P.O. Box 25040
Honolulu, HI 96825-0040

Established in 2001 in Hawaii.
Donors: Ron Higgins; Sanne Higgins; The Higgins Community Property Trust.
Foundation type: Independent foundation.
Financial data (yr. ended 12/31/13): Assets, $2,886,896 (M); expenditures, $271,563; qualifying distributions, $242,669; giving activities include $225,001 for 3 grants (high: $200,000; low: $1).
Fields of interest: Education; Community and economic development.
Type of support: General support.
Limitations: Applications accepted. Giving primarily in HI.
Application information:
  Initial approach: Letter of inquiry (no more than 2 pages)
  Deadline(s): None
  Board meeting date(s): Mar. and Sept.
Trustees: Ron Higgins; Sanne Higgins.
EIN: 990353608

2636
The Kahiau Foundation
2969 Kalakaua Ave., Ste. 1101
Honolulu, HI 96815-4626

Established in 2005 in California.
Donors: Allene Wong; David Eckles.
Foundation type: Independent foundation.
Financial data (yr. ended 12/31/13): Assets, $3,509,958 (M); expenditures, $217,985; qualifying distributions, $178,889; giving activities include $176,500 for 3 grants (high: $100,000; low: $1,500).
Fields of interest: Cultural awareness; Elementary education; Foundations; Science.
Type of support: Individual development.
Limitations: Applications not accepted. Giving primarily in HI.
Application information: Contributes only to pre-selected organizations.
Officers: Allene Wong, Chair. and Pres.; Colleen Wong, Secy.
Directors: Morgan Eckles; Zachary Kau.
EIN: 050629872

2637
Kaneta Foundation
(formerly Kaneta Charitable Foundation)
827 Fort Street Mall
Honolulu, HI 96813-4317   (808) 566-5550
Contact: Lester Kaneta, Pres.; Amy Luersen, Dir. Phil. Svcs.

FAX: (808) 521-6286;
E-mail: info@kanetafoundation.org; Main
URL: http://kanetafoundation.org
Grants List: http://www.kanetafoundation.org/
grants

Established in 1999 in Hawaii.
Donors: Lester Kaneta; Marian Kaneta; JII Capital,
Inc.
Foundation type: Independent foundation.
Financial data (yr. ended 12/31/13): Assets,
$4,186,481 (M); gifts received, $203,574;
expenditures, $395,882; qualifying distributions,
$334,940; giving activities include $194,940 for 7
grants (high: $155,440; low: $3,000), and
$140,000 for grants to individuals.
Purpose and activities: Giving primarily for human
services, community development, religion and
spiritual development, and youth development;
funding also for scholarships to graduating Christian
high school seniors who are residents of HI.
Fields of interest: Education; Christianity; Human
services; Youth development.
Type of support: General support; Financial
sustainability; Annual campaigns; Program
development; Student aid.
Limitations: Applications not accepted. Giving
primarily in HI and NV. No support for political
organizations.
Application information: Unsolicited requests for
funds not accepted.
   Board meeting date(s): Apr. 15
Officers: Lester Kaneta, Pres. and V.P.; Marian
Kaneta, Secy.-Treas.
EIN: 311655882

2638
Locations Foundation
614 Kapahulu Ave., 3rd Fl.
Honolulu, HI 96815-3846 (808) 735-4200

Established in 1988 in Hawaii.
Donors: RESCO, Inc.; William Chee; Corinda Wong.
Foundation type: Company-sponsored foundation.
Financial data (yr. ended 12/31/13): Assets,
$910,154 (M); gifts received, $236,766;
expenditures, $167,606; qualifying distributions,
$164,753; giving activities include $142,405 for 29
grants (high: $30,366; low: $1,004).
Purpose and activities: The foundation supports
organizations involved with health, diabetes, youth,
and human services.
Fields of interest: Education; Reading promotion;
Nonprofits; Health; Diabetes; Cancers; Housing
development; Human services; Family services;
Child welfare; Adult and child mentoring; Females.
Type of support: General support; Scholarships;
Regranting.
Limitations: Applications accepted. Giving primarily
in Honolulu, HI. No grants to individuals.
Application information:
   Initial approach: Proposal
   Deadline(s): None
Officers and Directors: Jodee Farm, Pres. and
Director; Dolores Bediones, V.P. and Director; Toan
Doran, V.P. and Director; Chad Takesue, V.P. and
Director; Corinda Wong, V.P. and Director; Noele
Kanemoto, Secy.; Joann Lumsden, Co-Treas.; Dan
Tabori, Co-Treas. and Director; James Chan;
Stephanie Chan.
EIN: 990267351

2639
The Makana Aloha Foundation
P.O. Box 342190
Kailua, HI 96734-8998 (808) 683-8363
Contact: Jami Lynn Burks, Pres.
E-mail: makanaalohafoundation@gmail.com; Main
URL: http://makanaalohafoundation.org
Grants List: http://makanaalohafoundation.org/
page5.html

Established in 2008 in California.
Donors: Gunars E. Valkirs; Jorene Valkirs.
Foundation type: Independent foundation.
Financial data (yr. ended 03/31/13): Assets,
$6,549,582 (M); expenditures, $430,653;
qualifying distributions, $383,758; giving activities
include $338,043 for 16 grants (high: $51,750;
low: $1,969).
Purpose and activities: Giving primarily for
education, health, and human services.
Fields of interest: Education; Higher education;
Health; Human services.
Limitations: Giving primarily in CA and HI.
Application information: Application form required.
   Initial approach: Letter requesting application
   form
   Deadline(s): None
Officers: Jami Lynn Burks, Pres. and Secy.; Gunars
E. Valkirs, V.P.
Director: JoRene Valkirs.
EIN: 208877756

2640
Michael J. Marks Foundation
c/o E. Gunner Schull
1000 Bishop St., Ste. 1200
Honolulu, HI 96813-4298

Established in 2007 in Hawaii.
Donors: Michael J. Marks†; E. Gunner Schull.
Foundation type: Independent foundation.
Financial data (yr. ended 12/31/14): Assets,
$764,206; expenditures, $370,118; qualifying
distributions, $355,000.
Fields of interest: Law education.
Limitations: Applications not accepted. Giving
primarily in Chicago, IL.
Application information: Unsolicited requests for
funds not accepted.
Officers and Directors: David Skudneski, V.P. and
Director; E. Gunner Schull, Treas. and Director;
Susan Roberts.
EIN: 711023900

2641
Dolores Furtado Martin Foundation
1088 Bishop St., Ste. 1206
Honolulu, HI 96813 (808) 923-3050
Contact: Watters O. Martin Jr., Pres. and Dir.

Established in 2000 in Hawaii.
Donors: Dolores F. Martin; Walter O. Martin, Jr.
Foundation type: Independent foundation.
Financial data (yr. ended 12/31/13): Assets,
$4,421,909 (M); expenditures, $321,162;
qualifying distributions, $239,861; giving activities
include $238,098 for 32 grants (high: $50,000;
low: $100).
Fields of interest: Arts and culture; Ethnic
museums; Education; Children's hospital care;

Community and economic development;
Christianity; Children.
Limitations: Applications accepted. Giving primarily
in HI. No grants to individuals.
Application information:
   Initial approach: Proposal
   Deadline(s): None
Officers and Directors: Watters O. Martin, Jr., Pres.
and Director; Martha Ann Mahealani Riley, V.P. and
Secy. and Director; Thomas Skye.
EIN: 990348924

2642
Minami Community Foundation
45-558 C Kamehameha Hwy., Ste. 14
Kaneohe, HI 96744-1944
Contact: Henry T. Iida, Pres.

Established in 1992 in Hawaii.
Donor: American Golf Corp.
Foundation type: Independent foundation.
Financial data (yr. ended 12/31/14): Assets,
$2,815,482 (M); gifts received, $18,902;
expenditures, $174,930; qualifying distributions,
$144,536; giving activities include $140,348 for 12
grants (high: $20,000; low: $1,848).
Fields of interest: Secondary education; Higher
education; Environment; Youth development.
Limitations: Applications accepted. Giving limited to
the Kaneohe and Kahaluu areas of Oahu, HI.
Application information: Application form required.
   Initial approach: Letter
   Deadline(s): None
Officers: Henry T. Iida, Pres.; Fred Shiroma, V.P.;
Tom Enomoto, Secy.; John Reppun, Treas.
Directors: Rick Towill; Rich Vermeesch; Patricia
Yamashiro.
EIN: 990292394

2643
The O. L. Moore Foundation
129 Kualapa Pl.
Lahaina, HI 96761-2902
Contact: William E. Moore

Established in 1959 in Illinois.
Donor: O.L. Moore†.
Foundation type: Independent foundation.
Financial data (yr. ended 12/31/13): Assets,
$3,045,101 (M); expenditures, $187,598;
qualifying distributions, $149,000; giving activities
include $149,000 for 36 grants (high: $10,000;
low: $2,000).
Purpose and activities: Support primarily for higher
education; giving also for health associations and
services, and cultural programs; giving also to
Hawaiian immersion programs to support cultural
re-emergence and identity.
Fields of interest: Arts and culture; Higher
education; Health; Human services.
Type of support: General support; Continuing
support; Annual campaigns; Capital campaigns;
Emergency funds.
Limitations: Applications accepted. Giving primarily
in Maui County, HI and the Greater Portland, OR. No
support for political organizations. No grants to
individuals.
Application information:
   Initial approach: Letter
   Deadline(s): None
   Board meeting date(s): Dec.

Officers and Directors: William E. Moore, Pres. and Treas. and Director; Dee Anne Mahuna, V.P. and Director; Patricia Dodd; Peter E. Mahuna; Joshua Moore; Rebekah Lynn Sims; Thomas C. Thayer.
Trustee: Bank of Hawaii.
Number of staff: None.
EIN: 366101149

2644
Bouslog Sawyer Charitable Trust
63 Merchant St.
Honolulu, HI 96813

Donor: Stephen Sawyer.
Foundation type: Independent foundation.
Financial data (yr. ended 12/31/13): Assets, $9,763,802 (M); expenditures, $536,838; qualifying distributions, $389,542; giving activities include $375,999 for 1 grant.
Fields of interest: Education.
Limitations: Applications not accepted.
Application information: Unsolicited requests for funds not accepted.
Trustee: Mark D. Bernstein.
EIN: 276061515

2645
Servco Foundation
P.O. Box 2788
Honolulu, HI 96803-2788 (800) 564-1386
FAX: (808) 523-3937;
E-mail: donations@servco.com; Main URL: http://servco.com/philanthropy/servco_foundation.php

Established in 1986 in Hawaii.
Donor: Servco Pacific Inc.
Foundation type: Company-sponsored foundation.
Financial data (yr. ended 06/30/13): Assets, $5,370,037 (M); gifts received, $75,550; expenditures, $348,566; qualifying distributions, $318,036; giving activities include $272,798 for 62 grants (high: $70,000; low: $74), and $40,001 for 23 grants to individuals (high: $2,000; low: $1,333).
Purpose and activities: The foundation supports museums and organizations involved with education, youth development, and human services.
Fields of interest: Arts and culture; Education; Diseases and conditions.
Type of support: General support; Employee matching gifts; Annual campaigns; Capital campaigns; Scholarships.
Limitations: Applications accepted. Giving limited to HI and the U.S. Pacific region. No support for political organizations.
Publications: Application guidelines.
Application information: Application form required.
    Initial approach: Completed application form
    Copies of proposal: 1
    Deadline(s): Mar. 1
Officers and Directors: Mark H. Fukunaga, Chair. and Director; Eric S. Fukunaga, Pres. and Director; Patrick D. Ching, V.P. and Treas.; Glenn K. Inouye, V.P. and Director; Sandra C.H. Wong, Secy.
Number of staff: None.
EIN: 990248256

2646
The Shidler Family Foundation
841 Bishop St.
Honolulu, HI 96813
Contact: Jay H. Shidler, Tr.

Donor: Jay H. Shidler.
Foundation type: Independent foundation.
Financial data (yr. ended 12/31/13): Assets, $4,450 (M); gifts received, $200,827; expenditures, $196,377; qualifying distributions, $196,377; giving activities include $183,150 for 8 grants (high: $86,250; low: $1,900).
Fields of interest: Arts and culture; Nonprofits; Radio; Community and economic development; Youth development.
Type of support: Regranting.
Limitations: Applications not accepted. Giving primarily in HI.
Application information: Contributes only to pre-selected organizations.
Trustee: Jay H. Shidler.
EIN: 461980574

2647
The Shields Animal Shelter Foundation
P. O. Box 482190
Kaunakakai, HI 96748-2190

Donor: Kathleen Shields†.
Foundation type: Independent foundation.
Financial data (yr. ended 06/30/13): Assets, $1,683,298 (M); expenditures, $368,029; qualifying distributions, $283,259; giving activities include $283,259 for 34 grants (high: $143,402; low: $500).
Fields of interest: Education; Domesticated animals; Animal welfare; Human services.
Type of support: General support.
Limitations: Applications not accepted. Giving primarily in HI.
Application information: Unsolicited requests for funds not accepted.
Officer: Debra Buechel, Mgr.
EIN: 270274579

2648
Shiraki Memorial Foundation
2020 Vancouver Dr.
Honolulu, HI 96822
Application address: Stanley Togikawa, 3165 Oahu Ave., Honolulu, HI 96822, tel.:(808) 284-5413

Established in 1997 in Hawaii.
Donor: Hilda Kikuno Shiraki Trust.
Foundation type: Independent foundation.
Financial data (yr. ended 12/31/14): Assets, $5,701,361 (M); gifts received, $8,490; expenditures, $279,931; qualifying distributions, $155,217; giving activities include $155,217 for 5 + grants.
Purpose and activities: Scholarships are limited to Hawaii residents who are attending Southern Baptist seminaries or schools, and who are also Southern Baptist church members.
Fields of interest: Graduate and professional education; Baptist; Theology.
International interests: Southeastern Asia.
Type of support: Scholarships.
Limitations: Applications accepted. Giving limited to residents of HI. No grants to individuals directly.

Application information: Application form required.
    Initial approach: Proposal
    Deadline(s): None
Officers: Stanley Togikawa, Pres.; Clyde Kakiuchi, V.P.; Danette Kong, Secy.
Number of staff: None.
EIN: 943274547

2649
Gertrude S. Straub Trust Estate
P.O. Box 3170, Dept. 715
Honolulu, HI 96802-3170

Donor: Gertrude S. Straub†.
Foundation type: Independent foundation.
Financial data (yr. ended 03/31/15): Assets, $7,486,571 (M); expenditures, $406,330; qualifying distributions, $344,208; giving activities include $280,040 for 127 grants to individuals (high: $3,000; low: $500).
Purpose and activities: Scholarship grants to HI public high school graduates to attend mainland colleges and major in a subject relating to the better understanding of peace and the promotion of international peace.
Fields of interest: International studies; International relations; International peace and security.
Type of support: Student aid.
Limitations: Applications accepted. Giving primarily to residents of HI.
Publications: Informational brochure (including application guidelines).
Application information: See web site for complete application policies and forms. Applicants must be graduates of public high schools in HI. Application form required.
    Initial approach: Complete online application form
    Copies of proposal: 1
    Deadline(s): Feb. 18
    Board meeting date(s): Apr.
    Final notification: Apr.
Trustee: Bank of Hawaii.
EIN: 996003243

2650
Mamoru & Aiko Takitani Foundation, Inc.
(formerly Takitani Foundation, Inc.)
81 S. Hotel St., Ste. 300
Honolulu, HI 96813-3145 (808) 228-0209
Main URL: http://www.takitani.org

Established in 1976 in Hawaii.
Donors: Hawaiian Host, Inc.; Aiko Takitani.
Foundation type: Company-sponsored foundation.
Financial data (yr. ended 12/31/13): Assets, $6,888,814 (M); gifts received, $353,328; expenditures, $183,276; qualifying distributions, $173,276; giving activities include $30,000 for 6 grants (high: $8,000; low: $1,000), and $105,350 for 77 grants to individuals (high: $5,000; low: $500).
Purpose and activities: The foundation awards college scholarships to high school seniors living in Hawaii.
Fields of interest: Education; Human services; Youth development.
Type of support: Scholarships; Student aid.
Limitations: Applications accepted. Giving limited to HI.

Application information: Application form required.
Initial approach: Contact school administrator for an application form
Deadline(s): None
Officers: Michael W. Perry, Chair.; Hideo Kondo, Pres.; Janice Luke Loo, V.P.; Mildred Higashi, Secy.; Stuart Ho, Treas.
Directors: Brett G. Schlemmer; Karen Uno.
EIN: 510212114

2651
Albert T. & Wallace T. Teruya Foundation
1276 Young St.
Honolulu, HI 96814-1867 (808) 591-8946

Established in 1968 in Hawaii.
Foundation type: Independent foundation.
Financial data (yr. ended 12/31/13): Assets, $3,675,043 (M); expenditures, $160,647; qualifying distributions, $150,000; giving activities include $150,000 for 4 grants (high: $40,000; low: $35,000).
Purpose and activities: Support is largely for secondary and other education, the arts, including a theater and cultural center, and building campaigns.
Fields of interest: Education.
Type of support: General support; Building and renovations.
Limitations: Applications accepted. Giving primarily in Honolulu, HI. No grants to individuals.
Application information: Application form required.
Initial approach: Letter
Deadline(s): None
Officers and Trustees: Raymond T. Teruya, Pres.; Roy T. Uyehara, Secy. and Trustee; Wayne T. Teruya, Treas. and Trustee; John Love; Rosemarie J. Love; Dexter T. Teruya; Ethel M. Teruya.
EIN: 996014692

2652
Ululani Foundation
75-853 Keaolani Dr.
Kailua Kona, HI 96740-8815 (808) 327-0144
Contact: Diane S. Heiman, V.P., Treas., and Dir.

Established in 2005 in Hawaii.
Donors: Diane S. Heiman; Stephen E. Heiman.
Foundation type: Independent foundation.
Financial data (yr. ended 12/31/13): Assets, $4,761,040 (M); expenditures, $193,245; qualifying distributions, $154,162; giving activities include $144,487 for 9 grants (high: $100,000; low: $465).
Fields of interest: Education; Nonprofits; Hospital care; Eye diseases.
Type of support: Regranting.
Application information:
Initial approach: Proposal
Deadline(s): None
Officers and Directors: Stephen E. Heiman, Pres. and Secy. and Director; Diane S. Heiman, V.P. and Treas. and Director; Harry Welch.
EIN: 203283739

2653
Antone & Edene Vidinha Charitable Trust
c/o Bank of Hawaii, N.A.
P.O. Box 3170, Dept. 715
Honolulu, HI 96802-3170
Contact: Paula Boyce, Asst. V.P.

E-mail: paula.boyce@boh.com; Additional e-mail: elaine.moniz@boh.com; Main URL: http://www.boh.com/philanthropy

Established in 1989 in Hawaii.
Donors: Antone Vidinha†; Edene Vidinha†.
Foundation type: Independent foundation.
Financial data (yr. ended 06/30/13): Assets, $7,723,437 (M); expenditures, $453,079; qualifying distributions, $401,490; giving activities include $340,875 for 11 grants (high: $70,000; low: $10,000).
Fields of interest: Education; Health; Diseases and conditions; Cancers; Religion; Human services.
Type of support: General support; Capital and infrastructure; Equipment; Individual development; Program development; Scholarships.
Limitations: Applications not accepted. Giving limited to Kauai Island, HI, only. No grants to individuals, or for endowments or multi-year pledges.
Publications: Occasional report.
Application information: Contributes only to pre-selected organizations.
Board meeting date(s): May or June
Trustee: Bank of Hawaii, N.A.
Number of staff: None.
EIN: 990273993

2654
S. W. Wilcox Trust
c/o Bank of Hawaii
P.O. Box 3170, Dept. 715
Honolulu, HI 96802-3180 (808) 694-4944
Contact: Paula Boyce; Elaine Moniz

Established in 1921 in Hawaii.
Donor: Samuel Whitney Wilcox†.
Foundation type: Independent foundation.
Financial data (yr. ended 12/31/13): Assets, $4,993,373 (M); expenditures, $280,082; qualifying distributions, $243,851; giving activities include $210,000 for 17 grants (high: $30,000; low: $5,000).
Purpose and activities: Giving to support local health, welfare, and educational organizations on Kauai, Hawaii.
Fields of interest: Education; Health; Diseases and conditions; Human services.
Type of support: General support; Continuing support; Capital campaigns; Capital and infrastructure; Seed money; Scholarships.
Limitations: Applications accepted. Giving limited to Kauai and Big Island, HI. No grants to individuals, or for research programs, fellowships, or matching gifts; no loans.
Application information: Contact Foundation for scholarship application. Application form required.
Initial approach: Proposal
Copies of proposal: 4
Deadline(s): None
Trustees: Gale Fisher Carswell; Pamela W. Dohrman; David W. Pratt.
Number of staff: None.
EIN: 996002547

2655
The Robert and Betty Wo Foundation
702 S. Beretania St.
Honolulu, HI 96813-2581 (808) 545-5966

Established in 1990 in Hawaii.
Donor: C.S. Wo Foundation.
Foundation type: Independent foundation.
Financial data (yr. ended 03/31/14): Assets, $559,798 (M); gifts received, $392,923; expenditures, $143,591; qualifying distributions, $139,500; giving activities include $139,500 for 22 grants (high: $52,500; low: $500).
Purpose and activities: Giving primarily for the arts, education, and rehabilitation hospitals.
Fields of interest: Education; Diseases and conditions; Human services.
Limitations: Applications accepted. Giving primarily in HI. No grants to individuals.
Application information:
Initial approach: Proposal
Deadline(s): None
Officers and Directors: Robert C. Wo, Pres.; Robert W. Wo, V.P. and Director; Wendell Wo, Secy. and Director; Michael Wo, Treas. and Director; Craig Scott Wo.
EIN: 990281956

2656
Harry Chow & Nee-Chang Chock Wong Foundation
1164 Bishop St., Ste. 530
Honolulu, HI 96813-2815

Established in 1970 in Hawaii.
Donors: Harry C. Wong†; Nee-Chang Chock Wong†.
Foundation type: Independent foundation.
Financial data (yr. ended 12/31/14): Assets, $12,427,762 (M); expenditures, $658,287; qualifying distributions, $510,790; giving activities include $438,220 for 54 grants (high: $250,000; low: $70).
Fields of interest: Education; Higher education; Foundations; Christianity; Human services.
Type of support: General support; Continuing support; Curriculum development; Scholarships.
Limitations: Applications not accepted. Giving limited to HI. No grants to individuals.
Application information: Contributes only to pre-selected organizations.
Officers and Directors: Robert H.Y. Leong, Pres. and Secy.-Treas. and Director; Maxine W. Leong, V.P. and Director; Toni L. Parastie, V.P. and Director.
EIN: 996012585

2657
Henry & Colene Wong Foundation
2250 Kalakaua Ave., Ste. 513
Honolulu, HI 96815-2547 (808) 922-7876
Contact: Gordon J. Mau, V.P.

Established in 1991 in Hawaii.
Donor: Henry H. Wong.
Foundation type: Independent foundation.
Financial data (yr. ended 12/31/13): Assets, $4,638,595 (M); expenditures, $259,060; qualifying distributions, $231,910; giving activities include $200,000 for 10 grants (high: $46,500; low: $2,500).
Fields of interest: Human services; Food aid.
Type of support: Volunteer development.
Limitations: Applications accepted. Giving primarily in HI.
Application information: Application form required.
Initial approach: Letter
Deadline(s): None

Officers: Gordon J. Mau, Pres. and Secy.; Dominic Dias, V.P.; Harlan J. Cadinha, Treas.
Directors: Sheri-Dee Garboden; Jan Harada; Colene S. Wong.
EIN: 990292290

2658
W. T. Yoshimoto Foundation Charitable Trust

P.O. Box 3708
Honolulu, HI   96811-3708

Foundation type: Independent foundation.
Financial data (yr. ended 12/31/14): Assets, $5,575,441 (M); expenditures, $267,590; qualifying distributions, $207,732; giving activities include $172,000 for 4 grants (high: $125,000; low: $5,000).
Fields of interest: Arts and culture; Science museums; Zoology; Human services; Youth development.
International interests: Japan.
Limitations: Applications not accepted. Giving primarily in HI; some giving in Tokyo, Japan.
Application information: Unsolicited requests for funds not accepted.
Officers: Randy A. Harris, Pres.; Wendell W.S. Kam, V.P.; Jeannie V. Davidson, Treas.
Trustee: First Hawaiian Bank.
EIN: 456717935

2659
Beatrice M. H. Young Foundation, Inc.

1268 Young St., Ste. 302
Honolulu, HI   96814-1801   (808) 591-9799
Contact: Douglas K.T. Ho, Pres.

Established in 2004 in Hawaii.
Donor: Beatrice M.H. Young.
Foundation type: Independent foundation.
Financial data (yr. ended 12/31/13): Assets, $7,570,998 (M); expenditures, $774,132;

qualifying distributions, $379,915; giving activities include $379,915 for 19 grants (high: $300,000; low: $250).
Fields of interest: Arts and culture; Education; Community and economic development.
Limitations: Applications accepted. Giving primarily in Honolulu, HI.
Application information:
Initial approach: Letter
Deadline(s): None
Officers and Directors: Douglas K.T. Ho, Pres. and Director; Gregory Leong, V.P. and Director; Randolph Leong, Secy. and Director; Frank Allen Williams; Reuben Wong.
EIN: 300180163

2660
John Chin Young Foundation

4558 Malia St.
Honolulu, HI   96821-1157   (808) 737-9776
Contact: Deborah Li Young, Tr.

Foundation type: Independent foundation.
Financial data (yr. ended 12/31/14): Assets, $5,190,495 (M); expenditures, $383,018; qualifying distributions, $266,816; giving activities include $266,816 for 11 grants (high: $126,316; low: $1,500).
Fields of interest: Arts and culture; Education.
Type of support: Scholarships; General support.
Limitations: Applications accepted. Giving primarily in Honolulu, HI. No grants to individuals directly.
Application information:
Initial approach: Proposal
Deadline(s): None
Trustees: Roger Bellinger; Wesley Park; Deborah Li Young.
EIN: 996081402

2661
The Zierk Family Foundation

c/o Kukio
72-3207 Manini' Owali Dr.
Kailua-Kona, HI   96740

Donor: David K. Zierk.
Foundation type: Independent foundation.
Financial data (yr. ended 12/31/13): Assets, $10,305,396 (M); gifts received, $8,500,000; expenditures, $429,244; qualifying distributions, $424,200; giving activities include $424,200 for 14 grants (high: $250,000; low: $1,000).
Fields of interest: Health; Community and economic development; Human services.
Limitations: Applications not accepted. Giving primarily in CA; funding also in HI.
Application information: Unsolicited requests for funds not accepted.
Officers: David K. Zierk, Pres. and Treas.; Davn M. Zierk, V.P. and Secy.
EIN: 462243181

2662
Zwaanstra Foundation

P.O. Box 790387
Paia, HI   96779-0387
Contact: David Houde, CPA

Donor: John Zwaanstra IV.
Foundation type: Independent foundation.
Financial data (yr. ended 12/31/14): Assets, $50,905 (M); expenditures, $177,390; qualifying distributions, $177,375; giving activities include $176,585 for 1 grant.
Fields of interest: Education; University education.
Limitations: Applications not accepted. Giving primarily in MA and NJ. No grants to individuals.
Application information: Contributes only to pre-selected organizations.
Trustees: John Zwaanstra III; John Zwaanstra IV; Shizuka Zwaanstra.
EIN: 911751312

IDAHO

2663
Ambrosiani-Pastore Foundation Inc.
1075 W. Oden Bay Rd.
Sandpoint, ID 83864-6496   (208) 265-8694

Donors: Jack Ambrosiani; Irene Ambrosiani†;
Ambrosiani Foundation; Mary J. Ambrosiani.
Foundation type: Independent foundation.
Financial data (yr. ended 12/31/13): Assets,
$14,821,513 (M); gifts received, $1,429,290;
expenditures, $198,722; qualifying distributions,
$198,722; giving activities include $157,356 for 11
grants (high: $26,386; low: $1,310).
Fields of interest: Secondary education;
Christianity; Human services; Food delivery; Child
welfare; Homeless services.
Limitations: Applications not accepted. Giving
primarily in ID. No grants to individuals.
Application information: Contributes only to
pre-selected organizations.
Officers: Jack Ambrosiani, Pres. and Treas.; Mary J.
Ambrosiani, V.P. and Secy.
EIN: 820510166

2664
Angels Among Us, Inc.
10151 River Rock Ln.
Garden City, ID 83714-8088
Contact: Angie Harrison, Pres.
Main URL: http://www.aauinc.org

Donor: Angie Harrison.
Foundation type: Independent foundation.
Financial data (yr. ended 12/31/13): Assets,
$192,350 (M); gifts received, $379,815;
expenditures, $198,494; qualifying distributions,
$198,493; giving activities include $198,277 for 25
grants (high: $83,629; low: $10).
Fields of interest: Education; Health; Housing
development; Human services; Homeless services.
Type of support: Capital and infrastructure.
Limitations: Applications accepted. Giving primarily
in the Boise, ID, area.
Publications: Application guidelines.
Application information: Complete application
guidelines available on grantmaker web site.
Application form required.
Initial approach: See grantmaker web site for
application form
Deadline(s): None
Officers and Directors: Angie Harrison, Pres. and
Director; Kirsten Heffner, V.P. and Director; Amber
Mallett, Secy. and Director; Sharon Burke, Treas.
and Director; Teresa Tavelli.
EIN: 264682140

2665
Camille Beckman Foundation, Inc.
175 S. Rosebud Ln.
Eagle, ID 83616-4500   (208) 344-7150

Established in 1994 in Idaho.
Donors: Foad Roghani; Susan Camille Roghani;
Camille Beckman Corp.
Foundation type: Independent foundation.

Financial data (yr. ended 12/31/13): Assets,
$5,169,447 (M); gifts received, $75,000;
expenditures, $268,723; qualifying distributions,
$223,378; giving activities include $221,459 for 28
grants (high: $50,000; low: $9).
Purpose and activities: Giving primarily for
disadvantaged children, financially disadvantaged
elderly persons, the homeless, and persons with
disabilities. The foundation will also provide funding
to qualified charities offering training experience and
education to allow targeted people to become more
productive and self-sufficient.
Fields of interest: Agriculture; Housing
development; Human services.
Limitations: Applications accepted. Giving primarily
in ID. No grants to individuals.
Application information: Application form required.
Initial approach: Letter
Deadline(s): None
Officers: Susan Camille Roghani, Pres.; Foad
Roghani, V.P.; Albert P. Barker, Secy.; Michael R.
Lindstrom, Treas.
Directors: Paul A. Beckman; Roshan Roghani.
EIN: 820484130

2666
Boise Legacy Constructors Foundation Inc.
(formerly Washington Group Foundation)
102 S. 17th St., Ste. 200
Boise, ID 83702-5172   (208) 424-7622
Contact: Marlene M. Puckett, Secy. and Exec. Dir.
FAX: (208) 424-7627;
E-mail: blcfoundation@qwestoffice.net; *Main
URL:* http://
boiselegacyconstructorsfoundation.com

Established in 1947 in Idaho.
Donors: Morrison Knudsen Corp.; Washington
Group International, Inc.; WGI Holdings England.
Foundation type: Operating foundation.
Financial data (yr. ended 12/31/13): Assets,
$8,775,196 (M); gifts received, $16,348;
expenditures, $355,444; qualifying distributions,
$351,131; giving activities include $46,615 for 35
+ grants (high: $11,240; low: $25), and $181,187
for 276 grants to individuals (high: $7,250).
Purpose and activities: The foundation supports
programs designed to promote health and human
services, civic and community issues, education,
and culture and arts, and awards grants to needy
individuals to assist with basic necessities.
Fields of interest: Arts and culture; Visual arts;
Performing arts; Education; Environment; Health;
Science; Technology; Mathematics; Public affairs;
Community and economic development; Human
services; Adolescents; Seniors; Low-income and
poor people.
Type of support: Equipment; Grants to individuals;
Emergency funds; Program development;
Sponsorships.
Limitations: Applications accepted. Giving limited to
areas of company operations in Boise and Treasure
Valley, ID. No support for political, labor, or fraternal
organizations, merchant associations, civic clubs,
memberships, lobbying, or discriminatory
organizations, or churches or religious
organizations. No grants for trust funds, sporting
events, seminars, contests, sponsorships, travel,
student trips or tours, books, films, television or
video production, research or feasibility studies, or
tickets for raffles or other prize-oriented activities.
Publications: Application guidelines.

Application information:
Initial approach: E-mail the foundation for
application information
Deadline(s): None
Officers: Frank Finlayson, Pres.; Marlene Puckett,
Secy. and Exec. Dir.; Russell Strong, Treas.
Directors: Mary Ann Arnold; Mac Hartley; James
McCallum; Matthew Reece; Tony Sander; Scott
Wilson; Dawn Yantek.
Number of staff: 1 full-time professional.
EIN: 826005410

2667
Boswell Family Foundation
P.O. Box 413
Ketchum, ID 83340-0413

Donor: J.G. Boswell II.
Foundation type: Independent foundation.
Financial data (yr. ended 12/31/13): Assets,
$5,498,099 (M); expenditures, $437,412;
qualifying distributions, $351,330; giving activities
include $282,992 for 43 grants (high: $50,000;
low: $250).
Fields of interest: Education; Community service;
Child welfare.
Limitations: Applications not accepted. Giving
primarily in CA and Hailey, ID. No grants to
individuals.
Application information: Unsolicited requests for
funds not accepted.
Officers: Lorraine Wilcox, Pres.; Barbara W. Boswell,
V.P.; Theresa E. Williams, Secy.-Treas.
EIN: 820514966

2668
The Wattis Dumke Foundation, Inc.
c/o Ed Dumke
P.O. Box 3118
Ketchum, ID 83340-3118

Established in 2002 in Idaho.
Donor: Edmund W. Dumke.
Foundation type: Independent foundation.
Financial data (yr. ended 12/31/14): Assets,
$8,304,760; expenditures, $530,316; qualifying
distributions, $428,000.
Fields of interest: Education; Animal welfare;
Foundations; Human services.
Limitations: Applications not accepted. Giving
primarily in CA, ID, and NV. No grants to individuals.
Application information: Contributes only to
pre-selected organizations.
Officer: Edmund E. Dumke, Pres.
Directors: Andrew B. Dumke; Carol B. Dumke;
Edmund W. Dumke; Michelle Praggastis.
EIN: 820555363

2669
The Emelco Foundation
9030 N. Hess St.
P.O. Box 354
Hayden, ID 83835

Established in 1983 in California.
Donors: Lynn A. Smith†; Mary McKay Smith†.
Foundation type: Independent foundation.
Financial data (yr. ended 12/31/13): Assets,
$5,252,174 (M); expenditures, $225,032;
qualifying distributions, $218,255; giving activities

include $211,000 for 21 grants (high: $25,000; low: $5,000).

Purpose and activities: Giving primarily for Christian organizations and human services.

Fields of interest: Education; Christianity; Human services.

Limitations: Applications not accepted. Giving primarily in CA.

Application information: Unsolicited requests for funds not accepted.

Officers: Julie Johnson, Pres.; Erik Johnson, Secy.; Katherine M. Norman, Treas.

EIN: 953863839

2670
Equinox Foundation, Inc.
(formerly Fenton Family Foundation, Inc.)
P.O. Box 2021
Sandpoint, ID   83864-2021
E-mail: info@theequinoxfoundation.org; Main URL: http://theequinoxfoundation.org

Established in 2006 in Idaho.

Donors: Joyce R. Fenton; Steven Fenton.

Foundation type: Independent foundation.

Financial data (yr. ended 12/31/14): Assets, $6,448,767 (M); expenditures, $316,877; qualifying distributions, $278,805; giving activities include $278,000 for 14 grants (high: $235,000; low: $500).

Purpose and activities: The foundation partners with the Inland Northwest Community Foundation to provide a grant program for the benefit of the communities in Bonner and Boundary counties of North Idaho.

Fields of interest: Environment; Youth development.

Limitations: Applications accepted. Giving primarily in Boundary and Bonner counties, ID. No grants to individuals.

Application information: To learn more about applying for a grant, visit the web site of the Inland Northwest Community Foundation: http://www.inwcf.org.

Officers: Julie R. Kubiak, Pres.; Susan L. Kubiak, V.P. and Treas.; J. Ted Diehl, Secy.

Directors: Mark S. Kubiak; Steve Meyer.

EIN: 203751438

2671
John and Elaine French Family Foundation
114 Wall St.
P.O. Box 4984
Ketchum, ID   83340

Established in 2001 in California.

Donors: Elaine A. French; John K. French.

Foundation type: Independent foundation.

Financial data (yr. ended 12/31/13): Assets, $4,689,915 (M); expenditures, $293,996; qualifying distributions, $250,000; giving activities include $250,000 for 16 grants (high: $50,000; low: $2,500).

Fields of interest: Education; Natural resources; Family planning.

Limitations: Applications not accepted. Giving primarily in CA, ID, MA, and VA. No support for religious and health organizations, with the exception of family planning organizations. No grants to individuals.

Application information: Contributes only to pre-selected organizations.

Officers: Elaine A. French, Pres.; John K. French, C.F.O. and Secy.

Directors: Charles H. French; Duncan A. French; Eric R. French.

EIN: 912169139

2672
Robert M. Golden Foundation
c/o Morley Golden
P.O. Box 286
Sun Valley, ID   83353-0286

Foundation type: Independent foundation.

Financial data (yr. ended 12/31/13): Assets, $5,975,748 (M); expenditures, $401,570; qualifying distributions, $366,588; giving activities include $361,830 for 105 grants (high: $20,000; low: $5).

Purpose and activities: Giving primarily for the arts, health organizations, and human services.

Fields of interest: Arts and culture; Historic preservation; Environment; Foundations; Diseases and conditions; Community and economic development; Human services.

Limitations: Applications not accepted. Giving limited to CA and ID. No grants to individuals.

Application information: Contributes only to pre-selected organizations.

Officers: Connie Golden, Pres.; Marilyn Golden Kelley, V.P.; Morley Golden, Secy.-Treas.

EIN: 956099985

2673
The Good Works Institute, Inc.
P.O. Box 1811
Sun Valley, ID   83353-1811   (208) 726-4421
Contact: Ann M. Down, Pres.
FAX: (208) 622-8003; E-mail: anndown@yahoo.com

Established in 1999 in Idaho.

Donor: Ann M. Down.

Foundation type: Independent foundation.

Financial data (yr. ended 09/30/14): Assets, $57,957 (M); gifts received, $348,012; expenditures, $465,483; qualifying distributions, $441,042; giving activities include $439,839 for 24 grants (high: $96,043; low: $5,000).

Purpose and activities: Giving in support of the health and welfare of children and the preservation and protection of the environment.

Fields of interest: Health; Religion; Human services.

Application information: Contact foundation for complete application requirements.

  Initial approach: Letter, e-mail, or fax
  Deadline(s): None

Officers: Ann M. Down, Pres.; Douglas I. Aanestad, Secy.; Sandra Clapp, Treas.

Director: Phylis Hockett.

EIN: 820518035

2674
Lola and Duane Hagadone Foundation, Inc.
P.O. Box 6200
Coeur d'Alene, ID   83816-1937

Donor: Hagadone Helicopters, LLC.

Foundation type: Independent foundation.

Financial data (yr. ended 12/31/13): Assets, $3,155,018 (M); gifts received, $3,324,415;

expenditures, $171,775; qualifying distributions, $150,000; giving activities include $150,000 for 1 grant.

Fields of interest: Education.

Limitations: Applications not accepted.

Application information: Unsolicited requests for funds not accepted.

Officers and Directors: Duane B. Hagadone, Pres. and Director; Lola C. Hagadone, V.P. and Director; Bradley D. Hagadone, Secy.-Treas. and Director.

EIN: 462790265

2675
The Susan and Richard Hare Family Foundation Inc.
P.O. Box 2508
Sun Valley, ID   83353-2508

Established in 2002 in Idaho.

Donors: Richard Hare; Susan Hare.

Foundation type: Independent foundation.

Financial data (yr. ended 12/31/13): Assets, $626,953 (M); expenditures, $158,535; qualifying distributions, $156,700; giving activities include $156,700 for 50 grants (high: $20,000; low: $100).

Fields of interest: Arts and culture; Orchestral music; Education; Elementary and secondary education; Natural resources; Biodiversity; Wildlife biodiversity; Domesticated animals; Animal training; Health; Hospice care; Diseases and conditions; Community and economic development; Sports and recreation; Human services.

Type of support: Advocacy.

Limitations: Applications not accepted. Giving primarily in Washington, DC and ID. No grants to individuals.

Application information: Contributes only to pre-selected organizations.

Officers: Richard Hare, Pres.; Susan F. Hare, Secy.

Directors: Melinda H. Bush; Michelle H. Gillern; Daniel P. Hare.

EIN: 810547042

2676
Hecla Charitable Foundation
6500 N. Mineral Dr., Ste. 200
Coeur d'Alene, ID   83815-9408   (208) 769-4100
Contact: Carolyn Turner, Treas.

Foundation type: Independent foundation.

Financial data (yr. ended 12/31/13): Assets, $6,334,253 (M); expenditures, $369,584; qualifying distributions, $349,014; giving activities include $349,014 for 86 grants (high: $34,000; low: $100).

Fields of interest: Education; Nonprofits; Human services.

Type of support: Regranting.

Limitations: Applications accepted. Giving primarily in CO.

Application information: Application form required.

  Initial approach: Proposal
  Deadline(s): None

Officers and Directors: Luther J. Russell, Pres. and Director; Mike Satre, V.P. and Director; Tami Whitman, Secy.; Carolyn Turner, Treas.; James A. Sabala; Dean McDonald; Mike Dexter.

EIN: 261728023

2677
Intermountain Industries Petroglyph Energy Foundation, Inc.
(formerly Intermountain Gas Industries Foundation, Inc.)
P.O. Box 70019
Boise, ID 83707-1608 (208) 685-7600
Contact: Nancy Murrin
Application address: 960 Broadway Ave., Ste. 500
Boise, ID 83706, tel.: (208) 685-7600; Main
URL: http://www.intermountainindustries.com/
community.php

Established in 1988 in Idaho.
Donors: Intermountain Gas Co.; IGI Resources, Inc.; Petroglyph Operating Co.; Intermountain Industries, Inc.
Foundation type: Company-sponsored foundation.
Financial data (yr. ended 09/30/13): Assets, $626,611 (M); gifts received, $215,000; expenditures, $208,789; qualifying distributions, $208,466; giving activities include $208,466 for 48 grants (high: $23,300; low: $100).
Purpose and activities: The foundation supports organizations involved with arts and culture, education, health, human services, community development, and civic affairs.
Fields of interest: Education; Health; Human services.
Type of support: General support; Scholarships.
Limitations: Applications accepted. Giving primarily in areas of company operations, with emphasis on ID. No grants to individuals.
Application information: Application form required.
Initial approach: Request application form
Deadline(s): None
Officers and Directors: William C. Glynn, Pres. and Director; Michael E. Rich, V.P. and Secy.; Paul Powell, V.P. and Director; Richard Hokin.
EIN: 820431608

2678
The Joan Leidy Foundation, Inc.
P.O. Box 1709
Hailey, ID 83333-1709

Established in 1993 in Idaho.
Donors: Helen Leidy Samson; Leidy Sue Samson.
Foundation type: Independent foundation.
Financial data (yr. ended 12/31/13): Assets, $4,477,108 (M); gifts received, $100,000; expenditures, $256,534; qualifying distributions, $225,000; giving activities include $225,000 for 24 grants (high: $16,000; low: $5,000).
Fields of interest: Hospice care; Family planning; Legal services; Housing development; Human services; Homeless services.
Limitations: Applications accepted. Giving primarily in CA and ID. No grants to individuals.
Application information: Application form required.
Initial approach: Letter
Deadline(s): None
Officers: Christopher Heiser, Pres.; Leidy Sue Samson, V.P.; Megan Heiser, Secy.; K.C. Samson Brittenham, Treas.
Directors: Ann Erickson; Shelley Seibel.
EIN: 943184527

2679
Melaleuca Foundation
3910 S. Yellowstone Hwy.
Idaho Falls, ID 83402-4342
E-mail: info@melaleucafoundation.org; Main
URL: http://www.melaleuca.org

Established in 2003 in Idaho.
Donor: Melaleuca, Inc.
Foundation type: Company-sponsored foundation.
Financial data (yr. ended 12/31/13): Assets, $319,532 (M); gifts received, $252,718; expenditures, $225,261; qualifying distributions, $214,632; giving activities include $159,832 for grants, and $54,800 for grants to individuals.
Purpose and activities: The foundation supports organizations involved with education and the Saint Lucia Children's Home in Quito, Ecuador.
Fields of interest: Education; Child welfare; Shelter and residential care.
International interests: Ecuador.
Type of support: General support; Scholarships.
Limitations: Applications not accepted. Giving primarily in ID and Quito, Ecuador. No grants to individuals.
Application information: Contributes only to pre-selected organizations.
Officers: Frank L. VanderSloot, Pres.; Damon Watkins, Secy.; Thomas K. Knutson, Treas.
EIN: 200513976

2680
Bruce Mitchell Foundation
12038 W. Mesquite Dr.
Boise, ID 83713-0814
Application address: c/o Glenda Leigh, P.O. Box 443, Parma, ID 83660, tel.: (208) 722-5295

Established in 1989 in Idaho.
Donor: W. Bruce Mitchell†.
Foundation type: Independent foundation.
Financial data (yr. ended 06/30/13): Assets, $5,377,723 (M); expenditures, $261,293; qualifying distributions, $244,445; giving activities include $221,512 for 92 grants to individuals (high: $3,000; low: $833).
Purpose and activities: Scholarships primarily to graduates of Parma High School, Parma, ID; support also for the Parma local public school district and a vocational education scholarship fund program.
Fields of interest: Elementary and secondary education; Vocational education; Higher education.
Type of support: Equipment; Scholarships; Student aid.
Limitations: Applications accepted. Giving primarily in Parma, ID.
Application information: Application form required.
Initial approach: Contact Foundation
Deadline(s): Apr. 15 for scholarships
Trustees: Pat Gotsch; Ed Johnson; Cari Magette; Larry Sorenson; Jon Watson.
EIN: 943107820

2681
Frank A. Morbeck Community Foundation Inc.
P.O. Box 709
Wallace, ID 83873-0709 (208) 752-1154
Contact: Marilyn White, Secy. and Dir.

Established in 1999 in Idaho.

Donor: Frank A. Morbeck†.
Foundation type: Independent foundation.
Financial data (yr. ended 12/31/13): Assets, $3,411,056 (M); expenditures, $200,005; qualifying distributions, $179,255; giving activities include $168,858 for 24 grants (high: $45,900; low: $375).
Fields of interest: Arts and culture; Education; University education; Youth development.
Type of support: General support; Scholarships.
Limitations: Applications accepted. Giving primarily in Wallace, ID.
Application information: Application form required.
Initial approach: Contact foundation for application form
Deadline(s): Mar. 1
Officers and Directors: Michael K. Branstetter, Pres. and Director; Dick L. Vester, V.P. and Director; Marilyn White, Secy. and Director; Jennifer Carrico; Bill Mooney; Robert Rannells; Kathy Zanetti.
EIN: 820509175

2682
Harry W. Morrison Foundation, Inc.
827 E. Park Blvd.
Boise, ID 83712-7781
Contact: Bernice Hays
E-mail: bernicehwm@gmail.com

Established in 1952 in Idaho.
Donors: Harry W. Morrison†; Velma V. Morrison.
Foundation type: Independent foundation.
Financial data (yr. ended 12/31/13): Assets, $10,296,140 (M); gifts received, $250; expenditures, $660,478; qualifying distributions, $415,657; giving activities include $325,496 for grants.
Purpose and activities: Giving primarily to improve the quality of life in Idaho.
Fields of interest: Arts and culture; Higher education; Christianity; Human services; Child welfare.
Type of support: Research; Matching grants; Equipment; Capital campaigns; General support; Capital and infrastructure; Scholarships.
Limitations: Applications accepted. Giving primarily in the greater ID area. No grants to individuals.
Publications: Annual report.
Application information: Application form required.
Initial approach: Proposal
Copies of proposal: 1
Deadline(s): None
Board meeting date(s): Annually during summer
Final notification: 0-60 days
Officers: Velma V. Morrison, Chair.; Justin Wilkerson, C.E.O. and Pres.; Judith V. Roberts, V.P.; Linda L. Klingner, Secy.
Directors: Bernice Wilkerson; Frank Winsor.
Number of staff: 1 part-time professional; 1 part-time support.
EIN: 826008111

2683
The Kipp Nelson Foundation
P.O. Box 10021
Ketchum, ID 83340-8021

Established in 1998 in New York.
Donors: Eddie Bauer; Kipp N. Nelson.
Foundation type: Independent foundation.

Financial data (yr. ended 12/31/13): Assets, $2,734,688 (M); expenditures, $196,728; qualifying distributions, $188,235; giving activities include $188,235 for 10 grants (high: $99,340; low: $500).
Fields of interest: Historic preservation; Natural resources; Winter sports.
Limitations: Applications not accepted. Giving primarily in ID. No grants to individuals.
Application information: Unsolicited requests for funds not accepted.
Directors: Carlos A. Cordeiro; Kipp N. Nelson.
EIN: 133936467

2684
The Palmedo Family Foundation Inc.
P.O. Box 2211
Ketchum, ID   83340-2211

Donors: Peter Palmedo; Jane Palmedo.
Foundation type: Independent foundation.
Financial data (yr. ended 12/31/14): Assets, $2,547,942; expenditures, $152,479; qualifying distributions, $149,000.
Fields of interest: Education; Religion; Human services.
Limitations: Applications not accepted.
Application information: Unsolicited requests for funds not accepted.
Directors: Brittain E. Palmedo; Jane B. Palmedo; Peter F. Palmedo; Peter F. Palmedo, Jr.; Whitney J. Palmedo.
EIN: 263934465

2685
J. R. Simplot Foundation, Inc.
P.O. Box 27
Boise, ID   83707-0027
Main URL: http://jacksurbanmeetingplace.org

Established in 1953 in Idaho.
Donors: J. R. Simplot†; JR Simplot Co.
Foundation type: Independent foundation.
Financial data (yr. ended 09/30/13): Assets, $204,554,385 (M); gifts received, $29,400; expenditures, $1,632,038; qualifying distributions, $8,100,978; giving activities include $400,000 for 21+ grants (high: $131,200).
Fields of interest: Arts and culture; Foundations.
Type of support: General support; In-kind gifts; Matching grants; Continuing support; Capital campaigns; Capital and infrastructure; Endowments; Scholarships.
Limitations: Applications not accepted. Giving primarily in Boise, ID. No grants to individuals.
Publications: Informational brochure.
Application information: Contributes only to pre-selected organizations.
Officers and Directors: Debbie McDonald, Pres. and Director; Scott Simplot, V.P. and Director; Ron Graves, Secy.; Annette Elg, Treas.; Don Simplot; Gay Simplot; Ted Simplot.
EIN: 826003437

2686
Smeed Memorial Foundation
1201 S. Kimball Ave.
Caldwell, ID   83605-4626
E-mail: rcoffman@cableone.net; Application address: c/o Smeed Memorial Foundation, 3509 Malibu Pl., Caldwell, ID 83605 tel.: (208) 455-9040

Donor: Ralph E. Smeed†.
Foundation type: Independent foundation.
Financial data (yr. ended 12/31/13): Assets, $4,988,074 (M); gifts received, $2,901,695; expenditures, $498,591; qualifying distributions, $435,500; giving activities include $435,500 for 8 grants (high: $250,000; low: $5,000).
Fields of interest: Education; Human services.
Type of support: General support.
Limitations: Applications accepted. Giving primarily in ID and TX.
Application information: Application form required.
   Initial approach: Completed Application form
   Deadline(s): None
Officers: Rick Coffman, Pres.; Dan Symms, V.P.; Elizabeth Allan-Hodge, Secy.; Dick Anderson, Treas.
Directors: Maurice Clements; Chris Derry; Stan Hawkins; Phil Hurley; Laird Maxwell; Monte Munn; Theron Nelson; Steve Symms.
EIN: 453753483

2687
Harold E. & Phyllis S. Thomas Foundation
12549 W. Bowmont Ct.
Boise, ID   83713-0023
Contact: Judy Rasmussen, Dir.

Established in 1995 in Idaho.
Donors: Phyllis Thomas; Harold Thomas; Patrick W. Feenstra.
Foundation type: Independent foundation.
Financial data (yr. ended 12/31/13): Assets, $0 (M); gifts received, $1,391,097; expenditures, $512,203; qualifying distributions, $440,823; giving activities include $440,823 for 28+ grants (high: $50,000).
Purpose and activities: Grants are awarded for Christian evangelical work with particular consideration for missions and organizations engaged in missionary teachings and work. Some giving also for other religious philanthropic organizations.
Fields of interest: Christianity.
Limitations: Applications not accepted. Giving in the U.S., with emphasis on ID and WA.
Application information: Contributes only to pre-selected organizations. Unsolicited requests for funds not accepted.
Trustees: Don Anderson; Dave Hills; James Mitchell; Robert Renfro; Harold E. Thomas; Rick Thomas.
Director: Judy Rasmussen.
EIN: 820477243

2688
Troxell Fund Inc.
827 Balsam St.
Boise, ID   83706-2511   (208) 344-1006
Contact: Ann Troxell Murdoch, Pres. and Dir.

Established in 1991 in Idaho.

Donors: Robert I. Troxell†; Barbara Noble Troxell; Ann Troxell Murdoch.
Foundation type: Independent foundation.
Financial data (yr. ended 12/31/13): Assets, $2,308,605 (M); gifts received, $14; expenditures, $394,195; qualifying distributions, $361,538; giving activities include $350,000 for 16 grants (high: $60,000; low: $5,000).
Fields of interest: Education; Animal welfare; Human services; Child welfare; Females.
Limitations: Applications accepted. Giving primarily in ID. No grants to individuals.
Application information:
   Initial approach: Proposal
   Deadline(s): None
   Board meeting date(s): Annually
Officer and Directors: Ann Troxell Murdoch, Pres. and Director; Susan Ashla; Jane Crane; Mary Jane Hill.
Number of staff: 1 part-time professional.
EIN: 943135977

2689
Claude R. and Ethel B. Whittenberger Foundation
P.O. Box 1073
Caldwell, ID   83606-1073   (208) 459-4649
Contact: Coralie Weston, Chair.
Grants List: http://www.whittenberger.org/awardedgrants.html

Established in 1970 in Idaho.
Donor: Ethel B. Whittenberger†.
Foundation type: Independent foundation.
Financial data (yr. ended 12/31/13): Assets, $5,657,086 (M); expenditures, $216,604; qualifying distributions, $176,918; giving activities include $172,324 for 43 grants (high: $34,475; low: $1,000).
Purpose and activities: The Whittenberger Foundation currently gives priority to innovative and enriching projects which significantly improve the quality of life for children and young people. The foundation's areas of interest relating to children and young people are education, arts and culture, health, social welfare, recreation and the environment.
Fields of interest: Arts and culture; Education; Environment; Health; Libraries; Sports and recreation; Human services; Child welfare; Children and youth; Children; Adolescents; Young adults.
Type of support: Equipment; Program development; Publications; Seed money; Curriculum development; Scholarships.
Limitations: Applications accepted. Giving limited to ID, with emphasis on the southwestern area. No support for political involvement of any kind. No grants to individuals, or for endowment funds, general operating funds, research, individual scholarships, fundraisers, capital campaigns, construction or advertising.
Publications: Application guidelines; Grants list; Multi-year report; Program policy statement.
Application information: No audio or videotapes accepted. Application form required.
   Initial approach: Letter requesting application form
   Copies of proposal: 8
   Deadline(s): None
   Board meeting date(s): Apr., July, Oct., and Jan.
   Final notification: Second week in Nov.
Officer: Coralie Weston, Chair.

Directors: Elaine Carpenter; Scott Gipson; Michael Groff; Joe Miller; Laura Moylan; Estella Zamora.
Number of staff: 2 part-time support.
EIN: 237092604

2690
The Robert I. Wishnick Foundation
(doing business as The William Wishnick Foundation)
(formerly The Witco Foundation)
P.O. Box 447
Ponderay, ID   83852

Established in 1951 in Illinois.
Donor: William Wishnick.
Foundation type: Independent foundation.
Financial data (yr. ended 12/31/13): Assets, $7,960,551 (M); expenditures, $480,656; qualifying distributions, $444,372; giving activities include $433,400 for 66 grants (high: $67,500; low: $150).
Fields of interest: Arts and culture; Animal welfare; Nonprofits; Judaism; Human services.
Type of support: General support; Annual campaigns; Capital campaigns; Endowments; Regranting; Research.

Limitations: Applications not accepted. Giving primarily in UT. No grants to individuals.
Application Information: Contributes only to pre-selected organizations.
  Board meeting date(s): 4 to 5 times a year
Officers: Lisa Wishnick, Pres. and Treas.; Ami Jo Gibson, Secy.
Directors: Kendall Wishnick Adams; Gina Grossman; Howard Schur.
EIN: 136068668

ILLINOIS

2691
1335 Foundation

c/o Brown & Brown, LLC
225 W. Washington St., Ste. 1650
Chicago, IL 60606-3486

Established in 1989 in Illinois.
Donors: Howard J. Brown; Elizabeth K. Brown.
Foundation type: Independent foundation.
Financial data (yr. ended 12/31/13): Assets,
$4,129,631 (M); gifts received, $352,824;
expenditures, $205,442; qualifying distributions,
$178,268; giving activities include $178,268 for 33
grants (high: $50,000; low: $100).
Purpose and activities: Giving primarily for
education, human services, and community
development.
Fields of interest: Secondary education; Higher
education; Nonprofits; Public libraries; Community
and economic development; Human services; Child
welfare.
Type of support: Regranting.
Limitations: Applications not accepted. Giving
primarily in Kenosha, WI. No grants to individuals.
Application information: Contributes only to
pre-selected organizations.
Officer: Elizabeth K. Brown, Pres. and Treas.
Directors: Sarah M. Brown-Russ; Amy I.
Brown-Tuchler; Lucille Brown Minn; Steven Minn;
Mark J. Russ; James Tuchler.
EIN: 363701371

2692
Stuart & Benjamin Abelson Foundation

c/o H. Debra Levin
131 S. Dearborn, Ste. 2400
Chicago, IL 60603-5577

Established in 2005 in Illinois.
Foundation type: Independent foundation.
Financial data (yr. ended 12/31/13): Assets,
$5,608,431 (M); expenditures, $262,472;
qualifying distributions, $224,652; giving activities
include $221,000 for 14 grants (high: $90,000;
low: $1,000).
Fields of interest: Environment; Foundations;
Human services; International relations.
Limitations: Applications not accepted. No grants to
individuals.
Application information: Unsolicited requests for
funds not accepted.
Trustees: Benjamin Abelson; H. Debra Levin.
EIN: 201704170

2693
Stuart & Jesse Abelson Foundation

c/o H. Debra Levin
131 S. Deerborn St., Ste. 2400
Chicago, IL 60603-5577

Established in 2005 in Illinois.
Foundation type: Independent foundation.
Financial data (yr. ended 12/31/13): Assets,
$5,969,426 (M); expenditures, $265,054;
qualifying distributions, $243,575; giving activities

include $241,210 for 7 grants (high: $120,000;
low: $1,210).
Fields of interest: Domesticated animals; Health;
Human rights.
Limitations: Applications not accepted. Giving
primarily in IL. No grants to individuals.
Application information: Unsolicited requests for
funds not accepted.
Trustees: Jesse F. Abelson; H. Debra Levin.
EIN: 201704222

2694
The Acorn Foundation

c/o Cottle
1160 S. Michigan Ave., Ste. 3002
Chicago, IL 60605-3047 3126631160

Established in 1995 in Illinois.
Donors: Ralph L. Wanger; Leah Zell Wanger;
Kathleen Tucker.
Foundation type: Independent foundation.
Financial data (yr. ended 12/31/14): Assets,
$898,212; gifts received, $819,675; expenditures,
$164,526; qualifying distributions, $161,296.
Fields of interest: Arts and culture; Museums;
Education; Judaism; Human services.
Limitations: Applications not accepted. Giving
primarily in New York, NY and Chicago, IL. No grants
to individuals.
Application information: Contributes only to
pre-selected organizations.
Officers: Ralph Wanger, Pres.; Kathleen Tucker,
Treas.
Directors: Eric David Wanger; Leonard Ralph
Wanger; Debra Wanger Yaruss.
EIN: 363991208

2695
Acorn Investing, Inc.

(formerly World-Christian Mobilization, Inc.)
372 Rolling Wood Ln., Apt. C
Barrington, IL 60010

Established in 1993 in Illinois.
Donor: Carol Eich.
Foundation type: Independent foundation.
Financial data (yr. ended 12/31/14): Assets,
$1,675,299 (M); expenditures, $290,471;
qualifying distributions, $280,955; giving activities
include $270,670 for 38 grants (high: $25,230;
low: $1,000).
Fields of interest: Education; Radio; Christianity;
Human services.
Limitations: Applications not accepted. Giving on a
national basis. No grants to individuals.
Application information: Contributes only to
pre-selected organizations.
Officers and Directors: Carol Eich, Pres. and Treas.
and Director; Lynne Walters, V.P. and Director; Beth
Mann, Secy. and Director; Katie DeLaere; Kenneth
Piercey; Sara Piercey.
EIN: 363905593

2696
Marjorie C. Adams Charitable Trust

c/o JPMorgan Chase Bank, N.A.
10 S. Dearborn St., 21st Fl.
Chicago, IL 60603-2300
Application address: c/o JPMorgan Chase Bank,
N.A., Attn.: Frank Lemma, 270 Park Ave., 16th Fl.,
New York, NY 10017, tel.: (212) 648-1477

Established in 1987 in New York.
Donor: Marjorie Carr Adams†.
Foundation type: Independent foundation.
Financial data (yr. ended 08/31/13): Assets,
$3,773,967 (M); expenditures, $228,309;
qualifying distributions, $185,862; giving activities
include $172,000 for 2 grants (high: $122,000;
low: $50,000).
Purpose and activities: Giving primarily for care and
treatment of deaf and blind people, research into
the causes and the treatment of deafness and
blindness, and K-12 education.
Fields of interest: Education; People with vision
impairments; People with hearing impairments.
Type of support: Capital campaigns; Capital and
infrastructure; Endowments.
Limitations: Applications accepted. Giving primarily
in NY. No grants to individuals; no loans or
program-related investments.
Publications: Grants list.
Application information:
  Deadline(s): None
Trustee: JPMorgan Chase Bank, N.A.
EIN: 136897539

2697
Adreani Foundation

7458 N. Harlem Ave.
Chicago, IL 60631-4404

Established in 1978 in Illinois.
Donors: Raymond J. Adreani; RJA Investment Fund,
L.P.
Foundation type: Independent foundation.
Financial data (yr. ended 11/30/13): Assets,
$7,441,697 (M); expenditures, $392,584;
qualifying distributions, $381,550; giving activities
include $381,550 for 82 grants (high: $55,000;
low: $100).
Purpose and activities: Giving primarily for the arts,
education, health organizations, children and social
services, YMCAs, and Christian churches.
Fields of interest: Arts and culture; Education;
Elementary and secondary education; Higher
education; Diseases and conditions; Christianity;
Human services; Child welfare.
Limitations: Applications not accepted. Giving
primarily in IL. No grants to individuals.
Application information: Unsolicited requests for
funds not accepted.
Officers: Raymond J. Adreani, Pres.; Susan J. Smith,
Treas.
EIN: 363059439

2698
Agape Foundation

333 N. Michigan Ave., Ste. 510
Chicago, IL 60601-3934 (312) 641-5765
Contact: Iris Krieg

Established in 2002 in Illinois.
Donor: Michael J. Romano III.

Foundation type: Independent foundation.
Financial data (yr. ended 12/31/13): Assets, $4,007,000 (M); expenditures, $230,876; qualifying distributions, $185,737; giving activities include $171,975 for 24 grants (high: $52,975; low: $500).
Purpose and activities: Giving primarily for health and human services.
Fields of interest: Secondary education; Higher education; Human services.
Type of support: General support; Continuing support; Annual campaigns; Capital campaigns; Capital and infrastructure; Program development; Seed money.
Limitations: Applications accepted. Giving primarily in IL. No grants to individuals.
Application information:
  Initial approach: Letter
  Copies of proposal: 1
  Deadline(s): None
  Final notification: 3-4 weeks
Officers: Michael J. Romano III, Chair. and Director; Benita Romano, Vice-Chair. and Treas.; Stephen L. Golan, Secy.
Number of staff: None.
EIN: 320048185

2699
Agent F Leslye H Phillips Fam Fdn
10 S. Dearborn IL1-0117
Chicago, IL   60603

Foundation type: Independent foundation.
Financial data (yr. ended 12/31/13): Assets, $7,066,083 (M); expenditures, $219,814; qualifying distributions, $169,469; giving activities include $160,743 for 6 grants (high: $75,000; low: $2,250).
Fields of interest: Arts and culture; Education; Religion.
Limitations: Applications not accepted. Giving primarily in MN and NJ.
Application information: Unsolicited requests for funds not accepted.
Officers: Leslye Hutton Phillips, Pres. and Treas.; Elizabeth Fitzpatrick, V.P. and Secy.
Director: Sidney Kaplan.
EIN: 274817621

2700
Armer F. Ahlstrand Charitable Foundation Trust
111 W. Monroe St., Tax Div 10C
Chicago, IL   60603

Established in 1997 in Illinois.
Donor: Armer F. Ahlstrand†.
Foundation type: Independent foundation.
Financial data (yr. ended 08/31/14): Assets, $3,821,037 (M); expenditures, $217,987; qualifying distributions, $193,977; giving activities include $172,742 for 30 grants (high: $17,275; low: $1,919).
Fields of interest: Arts and culture; Theater; Art museums; Education; Diseases and conditions; Cancers; Religion; Christianity; Human services; Child welfare.
Limitations: Applications not accepted. Giving primarily in Rockford, IL. No grants to individuals.
Application information: Contributes only to pre-selected organizations.

Trustee: Harris Bank, N.A.
EIN: 367201890

2701
Allen-Heath Memorial Foundation
222 N. LaSalle St., Ste. 300
Chicago, IL   60601-1081

Established in 1947 in California.
Donors: Harriet A. Heath†; John E.S. Heath†.
Foundation type: Independent foundation.
Financial data (yr. ended 12/31/13): Assets, $6,160,502 (M); expenditures, $258,292; qualifying distributions, $207,680; giving activities include $185,000 for 24 grants (high: $50,000; low: $1,000).
Fields of interest: Arts and culture; Theater; Higher education; Health; Diseases and conditions; Public libraries; Abuse prevention; Fire prevention and control; Public affairs; Human services; Food aid; Child welfare; Women's services.
Type of support: General support; Program development.
Limitations: Applications not accepted.
Application information: Unsolicited requests for funds not accepted.
Officers: Charles K. Heath, Pres.; Lisa Burman, Secy.; James Harbert, Treas.
Directors: Alexandra K. Heath Brezinski; Edwin Brezinski; Elizabeth Phillips.
EIN: 363056910

2702
Alliant Credit Union Foundation
11545 W. Touhy Ave.
Chicago, IL   60666   (800) 328-1935; 8635
Contact: Wayne Rosenwinkel, V.P. and Dir.
E-mail: foundation@alliantcreditunion.com; Main URL: http://www.alliantcreditunionfoundation.org

Donor: Alliant Credit Union.
Foundation type: Company-sponsored foundation.
Financial data (yr. ended 06/30/13): Assets, $4,061,130 (M); gifts received, $500,000; expenditures, $263,472; qualifying distributions, $263,472; giving activities include $261,729 for 129 grants (high: $30,000).
Purpose and activities: The foundation promotes financial literacy, economic empowerment, and self-sufficiency in people, especially in communities where Alliant Credit Union members and employees live and work.
Fields of interest: Education; Elementary and secondary education; Reading promotion; Community and economic development; Financial counseling; Children; Low-income and poor people.
Type of support: Annual campaigns; Employee volunteer services; General support; Program development.
Limitations: Applications accepted. Giving primarily in areas of company operations in Chicago, IL.
Publications: Informational brochure.
Application information: Application form required.
  Initial approach: E-mail foundation
  Deadline(s): None
Officers and Directors: David Mooney, Chair. and Director; Wayne Rosenwinkel, Pres. and Director; Robert Russell, V.P.; Meredith Ritchie, Secy.; Michael Gard, Treas. and Director; Rich Holke; Albert Obay.
EIN: 711052113

2703
The Allyn Foundation, Inc.
539 Princeton Rd.
Hinsdale, IL   60521

Foundation type: Independent foundation.
Financial data (yr. ended 12/31/14): Assets, $6,257,745 (M); expenditures, $304,765; qualifying distributions, $300,865; giving activities include $300,000 for 88 grants (high: $10,000; low: $1,000).
Purpose and activities: Giving primarily for the arts, health, and human services.
Fields of interest: Arts and culture; Higher education; Hospital care; Diseases and conditions; Human services; Child welfare.
Limitations: Applications not accepted. No grants to individuals.
Application information: Unsolicited requests for funds not accepted.
Officers and Directors: Cynthia A. Stuhley, Pres. and Director; John W. Allyn, Jr., V.P. and Director; Sharon A. Taylor.
EIN: 237025589

2704
Almeida Family Foundation
440 W. Randolph St., Ste. 500
Chicago, IL   60606-1507

Established in 2001 in Illinois.
Donors: Jill F. Almeida; Richard J. Almeida.
Foundation type: Independent foundation.
Financial data (yr. ended 12/31/13): Assets, $725,598 (M); gifts received, $225,914; expenditures, $166,406; qualifying distributions, $162,431; giving activities include $159,770 for 39 grants (high: $50,000; low: $70).
Fields of interest: Arts and culture; Art museums; Elementary and secondary education; Rehabilitation; Human services; Child welfare; Youth development.
Limitations: Applications not accepted. Giving primarily in Chicago, IL. No grants to individuals.
Application information: Contributes only to pre-selected organizations.
Officers: Jill F. Almeida, Pres.; Richard J. Almeida, Secy.-Treas.
Director: Alexis Almeida.
EIN: 364480855

2705
The Alton Foundation
400 S. Main St.
P.O. Box 349
Wood River, IL   62095-1426

Established in 1947 in Illinois.
Donors: Louise K. Barth Memorial Fund; Edna & Emma O. Sawyer Trust; Louise K. Barth Memorial Trust.
Foundation type: Independent foundation.
Financial data (yr. ended 12/31/14): Assets, $3,479,714 (M); gifts received, $138,173; expenditures, $290,728; qualifying distributions, $272,193; giving activities include $253,416 for 36 grants (high: $38,400; low: $360).
Purpose and activities: Giving primarily to Christian agencies and churches, and for higher education, children's services, boys and girls clubs, and human services.

Fields of interest: Arts and culture; Higher education; Christianity; Human services; Child welfare; Youth services.
Type of support: Annual campaigns; Program-related investments; Equipment; Emergency funds; Scholarships.
Limitations: Applications accepted. Giving limited to Madison County, IL, and adjoining counties. No grants to individuals.
Application information: Application form required.
  Initial approach: Letter
  Copies of proposal: 1
  Deadline(s): None
  Board meeting date(s): Dec. 15 and June 15
Officers: Francis Mazenko, Chair.; Mark Kratschmer, Vice-Chair.; Robert J. Walters, Secy.
Directors: Dr. Leo Green; Gary Osborne; Jeannine Kelly; Emert Wyss.
Number of staff: 2 part-time support.
EIN: 376045370

2706
Alton Woman's Home Association
P.O. Box 552
Alton, IL 62002-0552

Established in 1897 in Illinois.
Foundation type: Operating foundation.
Financial data (yr. ended 12/31/14): Assets, $3,274,698; gifts received, $2,815; expenditures, $207,539; qualifying distributions, $192,000.
Purpose and activities: Giving for local-area needy women and children, services for the aged, and welfare agencies.
Fields of interest: Human services; Child welfare; Women's services; Children; Seniors; Females.
Type of support: Continuing support.
Limitations: Applications accepted. Giving limited to Madison County, IL. No support for profit-making organizations. No grants to individuals.
Publications: Financial statement.
Application information: Application form required.
  Initial approach: Letter
  Copies of proposal: 1
  Board meeting date(s): Mar., June, Sept., Nov., and Dec.
Officers: Saundra Hudson, Pres.; Julie Harper, V.P.; Mary Ruth Kettenbach, Corresponding Secy.; Angela McDowell, Recording Secy.; Joanne Adams, Treas.
EIN: 370799839

2707
American Friends of the National Institute for Psychobiology in Israel
(also known as AFNIPI)
5825 S. Dorchester Ave., Ste. 9W
Chicago, IL 60637-1701   (773) 546-8037
FAX: (773) 834-3562;
E-mail: egershon@yoda.bsd.uchicago.edu;
Application address: c/o Nipi Scientific Advisory Committee, 5841 S. Maryland Ave., MC 3077, Chicago, IL 60637; Main URL: http://www.afnipi.org
Grants List: http://www.afnipi.org/grants/byyear/2012

Donors: Charles E. Smith Family Foundation; Morton B. & Blance S. Prince Philanthropic Fund.
Foundation type: Independent foundation.
Financial data (yr. ended 12/31/12): Assets, $9,919 (M); gifts received, $219,360; expenditures, $209,441; qualifying distributions,

$209,441; giving activities include $209,426 for 1 grant.
Fields of interest: Education; Brain and nervous system disorders; Judaism.
International interests: Israel.
Type of support: Research.
Limitations: Applications accepted. Giving limited to Jerusalem, Israel.
Application information: Application form required.
  Initial approach: Letter or E-mail
  Deadline(s): 1st year funding Dec. 31, 2nd & 3rd year funding Apr. 30
Officers and Directors: Elliot S. Gershon, Pres. and Director; Shaul Hochstein, Secy.-Treas. and Director; Lisa Adler Covitz; Orley M. Desser; Vance Liebman; Anita Roe; Leona Z. Rosenberg; David Bruce Smith; Joseph Walder.
EIN: 900794238

2708
Amsted Industries Foundation
180 N. Stetson Ave., Ste. 1800
Chicago, IL 60601-6808   (312) 819-1700
Contact: Shirley Whitesell, Tr.

Established in 1953 in Illinois.
Donor: Amsted Industries Inc.
Foundation type: Company-sponsored foundation.
Financial data (yr. ended 09/30/13): Assets, $63,564 (M); gifts received, $405,460; expenditures, $342,848; qualifying distributions, $341,638; giving activities include $3,000 for 2 grants, and $338,638 for 485 employee matching gifts.
Purpose and activities: The foundation supports organizations involved with arts and culture, education, health, and human services.
Fields of interest: Arts and culture; Education; Health.
Type of support: General support; Employee matching gifts; Continuing support; Capital and infrastructure.
Limitations: Applications accepted. Giving limited to areas of company operations, with some emphasis on Chicago, IL. No support for religious organizations or veterans' organizations. No grants to individuals, or for endowments, scholarships, fellowships, or advertising; no loans.
Application information: Application form required.
  Initial approach: Letter
  Deadline(s): 15 days after the month of receipt
Trustees: Glenn Chamberlin; W. Robert Reum; Shirley J. Whitesell.
Number of staff: 1 part-time professional; 1 part-time support.
EIN: 366050609

2709
Anschel Eilian Family Charitable Foundation
c/o C. Eilian
3470 N. Lake Shore Dr., Ste. 27
Chicago, IL 60657-2892

Established in 2002 in Illinois.
Donors: Trude Anschel; Jonathan Eilian.
Foundation type: Independent foundation.
Financial data (yr. ended 12/31/14): Assets, $797,512 (M); expenditures, $444,514; qualifying distributions, $441,985; giving activities include

$441,985 for 31 grants (high: $200,000; low: $100).
Purpose and activities: Giving primarily for Jewish organizations; funding also for cancer research.
Fields of interest: Nonprofits; Diseases and conditions; Judaism; Human services.
Type of support: Regranting; Research.
Limitations: Applications not accepted. Giving primarily in IL and NY; funding also in Washington, DC. No grants to individuals.
Application information: Contributes only to pre-selected organizations.
Officers: Charlene Eilian, Pres. and Treas; Daniel Anschel, Secy.
EIN: 320002986

2710
Aon Memorial Education Fund
(formerly Aon Assistance Fund)
200 E. Randolph St., 8th Fl.
Chicago, IL 60601-6419   (312) 381-3551
Contact: Beth Gallagher, V.P.
E-mail: beth.gallagher@aon.com; Main URL: http://www.aon.com/usa/about-aon/aon-memorial-education-fund.jsp

Foundation type: Company-sponsored foundation.
Financial data (yr. ended 12/31/13): Assets, $5,031,226 (M); expenditures, $426,093; qualifying distributions, $371,893; giving activities include $330,031 for grants to individuals.
Purpose and activities: The fund provides scholarships to children of Aon employees lost on September 11th. Scholarships are awarded to individuals for post-secondary education, as well as funding for education at various levels for individuals with special needs.
Fields of interest: Education; Higher education; Non-natural disasters; People with disabilities.
Type of support: Scholarships; Grants to individuals; Student aid.
Limitations: Applications not accepted.
Officers and Directors: Ram Padmanabhan, V.P. and Secy.; Justin Dygert, V.P.; Beth Gallagher, V.P.; Paul A. Hagy, V.P. and Director; Robert E. Lee, V.P.; Katie Rooney, V.P.; Jeremy G.O. Farmer; Harvey N. Medvin.
EIN: 364468038

2711
Scott B. & Annie P. Appleby Charitable Trust
c/o The Northern Trust Co.. N.A.
50 S. Lasalle St., Ste. L-5
Chicago, IL 60603
Application address: c/o The Northern Trust Co., 1515 Ringling Blvd, Sarasota, Fl 34236, tel.: (941) 329-2628

Established in 1948 in District of Columbia.
Donor: Scott B. Appleby†.
Foundation type: Independent foundation.
Financial data (yr. ended 12/31/13): Assets, $4,247,517 (M); expenditures, $249,301; qualifying distributions, $198,489; giving activities include $188,750 for 14 grants (high: $100,000; low: $250).
Purpose and activities: Emphasis on higher education for the handicapped, primarily in GA; some grants for cultural programs and child welfare

in FL; support also for adult and other education, including religious schools, and the environment.
Fields of interest: Arts and culture; Education; Elementary and secondary education; Higher education; Adult education; Environment; Religion; Child welfare; People with disabilities.
Type of support: Research; General support; Continuing support; Capital campaigns; Capital and infrastructure; Scholarships.
Limitations: Applications accepted. Giving on a national basis, with some emphasis on CA, FL, GA, NM, and NY. No grants to individuals.
Application information: Application form required.
Initial approach: Letter
Deadline(s): None
Board meeting date(s): Fall
Trustees: Benjamin N. Colby; F. Jordan Colby; Sarah Rob Colby Pierce; The Northern Trust Co.
Number of staff: 1 part-time support.
EIN: 526334302

2712
AptarGroup Charitable Foundation
475 W. Terra Cotta Ave., Ste. E
Crystal Lake, IL   60014-3407   (815) 477-0424
Contact: Matthew DellaMaria, Secy. and Dir.

Established in 1994 in Illinois.
Donor: AptarGroup, Inc.
Foundation type: Company-sponsored foundation.
Financial data (yr. ended 12/31/13): Assets, $70,746 (M); gifts received, $250,000; expenditures, $291,272; qualifying distributions, $291,272; giving activities include $291,272 for 174 grants (high: $39,300; low: $100).
Purpose and activities: The foundation supports organizations involved with arts and culture, education, health, and human services.
Fields of interest: Education; Health; Human services.
Limitations: Applications accepted. Giving primarily in areas of company operations in CT, IL, MA, and WI. No support for nursing homes, animal welfare groups, national or international relief organizations, primary, secondary, or theological schools, or religious, civic, fraternal, veterans', social, or political organizations. No grants to individuals (except for scholarships), or for testimonial dinners, fundraising events, courtesy advertising, or trips or tours.
Publications: Application guidelines.
Application information: Application form required.
Initial approach: Completed application form
Deadline(s): Mar. 15 for Spring and Oct. 15 for Winter meeting
Board meeting date(s): June and Dec.
Officers and Directors: Stephen J. Hagge, Chair., Pres., and Treas.; Matthew DellaMaria, Secy. and Director; Patrick Doherty; Robert Kuhn; Eldon Schaffer.
EIN: 363927834

2713
Guy A. & N. Kay Arboit Charitable Trust
c/o First American Bank
218 W. Main St.
Dundee, IL   60118-2093   (847) 403-8111

Established in 1997 in Illinois.
Donors: Guy A. Arboit†; N. Kay Arboit†.
Foundation type: Independent foundation.

Financial data (yr. ended 12/31/14): Assets, $4,340,833; expenditures, $266,336; qualifying distributions, $224,467.
Purpose and activities: Giving primarily for education, and to Roman Catholic organizations and churches.
Fields of interest: Education; Religion; Catholicism; Human services.
Type of support: Capital campaigns; Matching grants; Capital and infrastructure; Land acquisitions; Scholarships.
Application information: Application form required.
Initial approach: Letter
Deadline(s): Apr. 1 and Oct. 1
Trustee: First American Bank.
EIN: 367164572

2714
Argo Foundation Inc.
c/o The Northern Trust Co.
P.O. Box 803878
Chicago, IL   60680-3537

Donors: Mrs. Lamar Oglesby; Richard A. Oglesby, Sr.; Chatham Investment Partners; John Oglesby.
Foundation type: Independent foundation.
Financial data (yr. ended 12/31/13): Assets, $1,950,151 (M); gifts received, $138,268; expenditures, $233,461; qualifying distributions, $227,461; giving activities include $226,461 for 30 grants (high: $50,000; low: $1,000).
Fields of interest: Education; Foundations; Religion; Human services.
Type of support: Scholarships.
Limitations: Applications not accepted. Giving limited to GA and IL.
Application information: Unsolicited requests for funds not accepted.
Officers: Richard A. Oglesby, Jr., Chair.; John F. Oglesby, Treas.
EIN: 582020943

2715
B&D Foundation
191 N. Wacker Dr., Ste. 1500
Chicago, IL   60606-1899

Established in 2005 in Illinois.
Donors: Summit Charitable Lead Trust; William H. Barrows; Donna E. Barrows.
Foundation type: Independent foundation.
Financial data (yr. ended 12/31/13): Assets, $2,613,605 (M); gifts received, $90,200; expenditures, $238,595; qualifying distributions, $165,425; giving activities include $158,000 for 30 grants (high: $50,000; low: $1,000).
Fields of interest: Arts and culture; Education; Higher education; Judaism; Human services; Child welfare.
Type of support: General support.
Limitations: Applications not accepted. Giving primarily in IL. No grants to individuals.
Application information: Unsolicited requests for funds not accepted.
Officers and Directors: William H. Barrows, Pres. and Director; Donna E. Barrows, V.P. and Secy. and Director; Jack Polsky, V.P.; Beth Stephens, Treas.; Robert Lewis Barrows.
EIN: 421652722

2716
Cicero Milo Bailey Trust f/b/o Riley Hospital
10 S. Dearborn, IL1-0117
Chicago, IL   60603

Foundation type: Independent foundation.
Financial data (yr. ended 12/31/13): Assets, $8,811,771 (M); expenditures, $376,734; qualifying distributions, $328,627; giving activities include $313,555 for 1 grant.
Fields of interest: Health; Children.
Limitations: Applications not accepted. Giving primarily in IN.
Application information: Unsolicited requests for funds not accepted.
Trustee: JPMorgan Chase Bank, N.A.
EIN: 356010734

2717
Baird Foundation
120 S. LaSalle St., Ste. 2000
Chicago, IL   60603-3594

Established in 1996 in Illinois.
Donors: Baird & Warner, Inc.; Neil McKay; Olive B. McKay; John Baird.
Foundation type: Company-sponsored foundation.
Financial data (yr. ended 02/28/14): Assets, $1,565,768 (M); expenditures, $342,173; qualifying distributions, $331,300; giving activities include $331,300 for 10 grants (high: $250,000; low: $100).
Purpose and activities: The foundation supports arboretums and organizations involved with arts and culture, education, land conservation, crime and law enforcement, civic affairs, and Christianity.
Fields of interest: Arts and culture; Religion; Human services.
Limitations: Applications not accepted. Giving primarily in Chicago, IL. No grants to individuals.
Application information: Contributes only to pre-selected organizations.
Officers: Stephen W. Baird, Pres. and C.E.O.; Olive B. McKay, Secy.; Katharine Mann, Treas.
EIN: 366042924

2718
Stephen W. & Susan M. Baird Foundation
c/o Stephen W. Baird
1154 Pine St.
Winnetka, IL   60093-2026

Donors: Stephen W. Baird; Susan M. Baird.
Foundation type: Independent foundation.
Financial data (yr. ended 11/30/14): Assets, $4,551,729 (M); expenditures, $149,891; qualifying distributions, $135,550; giving activities include $135,450 for 49 grants (high: $35,000; low: $100), and $100 for 1 grant to an individual.
Fields of interest: Museums; Education; University education; Environment; Land resources; Hospital care; Diseases and conditions; Radio; Child welfare.
Limitations: Applications not accepted. Giving primarily in IL and MA.
Application information: Unsolicited requests for funds not accepted.
Officers and Directors: Stephen W. Baird, Pres. and Director; Susan M. Baird, Secy. and Director.
EIN: 200478557

2719
Banta Family Foundation
161 E. Chicago Ave., Ste. 41-G
Chicago, IL 60611-2624

Established in 1997 in Illinois.
Donors: June M. Banta; Merle H. Banta.
Foundation type: Independent foundation.
Financial data (yr. ended 12/31/13): Assets,
$817,751 (M); gifts received, $209,815;
expenditures, $356,979; qualifying distributions,
$348,540; giving activities include $348,500 for 11
grants (high: $215,000; low: $500).
Fields of interest: Education; Elementary education;
Hospital care; Christianity; Human services.
Limitations: Applications not accepted. Giving
primarily in CA. No grants to individuals.
Application information: Unsolicited requests for
funds not accepted.
Officers: Merle H. Banta, Pres. and Treas.; June M.
Banta, V.P. and Secy.
Directors: Berton M. Banta; Bradford C. Banta;
Brenda Banta Williams.
EIN: 364141026

2720
The Barr Fund
(formerly Kristina Barr and George Barr Foundation)
c/o Philip C. Ravid, Jesser Ravid
150 N. Wacker Dr., Ste. 3100
Chicago, IL 60606-4701

Donor: George Barr Residuary Trust.
Foundation type: Independent foundation.
Financial data (yr. ended 12/31/14): Assets,
$5,313,940 (M); expenditures, $328,502;
qualifying distributions, $267,600; giving activities
include $250,950 for 86 grants (high: $25,000;
low: $200).
Fields of interest: Arts and culture; Education;
Health; Mental health care; Religion.
Type of support: General support.
Limitations: Applications accepted. Giving primarily
in IL. No grants to individuals.
Application information:
  Initial approach: Letter
  Deadline(s): None
Officers and Directors: Donald G. Lubin, Pres. and
Director; Howard Isenberg, Treas. and Director; Amy
S. Lubin, Secy. and Director; Alan L. Isenberg; Marc
S. Isenberg; Alice L. Spahr.
EIN: 366111449

2721
Bill Bartholomay Foundation
c/o William C. Bartholomay
233 S. Wacker Dr., Ste. 2000
Chicago, IL 60606-6400

Established in 1989 in Illinois.
Donor: William C. Bartholomay.
Foundation type: Independent foundation.
Financial data (yr. ended 12/31/13): Assets,
$5,448,199 (M); gifts received, $4,225;
expenditures, $208,315; qualifying distributions,
$164,650; giving activities include $164,650 for 41
grants (high: $55,000; low: $25).
Fields of interest: Arts and culture; Science
museums; Education; Higher education; Zoos;
Diseases and conditions; Community and economic

development; Christianity; Human services; Child
welfare.
Limitations: Applications not accepted. Giving
primarily in IL. No grants to individuals.
Application information: Contributes only to
pre-selected organizations.
Trustee: William C. Bartholomay.
EIN: 363679496

2722
Bartsch Memorial Trust
(formerly Ruth Bartsch Memorial Bank Trust)
10 S. Dearborn St., MC IL1-0117
Chicago, IL 60603-2300
Application address: c/o Peggy Swarzman, V.P., 270
Park Ave., Fl. 16, New York, NY 10017-2014,
tel.: (212) 648-2394

Established in 1983 in New York.
Donor: Ruth Bartsch†.
Foundation type: Independent foundation.
Financial data (yr. ended 11/30/13): Assets,
$9,600,423 (M); expenditures, $504,627;
qualifying distributions, $425,181; giving activities
include $395,726 for 11 grants (high: $75,000;
low: $10,000).
Purpose and activities: Giving primarily for
education, and children, youth, and social services.
Fields of interest: Elementary and secondary
education; Special needs education; Human
services; Scouting programs; Low-income and poor
people; People with vision impairments.
Limitations: Applications accepted. Giving primarily
in CT, FL, IL, MA, MI, and NY. No grants to
individuals.
Application information:
  Initial approach: Proposal
  Deadline(s): None
Trustees: Mark S. Richards; JPMorgan Chase Bank,
N.A.
EIN: 133188775

2723
Robert and Isabelle Bass Foundation
Inc.
P.O. Box 81350
Chicago, IL 60681-0350

Established in 1986 in Illinois.
Donor: Robert O. Bass.
Foundation type: Independent foundation.
Financial data (yr. ended 12/31/14): Assets,
$2,781,698; expenditures, $166,756; qualifying
distributions, $132,417.
Fields of interest: Arts and culture; Education.
Limitations: Giving primarily in Chicago, IL. No
grants to individuals.
Officers: Susan Bass Noel, Pres.; Chris Noel
Dewald, V.P.
Director: Jay P. Tarshis.
EIN: 363487098

2724
Alben F. & Clara G. Bates Foundation
159 Cottage Hill Rd., Apt. 113
Elmhurst, IL 60126-3347

Established in 1952 in Illinois.
Donor: Henry G. Bates.
Foundation type: Independent foundation.

Financial data (yr. ended 12/31/13): Assets,
$5,033,761 (M); expenditures, $379,728;
qualifying distributions, $356,100; giving activities
include $356,100 for 125 grants (high: $38,750;
low: $250).
Purpose and activities: Giving primarily for
education, health care, and social services.
Fields of interest: Arts and culture; Education;
Higher education; Health; Hospital care; Cystic
fibrosis; Human services; Child welfare.
Limitations: Applications not accepted. Giving
primarily in IL. No grants to individuals.
Application information: Contributes only to
pre-selected organizations.
Officers: Christine B. Crum, Pres.; Josephine B.
Prasil, V.P. and Secy.; Jill E. Dickens, V.P.; Henry G.
Bates, Treas.
Director: Robert Wier.
EIN: 366081072

2725
The George A. Bates Memorial Foundation
P.O. Box 728
Roscoe, IL 61073-0728   (815) 986-4481

Established in 1991 in Illinois.
Donor: George A. Bates†.
Foundation type: Independent foundation.
Financial data (yr. ended 12/31/14): Assets,
$5,020,206; expenditures, $266,814; qualifying
distributions, $224,641.
Fields of interest: Higher education; Hospital care;
Rehabilitation; Human services; Family services;
Children and youth.
Limitations: Applications accepted. Giving primarily
in IL.
Application information: Application form required.
  Initial approach: Letter
  Deadline(s): None
Trustees: Constance Bates McGregor; Michael C.
Murray, Ph.D; Carol Schroeder; James H. Stacke.
EIN: 363747609

2726
Ralph J. Baudhuin Foundation
1616 Arden Ave.
Rockford, IL 61107-2028   (815) 229-3661
Contact: Paul F. Baudhuin, Tr.

Established in 1959 in Illinois.
Foundation type: Independent foundation.
Financial data (yr. ended 12/31/14): Assets,
$6,729,150 (M); expenditures, $332,523;
qualifying distributions, $313,000; giving activities
include $313,000 for 125 grants (high: $30,000;
low: $500).
Purpose and activities: Giving primarily for a
mission and Roman Catholic churches; support also
for universities and health and religious
organizations.
Fields of interest: Higher education; Diseases and
conditions; Christianity; Catholicism.
Limitations: Applications accepted. Giving primarily
in IL.
Application information: Application form required.
  Initial approach: Letter
  Deadline(s): None
Trustees: Annette Baudhuin; Mike Baudhuin; Paul
Baudhuin; Tom Baudhuin; Pat Naruz.
EIN: 366046399

2727
Melvin R. Baum Private Foundation
866 N. Main St.
Morton, IL 61550-1602

Established in 1999 in Illinois.
Donor: Melvin R. Baum.
Foundation type: Independent foundation.
Financial data (yr. ended 12/31/13): Assets, $3,003,768 (M); gifts received, $90,889; expenditures, $277,828; qualifying distributions, $248,800; giving activities include $248,800 for 14 grants (high: $120,000; low: $100).
Fields of interest: Agriculture; Religion; Christianity; Human services.
Limitations: Applications not accepted. Giving primarily in IL. No grants to individuals.
Application information: Contributes only to pre-selected organizations.
Officers and Directors: Melvin R. Baum, Pres. and Director; Gregory Hunziker, Secy. and Director; Linda Baum, Treas. and Director.
EIN: 371379627

2728
Lucy & Emily Beasley Charitable Trust
10 S. Dearborn, IL1-0117
Chicago, IL 60603
Application address: JPMorgan Chase Bank, N.A., 1300 E. 9th St., Cleveland, OH 44114, tel.: (216) 781-2204

Established in 1981 in Ohio.
Donors: Robert P. Beasley Trust; Emily T. Beasley Trust.
Foundation type: Independent foundation.
Financial data (yr. ended 09/30/13): Assets, $7,931,495 (M); expenditures, $515,525; qualifying distributions, $381,982; giving activities include $360,000 for 23 grants (high: $50,000; low: $1,000).
Purpose and activities: Giving primarily for higher education.
Fields of interest: Higher education; Human services; Developmental disability services.
Limitations: Applications accepted. Giving primarily in Akron and Kent, OH.
Application information: Application form required.
  Initial approach: Letter
  Deadline(s): None
Trustee: Howard W. Cable, Jr.
Board Members: Gay W. Cable; Robert E. Hissong; A. Russell Smith.
EIN: 341350747

2729
John and Frances Beck Foundation
(formerly The Frances Mottey Beck Reading Center, Inc.)
9529 Bronx Pl., Apt. 319
Skokie, IL 60077-1364
Application address: c/o John Frances Beck Foundation, 2200 Ross Ave., Dallas, TX 75201-2787 tel.: (866) 300-6222

Established in 1998 in Illinois.
Donors: John M. Beck; Marianne Friedman.
Foundation type: Independent foundation.
Financial data (yr. ended 12/31/13): Assets, $840,623 (M); expenditures, $328,253; qualifying

distributions, $310,824; giving activities include $297,150 for 9 grants (high: $150,000; low: $150).
Fields of interest: Education.
Limitations: Applications accepted. Giving primarily in IL. No grants to individuals.
Application information:
  Initial approach: Proposal
  Deadline(s): None
Officers: Herbert Walberg, Chair.; Marianne Friedman, Pres.; Winifred Stariha, V.P.
Board Members: Charles W. Laabs; Timothy Sares; Trudy Wallace.
EIN: 364205800

2730
Bruce R. & Nancy W. Beeghly Family Foundation
c/o JPMorgan Chase Bank
10 S. Dearborn St., 21st Fl.
Chicago, IL 60603-2300 (330) 533-8310
Contact: Patrick A. Sebastiano Esq.
Application address: 6600 Summit Dr., Canfield, OH 44406

Foundation type: Independent foundation.
Financial data (yr. ended 09/30/13): Assets, $2,054,998 (M); expenditures, $230,416; qualifying distributions, $217,083; giving activities include $211,000 for 25 grants (high: $50,000; low: $1,000).
Fields of interest: Historic preservation; Education; University education; Philanthropy; Nonprofits; Human services.
Type of support: Regranting.
Application information: Application form required.
  Initial approach: Contact foundation
  Deadline(s): None
Trustee: JPMorgan Chase Bank, N.A.
Directors: Bruce R. Beeghly; Nancy W. Beeghly.
EIN: 263853336

2731
Bellebyron Foundation
c/o Briar Hall LLC
200 W. Madison St., Ste. 3400
Chicago, IL 60606-3600

Established in 1983 in Illinois.
Donor: Harold Byron Smith, Jr.
Foundation type: Independent foundation.
Financial data (yr. ended 12/31/14): Assets, $575,058; expenditures, $435,810; qualifying distributions, $434,885.
Fields of interest: Historic preservation; Aquariums; Botanical gardens; Hospital care.
Limitations: Applications not accepted. Giving primarily in CA and FL. No grants to Individuals.
Application information: Contributes only to pre-selected organizations.
Officers and Directors: Stephen B. Smith, Pres. and Director; David B. Smith, Secy. and Director; Christopher B. Smith.
EIN: 366058056

2732
The Bellick Foundation
c/o Wolverine Trading, LLC
175 W. Jackson Blvd., 2nd Fl.
Chicago, IL 60604-3034

Established in 2001 in Illinois.
Donors: Robert R. Bellick; Sheryl D. Bellick.
Foundation type: Independent foundation.
Financial data (yr. ended 12/31/13): Assets, $93,505 (M); gifts received, $439,439; expenditures, $376,254; qualifying distributions, $374,282; giving activities include $374,282 for 34 grants (high: $92,500; low: $100).
Purpose and activities: Giving primarily for education, health organizations, and to Jewish organizations.
Fields of interest: Education; Elementary education; Higher education; Nonprofits; Diseases and conditions; Judaism; Children.
Type of support: General support; Regranting.
Limitations: Applications not accepted. Giving primarily in IL. No grants to individuals.
Application information: Unsolicited requests for funds not accepted.
Officers and Directors: Sheryl D. Bellick, Pres. and Director; Robert R. Bellick, Secy.-Treas. and Director; Christopher L. Gust.
EIN: 300064562

2733
Albert & Pamela Bendich Charitable Trust
2700 Patriot Blvd., Ste. 170
Glenview, IL 60026-8080 (847) 729-0600
Contact: Alan H. Hammerman, Tr.

Established in 2003 in Illinois.
Donors: Albert Bendich; Pamela Bendich.
Foundation type: Independent foundation.
Financial data (yr. ended 12/31/13): Assets, $630,546 (M); gifts received, $137,794; expenditures, $199,815; qualifying distributions, $197,000; giving activities include $197,000 for 64 grants (high: $50,000; low: $250).
Fields of interest: Animal welfare; Human services.
Limitations: Applications accepted. Giving primarily in CA.
Application information: Application form required.
  Initial approach: Letter
  Deadline(s): None
Trustees: Alan H. Hammerman; Adrienne Keffeler.
EIN: 206085782

2734
Barbara Bere Foundation Inc.
641 S. Elm St.
Hinsdale, IL 60521-4623

Established in 1983 in Illinois.
Donors: James F. Bere†; Barbara L. Bere.
Foundation type: Independent foundation.
Financial data (yr. ended 12/31/13): Assets, $4,828,146 (M); expenditures, $391,788; qualifying distributions, $347,500; giving activities include $347,500 for 37 grants (high: $69,200; low: $200).
Fields of interest: Arts and culture; Education; Higher education; Graduate and professional education; Diseases and conditions; Christianity; Theology; Human services.
Type of support: General support; Continuing support; Annual campaigns; Capital campaigns.
Limitations: Applications not accepted. No grants to individuals.
Application information: Unsolicited requests for funds not accepted.

Officers and Directors: Barbara V. Bere, Pres. and Director; James F. Bere, Jr., V.P. and Director; Robert P. Bere, V.P. and Director; Becky B. Sigfusson, V.P. and Director; Lynn B. Stine, V.P. and Director; David L. Bere, Secy.-Treas. and Director.
EIN: 363272779

2735
Bergstein Family Foundation
271 White Oak Ln.
Winnetka, IL   60093-3629

Donor: Melvyn Bergstein.
Foundation type: Independent foundation.
Financial data (yr. ended 12/31/14): Assets, $2,178,380; expenditures, $277,965; qualifying distributions, $263,000.
Fields of interest: Arts and culture; Cancers; Public affairs; Judaism.
Type of support: General support.
Limitations: Applications not accepted. Giving primarily in IL and NY.
Application information: Unsolicited requests for funds not accepted.
Officers and Directors: Melvyn Bergstein, Pres. and Director; Adam Bergstein, Secy. and Director; Seth Bergstein, Treas. and Director; Bertini Bergstein.
EIN: 273008211

2736
Bergstrom Inc. Charitable Foundation
10 S. Dearborn, IL1-0117
Chicago, IL   60603   (815) 394-4655

Donors: Bergstrom Manufacturing Co., Inc.; Bergstrom Climate Systems, Inc.; Bergstrom Inc.
Foundation type: Company-sponsored foundation.
Financial data (yr. ended 04/30/13): Assets, $1,446,442 (M); gifts received, $180,868; expenditures, $360,425; qualifying distributions, $355,988; giving activities include $354,560 for 48 grants (high: $37,500; low: $1,000).
Purpose and activities: The foundation supports history museums, parks, and community foundations and organizations involved with education, health, golf, and human services.
Fields of interest: Education; Health; Human services.
Type of support: Program development.
Limitations: Applications accepted. Giving primarily in Rockford, IL. No grants to individuals.
Application information: Application form required.
 Initial approach: Letter
 Deadline(s): None
Trustees: David R. Rydell; JPMorgan Chase Bank, N.A.
EIN: 366692339

2737
Craig and Donna Bernfield Family Foundation
1755 Overland Trail
Deerfield, IL   60015-1811

Donor: Craig M. Bernfield.
Foundation type: Independent foundation.
Financial data (yr. ended 12/31/13): Assets, $2,572,921 (M); expenditures, $239,895; qualifying distributions, $227,379; giving activities

include $225,571 for 5 grants (high: $109,533; low: $6,038).
Fields of interest: Judaism; Human rights; Human services.
Limitations: Applications not accepted.
Application information: Unsolicited requests for funds not accepted.
Trustees: Craig Bernfield; Donna Bernfield.
EIN: 266447164

2738
Gertrude and William A. Bernoudy Foundation
c/o The Northern Trust Co.
P.O. Box 803878
Chicago, IL   60608

Established in 1994 in Missouri.
Donor: G. Bernoudy Interim Trust.
Foundation type: Independent foundation.
Financial data (yr. ended 11/30/13): Assets, $10,539,045 (M); expenditures, $453,381; qualifying distributions, $386,261; giving activities include $378,500 for 19 grants (high: $62,500; low: $5,000).
Purpose and activities: Giving primarily for animal welfare, architecture, art, civic projects, education, health services and human services.
Fields of interest: Performing arts; Historic preservation; Education; Higher education; Health; Antidiscrimination; Child welfare.
Type of support: General support; Capital campaigns.
Limitations: Applications not accepted. Giving primarily in St. Louis, MO. No support for film/video (unless film is an integral part of the organization's activities). No grants for endowment scholarship funds, fundraising activities, loans, travel, medical research or to individuals.
Application information: Unsolicited requests for funds not accepted.
Trustees: Edwin M. Meissner, Jr.; John D. Schaperkotter; Stuart Symington, Jr.; The Northern Trust Co.
EIN: 436512119

2739
Jacob Best Foundation
c/o The Northern Trust Co.
P.O. Box 803878
Chicago, IL   60680-3878

Established in 1958 in Illinois.
Donors: Jacob H. Best Trust; Thilo M. Best Charitable Trust.
Foundation type: Independent foundation.
Financial data (yr. ended 02/28/15): Assets, $3,779,855 (M); expenditures, $201,027; qualifying distributions, $167,558; giving activities include $166,509 for 42 grants (high: $9,566; low: $1,755).
Purpose and activities: Giving for education, youth services, and Protestant organizations.
Fields of interest: Education; Health; Protestantism; Human services; Child welfare; Youth services; Adult and child mentoring.
Limitations: Applications not accepted. Giving primarily in CA, IL, and TN. No grants to individuals.
Application information: Unsolicited requests for funds not accepted.

Officers: Thilo H. Best, Pres.; Bryan Best, Secy.; Thomas S. Bridges, Treas.
Director: Peter Best.
EIN: 366052049

2740
Walter J. and Edith E. Best Foundation
111 W. Monroe St., Tax Div 16W
Chicago, IL   60603

Established in 1986 in Illinois.
Donors: Walter Best†; Edith Best†.
Foundation type: Independent foundation.
Financial data (yr. ended 11/30/13): Assets, $5,608,249 (M); expenditures, $470,653; qualifying distributions, $420,437; giving activities include $378,061 for 42 grants (high: $50,000; low: $1,500).
Purpose and activities: Giving primarily for health and youth services.
Fields of interest: Hospital care; Diseases and conditions; Child welfare; Children.
Type of support: General support; Continuing support; Capital campaigns; Program development; Curriculum development; Scholarships; Research.
Limitations: Applications accepted. Giving primarily in the Chicago, IL, area. No grants to individuals.
Publications: Application guidelines.
Application information:
 Initial approach: Letter requesting application form and guidelines
 Deadline(s): Apr. 30
 Board meeting date(s): June and Oct.
Trustees: Thomas Kuhn; BMO Harris Bank, N.A.
EIN: 366857916

2741
Charles W. & Patricia S. Bidwill Charitable Foundation
c/o Particia M. Bidwill
P.O. Box 2541
Glenview, IL   60025-6541

Established in 2004 in Illinois.
Donors: Charles W. Bidwill, Jr.; Patricia S. Bidwill.
Foundation type: Independent foundation.
Financial data (yr. ended 12/31/13): Assets, $2,682,801 (M); expenditures, $226,671; qualifying distributions, $194,069; giving activities include $173,000 for 13 grants (high: $33,000; low: $2,500).
Fields of interest: Education; Pediatrics; Youth development.
Limitations: Applications not accepted. Giving primarily in CA and IL. No grants to individuals.
Application information: Contributes only to pre-selected organizations.
Officers and Directors: Charles W. Bidwill, Jr., Pres. and Director; Patricia S. Bidwill, Secy. and Director; Brian R. Bidwill; Patricia M. Bidwill; Shauna B. Valenzuela.
EIN: 364479735

2742
Bisco Charitable Foundation
1100 W. Irving Park Rd.
Schaumburg, IL   60193-3569   (847) 534-6046
Contact: Minsook Suh, Dir.

Established in 1997 in Illinois.

Donors: Byoung Suh; Minsook Suh; Bisco, Inc.
Foundation type: Independent foundation.
Financial data (yr. ended 12/31/13): Assets, $4,794,327 (M); gifts received, $1,303,206; expenditures, $344,380; qualifying distributions, $289,231; giving activities include $281,000 for 12 grants (high: $110,000; low: $1,000).
Fields of interest: Education; Higher education.
Type of support: General support; Individual development.
Limitations: Applications accepted. Giving primarily in CA and IL. No grants to individuals.
Application information:
  Initial approach: Letter
  Deadline(s): None
Directors: Colleen M. Suh; Julienne S. Suh; Minsook Suh.
EIN: 364198175

2743
A.G. Bishop Charitable Trust
10 S. Dearborn, IL1-0117
Chicago, IL   60603
Application address: c/o Jomorgan Chase Bank, N.A., 1116 W. Long Lake Fl. 2, Bloomfield Hills, MI 48302, tel.:(248) 645-7308

Established in 1944 in Michigan.
Donor: Arthur Giles Bishop†.
Foundation type: Independent foundation.
Financial data (yr. ended 12/31/13): Assets, $11,707,257 (M); expenditures, $381,337; qualifying distributions, $308,378; giving activities include $285,500 for 19 grants (high: $50,000; low: $2,500).
Purpose and activities: Giving primarily for education, the arts, and youth and social services.
Fields of interest: Arts and culture; Higher education; Foundations; Nonprofits; Human services; Child welfare.
Type of support: General support; Continuing support; Annual campaigns; Capital and infrastructure; Equipment; Land acquisitions; Regranting; Debt reduction; Emergency funds; Seed money; Research.
Limitations: Applications accepted. Giving limited to the Flint and Genesee County, MI, community. No grants to individuals, or for endowment funds, scholarships, fellowships, or matching gifts; no loans.
Publications: Application guidelines.
Application information: Application form required.
  Initial approach: Letter
  Copies of proposal: 3
  Deadline(s): None
Trustees: Robert J. Bellairs, Jr.; Elizabeth B. Wentworth; JPMorgan Chase Bank, N.A.
EIN: 386040693

2744
Harold C. & Jacqueline F. Bladel Foundation, Inc.
c/o The Northern Trust, N.A.
P.O. Box 803878
Chicago, IL   60680-3878
Application address: c/o Northern Trust Bank, P.O. Box 4097, Sarasota, FL 34230, tel.: (941) 957-3660

Established in 1997 in Florida.
Foundation type: Independent foundation.

Financial data (yr. ended 12/31/13): Assets, $3,327,867 (M); expenditures, $202,390; qualifying distributions, $168,483; giving activities include $166,200 for 26 grants (high: $40,000; low: $2,500).
Fields of interest: Human services; Family services; Child welfare; Senior services.
Limitations: Applications accepted. Giving primarily in FL.
Application information: Application form required.
  Initial approach: Proposal
  Deadline(s): None
Trustee: Northern Trust Bank, N.A.
EIN: 911910210

2745
Block Family Foundation
(formerly Block Electric Company, Inc. Foundation)
7107 N. Milwaukee Ave.
Niles, IL   60714-4424

Established in 1991 in Illinois.
Donors: Block Electric Co., Inc.; John G. Block.
Foundation type: Company-sponsored foundation.
Financial data (yr. ended 12/31/13): Assets, $1,626,486 (M); gifts received, $149,966; expenditures, $163,592; qualifying distributions, $151,600; giving activities include $151,600 for 27 grants (high: $50,000; low: $200).
Purpose and activities: The foundation supports organizations involved with higher education, medical education, health, cancer, and human services.
Fields of interest: Education; Health; Human services.
Limitations: Applications not accepted. Giving limited to IL. No grants to individuals.
Application information: Contributes only to pre-selected organizations.
Directors: John G. Block; Michael Block; Jeffrey Underwood.
EIN: 363811476

2746
Margaret S. & Philip D. Block, Jr. Family Foundation
100 E. Walton, Ste. 600W
Chicago, IL   60611-1513

Established in 1959 in Illinois.
Donors: Andrew K. Block; Margaret S. Block; Shaun C. Block; Philip D. Block III.
Foundation type: Independent foundation.
Financial data (yr. ended 12/31/13): Assets, $4,215,216 (M); gifts received, $50,563; expenditures, $247,251; qualifying distributions, $232,771; giving activities include $229,808 for 127 grants (high: $10,000; low: $98).
Fields of interest: Arts and culture; Humanities; Education; Higher education; Zoos; Nonprofits; Diseases and conditions.
Type of support: Regranting.
Limitations: Applications accepted. Giving primarily in Chicago, IL and MA. No grants to individuals.
Application information:
  Initial approach: Letter
  Deadline(s): None
Officers: Andrew K. Block, Pres.; Philip D. Block III, Secy.
Directors: Judith S. Block; Shaun C. Block.
EIN: 366047602

2747
The Robert Thomas Bobins Foundation
(formerly Bobins Foundation)
209 E. Lake Shore Dr., Ste. 10E
Chicago, IL   60611-1340

Established in 2007 in Illinois.
Donors: Norman Bobins; Virginia Bobins.
Foundation type: Independent foundation.
Financial data (yr. ended 12/31/13): Assets, $333,047 (M); gifts received, $425,000; expenditures, $358,353; qualifying distributions, $358,353; giving activities include $358,338 for 105 grants (high: $35,000; low: $100).
Fields of interest: Museums.
Limitations: Applications not accepted. Giving primarily in IL. No grants to individuals.
Application information: Contributes only to pre-selected organizations.
Trustees: Norman Bobins; Virginia Bobins.
EIN: 261569990

2748
Herbert B. Boehl Charitable Trust
c/o JPMorgan Chase Bank N.A.
10 S. Dearborn, IL1-0117
Chicago, IL   60603

Foundation type: Independent foundation.
Financial data (yr. ended 12/31/14): Assets, $4,136,298; expenditures, $219,208; qualifying distributions, $196,885.
Fields of interest: Education; Health; Religion.
Limitations: Applications not accepted. Giving primarily in KY.
Application information: Unsolicited requests for funds not accepted.
Trustee: JPMorgan Chase Bank, N.A.
EIN: 611345132

2749
Charles H. and Bertha L. Boothroyd Foundation
175 W. Jackson Blvd., Ste. 1600
Chicago, IL   60604-2827
Contact: Thomas C. Kaufmann, Pres.

Established in 1958 in Illinois.
Donors: Mary T. Palzkill†; Agnes K. McAvoy Trust; Gudrun Alcock.
Foundation type: Independent foundation.
Financial data (yr. ended 06/30/14): Assets, $5,095,371 (M); expenditures, $388,390; qualifying distributions, $322,048; giving activities include $272,000 for 18 grants (high: $40,000; low: $3,000).
Purpose and activities: Giving primarily for the arts and education.
Fields of interest: Arts and culture; Education; Diseases and conditions; Human services.
Type of support: General support; Continuing support; Program development; Scholarships; Research.
Limitations: Applications accepted. Giving primarily in IL.
Application information: Application form required.
  Initial approach: Proposal
  Deadline(s): None
Officers: Thomas C. Kaufmann, Pres. and Treas.; Owen Beacon, V.P.; Dennis A Marks, Secy.

Number of staff: 1 part-time support.
EIN: 366047045

2750
Walter and Phyllis Ann Borten Foundation
c/o Kathleen D. Fuhr, Barbara D. Jonas
10 S. Dearborn St., IL1-0117
Chicago, IL 60603-2024

Foundation type: Independent foundation.
Financial data (yr. ended 12/31/13): Assets,
$3,148,169 (M); expenditures, $210,022;
qualifying distributions, $158,966; giving activities
include $143,000 for 19 grants (high: $65,500;
low: $500).
Fields of interest: Health; Diseases and conditions;
Youth development.
Type of support: Research.
Limitations: Applications not accepted. Giving
primarily in CT.
Application information: Unsolicited requests for
funds not accepted.
Trustees: Kathleen D. Fuhr; Barbara D. Joans;
JPMorgan Chase Bank, N.A.
EIN: 272269154

2751
Bound To Stay Bound Books Foundation
c/o Jacksonville Savings Bank
1211 W. Morton Ave.
Jacksonville, IL 62650-2770
Main URL: http://www.btsb.com/about-us

Established in 1984 in Illinois.
Donor: Bound To Stay Bound Books, Inc.
Foundation type: Company-sponsored foundation.
Financial data (yr. ended 12/31/14): Assets,
$4,366,276; expenditures, $230,579; qualifying
distributions, $208,250.
Purpose and activities: The foundation supports
programs designed to address promote literature
and media and awards scholarships to students
pursuing graduate library degrees.
Fields of interest: Arts and culture; Education;
Reading promotion; Public libraries; Communication
media.
Type of support: General support; Program
development; Scholarships.
Limitations: Applications not accepted. Giving
primarily in IL.
Application information: Unsolicited requests for
funds not accepted.
Trustee: Jacksonville Savings Bank, N.A.
EIN: 376227827

2752
Ferdinand A. and Agnes M. Bower Charitable Trust
10 S. Dearbor St., IL1-0117
Chicago, IL 60603-2024

Foundation type: Independent foundation.
Financial data (yr. ended 09/30/13): Assets,
$4,928,201 (M); expenditures, $258,371;
qualifying distributions, $229,473; giving activities
include $220,422 for 13 grants (high: $142,622;
low: $100).
Fields of interest: Arts and culture; Education;
Catholicism.

Limitations: Applications not accepted. Giving
primarily in MI.
Application information: Unsolicited requests for
funds not accepted.
Trustee: JPMorgan Chase Bank, N.A.
EIN: 386194577

2753
Thomas Sidlik & Rebecca Boylan Foundation
P.O. Box 803878
Chicago, IL 60680-3878

Established in 1998 in Michigan.
Donors: Rebecca A. Boylan; Thomas W. Sidlik.
Foundation type: Independent foundation.
Financial data (yr. ended 12/31/13): Assets,
$1,287,062 (M); gifts received, $997,181;
expenditures, $374,242; qualifying distributions,
$362,715; giving activities include $361,715 for 57
grants (high: $50,000; low: $50).
Fields of interest: Education; Higher education;
Christianity; Human services.
Limitations: Applications not accepted. Giving
primarily in Ann Arbor, MI; funding also in Chicago,
IL. No grants to individuals.
Application information: Contributes only to
pre-selected organizations.
Directors: Rebecca A. Boylan; James Fontichiaro;
Thomas W. Sidlik.
EIN: 383447404

2754
Boyle Family Foundation
1133 W. 35th St.
Chicago, IL 60609

Donors: Patrick J. Boyle†; Boyle Desendants
Charitable Lead Trust; Schulze & Burche.
Foundation type: Operating foundation.
Financial data (yr. ended 12/31/13): Assets,
$9,676,402 (M); gifts received, $1,116,656;
expenditures, $358,936; qualifying distributions,
$330,685; giving activities include $328,310 for 23
grants (high: $60,000; low: $310).
Fields of interest: Out-patient medical care.
Type of support: Scholarships.
Limitations: Applications not accepted. Giving
primarily in NY. No grants to individuals.
Application information: Unsolicited requests for
funds not accepted.
Officers: Theresa Boyle, Secy.; Patricia Boyle
Wheeler, Treas.
Directors: Brian Boyle; Kevin Boyle; Michael Boyle;
Karen Boyle Conboy; Caroline Boyle Salina.
EIN: 364057351

2755
Christine & Paul Branstad Family foundation
c/o Jean Einstein
400 W. Erie St., Ste. 100
Chicago, IL 60654-6911

Donor: Paul A. Branstad.
Foundation type: Independent foundation.
Financial data (yr. ended 12/31/13): Assets,
$6,530,158 (M); expenditures, $547,422;
qualifying distributions, $489,398; giving activities

include $415,009 for 9 grants (high: $125,000;
low: $10,000).
Fields of interest: Higher education; Protestantism.
Limitations: Applications not accepted. Giving
primarily in AZ and IL.
Application information: Unsolicited requests for
funds not accepted.
Directors: Christine W. Branstad; Paul A. Branstad;
Jean M. Einstein.
EIN: 263171796

2756
The Abe & Miriam Brenner Foundation
c/o The Northern Trust Co.
P.O. Box 803878
Chicago, IL 60680-3878

Established in 1993 in North Carolina.
Donors: Abe Brenner; Miriam Brenner.
Foundation type: Independent foundation.
Financial data (yr. ended 12/31/14): Assets,
$3,291,549 (M); expenditures, $193,462;
qualifying distributions, $161,500; giving activities
include $160,500 for grants (high: $80,000; low:
$3,500).
Fields of interest: Higher education; Health;
Children's hospital care; Judaism; Human services;
Children.
Limitations: Applications not accepted. Giving
primarily in NC. No grants to individuals.
Application information: Contributes only to
pre-selected organizations.
Directors: Francis Brenner; Frank Brenner; Michael
Brenner; Miriam Brenner; Susan Brenner.
EIN: 561855206

2757
Cornell Brewer Foundation
c/o David Jackson
1300 E. Woodfield Rd., Ste. 300
Schaumburg, IL 60173-4984

Foundation type: Independent foundation.
Financial data (yr. ended 12/31/13): Assets,
$12,196,672 (M); expenditures, $680,673;
qualifying distributions, $609,921; giving activities
include $418,950 for 35 grants (high: $100,000;
low: $1,000).
Fields of interest: Diseases and conditions;
Christianity.
Limitations: Applications not accepted.
Application information: Unsolicited requests for
funds not accepted.
Officers: Charles H. Brewer, Pres.; David D.
Jackson, V.P. and Treas; Lynn P. Brewer, Secy.
EIN: 263205517

2758
T. Kimball Brooker Foundation
21 S. Clark St., Ste. 3990
Chicago, IL 60603-2008

Established in 1986 in Illinois.
Donors: T. Kimball Brooker; Barbara Oil Co.
Foundation type: Independent foundation.
Financial data (yr. ended 10/31/14): Assets,
$2,733,784 (M); gifts received, $50,000;
expenditures, $162,805; qualifying distributions,
$136,685; giving activities include $136,685 for 13
grants (high: $103,000; low: $25).

Purpose and activities: Giving primarily for private and university libraries.
Fields of interest: Arts and culture; Museums; University education; Academic libraries; School libraries and media centers.
Limitations: Applications not accepted. Giving primarily in Chicago, IL, and New York, NY. No grants to individuals.
Application information: Contributes only to pre-selected organizations.
Officers: T. Kimball Brooker, Pres. and Treas.
EIN: 363481541

2759
Clayton Brown Family Foundation
1555 Wadsworth Rd.
Wheaton, IL 60187-7439

Established in 1983 in Illinois.
Donors: Clayton Brown and Associates, Inc.; Clayton F. Brown.
Foundation type: Independent foundation.
Financial data (yr. ended 06/30/13): Assets, $5,284,100 (M); gifts received, $137,952; expenditures, $361,788; qualifying distributions, $328,875; giving activities include $328,875 for 53 grants (high: $49,000; low: $175).
Purpose and activities: Giving primarily for religious purposes, especially in relation to youth.
Fields of interest: Religion; Youth services.
Type of support: General support.
Limitations: Applications not accepted. Giving primarily in CO and IL. No grants to individuals.
Application information: Contributes only to pre-selected organizations.
Officers: Clayton F. Brown, Pres.; Charlotte G. Brown, V.P.; Steven C. Brown, Secy.-Treas.
EIN: 363250579

2760
Bruce Foundation
20 N. Wacker Dr., Ste. 2414
Chicago, IL 60606-3004 3122369162

Established in 1998 in Illinois.
Donor: Robert B. Bruce.
Foundation type: Independent foundation.
Financial data (yr. ended 12/31/14): Assets, $2,749,955; gifts received, $6,046; expenditures, $215,536; qualifying distributions, $206,000.
Fields of interest: Education; Community and economic development; Human services.
Limitations: Applications not accepted. Giving primarily in IL and MI. No grants to individuals.
Application information: Unsolicited requests for funds not accepted.
Officer: Robert Bruce, Mgr.
EIN: 364257410

2761
Julia Harrison Bruce Foundation
101 S. Park Ave.
Herrin, IL 62948-3609 (618) 942-6666

Donors: Carl Bruce; Julia H. Bruce; Tony Galines Foundation; Julia Bruce Living Trust.
Foundation type: Independent foundation.
Financial data (yr. ended 12/31/13): Assets, $12,075,074 (M); expenditures, $829,137; qualifying distributions, $376,247; giving activities

include $199,415 for 9 grants (high: $131,960; low: $53).
Fields of interest: Education; Higher education; Community and economic development; Human services.
Type of support: Scholarships.
Limitations: Applications accepted. Giving primarily in IL.
Application information: Application form required.
Initial approach: Letter
Deadline(s): None
Trustee: The Bank of Herrin, N.A.
Advisors: Carl Goodwin; Clay Goodwin; Ed Goodwin; Barbara Jacobs.
EIN: 376085206

2762
The Brunswick Foundation, Inc.
1 N. Field Ct.
Lake Forest, IL 60045-4811 (847) 735-4344
Contact: Judith P. Zelisko, Pres. and Dir.
Main URL: http://www.brunswick.com/company/community/brunswickfoundation.php

Donors: Brunswick Corp.; Peter N. Larson.
Foundation type: Company-sponsored foundation.
Financial data (yr. ended 12/31/14): Assets, $2,502,048 (M); gifts received, $300,000; expenditures, $220,450; qualifying distributions, $220,425; giving activities include $28,675 for grants, and $186,250 for grants to individuals.
Purpose and activities: The foundation supports organizations involved with arts and culture, education, health, and welfare; and programs that promote boating, indoor recreation, fitness and related industry interests.
Fields of interest: Arts and culture; Education; Higher education; Health; Sports and recreation; Boating; Human services; Scouting programs.
Type of support: General support; Employee volunteer services; Employee matching gifts; Continuing support; Capital campaigns; Capital and infrastructure; Program development; Scholarships.
Limitations: Applications accepted. Giving primarily in areas of company operations in FL, IL, MI, OH, and W. No support for religious organizations, preschools, primary or secondary schools, fraternal orders, or veterans' or labor organizations. No grants to individuals (except for employee-related scholarships), or for endowments or capital campaigns, trips, tours, tickets, or advertising; no in-kind product or equipment donations.
Publications: Application guidelines.
Application information: Application form required.
Initial approach: Request grant application form
Deadline(s): None
Board meeting date(s): Quarterly
Officers and Directors: Judith P. Zelisko, Pres. and Director; B. Russell Lockridge, V.P. and Director; Marsha T. Vaughn, Secy.; William L. Metzger, Treas. and Director.
Number of staff: 1 full-time professional.
EIN: 366033576

2763
The Bufka Foundation
(formerly The Bufka Family Foundation)
2118 Plum Grove Rd., Ste. 284
Rolling Meadows, IL 60008-1932 (800) 779-2516
Contact: Andrea Bufka, Dir.

E-mail: info@bufkafoundation.org; *Main URL:* http://www.bufkafoundation.org
Grants List: http://www.bufkafoundation.org/The_Bufka_Foundation/Recent_Grants.html

Established in 1995 in Illinois.
Donors: Carl K. Bufka; 687 BR.
Foundation type: Independent foundation.
Financial data (yr. ended 11/30/14): Assets, $946,033 (M); gifts received, $65,025; expenditures, $281,745; qualifying distributions, $279,020; giving activities include $259,839 for 39 grants (high: $35,000; low: $100).
Purpose and activities: The foundation's mission is helping people in desperate need.
Fields of interest: Housing development; Human services; Homeless people.
Type of support: Continuing support; Matching grants; Annual campaigns.
Limitations: Applications accepted. Giving primarily in the northwest suburbs of Chicago, IL and in northeastern VT. No grants to individuals, or for capital campaigns or endowments.
Application information: The foundation is not accepting unsolicited proposals at this time, but if an organization would like to be considered for an application request, it may submit a letter of inquiry with some brief general information, including its program and support. Email correspondence preferred; CAGA Chicago Area Grant Application Form accepted. Application form required.
Initial approach: Letter
Deadline(s): None
Officer: Carl K. Bufka, Pres.
Directors: Andrea Bufka; Karen L. Bufka; Michael Hughes.
Number of staff: 2 part-time professional.
EIN: 364064204

2764
Build Cambodia, Inc.
1555 N. Astor St., Apt. 45W
Chicago, IL 60610-5787 (312) 751-1591
E-mail: edbachrach@aol.com; *Main URL:* http://www.buildcambodia.org

Established in 2006 in Illinois.
Donor: Ed Bachrach.
Foundation type: Independent foundation.
Financial data (yr. ended 12/31/13): Assets, $27,301 (M); gifts received, $230,709; expenditures, $265,541; qualifying distributions, $265,541; giving activities include $228,319 for 7 grants (high: $103,775; low: $2,000), and $8,918 for 1 grant to an individual.
Purpose and activities: The organization is dedicated to helping Cambodians build their lives and society and ensuring that a steady flow of attention and resources for worthwhile efforts in Cambodia.
Fields of interest: Philanthropy; Health; Human services.
International interests: Cambodia.
Limitations: Applications not accepted. Giving primarily to Concord, MA.
Application information: Unsolicited requests for funds not accepted.
Officers and Directors: Ed Bachrach, Chair. and Director; Laurie Bachrach, Treas. and Director; David Prichard; Kheang Un.
EIN: 204864316

2765
Everett S. Bulkley, Jr. Trust
(formerly The Bulkley Foundation Trust)
c/o JPMorgan Chase Bank, N.A.
10 S. Dearborn St., IL1-0117
Chicago, IL 60603-2300 8668885157
Application address: c/o JPMorgan Chase Bank,
N.A., Attn.: Edward Marks, V.P., 122 Main St., New
Canaan, CT, 06480-4709, tel.: (203) 972-2205

Established in 1989 in Connecticut.
Donor: Everett S. Bulkley, Jr.†.
Foundation type: Independent foundation.
Financial data (yr. ended 12/31/14): Assets,
$3,758,699; expenditures, $220,337; qualifying
distributions, $185,515.
Purpose and activities: Primary areas of interest
include welfare and family services, cancer and
heart disease, and community funds.
Fields of interest: Historic preservation; Education;
Voluntarism; Hospice care; Muscular dystrophy;
Heart and circulatory system diseases; Respiratory
system diseases; Cancers; Food aid; Family
services; Child welfare; Homeless services; Children
and youth; Females; Female children and youth;
Males; Male children and youth; Homeless people;
Low-income and poor people; People with
disabilities; People with vision impairments; People
with psychosocial disabilities; Terminally ill people.
Type of support: Annual campaigns; Capital
campaigns; Capital and infrastructure;
Scholarships; Student aid; Research.
Limitations: Giving limited to the Greater Norwalk,
CT, area.
Application information:
Copies of proposal: 1
Trustee: JPMorgan Chase Bank, N.A.
EIN: 066332021

2766
Dean L. & Rosemarie Buntrock Foundation
Oakbrook Terrace Twr.
One Tower Ln., Ste. 2242
Oakbrook Terrace, IL 60181-4636

Established in 1979 in Illinois.
Donors: Dean L. Buntrock; Rosemarie Buntrock.
Foundation type: Independent foundation.
Financial data (yr. ended 12/31/13): Assets,
$688,953 (M); expenditures, $221,290; qualifying
distributions, $211,815; giving activities include
$211,815 for 87 grants (high: $42,250; low: $50).
Fields of interest: Arts and culture; Museums;
Education; Hospital care; Diseases and conditions;
Protestantism; Human services.
Limitations: Applications not accepted. Giving
primarily in CA. No grants to individuals.
Application information: Contributes only to
pre-selected organizations.
Officer: Donovan A. Langford III, Treas.
Directors: Dean L. Buntrock; Rosemarie Buntrock.
EIN: 363001925

2767
William, Agnes & Elizabeth Burgess Memorial Scholarship Fund
c/o First Mid-Illinois Bank & Trust
P.O. Box 529
Mattoon, IL 61938-0529 (217) 258-0633
Contact: Laura Walk

Established in 1943 in Illinois.
Foundation type: Independent foundation.
Financial data (yr. ended 03/31/15): Assets,
$4,248,293 (M); expenditures, $300,638;
qualifying distributions, $204,851; giving activities
include $200,000 for 100 grants to individuals
(high: $2,000; low: $2,000), and $4,851 for
foundation-administered programs.
Purpose and activities: Scholarship awards for
graduates of Mattoon Community High School,
Illinois.
Fields of interest: Higher education.
Type of support: Student aid.
Limitations: Applications accepted. Giving limited to
residents of Mattoon, IL.
Application information: Application form required.
Initial approach: Proposal
Deadline(s): Mar. 15
Trustee: First Mid-Illinois Bank & Trust.
EIN: 376024599

2768
Henrietta Lange Burk Fund
c/o U.S. Trust, Philanthropic Solutions
231 S. LaSalle St., IL-1-231-13-32
Chicago, IL 60604 (312) 828-4154
Contact: George Thorn, Market Director
E-mail: ilgrantmaking@ustrust.com; Main
URL: http://www.bankofamerica.com/grantmaking

Established in 1995 in Illinois.
Donor: Henrietta Lange Burk Trust.
Foundation type: Independent foundation.
Financial data (yr. ended 09/30/13): Assets,
$8,921,788 (M); expenditures, $461,011;
qualifying distributions, $393,605; giving activities
include $326,000 for 19 grants (high: $30,000;
low: $5,000).
Purpose and activities: Giving primarily for the arts
and human services.
Fields of interest: Arts and culture; Education;
Health; Religion; Human services; Child welfare.
Limitations: Applications accepted. Giving primarily
in Chicago, IL.
Application information: Application guidelines
available at Fund web site. Application form
required.
Initial approach: E-mail
Copies of proposal: 1
Deadline(s): June 1 and Nov. 1
Final notification: Varies
Trustee: Bank of America, N.A.
EIN: 367092200

2769
Leo Burnett Company Charitable Foundation
35 W. Wacker Dr., 4th Fl.
Chicago, IL 60601-1608

Established in 1985 in Illinois.
Donors: Leo Burnett Co.; Leo Burnett USA, Inc.; Alice
O'Hara.
Foundation type: Company-sponsored foundation.
Financial data (yr. ended 12/31/13): Assets,
$813,796 (M); gifts received, $241,840;
expenditures, $277,903; qualifying distributions,
$277,903; giving activities include $277,095 for
grants.

Purpose and activities: The foundation supports
organizations involved with advertising and
education.
Fields of interest: Arts and culture; Education.
Type of support: General support; Employee
matching gifts.
Limitations: Applications not accepted. Giving
primarily in CO, GA, KS, and Richmond, VA. No
grants to individuals.
Application information: Unsolicited requests for
funds not accepted.
Officers: Thomas Bernardin, Pres.; Richard
Stoddart, Exec. V.P.; Suellen Ravanas, V.P.; Carla
Michelotti, Secy.; Patrick Dumouchel, Treas.
Number of staff: 1 full-time professional; 1 part-time
professional; 1 full-time support.
EIN: 363379336

2770
Burt Family Foundation
412 Fox Meadow Dr.
Northfield, IL 60093-4301

Established in 1997 in Illinois.
Donor: Robert N. Burt.
Foundation type: Independent foundation.
Financial data (yr. ended 04/30/13): Assets,
$2,814,108 (M); expenditures, $382,743;
qualifying distributions, $350,063; giving activities
include $332,500 for 21 grants (high: $62,000;
low: $500).
Purpose and activities: Giving for medical research,
youth programs, and women's services.
Fields of interest: Arts and culture; Education;
Diseases and conditions; Human services; Youth
services; Women's services; Females.
Type of support: Research.
Limitations: Applications not accepted. Giving
primarily in CA and IL. No grants to individuals.
Application information: Contributes only to
pre-selected organizations.
Trustees: Charles R. Burt; Lynn C. Burt; Randolph N.
Burt; Robert N. Burt; Tracy C. Burt.
EIN: 367190233

2771
Caccomo Family Foundation
c/o Martin Tish, Neal Gerber & Eisenberg
2 N. LaSalle St., Ste. 1700
Chicago, IL 60602-3963

Established in 2001 in Illinois.
Donor: Aurelio Caccomo.
Foundation type: Independent foundation.
Financial data (yr. ended 12/31/14): Assets,
$5,731,213 (M); expenditures, $435,349;
qualifying distributions, $310,000; giving activities
include $310,000 for 11 grants (high: $132,000;
low: $3,000).
Fields of interest: Higher education; Zoos; Animal
welfare; Veterinary medicine.
Limitations: Applications not accepted. Giving
primarily in IL. No grants to individuals.
Application information: Unsolicited requests for
funds not accepted.
Officers: Martin H. Tish, Pres.; Lynne Caruso
McIlquham, Secy.
Director: Riad Barmada.
EIN: 364462798

2772
Cafaro-Livingston Charitable Trust
c/o Debra A. Cafaro, Terrance Livingston
353 N. Clark St., Ste. 3300
Chicago, IL 60654-4704

Donor: Debra A. Cafaro.
Foundation type: Independent foundation.
Financial data (yr. ended 12/31/13): Assets, $386,432 (M); gifts received, $351,550; expenditures, $445,937; qualifying distributions, $445,415; giving activities include $440,700 for 25 grants (high: $200,000; low: $200).
Fields of interest: Arts and culture; Education; Higher education; Housing development; Food banks.
Limitations: Applications not accepted. Giving primarily in IL and OH.
Application information: Unsolicited requests for funds not accepted.
Trustees: Debra A. Cafaro; Terrance K. Livingston.
EIN: 276182324

2773
Tyler R. Cain Family Foundation
c/o Friedman and Huey Assoc., LLP
1313 W. 175th St.
Homewood, IL 60430-4606
Application address: c/o Tyler R. Cain, Pres., 316 S. Beach Rd., Hobe Sound, FL 33455, tel.: (708) 799-6800

Established in 1986 in Illinois.
Foundation type: Independent foundation.
Financial data (yr. ended 12/31/13): Assets, $2,213,844 (M); expenditures, $280,092; qualifying distributions, $277,142; giving activities include $274,753 for 41 grants (high: $102,000; low: $100).
Purpose and activities: Giving primarily for education, the environment, and Christian organizations.
Fields of interest: Education; Environment; Health.
Type of support: General support; Annual campaigns; Capital campaigns.
Limitations: Applications accepted. Giving primarily in IL, including Chicago and Lake Forest. No grants to individuals.
Application information:
   Initial approach: Letter
   Deadline(s): None
Officers: Tyler R. Cain, Pres.; Dulany Anning, Treas.
EIN: 363496960

2774
The Canterbury Foundation Ltd.
(formerly Episcopal Foundation of Dixon, Illinois, Ltd.)
5624 N. Virginia Ave.
Chicago, IL 60659-3717 (773) 330-0201
Contact: Curt Schmitt, Pres.

Foundation type: Independent foundation.
Financial data (yr. ended 12/31/13): Assets, $4,792,834 (M); expenditures, $371,090; qualifying distributions, $293,870; giving activities include $267,185 for 7+ grants (high: $215,900; low: $120), and $26,685 for 1 grant to an individual (high: $26,685).

Purpose and activities: The organization supports various charitable, religious, and educational purposes, including scholarships.
Fields of interest: Education; Christianity.
Type of support: General support; Capital and infrastructure; Student aid.
Limitations: Applications accepted. Giving primarily in IL.
Application information: Application form required.
   Initial approach: Letter
   Deadline(s): None
Officers: Curt Schmitt, Pres.; Katie Heisinger, V.P.; Barbara Sullivan, Secy.-Treas.
EIN: 363614304

2775
Mullooly Carey Foundation
440 W. Randolph St., Ste. 500
Chicago, IL 60606-1507 (312) 651-2400
Contact: Edward J. McGillen, Tr.

Donor: Jeanne M. Carey Trust.
Foundation type: Independent foundation.
Financial data (yr. ended 12/31/13): Assets, $4,016,720 (M); gifts received, $5,000; expenditures, $231,213; qualifying distributions, $204,018; giving activities include $189,000 for 11 grants (high: $50,000; low: $1,000).
Fields of interest: Education; Health; Human services.
Application information:
   Initial approach: Proposal
   Deadline(s): None
Trustee: Edward J. McGillen.
EIN: 272313839

2776
The Evelyn C. Carter Foundation Corp.
351 W. Glade Rd.
Palatine, IL 60067-6831
Contact: Scot A. Leonard

Established in 1999 in Illinois.
Donor: Evelyn Carter.
Foundation type: Independent foundation.
Financial data (yr. ended 05/31/13): Assets, $4,206,370 (M); expenditures, $194,801; qualifying distributions, $178,350; giving activities include $168,500 for 19 grants (high: $20,000; low: $2,500).
Fields of interest: Diseases and conditions; Alzheimer's disease; Diabetes; Cancers.
Type of support: Research.
Limitations: Applications not accepted. Giving primarily in IL. No grants to individuals.
Application information: Contributes only to pre-selected organizations.
Officers: Scot A. Leonard, Pres.; Robert Dion, Treas.
Directors: William Arendt; James Devine; Jeanine Holtsford.
EIN: 364292352

2777
The Cashel Foundation
401 N. Michigan Ave., Ste. 1200
Chicago, IL 60611-4264 3129460021
Application address: c/o Mary Ellen Cooney, 625 N. Michigan Ave., Chicago, IL 60611

Established in 1997 in Illinois.

Donor: Mary E. Cooney.
Foundation type: Independent foundation.
Financial data (yr. ended 12/31/14): Assets, $185,523; expenditures, $231,836; qualifying distributions, $227,000.
Purpose and activities: Giving for the education of disadvantaged children, long-term community-supported homes for children, and medical care for children and their families.
Fields of interest: Arts and culture; Higher education; Human services; Child welfare.
Limitations: Applications accepted. Giving primarily in IL. No grants to individuals.
Application information:
   Initial approach: Proposal
   Deadline(s): None
Officers: Mary E. Cooney, Pres.; Christopher L. Cooney, V.P.; Brendan H. Cooney, Secy.-Treas.
EIN: 364154116

2778
The Catalyst Foundation
191 N. Wacker Dr., Ste. 1500
Chicago, IL 60606-1899

Established in 2005 in Illinois.
Donors: Patricia Jane Rosbrow; June H. Barrows; Donna E. Barrows; The Irving Harris Foundation; Mary Ann Wark; The Sidney and June Barrows Foundation; Robert Lewis Barrows; William H. Barrows; Generativity Charitable Lead Trust.
Foundation type: Independent foundation.
Financial data (yr. ended 12/31/13): Assets, $2,653,454 (M); gifts received, $90,200; expenditures, $314,533; qualifying distributions, $249,415; giving activities include $242,000 for 25 grants (high: $30,000; low: $2,000).
Fields of interest: Higher education; Child welfare.
Limitations: Applications not accepted. Giving primarily in CA, IL, MI, and NY. No grants to individuals.
Application information: Contributes only to pre-selected organizations.
Officers and Directors: Thomas W. Rosbrow, Pres. and Director; Jack Polsky, V.P.; Benjamin Rosbrow, V.P. and Director; Jesse Rosbrow, V.P. and Director; Laura Rosbrow, V.P. and Director; Patricia Jane Rosbrow, Secy.-Co-Treas. and Director; Beth Stephens, Co-Treas.
EIN: 300286950

2779
Ceres Foundation
1046 Happ Rd.
Northfield, IL 60093-1009

Established in 1991 in Illinois.
Donors: Burton W. Hales; Daniel B. Hales; Marion J. Hales; Hales Charitable Fund, Inc.
Foundation type: Independent foundation.
Financial data (yr. ended 12/31/14): Assets, $6,537,761; expenditures, $315,415; qualifying distributions, $258,838.
Fields of interest: Arts and culture; Education; Environment; Foundations; Nonprofits; Hospital care; Diseases and conditions; Christianity; Human services; Child welfare.
Type of support: Regranting.
Limitations: Applications not accepted. Giving primarily in IL. No grants to individuals.

Application information: Unsolicited requests for funds not accepted.
Officers and Directors: Daniel R.J. Hales, Pres. and Director; Florence H. Testa, V.P. and Secy. and Director; Marion H. Chardoul, Treas. and Director.
EIN: 363735653

2780
Naomi B. Chambers Charitable Trust
10 S. Dearborn St., IL1-0117
Chicago, IL 60603-2300

Foundation type: Independent foundation.
Financial data (yr. ended 12/31/13): Assets, $12,309,489 (M); expenditures, $375,355; qualifying distributions, $294,389; giving activities include $267,992 for 6 grants (high: $80,398; low: $26,799).
Fields of interest: Education; Health; Human services.
Limitations: Applications not accepted.
Application information: Unsolicited requests for funds not accepted.
Trustee: JPMorgan Chase Bank, N.A.
EIN: 376410705

2781
The Chapin Foundation
(formerly The Bracknell Court Foundation)
c/o Craig Heimark, O'Connor Partners
135 S. Lasalle St., Ste. 3250
Chicago, IL 60603-4130

Established in 1993 in Illinois.
Donor: Craig F. Heimark.
Foundation type: Independent foundation.
Financial data (yr. ended 12/31/13): Assets, $701,049 (M); expenditures, $266,691; qualifying distributions, $260,020; giving activities include $260,020 for 22 grants (high: $75,000; low: $125).
Purpose and activities: Giving for education institutions and fine arts programs focused on children.
Fields of interest: Arts and culture; Ballet; Elementary and secondary education; University education; Judaism; Child welfare.
International interests: Canada.
Limitations: Applications not accepted. Giving primarily in CA and RI. No grants to individuals.
Application information: Contributes only to pre-selected organizations.
Trustee: Craig F. Heimark.
EIN: 367058074

2782
Chapin-May Foundation of Illinois
c/o The Northern Trust Co.
P.O. Box 803878
Chicago, IL 60680-3878

Established in 1944 in Illinois.
Donors: Simeon B. Chapin; Alice Chapin May†.
Foundation type: Independent foundation.
Financial data (yr. ended 12/31/14): Assets, $3,696,987 (M); expenditures, $211,448; qualifying distributions, $184,787; giving activities include $177,000 for 25 grants (high: $35,000; low: $1,000).
Fields of interest: Elementary and secondary education; Higher education; Graduate and

professional education; Hospital care; Religion; Theology; Human services.
Type of support: Scholarships.
Limitations: Applications not accepted. Giving primarily in the Chicago, IL, area. No grants to individuals.
Application information: Unsolicited requests for funds not accepted.
Trustee: The Northern Trust Co.
EIN: 366039390

2783
Charles Foundation Charitable Trust
135 S. LaSalle St.
Chicago, IL 60603-4177
Application Address: Maria I. Botelho, 100 Westminister St., Providence, RI 02903, tel.: (401) 278-02903

Established in 1998 in Missouri.
Donor: C. Osiek.
Foundation type: Independent foundation.
Financial data (yr. ended 12/31/14): Assets, $6,791,978 (M); expenditures, $334,417; qualifying distributions, $277,976; giving activities include $259,000 for 16 grants (high: $68,000; low: $1,000).
Purpose and activities: Giving primarily for human welfare and religious education.
Fields of interest: Religion; Human services.
Limitations: Applications accepted. Giving primarily in MO.
Application information: Application form required.
Initial approach: Letter
Deadline(s): None
Trustees: K. Hughes; C. Osiek; Bank of America, N.A.
EIN: 436801942

2784
Samuel M. Cherry Memorial Charitable Trust
c/o Deloitte Tax LLP
111 S. Wacker Dr., 26th Fl.
Chicago, IL 60606-4309

Donors: Virginia B. Cherry Trust; Walter L. Cherry Jr. Trust; Virginia B. Cherry†.
Foundation type: Independent foundation.
Financial data (yr. ended 12/31/14): Assets, $5,156,642; expenditures, $217,589; qualifying distributions, $207,115.
Fields of interest: Arts and culture; Education; Science.
Limitations: Applications not accepted. Giving primarily in IL.
Application information: Unsolicited requests for funds not accepted.
Trustee: Peter B. Cherry.
EIN: 266541160

2785
Chez Family Foundation
1524 N. Astor St.
Chicago, IL 60610-2057
Application address: c/o University of Illinois, Attn.: Stacey Kostell, 901 W. Illinois St., Ste. 103, Urbana, IL 61801, tel.: (217) 333-0302, Email: uischolarships@illinois.edu

Donor: Ronald L. Chez.
Foundation type: Independent foundation.
Financial data (yr. ended 12/31/13): Assets, $1,718,728 (M); gifts received, $1,219,500; expenditures, $305,379; qualifying distributions, $285,787; giving activities include $267,908 for 1 grant.
Fields of interest: Education; University education.
Limitations: Applications accepted. Giving primarily in IL.
Application information:
www.admissions.illinois.edu/chez/application.pdf.
Application form required.
Initial approach: See website or e-mail
Deadline(s): Jan. 1
Trustees: Eric J. Chez; Ronald L. Chez; Elizabeth A. MacKnin.
EIN: 264654718

2786
Chicago Title and Trust Company Foundation
c/o John Rau Miami Corp.
410 N. Michigan Ave., Ste. 590
Chicago, IL 60611-4220 (312) 644-6720

Established in 1951 in Illinois.
Donor: Chicago Title and Trust Co.
Foundation type: Company-sponsored foundation.
Financial data (yr. ended 12/31/14): Assets, $606,237; expenditures, $265,316; qualifying distributions, $244,140.
Purpose and activities: The foundation supports libraries, hospitals, aquariums, and festivals and organizations involved with arts and culture, higher education, youth development business, human services, and community development.
Type of support: General support; Annual campaigns; Capital and infrastructure; Program development.
Limitations: Applications accepted. Giving primarily in Chicago, IL. No support for religious organizations. No grants to individuals, or for debt reduction.
Application information:
Initial approach: Proposal
Copies of proposal: 1
Deadline(s): None
Officers and Trustees: John Rau, Chair. and Trustee; Eileen Hughes, Treas.; Norman R. Bobins; Robert Stucker.
Number of staff: 1 part-time support.
EIN: 366036809

2787
Chicago Tribune Foundation
435 N. Michigan Ave., 2nd Fl.
Chicago, IL 60611-4041 (312) 222-3928
Contact: Jan Ellen Woelffer
FAX: (312) 222-3882;
E-mail: jwoelffer@tribune.com; Main URL: http://www.chicagotribune.com/communitygiving
Facebook: http://www.facebook.com/ChicagoTribuneCommunityGiving

Established in 1958 in Illinois.
Donor: Chicago Tribune Co.
Foundation type: Company-sponsored foundation.
Financial data (yr. ended 12/31/13): Assets, $531,376 (M); gifts received, $7,779; expenditures, $2,587; qualifying distributions,

$268,412; giving activities include $221,770 for 28 grants (high: $100,000; low: $500), and $46,642 for 1 employee matching gift.

Purpose and activities: The foundation supports organizations involved with journalism, arts and culture, and civic affairs. Special emphasis is directed toward programs that foster education for under-served populations.

Fields of interest: Arts and culture; Education; Publishing; Public affairs; Community and economic development; Freedom of association and expression; Human services; Adolescents; Adults; Ethnic and racial groups.

Type of support: General support; Employee matching gifts; Program development.

Limitations: Applications accepted. Giving primarily in the metropolitan Chicago, IL, area; giving also to national organizations for Journalism. No support for high school or college newspapers or international organizations. No grants to individuals, or for capital campaigns.

Publications: Application guidelines; Grants list.

Application information: Application form required.

Initial approach: Letter, e-mail, or telephone

Copies of proposal: 1

Deadline(s): Feb. 1 for Culture; Aug. 1 for Journalism

Board meeting date(s): June for Culture; Nov. for Journalism

Officers and Directors: Tony Hunter, Chair.; Joseph Schiltz, Pres.; Joetta Fields-Taylor, Secy.; Phil Doherty, Treas.; Maggie Wartik; Joyce Winnecke.

Number of staff: None.

EIN: 366050792

2788
Albert A. Christ Scholarship Fund

10 S. Dearborn St., IL1-0117
Chicago, IL 60603-2300

Established in 1995 in West Virginia.

Donor: Helen Christ†.

Foundation type: Independent foundation.

Financial data (yr. ended 06/30/13): Assets, $4,628,889 (M); expenditures, $240,385; qualifying distributions, $208,790; giving activities include $198,800 for grants to individuals.

Purpose and activities: Scholarship awards to deserving young people residing in the Wheeling, West Virginia, area, to attend college or university or to pursue graduate studies.

Fields of interest: Higher education.

Type of support: Student aid.

Limitations: Applications not accepted. Giving limited to residents of the Wheeling, WV area.

Application information: Unsolicited requests for funds not accepted.

Trustee: JPMorgan Chase Bank, N.A.

EIN: 556129775

2789
C. W. Christian Foundation

18900 Panduit Dr.
Tinley Park, IL 60487

Established in 2007 in Illinois.

Donor: Caveney Family Enterprises, LP.

Foundation type: Company-sponsored foundation.

Financial data (yr. ended 12/31/14): Assets, $2,442,298; gifts received, $38,500;

expenditures, $187,298; qualifying distributions, $185,760.

Fields of interest: Cancers; Catholicism; Human services.

Limitations: Applications not accepted.

Application information: Unsolicited requests for funds not accepted.

Trustee: Donald Mrozek.

EIN: 261333690

2790
Marjorie L. Christiansen Foundation

(formerly Arthur J. & Cecelia L. Christiansen Foundation)
10 S. Dearborn St., IL1-0117
Chicago, IL 60603-2300

Established in 1960 in Wisconsin.

Foundation type: Independent foundation.

Financial data (yr. ended 05/31/14): Assets, $3,788,076 (M); expenditures, $203,235; qualifying distributions, $164,613; giving activities include $154,500 for 29 grants (high: $24,500; low: $1,500).

Purpose and activities: Giving primarily in the area of health care and support of programs geared toward the elderly in the Racine, WI, area; priority given to organizations supported by the founder during her lifetime.

Fields of interest: Music; Botanical gardens; Health; Geriatrics; Eye diseases; Christianity; Cemeteries and burial services; Senior services; Seniors; Christians.

Limitations: Applications accepted. Giving limited to the Racine, WI, area. No grants to individuals.

Application information: Application form required.

Initial approach: Letter

Copies of proposal: 2

Deadline(s): None

Board meeting date(s): May and Nov.

Trustees: Scott Stewart; JPMorgan Chase Bank, N.A.

EIN: 396037585

2791
Citadel Foundation

(formerly Citadel Group Foundation)
c/o Min Sok Lee
131 S. Dearborn St.
Chicago, IL 60603-5517

Established in 2001 in Illinois.

Donors: Kenneth C. Griffin; Gerald A. Beeson; Adam C. Cooper; Nessan Fitzmaurice; Thomas Miglis; H. Michael Pyles; Joseph Russell; Mark Stainton; Ervin Shindell; Tim Throsby; C. James Yen.

Foundation type: Independent foundation.

Financial data (yr. ended 12/31/13): Assets, $406,949 (M); gifts received, $660,000; expenditures, $286,224; qualifying distributions, $286,224; giving activities include $275,477 for 16 grants (high: $67,200; low: $1,500).

Purpose and activities: Giving primarily for the arts, education, and for children, youth, and social services.

Fields of interest: Arts and culture; Education; Foundations; Public libraries; Human services; Food banks; Child welfare.

Limitations: Applications not accepted. Giving primarily in Chicago, IL and New York, NY. No grants to individuals.

Application information: Contributes only to pre-selected organizations.

Officers and Directors: Kenneth C. Griffin, Pres. and Director; Min Sok Lee, Secy. and Director; Catherine Stickrod, Treas. and Director; Gerald Beeson; Adam C. Cooper; Scott Rafferty.

EIN: 364482467

2792
Clarks Fork Foundation

270 Westminster Rd., Ste. 300
Lake Forest, IL 60045-1899

Established in 1989 in Illinois.

Donors: Margaret S. Hart; Augustin Hart.

Foundation type: Independent foundation.

Financial data (yr. ended 12/31/13): Assets, $3,542,985 (M); expenditures, $229,048; qualifying distributions, $185,209; giving activities include $176,689 for 101 grants (high: $35,000; low: $35).

Fields of interest: Arts and culture; Education; Undergraduate education; Health; Hospital care; Religion; Human services.

Limitations: Applications not accepted. Giving primarily in Chicago, IL and MT. No grants to individuals.

Application information: Unsolicited requests for funds not accepted.

Officers and Directors: Margaret S. Hart, Pres. and Director; Kathryn H. Lansing, Secy. and Director; Heather Hart Goldstein, Treas. and Director.

EIN: 363674219

2793
Cless Family Foundation

(formerly Karl Cless Foundation)
2100 Mallard Dr.
Northbrook, IL 60062-6643

Established in 1991 in Illinois.

Donor: Gerhard Cless.

Foundation type: Independent foundation.

Financial data (yr. ended 12/31/13): Assets, $19,761,062 (M); gifts received, $1,813,225; expenditures, $428,405; qualifying distributions, $426,528; giving activities include $426,500 for 9 grants (high: $220,000; low: $3,000).

Purpose and activities: Giving primarily for education and medical research.

Fields of interest: Education; Higher education; Diseases and conditions.

Type of support: Research.

Limitations: Applications not accepted. Giving primarily in IL; some funding in FL and NC. No grants to individuals.

Application information: Contributes only to pre-selected organizations.

Officers and Directors: Gerhard Cless, Pres. and Treas. and Director; Ruth I. Cless, V.P. and Secy. and Director; Bryan C. Cless; Martin Cless; Stephen G. Cless; Jennifer U. Zehr.

EIN: 363796675

2794
Clingen Foundation Ltd

c/o Brian T. Clingen
5101 Darmstadt Rd.
Hillside, IL 60162-1424

Established in 1997 in Illinois.
Donor: Brian T. Clingen.
Foundation type: Independent foundation.
Financial data (yr. ended 12/31/13): Assets, $1,501,506 (M); gifts received, $1,600,000; expenditures, $199,306; qualifying distributions, $192,500; giving activities include $192,500 for 8 grants (high: $84,000; low: $500).
Purpose and activities: Giving primarily for education, youth and family services, and social services; funding also for Roman Catholic education, organizations, and churches.
Fields of interest: Higher education; Nonprofits; Catholicism; Human services; Family services; Child welfare.
Type of support: Regranting.
Limitations: Applications not accepted. Giving primarily in IL and IN. No grants to individuals.
Application information: Contributes only to pre-selected organizations.
Officers and Directors: Brian T. Clingen, Pres. and Treas. and Director; Kenneth W. Clingen, Secy. and Director; Deidre M. Clingen.
EIN: 364200766

2795
Robert & Terri Cohn Family Foundation
2135 Larkdale Dr.
Glenview, IL 60025-4106

Established in 1982 in Illinois.
Donors: Robert Cohn; Terri L. Cohn; Jonathan Cohn; Andrew Cohn; Jamie Cohn; Lawrence Cohn.
Foundation type: Independent foundation.
Financial data (yr. ended 12/31/14): Assets, $6,502,456; expenditures, $367,610; qualifying distributions, $322,815.
Fields of interest: Arts and culture; Higher education; Zoos; Hospital care; Diseases and conditions; Judaism; Human services.
Type of support: General support; Annual campaigns; Scholarships.
Limitations: Applications not accepted. Giving primarily in Chicago, IL. No grants to individuals.
Application information: Unsolicited requests for funds not accepted.
Officers: Terri L. Cohn, Pres.; Jonathan Cohn, V.P.; Lawrence Cohn, V.P.; Jamie Kost, V.P.; Andrew Cohn, Secy.
EIN: 363192296

2796
Jacob & Rosaline Cohn Foundation
c/o The Northern Trust Co.
P.O. Box 803878
Chicago, IL 60680-3878

Established in 1950 in Illinois.
Donors: Rosaline Cohn; Marcia Cohn.
Foundation type: Independent foundation.
Financial data (yr. ended 12/31/13): Assets, $8,077,411 (M); gifts received, $500,000; expenditures, $301,896; qualifying distributions, $290,015; giving activities include $289,000 for 15 grants (high: $175,000; low: $500).
Fields of interest: Arts and culture; Arts education; Historic preservation; Higher education; Hospital care; Libraries; Judaism; Human services; Child welfare.

Limitations: Applications not accepted. Giving primarily in Chicago, IL and NY. No grants to individuals.
Application information: Contributes only to pre-selected organizations.
Trustee: Marcia Cohn.
EIN: 367012504

2797
Lizanell and Colbert Coldwell Foundation
c/o JPMorgan Chase Bank, N.A.
10 S. Dearborn, ILI-0117
Chicago, IL 60603
Application address: c/o JPMorgan Chase Bank, Attn.: Larry Bothe, 420 Throckmorton, Fl. 3, Fort Worth, TX 76102, tel.: (817) 884-4022

Established in 1990 in Texas.
Donor: Lizanell Coldwell†.
Foundation type: Independent foundation.
Financial data (yr. ended 03/31/13): Assets, $4,886,648 (M); expenditures, $289,428; qualifying distributions, $245,852; giving activities include $233,238 for 5 grants (high: $100,232; low: $10,000).
Purpose and activities: Giving limited to TX organizations furthering the advancement of medical sciences, and research institutions dedicated to medical research, especially for the cure and prevention of heart disease and cancer.
Fields of interest: Higher education; Diseases and conditions.
Type of support: General support; Research; Equipment; Research and evaluation.
Limitations: Giving limited to TX, with emphasis on El Paso. No support for political organizations. No grants to individuals, or for endowment funds.
Trustees: Colbert Coldwell; Annette Hoy, MD; JPMorgan Chase Bank, N.A.
EIN: 742576133

2798
The Cole Charitable Trust
P.O. Box 803878
Chicago, IL 60680-3878

Established in 2000 in Georgia.
Donors: Madison F. Cole; Cole Family Investements; MFC Family Trust.
Foundation type: Independent foundation.
Financial data (yr. ended 12/31/13): Assets, $3,668,453 (M); gifts received, $217,888; expenditures, $202,970; qualifying distributions, $195,667; giving activities include $194,917 for 6 + grants.
Fields of interest: Education; Religion; Youth development.
Type of support: Annual campaigns; Capital campaigns; Endowments.
Limitations: Applications not accepted. Giving primarily in GA; some giving in VA. No grants to individuals.
Application information: Unsolicited requests for funds not accepted.
Board meeting date(s): Sept.
Trustees: Madison F. Cole, Jr.; Sharon J. Cole.
Number of staff: None.
EIN: 586400414

2799
The Collins Family Foundation
c/o Robert T. Napier, Harrison & Held, LLP
333 W. Wacker Dr., Ste. 1700
Chicago, IL 60606-1247

Established in 1994 in Minnesota.
Donors: Arthur D. Collins, Jr.; Anne B. Collins; Elizabeth Collins.
Foundation type: Independent foundation.
Financial data (yr. ended 12/31/13): Assets, $5,340,583 (M); expenditures, $270,641; qualifying distributions, $257,950; giving activities include $217,600 for 9 grants (high: $149,000; low: $100).
Fields of interest: Arts and culture; Education; Higher education; Business education; Nonprofits; Family planning; Diseases and conditions; Human services.
Type of support: Regranting.
Limitations: Applications not accepted. Giving primarily in MN and PA. No grants to individuals.
Application information: Contributes only to pre-selected organizations.
Officer: Elizabeth Collins, Pres.
Trustees: Anne B. Collins; Arthur D. Collins, Jr.
EIN: 411792606

2800
Earle M. & Virginia M. Combs Foundation
2384 Oak Hill Rd.
Barrington, IL 60010-3898

Established in 1967 in Illinois.
Donors: Earle M. Combs III; Virginia M. Combs; Earle M. Combs IV; CME Group, Inc.
Foundation type: Independent foundation.
Financial data (yr. ended 12/31/13): Assets, $10,046,211 (M); gifts received, $564,579; expenditures, $422,388; qualifying distributions, $383,138; giving activities include $328,794 for 74 grants (high: $67,000; low: $500).
Purpose and activities: Giving primarily for Christian and Baptist organizations; funding also for education and human services, including a YMCA.
Fields of interest: Higher education; Graduate and professional education; Christianity; Baptist; Theology; Human services; Youth services.
International interests: Australia; Fiji; Zambia.
Type of support: General support.
Limitations: Applications not accepted. Giving on a national and international basis, with emphasis on IL and WI; funding also in Australia, Fiji, and Zambia. No grants to individuals.
Application information: Contributes only to pre-selected organizations.
Officers and Directors: Earle M. Combs III, Pres. and Director; Virginia M. Combs, Secy.-Treas.; Earle M. Combs IV; Bonnie C. Etters.
EIN: 366168454

2801
Communitas Charitable Trust
c/o Harold M. Baron
5555 N. Sheridan Rd., Ste. 1011
Chicago, IL 60640-1624

Established in 1991 in Illinois.
Donors: Harold M. Baron; Paula L. Baron.
Foundation type: Independent foundation.

Financial data (yr. ended 12/31/13): Assets, $1,717,407 (M); expenditures, $206,084; qualifying distributions, $203,319; giving activities include $184,000 for 13 grants (high: $70,500; low: $1,000).
Fields of interest: Arts and culture; Education; Public affairs; Judaism; Human services; International relations; International peace and security.
Type of support: General support.
Limitations: Applications not accepted. Giving primarily in IL. No grants to individuals.
Application information: Unsolicited requests for funds not accepted.
Trustees: Harold M. Baron; Paula L. Baron.
EIN: 366947593

2802
Community Foundation of Kankakee River Valley

(formerly Kankakee River Valley Foundation)
701 S. Harrison Ave.
Kankakee, IL 60901   (815) 939-1611
FAX: (815) 936-9633;
E-mail: info@endowthefuture.org; Main URL: http://www.endowthefuture.org
Facebook: https://www.facebook.com/CommunityFoundationKankakeeRiverValley
Parent's Page -Success by 6, an early childhood initiative: http://www.parentspage.org

Established in 1982 in Illinois.
Foundation type: Community foundation.
Financial data (yr. ended 12/31/12): Assets, $6,703,442 (M); gifts received, $74,145; expenditures, $963,325; giving activities include $198,543 for 4+ grants (high: $12,500).
Purpose and activities: The foundation: 1) promotes visionary philanthropy to create and support vital and caring communities; 2) builds and preserves funds of many individuals and institutions; 3) distributes to nonprofit organizations that serve members of the community; and 4) convenes concerned individuals to shape flexible responses to changing needs of the community.
Fields of interest: Arts and culture; Education; Land resources; Health; Employment; Human services; Child care.
Type of support: Equipment; Pro bono consulting services; Program development; Matching grants; Seed money.
Limitations: Applications accepted. Giving for the benefit of residents of the area, including Aroma Park, Bourbonnais, Bradley, and Kankakee in Kankakee County, IL.
Publications: Application guidelines; Informational brochure; Newsletter.
Application information: Visit foundation web site for application form and guidelines. Application form required.
  Initial approach: Submit online application
  Deadline(s): Mar. 6
  Board meeting date(s): 3rd Thurs. of each month
Officers and Directors: Kari Nugent, Chair. and Director; Roger Benson, Secy. and Director; Dale Gerretse, Treas. and Director; Nicole Smolkovich, Exec. Dir.; Hollice Clark; Karl Kruse; Elizabeth Kubal; Lawrence Mahoney; Dr. Stonewall McCuiston; Mike O'Brien; Lyndsay Parkhurst; Cindi Reddish; Paul Snellenberger; Mike Van Mill.

Number of staff: 1 full-time professional; 1 part-time professional; 1 full-time support.
EIN: 363235540

2803
Community Foundation of the Quincy Area

(formerly Quincy Area Community Foundation)
4531 Maine, Ste. A
Quincy, IL 62305   (217) 222-1237
Contact: Jill Arnold Blickhan, Exec. Dir.; Amy Meyer Lehenbauer, Outreach Coord.
FAX: (217) 222-2260;
E-mail: info@mycommunityfoundation.org; Mailing address: P.O. Box 741, Quincy, IL 62306-0741; Additional e-mail: execdir@mycommunityfoundation.org; Grant inquiry e-mail: grants@mycommunityfoundation.org; Main URL: http://www.mycommunityfoundation.org
Facebook: http://www.facebook.com/mycommunityfoundation
YouTube: http://www.youtube.com/user/qacf2010?feature=watch

Established in 1997 in Illinois.
Foundation type: Community foundation.
Financial data (yr. ended 12/31/13): Assets, $19,261,280 (M); gifts received, $2,107,378; expenditures, $590,473; giving activities include $329,752 for 14+ grants (high: $30,000), and $7,300 for 9 grants to individuals.
Purpose and activities: The foundation seeks to enrich the quality of life in the tri-state area by offering a way for people from all walks of life to easily and effectively support the groups and issues they care about most.
Fields of interest: Arts and culture; Education; Health; Community and economic development; Human services.
Type of support: Capacity-building and technical assistance; Matching grants; General support; Capital and infrastructure; Equipment; Program development; Publications; Seed money; Curriculum development; Scholarships.
Limitations: Applications accepted. Giving limited to Adams, Brown, Hancock, and Pike counties, IL, Lee County, IA, and Clark, Knox, Lewis, Marion, Monroe, Pike, Ralls, and Shelby counties, MO. No support for religious purposes. No grants to individuals (except for scholarships), or for annual campaigns, endowments, debt reductions, national fundraising efforts, sponsorships for fundraising or for-profit events or recurring events.
Publications: Application guidelines; Annual report; Grants list; Informational brochure; Newsletter.
Application information: Visit foundation web site for guidelines and to access online application. Grants from the foundation's competitive fund are generally limited to $1,000 or less. Application form required.
  Initial approach: Submit online application
  Deadline(s): June 1
  Board meeting date(s): 4th Tues. of each month
  Final notification: Sept.-Nov.
Officers and Directors: Andy Sprague, Chair. and Director; William McCleery, Jr., Vice-Chair. and Director; Lydia Ahrens, Secy. and Director; Erin Wharton, CPA, Treas. and Director; Jill Arnold Blickhan, Exec. Dir.; Leah Berry; Julie Bowen; Tony Crane; Tom Dale; Larry Fischer; Lance Grady; Tanya Harvey; Philip Krupps; Laura McReynolds; Blake Roderick; Steve Siebers; Sharon Tenhouse; Byron Webb III.

Number of staff: 1 full-time professional; 1 part-time professional; 1 part-time support.
EIN: 371366611

2804
Frank W. & Nancy S. Considine Foundation

1504 Primrose Ln.
Glenview, IL 60026-7772

Established in 1992 in Illinois.
Donors: Frank W. Considine; Nancy Considine.
Foundation type: Independent foundation.
Financial data (yr. ended 12/31/13): Assets, $990,487 (M); expenditures, $423,516; qualifying distributions, $413,511; giving activities include $413,511 for 29 grants (high: $300,000; low: $30).
Fields of interest: Arts and culture; Health; Catholicism.
Limitations: Applications not accepted. Giving primarily in Chicago, IL. No grants to individuals.
Application information: Unsolicited requests for funds not accepted.
Officers: Frank W. Considine, Pres. and Secy.; Nancy Considine, V.P.
Directors: Nancy Considine Clark; Kevin S. Considine.
EIN: 363864286

2805
Constans-Culver Foundation

10 S. Dearborn, IL1-0117
Chicago, IL 60603

Established in 1965 in New York.
Donor: Erne Constans Culver†.
Foundation type: Independent foundation.
Financial data (yr. ended 12/31/13): Assets, $5,926,316 (M); expenditures, $328,063; qualifying distributions, $269,269; giving activities include $250,000 for 9 grants (high: $35,000; low: $5,000).
Fields of interest: Arts and culture; Music; Museums; Education; Higher education; Business education; Diseases and conditions; Libraries; Public administration; National defense; Christianity; Human services; Low-income and poor people.
Type of support: General support; Continuing support.
Limitations: Applications accepted. Giving primarily in NY and PA. No grants to individuals, or for endowment funds.
Application information:
  Initial approach: Proposal
  Deadline(s): None
Trustees: Janna C. Collins; Victoria Prescott Herd; Elizabeth Scholtz; JPMorgan Chase Bank, N.A.
Number of staff: None.
EIN: 136048059

2806
John D. & Barbara C. Cooney Family Foundation

c/o John D. Cooney
120 N. LaSalle St., 30th Fl.
Chicago, IL 60602-2492

Established in 2000 in Illinois.
Donors: Barbara C. Cooney; John D. Cooney.
Foundation type: Independent foundation.

Financial data (yr. ended 12/31/13): Assets, $6,714,662 (M); expenditures, $223,518; qualifying distributions, $184,968; giving activities include $184,968 for 15 grants (high: $100,000; low: $500).
Purpose and activities: Giving primarily for education.
Fields of interest: Elementary and secondary education; Higher education; Law education; Health.
Limitations: Applications not accepted. Giving primarily in IL. No grants to individuals.
Application information: Contributes only to pre-selected organizations.
Directors: Barbara C. Cooney; John D. Cooney.
EIN: 364408630

2807
Leslie & Loretta Copeland Foundation
10 S. Dearborn St., IL1-0117
Chicago, IL 60603-2300

Established in 1999 in Illinois.
Donor: Loretta M. Copeland†.
Foundation type: Independent foundation.
Financial data (yr. ended 12/31/13): Assets, $9,476,974 (M); expenditures, $480,907; qualifying distributions, $420,715; giving activities include $403,156 for 13 grants (high: $31,012; low: $31,012).
Fields of interest: Higher education; Protestantism.
Limitations: Applications not accepted. Giving primarily in IL. No grants to individuals.
Application information: Contributes only to pre-selected organizations.
Trustee: JPMorgan Chase Bank, N.A.
EIN: 367278445

2808
Willard J. and Alice C. Corbett Charitable Trust
111 W. Monroe St., Tax Div. 10C
Chicago, IL 60603-4096

Foundation type: Independent foundation.
Financial data (yr. ended 07/31/14): Assets, $5,537,607 (M); expenditures, $457,046; qualifying distributions, $410,032; giving activities include $386,787 for 12 grants (high: $64,465; low: $16,116).
Fields of interest: Higher education; Foundations; Nonprofits; Human services.
Type of support: Regranting.
Limitations: Applications not accepted. Giving primarily in IL. No grants to individuals.
Application information: Contributes only to pre-selected organizations.
Trustee: BMO Harris Bank, N.A.
EIN: 367122094

2809
Willard J. & Alice C. Corbett Foundation
111 W. Monroe St., Ste. 10C
Chicago, IL 60603-4098 (312) 461-5154

Established in 1995 in Illinois.
Donor: Alice Corbett†.
Foundation type: Independent foundation.
Financial data (yr. ended 07/31/14): Assets, $2,134,301 (M); expenditures, $176,231; qualifying distributions, $157,557; giving activities

include $148,071 for 8 grants (high: $50,000; low: $5,000).
Fields of interest: Medical education; Foundations; Hospice care; Community recreation; Human services.
Limitations: Applications accepted. Giving primarily in Rockford, IL. No grants to individuals.
Application information: Application form required.
  Initial approach: Letter
  Deadline(s): Apr. 30
  Final notification: July 1
Trustee: Harris Bank, N.A.
EIN: 364099445

2810
Corcoran Family Foundation
523 Hoyt Ln.
Winnetka, IL 60093-2622 8476775831

Established in 2007 in Illinois.
Donors: Gerald F. Corcoran; Maureen A. Corcoran.
Foundation type: Independent foundation.
Financial data (yr. ended 12/31/14): Assets, $4,464,183; expenditures, $256,354; qualifying distributions, $237,158.
Fields of interest: Education; Catholicism; Child welfare; People with disabilities.
Application information:
  Initial approach: Proposal
  Deadline(s): None
Officers: Gerald Corcoran, Pres. and Secy.; Maureen Corcoran, V.P. and Treas.
EIN: 261508742

2811
Cord Vanderpool Foundation
10470 W. 163rd Pl.
Orland Park, IL 60467-5445 (708) 590-6253
FAX: (708) 873-5509; Main URL: http://www.cordvanderpool.com
Facebook: https://www.facebook.com/Cord.Vanderpool

Established in 2009 in Illinois.
Donors: Floridamae Vanderpool 2005 Trust; Parkview Christian Church.
Foundation type: Independent foundation.
Financial data (yr. ended 12/31/13): Assets, $3,389,496 (M); gifts received, $81,344; expenditures, $777,845; qualifying distributions, $331,711; giving activities include $150,128 for 10 grants (high: $103,700; low: $500).
Fields of interest: Education; Human services.
Limitations: Applications not accepted. Giving primarily in IL.
Application information: Unsolicited requests for funds not accepted.
Officers: Gary Bertacchi, Pres. and Director; Therese Foster, V.P. and Director; Thomas Lavin, V.P.
EIN: 204817193

2812
Cornerstone Center Foundation
0s280 Bauman Ct.
West Chicago, IL 60185

Established in 1998 in Illinois.
Donor: Henrietta Van Der Molen†.
Foundation type: Operating foundation.

Financial data (yr. ended 12/31/13): Assets, $3,277,953 (M); gifts received, $5,068; expenditures, $387,703; qualifying distributions, $208,715; giving activities include $161,710 for 44 grants (high: $20,200; low: $100).
Fields of interest: Christianity; Human services; Child welfare.
Limitations: Applications not accepted. Giving primarily in IL and IN. No grants to individuals.
Application information: Contributes only to pre-selected organizations.
Trustees: Virginia Johnson; Jeffrey Vandermolen.
EIN: 364248583

2813
Wyman R. Coulter Trust
c/o Kathie J. Butts
1 S. Wacker, 24th Fl.
Chicago, IL 60606-4654
Application address: c/o Distribution Comm., 1000 3rd St., P.O. Box 55, Orion IL 61273, tel.: (309) 526-3374

Established in 2006 in Illinois.
Donor: June G. Coulter†.
Foundation type: Independent foundation.
Financial data (yr. ended 12/31/14): Assets, $2,710,002; expenditures, $153,762; qualifying distributions, $133,818.
Fields of interest: Education; Protestantism; Human services.
Limitations: Applications accepted. Giving primarily in Orion, IL. No grants to individuals.
Application information: Application form required.
  Initial approach: Proposal
  Deadline(s): None
Trustee: ATG Trust Company.
Distribution Committee: Donna M. Boehm; James R. Dingman; Gerald L. Meyer.
EIN: 366045031

2814
Gerry and Bill Cowlin Foundation
c/o The Northern Trust Company
P.O. Box 803878
Chicago, IL 60680-3878

Established in 2003 in Illinois.
Donors: W.J. Cowlin Charitable Trust; Cowlin Charitable Lead Trust.
Foundation type: Independent foundation.
Financial data (yr. ended 12/31/13): Assets, $6,913,755 (M); gifts received, $2,349,521; expenditures, $333,953; qualifying distributions, $315,015; giving activities include $314,000 for 6 grants (high: $150,000; low: $1,000).
Fields of interest: Arts and culture; Student services; Genetic conditions and birth defects; Food banks; Family services; International development.
Limitations: Applications not accepted. Giving primarily in CA, IL and MI. No grants to individuals.
Application information: Unsolicited requests for funds not accepted.
Officer: Geraldine Cowlin, Pres.
Directors: Bill Cowlin; Bridget Cowlin; David A. Cowlin; Martha Ratzner; Sarah Towne.
EIN: 562403559

2815
Cremer Foundation Inc.
111 W. Monroe St., Tax Div., Ste. 10C
Chicago, IL 60603 3124615154
Application address: c/o James Berkenstadt, P.O.
Box 1, Madison, WI 53701, tel.: (608) 837-5166

Established in 1965 in Wisconsin.
Donor: Frances Cremer.
Foundation type: Independent foundation.
Financial data (yr. ended 12/31/14): Assets,
$4,281,284; expenditures, $388,570; qualifying
distributions, $356,125.
Purpose and activities: Giving primarily to social
service agencies, especially those aiding troubled
youth, the homeless, the handicapped and senior
citizens.
Fields of interest: Child educational development;
Biomedicine; Diseases and conditions; Alcoholism;
Housing development; Human services; Family
services; Child welfare; Child development; Senior
services; Seniors; People with disabilities.
Type of support: General support; Matching grants;
Seed money; Scholarships; Research; Research
and evaluation.
Limitations: Applications accepted. Giving primarily
in the Madison, WI, area. Generally no support for
religious-based programs. No grants to individuals
or generally for deficit financing or conferences or
seminars.
Publications: Application guidelines.
Application information:
Initial approach: Letter
Copies of proposal: 1
Deadline(s): None
Board meeting date(s): 2 times per year; usually
in Mar. and Aug.
Officers: Holly L. Cremer, Pres. and Treas.; Robert
R. Stroud, V.P.; Helen A. George, Secy.
Directors: James A. Berkenstadt; Rebecca
Berkenstadt; James T. Sykes.
EIN: 396086822

2816
William J. Cronin Foundation
111 W. Monroe St. Tax Div. 10C
Chicago, IL 60603-5000
Application address: c/o James P. McGuire, P.O. Box
2574, Janesville, WI 53547-2574, tel.: (608)
752-7615

Established in 1979 in Wisconsin.
Donor: William J. Cronin†.
Foundation type: Independent foundation.
Financial data (yr. ended 11/30/13): Assets,
$2,769,991 (M); expenditures, $178,726;
qualifying distributions, $166,448; giving activities
include $153,001 for 25 grants (high: $15,300;
low: $1,000).
Fields of interest: Health; Christianity; Human
services; Family services; Child welfare; Youth
development.
Limitations: Applications accepted. Giving
exclusively for the benefit of the residents of
Janesville, WI.
Application information:
Initial approach: Letter
Deadline(s): Nov. 1
Trustee: BMO Harris Bank, N.A.
EIN: 930782568

2817
Cronk Family Foundation
c/o M. Cronk
13 Natoma Dr.
Oak Brook, IL 60523-7711

Established in 2002 in Illinois.
Donors: Gerald M. Cronk; Lidia E. Cronk.
Foundation type: Independent foundation.
Financial data (yr. ended 12/31/13): Assets,
$1,665,538 (M); expenditures, $340,986;
qualifying distributions, $337,261; giving activities
include $337,261 for 142 grants (high: $50,000;
low: $15).
Fields of interest: Higher education; Graduate and
professional education; Christianity; Theology;
Human services.
Limitations: Applications not accepted. No grants to
individuals.
Application information: Contributes only to
pre-selected organizations.
Officers and Directors: Gerald M. Cronk, Pres. and
Director; Lidia E. Cronk, Secy.-Treas. and Director;
John Norbut.
EIN: 753025533

2818
Duane A. Cullinan Memorial Trust
P.O. Box 166
Tremont, IL 61568-0166

Established in 1983 in Illinois.
Donors: Libby Mathers; Stephen A. Cullinan;
Michael N. Cullinan; Elizabeth A. Mathers.
Foundation type: Independent foundation.
Financial data (yr. ended 12/31/13): Assets,
$509,425 (M); gifts received, $145,632;
expenditures, $183,817; qualifying distributions,
$179,002; giving activities include $178,500 for 8
grants (high: $75,000; low: $2,000).
Fields of interest: Arts and culture; Education;
Catholicism.
Limitations: Applications not accepted. Giving
primarily in Peoria, IL. No grants to individuals.
Application information: Unsolicited requests for
funds not accepted.
Trustees: Michael N. Cullinan; Stephen A. Cullinan;
Elizabeth A. Mathers.
EIN: 371139997

2819
Carlie Cunningham Foundation
c/o JPMorgan Bank, N.A.
10 S. Dearborn St., IL1-0117
Chicago, IL 60603-2024

Established in 1997 in Indiana.
Donor: Carlie Cunningham†.
Foundation type: Independent foundation.
Financial data (yr. ended 06/30/13): Assets,
$201,868 (M); expenditures, $243,585; qualifying
distributions, $240,080; giving activities include
$234,100 for 8 grants (high: $100,000; low:
$3,000).
Fields of interest: Arts and culture; Youth services.
Limitations: Applications not accepted. Giving
primarily in IN. No grants to individuals.
Application information: Unsolicited requests for
funds not accepted.
Trustee: JPMorgan Chase Bank, N.A.
EIN: 352053212

2820
**D.A.S. Charitable Fund for the
Preservation of Feline Animal Life**
P.O. Box 6630
Libertyville, IL 60048-6630 (847) 680-4024
E-mail: dennisryan@dasfund.com; Main URL: http://
www.dasfund.com

Established in 2002 in Illinois.
Donor: Steven C. Pearson†.
Foundation type: Independent foundation.
Financial data (yr. ended 12/31/14): Assets,
$6,314,223; expenditures, $642,137; qualifying
distributions, $583,146.
Purpose and activities: Giving limited to the
promotion and preservation of animal life in Lake
County, IL.
Fields of interest: Animal welfare.
Limitations: Applications accepted. Giving limited to
Lake County, IL. No grants to individuals.
Application information:
Initial approach: Letter
Deadline(s): None
Trustee: Dennis Ryan.
EIN: 300068578

2821
Harvey and Ethel Daeumer Foundation
c/o Dobosz Law Offices, PC
2175 Point Blvd., Ste. 150
Elgin, IL 60123-5262 8476288310
Contact: Glen T. Dobosz
E-mail: HEDFnd@gmail.com; Application address: c/
o Laurie A.Z. Bitter, 72 N. Alfred Ave., Ste. 2, Elgin,
IL 60123, tel.: (847) 888-2555; Main URL: http://
www.daeumer.org

Established in 2001 in Illinois.
Donors: Harvey E. Daeumer; Harvey Daeumer Trust
No. 1.
Foundation type: Independent foundation.
Financial data (yr. ended 12/31/14): Assets,
$4,233,597; gifts received, $1,735; expenditures,
$196,575; qualifying distributions, $189,132.
Fields of interest: Religion; Human services; Youth
development.
Limitations: Applications accepted. Giving primarily
in IL.
Application information: Application form required.
Initial approach: Proposal
Deadline(s): None
Officers and Directors: Bonnie L. Emberton, Pres.
and Director; Laurie A.Z. Bitter, Secy. and Director;
Glen T. Dobosz, Treas. and Director.
EIN: 364462103

2822
Dancing Skies Foundation
134 N. Lasalle St., No. 1050
Chicago, IL 60602-2318

Established in 2008 in Illinois.
Foundation type: Independent foundation.
Financial data (yr. ended 12/31/13): Assets,
$6,735,988 (M); expenditures, $348,322;
qualifying distributions, $342,955; giving activities
include $340,000 for 8 grants (high: $140,000;
low: $5,000).
Fields of interest: Performing arts; Health; Human
services.

Limitations: Applications not accepted. Giving primarily in Chicago and Highland Park, IL. No grants to individuals.
Application information: Contributes only to pre-selected organizations.
Officer: Audrey Weaver, Pres.
Directors: Meredith Erickson; Karl Leinberger.
EIN: 263286007

2823
Danielson Foundation
410 N. Michigan Ave., Ste. 590
Chicago, IL 60611-4220

Established in 1964 in Illinois.
Donors: Deering Foundation; Christopher Massey.
Foundation type: Independent foundation.
Financial data (yr. ended 11/30/13): Assets, $1,899,118 (M); gifts received, $150,000; expenditures, $241,867; qualifying distributions, $244,332; giving activities include $228,000 for 44 grants (high: $25,000; low: $1,000).
Fields of interest: Arts and culture; Education; Higher education; Environment; Foundations; Health; Diseases and conditions; Human services.
Limitations: Applications not accepted. Giving primarily in CA and FL; some funding nationally. No grants to individuals, or for scholarships, fellowships, or loans.
Application information: Contributes only to pre-selected organizations.
Officers and Directors: John Rau, Pres. and Director; Candida D. Burnap, V.P. and Director; Susan D. Pattock, Secy.-Treas.; Catherine Andrea Massey; Christopher Massey; Richard S. Massey.
EIN: 362540494

2824
James Deering Danielson Foundation
410 N. Michigan Ave., Ste. 590
Chicago, IL 60611-4220

Established in 1969 in Illinois.
Donors: Deering Foundation; Miami Corp.; Beverly Danielson.
Foundation type: Independent foundation.
Financial data (yr. ended 12/31/13): Assets, $1,661,887 (M); gifts received, $150,000; expenditures, $238,819; qualifying distributions, $225,500; giving activities include $225,500 for 45 grants (high: $50,000; low: $1,000).
Purpose and activities: Giving primarily for social organizations, cultural programs, public and international policy, and civil rights. Funding also for education.
Fields of interest: Museums; Education; Elementary and secondary education; Undergraduate education; Public libraries; Public policy.
Type of support: General support; Policy, advocacy and systems reform.
Limitations: Applications not accepted. Giving primarily in Washington, DC, FL and ME. No grants to individuals, or for scholarships or fellowships; no loans.
Application information: Generally contributes only to pre-selected organizations.
Officers and Directors: John Rau, Pres. and Director; Barbara S. Danielson, V.P. and Director; Beverly Danielson, V.P. and Director; Charles E.

Seitz III, V.P. and Director; Jocelyn D. Tennille, V.P. and Director; Susan D. Pattock, Secy.-Treas.
EIN: 237042530

2825
Nelson B. Delavan Foundation
10 S. Dearborn IL1-0117
Chicago, IL 60603
Application Address: c/o JPMorgan Chase Bank, 1 Chase Sq., Rochester, NY, 14643, Application Phone: (585) 797-1925

Established in 1983 in New York.
Foundation type: Independent foundation.
Financial data (yr. ended 12/31/14): Assets, $5,858,983 (M); expenditures, $454,446; qualifying distributions, $407,305; giving activities include $397,257 for 57 grants (high: $118,000; low: $200).
Purpose and activities: Giving primarily to organizations that support performances of fine arts.
Fields of interest: Arts and culture; Performing arts; Medical education; Animal welfare; Health; Diseases and conditions; Human services; Child welfare; Women's services; International relations; Females.
Type of support: General support.
Limitations: Applications accepted. Giving primarily in the Finger Lakes area and Monroe County, NY. No grants to individuals.
Application information: Application form required.
Initial approach: Letter
Copies of proposal: 2
Deadline(s): Most applications reviewed between Feb. 1 and Mar. 15, and between Sept. 1 and Oct. 15
Trustee: JPMorgan Chase Bank, N.A.
EIN: 166260274

2826
Delta Foundation
1249 Waukegan Rd.
Glenview, IL 60025-3077
Contact: Michael O'Brien

Established in 1994 in Illinois.
Donor: Jean F. Deal.
Foundation type: Independent foundation.
Financial data (yr. ended 05/31/13): Assets, $5,466,419 (M); expenditures, $283,256; qualifying distributions, $283,256; giving activities include $187,997 for 23 grants (high: $17,533; low: $833).
Fields of interest: Education; Higher education; Arthritis; Community and economic development; Christianity; Sports and recreation; Human services; Child welfare.
Type of support: Endowments; Research; Equipment; Capital and infrastructure; Program development; General support.
Limitations: Applications not accepted. Giving primarily in IL, with emphasis on Cook and Morgan counties, and MI, with some emphasis on Ludington and Saginaw. No grants to individuals.
Application information: Contributes only to pre-selected organizations.
Trustees: Harmon B. Deal III; Jean F. Deal; Michael O'Brien; Nancy D. Walch.
EIN: 363917119

2827
N. Demos Foundation, Inc.
50 S. LaSalle St., Apt. B-3
Chicago, IL 60603-1008 (312) 444-5933
Application Phone: (312) 630-6047

Established in 1964 in New York.
Donor: Nicholas Demos†.
Foundation type: Independent foundation.
Financial data (yr. ended 06/30/14): Assets, $3,786,154 (M); expenditures, $226,451; qualifying distributions, $215,218; giving activities include $167,000 for 28 grants (high: $15,000; low: $3,000).
Purpose and activities: Grants for educational projects, social work activities, and health care assistance in Greece.
Fields of interest: Education; Child welfare.
International interests: Greece.
Type of support: General support; Scholarships.
Limitations: Applications accepted. Giving limited to Greece. No grants to individuals.
Publications: Application guidelines.
Application information: Application form required.
Initial approach: Proposal
Copies of proposal: 1
Deadline(s): None
Board meeting date(s): Fall
Officers and Directors: Judge Paul Lillios, Chair. and Director; Desi Bakalis, Pres. and Director; R. Hugh Magill, Treas.; Elizabeth Gebhard; Metropolitan Iakovos; Martha T. Roth; Amy Cunningham, Secy. and Director; Frederick Chapekis; Alexander Zagoreos.
EIN: 366165689

2828
James and Catherine Denny Foundation
1 N. Wacker Dr., Ste. 4125
Chicago, IL 60606-2834

Established in 1993 in Illinois.
Donors: James M. Denny; Catherine M. Denny.
Foundation type: Independent foundation.
Financial data (yr. ended 12/31/13): Assets, $4,099,319 (M); gifts received, $100,000; expenditures, $445,530; qualifying distributions, $415,100; giving activities include $415,100 for 43 grants (high: $40,000; low: $100).
Purpose and activities: Giving primarily for Roman Catholic education, organizations and churches; funding also for social services.
Fields of interest: Education; Higher education; Foundations; Catholicism; Human services.
Limitations: Applications not accepted. Giving primarily in Chicago, IL. No grants to individuals.
Application information: Contributes only to pre-selected organizations.
Trustees: Catherine M. Denny; James M. Denny.
EIN: 367067862

2829
The Diamond Family Foundation
1 N. Franklin, Ste. 900
Chicago, IL 60606-3461
Contact: Jennifer Diamond, Dir.

Established in 1994 in Illinois.
Donor: Terry Diamond.
Foundation type: Independent foundation.

Financial data (yr. ended 12/31/13): Assets, $6,351,032 (M); expenditures, $309,671; qualifying distributions, $309,671; giving activities include $220,977 for grants.
Fields of interest: Arts and culture; Museums; Education; Education services; Nonprofits; Public affairs; Judaism; Human services.
Type of support: Regranting.
Limitations: Applications accepted. Giving primarily in IL. No grants to individuals.
Application information: Application form required.
  Initial approach: Letter
  Deadline(s): None
Officers and Directors: Terry Diamond, Pres. and Treas.; Marilyn Diamond, V.P. and Secy. and Director; Jennifer Diamond; John Diamond; Jamie Diamond Schwartz.
EIN: 363991910

2830
The Dick Family Foundation
273 Market Sq.
P.O. Box 312
Lake Forest, IL 60045-1892

Established in 1979 in Illinois.
Foundation type: Independent foundation.
Financial data (yr. ended 12/31/14): Assets, $3,412,579 (M); expenditures, $168,736; qualifying distributions, $166,098; giving activities include $137,500 for 32 grants (high: $35,000; low: $500).
Fields of interest: Education; Health; Human rights.
Limitations: Applications not accepted. Giving primarily in IL, with emphasis on Chicago and Lake Forest. No grants to individuals.
Application information: Unsolicited requests for funds not accepted.
Officers and Directors: John H. Dick, Pres. and Treas.; Mrs. Natalie C. Culley, Secy. and Director; Edison W. Dick; John H. Dick, Jr.; Anne Culley Wise.
EIN: 366057056

2831
Mary, Martha & Emmett J. Doerr Charitable Trust
111 W. Monroe St., Ste. 10C
Chicago, IL 60603-4098
Application Address: c/o BMO Harris Bank, N.A., P.O. Box 2977, Milwaukee, WI, 53201, Application Phone: (414) 815-3570

Foundation type: Independent foundation.
Financial data (yr. ended 06/30/14): Assets, $4,235,734 (M); expenditures, $203,803; qualifying distributions, $175,008; giving activities include $158,100 for 18 grants (high: $25,000; low: $1,500).
Purpose and activities: Giving primarily for Roman Catholic education.
Fields of interest: Education; Health; Catholicism; Human services; Scouting programs.
Limitations: Applications accepted. Giving primarily in WI.
Application information: Application form required.
  Initial approach: Letter
  Deadline(s): None
  Board meeting date(s): Feb.
Trustee: BMO Harris Bank, N.A.
EIN: 396756635

2832
Donovan Family Foundation
211 W. Westminster Rd.
Lake Forest, IL 60045-2126

Established in 2006 in Illinois.
Donors: David E. Donovan; Nancy S. Donovan.
Foundation type: Independent foundation.
Financial data (yr. ended 12/31/13): Assets, $1,786,153 (M); gifts received, $80,000; expenditures, $281,600; qualifying distributions, $261,250; giving activities include $260,250 for 8 grants (high: $120,000; low: $5,000).
Fields of interest: Science museums; University education.
Limitations: Applications not accepted. Giving primarily in DC, IL and WY. No grants to individuals.
Application information: Contributes only to pre-selected organizations.
Trustees: David E. Donovan; Nancy S. Donovan.
EIN: 367463172

2833
R. & C. Donovan Family Foundation, Inc.
10 S. Dearborn, IL1-0117
Chicago, IL 60603

Established in 2001 in New Jersey.
Donor: Raymond J. Donovan.
Foundation type: Independent foundation.
Financial data (yr. ended 12/31/13): Assets, $3,397,808 (M); expenditures, $158,064; qualifying distributions, $154,500; giving activities include $154,500 for 13 grants (high: $55,000; low: $1,000).
Fields of interest: Education; Religion; Human services.
Limitations: Applications not accepted. Giving primarily in NJ. No grants to individuals.
Application information: Unsolicited requests for funds not accepted.
Officers: Raymond C. Donovan, Pres.; Keith Donovan, V.P; Mary Ellen Stewart, V.P.; Catherine Donovan, Secy.; Kenneth M. Donovan, Treas.
Trustee: JPMorgan Chase Bank, N.A.
EIN: 223844249

2834
Sally and James Dowdle Family Foundation
c/o Madden, Jiganti, Moore & Sinars LLP
190 S. LaSalle St., Ste. 1700
Chicago, IL 60603-3496

Established in 1997 in Illinois.
Donor: James C. Dowdle.
Foundation type: Independent foundation.
Financial data (yr. ended 03/31/13): Assets, $108,250 (M); gifts received, $100,000; expenditures, $326,141; qualifying distributions, $321,850; giving activities include $321,850 for 30 grants (high: $100,000; low: $150).
Purpose and activities: Giving primarily for education, Roman Catholic agencies and churches, health and human services, and youth organizations.
Fields of interest: Education; Secondary education; Graduate and professional education; Medical education; Health; Diseases and conditions; Catholicism; Theology; Human services; Child welfare; Youth development.

Limitations: Applications not accepted. Giving primarily in IL. No grants to individuals.
Application information: Unsolicited requests for funds not accepted.
Officers and Directors: Sally S. Dowdle, Pres. and Director; Colleen D. Burke, V.P. and Director; James C. Dowdle, Jr., V.P. and Director; Jeanne D. Dwyer, V.P. and Director; Sarah D. Tyrrell, V.P. and Director; James C. Dowdle, Secy.-Treas. and Director.
EIN: 364157838

2835
Thomas W. Dower Foundation
P.O. Box 416
Kenilworth, IL 60043-0416
Contact: Mary K. Hartigan, Tr.

Established in 1951 in Illinois.
Donor: Thomas W. Dower†.
Foundation type: Independent foundation.
Financial data (yr. ended 04/30/14): Assets, $7,194,360 (M); expenditures, $392,512; qualifying distributions, $299,229; giving activities include $269,000 for 65 grants (high: $20,000; low: $500).
Purpose and activities: Giving primarily for education, health care, and to Roman Catholic organizations.
Fields of interest: Arts and culture; Education; Human services.
Limitations: Applications not accepted. Giving primarily in IL, with emphasis on Chicago. No grants to individuals.
Application information: Contributes only to pre-selected organizations.
Trustees: Mary Hartigan, Esq.; Mary K. Hartigan; Eileen Madigan.
EIN: 366071665

2836
Mildred & Bernard Doyle Charitable Trust
P.O. Box 803878
Chicago, IL 60680-3878

Established in 1997 in Florida.
Foundation type: Independent foundation.
Financial data (yr. ended 05/31/15): Assets, $3,562,350 (M); expenditures, $186,010; qualifying distributions, $168,835; giving activities include $165,500 for 19 grants (high: $20,000; low: $5,000).
Purpose and activities: Giving for the arts, education, and women's services.
Fields of interest: Arts and culture; Historic preservation; Education; Higher education; Human services; Adult and child mentoring; Women's services.
Limitations: Applications not accepted. Giving primarily in FL. No grants to individuals.
Application information: Unsolicited requests for funds not accepted.
Trustee: The Northern Trust Co., N.A.
EIN: 656232467

2837
The Drugas Family Legacy Foundation
17760 S. Iroquois Terr.
Tinley Park, IL 60477-7848

Donor: Theodore G. Drugas†.

Foundation type: Independent foundation.
Financial data (yr. ended 12/31/13): Assets, $1,137,357 (M); expenditures, $312,297; qualifying distributions, $300,000; giving activities include $300,000 for 1 grant.
Fields of interest: University education.
Limitations: Applications not accepted. Giving primarily in Urbana, IL.
Application information: Unsolicited requests for funds not accepted.
Directors: George Drugas; Peter Drugas; Diane Drugas Keen.
EIN: 273954565

2838
The Howard and Ursula Dubin Foundation
c/o Howard S. Dubin
1633 Central Ave.
Evanston, IL   60201-1569   (847) 864-7000
Contact: Howard S. Dubin, Pres.

Established in 1997 in Illinois.
Donor: Howard S. Dubin.
Foundation type: Independent foundation.
Financial data (yr. ended 12/31/13): Assets, $6,977,639 (M); gifts received, $207,800; expenditures, $334,027; qualifying distributions, $315,130; giving activities include $315,038 for 55 grants (high: $60,000; low: $250).
Purpose and activities: The foundation mainly supports journalism groups, animal protection, including a low-cost spay-neuter clinic, and religious organizations.
Fields of interest: Education; Animal welfare; Religion; Human services.
Type of support: Continuing support; Annual campaigns; Capital campaigns; Capital and infrastructure; Internships.
Limitations: Applications accepted. Giving primarily in IL and IN. No grants to individuals.
Publications: Annual report.
Application information: Application form required.
   Initial approach: Proposal
   Deadline(s): None
Officers: Howard S. Dubin, Pres.
Directors: Anne E. Dubin; Thomas G. Dubin.
Number of staff: None.
EIN: 364161932

2839
Duncan Family Foundation
800 N. Michigan Ave., Ste. 2001
Chicago, IL   60611-2149   (312) 337-9633
Contact: Bruce W. Duncan, Pres.

Established in 2005 in Illinois.
Donor: Bruce W. Duncan.
Foundation type: Independent foundation.
Financial data (yr. ended 12/31/13): Assets, $9,431,556 (M); gifts received, $384,693; expenditures, $338,339; qualifying distributions, $336,000; giving activities include $336,000 for 27 grants (high: $50,000; low: $1,000).
Fields of interest: Education.
Limitations: Applications accepted. Giving primarily in IL and OH. No grants to individuals.
Application information:
   Initial approach: Letter
   Deadline(s): None

Officers: Bruce W. Duncan, Pres.; Deborah E. Duncan, V.P.
EIN: 203871657

2840
Louise Head Duncan Trust
(also known as The Peyton Samuel Head Family Trust)
c/o JPMorgan Chase Bank, N.A.
10 S. Dearborn St., IL1-0117
Chicago, IL   60603-2300
Application address: c/o The Peyton Samuel Head Family Trust, P.O. Box 248, LaGrange, KY 40031, tel.: (859) 231-2408

Donor: Louise Head Duncan†.
Foundation type: Independent foundation.
Financial data (yr. ended 12/31/13): Assets, $8,350,973 (M); expenditures, $460,081; qualifying distributions, $366,468; giving activities include $348,964 for 23 grants (high: $72,000; low: $2,000).
Purpose and activities: Giving for the overall improvement of the quality of life of the people of Oldham County, KY.
Fields of interest: Historic preservation; Education; Community and economic development; Human services.
Type of support: General support.
Limitations: Applications accepted. Giving limited to Oldham County, KY. No grants to individuals.
Application information: One request per year per organization. Include cover letter with application. Application form required.
   Initial approach: Letter requesting application form
   Copies of proposal: 3
   Deadline(s): None
   Board meeting date(s): July and Nov.
Trustee: JPMorgan Chase Bank, N.A.
Advisory Committee: Thomas W. Gaines, Jr.; Joseph William Hall; Lane A. Richie.
EIN: 616183556

2841
Mildred H. Dunning Memorial Fund Trust
10 S. Dearborn IL1-0117
Chicago, IL   60603-2300

Foundation type: Independent foundation.
Financial data (yr. ended 12/31/13): Assets, $3,966,590; expenditures, $174,361; qualifying distributions, $143,424.
Fields of interest: Philanthropy; Health; Hospital care; Human services.
Limitations: Applications not accepted. Giving primarily in KY.
Application information: Unsolicited requests for funds not accepted.
Trustee: JPMorgan Chase Bank, N.A.
EIN: 616241891

2842
James Dyson Foundation North America
600 W. Chicago Ave., Ste. 275
Chicago, IL   60654-2813   (312) 469-5933
E-mail: jamesdysonfoundationus@dyson.com; UK headquarters contact: Tetbury Hill, Malmesbury, Wiltshire SN16 0RP, tel.: +44 1666 828001;

Australia and New Zealand contact: e-mail: jamesdysonawardAU@dyson.com; Austria, Ireland and Italy contact: e-mail: jamesdysonaward@dyson.com; Belgium contact: e-mail: jamesdysonawardBE@dyson.com; Canada contact: e-mail: jamesdysonawardCA@dyson.com; France contact: e-mail: jamesdysonawardFR@dyson.com; Germany contact: e-mail: jamesdysonawardDE@dyson.com; Japan contact e-mail: jamesdysonawardJP@dyson.com; Malaysia contact: e-mail: jamesdysonawardMY@dyson.com; Netherlands contact: e-mail: jamesdysonawardNL@dyson.com; Russia contact: e-mail: jamesdysonawardRU@dyson.com; Singapore contact: e-mail: jamesdysonawardSG@dyson.com; Spain contact: e-mail: jamesdysonawardES@dyson.com; Switzerland contact: e-mail: jamesdysonawardCH@dyson.com; Main URL: http://www.jamesdysonfoundation.com

Foundation type: Independent foundation.
Financial data (yr. ended 12/31/13): Assets, $216,617 (M); gifts received, $473,535; expenditures, $604,913; qualifying distributions, $604,913; giving activities include $266,390 for 6 + grants (high: $90,000), and $51,612 for 5 grants to individuals (high: $12,571; low: $3,262).
Purpose and activities: Giving primarily for higher education, particularly for scholarships in engineering. James Dyson Awards celebrate and publicize the work of young designers on a global platform. Entrants must be, or have been within the last 4 years, enrolled for at least one semester in an undergraduate or graduate engineering or design program at a university in a country chosen to participate in the Award (Australia, Austria, Belgium, Canada, France, Germany, Hong Kong, Ireland, Italy, Japan, Malaysia, the Netherlands, New Zealand, Russia, Singapore, Spain, Switzerland, Taiwan, the U.K. and the U.S.).
Fields of interest: Design; Higher education; Engineering.
International interests: Australia; Austria; Belgium; Canada; France; Germany; Hong Kong; Ireland; Italy; Japan; Malaysia; Netherlands; New Zealand; Russia; Singapore; Spain; Switzerland; Taiwan; United Kingdom of Great Britain and Northern Ireland.
Type of support: Scholarships.
Limitations: Applications not accepted. Giving on a national and international basis.
Application information: Unsolicited requests for funds not accepted. See foundation web site for Dyson Award application information and for countries currently connected to the award.
Officers: Anthony Jones, Pres.; Kim Hoffman, Secy.; Robert Cherry, Treas.
Director: Louis Foreman.
EIN: 453114281

2843
Theodore Eckert Foundation
5757 W. Howard St.
Niles, IL   60714-4012

Established in 1999 in Illinois.
Foundation type: Independent foundation.
Financial data (yr. ended 12/31/13): Assets, $7,349,320 (M); expenditures, $471,759; qualifying distributions, $423,148; giving activities

include $368,922 for 102 grants (high: $10,000; low: $7).
Fields of interest: Arts and culture; Education; Higher education; Nonprofits; Alzheimer's disease; Cystic fibrosis; Orthodox Christianity; Food banks.
Type of support: Regranting.
Limitations: Applications not accepted. Giving primarily in IL. No grants to individuals.
Application information: Contributes only to pre-selected organizations.
Officers and Directors: Theodore H. Eckert, Pres. and Director; Elizabeth A. Eckert, Secy.-Treas. and Director; Katherine Elizabeth Eckert; Theodore Mark Eckert.
EIN: 364333970

2844
Eclipse Foundation
1665 Elmwood Rd.
Rockford, IL   61103-1211   (815) 877-3031
Contact: Wendy Perks Fisher, Pres.

Donors: Eclipse Inc.; A. C. Perks†; Blackman Kallick; ACP Loan Repayment; ECLIPSE INC.
Foundation type: Company-sponsored foundation.
Financial data (yr. ended 03/31/14): Assets, $1,249,678 (M); gifts received, $100,809; expenditures, $172,405; qualifying distributions, $160,500; giving activities include $160,500 for 6 grants (high: $90,000; low: $2,000).
Purpose and activities: The foundation supports museums and conservatories and organizations involved with secondary education and homelessness.
Fields of interest: Education; Sports and recreation; Human services.
Type of support: General support.
Limitations: Applications accepted. Giving primarily in Rockford and Winnebago County, IL, and surrounding areas. No grants to individuals.
Application information: Application form required.
  Initial approach: Letter
  Copies of proposal: 1
  Deadline(s): None
Officers: Wendy Perks Fisher, Pres.; Douglas C. Perks, V.P.; Jim Corbett, Secy.-Treas.
Directors: Anna Perks; Luke Perks; Wade Perks.
EIN: 366056968

2845
D. J. Edelman Family Foundation
200 E. Randolph Dr., Ste. 6300
Chicago, IL   60601-6410   (312) 240-2755

Established in 1997 in Illinois.
Donors: Daniel J. Edelman; Ruth A. Edelman; Daniel J. Edelman, Inc. and Subsidiaries.
Foundation type: Independent foundation.
Financial data (yr. ended 12/31/14): Assets, $1,885,066; gifts received, $0; expenditures, $171,607; qualifying distributions, $167,265 and $0 for set-asides.
Fields of interest: Education; Higher education; Nonprofits; Diseases and conditions; Judaism; Human services.
Type of support: General support; Scholarships; Regranting.
Limitations: Applications accepted. Giving primarily in IL and NY. No grants to individuals.
Application information: Application form required.

Initial approach: Letter
Deadline(s): Dec. 1
Trustees: John D. Edelman; Renee Edelman; Richard W. Edelman.
EIN: 367184921

2846
Marian & Arthur Edelstein Foundation
(formerly Edelstein Foundation)
750 N. Rush St., Ste. 603
Chicago, IL   60611-2553

Established in 1959 in Illinois.
Donors: Bohemian Distributing Co.; Arthur Edelstein; James Edelstein; Marian Edelstein.
Foundation type: Independent foundation.
Financial data (yr. ended 12/31/12): Assets, $3,248,784 (M); expenditures, $311,759; qualifying distributions, $301,216; giving activities include $297,191 for 49 grants (high: $100,000; low: $50).
Fields of interest: Arts and culture; Nonprofits; Diseases and conditions; Judaism; Youth development.
Type of support: Regranting.
Limitations: Applications not accepted. Giving primarily in IL. No grants to individuals.
Application information: Unsolicited requests for funds not accepted.
Officers: James Edelstein, Pres.; Marian Edelstein, V.P.
EIN: 366056582

2847
The Edgerly Foundation
(formerly Foundation for Partnerships Trust)
P.O. Box 803878
Chicago, IL   60680-3878

Established in 1992 in Massachusetts.
Donors: William S. Edgerly; Lois Stiles Edgerly.
Foundation type: Independent foundation.
Financial data (yr. ended 12/31/13): Assets, $1,941,462 (M); expenditures, $351,348; qualifying distributions, $344,174; giving activities include $342,000 for 42 grants (high: $100,000; low: $1,000).
Purpose and activities: Giving primarily for education and community development.
Fields of interest: Education; Elementary and secondary education; Higher education; Nonprofits; Legal services; Community and economic development; Organized labor; Protestantism; Foreign policy.
Type of support: Regranting.
Limitations: Applications not accepted. Giving primarily in MA. No grants to individuals.
Application information: Contributes only to pre-selected organizations.
Trustees: Lois Stiles Edgerly; William S. Edgerly; Edward P. Lawrence; The Northern Trust Co.
EIN: 043165980

2848
Harding Educational and Charitable Foundation
(formerly The Harding Educational and Charitable Foundation)
10 S. Dearborn IL1-0117
Chicago, IL   60603
Application address: Thomas Thompson, Esq., 88 Pine St., 21st Fl., New York, NY 10005, tel.: (212) 943-0280

Established in 1945 in New York.
Donors: Henry J. Harding; Robert L. Harding; Martha Harding†.
Foundation type: Independent foundation.
Financial data (yr. ended 12/31/13): Assets, $6,403,037 (M); expenditures, $349,523; qualifying distributions, $282,510; giving activities include $261,000 for 36 grants (high: $30,000; low: $500).
Purpose and activities: Giving primarily for wilderness and wildlife conservation, education, and human services.
Fields of interest: Arts and culture; Museums; Education; Higher education; Natural resources; Domesticated animals; Hospital care; Human services; Child welfare.
Limitations: Applications accepted. Giving primarily in MA and NY. No grants to individuals.
Application information:
  Initial approach: Proposal
  Deadline(s): None
Trustees: Robert L. Harding, Jr.; Faith Harding Mori; Timothy L. Thompson, Esq.; JPMorgan Chase Bank, N.A.
EIN: 136083440

2849
Ira A. & Barbara R. Eichner Foundation
1 AAR Pl.
1100 N. Wood Dale Rd.
Wood Dale, IL   60191-1159

Established in 1996 in Illinois.
Donor: Ira A. Eichner.
Foundation type: Independent foundation.
Financial data (yr. ended 01/31/13): Assets, $1,060,569 (M); gifts received, $299,084; expenditures, $208,264; qualifying distributions, $208,146; giving activities include $208,131 for 40 grants (high: $40,000; low: $25).
Purpose and activities: Giving primarily for Jewish organizations and the arts.
Fields of interest: Arts and culture; Education; Religion.
Limitations: Applications not accepted. Giving primarily in IL. No grants to individuals.
Application information: Contributes only to pre-selected organizations.
Trustees: Barbara R. Eichner; Ira A. Eichner.
EIN: 367167187

2850
Eisenberg Family Charitable Trust
c/o JPMorgan Chase Bank, N.A.
10 S. Dearborn St., IL1-0117
Chicago, IL   60603-2300
Application address: c/o Carolyn O'Brien, Program Officer, 270 Park Ave., NY1-K348, New York, NY 10017, tel.: (212) 464-2350

Established in 1996 in New York.
Donor: Estelle Eisenberg†.
Foundation type: Independent foundation.
Financial data (yr. ended 04/30/13): Assets, $7,200,784 (M); expenditures, $404,909; qualifying distributions, $344,644; giving activities include $325,000 for 1 grant.
Fields of interest: Health; Alzheimer's disease.
Limitations: Applications accepted. Giving primarily in FL; some funding also in IL. No grants to individuals.
Publications: Grants list.
Application information:
  Deadline(s): None
  Board meeting date(s): Apr.
Trustee: JPMorgan Chase Bank, N.A.
EIN: 527091392

2851
Eiszner Family Foundation
1 S. Dearborn St.
Chicago, IL 60603-2304
Contact: S. Bart

Established in 2004 in Illinois.
Donor: Joyce C. Eiszner.
Foundation type: Independent foundation.
Financial data (yr. ended 12/31/14): Assets, $3,009,065 (M); expenditures, $175,778; qualifying distributions, $161,471; giving activities include $150,000 for 7 grants (high: $55,000; low: $3,000).
Fields of interest: Medical education; Diseases and conditions; Multiple sclerosis; Human services.
Limitations: Applications not accepted. Giving primarily in IL. No grants to individuals.
Application information: Unsolicited requests for funds not accepted.
Officers and Directors: Joyce C. Eiszner, Pres. and Secy. and Director; James R. Eiszner, Jr., V.P. and Secy. and Director; Timothy J. Eiszner, V.P. and Treas. and Director.
EIN: 043801691

2852
Baisley Powell Elebash Fund
10 S. Dearborn St.
Chicago, IL 60603-2300 (212) 464-2487
Contact: Jonathan Horowitz; Erin K. Hogan, V.P., JPMorgan Chase Bank, N.A.
FAX: (212) 464-2305; E-mail for Jonathan Horowitz: jonathan.g.horowitz@jpmchase.com; E-mail for Erin Hogan: erin.hogan@jpmorgan.com

Established in 1997 in New York.
Foundation type: Independent foundation.
Financial data (yr. ended 10/31/13): Assets, $8,389,977 (M); expenditures, $499,675; qualifying distributions, $420,987; giving activities include $400,000 for 4 grants (high: $200,000; low: $30,000).
Purpose and activities: Giving primarily for music and health care for low-income adults.
Fields of interest: Music; Health.
Limitations: Applications accepted. Giving primarily in New York, NY; giving also in Birmingham, AL. No grants to individuals.
Publications: Grants list; Informational brochure.
Application information:
  Copies of proposal: 1

Deadline(s): Aug. 1
Board meeting date(s): Oct.
Trustee: JPMorgan Chase Bank, N.A.
EIN: 137125140

2853
Gail G. Ellis Foundation, Inc.
c/o David Friedlander, FGMK
2801 Lakeside Dr., 3rd Fl.
Bannockburn, IL 60015-1275

Established in 1995 in Illinois.
Donor: Gail G. Ellis.
Foundation type: Independent foundation.
Financial data (yr. ended 12/31/13): Assets, $11,760,694; expenditures, $598,891; qualifying distributions, $429,700.
Fields of interest: Arts and culture; Education; Higher education; Health; Diseases and conditions; Human services.
Limitations: Applications not accepted. No grants to individuals.
Application information: Unsolicited requests for funds not accepted.
Directors: Gail G. Ellis; Brian C. Sullivan; Carrie E. Sullivan.
EIN: 364076867

2854
EMA Foundation
(formerly Eugene M. Adler Family Fund)
c/o Joe Palmer
7809 W. 159th St.
Tinley Park, IL 60477-1343

Established in 1969 in Illinois.
Foundation type: Independent foundation.
Financial data (yr. ended 04/30/13): Assets, $3,403,620 (M); expenditures, $197,359; qualifying distributions, $185,000; giving activities include $185,000 for 15 grants (high: $33,000; low: $500).
Fields of interest: Education; Environment; Nonprofits; Human rights.
Type of support: General support; Matching grants; Regranting; Annual campaigns; Capital and infrastructure; Equipment; Land acquisitions; Program development; Convening; Seed money; Curriculum development.
Limitations: Applications not accepted. Giving primarily in HI, NM and OH.
Application information: Contributes only to pre-selected organizations.
Officers: Constance Adler, Pres.; Jackie Myer Thorman, Treas.
EIN: 366063024

2855
Engle Family Foundation
610 W. Belden Ave.
Chicago, IL 60614-3306

Donors: S. Cody Engle; Catherine C. Engle.
Foundation type: Independent foundation.
Financial data (yr. ended 12/31/13): Assets, $615,162 (M); expenditures, $185,834; qualifying distributions, $176,081; giving activities include $175,181 for 47 grants (high: $38,001; low: $30).

Fields of interest: Arts and culture; Theater; Humanities; Education; Diseases and conditions; Religion.
Limitations: Applications not accepted. Giving primarily in Tucson, AZ and Chicago, IL. No grants to individuals.
Application information: Contributes only to pre-selected organizations.
Officers and Directors: S. Cody Engle, Pres. and Director; Deborah Engle, V.P. and Director.
EIN: 363497311

2856
Enivar Charitable Fund
118 S. Clinton, Ste. 550
Chicago, IL 60661-5770 (312) 201-8999

Established in 1956 in Illinois.
Donors: Nancy R. Florsheim; Enivar Enterprises, Inc.
Foundation type: Independent foundation.
Financial data (yr. ended 12/31/13): Assets, $1,328,855 (M); expenditures, $181,782; qualifying distributions, $168,035; giving activities include $163,800 for 100 grants (high: $30,000; low: $50).
Purpose and activities: Giving primarily for arts and culture, education, and human services.
Fields of interest: Arts and culture; Museums; Education; Nonprofits; Diseases and conditions; Human services.
Type of support: Regranting.
Limitations: Applications accepted. Giving primarily in Chicago, IL. No grants to individuals.
Application information:
  Initial approach: Proposal
  Deadline(s): None
Officers: Nancy R. Florsheim, Pres.; Vance Liebman, Secy.
Director: Wilson P. Funkhouser.
EIN: 366049235

2857
Epaphroditus Foundation
860 Tollgate Rd.
Elgin, IL 60123-9300

Established in 1945 in Illinois.
Foundation type: Independent foundation.
Financial data (yr. ended 02/28/13): Assets, $3,984,417 (M); expenditures, $205,764; qualifying distributions, $199,243; giving activities include $189,000 for 22 grants (high: $19,000; low: $1,000).
Purpose and activities: Giving primarily to Christian organizations and for human services.
Fields of interest: Education; Religion; Christianity; Human services; Food aid; Low-income and poor people.
Limitations: Applications not accepted. Giving primarily in IL. No grants to individuals.
Application information: Contributes only to pre-selected organizations.
Officers: Ronald Michaelson, Pres. and C.E.O.; Lynn Worster, Secy.; Gary Gundersen, Treas.
Directors: Gayle Dougherty; Wes Granberg-Michaelson; Carl Gundersen; David Heidlauf; Valerie Heidlauf; Joan Johnson; Jeanne Lunden.
EIN: 366072198

2858
Equity Residential Foundation
(formerly Equity Community Foundation)
2 N. Riverside Plz.
Chicago, IL 60606-2652
Contact: Robert Garechana

Established in 2002 in Illinois.
Donor: Samuel Zell.
Foundation type: Independent foundation.
Financial data (yr. ended 12/31/13): Assets, $3,898,788 (M); expenditures, $275,299; qualifying distributions, $246,531; giving activities include $238,856 for 14 grants (high: $75,000; low: $2,000).
Fields of interest: Human services; Child welfare.
Limitations: Applications not accepted. Giving primarily in Denver, CO, Chicago, IL, with some giving in AZ. No grants to individuals.
Application information: Unsolicited requests for funds not accepted.
Officers: David J. Neithercut, Pres.; Michael Gast, V.P.; Marty McKenna, V.P.; Bruce C. Strohm, V.P.; Robert Garechana, Treas.
Director: Samuel Zell.
EIN: 364478772

2859
Harry and Dorothy Espenscheid Charitable Foundation
c/o BMO Harris Bank, N.A.
111 W. Monroe St., Ste. 10C
Chicago, IL 60603 (312) 461-7271

Established in 2005 in Illinois.
Donors: Harry Espenscheid; Dorothy Espenscheid.
Foundation type: Independent foundation.
Financial data (yr. ended 09/30/13): Assets, $2,068,055 (M); expenditures, $212,225; qualifying distributions, $198,455; giving activities include $190,727 for 5 grants (high: $143,227; low: $5,000).
Fields of interest: Domesticated animals; Human services; Scouting programs.
Limitations: Applications accepted. Giving primarily in Rockford, IL. No grants to individuals.
Application information: Application form required.
  Initial approach: Letter
  Deadline(s): None
Trustee: BMO Harris Bank, N.A.
EIN: 203655481

2860
Estate of Mildred Bancroft Charitable Trust
10 S. Dearborn IL1-0117
Chicago, IL 60603-3038

Foundation type: Independent foundation.
Financial data (yr. ended 12/31/13): Assets, $1,257,472 (M); expenditures, $419,992; qualifying distributions, $352,494; giving activities include $352,494 for 2 grants (high: $176,247; low: $176,247).
Fields of interest: Education; Human services.
Limitations: Applications not accepted. Giving primarily in LA.
Application information: Unsolicited requests for funds not accepted.
Trustee: JPMorgan Chase Bank, N.A.
EIN: 726096396

2861
Esther M. & Freeman E. Everett Charitable Foundation
10 S. Dearborn IL1-0117
Chicago, IL 60603 8668885157
Application address: 730 N. Nevada Ave., Colorado Springs, CO 80903, tel.: (719) 389-1251

Established in 2001 in Colorado.
Foundation type: Independent foundation.
Financial data (yr. ended 12/31/14): Assets, $2,952,038; expenditures, $237,875; qualifying distributions, $208,424.
Fields of interest: Arts and culture; Education; Foundations; Human services; Child welfare.
Limitations: Applications accepted. Giving primarily in CO and WI. No grants to individuals.
Application information: Application form required.
  Initial approach: Letter
  Deadline(s): None
Trustee: JPMorgan Chase Bank, N.A.
EIN: 527246146

2862
Fabyan Foundation
P.O. Box 472
Geneva, IL 60134-0472

Established in 1991 in Illinois.
Donor: Nelle Fabyan†.
Foundation type: Independent foundation.
Financial data (yr. ended 12/31/13): Assets, $7,110,470 (M); expenditures, $392,520; qualifying distributions, $347,000; giving activities include $326,000 for 5 grants (high: $220,000; low: $5,000).
Purpose and activities: Support primarily for educational scholarships and programs.
Fields of interest: Historic preservation; Education; Public libraries.
Type of support: Scholarships; General support.
Limitations: Applications not accepted. Giving primarily in Geneva, IL. No grants to individuals.
Application information: Contributes only to pre-selected organizations.
Officers and Directors: Debra Campbell, Pres. and Director; Carol Peterson, Secy.-Treas. and Director; Kate McCracken.
EIN: 363736909

2863
Family Alliance Foundation
333 N. Michigan Ave., Ste. 510
Chicago, IL 60601-3934

Established in 2009 in Illinois.
Foundation type: Independent foundation.
Financial data (yr. ended 12/31/12): Assets, $6,248,166 (M); expenditures, $417,919; qualifying distributions, $322,500; giving activities include $322,500 for grants.
Fields of interest: Diseases and conditions; Human services.
Type of support: General support; Research.
Limitations: Applications not accepted. Giving primarily in IL. No grants to individuals.
Application information: Unsolicited requests for funds not accepted.
Officers: Barbara W. Kessler, Pres.; Eric J. Kessler, Secy.; Dennis L. Kessler, Treas.
EIN: 264568728

2864
Hoellen Family Foundation
1940 W. Irving Park Rd.
Chicago, IL 60613 (773) 327-4700
Contact: R. Hoellen, Dir.

Donor: John J. Hoellen.
Foundation type: Independent foundation.
Financial data (yr. ended 12/31/13): Assets, $8,029,874 (M); expenditures, $393,964; qualifying distributions, $382,725; giving activities include $276,463 for grants.
Purpose and activities: Giving primarily for education in Chicago's Ravenswood community.
Fields of interest: Museums; Historic preservation; Elementary and secondary education; Secondary education; University education; Zoos; Libraries; Protestantism; Children and youth; Children; Adolescents; Adults; Young adults; Seniors; Females; Female children and youth; Female adults; Female young adults; Males; Male children and youth; Male adults; Male young adults; Homeless people; Low-income and poor people; People with disabilities; People with physical disabilities; People with psychosocial disabilities.
Type of support: Scholarships; Grants to individuals; Research; Matching grants.
Limitations: Applications accepted. Giving primarily in the Ravenswood area of Chicago, IL. No support for political organizations.
Application information: Application form required.
  Initial approach: Letter
  Deadline(s): Oct.
Officers: George Rice, V.P.; Allan Pallante, Treas.
Directors: R. Hoellen; Catherine Phelps; Elizabeth J. Ward.
Number of staff: 4 part-time professional; 1 part-time support.
EIN: 363209348

2865
Farnham Foundation
c/o Joel Ashmus
315 Quail Ridge Dr.
Westmont, IL 60559-6144

Established in 1989 in Illinois.
Donor: Viola D. Hank†.
Foundation type: Independent foundation.
Financial data (yr. ended 12/31/13): Assets, $4,580,937 (M); expenditures, $446,440; qualifying distributions, $439,000; giving activities include $439,000 for 4 grants (high: $200,000; low: $3,000).
Fields of interest: Arts and culture; Education; Religion.
Type of support: General support.
Limitations: Applications not accepted. Giving primarily in Chicago, IL and IN. No grants to individuals.
Application information: Unsolicited requests for funds not accepted.
Officer: Celeste Hank Wright, Chair.
Trustees: Allen B. Hank; John C. Hank; J. Luke McGuinness; Cynthia H. Stark.
EIN: 363684134

2866
Peter & Paula Fasseas Foundation
c/o Peter Fasseas
1933 Marcey St.
Chicago, IL 60614

Established in 1995 in Illinois.
Donors: Alpha Bancorp; Metropolitan Bancorp; Plaza Bancorp; Metropolitan Bank Group; North Community Bank.
Foundation type: Company-sponsored foundation.
Financial data (yr. ended 12/31/13): Assets, $41,208,241 (M); expenditures, $426,673; qualifying distributions, $313,672; giving activities include $238,045 for 31 grants (high: $75,343; low: $200).
Purpose and activities: The foundation supports hospitals and organizations involved with education, animal welfare, and cancer.
Fields of interest: Education; Domesticated animals; Diseases and conditions.
Type of support: General support.
Limitations: Applications not accepted. Giving limited to Chicago, IL. No grants to individuals.
Application information: Contributes only to pre-selected organizations.
Officer: Peter A. Fasseas, Pres.
Directors: Alexis Fasseas; Drew Fasseas; Paula Fasseas.
EIN: 364010374

2867
Marianne G. Faulkner Trust
(formerly Marianne Galliard Faulkner Trust)
10 S. Dearborn St., IL1-0117
Chicago, IL 60603-2300
Application address: c/o Connie A. Brandeis, 270 Park Ave., 16th Fl., New York, NY 10017, tel.: (212) 648-1494

Established in 1959 in Vermont.
Donor: Marianne Gaillard Faulkner†.
Foundation type: Independent foundation.
Financial data (yr. ended 12/31/13): Assets, $9,446,126 (M); expenditures, $507,225; qualifying distributions, $457,844; giving activities include $405,000 for 2 grants (high: $385,000; low: $20,000).
Purpose and activities: Annual funding for groups identified by the donor; limited funding available to other groups primarily near or in Woodstock, VT within program areas.
Fields of interest: Education; Environment; Senior services.
Type of support: Capital and infrastructure; General support; Program development.
Limitations: Applications accepted. Giving primarily in the Woodstock, VT, area, with emphasis on organizations identified by the donor. No grants to individuals, or for endowment funds.
Publications: Application guidelines; Grants list.
Application information: Application form required.
Initial approach: Letter
Copies of proposal: 1
Deadline(s): None
Trustee: JPMorgan Chase Bank, N.A.
Number of staff: None.
EIN: 136047458

2868
Federation of Protestant Welfare Agencies Trust
10 S. Dearborn IL1-0117
Chicago, IL 60603

Foundation type: Independent foundation.
Financial data (yr. ended 07/31/14): Assets, $8,638,603 (M); expenditures, $450,675; qualifying distributions, $375,612; giving activities include $355,144 for 1 grant.
Fields of interest: Christianity; Human services.
Limitations: Applications not accepted. Giving primarily in New York, NY.
Application information: Unsolicited requests for funds not accepted.
Trustee: JPMorgan Chase Bank, N.A.
EIN: 136036355

2869
Tim and Karla Feltes Family Foundation
1207 N. West St.
Wheaton, IL 60187-3577

Established in 2007 in Illinois.
Donors: Timothy Feltes; Karla Feltes.
Foundation type: Independent foundation.
Financial data (yr. ended 12/31/13): Assets, $2,895,274 (M); expenditures, $182,251; qualifying distributions, $155,731; giving activities include $155,000 for 4 grants (high: $90,000; low: $5,000).
Fields of interest: Education; Maternal and perinatal health; Diseases and conditions; Human services.
Limitations: Applications not accepted. Giving primarily in IL. No grants to individuals.
Application information: Contributes only to pre-selected organizations.
Officers and Directors: Timothy Feltes, Pres. and Secy. and Director; Karla Feltes, Treas. and Director; Barbara Wisdom.
EIN: 261115240

2870
The Earl and Bettie Fields Automotive Group Foundation, Inc.
(formerly Earl and Bettie Fields Charitable Foundation, Inc.)
2100 Frontage Rd.
Glencoe, IL 60022-2201 (847) 446-5100
Contact: John R. Fields

Established in 1995 in Illinois.
Donors: Fields Imports, Inc.; Fields Pag, Inc.; Fields Motorcars of Florida; Fields Jeep.
Foundation type: Independent foundation.
Financial data (yr. ended 12/31/13): Assets, $2,617,177 (M); gifts received, $336,437; expenditures, $203,454; qualifying distributions, $203,344; giving activities include $203,344 for 82 grants (high: $25,000; low: $75).
Fields of interest: Education; Health; Christianity; Human services; Family services; Child welfare.
Type of support: General support.
Limitations: Applications accepted. Giving primarily in IL. No grants to individuals.
Application information:
Deadline(s): None
Officer and Directors: John R. Fields, Treas.; Earl D. Klein.
EIN: 364006933

2871
Fifield Family Foundation
222 S. Riverside Plz., Ste. 600
Chicago, IL 60606-6173

Donors: Steven D. Fifield; Randy A. Fifield.
Foundation type: Independent foundation.
Financial data (yr. ended 12/31/13): Assets, $42 (M); gifts received, $254,900; expenditures, $261,043; qualifying distributions, $257,500; giving activities include $257,500 for 2 grants (high: $250,000; low: $7,500).
Purpose and activities: Giving primarily to a children's hospital.
Fields of interest: Children's hospital care; Children.
Limitations: Applications not accepted. Giving primarily in Chicago, IL. No grants to individuals.
Application information: Unsolicited requests for funds not accepted.
Trustees: Randy A. Fifield; Steven D. Fifield.
EIN: 201074711

2872
The Johnsie Fiock Fildes Foundation, Ltd.
P.O. Box 357
Olney, IL 62450-0357
Application address: c/o Jeffrey E. Fleming, 420 Whittle Ave., Olney, IL 62450, tel.: (618) 395-8491

Established in 2007 in Illinois.
Foundation type: Independent foundation.
Financial data (yr. ended 12/31/13): Assets, $6,002,142 (M); expenditures, $206,114; qualifying distributions, $165,378; giving activities include $130,378 for 6 grants (high: $50,000; low: $5,000), and $35,000 for 27 grants to individuals (high: $3,000; low: $1,000).
Purpose and activities: Giving primarily for education and health care; giving also for scholarships to Richland County, Illinois, high school graduates entering the medical field.
Fields of interest: Education; Hospital care.
Type of support: General support; Student aid.
Limitations: Applications accepted. Giving limited to Richland County, IL.
Application information:
Initial approach: Proposal
Deadline(s): Mar. 10 and Jun. 30
Officers and Directors: Robert David, Pres. and Director; Jeffrey Fleming, V.P. and Director; Harvey Pettry, Secy. and Director; Marilyn Holt, Treas. and Director; Fred Wells.
EIN: 364542462

2873
Jacob J. Fink Charitable Foundation
c/o Baker Tilly Virchow Krause, LLP
205 N. Michigan Ave.
Chicago, IL 60601

Established in 2000 in Illinois.
Foundation type: Independent foundation.
Financial data (yr. ended 12/31/13): Assets, $3,492,247 (M); expenditures, $325,002; qualifying distributions, $275,757; giving activities include $258,175 for 13 grants (high: $40,000; low: $4,000).
Fields of interest: Education; Judaism; Human services.
Limitations: Applications not accepted. Giving primarily in IL. No grants to individuals.

Application information: Unsolicited requests for funds not accepted.
Trustees: Stephen D. Levin; Eric Rein.
EIN: 364176379

2874
Sonja and F. Conrad Fischer Foundation
1050 Crescent Ln.
Winnetka, IL 60093-1501
Application address: c/o F. Conrad Fischer, W. Blair Co., 222 W. Adams St., Chicago, IL 60606, tel.: (312) 236-1600

Established in 1990 in Illinois.
Donors: Sylvia Fischer; F. Conrad Fisher; Sonja H. Fischer.
Foundation type: Independent foundation.
Financial data (yr. ended 12/31/13): Assets, $2,962,022 (M); expenditures, $171,658; qualifying distributions, $168,900; giving activities include $168,900 for 35 grants (high: $35,000; low: $300).
Fields of interest: Performing arts; Education; Foundations; Human services.
Limitations: Applications accepted. Giving primarily in IL.
Application information: Application form required.
Initial approach: Proposal
Deadline(s): Nov. 15
Trustees: F. Conrad Fisher; Sonja H. Fisher.
EIN: 366941059

2875
Patrick & Robyn Flinn Family Foundation
c/o Patrick J. Flinn
37W204 Grandmas Ln.
Saint Charles, IL 60175-4725

Established in 2005 in Illinois.
Donors: Robyn Flinn; Patrick J. Flinn.
Foundation type: Independent foundation.
Financial data (yr. ended 12/31/13): Assets, $1,837,539 (M); gifts received, $299,419; expenditures, $179,750; qualifying distributions, $173,000; giving activities include $173,000 for 6 grants (high: $120,000; low: $3,000).
Fields of interest: Elementary education; Foundations; Community health care.
Limitations: Applications not accepted. Giving primarily in IL. No grants to individuals.
Application information: Contributes only to pre-selected organizations.
Trustees: Patrick J. Flinn; Robyn Flinn.
EIN: 203949497

2876
Foley Family Foundation
930 S. Westwood Ave.
Addison, IL 60101-4917

Established in 1999 in Illinois.
Donors: James F. Foley; J. Justin Foley.
Foundation type: Independent foundation.
Financial data (yr. ended 12/31/13): Assets, $3,803,433 (M); expenditures, $233,194; qualifying distributions, $216,775; giving activities include $215,700 for 56 grants (high: $100,000; low: $100).
Fields of interest: Arts and culture; Education; Health; Human services.

Limitations: Applications not accepted. Giving primarily in IL. No grants to individuals.
Application information: Contributes only to pre-selected organizations.
Officer: James F. Foley, Pres.
Directors: Kathryn Fitch; Jean I. Foley; J. Justin Foley.
EIN: 364263312

2877
Follett Educational Foundation
3 Westbrook Corp Ctr., Ste. 200
Westchester, IL 60154 (708) 437-2402
Main URL: http://www.folletteducationalfoundation.org

Established in 1964 in Illinois.
Donors: Dwight W. Follett†; Follett Corp.; Mildred Follett; Kent Follett; Nancy Follett; Virginia Faesen; Robert Follett; Jean Thompson; Doug Thompson; Ariel O'Hara; Julie Follett.
Foundation type: Company-sponsored foundation.
Financial data (yr. ended 07/31/13): Assets, $3,594,191 (M); gifts received, $303,475; expenditures, $300,954; qualifying distributions, $235,038; giving activities include $235,038 for 118 grants to individuals (high: $13,250; low: $194).
Purpose and activities: The foundation awards college scholarships to children of employees of Follett Corporation.
Type of support: Scholarships.
Limitations: Applications not accepted. Giving limited to areas of company operations, with emphasis on IL.
Application information: Contributes only through employee-related scholarships.
Board meeting date(s): June
Officers and Trustees: Britten Follett, Pres. and Trustee; Keith O'Hara, V.P.; Joe Skaggs, Secy.; Ron Griffin, Treas. and Trustee; Elio Distaola; Matthew Follett; Alison O'Hara; Suzanne Stegeman; Alan Stratman; Christopher D. Traut; Iris Waichler.
EIN: 366104348

2878
Herman Forbes Charitable Trust
c/o JPMorgan Chase Bank, N.A.
10 S. Dearborn St., IL1-0117
Chicago, IL 60603-2300
Application address: c/o JPMorgan Chase Bank, N.A., 270 Park Ave., 16th Fl., New York, NY 10017-2014, tel.: (212) 464-1020

Established in 1982 in New York.
Donor: Herman Forbes†.
Foundation type: Independent foundation.
Financial data (yr. ended 03/31/13): Assets, $7,188,033 (M); expenditures, $476,039; qualifying distributions, $387,779; giving activities include $360,000 for 31 grants (high: $43,000; low: $2,000).
Fields of interest: Education; Judaism.
Limitations: Applications accepted. Giving primarily in FL and New York, NY; some giving in NH. No grants to individuals or for matching gifts or loans.
Publications: Grants list.
Application information:
Deadline(s): None
Board meeting date(s): Mar. and Dec.

Trustees: William H. Fleece, Esq.; Benjamin Ari Herring; Gerald Moss; JPMorgan Chase Bank, N.A.
EIN: 136814404

2879
Frank Foster Charitable Trust
10 S. Dearborn St., IL1-0117
Chicago, IL 60603-3038

Established in 2007 in Illinois.
Donor: Frank Foster†.
Foundation type: Independent foundation.
Financial data (yr. ended 12/31/13): Assets, $891,171 (M); expenditures, $251,780; qualifying distributions, $236,384; giving activities include $227,498 for 22 grants (high: $125,000; low: $250).
Fields of interest: Arts and culture; Human services.
Limitations: Applications not accepted. Giving primarily in IL. No grants to individuals.
Application information: Unsolicited requests for funds not accepted.
Trustees: Timothy D. Foster; Marc Muskat; JPMorgan Chase Bank, N.A.
EIN: 306145816

2880
The Foundation for Peripheral Neuropathy
485 Half Day Rd., Ste. 200
Buffalo Grove, IL 60089-8806
Main URL: www.foundationforpn.org

Established in 2007 in Illinois.
Donor: Jack Miller.
Foundation type: Independent foundation.
Financial data (yr. ended 12/31/13): Assets, $375,973 (M); gifts received, $1,213,558; expenditures, $997,311; qualifying distributions, $958,494; giving activities include $228,195 for 3 grants (high: $93,395; low: $66,050).
Purpose and activities: The foundation's mission is to dramatically improve the lives of people living with Peripheral Neuropathy. The foundation will be the catalyst for advancing innovative therapeutic developments and accelerating a cure for painful neuropathies by funding collaborative efforts of leading scientists and physicians. It will strive to raise awareness of peripheral neuropathy through outreach programs to patients, their families, and healthcare professionals.
Fields of interest: Neurology; Diseases and conditions; Musculoskeletal diseases.
Type of support: Research.
Limitations: Applications not accepted. Giving on a national basis. No grants to individuals.
Application information: Contributes only to pre-selected organizations.
Officers: Pam Shlemon, Pres. and Exec. Dir.; Scott Hirsch, Treas.
Directors: Randy Bull; David Cornblath, MD; Richard Easley; John A. Kessler, MD; Goldie Wolfe Miller; Jack Miller; Ron Shaw.
Scientific Advisory Board: Eva Feldman, M.D., Ph.D.; Roy Freedman, MD; Deborah Lee, M.D., Ph.D.; David Simpson, MD.
EIN: 261195248

2881
Foundation for Retinal Research
666 Dundee Rd., Ste. 1104
Northbrook, IL 60062-2735 (224) 927-5063
Contact: David Brint, Pres.
FAX: (847) 562-9401; E-mail: info@tfrr.org; Main
URL: http://www.tfrr.org
Facebook: http://www.facebook.com/pages/
Foundation-for-Retinal-Research/
132181800132766

Established in 1998 in Illinois.
Donors: Brinshore Development, LLC; William
Dutton; Richard Cortessi; Claire Cortessi; Alan
Schwartz; Jimmy Brendle; Heather Brendle.
Foundation type: Independent foundation.
Financial data (yr. ended 12/31/13): Assets,
$1,404,974 (M); gifts received, $1,127,976;
expenditures, $486,089; qualifying distributions,
$427,215; giving activities include $267,573 for 3
grants (high: $166,333; low: $26,240).
Purpose and activities: Giving primarily for research
to find treatments and cures for retinal degenerative
diseases and for the support of affected families.
Fields of interest: Diseases and conditions; Eye
diseases.
International interests: Netherlands.
Type of support: Research; Research and
evaluation.
Limitations: Applications accepted. Giving primarily
in CA, MA, MD, ME, PA and the Netherlands. No
grants to individuals.
Application information: Requests should be in
standard format for medical research; written or
electronic formats are acceptable.
  Deadline(s): None
Officers: David Brint, Pres.; Elizabeth Brint, V.P.;
Sally Lewinski, Exec. Dir.
Advisory Board: Jean Bennett, MD; Constance
Cepko, Ph.D; Gerald J. Chader, Ph.D; Stephan
Daiger, Ph.D; Eugene de Juan; Mark Humayun, MD;
Edwin Stone, M.D., Ph.D.; Weng Tao, M.D., Ph.D.
EIN: 364232603

2882
The Four T's Foundation
c/o The Northern Trust Co.
P.O. Box 803878
Chicago, IL 60680-3878

Established in 2000 in New York.
Donor: John S. Reed.
Foundation type: Independent foundation.
Financial data (yr. ended 12/31/13): Assets,
$1,954,945 (M); expenditures, $178,047;
qualifying distributions, $164,438; giving activities
include $163,388 for 4 grants (high: $100,000;
low: $5,000).
Fields of interest: Education; Disasters and
emergency management; Human services.
Limitations: Applications not accepted. Giving
primarily in Washington, DC and New York, NY.
Application information: Unsolicited requests for
funds not accepted.
Trustees: Cynthia L. Reed; John S. Reed.
EIN: 137219393

2883
Flora Foust Educational Fund
10 S. Dearborn IL1-0117
Chicago, IL 60603

Foundation type: Independent foundation.
Financial data (yr. ended 03/31/14): Assets,
$4,448,539 (M); expenditures, $169,034;
qualifying distributions, $147,345; giving activities
include $140,564 for 1 grant.
Fields of interest: Religion.
Limitations: Applications not accepted. Giving
primarily in TX.
Application information: Unsolicited requests for
funds not accepted.
Trustee: JPMorgan Chase Bank, N.A.
EIN: 756326288

2884
The Fraida Foundation
c/o Popowcer Katten, Ltd.
35 E. Wacker Dr., Ste. 1550
Chicago, IL 60601-2124

Donors: Hy Greenhill; Michael L. Greenhill; Mark A.
Greenhill.
Foundation type: Independent foundation.
Financial data (yr. ended 04/30/13): Assets,
$4,280,774 (M); expenditures, $258,696;
qualifying distributions, $240,500; giving activities
include $240,500 for 19 grants (high: $40,000;
low: $1,000).
Purpose and activities: Funding primarily for
education, Jewish agencies and temples, and
human services.
Fields of interest: Education; Nonprofits; Diseases
and conditions; Judaism; Human services; Child
welfare; Senior services; Homeless people.
Type of support: Research; Research and
evaluation; Regranting.
Limitations: Applications not accepted. Giving
primarily in IL. No grants to individuals.
Application information: Unsolicited requests for
funds not accepted.
Officers: Michael L. Greenhill, Pres.; Mark A.
Greenhill, V.P.; Leonard H. Popowcer, V.P.
EIN: 363126643

2885
Zollie & Elaine Frank Fund
(doing business as Mrs. Zollie S. Frank Fund)
666 Garland Pl.
Des Plaines, IL 60016-4725 (847) 982-0333
Contact: Elaine S. Frank, Pres.

Established in 1953 in Illinois.
Donors: Zollie S. Frank; Elaine S. Frank; Z. Frank,
Inc.; Four Wheels, Inc.; Wheels, Inc.; Frank
Consolidated Enterprises.
Foundation type: Independent foundation.
Financial data (yr. ended 12/31/13): Assets,
$5,523,218 (M); gifts received, $25,000;
expenditures, $270,225; qualifying distributions,
$245,776; giving activities include $245,776 for 82
grants (high: $38,500; low: $20).
Purpose and activities: Giving primarily for higher
education and Jewish federated giving programs,
agencies, and temples; funding also for arts and
culture, health care and health associations,
children and youth services, and social services.
Fields of interest: Arts and culture; Arts education;
Performing arts; Higher education; Nonprofits;
Health; Diseases and conditions; Judaism; Human
services; Child welfare.
Type of support: General support; Regranting.

Limitations: Applications accepted. Giving primarily
in IL, with emphasis on Chicago.
Application information: Application form required.
  Initial approach: Letter
  Deadline(s): None
Officers: Elaine S. Frank, Pres.; James S. Frank,
V.P.; Laurie A. Lieberman, V.P.; Nancy Schechtman,
Secy.; Charles E. Frank, Treas.
EIN: 366118400

2886
The Marshall Frankel Foundation
c/o Caruso & Co., Ltd.
319 Lafayette St.
Sandwich, IL 60548-1637

Established in 1979 in Illinois.
Donors: Marshall Frankel†; Susan Ruder.
Foundation type: Independent foundation.
Financial data (yr. ended 12/31/14): Assets,
$7,111,943; gifts received, $10,548;
expenditures, $384,222; qualifying distributions,
$320,000.
Fields of interest: Performing arts; Museums;
Elementary and secondary education; Higher
education; Abortion; Human services; Females.
Limitations: Applications not accepted. Giving
primarily in ID, IL, MA, and NY. No grants to
individuals.
Application information: Contributes only to
pre-selected organizations.
Officers and Directors: Elizabeth Frankel, Pres. and
Director; Rebecca Frankel Wilkinson, Secy. and
Director; Lynne Caruso McIlquham, Treas. and
Director.
EIN: 363012367

2887
Franklin Philanthropic Foundation
180 N. Stetson Ave., Ste. 1940
Chicago, IL 60601-6750

Established in 1989 in Illinois.
Donor: Morris F. Goodman.
Foundation type: Independent foundation.
Financial data (yr. ended 12/31/14): Assets,
$6,075,616 (M); gifts received, $600,000;
expenditures, $444,414; qualifying distributions,
$315,000; giving activities include $310,000 for 81
grants (high: $10,000; low: $500).
Fields of interest: Education; University education;
Environment; Nonprofits; Family planning; Human
services.
Type of support: General support; Regranting.
Limitations: Applications not accepted. Giving
primarily in NY and WI. No grants to individuals.
Application information: Unsolicited requests for
funds not accepted.
Officers and Directors: Morris F. Goodman, Pres.
and Director; Deborah Goodman, V.P. and Director;
Joyce Goodman, V.P. and Director; Linda Goodman,
V.P. and Director; Stanley Goodman, V.P. and
Director; William Michael Goodman, V.P. and
Director; Jenny Goodman-Bowden, V.P. and Director;
Charles F. Moles, Secy. and Director; John A. Shea,
Treas. and Director.
EIN: 363668125

2888
Franklin Square Foundation
835 Westerfield Dr.
Wilmette, IL 60091-1809

Donors: Jacqueline L. Quern Berry; Margaret Quern Atkins; Susannah Quern Pratt.
Foundation type: Independent foundation.
Financial data (yr. ended 12/31/13): Assets, $2,118,308 (M); gifts received, $98,039; expenditures, $149,396; qualifying distributions, $140,500; giving activities include $140,500 for 13 grants (high: $25,000; low: $3,000).
Fields of interest: Education; Botanical gardens; Archives and special collections; Christianity; Camps; Human services; Youth development.
Type of support: Individual development.
Limitations: Applications not accepted. Giving primarily in IL. No grants to individuals.
Application information: Contributes only to pre-selected organizations.
Directors: Margaret Quern Atkins; Susannah Quern Pratt; Jacqueline L. Quern Berry.
EIN: 010746539

2889
C. Lydia Frederick Foundation
c/o The North Trust Company
P.O. Box 803878
Chicago, IL 60680-3878

Foundation type: Independent foundation.
Financial data (yr. ended 07/31/13): Assets, $2,923,031 (M); expenditures, $192,823; qualifying distributions, $159,812; giving activities include $156,127 for 10 grants (high: $35,399; low: $483).
Fields of interest: Health; Religion; Human services.
Limitations: Applications not accepted. Giving primarily in IL.
Application information: Unsolicited requests for funds not accepted.
Trustee: The Northern Trust Company.
EIN: 366028568

2890
Fredman Family Charitable Trust
P.O. Box 512
Collinsville, IL 62234-0512 (618) 344-4267
Contact: Yoseph Fredman, Tr.

Established in 1987 in Illinois.
Donors: Fredman Bros. Furniture Co., Inc.; Favish Krywat; Harry Morgenstern; Andrew Epstein.
Foundation type: Independent foundation.
Financial data (yr. ended 09/30/13): Assets, $16,891 (M); gifts received, $186,905; expenditures, $202,470; qualifying distributions, $201,339; giving activities include $200,269 for 173 grants (high: $14,948; low: $10).
Purpose and activities: Giving for education and Jewish agencies, temples and schools.
Fields of interest: Education; Elementary and secondary education; Nonprofits; Judaism; Human services; Family services; Child welfare.
Type of support: Regranting.
Limitations: Applications accepted. Giving primarily in IL, MO, and NY.
Application information: Application form required.
Initial approach: Letter
Deadline(s): None

Trustees: Aaron Fredman; Yoseph Fredman.
EIN: 371226214

2891
Fremont Foundation
610 Brierhill Rd.
Deerfield, IL 60015-4406

Established in 1988 in Illinois.
Donors: Robert S. Fremont; Barbara Fremont.
Foundation type: Independent foundation.
Financial data (yr. ended 12/31/13): Assets, $2,656,771 (M); gifts received, $10,548; expenditures, $422,222; qualifying distributions, $415,544; giving activities include $414,728 for 76 grants (high: $150,000; low: $36).
Purpose and activities: Giving primarily to Jewish federated giving programs; some funding for the arts and human services.
Fields of interest: Arts and culture; Museums; Elementary and secondary education; Nonprofits; Hospital care; Human services.
Type of support: Regranting.
Limitations: Applications not accepted. Giving primarily in Chicago, IL. No grants to individuals.
Application information: Contributes only to pre-selected organizations.
Officer and Directors: Barbara Fremont, Pres. and Director; Lisa Fremont Boyle.
EIN: 363611956

2892
Maurice & Henry Freund Charitable Foundation
123 N. Wacker Dr., Ste. 1550
Chicago, IL 60606-1918

Donors: Henry Freund; Dorothy Freund†; Joyce Freund.
Foundation type: Independent foundation.
Financial data (yr. ended 12/31/13): Assets, $2,514,379 (M); gifts received, $419,283; expenditures, $154,414; qualifying distributions, $153,827; giving activities include $153,827 for 30 grants (high: $105,830; low: $36).
Fields of interest: Arts and culture; Art museums; Education; Human services.
Limitations: Applications not accepted. Giving primarily in Palm Springs, CA. No grants to individuals.
Application information: Unsolicited requests for funds not accepted.
Officers: Henry Freund, Mgr.; Joyce Freund, Mgr.; Marilyn Freund, Mgr.
EIN: 366069946

2893
Robert J. Frisby Foundation
333 W. Wacker Dr., Ste. 1700
Chicago, IL 60606-1250

Donor: R. J. Frisby.
Foundation type: Independent foundation.
Financial data (yr. ended 12/31/13): Assets, $3,292,408 (M); expenditures, $227,053; qualifying distributions, $194,014; giving activities include $166,289 for grants.
Purpose and activities: Giving primarily for Christian and Roman Catholic organizations, and social services.

Fields of interest: Christianity; Catholicism; Human services; Food aid; Child welfare; Low-income and poor people.
Limitations: Applications not accepted.
Application information: Contributes only to pre-selected organizations.
Officers: Michael Frisby, Pres.; Timothy G. Carroll, Secy.
Directors: Daniel Frisby; Kent Frisby; Timothy Frisby.
EIN: 043785583

2894
Full Circle Family Foundation
c/o Terrance K. Holt
5215 Old Orchard Rd., Ste. 675
Skokie, IL 60077

Established in 2000 in Illinois.
Donors: Virginia R. Holt; Terrance Holt.
Foundation type: Independent foundation.
Financial data (yr. ended 12/31/13): Assets, $2,554,893 (M); expenditures, $158,325; qualifying distributions, $155,350; giving activities include $155,350 for 25 grants (high: $42,500; low: $300).
Fields of interest: Arts and culture; Education; Religion.
Limitations: Applications not accepted. Giving primarily in IL. No grants to individuals.
Application information: Unsolicited requests for funds not accepted.
Officers: Virginia R. Holt, Pres.; Terrance K. Holt, V.P. and Treas.
EIN: 364391114

2895
Full Circle Foundation
P.O. Box 387
Richmond, IL 60071-0387
E-mail: grants@fullcircleinc.org; Main URL: http://fullcircleinc.org

Established in 1998 in Illinois.
Donors: Russell Foszcz; Sara Foszcz.
Foundation type: Independent foundation.
Financial data (yr. ended 12/31/14): Assets, $1,172,394; gifts received, $200,000; expenditures, $348,612; qualifying distributions, $340,673.
Purpose and activities: The foundation focuses its grants on educational opportunities, environmental and natural resource issues, health organizations, housing and shelter, and basic human services.
Fields of interest: Education; Natural resources; Diseases and conditions; Housing development; Human services.
Type of support: General support.
Limitations: Applications accepted. Giving emphasis is strongly on local organizations in McHenry County, IL, but some grants are awarded to national organizations. No support for religious organizations. No grants to individuals.
Application information: Grant applicants must submit a grant request form obtained from the foundation. Do not share grant request forms as they are dated and coded. Forms (and proposals) submitted without code will be automatically rejected. Application form required.
Initial approach: Letter or e-mail
Copies of proposal: 1
Deadline(s): Nov. 30

Board meeting date(s): Dec. 15
Final notification: 60 days
Officers: Sara Foszcz, Pres.; Russell Foszcz, V.P.
Directors: Cooper Foszcz; Joshua Foszcz.
Number of staff: None.
EIN: 364265265

2896
Fund for Enlightenment
875 N. Michigan Ave., Ste. 3350
Chicago, IL 60611-1905
Contact: Harry Drexler, Chair.

Donors: Harry Drexler; Lloyd Drexler; Arthur N. Jaye; Richard Drexler; Dan Drexler; Jason Drexler.
Foundation type: Independent foundation.
Financial data (yr. ended 12/31/13): Assets, $837,665 (M); gifts received, $150,000; expenditures, $276,053; qualifying distributions, $248,100; giving activities include $209,400 for 4 grants (high: $200,000; low: $400).
Fields of interest: Education; Catholicism; Human services.
Limitations: Applications accepted. Giving primarily in Chicago, IL, Washington, DC and New York, NY.
Application information:
Initial approach: Contact foundation
Deadline(s): None
Officers: Harry Drexler, Chair.; Dan Drexler, Treas.
EIN: 366063973

2897
Paul A. Funk Foundation
115 W. Jefferson St., Ste. 200
Bloomington, IL 61702-3217

Established in 1967 in Illinois.
Foundation type: Independent foundation.
Financial data (yr. ended 06/30/13): Assets, $10,531,927 (M); gifts received, $100; expenditures, $414,719; qualifying distributions, $465,313; giving activities include $213,400 for 40 grants (high: $50,000; low: $500), and $251,913 for foundation-administered programs.
Purpose and activities: Giving primarily for education, health, human services, and to a nature center foundation.
Fields of interest: Higher education; Foundations; Diseases and conditions; Community and economic development; Human services; Child welfare.
Limitations: Applications not accepted. Giving primarily in McLean County, IL. No grants to individuals.
Application information: Unsolicited requests for funds not accepted.
Trustees: Duncan Funk; Rey Jannusch; Justin McLaughlin; Clint Rehtmeyer; Leigh Ann Sharp.
EIN: 376075515

2898
The Gallagher 312 Foundation
1821 Walden Office Sq., No. 400
Schaumburg, IL 60173-4158

Established in 1985 in Illinois.
Donors: A. James Gallagher; Marie P. Gallagher.
Foundation type: Independent foundation.
Financial data (yr. ended 12/31/14): Assets, $3,245,910 (M); expenditures, $211,631; qualifying distributions, $166,299.

Fields of interest: Arts and culture; Elementary and secondary education; Christianity; Human services.
Limitations: Applications not accepted. Giving primarily in IL and MI. No grants to individuals.
Application information: Contributes only to pre-selected organizations.
Officers: Kevin P. Gallagher, Pres.; Marie P. Gallagher, Secy.-Treas.
EIN: 363373685

2899
The Galter Foundation
P.O. Box 480752
Niles, IL 60714-0752

Established in 1943 in Illinois.
Donors: Dollie Galter†; Jack Galter†; Spartus Corp.; William Galter†; The Galter Corp.; HSDC.
Foundation type: Independent foundation.
Financial data (yr. ended 12/31/13): Assets, $9,405,098 (M); expenditures, $269,555; qualifying distributions, $235,000; giving activities include $235,000 for 16 grants (high: $40,000; low: $2,500).
Purpose and activities: Giving primarily for education, hospitals, children and youth services, including children's hospitals, social services, and Jewish organizations.
Fields of interest: Health; Religion; Human services.
Limitations: Applications not accepted. Giving primarily in Chicago, IL. No grants to individuals; no loans or program-related investments.
Application information: Unsolicited requests for funds not accepted.
Directors: Hirshel Goodman; Karen Goodman; Robert Joseph.
EIN: 366082419

2900
Judy Gantz Charitable Trust
111 W. Monroe St., Tax Div. 10C
Chicago, IL 60603-4026   (312) 461-5154

Established in 2003 in Illinois.
Donor: Louis Gantz Trust.
Foundation type: Independent foundation.
Financial data (yr. ended 12/31/14): Assets, $3,848,004; expenditures, $404,617; qualifying distributions, $375,729.
Purpose and activities: Giving to organizations that provide residence for physically handicapped, mentally retarded and emotionally disturbed persons.
Fields of interest: People with disabilities; People with physical disabilities.
Limitations: Applications accepted. Giving primarily in IL. No grants to individuals.
Application information: Application form required.
Initial approach: Proposal
Deadline(s): None
Trustees: Barbara Ann Smith; BMO Harris Bank, N.A.
EIN: 367429638

2901
Gantz Family Foundation
72 Indian Hill Rd.
Winnetka, IL 60093-3937

Established in 1986 in Illinois.

Donors: Wilbur H. Gantz; Linda Gantz.
Foundation type: Operating foundation.
Financial data (yr. ended 12/31/13): Assets, $8,202,652 (M); expenditures, $434,005; qualifying distributions, $353,568; giving activities include $353,568 for 28 grants (high: $126,068; low: $150).
Fields of interest: Arts and culture; Religion; Youth development.
Limitations: Applications not accepted. Giving primarily in IL. No grants to individuals.
Application information: Unsolicited requests for funds not accepted.
Officers and Directors: Wilbur Gantz, Pres. and Director; Linda Gantz, V.P. and Director; Caroline Burns, Treas. and Director; Matthew Gantz; Leslie McLamore.
EIN: 363484258

2902
James L. Garard, Jr. Charitable Trust
c/o Rose McBride
3 First National Plz., Ste. 5100
Chicago, IL 60602-5011

Established in 1991 in Illinois.
Donor: James L. Garard, Jr.
Foundation type: Independent foundation.
Financial data (yr. ended 12/31/14): Assets, $2,230,449; expenditures, $365,128; qualifying distributions, $358,365.
Fields of interest: Education; Higher education; Botanical gardens; Hospital care; Diseases and conditions; Christianity; Human services.
Limitations: Applications not accepted. No grants to individuals.
Application information: Unsolicited requests for funds not accepted.
Trustee: James L. Garard, Jr.
EIN: 366971311

2903
Gary & Denise Gardner Family Foundation
10540 S. Longwood Dr.
Chicago, IL 60643-2667

Established in 1999 in Illinois.
Donors: Gary E. Gardner; Denise B. Garder; Gardner Equity Investments L.P.
Foundation type: Independent foundation.
Financial data (yr. ended 12/31/13): Assets, $910,927 (M); gifts received, $200,000; expenditures, $236,802; qualifying distributions, $235,665; giving activities include $235,650 for 19 grants (high: $125,000; low: $500).
Fields of interest: Education.
Type of support: General support.
Limitations: Applications not accepted. Giving primarily in Chicago, IL. No grants to individuals.
Application information: Unsolicited requests for funds not accepted.
Officers: Gary E. Gardner, Pres.; Denise B. Gardner, Secy.; Betty B. Barnett, Treas.
EIN: 364318040

2904
The J. W. Gardner II Foundation
510 Maine St., 9th Fl.
P.O. Box 140
Quincy, IL 62306-3941 (217) 277-2526
Contact: John G. Stevenson Jr., Dir.

Established in 2002 in Illinois.
Foundation type: Operating foundation.
Financial data (yr. ended 12/31/13): Assets, $4,821,899 (M); expenditures, $244,089; qualifying distributions, $197,070; giving activities include $197,070 for 14 grants (high: $50,000; low: $1,500).
Fields of interest: Museums; Education; Animal welfare; Housing development; Human services; Child welfare; Scouting programs; Adult and child mentoring.
Limitations: Applications accepted. Giving primarily in Quincy, IL, and the surrounding tri-state area. No grants to individuals.
Application information: Application form required.
Initial approach: Letter
Deadline(s): June 30
Directors: Robert S. Black; John G. Stevenson, Jr.
EIN: 371404507

2905
T.J. Gardner Trust
10 S. Dearborn IL1-0117
Chicago, IL 60603

Foundation type: Independent foundation.
Financial data (yr. ended 06/30/13): Assets, $6,615,090 (M); expenditures, $307,574; qualifying distributions, $220,595; giving activities include $202,328 for 2 grants (high: $101,164; low: $101,164).
Fields of interest: Health; Human services.
Limitations: Applications not accepted.
Application information: Unsolicited requests for funds not accepted.
Trustee: JPMorgan Chase Bank, N.A.
EIN: 756347666

2906
Gassin Family Foundation
c/o Friedman & Huey Assocs., LLP
1313 W. 175th St.
Homewood, IL 60430-4606

Established in 1990 in Illinois.
Donors: Bernard Gassin; Benny Gassin.
Foundation type: Independent foundation.
Financial data (yr. ended 05/31/13): Assets, $2,615,977 (M); expenditures, $191,442; qualifying distributions, $169,000; giving activities include $165,000 for 4 grants (high: $100,000; low: $5,000).
Fields of interest: Diseases and conditions; Alzheimer's disease; Autism; Judaism.
Type of support: General support.
Limitations: Applications not accepted. Giving primarily in IL and NJ. No grants to individuals.
Application information: Unsolicited requests for funds not accepted.
Officer: Amy Gassin Savitz, Pres.
Directors: Nancy Gassin Molesworth; Stuart Savitz.
EIN: 363711224

2907
General Iron Industries Charitable Foundation
1909 N. Clifton Ave.
Chicago, IL 60614-4803

Established in 2007 in Illinois.
Donor: General Iron Holdings Inc.
Foundation type: Independent foundation.
Financial data (yr. ended 12/31/13): Assets, $68,260 (M); gifts received, $200,000; expenditures, $351,895; qualifying distributions, $350,300; giving activities include $350,300 for 35 grants (high: $100,000; low: $500).
Fields of interest: Hospital care; Diseases and conditions; Judaism; Human services.
Limitations: Applications not accepted. No grants to individuals.
Application information: Unsolicited requests for funds not accepted.
Directors: Adam Labkon; Howard Labkon; Lindsey Levin Labkon; Marilyn Labkon; Mark Labkon.
EIN: 260367916

2908
The Generations Fund
1000 Skokie Blvd., Ste. 540
Wilmette, IL 60091-1187
E-mail: adowney@genmin.com; Additional e-mail: Questions@Generationsfund.org

Established in 1977 in Illinois.
Donors: Felt Products Manufacturing Co.; Fel-Pro Inc.; Richard Morris; Bruce Morris; Bruce Morris 1993 Descendants Trust; Robert Morris; Ellen Morris.
Foundation type: Independent foundation.
Financial data (yr. ended 12/31/13): Assets, $3,441,005 (M); gifts received, $10; expenditures, $213,367; qualifying distributions, $172,447; giving activities include $168,828 for 56 grants (high: $18,328; low: $250).
Purpose and activities: Primary areas of interest include education, community development, social services, and Jewish organizations, including welfare funds.
Fields of interest: Arts and culture; Visual arts; Performing arts; Education; Nonprofits; Community and economic development; Judaism; Human services; Family services; Youth services; Senior services; Seniors; People with disabilities.
Type of support: General support; Program development; Regranting.
Limitations: Applications not accepted. Giving primarily in Chicago, IL. No grants to individuals.
Application information: Unsolicited requests for funds not accepted.
Board meeting date(s): Aug.
Officers: Robert Morris, Pres.; Ellen Morris, Secy.; Bruce Morris, Treas.
Number of staff: 1 part-time professional.
EIN: 770609737

2909
Geneseo Foundation
P.O. Box 89
Geneseo, IL 61254-0089
Application address: c/o Central Bank Illinois, Attn.: Michael Kelly, Trust Off., 101 N. State St., Geneseo, IL 61254, tel.: (309) 944-5601
Grants List: http://www.geneseofoundation.org/GiftsAwarded.html

Established in 1961 in Illinois.
Donors: George B. Dedrick; Walter & Carol Keppy Memorial Trust; Geneseo Lions Club; Hayden Dedecker; Faith Dedecker; Catherine Cambell†.
Foundation type: Independent foundation.
Financial data (yr. ended 03/31/15): Assets, $8,884,541 (M); gifts received, $134,609; expenditures, $428,994; qualifying distributions, $420,745; giving activities include $338,210 for 31 grants (high: $100,000; low: $500), and $50,112 for 90 grants to individuals.
Purpose and activities: Giving for civic organizations, social services, youth, recreation, and education, including for scholarships for graduates of Geneseo High School.
Fields of interest: Arts and culture; Education; Public administration; Community and economic development; Sports and recreation; Human services; Child welfare.
Type of support: General support; Student aid.
Limitations: Applications accepted. Giving primarily in Geneseo, IL.
Application information: Application form required.
Initial approach: Letter or telephone to request application form
Copies of proposal: 1
Board meeting date(s): Monthly
Managers: Bryce B. Chamberlain; John J. DuBois; Michael L. Gernant; John T. Greenwood; Eric Johnson; Brett Lohman; Central Bank Illinois; Todd W. Sieben; Bruce Fehlman.
EIN: 366079604

2910
Genesis Philanthropic Fund
200 S. Wacker Dr., Ste. 4000
Chicago, IL 60606-5829

Established in 1996 in Illinois.
Donor: Betsy R. Gidwitz.
Foundation type: Independent foundation.
Financial data (yr. ended 12/31/14): Assets, $2,474,441; expenditures, $185,717; qualifying distributions, $147,485.
Fields of interest: Judaism.
Limitations: Applications not accepted. Giving primarily in Chicago, IL.
Application information: Unsolicited requests for funds not accepted.
Officers: Betsy R. Gidwitz, Pres.; Teri Gidwitz, V.P.
Director: Steven Gidwitz.
EIN: 364118456

2911
George H.Parr Trust
c/o The Gerber State Bank
110 E. Elm
P.O. Box 410
Argenta, IL 62501-0410

Foundation type: Independent foundation.

Financial data (yr. ended 12/31/14): Assets, $7,898,347 (M); expenditures, $298,008; qualifying distributions, $227,652; giving activities include $224,964 for 13 grants (high: $44,993; low: $2,250).
Fields of interest: Hospital care; Public libraries.
Limitations: Applications not accepted. Giving primarily in IL.
Application information: Unsolicited requests for funds not accepted.
Trustee: The Gerber State Bank.
EIN: 376113187

2912
Gibbet Hill Foundation
410 N. Michigan Ave., Ste. 590
Chicago, IL 60611-4220

Established in 1976 in Illinois.
Donors: Deering Foundation; Miami Corp.
Foundation type: Independent foundation.
Financial data (yr. ended 12/31/14): Assets, $2,107,909 (M); gifts received, $200,000; expenditures, $242,080; qualifying distributions, $234,454; giving activities include $230,000 for 10 grants (high: $50,000; low: $10,000).
Purpose and activities: Giving primarily for higher and other education; funding also for the environment and social services.
Fields of interest: Education; Higher education; Environment; Family planning; Archives and special collections; Sports and recreation.
Type of support: General support.
Limitations: Applications not accepted. Giving primarily in CO, IL, LA, MA, and NY. No grants to individuals.
Application information: Contributes only to pre-selected organizations.
Officers and Directors: John Rau, Pres. and Director; Richard F. Hogan, V.P. and Director; Stephen Strachan, V.P. and Director; Susan D. Pattock, Secy.-Treas.
EIN: 510189357

2913
Christina and Ronald Gidwitz Charitable Foundation
200 S. Wacker Dr., Ste. 4000
Chicago, IL 60606-5849

Established in 2001 in Illinois.
Donors: Christina K. Gidwitz; Ronald J. Gidwitz.
Foundation type: Independent foundation.
Financial data (yr. ended 12/31/14): Assets, $1,169; gifts received, $342,625; expenditures, $338,900; qualifying distributions, $335,000.
Purpose and activities: Giving primarily for museums, education and a Boys and Girls Club.
Fields of interest: Arts and culture; Education; Health.
Limitations: Applications accepted. Giving primarily in Chicago, IL.
Application information: Application form required.
  Initial approach: Letter
  Deadline(s): None
Officers: Christina K. Gidwitz, Chair.; Ronald J. Gidwitz, Pres.; Kevin O'Keefe, Treas.
EIN: 364430172

2914
Gidwitz Family Foundation
200 S. Wacker Dr., Ste. 4000
Chicago, IL 60606-5849

Established in 1996 in Illinois.
Donors: James G. Gidwitz; Ronald J. Gidwitz; Nancy Gidwitz; Jane B. Gidwitz; Alan Gidwitz; Ralph Gidwitz; Gail Gidwitz.
Foundation type: Independent foundation.
Financial data (yr. ended 12/31/14): Assets, $1,791,845; gifts received, $80,000; expenditures, $119,569; qualifying distributions, $114,139.
Purpose and activities: Giving primarily for Jewish organizations.
Fields of interest: Arts and culture; Education; Higher education; Environment; Nonprofits; Diseases and conditions; Judaism.
Type of support: Research; Regranting.
Limitations: Applications accepted. Giving primarily in IL.
Application information: Application form required.
  Initial approach: Letter
  Deadline(s): None
Officers and Directors: Betsy R. Gidwitz, Pres. and Director; Ronald J. Gidwitz, V.P. and Director; Nancy Gidwitz, Secy. and Director; James G. Gidwitz; Peter E. Gidwitz; Ralph W. Gidwitz; Teri Gidwitz; Thomas R. Gidwitz; Linda Karamitis.
EIN: 364118455

2915
The Dorothy and Lillian Gish Prize
c/o JPMorgan Chase Bank, N.A.
10 S. Dearborn St., 21st Fl.
Chicago, IL 60603-2300
Contact: Jonathan G. Horowitz, JPMorgan Chase Bank, N.A.
E-mail: jonathan.g.horowitz@jpmorgan.com; *Main URL:* http://www.gishprize.com
Grants List: http://www.gishprize.com/recipients

Established in 1994 in New York.
Donor: Lillian D. Gish†.
Foundation type: Independent foundation.
Financial data (yr. ended 06/30/14): Assets, $7,711,167 (M); expenditures, $526,127; qualifying distributions, $438,010; giving activities include $300,000 for 1 grant.
Purpose and activities: Awards an annual prize in Nov. for lifetime achievement in the arts to one individual who has made an outstanding contribution to the beauty of the world and to mankind's enjoyment and understanding of life.
Fields of interest: Arts and culture.
Type of support: Grants to individuals.
Limitations: Giving on a national and international basis.
Application information:
  Board meeting date(s): Mar.
Trustee: JPMorgan Chase Bank, N.A.
Number of staff: 1 part-time professional.
EIN: 133751413

2916
The Joseph B. Glossberg Foundation
455 Cityfront Plz., Ste. 3000
Chicago, IL 60611-5327

Established in 1997 in Illinois.

Donor: Joseph B. Glossberg.
Foundation type: Independent foundation.
Financial data (yr. ended 12/31/14): Assets, $12,914; gifts received, $142,500; expenditures, $144,834; qualifying distributions, $142,950.
Purpose and activities: Giving primarily for higher education, the humanities, athletic programs, libraries, youth music education, music programs and human services.
Fields of interest: Arts services; Music; Orchestral music; Performing arts education; Humanities; Higher education; Education services; Rehabilitation; School libraries and media centers; School athletics; Human services.
Limitations: Applications not accepted. Giving primarily in IL and PA. No grants to individuals.
Application information: Contributes only to pre-selected organizations.
Officers and Directors: Joseph B. Glossberg, Pres. and Treas. and Director; Madeleine K.B. Glossberg, V.P. and Secy. and Director; John C. Stiefel, V.P. and Director.
EIN: 364119754

2917
Gloyd Family Foundation
809 Detweiller Dr.
Peoria, IL 61614

Established in 1997 in Illinois.
Donor: Lawrence E. Gloyd.
Foundation type: Independent foundation.
Financial data (yr. ended 12/31/13): Assets, $4,057,887 (M); expenditures, $317,393; qualifying distributions, $317,393; giving activities include $233,500 for 29 grants (high: $50,000; low: $500).
Fields of interest: Arts and culture; Education; Diseases and conditions; Protestantism; Human services; Child welfare; Youth development.
Limitations: Applications not accepted. No support for political campaigns . No grants to individuals, or for loans.
Application information: Unsolicited requests for funds not accepted.
Directors: Julia G. Buchanan; Sheryl J. Burdick; Susan M. Crowell.
EIN: 364140796

2918
Gochnauer Family Foundation
335 Woodley Rd.
Winnetka, IL 60093-3740

Established in 1998 in California.
Donor: Richard W. Gochnauer.
Foundation type: Independent foundation.
Financial data (yr. ended 12/31/12): Assets, $4,752,843 (M); expenditures, $251,311; qualifying distributions, $211,590; giving activities include $211,590 for 28 grants (high: $65,000; low: $90).
Purpose and activities: Giving to provide financial help for families and children, by supporting organizations and programs that promote spiritual, medical, cultural, and educational growth or provide essential services.
Fields of interest: Arts and culture; Nonprofits; Christianity; Human services; Child welfare; International development.

Type of support: General support; Capital campaigns; Regranting.
Limitations: Applications accepted. Giving primarily in southern CA, the greater Chicago, IL, area, and in MT. No grants to individuals.
Application information: Larger requests, in amounts of $5,000 or more, must include additional information. Contact foundation for complete application details.
　Initial approach: Letter
　Copies of proposal: 2
　Deadline(s): None
　Board meeting date(s): Quarterly
Officers: Beth A. Gochnauer, Chair. and Secy.; Richard W. Gochnauer, Pres. and Treas.; Grant D. Gochnauer, V.P.; Meg Gochnauer, V.P.
EIN: 330833479

2919
Goldberg Kohn Foundation

(formerly Goldberg, Kohn, Bell, Black, Rosenbloom & Moritz Foundation)
55 E. Monroe St., Ste. 3300
Chicago, IL　60603-5806　(312) 201-4000
Contact: Joel F. Brown, Dir.

Established in 1993 in Illinois.
Donors: Steve Bell; Dennis Black; Wayne Gilmartin; Richard Kohn; Terry Moritz; James Rosenbloom; Alan Solow; Randall L. Klein; David L. Dranoff; Gary T. Zussman; David M. Mason; Joel F. Brown; Denise B. Caplan.
Foundation type: Company-sponsored foundation.
Financial data (yr. ended 12/31/13): Assets, $38,080 (M); gifts received, $198,379; expenditures, $144,911; qualifying distributions, $144,275; giving activities include $144,250 for 35 grants (high: $25,000; low: $100).
Purpose and activities: Giving primarily for education and legal services.
Fields of interest: Education; Human services; Youth development.
Type of support: General support.
Limitations: Applications accepted. Giving primarily in IL.
Application information: Application form required.
　Initial approach: Letter
　Deadline(s): None
Officers and Directors: Steven A. Levy, Chair. and Pres.; Oscar L. Alcantara, Secy. and Director; Joel F. Brown; Seth H. Good; Michael B. Manuel.
EIN: 363879526

2920
Max Goldenberg Foundation

111 W. Monroe St., Tax Div. 10C
Chicago, IL　60603-4096　(312) 461-5154

Established in 1946 in Illinois.
Donor: Max Goldenberg‡.
Foundation type: Independent foundation.
Financial data (yr. ended 12/31/14): Assets, $7,665,905 (M); expenditures, $482,623; qualifying distributions, $357,403; giving activities include $315,000 for 28 grants (high: $25,005; low: $2,500).
Fields of interest: Higher education; Nonprofits; Specialty hospital care; Diseases and conditions; Catholicism; Human services.
Type of support: Research; Research and evaluation; Regranting.

Limitations: Applications accepted. Giving primarily in IL.
Publications: Annual report.
Application information: Application form required.
　Initial approach: Letter
　Copies of proposal: 1
　Deadline(s): None
　Board meeting date(s): Oct. and Nov.
Trustee: BMO Harris Bank, N.A.
EIN: 362471625

2921
Golder Family Foundation

254 Scott Ave.
Winnetka, IL　60093-1560　(847) 242-0500
Contact: David B. Golder, V.P. and Treas.

Established in 1985 in Illinois.
Donors: Stanley C. Golder; Joan J. Golder; Golder Family Partnership.
Foundation type: Independent foundation.
Financial data (yr. ended 12/31/13): Assets, $6,350,331 (L); gifts received, $28,000; expenditures, $384,425; qualifying distributions, $293,000; giving activities include $293,000 for 17 grants (high: $40,000; low: $1,000).
Purpose and activities: Giving primarily to Jewish agencies and temples; funding also for other social service organizations.
Fields of interest: Education; Nonprofits; Judaism; Human services; Child welfare.
Type of support: Regranting.
Limitations: Applications accepted. Giving primarily in the Chicago, IL, area. No grants to individuals.
Application information:
　Initial approach: Proposal
　Deadline(s): None
Officers: Joan J. Golder, Pres. and Secy.; David B. Golder, V.P. and Treas.; Kenneth Golder, V.P.; Nancy Northrip, V.P.
EIN: 363485592

2922
Peter D. & Carol Goldman Foundation

219 Cary Ave.
Highland Park, IL　60035-4335

Established in 1990 in Illinois.
Donors: Peter D. Goldman; Carol Goldman.
Foundation type: Independent foundation.
Financial data (yr. ended 12/31/14): Assets, $5,911,315; gifts received, $15; expenditures, $267,907; qualifying distributions, $231,593.
Fields of interest: Higher education; Judaism.
Type of support: General support.
Limitations: Applications not accepted. Giving primarily in IL. No grants to individuals.
Application information: Contributes only to pre-selected organizations.
Officers: Peter D. Goldman, Pres.; Carol Goldman, Secy.
EIN: 363730772

2923
Good Heart Work Smart Foundation

830 North Blvd.
Oak Park, IL　60301-1354

Established in 2006 in Illinois.

Donors: Stephen G. Schuler; Mary Jo Schuler; Shu Trading, Inc.
Foundation type: Independent foundation.
Financial data (yr. ended 12/31/13): Assets, $1,313,911 (M); gifts received, $440,000; expenditures, $352,031; qualifying distributions, $328,807; giving activities include $328,807 for 225 grants (high: $19,783; low: $41).
Fields of interest: Education; Foundations; Catholicism; Human services.
Limitations: Applications not accepted. Giving primarily in IL.
Application information: Unsolicited requests for funds not accepted.
Trustees: Susan Mika; Melvin P. Phillips, Jr.; Mary Jo Schuler; Stephen G. Schuler; Stacy Wettstein.
EIN: 205836042

2924
Albert Goodstein Family Foundation

c/o Marilyn Kushen
1600 Green Bay Rd., Ste. 104
Highland Park, IL　60035

Established in 1993 in Illinois.
Foundation type: Independent foundation.
Financial data (yr. ended 12/31/14): Assets, $3,468,012; expenditures, $257,312; qualifying distributions, $224,038.
Purpose and activities: Giving for Jewish federated giving programs, education, health and medical services, and art programs.
Fields of interest: Art museums; Higher education; Nonprofits; Diseases and conditions; Alzheimer's disease; Heart and circulatory system diseases; Cancers; Judaism.
Type of support: Research; Research and evaluation; Regranting.
Limitations: Applications not accepted. Giving primarily in Chicago, IL.
Application information: Unsolicited requests for funds not accepted.
Officers: Marilyn Kushen, Pres. and Treas.; Ivan Kushen, V.P.; Alisa Kagan, Secy.
EIN: 363780985

2925
The Gostomski Foundation

c/o H&H, LLP
333 W. Wacker Dr., Ste. 1700
Chicago, IL　60606-1247
Contact: Robert T. Napier

Donors: Michael M. Gostomski; Gostomski Family Foundation.
Foundation type: Independent foundation.
Financial data (yr. ended 12/31/13): Assets, $3,640,213 (M); gifts received, $3,699,821; expenditures, $249,658; qualifying distributions, $230,000; giving activities include $230,000 for 3 grants (high: $200,000; low: $10,000).
Fields of interest: Education; Religion.
Limitations: Applications not accepted. Giving primarily in MN.
Application information: Unsolicited requests for funds not accepted.
Trustee: Michael M. Gostomski.
EIN: 466976292

2926
Elizabeth Firestone Graham Foundation
10 S. Dearborn, IL1-0117
Chicago, IL 60603

Established in 1983 in Ohio.
Foundation type: Independent foundation.
Financial data (yr. ended 11/30/13): Assets, $4,956,929 (M); expenditures, $238,431; qualifying distributions, $216,680; giving activities include $208,500 for grants.
Purpose and activities: Giving for contemporary visual arts projects, with emphasis on exhibition publications (catalogues) for early- and mid-career artists.
Fields of interest: Arts and culture; Arts education; Visual arts; Museums; Art museums.
Type of support: Program development; Publications.
Limitations: Applications not accepted. Giving primarily in IL, NC, and VA. No grants to individuals or for general operating budgets or endowment funds.
Application information: Contributes only to pre-selected organizations.
Trustees: Barbara F. Graham; Ray A. Graham III.
EIN: 341388252

2927
Avrum Gray Family Fund
440 S. LaSalle St., Ste. 650
Chicago, IL 60605-1028   3129674211

Established in 2004 in Illinois.
Donors: Mae K. Gray Revocable Trust; Joseph J. Gray Fund; AG 1991 Trust; G-Bar Limited Partnership.
Foundation type: Independent foundation.
Financial data (yr. ended 12/31/14): Assets, $10,922,620; gifts received, $4,862,660; expenditures, $277,988; qualifying distributions, $277,988.
Fields of interest: Performing arts; Education; Diseases and conditions; Judaism; Human services.
Type of support: Research; Research and evaluation.
Limitations: Applications accepted. Giving primarily in Chicago, IL.
Application information: Application form required.
　Initial approach: Request application form
　Deadline(s): None
Officers: Lori Gray Faversham, Pres.; Avrum Gray, V.P. and Treas.; James Gray, V.P.; Matthew Gray, V.P.
EIN: 201533159

2928
The Sue and Melvin Gray Foundation
(formerly Melvin and Susanne Gray Foundation)
2 Mid America Plz., Ste. 400
Oakbrook Terrace, IL 60181-4714

Established in 1986 in Illinois.
Donor: Graycor, Inc.
Foundation type: Company-sponsored foundation.
Financial data (yr. ended 12/31/14): Assets, $1,037,909; expenditures, $231,811; qualifying distributions, $220,500.
Purpose and activities: The foundation supports organizations involved with arts and culture, education, health, and human services.

Fields of interest: Arts and culture; Education; Health.
Type of support: General support.
Limitations: Applications accepted. Giving primarily in Chicago, IL. No grants to individuals.
Application information:
　Initial approach: Letter
　Deadline(s): None
Officers: Melvin Gray, Pres.; Susanne Gray, V.P.; Steven F. Gray, Secy.
EIN: 363485579

2929
The Dean and Lois Griffith Foundation
(formerly The Griffith Family Foundation)
1 Griffith Ctr.
Alsip, IL 60803-3495   (708) 371-0900
Contact: Joseph R. Maslick Jr., Treas. and Tr.

Established in 1967 in Illinois.
Donors: Dean L. Griffith; Lois Jo Griffith.
Foundation type: Independent foundation.
Financial data (yr. ended 12/31/13): Assets, $1,253,481 (M); gifts received, $637,599; expenditures, $239,173; qualifying distributions, $239,173; giving activities include $239,148 for 37 grants (high: $87,923; low: $90).
Fields of interest: Higher education; Christianity; Human services.
Limitations: Applications accepted. Giving primarily in IL and WI. No grants to individuals.
Application information: Application form required.
　Initial approach: Letter
　Copies of proposal: 1
　Deadline(s): Oct. 1
Officers and Trustees: Dean L. Griffith, Pres. and Trustee; James S. Legg, Secy.; Joseph R. Maslick, Jr., Treas. and Trustee; Lois Jo Griffith.
EIN: 366162494

2930
Griffith Laboratories Inc. Foundation
1 Griffith Ctr.
Alsip, IL 60803-3495   (708) 371-0900
Contact: Joseph R. Maslick Jr., V.P. and Treas.

Donors: Griffith Laboratories U.S.A., Inc.; Griffith Micro Science, Inc.; Griffith Laboratories, Inc.; Griffith Labs Worldwide.
Foundation type: Company-sponsored foundation.
Financial data (yr. ended 09/30/13): Assets, $791,473 (M); gifts received, $174,000; expenditures, $333,710; qualifying distributions, $333,710; giving activities include $333,700 for 12 grants (high: $115,700; low: $500).
Purpose and activities: The foundation supports organizations involved with diabetes, children and youth, and Christianity.
Fields of interest: Education; Religion; Human services.
Type of support: General support.
Limitations: Applications accepted. Giving primarily in GA, IL, and WI. No grants to individuals.
Application information: Application form required.
　Initial approach: Letter
　Copies of proposal: 1
　Deadline(s): July 1
Officers: Dean L. Griffith, Pres.; Joseph R. Maslick, Jr., V.P. and Treas.; James S. Legg, Secy.
EIN: 510195285

2931
Jessie E. Griswold Trust
520 N. Main St.
White Hall, IL 62092-1151   (217) 374-2306
Contact: Howard Piper, Tr.

Foundation type: Independent foundation.
Financial data (yr. ended 12/31/14): Assets, $13,822,929 (M); expenditures, $353,954; qualifying distributions, $390,842; giving activities include $244,626 for grants.
Purpose and activities: Loan awards for students of Green County, Illinois, for higher education.
Fields of interest: Education.
Type of support: Student aid; Loans to individuals; Individual development.
Limitations: Giving limited to IL residents.
Application information: Application form required.
　Deadline(s): None
Trustees: Ron Hetelle; Howard Piper.
EIN: 376105072

2932
Grace Elizabeth Groner Scholarship Foundation
585 Bank Ln., Ste. 3000
Lake Forest, IL 60045-5308
Application address: c/o Daniela Resendiz, 555 N. Sheridan Rd., Lake Forest, IL 60045, tel.: (847) 735-6162

Donors: Grace Groner; Grace Groner Trust; John Lilly; Diana Hickert-Hill.
Foundation type: Independent foundation.
Financial data (yr. ended 12/31/13): Assets, $7,932,005 (M); gifts received, $204,080; expenditures, $570,936; qualifying distributions, $483,024; giving activities include $24,296 for 3 grants (high: $10,000; low: $4,296), and $315,122 for 40 grants to individuals (high: $46,335; low: $400).
Fields of interest: Education.
Type of support: Student aid; General support.
Limitations: Applications accepted. Giving primarily in Lake Forest, IL.
Trustees: William C. Marlatt; L. Robert Pasquesi.
EIN: 266687616

2933
Sam & Sarah Grossinger Foundation
6900 N. McCormick Blvd.
Lincolnwood, IL 60712   (857) 675-8300
Contact: Sharon Grossinger, V.P.

Established in 1963 in Illinois.
Donors: Grossinger Motorcorp; Irwin Grossinger; Sharon Grossinger.
Foundation type: Independent foundation.
Financial data (yr. ended 09/30/13): Assets, $3,990,229 (M); expenditures, $155,912; qualifying distributions, $128,178; giving activities include $121,243 for 33 grants (high: $20,000; low: $50).
Fields of interest: Music; Education; Higher education; Graduate and professional education; Nonprofits; Prostate cancer; Science; Judaism; Theology.
Type of support: General support; Student aid; Regranting.
Limitations: Applications accepted. Giving primarily in the Chicago, IL area.

Application information: Application form required.

Initial approach: Proposal

Deadline(s): None

Officers: Caroline Grossinger-Schiller, Pres.; Suzanne Grossinger Gould, V.P.; Gary Grossinger, V.P.; Sharon Grossinger, V.P.

EIN: 366108185

2934
The Jennifer and David Dean Grumhaus, Jr. Foundation
487 Walnut Rd.
Lake Forest, IL 60045-2245

Established in 2007 in Illinois.

Donors: David D. Grumhaus, Jr.; Jennifer K. Grumhaus; Gorter Family Foundation.

Foundation type: Independent foundation.

Financial data (yr. ended 12/31/13): Assets, $953,318 (M); gifts received, $25,000; expenditures, $184,135; qualifying distributions, $182,250; giving activities include $182,250 for 30 grants (high: $40,000; low: $250).

Fields of interest: Education; Religion; Human services.

Limitations: Applications not accepted. Giving primarily in IL and NY. No grants to individuals.

Application information: Unsolicited requests for funds not accepted.

Officers: David D. Grumhaus, Jr., Pres.; Jennifer K. Grumhaus, Secy.

Director: Daid Kahl.

EIN: 261479932

2935
James P. and Brenda S. Grusecki Family Foundation
840 N. Lake Shore Dr., Ste. 2301
Chicago, IL 60611-2490

Established in 2002 in Illinois.

Donor: James P. Grusecki.

Foundation type: Independent foundation.

Financial data (yr. ended 12/31/13): Assets, $9,860,454 (M); gifts received, $599,286; expenditures, $409,466; qualifying distributions, $376,520; giving activities include $376,520 for 25 grants (high: $100,000; low: $1,500).

Purpose and activities: The purpose of the Foundation is to fund programs and initiatives in education, the performing arts, and housing and social services in the Chicago, Illinois area. Educational funding ranges from pre-school to after school to public and private. Additional specific interests include women's issues, mental health, transformational housing, and theater. Programs that combine these fields of interest receive consideration, especially those that introduce targeted underserved populations to performing arts.

Limitations: Applications not accepted. Giving primarily in the Chicago, IL area. No grants to individuals.

Application information: Contributes only to pre-selected organizations.

Officers and Directors: James P. Grusecki, Pres. and Treas and Director; Brenda S. Grusecki, V.P. and Secy. and Director; Robert D. Tuerk.

EIN: 161639401

2936
The Christopher L. & M. Susan Gust Foundation
c/o Wolverine Trading, LLC
175 W. Jackson Blvd., 2nd Fl.
Chicago, IL 60604-3034 (312) 884-3724
Contact: Christopher L. Gust, Dir.

Established in 2001 in Illinois.

Donors: Christopher L. Gust; M. Susan Gust.

Foundation type: Independent foundation.

Financial data (yr. ended 12/31/13): Assets, $17,020,427 (M); expenditures, $679,925; qualifying distributions, $596,299; giving activities include $253,112 for 10 grants (high: $166,987; low: $2,000).

Fields of interest: Elementary and secondary education; Higher education; Human services.

Type of support: Program development; General support; Capital campaigns.

Limitations: Applications accepted. Giving primarily in Chicago, IL; some funding also in Ann Arbor, MI.

Application information: Application form required.

Initial approach: Letter

Deadline(s): None

Directors: Diane Edmundson; Christopher L. Gust; M. Susan Gust.

EIN: 611405669

2937
H & H Charitable Foundation
c/o O'Connor Partners, Herbert E. Seif
135 S. Lasalle St., Ste. 3250
Chicago, IL 60603-4130

Established in 1990 in Illinois.

Donors: Herbert E. Seif; Harriet Seif.

Foundation type: Independent foundation.

Financial data (yr. ended 11/30/13): Assets, $4,718,900 (M); gifts received, $300,747; expenditures, $267,297; qualifying distributions, $212,220; giving activities include $212,220 for 24 grants (high: $75,000; low: $100).

Fields of interest: Elementary and secondary education; Judaism; Child welfare.

Limitations: Applications not accepted. Giving primarily in NY. No grants to individuals.

Application information: Contributes only to pre-selected organizations.

Officers and Directors: Herbert E. Seif, Pres. and Director; Hyman Muller, V.P. and Director; Harriet R. Seif, Secy.-Treas. and Director; Jonathan A. Seif.

EIN: 363426895

2938
H. W. R. Foundation
c/o The Northern Trust Co.
P.O. Box 803878
Chicago, IL 60680-3878

Foundation type: Independent foundation.

Financial data (yr. ended 08/31/12): Assets, $5,022,789 (M); expenditures, $340,960; qualifying distributions, $314,155; giving activities include $311,482 for 1 grant.

Fields of interest: Human services.

Limitations: Applications not accepted.

Application information: Unsolicited requests for funds not accepted.

Trustee: Northern Trust Co.

EIN: 946623056

2939
H.C.D. Foundation
1370 Shagbark Dr.
Des Plaines, IL 60018-1656

Established in 1989 in Illinois.

Donors: Harriet C. Dennis†; Jeffrey Dennis.

Foundation type: Independent foundation.

Financial data (yr. ended 12/31/14): Assets, $8,140,433; gifts received, $24,040; expenditures, $336,694; qualifying distributions, $328,978.

Fields of interest: Nonprofits; Religion; Catholicism; Human services; Youth services.

Type of support: Regranting.

Limitations: Applications not accepted. Giving primarily in CA and IL. No grants to individuals.

Application information: Unsolicited requests for funds not accepted.

Trustees: Timothy G. Carroll; Jeffrey Dennis.

EIN: 363669822

2940
Haarlow Family Charitable Foundation
112 N. Lincoln
Hinsdale, IL 60521-3439

Established in 1992 in Illinois.

Donors: A. William Haarlow III; Evangeline R. Haarlow.

Foundation type: Independent foundation.

Financial data (yr. ended 12/31/13): Assets, $2,228,854 (M); expenditures, $141,855; qualifying distributions, $115,028; giving activities include $115,000 for 7 grants (high: $40,000; low: $500).

Fields of interest: Education; Diseases and conditions; ALS; Human services.

Limitations: Applications not accepted. Giving primarily in IL. No grants to individuals.

Application information: Unsolicited requests for funds not accepted.

Officers: Evangeline Rupp Haarlow, Pres.; William Noble Haarlow, Secy.; Blair Richlay Haarlow, Treas.

EIN: 363848959

2941
William M. Hales Foundation
408 Greenbay Rd.
P.O. Box 63
Kenilworth, IL 60043-1098

Established in 1991 in Illinois.

Donors: William M. Hales; Mary C. Hales; Lynn H. Jacob; John W. Hales.

Foundation type: Independent foundation.

Financial data (yr. ended 12/31/14): Assets, $6,122,529 (M); expenditures, $317,200; qualifying distributions, $256,021; giving activities include $254,900 for 39 grants (high: $50,000; low: $500).

Fields of interest: Arts and culture; Higher education; Nonprofits; Health; Human services.

Type of support: Regranting.

Limitations: Applications not accepted. Giving primarily in IL. No grants to individuals.

Application information: Unsolicited requests for funds not accepted.

Officers and Directors: Catherine L. Hales, Pres.; John W. Hales, Secy.-Treas.; Erick W. Hales.

EIN: 363735095

2942
Half Moon Foundation
c/o Edward Fellin McGladery
1 S. Wacker Dr., No. 800
Chicago, IL 60606

Established in 1990 in Illinois.
Donors: Tracy Louis Merrill; Joe Merrill.
Foundation type: Independent foundation.
Financial data (yr. ended 12/31/14): Assets, $692,848; gifts received, $375,000; expenditures, $436,591; qualifying distributions, $428,315.
Fields of interest: Education; Elementary and secondary education; Higher education; Environment; Hospital care; Diseases and conditions; Cancers; Human services.
Type of support: Annual campaigns.
Limitations: Applications not accepted. Giving primarily in CT, MA, NY, and WI. No grants to individuals.
Application information: Contributes only to pre-selected organizations.
Officers and Directors: Tracy Louis Merrill, Pres. and Director; Joseph W. Merrill, V.P. and Director; Oliver Merrill, Secy.-Treas. and Director.
EIN: 363715158

2943
Hallene Family Foundation Inc.
1903 Glenwood Dr.
Moline, IL 61265-5233 (309) 762-3595

Established in 1995 in Illinois.
Donor: Phyllis W. Hallene.
Foundation type: Independent foundation.
Financial data (yr. ended 12/31/14): Assets, $4,193,377; gifts received, $169,415; expenditures, $279,997; qualifying distributions, $258,938.
Fields of interest: Arts and culture; Education; Cancers; Religion.
Limitations: Applications accepted. Giving primarily in FL, IL, and MN.
Application information:
  Initial approach: Proposal
  Deadline(s): None
Officers: Phyllis W. Hallene, Pres. and Secy.; Alan M. Hallene, Jr., Treas.
Directors: James N. Hallene; Carol H. King; Janet O'Hern.
EIN: 371335373

2944
The Halstead Foundation Inc.
10 S. Dearborn IL1-0117
Chicago, IL 60603

Established in 1987 in Arizona.
Donors: J.D. Halstead Lumber Co.; Halstead Trust; Halstead Charitable Trust; Malabar J&J Halstead Survivors Trust; Joanne S. Halstead‡.
Foundation type: Independent foundation.
Financial data (yr. ended 12/31/13): Assets, $8,955,310 (M); gifts received, $1,289,482; expenditures, $343,049; qualifying distributions, $288,505; giving activities include $175,000 for 13 grants (high: $52,500; low: $1,500).
Fields of interest: Education; Higher education.
Type of support: Scholarships; Individual development.

Limitations: Applications not accepted. No grants to individuals.
Application information: Contributes only to pre-selected organizations.
Trustee: JPMorgan Chase Bank, N.A.
Board Members: Sandra Alpizar; Dawn Bergford; Jeffrey Bergford; Elaine Klesius; Patrick Klesius; Stephen Klesius.
EIN: 866052836

2945
William P. Hamilton Fund Trust
10 S. Dearborn, IL1-0117
Chicago, IL 60603

Foundation type: Independent foundation.
Financial data (yr. ended 11/30/13): Assets, $9,904,915 (M); expenditures, $497,564; qualifying distributions, $423,649; giving activities include $401,055 for 1 grant.
Fields of interest: Community and economic development.
Limitations: Applications not accepted.
Application information: Unsolicited requests for funds not accepted.
Trustee: JPMorgan Chase Bank, N.A.
EIN: 136846411

2946
George A. Hamlin
c/o The Northern Trust Company
P.O. Box 803878
Chicago, IL 60680-3878

Foundation type: Independent foundation.
Financial data (yr. ended 09/30/14): Assets, $3,121,703 (M); expenditures, $237,675; qualifying distributions, $207,272; giving activities include $203,715 for 4 grants (high: $81,486; low: $40,743).
Fields of interest: Sports and recreation; Human services; Youth development.
Limitations: Applications not accepted. Giving primarily in IL.
Application information: Unsolicited requests for funds not accepted.
Trustee: The Northern Trust Company.
EIN: 366035858

2947
Harold G. and Sue Ann Hamm Foundation
P.O. Box 803878
Chicago, IL 60680-3878
Application address: James J. Van Stone, 101 N. Robinson, Ste. 920, Oklahoma City, OK 73116
Harold and Sue Ann Hamm's Giving Pledge Profile: http://glasspockets.org/ philanthropy-in-focus/eye-on-the-giving-pledge/ profiles/hamm

Established in 2006 in Oklahoma.
Donors: Harold G. Hamm; Sue A. Hamm.
Foundation type: Independent foundation.
Financial data (yr. ended 03/31/13): Assets, $126 (M); expenditures, $205,586; qualifying distributions, $204,483; giving activities include $203,420 for 1 grant.
Purpose and activities: Giving primarily to a pre-K through grade 12, independent Episcopal school.

Fields of interest: Elementary and secondary education.
Limitations: Applications accepted. Giving primarily in Oklahoma City, OK. No grants to individuals.
Application information:
  Initial approach: Letter
  Deadline(s): None
Officers: Harold G. Hamm, Pres.; Sue Ann Hamm, Secy.-Treas.; James J. Van Stone, C.I.O.; Bert Mackie.
EIN: 208084833

2948
Irving A. Hansen Memorial Foundation
10 S. Dearborn St., IL1-0117
Chicago, IL 60603-2300

Established in 1983 in New York.
Donors: Irving A. Hansen‡; Elizabeth A. Hansen Irrevocable Trust; Elizabeth A. Hansen Revocable Trust; Elizabeth A. Hansen Trust.
Foundation type: Independent foundation.
Financial data (yr. ended 07/31/13): Assets, $6,941,159 (M); expenditures, $488,959; qualifying distributions, $400,035; giving activities include $375,000 for 15 grants (high: $30,000; low: $20,000).
Fields of interest: University education; Libraries; Human services; Child welfare.
Type of support: General support.
Limitations: Applications not accepted. Giving primarily in CA, ME and NY. No grants to individuals; no loans.
Application information: Unsolicited requests for funds not accepted.
Trustees: Louis B. Frost, Esq.; William F. Hibberd; JPMorgan Chase Bank, N.A.
EIN: 133177338

2949
Alice G. Hanson Family Foundation
P.O. Box 803878
Chicago, IL 60680-3878

Foundation type: Independent foundation.
Financial data (yr. ended 12/31/13): Assets, $9,152,974 (M); expenditures, $657,785; qualifying distributions, $573,250; giving activities include $440,000 for 3 grants (high: $300,000; low: $40,000).
Purpose and activities: Giving primarily for Jewish organizations as well as to a charitable gift fund; funding also for a children's hospital.
Fields of interest: Foundations; Specialty hospital care; Judaism; Human services; Child welfare.
Limitations: Applications not accepted. Giving primarily in MA and NY, with some giving in IL and NM. No grants to individuals.
Application information: Contributes only to pre-selected organizations.
Officers and Directors: Burton Rottman, Pres. and Director; Howard Rottman, Secy. and Director; Michael Rottman, Treas. and Director.
EIN: 363215192

2950
Anna Emery Hanson Testamentary Charitable Trust
c/o The Northern Trust Co.
P.O. Box 803878
Chicago, IL 60680-3878

Established in 1986 in Illinois.
Donor: Anna Emery Hanson†.
Foundation type: Independent foundation.
Financial data (yr. ended 09/30/13): Assets, $4,127,682 (M); expenditures, $209,958; qualifying distributions, $186,746; giving activities include $183,798 for 79 grants (high: $18,912; low: $200).
Fields of interest: Elementary and secondary education; Higher education; Environment; Health; Hospital care; Mental health care; Community and economic development; Christianity; Human services; Family services; Child welfare.
Type of support: General support; Matching grants; Endowments; Seed money; Research and evaluation.
Limitations: Applications not accepted. Giving primarily in CT, WI, and WY. No grants to individuals.
Application information: Contributes only to pre-selected organizations.
Trustees: Marjorie Hanson Greenfield; Mary Anna Hanson MacLean; Rainer R. Weigel; The Northern Trust Co.
EIN: 366854655

2951
George & Barbara Hanus Foundation
200 W. Madison St., 42nd Fl.
Chicago, IL 60606-3402

Established in 1986 in Illinois.
Donor: George D. Hanus.
Foundation type: Independent foundation.
Financial data (yr. ended 11/30/14): Assets, $60,716 (M); gifts received, $392,250; expenditures, $393,226; qualifying distributions, $393,226; giving activities include $391,690 for 30 grants (high: $83,000).
Purpose and activities: Giving primarily to Jewish organizations, including a Jewish broadcasting network and a Jewish publication; funding also for scholarships and yeshivas.
Fields of interest: Education; Elementary and secondary education; Higher education; Religion.
Limitations: Applications not accepted. Giving primarily in IL. No grants to individuals.
Application information: Contributes only to pre-selected organizations. .
Officers: George D. Hanus, Pres.; Barbara A. Hanus, Secy.
Director: Magda Hanus.
EIN: 363485278

2952
Harry J. Harczak, Sr. Memorial Foundation
65 E. Monroe, Ste. 4809
Chicago, IL 60603-5755

Established in 2007 in Illinois.
Donors: Harry J. Harczak, Jr.; Marcy A. Harczak.
Foundation type: Independent foundation.
Financial data (yr. ended 12/31/14): Assets, $981,944 (M); expenditures, $177,251; qualifying distributions, $168,450; giving activities include $168,450 for 31 grants (high: $38,000; low: $250).
Fields of interest: Arts and culture; Education; Higher education; Food aid; Child welfare; Youth development.
Type of support: General support; Endowments.
Limitations: Applications not accepted. Giving primarily in IL. No grants to individuals.
Application information: Unsolicited requests for funds not accepted.
Officers: Harry J. Harczak, Jr., Co-Pres. and Secy.; Marcy A. Harczak, Co-Pres. and Treas.
Director: Jason Harczak.
EIN: 260566418

2953
Hardiek Family Foundation
c/o Bernard Hardiek
3454 52nd St.
Moline, IL 61265-6627

Established in 2003 in Illinois.
Donor: Bernard Hardiek.
Foundation type: Independent foundation.
Financial data (yr. ended 12/31/14): Assets, $2,456,338 (M); expenditures, $170,964; qualifying distributions, $170,964; giving activities include $155,338 for 15 grants (high: $43,825; low: $1,000).
Fields of interest: Secondary education; Public libraries; Catholicism.
Type of support: General support.
Limitations: Applications not accepted. No grants to individuals.
Application information: Contributes only to pre-selected organizations.
Directors: Kathy Dougherty; Bernard Hardiek; Greg Hardiek; Mark Hardiek.
EIN: 806024613

2954
Laura Hare Charitable Trust
c/o Tax Div.
111 W. Monroe St., Ste. 10C
P.O. Box 2977
Chicago, IL 60603 3124615154
Application address: c/o BMO Harris Bank N.A., 3929 River Crossing Pkwy., Ste. 200, Indianapolis, IN 46240, tel.: (317) 472-3570

Established in 2007 in Wisconsin.
Donor: Laura Hare†.
Foundation type: Independent foundation.
Financial data (yr. ended 12/31/14): Assets, $8,057,291 (M); expenditures, $322,392; qualifying distributions, $280,474.
Purpose and activities: Giving primarily to maintain ecologically-significant undeveloped land for purposes of preserving it in its natural state.
Fields of interest: Natural resources; Land resources; Environmental studies.
Type of support: Individual development.
Limitations: Applications accepted. Giving primarily in IN and NJ.
Application information:
    Initial approach: Proposal
    Deadline(s): None
Trustee: BMO Harris Bank, N.A.
Selection Committee Members: Helga Behroozi; Valita M. Fredland; Lenore Tedesco.
EIN: 206955819

2955
Marguerite Delany Hark Foundation
325 W. Wellington Ave.
Chicago, IL 60657-5636

Established in 1988 in Illinois.
Donor: Marguerite Delany Hark.
Foundation type: Independent foundation.
Financial data (yr. ended 12/31/14): Assets, $3,963,564; expenditures, $238,455; qualifying distributions, $220,015.
Purpose and activities: Giving primarily for education and housing.
Fields of interest: Education; Housing development.
Limitations: Applications not accepted. Giving in the U.S., with some emphasis on GA, IL, and WI. No grants to individuals.
Application information: Unsolicited requests for funds not accepted.
Trustees: William P. Eftax; Marguerite Delany Hark; Richard C. Ruwe.
EIN: 363617116

2956
E. F. Harris Family Foundation
807 Chestnut Ave.
Wilmette, IL 60091-1743
Contact: Robert J. Reichner
Application address: c/o Mark Harris, 1417 Dana Ave., Palo Alto, CA 94301-3116

Donors: Edward F. Harris; Vera Harris; Edward F. Harris Charitable Lead Trust.
Foundation type: Independent foundation.
Financial data (yr. ended 12/31/13): Assets, $3,489,369 (M); gifts received, $343,392; expenditures, $212,673; qualifying distributions, $197,182; giving activities include $197,097 for 54 grants (high: $82,500; low: $30).
Fields of interest: Education; Religion; Human services.
Application information:
    Initial approach: Proposal
    Deadline(s): None
Officers and Directors: Mark Harris, Pres. and Director; Jane Harris, V.P. and Director; Mary Ann Harris, Secy.-Treas. and Director.
EIN: 366108528

2957
Hunt and Diane Harris Family Foundation
901 46th St.
Moline, IL 61265-2685 (309) 764-0123
Contact: John Harris II, Pres. and Treas.

Established in 1986 in Illinois.
Donors: Diane B. Harris; John H. Harris II.
Foundation type: Independent foundation.
Financial data (yr. ended 12/31/13): Assets, $5,483,916 (M); expenditures, $288,179; qualifying distributions, $275,795; giving activities include $275,000 for 5 grants (high: $160,000; low: $10,000).
Purpose and activities: Support for capital programs, and non-ongoing support for health, human services, and the arts, in the IA and IL Quad Cities area.
Fields of interest: Arts and culture; Education; Nonprofits; Human services; Youth services.

Type of support: Capital campaigns; Matching grants; Capital and infrastructure; Equipment; Program development; Regranting.
Limitations: Applications accepted. Giving limited to the IA and IL Quad cities areas. No grants to individuals.
Application information:
Initial approach: Proposal
Deadline(s): None
Board meeting date(s): As needed
Officers: John H. Harris II, Pres. and Treas.; Diane B. Harris, Secy.
Directors: Alexander W. Harris; Jennifer M. Harris; Molly K. Harris.
Number of staff: None.
EIN: 363488560

2958
John H. Hart Foundation
1500 N. Lake Shore Dr., Apt. 13A
Chicago, IL   60610-6686

Established in 2003 in Illinois.
Foundation type: Independent foundation.
Financial data (yr. ended 12/31/13): Assets, $1,996,210 (M); expenditures, $326,869; qualifying distributions, $321,524; giving activities include $314,885 for 45 grants (high: $78,100; low: $200).
Fields of interest: Arts and culture; Education.
Limitations: Applications not accepted. Giving primarily in IL.
Application information: Unsolicited requests for funds not accepted.
Officers and Directors: John H. Hart, Pres. and Treas. and Director; Carol Prins, V.P. and Director; Ronald Schreiber, Secy. and Director.
EIN: 200156873

2959
Amherst F. Hary Foundation
130 N. Water St.
Decatur, IL   62523-1310

Established in 2004 in Illinois.
Foundation type: Independent foundation.
Financial data (yr. ended 12/31/13): Assets, $5,333,717 (M); expenditures, $286,041; qualifying distributions, $230,565; giving activities include $230,565 for 6 grants (high: $130,951; low: $6,000).
Fields of interest: Education; Health.
Limitations: Applications not accepted. Giving primarily in Decatur, IL.
Application information: Unsolicited requests for funds not accepted.
Advisors: Becky Colker; Gary Davis; Peg Luy; Julie Moore; Louise Stewart.
EIN: 300185703

2960
Oris B. Hastings Charitable Foundation
c/o John G. Holland, Jr.
230 8th St.
P.O. Box 186
Cairo, IL   62914-2135

Established in 1988 in Illinois.
Foundation type: Independent foundation.

Financial data (yr. ended 12/31/14): Assets, $6,219,588; expenditures, $509,717; qualifying distributions, $453,105.
Fields of interest: Museums; Historic preservation; Education; Specialty hospital care; Community and economic development; Catholicism; Human services; Child welfare.
Limitations: Applications not accepted. Giving primarily in Cairo, IL. No grants to individuals.
Application information: Unsolicited requests for funds not accepted.
Trustee: John G. Holland, Jr.
EIN: 371105036

2961
John I. Hay Foundation
c/o The Northern Trust Co.
P.O. Box 803878
Chicago, IL   60680-3878

Established in 1955 in Illinois.
Donor: John I. Hay Trust.
Foundation type: Independent foundation.
Financial data (yr. ended 12/31/13): Assets, $5,068,874 (M); expenditures, $251,644; qualifying distributions, $227,210; giving activities include $226,135 for 2 grants (high: $206,700; low: $19,435).
Fields of interest: Arts and culture; Human services; Youth services.
Type of support: General support; Equipment.
Limitations: Applications not accepted. Giving primarily in IL and Jackson, MS. No grants to individuals.
Application information: Unsolicited requests for funds not accepted.
Officers: John C. Goodall, Jr., Pres.; John C. Goodall III, Secy.; Roberta J. Ellerman, Treas.
EIN: 366103629

2962
Mary Heath Foundation
P.O. Box 217
Robinson, IL   62454-0217   (618) 544-3900
Contact: Stewart Schutte

Established in 1994 in Illinois.
Foundation type: Independent foundation.
Financial data (yr. ended 12/31/13): Assets, $5,390,836 (M); expenditures, $275,582; qualifying distributions, $259,775; giving activities include $217,996 for 30 grants (high: $20,000; low: $1,064).
Purpose and activities: Support primarily for organizations sponsoring projects in the areas of public health, safety, recreation, and education in IL.
Fields of interest: Arts and culture; Adult education; Parent-teacher involvement; Libraries; Fire prevention and control; Community improvement; Housing development; Food banks; Youth development; Shelter and residential care; Senior services.
Type of support: Capital and infrastructure; Equipment; Program development; Curriculum development.
Limitations: Applications accepted. Giving limited to IL. No grants to individuals, or for endowments, deficit reduction, fundraising, or political campaigns.
Publications: Application guidelines; Program policy statement.
Application information: Application form required.

Initial approach: Proposal
Copies of proposal: 6
Deadline(s): May 1 and Nov. 1
Advisory Committees: Radford Burkett; Todd Musgrave; Thomas Pearce; Randy Rich; Rodney Stewart.
EIN: 371330907

2963
Julius W. Hegeler II Foundation
1521 N. Vermilion St.
Danville, IL   61832-2370   (217) 442-1521
Contact: Julius W. Hegeler II, Pres.

Established in 1992 in Illinois.
Donor: Julius W. Hegeler II.
Foundation type: Operating foundation.
Financial data (yr. ended 06/30/13): Assets, $14,247,714 (M); expenditures, $749,353; qualifying distributions, $710,172; giving activities include $364,385 for 17 grants (high: $50,000; low: $1,000).
Fields of interest: Arts and culture; Education; Higher education; Health; Hospital care; Human services.
Limitations: Applications accepted. Giving primarily in Danville, IL. No grants to individuals.
Application information:
Initial approach: Proposal
Deadline(s): None
Officers and Directors: Julius W. Hegeler II, Pres. and Director; Alix S. Hegeler, V.P. and Director; Lois Wise, Secy.-Treas. and Director; F. Jay Foster.
EIN: 371302455

2964
Gussie Heins Residuary Trust
10 S. Dearborn, IL1-0117
Chicago, IL   60603

Established in 2005 in Illinois.
Foundation type: Independent foundation.
Financial data (yr. ended 12/31/14): Assets, $7,747,693; expenditures, $440,532; qualifying distributions, $371,723.
Fields of interest: Human services; Child welfare; Shelter and residential care.
Limitations: Applications not accepted. Giving primarily in IL.
Application information: Unsolicited requests for funds not accepted.
Trustee: JPMorgan Chase Bank, N.A.
EIN: 366016975

2965
Henderson Education Fund f/bo Tulane University
10 S. Dearborn IL1-0117
Chicago, IL   60603   8668885157

Foundation type: Independent foundation.
Financial data (yr. ended 12/31/14): Assets, $1,881,771; expenditures, $177,505; qualifying distributions, $158,966.
Fields of interest: Education.
Limitations: Applications not accepted.
Application information: Unsolicited requests for funds not accepted.
Trustee: JPMorgan Chase Bank, N.A.
EIN: 726017995

2966
Bernard & Pauline Herbert Scholarship Trust

10 S. Dearborn IL1-0117
Chicago, IL 60603

Established in 2006 in Arizona.
Donors: Dr. Bernard E. Herbert; Pauline I. Herbert†.
Foundation type: Independent foundation.
Financial data (yr. ended 12/31/14): Assets, $4,249,226; expenditures, $246,057; qualifying distributions, $202,418.
Purpose and activities: Giving for scholarships to students of osteopathic medicine at Des Moines University, Iowa.
Fields of interest: Medical education.
Type of support: Scholarships.
Limitations: Applications not accepted. Giving limited to Des Moines, IA.
Application information: Unsolicited requests for funds not accepted.
Trustee: JPMorgan Chase Bank, N.A.
EIN: 206945564

2967
The Heritage Foundation of First Security Federal Savings Bank, Inc.

2329 W. Chicago Ave.
Chicago, IL 60622-4723 (773) 486-6645

Established in 1997 in Illinois.
Donors: First Security Federal Savings Bank; Maria Olijnyk.
Foundation type: Company-sponsored foundation.
Financial data (yr. ended 12/31/14): Assets, $13,525,927; expenditures, $543,068; qualifying distributions, $403,010.
Purpose and activities: The foundation supports programs designed to preserve Ukrainian culture and heritage; and promote democracy and a free market economy.
Fields of interest: Arts and culture; Education; Human services.
International interests: Ukraine.
Type of support: General support; Program development; Convening; Publications.
Limitations: Applications accepted. Giving primarily in IL. No grants to individuals.
Application information:
    Initial approach: Proposal
    Deadline(s): None
Officers: Julian E. Kulas, Pres. and Director; Paul Nadzikewycz, V.P.; Terry Gawryk, Secy.
Trustees: Taras Drozd; Dmytro Shtohryn; Chrysta Wereszczak.
Number of staff: 1 part-time support.
EIN: 364135415

2968
Skip & Meg Herman Family Foundation

3800 N. Lake Shore Dr., Ste. 15B
Chicago, IL 60613-3301

Donors: Sidney N. Herman; Margaret Herman.
Foundation type: Independent foundation.
Financial data (yr. ended 12/31/14): Assets, $1,159,686; gifts received, $2,028; expenditures, $397,561; qualifying distributions, $394,333.
Fields of interest: Education; University education; Land resources; Nonprofits.
Type of support: Regranting.

Limitations: Applications not accepted.
Application information: Unsolicited requests for funds not accepted.
Officers and Directors: Sidney N. Herman, Pres. and Director; Margaret Herman, Secy.-Treas. and Director; Rockney W. Hudson.
EIN: 263033542

2969
Myrtle E. & William G. Hess Charitable Trust

c/o JPMorgan Chase Bank, N.A.
10 S. Dearborn St., 21st Fl.
Chicago, IL 60603-2300
E-mail: matthew.h.wasmund@jpmorgan.com;
Application address: c/o JPMorgan Chase Bank, N.A., 1116 West Long Lake, 2nd Fl., Bloomfield Hills, MI 48302-1963, tel.: (248) 645-7308

Established in 1984 in Michigan.
Donor: Myrtle E. Hess†.
Foundation type: Independent foundation.
Financial data (yr. ended 09/30/13): Assets, $7,214,903 (M); expenditures, $395,311; qualifying distributions, $336,009; giving activities include $319,120 for 17 grants (high: $100,000; low: $5,000).
Purpose and activities: Giving only to Roman Catholic institutions and agencies located in Oakland County, MI, including Roman Catholic hospitals and schools, or to those institutions that received grants during the donor's lifetime or that were designated for support in the donor's will.
Fields of interest: Education; Elementary and secondary education; Child educational development; Nonprofits; Hospital care; Alcoholism; Religion; Catholicism; Sports and recreation; Human services; Child development.
Type of support: General support; Annual campaigns; Capital and infrastructure; Endowments; Program development; Scholarships; Regranting.
Limitations: Applications accepted. Giving limited to Oakland County, MI.
Application information:
    Initial approach: Proposal
    Copies of proposal: 2
    Board meeting date(s): Mar.
Trustees: Thomas W. Payne; JPMorgan Chase Bank, N.A.
EIN: 382617770

2970
Highland Park Community Foundation

P.O. Box 398
Highland Park, IL 60035-0398 (847) 433-4100
E-mail: info@hpcommunityfoundation.com; Main URL: http://www.hpcommunityfoundation.com

Established in 1992 in Illinois.
Foundation type: Community foundation.
Financial data (yr. ended 12/31/13): Assets, $3,292,400 (M); gifts received, $161,362; expenditures, $179,343; giving activities include $145,850 for 10+ grants (high: $21,500).
Purpose and activities: The foundation seeks to meet the unmet social service, cultural, educational and environmental needs of Highland Park and Highwood, and to promote philanthropy in the community.

Fields of interest: Arts and culture; Theater; Education; Early childhood education; Environment; Public libraries; Family services; Youth services.
Limitations: Applications accepted. Giving limited to Highland Park, IL. No grants to individuals.
Publications: Application guidelines.
Application information: Visit foundation web site for application form and guidelines. After submitting application online, send attachments by U.S. Mail. Application form required.
    Initial approach: Complete online grant application and mail attachments to foundation office
    Deadline(s): July 15
Officers and Directors: Wally R. Nathan, Chair. and Director; Peter Flanzer, Vice-Chair. and Director; Charles Dobrusin, Secy. and Director; David Fairman, Treas. and Director; Sofia Alvarez; Jack B. Blane; Betsy Brint; Bruce K. Goodman; Steven A. Hirsh; Cookie Anspach Kohn; Laurie Levin; Frank Lieber; Andrew M. Livingston; Jean Meadows; Nancy Mills; David Reich; Virginia Schulte; David B. Small; Donald Stewart; Sallyan Windt; Cynthia Witten.
EIN: 363819818

2971
Arthur W. Hill Foundation

c/o Robert W. Gillett
1400 Burr Oak Dr.
Glenview, IL 60025

Foundation type: Independent foundation.
Financial data (yr. ended 10/31/13): Assets, $6,251,382 (M); expenditures, $265,718; qualifying distributions, $211,217; giving activities include $182,523 for 46 grants (high: $31,500; low: $65).
Fields of interest: Education; Housing development; Religion.
Limitations: Applications not accepted. Giving primarily in IL and MI. No grants to individuals.
Application information: Unsolicited requests for funds not accepted.
Officers: Robert W. Gillett, Pres.; Mary H. Gillett, V.P.; Nancy Tefft, V.P.
EIN: 366050191

2972
The George F. and Helen M. Hirschmann Charitable Foundation

c/o Mark D. Toljanic
2215 York Rd., Ste. 550
Oak Brook, IL 60523-4013

Established in 1994 in Illinois.
Donors: George F. Hirschmann; Linda H. Hanson; Vanguard Windsor II Fund.
Foundation type: Independent foundation.
Financial data (yr. ended 12/31/14): Assets, $4,884,456; expenditures, $266,834; qualifying distributions, $246,000 and $0 for set-asides.
Fields of interest: Animal welfare.
Limitations: Applications not accepted. Giving primarily in IL. No grants to individuals.
Application information: Unsolicited requests for funds not accepted.
Officer and Directors: Mark D. Toljanic, Pres. and Secy. and Director; Andrew Hanson; Christy Hanson; Linda H. Hanson; Donna Wilbert.
EIN: 363961987

2973
Doris & Jerome Hirschmann Family Foundation
1410 Sheridan Rd., Apt. 6C
Wilmette, IL 60091-1896

Established in 1990 in Illinois.
Donors: Doris Hirschman; Jerome Hirschman.
Foundation type: Independent foundation.
Financial data (yr. ended 12/31/14): Assets, $3,636,497 (M); expenditures, $250,731; qualifying distributions, $233,341; giving activities include $230,600 for 38 grants (high: $52,500; low: $15).
Fields of interest: Diseases and conditions; Religion; Human services.
Limitations: Applications accepted. Giving primarily in IL. No grants to individuals.
Application information: Application form required.
  Initial approach: Letter
  Deadline(s): None
Officers and Directors: Richard A. Hirschmann, Pres. and Secy. and Director; Doris Hirschmann, Treas. and Director; Louis W. Hirschmann.
EIN: 363678232

2974
Hodes Family Foundation
P.O. Box 803878
Chicago, IL 60680-3878 3129253784

Established in 1984 in Illinois.
Donor: Scott Hodes.
Foundation type: Independent foundation.
Financial data (yr. ended 12/31/14): Assets, $1,692,576; expenditures, $204,932; qualifying distributions, $175,601.
Purpose and activities: Giving for the arts, Jewish organizations, and human services.
Fields of interest: Arts and culture; Education; Religion.
Limitations: Applications not accepted. Giving primarily in Chicago, IL. No grants to individuals.
Application information: Unsolicited requests for funds not accepted.
Officers: Maria Becily-Hodes, Pres.; Scott Hodes, Secy.-Treas.
Directors: Anthony S. Hodes; Valery H. Lodato.
EIN: 363296044

2975
Hoffer Foundation
500 N. Collins St.
South Elgin, IL 60177-1104 (847) 741-5740
Contact: Gretchen Hoffer Farb, Dir.

Established in 1966 in Illinois.
Donors: Hoffer Plastics Corp.; Robert A. Hoffer†.
Foundation type: Company-sponsored foundation.
Financial data (yr. ended 11/30/13): Assets, $2,167,135 (M); gifts received, $1,890; expenditures, $384,413; qualifying distributions, $357,702; giving activities include $357,702 for 27 + grants (high: $11,073).
Purpose and activities: The foundation supports organizations involved with education, health, and human services.
Fields of interest: Education; Higher education; Nonprofits; Health; Hospital care; Hospice care; Human services; Youth services; Domestic violence shelters.

Type of support: General support; Regranting.
Limitations: Applications accepted. Giving primarily in IL, with emphasis on Elgin and South Elgin. No support for political or religious organizations.
Application information: Application form required.
  Initial approach: Letter
  Deadline(s): None
Directors: Charlotte H. Canning; Mary Hoffer Eagin; Sara Eagin; Gretchen Hoffer Farb; Helen C. Hoffer; Robert A. Hoffer, Jr.; William A. Hoffer; William Alex Hoffer.
EIN: 366160991

2976
The Holden Foundation
500 Lake Cook Rd., Ste. 200
Deerfield, IL 60015-4937

Established in 1995 in Illinois.
Donors: D.H. Carroll; Catharine A. Carroll.
Foundation type: Independent foundation.
Financial data (yr. ended 12/31/13): Assets, $4,488 (M); gifts received, $306,371; expenditures, $301,973; qualifying distributions, $301,958; giving activities include $301,350 for 44 grants (high: $60,000; low: $100).
Purpose and activities: Giving primarily for cowboy and Western heritage museums as well as rodeo organizations; some funding also for education, human services, and youth organizations.
Fields of interest: Museums; Education; Human services; Youth development.
Limitations: Applications not accepted. Giving primarily in CA, IL, OK and WY. No grants to individuals.
Application information: Unsolicited requests for funds not accepted.
Trustee: D.H. Carroll.
EIN: 367093502

2977
Bertrand Hopper Memorial Foundation
c/o U.S. Bank, N.A., Trust Dept.
108 W. Market St.
Taylorville, IL 62568-0350 2172871820
Application address: William B. Hopper, P.O. Box 350 - Trust Dept., Taylorville, IL 62568-0530, tel.: (217) 287-1820

Established in 1956 in Illinois.
Donors: Bertrand C. Hopper; Hopper Paper Co.; John S. Corzine Foundation.
Foundation type: Independent foundation.
Financial data (yr. ended 12/31/13): Assets, $5,036,958 (M); gifts received, $6,000; expenditures, $278,214; qualifying distributions, $261,094; giving activities include $245,500 for 34 grants (high: $45,000; low: $500).
Fields of interest: Education; Nonprofits; Health; Hospital care; Cancers; Human services; Child welfare.
Type of support: Annual campaigns; Capital campaigns; Scholarships; Regranting.
Limitations: Applications accepted. Giving primarily in IL. No grants to individuals.
Application information: Application form required.
  Initial approach: Letter
  Deadline(s): None
Officers: William B. Hopper, Pres.; Ronald E. Mizer, V.P.; Bonnie Bruns, Secy.-Treas.

Directors: Stephanie Hopper Denby; Kenneth A. Hart; Austin W. Hopper; David W. Hopper; Marilyn M. Hopper; Randal B. Hopper; Randall K. Perry.
EIN: 376026794

2978
Irvin E. Houck Charitable Trust
c/o PrivateBank
120 S. Lasalle St., 7th Fl.
Chicago, IL 60603

Established in 1970 in Illinois.
Foundation type: Independent foundation.
Financial data (yr. ended 11/30/14): Assets, $155,848 (M); expenditures, $155,848; qualifying distributions, $152,118; giving activities include $151,300 for 53 grants (high: $21,000; low: $300).
Fields of interest: Christianity; Human services.
Limitations: Applications not accepted. Giving in the U.S., with emphasis on IL and RI. No grants to individuals.
Application information: Unsolicited requests for funds not accepted.
Trustees: Richard I. Houck; Mary Houck Olson; Margaret H. Smith; The PrivateBank.
EIN: 237128830

2979
The Francis J. and Patricia A. Houlihan Foundation
c/o Grubich Consultants, LTD
728 Florsheim Dr., Ste. 13
Libertyville, IL 60048-5273

Established in 1996 in Illinois.
Donor: Francis J. Houlihan.
Foundation type: Independent foundation.
Financial data (yr. ended 12/31/13): Assets, $3,507,252 (M); gifts received, $100,000; expenditures, $185,289; qualifying distributions, $158,812; giving activities include $158,812 for 41 grants (high: $29,000; low: $100).
Fields of interest: Education; Elementary and secondary education; Hospital care; Christianity; Human services; Child welfare.
Limitations: Applications not accepted. Giving primarily in IL. No grants to individuals.
Application information: Contributes only to pre-selected organizations.
Officers: Francis J. Houlihan, Pres.; Patricia A. Houlihan, V.P.; Kenneth E. Grubich, Treas.
EIN: 364121030

2980
Susan Cook House Educational Trust
10 S. Dearborn St., IL1-0117
Chicago, IL 60603-2300
Application address: c/o Heather Smith, 1 East Old State Capitol Plz., 3rd Fl., Springfield, IL 62701, tel.: (217) 525-9737

Established in 1969 in Illinois.
Foundation type: Independent foundation.
Financial data (yr. ended 11/30/13): Assets, $4,505,735 (M); expenditures, $307,482; qualifying distributions, $262,788; giving activities include $255,066 for 20 grants (high: $28,500; low: $1,637).

Purpose and activities: Giving primarily for the arts and wildlife. Scholarship awards to residents of Sangamon County, Illinois.
Fields of interest: Arts councils; Orchestral music; University education; Wildlife sanctuaries.
Type of support: Student aid; General support; Scholarships.
Limitations: Applications accepted. Giving limited to Sangamon County, IL.
Application information: Application form required.
  Initial approach: Proposal
  Copies of proposal: 2
  Deadline(s): None
Trustee: JPMorgan Chase Bank, N.A.
EIN: 376087675

2981
Howard Family Foundation
1624 Wesley Ave.
Evanston, IL 60201-4106 (847) 864-6767
Contact: Barbara H. Howard, Tr.

Established in 1993 in Illinois.
Donor: Barbara H. Howard.
Foundation type: Independent foundation.
Financial data (yr. ended 12/31/13): Assets, $5,763,832 (M); expenditures, $265,307; qualifying distributions, $221,000.
Fields of interest: Arts and culture; Opera; University education; Foundations; Nonprofits; Diabetes; Christianity; Human services; Child welfare; Women's services.
Type of support: Research; Regranting.
Limitations: Applications accepted. Giving primarily in IL. No grants to individuals.
Application information: Application form required.
  Initial approach: Letter
  Deadline(s): None
Trustee: Barbara H. Howard.
EIN: 367041179

2982
Leola W. and Charles H. Hugg Trust
c/o JPMorgan Chase Bank, N.A.
10 S. Dearborn St., IL1-0117
Chicago, IL 60603-2300

Foundation type: Independent foundation.
Financial data (yr. ended 12/31/13): Assets, $8,609,327 (M); expenditures, $531,238; qualifying distributions, $436,882; giving activities include $403,175 for grants to individuals.
Purpose and activities: Grants for scholarships to students from Williamson County, TX, to attend colleges and universities in TX.
Fields of interest: Higher education.
Limitations: Applications not accepted.
Application information: Unsolicited requests for funds not accepted.
  Board meeting date(s): Annually
Trustees: Richard L. Anderson; Ronald L. Swain; JPMorgan Chase Bank, N.A.
EIN: 741907673

2983
John E. & Jeanne T. Hughes Charitable Foundation
1057 W. Monroe St.
Chicago, IL 60607-2603

Established in 1991 in Illinois.
Donors: John E. Hughes; Jeanne T. Hughes.
Foundation type: Independent foundation.
Financial data (yr. ended 09/30/14): Assets, $4,762,919; expenditures, $207,291; qualifying distributions, $199,911.
Purpose and activities: Primary areas of interest include self-employment education and training, entrepreneurship and educational research, primary through graduate education, business start-up education, cancer care, and medical treatment.
Fields of interest: Education; Voluntarism; Diseases and conditions; Cancers.
Type of support: General support; Matching grants; Capital campaigns; Research; Program development; Research and evaluation; Convening; Curriculum development; Scholarships.
Limitations: Applications not accepted. Giving primarily in AZ, Chicago, IL, and NM. No support for religious or political organizations. No grants to individuals, or loans to individuals.
Application information: Unsolicited requests for funds not accepted.
  Board meeting date(s): Varies
Officers and Directors: John E. Hughes, Pres. and Director; Jeanne T. Hughes, V.P. and Exec. Dir.; Carole J. Hennessy, Secy. and Director; Michael W. Hennessy, Treas. and Director; Jonathan M. Hennessy; Matthew H. Hennessy.
EIN: 363798525

2984
Virginia Hunt Trust for Episcopal Charitable Institutions
10 S. Dearborn St., IL1-0117
Chicago, IL 60603-2300
Application address: c/o JPMorgan Chase Bank, Attn.: Edward Rudawitz, 270 Park Ave., 16th Fl., New York, NY 10017, tel.: (212) 648-1494

Donor: Virginia Hunt†.
Foundation type: Independent foundation.
Financial data (yr. ended 03/31/13): Assets, $4,912,195 (M); expenditures, $267,451; qualifying distributions, $233,197; giving activities include $220,000 for 5 grants (high: $120,000; low: $15,000).
Purpose and activities: Giving limited to Episcopal charitable institutions, especially to those organizations that were known to the donor.
Fields of interest: Nonprofits; Episcopalianism and Anglicanism; Lutheranism; Human services.
Type of support: Program development; Capital and infrastructure; Regranting; General support.
Limitations: Giving primarily in NY and VT, with emphasis on Burlington. No grants to individuals.
Publications: Application guidelines; Grants list.
Application information: Contributes primarily to organizations known to donor.
  Initial approach: Letter of inquiry
  Copies of proposal: 1
  Deadline(s): Jan. 1
  Board meeting date(s): Mar.
  Final notification: Mar. 31
Trustee: JPMorgan Chase Bank, N.A.
Number of staff: None.
EIN: 237426415

2985
Ed E. & Gladys Hurley Foundation
c/o JPMorgan Chase Bank, N.A.
10 S. Dearborn, IL1-0117
Chicago, IL 60603
Application address: c/o JPMorgan Chase Bank, N.A., Attn.: Debbie Ottinger, P.O. Box 227237, Dallas, TX 75222-7237, tel.: (214) 965-2914

Established in 1954 in Louisiana.
Donor: Ed E. Hurley†.
Foundation type: Independent foundation.
Financial data (yr. ended 12/31/13): Assets, $4,278,727 (M); expenditures, $219,425; qualifying distributions, $184,880; giving activities include $175,600 for 27 grants to individuals (high: $1,500; low: $500).
Purpose and activities: Support for higher education through grants to colleges and universities and scholarships awarded to students residing in AR, LA, and TX.
Fields of interest: Higher education.
Type of support: Student aid; General support.
Limitations: Giving primarily to residents and organizations of AR, LA, and TX.
Application information: Application form required.
  Initial approach: Letter, including past grades and loan request
  Deadline(s): June 30
Trustee: JPMorgan Chase Bank, N.A.
EIN: 726018854

2986
Ideal Industries Foundation
Becker Pl.
Sycamore, IL 60178 (815) 895-5181
Contact: James Pfotenhauer, V.P. and Secy.

Established in 1986 in Illinois.
Donors: Ideal Industries Inc.; Sally Juday; Susan Golding; Dave Juday; Nancy Juday; Patricia Juday; David W. Juday; Chris Lamb; Roberta McQuade.
Foundation type: Company-sponsored foundation.
Financial data (yr. ended 12/31/13): Assets, $2,348,375 (M); gifts received, $175,881; expenditures, $186,357; qualifying distributions, $170,500; giving activities include $170,500 for 35 grants (high: $25,000; low: $75).
Purpose and activities: The foundation supports history museums and organizations involved with child welfare, children and youth, disability services, homelessness, and economic development.
Fields of interest: Arts and culture; Health; Human services.
Type of support: General support; Continuing support.
Limitations: Applications accepted. Giving primarily in IL.
Application information: Application form required.
  Initial approach: Proposal
  Copies of proposal: 1
  Deadline(s): None
Officers: Chris Lamb, Pres.; James Pfotenhauer, V.P. and Secy.; Sheila Johnsen, V.P. and Treas.
Directors: Jessica Baack; David W. Juday; Carpice Perez; Anita Zurburgg.
EIN: 363449960

2987
Ingredion Charitable Foundation
5 Westbrook Corporate Ctr.
Westchester, IL 60154-5749

Donor: Ingredion Inc.
Foundation type: Independent foundation.
Financial data (yr. ended 12/31/13): Assets, $1,853,223 (M); expenditures, $147,700; qualifying distributions, $146,823; giving activities include $146,808 for 8 grants (high: $65,711; low: $1,730).
Fields of interest: Diseases and conditions; Agriculture; Human services.
Limitations: Applications not accepted.
Application information: Unsolicited requests for funds not accepted.
Officers and Directors: Diane Frisch, Pres. and Director; Christine Castellano, Secy. and Director; James Kreider, Treas.; Cheryl K. Beebe; Richard O'Shanna.
EIN: 800877126

2988
Ingredion Educational Foundation
5 Westbrook Corporate Ctr.
Westchester, IL 60154-5749 (507) 931-1682

Established in 2001 in Delaware.
Donors: Konrad Schlatter; James W. & Jayne A. McKee Foundation; Best Foods Educational Foundation.
Foundation type: Company-sponsored foundation.
Financial data (yr. ended 12/31/14): Assets, $3,970,761 (M); expenditures, $291,837; qualifying distributions, $242,950; giving activities include $229,600 for grants to individuals.
Purpose and activities: The foundation awards college scholarships to children of full-time employees of Corn Products International, Inc. and its affiliates.
Fields of interest: Higher education.
International interests: Australia; Brazil; Canada; Chile; China; Kenya; Mexico; Pakistan; Peru; South Korea; Thailand.
Type of support: Scholarships; Employee-related scholarships.
Limitations: Applications not accepted. Giving primarily in areas of company operations in IL, IN, NJ, Australia, Brazil, Canada, Chile, China. Kenya, Mexico, Pakistan, Peru, South Korea, and Thialand.
Application information: Contributes only through employee-related scholarships. Application form required.
Officers and Directors: Diane J. Frisch, Pres. and Director; Mary Ann Hynes, Secy. and Director; Cheryl K. Beebe, Treas. and Director.
EIN: 364477522

2989
Iroquois Federal Foundation Inc.
201 Cherry St.
Watseka, IL 60970-1661 (815) 432-2476

Donor: IF Bancorp Inc.
Foundation type: Independent foundation.
Financial data (yr. ended 12/31/14): Assets, $5,196,344 (M); expenditures, $246,124; qualifying distributions, $261,601.
Fields of interest: Arts and culture; Education; Human services.

Limitations: Applications accepted. Giving primarily in IL.
Application information: Application form required.
Initial approach: Completed application form *Deadline(s):* Mar. 1 and Sept. 30
Officers: Alan Martin, Pres.; Beth Warren, Secy.; Pamela Verkler, Treas.
Directors: James D. Anderson; Thomas Chamberlain; Robert L. Cotter, Jr.; Gary Martin; Frank Simutis.
EIN: 452255196

2990
Sultan and Sakeba Issa Family Foundation
161 North Tower Dr., Ste. J.
Burr Ridge, IL 60527-7818

Donor: Sultan Issa.
Foundation type: Independent foundation.
Financial data (yr. ended 10/31/13): Assets, $40,418 (M); gifts received, $263,383; expenditures, $225,114; qualifying distributions, $208,897; giving activities include $208,897 for 17 grants (high: $46,000; low: $350).
Fields of interest: Zoos; Domesticated animals; Sports and recreation; Youth development.
Limitations: Applications not accepted. Giving primarily in IL.
Application information: Unsolicited requests for funds not accepted.
Officers: Sultan Issa, Pres.; Sakeba Issa, V.P. and Treas.; Suad Issa, Secy.
EIN: 453845340

2991
Verne G. and Judith A. Istock Foundation
Chase Tower
10 S. Dearborn, Ste. 0554
Chicago, IL 60603-2003

Established in 2001 in Illinois.
Donors: Judith A. Istock; Verne G. Istock.
Foundation type: Independent foundation.
Financial data (yr. ended 12/31/13): Assets, $1,511,222 (M); gifts received, $281,500; expenditures, $358,447; qualifying distributions, $358,447; giving activities include $346,000 for 53 grants (high: $110,000; low: $500).
Fields of interest: Arts and culture; Education; Philanthropy.
Limitations: Applications not accepted. Giving primarily in Chicago, IL. No grants to individuals.
Application information: Unsolicited requests for funds not accepted.
Trustees: Judith A. Istock; Verne G. Istock.
EIN: 367362355

2992
Reinhardt H. & Shirley R. Jahn Foundation
2737 Eastwood Ave.
Evanston, IL 60201-1544

Established in 1992 in Illinois.
Donors: Shirley R. Jahn; Reinhardt H. Jahn†.
Foundation type: Independent foundation.
Financial data (yr. ended 12/31/13): Assets, $3,506,805 (M); expenditures, $338,863; qualifying distributions, $321,000; giving activities

include $321,000 for 9 grants (high: $250,000; low: $5,000).
Fields of interest: Arts and culture; History; Environment; Botanical gardens; Archaeology; Youth development; Youth services.
Limitations: Applications not accepted. Giving primarily in IL. No grants to individuals.
Application information: Unsolicited requests for funds not accepted.
Officers and Directors: Shirley R. Jahn, Chair. and Treas.; Reinhardt E. Jahn, Pres. and Director; Carolyn L. Jahn, Secy.; Charles L. Jahn.
EIN: 363857635

2993
Arthur G. & Dawn L. Jaros Sr. Charitable Trust
5916 Longview Dr.
Countryside, IL 60525-3953

Established in 2004 in Illinois.
Donor: Arthur G. Jaros Declaration of Trust, Sr.
Foundation type: Independent foundation.
Financial data (yr. ended 12/31/13): Assets, $5,011,735 (M); gifts received, $1,920,186; expenditures, $319,113; qualifying distributions, $271,185; giving activities include $210,860 for 44 grants (high: $31,240; low: $50).
Fields of interest: Education; Diseases and conditions; Cancers; Christianity; Human services; Child welfare.
Type of support: Research.
Limitations: Applications not accepted. Giving primarily in IL. No grants to individuals.
Application information: Unsolicited requests for funds not accepted.
Trustees: Arthur G. Jaros, Jr.; Randall S. Jaros; Wesley A. Jaros.
EIN: 206090921

2994
JBS Foundation
150 Aspen Way
Deerfield, IL 60015-4752

Established in 2004 in Illinois.
Donors: Lisa Lavin; Ronald Lavin.
Foundation type: Independent foundation.
Financial data (yr. ended 12/31/13): Assets, $4,308,327 (M); expenditures, $266,605; qualifying distributions, $201,190; giving activities include $201,190 for 49 grants (high: $27,000; low: $300).
Fields of interest: Nonprofits; Judaism; Human services; Youth development.
Type of support: Regranting.
Limitations: Applications not accepted. Giving primarily in IL. No grants to individuals.
Application information: Contributes only to pre-selected organizations.
Officers: Ronald Lavin, Pres.; Lisa Lavin, Secy.-Treas.
Director: Nelida Bernheim.
EIN: 383713152

2995
Jentes Family Foundation
c/o William R. Jentes
1500 N. Lake Shore Dr., Ste. 4C
Chicago, IL 60610-6686

Established in 1987 in Illinois.
Donors: William R. Jentes; Janet O. Jentes.
Foundation type: Independent foundation.
Financial data (yr. ended 12/31/14): Assets,
$4,897,022; gifts received, $3,465; expenditures,
$247,871; qualifying distributions, $242,468 and
$0 for set-asides.
Fields of interest: Arts and culture; Higher
education.
Limitations: Applications not accepted. Giving
primarily in Chicago, IL. No grants to individuals.
Application information: Unsolicited requests for
funds not accepted.
Officers and Directors: William R. Jentes, Pres. and
Treas. and Director; Donald G. Kempf, Jr., Secy. and
Director; Janet O. Jentes; Justine O. Jentes.
EIN: 363566107

2996
Jephson Educational Trust No. 1
10 S. Dearborn, IL1-0117
Chicago, IL 60603

Established in 1946 in New York.
Donor: Lucretia Davis Jephson†.
Foundation type: Independent foundation.
Financial data (yr. ended 12/31/14): Assets,
$5,933,774; expenditures, $315,554; qualifying
distributions, $256,348.
Purpose and activities: To support four-year
educational institutions through scholarship aid for
youth throughout the U.S.
Fields of interest: Higher education.
Type of support: Scholarships.
Limitations: Applications not accepted. Giving in the
U.S., primarily in MA, NY and VT. No grants to
individuals, or for matching gifts; no loans.
Publications: Grants list; Informational brochure.
Application information: Contributes only to
pre-selected organizations.
   Board meeting date(s): June and Oct.
Trustees: John F. Parkin; Robert D. Taisey;
JPMorgan Chase Bank, N.A.
EIN: 136023169

2997
JKP Family Foundation
300 N. LaSalle St., Ste. 1500
Chicago, IL 60654-3413

Donor: J.K. Poorman.
Foundation type: Independent foundation.
Financial data (yr. ended 12/31/13): Assets,
$5,135,590 (M); gifts received, $134,973;
expenditures, $232,810; qualifying distributions,
$231,750; giving activities include $231,750 for 14
grants (high: $115,000; low: $1,000).
Fields of interest: Arts and culture; Orchestral
music; Education; Higher education; Youth
development.
Type of support: Scholarships.
Limitations: Applications not accepted.
Application information: Unsolicited requests for
funds not accepted.
Trustee: J.K. Poorman.
EIN: 263930130

2998
JLH Foundation
352 Deepwood Rd.
Barrington, IL 60010-8618

Established in 2007 in Illinois.
Donor: Jerry L. Hayden.
Foundation type: Independent foundation.
Financial data (yr. ended 12/31/13): Assets,
$630,691 (M); gifts received, $200,000;
expenditures, $203,648; qualifying distributions,
$203,648; giving activities include $200,000 for 1
grant.
Limitations: Applications not accepted. Giving
primarily in Peoria, IL and MI. No grants to
individuals.
Application information: Unsolicited requests for
funds not accepted.
Officers: Jerry L. Hayden, Pres.; Douglas Hayden,
V.P.; Marilyn J. Hayden, Secy.
Director: Stephen M. Margolin.
EIN: 421692014

2999
JMR Charities, Inc.
333 W. 35th St.
Chicago, IL 60616-3651

Donor: Jerry Reinsdorf.
Foundation type: Independent foundation.
Financial data (yr. ended 12/31/13): Assets,
$229,823 (M); gifts received, $350,000;
expenditures, $339,665; qualifying distributions,
$339,664; giving activities include $338,915 for 18
+ grants (high: $209,230; low: $500).
Fields of interest: Domesticated animals; Hospital
care; Judaism.
Limitations: Applications not accepted. Giving
primarily in Phoenix, AZ. No grants to individuals.
Application information: Contributes only to
pre-selected organizations.
Officers: Jerry Reinsdorf, Pres.; Allan Muchin, Secy.
Trustee: Jonathan Reinsdorf.
EIN: 363218989

3000
Jocarno Fund
333 North Michigan, Ste. 510
Chicago, IL 60601-3934
Contact: John Schlossman

Established in 1959 in Illinois.
Donors: Shirley Schlossman; John Schlossman.
Foundation type: Independent foundation.
Financial data (yr. ended 12/31/12): Assets,
$1,759,258 (M); gifts received, $129,396;
expenditures, $223,139; qualifying distributions,
$204,567; giving activities include $195,650 for
105 grants (high: $10,000; low: $250).
Purpose and activities: Giving primarily for the arts,
education, and health and human services.
Fields of interest: Arts and culture; Higher
education; Natural resources; Foundations;
Nonprofits; Health; Religion; Human rights; Human
services; Youth development; International peace
and security.
Type of support: General support; Continuing
support; Annual campaigns; Land acquisitions;
Emergency funds; Regranting.
Application information:

Initial approach: Letter
   Copies of proposal: 1
Officers: Marc Schlossman, Pres.; Gail Mewhort,
V.P.; Shirley Schlossman, Secy.; Peter Schlossman,
Treas.
Number of staff: 2 part-time support.
EIN: 366062019

3001
A. D. Johnson Foundation
1 N. LaSalle St., Ste. 3000
Chicago, IL 60602-4003 (312) 782-7320

Established in 1965 in Illinois.
Donor: A.D. Johnson†.
Foundation type: Independent foundation.
Financial data (yr. ended 12/31/14): Assets,
$1,681,282 (M); expenditures, $186,024;
qualifying distributions, $155,132; giving activities
include $150,000 for 11 grants (high: $30,000;
low: $5,000).
Fields of interest: Arts and culture; Education;
Nonprofits; Hospital care; Hospice care; Diseases
and conditions; Cystic fibrosis; Human services.
Type of support: General support; Capital and
infrastructure; Research; Endowments; Research
and evaluation; Regranting.
Limitations: Applications accepted. Giving primarily
in FL. No grants to individuals.
Application information:
   Initial approach: Proposal
   Deadline(s): None
Officers: Diane T. Johnson, Pres.; Martha C.
Johnson, V.P. and Secy.-Treas.; Herbert J. Theisen,
Genl. Counsel.
EIN: 366124270

3002
Jones Family Foundation
(formerly John Davidson Jones Memorial Fund)
891 Feehanville Dr.
Mount Prospect, IL 60056-6002

Established in 1993 in Illinois.
Donors: Mary Beth Olsen; Brad Olsen;
Cummins-Allison Corp.; Ronald M. Cameron; Rich E.
Start; Same Day Delivery Inc; The Jesus Fund.
Foundation type: Independent foundation.
Financial data (yr. ended 01/31/13): Assets,
$12,296 (M); gifts received, $158,915;
expenditures, $180,644; qualifying distributions,
$180,644; giving activities include $174,052 for 9
grants (high: $38,173; low: $1,033).
Fields of interest: Secondary education; Higher
education.
Type of support: Scholarships.
Limitations: Applications not accepted. Giving
primarily in CA, IL, MD, NC, SC, TX and VA. No grants
to individuals.
Application information: Contributes only to
pre-selected organizations.
Officers and Directors: William J. Jones, Pres. and
Secy. and Director; John E. Jones, V.P. and Director;
Paul A. Jones, Treas. and Director.
Number of staff: None.
EIN: 363936011

3003
Judy Family Foundation

(formerly Green Pond Foundation)
14 Country Ln.
Northfield, IL 60093-1003

Donor: Paul R. Judy.
Foundation type: Independent foundation.
Financial data (yr. ended 12/31/12): Assets, $6,134,868 (M); expenditures, $367,210; qualifying distributions, $303,769; giving activities include $295,308 for 56 grants (high: $25,000; low: $200).
Fields of interest: Arts and culture; Music; Higher education; Environment; Human services.
Type of support: General support.
Limitations: Applications not accepted. Giving primarily in IL and MA. No grants to individuals.
Application information: Contributes only to pre-selected organizations.
Officers: Paul R. Judy, Chair. and Treas.; Mary Ann Judy, Vice-Chair.; Carol Cronin, C.E.O. and Pres.; Hannah Judy Gretz, Secy.
Trustees: David Cronin; Catriona Duncan; Stephen R. Gretz.
EIN: 366168607

3004
Kainz Family Foundation

(formerly Joseph A. & Susan J. Kainz Foundation)
c/o Kutchins, Robbins, & Diamond, Ltd.
1101 Perimeter Dr., Ste. 760
Schaumburg, IL 60173-5025

Established in 2000 in Illinois.
Donors: Joseph A. Kainz; Susan J. Kainz.
Foundation type: Independent foundation.
Financial data (yr. ended 06/30/13): Assets, $3,982,642 (M); expenditures, $277,425; qualifying distributions, $196,000; giving activities include $196,000 for 21 grants (high: $30,000; low: $500).
Purpose and activities: Giving primarily for children's services including health care.
Fields of interest: Environment; Natural resources; Zoos; Health; Hospital care; Hospice care; Child welfare.
Limitations: Applications not accepted. Giving primarily in IL, MT, and VA. No grants to individuals.
Application information: Contributes only to pre-selected organizations.
Directors: John Kainz; Joseph A. Kainz; Michael J. Kainz; Patrick J. Kainz; Susan J. Kainz.
EIN: 364394506

3005
Robert S. and Mary Ann Kaminski Family Foundation

c/o Lawrence H. Brenman
11411 Swinford Ln.
Mokena, IL 60448-9242

Established in 2000 in Illinois.
Donors: Robert S. Kaminski; Mary Ann Kaminski; Robert S. Kaminski Trust.
Foundation type: Independent foundation.
Financial data (yr. ended 12/31/13): Assets, $4,772,012 (M); gifts received, $986,981; expenditures, $187,346; qualifying distributions, $160,025; giving activities include $160,000 for 3 grants (high: $100,000; low: $10,000).

Fields of interest: Education.
Limitations: Applications not accepted. Giving primarily in IL and OH. No grants to individuals.
Application information: Unsolicited requests for funds not accepted.
Officers: Robert S. Kaminski, Pres.; Janice Blaesing, V.P.; David M. Kaminski, V.P.; Robert M. Kaminski, V.P.; Mary Ann Kaminski, Secy.-Treas.
Director: Lawrence H. Brenman.
EIN: 367338457

3006
The Max and Yetta Karasik Family Foundation

P.O. Box 803878
Chicago, IL 60680-3878

Established in 2001 in Florida.
Donor: Marshall Karasik†.
Foundation type: Independent foundation.
Financial data (yr. ended 12/31/13): Assets, $5,049,535 (M); expenditures, $250,297; qualifying distributions, $211,863; giving activities include $160,000 for 9 grants (high: $25,000; low: $5,000).
Fields of interest: Environment; Zoos; Foundations; Health; Hospital care; Hospice care; Diseases and conditions; Diabetes; Judaism; Human services.
Type of support: General support; Research.
Limitations: Applications not accepted. Giving primarily in CA, CO, FL, HI, and NY. No grants to individuals.
Application information: Contributes only to pre-selected organizations.
Officers: Jean Sanson, Secy.; Leslie Robbins Rudawsky, Treas.
Trustees: Lois G. Robbins; Richard Robbins, MD.
EIN: 311667792

3007
Hattie Hannah Keeney Trust

10 S. Dearborn IL1-0117
Chicago, IL 60603
Application address: JPMorgan Chase Bank, N.A., 21805 Field Pkwy., 1st Fl., Deer Park, IL 60010, tel.: (847) 726-3619

Established in 1950 in Illinois.
Donor: Hattie Hannah Keeney†.
Foundation type: Independent foundation.
Financial data (yr. ended 12/31/13): Assets, $5,081,715 (M); expenditures, $257,801; qualifying distributions, $221,052; giving activities include $209,500 for 4 grants (high: $150,000; low: $5,000).
Fields of interest: Health; Hospital care; Mental health care; Child welfare; People with disabilities.
Type of support: General support.
Limitations: Applications accepted. Giving primarily in the Traverse City, MI, area. No grants to individuals.
Application information: Application form required.
  Initial approach: Proposal
  Deadline(s): None
Trustee: JPMorgan Chase Bank, N.A.
EIN: 366016171

3008
The Kellcie Fund

1603 Orrington Ave., Ste. 1275
Evanston, IL 60201-5064 (847) 328-2383
Contact: Kenneth A. Lehman, Co-Pres.

Established in 1999 in Illinois.
Donors: New Prospect Foundation; Kenneth A. Lehman.
Foundation type: Independent foundation.
Financial data (yr. ended 12/31/13): Assets, $2,953,320 (M); gifts received, $100,000; expenditures, $248,675; qualifying distributions, $245,223; giving activities include $243,496 for 126 grants (high: $35,000; low: $43).
Fields of interest: Education; Higher education; Hospital care; Human services; Low-income and poor people.
Type of support: Equal access.
Limitations: Applications accepted. Giving primarily in Chicago, IL.
Application information:
  Initial approach: Letter
  Deadline(s): None
Officers: Kenneth A. Lehman, Co-Pres.; Lucy G. Lehman, Co-Pres.; Amy G. Lehman, Secy.; Peter G. Lehman, Treas.
EIN: 364267581

3009
Keller Family Foundation

c/o Ginsberg Myers
1264 Derby Ln.
Mundelein, IL 60060-4619

Established in 1997 in Illinois.
Donor: Dennis J. Keller.
Foundation type: Independent foundation.
Financial data (yr. ended 12/31/13): Assets, $540,288 (M); expenditures, $184,215; qualifying distributions, $184,185; giving activities include $184,185 for 69 grants (high: $25,000; low: $40).
Purpose and activities: Giving primarily for education, conservation, and health and human services.
Fields of interest: Education; Domesticated animals; Human services.
Limitations: Applications not accepted. Giving primarily in IL. No grants to individuals.
Application information: Unsolicited requests for funds not accepted.
Trustees: Constance T. Keller; David M. Keller; Dennis J. Keller; Jeffrey B. Keller; John T. Keller; Gene R. Myers.
EIN: 364209206

3010
William M. Keller Trust

10 S. Dearborn IL1-0117
Chicago, IL 60603 8668885157
Application address: c/o JPMorgan Chase Bank, N.A., 1 E. Ohio St., Indianapolis, IN 46277-1916, tel.: (317) 684-3017

Foundation type: Independent foundation.
Financial data (yr. ended 12/31/14): Assets, $4,139,752; expenditures, $204,098; qualifying distributions, $174,619.
Purpose and activities: Grant awards to high school students and high school graduates residing in Bartholomew County, Indiana, who intend to pursue

careers in the medical, nursing, scientific, engineering, or technical fields.

Fields of interest: Graduate and professional education; Medical education; Nursing care; Engineering.

Type of support: Scholarships; Student aid.

Limitations: Applications accepted. Giving limited to graduating high school students residing in Bartholomew County, IN.

Publications: Application guidelines.

Application information: Application form required.

   Initial approach: Letter

   Deadline(s): Mar. 31

   Board meeting date(s): Quarterly

Trustee: JPMorgan Chase Bank, N.A.

EIN: 351035651

3011
Kelly Foundation
1925 Enterprise Ct.
Libertyville, IL   60048-9764

Donors: Fabrication Technologies, Inc.; Paul Kelly.

Foundation type: Independent foundation.

Financial data (yr. ended 12/31/13): Assets, $1,045,696 (M); gifts received, $800,000; expenditures, $154,758; qualifying distributions, $147,450; giving activities include $147,450 for 18 grants (high: $30,000; low: $175).

Fields of interest: Education; Religion; Human services.

Limitations: Applications not accepted. Giving primarily in IL.

Application information: Unsolicited requests for funds not accepted.

Officers: Paul Kelly, Pres.; Michele Kelly, Secy.

Director: Frederick M. Lerner.

EIN: 461625964

3012
T. Lloyd Kelly Foundation
c/o Bank of America, N.A.
231 S. LaSalle St.
Chicago, IL   60697-0001   (312) 828-8166
Contact: Srilatha V. Lakkaraju

Established in 1951 in Illinois.

Donor: Mildred Wetten Kelly McDermott.

Foundation type: Independent foundation.

Financial data (yr. ended 12/31/13): Assets, $4,961,144 (M); expenditures, $245,431; qualifying distributions, $210,449; giving activities include $190,000 for 42 grants (high: $30,000; low: $500).

Fields of interest: Secondary education; Higher education; Business education; Hospital care; Family planning; Human services.

Application information:

   Initial approach: Proposal

   Deadline(s): None

Officers and Directors: Robert A. Malstrom, Pres. and Director; Arthur L. Kelly, V.P. and Director; H. Blair White, Secy. and Director; Barbara Kelly Hull.

EIN: 366050341

3013
Parker Kemp Foundation
P.O. Box 169
Lexington, IL   61753-0169

Donor: G. Parker Kemp.

Foundation type: Independent foundation.

Financial data (yr. ended 12/31/14): Assets, $3,879,223; expenditures, $219,780; qualifying distributions, $203,120.

Fields of interest: Education; Religion; Human services.

Limitations: Applications not accepted. Giving primarily in IL and CO. No grants to individuals.

Application information: Unsolicited requests for funds not accepted.

Trustees: Christopher Kemp; Parker Kemp; Rene M. Shaffer.

EIN: 237037957

3014
Jackson Kemper Foundation
6 Bruce Cir.
Hawthorn Woods, IL   60047-9019

Established in 1997 in Illinois.

Donors: Jackson Kemper Enterprises; Jackson Kemper.

Foundation type: Independent foundation.

Financial data (yr. ended 12/31/13): Assets, $3,213,980 (M); expenditures, $173,174; qualifying distributions, $155,014; giving activities include $155,000 for 23 grants (high: $35,000; low: $1,000).

Fields of interest: Health; Housing development; Human services.

Limitations: Applications not accepted. No grants to individuals.

Application information: Contributes only to pre-selected organizations.

Directors: Mark Costa; Jackson Kemper, Jr.; Sharon J. Kemper.

EIN: 364152920

3015
Roy G. Kerr Foundation
1993 Westgate Terr.
Highland Park, IL   60035-2937   (847) 831-2905
Contact: Holly Kerr, Treas.

Donor: Holly Kerr.

Foundation type: Independent foundation.

Financial data (yr. ended 12/31/14): Assets, $495,288 (M); expenditures, $154,013; qualifying distributions, $154,013; giving activities include $152,203 for 10 grants (high: $47,070; low: $1,308).

Fields of interest: Education; Higher education.

Type of support: Individual development.

Limitations: Applications accepted. Giving limited to IL. No grants to individuals.

Application information: Application form required.

   Initial approach: Proposal

   Deadline(s): Mar. 31 and Oct. 31

Officers: Ginny Fagen, Pres.; Debby Farmer, Secy.; Holly Kerr, Treas.

EIN: 363956083

3016
Keyes Charitable Trust
c/o The Northern Trust Co.
P.O. Box 803878
Chicago, IL   60680-3878

Established in 2004 in Wisconsin.

Donor: James H. Keyes.

Foundation type: Independent foundation.

Financial data (yr. ended 10/31/14): Assets, $8,363,353; gifts received, $1,220,541; expenditures, $405,678; qualifying distributions, $354,600.

Fields of interest: Arts and culture; Education; Higher education; Hospital care; Christianity; Human services.

Limitations: Applications not accepted. Giving primarily in GA, TX and WI. No grants to individuals.

Application information: Contributes only to pre-selected organizations.

Trustees: James H. Keyes; James P. Keyes; Kevin W. Keyes; Timothy D. Keyes.

EIN: 206329312

3017
The Kilrea Foundation
c/o The Northern Trust Co.
P.O. Box 803878
Chicago, IL   60680-3878

Established in 2000 in Illinois.

Donors: Scott Kilrea; Mary Beth Kilrea.

Foundation type: Independent foundation.

Financial data (yr. ended 12/31/13): Assets, $4,023,462 (M); expenditures, $236,963; qualifying distributions, $195,175; giving activities include $194,150 for 23 grants (high: $50,000; low: $500).

Fields of interest: Arts and culture; Education; University education; Christianity; Human services; Child welfare; Homeless shelters; Military personnel.

Type of support: Individual development.

Limitations: Applications not accepted. Giving primarily in IL. No grants to individuals.

Application information: Contributes only to pre-selected organizations.

Officer: Scott Kilrea, Pres.

Directors: Mary Beth Kilrea; Lewis M. Schneider.

EIN: 367339715

3018
The Kipper Family Foundation
(formerly Chas. and Ruth Levy Foundation)
20 N. Martingale Rd., No. 500
Schaumburg, IL   60173-2419
Contact: B. Pitstick

Established in 1959 in Illinois.

Donors: Barbara Levy Kipper; David Kipper.

Foundation type: Independent foundation.

Financial data (yr. ended 06/30/13): Assets, $779,773 (M); gifts received, $275,925; expenditures, $366,391; qualifying distributions, $364,093; giving activities include $364,093 for 21 grants (high: $110,000; low: $280).

Fields of interest: Arts and culture; Health care clinics.

Type of support: General support.

Limitations: Applications not accepted. Giving primarily in Chicago, IL. No grants to individuals.

Application information: Contributes only to pre-selected organizations.

Directors: Talia K. Ausiello; Linda C. Harris; Barbara Kipper; Donald Lubin; Tamar K. Jacoby.

EIN: 366032324

3019
The Kjellstrom Family Foundation

5901 Churchview Dr.
Rockford, IL 61107-6105

Established in 2004 in Illinois.
Donor: Janet Ann Kjellstrom.
Foundation type: Independent foundation.
Financial data (yr. ended 12/31/13): Assets, $2,682,393 (M); expenditures, $262,875; qualifying distributions, $232,531; giving activities include $232,531 for 9 grants (high: $115,531; low: $2,000).
Fields of interest: Community and economic development; Housing development; Religion.
Limitations: Applications not accepted. Giving primarily in Rockford, IL. No grants to individuals.
Application information: Unsolicited requests for funds not accepted.
Trustee: Janet Ann Kjellstrom; Dan Loescher; Paul Logli; Gloria Lundeen.
EIN: 206368876

3020
Louis & Rose Klosk Fund

10 S. Dearborn IL1-0117
Chicago, IL 60603

Established in 1970 in New York.
Donor: Louis Klosk†.
Foundation type: Independent foundation.
Financial data (yr. ended 12/31/13): Assets, $6,350,415 (M); expenditures, $333,210; qualifying distributions, $287,931; giving activities include $268,000 for 28 grants (high: $40,000; low: $500).
Purpose and activities: Giving primarily for health associations and Jewish organizations.
Fields of interest: Higher education; Nonprofits; Health; Diseases and conditions; Judaism; Human services; Senior services.
Type of support: General support; Regranting.
Limitations: Applications not accepted. Giving primarily in NY. No grants to individuals.
Application information: Contributes only to pre-selected organizations.
Trustees: Barry C. Cooper; Herbert L. Cooper; JPMorgan Chase Bank, N.A.
EIN: 136328994

3021
Burdette and Kathryn Knappenberger
Charitable Trust

1705 Towanda Ave.
P.O. Box 2020
Bloomington, IL 61701-2040
Contact: David W. Wilson

Established in 2004 in Illinois.
Donor: Burdette Knappenberger†.
Foundation type: Independent foundation.
Financial data (yr. ended 12/31/14): Assets, $6,271,937 (M); expenditures, $334,525; qualifying distributions, $301,816; giving activities include $298,775 for 8 grants (high: $59,755; low: $14,939).
Fields of interest: Education; Christianity; Human services.
Limitations: Applications not accepted. Giving primarily in IL. No grants to individuals.

Application information: Contributes only to pre-selected organizations.
Trustee: Country Trust Bank.
EIN: 206060700

3022
Knight Family Foundation

(formerly Robert and Mary Knight Family Foundation)
c/o The Northern Trust Co.
P.O. Box 803878
Chicago, IL 60680-3878

Established in 1998 in Illinois.
Donors: Robert G. Knight, Jr.; Robert G. Knight, Jr. Trust.
Foundation type: Independent foundation.
Financial data (yr. ended 03/31/15): Assets, $14,227,244 (M); expenditures, $280,783; qualifying distributions, $226,030; giving activities include $225,000 for 5 grants (high: $75,000; low: $12,500).
Fields of interest: Education; Undergraduate education; Philanthropy; Health.
Limitations: Applications not accepted. Giving primarily in IL and IN. No grants to individuals.
Application information: Unsolicited requests for funds not accepted.
Officers: Mary K. Knight, Treas.; Andrew M. Knight, Pres.; Robert G. Knight III, Secy.; Robert T. Gratzer, V.P.
EIN: 364265122

3023
The Knowles Foundation

c/o Michael Powers
200 S. Michigan Ave., Ste. 1100
Chicago, IL 60604-2461

Established in 1955 in Illinois.
Donors: Knowles Electronics, Inc.; Nancy Knowles.
Foundation type: Independent foundation.
Financial data (yr. ended 09/30/14): Assets, $5,620,626; expenditures, $283,298; qualifying distributions, $257,018.
Purpose and activities: Giving primarily for higher education, and for the arts; funding also for medical associations.
Fields of interest: Arts education; Opera; Museums; Art museums; Education; University education; Hospital care; Diseases and conditions.
Limitations: Applications not accepted. Giving primarily in IL. No grants to individuals; no program-related investments.
Application information: Contributes only to pre-selected organizations.
Officers and Directors: Nancy W. Knowles, Pres. and Treas. and Director; Michael J. Powers, Secy. and Director; David J. Hill.
EIN: 366051968

3024
Kobe College Corporation

540 W. Frontage Rd., Ste. 3335
Northfield, IL 60093-1233
Main URL: http://www.kccjee.org

Donor: Mary Longbrake Trust.
Foundation type: Independent foundation.
Financial data (yr. ended 03/31/15): Assets, $4,658,638; gifts received, $23,870;

expenditures, $285,719; qualifying distributions, $272,137.
Fields of interest: Higher education.
International interests: Japan.
Type of support: Student aid.
Limitations: Applications not accepted. Giving primarily in Nishinomiya, Hyogo, Japan.
Application information: Unsolicited requests for funds not accepted.
Officers: Go Sugiura, Pres.; Angie Gaspar, V.P., Admin. and Secy.; Ken Tornheim, Treas.
Directors: Lynn Cohee; Robert Head; Takuzo Ishida; Bradley Knotts; Robert Mason; Reiko Mrozik; Jeanne Sokolowski; Cindi Sturtz-Sreetharan; Roberta Wollons; Fumiyo Young.
EIN: 362110366

3025
Koch Family Foundation

c/o Dolgin Law Group, LLC
30 N. La Salle St., Ste. 2610
Chicago, IL 60602-3357
Contact: Steven Koch, Pres.
Application Address: 2012 N. Mohawk, Chicago, IL 60614;

Donor: Steven Koch.
Foundation type: Independent foundation.
Financial data (yr. ended 12/31/13): Assets, $1,605,569 (M); expenditures, $301,152; qualifying distributions, $289,515; giving activities include $289,500 for 20 grants (high: $250,000; low: $250).
Fields of interest: Health; Agriculture; Human services.
Limitations: Applications accepted. Giving primarily in Chicago, IL.
Application information: Application form required.
   Initial approach: Letter
   Deadline(s): None
Officers: Steven Koch, Pres.; Jay Dolgin, Secy.
Directors: Jacob Koch; Leah Koch; Rebecca Koch.
EIN: 274274285

3026
Robert August Koranda Memorial
Foundation

c/o Kenneth R. Koranda
7S541 Donwood Dr. E.
Naperville, IL 60540-9444

Established in 2003 in Illinois.
Donors: Kenneth R. Koranda; Susan W. Koranda; Koranda Family Foundation.
Foundation type: Independent foundation.
Financial data (yr. ended 12/31/13): Assets, $325,338 (M); expenditures, $259,210; qualifying distributions, $256,100; giving activities include $256,100 for 10 grants (high: $200,000; low: $1,000).
Fields of interest: Education; Environment; Human services.
Limitations: Applications not accepted. No grants to individuals.
Application information: Unsolicited requests for funds not accepted.
Trustees: John Koranda; Katherine Koranda; Kenneth R. Koranda; Susan W. Koranda.
EIN: 367417497

3027
Kott Gerontology Institute
1049 Lake St., Ste. 204
Oak Park, IL 60301-6708

Donor: Kott Memorial Charitable Trust.
Foundation type: Independent foundation.
Financial data (yr. ended 06/30/13): Assets, $23,729 (M); gifts received, $332,748; expenditures, $310,041; qualifying distributions, $310,041; giving activities include $82,550 for 8 grants (high: $19,200; low: $4,250), and $173,831 for 19 grants to individuals.
Fields of interest: Education.
Type of support: Student aid.
Limitations: Applications not accepted. Giving primarily in IL.
Application information: Unsolicited requests for funds not accepted.
Officers: Glenn Green, Pres.; Catherine Swan, Secy.-Treas.; Benjamin Friedman, Exec. Dir.
Directors: Mary Constantino; Joseph Mikels; Jay Miller.
EIN: 455081047

3028
KPW Family Foundation
1420 N. Lake Shore Dr., Ste. 10B
Chicago, IL 60610-6690

Donor: Patricia O'Neill Cox.
Foundation type: Independent foundation.
Financial data (yr. ended 12/31/14): Assets, $783,432; expenditures, $257,807; qualifying distributions, $257,430.
Fields of interest: Arts and culture; Education; Community and economic development.
Limitations: Applications not accepted. Giving primarily in IL. No grants to individuals.
Application information: Unsolicited requests for funds not accepted.
Directors: Patricia O'Neill Cox; Katherine Patricia Hunckler; Lawrence I. Richman.
EIN: 261508438

3029
Krasberg-Mason Foundation
c/o Margaret K. Mason
170 Dickens Rd.
Northfield, IL 60093-3229

Established in 1992 in Illinois.
Donors: Corinne Krasberg†; David E. Mason; Margaret K. Mason.
Foundation type: Operating foundation.
Financial data (yr. ended 12/31/14): Assets, $1,749,778; expenditures, $161,973; qualifying distributions, $160,500 and $0 for set-asides.
Fields of interest: Arts and culture; Higher education; Protestantism.
Type of support: Scholarships; General support; Continuing support; Capital campaigns; Capital and infrastructure; Annual campaigns.
Limitations: Applications not accepted. Giving on a national basis, primarily east of the Mississippi River. No grants to individuals, or for conferences/seminars, consulting services, curriculum development, debt reduction, emergency funds, employee matching gifts, employee-related scholarships, endowments, equipment, exchange programs, fellowships, in-kind gifts, income

development, internship funds, land acquisition, management development, matching/challenge support, professorships, program development, program evaluation, program-related investments/loans, publication, research, scholarships to individuals, seed money, student loans to individuals, or for technical assistance.
Application information: Contributes only to pre-selected organizations.
Officers and Directors: Margaret K. Mason, Pres. and Director; David E. Mason, Secy.-Treas. and Director; Bruce E. Mason; Sarah C. Mason.
Number of staff: None.
EIN: 363807993

3030
Krehbiel Family Foundation
c/o Robert J. Reichner & Assoc., Inc.
807 Chestnut Ave.
Wilmette, IL 60091-1743

Established in 2003 in Illinois.
Foundation type: Independent foundation.
Financial data (yr. ended 10/31/14): Assets, $8,075,542; expenditures, $456,796; qualifying distributions, $361,925.
Fields of interest: Art museums; Higher education; Environment; Children's hospital care; Child welfare; International relations; Children.
Limitations: Applications not accepted. Giving primarily in IL, NH and NY.
Application information: Unsolicited requests for funds not accepted.
Officers and Directors: Margaret V. Krehbiel-Ellsworth, Pres. and Secy. and Director; William V. Krehbiel, Treas. and Director; Frederick L. Krehbiel; Jay F. Krehbiel; John H. Krehbiel III.
EIN: 841621866

3031
The Anstiss & Ronald Krueck
Foundation
18 E. Pearson St.
Chicago, IL 60611-2002

Established in 1992 in Illinois.
Donors: Ronald Krueck; Anstiss Krueck.
Foundation type: Independent foundation.
Financial data (yr. ended 12/31/13): Assets, $911,667 (M); expenditures, $268,943; qualifying distributions, $259,850; giving activities include $259,850 for 11 grants (high: $217,000; low: $100).
Purpose and activities: Giving primarily for the arts, as well as for education.
Fields of interest: Arts and culture; Education; Religion.
Limitations: Applications accepted. Giving primarily in Chicago, IL.
Application information:
Initial approach: Proposal
Deadline(s): None
Trustees: Anstiss Krueck; Ronald Krueck.
EIN: 363855553

3032
Lakonishok Foundation
1943 N. Burling St.
Chicago, IL 60614-5123

Donor: Josef Lakonishok.
Foundation type: Independent foundation.
Financial data (yr. ended 12/31/13): Assets, $2,988,423 (M); gifts received, $1,023,523; expenditures, $150,000; qualifying distributions, $150,000; giving activities include $150,000 for 1 grant.
Fields of interest: Arts and culture.
Limitations: Applications not accepted.
Application information: Unsolicited requests for funds not accepted.
Officer: Josef Lakonishok, Pres.
EIN: 463460720

3033
Lakshmi Foundation
858 W. Armitage, Ste. 410
Chicago, IL 60614-4370
Contact: Steve Levin

Established in 2005 in Illinois.
Donors: Hana Foundation; Kemery Bloom.
Foundation type: Independent foundation.
Financial data (yr. ended 04/30/14): Assets, $1,433,853 (M); expenditures, $254,877; qualifying distributions, $253,654; giving activities include $243,000 for 21 grants (high: $80,000; low: $1,000).
Fields of interest: Arts and culture; Education; Human services.
Limitations: Applications not accepted. Giving primarily in Chicago, IL; some funding also in Washington, DC and St. Louis, MO. No grants to individuals.
Application information: Contributes only to pre-selected organizations.
Officers and Directors: Kemery Bloom, Pres. and Treas. and Director; Kara Bloom, V.P. and Director; Matthew Chapman, Secy. and Director.
Number of staff: None.
EIN: 201746794

3034
Mitchell J. And Mary Ellen Lamka
Foundation
P.O. Box 5799
River Forest, IL 60305-5799

Donor: Mary Ellen Lamka Trust.
Foundation type: Independent foundation.
Financial data (yr. ended 12/31/13): Assets, $5,223,120 (M); expenditures, $272,420; qualifying distributions, $188,530; giving activities include $188,530 for 3 grants (high: $89,880; low: $32,000).
Fields of interest: Education; Religion; Christianity.
Limitations: Applications not accepted. Giving primarily in IL.
Application information: Unsolicited requests for funds not accepted.
Officer: Jean M. Finnegan, Exec. Dir.
Trustee: Daniel Finnegan.
EIN: 273181533

3035
Lancaster Family Foundation
3000 Garlands Ln., Unit 3466
Barrington, IL 60010-6848

Established in 1991 in Illinois.

Donor: James R. Lancaster.

Foundation type: Independent foundation.

Financial data (yr. ended 12/31/13): Assets, $4,913,001 (M); gifts received, $1,935; expenditures, $320,838; qualifying distributions, $282,820; giving activities include $282,820 for 70 grants (high: $65,100; low: $50).

Fields of interest: Arts and culture; Higher education; Health; Protestantism; Human services; Child welfare.

Limitations: Applications not accepted. Giving primarily in IL. No grants to individuals.

Application information: Contributes only to pre-selected organizations.

Officer: James R. Lancaster, Pres.

Directors: Amy S. Lancaster; Craig J. Lancaster; Mark T. Lancaster; Nancy L. Liskevych; Anne M. Springer.

EIN: 363794645

3036
Landau Family Foundation

P.O. Box 577880
Chicago, IL 60657-7880

Established in 1955 in Illinois.

Donor: Howard M. Landau†.

Foundation type: Independent foundation.

Financial data (yr. ended 11/30/13): Assets, $8,640,894 (M); expenditures, $518,731; qualifying distributions, $430,000; giving activities include $430,000 for 26 grants (high: $50,000; low: $3,000).

Purpose and activities: Support primarily for social and economic justice.

Fields of interest: Nonprofits; Public interest law; Public affairs; Judaism; Human rights; Human services; Immigrants and migrants; Low-income and poor people.

International interests: Israel; Middle East.

Type of support: General support; Program-related investments; Continuing support; Emergency funds; Program development; Seed money; Regranting.

Limitations: Applications accepted. Giving primarily in Chicago, IL. No grants to individuals.

Application information:
  Initial approach: Proposal
  Deadline(s): None

Officers and Directors: Kay Berkson, Pres. and Director; Kenneth J. Landau, Secy. and Director; Sidney Hollander, Treas. and Director; Daniel Berkson.

EIN: 366089098

3037
Louise H. Landau Foundation

c/o M. Katten
525 N. Monroe St., Ste. 1600
Chicago, IL 60661-3693

Established in 1989 in Illinois.

Foundation type: Independent foundation.

Financial data (yr. ended 12/31/13): Assets, $378,930 (M); expenditures, $228,114; qualifying distributions, $228,114; giving activities include $222,500 for 15 grants (high: $25,000; low: $2,500).

Fields of interest: Arts and culture; Theater; Education; Land resources; Health; Hospice care; Cancers; Judaism; Senior services.

Type of support: General support.

Limitations: Applications not accepted. Giving primarily in Chicago, IL. No grants to individuals.

Application information: Contributes only to pre-selected organizations.

Officers: Melvin L. Katten, Pres.; Patricia Taylor, Secy.; Melvin Katten, Treas.

EIN: 363648892

3038
The Larsen Foundation

10 S. Dearborn IL1-0117
Chicago, IL 60603

Donors: Marilyn Larsen; Terrence Larsen.

Foundation type: Independent foundation.

Financial data (yr. ended 12/31/14): Assets, $3,922,575; expenditures, $220,415; qualifying distributions, $188,169.

Fields of interest: Performing arts; Education; Higher education; Nonprofits.

Type of support: Regranting.

Limitations: Applications not accepted. No grants to individuals.

Application information: Unsolicited requests for funds not accepted.

Trustees: Ashley Murphy; Craig Larsen; Terrence Larsen; JPMorgan Chase Bank, N.A.

EIN: 516507234

3039
Orville H. and Shirley I. Larson Charitable Trust

21 E. Main St.
Galesburg, IL 61401-4525

Donor: Orville H. Larson†.

Foundation type: Independent foundation.

Financial data (yr. ended 12/31/14): Assets, $8,161,667 (M); expenditures, $506,546; qualifying distributions, $424,000; giving activities include $424,000 for 4 grants (high: $141,333; low: $70,667).

Fields of interest: Diseases and conditions; Religion.

Limitations: Applications not accepted. Giving primarily in IL.

Application information: Unsolicited requests for funds not accepted.

Trustees: Lynn Bowman; Farmers & Mechanics Bank.

EIN: 367517145

3040
Michael Lascaris Scholarship Trust

c/o Schiff Hardi
233 S. Wacker Dr.
Chicago, IL 60606-5096
Contact: Sarah K. Severson
E-mail: info@lascaristrust.gr; *Main URL:* http://lascaristrust.gr
Facebook: http://www.facebook.com/Lascaris.Trust
Grants List: http://lascaristrust.gr/?cmd=receipients

Established in 1997 in Illinois.

Foundation type: Independent foundation.

Financial data (yr. ended 12/31/13): Assets, $5,076,337 (M); expenditures, $465,564; qualifying distributions, $440,275; giving activities

include $206,400 for 173 grants to individuals (high: $1,720; low: $860).

Purpose and activities: Scholarship awards to individuals of Greek ancestry from Greece, Cyprus and Istanbul for the purpose of learning the English language. The scholarships are only for English language instruction at all levels from beginner up to and including the Certificate of Proficiency (Universities of Cambridge and Michigan) and are applicable to candidates of all ages, provided they have had their 12th birthday. Candidates must also be Greek Orthodox. The scholarships cover all tuition and educational materials for one year, with the possibility of renewal for further years for those recipients who are conscientious in their study and attendance.

Fields of interest: Education; Human services.

International interests: Cyprus; Greece.

Type of support: Student aid.

Limitations: Applications accepted. Giving primarily in Cyprus, Greece and Istanbul.

Application information: See web site for scholarship application information and guidelines. Application form required.
  Initial approach: Telephone or e-mail
  Deadline(s): May 4

Officers: Sherry Cossyphas, Mgr.; Evangelia Laiou, Mgr.; Maria Rallis, Mgr.

Trustee: Koula Pagonis.

EIN: 367144785

3041
Herman & Debbie Lazar Charitable Foundation

6600 N. California Ave., Ste. 3N
Chicago, IL 60645

Established in 1991 in Illinois.

Donor: Herman Lazar.

Foundation type: Independent foundation.

Financial data (yr. ended 12/31/13): Assets, $244,657 (M); gifts received, $205,000; expenditures, $290,664; qualifying distributions, $290,664; giving activities include $290,664 for 17 grants (high: $80,000; low: $360).

Fields of interest: Education; Judaism; Human services.

Limitations: Applications not accepted. No grants to individuals.

Application information: Contributes only to pre-selected organizations.

Officer: Samuel Brandman, Pres. and Secy.-Treas.

EIN: 363767237

3042
The Lazzara Family Foundation

7951 S. Drew Ave.
Burr Ridge, IL 60527-5932

Established in 1983 in Illinois.

Donors: Jack R. Lazzara; Antoinette Lazzara; Philip Lazzara†; Angelo J. Lazzara†; Alan A. Lazzara.

Foundation type: Independent foundation.

Financial data (yr. ended 12/31/13): Assets, $2,177,106 (M); gifts received, $43,002; expenditures, $201,503; qualifying distributions, $200,000; giving activities include $200,000 for 16 grants (high: $37,500; low: $2,500).

Purpose and activities: Giving primarily for education, human services, medical research and for health care.

Fields of interest: Higher education; Health; Hospital care; Diseases and conditions; Human services.

Type of support: Capital campaigns; Endowments; Equipment; Research; Fellowships; Research and evaluation; General support; Scholarships.

Limitations: Applications not accepted. Giving on a national basis. No support for political organizations, or non-501(c)3 organizations. No grants to individuals.

Application information: Unsolicited requests for funds not accepted.

Trustees: Alan A. Lazzara; Angelo J. Lazzara; Antoniette Lazzara; Jack R. Lazzara; Nancy P. Stevens.

EIN: 363248699

3043
Bertha Lebus Charitable Trust
P.O. Box 803878
Chicago, IL 60680-3878

Foundation type: Independent foundation.

Financial data (yr. ended 12/31/14): Assets, $4,401,416; expenditures, $315,593; qualifying distributions, $235,920.

Purpose and activities: Giving primarily for higher education; funding also for the arts, health, and human services.

Fields of interest: Arts and culture; Natural history museums; Education; Higher education; Health; Hospital care; Hospice care; Cancers; Public libraries; Gardening; Human services; Family services.

Limitations: Applications not accepted. Giving primarily in IL and KY. No grants to individuals.

Application information: Contributes only to pre-selected organizations.

Trustee: Northern Trust, N.A.

Directors: Sally Ann Hagan; Frazer D. Lebus, Jr.; Jessica Robbins.

EIN: 956022085

3044
Leestma Family Foundation
333 N. Canal 1903
Chicago, IL 60606 (312) 988-2500

Established in 1990 in Illinois.

Donor: I.H. Marsilje Irrevocable Trust.

Foundation type: Independent foundation.

Financial data (yr. ended 12/31/14): Assets, $8,598,946; expenditures, $490,803; qualifying distributions, $425,483.

Fields of interest: Christianity; Human services; Family services; Child welfare.

Application information: Application form required.

Initial approach: Letter

Deadline(s): None

Officers: Louise M. Leestma, Pres.; Jan E. Leestma, Secy.-Treas.

Board Members: James LaFleur; Johanna Leestma LaFleur.

EIN: 363701346

3045
The Lehman-Stamm Family Fund
(formerly Goodworks Fund)
101 Hamilton St.
Evanston, IL 60202 (847) 328-0182
Contact: Ronna Stamm, Pres.
FAX: (847) 328-0417; E-mail: lsffund@gmail.com

Established in 1999 in Illinois.

Donors: Paul Lehman; KKP Holdings LLC; New Prospect Foundation.

Foundation type: Independent foundation.

Financial data (yr. ended 12/31/13): Assets, $2,584,737 (M); expenditures, $334,131; qualifying distributions, $318,727; giving activities include $315,745 for 69 grants (high: $30,000; low: $250).

Purpose and activities: Giving primarily focused on civil rights and civil liberties, LGBT issues, and reproductive health.

Fields of interest: Theater; Reproductive health care; Individual liberties; Freedom of association and expression; Reproductive rights; Marriage equality; Antidiscrimination; Immigrant rights; Minority rights; Women's rights; LGBTQ rights.

Type of support: General support; Annual campaigns.

Limitations: Applications accepted. Giving primarily in IL.

Application information:

Initial approach: Letter

Copies of proposal: 1

Deadline(s): Sept. 1

Officers: Ronna Stamm, Pres.; Jonathan Lehman, Secy.; Paul Lehman, Treas.

EIN: 364267578

3046
Sheldon L. and Pearl R. Leibowitz Foundation
2800 Lakeside Dr.
Bannockburn, IL 60015-1246

Established in 1986 in Illinois.

Donors: Sheldon L. Leibowitz; Pearl R. Leibowitz.

Foundation type: Independent foundation.

Financial data (yr. ended 09/30/14): Assets, $234,015 (M); expenditures, $262,530; qualifying distributions, $262,530; giving activities include $262,500 for 61 grants (high: $25,000; low: $500).

Purpose and activities: Giving for human services, Jewish federated programs, and health associations.

Fields of interest: Arts and culture; Education; Graduate and professional education; Nonprofits; Hospital care; Diseases and conditions; Judaism; Theology; Human services; Child welfare.

Type of support: Regranting.

Limitations: Applications not accepted. Giving primarily in Chicago, IL. No grants to individuals.

Application information: Contributes only to pre-selected organizations.

Directors: Dale Leibowitz; Lew Leibowitz.

EIN: 363480213

3047
Phillip and Edith Leonian Foundation
(formerly Paul & Gabriella Rosenbaum Foundation)
1723 S. Michigan Ave.
Chicago, IL 60616-1211 (312) 987-9500
Contact: Phillip Leonian, Treas.

Established in 1983 in Illinois.

Donors: Gabriella Rosenbaum; Gabriella Rosenbaum Trust; Phillip Leonian; Edith Leonian.

Foundation type: Independent foundation.

Financial data (yr. ended 09/30/13): Assets, $9,013,423 (M); gifts received, $1,198,603; expenditures, $607,496; qualifying distributions, $559,635; giving activities include $425,159 for 7 grants (high: $125,000; low: $10,000).

Fields of interest: Museums; Art museums.

Limitations: Applications accepted. Giving primarily in Chicago, IL.

Application information: Application form required.

Initial approach: Proposal

Deadline(s): None

Officers: Edith Leonian, Pres.; Phillip Leonian, Treas.

Director: Allan J. Riech.

EIN: 363204862

3048
The Nathan and Kiyoko Lerner Foundation
500 W. Superior, Ste. 2401
Chicago, IL 60610-8151
Contact: Kiyoko Lerner, Pres.

Foundation type: Independent foundation.

Financial data (yr. ended 12/31/12): Assets, $0 (M); expenditures, $158,502; qualifying distributions, $156,476; giving activities include $156,476 for 2 grants (high: $83,000; low: $73,476).

Fields of interest: Arts and culture; Mental health care.

International interests: France.

Limitations: Applications accepted. Giving primarily in IL and Paris, France.

Application information: Application form required.

Initial approach: Letter

Deadline(s): None

Officers: Kiyoko Lerner, Pres.; Michael Lerner, V.P.; Alan Aronson, Secy.

EIN: 367167086

3049
Elaine and Donald Levinson Foundation
111 E. Oak St.
Chicago, IL 60611-1202
Contact: Donald Levinson, Pres., Treas. and Dir

Donors: Donald Levinson; Elaine Levinson.

Foundation type: Independent foundation.

Financial data (yr. ended 12/31/14): Assets, $63,449 (M); gifts received, $250,000; expenditures, $236,762; qualifying distributions, $236,762; giving activities include $236,737 for 31 grants (high: $113,250; low: $25).

Purpose and activities: Giving for the arts, education, health, human services, and Jewish organizations.

Fields of interest: Arts and culture; Education; Higher education; Nonprofits; Health; Diseases and conditions; Judaism; Human services.

Type of support: Regranting; Fundraising.

Limitations: Applications not accepted. No grants to individuals.

Application information: Contributes only to pre-selected organizations.

Officers and Directors: Donald Levinson, Pres. and Treas. and Director; Elaine Levinson, V.P. and Director.
EIN: 363484269

3050
Robert M. and Diane V. S. Levy Family Foundation
c/o Robert M. Levy
2 N. LaSalle St., Ste. 500
Chicago, IL 60602-3703

Established in 1997 in Illinois.
Donor: Robert M. Levy.
Foundation type: Independent foundation.
Financial data (yr. ended 12/31/13): Assets, $8,819,250 (M); gifts received, $301,768; expenditures, $521,975; qualifying distributions, $438,515; giving activities include $433,500 for 19 grants (high: $90,000; low: $1,000).
Fields of interest: Higher education; Nonprofits; Human services.
Type of support: Scholarships; Capital campaigns; Regranting.
Limitations: Applications not accepted. Giving primarily in Chicago, IL. No grants to individuals.
Application information: Contributes only to pre-selected organizations.
Trustees: Diane V.S. Levy; Robert M. Levy.
EIN: 367190582

3051
John & Anne Lichner Foundation
631 Burno Dr.
Palatine, IL 60067-6713

Established in 2002 in Illinois.
Donor: Anne Lichner Trust.
Foundation type: Independent foundation.
Financial data (yr. ended 12/31/13): Assets, $1,749,421 (M); expenditures, $169,420; qualifying distributions, $167,500; giving activities include $167,500 for 28 grants (high: $10,000; low: $2,500).
Fields of interest: Diseases and conditions; Christianity; Human services; Child welfare.
Type of support: Research.
Limitations: Applications not accepted. Giving primarily in IL. No grants to individuals.
Application information: Contributes only to pre-selected organizations.
Officers: Kathleen A. Marsh, Pres.; John A. Lichner, Jr., Secy.; Lee M. Marsh, Treas.
EIN: 352170182

3052
Marvin and Kay Lichtman Foundation
c/o Judge Edwin M. Berman
410 S. Michigan Ave., Ste. 626
Chicago, IL 60605-1452

Established in 1991 in Illinois.
Donors: Kay Lichtman; Marvin Lichtman.
Foundation type: Independent foundation.
Financial data (yr. ended 12/31/14): Assets, $10,493,622; gifts received, $0; expenditures, $561,956; qualifying distributions, $470,396.
Fields of interest: Arts and culture; Higher education; Hospital care; Diseases and conditions; Television; Human services; Youth services.

Type of support: General support.
Limitations: Applications not accepted. Giving primarily in Chicago, IL. No grants to individuals.
Application information: Contributes only to pre-selected organizations.
Officers: Sheila Burns, Pres.; Edwin M. Berman, Secy.-Treas. and Exe. Dir.
Directors: Richard L. Curry; Floyd D. Perkins.
EIN: 363795280

3053
Lifetract Foundation
350 N. Orleans St., 7th Fl.
Chicago, IL 60654

Established in 2008 in Illinois.
Donor: Brian R. Gelber.
Foundation type: Independent foundation.
Financial data (yr. ended 12/31/13): Assets, $1,548,008 (M); expenditures, $285,678; qualifying distributions, $282,663; giving activities include $282,663 for 1 grant.
Fields of interest: Education; Digestive system diseases.
Type of support: Research.
Limitations: Applications not accepted.
Application information: Unsolicited requests for funds not accepted.
Officers: Brian R. Gelber, Pres.; Franklin A. Gelber, V.P.; Sandra Gelber, Secy.
EIN: 262643205

3054
Elick and Charlotte Lindon Foundation
c/o Charlotte Lindon
2500 Indigo Ln., Ste. 337
Glenview, IL 60025-8306

Established in 1978 in Illinois.
Donors: Charlotte Lindon; Elick Lindon†.
Foundation type: Independent foundation.
Financial data (yr. ended 12/31/13): Assets, $4,889,445 (M); gifts received, $60,000; expenditures, $301,141; qualifying distributions, $270,805; giving activities include $270,805 for 54 grants (high: $30,000; low: $20).
Fields of interest: Arts and culture; Foundations; Housing development; Judaism; Human services; Senior services; Low-income and poor people; People with disabilities.
International interests: Israel.
Type of support: General support; Continuing support; Annual campaigns; Capital campaigns; Emergency funds; Program development; Seed money.
Limitations: Applications not accepted. No support for political organizations . No grants to individuals.
Application information: Unsolicited requests for funds not accepted.
Board meeting date(s): Varies
Director: Charlotte Lindon.
EIN: 363071211

3055
Marguerite Listeman Fund
c/o The Northern Trust Co.
P.O. Box 803878
Chicago, IL 60680-3878

Established in 1958 in Illinois.

Donors: Kurt Listeman†; Harold Naeder.
Foundation type: Independent foundation.
Financial data (yr. ended 12/31/14): Assets, $4,813,138; expenditures, $277,688; qualifying distributions, $231,103.
Purpose and activities: Grants primarily for community development, including support for buildings and equipment for parks and recreation areas and cultural facilities.
Fields of interest: Arts and culture; Public administration; Community and economic development; Sports and recreation.
Type of support: General support; Building and renovations; Equipment.
Limitations: Applications not accepted. Giving primarily in WI. No grants to individuals.
Application information: Unsolicited requests for funds not accepted.
Officers: Tim Voigt, Chair.; Benjamin Urlaub, Secy.
Advisors: Wayne Gross; Dan Patey; Donald Quicker; Tim R. Harvey.
Trustee: The Northern Trust Co.
EIN: 366028439

3056
Livney Foundation
1 N. LaSalle St., Ste. 1620
Chicago, IL 60602-3936
Contact: Roland Livney

Established in 1990 in Illinois.
Donors: Roland Livney; David Connelly.
Foundation type: Independent foundation.
Financial data (yr. ended 12/31/13): Assets, $942,122 (M); gifts received, $100,512; expenditures, $176,276; qualifying distributions, $124,796; giving activities include $124,796 for 5 grants (high: $105,000; low: $2,500).
Fields of interest: Arts and culture; Health; Diseases and conditions.
Type of support: Research.
Limitations: Applications not accepted. Giving primarily in IL and PA. No grants to individuals.
Application information: Contributes only to pre-selected organizations.
Officers: Roland Livney, Pres.; Patrick Livney, Secy.
Director: Joy Largent.
EIN: 363734084

3057
Joseph Lizzadro Family Foundation
2215 York Rd., Ste. 304
Oak Brook, IL 60523-4004 (630) 571-7200
Contact: Joseph F. Lizzadro, Pres.

Established in 1957 in Illinois.
Donor: John S. Lizzadro.
Foundation type: Independent foundation.
Financial data (yr. ended 12/31/12): Assets, $5,708,840 (M); expenditures, $165,675; qualifying distributions, $165,025; giving activities include $165,000 for 1 grant.
Purpose and activities: Giving primarily for a family affiliated museum.
Fields of interest: Museums.
Type of support: General support.
Limitations: Applications accepted. Giving on a national basis. No grants to individuals.
Application information: Application form required.
Initial approach: Letter

Copies of proposal: 1
Deadline(s): Nov.
Officers and Directors: Joseph F. Lizzadro, Pres. and
Director; Angela L. Anderson, V.P. and Director;
Louis L. Lizzadro, Secy.; John S. Lizzadro, Treas. and
Director; Bonita Hay; Gina Nicholas.
Number of staff: None.
EIN: 366047939

3058
Logos Charitable Fund, Inc.
200 W. Monroe St., Ste. 1440
Chicago, IL 60606-5015

Donors: Mr. Noel G. Moore; Mrs. Michele Moore.
Foundation type: Independent foundation.
Financial data (yr. ended 11/30/13): Assets,
$2,956,746 (M); gifts received, $500,000;
expenditures, $190,082; qualifying distributions,
$160,985; giving activities include $160,985 for 33
grants (high: $50,000; low: $150).
Purpose and activities: Giving primarily to Catholic
agencies and churches, and for human services.
Fields of interest: Education; University education;
Christianity; Catholicism; Human services;
International development.
Type of support: Continuing support; Annual
campaigns; Individual development; Program
development; Curriculum development;
Scholarships.
Limitations: Applications not accepted. Giving
primarily in IL. No grants to individuals.
Application information: Contributes only to
pre-selected organizations.
Officers and Directors: Noel G. Moore, Pres. and
Director; Jeff McKinley, Secy. and Director; Michele
Moore.
EIN: 363994192

3059
Lohengrin Foundation Inc
c/o Peter & Lucy Ascoli
5744 S. Kimbark Ave.
Chicago, IL 60637-1615

Donors: Peter M. Ascoli; Lucy B. Ascoli.
Foundation type: Independent foundation.
Financial data (yr. ended 12/31/13): Assets,
$109,549 (M); gifts received, $253,746;
expenditures, $232,092; qualifying distributions,
$228,698; giving activities include $226,633 for 34
grants (high: $14,000; low: $1,000).
Fields of interest: Arts and culture; Performing arts;
Humanities; Secondary education; Higher
education; Community and economic development;
Judaism; Basic and emergency aid; International
development.
Type of support: General support.
Limitations: Applications not accepted. Giving
primarily in Chicago, IL. No grants to individuals.
Application information: Unsolicited requests for
funds not accepted.
Officers: Peter M. Ascoli, Pres. and Treas.; Elizabeth
Tsapira, V.P.; Lucy B. Ascoli, Secy.
EIN: 136141339

3060
Loudoun Hospital Trust 3
10 S. Dearborn St., IL1-0117
Chicago, IL 60603-2300

Foundation type: Independent foundation.
Financial data (yr. ended 12/31/14): Assets,
$4,521,157; expenditures, $264,160; qualifying
distributions, $214,581.
Fields of interest: Health.
Limitations: Applications not accepted.
Application information: Unsolicited requests for
funds not accepted.
Trustee: JPMorgan Chase Bank, N.A.
EIN: 136023376

3061
Loudoun Hospital Trust f/b/o Eleanor
10 S. Dearborn IL1-0117
Chicago, IL 60603   8668885157

Foundation type: Independent foundation.
Financial data (yr. ended 12/31/14): Assets,
$7,299,379; expenditures, $412,910; qualifying
distributions, $341,268.
Fields of interest: Health.
Limitations: Applications not accepted. Giving
primarily in VA.
Application information: Unsolicited requests for
funds not accepted.
Trustee: JPMorgan Chase Bank, N.A.
EIN: 136023375

3062
Loudoun Memorial Hospital Trust 2
10 S. Dearborn St., IL1-0117
Chicago, IL 60603-2300

Foundation type: Independent foundation.
Financial data (yr. ended 12/31/14): Assets,
$7,541,891; expenditures, $424,217; qualifying
distributions, $352,040.
Fields of interest: Health.
Limitations: Applications not accepted.
Application information: Unsolicited requests for
funds not accepted.
Trustee: JPMorgan Chase Bank, N.A.
EIN: 136257810

3063
Elizabeth and Jeff Louis Foundation
(formerly John Jeffry Louis III Foundation)
c/o Bell & Anderson LLC
135 S. Lasalle St., Ste. 2350
Chicago, IL 60603   2623843700
Application address: Lauren McGrath, c/o Credit
Suisse, 227 W. Monroe St., Ste. 4350, Chicago, IL
60606, tel.: (312) 345-6800

Established in 1992 in Illinois.
Donors: John Jeffry Louis III; John J. Louis
Foundation; John Jeffry Louis.
Foundation type: Independent foundation.
Financial data (yr. ended 12/31/14): Assets,
$21,587; gifts received, $135,000; expenditures,
$136,952; qualifying distributions, $126,284.
Purpose and activities: Giving for art and cultural
institutes, education, and religion.
Fields of interest: Arts and culture; Education;
Higher education; Undergraduate education;
Hospital care; Religion.
Type of support: Annual campaigns.
Limitations: Applications accepted. Giving primarily
in the Chicago, IL, area and in MA. No grants to
individuals.

Application information:
Initial approach: Proposal
Deadline(s): None
Directors: Walter W. Bell; J. Jeffry Louis; Timothy C.
Louis.
EIN: 363849306

3064
Jeff B. and Katherine B. Love Foundation
(formerly Ben and Margaret Love Foundation)
10 S. Dearborn, IL1-0111
Chicago, IL 60603
Application address: Jeff B. Love, c/o Kevin Biekert,
712 Main St., 11th Fl., Houston, TX 77002-3224,
tel.: (713) 216-6009

Established in 1986 in Texas.
Donors: Ben F. Love; Margaret M. Love.
Foundation type: Independent foundation.
Financial data (yr. ended 12/31/14): Assets,
$1,032,010 (M); expenditures, $299,590;
qualifying distributions, $290,128; giving activities
include $288,683 for 49 grants (high: $54,500;
low: $300).
Purpose and activities: Giving primarily for religious
and civic organizations, medical research, and
education.
Fields of interest: Arts and culture; Museums;
Education; Higher education; Nonprofits; Diseases
and conditions; Human services; Child welfare.
Type of support: General support; Research;
Endowments; Regranting.
Limitations: Applications accepted. Giving primarily
in Houston, TX.
Application information: Application form required.
Initial approach: Letter
Deadline(s): None
Officers: Jeff B. Love, Pres.; Katherine Love, V.P.
Directors: Benton Love; Elizabeth Love Ross.
Trustee: JPMorgan Chase Bank, N.A.
EIN: 760220082

3065
Wesley Luehring Foundation
807 Cherry St.
Wheaton, IL 60187-4303   (630) 668-7663
Contact: Gary E. Crocus, Pres.

Established in 1989 in Illinois.
Donors: Marian D. Luehring Trust; Ruth E. Luehring
Irrevocable Trust.
Foundation type: Independent foundation.
Financial data (yr. ended 12/31/13): Assets,
$7,807,584 (M); expenditures, $465,082;
qualifying distributions, $402,471; giving activities
include $400,000 for 17 grants (high: $50,000;
low: $5,000).
Fields of interest: Historic preservation; Specialty
hospital care; Diseases and conditions; Cancers;
Christianity; Protestantism; Human services; Youth
development; Scouting programs; People with vision
impairments.
Limitations: Applications accepted. Giving primarily
in IL. No grants to individuals.
Application information: Application form required.
Initial approach: Letter
Deadline(s): None
Officers: Gary E. Crocus, Pres.; R. Terence Kalina,
Secy.; Michael Celer, Treas.

Directors: Lisa Patterson; Corinne Schaefer; Joseph M. Schaefer, Sr.
EIN: 363616086

3066
The Robert Lyon Leukemia Foundation
1406 N. Astor St.
Chicago, IL 60610-1615
Main URL: http://rhlfoundation.com

Donor: Donna Lyon.
Foundation type: Independent foundation.
Financial data (yr. ended 12/31/12): Assets, $3,445,204 (M); gifts received, $138,758; expenditures, $267,208; qualifying distributions, $208,500; giving activities include $208,500 for 9 grants (high: $120,000; low: $2,500).
Purpose and activities: Giving primarily for research programs delivering treatment improvements for patients struggling with leukemia.
Fields of interest: Diseases and conditions; Leukemia; Housing development.
Limitations: Applications not accepted. Giving primarily in IL.
Application information: Unsolicited requests for funds not accepted.
Officer: Donna Lyon, Exec. Dir.
Director: David Lyon.
EIN: 261500324

3067
Maak Foundation
c/o Friedman and Huey Assocs., LLP
1313 W. 175th St.
Homewood, IL 60430-4606

Established in 2001 in District of Columbia.
Donor: Madeleine K. Albright.
Foundation type: Independent foundation.
Financial data (yr. ended 06/30/14): Assets, $1,084,171 (M); gifts received, $126,561; expenditures, $212,829; qualifying distributions, $206,000; giving activities include $206,000 for 14 grants (high: $50,000; low: $2,500).
Fields of interest: Higher education; International relations.
Limitations: Applications not accepted. Giving primarily in CO, DC and MA. No grants to individuals.
Application information: Contributes only to pre-selected organizations.
Officers: Madeleine K. Albright, Pres.; Alice Albright, V.P.; Katharine Albright, Co-Secy.; Elliott Friedman, Co-Secy.; Anne Albright, Treas.
EIN: 010556625

3068
Marquis George MacDonald Foundation
P.O. Box 803878
Chicago, IL 60680-3878

Established in 1951 in New York.
Donor: Marquis George MacDonald†.
Foundation type: Independent foundation.
Financial data (yr. ended 12/31/13): Assets, $8,178,943 (M); expenditures, $518,019; qualifying distributions, $445,318; giving activities include $391,000 for 9 grants (high: $15,000; low: $2,400).
Fields of interest: Arts and culture; Visual arts; Performing arts; Dance; Theater; Music; Museums;

Secondary education; Higher education; Environment; Natural resources; Animal welfare; Health; Hospital care; Diseases and conditions; HIV/AIDS; Alcoholism; Cancers; Communication media; Community and economic development; Religion; Christianity; Human services; Food aid; Senior services; Women's services; Arms control; Seniors; Females; People with disabilities.
Type of support: Continuing support; Program development; Scholarships; Research.
Limitations: Applications not accepted. Giving primarily in FL, NY and PA. No grants to individuals, or for matching gifts; no loans.
Application information: Contributes only to pre-selected organizations.
Officers and Directors: Lee McDonald, Pres. and Director; Catherine MacDonald, V.P. and Director; Joseph MacDonald, V.P. and Director; Albert McDonald, V.P. and Director; Kristen McDonald, V.P. and Director; Helen McDonald, V.P.; Lauren McDonald, Secy. and Director; Kevin McDonald, Treas. and Director.
Number of staff: 1 part-time professional.
EIN: 131957181

3069
Web Maddox Trust
c/o JP Morgan Chase Bank N.A.
10 S. Dearborn St., IL1-0117
Chicago, IL 60603-2300
Application address: P.O. Box 2050, Fort Worth, TX 76113-2050, tel.: (817) 884-4159

Established in 1986 in Texas.
Foundation type: Independent foundation.
Financial data (yr. ended 03/31/13): Assets, $4,384,016 (M); expenditures, $280,478; qualifying distributions, $208,791; giving activities include $196,000 for 10 grants (high: $50,000; low: $3,000).
Fields of interest: Arts and culture; Performing arts; Opera; Orchestral music; Museums; Higher education; Human services.
Type of support: General support.
Limitations: Applications accepted. Giving primarily in Tarrant County, TX. No support for organizations supported by the United Way. No grants to individuals.
Application information: Application form required.
Initial approach: Letter
Deadline(s): None
Trustee: JPMorgan Chase Bank, N.A.
EIN: 756347669

3070
Mako Foundation
191 N. Wacker Dr., Ste. 1500
Chicago, IL 60606-1899

Established in 2005 in Illinois.
Donor: Nancy Meyer.
Foundation type: Independent foundation.
Financial data (yr. ended 12/31/13): Assets, $5,460,165 (M); expenditures, $374,201; qualifying distributions, $237,073; giving activities include $229,658 for 45 grants (high: $20,000; low: $158).
Fields of interest: Arts and culture; Education; Human services; Child welfare.
Limitations: Applications not accepted. Giving primarily in CA and NY. No grants to individuals.

Application information: Unsolicited requests for funds not accepted.
Officers and Directors: Thomas W. Meyer, Pres. and Director; Jack Polsky, V.P.; Julie Stevenson, Secy. and Director; Beth Stephens, Treas.; Nancy Meyer.
EIN: 300286945

3071
Mallon Family Foundation
6 N. Michigan Ave., Ste. 803
Chicago, IL 60602-4885

Established in 1998 in Illinois.
Donors: Margaret Mallon; Thomas J. Mallon; Regent Management Services LLC.
Foundation type: Independent foundation.
Financial data (yr. ended 12/31/13): Assets, $17,194 (M); gifts received, $163,386; expenditures, $151,033; qualifying distributions, $145,818; giving activities include $143,953 for grants.
Fields of interest: Christianity; Human services.
Type of support: General support.
Limitations: Applications not accepted. No grants to individuals.
Application information: Unsolicited requests for funds not accepted.
Officer: Thomas J. Mallon, Pres.
EIN: 364261662

3072
The Henry & Belle Mann Charitable Foundation
1186 Linden Ave.
Highland Park, IL 60035-4150

Established in 1961 in Illinois.
Donors: Sheldon Mann; H. George Mann.
Foundation type: Independent foundation.
Financial data (yr. ended 12/31/14): Assets, $3,298,458; expenditures, $197,278; qualifying distributions, $170,400.
Fields of interest: Nonprofits.
Type of support: Regranting.
Limitations: Applications not accepted. Giving primarily in the Chicago, IL, area. No grants to individuals.
Application information: Unsolicited requests for funds not accepted.
Trustees: H. George Mann; Sheldon Mann.
EIN: 366136141

3073
The Manne Family Foundation
c/o Stanley Manne
123 N. Wacker Dr., Ste. 810
Chicago, IL 60606-1712

Established in 1997 in Illinois.
Donor: Stanley Manne.
Foundation type: Independent foundation.
Financial data (yr. ended 12/31/14): Assets, $18,849,663; gifts received, $2,049,934; expenditures, $446,728; qualifying distributions, $418,375 and $0 for set-asides.
Fields of interest: Education; Nonprofits; Human services; Child welfare; Homeless services.
Type of support: Regranting.
Limitations: Applications not accepted. Giving primarily in FL and IL. No grants to individuals.

Application information: Unsolicited requests for funds not accepted.
Officer: Stanley Manne, Chair.
Director: Sharon Manne.
EIN: 364131393

3074
Albert and Anne Mansfield Foundation
c/o Marlene Hopmayer
999 N. Lake Shore Dr.
Chicago, IL 60611-1305   3127511124
Application address: c/o Focused Philanthropy, Attn.: Celene Peurye, 122 4th St., Wilmette, IL 60091, tel.: (202) 624-3500

Established in 1999 in Illinois.
Foundation type: Independent foundation.
Financial data (yr. ended 12/31/14): Assets, $7,036,407; expenditures, $347,910; qualifying distributions, $242,628.
Fields of interest: Higher education; Law education; Reading promotion; Community and economic development.
Limitations: Applications accepted. Giving primarily in IL, with some giving in MN. No grants to individuals.
Application information: Application form required.
  Initial approach: Letter
  Deadline(s): None
Officers: Alec Hopmayer, Pres. and C.E.O.; Marlene Hopmayer, Exec. Dir.
Directors: Jeffrey Hopmayer; Alexis Mansfield; Benetta Mansfield; Justin Mansfield; Seymour Mansfield; Adam Nichols; Briana Nichols; Marcy Shinbaum.
EIN: 364244272

3075
Michael J. Marchese Foundation
4104 N. Harlem Ave.
Norridge, IL 60706-1244
Contact: Michael Marchese, Pres. and Dir.

Established in 1986 in Illinois.
Donors: Margaret Marchese; Michael Marchese; Marianne Marchese; Forest Harlem Properties; Harlem Irving Companies, Inc.
Foundation type: Independent foundation.
Financial data (yr. ended 12/31/13): Assets, $1,015,220 (M); gifts received, $162,100; expenditures, $181,396; qualifying distributions, $169,034; giving activities include $169,034 for 6 grants (high: $2,750; low: $300).
Fields of interest: Arts and culture; Health; Catholicism.
Limitations: Applications accepted. Giving primarily in Chicago, IL.
Application information:
  Initial approach: Proposal
  Deadline(s): None
Officer and Director: Michael Marchese, Pres. and Director.
EIN: 363486786

3076
Joseph L. & Sarah S. Marcum Foundation
P.O. Box 803878
Chicago, IL 60680

Established in 1987 in Ohio.

Donors: Joseph L. Marcum; Sarah Marcum.
Foundation type: Independent foundation.
Financial data (yr. ended 12/31/13): Assets, $8,589,847 (M); gifts received, $999,960; expenditures, $446,819; qualifying distributions, $411,727; giving activities include $362,500 for 40 grants (high: $226,500; low: $500).
Fields of interest: Arts and culture; Higher education; Foundations; Nonprofits; Community and economic development; Christianity; Human services.
Type of support: Regranting.
Limitations: Applications not accepted. Giving primarily in OH. No grants to individuals.
Application information: Unsolicited requests for funds not accepted.
Officer: Joseph L. Marcum, Chair.
Trustees: Catharine M. Lowe; M. Christina Manchester; Sarah S. Marcum; Stephen S. Marcum; Sarah S. Shuffield.
EIN: 311190243

3077
Ellen Marks Cancer Foundation
835 N. Church Ct.
Elmhurst, IL 60126-1036

Donors: David Marks; Party City; R. Myles Financial, Inc.; D.M. Merchandising, Inc.; Richard Schwartz; Jeffrey Kaufmann; PFI Distributors, Inc.
Foundation type: Independent foundation.
Financial data (yr. ended 12/31/14): Assets, $384,387 (M); gifts received, $158,069; expenditures, $156,319; qualifying distributions, $155,344; giving activities include $155,344 for 13 grants (high: $100,000; low: $200).
Fields of interest: Higher education; Diseases and conditions; Cancers.
Limitations: Applications not accepted. Giving primarily in Evanston, IL.
Application information: Unsolicited requests for funds not accepted.
Directors: Jason Mann; David Marks; Brianna Meade.
EIN: 273494555

3078
Marquette Bank Affordable Housing Foundation
6316 S. Western Ave.
Chicago, IL 60636-2443

Established in 2007 in Illinois.
Foundation type: Independent foundation.
Financial data (yr. ended 12/31/13): Assets, $2,655,057 (M); expenditures, $272,586; qualifying distributions, $245,530; giving activities include $50,750 for 24 grants (high: $10,000; low: $500), and $194,780 for 31 grants to individuals (high: $12,500; low: $2,200).
Fields of interest: Community and economic development; Housing development; Youth development.
Limitations: Applications not accepted. Giving primarily in Chicago, IL.
Application information: Unsolicited requests for funds not accepted.
Officers: Michael Mangin, Pres.; Betty Kosky, V.P.; Thomas Burgin, Secy.; Paul Eckroth, Treas.

Directors: Theodore Cachey; James Capraro; Paul McCarthy; George Moncada; Barry Sabloff; William Sullivan; Mark Zelisko.
EIN: 261566453

3079
Marsteller Family Foundation
c/o Harris Bank, N.A.
111 W. Monroe St., Ste. 10E
Chicago, IL 60603-4096   (312) 461-5691
Contact: Elizabeth M. Gorden, Pres. and Dir.; Jane Barnett

Established in 1982 in Illinois.
Donor: Gloria C. Marsteller Trust.
Foundation type: Independent foundation.
Financial data (yr. ended 12/31/13): Assets, $2,574,007 (M); expenditures, $348,134; qualifying distributions, $330,375; giving activities include $330,375 for 35 grants (high: $100,000; low: $500).
Purpose and activities: Giving primarily for the arts and education.
Fields of interest: Arts and culture; Dance; Art museums; Education; Higher education.
Type of support: General support; Continuing support; Program development; Professorships.
Limitations: Applications accepted. Giving primarily in CA and NY. No grants to individuals.
Application information: Application form required.
  Initial approach: Proposal
  Deadline(s): None
Officers and Directors: Elizabeth M. Gordon, Pres. and Director; Charlie O'Connell, Secy.-Treas.; John Gordon; Jay Owen.
Number of staff: 1 part-time support.
EIN: 363193322

3080
Mary's Alabaster Jar Perpetual Charitable Foundation
528 N. Market St.
Mount Carmel, IL 62863-1558

Established in 2010 in Illinois.
Foundation type: Independent foundation.
Financial data (yr. ended 12/31/14): Assets, $6,722,718 (M); expenditures, $266,555; qualifying distributions, $220,542; giving activities include $220,500 for 10 grants (high: $70,000; low: $5,000).
Fields of interest: Christianity.
Limitations: Applications not accepted.
Application information: Unsolicited requests for funds not accepted.
Officers: Mark Wankel, Pres.; Jordan Wankel, Secy.; William V. Brown, Treas.
EIN: 276701338

3081
Mary's Foundation
1455 N.E. Windermere Dr.
Tremont, IL 61568-9769

Donor: Jerome Green.
Foundation type: Independent foundation.
Financial data (yr. ended 12/31/14): Assets, $514,180; gifts received, $372,711; expenditures, $148,929; qualifying distributions, $144,308.
Fields of interest: Education; Children.

Limitations: Applications not accepted. Giving primarily in IL.
Application information: Unsolicited requests for funds not accepted.
Officer: Jerome Green, Pres.
Directors: Joyce Boone; Connie Dullard; Nancy Green; Mary Jo Palmer.
EIN: 263730953

3082
Richard J. Massey Foundation for Arts and Science
c/o Madden, Jiganti, Moore & Sinars LLP
190 S. LaSalle St., Ste. 1700
Chicago, IL 60603-3496

Foundation type: Independent foundation.
Financial data (yr. ended 12/31/13): Assets, $2,389,186 (M); gifts received, $149; expenditures, $397,818; qualifying distributions, $392,655; giving activities include $392,655 for 32 grants (high: $100,000; low: $400).
Fields of interest: Arts and culture; Opera; Art museums; Human services.
Limitations: Applications not accepted. Giving primarily in New York, NY. No grants for individuals.
Application information: Contributes only to pre-selected organizations.
Trustees: Gene Major; Richard J. Massey.
EIN: 206391730

3083
Mazzetta Family Foundation
1990 St. Johns Ave.
Highland Park, IL 60035-3103

Established in 2002 in Illinois.
Donors: Zachary D. Mazzetta; Cynthia L. Mazzetta; Jordan J. Mazzetta; Thomas J. Mazzetta; Mazzetta Company, LLC.
Foundation type: Independent foundation.
Financial data (yr. ended 12/31/13): Assets, $338,995 (M); gifts received, $240,000; expenditures, $169,654; qualifying distributions, $169,551; giving activities include $169,500 for 6 grants (high: $100,000; low: $500).
Fields of interest: Judaism.
Limitations: Applications not accepted. No grants to individuals.
Application information: Unsolicited requests for funds not accepted.
Officers and Directors: Thomas J. Mazzetta, Pres. and Treas. and Director; Cynthia L. Mazzetta, V.P. and Secy. and Director; Jordan J. Mazzetta, V.P. and Director; Zachary D. Mazzetta, V.P.
EIN: 820575950

3084
Roger & Nancy McCabe Foundation
c/o The Northern Trust Company
P.O. Box 803878
Chicago, IL 60680-3878

Established in 2005 in Minnesota.
Donors: Nancy McCabe; Roger McCabe.
Foundation type: Independent foundation.
Financial data (yr. ended 12/31/13): Assets, $10,419,619 (M); gifts received, $499,074; expenditures, $414,059; qualifying distributions,

$390,307; giving activities include $388,800 for 21 grants (high: $90,000; low: $350).
Fields of interest: Arts and culture; University education; Domesticated animals; Diseases and conditions; Cancers; Human services; Family services; Child welfare; Youth development; Women's services.
Type of support: Research.
Limitations: Applications not accepted. Giving primarily in FL, MA, and MN. No grants to individuals.
Application information: Contributes only to pre-selected organizations.
Officers: Roger McCabe, Pres.; Nancy McCabe, Treas.
Director: Darla Huff.
EIN: 202990948

3085
Luther T. McCauley Charitable Trust
c/o JPMorgan Chase Bank, N.A.
10 S. Dearborn St., IL1-0117
Chicago, IL 60603-2300
Application address: c/o JPMorgan Chase Bank, N.A., 370 17th St., Denver, CO 80202-1370, tel.: (303) 607-7710

Established in 1978 in Colorado.
Foundation type: Independent foundation.
Financial data (yr. ended 04/30/14): Assets, $5,748,983 (M); expenditures, $301,857; qualifying distributions, $261,600; giving activities include $249,000 for 23 grants (high: $25,000; low: $2,500).
Purpose and activities: Support primarily for programs benefiting economically deprived, socially disadvantaged, and mentally or physically handicapped citizens of El Paso County, Colorado.
Fields of interest: Zoos; Diseases and conditions; Public administration; Human services; Family services.
Type of support: General support; Matching grants; Equipment.
Limitations: Applications accepted. Giving primarily in El Paso County, CO. No grants to individuals.
Publications: Application guidelines.
Application information: Application form required.
  Initial approach: Letter
  Copies of proposal: 1
  Deadline(s): None
  Board meeting date(s): Quarterly
Trustee: JPMorgan Chase Bank, N.A.
EIN: 846152258

3086
The Robert McCormack Family Charitable Foundation
P.O. Box 803878
Chicago, IL 60680-3878

Established in 2004 in Illinois.
Donor: McCormack Charitable Lead Trust.
Foundation type: Independent foundation.
Financial data (yr. ended 12/31/13): Assets, $6,878,269 (M); gifts received, $260,509; expenditures, $257,938; qualifying distributions, $214,164; giving activities include $212,450 for 25 grants (high: $60,000; low: $100).
Fields of interest: Education; Zoos; Botanical gardens; Animal welfare; Nonprofits; Gardening; Christianity; Human services.
Type of support: Regranting.

Limitations: Applications not accepted. Giving primarily in CT and Chicago, IL. No grants to individuals.
Application information: Unsolicited requests for funds not accepted.
Trustee: The Northern Trust Co.
EIN: 367410704

3087
P&F McCourtney Foundation
(formerly Flora S. McCourtney Trust)
c/o Bank of America, N.A.
231 S. LaSalle St., IL1-231-10-05
Chicago, IL 60697-0001
Application address: Robert J. (Bob) Glew, 111 Westminster St., Providence, RI 02903; tel.: (401) 278-6035

Established in 1953 in Illinois.
Donors: Plato McCourtney†; Flora McCourtney†.
Foundation type: Independent foundation.
Financial data (yr. ended 09/30/13): Assets, $7,619,422 (M); gifts received, $421; expenditures, $330,134; qualifying distributions, $313,401; giving activities include $303,000 for 47 grants to individuals (high: $69,000; low: $3,000).
Purpose and activities: Scholarship awards paid through the college or university for graduating seniors Sangamon County high schools in Illinois, who wish to continue their education.
Fields of interest: Higher education.
Type of support: Student aid.
Limitations: Giving limited to residents of Sangamon County, IL.
Application information: Application form available at qualifying high schools. Application form required.
  Initial approach: Completed application
  Deadline(s): Mar. 31
  Board meeting date(s): Early Apr.
  Final notification: May
Trustee: Bank of America, N.A.
EIN: 436023586

3088
McCrea Foundation
P.O. Box 803878
Chicago, IL 60680-3878   3126306000

Established in 1960 in Virginia.
Donors: Mary Corling McCrea†; The Phoebe Welsh Crut.
Foundation type: Independent foundation.
Financial data (yr. ended 02/28/14): Assets, $7,101,783; expenditures, $461,210; qualifying distributions, $411,095.
Purpose and activities: Giving primarily for education and health, including a children's hospital; funding also for human services and religion.
Fields of interest: Museums; Education; Secondary education; Animal welfare; Specialty hospital care; Hospice care; Community and economic development; Religion; Judaism; Human services; Child welfare.
Type of support: General support; Scholarships.
Limitations: Applications not accepted. Giving primarily in Minden, NV; Portland, OR; and Houston, TX. No grants to individuals.
Application information: Contributes only to pre-selected organizations.
  Board meeting date(s): Generally in May

Officers: Phoebe W. Welsh, Pres.; David D. Welsh, V.P. and Secy.; John L. Welsh III, V.P.; Edward C. Welsh, V.P. and Treas.
Agent: The Northern Trust Co.
EIN: 546052010

3089
McCune Family Foundation
P.O. Box 803878
Chicago, IL 60680-3878

Established in 2007 in Illinois.
Donor: Mary W. McCune.
Foundation type: Independent foundation.
Financial data (yr. ended 12/31/13): Assets, $26,178,155 (M); gifts received, $24,868,827; expenditures, $379,610; qualifying distributions, $333,376; giving activities include $328,500 for 3 grants (high: $121,000; low: $100,000).
Fields of interest: Environment; Animal training.
Limitations: Applications not accepted. Giving primarily in FL and MA.
Application information: Unsolicited requests for funds not accepted.
Trustee: The Northern Trust Co.
EIN: 261595257

3090
James J. & Jacqualine A. McDonough Foundation
c/o the Northern Trust Co.
1501 N. State Pkwy., Apt. 21D
Chicago, IL 60610-1676

Established in 1989 in Illinois.
Donors: James J. McDonough; Jacqualine A. McDonough.
Foundation type: Independent foundation.
Financial data (yr. ended 12/31/14): Assets, $6,074,969 (M); expenditures, $284,818; qualifying distributions, $258,515; giving activities include $257,500 for 6 grants (high: $75,000; low: $7,500).
Fields of interest: University education.
Limitations: Applications not accepted. Giving primarily in Chicago, IL. No grants to individuals.
Application information: Unsolicited requests for funds not accepted.
Officers: James J. McDonough, Pres.; Jacqualine A. McDonough, V.P.; James P. Mcdonough, Treas.; Maureen M. Curley, Secy.
EIN: 363689173

3091
Nancy A. Lauter & Alfred L. McDougal Charitable Fund
737 N. Michigan Ave.
Chicago, IL 60611-4130 (312) 255-0936
Contact: Nancy S. Lowenthal

Foundation type: Independent foundation.
Financial data (yr. ended 12/31/13): Assets, $6,828,708 (M); expenditures, $217,224; qualifying distributions, $188,541; giving activities include $176,850 for grants.
Fields of interest: Arts and culture; Education; Individual liberties; Human services.
Limitations: Applications accepted. Giving primarily in Chicago, IL.
Application information:

Initial approach: Proposal
Deadline(s): None
Trustees: Nancy A. Lauter; Alfred L. McDougal.
EIN: 527240158

3092
Max McGraw Wildlife Foundation
P.O. Box 9, Rte. 25
Dundee, IL 60118-0009 (847) 741-8000
Contact: Charles S. Potter, Exec. Dir.
Main URL: http://www.mcgrawwildlife.org

Established in 1962 in Illinois.
Donor: McGraw Foundation.
Foundation type: Operating foundation.
Financial data (yr. ended 04/30/13): Assets, $24,024,822 (M); gifts received, $2,933,414; expenditures, $5,780,733; qualifying distributions, $2,251,111; giving activities include $65,830 for 2 grants (high: $65,800; low: $30), $96,146 for 9 grants to individuals (high: $20,350; low: $3,200), and $1,480,912 for 2 foundation-administered programs.
Purpose and activities: Giving primarily to organizations that sponsor wildlife research projects, especially those related to upland game birds, song birds, waterfowl, fisheries, and endangered species.
Fields of interest: Higher education; Natural resources; Biodiversity; Wildlife biodiversity.
Type of support: Internships; Donated land; Technical assistance.
Publications: Informational brochure.
Application information:
Initial approach: Letter
Deadline(s): None
Board meeting date(s): Mid-June
Officers: Scott M. Elrod, Chair.; J. Stanley Pepper, Vice-Chair.; Charles S. Potter, Jr., C.E.O. and Pres.; Wendy Romero, C.O.O. and V.P.; Clark E. Ganshirt, V.P.; Joseph J. Slawek, Secy.; Bruce Crowther, Treas.
Directors: Thomas Anderson; Robert G. Donnelley; Thomas G. Fitzgerald; Terence M. Graunke; Michael C. Hillstrom; Eugene M. Lerner; Lawrence R. Lucas; Carol E. Moorman; Timothy N. Thoelecke; Allen M. Turner.
EIN: 362519612

3093
McKee Family Foundation
53 W. Jackson Blvd., No. 1218
Chicago, IL 60604-3606

Established in 2000 in Illinois.
Donor: Howard A. McKee.
Foundation type: Independent foundation.
Financial data (yr. ended 12/31/14): Assets, $6,626,500 (M); expenditures, $358,742; qualifying distributions, $344,043; giving activities include $317,000 for 59 grants (high: $26,000; low: $100).
Fields of interest: Arts and culture; Education; Christianity; Human services; Victim aid; Family services.
Limitations: Applications not accepted. Giving on a national basis; with emphasis on CO, IA, and IL. No grants to individuals.
Application information: Contributes only to pre-selected organizations.

Officers and Directors: Jean M. Barry, Pres. and Director; John Barry, Secy. and Director; Gregory A. McKee, Treas. and Director; Barbara M. Bays; Timothy Barry; Janet M. Griesinger; Jessica D. Heydt; Meredith B. McKee; William A. McKee; Lael H. Stanzcak.
EIN: 364329457

3094
Ella G. McKee Foundation
c/o First National Bank Trust Dept.
311 Banker Blvd.
Vandalia, IL 62471-1941

Foundation type: Independent foundation.
Financial data (yr. ended 12/31/13): Assets, $1,969,604 (M); gifts received, $191,114; expenditures, $275,490; qualifying distributions, $250,677; giving activities include $234,325 for 132 grants to individuals (high: $3,600; low: $300).
Purpose and activities: Awards scholarships and interest-free loans to students who have resided in Fayette County, IL, for at least four years.
Fields of interest: Education.
Type of support: Student aid; Loans to individuals.
Limitations: Applications not accepted. Giving limited to residents of Fayette County, IL.
Application information: Unsolicited request for funds not accepted.
Trustee: First National Bank.
EIN: 376099863

3095
McLaughlin Family Foundation
2430 River Dr.
Moline, IL 61265-1564 (309) 736-6005
Contact: Peter Britt

Established in 1997 in Illinois.
Donors: McLaughlin Body Company; Raymond L. McLaughlin; Peter J. McLaughlin.
Foundation type: Company-sponsored foundation.
Financial data (yr. ended 12/31/13): Assets, $3,247,646 (M); expenditures, $310,292; qualifying distributions, $283,055; giving activities include $282,415 for 23 grants (high: $100,000; low: $1,000).
Purpose and activities: The foundation supports community foundations and organizations involved with secondary and higher education, human services, community development, and Catholicism.
Fields of interest: Secondary education; Higher education; Foundations; Community and economic development; Catholicism; Human services.
Type of support: General support; Capital campaigns.
Limitations: Applications accepted. Giving primarily in the Moline, IL, area. No grants to individuals.
Application information:
Initial approach: Proposal
Deadline(s): None
Trustees: Peter J. McLaughlin; Raymond L. McLaughlin.
EIN: 364158320

3096
Robert G. and Rebecca A. McLennan Foundation
1670 S. Wolf Rd.
Wheeling, IL 60090-6516

Established in 2001 in Illinois.
Donors: Robert G. McLennan; Rebecca A. McLennan.
Foundation type: Independent foundation.
Financial data (yr. ended 12/31/13): Assets, $406,725 (M); expenditures, $356,991; qualifying distributions, $355,000; giving activities include $355,000 for 3 grants (high: $250,000; low: $5,000).
Fields of interest: Arts and culture; Education; Youth services.
Limitations: Applications not accepted. Giving primarily in IL. No grants to individuals.
Application information: Contributes only to pre-selected organizations.
Officers and Directors: Robert G. McLennan, Pres. and Director; Rebecca A. McLennan, V.P. and Director; Douglas A. McLennan; Robert M. McLennan.
EIN: 364482912

3097
Andrew & Jeanine McNally Charitable Foundation
333 N. Michigan Ave.
Chicago, IL 60601-4104

Established in 1993 in Illinois.
Donors: A. McNally III Trust; Andrew McNally IV.
Foundation type: Independent foundation.
Financial data (yr. ended 06/30/14): Assets, $739,408 (M); gifts received, $158,980; expenditures, $156,417; qualifying distributions, $156,254; giving activities include $156,000 for 32 grants (high: $45,000; low: $250).
Fields of interest: Arts and culture; Performing arts; Maritime museums; Natural history museums; Secondary education; Higher education; Zoos; Domesticated animals; Foundations; Hospital care; Rehabilitation; Libraries; Community improvement; Human services; Children; People with disabilities.
Limitations: Applications not accepted. Giving primarily in Chicago, IL and NY. No grants to individuals.
Application information: Contributes only to pre-selected organizations.
Trustees: Andrew McNally IV; Jeanine S. McNally.
EIN: 367056039

3098
George Reed McNeill Animal Welfare Fund
7000 W. 127th St.
Palos Heights, IL 60463-1558

Donor: George Reed McNeill†.
Foundation type: Independent foundation.
Financial data (yr. ended 08/31/13): Assets, $7,536,437 (M); gifts received, $3,448; expenditures, $532,883; qualifying distributions, $441,796; giving activities include $396,710 for 8 grants (high: $100,000; low: $9,743).
Fields of interest: Domesticated animals.
Type of support: General support.
Limitations: Applications not accepted. Giving primarily in IL.
Application information: Unsolicited requests for funds not accepted.
Officers: Paul Galinski, Pres.; Sister Anna Doyle, V.P.; Thomas F. Courtney, Sr., Secy.-Treas.
EIN: 271045290

3099
James J. and Jamie Thorsen McNulty Foundation
c/o James J. McNulty
6 Kent Rd.
Winnetka, IL 60093-1816

Established in 1996 in Illinois.
Donor: James J. McNulty.
Foundation type: Independent foundation.
Financial data (yr. ended 12/31/13): Assets, $620,633 (M); gifts received, $200,000; expenditures, $292,523; qualifying distributions, $290,000; giving activities include $290,000 for 12 grants (high: $75,000; low: $600).
Fields of interest: Education; Higher education; Foundations; Christianity; Human services.
Limitations: Applications not accepted. Giving primarily in IL and Granville, OH. No grants to individuals.
Application information: Contributes only to pre-selected organizations.
Trustees: James McNulty; Kyle J. McNulty; Lucas H. McNulty; Jamie K. Thorsen.
EIN: 367129915

3100
Nelson Mead Fund
c/o Adwell Svcs., LLC
102 N. Westgate Ave.
Jacksonville, IL 62650-1718
Contact: Ruth C. Mead, Tr.; Dana Bangert, C.P.A.
E-mail: bangert@adwellcorporation.com

Established in 1965 in Ohio.
Donors: Ioka Fund; Ruth C. Mead; Nelson & Ruth Mead Charitable Remainder Trust.
Foundation type: Independent foundation.
Financial data (yr. ended 11/30/13): Assets, $6,554,121 (M); expenditures, $380,490; qualifying distributions, $324,394; giving activities include $305,788 for grants.
Purpose and activities: Giving to contribute to education, the environment, health and religion.
Fields of interest: Arts and culture; Education; Natural resources; Biodiversity; Wildlife biodiversity; Diseases and conditions; Public administration; Religion; Christianity; Children; Seniors; Low-income and poor people; Victims of crime and abuse; People with psychosocial disabilities.
Type of support: Continuing support; Annual campaigns; Capital campaigns; Capital and infrastructure; Equipment; Emergency funds; Research.
Limitations: Applications not accepted. Giving on a national basis. No grants to individuals.
Application information: Contributes only to pre-selected organizations.
 Board meeting date(s): June 15 and Nov. 30
Trustee: Ruth C. Mead.
Number of staff: None.
EIN: 316064591

3101
Meier Family Foundation
10 S. Dearborn IL1-0117
Chicago, IL 60603

Established in 2007 in Delaware.
Donor: Arlene Meier.
Foundation type: Independent foundation.

Financial data (yr. ended 12/31/13): Assets, $6,106,625 (M); expenditures, $332,788; qualifying distributions, $307,035; giving activities include $306,000 for 28 grants (high: $150,000; low: $1,000).
Fields of interest: Foundations; Nonprofits; Hospital care; Women's services; Children.
Type of support: Regranting.
Limitations: Applications not accepted. Giving primarily in WI. No grants to individuals.
Application information: Contributes only to pre-selected organizations.
Officers and Directors: Arlene Meier, Pres. and Director; Marshall Meier, V.P.
EIN: 208762273

3102
The Merchantz Family Foundation
723 W. North St.
Hinsdale, IL 60521-3001

Established in 1991 in Illinois.
Donors: William Merchantz; Cathy Jo Merchantz.
Foundation type: Independent foundation.
Financial data (yr. ended 12/31/14): Assets, $4,327,923 (M); gifts received, $635,000; expenditures, $247,930; qualifying distributions, $208,782; giving activities include $193,000 for 10 grants (high: $100,000; low: $2,000).
Fields of interest: Education; Christianity; Sports and recreation.
Limitations: Applications not accepted. Giving primarily in IL. No grants to individuals.
Application information: Unsolicited requests for funds not accepted.
Officers and Directors: William Merchantz, Pres. and Director; Cathy Jo Merchantz, Secy. and Director.
EIN: 363739087

3103
Henry and Louise Mermelstein Charitable Foundation
6500 North Hamlin
Lincolnwood, IL 60712-3904

Established in 1986 in Illinois.
Donors: Henry Mermelstein; Louise Mermelstein; Doreen Mermelstein; Marvin Mermelstein.
Foundation type: Independent foundation.
Financial data (yr. ended 06/30/13): Assets, $1,681,058 (M); gifts received, $196,173; expenditures, $183,218; qualifying distributions, $182,454; giving activities include $182,454 for 285 grants (high: $44,000; low: $25).
Purpose and activities: Support for Jewish organizations, including yeshivas and congregations.
Fields of interest: Education; Judaism.
International interests: Canada; Israel.
Limitations: Applications not accepted. Giving primarily in the U.S., with some emphasis on Chicago, IL, NJ and NY. No grants to individuals.
Application information: Unsolicited requests for funds not accepted.
Officer: Henry Mermelstein, Pres.
Directors: Joseph Mermelstein; Louise Mermelstein; Marvin Mermelstein.
EIN: 363481731

3104
Metzner Family Foundation
3 Lakewood Dr.
Glencoe, IL 60022-1326
Contact: Mark J. Metzner

Established in 1998 in Illinois.
Donor: Mark J. Metzner.
Foundation type: Independent foundation.
Financial data (yr. ended 12/31/13): Assets, $3,335,488 (M); expenditures, $144,166; qualifying distributions, $138,100; giving activities include $135,900 for 61 grants (high: $40,000; low: $25).
Fields of interest: Arts and culture; Philanthropy; Human services.
Limitations: Applications not accepted. Giving primarily IL and NY. No grants to individuals.
Application information: Unsolicited requests for funds not accepted.
Officers: Mark J. Metzner, Pres.; Joan S. Henson, V.P.; Gary F. Metzner, Secy.; David B. Metzner, Treas.
EIN: 364264868

3105
Lucille Meusel Trust
10 S. Dearborn St., IL1-0117
Chicago, IL 60603-2300

Foundation type: Independent foundation.
Financial data (yr. ended 11/30/13): Assets, $17,515,843 (M); expenditures, $385,932; qualifying distributions, $270,803; giving activities include $236,945 for 14 grants (high: $33,125; low: $5,521).
Fields of interest: Health; Catholicism; Human services.
Limitations: Applications not accepted. Giving primarily in Green Bay, WI.
Application information: Unsolicited requests for funds not accepted.
Trustee: JPMorgan Chase Bank, N.A.
EIN: 396435763

3106
C. Louis Meyer Family Foundation
c/o Carol Barrett, Admin.
P.O. Box 854
Huntley, IL 60142-0854
E-mail: CLMFF@foxvalley.net; *Main URL:* http://www.clmff.com
Facebook: https://www.facebook.com/pages/C-Louis-Meyer-Family-Foundation/134094546648658

Established in 1999 in Illinois.
Foundation type: Independent foundation.
Financial data (yr. ended 12/31/13): Assets, $3,616,664 (M); expenditures, $393,542; qualifying distributions, $338,419; giving activities include $249,995 for 68 grants (high: $27,000; low: $300).
Purpose and activities: To further public welfare through the relief of poverty and suffering, the advancement of education, the promotion of health, and the extension of the influence of religion.
Fields of interest: Arts and culture; Education; Health; Diseases and conditions; Christianity; Human services; Youth services; Children and youth; Infants and toddlers; Children; Adolescents;

Adults; Young adults; Female children and youth; Female adults; Male children and youth; Male adults; Single parents; Ethnic and racial groups; Homeless people; Low-income and poor people; Victims of crime and abuse; People with disabilities; People with psychosocial disabilities; Substance abusers.
Type of support: General support; Matching grants; Continuing support; Capital campaigns; Capital and infrastructure; Emergency funds; Program development; Scholarships; Research.
Limitations: Applications accepted. Giving primarily in Chicago, IL, Pinehust, NC, and SC; some giving on a national basis. No support for political causes. No grants to individuals, or for ads in charitable publications, purchase of special events tickets, seed money for new businesses, or political causes.
Publications: Application guidelines; Grants list.
Application information: Application form available on foundation web site. Chicago Area Grant Application Form accepted. Application form required.
> *Initial approach:* Letter or e-mail
> *Copies of proposal:* 1
> *Deadline(s):* Applications are accepted starting Aug. 1 and must be postmarked no later than Oct. 31
> *Board meeting date(s):* Quarterly, dates vary within each quarter
> *Final notification:* 4 months

Officers and Directors: C. Foster Brown III, Pres. and Director; Louis M. Brown II, V.P.; Angeline Brown Leonard, Secy.; Nicholas C. Brown, Treas.; C. Foster Brown IV; Jennifer Brown; Whitney Brown.
Number of staff: 1 full-time professional; 1 part-time support.
EIN: 364304695

3107
Meyers Charitable Family Fund
8748 Kells Dr.
Hickory Hills, IL 60457-1793 (708) 598-8111

Established in 1988 in Illinois.
Foundation type: Independent foundation.
Financial data (yr. ended 12/31/14): Assets, $398,876; expenditures, $213,978; qualifying distributions, $200,175.
Fields of interest: Arts and culture; Museums; Education; Environment; Wildlife biodiversity; Zoos; Foundations; Hospital care; Christianity; Human services; Child welfare; Unknown or not classified.
Limitations: Applications accepted. Giving primarily in CA, DC, ID and IL. No grants to individuals.
Application information:
> *Initial approach:* Proposal
> *Deadline(s):* None

Officers and Directors: David R. Meyers, Pres. and Director; Frederick C. Meyers, Secy.-Treas.; Margery McGrew.
EIN: 363610777

3108
Micole Foundation
28 Elmwood Dr.
Naperville, IL 60540

Established in 2000 in Illinois.
Donor: Richard C. Notebaert.
Foundation type: Independent foundation.

Financial data (yr. ended 12/31/14): Assets, $5,489,642; expenditures, $388,179; qualifying distributions, $337,739.
Fields of interest: Ballet; Museums; Education; Environment; Diabetes; Christianity; Child welfare.
Limitations: Applications not accepted. Giving primarily in IL. No grants to individuals.
Application information: Unsolicited requests for funds not accepted.
Trustees: Michelle Hawver; Nicole Lacy.
EIN: 367309675

3109
Adah K. Millard Charitable Trust
c/o The Northern Trust Co.
P.O. Box 803878
Chicago, IL 60680-3878

Established in 1976 in Illinois.
Donor: Adah K. Millard†.
Foundation type: Independent foundation.
Financial data (yr. ended 12/31/14): Assets, $6,758,944; expenditures, $413,230; qualifying distributions, $348,488.
Fields of interest: Arts and culture; Performing arts; Art museums; Education; Higher education; Animal welfare; Nonprofits; Hospital care; Christianity; Human services; Food banks; Child welfare.
Type of support: General support; Continuing support; Capital and infrastructure; Equipment; Program development; Seed money; Regranting.
Limitations: Applications not accepted. Giving limited to Douglas County, NE. No grants to individuals, or for endowment funds, scholarships, or fellowships; generally no grants for operating budgets; no loans.
Application information: Contributes only to pre-selected organizations.
> *Board meeting date(s):* Apr. and Nov.

Trustee: The Northern Trust Co.
EIN: 366629069

3110
Leon J. Millard Foundation
c/o The Northern Trust Co.
P.O. Box 803878
Chicago, IL 60680-3878

Foundation type: Independent foundation.
Financial data (yr. ended 12/31/13): Assets, $5,398,113 (M); expenditures, $264,743; qualifying distributions, $226,787; giving activities include $214,150 for 10 grants (high: $35,000; low: $4,000).
Fields of interest: Arts and culture; Museums; Education; Foundations; In-patient medical care; Hospital care; Police agencies; Human services; Youth development.
Limitations: Applications not accepted. Giving primarily in Omaha, NE. No grants to individuals.
Application information: Contributes only to pre-selected organizations.
Trustee: The Northern Trust Co.
EIN: 366027449

3111
Mark and Maureen Miller Family Foundation Fund
28161 N. Keith Dr.
Lake Forest, IL 60045-4528

Donor: Mark C. Miller.
Foundation type: Independent foundation.
Financial data (yr. ended 12/31/13): Assets, $9,566,135 (M); expenditures, $546,963; qualifying distributions, $432,889; giving activities include $429,000 for 35 grants (high: $200,000; low: $500).
Fields of interest: Domesticated animals; Health; Diseases and conditions; Religion.
Type of support: Research.
Limitations: Applications not accepted. Giving primarily in IL and PA.
Application information: Unsolicited requests for funds not accepted.
Officers: Mark C. Miller, Pres. and Treas.; Maureen E. Miller, V.P. and Secy.
Directors: Jonathan D. Miller; Sean M. Miller.
EIN: 261828406

3112
Miller Family Foundation, Inc.
P.O. Box 803878
Chicago, IL 60680-3878

Established in 1996 in Georgia.
Donor: William G. Miller.
Foundation type: Independent foundation.
Financial data (yr. ended 08/31/14): Assets, $6,029,463; expenditures, $360,182; qualifying distributions, $291,530.
Fields of interest: Arts and culture; Museums; Education; Specialty hospital care; National defense; Human services.
Type of support: Individual development.
Limitations: Applications not accepted. Giving primarily in FL and TN, with some giving in GA. No grants to individuals.
Application information: Contributes only to pre-selected organizations.
Officers: William G. Miller, Pres.; Carol Short, Secy.
EIN: 582261960

3113
Miller, Cooper & Co., Ltd. Charitable Foundation
1751 Lake Cook Rd., Ste. 400
Deerfield, IL 60015-5286
Contact: Pete Cieslak

Established in 1992 in Illinois.
Donors: Miller, Cooper & Co., Ltd.; Ross S. Pearlstein; Julian Levy; Charles Cohen; Peter F. Cieslak; Jeffrey Feld; Ricky L. Max; Brian Kayman; James G. Rediger; Robert L. Sabin; Marianne E. Phalin; William Wiersema; Kristen L. Fitzpatrick; Steven R. Madden.
Foundation type: Independent foundation.
Financial data (yr. ended 09/30/14): Assets, $19,477 (M); gifts received, $149,200; expenditures, $176,947; qualifying distributions, $176,932; giving activities include $176,932 for 70 grants (high: $90,000; low: $50).
Fields of interest: Nonprofits; Agriculture; Religion; Human services.
Type of support: General support; Regranting; Scholarships; Research.
Limitations: Applications not accepted. Giving primarily in IL. No grants to individuals.
Application information: Unsolicited requests for funds not accepted.

Officers: Ross Pearlstein, Pres.; Robert Sabin, Secy.; Peter Cieslak, Treas.
Director: Marianne Phalin.
EIN: 363851204

3114
Juanita & Henry S. Miller, Jr. Arts Foundation
P.O. Box 803878
Chicago, IL 60680-3878
Application address: c/o Anne B. Turner, 5959 Royal Ln., Ste. 634-205, Dallas, TX 75230

Established in 1992 in Texas.
Donors: Juanita Miller; Henry S. Miller, Jr.
Foundation type: Independent foundation.
Financial data (yr. ended 06/30/13): Assets, $0 (M); expenditures, $216,739; qualifying distributions, $215,130; giving activities include $214,739 for 3 grants (high: $184,439; low: $300).
Fields of interest: Arts and culture; Orchestral music.
Type of support: General support.
Limitations: Applications accepted. Giving primarily in Dallas, TX. No grants to individuals.
Application information:
Initial approach: Contact foundation
Deadline(s): None
Officers: Vance C. Miller, Sr., Chair; Jacqueline Miller Stewart, Pres.; Henry S. Miller III, Secy.; Patricia Miller Donosky, Treas.
EIN: 752456360

3115
Gordon H. & Karen M. Millner Family Foundation
3535 Patten Rd., Ste. 7A
Highland Park, IL 60035-5960

Established in 1995 in Illinois.
Donors: Gordon H. Millner; Millner Charitable Lead Annuity Trust; Karen M. Millner.
Foundation type: Independent foundation.
Financial data (yr. ended 11/30/14): Assets, $4,454,017 (M); gifts received, $100,000; expenditures, $410,710; qualifying distributions, $361,466; giving activities include $358,750 for 61 grants (high: $75,000; low: $50).
Fields of interest: Higher education; Nonprofits; Diseases and conditions; Arthritis; Judaism.
Type of support: Regranting.
Limitations: Applications not accepted. Giving primarily in IL. No grants to individuals.
Application information: Unsolicited requests for funds not accepted.
Officers: Gordon H. Millner, Pres.; Karen M. Millner, Secy.-Treas.
EIN: 363998692

3116
Miner Family Charitable Trust
6838 E. State St.
Rockford, IL 61107-4610

Donor: Jerry Miner‡.
Foundation type: Independent foundation.
Financial data (yr. ended 12/31/13): Assets, $3,997,757 (M); expenditures, $229,644; qualifying distributions, $193,180; giving activities

include $167,041 for 13 grants (high: $16,704; low: $1,000).
Fields of interest: Domesticated animals; Christianity; Human services.
Limitations: Applications not accepted. Giving primarily in IL. No grants to individuals.
Application information: Unsolicited requests for funds not accepted.
Trustees: Brian Reese, Esq.; Alpine Bank & Trust Co., Inc.
EIN: 367414569

3117
The Edward and Lucy Minor Family Foundation
(formerly Edward & Lucy R. Minor Family Foundation, Inc.)
326 Ravine Dr.
Highland Park, IL 60035-3344 8475590661

Established in 1970 in Illinois.
Donor: Robinson Steel Co.
Foundation type: Independent foundation.
Financial data (yr. ended 12/31/14): Assets, $3,976,331; expenditures, $287,193; qualifying distributions, $223,050.
Fields of interest: Arts and culture; Opera; Museums; Education; Nonprofits; Diseases and conditions; Judaism; Antidiscrimination; Human services; Child welfare.
Type of support: Research; Regranting.
Limitations: Applications not accepted. Giving primarily in IL. No grants to individuals.
Application information: Unsolicited requests for funds not accepted.
Officers and Directors: Lucy Minor, Pres. and Director; Jennifer Minor Lansing; Judith Minor.
Number of staff: None.
EIN: 237071065

3118
Minow Family Foundation
c/o Sidley Austin Brown & Wood, LLP
1 S. Dearborn St.
Chicago, IL 60603-2302 (312) 853-7555

Established in 1967 in Illinois.
Donors: Josephine B. Minow; Newton N. Minow.
Foundation type: Independent foundation.
Financial data (yr. ended 12/31/14): Assets, $3,643,815; expenditures, $216,617; qualifying distributions, $195,480.
Purpose and activities: Giving primarily for education, arts and culture, and Jewish agencies.
Fields of interest: Arts and culture; Music; History; Education; Higher education; Archaeology; Communication media; Judaism.
Type of support: General support.
Limitations: Applications accepted. Giving primarily in Chicago, IL.
Application information:
Initial approach: Letter
Deadline(s): None
Officers and Directors: Josephine B. Minow, Pres. and Director; Newton N. Minow, V.P. and Secy. and Director; Franklin A. Chanen, V.P. and Treas. and Director; Martha L. Minow; Mary R. Minow; S. Nell Minow.
EIN: 366169301

3119
Mirapaul Foundation
1187 Wilmette Ave., Apt. 102
Wilmette, IL 60091-2719 3307629785
Application address: c/o Matthew R. Mirapaul, 3421 Ridgewood Rd., Ste. 300, Akron, OH 44333, tel.: (330) 762-9785

Established in 1988 in Ohio.
Donors: Walter N. Mirapaul; Matthew R. Mirapaul; Evan D. Mirapaul; Walter N. Mirapaul Charitable Lead Trust.
Foundation type: Independent foundation.
Financial data (yr. ended 09/30/14): Assets, $1,462,419; gifts received, $0; expenditures, $188,499; qualifying distributions, $158,013.
Fields of interest: Arts and culture; Philanthropy; Human services.
Type of support: Annual campaigns; Endowments.
Limitations: Applications accepted. Giving primarily in CA, IL, OH, and NY. No grants to individuals.
Application information: Application form required.
  Initial approach: Letter
  Deadline(s): None
Trustees: Evan D. Mirapaul; Matthew R. Mirapaul.
EIN: 341602913

3120
Bernard & Marjorie Mitchell Family Foundation
5 Revere Dr.
Ste. 400
Northbrook, IL 60062-1570

Established in 1969 in Illinois.
Donors: Bernard A. Mitchell Trust; Lee H. Mitchell; Marjorie I. Mitchell.
Foundation type: Independent foundation.
Financial data (yr. ended 12/31/14): Assets, $2,786,593 (M); expenditures, $146,023; qualifying distributions, $136,015; giving activities include $135,000 for 4 grants (high: $102,500; low: $2,500).
Fields of interest: Arts and culture; Performing arts; Higher education; Nonprofits; Hospital care; Human services.
Type of support: Regranting.
Limitations: Applications not accepted. Giving primarily in Chicago, IL. No grants to individuals.
Application information: Contributes only to pre-selected organizations.
Trustees: David Kohn; Lee Mitchell; Victoria C. Kohn; Valerie Kohn Meyer.
EIN: 237007014

3121
The Jean Whyte and Frank T. Mohr Charitable Trust
101 N. Mayflower Rd.
Lake Forest, IL 60045-2422

Established in 1988 in Illinois.
Donors: Frank T. Mohr; Jean Whyte Mohr.
Foundation type: Independent foundation.
Financial data (yr. ended 12/31/14): Assets, $4,569,882 (M); gifts received, $7,250; expenditures, $286,502; qualifying distributions, $277,915; giving activities include $274,250 for 3 grants (high: $199,250; low: $20,000).

Fields of interest: Education; Higher education; Hospital care; Family planning; Christianity; Human services.
Limitations: Applications not accepted. Giving primarily in IL; Support Limitations: No grants to individuals. No grants to individuals.
Application information: Unsolicited requests for funds not accepted.
Trustees: Frank T. Mohr; Jean Whyte Mohr.
EIN: 363649835

3122
Monroe Fund Inc.
225 Woodlawn Ave.
Hubbard Woods, IL 60093-1552 (847) 507-8020
Contact: Marjorie Gordon Schaye, V.P.

Established in 1956 in Illinois.
Donors: Mayme Gordon; Marjorie G. Schaye; Marshall Gordon; Eugene Gordon.
Foundation type: Independent foundation.
Financial data (yr. ended 08/31/13): Assets, $0 (M); expenditures, $178,800; qualifying distributions, $174,695; giving activities include $174,695 for 10 grants (high: $68,049; low: $500).
Fields of interest: Arts and culture; Education; Religion.
Type of support: General support.
Limitations: Applications accepted. Giving primarily in FL. No grants to individuals.
Application information: Application form required.
  Initial approach: Proposal
  Deadline(s): None
Officers: Charlotte A. Gordon, Pres.; Raymond P. Gordon, V.P.; Marjorie G. Schaye, V.P.
EIN: 366064590

3123
Moore Family Foundation
1710 N. Waukegan Rd.
Lake Forest, IL 60045-1155
Contact: Annette M. Moore, Treas.

Donor: Everett H. Moore.
Foundation type: Independent foundation.
Financial data (yr. ended 06/30/13): Assets, $300,576 (M); expenditures, $283,070; qualifying distributions, $275,278; giving activities include $241,116 for grants.
Fields of interest: Education; Religion; Human services.
Limitations: Applications accepted. Giving primarily in WI. No grants to individuals.
Application information: Application form required.
  Initial approach: Letter
  Deadline(s): None
Officers and Directors: Douglas D. Moore, Pres. and Director; Laura J. Moore, Secy. and Director; Annette M. Moore, Treas. and Director; Peter M. Moore.
EIN: 366117705

3124
The Robert D. and Alma Moreton Foundation
10 S. Dearborn, IL1-0117
Chicago, IL 60603
Application address: c/o JPMorgan Chase Bank, N.A., Attn.: Adrean Williams-Boyd, 420 Throckmorton St., 3rd Fl., Fort Worth, TX 76102,

tel.: (817) 884-5155, web site: www.jpmorgan.com/onlinegrants

Donors: Alma Moreton†; Robert Moreton Trust A; JPMorgan Chase Bank, N.A.
Foundation type: Independent foundation.
Financial data (yr. ended 12/31/13): Assets, $17,093,112 (M); gifts received, $450,408; expenditures, $410,284; qualifying distributions, $322,451; giving activities include $300,000 for 8 grants (high: $100,000; low: $10,000).
Fields of interest: Arts and culture; Orchestral music; Education; Human services; Youth development.
Type of support: Advocacy.
Limitations: Applications accepted. Giving primarily in TX.
Application information: See online application form. Application form required.
  Deadline(s): None
Trustee: JPMorgan Chase Bank, N.A.
EIN: 387008245

3125
Morris Community Foundation
(doing business as Community Foundation of Grundy County)
(formerly Morris Community Foundation)
102 Liberty St.
Morris, IL 60450 (815) 941-0852
Contact: Julianne Buck, Exec. Dir.
FAX: (815) 941-9110;
E-mail: info@cfgrundycounty.com; Additional e-mail: julie@cfgrundycounty.com; Main URL: http://cfgrundycounty.com
Facebook: http://www.facebook.com/pages/Community-Foundation-of-Grundy-County/122315711112349
RSS feed: http://www.cfgrundycounty.com/comments/feed

Established in 1999 in Illinois.
Foundation type: Community foundation.
Financial data (yr. ended 12/31/13): Assets, $6,111,272 (M); gifts received, $272,674; expenditures, $514,640; giving activities include $314,078 for 9+ grants (high: $133,370).
Purpose and activities: The mission of the foundation is to provide vision for Morris County and the surrounding area in order to preserve and enhance quality of life.
Fields of interest: Early childhood education; Land resources; Employment; Human services.
Limitations: Applications accepted. Giving primarily in Morris County, IL. No support for disease-specific organizations or religious denominations. No grants to individuals, or for operational budgets.
Publications: Application guidelines.
Application information: Grant applications are reviewed by Grants Committee on the 1st Wednesday of the month; application packets are due one week in advance in order to be shared and reviewed before the committee meeting. Visit foundation web site for application forms and guidelines.
  Initial approach: Submit proposal
Officers and Directors: Ralph Wolter, Pres. and Director; Tom Tesdal, V.P. and Director; Kristi Bennington, Secy.-Treas. and Director; Julianne Buck, Exec. Dir.; Jim Baum; Nancy Bjelland; Lorraine Davidson; Dave Ferguson; Jay Fillman; Chris Breisch

Harty; Shantel Leasure; Dr. Ann Marie Struck; Dick Walker; Al Yancey.
EIN: 364299824

3126
Morton Community Foundation
105 E. Jefferson St.
Morton, IL 61550 (309) 291-0434
Contact: Scott A. Witzig, Exec. Dir.
FAX: (309) 291-0434;
E-mail: info@mortoncommunityfoundation.org; Main URL: http://www.mortoncommunityfoundation.org

Foundation type: Community foundation.
Financial data (yr. ended 06/30/13): Assets, $2,612,779 (M); gifts received, $308,419; expenditures, $408,465; giving activities include $237,356 for grants.
Application information: Visit website for more information.
 Initial approach: Submit Application
 Deadline(s): Mar. 14
Officers and Trustees: Michele Kuhl, Pres. and Trustee; Carol Jankowski, V.P. and Trustee; Janice Sherman, Secy. and Trustee; David Mills, Treas. and Trustee; Scott A. Witzig, Exec. Dir.; Julie Albers; Craig H. Barley; Laura Elam; Kim Gryl; Phil Kuhl; Linda Martin; Wayne Menold; Mike Murphy; Rob Personett; Tyler Petersen; Christina Taylor; Katie VandenBerg.
EIN: 371397503

3127
Morton Family Foundation
420 E. Ohio St., Apt. 4F
Chicago, IL 60611-3314

Established in 1988 in Illinois.
Donor: John B. Morton.
Foundation type: Independent foundation.
Financial data (yr. ended 12/31/14): Assets, $3,867,423; gifts received, $0; expenditures, $470,704; qualifying distributions, $364,837 and $0 for set-asides.
Fields of interest: Education; Natural resources; Television; Christianity; Human services; Scouting programs.
Type of support: Scholarships; Capital campaigns; Annual campaigns.
Limitations: Applications accepted. Giving primarily in Libertyville IL, Deerfield, MA, Durham, NC, and Jackson Hole, WY.
Application information: Application form required.
 Initial approach: Letter
 Deadline(s): None
Officers: Charles Frey, Pres.; William P. O'Keefe, Secy.-Treas.
EIN: 363605391

3128
Mouat Charitable Trust
c/o Tax Division
111 W. Monroe St., Ste. 10C
Chicago, IL 60603
Application address: BMO Harris Bank, N.A., P.O. Box 5000, Janesville, WI 53547, tel.: (608) 755-4265

Established in 2003 in Wisconsin.
Foundation type: Independent foundation.

Financial data (yr. ended 10/31/13): Assets, $2,066,089 (M); expenditures, $198,693; qualifying distributions, $186,766; giving activities include $178,400 for 8 grants (high: $90,000; low: $5,000).
Fields of interest: Historic preservation; Education; Human services.
Limitations: Applications accepted. Giving primarily in MA and WI.
Application information: Application form required.
 Initial approach: Letter
 Deadline(s): None
Trustee: BMO Harris Bank, N.A.
EIN: 396759291

3129
The Mullen Family Foundation
c/o Harrison & Held, LLP
333 W. Wacker Dr., Ste. 1700
Chicago, IL 60606-1247

Established in 1998 in Illinois.
Donor: Timothy R. Mullen.
Foundation type: Independent foundation.
Financial data (yr. ended 09/30/13): Assets, $3,876,458 (M); expenditures, $403,960; qualifying distributions, $377,510; giving activities include $377,500 for 14 grants (high: $207,000; low: $2,000).
Fields of interest: Arts and culture; Theater; Education; Elementary and secondary education; Zoos; Human services; Child welfare.
Type of support: General support.
Limitations: Applications not accepted. Giving primarily in IL. No grants to individuals.
Application information: Contributes only to pre-selected organizations.
Officers and Directors: Timothy R. Mullen, Pres. and Treas. and Director; Alicia C. Mullen, V.P. and Secy. and Director; Mary L. Mullen; Joseph Mullen.
EIN: 364270223

3130
W. B. Munson Foundation
c/o JPMorgan Chase Bank, N.A.
10 S. Dearborn St.
Chicago, IL 60603-2300 8668885157
Application address: c/o JPMorgan Chase Bank, N.A., 2200 Ross Ave., 7th Fl., Dallas, TX 75201

Established in 1943 in Texas.
Foundation type: Independent foundation.
Financial data (yr. ended 12/31/14): Assets, $8,461,640; expenditures, $449,871; qualifying distributions, $377,556.
Purpose and activities: Giving primarily for health care, the arts and education, including scholarship awards to high school graduates from Denison, Texas.
Fields of interest: Arts and culture; Performing arts; Education; Higher education; Hospital care; Family planning; Public libraries; Community and economic development; Camps; School athletics; Human services; Child welfare.
Type of support: General support; Employee matching gifts; Capital and infrastructure; Equipment; Endowments; Student aid.
Limitations: Giving primarily in Grayson County, TX.
Application information: Application form required.
 Initial approach: Letter
 Copies of proposal: 7

Deadline(s): None
 Board meeting date(s): Quarterly
Trustee: JPMorgan Chase Bank, N.A.
Number of staff: None.
EIN: 756015068

3131
The Murnane Family Foundation
c/o Frank Murnane, Sr.
607 Northwest Ave.
Northlake, IL 60164-1301

Established in 1997 in Illinois.
Donors: Frank Murnane, Sr.; Murnane Specialities.
Foundation type: Independent foundation.
Financial data (yr. ended 12/31/13): Assets, $546,469 (M); gifts received, $30,000; expenditures, $149,025; qualifying distributions, $149,000; giving activities include $149,000 for 5 grants (high: $90,000; low: $5,000).
Fields of interest: Education.
Limitations: Applications not accepted. Giving primarily in IN. No grants to individuals.
Application information: Contributes only to pre-selected organizations.
Director: Frank Murnane, Sr.
EIN: 364147114

3132
Michael E. Murphy Foundation
1242 N. Lake Shore Dr., Ste. 25
Chicago, IL 60610-2332

Established in 1986 in Illinois.
Donors: Michael E. Murphy; Adele A. Murphy.
Foundation type: Independent foundation.
Financial data (yr. ended 12/31/13): Assets, $4,746,311 (M); gifts received, $200,000; expenditures, $226,876; qualifying distributions, $222,250; giving activities include $222,250 for 18 grants (high: $54,000; low: $1,000).
Fields of interest: Performing arts; Historic preservation; Education; Higher education; Nonprofits; Christianity; Catholicism; Human services; Developmental disability services.
Type of support: General support; Regranting.
Limitations: Applications not accepted. No grants to individuals.
Application information: Unsolicited requests for funds not accepted.
Officers and Directors: Leslie M. Barker, Pres. and Director; Adele A. Murphy, V.P. and Secy.-Treas. and Director; Michael E. Murphy, V.P. and Director; Christopher M. Murphy; Glenn S. Murphy.
EIN: 363436624

3133
Nayak Foundation Charitable Trust
1906 Crimson Ln.
Bloomington, IL 61704-2737 (309) 663-7160
Contact: Nicholas Nayak MD, Exec. Dir.

Established in 1998 in Illinois.
Donors: Nicholas A. Nayak, MD; Anjuli S. Nayak, MD.
Foundation type: Independent foundation.
Financial data (yr. ended 12/31/13): Assets, $5,531,138 (M); gifts received, $500,100; expenditures, $279,994; qualifying distributions, $267,357; giving activities include $267,357 for grants.

Fields of interest: Education; Medical education; Health; Religion.
Type of support: General support; Grants to individuals; Student aid.
Limitations: Applications not accepted. Giving primarily in IL.
Application information: Contributes only to pre-selected organizations.
Officer: Nicholas A. Nayak, MD, Exec. Dir.
Trustee: Anjuli S. Nayak, MD.
EIN: 371378892

3134
NCI Lending a Hand
30 S. Wacker Dr., Ste. 3550
Chicago, IL 60606-7481

Donors: Erik Linn; Timothy Hart; Patrick Hurley; John McDonald; Avram Tucker; Navigant Consulting, Inc.
Foundation type: Independent foundation.
Financial data (yr. ended 12/31/13): Assets, $98,182 (M); gifts received, $380,000; expenditures, $307,912; qualifying distributions, $291,660; giving activities include $291,660 for 127 grants (high: $17,320; low: $100).
Fields of interest: Arts and culture; Higher education; Health; Hospital care; Diseases and conditions; Human services; Child welfare.
Limitations: Applications not accepted. Giving primarily in Washington, DC and LA.
Application information: Unsolicited outside requests are not accepted or responded to. Applications will not be accepted.
Trustees: Pat McGrath; Shannon Prown; Pia Thompson.
EIN: 367449584

3135
Bell B. Neel Charitable Trust
10 S. Dearborn, IL1-0117
Chicago, IL 60603

Foundation type: Independent foundation.
Financial data (yr. ended 12/31/14): Assets, $4,885,895; expenditures, $249,189; qualifying distributions, $224,020.
Fields of interest: Nonprofits.
Type of support: Regranting.
Limitations: Applications not accepted. Giving limited to Louisville, KY.
Application information: Unsolicited requests for funds not accepted.
Trustee: JPMorgan Chase Bank, N.A.
EIN: 616074004

3136
New Directions Foundation
c/o KKP Group, LLC
1603 Orrington Ave., No. 1275
Evanston, IL 60201-5064 (847) 328-2383
Contact: Stanley Schlozman, Secy.; Kay Schlozman, Pres.

Established in 1999 in Illinois.
Donors: Schlozman 1993 Descendants Trust; F. Lehman; Lehman 93F Descendants Trust; Lehman 93E Descendants Trust; New Prospect Foundation; KKP Holdings LLC; Stanley Schlozman.
Foundation type: Independent foundation.

Financial data (yr. ended 12/31/13): Assets, $5,995,296 (M); gifts received, $486,400; expenditures, $293,266; qualifying distributions, $279,417; giving activities include $277,750 for 67 grants (high: $25,000; low: $250).
Fields of interest: Arts and culture; Children's museums; Education; Higher education; Nonprofits; Hospital care; Family planning; Diseases and conditions; Legal services; Public affairs; Human services; Child welfare; Youth services; Females.
Type of support: Regranting.
Limitations: Applications accepted. Giving primarily in the greater metropolitan Boston, MA, and New York, NY, areas. No grants to individuals.
Application information:
Initial approach: Proposal
Deadline(s): None
Officers: Kay Schlozman, Pres.; Stanley Schlozman, Secy.
Directors: Paul A. Lehman; Daniel A. Schlozman; Julia E. Schlozman.
EIN: 364267729

3137
New Horizon Foundation
1625 Hinman Ave., No. 202
Evanston, IL 60201-4522
E-mail: nhf@revelle.net

Established in 1985 in Illinois.
Donors: Roger R. Revelle†; Ellen C. Revelle; William R. Revelle; Eleanor M. Revelle; Piero F. Paci†; Mary Paci; Carolyn R. Revelle; Gary C. Hufbauer.
Foundation type: Independent foundation.
Financial data (yr. ended 08/31/13): Assets, $4,084,923 (M); gifts received, $3,475,362; expenditures, $379,297; qualifying distributions, $361,421; giving activities include $353,750 for 66 grants (high: $77,500; low: $500).
Purpose and activities: The foundation is interested in developing and funding direct and indirect programs in which it can encourage interest and foster education in the arts and sciences. It also funds projects concerned with issues in human rights, social welfare and global security.
Fields of interest: Arts and culture; Education; Public policy; Human rights; Human services; International peace and security.
Type of support: General support; Continuing support; Annual campaigns; Capital campaigns; Endowments; Scholarships; Policy, advocacy and systems reform; Research.
Limitations: Applications not accepted. Giving on a national basis. No grants to individuals.
Publications: Annual report.
Application information: Contributes only to pre-selected organizations.
Officers and Directors: William R. Revelle, Pres. and Director; Mary Paci, V.P. and Director; Carolyn Revelle, V.P. and Director; Ethelyn C. Bond, Secy.-Treas.; Ellen Hufbauer; Eleanor M. Revelle.
Number of staff: 1 part-time professional.
EIN: 363406294

3138
New Visions Foundation
485 E. Half Day Rd., Ste. 350
Buffalo Grove, IL 60089-8806

Established in 1999 in Illinois.
Donors: HLM & JM Charitable Lead Trust; R. Miller.

Foundation type: Independent foundation.
Financial data (yr. ended 12/31/13): Assets, $3,778,373 (M); gifts received, $716,326; expenditures, $482,322; qualifying distributions, $480,813; giving activities include $419,500 for 47 grants (high: $35,000; low: $500).
Purpose and activities: The primary mission of the foundation is to catalyze and support diverse efforts. It seeks to help visionary organizations promote wider recognition and acceptance of cultural alternatives that address the challenges of our time, and to establish working models of engaged, effective action. It recognizes that this task requires outreach to the public as well as efforts to inform and inspire those already involved in cultural change. Major program areas are economic reform, education, peace, and sustainability.
Fields of interest: Arts and culture; Education; Environment; Social enterprise; Spirituality; Human rights; International peace and security.
Limitations: Applications not accepted. Giving on a national and international basis, with some emphasis on VT. No support for non public charities. No grants to individuals.
Application information: Unsolicited requests for funds not accepted.
Board meeting date(s): Three times per year
Officers and Directors: R. Miller, Pres. and Director; J. Kristel, V.P. and Director; E. Versten, Secy. and Director; E. Achepohl, Treas. and Director.
EIN: 364291720

3139
Nickum Foundation
724 S. Madison St.
Hinsdale, IL 60521-4361

Established in 1993 in Michigan.
Foundation type: Independent foundation.
Financial data (yr. ended 12/31/13): Assets, $3,213,270 (M); expenditures, $174,110; qualifying distributions, $151,779; giving activities include $150,000 for 8 grants (high: $35,000; low: $10,000).
Fields of interest: Higher education; Specialty hospital care.
Type of support: General support.
Limitations: Applications not accepted. Giving primarily in IL and MI. No grants to individuals.
Application information: Unsolicited requests for funds not accepted.
Officers: Johanna N. McClear, Pres.; Kevin R. McClear, V.P.; Richard J. McClear, Secy.; Chris R. McClear, Treas.
EIN: 383141920

3140
Night Owl Foundation
485 Half Day Rd., Ste. 350
Buffalo Grove, IL 60089-8806
Contact: Elizabeth Versten, Exec. Dir.

Established in 2006 in Illinois.
Donors: L. Khanuk; HLM and JM 2006 Charitable Lead Trust.
Foundation type: Independent foundation.
Financial data (yr. ended 12/31/13): Assets, $7,697,118 (M); gifts received, $1,316,326; expenditures, $489,967; qualifying distributions, $482,032; giving activities include $428,000 for 15 grants (high: $75,000; low: $5,000).

Purpose and activities: The foundation aims to support effective organizations that foster innovative research and development in medicine, with an emphasis on pediatrics and cancer, and organizations that provide assistance to Jewish refugees and immigrants from the former Soviet Union to the Chicago, Illinois area and Israel.
Fields of interest: Health; Human services.
Limitations: Applications not accepted. No grants to individuals.
Application information: Contributes only to pre-selected organizations.
Officers and Directors: L. Khanuk, Pres. and Director; T. Khanuk, V.P. and Secy. and Director; E. Achepohl, Treas. and Director.
Number of staff: None.
EIN: 205905161

3141
The Eric and Joan Norgaard Charitable Trust
3906 Steeple Run Dr.
Crystal Lake, IL   60014-6568

Established in 2003 in Illinois.
Donors: Steven A. Kadish; Eric Norgaard†; The Eric Norgaard Living Trust.
Foundation type: Independent foundation.
Financial data (yr. ended 12/31/13): Assets, $2,622,487 (M); gifts received, $50,000; expenditures, $189,151; qualifying distributions, $186,651; giving activities include $151,500 for 46 grants (high: $18,000; low: $1,000).
Fields of interest: Music; Museums; Environment; Domesticated animals; Health care administration and financing; Medical specialties.
Type of support: General support; Research.
Limitations: Applications not accepted. Giving primarily in CA, Washington, DC, MA, MD and NY.
Application information: Unsolicited requests for funds not accepted.
Trustee: Steven A. Kadish.
EIN: 367386936

3142
Francis S. North Foundation
P.O. Box 803878
Chicago, IL   60680-3878

Donor: North Family Voting Trust.
Foundation type: Independent foundation.
Financial data (yr. ended 06/30/14): Assets, $3,631,131 (M); expenditures, $187,354; qualifying distributions, $151,684; giving activities include $147,500 for 11 grants (high: $25,000; low: $5,000).
Fields of interest: University education; Law education; Health; Health care clinics; Hospice care; Youth services.
Type of support: General support; Research and evaluation.
Limitations: Applications not accepted. Giving primarily in CA. No grants to individuals; no loans or program-related investments.
Application information: Contributes only to pre-selected organizations.
Trustee: The Northern Trust Co.
EIN: 366125418

3143
The Novick Family Foundation
30 E. North Ave.
Northlake, IL   60164-2516

Established in 1989 in Illinois.
Donor: Rose A. Novick.
Foundation type: Independent foundation.
Financial data (yr. ended 12/31/14): Assets, $4,070,013; expenditures, $177,674; qualifying distributions, $136,697.
Fields of interest: Arts and culture; Education; University education; Human services.
Limitations: Applications not accepted. Giving primarily in IL and NY, with some giving in SC. No grants to individuals.
Application information: Unsolicited requests for funds not accepted.
Directors: Baron D. Harmon; Oscar A. Novick; Robert W. Matanky.
EIN: 363672351

3144
Nth Dimensions Education Solutions, Inc.
22 N. Morgan St., Ste. 113
Chicago, IL   60607-2622   (202) 421-4115

Donors: Zimmer, Inc.; American Academy of Orthopaedic Surgeons.
Foundation type: Independent foundation.
Financial data (yr. ended 12/31/13): Assets, $12,813 (M); gifts received, $238,435; expenditures, $312,921; qualifying distributions, $154,470; giving activities include $154,470 for grants.
Fields of interest: Orthopedics.
Application information: Application form required.
Initial approach: Letter
Deadline(s): Jan. 31
Officer: Bonnie Simpson Mason, Exec. Dir.
Directors: Katrina Adams; J. Kevin Franks; Ebony Halliburton.
EIN: 260116813

3145
Rudolf Nureyev Dance Foundation
308 W. Erie St., Ste. 700
Chicago, IL   60610-3537   (312) 649-0700
Contact: Barry L. Weinstein, Pres.
FAX: (312) 787-7534;
E-mail: barry@rudolfnureyevdancefoundation.org;
E-mail for Barry Weinstein:
barry@rudolfnureyevdancefoundation.org; Main URL: http://www.rudolfnureyevdancefoundation.org
Grants List: http://www.rudolfnureyevdancefoundation.org/RNDF/Grants_files/RNDF%20Awards.pdf

Established in 1991 in Illinois.
Donor: Rudolf Nureyev†.
Foundation type: Independent foundation.
Financial data (yr. ended 06/30/14): Assets, $6,756,501 (M); expenditures, $318,173; qualifying distributions, $254,385; giving activities include $221,800 for 5 grants (high: $100,000; low: $20,000).
Purpose and activities: The foundation provides grants in the U.S. for ballet and modern dance performances, funds dance schools and dance scholarships, provides financial assistance for the creation of new choreography, and supports the

establishment of dance collections and film archives to preserve the history, tradition and appreciation of dance.
Fields of interest: Arts and culture.
Type of support: General support; Scholarships.
Limitations: Applications accepted. Giving on a national basis. No support for health or medical research. No grants to individuals, or for maintenance, construction, office expenses, or for administrative costs.
Application information: See grantmaker web site for complete application guidelines. Application form required.
Initial approach: See Website
Deadline(s): Aug. 31
Board meeting date(s): Between Sept. and Oct.
Officers: Barry L. Weinstein, Pres.; Jeannette Etheredge, V.P.; Joyce A. Moffatt, V.P.; Hilary Weinstein, V.P.; Paul Horowitz, Secy.-Treas.
EIN: 363822516

3146
Bill Nygren Foundation
(formerly William & Sara Nygren Charitable Foundation)
2 N. LaSalle St., Ste. 500
Chicago, IL   60602-3703

Established in 1994 in Illinois.
Donors: William C. Nygren; Sara Nygren.
Foundation type: Independent foundation.
Financial data (yr. ended 12/31/14): Assets, $12,609,951; expenditures, $407,125; qualifying distributions, $391,840.
Purpose and activities: Giving primarily for education, children, youth and social services, and federated giving programs.
Fields of interest: Education; Higher education; Nonprofits; Human services; Child welfare.
Type of support: Regranting.
Limitations: Applications not accepted. Giving primarily in Chicago, IL; some funding also in WI. No grants to individuals.
Application information: Unsolicited requests for funds not accepted.
Officer and Directors: William C. Nygren, Pres. and Treas. and Director; Henry Berghoef; Robert Levy.
EIN: 363987600

3147
Oberweiler Foundation
1250 S. Grove St., Ste. 200
Barrington, IL   60010-5011
FAX: (847) 277-7446;
E-mail: oberw1@ameritech.net
Google Plus: https://plus.google.com/110987600611257280915/about?gl=us&hl=en

Established in 2000 in Illinois.
Donor: Siegfried Weiler.
Foundation type: Independent foundation.
Financial data (yr. ended 12/31/12): Assets, $10,115,544 (M); expenditures, $687,237; qualifying distributions, $509,760; giving activities include $409,771 for 30 grants (high: $35,000; low: $178).
Purpose and activities: Giving primarily to 1) help individuals achieve higher levels of wellness through the application of alternative medicine procedures, 2) prevent the demise of America's wilderness/wetlands as a result of private exploitation and/or

public encroachment, and 3) assist disadvantaged, sick, and/or abused children.
Fields of interest: Environment; Health; Diseases and conditions; Child welfare; Children and youth; Children.
Type of support: Equipment; Matching grants; Land acquisitions; Emergency funds; Internships; Research.
Limitations: Applications not accepted. Giving primarily in northern IL. No grants for operational support.
Application information: Contributes only to pre-selected organizations.
Board meeting date(s): Feb.
Officers: Siegfried Weiler, Pres.; James R. Bartell, V.P.; Anna Weiler, Secy.-Treas.
Directors: Ruth S. Flynn; Ronald Ohlsen; Martha Heylin.
Number of staff: 1 full-time professional.
EIN: 364376705

3148
O'C Family Foundation
c/o Martin M. O'Connor
770 Lake Cook Rd., Ste. 130
Deerfield, IL 60015-4920

Established in 1995 in Illinois.
Donors: Martin O'Connor; Christine O'Connor Lane; Patricia O'Connor Mergener.
Foundation type: Independent foundation.
Financial data (yr. ended 12/31/13): Assets, $369,203 (M); expenditures, $310,586; qualifying distributions, $310,000; giving activities include $310,000 for 3 grants (high: $300,000; low: $5,000).
Fields of interest: Education; Agriculture; Religion.
Type of support: General support.
Limitations: Applications not accepted. Giving primarily in IL. No grants to individuals.
Application information: Unsolicited requests for funds not accepted.
Officers and Directors: Christine O'Connor Lane, Pres. and Director; Martin O'Connor, Secy.-Treas. and Director; Patricia O'Connor Mergener, Director; Daniel O'Connor; Matthew O'Connor.
EIN: 363999340

3149
The William F. O'Connor Foundation
c/o Ryan and Juraska
141 W. Jackson Blvd., Ste. 2250
Chicago, IL 60604-3328
Contact: Carol Hennessy, Treas.

Donor: William F. O'Connor†.
Foundation type: Independent foundation.
Financial data (yr. ended 06/30/13): Assets, $23,860,924 (M); expenditures, $498,782; qualifying distributions, $404,684; giving activities include $350,000 for 12 grants (high: $125,000; low: $10,000).
Purpose and activities: Giving primarily for medical research, focusing on cancer prevention and cure. Giving also for arts, culture, and education in the Chicago, Illinois, area.
Fields of interest: Arts and culture; Education; Higher education; Specialty hospital care; Diseases and conditions; Cancers; Communication media; Catholicism.
Type of support: Research.

Limitations: Applications not accepted. Giving primarily in IL. No grants to individuals.
Application information: Unsolicited requests for funds not accepted.
Board meeting date(s): Monthly
Officers and Directors: Carol Hennessy, Pres. and Treas. and Director; Mark Cermak; Mary Jo McGuire; Mary Jane O'Connor; Joanne Unkovsky.
EIN: 363593445

3150
The O'Donnell Green Music and Dance Foundation
(formerly Music and Dance Foundation, Inc.)
c/o JPMorgan Chase Bank, N.A.
10 S. Dearborn, 21st Fl.
Chicago, IL 60603
Application address: c/o JPMorgan Chase Bank, N.A., 2200 Ross Ave., 5th Fl., Dallas, TX 75201

Donor: May O' Donnell Green†.
Foundation type: Independent foundation.
Financial data (yr. ended 06/30/13): Assets, $3,399,041 (M); gifts received, $40,000; expenditures, $288,716; qualifying distributions, $261,356; giving activities include $240,000 for 10 grants (high: $40,000; low: $10,000).
Fields of interest: Dance.
Type of support: Student aid.
Limitations: Applications accepted. Giving primarily in NY.
Application information: Application form required.
Initial approach: Proposal
Deadline(s): None
Officers: Norton Owen, Chair.; Wanda Fleck, Secy.; Roberta Garcia, Co-Treas.; Jo-Ann B. Victor, Co-Treas.
EIN: 133574289

3151
George and Sarah Ohlhausen Foundation
c/o Much Shelist
191 N. Wacker Dr., 1800
Chicago, IL 60606-1615 (312) 521-2435
E-mail: jrubenstein@muchshelist.com

Established in 2002 in Illinois.
Donors: George Ohlhausen; Sarah Ohlhausen.
Foundation type: Independent foundation.
Financial data (yr. ended 12/31/14): Assets, $3,614,653; gifts received, $0; expenditures, $203,866; qualifying distributions, $165,440.
Fields of interest: Arts and culture; Judaism; Human services.
Limitations: Applications accepted. Giving primarily in FL, IL, and NY.
Application information: Application form required.
Initial approach: Letter
Deadline(s): None
Officers: Jeffrey Rubenstein, Pres.; Howard M. Cohen, Secy.; Norman Bobins, Treas.
EIN: 364267872

3152
The Okner-Robbins Foundation
(formerly The Okner Foundation)
1755 Wild Rose
Highland Park, IL 60035-5517

Established in 1996 in Illinois.

Donor: Seymour Okner†.
Foundation type: Independent foundation.
Financial data (yr. ended 12/31/14): Assets, $1,790,752; expenditures, $409,363; qualifying distributions, $387,625.
Fields of interest: Education; Diseases and conditions; Judaism; Child welfare.
Limitations: Applications not accepted. Giving primarily in IL; some funding also in NY. No grants to individuals.
Application information: Unsolicited requests for funds not accepted.
Officers and Directors: David Robbins, Pres. and Treas. and Director; Joel C. Okner, Secy. and Director; Ellyn Robbins.
EIN: 363870305

3153
Evelyn B. Olin Charitable Trust
231 S. LaSalle St., IL1-231-10-05
Chicago, IL 60697-0001 (314) 898-9323
Contact: Paula J. Curtit
Application address: 7800 Forsyth Blvd., Clayton, MO 63105-3311, tel.: (314) 898-9323

Established in 1971 in Missouri.
Foundation type: Independent foundation.
Financial data (yr. ended 12/31/13): Assets, $1,652,440 (M); expenditures, $149,739; qualifying distributions, $145,245; giving activities include $143,000 for 10 grants (high: $50,000; low: $1,000).
Purpose and activities: Giving to organizations that have programs and services which promote and enhance the development of boys and girls by instilling a sense of competence, usefulness, belonging, and influence.
Fields of interest: Education; Youth services.
Type of support: General support; Public engagement and education.
Limitations: Applications accepted. Giving primarily in MO. No grants to individuals.
Application information:
Initial approach: Proposal
Deadline(s): None
Trustee: Bank of America, N.A.
EIN: 436025747

3154
The Delmar and Audria M. Olson Family Foundation
c/o The Northern Trust Co.
P.O. Box 803878
Chicago, IL 60680-3878

Foundation type: Independent foundation.
Financial data (yr. ended 12/31/14): Assets, $3,060,052 (M); expenditures, $166,853; qualifying distributions, $141,486; giving activities include $140,471 for 24 grants (high: $56,000; low: $500).
Fields of interest: Arts and culture; Religion; Human services.
Limitations: Applications not accepted. Giving primarily in Sarasota, FL. No grants to individuals.
Application information: Unsolicited requests for funds not accepted.
Trustees: Gary A. Olson; Barbara L. Raifall III.
EIN: 367253495

3155
The Oppenheimer Family Foundation
c/o E.H. Oppenheimer
1501 N. State Pkwy., Ste. 11B
Chicago, IL 60610-5737
Application address: c/o E.H. Oppenheimer, P.O. Box 14771, Chicago, IL 60614; fax: (312) 943-9472

Established in 1953 in Illinois.
Donors: Edward H. Oppenheimer; James K. Oppenheimer; Harry D. Oppenheimer; Seymour Oppenheimer†.
Foundation type: Independent foundation.
Financial data (yr. ended 12/31/13): Assets, $4,590,326 (M); gifts received, $200; expenditures, $500,936; qualifying distributions, $437,625; giving activities include $437,625 for 202 grants (high: $26,000; low: $300).
Purpose and activities: Giving primarily for the arts, education, the environment, and social services.
Fields of interest: Arts and culture; Arts education; Education; Environment; Nonprofits; Communication media; Human services.
Type of support: Regranting.
Limitations: Applications accepted. Giving primarily in Chicago, IL.
Application information: Guidelines for the Teacher Incentive Grant may be found at: http://www.offtig.org/contactus.php. Application form required.
Initial approach: Letter
Copies of proposal: 1
Deadline(s): None
Officers: Edward H. Oppenheimer, Pres.; Harry J. Oppenheimer, V.P.; James Oppenheimer, V.P.; William J. Garmisa, Secy.
EIN: 366054015

3156
Orsini Charitable Foundation, Inc.
1111 Nicholas Blvd.
Elk Grove Village, IL 60007-2516

Established in 2008 in Illinois.
Donors: Tony Orsini; Howard Manzuk; Orsini Home Medical; Orsini Pharmaceutical Services, Inc.
Foundation type: Operating foundation.
Financial data (yr. ended 12/31/13): Assets, $0 (M); gifts received, $290,301; expenditures, $225,691; qualifying distributions, $225,691; giving activities include $212,538 for 6 grants (high: $133,114; low: $1,551).
Fields of interest: Religion; Human rights; Human services.
Limitations: Applications not accepted. Giving primarily in IL and VA.
Application information: Unsolicited requests for funds not accepted.
Directors: Rebecca Orsini; Tony Orsini; Carla Sawa.
EIN: 753265430

3157
The OSA Foundation
351 W. Hubbard St., Ste. 600
Chicago, IL 60654-4486
E-mail: robin@theosafoundation.org; Main
URL: http://theosafoundation.org

Established in 2004 in Illinois.
Foundation type: Independent foundation.

Financial data (yr. ended 12/31/13): Assets, $7,692,792 (M); expenditures, $475,428; qualifying distributions, $402,376; giving activities include $400,000 for 19 grants (high: $30,000; low: $10,000).
Purpose and activities: Giving primarily for education through technology in under-resourced communities.
Fields of interest: Education; Higher education; Graduate and professional education; Technology; Engineering.
Limitations: Applications not accepted. Giving primarily in IL. No grants to individuals.
Application information: Contributes only to pre-selected organizations.
Officers: Robin Lavin, Pres. and Secy.; Jack Lavin, V.P. and Treas.
Directors: Mitchell Kent; Eric Lavin.
EIN: 721589724

3158
The Osi Group Foundation
1225 Corporate Blvd.
Aurora, IL 60505-7616

Donor: OSI Group, LLC.
Foundation type: Independent foundation.
Financial data (yr. ended 12/31/14): Assets, $32,628 (M); gifts received, $150,000; expenditures, $152,099; qualifying distributions, $151,419; giving activities include $151,419 for 23 grants (high: $121,666; low: $200).
Fields of interest: Education; Health; Human services.
Limitations: Applications not accepted. Giving primarily in IL.
Application information: Unsolicited request for funds not accepted.
Directors: Donna B. Coaxum; Sheldon Lavin; David G. McDonald; Kristina L. Swanson; William J. Weimer, Jr.
EIN: 273722112

3159
Our Lady of Perpetual Help Trust
10 S. Dearborn IL1-0117
Chicago, IL 60603 8668885157

Foundation type: Independent foundation.
Financial data (yr. ended 12/31/14): Assets, $2,188,894; expenditures, $274,490; qualifying distributions, $246,626.
Fields of interest: Human services.
Limitations: Applications not accepted. Giving primarily in NJ.
Application information: Unsolicited requests for funds not accepted.
Trustee: JPMorgan Chase Bank, N.A.
EIN: 136046790

3160
The Owen Foundation
1706 E. Washington
Bloomington, IL 61701-4237 (309) 826-1141
Contact: Frances M. Owen, V.P.

Established in 1994 in Illinois.
Donors: Richard B. Owen; Frances M. Owen.
Foundation type: Independent foundation.

Financial data (yr. ended 12/31/13): Assets, $3,329,835 (M); gifts received, $250; expenditures, $177,270; qualifying distributions, $143,227; giving activities include $137,235 for 12 grants (high: $55,000; low: $80).
Purpose and activities: Giving for higher education, religion, and health and medical services.
Fields of interest: Education; University education; Health; Diseases and conditions.
Limitations: Applications accepted. Giving primarily in Bloomington and Normal, IL.
Application information: Application form required.
Initial approach: Contact foundation for application
Deadline(s): None
Officers and Directors: Frances M. Owen, Pres. and Treas. and Director; Brent R. Alsman, V.P. and Director; Andrew Owen Beyer, Secy. and Director.
EIN: 371335069

3161
The Pangburn Foundation
c/o JPMorgan Chase Bank, N.A.
10 S. Dearborn St., IL1-0117
Chicago, IL 60603-2300
Application address: c/o JPMorgan Chase Bank, N.A., Attn.: Larry Bothe, P.O. Box 2050, Fort Worth, TX 76113, tel.: (817) 884-4022

Established in 1962 in Texas.
Foundation type: Independent foundation.
Financial data (yr. ended 03/31/13): Assets, $7,036,502 (M); expenditures, $387,810; qualifying distributions, $340,309; giving activities include $325,000 for 6 grants (high: $100,000; low: $30,000).
Purpose and activities: Emphasis on cultural programs, especially music and the performing arts; funding also for education and human services.
Fields of interest: Performing arts; Ballet; Theater; Opera; Orchestral music; Museums; Education; Human services.
Limitations: Applications accepted. Giving primarily in the Fort Worth, TX, area. No grants to individuals.
Application information:
Initial approach: Letter
Copies of proposal: 1
Deadline(s): Sept. 30
Board meeting date(s): Oct. or Nov.
Trustee: JPMorgan Chase Bank, N.A.
EIN: 756042630

3162
Parker Family Foundation
P.O. Box 803878
Chicago, IL 60680-3878

Established in 1999 in California.
Donors: Gerald Hans Parker; Carol Ellen Parker.
Foundation type: Independent foundation.
Financial data (yr. ended 09/30/13): Assets, $1,902,090 (M); expenditures, $208,426; qualifying distributions, $193,546; giving activities include $191,000 for 9 grants (high: $110,000; low: $1,000).
Fields of interest: Arts and culture; Education; University education; Human services.
Limitations: Applications not accepted. Giving primarily in CA. No grants to individuals.
Application information: Unsolicited requests for funds not accepted.

Trustees: Carol Ellen Parker; Gerald Hans Parker; Northern Trust, N.A.
EIN: 946746143

3163
George R. Parker Trust
10 S. Dearborn St., IL1-0117
Chicago, IL 60603-2300

Foundation type: Independent foundation.
Financial data (yr. ended 12/31/13): Assets, $7,023,226 (M); expenditures, $281,830; qualifying distributions, $254,256; giving activities include $245,973 for 1 grant.
Fields of interest: Education.
Limitations: Applications not accepted.
Application information: Unsolicited requests for funds not accepted.
Trustee: JPMorgan Chase Bank, N.A.
EIN: 616030614

3164
James K. Patterson Trust
10 S. Dearborn St., IL1-0117
Chicago, IL 60603

Foundation type: Independent foundation.
Financial data (yr. ended 12/31/14): Assets, $6,288,336 (M); expenditures, $301,797; qualifying distributions, $241,449; giving activities include $228,565 for 1 grant.
Fields of interest: Education; University education.
Type of support: General support.
Limitations: Applications not accepted. Giving primarily in KY.
Application information: Unsolicited requests for funds not accepted.
Trustee: JPMorgan Chase Bank, N.A.
EIN: 616018232

3165
The Pawlowski Family Foundation
2015 Mitchell Blvd., Ste. A
Schaumburg, IL 60193-4563

Established in 1996 in Illinois.
Donors: Frank J. Pawlowski; Mary Lou Pawlowski.
Foundation type: Independent foundation.
Financial data (yr. ended 12/31/13): Assets, $4,337,783 (M); gifts received, $50,000; expenditures, $177,888; qualifying distributions, $176,446; giving activities include $175,032 for 10 grants (high: $35,000; low: $1,200).
Fields of interest: Health; Housing development; Catholicism.
Limitations: Applications not accepted. No grants to individuals.
Application information: Unsolicited requests for funds not accepted.
Officers: Frank J. Pawlowski, Pres.; Glenn Pawlowski, Secy.; Gayle Engels, Treas.
EIN: 364118188

3166
Sheila A. Penrose & R. Ernest Mahaffey Charitable Foundation
c/o Gregory M. Winters
330 N. Wabash, Ste. 2100
Chicago, IL 60611

Established in 1998 in Illinois.
Donors: Sheila A. Penrose; R. Ernest Mahaffey.
Foundation type: Independent foundation.
Financial data (yr. ended 12/31/13): Assets, $2,872,629 (M); expenditures, $188,326; qualifying distributions, $166,595; giving activities include $163,562 for 18 grants (high: $28,500; low: $500).
Fields of interest: Education; Higher education; Nonprofits; Health; Human services; International relations.
Type of support: Regranting.
Limitations: Applications not accepted. Giving primarily in FL and IL. No grants to individuals.
Application information: Contributes only to pre-selected organizations.
Officers and Directors: R. Ernest Mahaffey, Pres. and Director; Sheila A. Penrose, Secy. and Director; Barbara Gaines.
EIN: 364220588

3167
Pepper Family Foundation
c/o Richard S. Pepper
643 N. Orleans St.
Chicago, IL 60654-3608

Established in 1987 in Illinois.
Donors: The Pepper Cos., Inc.; Richard S. Pepper; Roxelyn M. Pepper; Richard S. Pepper Trust.
Foundation type: Independent foundation.
Financial data (yr. ended 12/31/14): Assets, $6,707,728 (M); gifts received, $202,500; expenditures, $327,068; qualifying distributions, $264,500; giving activities include $264,500 for 20 grants (high: $50,000; low: $1,000).
Fields of interest: Arts and culture; Elementary and secondary education; Higher education; Foundations; Hospital care; Christianity.
Type of support: General support; Scholarships.
Limitations: Applications not accepted. Giving primarily in IL, with emphasis on Chicago and Barrington. No grants to individuals.
Application information: Contributes only to pre-selected organizations.
Officers and Directors: Richard S. Pepper, Pres. and Treas. and Director; Thomas M. O'Leary, Exec. V.P. and Secy.; Roxelyn M. Pepper, V.P. and Director; J. David Pepper; Lisa Pepper.
EIN: 363540747

3168
Edwin E. Perkins Foundation
10 S. Dearborn, IL1-0117
Chicago, IL 60603 8668885157
Application address: c/o JPMorgan Chase Bank, N.A., Attn.: Neil V. Meltzer, 1101 Skokie Blvd., 260, IL 60062, tel.: (847) 239-8357

Established in 1961 in Illinois.
Donor: Edwin E. Perkins†.
Foundation type: Independent foundation.

Financial data (yr. ended 01/31/15): Assets, $3,788,500; expenditures, $234,763; qualifying distributions, $189,227.
Fields of interest: Arts and culture; Education; Human services.
Type of support: General support.
Limitations: Applications accepted. Giving primarily in ID; some giving in CA.
Application information: Application form required.
Initial approach: Letter
Copies of proposal: 1
Deadline(s): None
Trustees: Thomas J. O'Neil; Catherine Williford; JPMorgan Chase Bank, N.A.
EIN: 366090223

3169
Perkins Hunter Foundation
311 S. Wacker Dr., Ste. 6000
Chicago, IL 60606-6696

Established in 1988 in Illinois.
Donors: Robert H. Perkins; Thomas Perkins.
Foundation type: Independent foundation.
Financial data (yr. ended 12/31/13): Assets, $7,434,539 (M); gifts received, $1,292,298; expenditures, $396,875; qualifying distributions, $395,000; giving activities include $395,000 for 19 grants (high: $150,000; low: $5,000).
Fields of interest: Arts and culture; Higher education; Foundations; Human services; Family services; Low-income and poor people.
Limitations: Applications not accepted. Giving primarily in CA. No grants to individuals.
Application information: Contributes only to pre-selected organizations.
Directors: Alec Perkins; Jamel Perkins; Thomas Perkins.
EIN: 363486609

3170
Perry Family Trust
c/o Harris Bank
111 W. Monroe St., Ste. 16W, Tax Div. 10C
Chicago, IL 60603-4026

Foundation type: Independent foundation.
Financial data (yr. ended 12/31/14): Assets, $4,612,565; expenditures, $264,979; qualifying distributions, $234,106.
Fields of interest: Diseases and conditions; Religion.
Limitations: Applications not accepted. Giving primarily in IL.
Application information: Unsolicited requests for funds not accepted.
Trustee: BMO Harris Bank, N.A.
EIN: 261634350

3171
The Herman & Katherine Peters Foundation, Corp.
351 W. Glade Rd.
Palatine, IL 60067-6831 (847) 909-3130
Contact: Scot A. Leonard, Pres.

Established in 1998 in Illinois.
Donors: Katherine Peters†; Katherine Peters Trust.
Foundation type: Independent foundation.

Financial data (yr. ended 12/31/14): Assets, $7,129,041 (M); expenditures, $399,244; qualifying distributions, $342,289; giving activities include $166,000 for 30 grants (high: $22,500; low: $1,000), and $47,500 for 15 grants to individuals (high: $2,500; low: $2,500).
Purpose and activities: Scholarship awards to financially needy students pursuing studies relating to environmental concerns or Christian-based religious instruction. Some giving for educational field trips for underprivileged children to heighten their awareness about the importance of conservation.
Fields of interest: Higher education; Environmental education; Christianity.
Type of support: Student aid.
Limitations: Applications accepted. Giving primarily in AZ, CO, IL, MI, and WI.
Application information: Application form required.
  Initial approach: Completed application form
  Deadline(s): None
Officers and Directors: Scot A. Leonard, Pres. and Director; George Carroll, V.P. and Director; Jeanine Holtsford, Secy.-Treas. and Director; James P. Devine, Jr.; Cindy Hass.
Number of staff: 1 full-time professional.
EIN: 364180010

3172
R. D. & Linda Peters Foundation
10 S. Dearborn, IL1-0117
Chicago, IL 60603
Appliaction address: Richard Hugo, 10502 N. Burning Bush Ln., Mequon, WI 53092, tel.: (866) 888-5157

Donors: R.D. Peters†; Linda Peters†.
Foundation type: Independent foundation.
Financial data (yr. ended 12/31/13): Assets, $5,835,481 (M); expenditures, $320,475; qualifying distributions, $271,427; giving activities include $261,723 for 17 grants (high: $151,367; low: $2,000).
Purpose and activities: Emphasis normally restricted to conservation endeavors, an educational scholarship fund, and youth activities; support also for a medical college.
Fields of interest: Orchestral music; Education; Graduate and professional education; Medical education; Natural resources; Engineering; Youth services.
Type of support: General support; Capital campaigns; Equipment; Research.
Limitations: Applications accepted. Giving primarily in Brillion and Chilton, WI area.
Application information: Application form required.
  Initial approach: Letter
  Copies of proposal: 3
  Deadline(s): None
  Board meeting date(s): Quarterly
Officers: Michael Best, Pres.; Kenneth J. Wagner, V.P.; Richard G. Hugo, Secy.-Treas.
EIN: 396097994

3173
David C. and Ellen R. Petrick Foundation
416 W. Cuttriss St.
Park Ridge, IL 60068-2707

Established in 1999 in Illinois.
Donors: David C. Petrick; Ellen Patrick.

Foundation type: Independent foundation.
Financial data (yr. ended 12/31/13): Assets, $11,384,016 (M); gifts received, $2,754,656; expenditures, $354,241; qualifying distributions, $325,000; giving activities include $325,000 for 23 grants (high: $247,250; low: $200).
Fields of interest: Education; Higher education; Domesticated animals; Animal welfare; Human services.
Type of support: General support.
Limitations: Applications not accepted. Giving primarily in IL. No grants to individuals.
Application information: Unsolicited requests for funds not accepted.
Officers: David C. Petrick, Mgr.; Ellen Petrick, Mgr.
EIN: 364281619

3174
Petrovich Family Foundation
6618 St. James Ct.
Downers Grove, IL 60516-3032

Donor: Dushan Petrovich.
Foundation type: Independent foundation.
Financial data (yr. ended 12/31/13): Assets, $1,665,234 (M); gifts received, $200,000; expenditures, $254,250; qualifying distributions, $240,663; giving activities include $240,000 for 4 grants (high: $125,000; low: $3,000).
Fields of interest: Planetariums; Education; Undergraduate education; Science; Human services.
Type of support: Advocacy.
Limitations: Applications not accepted. Giving primarily in IL.
Application information: Unsolicited requests for funds not accepted.
Directors: Dushan Petrovich; Lisa Petrovich; Nancy Petrovich; Steven Petrovich.
EIN: 263301164

3175
The Pharmore Drugs Charitable Foundation
3531 W. Howard St.
Skokie, IL 60076-4012

Donors: Avrom Goldfeder; Pharemore Drugs LLC.
Foundation type: Independent foundation.
Financial data (yr. ended 12/31/13): Assets, $30,296 (M); gifts received, $441,152; expenditures, $374,989; qualifying distributions, $373,700; giving activities include $373,700 for 42 grants (high: $37,600; low: $1,000).
Fields of interest: Education; Judaism; Human services.
Limitations: Applications not accepted.
Application information: Unsolicited requests for funds not accepted.
Officers and Directors: Avrom Goldfeder, Pres. and Director; Ari Shabat, V.P. and Director; Steve Brueggeman, Treas. and Director.
EIN: 261198676

3176
Pinnell Foundation
20 N. Wacker Dr., Ste. 2800
Chicago, IL 60606-3101

Established in 1988 in Illinois.

Donors: H.P. Pinnell; Curtis G. Pinnell; Emilysue Pinnell.
Foundation type: Independent foundation.
Financial data (yr. ended 12/31/14): Assets, $5,152,011; expenditures, $295,894; qualifying distributions, $247,650.
Fields of interest: Arts and culture; Protestantism; Human services.
Limitations: Applications not accepted. Giving primarily in IL and TX. No grants to individuals.
Application information: Unsolicited requests for funds not accepted.
Officers and Directors: H.P. Pinnell, Pres. and Director; Emilysue Pinnell, V.P. and Director; Richard John Williams, Secy. and Director; Paul S. Vander Woude.
EIN: 363621711

3177
Frederick Pitzman Fund
(formerly Pitzman Fund)
c/o Bank of America, N.A.
231 S. LaSalle St., IL1-231-10-05
Chicago, IL 60697-0001
Application address: c/o Bank of America, N.A., Attn.: Spencer Heddens, 100 N. Broadway, St. Louis, MO 63102-2728, tel.: (816) 292-4300

Established in 1944 in Missouri.
Donor: Frederick Pitzman†.
Foundation type: Independent foundation.
Financial data (yr. ended 09/30/13): Assets, $5,008,822 (M); expenditures, $238,127; qualifying distributions, $228,148; giving activities include $225,800 for 17 grants (high: $150,000; low: $500).
Fields of interest: Education; Environment; Zoos; Botanical gardens; Health; Family planning; Addiction services; Protestantism; Human services; Child welfare.
Type of support: General support; Continuing support; Annual campaigns.
Limitations: Applications accepted. Giving primarily in St. Louis, MO. No grants to individuals.
Application information:
  Deadline(s): None
Trustees: Caroline P. Early; Gilbert Gordon Early; Bank of America, N.A.
EIN: 436023901

3178
Podolsky Family Foundation
c/o Podolsky Northstar
2610 Lake Cook Rd., Ste. 100
Riverwoods, IL 60015-5710

Established in 1988 in Illinois.
Donors: Milton Podolsky; Randy Podolsky; Steven Podolsky.
Foundation type: Independent foundation.
Financial data (yr. ended 11/30/13): Assets, $2,566,354 (M); gifts received, $28,418; expenditures, $147,122; qualifying distributions, $138,375; giving activities include $138,375 for 43 grants (high: $25,000; low: $100).
Fields of interest: Philanthropy; Religion; Judaism; Human services.
Limitations: Applications not accepted. No grants to individuals.
Application information: Unsolicited requests for funds not accepted.

Officers: Steven Podolsky, Pres.; Randy Podolsky, V.P. and Secy.; Milton Podolsky, Treas.
EIN: 363648282

3179
Polk Family Charitable Fund

(formerly Polk Bros. Fifty-Five Plus)
333 N. Michigan Ave., Ste. 510
Chicago, IL 60601-2417
Contact: Iris Krieg

Established in 1984 in Illinois.
Foundation type: Independent foundation.
Financial data (yr. ended 08/31/13): Assets, $3,135,372 (M); expenditures, $261,510; qualifying distributions, $260,174; giving activities include $241,250 for 95 grants (high: $40,000; low: $250).
Purpose and activities: Giving primarily for higher education and human services.
Fields of interest: Arts and culture; Museums; Higher education; Judaism; Human services; Child welfare.
Limitations: Applications not accepted. Giving on a national basis. No grants to individuals.
Application information: Unsolicited requests for funds not accepted.
Board meeting date(s): Sept.
Officers: Linda Cutler, Pres.; Jeffrey A. Lewis, V.P.; Ellen Multack, Secy.-Treas.
Directors: Bruce R. Bachmann; Sandra P. Guthman; E. Richard Polk; Edward M. Polk; Howard J. Polk; Jeffrey A. Polk; Jennifer Polk.
Number of staff: None.
EIN: 363332896

3180
Pollack Family Foundation

c/o JPMorgan Services, Inc.
10 S. Dearborn, IL1-0117
Chicago, IL 60603 8668885157

Established in 1998 in New York.
Donors: Leon Pollack; Marsha Pollack Charitable Trust.
Foundation type: Independent foundation.
Financial data (yr. ended 12/31/13): Assets, $1,090,309; gifts received, $83,787; expenditures, $241,647; qualifying distributions, $229,100.
Fields of interest: Higher education; Medical education; Nonprofits; Health; Judaism.
Type of support: Regranting.
Limitations: Applications not accepted. Giving primarily in NJ and NY. No grants to individuals.
Application information: Contributes only to pre-selected organizations.
Trustees: Andrea Gabay; Michael Gabay; Robin Perlman; Leon Pollack.
EIN: 137157336

3181
Jerry E. Poncher Family Foundation

c/o RSM McGladrey, Inc.
20 N., Martingale Rd., Ste. 500
Schaumburg, IL 60173-2420

Established in 1965 in Illinois.
Donors: Jerry E. Poncher; Lyle Poncher; Great River Productions, Inc. Profit Sharing Plan.

Foundation type: Independent foundation.
Financial data (yr. ended 12/31/12): Assets, $2,508,680 (M); expenditures, $220,534; qualifying distributions, $172,350; giving activities include $172,350 for grants.
Fields of interest: Education; Judaism; Human rights; Human services.
Type of support: General support.
Limitations: Applications not accepted. Giving primarily in CA and NY. No grants to individuals.
Application information: Unsolicited requests for funds not accepted.
Officers and Directors: Lyle Poncher, Pres. and Treas. and Director; Kathleen P. Poncher, V.P.
EIN: 366140417

3182
Pond Family Foundation

2920 N. Commonwealth Ave.
Chicago, IL 60657-6233

Established in 1998 in Illinois.
Donors: Peter Pond; Alicia Pond.
Foundation type: Independent foundation.
Financial data (yr. ended 12/31/13): Assets, $4,759,581 (M); expenditures, $240,958; qualifying distributions, $195,916; giving activities include $195,916 for 35 grants (high: $35,000; low: $250).
Fields of interest: Arts and culture; Theater; Museums; Higher education; Nonprofits; Diseases and conditions; Human services; Child welfare.
Type of support: Regranting.
Limitations: Applications not accepted. Giving primarily in Chicago, IL. No grants to individuals.
Application information: Unsolicited requests for funds not accepted.
Directors: Alicia Pond; Peter Pond.
EIN: 367238359

3183
Powell Foundation

6843 N. Knox Ave.
Lincolnwood, IL 60712-2415

Established in 2006 in Illinois.
Donor: Kenneth Powell Trust.
Foundation type: Independent foundation.
Financial data (yr. ended 12/31/14): Assets, $2,192,066 (M); expenditures, $337,614; qualifying distributions, $337,221; giving activities include $320,000 for 18 grants (high: $50,000; low: $5,000).
Fields of interest: Animal welfare.
Limitations: Applications not accepted. Giving primarily in CO, IL, MA and UT.
Application information: Unsolicited requests for funds not accepted.
Trustees: Michael Miller; Marita Powell.
EIN: 204747466

3184
Pritzker Early Childhood Foundation

(formerly Pritzker Early Childhood Development Fund)
333 N. Michigan Ave., Ste. 510
Chicago, IL 60601-3934 (312) 641-5440
Contact: Iris Krieg

FAX: (312) 641-5736; E-mail: pritzkerecf@aol.com; Main URL: http://www.pecfound.org
Grants List: http://www.pecfound.org/our_grantees0.aspx

Established in 2002 in Illinois.
Foundation type: Independent foundation.
Financial data (yr. ended 12/31/13): Assets, $6,969,214 (M); expenditures, $403,374; qualifying distributions, $329,015; giving activities include $268,000 for 11 grants (high: $50,000; low: $10,000).
Purpose and activities: The foundation supports initiatives in the field of early childhood development, and focuses both on expanding and increasing the effectiveness of programs and practices that have proven successful in providing high-quality services to youngsters in underserved communities. The foundations goal is to furnish children from the prenatal stage to age five with the tools that will help them succeed in school, a goal the foundation feels can only be realized by nurturing them from the earliest weeks and months of their lives. The foundation's primary focus for grantmaking includes: 1) Replication Grants, which support organizations that assist multiple sites, generally in more than one state, in broadening the reach and effectiveness of their evidence-based programs and practices; 2) Professional Development Grants, which support the provision of technical assistance and training in proven programs and practices to staff in multiple sites, often in more than one state, and 3) the foundation's Early Childhood Quality Improvement Program (EQUIP).
Fields of interest: Child welfare; Youth development.
Limitations: Giving primarily in Illinois, with emphasis on Chicago. No support for fraternal or political organizations, private foundations, or for workshops or the production and/or distribution of materials that are not part of a comprehensive training. No grants to individuals, or for capital campaigns, conferences, or ticket purchases for benefits; no loans.
Publications: Application guidelines.
Application information: Guidelines and application forms for EQUIP grants may be requested by tel. Application information and complete guidelines for all of the foundation's programs are available on foundation web site.
Initial approach: For Replication and Professional Development Grants: Cover letter and executive summary (no more than 2 pages)
Deadline(s): For Replication and Professional Development Grants: Feb. 15 and Aug. 15. For EQUIP: June 1
Board meeting date(s): May, Oct.
Final notification: For Replication and Professional Development Grants: generally in Nov. and May. For EQUIP: generally in July
Officers and Directors: Gigi Pritzker Pucker, Pres. and Director; Ronald D. Wray, V.P.; Karen Pritzker, Secy. and Director; Penny Pritzker, Treas. and Director; Margot Pritzker; Susan Pritzker.
EIN: 412051114

3185
Pugdin Memorial Fund

10 S. Dearborn IL1-0117
Chicago, IL 60603

Foundation type: Independent foundation.

Financial data (yr. ended 12/31/14): Assets, $4,901,748; expenditures, $288,735; qualifying distributions, $235,935.
Fields of interest: Nonprofits; Judaism.
Type of support: Regranting.
Limitations: Applications not accepted. Giving primarily in New York, NY.
Application information: Unsolicited requests for funds not accepted.
Trustee: JPMorgan Chase Bank, N.A.
EIN: 311663740

3186
Putnam Family Foundation
326 Essex Rd.
Kenilworth, IL   60043-1124

Established in 2005 in Illinois.
Donor: Gerald D. Putnam.
Foundation type: Independent foundation.
Financial data (yr. ended 12/31/13): Assets, $3,263,463 (M); expenditures, $304,209; qualifying distributions, $280,000; giving activities include $280,000 for 9 grants (high: $130,000; low: $1,000).
Fields of interest: Education; Children's hospital care; Children.
Type of support: General support.
Limitations: Applications not accepted. Giving primarily in IL. No grants to individuals.
Application information: Unsolicited requests for funds not accepted.
Officers: Gerald D. Putnam, Pres. and Treas.; Sharron Putnam, V.P. and Secy.
Directors: Rachel Putnam.
EIN: 204000349

3187
Reade Industrial Fund
111 W. Monroe St., Tax Div. 10C
Chicago, IL   60603-4026   (312) 461-5154

Established in 1946 in Illinois.
Donor: Edith M. Reade†.
Foundation type: Independent foundation.
Financial data (yr. ended 12/31/14): Assets, $4,117,326 (M); expenditures, $219,048; qualifying distributions, $192,997; giving activities include $175,000 for 4 grants (high: $60,000; low: $25,000).
Purpose and activities: Grants are given to organizations to provide up to $5,000 in aid to individuals of good moral character, who are or have been employed in industry in the state of Illinois, and who shall by reason of an emergency beyond their control, such as accidental injury, illness of themselves or family members, inability to obtain any employment, or sudden and involuntary cessation of employment, be unable to care for themselves and their spouse and children and be in need of aid.
Fields of interest: Family services; Low-income and poor people.
Limitations: Applications accepted. Giving primarily in IL.
Application information: Application form required.
  Initial approach: Contact foundation for
    application form
  Deadline(s): None
Trustee: BMO Harris Bank, N.A.
EIN: 366048673

3188
Red Bird Hollow Foundation
c/o Paula Lillard
1340 N. Waukegan Rd.
Lake Forest, IL   60045-1147

Established in 1991 in Illinois.
Donors: John S. Lillard; Paula Polk Lillard; Polk Foundation.
Foundation type: Independent foundation.
Financial data (yr. ended 06/30/13): Assets, $2,223,195 (M); gifts received, $266,920; expenditures, $372,616; qualifying distributions, $366,350; giving activities include $366,350 for 59 grants (high: $150,000; low: $250).
Purpose and activities: Giving primarily for education and youth programs.
Fields of interest: Arts and culture; Education; Human services.
Limitations: Applications not accepted. Giving primarily in IL. No grants to individuals.
Application information: Contributes only to pre-selected organizations.
Officers: Paula Polk Lillard, Pres.; Howard Jessen, V.P. and Treas.; John Lillard, V.P.; Helen Jessen, Secy.
EIN: 363747664

3189
Red Lodge Foundation
1191 Lindenwood Dr.
Winnetka, IL   60093-3721

Established in 2007 in Illinois.
Donors: Colleen Mitchell Knupp; Jeffrey Knupp.
Foundation type: Independent foundation.
Financial data (yr. ended 09/30/14): Assets, $4,759,554; expenditures, $261,574; qualifying distributions, $224,610.
Fields of interest: Education; Nonprofits; Cancers; Human services; Child welfare.
Type of support: Regranting.
Limitations: Applications not accepted. No grants to individuals.
Application information: Contributes only to pre-selected organizations.
Officers and Directors: Colleen Mitchell Knupp, Pres. and Secy. and Director; Jeffrey Knupp, V.P. and Treas. and Director; Gerry Corcoran.
EIN: 261509357

3190
Reed Family Foundation
135 S. LaSalle St., Ste. 2350
Chicago, IL   60603-4153

Established in 2007 in Illinois.
Donor: John Shedd Reed.
Foundation type: Independent foundation.
Financial data (yr. ended 12/31/13): Assets, $9,773,179 (M); gifts received, $1,490,000; expenditures, $367,657; qualifying distributions, $334,000; giving activities include $334,000 for 144 grants (high: $50,000; low: $10).
Fields of interest: Arts and culture; Human services.
Limitations: Applications not accepted. Giving primarily in NY and OR. No grants to individuals.
Application information: Unsolicited requests for funds not accepted.
Officers and Directors: Marjorie Lindsay Reed, Pres. and Director; Walter W. Bell, Secy.-Treas. and

Director; Ginevra R. Ralph; Helen S. Reed; John S. Reed, Jr.; L. Keith Reed; Peter S. Reed.
EIN: 261247721

3191
Sam and Victoria Reed Family Foundation
622 W. Maple St.
Hinsdale, IL   60521-3141   (630) 850-9385
Contact: Sam K. Reed, Tr.

Established in 2000 in Illinois.
Donor: Sam K. Reed.
Foundation type: Independent foundation.
Financial data (yr. ended 12/31/13): Assets, $5,021,332 (M); expenditures, $295,881; qualifying distributions, $279,000; giving activities include $279,000 for 54 grants (high: $25,000; low: $500).
Fields of interest: Arts and culture; Museums; University education; Business education; Animal welfare; Diseases and conditions; Housing development; Human services.
Limitations: Applications accepted. Giving primarily in MO and TX.
Application information:
  Initial approach: Letter
  Deadline(s): None
Trustees: Sam K. Reed; Victoria P. Reed.
EIN: 364393893

3192
Reichert Foundation
580 Douglas Dr.
Lake Forest, IL   60045-3342
Contact: Susan Milanak, Treas. and Exec. Dir.
E-mail: info@thereichertfoundation.org; E-mail for Susan Milanak: susan@thereichertfoundation.org; Main URL: http://www.thereichertfoundation.org
Grant Database: http:// www.thereichertfoundation.org/ CurrentGrantees.aspx
Knowledge Center: http:// www.thereichertfoundation.org/ AnnualReports.aspx

Established in 1986 in Illinois.
Donors: Jack F. Reichert†; Corrine V. Reichert.
Foundation type: Independent foundation.
Financial data (yr. ended 12/31/14): Assets, $4,225,091; gifts received, $200; expenditures, $247,335; qualifying distributions, $210,525.
Purpose and activities: The foundation principally donates to organizations that provide food, clothing and shelter to disadvantaged persons. Also giving to disaster relief organizations and organizations that provide care to critically ill children.
Fields of interest: Health; Human services; Child welfare.
Type of support: General support; Continuing support; Annual campaigns; Capital and infrastructure; Emergency funds; Program development.
Limitations: Applications not accepted. Giving primarily in the Chicago area and Lake County, IL. No support for colleges. No grants to individuals.
Publications: Grants list.
Application information: The foundation does not accept unsolicited requests for funds. Currently the foundation is not accepting letters of inquiry.
  Board meeting date(s): Sept.

Officers and Directors: Corrine V. Reichert, Chair. and Pres. and Director; John Reichert, V.P. and Director; Susan Reichert Milanak, Treas. and Exec. Dir.; Drew Brooks.
Number of staff: None.
EIN: 363487139

3193
Richard and Marianne Reinisch Foundation
c/o Marianne Reinisch
950 Augusta Way, No. 303
Highland Park, IL 60035-1843

Established in 1999 in Illinois.
Donors: Richard Reinisch; Marianne Reinisch.
Foundation type: Independent foundation.
Financial data (yr. ended 12/31/13): Assets, $318,574 (M); gifts received, $100,000; expenditures, $222,132; qualifying distributions, $222,132; giving activities include $222,100 for 39 grants (high: $40,000; low: $1,000).
Fields of interest: Education; Nonprofits; Diseases and conditions; Human services.
Type of support: Regranting.
Limitations: Applications not accepted. Giving primarily in CO and IL. No grants to individuals.
Application information: Unsolicited requests for funds not accepted.
Officer: Marianne Reinisch, Pres.
Trustee: Steven W. Reinisch.
EIN: 364336221

3194
The William R. Rich Foundation
c/o Lynne Kaplan
9450 W. Bryn Mawr Ave., Ste. 310
Rosemont, IL 60018-5272

Established in 1993 in Illinois.
Foundation type: Independent foundation.
Financial data (yr. ended 12/31/13): Assets, $8,360,624 (M); expenditures, $401,981; qualifying distributions, $343,000; giving activities include $343,000 for 6 grants (high: $200,000; low: $5,000).
Fields of interest: Education; University education; Medical education; Specialty hospital care; Child welfare; Women's services.
Type of support: Research.
Limitations: Applications not accepted. Giving primarily in CA and IL. No grants to individuals.
Application information: Contributes only to pre-selected organizations.
Trustees: Lynne Kaplan; Elizabeth Reardon; Mark Reardon.
EIN: 363885448

3195
Richard Benevolent Foundation
720 Hampton Course
West Chicago, IL 60185-5807

Established in 2002 in Illinois.
Donors: Betty J. Richard; Elwood Richard.
Foundation type: Independent foundation.
Financial data (yr. ended 06/30/13): Assets, $398,008 (M); gifts received, $300,000; expenditures, $309,869; qualifying distributions,

$307,600; giving activities include $301,500 for 8 grants (high: $125,000; low: $5,000).
Purpose and activities: Giving primarily for missionary work, health research, and for the disabled.
Fields of interest: Nonprofits; Health; Christianity; Human services; People with disabilities.
Type of support: Research and evaluation; Regranting.
Limitations: Applications not accepted. Giving primarily in IL and VA. No grants to individuals.
Application information: Contributes only to pre-selected organizations.
Officers and Directors: Elwood Richard, Pres. and Director; Beth Richard, V.P. and Director; Betty J. Richard, V.P. and Director; Sharon Wong, Secy. and Director.
EIN: 753089935

3196
Ronald H. Ringer Foundation
c/o Daniel R. Swett
615 Crofton Ave. S.
Highland Park, IL 60035-3909
E-mail: danrswett@comcast.net

Established in 2001 in Illinois.
Donor: Ronald H. Ringer.
Foundation type: Independent foundation.
Financial data (yr. ended 12/31/13): Assets, $4,285,345 (M); expenditures, $399,071; qualifying distributions, $375,500; giving activities include $375,500 for 13 grants (high: $150,000; low: $2,500).
Purpose and activities: The foundation supports primary grade education of underprivileged children in the Chicago, IL area.
Fields of interest: Education; Elementary education; Child educational development; Youth services.
Limitations: Applications not accepted. Giving primarily in the Chicago, IL, area. No grants to individuals.
Application information: Contributes only to pre-selected organizations.
Trustee: Daniel R. Swett.
EIN: 367334016

3197
Elizabeth N. Robb Charitable Foundation
10 S. Dearborn IL1-0117
Chicago, IL 60603-2300

Foundation type: Independent foundation.
Financial data (yr. ended 12/31/14): Assets, $9,047,444; expenditures, $331,182; qualifying distributions, $250,914.
Fields of interest: Education; Health.
Limitations: Applications not accepted.
Application information: Unsolicited requests for funds not accepted.
Trustee: JPMorgan Chase Bank, N.A.
EIN: 776238653

3198
Helen Roberti Charitable Trust
111 W. Monroe St., Tax Div. 10C
Chicago, IL 60603-4026 (312) 461-5154

Established in 1994 in Illinois.

Foundation type: Independent foundation.
Financial data (yr. ended 12/31/14): Assets, $5,394,574; expenditures, $292,186; qualifying distributions, $250,235.
Purpose and activities: The trust makes distributions to organizations that maintain scholarship programs to enable Native Americans to obtain professional degrees.
Fields of interest: Higher education; American Indians.
Limitations: Applications accepted. Giving primarily in AZ and SD. No grants to individuals.
Application information: Application form required.
  Initial approach: Letter
  Deadline(s): None
Trustee: BMO Harris Bank, N.A.
EIN: 367056111

3199
Douglas C. & Lynn M. Roberts Family Foundation
P.O. Box 218
Sycamore, IL 60178-0218

Established in 2007 in Illinois.
Donor: Douglas C. Roberts Trust.
Foundation type: Independent foundation.
Financial data (yr. ended 12/31/13): Assets, $3,980,368 (M); expenditures, $196,692; qualifying distributions, $175,800; giving activities include $175,800 for 19 grants (high: $58,000; low: $100).
Fields of interest: Human services; Adolescents.
Limitations: Applications not accepted. No grants to individuals.
Application information: Unsolicited requests for funds not accepted.
Trustee: Douglas C. Roberts.
EIN: 376421756

3200
The Nick and Alma Robson Foundation
10 S. Dearborn IL1-0117
Chicago, IL 60603
Application address: c/o Sybil Ann Robson, V.P., 2021 S. Lewis Ave., Ste. 740, Tulsa, OK 74104-5713

Established in 1992 in Texas.
Donors: Alma Lavon Robson; John N. Robson.
Foundation type: Independent foundation.
Financial data (yr. ended 06/30/13): Assets, $7,166,798 (M); expenditures, $368,750; qualifying distributions, $345,000; giving activities include $345,000 for 7 grants (high: $115,000; low: $5,000).
Fields of interest: Special needs education; Christianity; People with disabilities.
Limitations: Applications accepted. Giving primarily in AL, MO, and OK.
Application information: Application form required.
  Initial approach: Letter
  Deadline(s): None
Officers: Bruce Allen Robson, Pres.; Sybil Ann Robson, V.P.; John Joseph Robson, Secy.-Treas.
EIN: 752438350

3201
The Roche Family Foundation Inc.
10540 S. Lorel
Oak Lawn, IL 60453-5155

Established in 2008 in Illinois.
Donors: Acorn Composite Corporation; Robert W. Roche; The Moore Bay Trust.
Foundation type: Independent foundation.
Financial data (yr. ended 07/31/14): Assets, $10; gifts received, $436,081; expenditures, $417,811.
Fields of interest: Education.
Limitations: Applications not accepted. Giving primarily in CO, IL and NJ.
Application information: Unsolicited requests for funds not accepted.
Officers and Directors: Robert Roche, Pres. and Director; Ritsuko Hattori-Roche, V.P. and Director; Theresa Roche, Secy.
EIN: 260832023

3202
Lon & Jessie Rogers Educational Trust
c/o JPMorgan Chase Bank, N.A.
10 S. Dearborn St., IL1-0117
Chicago, IL 60603-2317
Application address: JPMorgan Chase Bank, N.A., 2200 Ross Ave., Dallas, TX 75201, tel.: (214) 965-2914

Foundation type: Independent foundation.
Financial data (yr. ended 09/30/13): Assets, $12,994,634 (M); expenditures, $456,920; qualifying distributions, $585,634; giving activities include $392,759 for 3 grants (high: $331,730; low: $29,529).
Purpose and activities: The foundation awards low-interest loans and scholarships to students who are residents of Muhlenberg, Pike, and Ohio Counties, KY. Preference is given to students who are attending Centre College. Loans and scholarship awards are limited to students who are attending non-publicly-funded universities and colleges.
Fields of interest: Higher education.
Type of support: Student aid; Loans to individuals.
Limitations: Applications accepted. Giving primarily to residents of Ohio, Muhlenberg, and Pike counties, KY.
Application information: Application form required.
Initial approach: Application form is available from JPMorgan Chase Bank, N.A.
Deadline(s): Reasonable time before tuition due date
Trustee: JPMorgan Chase Bank, N.A.
EIN: 616019469

3203
The Richard and Margaret Romano Charitable Trust
1 Rotary Ctr., Ste. 1300
Evanston, IL 60201-4469

Established in 2005 in Illinois.
Donor: Richard C. Romano.
Foundation type: Independent foundation.
Financial data (yr. ended 12/31/13): Assets, $872,418 (M); gifts received, $287,491; expenditures, $198,169; qualifying distributions, $196,154; giving activities include $189,230 for 44 grants (high: $100,000; low: $50).
Fields of interest: Education; Catholicism; Child welfare.
Limitations: Applications not accepted. No grants to individuals.
Application information: Unsolicited requests for funds not accepted.
Trustees: Kathryn R. Mayer; James D. Romano; Joseph R.V. Romano; Margaret V. Romano; Richard C. Romano.
EIN: 686251318

3204
Rosebud Foundation
c/o Thomas Wilson
195 Birch St.
Winnetka, IL 60093

Foundation type: Independent foundation.
Financial data (yr. ended 12/31/13): Assets, $358,710 (M); expenditures, $124,288; qualifying distributions, $121,200; giving activities include $121,200 for 18 grants (high: $35,200; low: $200).
Fields of interest: Education; Employment; Sports and recreation.
Limitations: Applications not accepted. Giving primarily in IL.
Application information: Unsolicited requests for funds not accepted.
Officers and Directors: Thomas Wilson, Pres. and Director; C. Page O'Donohue, Secy.-Treas. and Director; Christine M. Wilson; Kathryn Wilson.
EIN: 262250986

3205
The Claire Rosen & Samuel Edes Foundation
c/o Quarles & Brady
300 N. Lasalle St., Ste. 4000
Chicago, IL 60654-3422

Established in 1986 in Illinois.
Donor: Claire Rosen Edes.
Foundation type: Independent foundation.
Financial data (yr. ended 12/31/13): Assets, $0 (M); expenditures, $237,852; qualifying distributions, $213,851; giving activities include $180,000 for 5 grants (high: $40,000; low: $35,000).
Fields of interest: Arts and culture.
Type of support: General support.
Limitations: Applications not accepted. Giving primarily in Chicago, IL. No grants to individuals.
Application information: Unsolicited requests for funds not accepted.
Officers: Nik B. Edes, Pres.; Stephen Netburn, V.P.; Sarah M. Linsley, Treas.
Director: Charles S. Stark.
EIN: 363514607

3206
Michael Alan Rosen Foundation
10 S. Dearborn, ILI-0117
Chicago, IL 60603

Established in 1986 in California.
Donors: Tobi Haleen; Conrad Hilton Foundation; The AGR Trust; Arlene Rosen.
Foundation type: Operating foundation.
Financial data (yr. ended 12/31/13): Assets, $5,413,259 (M); gifts received, $250,050; expenditures, $317,835; qualifying distributions, $269,396; giving activities include $257,850 for 15 grants (high: $125,000; low: $150).
Fields of interest: University education; Hospital care; Addiction services; Substance abuse treatment.
Type of support: General support; Program-related investments.
Limitations: Applications not accepted. Giving primarily in CA. No grants to individuals.
Application information: Contributes only to pre-selected organizations.
Officers: Arlene Rosen, Pres. and Treas.; William Kroger, V.P.; Tobi Haleen, Secy.
Number of staff: 2 full-time professional; 7 full-time support; 6 part-time support.
EIN: 943024736

3207
Harry & Bessye Rosenberg Charitable Trust
c/o The Northern Trust Co.
P.O. Box 803878
Chicago, IL 60680-3878

Established in 1994 in Illinois.
Foundation type: Independent foundation.
Financial data (yr. ended 09/30/13): Assets, $3,986,544 (M); expenditures, $227,703; qualifying distributions, $174,614; giving activities include $168,000 for 37 grants (high: $30,000; low: $500).
Fields of interest: Arts and culture; Nonprofits; Health; Diseases and conditions; Judaism.
Type of support: Research; Research and evaluation; Regranting.
Limitations: Applications not accepted. Giving primarily in IL. No grants to individuals.
Application information: Unsolicited requests for funds not accepted.
Trustees: Lawrence Glick; The Northern Trust Co.
EIN: 367139417

3208
Lee and Nathan Rosenmutter Family Foundation
(formerly Rosenmutter Foundation)
1909 N. Clifton Ave.
Chicago, IL 60614-4803

Donors: General Iron Industries, Inc.; Price Watson.
Foundation type: Company-sponsored foundation.
Financial data (yr. ended 01/31/14): Assets, $675,258 (M); expenditures, $219,433; qualifying distributions, $219,100; giving activities include $219,100 for 5 grants (high: $200,000; low: $100).
Purpose and activities: The foundation supports organizations involved with film, education, human services, military and veterans, and Judaism.
Fields of interest: Education; Secondary education; Graduate and professional education; Film and video; National defense; Religion; Judaism; Theology; Human services; Developmental disability services.
International interests: Israel.
Type of support: General support.
Limitations: Applications not accepted. No grants to individuals.
Application information: Unsolicited requests for funds not accepted.

Directors: Eva Braverman; Adam Labkon; Howard Labkon; Marilyn Labkon.
EIN: 366110084

3209
The Rosenson Family Foundation
2021 St. Johns Ave., Ste. 3C
Highland Park, IL   60035-6104

Established in 1990 in Illinois.
Donor: Harold Rosenson.
Foundation type: Independent foundation.
Financial data (yr. ended 12/31/14): Assets, $2,716,870 (M); expenditures, $147,320; qualifying distributions, $144,020; giving activities include $144,020 for 173 grants (high: $6,000; low: $100).
Fields of interest: Education; Religion; Judaism; Human services.
Type of support: General support; Continuing support; Annual campaigns; Capital campaigns; Capital and infrastructure; Emergency funds; Scholarships.
Limitations: Applications not accepted. Giving primarily in IL. No grants to individuals.
Application information: Unsolicited requests for funds not accepted.
Directors: Alan D. Rosenson; Harold Rosenson; Kenneth B. Rosenson; Linda J. Rosenson; Michael E. Rosenson.
EIN: 363677314

3210
Benjamin J. Rosenthal Foundation
P.O. Box 410
Deerfield, IL   60615

Established in 1922 in Illinois.
Donor: Benjamin J. Rosenthal†.
Foundation type: Independent foundation.
Financial data (yr. ended 12/31/14): Assets, $3,953,446 (M); expenditures, $235,681; qualifying distributions, $172,248; giving activities include $138,000 for 55 grants (high: $5,000; low: $1,000).
Purpose and activities: Support primarily for youth, child welfare, human services, arts and culture, and protection of animals.
Fields of interest: Arts and culture; Education; Natural resources; Animal welfare; Social sciences; Human services; Child welfare; International relations.
Type of support: Individual development; Policy, advocacy and systems reform.
Limitations: Applications not accepted. Giving primarily in Chicago, IL. No grants to individuals.
Application information: Unsolicited requests for funds not accepted.
Officers: Elaine Broadhead, Pres.; Walter Roth, Secy.; Rodger Mandel, Treas. and Admin.
Trustees: Joseph Glossberg; Thomas Foulke.
EIN: 362523643

3211
Rossman Family Foundation
c/o Harrison & Held, LLP
333 W. Wacker Dr., Ste. 1700
Chicago, IL   60606

Established in 2005 in Illinois.

Donors: Howard M. Rossman; Beverly G. Rossman.
Foundation type: Independent foundation.
Financial data (yr. ended 12/31/13): Assets, $10,913,377 (M); gifts received, $200,000; expenditures, $453,465; qualifying distributions, $399,010; giving activities include $399,000 for 11 grants (high: $220,000; low: $5,000).
Fields of interest: Charter school education; University education; Public policy; Leadership development; International development.
Type of support: Policy, advocacy and systems reform.
Limitations: Applications not accepted. Giving primarily in Washington, DC, and the greater metropolitan Chicago, IL, area. No grants to individuals.
Application information: Unsolicited requests for funds not accepted.
Officers: Howard M. Rossman, Pres. and Treas.; Erin Rossman, V.P.; Jeremy Rossman, V.P.; Beverly G. Rossman, Secy.
EIN: 203928172

3212
Albert J. and Susan E. Rot Foundation
P.O. Box 222
Naperville, IL   60565-0222   (630) 416-2100
Contact: Albert J. Rot, Pres.

Established in 1989 in Illinois.
Donors: Albert J. Rot; Susan E. Rot; Keith A. Rot.
Foundation type: Independent foundation.
Financial data (yr. ended 12/31/13): Assets, $1,119,812 (M); expenditures, $141,605; qualifying distributions, $132,785; giving activities include $80,000 for 6 grants (high: $20,000; low: $5,000), and $48,379 for 13 grants to individuals (high: $6,767; low: $1,000).
Fields of interest: Religion; Sports and recreation; Human services.
Type of support: General support; Student aid.
Limitations: Applications accepted. Giving in the U.S., with preference given to residents of IL.
Application information: Application form required.
Initial approach: Proposal
Deadline(s): None
Officers: Albert J. Rot, Pres.; Susan E. Rot, V.P.
Directors: Keith A. Rot; Richard K. Rot.
EIN: 363653679

3213
Rothman Family Foundation
311 S. Wacker Dr., Ste. 4190
Chicago, IL   60606-6621   (312) 663-4700
Contact: Patricia C. Rothman, V.P. and Secy.

Established in 1986 in Illinois.
Donors: Florence C. Rothman; Gregory C. Rothman; Patricia C. Rothman; Noel N. Rothman; Michael C. Rothman; Hermine C. Rothman.
Foundation type: Independent foundation.
Financial data (yr. ended 12/31/13): Assets, $4,253,220 (M); gifts received, $480,000; expenditures, $447,704; qualifying distributions, $389,500; giving activities include $389,500 for 39 grants (high: $71,000; low: $500).
Fields of interest: Arts and culture; Judaism; Human rights; Antidiscrimination; Human services; Basic and emergency aid; International development.

Limitations: Applications accepted. Giving primarily in IL, some giving also in NY. No grants to individuals.
Application information: Application form required.
Initial approach: Letter
Deadline(s): None
Final notification: 90 days
Officers: Florence C. Rothman, Pres.; Patricia C. Rothman, V.P. and Secy.; Gregory C. Rothman, V.P.; Hermine C. Rothman, V.P.; Michael C. Rothman, V.P.; Noel N. Rothman, V.P.
EIN: 363490566

3214
Beryl O. and Wilma Sime Roundy Charitable Foundation
P.O. Box 803878
Chicago, IL   60680-3878

Established in 2006 in Illinois.
Donors: Beryl O. Roundy; Wilma Sime Roundy Marital Election; Roundy Marital Trust.
Foundation type: Independent foundation.
Financial data (yr. ended 12/31/13): Assets, $9,911,867 (M); expenditures, $220,786; qualifying distributions, $203,220; giving activities include $200,731 for 9 grants (high: $37,737; low: $4,912).
Fields of interest: Education; Religion; Human services.
Limitations: Applications not accepted. No grants to individuals.
Application information: Unsolicited requests for funds not accepted.
Trustee: Northern Trust, N.A.
EIN: 203993988

3215
The Dennis and Joyce Ruben Foundation
6519 N. Central Park Ave.
Lincolnwood, IL   60712-4013

Established in 1986 in Illinois.
Donors: Dennis Ruben; Joyce Ruben.
Foundation type: Independent foundation.
Financial data (yr. ended 12/31/13): Assets, $6,009 (M); gifts received, $319,450; expenditures, $318,411; qualifying distributions, $312,208; giving activities include $312,208 for 59 grants (high: $141,800; low: $18).
Purpose and activities: Giving primarily to Jewish agencies, temples, and schools.
Fields of interest: Elementary and secondary education; Judaism; Human services.
Limitations: Applications not accepted. Giving primarily in IL and NY. No grants to individuals.
Application information: Contributes only to pre-selected organizations.
Trustees: Dennis Ruben; Joyce Ruben.
EIN: 363486610

3216
Eluned & Edward Russell Charitable Foundation
P.O. Box 803878
Chicago, IL   60680-3878

Established in 1999 in Florida.
Donors: Edward W. Russell Irrevocable Trust; Eluned Russell Irrevocable Trust.

Foundation type: Independent foundation.

Financial data (yr. ended 02/28/15): Assets, $4,337,639; expenditures, $278,949; qualifying distributions, $220,212.

Fields of interest: Education; Nonprofits; Hospital care; Diseases and conditions; Housing development; Human services; Child welfare; Scouting programs.

Type of support: Regranting.

Limitations: Applications not accepted. Giving primarily in Sarasota, FL. No grants to individuals.

Application information: Unsolicited requests for funds not accepted.

Trustee: The Northern Trust Co.

EIN: 656294158

3217
Biff Ruttenberg Foundation
55 E. Monroe St., Ste. 2910
Chicago, IL 60603-5843

Established in 2004 in Illinois.

Donors: Roger F. Ruttenberg; Biff Ruttenberg.

Foundation type: Independent foundation.

Financial data (yr. ended 12/31/13): Assets, $1,719,087 (M); gifts received, $136,725; expenditures, $215,464; qualifying distributions, $201,804; giving activities include $200,425 for 43 grants (high: $50,000; low: $100).

Fields of interest: Education; Diseases and conditions; Judaism.

Type of support: General support.

Limitations: Applications not accepted. Giving primarily in IL. No grants to individuals.

Application information: Unsolicited requests for funds not accepted.

Officers: Roger F. Ruttenberg, Pres.; Gwen Callans, V.P.; Dawn Stevenson, Secy.; Lisa Kovar, Treas.

EIN: 201762284

3218
The Ruttenberg Foundation
c/o David W. Ruttenberg
833 N. Orleans St., Ste. 400
Chicago, IL 60610-3181

Established in 1999 in Illinois.

Donor: David W. Ruttenberg.

Foundation type: Independent foundation.

Financial data (yr. ended 11/30/13): Assets, $2,732,476 (M); gifts received, $205,000; expenditures, $225,409; qualifying distributions, $415,244; giving activities include $207,500 for 8 grants (high: $100,000; low: $500).

Fields of interest: Arts and culture; Education; Higher education; Foundations; Storms.

Limitations: Applications not accepted. Giving primarily in Chicago, IL. No grants to individuals.

Application information: Unsolicited requests for funds not accepted.

Officers: David W. Ruttenberg, Pres.; Jonathon McCulloch, Secy.; Pamela I. Kaji, Treas.

EIN: 364264024

3219
William G. & Mary A. Ryan Foundation
12 Salt Creek Ln., Ste. 200
Hinsdale, IL 60521-8611

Established in 1993 in Illinois.

Donors: Mary A. Ryan; William G. Ryan.

Foundation type: Independent foundation.

Financial data (yr. ended 11/30/13): Assets, $1,548,493 (M); gifts received, $500,000; expenditures, $202,208; qualifying distributions, $198,500; giving activities include $198,500 for 34 grants (high: $46,000; low: $100).

Purpose and activities: Giving primarily for a medical center, as well as for the arts, education, social services, and Roman Catholic churches.

Fields of interest: Performing arts; Education; Nonprofits; Hospital care; Diseases and conditions; Catholicism; Human services.

Type of support: Regranting.

Limitations: Applications not accepted. Giving primarily in IL; some funding also in FL. No grants to individuals.

Application information: Contributes only to pre-selected organizations.

Directors: Mary A. Ryan; William G. Ryan.

EIN: 363870010

3220
Franklin I. and Irene List Saemann Foundation
(formerly Franklin I. Saemann Foundation)
14932 Norrish Rd.
Morrison, IL 61270-9746
Application address: P.O. Box 105, Morrison, IL 61270-0105

Established in 1983 in Indiana.

Donors: Franklin I. Saemann†; Irene L. Saemann†.

Foundation type: Independent foundation.

Financial data (yr. ended 06/30/13): Assets, $7,251,034 (M); expenditures, $586,557; qualifying distributions, $439,200; giving activities include $415,800 for 12 grants (high: $295,000; low: $500).

Purpose and activities: Giving primarily for higher education and human services, with an emphasis on funding for libraries and literacy programs.

Fields of interest: Higher education; Public libraries; Human services.

Limitations: Applications accepted. Giving primarily in Waverly, IA, Warsaw, IN, and Kenosha, WI. No grants to individuals.

Publications: Informational brochure (including application guidelines).

Application information:
  Initial approach: Letter
  Deadline(s): Apr. 1
  Board meeting date(s): Quarterly; June for considering grant applications

Trustees: Amy C. Kilgus Chamley; Katherine A. Kauffman; Adam Kilgus; Joann A. Kilgus; Robert List; Jonathan Waller; June I. Waller.

Number of staff: 1 full-time professional; 3 full-time support.

EIN: 626171002

3221
Saliba Family Charitable Foundation, Inc.
135 S. LaSalle, Ste. 3914
Chicago, IL 60603-4133

Foundation type: Independent foundation.

Financial data (yr. ended 12/31/13): Assets, $1,170,756 (M); expenditures, $230,917; qualifying distributions, $229,500; giving activities

include $229,500 for 6 grants (high: $100,000; low: $1,000).

Fields of interest: Education; Housing development; Golf; Human services.

Type of support: General support; Scholarships.

Limitations: Applications not accepted. Giving primarily in CA, DC and IL.

Application information: Unsolicited requests for funds not accepted.

Officers: Anthony Saliba, Pres.; Robert Saliba, Secy.

Director: Moira Saliba.

EIN: 263189604

3222
Sasco Foundation
10 S. Dearborn IL1-0117
Chicago, IL 60603
Application address: c/o, John J. Powers, Mgr. Dir., JPMorgan Chase Bank, 270 Park Ave., New York, NY 10017

Established in 1951 in New York.

Donors: Leila E. Riegel†; Katherine R. Emory†.

Foundation type: Independent foundation.

Financial data (yr. ended 12/31/13): Assets, $6,289,550 (M); expenditures, $355,259; qualifying distributions, $300,190; giving activities include $282,500 for 51 grants (high: $100,000; low: $500).

Fields of interest: Arts and culture; Natural resources; Foundations; Health; Human services; Family services; Females.

Type of support: General support; Continuing support.

Limitations: Applications accepted. Giving primarily in CT, ME, and NY. No grants to individuals.

Application information: Application form required.
  Initial approach: Letter
  Deadline(s): Sept. 30

Trustees: Lucy E. Ambach; Benjamin Emory; Katherine Emory Stookey; JPMorgan Chase Bank, N.A.

EIN: 136046567

3223
Paul & Norma Schaumburg Charitable Trust
P.O. Box 67
Milford, IL 60953-0067 (815) 889-4140

Donor: Norma L. Schaumburg†.

Foundation type: Independent foundation.

Financial data (yr. ended 12/31/13): Assets, $6,350,346 (M); expenditures, $327,711; qualifying distributions, $233,000; giving activities include $233,000 for 12 grants (high: $60,000; low: $2,500).

Purpose and activities: Scholarship awards to high school graduates in the Milford and Sheldon, Illinois, area; giving also to religious, human services and educational organizations in Iroquois County.

Fields of interest: Arts and culture; Education; Religion.

Type of support: Scholarships; Student aid.

Limitations: Applications accepted. Giving primarily in Milford, Sheldon and Iroquois County, IL.

Application information: Application form required.
  Initial approach: Contact foundation for application
  Deadline(s): For Scholarships May 1; For Other Grants Nov. 1

Trustees: Cheryl Knake; Craig Luke; Gayle van Vickle.
EIN: 456918419

3224
Schiff Hardin & Waite Foundation
(formerly Schiff Hardin & Waite Foundation)
233 S. Wacker Dr., Ste. 6600
Chicago, IL   60606-6360

Established in 1986 in Illinois.
Donors: Schiff Hardin LLP; Bruce Weisenthal.
Foundation type: Company-sponsored foundation.
Financial data (yr. ended 11/30/13): Assets, $119,936 (M); gifts received, $261,615; expenditures, $297,698; qualifying distributions, $297,698; giving activities include $296,500 for 76 grants (high: $75,000; low: $100).
Purpose and activities: The foundation supports hospitals and organizations involved with education, cancer, crime and law enforcement, automotive safety, and civil rights.
Fields of interest: Education; Diseases and conditions; Human services.
Type of support: General support.
Limitations: Applications not accepted. Giving primarily in Chicago, IL. No grants to individuals.
Application information: Contributes only to pre-selected organizations.
Officer: Joseph A. Vasquez, Jr., Treas.
Directors: Marci A. Eisenstein; Stephen M. Hankins; Robert H. Riley; Kenneth M. Roberts; Peter L. Rossiter; Ronald S. Safer; Bruce P. Weisenthal.
EIN: 363465740

3225
Morris Schinasi International Hospital
10 S. Dearborn IL1-0117
Chicago, IL   60603

Foundation type: Independent foundation.
Financial data (yr. ended 12/31/13): Assets, $3,525,916 (M); expenditures, $192,283; qualifying distributions, $158,991; giving activities include $148,000 for 1 grant.
Fields of interest: Health.
Limitations: Applications not accepted.
Application information: Unsolicited requests for funds not accepted.
Trustee: JPMorgan Chase Bank, N.A.
EIN: 136029118

3226
The John D. and Minnie R. Schneider Charitable Trust
(formerly John D. Schneider Charitable Trust)
c/o Richard T. Zwirner
180 N. Stetson Ave., Ste. 3700
Chicago, IL   60601-6701

Established in 1985 in Illinois.
Donor: Hollister Inc.
Foundation type: Independent foundation.
Financial data (yr. ended 12/31/13): Assets, $6,537,153 (M); gifts received, $52,732; expenditures, $265,629; qualifying distributions, $250,000; giving activities include $250,000 for 2 grants (high: $225,000; low: $25,000).

Fields of interest: Higher education; Spinal cord injuries and diseases; International development; People with disabilities.
Limitations: Applications not accepted. Giving primarily in IL and Washington, DC. No grants to individuals.
Application information: Contributes only to pre-selected organizations.
Officer and Trustees: Richard T. Zwirner, Pres. and Trustee; Loretta L. Stempinski.
EIN: 363388493

3227
Schneider Family Foundation
620 W. Burlington Ave.
La Grange, IL   60525-2228

Established in 1996 in Illinois.
Donor: Kent Schneider‡.
Foundation type: Independent foundation.
Financial data (yr. ended 12/31/14): Assets, $2,365,254; expenditures, $149,457; qualifying distributions, $137,970.
Limitations: Applications not accepted. No grants to individuals.
Application information: Unsolicited requests for funds not accepted.
Trustee: First National Bank of La Grange.
EIN: 367121646

3228
Robert E. Schneider Foundation
P.O. Box 11452
Chicago, IL   60611-0452

Established in 1968 in Illinois.
Donors: Phyllis Schneider; Melvin Schneider.
Foundation type: Independent foundation.
Financial data (yr. ended 12/31/14): Assets, $3,395,952 (M); expenditures, $228,241; qualifying distributions, $221,468; giving activities include $195,000 for 16 grants (high: $60,000; low: $2,000).
Fields of interest: Philanthropy; Health; Diseases and conditions.
Limitations: Applications not accepted. Giving primarily in FL and IL. No grants to individuals.
Application information: Unsolicited requests for funds not accepted.
Officers and Directors: Richard Schneider, Pres. and Director; Claudia Schneider, V.P. and Director; Frederic Schneider, V.P. and Director; Marilyn R. Moss, Secy.-Treas. and Director.
EIN: 366212061

3229
Schorr-Lieberman Family Foundation
c/o Harrison A. Held, LLP
333 W. Wacker Dr., Ste. 1700
Chicago, IL   60606-1250

Established in 1997 in Illinois.
Donors: Melvin Lieberman; Phyllis Lieberman; Marny Dixon; Dana Price; Seth Dixon; Dawn Lieberman; Kenneth Lieberman.
Foundation type: Independent foundation.
Financial data (yr. ended 12/31/13): Assets, $1,728,108 (M); gifts received, $100,000; expenditures, $238,841; qualifying distributions,

$225,118; giving activities include $225,118 for 21 grants (high: $100,000; low: $100).
Fields of interest: Education; Nonprofits; Cancers; Judaism; Children.
Type of support: General support; Regranting.
Limitations: Applications not accepted. Giving primarily in Chicago, IL. No grants to individuals.
Application information: Unsolicited requests for funds not accepted.
Officers and Directors: Kenneth Lieberman, Pres. and Treas. and Director; Marny Dixon, Secy. and Director; Seth Dixon; Barbara Lieberman; Dana Price; Dawn Lieberman.
EIN: 364172057

3230
Scott Family Foundation
c/o Jones Lang Las.
200 E. Randolph St., 44th Fl.
Chicago, IL   60601-6436

Established in 1999 in Illinois.
Donor: Stuart L. Scott.
Foundation type: Independent foundation.
Financial data (yr. ended 12/31/13): Assets, $5,027,212 (M); gifts received, $505,306; expenditures, $396,525; qualifying distributions, $306,750; giving activities include $306,750 for 42 grants (high: $120,000; low: $50).
Purpose and activities: Giving primarily for higher education, human services, and to a wildlife foundation.
Fields of interest: Education; Higher education; Domesticated animals; Human services.
Limitations: Applications not accepted. Giving in the U.S., with some emphasis on Washington, DC, FL, IL, and NY. No grants to individuals.
Application information: Contributes only to pre-selected organizations.
Trustees: Ann O. Scott; Stuart Scott.
EIN: 367287571

3231
Anthony J. & Elaine M. Scrugli Charitable Trust
15 Salt Creek Ln.,Ste.312
Hinsdale, IL   60521-2926

Donor: Anthony & Elaine Scrugli Trust.
Foundation type: Operating foundation.
Financial data (yr. ended 12/31/13): Assets, $2,041,879 (M); expenditures, $235,871; qualifying distributions, $195,258; giving activities include $195,258 for 1 grant.
Fields of interest: Health.
Limitations: Applications not accepted.
Application information: Unsolicited requests for funds not accepted.
Directors: Peter Coules; Mark R. Donatelli; LeRoy Rosasco.
EIN: 274405237

3232
Ruth O. Secord Perpetual Charitable Trust
10 S. Dearborn IL1-0117
Chicago, IL   60603

Donor: Ruth O. Secord Trust.
Foundation type: Independent foundation.

Financial data (yr. ended 02/28/13): Assets, $5,333,935 (M); expenditures, $286,147; qualifying distributions, $230,066; giving activities include $212,286 for 11 grants (high: $50,000; low: $8,000).
Fields of interest: Education; Environment; Religion.
Limitations: Applications not accepted. Giving primarily in IL.
Application information: Unsolicited requests for funds not accepted.
Trustees: Robert A. Berghoff; JPMorgan Chase Bank, N.A.
EIN: 452684146

3233
The Janet Prindle Seidler Foundation
c/o The Northern Trust Co.
P.O. Box 803878
Chicago, IL 60680-3878

Established in 2001 in New York.
Donor: Janet Prindle Seidler.
Foundation type: Independent foundation.
Financial data (yr. ended 10/31/13): Assets, $6,533,149 (M); expenditures, $245,391; qualifying distributions, $237,000; giving activities include $237,000 for grants.
Fields of interest: Arts and culture; Museums; Higher education; Health; Christianity.
Limitations: Applications not accepted. Giving primarily in IN and NY. No grants to individuals.
Application information: Contributes only to pre-selected organizations.
Trustees: Charles J. Seidler, Jr.; Janet Prindle Seidler; The Northern Trust Co.
EIN: 137304477

3234
The Self Reliance Foundation
2332 W. Chicago Ave.
Chicago, IL 60622 (773) 328-7500
Contact: Oresta Fedyniak, Chair.

Donor: SelfReliance Ukrainian Fed C U.
Foundation type: Independent foundation.
Financial data (yr. ended 12/31/13): Assets, $6,063,088 (M); gifts received, $602,000; expenditures, $320,310; qualifying distributions, $313,900; giving activities include $313,900 for 41 grants (high: $31,000; low: $1,000).
Purpose and activities: Giving primarily to Ukrainian organizations and Ukrainian Catholic and Ukrainian Orthodox churches.
Fields of interest: Arts and culture; Education; Catholicism; Orthodox Christianity.
Limitations: Applications accepted. Giving primarily in IL, with emphasis on Chicago; some funding also in New York, NY.
Application information: Application form required.
   Initial approach: Letter
   Deadline(s): None
Officers: Oresta Fedyniak, Chair.; Oleh Karawan, Vice-Chair.; Victor Wojtychiw, Secy.-Treas.
EIN: 205423872

3235
Sequoia Farm Foundation
145 N. Merchant St.
Decatur, IL 62523 2173628600
Main URL: http://www.sequoiafarmfoundation.org

Donor: Howard G. Buffett Foundation.
Foundation type: Independent foundation.
Financial data (yr. ended 12/31/13): Assets, $67,655,956 (M); gifts received, $21,642,667; expenditures, $5,117,556; qualifying distributions, $22,674,882; giving activities include $208,593 for 2 grants (high: $184,738; low: $23,855).
Fields of interest: Human services.
Type of support: Research.
Limitations: Applications not accepted. Giving primarily in NE.
Application information: Unsolicited requests for funds not accepted.
Officers: Howard G. Buffett, Pres.; Howard W. Buffett, Secy.; Trisha Cook, Treas.
EIN: 455160833

3236
W. L. & Louise E. Seymour Foundation
c/o JPMorgan Chase Bank, N.A.
10 S. Dearborn St., IL1-0117
Chicago, IL 60603-2300
Application address: 420 Throckmorton St., 3rd Fl., Fort Worth, TX 76102, tel.: (817) 884-4022

Established in 1983 in Texas.
Donor: Louise E. Seymour†.
Foundation type: Independent foundation.
Financial data (yr. ended 03/31/13): Assets, $4,468,435 (M); expenditures, $239,693; qualifying distributions, $204,468; giving activities include $193,946 for 7 grants (high: $75,000; low: $500).
Purpose and activities: Grants only for crippled children, mentally retarded children, handicapped and homeless children, and the elderly.
Fields of interest: Human services; Family services; Child welfare; Shelter and residential care; Developmental disability services; Homeless services; Seniors.
Type of support: General support; Equipment; Program development; Research.
Limitations: Applications accepted. Giving limited to TX, with emphasis on El Paso. No support for political organizations. No grants to individuals or for endowments.
Application information: Application form required.
   Initial approach: Letter
   Deadline(s): None
Trustee: JPMorgan Chase Bank, N.A.
EIN: 746315820

3237
Avi Shaked and Babs Waldman Family Foundation, Inc.
8 Milburn St.
Evanston, IL 60201-1744
Application address: c/o Avi Shaked Babs Waldman Family Foundation, 8 Milburn Park, Evanston, IL 60201 tel.: (847) 782-8797

Established in 2005 in Illinois.
Donors: Avi Shaked; Babs Waldman.
Foundation type: Independent foundation.
Financial data (yr. ended 12/31/13): Assets, $157,052 (M); expenditures, $199,275; qualifying distributions, $198,750; giving activities include $198,750 for 5 grants (high: $165,000; low: $750).
Fields of interest: Higher education.
Limitations: Applications accepted. Giving primarily in IL, NY, and WI.

Application information: Application form required.
   Initial approach: Letter
   Deadline(s): None
Officers: Avi A. Shaked, Pres. and Treas.; Babs H. Waldman, V.P.; Gerald J. Kahn, Secy.
EIN: 203995403

3238
Joseph R. and Helen Shaker Family Foundation
(formerly The Shaker Family Foundation)
1100 W. Lake St.
Oak Park, IL 60301-1015
Main URL: http://www.shaker.com/about/philanthropy

Established in 1986 in Illinois.
Donors: Shaker Advertising Agency, Inc.; Joseph R. Shaker; Anthony R. Shaker; Elizabeth A. Shaker; Joseph G. Shaker; John E. Shaker; Catherine S. Breit; Anthony Abraham Foundation; Helen E. Shaker.
Foundation type: Independent foundation.
Financial data (yr. ended 11/30/13): Assets, $23,736 (M); gifts received, $257,149; expenditures, $257,336; qualifying distributions, $256,659; giving activities include $183,806 for 47 grants (high: $85,905; low: $20).
Purpose and activities: Giving primarily for social services, health care, education, human rights, and child welfare.
Fields of interest: Education; Catholicism; Human services.
Type of support: General support; Annual campaigns; Capital and infrastructure; Scholarships.
Limitations: Applications not accepted. Giving primarily in IL, with some emphasis on the Chicago area. No grants to individuals.
Application information: Unsolicited requests for funds not accepted.
Trustee: Anthony R. Shaker.
Number of staff: 1
EIN: 363572999

3239
Shamrock Foundation
747 Sheridan Rd.
Wilmette, IL 60091-1959
Main URL: http://www.shamrockfound.org
Blog: http://www.shamrockfound.org/?page_id=7

Established in 2004 in Illinois.
Donors: Edwardson Family Foundation; Catharine O. Edwardson; Catherine O. Edwardson Charitable Lead Annuity Trust 2; Catherine O. Edwardson Charitable Lead Annuity Trust.
Foundation type: Independent foundation.
Financial data (yr. ended 12/31/13): Assets, $4,990,302 (M); gifts received, $250,000; expenditures, $238,463; qualifying distributions, $216,530; giving activities include $216,530 for 13 grants (high: $50,000; low: $10,000).
Fields of interest: Economic development; Christianity; International development.
Limitations: Applications not accepted. Giving primarily in DC, IL and TX. No grants to individuals.
Application information: Contributes only to pre-selected organizations.
Officer: Catharine O. Edwardson, Pres.

Trustees: Laura K. Barrett; Anne L. Edwardson; Shelly M. Edwardson.
EIN: 061720127

3240
Joan and James Shapiro Foundation, Inc.
5614 S. Dorchester Ave.
Chicago, IL 60637-1722

Established in 1986 in Illinois.
Donors: Joan Shapiro; James Shapiro.
Foundation type: Independent foundation.
Financial data (yr. ended 12/31/13): Assets, $3,844,031 (M); expenditures, $189,420; qualifying distributions, $170,545; giving activities include $170,257 for 52 grants (high: $40,000; low: $40).
Fields of interest: Arts and culture; Higher education; Environment; Hospital care; Judaism; Human services.
Limitations: Applications not accepted. Giving primarily in Chicago, IL and NY. No grants to individuals.
Application information: Contributes only to pre-selected organizations.
Officers and Directors: James Shapiro, Pres. and Director; Joan Shapiro, Secy.-Treas. and Director; Sandra Panem.
EIN: 363486763

3241
Share Foundation
123 S.W. Jefferson Ave., Ste. 108
Peoria, IL 61602-1221

Established in 1997 in Illinois.
Donor: Kenneth D. Baum.
Foundation type: Independent foundation.
Financial data (yr. ended 12/31/13): Assets, $133,177 (M); gifts received, $80,000; expenditures, $159,145; qualifying distributions, $159,125; giving activities include $158,975 for 39 grants (high: $24,700; low: $100).
Fields of interest: Christianity; Human services.
Limitations: Applications not accepted. Giving primarily in IL, with emphasis on Morton and Peoria. No grants to individuals.
Application information: Contributes only to pre-selected organizations.
Officers and Directors: Kenneth D. Baum, Pres. and Director; Jody L. Baum, V.P. and Director; Terry L. Baum, Secy.-Treas.
EIN: 371357922

3242
Seyfarth Shaw Charitable Foundation
131 S. Dearborn St., Ste. 2400
Chicago, IL 60603
Main URL: http://www.seyfarth.com

Established in 2004 in Illinois.
Donors: Seyfarth Shaw LLP; Joel Kaplan.
Foundation type: Company-sponsored foundation.
Financial data (yr. ended 12/31/13): Assets, $139,761 (M); gifts received, $300,000; expenditures, $187,700; qualifying distributions, $187,700; giving activities include $187,700 for 68 grants (high: $15,000; low: $1,000).
Fields of interest: Diseases and conditions; Human rights.

Limitations: Applications not accepted.
Application information: Unsolicited requests for funds not accepted.
Officers: Joan Larkin, Pres.; Nathaniel Sack, V.P. and Treas.
Trustees: Brian T. Ashe; Sara Beiro Farabow; Ameena Majid; Robert Nobile; William Prickett.
EIN: 201076114

3243
Ilene & Michael Shaw Charitable Trust I
833 Rice St.
Highland Park, IL 60035-4738

Established in 1995 in Illinois.
Donors: Ilene Shaw; Michael Shaw; Sarita Warshawsky.
Foundation type: Independent foundation.
Financial data (yr. ended 12/31/14): Assets, $3,567,642 (M); gifts received, $123,459; expenditures, $169,803; qualifying distributions, $155,389; giving activities include $153,024 for 75 grants (high: $30,000; low: $50).
Fields of interest: Arts and culture; Education; Human services.
Limitations: Applications not accepted. No grants to individuals.
Application information: Unsolicited requests for funds not accepted.
Trustee: Ilene Shaw.
EIN: 364054433

3244
Charles H. & Beverly E. Shaw Foundation
316 Oak Hill Rd.
Barrington, IL 60010-1640

Established in 1999 in Illinois.
Donors: Charles H. Shaw†; Beverly E. Shaw.
Foundation type: Independent foundation.
Financial data (yr. ended 12/31/13): Assets, $52,472 (M); gifts received, $275,000; expenditures, $259,675; qualifying distributions, $258,475; giving activities include $258,475 for 128 grants (high: $20,000; low: $50).
Fields of interest: University education; Diseases and conditions; Human services.
Limitations: Applications not accepted. Giving primarily in Chicago, IL. No grants to individuals.
Application information: Unsolicited requests for funds not accepted.
Trustee: Beverly E. Shaw.
EIN: 367295674

3245
Virginia Lee Shirley Private Foundation
333 W. Wacker Dr., Ste. 1700
Chicago, IL 60606-1247

Donor: Virginia Lee Shirley†.
Foundation type: Independent foundation.
Financial data (yr. ended 12/31/13): Assets, $7,767,729 (M); gifts received, $1,043,966; expenditures, $483,744; qualifying distributions, $416,600; giving activities include $416,600 for 43 grants (high: $50,000; low: $1,000).
Fields of interest: Education; Health; Human services.
Type of support: General support.

Limitations: Applications not accepted. Giving primarily in IL.
Application information: Unsolicited requests for funds not accepted.
Officers and Directors: Louis S. Harrison, Pres. and Director; Lynne Kaplan, Secy. and Director; Carole J. Walther, Treas. and Director.
EIN: 272545558

3246
Shodeen Family Foundation
17 N. 1st St.
Geneva, IL 60134-2220

Established in 1999 in Illinois.
Donor: Kent W. Shodeen.
Foundation type: Independent foundation.
Financial data (yr. ended 12/31/13): Assets, $3,488,866 (M); expenditures, $311,624; qualifying distributions, $275,050; giving activities include $257,050 for 44 grants (high: $50,000; low: $200).
Fields of interest: Children's museums; Natural resources; Health; Human services; Food banks; Family services.
Limitations: Applications not accepted. Giving primarily in IL. No grants to individuals.
Application information: Unsolicited requests for funds not accepted.
Officers and Directors: Kent W. Shodeen, Pres. and Director; Anna S. Harmon, Secy. and Director; Beth C. Shodeen; Craig A. Shodeen; Eric M. Shodeen.
EIN: 364294720

3247
Esther Simon Charitable Trust
10 S. Dearborn IL1-0117
Chicago, IL 60603
Application address: c/o Stephen A. Simon, JPMorgan Chase Bank, 270 Park Ave., New York, NY, 10017

Established in 1952 in New York.
Donor: Esther Simon†.
Foundation type: Independent foundation.
Financial data (yr. ended 12/31/13): Assets, $8,197,189 (M); expenditures, $437,642; qualifying distributions, $420,324; giving activities include $416,000 for grants.
Purpose and activities: Primary areas of interest include cultural programs and the arts, education, social services, and medical research.
Fields of interest: Arts and culture; Performing arts; Art museums; Historic preservation; Education; Undergraduate education; Natural resources; Hospital care; Diseases and conditions; Community and economic development; Human services; Child welfare.
Type of support: General support; Annual campaigns; Research; Research and evaluation.
Limitations: Applications accepted. Giving primarily in CA, Washington, DC, MA, New York, NY and OH. No grants to individuals.
Application information:
   Initial approach: Letter
   Deadline(s): None
Trustees: Stephen A. Simon; JPMorgan Chase Bank, N.A.
EIN: 236286763

3248
John M. Simpson Foundation
30 N. LaSalle St., Ste. 1232
Chicago, IL 60602-3344

Established in 1961 in Illinois.
Donors: Susan S. Cavender; Patricia S. O'Kieffe; Michael Simpson; S.S. Cavender Charitable Lead Annuity Trust; P.S. O'Kieffe Charitable Lead Annuity Trust.
Foundation type: Independent foundation.
Financial data (yr. ended 12/31/13): Assets, $6,598,713 (M); expenditures, $346,931; qualifying distributions, $310,000; giving activities include $310,000 for 29 grants (high: $25,000; low: $1,000).
Purpose and activities: Giving primarily for hospitals, clinics, health services, including family planning, and social services; some support also for a nature conservatory.
Fields of interest: Natural history museums; Elementary education; Natural resources; Biodiversity; Wildlife biodiversity; Health; Hospital care; Hospice care; Family planning; Diabetes; Protestantism; Human services; Child welfare.
Type of support: Research.
Limitations: Applications not accepted. Giving primarily in AZ; some giving also in HI and IL. No grants to individuals.
Application information: Contributes only to pre-selected organizations.
Officers: Jonathan B. Mellin, Pres.; Debra M. Coy, Secy.; Timothy M. Crenshaw, Treas.
Directors: Susan S. Cavender; Patricia S. O'Kieffe; Howard Simpson.
EIN: 366071621

3249
William & Hope Simpson Foundation
30 N. LaSalle St., Ste. 1232
Chicago, IL 60602-3344

Donors: William Simpson; Patrick J. Herbert III; U.S. Trust.
Foundation type: Independent foundation.
Financial data (yr. ended 12/31/13): Assets, $4,385,986 (M); expenditures, $231,610; qualifying distributions, $209,300; giving activities include $209,300 for 25 grants (high: $30,000; low: $500).
Fields of interest: Education; Health; Youth development.
Limitations: Applications not accepted. Giving primarily in MA and NY. No grants to individuals.
Application information: Unsolicited requests for funds not accepted.
Officers and Directors: Jonathan B. Mellin, Pres.; Debra M. Coy, Secy.; Maxwell F. Youngquist, Treas.; James F. Curtis III; Patrick J. Herbert III; Sheila C. Issenberg; Hope G. Simpson; Howard B. Simpson.
EIN: 366071622

3250
The Skylark Foundation
(formerly Sharen and Marc Berman Charitable Foundation)
180 E. Pearson St., Ste. 5604
Chicago, IL 60611-2185

Established in 1993 in Illinois.
Donors: Marc L. Berman; Sharen Berman.

Foundation type: Independent foundation.
Financial data (yr. ended 12/31/13): Assets, $1,087,896 (M); gifts received, $30,000; expenditures, $180,513; qualifying distributions, $162,266; giving activities include $162,266 for 9 grants (high: $79,366; low: $500).
Purpose and activities: Giving primarily for Jewish organizations and art and culture.
Fields of interest: Arts and culture; Education; Judaism.
Limitations: Applications not accepted. Giving primarily in IL. No grants to individuals.
Application information: Unsolicited requests for funds not accepted.
Trustee: Marc L. Berman.
EIN: 367055540

3251
Frances C. & William P. Smallwood Foundation
(also known as Smallwood Foundation)
P.O. Box 2050
Chicago, IL 60603-2050
Application address: c/o JPMorgan Chase Bank, NA, 420 Throckmorton, Fort Worth, TX 76102, tel.: (817) 884-4772

Donor: William P. Smallwood Trust.
Foundation type: Independent foundation.
Financial data (yr. ended 12/31/13): Assets, $9,321,582 (M); expenditures, $457,688; qualifying distributions, $403,345; giving activities include $395,190 for 35 grants (high: $50,000; low: $2,500).
Purpose and activities: Giving primarily for higher and other education, the arts, health care, and children, youth, and social services.
Fields of interest: Arts and culture; Education; Higher education; Health; Human services; Family services; Child welfare.
Limitations: Applications accepted. Giving primarily in FL, NV and TX. No grants to individuals.
Application information: Application form required.
  Initial approach: Request application form
  Deadline(s): None
Trustees: Saul Baker; Harry Bartel; Sally Muller; Rick Piersall; Suzy Stockdale; JPMorgan Chase Bank, N.A.
EIN: 237000306

3252
Lemon L. Smith Clinic Trust 2
10 S. Dearborn St., IL1-0117
Chicago, IL 60603-2300

Foundation type: Independent foundation.
Financial data (yr. ended 12/31/14): Assets, $5,133,247; expenditures, $247,935; qualifying distributions, $201,249.
Fields of interest: Health.
Limitations: Applications not accepted.
Application information: Unsolicited requests for funds not accepted.
Trustee: JPMorgan Chase Bank, N.A.
EIN: 131946319

3253
Hal & John Smith Family Foundation, Inc.
(formerly Hal & John Smith Family Foundation)
P.O. Box 803878
Chicago, IL 60680

Established in 1960 in Georgia.
Donors: Hal L. Smith†; Julia T. Smith†.
Foundation type: Independent foundation.
Financial data (yr. ended 12/31/14): Assets, $6,057,912; expenditures, $358,284; qualifying distributions, $315,292.
Fields of interest: Education; Undergraduate education; Religion; Human services.
Type of support: Capital campaigns; Matching grants; Endowments; Fellowships; Scholarships.
Limitations: Applications not accepted. Giving primarily in Atlanta, GA. No support for art organizations. No grants to individuals.
Application information: Contributes only to pre-selected organizations.
Officers: John E. Smith II, Chair.; Claiborne S. Jones, Vice-Chair.; Claiborne B. Smith, Secy.-Treas.
Board Member: Hayden P. Smith.
EIN: 205912128

3254
Smithburg Family Foundation
676 N. Michigan Ave., Ste. 3860
Chicago, IL 60611-4953

Established in 2001 in Illinois.
Donor: William D. Smithburg.
Foundation type: Independent foundation.
Financial data (yr. ended 12/31/13): Assets, $5,152,628 (M); expenditures, $355,591; qualifying distributions, $292,350; giving activities include $292,350 for 32 grants (high: $42,350; low: $500).
Fields of interest: Art museums; Education; Environment; Botanical gardens; Health; Hospital care; Religion; Human services.
Limitations: Applications not accepted. Giving primarily in CO and IL. No grants to individuals.
Application information: Contributes only to pre-selected organizations.
Officer and Directors: William D. Smithburg, Pres., V.P., and Secy.-Treas. and Director; Thomas A. Smithburg; Thomas W. Smithburg; Susan S. Sullivan.
EIN: 364475690

3255
Elizabeth A. Smysor Charitable Trust
1301 Walnut St.
P.O. Box 1389
Murphysboro, IL 62966-2026
Application address: P.O. Box 1166, Murphysboro, IL 62966-1166, tel.: (618) 684-5911

Established in 1994 in Illinois.
Foundation type: Independent foundation.
Financial data (yr. ended 07/31/13): Assets, $8,346,319 (M); expenditures, $306,782; qualifying distributions, $181,400; giving activities include $181,400 for grants.
Purpose and activities: Giving only for projects within the cities of Ava and Murphysboro, Illinois.
Fields of interest: Arts and culture; Secondary education; Public libraries; Community

improvement; Food banks; Cemeteries and burial services.
Type of support: General support; Program development; Scholarships.
Limitations: Applications accepted. Giving limited to Ava and Murphysboro, IL. No grants to individuals.
Application information: Application form required.
Initial approach: Request application
Deadline(s): Mar. 1
Officers: Frank W. Cheatham, Vice-Chair.; James A. Lawder, Secy.
Directors: L.D. Allen; Scott R. Maloney; Thomas Jones, Esq.; Bert Ozburn; William Wilson.
Trustee: Regions Bank.
EIN: 376243123

3256
The Sondheimer Family Charitable Foundation
2630 Laurel Ln.
Wilmette, IL   60091-2202

Established in 2008 in Illinois.
Donor: Ida Sondheimer.
Foundation type: Independent foundation.
Financial data (yr. ended 12/31/13): Assets, $6,390,754 (M); expenditures, $346,877; qualifying distributions, $325,215; giving activities include $322,035 for 40 grants (high: $50,000; low: $1,000).
Fields of interest: Nonprofits; Judaism.
Type of support: Regranting.
Limitations: Applications not accepted. Giving primarily in IL.
Application information: Unsolicited requests for funds not accepted.
Officers: Ida N. Sondheimer, Pres.; Stuart P. Sondheimer, Secy.-Treas.
EIN: 263060552

3257
The Speiser Family Foundation
135 S. Kensington Ave.
La Grange, IL   60525-2214

Established in 1996 in Illinois.
Donors: Texor Petroleum Co.; Anthony E. Speiser; Christine A. Speiser; Exron Capital, Inc.
Foundation type: Company-sponsored foundation.
Financial data (yr. ended 12/31/13): Assets, $1,186,085 (M); gifts received, $116,267; expenditures, $251,726; qualifying distributions, $242,602; giving activities include $242,602 for 16 grants (high: $131,602; low: $1,000).
Purpose and activities: The foundation supports organizations involved with K-12 education, housing, youth development, and human services.
Fields of interest: Education; Housing development; Youth development.
Limitations: Applications not accepted. Giving primarily in IL. No grants to individuals.
Application information: Unsolicited requests for funds not accepted.
Officers and Directors: Matthew B. Spieser, Secy. and Director; Anthony E. Speiser, Treas.; Christine A. Speiser, Fdn. Mgr.; Kate Speiser.
EIN: 364117679

3258
The Sarah Spencer Foundation
50 S. LaSalle St., 3rd Fl.
Chicago, IL   60675-0001

Established in 1985 in Illinois.
Donors: George S. Trees, Sr.; George S. Trees, Jr.; Edith M. Trees.
Foundation type: Independent foundation.
Financial data (yr. ended 12/31/13): Assets, $1,258,985 (M); expenditures, $205,911; qualifying distributions, $190,000; giving activities include $190,000 for 25 grants (high: $50,000; low: $250).
Purpose and activities: Giving primarily for education and human services.
Fields of interest: Arts and culture; Opera; Education; Environment; Foundations; Cancers; Television; Christianity; Human services.
Limitations: Applications not accepted. Giving primarily in Palm Beach, FL and Chicago, IL. No grants to individuals.
Application information: Contributes only to pre-selected organizations.
Officers: George S. Trees, Jr., Pres.; M. Jay Trees, Secy.-Treas.
Director: Susan Trees.
EIN: 363444748

3259
Elmer & Sylvia Sramek Charitable Trust
c/o Northern Trust Company
P.O. Box 803878
Chicago, IL   60680-3878

Established in 1995 in Illinois.
Donor: Elmer D. Sramek Trust.
Foundation type: Independent foundation.
Financial data (yr. ended 11/30/13): Assets, $4,519,591 (M); expenditures, $243,405; qualifying distributions, $204,294; giving activities include $200,000 for 2 grants (high: $180,000; low: $20,000).
Fields of interest: Higher education; Hospital care; Eye diseases.
Type of support: Research.
Limitations: Applications not accepted. Giving primarily in Chicago, IL, and Ann Arbor, MI. No grants to individuals.
Application information: Contributes only to pre-selected organizations.
Trustee: Northern Trust Company.
EIN: 367123072

3260
SSAB North American Foundation
(formerly Ipsco Charitable Foundation)
801 Warrenville Rd., Ste. 800
Lisle, IL   60532-0912

Established in 2005 in Illinois.
Foundation type: Independent foundation.
Financial data (yr. ended 12/31/13): Assets, $776,648 (M); expenditures, $380,673; qualifying distributions, $379,615; giving activities include $379,615 for 100 grants (high: $46,576; low: $50).
Fields of interest: Arts and culture; Nonprofits; Diseases and conditions; Human services.
Type of support: Regranting.
Limitations: Applications not accepted. Giving primarily in AL and IA.

Application information: Unsolicited requests for funds not accepted.
Officers: Chuck Schmitt, Pres.; Michele Klebuc-Simes, Secy.; Phil Marusarz, Treas.
EIN: 412191056

3261
The Stairway Fund
191 N. Wacker Dr., Ste. 1500
Chicago, IL   60606-1899

Established in 2005 in Illinois.
Foundation type: Independent foundation.
Financial data (yr. ended 12/31/13): Assets, $5,376,464 (M); expenditures, $336,753; qualifying distributions, $208,723; giving activities include $201,308 for 37 grants (high: $50,000; low: $250).
Fields of interest: Arts and culture; Education; Undergraduate education; Christianity; Human services.
Type of support: General support.
Limitations: Applications not accepted. Giving primarily in CT and New York, NY. No grants to individuals.
Application information: Contributes only to pre-selected organizations.
Officers and Directors: Daniel H. Meyer, Pres. and Director; Jack Polsky, V.P. and Director; Audrey H. Meyer, Secy. and Director; Beth Stephens, Treas.
EIN: 300286949

3262
Henry M. Staley Charitable Trust
3301 Embassy Dr.
Springfield, IL   62711-7411
Contact: Henry M. Staley, Tr.
Application address: c/o Mark E. Staley, 2700 Westport Dr., Springfield, IL 62711

Established in 1965 in Illinois.
Donors: Henry M. Staley; Violet L. Staley.
Foundation type: Independent foundation.
Financial data (yr. ended 12/31/13): Assets, $4,189,971 (M); expenditures, $246,044; qualifying distributions, $220,850; giving activities include $220,850 for 59 grants (high: $20,000; low: $250).
Purpose and activities: Giving for development and promotion of free enterprise, free trade, and minimal government. Organizations that are national in scope must meet all standards of BBB Wise Giving Alliance.
Fields of interest: Education; Health; Community and economic development; Religion; Human services.
Type of support: General support; Continuing support; Annual campaigns; Capital campaigns; Capital and infrastructure; Equipment; Emergency funds; Program development; Seed money; Research.
Limitations: Applications accepted. Giving primarily in Decatur, IL. No support for political organizations. No grants to individuals.
Publications: Annual report.
Application information:
Initial approach: Letter of proposal
Copies of proposal: 1
Deadline(s): None
Board meeting date(s): Varies
Final notification: Varies

Trustee: Mark E. Staley.
Number of staff: 1 part-time support.
EIN: 376055935

3263
The Bill and Orli Staley Foundation
c/o Lynne Kaplan
9450 W. Bryn Mawr Ave., Ste. 310
Rosemont, IL   60018-5272

Established in 1993 in Illinois.
Donor: William D. Staley.
Foundation type: Independent foundation.
Financial data (yr. ended 12/31/13): Assets,
$1,629,105 (L); expenditures, $198,406;
qualifying distributions, $184,038; giving activities
include $184,038 for 12 grants (high: $45,000;
low: $1,000).
Purpose and activities: Giving primarily for the arts
and culture.
Fields of interest: Arts education; Performing arts;
Art museums; Natural resources; Zoos; Nonprofits.
Limitations: Applications not accepted. Giving
primarily in Chicago, IL. No grants to individuals.
Application information: Contributes only to
pre-selected organizations.
Trustees: Arlene D. Staley; William D. Staley.
EIN: 363925847

3264
A.E. Staley Jr. Foundation
c/o Soy Capital Bank & Trust Co.
455 N. Main St.
Decatur, IL   62523-1103

Established in 1955 in Illinois.
Donor: Augustus Eugene Staley, Jr.
Foundation type: Independent foundation.
Financial data (yr. ended 12/31/14): Assets,
$4,853,933; gifts received, $0; expenditures,
$343,078; qualifying distributions, $274,181 and
$0 for set-asides.
Purpose and activities: Giving primarily for
education and for health care.
Fields of interest: Higher education; Community
college education; University education;
Environment; Animal welfare; Nonprofits; Health;
Hospital care; Cancers; Human services.
Type of support: Regranting.
Limitations: Applications not accepted. Giving
primarily in IL. No grants to individuals.
Application information: Contributes only to
pre-selected organizations.
Trustee: Soy Capital Bank & Trust Co.
EIN: 376023961

3265
Donna Wolf Steigerwaldt Foundation, Inc.
c/o Gregory G. Palmer
227 W. Monroe St., Ste. 4700
Chicago, IL   60606-5096

Established in 1980 in Illinois.
Donors: Donna Wolf Steigerwaldt†; Jockey
International, Inc.
Foundation type: Independent foundation.
Financial data (yr. ended 10/31/13): Assets,
$2,093,495 (M); expenditures, $134,006;
qualifying distributions, $134,006; giving activities

include $124,300 for 9 grants (high: $100,000;
low: $500).
Fields of interest: Arts and culture; Education;
Diseases and conditions.
Type of support: Continuing support; Annual
campaigns; Research; Capital and infrastructure;
Scholarships.
Limitations: Applications not accepted. Giving
primarily in Sarasota, FL, and Kenosha, WI. No
grants to individuals.
Application information: Unsolicited requests for
funds not accepted.
Officers and Directors: William Steigerwaldt, Pres.
and Treas. and Director; Debra Steigerwaldt Waller,
V.P. and Director; Noreen A. Wilkinson, Secy. and
Director.
EIN: 363104409

3266
Avy and Marcie Stein Foundation
c/o Avy Stein
1101 Skokie Blvd., Ste. 260
Northbrook, IL   60062-4122

Established in 1995 in Illinois.
Donors: Avy Stein; Marcie Stein.
Foundation type: Independent foundation.
Financial data (yr. ended 12/31/13): Assets,
$1,359 (M); gifts received, $244,390;
expenditures, $333,436; qualifying distributions,
$331,048; giving activities include $328,636 for 89
grants (high: $50,000; low: $100).
Purpose and activities: Giving primarily for the arts,
education, and health organizations, including
children's health; funding also for other children's
services, and to Jewish organizations.
Fields of interest: Arts and culture; Education;
Higher education; Nonprofits; Diseases and
conditions; Judaism; Child welfare.
Type of support: Regranting.
Limitations: Applications not accepted. Giving
primarily in IL. No grants to individuals.
Application information: Contributes only to
pre-selected organizations.
Directors: Avy Stein; Marcie Stein.
EIN: 363993406

3267
Matthew Steinmetz Charitable Trust
1235 W. Webster Ave.
Chicago, IL   60614-3139   (773) 404-8480
Contact: Matthew E. Steinmetz, Tr.

Donor: Matthew Steinmetz.
Foundation type: Independent foundation.
Financial data (yr. ended 06/30/13): Assets,
$171,917 (M); expenditures, $353,192; qualifying
distributions, $353,192; giving activities include
$353,192 for 55 grants (high: $41,083; low: $70).
Fields of interest: Education; Philanthropy; Housing
development; Homeless people.
Limitations: Applications accepted. Giving primarily
in IL.
Application information:
Initial approach: Proposal
Deadline(s): None
Trustee: Matthew Steinmetz.
EIN: 276988480

3268
A. J. & S. L. Stern Family Foundation
9049 N. Karlov Ave.
Skokie, IL   60076-1715

Established in 1999 in Illinois.
Donors: Abraham J. Stern; Susan L. Stern.
Foundation type: Independent foundation.
Financial data (yr. ended 12/31/13): Assets,
$648,146 (M); gifts received, $550,000;
expenditures, $417,586; qualifying distributions,
$415,091; giving activities include $415,091 for
252 grants (high: $25,000; low: $25).
Fields of interest: Nonprofits; Judaism.
Type of support: Regranting.
Limitations: Applications not accepted. No grants to
individuals.
Application information: Contributes only to
pre-selected organizations.
Officers: Abraham J. Stern, Pres.; Susan L. Stern,
V.P.
EIN: 364316434

3269
Jerome H. Stone Family Foundation
c/o Jerome H. Stone Alzheimer's Assoc.
225 N. Michigan Ave., 17th Fl.
Chicago, IL   60601-7757   (312) 335-5808
Contact: Jerome H. Stone, Pres.

Established in 1963 in Illinois.
Donors: Jerome H. Stone; Cynthia Raskin; Ellen
Stone Belic; Cynthia Stone; James H. Stone.
Foundation type: Independent foundation.
Financial data (yr. ended 12/31/13): Assets,
$5,808,440 (M); gifts received, $1,125,142;
expenditures, $318,264; qualifying distributions,
$285,479; giving activities include $281,794 for 71
grants (high: $50,000; low: $20).
Purpose and activities: Giving primarily for the arts,
particularly museums, as well as for education,
health organizations, and Jewish organizations.
Fields of interest: Arts and culture; Museums;
Education; Higher education; Nonprofits; Diseases
and conditions; Alzheimer's disease; Judaism;
Human services.
Type of support: Regranting.
Limitations: Applications accepted. Giving primarily
in IL, with emphasis on Chicago. No grants to
individuals.
Application information:
Initial approach: Proposal
Deadline(s): None
Officers: Jerome H. Stone, Pres.; Ellen Stone Belic,
V.P.; Cynthia Raskin, Secy.; James H. Stone, Treas.
EIN: 366061300

3270
H. Chase Stone Trust B
10 S. Dearborn, IL1-0117
Chicago, IL   60603   8668885157
Application address: c/o JPMorgan Chase Bank,
N.A., 402 N. Tejon St., Colorado Springs, CO 80903,
tel. (719) 227-6445

Established in 1974 in Colorado.
Foundation type: Independent foundation.
Financial data (yr. ended 12/31/14): Assets,
$3,596,098; expenditures, $215,872; qualifying
distributions, $176,267.

Fields of interest: Arts and culture; Education; Environment; Nonprofits; Human services; Child welfare; Youth services.
Type of support: General support; Capital and infrastructure; Equipment; Regranting.
Limitations: Applications accepted. Giving limited to El Paso County, CO. No grants to individuals.
Publications: Application guidelines.
Application information: Application form required.
  Initial approach: Letter
  Copies of proposal: 1
  Deadline(s): Apr. 30th and Oct. 31st
  Board meeting date(s): Quarterly
Trustee: JPMorgan Chase Bank, N.A.
EIN: 846066113

3271
Oliver W. Storer Scholarship Foundation
c/o JPMorgan Chase Bank, N.A.
10 S. Dearborn, IL1-0117
Chicago, IL 60603
Contact: Jean Landy, Fiduciary Off.
Application address: c/o Beasley, Gilkison, Retherford & Buckles, Attn.: Charles E. Retherford, 110 E. Charles St., Muncie, IN 47308, tel.: (765) 289-0661

Established in 1952 in Indiana.
Donor: Oliver W. Storer†.
Foundation type: Independent foundation.
Financial data (yr. ended 02/28/14): Assets, $5,384,710 (M); expenditures, $281,251; qualifying distributions, $233,572; giving activities include $209,664 for 16 grants to individuals (high: $78,564; low: $5,250).
Purpose and activities: Primarily awards scholarships to high school seniors of Delaware County, Indiana.
Fields of interest: Higher education.
Type of support: Student aid.
Limitations: Applications accepted. Giving limited to residents of Delaware County, IN.
Application information: Application form required.
  Initial approach: Letter
  Deadline(s): 60 days prior to start of school year
  Board meeting date(s): Summer
Trustee: JPMorgan Chase Bank, N.A.
EIN: 356012044

3272
STS Foundation
c/o The Northern Trust Co.
P.O. Box 803878
Chicago, IL 60680-3878

Established in 2007 in Wyoming.
Foundation type: Independent foundation.
Financial data (yr. ended 12/31/13): Assets, $9,798,834 (M); expenditures, $500,050; qualifying distributions, $442,148; giving activities include $436,000 for 145 grants (high: $25,000; low: $1,000).
Fields of interest: Museums; Education; Higher education.
Limitations: Applications not accepted. No grants to individuals.
Application information: Contributes only to pre-selected organizations.
Officers: Jennifer H. Wilson, Pres.; Virginia Bartholomay, V.P.; Phelps H. Swift, Secy.
EIN: 202045581

3273
W.B. and Ellen Gordon Stuart Trust
10 S. Dearborn St., IL1-0117
Chicago, IL 60603-2300 (817) 884-5155

Established in 1970 in Texas.
Donor: Ellen G. Stuart Trust.
Foundation type: Independent foundation.
Financial data (yr. ended 06/30/13): Assets, $8,108,375 (M); gifts received, $25,777; expenditures, $486,890; qualifying distributions, $385,195; giving activities include $364,180 for 8 grants (high: $104,000; low: $10,000).
Purpose and activities: Giving primarily for the treatment or study of heart disease, cancer, and infant paralysis.
Fields of interest: Hospital care; Diseases and conditions; Heart and circulatory system diseases; Children.
Type of support: General support; Equipment; Research; Research and evaluation.
Limitations: Applications accepted. Giving primarily in TX.
Application information: Application form required.
  Initial approach: Proposal
  Deadline(s): Sept. 30
Trustee: JPMorgan Chase Bank, N.A.
EIN: 756014224

3274
Margaret A. Stutsman Charitable Trust
c/o Quad City Bank
3551 7th St., Ste. 100
Moline, IL 61265-6156 3097363889

Foundation type: Independent foundation.
Financial data (yr. ended 12/31/14): Assets, $3,460,203; expenditures, $234,516; qualifying distributions, $234,516 and $0 for set-asides.
Fields of interest: Education; Human services.
Limitations: Applications not accepted. Giving primarily in IA and IL.
Application information: Unsolicited requests for funds not accepted.
Trustee: Quad City Bank & Trust Co.
EIN: 206734309

3275
Karen Sue Lavin Foundation
c/o Polished Nickel Capital MGMT
155 N Wacker Dr., Ste. 840
Chicago, IL 60606-1723

Donor: Karen S. Lavin.
Foundation type: Independent foundation.
Financial data (yr. ended 12/31/13): Assets, $400,281 (M); gifts received, $100,000; expenditures, $177,326; qualifying distributions, $173,100; giving activities include $173,100 for 8 grants (high: $85,000; low: $3,000).
Fields of interest: Arts and culture; Agriculture; Human services.
Limitations: Applications not accepted.
Application information: Unsolicited requests for funds not accepted.
Officers and Directors: Karen Sue Lavin, Pres. and Director; Andrew Langert, V.P. and Secy. and Director; Theodre Hanson, Treas. and Director.
EIN: 454331278

3276
Hugh D. and Julie H. Sullivan Family Foundation
11 E. Walton St., Ste. 4600
Chicago, IL 60611-5440

Established in 2006 in New York.
Donors: Hugh D. Sullivan; Julie H. Sullivan.
Foundation type: Independent foundation.
Financial data (yr. ended 12/31/13): Assets, $144,471 (M); gifts received, $400,000; expenditures, $324,370; qualifying distributions, $324,220; giving activities include $322,520 for 11 grants (high: $250,000; low: $100).
Fields of interest: Arts and culture; Education; Diseases and conditions.
Type of support: General support; Research.
Limitations: Applications not accepted. Giving primarily in New Haven, CT and New York, NY. No grants to individuals.
Application information: Contributes only to pre-selected organizations.
Trustees: Hugh D. Sullivan; Julie H. Sullivan.
EIN: 137553616

3277
Sulzer Family Foundation
1940 W. Irving Park Rd.
Chicago, IL 60613-2468 (773) 329-4700
Contact: George A. Rice, Pres.

Established in 1956 in Illinois.
Donor: Grace E. Sulzer†.
Foundation type: Independent foundation.
Financial data (yr. ended 12/31/13): Assets, $6,198,151 (M); expenditures, $328,110; qualifying distributions, $301,301; giving activities include $232,113 for grants.
Purpose and activities: Giving for education, including higher, secondary, elementary, and adult education; programs for youth and the aged; community development and libraries.
Fields of interest: Education; Elementary and secondary education; Higher education; Public libraries; Community and economic development; Religion; Human services; Youth services; Senior services; Seniors.
Type of support: General support; Continuing support.
Limitations: Applications accepted. Giving primarily in the Ravenswood area of Chicago, IL. No grants to individuals.
Application information:
  Initial approach: Letter
  Deadline(s): Oct.
  Board meeting date(s): Nov.
Officers: George A. Rice, Pres.; Allan Pallante, Treas.
Director: Robert B. Hoellen.
Number of staff: 1 full-time support.
EIN: 362466016

3278
The Sumac Foundation
c/o JPMorgan Services Inc.
10 S. Dearborn, IL1-0117
Chicago, IL 60603

Donor: Freebairn Char Lead Annuity Trust.
Foundation type: Independent foundation.

Financial data (yr. ended 03/31/13): Assets, $4,507,824 (M); gifts received, $353,306; expenditures, $199,115; qualifying distributions, $188,968; giving activities include $188,000 for 8 grants (high: $50,000; low: $5,000).
Fields of interest: Legal services; Immigrant rights; Ethnic and racial groups; People of Latin American descent.
Limitations: Applications not accepted. Giving primarily in AR, CA and IL. No grants to individuals.
Application information: Contributes only to pre-selected organizations.
Trustees: Elizabeth A. Freebairn; Kenneth T. Freebairn; William A. Freebairn.
EIN: 137115395

3279
Summer Fund II
191 N. Wacker Dr., Ste. 1500
Chicago, IL 60606-1899

Established in 2005 in Illinois.
Donor: Nancy Meyer.
Foundation type: Independent foundation.
Financial data (yr. ended 12/31/13): Assets, $4,173,282 (M); gifts received, $50,050; expenditures, $459,736; qualifying distributions, $357,804; giving activities include $250,150 for 32 grants (high: $26,170; low: $1,500).
Fields of interest: Arts and culture; Education; Judaism; Human services; Family services; Child welfare.
Type of support: General support.
Limitations: Applications not accepted. Giving primarily in NY. No grants to individuals.
Application information: Unsolicited requests for funds not accepted.
Officers and Directors: Nancy Meyer, Pres. and Director; Jack Polsky, V.P.; Marc Weiss, Secy. and Director; Beth Stephens, Treas.; David Harris.
EIN: 141919035

3280
James B. Tafel Foundation
86 Paganica Dr.
Barrington, IL 60010-2644 (847) 382-6930
Contact: James B. Tafel, Tr.

Established in 1986 in Illinois.
Donor: James B. Tafel.
Foundation type: Independent foundation.
Financial data (yr. ended 09/30/13): Assets, $3,339,128 (M); expenditures, $171,981; qualifying distributions, $170,200; giving activities include $170,200 for grants.
Purpose and activities: Giving primarily for education and human services.
Fields of interest: Education; Higher education; Hospital care; Human services.
Limitations: Applications accepted. Giving primarily in FL and IL, some giving in CA. No grants to individuals.
Application information:
  Initial approach: Letter
  Deadline(s): None
Trustees: Ida May Tafel; James B. Tafel; James B. Tafel, Jr.; Julie K. Tafel-Klaus.
EIN: 363475140

3281
Takiff Family Foundation
(formerly Sanford & Bobette Takiff Charities, Ltd.)
313 Shoreline Ct.
Glencoe, IL 60022-1944 (847) 835-6500
Contact: Bobette Takiff, Dir.

Established in 1984 in Illinois.
Donors: Bobette Takiff; Sanford Takiff.
Foundation type: Independent foundation.
Financial data (yr. ended 12/31/13): Assets, $7,594,541 (M); expenditures, $420,703; qualifying distributions, $392,640; giving activities include $385,438 for 60 grants (high: $50,150; low: $25).
Purpose and activities: Giving primarily for Jewish organizations, as well as for education and health.
Fields of interest: Arts and culture; Museums; Education; Nonprofits; Diseases and conditions; Judaism; Human services.
Type of support: Continuing support; Annual campaigns; Capital campaigns; Capital and infrastructure; Program development; Curriculum development; Regranting; Scholarships.
Limitations: Applications accepted. Giving primarily in Chicago, IL. No grants to individuals.
Application information:
  Initial approach: Letter
  Deadline(s): None
  Board meeting date(s): 3rd Tues. of each month
Directors: Jill Hirsh; Elizabeth Scheinfeld; Bobette Takiff; Sherri Zirlin.
EIN: 363307589

3282
Bud Tarrson Foundation for Dental Research
(formerly Butler/Tarrson Dental Research Foundation)
10 S. Wacker Dr., Ste. 4000
Chicago, IL 60606-7507
Contact: H. Rosenberg
Application address: c/o Ronald E. Tarrson, 3930 N. Pine Grove, Chicago, IL 60601

Foundation type: Independent foundation.
Financial data (yr. ended 12/31/13): Assets, $1,458,888 (M); expenditures, $329,283; qualifying distributions, $311,715; giving activities include $311,715 for 3 grants (high: $301,663; low: $5,000).
Purpose and activities: Grants primarily restricted to dental health, education and research.
Fields of interest: Education.
Type of support: General support; Research.
Limitations: Applications accepted. Giving primarily in Chicago, IL and Stony Brook, NY. No grants to individuals.
Application information:
  Initial approach: Contact foundation
  Deadline(s): None
Directors: Dr. Nolan Levine; Linda C. Tarrson; Ronald E. Tarrson.
EIN: 362983183

3283
Taxman Family Foundation
c/o Seymour Taxman
5215 Old Orchard Rd., Ste. 130
Skokie, IL 60077-1098

Donor: Nancy Taxman.
Foundation type: Independent foundation.
Financial data (yr. ended 12/31/13): Assets, $2,915,416 (M); gifts received, $1,367,222; expenditures, $184,106; qualifying distributions, $178,023; giving activities include $178,023 for 34 grants (high: $90,000; low: $50).
Fields of interest: Internal medicine; Diseases and conditions; Multiple sclerosis; Judaism.
Type of support: Research.
Limitations: Applications not accepted. No grants to individuals.
Application information: Unsolicited requests for funds not accepted.
Officers: Seymour Taxman, Pres.; Nancy R. Taxman, Secy.; Mitchell Roth, Treas.
EIN: 204568076

3284
Paul and Patricia Taylor Family Foundation
c/o The Northern Trust Co.
P.O. Box 803878
Chicago, IL 60680-3878

Established in 2002 in Missouri.
Donors: Paul M. Taylor; Patricia N. Taylor.
Foundation type: Independent foundation.
Financial data (yr. ended 12/31/14): Assets, $1,321,807 (M); expenditures, $231,879; qualifying distributions, $221,000; giving activities include $220,000 for 19 grants (high: $25,000; low: $5,000).
Fields of interest: Arts and culture; Health; Human services.
Limitations: Applications not accepted. Giving primarily in the U.S., with emphasis in Phoenix and Scottsdale, AZ, and St. Louis, MO. No grants to individuals.
Application information: Contributes only to pre-selected organizations.
Officers: Cory Newport Taylor, V.P., Opers.; Pamela Joy Taylor, V.P., Public Rels.; Patricia N. Taylor, Secy.-Treas.
EIN: 481269165

3285
Fred and Harriett Taylor Foundation
10 S. Dearborn, IL1-0117
Chicago, IL 60603
Application address: c/o JPMorgan Chase Bank, N.A., Attn.: Deborah Ottinger, 5500 Ross Ave., Dallas, TX 75201, tel.: (214) 965-2914

Established in 1976 in New York.
Donor: Fred C. Taylor†.
Foundation type: Independent foundation.
Financial data (yr. ended 12/31/13): Assets, $9,533,957 (M); expenditures, $330,503; qualifying distributions, $259,917; giving activities include $238,400 for 19 grants (high: $100,000; low: $1,500).
Fields of interest: Education; Hospital care; Community and economic development; Human services; Scouting programs.
Type of support: General support.
Limitations: Applications accepted. Giving primarily in Hammondsport, NY. No grants to individuals.
Application information: Visit http://www.jpmorgan.com/ for complete application guidelines. Application form required.

Initial approach: See website
Deadline(s): None
Trustee: JPMorgan Chase Bank, N.A.
EIN: 166205365

3286

Maurice and Michelle Taylor Foundation

c/o Gray Hunter Stenn LLP
500 Maine St.
Quincy, IL 62301-3949

Established in 1998 in Illinois.
Donors: Maurice M. Taylor, Jr.; Michelle Taylor.
Foundation type: Independent foundation.
Financial data (yr. ended 12/31/13): Assets,
$1,115,703 (L); gifts received, $1,615;
expenditures, $224,295; qualifying distributions,
$222,920; giving activities include $222,500 for 7
grants (high: $200,000; low: $1,000).
Fields of interest: Education; Diseases and
conditions.
Type of support: General support; Scholarships.
Limitations: Applications not accepted. Giving
primarily in IL and MI. No grants to individuals.
Application information: Contributes only to
pre-selected organizations.
Directors: Cheri T. Holley; Maureen McClayton;
Anthony Soave; Maurice M. Taylor, Jr.; Michelle
Taylor.
EIN: 364224065

3287

Brent Taylor Perpetual Charitable Trust

c/o Mercantile Trust & Savings Bank
200 N. 33rd St.
P.O. Box 3455
Quincy, IL 62305-3714 2172237310
Application address: c/o Titan International,
Attn.: Courtney Leeser, 2701 Spruce St., Quincy, IL
62301-3473, tel.: (217) 221-4489

Donors: Maurice Taylor; Michelle Taylor.
Foundation type: Independent foundation.
Financial data (yr. ended 12/31/14): Assets,
$386,538; gifts received, $206,409; expenditures,
$204,260; qualifying distributions, $199,310.
Purpose and activities: Scholarship awards paid
directly to the college or university for persons who
are enrolled in a qualified educational institution on
a full-time basis for the succeeding semester or
quarter, and are either qualified employees or
children of qualified employees of Titan
International, Inc., or any of its subsidiaries, OTR
Wheel, Inc., or any of its subsidiaries or affiliates, or
residents of Quincy, Illinois, Ellsworth, Michigan, or
Saltville, Virginia.
Fields of interest: Higher education.
Type of support: Scholarships; Student aid.
Limitations: Applications accepted. Giving primarily
to benefit of residents of Quincy, IL, Ellsworth, MI,
or Saltville, VA.
Application information: Application form required.
Initial approach: Letter requesting application
form
Deadline(s): None
Trustee: Mercantile Trust & Savings Bank.
EIN: 376353965

3288

Tengelsen Family Foundation

1800 N. Hermitage Ave.
Chicago, IL 60662

Established in 2007 in Illinois.
Donors: Erich W. Tengelsen; Jennifer Tengelsen.
Foundation type: Independent foundation.
Financial data (yr. ended 12/31/13): Assets,
$1,433,699 (M); gifts received, $1,123,957;
expenditures, $359,741; qualifying distributions,
$353,500; giving activities include $257,747 for 25
grants (high: $56,294; low: $105).
Fields of interest: Arts and culture; Education;
Religion.
Limitations: Applications not accepted. Giving
primarily in IL. No grants to individuals.
Application information: Unsolicited request for
funds not accepted.
Officers: Jennifer Tengelsen, Pres.; Erich W.
Tengensen, Secy.; Sabrina Guthrie, Treas.
EIN: 205950073

3289

Thaman Family Foundation

c/o The Northern Trust Co.
P.O. Box 803878
Chicago, IL 60680—3878

Donors: Michael H. Thaman; Lisa Gathard.
Foundation type: Independent foundation.
Financial data (yr. ended 12/31/14): Assets,
$764,303; expenditures, $288,395; qualifying
distributions, $280,025.
Fields of interest: Arts and culture; Education;
Human services.
Limitations: Applications not accepted.
Application information: Unsolicited requests for
funds not accepted.
Officers: Lisa Gathard, Chair. and Pres.; Michael H.
Thaman, Secy.-Treas.
Director: John Melick.
EIN: 450669361

3290

The Tobey Foundation

c/o Ann T. Rowlands
1227 Canterbury Ln.
Glenview, IL 60025-3138

Established in 1994 in Illinois.
Donors: William R. Tobey, Jr.; Anne C. Tobey.
Foundation type: Independent foundation.
Financial data (yr. ended 12/31/13): Assets,
$2,540,990 (M); gifts received, $25,101;
expenditures, $250,220; qualifying distributions,
$231,153; giving activities include $226,518 for 55
grants (high: $36,018; low: $500).
Fields of interest: Arts and culture; Education;
Higher education; Human services.
Type of support: General support; Scholarships.
Limitations: Applications not accepted. Giving
primarily in IL. No grants to individuals.
Application information: Contributes only to
pre-selected organizations.
Directors: Ann T. Rowlands; Anne C. Tobey; William
H. Tobey; William R. Tobey, Jr.
EIN: 363989019

3291

Townsend Family Foundation

321 N. Clark St., Ste. 930
Chicago, IL 60654-6464

Established in 1998 in Illinois.
Donors: MarrGwen Townsend; Stuart Townsend.
Foundation type: Independent foundation.
Financial data (yr. ended 12/31/14): Assets,
$2,351,009 (M); expenditures, $259,041;
qualifying distributions, $243,150; giving activities
include $243,150 for 20 grants (high: $51,500;
low: $250).
Fields of interest: Arts and culture; Education;
Economics; Human services.
Limitations: Applications not accepted. Giving
primarily in Chicago, IL. No grants to individuals.
Application information: Unsolicited requests for
funds not accepted.
Directors: MarrGwen Townsend; Stuart Townsend.
EIN: 364199459

3292

Trio Foundation

45 Indian Hill Rd.
Winnetka, IL 60093-3939

Established in 2007 in Illinois.
Donors: John P. Amboian, Jr.; Ann L. Amboian.
Foundation type: Independent foundation.
Financial data (yr. ended 12/31/14): Assets,
$4,987,477; expenditures, $207,038; qualifying
distributions, $161,500.
Fields of interest: University education; Specialty
hospital care; Pediatrics; Youth services.
Limitations: Applications not accepted. Giving
primarily in IL. No grants to individuals.
Application information: Contributes only to
pre-selected organizations.
Officers and Directors: Ann L. Amboian, Pres. and
Director; John P. Amboian, Jr., V.P. and Treas.;
Michael S. Lee, Secy. and Director; Andrew L.
Amboian.
EIN: 261115900

3293

Trust for Aging in America Inc.

10 S. Dearborn St., IL1-0117
Chicago, IL 60603-2300

Foundation type: Independent foundation.
Financial data (yr. ended 12/31/14): Assets,
$7,276,127 (M); expenditures, $352,887;
qualifying distributions, $275,359; giving activities
include $255,321 for 1 grant.
Fields of interest: Senior services; Seniors.
Limitations: Applications not accepted. Giving
primarily in The Bronx, NY. No grants to individuals.
Application information: Unsolicited requests for
funds not accepted.
Trustee: JPMorgan Chase Bank, N.A.
EIN: 136046634

3294

Trust Under the Will of James Deering Charitable Trust

c/o The Northern Trust Co.
P.O. Box 803878
Chicago, IL 60680-3878

Foundation type: Independent foundation.
Financial data (yr. ended 12/31/13): Assets,
$5,987,725 (M); expenditures, $326,402;
qualifying distributions, $272,767; giving activities
include $266,065 for 5 grants (high: $64,213; low:
$39,213).
Fields of interest: Health; Human services.
Limitations: Applications not accepted.
Application information: Unsolicited requests for
funds not accepted.
Trustee: The Northern Trust Company.
EIN: 596123810

3295
Tully Family Foundation
33 N. Dearborn St., No. 2450
Chicago, IL 60602-3109 3129178700

Established in 1997 in Illinois.
Donor: Thomas M. Tully.
Foundation type: Operating foundation.
Financial data (yr. ended 12/31/14): Assets,
$9,348,294; gifts received, $1,211,149;
expenditures, $260,194; qualifying distributions,
$249,000.
Fields of interest: Education; Diseases and
conditions; Human services.
Type of support: Research.
Limitations: Applications not accepted. Giving
primarily in IL, with emphasis on Chicago. No grants
to individuals.
Application information: Unsolicited requests for
funds not accepted.
Officers: Thomas M. Tully, Pres. and Director; Ellen
Danaher Tully, Secy. and Director.
Director: Kenneth G. Pigott.
EIN: 364156972

3296
The Walter & Mary Tuohy Foundation
c/o John L. Tuohy, Chapman and Cutler
111 W. Monroe St., Ste. 1400
Chicago, IL 60603-4080

Established in 1960 in Ohio.
Donors: Mary Frances Tuohy†; Walter Joseph
Tuohy†.
Foundation type: Independent foundation.
Financial data (yr. ended 12/31/14): Assets,
$227,332; expenditures, $74,265; qualifying
distributions, $186,728.
Fields of interest: Education; Religion; Human
services.
Type of support: Annual campaigns; Capital
campaigns; Capital and infrastructure; Curriculum
development; Research.
Limitations: Applications not accepted. Giving
primarily in IL. No grants to individuals.
Application information: Unsolicited requests for
funds not accepted.
Officers and Trustees: John L. Tuohy, Pres. and
Treas. and Trustee; Walter J. Tuohy, Jr., V.P. and
Secy. and Trustee; Mary Ann Kundtz, V.P. and
Trustee; Patricia J. Tuohy, V.P. and Trustee.
EIN: 346558081

3297
The Turner Foundation
10 S. Dearborn IL1-0117
Chicago, IL 60603 (225) 332-4443
Contact: Jules Ellender
Application address: C/o. JPMorgan Chase Bank,
N.A., 451 Florida St., 6th Fl., Baton Rouge, LA
70801, tel.: (225) 332-4443

Established in 1989 in Louisiana.
Donors: Turner Industries, Inc.; National
Maintenance Corp.; International Piping Systems;
Nichols Construction; International Maintenance
Corp.; Burt S. Turner; Suzanne W. Turner.
Foundation type: Company-sponsored foundation.
Financial data (yr. ended 12/31/13): Assets,
$5,297,150 (M); expenditures, $352,002;
qualifying distributions, $311,609; giving activities
include $300,000 for 2 grants (high: $200,000;
low: $100,000).
Purpose and activities: The foundation supports
organizations involved with historic preservation,
education, recreation, and Catholicism.
Fields of interest: Health; Sports and recreation;
Human services.
Type of support: Program development.
Limitations: Applications accepted. Giving primarily
in Washington, DC, Baton Rouge, LA, and New York,
NY. No grants to individuals.
Application information:
 Initial approach: Proposal
 Deadline(s): None
Trustee: JPMorgan Chase Bank, N.A.
EIN: 581875562

3298
Twomey Foundation
P.O. Box 158
Smithshire, IL 61478-0158

Established in 1994 in Illinois.
Donors: Twomey Company; John Twomey; Norma L.
Kirkpatrick; Charles Kirkpatrick; John E. Twomey;
Melba A. Twomey; Norma L. Kirkpatrick.
Foundation type: Independent foundation.
Financial data (yr. ended 03/31/15): Assets,
$8,103,055 (M); gifts received, $50,000;
expenditures, $419,845; qualifying distributions,
$374,018; giving activities include $369,930 for 69
grants (high: $75,400; low: $200).
Purpose and activities: Giving primarily for human
services, religion and education.
Fields of interest: Arts and culture; Historic
preservation; Education; Elementary and secondary
education; Health; Religion; Protestantism; Human
services; Youth development; Youth services.
Limitations: Applications not accepted. Giving
primarily in IL. No grants to individuals.
Application information: Unsolicited requests for
funds not accepted.
Officers and Directors: John E. Twomey, Pres. and
Director; Melba A. Twomey, Secy. and Director;
Norma L. Kirkpatrick; Victor L. Twomey.
EIN: 371330616

3299
Ulm Family Foundation
10 S. Dearborn IL1-0117
Chicago, IL 60603-6089

Established in 2006 in Unspecified.

Donors: Marcia L. Ulm; William Lee Ulm, Sr.
Foundation type: Independent foundation.
Financial data (yr. ended 12/31/13): Assets,
$3,864,052 (M); expenditures, $324,430;
qualifying distributions, $297,500; giving activities
include $297,500 for 20 grants (high: $55,000;
low: $2,500).
Fields of interest: Health; Agriculture; Religion.
Type of support: General support; Student aid.
Limitations: Applications not accepted. Giving
primarily in GA and SC.
Application information: Unsolicited requests for
funds not accepted.
Officers: William Lee Ulm, Sr., Pres.; Marcia L. Ulm,
Secy.-Treas.
Directors: Elizabeth A. Ulm; Joseph Ian Alexander
Ulm; William L. Ulm, Jr.
EIN: 205745473

3300
United Conveyor Foundation
2100 Norman Dr. W.
Waukegan, IL 60085-6752 (847) 473-5900

Established in 1957 in Illinois.
Donor: United Conveyor Corp.
Foundation type: Company-sponsored foundation.
Financial data (yr. ended 12/31/14): Assets,
$5,442,861; gifts received, $75,000;
expenditures, $186,691; qualifying distributions,
$173,950.
Purpose and activities: The foundation supports
festivals and organizations involved with arts and
culture, education, child welfare, and human
services.
Fields of interest: Arts and culture; Education;
Human services.
Type of support: General support; Employee
matching gifts; Scholarships.
Limitations: Applications accepted. Giving primarily
in IL.
Application information: Application form required.
 Initial approach: Proposal
 Deadline(s): July 1
Trustees: Donald N. Basler; David S. Hoyem.
EIN: 366033638

3301
Vail Family Foundation
c/o Robert J. Vechiola, Foley & Lardner LLP
321 N. Clark St., Ste. 2800
Chicago, IL 60654-5313

Established in 1985 in Illinois.
Donors: James D. Vail III; Foster M. Vail.
Foundation type: Independent foundation.
Financial data (yr. ended 12/31/14): Assets,
$2,233,049 (M); expenditures, $190,742;
qualifying distributions, $168,864; giving activities
include $163,850 for 28 grants (high: $42,500;
low: $850).
Purpose and activities: Giving primarily for
education and human services.
Fields of interest: Arts and culture; Music; Historic
preservation; Education; Elementary and secondary
education; Higher education; Hospital care; Public
libraries; Christianity; Judaism; Human services.
Type of support: General support; Capital
campaigns.

Limitations: Applications not accepted. Giving primarily in the Chicago, IL, area. No grants to individuals.
Application information: Unsolicited requests for funds not accepted.
Officers and Directors: Margaret C. Vail, Pres. and Director; James D. Vail IV, Exec. V.P. and Director; John F. Vail, V.P. and Treas. and Director; James D. Vail, V, V.P. and Director; Robert J. Vechiola, Secy.
EIN: 363441436

3302
Valenti Charitable Foundation
875 N. Michigan Ave., Ste. 3100
Chicago, IL   60611-1962

Established in 1981 in Illinois.
Donors: Joseph E. Valenti, Sr.; Marcelline H. Valenti; Kevin Tracy; Constance V. Tracy; Christopher P. Valenti.
Foundation type: Independent foundation.
Financial data (yr. ended 11/30/14): Assets, $2,765,369 (M); expenditures, $219,694; qualifying distributions, $189,036; giving activities include $186,036 for 5 grants (high: $175,000; low: $375).
Fields of interest: Education; Human services.
Limitations: Applications not accepted. Giving primarily in IL, with some emphasis on Chicago. No grants to individuals.
Application information: Unsolicited requests for funds not accepted.
Officers: Christopher P. Valenti, V.P. and Secy.; Constance V. Tracy, V.P.; Thomas Valenti, Treas.
Trustees: Lisa V. Burke; Meghan T. Manchon; James Valenti; Joseph E. Valenti, Jr.; Marcelline H. Valenti; Mark T. Valenti.
EIN: 363155159

3303
Vibern Foundation
c/o Joel Ashmus
315 Quail Ridge Dr.
Westmont, IL   60559-6144

Established in 1995 in Illinois.
Donor: Viola D. Hank.
Foundation type: Independent foundation.
Financial data (yr. ended 12/31/13): Assets, $5,361,007 (M); expenditures, $282,885; qualifying distributions, $270,000; giving activities include $270,000 for 7 grants (high: $110,000; low: $15,000).
Fields of interest: Education; Catholicism.
Limitations: Applications not accepted. Giving limited to IL. No grants to individuals.
Application information: Unsolicited requests for funds not accepted.
Trustees: William H. Dale, Jr.; Cynthia H. Stark; Celeste H. Wright.
EIN: 363996796

3304
The Victor Foundation
191 N. Wacker Dr., Ste. 1500
Chicago, IL   60606-1899

Established in 2005 in Illinois.
Donors: Victor Charitable Lead Trust; Robert Lewis Barrows.

Foundation type: Independent foundation.
Financial data (yr. ended 12/31/13): Assets, $2,228,374 (M); gifts received, $90,200; expenditures, $266,918; qualifying distributions, $202,030; giving activities include $194,615 for 32 grants (high: $100,000; low: $100).
Fields of interest: Higher education; Nonprofits; Judaism; Human services.
Type of support: Regranting.
Limitations: Applications not accepted. Giving primarily in MN and NY. No grants to individuals.
Application information: Unsolicited requests for funds not accepted.
Officers and Directors: Robert Lewis Barrows, Pres. and Director; Erin Lin Frautschy Barrows, V.P.; Geoffrey M. Barrows, V.P. and Director; Stephen H. Barrows, V.P. and Director; Jack Polsky, V.P.; Linda Masters Barrows, Secy.-Treas. and Director.
EIN: 421652732

3305
Charles & Marie Von Weise
111 W. Monroe St., Tax Div. 10C
Chicago, IL   60603-4096

Foundation type: Independent foundation.
Financial data (yr. ended 12/31/14): Assets, $6,081,118 (M); expenditures, $342,018; qualifying distributions, $306,960; giving activities include $276,276 for 17 grants (high: $27,661; low: $3,661).
Fields of interest: Education; Health; Housing development.
Limitations: Applications not accepted. Giving primarily in Rockford, IL.
Application information: Unsolicited requests for funds not accepted.
Trustee: BMO Harris Bank, N.A.
EIN: 366046587

3306
The Wagner Foundation
1900 Barberry Rd.
Northbrook, IL   60062-5805

Established in 1953 in Illinois.
Foundation type: Independent foundation.
Financial data (yr. ended 02/28/14): Assets, $3,034,991 (M); expenditures, $214,677; qualifying distributions, $158,100; giving activities include $155,000 for 33 grants (high: $35,000; low: $500).
Purpose and activities: Giving primarily for human services, health and medical organizations, and Jewish agencies.
Fields of interest: Nonprofits; Diseases and conditions; Judaism; Human services.
Type of support: Regranting.
Limitations: Applications not accepted. Giving primarily in Chicago, IL. No grants to individuals.
Application information: Contributes only to pre-selected organizations.
Officers: William R. Wagner, Pres.; Ralph E. Satoloe, Secy.; Paul R. Wagner, Treas.
Director: David Wagner.
EIN: 366055674

3307
Maurice Walk Fine Arts Foundation
135 S. LaSalle St., Ste. 2350
Chicago, IL   60603-4153

Established in 1999 in Illinois.
Donor: Maurice Walk Trust.
Foundation type: Independent foundation.
Financial data (yr. ended 12/31/13): Assets, $6,459,512 (M); expenditures, $306,127; qualifying distributions, $231,860; giving activities include $231,860 for 6 grants (high: $97,000; low: $5,000).
Fields of interest: Arts education; Music; Musical ensembles and groups.
Limitations: Applications not accepted. Giving primarily in WY. No grants to individuals.
Application information: Contributes only to pre-selected organizations.
Officers and Directors: Margaretha Walk, Pres. and Director; Cynthia Walk, Secy. and Director; Marguerite A. Walk, Treas. and Director; Richard Palmer.
EIN: 364327696

3308
Cecil I. Walker Machinery Company Charitable Trust
10 S. Dearborn St., Fl. 21
Chicago, IL   60603-2300

Donor: Cecil I. Walker Machinery Co.
Foundation type: Company-sponsored foundation.
Financial data (yr. ended 05/31/14): Assets, $5,237,312 (M); expenditures, $297,902; qualifying distributions, $245,192; giving activities include $242,500 for 10 grants (high: $65,000; low: $1,500).
Purpose and activities: The foundation supports organizations involved with arts and culture, higher education, and Christianity.
Fields of interest: Arts and culture; Performing arts; Higher education; Christianity; Human services; Scouting programs.
Type of support: General support; Continuing support; Annual campaigns; Scholarships; Sponsorships.
Limitations: Applications not accepted. Giving limited to Charleston, WV. No grants to individuals.
Application information: Contributes only to pre-selected organizations.
Trustee: JPMorgan Chase Bank, N.A.
EIN: 556050733

3309
David M. and Mary Ann Barrows Wark Foundation
191 N. Wacker Dr., Ste. 1500
Chicago, IL   60606-1899

Established in 2000 in Illinois.
Donors: Mary Ann Barrows Wark; Mada Charitable Lead Trust.
Foundation type: Independent foundation.
Financial data (yr. ended 12/31/13): Assets, $1,804,187 (M); gifts received, $80,200; expenditures, $261,137; qualifying distributions, $209,415; giving activities include $202,000 for 8 grants (high: $100,000; low: $1,000).
Fields of interest: Judaism.

Limitations: Applications not accepted. Giving primarily in St. Paul, MN. No grants to individuals.
Application information: Contributes only to pre-selected organizations.
Officers and Directors: Mary Ann Barrows Wark, Pres. and Director; Jack Polsky, V.P. and Secy.; Beth Stephens, Treas.; Barry J. Wark; David M. Wark.
EIN: 364383745

3310
The Warner Family Foundation
10 S. Dearborn, IL1-0117
Chicago, IL 60603

Established in 2001 in New York.
Donors: Douglas A. Warner III; Patricia G. Warner.
Foundation type: Independent foundation.
Financial data (yr. ended 12/31/14): Assets, $5,450,312; expenditures, $319,180; qualifying distributions, $257,888.
Fields of interest: Education; Foundations; Health; Specialty hospital care; Cancers.
Type of support: General support.
Limitations: Applications not accepted. Giving primarily in CT, DE, FL and NY. No grants to individuals.
Application information: Contributes only to pre-selected organizations.
Trustees: Douglas A. Warner III; Patricia G. Warner; JPMorgan Chase Bank, N.A.
EIN: 516522857

3311
William J. Watson Irrevocable Trust
10 S. Dearborn, IL1-0117
Chicago, IL 60603 8668885157

Foundation type: Independent foundation.
Financial data (yr. ended 12/31/14): Assets, $9,110,839; expenditures, $527,093; qualifying distributions, $433,738.
Fields of interest: Education; Diseases and conditions; Human services; Family services.
Type of support: General support.
Limitations: Applications not accepted. Giving primarily in IL.
Application information: Unsolicited requests for funds not accepted.
Trustee: JPMorgan Chase Bank, N.A.
EIN: 366014834

3312
Weaver Family Private Foundation
1780 Happ Rd.
Northbrook, IL 60062-5606

Established in 2002 in Illinois.
Donor: William Weaver.
Foundation type: Independent foundation.
Financial data (yr. ended 12/31/13): Assets, $7,810,725 (M); expenditures, $370,749; qualifying distributions, $351,073; giving activities include $348,450 for 18 grants (high: $65,200; low: $1,000).
Fields of interest: Undergraduate education; Diseases and conditions; Community and economic development.
Type of support: Research.

Limitations: Applications not accepted. Giving primarily in CO, CA, IL and VT. No grants to individuals.
Application information: Contributes only to pre-selected organizations.
Directors: Annamarie Weaver; Leslie A. Weaver; Hilton Weinberg.
EIN: 371423304

3313
Webb Foundation
P.O. Box 432
Winthrop Harbor, IL 60096-0432 2629481033
Application address: P.O. Box 423, Winthrop Harbor, IL 60096, tel.: (262) 948-1033

Established in 1969 in Missouri.
Donors: Francis M. Webb†; Pearl M. Webb†.
Foundation type: Independent foundation.
Financial data (yr. ended 12/31/14): Assets, $6,460,990; expenditures, $341,179; qualifying distributions, $285,981.
Fields of interest: Secondary education; Higher education; Health; Hospital care; Diseases and conditions; Christianity; Human services; Child welfare; Seniors; Low-income and poor people.
Type of support: General support; Continuing support; Annual campaigns; Capital and infrastructure; Equipment; Seed money; Scholarships; Research.
Limitations: Applications accepted. Giving limited to the metropolitan area of Chicago, IL, and St. Louis, MO; Chicago grants limited to pre-selected organizations. No grants to individuals, or for emergency funds, deficit financing, land acquisition, endowment funds, matching gifts, special projects, publications, conferences, or fundraising or special events; no loans.
Publications: Informational brochure (including application guidelines).
Application information: Awardees must submit final report before next application.
Initial approach: Proposal
Copies of proposal: 1
Deadline(s): Feb. 28 and Aug. 31
Board meeting date(s): June and Nov.
Final notification: After board meetings
Officer: Greg Preves, Secy.; Linda Barry, Admin.
Advisors: John Barry; Evelyn M. McDonald; Donna Sue Preves; Robert Preves.
Number of staff: 1 part-time professional.
EIN: 237028768

3314
Robert G. Wehle Charitable Trust
10 S. Dearborn, IL1-0117
Chicago, IL 60603

Established in 1965 in New York.
Donors: Elizabeth Wehle Charitable Trust; Robert G. Wehle†; Louis A. Wehle Residual Trust.
Foundation type: Independent foundation.
Financial data (yr. ended 12/31/13): Assets, $6,252,801 (M); gifts received, $4,385; expenditures, $425,049; qualifying distributions, $365,011; giving activities include $345,259 for 2 grants (high: $232,259; low: $113,000).
Fields of interest: Environment; Natural resources; Sports and recreation.
Type of support: General support.

Limitations: Applications not accepted. Giving primarily in AL; funding also in NY. No grants to individuals.
Application information: Contributes only to pre-selected organizations.
Trustee: JPMorgan Chase Bank, N.A.
EIN: 166065271

3315
Wein Family Foundation
(formerly Hyman & Susan Wein Foundation)
1550 W. Carroll Ave.
Chicago, IL 60607-1012

Donors: Irving L. Wein; Zahava Wein; Fantasy Diamond Co.
Foundation type: Independent foundation.
Financial data (yr. ended 12/31/13): Assets, $3,315,561 (M); expenditures, $147,043; qualifying distributions, $129,912; giving activities include $129,912 for 19 grants (high: $50,000; low: $100).
Purpose and activities: Giving primarily to Jewish organizations, as well as for education.
Fields of interest: Education; Nonprofits; Diseases and conditions; Judaism; Human services.
International interests: Israel.
Type of support: Capital campaigns; Regranting.
Limitations: Applications not accepted. Giving primarily in Chicago, IL. No grants to individuals.
Application information: Unsolicited requests for funds not accepted.
Officers: Joseph Wein, Pres.; Susan Wein-Bernhardt, Secy.; Zahava Wein, Treas.
EIN: 366065421

3316
Marc Weiner Foundation
55 E. Jackson Blvd., Ste. 500
Chicago, IL 60604-4396

Established in 2004 in Illinois.
Donors: Elliot M. Weiner; Laurence Weiner.
Foundation type: Independent foundation.
Financial data (yr. ended 12/31/14): Assets, $13,108 (M); gifts received, $157,500; expenditures, $146,658; qualifying distributions, $146,658; giving activities include $146,620 for 27 grants (high: $41,000; low: $500).
Fields of interest: Education; Judaism; Human services.
Limitations: Applications not accepted. Giving primarily in Chicago, IL. No grants to individuals.
Application information: Contributes only to pre-selected organizations.
Officers: Elliot M. Weiner, Pres.; Laurence Weiner, V.P.; Steven Wold, Secy.
EIN: 421653879

3317
Robert G. Weiss Family Foundation
c/o Robert G. Weiss
100 E. Walton St., Ste. 600E
Chicago, IL 60611-1448

Donor: Robert G. Weiss.
Foundation type: Independent foundation.
Financial data (yr. ended 12/31/13): Assets, $1,414,702 (M); expenditures, $233,578; qualifying distributions, $211,105; giving activities

include $209,733 for 35 grants (high: $34,068; low: $600).

Fields of interest: Arts and culture; Opera; Education; Nonprofits; Hospital care; Judaism.

Type of support: Regranting.

Limitations: Applications not accepted. Giving primarily in the Chicago, IL area; some giving in NM. No grants to individuals.

Application information: Contributes only to pre-selected organizations.

Officers: Robert A. Weiss, V.P.; Floretta A. Weiss, Secy.; Louis A. Weiss, Treas.

EIN: 366090520

3318
Wessel Family Foundation
c/o The Northen Trust Company
P.O. Box 803878
Chicago, IL 60680-3878

Established in 2003 in Florida.

Donors: Jeffrey H. Wessel; Elizabeth K. Wessel.

Foundation type: Independent foundation.

Financial data (yr. ended 08/31/13): Assets, $2,025,854 (M); gifts received, $271,321; expenditures, $147,025; qualifying distributions, $140,561; giving activities include $140,500 for 12 grants (high: $51,800; low: $500).

Fields of interest: Education; Health; Human services.

Limitations: Applications not accepted. No grants to individuals.

Application information: Unsolicited requests for funds not accepted.

Officers and Directors: Elizabeth K. Wessel, Chair. and Director; Jeffrey H. Wessel, Pres. and Director; Katherine W. Mitchell, Secy. and Director; Brandon J. Wessel, Treas. and Director.

EIN: 550799320

3319
Wesselink Family Foundation
1133 Western Ave.
Northbrook, IL 60062-4457

Established in 2000 in Illinois.

Donors: David D. Wesselink; Linda R. Wesselink.

Foundation type: Independent foundation.

Financial data (yr. ended 12/31/14): Assets, $4,475,143; expenditures, $154,928; qualifying distributions, $152,834.

Fields of interest: Higher education; Protestantism.

Limitations: Applications not accepted. Giving primarily in IA, with emphasis on Pella; giving also in IL and MI. No grants to individuals.

Application information: Unsolicited requests for funds not accepted.

Officers and Directors: David D. Wesselink, Pres. and Director; William J. Wesselink, V.P. and Director; Linda R. Wesselink, Secy. and Director; Catherine E. Wesselink, Treas. and Director.

EIN: 364405466

3320
Weston Foundation
360 W. Illinois St., Ste. 11C
Chicago, IL 60654-5246 (312) 755-0600
Contact: Kathleen McDaniel

Donor: Roger L. Weston.

Foundation type: Independent foundation.

Financial data (yr. ended 12/31/13): Assets, $6,327,531 (M); gifts received, $319,273; expenditures, $323,255; qualifying distributions, $316,116; giving activities include $316,116 for 50 grants (high: $80,900; low: $250).

Fields of interest: Arts and culture; Education; Higher education; Human services.

Limitations: Applications accepted. Giving primarily in IL.

Application information: Application form required.
Initial approach: Completed application form
Deadline(s): Dec. 15

Officer: Sultan S. Issa, C.F.O.

Trustee: Roger L. Weston.

EIN: 367483664

3321
David & Barbara Whitwam Foundation
c/o Northern Trust Co.
P.O. Box 803878
Chicago, IL 60680-3878

Established in 1986 in Michigan.

Donors: David R. Whitwam; Barbara Whitwam.

Foundation type: Independent foundation.

Financial data (yr. ended 12/31/14): Assets, $1,847,316 (M); expenditures, $166,289; qualifying distributions, $150,500; giving activities include $149,500 for 11 grants (high: $60,000; low: $500).

Fields of interest: Education; Nonprofits; Protestantism; Human services.

Type of support: Regranting.

Limitations: Applications not accepted. Giving primarily in Benton Harbor, MI. No grants to individuals.

Application information: Unsolicited requests for funds not accepted.

Officers: David R. Whitwam, Pres.; Laura Ridgeway, V.P.; Mark Whitwam, Treas.

EIN: 382712616

3322
The Will Foundation
1320 Elm Tree Rd.
Lake Forest, IL 60045-1418
Contact: Molly McKenna

Established in 1994 in Illinois.

Donors: Andrew J. McKenna; William J. McKenna; John Crowe.

Foundation type: Independent foundation.

Financial data (yr. ended 09/30/13): Assets, $20,083 (M); gifts received, $196,567; expenditures, $182,520; qualifying distributions, $182,520; giving activities include $180,000 for 2 grants (high: $123,750; low: $56,250).

Fields of interest: University education; Health; Hospital care; Diseases and conditions.

Type of support: General support.

Limitations: Applications not accepted. Giving primarily in Chicago, IL and New York, NY. No grants to individuals.

Application information: Unsolicited requests for funds not accepted.

Officers: William J. McKenna, Pres.; Molly C. McKenna, Secy.-Treas.

EIN: 363994814

3323
Susan & Robert Wislow Charitable Foundation
20 N. Michigan Ave., Ste. 400
Chicago, IL 60602-4828

Established in 1986 in Illinois.

Donors: Robert A. Wislow; Susan Wislow; U.S. Equities Realty LLC.

Foundation type: Independent foundation.

Financial data (yr. ended 12/31/13): Assets, $913,059 (M); gifts received, $100,000; expenditures, $281,026; qualifying distributions, $279,821; giving activities include $278,585 for 43 grants (high: $40,000; low: $100).

Fields of interest: Arts and culture; Education; Undergraduate education; Natural resources; Health; Christianity; Human services; Child welfare.

Type of support: General support.

Limitations: Applications not accepted. Giving primarily in Chicago, IL. No grants to individuals.

Application information: Contributes only to pre-selected organizations.

Officers: Robert A. Wislow, Pres. and Treas.; Susan Wislow, V.P. and Secy.

Director: Leonard A. Wislow.

EIN: 363496206

3324
Witz-Mallinger Charitable Foundation
10 S. Dearborn St., IL1-0117
Chicago, IL 60603-2300

Established in 2004 in Arizona.

Donor: Jeanette Witz Mallinger.

Foundation type: Independent foundation.

Financial data (yr. ended 08/31/13): Assets, $5,005,093 (M); expenditures, $347,457; qualifying distributions, $303,875; giving activities include $288,000 for 11 grants (high: $54,000; low: $10,000).

Fields of interest: Education; Health; Christianity; Human services; Child welfare.

Limitations: Applications not accepted. Giving primarily in AZ. No grants to individuals.

Application information: Contributes only to pre-selected organizations.

Trustee: JPMorgan Chase Bank, N.A.

EIN: 206412740

3325
John T. Wolf Charitable Trust II
c/o Alpine Bank & Trust Co.
P.O. Box 6086
Rockford, IL 61125-1086

Established in 2003 in Illinois.

Donors: John T. Wolf; John T. & Peggy L. Wolf Charitable Lead Trust.

Foundation type: Independent foundation.

Financial data (yr. ended 12/31/13): Assets, $1,487,644 (M); gifts received, $51,595; expenditures, $240,536; qualifying distributions, $225,375; giving activities include $225,375 for 26 grants (high: $106,000; low: $300).

Fields of interest: Education; Health; Religion; Human services.

Limitations: Applications not accepted. Giving primarily in Boone County and Belvidere, IL. No grants to individuals.

Application information: Unsolicited requests for funds not accepted.
Trustee: Alpine Bank & Trust Co.
EIN: 367414566

3326
Marie E. Wolf Charitable Trust
111 W. Monroe St., Tax Div. 10C
Chicago, IL 60603 (312) 461-5154

Established in 1996 in Illinois.
Foundation type: Independent foundation.
Financial data (yr. ended 12/31/14): Assets, $7,429,691 (M); expenditures, $385,084; qualifying distributions, $354,846; giving activities include $313,190 for 5 grants (high: $125,276; low: $31,319).
Fields of interest: Undergraduate education; Hospital care; Hospice care; Christianity; Human services.
Limitations: Applications accepted. Giving primarily in IL. No grants to individuals.
Application information: Application form required.
  Initial approach: Proposal
  Deadline(s): None
Trustee: BMO Harris Bank, N.A.
EIN: 367160372

3327
Geary Rimmer Vincent Wolf Foundation
1555 N. Astor St., 21 NE
Chicago, IL 60610-1673

Established in 1999 in Illinois.
Donors: Linda G. Wolf; Gregory E. Wolf.
Foundation type: Independent foundation.
Financial data (yr. ended 12/31/13): Assets, $5,627,390 (M); gifts received, $624,928; expenditures, $248,089; qualifying distributions, $207,760; giving activities include $207,760 for 26 grants (high: $30,500; low: $30).
Fields of interest: Education; Housing development; Christianity; Human services; Child welfare.
Limitations: Applications not accepted. Giving primarily in IL. No grants to individuals.
Application information: Unsolicited requests for funds not accepted.
Directors: Gregory E. Wolf; Linda G. Wolf; Ryan G. Wolf.
EIN: 364333148

3328
Noah Wolff Family Foundation, Inc.
7061 N. Kedzie Ave., Ste. 201
Chicago, IL 60645-2818

Established in 1987 in Illinois.
Donor: Noah Wolff.
Foundation type: Independent foundation.
Financial data (yr. ended 12/31/13): Assets, $2,499,181 (M); expenditures, $379,894; qualifying distributions, $379,894; giving activities include $376,913 for 52 grants (high: $61,808; low: $1,000).
Fields of interest: Education; Judaism.
Limitations: Applications not accepted. No grants to individuals.
Application information: Unsolicited requests for funds not accepted.

Officers and Directors: Noah Wolff, Pres. and Director; Marilyn Wolff, Secy. and Director; Ranan Wolff.
EIN: 363496915

3329
L. S. Wood Charitable Trust
c/o Bank of America, N.A.
231 S. LaSalle St.
Chicago, IL 60697-0001
Application address: c/o Donald H. Parkison, Admin., 1317 Grand Ave., Ste. 228, Glenwood Springs, CO 81601-3841, tel.: (970) 945-4952, fax: (970) 947-9215, e-mail: parkison@sopris.net

Foundation type: Independent foundation.
Financial data (yr. ended 12/31/13): Assets, $7,120,366 (M); expenditures, $535,797; qualifying distributions, $469,788; giving activities include $381,000 for 157 grants (high: $5,000; low: $500).
Purpose and activities: Scholarship awards to individuals for undergraduate degree programs.
Fields of interest: Higher education.
Type of support: Student aid.
Limitations: Applications accepted. Giving primarily to residents of CO.
Application information: Application form required.
  Initial approach: Proposal
  Deadline(s): Feb. 1
Trustees: Diane Delaney; Thomas E. Gibbs; Katherine Gossard; Joseph Edward Harker; John A. Reeves; John A. Reeves, Jr.; Bank of America, N.A.
EIN: 366146230

3330
Sara H. Woodruff Foundation
P.O. Box 803878
Chicago, IL 60680-3878

Donor: Sarah H. Woodruff.
Foundation type: Independent foundation.
Financial data (yr. ended 12/31/13): Assets, $5,707,870 (M); expenditures, $311,284; qualifying distributions, $260,459; giving activities include $255,017 for 40 grants (high: $20,000; low: $2,500).
Fields of interest: Arts and culture; Higher education; Zoos; Housing development; Christianity; Human services; Youth services; Homeless services.
Limitations: Applications not accepted. Giving primarily in FL, GA, NC, and NY. No grants to individuals.
Application information: Contributes only to pre-selected organizations.
Trustee: The Northern Trust Co.
EIN: 596123443

3331
Elizabeth Holloway Woods Foundation
120 S. LaSalle St., 7th Fl.
Chicago, IL 60603

Foundation type: Independent foundation.
Financial data (yr. ended 11/30/13): Assets, $4,427,334 (M); expenditures, $257,905; qualifying distributions, $199,893; giving activities include $189,000 for 18 grants (high: $30,000; low: $500).

Fields of interest: Arts and culture; Education; Protestantism.
Limitations: Applications not accepted. Giving primarily in MO.
Application information: Unsolicited requests for funds not accepted.
Trustees: Elizabeth W. Bradbury; PrivateBank.
EIN: 276155847

3332
John R. Woods Foundation
c/o The PrivateBank
120 S. LaSalle St., 7th Fl.
Chicago, IL 60603-3403

Foundation type: Independent foundation.
Financial data (yr. ended 11/30/13): Assets, $4,471,289 (M); expenditures, $260,213; qualifying distributions, $201,416; giving activities include $190,000 for 34 grants (high: $39,000; low: $500).
Fields of interest: Arts and culture; Education; Human services.
Limitations: Applications not accepted. Giving primarily in CO.
Application information: Unsolicited requests for funds not accepted.
Trustees: Catherine Woods Hill; The PrivateBank.
EIN: 276155799

3333
The Wright Foundation
3504 Cattail Cove
Pekin, IL 61554-9001 3096208024
Application address: Robert M. Wright, M.D., 1510 W. Shore Dr., Pekin, IL 61554, tel.: (309) 620-8024

Established in 1992 in Illinois.
Donors: Nelson A. Wright, Jr., MD†; Robert M. Wright, MD; Nelson A. Wright III, MD.
Foundation type: Independent foundation.
Financial data (yr. ended 12/31/14): Assets, $4,092,042; gifts received, $0; expenditures, $308,301; qualifying distributions, $274,992.
Purpose and activities: Giving primarily for education, health, and religious organizations.
Fields of interest: Education; Higher education; Nonprofits; Health; Hospital care; Protestantism; Catholicism.
Type of support: General support; Regranting.
Limitations: Applications accepted. Giving primarily in Pekin and Peoria, IL and OH. No grants to individuals.
Application information:
  Initial approach: Proposal
  Deadline(s): None
  Board meeting date(s): 1st week in Dec.
Officers and Directors: Nelson A. Wright III, MD, Pres. and Director; Robert M. Wright, MD, V.P. and Director; Barbara J. Wright, Secy.
EIN: 371291533

3334
Morton & Helen Yulman Charitable Trust
(formerly Yulman Foundation)
c/o The Northern Trust Co.
P.O. Box 803878
Chicago, IL 60680-3878

Donors: Morton Yulman; Helen Yulman.
Foundation type: Independent foundation.
Financial data (yr. ended 12/31/13): Assets, $14,070,606; expenditures, $726,382; qualifying distributions, $436,900.
Purpose and activities: Giving primarily to Jewish organizations.
Fields of interest: Art museums; Nonprofits; Judaism; Human services.
Type of support: Regranting.
Limitations: Applications not accepted. Giving primarily in FL and NY. No grants to individuals.
Application information: Contributes only to pre-selected organizations.
Trustees: Nedra Y. Oren; E. Richard Yulman; Helen B. Yulman.
EIN: 146015572

3335
Zaccone Family Foundation
729 Wilson Ln.
Hinsdale, IL   60521
Main URL: http://www.zacconefamilyfoundation.com

Established in 2007 in Delaware.
Donors: Suzanne M. Zaccone; Loretta Zaccone; D.R. Zaccone.
Foundation type: Independent foundation.
Financial data (yr. ended 12/31/13): Assets, $576,657 (M); gifts received, $218,425; expenditures, $281,955; qualifying distributions, $275,327; giving activities include $246,597 for 4 grants (high: $100,000; low: $21,597).
Fields of interest: Cancers.
Limitations: Applications not accepted. Giving primarily in IL. No grants to individuals.
Application information: Contributes only to pre-selected organizations.
Officers and Directors: Suzanne M. Zaccone, Pres. and Director; Dominic R. Zaccone II, V.P. and

Director; Shere Zaccone, Secy. and Director; Loretta Zaccone.
EIN: 261595390

3336
Saul Zaentz Charitable Trust
2700 Patriot Blvd., Ste. 170
Glenview, IL   60026-8080

Established in 2004 in California.
Donor: Saul Zaentz.
Foundation type: Independent foundation.
Financial data (yr. ended 12/31/13): Assets, $511,697 (M); expenditures, $116,740; qualifying distributions, $115,000; giving activities include $115,000 for 6 grants (high: $50,000; low: $5,000).
Fields of interest: Higher education; Community health care; Film and video; Human services; Food aid.
Limitations: Applications not accepted. Giving primarily in CA and GA. No grants to individuals.
Application information: Contributes only to pre-selected organizations.
Trustees: Alan H. Hammerman; Elliott G. Steinberg; Saul Zaentz.
EIN: 367192460

3337
Eugene & Delores Zemsky Charitable Foundation
113 Radcliffe Ct.
Glenview, IL   60025   (773) 247-4600
Contact: Eugene M. Zemsky, Tr.

Established in 1974 in Illinois.
Donors: Eugene M. Zemsky; Delores Zemsky; The Zemsky Corp.; Zemsky Charitable Remainder Trust.
Foundation type: Independent foundation.

Financial data (yr. ended 11/30/13): Assets, $1,562,272 (M); gifts received, $25,000; expenditures, $144,429; qualifying distributions, $144,429; giving activities include $144,226 for 7 grants (high: $140,000; low: $50).
Fields of interest: Arts and culture; Nonprofits; Health.
Type of support: Regranting.
Limitations: Applications accepted. Giving primarily in Chicago, IL. No grants to individuals.
Application information: Application form required.
  Initial approach: Letter
  Deadline(s): None
Trustees: Delores Zemsky; Eugene M. Zemsky.
EIN: 237411882

3338
Zuckerman Family Foundation
1049 Bluff Rd.
Glencoe, IL   60022-1120

Established in 1996 in Illinois.
Donors: Sheri Zuckerman; Sherwin Zuckerman.
Foundation type: Independent foundation.
Financial data (yr. ended 12/31/14): Assets, $1,744,220; gifts received, $590,237; expenditures, $439,914; qualifying distributions, $409,185.
Fields of interest: Education; Nonprofits; Human services.
Type of support: Regranting.
Limitations: Applications not accepted. Giving primarily in IL. No grants to individuals.
Application information: Contributes only to pre-selected organizations.
Officers and Directors: Sherwin Zuckerman, Pres. and Secy. and Director; Sheri Zuckerman, Treas. and Director; Nathan M. Grossman.
EIN: 364120779

INDIANA

3339
The Ackerman Foundation

280 E. 96th St., Ste. 350
Indianapolis, IN 46240-3858 (317) 663-0205
Contact: John F. Ackerman, Tr.
FAX: (317) 663-0215;
E-mail: jdisbro@cardinalep.com; Main URL: http://ackermanfoundation.com
Grants List: http://ackermanfoundation.com/2013grants.html

Established in 1992 in Indiana.
Donor: James F. Ackerman.
Foundation type: Independent foundation.
Financial data (yr. ended 12/31/13): Assets, $8,846,665 (M); gifts received, $75; expenditures, $590,043; qualifying distributions, $414,700; giving activities include $414,700 for 43 grants (high: $50,000; low: $1,000).
Purpose and activities: Giving primarily to central Indiana organizations as well as a few national medical research institutions. Specifically, the foundation focuses on Indiana cultural institutions and organizations benefiting health and human services, community development, and education.
Fields of interest: Arts and culture; Higher education; Nonprofits; Health; Diseases and conditions; Judaism; Human services; Seniors.
Type of support: General support; Continuing support; Annual campaigns; Capital campaigns; Capital and infrastructure; Equipment; Research; Endowments; Regranting.
Limitations: Giving primarily in IN, with some giving on a national basis. No grants to individuals.
Publications: Application guidelines; Financial statement; Grants list.
Application information:
  Initial approach: Brief one or two page letter describing proposal
  Copies of proposal: 1
  Deadline(s): Thirty days prior to the meeting date
  Board meeting date(s): The business day that falls on or closest to June 15 and Dec. 15
Trustee: John F. Ackerman.
Number of staff: 2 full-time professional.
EIN: 356567579

3340
Terry D. and Carol A. Agness Family Foundation

13 Ridgeline Dr.
Brownsburg, IN 46112-8833

Foundation type: Independent foundation.
Financial data (yr. ended 12/31/14): Assets, $3,971,796 (M); expenditures, $189,420; qualifying distributions, $189,420; giving activities include $161,000 for 7 grants (high: $30,000; low: $1,000).
Fields of interest: Philanthropy; Religion; Human services.
Limitations: Applications not accepted. Giving primarily in IN.
Application information: Unsolicited requests for funds not accepted.
Trustees: Lance Agness; Lana Barnhisel.
EIN: 262521253

3341
Tim and Libby Ash Family Foundation, Inc.

7609 W. Jefferson Blvd.
Fort Wayne, IN 46804-4133 (260) 470-0604
Contact: Timothy E. Ash

Donor: Timothy E. Ash.
Foundation type: Independent foundation.
Financial data (yr. ended 12/31/13): Assets, $1,570,414 (M); gifts received, $250,682; expenditures, $219,036; qualifying distributions, $211,245; giving activities include $211,245 for 24 grants (high: $131,550; low: $45).
Fields of interest: Education; Human services.
Limitations: Applications not accepted. Giving primarily in Fort Wayne, IN.
Application information: Unsolicited requests for funds not accepted.
Board Members: Elizabeth A. Ash; Timothy E. Ash; Jason Grover.
EIN: 271243709

3342
Ayres Foundation Inc.

545 W. 93rd St.
Indianapolis, IN 46260-1415 (317) 443-1868
Contact: John Ed Peacock Jr., Treas.
E-mail: ayresfoundationinc@gmail.com

Established in 1944 in Indiana.
Donors: L.S. Ayres and Co.; Theodore B. Griffith†; Mrs. Theodore B. Griffith†.
Foundation type: Independent foundation.
Financial data (yr. ended 12/31/13): Assets, $0 (M); expenditures, $216,174; qualifying distributions, $203,650; giving activities include $203,650 for 53 grants (high: $22,250; low: $50).
Purpose and activities: Giving primarily for community services, and to educational and cultural organizations in the Indianapolis, IN area.
Fields of interest: Arts and culture; Secondary education; Higher education; Community and economic development; Human services; Low-income and poor people; People with disabilities; People with physical disabilities; People with psychosocial disabilities.
Type of support: General support; Continuing support; Annual campaigns; Capital campaigns; Capital and infrastructure; Equipment; Emergency funds; Program development; Seed money.
Limitations: Applications accepted. Giving primarily in central IN, with emphasis on Indianapolis. No grants to individuals.
Publications: Application guidelines.
Application information: Application form required.
  Initial approach: Brief proposal using the foundation's guidelines
  Copies of proposal: 1
  Deadline(s): Apr. 15 and Oct. 15
  Board meeting date(s): Late spring and late fall
  Final notification: 8 weeks; positive responses only
Officers: Jay Ed Peacock, Jr., Pres.; Nancy Ayres, V.P.; Bert M. Wilhoite, Secy.; John Ed Peacock, Treas.
Director: Alma Lathrop.
Number of staff: None.
EIN: 356018437

3343
BAJ Foundation Inc.

6900 S. Gray Rd.
Indianapolis, IN 46237-3209

Established in 2000 in Indiana.
Donors: Blake Renata Jackson; Abishai Financial II, LP.
Foundation type: Independent foundation.
Financial data (yr. ended 12/31/13): Assets, $0 (M); gifts received, $68,225; expenditures, $240,313; qualifying distributions, $239,733; giving activities include $239,733 for 61 grants (high: $57,560; low: $50).
Fields of interest: Education; Christianity.
Limitations: Applications not accepted. Giving primarily in IN.
Application information: Unsolicited requests for funds not accepted.
Directors: James Conner; Blake A. Jackson; Wess Jackson.
EIN: 352123626

3344
Benton Community Foundation

P.O. Box 351
Fowler, IN 47944-0351 (765) 884-8022
Contact: Ashley Bice, Exec. Dir.
FAX: (765) 884-8023; E-mail: info@bentoncf.org;
Additional e-mail: ashley@bentoncf.org; Main
URL: http://www.bentoncf.org
Blog: http://www.bentoncf.org/blog
Facebook: http://www.facebook.com/pages/Fowler-In/Benton-Community-Foundation/45746243950

Established in 2003 in Indiana.
Foundation type: Community foundation.
Financial data (yr. ended 12/31/12): Assets, $4,757,089 (M); gifts received, $256,102; expenditures, $316,604; giving activities include $117,549 for 1+ grant (high: $8,000), and $75,650 for 30 grants to individuals.
Purpose and activities: The foundation seeks to enhance the community through civic leadership, philanthropy, and charitable development initiatives.
Fields of interest: Arts and culture; Higher education; Land resources; Health; Community and economic development; Sustainable development; Economic development; Human services.
Type of support: Capital and infrastructure; Program development; Student aid.
Limitations: Applications accepted. Giving primarily in Benton County, IN. No grants to individuals (except for scholarships), or for endowments, ongoing operating expenses, programs already completed, or debt reduction or elimination; no multi-year programs.
Publications: Application guidelines; Annual report; Grants list; Informational brochure; Newsletter.
Application information: Visit foundation web site for application forms and guidelines per grant type. Application form required.
  Initial approach: Submit application form and attachments
  Copies of proposal: 1
  Deadline(s): Varies
  Board meeting date(s): 3rd Wed. of each month (except July)
Officers and Board Members: Laurel Strasburger, Pres. and Director; Laurie Phillips, Secy. and Director; Ashley Bice, Exec. Dir.; Steve Brunton;

Jayme Buchanan; Cathy Coats; Natasha Cox; Dave Guthridge; Destin Haas; Tom Luce; Chris Sheetz; John Wright.
Number of staff: 1 part-time professional; 1 part-time support.
EIN: 260074023

3345
Bill Deputy Foundation
4200 Middlebury St.
Elkhart, IN 46516-5596

Established in 2008 in Unspecified.
Donor: William J. Deputy Charitable Lead Annuity Trust.
Foundation type: Independent foundation.
Financial data (yr. ended 12/31/13): Assets, $6,075,583 (M); gifts received, $928,058; expenditures, $364,673; qualifying distributions, $229,941; giving activities include $203,781 for 36 grants (high: $70,000; low: $500).
Fields of interest: European football; Youth services.
Limitations: Applications not accepted. Giving primarily in IN. No grants to individuals.
Application information: Unsolicited requests for funds not accepted.
Officers: Robert J. Deputy, Pres. and Treas.; Lawrence P. Deputy, V.P. and Secy.
EIN: 262480796

3346
Blackford County Community Foundation, Inc.
121 N. High St.
P.O. Box 327
Hartford City, IN 47348-0327 (765) 348-3411
Contact: Patricia D. Poulson, Exec. Dir.
FAX: (765) 348-4945;
E-mail: foundation@blackfordcounty.org; Additional e-mail: ppoulson@blackfordcounty.org; Main URL: http://www.blackfordcofoundation.org
Facebook: http://www.facebook.com/BlackfordCoFoundation

Established in 1989 in Indiana.
Foundation type: Community foundation.
Financial data (yr. ended 12/31/13): Assets, $6,066,589 (M); gifts received, $237,505; expenditures, $497,297; giving activities include $126,035 for 7+ grants (high: $25,652), and $134,130 for 192 grants to individuals.
Purpose and activities: The foundation's mission is to enhance and improve the quality of life in Blackford County, Indiana. The foundation accomplishes this by continually increasing their endowed assets so that they can better meet to the needs of the community.
Fields of interest: Arts and culture; Education; Health; Mental health care; Community and economic development; Community beautification; Neighborhood associations; Human services; Family services; Child welfare; Senior services.
Type of support: General support; Student aid; Individual development.
Limitations: Applications accepted. Giving primarily in Blackford County, IN. No support for sectarian or religious purposes. No grants for building campaigns, endowments or operating budgets.

Publications: Application guidelines; Annual report; Financial statement; Grants list; Informational brochure; Newsletter.
Application information: Visit foundation web site for application guidelines. Application form required.
Initial approach: Contact foundation
Copies of proposal: 6
Deadline(s): Feb. 19 and July 20
Board meeting date(s): Monthly
Final notification: Mar. and Aug.
Officers and Directors: Maxie A. Malott, Pres. and Director; Diana L. Holsten, V.P. and Director; Julie A. Forcum, Secy. and Director; Peggy L. Fisher, Treas. and Director; Patricia D. Poulson, Exec. Dir.; Robert Benbow; Gary D. Cheesman; Jon Creek; David K. Neff; Lisa C. Weeks; J. Nolan Willman.
EIN: 351772356

3347
The Bos Family Foundation
10420 Mulligan Dr.
Wheatfield, IN 46392-7057 (219) 987-5696
Contact: Lynn Marie Schakel, Secy.

Established in 2006 in Texas.
Donors: Tony Bos; Martha Tynan; Mary Beth Bos; Gavin Herrema; Lynn Schakel; Lara Herrema; Derek Herrema; Fred Schakel; Caleb Herrema; Newberry Farms, LLC; T & M Limited Partnership; T & M Properties; Fair Oaks Dairy Farm, LLC.
Foundation type: Independent foundation.
Financial data (yr. ended 12/31/13): Assets, $227,735 (M); gifts received, $181,000; expenditures, $202,356; qualifying distributions, $188,883; giving activities include $188,883 for 9 grants (high: $50,000; low: $5,000).
Purpose and activities: Scholarship awards to individuals attending a seminary educational institution.
Fields of interest: Graduate and professional education; Theology.
Type of support: Scholarships.
Limitations: Applications accepted. Giving primarily in CA, IL, IN, and TX.
Application information: Application form required.
Initial approach: Completed application form
Deadline(s): None
Officers: Mary Beth Bos, Pres. and Treas.; Lynn Schakel, Secy.
EIN: 203716147

3348
Elba L. and Gene Portteus Branigin Foundation Inc.
111 Monument Cir., Ste. 2700
Indianapolis, IN 46204-5120

Established in 1987 in Indiana.
Foundation type: Independent foundation.
Financial data (yr. ended 12/31/13): Assets, $5,372,750 (M); expenditures, $328,471; qualifying distributions, $288,637; giving activities include $263,600 for 22 grants (high: $100,000; low: $1,000).
Fields of interest: Arts and culture; Education; Higher education; Health; Christianity; Human services; Youth organizing.
Type of support: General support; Endowments; Scholarships.
Limitations: Applications not accepted. Giving primarily in Franklin, IN. No grants to individuals.

Application information: Contributes only to pre-selected organizations.
Officers and Directors: Eugene L. Henderson, Chair. and Director; John M. Chiarotti, Pres. and Treas. and Director; Stephen E. Devoe, Secy. and Director.
EIN: 351697364

3349
Alan W. and Sharon A. Braun Family Foundation, Inc.
949 Cedar Hill Dr.
Evansville, IN 47710-5401

Donors: Alan Braun; Sharon Braun.
Foundation type: Independent foundation.
Financial data (yr. ended 12/31/13): Assets, $7,774,612 (M); gifts received, $700,000; expenditures, $226,387; qualifying distributions, $192,868; giving activities include $189,850 for 24 grants (high: $53,000; low: $100).
Fields of interest: Education; Basketball; Human services.
Limitations: Applications not accepted. Giving primarily in IN.
Application information: Unsolicited requests for funds not accepted.
Officers: Alan W. Braun, Pres. and Treas.; Sharon A. Braun, V.P. and Secy.
Directors: Mathew A. Braun; Molly A. Russell.
EIN: 454122368

3350
The Brave Heart Foundation Inc
8425 Woodfield Crossing Blvd., Ste. 100
Indianapolis, IN 46240

Donors: William Griffith; Gerry Griffith.
Foundation type: Independent foundation.
Financial data (yr. ended 12/31/13): Assets, $3,819,228 (M); gifts received, $225,046; expenditures, $305,455; qualifying distributions, $275,380; giving activities include $275,380 for 62 grants (high: $27,500; low: $500).
Fields of interest: Housing development; Religion; Human services.
Limitations: Applications not accepted.
Application information: Unsolicited requests for funds not accepted.
Officers: William Griffith, Chair.; James Mulholland, Secy.; Gerry Griffith, Treas.
Board Members: David McDaniel; Kim Walton.
EIN: 270720856

3351
The Sol & Arlene Bronstein Foundation
c/o Old National Bank
P.O. Box 207
Evansville, IN 47702-2966 (812) 464-1399
Contact: Linda Thompsan, Trust Off., Old National Bank

Established in 1979 in Indiana.
Donors: Sol Bronstein†; Laketon Asphalt Refining Co.
Foundation type: Independent foundation.
Financial data (yr. ended 12/31/13): Assets, $2,669,186 (M); expenditures, $192,041; qualifying distributions, $176,696; giving activities include $162,000 for 14 grants (high: $76,500; low: $250).

Purpose and activities: Giving primarily for Jewish organizations, with emphasis on temple support, Jewish education, and Jewish welfare funds.
Fields of interest: Arts and culture; Higher education; Nonprofits; Judaism; Human services; Low-income and poor people.
Type of support: General support; Continuing support; Program development; Research; Regranting.
Application information:
    Initial approach: Proposal
    Deadline(s): None
Trustee: Old National Bank.
EIN: 356313412

3352
Jerry L. and Barbara J. Burris Foundation, Inc.
c/o Jeffrey H. Thomasson
P.O. Box 80238
Indianapolis, IN 46280-0238 (317) 843-5678
Contact: Jeffrey H. Thomasson, Secy.

Established in 1994 in Indiana.
Donor: Jerry L. Burris†.
Foundation type: Independent foundation.
Financial data (yr. ended 12/31/13): Assets, $3,291,453 (M); expenditures, $227,110; qualifying distributions, $141,908; giving activities include $130,000 for 20 grants (high: $30,000; low: $1,000).
Purpose and activities: Giving primarily for youth services, human services, museums, and education.
Fields of interest: Arts and culture; Museums; Education; Zoos; Specialty hospital care; Protestantism; Human services; Child welfare.
Type of support: General support; Scholarships.
Limitations: Applications not accepted. Giving primarily in Indianapolis, IN; some giving in Naples, FL and in GA.
Application information: Unsolicited requests for funds not accepted.
Officers: Barbara J. Burris, Pres.; Stacey L. Burris Ice, V.P.; Jeffrey H. Thomasson, Secy.
EIN: 351914399

3353
Bussing-Koch Foundation, Inc.
2905 Bayard Park Dr.
Evansville, IN 47714-2507
Contact: Wilfred C. Bussing III, Pres.

Established in 1995 in Indiana.
Donor: Loretta M. Koch†.
Foundation type: Independent foundation.
Financial data (yr. ended 12/31/14): Assets, $3,913,607 (M); gifts received, $1,000; expenditures, $371,090; qualifying distributions, $366,051; giving activities include $317,605 for 61 grants (high: $100,000; low: $75).
Fields of interest: Arts and culture; Art museums; Higher education; Rehabilitation; Catholicism; Human services; Youth services; Scouting programs.
Type of support: General support; Continuing support; Annual campaigns; Capital campaigns; Capital and infrastructure; Equipment; Land acquisitions; Endowments; Debt reduction; Emergency funds; Program development; Convening; Professorships; Publications; Seed

money; Curriculum development; Fellowships; Scholarships; Research; Technical assistance; Program evaluations.
Limitations: Applications not accepted. Giving primarily in southwestern IN.
Application information: Unsolicited requests for funds not accepted.
    Board meeting date(s): As needed
Officers: Wilfred C. Bussing III, Pres.; Marie A. Bussing, V.P.; Constance K. Bussing, Secy.-Treas.
EIN: 351780862

3354
Florence V. Carroll Charitable Trust
c/o Wells Fargo Bank Indiana, N.A.
1251 N. Eddy St., Ste. 203
South Bend, IN 46617-1478
Contact: Mary Naragan, Trust Assoc.

Established in 1989 in Indiana.
Donor: Florence V. Carroll Trust.
Foundation type: Independent foundation.
Financial data (yr. ended 12/31/13): Assets, $9,894,771 (M); expenditures, $521,475; qualifying distributions, $413,986; giving activities include $388,007 for 31 grants (high: $26,667; low: $4,500).
Fields of interest: Arts and culture; Higher education; Human services.
Limitations: Applications accepted. Giving limited to St. Joseph County, IN.
Application information:
    Initial approach: Letter
    Copies of proposal: 7
    Deadline(s): Apr. 1 and Oct. 1
    Board meeting date(s): May and Nov.
    Final notification: May and Nov.
Trustee: Wells Fargo Bank, N.A.
EIN: 356495556

3355
CDM Foundation, Inc.
P.O. Box 1655
South Bend, IN 46634-1655

Established in 1989 in Illinois.
Donor: Anne C. McClure.
Foundation type: Independent foundation.
Financial data (yr. ended 12/31/13): Assets, $3,594,786 (M); expenditures, $202,144; qualifying distributions, $194,700; giving activities include $194,700 for 52 grants (high: $100,000; low: $250).
Purpose and activities: Giving primarily for the arts, education, and health and human services.
Fields of interest: Arts and culture; Elementary and secondary education; Higher education; Hospital care; Christianity; Human services.
Type of support: Annual campaigns; Capital campaigns.
Limitations: Applications not accepted. No grants to individuals.
Application information: Unsolicited requests for funds not accepted.
Officers and Directors: Anne C. McClure, Pres. and Director; Archibald McClure, Secy. and Director; Ross J. Mangano, Treas. and Director; Walter W. Bell.
EIN: 363656304

3356
Judith Clark-Morrill Foundation, Inc.
701 W. King St.
P.O. Box 180
Garrett, IN 46738-1350 (260) 357-4141

Donor: Judith Morrill.
Foundation type: Independent foundation.
Financial data (yr. ended 12/31/13): Assets, $524,689 (M); expenditures, $208,098; qualifying distributions, $204,270; giving activities include $202,483 for 10 grants (high: $58,480; low: $500).
Fields of interest: Arts and culture; Education; Health.
Limitations: Applications accepted. Giving primarily in IN. No grants to individuals, or for student groups, scholarships, annual campaigns, general operating support, travel, or advertising; no loans or multi-year funding.
Application information: Application form required.
    Initial approach: Proposal
    Deadline(s): Last working day of May and Nov.
    Board meeting date(s): June 1 and Dec. 1
Officers: Judith Morrill, Pres.; Craig T. Benson, Secy.-Treas.
Directors: Alelia Barry; Byron Braun; Mark Fogt; Donald E. Smith.
EIN: 300046592

3357
The Cohen Family Foundation, Inc.
10360 Charter Oaks
Carmel, IN 46032-8305 (317) 259-0157

Established in 1996 in Indiana.
Donors: Alan H. Cohen; David I. Klapper; Linda M. Cohen.
Foundation type: Independent foundation.
Financial data (yr. ended 12/31/14): Assets, $7,403,526; expenditures, $588,661; qualifying distributions, $352,870.
Fields of interest: Arts and culture; Theater; Education; Zoos; Hospital care; Judaism; Child welfare.
Limitations: Applications accepted. Giving primarily in IN. No grants to individuals.
Application information: Application form required.
    Initial approach: Proposal
    Deadline(s): None
Officers: Alan H. Cohen, Pres. and Treas.; Linda M. Cohen, VP. and Secy.; Nathan Cohen, V.P.; Lauren Cohen Edmundson, Mgr.
Director: David I. Klapper.
EIN: 352003440

3358
The Community Covenant Foundation, Inc.
6310 Ferguson St.
Indianapolis, IN 46220-1708

Established in 2000 in Indiana.
Donors: Thomas L. Hefner; Patty M. Hefner; TLH Charitable Lead Trust.
Foundation type: Independent foundation.
Financial data (yr. ended 12/31/14): Assets, $3,377,138 (M); gifts received, $61,469; expenditures, $180,351; qualifying distributions, $163,000; giving activities include $155,000 for 24 grants (high: $50,000; low: $5,000).
Fields of interest: Education; Religion; Human services.

Limitations: Applications not accepted. Giving primarily in Indianapolis, IN. No grants to individuals.
Application information: Unsolicited requets for funds not accepted.
Officer and Directors: Thomas L. Hefner, Pres. and Director; Henry Mason Hefner; James Curtis Hefner; Patty M. Hefner.
EIN: 352117707

3359
Community Foundation of Madison and Jefferson County, Inc.
416 W. St., Ste. B
P.O. Box 306
Madison, IN 47250-0306 (812) 265-3327
Contact: Bill Barnes, Pres. and C.E.O.
FAX: (812) 273-0181; E-mail: info@cfmjc.org; Main URL: http://www.cfmjc.org
Facebook: http://www.facebook.com/cfmjc
Scholarship e-mail: kelly@cfmjc.org

Established in 1992 in Indiana.
Foundation type: Community foundation.
Financial data (yr. ended 12/31/12): Assets, $18,126,846 (M); gifts received, $273,207; expenditures, $731,134; giving activities include $369,584 for 19+ grants (high: $42,615), and $71,845 for 51 grants to individuals.
Purpose and activities: The mission of the foundation is to build a strong, vibrant community by helping donors provide perpetual funding for the people, projects and passions of Jefferson County, IN.
Fields of interest: Arts and culture; Education; Environment; Animal welfare; Diseases and conditions; Community and economic development; Human services; Adolescents; Seniors.
Type of support: Capacity-building and technical assistance; Pro bono consulting services; Matching grants; Capital campaigns; Building and renovations; Equipment; Endowments; Emergency funds; Program development; Convening; Seed money; Scholarships; Technical assistance; Student aid.
Limitations: Applications accepted. Giving limited to Jefferson County, IN. No support for religious purposes or programs requiring religious participation, public or private educational institutions, or government agencies. No grants to individuals (except for scholarships), or for debt reduction, annual appeals or membership contribution, ongoing operating expenses or regular programming of well-established agencies, or travel expenses.
Publications: Application guidelines; Annual report; Financial statement; Grants list; Informational brochure; Newsletter; Program policy statement.
Application information: Visit foundation web site for the Initial Proposal form and application information. Application form required.
  Initial approach: Contact foundation
  Deadline(s): Aug. 1 for Initial Proposal, Sept. 5 for full application
  Board meeting date(s): 1st Wed. of each month
  Final notification: Mar. 19
Officers and Directors: Bonnie Hare, Chair. and Director; Carri Dirksen, Vice-Chair. and Director; Bill Barnes, C.E.O. and Pres. and Director; Darleen Connolly, Secy. and Director; Anthony D. Brandon, Treas. and Director; Mark Wynn, Counsel; Dr. Ben Canida; Clifford Carnes; Al Huntington; Chuck

McKay; Eric Phagan; Margaret Seifert-Russell; Ann Suchocki; Steve Telfer.
Number of staff: 2 full-time professional; 1 full-time support; 1 part-time support.
EIN: 351847297

3360
Community Foundation of Morgan County, Inc.
56 N. Main St.
Martinsville, IN 46151-1415 (765) 813-0003
Contact: Edward Kominowski, Exec. Dir.
FAX: (765) 813-0017; E-mail: info@cfmconline.org;
Toll Free Tel.: (855) 280-3095; Mooresville office address: 250 N. Monroe St., Mooresville, IN 46158;
Phone: (317)-831-1232; Fax: (765)-813-0017;
Main URL: http://cfmconline.org
Facebook: https://www.facebook.com/CFMorganCounty
Google Plus: https://plus.google.com/+YourcfmcOrg/posts

Established in 1995 in Indiana.
Foundation type: Community foundation.
Financial data (yr. ended 12/31/13): Assets, $6,981,178 (M); gifts received, $1,049,979; expenditures, $1,330,980; giving activities include $109,896 for 1+ grant, and $113,202 for 74 grants to individuals.
Purpose and activities: The foundation works with citizens to enhance the quality of life for current and future generations. It accepts gifts, administers funds, and makes grants to meet needs throughout Morgan County, IN.
Fields of interest: Arts and culture; Education; Environment; Health; Community and economic development; Human services; Youth development.
Type of support: Capital and infrastructure; In-kind gifts; Matching grants; Equipment; Endowments; Program development; Publications; Seed money; Curriculum development; Scholarships; Technical assistance; Student aid.
Limitations: Applications accepted. Giving limited to the Morgan County, IN, area.
Publications: Application guidelines; Annual report; Financial statement; Grants list; Informational brochure; Newsletter.
Application information: The foundation hosts a free "How to Apply for Grants" seminar; visit foundation web site for more information and complete application forms, guidelines, and deadlines. Application form required.
  Initial approach: Contact foundation
  Deadline(s): Varies
  Board meeting date(s): 2nd Mon. of each month
  Final notification: Within 1 month
Officers and Directors: Chris Branson, Pres. and Director; Lisa Arnold, V.P. and Director; Frank Rowe, Secy. and Director; James Johnson, Treas. and Director; Ed Kominowski, Exec. Dir.; Tim Currens; Susan Haynes; William Meredith; Steve Sonnega; Judith Strode; Judy Williams; Patty Wood.
Number of staff: 2 full-time professional; 1 part-time professional.
EIN: 351956929

3361
Community Foundation of Randolph County, Inc.
213 S. Main St.
Winchester, IN 47394-1824 (765) 584-9077
Contact: Ruth B. Mills, Exec. Dir.
FAX: (765) 584-7710;
E-mail: info@cfrandolphcounty.org; Additional e-mail: rmills@cfrandolphcounty.org; Main URL: http://www.randolphcountyfoundation.org
Facebook: https://www.facebook.com/#!/pages/Community-Foundation-of-Randolph-County/205746446129959
Twitter: http://www.twitter.com/CFofRC

Established in 1992 in Indiana.
Foundation type: Community foundation.
Financial data (yr. ended 12/31/13): Assets, $8,262,514 (M); gifts received, $725,251; expenditures, $628,515; giving activities include $314,860 for 23+ grants (high: $57,888), and $126,169 for 68 grants to individuals.
Purpose and activities: The Community Foundation of Randolph County, Inc. seeks to bring people and resources together to enrich the lives of Randolph County residents. .
Fields of interest: Arts and culture; Historic preservation; Education; Higher education; Environment; Health; Community and economic development; Economic development; Human services; Adolescents; Seniors.
Type of support: Program development; Curriculum development; Scholarships; Individual development.
Limitations: Applications accepted. Giving limited to Randolph County, IN. No support for religious or sectarian purposes. No grants to individuals (except for scholarships), or for make-up of operating deficits, post-event or after-the-fact situations, or endowments campaigns.
Publications: Application guidelines; Annual report; Newsletter; Occasional report (including application guidelines).
Application information: Visit foundation web site for application cover sheet and guidelines. Completed typewritten application forms should be sent or delivered to the foundation's office. Applications cannot be submitted online. Application form required.
  Initial approach: Submit application
  Copies of proposal: 11
  Deadline(s): Mar. 31 and Sept. 30
  Board meeting date(s): 3rd Thursday of each month
  Final notification: 4 to 6 weeks
Officers and Directors: Chip Loney, Pres. and Director; Cheryl Jones, V.P. and Director; Sheryl Thurston, Secy. and Director; Lisa Jennings, Treas. and Director; Ruth B. Mills, Exec. Dir.; Christen Commers; Dick Gause; Richard Gough; Jane Grove; Joyce Husmann; James Meinerding; Janice Powers; Ronn Shumaker; Cathy Stephen; Kent Thornburg; Linda Wilcox.
Number of staff: 2 full-time professional.
EIN: 351903148

3362
Community Foundation of Switzerland County, Inc.

303 Ferry St.
P.O. Box 46
Vevay, IN 47043-1103 (812) 427-9160
Contact: Pam W. Acton, Exec. Dir.
E-mail: info@cfsci.org; Grants E-mail:
pacton@cfsci.org; Scholarship E-mail:
mandrew@cfsci.org; Main URL: http://
www.cfsci.org
Facebook: http://www.facebook.com/cfsci

Established in 1999 in Indiana.
Foundation type: Community foundation.
Financial data (yr. ended 12/31/13): Assets,
$11,749,682 (M); gifts received, $439,638;
expenditures, $672,955; giving activities include
$322,221 for 8+ grants (high: $132,013), and
$54,075 for grants to individuals.
Purpose and activities: The mission of the
foundation is to connect people who care with
causes that matter for good, for ever, for Switzerland
County.
Fields of interest: Arts and culture; Education;
Environment; Health; Community and economic
development; Human services.
Limitations: Applications accepted. Giving limited to
Switzerland County, IN. No support for religious
organizations for direct religious activities. No grants
to individuals (except for scholarships), operating
expenses, debt reduction, endowments, annual
appeals or memberships, travel expenses, or
endowment building.
Publications: Application guidelines; Annual report;
Grants list; Informational brochure; Program policy
statement; Program policy statement (including
application guidelines).
Application information: Visit foundation web site
for grant application and guidelines. Application
form required.
  Initial approach: Complete online application
    through web site
  Deadline(s): Feb. 2
  Board meeting date(s): 3rd Tues. of month
Officers and Directors: Steve Lyons, Pres. and
Director; Wilma Swango, V.P. and Director; Ruth
Lohide, Secy. and Director; Phyllis Collier, Treas.
and Director; Pam W. Acton, Exec. Dir.; Jessica
Archer; Adam Cole; Nancy Craig; Ginger Furnish;
Michelle Hicks; Roy Leap; Jim Phipps.
Number of staff: 2 full-time professional.
EIN: 352087649

3363
Community Foundation Partnership, Inc.

(doing business as Lawrence County Community
Foundation)
(also known as CFP)
1324 K St., Ste. 150
P.O. Box 1235
Bedford, IN 47421-3732 (812) 279-2215
Contact: Hope Flores, Exec. Dir.
FAX: (812) 279-1984; E-mail: hope@cfpartner.org;
Main URL: http://www.cfpartner.org

Established in 1992 in Indiana.
Foundation type: Community foundation.
Financial data (yr. ended 12/31/12): Assets,
$8,388,472 (M); gifts received, $723,249;
expenditures, $692,796; giving activities include

$287,786 for grants, and $360,007 for
foundation-administered programs.
Purpose and activities: The foundation's mission is
to enhance the quality of life for the citizens of
Lawrence and Martin Counties, IN, in the areas of
education, health and human services, civic and
historical affairs, the arts and culture, and
recreational activities.
Fields of interest: Arts and culture; Historical
activities; Education; Health; Community and
economic development; Sports and recreation;
Human services.
Type of support: Endowments; Matching grants;
Scholarships.
Limitations: Applications accepted. Giving primarily
in Lawrence and Martin counties, IN. No support for
religious instruction or doctrine. No grants to
individuals (except for scholarships), or for debt
retirement, capital campaigns, or endowments.
Publications: Informational brochure; Newsletter.
Application information: Visit foundation web site
for application forms, guidelines, and specific
deadline dates. The foundation offers Grantseeker
Workshops approximately 1 month prior to grant
application deadline; attendance is strongly
encouraged. Application form required.
  Copies of proposal: 7
  Deadline(s): Varies
  Final notification: Varies
Officers and Directors: Vernita Williams, Pres. and
Director; John Drake, V.P. and Director; Beth Lett,
Secy. and Director; Hope Flores, Exec. Dir.; Deanna
Bauernfiend; Lynn Gee; Terry Hasler; Kate Hawkins;
Stevie Horton; Kim Howell; Rita Poirier; Chris
Stevens.
Number of staff: 2 full-time professional; 2 full-time
support.
EIN: 351889139

3364
Jay & Phyllis Conrad Family Foundation Inc.

400 S. Harrison St.
Berne, IN 46711-2004

Established in 1993 in Unspecified.
Donors: Phyllis Conrad‡; Mark Conrad; Jean Conrad;
Beth Conrad; Arlene Conrad.
Foundation type: Independent foundation.
Financial data (yr. ended 12/31/13): Assets,
$3,117,665 (M); gifts received, $130,321;
expenditures, $165,909; qualifying distributions,
$162,600; giving activities include $162,600 for 24
grants (high: $56,300; low: $100).
Fields of interest: Christianity.
Limitations: Applications not accepted. Giving
primarily in CA and TN.
Application information: Unsolicited requests for
funds not accepted.
Officers: Arlene Conrad, Pres.; Beth Conrad, Secy.;
Jean Conrad, Treas.
EIN: 351899472

3365
Crescent-Cresline-Wabash Plastics Foundation, Inc.

600 Cross Pointe Blvd.
Evansville, IN 47715-9119

Established in 1986 in Indiana.

Donors: Crescent Plastics, Inc.; Wabash Plastics,
Inc.; Cresline Plastics Pipe Co., Inc.;
Cresline-Northwest LLC; Cresline-West, Inc.
Foundation type: Company-sponsored foundation.
Financial data (yr. ended 12/31/14): Assets,
$5,896,296; gifts received, $1,810; expenditures,
$279,061; qualifying distributions, $269,485 and
$0 for set-asides.
Purpose and activities: The foundation supports
museums and organizations involved with
performing arts, education, and youth development.
Fields of interest: Performing arts; Orchestral
music; Museums; Education; Higher education;
Nonprofits; Youth development; Scouting programs;
Economics for youth.
Type of support: General support; Regranting.
Limitations: Applications not accepted. Giving
primarily in areas of company operations in
Evansville, IN. No grants to individuals.
Application information: Contributes only to
pre-selected organizations.
Officer: Belle Fahrer, Secy.
Directors: John C. Schroeder; Richard A. Schroeder.
EIN: 311196890

3366
Clarence E. & Inez R. Custer Foundation, Inc.

P.O. Box 929
Columbus, IN 47202-0929 (812) 376-1795
Contact: William Helmbrecht, Pres.,Treas. and Dir.

Established in 1988 in Indiana.
Foundation type: Independent foundation.
Financial data (yr. ended 12/31/13): Assets,
$8,118,331 (M); expenditures, $432,567;
qualifying distributions, $245,139; giving activities
include $226,105 for 40 grants (high: $57,000;
low: $500).
Fields of interest: Education; Zoos; Foundations;
Hospital care; Hospice care; Human services;
Family services; Youth development.
Limitations: Applications accepted. Giving primarily
within a 50-mile radius of Columbus, IN. No grants
to individuals.
Application information: Application form required.
  Initial approach: Completed application Form
  Deadline(s): None
  Board meeting date(s): As required, generally 4
    times per year
Officers and Directors: William Helmbrecht, Pres.
and Treas. and Director; James W. Holland, Secy.
and Director; Dianne Bardley; Max E. Carothers;
Dick Weaver.
Trustee: First Financial Bank, N.A.
EIN: 311130385

3367
Decatur County Community Foundation, Inc.

101 E. Main St., Ste. 1
P.O. Box 72
Greensburg, IN 47240-2031 (812) 662-6364
Contact: Tami Wenning, Exec. Dir.
FAX: (812) 662-8704;
E-mail: contact@dccfound.org; Main URL: http://
www.dccfound.org
Facebook: https://www.facebook.com/dccfound

Established in 1992 in Indiana.
Foundation type: Community foundation.

Financial data (yr. ended 12/31/13): Assets, $18,483,933 (M); gifts received, $432,148; expenditures, $773,656; giving activities include $257,743 for 9+ grants (high: $25,000), and $155,541 for 75 grants to individuals.

Purpose and activities: The foundation seeks to provide a general depository for charitable contributions that will service Decatur County. The foundation supports the following areas of interest: civic and community, education, health and human services, arts and literacy, historic preservation, safety, and youth and recreation.

Fields of interest: Arts and culture; Historic preservation; Education; Reading promotion; Health; Public health; Safety education; Community and economic development; Sports and recreation; Human services; Youth development; Youth organizing.

Type of support: Capital and infrastructure; Grants to individuals; Program-related investments; Equipment; Emergency funds; Matching grants; Program development; Seed money; Scholarships; Technical assistance; Student aid.

Limitations: Applications accepted. Giving primarily in Decatur County, IN. No support for religious purposes. No grants for debt reduction, post-event or after the fact funding, make-up operating deficits, or ongoing operating expenses.

Publications: Application guidelines; Annual report (including application guidelines); Financial statement; Informational brochure; Informational brochure (including application guidelines); Newsletter; Occasional report.

Application information: Visit foundation web site for Letter of Intent form and additional guidelines per grant type. Upon approval of Letter of Intent, grant applications will be sent to eligible applicants. Organizations may not receive foundation grants more than once in a 12-month period; maximum grant amount is $15,000. Application form required.
  Initial approach: Submit Letter of Intent form
  Copies of proposal: 10
  Deadline(s): Feb. 15, May 15, and Sept. 15 for large grants; 10th of each month for grants under $1,500; Oct. 1 and Feb. 1 for Teacher Grants.
  Board meeting date(s): 3rd Fri. monthly
  Final notification: Normally within 2 months

Officers and Directors: Gail Rueff, Pres. and Director; Dennis Wilson, V.P. and Director; Bob Cupp, Secy.-Treas. and Director; Deb Locke, Exec. Dir.; Steve Doerflinger; Sharon Hollowell; Roland Shirk; Lynda Smith; Carrie Stapp; Dave Stults; Mark Vice.

Number of staff: 1 full-time professional; 1 part-time support.

EIN: 351870979

3368
W.M. Craig and Teneen L. Dobbs Charitable Foundation
2360 Treesdale Cir.
Carmel, IN 46032-7934 (317) 848-5377
Contact: Wm. Craig Dobb, Tr.

Established in 2010 in Indiana.
Donors: W.M. Craig Dobbs; Teneen L. Dobbs.
Foundation type: Independent foundation.
Financial data (yr. ended 12/31/13): Assets, $95,613 (M); gifts received, $404,000; expenditures, $304,878; qualifying distributions, $300,886; giving activities include $300,886 for 26 grants (high: $125,500; low: $250).

Fields of interest: Arts and culture; Education; Human services.
Limitations: Applications accepted. Giving primarily in IN and KY.
Application information: Application form required.
  Initial approach: Letter
  Deadline(s): None
Trustees: Wm. Craig Dobbs; Teneen L. Dobbs.
EIN: 276429985

3369
Dorsey Foundation Inc.
5868 E. 71st St., Ste. E-217
Indianapolis, IN 46220-5859

Donors: Scott Dorsey; Erin Dorsey.
Foundation type: Independent foundation.
Financial data (yr. ended 12/31/13): Assets, $10,099,331 (M); gifts received, $10,093,288; expenditures, $556,818; qualifying distributions, $268,890; giving activities include $257,102 for 7 grants (high: $185,352; low: $500).
Fields of interest: Education; Domesticated animals; Sports and recreation.
Limitations: Applications not accepted. Giving primarily in Indianapolis, IN.
Application information: Unsolicited requests for funds not accepted.
Officers: Erin Dorsey, Pres.; Carol Dorsey, Secy.; Scott Dorsey, Treas.
EIN: 463002776

3370
Dubois County Community Foundation, Inc.
600 McCrillus St.
P.O. Box 269
Jasper, IN 47547-0269 (812) 482-5295
Contact: Brad Ward, C.E.O.
FAX: (812) 482-7461; *E-mail:* dccf@fullnet.com;
Main URL: http://www.dccommunityfoundation.org
Facebook: https://www.facebook.com/pages/Dubois-County-Community-Foundation/167434679983027
YouTube: http://www.youtube.com/channel/UCREO6Qt3VjpWgnkSS12AHqw?feature=watch

Established in 1996 in Indiana.
Foundation type: Community foundation.
Financial data (yr. ended 12/31/13): Assets, $25,493,192 (M); gifts received, $1,755,597; expenditures, $965,648; giving activities include $336,773 for 12+ grants (high: $17,145), and $46,600 for 52 grants to individuals.
Purpose and activities: The foundation believes every Dubois County citizen now and in future generations deserves a community that is vibrant, healthy and sustainable. They facilitate this belief by connecting people with the needs they care about most and empowering them to make a difference in the county through philanthropy and endowment building.
Fields of interest: Arts and culture; Education; Environment; Health; Community beautification; Sports and recreation; Human services; Youth development.
Type of support: Equipment; Program development; Convening; Publications; Seed money; Curriculum development; Scholarships; Technical assistance; Student aid.

Limitations: Applications accepted. Giving concentrated in Dubois County, IN. No support for the operational expenses of government units or agencies. No grants for operating expenses of nonprofits, funding after the fact, annual fundraising, sponsorship of events, or debt retirement; no loans.
Publications: Application guidelines; Annual report; Financial statement; Grants list; Informational brochure; Newsletter.
Application information: Visit foundation web site for application forms and guidelines. Application form required.
  Initial approach: Submit application forms and attachments
  Copies of proposal: 10
  Deadline(s): Sept. 15
  Board meeting date(s): 4th Mon. of Feb., Apr., June, Aug., Oct., and Dec.
  Final notification: Within 3 or 4 months
Officers and Directors: Pat Miller, Pres. and Director; Jen Verkamp, V.P. and Director; Brad Ward, C.E.O. and Director; Kurt Fuhs, Secy. and Director; Ray Schwenk, Treas. and Director; Jeryl Luegers, Emeritus; Gary Brick; Mitch Clark; Matt Eckert; Larry Fuesler; Kim Gunderson; Bill Kaiser; Tom Krodel; Debbie Seger; Brent Sternberg; Andrea Tooley; Brian Tretter; Nancy Wilson.
Number of staff: 2 full-time professional; 1 full-time support.
EIN: 351990305

3371
Dukes Health Care Foundation of Miami County Inc.
c/o Comerford Co.
35 W. 5th St.
Peru, IN 46970
Application address: 13 E. Main St., Peru, IN 46970, tel.: (765) 472-2236

Donors: Clarence C. Holmes Trust; Lyman Banks Trust.
Foundation type: Independent foundation.
Financial data (yr. ended 12/31/13): Assets, $7,812,215 (M); gifts received, $22,176; expenditures, $294,678; qualifying distributions, $251,878; giving activities include $246,638 for 14 grants (high: $130,492; low: $549).
Fields of interest: Health; Religion; Human services.
Limitations: Applications accepted. Giving primarily in IN.
Application information: Application form required.
  Initial approach: Proposal
  Deadline(s): Nov. 30
Officers: Sally Keith, Pres.; John Claxton, V.P.; Bob Schwartz, Secy.; Kevin Comerford, Treas.
Trustees: Jon Faust; Ralph Duckwall; Richard Wiles.
EIN: 201672681

3372
Duneland Health Council, Inc.
P.O. Box 9327
Michigan City, IN 46361-9327 (219) 874-4193

Established in 1997 in Indiana.
Donor: Alverno Health Care Corp.
Foundation type: Independent foundation.
Financial data (yr. ended 12/31/13): Assets, $7,554,523 (M); expenditures, $581,872; qualifying distributions, $428,073; giving activities

include $428,073 for 23 grants (high: $57,000; low: $500).
Purpose and activities: To improve the health and general welfare of the greater Michigan City, IN, community.
Fields of interest: Education; Graduate and professional education; Health; Health care clinics; Nursing care; Community and economic development; Children's rights; Human services; Family services.
Type of support: Advocacy.
Limitations: Applications accepted. Giving primarily in the metropolitan Michigan City, IN, area. No support for religious organizations. No grants to individuals, or for fund-raising, endowments, or advertising.
Application information: Duneland Health Council Grant Application Form required. Application form required.
  Initial approach: Proposal
  Deadline(s): None
Officers: Gil Pontius, Chair.; George R. Averitt, Vice-Chair.; Tom Cipares, Secy.; H. Fred Miller, Treas.; Norman D. Steider, Exec. Dir.
Directors: Linda Anast-May; Linda Bechinski; Barbara Eason-Watkins; Judy Jacobi; Allan Whitlow.
EIN: 352021548

3373
James W. & Betty Dye Foundation, Inc.
900 Ridge Rd., Ste. M
Munster, IN 46321-1727 (219) 836-1100
Contact: Scholarship Comm.
FAX: (219) 836-6128;
E-mail: info@dyescholarships.org; Main URL: http://jimandbettydyescholarships.org

Established in 1993 in Indiana.
Donors: James W. Dye; Betty Dye.
Foundation type: Independent foundation.
Financial data (yr. ended 12/31/14): Assets, $15,540,849 (M); gifts received, $3,625,655; expenditures, $484,748; qualifying distributions, $465,154; giving activities include $438,859 for 196 grants to individuals (high: $7,000; low: $50).
Purpose and activities: Provides tuition scholarships to qualified high school graduates of participating high schools in northwest Indiana to attend Indiana University Bloomington, Indiana University Northwest, Purdue University West Lafayette, Purdue University Calumet, Indiana University or Purdue University Indianapolis, or Ball State University Muncie.
Fields of interest: University education.
Type of support: Student aid.
Limitations: Applications accepted. Giving limited to residents of IN.
Application information: See foundation web site for complete application guidelines. Application form required.
  Deadline(s): Mar. 1
  Final notification: May 15
Officer and Director: James W. Dye, Pres. and Director.
EIN: 351884798

3374
Jack and Debra Edelman Foundation, Inc.
3274 Lantern Trail
Richmond, IN 47374-7195

Established in 2006 in Indiana.
Foundation type: Operating foundation.
Financial data (yr. ended 12/31/13): Assets, $112,254 (M); expenditures, $354,512; qualifying distributions, $350,000; giving activities include $350,000 for 2 grants (high: $250,000; low: $100,000).
Fields of interest: Judaism; Youth services.
Limitations: Applications not accepted. Giving primarily in Richmond, IN, and Dayton, OH.
Application information: Unsolicited requests for funds not accepted.
Trustees: Debra Edelman; Jack Edelman.
EIN: 208022209

3375
Elder Foundation
4251 W. Industries Rd.
Richmond, IN 47374-1385

Established in 1994 in Indiana.
Donors: Elder Groups, Inc.; Bruce E. Elder Trust; Vandor Corp.
Foundation type: Company-sponsored foundation.
Financial data (yr. ended 06/30/14): Assets, $571,199 (M); gifts received, $6,000; expenditures, $215,360; qualifying distributions, $211,000; giving activities include $211,000 for 3 grants (high: $205,000; low: $1,000).
Purpose and activities: The foundation supports organizations involved with youth development and Christianity.
Fields of interest: Christianity; Youth services.
Type of support: General support.
Limitations: Applications not accepted. Giving primarily in Richmond, IN and Rochester, MI.
Application information: Contributes only to pre-selected organizations.
Trustees: Alan H. Elder; Amy Elder; Jack E. Elder; Julie Elder; Louise Elder; Paul A. Elder.
EIN: 351944291

3376
Niel C. and Karen Ma Ellerbrook Family Foundation, Inc.
35 Johnson Pl.
Evansville, IN 47714-1605

Established in 2007 in Indiana.
Donors: Niel C. Ellerbrook; Karen Ellerbrook.
Foundation type: Independent foundation.
Financial data (yr. ended 12/31/13): Assets, $2,709,432 (M); gifts received, $296,278; expenditures, $304,838; qualifying distributions, $301,452; giving activities include $300,330 for 13 grants (high: $126,775; low: $2,500).
Fields of interest: Arts and culture; Education; Higher education; Environment.
Limitations: Applications not accepted. Giving primarily in IN. No grants to individuals.
Application information: Unsolicited requests for funds not accepted.
Officers: Niel C. Ellerbrook, Pres. and Treas.; Karen M. Ellerbrook, V.P. and Secy.
Director: Jennifer A. Warfel.
EIN: 260431032

3377
Eskenazi Family Foundation, Inc.
10689 N. Pennsylvania St.
Indianapolis, IN 46208-5728

Donor: Sidney Lois Eskenazi.
Foundation type: Independent foundation.
Financial data (yr. ended 09/30/13): Assets, $3,740,164; gifts received, $1,198,359; expenditures, $167,730; qualifying distributions, $142,268.
Fields of interest: Foundations; Diseases and conditions; Judaism; Human services.
Limitations: Applications not accepted. Giving primarily in Indianapolis, IN.
Application information: Unsolicited requests for funds not accepted.
Officers: Sidney Eskenazi, Pres.; Lois Eskenazi, Secy.; Sandra Eskenazi, Mgr.; Dori Meyers, Mgr.
EIN: 371500990

3378
Eternal Abundance Foundation, Inc.
6900 S. Gray Rd.
Indianapolis, IN 46237-3209

Established in 1994 in Indiana.
Donor: Mark A. Jackson.
Foundation type: Independent foundation.
Financial data (yr. ended 12/31/13): Assets, $100,231 (M); expenditures, $271,390; qualifying distributions, $271,390; giving activities include $271,390 for 21 grants (high: $55,400; low: $350).
Fields of interest: Religion; Human services.
Limitations: Applications not accepted. Giving primarily in FL and IN. No grants to individuals.
Application information: Contributes only to pre-selected organizations.
Officer: Mark A. Jackson, Pres.
EIN: 351940184

3379
Fayette County Foundation
521 N. Central Ave., Ste. A
P.O. Box 844
Connersville, IN 47331 (765) 827-9966
Contact: Anna Dungan, Exec. Dir.; Katherine Good, Prog. Off.
FAX: (765) 827-5836;
E-mail: info@fayettefoundation.com; Grant application e-mail: kgood@fayettefoundation.com; Main URL: http://www.fayettefoundation.com Facebook: http://www.facebook.com/pages/Connersville-IN/Fayette-County-Foundation/369719452177

Established in 1985 in Indiana.
Foundation type: Community foundation.
Financial data (yr. ended 12/31/13): Assets, $5,837,412 (M); gifts received, $59,941; expenditures, $368,226; giving activities include $174,056 for grants.
Purpose and activities: The foundation seeks to inspire a spirit of philanthropy in Fayette County, IN, by enhancing the quality of life through impacting grantmaking, strategic endowment building, and community leadership.
Fields of interest: Arts and culture; Education; Higher education; Environment; Animal welfare; Health; Diseases and conditions; Community and economic development; Sustainable development;

Economic development; Religion; Human services; Youth mentoring; Adolescents.

Type of support: Building and renovations; In-kind gifts; Endowments; Emergency funds; Convening; Scholarships; Student aid.

Limitations: Applications accepted. Giving limited to Fayette County, IN. No support for religious organizations. No grants for deficit funding, or for salaries, annual campaigns, repeat funding, or for travel expenses.

Publications: Annual report; Grants list; Informational brochure; Newsletter.

Application information: Visit foundation web site for application information. Application form required.

   Initial approach: Letter of intent
   Copies of proposal: 9
   Deadline(s): Feb. 27 for Spring Grants, Oct. 31 for Fall Grants, Oct. 1 for Letter of intent for Fall Grants, Jun. 2 for Letter of Intent Summer Grants, Feb. 2 for Letter of Intent Spring Grants.
   Board meeting date(s): Once a month
   Final notification: 4 weeks

Officers and Directors: Andy Yaryan, Pres. and Director; Anna Dungan, Exec. Dir.; Brett Adams; Jon Eakins; Mahershall Gardner; Becky Gibson; Doug Hornsby; Duane Keaffaber; Cyndi Nesbitt; Jane Oakley; Donna Stern; Nick Thomas.

Number of staff: 2 full-time professional.

EIN: 311185980

3380

Ron and Lisa Fenech Foundation

11390 County Rd. 14
Middlebury, IN 46540-1512
Application address: P.O. Box 1512, Middlebury, IN 46540, tel.: (574) 825-5310

Established in 2004 in Indiana.

Donors: Lisa R. Fenech; Ronald J. Fenech.

Foundation type: Independent foundation.

Financial data (yr. ended 12/31/13): Assets, $3,675,223 (M); expenditures, $193,140; qualifying distributions, $144,950; giving activities include $144,950 for 29 grants (high: $36,250; low: $100).

Purpose and activities: Giving primarily for higher education, Protestant churches, health care, and human services; scholarship awards to the children of employees of Keystone RV Company for colleges and universities.

Fields of interest: Education; Elementary education; Protestantism; Human services.

Type of support: Scholarships; General support; Student aid.

Limitations: Applications accepted. Giving primarily in IN.

Application information: Application form required.

   Initial approach: Completed application form
   Deadline(s): June 15

Directors: Lisa R. Fenech; Michael J. Fenech; Ronald J. Fenech; Taylor R. Fenech.

EIN: 201944647

3381

Russell & Penny Fortune Foundation Inc.

c/o Russell Fortune III
320 N. Meridian St., Ste. 410
Indianapolis, IN 46204-1723

Established in 1998 in Indiana.

Donors: Russell Fortune III; Martha Murray Fortune Foundation.

Foundation type: Independent foundation.

Financial data (yr. ended 12/31/13): Assets, $2,619,784 (M); gifts received, $222,321; expenditures, $246,670; qualifying distributions, $215,472; giving activities include $212,720 for 4 grants (high: $71,570; low: $29,200).

Fields of interest: Elementary and secondary education.

Limitations: Applications not accepted.

Application information: Unsolicited requests for funds not accepted.

Officers: Russell Fortune III, Chair.; Paul Lindemann, Secy.; James P. Fadley, Exec. Dir.

Directors: Penny Fortune; Marc A. Hetzner; William C. Metzger.

EIN: 352041399

3382

Franklin Electric Charitable & Educational Foundation

(formerly The Franklin Electric—Edward J. Schaefer and T. W. Kehoe Charitable and Educational Foundation, Inc.)
9255 Coverdale Rd.
Fort Wayne, IN 46809 (260) 824-2900
Contact: John J. Haines, Secy.

Established in 1964 in Indiana.

Donor: Franklin Electric Co., Inc.

Foundation type: Company-sponsored foundation.

Financial data (yr. ended 12/31/13): Assets, $1,829 (M); gifts received, $156,255; expenditures, $192,053; qualifying distributions, $191,667; giving activities include $165,631 for 48 grants (high: $22,372; low: $250), and $23,000 for 13 grants to individuals (high: $2,000; low: $1,000).

Purpose and activities: The foundation supports orchestras and organizations involved with television, education, and youth development.

Fields of interest: Education; Community and economic development; Religion.

Type of support: General support; Scholarships.

Limitations: Applications accepted. Giving primarily in areas of company operations, with emphasis on AR, IN, and OK.

Application information: Application form required.

   Initial approach: Contact foundation for application form
   Deadline(s): None

Officers: R. Scott Trumbull, Pres. and C.E.O.; Thomas J. Strupp, V.P.; John J. Haines, Co-Secy.; Angela M. Hughes, Co-Secy.

EIN: 237399324

3383

The Froderman Foundation, Inc.

4325 U.S. Highway 41
P.O. Box 10039
Terre Haute, IN 47802-4406
Contact: Mark Fuson, Pres.
FAX: (812) 232-8414;
E-mail: markfuson@drivefuson.com; Main URL: http://www.frodermanfoundation.com

Established in 1962 in Indiana.

Donors: Harvey Froderman†; Mrs. Harvey Froderman.

Foundation type: Independent foundation.

Financial data (yr. ended 12/31/14): Assets, $12,015,249 (M); expenditures, $473,253; qualifying distributions, $404,069; giving activities include $404,069 for 18 grants (high: $128,571; low: $1,600).

Purpose and activities: The foundation's mission is to provide funds to qualified applicants whose emphasis is to promote religious, educational, medical, and/or charitable causes.

Fields of interest: Higher education; Diseases and conditions; Christianity; Human services.

Type of support: Capital and infrastructure; Equipment; Publications; Scholarships.

Limitations: Applications accepted. Giving primarily in Indianapolis and Terre Haute, IN. No grants to individuals, or for operating budgets.

Application information: Application form required.

   Initial approach: Request application
   Copies of proposal: 1
   Deadline(s): None
   Board meeting date(s): Apr., June, Sept., and Dec.

Officers: Mark Fuson, Pres.; Carl Froderman, V.P.; Chris Froderman, Secy.; Brad Fuson, Treas.

EIN: 356025283

3384

Gaither Charitable Foundation, Inc.

P.O. Box 737
Alexandria, IN 46001-0737 (765) 724-8278
Contact: Gina Brisco

Donors: William J. Gaither; Gloria Gaither; Bill Gaither.

Foundation type: Independent foundation.

Financial data (yr. ended 12/31/13): Assets, $6,713,753 (M); expenditures, $475,757; qualifying distributions, $408,915; giving activities include $408,915 for 23 grants (high: $300,000; low: $25).

Fields of interest: Education; University education; Christianity; Human services.

Limitations: Applications accepted. Giving primarily in IN.

Application information:

   Initial approach: Proposal
   Deadline(s): None

Officers: William J. Gaither, Pres.; Barry W. Jennings, Secy.

Directors: Gloria L. Gaither; Suzanne G. Jennings.

EIN: 352020501

3385

J. A. Gammon Charitable Foundation, Inc.

c/o George Carberry
9191 Broadway
Merrillville, IN 46410-7043

Established in 1991 in Indiana.

Foundation type: Independent foundation.

Financial data (yr. ended 12/31/13): Assets, $3,856,154 (M); expenditures, $223,710; qualifying distributions, $207,210; giving activities include $181,520 for 11 grants (high: $123,520; low: $1,000).

Fields of interest: Performing arts; Education; Hospital care; Diabetes; Communication media; Housing development; Human services; Family services; Child welfare; Scouting programs; Low-income and poor people.

Type of support: Research.

Limitations: Applications not accepted. Giving primarily in IN and New York, NY; some funding also in Chicago, IL. No grants to individuals.
Application information: Contributes only to pre-selected organizations.
Officers and Directors: Viola Ann Gammon Botterman, Pres. and Director; James A. Gammon III, V.P. and Director; George Carberry, Secy. and Director.
EIN: 621474246

3386
Max L. & Jacqueline Gibson Foundation
P.O. Box 9629
Terre Haute, IN   47808-9629   (812) 234-4864
Contact: John Perry, Trust Off., Terre Haute Savings Bank

Established in 1984 in Indiana.
Donors: Max L. Gibson; Jacqueline Gibson; Gregory Gibson; Jami Patterson.
Foundation type: Independent foundation.
Financial data (yr. ended 11/30/13): Assets, $2,625,950 (M); gifts received, $7,800; expenditures, $238,732; qualifying distributions, $235,900; giving activities include $235,900 for 97 grants (high: $24,500; low: $100).
Fields of interest: Education; Protestantism; Human services.
Type of support: General support; Emergency funds.
Limitations: Applications accepted. Giving primarily in Terre Haute, IN. No grants to individuals.
Application information: Application form required.
   Initial approach: Letter
   Copies of proposal: 2
   Deadline(s): None
   Board meeting date(s): Nov.
Officers: Gregory Gibson, Mgr.; Lisa Gibson, Mgr.; Max L. Gibson, Mgr.; Jami Patterson, Mgr.; Jill Short, Mgr.
Trustee: Terre Haute Savings Bank.
EIN: 356417568

3387
Globe Foundation Limited
3392 Eden Hollow Pl.
Carmel, IN   46033-3033
E-mail: info@globefoundation.org; *Main URL:* http://www.globefoundation.org
Flickr: https://www.flickr.com/photos/77184629@N08
Twitter: http://twitter.com/GlobeFoundation

Established in 2008 in Indiana.
Donors: Suzanne Fehsenfeld; Fred M. Fehsenfeld, Jr.
Foundation type: Independent foundation.
Financial data (yr. ended 12/31/13): Assets, $5,373 (M); gifts received, $253,700; expenditures, $419,369; qualifying distributions, $382,500; giving activities include $382,500 for 6 grants (high: $150,000; low: $2,500).
Purpose and activities: Giving primarily to organizations and individuals addressing humanitarian, animal and environmental conservation needs worldwide.
Fields of interest: Environment; Domesticated animals; Human services.
Limitations: Applications not accepted. Giving primarily in IN.

Application information: Unsolicited requests for funds not accepted.
Officers: Suzanne Fehsenfeld, Chair.; Fred M. Fehsenfeld, Jr., Vice-Chair.; Karen A. Kennelly, Secy.-Treas.
EIN: 263282195

3388
God's Provision Inc.
c/o L.M. Henderson & Company LLP
450 E. 96th St., Ste. 200
Indianapolis, IN   46240-3797

Established in 2004 in Indiana.
Donors: Timothy L. Wagner; Carol A. Wagner.
Foundation type: Independent foundation.
Financial data (yr. ended 06/30/14): Assets, $1,111,587; gifts received, $1,420; expenditures, $140,568; qualifying distributions, $131,750.
Fields of interest: Christianity.
Type of support: General support.
Limitations: Applications not accepted. Giving primarily in Indianapolis, IN. No grants to individuals.
Application information: Unsolicited requests for funds not accepted.
Officers: Timothy L. Wagner, Pres.; Carol A. Wagner, V.P.; Stephanie Wagner, Secy.; Erica Iles, Treas.
EIN: 202016970

3389
The Green Family Charitable Foundation
4449 Hickory Grove Blvd.
Greenwood, IN   46143   (317) 496-1121
Contact: Jennifer Kent, Exec. Dir.

Donors: Patricia Green; Larry Green.
Foundation type: Operating foundation.
Financial data (yr. ended 12/31/13): Assets, $202,522 (M); gifts received, $300,000; expenditures, $398,394; qualifying distributions, $374,500; giving activities include $374,500 for 7 grants (high: $260,000; low: $1,000).
Fields of interest: Christianity.
Limitations: Applications accepted. Giving primarily in IN and MO.
Application information:
   Initial approach: Proposal
   Deadline(s): None
Officer: Jennifer Kent, Exec. Dir.
EIN: 200405852

3390
Greene County Foundation, Inc.
(formerly Greene County Community Foundation)
4513 W. State Hwy. 54
Bloomfield, IN   47424   8126593142
Contact: Cam Trampke, Exec. Dir.
E-mail: gcf@greenecountyfoundation.org; *Additional e-mail:* ctrampke@greenecountyfoundation.org; *Tel./Fax:* (812) 659-3142; *Main URL:* http://www.greenecountyfoundation.org
Facebook: https://www.facebook.com/GreeneCountyFoundation

Established in 1990 in Indiana.
Foundation type: Community foundation.
Financial data (yr. ended 12/31/13): Assets, $5,931,242 (M); gifts received, $249,728; expenditures, $381,830; giving activities include

$198,316 for 3+ grants (high: $83,815), and $25,121 for 11 grants to individuals.
Purpose and activities: The foundation seeks to work with charitably minded individuals and organizations to strengthen Greene County now and for future generations to come.
Fields of interest: Arts and culture; Philanthropy; Health; Community and economic development; Community beautification; Sports and recreation; Human services.
Type of support: Program development.
Limitations: Applications accepted. Giving limited to Greene County, IN. No support for religious purposes. No grants for annual appeals or membership contributions.
Publications: Application guidelines; Annual report; Occasional report.
Application information: Visit foundation web site for more information.
   Initial approach: Contact foundation
   Copies of proposal: 6
   Deadline(s): July 22
   Board meeting date(s): 2nd Mon. of every month
   Final notification: Aug.
Officers and Directors: Kevin Kramer, Pres. and Director; John Wells, V.P. and Director; Patti Jones, Secy. and Director; Melonie Graves, Treas. and Director; Cam Trampke, Exec. Dir.; beth Clark; Grace Hayes; Kim Hughes; Tom Roberts; Dan Sichting; Linda Thomas; Bob Weeks.
Number of staff: 1 part-time professional; 1 part-time support.
EIN: 351815060

3391
The Harlan Family Foundation
7597 E. U.S. Hwy. 36
Avon, IN   46123-7171

Donors: Hal P. Harlan; Hal P. Harlan Charitable Lead Trust.
Foundation type: Independent foundation.
Financial data (yr. ended 12/31/13): Assets, $6,159,668 (M); gifts received, $73,317; expenditures, $272,515; qualifying distributions, $223,999; giving activities include $223,199 for 15 grants (high: $42,784; low: $250).
Fields of interest: Museums; Children's museums; Zoos; Foundations; Nonprofits; Community service.
Type of support: General support; Capital campaigns; Regranting.
Limitations: Applications not accepted. Giving primarily in AR and IN. No grants to individuals.
Application information: Contributes only to pre-selected organizations.
Trustees: Doug Harlan; Hal P. Harlan; Hugh Harlan.
EIN: 203994043

3392
Herr Family Foundation, Inc.
7113 Bentgrass Dr.
Indianapolis, IN   46236-8120

Established in 1997 in Indiana.
Foundation type: Independent foundation.
Financial data (yr. ended 12/31/14): Assets, $2,264,297; expenditures, $170,351; qualifying distributions, $151,920.
Fields of interest: Christianity; Family services; Youth services.
Type of support: General support.

Limitations: Applications not accepted. Giving primarily in Indianapolis, IN. No grants to individuals.
Application information: Unsolicited requests for funds not accepted.
Officers: Audrey C. Williams, Pres.; Linda Dison, V.P.
Trustees: Emily Williams; Robert Williams.
EIN: 352016101

3393
John A. Hillenbrand Foundation, Inc.
300 Winding Way, Ste. 200
Batesville, IN   47006-7611   (812) 934-8274
Contact: W. August Hillenbrand, Pres.

Established in 1950 in Indiana.
Donor: Hillenbrand Industries, Inc.
Foundation type: Independent foundation.
Financial data (yr. ended 11/30/12): Assets, $4,384,037 (M); expenditures, $240,825; qualifying distributions, $235,850; giving activities include $233,350 for 12 grants (high: $100,000; low: $1,250).
Purpose and activities: Giving primarily for community development, particularly to support computer literacy in schools in the Batesville, Indiana, area; giving also for local arts organizations.
Fields of interest: Arts and culture; Performing arts; Education; Foundations; Community and economic development; European football; Scouting programs; Females.
Type of support: Advocacy.
Limitations: Applications accepted. Giving limited to Batesville, IN, and surrounding areas.
Application information:
Initial approach: Typed letter
Deadline(s): Early Apr.
Board meeting date(s): May
Officers: W. August Hillenbrand, Pres.; John A. Hillenbrand II, 1st V.P.; William A. Hillenbrand II, 2nd V.P.; J. Claire Sherman, Secy.; George E. Brinkmoeller, Treas.
EIN: 356042242

3394
J. Herbert Hoch & Martha Hoch Memorial Trust
P.O. Box 188
Francesville, IN   47946-0188
Application address: Winamac Jr.-Sr. High School, 715 School Dr., Winamac, IN 46996, tel.: (219) 946-6151

Established in 2004 in Indiana.
Donor: J. Herbert Hoch.
Foundation type: Operating foundation.
Financial data (yr. ended 12/31/13): Assets, $6,194,731 (M); expenditures, $270,116; qualifying distributions, $482,235; giving activities include $249,459 for 33 grants to individuals (high: $18,206; low: $245).
Purpose and activities: Scholarship awards to graduating seniors from Eastern Pulaski Community School Corporation of Winamac, IN, who will attend a college or university in the fall immediately following graduation.
Fields of interest: Higher education.
Type of support: Student aid.
Limitations: Applications accepted. Giving primarily in Winamac, IN.
Application information: Application form required.

Initial approach: Proposal
Deadline(s): Apr. 1
Trustee: Alliance Bank, N.A.
EIN: 776236699

3395
Hoffman Legacy Foundation, Inc.
2925 Chichester Ln.
Fort Wayne, IN   46815-8550

Established in 2002 in Indiana.
Donors: Gregory Hoffman; Susan Hoffman.
Foundation type: Independent foundation.
Financial data (yr. ended 12/31/14): Assets, $287,607 (M); gifts received, $93,375; expenditures, $123,736; qualifying distributions, $117,500; giving activities include $117,500 for 10 grants (high: $45,000; low: $1,000).
Fields of interest: Higher education; Health; Catholicism; Catholics.
Limitations: Applications not accepted. Giving primarily in IN. No grants to individuals.
Application information: Unsolicited requests for funds not accepted.
Directors: Gregory Hoffman; Susanne Hoffman; Jeffrey Moheban.
EIN: 300024915

3396
Hulman & Company Foundation, Inc.
P.O. Box 150
Terre Haute, IN   47808-0150   (812) 232-9446

Established in 1998 in Indiana.
Donor: Hulman & Co.
Foundation type: Company-sponsored foundation.
Financial data (yr. ended 12/31/14): Assets, $3,728,659; expenditures, $168,708; qualifying distributions, $160,000.
Purpose and activities: The foundation supports community foundations and organizations involved with engineering education, animal welfare, and youth services.
Fields of interest: Graduate and professional education; Animal welfare; Foundations; Engineering; Human services; Youth services.
Type of support: General support.
Application information:
Initial approach: Proposal
Deadline(s): None
Officers: W. Curtis Brighton, Pres.; Gretchen E. Snelling, Secy.; Jeffrey G. Belskus, Treas.
Directors: Anton H. George; M. Josephine George; Katherine M. George; Mari H. George; Nancy L. George.
EIN: 352063427

3397
Huntington County Community Foundation, Inc.
(formerly Heritage Fund of Huntington County, Inc.)
356 W. Park Dr.
P.O. Box 5037
Huntington, IN   46750-2636   (260) 356-8878
Contact: Michael Howell, Exec. Dir.
FAX: (260) 356-0921;
E-mail: info@huntingtonccf.org; Main URL: http://huntingtonccf.org
E Newsletter: http://huntingtonccf.org/newsletter.html

Facebook: http://www.facebook.com/pages/Huntington-County-Community-Foundation/241568909220594
Scholarship e-mail: scholarship@huntingtonccf.org

Established in 1991 in Indiana.
Foundation type: Community foundation.
Financial data (yr. ended 12/31/13): Assets, $13,786,715 (M); gifts received, $315,416; expenditures, $663,525; giving activities include $338,538 for 4+ grants (high: $100,000), and $83,438 for 108 grants to individuals.
Purpose and activities: The foundation funds charitable projects that will make a positive impact on Huntington County, IN, and its people, and is particularly interested in ideas that shed new light on local needs and provide innovative, long term solutions. Grantmaking areas of interest include arts and culture, community development, education, environment, health, human services, and youth development.
Fields of interest: Arts and culture; Education; Elementary and secondary education; Higher education; Environment; Health; Community and economic development; Sports and recreation; Human services; Youth development.
Type of support: Capacity-building and technical assistance; Pro bono consulting services; Annual campaigns; Program-related investments; Matching grants; Capital and infrastructure; Equipment; Land acquisitions; Endowments; Program development; Convening; Professorships; Publications; Seed money; Curriculum development; Scholarships; Technical assistance; Program evaluations; Student aid.
Limitations: Applications accepted. Giving primarily in Huntington County, IN. No grants for operating funds.
Publications: Application guidelines; Annual report; Annual report (including application guidelines); Financial statement; Grants list; Informational brochure; Informational brochure (including application guidelines); Newsletter; Newsletter (including application guidelines); Program policy statement; Program policy statement (including application guidelines).
Application information: Visit foundation web site for application form and guidelines. Application form required.
Initial approach: Submit application
Copies of proposal: 8
Deadline(s): Apr. 15 and Oct. 15; Mar. 25 for Scholarships
Board meeting date(s): Bimonthly
Final notification: 2 weeks
Officers and Directors: Jim Scheiber, Pres. and Director; Rick Delaney, 1st V.P. and Director; Steve Eisenhut, 2nd V.P. and Treas. and Director; Michael Howell, Exec. Dir.; Nancy Breiner; Gina Canady; David Daugherty; Midge Decker; Roger Dyson; Bill Hancher; Steve Kimmel; John Niederman; Marshall Sanders; Fred Scheiber; Greg Smitley.
Number of staff: 1 full-time professional; 1 part-time professional; 1 part-time support.
EIN: 351838709

3398
Interactive Intelligence Foundation Corp.
c/o Ashley Vukovits
7601 Interactive Way
Indianapolis, IN   46278-2727   (317) 872-3000
E-mail: info@inin.com; Main URL: http://interactivefoundation.org

Donors: Donald Brown; Interactive Intelligence Inc.; The Indianapolis Foundation Legacy; Audiocodes Inc.; Karen Hill; Mark Hill.
Foundation type: Independent foundation.
Financial data (yr. ended 12/31/13): Assets, $259,986 (M); gifts received, $236,430; expenditures, $190,141; qualifying distributions, $188,390; giving activities include $154,709 for 14 grants (high: $50,382; low: $350).
Fields of interest: Education; Human services; Youth development.
Limitations: Applications accepted. Giving primarily in IN.
Application information: Application form required.
 Initial approach: See website for application form and submit via e-mail
 Deadline(s): Nov. 15
Officers and Directors: Donald Brown, Chair. and Director; Joseph Staples, Pres. and Director; Ashley Vukovits, Secy.-Treas. and Director.
EIN: 274265697

3399
J & S Laidig Family Foundation, Inc.
14450 Madison Rd.
Mishawaka, IN 46544-9103

Donors: Jon & Sonja Laidig Charitable Trust; Jon Laidig; Laidig Systems Inc.; Sonja Laidig; Wynn Laidig.
Foundation type: Independent foundation.
Financial data (yr. ended 12/31/14): Assets, $5,192,810; expenditures, $249,428; qualifying distributions, $228,000.
Fields of interest: Philanthropy; Religion; Human services.
Limitations: Applications not accepted.
Application information: Unsolicited requests for funds not accepted.
Officers: Wynn Laidig, Pres. and Secy.; Lyn Rich, V.P. and Treas.
EIN: 273191498

3400
The J. & J. Foundation, Inc.
2925 Anniston Dr.
Indianapolis, IN 46227

Established in 2003 in Indiana.
Donor: Ober Foundation.
Foundation type: Independent foundation.
Financial data (yr. ended 10/31/12): Assets, $231,654 (M); expenditures, $121,202; qualifying distributions, $118,750; giving activities include $118,750 for 6 grants (high: $52,900; low: $200).
Fields of interest: Foundations; Christianity; Human services.
Limitations: Applications not accepted. Giving primarily in IN. No grants to individuals.
Application information: Unsolicited requests for funds not accepted.
Officers: John Howell, Pres.; Mary Ann Reed, Secy.
Director: Janet Dunn.
EIN: 900117924

3401
Jasper Foundation, Inc.
301 N. Van Rensselaer St.
P.O. Box 295
Rensselaer, IN 47978-2630 (219) 866-5899
Contact: Kristen Ziese, Exec. Dir.
FAX: (219) 866-0555; E-mail: jasper@liljasper.com;
Additional e-mail: kziese@jasperfdn.org; Main URL: http://www.jasperfdn.org

Established in 1992 in Indiana.
Foundation type: Community foundation.
Financial data (yr. ended 12/31/12): Assets, $13,957,576 (M); gifts received, $1,528,430; expenditures, $449,059; giving activities include $248,193 for 1+ grant (high: $18,209).
Purpose and activities: The foundation seeks to assist donors in creating a source of assets to meet the ongoing and changing charitable needs and interests of the people living in all of the Jasper County communities. The foundation seeks to make philanthropic grants in response to community needs for education, arts and culture, health, social concerns, and historic preservation.
Fields of interest: Arts and culture; Historic preservation; Education; Higher education; Environment; Health; Hospital care; Community and economic development; Sports and recreation; Human services.
Type of support: Seed money; Matching grants; Scholarships; Individual development.
Limitations: Applications accepted. Giving limited to Jasper County, IN. No support for religious purposes or for national organizations (unless the monies are to be used solely to benefit citizens of Jasper County). No grants for budget deficits, endowments, annual giving campaigns, or for projects normally the responsibility of a government agency; generally no grants for travel.
Publications: Application guidelines; Annual report.
Application information: Visit foundation web site for application form and guidelines. Application form required.
 Initial approach: Contact Exec. Dir. before submitting application
 Copies of proposal: 6
 Deadline(s): Apr. 1 and Oct. 1
Officers and Directors: Dr. Kathy Parkison, Pres. and Director; Stephen J. Kinsell, V.P. and Director; Dawn Kearney, Secy. and Director; David F. Schrum, Treas. and Director; Kristen Ziese, Exec. Dir.; Norman P. Chappell; Russell Collins; Hubert Doughty; Dr. Jack Drone; Brian Egan; Ashley Hayworth-Hopp; Craig Hooker; Calvin Ilingworth; Ron Jordan; Gene Lehman; Todd Sammons; Patty Stringfellow; John Tillema; Gina Van Baren.
EIN: 351842404

3402
Jennings County Community Foundation, Inc.
111 N. State St.
North Vernon, IN 47265 (812) 346-5553
Contact: Barbara Shaw, Exec. Dir.
FAX: (812) 352-4061;
E-mail: jccf@jenningsfoundation.net; Main URL: http://www.jenningsfoundation.net
Facebook: https://www.facebook.com/pages/Jennings-County-Community-Foundation/144210068953807?ref=ts

Established in 1994 in Indiana.

Foundation type: Community foundation.
Financial data (yr. ended 12/31/13): Assets, $4,319,856 (M); gifts received, $424,811; expenditures, $476,534; giving activities include $219,152 for 3+ grants (high: $25,505), and $102,370 for 63 grants to individuals.
Purpose and activities: The foundation seeks to serve philanthropic and charitable needs in Jennings County, IN, by offering endowment services, grantmaking, scholarships, donor estate and planned gift services to individuals and qualified organizations serving the community.
Fields of interest: Arts and culture; Education; Environment; Health; Community and economic development; Human services.
Type of support: Capital and infrastructure; Pro bono consulting services; Program-related investments; Equipment; Endowments; In-kind gifts; Matching grants; Program development; Curriculum development; Scholarships.
Limitations: Applications accepted. Giving primarily in Jennings County, IN. No grants to individuals (except for scholarships).
Publications: Application guidelines; Annual report; Financial statement; Informational brochure; Newsletter.
Application information: Visit the foundation's web site for application form, guidelines and specific deadline dates. Application form required.
 Initial approach: Submit application and attachments
 Copies of proposal: 10
 Deadline(s): Mar. and Sept.
 Board meeting date(s): Monthly
Officers and Board Members: Greg Hicks, Pres. and Director; Linda Erler, V.P. and Director; Brenda Habenicht, Secy. and Director; Carolyn Frey, Treas. and Director; Barb Shaw, Exec. Dir.; Darlene Bradshaw; Dr. Bill Burnett; Bill Dillon; Kathy Dove; Teri Doran; Jennifer Franklin; Kathryn Johnson; Dixie Tempest; Sandy Vance; Bob Weeks.
Number of staff: 1 full-time professional; 2 part-time support.
EIN: 351922885

3403
Jack Jennings Foundation
9910 Cumberland Rd.
Fishers, IN 46038-9216

Established in 1995 in Indiana.
Donors: Bonnie McGinnis; Craig McGinnis.
Foundation type: Independent foundation.
Financial data (yr. ended 12/31/13): Assets, $2,872,320 (M); expenditures, $193,028; qualifying distributions, $180,665; giving activities include $180,665 for 29 grants (high: $88,550; low: $100).
Fields of interest: Education; Health; Diseases and conditions; Christianity.
Type of support: Research; Research and evaluation.
Limitations: Applications not accepted. Giving primarily in IN. No grants to individuals.
Application information: Unsolicited requests for funds not accepted.
Trustees: Bonnie McGinnis; Craig McGinnis.
EIN: 356627471

3404
Jolan Foundation Corp.
1312 Fran Lin Pkwy.
Munster, IN 46321-3706

Established in 2007 in Indiana.
Donor: Eugene H. Deutsch.
Foundation type: Independent foundation.
Financial data (yr. ended 12/31/14): Assets, $8,167 (M); gifts received, $230,000; expenditures, $226,049; qualifying distributions, $226,049; giving activities include $226,049 for 27 grants (high: $100,000; low: $500).
Fields of interest: Nonprofits; Hospital care; Diseases and conditions.
Type of support: Regranting.
Limitations: Applications not accepted. Giving primarily in IN. No grants to individuals.
Application information: Unsolicited requests for funds not accepted.
Officers: Eugene H. Deutsch, Pres.; Joseph Deutsch, V.P.; Shirley Deutsch, Secy.-Treas.
EIN: 261392912

3405
Emil E. Keck Charitable Trust
c/o Old National Bank
1 Main St.
Evansville, IN 47708-1464

Established in 1968 in Indiana.
Foundation type: Independent foundation.
Financial data (yr. ended 12/31/13): Assets, $3,262,498 (M); expenditures, $288,787; qualifying distributions, $254,725; giving activities include $254,725 for 3 grants (high: $84,910; low: $84,905).
Fields of interest: Education; Religion; Human services.
Limitations: Applications not accepted. No grants to individuals.
Application information: Unsolicited requests for funds not accepted.
Trustee: Old National Trust Co.
EIN: 356434803

3406
KEJ Foundation, Inc.
6900 S. Gray Rd.
Indianapolis, IN 46237-3209

Established in 2000 in Indiana.
Donor: Kyle Jackson.
Foundation type: Independent foundation.
Financial data (yr. ended 12/31/13): Assets, $0 (M); gifts received, $499,175; expenditures, $408,264; qualifying distributions, $395,102; giving activities include $395,102 for 114 grants (high: $62,560; low: $50).
Fields of interest: Education; Christianity.
Limitations: Applications not accepted. Giving primarily in FL and IN. No grants to individuals.
Application information: Contributes only to pre-selected organizations.
Directors: Thomas Conner; Blake A. Jackson; Kyle Jackson.
EIN: 352123727

3407
The Kharis Foundation Inc.
1332 Wilderness Dr.
Schererville, IN 46375-2944 (219) 865-1261
Contact: Diane Aardema, Secy.-Treas. and Dir.

Donors: Norman Aardema; Diane Aardema.
Foundation type: Independent foundation.
Financial data (yr. ended 12/31/12): Assets, $116,366 (M); gifts received, $100,000; expenditures, $113,145; qualifying distributions, $112,900; giving activities include $112,900 for 17 grants (high: $50,000; low: $200).
Fields of interest: Arts and culture; Housing development; Religion.
Limitations: Applications accepted. Giving primarily in IL and SD.
Application information: Application form required.
 Initial approach: Letter
 Deadline(s): None
Officers and Directors: Norman Aardema, Pres. and Director; Diane Aardema, Secy.-Treas. and Director; Peter Aardema.
EIN: 020814904

3408
The Klapper Family Foundation, Inc.
8730 Williamshire East Dr.
Indianapolis, IN 46260 (317) 844-7324

Established in 1996 in Indiana.
Donor: David I. Klapper.
Foundation type: Independent foundation.
Financial data (yr. ended 12/31/14): Assets, $9,949,933; expenditures, $442,595; qualifying distributions, $440,024.
Purpose and activities: Giving primarily to a university; some giving also to Jewish organizations and temples as well as for children, youth, families, and social services, including an emergency shelter for homeless families with children.
Fields of interest: Theater; Education; University education; Nonprofits; Hospital care; Judaism; Human services; Family services; Child welfare; Youth organizing.
Type of support: Regranting.
Limitations: Applications accepted. Giving primarily in Bloomfield and Indianapolis, IN.
Application information: Application form required.
 Initial approach: Proposal
 Deadline(s): None
Officers: David I. Klapper, Pres. and Treas.; Mary Elizabeth Klapper, V.P. and Secy.
Director: Alan H. Cohen.
EIN: 351999306

3409
Charles W. Kuhne Foundation Trust
c/o Wells Fargo Bank N.A., MAC 8622-031
P.O. Box 960
Fort Wayne, IN 46801-6632
Application address: c/o Wells Fargo Bank, Attn.: Jennifer King, 111 E. Wayne St., Fort Wayne, IN 46802, tel.: (260) 461-6458, email: jennifer.i.king@wellsfargo.com

Foundation type: Independent foundation.
Financial data (yr. ended 07/31/13): Assets, $6,512,226 (M); expenditures, $387,906; qualifying distributions, $359,434; giving activities

include $306,984 for 39 grants (high: $25,000; low: $2,009).
Purpose and activities: Giving primarily for education, the arts, particularly theater and public television, community development, and social services.
Fields of interest: Arts and culture; History museums; Education; Higher education; Community and economic development; Human services; Food banks; Child welfare.
Type of support: General support; Matching grants; Annual campaigns; Capital campaigns; Capital and infrastructure; Equipment; Program development.
Limitations: Applications accepted. Giving limited to Allen County, IN. No grants to individuals, or for scholarships, exhibitions or seminars.
Application information:
 Initial approach: Letter
 Copies of proposal: 4
 Deadline(s): None
 Board meeting date(s): Quarterly
Trustee: Wells Fargo Bank, N.A.
EIN: 356011137

3410
Lacy Foundation
54 Monument Cir., Ste. 900
Indianapolis, IN 46204-2942

Donors: Andre B. Lacy; Edna B. Lacy Memorial; Margot L. Eccles†; Andre B. Lacy Charitable Trust; Indianapolis Motor Speedway.
Foundation type: Independent foundation.
Financial data (yr. ended 12/31/13): Assets, $8,331,161 (M); gifts received, $164,124; expenditures, $359,815; qualifying distributions, $357,162; giving activities include $351,489 for 50 grants (high: $70,000; low: $75).
Purpose and activities: Support primarily for an executive leadership series administered by a chamber of commerce; giving also for community funds and education.
Fields of interest: Arts and culture; Education; Environment; Nonprofits; Community and economic development.
Type of support: Continuing support; Annual campaigns; Regranting; Capital campaigns; Endowments; Program development.
Limitations: Applications not accepted. Giving limited to the greater Indianapolis, IN, area. No grants to individuals.
Application information: Contributes only to pre-selected organizations.
Officers: Andre B. Lacy, Chair.; Jill S. Lacy, Pres.
Trustees: Jeffery Dible; M. E. Eccles; Robert J. Kaspar.
Number of staff: 1 full-time professional; 1 full-time support.
EIN: 237415837

3411
Lafayette Life Foundation, Inc.
508 Vermont Dr.
Lafayette, IN 47905-4679
Application address: c/o Jan Cavendish, 400 Broadway, MS L2 Cincinnati, OH 45202, tel.: (513) 362-4937

Established in 2004 in Indiana.
Foundation type: Independent foundation.

Financial data (yr. ended 12/31/13): Assets, $3,412,525 (M); expenditures, $173,872; qualifying distributions, $172,300; giving activities include $166,300 for 29 grants (high: $35,000; low: $1,000).

Fields of interest: Nonprofits; Mental health care; Agriculture; Human services.

Type of support: Regranting.

Application information: Application form required.
Initial approach: Grant application form
Deadline(s): None

Officers and Directors: William F. Olds, Pres. and Director; Bryan C. Dunn, V.P.; Mark J. Snyder, Secy.; Dan Haneline, Treas.; Jerry B. Stillwell.

EIN: 510524801

3412
LaGrange County Community Foundation, Inc.
109 E. Central Ave., Ste. 3
Lagrange, IN 46761-2301 (260) 463-4363
Contact: Laura Lemings, Exec. Dir.; Laney Kratz, Prog. Off.
FAX: (260) 463-4856; E-mail: lccf@lccf.net; Additional e-mail: llemings@lccf.net; Main URL: http://www.lccf.net

Established in 1991 in Indiana.

Foundation type: Community foundation.

Financial data (yr. ended 12/31/13): Assets, $12,409,532 (M); gifts received, $240,001; expenditures, $831,534; giving activities include $191,972 for 10+ grants (high: $35,680), and $46,000 for 59 grants to individuals.

Purpose and activities: The foundation seeks to encourage philanthropy and charitable giving throughout LaGrange County, IN.

Fields of interest: Arts and culture; Education; Higher education; Environment; Community and economic development; Human services; Child welfare; Youth development.

Type of support: General support; Pro bono consulting services; In-kind gifts; Capacity-building and technical assistance; Capital and infrastructure; Matching grants; Equipment; Land acquisitions; Endowments; Emergency funds; Program development; Convening; Seed money; Scholarships; Technical assistance; Program evaluations; Student aid.

Limitations: Applications accepted. Giving limited to LaGrange County, IN.

Publications: Annual report; Financial statement; Grants list; Informational brochure; Newsletter; Occasional report.

Application information: Visit foundation web site for updates.
Initial approach: Mail or hand-deliver grant proposal
Copies of proposal: 8
Deadline(s): Varies
Board meeting date(s): 4th Tues. of each month
Final notification: 30 - 45 days

Officers and Directors: Steve Scott-Welty, Pres. and Director; Jeff Wible, Secy. and Director; Dr. Rhonda Sharp, Treas. and Director; Laura Lemings, Exec. Dir.; Mahlon Bontrager; Vickie Guyas; Jama Keaffaber; Sue Keenan; Crystal Leu; Jayne Perkins.

Number of staff: 2 full-time professional; 2 part-time professional; 1 full-time support.

EIN: 351834679

3413
M.C.R. Charitable Foundation, Inc.
(formerly Margaret Cole Richards Charitable Foundation, Inc.)
7643 William Penn Pl.
Indianapolis, IN 46256-2289

Established in 1998 in Indiana.

Donors: Margaret Cole Richards; Margaret C. Russell.

Foundation type: Independent foundation.

Financial data (yr. ended 12/31/13): Assets, $2,099,586 (M); expenditures, $187,703; qualifying distributions, $166,121; giving activities include $136,119 for 28 grants (high: $22,617; low: $100).

Fields of interest: Arts and culture; Sports and recreation; Human services.

Type of support: General support.

Limitations: Applications not accepted. Giving primarily in IN. No grants to individuals.

Application information: Unsolicited requests for funds not accepted.

Officers: Margaret C. Russell, Pres. and Treas.; E. Frances Eickhoff, V.P.; Patricia Alvis, Secy.; Janice Nichols, Exec. Dir.; Marjorie Wilkerson, Exec. Dir.

EIN: 352063157

3414
Magee-O'Connor Foundation Inc.
201 W. Wayne St.
Fort Wayne, IN 46802 (260) 422-0488
Contact: Douglas E. Miller, Tr.

Established in 1963 in Indiana.

Foundation type: Independent foundation.

Financial data (yr. ended 12/31/13): Assets, $5,404,214 (M); expenditures, $233,955; qualifying distributions, $214,500; giving activities include $214,500 for 32 grants (high: $25,000; low: $1,000).

Purpose and activities: Giving primarily for education, health care, social services, including services for people who are blind, children and youth services, and Roman Catholic organizations and churches.

Fields of interest: Education; Higher education; Health; Catholicism; Human services; Child welfare; Adult and child mentoring.

Limitations: Applications accepted. Giving primarily in Fort Wayne, IN. No grants to individuals.

Application information:
Initial approach: Proposal
Deadline(s): None

Trustee: Douglas E. Miller.

EIN: 237087967

3415
Maurer Family Foundation
c/o Jill Burnett
2422 Londonberry Blvd.
Carmel, IN 46032-8219

Established in 1989 in Indiana.

Donor: Michael S. Maurer.

Foundation type: Independent foundation.

Financial data (yr. ended 12/31/12): Assets, $994,351 (M); gifts received, $176,013; expenditures, $371,547; qualifying distributions, $193,852; giving activities include $193,852 for grants.

Fields of interest: Arts and culture; Education; University education; Nonprofits; Cancers; Christianity; Judaism; Human services; Child welfare.

Type of support: General support; Regranting.

Limitations: Applications not accepted. Giving primarily in IN. No grants to individuals.

Application information: Contributes only to pre-selected organizations.

Directors: Jill Burnett; Matthew Burnett; Greg Maurer; Janie Maurer; Linda Maurer; Michael S. Maurer; Todd J. Maurer.

EIN: 351787262

3416
McKinney Family Foundation Inc.
135 N. Pennsylvania St., 10th Fl.
Indianapolis, IN 46204-2400

Established in 2007 in Indiana.

Donor: Robert N. McKinney.

Foundation type: Independent foundation.

Financial data (yr. ended 12/31/14): Assets, $6,279,269; expenditures, $360,934; qualifying distributions, $328,410.

Fields of interest: Foundations.

Limitations: Applications not accepted. Giving primarily in IN. No grants to individuals.

Application information: Contributes only to pre-selected organizations.

Officers and Directors: Robert H. McKinney, Chair. and Director; Marni McKinney, Pres. and Treas. and Director; Kevin K. McKinney, V.P. and Director; Lisa C. McKinney, Secy. and Director; Kent McKinney; Robert C. McKinney.

EIN: 261585667

3417
Mervis Family Foundation
10000 Summer Lakes Dr.
Carmel, IN 46032-9332
Contact: Michael J. Mervis, Pres.
E-mail: foundation@mervis.com

Established in 1994 in Indiana.

Donors: Louis L. Mervis; Sybil S. Mervis; Michael J. Mervis; Mervis Industries; Adam Mervis.

Foundation type: Independent foundation.

Financial data (yr. ended 12/31/13): Assets, $84,751 (M); gifts received, $305,548; expenditures, $276,729; qualifying distributions, $270,002; giving activities include $270,002 for grants.

Fields of interest: Arts and culture; Education; Environment; Nonprofits; Health; Judaism; Human services; Youth services.

Type of support: Regranting.

Limitations: Applications not accepted. Giving on a national basis, with some emphasis on IL and IN. No grants to individuals.

Application information: Unsolicited requests for funds not accepted.

Officer: Michael J. Mervis, Pres.

Directors: Ellen J. Deluca; Laurel Kroack; Louis L. Mervis; Sybil S. Mervis.

EIN: 351921800

3418
Robert P. & Clara I. Milton Charitable Trust Foundation

c/o Wells Fargo Bank, N.A.
112 W. Jefferson Blvd.
South Bend, IN 46601-1923

Established in 1989 in Indiana.
Donor: Milton Home, Inc.
Foundation type: Independent foundation.
Financial data (yr. ended 12/31/14): Assets, $6,155,895 (M); expenditures, $316,892; qualifying distributions, $275,917; giving activities include $257,207 for 6 grants (high: $102,160; low: $25,000).
Purpose and activities: Giving only to organizations in St. Joseph County, IN, that assist persons aged 65 or over in finding and maintaining housing.
Fields of interest: Diseases and conditions; Alzheimer's disease; Community and economic development; Housing services.
Limitations: Applications accepted. Giving limited to St. Joseph County, IN. No grants to individuals.
Application information:
  Initial approach: Proposal
  Copies of proposal: 7
  Deadline(s): June 1
  Board meeting date(s): June
  Final notification: 4-8 weeks
Trustee: Wells Fargo Bank, N.A.
EIN: 356502846

3419
The Mothershead Foundation

c/o Jon F. Spadorcia
1 American Sq., Ste. 2000
Indianapolis, IN 46282-0004
Application address: c/o Julie Brooks, 6311 Westfield Blvd., Ste. 205, Indianapolis, IN 46220, tel.: (317) 257-8208

Established in 1991 in Indiana.
Donor: Katharine B. Mothershead.
Foundation type: Independent foundation.
Financial data (yr. ended 12/31/13): Assets, $4,133,771 (M); gifts received, $2,160; expenditures, $437,435; qualifying distributions, $344,558; giving activities include $306,931 for 17 grants (high: $70,000; low: $100).
Fields of interest: Museums; Children's museums; History; Education; Archaeology; Housing development; Human services.
Type of support: Regranting; Fundraising.
Limitations: Applications accepted. Giving primarily in Indianapolis, IN. No grants to individuals.
Application information:
  Initial approach: Letter
  Deadline(s): None
Trustees: Katharine M. Kruse; Richard D. Kruse.
EIN: 351844375

3420
Edgar and Roberta Mulzer Foundation

(formerly The Mulzer Foundation, Inc.)
401 10th St.
Tell City, IN 47586-0307
Application address: P.O. Box 307, Tell City, IN 47586, tel.: (812) 547-2337

Established in 1998 in Indiana.
Donor: Edgar C. Mulzer.
Foundation type: Independent foundation.
Financial data (yr. ended 12/31/13): Assets, $5,193,220 (M); expenditures, $263,666; qualifying distributions, $227,500; giving activities include $227,500 for 63 grants (high: $10,000; low: $500).
Fields of interest: Nonprofits; Protestantism; Human services; Scouting programs; Adult and child mentoring.
Type of support: Regranting.
Limitations: Applications accepted. Giving primarily in IN.
Application information:
  Initial approach: Proposal
  Deadline(s): None
Officer: Bill H. Bradley, V.P. and Secy.-Treas.
Directors: Beverly K. Bradley; Angela Erwin; Rebecca Mulzer; Roberta Mulzer; Jean Ryan.
EIN: 352049784

3421
MutualBank Charitable Foundation Inc.

(formerly Mutual Charitable Foundation Inc.)
110 E. Charles St.
P.O. Box 551
Muncie, IN 47308-0551

Established in 1998 in Indiana.
Donors: Mutual Financial, Inc.; Mutual Bank.
Foundation type: Company-sponsored foundation.
Financial data (yr. ended 06/30/14): Assets, $5,404,130 (M); gifts received, $25,000; expenditures, $227,381; qualifying distributions, $225,609; giving activities include $212,297 for 49 grants (high: $30,000; low: $500).
Purpose and activities: The foundation supports food banks and organizations involved with education, housing development, human services, and economic development.
Fields of interest: Theater; Education; Higher education; Community college education; Nonprofits; Economic development; Housing development; Human services; Food banks; Homeless services.
Type of support: General support; Continuing support; Equipment; Program development; Scholarships; Sponsorships; Regranting.
Limitations: Applications not accepted. Giving primarily in Indianapolis, Marion, Muncie, and Warsaw, IN. No grants to individuals.
Application information: Contributes only to pre-selected organizations.
Officers and Directors: Richard Benson; Sam Abram; Linn A. Crull; Patrick Botts, Pres.; David Heeter, V.P.; Christopher Cook, Treas.; Ray Down Roberts, Chair.; Chris Caldwell, Secy.
EIN: 352064221

3422
The Namaste Foundation Inc.

9704 W. Raintree Dr.
Columbus, IN 47201-9295

Established in 1990 in Indiana.
Donors: Constance Marbach; Terry Marbach.
Foundation type: Independent foundation.
Financial data (yr. ended 12/31/13): Assets, $9,023,646 (M); gifts received, $431,860; expenditures, $346,269; qualifying distributions, $332,634; giving activities include $330,785 for 62 grants (high: $30,000; low: $500).

Fields of interest: Environment; Nonprofits; Family planning; Child welfare.
Type of support: General support; Regranting; Capital campaigns; Land acquisitions; Endowments; Seed money.
Limitations: Applications not accepted. No support for religious organizations. No grants to individuals or to organizations that discriminate on the basis of gender, race, religion, or sexual orientation.
Publications: Annual report; Grants list.
Application information: Contributes only to pre-selected organizations.
  Board meeting date(s): Quarterly
Officers: Terry Marbach, Pres.; Constance Marbach, V.P.
Directors: Jill Griffen; Beth Marbach.
Number of staff: None.
EIN: 351814583

3423
Daniel M. Niblick Family Foundation

3470 Stellhorn Rd.
Fort Wayne, IN 46815-4630

Established in 1997 in Indiana.
Donor: Harold W. Niblick.
Foundation type: Independent foundation.
Financial data (yr. ended 06/30/13): Assets, $2,067,797 (M); expenditures, $280,795; qualifying distributions, $274,190; giving activities include $266,865 for 13 grants (high: $97,500; low: $500).
Purpose and activities: Giving primarily for education, youth and social services, and Christian and Roman Catholic churches and organizations.
Fields of interest: Community and economic development; Christianity; Catholicism; Youth development.
Limitations: Applications not accepted. Giving primarily in IN. No grants to individuals.
Application information: Unsolicited requests for funds not accepted.
Trustee: Galen D. Maust, CPA.
EIN: 352005094

3424
The Carson and Rosemary Noecker Family Foundation

c/o Tower Trust Co.
P.O. Box 11080
Fort Wayne, IN 46855 (260) 427-7130

Established in 2004 in Indiana.
Donors: Carson Noecker; Rosemary Noecker.
Foundation type: Independent foundation.
Financial data (yr. ended 06/30/13): Assets, $1,818,204 (M); gifts received, $320,051; expenditures, $342,141; qualifying distributions, $330,894; giving activities include $328,000 for 9 grants (high: $175,000; low: $3,000).
Fields of interest: Orchestral music; Cancers; Human services; People with disabilities; People with vision impairments.
Type of support: General support; Capital campaigns.
Limitations: Applications accepted. Giving primarily in IN.
Application information: Application form required.
  Initial approach: Letter
  Deadline(s): None
Trustee: Tower Trust Co.

Committee Members: Debra L. Breunling; George R. Donner; Robert A. Wagner.
EIN: 386826742

3425
Elizabeth Ruddick Nugent Foundation

P.O. Box 929
Columbus, IN 47202-0929 (812) 376-1759
Contact: William Helmbrecht, Treas.; Melissa Fleetwood

Established in 1961 in Indiana.
Donor: Elizabeth R. Nugent.
Foundation type: Independent foundation.
Financial data (yr. ended 12/31/13): Assets, $8,937,230 (M); expenditures, $383,405; qualifying distributions, $356,869; giving activities include $315,758 for 34 grants (high: $45,000; low: $1,000).
Fields of interest: Arts and culture; Health; Hospice care; Diseases and conditions; Community and economic development; Protestantism; Human services; Family services.
Limitations: Applications accepted. Giving primarily in Columbus, IN. No grants to individuals.
Application information: Application form required.
Initial approach: Completed application form
Deadline(s): Prior to annual meeting
Officers: Judith R. Jones, Pres.; A. Samuel Pentzer, V.P.; Thomas C. Bigley, Jr., Secy.; William Helmbrecht, Treas.
Director: Robert L. Spurgin.
Trustee: First Financial Bank, N.A.
EIN: 356049600

3426
Hollie & Anna Oakley Foundation, Inc.

18 S. 16th St.
Terre Haute, IN 47807-4102 (812) 232-4437

Established in 1954 in Indiana.
Donors: Hollie N. Oakley‡; H.N. Oakley Testamentary Trust.
Foundation type: Independent foundation.
Financial data (yr. ended 12/31/13): Assets, $10,760,649 (M); expenditures, $582,002; qualifying distributions, $475,583; giving activities include $390,500 for 18 grants (high: $100,000; low: $500).
Fields of interest: Arts and culture; Children's museums; Education; Higher education; Hospital care; Diseases and conditions; Human services.
Type of support: Capital and infrastructure; Capital campaigns; General support; Scholarships.
Limitations: Applications accepted. Giving primarily in IN, with emphasis on Terre Haute. No grants to individuals.
Application information: Application form required.
Initial approach: Letter
Deadline(s): Apr. 10, July 10, Oct. 10, and Dec. 10
Officers: Alice Ann Perry, Pres.; Eston L. Perry, V.P. and Treas.; Julie Heck, Secy.
Directors: Doris Kiburis; Jennifer Norris; Jennifer Perry; Travis Norris.
EIN: 237008034

3427
Ohio County Community Foundation, Inc.

330 Industrial Access Dr.
P.O. Box 170
Rising Sun, IN 47040 (812) 438-9401
Contact: Peggy Dickson, Exec. Dir.; Stephanie Scott, Prog. Coord.
FAX: (812) 438-9488;
E-mail: pdickson@occfrisingsun.com; Grant inquiry e-mail: sscott@occfrisingsun.com; Main
URL: http://www.occfrisingsun.com

Established in 1998 in Indiana.
Foundation type: Community foundation.
Financial data (yr. ended 12/31/13): Assets, $27,697,842 (M); gifts received, $375,742; expenditures, $794,823; giving activities include $168,352 for 9+ grants (high: $28,510), and $101,972 for 130 grants to individuals.
Purpose and activities: The foundation seeks to assist donors with building, managing and distributing a lasting source of charitable resources for Ohio County, IN. The foundation makes grants in the fields of community development, education, human services, cultural affairs and health.
Fields of interest: Arts and culture; Education; Environment; Health; Community and economic development; Human services.
Type of support: Grants to individuals.
Limitations: Applications accepted. Giving limited to Ohio County, IN. No support for sectarian religious purposes. No grants to individuals (except for scholarships).
Publications: Application guidelines; Annual report; Grants list; Informational brochure; Newsletter.
Application information: Visit foundation web site for application form and guidelines. Application form required.
Initial approach: Submit application form
Copies of proposal: 10
Deadline(s): Apr. 15 and Oct. 15
Board meeting date(s): 10 times per year
Final notification: May and Dec.
Officers and Board Members: Monte Denbo, Pres. and Director; Ken McIntosh, V.P. and Director; Nancy Gilliland, Secy. and Director; April Hautman, Treas. and Director; Peggy Dickson, Exec. Dir.; Douglas Baker; Wayne Chipman; Rosie Hewitt; Barb Scranton; John Spina.
Number of staff: 1 full-time professional; 1 part-time support.
EIN: 352038531

3428
Oliver Memorial Trust Foundation

c/o Wells Fargo Bank, N.A.
112 W. Jefferson Blvd.
South Bend, IN 46601-1923
Contact: Karen L. Nevorski, Trust Off., Wells Fargo Bank, N.A.

Established in 1959 in Indiana.
Donors: C. Frederick Cunningham‡; Gertrude Oliver Cunningham‡; Walter C. Steenburg‡; Jane Cunningham Warriner; J. Oliver Cunningham; John Warriner; Jane Warriner.
Foundation type: Independent foundation.
Financial data (yr. ended 12/31/13): Assets, $10,480,811 (M); gifts received, $10,000; expenditures, $386,421; qualifying distributions, $352,396; giving activities include $341,741 for 14 grants (high: $207,441; low: $300).

Purpose and activities: Emphasis on hospitals, higher education, particularly college endowments, community funds, and youth agencies.
Fields of interest: Higher education; Nonprofits; Hospital care; Youth services.
Type of support: Continuing support; Matching grants; Annual campaigns; Capital campaigns; Capital and infrastructure; Regranting; Equipment; Endowments; Program development; Seed money; Research.
Limitations: Applications not accepted. Giving primarily in the South Bend, IN, area. No grants to individuals, or for land acquisition, conferences, scholarships, or fellowships; no loans.
Application information: Unsolicited requests for funds not accepted.
Board meeting date(s): Quarterly or as required
Trustee: Wells Fargo Bank, N.A.
EIN: 356013076

3429
O'Rourke-Schof Family Foundation

c/o Tower Trust Company
P.O. Box 11080
Fort Wayne, IN 46855-1080 (260) 427-7130
Contact: David Fee

Established in 1985 in Indiana.
Donor: Rejean O'Rourke‡.
Foundation type: Independent foundation.
Financial data (yr. ended 04/30/13): Assets, $4,654,943 (M); expenditures, $234,808; qualifying distributions, $213,920; giving activities include $191,000 for 13 grants (high: $25,000; low: $5,000).
Purpose and activities: Giving primarily for Roman Catholic churches, and human services.
Fields of interest: Orchestral music; Zoos; Hospice care; Catholicism; Human services.
Type of support: General support.
Limitations: Giving primarily in Fort Wayne, IN. No grants to individuals.
Application information: Application form required.
Initial approach: Letter
Deadline(s): None
Officers: Marlene Buesching, Chair.; Marjorie Motherwell, Vice-Chair.; Daniel Nieter, Secy.
Trustee: Tower Trust Company.
EIN: 356437238

3430
The OTT Foundation Inc.

1800 N. Wabash Rd., Ste. 300
Marion, IN 46952

Donors: TLC Management, Inc.; Ryan Ott; Gary Ott; Connie Ott; Amie Ott.
Foundation type: Independent foundation.
Financial data (yr. ended 12/31/13): Assets, $621,552 (M); gifts received, $300,200; expenditures, $276,794; qualifying distributions, $271,412; giving activities include $271,412 for 20 grants (high: $100,000; low: $200).
Fields of interest: Christianity.
Limitations: Applications not accepted. Giving primarily in CO, DC and IN.
Application information: Unsolicited requests for funds not accepted.
Officers: Gary Ott, Pres.; Bradley Ott, V.P.; Connie Ott, Treas.

Directors: Amie Ott; Ryan Ott; Sarah Ott; Daniel Showalter; Jennifer Showalter.
EIN: 263299645

3431
PHP Foundation, Inc.
c/o Old National Trust Co.
P.O. Box 207
Evansville, IN 47702-0207

Established in 2006 in Indiana.
Donor: PHP.
Foundation type: Independent foundation.
Financial data (yr. ended 12/31/14): Assets, $3,016,386 (M); gifts received, $390,165; expenditures, $410,388; qualifying distributions, $401,072; giving activities include $396,000 for 14 grants (high: $110,000; low: $5,000).
Fields of interest: Health; Health care clinics; Human services.
Limitations: Applications not accepted. Giving primarily in Fort Wayne, IN. No grants to individuals.
Application information: Contributes only to pre-selected organizations.
Officers and Directors: Rick Cochran, Chair.; James A. Brunnemer, Secy.-Treas. and Director; Gail Doran; David W. Stein, MD; Phillip C. Wright, MD.
Trustee: Old National Trust Co.
EIN: 204615314

3432
Pulaski County Community Foundation, Inc.
(also known as Pulaski Community Foundation)
127 E. Pearl St.
P.O. Box 407
Winamac, IN 46996   (574) 946-0906
Contact: Wendy Rose, Exec. Dir.
FAX: (574) 946-0971; E-mail: pccf@pulaskiccf.org;
Main URL: http://www.pulaskiccf.org/?view=mobile
Facebook: https://www.facebook.com/pages/Pulaski-County-Community-Foundation-Inc/156090961089507
YouTube: http://www.youtube.com/user/PCCFVideo

Established in 2002 in Indiana.
Foundation type: Community foundation.
Financial data (yr. ended 12/31/13): Assets, $7,888,691 (M); gifts received, $151,745; expenditures, $513,244; giving activities include $237,154 for 5+ grants (high: $49,611), and $45,247 for 53 grants to individuals.
Purpose and activities: The foundation encourages the establishment of endowed funds to serve and support the charitable interests of local citizens and community.
Fields of interest: Education; Community and economic development; Female young adults; Male young adults.
Type of support: Equipment; Emergency funds; Program development; Scholarships.
Limitations: Applications accepted. Giving limited to Pulaski County, IN. No grants to individuals (except for scholarships), or for ongoing operating expenses, annual fundraising drives, existing obligations, debt reduction, building campaigns, travel, or endowments; no loans or multi-year grants.
Publications: Application guidelines; Annual report; Financial statement; Grants list.

Application information: Visit foundation web site for application guidelines. Application form required.
  Initial approach: Complete online application
  Board meeting date(s): 3rd Tues. of every month
Officers and Directors: Don Street, Pres. and Director; Ron Kruger, V.P. and Director; Peach Roth, Secy. and Director; Robert Simpson, Treas. and Director; Wendy Rose, Exec. Dir.; Robert Conn; Missy Culp; Katie DeGroot; Carola Forsythe; Julie Hanus; Jim Ketchen; Gregg Malott; Darlene Mellon; Tim Murray; Shane Pilarski; Mary Welker.
Number of staff: 1 full-time professional; 1 part-time support.
EIN: 352127564

3433
Quigg Fund, Inc.
P.O. Box 698
Richmond, IN 47375   (765) 962-8535
Contact: Rob Quigg

Established in 1962 in Indiana.
Foundation type: Independent foundation.
Financial data (yr. ended 12/31/14): Assets, $2,008,885 (M); gifts received, $100,000; expenditures, $145,802; qualifying distributions, $144,255; giving activities include $144,255 for 30 grants (high: $50,000; low: $5).
Fields of interest: Youth services.
Limitations: Applications accepted. Giving limited to Wayne County, IN. No grants to individuals.
Application information:
  Initial approach: Letter
  Deadline(s): Dec. 1
Officers: James R. Quigg, Jr., Pres.; William M. Quigg, V.P.; James R. Quigg III, Secy.-Treas.
EIN: 356022680

3434
M. E. Raker Foundation, Inc.
6207 Constitution Dr.
Fort Wayne, IN 46804-1517
Contact: Jennifer J. Pickard, Secy.

Established in 1984 in Indiana.
Donor: M.E. Raker†.
Foundation type: Independent foundation.
Financial data (yr. ended 06/30/13): Assets, $9,867,422 (M); expenditures, $518,193; qualifying distributions, $426,366; giving activities include $369,799 for 50 grants (high: $15,000; low: $1,000).
Fields of interest: Arts and culture; Education; Human services.
Type of support: General support; Matching grants; Capital and infrastructure; Program development.
Limitations: Applications accepted. Giving primarily in Allen County, IN. No support for the arts. No grants to individuals.
Application information: Application form required.
  Initial approach: Letter requesting application
  Deadline(s): None
Officers: Stephen J. Williams, Pres.; Jennifer J. Pickard, Secy.; Emily Pichon, Treas.
Director: John N. Pichon.
EIN: 311040474

3435
Tom Raper Foundation, Inc.
43 S. 8th St.
Richmond, IN 47374-5575   (765) 935-0900
Contact: Thomas R. Raper, Pres.

Donor: Thomas R. Raper.
Foundation type: Independent foundation.
Financial data (yr. ended 11/30/13): Assets, $6,325,393 (M); gifts received, $131,607; expenditures, $321,000; qualifying distributions, $258,127; giving activities include $249,290 for 20 grants (high: $50,000; low: $150).
Purpose and activities: Grants primarily for Christian ministries, including support for Baptist churches.
Fields of interest: Education; Christianity; Human services.
Type of support: General support.
Limitations: Applications accepted. Giving primarily in FL and IN.
Application information: Application form required.
  Initial approach: Completed application form
  Deadline(s): None
Officers: Thomas R. Raper, Pres.; Nancy Brookbank, Secy.
Director: Suzanne D. Raper.
EIN: 310999060

3436
Raymond Foundation Inc.
P.O. Box 3082
Bloomington, IN 47402-3082   (812) 824-9693
Contact: Linda A. Raymond, Pres.

Established in 1993 in Kentucky.
Donor: Raymond Equipment Co.
Foundation type: Independent foundation.
Financial data (yr. ended 12/31/13): Assets, $2,987,895 (M); expenditures, $267,426; qualifying distributions, $250,113; giving activities include $245,201 for 11 grants (high: $40,000; low: $4,570).
Purpose and activities: Giving primarily for higher education (for scholarships, faculty chairs, and research), medical care for the young, and science education at primary and secondary levels.
Fields of interest: Education; Higher education; Health; Religion; Protestantism; Human services.
Type of support: Seed money; Program development; General support; Equipment; Continuing support; Professorships; Research; Scholarships; Technical assistance.
Limitations: Applications accepted. Giving primarily in KY and IN. No support for political organizations.
Application information: Application form required.
  Initial approach: Letter
  Deadline(s): None
Officers and Directors: Linda A. Raymond, Pres. and Director; Michael Cain, V.P. and Director; Anne H. Raymond, Secy.-Treas. and Director.
EIN: 611229966

3437
Rifkin Family Foundation
5642 Coventry Ln.
Fort Wayne, IN 46804-7140

Established in 1986 in Indiana.
Donors: OmniSource Corp.; Gopher Smelting & Refining Corp.; Daniel M. Rifkin; Associated Media

Group LLC; Richard S. Rifkin; Martin S. Rifkin; Mezuman Associates LLC.
Foundation type: Independent foundation.
Financial data (yr. ended 12/31/13): Assets, $8,234,478 (M); expenditures, $474,130; qualifying distributions, $420,172; giving activities include $420,172 for 52 grants (high: $107,900; low: $100).
Purpose and activities: Giving primarily for education, children and social services, and Jewish organizations.
Fields of interest: Education; Nonprofits; Diseases and conditions; Judaism; Human services; Child welfare.
Type of support: Regranting.
Limitations: Applications not accepted. Giving primarily in Fort Wayne, IN. No grants to individuals.
Application information: Contributes only to pre-selected organizations.
Trustee: Daniel M. Rifkin.
EIN: 311192429

3438
Rinker Family Foundation, Inc.
121 W. Franklin St., Ste. 400
Elkhart, IN 46516-3201

Established in 2004 in Indiana.
Donors: Beverly Rinker; John J. Rinker.
Foundation type: Independent foundation.
Financial data (yr. ended 06/30/13): Assets, $2,447,234 (M); expenditures, $326,273; qualifying distributions, $310,539; giving activities include $308,739 for 10 grants (high: $250,000; low: $2,000).
Fields of interest: Health care administration and financing; Hospital care; Human services; Child welfare; Senior assisted living.
Limitations: Applications not accepted. Giving primarily in IN. No grants to individuals.
Application information: Contributes only to pre-selected organizations.
Officers: Raeni Rinker-Dumford, Pres.; John J. Rinker, V.P.; Resia Rinker, V.P.; Lori Rinker, Secy.-Treas.
EIN: 202038798

3439
Roberts Family Foundation, Inc.
90 E. Cedar St.
Zionsville, IN 46077-1501

Donor: John T. Roberts.
Foundation type: Independent foundation.
Financial data (yr. ended 12/31/14): Assets, $3,641,179; expenditures, $220,055; qualifying distributions, $180,000.
Fields of interest: Education; Health; Youth development.
Limitations: Applications not accepted. Giving primarily in IN.
Application information: Unsolicited requests for funds not accepted.
Officers and Directors: John T. Roberts, Pres. and Director; Robin R. Roberts, V.P. and Director; Alan McLaughlin.
EIN: 271529236

3440
M. A. Rooney Foundation, Inc.
9333 N. Meridian St., Ste.150
Indianapolis, IN 46260

Donors: Theresa A. Rooney; Cathleen L. Rooney; Republican Leadership Coalition; Fairness Foundation; American Seniors; J. Patrick Rooney†.
Foundation type: Independent foundation.
Financial data (yr. ended 12/31/14): Assets, $367,051 (M); gifts received, $796,126; expenditures, $1,267,580; qualifying distributions, $229,535; giving activities include $229,535 for 3 grants (high: $227,739; low: $651).
Fields of interest: Education.
Type of support: Scholarships.
Limitations: Applications not accepted. Giving primarily in IN. No grants to individuals.
Application information: Unsolicited requests for funds not accepted.
Officers and Directors: Therese A. Rooney, Pres. and Director; Frank B. Fults, Secy.-Treas.; Cathleen L. Rooney; David J. West.
EIN: 362673952

3441
Rush County Community Foundation, Inc.
c/o Alisa Henderson
117 N. Main St.
Rushville, IN 46173-1927 (765) 938-1177
Contact: Alisa Henderson, Exec. Dir.
FAX: (765) 938-1719;
E-mail: info@rushcountyfoundation.org; Main URL: http://www.rushcountyfoundation.org
Facebook: https://www.facebook.com/rushcountyfoundation
Instagram: https://instagram.com/rushcofoundation
Twitter: https://twitter.com/GiveINRush

Established in 1991 in Indiana.
Foundation type: Community foundation.
Financial data (yr. ended 12/31/13): Assets, $11,952,389 (M); gifts received, $168,407; expenditures, $457,881; giving activities include $188,372 for 7+ grants (high: $33,086), and $101,823 for 115 grants to individuals.
Purpose and activities: The foundation seeks to enrich and enhance the quality of life in Rush County, Indiana.
Fields of interest: Arts and culture; Education; Nonprofits; Hospital care; Public affairs; European football; Human services.
Type of support: Capital and infrastructure; Matching grants; Equipment; Program development; Seed money; Scholarships; Technical assistance; Regranting.
Limitations: Applications accepted. Giving limited to Rush County, IN. No support for religious purposes. No grants to individuals (except for scholarships), or for operating expenses, annual drives, building campaigns, debt reduction, endowments, multi-year grants, or travel expenses; no loans.
Publications: Application guidelines; Annual report; Financial statement; Grants list; Informational brochure; Newsletter.
Application information: Contact the foundation's Grants Prog. Dir. or Exec. Dir. for a current set of grant guidelines and application form. Application form required.
  Initial approach: Telephone or e-mail
  Copies of proposal: 14

Deadline(s): Feb. 1, Jun. 1 and Oct. 1
Board meeting date(s): 4th Tues. of the month
Officers and Directors: Alisa Winters, Exec. Dir.; Terry VanNatta, C.F.O. and Director; Robert Bridges; David Burkhardt; J.B. Gardner; Michele King; Greg Krodel; Tony Laird; Tom Mahan; Dr. Amy Meyer-Ploeger; Phillip Morgan; Keith Perin; Cindy Powers; Suellen Reed; Charlie Smith; Diana White.
Number of staff: 1 full-time professional; 1 full-time support.
EIN: 351835950

3442
Salin Foundation, Inc.
10587 Coppergate Dr.
Carmel, IN 46032-9204 (317) 532-2260
Contact: Sherri Fritsch, Secy.-Treas.

Established in 1998 in Indiana.
Donors: Bill Salin, Sr.; William N. Salin, Sr.
Foundation type: Independent foundation.
Financial data (yr. ended 12/31/14): Assets, $2,687,860 (M); gifts received, $55,830; expenditures, $179,295; qualifying distributions, $173,070; giving activities include $170,400 for 20 grants (high: $35,000; low: $100).
Fields of interest: Education; Domesticated animals; Protestantism.
Limitations: Applications accepted. Giving primarily in IN.
Application information: Application form required.
  Initial approach: Proposal
  Deadline(s): None
Officers: William N. Salin, Sr., Pres.; Sherri Fritsch, Secy.-Treas.
Directors: Susie McClain; M. Jane Salin; William N. Salin II.
EIN: 352047694

3443
Edgar & Lucile Schergens Foundation, Inc.
727 Main St.
Tell City, IN 47586-1934 (812) 547-5592
Contact: J. David Huber, Secy.-Treas.

Established in 1995 in Indiana.
Donor: Lucile E. Schergens.
Foundation type: Independent foundation.
Financial data (yr. ended 12/31/13): Assets, $6,530,461 (M); expenditures, $329,051; qualifying distributions, $227,045; giving activities include $9,545 for 2 grants (high: $7,700; low: $1,845), and $217,500 for 27 grants to individuals (high: $8,500; low: $2,500).
Fields of interest: Higher education; Community and economic development.
Type of support: General support; Student aid.
Limitations: Applications accepted. Giving primarily in Perry County, IN.
Application information: Application form required.
  Initial approach: Proposal
  Deadline(s): None
Officers: William Borders, Pres.; John Werner, V.P.; J. David Huber, Secy.-Treas.
EIN: 351848445

3444
Schurz Communications Foundation, Inc.
1301 E. Douglas Rd.
Mishawaka, IN 46545-1732 (574) 235-6243

Established in 1940 in Indiana.
Donors: South Bend Tribune Corp.; WSBT, Inc.; Schurz Communications, Inc.; West United Way Pledge.
Foundation type: Company-sponsored foundation.
Financial data (yr. ended 12/31/13): Assets, $713,450 (M); gifts received, $165,000; expenditures, $154,549; qualifying distributions, $146,100; giving activities include $146,100 for 8 grants (high: $65,000; low: $1,100).
Purpose and activities: The foundation supports museums and medical centers and organizations involved with higher education, Christianity, and disabled people.
Fields of interest: Education; Religion; Human services.
Type of support: General support; Annual campaigns; Capital campaigns; Endowments.
Limitations: Applications accepted. Giving limited to South Bend, IN.
Application information:
Initial approach: Proposal
Deadline(s): None
Officers and Directors: David C. Ray, Pres. and Director; Sally Brown, V.P. and Director; Marci Burdick, Secy. and Director; Charles Pittman, Treas. and Director.
Trustee: 1st Source Bank, N.A.
EIN: 356024357

3445
Olin B. and Desta Schwab Foundation, Inc.
c/o Michael Earls, C.P.A.
200 E. Main St.
Fort Wayne, IN 46802-2316
Application address: 110 W. Berry St., Ste. 2401, Fort Wayne, IN 46802, tel.: (260) 461-6128

Established in 2008 in Indiana.
Foundation type: Independent foundation.
Financial data (yr. ended 06/30/13): Assets, $7,197,965 (M); expenditures, $360,587; qualifying distributions, $276,973; giving activities include $221,418 for 7 grants (high: $63,000; low: $10,000).
Purpose and activities: Grants are made for the following purposes: 1) To assist people, especially youth, in the process of career development decision-making; 2) To provide career services; and 3) To provide funding to services as a common community good that impacts the greatest number of clients.
Fields of interest: Employment.
Limitations: Applications accepted. Giving primarily in IN. No grants for salaries, or for curriculum development.
Application information: Application form required.
Initial approach: Contact foundation for application guidelines
Deadline(s): Mar. 31 and Aug. 31
Officers: M. James Johnston, Pres. and Director; Jerrilee K. Mosier, Secy.; Michael Earls, Treas.
Directors: Holly Brady; John Ferguson; Courtney Tritch; Bill Zielke.
EIN: 352284008

3446
Scott County Community Foundation, Inc.
(also known as Scott County Community Foundation)
60 N. Main St.
P.O. Box 25
Scottsburg, IN 47170-1129 (812) 752-2057
Contact: Jaime Toppe, Exec. Dir.
FAX: (812) 752-9257;
E-mail: info@scottcountyfoundation.org; Main URL: http://www.scottcountyfoundation.org
Facebook: http://www.facebook.com/ScottCountyCommunityFoundation
RSS feed: http://www.scottcountyfoundation.org/feed
Twitter: https://twitter.com/ScottCountyCF
YouTube: http://www.youtube.com/user/scottcountyfound?feature=mhee

Established in 1996 in Indiana.
Foundation type: Community foundation.
Financial data (yr. ended 09/30/13): Assets, $7,221,691 (M); gifts received, $107,663; expenditures, $366,820; giving activities include $143,207 for 8+ grants (high: $49,275), and $27,004 for grants to individuals.
Purpose and activities: The mission of Scott County Community Foundation is: "Growing and preserving charitable gifts to strengthen Scott County by looking forward and giving back." .
Fields of interest: Arts and culture; Education; Higher education; Environment; Philanthropy; Health; Hospital care; Community and economic development; Sports and recreation; Human services; Family services.
Type of support: Equipment; Scholarships; Emergency funds; General support; Program development.
Limitations: Applications accepted. Giving limited to organizations that benefit residents in Scott County, IN. No support for religious or sectarian purposes. No grants for travel expenses, or typically for ongoing operational expenses, existing obligations, or endowments; no loans.
Publications: Application guidelines; Annual report; Financial statement; Newsletter.
Application information: Visit foundation web site for application forms and guidelines. Application form required.
Initial approach: Contact foundation
Copies of proposal: 10
Deadline(s): Apr. 30
Board meeting date(s): Second Thursday of every month, 10 times per year
Officers and Directors: L.L. Lowry, Chair. and Director; Melinda Sparkman, Vice-Chair. and Director; Barbara Broady, Secy. and Director; Charlotte Boswell, C.F.O. and Director; Lisa Conder, Treas. and Director; Jaime Toppe, Exec. Dir.; Nancy Barr; Michael Everett; Hank Jentzen; Josh Stigdon; Christa West; Dennis Wilson; Terril Wolka.
Number of staff: 2 full-time professional.
EIN: 352014369

3447
Steven M. Seger Memorial Foundation, Inc.
1365 W. 15th St.
Jasper, IN 47546-9107 (812) 678-2891
Contact: Thomas W. Seger, Secy. and Dir.

Established in 1993 in Indiana.

Donors: Thomas W. Seger; Cynthia J. Seger; Kelly Seger; Andy Seger; Audrey Seger; Wabash Valley Produce.
Foundation type: Independent foundation.
Financial data (yr. ended 12/31/13): Assets, $1,551,914 (M); gifts received, $94,671; expenditures, $137,767; qualifying distributions, $134,156; giving activities include $134,156 for 8 grants (high: $60,000; low: $250).
Fields of interest: Education; Health; Christianity; Human services.
Type of support: Capital and infrastructure.
Limitations: Applications accepted. Giving primarily in IN, PA, and TX.
Application information: Application form required.
Initial approach: Letter
Deadline(s): None
Officers and Directors: Cynthia J. Seger, Pres. and Director; Thomas W. Seger, Secy. and Director; Randolph L. Seger.
EIN: 351906210

3448
Greater Seymour Trust Fund
P.O. Box 1001
Seymour, IN 47274-1001 (812) 522-3607
Main URL: http://greaterseymourtrustfund.com

Established in 1969 in Indiana.
Donors: Waldron Berry; Irene Bunker†; Nellie Kloeker†; Mary H. Glasson; Arletta Cobb†; Willard Klakamp†; Ivan Frische†; Fredrick Kasting†; Gilbert Kovener†; Ruth Frische; Joanna L. Myers.
Foundation type: Independent foundation.
Financial data (yr. ended 06/30/13): Assets, $8,435,368 (M); gifts received, $6,615; expenditures, $347,964; qualifying distributions, $247,964; giving activities include $247,964 for grants.
Purpose and activities: Awards scholarships to high school seniors at Jackson County, Indiana, high schools and Washington High School, Wisconsin, and provides professional educational support for Jackson County, Indiana, nurses; support also for youth organizations.
Fields of interest: Arts and culture; Higher education; Graduate and professional education; Nursing care; Youth development; Children and youth; Adults; Homeless people; Low-income and poor people.
Type of support: General support; Continuing support; Equipment; Convening; Student aid.
Limitations: Applications accepted. Giving limited to the greater Jackson County, IN area; scholarships limited to Jackson County, IN high schools and Washington High School, WI seniors.
Publications: Annual report; Informational brochure.
Application information: See foundation web site for complete application guidelines. Application form required.
Initial approach: Proposal
Deadline(s): Mar. 1
Board meeting date(s): 2nd Tues. in Nov. annually
Officers: Robert Von Dielingen, Pres.; Jan Warren, Secy.
Directors: Ralph Blomenberg; Max W. Ernest; David M. Geis; Brett Hayes; Craig Luedeman; Jacqueline F. Sciarra; George Spray.
Trustee: Jackson County Bank.
Number of staff: None.
EIN: 356208884

3449
Hamer D. & Phyllis C. Shafer Foundation Charitable Trust
P.O. Box 548
Muncie, IN 47308-0458
Contact: Liz Ludwick
E-mail: lludwick@munciepower.com

Donor: Phyllis C. Shafer†.
Foundation type: Independent foundation.
Financial data (yr. ended 12/31/13): Assets, $7,859,724 (M); gifts received, $5,725,843; expenditures, $366,419; qualifying distributions, $335,709; giving activities include $329,750 for 14 grants (high: $100,000; low: $3,000).
Fields of interest: Arts and culture; Education; Health; Radio; Religion; Youth development.
Type of support: General support.
Limitations: Applications not accepted. Giving primarily in IN and MI.
Application information: Unsolicited requests for funds not accepted.
Officers and Trustees: Terry L. Walker, Chair. and Pres. and Trustee; Ray L. Chambers, V.P. and Trustee; Christopher D. Fancher, Secy. and Trustee; Kenneth R. Briner, Treas. and Trustee.
EIN: 351997098

3450
Share the Warmth, Inc.
1 Vectren Sq.
Evansville, IN 47708-1209
E-mail: info@sharethewarmthinc.com; Application address: Attn.: Vectren Corporation, c/o Beth Pace, 100 N. Governor St., Evansville, IN 47711-5540, tel.: (812) 491-4403; Main URL: http://www.sharethewarmthinc.com

Donors: Vectren Energy Delivery; Vectren Utility Holding, Inc.; Ritter Plumbing Co, Inc.
Foundation type: Independent foundation.
Financial data (yr. ended 01/01/15): Assets, $439,869 (M); gifts received, $490,658; expenditures, $264,924; qualifying distributions, $264,924; giving activities include $254,400 for 2 grants (high: $203,300; low: $51,100).
Purpose and activities: Giving to organizations that offer comprehensive long-term energy conservation benefits to single family homeowners that meet the state and federal guidelines for low-income, weatherization initiative program.
Fields of interest: Community and economic development.
Limitations: Applications accepted. Giving primarily in IN. No grants to individuals.
Application information: Application form required.
  Initial approach: Proposal
  Deadline(s): None
Officers and Directors: Jeffrey W. Whiteside, Pres. and Director; Ronald E. Christian, V.P. and Secy. and Director; Robert L. Goocher, V.P. and Treas.; Jerome A. Benkert, Jr.; Carl L. Chapman.
EIN: 352152987

3451
The Ned and Emily Sherwood Family Foundation
One Indiana Sq., Ste. 1200
Indianapolis, IN 46204

Donors: Ned L. Sherwood; Emily Layzer Sherwood.

Foundation type: Independent foundation.
Financial data (yr. ended 05/31/14): Assets, $6,908,345 (M); expenditures, $410,296; qualifying distributions, $390,853; giving activities include $390,853 for 38 grants (high: $80,100; low: $100).
Fields of interest: Education; Higher education; Mental health care; Human rights.
Type of support: Endowments; Scholarships; Research.
Limitations: Applications not accepted. Giving primarily in NY. No grants to individuals.
Application information: Unsolicited requests for funds not accepted.
Officers and Directors: Ned L. Sherwood, Pres. and Director; Emily Layzer Sherwood, V.P. and Director; Matthew F. Sherwood, Secy. and Director; Richard I. Sherwood, Treas. and Director.
EIN: 364273196

3452
Herbert & Bui Simon Foundation Inc.
P.O. Box 7033
Indianapolis, IN 46207-7033

Donor: Herbert Simon.
Foundation type: Independent foundation.
Financial data (yr. ended 12/31/13): Assets, $1,803,317 (M); gifts received, $1,997,398; expenditures, $292,203; qualifying distributions, $287,000; giving activities include $287,000 for 10 grants (high: $75,000; low: $500).
Fields of interest: Arts and culture; Education; Diseases and conditions.
Limitations: Applications not accepted. Giving primarily in CA.
Application information: Unsolicited requests for funds not accepted.
Officers: Porntip Bui Simon, Pres.; Herbert Simon, V.P.; Len Freedman, Secy.-Treas.
EIN: 462577284

3453
The Smith Family Foundation Inc.
11711 N. Meridian St., Ste. 600
Carmel, IN 46032-4534
Contact: Jeffrey H. Thomasson
Application address: c/o Jeffrey H. Thomasson, P.O. Box 40856, Indianapolis, IN 46240 tel.: (317) 805-5000

Established in 1997 in Indiana.
Donor: Lonnie M. Smith.
Foundation type: Independent foundation.
Financial data (yr. ended 03/31/15): Assets, $9,027,249 (M); gifts received, $2,556,900; expenditures, $440,264; qualifying distributions, $427,947; giving activities include $427,947 for 22 grants (high: $100,000; low: $1,000).
Fields of interest: Education; Health; Human services.
Type of support: General support.
Limitations: Applications accepted. Giving primarily in CA. No grants to individuals.
Application information: Application form required.
  Initial approach: Letter
  Deadline(s): None
Officers and Directors: Lonnie M. Smith, Pres. and Director; Cheryl D. Smith, V.P. and Director; Jeffrey H. Thomasson, Secy.-Treas. and Director.
EIN: 352015637

3454
The Patricia H. Snyder Family Foundation
c/o Norman E. Snyder
315 W. Wortman Rd.
Evansville, IN 47725-8615

Established in 2001 in Indiana.
Donor: The Patricia Snyder Foundation.
Foundation type: Independent foundation.
Financial data (yr. ended 12/31/14): Assets, $4,551,070; gifts received, $140,000; expenditures, $251,194; qualifying distributions, $212,540 and $0 for set-asides.
Fields of interest: Arts and culture; Education; Health; Religion.
Limitations: Applications not accepted. Giving primarily in Evansville, IN. No grants to individuals.
Application information: Unsolicited requests for funds not accepted.
Officers: Joseph H. Snyder, Mgr.; Luke E. Snyder, Mgr.; Susan H. Snyder, Mgr.; Zachary H. Snyder, Mgr.
Trustee: Norman E. Snyder.
EIN: 356710105

3455
Springleaf Finance Foundation, Inc.
(formerly American General Finance, Inc.—Richard E. Meier Foundation, Inc.)
601 N.W. 2nd St.
P.O. Bos 59
Evansville, IN 47701-0059 (812) 468-5413
Contact: Michelle Dixon

Established in 1958 in Illinois.
Donors: American General Finance, Inc.; Springlea finance, Inc.
Foundation type: Company-sponsored foundation.
Financial data (yr. ended 12/31/13): Assets, $84,849 (M); gifts received, $360,000; expenditures, $341,063; qualifying distributions, $364,367; giving activities include $364,367 for 10 + grants (high: $125,000).
Purpose and activities: The foundation supports organizations involved with arts and culture, education, patient services, housing development, children and youth, and community development.
Fields of interest: Human services; Youth development.
Type of support: General support; Continuing support; Annual campaigns; Capital and infrastructure.
Limitations: Applications accepted. Giving primarily in Evansville, IN. No support for religious organizations not of direct benefit to the entire community or health care organizations. No grants to individuals (except for employee-related scholarships), or for start-up needs, emergency needs or endowments, debt reduction, equipment, land acquisition, special projects, research, publications, tickets or advertising for benefit purposes, or conferences; no loans; no matching or challenge grants.
Publications: Application guidelines.
Application information: Application form required.
  Initial approach: Letter
  Copies of proposal: 1
  Deadline(s): None
  Board meeting date(s): Quarterly
  Final notification: 4 to 6 weeks
Officers and Directors: Minchung Kgil, Chair., Pres., and C.F.O. and Director; David Patrick Hogan, Sr. V.P.; Vincent Ciuffetelli, Sr. V.P. and C.I.O.; William

Kandel, V.P. and Cont.; Clifford N. Pederson, V.P.; David R. Schulz, Treas.; Scott D. McKinlay, Genl. Counsel and Director; Scott Lascelles.

EIN: 356042566

3456
The Stamm Koechlein Family Foundation
(formerly The Stamm Family Foundation)
2320 Reeveston
Richmond, IN 47374-5834
Contact: Monica Koechlein

Established in 2000 in California.
Donors: David A. Stamm; Teresa Stamm Batsel; Institutional Venture Partners.
Foundation type: Independent foundation.
Financial data (yr. ended 12/31/13): Assets, $3,774,744 (M); expenditures, $199,476; qualifying distributions, $182,563; giving activities include $176,954 for 20 grants (high: $32,500; low: $2,000).
Fields of interest: Education; Foundations; Community and economic development; Youth services.
Limitations: Applications not accepted. Giving primarily in IN, with emphasis on Richmond. No grants to individuals.
Application information: Unsolicited requests for funds not accepted.
Officers: Monica Koechlein, Pres.; Maggie Johnson, Secy.; David Stamm, C.F.O and Treas.
Board Members: Kathy Gage; Curtis Johnson; Linda Johnson; John H. Koechlein; Laura Stamm.
EIN: 943376479

3457
Mary Margaret Stucky Testamentary Trust
c/o Clark D. Valentine
434 W. Wayne St.
Fort Wayne, IN 46802-2122

Established in 2004 in Indiana.
Donor: Mary Margaret Stucky Trust.
Foundation type: Independent foundation.
Financial data (yr. ended 12/31/14): Assets, $4,249,108; expenditures, $249,134; qualifying distributions, $202,048.
Fields of interest: Christianity.
Limitations: Applications not accepted. Giving primarily in IN. No grants to individuals.
Application information: Unsolicited requests for funds not accepted.
Trustee: Clark D. Valentine.
EIN: 206300140

3458
TCU Foundation Inc.
110 S. Main St.
P.O. Box 1395
South Bend, IN 46624 (800) 333-3828
Contact: Karol Griffin, Exec. Dir.

Established in 1995 in Indiana.
Donors: Teacher's Credit Union; Community Foundation of St. Joseph County.
Foundation type: Company-sponsored foundation.
Financial data (yr. ended 12/31/13): Assets, $613,815 (M); gifts received, $130,505; expenditures, $189,361; qualifying distributions,

$182,016; giving activities include $182,016 for 45 grants (high: $28,476; low: $500).
Purpose and activities: The foundation supports organizations involved with education and other member-driven initiatives. Special emphasis is directed toward programs that promote life-long learning and financial literacy.
Fields of interest: Arts and culture; Art museums; Education; Reading promotion; Voluntarism; Health; Child welfare.
Type of support: Endowments; Employee matching gifts; Donated equipment; Program development; Curriculum development; Matching grants; Scholarships; Research; Student aid.
Limitations: Applications accepted. Giving limited to areas of company operations in IN.
Application information:
Initial approach: Proposal
Copies of proposal: 1
Deadline(s): None
Officers: David Sage, Chair.; William Hojnacki, Vice-Chair.; Roger Thornton, Secy.; Paul Marsh, Treas.; Karol Griffin, Exec. Dir.
Directors: Jim Dubois; Shirley Golichowski; Vincent Henderson; Thea Kelly; Diane Maas; John R. Myers.
Number of staff: None.
EIN: 351939838

3459
The Thomasson Foundation
(formerly Oxford Foundation, Inc.)
P.O. Box 80238
Indianapolis, IN 46280-0238
Contact: Jeffery H. Thomasson

Established in 1992 in Indiana.
Donor: Jeffrey H. Thomasson.
Foundation type: Independent foundation.
Financial data (yr. ended 12/31/13): Assets, $29,616 (M); gifts received, $100,580; expenditures, $193,062; qualifying distributions, $192,262; giving activities include $187,500 for 51 grants (high: $10,000; low: $750).
Purpose and activities: Giving primarily to Christian organizations and churches; giving also for scholarships.
Fields of interest: Higher education; Christianity.
Type of support: General support; Student aid.
Limitations: Applications accepted. Giving primarily in FL, IL and IN.
Application information: Include academic transcript, test scores, proof of financial need, personal essay, extracurricular activities, academic honors and achievement awards, recommendation, and list of institutions to which applicant will apply.
Initial approach: Letter
Deadline(s): None
Officers and Directors: Jeffrey H. Thomasson, Pres. and Secy.-Treas. and Director; Benita Thomasson, V.P. and Director; Brittany Thomasson, V.P.; J. Elliott Thomasson, V.P.; Robert Elzer.
EIN: 351870799

3460
Thrush-Thompson Foundation, Inc.
(formerly H. A. Thrush Foundation, Inc.)
P.O. Box 670
Westfield, IN 46074-0670

Established in 1936 in Delaware.
Donors: Paul F. Thompson; Homer A. Thrush†.

Foundation type: Independent foundation.
Financial data (yr. ended 07/31/15): Assets, $6,749,015 (M); expenditures, $359,328; qualifying distributions, $329,296; giving activities include $285,000 for 30 grants (high: $105,000; low: $2,500).
Fields of interest: Arts and culture; Higher education; Nonprofits; Diseases and conditions; Christianity; Protestantism; Sports and recreation; Human services; Child welfare; Males.
Type of support: Regranting.
Limitations: Applications accepted. Giving primarily in IN. No grants to individuals.
Officers: Jerry Thompson, Chair. and Pres.; Stanley T. Thompson, V.P. and Secy.; Scott A. Thompson, V.P.; Sterling A. Thompson, V.P.; Stuart K. Thompson, V.P.; Steven S. Thompson, V.P. and Treas.
EIN: 352133120

3461
The Vann Family Foundation, Inc.
11008 Carnoustie Ln.
Ft. Wayne, IN 46814 2603414777

Established in 1997 in Indiana.
Donors: James M. Vann; Mrs. James M. Vann.
Foundation type: Independent foundation.
Financial data (yr. ended 12/31/14): Assets, $6,560,072; expenditures, $280,369; qualifying distributions, $233,190.
Fields of interest: Arts and culture; Museums; Higher education; Medical education; Health; Specialty hospital care; Libraries; Protestantism; Human services.
Type of support: General support.
Limitations: Applications accepted. Giving primarily in IN, MN, and NC.
Application information: Application form required.
Initial approach: Letter
Deadline(s): Sept. 1
Officers: James M. Vann, Chair.; Majorie Lee Vann, Pres.; Sherry S. Connelly, Secy.-Treas.
Directors: Debbie Gilreath; Stephanie Moen; James Vann III; Michael Vann.
EIN: 352008538

3462
Vevay-Switzerland County Foundation, Inc.
P.O. Box 193
Vevay, IN 47043-0193 (812) 427-2533
Contact: Steve Crabtree

Established in 1985 in Indiana.
Donors: Paul W. Ogle; Switzerland County.
Foundation type: Independent foundation.
Financial data (yr. ended 12/31/13): Assets, $3,743,961 (M); gifts received, $229,884; expenditures, $285,723; qualifying distributions, $220,963; giving activities include $126,244 for 20 grants (high: $25,000; low: $413).
Purpose and activities: Giving primarily for exterior renovation or restoration of civic and commercial structures.
Fields of interest: Education; Philanthropy; Public affairs.
Type of support: Building and renovations; Matching grants.
Limitations: Applications accepted. Giving limited to the town of Vevay and Switzerland County, IN.

Application information: Application form required.
  Initial approach: Proposal
  Deadline(s): None
Officers: Judy Firth, Pres.; Janet Hendricks, Secy.; Tammy Hayes, Treas.; Thomas S. Crabtree II, Exec. Dir.
Directors: Jon Bond; Mike Busch; Rose Leap; Mark Lohide; Josh South.
EIN: 351472069

3463
Vision of Hope Custody
(formerly Vision of Hope Foundation)
c/o Greenfield Banking Co.
1920 N. State St.
Greenfield, IN   46140-1088

Established in 1986 in Indiana.
Foundation type: Independent foundation.
Financial data (yr. ended 09/30/14): Assets, $370,103 (M); expenditures, $162,082; qualifying distributions, $154,500; giving activities include $154,500 for 5 grants (high: $125,000; low: $1,500).
Purpose and activities: Giving primarily for higher education, Baptist churches and organizations, and for human services.
Fields of interest: Higher education; Christianity; Baptist; Human services.
Limitations: Applications not accepted. Giving primarily in IN, with emphasis on Lafayette. No grants to individuals.
Application information: Contributes only to pre-selected organizations.
Officer: Linda Rohrman, Pres.
EIN: 311195123

3464
Von Tobel Foundation, Inc.
P.O. Box 1819
Valparaiso, IN   46384-1819
Contact: Paul J. Von Tobel III, Pres.

Established in 1980 in Indiana.
Donors: Von Tobel Corp.; Paul and Candance Von Tobel Trust.
Foundation type: Independent foundation.
Financial data (yr. ended 12/31/13): Assets, $3,289,712 (M); gifts received, $336,674; expenditures, $266,169; qualifying distributions, $249,000; giving activities include $249,000 for 36 grants (high: $85,000; low: $400).
Fields of interest: Higher education; Christianity; Human services.
Type of support: General support.
Limitations: Applications accepted. Giving primarily in IL and IN. No grants to individuals.
Application information:
  Initial approach: Contact foundation for application information
  Deadline(s): None
Officers and Directors: Paul J. Von Tobel III, Pres. and Director; Candace J. Von Tobel, Secy.-Treas. and Director.
EIN: 310981036

3465
Welter Foundation, Inc.
21027 Riverbrook Ln.
Bristol, IN   46507-9417   (574) 596-2543
Contact: Jill Richardson
E-mail: jrr22123@msn.com

Established in 1997 in Indiana.
Donors: Edward P. Welter; Wilhelmina J. Welter.
Foundation type: Operating foundation.
Financial data (yr. ended 12/31/13): Assets, $6,453,892 (M); expenditures, $367,304; qualifying distributions, $312,926; giving activities include $312,926 for 29 grants (high: $55,000; low: $500).
Fields of interest: University education; Foundations; Nonprofits; Diabetes; Child abuse; Christianity; Human services.
Type of support: Research; Regranting.
Limitations: Applications accepted. Giving primarily in IN and MI.
Application information:
  Initial approach: Letter
  Deadline(s): None
Officers and Directors: Edward P. Welter, Pres. and Director; Cynthia S. Gillard, Secy. and Director; Wilhelmina J. Welter, Treas. and Director.
EIN: 352023590

3466
Western Indiana Community Foundation, Inc.
(formerly Covington Community Foundation)
135 S. Stringtown Rd.
P.O. Box 175
Covington, IN   47932-0175   (765) 793-0702
Contact: Dale A. White, Exec. Dir.
FAX: (765) 793-0703; *E-mail:* info@wicf-inc.org;
Main URL: http://www.wicf-inc.org
Scholarship tel.: (765) 793-0702 ext. 3,
e-mail: keaton@wicf-inc.org

Established in 1990 in Indiana.
Foundation type: Community foundation.
Financial data (yr. ended 12/31/12): Assets, $10,457,381 (M); gifts received, $447,636; expenditures, $484,766; giving activities include $203,098 for grants, and $72,053 for grants to individuals.
Purpose and activities: The foundation seeks to support, encourage, and maintain core Christian values leading to a community which recognizes the benefits of individual commitment to honesty, integrity, reliability, marriage, respect for others, church and traditional family, and to provide public-spirited donors a vehicle for using their gifts in the best possible way now and in the future as conditions inevitably change.
Fields of interest: Arts and culture; Education; Health; Economic development; Community improvement; Sports and recreation.
Type of support: Capital campaigns; Matching grants; Capital and infrastructure; Equipment; Emergency funds; Program development; Seed money; Curriculum development; Scholarships; Student aid.
Limitations: Applications accepted. Giving limited to the Attica, Covington, and Southeast Fountain school districts, IN. No grants for individuals (except for scholarships), or for operating budgets, endowments, apparel such as school/sport uniform, or long-term funding.

Publications: Application guidelines; Annual report; Financial statement; Informational brochure; Newsletter; Occasional report (including application guidelines).
Application information: Visit foundation web site for application form and guidelines. Application form required.
  Initial approach: Submit application form and attachments
  Copies of proposal: 1
  Deadline(s): None
  Board meeting date(s): Monthly
  Final notification: 2 to 4 weeks
Officers and Directors: Kevin Martin, Pres. and Director; Dick Minnette, V.P. and Director; Kim Eaton, Secy. and Director; Raquel Stultz, Treas. and Director; Dale A. White, Exec. Dir.; Beth Mason; Thomas A. McGurk, Jr.; Susan Reynolds; John L. Shambach; Robert C. Wright.
Number of staff: 2 full-time professional; 1 part-time support.
EIN: 351814927

3467
The Weston Wabash Foundation
c/o Old National Trust Co.
P.O. Box 1447
Terre Haute, IN   47808-1447

Foundation type: Independent foundation.
Financial data (yr. ended 12/31/14): Assets, $5,781,694 (M); expenditures, $319,403; qualifying distributions, $295,000; giving activities include $295,000 for 27 grants (high: $50,000; low: $1,500).
Fields of interest: Children's museums; Higher education; Foundations; Nonprofits; Hospital care; Human services; Child welfare; Scouting programs.
Type of support: General support; Scholarships; Regranting.
Limitations: Applications not accepted. Giving primarily in Terre Haute, IN. No grants to individuals, or for direct charitable activities or program-related investments.
Application information: Contributes only to pre-selected organizations.
Officers and Trustees: Ward M. Hubbard, Pres. and Treas. and Trustee; Curtis W. Stephens, V.P. and Trustee; Edward T. Turner, Jr.
EIN: 316023751

3468
The Wilmes Family Charitable Foundation, Inc
7904 Traders Hollow Ln.
Indianapolis, IN   46278-1291   3172917255

Donors: Arthur L. Wilmes; Cecelia A. Wilmes.
Foundation type: Independent foundation.
Financial data (yr. ended 12/31/14): Assets, $4,043,232; gifts received, $25,000; expenditures, $332,527; qualifying distributions, $252,200.
Fields of interest: Education.
Application information: Application form required.
  Initial approach: Letter
  Deadline(s): None
Officers: Arthur L. Wilmes, Pres.; Cecelia A. Wilmes, V.P.; Mary E. Wilmes, Secy.; Katherine A. Wilmes, Treas.
EIN: 461620511

3469
The Winchester Foundation
8335 Allison Pointe Trail., Ste. 300
Indianapolis, IN 46250-1687 (317) 842-0880
Contact: Chris L. Talley, Chair.

Established in 1946 in Indiana.
Foundation type: Independent foundation.
Financial data (yr. ended 12/31/13): Assets,
$4,767,454 (M); expenditures, $268,530;
qualifying distributions, $235,835; giving
activities include $222,185 for 25 grants to individuals (high:
$20,000; low: $1,400).

Purpose and activities: Grants primarily to
educational and cultural organizations. The
foundation also administers several scholarship
funds. Of these, the Pierre Goodrich Scholarship
Fund is open to applicants who have attended
Winchester Community High School, Indiana, for at
least two years prior to graduation.
Fields of interest: Arts and culture; Higher
education; Human services.
Type of support: General support; Student aid.

Limitations: Applications accepted. Giving primarily
in IN; scholarships limited to residents of Randolph
County, IN.
Application information: Application form required.
  Initial approach: Letter
  Deadline(s): None
Officers: Chris L. Talley, Chair.; Terri E. Matchett,
Secy.
Trustees: Ruth Connally; Helen Garlotte; Dane
Starbuck; Old National Trust.
EIN: 237422941

IOWA

3470
Andringa Family Foundation, Inc.
10682 N.E. 46th Ave.
Mitchellville, IA 50169-9500

Donors: Dale J. Andringa; Mary A. Andringa; Mindi Vanden Bosch; Franklin Vanden Bosch.
Foundation type: Independent foundation.
Financial data (yr. ended 12/31/14): Assets, $540,346 (M); gifts received, $300,679; expenditures, $159,556; qualifying distributions, $156,000; giving activities include $156,000 for 9 grants (high: $75,000; low: $1,000).
Fields of interest: Secondary education; Higher education; Graduate and professional education; Religion; Theology.
Type of support: General support.
Limitations: Applications not accepted. Giving primarily in CA and IA. No grants to individuals.
Application information: Unsolicited requests for funds not accepted.
Officers and Directors: Dale J. Andringa, Pres. and Director; Mary A. Andringa, Secy.-Treas. and Director; Franklin Vanden Bosch; Mindi Vanden Bosch.
EIN: 421240932

3471
Foster & Evelyn Barkema Charitable Trust
P.O. Box 461
Hampton, IA 50441-0461
Application address: c/o Zoe Brown, Tr., 700 S. Federal St., Hampton, IA 50441, tel.: (641) 456-5196

Donors: Foster Barkema; Evelyn Barkema.
Foundation type: Independent foundation.
Financial data (yr. ended 12/31/13): Assets, $3,877,379 (M); gifts received, $1,479,479; expenditures, $316,303; qualifying distributions, $255,888; giving activities include $252,382 for 50 grants (high: $41,000; low: $500).
Fields of interest: Education; Higher education; Christianity; Human services.
Type of support: Scholarships.
Limitations: Applications accepted. Giving primarily in IA.
Application information: Application form required.
  Initial approach: Letter
  Deadline(s): Sept. 30
Trustee: Zoe Brown.
EIN: 466233696

3472
Becker Family Foundation
102 S. Harrison, Ste. 200
Davenport, IA 52801

Established in 2004 in Iowa.
Donors: Sharon Becker; Jeffrey Becker.
Foundation type: Independent foundation.
Financial data (yr. ended 12/31/13): Assets, $9,528,751 (M); gifts received, $453,200; expenditures, $186,294; qualifying distributions, $130,460; giving activities include $126,560 for 25 grants (high: $56,000; low: $100).

Fields of interest: Education; Diseases and conditions; Religion.
Type of support: General support; Research.
Limitations: Applications not accepted. No grants to individuals.
Application information: Unsolicited requests for funds not accepted.
Directors: Jeffrey Becker; Sharon Becker.
EIN: 201648227

3473
F. William Beckwith Charitable Foundation
(formerly F. William Beckwith & Leola I. Beckwith Charitable Foundation)
1502 220th St.
Boone, IA 50036-7523
Application address: c/o F. William Beckwith, P.O. Box 70, Boone, IA 50036, tel.: (515) 432-9164

Established in 1995 in Iowa.
Donors: F. William Beckwith; Leola I. Beckwith†.
Foundation type: Operating foundation.
Financial data (yr. ended 12/31/13): Assets, $4,523,603 (M); gifts received, $299,597; expenditures, $232,273; qualifying distributions, $200,000; giving activities include $200,000 for 1 grant.
Fields of interest: Education; Botanical gardens; Public libraries; Christianity; Camps; Family services; Agriculture for youth.
Limitations: Giving primarily in IA and TN. No grants to individuals.
Application information:
  Initial approach: Letter
  Deadline(s): None
Officer: F. William Beckwith, Pres. and Treas.
EIN: 421448419

3474
Michael L. And Margie A . Bennett Foundation
4280 Sergeant Rd., Ste. 250
Sioux City, IA 51106-4612

Donor: Michael L. Bannett.
Foundation type: Independent foundation.
Financial data (yr. ended 12/31/13): Assets, $2,557,650 (M); expenditures, $267,606; qualifying distributions, $265,341; giving activities include $265,341 for 12 grants (high: $50,000; low: $2,450).
Fields of interest: Education; Undergraduate education; Nonprofits; Human services.
Type of support: Regranting.
Limitations: Applications not accepted. Giving primarily in IA.
Application information: Unsolicited Requests for funds not accepted.
Officers: Michael L. Bennett, Chair.; Margie Bennett, Vice-Chair.; Mary Weaver, Secy.
EIN: 273630915

3475
Bishop Educational Trust
c/o First National Bank
300 E. 2nd St.
Muscatine, IA 52761-4121
Contact: Scott Snow

Foundation type: Independent foundation.
Financial data (yr. ended 12/31/13): Assets, $2,964,186 (M); expenditures, $175,133; qualifying distributions, $161,441; giving activities include $147,750 for 74 grants to individuals (high: $5,500; low: $500).
Purpose and activities: Scholarships given to residents of Louisa and Muscatine counties, Iowa, to attend college in Iowa. The scholarships can be used toward an undergraduate degree or for a technical or trade school.
Fields of interest: Vocational post-secondary education; Higher education.
Type of support: Student aid.
Limitations: Applications accepted. Giving limited to residents of Louisa and Muscatine counties, IA.
Application information: Application form required.
  Initial approach: Proposal
  Deadline(s): June 1 of each academic year
  Board meeting date(s): Summer before the school year
Trustee: First National Bank of Muscatine.
EIN: 426531722

3476
The Blin Foundation, Inc.
(formerly Blin Family Foundation of Independence, Iowa, Inc.)
2300 Swan Lake Blvd., Ste. 303
Independence, IA 50644-9708

Established in 2000 in Iowa.
Donors: James L. Blin; Christopher Burgard; Randy Blin.
Foundation type: Independent foundation.
Financial data (yr. ended 12/31/13): Assets, $3,780,680 (M); gifts received, $50,000; expenditures, $240,023; qualifying distributions, $208,750; giving activities include $208,750 for 5 grants (high: $200,000; low: $250).
Fields of interest: Arts and culture; Education; Philanthropy.
Limitations: Applications not accepted. Giving primarily in IA.
Application information: Unsolicited requests for funds not accepted.
Directors: James L. Blin; Judy R. Blin; Randy A. Blin; Timothy L. Blin; Sandra L. Blin Burgard; Tamara K. Blin Diamond.
EIN: 421504887

3477
Burke Family Foundation
P.O. Box 723
Ames, IA 50010-0723

Donor: William J. Burke, Sr.†.
Foundation type: Independent foundation.
Financial data (yr. ended 03/31/13): Assets, $7,073,022 (M); gifts received, $6,435,194; expenditures, $165,669; qualifying distributions, $141,784; giving activities include $140,000 for 2 grants (high: $130,000; low: $10,000).
Fields of interest: Education; Health.
Limitations: Applications not accepted. Giving primarily in IA.
Application information: Unsolicited requests for funds not accepted.
Officers: Kathleen A. Burke, Pres. and Exec. Dir.; Thomas R. Burke, V.P.; Karen A. Burianek, Secy.; Kristine A. Holmes, Treas.

Director: William J. Burke, Jr.
EIN: 455592432

3478
Lavern T. Busse & Audrey Busse Foundation
2129 N. Towne Ln. N.E., Ste. B
Cedar Rapids, IA 52402-1968

Established in 1990 in Texas.
Donors: Lavern T. Busse; Audrey Busse.
Foundation type: Independent foundation.
Financial data (yr. ended 12/31/13): Assets,
$9,880,292 (M); gifts received, $596,853;
expenditures, $349,589; qualifying distributions,
$324,499; giving activities include $322,749 for 27
grants (high: $85,850; low: $50).
Fields of interest: Arts and culture; Higher
education; Nonprofits; Diseases and conditions;
Libraries; Protestantism; Camps.
Type of support: Regranting.
Limitations: Applications not accepted. No grants to
individuals.
Application information: Unsolicited requests for
funds not accepted.
Trustees: Audrey Busse; Jeffrey Busse; Lavern T.
Busse; Lori Ann Busse; Lisa Busse Carpenter.
EIN: 752342746

3479
Dean & Sandra Carlson Foundation
3811 127th St.
Urbandale, IA 50323-2349

Established in 1997 in Iowa.
Donors: C. Dean Carlson; Sandra S. Carlson.
Foundation type: Independent foundation.
Financial data (yr. ended 12/31/14): Assets,
$8,374,207; gifts received, $128,100;
expenditures, $360,284; qualifying distributions,
$355,000.
Fields of interest: Nonprofits; Family planning;
Libraries; Human services; Women's services.
Type of support: General support; Regranting.
Limitations: Applications not accepted. Giving
primarily in IA and KS. No grants to individuals.
Application information: Contributes only to
pre-selected organizations.
Officers: C. Dean Carlson, Pres.; Sandra S. Carlson,
V.P.
EIN: 391891960

3480
Cole-Belin Education Foundation
(formerly Marlin Cole and Connie Belin Charitable
Foundation)
13607 169th Ln.
Indianola, IA 50125-9490

Established in 1985 in Iowa.
Foundation type: Independent foundation.
Financial data (yr. ended 12/31/13): Assets,
$4,816,096 (M); expenditures, $380,286;
qualifying distributions, $290,676; giving activities
include $276,500 for 30 grants (high: $10,000;
low: $1,000).
Purpose and activities: Giving primarily for
educational institutions and programs.
Fields of interest: Education; Gifted education;
Higher education.

Type of support: General support; Scholarships.
Limitations: Applications not accepted. Giving
primarily in IA. No grants to individuals.
Application information: Unsolicited requests for
funds not accepted.
Officers: Laurie Belin, Pres.; Thomas Richard Belin,
V.P.; James M. Belin, Secy.-Treas.
Director: Joy Elizabeth Belin.
EIN: 421263748

3481
The Coons Foundation
c/o Kenton R. Coons
17112 480th Ln.
Chariton, IA 50049-8647

Established in 1997 in Louisiana.
Donors: Margaret L. Coons; Marion M. Coons;
Christine S. Coons; Kenton R. Coons.
Foundation type: Independent foundation.
Financial data (yr. ended 12/31/13): Assets,
$4,981,228 (M); gifts received, $3,434;
expenditures, $267,582; qualifying distributions,
$256,182; giving activities include $253,300 for 32
grants (high: $51,000; low: $1,000).
Fields of interest: Arts and culture; Undergraduate
education; Hospital care; Christianity; Human
services.
Limitations: Applications not accepted. Giving
primarily in IA. No grants to individuals.
Application information: Unsolicited requests for
funds not accepted.
Officers and Directors: Kenton R. Coons, Pres. and
Director; Christine S. Coons, Secy.-Treas. and
Director; Kevin Coons; Kyle Coons; Karen Dixson.
EIN: 391898965

3482
Gardner and Florence Call Cowles Foundation
1501 42nd St.
West Des Moines, IA 50266-1005

Established in 1934 in Iowa.
Donors: Gardner Cowles, Sr.†; Florence C. Cowles†.
Foundation type: Independent foundation.
Financial data (yr. ended 12/31/13): Assets,
$6,697,508 (M); expenditures, $328,481;
qualifying distributions, $250,000; giving activities
include $250,000 for 1 grant.
Fields of interest: Orchestral music; Art museums;
Family planning.
Type of support: General support; Matching grants;
Continuing support; Capital and infrastructure;
Endowments; Seed money.
Limitations: Applications not accepted. Giving
primarily in IA. No grants to individuals, or for
scholarships or fellowships; no loans.
Publications: Annual report.
Application information: Contributes only to
pre-selected organizations.
 Board meeting date(s): Annually, and as required
Officers: Charles C. Edwards, Jr., Pres.; Elizabeth
Ballantine, V.P.; Lisa Kruidenier, Secy.
Trustees: Katie Nichols; Nancy Schned.
Number of staff: None.
EIN: 426054609

3483
Daniels Family Foundation
(formerly The Ronald L. Daniels and June E. Daniels
Foundation)
3101 Ingersoll Ave.
Des Moines, IA 50312-3918 (515) 277-4000
Contact: Ronald L. Daniels, Dir.

Established in 1990 in Iowa.
Donors: Ronald L. Daniels; Selma S. Daniels 1986
Irrevocable Trust.
Foundation type: Independent foundation.
Financial data (yr. ended 12/31/13): Assets,
$580,281 (M); gifts received, $581,439;
expenditures, $254,155; qualifying distributions,
$253,260; giving activities include $253,260 for 20
grants (high: $100,000; low: $18).
Fields of interest: Education; University education;
Judaism.
Limitations: Applications accepted. Giving primarily
in FL, IA and NY. No grants to individuals.
Application information: Application form required.
 Initial approach: Letter
 Deadline(s): None
Directors: June E. Daniels; Ronald L. Daniels.
EIN: 421361018

3484
Mark & Kay De Cook Foundation
1349 Northwest Dr.
Pella, IA 50219-1101 (641) 628-4840
Contact: Mark De Cook, V.P.

Established in 1997 in Iowa.
Donors: Kay De Cook; Mark De Cook.
Foundation type: Independent foundation.
Financial data (yr. ended 12/31/13): Assets,
$183,879 (M); expenditures, $167,149; qualifying
distributions, $166,516; giving activities include
$165,881 for 57 grants (high: $42,000; low: $25).
Fields of interest: Education; Religion; Human
services.
Limitations: Applications accepted. Giving primarily
in IA and MI.
Application information: Application form required.
 Initial approach: Request application form
 Deadline(s): None
Officers: Kay De Cook, Pres.; Mark De Cook, V.P.;
Daniel De Cook, Secy.-Treas.
EIN: 421465821

3485
The Catherine Vincent Deardorf Charitable Foundation
1207 Central Ave.
Fort Dodge, IA 50501-0798 (515) 573-2154
Contact: Kim Stuhrenberg

Established in 1994 in Iowa.
Foundation type: Independent foundation.
Financial data (yr. ended 12/31/13): Assets,
$8,220,970 (M); expenditures, $474,098;
qualifying distributions, $387,576; giving activities
include $387,576 for 28 grants (high: $61,815;
low: $1,000).
Purpose and activities: Giving primarily for the
community, including arts and culture, education,
and health and human services.
Fields of interest: Arts and culture; Visual arts;
Performing arts; Literature and writing; Elementary

and secondary education; Reproductive health care; Libraries; Human services; Child welfare.
Limitations: Applications accepted. Giving limited to Webster County, IA. No support for religious activities and groups. No grants to individuals.
Application information: Application form required.
Initial approach: Telephone call
Copies of proposal: 1
Deadline(s): None
Directors: Rhonda Chambers; Jane Gibb; Doug Harrell; Joseph Heffernan; Judy Perkins; Peg Trevino.
EIN: 426496438

3486
deStwolinski Family Foundation
2911 Hamilton Blvd.
P.O. Box 270
Sioux City, IA 51104-2405

Established in 1998 in Nebraska.
Donor: Lance W. deStwolinski.
Foundation type: Independent foundation.
Financial data (yr. ended 05/31/13): Assets, $1,931,617 (M); expenditures, $203,517; qualifying distributions, $203,517; giving activities include $174,566 for grants.
Fields of interest: Education; National defense.
Type of support: Capital campaigns; Endowments; Scholarships.
Limitations: Applications not accepted. Giving primarily in AZ, IA, NE and NM.
Application information: Unsolicited requests for funds not accepted.
Board meeting date(s): Nov. and May
Officers: Lance W. deStwolinski, Pres.; Elizabeth H. deStwolinski, V.P. and Secy.-Treas.
Directors: Matthew deStwolinski; Kim Sealey; Pat Sealey.
EIN: 470812539

3487
Carl and Martha Drost Charitable Foundation
2352 Kirby Ave.
Oskaloosa, IA 52577-8708

Donors: Barb De Jong; Dave De Jong; Young Development; Martha Dorst; Carl Drost.
Foundation type: Independent foundation.
Financial data (yr. ended 12/31/13): Assets, $186,268 (M); gifts received, $185,000; expenditures, $138,396; qualifying distributions, $138,071; giving activities include $137,746 for 20 grants (high: $37,300; low: $20).
Fields of interest: Diseases and conditions; Religion; Human services.
Limitations: Applications not accepted. Giving primarily in MO and NE. No grants to individuals.
Application information: Unsolicited requests for funds not accepted.
Directors: Carl Drost; Martha Drost.
EIN: 141945040

3488
Cornelius Duggan Scholarship Trust
c/o Security National Bank, Trust Dept.
P.O. Box 147
Sioux City, IA 51102-0147

Established in 1991 in Iowa.
Foundation type: Independent foundation.
Financial data (yr. ended 12/31/13): Assets, $3,415,773 (M); expenditures, $265,665; qualifying distributions, $214,265; giving activities include $213,750 for 46 grants to individuals (high: $4,500; low: $4,500).
Purpose and activities: Provides scholarships only to Sioux City, Iowa, graduates attending a private Iowa college.
Fields of interest: Higher education.
Type of support: Student aid.
Limitations: Applications not accepted. Giving restricted to Sioux City, IA.
Application information: Unsolicited requests for funds not accepted.
Trustee: Security National Bank.
EIN: 426136907

3489
Mark and Mary Ellen Stinski Foundation
3590 Point Rd., N.E.
North Liberty, IA 52317-9361

Donors: Mary Ellen Stinski; Mark Stinski.
Foundation type: Independent foundation.
Financial data (yr. ended 12/31/12): Assets, $1,126,721 (M); gifts received, $250,000; expenditures, $146,388; qualifying distributions, $145,512; giving activities include $145,512 for grants.
Fields of interest: Health; Religion; Human services.
Limitations: Applications not accepted. Giving primarily in IA.
Application information: Unsolicited requests for funds not accepted.
Officers: Mark Stinski, Pres.; Mary Ellen Stinski, Treas.
EIN: 271247050

3490
Farrer Endowment Foundation
P.O. Box 1567
Mason City, IA 50402-1567 (641) 423-5154
Contact: Gerald M. Stambaugh, Secy.

Established in 1986 in Iowa.
Foundation type: Independent foundation.
Financial data (yr. ended 12/31/13): Assets, $5,814,955 (M); expenditures, $255,656; qualifying distributions, $251,326; giving activities include $232,200 for 54 grants (high: $35,000; low: $1,000).
Fields of interest: Libraries; Human services; Child welfare.
Limitations: Applications accepted. Giving primarily in Mason, IA.
Application information: Application form required.
Initial approach: Letter
Deadline(s): Jan. thru Apr. 30
Officers: James R. Heiny, Pres.; Frank B. Inghram, V.P. and Treas.; Gerald M. Stambaugh, Secy.
EIN: 421214699

3491
Joan Kuyper Farver Foundation
604 Liberty St., Ste. 311
Pella, IA 50219-1777 (641) 621-6000

Donors: Mary Joan Farver; Pella Corporation.

Foundation type: Independent foundation.
Financial data (yr. ended 12/31/13): Assets, $535,975 (M); gifts received, $360,000; expenditures, $385,980; qualifying distributions, $385,500; giving activities include $385,500 for 42 grants (high: $110,000; low: $500).
Fields of interest: Arts and culture; Opera; Higher education; Health; Hospital care; Protestantism; Human services.
Type of support: General support; Continuing support; Annual campaigns; Capital campaigns; Capital and infrastructure; Endowments; Emergency funds; Curriculum development.
Publications: Program policy statement.
Application information: Application form required.
Initial approach: Contact foundation for application form
Deadline(s): Contact foundation for deadline
Board meeting date(s): Apr. and as needed
Officers: Mary Joan Farver, Pres.; Charles S. Farver, V.P.; Mary Farver Griffith, Secy.
EIN: 841205184

3492
V.O. Figge and Elizebeth Kahl Figge Charitable Foundation
326 W. 3rd St., Ste. 714
Davenport, IA 52801-1220 (563) 336-8902

Established in 1992 in Iowa.
Donor: Vivian Otto Figge†.
Foundation type: Independent foundation.
Financial data (yr. ended 12/31/13): Assets, $0 (M); expenditures, $380,502; qualifying distributions, $380,502; giving activities include $371,260 for 4 grants (high: $366,260; low: $1,000).
Purpose and activities: Giving primarily for education and Catholic agencies and services.
Fields of interest: Art museums; Education; Human services.
Limitations: Applications accepted. Giving primarily in IA.
Application information: Application form required.
Initial approach: Letter
Deadline(s): None
Trustees: Thomas K. Figge; Richard Horst.
EIN: 421398444

3493
First Citizens National Bank Charitable Foundation, Inc.
2601 4th St. S.W.
P.O. Box 1708
Mason City, IA 50402-1708 (641) 423-1600
Contact: Patricia A. Tomson, Exec. Dir.
E-mail: ojt2@mchsi.com; *Main URL:* https://www.firstcitizensnb.com

Established in 1996 in Iowa.
Donors: O. Jay Tomson; First Citizens National Bank; First Citizens Financial Corp.
Foundation type: Company-sponsored foundation.
Financial data (yr. ended 12/31/13): Assets, $1,197,910 (M); gifts received, $350,000; expenditures, $413,743; qualifying distributions, $404,350; giving activities include $401,350 for 76 grants (high: $60,000; low: $500).
Purpose and activities: The foundation supports fire departments and organizations involved with arts and culture, education, animal welfare, health,

human services, community development, and low-to-moderate income individuals.

Fields of interest: Arts and culture; Education; Human services.

Type of support: General support; Annual campaigns; Capital campaigns; Capital and infrastructure; Equipment; Debt reduction; Emergency funds; Program development; Curriculum development; Scholarships; Sponsorships.

Limitations: Applications accepted. Giving primarily in areas of company operations in North IA, with emphasis on Chickasaw, Cerro Gordo, Floyd, Franklin, Hancock, Mitchell, and Wright. No grants for endowments.

Publications: Application guidelines.

Application information: Application form required.

  Initial approach: Complete online application form

  Deadline(s): None

  Board meeting date(s): June and Nov.

Officers: O. Jay Tomson, Pres.; Patricia A. Tomson, Exec. Dir.

Directors: Gordon Anderson; Marti T. Rodamaker; Catherine Rottinghaus; Kristine Schultz.

Number of staff: 1 part-time professional.

EIN: 421451615

3494
James W. and Ella B. Forster Charitable Trust

c/o Frontier Bank
P.O. Box 551
Rock Rapids, IA 51246-0551
Application Address: c/o Frontier Bank, 301 1st Ave., Rock Rapids, IA, 51246, Application
Phone: (712) 472-2537

Established in 1987 in Iowa.

Donors: James W. Forster†; Ella B. Forster†.

Foundation type: Independent foundation.

Financial data (yr. ended 12/31/14): Assets, $7,857,685 (M); expenditures, $405,361; qualifying distributions, $375,328; giving activities include $366,965 for 10 grants (high: $130,000; low: $2,500).

Purpose and activities: Giving primarily for community improvement.

Fields of interest: Elementary and secondary education; Hospital care; Public libraries; Economic development; Community improvement.

Type of support: Capital and infrastructure; Matching grants; Program development; Seed money.

Limitations: Applications accepted. Giving primarily in Rock Rapids, IA. No grants to individuals.

Application information: Application form required.

  Initial approach: Proposal

  Deadline(s): Sept. 30

Directors: Bruce Jennings; Bruce Kammermeyer; George Schneidermann.

EIN: 421305882

3495
William C. and Dorotha Gaedke Charitable Trust

425 Cedar St.
Waterloo, IA 50701-1351
Contact: LuAnn Ray, Trust Off., U.S. Bank, N.A.

Established in 2002 in Iowa.

Donor: Dorotha Gaedke†.

Foundation type: Independent foundation.

Financial data (yr. ended 06/30/13): Assets, $4,116,242 (M); expenditures, $246,600; qualifying distributions, $205,251; giving activities include $200,000 for 7 grants (high: $40,000; low: $20,000).

Fields of interest: University education; Foundations; Diseases and conditions; Parkinson's disease.

Limitations: Applications not accepted. Giving primarily in IA. No grants to individuals.

Application information: Contributes only to pre-selected organizations.

Trustee: U.S. Bank, N.A.

Directors: Vicki Angove; Sharon I. Chin; John Harris.

EIN: 396767863

3496
Gartner Family Foundation

100 Market St., Ste. 515
Des Moines, IA 50309-4766 (515) 279-6155
Contact: Michael G. Gartner

Established in 1994 in Iowa.

Donors: Michael G. Gartner; Barbara Gartner; Melissa Gartner; Carl Gartner†.

Foundation type: Independent foundation.

Financial data (yr. ended 12/31/13): Assets, $6,378,803 (M); gifts received, $144,775; expenditures, $302,360; qualifying distributions, $276,150; giving activities include $276,150 for 25 grants (high: $30,000; low: $1,000).

Fields of interest: Arts and culture; Higher education; Protestantism; Youth development; Youth services; Children and youth.

Limitations: Applications accepted. Giving primarily in IA. No grants to individuals.

Application information: Application form required.

  Initial approach: Contact foundation for application

  Deadline(s): None

  Board meeting date(s): Quarterly

Officers: Michael C. Gartner, Pres.; Melissa M. Gartner, V.P.; Barbara Gartner, Secy.; Michael G. Gartner, Treas.

Number of staff: None.

EIN: 421422699

3497
The Gazette Foundation

500 2nd Ave. S.E.
Cedar Rapids, IA 52401-1608
Main URL: http://www.gcrcf.org

Established in 1960 in Iowa.

Donor: The Gazette Co.

Foundation type: Company-sponsored foundation.

Financial data (yr. ended 12/31/13): Assets, $21,859 (M); gifts received, $148,000; expenditures, $191,930; qualifying distributions, $189,074; giving activities include $189,074 for grants.

Purpose and activities: The foundation supports community foundations, the United Way, and organizations involved with higher education and other areas. The foundation's programs are administered by the Greater Cedar Rapids Community Foundation.

Fields of interest: Arts and culture; Health; Human services.

Type of support: Annual campaigns; Capital campaigns; Capital and infrastructure.

Limitations: Applications accepted. Giving limited to the Cedar Rapids, IA, area. No support for public schools or religious organizations. No grants to individuals, or for endowments, advertising, city or municipal projects, fundraising dinners, band uniforms, trips, conferences, group travel, or honoraria for distinguished guests.

Publications: Application guidelines.

Application information: Application form required.

  Initial approach: See website for application form

  Deadline(s): See website for deadline

  Board meeting date(s): Quarterly or as needed

Officers and Directors: Charles Peters, Pres. and Director; Elizabeth Schott, Secy. and Director; Scott Grasso, Treas.; Cathy Terukina.

EIN: 426075177

3498
Geisler Penquite Corporation

P.O. Box 924
Newton, IA 50208 (641) 791-2874
Contact: Dan Skokan, Pres.

Established in 1969 in Iowa.

Donors: Gertrude Geisler†; Harold Geisler†; John Geisler†; Mavis Geisler; Cecil Geisler Penquite†; Loren Penquite†.

Foundation type: Independent foundation.

Financial data (yr. ended 12/31/13): Assets, $10,659,499 (M); expenditures, $500,001; qualifying distributions, $440,000; giving activities include $440,000 for 17 grants (high: $264,000; low: $11,000).

Fields of interest: Education; Higher education; Human services.

Type of support: Endowments.

Limitations: Applications accepted. Giving primarily in Pella, IA.

Publications: Application guidelines; Program policy statement.

Application information: Application form required.

  Initial approach: Letter

  Copies of proposal: 1

  Deadline(s): None

Officers: Dan Skokan, Pres. and Treas.; Eric Sickler, V.P.; Maureen Timmer, Secy.

Directors: Eugene Knopf; Jean Schnell; Margaret Tungseth.

EIN: 237103845

3499
John P. and Lawrence J. Giacoletto Foundation

1175 8th Ave.
Marion, IA 52302-3503 (319) 363-1910
FAX: (319) 377-9406; *E-mail:* info@giacoletto.org
Main URL: http://www.giacoletto.org

Donor: Giacoletto Living Trust.

Foundation type: Operating foundation.

Financial data (yr. ended 12/31/13): Assets, $8,165,745 (M); expenditures, $492,836; qualifying distributions, $492,836; giving activities include $422,500 for 30 grants (high: $100,000; low: $1,000).

Fields of interest: Education; Nonprofits; Libraries; Public libraries.

Type of support: Regranting.

Limitations: Applications accepted. Giving primarily in IA and IN.
Application information: See foundation web site for complete application guidelines. Application form required.
  Initial approach: Submit online Grant Letter of Inquiry through foundation web site
  Deadline(s): Quarterly
Trustees: Barbara Robison; E. Wayne Scott; Alex Taylor.
EIN: 201777917

3500
Gleeson Family Foundation
(formerly Gleeson Foundation)
P.O. Box 8800
Sioux City, IA 51102-8800

Donors: Gleeson Constructors; Robert E. Gleeson; Klinger Co.; Helen K. Gleeson; John W. Gleeson; Klinger Co., Inc.
Foundation type: Independent foundation.
Financial data (yr. ended 12/31/12): Assets, $3,213,464 (M); gifts received, $300,000; expenditures, $156,216; qualifying distributions, $141,000; giving activities include $141,000 for 15 grants (high: $25,000; low: $500).
Fields of interest: Education; Religion; Human services.
Limitations: Applications not accepted. Giving primarily in Sioux City, IA. No grants to individuals.
Application information: Unsolicited requests for funds not accepted.
Officers: John W. Gleeson, Pres. and Treas.; Karen Gleeson, Secy.
EIN: 420933162

3501
Grinnell Mutual Group Foundation
(formerly GMG Foundation)
4215 Hwy., Ste.146
Grinnell, IA 50112-0790 (641) 269-8000
Contact: Barbara Baker, Mgr.
E-mail: jwoods@gmrc.com

Established in 1987 in Iowa.
Donor: Grinnell Mutual Reinsurance Co.
Foundation type: Company-sponsored foundation.
Financial data (yr. ended 12/31/13): Assets, $9,413 (M); gifts received, $140,000; expenditures, $137,605; qualifying distributions, $137,605; giving activities include $96,988 for 37 grants (high: $20,000; low: $250), and $40,617 for 50 employee matching gifts.
Purpose and activities: The foundation supports organizations involved with education, natural resources, agriculture, community development, and civic affairs.
Fields of interest: Health; Community and economic development; Human services.
Type of support: General support; Grants to individuals; Employee matching gifts; Annual campaigns; Program development.
Limitations: Applications accepted. Giving primarily in areas of company operations, with emphasis on Grinnell, IA. No support for religious or political organizations.
Publications: Annual report.
Application information: Application form required.
  Initial approach: Completed Application form
  Deadline(s): None

Officers: Larry Jansen, Pres.; Shawn McKay, V.P.; Adam Smith, Secy.; Hutch Kracht, Treas.
Directors: Stacy Heinen; Carla Kelling; Brent Larsen; Lynn Mawe; Phyllis Steffen; Ray Spriggs.
Number of staff: None.
EIN: 421308146

3502
The John R. and Zelda Z. Grubb Charitable Foundation
14914 Brookview Dr.
Urbandale, IA 50323-2460

Established in 1995 in Iowa.
Donors: John R. Grubb†; John R. Grubb, Inc.
Foundation type: Operating foundation.
Financial data (yr. ended 12/31/13): Assets, $11,865,106 (M); expenditures, $4,493,686; qualifying distributions, $334,786; giving activities include $334,786 for 23 grants (high: $100,090; low: $1,000).
Purpose and activities: Giving primarily for health as well as children, youth and social services. The grantmaker also operates two nursing homes for the elderly, as well an assisted living facility for the elderly.
Fields of interest: Education; Foundations; Health; Diseases and conditions; Christianity; Human services; Child welfare; Seniors.
Limitations: Applications not accepted. Giving primarily in IA. No grants to individuals.
Application information: Contributes only to pre-selected organizations.
Officer: John W. Grubb, Pres. and Secy.-Treas.
EIN: 426521745

3503
The GuideOne Insurance Foundation, Inc.
1111 Ashworth Rd., M.S. A27
West Des Moines, IA 50265-3544
Contact: Sarah Buckley, V.P., Corp. Comms. and Mktg.
Main URL: http://www.guideone.com/AboutUs/foundation.htm

Established in 2000 in Iowa.
Donor: GuideOne Life Insurance Co.
Foundation type: Operating foundation.
Financial data (yr. ended 12/31/12): Assets, $2,151,567 (M); gifts received, $72,517; expenditures, $425,577; qualifying distributions, $425,577; giving activities include $425,577 for 35 grants (high: $161,898; low: $1,000).
Purpose and activities: The foundation supports food banks and organizations involved with housing development, human services, community development, and Christianity. Special emphasis is directed toward programs designed to promote mission and community development; provide assistance for immediate needs; and promote prevention of drinking and driving and underage drinking.
Fields of interest: Nonprofits; Impaired driving; Disaster relief; Automotive safety; Community and economic development; Housing development; Christianity; Human services; Food banks; Child welfare; Victims of disaster.
Type of support: General support; Emergency funds; Program development; Sponsorships; Regranting.

Limitations: Giving primarily in IA; giving also to national organizations. No grants to individuals.
Officers and Directors: James D. Wallace, Chair. and Pres. and Director; Brian Hughes, Treas.; Tom Fischer.
EIN: 391910630

3504
Bruce & Sandy Heerema Charitable Foundation
1111 Sunset St.
Pella, IA 50219-1043 (641) 628-2351
Contact: Bruce Heerema, Pres.

Established in 1997 in Iowa.
Donors: Bruce Heerema; Sandy Heerema.
Foundation type: Independent foundation.
Financial data (yr. ended 12/31/13): Assets, $1,037,232 (M); gifts received, $561,695; expenditures, $208,012; qualifying distributions, $207,506; giving activities include $207,000 for 12 grants (high: $75,500; low: $300).
Purpose and activities: Giving primarily for Christian organizations and schools.
Fields of interest: Education; Employment; Religion.
Limitations: Applications accepted. Giving primarily in CT and IA.
Application information: Application form required.
  Initial approach: Contact foundation for the application form
  Deadline(s): None
Officers: Bruce Heerema, Pres.; Sandy Heerema, V.P.
Directors: M. Timothy Heerema; Steven Heerema.
EIN: 391910689

3505
Henry Family Foundation
195 S. Grandview Ave.
Dubuque, IA 52003-7224 (563) 556-4011
Contact: Douglas M. Henry, Treas.

Established in 2000 in Florida.
Donor: Allen S. Henry.
Foundation type: Independent foundation.
Financial data (yr. ended 12/31/13): Assets, $4,122,617 (M); expenditures, $208,995; qualifying distributions, $161,625; giving activities include $161,625 for 28 grants (high: $15,000; low: $1,000).
Fields of interest: Arts and culture; Education; Nonprofits; Protestantism; Golf; Human services.
Type of support: Regranting.
Limitations: Applications accepted. Giving primarily in IA.
Application information: Application form required.
  Initial approach: Letter
  Deadline(s): None
Officers: Allen S. Henry, Pres.; James B. Henry, V.P.; Charles S. Henry, Secy.; Douglas M. Henry, Treas.
EIN: 593677987

3506
John Herr Foundation Trust
P.O. Box 337
Fairfield, IA 52556-0006

Donors: Bryan Herr; Delinda Herr.
Foundation type: Independent foundation.

Financial data (yr. ended 12/31/13): Assets, $6,156,832 (M); expenditures, $402,375; qualifying distributions, $396,305; giving activities include $360,000 for 5 grants (high: $165,000; low: $15,000), and $34,477 for 1 foundation-administered program.
Fields of interest: Community and economic development; Religion; Christianity; Human services.
Limitations: Applications not accepted. Giving primarily in TX.
Application information: Unsolicited requests for funds not accepted.
Trustees: Bryan Herr; Dale Long; Michael Marx.
EIN: 546587688

3507
The Jared & Carol Hills Foundation
c/o Darrell A. Morf
115 3rd St. S.E., Ste. 1200
Cedar Rapids, IA 52401-1222
Application address: c/o Carol T. Hills, 2008 Balsam Dr. S.W., Cedar Rapids, IA 52404; tel.: (319) 366-7641

Established in 1997 in Iowa.
Donors: Jared S. Hills; Carol T. Hills.
Foundation type: Independent foundation.
Financial data (yr. ended 12/31/14): Assets, $3,984,382 (M); gifts received, $22; expenditures, $176,256; qualifying distributions, $170,635; giving activities include $170,635 for 56 grants (high: $30,000; low: $135).
Fields of interest: Philanthropy; Religion; Christianity; Human services.
Limitations: Applications accepted. Giving primarily in Cedar Rapids, IA. No grants to individuals.
Application information: Application form required.
 Initial approach: Letter
 Deadline(s): None
Officers: Carol T. Hills, Pres.; Jared S. Hills, V.P.; Darrel A. Morf, Secy.; Roger J. Schmidt, Treas.
Directors: John Botkin; Kari Dirks; Paul Hills.
EIN: 391896077

3508
William M. & Donna J. Hoaglin Foundation, Inc.
800 Alter Ct.
Mount Pleasant, IA 52641-2404
Application address: c/o Donna J. Hoaglin, P.O. Box 791, Mount Pleasant, IA 52641-0791

Donors: William M. Hoaglin; Donna J. Hoaglin.
Foundation type: Independent foundation.
Financial data (yr. ended 01/31/14): Assets, $5,842,097 (M); expenditures, $289,606; qualifying distributions, $289,606; giving activities include $282,306 for 24 grants (high: $78,000; low: $792).
Purpose and activities: Giving primarily to promote the literary and educational welfare of people in Henry and Van Buren counties, Iowa.
Fields of interest: Historical activities; Education; Natural resources; Community and economic development; Swimming; Human services.
Limitations: Applications accepted. Giving primarily in Henry and Van Buren counties, IA. No grants to individuals.
Application information: Application form required.

Deadline(s): Jan. 1 and July 1
 Board meeting date(s): 3rd Mon. of July and Jan.
Officers: Donna J. Hoaglin, Pres.; Joe Remick, V.P.; Carmen Heaton, Secy.; David H. Carrick, Treas.
Directors: Norman Kisling; Larry Remick.
EIN: 421121634

3509
Dale & Marilyn Howard Charitable Foundation
615 Railroad St.
Iowa Falls, IA 50126-2209

Established in 2006 in Iowa.
Donor: Dale A. Howard.
Foundation type: Independent foundation.
Financial data (yr. ended 12/31/14): Assets, $0 (M); gifts received, $188,080; expenditures, $205,683; qualifying distributions, $205,183; giving activities include $205,183 for 6 grants (high: $195,038; low: $245).
Fields of interest: Higher education.
Limitations: Applications not accepted. Giving primarily in IA. No grants to individuals.
Application information: Contributes only to pre-selected organizations.
Officers: Dale A. Howard, Pres. and Treas.; Marilyn J. Howard, V.P.; Steven M. Howard, Secy.
Directors: Diane S. Gulick; Donna A. Embree; Scott A. Howard.
EIN: 204960221

3510
The Howe Foundation
101 W. Mississippi Dr., Ste. 600
Muscatine, IA 52761-5564
Contact: Stanley M. Howe, Pres.; Helen H. Howe

Established in 1992 in Iowa.
Donor: Stanley M. Howe.
Foundation type: Independent foundation.
Financial data (yr. ended 06/30/14): Assets, $6,437,252 (M); expenditures, $142,463; qualifying distributions, $131,980; giving activities include $128,140 for 7 grants (high: $85,000; low: $240).
Fields of interest: Performing arts; Education; Higher education; Protestantism; Human services.
Limitations: Applications not accepted. Giving primarily in IA; some funding also in Alpharetta, GA. No grants to individuals.
Application information: Contributes only to pre-selected organizations.
Directors: James Howe; Stanley M. Howe; Helen H. Howe.
Number of staff: None.
EIN: 421395312

3511
Iowa Foundation for Agricultural Advancement
1440 N.W. 134th Ave.
Slater, IA 50244
Application address: c/o Winner's Circle Scholarship, 30805 595th Ave., Cambridge, IA 50046, tel.: (515) 383-4386
Facebook: https://www.facebook.com/IowaFoundationforAgAdvancement

Donors: Robert Schlutz; Iowa Select Farms; Sinclair Tractor; Beef Promotions of Iowa; Rastetter Foundation; Mike Pentzenhauser.
Foundation type: Independent foundation.
Financial data (yr. ended 12/31/13): Assets, $0 (M); gifts received, $133,886; expenditures, $259,500; qualifying distributions, $173,700; giving activities include $173,700 for 128 grants to individuals (high: $8,000; low: $200).
Purpose and activities: Scholarship awards to students pursuing a degree relating to the animal industry at any 2-year or 4-year post secondary educational institution in Iowa.
Fields of interest: Education; Agriculture.
Type of support: Student aid.
Limitations: Applications accepted. Giving primarily in IA.
Application information: Application form required.
 Initial approach: Contact foundation for application
 Deadline(s): June 1
Officers: Jack Bair, Pres.; Stephen Weldon, V.P.; Shelley Wing, Secy.; Scott Wiley, Treas.
Directors: Rob Bohnsack; Dick Danielson; Dustin Ford; Lindsay Greiner; Harold Hodson; Taylor Sweeney; Gary Vanaernam; Linda Weldon; Cat Wood.
EIN: 421183067

3512
The Iowa Foundation for Education, Environment and the Arts
13607 169th Ln.
Indianola, IA 50125-9490

Established in 1992 in Iowa.
Donor: David W. Belin.
Foundation type: Independent foundation.
Financial data (yr. ended 12/31/14): Assets, $4,711,616; expenditures, $342,986; qualifying distributions, $242,970.
Fields of interest: Arts and culture; Music; Museums; Education; Judaism; Human services; Youth services.
Type of support: General support.
Limitations: Applications not accepted. Giving primarily in IA. No grants to individuals.
Application information: Contributes only to pre-selected organizations.
Officers: Laurie Belin, Pres.; Thomas Richard Belin, V.P.; James M. Belin, Secy.-Treas.
Director: Joy Elizabeth Belin.
EIN: 421333063

3513
Iowa P.E.O. Project Fund, Inc.
1706 Pikes Peak Ct. NE
Cedar Rapids, IA 52402
Contact: Gaye Roberts, Pres.
E-mail: gaye.roberts@mchsi.com

Established in 1997 in Iowa.
Donor: Iowa State Chapter, P.E.O. Sisterhood.
Foundation type: Independent foundation.
Financial data (yr. ended 03/31/13): Assets, $3,779,440 (M); gifts received, $353,759; expenditures, $327,581; qualifying distributions, $327,581; giving activities include $68,370 for 1+ grant, and $242,956 for 82 grants to individuals (high: $5,000).

Purpose and activities: Giving to provide for the health, education, welfare, maintenance, and support of any deserving person; also provides scholarships to Iowa women to attend Cottey College in Nevada, Missouri.

Fields of interest: Education; Human services; Children; Adults; Low-income and poor people.

Type of support: General support; Grants to individuals; Loans to individuals; Continuing support; Debt reduction; Individual development; Emergency funds; Student aid.

Limitations: Giving limited to female residents (and families) of IA.

Publications: Annual report; Financial statement; Informational brochure.

Application information: Applications not accepted directly. Applicant must be supported by a local chapter and contact must be made only through a local chapter. Application form required.

Initial approach: Proposal

Deadline(s): None

Officers: Gaye Roberts, Pres.; Zoe-Ann Helgerson, V.P.; Susan Voss, Secy.; Debra Beach, Treas.

Board Members: Judy Hughes; Jill Mortenson; Judy Sievers.

Number of staff: 1 part-time professional.

EIN: 420722695

3514
Greater Jefferson County Community Foundation

P.O. Box 1325
Fairfield, IA 52556-1325 (641) 472-0758
Contact: Barbara Kistler, Admin.
FAX: (641) 472-0758;
E-mail: gjcf0758@iowatelecom.net; Main
URL: http://greaterjeffersoncountyfoundation.org

Established in 1975 in Iowa.

Foundation type: Community foundation.

Financial data (yr. ended 03/31/13): Assets, $2,521,792 (M); gifts received, $418,038; expenditures, $208,849; giving activities include $95,172 for grants, and $79,778 for grants to individuals.

Purpose and activities: The Greater Jefferson County Foundation receives, accepts and distributes funds for educational, cultural, civic and charitable purposes for the benefit of the greater community of Jefferson County, Iowa.

Fields of interest: Arts and culture; Humanities; Education; Disasters and emergency management; Sports and recreation; Baseball and softball; Child welfare; Youth development.

Type of support: Capital and infrastructure; Equipment; Endowments; Student aid; Individual development.

Limitations: Applications accepted. Giving limited to Jefferson County, IA. No support for churches. No grants for operating expenses.

Publications: Application guidelines; Annual report; Financial statement; Grants list; Informational brochure.

Application information: Visit foundation's web site for additional guidelines and online application. Application form required.

Initial approach: Complete online grant application

Copies of proposal: 1

Deadline(s): June 1

Board meeting date(s): May and Nov.

Final notification: 30 days

Officers and Directors: Bob Wiegert, Pres. and Director; Ken Malloy, V.P. and Director; Peggy Small, Secy. and Director; Dave Eastburn, Treas. and Director; Joe Carr; Dave Dickey; David Eastburn; Sarah Flattery; Marty Gleason; Nancy Horras; Tim Kuiken; Greg Lowenbery; Ken Malloy; Pat McMahon; Pam Mitchell; Linda Pettit; Renee Rebling; Peggy Small; Bob Wiegert.

Number of staff: 1 part-time support.

EIN: 510172078

3515
K2 Charitable Foundation

2400 86th St., Ste. 24
Urbandale, IA 50322-4306 (515) 276-3456
Contact: Kenneth L. Smith, Pres.

Donors: Kenneth L. Smith; Irrevocable K-2 Trust.

Foundation type: Independent foundation.

Financial data (yr. ended 12/31/13): Assets, $498,859 (M); gifts received, $650,627; expenditures, $155,248; qualifying distributions, $147,500; giving activities include $147,500 for 5 grants (high: $60,000; low: $6,000).

Fields of interest: Health; Religion; Youth development.

Application information: Application form required.

Initial approach: Contact foundation for application form

Deadline(s): None

Officers: Kenneth L. Smith, Pres.; Scott Temple, V.P.; Dave Harmeyer, Secy.; John Lamale, Treas.

EIN: 461208733

3516
Krause Gentle Foundation

6400 Westown Pkwy.
West Des Moines, IA 50266-7709

Established in 1994 in Iowa.

Donors: William A. Krause; KG Investments; Krause Gentle Corporation; Kum & Go LC; Cheiftain.

Foundation type: Independent foundation.

Financial data (yr. ended 12/31/13): Assets, $7,670,769 (M); gifts received, $3,100,000; expenditures, $403,120; qualifying distributions, $400,095; giving activities include $397,837 for 108 grants (high: $135,535; low: $50).

Purpose and activities: Giving primarily for Catholic schools, churches and organizations; giving also for youth services and programs and for education.

Fields of interest: Arts and culture; Elementary and secondary education; Higher education; Nonprofits; Multiple sclerosis; Community and economic development; Protestantism; Catholicism; Human services; Youth services.

Type of support: Regranting.

Limitations: Applications not accepted. Giving primarily in IA. No grants to individuals.

Application information: Contributes only to pre-selected organizations.

Directors: Dennis Folden; William A. Krause.

EIN: 421414004

3517
Daniel J. & Ann L. Krumm Charitable Trust

122 S. Linn St.
Iowa City, IA 52240-1802 (888) 222-0814
Contact: Timothy J. Krumm, Tr.

Established in 1986 in Iowa.

Donors: Daniel J. Krumm; Ann L. Krumm.

Foundation type: Independent foundation.

Financial data (yr. ended 12/31/13): Assets, $4,827,655 (M); expenditures, $237,980; qualifying distributions, $189,300; giving activities include $188,500 for 11 grants (high: $30,000; low: $1,500).

Purpose and activities: Giving primarily for Lutheran social services and to a camp; funding also for the arts.

Fields of interest: Opera; Education; Television; Methodism; Camps; Human services.

Type of support: General support; Annual campaigns; Capital campaigns.

Limitations: Applications accepted. Giving primarily in IA. No grants to individuals.

Application information:

Initial approach: Proposal

Deadline(s): None

Trustees: David J. Krumm; Timothy J. Krumm.

EIN: 421308651

3518
Lucile Latta Charitable Trust

P.O. Box 147
Sioux City, IA 51102-0147

Established in 1997 in Iowa.

Donor: Lucile Latta†.

Foundation type: Independent foundation.

Financial data (yr. ended 12/31/13): Assets, $6,559,380 (M); expenditures, $263,257; qualifying distributions, $210,389; giving activities include $208,513 for 42 grants (high: $6,100; low: $937).

Purpose and activities: Giving primarily for college scholarships.

Fields of interest: Education.

Type of support: Student aid.

Limitations: Applications not accepted. Giving limited to residents of Harrison County, IA.

Application information: Unsolicited requests for funds not accepted.

Trustee: Security National Bank.

EIN: 426554228

3519
McCarthy/Bush Foundation

5401 Victoria Ave.
Davenport, IA 52807-3932

Established in 1989 in Iowa.

Donors: Linwood Mining & Minerals Corp.; McCarthy Improvement Co.; John L. Bush; McCarthy Bush Corp.

Foundation type: Company-sponsored foundation.

Financial data (yr. ended 12/31/13): Assets, $794 (M); gifts received, $189,000; expenditures, $188,806; qualifying distributions, $185,469; giving activities include $185,469 for 31 grants (high: $50,000; low: $100).

Purpose and activities: The foundation supports organizations involved with arts and culture, education, school athletics, human services, and religion.

Fields of interest: Education; Religion; Human services.

Limitations: Applications not accepted. Giving primarily in Davenport, IA. No grants to individuals.

Application information: Contributes only to pre-selected organizations.
Trustees: Tom Bush; Barbara J. Johnson; Mary Walsh.
EIN: 421322400

3520
A. Y. McDonald Manufacturing Company Charitable Foundation
P.O. Box 508
Dubuque, IA 52004-0508

Established in 1967 in Iowa.
Donor: A.Y. McDonald Industries, Inc.
Foundation type: Company-sponsored foundation.
Financial data (yr. ended 12/31/13): Assets, $5,481,212 (M); gifts received, $850,000; expenditures, $313,900; qualifying distributions, $313,900; giving activities include $313,900 for 61 grants (high: $37,000; low: $100).
Purpose and activities: The foundation supports orchestras and recreation centers and organizations involved with education, health, medical research, and human services.
Fields of interest: Orchestral music; Education; Higher education; Nonprofits; Health; Patient social services; Health care clinics; Diseases and conditions; Public libraries; Community recreation; Human services; Child welfare; Youth services; Economics for youth.
Type of support: Program development; Capital campaigns; General support; Research; Regranting.
Limitations: Applications not accepted. Giving primarily in eastern IA, with emphasis on Dubuque. No grants to individuals.
Application information: Contributes only to pre-selected organizations.
Officers: R. D. McDonald II, Pres.; Sarah Hasken, V.P. and Corp. Secy.; Scott Knapp, V.P.; J. M. McDonald III, Treas.
Director: John Schmidt.
EIN: 426119514

3521
Medical Associates Clinic Foundation of Dubuque
1605 Associates Dr., Ste. 101
Dubuque, IA 52002-2270

Established in 1993 in Iowa.
Donor: Medical Associates Clinic, P.C.
Foundation type: Independent foundation.
Financial data (yr. ended 12/31/13): Assets, $2,015,344 (M); gifts received, $200,102; expenditures, $190,899; qualifying distributions, $183,156; giving activities include $171,595 for 8 grants (high: $68,400; low: $500).
Fields of interest: Education; Health; Human services.
Type of support: General support; Scholarships.
Limitations: Applications not accepted. Giving primarily in Dubuque, IA.
Application information: Unsolicited requests for funds not accepted.
Officers: Mark Moore, Chair.; Jill Mitchell, Treas.; John Tallent, Exec. Dir.
Directors: John Dolehide; Jared Freiburger; Lawrence Kukla; John Moore.
EIN: 421172640

3522
Mount Saint Clare Education Charitable Trust
235 6th Ave. S.
Clinton, IA 52732-4305

Donors: Whitten-Welch Foundation; Mount Saint Clare Education Foundation.
Foundation type: Independent foundation.
Financial data (yr. ended 12/31/13): Assets, $3,213,326 (M); gifts received, $3,160,291; expenditures, $158,696; qualifying distributions, $153,650; giving activities include $153,650 for 1 grant.
Fields of interest: Higher education.
Limitations: Applications not accepted. Giving primarily in IA.
Application information: Unsolicited requests for funds not accepted.
Trustee: Clinton National Bank, N.A.
EIN: 455445734

3523
Muscatine Health Support Foundation
209 Iowa Ave.
Muscatine, IA 52761-3730
Contact: Betty J. Anders, Admin. Asst.

Established in 1984 in Iowa.
Foundation type: Independent foundation.
Financial data (yr. ended 06/30/13): Assets, $2,955,655 (M); expenditures, $277,613; qualifying distributions, $212,556; giving activities include $210,623 for 6 grants (high: $171,000; low: $395).
Purpose and activities: Support of projects that will improve the community health and aid the growth and development of the medical care system in Muscatine County, IA.
Fields of interest: Health; Diseases and conditions.
Type of support: Equipment; Matching grants; Program development; Seed money.
Limitations: Applications not accepted. Giving limited to the Muscatine, IA, area.
Application information: Unsolicited requests for funds not accepted.
Board meeting date(s): Apr. and Oct.
Officers and Trustees: Richard H. Stanley, Pres. and Trustee; William B. Trent, Jr., V.P. and Trustee; Charles R. Coulter, Secy.-Treas. and Trustee.
Number of staff: 1 part-time support.
EIN: 421005290

3524
The Nelson Foundation
4105 Timberwood Dr.
West Des Moines, IA 50265-5366 (515) 266-2111

Established in 1983 in Iowa.
Donors: R.W. Nelson; Mary Nelson.
Foundation type: Independent foundation.
Financial data (yr. ended 12/31/14): Assets, $1,732,868; expenditures, $273,950; qualifying distributions, $271,975.
Fields of interest: Higher education; Nonprofits; Christianity.
Type of support: Continuing support; Scholarships; Regranting.
Limitations: Applications accepted. Giving primarily in IA.

Publications: Annual report.
Application information: Application form required.
Initial approach: Request application form
Deadline(s): None
Board meeting date(s): Jan.
Officers: R.W. Nelson, Pres. and Treas.; Mary A. Nelson, V.P. and Secy.
EIN: 421207818

3525
John & Mary Pappajohn Scholarship Foundation
666 Walnut St.
2116 Financial Center
Des Moines, IA 50309-3907

Foundation type: Independent foundation.
Financial data (yr. ended 09/30/14): Assets, $539,416 (M); expenditures, $280,855; qualifying distributions, $279,853; giving activities include $278,850 for 36 grants (high: $80,000; low: $100).
Fields of interest: Education; Higher education; Religion.
Type of support: Individual development.
Limitations: Applications not accepted. Giving primarily in Des Moines, IA; some funding also in VA. No grants to individuals.
Application information: Contributes only to pre-selected organizations.
Directors: John Pappajohn; Mary Pappajohn; Ann Vassiliou.
EIN: 421645551

3526
Peace Foundation
103 Full Moon Ln.
Fairfield, IA 52556-2062

Donors: John Fagan; Susel A. Fagan.
Foundation type: Independent foundation.
Financial data (yr. ended 12/31/13): Assets, $1,771,478 (M); gifts received, $1,931,509; expenditures, $152,818; qualifying distributions, $140,000; giving activities include $140,000 for 2 grants (high: $100,000; low: $40,000).
Fields of interest: Education; Diseases and conditions.
Limitations: Applications not accepted. Giving primarily in KY and IA.
Application information: Unsolicited requests for funds not accepted.
Directors: John Fagan; Susel A. Fagan; Bhavani Mair; Victor Raymond.
EIN: 463789772

3527
Pottawattamie County Community Foundation
536 E. Broadway
Council Bluffs, IA 51503 (712) 256-7007
Contact: Jerry Mathiasen, Pres. and C.E.O.
FAX: (712) 256-5007; E-mail: info@ourpccf.org;
Main URL: http://www.ourpccf.org
Facebook: http://www.facebook.com/pages/Pottawattamie-County-Community-Foundation/120183394687048

Foundation type: Community foundation.
Financial data (yr. ended 12/31/13): Assets, $10,205,047 (M); gifts received, $204,979;

expenditures, $502,538; giving activities include $101,286 for grants, and $94,684 for 95 grants to individuals.

Purpose and activities: The Pottawattamie County Community Foundation is a partnership of rural and urban citizens dedicated to improving the lives of all residents of the county's communities by: 1) serving as an effective catalyst for responses to community issues; 2) supporting continuous efforts to meet changing needs stimulating donor-driven philanthropy; 3) raising the capacity of nonprofit organizations in the county; and 4) providing careful stewardship of the foundation's resources.

Fields of interest: Disasters and emergency management; Community and economic development.

Limitations: Applications accepted. Giving primarily in Pottawattamie County, IA. No grants for clinical or medical research, capital campaigns, operating deficits or retirement of debt, construction projects or real estate acquisitions, gift cards or prizes, or vehicles, such as vans or buses, or emergency medical services equipment; endowment programs are typically not funded.

Publications: Application guidelines; Annual report.

Application information: Visit foundation web site for application forms and guidelines per grant type. Application form required.

> *Initial approach:* Submit application and attachments
> *Deadline(s):* Mar. 1 and Sept. 1 for the Community Grants Program
> *Final notification:* 45 days for Community Grants Program

Officers and Directors: Kelly Summy, Chair. and Director; Marie Knedler, Vice-Chair. and Director; Jerry Mathiasen, Pres. and C.E.O. and Director; Jerry Banks, Secy. and Director; Robert McCarthy, Treas. and Director; Bobbette Behrens; Dean R. Fischer; Walter Keast; Frank Pechacek; A.W. Tauke.

EIN: 261382215

3528
Premier Communications Foundation

(formerly MTC Foundation, Inc.)
c/o Mutual Telephone Company
P.O. Box 200
Sioux Center, IA 51250-0200

Established in 1990 in Iowa.

Donor: Mutual Telephone Co.

Foundation type: Company-sponsored foundation.

Financial data (yr. ended 12/31/13): Assets, $4,479,158 (M); gifts received, $50,000; expenditures, $328,881; qualifying distributions, $285,250; giving activities include $285,250 for 44 grants (high: $70,000; low: $250).

Purpose and activities: The foundation supports fire departments and organizations involved with education, health, human services, and community development.

Fields of interest: Education; Disasters and emergency management; Community and economic development.

Type of support: General support; Scholarships.

Limitations: Applications not accepted. Giving primarily in IA.

Application information: Unsolicited requests for funds not accepted.

Officers: Howard Beernink, Pres.; Owen Dykshorn, V.P.; Glen Vermeer, Secy.; Douglas Boone, Treas.

Directors: Ted Hengeveld; John Koerselman; David Krahling; Michael D. McAlpine; Jim Mouw; Lauren Vos.

EIN: 421358494

3529
R & R Realty Group Foundation

1225 Jordan Creek Pkwy., Ste. 200
West Des Moines, IA 50266-2346

Established in 1999 in Iowa.

Donors: R&R Investors Inc.; Daniel P. Rupprecht.

Foundation type: Company-sponsored foundation.

Financial data (yr. ended 06/30/14): Assets, $93,632 (M); gifts received, $352,629; expenditures, $315,459; qualifying distributions, $313,747; giving activities include $312,847 for 49 grants (high: $35,000; low: $250).

Purpose and activities: The foundation supports organizations involved with education, health, athletics, human services, and Catholicism.

Fields of interest: Education; Secondary education; Higher education; Nonprofits; Health; Catholicism; Golf; Track and field.

Type of support: General support; Regranting.

Limitations: Applications not accepted. Giving primarily in Ames, Des Moines, Urbandale, and West Des Moines, IA. No grants to individuals.

Application information: Contributes only to pre-selected organizations.

Officers: Judy A. Price, Pres.; Mark A. Rupprecht, Secy.; Anthony J. Rogers, Treas.

Directors: Susan M. Bosworth; Daniel P. Rupprecht; Paul S. Rupprecht; Phyllis M. Rupprecht; Thomas P. Rupprecht.

EIN: 421494641

3530
Rohde Family Charitable Foundation

c/o Sara Sauter
2401 White Eagle Trail S.E.
Cedar Rapids, IA 52403-1545

Established in 1996 in Iowa.

Donor: Charles P. Rohde.

Foundation type: Independent foundation.

Financial data (yr. ended 12/31/13): Assets, $3,809,227 (M); gifts received, $750; expenditures, $199,820; qualifying distributions, $159,470; giving activities include $158,200 for 17 grants (high: $65,000; low: $200).

Fields of interest: Undergraduate education; Graduate and professional education; Nursing care.

Type of support: Scholarships.

Limitations: Applications not accepted. Giving primarily in IA. No grants to individuals.

Application information: Unsolicited requests for funds not accepted.

Officers and Directors: Sara Sauter, Pres. and Director; Charles A. Rohde, Secy.-Treas. and Director.

EIN: 421452341

3531
The Joseph and Edward Ryan Memorial

103 E. 3rd St.
West Liberty, IA 52776-0346 3196272713
Application address: c/o Tim Putney, 101 E. 4th St., West Liberty, IA 52776, tel.: (319) 627-2191

Donor: Joseph Ryan†.

Foundation type: Independent foundation.

Financial data (yr. ended 12/31/14): Assets, $5,361,541; expenditures, $323,058; qualifying distributions, $299,399.

Fields of interest: Education; Foundations; Public libraries; Fire prevention and control; Community and economic development.

Limitations: Applications accepted. Giving primarily in West Liberty, IA.

Application information: Application form required.

> *Initial approach:* Letter
> *Deadline(s):* None
> *Board meeting date(s):* Quarterly

Officer: Tim Putney, Pres.

Directors: Robert Cline; Priscilla Haessig.

EIN: 870693977

3532
Schildberg Foundation

P.O. Box 358
Greenfield, IA 50849 8166405461

Established in 1986 in Iowa.

Donors: S.K. Schildberg; Sylvia K. Schildberg Irrev. Trust.

Foundation type: Independent foundation.

Financial data (yr. ended 04/30/14): Assets, $4,215,013; expenditures, $230,535; qualifying distributions, $191,765.

Fields of interest: Education; Graduate and professional education; Voluntarism; Nursing care; Public libraries; Fire prevention and control; Christianity; Human services.

Type of support: General support; Volunteer development.

Limitations: Applications not accepted. Giving primarily in IA. No grants to individuals.

Application information: Unsolicited requests for funds not accepted.

Officers: Bernadette M. Youngblood, Pres.; Mark Schildberg, V.P.; Marlene Schildberg, Secy.

Director: Kathy Hellebuyck.

EIN: 421282794

3533
Dale D. Schroeder Trust

12086 120th St.
Rippey, IA 50235-4703 (866) 228-8142
E-mail: daleschroeder@act.org; Main URL: http://www.act.org/daleschroeder

Established in 2004 in Iowa.

Foundation type: Independent foundation.

Financial data (yr. ended 12/31/14): Assets, $863,986; expenditures, $276,150; qualifying distributions, $212,652.

Purpose and activities: Scholarship awards to qualifying graduating high school seniors in Iowa with a G.P.A. of at least 2.5, who plan to attend Iowa State University, University of Iowa, or University of Northern Iowa. Applicants must be legal residents of Iowa and must live in an Iowa community with a population between 1 and 10,000.

Fields of interest: Higher education.

Type of support: Student aid.

Limitations: Applications accepted. Giving limited to residents of IA.

Application information: Complete application guidelines available on Trust web site.

> *Deadline(s):* Mar. 26

Trustee: Walt Tomenga.
EIN: 206519954

3534
Security National Bank Charitable Foundation
(formerly SNB Charitable Foundation Trust)
P.O. Box 147
Sioux City, IA 51102-0147

Established in 1995 in Iowa.
Donors: Security National Bank; Security National Corp.
Foundation type: Company-sponsored foundation.
Financial data (yr. ended 12/31/13): Assets, $961,410 (M); gifts received, $200,000; expenditures, $251,621; qualifying distributions, $250,911; giving activities include $250,911 for 33 grants (high: $27,778; low: $250).
Purpose and activities: The foundation supports organizations involved with arts and culture, education, health, youth development, and community development.
Fields of interest: Education; Diseases and conditions; Human services.
Type of support: General support.
Limitations: Applications not accepted. Giving primarily in Sioux City, IA. No grants to individuals.
Application information: Unsolicited requests for funds not accepted.
Directors: Steve Corrie; D. Douglas Rice; Richard Waller.
EIN: 364063036

3535
Ann Smeltzer Charitable Trust
P.O. Box 791
Fort Dodge, IA 50501-0791

Established in 2003 in Iowa.
Donor: Ann Smeltzer†.
Foundation type: Operating foundation.
Financial data (yr. ended 12/31/13): Assets, $9,288,075 (M); expenditures, $840,953; qualifying distributions, $263,793; giving activities include $263,793 for 33 grants (high: $38,790; low: $75).
Purpose and activities: Giving primarily for the upkeep of the Ann Smeltzer Home; some giving for public programs and for scholarship awards to Fort Dodge music arts students.
Fields of interest: Arts education; Museums.
Limitations: Applications not accepted. Giving primarily in Fort Dodge, IA.
Application information: Contributes only to pre-selected organizations.
Officers: William "Bill" Griffel, Pres.; Jack Christensen, Secy.
Board Members: Ken Adams; Bottorff; Stephen Kersten; Larry Lee; Jim Patton; Drew Sieben; Barbara Shultz.
EIN: 426586947

3536
C. Richard Stark, Jr. & Joan E. Stark Foundation
1422 Central Ave.
Fort Dodge, IA 50501-4252

Established in 1989 in Iowa.

Donors: C. Richard Stark, Jr.; Joan E. Stark.
Foundation type: Independent foundation.
Financial data (yr. ended 12/31/13): Assets, $2,353,421 (M); expenditures, $346,990; qualifying distributions, $328,500; giving activities include $328,500 for 14 grants (high: $100,000; low: $1,000).
Purpose and activities: Giving primarily for education, social services, health, and to Roman Catholic churches and organizations.
Fields of interest: Elementary and secondary education; Higher education; Diseases and conditions; Catholicism; Human services.
Type of support: Research; Research and evaluation.
Limitations: Applications not accepted. Giving primarily in IA. No grants to individuals.
Application information: Contributes only to pre-selected organizations.
Trustee: First American Bank.
Directors: C. Richard Stark, Jr.; Joan E. Stark.
EIN: 421345092

3537
Tomson Family Foundation Trust
2601 4th St. S.W.
Mason City, IA 50401-4650   (641) 423-1600

Donors: O. Jay Tomson; Patricia A. Tomson.
Foundation type: Independent foundation.
Financial data (yr. ended 12/31/14): Assets, $6,096,280 (M); gifts received, $329,745; expenditures, $429,767; qualifying distributions, $426,000; giving activities include $426,000 for 12 grants (high: $200,000; low: $100).
Purpose and activities: Giving primarily for education, particularly Lutheran colleges; funding also for human services, and to a medical center foundation.
Fields of interest: Education; Higher education; Foundations; Health; Human services; Lutherans.
Limitations: Applications accepted. Giving primarily in Mason City, IA, and MN.
Application information:
   Initial approach: Proposal
   Deadline(s): None
Officers: O. Jay Tomson, Pres. and Secy.; Patricia A. Tomson, V.P.
EIN: 356947483

3538
Linda Glazer Toohey Foundation
3737 River Oaks Dr.
Des Moines, IA 50312-4614

Established in 1985 in Iowa.
Donors: Linda Glazer Toohey; Madelyn M. Levitt†.
Foundation type: Independent foundation.
Financial data (yr. ended 12/31/14): Assets, $8,572,158 (M); gifts received, $40,470; expenditures, $396,535; qualifying distributions, $386,079; giving activities include $386,079 for 8 grants (high: $207,579; low: $1,000).
Fields of interest: Arts and culture; Education; Health; Human services.
Type of support: General support.
Limitations: Applications not accepted. Giving primarily in NY. No grants to individuals.
Application information: Unsolicited requests for funds not accepted.

Officers: Linda Glazer Toohey, Pres. and Treas.; Michael J. Toohey, Secy.
EIN: 421258467

3539
The Van Buren Foundation, Inc.
c/o Community First Bank
714 First St.
Keosauqua, IA 52565-0130
Contact: George Manning
Application address: c/o Jon Finney, P.O. Box 475, Keosauqua, Iowa 52565, tel.: (319) 293-3129

Established in 1959 in Iowa.
Donors: Ralph S. Roberts; Lawrence Finney Trust; Robert L. Vickerman.
Foundation type: Independent foundation.
Financial data (yr. ended 12/17/14): Assets, $7,395,868 (M); gifts received, $274,546; expenditures, $352,327; qualifying distributions, $295,985; giving activities include $212,554 for 34 grants (high: $70,000; low: $189), and $30,982 for 15 grants to individuals (high: $7,554; low: $500).
Purpose and activities: Grants for local community development and education.
Fields of interest: Education; Hospital care; Public administration; Community and economic development.
Type of support: General support; Loans to individuals; Capital and infrastructure; Program development; Student aid.
Limitations: Applications accepted. Giving primarily in Van Buren County, IA.
Application information:
   Initial approach: Call or write for complete application guidelines
   Copies of proposal: 1
   Deadline(s): None
   Board meeting date(s): Biannually, and as needed
Officers and Directors: Ben Koellner; Jeanne Erickson.
EIN: 426062589

3540
Arlan J. Van Wyk Family Foundation
P.O. Box 389
Sheldon, IA 51201-0389

Established in 1999 in Iowa.
Donors: Arlan J. Van Wyk; Dave Van Wyk; Gina Van Wyk.
Foundation type: Independent foundation.
Financial data (yr. ended 12/31/13): Assets, $105,674 (M); gifts received, $120,000; expenditures, $116,153; qualifying distributions, $115,600; giving activities include $115,600 for 28 grants (high: $25,000; low: $100).
Fields of interest: Education; Christianity; Human services; Child welfare.
Limitations: Applications not accepted. Giving primarily in IA. No grants to individuals.
Application information: Unsolicited requests for funds not accepted.
Officers: Arlan J. Van Wyk, Pres.; Darla Arends, Treas.
Director: Dave Van Wyk.
EIN: 421484434

3541
Harry Vermeer Family Foundation
(formerly Vermeer Investment Company Foundation)
608 E. 2nd St., Ste. 202
Pella, IA 50219-1761

Established in 1976 in Iowa.
Donors: Harry G. Vermeer; Michael Vermeer; Marion County State Bank; Bernice Vermeer.
Foundation type: Independent foundation.
Financial data (yr. ended 12/31/14): Assets, $5,577,851 (M); gifts received, $100,000; expenditures, $466,086; qualifying distributions, $270,000; giving activities include $270,000 for 22 grants (high: $28,000; low: $1,000).
Fields of interest: Secondary education; Higher education; Nonprofits; Hospital care; Religion; Christianity; Human services.
Type of support: Regranting.
Limitations: Applications not accepted. Giving primarily in AZ, IA, MI and SD. No grants to individuals.
Application information: Unsolicited requests for funds not accepted.
Officers: Nancy Vermeer, Chair.; Melinda Papadeas, Vice-Chair.; Bernice Vermeer, Secy.; Michael Vermeer, Treas.
EIN: 510182729

3542
R. & L. Vermeer Foundation, Inc.
666 Grand Ave., Ste. 2000
Des Moines, IA 50309-2510

Established in 1984 in Iowa.
Donors: Lois J. Vermeer; Robert L. Vermeer; Vermeer Farms, Inc.
Foundation type: Independent foundation.
Financial data (yr. ended 12/31/14): Assets, $338,543 (M); gifts received, $302,948; expenditures, $152,515; qualifying distributions, $151,850; giving activities include $151,850 for 32 grants (high: $28,000; low: $50).
Fields of interest: Historic preservation; Education; Undergraduate education; Hospice care; Religion; Christianity; Human services.
Limitations: Applications not accepted. Giving primarily in Pella, IA. No grants to individuals.
Application information: Unsolicited requests for funds not accepted.
Officers: Robert L. Vermeer, Pres. and Treas.; Lois J. Vermeer, V.P. and Secy.
EIN: 421240931

3543
The Vonderhaar Family Foundation
6 Summer Pl.
Bettendorf, IA 52722-7544
Contact: James J. Vonderharr, Dir.; Collette C. Vonderharr, Dir.

Established in 1995 in Iowa.
Donors: James J. Vonderhaar; Collette C. Vonderhaar.
Foundation type: Independent foundation.
Financial data (yr. ended 12/31/13): Assets, $2,535,043 (M); gifts received, $50,000; expenditures, $154,247; qualifying distributions, $151,777; giving activities include $151,777 for 26 grants (high: $35,500; low: $1,000).

Purpose and activities: Giving primarily for education and human services.
Fields of interest: Education; Catholicism; Sports and recreation.
Type of support: General support.
Limitations: Applications accepted. Giving primarily in IA. No grants to individuals.
Application information:
Initial approach: Proposal
Deadline(s): None
Directors: Collette C. Vonderhaar; James J. Vonderhaar.
EIN: 421447723

3544
Wahlert Foundation
P.O. Box 736
Dubuque, IA 52004-0736
Contact: Amy Principi, Pres.; R.H. Wahlert, V.P. and Treas.
E-mail: info@wahlertfoundation.org; Summer address: P.O. Box 736, Dubuque, IA 52004-0736. E-mail: Bob16307@aol.com; Main URL: http://www.wahlertfoundation.org

Established in 1948 in Iowa.
Donor: H.W. Wahlert†.
Foundation type: Independent foundation.
Financial data (yr. ended 07/31/13): Assets, $6,401,270 (M); gifts received, $6,692; expenditures, $413,645; qualifying distributions, $334,544; giving activities include $334,544 for 43 grants (high: $60,000; low: $500).
Purpose and activities: Support primarily for higher, secondary, and medical education; grants also for health services and hospitals, including medical and cancer research, social service agencies, including drug abuse prevention programs and services for families, the homeless and the handicapped, child welfare programs for minorities, cultural activities, including the arts and museums, and Catholic welfare organizations and schools.
Fields of interest: Secondary education; Higher education; Health; Catholicism; Human services; Senior services; Children; Seniors; Females; People of Latin American descent; American Indians; Migrant workers; Homeless people; Low-income and poor people; Terminally ill people.
International interests: Honduras.
Type of support: General support; Annual campaigns; Capital campaigns; Capital and infrastructure; Equipment; Emergency funds; Program development; Scholarships.
Limitations: Applications accepted. Giving primarily in IA, IL and WI. No grants to individuals, or for publications, conferences, or matching gifts; no loans.
Publications: Application guidelines.
Application information: Complete application procedures and guidelines available on foundation web site. Application form required.
Initial approach: Application form on foundation web site
Copies of proposal: 1
Board meeting date(s): 2nd Sat. of Sept.
Officers: Amy Wahlert Principi, Pres. and Director; Robert H. Wahlert, Exec. V.P. and Treas. and Director; David Wahlert, V.P. and Director; Mark Wahlert, V.P.; Brian J. Kane, Secy. and Director.
Directors: Kathleen C. Chameli; Marni L. Peck; Alan Wahlert; Donna Wahlert; Nancy Wahlert; James R. Wahlert; Robert C. Wahlert; Susan Wahlert.

Number of staff: 1 part-time professional.
EIN: 426051124

3545
Weathertop Foundation
(formerly Thomas Nelson Urban, Jr. and Mary Bright Urban Foundation)
5320 Grand Ave.
Des Moines, IA 50312-2124

Established in 1994 in Iowa.
Donors: Thomas Nelson Urban; Mary Bright Urban.
Foundation type: Independent foundation.
Financial data (yr. ended 07/31/13): Assets, $11,272,721 (M); gifts received, $2,550; expenditures, $477,825; qualifying distributions, $442,675; giving activities include $436,880 for 66 grants (high: $120,000; low: $250).
Fields of interest: Arts and culture; Orchestral music; Education; Higher education; Botanical gardens; Foundations; Nonprofits; Diseases and conditions; Christianity; Human services.
Type of support: General support; Regranting.
Limitations: Applications not accepted. Giving primarily in FL, IA, OH, and MA.
Application information: Unsolicited requests for funds not accepted.
Board meeting date(s): Aug.
Officers: Thomas Nelson Urban, Jr., Chair. and Pres.; Mary Bright Urban, V.P.; Victoria Urban Broer, Secy.; William G. Urban, Treas.
Directors: Cornelia Urban Sawczuk; Thomas N. Urban III.
EIN: 421431036

3546
Weigle Family Foundation
(formerly David Weigle Foundation)
2611 State St.
Bettendorf, IA 52722-5207

Established in 1990 in Iowa.
Donors: David B. Weigle; Jonathan H. Weigle; Benjamin J. Weigle; Nancy B. Weigle; Joan W. McGee.
Foundation type: Independent foundation.
Financial data (yr. ended 12/31/13): Assets, $156,372 (M); gifts received, $67,577; expenditures, $146,898; qualifying distributions, $146,229; giving activities include $146,229 for 26 grants (high: $100,776; low: $25).
Fields of interest: Education; Judaism; Human services.
Limitations: Applications not accepted. Giving primarily in IA. No grants to individuals.
Application information: Unsolicited requests for funds not accepted.
Officers and Directors: Joan W. McGee, Mgr. and Director; Benjamin J. Weigle, Mgr. and Director; David B. Weigle, Mgr. and Director; Jonathan H. Weigle, Mgr. and Director.
EIN: 363745791

3547
The West Bancorporation Foundation, Inc.
1601 22nd St.
West Des Moines, IA 50266-1408 (515) 222-2300
Contact: Jill T. Hansen, Exec. Dir.

Established in 2003 in Iowa.
Donor: West Bank.
Foundation type: Company-sponsored foundation.
Financial data (yr. ended 12/31/13): Assets, $1,493,963 (M); gifts received, $575,603; expenditures, $300,968; qualifying distributions, $290,740; giving activities include $290,740 for 84 grants (high: $41,000; low: $640).
Purpose and activities: The foundation supports organizations involved with arts and culture, education, and human services. Special emphasis is directed toward programs designed to benefit low- and moderate-income individuals.
Fields of interest: Education; Environment; Human services.
Type of support: General support; Annual campaigns; Capital campaigns; Capital and infrastructure; Program development; Scholarships; Sponsorships.
Limitations: Applications accepted. Giving primarily in central and eastern IA. No support for athletic organizations, fraternal organizations, K-12 schools, pass-through organizations (with the exception of United Way and independent college funds), political organizations, private foundations, sectarian, religious or denominational organizations, social organizations, tax-supported city, county, or state organizations, trade, industry, or professional organizations, United Way organizations for United Way-funded programs, or veterans' organizations. No grants to individuals, or for conference or seminar attendance, courtesy or goodwill advertising in benefit publications, endowments or memorials, fellowships, festival participation, or capital campaigns for hospitals or healthcare facilities.
Publications: Application guidelines.
Application information: Application form required.
Initial approach: Letter
Deadline(s): Jan. 1, Apr. 1, July 1, and Oct. 1
Officers and Directors: Alice A. Jensen, Secy.; Douglas R. Gulling, Treas. and Director; Jill T. Hansen, Exec. Dir.; Peggy J. Fleming; Steve R. Hall; Kaye R. Lozier; David D. Nelson; Harlee N. Olafson; Sharen K. Surber; Ashley L. Wear; Rodney S. Wiekert; Brad L. Winterbottom.
EIN: 200523259

3548
The Jim and Marie Wood Foundation
c/o Alan Anderson
110 N. 2nd Ave.
Logan, IA 51546-1332

Established in 1990 in Oregon.
Donor: James N. Wood.
Foundation type: Independent foundation.
Financial data (yr. ended 12/31/12): Assets, $3,730,752 (M); expenditures, $190,154; qualifying distributions, $155,354; giving activities include $155,354 for grants.
Purpose and activities: Giving limited for the betterment of the city of Logan, IA, including scholarships to residents.
Fields of interest: Museums; Education; Community and economic development.
Type of support: General support; Student aid.
Limitations: Applications not accepted. Giving limited to Logan, IA.
Application information: Unsolicited requests for funds not considered.

Directors: Alan J. Anderson; Michael Massman; Thomas Stoner; Helen M. Wood.
EIN: 931044500

3549
Woodward Foundation, Inc.
801 Bluff St.
Dubuque, IA 52001-4661
Contact: Thomas Woodward, Pres.

Established in 1956 in Iowa.
Donor: Woodward Communications, Inc.
Foundation type: Independent foundation.
Financial data (yr. ended 12/31/13): Assets, $57,317 (M); gifts received, $130,000; expenditures, $169,479; qualifying distributions, $165,600; giving activities include $165,600 for 16 grants (high: $40,600; low: $1,000).
Fields of interest: Opera; Art museums; Higher education; Undergraduate education; Nonprofits; Public libraries; Community recreation; Human services.
Type of support: Regranting.
Limitations: Applications accepted. Giving primarily in Dubuque, IA; some giving in WI. No grants to individuals or for scholarships or endowments; no loans or program-related investments.
Application information: Application form required.
Initial approach: Letter
Deadline(s): Apr. 1 and Nov. 1
Board meeting date(s): Annually
Officers: Thomas Woodward, Pres.; Barbara Sullivan Woodward, V.P.; Cheri Phipps, Secy.; Steve Larson, Treas.
Directors: Mary Anne Drewek; Jim Normandin; Kristin Woodward.
EIN: 426070224

3550
World Food Prize Foundation
666 Grand Ave., Ste. 1700
Des Moines, IA 50309-2500 (515) 245-3783
Contact: Judith Pim, Dir., Secretariat Operations
FAX: (515) 245-3785;
E-mail: wfp@worldfoodprize.org; Main URL: http://www.worldfoodprize.org
Facebook: http://www.facebook.com/pages/The-World-Food-Prize/51072466793
RSS feed: http://www.worldfoodprize.org/RSS/newsfeed.xml
Twitter: http://twitter.com/worldfoodprize
YouTube: http://www.youtube.com/user/WorldFoodPrize
E-mail for Judith Pim: jpim@worldfoodprize.org

Established in 1990 in Iowa.
Foundation type: Independent foundation.
Financial data (yr. ended 12/31/13): Assets, $51,834,480 (M); gifts received, $7,757,755; expenditures, $4,773,179; qualifying distributions, $3,438,552; giving activities include $250,000 for 3 grants to individuals (high: $83,334; low: $83,333).
Purpose and activities: Awards prizes to individuals for achievement in improving the world food supply.
Fields of interest: Agriculture.
International interests: Belgium.
Type of support: General support; Grants to individuals; In-kind gifts; Capital campaigns; Endowments; Internships.

Limitations: Applications accepted. Giving primarily in MO and NC.
Publications: Informational brochure; Informational brochure (including application guidelines).
Application information: See foundation web site for application and nomination information.
Copies of proposal: 1
Deadline(s): Apr. 1
Officers: John Ruan III, Chair.; Kenneth Quinn, Pres.; John Ruan IV, Secy.; Tracey Ball, Treas.
Number of staff: 7 full-time professional.
EIN: 421356715

3551
John R. and Eloise Mountain Wright Foundation
222 S. Linn St.
Iowa City, IA 52240-1601
Contact: Tim Grady

Established in 1995 in Missouri.
Donors: John R. Wright; Eloise M. Wright.
Foundation type: Independent foundation.
Financial data (yr. ended 12/31/13): Assets, $4,901,558 (M); gifts received, $75,000; expenditures, $211,527; qualifying distributions, $203,242; giving activities include $195,000 for 16 grants (high: $53,000; low: $500).
Fields of interest: Arts and culture; Education; Christianity.
International interests: Africa; Central America; Ireland.
Type of support: Annual campaigns; Matching grants; Capital and infrastructure; Emergency funds; Scholarships.
Limitations: Applications not accepted. Giving primarily in IA; some giving also in CA, MI and OR. Funding also in Africa, Central America and Ireland. No grants to individuals.
Application information: Contributes only to pre-selected organizations.
Directors: Eloise M. Wright; Graciela C. Wright.
EIN: 431698425

3552
Young Family Foundation of Waterloo, Iowa
P.O. Box 1077
Waterloo, IA 50704-1077 (319) 234-4411
Contact: Richard C. Young, Pres.

Established in 1990 in Iowa.
Donor: Richard C. Young.
Foundation type: Independent foundation.
Financial data (yr. ended 12/31/13): Assets, $8,263,579 (M); expenditures, $477,850; qualifying distributions, $325,054; giving activities include $315,000 for 7 grants (high: $250,000; low: $5,000).
Purpose and activities: Giving primarily for conservation and for the purchase, development, operation, and enhancement of the natural and recreational resources in northeast IA.
Fields of interest: Science museums; Environment; Wildlife biodiversity; Community and economic development; Sports and recreation.
Type of support: Annual campaigns; Employee matching gifts; Capital campaigns; Capital and infrastructure; Equipment; Land acquisitions; Emergency funds; Curriculum development; Internships; Research.

Limitations: Applications accepted. Giving primarily in Ames, IA.
Application Information: Application form required.

Initial approach: Letter

Deadline(s): None
Board meeting date(s): Quarterly
Officers: Richard C. Young, Pres.; Thomas S. Young, V.P.; Travis Young, Secy.-Treas.
EIN: 421356506

KANSAS

3553
Adair-Exchange Bank Foundation
P.O. Box 189
Atchison, KS   66002-0189

Donors: First National Bank; Exchange National Bank; Exchange Bankshares Corp.
Foundation type: Company-sponsored foundation.
Financial data (yr. ended 12/31/13): Assets, $892,463 (M); gifts received, $200,000; expenditures, $174,619; qualifying distributions, $172,000; giving activities include $172,000 for 32 grants (high: $100,000; low: $500).
Purpose and activities: The foundation supports organizations involved with education, animal welfare, human services, and religion.
Fields of interest: Education; Religion; Human services.
Type of support: General support.
Limitations: Applications not accepted. Giving primarily in KS. No grants to individuals.
Application information: Unsolicited requests for funds not accepted.
Officers and Directors: Paul H. Adair, Pres. and Director; Richard R. Dickason, V.P. and Director; Sharon Baldridge, Secy. and Director; Marsha A. Adair, Treas. and Director.
EIN: 237389214

3554
The Atterbury Family Foundation
2001 Shawnee Mission Pkwy.
Shawnee Mission, KS   66205-2051
Main URL: http://www.atterburyfoundation.org

Established in 1998 in Missouri.
Donors: Alan L. Atterbury; Mary P. Atterbury.
Foundation type: Independent foundation.
Financial data (yr. ended 12/31/13): Assets, $4,869,693 (M); expenditures, $340,569; qualifying distributions, $319,050; giving activities include $319,050 for 49 grants (high: $70,000; low: $500).
Purpose and activities: Support primarily for a community foundation; giving also for the arts, education, and human services.
Fields of interest: Arts and culture; Education; Foundations; Human services.
Type of support: General support.
Limitations: Applications not accepted. Giving limited to KS and MO, with emphasis on the bi-state Kansas City area. No grants to individuals.
Application information: Unsolicited requests for funds not accepted.
Officers: Alan L. Atterbury, Chair.; Mary P. Atterbury, Pres.; Jennifer L. Atterbury, V.P. and Secy.; Andrew L. Atterbury, V.P. and Treas.; David A. Atterbury, V.P.
EIN: 481202943

3555
Emil Babinger Charitable Trust
P.O. Box 807
Emporia, KS   66801-0807   (620) 342-3454

Established in 1988 in Kansas.
Donor: Emil Babinger.

Foundation type: Independent foundation.
Financial data (yr. ended 12/31/14): Assets, $6,989,449; expenditures, $416,002; qualifying distributions, $290,734.
Fields of interest: Arts and culture; Education; Catholicism; Human services.
Type of support: General support.
Limitations: Applications accepted. Giving limited to Emporia and Olpe, KS. No grants to individuals.
Application information:
  Initial approach: Proposal
  Deadline(s): None
Trustees: John E. Kuhlmann; George C. Osborn; Todd Osborn; ESB Financial.
EIN: 481061932

3556
Louis W. & Dolpha Baehr Foundation
c/o First Option Trust Dept.
P.O. Box B
Paola, KS   66071   (913) 294-3811

Established in 1967 in Kansas.
Donors: L.W. Baehr†; Dolpha Baehr†.
Foundation type: Independent foundation.
Financial data (yr. ended 04/30/13): Assets, $4,926,644 (M); expenditures, $246,845; qualifying distributions, $221,971; giving activities include $155,700 for 15 grants (high: $35,000; low: $1,000), and $25,000 for 1 employee matching gift.
Purpose and activities: Primary areas of interest include education, health, including mental health, recreation, and community improvement.
Fields of interest: Education; Elementary education; Hospital care; Mental health care; Community and economic development; Sports and recreation; Children and youth; People with hearing impairments.
Type of support: General support; Matching grants; Capital and infrastructure; Equipment; Endowments; Program development; Seed money; Research.
Limitations: Applications accepted. Giving limited to eastern KS, including the greater Kansas City area. No support for sectarian or religious organizations whose services are limited to members of any one religious group, or for agencies operating as chapters of a state or national organization. No grants to individuals, or for advertising; no loans.
Publications: Application guidelines.
Application information: Application form required.
  Initial approach: Letter
  Copies of proposal: 8
  Deadline(s): None
  Board meeting date(s): Jan. and July
Trustee: First Option Bank.
Number of staff: None.
EIN: 486129741

3557
Earl Bane Foundation
P.O. Box 201
Salina, KS   67402-0201
Application address: c/o Robert Buster, 315 N. 9th St., Salina, KS 67401, tel.: (785) 827-1492

Established in 1994 in Kansas.
Donor: Earl Bane†.
Foundation type: Independent foundation.

Financial data (yr. ended 04/30/13): Assets, $15,203,786 (M); expenditures, $482,399; qualifying distributions, $437,043; giving activities include $383,600 for 58 grants (high: $75,000; low: $100).
Purpose and activities: Giving primarily for higher education, children, youth, and social services, and to other qualified organizations for the educational, economic, scientific, and religious benefit of Salina and Saline County, KS.
Fields of interest: Education; Higher education; Nonprofits; Human services; Child welfare; Senior services.
Type of support: Annual campaigns; Program-related investments; Capital and infrastructure; Equipment; Endowments; Program development; Scholarships; Regranting; Student aid.
Limitations: Applications accepted. Giving primarily in Salina and Saline County, KS.
Application information: Application form required.
  Initial approach: Letter
  Copies of proposal: 3
  Deadline(s): None
Officers and Trustees: Robert Buster, Pres. and Trustee; Melanie Bailey, V.P. and Treas.; Mindy Tillberg, Secy. and Trustee; Gerald L. Hunter; Corlene Lange.
Number of staff: 1 part-time professional.
EIN: 481152429

3558
Berry Foundation Inc.
c/o Judy Worrell
3223 N. Hydraulic
P.O. Box 829
Wichita, KS   67201-0829

Established in 2006 in Kansas.
Donor: Berry Companies.
Foundation type: Company-sponsored foundation.
Financial data (yr. ended 12/31/13): Assets, $376,023 (M); gifts received, $406,071; expenditures, $206,494; qualifying distributions, $206,394; giving activities include $204,681 for 103 grants (high: $20,000; low: $90).
Purpose and activities: The foundation supports nonprofit organizations involved with arts, education, and human services.
Fields of interest: Arts and culture; Education; Early childhood education; Secondary education; Zoos; Nonprofits; Business and industry; Christianity; Human services; Child welfare; Youth services; Developmental disability services.
Type of support: General support; Annual campaigns; Capital and infrastructure; Endowments; Scholarships; Regranting.
Limitations: Applications accepted. Giving primarily in KS. No grants to individuals.
Application information:
  Initial approach: Proposal
  Deadline(s): None
Officers and Directors: Fred F. Berry, Jr., Pres. and Director; Judy Worrell, Secy.-Treas. and Director; Walter T. Berry; Daniel J. Scheer.
EIN: 203942107

3559
Bramlage Family Foundation
P.O. Box 1005
Junction City, KS   66441-1005

Established in 1997 in Kansas.
Donors: Fred C. Bramlage; Dorothy O. Bramlage; F. Robert Bramlage.
Foundation type: Independent foundation.
Financial data (yr. ended 12/31/13): Assets, $1,904,525 (M); gifts received, $1,500,000; expenditures, $295,067; qualifying distributions, $178,950; giving activities include $178,950 for 35 grants (high: $12,600; low: $500).
Purpose and activities: Giving for education, scouting organizations, and for public institutes.
Fields of interest: Elementary and secondary education; Higher education; Natural resources; Crisis intervention; Youth development.
Limitations: Applications not accepted. Giving primarily in KS and MO. No grants to individuals.
Application information: Unsolicited requests for funds not accepted.
Officers: Dorothy B. Willcoxon, Pres.; Jeff Tate, Secy.; F. Robert Bramlage, Treas.
EIN: 742822314

3560
The Breidenthal-Snyder Foundation
(formerly Ruth B. and Willard B. Snyder Foundation, Inc.)
8014 State Line Rd., Ste. 203
Shawnee Mission, KS 66208-3710
Contact: Willard B. Snyder, Pres.

Established in 1984 in Kansas.
Donors: Ruth B. Snyder†; Willard B. Snyder; Julie Breidenthal Gold†.
Foundation type: Independent foundation.
Financial data (yr. ended 12/31/13): Assets, $9,895,366 (M); gifts received, $3,255; expenditures, $479,614; qualifying distributions, $381,365; giving activities include $373,052 for 83 grants (high: $21,000; low: $12).
Fields of interest: Arts and culture; Education; Human services.
Limitations: Applications accepted. Giving primarily in the Kansas City, KS, area. No grants to individuals.
Application information: Generally contributes only to pre-selected organizations. Only 1 grant to any recipient within a calendar year. Application form required.
   Initial approach: Letter requesting application
   Copies of proposal: 1
   Deadline(s): None
   Board meeting date(s): June and Dec.
   Final notification: Positive responses only
Officers: Willard B. Snyder, Pres.; Rolf D. Snyder, Secy.-Treas.
Directors: Pat Lockerby; T.J. Snyder; Patrick Wong.
Number of staff: None.
EIN: 480979412

3561
Samuel M. and Laura H. Brown Charitable Trust
P.O. Box 1, Trust Tax Dept.
Wichita, KS 67201-5001 (316) 383-1912
Contact: Stephanie Clausen

Established in 1974 in Kansas.
Donor: S.M. Brown†.
Foundation type: Independent foundation.
Financial data (yr. ended 11/30/13): Assets, $980,945 (M); expenditures, $419,112; qualifying

distributions, $406,252; giving activities include $394,882 for 32 grants (high: $50,000; low: $2,000).
Purpose and activities: Giving for the arts and human services.
Fields of interest: Arts and culture; Music; Human services; Senior services.
Type of support: Capital campaigns; Equipment; Program development.
Limitations: Applications accepted. Giving primarily in Sedgwick County, KS, with emphasis on Wichita. No grants to individuals.
Application information:
   Initial approach: Proposal
   Deadline(s): None
Trustees: Doris Nelson; Martin Pringle Law Firm; INTRUST Bank, N.A.
EIN: 486193416

3562
Buford Family Foundation
9176 E. 13th St.
Witchita, KS 67206

Donor: Martha C. Buford.
Foundation type: Independent foundation.
Financial data (yr. ended 12/31/14): Assets, $1,145,506 (M); expenditures, $355,432; qualifying distributions, $335,620; giving activities include $335,260 for 16 grants (high: $95,000; low: $1,000).
Fields of interest: Philanthropy; Nonprofits; Diseases and conditions; Diabetes; Human rights; Human services; Child welfare.
Type of support: Research; Regranting.
Limitations: Applications not accepted. Giving primarily in Wichita, KS; Tulsa, OK; and San Antonio, TX. No grants to individuals.
Application information: Unsolicited requests for funds not accepted.
Officers and Directors: Martha C. Buford, Pres. and Secy. and Director; Josephine B. Siegfried, V.P. and Treas. and Director; Anne S. Buford; C. Robert Buford; R.C. Buford.
EIN: 731519009

3563
Cape Flattery Foundation
c/o Heritage Group, LLC
7309 E. 21st St. N., Ste. 120
Wichita, KS 67206-1178

Established in 1983 in Kansas.
Donors: Diana C. Broze; CGF Industries, Inc.; Ruth G. Fink†; Ruth G. Fink Charity Trust.
Foundation type: Independent foundation.
Financial data (yr. ended 12/31/13): Assets, $8,433,088 (M); gifts received, $302,066; expenditures, $297,883; qualifying distributions, $257,817; giving activities include $254,100 for 21 grants (high: $25,000; low: $1,000).
Purpose and activities: Giving for education, religion, medical care, and community funds.
Fields of interest: Museums; Education; Higher education; Health; Radio; Community and economic development; Human services.
Type of support: General support; Capital and infrastructure; Scholarships.
Limitations: Applications not accepted. Giving limited to Seattle, WA. No grants to individuals.

Application information: Contributes only to pre-selected organizations.
Trustee: Diana C. Broze.
EIN: 480948600

3564
Central Charities Foundation Inc.
P.O. Box 700
Junction City, KS 66441-0700 (785) 238-4114

Established in 1997 in Kansas.
Donors: Central National Bank; Edward C. Rolfs; Edward J. Rolfs; Mary Beerhalter; Ralph Dietrich.
Foundation type: Company-sponsored foundation.
Financial data (yr. ended 12/31/13): Assets, $2,954,922 (M); gifts received, $61,414; expenditures, $317,680; qualifying distributions, $298,146; giving activities include $296,255 for 41 grants (high: $101,200; low: $10).
Purpose and activities: The foundation supports organizations involved with education, youth development, children and youth, senior citizen services, and Christianity.
Fields of interest: Education; Religion; Human services.
Type of support: General support.
Limitations: Applications accepted. Giving limited to Junction City and Geary County, KS.
Application information: Application form required.
   Initial approach: Contact foundation for application form
   Deadline(s): None
Board Members: Sara Girard; Christine A. Munson; Edward J. Rolfs; Betty Waters.
EIN: 486143983

3565
Bruce G. Cochener Foundation
2420 N. Woodlawn Bldg., Ste. 500
Wichita, KS 67220-3960

Established in 1968 in Kansas.
Donors: Bruce G. Cochener; Ruth G. Fink Charitable Reminder Unitrust.
Foundation type: Independent foundation.
Financial data (yr. ended 12/31/13): Assets, $5,441,374 (M); gifts received, $302,067; expenditures, $282,388; qualifying distributions, $256,144; giving activities include $205,147 for 57 grants (high: $65,000; low: $25).
Fields of interest: Arts and culture; Education; Human services.
Type of support: General support; Capital and infrastructure.
Limitations: Applications not accepted. Giving primarily in Wichita, KS. No grants to individuals.
Application information: Unsolicited requests for funds not accepted.
Officers and Trustees: Nancy M. Cochener, Pres. and Trustee; Donna M. Cochener-Metcalfe, V.P. and Trustee; Jessi B. Stang, Secy; Christine M. Widrig, Treas.; Todd M. Connell.
EIN: 237255404

3566
Coffeyville Area Community Foundation
P.O. Box 635
Coffeyville, KS 67337 (620) 251-4769
Contact: Janie DeVore Gillis, Exec. Dir.

E-mail: janie@coffeyvillefoundation.org; Main
URL: http://www.coffeyvillefoundation.org
Facebook: http://www.facebook.com/pages/
Coffeyville-Area-Community-Foundation/
113845465333050
Twitter: https://twitter.com/cacf_marci

Established in 2001 in Kansas.
Foundation type: Community foundation.
Financial data (yr. ended 12/31/13): Assets,
$4,740,378 (M); gifts received, $228,654;
expenditures, $272,265; giving activities include
$144,138 for 7+ grants (high: $17,650).
Purpose and activities: The mission of the
Coffeyville Area Community Foundation is to endow
funds to improve the quality of life for people of the
Coffeyville Area.
Fields of interest: Arts and culture; Education;
Environment; Health; Human services; Child
welfare.
Limitations: Applications accepted. Giving primarily
in Coffeyville, KS. No support for religious purposes.
No grants to individuals, or for administrative or
general operating expenses, marketing plans,
purchase of tickets or tables at special events,
memberships, or advertising, annual campaigns,
endowment funds, or debt retirement.
Publications: Application guidelines; Newsletter.
Application information: Visit foundation web site
for application form. Application form required.
　Initial approach: Submit application form and
　　attachments
　Copies of proposal: 1
Officers and Trustees: Debbie Allen, Pres. and
Trustee; Fawn Lin, V.P. and Trustee; Renee Sharpe,
Secy. and Trustee; Larry Fischer, Treas. and Trustee;
Janie DeVore Gillis, Exec. Dir.; Joan Fons; Paul Kritz;
Mark Muller; Dickie Rolls; Ann Marie Vannoster.
EIN: 311765700

3567

The Community Foundation of Dickinson County, Inc.

(formerly Abilene Community Foundation)
213 N. Bdwy.
P.O. Box 735
Abilene, KS　67410　(785) 263-1863
Contact: Kristine Meyer, Pres.
E-mail: info@communityfoundation.us; Main
URL: http://www.communityfoundation.us

Established in 1999 in Kansas.
Foundation type: Community foundation.
Financial data (yr. ended 12/31/13): Assets,
$7,407,211 (M); gifts received, $1,625,561;
expenditures, $508,609; giving activities include
$245,791 for 14+ grants (high: $28,835), and
$23,512 for 34 grants to individuals.
Purpose and activities: The foundation seeks to
connect donors to charitable giving priorities, serve
as a resource for local nonprofit organizations and
provide leadership to the community.
Fields of interest: Arts and culture; Education;
Environment; Health; Community and economic
development; Human services; Child welfare.
Type of support: Program development.
Limitations: Applications accepted. Giving primarily
in Dickinson County, KS. No grants to individuals
(except for designated scholarship funds), general
operating expenses, capital campaigns, endowment
campaigns, annual campaigns, fundraising events,
travel, or debt retirement.
Publications: Application guidelines; Annual report.

Application information: Application form required.
　Initial approach: Telephone
　Deadline(s): Oct. 30 for Fall Grants
　Final notification: Dec. 19 for Fall Grants
Officers and Directors: David Mills, Chair. and
Director; Bruce Taylor, Vice-Chair. and Director;
Kristine Meyer, Pres. and Director; Ron Shouse,
Secy.-Treas. and Director; Loren Barten; Julie
Beswick; Craig Chamberlin; Larry Coulson; Bruce
Dale; Diana Floyd; Elinor Haas; Brenda Holm; Mike
Johnson; Tim Johnson; Dennis Riordan; Debbie
Smart; Dennis Weishaar; Marcia Williamson; Mark
Wilson; Kent Wyatt; Tate Wyatt.
EIN: 481214850

3568

CPS Foundation Inc.

9905 W. 144th St.
Overland Park, KS　66221-7503　(913) 681-8265
Contact: Penny Boles, Pres.
Main URL: http://www.cps-foundation.com

Foundation type: Independent foundation.
Financial data (yr. ended 12/31/13): Assets,
$3,265,907 (M); expenditures, $234,744;
qualifying distributions, $147,920; giving activities
include $147,920 for 14 grants (high: $25,000;
low: $2,500).
Fields of interest: Education; Religion; Sports and
recreation; Human services.
Limitations: Applications accepted. Giving primarily
in KS and MO.
Application information: Application form required.
　Initial approach: Letter
　Deadline(s): None
Officers: Penny Boles, Pres.; Carmen Terry, Secy.;
Scott Terry, Jr., Treas.
Director: Ryan C. Terry.
EIN: 262219593

3569

The Cloud L. & Sara J. Cray Family Foundation

20045 266th Rd.
Atchison, KS　66002-6147　(913) 367-2707
Contact: Cloud L. Cray, Tr.

Donors: Cloud L. Cray, Jr.; Sara Jane Cray; Cloud L.
Cray Family Trust; Sara J. Cray Estate.
Foundation type: Independent foundation.
Financial data (yr. ended 12/31/13): Assets,
$1,898,020 (M); gifts received, $314,700;
expenditures, $277,350; qualifying distributions,
$274,727; giving activities include $274,700 for 17
grants (high: $150,000; low: $1,000).
Fields of interest: Arts and culture; Education;
Higher education; Religion.
Type of support: General support.
Limitations: Applications accepted. Giving primarily
in KS.
Application information: Application form required.
　Initial approach: Contact foundation
　Deadline(s): Nov. 30
Trustee: Cloud L. Cray.
EIN: 481140738

3570

Roderick J. & Jo Anne Cyr Foundation

5188 W. 150th Pl.
Leawood, KS　66224

Established in 1999 in Kansas.
Donor: Roderick J. Cyr.
Foundation type: Independent foundation.
Financial data (yr. ended 12/31/14): Assets,
$7,430,431; expenditures, $523,945; qualifying
distributions, $429,604.
Fields of interest: Education; Christianity;
Catholicism; Human services.
Limitations: Applications not accepted. No grants to
individuals.
Application information: Unsolicited requests for
funds not accepted.
Trustees: Catherine A. Nigro; Christopher Nigro;
Suzanne T. Whitmer.
EIN: 486364680

3571

James A. and Juliet L. Davis Foundation Inc.

1 Compound Dr.
Hutchinson, KS　67502-4349　(620) 662-8331
Contact: Merl F. Sellers, Pres.

Established in 1954 in Kansas.
Foundation type: Independent foundation.
Financial data (yr. ended 12/31/13): Assets,
$4,752,929 (M); expenditures, $232,915;
qualifying distributions, $209,629; giving activities
include $187,500 for 44 grants (high: $39,000;
low: $500).
Purpose and activities: Support primarily for higher
education, including scholarships for students
graduating from Hutchinson High School, Kansas.
Fields of interest: Education; Foundations; Youth
services.
Type of support: General support; Scholarships;
Student aid.
Limitations: Applications accepted. Giving primarily
in KS. No grants to individuals directly (except
limited scholarships to designated students); no
loans.
Application information: Scholarships limited to
students graduating from Hutchinson High School,
KS, who will attend college in KS or MO.
Scholarships are awarded to persons designated by
a review committee and are not available on the
basis of application. Scholarship awards announced
at high school awards assembly.
　Initial approach: Proposal
　Deadline(s): Mar. 15
　Board meeting date(s): 3rd Mon. of each month
Officers: Merl F. Sellers, Pres.; Kent Longenecker,
V.P.; Ray E. Dillon III, Secy.-Treas.
Trustees: R.A. Edwards; Allen K. Fee; Edward A.
Hobart, MD.
EIN: 486105748

3572

The Dehaemers Family Charitable Trust

14747 Mission Rd.
Overland Park, KS　66224-9506

Established in 2006 in Kansas.
Donors: David Dehaemers; Barbara Dehaemers.
Foundation type: Independent foundation.
Financial data (yr. ended 12/31/13): Assets,
$2,495,159 (M); expenditures, $348,329;
qualifying distributions, $339,150; giving activities
include $338,500 for 16 grants (high: $140,000;
low: $5,000).

Fields of interest: Elementary and secondary education; Youth services.
Type of support: General support.
Limitations: Applications not accepted. Giving primarily in MO. No grants to individuals.
Application information: Unsolicited requests for funds not accepted.
Directors: Barbara Dehaemers; David Dehaemers.
EIN: 436931676

3573
DeVore Foundation, Inc.
9020 E. 35th St. N., Ste. A
Wichita, KS   67226-2017

Established in 1953 in Kansas.
Donors: Floyd DeVore†; Richard A. DeVore; William D. DeVore.
Foundation type: Independent foundation.
Financial data (yr. ended 11/30/13): Assets, $7,498,747 (M); expenditures, $317,767; qualifying distributions, $287,605; giving activities include $286,320 for 44 grants (high: $145,000; low: $100).
Fields of interest: Arts and culture; Higher education; Foundations; Nonprofits; Health; Diseases and conditions; Protestantism; Human services; Child welfare.
Type of support: General support; Continuing support; Annual campaigns; Capital campaigns; Capital and infrastructure; Equipment; Endowments; Program development; Regranting; Seed money.
Limitations: Applications not accepted. Giving restricted to the Wichita, KS, area.
Application information: Unsolicited requests for funds not accepted.
Officers: Richard A. DeVore, Pres. and Secy.; William D. DeVore, V.P. and Treas.
EIN: 486109754

3574
Elsberry Family Foundation
11521 Pawnee Cir.
Leawood, KS   66211-2944   (913) 661-2578

Established in 2006 in Kansas.
Donors: Anne W. Elsberry; Howard Elsberry.
Foundation type: Independent foundation.
Financial data (yr. ended 12/31/14): Assets, $1,148,108; expenditures, $237,063; qualifying distributions, $224,702.
Fields of interest: Arts and culture; Education; Catholicism.
Limitations: Applications accepted. Giving primarily in MO, with some giving in KS.
Application information:
  Initial approach: Letter
  Deadline(s): None
Officers and Directors: Anne W. Elsberry, Pres. and Secy. and Director; Howard Elsberry, V.P. and Treas. and Director.
EIN: 203956294

3575
Hoffman Family Foundation
17960 Bond Ave.
Bucyrus, KS   66013-9601
Contact: John Hoffman

Established in 1999 in Kansas.
Donors: John Hoffman; Linda Hoffman.
Foundation type: Independent foundation.
Financial data (yr. ended 03/31/13): Assets, $2,482,589 (M); gifts received, $30,000; expenditures, $276,966; qualifying distributions, $262,247; giving activities include $260,000 for 17 grants (high: $75,000; low: $2,500).
Fields of interest: Elementary and secondary education; University education; Animal welfare; Children's hospital care; Family services; Child welfare; Youth services; Scouting programs; Children; People with vision impairments.
Type of support: General support; Annual campaigns; Capital campaigns.
Limitations: Applications not accepted. Giving primarily in MO. No grants to individuals.
Application information: Contributes only to pre-selected organizations.
  Board meeting date(s): End of year
Trustees: Heather A. Bahora; John R. Hoffman; Linda Hoffman.
EIN: 436827233

3576
Virginia H. Farah Foundation
P.O. Box 457
Wichita, KS   67201-0457   (316) 682-1939
Contact: Eric S. Namee, Pres.
E-mail: contact@farahfoundation.org; Main URL: http://www.farahfoundation.org
Grants List: http://www.farahfoundation.org/pastrecipients.html

Foundation type: Independent foundation.
Financial data (yr. ended 12/31/13): Assets, $786,576 (M); gifts received, $813; expenditures, $319,231; qualifying distributions, $268,407; giving activities include $268,407 for 26 grants (high: $25,000; low: $125).
Purpose and activities: Giving primarily for the maintenance and growth of the Orthodox Christian Church in the U.S. and the world.
Fields of interest: Orthodox Christianity.
Type of support: Capacity-building and technical assistance; Capital campaigns; Capital and infrastructure; Program development; Publications; Seed money.
Application information: See foundation web site for current information. Application form required.
  Initial approach: Letter
  Copies of proposal: 4
  Deadline(s): July 1
  Board meeting date(s): Fall
Officers and Trustees: Eric S. Namee, Pres. and Trustee; Valerie DeBolt, V.P. and Trustee; Bruce Ferris, Secy.-Treas.
EIN: 760067300

3577
The Fidelity Bank Foundation
(formerly Bastian Foundation)
100 E. English St.
Wichita, KS   67202-3706

Established in 1961 in Kansas.
Donors: H. Marvin Bastian; Fidelity Bank.
Foundation type: Independent foundation.
Financial data (yr. ended 03/31/14): Assets, $5,524,273 (M); gifts received, $8,682; expenditures, $238,740; qualifying distributions,

$221,960; giving activities include $221,960 for 27 grants (high: $25,000; low: $100).
Fields of interest: Arts and culture; Higher education; Zoos; Nonprofits; Christianity; Human services; Child welfare.
Type of support: General support; Continuing support; Annual campaigns; Capital campaigns; Capital and infrastructure; Endowments; Regranting; Program development; Curriculum development.
Limitations: Applications not accepted. Giving limited to KS, with emphasis on Wichita. No grants to individuals.
Application information: Unsolicited requests for funds not accepted.
  Board meeting date(s): Bimonthly
Officers: H. Clay Bastian, Pres. and Secy.; M. Clark Bastian, Treas.
Directors: Aaron C. Bastian; Christine C. Bastian.
EIN: 486112483

3578
The Fox Family Foundation
2904 W. 112th St.
Leawood, KS   66211-3087

Established in 2007 in Kansas.
Donors: Kevin J. Fox; Amelia L. Fox.
Foundation type: Independent foundation.
Financial data (yr. ended 12/31/13): Assets, $6,086,281 (M); expenditures, $308,947; qualifying distributions, $304,282; giving activities include $301,392 for 37 grants (high: $120,500; low: $50).
Fields of interest: Human services; Family services; Child welfare.
Limitations: Applications not accepted.
Application information: Contributes only to pre-selected organizations.
Directors: Amelia L. Fox; Gregory P. Fox; Joseph P. Fox; Kenneth J. Fox; Kevin J. Fox.
EIN: 261277915

3579
R. E. French Family Educational Foundation
P.O. Box 203
Gridley, KS   66852-0203

Foundation type: Independent foundation.
Financial data (yr. ended 06/30/14): Assets, $11,483,027 (M); gifts received, $500; expenditures, $663,804; qualifying distributions, $555,679; giving activities include $15,152 for 5 grants (high: $5,000; low: $75), and $425,450 for 296 grants to individuals (high: $1,550; low: $750).
Purpose and activities: The foundation provides scholarships to graduates of Kansas high schools, who have demonstrated the desire to attend a college or university, or who seek vocational training in an accredited vocational training institution. The foundation also awards grants to Kansas schools, libraries, and other educational institutions to provide or improve facilities, equipment, or books.
Fields of interest: Education.
Type of support: Equipment; Student aid.
Limitations: Applications accepted. Giving limited to KS.
Application information: Completion of application form required for scholarships. Application form required.

Initial approach: E-mail
Deadline(s): None
Trustees: Gregory L. Arnold; Sarah K. Grimm; Joann Osborn.
EIN: 480926521

3580
Goebel Family Star Lumber Charitable Foundation
(formerly Star Lumber & Supply Charitable Foundation)
P.O. Box 7712
Wichita, KS 67277-7712 (316) 942-2221
Contact: Jenny L. Stephens, Treas.
FAX: (316) 942-0690; Main URL: http://www.starlumber.com/starlumbercharitabletrust.html

Established in 1989 in Kansas.
Donor: Star Lumber & Supply Co., Inc.
Foundation type: Company-sponsored foundation.
Financial data (yr. ended 12/31/13): Assets, $870,147 (M); gifts received, $206,000; expenditures, $392,008; qualifying distributions, $390,585; giving activities include $390,585 for 49 grants (high: $51,909; low: $100).
Purpose and activities: The foundation supports medical centers and organizations involved with arts and culture, education, animal welfare, human services, and Catholicism.
Fields of interest: Arts and culture; Education; Human services.
Type of support: Continuing support; Annual campaigns; Capital and infrastructure; Scholarships.
Limitations: Applications accepted. Giving limited to central KS. No grants to individuals.
Publications: Grants list.
Application information: Application form required.
   Initial approach: Complete online application form
   Deadline(s): None
   Board meeting date(s): Jan., Mar., May, July, Sept., and Nov.
Officers: Robert L. Goebel, Pres.; Connie M. Armstrong, Secy.; Jennifer L. Stephens, Treas.
Trustees: Jess Brearton; Patrick M. Goebel; Kathleen Goebel; Jacqueline A. Jolly; Jeanette Jones; David McDaneld; Brian Schawe; Allen Spurgeon; Rebecca Stuhlsatz; Jerry Warren.
EIN: 481065296

3581
Goldberg Family Foundation
c/o Lynn G. Intrater
10412 Metcalf Ave.
Overland Park, KS 66212-1806

Established in 2002 in Kansas.
Donors: Geraldine D. Goldberg; John M. Goldberg; Robert A. Goldberg; Lynn G. Intrater.
Foundation type: Independent foundation.
Financial data (yr. ended 12/31/13): Assets, $3,313,197 (M); expenditures, $254,310; qualifying distributions, $241,914; giving activities include $232,156 for 52 grants (high: $102,500; low: $180).
Fields of interest: Higher education; Nonprofits; Judaism; Human services.
Type of support: Regranting.

Limitations: Applications not accepted. Giving primarily in Overland Park, KS, and Kansas City, MO. No grants to individuals.
Application information: Unsolicited requests for funds not accepted.
Trustee: Lynn G. Intrater.
Advisory Committee Members: Geraldine D. Goldberg; John M. Goldberg; Robert A. Goldberg.
EIN: 436884613

3582
Golden Belt Community Foundation
(also known as Golden Belt Foundation)
1307 Williams St.
P.O. Box 1911
Great Bend, KS 67530 (620) 792-3000
Contact: Christy L. Tustin, Exec. Dir.
FAX: (620) 792-7900;
E-mail: gbcf@goldenbeltcf.org; Main URL: http://www.goldenbeltcf.org
Facebook: https://www.facebook.com/pages/Golden-Belt-Community-Foundation/123961677703858
Twitter: https://twitter.com/goldenbeltcf

Established in 1996 in Kansas.
Foundation type: Community foundation.
Financial data (yr. ended 12/31/12): Assets, $10,629,065 (M); gifts received, $1,977,141; expenditures, $472,850; giving activities include $218,993 for 11+ grants (high: $25,444), and $15,850 for 23 grants to individuals.
Purpose and activities: The foundation exists to provide non-profit organizations in central Kansas with a permanent source of support and to serve as a vehicle for charitable giving for donors. The foundation serves the counties of Barton, Pawnee, Rush, and Stafford.
Fields of interest: Arts and culture; Environment.
Type of support: Program development; Student aid.
Limitations: Applications accepted. Giving primarily in Barton, Pawnee, Rush, and Strafford counties, KS. No support for recreational, sporting events or athletic associations, leisure and entertainment, or religious organizations for religious activities. No grants to individuals (except for scholarships), or for travel, endowment, debt retirement, or annual campaigns.
Publications: Application guidelines; Annual report.
Application information: Visit foundation website for additional application information.
   Initial approach: Submit application
   Copies of proposal: 1
   Deadline(s): Mar. 1, July 1, and Nov. 1
   Board meeting date(s): Mar., July and Nov.
   Final notification: Mar. 31, July 30, and Nov. 30
Officer and Directors: Christy L. Tustin, Exec. Dir.; Mark Bitter; Melanie Calcara; Joan Dreher; Misty Fisher; Randy Goering; Sarah Johnson; Steve Miller; Richelle Roth; Tammy Rosenberg; Amber Rugan; Dr. Ron Sandstrom; Gary Seibert; Kathy Straub; Paul Snapp; Ardis Viegra.
EIN: 742804940

3583
Green Mountain Charitable Foundation
6017 Windsor Dr.
Fairway, KS 66205-3348

Established in 1997 in Kansas.
Donor: John C. Kornitzer.

Foundation type: Independent foundation.
Financial data (yr. ended 12/31/13): Assets, $7,063,067 (M); expenditures, $328,797; qualifying distributions, $322,500; giving activities include $322,500 for 9 grants (high: $150,000; low: $1,500).
Fields of interest: Arts and culture; Education; Health; Christianity; Human services.
Limitations: Applications not accepted. Giving primarily in KS, MD and MO. No grants to individuals.
Application information: Contributes only to pre-selected organizations.
Officers and Directors: John C. Kornitzer, Pres. and Treas.; Carol W. Kornitzer, V.P. and Secy. and Director; Nicole M. Kornitzer, V.P.
EIN: 742833070

3584
Haglage Charitable Trust Agency
5442 W. 100th Terr.
Overland Park, KS 66207-3120 (913) 338-4455
Contact: Randall Leonard, Tr.

Donors: Dorothy Claire Haglage†; Daniel Hutchins.
Foundation type: Independent foundation.
Financial data (yr. ended 12/31/13): Assets, $3,107,174 (M); expenditures, $404,890; qualifying distributions, $381,131; giving activities include $377,500 for 15 grants (high: $60,000; low: $2,000).
Fields of interest: Christianity; Human services.
Limitations: Applications accepted. Giving primarily in MO. No grants to individuals.
Application information:
   Initial approach: Proposal
   Deadline(s): None
Trustees: Daniel F. Hutchins; Randall Leonard; Gordon Peterson.
EIN: 486375911

3585
The Pete Henry Foundation
P.O. Box 504
Colby, KS 67701-0504 (785) 462-6553

Donor: Pierre C. Henry.
Foundation type: Independent foundation.
Financial data (yr. ended 06/30/13): Assets, $9,664,027 (M); expenditures, $337,374; qualifying distributions, $321,022; giving activities include $307,125 for 48 grants (high: $54,500; low: $375).
Purpose and activities: Giving primarily for education and scholarship funds.
Fields of interest: Higher education.
Type of support: General support; Scholarships.
Limitations: Applications accepted. Giving limited to the following KS counties: Decatur, Gove, Logan, Rawlins, Sheridan, Sherman, Cheyenne, Thomas, and Wallace.
Application information: Scholarship awards paid directly to school of admissions for qualified graduating senior. Application form required.
   Initial approach: Proposal
   Deadline(s): Mar. 1
Officers and Directors: Kenton K. Krehbiel, Pres. and Director; William Dowell, Secy.; William H. Biel; Wayne L. Carpenter; Richard Epard.
EIN: 481201942

3586

E. L. and Z. Irene Hopkins Private Foundation

P.O. Box 807
Emporia, KS 66801-0807

Established in 1997 in Kansas.
Donors: E.L. Hopkins; Z. Irene Hopkins.
Foundation type: Independent foundation.
Financial data (yr. ended 12/31/13): Assets, $8,374,406 (M); expenditures, $378,092; qualifying distributions, $356,246; giving activities include $208,285 for 38 grants (high: $56,849; low: $50).
Purpose and activities: Giving for public education and social service organizations.
Fields of interest: Education; Secondary education; Health; Child welfare.
Type of support: Public engagement and education.
Limitations: Applications not accepted. Giving primarily in Emporia, KS. No grants to individuals.
Application information: Unsolicited requests for funds not accepted.
Officers: Kenneth L. Hopkins, Pres.; Michelle R. Molinaro, Secy.-Treas.
Directors: Ruby Butcher; Tom Krueger.
EIN: 742831255

3587

Insurance Management Associates Foundation

(also known as IMA Foundation)
8200 E. 32nd St. North
Wichita, KS 67226 (316) 267-9221
Contact: Ruth Rohs, Exec. Dir.
FAX: (316) 266-6254;
E-mail: foundation@imacorp.com; Main URL: http://www.imafg.com/ima-foundation

Donors: Insurance Management Associates, Inc.; The IMA Financial Group Inc.
Foundation type: Company-sponsored foundation.
Financial data (yr. ended 12/31/13): Assets, $2,631,723 (M); gifts received, $595,990; expenditures, $347,003; qualifying distributions, $314,062; giving activities include $314,062 for 48 grants (high: $30,000; low: $500).
Purpose and activities: The foundation supports programs designed to advance youth; promote arts and culture; enhance economic vitality; and promote health and wellness.
Fields of interest: Arts and culture; Performing arts; Art museums; Education; Elementary and secondary education; Early childhood education; Higher education; Nonprofits; Health; Hospital care; Leadership development; Community and economic development; Employment; Business and industry; Human services; Child welfare; Scouting programs; Senior services; Adolescents.
Type of support: General support; Capital campaigns; Program development; Scholarships; Regranting.
Limitations: Applications accepted. Giving primarily in areas of company operations in Denver, CO, Kansas City, Topeka, and Wichita, KS, and Dallas TX. No support for fiscal agents or sponsors. No grants to individuals.
Publications: Application guidelines; Program policy statement.
Application information: Applicants are encouraged to email the foundation in advance of submitting a letter of inquiry to ensure that the organization's

request is a fit for the IMA Foundation. Letters of inquiry should not exceed 4 pages. Average grant awards range from $5,000 to $10,000.
  Initial approach: E-mail letter of inquiry
  Deadline(s): Apr. 1 and Oct. 1
Trustees: Anita Bourke; Robert L. Cohen; William C. Cohen, Jr.; Robert Reiter; Kurt D. Watson.
EIN: 237432160

3588

Jeffcoat Memorial Foundation

101 1/2 N.W. Third
P.O. Box 413
Abilene, KS 67410-2361

Foundation type: Independent foundation.
Financial data (yr. ended 12/31/13): Assets, $4,557,087 (M); expenditures, $213,778; qualifying distributions, $208,002; giving activities include $206,403 for 15 grants (high: $35,000; low: $4,066).
Fields of interest: Historic preservation; Education; Foundations.
Limitations: Applications not accepted. Giving primarily in Abilene and Salina, KS. No grants to individuals.
Application information: Contributes only to pre-selected organizations.
Officers: Wayne Burklund, Pres.; Robert H. Royer, Jr., Secy.
EIN: 481200599

3589

Jellison Benevolent Society Inc.

P.O. Box 145
Junction City, KS 66441-0145 (785) 762-5566
Contact: Susan E. Williams
FAX: (785) 762-4242;
E-mail: s_williams1948@yahoo.com

Established in 1947 in Kansas.
Donors: A.D. Jellison†; Maude S. Jellison†.
Foundation type: Independent foundation.
Financial data (yr. ended 12/31/12): Assets, $3,821,518 (M); expenditures, $223,338; qualifying distributions, $156,600; giving activities include $156,600 for grants.
Purpose and activities: Support for YMCA and other social service and youth groups; also awards scholarships to local-area students for undergraduate study.
Fields of interest: Education; Human services; Child welfare.
Type of support: Scholarships; General support; Student aid.
Limitations: Applications accepted. Giving limited to KS, with emphasis on Geary County residents and/or organizations.
Publications: Application guidelines.
Application information: Application form required for students applying for educational grants; charitable organizations must submit request for funds along with IRS Determination Letter. Application form required.
  Initial approach: Letter, telephone or e-mail
  Copies of proposal: 1
  Deadline(s): For scholarships: June 20 for fall semester, Nov. 20 for spring semester; for charitable organizations, Nov. 20
  Board meeting date(s): July and Dec.
  Final notification: Within 10 days of meeting

Directors: Barbara Craft; Dorothy J. Cassity; Dale Ann Clore; Ted Hayden; Janet Vogelsang; James Ward.
Number of staff: None.
EIN: 486106092

3590

Verla Nesbitt Joscelyn Foundation

P.O. Box 975
Salina, KS 67402-0975

Established in 1968 in Kansas.
Donor: Verla Nesbitt Joscelyn.
Foundation type: Independent foundation.
Financial data (yr. ended 12/31/13): Assets, $7,397,120 (M); expenditures, $603,206; qualifying distributions, $461,539; giving activities include $438,004 for 42 grants (high: $40,000; low: $1,000).
Fields of interest: Arts and culture; Higher education; Nonprofits; Human services; Child welfare.
Type of support: Regranting.
Limitations: Applications not accepted. Giving primarily in Salina, KS. No grants to individuals.
Application information: Contributes only to pre-selected organizations.
Officers: Janice L. Doherty, Pres.; George W. Yarnevich, V.P.; Mark Zimmerman, V.P.; Thomas A. Williamson, Treas.
Director: Leroy Baumberger.
EIN: 237067278

3591

Kammco Foundation, Inc.

623 S.W. 10th Ave.
Topeka, KS 66612

Donors: Kansas Medical Mutual Insurance Co.; Daniel J. Suiter, MD; Jerry Slaughter; Donald W. Hatton, MD; Kurt Scott; Craig A. Concannon, MD.
Foundation type: Independent foundation.
Financial data (yr. ended 12/31/13): Assets, $4,042,161 (M); expenditures, $207,120; qualifying distributions, $192,043; giving activities include $189,505 for 2 grants (high: $187,005; low: $2,500).
Fields of interest: Education; Health.
Type of support: General support.
Limitations: Applications not accepted. Giving primarily in KS.
Application information: Unsolicited requests for funds not accepted.
Officers and Directors: Donald W. Hatton, MD, Chair. and Director; Kurt Scott, Pres.; Jerry Slaughter, Secy.; Daniel J. Suiter, MD, Treas.; Craig A. Concannon, MD.
EIN: 271401043

3592

Kansas Rural Communities Foundation

P.O. Box 25
Wamego, KS 66547 (785) 456-8444
Contact: Glenn Brunkow, Exec. Dir.
FAX: (785) 456-8443; E-mail: krcf@wamego.net;
Additional address: 1003 Lincoln St., Farm Bureau

Bldg., Wamego, KS 66547; Main URL: http://www.thekrcf.org
Facebook: https://www.facebook.com/pages/Kansas-Rural-Communities-Foundation/246611292059

Established in 2006 in Kansas.
Foundation type: Community foundation.
Financial data (yr. ended 12/31/13): Assets, $1,609,214 (M); gifts received, $445,237; expenditures, $310,745; giving activities include $223,859 for 11 grants (high: $20,000), and $5,670 for 8 grants to individuals.
Purpose and activities: The foundation seeks to enrich the quality of life in all Kansas communities, build statewide awareness of community needs and opportunities, provide a vehicle by which individuals, families, businesses, and organizations can financially support the needs of their communities, solicit funds and educate potential donors about the advantages of giving for both the donor and their community, and ensure professional management of perpetually endowed funds.
Fields of interest: Historic preservation; Education; Environment; Health; Libraries; Telecommunications; Sustainable development; Rural development; Human services; Family disability resources; Children and youth; People with disabilities.
Type of support: Program development; Building and renovations.
Limitations: Applications not accepted. Giving primarily in rural Kansas, including Havensville, Manhattan, Norton, Olsburg, Onaga, St. George, St. Marys, Wamego, Westmoreland, and Wheaton.
Publications: Annual report; Newsletter.
Officers and Directors: Laura Pearl, Co-Pres. and Director; James Waters, Co-Pres. and Director; Abby Amick, V.P. and Director; Kally McConkey, Secy. and Director; Julie Roller, Treas. and Director; Glenn Brunkow, Exec. Dir.; Casey Blume; Chris Flattery; Suzanne Hemphill; Ron Hinrichsen; Steve Hund; Joe Minihan; Ann Walter.
Community Advisors: Bob Cole; Tom Nelson.
EIN: 203579294

3593
Kejr Foundation Inc.
P.O. Box 1812
Salina, KS 67402-1812

Established in 1959 in Colorado.
Donors: Joseph Kejr†; Mary Kejr; Kejr Trust; Kejr Family Foundation of Brookville, KS; Maurice Kapsner; William Smith; Ralph Pugh; David Mulder; Spencer Bower; Lee Ann Christy; Thomas Christy; Kejr, Inc.; Great Plains Manufacturing Inc.; John D. Bower; Thomas and Lee Ann Christy.
Foundation type: Independent foundation.
Financial data (yr. ended 12/31/13): Assets, $3,725,736 (M); gifts received, $40,000; expenditures, $369,105; qualifying distributions, $265,584; giving activities include $265,584 for 35 grants (high: $26,584; low: $500).
Purpose and activities: Support of interdenominational, evangelical religious programs, including radio broadcasting, church extension, and missionary projects. The foundation also sponsors a consultation and evaluation service and a retreat facility for church and educational personnel.
Fields of interest: Religion; Christianity.
International interests: Congo, Republic of the.

Type of support: Convening.
Limitations: Applications not accepted. Giving primarily in IL, MN, and NY. No grants to individuals.
Application information: Contributes only to pre-selected organizations.
Officers: Harry J. Kejr, Pres.; George Lewis, V.P.; Melvin Kejr, Secy.; Larry Kejr, Treas.
EIN: 846023358

3594
Kiersznowski Family Charitable Trust
6538 Wenonga Rd.
Mission Hills, KS 66208-1724

Established in 1998 in Kansas.
Donors: David Kiersznowski; Demi Lloyd; Patricia Lloyd Land Charitable Lead Trust; Pat Lloyd†; Demi Lloyd Revocable Trust; David Kiersznowski Revocable Trust.
Foundation type: Independent foundation.
Financial data (yr. ended 12/31/13): Assets, $23,740,854 (M); gifts received, $1,396,689; expenditures, $555,998; qualifying distributions, $344,500; giving activities include $344,500 for 8 grants (high: $200,000; low: $5,000).
Fields of interest: Christianity.
Limitations: Applications not accepted. Giving primarily in VA. No grants to individuals.
Application information: Contributes only to pre-selected organizations.
Trustee: Chad Battison.
Directors: David Kiersznowski; Demi Lloyd.
EIN: 436789722

3595
Legacy, A Regional Community Foundation
(also known as Legacy Foundation)
1216 Main St.
P.O. Box 713
Winfield, KS 67156 (620) 221-7224
Contact: Pamela Moore, Exec. Dir.
FAX: (620) 221-0532;
E-mail: admin@legacyregionalfoundation.org;
Additional tel.: (855) 470-7224; Main URL: http://www.legacyregionalfoundation.org
Facebook: https://www.facebook.com/legacycommunityfoundation

Established in 1996 in Kansas.
Foundation type: Community foundation.
Financial data (yr. ended 12/31/13): Assets, $5,205,613 (M); gifts received, $473,330; expenditures, $491,344; giving activities include $192,029 for 9+ grants (high: $36,600), and $63,330 for 68 grants to individuals.
Purpose and activities: Giving primarily for the health and well being of children, and for the betterment of South Central Kansas.
Fields of interest: Health; Community and economic development; Child welfare; Infants and toddlers; Children; People with disabilities.
Type of support: Continuing support; Matching grants; Equipment; Endowments; Emergency funds; Program development; Publications; Seed money; Curriculum development; Scholarships.
Limitations: Applications accepted. Giving limited to Cowley, Sumner, and Chautauqua, KS. No support for sectarian religious purposes. No grants for individuals (except for scholarships), or for operating

support, travel including school field trips, or conferences.
Publications: Application guidelines; Annual report; Financial statement; Grants list; Informational brochure; Newsletter.
Application information: Visit foundation web site for application form and guidelines. Application form required.
> *Initial approach:* Submit application and attachments
> *Copies of proposal:* 1
> *Deadline(s):* None
> *Board meeting date(s):* 3rd Thurs. of every month
> *Final notification:* Within 6 weeks
Officers and Directors: Steven Hill, Chair. and Director; Sid Regnier, Vice-Chair. and Director; Greg Thompson, Secy.-Treas. and Director; Pamela Moore, Exec. Dir.; Judy Clark; Carol House; Steve Perkins; Dared Price; Terry Sisson; Tom Wallrabenstein; Karen Zeller.
Number of staff: 1 full-time professional; 1 full-time support.
EIN: 481187957

3596
Mosby Lincoln Foundation
7309 E. 21st St. N., Ste. 120
Wichita, KS 67206-1178

Established in 1987 in Kansas.
Donor: Edward M. Lincoln.
Foundation type: Independent foundation.
Financial data (yr. ended 12/31/13): Assets, $3,538,639 (M); expenditures, $156,469; qualifying distributions, $132,083; giving activities include $130,105 for 48 grants (high: $30,000; low: $100).
Fields of interest: Community and economic development; Religion; Human services.
Limitations: Applications not accepted. Giving primarily in KS. No grants to individuals.
Application information: Contributes only to pre-selected organizations.
Trustee: Edward M. Lincoln.
EIN: 470692538

3597
The Logan Foundation
c/o Eugene T. Logan
10501 E. Genova
Wichita, KS 67206

Established in 1988 in Kansas.
Donor: Robert E. Logan.
Foundation type: Independent foundation.
Financial data (yr. ended 12/31/13): Assets, $1,938,651 (M); expenditures, $174,275; qualifying distributions, $161,050; giving activities include $161,050 for 29 grants (high: $30,000; low: $300).
Purpose and activities: Giving primarily for Christian churches, ministries, missions and Bible class.
Fields of interest: Higher education; Christianity.
Limitations: Applications not accepted. Giving primarily in KS. No grants to individuals.
Application information: Contributes only to pre-selected organizations.
Officers: Eugene T. Logan, Pres.; Margaret E. Logan, Secy.-Treas.
Directors: James Logan; Peter L. Peterson.
EIN: 481061492

3598
Lowenstein Brothers Foundation
5248 W. 126th Terr.
Leawood, KS   66209-3126   (913) 498-2202
Contact: William B. Lowenstein, Tr.

Established in 1956 in Missouri.
Donor: William B. Lowenstein.
Foundation type: Independent foundation.
Financial data (yr. ended 10/31/13): Assets,
$4,124,551 (M); expenditures, $261,463;
qualifying distributions, $238,007; giving activities
include $235,000 for 2 grants (high: $230,000;
low: $5,000).
Fields of interest: Education; Nonprofits; Judaism;
Human services.
Type of support: Regranting.
Limitations: Applications accepted. Giving primarily
in KS and MO.
Application information: Application form required.
   Initial approach: Letter
   Deadline(s): None
Trustees: Marjorie Sue Kaplan; Glenn L.
Lowenstein; John Lowenstein; Lon J. Lowenstein;
Reed Lowenstein; William B. Lowenstein.
EIN: 436055404

3599
Mann Family Foundation
3260 N. Jabara Rd.
Wichita, KS   67226-8935   (316) 351-7500

Donors: Ronald D. Mann; Barbara L. Mann.
Foundation type: Independent foundation.
Financial data (yr. ended 12/31/14): Assets,
$3,523,991; gifts received, $141,439;
expenditures, $350,469; qualifying distributions,
$333,222.
Fields of interest: Education; Health; Human
services.
Limitations: Applications accepted. Giving primarily
in KS.
Application information: Application form required.
   Initial approach: Letter
   Deadline(s): None
Trustees: Barbara L. Mann; Ronald D. Mann.
EIN: 263881101

3600
Master Craftsmen Foundation
c/o National Advisors Trust Co.
8717 W. 110th St., Ste. 700
Overland Park, KS   66210-2127   (913) 234-8238
Contact: Sherrill Ann Mulhern, Pres. and Dir.

Established in 1986 in Missouri.
Donors: American Standard Inc.; Kraft Foods Inc.
Foundation type: Independent foundation.
Financial data (yr. ended 12/31/13): Assets,
$2,384,602 (M); expenditures, $148,663;
qualifying distributions, $147,522; giving activities
include $143,825 for 20 grants (high: $15,000;
low: $325).
Purpose and activities: Giving primarily for the arts,
education, and hospitals.
Fields of interest: Arts and culture; Education;
Religion.
Type of support: Capital campaigns.
Limitations: Applications accepted. Giving primarily
in Kansas City, MO. No grants to individuals.
Application information:

Initial approach: Proposal
   Deadline(s): None
Officer and Directors: Sherrill Ann Mulhern, Pres.
and Director; Estelle Sosland; Kathleen L. Szleper.
EIN: 431377578

3601
McFadden Charitable Trust
c/o The Peoples Bank
P.O. Box 307
Smith Center, KS   66967-0307

Established in 2002 in Kansas.
Foundation type: Independent foundation.
Financial data (yr. ended 12/31/14): Assets,
$9,882,086; expenditures, $318,461; qualifying
distributions, $318,461.
Purpose and activities: Giving primarily for
scholarships.
Fields of interest: Education; Hospital care;
Community and economic development;
Christianity; Child welfare.
Type of support: General support; Individual
development.
Limitations: Applications accepted. Giving primarily
in Osborne County, KS.
Application information:
   Initial approach: Proposal
   Deadline(s): Scholarships by Apr. 1, other
      organizations by Dec. 1
Trustee: The Peoples Bank.
Directors: Paul Gregory; Olin Hyde; Gregory Mick;
Donald Weis; Terry Zvolanek.
EIN: 486319389

3602
Catherin V. Merrill Foundation
8010 State Line Rd., Ste. 220
Prairie Village, KS   66208-3711   (913) 341-8185
Contact: Charles Wheeler, Tr.

Donor: Catherin V. Merrill.
Foundation type: Independent foundation.
Financial data (yr. ended 12/31/13): Assets,
$10,148,775 (M); expenditures, $477,436;
qualifying distributions, $441,344; giving activities
include $377,466 for 27 grants (high: $60,216;
low: $750).
Fields of interest: Education; Undergraduate
education; University education; Graduate and
professional education; Christianity; Theology;
Human services.
Limitations: Applications accepted. Giving limited to
the greater Kansas City, MO, area. No grants to
individuals.
Application information: Application form required.
   Initial approach: Letter
   Deadline(s): None
Trustees: Christine DeMarea; H. Elvin Knight, Jr.; W.
H. Madden; Charles Wheeler.
EIN: 237066845

3603
Mildred and Rolland Middlekauff
Foundation
P.O. Box 198
Salina, KS   67402-0198
Application address: c/o Sidney A. Reitz, 119 W. Iron
Ave., Salina, KS 67401, tel.: (785) 827-7251

Donor: Mildred Middlekauff Trust.
Foundation type: Independent foundation.
Financial data (yr. ended 06/30/14): Assets,
$7,363,309 (M); expenditures, $223,664;
qualifying distributions, $298,325; giving activities
include $277,175 for 23 grants (high: $60,000;
low: $1,000).
Fields of interest: Arts and culture; Theater;
Education; University education; Domesticated
animals; Foundations; Hospice care; Christianity;
Human services.
Type of support: Scholarships.
Limitations: Applications accepted. Giving primarily
in Manhattan and Salina, KS.
Application information: Application form required.
   Initial approach: Letter
   Deadline(s): None
Officers: Sidney A. Reitz, Pres.; Susan N. Reitz,
Secy.-Treas.
EIN: 352199154

3604
Miller-Mellor Association
5301 W. 67th St.
Prairie Village, KS   66208-1409   (913) 432-5301
Contact: Craig W. Patterson, Dir.

Established in 1950 in Missouri.
Foundation type: Independent foundation.
Financial data (yr. ended 06/30/13): Assets,
$6,248,980 (M); expenditures, $332,691;
qualifying distributions, $317,300; giving activities
include $317,300 for 52 grants (high: $50,000;
low: $100).
Purpose and activities: Grants primarily for higher
education and cultural programs; support also for
Roman Catholic churches and health services.
Fields of interest: Arts and culture; Higher
education; Hospital care; Specialty hospital care;
Catholicism; Human services.
Limitations: Applications accepted. Giving primarily
in Kansas City, MO.
Application information:
   Initial approach: Proposal
   Deadline(s): None
Officers and Directors: Anne Patterson, Pres. and
Director; JoZach James Miller, V.P. and Director;
James Ludlow Miller, Secy.-Treas. and Director;
Marika Ivanko; Craig W. Patterson; Mark Elliot
Patterson.
EIN: 446011906

3605
Julia J. Mingenback Foundation Inc.
c/o Peoples Bank Trust
P.O. Box 1226
McPherson, KS   67460-1226   6202415023
Application address: c/o James Ketcherside, 609
Wickersham Dr., McPherson, KS 67460, tel.: (620)
241-3893

Established in 1959 in Kansas.
Donor: E.C. Mingenback†.
Foundation type: Independent foundation.
Financial data (yr. ended 12/31/14): Assets,
$4,331,178; expenditures, $275,866; qualifying
distributions, $202,500.
Purpose and activities: Giving is generally limited to
educational and cultural activities.

Fields of interest: Arts and culture; Elementary and secondary education; Higher education; Hospital care; Religion; Senior services; Seniors.
Type of support: Capital campaigns; Capital and infrastructure; Equipment.
Limitations: Applications accepted. Giving limited to McPherson County, KS. No grants to individuals, or for operating funds.
Application information: Application form required.
Initial approach: Letter
Deadline(s): None
Officers: James Ketcherside, Pres.; Brett Reber, V.P.; Bev Hess, Secy.-Treas.; Peoples Bank & Trust Co., Mgr.
Directors: Don C Steffes; B Carver Swindoll.
Number of staff: None.
EIN: 486109567

3606
The Mistler Family Foundation
4200 Somerset Dr., Ste. 208
Prairie Village, KS   66208

Established in 1991 in Missouri.
Donors: Richard E. Mistler; Thomas E. Mistler; Alvin J. Mistler†.
Foundation type: Independent foundation.
Financial data (yr. ended 12/31/13): Assets, $9,474,475 (M); gifts received, $29,985; expenditures, $288,510; qualifying distributions, $280,760; giving activities include $280,760 for 128 grants (high: $110,500; low: $79).
Fields of interest: Education; University education; Foundations; Community and economic development; Religion; Protestantism; Human services.
Type of support: General support.
Limitations: Applications not accepted. Giving primarily in KS and Kansas City, MO. No grants to individuals.
Application information: Contributes only to pre-selected organizations.
Officers and Directors: Richard E. Mistler, Pres. and Secy. and Director; Thomas E. Mistler, V.P. and Director.
Number of staff: None.
EIN: 481101420

3607
Albert Morgan and Leona A. Morgan Charitable Foundation
711 3rd St.
P.O. Box 266
Phillipsburg, KS   67661-1915   (785) 543-6561
Contact: Denis Miller, Dir.

Established in 1992 in Kansas.
Donors: Albert Morgan†; Leona Morgan†.
Foundation type: Independent foundation.
Financial data (yr. ended 09/30/13): Assets, $10,643,839 (M); expenditures, $623,479; qualifying distributions, $448,642; giving activities include $386,045 for 25+ grants (high: $90,901).
Purpose and activities: Giving primarily to benefit the residents of Phillips County, KS.
Fields of interest: Historic preservation; Specialty hospital care; Human services; Scouting programs.
Limitations: Applications accepted. Giving limited to Phillipsburg, KS. No grants to individuals.
Application information: Application form required.
Initial approach: Request application

Copies of proposal: 6
Deadline(s): 2 weeks prior to board meeting
Board meeting date(s): Semi-monthly
Final notification: 1 week following board meeting
Officers: Denis Miller, Chair.; Lowell Hahn, Secy.; Lori Ferguson, Treas.
Directors: John Beim; Daniels Heinze.
EIN: 481126706

3608
Dorothy M. Morrison Foundation
10343 S. Highland Cir.
Olathe, KS   66061-8441   (913) 302-5451

Established in 1993 in Kansas.
Donors: Dorothy M. Morrison Crut; Dorothy M. Morrison Crut No. 2.
Foundation type: Independent foundation.
Financial data (yr. ended 10/31/14): Assets, $6,490,476 (M); expenditures, $436,288; qualifying distributions, $311,000; giving activities include $311,000 for 1 grant.
Fields of interest: Domesticated animals; Human services.
Limitations: Applications accepted. Giving limited to Great Bend, KS. No grants to individuals.
Application information:
Initial approach: Proposal
Deadline(s): None
Director: Katherine Opie; Sandra Opie.
EIN: 481140332

3609
Muchnic Foundation
704 N. 4th St.
P.O. Box 329
Atchison, KS   66002-1924   (913) 367-4164
Contact: Sharon Meier

Established in 1946 in Kansas.
Donors: Valley Co., Inc.; Helen Q. Muchnic†; H.E. Muchnic†.
Foundation type: Independent foundation.
Financial data (yr. ended 11/30/13): Assets, $9,675,237 (M); expenditures, $532,865; qualifying distributions, $500,139; giving activities include $397,704 for 64 grants (high: $45,000; low: $1,000).
Purpose and activities: Giving primarily for higher education and cultural programs, including museums, and civic affairs; support also for health associations and medical research.
Fields of interest: Arts and culture; Museums; Higher education; Diseases and conditions.
Type of support: Research; Research and evaluation.
Limitations: Applications accepted. Giving on a national basis. No grants to individuals.
Application information: Large brochures are not helpful.
Initial approach: Letter
Deadline(s): Oct. 31
Board meeting date(s): As required
Officer: David C. Mize, Pres.; Sharon Meier, Secy.-Treas.
Directors: Ann Mize; Daphne Nan Muchnic.
Number of staff: 1
EIN: 486102818

3610
Chester Edwin & Mary Nash Charitable Foundation
P.O. Box 751
Hugoton, KS   67951-0751

Foundation type: Independent foundation.
Financial data (yr. ended 12/31/13): Assets, $6,429,893 (M); expenditures, $240,675; qualifying distributions, $162,216; giving activities include $162,216 for 2 grants (high: $144,600; low: $17,616).
Fields of interest: Domesticated animals.
Type of support: General support.
Limitations: Applications not accepted. No grants to individuals.
Application information: Unsolicited requests for funds not accepted.
Trustees: Brenda Kinser; David Petty.
EIN: 736331357

3611
George H. Nettleton Foundation
(formerly George H. Nettleton Home)
P.O. Box 8707
Prairie Village, KS   66208-0707
Contact: Susann Riffe, Pres.
E-mail: susannriffe@aol.com; Application address: 13820 W. 77th Terr., Lenexa, KS 66216; Main URL: http://www.gnettleton.org

Donors: Nettleton Trust; Aduh Hudson-Jaccard Charitable Trust Fund; Susie M. Root Charitable Trust; A.H. Jaccard Memorial Trust; TUW Minerva Gundelfinger; L.A. Jaccard Memorial Trust.
Foundation type: Independent foundation.
Financial data (yr. ended 12/31/13): Assets, $4,381,518 (M); gifts received, $48,604; expenditures, $346,282; qualifying distributions, $310,418; giving activities include $310,013 for 11 grants (high: $75,000; low: $500).
Purpose and activities: Giving limited to organizations providing services for the elderly.
Fields of interest: Seniors.
Type of support: General support.
Limitations: Applications accepted. Giving limited to the greater Kansas City, MO area. No support for faith-based organizations.
Application information: Application form required.
Initial approach: Letter
Copies of proposal: 10
Deadline(s): Oct. 1
Board meeting date(s): 6 times per year
Officers: Susann Riffe, Pres.; Teresa L. Clark, V.P.; Jody Carroll, Secy.; Ken Lawrence, Treas.
Board Members: Paul Becker; Don Davis; Bob Frazier; David Ross; Lucina Noches Talbert.
EIN: 440369625

3612
O' Brate Foundation
P.O. Box 1271
Garden City, KS   67846-1271   (620) 408-8381
Contact: Deanna Kuder
E-mail: deanna@obratefoundation.org; Main URL: http://www.obratefoundation.org

Donors: Cecil O'Brate; American Warrior; Palmer American Holding.
Foundation type: Independent foundation.

Financial data (yr. ended 12/31/13): Assets, $183,600 (M); gifts received, $476,867; expenditures, $290,429; qualifying distributions, $286,919; giving activities include $189,739 for grants to individuals.
Fields of interest: Education; Youth development.
Type of support: Student aid.
Limitations: Applications accepted. Giving primarily in KS.
Application information: Application form required.
  Initial approach: E-mail
  Deadline(s): None
Trustees: Edward Condon; Joseph L. Erskin; Cecil O'Brate; Jennifer O'Brate; Mark O'Brate; Thomas M. Willis.
EIN: 461631934

3613
Tom W. and Jeanne H. Olofson Foundation

501 Kansas Ave.
Kansas City, KS 66105-1309
Contact: Tom Olofson

Established in 2001 in Missouri.
Donors: Tom W. Olofson; Jeanne H. Olofson.
Foundation type: Independent foundation.
Financial data (yr. ended 12/31/13): Assets, $2,980,510 (M); gifts received, $250,000; expenditures, $333,674; qualifying distributions, $331,463; giving activities include $330,000 for 2 grants (high: $180,000; low: $150,000).
Purpose and activities: Giving primarily for higher education, and to a Presbyterian church.
Fields of interest: Philanthropy; Religion.
Limitations: Applications not accepted. Giving primarily in KS, MO and PA. No grants to individuals.
Application information: Unsolicited requests for funds not accepted.
Officers: Tom W. Olofson, Chair.; Jeanne H. Olofson, Pres.
Directors: Christopher E. Olofson; Scott W. Olofson.
EIN: 431945167

3614
Payless Shoesource Foundation

(formerly Collective Brands Foundation)
3231 S.E. 6th St.
Topeka, KS 66607-2207
Main URL: http://www.paylesscorporate.com

Established in 1998 in Kansas.
Donors: Payless ShoeSource, Inc.; Collective Brands, Inc.
Foundation type: Company-sponsored foundation.
Financial data (yr. ended 02/01/14): Assets, $602,446 (M); gifts received, $266,000; expenditures, $387,099; qualifying distributions, $384,550; giving activities include $348,650 for 71 grants (high: $42,500; low: $50).
Purpose and activities: The foundation supports programs designed to address women's preventative health; promote children's physical activity and fitness; improve the lives of children and youth in need; preserve the environment; and support the footwear industry.
Fields of interest: Arts and culture; Education; Environment; Nonprofits; Health; Physical fitness; Business and industry; Human services; Child welfare; Children; Females.

Type of support: Continuing support; In-kind gifts; Annual campaigns; Capital campaigns; Capital and infrastructure; Program development; Scholarships; Sponsorships; Regranting.
Limitations: Applications accepted. Giving primarily in areas of company operations, with emphasis on Redlands, CA, Denver, CO, Topeka, the Kansas City metropolitan area, and Lawrence, KS, greater Boston and Lexington, MA, New York, NY, and Brookville, OH. No support for private charities or foundations, private schools, or religious or political organizations. No grants to individuals, or for capital campaigns, debt reduction, travel, or conferences.
Publications: Application guidelines.
Application information: Application form required.
  Initial approach: See website for application form
  Deadline(s): None
  Board meeting date(s): Quarterly
Officers and Directors: W. Paul Jones, Pres. and Director; Miguel R. Rivera, Sr., V.P. and Secy. and Director; Nicole Sloup, V.P. and Exec. Dir.; Cristi Allen, V.P.; Betty J. Click, V.P. and Director; Gary C. Madsen, Treas. and Director; Kaci Brady, Admin.; Virginia Peterson Carosso; Paul Fenaroli; Stephen J. Gish; Darrel J. Pavelka; Bruce Pettet; Douglas J. Treff.
EIN: 481196508

3615
Price Family Foundation

12721 Metcalf Ave., Ste. 200
Overland Park, KS 66213-2619

Established in 2001 in Kansas.
Donors: Steve Price Charitable Lead Trust; Steve Price; Kent Price.
Foundation type: Independent foundation.
Financial data (yr. ended 12/31/13): Assets, $2,008,580 (M); gifts received, $700,000; expenditures, $180,140; qualifying distributions, $161,642; giving activities include $161,642 for 3 grants (high: $158,542; low: $600).
Fields of interest: Judaism.
Type of support: General support.
Limitations: Applications not accepted. No grants to individuals.
Application information: Unsolicited requests for funds not accepted.
Trustees: Doug Price; Kent Price; Steve Price.
EIN: 436855563

3616
Sam Price Family Foundation

c/o Kimberly S. Zellmer
11150 Overbrook Rd., Ste. 350
Leawood, KS 66211-2298

Established in 2003 in Kansas.
Donors: Sam Price; Sam Price Charitable Lead Annuity Trust.
Foundation type: Independent foundation.
Financial data (yr. ended 12/31/14): Assets, $9,536,698 (M); gifts received, $622,559; expenditures, $437,491; qualifying distributions, $385,073; giving activities include $348,700 for 38 grants (high: $50,000; low: $2,000).
Purpose and activities: Giving primarily for health care, children, youth and social services, and Jewish organizations.

Fields of interest: Nonprofits; Health; Hospice care; Diseases and conditions; Judaism; Human services; Child welfare.
Type of support: Research; Research and evaluation; Regranting; General support.
Limitations: Applications not accepted. Giving primarily in CO, KS and MO. No grants to individuals.
Application information: Unsolicited requests for funds not accepted.
Trustees: Barry Price; Donna Price; Peggy Jo Price.
EIN: 300086435

3617
Rathert Foundation

P.O. Box 265
Smith Center, KS 66967-0265
Application address: c/o The Peoples Bank, 136 S. Main, Smith Center, KS 66967, tel.: (785) 282-6682

Foundation type: Independent foundation.
Financial data (yr. ended 04/30/13): Assets, $875,086 (M); expenditures, $353,268; qualifying distributions, $334,763; giving activities include $333,373 for 26 grants (high: $55,159; low: $150).
Purpose and activities: Giving primarily for disaster or medical hardship cases.
Fields of interest: Education; Health; Hospital care; Religion.
Limitations: Applications accepted. Giving primarily in Phillips and Smith counties, KS.
Application information: Application form required.
  Initial approach: Letter
  Deadline(s): May 1
Officer: Jolene Beckman, Secy.
Trustees: Lovelle Kirchhoff; Alice Rietzke; John Terrill; Donald Wiens.
EIN: 480963083

3618
Jane & Bernard Reeble Foundation

2045 Huntington Rd.
Emporia, KS 66801-5423   (609) 999-9999
Contact: Jane H. Reeble, Pres. and Secy.-Treas.

Established in 1992 in Kansas.
Donor: Bernard K. Reeble.
Foundation type: Independent foundation.
Financial data (yr. ended 06/30/13): Assets, $4,800,536 (M); expenditures, $222,015; qualifying distributions, $220,250; giving activities include $220,250 for grants.
Fields of interest: Vocational education; Higher education; Christianity; Human services.
Type of support: General support.
Limitations: Applications accepted. Giving primarily in Emporia, KS. No grants to individuals.
Application information: Application form required.
  Initial approach: Letter
  Deadline(s): None
Officer: Jane H. Reeble, Pres. and Secy.-Treas.
EIN: 481122830

3619
Ross Foundation

100 N. Broadway, Ste. 455
Wichita, KS 67202-2212   (316) 264-4981
Contact: Hal Ross, V.P.

Established in 1961 in Kansas.

Donor: G. Murray Ross†.
Foundation type: Independent foundation.
Financial data (yr. ended 12/31/13): Assets, $5,631,532 (M); expenditures, $283,436; qualifying distributions, $233,459; giving activities include $186,431 for 28 grants (high: $58,000; low: $500).
Purpose and activities: Support primarily for cultural organizations, including the fine arts, a historical organization, and museums; support also for youth and science and technology.
Fields of interest: Arts and culture; Museums; Historic preservation; Education; Science; Technology; Child welfare.
Type of support: Capital and infrastructure; Equipment; Professorships; Scholarships; Individual development.
Limitations: Applications accepted. Giving primarily in KS.
Application information:
  Initial approach: Proposal
  Copies of proposal: 1
  Deadline(s): None
  Board meeting date(s): Early Mar., June, Sept., and Dec.
Officers: Hal Ross, V.P.; Susan Ross Sheets, Secy.-Treas.
Director: William M. Sheets.
Number of staff: 1 full-time professional.
EIN: 486125814

3620
David and Mary P. Rush Educational Trust
c/o Dennis Bieker
P.O. Box 579
Hays, KS   67601-0579   (785) 625-3537

Established in 1993 in Kansas.
Foundation type: Independent foundation.
Financial data (yr. ended 01/31/15): Assets, $5,729,654; expenditures, $391,662; qualifying distributions, $271,515.
Purpose and activities: Scholarships only available to graduates of Graham County High School in Kansas, who are full-time students, have involvement in high school and community activities, maintain a 2.0 GPA or better, and are in financial need.
Fields of interest: Higher education.
Type of support: Scholarships.
Limitations: Applications accepted. Giving limited to residents of Graham County, KS.
Application information: Application form required.
  Initial approach: Request application form
  Deadline(s): May 1
Trustees: Dennis L. Bieker; Keith Riley; Brad Trexler.
EIN: 486243254

3621
Nicolas M. Salgo Charitable Trust
c/o Heritage Group LC
7309 E. 21 St. N., Ste. 120
Wichita, KS   67206-1178

Established in 1982 in Kansas.
Donor: Nicolas M. Salgo.
Foundation type: Independent foundation.
Financial data (yr. ended 11/30/13): Assets, $202,152 (M); expenditures, $205,271; qualifying distributions, $202,323; giving activities include $200,000 for 1 grant.

Fields of interest: Arts and culture; Education; Health; Community and economic development; Catholicism.
Type of support: General support; Scholarships.
Limitations: Applications not accepted. Giving primarily in NJ and NY. No grants to individuals.
Application information: Contributes only to pre-selected organizations.
Trustee: Miklos P. Salgo.
EIN: 486250539

3622
Robert E. and Patricia Schmidt Foundation
P.O. Box 916
Hays, KS   67601-0916
Contact: Robert E. Schmidt, Treas.

Established in 1989 in Kansas.
Donors: Robert E. Schmidt; Patricia A. Schmidt.
Foundation type: Independent foundation.
Financial data (yr. ended 11/30/13): Assets, $11,731,740 (M); expenditures, $485,479; qualifying distributions, $359,964; giving activities include $359,964 for 45 grants (high: $50,000; low: $1,000).
Fields of interest: Arts councils; Museums; Elementary and secondary education; Cerebral palsy; Christianity.
Type of support: Capital campaigns; Endowments; Scholarships; Research.
Limitations: Applications accepted. Giving primarily in KS. No grants to individuals.
Publications: Annual report; Financial statement.
Application information: Application form required.
  Initial approach: Proposal
  Copies of proposal: 1
  Deadline(s): None
  Final notification: Within 1 month
Officer and Trustees: Robert E. Schmidt, Treas. and Trustee; Ann E. Barry; Joseph W. Jeter; Anthony A. Schmidt; Patricia A. Schmidt; Sue K. Schmidt.
Number of staff: None.
EIN: 481077463

3623
Scott Community Foundation
303 Court St., 3rd Fl.
Scott City, KS   67871   (620) 872-3790
Contact: Ryan Roberts, Exec. Dir.
E-mail: ryan@scottcf.org; Additional e-mail: jennifer@scottcf.org; Main URL: http://www.scottcf.org
Facebook: https://www.facebook.com/scottcommunityfoundation

Established in 1987 in Kansas.
Foundation type: Community foundation.
Financial data (yr. ended 12/31/13): Assets, $6,415,046 (M); gifts received, $880,512; expenditures, $709,928; giving activities include $364,861 for 10+ grants (high: $138,371), and $55,000 for 3 grants to individuals.
Purpose and activities: The foundation is dedicated to preserving local wealth so the communities in and around Scott County will forever remain attractive places to live, work, and raise a family.
Fields of interest: Education; Health; Community and economic development; Sports and recreation.
Limitations: Applications accepted. Giving primarily in Scott County, KS and the surrounding area. No grants to individuals (except for scholarships), or for

debt reduction, capital campaigns, or endowment programs.
Application information: Applications for grants from the General Fund and non-restricted component funds are available in the Fall of each year; visit foundation web site for updates. Application form required.
Officers and Trustees: Lori Krause, Chair. and Trustee; Clint Pearson, Vice-Chair. and Trustee; Nancy Hess, Secy. and Trustee; Dorothy Hutchins, Treas. and Trustee; Ryan Roberts, Exec. Dir.; Natalie Armantrout; Josh Bailey; Hugh Binns; Nancy Hess; Kelly Hoeme; Cody Palen; Myles Vulgamore.
EIN: 480995697

3624
The Arthur E. & Cornelia C. Scroggins Foundation, Inc.
P.O. Box 1112
Dodge City, KS   67801-1112   (620) 662-5319

Established in 1983 in Kansas.
Foundation type: Independent foundation.
Financial data (yr. ended 12/31/13): Assets, $5,525,996 (M); expenditures, $253,973; qualifying distributions, $187,016; giving activities include $177,400 for 19 grants (high: $87,000; low: $1,000).
Purpose and activities: Giving for children's hospitals and services, human services, and education.
Fields of interest: Education; Graduate and professional education; Health; Nursing care; Diseases and conditions; Human services; Child welfare.
Type of support: Scholarships.
Limitations: Applications accepted. Giving primarily within Ford and Gray counties, KS. No support for veterans', labor, fraternal, or athletic organizations (except for specific projects that benefit the broad community). No grants to individuals, or for capital campaigns or fundraising events.
Application information: Application form required.
  Initial approach: Completed application form
  Deadline(s): Dec. 31
Officers: George Voss, Pres.; Mitchell Counce, V.P.; Gaylene Friesen, Secy.; Stanley D. Simpson, Treas. and Mgr.
Directors: Roderic Simpson; Marilynne VenJohn; Fidelity State Bank and Trust Co.
Number of staff: 1 part-time professional.
EIN: 480945437

3625
The Ken and Jan Shannon Family Foundation
P.O. Box 3903
Wichita, KS   67201-3903

Donor: Kenneth F. Shannon.
Foundation type: Independent foundation.
Financial data (yr. ended 06/30/14): Assets, $140,419 (M); gifts received, $450,000; expenditures, $390,565; qualifying distributions, $390,500; giving activities include $390,500 for 12 grants (high: $225,000; low: $1,000).
Fields of interest: Nonprofits; Maternal and perinatal health; Christianity; Human services; Child welfare; International relations.
Type of support: Regranting.

Limitations: Applications not accepted. Giving primarily in Colorado Springs, CO and Wichita, KS. No grants to individuals.
Application Information: Unsolicited requests for funds not accepted.
Officers and Directors: Janet A. Shannon, Pres. and Director; Ken Shannon, Secy.-Treas. and Director; John Melhorn; Julie E. Melhorn; David J. Shannon; Kirsten Shannon.
EIN: 200438918

3626
James E. and Maude Sheetz Charitable Trust
P.O. Box 5049
Topeka, KS 66605-0049

Foundation type: Independent foundation.
Financial data (yr. ended 12/31/13): Assets, $3,285,786 (M); expenditures, $237,106; qualifying distributions, $233,728; giving activities include $208,062 for 2 grants (high: $104,031; low: $104,031).
Fields of interest: Education; Catholicism.
Limitations: Applications not accepted.
Application Information: Unsolicited requests for funds not accepted.
Trustee: Corefirst Bank & Trust.
EIN: 376454300

3627
Smoot Charitable Foundation
P.O. Box 678
Salina, KS 67402-0678
Contact: Robert W. Weber MD, Pres.

Foundation type: Independent foundation.
Financial data (yr. ended 06/30/14): Assets, $10,964,829 (M); expenditures, $574,770; qualifying distributions, $435,284; giving activities include $414,284 for 40 grants (high: $147,784; low: $1,000).
Fields of interest: Arts and culture; Higher education; Nonprofits; Human services; Child welfare.
Type of support: Regranting.
Limitations: Applications accepted. Giving limited to Saline County, KS. No grants to individuals.
Application Information: Application form required.
 Initial approach: Letter
 Deadline(s): None
Officers: Robert W. Weber, MD, Pres.; George W. Yarnevich, V.P.; Janice L. Doherty, Secy.; Tom A. Williamson, Treas.
EIN: 480851141

3628
South Central Community Foundation
114 W. 5th St.
P.O. Box 8624
Pratt, KS 67124 (620) 672-7929
Contact: Bekki Pribil, Exec. Dir.
FAX: (620) 672-7669;
E-mail: sccf@southcentralcommunityfoundation.com; Additional e-mail: ed@sccfks.org; Main URL: http://sccfks.org
Facebook: https://www.facebook.com/SouthCentralCommunityFoundation
Google Plus: https://plus.google.com/103991227431030153147/posts?fww=1

Twitter: http://twitter.com/sccfks
YouTube: http://www.youtube.com/user/SCCFKS?feature=mhee

Established in 1994 in Kansas.
Foundation type: Community foundation.
Financial data (yr. ended 12/31/13): Assets, $13,796,446 (M); gifts received, $414,773; expenditures, $482,476; giving activities include $286,826 for 14+ grants (high: $25,000).
Purpose and activities: The foundation seeks to receive and accept property to be administered exclusively for charitable purposes, primarily in, or for the benefit of, south central Kansas.
Fields of interest: Arts and culture; Education; Higher education; Public libraries; Community and economic development; Christianity; Human services; Youth development; Senior services.
Type of support: Capital campaigns; Endowments.
Limitations: Applications accepted. Giving limited to south central KS.
Publications: Application guidelines; Annual report; Informational brochure; Newsletter.
Application Information: Visit foundation web site for application form and additional information. Application form required.
 Initial approach: Submit application form and attachments
 Copies of proposal: 1
 Deadline(s): Aug. 31
 Board meeting date(s): Quarterly
Officers and Directors: Fred Dierksen, Chair. and Director; Kristi Molz, Vice-Chair. and Director; Nancy Kerr, Secy. and Director; Monica Hayse, Treas. and Director; Bekki Pribil, Exec. Dir.; Gail Boisseau, At-Large; Shawn Collins; Debbie Estes; Kelly Estes; Joyce Frazier; Mary Gordon; Kathy Hurst; Candy Murphy; Tom Murphy; Stan Robertson.
Number of staff: 1 full-time professional.
EIN: 481156704

3629
Herman, Esther & Henry Stallman Foundation
P.O. Box 913
Hutchinson, KS 67504-0913 (620) 560-6141
Contact: Karen S. Smart
Application address: 1 N. Main, Hutchinson, KS 67504-0913

Established in 2005 in Kansas.
Foundation type: Independent foundation.
Financial data (yr. ended 12/31/13): Assets, $3,564,341 (L); expenditures, $194,515; qualifying distributions, $164,775; giving activities include $163,800 for 27 grants (high: $13,500; low: $1,000).
Fields of interest: Museums; Diseases and conditions; Interfaith; Human services; Youth development.
Limitations: Applications accepted. Giving primarily in Reno County, KS. No grants to individuals.
Application Information:
 Initial approach: Proposal
 Deadline(s): None
Trustee: First National Bank.
EIN: 203625633

3630
The Stolzer Family Foundation
5124 Founders Way
Manhattan, KS 66503-8692

Established in 1994 in Kansas.
Donor: L.W. Stolzer.
Foundation type: Independent foundation.
Financial data (yr. ended 12/31/13): Assets, $6,043,764 (M); expenditures, $349,710; qualifying distributions, $343,570; giving activities include $343,570 for 9+ grants (high: $216,955).
Fields of interest: Higher education; Foundations; Religion; Human services.
Limitations: Applications not accepted. Giving primarily in CA and KS. No grants to individuals.
Application Information: Unsolicited requests for funds not accepted.
Officers: L.W. Stolzer, Pres.; Ellen Stolzer Bolen, Secy.; Mary Kevin Stolzer Giller, Treas.
EIN: 481158885

3631
The Swearingen Foundation
c/o Donald Friend II
4200 Somerset Dr., Ste. 208
Prairie Village, KS 66208

Established in 1996 in Illinois.
Donor: John E. Swearingen.
Foundation type: Independent foundation.
Financial data (yr. ended 12/31/14): Assets, $1,108,032; expenditures, $237,086; qualifying distributions, $220,000.
Fields of interest: Arts and culture; Museums; Education; Higher education; Nonprofits; Hospital care; Libraries; Religion; Protestantism; Human services; Youth services.
Type of support: Regranting.
Limitations: Applications not accepted. No grants to individuals.
Application Information: Contributes only to pre-selected organizations.
Directors: Matthew C. Arnold, Sr.; F. Gary Pfleeger; Linda Swearingen-Arnold; Marcia Swearingen-Pfleeger.
EIN: 367164493

3632
Daniel J. Taylor Family Charitable Foundation
1938 N. Woodlawn, Ste. 400
Wichita, KS 67208-1875

Established in 1998 in Kansas.
Donor: Daniel J. Taylor, Sr.
Foundation type: Independent foundation.
Financial data (yr. ended 12/31/13): Assets, $1,188,300 (M); expenditures, $333,155; qualifying distributions, $329,275; giving activities include $329,275 for 49 grants (high: $60,000; low: $500).
Purpose and activities: Giving primarily for education, Christian and Protestant churches and organizations, and children, youth and social services.
Fields of interest: Education; Diseases and conditions; Christianity; Protestantism; Human services; Child welfare; Youth organizing.
Type of support: Endowments.

Limitations: Applications not accepted. Giving primarily in KS, with emphasis on Wichita. No grants to individuals.
Application information: Contributes only to pre-selected organizations.
Officers and Directors: Daniel J. Taylor, Sr., Pres. and Director; Kathleen Baer Taylor, Secy.-Treas. and Director; Daniel J. Taylor, Jr.
EIN: 481203060

3633
Testamentary Trust of Nellie F. Estes

c/o V.E. Chance
P.O. Box 255
Fowler, KS 67844-0255

Foundation type: Independent foundation.
Financial data (yr. ended 12/31/13): Assets, $2,255,319 (M); expenditures, $167,709; qualifying distributions, $131,086; giving activities include $125,876 for 10 grants (high: $22,888; low: $11,440).
Fields of interest: Diseases and conditions; Religion; Human services.
Limitations: Applications not accepted. Giving primarily in KS.
Application information: Unsolicited requests for funds not accepted.
Trustee: V.E. Chance.
EIN: 486275829

3634
Thomas County Community Foundation

350 S. Range, Ste. 14
Colby, KS 67701 (785) 460-9152
Contact: Keesa Wright, Admin. Asst.
FAX: (785) 460-9153; E-mail: tccf@st-tel.net; Main URL: http://
www.thomascountycommunityfoundation.com
Facebook: https://www.facebook.com/pages/
Thomas-County-Community-Foundation/
121447101203969?ref=ts

Established in 2001 in Kansas.
Foundation type: Community foundation.
Financial data (yr. ended 12/31/12): Assets, $1,696,129 (M); gifts received, $454,892; expenditures, $236,901; giving activities include $168,838 for grants, and $6,644 for grants to individuals.
Purpose and activities: The foundation's mission is to endow funds to improve the quality of life for all citizens of Thomas County.
Fields of interest: Unknown or not classified.
Limitations: Applications accepted. Giving primarily in Thomas County, KS. No support for programs that promote specific religious beliefs. No grants to individuals, or for operating expenses, salaries, travel expenses.
Publications: Application guidelines.
Application information: Visit foundation web site for application form and guidelines. Application form required.
  Initial approach: Mail grant application packets to committee
  Copies of proposal: 2
  Deadline(s): Mar. 31, June 30, Sept. 30, and Dec. 31
  Final notification: 3-4 weeks
Officers and Directors: Jada Tubbs, Pres. and Director; Dr. Mark Wahlmeier, V.P. and Director;

Ranell Lunsway, Secy. and Director; Leland Wilson, Treas. and Director; Karla Haggard, Exec. Dir.; Mike Baughn; Corky Bellamy; Duane Cheney; Marla Crumrine; Quintin Flanagan; Nancy LePell; Judy McCarty; Jody Metcalf; Peggy Miller; Tammi Strutt.
EIN: 481241974

3635
The Trusler Foundation Inc.

P.O. Box 704
Emporia, KS 66801-0704
Application address: c/o Thomas D. Thomas, 1225 W. 6th Ave., Emporia, KS 66801-2576, tel.: (620) 342-7641

Established in 1957 in Kansas.
Foundation type: Independent foundation.
Financial data (yr. ended 12/31/13): Assets, $8,213,828 (M); expenditures, $474,083; qualifying distributions, $414,835; giving activities include $398,079 for 11 grants (high: $150,000; low: $2,050).
Fields of interest: Arts councils; Theater; Orchestral music; Elementary and secondary education; Higher education; Natural resources; Nonprofits; Community improvement; Camps; Human services; Senior services.
Type of support: Capital and infrastructure; Land acquisitions; Endowments; Regranting.
Limitations: Applications accepted. Giving primarily in Emporia, KS. No grants to individuals.
Application information:
  Initial approach: Proposal
  Deadline(s): None
Officers: Ken Buchele, Co-Pres.; J. Michael Turnbull, Co-Pres.; Mark Schreiber, V.P.; Thomas D. Thomas, Co-Secy.-Treas.; Shirley Antes, Co-Secy.; Jeff Debauge, Co-Treas.
Board Members: D.J. Glaser; Cynthia Kraft; Kay Lauer; Bob Symmonds.
Trustee: ESB Financial.
EIN: 486117374

3636
V & H Charitable Foundation

P.O. Box 26128
Overland Park, KS 66225-6128

Established in 1990 in Kansas.
Donors: Helen Regnier; Ranch Mart, Inc.
Foundation type: Independent foundation.
Financial data (yr. ended 03/31/13): Assets, $12,048,033 (M); expenditures, $291,578; qualifying distributions, $230,454; giving activities include $230,454 for grants.
Fields of interest: Education; Higher education.
Limitations: Applications not accepted. Giving primarily in KS and MO. No grants to individuals.
Application information: Contributes only to pre-selected organizations.
Trustees: Catherine M. Regnier; Robert B. Regnier; Victor A. Regnier.
EIN: 436378149

3637
Dwane L. and Velma Lunt Wallace Charitable Foundation

301 N. Main St., Ste. 600
Wichita, KS 67202-4806 (316) 263-8294
Contact: Robert M. Hughes, Tr.

Established in 1989 in Kansas.
Donors: Dwane L. Wallace†; Velma L. Wallace.
Foundation type: Independent foundation.
Financial data (yr. ended 12/31/13): Assets, $9,728,791 (M); expenditures, $445,186; qualifying distributions, $368,099; giving activities include $341,236 for 22 grants (high: $50,000; low: $5,000).
Purpose and activities: Giving primarily for health and human services, as well as to a children's home.
Fields of interest: Nonprofits; Diseases and conditions; Cancers; Interfaith; Human services; Child welfare; Shelter and residential care.
Type of support: Endowments; Regranting.
Limitations: Applications accepted. Giving primarily in the Wichita, KS, area. No grants to individuals.
Application information: Application form required.
  Initial approach: Proposal
  Copies of proposal: 2
  Deadline(s): None
Trustees: Jeffrey D. Arbuckle; Sarah W. Bracco; Robert M. Hughes; Karen W. Johnson; Linda Wallace Jones.
EIN: 481071478

3638
The Walsh Family Foundation

2421 W. 65th St.
Mission Hills, KS 66208-1926

Donors: Teresa K. Walsh; Thomas J. Walsh.
Foundation type: Independent foundation.
Financial data (yr. ended 12/31/13): Assets, $5,251,844 (M); expenditures, $384,846; qualifying distributions, $344,247; giving activities include $316,634 for 8 grants (high: $100,000; low: $9,834).
Fields of interest: Arts and culture; Education; Health.
Limitations: Applications not accepted. Giving primarily in MO.
Application information: Unsolicited requests for funds not accepted.
Officers and Directors: Teresa K. Walsh, Pres. and Director; Thomas J. Walsh, V.P. and Secy.-Treas. and Director; Hailee A. Bland-Walsh; Kelsey W. Perry; Spencer Walsh.
EIN: 263002122

3639
Thomas S. Watson Family Foundation

(formerly Thomas S. Watson Foundation)
c/o Assured Management Co.
1901 W. 47th Pl., Ste. 200
Westwood, KS 66205-1834 (913) 432-1020
Contact: Charles E. Rubin, Tr.

Donors: Linda T. Watson; Thomas S. Watson; Mastercard; Sprint.
Foundation type: Independent foundation.
Financial data (yr. ended 12/31/13): Assets, $51,398 (M); gifts received, $146,915; expenditures, $162,575; qualifying distributions, $160,975; giving activities include $159,375 for 82 grants (high: $25,000; low: $100).
Fields of interest: Education; Higher education; Nonprofits; Health; Specialty hospital care; Human services.
Type of support: General support; Continuing support; Annual campaigns; Capital campaigns;

Capital and infrastructure; Emergency funds; Regranting; Program development.
Limitations: Applications accepted. Giving primarily in KS and MO. No grants to individuals.
Publications: Annual report.
Application information: Application form required.
Initial approach: Letter
Copies of proposal: 1
Deadline(s): Nov. 1
Board meeting date(s): Mid-Dec. and as necessary
Trustees: Arnold H. Brown; Charles E. Rubin; Thomas S. Watson.
EIN: 431360667

3640
The Keith & Margie Weber Family Foundation
(formerly The Weber Family Foundation)
2001 Shawnee Mission Pkwy.
Shawnee Mission, KS 66205-2051

Established in 1998 in Missouri.
Donors: Keith Weber; Marjory Weber.
Foundation type: Independent foundation.
Financial data (yr. ended 12/31/13): Assets, $5,742,809 (M); expenditures, $260,415; qualifying distributions, $228,800; giving activities include $228,800 for 23 grants (high: $30,000; low: $1,000).
Fields of interest: Foundations; Health; Hospital care; American football; Human services.
Type of support: General support.
Limitations: Applications not accepted. Giving primarily in CA, CO, MO, and TX. No grants to individuals.
Application information: Contributes only to pre-selected organizations.
Officers: Marjory E. Weber, Pres.; Patricia C. Weber, V.P. and Secy.; Leslie L. Olrich, V.P. and Treas.
EIN: 481203265

3641
Weskan Charitable Foundation
P.O. Box 4
Lakin, KS 67860-0004

Established in 1996 in Kansas.
Donors: Don Nightingale; Ralph Reimer; Kearney County Gas Irrigators; Dave R. Unruh; Howard Reimer; Donovan Toews; Goodnews; Bear Berry; Nikkel Lee; Tema Foundation; Jerrell Nightingale; Rapid Span; Warren Eicher; Paul Estrada; Jack Garret; Don Hiebert; Elton Koehn; Kelly Koehn; Max Koehn; Manford Nichols; Kenneth Nightingale; Louis Penner; Dalys Thiessen; Bob Unruh; Curtis Unruh; Dave R. Unruh Trust; Eldon Schmidt; Plains State Bank.
Foundation type: Independent foundation.
Financial data (yr. ended 12/31/14): Assets, $244,523 (M); gifts received, $364,127; expenditures, $354,582; qualifying distributions,

$349,888; giving activities include $349,888 for 8 grants (high: $288,425; low: $475).
Fields of interest: Education; Christianity; International development.
International interests: Haiti.
Limitations: Applications not accepted. Giving primarily in KS, with some giving in Jacmel, Haiti. No grants to individuals.
Application information: Contributes only to pre-selected organizations.
Trustees: Don Nightingale; Ralph Reimer.
EIN: 481187938

3642
K. T. Wiedemann Foundation Inc.
P.O. Box 782499
Wichita, KS 67278-2499 (316) 650-5038
Contact: Douglas S. Pringle, Tr.

Established in 1959 in Kansas.
Donor: K.T. Wiedemann Trust.
Foundation type: Independent foundation.
Financial data (yr. ended 02/28/14): Assets, $13,185,988 (M); gifts received, $300; expenditures, $473,055; qualifying distributions, $368,416; giving activities include $337,616 for 14 grants (high: $183,900; low: $5,000).
Purpose and activities: Giving primarily for the arts, youth, families, at-risk children, the elderly, health, people who are mentally and physically challenged, and people who are low income. If an organization is religious or religious-affiliated, they should receive broad-based Christian support (Catholic and Protestant churches/organizations).
Fields of interest: Performing arts; Education; Health; Diseases and conditions; Protestantism; Child welfare.
Type of support: General support; Capital campaigns; Emergency funds; Program development.
Limitations: Applications accepted. Giving primarily in Butler, Chase, Cowley, Greenwood, Sedgwick and Sumner counties in KS. No support for churches or religious-affiliated organizations for direct religious activities or religious instruction; or for civic or trade associations, or veterans' organizations, fraternal societies or orders. No grants to individuals, or for endowment funds, scholarships, deficits, debt retirement, or national fundraising efforts. Conferences, seminars, media events, or workshops are not supported unless they are an integral part of a broader project.
Application information: The foundation does not provide explanation for the denial of a proposal. Application form required.
Initial approach: Proposal (not exceeding 2 pages); or contact foundation requesting application guidelines
Deadline(s): None
Board meeting date(s): Apr. 15, Aug. 15, and Dec. 15

Trustees: Lynne A. Hankins; Bruce A. Pringle; Douglas S. Pringle; Priscilla C. Pringle.
EIN: 486117541

3643
Mary Jo Williams Charitable Trust
P.O. Box 439
Garden City, KS 67846-0439
Application address: c/o Michael Collins, 607 N. 7th St., Garden City, KS 67846, tel.: (620) 276-3203

Established in 1988 in Kansas.
Foundation type: Independent foundation.
Financial data (yr. ended 12/31/13): Assets, $6,157,897 (M); expenditures, $337,752; qualifying distributions, $285,223; giving activities include $277,574 for 12 grants (high: $50,679; low: $2,500).
Purpose and activities: Giving primarily for the prevention of cruelty to children or animals.
Fields of interest: Higher education; Natural resources; Animal welfare; Nonprofits; Human services; Food aid; Child welfare.
Type of support: Capital campaigns; Equipment; Endowments; Regranting.
Limitations: Giving primarily in Garden City, KS. No support for the funding or promotion of athletics or athletic competition. No grants to individuals.
Application information:
Initial approach: Letter
Copies of proposal: 3
Deadline(s): None
Board meeting date(s): Quarterly
Trustees: Michael E. Collins; Leonard Rich; Jack Williamson.
EIN: 486276428

3644
Thomas & Sally Wood Family Foundation
c/o Thomas J. Wood III
2701 W. 69th St.
Mission Hills, KS 66208-2144

Established in 1993 in Kansas.
Donors: Thomas J. Wood, Jr.; Sally Kemper Wood; Thomas And Sally Wood Charitable Remainder Trust.
Foundation type: Independent foundation.
Financial data (yr. ended 12/31/13): Assets, $7,408,916 (M); gifts received, $2,871; expenditures, $303,948; qualifying distributions, $268,100; giving activities include $268,100 for 28 grants (high: $62,500; low: $1,000).
Purpose and activities: Support for scientific, artistic, religious and literary purposes.
Fields of interest: Arts and culture; Art museums; Health; Diseases and conditions.
Limitations: Applications not accepted. No grants to individuals.
Application information: Unsolicited requests for funds not accepted.
Trustees: Susan Wood Athens; Sharon Wood Orr; Sally Wood Shaffer; Thomas J. Wood III.
EIN: 436445255

KENTUCKY

3645
The Abercrombie Foundation
P.O. Box 68
Versailles, KY 40383-5472 8599834477

Established in 1988 in Texas.
Donor: Josephine E. Abercrombie.
Foundation type: Independent foundation.
Financial data (yr. ended 12/31/14): Assets, $5,320,782; expenditures, $212,788; qualifying distributions, $177,450.
Fields of interest: Education; Secondary education; Higher education; Medical education; Natural resources; Hospital care; Addiction services; Diseases and conditions; Child welfare.
Type of support: Research; General support; Capital and infrastructure; Research and evaluation; Regranting; Fundraising.
Limitations: Applications not accepted. Giving primarily in central KY and TX. No grants to individuals.
Publications: Annual report.
Application information: Unsolicited requests for funds not accepted.
Officers and Trustees: Josephine E. Abercrombie, Pres. and Trustee; John W. Backer, V.P.; Pam B. Kincaid.
Number of staff: 2 part-time support.
EIN: 760229183

3646
Barr Foundation, Inc.
9900 Corporate Campus Dr., Ste. 2100
Louisville, KY 40223-5010 (502) 326-5662

Established in 2000 in Kentucky.
Donors: Mary Louise Barr; Charles C. Barr; J. McFerran Barr II.
Foundation type: Independent foundation.
Financial data (yr. ended 12/31/14): Assets, $4,717,360; expenditures, $279,007; qualifying distributions, $252,115.
Fields of interest: Arts and culture; Museums; Education; Natural resources; Child welfare; Scouting programs.
Type of support: General support.
Limitations: Applications accepted. Giving primarily in KY.
Application information: Application form required.
　　Initial approach: Letter
　　Deadline(s): Dec. 1
Officers and Directors: J. McFerran Barr II, Chair. and Director; Charles C. Barr, Secy. and Director; Mary Louise Barr, Treas. and Director.
EIN: 611361347

3647
William E. Barth Foundation
325 W. Main St., Ste. 2000
Louisville, KY 40202 (502) 584-1108
Contact: Allen P. Dodd III, Pres.
FAX: (502) 587-7756;
E-mail: information@doddattorneys.net; Main URL: http://www.doddattorneys.com/CM/Custom/William-E-Barth-Foundation.asp

Established in 1994 in Kentucky.
Donors: Dorothy B. Jochell†; Louise B. Laffan†.
Foundation type: Independent foundation.
Financial data (yr. ended 12/31/13): Assets, $2,123,521 (M); expenditures, $228,814; qualifying distributions, $169,200; giving activities include $169,200 for 52 grants (high: $20,000; low: $1,000).
Purpose and activities: Giving to organizations that seek to improve the quality of life in the city of Louisville and in Jefferson County, KY.
Fields of interest: Arts and culture; Education; Human services.
Type of support: General support; Matching grants; Annual campaigns; Capital campaigns; Capital and infrastructure; Land acquisitions; Program development.
Limitations: Applications accepted. Giving limited to Jefferson County, KY, with priority given to the city of Louisville. No support for political organizations. No grants to individuals.
Publications: Application guidelines; Grants list; Program policy statement.
Application information: See web site for application policies and guidelines, as well as for downloadable application form. Application form required.
　　Initial approach: Completed application form preferred
　　Copies of proposal: 1
　　Deadline(s): May 31 (subject to discretion to extend)
　　Board meeting date(s): May
　　Final notification: 6 to 8 months
Officers: Allen P. Dodd III, Pres.; Elizabeth Dodd Lococo, Secy.; Allen Mckee Dodd, Treas.
Directors: Jacob Crouse; Mary S. Sachs.
EIN: 621328750

3648
Alex Boone Charitable Trust
376 S. Broadway
Lexington, KY 40508-2512

Established in 1998 in Kentucky.
Donor: Alex Boone.
Foundation type: Independent foundation.
Financial data (yr. ended 12/31/13): Assets, $3,569,326 (M); expenditures, $216,702; qualifying distributions, $200,950; giving activities include $200,000 for 14 grants (high: $150,000; low: $500).
Fields of interest: Arts and culture; Education; Human services.
Limitations: Applications not accepted. Giving primarily in KY. No grants to individuals.
Application information: Contributes only to pre-selected organizations.
Trustee: Alex Boone.
EIN: 616253244

3649
Hilary Boone Foundation, Inc.
(formerly Boone Family Foundation, Inc.)
376 S. Broadway
Lexington, KY 40508-9508

Established in 1997 in Kentucky.
Donors: Hilary J. Boone, Jr.; Hilary J. Boone Jr. Charitable Remainder Unitrust.
Foundation type: Independent foundation.

Financial data (yr. ended 12/31/13): Assets, $8,657,356 (M); gifts received, $1,373,575; expenditures, $266,023; qualifying distributions, $228,271; giving activities include $226,500 for 48 grants (high: $55,000; low: $500).
Fields of interest: Arts and culture; Higher education; Graduate and professional education; Environment; Foundations; Engineering; Equestrianism; Racquet sports; Human services.
Type of support: General support.
Limitations: Applications not accepted. Giving primarily in KY; with some giving in TN. No grants to individuals.
Application information: Unsolicited requests for funds not accepted.
Officers: Samuel A.B. Boone, Pres. and Treas.; Alyce B. Hoskins, V.P.; Dowell Hoskins.
EIN: 611249175

3650
Larry R. Coffey Charitable Trust
504 Bedfordshire Rd.
Louisville, KY 40222-5509 (502) 426-2751
Contact: Joan B. Coffey

Established in 1989 in Kentucky.
Donor: Larry R. Coffey.
Foundation type: Independent foundation.
Financial data (yr. ended 12/31/14): Assets, $9,126,952 (M); gifts received, $100,000; expenditures, $412,854; qualifying distributions, $409,572; giving activities include $385,900 for 33 grants (high: $81,500; low: $500).
Fields of interest: Higher education; Christianity; Protestantism; Christians; Protestants.
Type of support: Capital campaigns.
Limitations: Applications accepted. Giving primarily in FL and Louisville, KY and VA. No grants to individuals.
Application information: Application form required.
　　Initial approach: Proposal
　　Deadline(s): None
Trustee: Larry R. Coffey.
EIN: 616168546

3651
Margaret E. Dickins Foundation Inc.
7504 Chestnutt Hill
Prospect, KY 40059-9484
Application address: c/o, Laura Jenkins, 1010 Monterey Blvd. N.E., St. Petersburg, FL 33704, tel.: (727) 824-5609

Established in 2001 in Florida.
Donor: Margaret E. Dickins†.
Foundation type: Independent foundation.
Financial data (yr. ended 12/31/13): Assets, $7,894,708 (M); expenditures, $435,009; qualifying distributions, $364,109; giving activities include $317,980 for 35 grants (high: $50,000; low: $1,000).
Fields of interest: Arts and culture; Museums; Animal welfare; Diseases and conditions; Human services.
Type of support: Research; Research and evaluation.
Limitations: Applications accepted. Giving primarily in FL, with emphasis on St. Petersburg. No grants to individuals.
Application information: Application form required.

Initial approach: Letter
Deadline(s): None
Trustees: Jim Decker; Joyce Decker.
Directors: Margaret Decker; Norma Hanley; Laura Jenkins.
EIN: 651082411

3652

Margaret E. & Stephen E. Diebold Charitable Foundation, Inc.
210 Pepperbush Rd.
Louisville, KY 40207-5714

Established in 2000 in Kentucky.
Donors: Stephen E. Diebold; Margaret E. Diebold.
Foundation type: Independent foundation.
Financial data (yr. ended 06/30/13): Assets, $1,763,589 (M); gifts received, $250,000; expenditures, $213,616; qualifying distributions, $198,991; giving activities include $197,600 for 35 grants (high: $13,000; low: $500).
Fields of interest: Catholicism; Human services.
Limitations: Applications not accepted. No grants to individuals.
Application information: Unsolicited requests for funds not accepted.
Officers: Stephen E. Diebold, Pres.; Margaret E. Diebold, Secy.
Director: Paul G. Franz.
EIN: 912107857

3653

Dunbar Foundation, Inc.
36 Arrowhead Rd.
Louisville, KY 40207-1537
Application address: c/o Laura Dunbar, P.O. Box 7668, Louisville, KY 40257, tel.: (502) 896-0403

Donor: Wallace H. Dunbar.
Foundation type: Independent foundation.
Financial data (yr. ended 04/30/15): Assets, $4,269,122 (M); expenditures, $216,291; qualifying distributions, $189,215; giving activities include $185,000 for 27 grants (high: $34,000; low: $400).
Fields of interest: Education; Higher education; Health; Religion.
Limitations: Applications accepted. Giving primarily in KY. No grants to individuals.
Application information:
Initial approach: Proposal
Deadline(s): None
Officers: Laura J. Dunbar, Pres.; Thomas E. Dunbar, V.P.; Sarah Dunbar Parker, V.P.; Martha D. Hall, Secy.; Wallace H. Dunbar, Jr., Treas.
EIN: 616052957

3654

Irvin F. & Alice S. Etscorn Charitable Foundation
c/o Hilliard Lyons Trust Company
P.O. Box 32760
Louisville, KY 40232-2760 (502) 588-8623

Established in 1996 in Kentucky.
Donor: Alice S. Etscorn†.
Foundation type: Independent foundation.
Financial data (yr. ended 06/30/14): Assets, $8,283,430; gifts received, $17,000;

expenditures, $468,383; qualifying distributions, $437,000.
Purpose and activities: Giving to YMCAs, and for pediatrics, eye diseases, and Christian organizations.
Fields of interest: Higher education; Organ and tissue banks; Pediatrics; Eye diseases; Christianity; Human services.
Type of support: Capital campaigns; Matching grants; Capital and infrastructure; Equipment; Professorships; Fellowships; Scholarships.
Limitations: Applications accepted. Giving primarily in Louisville and Jefferson County, KY. No grants to individuals.
Application information: Application form required.
Initial approach: Letter
Copies of proposal: 1
Deadline(s): 2nd Thurs. in Nov.
Board meeting date(s): Nov.
Final notification: 4 weeks
Trustee: Hilliard Lyons Trust Co.
Number of staff: None.
EIN: 611314419

3655

Foundation for Appalachian Kentucky
(formerly Community Foundation of Hazard and Perry County)
P.O. Box 310
Chavies, KY 41727 (606) 439-1357
Contact: Gerry Roll, Exec. Dir.
E-mail: info@appalachianky.org; Main URL: http://www.appalachianky.org

Established in 2002 in Kentucky.
Foundation type: Community foundation.
Financial data (yr. ended 12/31/12): Assets, $5,798,773 (M); gifts received, $4,512,689; expenditures, $597,505; giving activities include $347,153 for grants.
Purpose and activities: To support collaborative work in the local community around a common vision that enhances the lives of all citizens and to create a permanent endowment to serve as a catalyst and resource to respond to changing community priorities.
Fields of interest: Arts and culture; Education; Environment; Health; Housing development; Sports and recreation.
Limitations: Giving primarily in Chavies, KY. No support for private foundations, national organizations, or religious organizations for religious purposes. No grants to individuals, or for endowments, debt retirement, substance abuse treatment programs.
Application information: Visit foundation web site for updates on application information.
Officers and Directors: Gerry Roll, Exec. Dir.; Robin Gabbard, Assoc. Exec. Dir.; Mack Baker; Wally Cornett; Bill Fields; Chris Gooch; Steve Jones; Deloris Justice; Danny Maggard; Frank Medaris, Jr.; Scott McReynolds; Hugh Mitchell; Dr. John Pray; Lynn Smith; Peggy Vires; Annie Williams.
EIN: 611329396

3656

The Gagarin Trust
105 Beechwold Pl.
Bardstown, KY 40004-2180
Contact: Kathleen Llewellyn, Tr.

Established in 1997 in Connecticut.
Donors: Andrew Gagarin; Jamie Gagarin.
Foundation type: Independent foundation.
Financial data (yr. ended 12/31/14): Assets, $2,021,952 (M); expenditures, $271,929; qualifying distributions, $250,961; giving activities include $241,966 for 1 grant.
Purpose and activities: Giving primarily for education, particularly international education.
Fields of interest: Higher education; International relations.
Type of support: General support; Public engagement and education.
Limitations: Applications not accepted. Giving primarily in CA and NY. No grants to individuals.
Application information: Contributes only to preselected organizations.
Trustees: Kathleen Llewellyn; Vincent McGee; Odile Segal; Nancy Lynn Wiltsek.
EIN: 066419374

3657

GB Foundation, Inc.
P.O. Box 1421
Somerset, KY 42501-1421 (606) 677-9164

Donor: Oasis Care Center.
Foundation type: Independent foundation.
Financial data (yr. ended 12/31/14): Assets, $0; gifts received, $2,000; expenditures, $162,704; qualifying distributions, $157,500.
Fields of interest: Health; Religion; Human services; Homeless people.
Limitations: Applications not accepted. Giving primarily in FL.
Application information: Unsolicited requests for funds not accepted.
Officer: Melvin Godby, Chair.
Directors: Lawrence J. Botzman; Janet Godby.
EIN: 271393433

3658

The GHH Charitable Foundation
113 W. Public Sq., Ste. 200
Glasgow, KY 42141-2438

Established in 2002 in Kentucky.
Donors: Gaunce Management Inc.; Wayne Gaunce.
Foundation type: Company-sponsored foundation.
Financial data (yr. ended 12/31/13): Assets, $948,473 (M); gifts received, $176,389; expenditures, $215,495; qualifying distributions, $213,200; giving activities include $213,200 for 16 grants (high: $45,000; low: $200).
Purpose and activities: The foundation supports hospices and organizations involved with theological education and Christianity.
Fields of interest: Graduate and professional education; Hospice care; Christianity; Theology.
Type of support: General support.
Limitations: Applications not accepted. No grants to individuals.
Application information: Unsolicited requests for funds not accepted.
Trustees: Chapatcha Gaunce; Wayne Gaunce; Nell Houchens; Jean Hunsaker.
EIN: 320048907

3659
Wood & Marie C. Hannah Foundation
c/o Stock Yards Bank & Trust Co.
P.O. Box 32890
Louisville, KY 40232-2890 (502) 625-2447
Contact: C. Mayfield

Established in 1977 in Kentucky.
Donors: Marie C. Hannah†; Wood Hannah†.
Foundation type: Independent foundation.
Financial data (yr. ended 07/31/13): Assets,
$4,009,603 (M); expenditures, $221,559;
qualifying distributions, $175,732; giving activities
include $164,071 for 19 grants (high: $25,000;
low: $250).
Purpose and activities: Giving primarily for
education, youth and family services, and to
Christian churches.
Fields of interest: Education; Higher education;
Hospice care; Christianity; Family services; Child
welfare.
Type of support: Capital campaigns; Capital and
infrastructure; Equipment; Scholarships.
Limitations: Applications accepted. Giving primarily
in Louisville, KY. No grants to individuals.
Publications: Annual report.
Application information: Application form required.
  Initial approach: Letter
  Copies of proposal: 1
  Deadline(s): Apr. 1 and Oct. 1
  Board meeting date(s): Apr. and Oct.
Officer: Wood Hannah III, Pres.
Directors: Catha Hannah; Judy H. Harris; Neil B.
Jesse; John Stough; Harry Troutman; Stephen T.
Wolford.
Number of staff: 1
EIN: 310914024

3660
John Burton Harter Foundation
295 N. Hubbards Ln., Ste. 302
Louisville, KY 40207-8205 5024006000

Established in 2003 in Kentucky.
Donor: John Burton Harter.
Foundation type: Independent foundation.
Financial data (yr. ended 12/31/14): Assets,
$4,125,961; expenditures, $274,429; qualifying
distributions, $258,333.
Fields of interest: Arts and culture; Art museums;
Education; Human services; LGBTQ people.
Type of support: General support.
Limitations: Applications not accepted. Giving
primarily in CA, LA and New York, NY. No grants to
individuals.
Application information: Unsolicited requests for
funds not accepted.
Trustee: First Kentucky Trust.
Directors: Michel G. Delhaise; George Jordan; John
J. Sullivan; Alan J. Williams.
EIN: 306048115

3661
Morris & Dorothy Haskins Foundation Inc.
1767 Chestnut St.
Bowling Green, KY 42101-3503

Established in 1994 in Kentucky.
Donors: Morris E. Haskins†; Paul D. Wedge, Jr.
Foundation type: Independent foundation.

Financial data (yr. ended 12/31/13): Assets,
$10,476,714 (M); expenditures, $592,715;
qualifying distributions, $455,905; giving activities
include $358,680 for 25 grants (high: $131,200;
low: $250).
Purpose and activities: Giving primarily for
education and to Presbyterian churches and
organizations; some funding also for the arts.
Fields of interest: Arts and culture; Education;
Higher education; Protestantism.
Limitations: Applications not accepted. Giving
primarily in KY and WV. No grants to individuals.
Application information: Contributes only to
pre-selected organizations.
Officer: Paul D. Wedge, Jr., Pres.
Directors: Carol H. Wedge; Jody H. Wedge; Julia
Wedge; Paul D. Wedge III.
EIN: 611267321

3662
Hayswood Foundation, Inc.
1 W. McDonald Pkwy., Ste. 3A
Maysville, KY 41056-1138 (606) 563-9333
Contact: Lloyd Schlitz, Exec. Dir.
FAX: (606) 563-9444;
E-mail: hfound@maysvilleky.net; Main URL: http://
www.hayswood.org
Grants List: http://www.hayswood.org/Recent%
20Grant%20Recipients.html

Foundation type: Independent foundation.
Financial data (yr. ended 12/31/13): Assets,
$9,142,289 (M); gifts received, $13,202;
expenditures, $405,055; qualifying distributions,
$337,510; giving activities include $298,612 for 20
+ grants.
Purpose and activities: Giving to support mental
and physical health, and education.
Fields of interest: Education; Health; Mental health
care.
Type of support: General support; Matching grants;
Capital campaigns; Capital and infrastructure;
Equipment; Program development; Scholarships;
Student aid.
Limitations: Applications accepted. Giving limited to
Bracken, Fleming, Lewis, Mason, and Robertson
Counties in KY, and Adams and Brown Counties in
OH. No support for religious or political
organizations. No grants to individuals (except for
scholarships) or for endowments.
Publications: Application guidelines.
Application information: Application forms are
available starting June 1 of each year, and are
available on foundation web site. Application form
required.
  Initial approach: See web site
  Copies of proposal: 1
  Deadline(s): Aug. 1
  Board meeting date(s): Jan., May, Aug. and Oct.
  Final notification: Oct.
Officers and Directors: Dave Wallingford, Pres. and
Director; Ronald Rice, V.P. and Director; Dr. Robert
Ross, Secy. and Director; Douglas Hendrickson,
Treas. and Director; Lloyd Schlitz, Exec. Dir.; Michael
Clarice; Dave Clarke; Romey Griffey; Dr. John
McDowell; William McNeill; John Parker; Dr. Robert
Ross; Kirk Tolle; Ann Tomlin; Debra Wallingford;
Sally Walton.
Number of staff: 1 part-time professional.
EIN: 237345996

3663
Elsa M. Heisel Sule Charitable Trust
250 Grandview Dr.
Fort Mitchell, KY 41017-5667

Donor: Elsa Suleelsa Marie Heise†.
Foundation type: Independent foundation.
Financial data (yr. ended 12/31/12): Assets,
$12,996,703 (M); gifts received, $7,188,420;
expenditures, $299,728; qualifying distributions,
$160,150; giving activities include $160,150 for
grants.
Fields of interest: Arts and culture; Education;
Human services.
Limitations: Applications not accepted. Giving
primarily in KY and OH.
Application information: Unsolicited requests for
funds not accepted.
Trustee: Ruth Klette.
EIN: 207277661

3664
Michael E. Horn Family Foundation Inc.
P.O. Box 1944
Owensboro, KY 42302-1944 (270) 313-0245
Contact: Kathryn Crowe, Dir.
Main URL: http://www.hornfamilyfoundation.org
Facebook: https://www.facebook.com/
hornfamilyfoundation

Established in 2007 in Pennsylvania.
Foundation type: Independent foundation.
Financial data (yr. ended 12/31/13): Assets,
$8,735,276 (M); expenditures, $528,312;
qualifying distributions, $447,993; giving activities
include $280,000 for 30 grants (high: $55,000;
low: $500), and $50,500 for 51 grants to
individuals (high: $1,000; low: $500).
Fields of interest: Elementary and secondary
education; Higher education; Christianity;
Protestantism; Catholicism; Youth services.
Type of support: Student aid.
Limitations: Applications accepted. Giving limited to
the Owensboro and Davies county and surrounding
areas in KY.
Publications: Application guidelines.
Application information: Complete application
guidelines and procedures available on foundation
web site. Application form required.
  Initial approach: Scholarship and grant
    application available to download on
    foundation web site
  Deadline(s): Mar. 1st for scholarship
    applications; Oct. 15th for grants
Directors: Kathryn R. Crowe; Michael Andrew Horn;
Michael E. Horn; Paula K. Horn; Kayla Horn Walker.
EIN: 261375584

3665
The Ruel and Nell Houchens Charitable
Foundation
113 W. Public Sq., Ste. 200
Glasgow, KY 42141-2438

Established in 2006 in Kentucky.
Donor: Ruel Houchens.
Foundation type: Independent foundation.
Financial data (yr. ended 12/31/13): Assets,
$288,110 (M); expenditures, $403,047; qualifying
distributions, $401,014; giving activities include

$401,014 for 4 grants (high: $330,000; low: $15,000).
Fields of interest: Education; Youth development.
Limitations: Applications not accepted. No grants to individuals.
Application information: Contributes only to pre-selected organizations.
Trustees: Patrick Gaunce; Nell Houchens.
EIN: 208075165

3666
Independence Foundation, Inc.
2425 Frederica St.
P.O. Box 988
Owensboro, KY   42302   (270) 686-1776

Donors: Independence Bank; Ernie Davis.
Foundation type: Company-sponsored foundation.
Financial data (yr. ended 12/31/13): Assets, $183,953 (M); gifts received, $493,247; expenditures, $424,474; qualifying distributions, $424,474; giving activities include $413,750 for 365 grants (high: $25,000; low: $40), and $10,724 for 6 grants to individuals (high: $3,900; low: $293).
Purpose and activities: The foundation supports service clubs and organizations involved with education, cancer, housing development, recreation, youth, and community development; provides relief grants to employees of Independence Bank; and awards college scholarships to high school seniors from a seven county area.
Fields of interest: Education; Community and economic development; Sports and recreation.
Type of support: General support; Grants to individuals; Equipment; Emergency funds; Program development; Scholarships; Sponsorships; Student aid.
Limitations: Applications accepted. Giving primarily in areas of company operations in KY, with emphasis on Daviess, Hancock, Henderson, McLean, McCracken, Warren, and Webster counties.
Application information: Application form required.
Initial approach: Letter
Deadline(s): 20th of each month for general funding
Officer: Cathy R. Switzer, Admin.
Directors: Christopher Reid; Marjorie A. Reid.
EIN: 261568393

3667
Brereton and Elizabeth Jones Charitable Family Foundation
P.O. Box 487
Midway, KY   40347-0487   (859) 873-7270

Established in 1999 in Kentucky.
Donor: Brereton C. Jones.
Foundation type: Independent foundation.
Financial data (yr. ended 12/31/14): Assets, $1,362,239; gifts received, $425,000; expenditures, $208,839; qualifying distributions, $207,700.
Fields of interest: Education; Foundations; Community health care; Protestantism.
Type of support: General support.
Limitations: Applications accepted. Giving primarily in KY. No grants to individuals.
Application information: Application form required.
Initial approach: Letter
Deadline(s): None

Trustees: Brereton C. Jones; Elizabeth L. Jones.
EIN: 611358458

3668
Keeneland Foundation, Inc.
4201 Versailles Rd.
P.O. Box 1690
Lexington, KY   40588-1690   (859) 288-4142
Contact: Sandy Chinn
FAX: (859) 255-2484;
E-mail: schinn@keeneland.com; Additional tel.: (859) 254-3412; Main URL: http://www.keeneland.com/about/keeneland-foundation

Established in 1999 in Kentucky.
Donors: Keeneland Association Inc.; Maker's Mark; Casner Family Fund.
Foundation type: Company-sponsored foundation.
Financial data (yr. ended 06/30/13): Assets, $181,736 (M); gifts received, $208,572; expenditures, $216,570; qualifying distributions, $213,739; giving activities include $202,000 for 10 grants (high: $175,000; low: $1,000).
Purpose and activities: The foundation supports organizations involved with arts and culture, education, health, human services, and community development. Special emphasis is directed toward programs designed to serve the equine industry, specifically in the areas of thoroughbred breeding and racing.
Fields of interest: Arts and culture; Education; Higher education; Veterinary medicine; Health; Community and economic development; Human services.
Type of support: General support; Capital campaigns; Capital and infrastructure; Equipment; Endowments; Program development; Scholarships; Research.
Limitations: Applications accepted. Giving primarily in central KY. No support for political organizations, primary or secondary schools, fraternal or veterans' organizations not of direct benefit to the entire community, religious organizations not of direct benefit to the entire community, or youth sports leagues. No grants to individuals, or for courtesy advertising, annual campaigns, general operating support for hospitals or patient care institutions, or tickets or sponsorships; no ticket or dining space contributions.
Publications: Application guidelines.
Application information: Application form required.
Initial approach: Download application form and mail or e-mail application form to foundation
Deadline(s): None, but applications are reviewed in Dec.
Board meeting date(s): Quarterly
Officers and Directors: L.L. Haggin III, Pres.; Nick Nicholson, V.P.; Vince Gabbert, Secy.; William Thomason, Treas.; William S. Farish; William M. Lear, Jr.
Number of staff: None.
EIN: 611358165

3669
Kentucky Foundation for Women, Inc.
1215 Heyburn Bldg.
332 W. Broadway
Louisville, KY   40202-2184   (502) 562-0045
FAX: (502) 561-0420; E-mail: team@kfw.org; Toll free tel.: (866) 654-7564; Main URL: http://www.kfw.org
Facebook: https://www.facebook.com/kentuckyfoundationforwomen
Google Plus: https://plus.google.com/116893371613490087266/about
Grants List: http://www.kfw.org/grants/grantees
YouTube: https://www.youtube.com/channel/UCbLnmDWlt8Oe8tEPSMo9wYg

Established in 1985 in Kentucky.
Donor: Sallie Bingham.
Foundation type: Independent foundation.
Financial data (yr. ended 06/30/13): Assets, $12,934,418 (M); gifts received, $10,522; expenditures, $637,884; qualifying distributions, $597,040; giving activities include $60,225 for 16 grants (high: $7,500; low: $500), $144,775 for 54 grants to individuals (high: $7,444; low: $1,000), and $74,434 for 1 foundation-administered program.
Purpose and activities: Support for feminist artists and arts-related organizations, with the goal of bringing about social change through the arts. Giving to 1) feminist visual art: painting, sculpture, puppetry, crafts, photography exhibits, multi-media, etc.; 2) feminist performing arts: dance, theater, music, including performers, directors, producers, composers, lyricists, choreographers, and conductors; 3) feminist writers and playwrights; and 4) feminist video/filmmakers.
Fields of interest: Arts and culture; Visual arts; Painting; Photography; Performing arts; Choreography; Theater; Composition; Literature and writing; Social sciences; Film and video; Women's rights; Females.
Type of support: Grants to individuals.
Limitations: Giving limited to persons who live or work in KY, or to persons and organizations whose projects directly affect the lives of women in KY. No grants for scholarships or for any expenses associated with work towards a college degree; or for endowments, capital campaigns or facilities renovation.
Publications: Application guidelines; Annual report; Grants list; Newsletter.
Application information: Applicants are requested to write a 4-page proposal addressing the relationship between their art activities and social change, and/or the direct impact of their art-making upon KY women and girls. Application form required.
Initial approach: Request application form by letter or telephone; also available on foundation web site
Copies of proposal: 4
Deadline(s): For the Artist Enrichment Program, typically the first Friday of September; for the Art Meets Activism Program, typically the first Friday of March
Final notification: Nov. 30 for Artist Enrichment program; May 30 for Art Meets Activism program
Officers and Board Members: Gail Martin, Chair and Director; Katie Ward, Treas. and Director; Judith Jennings, Dir.; Gabriela Alcalde; Sallie Bingham; Leah Ottersbach; Cynthia Resor; Mae Suramek.

Number of staff: 2 full-time professional; 1 part-time professional; 1 full-time support; 1 part-time support.
EIN: 611070429

3670
B. J. Killian Foundation
c/o Stock Yards Bank & Trust
P.O. Box 34290
Louisville, KY 40232-4290 5026251076

Established in 1983 in Kentucky.
Donor: Nancy F. Wilson Charitable Lead Trust.
Foundation type: Independent foundation.
Financial data (yr. ended 12/31/14): Assets, $4,219,964; expenditures, $241,778; qualifying distributions, $214,403.
Purpose and activities: Giving for the betterment of non-profit corporations who have demonstrated the highest degree of effectiveness and the efficient use of resources for the benefit of those who are in need.
Fields of interest: Arts and culture; Christianity; Human services; Children and youth; Infants and toddlers; Children; Adolescents; Adults; Young adults; Females; Female children and youth; Female infants and toddlers; Female adults; Female young adults; Males; Male children and youth; Male infants and toddlers; Male adults; Male young adults; Single parents; People of African descent; Homeless people; Low-income and poor people; Victims of crime and abuse; Terminally ill people.
Type of support: General support.
Limitations: Applications not accepted. Giving primarily in KY. No support to individuals.
Application information: Contributes only to pre-selected organizations.
  Board meeting date(s): Mar. and Oct.
Trustees: Charles F. Killian; Mildred A. Killian; James T. Toler; Nancy F. Wilson; David Yewell.
EIN: 311077598

3671
W. Frank Lebus Jr. Charitable Trust
P.O. Box 157
Paris, KY 40362

Donor: W. Frank Lebus, Jr.†.
Foundation type: Independent foundation.
Financial data (yr. ended 12/31/14): Assets, $7,664,905 (M); expenditures, $409,875; qualifying distributions, $356,087; giving activities include $328,836 for 12 grants (high: $164,418; low: $3,288).
Fields of interest: Education; Religion; Human services.
Limitations: Applications not accepted. Giving primarily in KY.
Application information: Unsolicited requests for funds not accepted.
Trustee: Kentucky Bank.
EIN: 206658002

3672
Longest Foundation
c/o Stock Yards Bank & Trust Co.
P.O. Box 3429
Louisville, KY 40232-4290

Established in 2005 in Kentucky.

Donor: Mary B. Longest.
Foundation type: Independent foundation.
Financial data (yr. ended 12/31/14): Assets, $4,987,941; expenditures, $313,438; qualifying distributions, $260,637.
Fields of interest: Education; Christianity.
Limitations: Applications not accepted. Giving primarily in KY, NJ and OH. No grants to individuals.
Application information: Contributes only to pre-selected organizations.
Trustees: Jackson I. Jones; Gerald A. Plappert, Jr.; Stock Yards Bank & Trust Co.; Wyatt, Tarrant & Combs, LLP.
EIN: 320157651

3673
Mackin Foundation, Inc.
545 S. Third St., Ste. 310
Louisville, KY 40202-1838

Established in 1999 in Kentucky.
Donors: Interlock Industries, Inc.; Virginia Mackin.
Foundation type: Company-sponsored foundation.
Financial data (yr. ended 12/31/13): Assets, $6,076,989 (M); gifts received, $103,000; expenditures, $438,971; qualifying distributions, $367,500; giving activities include $367,500 for 9 grants (high: $200,000; low: $5,000).
Purpose and activities: The foundation supports organizations involved with arts and culture, higher education, health, human services, economic development, civic affairs, and religion.
Fields of interest: Education; Diseases and conditions; Human services.
Type of support: General support; Capital and infrastructure; Scholarships.
Limitations: Applications accepted. Giving primarily in KY.
Publications: Application guidelines.
Application information:
  Initial approach: Proposal
  Deadline(s): None
Officers: Jay Lawrence Mackin, Pres.; Craig L. Mackin, Treas.
Directors: Jeffrey L. Mackin; Kimberly Ann Mackin; Michael J. Mackin.
EIN: 352069109

3674
Magee Christian Education Foundation
344 Reed Ln.
Simpsonville, KY 40067-7407
Contact: Jean Hawxhurst, Secy.-Treas.
E-mail: mageefoundation@gmail.com

Established in 1938 in Kentucky.
Donors: Ella G. Magee†; Magee Carpet Co.
Foundation type: Independent foundation.
Financial data (yr. ended 12/31/13): Assets, $4,792,430 (M); expenditures, $251,635; qualifying distributions, $236,498; giving activities include $193,000 for 20 grants (high: $15,000; low: $5,000).
Purpose and activities: Support exclusively for scholarship programs aimed at students preparing for full-time church-related vocations at accredited theological schools or seminaries.
Fields of interest: Graduate and professional education; Adult education; Continuing education; Theology.
Type of support: Internships; Scholarships.

Limitations: Applications accepted. Giving on a national and international basis. No grants to individuals, or for capital or building funds.
Publications: Application guidelines; Annual report (including application guidelines).
Application information: Application form required.
  Initial approach: Letter or e-mail requesting application
  Copies of proposal: 1
  Board meeting date(s): Nov. 1
Officers and Directors: Glen S. Bagby, Pres. and Director; Otis W. Erisman, V.P. and Director; Jean Hawxhurst, Secy.-Treas.; James Magee, Pres. Emeritus and Director; P. Jeffrey Hill; Justin Hummel; William R. Jennings; Robert H. Spain.
Number of staff: 1 part-time professional.
EIN: 616034760

3675
Marksbury Family Foundation, Inc.
2433 Olde Bridge Ln.
Lexington, KY 40513-9740

Donors: Davis L. Marksbury, Jr.; Davis L. Marksbury; Exstream, Inc.; Marksbury Gifting Trust.
Foundation type: Independent foundation.
Financial data (yr. ended 12/31/13): Assets, $10,364,593 (M); gifts received, $2,311,404; expenditures, $245,695; qualifying distributions, $242,352; giving activities include $235,388 for 4 grants (high: $200,000; low: $1,000).
Fields of interest: Higher education.
Limitations: Applications not accepted. Giving primarily in Lexington, KY.
Application information: Contributes only to pre-selected organizations.
Officers: Davis L. Marksbury, Jr., Chair. and Exec. Dir.; Beverly E. Marksbury, Secy.-Treas.
Directors: Davis L. Marksbury III; Logan Renee Marksbury.
EIN: 264737208

3676
Frances Masser Charitable Trust
909 Liliy Creek Rd., Ste. 101
Louisville, KY 40243

Donor: Frances Masser†.
Foundation type: Independent foundation.
Financial data (yr. ended 12/31/13): Assets, $9,358,259 (M); expenditures, $490,848; qualifying distributions, $393,682; giving activities include $393,682 for 7 grants (high: $78,736; low: $47,242).
Fields of interest: Education; Domesticated animals; Human services.
Limitations: Applications not accepted.
Application information: Unsolicited requests for funds not accepted.
Trustee: T. Craig Wilson.
EIN: 276548145

3677
Jessie Barker McKellar Charitable Foundation
4969 U.S. Hwy. 42, Ste. 2000
Louisville, KY 40222-6384 5022127800
Application address: Douglas H. McKellar, Jr., 26325 Isabella Ave., Carmel, CA 93923, tel.: (502) 212-7800

Established in 1997 in Kentucky.
Foundation type: Independent foundation.
Financial data (yr. ended 12/31/14): Assets, $7,160,083; expenditures, $364,512; qualifying distributions, $312,940.
Purpose and activities: Giving primarily for health organizations, including a foundation for children's diabetes; funding also for other children and youth services, and to an Episcopal church.
Fields of interest: University education; Nonprofits; Diseases and conditions; Diabetes; Episcopalianism and Anglicanism; Lutheranism; Child welfare.
Type of support: Regranting.
Limitations: Applications accepted. Giving primarily in CA and KY.
Application information: Application form required.
  Initial approach: Letter
  Deadline(s): None
Trustee: Glenview Trust Co.
EIN: 626323409

3678
MGM Charitable/Scholarship Foundation
2116 Broadway
Paducah, KY 42001-7110 (270) 443-4500

Established in 2000 in Kentucky.
Donor: Laxmaiah Manchikanti, MD.
Foundation type: Independent foundation.
Financial data (yr. ended 11/30/13): Assets, $226,604 (M); gifts received, $249,905; expenditures, $241,511; qualifying distributions, $215,135; giving activities include $195,500 for 28 grants (high: $164,000; low: $500).
Purpose and activities: Scholarship awards for post-secondary education for students from McCracken County, Kentucky, priority given to students seeking admittance to institutions outside the state of Kentucky.
Fields of interest: Higher education.
Type of support: Student aid.
Limitations: Applications accepted. Giving limited to residents of McCracken County, KY.
Application information: Application form required.
  Initial approach: Completed application form
Trustees: Laxmaiah Manchikanti, MD; Murali Manohar Manchikanti, MD; Ram Mohan Manchikanti, MD.
EIN: 616264013

3679
Morris Family Foundation
6302 Crest Creek Ct.
Louisville, KY 40241-5801

Donors: John Richard Morris; John Ryan Morris; Glendolyn M. Morris; John Morris.
Foundation type: Independent foundation.
Financial data (yr. ended 12/31/13): Assets, $8,715,259 (M); expenditures, $429,012; qualifying distributions, $344,263; giving activities include $344,263 for 43 grants (high: $45,000; low: $50).
Fields of interest: Education; Christianity; Human services; Child welfare.
Limitations: Applications not accepted. Giving in the U.S., with emphasis on KY. No grants to individuals.
Application information: Unsolicited requests for funds not accepted.

Officer: John R. Morris, Exec. Dir.
EIN: 237125352

3680
The Mulhollem Cravens Foundation
c/o Paul B. Mulhollem, Jr.
P.O. Box 192
Carlisle, KY 40311-0192

Established in 2005 in Illinois.
Donors: Valerie K. Cravens; Paul B. Mulhollem, Jr.
Foundation type: Independent foundation.
Financial data (yr. ended 12/31/13): Assets, $1,756,565 (M); gifts received, $180,916; expenditures, $253,183; qualifying distributions, $240,025; giving activities include $240,000 for 10 grants (high: $50,000; low: $10,000).
Fields of interest: Museums; University education; Animal welfare; Philanthropy; Nonprofits.
Type of support: Regranting.
Limitations: Applications not accepted. No grants to individuals.
Application information: Unsolicited requests for funds not accepted.
Directors: Sylvia J. Cravens; Valerie K. Cravens; Paul B. Mulhollem, Jr.
EIN: 203835578

3681
E. E. Murry Family Foundation
620 E. Euclid Ave., Ste. 202
Lexington, KY 40502-6429

Established in 1986 in Pennsylvania.
Donor: Emanuel E. Murry.
Foundation type: Independent foundation.
Financial data (yr. ended 12/31/13): Assets, $7,181,124 (M); gifts received, $548,560; expenditures, $307,536; qualifying distributions, $272,500; giving activities include $272,500 for 9 grants (high: $240,000; low: $500).
Fields of interest: Health; Human services.
Type of support: Annual campaigns; Capital campaigns; Capital and infrastructure.
Limitations: Applications not accepted. Giving primarily in CA and PA. No grants to individuals.
Application information: Contributes only to pre-selected organizations.
Trustees: Emanuel E. Murry; Wesley E. Murry.
EIN: 231948416

3682
Namaste Foundation
901 Squire Hill Ct.
Crescent Springs, KY 41017-1336 (859) 391-8187
Contact: Judith L. Cunningham, Tr.

Established in 2006 in Kentucky.
Donor: Rubye A. Cunningham Charitable Lead Annuity Trust.
Foundation type: Independent foundation.
Financial data (yr. ended 12/31/13): Assets, $363,361 (M); gifts received, $205,710; expenditures, $200,994; qualifying distributions, $200,000; giving activities include $200,000 for 5 grants (high: $50,000; low: $25,000).
Fields of interest: University education; Adult education; Specialty hospital care; Pediatrics;

Protestantism; Human services; Food banks; Child welfare.
Limitations: Applications accepted. Giving primarily in AZ, KY, NH and OH.
Application information: Application form required.
  Initial approach: Letter
  Deadline(s): None
Trustees: Judith L. Cunningham; Janet C. Spadora.
EIN: 616320802

3683
Ogden College Foundation
c/o Daryl Greattinger Regent
1894 N. Main St.
Monticello, KY 42633-2048
Application address: Leigh Jones, P.O. Box 3350, Bowling Green, KY 42102-3350, tel.: (606) 348-9329

Donor: Guy Thomas†.
Foundation type: Independent foundation.
Financial data (yr. ended 06/30/13): Assets, $4,554,241 (M); expenditures, $198,169; qualifying distributions, $154,000; giving activities include $154,000 for grants.
Purpose and activities: Scholarship awards to students residing in Kentucky and attending Ogden College of Western Kentucky University; some giving also for professorships.
Fields of interest: Education; Higher education.
Type of support: Professorships; Fellowships; Student aid.
Limitations: Applications accepted. Giving limited to KY.
Publications: Informational brochure (including application guidelines).
Application information: Application form required.
  Initial approach: Contact foundation for application form
  Deadline(s): Feb 1
Directors: David Hartman; Leigh Smith Jones; Herbert Smith, Jr.
Number of staff: 1 part-time professional; 1 part-time support.
EIN: 237078715

3684
Opera House Fund, Inc.
c/o Doug Dean
106 W. Vine St., Ste. 600
Lexington, KY 40507-1679

Established in 1983 in Kentucky.
Donor: William T. Young, Jr.
Foundation type: Independent foundation.
Financial data (yr. ended 06/30/14): Assets, $7,930,277 (M); gifts received, $6,700; expenditures, $458,529; qualifying distributions, $410,980; giving activities include $404,875 for 13 + grants (high: $76,498).
Purpose and activities: The fund supports performing arts groups that use the Lexington Opera House.
Fields of interest: Arts education; Performing arts; Dance; Ballet; Theater; Music.
Limitations: Applications not accepted. Giving limited to Lexington, KY. No grants to individuals.
Application information: Contributes only to pre-selected organizations.
Officers and Directors: William T. Young, Jr., Pres. and Director; Linda Carey, V.P. and Director; Doug

Dean, Secy.-Treas. and Director; W. James Host; Bob Warren; Christopher Young.
EIN: 510180177

3685
C. F. Pollard Foundation Inc.
6009 Brownsboro Park Blvd., Ste. G
Louisville, KY   40207   (502) 228-1426
Contact: Lisa A. Kaster, Secy.

Established in 1993 in Kentucky.
Donor: Carl F. Pollard.
Foundation type: Independent foundation.
Financial data (yr. ended 12/31/13): Assets, $4,507,077 (M); expenditures, $430,268; qualifying distributions, $415,050; giving activities include $410,050 for 19 grants (high: $250,000; low: $1,000).
Fields of interest: Museums; Education; Libraries; Community and economic development; Equestrianism.
Limitations: Applications accepted. Giving primarily in KY. No grants to individuals.
Application information: Application form required.
   Initial approach: Letter
   Deadline(s): None
Officers: Carl F. Pollard, Pres.; Stuart B. Pollard, V.P.; Lisa A. Kaster, Secy.
Director: Susan P. Beebe.
EIN: 611246295

3686
Price Foundation Inc.
3514 Hedgewick Pl.
Louisville, KY   40245-8497   (502) 245-1343

Established in 2005 in Kentucky.
Donors: Charles E. Price; Charah Inc.
Foundation type: Independent foundation.
Financial data (yr. ended 12/31/13): Assets, $6,773 (M); gifts received, $329,000; expenditures, $323,883; qualifying distributions, $323,271; giving activities include $323,271 for 16 grants (high: $72,000; low: $283).
Fields of interest: Religion; Human services.
Limitations: Applications accepted. Giving primarily in FL and KY.
Application information:
   Initial approach: Proposal
   Deadline(s): None
Officers: Charles E. Price, Pres.; Janet Price, V.P.; Sarah Price, Secy.; Sarah Atwood, Treas.
EIN: 203012911

3687
Public Life Foundation of Owensboro
(formerly The Community Life Foundation of Owensboro, KY)
401 Frederica St., Bldg. B, Ste. 203
Owensboro, KY   42301   (270) 685-2652
FAX: (270) 685-6074; Main URL: http://www.plfo.org

Established in 1995 in Kentucky.
Donors: John S. Hager; Frankie Hager; Larry Hager Jr.; Marjorie Hager.
Foundation type: Operating foundation.
Financial data (yr. ended 12/31/14): Assets, $8,302,666; gifts received, $9,700; expenditures, $644,359; qualifying distributions, $566,801.

Purpose and activities: The foundation will support two broad categories of projects: (a) the exploration of the relationship of values and public life in the Owensboro, Kentucky area, and (b) education, especially for at-risk children and their parents. Proposals may be either research-oriented, with preference in the research area given to projects with the potential for improving the quality of public life in the Owensboro, Kentucky area.
Fields of interest: Education; Community and economic development; Human services.
Type of support: Endowments; Program development; Research; Technical assistance.
Limitations: Applications not accepted. Giving primarily in KY.
Publications: Annual report.
Application information: Unsolicited requests for funds not accepted.
Officers and Directors: Sarah Hager Wood, Chair. and Director; Bruce William Hager, Vice-Chair. and Director; Rodney Berry, Pres.; Kathy Strobel, Secy.; Susan Hager Alford, Treas. and Director; John Stewart Hager, Jr.; William G. Speciale.
Number of staff: 1 full-time professional; 1 full-time support.
EIN: 616232654

3688
Reed Foundation
c/o David W. Reed
P.O. Box 67
Gilbertsville, KY   42044-0067

Established in 1990 in Kentucky.
Donor: David W. Reed.
Foundation type: Independent foundation.
Financial data (yr. ended 12/31/13): Assets, $5,242,708 (M); expenditures, $395,676; qualifying distributions, $377,355; giving activities include $377,355 for 27 grants (high: $100,000; low: $1,000).
Purpose and activities: Giving primarily for education, health care, and human services.
Fields of interest: Education; Higher education; Health; Hospital care; Human services.
Type of support: General support; Capital and infrastructure; Endowments.
Limitations: Applications not accepted. Giving primarily in KY. No grants to individuals.
Application information: Contributes only to pre-selected organizations.
Trustee: David W. Reed.
EIN: 611189284

3689
Kenneth H. & Sarah M. Renau Foundation, Inc.
c/o John R. Sheryak
6450 Dutchmans Pkwy.
Louisville, KY   40205

Foundation type: Independent foundation.
Financial data (yr. ended 12/31/13): Assets, $1,608,384 (M); expenditures, $327,380; qualifying distributions, $299,169; giving activities include $292,500 for 16 grants (high: $187,500; low: $2,000).
Fields of interest: Domesticated animals; Housing development; Human services.
Limitations: Applications not accepted. Giving primarily in KY.

Application information: Unsolicited requests for funds not accepted.
Directors: Bobbie Scofield; Cherie Suchy; John Sheryak.
EIN: 611563465

3690
Louis T. Roth Foundation
1113 Red Fox Rd.
Louisville, KY   40205-1903

Established in 1964 in Kentucky.
Donors: Louis T. Roth; Lee Benovitz; Evan Roth; Lindsay Roth.
Foundation type: Independent foundation.
Financial data (yr. ended 04/30/13): Assets, $6,093,361 (M); gifts received, $40,365; expenditures, $290,534; qualifying distributions, $253,267; giving activities include $245,906 for 69 grants (high: $75,000; low: $70).
Purpose and activities: Giving primarily for Jewish agencies and temples.
Fields of interest: Arts and culture; Education; Nonprofits; Judaism; Human services.
Type of support: Regranting.
Limitations: Applications not accepted. Giving primarily in Louisville, KY. No grants to individuals.
Application information: Contributes only to pre-selected organizations.
Officers: Bruce J. Roth, Pres.; David M. Roth, V.P.
EIN: 610624305

3691
Robert W. Rounsavall, Jr. Family Foundation Inc.
c/o Libby Case
P.O. Box 19799
Louisville, KY   40259

Established in 2004 in Kentucky.
Donor: Robert W. Rounsavall, Jr. Trust.
Foundation type: Independent foundation.
Financial data (yr. ended 12/31/14): Assets, $7,049,218 (M); expenditures, $374,432; qualifying distributions, $346,557; giving activities include $324,114 for 32 grants (high: $71,119; low: $10,000).
Fields of interest: Arts and culture; Specialty hospital care; Diseases and conditions; Children.
Type of support: Research; Research and evaluation.
Limitations: Applications not accepted. Giving primarily in Louisville, KY. No grants to individuals.
Application information: Unsolicited requests for funds not accepted.
Officers and Directors: Robert W. Rounsavall, Pres. and Director; G. Hunt Rounsavall, Secy. and Director; Gretchen R. Clark, Treas. and Director; Libby Case, Exec. Dir.
EIN: 200991327

3692
Rouse Family Foundation, Inc.
2201 Regency Rd., Ste. 602
Lexington, KY   40503-2342

Established in 2007 in Kentucky.
Donor: Barbara H. Rouse†.
Foundation type: Independent foundation.

Financial data (yr. ended 12/31/13): Assets, $2,010,853 (M); expenditures, $284,479; qualifying distributions, $270,000; giving activities include $270,000 for 1 grant.

Purpose and activities: Giving primarily to a Christian foundation.

Fields of interest: Nonprofits.

Type of support: Regranting.

Limitations: Applications not accepted. Giving primarily in Lexington, KY. No grants to individuals.

Application information: Contributes only to pre-selected organizations.

Officers: William Rouse III, Pres.; Robert W. Rouse, V.P.; Hunter R. Kessinger, Secy.

EIN: 208796783

3693
Shapira Foundation, Inc.
4500 Bowling Blvd., Ste. 300
Louisville, KY   40207-5147

Established in 1945 in Kentucky.

Donor: Heaven Hill Distilleries, Inc.

Foundation type: Independent foundation.

Financial data (yr. ended 07/31/13): Assets, $1,569,623 (M); gifts received, $100,000; expenditures, $183,283; qualifying distributions, $177,090; giving activities include $177,090 for 13 grants (high: $100,000; low: $40).

Fields of interest: Health; Diseases and conditions; Judaism.

Type of support: General support.

Limitations: Applications not accepted. Giving primarily in Louisville, KY. No grants to individuals.

Application information: Contributes only to pre-selected organizations.

Officers: Anne E. Shapira, V.P.; Max L. Shapira, Secy.-Treas.

EIN: 610601759

3694
Arthur K. Smith Family Foundation, Inc.
6344 Limewood Circle Rd.
Louisville, KY   40222-6151

Established in 2006 in Kentucky.

Donor: Marlene Marie Smith Bajandas.

Foundation type: Independent foundation.

Financial data (yr. ended 05/31/13): Assets, $3,566,252 (M); expenditures, $188,886; qualifying distributions, $168,720; giving activities include $165,240 for 42 grants (high: $12,000; low: $500).

Fields of interest: Arts and culture; Education.

Limitations: Applications not accepted. Giving primarily in KY. No grants to individuals.

Application information: Contributes only to pre-selected organizations.

Officers: Marlene Marie Smith Bajandas, Pres.; John Bajandas, Secy.-Treas.

Directors: Laura D. Bajandas; Robert A. Kohn; Bruce J. Roth.

EIN: 203867228

3695
William Guy Spriggs Charitable Trust
P.O. Box 1360
Ashland, KY   41105-1360
Application Address: c/o William Guy Spriggs, 2747 Greenup Ave., Ashland, KY 41101

Donor: William Guy Spriggs.

Foundation type: Independent foundation.

Financial data (yr. ended 12/31/13): Assets, $0 (M); gifts received, $80,033; expenditures, $247,059; qualifying distributions, $208,751; giving activities include $208,751 for 1+ grant.

Purpose and activities: Giving primarily for children, youth and social services, as well as to Baptist and United Methodist churches.

Fields of interest: Baptist; Presbyterianism; Human services; Child welfare; Adult and child mentoring.

Application information:
Initial approach: Proposal
Deadline(s): None

Trustee: William Guy Spriggs.

EIN: 311730773

3696
Paula M. Steiner Family Foundation Inc.
865 Rosewood Dr.
Villa Hills, KY   41017-1333

Established in 2002 in Kentucky.

Donor: Paula M. Steiner.

Foundation type: Independent foundation.

Financial data (yr. ended 12/31/13): Assets, $2,994,543 (M); expenditures, $241,302; qualifying distributions, $209,000; giving activities include $209,000 for 14 grants (high: $28,000; low: $6,000).

Fields of interest: Arts and culture; Education; Christianity; Human services.

Limitations: Applications not accepted. Giving primarily in IL, MO and OH. No grants to individuals.

Application information: Contributes only to pre-selected organizations.

Officers and Directors: Paula M. Steiner, Pres. and Director; Judith A. Mroz, Secy. and Director; Michael E. Steiner, Treas. and Director; Karen Mroz-Bremner; John D. Mroz; David A. Steiner; Deborah Stroh.

EIN: 371452090

3697
Stock Yards Bank Foundation Inc.
P.O. Box 34290
Louisville, KY   40232-4290

Donor: Stock Yards Bank & Trust Co.

Foundation type: Company-sponsored foundation.

Financial data (yr. ended 12/31/14): Assets, $318,666; expenditures, $210,020; qualifying distributions, $208,700.

Purpose and activities: The foundation supports organizations involved with arts and culture, education, health, and human services.

Fields of interest: Arts and culture; Education; Higher education; Health; Hospital care; Human services; Child welfare.

Type of support: Annual campaigns; Capital campaigns; Endowments; Sponsorships.

Limitations: Applications not accepted.

Application information: Unsolicited requests for funds not accepted.

Officers: David P. Heintzman, Pres.; Nancy B. Davis, Secy.-Treas.

Director: Kathy C. Thompson.

EIN: 611380342

3698
Mary L. Stockdell-Joseph J. Leary Trust
P.O. Box 309
Frankfort, KY   40602-0309

Donor: Mary L. Stockdell†.

Foundation type: Independent foundation.

Financial data (yr. ended 12/31/14): Assets, $3,654,521; expenditures, $176,610; qualifying distributions, $164,211.

Fields of interest: Education; Christianity; Human services; Seniors.

Limitations: Applications not accepted. Giving primarily in KY.

Application information: Unsolicited requests for funds not accepted.

Trustee: Farmers Bank Capital Trust.

EIN: 456597246

3699
The Sutherland Foundation, Inc.
710 W. Main St., 3rd Fl.
Louisville, KY   40202-2698

Established in 1989 in Kentucky.

Donor: Laura Lee Lyons Brown.

Foundation type: Independent foundation.

Financial data (yr. ended 03/31/13): Assets, $13,927,552 (M); expenditures, $494,185; qualifying distributions, $385,057; giving activities include $236,647 for 17 grants (high: $66,182; low: $4).

Fields of interest: Arts and culture; Museums; Education; Environment; Human services.

Type of support: General support; Continuing support; Annual campaigns; Capital campaigns; Capital and infrastructure; Land acquisitions; Endowments; Program development.

Limitations: Applications not accepted. Giving primarily in the greater Louisville, KY, area. No grants to individuals.

Application information: Contributes only to pre-selected organizations.

Officers and Directors: Garvin Deters, Chair. and Director; Laura Lee Gasits, Secy. and Director; Del Hayunga, Treas. and Director; Laura Lee Lyons Brown; Sarah P. Ashworth; Polk Deters; George Gastis; Eugenia Potter.

EIN: 616175862

3700
Taylor Family Foundation Inc.
12011 Hunting Crest Dr.
Prospect, KY   40059
Application address: The Glenview Trust Co., Attn.: Emily Ledford Lawrence, 4060 U.S. Hwy. 42, Ste. 2000, Louisville, KY 40222, tel.: (502) 212-7834

Established in 2004 in Kentucky.

Foundation type: Independent foundation.

Financial data (yr. ended 12/31/13): Assets, $2,268,016 (M); expenditures, $161,419; qualifying distributions, $148,682; giving activities include $148,000 for 16 grants (high: $50,000; low: $1,000).

Purpose and activities: Giving primarily for the benefit of children, the environment and health.

Fields of interest: Natural resources; Health; Human services; Family services; Child welfare.

Limitations: Applications accepted. Giving primarily in IN and KY. No grants to individuals.
Application information:
Initial approach: Proposal
Deadline(s): None
Officers: Leslie D. Taylor, Pres. and Treas.; Victoria D. Buster, V.P. and Director; Karen Hill, Secy. and Director.
Number of staff: None.
EIN: 201952426

3701
Trager Family Foundation Inc.
601 W. Market St.
Louisville, KY   40202-2745

Established in 1998 in Kentucky.
Donors: Bernard M. Trager; Steven E. Trager.
Foundation type: Independent foundation.
Financial data (yr. ended 12/31/14): Assets, $9,964,993 (M); gifts received, $1,688,496; expenditures, $409,395; qualifying distributions, $339,556; giving activities include for 14 grants (high: $150,000; low: $289).
Fields of interest: Higher education; Nonprofits; Hospital care.
Type of support: General support; Regranting.
Limitations: Applications not accepted. No grants to individuals.
Application information: Contributes only to pre-selected organizations.
Officers: Steven E. Trager, Pres.; Jean S. Trager, Secy.-Treas.
Trustees: Shelley Trager Kusman; Amy Trager.
EIN: 611337078

3702
Trim Masters Charitable Foundation, Inc.
118 Wetherburn Ct.
Danville, KY   40422   (859) 612-2044
Contact: Dale Kihlman, Pres.

Donor: Trim Masters Inc.
Foundation type: Company-sponsored foundation.
Financial data (yr. ended 06/30/14): Assets, $1,525,045 (M); expenditures, $196,513; qualifying distributions, $196,412; giving activities include $182,450 for 52 grants (high: $10,000; low: $300).
Purpose and activities: The foundation supports festivals and parks and organizations involved with arts and culture, education, health, cancer, child welfare, agriculture, athletics, and human services.
Fields of interest: Arts and culture; Cultural awareness; Education; Elementary and secondary education; Higher education; Nonprofits; Health; Cancers; Public libraries; Child abuse; Agriculture; Parks; Festivals; Track and field; Human services; Child welfare; Scouting programs.
Type of support: Capital campaigns; Matching grants; General support; Capital and infrastructure; Equipment; Program development; Scholarships; Sponsorships; Regranting.
Limitations: Applications accepted. Giving primarily in KY. No grants to individuals.
Application information: Application form required.
Initial approach: Contact foundation for application
Deadline(s): None
Officers: Dale Kihlman, Pres.; Steve Hesselbrock, V.P.; Scarlett Ingram, Secy.-Treas.

Directors: Larry Carter; Mike French; Haley Milholland.
EIN: 611225606

3703
Marie R. & Ervine Turner Educational Foundation, Inc.
P.O. Box 620
Jackson, KY   41339-0620   (606) 666-9366
Contact: Lesley Warrix-Allen, Exec. Dir.

Established in 1999 in Kentucky.
Donor: John R. Turner†.
Foundation type: Operating foundation.
Financial data (yr. ended 12/31/13): Assets, $12,533,388 (M); expenditures, $295,552; qualifying distributions, $295,273; giving activities include $199,000 for 27 grants (high: $106,000; low: $500).
Purpose and activities: Giving to provide financial assistance to residents of Breathitt County, KY to further their education.
Fields of interest: Education.
Limitations: Applications accepted. Giving limited to residents of Breathitt County, KY.
Application information: Application form required.
Initial approach: Proposal
Deadline(s): None
Officers: Darrell A. Herald, Chair.; Lewis H. Warrix, Secy.; Joy Rae Shelton, Treas.; Lesley Warrix-Allen, Exec. Dir.
Directors: Leon L. Hollon; Donald Ison; Marcus Mullins.
EIN: 611333558

3704
USA Equestrian Trust Inc.
P.O. Box 13321
Lexington, KY   40583-3321
E-mail: grants@trusthorses.org; *Main URL:* http://trusthorses.org

Foundation type: Independent foundation.
Financial data (yr. ended 11/30/13): Assets, $4,844,549 (M); expenditures, $486,081; qualifying distributions, $404,298; giving activities include $307,709 for 20 grants (high: $50,000; low: $1,500).
Purpose and activities: The trust is dedicated to furthering the legacy of horses and equestrian sport.
Fields of interest: Education; Employment; Equestrianism.
Limitations: Applications accepted. Giving on a national basis with emphasis on KY.
Publications: Application guidelines.
Application information: Inquiries about grant applications or the grant process are handled only by e-mail. See trust web site for complete application guidelines. Application form required.
Initial approach: Application form on trust web site
Officers: Alan F. Balch, Pres.; Lisa Blackstone, V.P.; Georgie F. Green, Secy.; Guy R. Warner, Treas.
Directors: Linda A. Allen; Karl V. Hart; Kate Jackson; Marianne Ludwig; Fred K. Sarver.
EIN: 131764840

3705
Charles L. Weisberg Family Foundation
295 N. Hubbards Ln., Ste. 102
Louisville, KY   40207-8206

Established in 1990 in Kentucky.
Donors: Charles Weisberg; Ronald Weisberg; Frank Weisberg; Alan Weisberg.
Foundation type: Independent foundation.
Financial data (yr. ended 06/30/13): Assets, $982,679 (M); gifts received, $11,327; expenditures, $196,775; qualifying distributions, $195,036; giving activities include $190,529 for 131 grants (high: $95,000; low: $15).
Fields of interest: Education; Religion; Human services.
Limitations: Applications not accepted. Giving primarily in KY. No grants to individuals.
Application information: Unsolicited requests for funds not accepted.
Officers: Ronald Weisberg, Pres.; Frank Weisberg, V.P.; Alan Weisberg, Treas.
EIN: 611190609

3706
Welchwood Foundation Inc.
100 Riverside Plz., Ste. 1004
Covington, KY   41011-5717

Established in 2005 in Ohio.
Donor: Marjorie W. Drackett.
Foundation type: Independent foundation.
Financial data (yr. ended 06/30/14): Assets, $4,038,988 (M); expenditures, $189,415; qualifying distributions, $157,000; giving activities include $157,000 for 17 grants (high: $25,000; low: $2,000).
Fields of interest: Arts and culture; Education; Environment.
Limitations: Applications not accepted. Giving primarily in Cincinnati, OH. No grants to individuals.
Application information: Contributes only to pre-selected organizations.
Officers: Marjorie W. Drackett, Pres.; Anne D. Thomas, V.P.; Charles M. Drackett, Jr., Secy.-Treas.
EIN: 203199483

3707
The Woodlands Foundation, Inc.
c/o Daniel Huffman
P.O. Box 1212
Ashland, KY   41105-1212
Contact: Dan Huffman
Application address: 1562 Eagle Dr., Ashland, KY 41102-9666, tel.: (606) 928-9893

Foundation type: Independent foundation.
Financial data (yr. ended 09/30/13): Assets, $3,141,604 (M); expenditures, $395,990; qualifying distributions, $317,837; giving activities include $240,382 for 4 grants (high: $112,248; low: $15,000).
Fields of interest: Secondary education; Community and economic development.
Limitations: Applications accepted. Giving primarily in Ashland, KY.
Application information: Application form required.
Initial approach: Proposal
Deadline(s): None
Officers and Directors: Daniel Huffman, Chair. and Director; Paul Leake, Secy. and Director; Thomas Burnette; Ben Cooksey; William H. Jones, Jr.; William A. Stinnett; Mary Witten Wiseman.
EIN: 611334469

3708
Fred B. & Opal S. Woosley Foundation, Inc.
239 S. 5th St., Ste. 900
Louisville, KY 40202-3257
Application address: Arthur C. Peter, c/o Hilliard
Lyons, 500 W. Jefferson St., Louisville, KY
40202-2823, tel.: (502) 588-9133

Established in 1986 in Kentucky.
Foundation type: Independent foundation.
Financial data (yr. ended 12/31/13): Assets,
$6,805,860 (M); expenditures, $423,317;
qualifying distributions, $423,317; giving activities
include $375,000 for 40 grants (high: $30,000;
low: $4,000).
Purpose and activities: Giving primarily for children,
youth and social services.
Fields of interest: Diseases and conditions; Human
services; Child welfare; People with disabilities.
Limitations: Applications accepted. Giving primarily
in the Jefferson County, KY, area. No grants to
individuals.
Application information: Application form required.
Initial approach: Letter
Copies of proposal: 1
Deadline(s): None
Board meeting date(s): Dec.
Final notification: After board meeting; positive
replies only

Officer and Directors: Arthur C. Peter, Pres. and
Director; John McFerran Barr; David A. Bell; Beverly
S. Clark; Donald E. Meyer.
EIN: 611104319

3709
William B. Yarmuth Family Foundation Inc.
4102 Oxnard Creek Dr.
Louisville, KY 40241

Established in 2007 in Kentucky.
Donor: William B. Yarmuth.
Foundation type: Independent foundation.
Financial data (yr. ended 12/31/13): Assets,
$1,556,091 (M); gifts received, $29,318;
expenditures, $429,960; qualifying distributions,
$391,536; giving activities include $388,500 for 3
grants (high: $238,500; low: $50,000).
Fields of interest: Judaism.
Limitations: Applications not accepted. Giving
primarily in Louisville, KY.
Application information: Unsolicited requests for
funds not accepted.
Officer: William B. Yarmuth, Pres.
Directors: Jacob Yarmuth; Jeffrey T. Yarmuth;
Robert N. Yarmuth; Susan Long Yarmuth.
EIN: 208662831

3710
Lester E. Yeager Charitable Trust B
P.O. Box 964
Owensboro, KY 42302-0964 (270) 686-8254

Established in 1989 in Kentucky.
Donor: Lester E. Yeager†.
Foundation type: Independent foundation.
Financial data (yr. ended 12/31/13): Assets,
$5,624,270 (M); expenditures, $260,571;
qualifying distributions, $242,972; giving activities
include $177,580 for 59 grants (high: $8,290; low:
$750).
Purpose and activities: Giving primarily for health
and human services.
Fields of interest: Arts and culture; Science
museums; Higher education; Environmental
education; Health; Hospice care; Human services.
Application information: Application form required.
Initial approach: Completed application form
Copies of proposal: 4
Deadline(s): Dec. 15
Trustees: Ruth F. Adkins; Donald W. Haas; Nancy
Kennedy.
Number of staff: 1 part-time professional.
EIN: 611159548

LOUISIANA

3711
Ainsley's Angels of America
562 W. Friesen Rd.
Lake Charles, LA 70607-0677
Main URL: http://www.ainsleysangels.org

Donors: Walter S. Johnson Foundation; The Frederick Foundation; I Run 4.
Foundation type: Independent foundation.
Financial data (yr. ended 12/31/14): Assets, $146,773 (M); gifts received, $249,378; expenditures, $302,753; qualifying distributions, $224,273; giving activities include $195,249 for grants.
Limitations: Applications not accepted.
Application information: Unsolicited requests for funds not accepted.
Officers and Directors: Kim R. Rossier, Pres. and Director; Shaun Evans, V.P.; Joe Orth, V.P. and Director; Kristine Seaward, V.P. and Director; Lori N. Rossiter, Secy.; Terry P. Hebert, Treas.
EIN: 453576353

3712
A-Kids-Choice Trust
106 Esplanade Ct.
Bossier City, LA 71111-5470

Donor: Denise M. Bankston.
Foundation type: Independent foundation.
Financial data (yr. ended 12/31/13): Assets, $466,937 (M); gifts received, $391,025; expenditures, $312,995; qualifying distributions, $211,681; giving activities include $211,681 for 9 grants (high: $85,350; low: $100).
Fields of interest: Education; Religion; Human services.
Limitations: Applications not accepted. Giving primarily in LA.
Application information: Unsolicited requests for funds not accepted.
Officer: Denise M. Bankston, Pres.
EIN: 456193224

3713
The Biedenharn Foundation
3635 Greenacres Place Dr., Unit 347
Bossier City, LA 71111-2160

Established in 1985 in Louisiana.
Donors: R.Z. Biedenharn†; Catherine Susan Biedenharn†.
Foundation type: Independent foundation.
Financial data (yr. ended 11/30/14): Assets, $9,970,621 (M); expenditures, $590,379; qualifying distributions, $409,750; giving activities include $409,750 for 39 grants (high: $35,000; low: $1,000).
Purpose and activities: Giving primarily for human services and environmental conservation.
Fields of interest: Higher education; Environment; Health; Human services.
Type of support: General support; Annual campaigns; Endowments; Research and evaluation; Emergency funds; Research.

Limitations: Applications not accepted. Giving primarily in LA. No grants to individuals.
Application information: Contributes only to pre-selected organizations.
Board meeting date(s): Varies
Officer: Sydney Biedenharn, Chair.
Board Members: Gia Morgan; Mary Cobb Thompson; David E. Tyrone; Ross Walker.
Trustee: Linda Tyrone.
Number of staff: 1 part-time support.
EIN: 721052971

3714
Ronnie & Gwen Briggs Foundation
c/o Money Hill
140 St. Charles Ct.
Abita Springs, LA 70420-4009 (985) 875-0332
Contact: Ronald P. Briggs, Pres.; V. Gwendolyn Briggs, Secy.

Established in 2003 in Louisiana.
Donors: Ronald P. Briggs; V. Gwendolyn Briggs.
Foundation type: Independent foundation.
Financial data (yr. ended 12/31/13): Assets, $1,647,624 (M); expenditures, $240,120; qualifying distributions, $236,122; giving activities include $236,122 for 23 grants (high: $100,000; low: $500).
Fields of interest: Education; Philanthropy; Religion.
Limitations: Applications accepted. Giving primarily in LA, MD and TX. No grants to individuals.
Application information: Application form required.
Initial approach: Letter or Telephone call
Deadline(s): None
Officers: Ronald P. Briggs, Pres.; V. Gwendolyn Briggs, Secy.
EIN: 200478943

3715
The Donald J. Broussard Charitable Foundation
17820 W. Augusta Dr.
Baton Rouge, LA 70810-5927 (225) 751-4173
Contact: Donald J. Broussard, Tr.

Established in 2005 in Louisiana.
Donors: Donald J. Broussard; Merieda Broussard.
Foundation type: Independent foundation.
Financial data (yr. ended 12/31/13): Assets, $74,872 (M); gifts received, $98,800; expenditures, $151,254; qualifying distributions, $148,875; giving activities include $148,875 for 61 grants (high: $25,000; low: $100).
Fields of interest: Education; Catholicism; Human services; Food aid.
Application information: Application form required.
Initial approach: Letter
Deadline(s): None
Trustees: Donald J. Broussard; Merieda Broussard; Michael Broussard; Stephen Broussard.
EIN: 203905614

3716
Cahn Family Foundation
P.O. Box 52005
New Orleans, LA 70152-2005
Contact: James L. Cahn

Established in 1957 in Louisiana.
Donors: Dixie Mill Supply Co., Inc.; June Cahn†.

Foundation type: Independent foundation.
Financial data (yr. ended 12/31/14): Assets, $6,732,147 (M); gifts received, $246,263; expenditures, $383,823; qualifying distributions, $261,000; giving activities include $261,000 for 34 grants (high: $80,000; low: $1,000).
Fields of interest: Education; Nonprofits; Judaism; Human services; Child welfare.
Type of support: Regranting.
Limitations: Applications not accepted. No grants to individuals.
Application information: Unsolicited requests for funds not accepted.
Directors: Adele Cahn; James L. Cahn; Richard M. Cahn.
EIN: 726020106

3717
The Catalyst Foundation
6038 St. Charles Ave.
New Orleans, LA 70118-6118

Donor: Leslie R. Jacobs.
Foundation type: Independent foundation.
Financial data (yr. ended 12/31/13): Assets, $5,870,759 (M); expenditures, $231,670; qualifying distributions, $213,835; giving activities include $210,000 for 5 grants (high: $100,000; low: $10,000).
Fields of interest: Education; Housing development; Human services.
Limitations: Applications not accepted. Giving primarily in New Orleans, LA.
Application information: Unsolicited requests for funds not accepted.
Board Members: Leslie R. Jacobs; Scott Jacobs; Stephen Rosenthal.
EIN: 263063640

3718
Chambers Medical Foundation
1807 Lake St.
Lake Charles, LA 70601-5771
Application address: c/o Jason R. Chambers, 3796 Parian Ridge Rd. N.W., Atlanta, GA 30327, tel.: (404) 784-0925; Main URL: http://www.chambersmedicalfoundation.org

Established in 1990 in Louisiana.
Donor: Russell C. Chambers.
Foundation type: Independent foundation.
Financial data (yr. ended 12/31/13): Assets, $4,492,428 (M); expenditures, $272,634; qualifying distributions, $200,000; giving activities include $200,000 for 7 grants (high: $100,000; low: $5,000).
Fields of interest: Diseases and conditions; Biology; Human services.
Type of support: General support; Research; Research and evaluation.
Limitations: Applications accepted. Giving in the U.S., with emphasis on CA and GA. No grants to individuals.
Application information:
Initial approach: Letter
Deadline(s): None
Trustees: Jason R. Chambers; Edwin K. Hunter.
EIN: 726134893

3719
Crossroads Foundation Inc.
(formerly Crossroads Youth Ranch, Inc.)
62300 Russell Town Rd.
Roseland, LA 70456-2030

Foundation type: Operating foundation.
Financial data (yr. ended 12/31/13): Assets,
$4,800,319 (M); expenditures, $271,249;
qualifying distributions, $223,057; giving activities
include $223,057 for 24 grants (high: $36,820;
low: $1,000).
Fields of interest: Animal welfare; Human services;
Family services; Domestic violence shelters;
Adolescents; People with disabilities.
Limitations: Applications not accepted. Giving
primarily in LA.
Application information: Contributes only to
pre-selected organizations.
Officers: Gary M. Martinez, Pres.; Leslie H. Martinez,
V.P.
Directors: Carl Hunter; Dianne Hunter.
EIN: 743013051

3720
Daybrook Foundation
365 Canal St.
New Orleans, LA 70130-1112 (504) 561-6163
Contact: Lauren Holt, Exec.Dir.

Donor: Daybrook Fisheries Inc.
Foundation type: Independent foundation.
Financial data (yr. ended 09/30/13): Assets,
$5,303,683 (M); gifts received, $1,200,000;
expenditures, $148,454; qualifying distributions,
$148,360; giving activities include $148,360 for 12
grants (high: $42,339; low: $1,000).
Fields of interest: Education; Higher education;
Environment; Human services.
Type of support: Scholarships.
Limitations: Applications accepted. Giving primarily
in LA.
Application information:
Deadline(s): None
Officers: Gregory F. Holt, Chair.; Charles Wallace,
Secy.; Stephen Morganstern, Treas.; Lauren Holt,
Exec.Dir.
Director: W.B. Wallace.
EIN: 203478127

3721
Kitty DeGree Foundation
2410 Trenton St.
West Monroe, LA 71291-5442 (318) 355-3480
Contact: Cindy Rogers, Pres.

Established in 1999 in Louisiana.
Donor: Kitty DeGree.
Foundation type: Independent foundation.
Financial data (yr. ended 12/31/13): Assets,
$2,683,580 (M); expenditures, $315,705;
qualifying distributions, $312,500; giving activities
include $312,500 for 10 grants (high: $200,000;
low: $500).
Fields of interest: Education; Health; Disasters and
emergency management.
Limitations: Applications accepted. Giving primarily
in northeastern LA. No support for political
organizations. No grants for student loans, or for any
loans to individuals.
Application information: Application form required.

Initial approach: Letter
Copies of proposal: 2
Deadline(s): None
Officers: Cindy Rogers, Pres.; Scottie Traylor, V.P.;
John D. Cameron, Treas.
EIN: 721441364

3722
Dujay Charitable Foundation
c/o Trust Tax Compliance
P.O. Box 61540
New Orleans, LA 70161

Established in 1994 in Texas.
Donor: Eva Dujay†.
Foundation type: Independent foundation.
Financial data (yr. ended 12/31/14): Assets,
$6,012,693; expenditures, $331,710; qualifying
distributions, $279,344.
Fields of interest: Arts and culture; Health;
Addiction services; Diseases and conditions;
Christianity.
Type of support: General support; Capital
campaigns; Capital and infrastructure; Equipment.
Limitations: Applications not accepted. Giving
primarily in southeast TX. No grants to individuals.
Application information: Contributes only to
pre-selected organizations.
Board meeting date(s): June and July
Trustee: Capital One, N.A.
EIN: 760416456

3723
Ellis Family Foundation Trust
2441 Frierson Rd.
Shreveport, LA 71115-9506

Donors: Martha F. Ellis; Imogen M. Frierson.
Foundation type: Independent foundation.
Financial data (yr. ended 12/31/13): Assets,
$492,795 (M); gifts received, $417,749;
expenditures, $219,441; qualifying distributions,
$214,296; giving activities include $214,296 for 9
grants (high: $194,621; low: $500).
Fields of interest: Education; Housing development;
Religion.
Limitations: Applications not accepted. Giving
primarily in LA.
Application information: Unsolicited requests for
funds not accepted.
Trustee: Screven H. Watson.
Director: Martha F. Ellis.
EIN: 266446821

3724
Wendell & Anne Gauthier Family Foundation
730 Copal St.
Mandeville, LA 70448-4510

Established in 2002 in Louisiana.
Donor: Anne S. Barrios Gauthier.
Foundation type: Independent foundation.
Financial data (yr. ended 12/31/13): Assets,
$2,921,722 (M); expenditures, $136,069;
qualifying distributions, $121,619; giving activities
include $121,619 for 14 grants (high: $100,000;
low: $25).
Fields of interest: Arts and culture; Education;
Undergraduate education; Environment.

Limitations: Applications not accepted. Giving
primarily in LA. No grants to individuals.
Application information: Unsolicited requests for
funds not accepted.
Directors: John C. Calhoun; Anne S. Barrios
Gauthier; Celeste A. Gauthier; Cherie A. Gauthier;
Michelle A. Gauthier; Deborah M. Sulzer.
EIN: 721518612

3725
Jack Webster Grigsby Foundation
333 Texas St., Ste. 2285
Shreveport, LA 71101-3665

Donor: Jack W. Grigsby.
Foundation type: Independent foundation.
Financial data (yr. ended 12/31/14): Assets,
$6,941,240 (M); expenditures, $256,402;
qualifying distributions, $251,500; giving activities
include $251,500 for 36 grants (high: $25,000;
low: $1,000).
Fields of interest: Education; Religion; Human
services.
Limitations: Applications not accepted. Giving
primarily in LA and WY. No grants to individuals.
Application information: Unsolicited requests for
funds not accepted.
Trustee: Morgan Grigsby.
EIN: 836050857

3726
Harper Family Foundation
5258 Marcia Ave.
New Orleans, LA 70124-1049 (504) 488-5460
Contact: Katherine V. Mattesky
E-mail: gvpartners@yahoo.com

Established in 1991 in Louisiana.
Foundation type: Independent foundation.
Financial data (yr. ended 12/31/13): Assets,
$2,959,717 (M); expenditures, $181,306;
qualifying distributions, $162,236; giving activities
include $162,236 for 9 grants (high: $35,000; low:
$7,157).
Fields of interest: Museums; Higher education;
Nonprofits; European football; Human services;
Youth services.
Type of support: General support; Regranting.
Limitations: Applications accepted. Giving primarily
in LA.
Application information: Application form required.
Initial approach: Proposal
Deadline(s): None
Officers: Mary Mattesky Sanders, Pres.; Mary K.
Crigler Besselman, V.P.; Katherine V. Mattesky,
Secy.
EIN: 581921771

3727
Prentiss C. and Dolores M. Havens Family Foundation
201 St. Charles Ave., Ste. 4300
New Orleans, LA 70170-4300

Donor: Prentiss C. Havens.
Foundation type: Independent foundation.
Financial data (yr. ended 12/31/13): Assets,
$1,951,377 (M); gifts received, $748,020;
expenditures, $253,015; qualifying distributions,

$253,000; giving activities include $253,000 for 21 grants (high: $105,000; low: $2,000).
Fields of interest: Education; Diseases and conditions; Protestantism.
Type of support: Research.
Limitations: Applications not accepted.
Application information: Unsolicited requests for funds not accepted.
Officers: Prentiss C. Havens, Pres.; Catherine Havens Cary, V.P.; John P. Havens, V.P.; Debra H. Patrick, V.P.; Edward R. Grady, Jr., Secy. and Treas.
EIN: 263854804

3728
The H. H. and Edna Houseman Charitable Trust
c/o Trust Tax Compliance
P.O. Box 61540
New Orleans, LA 70161-1540

Established in 1999 in Texas.
Donors: Edna Houseman; Jackie Houseman Charitable Trust.
Foundation type: Independent foundation.
Financial data (yr. ended 12/31/14): Assets, $8,511,963; expenditures, $316,359; qualifying distributions, $257,547.
Fields of interest: Education; Health; Diseases and conditions.
Limitations: Applications not accepted. Giving primarily in LA. No grants to individuals.
Application information: Unsolicited requests for funds not accepted.
Trustee: Capital One, N.A.
EIN: 760636804

3729
Huie-Dellmon Trust
P.O. Box 330
Alexandria, LA 71309-0330 (318) 748-8141
Contact: Richard L. Crowell Jr., Tr.

Foundation type: Independent foundation.
Financial data (yr. ended 12/31/13): Assets, $13,254,128 (M); expenditures, $551,723; qualifying distributions, $452,064; giving activities include $432,110 for 32 grants (high: $69,400; low: $250).
Purpose and activities: Giving primarily to Protestant organizations, as well as for social services, and historic preservation.
Fields of interest: Historic preservation; Foundations; Nonprofits; Libraries; Christianity; Protestantism; Human services.
Type of support: General support; Matching grants; Continuing support; Annual campaigns; Capital campaigns; Capital and infrastructure; Regranting; Equipment; Endowments; Program development; Professorships; Scholarships; Research.
Limitations: Applications accepted. Giving primarily in central LA. No grants to individuals.
Application information:
Initial approach: Proposal
Deadline(s): None
Trustees: Richard L. Crowell, Jr.; Nancy C. Owens.
EIN: 720809684

3730
Kavanagh Family Foundation
365 Canal St., Ste. 2000
New Orleans, LA 70130-6534

Established in 2006 in Louisiana.
Donor: Danielle H. Kavanagh.
Foundation type: Independent foundation.
Financial data (yr. ended 12/31/13): Assets, $4,562,076 (M); expenditures, $350,013; qualifying distributions, $306,561; giving activities include $306,561 for 9 grants (high: $100,000; low: $5,000).
Fields of interest: Arts and culture; Education.
Type of support: General support.
Limitations: Applications not accepted. Giving primarily in LA and TX.
Application information: Unsolicited requests for funds not accepted.
Officers and Directors: Danielle H. Kavanagh, Pres. and Director; Mark A. Fullmer, Secy. and Director; William H. Langenstein III, Treas. and Director; Darren K. Crumpton; Dylan M. Kavanagh; Zachary P. Kavanagh.
EIN: 371530850

3731
Knight Family Foundation
P.O. Box 52688
Lafayette, LA 70505-2688 (337) 233-0464
Contact: Kelley Sobiesk, Dir.

Established in 2000 in Louisiana.
Donors: Edward R. Knight†; Edward R. Knight Testamentary Clut.
Foundation type: Independent foundation.
Financial data (yr. ended 12/31/13): Assets, $5,978,596 (M); expenditures, $259,545; qualifying distributions, $206,576; giving activities include $206,576 for 27 grants (high: $25,000; low: $500).
Fields of interest: Arts and culture; Education; Diseases and conditions.
Type of support: General support.
Limitations: Applications accepted. Giving primarily in LA.
Application information: Application form required.
Initial approach: Letter
Deadline(s): None
Officer: Ann Knight, Pres.
Directors: Bryan Knight; Mark Knight; Kelley Sobiesk.
EIN: 721462097

3732
Lake Charles American Press Foundation
(formerly The Tom B. & Flora I. Shearman Foundation)
P.O. Box 2893
Lake Charles, LA 70602-2893

Established in 1982 in Louisiana.
Donors: Thomas B. Shearman, Sr.; Thomas B. Shearman, Jr.
Foundation type: Independent foundation.
Financial data (yr. ended 03/31/13): Assets, $5,597,927 (M); expenditures, $235,571; qualifying distributions, $168,505; giving activities include $168,505 for 109 grants (high: $40,000; low: $25).

Purpose and activities: Giving primarily for youth services.
Fields of interest: Arts and culture; Nonprofits; Protestantism; Human services; Child welfare; Scouting programs; Adult and child mentoring.
Type of support: Regranting.
Limitations: Applications not accepted. Giving primarily in Lake Charles, LA. No grants to individuals.
Application information: Unsolicited requests for funds not accepted.
Trustees: Susan Cook; Thad Cook; James S. Shearman; Thomas B. Shearman, Jr.; Thomas B. Shearman III.
EIN: 720920599

3733
The Fritz Lang Foundation
P.O. Box 6300
Lake Charles, LA 70606-6300 (337) 474-2840
Contact: Wanda N. Borel, Admin.
FAX: (337) 474-2838;
E-mail: wanda@fritzlangfoundation.org; Main URL: http://fritzlangfoundation.org

Established in 1989 in Louisiana.
Donor: Fritz Lang.
Foundation type: Independent foundation.
Financial data (yr. ended 06/30/13): Assets, $2,347,016 (M); gifts received, $1,325,315; expenditures, $300,387; qualifying distributions, $278,873; giving activities include $5,000 for 1 grant, and $212,900 for 103 grants to individuals (high: $3,000; low: $1,000).
Purpose and activities: Scholarships to graduates of Jefferson Davis and Vermillion Parish high schools in Louisiana; applicants must major in agriculture, agri-business, animal husbandry/science, forestry, environmental science, wildlife, management/conservation, veterinary science, or a related major benefiting the economy of the student's parish. Scholarships are currently $1,200 per fall and spring semesters. Selection will be based on academic achievement and financial need. Students must have and maintain a 2.5 GPA or better.
Fields of interest: Higher education.
Type of support: Professorships; Student aid.
Limitations: Applications accepted. Giving limited to residents and organizations in LA.
Publications: Application guidelines.
Application information: Application guidelines and form available on foundation web site. The foundation does not have a walk-in location at this time. Late applications may be considered and placed on a waiting list for unclaimed funds. Application form required.
Deadline(s): Apr. 1
Board meeting date(s): Annually in Apr.
Officer and Trustees: Louis O. Trahan, Jr., Pres. and Trustee; Edwin K. Hunter.
EIN: 581854369

3734
Live Oak Foundation
(formerly Frank & Mary Godchaux Foundation)
c/o Leslie K. Godchaux
502 5th St.
Abbeville, LA 70510

Donors: Frank A. Godchaux III; Charles R. Godchaux; Frank M. Godchaux; Leslie K. Godchaux.
Foundation type: Independent foundation.
Financial data (yr. ended 12/31/13): Assets, $2,327,894 (M); expenditures, $383,877; qualifying distributions, $366,335; giving activities include $366,335 for 49 grants (high: $100,000; low: $250).
Purpose and activities: Giving primarily for health organizations, as well as for nursing school education; funding also for the environment, education, and to Episcopal churches.
Fields of interest: Education; Graduate and professional education; Environment; Nonprofits; Hospital care; Nursing care; Diseases and conditions; Episcopalianism and Anglicanism; Lutheranism.
Type of support: Regranting.
Limitations: Applications not accepted. No grants to individuals.
Application information: Unsolicited requests for funds not accepted.
Officers: Frank K. Godchaux, Pres.; Theresa G. Payne, V.P.; Leslie K. Godchaux, Secy.
EIN: 726042163

3735
Magale Foundation, Inc.
400 Texas St., 12th Fl.
Shreveport, LA 71101-3525

Established in 1957 in Louisiana.
Donor: John F. Magale†.
Foundation type: Independent foundation.
Financial data (yr. ended 11/30/14): Assets, $3,106,470 (M); expenditures, $182,902; qualifying distributions, $149,805; giving activities include $148,000 for 18 grants (high: $25,000; low: $2,000).
Purpose and activities: Grants for higher education, social services, and the performing arts, principally in AR and LA. Student loans for residents of AR, LA, or TX.
Fields of interest: Education; Diseases and conditions; Youth development.
Type of support: Research; Loans to individuals.
Limitations: Applications accepted. Giving primarily in southern AR and northern LA.
Application information: Application form required.
  Initial approach: Letter
  Copies of proposal: 1
  Deadline(s): Apr. 1
Trustee: JPMorgan Chase Bank, N.A.
Directors: Robin Branam; Mike Epley; Homer Greer; Fred Longino.
EIN: 726025096

3736
Arlene & Joseph Meraux Charitable Foundation, Inc.
417 Friscoville Ave.
Arabi, LA 70032 (504) 439-8191
Contact: Rita O. Gue, Pres.
Main URL: http://merauxfoundation.org

Established in 1999 in Louisiana.
Donor: Arlene V. Meraux†.
Foundation type: Independent foundation.
Financial data (yr. ended 12/31/12): Assets, $58,996,797 (M); expenditures, $2,129,643; qualifying distributions, $956,973; giving activities

include $161,213 for 24 grants (high: $25,885; low: $300).
Purpose and activities: Giving primarily for education, human services, and programs benefiting needy and/or ill children; also giving scholarship funds to high school graduates of St. Bernard Parish, LA.
Fields of interest: Education; Human services; Shelter and residential care; Low-income and poor people.
Type of support: General support; Student aid.
Limitations: Applications accepted. Giving primarily in LA.
Application information: Application form required.
  Initial approach: Letter
  Deadline(s): None
Officers: Rita Gue, Pres.; Floyd Gue, 1st V.P.; William Haines, 2nd V.P.; Sidney D. Torres III, Secy.; Christopher Haines, Treas.
EIN: 721400981

3737
The Jess Merkle Foundation
7717 Creswell Rd., Ste. 18
Shreveport, LA 71106-6031

Established in 1997 in Louisiana.
Donor: Lyda T. Merkle†.
Foundation type: Independent foundation.
Financial data (yr. ended 06/30/13): Assets, $4,697,977 (M); expenditures, $226,637; qualifying distributions, $179,846; giving activities include $179,000 for 8 grants (high: $82,000; low: $1,000).
Purpose and activities: Primarily giving for human services; funding also for a United Methodist church.
Fields of interest: Education; Community and economic development; Presbyterianism; Human services.
Type of support: General support; Endowments.
Limitations: Applications not accepted. Giving primarily in LA. No grants to individuals.
Application information: Contributes only to pre-selected organizations.
Trustee: Paul E. Merkle.
EIN: 721336331

3738
Jean and Saul A. Mintz Foundation
(formerly Carolyn Rose Strauss Foundation, Inc.)
P.O. Box 6058
Monroe, LA 71211-6058 (318) 388-2000
Contact: Morris F. Mintz, Dir.

Established in 1944 in Louisiana.
Donors: Roselyn L. Strauss†; Jean S. Mintz; Saul a. Mintz; Sally M. Mann; Carolyn M. Kaplan; Morris F. Mintz.
Foundation type: Independent foundation.
Financial data (yr. ended 12/31/13): Assets, $8,251,923 (M); gifts received, $2,593,826; expenditures, $343,135; qualifying distributions, $321,808; giving activities include $321,808 for 86 grants (high: $70,000; low: $40).
Fields of interest: Arts and culture; Education; Religion; Judaism.
Type of support: Capital campaigns.
Limitations: Applications accepted. Giving primarily in LA.
Application information:

Initial approach: Proposal
  Deadline(s): None
Directors: Carolyn M. Kaplan; Jay M. Kaplan; Anthony E. Mann; Sally M. Mann; Jean S. Mintz; Melinda F. Mintz; Morris F. Mintz.
EIN: 726027911

3739
The James R. Moffett Family Foundation
1615 Poydras St., 22nd Fl.
New Orleans, LA 70112-1254
Contact: Cynthia M. Molyneux, Exec. Dir.

Established in 1997 in Louisiana.
Donors: James R. Moffett; Louise H. Moffett; Moffett Holdings, LLC.
Foundation type: Independent foundation.
Financial data (yr. ended 09/30/13): Assets, $419,325 (M); gifts received, $428,000; expenditures, $430,237; qualifying distributions, $430,237; giving activities include $428,000 for 97 grants (high: $50,000; low: $500).
Fields of interest: Education; Nonprofits; Diseases and conditions; Cancers; Christianity; Child welfare.
Type of support: Regranting.
Limitations: Applications accepted. Giving primarily in CA, LA, and TX.
Application information:
  Initial approach: Letter
  Deadline(s): None
Officers: James R. Moffett, Pres.; Louise H. Moffett, V.P.; Crystal L. Moffett-Lourd, Secy.; James R. Moffett, Jr., Treas.; Cynthia M. Molyneux, Exec. Dir.
EIN: 721345770

3740
William Edwin Montan Charitable Trust
c/o Trust Tax Compliance
P.O. Box 61540
New Orleans, LA 70161-1540

Established in 2005 in Louisiana.
Donor: Mary Elizabeth Agnew†.
Foundation type: Independent foundation.
Financial data (yr. ended 12/31/14): Assets, $6,550,107 (M); expenditures, $395,468; qualifying distributions, $344,109.
Fields of interest: Art museums; Science museums; Health; Human services; Scouting programs.
Limitations: Applications not accepted. Giving primarily in LA. No grants to individuals.
Application information: Contributes only to pre-selected organizations.
Trustee: Capital One Bank, N.A.
EIN: 202128402

3741
Monteleone Family Foundation
214 Royal St.
New Orleans, LA 70130-2227

Established in 2002 in Louisiana.
Donor: New Hotel Monteleone, LLC.
Foundation type: Company-sponsored foundation.
Financial data (yr. ended 12/31/13): Assets, $3,142,905 (M); expenditures, $336,380; qualifying distributions, $335,323; giving activities include $335,323 for 3 grants (high: $199,913; low: $10,000).

Purpose and activities: The foundation supports organizations involved with education, cancer, and crime and law enforcement.
Fields of interest: Education; Sports and recreation; Human services.
Type of support: General support.
Limitations: Applications not accepted. Giving limited to New Orleans, LA and Houston, TX. No grants to individuals.
Application information: Contributes only to pre-selected organizations.
Officers: William A. Monteleone III, Pres.; Ronald Pincus, V.P.; Charles Lacinak, Jr., Secy.-Treas.
Directors: Anna Monteleone Burr; David G. Monteleone.
EIN: 820569393

3742
The New Life Foundation, Inc.
P.O. Box 52592
Lafayette, LA 70505-2592

Established in 1989 in Louisiana.
Donors: William P. Mills III; WPM Exploration, Inc.
Foundation type: Independent foundation.
Financial data (yr. ended 12/31/13): Assets, $1,737,426 (M); gifts received, $312,166; expenditures, $312,897; qualifying distributions, $281,239; giving activities include $281,239 for 70 grants (high: $70,000; low: $25).
Fields of interest: Arts and culture; Education; Protestantism; Human services; Family services; Child welfare.
Limitations: Applications not accepted. Giving primarily in Lafayette, LA.
Application information: Unsolicited requests for funds not accepted.
Officers and Directors: William P. Mills III, Pres. and Director; Sandra T. Mills, Secy.
EIN: 581864700

3743
The Nanette Noland Foundation
P.O. Box 788
Baton Rouge, LA 70821-0788

Donor: Nanette Noland.
Foundation type: Independent foundation.
Financial data (yr. ended 12/31/13): Assets, $1,005,720 (M); gifts received, $300,000; expenditures, $176,824; qualifying distributions, $168,950; giving activities include $168,000 for 7 grants (high: $117,000; low: $1,000).
Fields of interest: Education; Health; Religion.
Limitations: Applications not accepted. Giving primarily in Baton Rouge, LA.
Application information: Unsolicited requests for funds not accepted.
Trustee: Nanette Noland.
EIN: 205104719

3744
Operation Merry Christmas
1100 Poydros St., Ste. 2300
New Orleans, LA 70163-2301

Foundation type: Independent foundation.
Financial data (yr. ended 12/31/12): Assets, $0 (M); gifts received, $1,000; expenditures,

$416,922; qualifying distributions, $414,076; giving activities include $414,076 for 1 grant.
Fields of interest: Philanthropy.
Limitations: Giving primarily in LA.
Officers: Paula Murla, Chair.; Kathy Roussell, Vice-Chair.; Gerry Borders, Secy.; Tim Doody, Treas.
EIN: 721124043

3745
Parkside Foundation
701 Poydras St., Ste. 5000
New Orleans, LA 70139-7758

Established in 1961 in Louisiana.
Donors: Thomas B. Lemann; Stephen B. Lemann; Diana M. Lewis; J. Thomas Lewis; George Villere.
Foundation type: Independent foundation.
Financial data (yr. ended 12/31/13): Assets, $2,309,374 (M); expenditures, $233,641; qualifying distributions, $207,648; giving activities include $207,648 for 55 grants (high: $25,000; low: $100).
Fields of interest: Arts and culture; Education; Philanthropy.
Type of support: General support.
Limitations: Applications not accepted. Giving primarily in LA, with emphasis on New Orleans. No grants to individuals.
Application information: Unsolicited requests for funds not accepted.
Officers: Thomas B. Lemann, Pres.; J. Thomas Lewis, V.P.; George Villere, V.P.; Wendy M. Farrelly, Secy.
EIN: 726019058

3746
Powers Foundation, Inc.
c/o Heard, McElroy & Vestal
P.O. Box 1607
Shreveport, LA 71165-1607   (318) 429-1525
Contact: C. Cody White Jr., Pres. and Treas.

Established in 1967 in Louisiana.
Donor: Gussie N. Power†.
Foundation type: Independent foundation.
Financial data (yr. ended 07/31/14): Assets, $6,499,161 (M); gifts received, $52,000; expenditures, $289,875; qualifying distributions, $272,350; giving activities include $265,500 for 47 grants (high: $30,000; low: $1,000).
Purpose and activities: Giving primarily for education, volunteer services, human services, and federated giving programs.
Fields of interest: Arts and culture; Education; Voluntarism; Nonprofits; Hospital care; Human services; Youth services.
Type of support: Public engagement and education; Volunteer development; Regranting.
Limitations: Applications accepted. Giving primarily in the Shreveport and Bossier City, LA, areas.
Application information:
    Initial approach: Letter
    Deadline(s): None
Officers: C. Cody White, Jr., Pres. and Treas.; Ellen H. White, V.P.; Stephen C. White, V.P.; Sara Margaret White, Secy.
EIN: 756080974

3747
Pugh Family Foundation
P.O. Box 51366
Lafayette, LA 70505-1366
E-mail: nanpugh@pughfamilyfoundation.org; Mailing address: P.O. Box 470, Driggs, ID 83422; Main URL: http://www.pughfamilyfoundation.org

Established in 2000 in Louisiana.
Donors: Francis Tillou Nicholls Pugh III; Jo Ann Lewis Pugh; Francis Nicholls Pugh IV; Michael Lewis Pugh; Nancy Lewis Marie Pugh.
Foundation type: Independent foundation.
Financial data (yr. ended 12/31/14): Assets, $8,080,455 (M); gifts received, $2,500,000; expenditures, $373,833; qualifying distributions, $348,584; giving activities include $306,835 for 5 grants (high: $300,000; low: $50).
Purpose and activities: The foundation supports educational programs that address the root causes of poverty in Acadiana, LA.
Fields of interest: Education; Higher education; Foundations; Nonprofits; Housing development; Human services.
Type of support: Regranting.
Limitations: Applications accepted. Giving primarily in LA. No grants to individuals.
Publications: Application guidelines.
Application information: Complete application guidelines and procedures available on foundation web site. Application form required.
    Initial approach: Access application via the foundation web site
    Deadline(s): See foundation web site for current deadline
    Final notification: 4 to 6 weeks after deadline
Officer: Nancy Pugh, Exec. Dir.
Directors: Francis T.N. Pugh III; Francis T.N. Pugh IV; JoAnn Pugh; Michael L. Pugh.
EIN: 721491038

3748
The Ruckstuhl Foundation
12508 Astolat Ave.
Baton Rouge, LA 70816-2405

Donors: Richard E. Ruckstuhl, Sr.; Patricia J. Ruckstuhl.
Foundation type: Independent foundation.
Financial data (yr. ended 12/31/12): Assets, $2,703,076 (M); gifts received, $2,652,700; expenditures, $169,149; qualifying distributions, $169,149; giving activities include $165,088 for 1 grant.
Fields of interest: Education; Religion.
International interests: Africa.
Limitations: Applications not accepted. Giving primarily in New Orleans, LA.
Application information: Unsolicited requests for funds not accepted.
Officers and Directors: Julie E. Ruckstuhl, Pres. and Director; Richard E. Ruckstuhl, Jr., Secy. and Director; Kenneth D. Ruckstuhl, Treas. and Director; J. Carville; D. Fanguy; B. MacKay; M. Ruckstuhl; R. Ruckstuhl; R. Stephens.
EIN: 451449345

3749
Salutare Deum Foundation
817 Hickory Ave.
Harahan, LA 70123-3110

Donors: Durr Heavy Construction, LLC; Amid Metro Partnership, LLC; Rhino Holdings, LLC.
Foundation type: Independent foundation.
Financial data (yr. ended 12/31/13): Assets, $3,967,031 (M); gifts received, $280,000; expenditures, $285,202; qualifying distributions, $281,673; giving activities include $276,750 for 51 grants (high: $50,000; low: $250).
Fields of interest: Education; Religion; Sports and recreation.
Limitations: Applications not accepted. Giving primarily in LA.
Application information: Unsolicited requests for funds not accepted.
Directors: Dana Stumpf; Donna D. Stumpf; Shana Stumpf; Stephen F. Stumpf; Stephen F. Stumpf, Jr.
EIN: 208115159

3750
Sci-Port Foundation
820 Clyde Fant Pkwy.
Shreveport, LA   71101-3667

Foundation type: Independent foundation.
Financial data (yr. ended 12/31/13): Assets, $697,005 (M); expenditures, $165,745; qualifying distributions, $150,502; giving activities include $150,000 for 1 grant.
Fields of interest: Science.
Limitations: Applications not accepted. Giving primarily in LA.
Application information: Unsolicited requests for funds not accepted.
Officers: W. Clinton Rasberry, Chair.; Sylvia Goodman, Secy.
Directors: Joe N. Averett, Jr.; Witt Caruthers; Rand H. Falbaum; Tem McElroy; Susan B, Muse.
EIN: 721499941

3751
The Aaron or Peggy Selber Foundation, Inc.
333 Texas St., Ste. 1250
Shreveport, LA   71101-3676

Established in 1992 in Louisiana.
Donors: Peggy B. Selber; Aaron Selber, Jr.†.
Foundation type: Independent foundation.
Financial data (yr. ended 12/31/13): Assets, $2,200,697 (M); gifts received, $30; expenditures, $174,387; qualifying distributions, $148,068; giving activities include $147,069 for 70 grants (high: $26,100; low: $25).
Fields of interest: Higher education; Foundations; Nonprofits; Hospital care; Diseases and conditions; Religion; Human services.
Type of support: Regranting.
Limitations: Applications not accepted. Giving primarily in CA, CO, and LA. No grants to individuals.
Application information: Contributes only to pre-selected organizations.
Officers: Peggy B. Selber, Pres.; Dewey W. Corley, Exec. V.P; Vanessa Holman, Secy.-Treas.
Trustees: Penny S. Autenreith; Poly S. Gleichenhaus; Pamela Selber; Patty S. Newton.
EIN: 582022065

3752
Hyslop Shannon Foundation
1100 Poydras St., Ste. 2100
New Orleans, LA   70163-2100
Contact: James R. Morton

Established in 2000 in Louisiana.
Donor: Hyslop Shannon†.
Foundation type: Independent foundation.
Financial data (yr. ended 12/31/12): Assets, $3,563,036 (M); expenditures, $186,418; qualifying distributions, $167,126; giving activities include $164,376 for 36 grants (high: $30,000; low: $16).
Fields of interest: Arts and culture; Musical ensembles and groups; Education; Diseases and conditions; Judaism.
Limitations: Applications not accepted. Giving primarily in IL and LA. No grants to individuals.
Application information: Unsolicited requests for funds not accepted.
Officers and Directors: James R. Morton, Pres. and Director; Thomas M. Morton, V.P. and Director; Carol Whipple, Secy.-Treas. and Director.
EIN: 721447443

3753
Showers of Blessing Foundation
12315 Morgan Meadow Ave.
Baton Rouge, LA   70818-3924

Donor: Stanley Eugene Cheatham.
Foundation type: Independent foundation.
Financial data (yr. ended 12/31/13): Assets, $4,108,577 (M); expenditures, $256,019; qualifying distributions, $239,969; giving activities include $236,124 for 18 grants (high: $69,500; low: $2,000).
Fields of interest: Education; Protestantism; Human services.
Limitations: Applications not accepted. Giving primarily in LA.
Application information: Unsolicited requests for funds not accepted.
Officers: Stanley Eugene Cheatham, Chair. and Pres.; Barbara Marlene M. Cheatham, Secy.; Steven Eugene Cheatham, Treas.
Board Members: Scott Eric Cheatham; Skye Edwards Cheatham; Stanley Earl Cheatham.
EIN: 611583666

3754
Special Children's Foundation Inc.
P.O Box 77314
Baton Rouge, LA   70879-7314   (225) 573-7768

Foundation type: Independent foundation.
Financial data (yr. ended 04/30/13): Assets, $9,227,532 (M); expenditures, $317,341; qualifying distributions, $225,880; giving activities include $225,880 for grants.
Fields of interest: Education; Higher education; Health; Arthritis; Community and economic development.
Limitations: Applications accepted. Giving primarily in LA.
Application information: Application form required.
  Initial approach: Letter
  Deadline(s): None

Directors: Lacey Holder; Sharon Holder; Susan Jeansonne; Caroline Messenger; Carolyn Pittman.
EIN: 720806577

3755
B. A. and Elinor Steinhagen Benevolent Trust
c/o Trust Tax Compliance
P.O. Box 61540
New Orleans, LA   70161-1540
Application address: c/o Capital One, Attn.: Jean Moncla, P.O. Box 3928, Beaumont, TX 77704-3928, tel.: (409) 880-1415

Donors: B.A. Steinhagen†; Elinor Steinhagen†.
Foundation type: Independent foundation.
Financial data (yr. ended 12/31/14): Assets, $7,603,041 (M); expenditures, $361,525; qualifying distributions, $299,307; giving activities include $262,164 for 13 grants (high: $45,000; low: $2,500).
Purpose and activities: Giving for the housing and general assistance of the elderly and the helpless and afflicted of any age.
Fields of interest: Arts and culture; Education; Health; Housing development; Human services; Senior services; Seniors; Low-income and poor people; People with disabilities.
Type of support: Capital and infrastructure; Matching grants; Equipment; Program development; Publications; Seed money; Research.
Limitations: Applications accepted. Giving primarily to LA. No grants to individuals, or for operating budgets, continuing support, annual campaigns, emergency funds, deficit financing, conferences, scholarships, or fellowships; no loans.
Publications: Application guidelines.
Application information: Application form required.
  Initial approach: Letter
  Copies of proposal: 1
  Deadline(s): May 31
  Board meeting date(s): June and July
  Final notification: Aug.
Trustee: Capital One Bank, N.A.
EIN: 746039544

3756
Kendall Vick Public Law Foundation
c/o J.J. Reso, Jr.
1100 Poydras St., Ste. 3600
New Orleans, LA   70163-3600
E-mail: reso@bhbmlaw.com

Established in 1998 in Louisiana.
Donor: Kendall Vick†.
Foundation type: Independent foundation.
Financial data (yr. ended 12/31/13): Assets, $3,455,733 (M); gifts received, $8,282; expenditures, $207,956; qualifying distributions, $176,000; giving activities include $176,000 for 6 grants (high: $45,000; low: $1,000).
Type of support: Continuing support; Program-related investments.
Limitations: Applications not accepted. Giving primarily in LA. No grants to individuals.
Application information: Contributes only to pre-selected organizations.
Officers and Directors: Jerome J. Reso, Jr., Pres. and Director; Leon H. Rittenberg, Jr., Secy.; Martha Guarisco; John A. Rouchell.
EIN: 721293729

3757
Charles & Elizabeth Wetmore Foundation
1101 Dealers Ave.
New Orleans, LA 70123-2203
E-mail: ketawetmore@gmail.com; Application
address: c/o Keta Lowe, 116 longwood Dr.,
Mandeville, LA 70471, tel.: (504) 779-1888

Established in 1969 in Louisiana.
Donor: Wetmore Foundation Charitable Trust.
Foundation type: Operating foundation.
Financial data (yr. ended 12/31/13): Assets,
$190,729 (M); gifts received, $176,519;
expenditures, $232,437; qualifying distributions,
$230,973; giving activities include $100,000 for 1
grant, and $43,000 for grants to individuals.
Purpose and activities: Giving primarily to indigent
victims of tubercular disease and their immediate
families; giving also to local health departments that
specialize in the treatment of tuberculosis.
Fields of interest: Health.
Type of support: General support; Grants to
individuals.
Limitations: Applications accepted. Giving limited to
the metropolitan New Orleans, LA, area.
Application information: Application form required.
Initial approach: Letter
Deadline(s): None
Officers: Henry Jackson, Pres.; William C. Norris,
MD, V.P.; Margaret Ferguson Washington, Secy.;
Keta Thornburg, Exec. Dir.
Trustee: SunTrust Bank, N.A.
Number of staff: 1 full-time professional.
EIN: 237120743

3758
The Wheless Foundation
c/o Regions Bank
333 Texas St., LASH30202J
Shreveport, LA 71101-3666
Contact: Barbara R. York

Established in 1945 in Louisiana.
Donor: N. Hobson Wheless†.
Foundation type: Independent foundation.
Financial data (yr. ended 10/31/13): Assets,
$8,927,545 (M); expenditures, $458,091;
qualifying distributions, $351,219; giving activities
include $338,200 for 67 grants (high: $28,100;
low: $100).
Purpose and activities: Giving primarily for health
and human services and to Christian churches.
Fields of interest: Higher education; Nonprofits;
Diseases and conditions; Community and economic
development; Christianity; Child welfare; Senior
services.
Type of support: General support; Continuing
support; Annual campaigns; Capital campaigns;
Capital and infrastructure; Program development;
Regranting; Research.
Limitations: Applications accepted. Giving primarily
in northwest LA. No grants to individuals.
Application information:
Initial approach: Letter

Copies of proposal: 1
Deadline(s): None
Board meeting date(s): Annually in Oct.
Board Members: Jim Devane; Elise W. Hogan;
Nicholas Hobson Wheless, Jr.
Number of staff: None.
EIN: 726017724

3759
The Whitman Family Foundation
423 Ridgeway Dr.
Metairie, LA 70001-3046

Established in 2006 in Louisiana.
Donor: Wayne Whitman.
Foundation type: Independent foundation.
Financial data (yr. ended 12/31/12): Assets,
$6,605,377 (M); expenditures, $286,654;
qualifying distributions, $249,240; giving activities
include $249,240 for 34 grants (high: $50,740;
low: $100).
Fields of interest: Education; Sustainable
development; Urban development; Catholicism;
Child welfare; Youth development.
Type of support: General support; Volunteer
development.
Limitations: Applications not accepted. Giving
primarily in LA. No grants to individuals.
Application information: Contributes only to
pre-selected organizations.
Officer: Leigh Whitman, Pres.
EIN: 205666003

3760
Fanny Edith Winn Educational Trust
P.O. Drawer 730
Crowley, LA 70527-0730 (337) 783-7000

Established in 1989 in Louisiana.
Foundation type: Independent foundation.
Financial data (yr. ended 12/31/14): Assets,
$5,305,466; expenditures, $411,551; qualifying
distributions, $187,600.
Purpose and activities: Giving primarily to Roman
Catholic churches and for Roman Catholic
education.
Fields of interest: Higher education; Catholicism.
Type of support: General support; Scholarships.
Limitations: Giving primarily in LA.
Application information:
Deadline(s): None
Trustees: Scott Broussard; Stephen A. Stefanski;
Laura Zaunbrecher.
EIN: 726130364

3761
The Mary Freeman Wisdom Foundation
c/o Andrew B. Wisdom
1100 Poydras St., Ste. 1502
New Orleans, LA 70163
Main URL: http://
www.maryfreemanwisdomfoundation.org

Established in 1986 in Louisiana.
Donor: Mary Freeman Wisdom†.
Foundation type: Independent foundation.
Financial data (yr. ended 12/31/13): Assets,
$4,801,306 (M); expenditures, $229,289;
qualifying distributions, $186,350; giving activities
include $181,000 for 19 grants (high: $25,000;
low: $1,000).
Purpose and activities: Giving for arts groups;
support also for education, conservation, and social
services.
Fields of interest: Arts and culture; Orchestral
music; Education; Elementary and secondary
education; Higher education; Environment; Natural
resources; Family planning; Human services.
Type of support: General support; Matching grants;
Continuing support; Annual campaigns; Capital
campaigns; Capital and infrastructure; Equipment;
Endowments; Program development; Convening;
Seed money; Scholarships.
Limitations: Applications accepted. Giving primarily
in New Orleans, LA.
Publications: Application guidelines.
Application information: Application form required.
Initial approach: Online application form
Copies of proposal: 2
Deadline(s): Apr. 1
Board meeting date(s): Late Apr.
Final notification: None
Officers: Stuart Benjamin, Pres.; Ned Benjamin,
Secy.; Andrew Wisdom, Treas.
Trustees: Adelaide Wisdom Benjamin; Arthur
Wisdom; Matthew Morgan Wisdom.
Number of staff: 1 part-time support.
EIN: 726123208

3762
Zuschlag Family Foundation
c/o Richard E. Zuschlag
108 Astoria Loop
Lafayette, LA 70508-7302

Established in 2001 in Louisiana.
Donors: Richard Zuschlag; Elaine Zuschlag.
Foundation type: Independent foundation.
Financial data (yr. ended 12/31/13): Assets,
$1,479,945 (M); expenditures, $220,136;
qualifying distributions, $213,368; giving activities
include $213,368 for 27 grants (high: $20,000;
low: $100).
Fields of interest: Museums; Art museums; Higher
education; Nonprofits; Christianity.
Type of support: Regranting.
Limitations: Applications not accepted. Giving
primarily in LA. No grants to individuals.
Application information: Contributes only to
pre-selected organizations.
Trustees: Elaine Zuschlag; Erin E. Zuschlag; Joseph
B. Zuschlag; Richard Zuschlag; Richard B. Zuschlag.
EIN: 522364513

MAINE

3763
The Aldermere Foundation
(also known as Albert H. Chatfield, Jr. & Marion W. Chatfield Trust f/b/o The Aldermere Foundation)
c/o Spinnaker Trust
123 Free St.
Portland, ME 04101

Established in 1977 in Maine.
Foundation type: Operating foundation.
Financial data (yr. ended 12/31/13): Assets, $5,817,299 (M); expenditures, $311,277; qualifying distributions, $279,219; giving activities include $279,219 for 17 grants (high: $192,719; low: $1,000).
Purpose and activities: Giving primarily to support the environment and youth services.
Fields of interest: Natural resources; Land resources; Biodiversity; Wildlife biodiversity; Youth development.
Type of support: General support.
Limitations: Applications not accepted. Giving primarily in ME. No grants to individuals.
Application information: Unsolicited request for funds not accepted.
Trustee: Spinnaker Trust.
EIN: 016059906

3764
The Peter Alfond Foundation
c/o Dexter Enterprises, Inc.
2 Monument Sq.
Portland, ME 04101-4093

Established in 1993 in Maine.
Donors: Peter G. Alfond; Berkshire Hathaway Inc.
Foundation type: Independent foundation.
Financial data (yr. ended 12/31/13): Assets, $13,124,430 (M); expenditures, $510,712; qualifying distributions, $501,171; giving activities include $414,410 for 23 grants (high: $265,000; low: $100).
Fields of interest: Education; Foundations; Human services.
Type of support: General support.
Limitations: Applications not accepted. Giving primarily in MA, ME, and PR. No grants to individuals.
Application information: Contributes only to pre-selected organizations.
Trustees: Peter G. Alfond; William Alfond; Gregory Powell.
Number of staff: None.
EIN: 223267949

3765
The Marjorie C. Bailey Charitable Foundation
P.O. Box 760
Damariscotta, ME 04543-0760

Foundation type: Independent foundation.
Financial data (yr. ended 12/31/13): Assets, $4,707,990 (M); gifts received, $131; expenditures, $255,826; qualifying distributions, $197,280; giving activities include $197,280 for 17 grants (high: $50,000; low: $500).
Fields of interest: Arts and culture; Secondary education; Diseases and conditions; Agriculture; Christianity.
Limitations: Applications not accepted. Giving primarily in ME. No grants to individuals.
Application information: Contributes only to pre-selected organizations.
Trustee: Robert B. Gregory.
EIN: 266103130

3766
The Bank of Maine Charitable Foundation
(formerly Savings Bank of Maine, FSB Charitable Foundation)
P.O. Box 190
Gardiner, ME 04345-2109 (207) 582-5550
Contact: Thomas B. Wiggins, Treas.

Established in 1988 in Maine.
Donors: Gardiner Savings Institution, F.S.B.; Savings Bank of Maine.
Foundation type: Company-sponsored foundation.
Financial data (yr. ended 12/31/13): Assets, $1,392,621 (M); expenditures, $191,065; qualifying distributions, $189,715; giving activities include $164,065 for 84 grants (high: $12,000; low: $100).
Purpose and activities: The foundation supports fire departments and festivals and organizations involved with arts and culture, education, the environment, health, human services, and community development.
Fields of interest: Arts and culture; Education; Environment.
Type of support: General support.
Limitations: Applications accepted. Giving primarily in Gardiner, ME.
Application information: Application form required.
Initial approach: Letter
Deadline(s): None
Officers: Renee Smyth, Pres.; Thomas Wiggins, Treas.
Board Members: Lorraine Boston; Larissa Darcy; John Everets; Anita Nored; Laurel Perkins; Theodore Scontras; Maureen St. John.
EIN: 010446023

3767
The Borman Family Foundation
166 Old Waterville Rd., Ste. 3
Oakland, ME 04963-5358

Established in 2000 in Maine.
Donor: Cornelius H. Borman.
Foundation type: Independent foundation.
Financial data (yr. ended 07/31/13): Assets, $6,735,256 (M); gifts received, $41,953; expenditures, $369,368; qualifying distributions, $328,823; giving activities include $301,549 for 38 grants (high: $34,000; low: $1,000).
Fields of interest: Arts and culture; Opera; Higher education; Natural resources; Diseases and conditions; Alzheimer's disease; Human services; People with disabilities.
Type of support: Annual campaigns; Capital campaigns; Equipment; Capital and infrastructure; Scholarships; Program development; General support.

Limitations: Applications not accepted. Giving primarily in IL, IN, ME and NJ. No grants to individuals.
Application information: Unsolicited requests for funds not accepted.
Officers: Cornelius H. Borman, Pres.; Robert Borman, V.P.; Donald Borman, Secy.-Treas.
Directors: Adam Borman; Kate Borman; Matthew Borman; Robert Borman, Jr.; Megan Frowery.
EIN: 010522171

3768
Boulos Family Charitable Foundation
c/o H.M. Payson & Co.
P.O. Box 31
Portland, ME 04112-0031
Application address: c/o Thomas M. Pierce, 1 Portland Sq., 5th Fl., P.O. Box 31, Portland, ME 04112, tel.: (207) 772-3761

Established in 2007 in Maine.
Donors: The Boulos Co.; Joseph F. Boulos; Cheryl R. Boulos.
Foundation type: Independent foundation.
Financial data (yr. ended 12/31/13): Assets, $37,021 (M); gifts received, $130,703; expenditures, $135,778; qualifying distributions, $134,500; giving activities include $134,500 for 10 grants (high: $50,000; low: $4,500).
Fields of interest: Education; Philanthropy; Health.
Limitations: Applications accepted. Giving primarily in ME. No grants to individuals.
Application information: Application form required.
Initial approach: Letter
Deadline(s): None
Officers: Joseph F. Boulos, Pres.; Gretchen C. Boulos, V.P.; Stephanie J. Boulos, V.P.; Thomas M. Pierce, Secy.; Richard P. Leblanc, Clerk; Cheryl R. Boulos, Treas.
EIN: 753202504

3769
Brook Family Foundation
9 Korhonen Rd.
Norway, ME 04268-4222

Established in 1995 in Maine.
Foundation type: Independent foundation.
Financial data (yr. ended 03/31/13): Assets, $1,569,213 (M); expenditures, $198,694; qualifying distributions, $174,887; giving activities include $163,700 for 35 grants (high: $25,000; low: $500).
Purpose and activities: Giving primarily for education and the environment.
Fields of interest: Education; Natural resources; Agriculture; Human services; Youth development.
Type of support: Endowments; Program development.
Limitations: Applications not accepted. Giving primarily in MA, ME and VT. No grants to individuals.
Application information: Unsolicited requests for funds not accepted.
Officers: Shirley Brook, Pres.; Paul Brook, Treas.
Directors: Anthony Brook; Nickolas Brook; Robert L. Brook.
EIN: 010499178

3770
Margaret E. Burnham Charitable Trust
P.O. Box 31
Portland, ME 04112-0031 (207) 772-3761
Main URL: http://www.megrants.org/Burnham.html

Established in 1995 in Maine.
Donor: Margaret E. Burnham†.
Foundation type: Independent foundation.
Financial data (yr. ended 12/31/14): Assets, $8,464,614; expenditures, $430,622; qualifying distributions, $402,596.
Purpose and activities: Giving primarily for community and social services, medical organizations, education, arts and culture, and the environment.
Fields of interest: Arts and culture; Environment; Diseases and conditions; Human services.
Type of support: Continuing support; Annual campaigns; Capital campaigns; Capital and infrastructure; Equipment; Land acquisitions; Program development; Publications; Research.
Limitations: Applications accepted. Giving limited to ME. No support for religious organizations. No grants to individuals.
Publications: Application guidelines.
Application information: Application form required.
Initial approach: Completed application form
Copies of proposal: 1
Deadline(s): Oct. 1
Board meeting date(s): Dec.
Trustee: Thomas M. Pierce.
EIN: 010496879

3771
Camden Home for Senior Citizens
8 Harrison Ave.
Camden, ME 04843-1804 (207) 236-9467
Contact: Jean Payne

Established in 1941 in Maine.
Foundation type: Independent foundation.
Financial data (yr. ended 05/31/13): Assets, $3,507,379 (M); gifts received, $1,500; expenditures, $180,876; qualifying distributions, $173,712; giving activities include $155,200 for 97 grants to individuals.
Purpose and activities: Giving for heating, food, prescription drugs, rent, real estate taxes, and medical needs of senior citizens in Camden, Hope, Lincolnville, and Rockport, Maine.
Fields of interest: Arts and culture; Human services; Seniors.
Type of support: Grants to individuals.
Limitations: Applications accepted. Giving limited to residents of Camden, Hope, Lincolnville, and Rockport, ME.
Application information: Application form required.
Initial approach: Proposal
Deadline(s): None
Officers: Sam Jones, Pres.; Vernon Hunter, V.P.; Jean Payne, Secy.-Treas.
Trustees: Linda Annis; Elaine Davis; Nellie Hart; Adele Hopkins; Richard Laine; Sheila McFarland; Rosemary Winslow; Elizabeth Young.
EIN: 010248064

3772
Tom and Kate Chappell Family Foundation
P.O. Box 920
Kennebunk, ME 04043-0920

Foundation type: Independent foundation.
Financial data (yr. ended 12/31/13): Assets, $1,495,585 (M); expenditures, $161,935; qualifying distributions, $153,000; giving activities include $153,000 for 18 grants (high: $25,000; low: $250).
Fields of interest: Education; University education; Environment; Human services.
Limitations: Applications not accepted. Giving primarily in ME.
Application information: Unsolicited requests for funds not accepted.
Officers and Directors: Thomas M. Chappell, Pres. and Director; Katherine C. Chappell, Secy. and Director; Barbara K. Wheaton, Treas.
EIN: 205949141

3773
Olive A. Coates Charitable Trust
P.O. Box 31
Portland, ME 04112-0031

Foundation type: Independent foundation.
Financial data (yr. ended 12/31/13): Assets, $5,418,133 (M); expenditures, $230,587; qualifying distributions, $209,892; giving activities include $198,457 for 6 grants (high: $74,422; low: $24,807).
Fields of interest: Domesticated animals; Public affairs; Community and economic development.
Limitations: Applications not accepted. Giving primarily in ME.
Application information: Unsolicited requests for funds not accepted.
Trustees: Richard A. McKittrick; H.M. Payson & Co.
EIN: 016149204

3774
George J. & Theresa L. Cotsirilos Family Foundation
150 Middle St., Apt. 2B
Portland, ME 04101-4150

Established in 1985 in Illinois.
Donor: George J. Cotsirilos.
Foundation type: Independent foundation.
Financial data (yr. ended 12/31/13): Assets, $6,237,051 (M); expenditures, $320,523; qualifying distributions, $267,053; giving activities include $267,000 for 35 grants (high: $51,000; low: $500).
Fields of interest: Arts and culture; Education; Higher education; Law education; Religion; Human services.
Limitations: Applications not accepted. Giving primarily in Chicago, IL. No grants to individuals.
Application information: Contributes only to pre-selected organizations.
Officers: Stephanie Cotsirilos, Pres.; George G. Cotsirilos, Jr., Secy.; John G. Cotsirilos, Treas.
EIN: 363413343

3775
George P. Davenport Trust Fund
65 Front St.
Bath, ME 04530-2508 (207) 443-3431
Contact: Barry M. Sturgeon, Tr.
E-mail: davenporttrust@myfairpoint.net

Established in 1927 in Maine.

Donor: George P. Davenport†.
Foundation type: Independent foundation.
Financial data (yr. ended 12/31/13): Assets, $6,885,832 (M); gifts received, $8,290; expenditures, $392,510; qualifying distributions, $342,920; giving activities include $307,455 for 44 grants (high: $12,500; low: $550).
Purpose and activities: Support for the benefit of young and needy children, and for religious, temperance, moral, educational, benevolent and charitable institutions and organizations; also grants scholarships to Bath, ME area high school graduates.
Fields of interest: Education; Higher education; Health; Community and economic development; Religion; Human services; Child welfare.
Type of support: General support; Loans to individuals; Matching grants; Capacity-building and technical assistance; Capital and infrastructure; Emergency funds; Seed money; Student aid.
Limitations: Applications accepted. Giving limited to Bath, ME. No grants to individuals (other than student scholarships to Bath, ME area high school graduates), or for continuing support, annual campaigns, deficit financing, research, demonstration projects, publications, or celebration events.
Application information: Maine Philanthropy Center Common Grant Application Form accepted. Application form required.
Initial approach: Telephone
Copies of proposal: 1
Deadline(s): None
Board meeting date(s): Semimonthly
Final notification: 1 month
Trustees: Eric R. Allen; Roberta F. Banks; Barry M. Sturgeon.
Number of staff: 1 part-time support.
EIN: 016009246

3776
The Dugas Family Foundation
c/o P. Dugas
243 State St.
Portland, ME 04101-7152 2078992409
Application address: c/o Normand Dugas, 94 Woodlands Rd., Alton Bay, NH 03810, tel.: (603) 875-3314

Established in 1997 in Maine.
Donors: Normand Dugas; Agnes Dugas; Peter Henrich.
Foundation type: Independent foundation.
Financial data (yr. ended 05/31/14): Assets, $247,969; gifts received, $12,700; expenditures, $198,451; qualifying distributions, $194,230.
Purpose and activities: Giving for housing and food services for the poor.
Fields of interest: Health; Housing development; Catholicism; Food aid; Low-income and poor people.
International interests: Africa; Haiti; South America.
Type of support: Continuing support; Seed money.
Limitations: Applications accepted. Giving primarily in ME and NH. No support for arts organizations, or for political groups.
Application information:
Initial approach: Letter
Copies of proposal: 2
Deadline(s): None
Board meeting date(s): Aug.
Officers: Peter Dugas, Pres. and Treas.; Dennis Molleur, V.P.

Directors: Felice Colliton; Agnes Dugas; Marc Dugas; Normand Dugas; Michelle McGarrity; Danielle Molleur.
Number of staff: None.
EIN: 010519633

3777
Elliotsville Plantation Inc

P.O. Box 148
Portland, ME 04112-0148 (207) 370-5813

Established in 2002 in Maine.
Donors: Burt's Bees, Inc.; Roxanne Quimby; Marion McConnell.
Foundation type: Operating foundation.
Financial data (yr. ended 12/31/14): Assets, $136,877,460 (M); expenditures, $2,343,533; qualifying distributions, $2,335,507; giving activities include $299,950 for grants (high: $100,000; low: $450).
Fields of interest: Arts and culture; Human services.
Limitations: Applications not accepted. Giving primarily in ME. No grants to individuals.
Application information: Contributes only to pre-selected organizations.
Officers and Directors: Daniel E. O'Leary, C.E.O.; Lucas St. Clair, Pres. and Director; Hannah Quimby, Secy. and Director; Roxanne Quimby, Exec. Dir.
EIN: 134223002

3778
Firebird Foundation for Anthropological Research

P.O. Box A
Phillips, ME 04966-1501

Donors: George N. Appell; Laura W.R. Appell; Charity Appell Mcnabb.
Foundation type: Operating foundation.
Financial data (yr. ended 03/31/13): Assets, $3,490,297 (M); gifts received, $187,748; expenditures, $431,618; qualifying distributions, $421,074; giving activities include $198,394 for 24 grants to individuals (high: $10,000; low: $3,670).
Fields of interest: Diseases and conditions.
Type of support: Research; Grants to individuals.
Limitations: Applications not accepted. Giving primarily in NY.
Application information: Unsolicited requests for funds not accepted.
Officers: George N. Appell, Pres.; Laura P.A. Warren, Treas.
Directors: Laura W. R. Appell; Amity A. Doolittle, Ph.D; Michael J. Doolittle; Alan C. McNab; Charity R. Appell McNabb; Anton Ploeg, Ph.D; John C. Warren.
EIN: 010524375

3779
Franklin Savings Bank Community Development Foundation

198 Front St.
P.O. Box 825
Farmington, ME 04938-0825 (207) 778-3339
Contact: Peter Judkins, Pres.

Established in 2000 in Maine.
Donor: Franklin Savings Bank.
Foundation type: Company-sponsored foundation.
Financial data (yr. ended 12/31/13): Assets, $2,354,507 (M); gifts received, $150,000;

expenditures, $190,231; qualifying distributions, $189,505; giving activities include $189,505 for 131 grants (high: $25,000; low: $10).
Purpose and activities: The foundation supports health centers and organizations involved with arts and culture, education, recreation, children services, and community economic development.
Fields of interest: Arts and culture; Historic preservation; Education; Secondary education; Nonprofits; School-based health care; Community and economic development; Economic development; Sports and recreation; Winter sports; Human services; Child welfare.
Type of support: General support; Annual campaigns; Program development; Sponsorships; Student aid; Regranting.
Limitations: Applications accepted. Giving limited to western central ME.
Publications: Application guidelines.
Application information: Application form required.
 Initial approach: Letter
 Deadline(s): None
Officers: William J. Bernard, Chair.; Peter Judkins, Pres.; Shelley W. Deane, Secy.; Timothy J. Thompson, Clerk and Treas.
Directors: Richard H. Smith; Richard M. Walker.
EIN: 311719226

3780
The Robert and Dorothy Goldberg Charitable Foundation

c/o Bernstein, Shur, Sawyer and Nelson
100 Middle St.
P.O. Box 9729
Portland, ME 04104-5029 (207) 774-1200

Established in 1999 in New Hampshire.
Donors: Robert Goldberg†; Dorothy Goldberg†.
Foundation type: Independent foundation.
Financial data (yr. ended 12/31/14): Assets, $4,909,787; expenditures, $439,487; qualifying distributions, $225,721.
Fields of interest: Arts and culture; Education; Natural resources; Human services.
Limitations: Applications accepted. Giving primarily in Conway, NH. No grants to individuals.
Application information: Application form required.
 Initial approach: Letter
 Copies of proposal: 6
 Deadline(s): Mar. 30 and Sept. 30
Trustees: Michael S. King; Leonard M. Nelson.
EIN: 311622560

3781
The Golden Rule Foundation, Inc.

P.O. Box 658
Camden, ME 04843-0658
E-mail: laurel@goldrule.org; *Main URL:* http://www.goldrule.org

Established in 1981 in District of Columbia.
Donor: Jack Evans†.
Foundation type: Independent foundation.
Financial data (yr. ended 10/31/14): Assets, $3,814,558 (M); expenditures, $334,452; qualifying distributions, $286,159; giving activities include $235,080 for 39 grants (high: $30,000; low: $500).
Purpose and activities: Giving primarily for the arts, environmental programs, and social services.

Fields of interest: Arts and culture; Education; Environment; Natural resources; Toxic substance control; Community and economic development; Human services; Child welfare.
International interests: Mexico.
Type of support: General support; Program development; Seed money; Advocacy.
Limitations: Applications not accepted. Giving on a national basis. No grants to individuals.
Publications: Informational brochure.
Application information: Unsolicited requests for funds not considered.
 Board meeting date(s): Late Aug.
Officers: Jean Evans, Pres.; Tegan Stephens, Secy.; Salvadore Messina, Treas.
Advisory Board: Sian Evans.
Directors: Gareth Evans; Trevor Evans.
Number of staff: 1 part-time support.
EIN: 599207701

3782
Anne R. Henry Charitable Foundation

P.O. Box 31
Portland, ME 04112-0031

Established in 2012 in Maine.
Donors: Anne R. Henry Funding Trust; Anne Randolph Henry Trust.
Foundation type: Independent foundation.
Financial data (yr. ended 12/31/14): Assets, $4,418,560; expenditures, $261,299; qualifying distributions, $235,797.
Fields of interest: Cultural awareness; Historic preservation; Basic and emergency aid; Food banks.
Limitations: Applications not accepted. Giving primarily in Portland, ME.
Application information: Unsolicited Requests for funds not accepted.
Trustee: Verrill Dana; H.M. Payson; Anne Stanley.
EIN: 276254411

3783
The Hudson Foundation

(formerly Schair Family Foundation)
P.O. Box 402
Portland, ME 04112-0402 (207) 781-7706
Contact: Gillian B. Schair, Pres.
Main URL: http://www.hudsonfoundationmaine.org

Established in 1993 in Maine.
Donor: Douglas M. Schair.
Foundation type: Independent foundation.
Financial data (yr. ended 12/31/13): Assets, $4,401,916 (M); expenditures, $214,880; qualifying distributions, $173,141; giving activities include $167,417 for 23 grants (high: $20,000; low: $560).
Purpose and activities: Giving for projects relating to medical research and services, direct services to individuals, services to needy people, anti-bias education and to religious organizations.
Fields of interest: Education; Philanthropy; Community and economic development; Religion; Youth development.
Limitations: Applications accepted. Giving primarily in ME; giving also in MA and NY. No grants to individuals, or for scholarships, fellowships, or travel; no loans.
Application information: Application form required.
 Initial approach: Letter

Deadline(s): None
Board meeting date(s): Mar., June, Sept., and Dec.
Officers: Gillian B. Schair, Pres.; Loriann Touchette, Secy.; Erica M. Schair, Treas.
Directors: Leslie Cohen; Cindy Fernandez; Annemieke L. Schair; Justin H. Schair.
EIN: 010482817

3784
Max Kagan Family Foundation

51 Pine St.
Orono, ME   04473—4049   (978) 546-1188
Contact: Leslie Kagan, Tr.
E-mail: lkagan@kaganassoc.com

Established in 1955 in Maine.
Donors: Paula Kagan; Candace Platz; Leslie Kagan.
Foundation type: Independent foundation.
Financial data (yr. ended 12/31/13): Assets, $3,814,473 (M); gifts received, $24,900; expenditures, $190,895; qualifying distributions, $191,385; giving activities include $146,900 for 118 grants (high: $16,350; low: $50).
Fields of interest: Education; Higher education; Nonprofits; Diseases and conditions; Libraries; Judaism; Human services.
Type of support: Regranting.
Limitations: Applications accepted. Giving primarily in MA, ME and NY.
Application information:
 Initial approach: Proposal
 Deadline(s): None
Trustees: Richard Grossman; Leslie Kagan; Candace Platz; Ronald Striar.
EIN: 016019033

3785
Kennebec Savings Bank Foundation

(formerly Kennebec Foundation)
P.O. Box 50
Augusta, ME   04332-0050

Established in 1985 in Maine.
Donor: Kennebec Savings Bank.
Foundation type: Company-sponsored foundation.
Financial data (yr. ended 12/31/14): Assets, $8,193,210; gifts received, $2,658,216; expenditures, $478,536; qualifying distributions, $413,035.
Purpose and activities: The foundation supports programs designed to foster education, family, and health.
Fields of interest: Education; Higher education; Nonprofits; Health; Hospital care; Public libraries; Human services; Family services; Youth services; Homeless services.
Type of support: General support; Capital and infrastructure; Regranting.
Limitations: Applications not accepted. Giving primarily in the Kennebec County, ME, area. No grants to individuals.
Application information: Contributes only to pre-selected organizations.
Officers: Mark L. Johnston, Pres., Secy. and Clerk; Andrew Silsby, V.P.; Debra A. Getchell, Treas.
Directors: Mary A. Denison; Norman S. Elvin; Diane F. Hastings; Charles W. Hays, Jr.; Laura J. Hudson; William E. Mitchell; Richard D. O'Connor; Douglas E. Reinhardt; William W. Sprague, Jr.
EIN: 222624600

3786
Kennebunk Savings Bank Foundation

104 Main St.
P.O. Box 28
Kennebunk, ME   04043-0028
Main URL: http://www.kennebunksavings.com/community.html

Established in 2001 in Maine.
Donors: Kennebunk Savings Bank; Autumn Health Svcs. of Kennebunk.
Foundation type: Company-sponsored foundation.
Financial data (yr. ended 12/31/13): Assets, $4,146,923 (M); gifts received, $127,285; expenditures, $236,528; qualifying distributions, $216,772; giving activities include $213,499 for 29 grants (high: $55,000; low: $499).
Purpose and activities: The foundation supports organizations involved with arts and culture, education, conservation, wildlife, human services, community development, civic affairs, and senior citizens.
Fields of interest: Arts and culture; Education; Human services.
Type of support: General support.
Limitations: Applications accepted. Giving limited to areas of company operations in ME. No support for religious or political organizations. No grants to individuals.
Publications: Application guidelines; Program policy statement.
Application information: Application form required.
 Initial approach: Complete online application form
 Deadline(s): None
 Board meeting date(s): Monthly
Officers and Directors: Andrew T. Furlong, Jr., Chair. and Director; Wayne F. Manchester, Vice-Chair. and Director; Bradford C. Paige, Pres. and Director; Dennis Byrd, Exec. V.P.; Stephen A. Morris, Exec. V.P. and Director; Stephen A. Soubble, Sr. V.P.; Robyn LeBuff, V.P.; Susan F. Hoctor, Secy. and Clerk; Pamela J. Drew, Treas. and Mgr. and Director; Richard V. Bibber; James J. Keating III; Raymond E. Mailhot; Geoffrey Titherington.
EIN: 010547392

3787
Lafayette Family Foundation

155 Littlefield Ave.
Bangor, ME   04401-7206   (207) 862-8000
Contact: Jacqueline A. Rawcliffe, Secy.-Treas.

Established in 2007 in Maine.
Donors: J. Daniel Lafayette; Carla J. Lafayette; Androscoggin Bank; Lafayette's Oceanfront Resort; David Witham.
Foundation type: Independent foundation.
Financial data (yr. ended 12/31/13): Assets, $471,127 (M); gifts received, $171,280; expenditures, $156,362; qualifying distributions, $155,079; giving activities include $153,573 for 1 grant.
Fields of interest: Health; Diseases and conditions.
Type of support: Research.
Limitations: Applications accepted. Giving primarily in ME.
Application information:
 Initial approach: Proposal
 Deadline(s): None
Officers: J. Daniel Lafayette III, Pres.; Carla J. Lafayette, V.P.; Jacqueline A. Rawcliffe, Secy.-Treas.
EIN: 261586475

3788
Hattie A. and Fred C. Lynam Trust

P.O. Box 1100
Ellsworth, ME   04605-1100   (877) 475-5399
E-mail for Julie Zimmerman, Trust Officer: jzimmerman@bhbt.com; E-mail for Alain Boudreau, Trust Asst.: aboudreau@bhbt.com; Main URL: http://www.lynamtrust.com
Grants List: http://www.lynamtrust.com/grant_recipients.html
Scholarship application address: c/o Maine Community Foundation, 245 Main St., Ellsworth, ME 04605-1613, tel.: (207) 667-9735, toll free: (877) 700-6800, fax: (207) 667-0447

Established in 2007 in Maine.
Donor: Fred C. Lynam†.
Foundation type: Independent foundation.
Financial data (yr. ended 12/31/14): Assets, $5,590,636; expenditures, $321,032; qualifying distributions, $284,636.
Purpose and activities: Giving primarily for charitable, religious, and educational organizations which are particularly beneficial to and advantageous for the people of Mount Desert Island, Maine; giving also for scholarships to graduates of Mount Desert Island High School.
Fields of interest: Education; Foundations; Religion; Human services.
Type of support: General support; Capital campaigns; Equipment.
Limitations: Applications accepted. Giving primarily in Mount Desert Island, ME. No grants to individuals (only scholarships).
Application information: Application guidelines available on Trust web site.
Trustee: Bar Harbor Trust Svcs.
EIN: 010222218

3789
The P.D. Merrill Charitable Trust

c/o Richard P. LeBlanc
P.O. Box 7950
Portland, ME   04112-7950

Established in 2007 in Maine.
Donor: Paul D. Merrill.
Foundation type: Independent foundation.
Financial data (yr. ended 12/31/13): Assets, $5,587,677 (M); expenditures, $677,303; qualifying distributions, $208,000; giving activities include $200,000 for 3 grants (high: $100,000; low: $50,000).
Fields of interest: Historic preservation; Higher education.
Type of support: General support.
Limitations: Applications not accepted. Giving primarily in GA and ME. No grants to individuals.
Application information: Contributes only to pre-selected organizations.
Trustees: John Achatz; Peter Vigue.
EIN: 207312061

3790
The Messier Family Foundation

P.O. Box 595
Camden, ME   04843-0595

Established in 1997 in Maine.
Donor: Joseph D. Messler, Jr.
Foundation type: Independent foundation.

Financial data (yr. ended 06/30/14): Assets, $2,880,453 (M); gifts received, $400; expenditures, $208,090; qualifying distributions, $183,000; giving activities include $183,000 for 18 grants (high: $60,000; low: $1,000).
Purpose and activities: Giving primarily for health and medical services and higher education.
Fields of interest: Arts and culture; Education; Higher education; Health; Human services.
Limitations: Applications not accepted. Giving primarily in ME. No grants to individuals.
Application information: Unsolicited requests for funds not accepted.
Officer: Joseph D. Messler, Jr., Pres.
Directors: Richard A. McKittrick; Timothy P. Messler.
EIN: 043371941

3791
MG Marland Trust f/b/o So Me Health Care
P.O. Box 31
Portland, ME   04112-0031

Foundation type: Independent foundation.
Financial data (yr. ended 08/31/14): Assets, $4,670,977 (M); expenditures, $219,938; qualifying distributions, $202,351; giving activities include $197,597 for 1 grant.
Fields of interest: Health.
Limitations: Applications not accepted.
Application information: Unsolicited requests for funds not accepted.
Trustee: H.M. Payson & Co.
EIN: 016006945

3792
The Mimi Foundation
(formerly Dead River Foundation)
80 Exchange St.
P.O. Box 1427
Bangor, ME   04402-1427   (207) 947-8641

Established in 2005 in Maine.
Donor: Dead River Co.
Foundation type: Company-sponsored foundation.
Financial data (yr. ended 12/31/13): Assets, $2,950,023 (M); gifts received, $175,000; expenditures, $192,048; qualifying distributions, $169,625; giving activities include $168,250 for 36 grants (high: $30,000; low: $500).
Purpose and activities: The foundation supports health centers and organizations involved with education, the environment, and youth development.
Fields of interest: Arts and culture; Education; Human services.
Type of support: General support.
Limitations: Applications accepted. Giving primarily in ME.
Application information: Application form required.
  Initial approach: Proposal
  Deadline(s): None
Officers: Julie H. Bracken, Pres.; Courtney H. McCollum, V.P.; Calvin E. True, Esq., Secy.; Karen K. Schacht, Treas.
EIN: 203957984

3793
Leonard and Renee Minsky Charitable Trust
114 Linden St.
Bangor, ME   04401-3446

Established in 1989 in Maine.
Donors: Leonard Minsky; Renee Minsky.
Foundation type: Independent foundation.
Financial data (yr. ended 12/31/14): Assets, $881,689; expenditures, $140,269; qualifying distributions, $134,387.
Fields of interest: Education; Health; Human services.
Type of support: General support.
Limitations: Applications not accepted. No grants to individuals.
Application information: Unsolicited requests for funds not accepted.
Trustees: Leonard Minsky; Renee Minsky.
EIN: 223003820

3794
Narragansett Number One Foundation
P.O. Box 779
Bar Mills, ME   04004-0779
Contact: Patricia M. Wales, Pres.
Main URL: http://www.nnof.org

Established in 2001 in Maine.
Donors: Patricia M. Wales; R. Erwin Wales†.
Foundation type: Independent foundation.
Financial data (yr. ended 06/30/13): Assets, $5,965,296 (M); expenditures, $347,098; qualifying distributions, $306,099; giving activities include $306,099 for 46 grants (high: $20,000; low: $600).
Fields of interest: Museums; Historic preservation; Education; Animal welfare; Veterinary medicine; Foundations; Community and economic development; Religion; Sports and recreation; Human services.
Type of support: General support.
Limitations: Applications accepted. Giving primarily in Buxton, ME, and surrounding areas. No grants to individuals or to political campaigns.
Publications: Application guidelines.
Application information: See web site for application policies, guidelines and forms. Application forms may also be obtained by stopping by the Buxton, Hollis, Limington or Standish Town Halls during normal business hours. Application form required.
  Initial approach: Letter
  Copies of proposal: 2
  Deadline(s): Nov. 1 - Mar. 1
  Final notification: June 30
Officers and Directors: Patricia M. Wales, Pres. and Director; Angela H. DesRuisseaux, Secy.-Treas. and Director; David DesRuisseaux; Libby DesRuisseaux; Reid DesRuisseaux; Pamela H. Haines; Thomas Charles Holding; Eric P. Wales; Wendy York Wales.
EIN: 010546133

3795
The Old Bug Light Charitable Foundation
c/o Spinnaker Trust
P.O. Box 7160
Portland, ME   04112-7160

Established in 1997 in Maine.

Donors: Charles G. Moore III; Emily E. Moore; Charles G. Moore Trust.
Foundation type: Independent foundation.
Financial data (yr. ended 03/31/13): Assets, $2,235,516 (M); gifts received, $3,584; expenditures, $239,405; qualifying distributions, $200,000; giving activities include $200,000 for 8 grants (high: $100,000; low: $4,000).
Fields of interest: Higher education; Human services.
Type of support: General support.
Limitations: Applications not accepted. Giving primarily in ME and NH. No grants to individuals.
Application information: Contributes only to pre-selected organizations.
Trustees: Richard E. Curran, Jr.; Charles G. Moore III; Christopher S. Moore; Nathaniel T. Moore; Jennifer M. Vandekreeke; Abigail J. Woodman.
EIN: 010514859

3796
Oxford Hills Scholarship Foundation
1570 Main St., No. 11
Oxford, ME   04270-3390

Donors: Caldwell Scholarship Fund; Caldwell Group Charitable Trust; John Lane Porter; West Paris Alumni Association; John Caldwell.
Foundation type: Independent foundation.
Financial data (yr. ended 06/30/14): Assets, $7,814,060 (M); gifts received, $1,526,700; expenditures, $288,166; qualifying distributions, $247,617; giving activities include $247,617 for grants to individuals.
Purpose and activities: Scholarship awards to applicants attending an accredited college or post-secondary program; priority given to residents of Maine School District 17. Applicants must be free of criminal convictions and drug or alcohol abuse.
Fields of interest: Higher education.
Type of support: Student aid.
Limitations: Applications not accepted. Giving primarily in ME.
Application information: Unsolicited requests for funds not accepted.
Officers: William L. Medd, Pres.; Richard P. Colpitts, Treas.
Directors: Gene Benner; Charlene Chase; Mark S. Eastman; Robert Harman; Robert Story.
EIN: 010523143

3797
Planet Dog Foundation
(formerly Planet Dog Philanthropy)
85 Bradley Dr.
Westbrook, ME   04092-4174   (207) 761-1515
Contact: Kristen E. Smith, Exec. Dir.
E-mail: pdf@planetdog.com; *Main URL:* http://www.planetdogfoundation.org
Facebook: https://www.facebook.com/pages/Planet-Dog/47926098709
Flickr: http://www.flickr.com/photos/planetdog/sets
Pinterest: http://www.pinterest.com/planetdog1997
Twitter: https://twitter.com/planetdog1997
YouTube: http://www.youtube.com/PlanetDogInc

Established in 2004 in Maine.
Donors: Planet Dog, LLC; Richard B. Fisher 1998 Revocable Trust.

Foundation type: Independent foundation.
Financial data (yr. ended 12/31/13): Assets, $527,375 (M); gifts received, $167,979; expenditures, $160,166; qualifying distributions, $156,342; giving activities include $142,533 for 34 grants (high: $7,500; low: $250).
Purpose and activities: The foundation promotes and celebrates programs in which dogs serve and support their 'best friends,' and funds canine service programs that provide support to people in need.
Fields of interest: Animal welfare; Human services.
Type of support: General support; Endowments; Emergency funds; Program development; Cause-related marketing; Program evaluations.
Limitations: Applications accepted. No support for religious or political organizations, or government agencies . No grants to individuals, or for animal testing, spay/neuter programs, adoption shelter operating expenses, or rescue project operating expenses.
Application information: Complete application guidelines available on foundation web site.
  Board meeting date(s): Mar. 1 and Oct. 1
Officers: Alex Fisher, Pres.; Stephanie Volo, V.P.; Katie Lebel, Secy.; Kate Kingston, Treas.; Kristen Smith, Exec. Dir.
Director: Denise Saaf.
Number of staff: 1 full-time professional.
EIN: 010537471

3798
Pond Family Foundation
c/o Kirk Pond
3 Canter Ln.
Cape Elizabeth, ME 04107-2028 (207) 767-4421
Contact: Ann St. John Pond, Pres.

Established in 2004 in Maine.
Donors: Ann E. St. John Pond; Kirk Pond.
Foundation type: Independent foundation.
Financial data (yr. ended 12/31/14): Assets, $4,933,075 (M); gifts received, $81,100; expenditures, $279,095; qualifying distributions, $246,314; giving activities include $224,753 for 29 grants (high: $50,000; low: $500).
Fields of interest: Education; Health; Religion.
Type of support: General support.
Limitations: Applications accepted. Giving primarily in ME. No grants to individuals.
Application information:
  Initial approach: Proposal
  Deadline(s): None
Officers and Directors: Ann E. St. John Pond, Pres. and Director; Kirk Pond, Treas. and Director; Joel Pond; Kyle Pond; Erin Pond Friedland.
EIN: 201131673

3799
Protein Foundation
10 Moulton St.
Portland, ME 04101

Donors: Ralph Rogers; House of Flavors, Inc.
Foundation type: Independent foundation.
Financial data (yr. ended 12/31/13): Assets, $197,544 (M); gifts received, $425,025; expenditures, $338,936; qualifying distributions, $338,936; giving activities include $215,000 for 6 grants (high: $110,000; low: $10,000).

Purpose and activities: Giving primarily to religious organizations that provide food and shelter to the needy.
Fields of interest: Christianity; Human services; Low-income and poor people.
Type of support: General support; Student aid.
Limitations: Applications not accepted. Giving primarily in ME. No support for non-religious groups.
Application information: Unsolicited requests for funds not accepted.
Trustees: Walter Baker; Carol Fuchella; Whit Gallagher; Stephen Lanfer; Dale McClinton; Ralph Rogers; Frank Starvel.
EIN: 061046591

3800
General E. R. Quesada Educational Foundation
P.O. Box 7525
Portland, ME 04112-7525

Established in 1993 in Florida.
Foundation type: Independent foundation.
Financial data (yr. ended 12/31/14): Assets, $4,923,000; expenditures, $309,353; qualifying distributions, $290,567.
Fields of interest: Higher education; Foundations.
Limitations: Applications not accepted. No grants to individuals.
Application information: Unsolicited requests for funds not accepted.
Trustees: Peter W. Quesada; Strand O. Quesada; Thomas R. Quesada.
EIN: 656154889

3801
Red Empress Foundation
34 Enchanted Way
Bar Harbor, ME 04609-7398 (207) 801-8149

Established in 2001 in Colorado.
Donors: Gayle Nosal; Ken Nordling; Sally Nordling; NFP Partnership; NFP Ltd.
Foundation type: Independent foundation.
Financial data (yr. ended 12/31/13): Assets, $806,513 (M); gifts received, $175,300; expenditures, $244,329; qualifying distributions, $217,318; giving activities include $168,301 for 25 grants (high: $20,000; low: $1,500).
Fields of interest: Education; Health; Human services.
Application information:
  Initial approach: Letter
Officers: Gayle Nosal, Pres.; Maryanne Mattson, Exec. Dir.
EIN: 841605718

3802
Reny Charitable Foundation
731 Rte. 1
Newcastle, ME 04553-3923

Established in 1993 in Maine.
Donors: R.H. Reny, Inc.; Downeast Wholesalers, Inc.
Foundation type: Independent foundation.
Financial data (yr. ended 12/31/13): Assets, $3,601,438 (M); expenditures, $234,914; qualifying distributions, $213,949; giving activities include $213,949 for 72 grants (high: $69,500; low: $500).

Fields of interest: Education; Secondary education; Hospital care; Libraries; Fire prevention and control; Protestantism; Human services.
Type of support: Land acquisitions.
Limitations: Applications not accepted. Giving limited to ME. No grants to individuals.
Application information: Contributes only to pre-selected organizations.
Trustees: Carolyn D. Reny; John E. Reny; Robert D. Reny.
EIN: 026095307

3803
Virginia Hodgkins Somers Foundation, Inc.
P.O. Box 367
Kennebunk, ME 04043-0367
E-mail: admin@vhsfoundation.org; Application address: c/o Gordon C. Ayer, Pres., 16 Locke St., Kennenbunkport, ME 04046, tel.: (207) 289-4109; Main URL: http://www.vhsfoundation.org

Established in 1991 in Maine.
Foundation type: Independent foundation.
Financial data (yr. ended 09/30/14): Assets, $6,694,532 (M); expenditures, $447,569; qualifying distributions, $352,561; giving activities include $339,400 for 25 grants (high: $30,000; low: $1,400).
Purpose and activities: Giving primarily for children and education.
Fields of interest: Education; Human services; Family services; Child welfare.
Type of support: Convening; Matching grants; Capital campaigns; General support; Continuing support; Annual campaigns; Equipment; Land acquisitions; Program development; Seed money; Curriculum development; Research.
Limitations: Applications accepted. Giving primarily in New England, with a focus on southern ME and York County. No support for political, religious or governmental organizations.
Publications: Application guidelines; Informational brochure (including application guidelines).
Application information: See foundation web site for application guidelines. Application form required.
  Initial approach: Read guidelines on foundation web site to determine eligibility
  Copies of proposal: 1
  Deadline(s): See foundation web site for current deadlines
  Board meeting date(s): Jan. 15 and June 15
Officers: Gordon C. Ayer, Pres.; Susan Ayer, V.P.; Carolyn B. May, Treas.
Number of staff: 1 full-time professional; 2 part-time professional.
EIN: 010537127

3804
St. Croix Valley Recreation Foundation
12 Bates Ln.
Robbinston, ME 04671-3028

Established in 2006 in Maine.
Donors: Sidney R. Unobskey; Nancy G. Unobskey.
Foundation type: Independent foundation.
Financial data (yr. ended 12/31/12): Assets, $897,653 (M); expenditures, $226,709; qualifying distributions, $214,042; giving activities include $198,675 for 19 grants (high: $150,000; low: $25).
Fields of interest: Arts and culture; Education; Undergraduate education; Domesticated animals.

International interests: Canada.
Type of support: General support.
Limitations: Applications not accepted. Giving primarily in CA, MD and ME; some giving in New Brunswick, Canada. No grants to individuals.
Application information: Unsolicited requests for funds not accepted.
Officers: Sidney R. Unobskey, Pres.; Nancy G. Unobskey, V.P.; Harry K. Eisenberg, Treas.
EIN: 161767386

3805
The S. Douglas and Rita C. Sukeforth Charitable Foundation
982 Lakeview Dr.
South China, ME   04358-4326

Established in 1998 in Maine.
Donors: Rita C. Sukeforth; S. Douglas Sukeforth.
Foundation type: Independent foundation.

Financial data (yr. ended 12/31/13): Assets, $6,210,389 (M); gifts received, $126,150; expenditures, $287,538; qualifying distributions, $247,589; giving activities include $246,214 for 40 grants (high: $90,600; low: $100).
Purpose and activities: Giving primarily for health associations, including children's health and hospitals, social services, and Christian and Baptist organizations.
Fields of interest: Hospital care; Specialty hospital care; Diseases and conditions; Libraries; Christianity; Baptist; Human services; Child welfare; Youth services.
Type of support: Research.
Limitations: Applications not accepted. Giving primarily in ME. No grants to individuals.
Application information: Contributes only to pre-selected organizations.
Trustees: Rita C. Sukeforth; S. Douglas Sukeforth.
EIN: 016148895

3806
Wellspring Charitable Foundation
P.O. Box 5089
Portland, ME   04101-0789

Established in 2006 in Maine.
Donors: Robert B. Chaffee; Marcia G. Chaffee.
Foundation type: Independent foundation.
Financial data (yr. ended 12/31/14): Assets, $5,278,348 (M); expenditures, $251,956; qualifying distributions, $250,955; giving activities include $250,000 for 1 grant.
Fields of interest: Community and economic development.
Limitations: Applications not accepted. Giving primarily in Portland, ME. No grants to individuals.
Application information: Unsolicited requests for funds not accepted.
Trustees: Marcia G. Chaffee; Robert B. Chaffee.
EIN: 208103381

MARYLAND

3807
The Acacia Foundation

(formerly Acacia Charitable Foundation)
7315 Wisconsin Ave.
Bethesda, MD 20814-3202 (301) 280-1223
Contact: Jim Harvey, Treas.

Established in 2004 in Delaware.
Donor: Acacia Life Insurance Co.
Foundation type: Company-sponsored foundation.
Financial data (yr. ended 12/31/13): Assets,
$5,700,437 (M); gifts received, $100,000;
expenditures, $381,881; qualifying distributions,
$377,500; giving activities include $377,500 for 21
grants (high: $100,000; low: $2,500).
Purpose and activities: The foundation supports
organizations involved with education and youth
development. Support is given primarily in the
Washington, D.C., area.
Fields of interest: Education; Secondary education;
Reading promotion; Human services; Youth
development; Youth services.
Type of support: General support; Annual
campaigns.
Limitations: Applications accepted. Giving primarily
in the Washington, DC, area. No support for political
organizations or candidates, or social organizations.
No grants to individuals.
Publications: Application guidelines.
Application information: Application form required.
  Initial approach: Letter
  Deadline(s): None
Officers and Directors: Salene Hitchcock-Gear,
Pres. and Director; Robert-John H. Sands, V.P. and
Director; Shawn Grosser, Corp. Secy.; Jim Harvey,
Treas.; Barbara Krumsiek; Patricia McGuire; Edward
J. Quinn, Jr.; D. Wayne Silby; Robert M. Willis.
EIN: 201257409

3808
The William L. and Victorine Q. Adams Foundation, Inc.

1040 Park Ave., Ste. 300
Baltimore, MD 21201-5635 (410) 783-3203
Contact: Blanche Rodgers, Prog. Off.

Donor: William L. Adams.
Foundation type: Operating foundation.
Financial data (yr. ended 09/30/13): Assets,
$3,140,514 (M); gifts received, $284,415;
expenditures, $426,373; qualifying distributions,
$405,067; giving activities include $280,710 for 50
grants (high: $25,000; low: $300), and $42,777 for
8 grants to individuals (high: $12,519; low: $814).
Purpose and activities: Awards scholarships only to
African-American residents of Baltimore City,
Maryland, for undergraduate study in a
business-related field. Giving also for schools,
human services, and community support.
Fields of interest: Education; Business education;
Community and economic development; Human
services.
Type of support: General support; Student aid.
Limitations: Applications accepted. Giving primarily
in Baltimore, MD.
Application information: The foundation is no longer
accepting applications for the Adams Future

Business Leadership Scholarship Program, but is
honoring previous awards.
  Initial approach: Letter
  Deadline(s): None
  Board meeting date(s): June
  Final notification: July
Officers and Trustees: Theo C. Rodgers, Pres. and
Treas. and Trustee; Marjorie J. Rodgers Cheshire,
V.P. and Secy. and Trustee; Blanche D. Rodgers.
EIN: 521369556

3809
The Adler Family Foundation

(formerly The Adler Foundation)
5530 Wisconsin Ave., Ste. 1460
Chevy Chase, MD 20815-4302

Established in 1998 in Maryland.
Donors: James B. Adler; Esther G. Adler.
Foundation type: Independent foundation.
Financial data (yr. ended 12/31/13): Assets,
$4,185,448 (M); gifts received, $155,475;
expenditures, $311,756; qualifying distributions,
$305,450; giving activities include $301,850 for 19
grants (high: $75,000; low: $500).
Fields of interest: Arts and culture; Orchestral
music; Education; Judaism; Human services.
Type of support: General support.
Limitations: Applications not accepted. Giving
primarily in MD and Washington, DC. No grants to
individuals.
Application information: Contributes only to
pre-selected organizations.
Officers and Directors: James B. Adler, Pres. and
Treas. and Director; Eric S. Adler, V.P. and Director;
Esthy Adler, V.P. and Director; Laura Adler McGrew,
V.P. and Director.
EIN: 522070476

3810
Akridge Family Foundation

28181 Harleigh Ln.
Oxford, MD 21654-1532

Established in 2006 in Maryland.
Donors: Cyclops Family Partnership, LP; John E.
Akridge III; Sarah B. Akridge.
Foundation type: Independent foundation.
Financial data (yr. ended 12/31/13): Assets,
$51,645 (M); gifts received, $299,900;
expenditures, $274,219; qualifying distributions,
$270,362; giving activities include $270,362 for 30
grants (high: $25,000; low: $50).
Fields of interest: Arts education; Historic
preservation; Higher education; Natural resources.
Type of support: Annual campaigns.
Limitations: Applications not accepted. Giving
primarily in Washington, DC, and MD. No grants to
individuals.
Application information: Contributes only to
pre-selected organizations.
Directors: John E. Akridge III; Sarah B. Akridge.
EIN: 204904639

3811
The Allemall Foundation, Inc.

P.O. Box 25
Libertytown, MD 21762-0025

Donor: Edward D. Scott.

Foundation type: Independent foundation.
Financial data (yr. ended 06/30/13): Assets,
$2,482,715 (M); gifts received, $942,006;
expenditures, $478,167; qualifying distributions,
$144,412; giving activities include $113,503 for 15
grants (high: $50,500; low: $1,000), and $29,000
for 11 grants to individuals (high: $4,000; low:
$1,500).
Purpose and activities: Giving for wildlife and
conservation education, including scholarship
awards to students interested in wildlife and nature
conservation.
Fields of interest: Education; Domesticated
animals; Human services.
Type of support: General support; Student aid.
Limitations: Applications not accepted. Giving
primarily in FL and MD.
Application information: Unsolicited requests for
funds not accepted.
Officers: Edward D. Scott, C.E.O. and Pres.; Julia
Soistman, V.P.; Catherine D. Scott, Secy.; Carl
Hildebrand, Treas.
EIN: 200514500

3812
AMDG Foundation

c/o Patrick J. Dean
3701 Leland St.
Chevy Chase, MD 20815-4903

Donors: Patrick J. Dean; Mary R. Dean.
Foundation type: Independent foundation.
Financial data (yr. ended 12/31/13): Assets,
$12,828,045 (M); gifts received, $1,260,000;
expenditures, $468,612; qualifying distributions,
$372,554; giving activities include $330,900 for 17
grants (high: $180,000; low: $2,000) and $3 for
set-asides.
Fields of interest: Education; Health; Human
services.
Limitations: Applications not accepted.
Application information: Unsolicited requests for
funds not accepted.
Officers and Directors: Patrick J. Dean, Pres. and
Director; Mary R. Dean, Secy. and Director.
EIN: 263566999

3813
The Ammerman Foundation

9013 Holly Leaf Ln.
Bethesda, MD 20817-2656 3019838530

Established in 1986 in Maryland.
Donors: Lenell Ammerman†; Bruce Ammerman; Joy
Ammerman.
Foundation type: Independent foundation.
Financial data (yr. ended 12/31/14): Assets,
$4,024,071; expenditures, $222,390; qualifying
distributions, $205,786.
Fields of interest: Graduate and professional
education; Medical education; Environment; Natural
resources; Nonprofits; Hospital care; Judaism;
Theology.
Type of support: General support; Grants to
individuals; Continuing support; Annual campaigns;
Capital campaigns; Capital and infrastructure;
Equipment; Regranting; Land acquisitions;
Endowments; Program development;
Professorships; Curriculum development;
Fellowships; Internships; Scholarships; Research.

Limitations: Applications not accepted. Giving primarily in the Washington, DC area, including MD and VA.
Application information: Unsolicited requests for funds not accepted.
Trustees: Joshua M. Ammerman; Joy Ammerman; Matthew D. Ammerman; Rebecca A. Shpigel.
Number of staff: None.
EIN: 521320467

3814
Pauline K. Anderson Foundation, Inc.
1110 Professional Ct., Ste. 300
Hagerstown, MD 21740-5946

Established in 2001 in Maryland.
Donors: P.K. Anderson†; Presbyterian Church of Hagerstown, Inc.
Foundation type: Operating foundation.
Financial data (yr. ended 12/31/13): Assets, $6,704,152 (M); expenditures, $350,210; qualifying distributions, $277,867; giving activities include $271,000 for 13 grants (high: $40,000; low: $5,000).
Fields of interest: Education; Higher education; Foundations; Health; Health care clinics; Religion; Children's rights; Human services; Child welfare; Youth services; Scouting programs; Developmental disability services.
Type of support: General support.
Limitations: Applications not accepted. Giving primarily in Hagerstown, MD; with some giving in State Line, PA. No grants to individuals.
Application information: Contributes only to pre-selected organizations.
Officers: Robert L. Harrell, Pres.; John Itell, V.P. and Treas.; Michael G. Day, Secy.
EIN: 300021069

3815
The Lenox D. and Frances W. Baker Foundation
901 S. Bond St.
Baltimore, MD 21231-3305

Established in 2003 in Virginia.
Donor: Baker Trust.
Foundation type: Independent foundation.
Financial data (yr. ended 12/31/14): Assets, $2,227,534; expenditures, $297,410; qualifying distributions, $281,000 and $0 for set-asides.
Fields of interest: Education; Foundations; Family planning; Diseases and conditions; Human services.
Limitations: Applications not accepted. Giving primarily in MD and VA.
Application information: Contributes only to pre-selected organizations.
Trustees: Frances W. Baker; Lenox D. Baker, Jr.; Margaret W. Baker; Sara F. Baker.
EIN: 541788401

3816
Baltimore Equitable Insurance Foundation
100 N. Charles St., Ste. 640
Baltimore, MD 21201-1794 (410) 727-1794

Established in 1990 in Maryland.
Donor: The Baltimore Equitable Society.
Foundation type: Company-sponsored foundation.

Financial data (yr. ended 12/31/13): Assets, $5,967,949 (M); expenditures, $285,196; qualifying distributions, $281,065; giving activities include $278,250 for 10 grants (high: $60,000; low: $3,250).
Purpose and activities: The foundation supports organizations involved with elementary education, health, human services, and community development.
Fields of interest: Health; Housing development; Human services.
Type of support: General support; Program development.
Limitations: Applications not accepted. Giving limited to the Baltimore, MD, area. No grants to individuals.
Application information: Unsolicited requests for funds not accepted.
Officers: Richard O. Berndt, Chair.; Sharon V. Woodward, Pres. and Treas.; Juliet A. Eurich, Secy.
Directors: George L. Bunting, Jr.; Betsy Nelson.
EIN: 521645633

3817
The Baltimore Orioles Foundation
333 W. Camden St.
Baltimore, MD 21201-2435
Main URL: http://baltimore.orioles.mlb.com

Established in 1965 in Maryland.
Donors: Baltimore Orioles L.P.; ARAMARK Corp.; Touch Em All Foundation; Teammates for Kids; Azek Trim Boards; Jeremy Fefel; Melvin Mora; Miguel Tejada; Kris Benson; Brian Roberts; Orioles Reach; Military Program; RBI Program; Bird License Plates Program; J.J. Hardy; Kevin Gregg; Fanfest Merchandise/Autographs; Nicholas Markakis; Players Alumini Auction; Jackie Robinson Online Auction; Tsuyoshia Wada; Delaware North; Art of the Game.
Foundation type: Company-sponsored foundation.
Financial data (yr. ended 10/31/13): Assets, $1,157,548 (M); gifts received, $792,406; expenditures, $348,022; qualifying distributions, $346,427; giving activities include $229,120 for 15 grants (high: $75,000; low: $150).
Purpose and activities: The foundation supports sports museums and community foundations and organizations involved with orchestras, higher education, health, baseball, youth development, and human services.
Fields of interest: Orchestral music; Sport and hobby museums; Higher education; Foundations; Health; Baseball and softball; Human services; Youth development.
Type of support: General support.
Limitations: Applications accepted. Giving primarily in the Baltimore, MD area. No grants to individuals.
Application information: Application form required.
  Initial approach: Letter
  Deadline(s): None
Directors: Georgia K. Angelos; John Peter Angelos; Louis Francis Angelos; Peter G. Angelos; Joseph E. Foss.
EIN: 526058645

3818
Helen S. & Merrill L. Bank Foundation, Inc.
8 Roland Mews
Baltimore, MD 21210-1560

Established in 1969 in Maryland.
Donors: Helen S. Bank; Merrill L. Bank.
Foundation type: Independent foundation.
Financial data (yr. ended 06/30/14): Assets, $5,701,499 (M); expenditures, $417,788; qualifying distributions, $332,318; giving activities include $332,318 for 42 grants (high: $47,500; low: $250).
Purpose and activities: Giving primarily to Jewish organizations and federated giving programs; giving also for education, and health and human services.
Fields of interest: Arts and culture; Education; Nonprofits; Health; Hospital care; Diseases and conditions; Judaism; Human services.
Type of support: Regranting.
Limitations: Applications not accepted. Giving primarily in Palm Beach, FL, and Baltimore, MD.
Application information: Unsolicited requests for funds not accepted.
Officers: Penny Bank, Pres.; Herbert M. Bank, V.P.
EIN: 237031791

3819
Elsie Seeger Barton Irrevocable Trust
c/o M&T Trust Co.
25 S. Charles St.
Baltimore, MD 21201

Established in 2008 in Maryland.
Foundation type: Independent foundation.
Financial data (yr. ended 12/31/14): Assets, $4,787,709; expenditures, $310,841; qualifying distributions, $180,727.
Fields of interest: Animal welfare.
Limitations: Applications not accepted. Giving primarily in Baltimore, MD.
Application information: Unsolicited requests for funds not accepted.
Trustee: M&T Trust Co.
EIN: 526241137

3820
The Beaufort Foundation, Inc.
3013 Caves Rd.
Owings Mills, MD 21117-2909

Established in 2007 in Maryland.
Donors: Peter S. Welles; Sondra T. Welles.
Foundation type: Independent foundation.
Financial data (yr. ended 12/31/14): Assets, $1,907,783 (M); gifts received, $130,000; expenditures, $171,257; qualifying distributions, $170,923; giving activities include $170,000 for 21 grants (high: $100,000; low: $1,000).
Fields of interest: Aquariums.
Limitations: Applications not accepted. Giving primarily in CO and MD. No grants to individuals.
Application information: Unsolicited requests for funds not accepted.
Officers: Peter S. Welles, Pres.; Sondra T. Welles, V.P.; Amanda C. Welles, Secy.; Christina W. Maron, Treas.
EIN: 261606616

3821
Leo V. Berger Fund
c/o Sigmund Kassap
3635 Old Ct. Rd., Ste. 309
Baltimore, MD 21208-3907

Donor: Leo V. Berger†.
Foundation type: Independent foundation.
Financial data (yr. ended 12/31/12): Assets, $8,299,382 (M); expenditures, $446,477; qualifying distributions, $441,418; giving activities include $441,418 for grants.
Purpose and activities: Primarily local giving, with emphasis on Jewish welfare funds, hospitals, health, and education.
Fields of interest: Education; Nonprofits; Health; Hospital care; Diseases and conditions; Judaism.
Type of support: Regranting.
Limitations: Applications not accepted. Giving primarily in FL, MD, and NY. No grants to individuals.
Application information: Contributes only to pre-selected organizations.
Officers and Directors: Harvey Schwartz, Esq., Pres. and Director; Sigmund Kassap, V.P. and Director; Harry Kassap; Jason Schwartz.
EIN: 510196887

3822
Bernard Family Foundation
P.O. Box 647
Riverdale, MD 20738-0647 (301) 277-3029
Contact: Cathy S. Bernard, Tr.

Established in 2005 in Maryland.
Donor: Cathy S. Bernard.
Foundation type: Independent foundation.
Financial data (yr. ended 12/31/13): Assets, $4,359,515 (M); expenditures, $228,834; qualifying distributions, $221,339; giving activities include $200,000 for 23 grants (high: $48,000; low: $1,000).
Fields of interest: Performing arts; Theater; Education.
Limitations: Applications accepted. Giving primarily in MD.
Application information: Applicants should include their e-mail address. Application form required.
   Initial approach: Proposal
   Deadline(s): Dec. 31
Trustee: Cathy S. Bernard.
EIN: 203850421

3823
Besson Cooper Fund, Inc.
9529 Nightsong Ln.
Columbia, MD 21046-2065
Contact: Rebecca L. Besson, Pres.
Application Address: 36 S. Charles St., Ste. 1800, Baltimore, MD 21201

Donors: Rebecca L. Besson; Stuart Cooper.
Foundation type: Independent foundation.
Financial data (yr. ended 12/31/13): Assets, $4,947,519 (M); expenditures, $309,656; qualifying distributions, $265,869; giving activities include $265,869 for 33 grants (high: $75,679; low: $1,000).
Fields of interest: Arts and culture; Education; Domesticated animals.
Officers: Rebecca L. Besson, Pres. and Treas.; Stuart Cooper, V.P.; David A. Goldner, Secy.
EIN: 454076695

3824
The Biophilia Foundation, Inc.
P.O. Box 1753
Easton, MD 21601-8935 (410) 268-1802
Contact: Richard G. Pritzlaff, Pres.
FAX: (410) 268-1803; E-mail: biophilia@verizon.net; Additional address: c/o The Pritzlaff Ranch HC 68, Box 11A Sapello, New Mexico 87745; tel.: (505) 454-8382; Main URL: http://www.biophiliafoundation.org

Established in 1999 in New Mexico.
Donors: Magothy River Land Trust; Mrs. John C. Pritzlaff, Jr.; Richard G. Pritzlaff.
Foundation type: Operating foundation.
Financial data (yr. ended 12/31/13): Assets, $5,143,256 (M); expenditures, $413,903; qualifying distributions, $201,754; giving activities include $142,665 for 3 grants (high: $100,000; low: $10,000), and $59,089 for 1 foundation-administered program.
Purpose and activities: Giving primarily to support efforts to protect and restore wildlife habitats; also giving to programs that help reconnect individuals with nature.
Fields of interest: Natural resources; Biodiversity; Wildlife biodiversity.
Type of support: Equipment; Matching grants; Land acquisitions; Program development; Convening; Seed money; Technical assistance.
Limitations: Applications not accepted. Giving primarily in Washington, DC, MD, and NM. No grants to individuals.
Publications: Multi-year report.
Application information: Contributes only to pre-selected organizations.
   Board meeting date(s): Feb. and Aug.
Officer and Directors: Richard G. Pritzlaff, Pres. and Director; John Edward Gerber, Treas. and Director; Christopher Pupke, Exec. Dir.
Number of staff: 6 full-time professional; 1 part-time professional.
EIN: 522199334

3825
The Blum Family Foundation Inc.
(formerly The Samuel Blum Foundation, Inc.)
233 E. Redwood St., Garrett Bldg., Ste. 100
Baltimore, MD 21202-3332 (410) 685-4606
Contact: Marc P. Blum, Pres.

Donors: Alvin H. Blum; Claire Stampfer; Alex D. Blum; Ari Blum; James D. Blum.
Foundation type: Independent foundation.
Financial data (yr. ended 06/30/14): Assets, $3,908,941 (M); gifts received, $603,632; expenditures, $327,232; qualifying distributions, $321,380; giving activities include $100,000 for 250 grants.
Fields of interest: Education; Judaism; Human services.
Limitations: Applications accepted. Giving primarily in Baltimore, MD.
Application information: Application form required.
   Initial approach: Proposal
   Deadline(s): None
Officers and Directors: Marc P. Blum, Pres. and Director; James Blum, V.P. and Treas. and Director; Ari Blum, V.P.; Claire Stampfer, V.P. and Director; Emily Clayton, Secy.
EIN: 526039023

3826
Hershel & Esther Boehm Charity Fund
5919 Winner Ave.
Baltimore, MD 21215-3801
Contact: Howard M. Boehm, Pres.

Established in 1997 in Maryland.
Donors: Howard M. Boehm; Esther Boehm; Hershel Boehm.
Foundation type: Independent foundation.
Financial data (yr. ended 12/31/13): Assets, $1,149,178 (M); gifts received, $400,000; expenditures, $429,593; qualifying distributions, $429,593; giving activities include $429,593 for 210 grants (high: $51,410; low: $5).
Purpose and activities: Giving primarily for Jewish agencies and temples.
Fields of interest: Education; Judaism; Human services.
International interests: Israel.
Limitations: Applications accepted. Giving primarily in Baltimore, MD and New York, NY; giving also in Israel.
Application information: Application form required.
   Initial approach: Letter
   Deadline(s): None
Officers: Howard M. Boehm, Pres.; Esther Boehm, V.P.; Ronny S. Retter, Secy.
EIN: 522005744

3827
The Braitmayer Foundation
4725 Dorsey Hall Dr., Ste. A308
Ellicott City, MD 21042-7713 (410) 480-2799
Contact: Sabina Taj, Advisor
E-mail: sabina@braitmayerfoundation.org; Main URL: http://www.braitmayerfoundation.org
Grants List: http://www.braitmayerfoundation.org/2012/2011-grant-recipients
Grants List: http://www.braitmayerfoundation.org/2013/2012-grant-recipients
Grants List: http://www.braitmayerfoundation.org/2014/2013-grant-recipients
Grants List: http://www.braitmayerfoundation.org/grant-recipients

Established in 1964 in Massachusetts.
Donor: Marian S. Braitmayer†.
Foundation type: Independent foundation.
Financial data (yr. ended 12/31/13): Assets, $4,318,784 (M); expenditures, $266,439; qualifying distributions, $201,290; giving activities include $153,000 for 12 grants (high: $36,000; low: $1,000).
Purpose and activities: Support primarily for K-12 education. Of particular interest are curricular and school reform initiatives and preparation of, and professional development opportunities for, K-12 teachers. In addition, the foundation provides modest support of activities in Marion, MA, and surrounding communities which will improve the quality of life for residents in the area.
Fields of interest: Education; Elementary and secondary education; Elementary education; Secondary education; Cooperative education.
Type of support: Program development; Matching grants; Seed money; Curriculum development; Systems reform.
Limitations: Applications accepted. Giving on a national basis; interest also in Marion, MA, and surrounding communities. No grants to individuals, or for building, general operating purposes, endowment funds, or multi-year grants. Unless a

small percentage of the total amount requested, normally the foundation does not make grants for childcare, pre-kindergarten, after school programs, or for equipment including hardware, software, and books.

Publications: Application guidelines; Grants list; Program policy statement.

Application information: Faxed or e-mailed applications are not accepted. Applications are to be sent online, through the foundation's web site only. See foundation web site for additional details.

Initial approach: 2-page Letter of Inquiry via foundation web site

Deadline(s): Invited organizations will need to submit full proposals by Oct. 15

Board meeting date(s): Biannually

Final notification: Mar. 15

Officer and Trustees: R. Davis Webb, Jr., Chair. and Trustee; Eric A. Braitmayer; John W. Braitmayer; Karen L. Braitmayer; Nancy W. Corkery; Kristina B. Hewey; Anne B. Webb.

Number of staff: 1 part-time professional.

EIN: 046112131

3828
The Bresler Foundation, Inc.
10401 Grosvenor Pl., Ste. 1703
Rockville, MD 20852-4644

Donor: Charles S. Bresler†.

Foundation type: Independent foundation.

Financial data (yr. ended 12/31/14): Assets, $4,978,896 (M); expenditures, $249,827; qualifying distributions, $248,000; giving activities include $248,000 for 78 grants (high: $27,500; low: $250).

Fields of interest: Museums; Philanthropy; Human services.

Type of support: General support.

Limitations: Applications not accepted. Giving primarily in the metropolitan Washington, DC, area, including MD. No grants to individuals.

Application information: Unsolicited requests for funds not accepted.

Officers: Edward Bresler, Pres.; Amanda Bresler, Secy.; Carol Bresler, Treas.

EIN: 521589693

3829
The Broadus Charitable Foundation
(formerly The Elizabeth H. and Thomas H. Broadus Charitable Foundation)
P.O. Box 16360
Baltimore, MD 21210-0360 (410) 377-0271
Contact: Thomas H. Broadus III, Tr.

Established in 1986 in Maryland.

Donors: Lucy E. Broadus; Thomas H. Broadus III.

Foundation type: Independent foundation.

Financial data (yr. ended 12/31/13): Assets, $4,914,682 (M); expenditures, $199,277; qualifying distributions, $198,502; giving activities include $195,000 for 20 grants (high: $53,500; low: $250).

Fields of interest: Arts and culture; Education; Secondary education; Foundations.

Type of support: General support; Annual campaigns; Capital campaigns; Scholarships.

Limitations: Applications accepted. Giving primarily in MD, MA and NC.

Application information: Application form required.

Initial approach: Letter

Copies of proposal: 1

Deadline(s): None

Trustees: Lucy E. Broadus; Thomas H. Broadus III.

EIN: 526287380

3830
The Buffy and William Cafritz Family Foundation, Inc.
7315 Wisconsin Ave., Ste. 250 E
Bethesda, MD 20814-3202

Established in 2006 in Maryland.

Donor: William N. Cafritz Trust.

Foundation type: Independent foundation.

Financial data (yr. ended 12/31/13): Assets, $1,687,036 (M); gifts received, $400,325; expenditures, $313,301; qualifying distributions, $300,500; giving activities include $300,500 for 42 grants (high: $65,500; low: $100).

Fields of interest: Performing arts; Academic libraries.

Limitations: Applications not accepted. No grants to individuals.

Application information: Unsolicited requests for funds not accepted.

Officers and Directors: William N. Cafritz, Pres. and Director; Charles C. Wilkes, Secy.-Treas. and Director; Buffy M. Cafritz; Pamela Anne Cafritz.

EIN: 205657328

3831
Campbell Foundation, Inc.
8 Candlelight Ct.
Timonium, MD 21093-2808
Application address: c/o Virginia T. Campbell, 705 York Rd., Baltimore, MD 21204

Donor: Nottingham Properties, Inc.

Foundation type: Independent foundation.

Financial data (yr. ended 12/31/13): Assets, $3,785,127 (M); expenditures, $197,408; qualifying distributions, $162,000; giving activities include $162,000 for 95 grants (high: $10,000; low: $500).

Purpose and activities: Grants primarily for culture and education; support also for child welfare, health and social services.

Fields of interest: Arts and culture; Education; Health; Human services; Child welfare.

Type of support: General support; Continuing support; Annual campaigns; Capital campaigns; Capital and infrastructure; Endowments; Scholarships.

Limitations: Applications accepted. Giving primarily in the greater Baltimore, MD, area. No support for religious organizations. No grants to individuals.

Application information:

Initial approach: Letter

Copies of proposal: 1

Deadline(s): None

Board meeting date(s): Nov. or early Dec.

Officers: Virginia T. Campbell, Pres.; Taber Campbell Hook, Secy.; Bruce S. Campbell III, Treas.

Directors: J. Tyler Campbell; Mary Jo Campbell; Lynn Kelz; Marcie McHale.

EIN: 520794348

3832
Caplan Family Foundation Inc.
11433 Crondridge Dr.
Owings Mills, MD 21117-3528 (443) 796-7373
Contact: Justine Fields

Established in 1996 in Maryland.

Donors: Caswell Caplan First Charitable Inc. Trust; Caswell Caplan Second Charitable Inc. Trust.

Foundation type: Independent foundation.

Financial data (yr. ended 12/31/13): Assets, $2,396,607 (M); expenditures, $183,178; qualifying distributions, $172,164; giving activities include $169,636 for grants.

Purpose and activities: Giving for education and socio-economic issues, culture, and the beautification of Baltimore, Maryland.

Fields of interest: Religion; Human services.

Type of support: Annual campaigns; Capital campaigns; Endowments; Program development; Curriculum development; Fellowships.

Limitations: Applications accepted. Giving primarily in Baltimore, MD.

Application information: Application form required.

Initial approach: Letter

Deadline(s): None

Officers: Constance R. Caplan, Pres. and Secy.; Mark M. Caplan, V.P. and Treas.

Directors: Catherine Caplan; Jonathan Caplan; Eugene Schreiber.

Number of staff: 1 part-time support.

EIN: 522005222

3833
Nelson & Michelle Carbonell Foundation
c/o John Carbonell
9901 Founders Way
Damascus, MD 20872-2900

Established in 2000 in Virginia.

Donors: Nelson Carbonell; Michelle Carbonell.

Foundation type: Independent foundation.

Financial data (yr. ended 12/31/13): Assets, $8,526,448 (M); gifts received, $431; expenditures, $449,715; qualifying distributions, $411,721; giving activities include $407,200 for 11 grants (high: $170,000; low: $2,000).

Fields of interest: Education; Diseases and conditions; Human services.

Limitations: Applications not accepted. Giving primarily in CA and the greater metropolitan Washington, DC, area, including MD and VA. No grants to individuals.

Application information: Contributes only to pre-selected organizations.

Officer: John N. Carbonell, Pres. and Secy.

EIN: 522272147

3834
Ruth Carol Fund, Inc.
830 W. 40th St., Apt. 408
Baltimore, MD 21211-2126

Established in 2004 in Maryland.

Donor: Ruth R. Marder.

Foundation type: Independent foundation.

Financial data (yr. ended 12/31/12): Assets, $23,502,257 (M); gifts received, $20,253,486; expenditures, $324,721; qualifying distributions, $180,000; giving activities include $180,000 for grants.

Fields of interest: Health; Specialty hospital care; Human services.
Limitations: Applications not accepted. Giving primarily in MD. No grants to individuals.
Application information: Contributes only to pre-selected organizations.
Officers and Directors: Donald R. Mering, Pres. and Secy. and Director; Sanford S. Donald, V.P. and Treas. and Director.
EIN: 202013753

3835
Chessie Foundation, Inc.
4701 Willard Ave., Ste. 225
Chevy Chase, MD 20815-4615
Contact: James E. Pollin

Established in 2007 in Maryland.
Donor: Abe Pollin†.
Foundation type: Independent foundation.
Financial data (yr. ended 12/31/13): Assets, $3,790,536 (M); expenditures, $267,569; qualifying distributions, $254,783; giving activities include $245,560 for 6 grants (high: $133,060; low: $5,000).
Fields of interest: Education; Judaism; Human services; Youth services.
Limitations: Applications not accepted. Giving primarily in CA, MD and MA. No grants to individuals.
Application information: Contributes only to pre-selected organizations.
Directors: Ilene Ellenbogen; James E. Pollin.
EIN: 204710139

3836
The Clifton Foundation Inc.
c/o Richard L. Goodall
1 Byford Ct.
Chestertown, MD 21620-1641

Established in 2000 in Maryland.
Donors: Richard L. Goodall; Richard T. Goodall; Laura K. Goodall; Rosalie L. Goodall†.
Foundation type: Independent foundation.
Financial data (yr. ended 09/30/13): Assets, $7,536,997 (M); gifts received, $3,000,000; expenditures, $217,705; qualifying distributions, $205,012; giving activities include $180,000 for 17 grants (high: $30,000; low: $1,000).
Fields of interest: Philanthropy; Human services.
Type of support: General support.
Limitations: Applications not accepted. Giving primarily in MD. No grants to individuals.
Application information: Unsolicited requests for funds not accepted.
Officers and Directors: Richard L. Goodall, Pres. and Treas. and Director; Lauralea T. Goodall, V.P. and Director; Laura K.G. Gray, Secy. and Director; Richard T. Goodall; James S. Maffitt, Esq.
EIN: 522256618

3837
The Blavatt Glazer Cogan Foundation, Inc.
(formerly The Benjamin and Belle Cogan Foundation, Inc.)
2700 Stone Cliff Dr., Ste. 407
Baltimore, MD 21209-3863

Established in 2001 in Maryland.
Donor: Cogan Charitable Trust.

Foundation type: Independent foundation.
Financial data (yr. ended 04/30/15): Assets, $3,529,309 (M); expenditures, $185,256; qualifying distributions, $173,650; giving activities include $173,650 for 29 grants (high: $45,300; low: $50).
Fields of interest: Education; Health; Religion; Judaism.
Limitations: Applications not accepted. Giving on a national basis, with emphasis on MD. No grants to individuals.
Application information: Unsolicited requests for funds not accepted.
Officers: Ronald Blavatt, Pres.; Jeffrey Blavatt, V.P.; Jason Blavatt, Secy.-Treas.
EIN: 522333696

3838
The Abraham J. Cohen Family Charitable Foundation Inc.
c/o Goldman & Goldman
2330 W. Joppa Rd., Ste. 300
Lutherville, MD 21093 (410) 296-0888
Contact: Brian A. Goldman, Chair., V.P. and Tr.

Established in 2007 in Maryland.
Donor: Abraham J. Cohen Trust.
Foundation type: Independent foundation.
Financial data (yr. ended 12/31/13): Assets, $4,017,481 (M); expenditures, $269,901; qualifying distributions, $201,000; giving activities include $201,000 for 8 grants (high: $75,000; low: $1,000).
Fields of interest: Judaism.
Limitations: Applications accepted. Giving primarily in MD and NY. No grants to individuals.
Application information: Application form required.
   Initial approach: Letter
   Deadline(s): None
Officers and Trustees: Brian A. Goldman, Chair. and V.P. and Trustee; Alan J. Denis, Pres. and Trustee; Marc B. Terrill.
EIN: 830489792

3839
The Cole Foundation Inc.
2106 Lippizan Ct.
Fallston, MD 21047-1627
Contact: Barbara S. Ford

Established in 1994 in Maryland.
Donor: Roland H. Cole.
Foundation type: Independent foundation.
Financial data (yr. ended 12/31/13): Assets, $3,456,790 (M); expenditures, $269,630; qualifying distributions, $230,000; giving activities include $230,000 for 24 grants (high: $30,000; low: $2,000).
Fields of interest: Nonprofits; Hospice care; Diseases and conditions; Heart and circulatory system diseases; Housing development; Catholicism; Human services; Food delivery; People with disabilities; People with vision impairments.
Type of support: Research; Regranting.
Limitations: Applications not accepted. Giving primarily in MD. No grants to individuals.
Application information: Contributes only to pre-selected organizations.
Officers: Barbara S. Ford, Pres.; Bette Ann Tassone, V.P.; Beth L. Mack, Secy.-Treas.

Directors: Bonnie J. Cole; Ellen L. Cole.
EIN: 521907361

3840
The Contino Family Foundation
c/o Neuman
575 S. Charles St., Ste. 402
Baltimore, MD 21201-2484

Donors: Francis A. Contino; Betty Contino.
Foundation type: Independent foundation.
Financial data (yr. ended 12/31/13): Assets, $1,369,468 (M); gifts received, $4,500; expenditures, $194,993; qualifying distributions, $189,470; giving activities include $186,000 for 7 grants (high: $100,000; low: $1,000).
Fields of interest: Nonprofits; Catholicism; Human services.
Type of support: General support; Regranting; Capital campaigns.
Limitations: Applications not accepted. Giving primarily in MD. No grants to individuals.
Application information: Contributes only to pre-selected organizations.
Trustee: Francis A. Contino.
EIN: 861116070

3841
L. Gordon Gordon Croft Foundation Inc.
(formerly Leominster-Croft Foundation, Inc.)
Canton House, 300 Water St.
Baltimore, MD 21202-3330 (410) 576-8231
Contact: L. Gordon Croft, V.P.

Established in 1990 in Maryland.
Donors: Leominster, Inc.; L. Gordon Croft; Jane Aurell Croft.
Foundation type: Company-sponsored foundation.
Financial data (yr. ended 12/31/13): Assets, $5,872,576 (M); expenditures, $314,953; qualifying distributions, $301,939; giving activities include $299,846 for 64 grants (high: $248,065; low: $50).
Purpose and activities: The foundation supports organizations involved with education, the environment, health, human services, economically disadvantaged people, and homeless people.
Fields of interest: Education; Agriculture; Community and economic development.
Type of support: General support; Capital and infrastructure.
Limitations: Applications accepted. Giving primarily in MD.
Application information: Application form required.
   Initial approach: Letter
   Deadline(s): None
Officers: Kent Gordon Croft, Pres.; L. Gordon Croft, V.P.; Jane Aurell Croft, Secy.
EIN: 521682796

3842
CSG Foundation, Inc.
8401 Connecticut Ave., Ste. 1204
Chevy Chase, MD 20815-5821 (301) 907-4606
Contact: Carol F. Doolan, Exec. Dir.
FAX: (301) 652-9173;
E-mail: cdoolan.csgfoundation@verizon.net

Established in 1986 in Maryland.

Donors: Christopher S. Abell; Gregory T. Abell; W. Shepherdson Abell.
Foundation type: Independent foundation.
Financial data (yr. ended 12/31/13): Assets, $225,263 (M); expenditures, $189,737; qualifying distributions, $189,383; giving activities include $172,301 for 1 grant.
Purpose and activities: The primary focus is on projects for children age 3 and under, especially in low-income populations, involving 1) prenatal, neonatal and early childhood health care, especially in community-based settings, and 2) the treatment of emotional, mental and developmental disorders in young children.
Fields of interest: Prenatal care; Infant care; Diseases and conditions; Human services; Child welfare; Child development; Low-income and poor people.
Type of support: Continuing support; Matching grants; Program development.
Limitations: Applications not accepted. Giving limited to Washington, DC, Prince George's and Montgomery counties, MD, and northern VA. No support for programs for children age 4 or older, or for organizations supporting abortion. No grants to individuals, or for scholarships or building funds; no consecutive-year grant making.
Publications: Grants list; Program policy statement.
Application information: Unsolicited requests for funds not accepted.
   Board meeting date(s): Mar. and Sept.
Officers: Gregory T. Abell, Pres.; Christopher S. Abell, V.P.; W. Shepherdson Abell, Secy.-Treas.
Number of staff: 1 part-time professional.
EIN: 521488382

3843
Darby Foundation
c/o Choptank Partners, Inc.
P.O. Box 1410
Easton, MD   21601-3196   (410) 820-4300
Contact: Katherine D. Brady, Secy.-Treas.

Established in 1966 in New Jersey.
Donor: Nicholas F. Brady.
Foundation type: Independent foundation.
Financial data (yr. ended 12/31/13): Assets, $5,215,191 (M); gifts received, $3,109,511; expenditures, $404,720; qualifying distributions, $401,500; giving activities include $401,500 for 8 grants (high: $250,000; low: $500).
Fields of interest: Higher education; Human services.
Type of support: Annual campaigns; Capital campaigns.
Limitations: Applications accepted. Giving primarily in CT, Washington, DC, NJ, and NY.
Application information: Application form required.
   Initial approach: Letter
   Deadline(s): None
Officers: Nicholas F. Brady, Pres.; Katherine D. Brady, Secy.-Treas.
Number of staff: None.
EIN: 136212178

3844
Cora and John H. Davis Foundation, Inc.
1401 Rockville Pike, Ste. 560
Rockville, MD   20852-1434
Application address: c/o Stuart L. Bindeman, 7101 Wisconsin Ave., Ste. 1203, Bethesda, MD 20814, tel.: (301) 907-7200

Established in 1983 in District of Columbia.
Donors: Cora Davis†; John H. Davis†.
Foundation type: Independent foundation.
Financial data (yr. ended 12/31/14): Assets, $12,037,575 (M); expenditures, $553,955; qualifying distributions, $479,574; giving activities include $395,000 for 31 grants (high: $35,000; low: $2,500).
Purpose and activities: Giving primarily for education, youth and social services, hospitals and health associations, and Jewish social service agencies.
Fields of interest: Arts and culture; Performing arts; Secondary education; Higher education; University education; Hospital care; Diseases and conditions; Judaism; Human services; Family services; Youth services.
Type of support: General support; Continuing support; Annual campaigns; Capital campaigns; Capital and infrastructure; Equipment; Emergency funds; Scholarships; Research.
Limitations: Applications accepted. Giving primarily in the Washington, DC, area, including MD.
Application information: Application form required.
   Initial approach: Letter
   Copies of proposal: 1
   Deadline(s): None
Officers: Stuart L. Bindeman, Pres.; Harold Zirkin, V.P.; Michael F. Glazer, Secy.-Treas.
Number of staff: 3 part-time professional.
EIN: 521282054

3845
The Daydreams Foundation, Inc.
8511 Rapley Preserve Cir.
Potomac, MD   20854-5475

Established in 2007 in Maryland.
Donor: Mary Grace Day.
Foundation type: Independent foundation.
Financial data (yr. ended 12/31/14): Assets, $2,660,667 (M); gifts received, $3,500; expenditures, $139,953; qualifying distributions, $125,000; giving activities include $125,000 for 2 grants (high: $100,000; low: $25,000).
Fields of interest: Education; Health.
Type of support: Research.
Limitations: Applications not accepted. Giving primarily in MD. No grants to individuals.
Application information: Unsolicited requests for funds not accepted.
Officers: Mary Grace Day, Pres.; Lynn Marie Brown, V.P.; Gary Wayne Day, V.P.
EIN: 208119196

3846
Joel Dean Foundation Inc.
c/o Jurrien Dean
7422 Hampden Ln.
Bethesda, MD   20814-1366

Established in 1957 in New York.
Donors: Joel Dean; Joel Dean Assoc. Corp.

Foundation type: Independent foundation.
Financial data (yr. ended 12/31/13): Assets, $6,257,415 (M); expenditures, $237,982; qualifying distributions, $231,750; giving activities include $231,500 for 48 grants (high: $57,000; low: $500).
Fields of interest: Arts and culture; Secondary education; Higher education; University education.
Type of support: General support; Scholarships.
Limitations: Applications not accepted. Giving primarily in CA, Washington, DC, MA and MD. No grants to individuals.
Application information: Contributes only to pre-selected organizations.
Officers and Directors: Jurrien Dean, Pres. and Treas.; Gillian Dean, V.P. and Director; Joel Dean, Jr., V.P. and Director.
EIN: 136097306

3847
The Carl DelSignore Foundation, Inc.
927 Braddock Rd.
Cumberland, MD   21502-2624   (301) 777-2772
Contact: G. Douglas Reinhard, Secy.

Established in 1986 in Maryland.
Donor: Carl DelSignore†.
Foundation type: Independent foundation.
Financial data (yr. ended 04/30/13): Assets, $4,185,680 (M); expenditures, $270,501; qualifying distributions, $171,347; giving activities include $171,347 for 38 grants (high: $52,000; low: $719).
Fields of interest: Higher education; Hospital care; Community and economic development; Protestantism; Catholicism; Child welfare.
Limitations: Applications accepted. Giving primarily in western MD and WV. No grants to individuals.
Application information:
   Initial approach: Proposal
   Deadline(s): None
Officers: R. Donald Cussins, Pres.; Carmen P. DelSignore, V.P.; G. Douglas Reinhard, Secy.; James L. Crickard, Treas.
EIN: 521489402

3848
The Devito Family Trust
(formerly The Beechmont Foundation)
c/o Mathias J. DeVito
Village Sq. 2, Ste. 220
5100 Falls Rd.
Baltimore, MD   21210-1935

Established in 1994 in Maryland.
Donor: Mathias J. DeVito.
Foundation type: Independent foundation.
Financial data (yr. ended 12/31/14): Assets, $5,589,941 (M); expenditures, $342,477; qualifying distributions, $278,150.
Fields of interest: Arts education; Elementary and secondary education; Higher education; Nonprofits; Hospital care; Diseases and conditions; Religion; Christianity; Human services; Youth services.
Type of support: Regranting.
Limitations: Applications not accepted. Giving primarily in Baltimore, MD. No grants to individuals.
Application information: Contributes only to pre-selected organizations.

Officer and Trustees: Ann DeVito Walker, Exec. Dir. and Trustee; Mathias J. DeVito; Rosetta K. DeVito.
EIN: 526705998

3849
Dockser Family Foundation, Inc.
c/o CRI, Inc.
11200 Rockville Pike, No. 300
Rockville, MD 20852-7101
Contact: William B. Dockser, Dir.
E-mail: billdockser@crimail.com

Donor: William B. Dockser.
Foundation type: Independent foundation.
Financial data (yr. ended 12/31/13): Assets, $2,963,542 (M); gifts received, $253,837; expenditures, $213,447; qualifying distributions, $210,701; giving activities include $210,701 for 34 grants (high: $50,000; low: $100).
Purpose and activities: Giving primarily to international women's advocacy groups.
Fields of interest: Arts and culture; Education; Nonprofits; Specialty hospital care; Human services; Females.
Type of support: Regranting.
Limitations: Applications not accepted. Giving primarily in the Washington, DC and MD. No grants to individuals.
Application information: Contributes only to pre-selected organizations.
Directors: Bradford H. Dockser; Saundra L. Dockser; William B. Dockser.
EIN: 521939143

3850
Doorstep Ministry Foundation, Inc.
(formerly Criste Family Foundation, Inc.)
P.O. Box 710
Riderwood, MD 21139-0710

Established in 1993 in Maryland.
Donors: Hildebert F. Criste; Mary Ellen Criste.
Foundation type: Independent foundation.
Financial data (yr. ended 12/31/14): Assets, $1,358,778; gifts received, $0; expenditures, $221,345; qualifying distributions, $211,644 and $0 for set-asides.
Purpose and activities: Giving primarily to Christian religious organizations and missions; funding also for human services and education.
Fields of interest: Secondary education; Higher education; Radio; Christianity; Human services; Family services; Youth services.
International interests: India; Nepal; South Africa; Thailand.
Limitations: Applications accepted. Giving primarily in FL, MD, and VA, as well as in India, Nepal, South Africa, and Thailand.
Application information: Application form required.
Initial approach: Proposal
Deadline(s): None
Officers: Mary Ellen Criste, Pres.; Hildebert F. Criste, V.P.; Walter F. Galbraith, Treas.
EIN: 521827165

3851
Harry F. Duncan Foundation, Inc.
409 Washington Ave., Ste. 900
Towson, MD 21204-4905

Established in 1955 in Delaware.
Donor: Harry F. Duncan.
Foundation type: Independent foundation.
Financial data (yr. ended 12/31/13): Assets, $4,315,489 (M); expenditures, $190,783; qualifying distributions, $171,300; giving activities include $127,300 for 32 grants (high: $22,500; low: $500), and $38,000 for 13 grants to individuals (high: $5,000; low: $2,000).
Purpose and activities: Grants primarily for church support and other religious programs. Also operates the Harry F. Duncan American Dream Scholarship program.
Fields of interest: Historic preservation; Education; Christianity; Human services; Food aid; Child welfare.
Limitations: Applications not accepted. Giving primarily in MO.
Application information: Unsolicited requests for funds not accepted.
Officers: Anneliese H. Duncan, Pres. and Treas.; Louis F. Friedman, V.P.; Phyllis C. Friedman, Secy.
EIN: 526054187

3852
The Eacho Family Foundation
c/o Santos, Postal and Co.
11 N. Washington St., Ste. 600
Rockville, MD 20850-4277 2404992040

Established in 1997 in Virginia.
Donor: William C. Eacho III.
Foundation type: Independent foundation.
Financial data (yr. ended 12/31/14): Assets, $2,032,485; gifts received, $200,000; expenditures, $154,331; qualifying distributions, $136,230.
Purpose and activities: Giving primarily for education.
Fields of interest: Elementary and secondary education; Higher education; Youth services.
Limitations: Applications not accepted. Giving primarily in the greater Washington, DC, area, with some emphasis on MD and MA. No grants to individuals.
Application information: Contributes only to pre-selected organizations.
Officer and Director: Donna W. Eacho, Pres. and Director.
EIN: 541879808

3853
The Eccles Family Foundation
3407 Raymond St.
Chevy Chase, MD 20815-3229

Established in 2001 in Maryland.
Donors: Robert Eccles; Mary Eccles.
Foundation type: Independent foundation.
Financial data (yr. ended 12/31/13): Assets, $4,774,224 (M); gifts received, $89,120; expenditures, $243,659; qualifying distributions, $237,480; giving activities include $237,480 for 21 grants (high: $35,000; low: $1,000).
Fields of interest: Education; Health; Human services; Family services; Children.
Limitations: Applications not accepted. No grants to individuals.
Application information: Unsolicited requests for funds not accepted.

Trustees: Mary Eccles; Robert Eccles.
EIN: 527132892

3854
The Ellasberg Family Foundation, Inc.
7 St. Paul St., Ste. 920
Baltimore, MD 21202-1687 (410) 752-7100

Established in 1980 in Maryland.
Donor: Richard A. Eliasberg.
Foundation type: Independent foundation.
Financial data (yr. ended 12/31/14): Assets, $8,386,903; expenditures, $494,096; qualifying distributions, $413,957.
Purpose and activities: Giving primarily for the arts, education, health and hospitals, including children's hospitals, and to Jewish organizations.
Fields of interest: Arts and culture; Education; Higher education; Nonprofits; Health; Specialty hospital care; Diseases and conditions; Judaism.
Type of support: General support; Annual campaigns; Endowments; Regranting.
Limitations: Applications accepted. Giving primarily in Baltimore, MD. No grants to individuals.
Application information:
Initial approach: Proposal
Deadline(s): None
Board meeting date(s): Quarterly
Officers and Trustees: Richard A. Eliasberg, Chair. and Pres. and Trustee; Benjamin Greenwald, Vice-Chair. and Trustee; H. Voss Eliasberg, V.P.; Gail E. Redtman, Secy. and Trustee; Ilona B. Winter, Treas.; Ann Betten; Douglas Hoffberger; Jeffrey Weiner.
EIN: 521199165

3855
Elno Family Foundation, Inc.
6705 Bonaventure Ct., Ste. 716
Bethesda, MD 20817-4026

Established in 1995 in Maryland.
Donors: Kathy Dweck; Morris Dweck; Elana Dweck; Noah Dweck; Susan Dweck.
Foundation type: Independent foundation.
Financial data (yr. ended 12/31/13): Assets, $4,957,071 (M); gifts received, $59,000; expenditures, $240,636; qualifying distributions, $222,684; giving activities include $217,681 for 75 grants (high: $41,525; low: $100).
Fields of interest: Judaism.
Limitations: Applications accepted. Giving primarily in Washington, DC, and New York, NY.
Application information:
Initial approach: Proposal
Deadline(s): None
Directors: Kathy Dweck; Morris Dweck; Susan Dweck.
EIN: 521937414

3856
Elsberg Family Foundation, Inc.
303 N. Queen St.
Chestertown, MD 21620-1629

Established in 1998 in Maryland.
Donors: Stuart M. Elsberg; Andrew Elsberg; Daniel Elsberg; Margery Elsberg; Jonathan S. Teller-Elsberg.
Foundation type: Independent foundation.

Financial data (yr. ended 12/31/14): Assets, $4,144,527; gifts received, $0; expenditures, $256,970; qualifying distributions, $209,400.
Fields of interest: Environment; Nonprofits; Health; Specialty hospital care; Judaism; Human services.
Type of support: Regranting.
Limitations: Applications not accepted.
Application information: Unsolicited requests for funds not accepted.
Officers and Trustees: Stuart M. Elsberg, Pres. and Trustee; Margery Elsberg, Secy.-Treas. and Trustee; Andrew Elsberg; Daniel Elsberg; Jonathan S. Teller-Elsberg.
EIN: 522103325

3857
The Feinberg Foundation
8014 Greentree Rd.
Bethesda, MD   20817-1304
Contact: Robert Feinberg, Dir.

Established in 1960 in Maryland.
Donors: Harry Feinberg†; Robert Feinberg.
Foundation type: Independent foundation.
Financial data (yr. ended 12/31/13): Assets, $7,670,618 (M); expenditures, $404,739; qualifying distributions, $350,000; giving activities include $350,000 for 5 grants (high: $100,000; low: $25,000).
Purpose and activities: Giving primarily for arts and cultural programs.
Fields of interest: Arts and culture; Orchestral music; Art museums.
Limitations: Applications not accepted. Giving primarily in Baltimore, MD, and in Washington, DC. No grants to individuals.
Application information: Unsolicited requests for funds not accepted.
Officers: Robert Feinberg, Pres. and Treas.; Besty Feinberg, V.P.; Ronald Dweck, Secy.
EIN: 237000380

3858
Gretchen V. & Samuel M. Feldman Private Foundation, Inc.
10045 Red Run Blvd., Ste. 250
Owings Mills, MD   21117-5907

Established in 1997 in Maryland.
Donors: Samuel M. Feldman; Gretchen V. Feldman; Samuel Feldman Revocable Trust.
Foundation type: Independent foundation.
Financial data (yr. ended 12/31/13): Assets, $2,317,016 (M); expenditures, $236,493; qualifying distributions, $219,422; giving activities include $219,422 for 106 grants (high: $25,000; low: $15).
Purpose and activities: Giving for education, health, medical and community services, and for Jewish organizations.
Fields of interest: Education; Land resources; Health; Community health care; Infant care; Eye diseases; Judaism; Human services.
Type of support: General support; Program-related investments.
Limitations: Applications not accepted. Giving primarily in MA. No grants to individuals.
Application information: Unsolicited requests for funds not accepted.

Officers: Gretchen V. Feldman, Chair.; Samuel M. Feldman, Pres.; Leigh E. Feldman, V.P. and Secy.; Dene E. Feldman, V.P. and Treas.
EIN: 522034763

3859
Constance and Carl Ferris Charitable Operating Foundation
901 S. Bond St., Ste. 400
Baltimore, MD   21231-3340   (410) 537-5458

Established in 2006 in Maryland.
Donors: Carl W. Ferris; Constance F. Ferris.
Foundation type: Operating foundation.
Financial data (yr. ended 12/31/13): Assets, $6,979,274 (M); expenditures, $332,055; qualifying distributions, $288,500; giving activities include $288,500 for 18 grants (high: $50,000; low: $5,000).
Fields of interest: University education; Hospital care.
Limitations: Applications accepted. Giving primarily in MD.
Application information:
  Initial approach: Letter
  Deadline(s): None
Officers: Constance F. Meyer, Pres.; Paul R. Alford, V.P.; John C. Poulton, Secy.-Treas.
EIN: 205568159

3860
The Ferris Family Foundation
(formerly George M. Ferris, Jr. Foundation)
6616 Lybrook Ct.
Bethesda, MD   20817-3029   (301) 922-2700
Contact: Karen Beardsly

Established in 1992 in Maryland.
Donors: George M. Ferris, Jr.†; Nancy S. Ferris.
Foundation type: Independent foundation.
Financial data (yr. ended 12/31/13): Assets, $7,653,845 (M); expenditures, $413,882; qualifying distributions, $374,985; giving activities include $374,985 for 63 grants (high: $94,375; low: $50).
Fields of interest: Education; Zoos; Specialty hospital care; Human services; Child welfare; Youth services.
Type of support: General support.
Limitations: Applications accepted. Giving primarily in the greater metropolitan Washington, DC, area including MD and VA. No grants to individuals.
Application information:
  Initial approach: Proposal
  Deadline(s): None
Trustee: Karen Beardsley.
EIN: 521774631

3861
Beverly K. & Jerome M. Fine Foundation, Inc.
409 Washington Ave., Ste. 900
Towson, MD   21204-4905

Established in 2010 in Maryland.
Donors: Jerome M. Fine†; Jerome M. Fine Rev. Trust.
Foundation type: Independent foundation.
Financial data (yr. ended 06/30/13): Assets, $7,616,885 (M); expenditures, $252,766;

qualifying distributions, $217,174; giving activities include $207,500 for 8 grants (high: $100,000; low: $2,500).
Fields of interest: Undergraduate education; Health; Hospital care; Human services.
Limitations: Applications not accepted. Giving primarily in MD.
Application information: Unsolicited requests for funds not accepted.
Officers: Louis F. Friedman, Pres. and Treas.; Phyllis C. Friedman, V.P. and Secy.
EIN: 352383776

3862
The Fischer Family Foundation
P.O. Box 34107
Bethesda, MD   20827-0107

Established in 2000 in Maryland.
Donors: Dr. Gerald Fischer; Marlene Kay Fischer.
Foundation type: Independent foundation.
Financial data (yr. ended 12/31/13): Assets, $35,163 (M); gifts received, $225,000; expenditures, $389,578; qualifying distributions, $389,578; giving activities include $387,654 for 8 grants (high: $189,404; low: $750).
Purpose and activities: Giving primarily for higher education, human services, and to Lutheran churches and organizations.
Fields of interest: Higher education; Specialty hospital care; Methodism; Human services.
Limitations: Applications not accepted. Giving primarily in Milwaukee, WI; some giving also in Washington, DC. No grants to individuals.
Application information: Contributes only to pre-selected organizations.
Officers: Gerald Fischer, Pres.; Marlene Kay Fischer, Exec. Dir.
EIN: 311726154

3863
Alice & Eugene Ford Foundation Inc.
20316 Seneca Meadows Pkwy.
Germantown, MD   20876-7004   (301) 562-1700
Contact: Eugene F. Ford, Pres.

Established in 2001 in Maryland.
Donors: Alice D. Ford†; Eugene F. Ford.
Foundation type: Independent foundation.
Financial data (yr. ended 12/31/13): Assets, $982,134 (M); gifts received, $350,000; expenditures, $245,722; qualifying distributions, $255,000; giving activities include $255,000 for 7 grants (high: $100,000; low: $5,000).
Fields of interest: Community and economic development; Housing development.
Limitations: Applications accepted. Giving primarily in Washington, DC. No grants to individuals.
Application information: Application form required.
  Initial approach: Proposal
  Deadline(s): None
Officers and Directors: Eugene F. Ford, Pres. and Director; Dennis Koubek, Secy.-Treas.; S. Lee Narrow.
EIN: 522271621

3864
The William and Eva Fox Foundation
7118 Arrowood Rd.
Bethesda, MD 20817-2809
Main URL: http://www.tcg.org/fox/index.htm
Grants List: http://www.tcg.org/fox/
fellows_past.htm

Established in 1987 in Delaware.
Donor: Belle Fox†.
Foundation type: Independent foundation.
Financial data (yr. ended 06/30/13): Assets,
$5,595,939 (M); expenditures, $259,367;
qualifying distributions, $251,806; giving activities
include $251,306 for 2 grants (high: $219,000;
low: $32,306).
Purpose and activities: The foundation's mission is
committed to the artistic development of theatre
actors as a strategy to strengthen live theatre.
Fields of interest: Performing arts; Theater.
International interests: United Kingdom of Great
Britain and Northern Ireland.
Type of support: Fellowships.
Limitations: Giving on a national basis and in
England.
Publications: Grants list.
Application information: Application guidelines and
form available on foundation web site.
Officer and Director: Robert P. Warren, Pres. and
Director.
EIN: 133497192

3865
Franey Family Foundation, Inc.
3 S. Acton Pl.
Annapolis, MD 21401

Established in 1994 in Maryland.
Donor: William G. Franey.
Foundation type: Independent foundation.
Financial data (yr. ended 12/31/14): Assets,
$872,095 (M); expenditures, $196,758; qualifying
distributions, $187,450; giving activities include
$187,450 for 25 grants (high: $48,450; low: $500).
Fields of interest: Education; ALS; Catholicism;
Human services; Child welfare.
Type of support: Research.
Limitations: Applications not accepted. Giving
primarily in MD.
Application information: Unsolicited requests for
funds not accepted.
Officer: William G. Franey, Pres.
EIN: 521909081

3866
Friedman Charitable Foundation, Inc.
(formerly The Friedman & Friedman Foundation, Inc.)
409 Washington Ave., Ste. 900
Towson, MD 21204-4905

Established in 1995 in Maryland.
Donors: Louis F. Friedman; Phyllis C. Friedman; D.
Sylvan Friedman; Miriam Friedman; Miriam S.
Friedman Revocable Trust.
Foundation type: Independent foundation.
Financial data (yr. ended 12/31/13): Assets,
$4,586,752 (M); gifts received, $355,351;
expenditures, $174,602; qualifying distributions,
$165,750; giving activities include $165,750 for 12
grants (high: $100,000; low: $1,000).

Fields of interest: Education; Health; Diseases and
conditions.
Limitations: Applications not accepted. Giving
primarily in Baltimore, MD. No grants to individuals.
Application information: Unsolicited requests for
funds not accepted.
Officers and Directors: Louis F. Friedman, Pres. and
Director; Samuel H. Friedman, V.P. and Director;
Phyllis C. Friedman, Secy. and Director; Robert A.
Fuld.
EIN: 521953450

3867
Fun-Raising Corporation
80001 Dewberry Ln., Apt.108
Pasadena, MD 21122

Established in 2011 in Maryland.
Donors: Delaware North Corporation; Sodexho Inc.
and Affiliates; Centerplate; Aramark.
Foundation type: Independent foundation.
Financial data (yr. ended 12/31/12): Assets,
$27,340 (M); gifts received, $225,613;
expenditures, $198,273; qualifying distributions,
$197,173.
Limitations: Applications not accepted.
Application information: Unsolicited requests for
funds not accepted.
Officers: Jennifer Schley, Pres.; Wayne Barth, Treas.
Directors: Samantha Appler; Dawn Labrecque.
EIN: 452646410

3868
Fusco Family Foundation, Inc.
1245 Cherry Tree Ln.
Annapolis, MD 21403-5023

Established in 2001 in Maryland.
Donors: Kristin A. Fusco; Jack A. Fusco.
Foundation type: Independent foundation.
Financial data (yr. ended 12/31/14): Assets,
$4,379,820; expenditures, $244,342; qualifying
distributions, $216,550.
Fields of interest: Education; University education;
Christianity; Human services.
Limitations: Applications not accepted. No grants to
individuals.
Application information: Contributes only to
pre-selected organizations.
Officers: Kristin A. Fusco, Pres. and Treas.; Jack A.
Fusco, Secy.
EIN: 522363816

3869
The Carl and Nancy Gewirz Fund, Inc.
7117 Glenbrook Rd.
Bethesda, MD 20814-1224

Donors: Carl Gewirz; Nancy Gewirz.
Foundation type: Independent foundation.
Financial data (yr. ended 11/30/13): Assets,
$5,300,690 (M); expenditures, $465,985;
qualifying distributions, $416,515; giving activities
include $338,495 for 97 grants (high: $52,662;
low: $20).
Fields of interest: Arts and culture; Museums;
Education; Higher education; Health; Hospital care.
Type of support: Capital campaigns.
Limitations: Applications not accepted. Giving
primarily in Washington, D.C.

Application information: Unsolicited requests for
funds not accepted.
Officer and Directors: Carl Gewirz, Pres. and
Director; Nancy Gewirz; Victoria Gewirz.
EIN: 521387044

3870
Adele & Willard Gidwitz Family Foundation
(formerly Adele & Willard Gidwitz Family Charitable
Foundation)
1829 Reisterstown Rd., Ste. 430
Baltimore, MD 21208-7107

Established in 1991 in Illinois.
Donors: Adele Gidwitz; Susan Gidwitz; Adele Gidwitz
Charitable Lead Annuity Trust; Susan Gidwitz
Charitable Lead Annuity Trust; John Gidwitz; Richard
Gidwitz 1999 Irrevocable Trust.
Foundation type: Independent foundation.
Financial data (yr. ended 12/31/13): Assets,
$10,164 (M); gifts received, $374,122;
expenditures, $373,228; qualifying distributions,
$373,228; giving activities include $364,800 for 51
grants (high: $85,000; low: $500).
Fields of interest: Arts and culture; Arts education;
Orchestral music; Higher education; Nonprofits;
Specialty hospital care; Cancers; Human services.
Type of support: Regranting.
Limitations: Applications not accepted. Giving
primarily in CT, IL, MD, OK and TN. No grants to
individuals.
Application information: Contributes only to
pre-selected organizations.
Officers: John D. Gidwitz, Pres.; Susan Gidwitz, V.P.;
Adele Gidwitz, Secy.-Treas.
EIN: 363745038

3871
Harry L. Gladding Foundation, Inc.
c/o Venable / ND Borden
750 E. Pratt St., Ste. 900
Baltimore, MD 21202-3157 (410) 244-7400
Contact: Neal D. Borden Esq., Tr.

Established in 1990 in Maryland.
Donor: Harry L. Gladding†.
Foundation type: Independent foundation.
Financial data (yr. ended 12/31/13): Assets,
$1,335,255 (M); expenditures, $168,414;
qualifying distributions, $148,647; giving activities
include $141,950 for 29 grants (high: $20,000;
low: $500).
Purpose and activities: Support primarily for arts
and cultural organizations.
Fields of interest: Arts and culture; Education;
Human services.
Type of support: General support; Matching grants;
Annual campaigns; Capital campaigns; Capital and
infrastructure; Equipment; Endowments; Convening;
Scholarships.
Limitations: Applications accepted. Giving primarily
in the Baltimore, MD, area.
Application information:
  Initial approach: Letter
  Copies of proposal: 1
  Deadline(s): None
  Board meeting date(s): May, Nov., and as needed
Trustees: Neal D. Borden, Esq.; Winifred Borden.
Number of staff: None.
EIN: 521672857

3872
The Stephen A. and Diana L. Goldberg Foundation, Inc.
7220 Wisconsin Ave., Ste. 200
Bethesda, MD 20814-3529

Established in 1994 in Delaware.
Donors: Stephen Goldberg; Diana Goldberg; Rae Goldberg†; Shadyside Assocs. Limited Partnership.
Foundation type: Independent foundation.
Financial data (yr. ended 12/31/13): Assets, $32,557 (M); gifts received, $325,000; expenditures, $338,144; qualifying distributions, $334,465; giving activities include $333,415 for 22 grants (high: $100,000; low: $100).
Purpose and activities: Support primarily for children's health care and development; giving also for the arts, the environment, civil rights, and public affairs.
Fields of interest: Arts and culture; Museums; Education; Nonprofits; Specialty hospital care; Pediatrics; Diseases and conditions; Public affairs; Human rights; Human services; Child welfare; Youth development.
Type of support: Research; Matching grants; Scholarships; Professorships; Program development; Endowments; Continuing support; Capital campaigns; Capital and infrastructure; Annual campaigns; General support; Regranting; Research and evaluation.
Limitations: Applications accepted. Giving on a national basis, with some emphasis on NY, RI, MT, and Washington, DC.
Application information:
  Initial approach: Proposal
  Deadline(s): None
Officers: Stephen A. Goldberg, Pres.; Diana L. Goldberg, V.P.; Martin J. Kirsch, Secy.
Directors: Brian L. Goldberg; Lauren B. Goldberg; Stuart W. Goldberg.
EIN: 510326473

3873
Peggy & Yale Gordon Charitable Trust
409 Washington Ave., Ste. 900
Towson, MD 21204-4905

Established in 1980 in Maryland.
Donor: Yale Gordon†.
Foundation type: Independent foundation.
Financial data (yr. ended 12/31/13): Assets, $4,903,149 (M); expenditures, $240,908; qualifying distributions, $206,249; giving activities include $193,250 for 15 grants (high: $35,150; low: $500).
Fields of interest: Performing arts; Music; Orchestral music; Education; Judaism.
Type of support: Continuing support.
Limitations: Applications not accepted. Giving primarily in Baltimore, MD.
Application information: Contributes only to pre-selected organizations.
Officer and Trustees: Phyllis C. Friedman, Exe. Dir. and Trustee; Charles J. Bishow; Louis F. Friedman; Sara R. Fuld; Hilda P. Sherr.
Number of staff: 3 full-time professional; 1 part-time support.
EIN: 521174287

3874
Gorlin Family Foundation
501 Hermleigh Rd.
Silver Spring, MD 20902-1607

Established in 2007 in Maryland.
Donor: Congressional Youth Leadership Council, Inc.
Foundation type: Independent foundation.
Financial data (yr. ended 12/31/13): Assets, $7,530,442 (M); expenditures, $461,852; qualifying distributions, $384,399; giving activities include $306,950 for 25 grants (high: $62,500; low: $850).
Fields of interest: University education; Judaism.
Limitations: Applications not accepted. Giving primarily in MD and NY. No grants to individuals.
Application information: Contributes only to pre-selected organizations.
Directors: David J. Butler; Jacques J. Gorlin; Susan J. Gorlin.
EIN: 260874184

3875
The Sanjay Govil Foundation, Inc.
c/o Ashoka Tankala
15201 Diamondback Dr., Ste. 125
Rockville, MD 20850-3695 (301) 355-7760
Contact: Sanjay Govil, Pres. and Treas.

Donor: Sanjay Govil.
Foundation type: Independent foundation.
Financial data (yr. ended 12/31/13): Assets, $1,668,950 (M); expenditures, $334,344; qualifying distributions, $330,000; giving activities include $330,000 for 1 grant.
Fields of interest: Education; Higher education; Human services.
Limitations: Applications accepted. Giving primarily in Philadelphia, PA.
Application information: Application form required.
  Initial approach: Letter
  Deadline(s): None
Officers: Sanjay Govil, Pres. and Treas.; Vidya Govil, V.P.; Ashoka Tankala, Secy.
EIN: 273455354

3876
The Greene-Milstein Family Foundation
(formerly Greene Foundation)
6608 Lybrook Ct.
Bethesda, MD 20817-3029 (301) 469-6737
Contact: Nancy G. Milstein, Treas.

Established in 1962 in Maine.
Donors: Myer Greene; Nancy G. Milstein; Herbert E. Milstein.
Foundation type: Independent foundation.
Financial data (yr. ended 12/31/14): Assets, $3,631,815 (M); gifts received, $28,500; expenditures, $189,104; qualifying distributions, $166,385; giving activities include $166,385 for 104 grants (high: $12,500; low: $35).
Fields of interest: Museums; Education; Higher education; Nonprofits; Hospital care; Judaism.
Type of support: Regranting.
Application information: Application form required.
  Initial approach: Letter
  Deadline(s): None
Officers: Herbert E. Milstein, Pres.; Nancy G. Milstein, Treas.

Trustee: Mark B. Milstein.
EIN: 016009341

3877
Gutman Family Foundation, Inc.
c/o Allan J. Gibber
1 South St., 27th Fl.
Baltimore, MD 21202-3282

Established in 1960 in Maryland.
Donors: Ernst Gutman; Menachem Gutman; Mannie Gutman†; Abraham Gutman; Allan J. Gibber; Bernard Steinharter; Elvia Diamonds, LLC; Miriam Steinharter; Abe Gutman; Debbie Gibber.
Foundation type: Independent foundation.
Financial data (yr. ended 12/31/13): Assets, $1,504,034 (M); gifts received, $151,500; expenditures, $287,941; qualifying distributions, $275,133; giving activities include $275,133 for 86 grants (high: $31,300; low: $485).
Fields of interest: Education; Nonprofits; Judaism; Human services.
Type of support: Regranting.
Limitations: Applications not accepted. No grants to individuals.
Application information: Contributes only to pre-selected organizations.
Officers: Allan J. Gibber, Pres.; Abraham Gutman, V.P.; Bernard Steinharter, Secy.-Treas.
Directors: Deborah S. Gibber; Marion Gutman; Miriam L. Steinharter.
EIN: 526056321

3878
Martha & Warren Halle Foundation, Inc.
2900 Linden Ln., Ste. 300
Silver Spring, MD 20910-1265 (301) 495-1520
Contact: Martha E. Halle, V.P. and Secy.

Donors: Warren E. Halle; Martha D. Halle.
Foundation type: Independent foundation.
Financial data (yr. ended 12/31/13): Assets, $666,433 (M); gifts received, $300,000; expenditures, $145,182; qualifying distributions, $145,000; giving activities include $145,000 for 4 grants (high: $50,000; low: $20,000).
Fields of interest: Health; Community and economic development; Housing development.
Application information:
  Initial approach: Proposal
  Deadline(s): None
Officers and Directors: Warren E. Halle, Pres. and Treas. and Director; Martha D. Halle, V.P. and Secy.
EIN: 208357937

3879
The Helm Foundation, Inc.
201 Woodbrook Ln.
Baltimore, MD 21212-1037 (410) 952-0078
Contact: Scott Helm, V.P. and Secy-Treas.

Established in 2002 in Illinois.
Donor: Scott Helm.
Foundation type: Independent foundation.
Financial data (yr. ended 06/30/13): Assets, $3,443,159 (M); gifts received, $5,463; expenditures, $447,211; qualifying distributions, $305,000; giving activities include $305,000 for 3 grants (high: $220,000; low: $35,000).

Fields of interest: Arts and culture; Theater; Education; Human services.
Application information:
 Initial approach: Proposal
 Deadline(s): None
Officers: Lesley Malin Helm, Pres.; Scott Helm, V.P. and Secy.-Treas.
Directors: Gladys M. Helm; JoAnne C. Malin.
Number of staff: None.
EIN: 260001014

3880
Corina Higginson Trust
c/o Wilton C. Corkern
3400 Bryan Point Rd.
Accokeek, MD 20607-9676
Application e-mail: info@corinahigginsontrust.org

Established in 1962 in District of Columbia.
Donor: Corina Higginson†.
Foundation type: Independent foundation.
Financial data (yr. ended 12/31/14): Assets, $4,105,385; expenditures, $454,077; qualifying distributions, $370,475.
Purpose and activities: The trust makes gifts primarily for the benefit of the Washington, DC, metropolitan area for charitable and educational purposes.
Fields of interest: Arts and culture; Education; Environment; Human services.
Type of support: General support; Matching grants; Continuing support; Program development; Convening; Publications; Seed money; Curriculum development; Internships; Research; Individual development.
Limitations: Applications accepted. Giving primarily in the Washington, DC, area, including portions of MD and VA. No support for medical or health-related programs or organizations. No grants to individuals, or for endowment funds or scholarship funds.
Publications: Application guidelines.
Application information: Proposals accepted by invitation only. Washington Grantmakers' Common Grant Application Form required for Letters of Intent and invited proposals; emailed PDF format strongly encouraged. Application form required.
 Initial approach: Letter of Intent
 Copies of proposal: 2
 Deadline(s): Jan. 1 and July 1 for Letter of Intent
 Board meeting date(s): May and Nov.
 Final notification: June and Dec.
Trustees: Damaris Abeles; Wilton C. Corkern, Jr.; Linda Cropp; Alexander Mackay-Smith, Jr.; Virginia L. Mackay-Smith; Floretta Dukes McKenzie.
EIN: 526055743

3881
Hittman Family Foundation, Inc.
3000 Stone Cliff Dr., Ste. 111
Baltimore, MD 21209-3780

Established in 1998 in Maryland.
Donors: Fred Hittman; Sandra Hittman.
Foundation type: Independent foundation.
Financial data (yr. ended 12/31/13): Assets, $3,827,726 (M); expenditures, $259,587; qualifying distributions, $238,495; giving activities include $227,500 for 16 grants (high: $80,000; low: $1,000).
Fields of interest: Education; Diseases and conditions; Human services.

Type of support: Research.
Limitations: Applications not accepted. Giving primarily in MD and NY. No grants to individuals.
Application information: Unsolicited requests for funds not accepted.
Officers and Directors: Stephen J. Hittman, Pres. and Director; Karen E. Gober, V.P. and Director; Judith E. Hittman, V.P. and Director; Sandra Hittman, Secy.-Treas. and Director; Jonathan D. Eisner; Shale D. Stiller.
EIN: 911937345

3882
The Emmert Hobbs Foundation, Inc.
409 Washington Ave., Ste. 900
Towson, MD 21204-4905

Established in 1983 in Maryland.
Donor: Emmert Hobbs†.
Foundation type: Independent foundation.
Financial data (yr. ended 07/31/13): Assets, $5,255,894 (M); expenditures, $247,727; qualifying distributions, $224,950; giving activities include $217,450 for 26 grants (high: $50,000; low: $500).
Fields of interest: Opera; Education; Undergraduate education; Health; Hospital care; Mental health care; Diseases and conditions; Human services; Child welfare; Youth services.
Type of support: Capital and infrastructure; Program development; Scholarships; Research; Research and evaluation.
Limitations: Applications not accepted. Giving primarily in the metropolitan Baltimore, MD, area. No grants to individuals.
Application information: Unsolicited requests for funds not accepted.
Officers: Louis F. Friedman, Pres. and Treas.; Samuel H. Friedman, V.P.; Phyllis C. Friedman, Secy.
EIN: 521285106

3883
The A. C. and Penney Hubbard Foundation, Inc.
1408 Walnut Hill Ln.
Baltimore, MD 21204-3662
Application address: c/o A.C. Hubbard, P.O. Box 482, Wilson, WY 83014, tel.: (410) 825-8221

Established in 1986 in Maryland.
Donors: A.C. Hubbard, Jr.; Penney Hubbard.
Foundation type: Independent foundation.
Financial data (yr. ended 10/31/12): Assets, $278,964 (M); gifts received, $174,041; expenditures, $202,264; qualifying distributions, $199,466; giving activities include $197,750 for 56 grants (high: $42,500; low: $100).
Fields of interest: Arts and culture; Music; Art museums; Education; Higher education; Nonprofits.
Type of support: General support; Matching grants; Regranting; Annual campaigns; Individual development.
Limitations: Applications accepted. Giving primarily in Baltimore, MD and WY.
Application information:
 Initial approach: Letter
 Deadline(s): None
Officers: A.C. Hubbard, Pres.; Penney Hubbard, Secy.
EIN: 521486929

3884
The Huether/McClelland Foundation, Inc.
(formerly The Huether Foundation, Inc.)
P.O. Box 370
1300 Brass Mill Rd.
Belcamp, MD 21017-0370
Contact: H. Douglas Huether, Chair.

Established in 1985 in Maryland.
Donors: H. Douglas Huether; George McClelland; Independent Can Co.; Richard D. Huether; Catherine McClelland; Ryan Huether; Ann Lee Huether; Mary Ellen Huether; William Armiger.
Foundation type: Independent foundation.
Financial data (yr. ended 12/31/13): Assets, $6,612,563 (M); gifts received, $297,000; expenditures, $309,763; qualifying distributions, $309,740; giving activities include $309,740 for 56 grants (high: $31,500; low: $5,000).
Purpose and activities: Scholarships limited to graduates of high schools in Harford County, MD, who plan to study engineering.
Fields of interest: Orchestral music; Museums; Historic preservation; Elementary and secondary education; Higher education; Hospice care; Pediatrics; Learning disorders; Christianity; Human services.
Type of support: General support; Scholarships; Student aid.
Limitations: Applications accepted. Giving primarily in Baltimore, MD; scholarships limited to residents of Harford County, MD. No support for political organizations. No grants to individuals (except for designated scholarship funds).
Application information:
 Initial approach: Proposal for grants
 Copies of proposal: 1
 Deadline(s): None
 Board meeting date(s): Triannually
Officers and Directors: H. Douglas Huether, Chair. and Pres. and Director; Richard D. Huether, Vice-Chair. and Director; George R. McClelland, Secy. and Director; Catherine H. McClelland, Treas. and Director.
Trustee: Mary Ellen M. Huether.
EIN: 521435090

3885
Humphreys Foundation, Inc.
24 N. Main St.
Berlin, MD 21811-1029
Application address: c/o Faw Casson & Co., LLP, P.O. Box 718, Ocean City, MD 21842, tel.: (410) 213-8700

Established in 1998 in Maryland.
Foundation type: Independent foundation.
Financial data (yr. ended 06/30/13): Assets, $7,399,130 (M); gifts received, $25; expenditures, $389,938; qualifying distributions, $357,545; giving activities include $357,545 for 13 grants (high: $100,000; low: $2,500).
Fields of interest: First aid training.
Limitations: Applications accepted. Giving primarily in MD. No grants to individuals.
Application information: Application form required.
 Initial approach: Completed application form
 Deadline(s): None
Officers: Ellen H. Lang, Pres.; Thomas K. Coates, V.P.; L. Susan Taylor, Secy.; William H. Mitchell, Treas.
EIN: 311639319

3886
Benno and Elayne Hurwitz Family Foundation, Inc.
100 E. Pratt St., 26th Fl.
Baltimore, MD 21202-1097 4107529737
Application address: c/o Marcy Jill Stempler, 40 Caveswood Ln., Owings Mills, MD 21117, tel.: (410) 902-5801

Established in 2008 in Maryland.
Donor: Benno & Elayne A. Hurwitz Charitable Lead Trust.
Foundation type: Independent foundation.
Financial data (yr. ended 12/31/14): Assets, $4,681,687; gifts received, $800,000; expenditures, $342,013; qualifying distributions, $274,260.
Purpose and activities: Giving primarily for Jewish organizations; funding also for health organizations.
Fields of interest: Arts and culture; Nonprofits; Hospital care; Diseases and conditions; Judaism; Human services.
Type of support: Regranting.
Limitations: Applications accepted. Giving primarily in MD.
Application information: Application form required.
   Initial approach: Letter
   Deadline(s): None
Officers and Directors: Elayne A. Hurwitz, Pres. and Director; Jan C. Hurwitz, V.P. and Director; Brian Balenson, Secy. and Director; Alfred L. Whiteman, Treas. and Director; William A. Hurwitz.
EIN: 201646666

3887
Mark & Carol Hyman Fund
c/o Susan Besharov
4518 Cumberland Ave.
Chevy Chase, MD 20815-5466

Established in 1991 in Massachusetts.
Donors: Mark Hyman, Jr.†; Mark Hyman Fund.
Foundation type: Independent foundation.
Financial data (yr. ended 12/31/13): Assets, $4,100,340 (M); expenditures, $230,565; qualifying distributions, $195,000; giving activities include $195,000 for 30 grants (high: $28,500; low: $1,000).
Fields of interest: Arts and culture; Performing arts; Museums; Education; Higher education; Health; Human services.
Limitations: Applications not accepted. Giving primarily in FL and MD. No grants to individuals.
Application information: Contributes only to pre-selected organizations.
Trustees: Douglas J. Besharov; Susan Hyman Besharov; Katherine Hyman Cook; Willard T. Cook.
EIN: 046677395

3888
Israelson Family Foundation, Inc.
409 Washington Ave., Ste. 900
Towson, MD 21204-4905

Established in 2000 in Maryland.
Donors: Bernice F. Israelson; Max R. Israelson†.
Foundation type: Independent foundation.
Financial data (yr. ended 06/30/13): Assets, $4,760,279 (M); expenditures, $221,543; qualifying distributions, $191,800; giving activities

include $191,800 for 7 grants (high: $60,000; low: $1,800).
Fields of interest: Philanthropy; Hospital care; Judaism; Children.
Type of support: Capital campaigns.
Limitations: Applications not accepted. Giving primarily in FL, MD and NJ. No grants to individuals.
Application information: Unsolicited requests for funds not accepted.
Officers and Directors: Stuart G. Israelson, Pres. and Treas. and Director; Wendy I. Carroll, V.P. and Director; Louis F. Friedman, Secy. and Director; Cynthia Israelson.
EIN: 522256896

3889
Izzo Family Foundation
4853 Cordell Ave., Ste. P-6
Bethesda, MD 20814-7015

Established in 2008 in Maryland.
Donors: Anthony J. Izzo, Jr.; Genco Masonry, Inc.
Foundation type: Independent foundation.
Financial data (yr. ended 06/30/13): Assets, $1,825,972 (M); gifts received, $550,000; expenditures, $220,156; qualifying distributions, $216,500; giving activities include $216,500 for 11 grants (high: $150,000; low: $500).
Fields of interest: Education; Health; Hospital care.
Limitations: Applications not accepted. Giving primarily in MD. No grants to individuals.
Application information: Contributes only to pre-selected organizations.
Directors: Anthony J. Izzo, Jr.; Anthony J. Izzo III; Mary Ann Richardson.
EIN: 260844190

3890
The Jake Foundation, Inc.
c/o Brian Leshner
Leshner Capital Mgmt.
42 State Cir.
Annapolis, MD 21401-1915

Established in 1998 in Virginia.
Donor: Joanne S. Barker.
Foundation type: Independent foundation.
Financial data (yr. ended 05/31/14): Assets, $7,830,779 (M); gifts received, $647,700; expenditures, $417,053; qualifying distributions, $414,617; giving activities include $413,400 for 33 grants (high: $100,000; low: $1,000).
Fields of interest: Theater; Elementary and secondary education; Higher education; Christianity.
Limitations: Applications not accepted. Giving primarily in the greater metropolitan Washington, DC, area (including MD and VA), and in MA. No grants to individuals.
Application information: Contributes only to pre-selected organizations.
Officers: Joanne S. Barker, Pres.; Brian Leshner, Treas.
EIN: 522107509

3891
Sheldon and Audrey Katz Foundation
P.O. Box 4337
Silver Spring, MD 20914-4337

Established in 1996 in Maryland.

Donors: Sheldon T. Katz; Audrey Katz.
Foundation type: Independent foundation.
Financial data (yr. ended 12/31/13): Assets, $7,342,901 (M); gifts received, $481,158; expenditures, $298,614; qualifying distributions, $270,000; giving activities include $270,000 for 11 grants (high: $100,000; low: $5,000).
Fields of interest: Theater; University education; Natural resources.
Limitations: Applications not accepted. Giving primarily in MD. No grants to individuals.
Application information: Unsolicited requests for funds not accepted.
Officers: Sheldon T. Katz, Pres.; Audrey Katz, Secy.
EIN: 522006607

3892
The Kay Family Foundation, Inc.
(formerly L & S Foundation)
8720 Georgia Ave., Ste. 410
Silver Spring, MD 20910-3638 (301) 589-8045
Contact: Lauren K. Pollin, V.P. and Secy.

Established in 1976 in Maryland.
Donors: Jack Kay†; Ina Kay†; Lauren Hawkins; Shelley Joan Kay.
Foundation type: Independent foundation.
Financial data (yr. ended 12/31/13): Assets, $15,784,509 (M); gifts received, $2,985,119; expenditures, $277,746; qualifying distributions, $244,366; giving activities include $244,366 for 8 grants (high: $156,366; low: $500).
Fields of interest: Foundations; Nonprofits; Hospital care; Judaism; Human services.
Type of support: Regranting.
Limitations: Applications accepted. Giving primarily in MD; some funding in New York, NY, and Washington, DC. No grants to individuals.
Application information: Application form required.
   Initial approach: Letter
   Deadline(s): None
Officer: Lauren K. Pollin, V.P. and Secy.
EIN: 521045650

3893
Ensign C. Markland Kelly, Jr. Memorial Foundation, Inc.
711 W. 40th St., Ste. 357
Baltimore, MD 21211-2109 (410) 366-8810
Contact: Carol W. Hunt, V.P. and Exec. Dir.

Established in 1946 in Maryland.
Donors: C. Markland Kelly†; Kelly Buick Sales Corp.
Foundation type: Independent foundation.
Financial data (yr. ended 12/31/14): Assets, $6,732,494 (M); expenditures, $398,242; qualifying distributions, $279,547; giving activities include $224,741 for 18 grants (high: $40,000; low: $700).
Fields of interest: Arts and culture; Orchestral music; Historic preservation; Secondary education; Health; Speech and hearing rehabilitation; Diseases and conditions; Child welfare; People with disabilities.
Type of support: Annual campaigns; Matching grants; Capital campaigns; Capital and infrastructure; Equipment; Endowments; Program development.
Limitations: Applications accepted. Giving limited to the greater metropolitan Baltimore, MD, area. No

grants to individuals, or for operating budgets, research, fellowships, or travel; no loans.
Publications: Application guidelines; Occasional report; Program policy statement.
Application information:
Initial approach: Letter requesting guidelines
Copies of proposal: 3
Deadline(s): None
Board meeting date(s): Monthly
Final notification: 6 months
Officers and Directors: Bowen P. Weisheit, Jr., Pres. and Director; Carol W. Hunt, V.P. and Exec. Dir.
Number of staff: 1 full-time professional.
EIN: 526033330

3894
The Kirk Family Foundation
P.O. Box 477
Ellicott City, MD 21041-0477

Established in 2001 in Maryland.
Donor: Donald H. Kirk, Jr.
Foundation type: Independent foundation.
Financial data (yr. ended 12/31/13): Assets, $1,262,157 (M); gifts received, $200,000; expenditures, $226,786; qualifying distributions, $212,072; giving activities include $208,650 for 11 grants (high: $100,000; low: $200).
Fields of interest: Education; Human services.
Type of support: Research.
Limitations: Applications not accepted. Giving primarily in MD. No grants to individuals.
Application information: Contributes only to pre-selected organizations.
Officers: Donald H. Kirk, Jr., Pres. and Treas.; Patricia M. Kirk, V.P. and Secy.
EIN: 522358200

3895
Knapp Educational Fund, Inc.
P.O. Box O
Saint Michaels, MD 21663-0450 (410) 745-5660

Established in 1979 in Maryland.
Donor: The Knapp Foundation, Inc.
Foundation type: Independent foundation.
Financial data (yr. ended 12/31/14): Assets, $5,593,901; expenditures, $431,196; qualifying distributions, $372,136.
Purpose and activities: Support for education, including scholarship awards.
Fields of interest: Education.
Type of support: Equipment; Scholarships.
Application information: Application form required.
Initial approach: Letter
Deadline(s): None
Officers: Antoinette P. Vojvoda, Pres.; Ruth M. Capranica, V.P. and Secy.; Steven F. Capranica, Treas.
EIN: 132970128

3896
Louis B. II and Josephine Kohn Family Foundation Inc.
c/o Gorfine Fiddle Co.
3635 Old Ct., Ste. 306
Baltimore, MD 21208-3908

Established in 2004 in Maryland.

Donor: Josephine L. Kohn.
Foundation type: Independent foundation.
Financial data (yr. ended 12/31/13): Assets, $4,306,932 (M); expenditures, $243,415; qualifying distributions, $195,000; giving activities include $195,000 for 8 grants (high: $50,000; low: $5,000).
Fields of interest: Arts education; Cancers.
Type of support: General support.
Limitations: Applications not accepted. Giving primarily in MD. No grants to individuals.
Application information: Unsolicited requests for funds not accepted.
Officers and Directors: Nancy Kohn Rabin, Pres. and Director; Jerome D. Carr, Secy.-Treas. and Director.
EIN: 201516339

3897
Irving Kohn Foundation, Inc.
c/o Nancy Kohn Rabin
26 Roland Green
Baltimore, MD 21210-2506 (410) 464-0064

Established in 1957 in Maryland.
Donor: Berkshire Hathaway Inc.
Foundation type: Independent foundation.
Financial data (yr. ended 12/31/13): Assets, $3,959,739 (M); expenditures, $204,350; qualifying distributions, $196,620; giving activities include $165,000 for 4 grants (high: $150,000; low: $5,000).
Purpose and activities: Giving primarily for art and cultural programs, education, and social service organizations.
Fields of interest: Arts and culture; Philanthropy; Human services.
Limitations: Applications accepted. Giving primarily in Baltimore, MD. No grants to individuals.
Application information: Application form required.
Initial approach: Letter
Deadline(s): None
Board meeting date(s): 3rd Thurs. in Nov.
Officers and Trustees: Nancy Kohn Rabin, Pres. and Trustee; Alan Bernstein, Jr., V.P. and Trustee; Leah Larson-Rabin, Secy. and Trustee; Karen Miel, Treas. and Trustee; Douglas Bernstein.
Number of staff: None.
EIN: 526034189

3898
Dr. Henry P. and Marion Page Durkee Laughlin Foundation, Inc.
(formerly National Psychiatric Endowment Fund, Inc.)
307 Upper College Terr.
Frederick, MD 21701-4818

Established in 1968 in Maryland.
Donors: Henry P. Laughlin, MD; M. P. Laughlin.
Foundation type: Independent foundation.
Financial data (yr. ended 12/31/13): Assets, $3,532,681 (M); gifts received, $2,390; expenditures, $195,079; qualifying distributions, $174,000; giving activities include $135,000 for 18 grants (high: $20,000; low: $5,000), and $39,000 for 26 grants to individuals (high: $1,200; low: $400).
Purpose and activities: Giving primarily to medical educational institutions. Also gives grants and certificates to outstanding psychiatric residents at leading medical schools and similar institutions.

Fields of interest: Education; Medical education; Religion.
Type of support: Student aid; General support; Fellowships.
Limitations: Applications not accepted. Giving primarily in MD.
Application information: Unsolicited requests for funds not accepted.
Officers: Henry P. Laughlin, MD, Pres.; M.P. Laughlin, V.P.; J.R. Laughlin, Secy.-Treas.
EIN: 526080760

3899
Legum Foundation, Inc.
1829 Reisterstown Rd.
Baltimore, MD 21208-6320

Donors: Jeffrey Legum; Laurie Legum; Michael Legum; Harriett Legum; Park Circle Motor Co.; Westminster Motor Co.
Foundation type: Independent foundation.
Financial data (yr. ended 12/31/14): Assets, $1,879,795; expenditures, $266,426; qualifying distributions, $243,707.
Fields of interest: Art museums; University education; Judaism.
Limitations: Applications not accepted. Giving primarily in Baltimore, MD.
Application information: Unsolicited requests for funds not accepted.
Trustees: Harriett Legum; Jeffrey Legum; Laurie Legum; Michael Legum.
EIN: 061772390

3900
The Charles & Margaret Levin Family Foundation Inc
11151 Veirs Mill Rd.
Wheaton, MD 20902-2533

Established in 1994 in Maryland.
Donors: Abbe Levin; Charles Levin; Margaret Levin.
Foundation type: Independent foundation.
Financial data (yr. ended 12/31/13): Assets, $9,272,248 (M); expenditures, $453,362; qualifying distributions, $415,450; giving activities include $415,450 for 87 grants (high: $150,000; low: $100).
Fields of interest: Diseases and conditions; Community and economic development; Judaism; Youth development.
Limitations: Applications not accepted. Giving primarily in MD. No grants to individuals.
Application information: Unsolicited requests for funds not accepted.
Directors: Abbe Levin; Alan Levin.
EIN: 521917299

3901
Liberty Giving Tree, Inc.
122 Defense Hwy., Ste. 201
Annapolis, MD 21401-7071

Donor: Dorothy K. Fitzgerald.
Foundation type: Independent foundation.
Financial data (yr. ended 12/31/13): Assets, $1,406,449 (M); expenditures, $289,100; qualifying distributions, $269,764; giving activities include $269,764 for 4 grants (high: $154,500; low: $7,030).

Fields of interest: Domesticated animals; Diseases and conditions; Human services.
Limitations: Applications not accepted. Giving primarily in FL.
Application information: Unsolicited requests for funds not accepted.
Officers: Dorothy K. Fitzgerald, Pres.; Alexandra K. Fitzgerald, V.P.
EIN: 271462754

3902
Loats Foundation, Inc.
c/o Draper & McGinley, P.A.
365 W. Patrick St.
Frederick, MD   21701-4854
Application address: 35 E. Church St., Frederick, MD, tel.: (301) 898-4000

Established in 1881 in Maryland.
Donor: John Loats†.
Foundation type: Independent foundation.
Financial data (yr. ended 05/31/13): Assets, $3,545,587 (M); expenditures, $201,688; qualifying distributions, $179,550; giving activities include $179,550 for 20 grants (high: $40,000; low: $1,300).
Purpose and activities: Giving primarily for scholarship funds and for the care of needy children.
Fields of interest: Education; Higher education; Human services; Child welfare; Adult and child mentoring; Domestic violence shelters.
Type of support: General support; Scholarships; Individual development.
Limitations: Applications accepted. Giving primarily in Frederick County, MD. No grants to individuals directly.
Publications: Application guidelines; Program policy statement.
Application information:
  Initial approach: Proposal
  Deadline(s): None
  Board meeting date(s): Annually and as required
Officers and Directors: Robert Driver-Bishop, Pres.; Marion D. Carmack, Jr., V.P. and Director; Helen F. Hahn, Secy. and Director; C. Richard Miller, Jr., Treas. and Director; Barbara Brittain; Kathleen A. Costlow; Rev. W. Phillip Fogarty; Lorraine Prete.
Number of staff: 1 part-time support.
EIN: 520610535

3903
Walter G. Lohr, Jr. Charitable Foundation, Inc.
c/o Katz Abosch
9690 Deereco Rd., Ste. 500
Timonium, MD   21093-6900

Established in 1985 in Maryland.
Donor: Walter G. Lohr, Jr.
Foundation type: Independent foundation.
Financial data (yr. ended 12/31/13): Assets, $4,144,786 (M); expenditures, $152,359; qualifying distributions, $150,030; giving activities include $148,270 for 2 grants (high: $148,020; low: $250).
Fields of interest: Arts and culture; Education; Human services.
Type of support: General support.
Limitations: Applications not accepted. Giving primarily in Baltimore, MD. No grants to individuals.

Application information: Unsolicited requests for funds not accepted.
Officer: Walter G. Lohr, Jr., Pres.
EIN: 521479394

3904
Lutheran Home and Hospital Foundation, Inc.
2571 Hanover Pike
Hampstead, MD   21074-1145   (410) 258-0398
Contact: Rev. Michael Dubsky, Exec. Dir.
E-mail: dubsky@aol.com

Donor: Catherine Stehman†.
Foundation type: Independent foundation.
Financial data (yr. ended 06/30/13): Assets, $2,086,755 (M); gifts received, $3,563; expenditures, $386,087; qualifying distributions, $366,360; giving activities include $364,177 for 18 grants (high: $150,000; low: $800).
Purpose and activities: Giving primarily for Lutheran and health organizations.
Fields of interest: Community college education; University education; Home health care; Substance abuse treatment; Methodism; Youth services.
Limitations: Applications accepted. Giving limited to Baltimore, MD. No grants to individuals.
Application information:
  Initial approach: Proposal
  Deadline(s): None
Officers and Directors: Pastor Robert Kretzschmar, Pres.; Claire Workneh, V.P.; Sue Fitzsimmons, Secy.; Gertrude Hinson, Treas. and Director; Rev. Michael Dubsky, Exec. Dir.
EIN: 521081449

3905
Morton and Sophia Macht Foundation, Inc.
15 E. Fayette St.
Baltimore, MD   21202-1606   (410) 539-2370
Contact: Amy Macht, Pres.

Established in 1956 in Maryland.
Donors: Sophia Macht†; Westland Gardens Co.; Mallview; Queensgate Co.; Windsor; Automatic Service Corp.; Baltoland Inc.; Conwill Co.; Dahley Co.; Builders; Compression; Developers; Halldane; Macwell; Patience; Realsearch; Tracery; Transmaryland Co.; Huron Co.; Outpost; Raintree; Scholar; Stranden; Lodestone; Masterplan, Inc.; Northrail; Walden Co.; Tensiltech Corp.; Thunderwood Co.; Talltimber; Wolfwind; College Gardens; Elmcroft Co.; Welsh Construction; Gradient; Folcroft Co.; Cosmo Co.; Lawford Co.; Park Grove Realty Co.; Cedlair Corp.; Philip Macht.
Foundation type: Independent foundation.
Financial data (yr. ended 04/30/13): Assets, $1,303,647 (M); gifts received, $360,800; expenditures, $460,115; qualifying distributions, $451,898; giving activities include $411,389 for 63 grants (high: $268,652; low: $50).
Fields of interest: Arts and culture; Education; Higher education; Environment; Human services; Child welfare.
Type of support: General support; Continuing support; Annual campaigns; Capital campaigns; Equipment; Program development; Convening; Publications; Seed money; Scholarships; Research.

Limitations: Applications accepted. Giving primarily in the metropolitan Baltimore, MD, area. No grants to individuals.
Application information: Application form required.
  Initial approach: Proposal
  Copies of proposal: 1
  Deadline(s): None
  Final notification: Letter
Officers and Trustees: Amy Macht, Pres. and Trustee; Katherine Kelly Howard, V.P. and Secy. and Trustee; Jill Gansler, V.P. and Treas. and Trustee; Bette D. Cohen, V.P. and Trustee; William A. Goodhardt, V.P. and Trustee; George R. Grose, V.P. and Trustee; Peter Grose, V.P. and Trustee; Robert W. Mastropieri, V.P. and Trustee.
EIN: 526035753

3906
Louise D. & Morton J. Macks Family Foundation, Inc.
4750 Owings Mills Blvd.
Owings Mills, MD   21117-4904

Established in 1989 in Maryland.
Donors: Morton J. Macks; Louise D. Macks; Martha Macks Charitable Lead Trust.
Foundation type: Independent foundation.
Financial data (yr. ended 09/30/13): Assets, $1,940,244 (M); gifts received, $47,581; expenditures, $175,767; qualifying distributions, $162,467; giving activities include $158,767 for 15 grants (high: $100,000; low: $600).
Purpose and activities: Giving primarily for Jewish causes, with emphasis on Jewish education.
Fields of interest: Education; Nonprofits; Judaism; Camps; Human services.
Type of support: General support; Regranting.
Limitations: Applications not accepted. Giving primarily in Baltimore, MD. No grants to individuals.
Publications: Annual report.
Application information: Contributes only to pre-selected organizations.
  Board meeting date(s): Oct./Nov.
Officers and Directors: Genine Macks Fidler, Pres. and Director; Lawrence M. Macks, V.P. and Director; Martha Macks-Kahn, V.P. and Director; Ellen A. Macks, Secy. and Director; Josh Fidler, Treas. and Director.
EIN: 521657510

3907
Mangione Family Foundation Inc.
1205 York Rd., 4th Fl.
Lutherville Timonium, MD   21093-6207   (410) 825-8400
Contact: Linda M. Licata, Treas.

Established in 1960 in Maryland.
Donors: Nicholas B. Mangione; Mary C. Mangione.
Foundation type: Independent foundation.
Financial data (yr. ended 12/31/13): Assets, $3,171,206 (M); gifts received, $450,000; expenditures, $435,369; qualifying distributions, $433,595; giving activities include $433,595 for 57 grants (high: $125,000; low: $55).
Fields of interest: Opera; Undergraduate education; Health; Hospital care; Diseases and conditions; Catholicism; Human services.
Type of support: General support; Scholarships.
Limitations: Applications accepted. Giving primarily in Baltimore, MD. No grants to individuals.

Application information:
Initial approach: Proposal
Deadline(s): None
Officers: Mary C. Mangione, Pres.; Louis Mangione, V.P.; Samuel Mangione, V.P.; Linda M. Licata, Treas.
EIN: 526054837

3908
Mann-Paller Foundation, Inc.
5404 Falmouth Rd.
Bethesda, MD   20816-1841   3012290777

Donors: Alan T. Paller; Marsha Paller.
Foundation type: Independent foundation.
Financial data (yr. ended 09/30/14): Assets, $6,732,805; gifts received, $2,200,000; expenditures, $373,389; qualifying distributions, $355,000.
Fields of interest: Dance; Education; Foundations.
Limitations: Applications not accepted. Giving in Washington, DC. No grants to individuals.
Application information: Contributes only to pre-selected organizations.
Officers: Marsha Paller, Pres. and Treas.; Channing Paller, V.P.; Alan T. Paller, Secy.
EIN: 521316829

3909
Marriott Daughters Foundation
10400 Fernwood Rd., Dept. 901
Bethesda, MD   20817-1102

Donor: The Richard E. Marriott Charitable Trust.
Foundation type: Independent foundation.
Financial data (yr. ended 10/31/14): Assets, $34,132,484 (M); gifts received, $8,060,046; expenditures, $482,833; qualifying distributions, $377,501; giving activities include $322,000 for 30 grants (high: $75,000; low: $2,500).
Fields of interest: Children's hospital care; Diseases and conditions; Human services; Child welfare.
Type of support: Research.
Limitations: Applications not accepted. Giving primarily in MA; with some giving to CA and UT.
Application information: Unsolicited requests for funds not accepted.
Officers and Directors: Julie Ann Marriott, Pres. and Director; Nancie Suzuki, Secy.; James A. Poulos, Treas.; Sandra Marriott Bertha; Mary Alice Marriott Hatch; Karen Christine Marriott.
EIN: 452590105

3910
The Sumner T. McKnight Foundation
901 S. Bond St.
Baltimore, MD   21231-3340

Established in 1956 in Maryland.
Donors: Sumner T. McKnight; H. Turney McKnight.
Foundation type: Independent foundation.
Financial data (yr. ended 12/31/13): Assets, $2,047,226 (M); expenditures, $303,542; qualifying distributions, $282,000; giving activities include $282,000 for 20 grants (high: $35,000; low: $1,000).
Fields of interest: Museums; Environment; Natural resources; Specialty hospital care; Diseases and conditions; Human services.

Type of support: Research; Research and evaluation.
Limitations: Applications not accepted. Giving in the U.S., with emphasis on MD and VA. No support for religion. No grants to individuals, or for endowment or capital funds or trips or tours.
Application information: Contributes only to pre-selected organizations.
Board meeting date(s): Apr.
Directors: H. Turney McKnight; Sumner T. McKnight; John T. Westrom.
Number of staff: 1
EIN: 416022360

3911
Alan & Amy Meltzer Family Foundation, Inc.
c/o R. Philipson & Co.
8601 Georgia Ave., Ste. 1001
Silver Spring, MD   20910-3440

Established in 1997 in Maryland.
Donors: Alan L. Meltzer; Greg Carroll; Amy Meltzer; Jack Abel.
Foundation type: Independent foundation.
Financial data (yr. ended 12/31/13): Assets, $3,182,582 (M); gifts received, $320,725; expenditures, $278,992; qualifying distributions, $212,938; giving activities include $208,188 for 52 grants (high: $31,250; low: $366).
Fields of interest: Education; Hospital care; Diabetes.
Limitations: Applications not accepted. Giving primarily in MD; also giving in VA and Washington, DC. No grants to individuals.
Application information: Contributes only to pre-selected organizations.
Officers: Alan L. Meltzer, Pres.; Amy Meltzer, V.P. and Secy.-Treas.
EIN: 522069235

3912
The Mental Wellness Foundation, Inc.
8171 Maple Lawn Blvd., Ste. 375
Fulton, MD   20759-2531

Established in 2000 in Maryland.
Donors: Barbara Bainum; Reality Investment Co., Inc.; Wilfried Busse.
Foundation type: Independent foundation.
Financial data (yr. ended 06/30/13): Assets, $3,825,588 (M); expenditures, $264,507; qualifying distributions, $236,851; giving activities include $230,500 for 20 grants (high: $33,250; low: $1,500).
Fields of interest: Education; Elementary education; Reading promotion; Mental health care; Human services.
Limitations: Applications not accepted. Giving primarily in San Francisco, CA, Baltimore, MD, Portland, OR, and Seattle, WA. No grants to individuals.
Application information: Contributes only to pre-selected organizations.
Officers: Barbara Bainum, Chair. and Pres.; Christine A. Shreve, Secy.-Treas.
Directors: Wilfried Busse; Amanda Renschler; Katherine Renschler; Scott Renschler; Todd Renschler.
EIN: 522287352

3913
The Robert Benson Meyer, Jr. Foundation, Inc.
9800 Sotweed Dr.
Potomac, MD   20854-4718   (301) 299-8236
Contact: Maria Teresa De Z. Meyer, Pres., Treas. and Dir.

Established in 1998 in Maryland.
Donor: Maria Teresa De Z. Meyer.
Foundation type: Independent foundation.
Financial data (yr. ended 12/31/13): Assets, $1,678,616 (M); gifts received, $552,845; expenditures, $396,557; qualifying distributions, $385,484; giving activities include $320,440 for 206 grants (high: $25,000; low: $50), and $65,044 for 20 grants to individuals (high: $30,734; low: $330).
Fields of interest: Education; Domesticated animals; Nonprofits; Catholicism; Human services; Basic and emergency aid; International development.
Type of support: General support; Grants to individuals; Regranting.
Limitations: Applications accepted. Giving primarily in Washington, DC, and MD.
Application information: Application form required.
Initial approach: Letter
Deadline(s): None
Officers and Directors: Maria Teresa De Z. Meyer, Pres. and Treas. and Director; Carlos Roberto Bensen Meyer, V.P. and Director; Katharine Maria Meyer, Secy. and Director.
EIN: 522104075

3914
The Lyn P. Meyerhoff Foundation, Inc.
1 South St., Ste. 1000
Baltimore, MD   21202-7301   (410) 727-3200
Contact: Misty Gibson
FAX: (410) 625-1075; E-mail: info@magnajm.com; Additional email: misty@magnajm.com; Main URL: http://www.meyerhoffcharitablefunds.org

Established in 1989 in Maryland.
Donor: Lenore P. Meyerhoff†.
Foundation type: Independent foundation.
Financial data (yr. ended 12/31/12): Assets, $5,208,034 (M); expenditures, $293,070; qualifying distributions, $209,664; giving activities include $196,237 for 12 grants (high: $100,000; low: $500).
Fields of interest: Education; Judaism; Human services.
Type of support: General support.
Limitations: Applications accepted. Giving primarily in MD and New York, NY. No grants to individuals.
Application information: See foundation web site for application guidelines. Application form required.
Initial approach: Letter
Deadline(s): None
Officers: Joseph Meyerhoff II, Pres.; Lee M. Hendler, V.P.; Jill M. Hieronimus, Secy.; Terry M. Rubenstein, Treas.
EIN: 521624876

3915
Leon & Marianne Minkoff Family Foundation
20457 Seneca Meadows Pkwy.
Germantown, MD   20876-7005

Established in 1986 in Maryland.
Donors: Leon P. Minkoff; Marianne Minkoff Lerner.
Foundation type: Independent foundation.
Financial data (yr. ended 12/31/13): Assets, $43,113 (M); gifts received, $231,841; expenditures, $243,750; qualifying distributions, $242,875; giving activities include $242,000 for 6 grants (high: $100,000; low: $1,000).
Fields of interest: Education; Nonprofits; Diseases and conditions; Archives and special collections; Judaism; Human services.
Type of support: Research; Research and evaluation; Regranting.
Limitations: Applications not accepted. Giving primarily in MD. No grants to individuals.
Application information: Unsolicited requests for funds not accepted.
Officers: Marianne Minkoff Lerner, Pres.; Paul N. Chod, Treas.
EIN: 521499816

3916
John Mitchell, Jr. Trust
7 St. Paul St., Ste. 1500
Baltimore, MD 21202-1626

Established in 2000 in Maryland.
Foundation type: Independent foundation.
Financial data (yr. ended 12/31/14): Assets, $4,449,729; expenditures, $214,696; qualifying distributions, $203,382.
Fields of interest: Health; Pediatrics; Ear, nose and throat diseases; Eye diseases; People with hearing impairments.
Type of support: Endowments; Equipment.
Limitations: Applications not accepted. Giving primarily in Baltimore, MD. No grants to individuals.
Application information: Contributes only to pre-selected organizations.
Trustees: Frederick Singley Koontz; John W. Payne; Robert Sloan.
EIN: 527005607

3917
The Clement C. Moore II and Elizabeth W. Y. Moore Charitable Trust
P.O. Box 1058
Chestertown, MD 21620-5058 (410) 788-5225

Established in 2001 in Delaware.
Donor: Clement C. Moore II.
Foundation type: Independent foundation.
Financial data (yr. ended 06/30/13): Assets, $2,620,569 (M); expenditures, $227,187; qualifying distributions, $179,241; giving activities include $175,451 for 12 grants (high: $53,951; low: $3,000).
Fields of interest: Arts and culture; Education; Veterinary medicine; Family planning; Public libraries; Community beautification; Human services; Food banks.
Limitations: Applications accepted. Giving primarily in NY.
Application information: Application form required.
Initial approach: Completed application form
Deadline(s): None
Trustees: Clement C. Moore II; Elizabeth W. Moore.
EIN: 527059395

3918
Moser Family Foundation, Inc.
10 E. Lee St., Apt. 2105
Baltimore, MD 21202-6023

Established in 2005 in Maryland.
Donors: Elizabeth K. Moser; M. Peter Moser.
Foundation type: Independent foundation.
Financial data (yr. ended 12/31/13): Assets, $10,228,572 (M); expenditures, $547,979; qualifying distributions, $456,892; giving activities include $240,801 for 44 grants (high: $30,000; low: $1).
Fields of interest: Education; Land resources; Human services.
Type of support: Capital campaigns.
Limitations: Applications not accepted. No grants to individuals.
Application information: Unsolicited requests for funds not accepted.
Officers and Trustees: Elizabeth K. Moser, Pres. and Trustee; Moriah Moser, V.P. and Trustee; Martin P. Moser, Jr., Secy. and Trustee; Jeremy R.H. Moser, Treas. and Trustee; Carolyn Goodman, Esq.; Laura Kittle; Daniel Morgenstern, MD.
EIN: 562567449

3919
Mpala Wildlife Foundation, Inc.
P.O. Box 137
Riderwood, MD 21139-0137 (410) 244-7507
Contact: Kay Berney
E-mail for Kay Berney: kberney@mpala.org;
Tel.: (410) 889-0194; Main URL: http://www.mpala.org
E Newsletter: http://www.mpala.org/Get_our_Newsletter.php

Established in 1989 in Maryland.
Donors: George L. Small†; Princeton University; Smithsonian Institute.
Foundation type: Operating foundation.
Financial data (yr. ended 12/31/13): Assets, $11,656,121 (M); gifts received, $367,779; expenditures, $348,869; qualifying distributions, $525,636; giving activities include $198,317 for 2 grants (high: $170,952; low: $27,365), and $285,636 for foundation-administered programs.
Purpose and activities: Giving primarily to a wildlife sanctuary and preserve, and operation of a scientific research center, as well as for the operation of a mobile clinic.
Fields of interest: Wildlife biodiversity.
International interests: Kenya.
Limitations: Applications not accepted. Giving primarily in Nanyuki, Kenya. No grants to individuals.
Application information: Contributes only to pre-selected organizations.
Officer: Margaret Kinnaird, Exec. Dir.
Trustees: Howard Ende; Jeffrey K. Gonya; Laurel Harvey; Dennis Keller; Dr. Ira Rubinoff; John Wreford-Smith.
EIN: 521656147

3920
The Thomas F. and Clementine L. Mullan Foundation, Inc.
2330 W. Joppa Rd., Ste. 210
Lutherville, MD 21093-4630

Established in 1958 in Maryland.

Donors: Thomas F. Mullan, Sr.; C. Louise Mullan.
Foundation type: Independent foundation.
Financial data (yr. ended 11/30/14): Assets, $4,752,976 (M); gifts received, $774,120; expenditures, $383,483; qualifying distributions, $300,110; giving activities include $296,310 for 60 grants (high: $120,000; low: $100).
Fields of interest: Secondary education; Higher education; Health; Hospital care; Diseases and conditions; Catholicism; Human services.
Limitations: Applications not accepted. Giving primarily in Baltimore, MD. No grants to individuals.
Application information: Contributes only to pre-selected organizations.
Officers: Thomas F. Mullan III, Pres. and Treas.; Norman Wilder, V.P.
EIN: 526050776

3921
The Murthynayak Foundation, Inc.
(formerly The Murthy Foundation, Inc.)
11 Cool Spring Ct.
Lutherville, MD 21093-3529
E-mail: info@murthynayak.org; Main URL: http://www.murthynayak.org
Blog: http://www.murthynayak.org/?cat=81

Established in 2001 in Maryland.
Donors: Sheela Murthy; Murthy Law Firm.
Foundation type: Independent foundation.
Financial data (yr. ended 12/31/13): Assets, $5,590,801 (M); gifts received, $100,000; expenditures, $311,503; qualifying distributions, $299,085; giving activities include $299,085 for 31 grants (high: $50,000; low: $158).
Fields of interest: Nonprofits; Human services.
Type of support: Regranting.
Limitations: Applications not accepted. Giving primarily in Washington, DC, and Baltimore, MD. No grants to individuals.
Application information: Unsolicited requests for funds not accepted.
Officers: Sheela Murthy, Pres.; Vasant Nayak, V.P.
Trustees: Kenneth B. Coehlo; Srinivas Murthy; Joseph E. Pollak.
EIN: 800016494

3922
Mustard Seed Foundation
7101 Wisconsin Ave., Ste. 1011
Bethesda, MD 20814-4805

Donor: Sandra P. Spedden.
Foundation type: Independent foundation.
Financial data (yr. ended 11/30/14): Assets, $819,399; gifts received, $125,000; expenditures, $253,963; qualifying distributions, $232,271.
Purpose and activities: Giving primarily for Christian organizations.
Fields of interest: Education; Religion; Christianity; Human services.
Type of support: Individual development.
Limitations: Applications not accepted. Giving primarily in MD. No grants to individuals.
Application information: Unsolicited requests for funds not accepted.
Officers: Sandra P. Spedden, Pres.; Yvonne Alexander Matthews, V.P.; John C. Hendricks, Secy.; Joann Knauer, Treas.
Directors: Ralph Scott; Blake Wise.
EIN: 521492276

3923
Alvin & Louise Myerberg Family Foundation, Inc.
335 N. Charles St.
Baltimore, MD 21201-4307 (410) 837-2900
Contact: Wendy M. Jachman, Pres.

Established in 1998 in Maryland.
Donor: Alvin J. Myerberg.
Foundation type: Independent foundation.
Financial data (yr. ended 12/31/12): Assets, $9,455,996 (M); expenditures, $404,361; qualifying distributions, $343,000; giving activities include $343,000 for grants.
Fields of interest: Arts and culture; Education; Judaism.
Limitations: Applications accepted. Giving primarily in Baltimore, MD, New York, NY, and Columbus, OH.
Application information:
  Initial approach: Proposal
  Deadline(s): None
Officers: Wendy M. Jachman, Pres.; Henry Myerberg, V.P. and Secy.; Jennifer Myerberg, V.P. and Treas.
EIN: 522136369

3924
The Nabit Foundation Inc.
20 Commerce St.
Baltimore, MD 21202-3208

Donors: Merwin J. Nabit; Charles J. Nabit; Great Chesapeake Bay Swim, Inc.
Foundation type: Independent foundation.
Financial data (yr. ended 06/30/14): Assets, $1,964,955 (M); gifts received, $5,500; expenditures, $332,716; qualifying distributions, $325,133; giving activities include $325,133 for 23 grants (high: $76,000; low: $500).
Fields of interest: Arts and culture; Art museums; Education; Higher education; Diseases and conditions; Human services.
Type of support: Research.
Limitations: Applications not accepted. Giving primarily in Baltimore, MD; some funding also in FL. No grants to individuals.
Application information: Contributes only to pre-selected organizations.
  Board meeting date(s): Periodically
Officers and Directors: Merwin J. Nabit, Pres. and Director; Charles J. Nabit, Secy. and Director; Michael C. Hodes.
EIN: 521756376

3925
Newday U.S.A. Foundation, Inc.
8160 Maple Lawn Blvd., Ste. 300
Fulton, MD 20759-2623
Contact: Robert I. Posner, Co-Chair.

Donor: Chrysalis Holdings, LLC.
Foundation type: Independent foundation.
Financial data (yr. ended 12/31/13): Assets, $0 (M); gifts received, $341,875; expenditures, $341,875; qualifying distributions, $295,820; giving activities include $295,820 for 7 grants (high: $100,000; low: $10,000).
Fields of interest: Education; Housing development; Human services.
Application information: Application form required.
  Initial approach: Letter
  Deadline(s): None

Officers: Thomas C. Lynch, Co.Chair. and Director; Robert I. Posner, Co-Chair. and Director; John Fenzel, Pres. and C.E.O.; Michael F. Shriver, V.P.; Nicole Jensen, Secy.-Treas.
EIN: 463282193

3926
The Nicholl Family Foundation, Inc.
1124 Day Rd.
Sykesville, MD 21784-5607

Established in 2001 in Maryland.
Donors: Teresa A. Nicholl; Peter T. Nicholl.
Foundation type: Independent foundation.
Financial data (yr. ended 12/31/13): Assets, $6,514,510 (M); gifts received, $1,002,475; expenditures, $455,024; qualifying distributions, $390,000; giving activities include $390,000 for 3 grants (high: $280,000; low: $50,000).
Fields of interest: Higher education; Hospital care; Diseases and conditions; Christianity.
Limitations: Applications not accepted. Giving primarily in Baltimore, MD and NY. No grants to individuals.
Application information: Contributes only to pre-selected organizations.
Officers: Teresa A. Nicholl, Pres. and Treas.; Peter T. Nicholl, V.P. and Secy.
EIN: 522347387

3927
No Plain Jane Foundation
(formerly The J. L. Stradley Foundation for the Protection of Independent Senior Women)
1006 S. Washington St.
Easton, MD 21601-4303

Established in 2001 in Delaware.
Donors: Jane L. Stradley; Diane Bradley.
Foundation type: Independent foundation.
Financial data (yr. ended 05/31/13): Assets, $3,681,278 (M); gifts received, $20,000; expenditures, $241,820; qualifying distributions, $225,000; giving activities include $225,000 for grants.
Fields of interest: Education; Christianity; Human services; Females; Female adults.
Type of support: Scholarships.
Limitations: Applications not accepted. Giving primarily in ME, MO, NY, and PA. No grants to individuals.
Application information: Contributes only to pre-selected organizations.
Officers: Diane Bradley, Pres.; Jo Rhea N. Wright, V.P.
EIN: 510411557

3928
Northern Kenya Fund
c/o Bunting Mgmt. Group
217 International Cir.
Hunt Valley, MD 21030-1332
E-mail: chris@northernkenyafund.org; *Main URL:* http://www.northernkenyafund.org
Facebook: https://www.facebook.com/pages/Northern-Kenya-Fund/204405872933612

Donors: Joseph J. Duffy, Jr.; Karen Jordan; The Bunting Family Foundation; Mary Ellen Kranzlin; Judith Needham; Anne R. Bunting; Arthur B. Schultz

Foundation; Marc Bunting; Samuel P. Pardoe Foundation; Travis Jordan; Dorothy B. Duffy; Christopher L. Bunting; George L. Bunting, Jr.; Mary Catherine Bunting.
Foundation type: Independent foundation.
Financial data (yr. ended 12/31/13): Assets, $52,280 (M); gifts received, $141,499; expenditures, $156,915; qualifying distributions, $155,515; giving activities include $154,500 for 6 grants (high: $130,000; low: $4,500).
Purpose and activities: Scholarship awards paid directly to the college for deserving and high-achieving students of Marsabit, Kenya, who have completed primary school but do not have the financial means to attend secondary school.
Fields of interest: Higher education.
International interests: Kenya.
Limitations: Applications not accepted. Giving primarily in Nairobi, Kenya. No grants to individuals.
Application information: Unsolicited requests for funds not accepted.
Officers and Directors: Christopher L. Bunting, Pres. and Director; Rebekah S. Bunting, Secy.-Treas. and Director; Deb Kmon Davidson.
EIN: 743196803

3929
Number Ten Foundation, Inc.
7902 Brynmor Ct., Ste. 606
Baltimore, MD 21208-4356 (410) 484-0002
Contact: Ralph A. Brunn, Pres.

Established in 1985 in Maryland.
Donors: Ralph A. Brunn; Simone Brunn.
Foundation type: Independent foundation.
Financial data (yr. ended 12/31/13): Assets, $3,065,790 (M); gifts received, $125,000; expenditures, $372,174; qualifying distributions, $364,095; giving activities include $364,095 for 110 grants (high: $152,000; low: $15).
Purpose and activities: Emphasis on Jewish welfare funds; some support for temples.
Fields of interest: Nonprofits; Judaism; Human services.
Type of support: Regranting.
Limitations: Applications accepted. Giving primarily in Baltimore, MD. No grants to individuals.
Application information: Application form required.
  Initial approach: Letter
  Deadline(s): None
Officers and Directors: Ralph A. Brunn, Pres. and Director; Simone Brunn, V.P. and Secy. and Director.
EIN: 521400791

3930
The O'Neil Family Foundation, Inc.
2 E. Read St.
Baltimore, MD 21202-2470
Application address: c/o Thomas F. O'Neil, Jr., 11325 John Carroll Rd., Owings Mills, MD 21117, tel.: (410) 837-2544

Established in 2007 in Maryland.
Donor: Thomas F. O'Neil, Jr.
Foundation type: Independent foundation.
Financial data (yr. ended 06/30/13): Assets, $8,972,136 (M); gifts received, $861,383; expenditures, $397,785; qualifying distributions, $385,000; giving activities include $383,065 for 21 grants (high: $111,065; low: $500).

Fields of interest: Foundations; Christianity; Female children and youth; Male children and youth.
Limitations: Applications accepted. Giving primarily in MD and VA.
Application information:
Deadline(s): None
Directors: Michael N. O'Neil; Pamela B. O'Neil; Stephen B. O'Neil; Thomas F. O'Neil, Jr.; Thomas F. O'Neil III.
EIN: 261313395

3931
The Anne Lindsey Otenasek Charitable Foundation, Inc.
405 E. Joppa Rd., Ste. 100
Baltimore, MD 21286-5465

Established in 2004 in Maryland.
Donors: Margaret B. Otenasek; Francis H. Otenasek; Catherine Otenasek Levitas; Richard J. Otenasek III.
Foundation type: Independent foundation.
Financial data (yr. ended 12/31/13): Assets, $654,151 (M); expenditures, $384,653; qualifying distributions, $327,000; giving activities include $327,000 for 14 grants (high: $115,500; low: $5,000).
Fields of interest: Education; Residential mental health care; Disasters and emergency management.
Type of support: Capital and infrastructure.
Limitations: Applications not accepted. Giving primarily to MA, MD and VA. No grants to individuals.
Application information: Contributes only to pre-selected organizations.
Officer and Directors: Margaret B. Otenasek, Pres. and Director; Catherine Otenasek Levitas; Francis H. Otenasek; John H. Otenasek; Page Otenasek Kozak; Richard J. Otenasek III.
EIN: 200702156

3932
The John B. Parsons Foundation
(also known as John B. Parsons-Salisbury Home for the Aged Trust)
P.O. Box 2916
Salisbury, MD 21801
Application address: c/o Ernest Cornbooks, 115 Broad St., Salisbury, MD 21801, tel.: (410) 742-3176, e-mail: ecornbrooks@webbnetlaw.com

Established in 1988 in Maryland.
Donors: John B. Parsons Trust; Katherine F. Parsons Trust.
Foundation type: Independent foundation.
Financial data (yr. ended 12/31/13): Assets, $5,867,980 (M); gifts received, $234,765; expenditures, $348,364; qualifying distributions, $282,094; giving activities include $279,600 for 11 grants (high: $74,400; low: $5,000).
Purpose and activities: The foundation funds organizations that assist needy elderly people to obtain housing, health care, clothing, and food.
Fields of interest: Convalescent care; Senior services.
Limitations: Applications accepted. Giving limited to the Salisbury, MD area. No grants to individuals.
Application information:
Initial approach: Proposal
Deadline(s): None

Officers: Ernest I. Cornbrooks III, Pres.; Jean H. Laws, V.P.; Gerald B. Truitt, Secy.; Robert C. Davis, Treas.
Trustees: Philip L. Bradshaw; Allen C. Brown; John M. Broyhill; David Downes; Gordon D. Gladden; Loudell Insley; Robert Long; Lynne Peverley; Carolyn Stegman; Jeffrey F. Turner; Gayle Widdowson; Pam Wierman.
EIN: 520591626

3933
The Paternotte Family Foundation, Inc.
215 Woodbrook Ln.
Baltimore, MD 21212-1037

Established in 1998 in Maryland.
Donors: William Paternotte; Nancy Paternotte.
Foundation type: Independent foundation.
Financial data (yr. ended 12/31/13): Assets, $216,029 (M); gifts received, $2,100; expenditures, $157,761; qualifying distributions, $154,717; giving activities include $153,567 for 8 grants (high: $67,000; low: $200).
Fields of interest: Arts and culture; Education; Environment.
Limitations: Applications not accepted. Giving primarily in MD. No grants to individuals.
Application information: Unsolicited requests for funds not accepted.
Officers: William Paternotte, Pres.; Nancy Paternotte, V.P.
EIN: 522101017

3934
The Pearlstone Fund, Inc.
(formerly The Esther S. Pearlstone Foundation, Inc.)
2 Village Sq., Ste. 212
Baltimore, MD 21210-1624
Application address: c/o Richard L. Pearlstone, P.O. Box 1860, Aspen, CO 81612-1860, tel.: (410) 532-2263

Established in 1999 in Maryland.
Foundation type: Independent foundation.
Financial data (yr. ended 02/28/13): Assets, $4,947,152 (M); expenditures, $292,626; qualifying distributions, $230,000; giving activities include $230,000 for 16 grants (high: $93,500; low: $250).
Purpose and activities: Giving primarily for arts, culture and education.
Fields of interest: Arts and culture; Arts education; Ballet; Higher education; Foundations; Nonprofits.
Type of support: Regranting.
Limitations: Applications accepted. Giving primarily in Baltimore, MD.
Application information: Application form required.
Initial approach: Letter
Deadline(s): None
Officers: Esther S. Pearlstone, Pres.; Richard L. Pearlstone, V.P. and Secy.-Treas.
Trustee: P. Justin Pearlstone.
EIN: 522179370

3935
Pettit Family Charitable Foundation
18205-D Flower Hill Way
Gaithersburg, MD 20879-5331 (301) 975-1020

Established in 1989 in Maryland.

Donors: Pettit and Griffin, Inc.; Pettit Family Charitable Trust; John H. Pettit†.
Foundation type: Independent foundation.
Financial data (yr. ended 12/31/13): Assets, $5,701,603 (M); gifts received, $123,716; expenditures, $302,923; qualifying distributions, $247,200; giving activities include $247,200 for 52 grants (high: $24,000; low: $200).
Purpose and activities: Giving for education, social services, and youth services.
Fields of interest: Education; Hospital care; Hospice care; Diseases and conditions; Community and economic development; Housing development; Christianity; Human services; Youth services.
Limitations: Applications accepted. Giving primarily in Washington, DC, and MD. No grants to individuals.
Application information: Application form required.
Initial approach: Letter
Deadline(s): None
Officers: Barbara Lynn Pettit, Mgr.; Jeanne Marie Pettit, Mgr.; John Stephen Pettit, Mgr.
Trustees: Carol Ann Pettit; Richard B. Pettit.
EIN: 521646923

3936
The Phase Foundation
2 Executive Park Ct.
Germantown, MD 20874-2645 (301) 540-0424

Established in 1989 in Maryland.
Donors: Norris C. Hekimian; Joan E. Hekimian.
Foundation type: Independent foundation.
Financial data (yr. ended 12/31/14): Assets, $5,720,141; expenditures, $449,517; qualifying distributions, $412,013.
Fields of interest: Education; Environment; Health; Human services.
Type of support: General support; Annual campaigns; Capital campaigns; Emergency funds.
Limitations: Applications accepted. No support for political or activist organizations . No grants to individuals.
Application information: Application form required.
Initial approach: Proposal
Copies of proposal: 1
Deadline(s): Aug.
Trustees: Catherine L. Hekimian; Christopher D. Hekimian; Joan E. Hekimian; A. Mark Knechtel; Allison H. Sitar.
Number of staff: 1 part-time professional.
EIN: 521611434

3937
The RCM & D Foundation
555 Fairmount Ave.
Towson, MD 21286-5417 (410) 339-7263
Contact: Albert R. Counselman, Chair. and Pres.

Established in 1999 in Maryland.
Donors: Riggs Conselman Michaels & Downes, Inc.; L. Patrick Deering; Charles C. Counselman; Catherine R. Counselman.
Foundation type: Independent foundation.
Financial data (yr. ended 03/31/15): Assets, $3,836,971 (M); gifts received, $100,000; expenditures, $215,676; qualifying distributions, $188,200; giving activities include $188,200 for 50 grants (high: $16,000; low: $100).

Fields of interest: Arts and culture; Orchestral music; Education; Higher education; Aquariums; Nonprofits; Hospital care; Cancers; Catholicism.
Type of support: Regranting.
Limitations: Applications accepted. Giving primarily in Baltimore, MD.
Application information: Application form required.
   Initial approach: Letter
   Deadline(s): None
Officers and Directors: Albert R. Counselman, Chair. and Pres. and Director; J. Kevin Carnell, Secy.; Price Poore, Treas.; Margaret K. Counselman.
EIN: 522204935

3938
RFI Foundation Inc.
7910 Woodmount Ave., No. 850
Bethesda, MD 20814-4885

Established in 2002 in Maryland.
Donors: Joshua B. Rales; Debra Rales.
Foundation type: Independent foundation.
Financial data (yr. ended 12/31/13): Assets, $2,227,418 (M); expenditures, $203,164; qualifying distributions, $196,494; giving activities include $194,348 for 33 grants (high: $60,000; low: $40).
Purpose and activities: Giving primarily for higher and other education, as well as to Jewish organizations and for Jewish federated programs; some funding for the arts, and cancer research.
Fields of interest: Arts and culture; Education; Elementary and secondary education; Higher education; Nonprofits; Judaism; Human services.
Type of support: Regranting.
Limitations: Applications not accepted. Giving primarily in Washington, DC and MD. No grants to individuals.
Application information: Contributes only to pre-selected organizations.
Officers and Directors: Joshua B. Rales, Pres. and Director; Maura Dyer, Secy. and Exec. Dir.; Norman Freidkin, Treas. and Director.
EIN: 542076962

3939
Rhona's Place Foundation
22 W. Pennsylvania Ave., Ste. 606
Towson, MD 21204-5005

Foundation type: Independent foundation.
Financial data (yr. ended 12/31/13): Assets, $7,961,067 (M); expenditures, $353,464; qualifying distributions, $292,948; giving activities include $230,030 for 32 grants (high: $60,080; low: $500).
Fields of interest: Graduate and professional education; Nursing care; Diseases and conditions; Human services.
Type of support: Research.
Limitations: Applications not accepted. Giving primarily in MD.
Application information: Unsolicited requests for funds not accepted.
Trustee: Jerry D. Focas.
EIN: 274477606

3940
Frederick W. Richmond Foundation, Inc.
31 S. Harrison St.
Easton, MD 21601-3020 (410) 820-7676

Established in 1962 in New York.
Donor: Frederick W. Richmond.
Foundation type: Independent foundation.
Financial data (yr. ended 06/30/13): Assets, $4,961,321 (M); expenditures, $216,367; qualifying distributions, $206,569; giving activities include $200,065 for 57 grants (high: $25,000; low: $250).
Purpose and activities: The foundation is interested in funding pilot projects, primarily in the arts, education, health, and the environment.
Fields of interest: Arts and culture; Education; Environment.
Type of support: Annual campaigns; Capital campaigns; Capital and infrastructure; Pilot programs; Professorships; Seed money; Fellowships; Scholarships.
Limitations: Applications accepted. Giving primarily in Talbot County, MD; some giving also in NY. No support for non-exempt organizations. No grants to individuals.
Publications: Program policy statement.
Application information:
   Initial approach: Proposal
   Deadline(s): None
   Board meeting date(s): Aug.
Officers: Timothy E. Wyman, Chair. and Treas.; Elizabeth Wyman, V.P.; James L. Myers, Secy.; Erin Geyelin, Exec. Dir.
Director: Karin W. Morgan.
Number of staff: 1 part-time professional.
EIN: 136124582

3941
Rogers-Wilbur Foundation, Inc.
P.O. Box 149
Gibson Island, MD 21056-0046 (410) 255-3757

Established in 1947 in Maryland.
Foundation type: Independent foundation.
Financial data (yr. ended 12/31/14): Assets, $4,435,714; expenditures, $283,641; qualifying distributions, $258,968.
Purpose and activities: Giving primarily for education, the arts, hospitals and health associations, and human services.
Fields of interest: Arts and culture; Museums; Historic preservation; Elementary education; Higher education; Hospital care; Specialty hospital care; Diseases and conditions; Religion; Human services.
Type of support: General support.
Limitations: Applications accepted. Giving primarily in MD, with emphasis on Baltimore and Annapolis. No grants to individuals.
Application information: Application form required.
   Initial approach: Letter
   Deadline(s): None
Officers and Directors: Leroy A. Wilbur, Jr., Pres. and Director; Lawrence A. Wilbur, V.P. and Director; Denise Wilbur, Secy. and Director; Scott E. Wilbur, Treas. and Director.
EIN: 136103945

3942
The Rothschild Charitable Foundation Inc.
100 E. Pratt St., Ste. 2550
Baltimore, MD 21202-1074

Established in 1986 in Maryland.
Donor: Stanford Z. Rothschild, Jr.
Foundation type: Independent foundation.
Financial data (yr. ended 12/31/13): Assets, $9,154,056 (M); gifts received, $50,700; expenditures, $412,739; qualifying distributions, $310,915; giving activities include $305,134 for 61 grants (high: $63,200; low: $100).
Fields of interest: Museums; Education; Nonprofits; Diseases and conditions; Judaism; Human services.
Type of support: Regranting.
Limitations: Applications not accepted. Giving primarily in Baltimore, MD. No grants to individuals; no loans or program-related investments.
Application information: Contributes only to pre-selected organizations.
Officers and Directors: Stanford Z. Rothschild, Jr., Pres. and Treas. and Director; Cory Rothschild, V.P. and Secy. and Director; David Rothschild.
EIN: 521492357

3943
The Jim and Patty Rouse Charitable Foundation, Inc.
(formerly The Jim Rouse Charitable Foundation, Inc.)
4537 Black Rock Rd.
Upperco, MD 21155-9544

Established in 1967 in Maryland.
Donor: James W. Rouse†.
Foundation type: Independent foundation.
Financial data (yr. ended 12/31/13): Assets, $7,119,053 (M); expenditures, $407,938; qualifying distributions, $336,135; giving activities include $326,500 for 102 grants (high: $25,000; low: $250).
Fields of interest: Zoos; Housing development; Human services; Low-income and poor people.
Type of support: General support.
Limitations: Applications not accepted. Giving primarily in Baltimore, MD. No grants to individuals.
Application information: Contributes only to pre-selected organizations.
   Board meeting date(s): Early Nov.
Officer: James W. Rouse, Pres.
Directors: Maria Gamper; James R. Norton; Molly Norton; John Rixey, Jr.; J. Barbour Rixey; Nancy Rouse; Winstead Rouse; James W. Rouse, Jr.
Number of staff: 1 part-time support.
EIN: 526074744

3944
S.B.E. & S. Clients' Consolidated Charitable Foundation
2191 Defense Hwy., Ste. 316
Crofton, MD 21114-2456
Contact: Thomas J. Egan, Pres.

Established in 1984 in District of Columbia.
Donors: Elizabeth M. Voight†; Paul J. Rohrich†; Hester M. Digges†; S.B.E. & S. Clients' Consolidated.
Foundation type: Company-sponsored foundation.
Financial data (yr. ended 09/30/14): Assets, $4,242,469 (M); expenditures, $233,853; qualifying distributions, $167,599; giving activities

include $167,500 for 17 grants (high: $50,000; low: $2,500).

Purpose and activities: The foundation supports bar associations and organizations involved with secondary education, cancer, multiple sclerosis, and disability services.

Fields of interest: Secondary education; Multiple sclerosis; Cancers; Legal services; Catholicism; Developmental disability services.

Type of support: General support.

Limitations: Applications accepted. Giving limited to the greater Washington, DC, area and MD. No grants to individuals.

Publications: Annual report.

Application information:
Initial approach: Proposal
Deadline(s): None

Officers: Thomas J. Egan, Pres.; Thomas J. Egan, Jr., V.P.; Katherine D. Egan, Secy.; Sharon E. Katula, Treas.

Directors: Herbert N. Harmon; Maurice J. Montaldo; Walter J. Murphy, Jr.

EIN: 521306077

3945
Salisbury Family Foundation Inc.

300 E. Lombard St., Ste. 620
Baltimore, MD 21202-3227

Established in 1996 in Maryland.

Donors: Charles Salisbury, Jr.; Edith Gans Salisbury.

Foundation type: Independent foundation.

Financial data (yr. ended 06/30/14): Assets, $4,763,070; expenditures, $277,945; qualifying distributions, $241,875.

Fields of interest: Arts and culture; Art museums; Education; Elementary and secondary education; Higher education; Medical education; Botanical gardens; Hospital care; Catholicism.

Type of support: Annual campaigns.

Limitations: Applications not accepted. Giving primarily in MD. No grants to individuals.

Application information: Unsolicited requests for funds not accepted.

Officers: Edith Gans Salisbury, Pres.; Katherine Gans Salisbury, V.P.; Anne S. Staley, Treas.

Director: Charles Harrison Salisbury, Jr.

EIN: 521999670

3946
Schuh Family Foundation, Inc.

P.O. Box 48
Gibson Island, MD 21056-0047

Established in 2000 in Maryland.

Donor: Steven R. Schuh.

Foundation type: Independent foundation.

Financial data (yr. ended 06/30/14): Assets, $2,568,780; expenditures, $203,903; qualifying distributions, $184,207.

Fields of interest: Arts and culture; Orchestral music; Elementary and secondary education; Higher education; Animal welfare; Nonprofits; Health; Catholicism; Human services; Youth development.

Type of support: Regranting.

Limitations: Applications not accepted. Giving primarily in MD. No grants to individuals.

Application information: Unsolicited requests for funds not accepted.

Officers: Steven R. Schuh, Pres.; Scott L. Schuh, Treas.

Directors: David J. Callan; Marilyn Hope Fisher; Brittany L. Schuh; J.P. Watson.

EIN: 522294448

3947
David M. Schwarz Architects Charitable Foundation Inc.

c/o R. Philipson & Co.
8601 Georgia Ave., Ste. 1001
Silver Spring, MD 20910-3440

Established in 2007 in District of Columbia.

Donors: David M. Schwarz; David M. Schwarz Architectural Services, Inc.

Foundation type: Independent foundation.

Financial data (yr. ended 09/30/14): Assets, $471,600 (M); gifts received, $280,381; expenditures, $186,815; qualifying distributions, $183,659; giving activities include $179,631 for 36 grants (high: $45,000; low: $250).

Fields of interest: Arts and culture; Education; University education; Domesticated animals.

Limitations: Applications not accepted. Giving primarily in Washington, DC, CT, FL, and IN. No grants to individuals.

Application information: Contributes only to pre-selected organizations.

Officers: Michael C. Swartz, Pres.; Gregory M. Hoss, Secy.-Treas.

Directors: Thomas H. Greene; David M. Schwarz; Craig P. Williams.

EIN: 261125220

3948
The Henry Sears Foundation, Inc.

300 Chino Farms Ln.
Chestertown, MD 21620-2344

Established in 1995 in Maryland.

Donors: Sears Family Clat; Henry F. Sears.

Foundation type: Independent foundation.

Financial data (yr. ended 12/31/13): Assets, $1,548,044 (M); expenditures, $200,337; qualifying distributions, $193,750; giving activities include $193,750 for 18 grants (high: $150,000; low: $250).

Fields of interest: Arts and culture; Education; Undergraduate education; Environment.

Type of support: General support.

Limitations: Applications not accepted. Giving primarily in MA and MD. No grants to individuals.

Application information: Unsolicited requests for funds not accepted.

Officers: Henry F. Sears, Pres.; Christopher Sears, V.P.; Philip W. Hoon, Esq., Secy.-Treas.

Board Members: Greg Cole; Henry Davis; Douglas Gill; James Gruber; James Judge; Evan Milles; John Seidel.

Director: Sharon Bushnell Sears.

EIN: 521933579

3949
Jacob S. Shapiro Foundation

2545 Wilkens Ave.
P.O. Box 4436
Baltimore, MD 21223-3333

Established in 1947 in Maryland.

Donors: Israel D. Shapiro†; Bernice S. Levinson; United Iron & Metal Co., Inc.

Foundation type: Independent foundation.

Financial data (yr. ended 12/31/13): Assets, $5,566,847 (M); expenditures, $299,500; qualifying distributions, $227,000; giving activities include $227,000 for 50 grants (high: $80,000; low: $250).

Fields of interest: Arts and culture; Performing arts education; Art museums; Education; Foundations; Nonprofits; Diseases and conditions; Judaism; Human services.

Type of support: Regranting.

Limitations: Applications not accepted. Giving primarily in Baltimore, MD. No grants to individuals.

Application information: Contributes only to pre-selected organizations.

Trustees: Jane Baum Rodbell; James R. Shapiro.

EIN: 526072215

3950
The Shattuck Family Foundation, Inc.

20 Blythewood Rd.
Baltimore, MD 21210-2402

Established in 1999 in Maryland.

Donor: Mayo A. Shattuck III.

Foundation type: Independent foundation.

Financial data (yr. ended 12/31/13): Assets, $822,028 (M); expenditures, $348,445; qualifying distributions, $343,650; giving activities include $343,650 for 15 grants (high: $250,000; low: $100).

Purpose and activities: Giving for higher education and medical research; funding also for the arts and social services.

Fields of interest: Arts education; Education; Nonprofits; Diseases and conditions; Human services.

Type of support: Research; Research and evaluation; Regranting.

Limitations: Applications not accepted. Giving in the U.S., with emphasis on Baltimore, MD. No grants to individuals.

Application information: Unsolicited requests for funds not accepted.

Officers and Trustees: Mayo A. Shattuck III, Pres. and Trustee; Molly Ann George Shattuck, Secy.-Treas. and Trustee; Mayo A. Shattuck IV.

EIN: 522165454

3951
Shrensky Foundation, Inc.

10708 Balantre Ln.
Potomac, MD 20854-1317

Established in 2000 in Maryland.

Donors: Lewis Shrensky; Barbara Shrensky.

Foundation type: Independent foundation.

Financial data (yr. ended 12/31/14): Assets, $1,384,036 (M); gifts received, $200,000; expenditures, $150,128; qualifying distributions, $141,407; giving activities include $141,000 for 6 grants (high: $60,000; low: $3,500).

Fields of interest: Arts and culture; Education; Religion.

Limitations: Applications not accepted. Giving primarily in Potomac, MD. No grants to individuals.

Application information: Unsolicited requests for funds not accepted.

Officers: Lewis F. Shrensky, Pres. and Treas.; Barbara Shrensky, V.P. and Secy.

EIN: 522284925

3952
The Jean and Sidney Silber Foundation, Inc.

11515 Woodland Dr.
Lutherville, MD 21093-1516 (410) 337-0070
Contact: Jean F. Silber, Secy.-Treas.

Established in 1996 in Maryland.
Donors: Jean F. Silber; Sidney Silber; Silber 73, LLC; Willard Hackerman.
Foundation type: Independent foundation.
Financial data (yr. ended 12/31/13): Assets, $7,932,413 (M); gifts received, $100,000; expenditures, $436,099; qualifying distributions, $384,500; giving activities include $384,500 for 26 grants (high: $100,000; low: $1,000).
Fields of interest: Higher education; Undergraduate education; Foundations; Community and economic development; Community recreation.
Limitations: Applications accepted. Giving primarily in Baltimore, MD.
Application information: Application form required.
Initial approach: Letter
Deadline(s): None
Officers: Sidney Silber, Co-Pres.; Jean F. Silber, Co=Pres.; Douglas Silber, Secy.-Treas.
Trustees: Janet D. Silber; Paul M. Silber.
EIN: 522005856

3953
The Robert and Christina Silberman Charitable Trust

10828 Alloway Dr.
Potomac, MD 20854-1503

Established in 2007 in Maryland.
Donors: Christina J. Silberman; Robert S. Silberman.
Foundation type: Independent foundation.
Financial data (yr. ended 12/31/13): Assets, $3,450,455 (M); gifts received, $74,637; expenditures, $233,577; qualifying distributions, $232,672; giving activities include $232,672 for 9 + grants (high: $200,000).
Fields of interest: Arts and culture; Education; Health.
Limitations: Applications not accepted. Giving primarily in Washington, DC, MD and NH. No grants to individuals.
Application information: Contributes only to pre-selected organizations.
Trustees: Christina J. Silberman; Robert S. Silberman.
EIN: 261500614

3954
Sanford and Doris Slavin Foundation, Inc.

c/o R. Philipson
8601 Georgia Ave., Ste. 1001
Silver Spring, MD 20910-3440

Established in 1970 in Maryland.
Donors: Doris Slavin; Sanford Slavin; Roni S. Pekins.
Foundation type: Independent foundation.
Financial data (yr. ended 05/31/13): Assets, $59,578 (M); gifts received, $5,000; expenditures, $267,664; qualifying distributions, $248,714; giving activities include $248,714 for 54 grants (high: $20,000; low: $100).
Purpose and activities: Giving primarily for education, the arts, hospitals and health care.

Fields of interest: Performing arts; Education; Foundations; Health; Hospital care; Judaism; Human rights; Reproductive rights; Human services.
Type of support: Individual development.
Limitations: Applications not accepted. Giving primarily in Washington, DC, MD and NY. No grants to individuals.
Application information: Contributes only to pre-selected organizations.
Officers: Sanford Slavin, Pres.; Jeffrey Z. Slavin, V.P. and Treas.; Doris Slavin, V.P.; Roni S. Pekins, Secy.
EIN: 237075323

3955
Albert & Lillian Small Foundation Inc.

7501 Wisconsin Ave., Ste. 1103E
Bethesda, MD 20814-6515 (301) 215-7997

Established in 1981 in District of Columbia.
Foundation type: Independent foundation.
Financial data (yr. ended 12/31/14): Assets, $3,294,098; expenditures, $362,334; qualifying distributions, $338,458.
Purpose and activities: Giving primarily to Reform Jewish organizations, as well as for education and health associations; funding also for the arts and human services.
Fields of interest: Arts and culture; Museums; Historic preservation; Education; Higher education; Specialty hospital care; Diseases and conditions; Reform Judaism; Human services.
Type of support: General support.
Limitations: Applications accepted. Giving primarily in Washington, DC, MD, and New York, NY. No grants to individuals.
Application information: Application form required.
Initial approach: Letter
Deadline(s): None
Officers: Albert H. Small, Pres.; Shirley Small, V.P.; Albert H. Small, Jr., Treas.
EIN: 521266289

3956
The Snyder Foundation for Animals Inc.

(formerly The William Snyder Foundation for Animals)
3600 Clipper Mill Rd., Ste. 224
Baltimore, MD 21211-2149
Main URL: http://www.snyderanimals.org

Established in 1898 in Maryland.
Foundation type: Independent foundation.
Financial data (yr. ended 04/30/14): Assets, $3,887,655 (M); gifts received, $170; expenditures, $764,108; qualifying distributions, $730,799; giving activities include $309,090 for grants, and $6,048 for foundation-administered programs.
Purpose and activities: The mission of the foundation is to promote the welfare of animals through philanthropic support and education. Pet overpopulation is the foundation's primary focus. Grant support includes giving for spay/neuter programs, wildlife rehabilitation, and shelter adoption. The foundation operates a full-time education program.
Fields of interest: Domesticated animals; Human services.
Limitations: Applications not accepted. Giving limited to MD. No support for political organizations.

No grants to individuals, or for personnel positions, capital campaigns, or general operating expenses.
Publications: Financial statement; Program policy statement.
Application information: Unsolicited requests for funds not accepted.
Board meeting date(s): 3rd Thurs. of each month
Officers: Bill W. Benson, Pres.; Barbara Feeser, V.P.; Paul Nastasi, Secy.-Treas.; Lora Dean Junkin, Exec. Dir.
Directors: Sharon A. Christie, Esq.; Sharon Chup; Maureen Pulver.
Number of staff: 3 full-time professional; 1 full-time support.
EIN: 526001538

3957
The Sonneborn Foundation Inc.

510 Garrison Forest Rd.
Owings Mills, MD 21117-4000
Contact: Mark D. Neumann

Established in 1999 in Maryland.
Donor: Patti Neumann.
Foundation type: Independent foundation.
Financial data (yr. ended 06/30/13): Assets, $1,156,120 (M); gifts received, $100,000; expenditures, $190,531; qualifying distributions, $175,000; giving activities include $175,000 for grants.
Fields of interest: Museums; Education; Community and economic development; Judaism.
Type of support: Individual development.
Limitations: Applications not accepted. Giving primarily in Baltimore, MD. No grants to individuals.
Application information: Contributes only to pre-selected organizations.
Officers: Mark D. Neumann, Pres. and Treas.; Patti Neumann, Secy.
Trustees: Ann Neumann Libov; Robin Neumann.
EIN: 911987558

3958
SPM Foundation, Inc.

c/o Suzanne P. Murphy
8300 Burdette Rd., Ste. E512
Bethesda, MD 20817-2801

Established in 1997 in Maryland.
Donor: Suzanne P. Murphy.
Foundation type: Independent foundation.
Financial data (yr. ended 12/31/13): Assets, $7,094,180 (M); expenditures, $429,340; qualifying distributions, $392,500; giving activities include $392,500 for 72 grants (high: $109,500; low: $500).
Fields of interest: Education; Hospital care; Christianity; Human services; Child welfare.
Limitations: Applications not accepted. No grants to individuals.
Application information: Contributes only to pre-selected organizations.
Officers: Suzanne P. Murphy, Pres.; Jamie Sue Schulte, V.P.; Douglas Pulliam McDaniel, Secy.; Margaret Ann Goldsmith, Treas.
EIN: 522038980

3959
Ruth and Robert St. John Foundation, Inc.
P.O. Box 2183
Easton, MD   21601-8932

Donor: Tidewater Titans Association.
Foundation type: Independent foundation.
Financial data (yr. ended 12/31/13): Assets, $4,170,315 (M); gifts received, $5,500; expenditures, $283,170; qualifying distributions, $221,000; giving activities include $221,000 for 38 grants (high: $15,000; low: $1,000).
Fields of interest: Historic preservation; Education; Public libraries; Human services; Child welfare; Scouting programs; Rent and mortgage assistance.
Type of support: General support.
Limitations: Applications not accepted. Giving primarily in MD.
Application information: Contributes only to pre-selected organizations.
Officers: Vernon J. Nily, Jr., Pres.; William H. Price II, Secy.; L. Stephen Satchell, Treas.
EIN: 521709184

3960
St. John of Shanghai and San Francisco Foundation, Inc.
11140 Rockville Pike, Ste. 620
Rockville, MD   20852-3117

Donors: Michael Rae; Anton Rae; Shahla Rae.
Foundation type: Independent foundation.
Financial data (yr. ended 12/31/14): Assets, $490,025 (M); gifts received, $100,000; expenditures, $235,888; qualifying distributions, $225,139; giving activities include $225,139 for 13 grants (high: $115,000; low: $500).
Fields of interest: Community and economic development; Religion; Tribal and indigenous religions; Indigenous peoples.
International interests: Russia.
Limitations: Applications not accepted. Giving primarily in Washington, DC; with some giving in Moscow, Russia.
Application information: Unsolicited requests for funds not accepted.
Officers and Directors: Michael Rae, Pres. and Director; Anton Rae, V.P. and Director; Shahla Rae, Secy.
EIN: 800207663

3961
The Stover Family Foundation
901 S. Bond St.
Baltimore, MD   21231-3339

Donors: Matt and Debra Stover Donor Advised; Debra Stover; John Stover.
Foundation type: Independent foundation.
Financial data (yr. ended 12/31/13): Assets, $1,807,145 (M); gifts received, $68,905; expenditures, $221,714; qualifying distributions, $209,527; giving activities include $206,360 for 37 grants (high: $100,000; low: $100).
Fields of interest: Education; Christianity.
Limitations: Applications not accepted. Giving primarily in MD.
Application information: Unsolicited requests for funds not accepted.

Officers: John Matthew Stover, Pres.; Debra Rogers Stover, V.P.; John C. Poulton, Treas.
EIN: 276189634

3962
Swenson Family Foundation
901 S. Bond St.
Baltimore, MD   21231-3339

Established in 2005 in Pennsylvania.
Donors: Madeline B. Swenson; Ralph G. Swenson.
Foundation type: Independent foundation.
Financial data (yr. ended 12/31/14): Assets, $1,113,059; expenditures, $184,065; qualifying distributions, $175,000 and $0 for set-asides.
Fields of interest: University education.
Limitations: Applications not accepted. Giving primarily in MD. No grants to individuals.
Application information: Unsolicited requests for funsd not accepted.
Officers and Directors: Carol A. Tanzola, V.P. and Secy.; Gary E. Swenson, V.P. and Director; Gregory E. Swenson, V.P. and Director.
EIN: 342053631

3963
Ten Talents Foundation, Inc.
P.O. Box 43547
Baltimore, MD   21236-0547   (410) 256-6316
Contact: Rachel Curtis, Dir.

Established in 2004 in Maryland.
Donors: Thomas Barbera; Mary Poppert Barbera.
Foundation type: Independent foundation.
Financial data (yr. ended 12/31/13): Assets, $3,268,474 (M); expenditures, $229,176; qualifying distributions, $191,091; giving activities include $181,000 for 15 grants (high: $40,000; low: $1,000).
Purpose and activities: Acknowledging that God is the author of life and the giver of all good things, the foundation will strive to aid those in desperate need, to comfort those who are sick in body or in spirit, to assist those who seek a better life through education, and to support those who defend our freedom.
Fields of interest: Health; Diseases and conditions; Christianity; Human services; Food delivery; Child welfare.
Type of support: Research; Research and evaluation.
Limitations: Applications accepted. Giving primarily in NY, PA, and the greater metropolitan Washington, DC, are, including portions of MD and VA.
Application information:
    Initial approach: Proposal
    Deadline(s): None
Officers and Directors: Thomas Barbera, Pres. and Director; Mary Poppert Barbera, V.P. and Secy. and Director; Robert P. Dushel, Treas.; Concetta Barbera; Rachel Curtis; William Curtis; Andrew Truszkowski; Madeline Truszkowski.
EIN: 300266863

3964
David P. Tenberg Charitable Foundation, Inc.
12206 Boxer Hill Rd.
Cockeysville, MD   21030-1740

Established in 2006 in Maryland.
Foundation type: Independent foundation.
Financial data (yr. ended 12/31/13): Assets, $1,347,386 (M); expenditures, $198,909; qualifying distributions, $197,028; giving activities include $197,028 for 23 grants (high: $25,000; low: $250).
Fields of interest: Wildlife biodiversity; Human services.
Limitations: Applications not accepted. Giving in the U.S., with emphasis on MD.
Application information: Contributes only to pre-selected organizations.
Trustee: Marvin Tenberg.
EIN: 203160444

3965
Thadikonda Research Foundation Inc.
7495 New Technology Way
Frederick, MD   21703-9401   (240) 629-1972
Contact: Krupaker Paul Thadikonda, Dir.

Established in 2003 in Maryland.
Donors: Krupakar Paul Thadikonda; Eminent Services Corp.; Kusalava International.
Foundation type: Independent foundation.
Financial data (yr. ended 12/31/13): Assets, $96,721 (M); gifts received, $240,000; expenditures, $316,325; qualifying distributions, $315,225; giving activities include $315,225 for 7 grants (high: $200,000; low: $225).
Purpose and activities: Giving to organizations that develop new treatments for rare disorders.
Fields of interest: Diseases and conditions; Interfaith; Spirituality.
International interests: India; Switzerland.
Type of support: General support; Research.
Limitations: Applications accepted. Giving primarily in Berne, Switzerland and Muri, India, with some giving in MD. No grants to individuals.
Application information: Application form required.
    Initial approach: Letter
    Deadline(s): None
Director: Krupakar Paul Thadikonda.
EIN: 522387319

3966
Louis B. Thalheimer and Juliet A. Eurich Charitable Fund, Inc.
(formerly The Louis B. Thalheimer Philanthropic Fund, Inc.)
c/o Louis B. Thalheimer
6225 Smith Ave., Ste. B100
Baltimore, MD   21209-3633   (410) 415-7660
Contact: Juliet A. Eurich, V.P.

Established in 1991 in Maryland.
Donors: Louis B. Thalheimer; Juliet A. Eurich; Baltimore Capital Corp.
Foundation type: Independent foundation.
Financial data (yr. ended 12/31/13): Assets, $2,504,763 (M); gifts received, $72,500; expenditures, $385,830; qualifying distributions, $381,250; giving activities include $381,250 for 18 grants (high: $200,000; low: $2,500).
Purpose and activities: Giving for the arts, education, and Jewish organizations.
Fields of interest: Arts and culture; Secondary education; Higher education; Nonprofits; Judaism.
Type of support: Regranting.

Limitations: Applications accepted. Giving primarily in MD and New York, NY. No grants to individuals.
Application information: Application form required.
Initial approach: Letter
Deadline(s): None
Officers and Directors: Louis B. Thalheimer, Pres. and Director; Juliet A. Eurich, V.P.; Monica Rovecamp, Secy.
EIN: 521755649

3967
Ernst & Gertrude Ticho Charitable Foundation
P.O. Box 672
Glen Echo, MD 20812-0672

Established in 2004 in Maryland.
Foundation type: Independent foundation.
Financial data (yr. ended 12/31/13): Assets, $7,150,130 (M); expenditures, $427,137; qualifying distributions, $368,706; giving activities include $331,500 for 32 grants (high: $56,000; low: $1,000).
Fields of interest: Arts and culture; Education; Mental health care; Diseases and conditions; Storms; Human services.
Type of support: Research.
Limitations: Applications not accepted. Giving primarily in Washington, DC, with some giving in CA and FL. No grants to individuals.
Application information: Unsolicited requests for funds not accepted.
Trustees: Marcia M. Allen; Gail L. Pasternack; Stefan A. Pasternack.
EIN: 546617185

3968
Sami and Annie Totah Family Foundation
8611 2nd Ave., Ste. 3A
Silver Spring, MD 20910

Foundation type: Independent foundation.
Financial data (yr. ended 12/31/14): Assets, $3,844,240 (M); expenditures, $231,947; qualifying distributions, $205,823; giving activities include $205,823 for 126 grants (high: $26,100; low: $85).
Fields of interest: Arts and culture; Education; Nonprofits; Diseases and conditions; Judaism; Human services.
Type of support: Regranting.
Limitations: Applications not accepted. Giving primarily in Washington, DC and MD. No grants to individuals.
Application information: Unsolicited requests for funds not accepted.
Trustees: Tamara Picache; Annie Totah; Elliott Totah; Karina Totah; Nicole Totah.
EIN: 522081895

3969
Marcia Brady Tucker Foundation, Inc.
P.O. Box 1149
Easton, MD 21601-8922
Main URL: http://mbtf.org

Established in 1941 in New York.
Donor: Marcia Brady Tucker†.
Foundation type: Independent foundation.

Financial data (yr. ended 12/31/13): Assets, $10,664,653 (M); expenditures, $624,491; qualifying distributions, $494,305; giving activities include $360,425 for 148 grants (high: $20,000; low: $100).
Purpose and activities: Giving primarily for the arts, education, the environment, social services, and religious institutions.
Fields of interest: Arts and culture; Museums; Higher education; Environment; Hospice care; Religion; Christianity; Judaism; Human services.
Type of support: General support; Matching grants; Annual campaigns; Capital campaigns; Capital and infrastructure; Endowments; Program development; Seed money.
Limitations: Applications not accepted. Giving primarily in CA, CO, MD, NY, and OH. No grants to individuals.
Application information: Unsolicited requests for funds not accepted.
Officers: Marcia B. Loughran, Pres.; Barbara Bartlett, V.P.; Emily Tucker, Secy.; David M. Randell, Jr., Treas.; Tracy L. Royston, Admin.
Directors: Carlos Alvarado; Marcia Boogaard; Thomas Boogaard; Elizabeth Sanders; Elizabeth Stoehr; Ben Tucker; Luther Tucker; Nick Tucker; Noah Tucker.
Number of staff: 1 part-time support.
EIN: 136161561

3970
The Tzedakah Fund
c/o Orin Z. Hirschman
6006 Berkeley Ave.
Baltimore, MD 21209-4014

Established in 2003 in Maryland.
Donors: Orin Z. Hirschman; Hershel Berkowitz; Ettil Berkowitz; Samuel Nebenzahl; Adina Nebenzahl; Aaron Martin; Alvin Hess.
Foundation type: Independent foundation.
Financial data (yr. ended 12/31/14): Assets, $6,257,032 (M); gifts received, $90,020; expenditures, $138,869; qualifying distributions, $129,175; giving activities include $127,500 for 17 grants (high: $54,000; low: $600).
Purpose and activities: Giving primarily to Jewish organizations.
Fields of interest: Education; Judaism; Jewish people.
Limitations: Applications not accepted. No grants to individuals.
Application information: Unsolicited requests for funds not accepted.
Trustees: Esther Hirschman; Orin Z. Hirschman.
EIN: 200386456

3971
The Aber D. Unger Foundation, Inc.
100 International Dr., 5th Fl.
Baltimore, MD 21202
Contact: Eileen Stoner

Established in 1960 in Maryland.
Foundation type: Independent foundation.
Financial data (yr. ended 02/28/14): Assets, $4,294,238 (M); expenditures, $344,445; qualifying distributions, $315,882; giving activities include $305,000 for 29 grants (high: $25,000; low: $1,000).

Purpose and activities: Giving primarily for music, medical research and services, and social welfare.
Fields of interest: Arts and culture; Music; Elementary and secondary education; University education; Health; Diseases and conditions; Community and economic development; Human services.
Type of support: Research.
Limitations: Applications accepted. Giving primarily in Baltimore, MD, and New York, NY. No grants to individuals.
Application information: Association of Baltimore Area Grantmakers Common Grant Application Format accepted. Application form required.
Initial approach: Letter
Deadline(s): None
Officer: John A. Feinblatt, Pres.
Director: Paul C. Wolman III.
EIN: 526034758

3972
V & S Foundation, Inc.
17700 Cliffbourne Ln.
Rockville, MD 20855-1102

Foundation type: Independent foundation.
Financial data (yr. ended 06/30/13): Assets, $3,377,651 (M); expenditures, $479,152; qualifying distributions, $435,536; giving activities include $373,345 for 11 grants (high: $56,750; low: $500).
Fields of interest: Domesticated animals; Sports and recreation; Human services.
Limitations: Applications not accepted. Giving primarily in MD.
Application information: Unsolicited requests for funds not accepted.
Officers: Stephanie R. Saturni, C.E.O.; Amanda C. Viragh, Pres.
EIN: 800160777

3973
Van Dyke Family Foundation, Inc.
23436 Lands End Rd.
Chestertown, MD 21620-5263 (410) 810-1812
Contact: Peter Van Dyke, Pres.

Established in 1997 in Maryland.
Donor: Peter Van Dyke.
Foundation type: Independent foundation.
Financial data (yr. ended 12/31/13): Assets, $8,020,725 (M); expenditures, $415,463; qualifying distributions, $385,325; giving activities include $369,825 for 79 grants (high: $102,125; low: $150).
Purpose and activities: Giving primarily for educational and environmental institutions.
Fields of interest: Arts and culture; Higher education; Environmental education.
Type of support: Annual campaigns; Capital campaigns.
Limitations: Applications accepted. Giving primarily in MD and NY. No grants to individuals.
Application information: Solicitations are generally ignored and are not encouraged. Most recipients are known without submissions. Application form required.
Initial approach: Proposal
Deadline(s): None

Officers: Peter Van Dyke, Pres.; Judith Ray Van Dyke, V.P.; George Ray Van Dyke, Secy.-Treas.
EIN: 522034301

3974
Van Strum Foundation
901 South Bond St.
Baltimore, MD   21231

Established in 1983 in California.
Donor: Van Strum Fam Tr. f/b/o Clarissa Van S.
Foundation type: Independent foundation.
Financial data (yr. ended 12/31/13): Assets, $3,253,659 (M); expenditures, $181,785; qualifying distributions, $143,060; giving activities include $143,000 for 13 grants (high: $27,500; low: $1,500).
Fields of interest: Education; Environment; Human services.
Type of support: Annual campaigns.
Limitations: Applications not accepted. Giving primarily in MD. No grants to individuals.
Application information: Unsolicited requests for funds not accepted.
Officers: Stevens Van Strum, Pres.; Laura H. Blewett, Secy.
Trustees: Cecilia Van Strum Nobel; Robert Nobel.
EIN: 942870047

3975
Wagner-Braunsberg Family Foundation, Inc.
6001 Montrose Rd., Ste. 606
Rockville, MD   20852-4899

Established in 1997 in Delaware.
Donors: K. Peter Wagner; Yvonne R. Wagner; Elizabeth Wagner.
Foundation type: Independent foundation.
Financial data (yr. ended 12/31/12): Assets, $3,117,144 (M); gifts received, $66,047; expenditures, $128,098; qualifying distributions, $122,293; giving activities include $122,293 for 29 grants (high: $50,000; low: $100).
Fields of interest: Science; Religion; Human services.
Limitations: Applications not accepted. Giving primarily in MD and NY. No grants to individuals.
Publications: Annual report.
Application information: Contributes only to pre-selected organizations.
Officers: Elizabeth S. Wagner, Pres.; Charles H.S. Wagner, V.P. and Director; K. Peter Wagner, V.P.; Wayne L.B. Wagner, V.P. and Director; Yvonne R. Wagner, V.P. and Director; Jason Lieberman, V.P.; Michael Lieberman, V.P.; Andrew L. Mann, Treas. and Director.
Number of staff: 1 part-time support.
EIN: 113373671

3976
The Robert A. Waidner Foundation
7 St. Paul St., Ste. 1500
Baltimore, MD   21202-1626

Established in 2001 in Maryland.
Foundation type: Independent foundation.
Financial data (yr. ended 12/31/14): Assets, $30,506,343; expenditures, $374,778; qualifying distributions, $189,068.

Fields of interest: Orchestral music.
Limitations: Applications not accepted. Giving primarily in Baltimore, MD. No grants to individuals.
Application information: Contributes only to pre-selected organizations.
Trustees: Frederick Singley Koontz; Robert Sloan.
EIN: 527195462

3977
Dorothy Wagner Wallis Charitable Trust
7 St. Paul St., Ste. 1500
Baltimore, MD   21202-1636   (410) 347-8770
Contact: Frederick Singley Koontz, Tr.

Foundation type: Independent foundation.
Financial data (yr. ended 12/31/14): Assets, $6,766,349 (M); expenditures, $343,835; qualifying distributions, $297,410; giving activities include $291,000 for 17 grants (high: $145,000; low: $5,000).
Purpose and activities: Giving primarily for art museums, historical preservation, higher education, and human services.
Fields of interest: Arts and culture; Art museums; Historic preservation; Higher education; Animal welfare; Human services.
Limitations: Applications accepted. Giving primarily in Baltimore, MD. No grants to individuals.
Application information:
 Initial approach: Proposal
 Deadline(s): None
Trustee: Frederick Singley Koontz.
EIN: 526605828

3978
Anna Emory Warfield Memorial Fund, Inc.
P.O. Box 674
Riderwood, MD   21139-0674   (410) 453-0345

Established in 1928 in Maryland.
Donor: S. Davies Warfield†.
Foundation type: Independent foundation.
Financial data (yr. ended 12/31/14): Assets, $5,479,247; expenditures, $306,086; qualifying distributions, $262,742.
Purpose and activities: Organized exclusively to assist aged and dependent women.
Fields of interest: Seniors; Females; Low-income and poor people.
Type of support: Grants to individuals.
Limitations: Applications accepted. Giving to residents of the metropolitan Baltimore, MD, area. No grants for capital or endowment funds, general support, matching gifts, scholarships, fellowships, or research; no loans.
Publications: Application guidelines.
Application information: Application form required.
 Initial approach: Letter
 Copies of proposal: 1
 Deadline(s): None
 Board meeting date(s): Apr. and Oct.
 Final notification: 2 months
Officers and Trustees: Louis W. Hargrave, Pres.; Jenny Washburne, V.P.; Anne S. DeMuth, Secy.; John D. Sullivan, Treas.; Howard Bernheim; Jessica Dorsey; Carter Franke; Betty Anne Howard; Fran Lodder; Betsy Mitchell; Braxton D. Mitchell; Charles B. Reeves; Esther Schmick; Janet R. Schmick; Lolly Strudwick; Paul Schmick; Sally Schmick; Paul Yanchus; Mary Yavalar.

Number of staff: 1 part-time support.
EIN: 520785672

3979
Carroll A. Weinberg, M.D., and Charlotte Cohen Weinberg Charitable Foundation Inc.
1233 W. Mount Royal Ave.
Baltimore, MD   21217-4133
Contact: Carroll A. Weinberg MD, Pres. and Treas.
Application address: Dr. and Mrs. Carroll A. Weinberg, 261 Indian Creek Rd., Wynnewood, PA 19096, tel.: (410) 727-4586

Established in 1989 in Maryland.
Donors: Charlotte Cohen Weinberg; Carroll A. Weinberg, MD.
Foundation type: Independent foundation.
Financial data (yr. ended 04/30/14): Assets, $3,406,995 (M); gifts received, $587,338; expenditures, $200,467; qualifying distributions, $200,340; giving activities include $200,340 for 9 + grants (high: $125,000).
Fields of interest: Arts and culture; Education; Religion.
Type of support: General support.
Limitations: Applications accepted. Giving primarily in MD and PA. No grants to individuals.
Application information: Application form required.
 Initial approach: Letter
 Deadline(s): None
Officers: Carroll A. Weinberg, MD, Pres. and Treas.; John C. Davidson, V.P. and Secy.; Gwynne A. Weinberg, V.P.
EIN: 521679498

3980
The Roz and Marvin H. Weiner Family Foundation, Inc.
P.O. Box 487
Owings Mills, MD   21117-0487

Donors: Florence Weiner†; Marvin H. Weiner.
Foundation type: Independent foundation.
Financial data (yr. ended 12/31/13): Assets, $5,933,166 (M); expenditures, $343,197; qualifying distributions, $317,250; giving activities include $317,250 for 17 grants (high: $175,000; low: $250).
Fields of interest: Education; Child welfare.
Type of support: Capital campaigns.
Limitations: Applications not accepted. Giving primarily in MD.
Application information: Unsolicited requests for funds not accepted.
Officers: Marvin H. Weiner, Pres. and Treas.; Rosalind A. Weiner, V.P.; Scott M. Weiner, Secy.
EIN: 263435899

3981
The Toby and Melvin Weinman Foundation, Inc.
(formerly Morris, Mary & Toby Weinman Memorial Foundation)
P.O. Box 530
Stevenson, MD   21153-0530
Application address: c/o Morris Mark Weinman, Pres., P.O. Box 5992, Baltimore, MD 21282

Donors: The Morris Weinman Co.; Melvin Weinman†.
Foundation type: Independent foundation.
Financial data (yr. ended 12/31/13): Assets, $7,317,383 (M); gifts received, $35,000; expenditures, $582,079; qualifying distributions, $493,497; giving activities include $353,718 for 45 grants (high: $75,000; low: $25).
Fields of interest: History museums; Education; Nonprofits; Hospital care; Diseases and conditions; Judaism.
Type of support: Regranting.
Limitations: Applications accepted. Giving primarily in Baltimore, MD; giving also in St. Petersburg, FL. No grants to individuals.
Application information:
  Initial approach: Letter
  Deadline(s): None
Officers: Morris Mark Weinman, Pres.; Jonathan H. Weinman, Secy.-Treas.
EIN: 526051197

3982
The Weiss Foundation
c/o Gelman Rosenberg & Freedman
4550 Montgomery Ave., Ste. 650 N.
Bethesda, MD 20814-3250

Established in 1993 in District of Columbia.
Donor: Stanley A. Weiss.
Foundation type: Operating foundation.
Financial data (yr. ended 09/30/13): Assets, $357,670 (M); gifts received, $250,000; expenditures, $235,340; qualifying distributions, $231,340; giving activities include $218,700 for 8 grants (high: $150,000; low: $1,000).
Purpose and activities: Focus on educating the public on issues concerning national and international security, including matters of defense policy and the promotion of democratic institutions and societies.
Fields of interest: Public policy; Child welfare; International relations; Arms control.
Type of support: Continuing support; Endowments; Program development; Research; Policy, advocacy and systems reform.
Limitations: Applications not accepted. Giving primarily in the greater metropolitan Washington, DC, area, and New York, NY. No grants to individuals.
Publications: Financial statement.
Application information: Contributes only to pre-selected organizations.
Officers: Stanley Weiss, Pres.; Lisa Weiss, V.P.; Anthony W. Weiss, Secy.
Director: Lori Christina Lurie.
Number of staff: 1 full-time professional; 1 part-time professional.
EIN: 521848413

3983
Widgeon Foundation, Inc.
26604 E. Bonfield Rd.
Oxford, MD 21654-1425 (410) 822-7707
Contact: Richard Robinson, Pres.

Established in 1963 in New York.
Donors: Elizabeth H. Robinson; John N. Robinson Trust.
Foundation type: Independent foundation.

Financial data (yr. ended 12/31/13): Assets, $3,216,241 (M); gifts received, $726,071; expenditures, $300,908; qualifying distributions, $260,807; giving activities include $216,297 for 37 grants (high: $41,670; low: $1,000).
Purpose and activities: Giving primarily to medical and educational organizations in the U.S.A.
Fields of interest: Museums; Historical activities; Education; Higher education; Health.
Type of support: Capital and infrastructure; Convening; Continuing support; Curriculum development; Equipment; Professorships; Program development; Research; Scholarships; Seed money.
Limitations: Applications accepted. Giving primarily in MD, VA, and PA. No support for supporting organizations. No grants to individuals.
Application information:
  Initial approach: Letter
  Deadline(s): None
  Board meeting date(s): 3rd Tues. in Nov.
Officers: Richard Robinson, Pres.; Katherine Moye, V.P.; Linda Morris Robinson, Secy.-Treas.
EIN: 136113927

3984
The Wieler Family Private Foundation
P.O. Box 65149
Baltimore, MD 21209-0149

Established in 1997 in Maryland.
Donors: Scott A. Wieler; Mary Baily Wieler.
Foundation type: Independent foundation.
Financial data (yr. ended 12/31/13): Assets, $2,155,068 (M); gifts received, $250,000; expenditures, $419,482; qualifying distributions, $406,578; giving activities include $406,285 for 25 grants (high: $85,347; low: $250).
Fields of interest: Arts and culture; Education; Human services.
Limitations: Applications not accepted. Giving primarily in Baltimore, MD. No grants to individuals.
Application information: Contributes only to pre-selected organizations.
Trustees: Mary Wieler; Scott A. Wieler.
EIN: 522034853

3985
Jack Wilen Foundation Inc.
2306 Cavesdale Rd.
Owings Mills, MD 21117-2305

Foundation type: Independent foundation.
Financial data (yr. ended 12/31/13): Assets, $5,013,809 (M); expenditures, $227,725; qualifying distributions, $226,750; giving activities include $226,750 for 40 grants (high: $18,500; low: $500).
Fields of interest: Arts and culture; Education; Nonprofits; Judaism; Human services.
Type of support: Regranting.
Limitations: Applications not accepted. No grants to individuals.
Application information: Unsolicited requests for funds not accepted.
Trustee: Jack Wilen.
EIN: 520794415

3986
Sylvia & Rip Williams Charitable Foundation
8218 Wisconsin Ave., Ste. 402
Bethesda, MD 20814-3107
Contact: Lee J. Miller

Established in 2003 in Maryland.
Donor: Sylvia L. Williams.
Foundation type: Independent foundation.
Financial data (yr. ended 06/30/13): Assets, $4,955,137 (M); expenditures, $235,010; qualifying distributions, $166,000; giving activities include $166,000 for grants.
Fields of interest: Protestantism; Child welfare.
Limitations: Applications not accepted. Giving primarily in FL and Washington, DC. No grants to individuals.
Application information: Unsolicited requests for funds not accepted.
Officers: Robert P. Sampson, Pres. and Secy.; Lee J. Miller, V.P. and Treas.
EIN: 141866661

3987
Alan D. and Wendy R. Wilson Foundation
11 Deep Run Ct.
Cockeysville, MD 21030-1600

Donor: Alan D. Wilson.
Foundation type: Independent foundation.
Financial data (yr. ended 12/31/13): Assets, $2,068,079 (M); gifts received, $145,404; expenditures, $200,178; qualifying distributions, $200,000; giving activities include $200,000 for 3 grants (high: $100,000; low: $10,000).
Fields of interest: Education; Religion; Human services.
Limitations: Applications not accepted. Giving primarily in MD and TN.
Application information: Unsolicited requests for funds not accepted.
Trustees: Alan D. Wilson; Wendy R. Wilson.
EIN: 263318655

3988
Windsor Foundation, Inc.
313 Talbot Blvd.
Chestertown, MD 21620-3000
Application address: c/o Joan Farrar, Dir., P.O. Box 92, Galena, MD 21635, tel.: (410) 648-5440

Established in 2004 in Maryland.
Donor: USA Fulfillment, Inc.
Foundation type: Independent foundation.
Financial data (yr. ended 12/31/13): Assets, $599,947 (M); gifts received, $165,780; expenditures, $403,326; qualifying distributions, $396,465; giving activities include $396,465 for 36 grants (high: $66,840; low: $225).
Purpose and activities: Giving primarily for Christian organizations.
Fields of interest: Community and economic development; Christianity.
International interests: Romania.
Limitations: Applications accepted. Giving primarily in FL, GA, MD, NC, and PA. No grants to individuals.
Application information: Application form required.
  Initial approach: Request application form
  Deadline(s): None

Officers: Will Larose, Pres.; Joan Farrar, Secy.; Robert R. Farrar, Treas.
Directors: Glenn Evans; Craig Moore; Shirley Moore.
EIN: 201484900

3989
The Witt/Hoey Foundation, Inc.
4215 Greenway
Baltimore, MD 21218-1135
Contact: Judy M. Phares, Pres.

Established in 1999 in Maryland.
Foundation type: Independent foundation.
Financial data (yr. ended 12/31/14): Assets, $1,345,676 (M); expenditures, $280,672; qualifying distributions, $273,831; giving activities include $273,831 for 24 grants (high: $79,000; low: $300).
Fields of interest: Arts and culture; Orchestral music; Education; University education; Hospital care; Human services; Family services.
Limitations: Applications accepted. Giving primarily in MD.
Application information: Application form required.
Initial approach: Letter
Deadline(s): Sept. 15
Officer: Judy M. Phares, Pres.
EIN: 522143620

3990
Wolpoff Family Foundation
9841 Washingtonian Blvd., Ste. 410
Gaithersburg, MD 20878-7339 (301) 917-2350
FAX: (301) 917-2398;
E-mail: info@wolpoff-familyfoundation.org; Main URL: http://www.wolpoff-familyfoundation.org

Foundation type: Independent foundation.
Financial data (yr. ended 10/31/13): Assets, $10,899,048 (M); expenditures, $486,873; qualifying distributions, $435,257; giving activities include $320,000 for 19 grants (high: $75,000; low: $850).
Fields of interest: Education; Nonprofits; Hospital care; Hospice care; Cancers.
Type of support: Regranting.
Limitations: Giving primarily in Washington, DC, MD and MA.
Publications: Application guidelines.
Application information: After letter of inquiry grant applications are extended by invitation only. Complete application guidelines available on foundation web site.
Initial approach: Letter of inquiry
Officers: Harry K. Wolpoff, Chair.; Carol Wolpoff, Vice-Chair.; Suzanne Oliwa, Exec. Dir.
EIN: 261419703

3991
Youth Shooting Sports Alliance
11265 Suffolk Dr.
Hagerstown, MD 21742-4054 (240) 347-4351
Contact: Stephen A. Miller
E-mail: proud2hunt@aol.com; Main URL: http://www.youthshootingsa.com

Established in 2008 in North Carolina.
Donors: National Shooting Sports Foundation; Savage Sports Corp.; Beretta U.S.A. Corp.; Leupold & Stevens, Inc.; O F Mossberg & Sons, Inc.; Daisy Outdoor Products; Hornady Manufacturing Co.; Sturm, Ruger & Co., Inc.; Winchester Ammunition; Henry Repeating Arms Co.; RSR Group, Inc.; Mule Deer Foundation; Cindy Flannigan; MidwayUSA;

Larry and Brenda Potterfield; Ellett Brothers; Big Rock Sport, LLC; NASGW; ATK; Henry Repeating Arms; Federal Catridge Co.; Baron Technology; Ellett Brothers, LLC; Bill Hick & Co., Ltd.
Foundation type: Operating foundation.
Financial data (yr. ended 12/31/13): Assets, $250,722 (M); gifts received, $281,066; expenditures, $539,407; qualifying distributions, $400,965; giving activities include $292,255 for 222 grants (high: $17,260; low: $29).
Fields of interest: Education; Health; Sports and recreation; Adolescents.
Type of support: Equipment.
Limitations: Applications accepted. Giving primarily in CA, MD and MN. No grants for Limited to youth shooting sports programs.
Application information: Application form required.
Initial approach: Contact foundation for application form
Deadline(s): Mid-Oct.
Officers: Joe Murfin, Pres.; Beth Merkel, V. P.; Chuck Walker, Secy.; Curt Borcherding, Treas.; Steve Miller, Exec. Dir.
Directors: John Anthon; Dave Baron; Jim Bequette; David Blenker; Ryan Bronson; Ron Coburn; Craig Dutton; Cyndi Flannigan; Lorraine Hellinghausen; Margaret Hornady-David; Greg Kosteck; Anthony Imperato; G. Patrick McDonald; Dick Placzek; Jay Scholes; Todd Seyfert; John Snow.
EIN: 260551145

MASSACHUSETTS

3992
2 Depot Square Ipswich Charitable Foundation

2 Depot Sq.
Ipswich, MA   01938-1914   (617) 356-3600
Contact: Stephen P. Cote, Treas.
Grants List: https://
www.institutionforsavings.com/
depot-square-recipients.htm

Established in 2005 in Massachusetts.
Donors: Ipswich Co-operative Bank; 1820 Security Corp.
Foundation type: Company-sponsored foundation.
Financial data (yr. ended 04/30/14): Assets, $2,105,278 (M); expenditures, $362,730; qualifying distributions, $362,730; giving activities include $360,815 for 77 grants (high: $50,000; low: $200).
Purpose and activities: The foundation supports organizations involved with arts and culture, education, health, housing, athletics, youth development, human services, and community economic development.
Fields of interest: Arts and culture; Education; Secondary education; Health; Community and economic development; Community improvement; Housing development; Track and field; Human services; Family services; Child welfare; Youth development.
Type of support: General support; Capital campaigns; Program development; Scholarships.
Limitations: Applications accepted. Giving primarily in areas of company operations in Ipswich, MA. No grants to individuals.
Publications: Application guidelines; Program policy statement.
Application information: Application form required.
  Initial approach: Contact foundation for application form
  Deadline(s): Contact foundation for deadline
  Board meeting date(s): Apr. and Nov.
Officers and Directors: Michael J. Jones, Pres. and Director; Tammy A. Roeger, Clerk; Stephen P. Cote, Treas.; Donald M. Greenough; Kimberly A. Rock; R. Drew March-Aurele; Ellen G. Nich; Ellen M. Rose; Richard J. Silverman.
EIN: 203950026

3993
The 484 Phi Alpha Foundation, Inc.

P.O. Box 1509
North Hampton, MA   01061-1509
Contact: Walter Colby
Application address: c/o Carl King, 33085 Nesika Rd., Gold Beach, OR 97444, tel.: (617) 816-3835

Established in 2001 in Massachusetts.
Donor: Massachusetts IOTA TAU, Inc.
Foundation type: Independent foundation.
Financial data (yr. ended 12/31/13): Assets, $3,529,141 (M); expenditures, $196,593; qualifying distributions, $178,042; giving activities include $160,000 for 20 grants (high: $35,000; low: $1,000).
Fields of interest: Education; Human services.

Limitations: Applications accepted. Giving primarily in Boston and Cambridge, MA. No grants to individuals.
Application information:
  Initial approach: Letter
  Deadline(s): None
Officers and Directors: Carl K. King, Pres.; William D. Putt, Clerk and Director; Walter F. Colby, Treas.; Edwin F. Brush; Thomas F. Comparato; Eric Fitch; John J. Golden, Director; James J. Latimer; Paul R. Marcus.
EIN: 043539065

3994
The A & A Fund

(formerly Alexander and Adelaide Hixon Fund for Religion and Education)
c/o R. Brinck Lowery
101 Arch St., 18th Fl.
Boston, MA   02110-1109

Established in 1991 in Massachusetts.
Donor: Alexander P. Hixon.
Foundation type: Independent foundation.
Financial data (yr. ended 12/31/13): Assets, $8,294,274 (M); expenditures, $508,246; qualifying distributions, $414,289; giving activities include $398,500 for 19 grants (high: $150,000; low: $5,000).
Fields of interest: Education; Community and economic development; Religion.
Limitations: Applications not accepted. Giving primarily in MA and NY. No grants to individuals.
Application information: Unsolicited requests for funds not accepted.
Trustee: Brinck Lowery.
Advisory Board: Alexandra H. Ballard; Dylan H. Hixon; Shanti S. Hixon; Sheila K. Hixon; India T. Radfar.
EIN: 043127721

3995
A Child Waits Foundation

1136 Barker Rd.
Pittsfield, MA   01201-8043   (866) 999-2445
FAX: (518) 794 6243;
E-mail: cnelson@achildwaits.org; Main URL: http://www.achildwaits.org

Established in 1998 in New York.
Donors: Cynthia Nelson; Randolph Nelson; Ira and Beth Leventhal Foundation; Dove Givings Foundation.
Foundation type: Operating foundation.
Financial data (yr. ended 12/31/12): Assets, $2,697,884 (M); gifts received, $114,196; expenditures, $441,606; qualifying distributions, $440,307; giving activities include $87,492 for 18 grants (high: $10,000; low: $26), and $228,241 for 63 grants to individuals (high: $9,090; low: $1,388).
Purpose and activities: Giving primarily to provide financial assistance to individuals adopting foreign-born children. Support for adoption, adoption funding, international adoption and child welfare and the child must meet special needs criteria, and adoptive family must meet financial criteria.
Fields of interest: Religion; Human services.
Type of support: Grants to individuals; Loans to individuals.

Limitations: Applications accepted. Giving on a national basis.
Application information: Application form required.
  Initial approach: Letter
  Copies of proposal: 1
  Deadline(s): None
  Board meeting date(s): Weekly
Officers: Cynthia Nelson, Pres.; Randolph Nelson, V.P.; Richard Cayne, Secy.
Number of staff: 2 full-time professional.
EIN: 133978652

3996
Noubar & Anna Afeyan Foundation

1 Sunset Ridge
Lexington, MA   02421-6031

Established in 1999 in Massachusetts.
Donors: Noubar B. Afeyan; Raffi Festekjian; Edwin Carol Kania.
Foundation type: Independent foundation.
Financial data (yr. ended 12/31/13): Assets, $1,679,289 (M); gifts received, $865,741; expenditures, $438,670; qualifying distributions, $437,422; giving activities include $418,163 for 17 grants (high: $125,000; low: $1,000).
Purpose and activities: Giving primarily for Armenian related projects and issues.
Fields of interest: Education; Human services.
International interests: Armenia.
Limitations: Applications not accepted. Giving primarily in Armenia, with some giving in MA. No grants to individuals.
Application information: Contributes only to pre-selected organizations.
Trustees: Noubar Afeyan; Anna Karin M. Gunnarson.
EIN: 043489109

3997
Ain Family Foundation, Inc.

297 Billerica Rd.
Chelmsford, MA   01824-4119

Established in 2005 in Massachusetts.
Donor: Mark S. Ain.
Foundation type: Independent foundation.
Financial data (yr. ended 12/31/13): Assets, $2,821,114 (M); expenditures, $219,841; qualifying distributions, $205,000; giving activities include $205,000 for 3 grants (high: $185,000; low: $5,000).
Fields of interest: Education; Women's services.
Limitations: Applications not accepted.
Application information: Unsolicited requests for funds not accepted.
Officer: Mark S. Ain, Pres., Clerk and Treas.
Director: Carolyn C. Ain.
EIN: 270134065

3998
Akamai Foundation Inc.

c/o Akamai Technologies Inc.
8 Cambridge Ctr.
Cambridge, MA   02142-1413   (617) 444-9748
Contact: Noelle Faris, Pres. and Secy.
E-mail: nfaris@akamai.com; Main URL: http://www.akamai.com/html/about/foundation.html

Established in 2000 in Massachusetts.

Donors: Paul Sagan; F. Thomson Leighton; Mrs. F. Thomson Leighton; George Conrades; ASU Foundation.
Foundation type: Company-sponsored foundation.
Financial data (yr. ended 12/31/13): Assets, $1,674,089 (M); gifts received, $300; expenditures, $387,927; qualifying distributions, $382,978; giving activities include $371,500 for 11 grants (high: $170,000; low: $2,500).
Purpose and activities: The foundation supports programs designed to promote mathematics education in grades K-12.
Fields of interest: Elementary and secondary education; Mathematics.
Type of support: General support.
Limitations: Applications accepted. Giving primarily in Washington, DC and MA.
Publications: Application guidelines.
Application information: Application form required.
Initial approach: Proposal
Deadline(s): Jan. 31
Officers and Directors: Noelle Faris, Pres. and Secy.; Jonathan Seelig, Treas. and Director.
EIN: 043530777

3999
John W. Alden Trust
225 Franklin St., 4th Fl.
Boston, MA 02110-2800 (866) 778-6859
Contact: Miki Akimoto, V.P.
FAX: (617) 542-7437;
E-mail: miki.akimoto@ustrust.com; For questions and information: Susan T. Monahan, Grants Coordinator, tel.: (617) 951-1108, email: susan.t.monahan@gmail.com; Main URL: http://www.cybergrants.com/alden
Grants List: http://www.cybergrants.com/alden/2009_final_grants.xls

Established in 1986 in Massachusetts.
Donor: Priscilla Alden†.
Foundation type: Independent foundation.
Financial data (yr. ended 09/30/13): Assets, $9,962,762 (M); expenditures, $475,400; qualifying distributions, $413,108; giving activities include $349,000 for grants.
Purpose and activities: Grant support directed toward organizations providing care and administering to the needs of children who are blind, retarded, disabled, or who are either mentally or physically ill, or to organizations engaged in medical and scientific research, directed toward the prevention or cure of diseases and disabilities particularly affecting children.
Fields of interest: Arts education; Education; Special needs education; Child educational development; Vocational education; Hospital care; Addiction services; Substance abuse treatment; Mental health counseling; Diseases and conditions; Musculoskeletal diseases; Mental and behavioral disorders; Depression; Stress; Genetic conditions and birth defects; Human services; Human services management; Child welfare; Adoption; Child development; Foster care; Youth services; Developmental disability services; People with disabilities.
Type of support: Program development; Seed money; Research; Research and evaluation; Capacity-building and technical assistance; Regranting; Advocacy; Fundraising.
Limitations: Applications accepted. Giving limited to eastern MA. No grants to individuals.
Publications: Application guidelines.

Application information: Applications must be submitted online at www.cybergrants.com/alden.
Initial approach: Email
Deadline(s): Jan. 5, Apr. 5, July 5, and Oct. 5
Board meeting date(s): Feb., May, Aug., and Nov.
Final notification: Within 1 month
Trustees: Susan T. Monahan; Bank of America, N.A.
Number of staff: 1 part-time professional; 1 part-time support.
EIN: 222719727

4000
Allison Family Charitable Foundation
69 Pinehurst Rd.
Belmont, MA 02478-1502

Established in 2007 in Massachusetts.
Donors: Graham Allison, Jr.; Elisabeth Allison.
Foundation type: Independent foundation.
Financial data (yr. ended 12/31/13): Assets, $2,071,307 (M); expenditures, $290,106; qualifying distributions, $289,653; giving activities include $289,200 for 20 grants (high: $80,000; low: $500).
Fields of interest: Education; Elementary and secondary education; Wildlife biodiversity; Animal welfare; Human services.
Limitations: Applications not accepted. Giving primarily in MA. No grants to individuals.
Application information: Contributes only to pre-selected organizations.
Trustees: Elisabeth Allison; Graham Allison, Jr.
EIN: 203848260

4001
The Altamira Foundation
401 Summer St.
Westwood, MA 02090-1059

Established in 2006 in Massachusetts.
Donor: Kenneth L. Abrams.
Foundation type: Independent foundation.
Financial data (yr. ended 12/31/13): Assets, $3,821,117 (M); gifts received, $249,624; expenditures, $369,285; qualifying distributions, $369,132; giving activities include $366,900 for 31 grants (high: $175,000; low: $100).
Fields of interest: Education; Undergraduate education; Foundations; Hospital care; Human services.
Limitations: Applications not accepted. Giving primarily in CA, IL and MA. No grants to individuals.
Application information: Contributes only to pre-selected organizations.
Trustees: Jessica L. Abrams; Kenneth L. Abrams; Susan N. Abrams.
EIN: 207190733

4002
Alvord Family Foundation
c/o Joel B. Alvord, Shawmut Capital Partners
75 Federal St., 18th Fl.
Boston, MA 02110-1913

Established in 1996 in Massachusetts.
Donor: Joel B. Alvord.
Foundation type: Independent foundation.
Financial data (yr. ended 11/30/14): Assets, $1,316,086 (M); gifts received, $250; expenditures, $229,695; qualifying distributions,

$211,810; giving activities include $211,810 for 31 grants (high: $83,000; low: $100).
Fields of interest: Arts and culture; Education; Human rights.
Limitations: Applications not accepted. Giving primarily in MA. No grants to individuals.
Application information: Unsolicited requests for funds not accepted.
Trustees: Joel B. Alvord; Sarah H. Alvord; Seth W. Alvord.
EIN: 046820195

4003
Ansin Foundation
c/o Rinet Co., LLC
101 Federal St., 14th Fl.
Boston, MA 02110-1859

Established in 1955 in Massachusetts.
Donors: Joan Fabrics Corp.; Harold S. Ansin.
Foundation type: Independent foundation.
Financial data (yr. ended 12/31/14): Assets, $5,061,549; expenditures, $297,476; qualifying distributions, $251,000.
Fields of interest: Health; Hospital care; Housing development; Religion.
Limitations: Applications not accepted. Giving primarily in FL and MA. No grants to individuals.
Application information: Contributes only to pre-selected organizations.
Officer: Patrick B. Maraghy, Fdn. Mgr.
Trustee: Joseph L. Ansin.
EIN: 046067779

4004
Arcadia Charitable Trust
c/o Hemenway & Barnes, LLP
P.O. Box 961209
Boston, MA 02196-1209

Established in 1997 in Massachusetts.
Donors: Lucy S. Moore; Marion R. Stone; Robert G. Stone, Jr.†.
Foundation type: Independent foundation.
Financial data (yr. ended 12/31/12): Assets, $6,433,504 (M); expenditures, $412,450; qualifying distributions, $325,564; giving activities include $308,654 for 7 grants (high: $100,000; low: $25,000).
Fields of interest: Education; Environment; Diseases and conditions; Cystic fibrosis; Cancers; Human services.
Type of support: Research; Research and evaluation.
Limitations: Applications not accepted. Giving primarily in CT, MA, and NY.
Application information: Unsolicited applications not accepted.
Board meeting date(s): July 14 and Nov. 17
Trustees: Sarah S. Fitzgerald; Catherine M. Stone; R. Gregg Stone III.
Number of staff: 1 part-time professional.
EIN: 137102310

4005
Archibald Family Charitable Foundation
c/o Nutter McClennen & Fish LLP
155 Seaport Blvd.
Boston, MA 02210-2698
Contact: David W. Lewis Jr.

Application address: c/o K&L Gates, Attn.: David W. Lewis, Jr., 1 Lincoln St., Boston, MA 02111-2950, tel.: (617) 261-3100

Established in 1998 in Massachusetts.
Donor: Anne G. Archibald.
Foundation type: Independent foundation.
Financial data (yr. ended 03/31/14): Assets, $4,454,310 (M); expenditures, $222,553; qualifying distributions, $199,981; giving activities include $180,000 for 31 grants (high: $45,000; low: $500).
Purpose and activities: Giving primarily for education; some funding for conservation, animal and wildlife protection, and health and human services.
Fields of interest: Historic preservation; Education; Higher education; Natural resources; Animal welfare; Health; Human services.
Type of support: General support.
Limitations: Applications accepted. Giving primarily in MA. No grants to individuals.
Application information:
  Initial approach: Proposal
  Deadline(s): None
Trustees: John L.G. Archibald; Mary A. Poor; Nutter McClennen & Fish LLP.
EIN: 043417222

4006
The Astra Foundation Inc.
524 Main St.
Acton, MA   01720-3301   (978) 266-3700
Contact: Bernard Haan, Pres. and Treas.
Main URL: http://www.astrafoundation.org

Established in 2000 in Massachusetts.
Donors: Bernard Haan; Jennifer Haan.
Foundation type: Operating foundation.
Financial data (yr. ended 05/31/14): Assets, $9,530,893 (M); expenditures, $778,440; qualifying distributions, $698,025; giving activities include $351,000 for 6 grants (high: $250,000; low: $2,000).
Purpose and activities: Giving to support programs and initiatives helping children thrive in their home and educational environments, with attention primarily on children with special needs and those who live in low-income urban areas.
Fields of interest: Philanthropy; Health; Human services.
Limitations: Applications accepted. Giving primarily in MA. No grants to individuals.
Application information: Application form required.
  Initial approach: Letter
  Deadline(s): None
Officer: Bernard Haan, Pres. and Treas.
EIN: 043526333

4007
Autism Consortium, Inc.
10 Shattuck St.
Boston, MA   02115-6030   (617) 432-7511
Contact: Deirdre B. Phillips, Exec. Dir.
FAX: (617) 432-6960;
E-mail: autismconsortium@hms.harvard.edu;
Toll-free tel.: (866) 518-0296; E-mail For Deirdre B. Phillips: deirdre_phillips@hms.harvard.edu; Main URL: http://www.autismconsortium.org

Established in 2006 in Massachusetts.

Foundation type: Independent foundation.
Financial data (yr. ended 12/31/12): Assets, $1,503,710 (M); gifts received, $1,392,443; expenditures, $1,004,071; qualifying distributions, $1,002,566; giving activities include $311,150 for 5 grants (high: $122,854; low: $17,285).
Purpose and activities: The consortium works to catalyze rapid advances in the understanding, diagnosis, and treatment of autism by engaging, supporting, and fostering collaboration among a community of clinicians, researchers, donors, and families, in order to improve the care of children and families affected by autism and other neurological disorders.
Fields of interest: Autism.
Type of support: Research.
Limitations: Applications not accepted. Giving limited to Boston, Cambridge, and Shrewsbury, MA; and Chicago, IL.
Publications: Informational brochure.
Application information: Contributes only to pre-selected organizations.
Officers and Directors: Peter Barrett, Ph.D, Pres. and Director; Alan L. Crane, MBA, V.P. and Director; John Graham, J.D., Secy. and Director; Paul R. Marcus, Treas. and Director; Deirdre B. Phillips, Exec. Dir.; Susan Whitehead.
EIN: 204765261

4008
Azadoutioun Foundation
c/o Gravestar Inc.
160 2nd St.
Cambridge, MA   02142-1515   (617) 492-4118

Established in 1985 in Massachusetts.
Donor: Carolyn G. Mugar.
Foundation type: Independent foundation.
Financial data (yr. ended 12/31/13): Assets, $2,360,604 (M); gifts received, $507,000; expenditures, $1,701,194; qualifying distributions, $1,007,649; giving activities include $314,907 for 2 grants (high: $300,000; low: $14,907).
Purpose and activities: Giving primarily for education and human services.
Fields of interest: Basic and remedial instruction; Reading promotion; Environment; Economic development; Human services; International development.
Type of support: General support; Program development.
Limitations: Applications accepted. Giving on a national basis. No grants to individuals; no loans.
Application information:
  Initial approach: Proposal
  Copies of proposal: 1
  Deadline(s): None
  Board meeting date(s): Annually
Officers: William Allen, Mgr.; Kathleen Duesterberg, Mgr.
Trustees: Anthony J. Barsamian; Janet Corpus; Carolyn G. Mugar; Sharryn Ross.
Number of staff: 1 part-time professional; 1 part-time support.
EIN: 042876245

4009
The Susan A. & Donald P. Babson Charitable Foundation
c/o GMA Foundations
77 Summer St., 8th Fl.
Boston, MA   02110-1006   (617) 391-3087
Contact: Michelle Jenney, Fdn. Admin.
FAX: (617) 523-8949;
E-mail: mjenney@gmafoundations.com; Main URL: http://www.babsonfoundation.org
Grants List: http://www.babsonfoundation.org/grants-awarded-2

Established in 1995 in Massachusetts.
Donor: Susan Babson†.
Foundation type: Independent foundation.
Financial data (yr. ended 12/31/13): Assets, $5,363,697 (M); expenditures, $266,204; qualifying distributions, $242,417; giving activities include $209,156 for 73 grants (high: $10,000; low: $1,000).
Purpose and activities: Giving primarily for the enrichment and empowerment of people of all ages around the world, so as to prevent exploitation, poverty, and injustice.
Fields of interest: Education; Human services; Youth development; Youth services.
Type of support: General support; Program development.
Publications: Application guidelines; Grants list.
Application information: Complete application information is available on foundation web site. Application form required.
  Initial approach: Letter of Inquiry using online application form
  Board meeting date(s): May and Oct.
Trustees: Averill Babson; Deborah E. Babson; James A. Babson; Richard L. Babson; Newell Flather; Wilmington Trust Co.
Number of staff: None.
EIN: 046782460

4010
Babson-Webber-Mustard Fund
434 Red Top Rd.
Brewster, MA   02631-1642   (508) 238-0321

Established in 1962 in Massachusetts.
Foundation type: Independent foundation.
Financial data (yr. ended 12/31/14): Assets, $5,379,169; expenditures, $260,008; qualifying distributions, $218,931.
Purpose and activities: Giving to aid needy residents of Massachusetts at Christmas time; support also for ministers' discretionary funds.
Fields of interest: Human services; Low-income and poor people.
Type of support: General support; Grants to individuals.
Limitations: Applications accepted. Giving primarily in the Gloucester and Wellesley, MA, areas.
Application information: Application form required.
  Initial approach: Letter or telephone
  Deadline(s): None
Trustees: Robert S. Hoffman III; Jesse M. Putney; Judith Rhome.
EIN: 042307820

4011
Charles F. Bacon Trust
c/o Bank of America, NA
225 Franklin St.
Boston, MA   02110   617-434-4847
Contact: Michealle Larkins
E-mail: kim.m.igoe-kasper@ustrust.comma.grantma
king@ustrust.com; *Main URL:* http://
www.bankofamerica.com/grantmaking

Established in 1928 in Massachusetts.
Donor: Charles F. Bacon†.
Foundation type: Independent foundation.
Financial data (yr. ended 12/31/14): Assets,
$4,774,299 (M); expenditures, $278,561;
qualifying distributions, $221,355; giving activities
include $183,500 for 14 grants (high: $20,000;
low: $6,000).
Purpose and activities: The Trust supports quality
educational, human services, and health care
programming for underserved populations. Special
consideration is given to organizations that serve
the needs of elderly women.
Type of support: General support; Program
development.
Limitations: Applications accepted. Giving limited to
MA. No grants to individuals.
Publications: Application guidelines.
Application information: Complete application and
guidelines available on web site. Application form
required.
   Initial approach: Proposal
   Copies of proposal: 1
   Deadline(s): Apr. 1
   Board meeting date(s): June
   Final notification: June 30
Trustee: Bank of America, N.A.
Number of staff: None.
EIN: 046024467

4012
Barakat, Inc.
689 Massachusetts Ave.
Cambridge, MA   02139-3302   (617) 301-4312
E-mail: info@barakatworld.org; *Main URL:* http://
barakatworld.org
Blog: https://barakatnews.wordpress.com
Community Blog: http://barakatblog.blogspot.com
Facebook: http://www.facebook.com/pages/
Barakat-Inc/8728933924?ref=ts
Flickr: https://www.flickr.com/photos/
barakatworld
Twitter: http://twitter.com/barakatinc
YouTube: http://www.youtube.com/barakatinc

Donors: Yayla Tribal Rugs, Inc.; Cultural Survival.
Foundation type: Independent foundation.
Financial data (yr. ended 09/30/13): Assets,
$353,753 (M); gifts received, $92,360;
expenditures, $333,785; qualifying distributions,
$332,839; giving activities include $156,252 for
grants.
Purpose and activities: Giving primarily for
education in South and Central Asia, with a focus on
providing basic education, increasing access to
higher education, and advancing literacy, especially
for women and children.
Fields of interest: Education; Environment; Water
resources; Land resources; Diseases and
conditions; Human services.
International interests: Afghanistan; India;
Pakistan.

Type of support: Research and evaluation.
Limitations: Giving primarily in South and Central
Asia.
Application information:
   Initial approach: Proposal
   Deadline(s): None
Officers: Ian Crowley, Pres.; Jennifer Z. Flanagan,
V.P.; Ike Syed, Secy.; William Mor, Treas.
Directors: Shereen Asmat; Thomas J. Barfield; Julie
Arcart Cook; Habibullah Karimi; Bilal Paracha;
Shweta Srivastava; Christopher K. Walter.
EIN: 043493675

4013
F. E. and A. R. Barstow Charitable Trust
P.O. Box 1089
Sherborn, MA   01770-7089

Established in 2000 in Massachusetts.
Donor: Frederick E. Barstow†.
Foundation type: Independent foundation.
Financial data (yr. ended 12/31/13): Assets,
$4,945,385 (M); expenditures, $271,035;
qualifying distributions, $270,035; giving activities
include $270,000 for 3 grants (high: $205,000;
low: $30,000).
Fields of interest: Arts and culture; Orchestral
music; Natural resources; Foundations; Human
services.
Limitations: Applications not accepted. Giving
primarily in CA, MA and OH. No grants to individuals.
Application information: Contributes only to
pre-selected organizations.
Trustees: James F. Barstow; John C. Barstow;
Thomas R. Barstow.
EIN: 043489662

4014
The Beaucourt Foundation, Inc.
c/o Goulston & Storrs
400 Atlantic Ave.
Boston, MA   02110-3331   (617) 574-4073
Contact: Peter A. Wilson, Pres., Treas. and Dir.

Established in 1987 in Massachusetts.
Foundation type: Independent foundation.
Financial data (yr. ended 12/31/14): Assets,
$1,963,029 (M); expenditures, $267,815;
qualifying distributions, $249,962; giving activities
include $245,000 for 2 grants (high: $145,000;
low: $100,000).
Fields of interest: Arts and culture; Education;
Nonprofits; Libraries.
Type of support: Regranting.
Limitations: Applications accepted. Giving primarily
in Boston, MA and New York, NY. No grants to
individuals.
Application information:
   Initial approach: Proposal
   Deadline(s): None
Officers and Directors: Peter A. Wilson, Pres. and
Treas. and Director; Mark M. Christopher, Secy.;
Matthew R. Hillery.
EIN: 042979426

4015
The Behrakis Foundation
80 Hayden Ave., Ste. 100
Lexington, MA   02421-7962   (781) 861-9114
Contact: Stephanie B. Liakos, Tr.

E-mail: sbliakos@behrprivfdn.com

Established in 1996 in Massachusetts.
Donors: George D. Behrakis; Margo Behrakis.
Foundation type: Independent foundation.
Financial data (yr. ended 09/30/13): Assets,
$3,952,404 (M); expenditures, $269,373;
qualifying distributions, $162,800; giving activities
include $162,800 for 45 grants (high: $20,000;
low: $250).
Fields of interest: Arts and culture; Education;
Health; Christianity.
Type of support: Continuing support;
Program-related investments; Matching grants;
Capital campaigns; Capital and infrastructure;
Program development; Convening; Scholarships;
Research.
Limitations: Applications accepted. Giving primarily
in Merrimack Valley, MA. No grants to individuals.
Publications: Informational brochure (including
application guidelines).
Application information: Application form required.
   Initial approach: Letter
   Copies of proposal: 1
   Deadline(s): Between Oct. 1 and June 30
   Board meeting date(s): Quarterly
Trustees: Drake Behrakis; George D. Behrakis;
Margo Behrakis; Stephanie B. Liakos.
Number of staff: 1 full-time professional.
EIN: 043348263

4016
The Benson Family Charitable Trust
c/o Moriarty & Primack P.C.
1 Monarch Pl., No. 900
Springfield, MA   01144-4006

Donors: Craig R. Benson; Denise A. Benson.
Foundation type: Independent foundation.
Financial data (yr. ended 12/31/14): Assets,
$11,562,834 (M); expenditures, $339,733;
qualifying distributions, $284,483; giving activities
include $284,333 for 11 grants (high: $150,000;
low: $5,000).
Fields of interest: Education; Higher education;
Health; Community and economic development;
Human services; Child welfare.
Type of support: General support.
Limitations: Applications not accepted. Giving
primarily in MA and NH. No grants to individuals.
Application information: Contributes only to
pre-selected organizations.
Trustee: Craig R. Benson.
EIN: 225017058

4017
Doris L. Benz Trust
c/o Wendell P. Weyland, Trustee
309 Ipswich Rd.
Boxford, MA   01921-1505
Scholarship application address: c/o New
Hampshire Charitable Fund Foundation,
Attn.: Student Aid Office, 37 Pleasant St., Concord,
NH 03301-4005, tel.: (603) 225-6641

Established in 1984 in New Hampshire.
Donor: Doris L. Benz†.
Foundation type: Independent foundation.
Financial data (yr. ended 06/30/13): Assets,
$9,151,176 (M); expenditures, $450,778;
qualifying distributions, $385,691; giving activities

include $357,302 for 24 grants (high: $195,052; low: $250).

Purpose and activities: Giving for scholarships for students graduating from Interlakes Regional High School, Sandwich, New Hampshire, and students graduating from any high school in Carroll County, New Hampshire; some giving also to organizations located in Massachusetts or New Hampshire.

Fields of interest: Education; Higher education; Hospital care; Human services; Child welfare; Domestic violence shelters.

Type of support: General support; Scholarships; Individual development.

Limitations: Applications accepted. Giving primarily in MA and NH; scholarship funds limited to residents of NH. No support for religious purposes.

Application information: Scholarship administered by New Hampshire Charitable Foundation. Application form required for scholarships. Application form required.

   Initial approach: Letter

   Deadline(s): Apr. 26 for scholarships; none for other grants

Trustee: Wendell P. Weyland.

EIN: 046504871

4018
Berger Family Charitable Foundation
2 Avery St., Apt. 34E
Boston, MA   02111-1018
Contact: Harvey Berger, M.D.

Established in 2007 in Massachusetts.

Donors: E. Edith Berger; Eva E. Berger.

Foundation type: Independent foundation.

Financial data (yr. ended 12/31/13): Assets, $51,642 (M); gifts received, $350,067; expenditures, $300,070; qualifying distributions, $300,000; giving activities include $300,000 for 1 grant.

Fields of interest: Education; Secondary education.

Type of support: Regranting; Capital campaigns; Fundraising.

Limitations: Applications not accepted. Giving primarily in Concord, MA. No grants to individuals.

Application information: Contributes only to pre-selected organizations.

Trustees: Eve Edith Berger; Harvey J. Berger, MD.

EIN: 208629538

4019
The Bergstrom Foundation
c/o Gary Bergstrom
220 Boylston St., Ste. 1516
Boston, MA   02116-3951

Established in 2000 in Massachusetts.

Donors: Gary L. Bergstrom; Joan L. Bergstrom†.

Foundation type: Independent foundation.

Financial data (yr. ended 07/31/14): Assets, $8,409,859 (M); expenditures, $444,801; qualifying distributions, $418,070; giving activities include $418,000 for 8 grants (high: $235,000; low: $3,000).

Fields of interest: Arts and culture; Education; Human services.

Limitations: Applications not accepted. Giving primarily in MA; funding also in New York, N. No grants to individuals.

Application information: Unsolicited requests for funds not accepted.

Trustee: Craig G. Bergstrom.

EIN: 066499658

4020
The Bigbird Fund
(formerly McQuillan-Criniti Charitable Fdoundation)
c/o Boylston Properties
800 Boylston St., Ste. 1390
Boston, MA   02199-7077

Donor: William P. McQuillan.

Foundation type: Independent foundation.

Financial data (yr. ended 12/31/13): Assets, $1,839,546 (M); expenditures, $290,118; qualifying distributions, $269,860; giving activities include $269,860 for 34 grants (high: $96,660; low: $250).

Fields of interest: Arts and culture; Theater; Public affairs; Human services.

Type of support: General support.

Limitations: Applications not accepted. Giving primarily in MA.

Application information: Unsolicited requests for funds not accepted.

Trustees: Linda M. Criniti; William P. McQuillan.

EIN: 454072533

4021
Helene B. Black Charitable Foundation
c/o Marvin Sparrow, N. Samiljan & R. Goldman
400 Atlantic Ave.
Boston, MA   02110-3333

Established in 1990 in Massachusetts.

Donor: Helene B. Black†.

Foundation type: Independent foundation.

Financial data (yr. ended 06/30/14): Assets, $3,231,928 (M); expenditures, $248,018; qualifying distributions, $227,631; giving activities include $215,050 for 40 grants (high: $120,000; low: $250).

Purpose and activities: Giving primarily for education, social services, and Jewish organizations.

Fields of interest: Education; Nonprofits; Legal services; Judaism; Human services; Child welfare.

Type of support: Regranting.

Limitations: Applications not accepted. Giving primarily in MA, with some emphasis on Boston. No grants to individuals.

Application information: Contributes only to pre-selected organizations.

Trustees: Marvin Sparrow; Nancy Samiljan; Robert P. Goldman.

EIN: 046667008

4022
The Blossom Fund
c/o Loring Wolcott Coolidge
230 Congress St.
Boston, MA   02110—2409   (617) 622-2216
Main URL: http://www.blossomfund.org

Established in 1994 in Massachusetts.

Foundation type: Independent foundation.

Financial data (yr. ended 03/31/13): Assets, $834,245 (M); gifts received, $100,000; expenditures, $173,263; qualifying distributions, $163,565; giving activities include $162,000 for 8 grants (high: $50,000; low: $10,000).

Purpose and activities: Support for the community and grassroots efforts of women in the Boston, MA area, Central America, and Mexico, and to encourage social and economic development of women and girls; support also for community-based educational and cultural projects in Boston, Brookline and Cambridge, MA, as well as for programs promoting the use of Boston-area outdoor space as described in foundation guidelines.

Fields of interest: Arts and culture; Education; Libraries; Archives and special collections; Economic development; Youth development; Women's services; International development; Females.

International interests: Central America; Mexico.

Type of support: General support; Seed money.

Limitations: Giving primarily in MA for local programs; giving nationally for programs benefiting Central America and Mexico. No support for health care or sports. No grants for scholarships, capital campaigns, or construction projects.

Application information:

   Board meeting date(s): Apr. 20 and Oct. 20

Trustees: Katherine Bowditch; Louise J. Bowditch; Robert S. Bowditch, Jr.; Amy L. Domini; Wendy S. Holding.

EIN: 223297205

4023
The Boger Charitable Trust
29 Irving St.
Cambridge, MA   02138-3009

Established in 1986 in Massachusetts.

Donors: Barbara C. Boger; The Crawford Trust for Grand Children Northern Trust; The Crawford Trust for Children Northern Trust.

Foundation type: Independent foundation.

Financial data (yr. ended 12/31/13): Assets, $2,859,413 (M); gifts received, $51,853; expenditures, $219,327; qualifying distributions, $180,533; giving activities include $180,533 for 63 grants (high: $129,629; low: $25).

Fields of interest: Arts and culture; Philanthropy; Health.

Type of support: General support.

Limitations: Applications not accepted. Giving primarily in MA. No grants to individuals.

Application information: Unsolicited requests for funds not accepted.

Trustees: Barbara C. Boger; William P. Boger III.

EIN: 222776296

4024
The Boyce Foundation
c/o Bowditch & Dewey, LLP
1 International Pl., 44th Fl.
Boston, MA   02110-2602   (617) 757-6517

Established in 2007 in Massachusetts.

Donor: Michael R. Boyce.

Foundation type: Independent foundation.

Financial data (yr. ended 12/31/14): Assets, $4,333,668 (M); gifts received, $19,560; expenditures, $245,476; qualifying distributions, $226,226.

Fields of interest: Domestic violence shelters.

Limitations: Applications accepted. Giving primarily in NC.

Application information: Application form required.

Initial approach: Letter
Deadline(s): None
Trustee: Samuel C. Sichko.
EIN: 261617992

4025

John W. Boynton Fund

c/o U.S. Trust, Bank of America, N.A.
225 Franklin St., 4th Fl.
Boston, MA 02110-2800 (866) 778-6859
Contact: Michealle Larkins, V.P.
E-mail: ma.grantmaking@ustrust.com; Main
URL: https://www.bankofamerica.com/
philanthropic/grantmaking.go

Donor: Dora C. Boynton†.
Foundation type: Independent foundation.
Financial data (yr. ended 12/31/14): Assets,
$3,976,149; expenditures, $233,153; qualifying
distributions, $210,445.
Purpose and activities: Grants principally to
organizations serving low-income elderly; special
consideration also to the town of Athol, MA.
Fields of interest: Housing development; Human
services; Youth services; Senior services; Seniors;
Low-income and poor people.
Type of support: General support; Continuing
support; Capital and infrastructure; Equipment;
Program development; Seed money.
Limitations: Applications accepted. Giving limited to
Athol and eastern MA. No grants to individuals, or
for endowment funds, research, scholarships,
fellowships, or matching gifts; no loans.
Publications: Application guidelines; Grants list.
Application information: Online application;
complete application guidelines available on Fund
web site.
Initial approach: Email
Trustee: Bank of America, N.A.
Number of staff: 2 part-time support.
EIN: 046036706

4026

Brabson Library & Educational Foundation

120 Sippewisset Rd.
Falmouth, MA 02540-1819
Contact: John Brabson, Pres.
E-mail: gatekeeper@brabsonfamilyfoundation.org;
Application address: c/o Elizabeth Feathers, V.P.,
4649 Country Rd. 9, East Nassau, NY 12062, tel.:
(812) 332-6507; Main URL: http://
www.brabsonfamilyfoundation.org

Established in 1990 in Florida.
Donors: George Brabson Trust; Evelyn Brabson
Trust.
Foundation type: Independent foundation.
Financial data (yr. ended 06/30/13): Assets,
$6,568,320 (M); gifts received, $398,189;
expenditures, $376,760; qualifying distributions,
$327,762; giving activities include $298,836 for 26
grants (high: $33,000; low: $500).
Fields of interest: Opera; Orchestral music; Science
museums; Education; Domesticated animals;
Children and youth; Children; Low-income and poor
people.
Type of support: General support; Annual
campaigns; Endowments; Seed money; Research.
Limitations: Applications accepted. Giving on a
national basis. No support for religious or political

organizations. No grants to individuals, or for food,
housing, clothing, or medical support.
Publications: Application guidelines; Grants list;
Occasional report; Program policy statement.
Application information: See foundation web site
for complete application guidelines. Application
form required.
Copies of proposal: 1
Deadline(s): Mar. 15
Final notification: Varies
Officers: John Brabson, Pres.; Elizabeth Feathers,
V.P.; Andrew Brabson, Treas.
Directors: Margaret Becker; Bennet Brabson; G.
Dana Brabson, Jr.; Jessica Brabson; Steve Brabson.
Number of staff: None.
EIN: 593021777

4027

Brock Family Foundation

c/o Castol Rock Advisors
200 Clarendon St., 35th Fl.
Boston, MA 02116-5040

Donors: Jack Brock-Wilson; Jane Brock-Wilson.
Foundation type: Independent foundation.
Financial data (yr. ended 12/31/13): Assets,
$7,222,069 (M); gifts received, $2,110;
expenditures, $298,829; qualifying distributions,
$250,500; giving activities include $250,000 for 2
grants (high: $200,000; low: $50,000).
Fields of interest: Education; Cancers.
Limitations: Applications not accepted. Giving
primarily in MA.
Application information: Unsolicited requests for
funds not accepted.
Trustee: Jane Brock-Wilson.
EIN: 276951581

4028

Harold Brooks Foundation

c/o Bank of America, N.A.
225 Franklin St.
Boston, MA 02110-2804 (866) 778-6859
E-mail: ma.grantmaking@ustrust.com; Main
URL: https://www.bankofamerica.com/
philanthropic/grantmaking.go

Established in 1984 in Massachusetts.
Donor: Harold Brooks†.
Foundation type: Independent foundation.
Financial data (yr. ended 12/31/14): Assets,
$10,565,899 (M); expenditures, $515,695;
qualifying distributions, $450,921; giving activities
include $395,000 for 19 grants (high: $125,000;
low: $10,000).
Purpose and activities: The foundation provides
assistance to causes and organizations that help
the largest possible number of residents of
Massachusetts' South Shore communities,
especially those that support the basic human
needs of South Shore residents. More specifically,
the foundation supports: 1) Educational programs
for all ages, including but not limited to academic
access, educational enrichment, and remedial
programming for children, youth, adults, and senior
citizens that focus on preparing individuals to
achieve while in school and beyond; 2) Health and
Mental Health programming that: a) makes possible
care or expands care in response to priority
community health needs of residents of the South
Shore, b) improves access to care (especially basic

services) for traditionally underserved individuals, or
c) prepares individuals to be independent and to
assist themselves; and 3) Food, Agriculture,
Nutrition and Housing and Shelter programs.
Fields of interest: Education; Health; Mental health
care; Agriculture; Housing development; Human
services.
Type of support: General support; Program
development.
Limitations: Giving limited to MA, with emphasis on
the South Shore area including Abington, Braintree,
Bridgewater, Brockton, Carver, Cohasset, Duxbury,
Hanover, Hanson, Hingham, Holbrook, Hull,
Marshfield, Norwell, Pembroke, Plymouth, Quincy,
Randolph, Rockland, Scituate, Weymouth, and
Whitman. No grants to individuals, or for general
operating expenses or endowments.
Publications: Application guidelines.
Application information: Complete application
guidelines available on foundation web site.
Initial approach: Letter
Copies of proposal: 1
Deadline(s): Apr. 1 and Oct. 1
Board meeting date(s): June and Dec.
Final notification: June 30 and Dec. 31
Trustees: Paul Taylor; Rev. M. James Workman;
Bank of America Merrill Lynch.
EIN: 046043983

4029

Stephanie L. Brown Foundation

c/o Joseph G. Imbriani, Esq.
160 Federal St.
Boston, MA 02110-1723

Established in 2005 in Massachusetts.
Donor: Stephanie L. Brown.
Foundation type: Independent foundation.
Financial data (yr. ended 12/31/14): Assets,
$2,845,631 (M); gifts received, $977,130;
expenditures, $394,585; qualifying distributions,
$346,500; giving activities include $346,500 for 11
grants (high: $235,000; low: $500).
Fields of interest: Education; Health; Human
services.
Limitations: Applications not accepted. Giving
primarily in MA. No grants to individuals.
Application information: Unsolicited requests for
funds not accepted.
Trustees: Joseph G. Imbriani; Stephanie L. Brown.
EIN: 203954546

4030

Bruner Foundation Inc.

130 Prospect St.
Cambridge, MA 02139-1844 (617) 492-8404
Contact: Emily Axelrod, Exec. Dir.
FAX: (617) 876-4002;
E-mail: info@brunerfoundation.org; Main
URL: http://www.brunerfoundation.org

Established in 1967 in New York.
Donors: Rudy Bruner†; Martha Bruner†.
Foundation type: Independent foundation.
Financial data (yr. ended 12/31/12): Assets,
$5,817,153 (M); expenditures, $485,932;
qualifying distributions, $288,695; giving activities
include $288,695 for grants.
Purpose and activities: Support primarily for the
Rudy Bruner Award for Excellence and evaluation of
nonprofit service delivery.

Fields of interest: Arts and culture; Architecture; Nonprofits; Community and economic development; Sustainable development; Urban development.
Type of support: Convening; Program development; Research; Capacity-building and technical assistance.
Limitations: Applications accepted. Giving on a national basis within the lower 48 states only. No grants to individuals, or for general support, building or endowment funds, scholarships, or fellowships.
Publications: Application guidelines; Informational brochure (including application guidelines); Program policy statement.
Application information: The foundation is not currently making any new grants. See foundation web site for application guidelines, procedures, and publications for the Rudy Bruner Award. Application form required.
   Initial approach: Letter
   Copies of proposal: 1
   Deadline(s): See Website
   Board meeting date(s): As required
Officers: Joshua E. Bruner, Pres.; R. Simeon Bruner, Treas.; Emily Axelrod, Exec. Dir.
Number of staff: 1 part-time professional; 1 part-time support.
EIN: 136180803

4031
The Gregory E. Bulger Foundation

12 Miller Hill Rd.
Dover, MA   02030-2332
Contact: Richard J. Dix, Mgr.
E-mail: GEBFoundation@aol.com

Established in 2002 in Massachusetts.
Donor: Gregory E. Bulger.
Foundation type: Independent foundation.
Financial data (yr. ended 12/31/13): Assets, $1,395,639 (M); expenditures, $384,040; qualifying distributions, $262,774; giving activities include $262,774 for 19 grants (high: $79,774; low: $500).
Fields of interest: Theater; Music; Orchestral music; Education; Health; Legal services; Child welfare.
Type of support: Annual campaigns; Matching grants; General support; Capital campaigns.
Limitations: Applications not accepted. Giving primarily in the Boston, MA area. No grants to individuals.
Application information: Contributes only to pre-selected organizations.
Officer: Richard J. Dix, Mgr.
Trustee: Gregory E. Bulger.
EIN: 331000434

4032
Florence Evans Bushee Foundation, Inc.

c/o Hemenway & Barnes, LLP
P.O. Box 961209
Boston, MA   02196-1209
Application address: c/o Arthur B. Page Esq., 60 State St., Boston, MA 02109-1899, tel.:(617) 227-7940

Established in 1953 in Massachusetts.
Donor: Florence Evans Bushee†.
Foundation type: Independent foundation.
Financial data (yr. ended 12/31/14): Assets, $5,663,728 (M); expenditures, $303,779; qualifying distributions, $275,312; giving activities

include $225,400 for 108 grants to individuals (high: $4,600; low: $500).
Purpose and activities: Giving primarily for undergraduate scholarships to residents of the Newburyport, Massachusetts, area.
Fields of interest: Higher education.
Type of support: Student aid.
Limitations: Applications accepted. Giving limited to Byfield, Newburyport, Newbury, West Newbury, and Rowley, MA. No grants for building funds, endowment funds, or operating budgets; no loans.
Publications: Application guidelines; Informational brochure.
Application information: Application form required.
   Initial approach: Letter
   Copies of proposal: 1
   Deadline(s): May 1
   Board meeting date(s): May, June, and as required
Officer and Directors: Judith A. Robertson, Pres. and Director; Sheila Christenson; Arthur B. Page.
Number of staff: 4 part-time professional.
EIN: 046035327

4033
Cabbadetus Foundation

c/o Hemenway & Barnes LLP
P.O. Box 961209
Boston, MA   02196-1209
Contact: Michael Elefante, Tr.

Established in 2007 in Florida.
Donor: Martha Robes Revocable Trust.
Foundation type: Independent foundation.
Financial data (yr. ended 12/31/14): Assets, $14,936,755 (M); gifts received, $42,000; expenditures, $461,177; qualifying distributions, $365,766; giving activities include $357,300 for 4 grants (high: $195,000; low: $40,000).
Fields of interest: Arts and culture; Education; Human services.
International interests: Virgin Islands of the United States.
Limitations: Applications not accepted. Giving primarily in ME, NH, VT, and St. John, U.S. Virgin Islands. No grants to individuals.
Application information: Unsolicited requests for funds not accepted.
Trustees: Michael B. Elefante; Martha S. Robes.
EIN: 266124255

4034
Paul & Virginia Cabot Charitable Trust

P.O. Box 55806
Boston, MA   02205-5806   6174825270

Established in 1994 in Massachusetts.
Donors: Paul C. Cabot†; Virginia Cabot†.
Foundation type: Independent foundation.
Financial data (yr. ended 01/31/15): Assets, $5,124,425; expenditures, $300,404; qualifying distributions, $259,820.
Purpose and activities: Giving primarily for natural resource conservation, the arts and education; funding also for health associations, particularly an eye research institute.
Fields of interest: Arts and culture; Historical activities; Education; Natural resources; Animal welfare; Hospital care; Diseases and conditions; Human services.
Type of support: General support; Continuing support; Annual campaigns; Capital campaigns;

Capital and infrastructure; Endowments; Program development.
Limitations: Applications not accepted. No grants to individuals.
Application information: Unsolicited requests for funds not accepted.
   Board meeting date(s): Annually
Trustees: Frederick C. Cabot; John M. Wood III; Fiduciary Trust Co.
EIN: 222929805

4035
Ella Lyman Cabot Trust Inc.

c/o GMA Foundations
77 Summer St., 8th Fl.
Boston, MA   02110   (617) 391-3087
Contact: Michelle Jenney, Administrator/Clerk
FAX: (617) 426-7087;
E-mail: mjenney@gmafoundations.com; Main
URL: http://www.cabottrust.org

Established in 1939 in Massachusetts.
Donor: Richard Cabot†.
Foundation type: Independent foundation.
Financial data (yr. ended 12/31/13): Assets, $3,460,004 (M); expenditures, $189,887; qualifying distributions, $172,309; giving activities include $40,000 for 4 grants (high: $18,070; low: $5,000), and $117,590 for 8 grants to individuals (high: $25,000; low: $5,000).
Purpose and activities: Grants primarily to individuals for projects (sometimes involving a departure from one's usual vocation or a creative extension of it) with a promise of good to others. Awards are usually made on a one-year basis and are not renewed.
Fields of interest: Arts and culture; Music; Humanities; Education; Child educational development; Environment; Health; Biomedicine; Religion; Human rights; Human services; Child development; Youth services; Women's services; International peace and security.
Type of support: General support; Grants to individuals.
Publications: Application guidelines.
Application information: Online preliminary application required. Grants are in the range of $15,000 to $25,000. The Trust does not grant renewals or follow-up grants. See Trust website for additional application information.
   Initial approach: Make email contact first, before submitting online preliminary application
   Deadline(s): Mar. 1 and Oct. 1
   Board meeting date(s): Spring and Fall
   Final notification: Usually 1 month
Officers and Trustees: Andrew G. Bodnar, MD, Chair. and Trustee; Michelle Jenney, Clerk; Jeffrey Swope, Treas. and Trustee; Gene A. Corbin; Sr. Carolyn Darr; Mary Jane Gibson; Helen Glikman; Ellen T. Harris; Robert M. Randolph; Hon. Byron Rushing; Constance W. Williams.
Number of staff: 1 part-time professional.
EIN: 042111393

4036
Cail Family Foundation

99 Florence St., 60 Apt. 3C, Bldg. N.
Chestnut Hill, MA   02467-1935

Established in 2006 in Massachusetts.
Donor: Milton Cail.

Foundation type: Independent foundation.
Financial data (yr. ended 12/31/12): Assets, $1,448,414 (M); gifts received, $250,000; expenditures, $199,588; qualifying distributions, $188,855; giving activities include $188,855 for grants.
Fields of interest: Diseases and conditions; Judaism.
Limitations: Applications not accepted. Giving primarily in MA. No grants to individuals.
Application information: Unsolicited requests for funds not accepted.
Trustees: Lois Cail; Milton Cail; Faith Kaplan.
EIN: 202034269

4037
The Eric & Barbara Carle Foundation

(formerly Eric Carle Foundation)
38 Main St.
Northampton, MA 01061-3197

Established in 1995 in Massachusetts.
Donors: Eric Carle; Barbara Carle.
Foundation type: Independent foundation.
Financial data (yr. ended 12/31/13): Assets, $2,869,337 (M); gifts received, $800,000; expenditures, $191,216; qualifying distributions, $179,304; giving activities include $177,755 for 16 grants (high: $158,000; low: $500).
Fields of interest: Museums; Education; Human services.
Type of support: General support.
Limitations: Applications not accepted. Giving primarily in MA. No grants to individuals.
Application information: Unsolicited requests for funds not accepted.
Trustees: Barbara Carle; Eric Carle.
EIN: 043296725

4038
Carlee Charitable Trust

c/o Loring, Wolcott, & Coolidge
230 Congress St.
Boston, MA 02110-2409 (617) 523-6531
Contact: Frederick D. Ballou, Tr.

Established in 1995 in Massachusetts.
Donor: Jane H. Carlee.
Foundation type: Independent foundation.
Financial data (yr. ended 12/31/13): Assets, $3,639,256 (M); expenditures, $287,209; qualifying distributions, $259,903; giving activities include $252,500 for 7 grants (high: $100,000; low: $7,500).
Purpose and activities: Giving for the protection and care of domestic animals, the protection of natural wildlife species, the conservation of areas of natural habitat and beauty, and the preservation of historic architecture in the New England area.
Fields of interest: Natural resources; Domesticated animals.
Type of support: Capital campaigns; Land acquisitions; Seed money.
Limitations: Applications accepted. Giving primarily in MA. No grants to individuals.
Application information: Application form required.
Initial approach: Contact foundation for application form
Deadline(s): Contact foundation for deadline

Trustees: Frederick D. Ballou; Caroline A. Ellis; Wendy S. Holding; Patricia H. Loring.
EIN: 046796657

4039
Casey Family Foundation

(formerly E. Paul & Patricia P. Casey Foundation)
3 Rainbow Rd.
Marblehead, MA 01945-1260

Established in 1964 in Massachusetts.
Donor: E. Paul Casey.
Foundation type: Independent foundation.
Financial data (yr. ended 12/31/13): Assets, $4,468,837 (M); expenditures, $224,573; qualifying distributions, $198,593; giving activities include $198,593 for 66 grants (high: $50,000; low: $50).
Fields of interest: Elementary and secondary education; Higher education; Health; Christianity; Human services.
Type of support: General support.
Limitations: Applications not accepted. Giving primarily in FL, CT, MA, ME, and NH. No grants to individuals.
Application information: Contributes only to pre-selected organizations.
Trustees: Jennifer P. Casey; Sheila C. McManus; Virginia C. Pettengill; Patricia C. Shepherd.
EIN: 026013556

4040
The Catino Family Foundation

800 Boylston St., 16th Fl.
Boston, MA 02199-1900
Application address: Catino Family Foundation, 312 Walnut St. Ste. 1600, Cincinnati, OH 45202
Tel.: (513) 563-3061

Donors: Theodore Catino; Beverly Catino.
Foundation type: Independent foundation.
Financial data (yr. ended 12/31/13): Assets, $3,114,419 (M); expenditures, $195,502; qualifying distributions, $176,025; giving activities include $174,250 for 6 grants (high: $124,675; low: $200).
Fields of interest: Education; Religion; Human services.
Application information: Application form required.
Initial approach: Letter
Deadline(s): None
Officers: Beverly Catino, Pres.; Theodore Catino, Secy.
EIN: 454104550

4041
The Davi-Ellen and Bruce Allen Chabner Family Foundation, Inc.

c/o Goulston & Storrs, P.C.
400 Atlantic Ave.
Boston, MA 02110-3333

Established in 2003 in Massachusetts.
Donors: Bruce Allan Chabner; Davi-Ellen Chabner; Zeltia Pharmaceuticals.
Foundation type: Independent foundation.
Financial data (yr. ended 12/31/13): Assets, $2,027,228 (M); gifts received, $20,585; expenditures, $218,119; qualifying distributions,

$187,452; giving activities include $178,740 for 39 grants (high: $100,000; low: $50).
Fields of interest: Arts and culture; Diseases and conditions; Cancers; Religion.
Limitations: Applications not accepted. Giving primarily in MA, with some giving in NY. No grants to individuals.
Application information: Contributes only to pre-selected organizations.
Officers and Directors: Davi-Ellen Chabner, Pres. and Treas. and Director; Bruce Allan Chabner, Clerk and Director; Brandon S. Chabner; Elizabeth C. Thompson.
EIN: 200509624

4042
The George & Marie Chabot Charitable Foundation

31 State St., 6th Fl.
Boston, MA 02109

Foundation type: Independent foundation.
Financial data (yr. ended 12/31/13): Assets, $3,813,171 (M); expenditures, $292,377; qualifying distributions, $260,390; giving activities include $260,390 for 27 grants (high: $75,000; low: $500).
Fields of interest: Arts and culture; Education; Housing development; Religion; Christianity.
Limitations: Applications not accepted. Giving primarily in MA.
Application information: Unsolicited requests for funds not accepted.
Trustees: Ann E. Polachi; Charles A. Polachi, Jr.; Peter V. Polachi.
EIN: 266382379

4043
The Change the World Foundation Trust

c/o SCS Financial Svcs,, LLC
1 Winthrop Sq., 4th Fl.
Boston, MA 02110-1209

Established in 2006 in Massachusetts.
Donors: Thomas Brady, Jr.; MMG; Best Buddies International.
Foundation type: Independent foundation.
Financial data (yr. ended 11/30/13): Assets, $1,091,363 (M); gifts received, $500,000; expenditures, $198,810; qualifying distributions, $195,000; giving activities include $195,000 for 9 grants (high: $50,000; low: $5,000).
Fields of interest: Education; Christianity.
Limitations: Applications not accepted. Giving primarily in Mateo, CA and Miami, FL. No grants to individuals.
Application information: Unsolicited requests for funds not accepted.
Trustee: Thomas Brady, Jr.
EIN: 256885307

4044
The Chartis Foundation

20 Bow St.
Cohasset, MA 02025-1330

Established in 2005 in Illinois.
Donor: Chartis Group LLC.
Foundation type: Company-sponsored foundation.

Financial data (yr. ended 12/31/13): Assets, $441,165 (M); gifts received, $145,500; expenditures, $181,570; qualifying distributions, $180,000; giving activities include $180,000 for 4 grants (high: $80,000; low: $25,000).

Purpose and activities: The foundation supports organizations involved with higher education and health.

Fields of interest: University education; Health; Infant care.

Type of support: General support.

Limitations: Applications not accepted. Giving primarily in CT, LA, and SD. No grants to individuals.

Application information: Contributes only to pre-selected organizations.

Directors: Ethan Arnold; Ken Graboys; Chris Regan.

EIN: 203996418

4045
Alfred E. Chase Charity Foundation
c/o Bank of America, N.A.
225 Franklin St.
Boston, MA   02110
E-mail: ma.grantmaking@ustrust.com; Main URL: http://www.bankofamerica.com/grantmaking

Established in 1956 in Massachusetts.

Donor: Alfred E. Chase†.

Foundation type: Independent foundation.

Financial data (yr. ended 10/31/13): Assets, $8,785,725 (M); expenditures, $466,660; qualifying distributions, $416,518; giving activities include $370,000 for 18 grants (high: $80,000; low: $10,000).

Purpose and activities: The foundation was established in 1956 to support and promote quality educational, human services, and health care programming for underserved populations. Special consideration is given to charitable organizations that serve the people of the city of Lynn and the North Shore of Massachusetts.

Fields of interest: Education; Human services; Child welfare; Youth services.

Type of support: General support; Program development.

Limitations: Giving limited to MA, with special consideration for Lynn and North Shore areas. No grants to individuals, or for research, scholarships, or fellowships; no loans.

Publications: Application guidelines.

Application information: Online application; complete guidelines available on foundation web site.

   Initial approach: E-mail
   Deadline(s): Mar. 1

Trustee: Bank of America, N.A.

Number of staff: None.

EIN: 046026314

4046
The Chickering Foundation
(formerly Dedham Temporary Home for Women & Children)
c/o Fiduciary Trust Co.
P.O. Box 55806
Boston, MA   02205-5806
Application address: c/o Susanne Coyne, 175 Federal St., Boston, MA 02110

Established in 1941 in Massachusetts.

Donors: Elisha V. Ashton Trust; Mary B. Fisher†.

Foundation type: Independent foundation.

Financial data (yr. ended 12/31/13): Assets, $3,019,270 (M); gifts received, $36,850; expenditures, $200,504; qualifying distributions, $176,478; giving activities include $174,500 for 12 grants (high: $18,000; low: $4,500).

Purpose and activities: Giving for the health and welfare of women and children.

Fields of interest: Family planning; Diseases and conditions; Human services; Family services; Women's services; Females.

Application information: Application form required.

   Initial approach: Letter
   Copies of proposal: 1
   Deadline(s): None
   Board meeting date(s): Feb., May and Oct.

Officers: Barbara Beal, Pres.; Darcy Fuguet, V.P.; Julia Terry, Rec. Secy.; Rali Weaver, Corr. Secy.; Juanita Allen Kingsley, Treas.

Number of staff: None.

EIN: 046012767

4047
Chicopee Savings Bank Charitable Foundation
70 Center St.
P.O. Box 300
Chicopee, MA   01014-0300   (413) 598-3107
Contact: Berdie Thompson, Coord.
E-mail: foundation@chicopeesavings.com; Main URL: http://www.chicopeesavings.com/default.asp?LINKNAME=COMMUNITY

Established in 2006 in Unspecified.

Donor: Chicopee Bancorp, Inc.

Foundation type: Company-sponsored foundation.

Financial data (yr. ended 12/31/14): Assets, $6,663,330 (M); expenditures, $435,520; qualifying distributions, $432,917.

Purpose and activities: The foundation supports programs designed to preserve and enhance quality of life within local neighborhoods and communities. Special emphasis is directed toward education; health and human services; youth; and affordable housing initiatives.

Fields of interest: Arts and culture; Education; Higher education; Health; Community and economic development; Housing development; Human services; Youth services; Adolescents; Low-income and poor people.

Type of support: General support; In-kind gifts; Continuing support; Annual campaigns; Program development; Scholarships; Sponsorships.

Limitations: Applications accepted. Giving primarily in areas of company operations in Chicopee, Ludlow, South Hadley, Ware, and West Springfield, MA. No support for political or fraternal organizations. No grants to individuals.

Publications: Application guidelines.

Application information: The foundation is currently accepting requests for general operating support from organizations that provide vital community services. Proposals should be no longer than 1 to 2 pages in length. A site visit may be requested. Multi-year funding is not automatic. Organizations receiving support are asked to submit periodic reports.

   Initial approach: Proposal
   Deadline(s): None; 90 days prior to need for sponsorships, events, or in-kind requests

Officers and Directors: William J. Wagner, Chair. and Pres. and Director; Theresa C. Szlosek, Secy.;

Guida R. Sajdak, Treas.; Douglas Engebretson; William J. Gikoas; Russell J. Omer; Gregg F. Orlen; Michael Sobon; James P. Lynch.

EIN: 223940271

4048
The Chirag Foundation
(formerly The Singhal Foundation)
c/o Anil and Abha Singhal
265 Kimball Rd.
Carlisle, MA   01741-1037

Established in 1999 in Massachusetts.

Donors: Anil Singhal; Abha Singhal.

Foundation type: Independent foundation.

Financial data (yr. ended 12/31/13): Assets, $4,936,747 (M); gifts received, $1,000,397; expenditures, $540,898; qualifying distributions, $438,831; giving activities include $438,831 for 8 grants (high: $250,000; low: $1,000).

Fields of interest: Health; Diseases and conditions; Human services.

Limitations: Applications not accepted. Giving primarily in MA. No grants to individuals.

Application information: Unsolicited requests for funds not accepted.

Trustees: Abha Singhal; Anil Singhal.

EIN: 046902382

4049
The John Clarke Trust
c/o US Trust, Bank of America, N.A.
225 Franklin St., MA1-225-04-02
Boston, MA   02110-2804
Contact: Emma Greene, Market Dir.; Charles, Tickner
E-mail: ma.ri.grantmaking@ustrust.com; Main URL: https://www.bankofamerica.com/philanthropic/grantmaking.go

Established in 1676 in Rhode Island.

Donor: John Clark†.

Foundation type: Independent foundation.

Financial data (yr. ended 12/31/14): Assets, $9,355,232 (M); expenditures, $451,817; qualifying distributions, $417,380; giving activities include $372,725 for 75 grants (high: $20,000; low: $2,000).

Purpose and activities: Giving primarily for education and to provide relief to people who are economically disadvantaged.

Fields of interest: Education; Higher education; Health care clinics; Community and economic development; Human services; Child welfare.

Type of support: General support; Matching grants; Equipment; Program development; Curriculum development; Scholarships.

Limitations: Applications accepted. Giving primarily in The trustees have established a policy of giving preference to organizations located on Aquidneck Island, RI, and within the East Bay area. However, applications from any RI 501(c)(3) are acceptable. The trustees will consider capital grant requests ONLY from Aquidneck Island.

Application information:
   Initial approach: Online
   Deadline(s): Apr. 1 and Nov. 1

Trustees: William W. Corcoran, Esq.; Barbara N. Watterson; Bank of America, N.A.

EIN: 056006062

4050
Clementi Family Charitable Trust
c/o Longview Development
80 Erdman Way, Ste. 301
Leominster, MA 01453-1818

Established in 1990 in Massachusetts.
Donor: Plastican, Inc.
Foundation type: Independent foundation.
Financial data (yr. ended 12/31/13): Assets, $4,113,615 (M); expenditures, $235,918; qualifying distributions, $206,000; giving activities include $206,000 for 14 grants (high: $70,000; low: $1,000).
Fields of interest: Art museums; Education; Diseases and conditions; Protestantism; Youth services.
Type of support: Scholarships.
Limitations: Applications not accepted. Giving primarily in the Leominster, MA, area. No grants to individuals.
Application information: Contributes only to pre-selected organizations.
Board Members: John Clementi; Anna Colangelo.
EIN: 043105942

4051
The Clifford Family Foundation Charitable Trust
c/o Frank P. Conrad
8 Cedar Rd.
Weston, MA 02493-2419

Established in 1989 in Massachusetts.
Donor: J. Christopher Clifford.
Foundation type: Independent foundation.
Financial data (yr. ended 12/31/13): Assets, $10,303,127 (M); gifts received, $229,229; expenditures, $284,260; qualifying distributions, $246,200; giving activities include $246,200 for 23 grants (high: $35,000; low: $1,000).
Fields of interest: Education; Higher education; Nonprofits; Human services; Youth services.
Type of support: Regranting.
Limitations: Applications not accepted. Giving primarily in MA and NY. No grants to individuals.
Application information: Unsolicited requests for funds not accepted.
Trustees: A. Keena Clifford; Caroline M. Clifford; Catherine K. Clifford; J. Christopher Clifford; John C. Clifford; Frank P. Conrad.
EIN: 223025894

4052
The Ogden Codman Trust
c/o Rackemann, Sawyer & Brewster
160 Federal St., 15th Fl.
Boston, MA 02110-1700
Contact: Susan T. Monahan, Tr.
E-mail: smonahan@rackemann.com; Main
URL: http://www.codmantrust.org

Established in 1968 in Massachusetts.
Donor: Dorothy S.F.M. Codman†.
Foundation type: Independent foundation.
Financial data (yr. ended 12/31/13): Assets, $4,602,426 (M); expenditures, $247,328; qualifying distributions, $211,827; giving activities include $180,000 for 9 grants (high: $50,000; low: $3,000).

Fields of interest: Museums; Historic preservation; Education; Agriculture; Community and economic development.
Type of support: General support; Matching grants; Capital and infrastructure; Equipment; Land acquisitions; Emergency funds.
Limitations: Applications accepted. Giving limited for the benefit of the residents of Lincoln, MA.
Publications: Application guidelines.
Application information: AGM Common Proposal Form accepted. See Trust web site for complete application information. Application form required.
  Initial approach: Email
  Copies of proposal: 1
  Deadline(s): None
  Board meeting date(s): 4th week of Feb., May, Aug., and Nov.
  Final notification: 2 to 3 weeks
Trustees: Maura E. Murphy; Susan T. Monahan; Michael F. O'Connell.
Number of staff: 1 part-time professional.
EIN: 046225360

4053
Ellen R. Cohen Charitable Trust
34 Monadnock Rd.
Newton, MA 02467

Established in 2001 in Massachusetts.
Donors: Julian Cohen†; Ellen Cohen.
Foundation type: Independent foundation.
Financial data (yr. ended 12/31/14): Assets, $5,346,937; gifts received, $6,153; expenditures, $344,764; qualifying distributions, $301,070.
Fields of interest: Higher education; Health.
Type of support: Ethics and accountability.
Limitations: Applications not accepted. Giving primarily in MA. No grants to individuals.
Application information: Unsolicited requests for funds not accepted.
Trustee: Ellen R. Cohen.
EIN: 046955867

4054
Ben And Rose Cole Charitable Pria Foundation
c/o Howland Capital
75 Federal St., No. 1100
Boston, MA 02110-1936

Donors: Ben Cole; Rose Cole.
Foundation type: Independent foundation.
Financial data (yr. ended 06/30/15): Assets, $6,697,255 (M); gifts received, $2,179,800; expenditures, $223,888; qualifying distributions, $185,000; giving activities include $185,000 for 2 grants (high: $135,000; low: $50,000).
Fields of interest: Health; Specialty hospital care.
Type of support: Research.
Limitations: Applications accepted. Giving primarily in MA.
Application information:
  Initial approach: Proposal
  Deadline(s): None
Trustees: Rose Cole; Barry Brown; Richard A.M. Lyon; Dr. Z. Myron Falchuk.
EIN: 453513929

4055
The William F. Connell Charitable Trust
c/o Lynch, Brewer, Hoffman & Sands, LLP
75 Federal St., 7th Fl.
Boston, MA 02110-1913

Established in 1986 in Massachusetts.
Donors: William F. Connell; William F. Connell Charitable Lead Annuity Trust; Margot C. Connell.
Foundation type: Independent foundation.
Financial data (yr. ended 12/31/13): Assets, $1,854,410 (M); gifts received, $135,000; expenditures, $187,885; qualifying distributions, $187,850; giving activities include $187,850 for 16 grants (high: $50,000; low: $350).
Fields of interest: Music; Secondary education; Higher education; Business education; Medical education; Hospital care; Cancers; Libraries.
Limitations: Applications not accepted. Giving primarily in MA. No grants to individuals.
Application information: Contributes only to pre-selected organizations.
Trustees: Courtenay E. Connell; Lisa T. McNamara; Monica C. Healey; Terence A. Connell; Timothy P. Connell; William C. Connell.
EIN: 222778156

4056
Gretchen Stone Cook Charitable Foundation
c/o Tyler & Reynolds, P.C.
77 Summer St., 6th Fl.
Boston, MA 02110-1006   (617) 695-9799
Contact: James L. Smithson, Tr.

Established in 2005 in Massachusetts.
Donor: Gretchen Stone Cook†.
Foundation type: Independent foundation.
Financial data (yr. ended 12/31/14): Assets, $7,449,609 (M); expenditures, $379,516; qualifying distributions, $320,214; giving activities include $320,000 for 5 grants (high: $100,000; low: $40,000).
Fields of interest: Education; Undergraduate education; Medical education; Specialty hospital care; Television.
Type of support: General support; Scholarships.
Limitations: Applications accepted. Giving primarily in MA. No grants to individuals.
Application information: Application form required.
  Initial approach: Proposal
  Deadline(s): None
Trustees: Gerald B. O'Grady III; James L. Smithson.
EIN: 206537290

4057
Coolidge Hill Foundation
75 Park St.
Lee, MA 01238-1701   (413) 243-0117
Contact: David J. Bruce, Treas.
E-mail: dbruce@leebank.com

Established in 1917 in Massachusetts.
Donors: Elizabeth S. Coolidge Trust; Coolidge Trust.
Foundation type: Independent foundation.
Financial data (yr. ended 12/31/14): Assets, $2,497,216 (M); gifts received, $51,064; expenditures, $152,189; qualifying distributions, $138,612; giving activities include $129,000 for 20 grants (high: $24,000; low: $500).

Purpose and activities: Giving primarily for programs for children and the handicapped.
Fields of interest: Health; Community and economic development; Human services.
Type of support: Program development; Seed money.
Limitations: Applications accepted. Giving primarily in MA. No grants to individuals.
Application information: Application form required.
Initial approach: Request application form
Deadline(s): Contact foundation for deadline
Officers: Anne Mcinerny Pinkston, Pres.; John C. Donna, V.P.; Ann Marie Miller, Secy.; David J. Bruce, Treas.
Directors: James B. Art; Maurice E. Callahan; Craig Cusson; Emil J. George; Deborah Georlach; Timothy Kiely; Jackie McNinch; Mary K. O'Brien; Cindy A. Shogry-Raimer; Colin Smith; Mary G. Tierney; Kathleen Tisdale; Sheri L. Quinn; Jeff Yeager.
EIN: 042121312

4058
The Crane & Co. Fund
30 South St.
Dalton, MA   01226-1751

Established in 1953 in Massachusetts.
Donors: Crane & Co., Inc.; Byron-Weston Co.
Foundation type: Company-sponsored foundation.
Financial data (yr. ended 12/31/13): Assets, $0 (M); gifts received, $350,450; expenditures, $350,450; qualifying distributions, $350,450; giving activities include $350,200 for 14 grants (high: $160,000; low: $200).
Purpose and activities: The foundation supports organizations involved with arts and culture, education, environmental conservation, health, human services, and government and public administration. Support is limited to Berkshire County, Massachusetts.
Fields of interest: Arts and culture; Museums; Education; Natural resources; Nonprofits; Health; Public administration; Human services.
Type of support: Annual campaigns; Capital campaigns; General support; Regranting.
Limitations: Applications not accepted. Giving limited to Berkshire County, MA. No grants to individuals, or for scholarships.
Application information: Unsolicited requests for funds not accepted.
Officers: Charles J. Kittredge, Pres.; Richard C. Kendall, Treas.
Trustee: John Kittredge.
EIN: 046057388

4059
The Crawford Idema Family Foundation
(formerly The Crawford Idema Foundation)
100 Main St., Ste. 325
Concord, MA   01742-2528   (978) 318-0505
Contact: Philip VanDerWilden, Exec. Dir.
FAX: (978) 318-0535;
E-mail: PhilipV@crawford-idema.org

Established in 1997 in California.
Foundation type: Independent foundation.
Financial data (yr. ended 12/31/13): Assets, $9,198,139 (M); gifts received, $50,000; expenditures, $670,598; qualifying distributions, $526,317; giving activities include $392,250 for 37 grants (high: $22,500; low: $2,500).

Purpose and activities: The foundation was established with the broad goal of benefiting society by strengthening institutions dedicated to helping individuals lead healthy and productive lives with dignity. Underlying this goal is the progressive belief in promoting the social and economic empowerment of all individuals. The foundation recognizes that not all individuals have access to the resources or support needed to lead lives of independence and dignity. Whether resulting from economic disparities, racial or gender prejudice, substance abuse or any other number of reasons, people often need a helping hand. This means not only helping those who are underprivileged, but also those who may not have the resources to afford basic necessities without help. Toward those ends, grantmaking seeks to support programs and projects which 1) Provide opportunities, services, and training for individuals to lead independent, productive, and healthy lives; 2) Enhance understanding, tolerance, compassion, and a sense of shared community between all people; 3) Promote a community of caring and compassion; and 4) Promote the preservation of the natural environment.
Fields of interest: Natural resources; Substance abuse prevention; Human services; Child development; LGBTQ people; Homeless people; Low-income and poor people.
Type of support: General support; Continuing support.
Limitations: Applications accepted. Giving limited to the Santa Barbara, CA and Concord, MA areas. No support for religious activities or programs that serve religious groups or denominations, or political candidates. No grants to individuals, general fund raising drives, endowment funds, or for debt reduction.
Publications: Informational brochure; Occasional report.
Application information: Unsolicited applications are not accepted. Interested parties must start with a 1-2 page letter of inquiry, which may be submitted anytime between Apr. 1 and Aug. 15. If invited to submit an application, the due date is usually the third Fri. in Sept.
Initial approach: Letter of inquiry
Copies of proposal: 1
Deadline(s): Second or third Fri. in Sept.
Board meeting date(s): Early Nov.
Final notification: Typically shortly after the early Nov. board meeting
Officers and Directors: Thomas Crawford, Jr., Pres. and Director; Nancy S. Crawford, Secy. and C.F.O. and Director; Philip VanDerWilden, Exec. Dir.; Susan C. Adams; Nancy R. Crawford; Peter T. Crawford; Thomas Crawford IV; Mary-Wren VanDerWilden; Peter Van Meeuwen.
Number of staff: 1 full-time professional.
EIN: 043473310

4060
The Cricket Foundation
50 Congress St., Ste. 832
Boston, MA   02109-4024
Contact: Michael M. Mikowski, Tr.
E-mail: gbutterworth@goodwinprocter.com

Established in 1978 in Massachusetts.
Foundation type: Independent foundation.
Financial data (yr. ended 09/30/14): Assets, $3,318,896 (M); expenditures, $177,279; qualifying distributions, $163,317; giving activities

include $152,100 for 21 grants (high: $20,000; low: $2,500).
Fields of interest: Arts and culture; Environment; Community and economic development.
Type of support: General support; Matching grants; Capital campaigns; Capital and infrastructure; Equipment; Land acquisitions; Program development; Convening; Publications; Seed money; Research.
Limitations: Applications accepted. No support for religious organizations. No grants to individuals.
Application information:
Initial approach: Letter
Deadline(s): May 1 and Nov. 1
Final notification: June and Dec.
Number of staff: 1 part-time professional.
EIN: 042655735

4061
Crowe Family Foundation
c/o Choate, LLP
P.O. Box 961019
Boston, MA   02196-1019

Donors: Kerridan Crowe; Michael K Crowe.
Foundation type: Independent foundation.
Financial data (yr. ended 06/30/14): Assets, $857,599 (M); gifts received, $116,200; expenditures, $224,818; qualifying distributions, $191,302; giving activities include $162,250 for 15 grants (high: $35,000; low: $250).
Fields of interest: Education; Health; Human services.
Limitations: Applications not accepted. Giving primarily in MA.
Application information: Unsolicited request for funds not accepted.
Trustees: Michael K. Crowe; Kerridan Crowe.
EIN: 273932476

4062
Curvey Family Foundation
82 Devonshire St., Ste. S9A
Boston, MA   02109-3605

Established in 2000 in Massachusetts.
Donors: James C. Curvey; J. Scott Curvey; Jeffrey C. Curvey.
Foundation type: Independent foundation.
Financial data (yr. ended 12/31/13): Assets, $3,547,336 (M); gifts received, $33,333; expenditures, $201,834; qualifying distributions, $185,517; giving activities include $164,850 for 37 grants (high: $20,000; low: $300).
Fields of interest: Arts and culture; Education; Health.
Limitations: Applications not accepted. Giving primarily in MA. No grants to individuals.
Application information: Unsolicited requests for funds not accepted.
Trustees: J. Scott Curvey; James C. Curvey; Jeffrey C. Curvey.
EIN: 043526188

4063
The Dalessandro Foundation
c/o Hemenway & Barnes
P.O. Box 961209
Boston, MA   02196-1209

Donors: Frances C. Dalessandro†; John J. Dalessandro†; Trust For Alfie.
Foundation type: Independent foundation.
Financial data (yr. ended 03/31/14): Assets, $10,249,589 (M); gifts received, $500,000; expenditures, $554,158; qualifying distributions, $432,750; giving activities include $432,500 for 11 grants (high: $100,000; low: $10,000).
Fields of interest: Education; Foundations; Health; Human services.
Limitations: Applications not accepted. Giving primarily in NY; funding also in OH. No grants to individuals.
Application information: Unsolicited requests for funds not accepted.
Trustees: Robert McCann; Walter D. O'Hearn, Jr.; Arthur B. Page; Timothy C. Withers.
EIN: 270210702

4064
The Gerald & Paul D'Amour Founders Scholarship for Academic Excellence
2145 Roosevelt Ave.
Springfield, MA   01104   (413) 504-4218
2012 Big Y Scholarship Recipients: http://www.bigy.com/Community/Scholarships/Awards#.UNCfpayrDTM

Established in 1994 in Massachusetts.
Donor: Big Y Foods, Inc.
Foundation type: Company-sponsored foundation.
Financial data (yr. ended 06/30/14): Assets, $2,148,355 (M); gifts received, $262,727; expenditures, $221,113; qualifying distributions, $215,578; giving activities include $215,578 for grants to individuals.
Purpose and activities: The foundation awards college scholarships to students residing in Big Y Foods, Inc. marketing areas.
Fields of interest: Higher education.
Type of support: Scholarships; Student aid.
Limitations: Applications accepted. Giving limited to areas of company operations in CT and central and western MA.
Publications: Application guidelines; Grants list.
Application information: Application form required.
   Initial approach: Proposal
   Deadline(s): Feb. 1
Trustees: Charles L. D'Amour; Donald H. D'Amour.
EIN: 223305742

4065
Robert E. Davoli & Eileen L. McDonagh Charitable Foundation
6 Winchelsea Ln.
Lincoln, MA   01773-5110

Established in 1993 in Massachusetts.
Donors: Robert E. Davoli; Eileen L. McDonagh.
Foundation type: Independent foundation.
Financial data (yr. ended 11/30/13): Assets, $875,016 (M); gifts received, $283,035; expenditures, $402,495; qualifying distributions, $396,492; giving activities include $396,492 for 38 grants (high: $100,000; low: $100).
Fields of interest: Arts and culture; Museums; Education; Higher education; Foundations; Health; Hospital care; Human services.
Type of support: General support; Scholarships.

Limitations: Applications not accepted. Giving primarily in MA, with emphasis on Boston. No grants to individuals.
Application information: Contributes only to pre-selected organizations.
Trustees: Robert E. Davoli; Eileen L. McDonagh.
EIN: 043210639

4066
The Taniguchi Deane Family Foundation
c/o Palmer Management Corp.
13 Elm St., Ste. 200
Cohasset, MA   02025-1828

Established in 2004 in Massachusetts.
Donor: Gordon L. Deane.
Foundation type: Independent foundation.
Financial data (yr. ended 12/31/13): Assets, $1,682,961 (M); expenditures, $388,322; qualifying distributions, $381,050; giving activities include $381,050 for 56 grants (high: $100,000; low: $100).
Fields of interest: Arts and culture; Arts education; Music; Education; Alzheimer's disease; ALS; HIV/AIDS.
Type of support: Research.
Limitations: Applications not accepted. Giving primarily in HI, MA and OH. No grants to individuals.
Application information: Contributes only to pre-selected organizations.
Trustees: Gordon L. Deane; Motoko T. Deane.
EIN: 421653917

4067
The Dedham Institution for Savings Foundation
45 School St., 5th Fl.
Boston, MA   02108-3204   (781) 461-0163
E-mail: glavoie@dedhamsavings.com; Application address: 55 Elm St., Dedham, MA 02026; Main URL: http://www.dedhamsavings.com/news-events-community-involvement.htm

Established in 1998 in Massachusetts.
Donor: Dedham Institution for Savings.
Foundation type: Company-sponsored foundation.
Financial data (yr. ended 12/31/14): Assets, $2,999,545; gifts received, $98,473; expenditures, $284,805; qualifying distributions, $257,379.
Purpose and activities: The foundation supports organizations involved with arts and culture, education, health, recreation, and human services.
Fields of interest: Arts and culture; Theater; Historical activities; Historic preservation; Education; Secondary education; Health; Public libraries; Sports and recreation; Baseball and softball; Human services; Youth services; Developmental disability services; Senior services.
Type of support: Annual campaigns; Capital campaigns; Capital and infrastructure; Equipment; Program development; Sponsorships.
Limitations: Applications accepted. Giving primarily in areas of company operations in Dedham, Needham, Norwood, Sharon, and Westwood, MA. No support for political or religious organizations. No grants to individuals.
Publications: Application guidelines.
Application information: Application form required.
   Initial approach: Request application form
   Deadline(s): Apr. 30 and Oct. 31

Board meeting date(s): May and Nov.
Final notification: June and Dec.
Trustees: Peter G. Brown; Judith G. Carver; Thomas J. Filbin; William G. Gothorpe; Robert B. Hanson; Juanita Allen Kingsley; Gerard R. Lavoie; Dean P. Plakias; Margot C. Pyle.
EIN: 043423462

4068
Felicia M. Delorenzo Scholarship Foundation, Inc.
c/o Nutter McClennen & Fish, LLP
P.O. Box 5140
Boston, MA   02205

Established in 2001 in Massachusetts.
Donor: Felicia DeLorenzo†.
Foundation type: Independent foundation.
Financial data (yr. ended 12/31/13): Assets, $8,047,814 (M); gifts received, $33,676; expenditures, $515,124; qualifying distributions, $390,387; giving activities include $322,427 for 55 grants (high: $22,000; low: $667).
Purpose and activities: Giving to provide scholarship assistance for post-secondary education to deserving high-school graduates who reside in Arlington, Massachusetts.
Fields of interest: Education; University education.
Type of support: Scholarships.
Limitations: Applications not accepted. No grants to individuals.
Application information: Unsolicited requests for funds not accepted.
Officers and Directors: Joann DeLorenzo Crimmings, Pres. and Director; John E. Fedele, Clerk and Director; James R. DeGiacomo, Treas. and Director.
EIN: 043557888

4069
The Devereaux Foundation
c/o Raphael and Raphael LLP
52 Church St.
Boston, MA   02216-5420

Established in 1988 in Massachusetts.
Donors: William Anderson Devereaux; Ann T. Devereaux.
Foundation type: Independent foundation.
Financial data (yr. ended 12/31/13): Assets, $789,686 (M); expenditures, $252,116; qualifying distributions, $240,035; giving activities include $239,000 for 22 grants (high: $100,000; low: $1,000).
Purpose and activities: Giving primarily for youth leadership and development programs and activities; support also for higher and other education.
Fields of interest: Education; Higher education; Child welfare; Youth organizing.
Type of support: Program development.
Limitations: Applications not accepted. Giving primarily in the Boston and North Shore, MA, area and PA. No grants to individuals or for capital campaigns or endowment funds.
Application information: Contributes only to pre-selected organizations.
   Board meeting date(s): Varies
Trustees: Ann Thompson Devereaux; William Anderson Devereaux.

Number of staff: None.
EIN: 046582339

4070
Donovan Family Foundation
86 Old Connecticut Path
Wayland, MA   01778-3302

Established in 2001 in Massachusetts.
Donors: Beverly A. Donovan; James R. Donovan; Donovan Charitable Lead Trust.
Foundation type: Independent foundation.
Financial data (yr. ended 12/31/13): Assets, $1,963,965 (M); gifts received, $111,000; expenditures, $319,354; qualifying distributions, $298,170; giving activities include $298,100 for 9 grants (high: $139,600; low: $3,000).
Fields of interest: Education; Hospital care; Cancers; Breast cancer; Catholicism; Child welfare; Youth services.
Limitations: Applications not accepted. Giving primarily in MA, with some giving in CT and NY. No grants to individuals.
Application information: Contributes only to pre-selected organizations.
Trustees: Beverly A. Donovan; James P. Donovan; James R. Donovan; Karen M. Donovan; Michael R. Donovan; Thidie Delaine Donovan.
EIN: 043584922

4071
Bertram A. and Ronald M. Druker Charitable Foundation
(formerly Druker Charitable Foundation)
c/o Goulston & Storrs
400 Atlantic Ave.
Boston, MA   02110-3331

Established in 1982 in Massachusetts.
Donors: Bertram A. Druker†; Ronald M. Druker.
Foundation type: Independent foundation.
Financial data (yr. ended 09/30/14): Assets, $12,081,939 (M); expenditures, $426,738; qualifying distributions, $375,948; giving activities include $345,000 for 5 grants (high: $200,000; low: $5,500).
Fields of interest: Arts and culture; Museums; Education; Hospital care.
Limitations: Applications not accepted. Giving primarily in the greater Boston, MA, area and in Lancaster, PA. No grants to individuals.
Application information: Contributes only to pre-selected organizations.
Trustees: Alan W. Rottenberg; Kimberly Druker Stockwell; Marvin Sparrow; Ronald M. Druker.
EIN: 042751060

4072
The Durant Family Foundation
c/o Nutter, McClennen & Fish, LLP
P.O. Box 51400
Boston, MA   02205-1400

Established in 1997 in Massachusetts.
Donor: Kingsley Durant.
Foundation type: Independent foundation.
Financial data (yr. ended 11/30/14): Assets, $3,762,740 (M); expenditures, $177,267; qualifying distributions, $175,535.

Fields of interest: Performing arts education; Education; Higher education; Medical education; Human services; Child welfare.
Limitations: Applications not accepted. Giving primarily in MA. No grants to individuals.
Application information: Contributes only to pre-selected organizations.
Trustees: John K. Dineen; Joan S. Durant; Kingsley Durant.
EIN: 043400633

4073
DWSS, Inc.
c/o Ballentine Partners LLC
230 3rd Ave., 5th Fl.
Waltham, MA   02451-7553

Established in 2006 in Massachusetts.
Donor: Louisa Putnam.
Foundation type: Independent foundation.
Financial data (yr. ended 12/31/13): Assets, $8,540,972 (M); expenditures, $476,403; qualifying distributions, $431,868; giving activities include $409,493 for 10 grants (high: $130,000; low: $5,000).
Fields of interest: Natural resources; Foundations.
Limitations: Applications not accepted. Giving in the U.S., with some emphasis on MA and Santa Fe, NM. No grants to individuals.
Application information: Contributes only to pre-selected organizations.
Officers and Directors: Louisa Putnam, Pres. and Secy. and Director; Rowan Finnegan, Treas. and Director.
EIN: 208104761

4074
Dwyer Foundation
9 Gina Way
Boxford, MA   01921-2732

Donors: William E. Dwyer III; Christine M. Dwyer.
Foundation type: Independent foundation.
Financial data (yr. ended 12/31/14): Assets, $3,294,013 (M); expenditures, $181,119; qualifying distributions, $159,925; giving activities include $159,925 for 34 grants (high: $43,200; low: $50).
Fields of interest: Education; Higher education; Human services; Youth services; Adult and child mentoring.
Limitations: Applications not accepted. Giving primarily in MA.
Application information: Contributes only to pre-selected organizations.
Trustees: Christine M. Dwyer; William E. Dwyer.
EIN: 274292722

4075
East Boston Savings Charitable Foundation Inc.
(formerly Meridian Charitable Foundation, Inc.)
c/o Kenneth Fisher
67 Prospect St.
Peabody, MA   01960-1604   (617) 567-1500
Contact: Deborah J. Jackson, Treas.
Additional tel.: (617) 567-1500; Main URL: http://www.ebsb.com
Grants List: http://ebsb.com/about-us/community/charitable-foundation/recipients.aspx

Established in 1998 in Massachusetts.
Donors: East Boston Savings Bank; Ralph R. Bagley, Esq.
Foundation type: Company-sponsored foundation.
Financial data (yr. ended 12/31/13): Assets, $6,812,814 (M); gifts received, $100,000; expenditures, $208,535; qualifying distributions, $208,535; giving activities include $208,500 for 49 grants (high: $5,000; low: $1,500).
Purpose and activities: The foundation supports camps and organizations involved with education, health, hunger, housing, human services, and community development.
Fields of interest: Education; Secondary education; Health; Hospice care; Community and economic development; Housing development; Camps; Human services; Food aid; Family services; Youth services; Homeless shelters; Developmental disability services; Homeless services; Senior services.
Type of support: Scholarships; Equipment; General support; Capital campaigns; Program development.
Limitations: Applications accepted. Giving limited to East Boston, Everett, Lynn, Lynnfield, Melrose, Peabody, Revere, Saugus, Wakefield, and Winthrop, MA, and other North Shore, MA, areas. No support for national organizations or city, town, state, or federal agencies. No grants to individuals or for annual campaigns or salaries.
Publications: Application guidelines; Grants list.
Application information: Grants range from $1,000 to $5,000. Proposal narratives should be no longer than 3 pages. If brochures or pamphlets are included with the application, the applicant must provide 10 copies of each. Support is limited to 1 contribution per organization during any given year. Application form required.
Initial approach: Download application form and mail proposal and form to foundation
Deadline(s): July
Final notification: 60 to 90 days
Officers and Directors: Richard J. Gavegnano, Pres.; Deborah J. Jackson, Treas.; Martha R. Bagley, Esq.; Paula M. Cotter; Grace Previte Magoon; Peter F. Scolaro; Ruth A. Sheets.
EIN: 043406328

4076
Easthampton Savings Foundation, Inc.
36 Main St.
Easthampton, MA   01027-2050   (413) 779-2296
Contact: Bozena C. Dabek, Treas.

Established in 1997 in Massachusetts.
Donors: Easthampton Savings Bank; ESB Securities Corp.
Foundation type: Company-sponsored foundation.
Financial data (yr. ended 12/31/13): Assets, $2,053,341 (M); gifts received, $117,663; expenditures, $226,705; qualifying distributions, $225,975; giving activities include $225,850 for 41 grants (high: $50,000; low: $1,000).
Purpose and activities: The foundation supports food banks and organizations involved with education, health, housing development, golf, and community economic development.
Fields of interest: Education; Higher education; Nonprofits; Health; Hospital care; Public libraries; Community and economic development; Housing development; Golf; Human services; Food banks; Youth services.
Type of support: General support; Continuing support; Annual campaigns; Capital campaigns;

Capital and infrastructure; Endowments; Program development; Sponsorships; Regranting.
Limitations: Applications accepted. Giving primarily in MA.
Application information: Application form required.
  Initial approach: Contact foundation for application form
  Deadline(s): None
Officers: Matthew Sosik, Pres.; Kenneth S. Cernak, Clerk; Bozena Dabek, Treas.
Directors: Peter Degrandpre; James G. Hayden; Anthony Villani.
EIN: 043371592

4077
Mary-Louise & Ruth N. Eddy Foundation
P.O. Box 55806
Boston, MA 02205-5806

Established in 1998 in Massachusetts.
Donors: Mary-Louise Eddy; Ruth N. Eddy†.
Foundation type: Independent foundation.
Financial data (yr. ended 12/31/13): Assets, $7,208,041 (M); expenditures, $390,359; qualifying distributions, $336,290; giving activities include $335,000 for 23 grants (high: $40,000; low: $2,500).
Fields of interest: Theater; Natural history museums; Historic preservation; Natural resources; Community and economic development; Christianity.
Type of support: General support.
Limitations: Applications not accepted. Giving primarily in MA. No grants to individuals.
Application information: Contributes only to pre-selected organizations.
Trustees: Sally Neese; Roger V. O'Day; Fiduciary Trust Co.
EIN: 222642870

4078
Edwards Scholarship Fund
89 South St., Ste. 603
Boston, MA 02111-2651 (617) 737-3400

Established in 1939 in Massachusetts.
Donor: Grace M. Edwards†.
Foundation type: Independent foundation.
Financial data (yr. ended 07/31/13): Assets, $8,598,329 (M); gifts received, $550; expenditures, $344,898; qualifying distributions, $294,930; giving activities include $206,250 for 97 grants to individuals (high: $5,000; low: $1,000).
Purpose and activities: Giving for scholarships to Boston, Massachusetts residents for higher education.
Fields of interest: Higher education.
Type of support: Student aid.
Limitations: Applications accepted. Giving limited to students residing in Boston, MA since the beginning of their junior year of high school.
Publications: Application guidelines.
Application information: Application form required.
  Initial approach: Letter requesting application
  Copies of proposal: 1
  Deadline(s): Mar. 1
  Board meeting date(s): Summer and winter
Trustees: Bernard Bonn III; Margaret Flanagan.
Number of staff: 1 part-time professional.
EIN: 046002496

4079
Chris & Jean Egan Foundation
116 Flanders Rd., Ste. 2000
Westborough, MA 01581-1072 (508) 898-3800

Established in 2004 in Massachusetts.
Donors: Donald Satterfield; Amb. Christopher F. Egan; Joe Zink; Richard Egan; Mike Brogan; Chris Choma; Antonio Frias; Brian Murphy; Kevin Giblin.
Foundation type: Independent foundation.
Financial data (yr. ended 12/31/14): Assets, $391,643; expenditures, $348,008; qualifying distributions, $348,008.
Fields of interest: Education; Christianity; Human services.
Type of support: General support.
Limitations: Applications accepted. Giving primarily in MA. No grants to individuals.
Application information: Application form required.
  Initial approach: Letter
  Deadline(s): None
Trustees: Amb. Christopher F. Egan; Jean Egan.
EIN: 721555517

4080
Dorothy Harrison Egan Foundation
c/o Gilmore, Rees & Carlson, P.C.
70 Walnut St.
Wellesley, MA 02481-2102
Application address: c/o Claire D. Graves, P.O. Box 3366, Nantucket, MA 02584-3366, tel.: (508) 228-9868

Established in 2004 in Massachusetts.
Donor: Dorothy Harrison Egan.
Foundation type: Independent foundation.
Financial data (yr. ended 09/30/13): Assets, $4,198,759 (M); gifts received, $2,000; expenditures, $333,223; qualifying distributions, $295,697; giving activities include $145,000 for 4 grants (high: $85,000; low: $5,000), and $123,727 for 25 grants to individuals (high: $10,000; low: $855).
Purpose and activities: Scholarship awards to qualified candidates who will be studying health care or any other related subjects in a college, medical school or institution.
Fields of interest: Education; Health; Human services.
Type of support: General support; Student aid.
Limitations: Applications accepted. Giving primarily in MA.
Application information: Application form required.
  Initial approach: Letter
  Deadline(s): Late winter, early spring
Trustees: Denis H. Gazaille; Claire Graves; William P. Hounhan; William J. Rees; Georgia A. Snell.
EIN: 571191002

4081
Elephant Rock Foundation Inc.
95 Hupi Rd.
P.O. Box 539
Monterey, MA 01245-9721
FAX: (413) 644-8940;
E-mail: marion.simon@no.mis.com

Established in 1998 in Massachusetts.
Donor: Leonard S. Simon.
Foundation type: Independent foundation.

Financial data (yr. ended 12/31/13): Assets, $3,068,460 (M); expenditures, $261,695; qualifying distributions, $239,340; giving activities include $233,700 for 25 grants (high: $50,700; low: $300).
Fields of interest: Arts and culture; Museums; Education; Health; Human services.
Limitations: Applications not accepted. Giving primarily in NY and MA. No grants to individuals.
Application information: Contributes only to pre-selected organizations.
Officers: Marion A. Simon, Pres.; Jeanine McAdam, Secy.; Andrew Simon, Treas.
Board Members: Patrice Battey-Simon; Miriam Goodman; Ethan Simon; Jonathan Simon.
EIN: 043451161

4082
Encourage, Inc.
c/o AccounTax Pros LLC
P.O. Box 675
Oxford, MA 01540

Established in 1986 in Florida.
Donors: Edward W. Poitras; Kay G. Poitras.
Foundation type: Independent foundation.
Financial data (yr. ended 12/31/13): Assets, $126,533 (M); gifts received, $450,000; expenditures, $458,634; qualifying distributions, $458,502; giving activities include $399,500 for 17 grants (high: $60,000; low: $500).
Fields of interest: Christianity; Protestantism.
Limitations: Applications not accepted. Giving primarily in CO, FL, IL, and PA. No grants to individuals.
Application information: Contributes only to pre-selected organizations.
Officer and Directors: Edward W. Poitras, Pres. and Co-Treas. and Director; Kay G. Poitras, V.P. and Co-Secy. and Director; Paula Miner, Co-Secy.-Treas.; Tim Boiling; David C. Bryan; Todd Hunter; George Comforted Keen; Thomas G. Riley; Barry Werner.
EIN: 592752833

4083
J. Irving & Jane L. England Charitable Trust
c/o F. Russell
370 Main St., Ste. 800
Worcester, MA 01608-1741 (508) 756-2423
Contact: Ann K. Molloy, Tr.

Established in 1997 in Massachusetts.
Foundation type: Independent foundation.
Financial data (yr. ended 12/31/13): Assets, $4,409,222 (M); expenditures, $241,889; qualifying distributions, $228,574; giving activities include $217,000 for 42 grants (high: $10,000; low: $1,500).
Purpose and activities: Giving primarily for health and human services.
Fields of interest: Arts and culture; Historical activities; Education; Health; Protestantism; Human services; Child welfare; Youth development.
Limitations: Applications accepted. Giving primarily in MA.
Application information: Application form required.
  Initial approach: Proposal
  Deadline(s): Dec. 1
Trustees: Ann K. Molloy; Francis J. Russell.
EIN: 046836265

4084

The Barbara Epstein Foundation Inc.
c/o Lewis Epstein
23 Joyce Rd.
Wayland, MA   01778-4515

Established in 2007 in New York.
Donor: Barbara Epstein†.
Foundation type: Independent foundation.
Financial data (yr. ended 12/31/13): Assets, $6,781,665 (M); expenditures, $350,776; qualifying distributions, $304,500; giving activities include $304,500 for 27 grants (high: $22,500; low: $1,000).
Fields of interest: Arts and culture; Diseases and conditions; Religion.
Limitations: Applications not accepted. No grants to individuals.
Application information: Contributes only to pre-selected organizations.
Officers: Lewis Epstein, Pres.; Jodi Epstein, Treas.
Director: Sidney D. Roseff.
EIN: 208355941

4085

Kahn Family Charitable Foundation
21 Peirce Rd.
Wellesley, MA   02481-1355   (781) 235-5415
Contact: Jordan A. Kahn, Tr.

Foundation type: Independent foundation.
Financial data (yr. ended 12/31/13): Assets, $1,752,563 (M); expenditures, $204,853; qualifying distributions, $194,128; giving activities include $192,985 for 22 grants (high: $50,000; low: $150).
Fields of interest: Judaism; Human services; Child welfare.
Limitations: Applications accepted. Giving primarily in MA.
Application information: Application form required.
  Initial approach: Letter
  Deadline(s): None
Trustees: Jordan A. Kahn; Kris D. Kahn; Lawrence M. Kahn; Susan R. Kahn; Toriano D. White.
EIN: 203946440

4086

The Fassino Foundation, Inc.
42 Eliot Hill Rd.
Natick, MA   01760-5534   (508) 653-4554
Contact: Edward G. Fassino, Pres.

Established in 1992 in Massachusetts.
Donor: Edward G. Fassino.
Foundation type: Independent foundation.
Financial data (yr. ended 12/31/12): Assets, $2,475,612 (M); expenditures, $248,605; qualifying distributions, $237,125; giving activities include $237,125 for grants.
Purpose and activities: Support for community-based organizations that aid women, children and the homeless; the foundation also grants college scholarships to specific high schools.
Fields of interest: Education; Hospital care; Family services; Child welfare; Females; Homeless people.
Type of support: General support; Student aid.
Limitations: Applications accepted. Giving primarily in the greater Boston, MA, area.
Application information: AGM Common Proposal Form accepted.

  Initial approach: Letter
  Deadline(s): None
Officers: Edward G. Fassino, Pres.; Alan L. Stanzler, Clerk; Lillian M. Fassino, Treas.
EIN: 043177633

4087

Aubert J. Fay Charitable Fund
P.O. Box 668
Lowell, MA   01852
Contact: Stephen L. Gervais, Tr.

Established in 1965 in Massachusetts.
Foundation type: Independent foundation.
Financial data (yr. ended 12/31/13): Assets, $5,166,485 (M); expenditures, $207,937; qualifying distributions, $199,082; giving activities include $172,000 for 48 grants (high: $15,000; low: $1,000).
Purpose and activities: Giving primarily for hospitals, and Roman Catholic education and organizations; funding also for children, youth and social services.
Fields of interest: Theater; Secondary education; Higher education; Hospital care; Housing development; Catholicism; Human services; Family services; Child welfare; Youth services.
Limitations: Applications accepted. Giving limited to Lowell, MA. No grants to individuals.
Application information: Application form required.
  Initial approach: Letter
  Deadline(s): None
Trustees: John F. Gervais; Stephen L. Gervais; Dexter Stevens.
EIN: 510203622

4088

FCTS Machine Technology Fund
15 Greenfield St.
Greenfield, MA   01301-1378
Contact: Steven Capshaw

Donors: William Dufraine; Applied Dynamics; Keo Mill Cutters; Judd Wire; Mayhew Steel Products; Hassay-Savage Broach Co.Inc.; Dumont Corp.; Bete Fog Nozzle; Steven Capshaw; Greenfield Savings Bank; Hillside Plastics; Valley Steel Stamp; Greenfield Cooperative Bank; Small Corp.
Foundation type: Independent foundation.
Financial data (yr. ended 08/31/14): Assets, $695 (M); gifts received, $77,973; expenditures, $214,751; qualifying distributions, $214,751; giving activities include $214,751 for 1 grant.
Fields of interest: Education.
Type of support: Equipment.
Limitations: Applications not accepted. Giving primarily in MA.
Application information: Unsolicited requests for funds not accepted.
Officers and Directors: William Dufraine, Pres. and Director; Daniel Graves, Clerk; Steven Capshaw, Treas. and Director; Jocelyn Croft; Doug Dziadzio; Richard Martin; Cody Sisson.
EIN: 460912507

4089

F. Felix Foundation
6 University Dr., Ste. 206
P.O. Box 240
Amherst, MA   01002-2265

Foundation type: Independent foundation.
Financial data (yr. ended 09/30/13): Assets, $4,175,722 (M); expenditures, $298,751; qualifying distributions, $261,529; giving activities include $182,755 for 25 grants (high: $50,000; low: $200).
Fields of interest: Foundations; Human services.
Limitations: Applications not accepted. Giving primarily in MA. No grants to individuals.
Application information: Contributes only to pre-selected organizations.
Officers and Directors: Robert Mazer, Pres. and Director; Magdalena Mazer, Secy.-Treas. and Director.
EIN: 043464255

4090

The Elizabeth T. Fessenden Charitable Foundation
c/o Northeast Investment Mgmt., Inc.
100 High St., Ste. 1000
Boston, MA   02110-1757

Established in 1995 in Massachusetts.
Foundation type: Independent foundation.
Financial data (yr. ended 07/31/13): Assets, $4,552,034 (M); expenditures, $397,277; qualifying distributions, $369,893; giving activities include $363,500 for 24 grants (high: $50,000; low: $1,000).
Purpose and activities: Giving primarily for environmental conservation and the arts.
Fields of interest: Arts and culture; Education; Natural resources; Botanical gardens; Health; Hospital care; Gardening.
Limitations: Applications not accepted. Giving primarily in MA. No grants to individuals.
Application information: Contributes only to pre-selected organizations.
Trustees: Thomas B. Moore; K. Davis Riemer; Louise C. Riemer.
EIN: 223432161

4091

Robert and Deborah First Family Foundation
22 Rockport Rd.
Weston, MA   02493-1428

Established in 1987 in Massachusetts.
Donors: Deborah First; Robert First.
Foundation type: Independent foundation.
Financial data (yr. ended 12/31/14): Assets, $2,470,154; expenditures, $221,263; qualifying distributions, $199,490.
Fields of interest: Arts and culture; Education; Diseases and conditions; Human services.
Type of support: Research.
Limitations: Applications not accepted. Giving primarily in MA. No grants to individuals.
Application information: Contributes only to pre-selected organizations.
Trustees: Deborah First; Robert First.
EIN: 222776314

4092

The Fleming Family Foundation
61 Meadowbrook Rd.
Weston, MA   02493-2407

Donor: Samuel C. Fleming.
Foundation type: Independent foundation.
Financial data (yr. ended 11/30/13): Assets, $4,713,980 (M); gifts received, $375,000; expenditures, $239,500; qualifying distributions, $212,500; giving activities include $212,500 for 7 grants (high: $76,500; low: $500).
Fields of interest: Education; Philanthropy; Diseases and conditions.
Limitations: Applications not accepted. Giving primarily in MA, NH and NY.
Application information: Unsolicited requests for funds not accepted.
Trustees: Nancy M. Fleming; Samuel C. Fleming.
EIN: 266201470

4093
Fletcher Family Charitable Foundation
22 Chestnut St.
Boston, MA   02108-3602

Established in 2003 in Massachusetts.
Donor: William C. Fletcher.
Foundation type: Independent foundation.
Financial data (yr. ended 10/31/13): Assets, $1,064,119 (M); gifts received, $201,268; expenditures, $380,935; qualifying distributions, $380,935; giving activities include $380,000 for 4 grants (high: $200,000; low: $5,000).
Fields of interest: Museums; Education.
Limitations: Applications not accepted. Giving primarily in MA, with some giving in ME. No grants to individuals.
Application information: Contributes only to pre-selected organizations.
Trustees: Elizabeth Elaine Fletcher Cooper; Joyce K. Fletcher; Pamela Fletcher; William C. Fletcher; William C. Fletcher III.
EIN: 256824995

4094
The Foundation for an American Vision
c/o Christina Dennis
29 Sawyer Rd.
Waltham, MA   02453-3467

Established in 1991 in Massachusetts.
Donors: Joseph Deitch; Robbie Lacritz.
Foundation type: Independent foundation.
Financial data (yr. ended 11/30/13): Assets, $4,356,700 (M); expenditures, $354,619; qualifying distributions, $338,905; giving activities include $338,905 for 25 grants (high: $250,000; low: $100).
Fields of interest: Early childhood education; Judaism; Human services.
Limitations: Applications not accepted. Giving primarily in MA. No grants to individuals.
Application information: Unsolicited requests for funds not accepted.
Trustee: Joseph Deitch.
EIN: 046694692

4095
Saint Francis Community Health Care, Inc.
c/o Stowe & Degon
95A Turnpike Rd.
Westborough, MA   01581-2878   (508) 755-8605
Contact: Michael D. Stowe, Vice-Chair.
Main URL: http://www.saintfrancischc.com

Foundation type: Independent foundation.
Financial data (yr. ended 12/31/13): Assets, $3,533,506 (M); gifts received, $2,811; expenditures, $191,762; qualifying distributions, $170,429; giving activities include $160,450 for 21 grants (high: $20,000; low: $1,000).
Fields of interest: Health; Catholicism; Human services.
Limitations: Applications accepted. Giving primarily in Worcester, MA.
Application information: See foundation web site for application guidelines. Application form required.
  Initial approach: Letter
  Deadline(s): Jan. 1 through Sept. 15
Officers: David Grenon, Chair. and Pres.; Michael D. Stowe, Vice-Chair. and V.P.; Lawrence Brodeur, Clerk; Jill Cosgrove Danksewicz, Treas.
Directors: Henry Braverman; Roger Dauphinais; Stephen Granger; Ralph D. Marois; Ronald Racine; E. Paul Tinsley.
EIN: 222755649

4096
The Churchill and Janet Franklin Family Foundation
40 Balls Hill Rd.
Concord, MA   01742-5301

Established in 2007 in Massachusetts.
Donors: Churchill G. Franklin; Janet H. Franklin.
Foundation type: Independent foundation.
Financial data (yr. ended 12/31/13): Assets, $973,510 (M); expenditures, $365,112; qualifying distributions, $357,611; giving activities include $350,500 for 13 grants (high: $175,000; low: $500).
Fields of interest: Museums; Higher education; Christianity.
Limitations: Applications not accepted. Giving primarily in MA, with emphasis on Concord, and Middlebury, VT. No grants to individuals.
Application information: Contributes only to pre-selected organizations.
Officer and Trustees: Churchill G. Franklin, Pres. and Trustee; Churchill H. Franklin; Janet H. Franklin; Katherine D. Franklin; Lindsey W. Franklin.
EIN: 261430103

4097
Fraser Family Foundation, Inc.
c/o Rinet Company, LLC
101 Federal St., 14th Fl.
Boston, MA   02110-1859

Established in 1988 in Massachusetts.
Donors: Richard M. Fraser; Richard M. & Helen T. Fraser Foundation.
Foundation type: Independent foundation.
Financial data (yr. ended 12/31/14): Assets, $601,463 (M); expenditures, $190,084; qualifying distributions, $178,425; giving activities include $178,425 for 32 grants (high: $30,000; low: $1,000).
Fields of interest: Arts and culture; Wildlife biodiversity; Animal welfare; Health; Protestantism.
Limitations: Applications not accepted. Giving primarily in FL, MA, and NY. No grants to individuals.
Application information: Contributes only to pre-selected organizations.

Officers: Richard M. Fraser, Pres.; Helen T. Fraser, Treas.
EIN: 043005593

4098
Friend Family Foundation
100 Federal St., 37th Fl.
Boston, MA   02110

Established in 2005 in Illinois.
Donor: Howard M. Friend.
Foundation type: Independent foundation.
Financial data (yr. ended 12/31/13): Assets, $441,010 (M); gifts received, $202,837; expenditures, $385,248; qualifying distributions, $383,478; giving activities include $382,893 for 34 grants (high: $139,500; low: $500).
Fields of interest: Judaism.
Type of support: General support.
Limitations: Applications not accepted. Giving primarily in IL. No grants to individuals.
Application information: Unsolicited requests for funds not accepted.
Officers and Directors: Howard M. Friend, Pres. and Secy. and Director; Loren Friend, V.P. and Treas. and Director; Barrie Friend; Charles Friend.
EIN: 342044584

4099
The Frisbie Family Foundation
c/o BGA Family Office
1 Marina Park Dr., Ste. 1150
Boston, MA   02210

Established in 2001 in Massachusetts.
Donor: Richard Frisbie.
Foundation type: Independent foundation.
Financial data (yr. ended 12/31/13): Assets, $6,277,093 (M); gifts received, $930,189; expenditures, $430,986; qualifying distributions, $362,825; giving activities include $362,825 for 25 grants (high: $250,000; low: $125).
Fields of interest: Arts and culture; Education; Hospital care; Diseases and conditions; Human services.
Limitations: Applications not accepted. Giving primarily in MA. No grants to individuals.
Application information: Contributes only to pre-selected organizations.
Trustee: Richard Frisbie.
EIN: 043558239

4100
Bulova Gale Foundation
c/o David L. Orenstein
75 North St.
Pittsfield, MA   01201

Established in 1997 in New York.
Foundation type: Independent foundation.
Financial data (yr. ended 12/31/12): Assets, $2,672,812 (M); expenditures, $162,921; qualifying distributions, $137,895; giving activities include $135,300 for 23 grants (high: $22,000; low: $300).
Purpose and activities: Giving primarily for education, health care, the arts, and Jewish organizations.
Fields of interest: Arts and culture; Education; Elementary and secondary education; Higher

education; Hospital care; Diseases and conditions; Judaism; Human services.
Limitations: Applications not accepted. No grants to individuals.
Application information: Unsolicited requests for funds not accepted.
Officers: Lynn Gale, Pres.; Peter Gale, V.P.; Barbara Maisel, Secy.-Treas.
EIN: 133866091

4101
Galileo Foundation for Community and Education, Inc.
c/o Hurwit & Associates
1150 Walnut St.
Newton, MA 02461-1229

Donor: Ruth & Amos Wilnai Foundation.
Foundation type: Independent foundation.
Financial data (yr. ended 12/31/13): Assets, $50,109 (M); gifts received, $220,340; expenditures, $183,755; qualifying distributions, $183,755; giving activities include $183,211 for 7 grants (high: $50,000; low: $14,900).
Fields of interest: Education; Health; Human services.
International interests: Israel.
Limitations: Applications not accepted. Giving primarily in Israel.
Application information: Unsolicited requests for funds not accepted.
Officers: Avigdor Willenz, Pres.; Adina Even-Zohar, Secy.
Trustee: Ben Zion Taube.
EIN: 043549606

4102
Frank Gerrity Charitable Trust
59 Cramond Rd.
Brookline, MA 02467-2830 (617) 916-0976

Established in 1968 in Massachusetts.
Donor: Ruth M. Gerrity.
Foundation type: Independent foundation.
Financial data (yr. ended 12/31/13): Assets, $5,125,131 (M); expenditures, $246,054; qualifying distributions, $196,479; giving activities include $196,479 for 62 grants (high: $50,000; low: $300).
Fields of interest: Arts and culture; Education; Higher education; Internal medicine; Human services; Child welfare.
Type of support: General support; Continuing support; Annual campaigns; Research.
Limitations: Applications accepted. Giving primarily in CT, MA, and ME. No grants to individuals.
Publications: Annual report.
Application information:
  Initial approach: Proposal
  Deadline(s): None
Trustees: James F. Gerrity III; Peter F. Gerrity; Ruth M. Gerrity.
EIN: 046195965

4103
The Gildea Family Foundation
36 Hubbard Rd.
Weston, MA 02493-2266
Contact: James Gildea

Foundation type: Independent foundation.
Financial data (yr. ended 04/30/13): Assets, $2,941,199 (M); expenditures, $341,781; qualifying distributions, $309,085; giving activities include $307,700 for 23 grants (high: $50,200; low: $250).
Fields of interest: Education; Housing development; Human services; Children; Homeless people.
Limitations: Applications not accepted. Giving primarily in MA.
Application information: Unsolicited requests for funds not accepted.
Trustees: Carol Gildea; James F. Gildea.
EIN: 800660362

4104
Gloria And Charles Clough Foundation
801 Main St.
Concord, MA 01742-4309

Donors: Charles I. Clough, Jr.; Gloria I. Clough.
Foundation type: Independent foundation.
Financial data (yr. ended 12/31/13): Assets, $9,130,650 (M); gifts received, $3,000,000; expenditures, $280,311; qualifying distributions, $278,000; giving activities include $275,000 for 4 grants (high: $100,000; low: $25,000).
Fields of interest: Education; Health; Human services.
Limitations: Applications not accepted. Giving primarily in MA.
Application information: Unsolicited requests for funds not accepted.
Trustees: Susan L. Brock; Kristin M. Canty; Charles I. Clough, Jr.; Charles I. Clough III; Gloria L. Clough; Kathryn A. Lorusso; Byron E. Woodman, Jr.
EIN: 276648632

4105
The William P. Goldman and Brothers Foundation, Inc.
47 Irving St.
Arlington, MA 02476 (781) 454-9000
Contact: Jeffrey Kraines, Pres.

Established in 1951 in New York.
Donors: William P. Goldman†; William P. Goldman and Brothers, Inc.; Byron Goldman.
Foundation type: Independent foundation.
Financial data (yr. ended 12/31/13): Assets, $7,493,335 (M); expenditures, $434,315; qualifying distributions, $396,179; giving activities include $396,179 for 108 grants (high: $28,500; low: $100).
Purpose and activities: Giving primarily to Jewish organizations.
Fields of interest: Education; Nonprofits; Hospital care; Diseases and conditions; Judaism; Human services.
Type of support: Research; Research and evaluation; Regranting.
Limitations: Applications accepted. Giving primarily in MA and NY.
Application information: Application form required.
  Initial approach: Proposal
  Deadline(s): None
Officers: Jeffrey L. Kraines, Pres.; Merrill M. Kraines, Treas.
EIN: 136163100

4106
The Jerry and Adi Greenberg Charitable Foundation
(formerly The Jerry A. Greenberg Charitable Foundation)
c/o Bowditch & Dewey
1 International Pl., 44th Fl.
Boston, MA 02110-2602 (617) 757-6517
Contact: Samuel C. Sichko, Tr.

Established in 1999 in Massachusetts.
Donors: Jerry A. Greenberg; The Jerry A. Greenberg Charitable Lead Trust-2000.
Foundation type: Independent foundation.
Financial data (yr. ended 12/31/13): Assets, $9,899,962 (M); expenditures, $378,231; qualifying distributions, $375,779; giving activities include $364,879 for 25 grants (high: $135,000; low: $500).
Fields of interest: Arts and culture; Theater; Education.
Limitations: Applications accepted. Giving primarily in CA. No grants to individuals.
Application information:
  Initial approach: Proposal
  Deadline(s): None
Trustees: Adi K. Greenberg; Jerry A. Greenberg; Marvin A. Greenberg; Samuel C. Sichko.
EIN: 043492171

4107
Griffin White Foundation Inc.
(formerly Griffin-White Home for Aged Men and Aged Couples, Inc.)
180 Merrimack St.
P.O. Box 6116
Haverhill, MA 01830-6128 (978) 372-1192

Foundation type: Independent foundation.
Financial data (yr. ended 12/31/13): Assets, $5,160,672 (M); expenditures, $175,508; qualifying distributions, $145,000; giving activities include $145,000 for 21 grants (high: $44,300; low: $645).
Purpose and activities: Giving primarily for organizations serving the aging.
Fields of interest: Housing development; Sports and recreation; Human services; Seniors.
Type of support: General support.
Limitations: Applications accepted. Giving limited to the greater Haverhill, MA, area. No grants to individuals.
Application information: Application form required.
  Initial approach: Letter
  Deadline(s): Aug. 31
Officers: James P. Cleary, Pres.; William J. Klueber, V.P.; Lucinda Nolet, Secy.; Thomas Faulkner, Sr., Treas.
Board Members: Melinda Barrett; Susan Cleary; Jefferson Davis; King Davis; Duncan C. Farmer; Thomas Faulkner, Jr.; Diane Galvin; Steven Jaskelevicus; David Shaw.
EIN: 042148009

4108
The Julia & Seymour Gross Foundation, Inc.
P.O. Box 506
Weston, MA 02493-0003

Donor: Inez Gross.

Foundation type: Independent foundation.
Financial data (yr. ended 06/30/14): Assets, $6,264,904 (M); expenditures, $482,603; qualifying distributions, $427,129; giving activities include $381,103 for 55 grants (high: $50,000; low: $250).
Fields of interest: Higher education; Medical education; Maternal and perinatal health; Human services.
International interests: Canada.
Type of support: General support.
Limitations: Applications not accepted. Giving primarily in CT, MA and NY, with some giving in Canada. No grants to individuals.
Application information: Contributes only to pre-selected organizations.
Officers and Directors: Jane Rogers Clark, MD, Pres. and Exec. Dir.; Clark Chessin Gertler, V.P.; Jonathan P. Gertler, MD, Secy.; Charles Garrison Gertler, Treas.
Board Members: William R. Gertler; Roger D. Kamm, Ph.D.
EIN: 136122092

4109
Guttag Family Foundation
273 Emerson Rd.
Lexington, MA   02420-1936   (212) 485-5500
Contact: John Guttag, Pres.

Established in 2007 in Delaware.
Donors: The Marjorie V. Guttag Trust; Guttag 2005 Annuity Trust A; Guttag 2005 Annuity Trust B; Guttag 2005 Annuity Trust C; Guttag 2005 Annuity Trust D; John Guttag.
Foundation type: Independent foundation.
Financial data (yr. ended 12/31/13): Assets, $5,646,221 (M); expenditures, $292,778; qualifying distributions, $266,765; giving activities include $258,800 for 30 grants (high: $63,000; low: $200).
Fields of interest: Higher education; Health; Hospital care; Females.
Limitations: Applications accepted. Giving primarily in MA and RI.
Application information:
Initial approach: Proposal
Deadline(s): None
Officer: John Guttag, Pres.
EIN: 208451379

4110
The Hagerty Family Foundation
c/o Thomas Hagerty
153 Brattle St.
Cambridge, MA   02138

Donors: Thomas M. Hagerty; Jeanne M. Hagerty.
Foundation type: Independent foundation.
Financial data (yr. ended 12/31/13): Assets, $1,736,455 (M); gifts received, $4,750; expenditures, $321,549; qualifying distributions, $315,300; giving activities include $314,800 for 19 grants (high: $50,000; low: $1,000).
Fields of interest: Art museums; University education; Diseases and conditions; Human services.
Limitations: Applications not accepted. Giving primarily in Boston, MA. No grants to individuals.
Application information: Unsolicited requests for funds not accepted.

Trustees: Jeanne M. Hagerty; Thomas M. Hagerty.
EIN: 200509132

4111
Jon L. Hagler Foundation
c/o Jon L. Hagler
2 Pleasant St.
Dover, MA   02030-2049

Established in 1984 in Massachusetts.
Donor: Jon L. Hagler.
Foundation type: Independent foundation.
Financial data (yr. ended 12/31/13): Assets, $5,213,698 (M); gifts received, $1,369,360; expenditures, $196,800; qualifying distributions, $193,150; giving activities include $193,150 for 31 grants (high: $150,000; low: $100).
Fields of interest: Education; Higher education; Foundations; Hospital care; Human services.
Limitations: Applications not accepted. Giving primarily in, but not limited to, MA and TX. No grants to individuals.
Application information: Contributes only to pre-selected organizations.
Trustee: Jon L. Hagler.
EIN: 222600563

4112
Charles S. & Carmen DeMora Hale Foundation
220 Boylston St., Ste. 1020
Boston, MA   02116-3949

Established in 1994 in California.
Foundation type: Independent foundation.
Financial data (yr. ended 06/30/13): Assets, $7,793,777 (M); expenditures, $463,947; qualifying distributions, $421,968; giving activities include $380,000 for 23 grants (high: $100,000; low: $1,700).
Fields of interest: Art museums; Historic preservation; Education; Hospital care; Specialty hospital care; Diseases and conditions; Cancers.
Type of support: Annual campaigns; Research.
Limitations: Applications not accepted. Giving primarily in MA. No grants to individuals.
Application information: Contributes only to pre-selected organizations.
Officers: Martin M. Hale, Pres.; Charles M. Hale, V.P.
EIN: 954480051

4113
The Martin and Deborah Hale Foundation
220 Boylston St., Ste. 1020
Boston, MA   02116-3949

Established in 1995 in Massachusetts.
Foundation type: Independent foundation.
Financial data (yr. ended 06/30/13): Assets, $4,651,393 (M); expenditures, $234,034; qualifying distributions, $209,274; giving activities include $184,550 for 33 grants (high: $45,000; low: $350).
Fields of interest: Performing arts; Art museums; Elementary and secondary education; Higher education; Student services; Protestantism; Child welfare.
Limitations: Applications not accepted. Giving primarily in MA. No grants to individuals.

Application information: Unsolicited requests for funds not accepted.
Trustee: Martin M. Hale.
EIN: 043294711

4114
Haley Family Foundation
c/o Steven and Kathleen Haley
148 Linden St., Ste. 303
Wellesley, MA   02482-7970

Established in 1998 in Massachusetts.
Donors: Steven Haley; Kathleen Powers Haley; Snows Hill, LLC.
Foundation type: Independent foundation.
Financial data (yr. ended 12/31/14): Assets, $15,903 (M); gifts received, $3,400; expenditures, $433,129; qualifying distributions, $418,600; giving activities include $417,400 for 5 grants (high: $250,000; low: $1,000).
Purpose and activities: Giving primarily for education and health.
Fields of interest: Performing arts; Elementary and secondary education; Higher education; Health; Diseases and conditions; Human services.
Type of support: Research.
Limitations: Applications not accepted. Giving primarily in MA. No grants to individuals.
Application information: Contributes only to pre-selected organizations.
Trustees: Kathleen Powers Haley; Steven Haley.
EIN: 043356222

4115
The Halfway Rock Foundation
c/o Eunice J. Panetta
33 Harbor St.
Manchester, MA   01944-1461

Established in 2000 in Massachusetts.
Donor: Eunice C. Johnson.
Foundation type: Independent foundation.
Financial data (yr. ended 06/30/13): Assets, $4,223,388 (M); expenditures, $529,882; qualifying distributions, $371,065; giving activities include $371,065 for 16 grants (high: $100,000; low: $500).
Fields of interest: Arts and culture; Education; Environment; Community and economic development.
Limitations: Applications not accepted. Giving primarily in MA. No grants to individuals.
Application information: Contributes only to pre-selected organizations.
Trustees: Eunice J. Panetta; Vincent J. Panetta.
EIN: 043542326

4116
Hampden Bank Charitable Foundation
P.O. Box 2048
Springfield, MA   01103-2048   (413) 452-5181
Contact: Robert M. Massey, Treas. and Dir.

Established in 2006 in Unspecified.
Donor: Hampden Bancorp.
Foundation type: Company-sponsored foundation.
Financial data (yr. ended 10/31/13): Assets, $5,350,112 (M); expenditures, $319,953; qualifying distributions, $317,936; giving activities

include $304,802 for 119 grants (high: $25,000; low: $100).

Purpose and activities: The foundation supports organizations involved with arts and culture, education, and human services.

Fields of interest: Arts and culture; Music; Orchestral music; Higher education; Human services; Child welfare; Developmental disability services; Senior services.

Type of support: General support; Continuing support; Program development.

Limitations: Applications accepted. Giving primarily in areas of company operations in the Springfield, MA, area. No grants to individuals.

Application information: Application form required.
  Initial approach: Contact foundation
  Deadline(s): None

Officers and Directors: Glenn S. Welch, Pres. and Director; Lynn S. Brunce, Secy.; Robert M. Massey, Treas. and Director; Anthony Caprio; James Shriver; Hector Toledo.

EIN: 331165388

4117

George Harrington Trust

c/o Choate Hall & Stewart LLP
2 International Pl.
Boston, MA 02110-4104   (617) 248-5028
Contact: John M. Cornish, Tr.

Established in 1936 in Massachusetts.

Donor: George Harrington†.

Foundation type: Independent foundation.

Financial data (yr. ended 08/31/13): Assets, $3,862,803 (M); expenditures, $230,003; qualifying distributions, $189,022; giving activities include $176,310 for 5 grants (high: $60,000; low: $16,310).

Fields of interest: Health; Diseases and conditions; Human services.

Type of support: Research.

Limitations: Applications accepted. Giving limited to MA. No grants to individuals.

Application information: Application form required.
  Initial approach: Completed application form
  Copies of proposal: 2
  Deadline(s): None
  Board meeting date(s): Mar., June, Sept., and Dec.

Trustees: John M. Cornish; William G. Cornish.

EIN: 046037725

4118

William H. Harris Foundation

19 Windemere Cir.
Braintree, MA 02184-4505

Donors: William H. Harris, MD; Johanna H. Harris.

Foundation type: Independent foundation.

Financial data (yr. ended 12/31/13): Assets, $8,328,873 (M); expenditures, $614,353; qualifying distributions, $467,815; giving activities include $435,565 for 23 grants (high: $250,000; low: $500).

Purpose and activities: Support for higher education, environmental sciences, and medical research, including orthopedic biomechanics and biomaterials research.

Fields of interest: Higher education; Natural resources; Domesticated animals; Orthopedics; Diseases and conditions.

Type of support: Research; Research and evaluation.

Limitations: Applications not accepted. Giving in the U.S., with some emphasis on PA. No grants to individuals.

Application information: Unsolicited requests for funds not accepted.

Trustees: Johanna H. Harris; William H. Harris, MD.

EIN: 046197960

4119

Charles E. Harwood Trust

309 Ipswich Rd.
Boxford, MA 01921-1505
Contact: Wendell P. Weyland
Application address: Kathy Adam, 2 Penny Ln., Peabody, MA 01960, tel.: (978) 887-0143

Established in 1992 in Massachusetts.

Donor: Charles E. Harwood†.

Foundation type: Independent foundation.

Financial data (yr. ended 06/30/13): Assets, $4,649,536 (M); expenditures, $250,384; qualifying distributions, $218,284; giving activities include $201,850 for 22 grants (high: $48,300; low: $500).

Fields of interest: Education; Elementary and secondary education; Hospital care; Human services.

Limitations: Applications accepted. Giving primarily in MA. No grants to individuals.

Application information: Application form required.
  Initial approach: Letter
  Deadline(s): None

Trustees: Kathy Adam; Wendell P. Weyland.

EIN: 046725545

4120

The Helen G. Hauben Foundation, Inc.

5 Apple Ridge Ln.
Littleton, MA 01460-2232

Established in 1999 in Massachusetts.

Foundation type: Independent foundation.

Financial data (yr. ended 06/30/13): Assets, $4,320,169 (M); expenditures, $212,959; qualifying distributions, $203,333; giving activities include $203,333 for 32 grants (high: $18,000; low: $1,000).

Fields of interest: Arts and culture; Performing arts; Performing arts education; Museums; Science museums; Higher education; Domesticated animals; Health; Diseases and conditions; Libraries; Radio; Television; Reproductive rights; Food banks.

Type of support: General support; Continuing support; Annual campaigns; Capital campaigns; Land acquisitions; Program development; Publications; Seed money; Curriculum development; Scholarships; Research.

Limitations: Applications not accepted. Giving primarily in MA. No grants to individuals.

Application information: Unsolicited requests for funds not accepted.
  Board meeting date(s): Mar.

Officer: Bruce M. Hauben, Pres.

Directors: Joyce Brinton; Craig Hauben; Jason Hauben; Michael Hauben.

EIN: 223658076

4121

The Hausman Family Charitable Trust

1 Avery St., Ste. 28D
Boston, MA 02111-1026

Established in 1987 in Massachusetts.

Donor: Jerry A. Hausman.

Foundation type: Independent foundation.

Financial data (yr. ended 12/31/13): Assets, $10,907,462 (M); expenditures, $385,120; qualifying distributions, $385,120.

Limitations: Applications not accepted. No grants to individuals.

Application information: Contributes only to pre-selected organizations.

Trustees: Jerry A. Hausman; Margaretta S. Hausman; Reed Shuldiner.

EIN: 222767736

4122

Haven Trust

50 Congress St., Rm. 800
Boston, MA 02109-4034   (617) 227-8660
Contact: George Lewis, Tr.

Established in 1960 in Massachusetts.

Donor: George Lewis.

Foundation type: Independent foundation.

Financial data (yr. ended 12/31/13): Assets, $175,944 (M); gifts received, $227,219; expenditures, $213,416; qualifying distributions, $208,067; giving activities include $204,975 for 112 grants (high: $50,000; low: $25).

Fields of interest: Arts and culture; Education; Health.

Type of support: Endowments.

Application information: Application form required.
  Initial approach: Proposal
  Deadline(s): None

Trustees: George Lewis; William N. Thorndike.

EIN: 046053996

4123

Hazard Family Foundation

23 Marlborough St.
Boston, MA 02116-2139

Established in 1996 in Massachusetts.

Donors: C. Michael Hazard; Susan G. Hazard; Hazard Limited Partnership.

Foundation type: Independent foundation.

Financial data (yr. ended 12/31/13): Assets, $6,830,581 (M); gifts received, $74,914; expenditures, $425,966; qualifying distributions, $378,495; giving activities include $377,000 for 54 grants (high: $100,000; low: $500).

Fields of interest: Visual arts; Education; Environment; Specialty hospital care.

Type of support: Annual campaigns; Capital campaigns; Land acquisitions.

Limitations: Applications not accepted. Giving primarily in MA and RI. No grants to individuals.

Application information: Unsolicited requests for funds not accepted.

Trustee: C. Michael Hazard.

EIN: 043338927

4124
Frank B. Hazard General Charity Fund
c/o U.S. Trust, Philanthropic Solutions
225 Franklin St., MA1-225-04-02
Boston, MA 02110-2801 8003577094
Contact: Emma Greene, Market Director
E-mail: ri.grantmaking@ustrust.com; Main
URL: http://www.bankofamerica.com/grantmaking

Foundation type: Independent foundation.
Financial data (yr. ended 12/31/14): Assets,
$5,238,544; expenditures, $258,622; qualifying
distributions, $217,428 and $0 for set-asides.
Purpose and activities: Giving primarily for human
services.
Fields of interest: Education; Nonprofits; Human
services; Family services; Child welfare; Women's
services; Low-income and poor people.
Type of support: General support; Endowments;
Regranting.
Limitations: Giving primarily in Providence, RI. No
grants to individuals.
Application information: Complete application
guidelines available on Fund web site.
  Initial approach: Online through Fund web site
  Deadline(s): Dec. 1
Trustee: Bank of America, N.A.
EIN: 056004659

4125
The Ulf B. and Elizabeth C. Heide Foundation Charitable Trust
c/o Frank P. Conrad
8 Cedar Rd.
Weston, MA 02493-2419

Established in 1991 in Massachusetts.
Donor: Ulf B. Heide.
Foundation type: Independent foundation.
Financial data (yr. ended 12/31/14): Assets,
$10,698,288 (M); expenditures, $440,470;
qualifying distributions, $347,990; giving activities
include $347,990 for 32 grants (high: $150,000;
low: $50).
Purpose and activities: Giving primarily for the arts,
particularly to an art museum; funding also for
education and human services.
Fields of interest: Orchestral music; Art museums;
Education; Higher education; Human services.
Limitations: Applications not accepted. Giving
primarily in MA. No grants to individuals.
Application information: Contributes only to
pre-selected organizations.
Trustees: Frank P. Conrad; Elizabeth C. Heide;
Elizabeth H. Heide; Ulf B. Heide.
EIN: 046665830

4126
Steven K. Helman Memorial Foundation
c/o Nutter McClennen & Fish, LLP
P.O. Box 51400
Boston, MA 02205-1400 6174392276
Application address: c/o Nutter, McClennen & Fish,
LLP, Attn.: Thomas P. Jalkut, 155 Seaport Blvd.,
Boston, MA 02110, tel.: (617) 439-2000

Established in 1990 in Massachusetts.
Donor: Irving J. Helman.
Foundation type: Independent foundation.

Financial data (yr. ended 01/31/15): Assets,
$336,954; expenditures, $197,411; qualifying
distributions, $191,271.
Fields of interest: Education; Higher education;
Undergraduate education; Hospice care; Cancers.
Application information: Application form required.
  Initial approach: Letter
  Deadline(s): None
Trustee: Thomas P. Jalkut.
EIN: 223106709

4127
Henderson Foundation
P.O. Box 420
Sudbury, MA 01776-0420 (978) 443-4646
Contact: Roberta Henderson, Tr.

Established in 1947 in Massachusetts.
Donors: Ernest Henderson†; George B.
Henderson†; J. Brooks Fenno†; Ernest Henderson
III.
Foundation type: Independent foundation.
Financial data (yr. ended 12/31/13): Assets,
$13,533,911 (M); expenditures, $669,912;
qualifying distributions, $406,359; giving activities
include $366,000 for 79 grants (high: $25,000;
low: $1,000).
Purpose and activities: Support for public policy
organizations in the fields of foreign policy, defense,
peace, and media issues, and higher and precollege
education; minor support for medical research.
Fields of interest: Arts and culture; Higher
education; Diseases and conditions; Public policy;
Human services.
Type of support: General support; Continuing
support; Research; Research and evaluation; Policy,
advocacy and systems reform.
Limitations: Applications accepted. Giving primarily
in Washington DC, MA, MD, NH and NY. No grants
to individuals, or for scholarships or fellowships.
Application information: Application form required.
  Initial approach: Letter
  Deadline(s): None
Trustees: Barclay Henderson; Roberta Henderson;
Augusta Petrone.
Number of staff: 1 part-time professional.
EIN: 046051095

4128
George B. Henderson Foundation
c/o Hemenway & Barnes, LLP
60 State St.
Boston, MA 02109
Contact: Gioia Perugini, Philanthropic Adv.
E-mail and tel. for Gioia Perugini:
gperugini@hembar.com; (617) 557-9777; Main
URL: http://thehendersonfoundation.com

Established in 1964 in Massachusetts.
Donor: George B. Henderson†.
Foundation type: Independent foundation.
Financial data (yr. ended 12/31/13): Assets,
$8,550,445 (M); expenditures, $389,852;
qualifying distributions, $306,482; giving activities
include $281,025 for 4 grants (high: $100,000;
low: $45,000).
Purpose and activities: Grants for enhancement of
the physical appearance of the city of Boston, MA.
Fields of interest: Historic preservation; Education;
Community and economic development;
Protestantism.

Type of support: Capital and infrastructure; Program
development.
Limitations: Applications accepted. Giving limited to
Boston, MA. No grants to individuals, or for
endowment funds, maintenance, operating budgets,
research, scholarships, fellowships, or general
purposes; no loans.
Publications: Application guidelines.
Application information: See foundation web site
for complete application guidelines and procedures.
Application form required.
  Initial approach: Submit proposal
  Copies of proposal: 9
  Deadline(s): See foundation web site for current
  deadlines
Trustees: Thomas E. Bator; Barclay C.S. Henderson;
Eric U. Henderson; John K. Herbert III.
EIN: 046089310

4129
The Hicks Family Charitable Foundation
c/o Day Pitney, LLP
1 International Pl.
Boston, MA 02110-2602
Contact: Jutta B. Hicks

Established in 2000 in Massachusetts.
Donor: Coleman S. Hicks.
Foundation type: Independent foundation.
Financial data (yr. ended 12/31/13): Assets,
$641,055 (M); expenditures, $150,970; qualifying
distributions, $149,800; giving activities include
$149,800 for 47 grants (high: $28,000; low: $300).
Fields of interest: Education; Human services.
Type of support: General support.
Limitations: Applications not accepted. Giving
primarily in MA, with emphasis on Boston. No grants
to individuals.
Application information: Contributes only to
pre-selected organizations.
Trustees: Jutta B. Hicks; Christian B. Hicks;
Darlington P. Hicks.
EIN: 043509776

4130
The Quaker Hill Foundation, Inc.
P.O. Box 111
North Andover, MA 01845-0111

Foundation type: Independent foundation.
Financial data (yr. ended 12/31/13): Assets,
$3,842,719 (M); expenditures, $234,195;
qualifying distributions, $189,626; giving activities
include $189,626 for 164 grants (high: $5,500;
low: $50).
Fields of interest: Community and economic
development; Religion; Human services.
Type of support: General support.
Limitations: Applications not accepted. Giving
primarily in MA, MN, NH, NY and PA.
Application information: Unsolicited requests for
funds not accepted.
Officers: Robert Wilcox, Chair.; Phebe Richards,
Secy.; Elizabeth Ducot, Treas.
Trustees: Andrew Currie; Daniel Miner; Mary
Stevens.
EIN: 273801257

4131
Hoffman Family Foundation
(formerly The John Ernest Hoffman Foundation)
c/o Stephen Moore & Roger Thomas, Loring,
Wolcott & Coolidge Office
230 Congress St., 12th Fl.
Boston, MA 02110-2409

Established in 1985 in Massachusetts.
Donor: Effe K.D. Hoffman†.
Foundation type: Independent foundation.
Financial data (yr. ended 12/31/13): Assets,
$3,698,243 (M); expenditures, $466,391;
qualifying distributions, $437,993; giving activities
include $431,500 for 41 grants (high: $70,000;
low: $1,000).
Fields of interest: Arts and culture; Higher
education; Human services.
Type of support: General support; Continuing
support; Annual campaigns; Capital campaigns;
Capital and infrastructure.
Limitations: Applications not accepted. Giving
primarily in NH. No grants to individuals.
Application information: Contributes only to
pre-selected organizations. Unsolicited requests for
funds not considered.
  Board meeting date(s): As needed
Trustees: John E. Hoffman, Jr.; Stephen A. Moore;
Roger M. Thomas.
EIN: 222677966

4132
Gisela B. Hogan Charitable Foundation
c/o Choate LLP
P.O. Box 961019
Boston, MA 02196-1019

Established in 1999 in Massachusetts.
Donor: Gisela B. Hogan.
Foundation type: Independent foundation.
Financial data (yr. ended 12/31/13): Assets,
$5,538,342 (M); expenditures, $371,511;
qualifying distributions, $310,279; giving activities
include $250,000 for 4 grants (high: $100,000;
low: $35,000).
Fields of interest: Christianity; Human services;
Females; Homeless people.
Type of support: General support.
Limitations: Applications not accepted. Giving
primarily in MA, NC and VA. No grants to individuals.
Application information: Contributes only to
pre-selected organizations.
Trustees: A. Silvana Giner; Jennifer C. Snyder.
EIN: 043484188

4133
The Honey Dew Family Foundation, Inc.
2 Taunton St., Ste. 261
Plainville, MA 02762 (508) 699-0079
E-mail: info@honeydewfamilyfoundation.org; Main
URL: http://www.honeydewfamilyfoundation.org
Facebook: https://www.facebook.com/pages/
Honey-Dew-Family-Foundation-Inc/
234823796534101?ref=ts&fref=ts
Grants List: http://
www.honeydewfamilyfoundation.org/
grant_recipients.html

Established in 2008 in Massachusetts.
Donors: Richard Bowen; Golf Tournament.
Foundation type: Independent foundation.

Financial data (yr. ended 06/30/14): Assets,
$12,178 (M); expenditures, $210,226; qualifying
distributions, $150,919; giving activities include
$150,919 for 36+ grants (high: $33,750).
Fields of interest: Human services.
Type of support: Student aid.
Limitations: Applications not accepted. Giving
primarily in MA.
Application information: Unsolicited requests for
funds not accepted.
Officers and Directors: Richard J. Bowen, Pres. and
Director; Kara J. Bowen, Clerk and Director; Amanda
J. Bowen; Stacy L. DeMaria; Jennifer A. Fellman;
Tracie L. Pond; Kelly A. Sofronas.
EIN: 261116810

4134
The Hopedale Foundation
43 Hope St.
Hopedale, MA 01747-0123
Application address: c/o Vincent J. Arone, Treas.,
P.O. Box 123, Hopedale, MA 01747, tel.: (508)
473-2871

Established in 1946 in Massachusetts.
Donors: Draper Corp.; Thomas H. West†; John D.
Gannett†; Richard B. Gannett†.
Foundation type: Independent foundation.
Financial data (yr. ended 10/31/14): Assets,
$10,938,614 (M); expenditures, $487,119;
qualifying distributions, $487,119; giving activities
include $264,500 for 14 grants (high: $100,000;
low: $500), $20,000 for 6 grants to individuals
(high: $5,000; low: $2,500), and $140,107 for
loans to individuals.
Purpose and activities: Emphasis on area
community funds and hospitals; support also for
museums and other cultural programs, health
agencies, youth services, and higher education;
student loans and scholarships are limited to
graduates of Hopedale High School in MA. New
grants only to organizations having direct impact on
the local community.
Fields of interest: Arts and culture; Museums;
Education; Higher education; Nonprofits; Health;
Hospital care; Social sciences; Child welfare.
Type of support: Student aid; Loans to individuals;
General support; Annual campaigns; Capital
campaigns; Regranting.
Limitations: Applications accepted. Giving primarily
in MA, with emphasis on Hopedale and Milford. No
grants for endowment funds.
Application information:
  Initial approach: Letter
  Copies of proposal: 1
  Deadline(s): June 1 for student loans; no set
    deadline for grants
  Board meeting date(s): Feb., June, and Oct.
Officers and Trustees: William B. Gannett, Chair.
and Trustee; Peter S. Ellis, Vice-Chair. and Trustee;
W. Gregory Burrill, Secy. and Trustee; Vincent J.
Arone, Treas. and Trustee; Steven G. Ellis; Alfred H.
Sparling, Jr.; Thomas H. West, Jr.
Number of staff: 1 part-time professional.
EIN: 046044779

4135
Henry Hornblower Fund, Inc.
P.O. Box 961269
Boston, MA 02196-1269 6175893286

Established in 1945 in Massachusetts.
Donor: Hornblower & Weeks-Lothrop Withington.
Foundation type: Operating foundation.
Financial data (yr. ended 12/31/14): Assets,
$7,888,499; expenditures, $443,672; qualifying
distributions, $357,150.
Purpose and activities: Emphasis on higher and
secondary education, hospitals, and cultural
programs; support also for needy individuals
presently or formerly employed by Hornblower &
Weeks.
Fields of interest: Arts and culture; Visual arts;
Museums; Secondary education; Higher education;
Land resources; Hospital care; Libraries;
Low-income and poor people.
Type of support: General support; Capital
campaigns; Endowments; Emergency funds;
Scholarships.
Limitations: Applications accepted. Giving primarily
in southeastern MA. No grants to individuals
directly; no loans.
Application information:
  Initial approach: Letter
  Copies of proposal: 1
  Deadline(s): Nov. 30
  Board meeting date(s): Mar., June, Sept., and
    Dec.
  Final notification: Dec. 31
Officer and Directors: Nathan N. Withington, Pres.
and Director; Orin H. Meyer.
Number of staff: 1 full-time support.
EIN: 237425285

4136
The Mabel A. Horne Fund
c/o U.S. Trust, Bank of America, N.A.
225 Franklin St., 4th Fl., MA1-225-04-02
Boston, MA 02110-2801 (866) 778-6859
Contact: Phung Pham, V.P.
E-mail: ma.grantmaking@ustrust.com; Main
URL: https://www.bankofamerica.com/
philanthropic/grantmaking.go

Established in 1964 in Massachusetts.
Donor: Mabel A. Horne†.
Foundation type: Independent foundation.
Financial data (yr. ended 09/30/13): Assets,
$6,468,769 (M); expenditures, $314,963;
qualifying distributions, $275,091; giving activities
include $238,000 for 24 grants (high: $15,000;
low: $1,000).
Purpose and activities: The Trust was established
in 1957 to support and promote quality educational,
human services, and health care programming for
underserved populations.
Fields of interest: Education; Health; Human
services.
Type of support: General support.
Limitations: Giving limited to MA. No support for
national organizations. No grants to individuals, or
for conferences, film production, scholarships,
travel, book publication, or research projects not
under the aegis of a recognized organization; no
loans.
Publications: Application guidelines.
Application information: Online application and
complete application guidelines available on Fund
web site.
  Initial approach: Online via Fund web site
  Deadline(s): Please consult Fund web site
Trustee: Bank of America, N.A.
EIN: 046089241

4137
Howard Home for Aged Men in the City of Brockton

71 Legion Pkwy., 3rd Fl.
Brockton, MA 02301-7225 (508) 584-4088
Contact: John F. Creedon, Pres.

Established in 1942 in Massachusetts.
Donors: Horace Howard†; Daniel W. Field Trust.
Foundation type: Operating foundation.
Financial data (yr. ended 03/31/13): Assets, $4,654,119 (M); expenditures, $330,927; qualifying distributions, $330,927; giving activities include $235,000 for 16 grants (high: $25,000; low: $5,000).
Purpose and activities: Giving for elderly situations (60 years or older).
Fields of interest: Human services.
Limitations: Applications accepted. Giving limited to within 35 miles of Boston, MA. No grants to individuals, salaries, or capital building projects.
Application information: Application form required.
  Initial approach: Letter
  Deadline(s): None
Officers: John F. Creedon, Pres.; Vaughn Boyajian, Clerk; Eugene Marrow, Treas.
EIN: 042103796

4138
Hurston Family Foundation, Inc.

29 Shaw Dr.
Wayland, MA 01778-3213

Established in 2007 in Maryland.
Foundation type: Independent foundation.
Financial data (yr. ended 12/31/12): Assets, $3,232,716 (M); expenditures, $168,219; qualifying distributions, $141,200; giving activities include $141,200 for 7 grants (high: $50,000; low: $1,200).
Fields of interest: Philanthropy; Religion; Human rights.
Limitations: Applications not accepted. Giving primarily in MA.
Application information: Unsolicited requests for funds not accepted.
Officers: Ronald O. Hurston, Pres.; Alan P. Kenney, Secy.
EIN: 260581018

4139
Hyde Charitable Foundation

54 Eastford Rd.
Southbridge, MA 01550-1875 (508) 764-4344
Contact: Richard B. Hardy, Tr.
Main URL: http://www.hydetools.com

Established in 1982 in Massachusetts.
Donors: Hyde Manufacturing Co.; Dexter-Russell, Inc.; Russell Harrington Cutlery, Inc.
Foundation type: Company-sponsored foundation.
Financial data (yr. ended 12/31/13): Assets, $4,150,656 (M); expenditures, $229,853; qualifying distributions, $214,580; giving activities include $209,500 for 36 grants (high: $38,000; low: $500).
Purpose and activities: The foundation supports organizations involved with education, human services, and community development.

Fields of interest: Education; Higher education; Hospital care; Community and economic development; Human services.
Type of support: General support; Annual campaigns; Capital campaigns; Capital and infrastructure; Equipment; Endowments; Emergency funds.
Limitations: Applications accepted. Giving primarily in Worcester County, MA.
Application information: Application form required.
  Initial approach: Letter
  Deadline(s): None
Trustees: Ronald P. Carlson; Richard R. Clemence; Richard B. Hardy; Susan H. Tretter.
EIN: 042752893

4140
Kathleen & Ronald J. Jackson Foundation

35 Paine Ave.
P.O. Box 170
Pride's Crossing, MA 01965-0170

Established in 1994 in Massachusetts.
Donors: Kathleen Jackson; Ronald J. Jackson.
Foundation type: Independent foundation.
Financial data (yr. ended 12/31/14): Assets, $4,132,899; gifts received, $1,000; expenditures, $213,120; qualifying distributions, $207,035.
Fields of interest: Arts and culture; Museums; Education; Hospital care; Libraries.
Limitations: Applications not accepted. No grants to individuals.
Application information: Unsolicited requests for funds not accepted.
Trustees: Kathleen Jackson; Ronald J. Jackson; Susan L. Jackson; Nancy A. Rushton.
EIN: 046762777

4141
The Janet Malser Humanities Trust

P.O. Box 458
Webster, MA 01570-0458
Main URL: http://www.janetmalsertrust.org

Donor: Janet E. Malser†.
Foundation type: Independent foundation.
Financial data (yr. ended 12/31/13): Assets, $4,265,262 (M); expenditures, $232,697; qualifying distributions, $232,697; giving activities include $192,901 for 27 grants (high: $40,250; low: $250).
Fields of interest: Arts and culture; Historic preservation; Education.
Limitations: Applications accepted. Giving primarily in Dudley, Oxford, and Webster, MA.
Application information: See Trust web site for application guidelines.
  Deadline(s): See Trust web site for deadline
Trustees: Kenneth J. Deary; Debra Horan; Keith Kirkland; Paul J. Macek; Margaret Pedersen; Ann L. Rada; Thomas G. Smith.
EIN: 264203944

4142
The Joe Lewis Jefferson Foundation Inc.

(formerly The D'Egville Foundation, Inc.)
c/o Steven A. Branson, Esq.
515 Providence Hwy., Ste. 103
Dedham, MA 02026-6817

Established in 1991 in Massachusetts.
Donor: Mark S. Ptashne.
Foundation type: Independent foundation.
Financial data (yr. ended 12/31/13): Assets, $2,252,320 (M); expenditures, $174,278; qualifying distributions, $166,275; giving activities include $166,275 for 25 grants (high: $50,000; low: $250).
Fields of interest: Arts and culture; Music; Orchestral music; Higher education; Natural resources; Foundations; Hospital care.
Limitations: Applications not accepted. Giving primarily in Boston, MA and NY. No grants to individuals.
Application information: Contributes only to pre-selected organizations.
Officers: Mark S. Ptashne, Pres. and Treas.; Steven A. Branson, Clerk.
Directors: James Doon; Lucy H. Gordon.
EIN: 223151628

4143
Esther B. Kahn Charitable Foundation

c/o Choate Hall & Stewart LLP
Two International Pl.
Boston, MA 02110 (617) 248-4814
Contact: John M. Cornish, Tr.
E-mail: estherbkahn@choate.com; Main
URL: http://www.estherbkahn.org
Grants List: http://www.estherbkahn.org/pdfs/2009_2010_SampleRecipients.pdf

Established in 1998 in Massachusetts.
Donor: Esther B. Kahn†.
Foundation type: Independent foundation.
Financial data (yr. ended 05/31/13): Assets, $4,499,403 (M); expenditures, $264,020; qualifying distributions, $225,893; giving activities include $190,000 for 24 grants (high: $12,500; low: $5,000).
Purpose and activities: The foundation supports and funds innovative approaches to education, the arts, and medical research.
Fields of interest: Theater; Opera; Performing arts education; Education; Specialty hospital care; Diseases and conditions.
Type of support: Annual campaigns; Capital campaigns; Convening; Continuing support; Curriculum development; Endowments; Research; Equipment; Fellowships; Internships; Program development; Program evaluations; Publications; Scholarships; Seed money; Technical assistance.
Limitations: Applications accepted. Giving on a national basis. No support for private foundations. No grants to individuals.
Publications: Application guidelines; Informational brochure (including application guidelines).
Application information: Preliminary application through foundation web site; final application by invitation only. See foundation web site for application policies, guidelines and application form. Application form required.
  Initial approach: E-mail
  Copies of proposal: 4
  Deadline(s): June 30 and Dec. 30
  Board meeting date(s): Jan. and July.
  Final notification: 3 weeks following board meeting
Trustees: John M. Cornish; Richard J. Eckstein; Robert A. Russo.
Number of staff: 2 part-time professional.
EIN: 046869254

4144
Peter H. Kamin Family Foundation
(formerly Peter & Loren Kamin Family Foundation)
40 Briarcliff Rd.
Longmeadow, MA   01106-1325

Established in 1998 in Massachusetts.
Donor: Peter H. Kamin.
Foundation type: Independent foundation.
Financial data (yr. ended 12/31/13): Assets,
$1,877,712 (M); expenditures, $158,840;
qualifying distributions, $156,520; giving activities
include $156,450 for 10 grants (high: $140,000;
low: $100).
Fields of interest: Education; Higher education;
Diseases and conditions; Religion.
Limitations: Applications not accepted. Giving
primarily in MA. No grants to individuals.
Application information: Unsolicited requests for
funds not accepted.
Trustees: Harriet Gilman; Peter H. Kamin.
EIN: 043398587

4145
Abraham Kaplan Charitable Foundation
c/o Donald Kaplan
P.O. Box 603
Marblehead, MA   01945   (781) 639-1910
Contact: Donald M. Kaplan, Mgr. and Tr.

Foundation type: Independent foundation.
Financial data (yr. ended 12/31/14): Assets,
$3,198,231 (M); expenditures, $257,317;
qualifying distributions, $145,475; giving activities
include $141,350 for 22 grants (high: $70,000;
low: $100).
Fields of interest: Arts and culture; Education;
Religion.
Limitations: Applications accepted. Giving on a
national basis, with emphasis on the East Coast.
Application information: Application form required.
  Initial approach: Letter
  Deadline(s): None
Officer and Trustees: Donald M. Kaplan, Mgr. and
Trustee; Shelley Driesman; Jonathan Kaplan.
EIN: 046067737

4146
Elia & Fannie Karas Foundation, Inc.
455 Dorchester Ave.
South Boston, MA   02127-2707   6172688800
Application address: c/o Leo Karas, Pres., 500
Atlantic Ave., Unit 21B, Boston, MA 02210,
tel.: (857) 277-0388

Donors: Karas & Karas Glass Co., Inc.; Leo Karas.
Foundation type: Independent foundation.
Financial data (yr. ended 08/31/14): Assets,
$402,417; gifts received, $300,000; expenditures,
$180,354; qualifying distributions, $177,690.
Fields of interest: Education; Health; Judaism.
Type of support: General support.
Limitations: Applications accepted. Giving primarily
in MA and NY. No grants to individuals.
Application information:
  Initial approach: Proposal
  Deadline(s): None
Officers: Leo Karas, Pres.; Joseph Karas, Clerk;
Barbara Karas, Treas.
EIN: 046074427

4147
Kelleher Family Charitable Trust
47 Crooked Ln.
Duxbury, MA   02332-3903
Contact: Richard M. Kelleher

Established in 1997 in Arizona.
Donors: Richard M. Kelleher; Nancy S. Kelleher.
Foundation type: Independent foundation.
Financial data (yr. ended 01/31/15): Assets,
$494,660 (M); gifts received, $223,774;
expenditures, $270,198; qualifying distributions,
$265,414; giving activities include $265,414 for 27
grants (high: $64,684; low: $490).
Fields of interest: Hospital care; Cancers;
Community and economic development;
Christianity; Youth services; Homeless shelters.
Type of support: Research.
Limitations: Applications not accepted. Giving
primarily in MA. No grants to individuals.
Application information: Unsolicited requests for
funds not accepted.
Trustees: M. Kristen Kelleher Hatten; Caroline F.
Kelleher; Nancy S. Kelleher; Patrick Kelleher;
Richard M. Kelleher; Elizabeth S. Sells.
EIN: 860874077

4148
The Kelsey Trust
99 Trapelo Rd.
Lincoln, MA   01773-2107

Established in 1988 in Massachusetts.
Donor: Sally Patrick Johnson.
Foundation type: Independent foundation.
Financial data (yr. ended 06/30/13): Assets,
$4,148,280 (M); expenditures, $221,545;
qualifying distributions, $196,500; giving activities
include $196,500 for 20 grants (high: $20,000;
low: $2,500).
Purpose and activities: Primary areas of interest
include the environment, children and families,
education, and health.
Fields of interest: Education; Child educational
development; Vocational education; Basic and
remedial instruction; Reading promotion;
Environment; Natural resources; Health; Family
planning; Nutrition; Housing development; Family
services; Child development; Youth services;
Children and youth; Infants and toddlers; Children;
Adolescents; Seniors; Single parents; Immigrants
and migrants; Homeless people; Low-income and
poor people.
Type of support: General support; Program-related
investments; Matching grants; Continuing support;
Capital campaigns; Land acquisitions; Emergency
funds; Publications; Seed money; Scholarships;
Technical assistance; Program evaluations; Policy,
advocacy and systems reform.
Limitations: Applications not accepted. Giving
limited to the Lake Champlain Drainage Basin. No
support for religious or political organizations. No
grants to individuals.
Application information: Unsolicited requests for
funds not accepted.
  Board meeting date(s): June and Dec.
Trustees: Paula D. Johnson; Sally P. Johnson;
Stephen P. Johnson.
Number of staff: None.
EIN: 046609917

4149
J. Henry Kendall Trust
c/o Enterprise Bank & Trust Co.
222 Merrimack St.
Lowell, MA   01852

Foundation type: Independent foundation.
Financial data (yr. ended 12/31/13): Assets,
$2,536,384 (M); expenditures, $154,145;
qualifying distributions, $154,145; giving activities
include $102,500 for 2 grants (high: $68,333; low:
$34,167), and $20,500 for 9 grants to individuals
(high: $4,300; low: $400).
Fields of interest: Education; Religion; Human
services.
Type of support: Grants to individuals.
Limitations: Applications not accepted. Giving
primarily in MA.
Application information: Unsolicited requests for
funds not accepted.
Trustee: Enterprise Bank & Trust Co.
EIN: 046035506

4150
Kenwood Foundation
45 School St., 5th Fl.
Boston, MA   02108-3204

Established in 1960 in Massachusetts.
Donors: Edith LaCroix Dabney; Fremont Street
Foundation, Inc.; Charles P. Knowles; Robert M.
Knowles; James T. Knowles; Jean L. Knowles; John
H. Knowles, Jr.; Edith K. Williams; Thomas M.
Williams; Jean Knowles-Hedlund; Jean Knowles
Hedlund; John H Knowles.
Foundation type: Independent foundation.
Financial data (yr. ended 12/31/13): Assets,
$366,429 (M); gifts received, $192,965;
expenditures, $213,747; qualifying distributions,
$194,089; giving activities include $193,965 for 86
grants (high: $30,000; low: $100).
Fields of interest: Arts and culture; Science
museums; Education; Higher education; Nonprofits;
Health; Hospital care; Diseases and conditions;
Communication media; Human services; Child
welfare.
Type of support: General support; Regranting.
Limitations: Applications not accepted. Giving
primarily in MA. No grants to individuals.
Application information: Contributes only to
pre-selected organizations.
Trustees: Edith LaCroix Dabney; Jean
Knowles-Hedlund; James T. Knowles; John H.
Knowles, Jr.; Robert M. Knowles; Theodore E. Ober;
Edith K. Williams; Thomas M. Williams.
EIN: 046012784

4151
Kershaw Foundation Charitable Trust
84 Beacon St.
Boston, MA   02108-3421   (617) 227-9600
Contact: Thomas A. Kershaw, Tr.

Established in 1993 in Massachusetts.
Donor: Thomas A. Kershaw.
Foundation type: Independent foundation.
Financial data (yr. ended 12/31/13): Assets,
$73,501 (M); gifts received, $79,397;
expenditures, $157,420; qualifying distributions,
$156,125; giving activities include $156,125 for 32
grants (high: $20,000; low: $100).

Fields of interest: Education; Higher education; Business education; Hospital care; Sports and recreation; Human services.
Limitations: Applications accepted. Giving primarily in MA. No grants to individuals.
Application information: Application form required.
Initial approach: Letter
Deadline(s): None
Trustees: John F. Bradley; Doris Gupa; Raymond Gupa; Thomas A. Kershaw.
EIN: 046744975

4152
Michael R. Kidder Family Foundation
(formerly Michael R. Kidder 1996 Charitable Trust)
c/o Family Office Mgmt. Services Inc.
18 Commerce Way, Ste. 4250
Woburn, MA 01801-1099

Established in 1996 in Massachusetts.
Donor: Michael R. Kidder.
Foundation type: Independent foundation.
Financial data (yr. ended 08/31/13): Assets, $10,202,263 (M); expenditures, $311,824; qualifying distributions, $307,750; giving activities include $300,000 for 2 grants (high: $200,000; low: $100,000).
Fields of interest: Foundations; Hospital care; Agricultural education; Human services.
Type of support: Individual development.
Limitations: Applications not accepted. Giving primarily in Boston and Martha's Vineyard, MA; some giving also in Keene, NH. No grants to individuals.
Application information: Contributes only to pre-selected organizations.
Trustee: Michael R. Kidder.
EIN: 046824225

4153
Oliver Killam Private Foundation Trust
c/o Welch & Muzio
27 Congress St., Ste. 512
Salem, MA 01970-5574

Donor: Oliver P. Killam†.
Foundation type: Independent foundation.
Financial data (yr. ended 12/31/13): Assets, $12,751,653 (M); expenditures, $339,398; qualifying distributions, $225,285.
Purpose and activities: Giving primarily for scholarships to Marblehead High School graduates.
Fields of interest: Education.
Type of support: General support; Student aid.
Limitations: Applications not accepted. Giving primarily in Marblehead, MA.
Application information: Unsolicited requests for funds not accepted.
Trustees: Robert Welch; Scott MacAllister.
EIN: 050566794

4154
Killian Family Foundation
(also known as Killian Family Foundation Charity)
c/o Raymond L. Killian, Sullivan & Worcester LLP
1 Post Office Sq.
Boston, MA 02109

Established in 2006 in Massachusetts.
Donors: Raymond L. Killian; Helen C. Killian.

Foundation type: Independent foundation.
Financial data (yr. ended 12/31/14): Assets, $1,340,407; gifts received, $2,556; expenditures, $311,176; qualifying distributions, $298,125.
Fields of interest: Arts and culture; Education; Elementary and secondary education; Housing development; Sports and recreation.
Limitations: Applications not accepted. Giving primarily in MA; funding also in FL. No grants to individuals.
Application information: Unsolicited requests for funds not accepted.
Trustees: Helen C. Killian; Raymond L. Killian.
EIN: 208039724

4155
Moses Kimball Fund
(also known as The Moses Kimball Fund for the Promotion of Good Citizenship)
(formerly Helen F. Kimball Trust)
c/o Loring, Wolcott and Coolidge
230 Congress St.
Boston, MA 02110-2409 (617) 523-6531
Contact: Susan Harrington, Grant Admin.
E-mail: moseskimballfund@lwcotrust.com; *Main URL:* http://www.moseskimballfund.org

Established in 1925 in Massachusetts.
Foundation type: Independent foundation.
Financial data (yr. ended 05/31/14): Assets, $4,229,030 (M); expenditures, $197,663; qualifying distributions, $169,158; giving activities include $153,000 for 37 grants (high: $14,000; low: $2,000).
Purpose and activities: The trustees emphasize grants to organizations which either provide jobs to minorities and disadvantaged members of the Greater Boston Community or links between educational institutions and needy members of the adjacent communities.
Fields of interest: Education; Employment; Human services; Family services; Youth organizing; Children and youth; Ethnic and racial groups; Low-income and poor people.
Type of support: Pro bono consulting services.
Limitations: Applications accepted. Giving primarily in MA.
Application information: See foundation's web site for application guidelines. Application form required.
Initial approach: Letter
Deadline(s): June 1
Trustees: C-F David Boit; Charles K. Cummings III; Paul Parravano.
EIN: 046061028

4156
King Spruce Company
50 Congress St., Ste. 410
Boston, MA 02109-4060

Established in 1952 in Maine.
Donors: M. Millicent Clapp; Eugene H. Clapp II; Maud M. Clapp.
Foundation type: Independent foundation.
Financial data (yr. ended 05/31/14): Assets, $6,041,108 (M); expenditures, $337,537; qualifying distributions, $279,000; giving activities include $279,000 for 77 grants (high: $33,000; low: $500).
Purpose and activities: Giving primarily for the arts, education, and hospitals.

Fields of interest: Arts and culture; Education; Higher education; Forest preservation; Hospital care; Protestantism; Human services; Family services; Child welfare.
Type of support: Capital campaigns; Endowments; Scholarships.
Limitations: Applications not accepted. Giving primarily in MA. No grants to individuals.
Application information: Contributes only to pre-selected organizations.
Officers and Trustees: Meredith P. Clapp, Pres. and Trustee; Marjorie G. Clapp, V.P. and Trustee; Thomas E. Needham, Clerk and Trustee; Eugene H. Clapp III, Treas. and Trustee.
EIN: 016009168

4157
The Kneisel Foundation, Inc.
c/o Glovsky & Glovsky
8 Washington St.
Beverly, MA 01915-5820

Donors: William J. Kneisel; Anne H. Kneisel.
Foundation type: Independent foundation.
Financial data (yr. ended 12/31/13): Assets, $3,974,301 (M); expenditures, $312,243; qualifying distributions, $239,000; giving activities include $239,000 for 78 grants (high: $50,000; low: $100).
Fields of interest: Elementary and secondary education; Higher education; Hospital care; Human services.
Limitations: Applications not accepted. Giving primarily in CT, MA, and NH. No grants to individuals.
Application information: Contributes only to pre-selected organizations.
Officers and Directors: William J. Kneisel, Pres. and Treas. and Director; Anne Hooper Kneisel, V.P. and Director; Anthony P. Fusco, Clerk; William Parsons, Jr.; Paula A. Ryan.
EIN: 043136120

4158
The Koha Family Foundation
c/o Valdur Koha
87 Hancock St.
Lexington, MA 02420-3422

Established in 2000 in Massachusetts.
Donor: Valdur Koha.
Foundation type: Independent foundation.
Financial data (yr. ended 12/31/13): Assets, $537,078 (M); expenditures, $182,018; qualifying distributions, $155,000; giving activities include $155,000 for 1 grant.
Fields of interest: Christianity.
Limitations: Applications not accepted. Giving primarily in MA. No grants to individuals.
Application information: Unsolicited requests for funds not accepted.
Trustees: Irene M. Koha; Valdur Koha; David M. Malutinok.
EIN: 043499731

4159
Florence & Richard Koplow Charitable Foundation
405 Waltham St., Ste. 115
Lexington, MA 02421-7934
Contact: Florence Koplow

Established in 1998 in Massachusetts.
Donors: Florence Koplow; Richard A. Koplow.
Foundation type: Independent foundation.
Financial data (yr. ended 12/31/14): Assets, $6,676,884 (M); expenditures, $370,795; qualifying distributions, $304,359; giving activities include $304,359 for 65 grants (high: $45,304; low: $12).
Fields of interest: Education; Medical education; Public health; Community and economic development; Youth development.
Limitations: Applications not accepted. Giving primarily in MA. No grants to individuals.
Application information: Contributes only to pre-selected organizations.
Trustee: Florence Koplow.
EIN: 046862775

4160
Krieger Charitable Trust
63 Beethoven Ave.
Waban, MA 02468-1732 (617) 467-5643
Contact: Roger M. Klein, Tr.
E-mail: rogerklein2000@yahoo.com

Established in 1986 in New Jersey.
Foundation type: Independent foundation.
Financial data (yr. ended 12/31/13): Assets, $10,931,503 (M); expenditures, $388,950; qualifying distributions, $388,950; giving activities include $375,537 for 32 grants (high: $100,000; low: $250).
Purpose and activities: Giving primarily to Jewish organizations, including Jewish education.
Fields of interest: Higher education; Nonprofits; Judaism; Human services.
Type of support: General support; Continuing support; Annual campaigns; Regranting; Capital campaigns; Endowments; Scholarships.
Limitations: Applications accepted. Giving primarily in northern NJ. No grants to individuals; no loans.
Application information: Application form required.
Initial approach: Proposal
Deadline(s): None
Trustees: Herbert C. Klein; Roger M. Klein.
EIN: 226374448

4161
Krupp Family Foundation
1 Beacon St., Ste. 1500
Boston, MA 02108-3116
FAX: (617) 556-1472;
E-mail: kruppfamilyfoundation@berkshire-group.com
; Main URL: http://kruppfamilyfoundation.org

Established in 2005 in Massachusetts.
Donor: George Krupp.
Foundation type: Independent foundation.
Financial data (yr. ended 12/31/14): Assets, $3,152,590 (M); gifts received, $304,625; expenditures, $298,591; qualifying distributions, $265,500; giving activities include $635,500 for 15 grants (high: $115,000; low: $2,500).
Purpose and activities: The mission of the foundation is to contribute to the common good of the Boston community through efforts that advance the arts, foster cultural expression, and improve, strengthen, and transform childrens futures. In addition, the foundation is dedicated to Jewish continuity, day school education, and local programs

that encourage Jewish identity and enrich the lives of disadvantaged Jews in the Boston community..
Fields of interest: Arts and culture; Education; Judaism; Human services; Jewish people.
Limitations: Applications not accepted. Giving primarily in the greater Boston, MA metropolitan area.
Application information: Unsolicited requests for funds not accepted.
Trustees: George Krupp; Lizbeth Krupp; Lawrence I. Silverstein.
EIN: 043812871

4162
The Kurian Foundation Trust
43 Delaney St.
Stow, MA 01775-1063

Established in 2005 in Massachusetts.
Donors: Thampy Kurian; HXI, LLC; Renaissance Electronics Corp.; Kurian Limited Partnership.
Foundation type: Independent foundation.
Financial data (yr. ended 09/30/13): Assets, $3,222,050 (M); gifts received, $2,849,155; expenditures, $177,528; qualifying distributions, $177,421; giving activities include $177,421 for 15 grants (high: $100,000; low: $100).
Fields of interest: Education; Health; Religion.
Limitations: Applications not accepted. Giving primarily in MA. No grants to individuals.
Application information: Unsolicited requests for funds not accepted.
Trustees: Molly Kurian; Thampy Kurian.
EIN: 161744447

4163
The Ladd Family Foundation
125 Claybrook Rd.
Dover, MA 02030-2116

Established in 1996 in Massachusetts.
Donors: Anne K. Ladd; Edward H. Ladd; Berthe K. Ladd.
Foundation type: Independent foundation.
Financial data (yr. ended 06/30/13): Assets, $4,270,914 (M); expenditures, $214,525; qualifying distributions, $198,822; giving activities include $195,500 for 13 grants (high: $30,000; low: $5,000).
Purpose and activities: Giving primarily for conservation.
Fields of interest: Education; Natural resources; Land resources; Foundations; Human services; Family services.
Limitations: Applications not accepted. No grants to individuals.
Application information: Unsolicited requests for funds not accepted.
Trustees: Leonard R. Carlman; Anne K. Ladd; Berthe K. Ladd; Edward H. Ladd; Edward L. Ladd; Laura Hewitt Ladd.
EIN: 043335235

4164
The Lalor Foundation, Inc.
c/o GMA Foundations
77 Summer St., 8th Fl.
Boston, MA 02110-1006 (617) 391-3088
Contact: Hannah Blaisdell

FAX: (617) 426-7087;
E-mail: hblaisdell@gmafoundations.com; Additional e-mail: fellowshipmanager@gmafoundations.com;
Main URL: http://www.lalorfound.org

Established in 1935 in Delaware.
Donor: Willard A. Lalor†.
Foundation type: Independent foundation.
Financial data (yr. ended 09/30/13): Assets, $14,285,790 (M); expenditures, $560,775; qualifying distributions, $478,919; giving activities include $416,500 for 21 grants (high: $47,000; low: $5,000).
Purpose and activities: The foundation awards fellowships to institutions for basic postdoctoral research in mammalian reproductive biology as related to the regulation of fertility.
Fields of interest: Family planning.
Type of support: Program development; Fellowships.
Limitations: Applications accepted. Giving on a national and international basis. No support for private organizations. No grants to individuals directly, or for operating budgets, capital or endowment funds, continuing support, annual campaigns, seed money, emergency funds, deficit financing, or matching gifts; no loans.
Publications: Application guidelines; Grants list.
Application information: Full proposals are by invitation only, upon review of initial concept paper. Only online applications are accepted. Application form required.
Initial approach: Submit concept paper through foundation web site
Copies of proposal: 1
Deadline(s): May 1 and Nov. 1
Board meeting date(s): June and Dec.
Final notification: Within 6-8 weeks for concept paper
Officers: Cynthia B. Patterson, Pres.; Lalor Burdick, Secy.-Treas.
Trustees: Andrew G. Braun; Christopher Burdick; Carol Chandler; Sally H. Zeckhauser.
Number of staff: None.
EIN: 516000153

4165
The Peter and Deborah Lamm Foundation
(formerly Peter Lamm Foundation)
c/o R. Bradford Malt, Ropes Gray LLP
800 Boylston St.
Boston, MA 02199-3600

Established in 1997 in Massachusetts.
Donor: Peter D Lamm.
Foundation type: Independent foundation.
Financial data (yr. ended 12/31/14): Assets, $414,861 (M); expenditures, $161,250; qualifying distributions, $154,614; giving activities include $150,450 for 42 grants (high: $40,000; low: $200).
Purpose and activities: Giving primarily for health organizations, human services, and the arts.
Fields of interest: Arts and culture; Education; Hospital care; Diseases and conditions; Judaism; Human rights; Human services; Housing services; Children.
Limitations: Applications not accepted. Giving primarily in Boston, MA, and New York, NY. No grants to individuals.
Application information: Contributes only to pre-selected organizations.

Trustees: Deborah Lamm; Peter D Lamm; R. Bradford Malt.
EIN: 043406251

4166
Langer Family Charitable Foundation
118 Huntington Ave., Apt. 2004
Boston, MA 02116-5777

Established in 1999 in Massachusetts.
Foundation type: Independent foundation.
Financial data (yr. ended 12/31/13): Assets, $129,285 (M); expenditures, $257,880; qualifying distributions, $250,000; giving activities include $250,000 for 1 grant.
Fields of interest: Health.
Limitations: Applications not accepted. No grants to individuals.
Application information: Unsolicited requests for funds not accepted.
Trustees: Molly A. Langer Gutcher; Carol B. Langer; Kurt W. Langer; Todd H. Langer.
EIN: 043492111

4167
The Melampy Lawrence Charitable Trust
1024 Main St.
Dunstable, MA 01827-1119

Donor: Patrick Melampy.
Foundation type: Independent foundation.
Financial data (yr. ended 12/31/13): Assets, $21,345,000 (M); gifts received, $19,962,402; expenditures, $736,473; qualifying distributions, $285,000; giving activities include $285,000 for 1 grant.
Fields of interest: University education.
Limitations: Applications not accepted. Giving primarily in MA.
Application information: Unsolicited requests for funds not accepted.
Trustees: Patrick Melampy; Priscilla Lawrence.
EIN: 387082935

4168
The Lawry Family Foundation
370 Concord Rd.
Weston, MA 02493-1313

Donors: Seth W. Lawry; Cynthia C. Lawry.
Foundation type: Independent foundation.
Financial data (yr. ended 12/31/13): Assets, $1,008,651 (M); expenditures, $154,648; qualifying distributions, $153,000; giving activities include $153,000 for 9 grants (high: $50,000; low: $3,000).
Fields of interest: Education; University education; Environment; Religion.
Limitations: Applications not accepted. Giving primarily in MA and ME.
Application information: Unsolicited requests for funds not accepted.
Trustees: Cynthia C. Lawry; Seth W. Lawry.
EIN: 464560816

4169
Learning by Giving Foundation Inc.
292 Newbury St., Ste. 335
Boston, MA 02115-2801 (650) 318-1091
E-mail: info@learningbygivingfoundation.org; Main URL: http://www.learningbygivingfoundation.org
Facebook: https://www.facebook.com/learningbygivingfoundation?fref=ts
Google Plus: https://plus.google.com/+LearningbygivingfoundationOrg/posts
Instagram: https://instagram.com/learngive
LinkedIn: http://www.linkedin.com/company/3037922?trk=tyah
Twitter: https://twitter.com/learngive
YouTube: https://www.youtube.com/channel/UC1dcJTrsjzE30Q8LmXamLOg

Donors: Doris Buffett; Kristen E. Williams.
Foundation type: Independent foundation.
Financial data (yr. ended 06/30/13): Assets, $5,001,510 (M); gifts received, $3,718,557; expenditures, $614,061; qualifying distributions, $315,000; giving activities include $315,000 for 33 grants (high: $20,000; low: $500).
Fields of interest: Education.
Limitations: Applications not accepted. Giving primarily in MA and NY.
Application information: Unsolicited requests for funds not accepted.
Officer: Louise Sawyer, Mgr.
Directors: Doris Buffett; Howard W. Buffett; Margaret Johnson; Alex Rozek; Mimi Rozek.
EIN: 452324555

4170
Leatherwood Foundation
100 Federal St., 37th Fl.
Boston, MA 02110-1802

Established in 2001 in Colorado.
Donor: Sarah R. Wagner.
Foundation type: Independent foundation.
Financial data (yr. ended 12/31/14): Assets, $3,777,257 (M); gifts received, $48,462; expenditures, $188,928; qualifying distributions, $163,405; giving activities include $158,500 for 28 grants (high: $15,000; low: $1,000).
Fields of interest: Natural resources; Sexual assault victim services; Human services.
Limitations: Applications not accepted. Giving primarily in CO. No grants to individuals.
Application information: Contributes only to pre-selected organizations.
Officers: Margaret Firth Waldon, Pres.; Colin E. Waldon, Treas.
EIN: 841592470

4171
Ledgeways Charitable Trust
c/o Daniel Carbonneau Castle Rock Adv.
200 Claredon St., 35th Fl.
Boston, MA 02116

Established in 2005 in Massachusetts.
Donors: Terrie F. Bloom; Bradley M. Bloom.
Foundation type: Independent foundation.
Financial data (yr. ended 12/31/14): Assets, $5,743,228 (M); gifts received, $2,130; expenditures, $288,728; qualifying distributions, $250,250.
Fields of interest: Arts and culture; Diseases and conditions; Agriculture.

Limitations: Applications not accepted. Giving primarily in MA. No grants to individuals.
Application information: Unsolicited requests for funds not accepted.
Trustees: Bradley M. Bloom; Eric N. Bloom; Matthew R. Bloom; Terrie F. Bloom; Jessica A. Bloom Galen.
EIN: 866341052

4172
Levangie Family Charitable Foundation
120 Commonwealth Ave., Ste. 4
Boston, MA 02116-2916 (617) 248-6690
Contact: Daniel J. Levangie, Tr.

Donors: Daniel J. Levangie; Joan Levangie.
Foundation type: Independent foundation.
Financial data (yr. ended 12/31/13): Assets, $2,817,274 (M); gifts received, $3,584; expenditures, $204,185; qualifying distributions, $162,035; giving activities include $150,000 for 2 grants (high: $125,000; low: $25,000).
Fields of interest: Education.
Type of support: General support.
Limitations: Applications accepted. Giving primarily in MA.
Application information: Application form required.
Initial approach: Letter
Deadline(s): None
Trustees: Aaron J. Levangie; Allison M. Levangie; Daniel J. Levangie; Joan Levangie.
EIN: 261619430

4173
The John Levy and Gail Rothenberg Family Foundation
c/o Feldberg Offices
P.O. Box 9175
Framingham, MA 01701-9175

Established in 1993 in Massachusetts.
Donors: John Levy; Gail Rothenberg.
Foundation type: Independent foundation.
Financial data (yr. ended 12/31/13): Assets, $4,280,965 (M); expenditures, $186,295; qualifying distributions, $184,385; giving activities include $184,350 for 29 grants (high: $30,000; low: $250).
Fields of interest: Health; Judaism; Human services.
Limitations: Applications not accepted. No grants to individuals.
Application information: Contributes only to pre-selected organizations.
Trustees: John Levy; Gail Rothenberg.
EIN: 043216914

4174
Shirley & Milton Levy Family Charitable Trust
P.O. Box 9175
Framingham, MA 01701-9175

Established in 1989 in Massachusetts.
Donor: Milton Levy.
Foundation type: Independent foundation.
Financial data (yr. ended 12/31/13): Assets, $6,079,657 (M); expenditures, $205,943; qualifying distributions, $205,216; giving activities include $205,181 for 37 grants (high: $70,181; low: $1,000).

Purpose and activities: Giving primarily for education and Jewish organizations.
Fields of interest: Higher education; Nonprofits; Diseases and conditions; Judaism; Human services.
Type of support: Regranting.
Limitations: Applications not accepted. No grants to individuals.
Application information: Unsolicited requests for funds not accepted.
Trustees: John F. Levy; Shirley Levy; Steven Levy.
EIN: 226480716

4175
George D. & Karen S. Levy Family Foundation
(formerly George & Karen Levy Private Foundation)
24 Carisbrooke Rd.
Wellesley Hills, MA 02481-1418 (781) 237-4445
Contact: Karen S. Levy, Mgr.

Established in 1995 in Massachusetts.
Donor: Karen S. Levy.
Foundation type: Independent foundation.
Financial data (yr. ended 12/31/12): Assets, $0 (M); expenditures, $244,507; qualifying distributions, $243,668; giving activities include $243,668 for 8 grants (high: $195,668; low: $500).
Fields of interest: Arts and culture; Education; Human services.
Type of support: General support.
Limitations: Applications accepted. Giving primarily in MA. No grants to individuals.
Application information:
Initial approach: Contact foundation
Deadline(s): None
Officer: Karen S. Levy, Mgr.
EIN: 046789959

4176
Margaret Stewart Lindsay Foundation of 1989
P.O. Box 55806
Boston, MA 02205-5806

Donors: Edwin B. Lindsay; Margaret S. Lindsay; Elizabeth S. Lindsay; E.L. Corbett Trust.
Foundation type: Independent foundation.
Financial data (yr. ended 12/31/13): Assets, $4,360,666 (M); gifts received, $5,145; expenditures, $436,830; qualifying distributions, $386,830; giving activities include $385,000 for 6 grants (high: $200,000; low: $10,000).
Fields of interest: Arts and culture; Education; Human services.
Limitations: Applications not accepted. Giving primarily in MA. No grants to individuals.
Application information: Contributes only to pre-selected organizations.
Trustees: Kathleen M. McCarthy; J. Brian Potts; Fiduciary Trust Co.
EIN: 043382858

4177
John and Sonia Lingos Family Foundation
32 Jacqueline Cir.
West Yarmouth, MA 02673-8343

Established in 1991 in Massachusetts.
Donors: John W. Lingos†; Sonia Tasha Lingos†.

Foundation type: Independent foundation.
Financial data (yr. ended 06/30/13): Assets, $5,659,603 (M); expenditures, $255,020; qualifying distributions, $246,250; giving activities include $246,250 for 33 grants (high: $75,000; low: $500).
Fields of interest: Art museums; Education; Higher education; Wildlife biodiversity; Public libraries; Christianity; Winter sports.
Type of support: General support; Capital and infrastructure; Scholarships.
Limitations: Applications not accepted. Giving primarily in MA. No grants to individuals.
Publications: Annual report.
Application information: Contributes only to pre-selected organizations.
Officers and Directors: Tania Lingos Webb, Pres. and Director; Tamara Lingos-Utley, Clerk and Treas. and Director; Sonia Tasha Lingos; Thalia I. Lingos.
Number of staff: 1 full-time professional.
EIN: 043134266

4178
Liswhit Foundation
200 Lexington St.
Weston, MA 02493-2146
Application address: c/o Charlotte D'Arcy Donaldson, Tr., P.O. Box 215, Weston, MA 02483, tel.: (508) 459-8037

Foundation type: Independent foundation.
Financial data (yr. ended 12/31/14): Assets, $4,884,632; expenditures, $328,638; qualifying distributions, $296,995.
Fields of interest: Arts and culture; Education; Human services.
Limitations: Applications accepted. Giving primarily in MA.
Application information: Application form required.
Initial approach: Completed application form
Deadline(s): None
Trustee: Charlotte D'Arcy Donaldson.
EIN: 273988759

4179
Longtine Charitable Foundation Trust 2001
263 Hammond St.
Chestnut Hill, MA 02467-3950

Established in 2001 in Massachusetts.
Donor: Janina Longtine.
Foundation type: Independent foundation.
Financial data (yr. ended 12/31/13): Assets, $2,870,922 (M); expenditures, $169,835; giving activities include $161,000 for 9 grants (high: $50,000; low: $1,000).
Fields of interest: Arts and culture; Education; Higher education; Maternal and perinatal health.
Limitations: Applications not accepted. Giving primarily in Boston, MA. No grants to individuals.
Application information: Contributes only to pre-selected organizations.
Trustee: Janina Longtine.
Number of staff: None.
EIN: 316655887

4180
The Lost and Foundation, Inc.
(formerly The O. & C. Curme Family Foundation)
314 Commonwealth Ave., Unit 1
Boston, MA 02115

Established in 2000 in Massachusetts.
Donors: Oliver D. Curme; Cynthia K. Curme.
Foundation type: Independent foundation.
Financial data (yr. ended 12/31/13): Assets, $2,794,924 (M); gifts received, $826,140; expenditures, $304,982; qualifying distributions, $286,500; giving activities include $286,500 for 11 grants (high: $236,600; low: $1,000).
Fields of interest: Music; Orchestral music; Education; Catholicism; Human services.
Limitations: Applications not accepted. Giving primarily in MA. No grants to individuals.
Application information: Contributes only to pre-selected organizations.
Officers: Cynthia K. Curme, Pres. and Clerk; Oliver D. Curme, Treas.
EIN: 043527006

4181
M & J Family Foundation
98 Arnold Rd.
Pelham, MA 01002-9791 (413) 256-4530
Contact: Jane Giat, Pres. & Dir.

Established in 1991 in New York.
Donor: The Kleinman Foundation.
Foundation type: Independent foundation.
Financial data (yr. ended 10/31/12): Assets, $0 (M); expenditures, $302,171; qualifying distributions, $301,551; giving activities include $296,389 for 1 grant.
Fields of interest: Human services.
Limitations: Applications accepted. Giving primarily in NY and OH. No grants to individuals.
Application information: Application form required.
Initial approach: Letter
Deadline(s): None
Officer and Directors: Jane Giat, Pres. and Director; Judith Hanlon; Joan Laser.
EIN: 113044190

4182
The Nicholas and Marion Madonna Foundation
886 Main St.
Osterville, MA 02655-2013

Established in 2007 in Massachusetts.
Donor: Robert P. Madonna.
Foundation type: Operating foundation.
Financial data (yr. ended 12/31/13): Assets, $4,156,084 (M); gifts received, $17,414; expenditures, $275,226; qualifying distributions, $251,035; giving activities include $251,000 for 6 grants (high: $200,000; low: $1,000).
Fields of interest: Education.
Limitations: Applications not accepted. Giving primarily in MA. No grants to individuals.
Application information: Contributes only to pre-selected organizations.
Trustee: Robert P. Madonna.
EIN: 510645638

4183
George W.P. Magee Trust
c/o U.S. Trust, Bank of America, N.A.
225 Franklin St., MA1-225-04-02
Boston, MA 02110
Contact: Augusta Haydock, Sr. V.P.
E-mail: augusta.k.haydock@ustrust.com; Main
URL: https://www.bankofamerica.com/
philanthropic/grantmaking.go

Foundation type: Independent foundation.
Financial data (yr. ended 09/30/14): Assets,
$7,746,058 (M); expenditures, $458,828;
qualifying distributions, $384,146; giving activities
include $329,700 for 10 grants (high: $50,000;
low: $17,300).
Purpose and activities: Supports the councils of the
Boy Scouts of America that are located in
Massachusetts.
Fields of interest: Scouting programs.
Limitations: Giving primarily in MA.
Application information: Complete application
guidelines available on Trust web site.
  Deadline(s): Sept. 15
Trustee: Bank of America, N.A.
EIN: 046011097

4184
**The Joan and Leo Mahoney Family
Foundation**
250 Westview Rd.
Lowell, MA 01851-3436

Established in 1999 in Massachusetts.
Donors: Leo D. Mahoney†; Eastern Minerals Inc.
Foundation type: Independent foundation.
Financial data (yr. ended 12/31/13): Assets,
$2,559,019 (M); gifts received, $300,000;
expenditures, $406,355; qualifying distributions,
$1,773,295; giving activities include $385,000 for
12 grants (high: $50,000; low: $5,000).
Fields of interest: Education.
Type of support: Capital campaigns.
Limitations: Applications not accepted. Giving
primarily in CT and MA. No grants to individuals.
Application information: Contributes only to
pre-selected organizations.
Trustees: Meghan L. Mahoney; Patrick L. Mahoney;
Shelagh E. Mahoney.
EIN: 043474541

4185
Isabelle Makepeace Charitable Trust
P.O. Box 1330
Hyannis, MA 02601-1330

Established in 1989 in Massachusetts.
Foundation type: Independent foundation.
Financial data (yr. ended 12/31/13): Assets,
$8,336,310 (M); expenditures, $441,412;
qualifying distributions, $375,987; giving activities
include $375,987 for 7 grants (high: $93,997; low:
$18,799).
Fields of interest: Arts and culture; Higher
education; Christianity; Youth services; People with
vision impairments.
Type of support: General support.
Limitations: Applications not accepted. Giving
limited to Watertown and Williamstown, MA; and
New York, NY. No grants to individuals.

Application information: Contributes only to
pre-selected organizations.
Trustee: TD Bank, N.A.
EIN: 046529891

4186
**The Maurice and Anne Makepeace Family
Foundation**
77 Piney Point Rd.
Marion, MA 02738-2037
Application address: c/o Christopher Makepeace,
200 Tihonet Rd., Wareham, MA 02571, tel.: (508)
748-1665

Established in 1998 in Massachusetts.
Donor: Maurice Makepeace.
Foundation type: Independent foundation.
Financial data (yr. ended 12/31/13): Assets,
$2,894,049 (M); expenditures, $147,487;
qualifying distributions, $121,035; giving activities
include $121,000 for 22 grants (high: $20,000;
low: $1,500).
Purpose and activities: Giving primarily for
education and social services.
Fields of interest: Education; Health; Youth
development.
Limitations: Applications accepted. Giving primarily
in MA. No grants to individuals.
Application information:
  Initial approach: Proposal
  Deadline(s): None
Trustees: Joanna Bennett; Christopher Makepeace.
EIN: 046863845

4187
Edward H. Mank Foundation
1430 Massachusetts Ave.
Cambridge, MA 02138-3831 (617) 576-3200
Contact: Donald Himmelsbach, Tr.

Established in 1984 in Massachusetts.
Donor: Edward H. Mank.
Foundation type: Independent foundation.
Financial data (yr. ended 12/31/13): Assets,
$501,952 (M); gifts received, $300,000;
expenditures, $411,777; qualifying distributions,
$372,427; giving activities include $350,602 for 8
+ grants (high: $200,000).
Purpose and activities: Giving primarily for hospitals
and health organizations; support also for Jewish
welfare.
Fields of interest: Higher education; Health;
Hospital care; Judaism; Human services.
Limitations: Applications accepted. Giving primarily
in MA.
Application information: Application form required.
  Initial approach: Letter
  Deadline(s): None
Trustees: Donald Himmelsbach; Matthew Horwitch;
Glen Iacqua.
EIN: 222580000

4188
**William and Cynthia Marcus Family
Charitable Trust**
(formerly Marcus Family Charitable Trust)
99-50 Florence St., Apt. 5B
Chestnut Hill, MA 02467-1941
Contact: William M. Marcus, Tr.

Established in 1985 in Massachusetts.
Donor: William M. Marcus.
Foundation type: Independent foundation.
Financial data (yr. ended 03/31/13): Assets,
$1,145,520 (M); gifts received, $270,386;
expenditures, $399,085; qualifying distributions,
$380,030; giving activities include $364,492 for 70
grants (high: $80,500; low: $25).
Purpose and activities: Giving primarily for
education and Jewish organizations.
Fields of interest: Education; Elementary and
secondary education; Higher education; Nonprofits;
Judaism.
Type of support: General support; Annual
campaigns; Capital campaigns; Research;
Regranting.
Limitations: Applications not accepted. Giving
primarily in MA. No grants to individuals.
Application information: Contributes only to
pre-selected organizations. Funds fully committed.
Trustees: Cynthia S. Marcus; Daniel H. Marcus;
Melanie L. Marcus; Richard S. Marcus; William M.
Marcus.
EIN: 046042910

4189
Marigold Charitable Trust
c/o Nixon Peabody LLP
100 Summer St.
Boston, MA 02110-2106 (617) 345-1000
Contact: Beverly G. Marram, Tr.

Established in 2005 in Massachusetts.
Donor: Beverly G. Marram.
Foundation type: Independent foundation.
Financial data (yr. ended 11/30/13): Assets,
$4,993,251 (M); gifts received, $8,302;
expenditures, $215,346; qualifying distributions,
$197,877; giving activities include $179,042 for 19
grants (high: $25,808; low: $38).
Fields of interest: Family services; Youth services.
Type of support: General support.
Limitations: Applications accepted. Giving primarily
in MA. No grants to individuals.
Application information:
  Initial approach: Letter
  Deadline(s): None
Trustees: Lawrence B. Cohen; Beverly G. Marram;
Meryl Rich; Susan Shamus.
EIN: 206748222

4190
**The Roger M. & Michelle S. Marino
Charitable Foundation**
254 Westfield St.
Dedham, MA 02026-5623 (781) 894-1117

Established in 1994 in Massachusetts.
Donors: Roger M. Marino; Michelle S. Marino.
Foundation type: Independent foundation.
Financial data (yr. ended 12/31/12): Assets,
$2,866,612 (M); expenditures, $412,559;
qualifying distributions, $334,350; giving activities
include $334,350 for grants.
Purpose and activities: Giving primarily for
education and human services.
Fields of interest: Education; Elementary and
secondary education; Higher education; Hospital
care; Human services.

Limitations: Applications not accepted. Giving primarily in MA, with some emphasis on Boston and Framingham and RI.
Application information: Unsolicited requests for funds not accepted.
Trustees: Michelle S. Marino; Roger M. Marino.
EIN: 046773605

4191
Massachusetts Maternity & Foundling Hospital Corporation

P.O. Box 600805
Newtonville, MA 02460-0008 (617) 928-1725
Contact: Cheryl Forte, Treas.
E-mail: info@massmaternity.org; *Main URL:* http://massmaternity.org
Grants List: http://massmaternity.org/grantsawarded.html

Established in 1893 in Massachusetts.
Foundation type: Independent foundation.
Financial data (yr. ended 10/31/13): Assets, $2,901,100 (M); expenditures, $149,941; qualifying distributions, $148,296; giving activities include $147,011 for 5 grants (high: $50,000; low: $10,136).
Purpose and activities: Giving to organizations that provide care for young unwed mothers of limited means and their infant children and for the prevention of teenage pregnancies.
Fields of interest: Diseases and conditions; Human services.
Type of support: Annual campaigns; Capital and infrastructure; Emergency funds; Program development; Convening.
Limitations: Applications accepted. Giving limited to the greater metropolitan Boston, MA, area. No support for day care programs. No grants to individuals.
Publications: Application guidelines.
Application information: See foundation web site for complete application guidelines. Application form required.
   Initial approach: Submit via e-mail the Associated Grant Makers Common Proposal Form, available on foundation web site, along with other requested items.
   Deadline(s): Nov. 1
   Final notification: Late Apr.
Officers and Directors: Thomas J. Connolly, MD, Pres. and Director; Douglas A. Morash, V.P. and Director; Nolly E. Corley, Secy. and Director; Cheryl Forte, Treas. and Director; Anne Groves; Lori B. Leeth.
EIN: 042628366

4192
Dennis and Marion Mavrogenis Trust Fund

c/o Eastern Bank Wealth Management
265 Franklin St.
Boston, MA 02110 (617) 897-1160
Contact: Daniel Hover

Established in 1992 in Massachusetts.
Donor: Marion Mavrogenis†.
Foundation type: Independent foundation.
Financial data (yr. ended 12/31/12): Assets, $2,236,123 (M); expenditures, $190,210; qualifying distributions, $147,209; giving activities include $146,200 for 14 grants to individuals (high: $14,300; low: $3,500).

Purpose and activities: Grants are awarded to residents of Salem, MA, who are high school graduates and wish to study to become doctors or nurses.
Fields of interest: Graduate and professional education; Medical education; Nursing care.
Type of support: Student aid.
Limitations: Applications accepted. Giving limited to residents of Salem, MA.
Application information: Application form required.
   Initial approach: Letter
   Deadline(s): May 1
Trustees: Arthur J. Frawley; Eastern Bank Wealth Management.
EIN: 043179137

4193
McCutchin-Collins Charitable Trust

(formerly McCutchin Charitable Trust)
30 Old Farm Rd.
Dover, MA 02030-2512

Established in 1990 in Massachusetts.
Donors: David S. Collins; John A. McCutchin.
Foundation type: Independent foundation.
Financial data (yr. ended 12/31/14): Assets, $6,350,396; expenditures, $289,772; qualifying distributions, $289,772.
Fields of interest: Higher education; Natural resources; Hospital care; Prostate cancer; Protestantism.
Limitations: Applications not accepted. Giving primarily in ME. No grants to individuals.
Application information: Unsolicited requests for funds not accepted.
Trustees: David S. Collins; Holiday M. Collins.
EIN: 223100739

4194
William J. McKee Charitable Foundation

370 Main St., 12th Fl.
Worcester, MA 01608

Foundation type: Independent foundation.
Financial data (yr. ended 12/31/13): Assets, $4,556,511 (M); expenditures, $229,999; qualifying distributions, $185,865; giving activities include $145,018 for 7 grants (high: $50,000; low: $18).
Fields of interest: Domesticated animals; Religion; Human services.
Limitations: Applications not accepted. Giving primarily in MA.
Application information: Unsolicited requests for funds not accepted.
Trustee: John E. Hodgson.
EIN: 046640238

4195
John A. McNeice, Jr. Charitable Foundation

c/o Choate
P.O. Box 96109
Boston, MA 02196

Established in 1997 in Massachusetts.
Donors: John A. McNeice, Jr.; John McNeice.
Foundation type: Independent foundation.
Financial data (yr. ended 04/30/14): Assets, $5,498,760 (M); expenditures, $425,822;

qualifying distributions, $390,781; giving activities include $310,000 for 8 grants (high: $252,500; low: $5,000).
Fields of interest: Elementary and secondary education; Hospital care; Diseases and conditions; Catholicism; Human services; Homeless shelters.
Limitations: Applications not accepted. Giving primarily in MA. No grants to individuals.
Application information: Unsolicited requests for funds not accepted.
Officer and Trustees: Margarete Anne Portanova, Exec. Dir. and Trustee; George Ashur; Edward G. Casey; A. Silvana Giner; John A. McNeice, Jr.; William B. Neenan, S.J.; John Shaughnessy, Jr.
EIN: 043371560

4196
James C. Melvin Trust

c/o Robert N. Shapiro Et Al, Ropes & Gray, LLP
800 Boylston St.
Boston, MA 02199-3600

Foundation type: Independent foundation.
Financial data (yr. ended 12/31/14): Assets, $5,646,400; expenditures, $293,031; qualifying distributions, $239,949.
Fields of interest: Elementary and secondary education; Medical education.
Type of support: Scholarships.
Limitations: Applications not accepted. Giving primarily to MA. No grants to individuals.
Application information: Contributes only to pre-selected organizations.
Trustees: Francis L. Coolidge; Brenda S. Diana; Edward P. Lawrence; Robert N. Shapiro.
EIN: 046029004

4197
Melvina Foundation

(formerly Eykamp Foundation)
c/o Diana Merewether, Esq.
171 Park Ave.
Arlington, MA 02476-5828

Donors: Dorothy Eykamp; D&G Eykamp Sons Trust; G.R. Eykamp; G&D Eykamp Grandchildren's Trust; William Eykamp; Rita Eykamp; Richard Eykamp.
Foundation type: Independent foundation.
Financial data (yr. ended 12/31/13): Assets, $12,204,060 (M); gifts received, $100,172; expenditures, $439,662; qualifying distributions, $399,367; giving activities include $395,567 for grants.
Purpose and activities: Giving primarily for the arts, human services, and to Christian organizations.
Fields of interest: Arts and culture; Performing arts; Higher education; Diseases and conditions; Film and video; Radio; Television; Christianity; Human services; Child welfare.
Limitations: Applications not accepted. Giving primarily in Evansville, IN and MA. No grants to individuals.
Application information: Contributes only to pre-selected organizations.
Officers: G.R. Eykamp, Chair.; William Eykamp, Pres.; Rita Eykamp, Secy.-Treas.
Director: Philip Eykamp.
EIN: 237001774

4198

Memorial Foundation for the Blind Inc.
(formerly Memorial Homes for the Blind)
799 W. Boylston St.
Worcester, MA 01606-3071 (508) 854-9980
E-mail: info@mfblind.org; Additional e-mail:
raymondlma@charter.net; Main URL: http://
www.mfblind.org

Established in 1951 in Massachusetts.
Foundation type: Independent foundation.
Financial data (yr. ended 03/31/13): Assets,
$3,986,492 (M); gifts received, $192,175;
expenditures, $257,312; qualifying distributions,
$227,537; giving activities include $221,742 for 3
+ grants (high: $105,000).
Purpose and activities: Support primarily for the
care of the visually handicapped.
Fields of interest: Eye diseases; Public libraries;
Radio; Special population support.
International interests: Greece.
Type of support: General support.
Limitations: Applications accepted. Giving primarily
to residents of the Worcester, MA, area.
Application information: Application form required.
  Initial approach: Proposal
  Copies of proposal: 1
  Deadline(s): None
Officers: Larry Raymond, Pres.; Elizabeth Myska,
V.P.; Jane Weisman, Secy.; Gary MacConnell, Treas.
Directors: Eleanor Brockway; T. Ashley Edwards;
Helen D. Fifield; James Gettens; Roger W. Greene;
Barbara Higgins; Nancy Jeppson; Maggie Lawler;
Diane MacConnell; Nicholas McNamara; Janice
Reidy; Joseph Reidy.
EIN: 041611615

4199

**The MENTOR Network Charitable
Foundation, Inc.**
313 Congress St., 5th Fl.
Boston, MA 02210-1218
E-mail: foundation@thementornetwork.com; Main
URL: http://www.thementornetwork.com/
foundation
Facebook: https://www.facebook.com/likementor
Grants List: http://
networkcharitablefoundation.org/grant-programs/
community-partners/community-partners
Twitter: https://twitter.com/The_MENTOR_Ntwk
YouTube: https://www.youtube.com/user/
TheMENTORNetwork

Established in 2006 in Massachusetts.
Donors: The MENTOR Network; Robert Digia;
Madison Dearborn Partners; Hugh R. Jones.
Foundation type: Independent foundation.
Financial data (yr. ended 09/30/13): Assets,
$1,036,336 (M); gifts received, $110,131;
expenditures, $271,720; qualifying distributions,
$263,288; giving activities include $248,493 for 40
grants (high: $59,334; low: $500).
Purpose and activities: The foundation works to
build on innovative approaches to human services
by seeking new solutions and creative ideas for
enhancing the lives of persons with disabilities and
youth and families facing emotional, behavioral and
other challenges, and by expanding opportunity.
Fields of interest: Education; Human services;
Family services; Adolescents; People with
disabilities.

Application information: Online application
process; paper-based applications no longer
accepted. Complete application guidelines available
on foundation web site. Application form required.
Officers and Directors: Gregory Torres, Chair. and
Director; Dwight D. Robson, Pres. and Director;
Linda DeRenzo, Secy. and Director; Chris M.
Kozakis, Treas. and Director; Kathleen Federico;
Denis Holler; Sarah Magazine; Edward Murphy;
Bruce Nardella.
EIN: 204935290

4200

Merrill Family Charitable Foundation Inc.
P.O. Box 990129
Boston, MA 02199-0129

Established in 1997 in New York.
Donor: Charles E. Merrill, Jr.
Foundation type: Independent foundation.
Financial data (yr. ended 12/31/13): Assets,
$2,884,271 (M); gifts received, $25,000;
expenditures, $228,132; qualifying distributions,
$211,552; giving activities include $196,676 for 50
grants (high: $27,087; low: $500).
Purpose and activities: Giving primarily for the arts,
education, the environment, and community
development.
Fields of interest: Dance; Music; Historical
activities; Education; Environment; Community and
economic development; Human services.
Limitations: Applications not accepted. Giving
primarily in MA and NY. No grants to individuals.
Application information: Contributes only to
pre-selected organizations.
Officers: Paul Merrill, Pres.; Amy Merrill, V.P.; Bruce
Merrill, Secy.-Treas.
EIN: 223494040

4201

Metanoia Fund
c/o Loring Wolcott & Coolidge
230 Congress St., 12th Fl.
Boston, MA 02110-2437

Established in 1990 in Massachusetts.
Donor: Frederick Morgan Taylor III.
Foundation type: Independent foundation.
Financial data (yr. ended 12/31/12): Assets,
$61,954 (M); expenditures, $120,864; qualifying
distributions, $115,395; giving activities include
$113,750 for 3 grants (high: $63,750; low:
$25,000).
Fields of interest: Education; Environment;
International relations; International development.
Type of support: General support.
Limitations: Applications not accepted. Giving
primarily in CA, MA, NY, RI, and WA. No grants to
individuals.
Application information: Contributes only to
pre-selected organizations.
Trustees: Florence Mavis Brown; Frederick Morgan
Taylor III; John F. Taylor; Lucy Farnsworth Taylor.
EIN: 046668886

4202

**Michael and Jill Stansky Family
Foundation**
36 Skyview Ln.
Sudbury, MA 01776-1147
Contact: Michael P. Stansky, Tr.

Established in 2006 in Massachusetts.
Donor: Michael P. Stansky.
Foundation type: Independent foundation.
Financial data (yr. ended 11/30/13): Assets,
$3,905,831 (M); gifts received, $1,688,386;
expenditures, $232,669; qualifying distributions,
$229,169; giving activities include $225,622 for 3
grants (high: $125,622; low: $10,000).
Fields of interest: Health; Diseases and conditions.
Type of support: Scholarships.
Limitations: Applications accepted. Giving primarily
in Boston, MA.
Application information: Application form required.
  Initial approach: Letter
  Deadline(s): None
Trustees: Jill Stansky; Michael P. Stansky.
EIN: 205944745

4203

**Middlesex Savings Charitable Foundation,
Inc.**
c/o Middlesex Savings Bank
6 Main St.
Natick, MA 01760-4506 (508) 315-5361
Contact: Mike Kuza, V.P.
E-mail: mkuza@middlesexbank.com; Main
URL: https://www.middlesexbank.com/
community-and-us/community-support/Pages/
charitable-foundation.aspx
Grants List: http://www.middlesexbank.com/
community/charitablefoundation/2012Grants.asp

Established in 2000 in Massachusetts.
Donor: Middlesex Savings Bank.
Foundation type: Company-sponsored foundation.
Financial data (yr. ended 12/31/13): Assets,
$11,168,136 (M); gifts received, $3,000,000;
expenditures, $462,447; qualifying distributions,
$414,037; giving activities include $404,540 for 44
grants (high: $37,500; low: $500).
Purpose and activities: The foundation supports
organizations involved with arts and culture, health
and wellness, employment training, youth
development, human services, and economically
disadvantaged people. Special emphasis is directed
toward programs designed to promote education;
capacity building; and community development.
Fields of interest: Arts and culture; Education;
Vocational education; Adult education; ESL and
second language acquisition; Community and
economic development; Job training; Financial
counseling; Human services; Youth development;
Low-income and poor people.
Type of support: General support; Financial
sustainability; Leadership and professional
development; System and operational
improvements; Equipment; Program development;
Technical assistance; Student aid.
Limitations: Applications accepted. Giving primarily
in areas of company operations in Acton, Ashland,
Ayer, Bedford, Bellingham, Berlin, Bolton,
Boxborough, Carlisle, Chelmsford, Concord, Dover,
Dunstable, Framingham, Franklin, Groton, Harvard,
Holliston, Hopedale, Hopkinton, Hudson, Lexington,
Lincoln, Littleton, Marlborough, Maynard, Medfield,

Medway, Milford, Millis, Natick, Needham, Newton, Norfolk, Northborough, Pepperell, Sherborn, Shirley, Southborough, Stow, Sudbury, Townsend, Tyngsborough, Upton, Walpole, Waltham, Wayland, Wellesley, Westborough, Westford, and Weston, MA. No support for religious, political, or discriminatory organizations. No grants for sponsorships, trips, or conferences; no in-kind donations.

Publications: Application guidelines; Grants list; Program policy statement.

Application information: Support is limited to 1 contribution per organization during any given year. Application form required.

   Initial approach: Complete online application
   Copies of proposal: 1
   Deadline(s): Apr. 1 and Aug. 1
   Board meeting date(s): June and Oct.

Officers: Dana M. Neshe, Pres.; William M. Kuza, V.P.; Brian D. Lanigan, Treas.

Directors: George F. Fiske, Jr.; Carrie Hatch Flood; Rudman J. Ham; John R. Heerwagen; Raymond Page; Arnold I. Zaltas.

Number of staff: 1 full-time support.

EIN: 043521246

4204
John Mirak Foundation

438 Massachusetts Ave., No. 127
Arlington, MA   02476

Established in 1972 in Massachusetts.

Donors: John Mirak; Arlington Center Service and Garage, Inc.; Mirak Building Trust; Artemis Mirak†.

Foundation type: Independent foundation.

Financial data (yr. ended 12/31/13): Assets, $8,960,276 (M); expenditures, $670,407; qualifying distributions, $359,561; giving activities include $323,070 for 24+ grants (high: $140,000).

Purpose and activities: Giving primarily for an Armenian cultural foundation and other Armenian organizations; funding also for the arts, and education.

Fields of interest: Arts and culture; Cultural awareness; Education; Forest preservation; Orthodox Christianity; Human services.

Limitations: Applications not accepted. Giving primarily in MA. No grants to individuals.

Application information: Contributes only to pre-selected organizations.

Officer: Robert Mirak, Mgr.

Trustees: Julia Mirak Kew; Jennifer Leach.

EIN: 237161662

4205
Everett W. & Marion E. Mitchell Foundation

c/o Nixon Peabody LLP
100 Summer St.
Boston, MA   02110-2131   (617) 345-1000
Contact: Ronald Garmey, Tr.

Established in 2007 in Massachusetts.

Donor: Everett W. Mitchell†.

Foundation type: Independent foundation.

Financial data (yr. ended 08/31/13): Assets, $7,595,936 (M); gifts received, $24; expenditures, $382,600; qualifying distributions, $343,927; giving activities include $152,206 for 2 grants (high: $150,000; low: $2,206), and $150,679 for 18 grants to individuals (high: $14,012; low: $4,950).

Purpose and activities: Giving primarily to students residing in the town of Middleton, PA on the basis of citizenship, academic proficiency, and financial need; giving also to a Congregational church.

Fields of interest: Protestantism.

Type of support: General support; Student aid.

Limitations: Applications accepted. Giving primarily to residents of Middleton, PA.

Application information:
   Initial approach: Letter
   Deadline(s): None

Trustee: Ronald Garmey.

EIN: 207088204

4206
Jacques Mohr Charitable Trust

P.O. Box 55806
Boston, MA   02205-5806

Foundation type: Independent foundation.

Financial data (yr. ended 12/31/14): Assets, $4,288,348 (M); expenditures, $217,504; qualifying distributions, $178,178; giving activities include $176,008 for 2 grants (high: $140,807; low: $35,201).

Fields of interest: Health; Hospital care.

Limitations: Applications not accepted. Giving primarily in MA.

Application information: Unsolicited requests for funds not accepted.

Trustees: Charles C.J. Platt; Fiduciary Trust Co.

EIN: 263797667

4207
The Morningstar Family Foundation

c/o Nixon Peabody LLP, Deborah Anderson
100 Summer St., Rm. 27
Boston, MA   02110-2131

Established in 1994 in Delaware.

Donors: Jane Morningstar; Otto Morningstar; Betty Morningstar.

Foundation type: Independent foundation.

Financial data (yr. ended 12/31/14): Assets, $3,995,030; expenditures, $269,792; qualifying distributions, $246,476.

Fields of interest: Arts and culture; Education; Higher education; Nonprofits; Hospital care; Judaism.

Type of support: Regranting.

Limitations: Applications not accepted. Giving primarily in CA, FL and MA. No grants to individuals.

Application information: Unsolicited requests for funds not accepted.

Officers: Betty Morningstar, Pres.; Deborah L. Anderson, Esq., Secy.-Treas.

EIN: 043236053

4208
Alfred L. & Annette S. Morse Foundation

c/o Ropes Gray LLP
800 Boylston St.
Boston, MA   02199-3600

Established in 1962 in Massachusetts.

Donors: Alfred L. Morse†; Annette S. Morse.

Foundation type: Independent foundation.

Financial data (yr. ended 12/31/13): Assets, $4,682,163 (M); expenditures, $257,312; qualifying distributions, $202,693; giving activities

include $200,000 for 51 grants (high: $60,000; low: $300).

Purpose and activities: Giving primarily to Jewish organizations and for health care.

Fields of interest: Education; Nonprofits; Health; Hospital care; Cancers; Judaism; Human services; International relations.

Type of support: Regranting.

Limitations: Applications not accepted. Giving primarily in Washington, DC, and FL. No grants to individuals.

Application information: Unsolicited requests for funds not accepted.

Trustees: Robert N. Shapiro; Harriet M. Zimmerman.

EIN: 046142795

4209
Richard P. & Claire W. Morse Foundation

240 Lee St.
Brookline, MA   02445-5915

Established in 1966 in Massachusetts.

Donors: Ruth Morse†; Claire W. Morse; Richard P. Morse.

Foundation type: Independent foundation.

Financial data (yr. ended 12/31/13): Assets, $6,666,820 (M); gifts received, $112,216; expenditures, $438,690; qualifying distributions, $436,205; giving activities include $434,635 for 41 grants (high: $110,250; low: $100).

Purpose and activities: Giving primarily to museums and a symphony orchestra; funding also for higher education and Jewish federated giving programs.

Fields of interest: Orchestral music; Museums; Education; Nonprofits; Hospital care; Human services.

Type of support: General support; Continuing support; Annual campaigns; Capital campaigns; Capital and infrastructure; Equipment; Regranting; Endowments; Emergency funds; Program development; Seed money; Curriculum development; Fellowships; Internships; Program evaluations.

Limitations: Applications not accepted. Giving primarily in Boston, MA. No grants to individuals.

Application information: Contributes only to pre-selected organizations.

Trustees: Claire W. Morse; Richard P. Morse.

EIN: 046142794

4210
The Morse Foundation

c/o David Gilmour
48 Stone Meadow Ln.
Hanover, MA   02339-3502

Established in 1998 in Massachusetts.

Donors: Phillip H. Morse; The Waterhouse Family Foundation.

Foundation type: Independent foundation.

Financial data (yr. ended 12/31/13): Assets, $741,367 (M); expenditures, $327,952; qualifying distributions, $315,100; giving activities include $315,100 for 30 grants (high: $200,000; low: $100).

Purpose and activities: Giving primarily for education, as well as for hospitals and health organizations, and youth and social services.

Fields of interest: Secondary education; Animal welfare; Hospital care; Diseases and conditions;

Baseball and softball; Human services; Child welfare.

Limitations: Applications not accepted. Giving primarily in MA and NY. No grants to individuals.

Application information: Contributes only to pre-selected organizations.

Trustees: David W. Gilmour; Phillip H. Morse; Susan K. Morse.

EIN: 046868099

4211
Mount Washington Charitable Foundation, Inc.
430 W. Broadway
South Boston, MA   02127-2216   (617) 269-5738

Established in 2002 in Massachusetts.

Donors: Fitzgerald Cleaning; Auburn Construction; Mt. Washington Co-operative Bank; East Boston Savings Bank.

Foundation type: Independent foundation.

Financial data (yr. ended 06/30/13): Assets, $770 (M); gifts received, $104,506; expenditures, $151,830; qualifying distributions, $151,830; giving activities include $151,760 for 214 grants (high: $5,000; low: $50).

Fields of interest: Education; Community and economic development; Human services.

Limitations: Applications accepted. Giving primarily in Boston, MA. No grants to individuals.

Application information:

Initial approach: Proposal
Deadline(s): None

Officers and Directors: Richard Gavegnano, Chair. and Director; Edward J. Merritt, Pres. and Director; James A. Morgan, V.P. and Clerk; Mary E. Hagen, V.P and Treas.; Thomas Henderson, V.P.; Vincent D. Basile; Marilyn A. Censullo; Anna R. DiMaria; Thomas J. Gunning; Edward Lynch; Gail Snowden.

EIN: 450488207

4212
Mountain Meadows Foundation, Inc.
c/o Capital Formation Companies
34 Washington St., Ste. 230
Wellesley Hills, MA   02481-1903

Donor: Carmine Capossela.

Foundation type: Independent foundation.

Financial data (yr. ended 12/31/12): Assets, $2,407,228 (M); expenditures, $192,588; qualifying distributions, $158,250; giving activities include $158,250 for grants.

Fields of interest: Education; Diseases and conditions; Sports and recreation.

Limitations: Applications not accepted. Giving primarily in NY and PA.

Application information: Unsolicited requests for funds not accepted.

Officers: Maura McDonnell, Pres.; Carmine Capossela, V.P.; John Williams, Secy.

EIN: 261471688

4213
The Mulberry Foundation, Inc.
370 Main St., 12th Fl.
Worcester, MA   01608-1723
E-mail: info@mulberryfoundation.org; Main
URL: http://www.mulberryfoundation.org

Established in 2000 in Massachusetts.

Donors: Leif N. Uptegrove; Carol Uptegrove.

Foundation type: Independent foundation.

Financial data (yr. ended 12/31/13): Assets, $3,523,723 (M); gifts received, $9,322; expenditures, $223,952; qualifying distributions, $191,621; giving activities include $175,000 for 13 grants (high: $30,000; low: $6,000).

Fields of interest: Education; Higher education; Christianity; Human services.

Limitations: Applications not accepted. Giving primarily in MA. No grants to individuals.

Application information: Unsolicited requests for funds not accepted.

Officers and Directors: Leif N. Uptegrove, Pres. and Treas. and Director; Carol L. Uptegrove, Clerk and Director; Laurel Phillips; Erin Uptegrove.

EIN: 043505849

4214
Cecile Higginson Murphy Charitable Foundation
c/o Choate LLP
P.O. Box 961019
Boston, MA   02196-1019

Established in 1998 in Massachusetts.

Donor: Cecile Higginson Murphy.

Foundation type: Independent foundation.

Financial data (yr. ended 06/30/15): Assets, $6,002,235 (M); gifts received, $129,943; expenditures, $463,226; qualifying distributions, $405,694; giving activities include $390,000 for 15 grants (high: $50,000; low: $2,000).

Fields of interest: Performing arts; Orchestral music; Human services.

Limitations: Applications not accepted. Giving primarily in MA. No grants to individuals.

Application information: Unsolicited requests for funds not accepted.

Trustees: John M. Cornish; Cecile Higginson Murphy.

EIN: 043447397

4215
1997 John & Mary Murphy Educational Foundation
600 Main St., Ste. 1
Winchester, MA   01890   (781) 721-0100
Contact: Patrick C. Hall, Tr.; John J. Sullivan, Tr.

Established in 2001 in Massachusetts.

Donor: Mary E. Murphy†.

Foundation type: Independent foundation.

Financial data (yr. ended 12/31/13): Assets, $3,517,278 (M); expenditures, $277,211; qualifying distributions, $240,831; giving activities include $236,835 for 16 grants (high: $49,335; low: $750).

Fields of interest: Higher education; Libraries.

Limitations: Applications accepted. Giving primarily in Winchester, MA.

Application information: Application form required.

Initial approach: Letter
Deadline(s): None

Trustees: Patrick C. Hall; John J. Sullivan.

EIN: 043399061

4216
MutualOne Charitable Foundation
(formerly Framingham Co-Operative Bank Charitable Foundation)
828 Concord St.
Framingham, MA   01701-4611   (508) 820-4000
FAX: (508) 872-1768; Application address: 160 Cochituate Rd., Framingham, MA 01701;

Established in 1998 in Massachusetts.

Donor: Mutualone Bank.

Foundation type: Company-sponsored foundation.

Financial data (yr. ended 12/31/14): Assets, $6,936,050; gifts received, $500,000; expenditures, $317,935; qualifying distributions, $313,890.

Purpose and activities: The foundation supports organizations involved with arts and culture, education, the environment, health, workforce development, housing, and community development. Special emphasis is directed toward programs designed to focus on disadvantaged and/ or underserved citizens of Framingham and Natick.

Fields of interest: Arts and culture; Education; Secondary education; Environment; Health; Community and economic development; Job training; Job creation and workforce development; Housing development; Human services; Food banks; Child welfare; Youth services; Low-income and poor people.

Type of support: Capital campaigns; Matching grants; Program development; Seed money.

Limitations: Applications accepted. Giving primarily in areas of company operations in Framingham and Natick, MA, area. No grants to individuals, or for political or sectarian activities.

Application information: Application form required.

Initial approach: Letter
Deadline(s): None

Trustees: Susan E. Acton; Paul V. Galvani; Mark R. Haranas; Clement T. Lambert; Robert P. Lamprey; Steven M. Sousa; Rachel A. Stewart.

EIN: 311595107

4217
NAID Foundation
P.O Box 821
Newburyport, MA   01950   9784626890
Application address: c/o Charles Morse, 19 Green St., Newbury, MA 01951

Foundation type: Independent foundation.

Financial data (yr. ended 12/31/14): Assets, $3,379,862; expenditures, $195,464; qualifying distributions, $181,500.

Fields of interest: Arts and culture; Education; Sustainable development; Urban development; Child welfare.

Limitations: Applications accepted. Giving primarily in Newburyport, MA. No grants to individuals.

Application information: Application form required.

Initial approach: Letter
Deadline(s): None

Officers: James C. Zampell, Pres.; Dorothy LaFrance, V.P.; Charles W. Morse, Jr., Treas.

Directors: Curtis L. Gerrish; Cindy M. Johnson; Arthur S. Page, Jr.; William Plante, Jr.; Michael Strem.

EIN: 223017922

4218
Neighborhood Partners Fund Inc.
35 Blake St.
Cambridge, MA   02140-1301

Established in 1999 in Massachusetts.
Donors: Debra Fox; William Traynor; RAF Foundation.
Foundation type: Operating foundation.
Financial data (yr. ended 12/31/13): Assets, $187,070 (M); gifts received, $266,593; expenditures, $407,017; qualifying distributions, $390,000; giving activities include $390,000 for 1 grant.
Fields of interest: Community and economic development.
Limitations: Applications not accepted. Giving primarily in Lawrence, MA. No grants to individuals.
Application information: Contributes only to pre-selected organizations.
Officers: Debra Fox, Pres. and Treas.; Amy Fox, Clerk.
EIN: 043476677

4219
John and Judith Nelson Family Foundation
c/o The Colony Group
2 Atlantic Ave.
Boston, MA   02110-3918

Established in 1999 in Massachusetts.
Donors: John Nelson; Christopher Lori Nelson; Scott Nelson.
Foundation type: Independent foundation.
Financial data (yr. ended 12/31/13): Assets, $532,923 (M); expenditures, $174,071; qualifying distributions, $169,435; giving activities include $169,435 for 21 grants (high: $74,150; low: $50).
Fields of interest: Philanthropy; Health; Diseases and conditions.
Limitations: Applications not accepted. Giving primarily in MA. No grants to individuals.
Application information: Unsolicited requests for funds not accepted.
Trustees: Christopher Nelson; John Nelson; Scott Nelson.
EIN: 046896202

4220
New England Biolabs Foundation
240 County Rd.
Ipswich, MA   01938-2723   (978) 998-7990
Contact: Susan Foster, Asst. Dir.; Jessica Brown, Exec. Dir.
FAX: (978) 356-3250; E-mail: info@nebf.org; Main URL: http://www.nebf.org
Grants List: http://www.nebf.org/previous.html

Established in 1982 in Massachusetts.
Donors: Donald G. Combs; New England Biolabs, Inc.; Martine Kellett.
Foundation type: Company-sponsored foundation.
Financial data (yr. ended 12/31/13): Assets, $8,711,658 (M); gifts received, $275,100; expenditures, $717,027; qualifying distributions, $667,300; giving activities include $437,900 for grants.
Purpose and activities: The foundation supports programs designed to promote conservation of biological diversity including terrestrial and marine; sustain cultural diversity including linguistic diversity and traditional knowledge systems and practices; maintain ecosystem services with emphasis on water, soil, and carbon sequestration; promote food security and economic vitality of local communities; and sustain healthy reefs and fisheries. The foundation also awards limited grants to individuals for small environmental research projects.
Fields of interest: Arts and culture; Elementary education; Environment; Coral reefs; Oceans and coastal waters; Biodiversity; Wildlife biodiversity; Aquatic wildlife protection; Environmental education; Biology; Ecology; Food security; Sustainable development; Food aid.
International interests: Belize; Bolivia; Cameroon; Central America; Developing Countries; Ecuador; El Salvador; Ghana; Guatemala; Honduras; Madagascar; Nicaragua; Papua New Guinea; Peru; South America; Tanzania.
Type of support: Program development; Grants to individuals; Matching grants; Seed money; Curriculum development; Research; Research and evaluation.
Limitations: Applications accepted. Giving primarily in New England, with emphasis on the Boston, MA, area, particularly the North Shore region; giving also in Belize, Bolivia, Cameroon, Central America, Ecuador, El Salvador, Ghana, Guatemala, Honduras, Madagascar, Nicaragua, Papua New Guinea, Peru, South America, and Tanzania. No support for organizations located in Argentina, Belize, Brazil, Chile, Columbia, Costa Rica, French Guiana, Mexico, Panama, the Philippines, Suriname, Uruguay, Venezuela, or Vietnam or private schools. No grants to individuals (except for environmental research), or for non-marine issues in the Caribbean or Madagascar, non-environmental education projects in Guatemala, non-environmental projects in Ghana, educational or community projects of U.S. organizations not located in the Boston, MA, area, art projects located outside the immediate community, capital campaigns, renovations or building funds, conferences, workshops, or travel, production of videos, movies, or books, religious activities, general operating support, scholarships, fellowships, or internships, scientific research eligible for funding by major agencies, services for senior citizens, economically disadvantaged people, or disabled people, or species-specific projects.
Publications: Application guidelines; Grants list.
Application information: Letters of inquiry should be no longer than 1 page. A full proposal may be requested at a later date. Local grants range from $1,000 to $5,000. International grants range from $3,000 to $8,000. Priority is given to organizations that have received prior funding. Organizations receiving support are asked to provide a final report.
  Initial approach: E-mail or mail letter of inquiry
  Copies of proposal: 1
  Deadline(s): Mar. 7 and July 14 for letters of inquiry; Apr. 18 and Sept. 12 for proposals
  Board meeting date(s): June and Dec.
  Final notification: 2 months following board meetings
Officer: Jessica Brown, Exec. Dir.
Trustees: David Comb; Heidi Ellard; Marcos Neto; Henry P. Paulus, Ph.D.
Number of staff: 2 part-time professional.
EIN: 042776213

4221
Newburyport Five Cents Savings Charitable Foundation Inc.
63 State St.
Newburyport, MA   01950-6615   (978) 462-3136
Contact: Timothy L. Felter, Treas.

Established in 2003 in Massachusetts.
Donor: Newburyport Five Cents Savings Bank.
Foundation type: Company-sponsored foundation.
Financial data (yr. ended 12/31/13): Assets, $4,244,031 (M); expenditures, $195,097; qualifying distributions, $192,597; giving activities include $191,027 for 32 grants (high: $20,000; low: $1,000).
Purpose and activities: The foundation supports arts associations and organizations involved with education, water conservation, and human services.
Fields of interest: Arts and culture; Housing development; Youth development.
Limitations: Applications accepted. Giving limited to areas of company operations in the greater Newburyport, MA, area.
Application information: Application form required.
  Initial approach: Completed application Form
  Deadline(s): None
Officers and Directors: Janice C. Morse, Pres. and Director; Lynne A. Carter, Clerk; Timothy L. Felter, Treas.; John Allison; James Connolly, Jr.; Edward Shephard.
EIN: 200318941

4222
Newburyport Society for the Relief of Aged Women, Inc.
P.O. Box 787
Newburyport, MA   01950-0987   (978) 463-8801
Contact: Melissa Foley, Co-Chair.
E-mail: nsraw1835@gmail.com; Main URL: http://www.nsraw.org

Established in 1835 in Massachusetts.
Foundation type: Independent foundation.
Financial data (yr. ended 04/01/14): Assets, $3,686,290 (M); expenditures, $216,213; qualifying distributions, $174,076; giving activities include $94,558 for 5 grants (high: $50,000; low: $3,058), and $79,518 for grants to individuals.
Purpose and activities: The mission is to serve needy women, sixty years and older.
Fields of interest: Health; Community and economic development; Human services; Female seniors; Low-income and poor people.
Limitations: Applications accepted. Giving primarily in Newburyport, MA.
Application information: Application form required.
  Initial approach: Proposal
  Deadline(s): None
Officers: Melissa Foley, Co-Chair.; Jocelyne Consentino, Co-Chair.; Ardis Campbell, Pres.; Dorothy Lafrance, V.P.; Lyn Parker, Secy.; Melissa Foley, Co-Chair.
Directors: Jean Coffman; Lori Davis; Jean Doyle; Linda Lynehan; Alice McLeod; Sally Plourde; Janet Sheenan; Elizabeth Swanson.
EIN: 042121771

4223
F.C. & C.W. Nichols Charity Fund
P.O. Box 55806
Boston, MA   02205-5806

Foundation type: Independent foundation.
Financial data (yr. ended 12/31/13): Assets, $6,280,881 (M); expenditures, $308,525; qualifying distributions, $262,580; giving activities include $260,000 for 3 grants (high: $130,000; low: $43,333).
Fields of interest: Museums; Hospital care; Religion.
Limitations: Applications not accepted.
Application information: Contributes only to pre-selected organizations; unsolicited requests for funds not considered or acknowledged.
Trustee: Fiduciary Trust Co.
EIN: 046007299

4224
Constance A. and George L. Noble Family Foundation, Inc
175 Monument Farm Rd.
Concord, MA 01742-5345

Established in 2008 in Massachusetts.
Donors: George L. Noble; Constance Noble.
Foundation type: Independent foundation.
Financial data (yr. ended 12/31/13): Assets, $3,461,040 (M); expenditures, $221,912; qualifying distributions, $221,912; giving activities include $213,633 for 21 grants (high: $105,633; low: $100).
Fields of interest: Higher education; Nonprofits; Judaism; Human services.
Type of support: Regranting.
Limitations: Applications not accepted. Giving in the U.S., with some emphasis on MA. No grants to individuals.
Application information: Contributes only to pre-selected organizations.
Officers: Constance A. Noble, Pres.; George L. Noble, Clerk and Treas.
EIN: 943459041

4225
Deborah Munroe Noonan Memorial Research Fund
(formerly Frank M. Noonan Trust)
c/o US Trust, Bank of America, N.A.
225 Franklin St., MA1-225-04-02
Boston, MA 02110-2801 (866) 778-6859
Contact: Miki Akimoto, Market Dir.
E-mail: ma.grantmaking@ustrust.com; E-mail regarding application process or for questions: ma.grantmaking@ustrust.com (indicate foundation name in subject line); Main URL: https://www.bankofamerica.com/philanthropic/grantmaking.go

Established in 1947 in Massachusetts.
Donor: Frank M. Noonan†.
Foundation type: Independent foundation.
Financial data (yr. ended 09/30/14): Assets, $10,623,628 (M); expenditures, $526,567; qualifying distributions, $461,118; giving activities include $399,900 for 4 grants (high: $160,000; low: $79,900).
Purpose and activities: Grants solely for organizations and hospitals directly serving children with disabilities.
Fields of interest: Education; Health; Human services.
Type of support: General support; Program development.

Limitations: Giving limited to the greater Boston, MA, area.
Publications: Application guidelines.
Application information: The fund's grant review process is externally administered by The Medical Foundation, a division of Health Resources in Action. Consult fund web site for more information. Application form required.
 Initial approach: See fund web site
 Copies of proposal: 16
 Deadline(s): Mar. 15
 Board meeting date(s): Distribution committee meets as required
 Final notification: June 30
Trustee: Bank of America, N.A.
Number of staff: None.
EIN: 046025957

4226
Novack Family Foundation
c/o Mintz, Levin
1 Financial Ctr.
Boston, MA 02111-2621

Established in 1999 in Massachusetts.
Donor: Kenneth J. Novack.
Foundation type: Independent foundation.
Financial data (yr. ended 12/31/13): Assets, $1,607,937 (M); gifts received, $132,571; expenditures, $344,523; qualifying distributions, $286,750; giving activities include $286,750 for 66 grants (high: $50,000; low: $250).
Purpose and activities: Giving to improve the lives of disadvantaged children and broaden their opportunities through education and direct support.
Fields of interest: Arts and culture; Education; Health; Child welfare.
Limitations: Applications not accepted. Giving primarily in MA, with emphasis on Boston. No grants to individuals.
Application information: Unsolicited requests for funds not accepted.
Trustee: Kenneth J. Novack.
EIN: 046896914

4227
Grace Swift Nye & Alfred Gibbs Nye Scholarship Trust
P.O. Box 55806
Boston, MA 02205-5806
Application address: P.O. Box 271369, West Hartford, CT 06127-1369, tel.: (806) 521-5694

Established in 1995 in Massachusetts.
Donor: Grace S. Nye†.
Foundation type: Independent foundation.
Financial data (yr. ended 12/31/13): Assets, $3,603,876 (M); expenditures, $256,061; qualifying distributions, $201,998; giving activities include $174,550 for 110 grants to individuals (high: $3,750; low: $1,250).
Purpose and activities: Giving to provide undergraduate financial assistance with renewable scholarships.
Fields of interest: Education.
Type of support: Student aid.
Limitations: Giving limited to graduating high school seniors of Bourne, Plymouth, Sandwich and Wareham, MA.
Publications: Application guidelines.
Application information: Application form required.

 Deadline(s): Early Apr.
 Board meeting date(s): Oct.
 Final notification: June
Trustees: Elaine H. LeLaurin; David E. Nye; Fiduciary Trust Co. Int'l.
Number of staff: 1 part-time support.
EIN: 066421534

4228
The Nypro Foundation, Inc.
c/o Nypro Inc.
101 Union St.
Clinton, MA 01510-2908 (978) 365-9721
Contact: Kenneth M. Flynn, Secy.

Donors: Gordon B. Lankton; Janet K. Lankton; Nypro Inc.
Foundation type: Independent foundation.
Financial data (yr. ended 12/31/13): Assets, $5,035,859 (M); gifts received, $226,000; expenditures, $269,099; qualifying distributions, $226,618; giving activities include $226,618 for 114 grants (high: $35,000; low: $100).
Fields of interest: Education; Diseases and conditions; Human services.
Limitations: Applications accepted. Giving primarily in MA. No grants to individuals.
Application information:
 Initial approach: Proposal
 Deadline(s): None
Officers: Theodore E. LaPres III, Pres.; Kenneth Flynn, Secy.; John Casali, Treas.
EIN: 043211993

4229
The O'Keefe Family Foundation
39 Grapevine Rd.
Wenham, MA 01984-1702
Contact: Karen M. O'Keefe

Donor: Karen M. O'Keefe.
Foundation type: Independent foundation.
Financial data (yr. ended 12/31/13): Assets, $0 (M); gifts received, $3,900; expenditures, $169,838; qualifying distributions, $164,903; giving activities include $164,778 for 17 grants (high: $36,000; low: $2,000).
Fields of interest: Education; Health.
Type of support: General support.
Limitations: Applications not accepted. Giving primarily in MA and New York, NY.
Application information: Unsolicited requests for funds not accepted.
Trustees: Laura Fandino; Katherine M. Ni Keefe; Andrew F. O'Keefe; David D. O'Keefe; Karen M. O'Keefe.
EIN: 263675448

4230
One Step Forward Education Foundation, Inc.
c/o RH&B, Inc.
50 Congress St., Ste. 900
Boston, MA 02109-4023
E-mail: info@osffoundation.com; Main URL: http://osffoundation.com

Donors: Mark S. Casady; Julia N. Casady.
Foundation type: Independent foundation.

Financial data (yr. ended 12/31/13): Assets, $5,673,838 (M); gifts received, $357; expenditures, $305,027; qualifying distributions, $275,801; giving activities include $266,500 for 13 grants (high: $150,000; low: $1,000).
Fields of interest: Arts and culture; Education; Human services.
Limitations: Applications not accepted. Giving primarily in MA.
Application information: Unsolicited request for funds not accepted.
Officers: Julia N. Casady, Pres.; Robert G. Bannish, Clerk; Mark S. Casady, Treas.
EIN: 271533374

4231
OneBeacon Charitable Trust
(formerly CGU Charitable Trust)
150 Royall St.
Canton, MA 02021-1030

Donor: General Accident Insurance Co. of America.
Foundation type: Company-sponsored foundation.
Financial data (yr. ended 12/31/13): Assets, $1,516,547 (M); expenditures, $388,118; qualifying distributions, $377,837; giving activities include $361,592 for 6 grants (high: $157,866; low: $23,250), and $16,245 for 1 employee matching gift.
Purpose and activities: The foundation supports food banks and organizations involved with arts and culture, education, health, cancer research, human services, community development, and other areas.
Fields of interest: Education; Agriculture; Human services.
Type of support: General support; Employee matching gifts; Sponsorships; Scholarships.
Limitations: Applications not accepted. Giving primarily in areas of company operations, with emphasis on Boston, MA. No grants to individuals (except for employee-related scholarships).
Application information: Contributes only to pre-selected organizations and through employee-related scholarships.
Trustees: Paul H. McDonough; Paul Romano; Thomas N. Schmitt.
EIN: 232441567

4232
Oristaglio Family Foundation
287 Commonwealth Ave., Ste. 4
Boston, MA 02115-2020   (617) 859-3088
Contact: Jeryl Oristaglio, Tr.

Established in 2000 in Massachusetts.
Donors: Stephen Oristaglio; Oristaglio Family Enhancement Trust.
Foundation type: Independent foundation.
Financial data (yr. ended 12/31/13): Assets, $65,093 (M); gifts received, $302,522; expenditures, $275,245; qualifying distributions, $272,590; giving activities include $272,590 for 47 grants (high: $60,000; low: $100).
Fields of interest: Education; Nonprofits; Hospital care; Diseases and conditions.
Type of support: Regranting.
Limitations: Applications accepted. Giving primarily in MA. No grants to individuals.
Application information: Application form required.
  Initial approach: Letter
  Deadline(s): None

Trustee: Jeryl Oristaglio.
EIN: 043541069

4233
Albert N. Parlin Trust
c/o Hemenway & Barnes
60 State St.
Boston, MA 02109-1209   6172277940

Foundation type: Independent foundation.
Financial data (yr. ended 12/31/14): Assets, $6,355,044; expenditures, $172,314; qualifying distributions, $135,234.
Fields of interest: Human services.
Type of support: General support.
Limitations: Applications not accepted. Giving limited to Boston and Somerville, MA. No grants to individuals.
Application information: Contributes only to pre-selected organizations.
Trustees: Timothy F. Fidgeon; Kurt F. Somerville.
EIN: 510150855

4234
The Patagonia Sur Foundation
P. O. Box 2428
Edgartown, MA 02539-2428   (917) 300-1076
Contact: Daniela Diaz, Exec. Dir.
FAX: (508) 503-3788;
E-mail: info@fundacionpatagoniasur.cl; Chilean Address: La Concepcion 141, Office 304, Providencia, Santiago, Chile, tel.: (56) 2-2897-3538; Main URL: http://patagoniasur.com/subpage.php?sid=47&l=e&l=e

Established in 2007 in Unspecified.
Donors: Warren Adams; Megan Adams; David Tufaro; Sharon Tufaro; Fred Mouawad; Jim Levitt; Jane Levitt; Brian Hoesterey; Dawn Hoesterey; Elizabeth Daisy Helman; Stephen Reifenberg; Chris Cervenak; Daniel Nowiszewski; Bechler River Partners, LLC; Tufaro Family Ltd. Partnership; BJP Ventures, LLC; Patagonia Resources, LLC; Small Pond Investments, Ltd.; Basant LTDA; Hvalbukta Ans.
Foundation type: Independent foundation.
Financial data (yr. ended 12/31/12): Assets, $22,755 (M); gifts received, $84,050; expenditures, $180,905; qualifying distributions, $176,458; giving activities include $176,458 for grants.
Purpose and activities: Giving primarily to encourage conservation and promote social and economic development in the Patagonia region of Chile.
Fields of interest: University education; Environment; International development.
International interests: Chile.
Type of support: General support.
Limitations: Applications not accepted. Giving primarily in Chile; some funding also in the U.S., with emphasis on Cambridge, MA and Portland, ME. No grants to individuals.
Application information: Contributes only to pre-selected organizations.
Directors: Steve Reifenberg; Pablo Allard; Francisca Cortes.
EIN: 208875388

4235
Pechet Foundation
c/o Streamline Family Office
60 Center St.
Dover, MA 02030-0174

Donors: Carol A. Pechet; Foundation for Medical Research; Maurice M. Pechet.
Foundation type: Independent foundation.
Financial data (yr. ended 12/31/13): Assets, $5,378,282 (M); expenditures, $321,050; qualifying distributions, $260,000; giving activities include $260,000 for 42 grants (high: $75,000; low: $500).
Purpose and activities: Giving primarily for higher education and the arts.
Fields of interest: Arts and culture; Education; Higher education; Diseases and conditions; Human services.
Type of support: Research; Research and evaluation.
Limitations: Applications not accepted. Giving primarily in MA. No grants to individuals.
Application information: Contributes only to pre-selected organizations.
Trustee: Carol A. Pechet.
EIN: 046059253

4236
The Pegasus Foundation
c/o Day, Pitney, LLP
One International Pl.
Boston, MA 02110-2602
Contact: John W. Grandy, Exec. Dir.
E-mail: info@pegasusfoundation.org; Main URL: http://www.pegasusfoundation.org

Established in 1996 in Massachusetts.
Donor: Barbara U. Birdsey.
Foundation type: Independent foundation.
Financial data (yr. ended 12/31/13): Assets, $1,106,320 (M); gifts received, $597,685; expenditures, $547,603; qualifying distributions, $327,050; giving activities include $327,050 for 32 grants (high: $100,000; low: $100).
Purpose and activities: The Pegasus Foundation was established in 1996 to fund initiatives that benefit animals and the environment. The Foundation's work is concentrated in several regions of the United States: the West and Southwest (Arizona and Montana), Florida, and Cape Cod, Massachusetts. Pegasus also funds animal welfare programs in the Caribbean and Kenya.
Fields of interest: Education services; Environment; Wildlife biodiversity; Animal welfare.
International interests: Caribbean; Kenya.
Type of support: Continuing support; Matching grants; Capacity-building and technical assistance; Program development; Convening; Program evaluations.
Limitations: Applications not accepted. Giving primarily in FL, MA, select western states, and in the Caribbean and Kenya. No grants to individuals, or for endowments, deficit reduction, or scholarships.
Publications: Annual report; Informational brochure.
Application information: Unsolicited proposals not accepted. Proposals accepted only from current grantees and those who have been invited to apply.
  Board meeting date(s): Quarterly
Officer: John W. Grandy, Exec. Dir.
Trustees: Charles J. Birdsey; David W. Fitts, Esq.; Karen B. Macleod; George W. Malloy; Stephen Ziobrowski.

Number of staff: 3 full-time professional; 1 part-time professional.
EIN: 223487149

4237
Peoples Federal Savings Bank Charitable Foundation

2036 Washington St.
Hanover, MA 02339-1617 (781) 982-6534
Contact: Maurice H. Sullivan Jr., Chair. and C.E.O.

Donor: Peoples Federal Savings Bank Foundation.
Foundation type: Independent foundation.
Financial data (yr. ended 12/31/14): Assets, $11,985,710 (M); expenditures, $440,791; qualifying distributions, $438,109; giving activities include $421,000 for 53 grants (high: $40,000; low: $1,000).
Fields of interest: Education; Health; Human services.
Application information: Application form required.
Initial approach: E-mail
Deadline(s): None
Officers and Directors: Maurice H. Sullivan, Jr., Chair. and C.E.O.; Thomas J. Leetch, Pres. and C.O.O.; James J. Gavin, Exec. V.P. and Director; Leann Cote, Secy. and Director; Christopher Lake, Treas. and Director; Andrea M. Howard.
EIN: 272499279

4238
PerkinElmer Foundation

(formerly EG&G Foundation)
940 Winter St.
Waltham, MA 02451-1457 (781) 663-6900
Contact: JoAnn Tupper
Main URL: http://www.perkinelmer.com

Established in 1979 in Massachusetts.
Donors: EG&G, Inc.; PerkinElmer, Inc.
Foundation type: Company-sponsored foundation.
Financial data (yr. ended 06/30/15): Assets, $8,077,187 (M); expenditures, $431,270; qualifying distributions, $336,350; giving activities include $336,350 for 35 grants (high: $75,000; low: $100).
Purpose and activities: The foundation supports programs designed to address human and environmental health. Special emphasis is directed toward the accurate diagnosis of disease; and protecting the environment.
Fields of interest: Arts and culture; Museums; Education; Elementary and secondary education; Aquariums; Health; School-based health care; Genetic conditions and birth defects; Human services; Homeless services.
Type of support: General support; Employee matching gifts.
Limitations: Applications accepted. Giving primarily in MA. No grants to individuals.
Application information: Application form required.
Initial approach: E-mail
Deadline(s): None
Trustees: Robert F. Friel; Joel S. Goldberg; John Letcher.
EIN: 042683042

4239
Permanent Endowment Fund for Martha's Vineyard

P.O. Box 1182
Oak Bluffs, MA 02557-0000 (508) 338-4665
Contact: Julie Anne McNary, Exec. Dir.
FAX: (508) 338-4665; E-mail: info@endowmv.org;
Main URL: http://www.permanentendowmv.org

Established in 1982 in Massachusetts.
Foundation type: Community foundation.
Financial data (yr. ended 12/31/13): Assets, $9,282,038 (M); gifts received, $442,605; expenditures, $419,007; giving activities include $117,968 for 5+ grants (high: $19,508), and $172,232 for 116 grants to individuals.
Purpose and activities: The foundation exists to give those who love the Vineyard an opportunity to make tax-deductible gifts to build an endowment designated to strengthen the quality of Vineyard life.
Fields of interest: Arts and culture; Visual arts; Performing arts; Education; Higher education; Environment; Natural resources; Health; Hospice care; Diseases and conditions; HIV/AIDS; Cancers; Community and economic development; Human services; Family services.
Type of support: Convening; Grants to individuals; Matching grants; Continuing support; Capital campaigns; Building and renovations; Equipment; Endowments; Emergency funds; Program development; Seed money; Scholarships; Research; Student aid.
Limitations: Applications accepted. Giving limited to Martha's Vineyard, MA. No grants for operating costs (except in emergency situations), or for endowments, debt reduction, or annual fund drives.
Publications: Application guidelines; Annual report.
Application information: Visit foundation web site for application form and guidelines. Application form required.
Initial approach: Telephone or letter
Copies of proposal: 10
Deadline(s): Feb. 15 and Sept. 15
Board meeting date(s): Usually 10 to 12 times per year
Final notification: 8 weeks
Officers and Board Members: Melissa M. Hackney, Chair. and Director; Edward F. Miller, Treas. and Director; Julie Anne McNary, Exec. Dir.; Kerry H. Alley; Emily B. Bramhall; Carlene J. Gatting; Sandra Grymes; Adriana Ignacio; Paul Karasik; Jennifer W. Marlin; Donald G. Ogilvie; Anne E. Williamson.
Trustee Bank: Dukes County Savings Bank.
Number of staff: 1 part-time support.
EIN: 042774790

4240
The Edward Lee and Slocumb Hollis Perry Foundation

214 Allandale Rd., Ste. A
Chestnut Hill, MA 02467 (617) 739-1298

Established in 1998 in Massachusetts.
Donors: Edward Lee Perry; Helen Wade Green Charitable Trust.
Foundation type: Independent foundation.
Financial data (yr. ended 12/31/14): Assets, $25,544; gifts received, $320,100; expenditures, $411,112; qualifying distributions, $410,762.
Purpose and activities: Giving primarily for the arts, particularly the performing arts and art museums.

Fields of interest: Arts and culture; Theater; Opera; Orchestral music; Performing arts education; Art museums; Secondary education; Hospital care; Radio.
Limitations: Applications accepted. Giving primarily in the greater Boston, MA, area. No grants to individuals.
Application information:
Initial approach: Proposal
Deadline(s): None
Officers and Trustees: Edward Lee Perry, Pres. and Trustee; Slocumb Hollis Perry, Treas. and Trustee; Anne H. Perkins.
EIN: 311621824

4241
Frank Reed & Margaret Jane Peters Memorial Fund I

c/o US Trust, Bank of America, N.A.
225 Franklin St., MA1-225-04-02
Boston, MA 02110-2801 (866) 778-6859
Contact: Phung Pham, V.P.
E-mail: ma.grantmaking@ustrust.com; Main
URL: https://www.bankofamerica.com/
philanthropic/grantmaking.go

Established in 1935 in Massachusetts.
Foundation type: Independent foundation.
Financial data (yr. ended 12/31/13): Assets, $9,561,412 (M); expenditures, $484,899; qualifying distributions, $394,762; giving activities include $352,000 for 20 grants (high: $85,000; low: $2,000).
Purpose and activities: Giving primarily to support and promote quality educational, human services, and health care programming for underserved populations. Special consideration is given to charitable organizations that serve youth and children.
Fields of interest: Education; Human services; Family services; Child welfare.
Limitations: Giving primarily in Boston, MA. No grants to individuals, for independent research projects, or for publications or national organizations.
Application information: Complete application guidelines available on fund's web site.
Initial approach: E-mail
Trustee: Bank of America, N.A.
EIN: 046012009

4242
Richard J. Phelps Charitable Foundation

599 North Ave., Door 8, 2nd Fl.
Wakefield, MA 01880-1648

Established in 1990 in Massachusetts.
Donor: Richard J. Phelps.
Foundation type: Independent foundation.
Financial data (yr. ended 06/30/13): Assets, $43,424 (M); gifts received, $26,829; expenditures, $253,651; qualifying distributions, $251,148; giving activities include $248,685 for 43 grants (high: $62,350; low: $100).
Fields of interest: Arts and culture; Secondary education; Higher education; University education; Housing development; Sports.
Type of support: General support; Capital and infrastructure; Scholarships.
Limitations: Applications not accepted. Giving primarily in CT, FL and MA.

Application information: Unsolicited requests for funds not accepted.
Trustees: Ann Jacobs; Richard J. Phelps.
EIN: 223090828

4243
Philips Electronics North American Foundation
(formerly North American Philips Foundation)
c/o Phillips Tax Dept.
3000 Minuteman Rd.
Andover, MA 01810-1032

Established in 1979 in New York.
Donors: Philips Electronics North America Corp.; Lifetime Systems Co.; Respironics, Inc.; Phillips Medical Systems (Cleveland), Inc.; Philips Medical Systems, Inc.; Philips Lumileds Holding BV.
Foundation type: Company-sponsored foundation.
Financial data (yr. ended 12/31/13): Assets, $305 (M); gifts received, $317,000; expenditures, $318,581; qualifying distributions, $318,581; giving activities include $317,000 for 87 grants (high: $10,000; low: $3,000).
Purpose and activities: The foundation awards college scholarships to children of employees of Philips Electronics North America Corporation.
Fields of interest: Education; Human services.
Limitations: Applications accepted. Giving primarily in IL, KS, KY, MA, NJ, NY, OH, PA, WA, and WI.
Application information: Application form required.
Initial approach: Contact foundation for application form
Deadline(s): Mar. 1
Officers: David A. Dripchak, Pres.; Paul Cavanaugh, V.P.; Joseph E. Innamorati, V.P.
EIN: 132961300

4244
Thomas S. Pierce Trust
P.O. Box 332
Middleboro, MA 02346-0332

Foundation type: Independent foundation.
Financial data (yr. ended 12/31/13): Assets, $5,599,116 (M); expenditures, $248,830; qualifying distributions, $231,103; giving activities include $231,103 for 5 grants (high: $67,000; low: $3,653).
Fields of interest: Education; Disasters and emergency management; Human services.
Limitations: Applications not accepted. Giving primarily in Middleboro, MA.
Application information: Unsolicited requests for funds not accepted.
Trustees: Donald K. Atkins; Bruce Atwood; Robert Desrosiers.
EIN: 042007122

4245
Pilgrim Foundation
P.O. Box 3400
Brockton, MA 02303-3400 (508) 586-6100
Contact: Jane Southworth

Established in 1926 in Massachusetts.
Donor: Edgar B. Davis†.
Foundation type: Independent foundation.
Financial data (yr. ended 12/31/13): Assets, $5,144,515 (M); gifts received, $50; expenditures,

$237,614; qualifying distributions, $207,671; giving activities include $128,219 for 12 grants (high: $50,000; low: $500), and $63,000 for grants to individuals.
Purpose and activities: Support primarily to aid children by assisting needy families through grants to individuals; provides camperships, memberships in character-building organizations, and scholarships for higher education; limited grants to organizations aiding adolescents.
Fields of interest: Arts and culture; Education; Public libraries; Catholicism; Human services; Youth services.
Type of support: General support; Grants to individuals; Student aid; Individual development.
Limitations: Applications accepted. Giving limited to residents of Brockton, MA.
Publications: Informational brochure.
Application information: Application form required.
Initial approach: Letter
Copies of proposal: 8
Deadline(s): June 30
Board meeting date(s): Last Sun. of the month
Officers: Joanne Johnson, Pres.; Betty Ann Grace, Secy.; David Orloff, Treas. and Director.
Trustees: George Asack, Jr.; Reinald Ledoux, Jr.; Kathleen Manson; James C. Pinkham; Edward Reservitz.
EIN: 042104834

4246
Poduska Family Foundation, Inc.
295 Meadowbrook Rd.
Weston, MA 02493-2450 (781) 893-3964
Contact: Susan M. Poduska, Pres. and Treas.
Main URL: http://poduskafamilyfoundation.org

Established in 1994 in Massachusetts.
Donor: John William Poduska.
Foundation type: Independent foundation.
Financial data (yr. ended 12/31/13): Assets, $108,166 (M); gifts received, $1,562; expenditures, $184,482; qualifying distributions, $177,250; giving activities include $177,250 for 27 grants (high: $60,000; low: $500).
Fields of interest: Ballet; Education; Health care clinics; Diseases and conditions; Cancers.
Type of support: Research.
Limitations: Applications accepted. Giving primarily in MA.
Application information:
Initial approach: Letter
Deadline(s): None
Officers and Directors: Susan M. Poduska, Pres. and Treas. and Director; Thomas Chase, Clerk and Director; Bonnie M. Menton; Mary Beth Pandiscio; Lily A. Poduska; John William Poduska, Jr.; John William Poduska, Sr.
EIN: 043235379

4247
The Progin Foundation
c/o Darmody, Merlino & Co., LLP
75 Federal St., Ste. 1500
Boston, MA 02110-1997

Established in 2007 in Massachusetts.
Donor: George K. Progin†.
Foundation type: Independent foundation.
Financial data (yr. ended 12/31/13): Assets, $3,581,399 (M); expenditures, $204,162;

qualifying distributions, $173,000; giving activities include $173,000 for 9 grants (high: $28,000; low: $10,000).
Fields of interest: Arts education; Education; Public libraries; Family services; Child welfare; Independent living for people with disabilities; People with vision impairments.
Limitations: Applications not accepted. Giving primarily in MA. No grants to individuals.
Application information: Contributes only to pre-selected organizations.
Trustees: A. Dennis Barbo; Brian D. Bixby.
EIN: 208919545

4248
Prokopis Charitable Foundation
c/o Edwards, Wildman, Palmer, LLP
111 Huntington Ave.
Boston, MA 02199-7610 (617) 239-0778
Contact: Peter A. Wilson, Tr.

Donor: Emmanuel C. Prokopis.
Foundation type: Independent foundation.
Financial data (yr. ended 12/31/13): Assets, $337,699 (M); expenditures, $164,678; qualifying distributions, $160,336; giving activities include $157,000 for 7 grants (high: $120,000; low: $2,000).
Fields of interest: Diseases and conditions; Cancers; Agriculture; Religion.
Type of support: General support; Research.
Application information: Application form required.
Initial approach: Request application form
Deadline(s): None
Trustees: Mark M. Christopher; Peter A. Wilson.
EIN: 043425084

4249
Ruth E. Proud Charitable Trust
87 Marshall St.
North Adams, MA 01247-0746

Established in 2002 in Massachusetts.
Foundation type: Independent foundation.
Financial data (yr. ended 12/31/13): Assets, $2,701,308 (M); expenditures, $237,874; qualifying distributions, $212,071; giving activities include $129,518 for 5 grants (high: $69,518; low: $5,000).
Fields of interest: Education; Computer science; Camps; Human services.
Limitations: Applications not accepted. Giving primarily in MA. No grants to individuals.
Application information: Contributes only to pre-selected organizations.
Trustee: Derosa Dohoney LLP.
EIN: 020691253

4250
The Provident Community Foundation, Inc.
5 Market St.
Amesbury, MA 01913-2408 (978) 834-8590
Contact: Beverly Ledoux, Dir.

Established in 1997 in Massachusetts.
Foundation type: Independent foundation.
Financial data (yr. ended 12/31/13): Assets, $1,511,960 (M); expenditures, $212,465; qualifying distributions, $179,785; giving activities

include $179,512 for 45 grants (high: $80,000; low: $55).

Purpose and activities: Giving for community services, economic development, youth programs, arts and culture, and social services in the Amesbury, Massachusetts, area.

Fields of interest: Arts and culture; Community and economic development; Human services; Youth development.

Limitations: Applications accepted. Giving limited to the Amesbury, MA, area. No grants to individuals.

Application information: Application form required.

Initial approach: Letter

Deadline(s): 1st Tues. in Mar., June, Sept. and Dec.

Officers and Directors: Wayne S. Tatro, Chair. and Director; Charles R. Cullen, Pres. and Director; Lorraine E. Sanborn, Secy. and Clerk.; David P. Mansfield, Treas.; Robert A. Becker; John K. Bosen; John J. Cameron; Frank G. Cousins, Jr.; Robert A. Gonthier, Jr.; Jay E. Gould; Lawrence C. Hoyt, Jr.; Laurie H. Knapp; Nancy M. Moore; Beverly Ledoux; Carl R. Lesage; Richard L. Peeke; Raymond E. Pouliot.

EIN: 043397455

4251
Puffin Foundation

50 Congress St., Ste. 800
Boston, MA 02109-4034

Donor: Levin H. Campbell.

Foundation type: Independent foundation.

Financial data (yr. ended 12/31/13): Assets, $7,228,878 (M); expenditures, $342,198; qualifying distributions, $292,256; giving activities include $241,000 for 10 grants (high: $61,000; low: $5,000).

Fields of interest: Human services.

Type of support: General support; Ethics and accountability.

Limitations: Applications not accepted. Giving primarily in MA.

Application information: Unsolicited requests for funds not accepted.

Trustees: Sarah H. C. Ambler; David Ambler; Levin H. Cambell, Jr.; Alexander Webb III.

EIN: 300674291

4252
Putnam Investments Foundation

1 Post Office Sq., Ste. A-16-B
Boston, MA 02109-2106

Established in 1992 in Massachusetts.

Donors: Putnam Investments, Inc.; Christine M. Halloran.

Foundation type: Company-sponsored foundation.

Financial data (yr. ended 12/31/13): Assets, $21,179 (M); gifts received, $65,196; expenditures, $230,717; qualifying distributions, $230,647; giving activities include $230,647 for 16 grants (high: $107,121; low: $26).

Purpose and activities: The foundation supports hospitals and organizations involved with education, children and youth, and family services.

Fields of interest: Arts and culture; Religion; Human services.

Limitations: Applications not accepted. Giving primarily in the greater metropolitan Boston, MA, area. No grants to individuals.

Application information: Contributes only to pre-selected organizations.

Trustees: Jonathan M. Goldstein; Clare S. Richer.

EIN: 043175266

4253
William Lowell Putnam Prize Fund for the Promotion of Scholarship

c/o Boston Family Office
88 Broad St., 2nd Fl.
Boston, MA 02110-3407

Donor: George Putnam.

Foundation type: Independent foundation.

Financial data (yr. ended 12/31/13): Assets, $11,395,919 (M); expenditures, $528,468; qualifying distributions, $501,765; giving activities include $225,000 for 1 grant, and $109,750 for 37 grants to individuals (high: $25,000; low: $200).

Purpose and activities: Giving primarily for higher education. The Putnam Prize Fund provides funds for mathematics competition and awards prizes to individuals and their schools.

Fields of interest: Higher education.

Type of support: Grants to individuals.

Limitations: Applications not accepted. Giving primarily in MA.

Application information: Unsolicited requests for funds not accepted.

Officers and Directors: George Putnam III, Pres. and Clerk. and Director; Warren Lowell Putnam, Treas. and Director.

EIN: 043414102

4254
The Francis J. Quirico Educational Foundation

c/o John C. Donna, Esq.
P.O. Box 1158
Pittsfield, MA 01202-1158
Contact: John C. Donna Esq.
Application address: c/o John C. Donna, Esq., 54 North St., Pittsfield, MA 01202, tel.: (413) 443-3440

Established in 2007 in Massachusetts.

Donor: Francis J. Quirico†.

Foundation type: Independent foundation.

Financial data (yr. ended 12/31/14): Assets, $4,912,409 (M); expenditures, $273,707; qualifying distributions, $270,195; giving activities include $251,210 for 50 grants to individuals (high: $14,000; low: $365).

Purpose and activities: Scholarship awards to residents of Pittsfield, Massachusetts, who are financially needy.

Fields of interest: Higher education.

Type of support: Student aid.

Limitations: Applications accepted. Giving primarily in Pittsfield, MA.

Application information: Application form required.

Initial approach: Letter

Deadline(s): Feb. 28

Trustees: John C. Donna, Esq.; Louis Giovanetti; Vincent P. Marinaro.

EIN: 207145260

4255
James M. Rabb Charitable Trust

10 Possum Rd.
Weston, MA 02493-2318

Donor: Irving W. Rabb†.

Foundation type: Independent foundation.

Financial data (yr. ended 12/31/13): Assets, $10,407,072 (M); expenditures, $172,504; qualifying distributions, $153,604; giving activities include $153,469 for 21 grants (high: $25,000; low: $25).

Fields of interest: Arts and culture; Education; Judaism.

Limitations: Applications not accepted. Giving primarily in MA.

Application information: Unsolicited requests for funds not accepted.

Trustee: Melinda A. Rabb.

EIN: 387032850

4256
Phillip and Susan Ragon Foundation

P.O. Box 380281
Cambridge, MA 02238-0281

Established in 2003 in Massachusetts.

Donors: Phillip T. Ragon; Susan M. Ragon.

Foundation type: Independent foundation.

Financial data (yr. ended 12/31/14): Assets, $1,003,457 (M); gifts received, $500,000; expenditures, $210,281; qualifying distributions, $207,100; giving activities include $205,000 for 15 grants (high: $25,000; low: $5,000).

Fields of interest: Education; Higher education; Diseases and conditions; Academic libraries; Christianity; Human services.

Limitations: Applications not accepted. Giving primarily in Boston and Cambridge, MA. No grants to individuals.

Application information: Contributes only to pre-selected organizations.

Trustees: Phillip T. Ragon; Susan M. Ragon.

EIN: 050547000

4257
George A. Ramlose Foundation, Inc.

P.O. Box 550
Sterling, MA 01564-0550 (978) 368-1200
Contact: David L. Taylor, Treas.
FAX: (978) 368-4312; *E-mail:* david@ramlose.org

Established in 1956 in New York.

Donor: George Ramlose Trust†.

Foundation type: Independent foundation.

Financial data (yr. ended 04/30/14): Assets, $3,167,672 (M); expenditures, $190,439; qualifying distributions, $147,971; giving activities include $147,971 for 57 grants (high: $10,322; low: $1,000).

Purpose and activities: Primary areas of interest include cultural programs, higher education, literacy, the disabled, and medical research.

Fields of interest: Orchestral music; Education; Teacher education; Education services; Diseases and conditions; Food aid; Child welfare; Women's services.

Type of support: General support; Equipment; Program development; Seed money; Scholarships; Research; Research and evaluation.

Limitations: Applications accepted. Giving primarily in New England, GA, and SC. No grants to individuals.
Application information: AGM Common Proposal Form accepted. Application form required.
   Initial approach: Proposal
   Copies of proposal: 2
   Deadline(s): Aug. 31
   Board meeting date(s): Oct.
   Final notification: Within 2 months
Officers: Peter F. Boyce, Pres.; Carole C. Boyce, V.P.; Linda M. Taylor, V.P.; David L. Taylor, Treas.
Number of staff: 1 part-time support.
EIN: 046048231

4258
The Ramsey McCluskey Family Foundation

P.O. Box 275
Lincoln, MA   01773-0275   (781) 259-9948
Contact: Margaret A. Ramsey, Tr.
E-mail: RMFndn@gmail.com; Main URL: http://www.ramseymccluskeyfndn.org
Grants List: http://www.ramseymccluskeyfndn.org/recentGrants.aspx

Established in 1999 in Massachusetts.
Donor: Margaret A. Ramsey.
Foundation type: Independent foundation.
Financial data (yr. ended 03/31/13): Assets, $3,119,953 (M); gifts received, $75,000; expenditures, $189,258; qualifying distributions, $165,014; giving activities include $155,600 for 32 grants (high: $75,000; low: $100).
Purpose and activities: Giving primarily to support projects in education and the arts.
Fields of interest: Arts and culture; Arts education; Museums; Education; Reading promotion; Domesticated animals; Food aid.
Type of support: Program development; Scholarships; Individual development.
Limitations: Applications accepted. Giving primarily in MA. No grants for capital campaigns, endowments, or general operating expenses.
Publications: Application guidelines.
Application information: Application form required.
   Initial approach: Letter or email (strongly encouraged over telephone calls)
   Copies of proposal: 1
   Deadline(s): Oct. 1
   Board meeting date(s): Late Mar.
Trustees: John M. McCluskey; Margaret A. Ramsey.
EIN: 043464899

4259
A.C. Ratshesky Foundation

c/o GMA Foundations
77 Summer St., 8th Fl.
Boston, MA   02110-1006   (617) 391-3092
Contact: Susan Haff, Fdn. Asst.; Prentice Zinn, Prog. Off.
FAX: (617) 426-7087;
E-mail: pzinn@gmafoundations.com; Main URL: http://www.ratsheskyfoundation.org
Grants List: http://www.ratsheskyfoundation.org/grants/past-grants

Established in 1916 in Massachusetts.
Donor: A.C. Ratshesky†.
Foundation type: Independent foundation.

Financial data (yr. ended 12/31/13): Assets, $7,412,195 (M); expenditures, $368,624; qualifying distributions, $283,890; giving activities include $227,000 for 20 grants (high: $25,000; low: $7,000).
Purpose and activities: The foundation is committed to fostering economic and social justice for low- and moderate-income families residing in Boston, Massachusetts and surrounding communities. The foundation gives priority consideration to programs from the following fields of interest: education and training, and arts and culture. Support for programs that serve disadvantaged Jewish populations is also of special interest, provided that these programs are aligned with one or more of the foundation's other fields of interest.
Fields of interest: Arts and culture; Arts education; Education; Vocational education; Basic and remedial instruction; Education services; Employment; Judaism; Family services; Child welfare; Low-income and poor people.
Type of support: General support; Continuing support; Program development; Seed money.
Limitations: Applications accepted. Giving limited to the metro Boston, MA, area, within Rte. 128. No support for public schools, or for health programs, national organizations, municipal, state or federal agencies, or religious programs. No grants to individuals, or for annual campaigns, general endowments, deficit financing, land acquisition, web sites, scientific or other research, publications, or conferences; no loans.
Publications: Application guidelines; Grants list.
Application information: The foundation uses an online application process. See foundation web site for complete application information. Associated Grant Makers Common Proposal Form accepted. Application form required.
   Initial approach: Proposal or telephone
   Copies of proposal: 1
   Deadline(s): Feb. 1, July 1, and Oct. 1
   Board meeting date(s): May, Oct., and Jan.
   Final notification: Following board meetings
Officers and Trustees: Laurie Morse Sprague, Pres. and Trustee; Rebecca Morse Steinfield, Secy. and Trustee; Linda G. Ortwein, Treas.; Craig Levy; Roberta Morse Levy; Alan R. Morse, Jr.; Eric Robert Morse; Jennifer Morse.
Number of staff: 2 part-time professional; 1 part-time support.
EIN: 046017426

4260
Red Acre Farm, Inc.

P.O. Box 278
Stow, MA   01775-0278
E-mail: grants@redacrefoundation.org; Main URL: http://www.redacrefoundation.org

Established in 1903 in Massachusetts.
Donors: Helen Hardenbrook†; Josephine Kibbey†.
Foundation type: Independent foundation.
Financial data (yr. ended 09/30/14): Assets, $8,156,451 (M); gifts received, $2,611; expenditures, $452,279; qualifying distributions, $393,540; giving activities include $355,000 for 46 grants (high: $20,000; low: $1,000).
Purpose and activities: Giving primarily for animal welfare, wildlife protection, and human and animal bond efforts.
Fields of interest: Wildlife biodiversity; Animal welfare.

Type of support: General support.
Limitations: Giving limited to southern New England (except CT), southern AZ, and some areas in southwestern CO. No grants to individuals.
Application information: See foundation web site for application guidelines and procedures. Application form required.
   Initial approach: E-mail to request proposal form
   Copies of proposal: 1
   Deadline(s): Varies
   Board meeting date(s): Summer and winter
Officers and Directors: Nathanael Shepherd, Pres. and Director; Jay Bowen, V.P. and Director; David Ayer, Clerk and Director; Walter M. Bird III, Treas. and Director; James G. Bird; Leonard W. Johnson; Quincey Simmons.
EIN: 042119492

4261
The Redwall Foundation Inc.

c/o Forrester Research Inc.
60 Acorn Park Dr.
Cambridge, MA   02140-2303

Established in 2005 in Massachusetts.
Donors: George F. Colony; Ann B. Colony.
Foundation type: Independent foundation.
Financial data (yr. ended 12/31/13): Assets, $5,116,480 (M); expenditures, $211,843; qualifying distributions, $200,085; giving activities include $200,000 for 2 grants (high: $100,000; low: $100,000).
Fields of interest: Higher education; Environment.
Limitations: Applications not accepted. Giving primarily in MA and NY. No grants to individuals.
Application information: Unsolicited requests for funds not accepted.
Officers and Directors: George F. Colony, Pres. and Director; Ann B. Colony, Clerk and Treas. and Director.
EIN: 161712932

4262
Howard & Robin Reisman Charitable Trust

165 Bay State Dr.
Braintree, MA   02184-5203

Established in 2002 in Massachusetts.
Donors: George C. Reisman; George C. and Evelyn R. Reisman Charitable Trust.
Foundation type: Independent foundation.
Financial data (yr. ended 12/31/13): Assets, $7,497,520 (M); expenditures, $283,701; qualifying distributions, $231,617; giving activities include $216,117 for 30 grants (high: $150,000; low: $35).
Fields of interest: Education; Higher education; Nonprofits; Judaism; Human services.
Type of support: Regranting.
Limitations: Applications not accepted. Giving primarily in MA and RI. No grants to individuals.
Application information: Contributes only to pre-selected organizations.
Trustees: Howard M. Reisman; Robin Reisman.
EIN: 046965548

4263
Robert S. & Maria J. Reisman Charitable Trust

131 Winding River Rd.
Needham, MA 02492-1024

Established in 2002 in Massachusetts.
Foundation type: Independent foundation.
Financial data (yr. ended 12/31/13): Assets, $8,520,129 (M); expenditures, $432,729; qualifying distributions, $376,450; giving activities include $341,450 for 33 grants (high: $255,000; low: $200).
Fields of interest: Domesticated animals; Health; Hospital care; Diseases and conditions.
Type of support: Research.
Limitations: Applications not accepted. Giving primarily in MA. No grants to individuals.
Application information: Unsolicited requests for funds not accepted.
Trustees: Maria Reisman; Robert Reisman.
EIN: 046965549

4264
Marjorie Harris Reynolds Foundation

c/o Atlantic Trust Co.
100 Federal St., 37th Fl.
Boston, MA 02110-1802

Established in 1996 in Massachusetts.
Donors: Eric Oddleifson; Eric Oddleifson Trust; GMO Renewable Resources LLC.
Foundation type: Independent foundation.
Financial data (yr. ended 12/31/13): Assets, $2,024,876 (M); gifts received, $50,000; expenditures, $193,365; qualifying distributions, $183,850; giving activities include $181,000 for 32 grants (high: $50,000; low: $400).
Fields of interest: Arts and culture; Education; Sports and recreation.
Limitations: Applications not accepted. Giving primarily in MA. No grants to individuals.
Application information: Unsolicited requests for funds not accepted.
Trustee: Janna Oddleifson.
EIN: 046820699

4265
Albert W. Rice Charitable Foundation

c/o Bank of America, N.A.
225 Franklin St., 4th Fl., MA1-225-04-02
Boston, MA 02110-2801 (866) 778-6859
E-mail: ma.grantmaking@ustrust.com; Main
URL: https://www.bankofamerica.com/philanthropic/grantmaking.go

Established in 1959 in Massachusetts.
Donors: Albert W. Rice†; Mary Gage Rice†.
Foundation type: Independent foundation.
Financial data (yr. ended 12/31/14): Assets, $6,908,896; expenditures, $462,240; qualifying distributions, $399,802.
Purpose and activities: The foundation supports and promotes quality educational, human services, and health care programming for underserved populations. Special consideration is given to charitable organizations that serve the people of Worcester, Massachusetts, and surrounding communities.
Fields of interest: Education; Health; Human services.

Type of support: General support; Program development.
Limitations: Giving primarily in Worcester, MA and surrounding communities. No grants to individuals.
Publications: Application guidelines.
Application information: Online application; complete application guidelines available on foundation web site. Application form required.
  Initial approach: E-mail
Trustee: Bank of America, N.A.
Number of staff: None.
EIN: 046028085

4266
The Robbins-de Beaumont Foundation

c/o Sullivan & Worcester LLP
1 Post Office Sq.
Boston, MA 02109-2106
Contact: John K. Graham
FAX: (617) 338-2880; *E-mail:* jrobbins@sandw.com

Established in 1992 in Massachusetts.
Donors: Joseph C. Robbins; Mary Deland de Beaumont; Mary Deland de Beaumont Trust.
Foundation type: Independent foundation.
Financial data (yr. ended 12/31/13): Assets, $10,310,072 (M); expenditures, $526,426; qualifying distributions, $461,526; giving activities include $393,750 for 27 grants (high: $30,000; low: $2,500).
Purpose and activities: The foundation seeks nonprofit organizations whose goals are helping people reach their full potential as contributing members of their family, neighborhoods, and society at large. Limited funds are available for unsolicited grants for new, innovative projects which address identified needs of the community served and have relatively modest operating budgets. The foundation also has an interest in the education of children and adults in the areas of parenting, volunteerism, employment/life skills, preservation of the environment, the performing and visual arts, and substance abuse.
Fields of interest: Arts and culture; Visual arts; Performing arts; Education; Natural resources; Community and economic development; Employment; Human services; Youth services.
Type of support: Seed money.
Limitations: Applications accepted. Giving on a national basis. No support for organizations whose primary focus is mental health, medical training, physical and mental disabilities, special programs, or for organizations whose annual operating budget exceeds $1,000,000, or which have been in existence for over 10 years. No grants to individuals, or for capital campaigns, debt reduction or cash reserves, endowments, multi-year pledges, seed money or start up costs.
Application information: Formal AGM proposal is by invitation only, after review of initial concept paper. Application form required.
  Initial approach: Letter of inquiry or concept paper (not to exceed 2 pages) before submission of a formal proposal
  Deadline(s): Mar. 1 for concept paper; June 30 for proposal
  Board meeting date(s): Semiannually, grant determinations usually in Nov.
Trustees: Joan H. Kopperl; Carol Massoni; Joseph C. Robbins.
EIN: 046719809

4267
Rockland Trust Charitable Foundation

(formerly Benjamin Franklin Bank Charitable Foundation)
288 Union St.
Rockland, MA 02370 (781) 982-6637
Contact: Jeanne Travers, Clerk
E-mail: jeanne.travers@rocklandtrust.com; Main
URL: https://www.rocklandtrust.com

Established in 2005 in Massachusetts.
Donor: Benjamin Franklin Bancorp, Inc.
Foundation type: Company-sponsored foundation.
Financial data (yr. ended 12/31/13): Assets, $6,779,075 (M); expenditures, $311,765; qualifying distributions, $308,321; giving activities include $275,726 for 106 grants (high: $30,000; low: $50), and $22,500 for 9 grants to individuals (high: $2,500; low: $2,500).
Purpose and activities: The foundation supports organizations involved with performing arts, education, health, human services, and community economic development.
Fields of interest: Performing arts; Education; Secondary education; Higher education; Nonprofits; Health; Community and economic development; Human services; Family services; Youth services; Scouting programs.
Type of support: General support; Annual campaigns; Capital campaigns; Program development; Publications; Sponsorships; Student aid; Regranting.
Limitations: Applications accepted. Giving primarily in areas of company operations in Bellingham, Blackstone, Foxboro, Franklin, Hopedale, Medfield, Medway, Mendon, Milford, Millis, Newton, Norfolk, Waltham and Wrentham, MA. No support for discriminatory organizations, religious organizations, candidates for political office, police or fire organizations, labor or fraternal organizations, or community or school sports teams. No grants to individuals (except for scholarships) or for political or government activities.
Application information: Support is limited to 1 contribution per organization during any given year. Application form required.
  Initial approach: Contact foundation for application form
  Deadline(s): None
Officers and Directors: Thomas R. Venables, Pres. and Director; Jeanne L. Travers, Clerk; Claire Bean, Treas. and Director; Jeffrey Smith; Ralph R. Valente; Arthur Viana.
EIN: 202668833

4268
Don and Marilyn Rodman Family Foundation

(formerly Don Rodman Family Foundation)
101 Washington St.
Foxboro, MA 02035-1357
Contact: Carolyn Chaplin, Tr.
E-mail: cchaplin@rodmanford.com; Application
address: c/o Rodman Ride for Kids, Attn.: Donald E. Rodman, 10 Lincoln Rd., Foxboro, MA 02035, tel.: (508) 698-4000

Established in 1999 in Massachusetts.
Donor: Donald E. Rodman.
Foundation type: Independent foundation.
Financial data (yr. ended 11/30/13): Assets, $1,924,989 (M); expenditures, $281,416; qualifying distributions, $259,816; giving activities

include $246,000 for 8 grants (high: $100,000; low: $5,000).
Fields of interest: Nonprofits; Human services; Child welfare.
Type of support: Regranting.
Limitations: Applications accepted. Giving primarily in MA. No grants to individuals.
Application information:
  Initial approach: Letter
  Deadline(s): None
Trustees: James Brett; Carolyn A. Chaplin; Joseph W. D'Arrigo; Nancy E. Dempze; Tracey Goulet; Brett J. Rodman; Curtis L. Rodman; Mary Scannell.
Director: Donald E. Rodman.
EIN: 043444155

4269
Rodman Ford Sales Inc. Charitable Trust
Route 1
Foxboro, MA 02035-1388 (508) 698-4001
Contact: Donald E. Rodman, Tr.

Established in 1986 in Massachusetts.
Donors: Rodman Ford Sales, Inc.; Donald E. Rodman; R. & R. Realty Co.; Rodman Five Realty Trust.
Foundation type: Company-sponsored foundation.
Financial data (yr. ended 12/31/13): Assets, $24,864 (M); gifts received, $286,433; expenditures, $321,997; qualifying distributions, $307,959; giving activities include $307,959 for 206 grants (high: $32,000; low: $100).
Purpose and activities: The foundation supports organizations involved with arts and culture, education, health, and human services.
Fields of interest: Arts and culture; Education; Health; Human services; Child welfare.
Limitations: Applications accepted. Giving primarily in MA. No grants to individuals.
Application information:
  Initial approach: Proposal
  Deadline(s): None
Trustees: Donald E. Rodman; Gene D. Rodman.
Number of staff: None.
EIN: 222780804

4270
Rollstone Charitable Foundation, Inc.
(formerly FSB Charitable Foundation, Inc.)
780 Main St.
Fitchburg, MA 01420-3112 (978) 345-1061
Contact: Martin F. Connors Jr., Pres.

Established in 2005 in Massachusetts.
Donors: Fitchburg Savings Bank; Rollstone Bank & Trust.
Foundation type: Independent foundation.
Financial data (yr. ended 12/31/14): Assets, $910,838 (M); gifts received, $218,347; expenditures, $169,838; qualifying distributions, $162,465; giving activities include $161,295 for 57 grants (high: $29,700; low: $250).
Fields of interest: Education; Philanthropy; Health.
Limitations: Applications accepted. Giving primarily in MA.
Application information: Application form required.
  Initial approach: Request application form
  Deadline(s): None
Officers and Directors: Martin F. Connors, Jr., Pres. and Director; Linda L. Racine, Clerk; Joseph B. Ruth

III, Treas.; Noel R. Bartsch; Anthony J. Mercadante; Michael E. Montuori.
EIN: 202843188

4271
Rose Foundation
c/o Goulston & Storrs
400 Atlantic Ave.
Boston, MA 02110-3333

Established in 2006 in Massachusetts.
Foundation type: Independent foundation.
Financial data (yr. ended 12/31/13): Assets, $9,329,305 (M); expenditures, $474,100; qualifying distributions, $387,469; giving activities include $360,000 for 6 grants (high: $100,000; low: $50,000).
Fields of interest: Public policy; Community and economic development; Human services.
Type of support: General support; Advocacy; Policy, advocacy and systems reform.
Limitations: Applications not accepted. Giving primarily in AR, Washington, DC, GA, MA, ME, MN, NC, NY, OH, OK, OR and VT. No grants to individuals.
Application information: Contributes only to pre-selected organizations.
Trustee: Adam Stein.
EIN: 204647579

4272
The Rosse Family Charitable Foundation
(formerly Thomas A. Rosse Family Charitable Foundation)
c/o Rosse Enterprises
10 Speen St., Ste. 4
Framingham, MA 01701-4661

Established in 1978 in Massachusetts.
Donor: Thomas A. Rosse.
Foundation type: Independent foundation.
Financial data (yr. ended 11/30/13): Assets, $9,386,824 (M); expenditures, $505,413; qualifying distributions, $417,052; giving activities include $416,600 for 59 grants (high: $100,000; low: $100).
Purpose and activities: Giving primarily for education, the arts, and health care.
Fields of interest: Arts and culture; Education; Higher education; Health; Hospital care.
Type of support: Annual campaigns; Scholarships; Research.
Limitations: Applications not accepted. Giving primarily in Concord and Boston, MA; some funding also in Annapolis, MD. No grants to individuals.
Application information: Contributes only to pre-selected organizations.
Officers and Directors: Thomas A. Rosse, Pres. and Director; Bennett S. Yee, Secy.-Treas.; Florence M. Rosse.
EIN: 042659411

4273
Josephine G. Russell Trust
59 Lucerne Dr.
Andover, MA 01810-1719 (978) 500-3171
E-mail: russelltrust@yahoo.com; Applications must also be sent to: Marsha E. Rich, 59 Lucerne Dr., Andover, MA 01810, Eileen Khoury, P.O. Box 5627, Salisbury, MA 01952, John T. Pollano, 861 Turnpike

St., North Andover, MA 01845, and Rev. Paul T. Keyes, 194 Main St., North Andover, MD 01845

Donor: Josephine G. Russell†.
Foundation type: Independent foundation.
Financial data (yr. ended 12/31/13): Assets, $10,388,079 (M); expenditures, $566,814; qualifying distributions, $454,935; giving activities include $417,125 for 40 grants (high: $30,000; low: $25).
Purpose and activities: The purpose of the trust is for the care, healing, and nursing of the sick and injured, the relief and aid of the poor, the training and education of the young, and any other manner of social service in the city of Lawrence, MA.
Fields of interest: Education; Hospital care; Human services; Youth development.
Type of support: General support; Annual campaigns; Emergency funds; Program development; Publications; Scholarships.
Limitations: Giving limited to the greater Lawrence, MA, area. No support for political organizations. No grants to individuals, or for matching gifts, capital, equipment, or construction; no loans.
Publications: Application guidelines.
Application information:
  Initial approach: Letter or proposal
  Copies of proposal: 5
  Deadline(s): Jan. 31
  Board meeting date(s): Quarterly
Trustees: Rev. Paul T. Keyes; Eileen M. Khoury; John T. Pollano, Esq.; Marsha E. Rich, Esq.
Number of staff: 1 part-time professional; 2 part-time support.
EIN: 042136910

4274
Sacajawea Charitable Foundation
(formerly Sacajawea Charitable Foundation Trust)
148 Linden St., Ste. 204
Wellesley, MA 02482-7904

Established in 2000 in Massachusetts.
Donors: Bartlett M. Hauthaway; Wrean Family.
Foundation type: Independent foundation.
Financial data (yr. ended 12/31/14): Assets, $6,683,169 (M); gifts received, $42,663; expenditures, $377,088; qualifying distributions, $351,000.
Fields of interest: Education; Wildlife biodiversity; Diseases and conditions; Religion; Human services.
Type of support: Research.
Limitations: Applications not accepted. Giving primarily in MA and ME.
Application information: Unsolicited requests for funds not accepted.
Director: William H. Wrean, Jr.
EIN: 046891321

4275
The Safe Family Foundation
45 School St., 5th Fl.
Boston, MA 02108-3204 (617) 523-1635
Contact: Elizabeth K. Safe, Tr.

Established in 2001 in Massachusetts.
Donor: Kenneth S. Safe, Jr.
Foundation type: Independent foundation.
Financial data (yr. ended 05/31/13): Assets, $4,393,876 (M); expenditures, $234,083; qualifying distributions, $210,000; giving activities

include $210,000 for 6 grants (high: $100,000; low: $10,000).

Fields of interest: Elementary and secondary education; Environment; Child welfare; Youth organizing.

Limitations: Applications accepted. Giving primarily in Boston, MA.

Application information:

Initial approach: Proposal

Deadline(s): None

Trustees: Elizabeth S. Bitting; Edith S. Devnew; Hope S. Nuland; Elizabeth K. Safe.

EIN: 306001640

4276
Sailors' Snug Harbor of Boston, Inc.

c/o GMA Foundations
77 Summer St., 8th Fl.
Boston, MA 02110-1006 (617) 426-7080
Contact: Gracelaw Simmons, Fdn. Admin.; Ruth Victorin, Fdn. Asst.
FAX: (617) 426-7087;
E-mail: info@gmafoundations.com; Tel. and e-mail for Gracelaw Simmons, Admin.: (617) 426-7080, ext. 312; gsimmons@gmafoundations.com; Main URL: http://www.sailorssnugharbor.org
Grants List: http://www.sailorssnugharbor.org/?page_id=6

Established in 1852 in Massachusetts.

Foundation type: Independent foundation.

Financial data (yr. ended 04/30/13): Assets, $7,494,785 (M); expenditures, $460,453; qualifying distributions, $415,171; giving activities include $373,200 for 31 grants (high: $25,000; low: $700).

Purpose and activities: Giving to help current and former fishing families in MA achieve sustainable self-sufficiency, as well as to help Greater Bostons low-income elderly population live independently.

Fields of interest: Health; Diseases and conditions; Human services; Family services; Senior services; Seniors; Low-income and poor people.

Type of support: General support; Matching grants; Continuing support; Capital and infrastructure.

Limitations: Applications accepted. Giving to agencies that serve seamen, fishermen, and their families is targeted toward MA organizations, with a particular focus on services in New Bedford, Gloucester, and Cape Cod. Grants for services to the elderly are awarded to agencies in greater Boston, with a preference for the City of Boston. No grants to individuals, or for conferences, seminars, debt reduction, cash reserves, multi-year pledges, or for publications, films or videos.

Publications: Application guidelines; Grants list; Occasional report; Program policy statement (including application guidelines).

Application information: All grantmaking guidelines are available on foundation web site.

Initial approach: Online proposal

Deadline(s): For Fishing Communities Initiative: Last Mon. in Aug. for Oct. meeting; for Elder Programs: Dec. 15, or the first Mon. after that date for Feb. meeting

Board meeting date(s): Usually in Feb., June, and Oct.

Officers and Trustees: William C. Eaton, Pres. and Trustee; William B. Perkins, V.P. and Trustee; Arthur Page, Clerk. and Trustee; Pamela S. Evans, Treas. and Trustee; William N. Bancroft; Herbert P. Dane; Charles R. Eddy; Tristan Eddy; Edward M. Howland; Amy E. Saltonstall Isaac; E. Amory Loring; Robert W.

Loring; Everett Morss, Jr.; George B. Motley; Jonathan Nash; Thomas Rogerson; G. West Saltonstall; Caroline Gates Slocum; Jo-Ann Watson; Benjamin J. Williams; David Willis.

Number of staff: None.

EIN: 042104430

4277
Salem Five Charitable Foundation, Inc.

210 Essex St.
Salem, MA 01970-3705 (978) 720-5322
Contact: Karen LaMesa, Mktg. Rep., Community Rels. & Events
FAX: (978) 498-0193;
E-mail: karen.lamesa@salemfive.com; Additional contact: Nicolas A. Caporale, Clerk, tel.: (978) 740-5772; Main URL: https://www.salemfive.com/index.php/in-the-community/charitable-foundations

Established in 1996 in Massachusetts.

Donor: Salem Five Cents Savings Bank.

Foundation type: Company-sponsored foundation.

Financial data (yr. ended 12/31/13): Assets, $1,359,641 (M); expenditures, $331,854; qualifying distributions, $317,351; giving activities include $315,332 for 248 grants (high: $10,000; low: $50).

Purpose and activities: The foundation supports organizations involved with economic self-sufficiency, workforce development, and financial literacy. Support is given primarily in areas of company operations in the North Shore, Massachusetts, area, with emphasis on Salem.

Fields of interest: Arts and culture; Education; Youth development.

Type of support: General support; Program development; Sponsorships.

Limitations: Applications accepted. Giving primarily in areas of company operations in the North Shore, MA, area, with emphasis on Salem. No support for discriminatory organizations. No grants for capital campaigns, equipment, or general operating support.

Publications: Application guidelines.

Application information: Grants range from $50 to $10,000. Application form required.

Initial approach: Complete online application or download application and mail to foundation

Deadline(s): None

Board meeting date(s): Monthly

Officers: Joseph M. Gibbons, Pres.; Nicholas A. Caporale, Clerk; Ping Yin Chai, Treas.

Directors: Richard Gourdeau; William J. Lundgren III.

EIN: 043342405

4278
The Reba Judith Sandler Foundation, Inc.

c/o Nixon Peabody, LLP
100 Summer St.
Boston, MA 02110-2106

Established in 1996 in New York.

Donors: Reba Sandler Charitable Lead Trust; Sheri C. Sandler.

Foundation type: Independent foundation.

Financial data (yr. ended 12/31/13): Assets, $5,417,448 (M); gifts received, $342,746; expenditures, $262,153; qualifying distributions, $230,210; giving activities include $227,650 for 24 grants (high: $30,000; low: $150).

Purpose and activities: Giving primarily for the arts and for health and human services.

Fields of interest: Arts and culture; Health; Judaism; Human services; Women's services.

Limitations: Applications not accepted. Giving primarily in NY. No grants to individuals.

Application information: Contributes only to pre-selected organizations.

Officers and Directors: Sherri C. Sandler, Pres. and Director; Jay D. Rosenbaum; Eva Sarah Sandler.

EIN: 133919640

4279
The Sandman Family Foundation

93 Abbott Rd.
Wellesley, MA 02481-6103

Established in 2003 in Massachusetts.

Donor: Paul Sandman.

Foundation type: Independent foundation.

Financial data (yr. ended 12/31/13): Assets, $135,390 (M); gifts received, $46,908; expenditures, $151,229; qualifying distributions, $146,500; giving activities include $146,500 for 9 grants (high: $50,000; low: $2,500).

Fields of interest: Arts and culture; Education; Religion.

Limitations: Applications not accepted. Giving primarily in MA. No grants to individuals.

Application information: Unsolicited requests for funds not accepted.

Trustees: Mary Elizabeth Sandman; Paul W. Sandman.

EIN: 736351444

4280
Savage Family Foundation

946 Great Plain Ave., Ste. 185
Needham, MA 02492-3030

Established in 1999 in Maine.

Donors: Michael T. Savage; Thomas W. Savage; The Savage Family CLAT.

Foundation type: Independent foundation.

Financial data (yr. ended 08/31/14): Assets, $3,386,091 (M); gifts received, $94,701; expenditures, $248,566; qualifying distributions, $237,806; giving activities include $217,000 for 16 grants (high: $50,000; low: $1,000).

Fields of interest: Arts and culture; Maritime museums; Education; Hospital care; Public libraries; Camps; Human services; Homeless services.

Limitations: Applications not accepted. Giving primarily in MA and ME. No grants to individuals.

Application information: Unsolicited requests for funds not accepted.

Officers and Directors: James B. Savage, Pres. and Director; Thomas W. Savage, V.P. and Director; Andrew T. Savage, Secy. and Director; Michael T. Savage, Treas. and Director; Jennifer S. McLean; Julie A. Savage; Priscilla B. Savage; Sally B. Savage.

EIN: 043492839

4281
Schechter Foundation

60 Kensington Cir.
Chestnut Hill, MA 02467-2624

Established in 1998 in Massachusetts.

Donors: David G. Schechter; Gail R. Schechter.

Foundation type: Independent foundation.
Financial data (yr. ended 12/31/14): Assets, $1,072,352; expenditures, $135,359; qualifying distributions, $135,359.
Fields of interest: Education; Health; Religion.
Limitations: Applications not accepted. No grants to individuals.
Application information: Unsolicited requests for funds not accepted.
Trustees: David Schechter; Gail Schechter.
EIN: 046855905

4282
The Susan F. Schiro and Peter J. Manus Foundation
40 Hawthorn Rd.
Brookline, MA   02445-7730

Established in 1993 in Massachusetts.
Donor: Schiro Fund, Inc.
Foundation type: Independent foundation.
Financial data (yr. ended 12/31/13): Assets, $4,021,738 (M); expenditures, $193,735; qualifying distributions, $171,750; giving activities include $171,750 for 10 grants (high: $42,500; low: $500).
Fields of interest: Diseases and conditions; Employment; Human services.
Limitations: Applications accepted. Giving primarily in MA. No grants to individuals.
Application information:
  Initial approach: Letter
  Deadline(s): None
Trustees: Peter J. Manus; Susan F. Schiro.
EIN: 223199042

4283
Schlager Family Foundation Inc
c/o Eric Schlager
250 1st Ave., Ste. 200
Needham, MA   02494-2885

Established in 2006 in Massachusetts.
Donors: Eric D. Schlager; Joan Schlager Weinsten; S. Lawrence Schlager; Robert D. Schlager; Judith P. Schlager; Robert A. Schlager; Bull Ventures Limited Partnership.
Foundation type: Independent foundation.
Financial data (yr. ended 06/30/13): Assets, $260,299 (M); gifts received, $204,250; expenditures, $395,403; qualifying distributions, $389,250; giving activities include $389,250 for 5 grants (high: $200,000; low: $4,250).
Fields of interest: Education; Hospital care; Cancers.
Limitations: Applications not accepted. Giving primarily in MA. No grants to individuals.
Application information: Unsolicited requests for funds not accepted.
Officers and Directors: Eric D. Schlager, Pres. and Director; S. Lawrence Schlager, Clerk and Director; Robert A. Schlager, Treas. and Director; Myra Kolton; Judith P. Schlager; Susan C. Skelley; Joan Schlager Weinsten.
EIN: 204002983

4284
Valerie Beth Schwartz Foundation
c/o Spielman Koenigsberg & Parker
P.O. Box 126
Belmont, MA   02478-0002

Established in 2000 in New York.
Donors: Bernard Schwartz; Ida Schwartz; Jonathan Schwartz.
Foundation type: Independent foundation.
Financial data (yr. ended 12/31/13): Assets, $9,494,458 (M); gifts received, $28,250; expenditures, $458,294; qualifying distributions, $437,961; giving activities include $432,175 for 40 grants (high: $80,000; low: $375).
Fields of interest: Arts and culture; Education; Judaism; Human services; Child welfare.
Limitations: Applications not accepted. No grants to individuals.
Application information: Contributes only to pre-selected organizations.
Trustees: Alexander Schwartz; Jonathan Schwartz.
EIN: 134117395

4285
The Robert G. Segel and Janice L. Sherman Family Foundation
125 High St., 23rd Fl.
Boston, MA   02110-2012

Established in 1997 in Massachusetts.
Donor: Robert G. Segel.
Foundation type: Independent foundation.
Financial data (yr. ended 11/30/13): Assets, $308,148 (M); gifts received, $201,200; expenditures, $227,800; qualifying distributions, $227,800; giving activities include $227,800 for 20 grants (high: $125,000; low: $500).
Fields of interest: Education; Sports and recreation; Human services.
Limitations: Applications not accepted. Giving primarily in FL and MA. No grants to individuals.
Application information: Unsolicited requests for funds not accepted.
Trustees: Ira J. Detisch; Noel G. Posternak; Robert G. Segel; Janice L. Sherman.
EIN: 046856264

4286
SER Family Charitable Foundation
846 University Ave.
Norwood, MA   02062-9108   (781) 461-1600
Contact: Shari E. Redstone, Tr.

Donors: National Amusements, Inc.; Northeast Theatre Corp.
Foundation type: Independent foundation.
Financial data (yr. ended 12/31/13): Assets, $10,868,163 (M); gifts received, $3,424,642; expenditures, $286,186; qualifying distributions, $198,250; giving activities include $198,250 for 12 grants (high: $50,000; low: $2,500).
Fields of interest: Education; Health; Community and economic development.
Limitations: Applications accepted. Giving primarily in CA and MA.
Application information: Application form required.
  Initial approach: Proposal
  Deadline(s): None
Trustee: Shari E. Redstone.
EIN: 262875287

4287
Shaich Family Foundation
c/o Ronald M. Shaich
23 Prescott St.
Brookline, MA   02446-4020

Established in 0 in Massachusetts.
Donor: Ronald M. Shaich.
Foundation type: Independent foundation.
Financial data (yr. ended 12/31/13): Assets, $10,075,702 (M); expenditures, $371,590; qualifying distributions, $341,638; giving activities include $341,638 for 1 grant.
Fields of interest: Elementary and secondary education; Judaism.
Limitations: Applications not accepted. Giving primarily in MA. No grants to individuals.
Application information: Contributes only to pre-selected organizations.
Trustee: Ronald M. Shaich.
EIN: 200499971

4288
Shanklin Foundation 2239788
c/o Cambridge Trust Co.
75 State St., 18th Fl.
Boston, MA   02109-1827

Established in 2007 in Massachusetts.
Donors: Garrett Shanklin; Sarah Shanklin.
Foundation type: Independent foundation.
Financial data (yr. ended 12/31/14): Assets, $3,804,509 (M); expenditures, $163,678; qualifying distributions, $136,135; giving activities include $135,000 for 1 grant.
Fields of interest: Music; Foundations.
Limitations: Applications not accepted.
Application information: Unsolicited requests for funds not accepted.
Trustee: Cambridge Trust Co.; Jay M. Decoteau; Norman D. Shanklin; Sarah W. Shanklin.
EIN: 260849353

4289
Abraham Shapiro Charity Fund Trust
c/o Morris & Morris
32 Kearney Rd.
Needham, MA   02494

Established in 1945 in Massachusetts.
Donor: Abraham Shapiro.
Foundation type: Independent foundation.
Financial data (yr. ended 12/31/13): Assets, $4,519,296 (M); expenditures, $208,105; qualifying distributions, $177,300; giving activities include $177,300 for 16 grants (high: $80,500; low: $500).
Purpose and activities: Giving primarily for higher education, and to Jewish organizations.
Fields of interest: Higher education; Nonprofits; Judaism.
Type of support: Regranting.
Limitations: Applications not accepted. No grants to individuals, or for scholarships, fellowships, or matching gifts; no loans.
Application information: Unsolicited requests for funds not accepted.
  Board meeting date(s): Quarterly
Trustees: Aron Ain; Joseph Michelson; Bram Shapiro.
EIN: 046043588

4290
Albert Shapiro Fund Inc.
975 Memorial Dr., Apt. 804
Cambridge, MA   02138-5755   (410) 561-4411
Contact: Eileen C. Shapiro, Pres. and Treas.

Established in 1983 in Maryland.
Donor: Albert Shapiro.
Foundation type: Independent foundation.
Financial data (yr. ended 03/31/15): Assets, $7,231,153 (M); gifts received, $27,260; expenditures, $348,976; qualifying distributions, $315,536; giving activities include $315,536 for 25 grants (high: $57,500; low: $1,000).
Purpose and activities: Giving primarily for Jewish organizations, especially welfare funds; support also for cultural programs and education.
Fields of interest: Performing arts; Museums; Higher education; Nonprofits; Judaism; Human services; Senior services.
Type of support: Regranting.
Limitations: Applications accepted. Giving primarily in West Palm Beach, FL, and Baltimore, MD. No grants to individuals.
Application information: Application form required.
Initial approach: Letter
Deadline(s): None
Officers: Eileen C. Shapiro, Pres. and Treas.; Reuben E. Eaves, V.P. and Secy.
EIN: 521300277

4291
The Clinton H. & Wilma T. Shattuck Charitable Trust
c/o Nutter McClennen & Fish, LLP
P.O. Box 51400
Boston, MA   02205

Established in 1985 in Massachusetts.
Foundation type: Independent foundation.
Financial data (yr. ended 08/31/14): Assets, $6,936,897 (M); expenditures, $383,956; qualifying distributions, $339,051; giving activities include $325,500 for 39 grants (high: $25,000; low: $4,000).
Fields of interest: Arts and culture; Museums; Education; Environment; Animal welfare; Hospice care; Law; Child welfare.
Limitations: Applications not accepted. Giving primarily in MA. No grants to individuals.
Application information: Contributes only to pre-selected organizations.
Trustee: Walter G. Van Dorn; Kevin Meuse; Elizabeth N. Van Dorn.
EIN: 222659654

4292
Shaughnessy Charitable Trust
(formerly John J. and Mary E. Shaughnessy Charitable Trust)
346 D St.
Boston, MA   02127

Established in 1988 in Massachusetts.
Donors: Shaughnessy Crane Service, Inc.; John J. Shaughnessy†; Mary E. Shaughnessy; Law Offices of Peter F. Davis; John J. Shaughnessy Trust; Shaughnessy & Ahearn Co.; Second Street Iron & Metal Co., Inc.; Estate of John Shaughnessy.
Foundation type: Company-sponsored foundation.

Financial data (yr. ended 08/31/14): Assets, $1,693,630 (M); gifts received, $845,951; expenditures, $140,080; qualifying distributions, $130,250; giving activities include $129,000 for 15 grants (high: $10,000; low: $1,000).
Purpose and activities: The foundation supports organizations involved with education, health, human services, Christianity, and Catholicism.
Fields of interest: Education; Religion; Human services.
Type of support: General support; Continuing support; Annual campaigns; Program development; Scholarships.
Limitations: Applications not accepted. Giving limited to Boston, MA. No grants to individuals.
Application information: Contributes only to pre-selected organizations.
EIN: 046595469

4293
George & Beatrice Sherman Family Charitable Trust
c/o G&S
400 Atlantic Ave.
Boston, MA   02110-3333

Established in 1969 in Massachusetts.
Donors: George Sherman†; Beatrice B. Sherman†.
Foundation type: Independent foundation.
Financial data (yr. ended 06/30/14): Assets, $1,393,904; gifts received, $500; expenditures, $139,859; qualifying distributions, $129,382.
Fields of interest: Elementary and secondary education; Nonprofits; Diseases and conditions; Judaism; Human services; Family services; Child welfare.
Type of support: Regranting.
Limitations: Applications not accepted. Giving primarily in CT and MA. No grants to individuals.
Application information: Unsolicited requests for funds not accepted.
Trustees: Robert P. Goldman; Amy Sherman Parets; Alan W. Rottenberg; Brian G. Sherman; Claire B. Sherman; Norton L. Sherman; Steven Sherman; Marvin Sparrow.
EIN: 046223350

4294
Sherman Hsu Family Foundation
21 Gibson Rd.
Newton, MA   02460-2214

Donors: Lynn Hsu; Paul Sherman.
Foundation type: Independent foundation.
Financial data (yr. ended 12/31/13): Assets, $7,544,908 (M); gifts received, $731,870; expenditures, $327,836; qualifying distributions, $327,800; giving activities include $327,800 for 23 grants (high: $80,000; low: $200).
Fields of interest: Education; Science; Community and economic development.
Limitations: Applications not accepted.
Application information: Unsolicited requests for funds not accepted.
Trustees: Lynn Hsu; Paul A. Sherman.
EIN: 276958071

4295
The Joseph & Agatha Sicari Charitable Trust
141 Kendall Hill Rd.
Sterling, MA   01564-1516   (978) 368-1200
Contact: David L. Taylor, Tr.

Established in 2000 in Massachusetts.
Donor: Helen Sicari†.
Foundation type: Independent foundation.
Financial data (yr. ended 12/31/13): Assets, $8,854,585 (M); expenditures, $559,492; qualifying distributions, $400,000; giving activities include $400,000 for 8 grants (high: $180,000; low: $5,000).
Fields of interest: Education; Housing development; Religion.
Type of support: Financial sustainability; Equipment; Seed money.
Limitations: Applications accepted. Giving primarily in CO and MA.
Application information:
Initial approach: Proposal
Deadline(s): None
Trustee: David Taylor.
Number of staff: 1 part-time professional; 1 part-time support.
EIN: 046922636

4296
Frank R. and Elizabeth Simoni Foundation, Inc.
29 Palmer Dr.
Canton, MA   02021-1828

Established in 1992 in Massachusetts.
Donors: Frank R. Simoni†; Elizabeth M. Simoni.
Foundation type: Independent foundation.
Financial data (yr. ended 12/31/13): Assets, $3,972,254 (M); gifts received, $50,000; expenditures, $211,827; qualifying distributions, $177,600; giving activities include $177,600 for 22 grants (high: $55,000; low: $1,000).
Purpose and activities: Giving to medical centers, and for education and human services.
Fields of interest: Education; Health; Community improvement; Youth development; Shelter and residential care; Developmental disability services; Senior services; People with disabilities.
Type of support: Capital and infrastructure; Matching grants; Equipment; Individual development; Scholarships.
Limitations: Applications not accepted. Giving primarily in MA. No grants to individuals.
Application information: Unsolicited requests for funds not accepted.
Officers: Elizabeth M. Simoni, Pres. and Treas.; Robert B. MacDonald, Clerk.
Director: Ann M. MacDonald.
Number of staff: None.
EIN: 043109508

4297
Singing Field Foundation Inc.
c/o Kahn, Litwin, Renza & Co., Ltd.
800 South St., Ste. 300
Waltham, MA   02453-1480

Established in 1998 in Massachusetts.
Donors: Jane Colburn†; Jonathan A. Scott.
Foundation type: Independent foundation.

Financial data (yr. ended 05/31/13): Assets, $4,192,088 (M); gifts received, $1,125; expenditures, $266,701; qualifying distributions, $229,652; giving activities include $221,000 for 37 grants (high: $30,000; low: $1,000).
Fields of interest: Environment; Animal welfare; Diseases and conditions.
Type of support: General support; Research.
Limitations: Applications not accepted. Giving primarily in CA, Washington, DC, MA, and NH. No grants to individuals.
Application information: Contributes only to pre-selected organizations.
Officers and Directors: Jonathan A. Scott, Pres. and Treas. and Director; Janet Bush, Secy.; Peter Dunlap-Shohl; Kathryn S. Scott; Barbara Wagner.
EIN: 043425998

4298
Robert and Dana Smith Family Foundation
(formerly Robert and Dana Smith Charitable Foundation)
c/o Castanea Partners
3 Newton Executive Park, Ste. 304
Newton, MA   02462-1433

Established in 2001 in Massachusetts.
Donors: Dana Weiss Smith; Robert A. Smith.
Foundation type: Independent foundation.
Financial data (yr. ended 11/30/13): Assets, $6,302,161 (M); gifts received, $221,109; expenditures, $355,311; qualifying distributions, $349,812; giving activities include $342,000 for 13 grants (high: $100,000; low: $2,000).
Fields of interest: Education; Elementary and secondary education; Health; Hospital care; Human services.
Limitations: Applications not accepted. Giving primarily in the Boston, MA, area. No grants to individuals.
Application information: Contributes only to pre-selected organizations.
Trustees: Dana Weiss Smith; Robert A. Smith.
EIN: 223850789

4299
The Horace Smith Fund
1441 Main St.
Springfield, MA   01103   (413) 739-4222
FAX: (413) 739-1108; Main URL: http://www.horacesmithfund.org

Established in 1898 in Massachusetts.
Donors: Horace Smith†; Jean M. Smith†.
Foundation type: Independent foundation.
Financial data (yr. ended 03/31/13): Assets, $6,700,423 (M); gifts received, $50; expenditures, $420,867; qualifying distributions, $219,750; giving activities include $219,750 for grants to individuals.
Purpose and activities: Scholarship grants for high school seniors in Hampden County, Massachusetts, and fellowships for Hampden County residents or qualified former residents.
Fields of interest: Higher education.
Type of support: Fellowships; Student aid.
Limitations: Applications accepted. Giving limited to Hampden County, MA, residents.
Application information: Application form required.

Initial approach: Contact foundation website for application form
Deadline(s): Dec. 20 for scholarship; Feb. 1 for fellowship
Officers: Michael P. Williams, Pres.; Anne Mahoney, V.P. and Admin.; Benjamin Bump, Exec. Secy.; Josephine Sarnelli, Clerk; Adonis E. Miller, Treas. and Director.
Trustees: Katleen Bourque; James W. Brodrick, Jr.; Samalid Hogan; Jerome Linehan; Michael E. Tucker; Wayne L. Webster.
Number of staff: 1 full-time professional; 1 part-time professional; 1 part-time support.
EIN: 042235130

4300
Justin Smith Morrill Scholarship Fund
P.O. Box 1330
Hyannis, MA   02601-1330
Application address: c/o Guidance Counselor, 122 Granite St., Leominster, MA 01453 tel.: (978) 534-7715; c/o Guidance Counselor, 9 Oakmont Dr., Ashuburnham, MA 01430 tel.: (978) 827-5907; c/o Guidance Counselor, 19 Main St., Townsend, MA 01469 tel.: (978) 597-8721

Foundation type: Independent foundation.
Financial data (yr. ended 12/31/13): Assets, $5,111,655 (M); gifts received, $29,590; expenditures, $426,810; qualifying distributions, $379,250; giving activities include $379,250 for 42 grants (high: $53,000; low: $500).
Fields of interest: Education; Higher education.
Type of support: Scholarships.
Limitations: Applications accepted. Giving limited to Fitchburg, Westminster, Ashby, and Ashburnham, MA.
Application information: Application form required.
Initial approach: Proposal
Deadline(s): May 1
Trustee: TD Bank, N.A.
EIN: 276509486

4301
The Lawrence and Lillian Solomon Foundation, Inc.
10 Laurel Ave.
Wellesley, MA   02481-7534

Established in 2005 in Massachusetts.
Foundation type: Independent foundation.
Financial data (yr. ended 12/31/13): Assets, $12,605,945 (M); expenditures, $1,085,879; qualifying distributions, $738,214; giving activities include $347,100 for 59 grants (high: $50,000; low: $250).
Fields of interest: Arts and culture; Education; Environment; Community and economic development.
Limitations: Applications not accepted. Giving primarily in MA, with emphasis on the Boston area.
Application information: Contributes only to pre-selected organizations.
Director: David Solomon.
EIN: 202631943

4302
Ahron M. and Sheera A. Solomont Family Foundation
531 Boylston St.
Brookline, MA   02445-5701

Established in 1997 in Massachusetts.
Donor: Ahron M. Solomont.
Foundation type: Independent foundation.
Financial data (yr. ended 12/31/13): Assets, $0 (M); expenditures, $198,286; qualifying distributions, $192,742; giving activities include $192,742 for 1 grant.
Fields of interest: Religion.
Limitations: Applications not accepted. Giving primarily in MA. No grants to individuals.
Application information: Unsolicited requests for funds not accepted.
Trustees: Patrick B. Maraghy; Ahron M. Solomont; Sheera A. Solomont.
EIN: 043390608

4303
Alan D. and Susan Lewis Solomont Family Foundation
c/o Rinet Co. LLC
101 Federal St., 14th Fl.
Boston, MA   02110-1859

Established in 1998 in Massachusetts.
Donors: Alan D. Solomont; Blanche Lewis; Leonard Lewis; Leonard D. Lewis Rollover Ira; Susan Lewis Solomont.
Foundation type: Independent foundation.
Financial data (yr. ended 12/31/13): Assets, $765,633 (M); expenditures, $191,876; qualifying distributions, $186,381; giving activities include $186,381 for 27 grants (high: $61,500; low: $100).
Purpose and activities: Giving primarily for education, hospitals and health care, human services, and Jewish agencies and temples.
Fields of interest: Education; Health; Religion; Judaism.
Limitations: Applications not accepted. Giving primarily in MA. No grants to individuals.
Application information: Contributes only to pre-selected organizations.
Trustee: Susan Lewis Solomont.
EIN: 043388562

4304
Spero Charitable Foundation
303 Brooksby Village, Ste. 301
Peabody, MA   01960-8573

Established in 1968 in Massachusetts.
Donor: Louis Spero†.
Foundation type: Operating foundation.
Financial data (yr. ended 12/31/13): Assets, $3,465,705 (M); expenditures, $231,474; qualifying distributions, $228,042; giving activities include $228,042 for 100 grants (high: $25,000; low: $47).
Fields of interest: Arts and culture; Child educational development; Higher education; Business education; Nonprofits; Health; Hospital care; Diseases and conditions; Heart and circulatory system diseases; Cancers; Public administration; Community and economic development; Judaism; Human services; Child welfare; Child development; Homeless services; Senior services; Unknown or not

classified; Seniors; Ethnic and racial groups; Homeless people.
International interests: Israel.
Type of support: General support; Annual campaigns; Research; Regranting.
Limitations: Applications not accepted. Giving primarily in MA. No grants to individuals.
Application information: Contributes only to pre-selected organizations.
Trustees: Janet Kouroubacalis; Shirley Spero.
EIN: 046183682

4305
Alan and Terri Spoon Family Foundation
11 Ledge Ways
Wellesley Hills, MA   02481-1409

Established in 2002 in Massachusetts.
Donor: Alan G. Spoon.
Foundation type: Independent foundation.
Financial data (yr. ended 12/31/13): Assets, $917,590 (M); expenditures, $313,820; qualifying distributions, $312,500; giving activities include $312,500 for 10 grants (high: $200,000; low: $500).
Fields of interest: Museums; Education; University education; Nonprofits; Health; Judaism.
Type of support: Regranting.
Limitations: Applications not accepted. Giving primarily in MA, with some giving in Washington, DC. No grants to individuals.
Application information: Contributes only to pre-selected organizations.
Trustees: Alan G. Spoon; Terri L. Spoon.
EIN: 510433601

4306
Phineas W. Sprague Memorial Foundation
P.O. Box 140
Mansfield, MA   02048-0140

Established in 1956 in Massachusetts.
Foundation type: Independent foundation.
Financial data (yr. ended 12/31/14): Assets, $3,497,760 (M); expenditures, $204,668; qualifying distributions, $184,583; giving activities include $171,717 for 45 grants (high: $25,000; low: $500).
Fields of interest: Arts and culture; Elementary and secondary education; Higher education; Human services.
Limitations: Applications not accepted. Giving primarily in ME. No grants to individuals.
Application information: Unsolicited requests for funds not accepted.
Officers: Cate S. Gilbane, Pres.; F. Whittington Foster, V.P.; Tilsley H. Kelly, Secy.; Eliza H.S. Rowe, Treas.
EIN: 046043554

4307
Marjorie Cohen Stanzler Charitable Trust
44 Highgate Rd.
Wellesley, MA   02481-1420

Established in 2001 in Massachusetts.
Donors: Julian Cohen; Marjorie Cohen Stanzler; Paul Stanzler.
Foundation type: Independent foundation.

Financial data (yr. ended 12/31/14): Assets, $5,962,375; gifts received, $2,070; expenditures, $404,681; qualifying distributions, $352,600.
Fields of interest: University education.
Type of support: General support.
Limitations: Applications not accepted. Giving limited to Boston, MA. No grants to individuals.
Application information: Contributes only to pre-selected organizations.
Trustees: Marjorie Cohen Stanzler; Paul Stanzler.
EIN: 046955868

4308
The Stare Fund
c/o Ropes & Gray
800 Boylston St.
Boston, MA   02199-3600

Established in 1959 in Massachusetts.
Donor: Fredrick J. Stare†.
Foundation type: Independent foundation.
Financial data (yr. ended 11/30/13): Assets, $9,673,557 (M); expenditures, $485,739; qualifying distributions, $445,410; giving activities include $438,967 for 31 grants (high: $68,167; low: $2,000).
Purpose and activities: Giving for health organizations; funding also for the arts and human services.
Fields of interest: Arts and culture; Orchestral music; Education; Hospital care; Diseases and conditions; Heart and circulatory system diseases; Human services.
Type of support: Research.
Limitations: Applications not accepted. Giving primarily in IL and MA. No grants to individuals.
Application information: Contributes only to pre-selected organizations.
Trustees: David S. Stare; Fredrick A. Stare; Mary S. Wilkinson.
EIN: 046026648

4309
Polly Thayer Starr Charitable Trust
c/o Hemenway & Barnes LLP
60 State St.
Boston, MA   02109-1800   (617) 227-7940
Contact: Arthur B. Page, Tr.

Donors: Polly Thayer Starr†; Donald Starr Charitable Lead Trust.
Foundation type: Independent foundation.
Financial data (yr. ended 06/30/14): Assets, $7,058,415 (M); expenditures, $349,948; qualifying distributions, $334,295; giving activities include $280,000 for 6 grants (high: $100,000; low: $25,000).
Fields of interest: Higher education; Nursing care; Libraries.
Limitations: Applications accepted. Giving primarily in KY and MA.
Application information: Application form required.
Initial approach: Letter
Deadline(s): None
Trustees: Nancy B. Gardiner; Arthur B. Page; Dinah Starr.
EIN: 222756435

4310
Stearns Charitable Trust
c/o Ropes & Gray, LLP
800 Boylston St.
Boston, MA   02199-3600

Established in 1947 in Massachusetts.
Donor: Russell B. Stearns†.
Foundation type: Independent foundation.
Financial data (yr. ended 12/31/13): Assets, $7,522,450 (M); expenditures, $390,047; qualifying distributions, $345,312; giving activities include $309,000 for 78 grants (high: $20,000; low: $1,000).
Purpose and activities: Emphasis on cultural programs, including a science museum; support also for libraries, community funds, the environment, an aquarium, and social services.
Fields of interest: Arts and culture; Museums; Environment; Nonprofits; Alcoholism; Libraries; Human services.
Type of support: General support; Continuing support; Annual campaigns; Capital campaigns; Capital and infrastructure; Land acquisitions; Program development; Regranting.
Limitations: Applications not accepted. Giving primarily in MA, IL, and RI. No grants to individuals.
Application information: Unsolicited requests for funds not accepted.
Trustees: Russell S. Beede; James Gassel; Anne B. Jencks.
EIN: 046036697

4311
Artemas W. Stearns Trust
9 Bartlet St., Ste. 343
Andover, MA   01810-3655   (978) 687-0156

Established in 1896 in Massachusetts.
Donor: Artemas W. Stearns†.
Foundation type: Independent foundation.
Financial data (yr. ended 12/31/14): Assets, $5,072,824; expenditures, $296,886; qualifying distributions, $220,680.
Purpose and activities: Support for organizations which service and benefit the deserving poor and indigent aged people, including hospitals, community projects, and secondary schools in the Lawrence, MA, area.
Fields of interest: Education; Secondary education; Hospital care; Community and economic development; Human services; Senior services; Seniors.
Type of support: General support; Annual campaigns; Emergency funds; Program development; Publications; Scholarships.
Limitations: Applications accepted. Giving limited to the Lawrence, MA, area. No grants to individuals, or for endowment funds, matching gifts, capital campaigns, equipment, or construction; no loans.
Publications: Application guidelines.
Application information:
Initial approach: Letter or proposal
Copies of proposal: 5
Deadline(s): Jan. 31
Board meeting date(s): Quarterly
Final notification: Within 3 months
Trustees: Rev. Paul T. Keyes; Eileen M. Khoury; Matthew A. Kraunelis; John T. Pollano; Marsha E. Rich.
Number of staff: 1 part-time professional; 1 part-time support.
EIN: 042137061

4312
Albert Steiger Memorial Fund, Inc.
P.O. Box 292
Springfield, MA   01102-0392   (413) 567-1017

Established in 1953 in Massachusetts.
Donors: Ralph A. Steiger; Chauncey A. Steiger; Albert Steiger, Inc.
Foundation type: Independent foundation.
Financial data (yr. ended 12/31/12): Assets, $0 (M); expenditures, $348,464; qualifying distributions, $345,128; giving activities include $323,469 for 16 grants (high: $120,000; low: $1,969).
Purpose and activities: Giving primarily for social service agencies, cultural programs, and higher education.
Fields of interest: Arts and culture; Environment; Health.
Type of support: Annual campaigns; Capital campaigns; Capital and infrastructure; Program development; Scholarships.
Limitations: Applications accepted. Giving limited to the Hampden County, MA, area. No grants to individuals or for endowment funds or operating budgets.
Application information: Grants recommended by the Community Funds Advisory Committee of the Community Council. Application form required.
   Initial approach: Contact foundation
   Copies of proposal: 1
   Deadline(s): None
Officers and Directors: Philip C. Steiger II, Pres. and Director; Ralph A. Steiger II, V.P. and Director; Allen Steiger, Treas. and Director; Richard S. Milstein, Clerk; Albert E. Steiger III.
EIN: 046051750

4313
Thomas G. Stemberg Charitable Foundation
c/o Brown Brothers Harriman & Co.
50 Post Office Sq.
Boston, MA   02110
Contact: C. Tierney

Established in 2006 in Massachusetts.
Donor: Thomas G. Stemberg.
Foundation type: Independent foundation.
Financial data (yr. ended 12/31/13): Assets, $6,628,484 (M); expenditures, $325,900; qualifying distributions, $234,250; giving activities include $234,250 for 10 grants (high: $55,000; low: $5,000).
Fields of interest: Orchestral music; Sport and hobby museums; Elementary and secondary education; Higher education; Basketball; People with vision impairments.
Type of support: General support.
Limitations: Applications not accepted. Giving primarily in MA. No grants to individuals.
Application information: Contributes only to pre-selected organizations.
Trustee: Thomas G. Stemberg.
EIN: 205672425

4314
The Storer Goodwin Decatur Foundation
c/o RH&B, Inc.
50 Congress St., Ste. 900
Boston, MA   02109-4023   6172271782

Donor: Mary Decatur Trust.
Foundation type: Independent foundation.
Financial data (yr. ended 09/30/14): Assets, $2,797,932; expenditures, $176,075; qualifying distributions, $156,341.
Fields of interest: Arts and culture; Museums.
Type of support: General support.
Limitations: Applications not accepted. Giving primarily in Portsmouth, NH.
Application information: Unsolicited requests for funds not accepted.
Trustees: Robert G. Bannish; Adrienne Smith.
EIN: 272849654

4315
Sullivan Family Foundation
15 Broad St., Ste. 502
Boston, MA   02109-3816
Application address: 117 Harbor View Rd., Milton, MA 02186-3522

Established in 2005 in Massachusetts.
Donor: James F. Sullivan.
Foundation type: Independent foundation.
Financial data (yr. ended 04/30/14): Assets, $2,809,652; expenditures, $216,735; qualifying distributions, $193,500.
Fields of interest: Education; Health; Human services.
Limitations: Applications accepted. Giving primarily in MA.
Application information: Application form required.
   Initial approach: Letter
   Deadline(s): Varies
Trustees: James F. Sullivan; Margaret Walsh Sullivan; Margaret Sullivan Walsh.
EIN: 203864725

4316
Summer Star Foundation for Nature, Art and Humanity Inc
(formerly Chin-Cheng Wu Foundation for Peace and Humanity, Inc.)
c/o Rinet Co
101 Federal St., 14th Fl.
Boston, MA   02110-1859
Contact: Shalin Liu, Pres. and Dir.

Established in 2000 in Massachusetts.
Donors: Chin-Cheng Wu; Shalin Liu.
Foundation type: Independent foundation.
Financial data (yr. ended 12/31/13): Assets, $1,520,073 (M); gifts received, $151,061; expenditures, $238,271; qualifying distributions, $218,942; giving activities include $218,942 for 18 grants (high: $87,175; low: $750).
Fields of interest: Education; Higher education; Domesticated animals; Human services.
International interests: Taiwan.
Type of support: General support.
Limitations: Applications accepted. Giving primarily in Boston, MA; some funding also in Taiwan. No grants to individuals.
Application information: Application form required.
   Initial approach: Proposal
   Deadline(s): None
Officers and Directors: Shalin Liu, Pres. and Director; Christopher Wu, Clerk.
EIN: 043504566

4317
Swan Society in Boston
(formerly Widows Society in Boston)
581 Boylston St., Ste. 705
Boston, MA   02116-3626   (617) 536-7951
Contact: Jackie Husid, Exec. Dir.

Established in 1816 in Massachusetts.
Foundation type: Operating foundation.
Financial data (yr. ended 10/31/14): Assets, $5,249,278 (M); gifts received, $1,000; expenditures, $293,037; qualifying distributions, $287,603; giving activities include $166,629 for 8 grants (high: $46,629; low: $10,000), and $64,611 for grants to individuals.
Purpose and activities: Support for widowed, divorced, or single women who are over 65 years old and in need of financial aid, and live within a 25 mile radius of the State House in Boston, MA.
Fields of interest: Senior services; Women's services; Seniors; Females; Low-income and poor people.
Type of support: Emergency funds.
Limitations: Applications accepted. Giving limited to applicants living within 25 miles of the State House in Boston, MA.
Publications: Application guidelines; Annual report; Informational brochure.
Application information: Application form required.
   Initial approach: Referrals from public and social organizations
   Copies of proposal: 1
   Deadline(s): None
   Board meeting date(s): Jan.
   Final notification: 1-2 weeks
Officers and Directors: Lucy Goreham, Pres. and Director; Jill Newman, Secy. and Director; Richard V. Howe, Treas.; Jackie Husid, Exec. Dir.; Eleanor Marsh; Lee Smith.
Number of staff: 1 part-time professional.
EIN: 042306840

4318
Sword and Spoon Foundation
138 Conant St., 1st Fl.
Beverly, MA   01915-1666

Donor: John Kingston.
Foundation type: Independent foundation.
Financial data (yr. ended 12/31/12): Assets, $1,958,636 (M); gifts received, $843,007; expenditures, $398,538; qualifying distributions, $364,956; giving activities include $364,956 for grants.
Fields of interest: Education; Housing development; Religion.
Limitations: Applications not accepted. Giving primarily in MA.
Application information: Unsolicited requests for funds not accepted.
Officers: John Kingston, Pres.; Jean Kingston, Clerk; Bradley Crate, Treas.
EIN: 207494902

4319
Symes Family Charitable Foundation
50 Dodge St.
Beverly, MA   01915-1711

Established in 1999 in Massachusetts.
Donors: Albert R. Symes; Barbara Symes.

Foundation type: Independent foundation.
Financial data (yr. ended 06/30/13): Assets, $2,080,404 (M); expenditures, $286,619; qualifying distributions, $200,872; giving activities include $200,872 for 2 grants (high: $190,872; low: $10,000).
Fields of interest: Theater.
Limitations: Applications not accepted. Giving primarily in MA. No grants to individuals.
Application information: Unsolicited requests for funds not accepted.
Officers and Directors: Albert R. Symes, Pres. and Director; Arica Symes-Elmer, V.P. and Treas. and Director; Landers Symes, Clerk; Barbara Symes.
EIN: 043494605

4320
Steven M. and Joyce E. Tadler Charitable Trust

c/o Joyce E. Tadler
P.O. Box 134
Manchester, MA   01944-0134

Donors: Steven M. Tadler; Joyce E. Tadler.
Foundation type: Independent foundation.
Financial data (yr. ended 12/31/13): Assets, $5,929,033 (M); gifts received, $1,594,170; expenditures, $322,234; qualifying distributions, $319,660; giving activities include $318,000 for 11 grants (high: $50,000; low: $5,000).
Fields of interest: Arts and culture; Education; Business education; Sports and recreation.
Limitations: Applications not accepted. Giving primarily in MA and VA.
Application information: Unsolicited requests for funds not accepted.
Trustees: Joyce E. Tadler; Steven M. Tadler.
EIN: 356797771

4321
Tapper Charitable Foundation

509 Falmouth Rd.
Mashpee, MA   02649-2699

Established in 1979 in Massachusetts.
Foundation type: Independent foundation.
Financial data (yr. ended 06/30/13): Assets, $3,373,316 (M); expenditures, $175,704; qualifying distributions, $170,860; giving activities include $170,860 for grants.
Fields of interest: Nonprofits; Health; Judaism.
Type of support: General support; Regranting.
Limitations: Applications not accepted. Giving primarily in MA and NY. No grants to individuals.
Application information: Unsolicited requests for funds not accepted.
Trustees: Albert Tapper; Charles Tapper; Eve Tapper; Lynne Tapper.
EIN: 042700063

4322
Eliot H. & June L. Tatelman Family Foundation

250 Boylston St., Ste. 7
Boston, MA   02116

Established in 2001 in Massachusetts.
Donors: Eliot H. Tatelman; Jordan Furniture Family Foundation.
Foundation type: Independent foundation.

Financial data (yr. ended 12/31/13): Assets, $5,829,878 (M); gifts received, $517,000; expenditures, $294,205; qualifying distributions, $248,320; giving activities include $248,250 for 8 grants (high: $100,000; low: $2,500).
Fields of interest: Nonprofits; Hospital care; Family planning; Basic and emergency aid; International development.
International interests: South Africa.
Type of support: Regranting.
Limitations: Applications not accepted. Giving primarily in MA, with some giving in NY. No grants to individuals.
Application information: Contributes only to pre-selected organizations.
Trustees: Eliot H. Tatelman; June L. Tatelman.
EIN: 456118546

4323
Susan and Barry Tatelman Family Foundation

9 Arlington St., Apt. 1
Boston, MA   02116-3413

Established in 2001 in Massachusetts.
Donors: Barry E. Tatelman; Jordan Furniture Foundation; Susan Tatelman.
Foundation type: Independent foundation.
Financial data (yr. ended 12/31/13): Assets, $2,013,362 (M); gifts received, $452,250; expenditures, $288,063; qualifying distributions, $251,884; giving activities include $251,634 for 38 grants (high: $66,634; low: $180).
Fields of interest: Nonprofits; Health; Hospital care; Judaism; Family services.
Type of support: Regranting.
Limitations: Applications not accepted. Giving primarily in MA, with emphasis on Boston. No grants to individuals.
Application information: Contributes only to pre-selected organizations.
Trustees: Barry E. Tatelman; Susan Tatelman.
EIN: 476242074

4324
Thee Mustard Seed Foundation

38 Newbury St., Ste. 6
Boston, MA   02116

Foundation type: Independent foundation.
Financial data (yr. ended 12/31/13): Assets, $3,741,613 (M); gifts received, $1,833,333; expenditures, $150,198; qualifying distributions, $143,800; giving activities include $143,800 for 6 grants (high: $100,000; low: $3,800).
Fields of interest: Health; Agriculture; Religion.
Limitations: Applications not accepted. Giving primarily in PA.
Application information: Unsolicited requests for funds not accepted.
Officer: Arthur S. Demoulas.
EIN: 260873247

4325
The Thompson Foster Street Foundation Inc.

c/o Goulston & Storrs, PC
400 Atlantic Ave.
Boston, MA   02110-3333

Established in 2000 in Massachusetts.
Donors: Elizabeth Thompson; David Thompson.
Foundation type: Independent foundation.
Financial data (yr. ended 12/31/14): Assets, $1,056,548 (M); gifts received, $600; expenditures, $193,038; qualifying distributions, $192,338; giving activities include $185,144 for 17 grants (high: $50,000; low: $500).
Fields of interest: Education; Diseases and conditions; Human services.
Type of support: Scholarships.
Limitations: Applications not accepted. Giving primarily in CT, MA and NY. No grants to individuals.
Application information: Unsolicited requests for funds not accepted.
Officers and Directors: Elizabeth Thompson, Pres. and Director; J. Robert Casey, Clerk; David Thompson, Treas. and Director.
EIN: 043501266

4326
The Thoracic Foundation

c/o Taylor, Ganson & Perrin, LLP
160 Federal St., 20th Fl.
Boston, MA   02110-1700   6179512777

Established in 1949 in Massachusetts.
Donors: Richard H. Overholt, MD†; The Greater Cincinnati Foundation.
Foundation type: Independent foundation.
Financial data (yr. ended 12/31/14): Assets, $7,133,573; expenditures, $447,202; qualifying distributions, $298,831.
Purpose and activities: Support for medical research in thoracic diseases.
Fields of interest: Medical education; Specialty hospital care; Smoking; Diseases and conditions; Heart and circulatory system diseases; Asthma; Child welfare.
Type of support: Convening; Publications; Research; Research and evaluation.
Limitations: Applications accepted. Giving primarily in MA, with emphasis on Boston.
Application information: Application form required.
Initial approach: Proposal
Copies of proposal: 1
Deadline(s): None
Trustees: Bradley R. Cook; Thomas J.S. Mikelson; Galen L. Stone.
EIN: 042226641

4327
Henry David Thoreau Foundation, Inc.

(formerly Northeast Educational Services, Inc.)
265 Medford St., Ste. 102
Somerville, MA   02143-1963   (617) 666-6900
Contact: John R. Galvin, Pres.
FAX: (617) 666-0345;
E-mail: jane@thoreauscholar.org; Main URL: http://www.thoreauscholar.org
LinkedIn: http://www.linkedin.com/groups?homeNewMember=&gid=1963069&trk=

Established in 1998 in Massachusetts.
Foundation type: Independent foundation.
Financial data (yr. ended 12/31/13): Assets, $10,765,601 (M); expenditures, $511,315; qualifying distributions, $490,154; giving activities include $178,353 for 19 grants (high: $23,644; low: $2,500), and $500 for 1 grant to an individual.

Purpose and activities: Giving for college and university scholarships to high school graduates who demonstrate strong interest in environmental fields of study and clear potential for leadership.
Fields of interest: Education; Higher education.
Type of support: Scholarships; Student aid.
Limitations: Applications accepted. Giving primarily in MA.
Application information: See web site for additional information. Application form required.
   Initial approach: Must use online application
   Deadline(s): Feb. 1
   Final notification: Apr. 30
Officers and Trustees: John R. Galvin, Pres. and Treas. and Trustee; Philip R. McCabe, Secy. and Clerk and Trustee; Scott D. Ellis; Jennifer P. Galvin; Marilee Jones; David R. Magnussen.
EIN: 042077934

4328
Willard C. Tilson Foundation
c/o Bayard Waring
3 Sandaba Rd.
Rockport, MA 01966-1812
Application address: c/o Bayard Waring, 30 Western Ave., Gloucester, MA 01930

Established in 1956 in Massachusetts.
Foundation type: Independent foundation.
Financial data (yr. ended 12/31/13): Assets, $4,750,007 (M); expenditures, $457,548; qualifying distributions, $419,378; giving activities include $408,000 for 9 grants (high: $225,000; low: $3,000).
Purpose and activities: Giving limited to programs helping brain-injured young people.
Fields of interest: Elementary and secondary education; Autism; Child welfare.
Limitations: Applications accepted. Giving limited to MA.
Application information: Application form required.
   Initial approach: Letter
   Copies of proposal: 1
   Deadline(s): None
Trustees: Bayard D. Waring; Philip B. Waring.
Number of staff: 1 full-time professional; 4 part-time professional.
EIN: 046036556

4329
The John H. and H. Naomi Tomfohrde Foundation
c/o Rackemann, Sawyer & Brewster
160 Federal St., 15th Fl.
Boston, MA 02110—1700 (617) 951-1108
Contact: Susan T. Monahan, Grants Coor.
E-mail: smonahan@gmail.com; Main URL: http://www.cybergrants.com/tomfohrde

Established in 1996 in Massachusetts.
Donor: John H. Tomfohrde†.
Foundation type: Independent foundation.
Financial data (yr. ended 12/31/13): Assets, $5,691,004 (M); expenditures, $276,984; qualifying distributions, $230,380; giving activities include $190,750 for 24 grants (high: $10,000; low: $3,000).
Purpose and activities: The foundation gives to charitable purposes or to charitable organizations, with particular focus on supporting the work of charitable institutions, organizations and agencies

in the New England area and particularly in Greater Boston, which are dedicated to the cultural, social and civic betterment of the community and particularly which foster the advancement of higher education, the classic arts, scientific research in biomedicine and the improvement of community health. Complete information on the foundation's current year focus can be found on the foundation's web site.
Fields of interest: Arts and culture; Education; Higher education; Health; Biomedicine; Women's services.
Type of support: Research.
Limitations: Applications accepted. Giving primarily in MA.
Application information: All applications must be submitted online at foundation web site. For trustees' current funding priorities, see foundation web site. Application form required.
   Initial approach: Submit concept paper online at foundation web site
   Deadline(s): See foundation web site
   Board meeting date(s): See foundation web site
Trustees: Maura E. Murphy; Michael F. O'Connell.
Number of staff: None.
EIN: 043338742

4330
Toocap Foundation
c/o Paul McCoy Family Office Svcs.
31 St. James Ave., Ste. 740
Boston, MA 02116-4186

Established in 2007 in Massachusetts.
Foundation type: Independent foundation.
Financial data (yr. ended 12/31/13): Assets, $5,630,387 (M); expenditures, $272,454; qualifying distributions, $242,000; giving activities include $242,000 for 32 grants (high: $75,000; low: $500).
Fields of interest: Education; Foundations; Human services.
Limitations: Applications not accepted. Giving primarily in FL, NH and VT. No grants to individuals.
Application information: Unsolicited requests for funds not accepted.
Trustees: Bayne Stevenson; Jean B. Stevenson.
EIN: 266130139

4331
Maria Torok Foundation, Inc.
(formerly Bernhard Sewald Foundation, Inc.)
c/o Nutter, McClennen & Fish, LLP
P.O. Box 51400
Boston, MA 02205-1400
Contact: Thomas P. Jalkut, Dir.

Established in 1997 in Massachusetts.
Donor: Maria E.W. Torok.
Foundation type: Independent foundation.
Financial data (yr. ended 09/30/13): Assets, $5,808,141 (M); expenditures, $290,714; qualifying distributions, $256,360; giving activities include $245,000 for 11 grants (high: $60,000; low: $10,000).
Fields of interest: Education; Nonprofits; Hospital care; HIV/AIDS; Human services.
Type of support: Regranting.
Limitations: Applications accepted. Giving primarily in MA.
Application information: Application form required.

   Initial approach: Letter
   Deadline(s): None
Officers and Directors: Thomas P. Jalkut, Pres. and Director; Jeffrey W. Roberts, Clerk and Director; Julia Satti Cosentino, Treas. and Director; John P. Dougherty; Carol J. Tsao.
EIN: 223555424

4332
Trefler Foundation
233 Needham St., No. 400B
Newton, MA 02464-1571 (617) 454-1135
Contact: Pamela L. Trefler, Tr.

Established in 1997 in Massachusetts.
Donors: Alan N. Trefler; Pamela L. Trefler.
Foundation type: Independent foundation.
Financial data (yr. ended 12/31/13): Assets, $5,180,045 (M); gifts received, $44; expenditures, $748,791; qualifying distributions, $503,928; giving activities include $344,235 for 5 grants (high: $266,000; low: $3,000).
Fields of interest: Education; Mental health care; Community and economic development.
Type of support: Student aid.
Limitations: Applications accepted. Giving primarily to residents of Boston, MA.
Application information:
   Initial approach: Contact foundation
   Deadline(s): None
Officer: Christine H. Green, Pres.
Trustees: Alan N. Trefler; Pamela L. Trefler.
EIN: 043369962

4333
Tresorelle Foundation
10 Derne St.
Boston, MA 02114-4203

Established in 2000 in Massachusetts.
Donor: Elizabeth H. Owens.
Foundation type: Independent foundation.
Financial data (yr. ended 12/31/13): Assets, $587,630 (M); gifts received, $164,461; expenditures, $304,708; qualifying distributions, $302,325; giving activities include $271,500 for 20 grants (high: $95,000; low: $1,500).
Purpose and activities: Giving primarily for education programs.
Fields of interest: Art museums; Education; Human services.
Type of support: General support; Program development; Scholarships.
Limitations: Applications not accepted. Giving primarily in Boston, MA. No grants to individuals.
Application information: Contributes only to pre-selected organizations.
Officers and Directors: Elizabeth H. Owens, Pres. and Director; Margaret F. Owens, Clerk and Director; Robert I. Owens, Treas. and Director; Elizabeth N.C. Owens; Julia H. Owens.
EIN: 043537378

4334
Ray Tye Medical Aid Foundation
175 Campanelli Dr.
P.O. Box 850376
Braintree, MA 02184-5206
Contact: Terri Carlson, Dir.

FAX: (781) 356-4551; E-mail: info@rtmaf.org; Additional e-mail: info@rtmaf.org; Main URL: http://www.rtmaf.org
Facebook: https://www.facebook.com/raytyemedicalaidfoundation
RSS feed: http://feeds.feedburner.com/TheRayTyeMedicalAidFoundation

Established in 2002 in Massachusetts.
Donors: Harvey R. Chaplin; Maurice Halter Foundation; National Distributing Co., Inc.
Foundation type: Independent foundation.
Financial data (yr. ended 12/31/13): Assets, $4,462,043 (M); gifts received, $71,331; expenditures, $432,406; qualifying distributions, $407,351; giving activities include $407,351 for 8 grants (high: $163,903; low: $3,581).
Purpose and activities: Grants are made for medical care of indigents in U.S. hospitals.
Fields of interest: Health; Hospital care; Low-income and poor people.
Limitations: Giving primarily in the Boston, MA, area, including Cambridge.
Publications: Newsletter.
Application information:
  Initial approach: Use Medical Aid Request form on foundation web site
  Copies of proposal: 1
  Board meeting date(s): As necessary
  Final notification: 30 days
Officers: Eileen Tye, Pres.; Terri Carlson, V.P.
EIN: 046958143

4335
Harold S. and Anna S. Ullian Charitable Foundation
800 Boylston St., 33rd Fl.
Boston, MA 02199-8001

Established in 1990 in Massachusetts.
Foundation type: Independent foundation.
Financial data (yr. ended 10/31/13): Assets, $2,957,136 (M); expenditures, $232,438; qualifying distributions, $195,000; giving activities include $195,000 for 18 grants (high: $40,000; low: $2,500).
Fields of interest: Nonprofits; Hospital care; Diseases and conditions; Judaism.
Type of support: Research; Regranting.
Limitations: Applications not accepted. Giving primarily in Boston, MA. No grants to individuals.
Application information: Unsolicited requests for funds not accepted.
Trustees: Steven A. Meyer; Eliot Snider; Robert Snider.
EIN: 043107591

4336
Ungar Foundation
31 W. Sheffield Rd.
Great Barrington, MA 01230-1933
Contact: Aine D. Ungar

Foundation type: Independent foundation.
Financial data (yr. ended 11/30/13): Assets, $11,623 (M); expenditures, $178,666; qualifying distributions, $174,975; giving activities include $174,975 for 6 grants (high: $115,475; low: $1,000).
Purpose and activities: The foundation promotes conscious living through tolerance, the elimination

of poverty through education and self-sufficiency, and the advancement of society as a whole. Its goal is to fund projects and organizations that will raise the consciousness of the community and promote social change.
Fields of interest: Education; Human services.
Type of support: Continuing support; Capital and infrastructure; Program development; Scholarships; Research.
Limitations: Applications not accepted. Giving primarily in New England. No support for political or religious organizations or for universities or charities outside of the U.S. No grants to individuals or for computers, annual campaigns, research or feasibility studies, consulting services, general endowment funds or operating budgets.
Application information: Unsolicited requests for funds not accepted.
Director: Aine D. Ungar.
Number of staff: 1 part-time support.
EIN: 136937282

4337
United Charitable Foundation
95 Elm St.
West Springfield, MA 01089-2704 (413) 787-1292
Contact: Dena M. Hall, Pres.
Main URL: https://www.bankatunited.com/about-us/united-bank-foundation

Established in 2005 in Massachusetts.
Donor: United Financial Bancorp, Inc.
Foundation type: Independent foundation.
Financial data (yr. ended 12/31/14): Assets, $6,977,231; expenditures, $417,427; qualifying distributions, $412,427.
Fields of interest: Arts and culture; Education; Health; Human services; Youth development.
Type of support: Technical assistance; Matching grants; Program development; Equipment; Capital campaigns; Capital and infrastructure.
Limitations: Applications accepted. Giving primarily in MA. No grants to individuals.
Application information: See foundation website for complete application guidelines. Application form required.
  Initial approach: Letter of intent
  Deadline(s): Jan. 15, Apr. 15, July 15., and Oct. 15
  Board meeting date(s): Quarterly in Feb., May, Aug., and Nov.
Officers: Dena M. Hall, Pres.; Mark A. Roberts, V.P. and Treas.; Jennifer Shaw, Secy.
Directors: Richard B. Collins; Carol Moore Cutting; Carol A. Leary; Kevin E. Ross; Robert A. Stewart, Jr.; Peter F. Straley; Thomas H. Themistos.
Number of staff: None.
EIN: 203128745

4338
The Upstream Foundation
95 Allen's Point Rd.
Marion, MA 02738-2300

Established in 1998 in Massachusetts.
Donor: Charles E. Bascom.
Foundation type: Independent foundation.
Financial data (yr. ended 12/31/13): Assets, $895,632 (M); expenditures, $278,446; qualifying

distributions, $262,930; giving activities include $250,845 for 77 grants (high: $30,000; low: $100).
Fields of interest: Arts and culture; Education; Females.
Limitations: Applications not accepted. Giving primarily in CA and MA. No grants to individuals.
Application information: Contributes only to pre-selected organizations.
Trustees: Charles E. Bascom; Christina M. Bascom.
EIN: 043408722

4339
The Michael and Helen Valerio Charitable Remainder Foundation
c/o Chiuve & Co.
100 Conifer Hill Dr., Ste. 106
Danvers, MA 01923

Established in 1999 in Massachusetts.
Donors: Michael Valerio; Helen Valerio.
Foundation type: Independent foundation.
Financial data (yr. ended 09/30/14): Assets, $1,902,195 (M); gifts received, $31,640; expenditures, $194,026; qualifying distributions, $173,166.
Fields of interest: Education; Catholicism.
Limitations: Applications not accepted. Giving primarily in MA.
Application information: Unsolicited requests for funds not accepted.
Officer: Michael Valerio, Pres.
Trustee: Helen Valerio.
EIN: 046903625

4340
Van Sloun Foundation
1787 E. Scotch Pine Ln.
P.O. Box 116
Westport, MA 02791 (508) 636-4573
Contact: Neil Van Sloun

Established in 1991 in Massachusetts.
Donors: Neil J. Van Sloun; Sylvia Van Sloun.
Foundation type: Independent foundation.
Financial data (yr. ended 12/31/13): Assets, $8,871,443 (M); expenditures, $465,916; qualifying distributions, $406,075; giving activities include $366,950 for 44 grants (high: $35,000; low: $250), and $9,000 for 9 grants to individuals (high: $1,000; low: $1,000).
Fields of interest: Secondary education; Higher education; Natural resources; Animal welfare; Cancers; Human services.
Type of support: General support; Student aid.
Limitations: Applications accepted. Giving primarily in MA.
Application information: Application form required.
  Initial approach: Letter
  Deadline(s): None
Officer: Joseph Van Sloun, Exec. Dir.
Directors: Everett M. Davis; Nancy Van Sloun.
Trustees: Eric H. Strand; David B. Titus; Dennis L. Van Sloun.
EIN: 046691809

4341

Vela Foundation

(formerly Bernadette T. Rehnert Charitable Trust)
129 Newbury St., Ste. 400
Boston, MA 02116 617-545-4282
Contact: Bernadette Rehnert, Trustee
Main URL: http://www.velafoundation.org
LinkedIn: https://www.linkedin.com/company/
vela-foundation
Twitter: https://twitter.com/vela_foundation

Established in 2007 in Massachusetts.
Donor: Bernadette T. Rehnert.
Foundation type: Independent foundation.
Financial data (yr. ended 12/31/13): Assets,
$4,922,917 (M); gifts received, $1,149,254;
expenditures, $196,857; qualifying distributions,
$177,990; giving activities include $177,990 for 16
grants (high: $50,000; low: $1,000).
Purpose and activities: The Vela Foundation is a
private grantmaking foundation dedicated to
promoting improved nutrition and wellness in
eastern Massachusetts, with an emphasis on
underserved communities. Supported organizations
are those whose missions include nutrition literacy
and education, improved fitness and a concern for
access to healthy foods. Preference is given to
nutrition education programs with strong family
engagement and programs working creatively to
effect systemic change. The Foundation promotes
collaboration among organizations and funders to
meet shared goals.
Fields of interest: Education; Physical fitness;
Nutrition; Obesity; Agriculture; Food aid; Food
banks.
Type of support: General support; Continuing
support; Program development.
Limitations: Applications accepted. Giving primarily
in eastern MA. No grants to individuals.
Application information: Please see
velafoundation.org for specific application
requirements. .
  Initial approach: E-mail
  Copies of proposal: 1
  Deadline(s): Mar. 2 and Sept. 15
  Final notification: Approximately 6-8 weeks
Trustee: Bernadette T. Rehnert.
EIN: 208117214

4342

Verrochi Family Charitable Trust

33 Beaver Pl.
Boston, MA 02108-3303

Established in 1993 in Massachusetts.
Donor: Paul M. Verrochi.
Foundation type: Independent foundation.
Financial data (yr. ended 07/31/13): Assets,
$2,409,017 (M); gifts received, $1,267,036;
expenditures, $217,993; qualifying distributions,
$211,539; giving activities include $206,940 for 34
grants (high: $53,625; low: $50).
Fields of interest: Arts and culture; Museums;
Education; Catholicism; Youth development;
Children.
Limitations: Applications not accepted. Giving
primarily in MA. No grants to individuals.
Application information: Contributes only to
pre-selected organizations.
Trustee: Paul M. Verrochi.
EIN: 046740855

4343

The Michael and Norah Videtta Charitable Trust

309 Ipswich Rd.
Boxford, MA 01921-1505 (978) 887-0143
Contact: Wendell P. Weyland, Tr.

Established in 2008 in Massachusetts.
Foundation type: Independent foundation.
Financial data (yr. ended 09/30/14): Assets,
$6,593,363 (M); expenditures, $353,804;
qualifying distributions, $298,284; giving activities
include $276,225 for 8 grants (high: $60,873; low:
$5,000).
Fields of interest: Specialty hospital care; Hospice
care; Protestantism; Human services.
Limitations: Applications accepted. Giving primarily
in Washington, DC, MA and NY. No grants to
individuals.
Application information: Application form required.
  Initial approach: Letter
  Deadline(s): None
Trustee: Wendell P. Weyland.
EIN: 306161369

4344

The Vine's Branch Foundation

c/o Nathan S. Abramson
14 Kelly Rd.
Cambridge, MA 02139-4404

Donors: Nathan S. Abramson; Sara D. Ontiveros.
Foundation type: Independent foundation.
Financial data (yr. ended 12/31/13): Assets,
$5,516 (M); gifts received, $206,481;
expenditures, $206,481; qualifying distributions,
$205,000; giving activities include $205,000 for 1
grant.
Fields of interest: Christianity.
Limitations: Applications not accepted. Giving
primarily in MA. No grants to individuals.
Application information: Contributes only to
pre-selected organizations.
Trustees: Nathan S. Abramson; Sara D. Ontiveros.
EIN: 206960359

4345

The Vingo Trust III

c/o LWC
230 Congress St., 12th Fl.
Boston, MA 02110-2409

Established in 1991 in Massachusetts.
Donor: Catherine Lastavica.
Foundation type: Independent foundation.
Financial data (yr. ended 12/31/13): Assets,
$3,764,322 (M); expenditures, $233,812;
qualifying distributions, $203,012; giving activities
include $200,000 for 1 grant.
Fields of interest: Historical activities.
Limitations: Applications not accepted. Giving
primarily in Boston, MA. No grants to individuals.
Application information: Contributes only to
pre-selected organizations.
Trustees: David W. Fitts, Esq.; Catherine C.
Lastavica; Peter Mulholland.
EIN: 223106692

4346

Maria C. Von Magnus Henderson Charitable Trust

3 Centennial Dr.
Peabody, MA 01960

Donor: Maria C. Von Magnus Henderson Irrev.
Foundation type: Independent foundation.
Financial data (yr. ended 12/31/14): Assets,
$2,675,168 (M); expenditures, $156,451;
qualifying distributions, $126,020; giving activities
include $116,554 for 2 grants (high: $58,277; low:
$58,277).
Fields of interest: Education; Higher education.
Limitations: Applications not accepted. Giving
primarily in MA.
Application information: Unsolicited requests for
funds not accepted.
Trustee: Family Capital Trust Co.
EIN: 356808786

4347

The George R. Wallace Foundation

c/o Goodwin Procter LLP
1 Exchange Pl.
Boston, MA 02109-2881
E-mail: lthompson@goodwinprocter.com

Established in 1963 in Massachusetts.
Donor: George R. Wallace‡.
Foundation type: Independent foundation.
Financial data (yr. ended 12/31/13): Assets,
$7,918,191 (M); expenditures, $449,924;
qualifying distributions, $404,932; giving activities
include $357,666 for 10 grants (high: $85,000;
low: $1,950).
Purpose and activities: Support for education
(particularly for programs that benefit low-income
students), and museums and libraries, particularly
those serving the Fitchburg and Leominster, MA,
area.
Fields of interest: Arts and culture; Education;
Higher education; Natural resources; Human
services.
Type of support: General support; Matching grants;
Annual campaigns; Capital campaigns; Capital and
infrastructure; Equipment; Endowments; Seed
money.
Limitations: Applications not accepted. Giving
primarily in the Fitchburg and Leominster, MA, area.
No support for religious organizations, except for
grants to support the education of disadvantaged
and/or disabled children. No grants to individuals,
or for scholarships or fellowships; no loans.
Application information: Unsolicited requests for
funds not accepted.
Trustees: Andre A. Gelinas; John Grado, Jr.; Regina
M. Pisa.
EIN: 046130518

4348

Blanche M. Walsh Charity Trust

P.O. Box 9531
Lowell, MA 01853-9531
Application address: c/o Cynthia A. Kelleher, Tr.,
P.O. Box 238, Chelmsford, MA 01824

Established in 1973 in Massachusetts.
Foundation type: Independent foundation.
Financial data (yr. ended 12/31/13): Assets,
$7,823,206 (M); expenditures, $260,682;

qualifying distributions, $260,682; giving activities include $199,500 for 57 grants (high: $11,000; low: $1,000).

Purpose and activities: Giving limited to Roman Catholic organizations, including educational institutions and welfare organizations.

Fields of interest: Arts and culture; Education; Elementary and secondary education; Graduate and professional education; Catholicism; Theology; Human services.

Type of support: General support; Capital and infrastructure; Equipment; Convening; Publications; Seed money; Scholarships.

Limitations: Applications accepted. Giving primarily in MA. No grants to individuals, or for endowment funds, continuing support, annual campaigns, deficit financing, or matching gifts; no loans.

Publications: Application guidelines.

Application information: Application form required.
Initial approach: Letter
Copies of proposal: 1
Deadline(s): Nov. 1
Final notification: Dec. 1

Trustees: John C. Donohoe; Cynthia A. Kelleher; Robert F. Murphy, Jr.

Number of staff: 3 part-time professional.

EIN: 046311841

4349
The Walske Charitable Foundation

(formerly Walske-Longtine Foundation)
c/o Loring Wolcott Coolidge Trust
230 Congress St., 12th Fl.
Boston, MA 02110-2409
Contact: Steven C. Walske, Tr.
Application address: c/o Steve Walske, 2118 Vallejo St., San Francisco, CA 94123, tel.: (415) 776-9005

Established in 1997 in Massachusetts.

Donor: Steven Walske.

Foundation type: Independent foundation.

Financial data (yr. ended 12/31/13): Assets, $6,059,961 (M); expenditures, $310,865; qualifying distributions, $258,070; giving activities include $256,000 for 14 grants (high: $70,000; low: $2,500).

Fields of interest: Museums; Historic preservation; Education; Undergraduate education; Family planning; Sustainable development; Urban development; Women's services.

Limitations: Applications accepted. Giving primarily in CA and Boston, MA.

Application information:
Initial approach: Proposal
Deadline(s): None

Trustees: Jennifer M. Walske; Steven C. Walske.

EIN: 046818329

4350
The Wapack Foundation

c/o Nochols & Pratt
50 Congress St.
Boston, MA 02109-4002 (617) 523-6800
Contact: James R. Nichols, Tr.

Established in 1992 in Massachusetts.

Donors: James R. Nichols; Elizabeth Nichols.

Foundation type: Independent foundation.

Financial data (yr. ended 12/31/13): Assets, $1,009,633 (M); gifts received, $96,706; expenditures, $214,600; qualifying distributions,

$207,175; giving activities include $202,750 for 18 grants (high: $75,000; low: $1,500).

Purpose and activities: Giving primarily for higher education and the environment.

Fields of interest: Arts and culture; Health; Catholicism.

Limitations: Applications accepted. Giving primarily in MA.

Application information:
Initial approach: Proposal
Deadline(s): None

Trustee: James R. Nichols.

EIN: 046178371

4351
Vila B. Webber 1985 Charitable Trust

c/o Choate LLP
P.O. Box 961019
Boston, MA 02196-1019

Established in 1989 in Massachusetts.

Foundation type: Independent foundation.

Financial data (yr. ended 06/30/13): Assets, $4,217,734 (M); expenditures, $261,236; qualifying distributions, $224,978; giving activities include $220,000 for grants.

Purpose and activities: Giving primarily for education and human services.

Fields of interest: Arts and culture; Languages; Education; Hospital care; Human services.

Limitations: Applications not accepted. Giving primarily in MA. No grants to individuals.

Application information: Unsolicited requests for funds not accepted.

Trustees: A. Silvana Giner; John J. Regan; Jennifer C. Snyder.

EIN: 222824617

4352
The Frederick E. Weber Charities Corporation

89 South St.
Boston, MA 02110 (617) 292-6264
Contact: Thanda Brassard, Pres.

Established in 1902 in Massachusetts.

Donor: Frederick E. Weber‡.

Foundation type: Independent foundation.

Financial data (yr. ended 03/31/14): Assets, $6,114,541 (M); expenditures, $349,307; qualifying distributions, $256,500; giving activities include $256,500 for 50 grants (high: $15,000; low: $1,000).

Purpose and activities: Giving primarily to social service agencies for emergency financial assistance to indigent families or individuals.

Fields of interest: Hospital care; Human services; Family services; Child welfare; Low-income and poor people.

Type of support: Emergency funds; Grants to individuals.

Limitations: Applications accepted. Giving limited to MA, with emphasis on Boston. No grants for research, capital projects, or equipment.

Publications: Annual report; Program policy statement.

Application information:
Initial approach: Letter
Copies of proposal: 1
Deadline(s): None

Board meeting date(s): Weekly except in Aug.
Final notification: 30 days

Officers: Thanda Brassard, Pres.; Lisa Van Vleck, Clerk; Nathaniel Butler, Treas.

Members: Elizabeth Aguilo; Linda Braun; Jeffrey Katz; Mitchell Pomerance; Kevin Queally; Jay Scollins; Kate Taylor.

Number of staff: 1 part-time support.

EIN: 042133244

4353
Webster Five Foundation, Inc.

10 A St.
Auburn, MA 01501-2102 (508) 943-9401
Contact: Sam Bitar, Treas. and Exec. Dir.
E-mail: foundation@web5.com

Established in 1995 in Massachusetts.

Donor: Webster Five Cents Savings Bank.

Foundation type: Company-sponsored foundation.

Financial data (yr. ended 10/31/13): Assets, $41,982 (M); gifts received, $150,000; expenditures, $149,477; qualifying distributions, $149,427; giving activities include $149,357 for 67 grants (high: $10,000; low: $500).

Purpose and activities: The foundation supports nonprofit organizations involved with arts and culture, education, health, human services, community economic development, and senior citizens.

Fields of interest: Arts and culture; Education; Human services.

Type of support: General support; Annual campaigns; Emergency funds; Program development.

Limitations: Applications accepted. Giving primarily in areas of company operations in MA. No support for political organizations or candidates, churches or synagogues or any affiliated organizations, fraternal organizations, employment unions, or tax-supported entities. No grants to individuals or for capital campaigns.

Publications: Application guidelines.

Application information: Application form required.
Initial approach: Contact foundation for application form
Deadline(s): None

Officers and Directors: Richard T. Leahy, Pres. and Director; Benjamin A. Craver, Clerk; Sam Bitar, Co-Treas. and Co-Exec. Dir.; Karen M. Kempskie-Aquino, Co-Treas. and Co-Exec. Dir.; Maura E. Aniello; David S. Bayer.

EIN: 043303760

4354
The John Leopold and Geraldine R. Weil Memorial Charitable Foundation Inc.

253 Riverview Ave., 1st Fl.
Newton, MA 02466-1358
Application address: c/o Jason A. Rosenberg, Esq., 246 Walnut St., Newtonville, MA 02460, tel.: (617) 964-7000

Foundation type: Operating foundation.

Financial data (yr. ended 12/31/13): Assets, $3,833,433 (M); expenditures, $278,925; qualifying distributions, $278,930; giving activities include $255,393 for 5 grants (high: $74,861; low: $15,000).

Purpose and activities: Giving to organizations that provide help and assistance for research, education

and training in, and to advance the knowldge and care given for, the fields of medicine, psychiatry, and psychology, and especially as they pertain to children.
Fields of interest: Child abuse; Family services; Child welfare; Child development.
Limitations: Applications accepted. Giving primarily in MA.
Application information: Application form required.
Initial approach: Proposal
Deadline(s): None
Officers and Directors: Richard C. Waters, Pres. and Director; Jason A. Rosenberg, Clerk and Director; Frank D. Micciantuono, Treas. and Director; Linda Helmig Bram; Tony Bram; Barbara Roop; Leonard Solomon; Patricia Waters.
EIN: 311662175

4355
Roberta & S.R. Weiner Family Foundation
c/o Alan W. Rottenberg Goulston & Storrs
400 Atlantic Ave.
Boston, MA   02110-3331

Donors: Stephen R. Weiner; Adam J. Weiner; Roberta S. Weiner.
Foundation type: Independent foundation.
Financial data (yr. ended 12/31/13): Assets, $0 (M); gifts received, $425,000; expenditures, $425,000; qualifying distributions, $425,000; giving activities include $425,000 for 4 grants (high: $250,000; low: $25,000).
Fields of interest: Education; Foundations; Religion; Judaism; Youth development.
Limitations: Applications not accepted. Giving primarily in MA.
Application information: Unsolicited requests for funds not accepted.
Trustees: Melissa Weiner Janfaza; Alan W. Rottenberg; Adam J. Weiner; Roberta S. Weiner; Stephen R. Weiner.
EIN: 462956417

4356
Weld Foundation
c/o Loring, Wolcott & Coolidge
230 Congress St., 12 Fl.
Boston, MA   02110-2437

Established in 1952 in Massachusetts.
Donor: Mary Weld Pingree†.
Foundation type: Independent foundation.
Financial data (yr. ended 12/31/13): Assets, $11,414,425 (M); expenditures, $485,173; qualifying distributions, $426,353; giving activities include $418,375 for 16 grants (high: $100,000; low: $5,000).
Purpose and activities: Giving primarily for education, museums, hospitals, including a children's hospital, and the environment.
Fields of interest: Museums; Elementary and secondary education; Natural resources; Health; Hospital care.
Limitations: Applications not accepted. Giving primarily in MA. No grants to individuals.
Application information: Contributes only to pre-selected organizations.
Trustees: Frederick D. Ballou; Peter B. Loring; Charles W. Pingree.
EIN: 046039173

4357
George W. Wells Foundation
c/o U.S. Trust, Bank of America, N.A.
225 Franklin St., 4th Fl.
Boston, MA   02110   (866) 778-6859
Contact: Michealle Larkins, V.P.
E-mail: ma.grantmaking@ustrust.com; Main
URL: http://www.bankofamerica.com/grantmaking

Foundation type: Independent foundation.
Financial data (yr. ended 12/31/14): Assets, $4,604,760; expenditures, $300,298; qualifying distributions, $249,456.
Purpose and activities: The Foundation was established in 1934 to support and promote quality educational, human services, and health care programming for underserved populations. Special consideration is given to charitable organizations that serve the people of Southbridge, Massachusetts and its surrounding communities.
Fields of interest: Education; Health; Human services.
Type of support: General support; Program development.
Limitations: Giving primarily in Southbridge, MA and surrounding communities. No grants to individuals.
Application information: Online application; complete application guidelines available on foundation web site.
Initial approach: Email
Trustee: Bank of America Merrill Lynch.
EIN: 046038039

4358
David P. Wheatland Charitable Trust
c/o Acadia Mgmt. Co., Inc.
111 Devonshire St., Ste. 620
Boston, MA   02109-5419   (617) 426-5755

Established in 1993 in Massachusetts.
Donor: David P. Wheatland Trust.
Foundation type: Independent foundation.
Financial data (yr. ended 12/31/14): Assets, $10,871,512; expenditures, $473,972; qualifying distributions, $469,818.
Purpose and activities: Giving primarily to a university's collection of historical scientific instruments, as well as to a museum. Preference is given to organizations that the donor and members of his family have historically supported, as well as referrals made by family members to the extent that funds are available.
Fields of interest: Museums; Art museums; Historical activities; Animal welfare; Christianity.
Type of support: General support.
Limitations: Applications accepted. Giving primarily in MA; some funding also in CA. No grants to individuals.
Application information: Application form required.
Initial approach: Letter
Deadline(s): None
Trustees: Eileen M. Balthazard; Martha W. Lunt; Peter O. Stauffer; Rebecca Wheatland; Timothy B. Biglow.
EIN: 046744379

4359
Ruth B. Whittemore Charitable Trust
c/o Erb & Southcotte
P.O. Box 827
Fitchburg, MA   01420-0024

Established in 2001 in Massachusetts.
Foundation type: Independent foundation.
Financial data (yr. ended 12/31/14): Assets, $5,744,745; expenditures, $297,125; qualifying distributions, $262,600.
Fields of interest: Foundations; Nonprofits; Public libraries; Christianity; Scouting programs.
Type of support: Regranting.
Limitations: Applications not accepted. Giving primarily in MA. No grants to individuals.
Application information: Unsolicited requests for funds not accepted.
Trustees: Donald R. Erb; Elisha W. Erb.
EIN: 046916255

4360
The Wilcox Family Foundation
100 Federal St., 37th Fl.
Boston, MA   02110

Established in 1989 in Connecticut.
Donors: George G. Wilcox; Christina H. Wilcox; Heroy Partners LLC.
Foundation type: Independent foundation.
Financial data (yr. ended 11/30/13): Assets, $3,467,970 (M); gifts received, $225,000; expenditures, $187,346; qualifying distributions, $171,111; giving activities include $165,699 for 37 grants (high: $20,000; low: $500).
Fields of interest: Arts and culture; Education; Health; Human services.
Type of support: General support.
Limitations: Applications not accepted. Giving primarily in MI, RI and VT. No grants to individuals.
Application information: Contributes only to pre-selected organizations.
Trustees: Christina W. McIntyre; G. Geer Wilcox; Peter B. Wilcox.
EIN: 226474493

4361
Windhorse Foundation
(formerly The Salem Family Foundation)
c/o Windhorse Capital Management
125 High St., 22nd Fl.
Boston, MA   02110-2704   (617) 850-9162
Contact: David A. Salem, Tr.

Established in 1992 in Virginia.
Donors: David A. Salem; Richard M. Salem; John F. Gifford.
Foundation type: Independent foundation.
Financial data (yr. ended 12/31/13): Assets, $5,147,614 (M); expenditures, $206,551; qualifying distributions, $164,105; giving activities include $157,300 for 26 grants (high: $50,000; low: $300).
Purpose and activities: Giving primarily for education, health care, and human services organizations.
Fields of interest: Arts and culture; Elementary and secondary education; Health; Human services.
Limitations: Applications accepted. Giving primarily in CO and MA. No grants to individuals.
Application information:
Initial approach: Letter
Deadline(s): None
Trustees: David A. Salem; Richard M. Salem.
EIN: 046707664

4362
Winning Home Inc.
c/o CFC Investments
P.O. Box 1308
Concord, MA 01742-1308   (978) 287-1414
Contact: Albert Chip Curran Jr.
FAX: (978) 287-6009; Main URL: http://
www.winninghome.org

Foundation type: Independent foundation.
Financial data (yr. ended 12/31/13): Assets,
$5,891,240 (M); expenditures, $360,035;
qualifying distributions, $319,507; giving activities
include $300,000 for 12 grants (high: $90,000;
low: $5,000).
Purpose and activities: Giving primarily for services
and support to children who are economically,
socially, physically, emotionally, or mentally
handicapped.
Fields of interest: Food aid; Child welfare; Youth
services; Low-income and poor people; People with
disabilities.
Limitations: Applications accepted. Giving primarily
in MA. No grants to individuals.
Application information: See foundation's web site
for application guidelines. Application form required.
Officers: Thomas Martin, Pres. and Director; Donald
Foley, V.P. and Director; Ernest Jones, Secy. and
Director; Albert F. Curran, Jr., Treas. and Director.
Directors: John Brophy; Larry Byron; Sean Coakley;
Robert Maguire; Steve Paladino; Mark Salvati;
Robert Simons; Mark Sullivan.
EIN: 046049776

4363
Clara B. Winthrop Charitable Trust
45 School St., 5th Fl.
Boston, MA 02108-3204   (617) 523-1635
Contact: Oliver A. Spalding, Tr.

Established in 1969 in Massachusetts.
Donor: Clara B. Winthrop†.
Foundation type: Independent foundation.
Financial data (yr. ended 12/31/13): Assets,
$3,335,521 (M); expenditures, $189,212;
qualifying distributions, $151,000; giving activities
include $151,000 for 29 grants (high: $10,000;
low: $1,000).
Fields of interest: Arts and culture; Museums;
Education; Natural resources; Community and
economic development.
Type of support: General support; Continuing
support; Annual campaigns; Capital campaigns.
Limitations: Applications accepted. Giving limited to
MA. No grants to individuals.
Application information: Application form required.
Initial approach: Proposal
Deadline(s): None
Board meeting date(s): Dec.
Trustees: Peter P. Brown; Theodore E. Ober; Oliver
A. Spalding.
EIN: 046039972

4364
Wyman-Gordon Foundation
370 Main St., 12th Fl.
Worcester, MA 01608-1723   (508) 459-8093

Established in 1966 in Delaware.
Donor: Wyman-Gordon Co.
Foundation type: Independent foundation.

Financial data (yr. ended 12/31/13): Assets,
$6,324,626 (M); expenditures, $333,304;
qualifying distributions, $286,129; giving activities
include $271,350 for 41 grants (high: $75,000;
low: $350).
Purpose and activities: The foundation supports
organizations involved with arts and culture,
education, health, human services, and community
development.
Fields of interest: Arts and culture; Museums;
Education; Higher education; Nonprofits; Hospital
care; Diseases and conditions; Community and
economic development; Human services.
Type of support: Capital campaigns; Capital and
infrastructure; Equipment; Regranting.
Limitations: Applications accepted. Giving primarily
in MA, with emphasis on the Grafton and Worcester
areas. No grants to individuals, or for endowment
funds, special projects, research, publications, or
conferences; no loans.
Application information: Application form required.
Initial approach: Proposal
Copies of proposal: 3
Deadline(s): None
Officers: David P. Gruber, Pres.; Wallace F. Whitney,
Jr., Secy.-Treas.
Director: Warner S. Fletcher.
Number of staff: 1 part-time professional; 1
part-time support.
EIN: 046142600

4365
Xeric Foundation
351 Pleasant St.
PMB 214
Northampton, MA 01060-3900   (413) 585-0671
E-mail: xericgrant@aol.com; Main URL: http://
www.xericfoundation.org
Grants List: http://www.xericfoundation.org/
xericchargrants.html

Established in 1991 in Massachusetts.
Donor: Peter A. Laird.
Foundation type: Independent foundation.
Financial data (yr. ended 09/30/14): Assets,
$3,994,813 (M); expenditures, $238,852;
qualifying distributions, $233,970; giving activities
include $199,720 for 48 grants (high: $21,000;
low: $500).
Purpose and activities: Giving to self-publishing
comic book creators in the U.S. and Canada;
support also for nonprofit organizations in western
MA, in the 413 area code, for unique projects or
services.
Fields of interest: Arts and culture; Education;
Housing development; Youth development.
Type of support: Continuing support; Grants to
individuals; Capital and infrastructure; Land
acquisitions; Program development; Publications;
Seed money; Scholarships; Technical assistance.
Limitations: Applications not accepted. Giving
limited to western MA for organizations. No grants
for operating budgets or capital costs.
Application information: The annual grant
application process is suspended until further
notice.
Officers: Peter A. Laird, Pres.; Christopher B. Milne,
V.P.; Kendall Clark Engelman, Secy.-Treas.;
Jeannine Atkins, Exec. V.P.
Number of staff: 1 part-time professional.
EIN: 223149258

4366
Alden N. Young Trust
1500 Worcester Rd., Ste. F
Framingham, MA 01702-8984   (603) 552-3373
Contact: Nancy S. Smith, Tr.
Application address: 2676 Wakefield Rd., Wakefield,
NH 03872, tel.: (603) 522-3373

Established in 1998 in California.
Foundation type: Independent foundation.
Financial data (yr. ended 12/31/13): Assets,
$2,845,674 (M); expenditures, $256,231;
qualifying distributions, $237,643; giving activities
include $173,180 for 14 grants (high: $35,820;
low: $900), and $51,820 for 25 grants to
individuals (high: $5,000; low: $500).
Fields of interest: Arts and culture; Education;
Christianity.
Type of support: General support; Student aid.
Limitations: Applications accepted. Giving primarily
in Wakefield NH and vicinity.
Application information: Application form required.
Initial approach: Proposal
Deadline(s): None
Officer: Arthur O. Ricci, Mgr.
Trustee: Nancy S. Smith.
EIN: 026117755

4367
Zampell Family Foundation
15 William Fairfield Dr.
Wenham, MA 01984-1123

Foundation type: Independent foundation.
Financial data (yr. ended 12/31/13): Assets,
$11,654 (M); gifts received, $147,078;
expenditures, $147,189; qualifying distributions,
$147,189; giving activities include $145,600 for 25
grants (high: $40,000; low: $500).
Fields of interest: Education; Health; Human
services.
Limitations: Applications not accepted. Giving
primarily in MA.
Application information: Unsolicited requests for
funds not accepted.
Trustees: Christine M. Zampell; James C. Zampell.
EIN: 263006687

4368
Zock Endowment Trust
c/o Cambridge Trust Co.
75 State St., 18th Fl.
Boston, MA 02109
Application address: c/o Robert A. Zock, Jr., 98 Birch
Hill Rd., Warner, NH 03278

Established in 1970 in New Jersey.
Donor: Sara M. Zock Charitable Remainder Unitrust.
Foundation type: Independent foundation.
Financial data (yr. ended 09/30/14): Assets,
$5,321,192 (M); expenditures, $314,240;
qualifying distributions, $245,964; giving activities
include $205,300 for 9 grants (high: $50,000; low:
$10,000).
Fields of interest: Education; Domesticated
animals; Veterinary medicine; Human services.
Application information:
Initial approach: None
Deadline(s): None

MICHIGAN

4369
Talbert & Leota Abrams Foundation
1412 Copper Cir.
Rochester, MI 48306-4592

Established in 1960 in Michigan.
Donors: Leota Abrams†; Talbert Abrams†.
Foundation type: Independent foundation.
Financial data (yr. ended 12/31/13): Assets, $9,785,068 (M); expenditures, $553,679; qualifying distributions, $485,219; giving activities include $338,000 for 10 grants (high: $50,000; low: $10,000).
Fields of interest: Higher education; Basic and remedial instruction; Reading promotion; Nonprofits; Libraries.
Type of support: Program development; Scholarships; Research; Regranting.
Limitations: Applications not accepted. Giving primarily in central MI. No support for churches for sectarian use, or for athletic activities. No grants to individuals, or for operating or traveling expenses; no loans.
Publications: Annual report.
Application information: Unsolicited requests for funds not accepted.
Board meeting date(s): June
Officers: Barbara J. Brown, Co-Pres.; Kyle C. Abbott, Co-Pres.; Craig C. Brown, V.P.; Tiffany L. Patzer, Secy.; Shane A. Patzer, Treas.
Director: Joe C. Foster.
Number of staff: 5 part-time professional.
EIN: 386082194

4370
Acheson Family Foundation
38710 Woodward Ave., Ste. 220
Bloomfield Hills, MI 48304

Established in 2006 in Michigan.
Donors: Michael H. Acheson; Adele F. Acheson.
Foundation type: Independent foundation.
Financial data (yr. ended 12/31/13): Assets, $1,238,878 (M); expenditures, $163,692; qualifying distributions, $157,646; giving activities include $155,300 for 6 grants (high: $125,000; low: $300).
Fields of interest: Elementary and secondary education; Higher education.
Limitations: Applications not accepted. Giving primarily in Wayne County, MI, with emphasis on the greater metropolitan Detroit area. No grants to individuals.
Application information: Contributes only to pre-selected organizations.
Officers and Directors: Michael H. Acheson, Pres. and Director; Marianne Brakora, Secy.-Treas.; Adele F. Acheson.
EIN: 205449358

4371
The Haiganoosh Mengushian Ajemian Foundation
2350 Franklin Rd.
Bloomfield Hills, MI 48302-0385

Donor: Robert Ajemian Trust.
Foundation type: Independent foundation.
Financial data (yr. ended 12/31/13): Assets, $7,199,105 (M); expenditures, $401,953; qualifying distributions, $325,506; giving activities include $249,500 for 39 grants (high: $50,000; low: $500).
Fields of interest: Arts and culture; Education; Catholicism; International development.
International interests: Armenia.
Limitations: Applications not accepted. Giving primarily in MI.
Application information: Unsolicited requests for funds not accepted.
Directors: Alex Sarkesian; Christopher Sarkesian; Lauren Sarkesian; Peter Sarkesian.
EIN: 270476819

4372
Tim Allen Foundation
(formerly The Laura Deibel and Tim Allen Foundation)
30600 Northwestern Hwy., Ste. 245
Farmington Hills, MI 48334-3171

Established in 1999 in Michigan.
Donor: Timothy Dick.
Foundation type: Independent foundation.
Financial data (yr. ended 12/31/13): Assets, $4,597,449 (M); expenditures, $230,000; qualifying distributions, $338,251; giving activities include $230,000 for 21 grants (high: $50,000; low: $500).
Purpose and activities: Giving primarily to museums and for human services.
Fields of interest: Museums; Education; Cancers; Communication media; Human services; Food aid; Homeless people.
Limitations: Applications not accepted. Giving primarily in CA; giving also in MI.
Application information: Unsolicited requests for funds not accepted.
Officer: Timothy A. Dick, Pres.
EIN: 383446053

4373
The Alnour Foundation
5031 Villa Linde Pkwy., Rm. 212
Flint, MI 48532

Established in 2000 in Michigan.
Foundation type: Independent foundation.
Financial data (yr. ended 12/31/12): Assets, $3,018,425 (M); expenditures, $151,080; qualifying distributions, $150,200; giving activities include $150,200 for 7 grants (high: $106,950; low: $250).
Purpose and activities: Giving for local Islamic centers.
Fields of interest: Community and economic development; Religion; Human services.
Limitations: Applications not accepted. Giving primarily in MI. No grants to individuals.
Application information: Unsolicited requests for funds not accepted.
Officers: Jamal Hammoud, MD, Pres.; Mai Hammoud, V.P.; Khaled Hammoud, Treas.
EIN: 382502540

4374
Alon and Shari Friendship Foundation, Inc.
3170 Walnut Lake, Crt. Ste.20
Commerce TWP, MI 48390-4143

Established in 1999 in Michigan.
Donors: Alon Kaufman; Shari Kaufman.
Foundation type: Independent foundation.
Financial data (yr. ended 12/31/13): Assets, $217,171 (M); gifts received, $510,000; expenditures, $357,744; qualifying distributions, $357,104; giving activities include $357,104 for 35 grants (high: $50,000; low: $50).
Purpose and activities: Giving primarily to Jewish agencies, temples, schools, and federated giving programs.
Fields of interest: Education; Nonprofits; Parkinson's disease; Judaism; Human services; Child welfare.
Type of support: Regranting.
Limitations: Applications not accepted. Giving primarily in Oakland County, MI. No grants to individuals.
Application information: Unsolicited requests for funds not accepted.
Officers: Alon Kaufman, Pres. and Director; Shari Kaufman, Secy.-Treas. and Director.
EIN: 383504283

4375
Amerisure Charitable Foundation
26777 Halsted Rd.
Farmington Hills, MI 48331-3577

Established in 2005 in Michigan.
Donors: Amerisure Mutual Insurance Co.; Guy Carpenter & Co., LLC; Amerisure Mutual Holdings, Inc.
Foundation type: Company-sponsored foundation.
Financial data (yr. ended 12/31/13): Assets, $1,919,155 (M); gifts received, $421,490; expenditures, $420,037; qualifying distributions, $411,600; giving activities include $411,600 for 33 grants (high: $75,000; low: $100).
Purpose and activities: The foundation supports organizations involved with arts and culture, education, health, mental health, housing development, athletics, human services, the insurance industry, and economics.
Fields of interest: Education; Sports and recreation; Youth development.
Limitations: Applications not accepted. Giving primarily in areas of company operations in MI. No grants to individuals.
Application information: Contributes only to pre-selected organizations.
Officers and Directors: Angela M. McBride, Pres. and C.E.O. and Director; Susan Gailey Vincent, V.P., Secy. and Genl. Counsel and Director; Matthew J. Simon, V.P. and Treas. and Director; Greg J. Crabb, V.P. and Director; Michael M. Dieterle, V.P. and Director; Daniel J. Graf, V.P.; Thomas E. Hoeg, V.P. and Director; Richard F. Russell, V.P. and Director; Edward H. Wagner, V.P. and Director.
EIN: 300289445

4376
The Anchor Foundation
3141 N. Lake Shore Dr.
Holland, MI 49424-6020

Established in 1997 in Michigan.
Donors: Elizabeth I. Huizenga; Herman Kanis; Suzanne Kanis.
Foundation type: Independent foundation.
Financial data (yr. ended 12/31/12): Assets, $1,618,667 (M); expenditures, $452,197; qualifying distributions, $428,500; giving activities include $428,500 for grants.
Purpose and activities: Giving primarily to Christian organizations, education, and ministries.
Fields of interest: Education; Christianity.
Limitations: Applications not accepted. Giving in the U.S., with some emphasis on MI. No grants to individuals.
Application information: Unsolicited requests for funds not accepted.
Officers and Directors: Suzanne Kanis, Pres. and Director; Herman Kanis, Mgr. and Director; Michael J. Kanis; Sally J. Morris; April L. Smith.
EIN: 383353871

4377
Frank N. Andersen Foundation
P.O. Box 225
Bridgeport, MI 48722-0225 (989) 772-2361
Contact: Michael Tate

Established in 1955 in Michigan.
Donor: Frank N. Andersen†.
Foundation type: Independent foundation.
Financial data (yr. ended 12/31/14): Assets, $7,421,491 (M); expenditures, $518,728; qualifying distributions, $440,018; giving activities include $440,018 for 33 grants (high: $146,920; low: $500).
Purpose and activities: Giving primarily for education, human services, and to community foundations.
Fields of interest: Education; Higher education; Foundations; Sports and recreation; Human services.
Type of support: Capital campaigns; Capital and infrastructure; Equipment; Scholarships.
Limitations: Applications accepted. Giving limited to Saginaw and Bay counties, MI. No grants to individuals.
Publications: Annual report.
Application information: Application form required.
  Initial approach: Letter requesting application form
  Copies of proposal: 1
  Deadline(s): None
  Board meeting date(s): Quarterly
Officers: Michael A. Tate, V.P.; John Gilmour, V.P.; Jeffrey W. McNally, Pres.
Trustees: Barbara Lincoln; Gerald Barber; Arnold L. Johnson.
Number of staff: 3 part-time professional.
EIN: 386062616

4378
The Andrah Foundation
9842 Fisk Rd.
Clinton, MI 49236

Established in 1996 in Michigan.
Donors: Thomas Knoll; Ruth Knoll.
Foundation type: Independent foundation.
Financial data (yr. ended 12/31/12): Assets, $5,402,017 (M); expenditures, $215,325;

qualifying distributions, $156,992; giving activities include $156,992 for grants.
Fields of interest: Arts and culture; Elementary and secondary education; Gifted education; Higher education.
Limitations: Applications not accepted. Giving primarily in CA and Ann Arbor, MI. No grants to individuals.
Application information: Contributes only to pre-selected organizations.
Officers: Gary Countryman, Pres.; Ruth S. Knoll, Secy.-Treas.
EIN: 383267840

4379
The Ave Maria Foundation
(formerly The Mater Christi Foundation)
P.O. Box 373
Ann Arbor, MI 48106-0373
Main URL: http://www.avemariafoundation.org
Thomas S. Monaghan's Giving Pledge
Profile: http://glasspockets.org/philanthropy-in-focus/eye-on-the-giving-pledge/profiles/monaghan

Established in 1983 in Michigan.
Donors: Domino's Pizza, Inc.; Thomas S. Monaghan; Lance Mudd; David Fischer; Lisa Fischer.
Foundation type: Independent foundation.
Financial data (yr. ended 12/31/13): Assets, $5,169,134 (M); gifts received, $3,211,200; expenditures, $1,546,000; qualifying distributions, $563,856; giving activities include $395,873 for 6 grants (high: $254,500; low: $720), and $77,467 for 3 foundation-administered programs.
Purpose and activities: Support primarily for a variety of organizations which bring Catholic life and culture to the world.
Fields of interest: Education; Human services; Youth development.
Type of support: Program development.
Limitations: Applications not accepted. Giving primarily in FL and MI. No grants to individuals.
Application information: Unsolicited applications not considered.
  Board meeting date(s): Annually
Officers and Directors: Thomas S. Monaghan, Pres. and Director; Jeff Randolph, Secy.; Paul Roney, Treas. and Director; Paul Fransway.
Number of staff: 1 part-time professional.
EIN: 382514364

4380
Avharas Avraham Foundation
c/o Grant Committee
333 W. Fort St.
Detroit, MI 48226

Donors: Gary Torgow; TF Foundation.
Foundation type: Independent foundation.
Financial data (yr. ended 12/31/13): Assets, $154,771 (M); gifts received, $447,874; expenditures, $293,236; qualifying distributions, $276,925; giving activities include $276,925 for 110 grants (high: $40,000; low: $25).
Fields of interest: Education; Religion; Human services.
Limitations: Applications accepted. Giving primarily in CA, MI and New York, NY.
Application information: Application form required.

Initial approach: Proposal
  Deadline(s): None
Officers and Directors: Gary Torgow, Pres. and Director; Malka Torgow, Secy. and Director; Yonah Torgow, Treas. and Director; Eliezer Torgow.
EIN: 462028020

4381
Baiardi Family Foundation Inc.
2328 Pinecrest St.
Harbor Springs, MI 49740-9261
E-mail: info@baiardifoundation.org; Additional email: grants@baiardifoundation.org; Main URL: http://www.baiardifoundation.org

Donors: Chris A. Baiardi; Cindy J. Baiardi; Angelo Baiardi†.
Foundation type: Independent foundation.
Financial data (yr. ended 12/31/13): Assets, $7,982,863 (M); expenditures, $383,595; qualifying distributions, $377,608; giving activities include $377,377 for 64 grants (high: $55,000; low: $500).
Purpose and activities: The foundation's mission remains to support and effect positive change within several main categories of giving. Specifically, the foundation has an interest in health care, education, the arts, environmental stewardship, land use and conservation, Catholic and Judeo-Christian traditions and values, and community resources.
Fields of interest: Arts and culture; Education; Natural resources; Land resources; Nonprofits; Hospital care; Diseases and conditions; Human services.
Type of support: Regranting.
Limitations: Applications accepted. Giving primarily in MI, with concentrations in the Detroit metropolitan area community and in northwest lower Michigan, specifically Emmet County. No grants to individuals.
Application information: Application guidelines available on foundation web site. Application form required.
  Initial approach: Review and complete Initial Contact Form on foundation web site
Officers: Chris A. Baiardi, Pres.; Kristen L. Baiardi, V.P.; Suzanne M. Baiardi, V.P.; Cindy J. Baiardi, Secy.-Treas.
EIN: 383430867

4382
Baldwin Foundation
c/o Founders Bank & Trust
P.O. Box 1828
Grand Rapids, MI 49501-1828 (616) 575-5704

Established in 1964 in Michigan.
Foundation type: Independent foundation.
Financial data (yr. ended 11/30/14): Assets, $3,375,373; expenditures, $195,540; qualifying distributions, $167,500.
Fields of interest: Arts and culture; Higher education; Hospital care; Christianity; Human services; Child welfare.
Type of support: Annual campaigns; Capital campaigns; Capital and infrastructure; Equipment; Professorships; Fellowships.
Limitations: Applications accepted. Giving primarily in western MI. No grants to individuals.
Application information:
  Initial approach: Proposal

Deadline(s): None
Board meeting date(s): July or Aug.
Officers: M. Dana Baldwin II, Pres.; Greg Conway, V.P.; Daniel G. Baas, Secy.-Treas.
Trustee: Founders Bank and Trust.
EIN: 386085641

4383
James & Shirley Balk Foundation
1230 Monroe Ave. N.W.
Grand Rapids, MI 49505-4620 (616) 458-1414
Contact: Shirley Balk

Established in 1984 in Michigan.
Donors: James H. Balk II; Shirley Balk.
Foundation type: Independent foundation.
Financial data (yr. ended 12/31/13): Assets, $6,299,095 (M); expenditures, $171,519; qualifying distributions, $169,885; giving activities include $169,885 for 25 grants (high: $38,115; low: $100).
Purpose and activities: Giving primarily for Christian education; support also for the arts, churches, human services, and botanical gardens.
Fields of interest: Education; Philanthropy; Human services.
Type of support: General support.
Limitations: Applications accepted. Giving primarily in Grand Rapids, MI. No grants to individuals.
Application information:
  Initial approach: Letter on organization's letterhead
  Deadline(s): None
Trustees: James H. Balk; James H. Balk II; Martin Balk; Shirley Balk; Steven Balk.
EIN: 382556356

4384
Barron Family Foundation
(formerly Nora Lee & Guy Barron Foundation)
5970 Wing Lake Rd.
Bloomfield Hills, MI 48301-1256

Established in 1980 in Michigan.
Donors: Nora Lee Barron; Guy L. Barron.
Foundation type: Independent foundation.
Financial data (yr. ended 11/30/13): Assets, $2,567,468 (M); gifts received, $100,000; expenditures, $189,105; qualifying distributions, $179,431; giving activities include $176,681 for 35 grants (high: $90,000; low: $300).
Fields of interest: Arts and culture; Philanthropy; Health; Judaism.
Type of support: General support; Financial sustainability; Annual campaigns; Capital campaigns; Scholarships.
Limitations: Applications not accepted. Giving primarily in MI and New York, NY. No grants to individuals.
Application information: Unsolicited requests for funds not accepted.
Trustees: Eric Barron; Guy Barron; Marc Barron; Nora Lee Barron.
EIN: 382346776

4385
Barstow Foundation
c/o Chemical Bank
235 E. Main St.
Midland, MI 48640-5137 (989) 839-5305

Established in 1967 in Michigan.
Donors: Florence K. Barstow†; Ruth M. Dixon.
Foundation type: Independent foundation.
Financial data (yr. ended 12/31/13): Assets, $7,795,261 (M); expenditures, $335,826; qualifying distributions, $294,244; giving activities include $294,244 for 35 grants (high: $30,000; low: $1,000).
Fields of interest: University education; Environment; Nonprofits; Public libraries; Human services; Food banks; Child welfare; Youth services; Domestic violence shelters.
Type of support: General support; Regranting; Capital campaigns; Program development; Scholarships.
Application information: Application form required.
  Initial approach: Letter
  Copies of proposal: 2
  Deadline(s): July 31
Officers: David O. Barstow, Co-Chair.; William R. Dixon, Co-Chair.; John E. Kessler, Secy.
Trustees: John C. Barstow; Robert G. Barstow; Ruth M. Dixon.
EIN: 386151026

4386
Barton-Malow Company Foundation
26500 American Dr.
Southfield, MI 48034-2252 (248) 436-5000

Established in 1954 in Michigan.
Donors: Barton-Malow Enterprises, Inc.; Cloverdale Equipment Co.; Barton Malow Company.
Foundation type: Company-sponsored foundation.
Financial data (yr. ended 03/31/14): Assets, $29,430 (M); gifts received, $100,000; expenditures, $176,400; qualifying distributions, $176,400; giving activities include $176,400 for 18 grants (high: $60,000; low: $100).
Purpose and activities: The foundation supports community foundations and organizations involved with education, health, heart disease, housing development, and children services.
Fields of interest: Education; Higher education; Foundations; Nonprofits; Health; Hospital care; Heart and circulatory system diseases; Housing development; Human services; Child welfare.
Type of support: General support; Scholarships; Regranting.
Limitations: Applications accepted. Giving primarily in FL, MD, MI, and VA. No grants to individuals.
Application information: Application form required.
  Initial approach: Letter
  Deadline(s): None
Trustee: Douglas Maibach.
EIN: 386088176

4387
The Baum Family Foundation
660 W. Indian Hills Dr.
Hastings, MI 49058-9480

Established in 1998 in Michigan.
Donors: Larry R. Baum; A. Earlene Baum.
Foundation type: Independent foundation.
Financial data (yr. ended 06/30/14): Assets, $6,733,291 (M); expenditures, $395,859; qualifying distributions, $875,700; giving activities include $385,700 for 12 grants (high: $161,000; low: $1,200).

Fields of interest: Sport and hobby museums; Education; Elementary and secondary education; Hospital care; Protestantism; Human services.
Limitations: Applications not accepted. Giving primarily in MI. No grants to individuals.
Application information: Contributes only to pre-selected organizations.
Officers and Directors: Larry R. Baum, Pres. and Director; David L. Baum, V.P. and Director; A. Earlene Baum, Secy. and Director; Arthur E. Albin, Treas.
EIN: 383443737

4388
Marvin Berlin Foundation
901 Wilshire Dr., Ste. 580
Troy, MI 48084

Established in 1986 in Michigan.
Donors: Marvin Berlin†; Alice Berlin.
Foundation type: Independent foundation.
Financial data (yr. ended 11/30/13): Assets, $11,804 (M); gifts received, $200,000; expenditures, $293,347; qualifying distributions, $293,347; giving activities include $293,197 for 11 grants (high: $200,000; low: $50).
Fields of interest: Judaism.
Limitations: Applications not accepted. Giving primarily in Southfield, MI. No grants to individuals.
Application information: Contributes only to pre-selected organizations.
Officers: Alice Berlin, Pres.; William E. Berlin, V.P. and Treas.; Kathie Ling, Secy.
EIN: 382731819

4389
Beson Family Foundation
c/o Alan J. Ferrara
32300 N.W. Hwy., No. 200
Farmington Hills, MI 48334-1567

Established in 1999 in Michigan.
Donor: Robert J. Beson Charitable Annuity Lead Trust.
Foundation type: Independent foundation.
Financial data (yr. ended 12/31/13): Assets, $1,177,092 (M); expenditures, $181,868; qualifying distributions, $180,734; giving activities include $179,600 for 7 grants (high: $135,000; low: $600).
Fields of interest: Education; Diseases and conditions.
Type of support: General support; Research.
Limitations: Applications not accepted. Giving primarily in MI. No grants to individuals.
Application information: Contributes only to pre-selected organizations.
Officers and Directors: Elizabeth C. Beson, Pres. and Director; Alan Ferrara, Secy. and Director; Gary Dabkowski, Treas. and Director.
EIN: 383308555

4390
Marion & Marlene Betten Foundation
(formerly The Betten Auto Family Foundation)
5901 28th St.
Grand Rapids, MI 49546-6907

Established in 1988 in Michigan.

Donors: Marion Betten; Marlene Betten; Courtsey Motors Inc.; Beten Imports Inc.; Laura Lamer; Alice Scholten.
Foundation type: Independent foundation.
Financial data (yr. ended 12/31/13): Assets, $3,667,964 (M); gifts received, $291,109; expenditures, $289,332; qualifying distributions, $263,335; giving activities include $260,450 for 53 grants (high: $107,400; low: $250).
Fields of interest: Graduate and professional education; Diseases and conditions; Christianity; Theology; Human services.
Type of support: General support.
Limitations: Applications not accepted. Giving primarily in Grand Rapids, MI. No grants to individuals.
Application information: Contributes only to pre-selected organizations.
Officers: Marlene Betten, Pres.; Laura Lamer, Secy.; Alice Scholten, Treas.
Directors: Gregory Betten; Rodney Betten.
EIN: 382848189

4391
The Les and Anne Biederman Foundation, Inc.
P.O. Box 564
Traverse City, MI   49685-0564
Contact: Chris Warren, Secy.

Established in 1986 in Michigan.
Donors: Lester M. Biederman†; Anna R. Biederman; Anne Biederman Trust.
Foundation type: Operating foundation.
Financial data (yr. ended 12/31/13): Assets, $7,338,050 (M); expenditures, $377,804; qualifying distributions, $345,700; giving activities include $345,700 for 34 grants (high: $50,000; low: $200).
Purpose and activities: Support for education, civic improvement, fine arts, health and human services, and recreation and youth services.
Fields of interest: Arts and culture; Education; Higher education; Nonprofits; Public administration; Sports and recreation; Human services; Youth services.
Type of support: General support; Continuing support; Capital and infrastructure; Equipment; Land acquisitions; Endowments; Program development; Regranting; Scholarships.
Limitations: Applications accepted. Giving primarily in northern MI. No support for fraternal organizations, societies, or orders, political organizations or campaigns, or for religious organizations for sectarian purposes. No grants to individuals (except selected scholarships), or for deficit financing or debt retirement, endowment funds, travel or conferences, normal operating expenses, scientific research, or writing, publication or production of articles, books or films.
Publications: Application guidelines.
Application information: Application form required.
Initial approach: Letter
Copies of proposal: 7
Deadline(s): 1 month prior to board meetings
Board meeting date(s): 2 to 3 times annually
Officers and Trustees: Ross Biederman, Pres. and Trustee; Lawrence E. Gorton, V.P.; Chris Warren, Secy.; Vojin Baic; Paul M. Biederman; Lee Russell.
Number of staff: None.
EIN: 382449838

4392
Bierlein Companies Foundation
2000 Bay City Rd.
Midland, MI   48642-6932

Established in 1985 in Michigan.
Donors: Bierlein Demolition Contractors, Inc.; Bierlein Environmental Services, Inc.; Bierlein Cos., Inc.; Bierlein Services, Inc.; Bierlein Companies, Inc.
Foundation type: Company-sponsored foundation.
Financial data (yr. ended 12/31/13): Assets, $1,849,102 (M); gifts received, $250,000; expenditures, $142,790; qualifying distributions, $142,695; giving activities include $142,695 for 98 grants (high: $15,000; low: $50).
Purpose and activities: The foundation supports organizations involved with arts and culture, education, health, children and youth, human services, community development, and Christianity.
Fields of interest: Arts and culture; Education; Higher education; Nonprofits; Health; Community and economic development; Christianity; Human services; Child welfare.
Type of support: General support; Annual campaigns; Capital campaigns; Regranting.
Limitations: Applications not accepted. Giving primarily in the Saginaw Valley, MI. No support for political organizations. No grants to individuals.
Application information: Contributes only to pre-selected organizations.
Officers: Michael D. Bierlein, Pres. and Director; Ryan Bierlein, V.P. and Director; Kenneth W. LeCureux, Secy.-Treas. and Director.
EIN: 382615341

4393
Blatt Family Foundation
(formerly Leland F. Blatt Family Foundation)
20416 Harper Ave.
Harper Woods, MI   48225-1644   3136421740

Established in 2000 in Michigan.
Donors: Elaine E. Blatt; John A. Blatt; Leland D. Blatt; Cheryl A. Saunders; Cheryl Blat.
Foundation type: Independent foundation.
Financial data (yr. ended 12/31/14): Assets, $0; gifts received, $248,300; expenditures, $249,075; qualifying distributions, $247,850.
Fields of interest: Arts and culture; University education; Hospital care; Diseases and conditions; Human services; Child welfare.
Limitations: Applications not accepted. Giving primarily in MI. No grants to individuals.
Application information: Unsolicited requests for funds not accepted.
Officers: Elaine E. Blatt, Pres.; Cheryl Saunders, V.P.; Leland D. Blatt, Secy.; John A. Blatt, Treas.
EIN: 383553310

4394
Seth Bonder Foundation
2723 S. State St., Ste. 400
Ann Arbor, MI   48104-6188

Donor: Seth Bonder Irrevocable Trust.
Foundation type: Independent foundation.
Financial data (yr. ended 12/31/12): Assets, $6,997,185 (M); gifts received, $7,302,578; expenditures, $395,215; qualifying distributions, $368,367; giving activities include $335,318 for 18 grants (high: $100,000; low: $644).

Fields of interest: Education; Health; Human services.
Limitations: Applications not accepted.
Application information: Unsolicited requests for funds not accepted.
Officer: Merrill Bonder, Pres.
EIN: 454929846

4395
Bostock Family Foundation
920 E. Lincoln St.
Birmingham, MI   48009-3608

Established in 2002 in Delaware.
Donor: Roy J. Bostock.
Foundation type: Independent foundation.
Financial data (yr. ended 12/31/14): Assets, $4,830,465; gifts received, $685,125; expenditures, $259,229; qualifying distributions, $209,863.
Fields of interest: Education; Higher education; Diseases and conditions; Human services.
Type of support: General support.
Limitations: Applications not accepted. Giving primarily in NY. No grants to individuals.
Application information: Contributes only to pre-selected organizations.
Officers and Directors: Roy J. Bostock, Chair. and Director; Merilee Bostock, Secy. and Director; Anne Louise Zachry Bostock; Kate Bostock; Matthew Bostock; Jesse Shefferman; Daniel Waters; Victoria Waters.
EIN: 522300953

4396
Branch County Community Foundation
2 W. Chicago St., Ste. E-1
Coldwater, MI   49036-1602   (517) 278-4517
Contact: Colleen Knight, Exec. Dir.
FAX: (888) 479-8640;
E-mail: info@brcofoundation.org; Additional E-mail: colleen@brcofoundation.org; Grant inquiry E-mail: grants@brcofoundation.org; Main URL: http://www.brcofoundation.org
Facebook: https://www.facebook.com/brcofoundation

Established in 1991 in Michigan.
Foundation type: Community foundation.
Financial data (yr. ended 09/30/13): Assets, $5,564,148 (M); gifts received, $433,747; expenditures, $560,000; giving activities include $298,410 for 6+ grants (high: $35,472), and $69,200 for grants to individuals.
Purpose and activities: The foundation serves the community by promoting charitable giving, building permanent endowments, and connecting community resource.
Fields of interest: Arts and culture; Humanities; Education; Early childhood education; Environment; Health; Community and economic development; Economic development; Employment; Human services; Family services; Youth development; Homeless shelters.
Type of support: General support; In-kind gifts; Matching grants; Equipment; Endowments; Convening; Scholarships; Technical assistance.
Limitations: Applications accepted. Giving limited to Branch County and Colon, MI. No support for sectarian religious programs. No grants to

individuals (except for scholarships); no loans or program-related investments.

Publications: Application guidelines; Annual report; Financial statement; Informational brochure; Newsletter; Occasional report.

Application information: Visit foundation web site for grant application guidelines. Applicants are strongly encouraged to meet with the foundation's staff prior to submitting an application. Application form required.

Initial approach: Submit a Pre-Application Questionnaire

Deadline(s): May 31 and Sept. 30 for Forever Fund and other Community Grant Funds; varies for others

Board meeting date(s): Monthly

Final notification: 2 months

Officers and Directors: Dave Wright, Pres. and Director; Wayne Reese, V.P. and Treas. and Director; Curt Proctor, Secy. and Director; Colleen Knight, Exec. Dir.; Paul Creal, Dir. Emeritus; Hillary Eley, Dir. Emeritus; Bob Mayer, Dir. Emeritus; Remus Rigg, Dir. Emeritus; Patricia Shoemaker, Dir. Emeritus; Jay Carlson; Joe Chase; Roberta Gagnon; Cheryl Globke; Rachel Hard; Josh Jones; Mary Jo Kranz; Chuck Lillis; Tyson McKinley; Kim Morgan; Dale Norton; Ron Rose; Connie Winbigler.

Number of staff: 1 full-time professional; 1 full-time support.

EIN: 383021071

4397

The Briggs-Fisher Foundation

46 Depetris Way

Grosse Pointe Farms, MI 48236-3701 (313) 886-9713

Established in 2005 in Michigan.

Donor: Mary Elizabeth Fisher Charitable lead Annuity Trust.

Foundation type: Independent foundation.

Financial data (yr. ended 12/31/14): Assets, $134,888; gifts received, $220,000; expenditures, $223,760; qualifying distributions, $220,000.

Fields of interest: Higher education; Medical education; Catholicism; Food aid.

Limitations: Applications accepted. Giving primarily in MI and MO. No grants to individuals.

Application information: Application form required.

Initial approach: Letter

Deadline(s): None

Officers: Charles T. Fisher III, Chair.; Walter B. Fisher, Pres. and Treas.; Sarah W. Fisher, Secy.

EIN: 203064253

4398

Wallace and Irene Bronner Family Charitable Foundation

P.O. Box 264

Frankenmuth, MI 48734-0264 (989) 652-9931

Established in 1989 in Michigan.

Donor: Wallace and Irene Bronner Family Trust.

Foundation type: Independent foundation.

Financial data (yr. ended 12/31/13): Assets, $5,971,837 (M); gifts received, $180,000; expenditures, $156,869; qualifying distributions, $152,497; giving activities include $152,497 for grants.

Purpose and activities: Giving primarily to Christian churches and organizations; funding also for education, health and human services.

Type of support: General support; Scholarships.

Limitations: Applications accepted. Giving primarily in MI, with emphasis on Frankenmuth and Saginaw. No loans or program-related investments.

Application information: Application form required.

Initial approach: Letter

Deadline(s): None

Officers: Wayne Bronner, Pres.; Carla Bronner, Secy.; Maria Bronner, Treas.

Directors: Irene R. Bronner; Randy Bronner.

EIN: 382834541

4399

Buffalo Bills Youth Foundation, Inc.

63 Kercheval Ave., Ste. 200

Grosse Pointe Farms, MI 48236-3652

Contact: Gretchen Geitter

Application address: 1 Bills Dr., Orchard Pk., NY 14127

Established in 1987 in New York.

Donors: Buffalo Bills Inc.; The Boston Beer Co.; Teammates for Kids Foundation; Jason Peters; Marcel Dareus; NFL Charities; NFL Youth Football Fund; NFL Foundation; Kelvin Sheppard; Steve Johnson; Tarvaris Jackson; Leodis McKelvin; Gasrth Brooks Teammates for Kids.

Foundation type: Company-sponsored foundation.

Financial data (yr. ended 12/31/13): Assets, $344,609 (M); gifts received, $323,507; expenditures, $283,699; qualifying distributions, $283,699; giving activities include $276,896 for 47 grants (high: $35,000; low: $1,000).

Purpose and activities: The foundation supports programs designed to promote education, health and fitness, and youth football. Special emphasis is directed toward programs designed to improve the lives of youth and young adults.

Fields of interest: Arts and culture; Education; Sports and recreation; American football; Adolescents.

Type of support: General support; Equipment; Program development; Research.

Limitations: Applications accepted. Giving primarily in western NY. No grants to individuals, or for fund drives, or political campaigns.

Publications: Application guidelines.

Application information: Application form required.

Initial approach: Completed application form

Copies of proposal: 1

Deadline(s): Apr. 30

Officers and Directors: Ralph C. Wilson, Jr., Chair. and Director; Mary M. Owen, Pres. and Secy. and Director; Jeffrey C. Littmann, V.P. and Treas. and Director.

EIN: 161291395

4400

The Buhr Foundation

637 Dornoch

Ann Arbor, MI 48103 (734) 996-2742

Contact: Martha B. Grimes, Pres. and Tr.

Established in 1953 in Michigan.

Donors: Buhr Machine Tool Co.; Dorothy B. Gackstatter Crut.

Foundation type: Independent foundation.

Financial data (yr. ended 12/31/13): Assets, $5,556,388 (M); expenditures, $353,698; qualifying distributions, $327,678; giving activities include $314,779 for 57 grants (high: $25,000; low: $500).

Fields of interest: Education; Higher education; Adult education; Hospital care; Christianity; Human services; Child welfare; Senior services.

Type of support: General support; Capital campaigns; Capital and infrastructure.

Application information: Application form required.

Initial approach: Letter

Deadline(s): None

Officers and Trustees: Martha B. Grimes, Pres. and Trustee; Richard J. Buhr, Secy. and Trustee; James D. Buhr, Treas. and Trustee; Thomas A. Buhr; C. Wendell Dunbar.

EIN: 386072288

4401

Buist Foundation

8650 Byron Center Ave. S.W.

Byron Center, MI 49315-9201 (616) 878-3315

Contact: Brent Brinks, Pres.

Main URL: http://www.buistelectric.com/company_info/community/buist_foundation.php

Donors: Buist Electric, Inc.; Larry G. Buist.

Foundation type: Operating foundation.

Financial data (yr. ended 12/31/13): Assets, $195,422 (M); gifts received, $389,108; expenditures, $264,503; qualifying distributions, $315,122; giving activities include $90,724 for 23 + grants (high: $20,000).

Purpose and activities: The foundation supports organizations involved with secondary education, health, housing, human services, and Christianity and awards grants to needy families.

Fields of interest: Education; Secondary education; Health; Maternal and perinatal health; Housing development; Christianity; Human services.

Type of support: Continuing support; Grants to individuals; General support; Scholarships.

Limitations: Applications accepted. Giving primarily in Grand Rapids, MI.

Publications: Application guidelines.

Application information: Application form required.

Initial approach: Letter

Deadline(s): None

Board meeting date(s): Monthly

Officers: Brent Brinks, Pres.; Matt DeVries, V.P.; Andy Vermunen, Secy.

Directors: Kathy Burgess; Aaron Cooper; Dave Houseman; Cindy Meengs; Jeff Maleport.

EIN: 383314509

4402

The Burdick-Thorne Foundation

c/o The Connable Office, Inc.

136 E. Michigan Ave., Ste. 1201

Kalamazoo, MI 49007-3918

Contact: David S. Kruis, Treas.

Established in 1990 in Michigan.

Donors: James M. Thorne†; Mary B. Thorne†.

Foundation type: Independent foundation.

Financial data (yr. ended 12/31/13): Assets, $11,324,339 (M); expenditures, $532,145; qualifying distributions, $485,577; giving activities include $405,250 for 63 grants (high: $30,000; low: $1,000).

Purpose and activities: Giving for higher education, the arts, social services, and natural resource preservation and enhancement.
Fields of interest: Arts councils; Performing arts; Music; Higher education; Natural resources; Human services.
Type of support: General support; Continuing support; Annual campaigns; Capital campaigns; Capital and infrastructure.
Limitations: Applications not accepted. Giving primarily in Kalamazoo, MI. No grants to individuals.
Application information: Contributes only to pre-selected organizations.
Board meeting date(s): Varies
Officers and Trustees: James C. Melvin, Pres. and Trustee; Loyal A. Eldridge III, V.P. and Secy. and Trustee; Bradley E. Weller, V.P. and Trustee; David S. Kruis, Treas. and Trustee; James S. Hilboldt, Trustee Emeritus; Andrea M. Thorne; Betsy V. Thorne.
EIN: 382904527

4403
Burt Foundation
c/o Erik H. Serr Miller Canfield
101 N. Main St., 7th Fl.
Ann Arbor, MI 48104-5507

Established in 1996 in Michigan.
Donor: Andrea L. Holmes.
Foundation type: Independent foundation.
Financial data (yr. ended 12/31/13): Assets, $13,287,244 (M); gifts received, $153,976; expenditures, $472,204; qualifying distributions, $441,500; giving activities include $441,500 for 20 grants (high: $50,000; low: $2,500).
Purpose and activities: Giving primarily for animal welfare; funding also for human services and the environment.
Fields of interest: Environment; Wildlife biodiversity; Wildlife sanctuaries; Animal welfare; Human services.
Limitations: Applications not accepted. Giving primarily in MI. No grants to individuals.
Application information: Contributes only to pre-selected organizations.
Officer and Directors: Andrea L. Holmes, Pres. and Secy.-Treas. and Director; Christine M. Holmes; Erik H. Serr.
EIN: 383309907

4404
Carls Endowment Trust
P.O. Box 75000
Detroit, MI 48275-7874

Foundation type: Independent foundation.
Financial data (yr. ended 12/31/13): Assets, $3,492,937 (M); expenditures, $196,687; qualifying distributions, $157,506; giving activities include $153,376 for 3 grants (high: $95,856; low: $18,670).
Fields of interest: Health.
Limitations: Applications not accepted. Giving primarily in MI.
Application information: Unsolicited requests for funds not accepted.
Trustee: Comerica Bank.
EIN: 386761927

4405
James F. Causley, Jr. Family Foundation
37910 Seaway Ct.
Harrison Township, MI 48045-6201

Established in 2000 in Michigan.
Donor: James F. Causley, Jr.
Foundation type: Independent foundation.
Financial data (yr. ended 12/31/13): Assets, $51,169 (M); gifts received, $285,000; expenditures, $241,722; qualifying distributions, $241,722; giving activities include $239,978 for 45 grants (high: $40,000; low: $100).
Fields of interest: Diseases and conditions; Catholicism; Human rights.
Type of support: General support.
Limitations: Applications not accepted. Giving primarily in MI. No grants to individuals.
Application information: Unsolicited requests for funds not accepted.
Officers: James F. Causley, Jr., Pres.; H. Rollin Allen, Secy.; William R. Cantwell, Treas.
Director: Hunter Wendt.
EIN: 383534503

4406
Bernard J. & Camille Cebelak Foundation
11931 Timberlane Dr.
Stanwood, MI 49346

Established in 1986 in Michigan.
Donors: Bernard J. Cebelak†; Camille L. Cebelak; Kent Manufacturing Co.
Foundation type: Independent foundation.
Financial data (yr. ended 12/31/13): Assets, $2,948,022 (M); expenditures, $348,146; qualifying distributions, $318,970; giving activities include $301,500 for 24 grants (high: $45,000; low: $3,000).
Purpose and activities: Giving primarily for education and for Christian and Roman Catholic organizations and agencies.
Fields of interest: Education; Secondary education; Health; Diseases and conditions; Christianity; Catholicism.
Type of support: Research; Research and evaluation.
Limitations: Applications not accepted. Giving primarily in MI. No grants to individuals.
Application information: Contributes only to pre-selected organizations.
Officers and Trustees: Camille L. Cebelak, Pres. and Trustee; Suzanne Singel, Secy. and Trustee; Michael J. Muraski, Treas. and Trustee; Patrice Konwinski; Lori Mitchell; Judy Siekman.
EIN: 382641979

4407
Christian Evangelical Foundation
3755 36th St. S.E., Ste. 400
Grand Rapids, MI 49512-3143

Established in 1987 in Illinois.
Donors: John C. Huizenga; Elizabeth I. Huizenga Foundation.
Foundation type: Independent foundation.
Financial data (yr. ended 12/31/14): Assets, $109,223; expenditures, $146,283; qualifying distributions, $146,000.
Purpose and activities: Giving primarily to Christian organizations and for Christian education.

Fields of interest: Education; Christianity; Human services.
Type of support: General support.
Limitations: Applications not accepted. Giving in the U.S., with emphasis on MI. No grants to individuals.
Application information: Contributes only to pre-selected organizations.
Officers and Directors: J.C. Huizenga, Pres. and Mgr. and Director; Jason Pater, Secy.-Treas. and Director; John R. Grant.
EIN: 363501198

4408
Christian Missionary Scholarship Foundation
3230 Lake Dr. S.E.
Grand Rapids, MI 49546-4444 (616) 526-7731
FAX: (616) 526-6777;
E-mail: info@christianmissionaryscholarship.org;
Main URL: http://www.christianmissionaryscholarship.org

Donors: Stanley Van Reken; Randall S. Van Reken; Capital Ventures of NV.
Foundation type: Independent foundation.
Financial data (yr. ended 12/31/13): Assets, $5,748,057 (M); gifts received, $500,861; expenditures, $408,015; qualifying distributions, $362,500; giving activities include $362,500 for grants.
Purpose and activities: Giving for scholarships to children of missionaries attending one of the following six colleges: Calvin College, Dordt College, Hope College, Kuyper College, Trinity Christian College and Wheaton College.
Fields of interest: Graduate and professional education; Christianity; Theology.
Type of support: Scholarships.
Limitations: Applications accepted. Giving primarily in IA, IL and MI. No grants to individuals.
Application information: See web site for complete application policies and guidelines and for an online application. Application form required.
Deadline(s): Feb. 15
Final notification: Apr. 1
Officers: Calvin P. Van Reken, Pres.; Walter Olsson, Secy.; Randall Van Reken, Treas.
Directors: Russell Bloem; Marge Hoogeboom; Thomas Stuit; Annie Valkema; Robert Weeldreyer.
EIN: 363553749

4409
Robert S. Clay Irrevocable Trust
c/o CNB Trust Department
1 S. Howell St., Ste. 03
P.O. Box 221
Hillsdale, MI 49242-1811

Foundation type: Operating foundation.
Financial data (yr. ended 12/31/13): Assets, $8,945,251 (M); expenditures, $372,364; qualifying distributions, $315,033; giving activities include $315,033 for 1 grant.
Fields of interest: Protestantism.
Limitations: Applications not accepted. Giving primarily in Hillsdale, MI. No grants to individuals.
Application information: Contributes only to pre-selected organizations.
Trustee: CNB Trust Dept.
EIN: 266519146

4410
Community Foundation of Greater Rochester

(formerly Greater Rochester Area Community Foundation)
303 E. St.
P.O. Box 80431
Rochester, MI 48308-0431 (248) 608-2804
Contact: Peggy Hamilton, Exec. Dir.
FAX: (248) 608-2826; E-mail: cfound@cfound.org;
Main URL: http://www.cfound.org
Facebook: https://www.facebook.com/pages/
Community-Foundation-of-Greater-Rochester/
1425820731017968

Established in 1983 in Michigan.
Foundation type: Community foundation.
Financial data (yr. ended 12/31/12): Assets, $7,257,570 (M); gifts received, $1,088,328; expenditures, $892,017; giving activities include $137,865 for 3+ grants (high: $65,000), and $97,145 for 75 grants to individuals.
Purpose and activities: To enhance the quality of life, the foundation is committed to act as the center for philanthropy and serve as the communitys endowment builder and grant maker by: 1) attracting charitable funds for permanent endowments; 2) encouraging charitable giving from a wide range of donors; 3) serving as a catalyst for change, innovator to resolve problems, a partner with other local groups and a resource to provide solutions for current and emerging community needs.
Fields of interest: Arts and culture; Performing arts; Music; Museums; Education; Elementary education; Environment; Natural resources; Health; Community and economic development; Sustainable development; Economic development; Sports and recreation; Human services; Family services; Youth services; Adolescents; People with disabilities.
Type of support: General support; Matching grants; Annual campaigns; Building and renovations; Equipment; Endowments; Emergency funds; Seed money; Scholarships; Student aid.
Limitations: Applications accepted. Giving limited to the greater Rochester, MI, area. No grants to individuals (except for designated scholarship funds), or for operating budgets.
Publications: Annual report (including application guidelines); Financial statement; Informational brochure; Newsletter.
Application information: Visit the foundation web site for application forms and specific guidelines per grant type. A foundation staff member will contact applicants who have submitted a letter of intent to discuss their submitted proposal and funding opportunities available. Application form required.
  Initial approach: Letter of Intent
  Copies of proposal: 7
  Deadline(s): Mar. 31 and Sept. 30 for grant application forms; Mar. 7 for scholarships
  Board meeting date(s): Quarterly
Officers and Trustees: Robert Justin, Chair. and Trustee; David Bray, Vice-Chair., Investments and Trustee; Mark Aiello, Vice-Chair., Devel. and Trustee; Mike Mackens, Secy. and Trustee; John Savio, Treas. and Trustee; Peggy Hamilton, Exec. Dir.; Linda Bermingham; Ken Bilodeau; Pat Botkin; Julie A. Byrd, MD; Tim Crawford; Ed Golick; Jason Hoffmeyer; Tom Mines; Vern Pixley; John Schultz; Beth Talbert.
Number of staff: 1 full-time professional; 1 part-time support.
EIN: 382476777

4411
Community Foundation of Monroe County

28 S. Macomb St., Ste. C
Monroe, MI 48161-2176 (734) 242-1976
Contact: Kathleen Russeau, Exec. Dir.
FAX: (734) 242-1234; E-mail: info@cfmonroe.org;
Main URL: http://www.cfmonroe.org
Facebook: https://www.facebook.com/cfmonroe/

Established in 1979 in Michigan.
Foundation type: Community foundation.
Financial data (yr. ended 03/31/14): Assets, $6,172,305 (M); gifts received, $267,875; expenditures, $822,035; giving activities include $147,299 for 6+ grants (high: $23,144), and $71,867 for 115 grants to individuals.
Purpose and activities: The foundation's mission is to encourage and facilitate philanthropy in Monroe County, MI.
Fields of interest: Arts and culture; Performing arts; Theater; Music; History; Historic preservation; Education; Elementary education; Higher education; Basic and remedial instruction; Reading promotion; Environment; Natural resources; Voluntarism; Health; Addiction services; Diseases and conditions; Archaeology; Public affairs; Community and economic development; Housing development; Human services; Food aid; Child welfare; Homeless services; Senior services; Seniors; Ethnic and racial groups; Low-income and poor people; People with disabilities.
Type of support: Capital campaigns; In-kind gifts; Capital and infrastructure; Matching grants; Equipment; Program development; Seed money; Curriculum development; Scholarships; Research; Technical assistance; Student aid; Individual development.
Limitations: Applications accepted. Giving limited to Monroe County, MI. No support for sectarian religious purposes. No grants to individuals (except through designated scholarship funds), or for annual fundraising drives, endowment campaigns, operational phases of established programs, conferences, travel, scholarly research, or for multi-year grant commitments; no loans.
Publications: Application guidelines; Annual report; Financial statement; Grants list; Informational brochure; Newsletter.
Application information: Visit foundation web site for online application and guidelines. Application form required.
  Initial approach: Telephone, letter or e-mail
  Copies of proposal: 10
  Deadline(s): Jan. 15, Apr. 15, July 15, and Oct. 15. or scholarships, Feb. 21 to school counselors and Feb. 28 to Community Foundation.
  Board meeting date(s): 4th Wed. of each month, except Dec.
  Final notification: One month
Officers and Trustees: Stephen McNew, Pres. and Trustee; Molly Luempert-Coy, V.P. and Trustee; Tom Schilling, Treas. and Trustee; Kathleen Russeau, Exec. Dir.; Teresa Beamsley; Paul Braunlich; Matt Budds; Barbara Harrington; Douglas Hassett; Steve Hudkins; Eric Hulsemann; Sr. Marie Gabriel Hungerman; Diane Kamprath; Joan Mahalak; Mike Newman; Brad Schreiber; Jan Vogelsang.
Number of staff: 1 full-time professional; 1 full-time support.
EIN: 382236628

4412
The H. P. and Genevieve Connable Fund

136 E. Michigan Ave., Ste. 1201
Kalamazoo, MI 49007-3936
Contact: David S. Kruis, Treas.

Established in 1987 in Michigan.
Donors: H.P. Connable†; Genevieve W. Connable†.
Foundation type: Independent foundation.
Financial data (yr. ended 12/31/13): Assets, $4,909,466 (M); expenditures, $253,154; qualifying distributions, $236,034; giving activities include $200,500 for 49 grants (high: $17,500; low: $1,250).
Fields of interest: Arts and culture; Higher education; Natural resources; Diseases and conditions; Human services.
Limitations: Applications not accepted. Giving primarily in Kalamazoo, MI. No grants to individuals.
Application information: Unsolicited requests for funds not accepted.
Officers and Trustees: James C. Melvin, Pres. and Trustee; Loyal A. Eldridge III, V.P. and Secy. and Trustee; Bradley E. Weller, V.P. and Trustee; David S. Kruis, Treas. and Trustee; James S. Hilboldt.
EIN: 382710894

4413
Conrad Charitable Foundation

504 W. Dunlap St.
Northville, MI 48167-1409

Established in 2001 in Michigan.
Donors: Beth Ann Beson; Beth Ann Beson Charitable Trust.
Foundation type: Independent foundation.
Financial data (yr. ended 12/31/13): Assets, $39,400 (M); gifts received, $258,000; expenditures, $233,598; qualifying distributions, $233,598; giving activities include $232,938 for 20 grants (high: $80,000; low: $422).
Fields of interest: Secondary education; Higher education; Christianity; Camps; Human services; Single parent support; Youth development; Housing services; Single parents.
Type of support: In-kind gifts.
Limitations: Applications not accepted. Giving primarily in Northville and Wayne County, MI.
Application information: Unsolicited requests for funds not accepted.
Officer: Beth Beson, Pres. and Secy.-Treas.
Director: Al Ferrara.
EIN: 383607715

4414
Raymond M. & Jane E. Cracchiolo Foundation

24055 Jefferson Ave., Ste. 200
Saint Clair Shores, MI 48080-1514
Contact: Maria Mitzel, Secy.

Established in 1984 in Michigan.
Donors: Raymond M. Cracchiolo; Jane E. Cracchiolo.
Foundation type: Independent foundation.
Financial data (yr. ended 12/31/13): Assets, $9,631,011 (M); gifts received, $501,228; expenditures, $238,269; qualifying distributions, $180,870; giving activities include $170,675 for 45 grants (high: $30,000; low: $25).

Purpose and activities: Giving primarily for youth and child welfare; support also for Christian organizations.

Fields of interest: Education; Christianity; Human services; Child welfare.

Type of support: General support.

Limitations: Applications not accepted. Giving primarily in MI. No grants to individuals.

Application information: Unsolicited requests for funds not accepted.

Officers: Raymond M. Cracchiolo, Pres.; Jane E. Cracchiolo, V.P.; Maria Mitzel, Secy.; Christi Cracchiolo Small, Treas.

Directors: Heidi Cracchiolo Bell; Natalie Ceniza; David Cracchiolo.

EIN: 382556359

4415
Thomas and Carol Cracchiolo Foundation
24055 Jefferson Ave., Ste. 200
Saint Clair Shores, MI   48080-1514

Established in 1984 in Michigan.

Donors: Carol A. Cracchiolo; Thomas A. Cracchiolo.

Foundation type: Independent foundation.

Financial data (yr. ended 06/30/14): Assets, $12,779,259 (M); gifts received, $792,848; expenditures, $501,499; qualifying distributions, $455,760; giving activities include $430,891 for 83 grants (high: $70,000; low: $50).

Purpose and activities: Giving primarily for education, health, human services, and to Roman Catholic agencies and churches.

Fields of interest: Education; Diseases and conditions; Catholicism; Human services; Child welfare.

Type of support: General support.

Limitations: Applications not accepted. Giving primarily in MI. No grants to individuals.

Application information: Unsolicited requests for funds not accepted.

Officers and Directors: Thomas A. Cracchiolo, Pres. and Director; Carol A. Cracchiolo, V.P. and Director; Ann Cracchiolo Caraway, Secy. and Director; Lisa Cracchiolo Peracchio, Treas. and Director; Bernadette M. Cracchiolo; Carol Cracchiolo Laub.

EIN: 382543263

4416
Marie Crowley Foundation
6400 Bowen Rd.
Saranac, MI   48881-9555   (616) 642-6841
Contact: Wilda J. Terrile, Tr.

Established in 1997 in Nevada.

Donors: Crowley Charitable Lead Trust; Marie Crowley Charitable Lead Trust.

Foundation type: Independent foundation.

Financial data (yr. ended 12/31/14): Assets, $4,501,550 (M); expenditures, $278,904; qualifying distributions, $236,426; giving activities include $236,426 for 39 grants (high: $20,000; low: $250).

Fields of interest: Education; Diseases and conditions; Human services.

Limitations: Applications accepted. Giving primarily in NV.

Application information: Application form required.

Initial approach: Proposal

Deadline(s): None

Trustees: Wilda J. Terrile; Avansino, Malarkey, Knobel and Mulli.

EIN: 880362044

4417
The Cummings Fund
c/o Hendon & Slate
P.O. Box 9
Fremont, MI   49412-0009

Established in 1963 in Michigan.

Donors: Harrington M. Cummings; Gay C. Cummings.

Foundation type: Independent foundation.

Financial data (yr. ended 12/31/13): Assets, $2,516,170 (M); expenditures, $247,543; qualifying distributions, $234,893; giving activities include $229,000 for 2 grants (high: $199,000; low: $30,000).

Fields of interest: Performing arts.

Type of support: General support; Capital campaigns; Seed money.

Limitations: Applications not accepted. Giving primarily in MI. No grants to individuals.

Application information: Unsolicited requests for funds not accepted.

Officers: Dan Slate, Pres.; Samuel Cummings, Secy.; Andrew Cummings, Treas.

Board Members: Gay C. Cummings; Mimi Cummings; Liss Flaherty.

EIN: 386079631

4418
William G. Currie Foundation
2801 E. Beltline N.E.
Grand Rapids, MI   49525

Established in 1985 in Michigan.

Donors: William G. Currie; Universal Forest Products, Inc.

Foundation type: Independent foundation.

Financial data (yr. ended 12/31/13): Assets, $578,154 (M); expenditures, $202,277; qualifying distributions, $193,013; giving activities include $193,013 for 35 grants (high: $50,000; low: $100).

Fields of interest: Education; Hospital care; Religion; Human services; Child welfare.

Limitations: Applications not accepted. Giving primarily in Grand Rapids, MI. No grants to individuals.

Application information: Contributes only to pre-selected organizations.

Officers and Directors: William G. Currie, Pres. and Director; Matthew J. Missad, Secy.-Treas.

EIN: 382641091

4419
Dana Foundation
1 Village Center Dr.
Van Buren Township, MI   48111   (419) 887-5141
Contact: Joe Stancati, Secy.
Application address: P.O. Box 1000, Maumee, OH 43537, Tel.: (419) 887-5141

Established in 1956 in Ohio.

Donors: Dana Corporation; Dana Holding Corporation.

Foundation type: Company-sponsored foundation.

Financial data (yr. ended 03/31/14): Assets, $323,317 (M); gifts received, $505,000;

expenditures, $254,177; qualifying distributions, $249,009; giving activities include $202,914 for 29 grants (high: $100,000; low: $500), and $46,095 for 1 employee matching gift.

Purpose and activities: The foundation supports organizations involved with arts and culture, education, cancer, food distribution, and human services.

Fields of interest: Arts and culture; Theater; Orchestral music; Art museums; Education; Nonprofits; Cancers; Human services; Food delivery; Child welfare; Youth services; Economics for youth.

Type of support: General support; Employee matching gifts; Continuing support; Annual campaigns; Capital campaigns; Capital and infrastructure; Equipment; Emergency funds; Scholarships; Regranting.

Limitations: Applications accepted. Giving primarily in areas of company operations in KY and OH. No grants to individuals (except for the Driveshaft Scholarship Fund), or for fellowships; no loans.

Application information:

Initial approach: Proposal

Copies of proposal: 1

Deadline(s): None

Officers and Directors: Marc Levin, Pres. and Director; Dave Benson, V.P. and Director; Joe Stancati, Secy. and Director; Rick Dyer, Treas. and Director; Jeffrey Cole; David Nash; Maureen Tackett.

Number of staff: 1 part-time professional.

EIN: 346544909

4420
The Dana Z Foundation
(formerly The Dana Foundation)
1806 N. Telegraph Rd.
Dearborn, MI   48128-1270

Established in 2007 in Michigan.

Foundation type: Independent foundation.

Financial data (yr. ended 12/31/12): Assets, $113,452 (M); gifts received, $263,000; expenditures, $152,534; qualifying distributions, $152,498; giving activities include $152,498 for 11 grants (high: $78,400; low: $250).

Fields of interest: Education; Religion; Islam; Human services.

Limitations: Applications not accepted. Giving primarily in MI. No grants to individuals.

Application information: Unsolicited requests for funds not accepted.

Officers: Opada Alzohaili, Pres.; Hala Alkhatib, V.P.

EIN: 260887540

4421
Robert C. Dart Foundation
500 Hogsback Rd.
Mason, MI   48854-9541

Established in 2006 in Michigan.

Donors: Dart Container Corporation of Kentucky; Dart Container Corporation of Georgia; Dart Container Corporation; Dart Container Sales Co., LLC; Robert C. Dart.

Foundation type: Company-sponsored foundation.

Financial data (yr. ended 10/31/13): Assets, $27,915,774 (M); expenditures, $252,577; qualifying distributions, $252,577; giving activities include $252,358 for 3 grants (high: $156,000; low: $34,818).

Purpose and activities: The foundation supports the Dart Foundation in Mason, Michigan.
Fields of interest: Foundations; Unknown or not classified.
Type of support: General support.
Limitations: Applications not accepted. Giving limited to Mason, MI. No grants to individuals.
Application information: Contributes only to a pre-selected organization.
Officers: Robert C. Dart, Pres. and Treas.; James D. Lammers, Secy.
Director: Ariane M. Dart.
EIN: 205973757

4422
Joie de Vivre Foundation
(formerly Dennis & Eileen Ellens Foundation)
345 E. 48th St., Ste. 200
Holland, MI 49423-5381

Established in 1989 in Michigan.
Donors: Dennis Ellens; Eileen Ellens; Prince Holding Corp.; Edgar Prince; Elsa Prince; Hudsonville Ice Cream.
Foundation type: Independent foundation.
Financial data (yr. ended 12/31/13): Assets, $62,072 (M); gifts received, $325,000; expenditures, $313,589; qualifying distributions, $313,520; giving activities include $313,500 for 14 grants (high: $100,000; low: $2,500).
Purpose and activities: Giving primarily to Christian organizations, including churches and schools, and for youth and family services.
Fields of interest: Education; Christianity; Human services; Family services; Child welfare.
Type of support: General support.
Limitations: Applications not accepted. Giving primarily in MI, with emphasis on Holland. No grants to individuals.
Application information: Contributes only to pre-selected organizations.
Officers: Eileen Ellens, Pres.; Curtis J. Ellens, V.P.; Brett Ellens, Secy.; Dennis Ellens, Treas.
EIN: 382902415

4423
Degroot Family Foundation
P.O Box 660
Watervliet, MI 49098-0660

Established in 2002 in Michigan.
Donor: Louise Degroot.
Foundation type: Independent foundation.
Financial data (yr. ended 12/31/13): Assets, $11,034,810 (M); gifts received, $8,205,775; expenditures, $209,009; qualifying distributions, $178,779; giving activities include $177,308 for 11 grants (high: $50,000; low: $1,000).
Purpose and activities: Giving primarily for cancer research; some funding also for a shelter for the homeless.
Fields of interest: Philanthropy; Housing development; Human services.
Limitations: Applications not accepted. Giving primarily in MI. No grants to individuals.
Application information: Unsolicited requests for funds not accepted.
Officers: Shirley Leith, Pres.; Eric Brown, Secy.; Shirley Leith, Treas.

Directors: Louise Degroot; Eric M Leith; Jessica M. Leith.
EIN: 061654753

4424
Lucille B. Deinzer Charitable Trust
c/o Monroe Bank & Trust
102 E. Front St.
Monroe, MI 48161
Application address: Deinzer Fund Committee, Trinity Lutheran Church, 323 Scott St., Monroe MI 48161, tel.:(734) 242-2734

Foundation type: Independent foundation.
Financial data (yr. ended 12/31/13): Assets, $1,508,144 (M); expenditures, $183,417; qualifying distributions, $181,119; giving activities include $164,991 for 1 grant.
Fields of interest: Religion.
Application information: Application form required.
    Initial approach: Contact foundation
    Deadline(s): None
Trustee: Monroe Bank & Trust.
EIN: 266251718

4425
Douglas & Sandra DeKock Family Foundation
c/o Douglas DeKock
806 N. Shore Dr.
Holland, MI 49424

Established in 2000 in Michigan.
Donors: Douglas DeKock; Sandra DeKock.
Foundation type: Independent foundation.
Financial data (yr. ended 12/31/13): Assets, $895,670 (M); expenditures, $269,496; qualifying distributions, $267,500; giving activities include $267,500 for 48 grants (high: $45,000; low: $500).
Fields of interest: Education; Graduate and professional education; Christianity; Theology.
Limitations: Applications not accepted. Giving primarily in Holland, MI.
Application information: Contributes only to pre-selected organizations.
Officers: Douglas DeKock, Pres. and Treas.; Sandra DeKock, Secy.
EIN: 383534244

4426
The Mignon Sherwood Delano Foundation
834 King Hwy., Ste. 110
Kalamazoo, MI 49001-2579 (269) 344-9236
Main URL: http://www.delanofoundation.com
Grants List: http://www.delanofoundation.com/recipients.html

Established in 1985 in Michigan.
Donor: Mignon Sherwood Delano†.
Foundation type: Independent foundation.
Financial data (yr. ended 12/31/13): Assets, $4,702,084 (M); expenditures, $229,023; qualifying distributions, $207,717; giving activities include $171,423 for 35 grants (high: $15,000; low: $1,000).
Purpose and activities: Giving for the furtherance of humanitarian, educational, cultural and environmental enrichment in the City of Allegan, Allegan County and southwestern Michigan.

Fields of interest: Arts and culture; Education; Health; Family planning; Diseases and conditions; Community and economic development; Housing development; Catholicism; Human services; Food banks; Youth development; Shelter and residential care.
Type of support: General support; Equipment; Program development.
Limitations: Applications accepted. Giving limited to the City of Allegan, Allegan County and southwestern MI. No grants to individuals.
Application information: See foundation web site for application policies and application form. Application form required.
    Deadline(s): 2nd Tues. in Sept.
Officers and Directors: Bernard Riker, Pres. and Director; Thomas Hunter, V.P. and Director; Thomas Berlin, Secy.; Rebecca Burnett, Treas.; Ellen Altamore.
Trustee: PNC Bank, N.A.
EIN: 382557743

4427
Delong-Sweet Family Foundation
c/o Comerica Bank
P.O. Box 75000, MC 4675
Detroit, MI 48275-4675

Established in 1998 in California.
Donor: Sweet Trust.
Foundation type: Independent foundation.
Financial data (yr. ended 05/31/14): Assets, $8,899,643 (M); expenditures, $493,807; qualifying distributions, $360,408; giving activities include $321,000 for 23 grants (high: $60,000; low: $1,000).
Fields of interest: Museums; Art museums; Education; Animal welfare; Foundations; Housing development; Special population support; Military personnel.
Type of support: General support.
Limitations: Applications not accepted. Giving primarily in CA; some giving also in GA. No grants to individuals.
Application information: Unsolicited requests for funds not accepted.
Trustees: James Wycliffe Delong; John Wycliffe Delong; Paul Ingalls; Peggy Ingalls Suckow.
EIN: 311605979

4428
The DeVlieg Foundation
(formerly The Charles DeVlieg Foundation)
500 Woodward Ave., Ste. 2500
Detroit, MI 48226-5499 (313) 961-0200
Contact: Curtis J. DeRoo, Secy.; Janet DeVlieg Pope, Pres.; Julia DeVlieg, V.P.

Established in 1961 in Michigan.
Donors: Charles B. DeVlieg†; Charles R. DeVlieg†; DeVlieg Machine Co.; Kathryn S. DeVlieg†.
Foundation type: Independent foundation.
Financial data (yr. ended 12/31/13): Assets, $6,426,927 (M); expenditures, $544,730; qualifying distributions, $394,007; giving activities include $308,500 for 16 grants (high: $119,000; low: $1,000).
Purpose and activities: Support largely for higher education, including education in engineering and technology, the environment, and wildlife; funding

also for other animal and wildlife organizations, the arts and youth services.

Fields of interest: Arts and culture; Higher education; Graduate and professional education; Natural resources; Domesticated animals; Engineering; Youth services.

Type of support: General support; Professorships; Scholarships.

Limitations: Applications accepted. Giving primarily in the ID, southeastern MI, and eastern WA, areas. No grants to individuals, or for endowment funds; no loans.

Publications: Annual report (including application guidelines).

Application information: Application form required.

Initial approach: Letter
Copies of proposal: 2
Deadline(s): None
Board meeting date(s): Semiannually

Officers and Directors: Janet DeVlieg Pope, Pres. and Director; Julia C. DeVlieg, V.P. and Director; Curtis J. DeRoo, Secy. and Director; James Pope; Gary Stetler.

Number of staff: 1 part-time professional.

EIN: 386075696

4429

Marvin G. and Jerene L. DeWitt Family Foundation

8065 Olive Shore Dr.
West Olive, MI 49460

Established in 1997 in Michigan.

Donors: Marvin Dewitt; Marilyn J. Norman; Nancy L. Haveman; Jerene L. Dewitt; Merle J. Dewitt.

Foundation type: Independent foundation.

Financial data (yr. ended 12/31/13): Assets, $937,548 (M); gifts received, $1,000,000; expenditures, $380,912; qualifying distributions, $378,929; giving activities include $377,000 for 36 grants (high: $100,000; low: $1,000).

Fields of interest: Christianity; Human services.

Limitations: Applications not accepted. No grants to individuals.

Application information: Unsolicited requests for funds not accepted.

Officers: Nancy L. Haveman, Pres.; Merle J. DeWitt, V.P. and Secy.; Marilyn J. Norman, Treas.

Trustees: Donald L. Dewitt; Gary D. Dewitt; Jack L. Dewitt; Keith A. Dewitt.

EIN: 383336470

4430

Edward and Evelyn Dik Family Foundation

P.O. Box 3636
Grand Rapids, MI 49501-3636
Application Address: c/o Fifth Third Private Bank, 640 Pasquinelli Dr., Ste. 200, Westmont, IL 60559; tel.: (630) 468-8938

Donors: Edward Dik; Evelyn Dik.

Foundation type: Independent foundation.

Financial data (yr. ended 12/31/13): Assets, $6,857,523 (M); expenditures, $447,238; qualifying distributions, $374,970; giving activities include $369,010 for 33 grants (high: $100,000; low: $250).

Fields of interest: Christianity; Human services.

Limitations: Applications accepted. Giving primarily in IL.

Application information: Application form required.

Initial approach: Letter
Deadline(s): Dec. 31

Trustee: Fifth Third Bank, N.A.

EIN: 466500183

4431

John D. & Jean E. Dinan Foundation

28815 8 Mile Rd., Ste. 101
Livonia, MI 48152-2042

Established in 1999 in Michigan.

Donors: Jean E. Dinan; John D. Dinan Irrevocable Trust.

Foundation type: Operating foundation.

Financial data (yr. ended 12/31/13): Assets, $5,285,056 (M); gifts received, $469,718; expenditures, $265,429; qualifying distributions, $233,190; giving activities include $233,190 for 29 grants (high: $30,000; low: $500).

Fields of interest: Education; Health; Catholicism.

Type of support: General support; Scholarships.

Limitations: Applications not accepted. Giving primarily in MI. No grants to individuals.

Application information: Contributes only to pre-selected organizations.

Officers: J. Denise Dinan, Secy.; Catherine A. Dillon, Treas.

EIN: 383419348

4432

The Angelo & Margaret DiPonio Foundation

14800 Farmington Rd., Ste. 102
Livonia, MI 48154-5464 (734) 458-1980
Contact: Charles E. Bietler, Dir.

Established in 1987 in Michigan.

Donor: Margaret E. DiPonio.

Foundation type: Independent foundation.

Financial data (yr. ended 10/31/14): Assets, $4,510,244 (M); expenditures, $312,187; qualifying distributions, $312,187; giving activities include $251,000 for 3 grants (high: $250,000; low: $500).

Fields of interest: Education; Undergraduate education; Health; Human services.

Type of support: Capital campaigns.

Limitations: Applications accepted. Giving limited to MI. No grants to individuals.

Application information: Application form required.

Initial approach: Proposal
Deadline(s): None

Directors: Charles E. Bietler; Margaret E. DiPonio; Ralph H. Houghton, Jr.

EIN: 382828486

4433

Doll-Loesel Foundation

1111 N. Water St., Ste. 401
Bay City, MI 48708-5677

Established in 1994 in Michigan.

Donors: George F. Loesel; Susan D. Loesel; Doris M. Doll.

Foundation type: Independent foundation.

Financial data (yr. ended 12/31/13): Assets, $1,281,097 (M); gifts received, $226,653; expenditures, $323,439; qualifying distributions,

---

$317,966; giving activities include $316,666 for 20 grants (high: $116,000; low: $500).

Purpose and activities: Giving primarily to food services for human services groups; support also for education and the arts.

Fields of interest: Arts and culture; Education; Human services; Food aid; Youth development.

Type of support: Continuing support; Equipment.

Limitations: Applications not accepted. Giving primarily in MI. No grants to individuals.

Application information: Contributes only to pre-selected organizations; unsolicited requests for funds not accepted.

Board meeting date(s): Nov.

Directors: George F. Loesel; Susan D. Loesel.

EIN: 383212771

4434

Milton H. Dresner Foundation, Inc.

28777 Northwestern Hwy., Ste. 100
Southfield, MI 48034-8321

Established in 2003 in Michigan.

Donor: Milton H. Dresner.

Foundation type: Independent foundation.

Financial data (yr. ended 12/31/13): Assets, $5,142,913 (M); expenditures, $434,079; qualifying distributions, $241,275; giving activities include $195,255 for 52 grants (high: $100,500; low: $60).

Fields of interest: Health; Judaism; Human services.

Limitations: Applications not accepted. Giving primarily in New York, NY. No grants to individuals.

Application information: Unsolicited requests for funds not accepted.

Officer: Milton H. Dresner, Pres.

Directors: Jane Dresner Sadaka; Mary Ann Dresner; Robert J. Dresner.

EIN: 352204352

4435

Doris J. & Donald L. Duchene Foundation

16845 Kercheval, Ste. 5
Grosse Pointe, MI 48230-1551
Contact: S. Gary Spicer Sr.

Established in 1997 in Michigan.

Donors: Doris Duchene; Donald L. Duchene, Sr.; Duchene CRUT.

Foundation type: Independent foundation.

Financial data (yr. ended 12/31/13): Assets, $2,763,541 (M); gifts received, $113,988; expenditures, $192,257; qualifying distributions, $153,967; giving activities include $142,750 for 30 grants (high: $42,150; low: $100).

Fields of interest: Education; Higher education; Religion; Human services.

Limitations: Applications accepted. Giving primarily in Detroit, MI.

Application information:

Initial approach: Contact foundation
Deadline(s): None

Officers and Trustees: Donald L. Duchene, Sr., Pres.; Barbara Duchene, V.P. and Trustee; S. Gary Spicer, Sr., Secy.; David Wind, Treas. and Trustee.

EIN: 383312705

4436
R. Hugh Elliott Family Foundation
1882 Pond Run Rd.
Auburn Hills, MI   48326-2768   (248) 475-2000

Established in 2007 in Michigan.
Donor: R. Hugh Elliott.
Foundation type: Independent foundation.
Financial data (yr. ended 12/31/14): Assets, $3,844,712; gifts received, $0; expenditures, $207,427; qualifying distributions, $176,000.
Fields of interest: Education; Higher education.
Limitations: Applications accepted. Giving primarily in MI.
Application information:
    Initial approach: Proposal
    Deadline(s): None
Directors: Chad K. Elliott; Nancy N. Elliott; R. Hugh Elliott.
EIN: 371557038

4437
The J. F. Ervin Foundation
P.O. Box 1168
Ann Arbor, MI   48406-1168   (734) 769-4600
Contact: John E. Pearson, Pres.

Foundation type: Independent foundation.
Financial data (yr. ended 12/31/13): Assets, $3,651,677 (M); expenditures, $179,521; qualifying distributions, $179,521; giving activities include $179,200 for 28 grants (high: $15,000; low: $1,200).
Fields of interest: Housing development; Catholicism; Youth development.
Application information: Application form required.
    Initial approach: Proposal
    Deadline(s): None
Officers and Trustees: John E. Pearson, Pres. and Trustee; Debra A. Pearson, V.P. and Treas. and Trustee; Heidi Becker, Secy. and Trustee; James Trent Pearson; Susan R. Pearson.
EIN: 356053755

4438
Fabiano Foundation
1885 Bevanda Ct.
Bay City, MI   48706

Established in 1997 in Michigan.
Donor: Fabiano Brothers, Inc.
Foundation type: Company-sponsored foundation.
Financial data (yr. ended 12/31/13): Assets, $1,188,280 (M); expenditures, $375,100; qualifying distributions, $374,800; giving activities include $374,800 for 18 grants (high: $186,000; low: $300).
Purpose and activities: The foundation supports organizations involved with historical activities, education, children services, and Catholicism.
Fields of interest: Historical activities; Education; Secondary education; Higher education; Health; Religion; Catholicism; Human services; Child welfare.
Type of support: General support; Capital campaigns.
Limitations: Applications not accepted. Giving primarily in areas of company operations in MI. No grants to individuals.
Application information: Contributes only to pre-selected organizations.

Officers: James C. Fabiano, Pres. and Treas.; James C. Fabiano II, V.P.; Joseph R. Fabiano II, V.P.; Evangeline L. Fabiano, Secy.
EIN: 383324462

4439
Callant Family Foundation
c/o Comerica Bank & Trust, N.A.
P.O. Box 75000, MC 7874
Detroit, MI   48275-7874   (303) 294-3349
Contact: Ted Stumpp

Established in 2009 in Montana.
Donor: Marcel Callant Estate Trust.
Foundation type: Independent foundation.
Financial data (yr. ended 09/30/13): Assets, $5,447,075 (M); expenditures, $292,307; qualifying distributions, $239,500; giving activities include $239,500 for 16 grants (high: $40,000; low: $3,000).
Fields of interest: Historic preservation; Education; Community and economic development.
Limitations: Applications accepted. Giving limited to Harlowton, MT.
Application information:
    Initial approach: Letter
    Deadline(s): None
Trustee: Comerica Bank and Trust, N.A.
EIN: 266582447

4440
Paul Farago Foundation
3508 Erie Dr.
Orchard Lake, MI   48324-1522   (248) 683-4010

Established in 1998 in Michigan.
Foundation type: Independent foundation.
Financial data (yr. ended 12/31/14): Assets, $2,826,309; expenditures, $420,467; qualifying distributions, $197,600.
Fields of interest: Education; Diseases and conditions; Human services.
Limitations: Applications accepted. Giving primarily in MI. No grants to individuals.
Application information: Application form required.
    Initial approach: Letter
    Deadline(s): None
Officer: Frank Campanale, Pres.
EIN: 383378111

4441
The Farver Foundation
626 Depot St.
Blissfield, MI   49228-1399   (517) 486-2121
Contact: Patrick Farver, Tr.
Main URL: http://www.farverfoundation.org

Established in 1988 in Michigan.
Donors: Orville W. Farver†; Constance Farver; Herbert Farver.
Foundation type: Independent foundation.
Financial data (yr. ended 12/31/13): Assets, $3,558,349 (M); expenditures, $345,896; qualifying distributions, $327,850; giving activities include $327,850 for 46 grants (high: $60,000; low: $250).
Fields of interest: Arts and culture; Education; Higher education; Foundations; Diseases and conditions; Community and economic development; Human services; Youth development.

Type of support: General support; Continuing support; Annual campaigns; Capital campaigns; Capital and infrastructure; Equipment; Emergency funds.
Publications: Application guidelines.
Application information: See foundation website for complete application guidelines. Application form required.
    Deadline(s): None
Trustees: Michael Farver; Patrick Farver; Cynthia Farver-Galiette.
EIN: 386540398

4442
Drusilla Farwell Foundation
675 E. Big Beaver, Ste. 111
Troy, MI   48083   (248) 817-2425

Established in 1937 in Michigan.
Foundation type: Independent foundation.
Financial data (yr. ended 08/31/14): Assets, $3,123,267; expenditures, $168,057; qualifying distributions, $133,329.
Fields of interest: Arts and culture; Education; Higher education; Diseases and conditions; Christianity; Human services; Child welfare.
Type of support: General support; Scholarships.
Application information:
    Initial approach: Proposal
    Deadline(s): None
Officers: Randolph Fields, Pres.; Leslie Wise, Secy.
Trustee: Charles Peltz.
EIN: 386082430

4443
The Ronda and Ron Ferber Foundation
3170 Walnut Lake Ct., Ste. 20
Commerce Township, MI   48390-1743

Established in 2000 in Michigan.
Donors: Roman S. Ferber; Ronda Ferber.
Foundation type: Independent foundation.
Financial data (yr. ended 12/31/13): Assets, $241,618 (M); gifts received, $510,000; expenditures, $300,021; qualifying distributions, $298,700; giving activities include $298,700 for 18 grants (high: $79,000; low: $500).
Purpose and activities: Giving primarily to Jewish organizations and federated giving programs.
Fields of interest: Nonprofits; Judaism; Human services.
Type of support: Regranting.
Limitations: Applications not accepted. Giving primarily in MI. No grants to individuals.
Application information: Unsolicited requests for funds not accepted.
Officers: Roman S. Ferber, Pres.; Ronda Ferber, Secy.-Treas.
EIN: 383557521

4444
Phillip & Elizabeth Filmer Memorial Charitable Trust
c/o Comerica Bank
P.O. Box 75000, MC 7874
Detroit, MI   48275-7874
Application address: c/o Michael Goellnitz, 101 N. Main St., Ste. 101, Ann Arbor, MI 48104, tel.: (734) 930-2417

Established in 2006 in Michigan.
Donor: Elizabeth Filmer Estate Trust.
Foundation type: Independent foundation.
Financial data (yr. ended 08/31/14): Assets, $6,291,939 (M); expenditures, $463,340; qualifying distributions, $394,800; giving activities include $394,800 for 35 grants (high: $24,100; low: $1,400).
Fields of interest: Education; Christianity; Human services; Family services; Child welfare.
Limitations: Applications accepted. Giving limited to Oakland County, MI.
Application information: Application form required.
Initial approach: Letter
Deadline(s): None
Trustee: Comerica Bank.
EIN: 203341412

4445
William and Martha Ford Fund

1901 Saint Antoine St., 6th Fl. at Ford Field
Detroit, MI 48226-2310 (313) 259-7777
Contact: David M. Hempstead, Secy. and Tr.

Established in 1953 in Michigan.
Donors: William Clay Ford†; Martha Firestone Ford.
Foundation type: Independent foundation.
Financial data (yr. ended 12/31/13): Assets, $4,528,687 (M); gifts received, $1,370,759; expenditures, $521,810; qualifying distributions, $452,584; giving activities include $440,540 for 64 grants (high: $200,000; low: $100).
Fields of interest: Education; Nonprofits; Health; Human services.
Type of support: Regranting.
Limitations: Applications accepted. Giving in the U.S., with emphasis on CT and MI. No grants to individuals.
Application information:
Initial approach: Letter
Deadline(s): None
Board meeting date(s): As necessary
Officers and Trustees: David M. Hempstead, Secy. and Trustee; Rodney P. Wood, Treas.; Martha F. Ford.
EIN: 386066335

4446
William C. Ford, Jr. Scholarship Program

1901 Saint Antoine St., 6th Fl.
Ford Field
Detroit, MI 48226-2310
Application address: Scholarship Management Services, 1 Scholarship Way, Saint Peter, MN 56082, tel.: (800) 537-4180

Established in 2005 in Michigan.
Donor: William C. Ford, Jr.
Foundation type: Independent foundation.
Financial data (yr. ended 12/31/13): Assets, $847,457 (M); gifts received, $200; expenditures, $328,891; qualifying distributions, $326,733; giving activities include $316,500 for 211 grants to individuals (high: $1,500; low: $1,500).
Purpose and activities: Grants scholarships to students who are a dependent of an active full-time Ford employee, not married, a U.S. citizen, under the age of 25, and enrolled to be a sophomore in the upcoming year.
Fields of interest: Higher education.
Type of support: Scholarships.

Limitations: Applications accepted. Giving primarily to children of Ford company employees.
Application information: Application form required.
Deadline(s): July 15
Officers: William C. Ford, Jr., Pres.; David M. Hempstead, Secy.; James G. Vella, Treas.
EIN: 202462203

4447
Allegra C. Ford-Thomas Foundation

2000 Brush St., Ste. 440
Detroit, MI 48226-2251 (313) 961-0500
Contact: Thomas J. Motschall, Dir.

Donor: Allegra C. Ford-Thomas.
Foundation type: Independent foundation.
Financial data (yr. ended 12/31/13): Assets, $6,908,687 (M); expenditures, $365,333; qualifying distributions, $324,920; giving activities include $316,500 for 16 grants (high: $50,000; low: $500).
Fields of interest: Education; Sports and recreation; Youth development.
Application information: Application form required.
Initial approach: Letter
Deadline(s): None
Officers and Directors: Anne Ford, Pres. and Director; Charlotte M. Ford, V.P. and Director; Alessandro F. Uzielli, Secy. and Director; Melinda Vanden Heuvel, Treas. and Director; Henry Ford III; Allegra C. Ford-Thomas; Thomas J. Motschall.
EIN: 263930880

4448
Foren Family Foundation

33 Bloomfield Hills Pkwy., Ste. 260
Bloomfield Hills, MI 48304-2946
Contact: John E. Grenke, Dir.

Established in 2005 in Michigan.
Donor: Frazier C. Foren Irrevocable Trust.
Foundation type: Independent foundation.
Financial data (yr. ended 12/31/13): Assets, $5,624,717 (M); expenditures, $331,264; qualifying distributions, $305,648; giving activities include $250,000 for 28 grants (high: $50,000; low: $600).
Fields of interest: Education; Higher education; Animal welfare; Christianity; Child welfare.
Type of support: Research.
Application information: Application form required.
Initial approach: Letter
Deadline(s): Aug. 1
Officers: Belinda Foren, Pres.; Donald Foren, V.P.; Jessica Trotter, Secy.
Directors: Robert Carlone; John E. Grenke.
EIN: 202766137

4449
Four County Community Foundation

(formerly Four County Foundation)
231 E. St. Clair
P.O. Box 539
Almont, MI 48003-0539 (810) 798-0909
Contact: Janet Bauer, Pres. and C.E.O.; Ross Moore, Prog. Asso.
FAX: (810) 798-0908; E-mail: info@4ccf.org;
Additional e-mail: janet@4ccf.org; Grant inquiry

e-mail: program@4ccf.org; Main URL: http://www.4ccf.org
Facebook: https://www.facebook.com/4CountyCommunityFoundation
Instagram: http://instagram.com/4ccf

Established in 1987 in Michigan.
Foundation type: Community foundation.
Financial data (yr. ended 12/31/13): Assets, $12,742,758 (M); gifts received, $477,735; expenditures, $583,896; giving activities include $204,737 for 13+ grants (high: $27,712), and $123,238 for 158 grants to individuals.
Purpose and activities: The foundation is committed to serving the current and emerging needs of the local community, continuing the tradition of philanthropy begun generations ago. The foundation is dedicated to bringing together human and financial resources to support progressive ideas in education, health, community, youth and adult programs. The foundation provides a secure, flexible vehicle for individuals, families, foundations and organizations to positively impact the quality of life in communities. The foundation recognizes that in order to meet its commitments to the community it serves it must seek growth through its permanent endowment funds from a wide range of donors.
Fields of interest: Education; Environment; Health; Diseases and conditions; Community and economic development; Sports and recreation; Child welfare.
Type of support: General support; Grants to individuals; Program development; Scholarships; Program evaluations.
Limitations: Applications accepted. Giving limited to northeast Oakland, northwest Macomb, southeast Lapeer, and southwest St. Clair counties, MI. No support for sectarian religious programs. No grants for operating expenses or basic educational or municipal functions (generally).
Publications: Application guidelines; Annual report; Informational brochure.
Application information: Visit foundation web site for application forms and additional guidelines per grant type. Faxed applications are not accepted. Application form required.
Initial approach: Submit application form
Copies of proposal: 9
Deadline(s): Jan. 1, Apr. 1, July 1, and Oct. 1 for Grants. and Apr. 1 for Scholarship.
Board meeting date(s): 6 meetings per year
Final notification: Within 1 month
Officers and Trustees: Sean O'Bryan, Chair. and Trustee; Jennifer Parker-Moore, Vice-Chair. and Trustee; Janet Bauer, C.E.O. and Pres. and Trustee; Meredith Moore, Pres., Youth Advisory Committee; John Brzozowski, Secy. and Trustee; Joe Worden, Treas. and Trustee; Peggy Domenick-Muscat; Randy Jorgensen; Denis McCarthy; Sheila McDonald; Dina Miramonti; Nancy Parmenter; Barb Redding; Dr. Gary Richards; Laura Schapman; Janaea Smith; Greg Tarr.
Number of staff: 2 full-time professional; 1 part-time professional.
EIN: 382736601

4450
Frankenmuth Community Foundation

(formerly Greater Frankenmuth Area Community Foundation)
P.O. Box 386
Frankenmuth, MI 48734-0386 (989) 284-4674
Contact: Scott Zimmer, Treas.; Stephen C. List, Exec. Dir.

E-mail: steve@frankenmuthcommunityfoundation.or g; Grant inquiry tel.: 989-652-3476; Main URL: http://www.frankenmuthfoundation.org Facebook: https://www.facebook.com/ FrankenmuthFoundation

Established in 1976 in Michigan.
Foundation type: Community foundation.
Financial data (yr. ended 12/31/13): Assets, $8,187,654 (M); gifts received, $1,755,266; expenditures, $289,247; giving activities include $186,254 for 7+ grants (high: $35,455), and $18,200 for 20 grants to individuals.
Purpose and activities: The foundation seeks to support the public, educational, recreational, charitable, and benevolent organizations of the greater Frankenmuth, MI, community.
Fields of interest: Education; Nonprofits; Leadership development; Community and economic development; Sustainable development; Urban development; Sports and recreation; Youth organizing; Unknown or not classified.
Type of support: Capital and infrastructure; Emergency funds; Program development; Scholarships; Student aid; Regranting.
Limitations: Applications accepted. Giving limited to the Frankenmuth, MI, area. No support for religious organizations for religious purposes. No grants to individuals (except through scholarship funds), annual fund drives, debt liability, or general operating expenses.
Publications: Application guidelines; Informational brochure.
Application information: Visit foundation web site for application form and guidelines. Application form required.
  Initial approach: Submit application
  Deadline(s): Jan. 17, Mar. 21, June 15, and Sept. 21
  Board meeting date(s): Feb., Apr., July and Oct.
  Final notification: After Board Meetings
Officers and Board Members: Jon Webb, Chair. and Director; Tim Hildner, Vice-Chair. and Director; Dennis Krafft, Secy. and Director; Scott Zimmer, Treas. and Director; Stephen C. List, Exec. Dir.; Joe Cramer; Julie Gafkay; Sue Piesko; W. Don Zehnder; Bob Zeilinger.
Trustee: Tri-Star Trust Bank.
EIN: 382140032

4451
The Richard J. Garber Foundation
1004 N. Michigan Ave.
Saginaw, MI 48602-4325

Established in 2007 in Michigan.
Donor: Richard J. Garber, Jr.
Foundation type: Independent foundation.
Financial data (yr. ended 12/31/12): Assets, $1,317,481 (M); gifts received, $500,069; expenditures, $270,080; qualifying distributions, $260,000; giving activities include $260,000 for grants.
Fields of interest: Arts and culture; Education; Youth development.
Limitations: Applications not accepted. Giving primarily in MI.
Application information: Unsolicited requests for funds not accepted.
Trustees: Anne M. Garber; Laura C. Garber; Richard J. Garber.
EIN: 261380405

4452
Barbara Garrett Charitable Trust
P.O. Box 3636
Grand Rapids, MI 49501-3636

Foundation type: Independent foundation.
Financial data (yr. ended 12/31/13): Assets, $3,434,239 (M); expenditures, $220,049; qualifying distributions, $166,310; giving activities include $161,746 for 4 grants (high: $53,915; low: $26,958).
Fields of interest: Education; Christianity.
Limitations: Applications not accepted.
Application information: Unsolicited requests for funds not accepted.
Trustee: Fifth Third Bank.
EIN: 456321841

4453
Charles H. Gershenson Foundation
2290 First National Bldg.
Detroit, MI 48226-3583

Established in 1984 in Michigan.
Foundation type: Independent foundation.
Financial data (yr. ended 04/30/14): Assets, $4,730,939 (M); expenditures, $318,497; qualifying distributions, $272,783; giving activities include $216,000 for 4 grants (high: $65,000; low: $36,000).
Fields of interest: Higher education; Hospital care; Judaism.
Type of support: Capital campaigns; Scholarships.
Limitations: Applications not accepted. Giving primarily in MI. No grants to individuals.
Application information: Contributes only to pre-selected organizations.
Trustee: Maurice S. Binkow.
EIN: 386454423

4454
Hal & Jean Glassen Memorial Foundation
P.O. Box 250
SunField, MI 48890-0250
Contact: Thomas Huggler

Established in 1991 in Michigan.
Donor: Harold Glassen†.
Foundation type: Independent foundation.
Financial data (yr. ended 12/31/13): Assets, $5,201,526 (M); expenditures, $304,550; qualifying distributions, $280,302; giving activities include $185,000 for 9 grants (high: $60,000; low: $1,500).
Purpose and activities: Giving primarily for higher education.
Fields of interest: Education; Environment.
Type of support: Capital and infrastructure; Program development; Scholarships.
Application information:
  Initial approach: Letter
  Deadline(s): None
Officers and Trustees: Tom Huggler, Pres. and Trustee; C. Allan Stewart, V.P. and Secy. and Trustee; Glen Miller, Treas. and Trustee; Thomas A. Baird.
EIN: 383012223

4455
Donald & Norma Golden Family Foundation
2000 Town Ctr., Ste. 1500
Southfield, MI 48075-1195   2483537620
Application address: c/o Donald L. Golden, Dir., 9999 Collins Ave., Apt. 4-J, Bal Harbor, FL 33154

Established in 2005 in Michigan.
Donors: Donald L. Golden; Richard S. Golden; Bradley Golden; Michael Golden; Randal E. Golden.
Foundation type: Independent foundation.
Financial data (yr. ended 12/31/14): Assets, $2,499,526; expenditures, $158,710; qualifying distributions, $150,298.
Fields of interest: Specialty hospital care; Diseases and conditions.
Type of support: Research; Research and evaluation.
Directors: Barry R. Bess; Donald L. Golden; Marion Golden.
EIN: 202354028

4456
Elizabeth Hekman Gordon Family Foundation
P.O. Box 532
Spring Lake, MI 49456-0532

Established in 2008 in Michigan.
Donor: Elizabeth Hekman Gordon.
Foundation type: Independent foundation.
Financial data (yr. ended 12/31/13): Assets, $5,674,291 (M); expenditures, $392,451; qualifying distributions, $252,910; giving activities include $247,166 for 30 grants (high: $60,000; low: $500).
Fields of interest: Arts and culture; Education; Christianity; Protestantism; Human services.
Limitations: Applications not accepted.
Application information: Unsolicited requests for funds not accepted.
Directors: Lisa Anne Cooper; Elizabeth Hekman Gordon; Laura M. Linger.
EIN: 262355707

4457
Robert and Mary Ann Gorlin Foundation
(formerly Robert Gorlin - Mary Ann Demattia Foundation)
19305 Gallant Fox Ln.
Northville, MI 48167-1127

Established in 2006 in Michigan.
Donors: Robert H. Gorlin; Mary Ann Demattia.
Foundation type: Independent foundation.
Financial data (yr. ended 12/31/13): Assets, $992,846 (M); gifts received, $4,004; expenditures, $127,715; qualifying distributions, $119,125; giving activities include $119,125 for 5 grants (high: $50,000; low: $3,000).
Fields of interest: Arts education; Education.
International interests: Canada.
Limitations: Applications not accepted. Giving primarily in MI; with some giving to Canada. No grants to individuals.
Application information: Unsolicited requests for funds not accepted.
Officers and Directors: Robert H. Gorlin, Pres. and Treas. and Director; Mary Ann Demattia, V.P. and Secy. and Director; Amy Demattia; Andrew Gorlin.
EIN: 205935870

4458
Grassland Trust
c/o West Michigan Bank & Trust
120 Cypress St.
Manistee, MI   49660-1753

Established in 1997 in Michigan.
Donors: Lorreva S. Foster; James R. Foster Trust.
Foundation type: Independent foundation.
Financial data (yr. ended 12/31/13): Assets, $11,427,678 (M); gifts received, $110,201; expenditures, $322,006; qualifying distributions, $313,659; giving activities include $285,000 for 4 grants (high: $140,000; low: $5,000).
Fields of interest: Nonprofits; Substance abuse treatment; Religion; Judaism; Human services.
Type of support: Regranting.
Limitations: Applications not accepted. Giving primarily in Livingston, MT and PA. No grants to individuals.
Application information: Contributes only to pre-selected organizations.
Trustees: Thomas A. Baither; James R. Foster; Lorreva S. Foster; Henry T. Mather.
EIN: 383357237

4459
Gratiot County Community Foundation
168 E. Center St.
P.O. Box 248
Ithaca, MI   48847-0248   (989) 875-4222
Contact: Tina M. Travis, Exec. Dir.
FAX: (989) 875-0016;
E-mail: gccf@gratiotfoundation.org; Main URL: http://www.gratiotfoundation.org
Facebook: https://www.facebook.com/GratiotCountyCommunityFoundation/

Established in 1992 in Michigan.
Foundation type: Community foundation.
Financial data (yr. ended 09/30/13): Assets, $10,705,543 (M); gifts received, $1,399,278; expenditures, $875,281; giving activities include $334,866 for 22+ grants (high: $24,742).
Purpose and activities: The foundation seeks to enhance the lives of Gratiot County citizens by identifying and addressing needs within the county, by building permanent endowments, and distributing grants in the fields of the arts, education, environment, health, youth development, human services and community development.
Fields of interest: Arts and culture; Education; Environment; Health; Community and economic development; Human services; Youth development.
Type of support: Building and renovations; Convening; Curriculum development; Emergency funds; General support; Internships; Program development; Scholarships; Seed money.
Limitations: Applications accepted. Giving limited to Gratiot County, MI. No support for religious or sectarian purposes. No grants for annual fundraising, ongoing operating expenses of established organizations, multi-year funding; no loans.
Publications: Application guidelines; Annual report; Informational brochure; Newsletter.
Application information: Visit foundation web site for application form and guidelines. Application form required.
Initial approach: Submit application and attachments
Copies of proposal: 1

Deadline(s): Feb. 1 and Jun. 1
Board meeting date(s): 1st Tues. of each month
Officers and Directors: Kevin Collison, Pres. and Director; Dan Rossman, Pres.-Elect. and Director; Dave McMacken, Secy. and Director; Rich Rice, Treas. and Director; Tina M. Travis, Exec. Dir.; Vicki Chessin; Tom Coulter; Chuck Fortino; Kelvin Grant; Janet Hunter; Roger Keck; Sue Malone; Barbara McKenzie; Tim Miller; Dan Raleigh; Becky Roslund; Dr. Jamey Seals; Heidi Sitts.
Number of staff: 1 full-time professional; 1 part-time professional; 1 part-time support.
EIN: 383087756

4460
Grosse Pointe Housing Foundation
1901 St. Antonie St., 6th Fl.
Detroit, MI   48226-2310   3132021290
E-mail: gphousingfoundation@gmail.com;
Application address: c/o Julie Secord, 777 Woodward Ave., Ste. 600, Detroit, MI 48226, tel.: (313) 324-3700; Main URL: http://gphousing.com/

Donors: Health Plan of Michigan Inc; Dr. Cotton.
Foundation type: Independent foundation.
Financial data (yr. ended 12/31/13): Assets, $81,793 (M); gifts received, $439,450; expenditures, $425,753; qualifying distributions, $425,121; giving activities include $416,165 for 151 grants to individuals (high: $4,550; low: $312).
Purpose and activities: Giving primarily for rent assistance awards to eligible students, medical residents, and student nurses who are renting living space in the Grosse Pointe Park, MI area.
Fields of interest: Housing development.
Type of support: Grants to individuals.
Limitations: Applications accepted. Giving primarily in MI.
Application information: Contact foundation for grant guidelines. Application form required.
Initial approach: Email
Deadline(s): None
Officers: Sean Cotton, Pres.; Michael Stines, Secy.; Jon Cotton, Treas.
Board Members: Michael Cotton; Shery Cotton.
EIN: 273976780

4461
Mort & Brigitte Harris Foundation
(formerly Harris Foundation)
36800 Woodward Ave., Ste. 230
Birmingham, MI   48009-6018

Established in 1983 in Michigan.
Donors: Brigitte P. Harris Charitable Lead Trust; Morton E. Harris.
Foundation type: Independent foundation.
Financial data (yr. ended 05/31/13): Assets, $1,866,285 (M); expenditures, $424,500; qualifying distributions, $414,405; giving activities include $414,405 for 48 grants (high: $155,000; low: $20).
Purpose and activities: Giving primarily for religious welfare organizations, including a Jewish welfare fund; giving also for health associations and medical research, hospitals, education, and family services.
Fields of interest: Orchestral music; Education; Nonprofits; Health; Religion; Human services; Family services; Youth services.
Type of support: Regranting.

Limitations: Applications not accepted. Giving primarily in FL and MI. No grants to individuals.
Application information: Contributes only to pre-selected organizations; unsolicited requests for funds not accepted.
Trustees: Brigitte P. Harris; Morton E. Harris.
EIN: 382499405

4462
Alice Kales Hartwick Foundation
P.O. Box 75000
Detroit, MI   48275-7874
Application address: c/o Peter A. Dow, 191 Ridge Rd., Grosse Pointe Farms, MI 48236, tel.: (305) 664-9093

Donor: Alice Kales Hartwick Unitrust.
Foundation type: Independent foundation.
Financial data (yr. ended 12/31/13): Assets, $770,231 (M); expenditures, $225,933; qualifying distributions, $215,000; giving activities include $215,000 for 27 grants (high: $20,000; low: $1,000).
Fields of interest: Arts and culture; Ceramic arts; Performing arts; Orchestral music; Education; Zoos; Nonprofits; Public libraries; Community and economic development; Human services.
Type of support: Regranting.
Application information:
Initial approach: Proposal
Deadline(s): None
Officers and Trustees: John O'Brien, Chair. and Trustee; Bruce Nichols, V.P. and Trustee; Peter A. Dow, Secy.-Treas. and Trustee.
EIN: 382248118

4463
Havirmill Foundation
(formerly Katherine P. & Jerry L. Miller Foundation)
136 E. Michigan Ave., Ste. 1201
Kalamazoo, MI   49007-3936

Established in 1984 in Michigan.
Donors: Susan Miller; Jerry Miller.
Foundation type: Independent foundation.
Financial data (yr. ended 12/31/13): Assets, $6,499,023 (M); expenditures, $262,294; qualifying distributions, $245,961; giving activities include $222,300 for 26 grants (high: $50,000; low: $500).
Fields of interest: Performing arts; Higher education; Nonprofits; Orthopedics; Economic development; Catholicism; Human services.
Type of support: Research; Regranting.
Limitations: Applications not accepted. Giving primarily in Kalamazoo, MI. No grants to individuals.
Application information: Unsolicited requests for funds not accepted.
Officers: Jerry L. Miller, Pres.; Susan L. Miller, V.P.; Kenneth V. Miller, Secy.-Treas.
EIN: 382480744

4464
Hayden Foundation
10260 Elk Lake Rd.
Williamsburg, MI   49690-0010

Established in 1964 in Florida.
Donors: Donald C. Hayden; ARH Trust; Agnes R. Hayden; ARH Revocable Trust.

Foundation type: Independent foundation.
Financial data (yr. ended 12/31/13): Assets, $5,095 (M); gifts received, $335,000; expenditures, $336,073; qualifying distributions, $334,566; giving activities include $330,457 for 135 grants (high: $100,000; low: $10).
Fields of interest: Education; Diseases and conditions; Protestantism; Human services; Child welfare.
Limitations: Applications not accepted. Giving in the U.S., with some emphasis on FL, MI, and NY. No grants to individuals.
Application information: Contributes only to pre-selected organizations.
Officers: Agnes R. Hayden, Pres.; Donald Hayden, Jr., V.P.
EIN: 386118718

4465
Vera and Imre Hecht Foundation Inc.
P.O. Box 75000
Detroit, MI 48275-7874

Established in 1999 in Florida.
Donor: Living Memorial Trust.
Foundation type: Independent foundation.
Financial data (yr. ended 12/31/14): Assets, $4,094,480; expenditures, $312,928; qualifying distributions, $244,512 and $0 for set-asides.
Fields of interest: Music; Education; Higher education; Science.
Type of support: General support.
Limitations: Applications not accepted. Giving primarily in NY.
Application information: Unsolicited requests for funds not accepted.
Officers: Diane Tauber, Pres.; Tom Marittai, V.P.; Ira Fox, Secy.; Veronica Simon, Treas.
EIN: 311652204

4466
The Herrington-Fitch Family Foundation Inc.
c/o Leslie Lee
P.O. Box 2210
Traverse City, MI 49685-2210
E-mail: leefamilyoffice@pinehollow.org

Established in 1996 in Michigan.
Donors: Leslie Lee; Maritime Heritage Alliance.
Foundation type: Independent foundation.
Financial data (yr. ended 12/31/13): Assets, $3,664,642 (M); expenditures, $191,092; qualifying distributions, $179,914; giving activities include $178,025 for 37 grants (high: $55,000; low: $25).
Purpose and activities: Giving for art and cultural programs, education, and nature conservation.
Fields of interest: Arts and culture; Education; Environment; Natural resources; Land resources.
Type of support: General support.
Limitations: Applications not accepted. Giving primarily in MI. No grants to individuals.
Application information: Contributes only to pre-selected organizations.
Officers: Leslie Lee, Pres.; Byrdie Butka, V.P.; Katherine Cowell, Secy.; Whitney Cowell, Treas.
Board Member: MacKenzie Cowell.
Number of staff: None.
EIN: 383331023

4467
James and Lynelle Holden Fund
802 E. Big Beaver Rd.
Troy, MI 48083-1404 (248) 689-5252
Contact: Donald J. Miller, Pres.
E-mail: hmmlaw@sbcglobal.net

Established in 1941 in Michigan.
Donors: James S. Holden†; Lynelle A. Holden†.
Foundation type: Independent foundation.
Financial data (yr. ended 10/31/14): Assets, $1,976,724 (M); expenditures, $249,317; qualifying distributions, $174,189; giving activities include $135,000 for 28 grants (high: $50,000; low: $1,000).
Purpose and activities: Support for medical research, including medical schools and children's hospitals, youth agencies, minority and underprivileged children, higher education, and cultural programs.
Fields of interest: Arts and culture; Higher education; Children's hospital care; Diseases and conditions; Child welfare; Children and youth; Children; Female children and youth; Male children and youth.
Type of support: General support; Matching grants; Continuing support; Capital and infrastructure; Equipment; Publications; Scholarships; Research; Research and evaluation.
Application information: Application form required.
Initial approach: Letter or proposal
Copies of proposal: 1
Deadline(s): None
Board meeting date(s): Feb., May, Aug., and Nov.
Officers and Trustees: Donald J. Miller, Pres. and Trustee; Ingrid O. Vernier, Secy.; William Buckley; Daniel T. Lis, V.P. , Treas. and Trustee.
Number of staff: 3 part-time professional; 1 part-time support.
EIN: 386052154

4468
Isabella Bank & Trust Foundation
400 N. Main
Mount Pleasant, MI 48858 (989) 772-9471

Established in 1997 in Michigan.
Donor: Isabella Bank and Trust.
Foundation type: Company-sponsored foundation.
Financial data (yr. ended 12/31/13): Assets, $1,814,664 (M); gifts received, $1,050,000; expenditures, $187,814; qualifying distributions, $184,302; giving activities include $180,800 for 8 grants (high: $90,800; low: $5,000).
Purpose and activities: The foundation supports hospitals and community foundations and organizations involved with arts and culture, higher education, and human services.
Fields of interest: Education; Community and economic development; Religion.
Type of support: General support; Sponsorships.
Limitations: Applications accepted. Giving primarily in Isabella County, MI, with emphasis on the Mt. Pleasant area. No grants to individuals.
Application information:
Initial approach: Proposal
Deadline(s): None
Officers and Directors: William J. Strickler, Chair. and Director; Richard J. Barz, Pres. and Director; Roxanne Schultz, Secy. and Director; Steven D. Pung, Treas. and Director; Dennis P. Angner.
EIN: 383348258

4469
JCT Foundation
6812 Farrell Dr.
Rockford, MI 49341

Established in 1997 in Michigan.
Donors: William W. Idema; P. Craig Welch, Jr.; Thomas J. Welch; Stephany Welch; Jason Flier; Patricia Flier.
Foundation type: Independent foundation.
Financial data (yr. ended 12/31/13): Assets, $12,115,885 (M); expenditures, $272,892; qualifying distributions, $257,970; giving activities include $257,500 for 17 grants (high: $40,000; low: $5,000).
Fields of interest: Education; Mental health counseling; Christianity.
Limitations: Applications not accepted. Giving primarily in FL and MI.
Application information: Unsolicited requests for funds not accepted.
Officers and Trustees: P. Craig Welch, Jr., Pres. and Secy.-Treas. and Trustee; Mary K. Welch, V.P. and Trustee; Julie W. Regan; P. Craig Welch III; Thomas J. Welch.
EIN: 383386697

4470
James R. and Anita Horne Jenkins Family Foundation
P.O. Box 1687
Midland, MI 48641-1687
Main URL: http://www.jenkinsstandinthegap.org
Grants List: http://www.jenkinsstandinthegap.org/grants/past-grant-recipients

Donors: James R. Jenkins; Anita H. Jenkins.
Foundation type: Independent foundation.
Financial data (yr. ended 12/31/13): Assets, $2,154,711 (M); gifts received, $1,498,000; expenditures, $168,087; qualifying distributions, $168,087; giving activities include $167,183 for grants.
Fields of interest: Cultural awareness; Literature and writing; Education; Disasters and emergency management; Leadership development; National defense; Community and economic development.
Limitations: Applications not accepted. Giving primarily in IA, IL, MI and TN. No grants to individuals.
Application information: Unsolicited requests for funds not accepted.
Officers: James R. Jenkins, Pres.; Andrea L. Jenkins, Secy.; Anita Horne Jenkins, Treas.
EIN: 454131764

4471
Paul T. & Frances B. Johnson Foundation
P.O. Box 203
Benzonia, MI 49616-0203 (231) 882-4681
FAX: (231) 882-9235; Application Address: 787 Michigan Ave., Benzonia, MI, 49616

Donors: Paul Johnson; Frances Johnson.
Foundation type: Independent foundation.
Financial data (yr. ended 06/30/14): Assets, $4,140,947 (M); expenditures, $158,467; qualifying distributions, $145,700; giving activities include $20,000 for 9 grants (high: $8,518; low: $500), and $125,700 for 71 grants to individuals (high: $7,000; low: $800).

Purpose and activities: Giving primarily for college scholarships; some giving also for human services and community services.
Fields of interest: Education; Community and economic development; Human services.
Type of support: General support; Student aid.
Limitations: Applications accepted. Giving limited to residents of Benzie, Grand Traverse, and Leelanau counties, MI.
Application information: Application form required for scholarships. Application form required.
  Initial approach: Letter
  Deadline(s): May 1, for scholarships and honoraria
  Final notification: No later than July 30 for scholarships and honoraria
Officers and Directors: Jon M. Haugen, Chair. and Treas. and Director; Lawrence I. McKay III, Secy. and Director; Ingrid K. Brey; James Kaiser; David Noonan.
EIN: 383382755

4472
The Jones Family Foundation
P.O. Box 575
Saline, MI 48176
E-mail: tamcarr@contltd.com

Established in 2008 in Michigan.
Donors: Wayne D. Jones; Shelly Jones.
Foundation type: Independent foundation.
Financial data (yr. ended 12/31/13): Assets, $7,959,667 (M); expenditures, $437,752; qualifying distributions, $424,299; giving activities include $323,789 for 30 grants (high: $150,000; low: $100).
Fields of interest: University education; Youth development.
Limitations: Applications not accepted. Giving primarily in FL and MI.
Application information: Unsolicited requests for funds not accepted.
Officers: Wayne D. Jones, Pres. and Treas.; Shelly Jones, V.P. and Secy.
Directors: Tamara Carr; Max Jones.
EIN: 261548355

4473
Marjorie and Maxwell Jospey Foundation
260 E. Brown St., No. 280
Birmingham, MI 48009-6231 (248) 647-4100
Contact: Neal F. Zalenko, Pres.

Established in 1948 in Michigan.
Donor: Maxwell Jospey.
Foundation type: Independent foundation.
Financial data (yr. ended 11/30/14): Assets, $6,097,040 (M); expenditures, $365,484; qualifying distributions, $325,116; giving activities include $293,616 for 56 grants (high: $65,000; low: $500).
Fields of interest: Arts and culture; Opera; Philanthropy; Foundations; Religion; Judaism.
Type of support: General support.
Limitations: Applications accepted. Giving primarily in MI. No grants to individuals.
Application information: Application form required.
  Initial approach: Proposal
  Deadline(s): None

Officers and Directors: Neal F. Zalenko, Pres. and Director; Michael W. Maddin, V.P. and Director; David C. Contorer, Secy. and Director.
EIN: 386061846

4474
JSJ Foundation
700 Robbins Rd.
Grand Haven, MI 49417-2603 (616) 842-6350
Contact: Lynne Sherwood, Chair. and Tr.
FAX: (616) 847-3112;
E-mail: plowmand@jsjcorp.com; *Main URL:* http://www.jsjcorp.com/community/philanthropy

Established in 1983 in Michigan.
Donor: JSJ Corp.
Foundation type: Company-sponsored foundation.
Financial data (yr. ended 12/31/13): Assets, $851,470 (M); gifts received, $400,000; expenditures, $232,049; qualifying distributions, $230,028; giving activities include $230,028 for 40 grants (high: $33,015; low: $500).
Purpose and activities: The foundation supports organizations involved with arts and culture, education, health, human services, and civic affairs.
Fields of interest: Education; Human services; Youth development.
Type of support: General support; Continuing support; Annual campaigns; Capital campaigns; Capital and infrastructure; Endowments; Program development; Scholarships.
Limitations: Applications accepted. Giving primarily in areas of company operations in Florence, AL, Ormond Beach, FL, Middleburg, IN, Grand Haven and Grand Rapids, MI, and La Crosse, WI. No support for political organizations or specific disease-related organizations. No grants to individuals, or for exchange programs, fellowships, internships, lectureships, professorships, or golf outings; no loans.
Publications: Application guidelines.
Application information:
  Initial approach: Proposal
  Copies of proposal: 1
  Deadline(s): None
Officers and Trustees: Lynne Sherwood, Chair. and Trustee; Erick P. Johnson, Secy.-Treas. and Trustee; Nelson C. Jacobson; Bari S. Johnson; Melinda E. Johnson; Robert J. Mesereau; Mark F. Sherwood.
Number of staff: None.
EIN: 382421508

4475
George W. & Sadie Marie Juhl Scholarship Fund
P.O. Box 309
Coldwater, MI 49036-0309
Contact: Mary Guthrie
Application Address: c/o Mary Guthrie, 51 W. Pearl St., Coldwater, MI 49036, tel.: (517) 279-5503

Established in 1983 in Michigan.
Foundation type: Independent foundation.
Financial data (yr. ended 03/31/15): Assets, $2,803,546 (M); expenditures, $162,666; qualifying distributions, $131,000; giving activities include $131,000 for 66 grants to individuals (high: $2,000; low: $1,000).
Purpose and activities: Scholarship awards for Branch County, Michigan, students to attend a local institution of higher education.

Fields of interest: Education; Higher education.
Type of support: Student aid.
Limitations: Applications accepted. Giving limited to residents of Branch County, MI.
Application information: Application form required.
  Initial approach: Request Application Form
  Deadline(s): May 1
Trustee: Southern Michigan Bank & Trust.
EIN: 386372257

4476
Jim and Ginger Jurries Foundation
347 Settlers Rd., Ste. 120
Holland, MI 49423

Donors: James L. Jurries; Virginia L. Jurries.
Foundation type: Independent foundation.
Financial data (yr. ended 12/31/13): Assets, $3,499,392 (M); gifts received, $16,356; expenditures, $304,686; qualifying distributions, $225,815; giving activities include $222,570 for 44 grants (high: $70,000; low: $500).
Fields of interest: Higher education; Christianity.
Limitations: Applications not accepted. Giving primarily in MI.
Application information: Unsolicited requests for funds not accepted.
Officer: Virginia L. Jurries, Fdn. Mgr.
Trustee: James L. Jurries.
EIN: 371467586

4477
Kalamazoo Community Foundation Charitable Trust
c/o PNC Bank, N.A.
245 North Rose St., 3rd Fl.
Kalamazoo, MI 49007-3823

Foundation type: Independent foundation.
Financial data (yr. ended 12/31/12): Assets, $3,480,552 (M); expenditures, $192,231; qualifying distributions, $171,875; giving activities include $171,875 for 1 grant.
Fields of interest: Foundations; Community and economic development.
Type of support: General support.
Limitations: Applications not accepted. Giving primarily in Kalamazoo, MI.
Application information: Unsolicited requests for funds not accepted.
Trustee: PNC Bank, N.A.
EIN: 386372488

4478
The Kantzler Foundation
1000 Adams St., Ste. 200
Bay City, MI 48708-5994
Application address: c/o Pere Marquette Depot, 919 Boutell Pl., Ste. 200, Bay City, MI 48708, tel.: (989) 892-0591

Established in 1974 in Michigan.
Donor: Leopold J. Kantzler†.
Foundation type: Independent foundation.
Financial data (yr. ended 12/31/13): Assets, $5,975,076 (M); expenditures, $195,515; qualifying distributions, $162,404; giving activities include $160,000 for 9 grants (high: $27,500; low: $2,000).

Purpose and activities: To support projects and capital improvements of charitable, artistic, educational, and cultural organizations in the greater metropolitan Bay City, MI, area.

Fields of interest: Arts and culture; Theater; Historical activities; Education; Natural resources; Foundations; Public libraries; Television; Community and economic development; Human services; Homeless shelters.

Type of support: Capital campaigns; Matching grants; Capital and infrastructure; Equipment; Land acquisitions; Program development; Seed money; Scholarships.

Limitations: Applications accepted. Giving limited to the greater Bay City, MI, area. No grants to individuals, or for operating budgets, continuing support, annual campaigns, special projects, publications, conferences, emergency funds, deficit financing, research, scholarships, or fellowships; no loans.

Publications: Financial statement; Informational brochure (including application guidelines).

Application information: Application form required.

Initial approach: Contact foundation for application form
Copies of proposal: 11
Deadline(s): 2-3 weeks before each board meeting
Board meeting date(s): Approximately 3 times per year

Officers: Dominic Monastiere, Pres.; Robert D. Sarow, Secy.; Jerome Yantz, Treas.; Kathy Czerwinski, Admin.

Trustees: Andrea Hales; Linda R. Heemstra; Ruth M. Jaffe; D. Brian Law; Michelle Vannest.

Number of staff: None.

EIN: 237422733

4479

Kaufman Foundation

4927 Stariha Dr., Ste. A
Muskegon, MI 49441-5576 (231) 798-7500
Contact: Richard F. Kaufman, Tr.; Sylvia C. Kaufman, Tr.

Established in 1959 in Michigan.

Donor: Amstore Corporation.

Foundation type: Independent foundation.

Financial data (yr. ended 12/31/14): Assets, $1,190,709 (M); gifts received, $25,000; expenditures, $166,408; qualifying distributions, $157,865; giving activities include $157,865 for 36 grants (high: $26,000; low: $50).

Purpose and activities: Giving primarily to museums, the arts, and Jewish agencies.

Fields of interest: Arts and culture; Museums; Nonprofits; Judaism.

Type of support: Regranting.

Limitations: Applications accepted. Giving in the U.S., with some emphasis on MI.

Application information: Application form required.

Initial approach: Letter
Deadline(s): None

Trustees: Richard F. Kaufman; Sylvia C. Kaufman.

EIN: 386091556

4480

Helen L. Kay Charitable Trust

(formerly Helen L. Kay Foundation)
c/o Comerica Bank
P.O. Box 75000, MC 3302
Detroit, MI 48275-3302
Application address: c/o Comerica Charitable Service Group, Attn.: Christopher Kelly, 101 N Main St ., Ste 100, Ann Arbor, MI 48104-5515, tel.: (734) 920-2413

Established in 2000 in Michigan.

Foundation type: Independent foundation.

Financial data (yr. ended 12/31/13): Assets, $8,106,592 (M); expenditures, $446,874; qualifying distributions, $385,901; giving activities include $375,000 for 50 grants (high: $35,000; low: $1,500).

Purpose and activities: Giving primarily for human services and health care, including a hospital.

Fields of interest: Elementary and secondary education; Health; Hospital care; Cancers; Protestantism; Human services; Vocational rehabilitation.

Limitations: Applications accepted. Giving primarily in MI and PA. No grants to individuals.

Application information:

Initial approach: Letter
Deadline(s): None

Trustee: Comerica Bank.

EIN: 383047073

4481

Keller Foundation

5225 33rd St. S.E.
Grand Rapids, MI 49512-2071
Contact: Zelene Wilkins, Exec. Dir.
E-mail: zelene@kellerfoundation.org; Main URL: http://www.kellerfoundation.org

Established in 1980 in Michigan.

Donors: Paragon Die & Engineering Co.; Bernedine Keller; Keller Charitable Remainder Annuity.

Foundation type: Independent foundation.

Financial data (yr. ended 06/30/13): Assets, $7,114,069 (M); gifts received, $6,198; expenditures, $342,799; qualifying distributions, $335,682; giving activities include $293,350 for 69 grants (high: $50,000; low: $100).

Purpose and activities: Giving to support innovative programs for city youth in Grand Rapids, Michigan, that foster nurturing environments, spark curiosity, enhance opportunities for self-sufficiency, and inspire high aspirations.

Fields of interest: Performing arts; Art museums; Education; Zoos; Health; Community beautification; Human services; Child welfare.

Type of support: General support; Matching grants; Continuing support; Capital campaigns; Capital and infrastructure; Program development; Seed money; Curriculum development; Scholarships.

Limitations: Applications accepted. Giving primarily in the Grand Rapids, MI, area. No support for political organizations. No grants to individuals.

Publications: Application guidelines.

Application information: Application form required.

Initial approach: Cover Letter
Deadline(s): May 15
Board meeting date(s): June

Officers: Kathleen Muir Laidlaw, Chair.; Andrew J. Keller, Vice-Chair.; David F. Muir, Treas.; Zelene Wilkins, Exec. Dir.; Lorissa K. MacAllister; Wesley MacAllister; Catherine L. Muir; Elizabeth M. Muir;

Lea Ann Muir; William M Muir; Christina L. Keller; Frederick P. Keller; Lars Whitman.

Number of staff: 1 part-time professional.

EIN: 382331693

4482

Edward and June Kellogg Foundation, Inc.

1250 Byron Rd.
Howell, MI 48843-1007 (517) 546-3330

Established in 2001 in Michigan.

Donor: June Kellogg.

Foundation type: Independent foundation.

Financial data (yr. ended 06/30/13): Assets, $5,160,088 (M); gifts received, $41,473; expenditures, $267,923; qualifying distributions, $212,201; giving activities include $196,875 for 27 grants (high: $25,000; low: $100).

Purpose and activities: Giving primarily in the areas of improving education and creating opportunities for careers in dentistry; advancing the dental health and well-being of youth in local communities as well as those underserved in other parts of the world; providing spiritual support in the process of these endeavors; supporting the humane treatment of animals; and promoting community stewardship.

Fields of interest: Elementary and secondary education; Graduate and professional education; Animal welfare; Dental care; Community and economic development; Christianity; Human services; Youth services; Scouting programs.

Type of support: General support; Capital campaigns; Equipment; Program development; Scholarships.

Limitations: Applications accepted. Giving primarily in MI.

Application information:

Initial approach: Letter
Deadline(s): None

Officer: Thomas A. Kellogg, Pres.

Directors: Ryan Kellogg; Sarah Tottingham.

EIN: 300057241

4483

Ronald and Eva Kinney Family Foundation

(formerly Ronald F. Kinney Foundation, Inc.)
c/o David S. Kruis, Treas.
136 E. Michigan Ave., Ste. 1201
Kalamazoo, MI 49007-3918

Established in 1990 in Michigan.

Donors: Ronald F. Kinney; Eva J. Kinney.

Foundation type: Independent foundation.

Financial data (yr. ended 12/31/13): Assets, $8,800,634 (M); expenditures, $401,493; qualifying distributions, $365,125; giving activities include $302,250 for 45 grants (high: $50,000; low: $250).

Purpose and activities: Giving primarily for education and medical research.

Fields of interest: Higher education; Mental health care; Diseases and conditions; Catholicism; Human services.

Type of support: General support; Research; Annual campaigns; Capital campaigns; Capital and infrastructure.

Limitations: Applications not accepted. Giving on a national basis, with emphasis on MI and MN.

Application information: Unsolicited requests for funds not accepted.

Officers and Trustees: Ronald F. Kinney, Chair. and Trustee; Eva J. Kinney, Pres. and Trustee; James C. Melvin, V.P. and Trustee; Bradley E. Weller, V.P.; Loyal A. Eldridge III, Secy.; David S. Kruis, Treas.
EIN: 382956566

4484
Kiwanis of Michigan Foundation
315 Kiwanis Dr.
Mason, MI   48854

Donors: Francis E. Moss; Kiwanis Club of Traverse City; Robert L. Carr Trust; Golden K. Kiwanis Club; Kiwanis Club of Ann Arbor.
Foundation type: Independent foundation.
Financial data (yr. ended 09/30/14): Assets, $786,821 (M); gifts received, $203,691; expenditures, $288,242; qualifying distributions, $281,734; giving activities include $265,377 for 4 grants (high: $114,277; low: $25,000).
Fields of interest: Health; Patient social services; Hospital care; Child welfare.
Limitations: Applications not accepted. Giving primarily in MI. No grants to individuals.
Application information: Contributes only to pre-selected organizations.
Officers: Mark Ott, Treas.; Paul Elsey, Pres.
EIN: 381723513

4485
Donald & Mary Kosch Foundation
(formerly Donald F. Kosch Foundation)
9 West Ln.
Dearborn, MI   48124-1193
Application address: c/o, Donald Kosch, 2450 Wyoming St., Dearborn, MI 48126-1518, tel.: (313) 842-2375

Established in 1994 in Michigan.
Donors: Donald F. Kosch; Donald Mary Kosch.
Foundation type: Independent foundation.
Financial data (yr. ended 12/31/13): Assets, $2,280,548 (M); gifts received, $351,629; expenditures, $375,122; qualifying distributions, $362,960; giving activities include $354,300 for 25 grants (high: $120,000; low: $300).
Fields of interest: Arts and culture; Museums; Health; Hospital care; Christianity.
Type of support: General support.
Limitations: Applications accepted. Giving primarily in MI, with emphasis on Ann Arbor, Dearborn, and Detroit.
Application information: Application form required.
Initial approach: Letter
Deadline(s): None
Officers: Donald F. Kosch, Pres. and Treas.; Mary T. Kosch, Secy.
EIN: 383147426

4486
Daniel J. & Ardith Koster Foundation
(also known as Ardith Stephenson)
7035 Ivanrest Ave., S.W.
Byron Center, MI   49315
Application address: c/o Greg Koster, 2015 8th Ave., Bryon Center, MI 49315, tel.: (616) 878-5554

Established in 1992 in Michigan.
Donors: NTB, Inc.; Ardith Stephenson; Daniel J. Koster†; Ardith A. Koster.

Foundation type: Independent foundation.
Financial data (yr. ended 12/31/13): Assets, $105,439 (M); gifts received, $192,410; expenditures, $218,629; qualifying distributions, $215,770; giving activities include $215,770 for 31 grants (high: $27,270; low: $500).
Purpose and activities: Giving primarily to Christian organizations; giving also for scholarships to full-time students who are engaged in substantial Christian service and who will attend a qualified Christian educational institution.
Fields of interest: Education; Christianity.
Limitations: Applications accepted. Giving primarily in MI. No grants to individuals.
Application information: Application form required.
Initial approach: Letter
Deadline(s): None
Board meeting date(s): Jan. and June
Officers: Ardith A. Stephenson, Pres.; Greg Koster, Exec. Dir.
Board Members: Cheryl Koster; Kurt Koster; Linda Koster; Rick Koster; Susan Koster.
EIN: 383067600

4487
L & L Educational Foundation
160 McLean Dr.
Romeo, MI   48065-4919   (586) 336-1608
Contact: Peggy Domenick-Muscat, Pres.
FAX: (586) 336-1635;
E-mail: edfoundation@llproducts.com; Main URL: http://fdnweb.org/landl/

Established in 1987 in Michigan.
Donors: Robert M. Ligon; W. Eugene Lane; Lane Texas Partners; Susan Lane Mulka; Lesle E. Cole.
Foundation type: Operating foundation.
Financial data (yr. ended 12/31/13): Assets, $10,669,157 (M); gifts received, $126,100; expenditures, $464,085; qualifying distributions, $421,378; giving activities include $418,503 for 98 grants to individuals (high: $11,923; low: $294).
Purpose and activities: The foundation provides financial grants to the employees of L&L Products, Inc., their spouse, and children, to support educational efforts specifically undertaken to prepare the individual for a future career or to enhance a current career.
Fields of interest: Higher education.
Type of support: Scholarships.
Limitations: Applications accepted. Giving limited to residents of MI.
Publications: Application guidelines.
Application information: Applications available in Jan. annually. See foundation web site for complete application guidelines. Application form required.
Initial approach: Complete and submit application online via foundation web site
Deadline(s): Apr. 1
Officers: Peggy Domenick-Muscat, Pres.; Heather Trombetta, V.P.; Sarah Fezzey, Secy.; Debbie Miner, Treas.
Trustees: Lesle E. Cole; Susan J. Lane; Arnold Kummerow; Justin L. Schupp.
EIN: 382785121

4488
Lamar Construction Foundation
4404 Central Pkwy.
Hudsonville, MI   49426-7831

Donor: Lamar Construction.
Foundation type: Independent foundation.
Financial data (yr. ended 12/31/12): Assets, $310 (M); gifts received, $236,050; expenditures, $399,740; qualifying distributions, $398,877; giving activities include $354,480 for 1 grant.
Limitations: Applications not accepted. Giving primarily in MI.
Application information: Unsolicited requests for funds not accepted.
Officers: Carl Blauwkamp, Pres.; George Holmes, Secy.; Matt Wickstra, Treas.
EIN: 454078022

4489
Lanting Foundation
151 Central Ave., Ste. 220
Holland, MI   49423-2831

Established in 1996 in Michigan.
Donor: Arlyn Lanting.
Foundation type: Independent foundation.
Financial data (yr. ended 12/31/13): Assets, $462,177 (M); expenditures, $355,892; qualifying distributions, $348,805; giving activities include $348,805 for 36 grants (high: $60,000; low: $1,000).
Purpose and activities: Giving to Christian schools and organizations.
Fields of interest: Education; Religion; Sports and recreation.
Limitations: Applications not accepted. Giving primarily in MI. No grants to individuals.
Application information: Unsolicited requests for funds not accepted.
Trustees: Arlyn Lanting; Marcia Lanting.
EIN: 383320436

4490
Lapeer County Community Foundation
(formerly Lapeer County Community Fund)
264 Cedar St.
Lapeer, MI   48446   (810) 664-0691
Contact: Ashley White, Exec. Dir.
E-mail: awhite@lapeercountycommunityfoundation.org; Main URL: http://www.lapeercountycommunityfoundation.org

Established in 1996 in Michigan.
Foundation type: Community foundation.
Financial data (yr. ended 12/31/13): Assets, $9,024,048 (M); gifts received, $211,393; expenditures, $474,190; giving activities include $174,585 for 10+ grants (high: $44,580), and $82,427 for 35 grants to individuals.
Purpose and activities: The foundation builds and manages permanent endowment funds from a wide variety of donors to provide grants that enhance the quality of life in Lapeer County, now and for future generations. Grants from unrestricted funds are made in the areas of education, arts and culture, the environment, health care, human services, recreation and other project topics.
Fields of interest: Arts and culture; Education; Environment; Health; Sports and recreation; Human services.
Type of support: Annual campaigns; In-kind gifts; Endowments; Matching grants; Scholarships.
Limitations: Applications accepted. Giving limited to Lapeer County, MI. No support for religious or sectarian purposes, or for legislative or political

purposes. No grants to individuals (except for scholarships).

Publications: Application guidelines; Annual report; Grants list; Informational brochure; Newsletter; Program policy statement.

Application information: The foundation encourages contacting the executive director to discuss the proposal prior to submitting an application. Full application guidelines and requirements are available at foundation web site, including downloadable application forms. Application form required.

Initial approach: Letter, telephone, e-mail or office visit

Copies of proposal: 4

Deadline(s): Final business day of each month

Board meeting date(s): 2nd Wed. of each month

Final notification: 8 weeks from submission

Officers and Trustees: Nick O. Holowka, Chair. and Trustee; Paul Bowman, Vice-Chair. and Trustee; Timothy Denney, Secy. and Trustee; Kim R. Brown, Treas. and Trustee; Ashley White, Exec. Dir.; Rick Burrough; Curt Carter; Ralph Deshetsky; Andrew Harrington; Kathryn L. Lawter; Dahna Loeding; Charlie Mann; Molly Muir; Jayme Resnik; Steve Zott.

Number of staff: 1 part-time professional.

EIN: 201271563

4491
C. & W. Lee Foundation

1902 Chevy Chase Blvd.
Kalamazoo, MI   49008-2255

Established in 1996 in Michigan.

Donor: Carl E. Lee.

Foundation type: Independent foundation.

Financial data (yr. ended 06/30/13): Assets, $0 (M); gifts received, $4,404; expenditures, $421,104; qualifying distributions, $419,667; giving activities include $416,467 for 6 grants (high: $402,167; low: $800).

Fields of interest: Foundations; Diseases and conditions; Religion; Christianity; Human services.

Limitations: Applications not accepted. Giving primarily in Kalamazoo, MI. No grants to individuals.

Application information: Unsolicited requests for funds not accepted.

Officers: Carl E. Lee, Pres. and Treas.; Cheryl Lee Weedman, Secy.

Director: Jeff Weedman.

EIN: 383352719

4492
The Myron P. Leven Foundation

25899 W. 12 Mile Rd., Ste. 350
Southfield, MI   48034-8315

Established in 1998 in Michigan.

Donors: Myron Leven Trust; Myron P. Leven†.

Foundation type: Independent foundation.

Financial data (yr. ended 12/31/13): Assets, $4,137,895 (M); gifts received, $75,994; expenditures, $465,455; qualifying distributions, $296,075; giving activities include $177,932 for 11 grants (high: $39,532; low: $1,000).

Fields of interest: Arts and culture; Performing arts; Higher education; Nonprofits; Economic development; Human services.

Type of support: Program development; Scholarships; Regranting.

Limitations: Applications not accepted. Giving primarily in MI, with some emphasis on Detroit. No grants to individuals.

Application information: Unsolicited requests for funds not accepted.

Officers: Aram Vosgerchian, Pres.; Arnold P. Garber, Secy.

EIN: 383443921

4493
The Linse Bock Foundation

(formerly The Ralph and Maggie Klingenmeyer Foundation)
c/o John M. Huff
333 Bridge St. N.W., Ste. 800
Grand Rapids, MI   49504-5320

Established in 1992 in Michigan.

Donors: Ralph E. Klingenmeyer; Maggie Klingenmeyer.

Foundation type: Independent foundation.

Financial data (yr. ended 12/31/13): Assets, $5,606,932 (M); expenditures, $307,809; qualifying distributions, $288,360; giving activities include $287,000 for 8 grants (high: $150,000; low: $7,500).

Fields of interest: Education; Elementary and secondary education; University education; Community health care; Christianity.

Type of support: General support.

Limitations: Applications not accepted. Giving primarily in Rochester, MN; giving also in MI, NC, and TN. No grants to individuals.

Application information: Contributes only to pre-selected organizations.

Officers and Directors: Maggie Klingenmeyer, Pres. and Director; Amy E. Iverson, Secy. and Director; John D. Klingenmeyer; Joseph R. Klingenmeyer.

EIN: 383078569

4494
Lois Walts-Farrell Family Foundation

200 Town Center, Ste. 1500
Southfield, MI   48075

Donor: Jeremiah E. Farrell.

Foundation type: Independent foundation.

Financial data (yr. ended 12/31/13): Assets, $13,163 (M); gifts received, $205,000; expenditures, $200,000; qualifying distributions, $200,000; giving activities include $200,000 for 1 grant.

Fields of interest: Health.

Limitations: Applications not accepted. Giving primarily in Royal Oak, MI.

Application information: Unsolicited requests for funds not accepted.

Directors: Barry R. Bess; Jeremiah E. Farrell; Bruce H. Seyburn.

EIN: 463299697

4495
Charles W. Loosemore Foundation

(formerly Loosemore Foundation)
100 th St., S.E., Ste. 646
Byron Center, MI   49315

Established in 1966 in Michigan.

Donor: Charles W. Loosemore.

Foundation type: Independent foundation.

Financial data (yr. ended 12/31/14): Assets, $3,499,918; expenditures, $202,742; qualifying distributions, $202,742.

Fields of interest: Arts and culture; Orchestral music; Education; University education; Community and economic development.

Limitations: Applications not accepted. Giving primarily in Grand Rapids, MI. No grants to individuals.

Application information: Contributes only to pre-selected organizations.

Officers: David M. Hecht, Pres.; Joyce F. Hecht, V.P.

EIN: 386140749

4496
LoPrete Family Foundation

(doing business as Louis and Nellie Sieg Fund)
40950 Woodward Ave., Ste. 306
Bloomfield Hills, MI   48304-5124   (248) 594-5770
Contact: James H. LoPrete, Pres.
E-mail: bqasawa@lopreteandlyneispc.com

Established in 2007 in Michigan.

Donors: Shirley Sieg†; Gertrude Dunlap†.

Foundation type: Independent foundation.

Financial data (yr. ended 01/31/13): Assets, $6,316,817 (M); expenditures, $355,485; qualifying distributions, $313,945; giving activities include $310,975 for 110 grants (high: $23,250; low: $500).

Fields of interest: Arts and culture; Education; Higher education; Natural resources; Health; Protestantism; Human services; Child welfare.

Type of support: Scholarships; General support; Individual development; Endowments; Continuing support; Capital campaigns; Capital and infrastructure.

Limitations: Applications not accepted. Giving primarily in Martin County, FL, and in IL and MI. No support for liberal and left-wing organizations. No grants to individuals.

Application information: Unsolicited requests for funds not accepted.

Board meeting date(s): Thanksgiving

Officers and Trustees: James H. LoPrete, Pres. and Treas. and Trustee; James S. LoPrete, V.P. and Trustee; Robert D. LoPrete, V.P. and Trustee; Mary M. Lyneis, Secy.

Number of staff: None.

EIN: 203641412

4497
M & M Area Community Foundation

1101 11th Ave., Ste. 2
P.O. Box 846
Menominee, MI   49858-0846   (906) 864-3599
Contact: Lisa K. Bayerl, Off. Mgr.
FAX: (906) 864-3657;
E-mail: info@mmcommunityfoundation.org; Main URL: http://www.mmcommunityfoundation.org
Facebook: http://www.facebook.com/pages/M-M-Area-Community-Foundation/284075872316
Twitter: https://twitter.com/MMACF1

Established in 1994 in Michigan.

Foundation type: Community foundation.

Financial data (yr. ended 12/31/13): Assets, $7,810,546 (M); gifts received, $678,051; expenditures, $570,252; giving activities include

$230,259 for 5+ grants (high: $44,886), and $48,190 for 33 grants to individuals.

Purpose and activities: The foundation's mission is to receive and administer funds and property in the form of permanent endowments from a wide range of donors for educational, environmental, cultural, recreational, and charitable purposes in a manner that promotes the spirit of philanthropy and meets the needs of the people of Menominee County, MI and Marinette County, WI.

Fields of interest: Arts and culture; Education; Higher education; Environment; Health; Addiction services; Community and economic development; Sports and recreation; Human services; Youth development; Adolescents.

Type of support: Continuing support; Employee matching gifts; Matching grants; Equipment; Program development; Seed money; Technical assistance; Student aid.

Limitations: Applications accepted. Giving limited to Menominee County, MI, and Marinette County, WI. No support for sectarian religious purposes. No grants to individuals (except for scholarships), or for routine operating expenses, endowments, annual campaigns, debt retirement, or for-profit enterprises.

Publications: Annual report; Financial statement; Grants list; Informational brochure; Newsletter.

Application information: Visit foundation web site for online Letter of Intent form, full grant application form, and guidelines. Full grant applications are accepted only after the project is deemed eligible based on Letter of Intent. Application form required.

　Initial approach: Complete online Letter of Intent
　Copies of proposal: 1
　Deadline(s): 1 month prior to full application deadline for Letter of Intent; Jan. 26 and June 15 for senior grants and Apr. 20 for youth grants
　Board meeting date(s): Quarterly; grants committee meets in Sept.
　Final notification: May for youth grants

Officers and Trustees: Drew May, Pres. and Trustee; Chuck Goddard, V.P. and Trustee; Dr. Jeffrey Orear, Secy. and Trustee; Lisa Fernstrum, Treas. and Trustee; Arthur Baron; Floyd Baum; Michele Biehl; Dr. Stephen Caselton; Mike Dama; Gene Davenport; Jerry Derusha; Lynn Dufrane; Deb Fisher; Dan Hannigan; Wesley Hoffman; John MacIntyre; Bruce Peters; Barb Peterson; Todd Schloegel; Karen Sebero; Dr. North Shetter; Daniel Ward; Robin Kinzer West; Gail Wright.

Number of staff: 1 full-time professional; 3 part-time professional.

EIN: 383264725

4498
Benard L. Maas Foundation
715 Barclay Ct.
Ann Arbor, MI　48105-3033

Established in 1942 in Michigan.
Donor: Benard L. Maas†.
Foundation type: Independent foundation.
Financial data (yr. ended 12/31/13): Assets, $7,636,047 (M); expenditures, $446,052; qualifying distributions, $383,302; giving activities include $250,460 for grants.

Purpose and activities: Giving primarily to Jewish organizations, as well as for the arts, children services, including children's hospitals, and social services.

Fields of interest: Arts and culture; Nonprofits; Specialty hospital care; Diseases and conditions; Judaism; Human services; Child welfare.

Type of support: Regranting.

Limitations: Applications not accepted. Giving primarily in MI. No grants to individuals.

Application information: Contributes only to pre-selected organizations.

Officers and Directors: Matthew T. Engelbert, Pres. and Director; David E. Engelbert, V.P. and Treas. and Director; Lynn H. Engelbert, Secy. and Director.

EIN: 386096405

4499
Mackinac Island Community Foundation
1391 Hoban Ave.
P.O. Box 1933
Mackinac Island, MI　49757-1933　(906) 847-3701
Contact: Robin Dorman, Exec. Dir.
FAX: (906) 847-3893; *E-mail:* info@micf.org;
Additional e-mail: rdorman@micf.org; Main
URL: http://www.micf.org
Facebook: http://www.facebook.com/pages/
Mackinac-Island-Community-Foundation/
297497672914

Established in 1994 in Michigan.
Foundation type: Community foundation.
Financial data (yr. ended 12/31/13): Assets, $8,353,540 (M); gifts received, $294,649; expenditures, $339,622; giving activities include $100,122 for 5+ grants (high: $54,718), and $94,222 for grants to individuals.

Purpose and activities: Recognizing the dignity and beauty of Mackinac Island, the foundation serves the general well-being of Island residents and visitors. The foundation is most interested in projects that focus on arts and humanities, social service, education, community enrichment, youth, environmental awareness and protection, health and wellness, or the horse tradition on Mackinac Island.

Fields of interest: Arts and culture; Humanities; History; Education; Higher education; Environment; Natural resources; Health; Archaeology; Community and economic development; Housing development; Sports and recreation; Equestrianism; Human services; Child welfare; Youth development; Children and youth; Adolescents; Low-income and poor people.

Type of support: General support; Continuing support; Emergency funds; Program development; Seed money; Scholarships.

Limitations: Applications accepted. Giving limited to the Mackinac Island area, MI. No support for organizations lacking 501(c)(3) status or for sectarian purposes. No grants to individuals (except for scholarships), or generally for deficit financing, operating expenses, or annual fundraising campaigns; no loans.

Publications: Application guidelines; Annual report (including application guidelines); Financial statement; Grants list; Informational brochure (including application guidelines); Newsletter.

Application information: Visit foundation web site for application form and guidelines. Application form required.

　Initial approach: Letter, e-mail, or telephone
　Copies of proposal: 1
　Deadline(s): Apr. 15 and Nov. 1

Board meeting date(s): Feb., May, June, July, Aug., Sept., and Dec.
Final notification: June and Dec.

Officers and Trustees: Carol Rearick, Chair. and Trustee; Jennifer King, Vice-Chair. and Trustee; Margaret M. Doud, Secy. and Trustee; Randy Stuck, Treas. and Trustee; Robin Dorman, Exec. Dir.; Bob Benser; Brenda Bunker; Bradley T. Chambers; Jack E. Dehring; George D. Goodman; Kristi Graham; Charles F. Kleber; R. Daniel Musser III; Lorna Puttkammer Straus; Jim Wynn.

Number of staff: 1 full-time professional.

EIN: 383179612

4500
Lorene and Ben Maibach Foundation
(formerly Maibach Foundation)
26500 American Dr.
Southfield, MI　48034-2252

Established in 1966 in Michigan.
Donors: Benjamin C. Maibach, Jr.†; Lorene M. Maibach Trust.
Foundation type: Independent foundation.
Financial data (yr. ended 12/31/13): Assets, $4,292,801 (M); expenditures, $295,921; qualifying distributions, $242,000; giving activities include $242,000 for 7 grants (high: $110,000; low: $500).

Fields of interest: Diseases and conditions; Christianity; Human services.

Limitations: Applications not accepted. Giving primarily in IN, KS, and MI. No grants to individuals.

Application information: Contributes only to pre-selected organizations.

Trustees: Douglas Maibach; Bahr Mark.

EIN: 386146651

4501
Anna Main Charitable Trust
c/o Victor R. Hayes and Gerald R. Gase
22811 Greater Mack Ave., Ste. 212
Saint Clair Shores, MI　48080-2054

Established in 1998 in Michigan.
Donor: Anna Main.
Foundation type: Independent foundation.
Financial data (yr. ended 09/30/13): Assets, $7,422,970 (M); expenditures, $330,970; qualifying distributions, $330,970; giving activities include $310,000 for 12 grants (high: $70,000; low: $5,000).

Fields of interest: Animal welfare; Catholicism; Human services; Child welfare; Developmental disability services; Senior services; Indigenous peoples; Homeless people; People with disabilities.

Limitations: Applications not accepted. Giving primarily in LA, KY, MI, MO, and OH. No grants to individuals.

Application information: Contributes only to pre-selected organizations.

Trustees: Gerald R. Gase; Victor R. Hayes.

EIN: 383336530

4502
The John Dykema and Michele Maly-Dykema Family Foundation
1345 Nottinghill Ct. S. E.
Grand Rapids, MI　49546-9038

Established in 2007 in Michigan.
Donors: John E. Dykema; Michele Maly-Dykema.
Foundation type: Independent foundation.
Financial data (yr. ended 12/31/13): Assets, $7,153,990 (M); expenditures, $479,349; qualifying distributions, $345,380; giving activities include $345,380 for 48 grants (high: $45,000; low: $250).
Fields of interest: Baseball and softball; Child welfare; Youth development.
Type of support: General support.
Limitations: Applications not accepted. Giving primarily in MI, with emphasis on Grand Rapids. No grants to individuals.
Application information: Contributes only to pre-selected organizations.
Officers: Michele Maly-Dykema, Chair. and Treas.; John E. Dykema, Pres. and Secy.; Adam Dykema, V.P.; Alex Dykema, V.P.; Gabrielle Dykema, V.P.
EIN: 261369140

4503
Manat Foundation
186 E. Main St., Ste. 300
Northville, MI 48167-2676

Established in 1986 in Michigan.
Donors: Manuel Charach; Natalie Charach; Jeffrey Charach; Michael Berman; Sherrill Berman.
Foundation type: Independent foundation.
Financial data (yr. ended 07/31/14): Assets, $6,030,208 (M); gifts received, $301,000; expenditures, $449,266; qualifying distributions, $430,600; giving activities include $430,600 for 30 grants (high: $160,000; low: $500).
Purpose and activities: Giving primarily for health associations, particularly for cancer, and to Jewish organizations; funding also for children, youth and social services.
Fields of interest: Nonprofits; Diseases and conditions; Judaism; Human services; Child welfare.
Type of support: Regranting.
Limitations: Applications not accepted. Giving primarily in NY. No grants to individuals.
Application information: Unsolicited requests for funds not accepted.
Officers: Manuel Charach, Mgr.; Natalie Charach, Mgr.
Trustee: Michael P. Berman.
EIN: 382710511

4504
Mariel Foundation
P.O. Box 6461
Traverse City, MI 49696-6461

Established in 1997 in Michigan.
Donors: Carolyn T. Hoagland; John T. Hoagland; James H. Hoagland; Anne H. Magoun; Nancy L. Hoagland; Peter R. Magoun.
Foundation type: Independent foundation.
Financial data (yr. ended 09/30/13): Assets, $9,634,149 (M); gifts received, $13; expenditures, $470,292; qualifying distributions, $426,159; giving activities include $407,000 for 41 grants (high: $50,000; low: $1,000).
Fields of interest: Performing arts; Museums; Higher education; Land resources; Child welfare; Youth development.
Limitations: Applications not accepted. Giving primarily in MI. No grants to individuals.

Application information: Contributes only to pre-selected organizations.
Officers and Directors: Nancy L. Hoagland, Pres. and Director; James H. Hoagland, V.P. and Director; Anne H. Magoun, Secy.-Treas. and Director; John T. Hoagland; Peter R. Magoun.
EIN: 383334050

4505
McClelland Foundation
(formerly The Pamela T. McClelland Family Foundation)
1111 W. Long Lake Rd., Ste. 202
Troy, MI 48098-6333

Established in 2000 in Michigan.
Donor: Pamela T. McClelland.
Foundation type: Independent foundation.
Financial data (yr. ended 06/30/14): Assets, $3,535,913 (M); expenditures, $188,490; qualifying distributions, $165,000; giving activities include $165,000 for 5 grants (high: $115,000; low: $2,000).
Fields of interest: Education; Domesticated animals; Human services.
Limitations: Applications not accepted. Giving primarily in MI. No grants to individuals.
Application information: Contributes only to pre-selected organizations.
Officers and Directors: James F. McClelland, Pres. and Director; Pamela K. McClelland, V.P. and Director; R. Keith Stark, Secy.-Treas. and Director.
EIN: 383568733

4506
The June and Cecil McDole Charitable Fund
24800 Denso Dr., Ste. 260
Southfield, MI 48033-7449

Donor: June McDole Trust.
Foundation type: Independent foundation.
Financial data (yr. ended 06/30/14): Assets, $8,647,963 (M); expenditures, $499,538; qualifying distributions, $380,500; giving activities include $380,500 for 55 grants (high: $27,500; low: $500).
Fields of interest: Education; Diseases and conditions; Human services.
Type of support: Research.
Limitations: Applications not accepted. Giving primarily in MI. No grants to individuals.
Application information: Contributes only to pre-selected organizations.
Officers: Konrad D. Kohl, Pres.; Paul F. Gamble, Secy.; Kevin J. Petras, Treas.
EIN: 203619178

4507
The June & Cecil McDole Foundation
24800 Denso Dr., Ste. 260
Southfield, MI 48033-7449

Established in 1993 in Michigan.
Donors: June McDole†; June McDole Charitable Remainder Trust.
Foundation type: Independent foundation.
Financial data (yr. ended 12/31/13): Assets, $5,284,461 (M); expenditures, $332,142; qualifying distributions, $240,750; giving activities

include $234,750 for 29 grants (high: $20,000; low: $1,000).
Fields of interest: Foundations; Nonprofits; Health; Hospice care; Cancers; Christianity; Human services; Food banks.
Type of support: General support; Regranting.
Limitations: Applications not accepted. Giving primarily in MI. No grants to individuals.
Application information: Contributes only to pre-selected organizations.
Officers: Konrad D. Kohl, Pres.; Kevin J. Petras, V.P. and Treas.; Paul F. Gamble, Secy.
EIN: 383145381

4508
McDonald Agape Foundation
380 N. Old Woodward Ave., Ste. 212
Birmingham, MI 48009-5314
Main URL: http://www.mcdonaldagape.org

Established in 1988 in Michigan.
Donors: Alonzo L. McDonald, Jr.; Egon Zehnder.
Foundation type: Independent foundation.
Financial data (yr. ended 12/31/13): Assets, $11,791,791 (M); gifts received, $26,200; expenditures, $896,999; qualifying distributions, $610,242; giving activities include $420,672 for 12 grants (high: $87,500; low: $2).
Purpose and activities: Giving primarily for Christian organizations and education.
Fields of interest: Higher education; Graduate and professional education; Christianity; Theology.
Limitations: Applications not accepted. Giving primarily in FL, GA, IA, MA, MI, NC, NY and VA. No grants to individuals.
Application information: Contributes only to pre-selected organizations.
Officers: Alonzo L. McDonald, Chair.; Peter McDonald, Vice-Chair.; R. Jamison Williams, Jr., Secy.; Mark A. Maurice, Treas.
Trustees: Jonathan Aitken; Suzanne M. McDonald; Jennifer McDonald Peters; Dr. Robert M. Pool.
EIN: 382840692

4509
The Michael F. McManus Foundation
(formerly The Header Foundation)
30600 Telegraph Rd., No. 3240
Bingham Farms, MI 48025

Established in 1969 in Michigan.
Donors: Header Products, Inc.; Michael F. McManus.
Foundation type: Independent foundation.
Financial data (yr. ended 12/31/13): Assets, $2,598,614 (M); expenditures, $293,912; qualifying distributions, $266,000; giving activities include $266,000 for 66 grants (high: $55,000; low: $100).
Fields of interest: Higher education; Catholicism; Human services.
Limitations: Applications not accepted. Giving primarily in the greater Detroit, MI, area. No grants to individuals.
Application information: Contributes only to pre-selected organizations.
Officers: William J. Harahan IV, Pres.; J. Rodney Guest, Treas.; Jordan H. Smith, Secy.
EIN: 386174305

4510
William F. McNally Family Foundation
(formerly William F. and Marjorie A. McNally
Memorial Foundation)
5825 Dixie Hwy.
Saginaw, MI 48601   (989) 777-2361
Contact: Jeff McNally, Pres. and Treas.

Established in 1982 in Michigan.
Donor: William F. McNally‡.
Foundation type: Independent foundation.
Financial data (yr. ended 12/31/13): Assets,
$9,746,581 (M); gifts received, $3,996,706;
expenditures, $293,898; qualifying distributions,
$276,590; giving activities include $273,590 for 30
grants (high: $50,000; low: $250).
Fields of interest: Art museums; Higher education;
Graduate and professional education; Hospital care;
Protestantism; Theology; Human services.
Type of support: Capital campaigns.
Limitations: Applications accepted. Giving primarily
in MI.
Application information:
 Initial approach: Letter
 Deadline(s): None
Officer: Jeff McNally, Pres. and Treas.
Trustees: Brian McNally; Dwight McNally.
EIN: 382429175

4511
Meritor, Inc. Trust
(formerly ArvinMeritor, Inc. Trust)
2135 W. Maple Rd.
Troy, MI 48084-7186
Contact: Krista Sohm, V.P.

Established in 1997 in Michigan.
Donors: Meritor Automotive, Inc.; ArvinMeritor, Inc.;
Meritor, Inc.
Foundation type: Company-sponsored foundation.
Financial data (yr. ended 09/29/13): Assets,
$262,575 (M); gifts received, $353,070;
expenditures, $348,720; qualifying distributions,
$348,720; giving activities include $348,720 for
113 grants (high: $50,000; low: $250).
Purpose and activities: The foundation supports
organizations involved with arts and culture,
education, health, human services, community
development, and civic affairs. Special emphasis is
directed toward engineering, science, and
technology education.
Fields of interest: Arts and culture; Opera;
Orchestral music; Education; Secondary education;
STEM education; Higher education; Nonprofits;
Health; Science; Technology; Engineering; Public
affairs; Community and economic development;
Business and industry; Human services; Youth
services; Economics for youth.
Type of support: Program development; Employee
volunteer services; Regranting; Employee matching
gifts.
Limitations: Applications accepted. Giving primarily
in areas of company operations, with emphasis on
MI. No support for discriminatory organizations,
religious or sectarian organizations not of direct
benefit to the entire community, labor, political, or
veterans' organizations, or fraternal, athletic, or
social clubs. No grants to individuals, or for general
operating support for local United Way agencies,
sponsorship of fundraising activities for individuals,
debt reduction, or seminars, conferences, trips, or
tours; no loans.
Publications: Application guidelines.

Application information: Application form required.
 Initial approach: Proposal
 Deadline(s): Aug.
Officers: Ivor J. Evans, Chair., Pres., and C.E.O.;
Jeffrey A. Craig, Pres. and C.O.O.; Kevin Nowlan, Sr.
V.P. and C.F.O.; Sandra Quick, Sr. V.P., Secy. and
Genl. Counsel.
EIN: 522089611

4512
Merkley Charitable Trust
328 S. Saginaw St., FNT 160
Flint, MI 48502-1923   (810) 342-7089

Donor: Martha K. Merkley‡.
Foundation type: Independent foundation.
Financial data (yr. ended 12/01/14): Assets,
$5,064,201 (M); expenditures, $221,194;
qualifying distributions, $215,251; giving activities
include $168,341 for 19 grants (high: $82,006;
low: $1,000).
Purpose and activities: Giving primarily to benefit
youth and the elderly.
Fields of interest: Education; Christianity; Human
services; Youth services; Seniors.
Type of support: Continuing support; Program
development.
Limitations: Applications accepted. Giving limited to
Genesee County, MI. No grants to individuals.
Publications: Application guidelines.
Application information:
 Initial approach: Letter
 Copies of proposal: 1
 Deadline(s): None
 Board meeting date(s): Quarterly
Trustee: FirstMerit Bank, N.A.
EIN: 386528749

4513
Roy G. Michell Charitable Foundation and Trust
c/o Janz & Knight, PLC
300 E. Long Lake Rd., Ste. 360
Bloomfield Hills, MI 48304-2377   2486469666

Established in 1963 in Michigan.
Donor: Roy G. Michell‡.
Foundation type: Independent foundation.
Financial data (yr. ended 04/30/15): Assets,
$6,084,393; expenditures, $350,386; qualifying
distributions, $277,500.
Fields of interest: Diseases and conditions;
Christianity; Human services.
Limitations: Applications not accepted. Giving
primarily in MI. No grants to individuals.
Application information: Contributes only to
pre-selected organizations.
Trustees: Roy G. Michell, Jr.; William Michell;
Kenneth E. Zink.
EIN: 386071109

4514
Michigan Gateway Community Foundation
(formerly Buchanan Area Foundation)
111 Days Ave.
Buchanan, MI 49107-1609   (269) 695-3521
Contact: Robert N. Habicht, C.E.O. and Pres.

FAX: (269) 695-4250; E-mail: info@mgcf.org; Main
URL: http://www.mgcf.org
Facebook: https://www.facebook.com/
Michigan-Gateway-Community-Foundation-2334499
13397034/
YouTube: https://www.youtube.com/user/
MGCF111days

Established in 1977 in Michigan.
Foundation type: Community foundation.
Financial data (yr. ended 03/31/13): Assets,
$7,729,400 (M); gifts received, $376,657;
expenditures, $522,236; giving activities include
$227,621 for 12+ grants (high: $40,000), and
$720 for grants to individuals.
Purpose and activities: The foundation provides
support for the arts, education, and social services.
Scholarships are for local-area high school seniors
for study in any field.
Fields of interest: Arts and culture; Education;
Health; Human services.
Type of support: General support; Matching grants;
Financial sustainability; Equipment; Program
development; Convening; Seed money; Curriculum
development; Program evaluations; Student aid.
Limitations: Applications accepted. Giving limited to
Berrien, Buchanan, Cass, and Niles Counties, MI.
Publications: Application guidelines; Annual report;
Financial statement; Informational brochure;
Newsletter.
Application information: Visit foundation web site
for application information. Use of the Common
Grant Application of the Council of Michigan
Foundations is encouraged. Application form
required.
 Initial approach: Telephone
 Copies of proposal: 1
 Deadline(s): Feb. 1, May 1, Aug. 1, and Nov. 1 for
   grants; Mar. 14 for scholarships
 Board meeting date(s): Mar., May, July, Aug., and
   Nov.
 Final notification: Within 1 month
Officers and Trustees: Louis A. Desenberg, Chair.
and Trustee; Robert N. Habicht, C.E.O. and Pres.
and Trustee; Robert Cochrane, Treas. and Trustee;
Celia Ash; Nancy Oare Butler; Karin Falkenstein;
Rudy Kappe; Paige Lamb; Pat McCollough; Kathy
Rossow; Judy Truesdell; Stephen K. Woods; James
Zaher.
Number of staff: 1 full-time professional; 1 part-time
support.
EIN: 382180730

4515
Frances Goll Mills Fund
328 S. Saginaw St., M/C 001065
Flint, MI 48502-1923   9897761416
Application address: c/o First Merit Bank, N.A.,
Attn.: Helen James, 101 N. Washington Ave., M/C
332021, Saginaw, MI 48607, tel.: (989) 776-7368

Established in 1982 in Michigan.
Donor: Frances Goll Mills‡.
Foundation type: Independent foundation.
Financial data (yr. ended 09/30/14): Assets,
$5,849,635; expenditures, $460,321; qualifying
distributions, $418,819.
Fields of interest: Elementary and secondary
education; Higher education; Environmental
education; Health; Health care financing;
Protestantism; Human services; Youth
development; Vocational rehabilitation.
Type of support: General support; Scholarships.

Limitations: Applications accepted. Giving limited to MI, with emphasis on Bay City, Midland, and Saginaw. No grants to individuals; no loans.
Publications: Application guidelines.
Application information: Application form required.
 Initial approach: Letter or proposal requesting application guidelines
 Copies of proposal: 1
 Deadline(s): None
 Board meeting date(s): 3rd Thurs. of Mar., June, Sept., and Dec.
Trustee: FirstMerit Bank, N.A.
EIN: 382434002

4516
Mojo Foundation
5940 Tahoe Dr. S.E.
Grand Rapids, MI 49546-7121 (616) 455-0200
Contact: Michael A. McGraw, Pres.

Established in 1996 in Michigan.
Donor: Michael A. McGraw.
Foundation type: Independent foundation.
Financial data (yr. ended 12/31/13): Assets, $9,273,747 (M); gifts received, $1,512,531; expenditures, $384,261; qualifying distributions, $326,520; giving activities include $326,500 for 29 grants (high: $125,000; low: $500).
Fields of interest: Christianity; Human services; Family services; Child welfare.
Limitations: Applications accepted. Giving primarily in Grand Rapids, MI. No grants to individuals.
Application information: Application form required.
 Initial approach: Letter
 Deadline(s): None
Officers: Michael A. McGraw, Pres.; Michael R. McGraw, V.P. and Secy.-Treas.; Joshua D. McGraw, V.P.
EIN: 383325750

4517
William and Marie Molnar Foundation Corp.
3565 Roland Dr.
Bloomfield Hills, MI 48301

Donors: Marie Molnar; William Molnar.
Foundation type: Independent foundation.
Financial data (yr. ended 12/31/14): Assets, $3,573,781 (M); gifts received, $200,023; expenditures, $186,547; qualifying distributions, $165,000; giving activities include $165,000 for 28 grants (high: $30,000; low: $1,000).
Fields of interest: Education; Religion; Human services.
Limitations: Applications not accepted. Giving primarily in MI. No grants to individuals.
Application information: Unsolicited requests for funds not accepted.
Officers: Marie Molnar, Mgr.; William Molnar, Mgr.
EIN: 383567851

4518
Morley Foundation
(formerly Morley Brothers Foundation)
P.O. Box 2485
Saginaw, MI 48605-2485 (989) 753-3438
Contact: David H. Morley, Pres.
Main URL: http://www.morleyfdn.org

Established in 1948 in Michigan.
Donors: Ralph Chase Morley, Sr.†; Mrs. Ralph Chase Morley, Sr.†.
Foundation type: Independent foundation.
Financial data (yr. ended 12/31/13): Assets, $4,695,891 (M); expenditures, $305,690; qualifying distributions, $231,188; giving activities include $213,455 for 67 grants (high: $25,000; low: $100).
Purpose and activities: Giving primarily in the areas of welfare, health, education, civic improvement, and the humanities in Michigan, with major emphasis on Saginaw County.
Fields of interest: Arts and culture; Performing arts; Museums; Education; Elementary education; Secondary education; Higher education; Business education; Health; Hospital care; Diseases and conditions; Community and economic development; Human services; Child welfare.
Type of support: General support; Employee matching gifts; Matching grants; Continuing support; Annual campaigns; Capital campaigns; Capital and infrastructure; Equipment; Emergency funds; Program development; Seed money; Research.
Limitations: Applications accepted. Giving primarily in the greater Saginaw County, MI, area. No grants to individuals, or for endowment funds, deficit financing, land acquisition, renovation projects, publications, or conferences; no loans.
Publications: Application guidelines; Informational brochure.
Application information: Application guidelines available on foundation web site. Application form required.
 Initial approach: Letter
 Copies of proposal: 1
 Board meeting date(s): Feb., May, Aug., and Nov.
 Final notification: 3 months
Officers and Trustees: David H. Morley, Pres. and Trustee; Carol Morley Beck, V.P. and Trustee; Christine Black, Secy. and Trustee; Peter Morley, Jr., Treas. and Trustee; Chase Brand; Michael Morley Brand; Jodona Morley Kinney; Sara Morley LaCroix; Burrows Morley, Jr.; Christopher Morley; George B. Morley, Jr.; Katharyn Morley; Michael Morley; Peter Morley; Lucy Thomson; Tom Thomson.
Number of staff: 1 part-time professional.
EIN: 386055569

4519
The Murdock Foundation
4298 Cedar Point Rd.
Manitou Beach, MI 49253-9622

Established in 1985 in Michigan.
Donors: Donald L. Murdock; Marcia Jean Murdock.
Foundation type: Independent foundation.
Financial data (yr. ended 11/30/14): Assets, $980,584 (M); expenditures, $259,658; qualifying distributions, $253,285; giving activities include $253,285 for 21 grants (high: $205,735; low: $100).
Fields of interest: Higher education; Nonprofits; Christianity.
Type of support: General support; Regranting.
Limitations: Applications not accepted. Giving primarily in MI. No grants to individuals.
Application information: Unsolicited requests for funds not accepted.
Officer and Director: Donald L. Murdock, Pres. and Secy.-Treas. and Director.

Trustees: Curtis J. Mann; Bart A. Murdock.
EIN: 382638239

4520
Judith & Edward Narens Family Foundation
29200 Northwestern Hwy., Ste. 200
Southfield, MI 48034-1060

Established in 1985 in Michigan.
Donors: Edward Narens; Judith Narens.
Foundation type: Independent foundation.
Financial data (yr. ended 11/30/13): Assets, $884,110 (M); gifts received, $150,000; expenditures, $158,454; qualifying distributions, $157,904; giving activities include $156,859 for 22 grants (high: $95,000; low: $300).
Purpose and activities: Giving primarily for Jewish agencies and services.
Fields of interest: Arts and culture; Nonprofits; Judaism; Human services.
Type of support: Regranting.
Limitations: Applications not accepted. Giving primarily in MI. No grants to individuals.
Application information: Unsolicited requests for funds not accepted.
Officers: Judith Narens, Pres.; Edward Narens, Secy.-Treas.
EIN: 382661323

4521
Nartel Family Foundation
(formerly Werner and Ruth Nartel Foundation)
141 Harrow Ln., Ste. 1
Saginaw, MI 48638-6093

Foundation type: Independent foundation.
Financial data (yr. ended 06/30/13): Assets, $4,734,849 (M); expenditures, $280,879; qualifying distributions, $280,879; giving activities include $227,017 for 20 grants (high: $66,667; low: $250).
Fields of interest: History museums; Nonprofits; Alzheimer's disease; Heart and circulatory system diseases; Breast cancer; Judaism; Human services; Child welfare.
Type of support: General support; Regranting.
Limitations: Applications not accepted. Giving primarily in IL and MI. No grants to individuals.
Application information: Contributes only to pre-selected organizations.
Officers: Evelyn Nartelski, Pres. and Treas.; Kathy Rembowski, V.P.
Trustees: Timothy Allen; Sherwood DeVisser; Sylvia McCown.
EIN: 382477768

4522
Allen E. & Marie A. Nickless Memorial Foundation
3023 Davenport Ave.
Saginaw, MI 48602-3652
Application address: c/o B.J. Humphreys, 5090 State St., Building A, Ste. 1, Saginaw, MI 48603, tel.: (989) 792-2552

Donors: Marie A. Nickless; Allen E. Nickless†.
Foundation type: Independent foundation.
Financial data (yr. ended 12/31/13): Assets, $6,012,871 (M); expenditures, $293,415; qualifying distributions, $264,726; giving activities

include $239,299 for 43 grants (high: $18,000; low: $500).

Fields of interest: Arts and culture; Education; Foundations; Christianity.

Type of support: General support.

Limitations: Applications accepted. Giving primarily in Saginaw County, MI. No loans or program-related investments.

Application information: Application form required.

Initial approach: Letter
Deadline(s): None

Officers: Charles Nickless, Pres.; Darcy Nickless, V.P.; B.J. Humphreys, Secy.; David A. Beyerlein, Treas.

Trustees: John Humphreys; John Kunitzer.

EIN: 237011258

4523
Noster Foundation
10596 Wellington Dr.
Plymouth, MI 48170-3429

Established in 2003 in Michigan.

Donor: Thomas J. Myler, Sr.

Foundation type: Independent foundation.

Financial data (yr. ended 12/31/13): Assets, $0 (M); expenditures, $163,900; qualifying distributions, $162,500; giving activities include $162,500 for 1+ grant.

Limitations: Applications not accepted.

Application information: Unsolicited requests for funds not accepted.

Officers: Marylyn Stanhope, Pres.; David G. Myler, Treas.

Board Member: John Fish.

EIN: 562434413

4524
Nusbaum Family Foundation
26575 Willowgreen Dr.
Franklin, MI 48025-1337 (248) 473-7570
Contact: Irving Nusbaum, Pres.

Established in 1990 in Michigan.

Donors: Irving Nusbaum; Barbara Nusbaum.

Foundation type: Independent foundation.

Financial data (yr. ended 12/31/12): Assets, $189,442 (M); gifts received, $2,245; expenditures, $360,259; qualifying distributions, $349,980; giving activities include $349,980 for grants.

Fields of interest: Child educational development; Nonprofits; Hospice care; Judaism.

Type of support: Regranting.

Limitations: Applications accepted. Giving primarily in MI.

Application information:

Initial approach: Letter
Deadline(s): None

Officers: Irving Nusbaum, Pres.; Barbara Nusbaum, Secy.

Directors: Michael Roth; Bruce H. Seyburn.

EIN: 382917028

4525
O'Donovan Family Foundation
4245 N. Oak Pointe Ct. N.E.
Grand Rapids, MI 49525-9415

Established in 2004 in Michigan.

Donors: Karen J. O'Donovan; Timothy J. O'Donovan.

Foundation type: Independent foundation.

Financial data (yr. ended 12/31/14): Assets, $6,705,186 (M); gifts received, $315,240; expenditures, $380,154; qualifying distributions, $358,560; giving activities include $357,320 for 21 grants (high: $100,000; low: $1,000).

Fields of interest: Arts and culture; Arts education; Education; University education; Medical education; Nonprofits; Children and youth.

Type of support: Regranting; Capital campaigns; Program development.

Limitations: Applications not accepted. Giving primarily in MA and MI. No grants to individuals.

Application information: Unsolicited requests for funds not accepted.

Officers: Timothy J. O'Donovan, Pres. and Secy.; Karen J. O'Donovan, Treas.

Trustees: Kevin M. O'Donovan; Ryan J. O'Donovan.

EIN: 383704443

4526
R. E. Olds Foundation
(formerly Ransom Fidelity Company)
P.O. Box 4900
East Lansing, MI 48826-4900 (517) 332-0234

Established in 1915 in Michigan.

Donor: Ransom E. Olds†.

Foundation type: Independent foundation.

Financial data (yr. ended 12/31/14): Assets, $4,020,298; expenditures, $244,728; qualifying distributions, $210,555.

Purpose and activities: Giving to community-based education programs focusing on youth, access to health care, animal welfare and environmental issues, greater Lansing Tri-County, Michigan.

Fields of interest: Education; Environment; Domesticated animals; Health; Youth development.

Type of support: Annual campaigns; Matching grants; Capital campaigns; Equipment; Emergency funds; Program development; Convening; Seed money.

Limitations: Applications accepted. Giving in the U.S., with emphasis on Lansing and the Tri-County, MI, area. No support for religious organizations. No grants to individuals.

Application information: Application form required.

Initial approach: Letter
Copies of proposal: 1
Deadline(s): None

Officers: Diana Tarpoff, Pres.; Patti Schafer, Secy.; Deborah Stephens, Treas.

Directors: Greggory Stephens; Emily Polo Tate.

Number of staff: 2 full-time professional.

EIN: 381485403

4527
Onequest Foundation
(formerly Jack and Mary DeWitt Family Foundation)
205 Norwood Dr.
Holland, MI 49424-2730

Established in 1992 in Michigan.

Donors: Jack L. DeWitt; Jacqueline Curtis; Laurie S. Wierda; Linda E. Berghorst; Ryan Berghorst; Steve DeWitt; Kyle Curtis; Jim DeWitt; Mary DeWitt; Lyne DeWitt; Jackie Curtis; Melissa DeWitt.

Foundation type: Independent foundation.

Financial data (yr. ended 12/31/13): Assets, $1,065,682 (M); gifts received, $21,807;

expenditures, $346,810; qualifying distributions, $327,053; giving activities include $319,500 for 34 grants (high: $50,000; low: $500).

Purpose and activities: Giving primarily for education, human services, and Christian agencies and churches.

Fields of interest: Higher education; Philanthropy; Christianity; Human services; Family services.

Type of support: Annual campaigns.

Limitations: Applications not accepted. Giving primarily in MI. No grants to individuals.

Application information: Unsolicited requests for funds not accepted.

Officers: Jack L. DeWitt, Pres. and Treas.; Mary E. DeWitt, V.P. and Secy.

Directors: Linda Ellen Berghorst; Jacqueline DeWitt Curtiss; James Russell DeWitt; Steven Lee DeWitt; Laurie Sue Wierda.

EIN: 383080740

4528
Paul F. and Franca G. Oreffice Foundation
c/o Gary Gudmunsen
224 E. Larkin St.
Midland, MI 48642

Established in 1986 in Michigan.

Donors: Paul F. Oreffice; Franca G. Oreffice.

Foundation type: Independent foundation.

Financial data (yr. ended 12/31/13): Assets, $2,842,832 (M); expenditures, $203,920; qualifying distributions, $190,420; giving activities include $190,420 for 32 grants (high: $60,000; low: $300).

Fields of interest: Hospital care; Diseases and conditions; Parkinson's disease; Cancers; Public policy; Equestrianism; People with physical disabilities; Military personnel.

Type of support: General support; Policy, advocacy and systems reform.

Limitations: Applications not accepted. Giving primarily in Washington, DC, FL and TX. No grants to individuals.

Application information: Contributes only to pre-selected organizations.

Officer: Paul F. Oreffice, Pres.

Director: Franca G. Oreffice.

EIN: 382705906

4529
Louis and Helen Padnos Foundation
P.O. Box 1979
Holland, MI 49422-1979

Established in 1999 in Michigan.

Donors: Louis & Helen Padnos Foundation; Louis Padnos Iron and Metal Co.; Two Dods Dancing LP; Jeffrey S. Padnos; Douglas B. Padnos; Park Avenue Partners LP.

Foundation type: Independent foundation.

Financial data (yr. ended 05/31/14): Assets, $6,104,135 (M); expenditures, $364,878; qualifying distributions, $318,177; giving activities include $315,467 for 45 grants (high: $80,000; low: $100).

Fields of interest: Arts and culture; Arts councils; Art museums; Education; Elementary and secondary education; Higher education; Foundations; Nonprofits; Hospital care; Specialty hospital care; Hospice care; Diseases and conditions; Cancers;

Housing development; Judaism; Human services; Youth services.

Type of support: Regranting.

Limitations: Applications not accepted. Giving primarily in MI, with emphasis on Grand Rapids and Holland. No grants to individuals.

Application information: Unsolicited requests for funds not accepted.

Officers and Trustees: Jeffrey S. Padnos, Pres. and Trustee; Shelley E. Padnos, Secy. and Trustee; Mitchell W. Padnos, Treas. and Trustee; Cynthia B. Padnos; Daniel P. Padnos; Douglas B. Padnos; William R. Padnos.

EIN: 383476218

4530
Rose and Lawrence C. Page, Sr. Family Charitable Foundation

(formerly Lawrence C. Page, Sr. Family Charitable Foundation)
c/o Mr. David C. Stone, Bodman LLP
201 W. Big Beaver, Ste. 500
Troy, MI   48084-4160

Established in 2007 in Michigan.

Donors: L.C. Page Char Tr f/b/o Page Fam Char; Lawrence C. Page, Sr.

Foundation type: Independent foundation.

Financial data (yr. ended 12/31/13): Assets, $4,196,832 (M); expenditures, $273,099; qualifying distributions, $191,707; giving activities include $188,000 for 15 grants (high: $50,000; low: $1,500).

Fields of interest: Elementary and secondary education; Human services.

Limitations: Applications not accepted. Giving primarily in MI.

Application information: Unsolicited requests for funds not accepted.

Directors: Marlene Holly Kunick; Michael N. Rice; David Stone.

EIN: 260367507

4531
Paine Family Foundation

c/o Northwest Investment and Trust
P.O. Box 1380
Traverse City, MI   49685-1380
Contact: Carol Paine-McGovern, Pres.
Application address: c/o Northwestern Bank, 625 S. Garfield Ave., Traverse City, MI 49686, tel.: (616) 285-0409

Established in 1991 in Michigan.

Donors: Martha L. Paine; G. William Paine; Carol Paine-McGovern.

Foundation type: Independent foundation.

Financial data (yr. ended 12/31/13): Assets, $6,572,512 (M); expenditures, $315,678; qualifying distributions, $280,635; giving activities include $256,529 for 38 grants (high: $27,722; low: $1,000).

Fields of interest: Historic preservation; Education; Higher education; Nonprofits; Health; Human services.

Type of support: General support; Endowments; Scholarships; Regranting.

Limitations: Applications accepted. Giving primarily in MI, with emphasis on Manistee, Ludington, Scottville, and Traverse City; giving also in Boulder, CO.

Application information:
  Initial approach: Proposal
  Deadline(s): None

Officers: Carol Paine-McGovern, Pres.; G. William Paine, V.P.; Martha L. Paine, Secy.-Treas.

EIN: 382996404

4532
Pappas Foundation, Inc.

30301 Northwestern Hwy., Ste. 200
Farmington Hills, MI   48334

Established in 1997 in Michigan.

Donor: Norman A. Pappas.

Foundation type: Independent foundation.

Financial data (yr. ended 12/31/14): Assets, $2,547,384 (M); gifts received, $384,715; expenditures, $210,785; qualifying distributions, $209,852; giving activities include $209,852 for 32 grants.

Fields of interest: Education; Religion; Sports and recreation.

Limitations: Applications not accepted. Giving primarily in MI. No grants to individuals.

Application information: Contributes only to pre-selected organizations.

Directors: Norman A. Pappas; Susan L. Pappas; Sydell Pappas.

EIN: 383386198

4533
Pardee Cancer Treatment Fund of Bay County

c/o County Michigan
P.O. Box 541
Bay City, MI   48707-0541   (989) 891-8815
Contact: Carol Wells

Donor: Elsa U. Pardee Foundation.

Foundation type: Operating foundation.

Financial data (yr. ended 09/30/13): Assets, $0 (M); gifts received, $164,581; expenditures, $203,082; qualifying distributions, $186,276; giving activities include $186,276 for grants.

Purpose and activities: Financial assistance provided to help pay medical bills of cancer patients who are residents of Bay County, Michigan.

Fields of interest: Health.

Type of support: Grants to individuals.

Limitations: Applications accepted. Giving limited to residents of Bay County, MI.

Publications: Annual report.

Application information: Application form required.
  Initial approach: Letter
  Deadline(s): None
  Board meeting date(s): Varies

Officers: Pastor Andreas Teich, Pres.; George Heron, V.P.; Dennis R. Geno, Secy.; Walter G. Szostak, Treas.

Directors: Kim Bejcek; Aaron Madzior; Cathleen Schell; Richard Steele; Carol VanderHarst.

Number of staff: 1 part-time professional.

EIN: 382877951

4534
Pardee Cancer Treatment Fund of Gratiot County

315 E. Warwick Dr., Ste. C
Alma, MI   48801-1014   9894661652
Contact: Lala Threloff

Donor: Elsa U. Pardee Foundation.

Foundation type: Operating foundation.

Financial data (yr. ended 09/30/14): Assets, $0 (M); gifts received, $195,865; expenditures, $201,291; qualifying distributions, $182,515; giving activities include $182,515 for 8+ grants.

Fields of interest: Hospital care; Diseases and conditions; Cancers.

Type of support: Research.

Limitations: Applications not accepted. Giving primarily in Gratiot County, MI.

Application information: Contributes only to pre-selected organizations.

Officers: Chuck Fortino, Chair.; Tom Steere, Vice-Chair.; Dale Nester, Secy.; Becky Hirschman, Treas.

Directors: Rick Beracy; Shelly Betancourt; Nancy Fenn; Topher Goggin; Mick Koutz; Jamey Seals; Bernard Siler; Brad Vibber; Robin Whitmore.

EIN: 383532130

4535
Anna Paulina Foundation

3400 W. Bristol Rd.
Flint, MI   48507-3112

Established in 1961 in Michigan.

Donors: Albert J. Koegel; Sunset Hills Assn.; Kathryn Koegel; John Koegel; Anne Rocco; Jane Koegel.

Foundation type: Independent foundation.

Financial data (yr. ended 12/31/13): Assets, $16,689,890 (M); gifts received, $555,325; expenditures, $454,377; qualifying distributions, $414,210; giving activities include $414,210 for 82 grants (high: $251,000; low: $100).

Fields of interest: Arts and culture; Education; Nonprofits; Christianity; Human services.

Type of support: Regranting.

Limitations: Applications not accepted. Giving primarily in the Genesee County, MI, area. No grants to individuals.

Application information: Contributes only to pre-selected organizations. Unsolicited applications not considered.
  Board meeting date(s): 3rd Wed. in June, annually

Officers: John C. Koegel, Pres.; Elizabeth M. Neithercut, V.P.; Jeffry D. Rocco, Secy.; Albert J. Koegel, Treas.

Trustees: Barbara L. Koegel; Jane Koegel; Kathryn Koegel; Lisa A. Koegel; Edward J. Neithercut; Mark E. Neithercut; Anne Rocco.

EIN: 386061335

4536
Peak Street Foundation

1985 Lalonde Rd.
East Jordan, MI   49727-9454   2319461722

Established in 1997 in Michigan.

Donors: Barbara Malpass; Frederick F. Malpass.

Foundation type: Independent foundation.

Financial data (yr. ended 12/31/14): Assets, $4,179,549; expenditures, $216,973; qualifying distributions, $186,300.

Fields of interest: Foundations.

Limitations: Applications not accepted. Giving limited to MI, with emphasis on East Jordan. No grants to individuals.

Application information: Contributes only to pre-selected organizations.

Officers: Barbara J. Malpass, Pres.; Frederick F. Malpass, Secy.-Treas.
EIN: 383350363

4537
The Karen & Drew Peslar Foundation
401 S. Old Woodward Ave., Ste. 433
Birmingham, MI 48009-6613

Established in 1997 in Michigan.
Donors: Drew Peslar; Karen Peslar.
Foundation type: Independent foundation.
Financial data (yr. ended 12/31/14): Assets, $6,625,227; expenditures, $417,990; qualifying distributions, $327,268.
Purpose and activities: Giving primarily for education, religion, human services, and arts and culture.
Fields of interest: Arts and culture; Museums; Secondary education; Christianity; Human services; Youth development.
Limitations: Applications not accepted. Giving limited to MI. No grants to individuals.
Application information: Contributes only to pre-selected organizations.
Officers and Directors: Drew Peslar, Pres.; Samantha Durokovic, Secy. and Director; Karen Peslar, Treas. and Director; Virginia Webster-Smith, Exec. Dir.
EIN: 383374272

4538
Phantom Foundation
113 W. Michigan Ave., Ste. 301
Jackson, MI 49201-1340

Established in 1998 in Michigan.
Donor: William B. Holmes.
Foundation type: Independent foundation.
Financial data (yr. ended 12/31/13): Assets, $892,257 (M); gifts received, $29,963; expenditures, $186,983; qualifying distributions, $185,000; giving activities include $185,000 for 5 grants (high: $125,000; low: $5,000).
Fields of interest: Health; Hospice care; Human services.
Type of support: General support.
Limitations: Applications not accepted. Giving limited to MI. No grants to individuals.
Application information: Unsolicited requests for funds not accepted.
Officers: William B. Holmes, Pres.; Wendy B. Holmes, Secy.-Treas.
Directors: Allison Holmes; Raleigh Holmes; Whitney Holmes.
EIN: 383353208

4539
Pilgrim Foundation
c/o S. Gunnar Klarr
1530 N. Cranbrook Rd.
Bloomfield Village, MI 48301-2314

Established in 1996 in Michigan.
Donors: Louise S. Klarr; S. Gunnar Klarr; Salwil Foundation.
Foundation type: Independent foundation.
Financial data (yr. ended 12/31/13): Assets, $5,476,583 (M); expenditures, $287,583;

qualifying distributions, $250,002; giving activities include $250,002 for 1 grant.
Fields of interest: Christianity; Human services; Basic and emergency aid; International development; Low-income and poor people.
Type of support: General support.
Limitations: Applications not accepted. Giving primarily in MI and NC. No grants to individuals.
Application information: Contributes only to pre-selected organizations.
Trustees: Louise S. Klarr; S. Gunnar Klarr.
EIN: 367159136

4540
Murray C. and Ina C. Pitt Charitable Trust
2000 Town Ctr., Ste. 1350
Southfield, MI 48075-1252

Established in 1995 in Michigan.
Donor: Murray C. Pitt.
Foundation type: Independent foundation.
Financial data (yr. ended 11/30/13): Assets, $1,628,643 (M); gifts received, $460,734; expenditures, $485,442; qualifying distributions, $310,918; giving activities include $310,248 for 37 grants (high: $201,000; low: $75).
Fields of interest: Arts and culture; Education; Elementary and secondary education; Higher education; Foundations; Nonprofits; Diseases and conditions; Human services.
Type of support: Research; Research and evaluation; Regranting.
Limitations: Applications not accepted. No grants to individuals.
Application information: Unsolicited requests for funds not accepted.
Officers: Murray C. Pitt, Pres.; Ina C. Pitt, V.P.
Director: Erin R. Frankel.
EIN: 383268352

4541
Albert and Doris Pitt Foundation
8019 Concord Rd.
Huntington Woods, MI 48070-1303

Established in 1992 in Michigan.
Donor: Doris Pitt.
Foundation type: Independent foundation.
Financial data (yr. ended 12/31/13): Assets, $1,834,007 (M); expenditures, $295,177; qualifying distributions, $279,600; giving activities include $279,600 for 46 grants (high: $20,000; low: $100).
Fields of interest: Nonprofits; Individual liberties; Human services.
Type of support: Regranting.
Limitations: Applications not accepted. Giving primarily in MI. No grants to individuals.
Application information: Unsolicited requests for funds not accepted.
Officers: Michael L. Pitt, Pres.; Janice B. Buchanan, Secy.; Peggy Pitt, Treas.
EIN: 383080424

4542
Plym Foundation
P.O. Box 906
Niles, MI 49120-0906
Application address: c/o James F. Keenan, 211 W. Washington St., South Bend, IN 46601, tel.: (574) 287-5977

Established in 1952 in Michigan.
Donor: Mrs. Francis J. Plym†.
Foundation type: Independent foundation.
Financial data (yr. ended 12/31/13): Assets, $6,223,410 (M); expenditures, $429,733; qualifying distributions, $334,900; giving activities include $300,000 for 38 grants (high: $50,000; low: $500).
Purpose and activities: Giving primarily for higher education and human services.
Fields of interest: Education; Higher education; Nonprofits; Public affairs; Community and economic development; Human services.
Type of support: Capital and infrastructure; Matching grants; Regranting; Program development.
Application information: Application form required.
Initial approach: Letter
Copies of proposal: 1
Deadline(s): None
Board meeting date(s): May
Officers and Trustees: J. Eric Plym, Pres.; James F. Keenan, Secy. and Trustee; Kate Campbell; John E. Plym, Jr.; Linda Plym; Robert Randall Plym.
EIN: 386069680

4543
Porter Foundation
1125 Santa Cruz Dr., S.E.
Grand Rapids, MI 49506-3468 (616) 459-9531
Contact: Margaret Beusse, Pres.

Donors: Burke E. Porter Machinery Co.; Burke Porter Trust.
Foundation type: Independent foundation.
Financial data (yr. ended 06/30/14): Assets, $3,091,284 (M); gifts received, $75,000; expenditures, $178,513; qualifying distributions, $153,000; giving activities include $153,000 for 14 grants (high: $45,000; low: $1,000).
Fields of interest: Arts and culture; Education; Youth development.
Type of support: General support; Matching grants.
Limitations: Applications accepted. Giving primarily in Grand Rapids, MI. Generally prefers programs with no religious affiliation.
Application information:
Initial approach: Letter, including letter from school counselor
Deadline(s): None
Officers and Directors: Margaret Beusse, Pres.and Secy. and Director; Heather Beusse, V.P.; Blake Beusse, Treas.
EIN: 386118663

4544
The Power Foundation
c/o James C. Melvin, Secy.
136 E. Michigan Ave., Ste. 1201
Kalamazoo, MI 49007-3918

Established in 1967 in Michigan.
Donors: Eugene B. Power†; Sadye H. Power†; Philip H. Power.

Foundation type: Independent foundation.
Financial data (yr. ended 12/31/13): Assets, $9,859,265 (M); gifts received, $300,000; expenditures, $524,482; qualifying distributions, $478,769; giving activities include $407,500 for 17 grants (high: $300,000; low: $500).
Purpose and activities: Giving for higher education, the arts, social services, and to natural resource preservation and enhancement.
Fields of interest: Arts and culture; Education; Higher education; Human services.
Type of support: General support; Continuing support; Annual campaigns; Capital campaigns; Capital and infrastructure; Research.
Limitations: Applications not accepted. Giving primarily in MI, with emphasis on Ann Arbor.
Application information: Unsolicited requests for funds not accepted.
Officers and Trustees: Philip H. Power, Pres. and Trustee; Kathleen K. Power, V.P. and Trustee; James C. Melvin, Secy. and Trustee; David S. Kruis, Treas.; James S. Hilboldt.
EIN: 386119490

4545
The Powers Family Foundation
4145 Embassy Dr. S.E.
Grand Rapids, MI   49546-2418

Established in 1997 in Michigan.
Donor: Robert J. Powers.
Foundation type: Independent foundation.
Financial data (yr. ended 12/31/13): Assets, $655,354 (M); gifts received, $373,866; expenditures, $232,011; qualifying distributions, $229,482; giving activities include $228,640 for 9 grants (high: $180,000; low: $240).
Purpose and activities: Giving primarily for Christian agencies and churches, for ministry support.
Fields of interest: Education; Religion; Human services.
Limitations: Applications not accepted. Giving primarily in MI. No grants to individuals.
Application information: Unsolicited requests for funds not accepted.
Officers: Robert J. Powers, Pres. and Treas.; Carol A. Powers, Secy.
Directors: Janet L. Jepsen; Sharon C. Meerman; Linda A. Powers; Lisa M. Wilbur.
EIN: 383377775

4546
The Robert E. Price Foundation, Inc.
P.O. Box 605
Adrian, MI   49221-0605   (517) 265-6160
Contact: Robert E. Price, Pres.

Established in 1995 in Michigan.
Donor: Robert E. Price.
Foundation type: Independent foundation.
Financial data (yr. ended 12/31/13): Assets, $3,341,626 (M); gifts received, $209,344; expenditures, $133,920; qualifying distributions, $133,920; giving activities include $133,900 for 14 grants (high: $35,000; low: $1,400).
Purpose and activities: Giving primarily for education.
Fields of interest: Orchestral music; Elementary and secondary education; Higher education; Undergraduate education; Cancers; Youth development.

Limitations: Applications accepted. Giving primarily in Adrian, MI. No grants to individuals.
Application information:
   Initial approach: Proposal
   Deadline(s): None
Officers: Robert E. Price, Pres.; Henry E. Mistele, Secy.
EIN: 383247629

4547
Ran Family Foundation
1425 Clarendon Rd.
Bloomfield Hills, MI   48302-2604

Established in 2000 in Michigan.
Donor: Gary L. Ran.
Foundation type: Independent foundation.
Financial data (yr. ended 08/31/13): Assets, $18,902 (M); gifts received, $205,850; expenditures, $187,085; qualifying distributions, $187,085; giving activities include $186,440 for 26 + grants (high: $80,095).
Fields of interest: Arts and culture; Education; Judaism.
Limitations: Applications not accepted. Giving primarily in MI. No grants to individuals.
Application information: Unsolicited requests for funds not accepted.
Officers: Gary L. Ran, Pres. and Treas.; Rhonda S. Ran, V.P. and Secy.
Trustee: Sheila Stone.
EIN: 383569240

4548
Milton M. Ratner Foundation
P.O. Box 250628
Franklin, MI   48025-0628
Contact: Therese M. Thorn, Treas.
E-mail: ratner_foundation@sbcglobal.net

Established in 1968 in Michigan.
Donor: Milton M. Ratner‡.
Foundation type: Independent foundation.
Financial data (yr. ended 08/31/13): Assets, $7,401,624 (M); expenditures, $414,178; qualifying distributions, $343,221; giving activities include $266,500 for 36 grants (high: $20,000; low: $1,000).
Purpose and activities: Giving primarily for higher education, and health and human services for children, families, and the elderly. Giving also for research to fight heart disease, for aid and training for the blind, and to aid physically handicapped children.
Fields of interest: Education; Higher education; Hospital care; Diseases and conditions; Heart and circulatory system diseases; People with vision impairments.
Type of support: General support; Matching grants; Individual development; Continuing support; Capital and infrastructure; Equipment; Endowments; Program development; Research; Research and evaluation; Scholarships.
Limitations: Applications accepted. Giving primarily in GA and MI. No grants to individuals.
Publications: Application guidelines; Grants list.
Application information: Council of Michigan Foundations Common Grant Application Form accepted.
   Initial approach: Letter no more than 3 pages
   Copies of proposal: 1

Deadline(s): Aug. 31
Board meeting date(s): Oct.
Final notification: Dec. 31
Officers and Trustees: Mary Jo Rossen, Pres. and Trustee; Charles R. McDonald, V.P. and Secy. and Trustee; Therese M. Thorn, Treas. and Trustee.
Agent: Meadowbrook Investment Advisors.
Number of staff: None.
EIN: 386160330

4549
Edward F. Redies Foundation Inc.
P.O. Box 411
Saline, MI   48176-0411   (517) 467-2042
E-mail: edredies@yahoo.com

Established in 1981 in Michigan.
Donor: R&B Machine Tool Co.
Foundation type: Company-sponsored foundation.
Financial data (yr. ended 12/31/13): Assets, $4,674,420 (M); expenditures, $273,887; qualifying distributions, $220,250; giving activities include $215,000 for 27 grants (high: $80,000; low: $1,000).
Purpose and activities: The foundation supports hospitals and parks and organizations involved with education, child welfare, and human services.
Fields of interest: Education; Public affairs; Human services.
Type of support: Annual campaigns; Capital campaigns; Capital and infrastructure; Equipment; Scholarships.
Limitations: Applications accepted. Giving primarily in the greater Washtenaw County, MI, area. No grants to individuals.
Publications: Application guidelines.
Application information: Application form required.
   Initial approach: Letter
   Copies of proposal: 1
   Deadline(s): Mar. 31
Officers: R. Edward Redies, Pres.; Karen Redies, Secy.-Treas.
Directors: Paul Bunten; Michelle Redies; Robert D. Redies; Thomas D. Redies; William D. Redies; Milton Stemen; Dennis Valenti.
EIN: 382391326

4550
The Riley Foundation
P.O Box 75000, MC 7874
Detroit, MI   48275-0001

Established in 1998 in Michigan.
Donors: George Riley; Dolores Riley.
Foundation type: Independent foundation.
Financial data (yr. ended 09/30/13): Assets, $1,554,490 (M); expenditures, $337,744; qualifying distributions, $323,442; giving activities include $281,019 for 17 grants (high: $100,000; low: $500).
Purpose and activities: Giving primarily to a public television station, as well as for health organizations and human services.
Fields of interest: Cancers; Television; Public affairs; Catholicism; Human services.
Limitations: Applications not accepted. Giving primarily in MI, with emphasis on Wixom and Farmington Hills. No grants or loans to individuals.
Application information: Contributes only to pre-selected organizations.
Trustees: Kimberly A. Fouts; Comerica Bank.

Board Members: Daniel G. Riley; George K. Riley; William D. Riley.
EIN: 383439851

4551
River City Foundation
3860 Rector Ave. N.E.
Rockford, MI 49341

Established in 1989 in Michigan.
Donors: Kenneth Betz; Judy Betz.
Foundation type: Independent foundation.
Financial data (yr. ended 11/30/14): Assets, $2,740,857; gifts received, $20; expenditures, $156,220; qualifying distributions, $140,520.
Fields of interest: Arts and culture; Hospital care; Housing development; Christianity; Human services.
Type of support: General support.
Limitations: Applications not accepted. Giving primarily in MI. No grants to individuals.
Application information: Contributes only to pre-selected organizations.
Officers: Kenneth Betz, Pres.; Judy Betz, Secy.
Directors: Anne Kittendorf; Heidi Thornton.
EIN: 382966996

4552
Roscommon County Community Foundation
701 Lake St.
P.O. Box 824
Roscommon, MI 48653 (989) 275-3112
Contact: Suzanne Luck, Exec. Dir.
FAX: (989) 275-3112; E-mail: info@myrccf.org;
Grant inquiry tel.: (989) 275-3112; Main
URL: http://
www.roscommoncountycommunityfoundation.org
Facebook: https://www.facebook.com/myrccf
RSS feed: http://myrccf.org/feed
Twitter: https://www.twitter.com/myRCCF

Established in 2001 in Michigan.
Donors: Rex Gillen†; Arlene Gillen†.
Foundation type: Community foundation.
Financial data (yr. ended 12/31/13): Assets, $7,053,543 (M); gifts received, $369,417; expenditures, $449,128; giving activities include $157,585 for grants, and $98,500 for 64 grants to individuals.
Purpose and activities: The foundation seeks to improve the quality of life for all present and future residents of Roscommon County by: 1) providing stewardship and leadership; 2) attracting and holding permanent endowment funds from a wide range of donors; and 3) by making grants of the income from its permanent endowment funds. The foundation is committed to protecting the personal investments that all residents have made, demonstrating concern for youth and many issues affecting their future, recognizing the value and importance of the natural environment now and for the future, and improving and building the future for families.
Fields of interest: Arts and culture; Arts education; Education; Child educational development; Graduate and professional education; Basic and remedial instruction; Cooperative education; Domesticated animals; Animal welfare; Animal training; HIV/AIDS; Missing persons; Police agencies; Search and rescue; Agriculture; Community and economic development; Community

service; Christianity; Baseball and softball; Basketball; American football; Golf; European football; School athletics; Human services; Child welfare; Child care; Scouting programs.
Type of support: Endowments; Scholarships; Public engagement and education; Capacity-building and technical assistance; Volunteer development; Research.
Limitations: Applications accepted. Giving limited to Roscommon County, MI. No support for religious or for-profit organizations. No grants to individuals (except for scholarships), or for endowment funds, administrative costs of fund-raising campaigns, routine operating expenses, or debt retirement.
Publications: Application guidelines; Annual report; Annual report (including application guidelines); Financial statement; Grants list; Informational brochure; Newsletter.
Application information: Visit foundation web site for application cover sheet and guidelines. Application form required.
  Initial approach: Submit application
  Copies of proposal: 8
  Deadline(s): Apr. 30 and Oct. 31
  Board meeting date(s): Varies
  Final notification: 2 months
Officers and Trustees: Ron Duquette, Chair. and Trustee; Tim Scherer, Vice-Chair. and Trustee; Mary Fry, Pres. and C.E.O. and Trustee; Susan Tyer, Secy. and Trustee; John Sinnaeve, Treas. and Trustee; Suzanne Luck, Exec. Dir.; Dave Harned; Matt Jernigan; Sonia Lake; Kathleen Lawrence, Jr.; Thomas Moreau; Greg Rogers.
Number of staff: 1 full-time professional; 2 part-time support.
EIN: 383612480

4553
Rottman Family Charitable Foundation
(formerly Fritz and Carol Rottman Charitable Foundation)
c/o Carol Rottman
1911 Thorn Run Ct. S.E.
Grand Rapids, MI 49546-8256

Established in 2000 in Michigan.
Donors: Francis M. Rottman; Carol J. Rottman.
Foundation type: Independent foundation.
Financial data (yr. ended 12/31/13): Assets, $3,477,856 (M); expenditures, $271,106; qualifying distributions, $205,902; giving activities include $182,000 for 26 grants (high: $36,000; low: $1,000).
Fields of interest: Education; Religion; Human rights.
Limitations: Applications not accepted. Giving primarily in MI. No grants to individuals.
Application information: Unsolicited requests for funds not accepted.
Officers: Carol Rottman, Pres. and Secy.-Treas.; Barbara Hoogenboom, Co-Secy.
Director: Doug Rottman.
EIN: 383566006

4554
The Steven F. and Melinda I. Roznowski Foundation
45 E. Grand River Rd.
Williamston, MI 48895-9343
Contact: Steven Roznowski, Pres.

Established in 2007 in Michigan.
Donors: Steven Roznowski; Melinda Roznowski.
Foundation type: Independent foundation.
Financial data (yr. ended 11/30/13): Assets, $1,644,538 (M); gifts received, $400,000; expenditures, $326,399; qualifying distributions, $313,600; giving activities include $313,600 for 9 grants (high: $250,000; low: $100).
Fields of interest: Arts education; Undergraduate education.
Limitations: Applications accepted. Giving primarily in MI.
Application information: Application form required.
  Initial approach: Letter
  Deadline(s): None
Officers: Steven Roznowski, Pres.; Melinda Roznowski, Secy.-Treas.
EIN: 261560327

4555
James R. Ryan Family Foundation
13313 E. Kingswood
Delton, MI 49046-9456

Established in 1999 in Michigan.
Donor: James Raymond Ryan†.
Foundation type: Independent foundation.
Financial data (yr. ended 12/31/13): Assets, $5,467,083 (M); gifts received, $5,132; expenditures, $306,857; qualifying distributions, $256,975; giving activities include $255,500 for 8 grants (high: $99,500; low: $1,000).
Fields of interest: Elementary and secondary education; Health; Diseases and conditions.
Type of support: General support; Research; Scholarships.
Limitations: Applications not accepted. Giving primarily in MI, with emphasis on Kalamazoo County. No grants to individuals.
Application information: Unsolicited requests for funds not accepted.
Officers: Thomas G. Ryan, Pres.; Debra Ryan, V.P.
Directors: Linda Bowman; Thomas M. Ryan.
EIN: 383495184

4556
Ghassan and Manal Saab Foundation
(formerly Ghassan M. Saab Foundation)
3407 Torrey Rd.
Flint, MI 48507-0718
E-mail: gmsaab@sgcs.net

Established in 1998 in Michigan.
Donor: Ghassan M. Saab.
Foundation type: Operating foundation.
Financial data (yr. ended 12/31/13): Assets, $2,864,632 (M); expenditures, $340,174; qualifying distributions, $331,836; giving activities include $323,500 for 19 grants (high: $200,000; low: $500).
Fields of interest: Arts and culture; Human services; International relations.
International interests: Lebanon; Middle East.
Limitations: Applications not accepted. Giving primarily in the U.S.; some giving in Lebanon. No grants to individuals.
Application information: Unsolicited requests for funds not accepted.
Directors: Ghassan M. Saab; Khalil Saab; Nadim Saab.

Number of staff: None.
EIN: 383416517

4557
Edward J. Sackerson Charitable Foundation
P.O. Box 716
Escanaba, MI 49829-0716 (906) 786-0220
Contact: Matt N. Smith Jr., Tr.

Established in 1997 in Michigan.
Donor: Edward J. Sackerson.
Foundation type: Independent foundation.
Financial data (yr. ended 12/31/13): Assets, $4,770,265 (M); expenditures, $240,881; qualifying distributions, $215,963; giving activities include $215,963 for 39 grants (high: $119,178; low: $500).
Fields of interest: Elementary and secondary education; Community and economic development; Christianity; Human services; Youth development.
Limitations: Applications accepted. Giving primarily in MI. No grants to individuals.
Application information:
    Initial approach: Letter
    Deadline(s): None
Trustees: Paul Kangas; Gary Olsen; Helen A. Sackerson; Matt N. Smith, Jr.
EIN: 383351811

4558
The Schalon Foundation
4418 Tanglewood Trail
Saint Joseph, MI 49085-9686
Application address: c/o Susan Schalon, 5694 Forest Glen Dr., Ada, MI 49301, tel.: (616) 318-9555

Established in 1997 in Michigan.
Donors: Edward I. Schalon†; Marcella J. Schalon.
Foundation type: Independent foundation.
Financial data (yr. ended 12/31/14): Assets, $4,925,963; expenditures, $421,517; qualifying distributions, $395,100.
Fields of interest: Arts and culture; Opera; Orchestral music; Human services.
Type of support: Capital and infrastructure.
Limitations: Applications accepted. Giving primarily in MI, with emphasis on St. Joseph. No grants to individuals.
Application information: Application form required.
    Initial approach: Letter
    Deadline(s): Dec. 1
Officers and Directors: Marcella J. Schalon, Pres. and Director; Susan K. Schalon, Secy. and Director; Scott Schalon, Treas. and Director.
EIN: 383341098

4559
The Art and Mary Schmuckal Family Foundation
6004 E. Gallivan Rd.
Cedar, MI 49621 (231) 935-1470
Contact: Evelyn K. Richardson, Secy.

Established in 1999 in Michigan.
Donors: Arthur M. Schmuckal; Schmuckal Land Co.
Foundation type: Independent foundation.
Financial data (yr. ended 06/30/14): Assets, $6,235,475 (M); gifts received, $593,642;

expenditures, $368,881; qualifying distributions, $335,324; giving activities include $328,100 for 28 grants (high: $78,000; low: $600).
Purpose and activities: Giving primarily to enhance the well-being of children, to strengthen the residents economically, and for community development.
Fields of interest: Graduate and professional education; Foundations; Community health care; Hospice care; Community and economic development; Theology; Human services; Children; Homeless people.
Type of support: Annual campaigns; Capital campaigns; Program development; Scholarships.
Limitations: Applications accepted. Giving primarily in Traverse City, MI.
Application information: Application form required.
    Initial approach: Letter
    Deadline(s): None
Officers: Barbara F. Benson, Pres.; Donald A. Schmuckal, V.P.; Evelyn K. Richardson, Secy.; Paul M. Schmuckal, Treas.
Directors: Andrew Benson; Jacob Richardson; Kevin P. Schmuckal.
EIN: 383498264

4560
The Schwarcz Foundation
26140 Raine St.
Oak Park, MI 48237-1024

Established in 2006 in Michigan.
Donors: Jack Schwarcz; Gail Schwarcz.
Foundation type: Independent foundation.
Financial data (yr. ended 12/31/12): Assets, $38,082 (M); gifts received, $144,700; expenditures, $143,131; qualifying distributions, $143,131; giving activities include $143,082 for 16 grants (high: $49,365; low: $500).
Purpose and activities: Grants awarded to promote Orthodox Jewish education and lifestyle.
Fields of interest: Graduate and professional education; Orthodox Judaism; Theology.
Limitations: Applications not accepted. Giving primarily in Oak Park and Southfield, MI; some giving also in Brooklyn, NY. No grants to individuals.
Application information: Contributes only to pre-selected organizations.
Directors: Aiden Gutis; Gail Schwarcz; Jack Schwarcz; Joseph P. Schwarcz.
EIN: 364564826

4561
John Scully Foundation
P.O. Box 75000
Detroit, MI 48275-7874
Application address: c/o Brenda Pearson, 60 S. 6th St., Ste. 2550, Minneapolis, MN 55402-4406, tel.: (612) 215-3603

Established in 2002 in South Dakota.
Donor: John Scully.
Foundation type: Independent foundation.
Financial data (yr. ended 12/31/13): Assets, $2,378,813 (M); expenditures, $276,997; qualifying distributions, $177,641; giving activities include $173,000 for 2 grants (high: $131,000; low: $42,000).
Fields of interest: Undergraduate education; Graduate and professional education; Theology.
Type of support: General support.

Limitations: Applications accepted. Giving primarily in IN, NH and SD. No grants to individuals.
Application information: Application form required.
    Initial approach: Letter
    Deadline(s): None
Trustee: Comerica Bank.
EIN: 266003516

4562
The SEED Foundation
P.O. Box 1243
Walled Lake, MI 48390-5243

Established in 2006 in Michigan.
Donor: Deborah A. Miesel.
Foundation type: Independent foundation.
Financial data (yr. ended 12/31/14): Assets, $25,766 (M); gifts received, $232,000; expenditures, $238,661; qualifying distributions, $238,000; giving activities include $238,000 for 10 grants (high: $75,000; low: $5,000).
Fields of interest: Arts and culture; Orchestral music; Religion; Human services.
Limitations: Applications not accepted. Giving primarily in Detroit, MI. No grants to individuals.
Application information: Contributes only to pre-selected organizations.
Officer: Deborah A. Miesel, Pres.
EIN: 205456221

4563
The Sehn Foundation
3515 Brookside Dr., Ste. A
Bloomfield Hills, MI 48302-2911

Established in 1968 in Michigan.
Donors: Francis J. Sehn; James T. Sehn; Barbara S. Day; Carole S. Laramie; Kathleen S. Lehman; Celestine Sehn.
Foundation type: Independent foundation.
Financial data (yr. ended 12/31/13): Assets, $3,056,268 (M); expenditures, $410,324; qualifying distributions, $379,099; giving activities include $359,270 for 25 grants (high: $200,000; low: $300).
Fields of interest: Education; Higher education; Graduate and professional education; Hospital care; Catholicism; Theology; Human services.
Type of support: General support.
Limitations: Applications not accepted. Giving primarily in MI. No grants to individuals.
Application information: Contributes only to pre-selected organizations.
Officers: Francis J. Sehn, Pres.; Barbara S. Day, Mgr.; Carole S. Laramie, Mgr.
EIN: 386160784

4564
The Seligman Family Foundation
1 Towne Sq., Ste. 1913
Southfield, MI 48076-3733

Established in 1991 in Michigan.
Donors: Irving Seligman; Scott Seligman; Kiss Investment Co., LLC; Sandra Seligman; Seth Meltzer; Irving R. Seligman Trust.
Foundation type: Independent foundation.
Financial data (yr. ended 12/31/13): Assets, $310,030 (M); expenditures, $256,439; qualifying

distributions, $256,254; giving activities include $256,254 for 34 grants (high: $40,000; low: $100).
Purpose and activities: Giving primarily to museums and to Jewish federated giving programs.
Fields of interest: Arts and culture; Art museums; Ethnic museums; Nonprofits; Human services.
Type of support: Regranting.
Limitations: Applications not accepted. Giving primarily in CA, FL, MI, and NY. No grants to individuals.
Application information: Contributes only to pre-selected organizations.
Officers and Trustees: Scott Seligman, Pres. and Trustee; Sandra Seligman, Secy. and Trustee; Seth Meltzer, Treas. and Trustee; Stephanie M. Zimmerman.
EIN: 382972397

4565
Serra Family Foundation
3118 E. Hill Rd.
Grand Blanc, MI   48439   (810) 694-1720
Contact: Lynne Parker, Treas.

Established in 1997 in Michigan.
Donors: Albert Serra; Lois Serra.
Foundation type: Independent foundation.
Financial data (yr. ended 12/31/13): Assets, $4,683,676 (M); expenditures, $235,683; qualifying distributions, $200,000; giving activities include $200,000 for 30 grants (high: $30,000; low: $1,000).
Fields of interest: Higher education; Natural resources; Health; Christianity.
Type of support: General support.
Limitations: Applications accepted. Giving primarily in MI.
Application information: Application form required.
Initial approach: Letter
Deadline(s): None
Officers and Directors: Amy Albright, V.P. and Director; Ann Lowney, V.P. and Director; Mary McMahon, V.P. and Director; Alice Serra Reid, V.P. and Director; Lynne Parker, Treas.
EIN: 383352324

4566
Mickey Shapiro Charitable Trust
31550 Northwestern Hwy., Ste. 200
Farmington Hills, MI   48334-2532

Established in 2003 in Michigan.
Donors: Mickey Shapiro; Asa Shapiro.
Foundation type: Independent foundation.
Financial data (yr. ended 12/31/13): Assets, $571,697 (M); gifts received, $650,000; expenditures, $420,404; qualifying distributions, $417,520; giving activities include $417,520 for 28 grants (high: $105,920; low: $50).
Fields of interest: Museums; Hospice care; Eye diseases; Prostate cancer; Judaism; Human services.
Type of support: Research.
Limitations: Applications not accepted. Giving primarily in MI. No grants to individuals.
Application information: Contributes only to pre-selected organizations.
Trustee: Mickey Shapiro.
Number of staff: None.
EIN: 306068151

4567
The Sherman Family Foundation
25001 River Dr.
Franklin, MI   48025-1172

Established in 2000 in Michigan.
Donors: Max M. and Marjorie S. Fisher Foundation, Inc.; Jane F. Sherman; D. Larry Sherman; Sylvia S. Wolf.
Foundation type: Independent foundation.
Financial data (yr. ended 12/31/13): Assets, $5,211,749 (M); gifts received, $19,558; expenditures, $269,114; qualifying distributions, $223,950; giving activities include $223,950 for 33 grants (high: $40,000; low: $200).
Fields of interest: Arts and culture; Education; Nonprofits; Judaism.
Type of support: Regranting.
Limitations: Applications not accepted. Giving primarily in MI. No grants to individuals.
Application information: Contributes only to pre-selected organizations.
Officers and Directors: D. Larry Sherman, Pres. and Director; Jane Sherman, Secy.-Treas. and Director; David F. Sherman; Scott R. Sherman; Sylvia S. Wolf.
EIN: 383505951

4568
Shiawassee Community Foundation
(formerly Shiawassee Foundation)
217 N. Washington St., Ste. 104
P.O. Box 753
Owosso, MI   48867-0753   (989) 725-1093
Contact: Carol Soule, Exec. Dir.
FAX: (989) 729-1358;
E-mail: shiafdn@michonline.net; Main URL: http://www.shiawasseecommunityfoundation.org
Facebook: http://www.facebook.com/pages/Shiawassee-Community-Foundation/221523204604399?fref=ts

Established in 1995 in Michigan.
Donor: John Northway.
Foundation type: Community foundation.
Financial data (yr. ended 09/30/13): Assets, $5,533,693 (M); gifts received, $400,826; expenditures, $268,702; giving activities include $71,484 for 1+ grant (high: $27,642), and $85,842 for 126 grants to individuals.
Purpose and activities: The mission of the foundation is to enrich the quality of life in Shiawassee County by building permanently endowed funds from a wide range of donors to fund emerging community needs.
Fields of interest: Arts and culture; Education; Higher education; Environment; Health; Community and economic development; Human services.
Type of support: Continuing support; Endowments; Program development; Convening; Curriculum development; Scholarships.
Limitations: Applications accepted. Giving limited to Shiawassee County, MI. No support for religious programs serving specific religious denominations. No grants to individuals (except for designated funds), or for routine operating expenses or expenses for established programs, fundraising drives, capital equipment, computers, video equipment, or vehicles, conference attendance, speakers, salaries, or projects that are primarily cause-related.
Publications: Annual report; Newsletter.
Application information: Upon review of letter of intent, organizations meeting the foundation's

funding and priority guidelines will be invited to submit a full grant application. Application form required.
Initial approach: Telephone
Copies of proposal: 2
Deadline(s): Varies
Board meeting date(s): Varies
Officers and Directors: Donald D. Levi, Chair. and Pres. and Director; Patrick A. Wegman II, V.P. and Director; Catherine Stevenson, Secy. and Director; Vearn Wenzlick, Treas. and Director; Carol Soule, Exec. Dir.; Larry D. Cook; Kevin J. Davis; Jacklyn C. Hurd; Glen T. Merkel; Roger A. Zick.
EIN: 383285624

4569
The Shine Foundation
P.O. Box 451
Zeeland, MI   49464-1085

Established in 2006 in Michigan.
Donors: Jeffrey Mulder; Jeri Mulder.
Foundation type: Independent foundation.
Financial data (yr. ended 12/31/13): Assets, $3,876,707 (M); gifts received, $58,941; expenditures, $443,164; qualifying distributions, $420,067; giving activities include $399,807 for 27 grants (high: $100,000; low: $100).
Fields of interest: Education; Nonprofits; Christianity; Youth services.
Type of support: Regranting.
Limitations: Applications not accepted. Giving primarily in MI. No grants to individuals.
Application information: Contributes only to pre-selected organizations.
Trustees: Jennifer Mesler; Jeffrey Mulder; Jeri Mulder.
EIN: 205940421

4570
Sinai Medical Staff Foundation
2000 Town Ctr., Ste. 1780
Southfield, MI   48075-1313   (248) 353-0150

Established in 2000 in Michigan.
Foundation type: Independent foundation.
Financial data (yr. ended 06/30/13): Assets, $3,620,844 (M); expenditures, $252,781; qualifying distributions, $195,200; giving activities include $195,200 for grants.
Purpose and activities: Support for medical research and dissemination of medical information in Michigan.
Fields of interest: Education; Health; Hospital care; Hospice care; Maternal and perinatal health; Diseases and conditions; Muscular dystrophy; Alzheimer's disease.
Type of support: Research; Research and evaluation.
Limitations: Applications accepted. Giving primarily in MI.
Application information: Application form required.
Initial approach: Proof of Request
Deadline(s): None
Officers: Robert S. Michaels, Pres.; Marc Feld, MD, V.P.; Gaylord D. Alexander, Secy.-Treas.; Robert A. Karbel, Mgr.
EIN: 237078893

4571
Skandalaris Family Foundation
c/o Robert J. Skandalaris
1030 Doris Rd.
Auburn Hills, MI 48326-2613 (248) 220-2004
FAX: (248) 220-2038;
E-mail: info@skandalaris.com; Main URL: http://www.skandalaris.com
College Scholarship tel.: (248) 220-2004, fax: (248) 220-2038

Established in 1997 in Michigan.
Foundation type: Independent foundation.
Financial data (yr. ended 12/31/14): Assets, $301,452; gifts received, $63,428; expenditures, $146,316; qualifying distributions, $145,900.
Purpose and activities: Scholarship awards to a group of students, characterized by their special talents, leadership skills, unselfish ways, strong values and commitment to excellence. Applicants must be high school seniors or undergraduate college students and U.S. citizens.
Fields of interest: Higher education.
Type of support: Student aid.
Limitations: Applications not accepted. Giving primarily to residents of MI. No support for candidates attending trade or foreign schools.
Application information: Unsolicited requests for funds not accepted for new applicants.
Officers: Robert J. Skandalaris, Pres.; Julie A. Skandalaris, V.P.; Kristin M. Puro, Secy.
EIN: 383394567

4572
The Skiles Foundation
c/o Comerica Bank
101 N. Main St.
Ann Arbor, MI 48104
Application address: c/o Ann Skiles McGinty, 1640 Harvard St., Houston, TX 77008, tel.: (713) 862-8408

Established in 1999 in Texas.
Donor: Elwin L. Skiles, Jr.
Foundation type: Independent foundation.
Financial data (yr. ended 12/31/13): Assets, $3,972,719 (M); expenditures, $178,758; qualifying distributions, $141,000; giving activities include $141,000 for 3+ grants (high: $101,000; low: $20,000).
Fields of interest: Arts and culture; Education; Natural resources; Public libraries.
Limitations: Applications accepted. Giving limited to San Antonio, TX. No grants to individuals.
Application information: Application form required.
    Initial approach: Letter
    Deadline(s): None
Officers: Ann Skiles McGinty, Pres. and Treas.; Sarah Skiles Zachry, V.P. and Secy.
EIN: 752845190

4573
Jean M. R. Smith Foundation
P.O. Box 42
Bad Axe, MI 48413-0042 (989) 860-8169
Contact: Rosemary Esch, V.P. and Exec. Dir.

Established in 1997 in Michigan.
Donor: Jean M.R. Smith†.
Foundation type: Independent foundation.

Financial data (yr. ended 12/31/14): Assets, $8,640,856 (M); expenditures, $517,535; qualifying distributions, $441,153; giving activities include $104,600 for 4 grants (high: $100,000; low: $500), and $297,784 for 65 grants to individuals (high: $7,500; low: $489).
Purpose and activities: Scholarships awards for residents of Huron County, Michigan.
Fields of interest: Higher education.
Type of support: Student aid.
Limitations: Applications accepted. Giving limited to residents of Huron County, MI.
Application information: Application form required.
    Initial approach: Proposal
    Deadline(s): Apr. 1
Officers: Robert Sajdak, Pres.; Rosemary Esch, V.P. and Exec. Dir.; John Schwedler, V.P.; Marion Herrington, Secy.; Nancy Smith, Treas.
Director: Richard M. Miettinen.
EIN: 383323030

4574
Speckhard-Knight Charitable Foundation
771 Bogey Ct.
Ann Arbor, MI 48103-8844 (734) 355-9926
Contact: Gerald Knight, Pres.
E-mail: zmjk@comcast.net; Main URL: http://www.speck-knight.org

Established in 1999 in Michigan.
Donors: Gerald C. Knight; Maureen Knight.
Foundation type: Independent foundation.
Financial data (yr. ended 12/31/13): Assets, $5,407,376 (M); expenditures, $284,402; qualifying distributions, $256,831; giving activities include $223,640 for 22 grants (high: $25,000; low: $2,000).
Purpose and activities: The foundation is dedicated to improving the quality of life in Jackson and Washtenaw counties in MI, and aiding environmental efforts in the third world. The foundation strives to assist nonprofit organizations that work in the important areas of adoption, foster care, at risk families and the environment.
Fields of interest: Environment; Human services; Adoption; Foster care.
Type of support: General support; Land acquisitions; Program development.
Limitations: Applications accepted. Giving primarily in MI.
Application information: Application form required.
    Initial approach: Letter
    Copies of proposal: 1
    Deadline(s): Mar., June and Nov.
    Board meeting date(s): Mar., July, and Nov.
Officers: Gerald C. Knight, Pres.; Maureen Knight, V.P.
Number of staff: None.
EIN: 383466344

4575
Springview Foundation
85 E. 8th St., Ste.150
Holland, MI 49423-9570 6162982231
Application address: c/o Virginia Conklin, 1 Haworth Ctr., Holland, MI 49423

Established in 1998 in Michigan.
Donors: Ethelyn L. Haworth; Richard G. Haworth; Richard and Ethelyn Haworth Foundation; Anna Haworth.

Foundation type: Independent foundation.
Financial data (yr. ended 12/31/14): Assets, $5,181,708; expenditures, $233,109; qualifying distributions, $223,160.
Fields of interest: Graduate and professional education; Christianity; Protestantism; Theology; Human services; Family services; Child welfare.
Limitations: Applications accepted. Giving primarily in Grand Rapids and Holland, MI.
Application information: Application form required.
    Initial approach: Contact foundation for application form
    Copies of proposal: 6
    Deadline(s): None
    Board meeting date(s): 1st half of Nov.
Trustees: Sara E. Dykema; Timothy J. Dykema; Anna C. Haworth; Ethelyn L. Haworth; Jennifer L. Haworth; Matthew R. Haworth; Richard G. Haworth.
Number of staff: None.
EIN: 383422204

4576
St. Clair Foundation
P.O. Box 3636
Grand Rapids, MI 49501-3636
Application address: c/o Fifth Third Bank, Attn.: Franklin H. Moore, Jr., 1000 Town Ctr. Dr., Ste. 1400, Southfield, MI 48075 tel.: (248) 603-0604

Established in 1956 in Michigan.
Donors: Alice W. Moore; John Emig Trust A; John Emig Trust B.
Foundation type: Independent foundation.
Financial data (yr. ended 12/31/14): Assets, $2,882,341 (M); expenditures, $179,683; qualifying distributions, $145,435; giving activities include $143,700 for 9 grants (high: $50,300; low: $300).
Fields of interest: Elementary education; Secondary education; Foundations; Hospital care; Public libraries; Public administration; Community and economic development; Human services; Youth development.
Type of support: Program development; Annual campaigns; Equipment; Scholarships.
Limitations: Applications accepted. Giving limited to the city of St. Clair, MI, and its immediate vicinity. No grants to individuals.
Application information: Application form required.
    Initial approach: Letter
    Deadline(s): None
Trustees: William Cedar; Gerald M. Emig; James Fredericks; Bernard Kuhn; Franklin H. Moore.
EIN: 386064622

4577
St. Michael's Self Help Wajda Project Trust
3905 Scenic Dr.
North Muskegon, MI 49445-8652

Foundation type: Independent foundation.
Financial data (yr. ended 12/31/14): Assets, $0 (M); gifts received, $300,000; expenditures, $300,003; qualifying distributions, $285,000; giving activities include $285,000 for 3 grants (high: $200,000; low: $25,000).
Fields of interest: Water resources; Health; Human services.

Limitations: Applications not accepted. Giving primarily in MI; with some giving to IL.
Application information: Unsolicited requests for funds not accepted.
Trustee: Stephen Nagengast.
EIN: 467447595

4578
Stern Family Foundation
24755 Franklin Park Dr.
Franklin, MI 48025-1227

Donors: Scott Stern; Lisa Stern.
Foundation type: Independent foundation.
Financial data (yr. ended 12/31/13): Assets, $1,049,066 (M); expenditures, $142,972; qualifying distributions, $133,830; giving activities include $133,830 for 16 grants (high: $50,000; low: $100).
Fields of interest: Education; University education; Religion; Human services.
Limitations: Applications not accepted. Giving primarily in IL.
Application information: Unsolicited requests for funds not accepted.
Officers and Directors: Scott Stern, Pres. and Treas. and Director; Lisa Stern, V.P. and Secy. and Director.
EIN: 263479263

4579
Stoddard Family Foundation, Inc.
29600 Southfield, No. 110
Southfield, MI 48076-2039

Established in 2000 in Michigan.
Donor: Stanford C. Stoddard.
Foundation type: Independent foundation.
Financial data (yr. ended 12/31/13): Assets, $1,523,933 (M); gifts received, $92,210; expenditures, $196,940; qualifying distributions, $212,296; giving activities include $211,494 for 9 grants (high: $50,294; low: $1,200).
Purpose and activities: Support primarily for higher education.
Fields of interest: Education; Diseases and conditions; Religion.
Type of support: General support; Program development; Scholarships.
Limitations: Applications not accepted. Giving primarily in Salt Lake City and Provo, UT; giving also in Traverse City, MI. No grants to individuals.
Application information: Unsolicited requests for funds not accepted.
Officers and Directors: Stanford C. Stoddard, Chair. and Director; Stanford D. Stoddard, Pres. and Treas and Director; Elizabeth S. Taggart, V.P. and Secy. and Director; Simeon H. Stoddard, V.P. and Director.
EIN: 383539927

4580
Margaret Jane Stoker Charitable Trust
328 S. Saginaw St., M/C 001065
Flint, MI 48502-1923
Application address: c/o Citizens Bank, Attn.: Karen McNish, 101 N. Washington Ave., Saginaw, MI 48607

Established in 2001 in Michigan.
Foundation type: Independent foundation.

Financial data (yr. ended 09/30/13): Assets, $2,821,162 (M); expenditures, $210,293; qualifying distributions, $174,500; giving activities include $174,500 for grants.
Fields of interest: Nonprofits; Community and economic development; Religion; European football; Human services; Adolescents.
Type of support: Regranting.
Limitations: Applications accepted. Giving primarily in the Saginaw County, MI, area.
Application information: Application form required.
Initial approach: Applications available through Citizens Bank
Deadline(s): None
Trustee: Citizens Bank.
EIN: 320000318

4581
The Joshua-Jim and Eunice Stone Foundation
27235 Ovid Ct.
Franklin, MI 48025-1036

Donors: Joshua J. Stone 20-Year Charitable Lead Unitrust; Joshua J. Stone 15-Year Charitable Lead Unitrust.
Foundation type: Independent foundation.
Financial data (yr. ended 12/31/13): Assets, $13,836,926 (M); gifts received, $2,057,124; expenditures, $318,504; qualifying distributions, $272,819; giving activities include $270,050 for 10 grants (high: $50,000; low: $1,000).
Fields of interest: Health; Agriculture; Human services.
Limitations: Applications not accepted.
Application information: Unsolicited requests for funds not accepted.
Officers and Directors: Gwen Weiner, Pres. and Director; Carol Depaul, V.P. and Secy. and Director; Marcia Klein, V.P. and Treas. and Director.
EIN: 270439220

4582
Maurice & Dorothy Stubnitz Foundation
4196 W. Maple Ave.
Adrian, MI 49221-2703

Established in 1981 in Michigan.
Foundation type: Independent foundation.
Financial data (yr. ended 09/30/13): Assets, $6,781,238 (M); expenditures, $369,964; qualifying distributions, $311,233; giving activities include $311,233 for 15 grants (high: $56,034; low: $2,000).
Purpose and activities: Giving primarily for higher education and human services.
Fields of interest: Opera; Orchestral music; Higher education; Community and economic development; Housing development; Human services.
Type of support: Capital and infrastructure; Equipment; Land acquisitions; Emergency funds; Program development; Seed money; Scholarships.
Limitations: Applications not accepted. Giving primarily in Adrian, MI. No grants to individuals.
Application information: Unsolicited requests for funds not accepted.
Officers: Karen Caine, V.P.; William Benz, Secy.; Michael Kapnick, Treas.
Directors: Michelle Force; Betty Gross; Hildreth Spencer; Charles E. Gross.
EIN: 382392373

4583
Sutaruk Foundation
3707 W. Maple Rd., Ste. 100B
West Bloomfield, MI 48301-3201

Established in 2003 in Michigan.
Donors: Catherine Sutar†; Alex Sutaruk Trust.
Foundation type: Independent foundation.
Financial data (yr. ended 12/31/14): Assets, $2,861,742 (M); expenditures, $320,730; qualifying distributions, $320,730; giving activities include $308,500 for 5 grants (high: $100,000; low: $31,000).
Fields of interest: Education; Hospital care; Diseases and conditions; Human services.
Type of support: Research.
Limitations: Applications not accepted. Giving primarily in MI, with emphasis on Detroit; giving also in Houston, TX. No grants to individuals.
Application information: Contributes only to pre-selected organizations.
Directors: Kathy Meyer Santamarina; Tom Meyer; Bradley Cwysyshyn.
EIN: 113673305

4584
Michael Talty and Helen Talty Charitable Trust
17199 N. Laurel Park Dr., Ste. 301
Livonia, MI 48152
Application address: c/o Kathleen Unetic, 30855 Harris Rd., Wickliffe, OH 44092, tel.: (734) 953-8600

Established in 2005 in Ohio.
Foundation type: Independent foundation.
Financial data (yr. ended 12/31/13): Assets, $4,832,681 (M); expenditures, $262,706; qualifying distributions, $233,940; giving activities include $211,600 for 23 grants (high: $51,200; low: $2,000).
Fields of interest: Education; Zoos; Sports and recreation.
Type of support: Scholarships.
Limitations: Applications accepted. Giving primarily in OH.
Application information: Application form required.
Initial approach: Request application form
Deadline(s): Aug. 15.
Trustees: Kevin J. Santa; Joseph E. Talty; Patrick E. Talty; Nari Talty-Schenkelberg; Thomas Talty, Jr.; Kathleen M. Unetic.
EIN: 226946772

4585
Tamer Foundation
1222 Balfour St.
Grosse Pointe Park, MI 48230-1020

Established in 1986 in Michigan.
Donors: James Tamer; James Tamer Restated Living Trust.
Foundation type: Independent foundation.
Financial data (yr. ended 04/30/13): Assets, $8,426,913 (M); expenditures, $510,147; qualifying distributions, $391,698; giving activities include $135,580 for 14 grants (high: $50,000; low: $100), and $256,118 for 35 grants to individuals (high: $12,000; low: $3,571).
Purpose and activities: Giving primarily for higher education, health and human services, and

Christian organizations, primarily Maronite Catholic agencies and churches.
Fields of interest: Higher education; Diseases and conditions; Christianity; Human services.
Type of support: General support; Grants to individuals; Scholarships; Student aid; Research.
Limitations: Applications not accepted. Giving primarily in Detroit, MI.
Application information: Unsolicited requests for funds not accepted.
Officer and Trustees: Josephine Saigh, Mgr. and Trustee; James George; Joseph Thomas.
EIN: 382679633

4586
Tarakji Foundation
26300 Telegraph Rd., 2nd Fl.
Southfield, MI 48033-2436 2483592305

Donor: N. Tarakji.
Foundation type: Independent foundation.
Financial data (yr. ended 12/31/14): Assets, $0; gifts received, $1,235,000; expenditures, $289,876; qualifying distributions, $288,825.
Fields of interest: Islam.
Limitations: Applications not accepted. Giving primarily in MI. No grants to individuals.
Application information: Contributes only to pre-selected organizations.
Officers: Nael Tarakji, Pres.; Lama Tarakji, V.P.; Bilal Tarakji, Secy.
EIN: 383478158

4587
Tassell-Wisner-Bottrall Foundation
(formerly The Leslie E. Tassell Foundation)
c/o Fifth Third Bank
111 Lyon St. N.W.
Grand Rapids, MI 49501-3636 8004000439
Application address: c/o Joyce Wisner, 3439 Quiggle Ave. S.E., Ada, MI 49301-9237, tel.: (616) 676-2570

Established in 1994 in Michigan.
Donors: The Leslie Metal Arts Co., Inc.; Leslie E. Tassell†.
Foundation type: Independent foundation.
Financial data (yr. ended 12/31/14): Assets, $8,415,076; expenditures, $474,502; qualifying distributions, $408,647.
Purpose and activities: Giving primarily for higher education, including scholarships to individuals; giving also for health care.
Fields of interest: Higher education; Health; Specialty hospital care.
Type of support: General support; Student aid.
Limitations: Applications accepted. Giving primarily in MI.
Application information: Application form required.
 Initial approach: Contact foundation for application
 Deadline(s): None
Trustees: David C. Bottrall; Michael R. Julien; Hilary F. Snell; Donald Wisner; Joyce S. Wisner; Leslie Wisner.
EIN: 383186818

4588
Technical Assistance Mission Inc.
2764 Lorraine St.
Marlette, MI 48453-1070

Donors: David Hall; Charlotte Hall.
Foundation type: Independent foundation.
Financial data (yr. ended 03/31/13): Assets, $6,548,542 (M); expenditures, $320,186; qualifying distributions, $260,231; giving activities include $235,387 for 25 grants (high: $89,900; low: $500), and $260,231 for 3 foundation-administered programs.
Fields of interest: Protestantism; Human services.
Type of support: General support.
Limitations: Applications not accepted. Giving primarily in FL.
Application information: Contributes only to pre-selected organizations.
Officers: David Hall, Pres.; Christy Hines, Secy.; Charlotte Hall, Treas.
EIN: 237241202

4589
Ben N. Teitel Charitable Trust
30348 Windingbrook Ln.
Farmington Hills, MI 48334

Established in 1987 in Michigan.
Donors: Ben N. Teitel†; Gerald S. Cook.
Foundation type: Independent foundation.
Financial data (yr. ended 09/30/13): Assets, $3,363,712 (M); expenditures, $203,322; qualifying distributions, $197,590; giving activities include $197,590 for 35 grants (high: $70,000; low: $100).
Purpose and activities: The trust supports a variety of Jewish community programs for children and the elderly, including camping, teen touring to Israel, and educational programs to train social workers for Jewish agency work.
Fields of interest: Nonprofits; Judaism; Human services; Senior services.
International interests: Israel.
Type of support: General support; Matching grants; Continuing support; Annual campaigns; Regranting; Capital campaigns; Capital and infrastructure; Endowments; Emergency funds; Program development; Seed money; Scholarships.
Limitations: Applications not accepted. Giving primarily in southeast MI and PA. No grants to individuals.
Application information: Contributes only to pre-selected organizations.
Trustee: Gerald S. Cook.
EIN: 386512136

4590
W. B. & Candace Thoman Foundation
222 N. Washington Sq., Ste. 400
Lansing, MI 48933-1800
Contact: Benjamin O. Schwendener Jr. Esq., Pres.

Established in 1968 in Michigan.
Donors: W.B. Thoman†; Candace Thoman†.
Foundation type: Independent foundation.
Financial data (yr. ended 12/31/13): Assets, $2,801,307 (M); expenditures, $182,369; qualifying distributions, $154,750; giving activities include $154,750 for 10 grants (high: $55,000; low: $600).

Purpose and activities: Giving primarily for education, orphans and the economically disadvantaged.
Fields of interest: Performing arts education; Education; Special needs education; Higher education; Basic and remedial instruction; Reading promotion; Camps; Human services; Low-income and poor people.
Type of support: General support; Program development.
Limitations: Applications accepted. Giving primarily in Ingham County, MI, with some emphasis on the Lansing area. No support for political organizations, churches, or religious organizations or programs. No grants to individuals.
Publications: Application guidelines; Program policy statement.
Application information: Application form required.
 Initial approach: Letter requesting guidelines
 Copies of proposal: 6
 Deadline(s): 2 weeks prior to board meetings
 Board meeting date(s): Quarterly
Officers and Trustees: Benjamin O. Schwendener, Jr., Pres. and Secy. and Trustee; Louis E. Legg, V.P. and Trustee; Frederick M. Baker, Treas. and Trustee; Rebecca Corner; Eva L. Evans, Ph.D; Helen Pratt Mickens.
Number of staff: 1 part-time support.
EIN: 237029842

4591
Thompson Educational Foundation
P.O. Box 6349
Plymouth, MI 48170-0353 7344536412

Established in 2002 in Michigan.
Donors: Ellen A. Thompson; Robert M. Thompson.
Foundation type: Independent foundation.
Financial data (yr. ended 12/31/14): Assets, $103,540,409; expenditures, $6,408,424; qualifying distributions, $3,566,254.
Fields of interest: Education.
Type of support: General support; Program-related investments.
Limitations: Applications not accepted. Giving primarily in MI. No grants to individuals.
Application information: Contributes only to pre-selected organizations.
Officers and Trustees: Robert M. Thompson, Chair. and Pres. and Trustee; Ellen A. Thompson, V.P. and Trustee; Joseph G. Horonzy, Secy.-Treas. and Trustee.
EIN: 300107259

4592
Mary Thompson Foundation
P.O. Box 75000
Detroit, MI 48275-7874
Application Address: c/o Mrs. Douglas F. Roby, Jr., P.O. Box 568, St. Clair Shores, MI 48080, tel.: (313) 886-2471

Established in 1979 in Michigan.
Donor: Mary Thompson†.
Foundation type: Independent foundation.
Financial data (yr. ended 12/31/13): Assets, $3,464,610 (M); expenditures, $192,021; qualifying distributions, $155,450; giving activities include $155,000 for 15 grants (high: $36,000; low: $500).

Purpose and activities: Giving primarily to assist the frail and elderly.
Fields of interest: Arts and culture; Education; Human services.
Type of support: General support; Continuing support; Equipment; Program development; Convening.
Limitations: Applications accepted. Giving limited to MI, with emphasis on Oakland and Wayne counties.
Application information: Application form required.
   Initial approach: Contact foundation for application form
   Copies of proposal: 1
   Deadline(s): None
Officers: Nena Dahling, Pres.; Mary Roby, V.P.; Gioconda McMillan, Secy.; Lynn Cameron, Treas.
Trustees: Jana Brownell; Jane Reuther.
EIN: 381359097

4593
The Richard K. Thompson Foundation
24417 Groesbeck Hwy.
Warren, MI   48089-4786

Donors: Orville K. Thompson Trust; Richard K. Thompson.
Foundation type: Independent foundation.
Financial data (yr. ended 12/31/13): Assets, $6,552,299 (M); gifts received, $2,996,827; expenditures, $178,532; qualifying distributions, $174,950; giving activities include $174,950 for 24 grants (high: $101,200; low: $100).
Fields of interest: Health care administration and financing; Respiratory system diseases; Down syndrome; Television; Human services; Food aid.
Type of support: General support.
Limitations: Applications not accepted. Giving primarily in Detroit, MI. No grants to individuals.
Application information: Contributes only to pre-selected organizations.
Officer: Richard K. Thompson, Pres. and Secy.-Treas.
Director: Linda Davis Vaughn.
EIN: 383447218

4594
Torgow Family Foundation
P.O. Box 31-0737
Detroit, MI   48231-0737

Established in 2000 in Michigan.
Donors: Malka Torgow; Gary Torgow; Bates Associates LLC; Sterling Group Limited LLC; Talmudical Yeshiva; 333 LP LLC; West Hampton Associates LLC.
Foundation type: Independent foundation.
Financial data (yr. ended 12/31/13): Assets, $5,245 (M); gifts received, $60,000; expenditures, $184,780; qualifying distributions, $184,715; giving activities include $179,339 for 81+ grants (high: $35,000; low: $54), and $5,376 for grants to individuals.
Purpose and activities: Giving primarily for Yeshivas.
Fields of interest: Nonprofits; Judaism.
Type of support: General support; Regranting.
Limitations: Applications accepted. Giving primarily in NY and MI.
Application information: Application form required.
   Initial approach: Letter
   Deadline(s): None

Officers and Trustees: Gary Torgow, Pres. and Trustee; Malka Torgow, Secy. and Trustee; Eliezer Torgow; Yonah Torgow.
EIN: 383560590

4595
Tremble Foundation, Inc.
(also known as St. Deny's Foundation, Inc.)
c/o Comerica Bank
99 Monroe Ave. N.W., Ste. 550
Grand Rapids, MI   49503-6211   (616) 752-4705
Contact: Kelly Deridder

Established in 1988 in Michigan.
Donor: Helen R. Tremble†.
Foundation type: Independent foundation.
Financial data (yr. ended 12/31/13): Assets, $6,022,026 (M); expenditures, $476,456; qualifying distributions, $313,070; giving activities include $313,070 for 32 grants (high: $61,000; low: $1,000).
Purpose and activities: Giving primarily for higher education, arts and art education programs, Christian agencies and health and hospice programs.
Fields of interest: Arts and culture; Education; Secondary education; Higher education; Environment; Domesticated animals; Hospital care; Christianity; Human services.
Type of support: General support; Program development; Scholarships.
Limitations: Applications accepted. Giving primarily in MI, with emphasis on the Dowagiac area.
Application information: Application form required.
   Initial approach: Letter
   Copies of proposal: 1
   Deadline(s): None
   Board meeting date(s): Spring and fall
   Final notification: 6 months
Trustee: Comerica Bank.
EIN: 382869889

4596
The Trico Foundation
29100 Northwestern Hwy., Ste. 290
Southfield, MI   48034

Established in 1986 in Michigan.
Donors: Warren J. Coville; Margot E. Coville; Trico Family Partnership; Joseph Blass.
Foundation type: Independent foundation.
Financial data (yr. ended 06/30/13): Assets, $6,933,201 (M); expenditures, $451,439; qualifying distributions, $307,422; giving activities include $280,060 for 43 grants (high: $100,000; low: $1,000).
Fields of interest: Arts and culture; Health; Diseases and conditions; Cancers.
Limitations: Applications not accepted. Giving primarily in MI. No grants to individuals.
Application information: Unsolicited requests for funds not accepted.
Officers: Warren J. Coville, Chair. and Treas.; Brent S. Triest, Pres.; Margot E. Coville, V.P.; Betsy Coville, Secy.
Board Members: Harold Berry; Claudia Coville; Barry Rosenbaum; Glenn Triest; Jonathan Triest.
EIN: 382702725

4597
Triford Foundation
13627 Heritage Rd.
Sterling Heights, MI   48312-6529

Established in 1968 in Michigan.
Foundation type: Independent foundation.
Financial data (yr. ended 12/31/13): Assets, $5,100,188 (M); expenditures, $255,180; qualifying distributions, $224,014; giving activities include $220,696 for 70 grants (high: $41,400; low: $246).
Fields of interest: Education; Elementary and secondary education; Health; Hospital care; Protestantism; Human services.
Type of support: General support; Annual campaigns.
Limitations: Applications not accepted. Giving on a national basis, with some emphasis on MI. No grants to individuals, or for building funds.
Application information: Contributes only to pre-selected organizations.
Officers and Trustees: Frederick S. Ford, Pres. and Secy. and Trustee; Horace C. Ford, V.P. and Treas.; Frederick B. Ford, V.P. and Trustee; James W. Ford, V.P. and Trustee.
Number of staff: 1 part-time professional; 1 part-time support.
EIN: 237003478

4598
Tuscola County Community Foundation
317 S. State St.
P.O. Box 534
Caro, MI   48723-0534   (989) 673-8223
Contact: Ken Micklash, Exec. Dir.
FAX: (989) 673-8223;
E-mail: tccf534@centurytel.net; Tel/fax: (989) 673-8223; Main URL: http://www.tuscolacountycommunityfoundation.org

Established in 1997 in Michigan.
Foundation type: Community foundation.
Financial data (yr. ended 12/31/13): Assets, $9,784,651 (M); gifts received, $217,591; expenditures, $605,992; giving activities include $274,273 for 12+ grants (high: $22,900), and $146,550 for grants to individuals.
Purpose and activities: The foundation is to make Tuscola County a better place to live by maintaining a permanent philanthropic endowment base which will assist and fund a variety of efforts, turning needs and dreams into realities.
Fields of interest: Education; Sports and recreation; Human services; Youth development; Children and youth; Children; Adolescents; Adults; Seniors; Homeless people; Low-income and poor people; Substance abusers.
Type of support: Capital and infrastructure; Matching grants; Equipment; Emergency funds; Program development; Seed money; Curriculum development; Scholarships.
Limitations: Applications accepted. Giving limited to Tuscola County, MI. No support for sectarian religious programs. No grants for operating budgets, previously incurred debt, endowment campaigns, or fundraising activities.
Publications: Application guidelines; Annual report; Financial statement; Grants list; Informational brochure; Newsletter.
Application information: Visit foundation web site for application form and guidelines. Application form required.

Initial approach: Letter or telephone
Copies of proposal: 6
Deadline(s): Mar. 1 and Oct. 1
Board meeting date(s): 4th Thurs., quarterly
Final notification: 3 months
Officers and Trustees: Gary Haas, Pres. and Trustee; Tim Lyons, V.P. and Trustee; Janet Thane, Secy. and Trustee; Ann Marie Ball, Treas. and Trustee; Ken Micklash, Exec. Dir.; Kurt Bender; Gary Crews; Pat Curtis; Denise Harrington; Dave Houghtaling; Amy Peters; Richard Ransford; Luther Stewart; Tom Striffler; Ben Varney; Susan Walker; Robert Worth; Rick Zimmer.
Number of staff: 1 part-time professional.
EIN: 383351315

4599
Tyler-Little Family Foundation
c/o Greenleaf Trust
1734 Embury Rd.
Kalamazoo, MI   49008-2246

Established in 2004 in Michigan.
Donor: J&M Tyler Assocs., LLC.
Foundation type: Independent foundation.
Financial data (yr. ended 03/31/13): Assets, $7,993,782 (M); expenditures, $373,541; qualifying distributions, $363,740; giving activities include $363,740 for grants.
Purpose and activities: Giving primarily for human services and a Presbyterian church.
Fields of interest: Community and economic development; Housing development; Protestantism; Human services; Youth development; Vocational rehabilitation.
Type of support: General support; Capital campaigns.
Limitations: Applications not accepted. No grants to individuals.
Application information: Contributes only to pre-selected organizations.
Officer: Mary L. Tyler, Pres. and Secy.
Directors: Sarah Tyler Chase; Steven Little Tyler; Timothy J. Tyler; Toni Lyn Tyler.
EIN: 200880483

4600
U.S.-China Cultural Foundation
920 E. Lincoln St.
Birmingham, MI   48009-3608

Established in 1993 in Michigan.
Donor: Shirley Young.
Foundation type: Independent foundation.
Financial data (yr. ended 12/31/13): Assets, $5,230,151 (M); gifts received, $41,860; expenditures, $251,103; qualifying distributions, $209,282; giving activities include $201,000 for 3 grants (high: $101,000; low: $50,000).
Fields of interest: International relations.
Limitations: Applications not accepted. Giving primarily in New York, NY. No grants to individuals.
Application information: Unsolicited requests for funds not accepted.
Officer and Trustees: Shirley Young, Pres. and Trustee; David Hsieh; Douglas Hsieh; William Hsieh; Min-Duo Li; Gene Young.
EIN: 383155351

4601
Van Curler Foundation
c/o Carol A. Van Curler
2008 Hogback Rd.
Ann Arbor, MI   48105-9768

Established in 2000 in Michigan.
Donors: Donald E. Van Curler; Carol Van Curler.
Foundation type: Independent foundation.
Financial data (yr. ended 12/31/13): Assets, $276,986 (M); gifts received, $331,075; expenditures, $215,811; qualifying distributions, $214,516; giving activities include $214,516 for 18 grants (high: $46,000; low: $1,000).
Fields of interest: Education; Health; Christianity.
Type of support: General support; Student aid.
Limitations: Applications not accepted. Giving primarily in FL and MI.
Application information: Unsolicited requests for funds not accepted.
Officers and Directors: Carol A. Van Curler, Pres. and Secy.-Treas.; Timothy R. Moore, V.P. and Director; Angela M. Templeton.
EIN: 383529339

4602
The W.S. and Lois Van Dalson Foundation
2347 W. Dowling Rd.
Delton, MI   49046-8663

Established in 2001 in Michigan.
Donors: William S. Van Dalson†; Lois A. Van Dalson Trust†; Virginia Van Dalson; William S. van Dalson Qtip Trust; Edward & Virginia van Dalson Irrevocable Trust.
Foundation type: Independent foundation.
Financial data (yr. ended 12/31/13): Assets, $12,784,982 (M); gifts received, $2,968,446; expenditures, $501,278; qualifying distributions, $405,104; giving activities include $393,500 for 20 grants (high: $155,000; low: $5,000).
Fields of interest: Education; Sports and recreation; Human services.
Type of support: General support; Capital campaigns.
Limitations: Applications not accepted. Giving primarily in Kalamazoo, MI. No grants to individuals.
Application information: Unsolicited requests for funds not accepted.
Officers: Alfred J. Gemrich, Chair., Pres. and Secy.; Sydney P. Waldorf, V.P.; Barbara L. James, Treas.
EIN: 383607246

4603
Vander Laan Family Foundation
2764 Beechtree Dr. S.W.
Byron Center, MI   49315-9475

Established in 1998 in Michigan.
Donors: Allen J. Vander Laan; Nancy D. Vander Laan.
Foundation type: Independent foundation.
Financial data (yr. ended 12/31/13): Assets, $5,061,824 (M); gifts received, $120,733; expenditures, $271,719; qualifying distributions, $226,000; giving activities include $226,000 for 40 grants (high: $50,000; low: $2,000).
Purpose and activities: Giving primarily for human services and religious organizations.
Fields of interest: Religion; Human services; Family services.
Type of support: General support.

Limitations: Applications not accepted. Giving primarily in Grand Rapids, MI. No grants to individuals.
Application information: Contributes only to pre-selected organizations.
Officers: Allen J. Vander Laan, Pres. and Treas.; Nancy D. Vander Laan, V.P. and Secy.
EIN: 383440120

4604
VanGilder Family Foundation Inc.
1065 Grant St.
Fenton, MI   48430-1715

Foundation type: Independent foundation.
Financial data (yr. ended 12/31/14): Assets, $2,534,271 (M); expenditures, $124,351; qualifying distributions, $112,500; giving activities include $112,500 for grants.
Fields of interest: Education.
Limitations: Applications not accepted. No grants to individuals.
Application information: Unsolicited requests for funds not accepted.
Officers: Russell B. VanGilder, Jr., Pres.; Shirley VanGilder, V.P.; Lisa VanGilder, Secy.-Treas.
EIN: 264128909

4605
The Vattikuti India Relief Foundation
1000 Town Ctr., No. 700
Southfield, MI   48075-1183

Established in 2008 in Michigan.
Donors: Rajendra B. Vattikuti; The Vattikuti Foundation.
Foundation type: Independent foundation.
Financial data (yr. ended 12/31/13): Assets, $738,411 (M); gifts received, $500,000; expenditures, $294,097; qualifying distributions, $291,915; giving activities include $291,915 for 1 grant.
Purpose and activities: Giving primarily to help alleviate poverty and to improve medical and educational services in India.
Fields of interest: Education; Health; Human services.
International interests: India.
Limitations: Applications not accepted. Giving primarily in India.
Application information: Unsolicited requests for funds not accepted.
Officers and Directors: Rajendra B. Vattikuti, Pres. and Treas. and Director; Padmaja Vattikuti, V.P. and Secy. and Director; Sarang Iyengar.
EIN: 263450613

4606
Vicksburg Foundation
P.O. Box 177
Vicksburg, MI   49097-0177
Contact: William Oswalt, Pres. and Secy.

Established in 1943 in Michigan.
Donor: Stanley H. Herman Charitable Unitrust.
Foundation type: Independent foundation.
Financial data (yr. ended 12/31/13): Assets, $3,833,068 (M); gifts received, $57,728; expenditures, $211,468; qualifying distributions,

$211,468; giving activities include $197,943 for 14 grants (high: $50,000; low: $1,300).

Purpose and activities: To coordinate and unify the charitable and benevolent activities of the incorporators; emphasis on community programs, education, and libraries.

Fields of interest: Education; Foundations; Libraries; Community and economic development; Human services.

Type of support: General support; Matching grants; Continuing support; Regranting; Annual campaigns; Fundraising; Capital campaigns; Capital and infrastructure; Equipment; Endowments; Program development; Convening; Seed money; Curriculum development; Scholarships.

Limitations: Applications accepted. Giving limited to MI, with emphasis on Vicksburg, Kalamazoo, and Schoolcraft. No grants to individuals.

Publications: Informational brochure.

Application information:
  Initial approach: Proposal
  Deadline(s): None
  Board meeting date(s): Mar., June, Sept., and Dec.

Officers: William Oswalt, Pres. and Secy.; Lloyd E. Appell, V.P.; Warren Lawrence, Treas.

Directors: Rudy Callen; Danna Downing; David Schriemer; James Shaw; Didik Soekarmoen.

Number of staff: None.

EIN: 386065237

4607

Vlasic Family Foundation
(formerly Vlasic Foundation)
38710 Woodward Ave., Ste. 100
Bloomfield Hills, MI 48304

Established in 1958 in Michigan.

Donors: Robert J. Vlasic; Joseph Vlasic†.

Foundation type: Independent foundation.

Financial data (yr. ended 12/31/13): Assets, $242,811 (M); expenditures, $133,463; qualifying distributions, $133,356; giving activities include $133,250 for 20 grants (high: $58,500; low: $200).

Purpose and activities: Giving primarily to educational, health, and cultural programs in which members of the Vlasic families have a personal interest.

Fields of interest: Arts and culture; Education; Higher education; Nonprofits; Health; Cancers; Catholicism; Human services.

Type of support: Regranting.

Limitations: Applications not accepted. Giving primarily in MI. No grants to individuals.

Application information: Contributes only to pre-selected organizations.

Officers: Paul A. Vlasic, Co-Pres. and Co-Treas.; Robert J. Vlasic, Co-Pres.; James J. Vlasic, V.P. and Co-Secy.; Richard R. Vlasic, V.P. and Co-Secy.; Michael A. Vlasic, V.P. and Co-Treas.; William J. Vlasic, V.P.

EIN: 386077329

4608

John W. and Rose E. Watson Foundation
c/o Tri-Star Trust Bank
1004 N. Michigan Ave.
Saginaw, MI 48602-4325 9899210010
Application address: c/o Jean Seman, 5800 Weiss St., Saginaw, MI 48602, tel.: (989) 792-2011

Established in 1959 in Michigan.

Foundation type: Independent foundation.

Financial data (yr. ended 12/31/14): Assets, $8,417,229; gifts received, $1,650; expenditures, $458,625; qualifying distributions, $411,099.

Purpose and activities: Support primarily for Roman Catholic organizations; scholarship awards limited to Saginaw, MI, residents graduating from local Roman Catholic high schools.

Fields of interest: Education; Catholicism; Human services; Child welfare.

Type of support: General support; Student aid.

Limitations: Applications accepted. Giving primarily in Saginaw, MI; scholarships limited to residents of Saginaw, MI.

Application information: Application form required.
  Deadline(s): 1 month prior to academic year

Officers: William L. Ruger, Pres.; Anne Hamilton, V.P.; Don Popielarz, Secy.; Jean Seman, Treas.

Board Members: Amy Dwyer; Richard Espinoza; Ruth Sawyers.

EIN: 386091611

4609

Lawrence & Idell Weisberg Foundation
(formerly Iodent Chemical Company Foundation)
4771 S. Chipping Glen
Bloomfield Hills, MI 48302-2305

Donors: Lawrence Weisberg; Idell Weisberg.

Foundation type: Independent foundation.

Financial data (yr. ended 09/30/14): Assets, $2,905,251 (M); expenditures, $180,850; qualifying distributions, $177,850; giving activities include $177,850 for 27 grants (high: $50,310; low: $200).

Fields of interest: Arts and culture; Religion; Human services.

Type of support: General support.

Limitations: Applications not accepted. Giving primarily in MI and NY. No grants to individuals.

Application information: Unsolicited requests for funds not accepted.

Trustees: Idell Weisberg; Lawrence Weisberg.

EIN: 382151372

4610

James & Jane Welch Foundation
P.O. Box 3636
Grand Rapids, MI 49501-3636

Established in 1990 in Michigan.

Donors: James C. Welch; Jane Welch.

Foundation type: Independent foundation.

Financial data (yr. ended 09/30/14): Assets, $7,467,900 (M); expenditures, $435,987; qualifying distributions, $390,460; giving activities include $387,240 for 21 grants (high: $75,000; low: $3,000).

Fields of interest: Arts and culture; Performing arts; Museums; Education; Nonprofits; Public libraries; Christianity; Protestantism; Child welfare.

Type of support: Regranting.

Limitations: Applications not accepted. Giving primarily in FL, MI and TX. No grants to individuals.

Application information: Contributes only to pre-selected organizations.

Officers: Jane N. Welch, Pres.; Thomas Brad Welch, V.P.; Elizabeth Welch Lykins, Secy.; Charles B. Welch, Treas.

Trustee: John Welch.

EIN: 382927749

4611

The Wetsman Foundation
132 N. Old Woodward Ave.
Birmingham, MI 48009-3375

Established in 1962 in Michigan.

Donors: Lillian R. Wetsman; William M. Wetsman; Janis B. Wetsman; David J. Wetsman.

Foundation type: Independent foundation.

Financial data (yr. ended 12/31/13): Assets, $3,489,829 (M); gifts received, $10,758; expenditures, $215,509; qualifying distributions, $191,955; giving activities include $191,955 for 24 grants (high: $50,000; low: $500).

Purpose and activities: Support primarily for federated giving programs and Jewish organizations; giving also for the arts and health.

Fields of interest: Arts and culture; Orchestral music; Art museums; Nonprofits; Health; Hospital care; Judaism; Human services.

Type of support: General support; Regranting.

Limitations: Applications not accepted. Giving primarily in CA and MI. No grants to individuals.

Application information: Contributes only to pre-selected organizations.

Officers: William M. Wetsman, Pres.; David J. Wetsman, V.P. and Secy.; Janis B. Wetsman, V.P. and Treas.; Adam F. Wetsman, V.P.

EIN: 386056692

4612

Wheeler Family Foundation, Inc.
201 W. Big Beaver Rd., Ste. 1420
Troy, MI 48084-4120

Established in 1997 in Delaware.

Donors: Thomas M. Wheeler; Michaelon A. Wright; Lisa Wheeler Huzella.

Foundation type: Independent foundation.

Financial data (yr. ended 06/30/13): Assets, $8,038,306 (M); expenditures, $520,169; qualifying distributions, $321,396; giving activities include $198,295 for 18 grants (high: $50,000; low: $100).

Fields of interest: Education; Christianity; Catholicism; Human services; Child welfare.

Limitations: Applications not accepted. Giving primarily in CO, FL, and MI. No grants to individuals.

Application information: Contributes only to pre-selected organizations.

Officers and Directors: Michaelon A. Wright, Pres. and Director; Robert Howard, Exec. V.P.; Douglas S. Soifer, Secy.; Paul Oster, Treas.; Lisa W. Huzella; Thomas R. Wheeler; Erin Wright; Morgan Wright.

EIN: 383392912

4613

The White Foundation
5530 Crabtree Rd.
Bloomfield Hills, MI 48301-1200

Established in 1945 in Michigan.

Donors: Glenn E. White; Ruth E. White; David B. White; Charles E. White; Nancy E. Bergsma.

Foundation type: Independent foundation.

Financial data (yr. ended 12/31/13): Assets, $1,921,756 (M); expenditures, $424,808;

qualifying distributions, $385,000; giving activities include $385,000 for 11 grants (high: $250,000; low: $5,000).

Purpose and activities: Grants primarily to organizations associated with the Free Methodist Church.

Fields of interest: Higher education; Christianity.

Limitations: Applications not accepted. Giving primarily in MI. No grants to individuals.

Application information: Contributes only to pre-selected organizations.

Officers: Glenn E. White, Pres. and Treas.; Nancy Bergsma, Secy.

Directors: Charles E. White; David B. White.

EIN: 386054883

4614
The Whiting Foundation

G9460 S. Saginaw Rd., Ste. J
Grand Blanc, MI 48439

Established in 1940 in Michigan.

Foundation type: Independent foundation.

Financial data (yr. ended 06/30/14): Assets, $11,432,077 (M); expenditures, $462,585; qualifying distributions, $406,805; giving activities include $358,000 for 31 grants (high: $25,000; low: $3,000).

Purpose and activities: Giving primarily for cultural activities, and for basic needs for people who are underprivileged.

Fields of interest: Arts and culture; Historic preservation; Education; Nonprofits; Diseases and conditions; Cancers; Community and economic development; Housing development; Child welfare.

Type of support: General support; Program development; Research; Research and evaluation; Regranting.

Limitations: Applications not accepted. Giving primarily in the Genesee County, MI, area, including the city of Flint.

Application information: Unsolicited requests for funds not accepted.

Officers: John T. Lindholm, Secy.-Treas.; Linda J. LeMieux, Pres.; Marsha A. Kump, Exec. Dir.

EIN: 386056693

4615
Whitman Family Foundation

c/o Northpoint Financial
920 E. Lincoln St.
Birmingham, MI 48009-3608

Established in 1994 in Michigan.

Donors: Marina V.N. Whitman; Robert F. Whitman.

Foundation type: Independent foundation.

Financial data (yr. ended 12/31/14): Assets, $2,442,817 (M); gifts received, $254,203; expenditures, $286,320; qualifying distributions, $257,770; giving activities include $255,100 for 37 grants (high: $80,000; low: $500).

Fields of interest: Performing arts; Higher education; Economics; Interdisciplinary studies; Public policy; Housing development; Basic and emergency aid; International development.

Type of support: Policy, advocacy and systems reform.

Limitations: Applications not accepted. Giving primarily in Washington, DC, Boston, MA, Ann Arbor, MI, Princeton, NJ, and Middlebury, VT. No grants to individuals.

Application information: Contributes only to pre-selected organizations.

Officers and Directors: Marina V.N. Whitman, Pres. and Director; Robert F. Whitman, V.P. and Treas. and Director; David L. Downie, Secy. and Director; Tracy Keller; Laura M. Whitman; Malcolm Whitman; William W. Downie.

EIN: 383191221

4616
Wickson-Link Memorial Foundation

3023 Davenport Ave.
Saginaw, MI 48602-3652 (989) 793-9830
Contact: David A. Beyerlein, Treas.

Established in 1973 in Michigan.

Donors: James Wickson†; Meta Wickson†.

Foundation type: Independent foundation.

Financial data (yr. ended 12/31/13): Assets, $5,662,831 (M); expenditures, $302,281; qualifying distributions, $274,064; giving activities include $245,530 for 39 grants (high: $30,000; low: $200).

Purpose and activities: Support for community funds, social services and programs for the disadvantaged, youth and child welfare, cultural organizations, health, education, and libraries.

Fields of interest: Arts and culture; Education; Human services.

Type of support: General support; Matching grants; Continuing support; Capacity-building and technical assistance; Capital campaigns; Capital and infrastructure; Equipment; Program development.

Limitations: Applications accepted. Giving primarily in Saginaw County, MI. No support for churches for building or operations. No grants to individuals.

Application information: Application form required.

Initial approach: Letter
Copies of proposal: 7
Deadline(s): None
Board meeting date(s): Quarterly

Officers: B.J. Humphreys, Pres.; David Beyerlein, Treas.

Trustees: Louis Hanisko; John Humphreys; Charles Nickless; Susan Piesko.

Number of staff: None.

EIN: 386083931

4617
The Wieczorek Family Foundation

9440 Grinnell St.
Detroit, MI 48213-1151

Established in 2001 in Michigan.

Donor: Dale M. Wieczorek.

Foundation type: Independent foundation.

Financial data (yr. ended 12/31/13): Assets, $1,280,598 (M); gifts received, $1,001,202; expenditures, $173,381; qualifying distributions, $171,558; giving activities include $132,500 for 11 grants (high: $35,000; low: $500), and $38,000 for 9 grants to individuals (high: $3,500; low: $3,000).

Fields of interest: Secondary education; Children's hospital care; Diseases and conditions; Human services; Child welfare; Children; Indigenous peoples.

Type of support: Student aid; Scholarships; Research.

Limitations: Applications not accepted. Giving primarily in MI.

Application information: Unsolicited requests for funds not accepted.

Officers: Dale M. Wieczorek, Chair.; Paulette Wieczorek, V.P.; Courtney Wieczorek, Secy.; Shannon Wieczorek, Treas.

EIN: 383625798

4618
The Williams Family Fund

(formerly The Jamison Williams Foundation)
380 N. Old Woodward Ave., Ste. 300
Birmingham, MI 48009-5322 (248) 642-0333
Contact: R. Jamison Williams Jr., Pres. and Dir.

Established in 1988 in Michigan.

Donors: R. Jamison Williams; Betty J. Williams.

Foundation type: Independent foundation.

Financial data (yr. ended 12/31/13): Assets, $4,893,837 (M); expenditures, $390,850; qualifying distributions, $257,750; giving activities include $257,750 for 23 grants (high: $54,250; low: $500).

Purpose and activities: Giving primarily for the arts.

Fields of interest: Arts and culture; Performing arts; Opera; Orchestral music; Museums; Education.

Type of support: General support.

Limitations: Applications accepted. Giving primarily in MI and NY. No grants to individuals.

Application information: Application form required.

Initial approach: Proposal
Deadline(s): None
Final notification: Within 2 months

Officer and Directors: R. Jamison Williams, Jr., Pres. and Director; Wendy J. Lynch.

EIN: 382837463

4619
The T. K. Zampetis Family Foundation

4829 W. Wickford
Bloomfield Hills, MI 48302-2384 (248) 792-7275
Contact: Theodore K. Zampetis, Pres.

Established in 2004 in Ohio.

Donor: Theodore K. Zampetis.

Foundation type: Independent foundation.

Financial data (yr. ended 12/31/14): Assets, $2,733,871 (M); expenditures, $198,415; qualifying distributions, $157,750; giving activities include $157,750 for 16 grants (high: $50,000; low: $750).

Fields of interest: Education; Catholicism; Human services.

Limitations: Applications accepted. Giving primarily in OH.

Application information: Application form required.

Initial approach: Letter
Deadline(s): None

Officers: Theodore K. Zampetis, Pres.; Constantine T. Zampetis, V.P.; Callie A. Zampetis-Budman, Secy.; Ann J. Zampetis, Treas.

EIN: 202057665

4620
Mary and George Herbert Zimmerman Foundation

200 Maple Park Blvd., Rm. 201
Saint Clair Shores, MI 48081-2211

Established in 1937 in Michigan.

Donors: Doris Z. Bato; Elaine Z. Peck.
Foundation type: Independent foundation.
Financial data (yr. ended 12/31/13): Assets,
$4,700,906 (M); expenditures, $218,721;
qualifying distributions, $187,970; giving activities
include $187,970 for 50 grants (high: $16,621;
low: $500).
Purpose and activities: Giving primarily for
education, health care, and human services.
Fields of interest: Education; Undergraduate
education; Foundations; Nonprofits; Health;
Hospital care; Alzheimer's disease; Catholicism;
Human services; Homeless services.
Type of support: Regranting.
Limitations: Applications not accepted. No grants to
individuals.
Application information: Unsolicited requests for
funds not accepted.
Officers and Directors: Georgia Z. Loftus, Pres. and
Director; James Loftus, V.P. and Director; Doris Z.
Bato, Secy. and Director; Elaine Z. Peck, Treas. and
Director; Douglas A. Cruikshank; Lisa P. Cruikshank;

Christopher Harris; Martha Harris; Maureen
Loftus-Mays; George R. Peck; Jennifer Peck; Sheila
P. Pettee; Timothy Pettee; Catherine B. Troy; Louis
G. Zimmerman; Mark L. Zimmerman.
EIN: 381685880

4621
P. J. and Mary Zondervan Foundation
(also known as Zondervan Foundation)
7140 Camino del Rey Dr. N.E.
Rockford, MI   49341-9463
Application address: Marilyn Faber, 281 Fremont St.,
Upland, CA 91784, tel.: (909) 982-6008

Established in 1981 in Michigan.
Donors: Peter J. Zondervan†; Mary Zondervan;
William J. Zondervan; William J. Zondervan
Charitable Remainder Trust.
Foundation type: Independent foundation.

Financial data (yr. ended 12/31/13): Assets,
$4,034,771 (M); expenditures, $216,113;
qualifying distributions, $176,329; giving activities
include $176,329 for 12 grants (high: $113,300;
low: $2,250).
Purpose and activities: To spread the gospel of
Jesus Christ.
Fields of interest: Graduate and professional
education; Christianity; Theology.
Type of support: Professorships; Equipment;
Program development; Convening; Curriculum
development; Scholarships; Research.
Limitations: Applications accepted. Giving primarily
in MI. No grants to individuals.
Application information: Application form required.
  Initial approach: Letter
  Deadline(s): None; requests are reviewed in Apr.
  and Sept.
  Final notification: Within 12 months
Officers and Directors: Robert Zondervan, Pres. and
Director; Marilyn Faber, Secy. and Director; Thomas
B. Kladder, Treas. and Director; Norman Pylman;
Mary Beth Schouten.
EIN: 382411884

MINNESOTA

4622
Aca Family Foundation
19955 Cottagewood Ave.
Deephaven, MN 55331-9238

Donors: Andrew Stillman; Ralph Stillman; Cassandra Stillman; Stillman Family Foundation; Faye Stillman.
Foundation type: Independent foundation.
Financial data (yr. ended 12/31/12): Assets, $4,910,151 (M); gifts received, $2,124,198; expenditures, $267,207; qualifying distributions, $263,880; giving activities include $261,535 for 4 grants (high: $198,535; low: $8,000).
Fields of interest: Religion; Human services; Children.
Limitations: Applications not accepted. Giving primarily in CA.
Application information: Unsolicited requests for funds not accepted.
Directors: Andrew Stillman; Cassandra Stillman; Faye Stillman; Ralph Stillman.
EIN: 274027513

4623
Acorn Foundation
350 Pleasant View Rd.
Chanhassen, MN 55317-9524
Contact: Shirley Sheldon, Pres.
Additional tel: (651) 439-1557

Established in 1997 in Minnesota.
Donors: Mark Hanson; Shirly Hanson.
Foundation type: Independent foundation.
Financial data (yr. ended 12/31/13): Assets, $5,617,445 (M); expenditures, $338,960; qualifying distributions, $299,576; giving activities include $265,000 for 15 grants (high: $100,000; low: $3,000).
Fields of interest: Hospice care; Protestantism; Children.
Type of support: General support.
Limitations: Applications not accepted. Giving primarily in MN.
Application information: Unsolicited requests for funds not accepted.
  Board meeting date(s): Annually
Officers: Shirley Sheldon, Pres.; Dan Sheldon, V.P.; Jamie Hanson, Secy.; Matthew Hanson, Treas.
EIN: 411891595

4624
Albany Mutual Telephone Foundation
131 6th St.
P.O. Box 570
Albany, MN 56307-0570 (320) 845-2101
Contact: Steve W. Katka, C.E.O. and Genl. Mgr.

Established in 2007 in Minnesota.
Donor: Central Stearns Comsis, Inc.
Foundation type: Company-sponsored foundation.
Financial data (yr. ended 12/31/13): Assets, $3,092,364 (M); expenditures, $168,912; qualifying distributions, $152,755; giving activities include $150,360 for 12 grants (high: $25,000; low: $4,360).

Purpose and activities: The foundation supports nonprofit organizations involved with education, community development, and religion.
Fields of interest: Education; Community and economic development; Religion.
Application information:
  Initial approach: Contact foundation application form
  Deadline(s): None
Officers: Steve Katka, C.E.O. and Genl. Mgr.; John Klaphake, Pres.; Joe Hennen, V.P.; Tony Reber, Secy.-Treas.
Directors: Norbert Overman; Dennis Sand; Dan Tomsche; David Waletzko; Jim Wimmer.
EIN: 261561849

4625
Albright Foundation
601 Carlson Pkwy., Ste. 610
Minnetonka, MN 55305-5215

Established in 2005 in Minnesota.
Donor: Robert Albright.
Foundation type: Independent foundation.
Financial data (yr. ended 12/31/13): Assets, $4,706,248 (M); gifts received, $752,450; expenditures, $200,600; qualifying distributions, $197,045; giving activities include $196,520 for 17 grants (high: $42,500; low: $1,020).
Fields of interest: Health; Public affairs; National defense; Religion.
Limitations: Applications not accepted. Giving primarily in CA, MN and VA. No grants to individuals.
Application information: Unsolicited requests for funds not accepted.
Officers: Robert Albright, Pres. and Treas.; Carolyn Albright, Secy.; Brian Haas, Mgr.
Directors: Jeanette Albright; Julie Albright; Robert Albright.
EIN: 203911328

4626
Elmer L. & Eleanor J. Andersen Foundation
2424 Territorial Rd.
Saint Paul, MN 55114-1556 (651) 642-0127
Contact: Mari Oyanagi Eggum, Fdn. Admin.
FAX: (651) 645-4684; *E-mail:* eandefdn@mtn.org

Established in 1957 in Minnesota.
Donors: Elmer L. Andersen†; Eleanor J. Andersen†; Anthony L. Andersen†.
Foundation type: Independent foundation.
Financial data (yr. ended 11/30/13): Assets, $5,304,022 (M); expenditures, $261,908; qualifying distributions, $229,875; giving activities include $183,200 for 76 grants (high: $25,000; low: $1,000).
Purpose and activities: The purpose of the foundation is to improve the quality of life through effective family grantmaking, honoring the legacy of its founders and investing in social change.
Fields of interest: Arts and culture; Education; Environment; Libraries; Communication media; Human services.
Type of support: General support; Continuing support; Annual campaigns; Program development.
Limitations: Applications accepted. Giving primarily in MN, with emphasis on the metropolitan St. Paul-Minneapolis area, primarily St. Paul. No support for health-related projects. No grants to individuals.

Publications: Annual report (including application guidelines).
Application information: Minnesota Common Grant Application Form accepted. The foundation accepts applications for Legacy Grants, but not for Trustee and Social Change Grants. Application form required.
  Initial approach: Request for guidelines
  Copies of proposal: 1
  Board meeting date(s): Middle of month in Mar., June, Sept., and Dec.
  Final notification: 21 days following board meeting
Officers and Directors: Julian Andersen, Pres. and Director; Terry Slye, Secy.; Amy Andersen, Treas. and Director; Charles Dayton.
Number of staff: 1 part-time professional.
EIN: 416032984

4627
The Anderson Trust
c/o Trust Tax Services
P.O. Box 64713
Saint Paul, MN 55164-0713

Foundation type: Independent foundation.
Financial data (yr. ended 12/31/13): Assets, $2,759,672 (M); expenditures, $203,362; qualifying distributions, $172,003; giving activities include $164,208 for 1 grant.
Fields of interest: Religion.
Limitations: Applications not accepted.
Application information: Unsolicited requests for funds not accepted.
Trustee: US Bank, N.A.
EIN: 416015218

4628
The Ankeny Foundation
601 Carlson Pkwy., Ste. 800
Minnetonka, MN 55305-5229

Established in 1963 in Minnesota.
Donors: DeWalt H. Ankeny, Jr.; Sally A. Anson; Kendall A. Mix; Michael H. Ankeny; Marie H. Ankeny Charitable Lead Trust; Dewalt Ankeny.
Foundation type: Independent foundation.
Financial data (yr. ended 03/31/13): Assets, $1,903,574 (M); gifts received, $505,187; expenditures, $260,947; qualifying distributions, $248,675; giving activities include $246,150 for 60 grants (high: $55,000; low: $100).
Fields of interest: Arts and culture; Education; Nonprofits; Diseases and conditions; Human services.
Type of support: General support; Annual campaigns; Capital campaigns; Endowments; Program development; Regranting.
Limitations: Applications not accepted. Giving primarily in MN, with emphasis on Minneapolis, and in NH. No grants to individuals.
Application information: Unsolicited general requests for funding not considered; grants to new organizations seldom considered.
Officers: Dewalt H. Ankeny, Jr., Pres.; Sally A. Anson, V.P.; Kendall A. Mix, Secy.; Michael H. Ankeny, Treas.
Number of staff: 1 part-time support.
EIN: 416024188

4629
Arctos Foundation
5201 Kellogg Ave.
Minneapolis, MN 55424-1304

Donor: George Vojta†.
Foundation type: Independent foundation.
Financial data (yr. ended 12/31/13): Assets, $10,616,879 (M); gifts received, $200,000; expenditures, $256,434; qualifying distributions, $198,410; giving activities include $157,400 for 8 grants (high: $68,000; low: $100).
Fields of interest: Education; Human services.
Limitations: Applications not accepted. Giving in the U.S., with some emphasis on GA and MN. No grants to individuals.
Application information: Unsolicited requests for funds not accepted.
Officer and Director: Christopher Vojta, Pres. and Director.
EIN: 800561039

4630
Arsher Charitable Trust
605 W. 37th St.
Hibbing, MN 55746-2829

Donors: James E. Rhude; Rhude & Fryberger Inc.; Joan Rhude.
Foundation type: Independent foundation.
Financial data (yr. ended 12/31/13): Assets, $9,867,347 (M); gifts received, $576,505; expenditures, $489,789; qualifying distributions, $409,855; giving activities include $405,300 for 45 grants (high: $60,000; low: $2,500).
Fields of interest: Diseases and conditions; Protestantism; Human services; Child welfare.
Limitations: Applications not accepted. Giving primarily in MN.
Application information: Contributes only to pre-selected organizations.
Trustees: John Nys; James E. Rhude.
EIN: 416331441

4631
Avocet Foundation
1660 S. Hwy. 100, Parkdale Plz., Ste. 426
Saint Louis Park, MN 55416-1533 (952) 512-1165
Contact: Joanne Kletscher, C.E.O., C.F.O., and Secy.

Established in 1996 in Minnesota.
Donors: Charles H. Bell†; Charles H. Bell Charitable Lead Annuity Trust; Charitable Lead Annuity Trust.
Foundation type: Independent foundation.
Financial data (yr. ended 12/31/13): Assets, $4,537,313 (M); gifts received, $190,106; expenditures, $252,872; qualifying distributions, $196,025; giving activities include $196,000 for 16 grants (high: $45,000; low: $5,000).
Fields of interest: Education; Environment; Human services; Adolescents.
Type of support: General support.
Limitations: Applications not accepted. Giving limited to MN. No grants to individuals.
Application information: Contributes only to pre-selected organizations.
Officer: Joanne Kletscher, C.E.O., C.F.O., and Secy.
EIN: 411859473

4632
The Bahl Foundation
P.O. Box 22094
Saint Paul, MN 55122-0094 (952) 895-8654

Established in 2002 in Connecticut.
Donors: Tracy L. Bahl; Felicia V. Bahl.
Foundation type: Independent foundation.
Financial data (yr. ended 12/31/13): Assets, $2,898 (M); gifts received, $272,856; expenditures, $337,846; qualifying distributions, $335,655; giving activities include $322,600 for 12 grants (high: $200,000; low: $1,200).
Purpose and activities: The foundation is dedicated to advancing the well being of children around the world through education, health, faith and the arts. .
Fields of interest: Education; Undergraduate education; Nonprofits; Youth services.
Type of support: Regranting.
Limitations: Applications accepted. Giving primarily in MN and NY.
Application information: Application form required.
 Initial approach: Letter
 Deadline(s): None
Officer: Penny Bailey, Exec. Dir.
Trustee: Tracy L. Bahl.
EIN: 146216533

4633
Gordon & Margaret Bailey Foundation
1323 Bohland Pl.
Saint Paul, MN 55119-6130 (651) 343-2050
Contact: Joseph Bailey, Pres. and Dir.

Established in 1991 in Minnesota.
Donor: Margaret Bailey.
Foundation type: Independent foundation.
Financial data (yr. ended 12/31/13): Assets, $4,556,232 (M); expenditures, $177,362; qualifying distributions, $166,089; giving activities include $154,700 for 24 grants (high: $20,000; low: $200).
Fields of interest: Education; Health; Community beautification; Christianity; Human services.
Limitations: Applications accepted. Giving primarily in MN.
Application information: See Minnesota Council on Foundations web site for complete application guidelines. Application form required.
 Initial approach: Letter
 Deadline(s): None
Officer and Directors: Joseph Bailey, Pres. and Director; Jerome Bailey; Chris Bartsch; Melissa Cullen; Laurie Grant.
EIN: 411704413

4634
Bame Foundation
900 Mendelssohn Ave. N.
Golden Valley, MN 55427-4309

Donors: Lamn, LLC; Christian Bame; Lubrication Technologies, Inc.; Insultation Distributors.
Foundation type: Independent foundation.
Financial data (yr. ended 12/31/13): Assets, $2,002,518 (M); gifts received, $711,990; expenditures, $254,750; qualifying distributions, $243,826; giving activities include $240,245 for 32 grants (high: $50,000; low: $100).
Fields of interest: Diseases and conditions; Sports and recreation; Human services.

Type of support: Research.
Limitations: Applications not accepted. Giving primarily in MN.
Application information: Unsolicited requests for funds not accepted.
Officers: Christian N. Bame, Pres.; Wendie M. Bame, Secy.; Marna Bame, Treas.
Directors: Kevin F. Bame; Stacey L. Bame; Merritt L. Geyen.
EIN: 274159707

4635
Baratz Family Foundation Inc.
600 South Hwy. 169, Ste. 701
Minneapolis, MN 55426
Contact: Stan Baratz, Pres.

Donors: Stan Baratz; Zollie Baratz; Shirley Baratz; Ken Fink.
Foundation type: Independent foundation.
Financial data (yr. ended 12/31/13): Assets, $488,075 (M); gifts received, $385,432; expenditures, $318,346; qualifying distributions, $314,331; giving activities include $314,331 for 139 grants (high: $27,500; low: $15).
Fields of interest: Education; Nonprofits; Hospital care; Judaism; Human services.
Type of support: General support; Capital and infrastructure; Regranting.
Limitations: Applications accepted. Giving primarily in FL and Minneapolis, MN.
Application information:
 Initial approach: Proposal
 Deadline(s): None
Officer: Stan Baratz, Pres.
EIN: 411295774

4636
Hugh C. Becker Foundation Inc.
13001 Shady Dale Rd.
Minnetonka, MN 55343-4904
Contact: George G. Selcke

Established in 2007 in Minnesota.
Donor: Hugh C. Becker†.
Foundation type: Independent foundation.
Financial data (yr. ended 12/31/14): Assets, $2,982,755 (M); expenditures, $192,485; qualifying distributions, $160,000; giving activities include $160,000 for 2 grants (high: $120,000; low: $40,000).
Fields of interest: Environment; Human services.
Limitations: Applications not accepted. Giving primarily in MN and WI. No grants to individuals.
Application information: Unsolicited request for funds not accepted.
Officer: George G. Selcke, Chair.
Board Members: Paul Hartman; Tim Hebert; Robert Hobbins; Greg Ide; Shawn Kellet; James Schultz.
EIN: 261117204

4637
David Winton Bell Foundation
1660 S. Hwy., 100 Parkdale Plz., Ste. 426
Saint Louis Park, MN 55416-1506

Established in 1955 in New York.
Foundation type: Independent foundation.
Financial data (yr. ended 12/31/13): Assets, $8,484,179 (M); expenditures, $504,837;

qualifying distributions, $400,356; giving activities include $400,306 for 35 grants (high: $40,000; low: $2,000).

Purpose and activities: Giving primarily to programs addressing environmental preservation and education, critical social education, and human service needs in Minneapolis.

Fields of interest: Education; Child educational development; Higher education; Environment; Natural resources; Biodiversity; Wildlife biodiversity; Community and economic development; Employment; Human services; Family services; Child welfare; Child development; Children; Adolescents; Ethnic and racial groups; Low-income and poor people; People with disabilities.

Type of support: General support; Continuing support; Capital campaigns; Capital and infrastructure; Program development; Seed money.

Limitations: Applications not accepted. Giving primarily in Minneapolis, MN.

Application information: Unsolicited requests for funds not accepted.

Board meeting date(s): May, June, Oct. and Nov.

Trustees: Charles B. Hartwell; David B. Hartwell; Lucy B. Hartwell; Penelope Bell Hatten.

EIN: 416023104

4638
James Ford Bell Foundation
c/o Family Philanthropy Advisors
1818 Oliver Ave. S.
Minneapolis, MN 55405-2208
E-mail: info@fpadvisors.com; Main URL: http://www.fpadvisors.com

Established in 1955 in Minnesota.

Donors: James Ford Bell†; Charles H. Bell†.

Foundation type: Independent foundation.

Financial data (yr. ended 12/31/14): Assets, $5,083,815; expenditures, $299,314; qualifying distributions, $262,452.

Purpose and activities: Emphasis on cultural programs; support also for wildlife preservation and conservation, youth agencies, the environment, education, health and human services.

Fields of interest: Arts and culture; Museums; Education; Early childhood education; Child educational development; Higher education; Adult education; Basic and remedial instruction; Reading promotion; Environment; Natural resources; Biodiversity; Wildlife biodiversity; Family planning; Biology; Population studies; Community and economic development; Urban development; Reproductive rights; Human services; Family services; Child welfare; Child development; Females; Ethnic and racial groups; People of Asian descent; People of African descent; People of Latin American descent; American Indians; Immigrants and migrants; Low-income and poor people; People with disabilities.

Type of support: General support; Continuing support; Program development; Seed money.

Limitations: Applications not accepted. No grants to individuals, or for fellowships, memberships, annual campaigns, or special events or fundraisers.

Application information: Unsolicited requests for funds not accepted.

Officer: Ellen George, Exec. Dir.

Trustees: Ford W. Bell; Samuel H. Bell, Jr.

EIN: 416023099

4639
Bend Foundation
730 2nd Ave. S., Ste. 1300
Minneapolis, MN 55402-2475   (612) 752-1770
Contact: Michael P. Hollern, Tr.

Established in 1947 in Illinois.

Donors: Brooks-Scanlon, Inc.; Brooks Resources Inc.

Foundation type: Company-sponsored foundation.

Financial data (yr. ended 12/31/13): Assets, $5,211,695 (M); gifts received, $18,972; expenditures, $287,623; qualifying distributions, $244,299; giving activities include $241,500 for 26 grants (high: $50,000; low: $1,000).

Purpose and activities: The foundation supports health clinics and organizations involved with arts and culture, education, land conservation, hunger, and human services.

Fields of interest: Arts and culture; Theater; Museums; Education; Higher education; Land resources; Health care clinics; Film and video; Human services; Food aid; Family services; Child welfare; Youth services; Domestic violence shelters.

Type of support: Annual campaigns; Capital and infrastructure; Equipment; Program development; Seed money.

Limitations: Applications accepted. Giving limited to central OR, with emphasis on Deschutes County. No grants for general operating support, debt reduction, endowments, special projects, research, publications, or conferences; no loans.

Application information: Application form required.

Initial approach: Letter
Copies of proposal: 1
Deadline(s): None
Board meeting date(s): Feb. or Mar.

Trustees: Colin Brooks; Conley Brooks, Jr.; Michael P. Hollern; Kirk Schueler; William L. Smith.

EIN: 416019901

4640
R. R. W. & Florence Berglund Family Foundation
c/o Snelson K. Berglund
665 N. Snelling Ave.
Saint Paul, MN 55104-1839

Established in 2003 in Minnesota.

Donor: Wesley E. Berglund†.

Foundation type: Independent foundation.

Financial data (yr. ended 12/31/13): Assets, $9,945,830 (M); expenditures, $466,475; qualifying distributions, $379,404; giving activities include $334,834 for 4 grants (high: $214,834; low: $15,000).

Fields of interest: Languages; Youth services.

Limitations: Applications not accepted. Giving primarily in MN. No grants to individuals.

Application information: Contributes only to pre-selected organizations.

Officer and Trustees: Stephen L. Nelson, Mgr. and Trustee; Kenneth J. Berglund.

EIN: 206126546

4641
Bieber Family Foundation
10025 Valley View Rd., Ste. 190
Eden Prairie, MN 55344

Established in 1990 in Minnesota.

Donors: William F. Bieber; Kathleen O'Connor.

Foundation type: Independent foundation.

Financial data (yr. ended 12/31/13): Assets, $10,812,202 (M); gifts received, $1,191,602; expenditures, $466,286; qualifying distributions, $400,525; giving activities include $400,500 for 91 grants (high: $30,000; low: $500).

Purpose and activities: Giving primarily for human services.

Fields of interest: Arts and culture; Education; Christianity; Human services; Child welfare.

Limitations: Applications not accepted. Giving primarily in MN. No grants to individuals.

Application information: Contributes only to pre-selected organizations.

Officers and Directors: William F. Bieber, Pres. and Director; Kathleen G. O'Connor, V.P. and Director; Christine Bieber Orris, Secy. and Director; Mark Osmanski, Treas.; Kerri Bieber McAfoos.

EIN: 411679484

4642
Archie C. & Jane McDonald Black Charitable Trust
c/o Archie C. Black III
924 Adeline Ln. N.
Golden Valley, MN 55422-4701

Established in 1997 in Minnesota.

Foundation type: Independent foundation.

Financial data (yr. ended 12/31/13): Assets, $4,701,043 (M); gifts received, $25; expenditures, $161,141; qualifying distributions, $159,050; giving activities include $159,050 for 17 grants (high: $30,000; low: $250).

Fields of interest: Education; Religion; Human services.

Limitations: Applications not accepted. Giving primarily in MN. No grants to individuals.

Application information: Unsolicited requests for funds not accepted.

Trustees: Archie C. Black; Jane McDonald.

EIN: 416426986

4643
Blank Family Foundation
P.O. Box 964
Long Lake, MN 55356-0964

Donors: Karen L. Blank; John P. Blank.

Foundation type: Independent foundation.

Financial data (yr. ended 12/31/13): Assets, $3,207,703 (M); expenditures, $233,535; qualifying distributions, $222,667; giving activities include $220,900 for 11 grants (high: $100,000; low: $1,000).

Fields of interest: Education; Health; Human services.

Limitations: Applications not accepted. Giving primarily in MN.

Application information: Unsolicited requests for funds not accepted.

Officers: Karen L. Blank, Pres.; John P. Blank, V.P. and Secy.-Treas.

Director: Meredith L. Blank.

EIN: 900410317

4644
Marvin & Betty Borman Foundation
3300 Wells Fargo Ctr.
90 S. 7th St.
Minneapolis, MN 55402-3903

Established in 1984 in Minnesota.
Donors: The Hendel Foundation; Elizabeth Borman; Marvin Borman†.
Foundation type: Independent foundation.
Financial data (yr. ended 12/31/13): Assets, $8,401,528 (M); gifts received, $2,632,209; expenditures, $441,584; qualifying distributions, $357,595; giving activities include $350,097 for 115 grants (high: $50,000; low: $25).
Purpose and activities: Giving to Jewish agencies, higher education, and youth development.
Fields of interest: Arts and culture; Higher education; Nonprofits; Judaism; Human services; Youth development.
Type of support: General support; Capital campaigns; Endowments; Regranting.
Limitations: Applications not accepted. Giving primarily in MN. No grants to individuals.
Application information: Contributes only to pre-selected organizations.
Officer: Elizabeth Borman, Pres., V.P. and Secy.-Treas.
EIN: 411506784

4645
Harlan Boss Foundation for the Arts
c/o W. Andrew Boss
332 Minnesota St., Ste. 2200
Saint Paul, MN 55101-1385

Established in 1994 in Minnesota.
Donor: Harlan Boss†.
Foundation type: Independent foundation.
Financial data (yr. ended 12/31/14): Assets, $4,206,874 (M); expenditures, $283,616; qualifying distributions, $257,518; giving activities include $254,500 for 18 grants (high: $45,000; low: $1,000).
Fields of interest: Arts and culture; Opera; Museums; Historic preservation; Education; Public libraries; Community and economic development; Human services.
Limitations: Applications not accepted. Giving primarily in Ramsey County, MN. No grants to individuals.
Application information: Unsolicited requests for funds not accepted.
Officers and Directors: Calvin W. Didier, V.P. and Director; Linda Boss, Secy.-Treas. and Director.
EIN: 411758708

4646
The Boss Foundation
5858 Centerville Rd.
Saint Paul, MN 55127-6804 (651) 653-0599
Contact: Daniel W. McKeown, Pres.

Donor: The Specialty Manufacturing Co.
Foundation type: Company-sponsored foundation.
Financial data (yr. ended 06/30/14): Assets, $7,456,327 (M); gifts received, $65,000; expenditures, $392,803; qualifying distributions, $342,025; giving activities include $342,000 for 58 grants (high: $15,000; low: $2,000).

Purpose and activities: The foundation supports zoos and organizations involved with arts and culture, higher education, and human services.
Fields of interest: Arts and culture; Performing arts; Theater; Opera; Museums; Historic preservation; Higher education; Zoos; Human services; Youth services.
Type of support: General support.
Limitations: Applications accepted. Giving primarily in the Minneapolis and St. Paul, MN, metropolitan area. No grants to individuals.
Publications: Application guidelines.
Application information: Application form required.
Initial approach: Letter
Deadline(s): June 30
Board meeting date(s): June
Officers: Heidi McKeown, Chair.; Daniel W. McKeown, Pres.; Isabella McKeown, Secy.; Desmond McKeown, Treas.
EIN: 416038452

4647
William E. Bradley Research Foundation
P.O. Box 5819
Rochester, MN 55903-5819

Established in 2002 in Washington.
Donor: William E. Bradley Family Foundation.
Foundation type: Independent foundation.
Financial data (yr. ended 12/31/13): Assets, $5,944,293 (M); expenditures, $265,650; qualifying distributions, $260,565; giving activities include $241,425 for 5 grants (high: $108,425; low: $10,000).
Fields of interest: Education; Higher education; Environment; Neurology; Diseases and conditions.
Type of support: Research.
Limitations: Applications not accepted. Giving primarily in MD, NC, and WA. No grants to individuals.
Application information: Contributes only to pre-selected organizations.
Trustees: David J. Bradley; Elizabeth A. Bradley.
EIN: 916558207

4648
Briggs and Morgan Foundation
(formerly Chancery Lane Foundation)
332 Minnesota St., Ste. 2200
Saint Paul, MN 55101
Main URL: http://www.briggs.com/about-leadership.html

Established in 1960 in Minnesota.
Donors: Alan Maclin; Joseph Roach; Jack Perry; Michael Krikava; Mary Ippel; Sam Hanson; Michael McEllistrem; Joseph Kinning; Terry Slye; Michael Grimes; Mark Ayotte; Lauren Lonergan; Frank Taylor; Brian Wenger; Charles Rogers; Timothy Thorton; Gregory Stemoe.
Foundation type: Company-sponsored foundation.
Financial data (yr. ended 12/31/13): Assets, $94,019 (M); gifts received, $339,769; expenditures, $371,032; qualifying distributions, $370,318; giving activities include $370,318 for 61 grants (high: $40,000; low: $600).
Purpose and activities: The foundation supports organizations involved with education, legal aid, and civil rights.

Fields of interest: Education; Higher education; Law education; Legal aid; Human rights; Human services.
Type of support: Continuing support; Annual campaigns; Capital campaigns; Program development.
Limitations: Applications not accepted. Giving primarily in the Minneapolis and St. Paul, MN, area. No grants to individuals.
Application information: Contributes only to pre-selected organizations.
Officers and Directors: Alan Maclin, Pres. and Director; Steve Ryan, V.P. and Director; Dawn Iacarella, Secy.; Terry Slye, Treas. and Director; Greg Stemoe.
EIN: 416009924

4649
The Bumgarner Family Foundation
6830 Newton Ave. S.
Richfield, MN 55423-2117

Established in 2003 in Minnesota.
Donors: Garnett I. Kirchner Trust I; Garnett I. Kirchner Trust II.
Foundation type: Independent foundation.
Financial data (yr. ended 12/31/13): Assets, $2,080,097 (M); expenditures, $134,736; qualifying distributions, $118,000; giving activities include $118,000 for 6 grants (high: $100,000; low: $2,000).
Fields of interest: Elementary and secondary education; Foundations; Nonprofits; Protestantism; Independent living for people with disabilities.
Type of support: General support; Regranting.
Limitations: Applications not accepted. Giving primarily in MN. No grants to individuals.
Application information: Unsolicited requests for funds not accepted.
Officers and Directors: John T. Bumgarner, Pres. and Treas. and Director; Terry L. Bumgarner, Secy. and Director; Carrie L. Bumgarner McLeod; Mariesa Ryan.
EIN: 743035482

4650
Rodney and Barbara Burwell Family Foundation
7901 Xerxes Ave. S., Ste. 201
Minneapolis, MN 55431-1219

Established in 1999 in Minnesota.
Donors: Rodney P. Burwell; Xerxes Corporation.
Foundation type: Independent foundation.
Financial data (yr. ended 12/31/13): Assets, $7,347,207 (M); expenditures, $368,860; qualifying distributions, $366,543; giving activities include $366,000 for 13 grants (high: $150,000; low: $500).
Fields of interest: Arts and culture; Education; Nonprofits; Religion; Human services.
Type of support: Regranting.
Limitations: Applications not accepted. Giving primarily in MN. No grants to individuals.
Application information: Contributes only to pre-selected organizations.
Officers and Directors: Rodney P. Burwell, Pres. and Director; Barbara E. Burwell, V.P. and Director; Janet R. Leuman, Secy.-Treas. and Director.
EIN: 411939337

4651
Butzow Family Foundation
9714 Brassie Cir.
Eden Prairie, MN 55347-2938

Established in 2007 in Minnesota.
Donor: Barry W. Butzow.
Foundation type: Independent foundation.
Financial data (yr. ended 12/31/13): Assets, $6,782,985 (M); gifts received, $2,275; expenditures, $410,254; qualifying distributions, $377,275; giving activities include $375,000 for 22 grants (high: $75,000; low: $3,500).
Fields of interest: Health care clinics; Infant care; Diabetes; Child welfare.
Limitations: Applications not accepted. Giving primarily in MN. No grants to individuals.
Application information: Contributes only to pre-selected organizations.
Officer: Barry W. Butzow, Pres. and Secy.-Treas.
Directors: Bryan A. Butzow; Joni Butzow; Jon Maruk.
EIN: 260178747

4652
Camara-Press Foundation
3515 Green Ridge Rd.
Minnetonka, MN 55305-4445

Foundation type: Independent foundation.
Financial data (yr. ended 12/31/13): Assets, $5,938,132 (M); gifts received, $1,300,000; expenditures, $152,809; qualifying distributions, $140,000; giving activities include $140,000 for 2 grants (high: $100,000; low: $40,000).
Fields of interest: Sports and recreation; Human services.
Limitations: Applications not accepted. Giving primarily in MN.
Application information: Unsolicited requests for funds not accepted.
Directors: Stella J. Camara Press; Thomas Press.
EIN: 271985444

4653
Caridad Corporation
2630 W. Lafayette Rd.
Excelsior, MN 55331-9417

Established in 1987 in Minnesota.
Donors: Thomas P. Lowe; Margaret L. Lowe; Finley Bros. Enterprises; Morgan Arundel.
Foundation type: Independent foundation.
Financial data (yr. ended 12/31/14): Assets, $465,972; expenditures, $362,916; qualifying distributions, $331,558.
Fields of interest: Arts and culture; Education; Community and economic development; Sports and recreation.
Limitations: Applications accepted. Giving primarily in Minneapolis, MN. No grants to individuals.
Application information: Application form required.
Initial approach: Letter
Deadline(s): Oct. 30
Officers: Thomas P. Lowe, Pres.; Margaret L. Lowe, V.P.; Thomas P. Lowe III, Treas.
EIN: 363505813

4654
Caroline's Kids Foundation
P.O Box 27247
Golden Valley, MN 55427-0247

Donor: Caroline Amplatz.
Foundation type: Independent foundation.
Financial data (yr. ended 12/31/13): Assets, $988,416 (M); expenditures, $286,458; qualifying distributions, $243,338; giving activities include $193,500 for 27 grants (high: $20,000; low: $1,000).
Fields of interest: Arts and culture; Education; Human services.
Limitations: Applications not accepted. Giving primarily in MN.
Application information: Unsolicited requests for funds not accepted.
Officers and Directors: Caroline Amplatz, Pres. and Secy. and Director; Kari Geurts, Treas. and Director; Bruce Larson.
EIN: 262424909

4655
Chadwick-Loher Foundation
1800 IDS Ctr.
80 S. 8th St.
Minneapolis, MN 55402-2100

Established in 1998 in Minnesota.
Foundation type: Independent foundation.
Financial data (yr. ended 12/31/13): Assets, $9,774,952 (M); expenditures, $546,398; qualifying distributions, $436,530; giving activities include $428,000 for grants.
Purpose and activities: Giving primarily for education and the arts.
Fields of interest: Arts and culture; Performing arts; Opera; Art museums; Education; Elementary and secondary education; Higher education; Foundations.
Limitations: Applications not accepted. Giving primarily in MN and TX. No grants to individuals.
Application information: Contributes only to pre-selected organizations.
Officers: John W. Dayton, Pres.; Arlene J. Dayton, Secy.-Treas.
Directors: Whitney D. Brunet; Chadwick L. Dayton.
EIN: 522390635

4656
Charity, Inc.
38 Minnesota Ave. S.
Aitkin, MN 56431-1621
Application address: c/o Deanne Hulme, 530 Williamsburg, Pl., New Richmond, WI 54017, tel.: (715) 246-6936

Established in 1962 in Minnesota.
Donors: Rose W. Totino; Pillsbury Co.
Foundation type: Independent foundation.
Financial data (yr. ended 12/31/13): Assets, $7,528,101 (M); expenditures, $492,446; qualifying distributions, $320,058; giving activities include $320,058 for 41 grants (high: $143,733; low: $500).
Purpose and activities: Primarily contributes to Christian religious and educational organizations.
Fields of interest: Elementary and secondary education; Higher education; Catholicism; Camps; Child welfare; Domestic violence shelters.

Limitations: Giving primarily in the Minneapolis-St. Paul, MN, area. No grants to individuals.
Application information:
Initial approach: Letter
Deadline(s): None
Officers and Directors: Joanne Elwell, Pres. and Secy.- Treas. and Director; Bonita Brenny, V.P. and Director; Donald Schwalm.
EIN: 410636273

4657
City of Rosemount-SKB
(formerly SKB Environmental, Inc. Rosemount Community Trust)
P.O. Box 392
Rosemount, MN 55068-0392 (651) 454-2533
Contact: Don Chapdelaine, Tr.

Established in 1993 in Minnesota.
Donors: USPCI, Inc.; Laidlaw Environmental Services, Inc.; Safety-Kleen Corp.; SKB Environmental Inc.; SKB, Inc.
Foundation type: Company-sponsored foundation.
Financial data (yr. ended 12/31/13): Assets, $1,847,373 (M); gifts received, $401,023; expenditures, $420,847; qualifying distributions, $417,974; giving activities include $417,974 for 8 grants (high: $355,974; low: $1,000).
Limitations: Applications accepted. Giving limited to the Rosemount, MN, area. No grants to individuals, or for political campaigns.
Application information: Application form required.
Initial approach: Proposal
Deadline(s): None
Officers: Heather Nosan, Pres.; Bill Olson, Secy.
Trustees: Donald Chapdelaine; John Domke.
EIN: 411739015

4658
Cook Waterfowl Foundation
7850 Metro Pkwy., Ste. 121
Minneapolis, MN 55425-1521

Donors: James R. Cook; Diane Cook; Roddy D. Ustipak; Crosslands Inc.; Investment Rarities Inc.
Foundation type: Operating foundation.
Financial data (yr. ended 11/30/13): Assets, $2,308,544 (M); gifts received, $44,500; expenditures, $287,797; qualifying distributions, $286,722; giving activities include $179,800 for 2 grants (high: $177,800; low: $2,000).
Fields of interest: Human services.
Type of support: General support.
Limitations: Applications not accepted. Giving primarily in MN. No grants to individuals.
Application information: Unsolicited requests for funds not accepted.
Officers: Joseph Tonnelli, Pres.; Diane Cook, Secy.; James Cook, Treas.
Number of staff: None.
EIN: 363327050

4659
Elbridge C. Cooke Trust
c/o Trust Tax Services
P.O. Box 64713
Saint Paul, MN 55164-0713

Foundation type: Independent foundation.

Financial data (yr. ended 12/31/13): Assets, $2,510,234 (M); expenditures, $141,254; qualifying distributions, $118,315; giving activities include $112,305 for 3 grants (high: $56,153; low: $28,076).

Fields of interest: Arts and culture; Health; Diseases and conditions.

Limitations: Applications not accepted. Giving limited to MN.

Application information: Unsolicited requests for funds not accepted.

Trustee: U.S. Bank, N.A.

EIN: 416015178

4660

The Cornwall Foundation

c/o Mary Anne J. Baker
90 S. 7th St., Ste. 5100
Minneapolis, MN 55402-4168

Established in 1999 in Minnesota.

Donor: LMB Family Trust.

Foundation type: Independent foundation.

Financial data (yr. ended 12/31/14): Assets, $5,096,808; expenditures, $233,511; qualifying distributions, $219,995.

Fields of interest: Education; Philanthropy; Health.

Limitations: Applications not accepted. Giving primarily in MN. No grants to individuals.

Application information: Unsolicited requests for funds not accepted.

Officers and Directors: Mary Ann Baker, Pres. and Secy.-Treas.; Looe Baker III, V.P. and Director; Looe Baker.

EIN: 411956489

4661

The Covenant Foundation

13777 40th St. N.
Stillwater, MN 55082-1210

Established in 1987 in Minnesota.

Donors: Gerald L. Haire; Industrial Lumber & Plywood; Woodgood, Inc.; Lucretia Haire; Wood Good Industries.

Foundation type: Independent foundation.

Financial data (yr. ended 11/30/14): Assets, $50,094 (M); gifts received, $145,000; expenditures, $120,164; qualifying distributions, $118,860; giving activities include $118,860 for 7 grants (high: $60,000; low: $360).

Purpose and activities: Giving primarily for Christian ministries.

Fields of interest: Education; Christianity; Human services; Christians.

Limitations: Applications not accepted. Giving primarily in MN. No grants to individuals.

Application information: Contributes only to pre-selected organizations.

Directors: Lucretia Haire; Steven Haire.

EIN: 363566128

4662

James M. Cox Foundation

c/o Trust Tax Svcs.
P.O. Box 64713
Saint Paul, MN 55164-0713 (402) 488-1951
Application address: 1500 Kingston Rd., Lincoln, NE 68506, tel.: (402) 488-1951

Established in 1989 in Nebraska.

Donor: James M. Cox†.

Foundation type: Company-sponsored foundation.

Financial data (yr. ended 12/31/14): Assets, $2,223,576; expenditures, $213,858; qualifying distributions, $197,965.

Purpose and activities: Assisting needy children to become productive adults through scholarships, grants to charitable organizations who have a similar purpose, and other methods of assistance.

Fields of interest: Education; Higher education; Child welfare.

Type of support: Emergency funds; Matching grants; Scholarships; Student aid.

Limitations: Applications accepted. Giving restricted to residents of eastern NE.

Publications: Application guidelines.

Application information: Application form required.

Initial approach: Request application form
Copies of proposal: 1
Deadline(s): Apr. 1
Board meeting date(s): Varies

Officers: Norman A. Otto, Pres.; Ronald C. Jensen, Secy.; Michael J. Lynch, Treas.

Trustee: US Bank, N.A.

EIN: 470719195

4663

The Deikel Family Foundation

(formerly The Ted Deikel Foundation)
1660 Highway 100 S., Ste. 500
Saint Louis Park, MN 55416-1551 (952) 697-4041
Contact: Theodore Deikel, Pres.
FAX: (952) 697-4042; E-mail: teddeikel@gmail.com

Established in 1989 in Minnesota.

Donor: Theodore Deikel.

Foundation type: Independent foundation.

Financial data (yr. ended 12/31/13): Assets, $9,224,623 (M); expenditures, $493,644; qualifying distributions, $393,422; giving activities include $369,282 for 15 grants (high: $100,000; low: $1,000).

Purpose and activities: Giving primarily to Jewish organizations and human service organizations.

Fields of interest: Nonprofits; Judaism; Human services.

Type of support: General support; Pro bono consulting services; Matching grants; Continuing support; Annual campaigns; Regranting; Capital campaigns; Capital and infrastructure; Equipment; Emergency funds; Program development; Seed money; Research.

Limitations: Applications accepted. Giving primarily in Minneapolis, MN. No grants to individuals.

Application information: The foundation requests that applicants limit their paper use and number of contacts.

Initial approach: Letter
Copies of proposal: 1
Deadline(s): None
Board meeting date(s): As needed
Final notification: Varies

Officer: Theodore Deikel, Pres. and Secy.

Number of staff: 1 part-time professional.

EIN: 411651703

4664

Roger L. & Agnes C. Dell Charitable Trust

c/o Trust Tax Services
P.O. Box 64713
Saint Paul, MN 55164-0713
Application address: c/o Richard L. Pemberton, Att.: U.S. Bank, 101 E. 5th St., St. Paul, MN 55101, tel.: (612) 303-3208

Established in 1970 in Minnesota.

Foundation type: Independent foundation.

Financial data (yr. ended 12/31/13): Assets, $4,521,371 (M); expenditures, $251,838; qualifying distributions, $214,309; giving activities include $198,888 for 26 grants (high: $50,000; low: $288).

Fields of interest: Higher education; Nonprofits; Protestantism; Youth services.

Type of support: General support; Scholarships; Regranting.

Limitations: Applications accepted. Giving primarily in the Fergus Falls, MN, area. No grants to individuals.

Application information: Application form required.

Initial approach: Letter
Deadline(s): None

Trustees: Morrie Kershner; Richard L. Pemberton; Stephen F. Rufer; U.S. Bank, N.A.

EIN: 416046675

4665

Dellwood Foundation, Inc.

3765 IDS Ctr., 80 S. 8th St.
Minneapolis, MN 55402

Established in 1958 in Minnesota.

Donor: John G. Ordway, Jr.

Foundation type: Independent foundation.

Financial data (yr. ended 12/31/13): Assets, $4,774,268 (M); expenditures, $256,471; qualifying distributions, $226,955; giving activities include $225,500 for 50 grants (high: $35,000; low: $500).

Fields of interest: Arts and culture; Performing arts; Museums; Education; Environment; Nonprofits; Hospital care; Human services.

Type of support: Regranting.

Limitations: Applications not accepted. Giving primarily in MN. No grants to individuals.

Application information: Unsolicited requests for funds not accepted.

Officers and Directors: Phillip W. Ordway, Pres. and Treas. and Director; John G. Ordway III, V.P. and Secy. and Director; J. Erik Ordway, V.P. and Director.

EIN: 416019244

4666

Greater Denfeld Foundation, Inc.

c/o Trust Tax Svcs.
P.O. Box 64713
Saint Paul, MN 55164-0713

Established in 1971 in Minnesota.

Foundation type: Independent foundation.

Financial data (yr. ended 04/30/13): Assets, $6,747,162 (M); gifts received, $132,736; expenditures, $362,747; qualifying distributions, $324,498; giving activities include $310,454 for grants to individuals.

Fields of interest: Education.

Type of support: Student aid.

Limitations: Giving limited in Duluth, MN.
Officers and Directors: William Westholm, Chair. and Director; Jon Helstrom, Vice-Chair. and Director; Claude Lutzka, Treas. and Director; Nancy Anderson; Don Annala; Harry Fisher; Gregory Fox; Marvin Heikkinen; Eille Martin.
EIN: 237182610

4667
The Depot Foundation
130 W. Superior St.
302 U.S. Bank Pl.
Duluth, MN 55802-2032   (218) 279-9913
FAX: (218) 279-9914;
E-mail: info@depotfoundation.org; Main
URL: http://www.depotfoundation.org

Foundation type: Independent foundation.
Financial data (yr. ended 06/30/13): Assets, $5,975,711 (M); gifts received, $201,804; expenditures, $292,603; qualifying distributions, $206,498; giving activities include $195,484 for 13 grants (high: $50,000; low: $53).
Purpose and activities: The foundation raises, manages, and distributes charitable capital to benefit primarily the St. Louis County Heritage and Arts Center and the nine arts and cultural organizations affiliated at the center.
Fields of interest: Arts and culture.
Type of support: General support; Capital and infrastructure; Program development.
Limitations: Giving primarily in northeastern MN and northwestern WI.
Publications: Annual report; Informational brochure; Newsletter.
Application information: Eligible applicants for all grants funding must have 501(c)(3) status and have a mission to preserve or present arts, culture, or history within northeastern Minnesota and/or northwestern Wisconsin. Application form required.
  Initial approach: Telephone or letter
  Copies of proposal: 6
  Deadline(s): Jan. 31 for Prindle/Wood Family Memorial Endowment Fund; Sept 30 for Designated Funds; Oct. 31 for Undesignated Funds
  Board meeting date(s): Bimonthly on the 4th Wed.
  Final notification: Feb. 28 for Prindle/Wood Family Memorial Endowment Fund; Oct. 31 for Designated Funds; Dec. 31 for Undesignated Fund
Officers and Directors: Richard Fischer, Chair. and Director; Jean B. Olsen, Vice-Chair. and Director; Thomas Whittaker, Secy. and Director; Melinda Machones, Treas. and Director; Linda Boben; Laura Budd; Pat Cutshall; Ben Fornear; Dexter Larson.
Number of staff: 1 full-time professional; 1 part-time support.
EIN: 411356072

4668
Desiring God Foundation
1801 11th Ave. S.
Minneapolis, MN 55404-2010

Established in 2001 in Minnesota.
Donor: John Piper.
Foundation type: Independent foundation.
Financial data (yr. ended 12/31/13): Assets, $980,726 (M); gifts received, $124,550; expenditures, $301,299; qualifying distributions,

$297,029; giving activities include $295,000 for 2 grants (high: $200,000; low: $95,000).
Fields of interest: Graduate and professional education; Christianity; Theology.
Limitations: Applications not accepted. Giving primarily in Minneapolis, MN. No grants to individuals.
Application information: Contributes only to pre-selected organizations.
Officers: John Piper, Pres.; Terry Kurschner, Treas.
Director: Noel Piper.
EIN: 412011129

4669
The Jaye F. and Betty F. Dyer Foundation
(formerly The Dyco Foundation)
527 Marquette Ave. S., Ste. 2450
Minneapolis, MN 55402-1333

Established in 1977 in Minnesota.
Donors: Dyco Petroleum Corp.; Jaye F. Dyer; The Jaye F. Dyer Family Charitable Lead Trust; Betty Faye Dyer Charitable Lead Trust.
Foundation type: Independent foundation.
Financial data (yr. ended 12/31/13): Assets, $5,222,579 (M); gifts received, $249,777; expenditures, $263,343; qualifying distributions, $234,326; giving activities include $208,000 for 24 grants (high: $50,000; low: $1,000).
Purpose and activities: Support for medicine and health, social service agencies, community development, and youth organizations. Primary focus: self-sufficiency through employment programs targeting the handicapped, minority teens, and the long-term unemployed.
Fields of interest: Health; Diseases and conditions; Agriculture; Community and economic development; Employment; Human services; Child welfare; Low-income and poor people; People with disabilities.
Type of support: General support; Emergency funds; Program development.
Limitations: Applications not accepted. Giving primarily in MN.
Application information: Unsolicited requests for funds not accepted.
Officers and Directors: Michael J. Dyer, Pres. and Director; Darlene L. McGee, V.P. and Admin.; Jill M. Dyer; Joe Selvaggio.
Number of staff: 1 part-time support.
EIN: 411390020

4670
Ecotrust Foundation
1976 Sheridan Ave. S.
Minneapolis, MN 55405-2211

Established in 1992 in Minnesota.
Donors: V. Wurtele; Peter Vaughan.
Foundation type: Independent foundation.
Financial data (yr. ended 12/31/13): Assets, $1,835,576 (M); gifts received, $150,000; expenditures, $257,398; qualifying distributions, $255,890; giving activities include $255,890 for 51 grants (high: $35,000; low: $100).
Purpose and activities: Giving primarily for environmental research, protection and conservation, including population control and family planning services.
Fields of interest: Environment; Natural resources; Family services.

Limitations: Applications not accepted. Giving primarily in NY and MN. No grants to individuals.
Application information: Contributes only to pre-selected organizations.
Officer and Directors: Peter Vaughan, Pres. and Director; Catherine K. Anson; Angus M. Vaughan.
EIN: 411735062

4671
The Edina Community Foundation
5280 Grandview Sq., Ste. 101
Edina, MN 55436-1755   (952) 833-9573
Contact: Dick Crockett, Exec. Dir.
FAX: (952) 833-9575;
E-mail: edfoundation@edinamn.gov; Main
URL: http://www.edinacommunityfoundation.org
Facebook: http://www.facebook.com/pages/
Edina-Community-Foundation/167404813358665

Established in 1977 in Minnesota.
Foundation type: Community foundation.
Financial data (yr. ended 06/30/13): Assets, $890,604 (M); gifts received, $256,668; expenditures, $310,724; giving activities include $158,885 for grants.
Purpose and activities: The foundation seeks to advance the community as a premier place for living, learning, raising families and nurturing leadership through the development of a strong program of philanthropy.
Fields of interest: Arts and culture; Disasters and emergency management; Community and economic development; Sports and recreation; Youth development.
Type of support: Scholarships.
Publications: Annual report.
Application information: Visit foundation web site for a grant application form and information. Application form required.
  Initial approach: Submit application form
  Deadline(s): Jan. 15, May 15, and Sept. 15
  Final notification: Within 6 weeks
Officers and Directors: Paul Mooty, Pres. and Director; Brenda Radichel Quaye, V.P. and Director; Scot Housh, Secy. and Director; Bernie Beaver, Treas. and Director; Dick Crockett, Exec. Dir.; Saturu Asato; Brad Beard; Ron Erhardt; James B. Hovland; Steven McDonald; Richard Olson; Mamie Segall; Maxine Wallin.
Emeriti: Carolyn Schroeder, Pres. and Director; Bonnie McGrath, Secy. and Director; Denny Maetzold; Fred Richards; Geof Workinger.
EIN: 411315037

4672
Edina Realty Foundation
6800 France Ave. S., Ste. 600
Minneapolis, MN 55435-2017   (952) 928-5356
Contact: Susan Cowsert, Dir.
Main URL: http://www.edinarealty.com/pages/
community-involvement-edina-realty-foundation

Established in 1996 in Minnesota.
Donor: Edina Realty, Inc.
Foundation type: Company-sponsored foundation.
Financial data (yr. ended 09/30/14): Assets, $402,694 (M); gifts received, $338,734; expenditures, $312,344; qualifying distributions, $302,454; giving activities include $302,454 for 130 grants (high: $22,902; low: $113).

Purpose and activities: The foundation supports programs designed to provide food, emergency shelter, medical care, job readiness training, and other services to the homeless.
Fields of interest: Health; Human services; Food aid; Food banks; Housing for the homeless; Housing services; Homeless services; Homeless people; Low-income and poor people.
Type of support: General support; Cash grants; Employee volunteer services; Capital campaigns; Capital and infrastructure; Emergency funds; Program development; Research.
Limitations: Applications accepted. Giving primarily in MN. No grants to individuals.
Publications: Application guidelines; Annual report; Program policy statement.
Application information: Grants range from $500 to $5,000 with the average grant being $2,000. Application form required.
  Initial approach: Download application form and mail to a local foundation representative
  Copies of proposal: 1
  Deadline(s): None
  Board meeting date(s): Quarterly
Directors: Michelle Cici; Mark Christopherson; Susan Cowsert; Kevin Folkerts; Scott Harris; Amy Kleinschmidt; Marc Kuhnley; Jodi Lucast; Debra Stumne.
Number of staff: 1 full-time support; 1 part-time support.
EIN: 411826980

4673
The Emmerich Foundation Charitable Trust
7700 Old Hwy., 169 Blvd.
Jordan, MN 55352

Established in 1992 in Minnesota.
Donors: Karol D. Emmerich; Richard J. Emmerich.
Foundation type: Independent foundation.
Financial data (yr. ended 12/31/14): Assets, $2,103,401; expenditures, $218,564; qualifying distributions, $211,575.
Fields of interest: Christianity.
Limitations: Applications not accepted. Giving on a national basis. No grants to individuals.
Application information: Unsolicited requests for funds not accepted.
Trustees: Karol D. Emmerich; Richard J. Emmerich.
Number of staff: None.
EIN: 411712553

4674
Alfred W. Erickson Foundation
P.O. Box 1224
Minneapolis, MN 55440-1224

Established in 1964 in Minnesota.
Donors: Holiday Stationstores, Inc.; Holiday Companies.
Foundation type: Independent foundation.
Financial data (yr. ended 12/31/14): Assets, $509,717; gifts received, $600,000; expenditures, $228,575; qualifying distributions, $228,575.
Fields of interest: Education; Law education; Nonprofits; Diseases and conditions; Cancers; Youth development; Children.
Type of support: Regranting; Research.
Limitations: Applications not accepted. Giving primarily in MN. No grants to individuals.

Application information: Unsolicited requests for funds not accepted.
Trustees: Brian A. Erickson; Neal D. Erickson; Ronald A. Erickson.
EIN: 416050856

4675
Arthur T. Erickson Foundation
P.O. Box 1224
Minneapolis, MN 55440-1224

Donor: Holiday Stationstores, Inc.
Foundation type: Company-sponsored foundation.
Financial data (yr. ended 12/31/13): Assets, $102,221 (M); gifts received, $300,000; expenditures, $344,556; qualifying distributions, $344,556; giving activities include $344,500 for 50 grants (high: $50,000; low: $500).
Purpose and activities: The foundation supports community foundations and organizations involved with arts and culture, K-12 and higher education, horticulture, health, equestrianism, disability services, and religion.
Fields of interest: Education; Health; Religion.
Type of support: General support; Annual campaigns; Program development; Research.
Limitations: Applications not accepted. Giving primarily in Minneapolis and St. Paul, MN. No grants to individuals.
Application information: Unsolicited requests for funds not accepted.
Trustees: Gerald A. Erickson; Marjorie J. Pihl.
EIN: 416050855

4676
Evert Foundation
c/o John Nelson
200 S. 6th St., Ste. 4000
Minneapolis, MN 55402-1431

Established in 2005 in Minnesota.
Donors: Lindsay McCabe; Ann McCabe.
Foundation type: Independent foundation.
Financial data (yr. ended 12/31/13): Assets, $4,946,919; expenditures, $156,552; qualifying distributions, $145,000.
Fields of interest: Arts and culture; Theater; Education; National defense; Christianity; Human services; Basic and emergency aid.
Type of support: Ethics and accountability.
Limitations: Applications not accepted. No grants to individuals.
Application information: Unsolicited requests for funds not accepted.
Trustees: Ann L. McCabe; Lindsay E. McCabe.
EIN: 416543299

4677
Faith, Hope and Love Foundation
1660 S. Hwy., 100 Parkdale Plz., Ste. 426
Saint Louis Park, MN 55416-1533 (952) 512-1165
Contact: Jill K.H. Geoffrion, Co-C.E.O.; Timothy Geoffrion, Co-C.E.O.

Established in 1996 in Minnesota.
Donor: Charitable Lead Annuity Trust No. 1.
Foundation type: Independent foundation.
Financial data (yr. ended 12/31/13): Assets, $4,214,617 (M); gifts received, $190,106;

expenditures, $226,113; qualifying distributions, $180,103; giving activities include $146,000 for 12 grants (high: $34,078; low: $1,000), and $34,078 for 7 grants to individuals (high: $9,434; low: $500).
Fields of interest: Health; Christianity; Human services.
Type of support: General support; Program development.
Limitations: Applications accepted. Giving on a national basis with an emphasis on MN. No grants for political or government units.
Application information:
  Initial approach: Letter
  Deadline(s): None
Officers: Jill K.H. Geoffrion, C.E.O.; Timothy C. Geoffrion, C.E.O.
EIN: 411852802

4678
Arlin Falck Foundation
12743 Buckley Rd.
Caledonia, MN 55921-2808 (507) 724-3348
Contact: Kathleen V. Nelson, Pres.

Established in 1999 in Minnesota.
Foundation type: Independent foundation.
Financial data (yr. ended 12/31/14): Assets, $5,324,804 (M); expenditures, $268,415; qualifying distributions, $250,463; giving activities include $205,786 for 33 grants (high: $27,440; low: $156).
Fields of interest: Education; Diseases and conditions; Community and economic development.
Type of support: General support; Scholarships; Research.
Limitations: Applications accepted. Giving primarily in IA and MN.
Application information: Application form required.
  Initial approach: Contact foundation
  Deadline(s): Nov. 1
Officers: Kathleen V. Nelson, Pres.; Dale Evavold, Secy.; Alan C. Anderson, Treas.
EIN: 411925877

4679
Farmers Union Industries Foundation Inc.
P.O. Box 319
Redwood Falls, MN 56283-0319 (320) 763-6561

Established in 1998 in Minnesota.
Donor: Farmers Union Marketing & Processing Assoc.
Foundation type: Company-sponsored foundation.
Financial data (yr. ended 06/30/14): Assets, $2,744,738 (M); expenditures, $329,131; qualifying distributions, $297,267; giving activities include $215,500 for 15 grants (high: $35,000; low: $2,000), and $8,000 for 6 grants to individuals (high: $1,500; low: $1,000).
Purpose and activities: The foundation supports research and education programs designed to promote agriculture production, management, and cooperative ventures.
Fields of interest: Education; Higher education; Agriculture; Farmlands; Sustainable agriculture.
Type of support: Equipment; Conference attendance; Seed money; Research; Program development; Sponsorships; Scholarships.
Limitations: Applications accepted. Giving primarily in MN, MT, ND, SD, and WI.

Publications: Annual report; Informational brochure.
Application information: Application form required.
  Initial approach: Request application form
  Copies of proposal: 3
  Deadline(s): None
Officers: Rollie Schlepp, Pres.; Dennis Rosen, Secy.-Treas.
Directors: Doug Peterson; Doug Sombke; Paul Symens.
EIN: 311634460

4680
Farview Foundation
c/o Trust Tax Services
P.O. Box 64713
Saint Paul, MN 55164-0713

Established in 1999 in Maryland.
Donor: Beatrice Wells Crosby†.
Foundation type: Independent foundation.
Financial data (yr. ended 06/30/13): Assets, $113,056 (M); gifts received, $11,830; expenditures, $141,526; qualifying distributions, $139,500; giving activities include $139,000 for 23 grants (high: $50,000; low: $1,000).
Fields of interest: Arts and culture; Education; Human services.
Limitations: Applications not accepted. Giving primarily in CA, Washington, DC, and NY. No grants to individuals.
Application information: Unsolicited requests for funds not accepted.
Trustee: Harriett Crosby.
EIN: 311633189

4681
Felhaber, Larson, Fenlon & Vogt Foundation
220 S. 6th St., Ste. 2200
Minneapolis, MN 55402-4504 (612) 339-6321
Main URL: http://www.felhaber.com/community.html

Established in 2005 in Minnesota.
Donor: Felhaber, Larson, Fenlon & Vogt, LLC.
Foundation type: Company-sponsored foundation.
Financial data (yr. ended 12/31/13): Assets, $95 (L); gifts received, $145,550; expenditures, $146,055; qualifying distributions, $146,030; giving activities include $143,450 for 44 grants (high: $25,000; low: $300).
Purpose and activities: The foundation supports nonprofit organizations involved with health care, human services, and philanthropy and voluntarism.
Fields of interest: Philanthropy; Health; Human services.
Limitations: Applications accepted. Giving primarily in MN.
Application information: Application form required.
  Initial approach: Letter
  Deadline(s): None
Officers and Directors: Richard C. Salmen, Chair. and Director; Christopher S. Hayhoe, Pres. and Director; Paul J. Zech, V.P. and Director; Sara G. McGrane, Secy. and Director; Stephen J. Burton, Treas. and Director.
EIN: 204907667

4682
Ferber Family Foundation
7760 France Ave. S., Ste. 700
Minneapolis, MN 55435-5844
Contact: Roy Ferber

Established in 2003 in Minnesota.
Donors: Roy R. Ferber; JoAnn B. Ferber.
Foundation type: Independent foundation.
Financial data (yr. ended 12/31/13): Assets, $2,692,124 (M); expenditures, $212,478; qualifying distributions, $186,095; giving activities include $183,170 for 14 grants (high: $49,800; low: $100).
Fields of interest: Education; Diseases and conditions; Religion; Youth organizing; Low-income and poor people.
Type of support: Capital campaigns; Research.
Limitations: Applications not accepted. Giving primarily in MN. No grants to individuals.
Application information: Contributes only to pre-selected organizations.
Officers: Roy R. Ferber, Pres.; JoAnn B. Ferber, Secy.-Treas.
EIN: 200228634

4683
Fingerhut Family Foundation
1660 Hwy. 100 S., Ste. 230
Minneapolis, MN 55416-1557 (952) 545-3000
Contact: Beverly Deikel, V.P. and Secy.-Treas.

Established in 1960 in Minnesota.
Donors: Manny Fingerhut†; Rose Fingerhut; Beverly Deikel; Ronald Fingerhut; RF Capital Trust.
Foundation type: Independent foundation.
Financial data (yr. ended 12/31/13): Assets, $104,771 (M); gifts received, $1,935,100; expenditures, $293,084; qualifying distributions, $292,802; giving activities include $291,350 for 14 grants (high: $250,000; low: $250).
Purpose and activities: Giving primarily to Jewish agencies, medical research, treatment centers and the United Way.
Fields of interest: Philanthropy; Health; Religion.
International interests: Israel.
Type of support: General support; Matching grants; Continuing support; Annual campaigns; Capital campaigns; Capital and infrastructure; Equipment; Emergency funds; Program development; Seed money; Research.
Limitations: Applications accepted. Giving primarily in MN, with emphasis on the Twin Cities. No grants to individuals.
Application information: Application form required.
  Initial approach: Letter
  Copies of proposal: 1
  Deadline(s): None
Officers and Directors: Ronald Fingerhut, Pres. and Director; Beverly Deikel, V.P. and Secy.-Treas.
Number of staff: 1 part-time professional; 1 part-time support.
EIN: 416030930

4684
Richard & Beverly Fink Family Foundation
c/o Wells Fargo Bank, N.A.
90 S. 7th St., Ste. 3300
Minneapolis, MN 55402-4104

Established in 1996 in Minnesota.

Donor: Richard Fink.
Foundation type: Independent foundation.
Financial data (yr. ended 12/31/13): Assets, $1,021,203 (M); gifts received, $25; expenditures, $177,807; qualifying distributions, $174,875; giving activities include $174,850 for 45 grants (high: $50,000; low: $200).
Fields of interest: Arts and culture; Nonprofits; Judaism.
Type of support: Regranting.
Limitations: Applications not accepted. Giving primarily in MN. No grants to individuals.
Application information: Unsolicited requests for funds not accepted.
Officers: Richard Fink, Pres.; Beverly Fink, Treas.
EIN: 411859799

4685
E. David Fischman Scholarship Fund
c/o Trust Tax Services
P.O. Box 64713
Saint Paul, MN 55164-0713

Established in 1998 in Minnesota.
Donor: E. David Fischman†.
Foundation type: Independent foundation.
Financial data (yr. ended 12/31/14): Assets, $7,395,345; expenditures, $423,659; qualifying distributions, $355,250 and $0 for set-asides.
Purpose and activities: Giving primarily for higher education scholarships.
Fields of interest: Education; University education.
Type of support: Scholarships; Individual development.
Limitations: Applications not accepted. Giving primarily in Boston, MA, and New York, NY. No grants to individuals.
Application information: Contributes only to pre-selected organizations. Unsolicited requests for funds not accepted.
Trustee: U.S. Bank, N.A.
EIN: 416438510

4686
Flaherty Family Foundation
8345 Crytal View Rd.
Eden Prairie, MN 55344-7636

Established in 1989 in Minnesota.
Donors: Edward F. Flaherty; Stephen Frey Foundation; Walsh Bishop Assoc. Inc.; George Frost; Tolomatic.
Foundation type: Independent foundation.
Financial data (yr. ended 12/31/13): Assets, $27,200 (M); gifts received, $239,000; expenditures, $225,726; qualifying distributions, $225,726; giving activities include $221,572 for 31 grants (high: $50,000; low: $50).
Fields of interest: Arts and culture; Education; Catholicism; Human services.
Limitations: Applications not accepted. Giving primarily in MN. No grants to individuals.
Application information: Unsolicited requests for funds not accepted.
Director: Edward F. Flaherty.
EIN: 411622611

4687
Fletcher Family Foundation
P.O. Box 1088
Forest Lake, MN 55025-7043
Main URL: http://fletcherfamilyfoundation.org

Established in 2003 in Minnesota.
Donors: Nancy J. Fletcher; Ronald R. Fletcher.
Foundation type: Independent foundation.
Financial data (yr. ended 12/31/13): Assets, $4,399,112 (M); gifts received, $50; expenditures, $349,636; qualifying distributions, $205,700; giving activities include $205,700 for 35 grants (high: $50,000; low: $100).
Purpose and activities: The foundation strives to help improve the human condition by empowering families and communities.
Fields of interest: Education; Christianity; Human services; Family services.
Limitations: Applications not accepted. Giving primarily in Washington, D.C. No grants to individuals.
Application information: Contributes only to pre-selected organizations.
Officers: Ronald R. Fletcher, Chair.; Nancy J. Fletcher, Pres.; Jacquelyn Fletcher, V.P. and Director; John Fletcher, V.P.
EIN: 562393836

4688
The Huelsmann Foundation
50 S. 6th St., Ste. 1500
Minneapolis, MN 55402-1498
Contact: Dean Barr

Established in 1998 in Minnesota.
Donor: Richard L. Huelsmann.
Foundation type: Independent foundation.
Financial data (yr. ended 12/31/13): Assets, $4,531,659 (M); expenditures, $241,023; qualifying distributions, $216,097; giving activities include $200,482 for 9 grants (high: $51,482; low: $3,000).
Fields of interest: Arts and culture; Public libraries; Catholicism.
Limitations: Applications not accepted. Giving primarily in MN. No grants to individuals.
Application information: Contributes only to pre-selected organizations.
Officers: Kristin M. Rossiter, Co-Pres. and Secy.; Jennifer A. Huelsmann, Co-Pres. and Treas.
EIN: 411893927

4689
Robert E. Fraser Foundation
90 S. 7th St., Ste. 4800
Minneapolis, MN 55402-4129

Established in 2005 in Minnesota.
Donor: Robert E. Fraser†.
Foundation type: Independent foundation.
Financial data (yr. ended 12/31/14): Assets, $4,773,751; expenditures, $410,189; qualifying distributions, $336,752.
Purpose and activities: Giving primarily for human services and health; funding also for higher education.
Fields of interest: Higher education; Hospice care; Human services.
Type of support: Research.

Limitations: Applications not accepted. Giving primarily in MN and MO. No grants to individuals.
Application information: Contributes only to pre-selected organizations.
Officers and Directors: William A. Haug, Pres. and Secy. and Director; Diane Carlson, V.P. and Treas. and Director; George P. Fraser, V.P. and Director.
EIN: 411710355

4690
Michael J. and Karen B. Frey Foundation
745 Ferndale Rd. N.
Wayzata, MN 55391-1010
Contact: Michael Frey

Established in 2003 in Minnesota.
Donors: Karen B. Frey; Michael J. Frey.
Foundation type: Independent foundation.
Financial data (yr. ended 12/31/13): Assets, $7,707,833 (M); expenditures, $402,348; qualifying distributions, $376,300; giving activities include $376,300 for 19 grants (high: $82,000; low: $1,100).
Fields of interest: Education; Elementary and secondary education; Diabetes; Religion; Christianity.
Type of support: Research.
Limitations: Applications not accepted. Giving primarily in MN. No grants to individuals.
Application information: Contributes only to pre-selected organizations.
Officers and Directors: Michael J. Frey, Pres. and Treas. and Director; Karen B. Frey, Secy. and Director; David J. Frey; Michael B. Frey; Sara J. Frey.
EIN: 753140739

4691
G&K Services Foundation
5995 Opus Pkwy., Ste. 500
Minnetonka, MN 55343-8387 (952) 912-5707
Contact: Colleen Keller, Exex. Asst.
E-mail: ckeller@gkservices.com; *Main URL:* http://www.gkservices.com/about/foundation.html

Established in 2005 in Minnesota.
Donor: G&K Services.
Foundation type: Company-sponsored foundation.
Financial data (yr. ended 12/31/13): Assets, $148,964 (M); gifts received, $4,533; expenditures, $221,523; qualifying distributions, $221,523; giving activities include $221,498 for 16 grants (high: $157,998; low: $3,000).
Purpose and activities: The foundation supports programs designed to promote education, human services, skills development, and self-sufficiency training. Special emphasis is directed toward community and workforce development.
Fields of interest: Education; Vocational education; Higher education; Adult literacy; High school equivalency; ESL and second language acquisition; Reading promotion; Nonprofits; Disaster relief; Leadership development; Employment; Job training; Human services; Child welfare; Vocational rehabilitation; Victims of disaster.
Type of support: General support; Grants to individuals; Program development; Regranting.
Limitations: Applications accepted. Giving primarily in areas of company operations in Minneapolis, MN. No support for political, lobbying, or advocacy organizations or candidates, fraternal, social, labor, veterans', or alumni organizations, athletic groups,

religious organizations not of direct benefit to the entire community, pre-schools, nursery schools, K-12 public or private educational institutions, economic development organizations. No grants to individuals or for scholarships, travel, conferences, conventions, sponsorships, recreation, sporting events, advertising, multi-year commitments, capital campaigns, endowments, academic, medical, or scientific research, or daycare programs.
Publications: Application guidelines.
Application information: Grants range from $1,000 to $5,000. The Minnesota Common Grant Application is also accepted. Proposal narratives should be no longer than 6 pages. Multi-year support is not automatic. Additional information may be requested at a later date. As site visit may be scheduled.
  Initial approach: E-mail or mail proposal to foundation
  Deadline(s): Sept. 30
  Board meeting date(s): Semi-annually
  Final notification: Jan. 31
Officers: Jeffrey L. Wright, Pres.; Jeffrey Louis Cotter, Secy.-Treas.
EIN: 743152076

4692
Gage Family Foundation
c/o Tonkawa Inc.
550 Tonkawa Rd.
Long Lake, MN 55356-9724 (952) 404-5636
Contact: C. David Nelson, Secy. and Tr.

Donors: Edwin C. Gage; Arleen M. Carlson Living Trust; Christine C. Gage; Barbara C. Gage.
Foundation type: Independent foundation.
Financial data (yr. ended 12/31/13): Assets, $345,862 (M); gifts received, $201,414; expenditures, $272,593; qualifying distributions, $267,909; giving activities include $263,834 for 19 grants (high: $75,000; low: $500).
Purpose and activities: Giving primarily for education, human services, youth services, and to a United Methodist church.
Fields of interest: Education; Higher education; Presbyterianism; Human services; Youth services.
Limitations: Applications accepted. Giving primarily in MN; some funding also in IL.
Application information: Application form required.
  Initial approach: Letter
  Deadline(s): Mar. 1 (for June grants) and Sept. 1 (for Dec. grants)
Officers and Trustees: Barbara C. Gage, Pres. and Trustee; C. David Nelson, Secy. and Trustee; Edwin C. Gage, Treas. and Trustee; Christine C. Gage.
EIN: 204900172

4693
Janice Gardner Foundation
60 S. 6th St., Ste. 3700
Minneapolis, MN 55402-4437
Application address: c/o Barbara Illies, 6050 Lake Rd., Ste. 114, Woodbury, MN 55125, tel.: (651) 731-0160

Established in 1987 in Minnesota.
Donors: George J. Gardner; Packaging, Inc.; George W. Gardner; Susan M. Gardner.
Foundation type: Independent foundation.
Financial data (yr. ended 12/31/13): Assets, $3,967,237 (M); gifts received, $387,245;

expenditures, $334,244; qualifying distributions, $284,334; giving activities include $268,930 for 14 grants (high: $75,000; low: $4,000).
Purpose and activities: Giving primarily for Roman Catholic education, agencies and churches.
Fields of interest: Elementary and secondary education; Higher education; Catholicism; Human services.
Limitations: Applications accepted. Giving primarily in MN.
Application information: Application form required.
Initial approach: Letter
Deadline(s): None
Officers and Directors: Elizabeth Glaeser, Co-Secy.-Co-Treas.; Barbara Illies, Co-Secy.-Co-Treas. and Director; George W. Gardner; Jacqui Gardner; Susan M. Khaury.
EIN: 411603464

4694
Garmar Foundation
65742 State Hwy. 56
Dodge Center, MN   55927-7750

Established in 1998 in Minnesota.
Donors: Denzil McNeilus; Marilee McNeilus; Garwin McNeilus.
Foundation type: Independent foundation.
Financial data (yr. ended 06/30/14): Assets, $1,655,953 (M); expenditures, $568,265; qualifying distributions, $673,938; giving activities include $214,564 for 8 grants (high: $106,904; low: $6,000).
Purpose and activities: Giving primarily for religious and missionary projects.
Fields of interest: Philanthropy; Christianity; Human services.
Limitations: Applications not accepted. Giving primarily in MD and TN. No grants to individuals.
Application information: Contributes only to pre-selected organizations.
Officers: Garwin McNeilus, Pres.; Denzil McNeilus, V.P.; Marilee McNeilus, Secy.-Treas.
EIN: 411914753

4695
Getsch Charitable Trust
10202 Berkshire Rd.
Bloomington, MN   55437-2265

Established in 2003 in Minnesota.
Foundation type: Independent foundation.
Financial data (yr. ended 12/31/13): Assets, $2,946,964 (M); expenditures, $208,281; qualifying distributions, $195,650; giving activities include $170,500 for 49 grants (high: $30,000; low: $250).
Fields of interest: Agriculture; Religion; Christianity; Sports and recreation; Human services.
Type of support: General support.
Limitations: Applications not accepted. Giving primarily in MN and WI. No grants to individuals.
Application information: Contributes only to pre-selected organizations.
Officer: David D. Getsch, Exec. Dir.
Trustees: Dianne H. Getsch; Edward W. Getsch; John H. Getsch; Marilyn R. Getsch; Marjorie D. Getsch.
EIN: 450510351

4696
Gilligan Foundation
2461 Park Ln.
Mendota Heights, MN   55120-1937

Established in 1985 in Minnesota.
Donor: Peter J. Gilligan.
Foundation type: Independent foundation.
Financial data (yr. ended 11/30/13): Assets, $4,044,439 (M); expenditures, $238,731; qualifying distributions, $214,546; giving activities include $208,000 for 29 grants (high: $35,000; low: $1,000).
Purpose and activities: Giving primarily for social welfare programs, including Catholic charity agencies and health projects designed to benefit the homeless, poor, and disadvantaged.
Fields of interest: Education; Elementary and secondary education; Catholicism; Human services.
Type of support: General support.
Limitations: Applications not accepted. Giving primarily in Minneapolis, MN. No grants to individuals.
Application information: Contributes only to pre-selected organizations.
Officers: Margaret Gilligan, Pres.; Ann Gilligan, V.P.; Michael Gilligan, Secy.; Joseph Lee-Gilligan, Treas.
EIN: 363418218

4697
Amy R. and Philip S. Goldman Foundation
c/o Adler Trust Co., Tax Dept.
10350 Bren Rd. W.
Minnetonka, MN   55343-9014

Established in 1999 in Minnesota.
Donors: Amy R. Goldman; Opus Corp.
Foundation type: Independent foundation.
Financial data (yr. ended 12/31/13): Assets, $3,760,774 (M); expenditures, $260,206; qualifying distributions, $259,031; giving activities include $254,500 for 9 grants (high: $125,000; low: $1,000).
Fields of interest: Elementary and secondary education.
Type of support: General support; Annual campaigns.
Limitations: Applications not accepted. Giving primarily in MN. No grants to individuals.
Application information: Unsolicited requests for funds not accepted.
Officers and Directors: Philip S. Goldman, Pres. and Director; Amy R. Goldman, Secy.-Treas. and Director.
EIN: 411925897

4698
Rosemary and David Good Family Foundation
1818 Oliver Ave. S.
Minneapolis, MN   55405-2224

Donors: Rosemary H. Good; David F. Good.
Foundation type: Independent foundation.
Financial data (yr. ended 12/31/13): Assets, $6,189,446 (M); expenditures, $394,437; qualifying distributions, $340,612; giving activities include $275,500 for 25 grants (high: $25,000; low: $5,000).
Fields of interest: Arts and culture; Health; Religion; Children.

Limitations: Applications not accepted. Giving primarily in MN.
Application information: Unsolicited requests for funds not accepted.
Officers: Rosemary H. Good, Pres.; David F. Good, V.P.; Teresa Bonner, Exec. Dir.
Directors: Veerle Arts; Allison G. Barosko; James Barosko; Adam P. Good.
EIN: 262294454

4699
Granite Foundation
1876 Gluek Ln.
Roseville, MN   55113-3851
Application address: c/o Timothy Madden, 690 Cleveland Ave. S., St. Paul, MN 55116, tel.: (651) 696-5605

Established in 2001 in Minnesota.
Donors: Timothy Madden; Diane Madden.
Foundation type: Independent foundation.
Financial data (yr. ended 12/31/13): Assets, $7,889,572 (M); gifts received, $349,651; expenditures, $463,425; qualifying distributions, $437,506; giving activities include $421,403 for 1 grant.
Fields of interest: Education; Christianity; Human services.
Type of support: General support; Program-related investments; Capital campaigns; Capital and infrastructure; Equipment; Land acquisitions; Endowments; Emergency funds; Program development; Convening; Professorships; Seed money; Curriculum development; Fellowships; Internships; Scholarships; Research; Program evaluations; Student aid; Individual development.
Limitations: Applications accepted. Giving primarily in MN and WI.
Application information: Application form required.
Initial approach: Letter
Copies of proposal: 1
Deadline(s): None
Officers and Directors: Timothy Madden, Pres. and Director; Diane Madden, Secy.-Treas. and Director; Francis T. Madden; Mallory L. Madden; Melanie M. Madden; Michaela Madden.
EIN: 260010320

4700
Griffiths Foundation
2717 Niagara Ln.
Minneapolis, MN   55447-4844

Established in 1991 in Minnesota.
Donor: Harold F. Griffiths.
Foundation type: Independent foundation.
Financial data (yr. ended 12/31/13): Assets, $3,056,513 (M); gifts received, $9,191; expenditures, $152,362; qualifying distributions, $145,688; giving activities include $145,663 for 1 grant.
Fields of interest: Education.
Limitations: Applications not accepted. Giving primarily in MN. No grants to individuals.
Application information: Unsolicited requests for funds not accepted.
Officers: Harold F. Griffiths, Pres.; Keith A. Griffiths, V.P.; Kenneth H. Griffiths, V.P.
EIN: 411628889

4701
N. Bud and Beverly Grossman Foundation
(formerly N. Bud Grossman Foundation)
4543 IDS Ctr.
80 S. 8th St.
Minneapolis, MN 55402-2100
Contact: Larry Waller

Established in 1973 in Minnesota.
Donors: N. Bud Grossman†; BNG Management; Beverly Grossman.
Foundation type: Independent foundation.
Financial data (yr. ended 12/31/13): Assets, $382,189 (M); expenditures, $404,670; qualifying distributions, $393,970; giving activities include $391,070 for 18 grants (high: $100,000; low: $70).
Purpose and activities: Giving primarily for the arts and Jewish organizations.
Fields of interest: Arts and culture; Education; Nonprofits; Human services.
Type of support: General support; Annual campaigns; Program development; Regranting.
Limitations: Applications accepted. Giving primarily in MN, with emphasis on the Minneapolis-St. Paul area. No support for fraternal organizations or for religious organizations for sectarian purposes. No grants to individuals, or for scholarships, fellowships, fundraising events, medical research, or matching gifts; no loans.
Publications: Annual report.
Application information: Telephone solicitations and form letters will not be considered. Application form required.
    Initial approach: Proposal
    Copies of proposal: 1
    Deadline(s): Apr. 16
    Board meeting date(s): Usually in Jan. and June
Directors: Bob Ezrilov; Beverly Grossman.
EIN: 237302799

4702
Grotto Foundation Inc.
1315 Red Fox Rd., Ste. 100
Arden Hills, MN 55112-6977 (651) 209-8010
FAX: (651) 209-8014;
E-mail: info@grottofoundation.org; Contact for questions regarding application process: Cullyn Richter, Grants and Off. Mgr., e-mail: crichter@grottofoundation.org; Main URL: http://www.grottofoundation.org
Grants List: http://www.grottofoundation.org/past-grants

Established in 1964 in Minnesota.
Donor: Louis W. Hill, Jr.†.
Foundation type: Independent foundation.
Financial data (yr. ended 04/30/13): Assets, $23,436,072 (M); expenditures, $1,051,225; qualifying distributions, $822,042; giving activities include $398,000 for 23 grants (high: $45,000; low: $500), and $637,363 for foundation-administered programs.
Purpose and activities: Giving primarily to improve the education and economic, physical and social well-being of citizens, with a special focus on families and culturally diverse groups. The foundation is further interested in increasing public understanding of American cultural heritage, the cultures of nations and the individuals responsibility to fellow human beings. Program areas include early childhood development and parenting, and Native language initiatives.
Fields of interest: Human services; Child welfare; Parent education; American Indians.
Type of support: General support; Program development.
Limitations: Applications accepted. Giving primarily in MN. No support for writing projects, non-operating foundations, nonprofit organizations that re-grant, government projects, or art programs. No grants to individuals, or for capital or endowment funds or programs, travel, operating budgets (except to aid in initiating occasional programs), annual campaigns, retroactive support, deficit financing, student research, scholarships, fellowships, publications, or conferences; no loans.
Publications: Annual report; Financial statement.
Application information: Application form required.
    Initial approach: Use online application process on foundation web site
    Deadline(s): Jan. 15, Mar. 15, July 15, and Nov. 15
    Board meeting date(s): Apr., June, Oct., and Feb.
Officers and Directors: Louis F. Hill, Pres. and Director; Malcolm W. McDonald, 2nd V.P. and Director; Ellis F. Bullock, Secy.; Mary Manuel Roman, Treas. and Director; Sonja Moore, Exec. Dir.; Richard Andolshek; Derek Benz; Erik Fors; Kathrine Hill; Louis Shea Hill; Nancy Randall-Dana; Barbara Slade.
Number of staff: 3 full-time professional; 2 part-time professional.
EIN: 416052604

4703
Groves Foundation
P.O. Box 1267
Minneapolis, MN 55440-1267 (952) 831-1597
Contact: F.N. Groves, Pres.

Donors: S.J. Groves and Sons Co.; Frank N. Groves†.
Foundation type: Company-sponsored foundation.
Financial data (yr. ended 09/30/13): Assets, $10,378,442 (M); expenditures, $716,503; qualifying distributions, $606,926; giving activities include $417,976 for 10 grants (high: $179,476; low: $500).
Purpose and activities: The foundation supports organizations involved with arts and culture, education, animal welfare, heart disease, employment, and athletics.
Fields of interest: Education; Employment; Sports and recreation.
Type of support: General support.
Limitations: Applications accepted. Giving primarily in the Minneapolis, MN, area. No grants to individuals or for capital or endowment funds; no loans; no matching gifts.
Application information: Application form required.
    Initial approach: Letter
    Deadline(s): None
Officers: Franklin N. Groves, Pres.; F. N. Groves, Jr., V.P.; David F. Cmiel, Secy.
Trustee: T. Asgrimson.
Number of staff: 1
EIN: 416038512

4704
Russell B. Hagen Foundation
(formerly Russell and Luaina Hagen Family Foundation)
100 2nd St. S.E., Ste. 1004
Minneapolis, MN 55414-9101

Established in 1999 in Minnesota.
Donors: Russell B. Hagen; Luaina R. Hagen.
Foundation type: Independent foundation.
Financial data (yr. ended 12/31/13): Assets, $2,393,158 (M); expenditures, $338,469; qualifying distributions, $317,000; giving activities include $305,000 for 5 grants (high: $200,000; low: $20,000).
Fields of interest: Higher education; Teacher education.
Limitations: Applications not accepted. Giving primarily in MN. No grants to individuals.
Application information: Unsolicited requests for funds not accepted.
Officer: Russell B. Hagen, Pres. and Treas.
Trustees: Alexander L. Hagen; Erin G. Hubbard.
EIN: 411941194

4705
Haggerty Family Foundation
c/o Ruth J. Haggerty
90 S. 7th St., Ste. 5100
Minneapolis, MN 55402-4168

Established in 1997 in Minnesota.
Donor: Daniel J. Haggerty.
Foundation type: Independent foundation.
Financial data (yr. ended 12/31/14): Assets, $3,737,083 (M); expenditures, $192,421; qualifying distributions, $174,017.
Fields of interest: Mental health care; Christianity; Human services.
Type of support: General support.
Limitations: Applications not accepted. Giving primarily in MN. No grants to individuals.
Application information: Unsolicited requests for funds not accepted.
Officers: Ruth Haggerty, Pres.; John Haggerty, V.P.; Kathleen Malone, V.P.; Maureen L. Mischinski, V.P.; Laurie Rivard, Secy.-Treas.
Director: Daniel J. Haggerty.
EIN: 411854247

4706
Jessie F. Hallett Charitable Trust
(formerly Hallett Charitable Trust)
c/o Trust Tax Services
P.O. Box 64713
Saint Paul, MN 55164-0713
Application address: c/o U.S. Bank, N.A., Att.: Sarah Godfrey, 101 East 5th St., 14th Fl., Saint Paul, MN 55101, tel.: (651) 466-8710

Established in 1984 in Minnesota.
Donor: Jessie F. Hallett†.
Foundation type: Independent foundation.
Financial data (yr. ended 11/30/13): Assets, $9,568,283 (M); expenditures, $516,030; qualifying distributions, $443,431; giving activities include $383,986 for 17 grants (high: $57,185; low: $250).
Purpose and activities: Giving for higher education and Protestant agencies.

Fields of interest: Education; Christianity; Youth development.
Limitations: Applications accepted. Giving primarily in the Midwest, with emphasis on MN. No grants to individuals.
Application information: Application form required.
Initial approach: Letter
Deadline(s): None
Trustees: Tom Jensen; Desiree Parker; Paul Schliesman; Kirk Springsted; U.S. Bank, N.A.
EIN: 416211994

4707
Helen Harrington Charitable Trust
c/o U.S. Bank, N.A.
101 E. 5th St., EP-MN-S14
Saint Paul, MN 55101-1801

Established in 1984 in Minnesota.
Foundation type: Independent foundation.
Financial data (yr. ended 12/31/13): Assets, $3,815,590 (M); expenditures, $224,314; qualifying distributions, $185,635; giving activities include $175,558 for 9 grants (high: $47,100; low: $1,713).
Fields of interest: Secondary education; Higher education; Nonprofits; Human services.
Type of support: Regranting.
Limitations: Applications not accepted. Giving primarily in St. Paul, MN. No grants to individuals.
Application information: Contributes only to pre-selected organizations.
Trustee: U.S. Bank, N.A.
EIN: 416094797

4708
Olga B. Hart Education Foundation
2094 Miller Creek Dr.
Duluth, MN 55811-1805

Established in 2002 in Minnesota.
Donor: Olga B. Hart Trust.
Foundation type: Independent foundation.
Financial data (yr. ended 12/31/13): Assets, $4,972,206 (M); expenditures, $308,700; qualifying distributions, $240,000; giving activities include $240,000 for 17 grants (high: $32,000; low: $3,000).
Fields of interest: Education.
Limitations: Applications not accepted. Giving primarily in MN. No grants to individuals.
Application information: Unsolicited requests for funds not accepted.
Trustee: Robert J. Wasko.
EIN: 412015095

4709
The Head Family Foundation
11100 Wayzata Blvd., Ste. 230
Minnetonka, MN 55305-5526 9526812891
Main URL: http://headfoundation.com

Established in 2004 in Minnesota.
Donors: Martha M. Head; Douglas M. Head.
Foundation type: Independent foundation.
Financial data (yr. ended 06/30/14): Assets, $6,101,577; expenditures, $217,665; qualifying distributions, $197,750.
Fields of interest: Arts and culture; Education; Human services.

Limitations: Applications not accepted. Giving primarily in MN. No grants to individuals.
Application information: Unsolicited requests for funds not accepted.
Officers: Martha M. Head, Pres.; Martha E.H. Kirwin, Secy.; Virginia R. Head, Treas.
Director: Christopher Kirwan.
EIN: 202032551

4710
Hegardt Foundation
500 IDS Ctr., 80 S. 8th St.
Minneapolis, MN 55402-2100

Established in 2007 in Minnesota.
Donor: Winifred J. and John M. Harris Charitable Lead Annuity Trust.
Foundation type: Independent foundation.
Financial data (yr. ended 12/31/13): Assets, $603,185 (M); gifts received, $401,113; expenditures, $394,758; qualifying distributions, $394,758; giving activities include $392,500 for 12 grants (high: $100,000; low: $5,000).
Fields of interest: Arts and culture; Dance; Education; Foundations; Health care clinics; Basic and emergency aid; International development.
Limitations: Applications not accepted. Giving primarily in MA and MN. No grants to individuals.
Application information: Contributes only to pre-selected organizations.
Officers: Carolyn B. Sundquist, Pres.; Marjorie E. Harris, V.P.; Katherine A. Harris, Secy.; W. Gordon Harris, Treas.
EIN: 205814715

4711
Heilicher Foundation
(formerly Menahem Heilicher Charitable Foundation)
c/o Jamie Heilicher
850 Decatur Ave. N.
Minneapolis, MN 55427-4324

Established in 1963 in Minnesota.
Donors: Amos Heilicher; Daniel Heilicher†; Advance Carter Co.; Elissa Heilicher.
Foundation type: Independent foundation.
Financial data (yr. ended 12/31/13): Assets, $5,365,793 (M); gifts received, $6,000; expenditures, $275,911; qualifying distributions, $223,830; giving activities include $220,960 for 13 grants (high: $120,600; low: $500).
Purpose and activities: Giving primarily to Jewish organizations.
Fields of interest: Arts and culture; Nonprofits; Judaism; Human services.
Type of support: Regranting.
Limitations: Applications not accepted. Giving primarily in Minneapolis, MN. No grants to individuals.
Application information: Contributes only to pre-selected organizations.
Officer: Elissa Heilicher, Pres.
Director: Matthew Heilicher.
EIN: 416043457

4712
Anna M. Heilmaier Charitable Foundation
c/o Trust Tax Services
P.O. Box 64173
Saint Paul, MN 55164-0713

Established in 1993 in Minnesota.
Donor: Anna M. Heilmaier†.
Foundation type: Independent foundation.
Financial data (yr. ended 12/31/13): Assets, $7,069,675 (M); expenditures, $336,426; qualifying distributions, $264,336; giving activities include $229,000 for 20 grants (high: $25,000; low: $3,000).
Purpose and activities: Giving primarily for medical research and the treatment of cancer, diseases of the eye, and other diseases; support also for classical and chamber music.
Fields of interest: Music; Diseases and conditions; Eye diseases; Cancers.
Type of support: General support; Capital campaigns; Research; Research and evaluation.
Limitations: Applications not accepted. Giving limited to the East Metro Region-St. Paul, and Ramsey, Washington, and Dakota counties, MN. No support for lobbying or political organizations. No grants to individuals, debt reduction, and for travel, or fundraising for re-granting to other organizations.
Application information: Unsolicited requests for funds not accepted.
Board meeting date(s): Mid-Sept.
Trustee: U.S. Bank, N.A.
EIN: 411761632

4713
Hickory Tech Corporation Foundation
(formerly Mankato Citizens Telephone Company Foundation)
P.O. Box 3248
Mankato, MN 56002-3248 (507) 387-3355
Main URL: http://www.enventis.com
Grants List: http://www.hickorytech.com/about-us/foundation/foundation-grant-awards-2010-11.aspx

Established in 1963 in Minnesota.
Donor: Hickory Tech Corp.
Foundation type: Company-sponsored foundation.
Financial data (yr. ended 02/28/14): Assets, $3,801,621 (M); expenditures, $172,728; qualifying distributions, $156,815; giving activities include $131,799 for 35 grants (high: $10,000; low: $1,000), and $24,291 for 70 employee matching gifts.
Purpose and activities: The foundation supports programs designed to promote culture, education, and community.
Fields of interest: Arts and culture; Education; Human services.
Type of support: Continuing support; Employee volunteer services; Scholarships; Employee matching gifts.
Limitations: Applications accepted. Giving limited to areas of company operations, with emphasis on the Mankato, MN, area. No support for discriminatory organizations, political organizations, religious organizations not of direct benefit to the entire community, or fraternal, veterans', or labor groups. No grants to individuals (except for employee-related scholarships), or for general operating support, capital campaigns, political activities, special occasion or goodwill advertising, sports programs or events, or cause-related marketing; no loans or loan guarantees.
Publications: Application guidelines.
Application information: Application form required.
Initial approach: Proposal
Copies of proposal: 1
Deadline(s): Dec. 1

Officers: Lyle G. Jacobson, Pres.; David A. Christensen, Secy.-Treas.
Directors: Myrita J. Craig; John W. Finke; Mike L. Olsen.
Number of staff: None.
EIN: 416034001

4714
HJ Promise Foundation
P.O. Box 5628
Minneapolis, MN 55440-5628

Donors: Peter Daitch; Alexa Daitch.
Foundation type: Independent foundation.
Financial data (yr. ended 12/31/13): Assets, $1,935,971 (M); gifts received, $299,000; expenditures, $435,113; qualifying distributions, $403,431; giving activities include $402,000 for 20 grants (high: $50,000; low: $5,000).
Fields of interest: Environment; Health; Agriculture.
Limitations: Applications not accepted. Giving primarily in CT.
Application information: Unsolicited requests for funds not accepted.
Officers: Peter Daitch, Pres.; Alexa Daitch, V.P.; Michella L. Johnson, Secy.; Lynn Wilde, Treas.
EIN: 262252708

4715
Hognander Foundation
c/o Wells Fargo Bank, N.A., PCS-MAC N9305-101
733 S. Marquette Ave.
Minneapolis, MN 55479-2025

Established in 1999 in Minnesota.
Donor: Gertrude Hognander.
Foundation type: Independent foundation.
Financial data (yr. ended 12/31/14): Assets, $4,409,401; expenditures, $331,927; qualifying distributions, $306,661.
Fields of interest: Arts and culture; Education; Health.
Type of support: General support.
Limitations: Applications not accepted. Giving primarily in Minneapolis, MN. No grants to individuals.
Application information: Unsolicited requests for funds not accepted.
Officers: Orville C. Hognander, Jr., Pres. and Treas.; Nadia Christensen, V.P. and Secy.
EIN: 411953881

4716
The Theodore G. Huisinga Charitable Foundation
P.O. Box 753
Willmar, MN 56201-0753

Established in 1988 in Minnesota.
Donors: Theodore G. Huisinga; Ruth Ann Houlthouse; Richard Huisinga; Ronald Huisinga; Randall Huisinga; Renae Chermak.
Foundation type: Independent foundation.
Financial data (yr. ended 12/31/13): Assets, $671,156 (M); gifts received, $232,000; expenditures, $211,346; qualifying distributions, $210,340; giving activities include $210,025 for 13 grants (high: $158,254; low: $100).
Purpose and activities: Giving primarily to Evangelical Christian organizations.

Fields of interest: Arts and culture; Education; Religion.
Limitations: Applications not accepted. Giving primarily in MN. No grants to individuals.
Application information: Contributes only to pre-selected organizations.
Trustees: Audrey Huisinga; Richard Huisinga; Theodore G. Huisinga.
EIN: 411639703

4717
Alfred A. Iversen and Family Foundation
1500 Park Rd.
Chanhassen, MN 55317-9593

Established in 2003 in Minnesota.
Donor: Alfred A. Iversen.
Foundation type: Independent foundation.
Financial data (yr. ended 12/31/13): Assets, $8,516,877 (M); gifts received, $424,831; expenditures, $424,697; qualifying distributions, $340,875; giving activities include $340,000 for 7 grants (high: $85,000; low: $25,000).
Fields of interest: Health; Christianity; Human services.
Limitations: Applications not accepted. Giving primarily in Washington, DC, MN, TN, and TX. No grants to individuals.
Application information: Contributes only to pre-selected organizations.
Officer and Directors: Alfred A. Iversen, Pres. and Director; Brenda C. Iversen; Emily A. Iversen.
EIN: 043781038

4718
Darren and Terry Jackson Foundation, Inc.
290 Woodlawn Ave.
Saint Paul, MN 55105-1237

Established in 2006 in Minnesota.
Donors: Darren R. Jackson; Theresa A. Jackson.
Foundation type: Independent foundation.
Financial data (yr. ended 12/31/13): Assets, $3,413,948 (M); gifts received, $1,999,900; expenditures, $417,801; qualifying distributions, $390,896; giving activities include $386,650 for 22 grants (high: $100,000; low: $500).
Fields of interest: Secondary education; Higher education; Human services.
Type of support: General support.
Limitations: Applications not accepted. Giving primarily in Minneapolis, MN. No grants to individuals.
Application information: Contributes only to pre-selected organizations.
Officers: Darren R. Jackson, Pres.; Theresa A. Jackson, Treas.
Director: Ryan D. Jackson.
EIN: 205941634

4719
Jeffers Foundation
2605 Fernbrook Ln., Ste. B-1
Plymouth, MN 55447-4736
Main URL: http://www.jeffersfoundation.org
Blog: http://www.jeffersfoundation.org/blog
YouTube: https://www.youtube.com/user/jeffersfoundation

Established in 2005 in Minnesota.

Foundation type: Operating foundation.
Financial data (yr. ended 12/31/13): Assets, $14,292,438 (M); expenditures, $799,489; qualifying distributions, $653,491; giving activities include $193,167 for 11 grants (high: $119,057; low: $585).
Purpose and activities: Giving primarily for education.
Fields of interest: Education; Environment; Human services.
Limitations: Applications accepted. Giving primarily in MN.
Application information: Application form required.
   Initial approach: See web site for application form
   Deadline(s): See web site for deadline
Directors: Galen Erickson; Michael Fairbourne; Darwin A. Fosse; Kelly Murray; Paul Oberg; Seliesa Pembleton; Fergus R. Wooley.
EIN: 202601947

4720
The Jostens Foundation, Inc.
3601 Minnesota Dr., Ste. 400
Minneapolis, MN 55435-5281   (952) 830-3235
Contact: Veronica Sanderson, Secy.
E-mail: foundation@jostens.com; Main URL: http://www.jostens.com/misc/aboutus/about_jostens_cp_involvement.html

Established in 1976 in Minnesota.
Donor: Jostens, Inc.
Foundation type: Company-sponsored foundation.
Financial data (yr. ended 12/31/13): Assets, $184,840 (M); gifts received, $500,000; expenditures, $436,103; qualifying distributions, $436,103; giving activities include $391,858 for 313 grants (high: $25,000; low: $25), and $30,000 for 13 grants to individuals (high: $5,000; low: $2,500).
Purpose and activities: The foundation supports organizations involved with education and youth development.
Fields of interest: Education; Elementary and secondary education; Higher education; Student retention; Reading promotion; Youth development.
Type of support: General support; Employee matching gifts; Program development; Scholarships.
Limitations: Applications accepted. Giving in areas of company operations, with emphasis on MN. No support for schools, school districts, or school foundations, organizations involved with highly political or controversial issues, churches or religious groups, or fraternal, veterans', or professional organizations. No grants to individuals (except for employee-related scholarships), or for personal needs, political campaigns or political lobbying activities, benefit fundraising events or tickets to fundraisers, recognition or testimonial events, disease-specific fundraising campaigns, athletic scholarships or activities, advertising, endowments, or capital campaigns.
Publications: Application guidelines; Informational brochure (including application guidelines); Program policy statement.
Application information: Requests may be submitted using the Minnesota Common Grant Form. Application form required.
   Initial approach: Proposal
   Copies of proposal: 1
   Deadline(s): Feb. 22, May 24, Aug. 23, and Nov. 22.

Board meeting date(s): Quarterly
Final notification: Within 1 month of board meetings

Officers and Directors: Charley Nelson, Pres.; Veronica Sanderson, Secy.; Randall Wilson, Treas.; Tricia Bishop; Sheri Hank; Aaron Kjolhaug; Marin Koentopf; Lindsey Robertson; Natalie Stute.
EIN: 411280587

4721
Kaplan Family Foundation

6566 France Ave. S., No. 701
Edina, MN 55435-1714
E-mail: aryeh1@aol.com

Established in 1994 in Minnesota.
Donors: Harvey Kaplan; Leah Kaplan; Marjorie Kaplan; Rachel Kaplan; Helen Kaplan; Ross Kaplan.
Foundation type: Independent foundation.
Financial data (yr. ended 12/31/13): Assets, $5,278,928 (M); expenditures, $268,055; qualifying distributions, $258,262; giving activities include $258,262 for 46 grants (high: $70,000; low: $100).
Purpose and activities: Giving primarily to Jewish agencies to support Jewish cultural arts, education and camping.
Fields of interest: Education; Nonprofits; Judaism; Human services; Family services.
International interests: Israel.
Type of support: Continuing support; Regranting; Annual campaigns; Endowments.
Limitations: Applications not accepted. Giving primarily in AZ, IL, MN, NY, PA, the Midwest, and Israel. No support for political organizations. No grants to individuals.
Application information: Contributes only to pre-selected organizations.
Board meeting date(s): July-Aug.
Officers and Directors: Harvey Kaplan, Pres. and Director; Marjorie Kaplan, V.P. and Director; Rachel Kaplan, Secy.; Helen Kaplan, Treas.; Laura Kaplan; Leah Kaplan; Ross Kaplan; Robert Riesman; Jon Smollen.
Number of staff: None.
EIN: 411794327

4722
H. & M. Kellogg Charitable Trust

c/o Trust Tax Svcs.
P.O. Box 64713
Saint Paul, MN 55164-0713

Established in 2000 in Minnesota.
Donor: Mildred H. Kellogg Trust†.
Foundation type: Independent foundation.
Financial data (yr. ended 12/31/14): Assets, $6,966,920; expenditures, $353,238; qualifying distributions, $292,072 and $0 for set-asides.
Fields of interest: Arts and culture; Museums; Elementary and secondary education; Graduate and professional education; Health; Diseases and conditions; Theology; People with hearing impairments.
Limitations: Applications not accepted. Giving primarily in IL, MA, MN and NY. No grants to individuals.
Application information: Contributes only to pre-selected organizations.

Trustees: Gary Johnson; Robert Struyk; U.S. Bank, N.A.
EIN: 311713052

4723
Kinman-Oldfield Family Foundation Trust

c/o Trust Tax Services
P.O. Box 64713
Saint Paul, MN 55164-0713
Application address: c/o U.S. Bank, N.A., Attn.: James Strasheim, 233 S. 13th St., Ste. 1011, Lincoln, NE 68508-2017, tel.: (402) 434-1584

Established in 1999 in Nebraska.
Donor: Col. A. Barney Oldfield.
Foundation type: Independent foundation.
Financial data (yr. ended 06/30/13): Assets, $4,275,669 (M); expenditures, $267,821; qualifying distributions, $226,296; giving activities include $162,049 for 5 grants (high: $124,049; low: $1,000), and $31,000 for 29 grants to individuals (high: $2,000; low: $1,000).
Purpose and activities: Giving for educational and medical research purposes.
Fields of interest: Education; Higher education; Foundations; Diseases and conditions.
Type of support: Research; Student aid; Research and evaluation; Individual development.
Limitations: Applications accepted. Giving primarily in MN and NE.
Application information: Application form required.
Initial approach: Letter
Deadline(s): None
Trustee: U.S. Bank, N.A.
EIN: 396720478

4724
Kinney Family Foundation

3001 Sandy Hook Dr.
Roseville, MN 55113-2168

Established in 2003 in Minnesota.
Donor: Madeleine B. Kinney†.
Foundation type: Independent foundation.
Financial data (yr. ended 12/31/14): Assets, $10,091,992 (M); expenditures, $464,984; qualifying distributions, $433,500; giving activities include $433,500 for 34 grants (high: $50,800; low: $400).
Purpose and activities:
Fields of interest: Education; Higher education; Nonprofits; Christianity; Catholicism; Human services; Child welfare.
Type of support: Regranting.
Limitations: Applications not accepted. Giving primarily in MN, with emphasis on Minneapolis-St. Paul.
Application information: Contributes only to pre-selected organizations.
Trustees: Barbara Winters; Evelyn Pallas.
EIN: 651205543

4725
The Knowlton Foundation

c/o Hormel Foods Corp.
1 Hormel Pl.
Austin, MN 55912-3680
Contact: Connie J. Nelson

Established in 1997 in Minnesota.

Donors: Richard L. Knowlton; Nancy V. Knowlton.
Foundation type: Independent foundation.
Financial data (yr. ended 12/31/13): Assets, $2,377,974 (M); expenditures, $194,940; qualifying distributions, $186,533; giving activities include $186,500 for 40 grants.
Fields of interest: Education; Hospital care; Diseases and conditions; Human services.
Type of support: General support; Research; Research and evaluation.
Limitations: Applications not accepted. Giving primarily in MN and VA. No grants to individuals.
Application information: Contributes only to pre-selected organizations.
Officers: Richard L. Knowlton, Pres. and Treas.; Nancy V. Knowlton, V.P. and Secy.
EIN: 411877113

4726
The Krisbin Foundation

1280 Bracketts Point Rd.
Wayzata, MN 55391-9530

Donors: B. Kristine Johnson; Robbin S. Johnson.
Foundation type: Independent foundation.
Financial data (yr. ended 12/31/13): Assets, $4,699,497 (M); gifts received, $2,500; expenditures, $298,772; qualifying distributions, $254,500; giving activities include $254,500 for 17 grants (high: $100,000; low: $1,000).
Fields of interest: Arts and culture; Education; Higher education; Nonprofits; Religion.
Type of support: Regranting.
Limitations: Applications not accepted. Giving primarily in MN. No grants to individuals.
Application information: Unsolicited requests for funds not accepted.
Trustees: B. Kristine Johnson; Robbin S. Johnson.
EIN: 416419749

4727
Winthrop and Frances Lane Foundation

c/o Trust Tax Services
P.O. Box 64713
Saint Paul, MN 55164-0713
Application address: 525 N. 132nd St., Omaha, NE 68154, tel.: (402) 963-2156

Foundation type: Independent foundation.
Financial data (yr. ended 12/31/13): Assets, $3,351,796 (M); expenditures, $211,224; qualifying distributions, $172,210; giving activities include $163,250 for 4 grants (high: $68,500; low: $11,250).
Purpose and activities: Giving primarily for scholarships to students enrolled at Creighton University School of Law, Omaha, Nebraska, and The University of Nebraska College of Law, Lincoln, Nebraska. Some giving also for general support of these institutions and for local Nebraska bar associations.
Fields of interest: Law education.
Type of support: General support; Convening; Research; Student aid.
Limitations: Applications accepted. Giving limited to residents of Omaha and Lincoln, NE. No loans or program-related investments.
Application information: Application form required.
Initial approach: Request application form
Deadline(s): None

Trustee: U.S. Bank, N.A.
EIN: 470581778

4728

John Larsen Foundation

2002 W. Lake of the Isles Pkwy.
Minneapolis, MN 55105-2438 (612) 377-9010
E-mail: johnlarsenfoundation@comcast.net; Main URL: http://johnlarsenfoundation.org
Grants List: http://johnlarsenfoundation.wordpress.com/past-grants

Established in 1991 in Minnesota.
Donors: John A. Larsen; Karen R. Larsen; Lillian Regenberg.
Foundation type: Independent foundation.
Financial data (yr. ended 12/31/13): Assets, $6,644,144 (M); expenditures, $374,066; qualifying distributions, $322,409; giving activities include $317,500 for 24 grants (high: $60,000; low: $500).
Purpose and activities: To better the lives of individuals and families, both traditional and non-traditional.
Fields of interest: Arts and culture; Education; Environment; Community and economic development; Human services; Children and youth; Adolescents; Adults; LGBTQ people; Homeless people; Incarcerated people; Victims of crime and abuse; Substance abusers.
Type of support: General support; Program-related investments; Matching grants; Continuing support; Capacity-building and technical assistance; Annual campaigns; Capital campaigns; Capital and infrastructure; Endowments; Recordings; Curriculum development; Equal access.
Limitations: Applications not accepted. Giving primarily in MN and WI. No support for religious or political organizations, umbrella organizations, or for fraternal societies. No grants to individuals.
Publications: Grants list; Multi-year report.
Application information: The foundation accepts grant requests by invitation only; unsolicited requests for funds are not accepted.
 Board meeting date(s): Varies
Officers: John E. Larsen, Pres.; John A. Larsen, Treas.
Board Member: Kristen L. Rose.
Director: Karen R. Larsen.
Number of staff: 1 part-time support.
EIN: 411715465

4729

Lillehei Family Charitable Foundation

400 Robert St. N.
Saint Paul, MN 55101-2098

Established in 2001 in Minnesota.
Donor: Katherine R. Lillehei.
Foundation type: Independent foundation.
Financial data (yr. ended 12/31/14): Assets, $3,963,405 (M); expenditures, $265,801; qualifying distributions, $217,155.
Fields of interest: Museums; Higher education; Diseases and conditions; Christianity; Human services.
Type of support: General support.
Limitations: Applications not accepted. Giving primarily in IL and MN. No grants to individuals.
Application information: Contributes only to pre-selected organizations.

Officer: Troy Loken, Pres.
Agent: Securian Trust Co.
Board Members: Craig Lillehei; Kevin Lillehei; Kimberle Loken.
EIN: 412009840

4730

Living Springs Foundation

708 S. 3rd St., Ste. 510
Minneapolis, MN 55415-1145 (612) 338-3255
Contact: Philip S. Sherburne

Established in 1998 in Minnesota.
Donors: Margaret Bullitt-Jonas; Robert A. Jonas.
Foundation type: Independent foundation.
Financial data (yr. ended 12/31/13): Assets, $1,966,065 (M); gifts received, $65,488; expenditures, $147,750; qualifying distributions, $132,507; giving activities include $126,435 for 34 grants (high: $30,000; low: $1,000).
Fields of interest: Education; Environment; Religion.
Limitations: Applications accepted. Giving primarily in MA. No grants to individuals.
Application information: Application form required.
 Initial approach: Contact foundation
 Copies of proposal: 2
 Deadline(s): None
Directors: Margaret Bullitt-Jonas; Robert Jonas.
EIN: 411904085

4731

Louis Foundation

1660 S. Hwy., 100 Parkdale, Ste. 426
Saint Louis Park, MN 55416 (952) 512-1165
Contact: Penelope B. Hatten, Pres.

Established in 1996 in Minnesota.
Donors: Charles H. Bell†; Charitable Lead Annuity Trust No. 1; Anita Gray Trust; Charles H. Bell Charitable Lead Annuity.
Foundation type: Independent foundation.
Financial data (yr. ended 12/31/13): Assets, $3,753,084 (M); gifts received, $190,106; expenditures, $277,787; qualifying distributions, $234,023; giving activities include $233,998 for 4 grants (high: $101,500; low: $20,000).
Purpose and activities: Giving primarily for education, animal welfare, and medical care.
Fields of interest: Elementary education; Wildlife biodiversity; Health.
Type of support: General support; Program development.
Limitations: Applications accepted. Giving in the U.S., with emphasis on MT; some giving also in Canada.
Application information: Application form required.
 Initial approach: Proposal
 Deadline(s): None
Officers: Penelope B. Hatten, Pres.; Dean E. Hatten, V.P. and Treas.
EIN: 411859474

4732

Lukis Foundation

125 Westwood Ln.
Wayzata, MN 55391-1532

Established in 1991 in Minnesota.
Donors: Donna Lukis; Lawrence Lukis.
Foundation type: Independent foundation.

Financial data (yr. ended 12/31/13): Assets, $32,151,804 (M); gifts received, $1; expenditures, $285,356; qualifying distributions, $230,150; giving activities include $230,150 for 17 grants (high: $20,000; low: $5,000).
Fields of interest: Education; Health; Human services.
Limitations: Applications not accepted. Giving primarily in MN and WI. No grants to individuals.
Application information: Unsolicited requests for funds not accepted.
Officers: Lawrence J. Lukis, Pres.; Donald Filareki, V.P.; Donna B. Lukis, Secy.-Treas.
EIN: 411708009

4733

The Luther Family Foundation

3701 Alabama Ave. S.
Saint Louis Park, MN 55416-5156 (952) 258-8800
Contact: Charles David Luther, Tr.

Established in 1994 in Minnesota.
Donors: Charles David Luther; Rudy Dan Luther; Luther Nissan Kia; Luther Family Ford; Bloomington Acura; Rudy Luther Toyota; Barb Hilbert.
Foundation type: Independent foundation.
Financial data (yr. ended 12/31/14): Assets, $10,957,833 (M); expenditures, $456,914; qualifying distributions, $373,953; giving activities include $373,453 for 28 grants (high: $112,013; low: $1,000).
Fields of interest: Diseases and conditions; Autism; Christianity; Human services.
Limitations: Applications accepted. Giving primarily in MN.
Application information: Application form required.
 Initial approach: Proposal
 Deadline(s): None
Trustees: Barb Hilbert; Charles David Luther; Rudy Dan Luther.
EIN: 411798367

4734

Lutheran Education Foundation of Minnesota

9201 Normandale Blvd.
Bloomington, MN 55437-1940

Donors: Mel Soderholm; Lucile Einess; Merlin Bretzman.
Foundation type: Independent foundation.
Financial data (yr. ended 12/31/13): Assets, $43,207 (M); gifts received, $11,165; expenditures, $206,739; qualifying distributions, $206,738; giving activities include $205,000 for 4 grants (high: $75,000; low: $15,000).
Fields of interest: Education.
Limitations: Applications not accepted. Giving primarily in MN.
Application information: Unsolicited requests for funds not accepted.
Officers: Mel Soderholm, Chair.; Merlin Bretzman, Vice-Chair.; Carol Radunz, Secy.; James Kelzer, Treas.
Board Members: Cheryl Chatman; Lucile Einess; Dennis Senne; Fran Wallin.
EIN: 200043655

4735
Lutheran Retirement Home of Southern Minnesota Inc.

2188 220th St.
Truman, MN 56088-2024   (507) 236-5461
Contact: Arnold Bentz, Pres.

Foundation type: Independent foundation.
Financial data (yr. ended 09/30/13): Assets, $1,395,128 (M); expenditures, $192,385; qualifying distributions, $170,848; giving activities include $167,993 for 4 grants (high: $105,593; low: $13,050).
Fields of interest: Education.
Limitations: Applications accepted. Giving primarily in MN.
Application information: Application form required.
  Initial approach: Letter
  Deadline(s): None
Officers: Arnold Bentz, Pres.; Robert Kosbab, 1st V.P.; Gilbert Zinke, 2nd V.P.; Martin Krause, Secy.-Treas.
Directors: Carol Berne; Larry Bremer; Oren Flours; Elroy Geistfeld; Timothy Hemp; John Hilgendorf; Wilbert Siege.
EIN: 416042564

4736
Luverne Area Community Foundation

P.O. Box 623
Luverne, MN 56156-0623   (507) 220-2424
E-mail: emily@luvacf.org; *Main URL:* http://www.luvacf.org
E Newsletter: http://www.luvacf.org/news.html
Facebook: https://www.facebook.com/pages/Luverne-Area-Community-Foundation/411709045510005

Established in 1992 in Minnesota.
Foundation type: Community foundation.
Financial data (yr. ended 12/31/12): Assets, $2,363,330 (M); gifts received, $321,783; expenditures, $285,012; giving activities include $198,400 for 5+ grants (high: $103,795).
Purpose and activities: The foundation seeks to develop and allocate financial resources to support area needs.
Fields of interest: Arts and culture; Environment; Community and economic development; Child welfare.
Limitations: Applications accepted. Giving primarily in the Luverne Area, MN. No support for religious organizations for religious purposes. No grants for annual appeals or membership drives, or for travel for individuals or groups.
Publications: Application guidelines.
Application information: Application form required.
  Initial approach: Submit application
  Deadline(s): Mar. 31 and Sept. 30
Officers and Directors: Michele Van Dyke, Pres. and Director; Ben Vander Kooi, Secy. and Director; Barb Berghorst, Treas. and Director; Beth Bartles; Greg Burger; Mike Cox; Doug Eisma; Jeff Hartquist; Karen Radisewitz; Nadine Schoep.
EIN: 411512905

4737
Mahon Foundation

c/o Peter M. Mahon, Jr.
3800 American Blvd. W., Ste. 990
Minneapolis, MN 55431-4424

Established in 2005 in Minnesota.
Donors: Peter M. Mahon, Jr.; Deborah P. Mahon.
Foundation type: Operating foundation.
Financial data (yr. ended 12/31/14): Assets, $47,488; expenditures, $146,703; qualifying distributions, $122,850.
Purpose and activities: Giving primarily for Christian organizations and ministries, as well as to a Baptist church.
Fields of interest: Christianity; Baptist; Human services.
Limitations: Applications not accepted. No grants to individuals.
Application information: Contributes only to pre-selected organizations.
Trustees: Deborah P. Mahon; Peter M. Mahon, Jr.
EIN: 416542523

4738
Judith Rauenhorst Mahoney Family Foundation

c/o Tax Dept.
10350 Bren Rd. W.
Minnetonka, MN 55343-9014

Established in 1998 in Minnesota.
Donors: Judith Rauenhorst Mahoney; Thomas Mahoney; Opus Corp.
Foundation type: Independent foundation.
Financial data (yr. ended 12/31/13): Assets, $3,980,683 (M); expenditures, $167,320; qualifying distributions, $165,689; giving activities include $161,000 for 7 grants (high: $96,300; low: $100).
Fields of interest: Education; Catholicism.
Type of support: General support.
Limitations: Applications not accepted. Giving primarily in IN and MN. No grants to individuals.
Application information: Contributes only to pre-selected organizations.
Officers and Directors: Judith Rauenhorst Mahoney, Pres. and Director; Anne Deanovic, Secy. and Director; Joseph Mahoney, Treas. and Director.
EIN: 411925964

4739
Maranatha Ministries Foundation

2719 Patton Rd.
Roseville, MN 55113-1139

Foundation type: Independent foundation.
Financial data (yr. ended 12/31/13): Assets, $5,048,578 (M); expenditures, $262,365; qualifying distributions, $213,185; giving activities include $209,000 for 9 grants (high: $45,000; low: $10,500).
Fields of interest: Education; Housing development; Religion.
Limitations: Applications not accepted.
Application information: Unsolicited requests for funds not accepted.
Officers: Roger Adams, Pres.; Kim Vander Werf, V.P.; Joanne Bettenga, Secy.; Larry Petersen, Treas.
Board Members: Miriam Hazzard; Dale Stephens.
EIN: 411586022

4740
March Family Foundation

4709 Townes Rd.
Edina, MN 55424-1237

Donors: John D. March; Sallie S. Mc
Foundation type: Independent foundatic
Financial data (yr. ended 12/31/13): Asse
$4,633,720 (M); gifts received, $296,288; expenditures, $300,121; qualifying distributions, $268,331; giving activities include $265,000 for 20 grants (high: $30,000; low: $5,000).
Fields of interest: Education; Housing development; Religion.
Type of support: General support.
Limitations: Applications not accepted. Giving primarily in MN.
Application information: Unsolicited requests for funds not accepted.
Officers: John D. Marsh, Pres. and Treas.; Sallie S. March, Secy.
Directors: John B. March; Mary Chung March; Timothy S. March; Daniel C. Mauer; Lisa M. Mauer.
EIN: 263296616

4741
Frank J. and Eleanor A. Maslowski Charitable Trust

c/o Larry Loeschen
9121 Baltimore St. N.E., Ste. 103
Blaine, MN 55449-4338

Foundation type: Independent foundation.
Financial data (yr. ended 12/31/13): Assets, $15,977,996 (M); expenditures, $612,391; qualifying distributions, $466,159; giving activities include $340,000 for 2 grants (high: $200,000; low: $140,000).
Purpose and activities: Giving primarily for medical research.
Fields of interest: Higher education; Hospital care.
Type of support: Research.
Limitations: Applications not accepted. Giving primarily in Minneapolis and Wadena, MN. No grants to individuals.
Application information: Unsolicited requests for funds not accepted.
Trustees: Mary Larson; Larry Loeschen; Maragret Schwartz.
EIN: 270915939

4742
Marcus McCoy Foundation

4610 Browndale Ave.
Edina, MN 55424-1143

Established in 2000 in Minnesota.
Donor: Jon M. Ashton.
Foundation type: Independent foundation.
Financial data (yr. ended 12/31/14): Assets, $4,404,623 (M); expenditures, $267,656; qualifying distributions, $245,075.
Fields of interest: Education; Environment; Protestantism; Interfaith; Human services; Women's services.
Limitations: Applications not accepted. Giving primarily in MN. No grants to individuals.
Application information: Unsolicited requests for funds not accepted.
Officers and Directors: Jon M. Ashton, Pres. and Director; Nancy Ashton, Secy.-Treas. and Director; Kreea Ashton; Sally Ann Story.
EIN: 411989867

4743
Richard F. McNamara Family Foundation
86 Woodland Cir.
Edina, MN 55424-1449

Established in 1992 in Minnesota.
Donor: Richard F. McNamara.
Foundation type: Independent foundation.
Financial data (yr. ended 12/31/13): Assets, $739,930 (M); expenditures, $180,860; qualifying distributions, $167,145; giving activities include $163,820 for 7 grants (high: $125,000; low: $1,000).
Purpose and activities: Giving primarily to Roman Catholic organizations, as well as for higher education, health organizations, and youth and social services.
Fields of interest: Education; Higher education; Nonprofits; Diseases and conditions; Alzheimer's disease; Catholicism; Human services; Child welfare.
Type of support: General support; Regranting.
Limitations: Applications not accepted. Giving limited to MN. No grants to individuals.
Application information: Unsolicited requests for funds not accepted.
Trustees: Emily McNamara; Robert J. McNamara.
EIN: 411725127

4744
Sam & Bertha Merritt Memorial Trust
c/o Trust Tax Services
P.O. Box 64713
Saint Paul, MN 55164-0713

Foundation type: Independent foundation.
Financial data (yr. ended 12/31/13): Assets, $3,354,501 (M); expenditures, $200,217; qualifying distributions, $162,170; giving activities include $154,126 for 2 grants (high: $77,063; low: $77,063).
Fields of interest: Higher education; Protestantism.
Limitations: Applications not accepted. Giving primarily in Bismarck, ND. No grants to individuals.
Application information: Unsolicited requests for funds not accepted.
Trustee: U.S. Bank, N.A.
EIN: 237035116

4745
Midcontinent Media Foundation
(formerly Midcontinent Foundation)
3600 Minnesota Dr., Ste. 700
Minneapolis, MN 55435-7979 (952) 844-2600
Contact: Patrick McAdaragh, Pres. and Dir.

Donors: Midcontinent Media, Inc.; Midcontinent Communications.
Foundation type: Company-sponsored foundation.
Financial data (yr. ended 12/31/13): Assets, $71,020 (M); gifts received, $179,996; expenditures, $190,495; qualifying distributions, $190,495; giving activities include $186,754 for 204 grants (high: $5,000; low: $25).
Purpose and activities: The foundation supports zoos and organizations involved with arts and culture, education, health, diabetes, crime and violence prevention, housing development, recreation, human services, and community economic development.

Fields of interest: Arts and culture; Education; Elementary education; Higher education; Zoos; Nonprofits; Health; Convalescent care; Diabetes; Crime prevention; Domestic violence; Fire prevention and control; Community and economic development; Housing development; Sports and recreation; Community recreation; Human services; Child welfare; Economics for youth.
Type of support: Capital and infrastructure; Employee matching gifts; Equipment; Emergency funds; Program development; Seed money; Regranting.
Limitations: Applications accepted. Giving primarily in areas of company operations in MN, ND, and SD. No support for organizations not endorsed by a Midcontinent Media employee.
Publications: Application guidelines.
Application information: The foundation gives priority to organizations endorsed by a Midcontinent Communications employee. Application form required.
Initial approach: Letter
Copies of proposal: 1
Deadline(s): None
Officers and Directors: Pat McAdaragh, Pres. and Director; Tom Simmons, Exec. Dir.; Steve Mattern; Brad Schoenfelder; Lance Schmidt; Debbie Stang.
EIN: 363556764

4746
The Doug & Martha Miller Foundation
c/o Phillip Strohm
601 Carlson Pkwy., Ste. 800
Minnetonka, MN 53305-5229

Established in 2004 in Minnesota.
Donor: Douglas V. Miller.
Foundation type: Independent foundation.
Financial data (yr. ended 12/31/13): Assets, $1,155,247 (M); expenditures, $153,949; qualifying distributions, $149,160; giving activities include $148,430 for grants.
Limitations: Applications not accepted. No grants to individuals.
Application information: Unsolicited requests for funds not accepted.
Officer: Douglas V. Miller, Pres. and Secy.-Treas.
Director: Weston Miller.
EIN: 201909215

4747
Melvin R. and Sally R. Mooty Family Foundation
5320 Kelsey Terr.
Edina, MN 55436-1021

Established in 2006 in Minnesota.
Donors: Melvin R. Mooty; Sally R. Mooty.
Foundation type: Independent foundation.
Financial data (yr. ended 12/31/13): Assets, $935,759 (M); expenditures, $121,995; qualifying distributions, $121,995; giving activities include $119,394 for 3 grants (high: $100,000; low: $9,144).
Fields of interest: Higher education; Christianity; Human services.
Limitations: Applications not accepted. Giving primarily in Minneapolis, MN. No grants to individuals.
Application information: Unsolicited requests for funds not accepted.

Trustees: Mary M. Kileen; Paul R. Mooty; Sally R. Mooty.
EIN: 205773931

4748
The Morning Foundation
(formerly The Holman Charitable Trust)
85 Langford Park
Saint Paul, MN 55108-1913

Donors: Thomas H. Holman, Jr.; Henry Holman; Janelle Holman; Kim D.L. Holman.
Foundation type: Independent foundation.
Financial data (yr. ended 12/31/13): Assets, $5,328,029 (M); gifts received, $117,558; expenditures, $329,132; qualifying distributions, $323,948; giving activities include $320,256 for 3 grants (high: $158,434; low: $35,000).
Fields of interest: Education; Elementary education; Business education; Foundations; Nonprofits; Diseases and conditions; Christianity; Catholicism; Human services; Child welfare.
Type of support: Regranting; Individual development.
Limitations: Applications not accepted. Giving primarily in MN. No grants to individuals.
Application information: Contributes only to pre-selected organizations.
Trustees: Kim D.L. Holman; Thomas H. Holman, Jr.
EIN: 742803921

4749
Diana Nelson and John Atwater Family Foundation
c/o Tonkawa Inc.
550 Tonkawa Rd.
Long Lake, MN 55356-9724 (952) 404-5636
Contact: C. David Nelson, Secy. and Tr.

Donors: Diana Nelson; John Atwater.
Foundation type: Independent foundation.
Financial data (yr. ended 12/31/13): Assets, $276,434 (M); gifts received, $252,381; expenditures, $121,908; qualifying distributions, $119,431; giving activities include $117,500 for 10 grants (high: $30,000; low: $500).
Fields of interest: Art museums; Education.
Type of support: General support.
Limitations: Applications accepted. Giving primarily in MA.
Application information: Application form required.
Initial approach: Proposal
Deadline(s): Mar. 1 and Sept. 1
Officers and Trustees: Diana Nelson, Pres. and Trustee; C. David Nelson, Secy. and Trustee; John Atwater, Treas. and Trustee.
EIN: 204900208

4750
Roger & Violet Noreen Charitable Trust
(formerly Noreen Family Charitable Trust)
c/o Trust Tax Services
P.O. Box 64713
Saint Paul, MN 55164-0713 6514668722
Application address: c/o Lisa Hiniker, 101 E. 5th St., St. Paul, MN 55101, tel.: (651) 466-8722

Established in 1989 in Minnesota.
Donor: Roger F. Noreen.
Foundation type: Independent foundation.

Financial data (yr. ended 12/31/14): Assets, $5,457,892; expenditures, $368,112; qualifying distributions, $291,550 and $0 for set-asides.
Purpose and activities: Giving primarily for human services, and to Christian and Protestant agencies and churches.
Fields of interest: Theater; Education; Health; Religion; Human services; Children.
Type of support: Capital campaigns.
Limitations: Applications accepted. Giving primarily in the Minneapolis-St. Paul, MN, area. No grants to individuals.
Application information: Application form required.
 Initial approach: Letter
 Deadline(s): None
Trustee: U.S. Bank, N.A.
EIN: 416309355

4751
Northern Star Foundation
408 St. Peter St., Ste. 434
Saint Paul, MN 55102-1119

Established in 1960 in Minnesota.
Foundation type: Independent foundation.
Financial data (yr. ended 10/31/13): Assets, $5,377,179 (M); expenditures, $243,171; qualifying distributions, $234,829; giving activities include $187,886 for 7 grants (high: $72,943; low: $1,000).
Purpose and activities: Emphasis on secondary and higher education, including scholarship funds, cultural programs, youth agencies, and a community fund.
Fields of interest: Arts and culture; Secondary education; Higher education; Nonprofits; Child welfare.
Type of support: General support; Scholarships; Regranting.
Limitations: Applications not accepted. Giving primarily in CA, FL and MN. No grants to individuals.
Application information: Contributes only to pre-selected organizations.
Officers: William H. Hamm, Pres.; Candace S. Hamm, V.P. and Secy.; Edward H. Hamm, V.P. and Treas.
EIN: 416030832

4752
Oak Grove Foundation
c/o Lowry Hill
90 S. 7th St., Ste. 5100
Minneapolis, MN 55402-4168

Established in 1998 in Minnesota.
Donors: Christine A. Morrison; John L. Morrison.
Foundation type: Independent foundation.
Financial data (yr. ended 12/31/13): Assets, $2,069,939 (M); gifts received, $301,186; expenditures, $193,256; qualifying distributions, $177,469; giving activities include $173,900 for 42 grants (high: $53,000; low: $100).
Fields of interest: University education; Hospital care; Human services.
Limitations: Applications not accepted. Giving primarily in MN. No grants to individuals.
Application information: Unsolicited requests for funds not accepted.
Officers: Christine A. Morrison, Pres.; John L. Morrison, V.P.
EIN: 411913047

4753
Alice M. O'Brien Foundation
1914 Nature View Ln.
West Saint Paul, MN 55118-4460
Main URL: http://www.aobfoundation.org

Established in 1951 in Minnesota.
Donor: Alice M. O'Brien†.
Foundation type: Independent foundation.
Financial data (yr. ended 12/31/14): Assets, $3,300,551; expenditures, $179,344; qualifying distributions, $156,500.
Purpose and activities: Giving primarily education; with some funding also for the arts and human services.
Fields of interest: Arts and culture; Historic preservation; Education; Higher education; Diseases and conditions; Catholicism; Human services.
Type of support: General support; Continuing support; Capital and infrastructure; Land acquisitions; Research.
Limitations: Applications not accepted. Giving primarily in MN. No grants to individuals, or for endowment funds, scholarships, fellowships, or matching gifts; no loans.
Application information: Contributes only to pre-selected organizations.
 Board meeting date(s): Sept. and Dec.
Officers: Alice O'Brien Berquist, Pres.; Alvina O'Brien, Secy.
Directors: Robin W. Brooksbank; Terence O'Brien, Jr.; Thomond R. O'Brien, Jr.
EIN: 416018991

4754
Onan Family Foundation
P.O. Box 50667
Minneapolis, MN 55405-0667 (952) 544-4702
Main URL: http://www.onanfamily.org/index.php?id=12
Grants List: http://www.onanfamily.org/index.php?id=10

Foundation type: Independent foundation.
Financial data (yr. ended 12/31/14): Assets, $5,521,004; expenditures, $251,561; qualifying distributions, $235,471.
Fields of interest: Arts and culture; Education; Public administration; Religion; Human services.
Type of support: General support; Continuing support; Emergency funds; Program development; Seed money.
Limitations: Applications not accepted. Giving primarily in Minneapolis and St. Paul, MN. No grants to individuals or for capital or endowment funds, research, scholarships, fellowships, trips, or matching gifts; generally, no loans.
Application information: Contributes only to pre-selected organizations; unsolicited grant requests not accepted.
 Board meeting date(s): Mar. and Aug.
Officers and Trustees: Sarah Boswell-Healey, Pres. and Trustee; Laura S. Girard, Secy. and Trustee; David W. Onan III, Treas. and Trustee; Patricia Onan, Exec. Dir.; Karen Onan Amundson; Judith O. Baragli; David W. Onan II.
Number of staff: 1 part-time professional.
EIN: 416033631

4755
The Casey Albert T. O'Neil Foundation
P.O. Box 64713
Saint Paul, MN 55164-0713
Application address: c/o U.S. Bank, N.A., Attn.: Sarah Godfrey, 800 Nicollet Mall, Minneapolis, MN 55402-7020; tel.: (612) 303-3208

Established in 1965 in Minnesota.
Donor: Albert T. O'Neil†.
Foundation type: Independent foundation.
Financial data (yr. ended 06/30/13): Assets, $12,678,158 (M); expenditures, $492,223; qualifying distributions, $388,886; giving activities include $329,000 for 40 grants (high: $30,000; low: $1,000).
Purpose and activities: Giving primarily for health associations and social services; funding also for children and youth, and Roman Catholic organizations.
Fields of interest: Arts and culture; Religion; Human services.
Type of support: General support; Continuing support; Annual campaigns; Emergency funds; Seed money.
Limitations: Applications accepted. Giving primarily in MN, with some emphasis on St. Paul. No grants to individuals, or for deficit financing, capital campaigns, endowment or scholarship funds, matching gifts, research, special projects, publications, or conferences; no loans.
Application information: Application form required.
 Initial approach: Letter
 Copies of proposal: 1
 Deadline(s): None
 Board meeting date(s): As required
 Final notification: 3 months
Trustees: Philip A. Gartner; John Kelley; Casey Albert O'Neil; U.S. Bank, N.A.
EIN: 416044079

4756
Open Door Foundation
1660 S. Hwy., 100 Parkdale Plz., Ste. 426
Saint Louis Park, MN 55416-1533 (952) 512-1165
Contact: David B. Hartwell, Pres.

Established in 1996 in Minnesota.
Donors: Charles H. Bell†; Anita Winton Gray Trust Dated May 1; Charitable Lead Annuity Trust No. 1; Charles H. Bell Charitable Lead Annu.
Foundation type: Independent foundation.
Financial data (yr. ended 12/31/13): Assets, $4,625,760 (M); gifts received, $190,106; expenditures, $269,530; qualifying distributions, $218,125; giving activities include $218,100 for 22 grants (high: $35,000; low: $100).
Fields of interest: Environment; Health; Human services.
Type of support: General support; Program development.
Limitations: Applications accepted. Giving primarily in MN. No grants to individuals.
Application information: Application form required.
 Initial approach: Proposal
 Deadline(s): None
Officers: David B. Hartwell, Pres. and Treas.; Elizabeth Debaut, V.P. and Secy.
EIN: 411859476

4757
Dr. William James And Winifred Joyce O'Rourke Family Charitable Trust
9450 Old Cedar Ave. S.
Bloomington, MN 55425—2418

Foundation type: Independent foundation.
Financial data (yr. ended 12/31/14): Assets, $276,870 (M); expenditures, $155,965; qualifying distributions, $152,366; giving activities include $152,366 for 3 grants (high: $150,000; low: $500).
Fields of interest: Secondary education; Higher education.
Limitations: Applications not accepted. Giving primarily in Madison, WI. No grants to individuals.
Application information: Unsolicited requests for funds not accepted.
Trustees: Kathleen Losardo; Colleen O'Rourke; Patrick O'Rourke; Sean O'Rourke; Timothy O'Rourke.
EIN: 461529496

4758
OSilas Foundation
2545 Manitou Island
White Bear Lake, MN 55110-3901
*Application address:*c/o Silas M.Ford, III, 309 Pondfield Rd., Bronxville, NY 10708, tel.: (914) 337-4044

Established in 1999 in Minnesota.
Donor: Silas M. Ford III.
Foundation type: Independent foundation.
Financial data (yr. ended 12/31/13): Assets, $6,195,067 (M); expenditures, $259,779; qualifying distributions, $259,779; giving activities include $234,400 for 46 grants (high: $30,000; low: $1,000).
Fields of interest: Education; Higher education; Environment; Hospital care; Human services.
Limitations: Applications accepted. Giving primarily in MN.
Application information: Application form required.
  Initial approach: Proposal
  Deadline(s): None
Officers and Directors: Silas M. Ford III, Pres. and Director; David C. Ford, V.P. and Secy. and Director; Olivia C. Ford, V.P. and Treas. and Director; Kimberly Ford-Werling, V.P. and Director; Nannette Bertschy; Durand G. Ford; Margaret Ford; Robert Werling.
EIN: 411955001

4759
The Pautsch Family Foundation
9077 Hidden Meadow Rd.
Woodbury, MN 55125-9198 (651) 738-9431
Contact: Mark P. Pautsch, Pres., Treas. and Dir.

Established in 2007 in Minnesota.
Donors: Mark G. Pautsch; Norma Jean Pautsch; Mark P. Pautsch.
Foundation type: Independent foundation.
Financial data (yr. ended 12/31/13): Assets, $4,265 (M); gifts received, $161,550; expenditures, $181,038; qualifying distributions, $180,300; giving activities include $180,300 for 5 grants (high: $132,000; low: $1,000).
Fields of interest: Education; Christianity; Human services.
Limitations: Applications accepted. Giving primarily in MN.

Application information:
  Initial approach: Proposal
  Deadline(s): None
Officers and Directors: Mark P. Pautsch, Pres. and Treas. and Director; Norma Jean Pautsch, Secy. and Director; Adam M. Pautsch; Bethany J. Pautsch; Matthew J. Pautsch.
EIN: 260150562

4760
Pax Christi Foundation
7900 Xerxes Ave. S., Ste. 928
Minneapolis, MN 55431-1123

Established in 1987 in Minnesota.
Donors: J.C. Pahl; J.M. Pahl.
Foundation type: Independent foundation.
Financial data (yr. ended 06/30/13): Assets, $768,230 (M); gifts received, $4,575; expenditures, $254,908; qualifying distributions, $229,700; giving activities include $222,500 for 1 grant.
Purpose and activities: Giving primarily to a foundation which supports a program that creates buildings to serve orphans and unwed mothers.
Fields of interest: Community and economic development.
International interests: Mauritius.
Limitations: Applications not accepted. Giving primarily in Mauritius. No grants to individuals.
Application information: Unsolicited requests for funds not accepted.
Officers: J.C. Pahl, Pres.; J.M. Pahl, Secy.-Treas.
EIN: 363550495

4761
Peace Shalom Foundation
1670 Robert St.
P.O. Box 357
Saint Paul, MN 55118-3918

Established in 1989 in Minnesota.
Donors: Janice E. Schiefelbein; Charles Schiefelbein.
Foundation type: Independent foundation.
Financial data (yr. ended 11/30/13): Assets, $2,291,045 (M); expenditures, $202,474; qualifying distributions, $202,091; giving activities include $192,750 for 30 grants (high: $19,750; low: $2,000).
Fields of interest: Religion.
Limitations: Applications not accepted. Giving primarily in MN. No grants to individuals.
Application information: Unsolicited requests for funds not accepted.
Directors: Charles Schiefelbein, Jr.; David M. Schiefelbein; Duane Schiefelbein.
EIN: 411654125

4762
Raymond B. Pinson Family Foundation
4297 138th Ct. W.
Rosemount, MN 55068-3311

Established in 2000 in Minnesota.
Donor: Raymond B. Pinson.
Foundation type: Independent foundation.
Financial data (yr. ended 12/31/12): Assets, $3,715,837 (M); gifts received, $538,600; expenditures, $258,104; qualifying distributions,

$215,000; giving activities include $215,000 for grants.
Fields of interest: Education; Protestantism.
Limitations: Applications not accepted. Giving primarily in CA and MN. No grants to individuals.
Application information: Unsolicited requests for funds not accepted.
Officers and Directors: Raymond B. Pinson, Pres. and Director; Kathleen A. Pinson, Secy.-Treas. and Director.
Board Members: Anne Pinson; Joshua Pinson; Noah Pinson; Robert Schmidt; Sarah Schmidt.
EIN: 411922232

4763
The Irwin Andrew Porter Foundation
7201 Ohms Ln., Ste. 100
Edina, MN 55439-2155
Main URL: http://www.iapfoundation.org
Domestic Grant Awards: http:// www.iapfoundation.org/?q=about/granthistory
International Grant Awards: http:// www.iapfoundation.org/?q=about/granthistory/ international

Established in 1996 in Minnesota.
Donor: Amy L. Hubbard.
Foundation type: Independent foundation.
Financial data (yr. ended 08/31/13): Assets, $3,036,556 (M); expenditures, $189,752; qualifying distributions, $179,721; giving activities include $179,721 for 20 grants (high: $34,000; low: $1,500).
Purpose and activities: The mission of the foundation is to fund innovative projects that foster connections between individuals, communities, the environment and the world at large.
Fields of interest: Arts and culture; Art museums; Education; Environment; Water resources; Health; Economic development; Human services; International development.
International interests: Africa; Caribbean; Central America; South America.
Type of support: Matching grants.
Limitations: Applications accepted. Giving primarily in the U.S., with a focus on IA, IL, MN, ND, SD, and WI; international giving limited to Central and South America, the Caribbean, and Africa. No support for political organizations or religious programs. No grants to individuals, or for operating expenses, capital campaigns, or endowments.
Application information: Complete application guidelines available on foundation web site.
  Copies of proposal: 1
  Board meeting date(s): Quarterly
Officer and Directors: Amy L. Hubbard, Chair. and Director; Arta Cheney; Scott Elkins; Jay Goldberg; Gloria Perez Jordan; Geoffrey Kehoe; Cari O'Brien.
EIN: 411852392

4764
The Elizabeth C. Quinlan Foundation, Inc.
801 Twelve Oaks Center Dr., Ste. 805B
Wayzata, MN 55391-4615 (952) 475-1550
Contact: Richard A. Klein, Pres.

Established in 1945 in Minnesota.
Donors: Elizabeth C. Quinlan†; Mary Elizabeth Lahiff†.
Foundation type: Independent foundation.

Financial data (yr. ended 12/31/13): Assets, $5,091,434 (M); expenditures, $315,351; qualifying distributions, $252,846; giving activities include $185,300 for 62 grants (high: $25,000; low: $200).
Purpose and activities: The foundation primarily supports educational institutions and their activities, and social service organizations and their programs. It also supports religious organizations and arts and humanities organizations and their activities.
Fields of interest: Arts and culture; Higher education; Nonprofits; Religion; Catholicism; Human services.
Type of support: General support; Matching grants; Continuing support; Annual campaigns; Capital and infrastructure; Equipment; Regranting; Land acquisitions; Endowments; Emergency funds; Program development; Seed money; Scholarships.
Limitations: Applications accepted. Giving limited to MN, with emphasis on the Twin Cities metro area. No support for political, fraternal, or sports organizations. No grants to individuals, or for goodwill advertising or benefit funding.
Publications: Annual report (including application guidelines).
Application information: Accepts Minnesota Common Grant Application Form.
  Initial approach: Letter
  Copies of proposal: 1
  Deadline(s): Submit proposal between Jan. 1 and Sept. 1
  Board meeting date(s): Oct.
  Final notification: Dec. 1
Officers and Trustees: Richard A. Klein, Pres. and Treas. and Trustee; Lucia L. Crane, V.P. and Trustee; Kathleen Leslie, Secy. and Trustee; Kathleen L. Budge; Mari Geis; Vincent Grundman; David Leslie.
Number of staff: 2 part-time support.
EIN: 410706125

4765
William D. Radichel Foundation
7301 Ohms Ln., Ste. 300
Edina, MN 55439-2350

Established in 2000 in Minnesota.
Donor: Radichel Family Intervivos Charitable Lead Trust.
Foundation type: Independent foundation.
Financial data (yr. ended 06/30/14): Assets, $92,671 (M); gifts received, $274,993; expenditures, $291,101; qualifying distributions, $276,650; giving activities include $276,650 for 34 grants (high: $65,000; low: $1,000).
Purpose and activities: Giving primarily for education, health care, children, youth, and social services, private grantmaking foundations, as well as to a community foundation, and to public broadcasting stations.
Fields of interest: Education; Elementary and secondary education; Higher education; Foundations; Health; Communication media; Human services; Child welfare.
Type of support: Regranting; Fundraising.
Limitations: Applications not accepted. Giving primarily in CO and MN. No grants to individuals.
Application information: Contributes only to pre-selected organizations.
Officers and Directors: Bradley P. Radichel, Pres. and C.E.O. and Director; Brenda Radichel Quaye,

V.P. and Director; Christina Radichel Caulkins, Secy.-Treas. and Director.
EIN: 411944317

4766
Rahr Foundation
800 W. 1st Ave.
Shakopee, MN 55379-1148 (952) 496-7003
Contact: Heidi Rahr Faris, Pres.
FAX: (952) 496-7055; E-mail: mtech@rahr.com

Donor: Rahr Malting Co.
Foundation type: Company-sponsored foundation.
Financial data (yr. ended 12/31/13): Assets, $4,374,464 (M); gifts received, $30,000; expenditures, $264,648; qualifying distributions, $200,776; giving activities include $182,000 for 42 grants (high: $10,000; low: $1,500).
Purpose and activities: The foundation supports health centers and organizations involved with performing arts, education, conservation, animal welfare, and human services.
Fields of interest: Education; Health; Human services.
Type of support: General support; Continuing support; Annual campaigns; Program development; Fellowships; Scholarships.
Limitations: Applications accepted. Giving primarily in MN. No grants for endowments or research programs; no loans.
Application information: Application form required.
  Initial approach: Request application form
  Copies of proposal: 1
  Deadline(s): Mar. 15
Officers: Heidi R. Faris, Pres.; Libby Jennings, V.P.; Marilyn T. Tech, Secy. and Admin.; William T. Rahr, Treas.
Director: Frederick W. Rahr.
Number of staff: 2 part-time support.
EIN: 396046046

4767
Mark and Karen Rauenhorst Foundation
c/o Tax Dept.
10350 Bren Rd. W.
Minnetonka, MN 55343-9014

Established in 1999 in Minnesota.
Donors: Mark Rauenhorst; Opus Corp.; Karen Rauenhorst.
Foundation type: Independent foundation.
Financial data (yr. ended 12/31/13): Assets, $5,162,906 (M); expenditures, $169,830; qualifying distributions, $168,317; giving activities include $163,500 for 13 grants (high: $50,000; low: $500).
Fields of interest: Education; Christianity; Human services.
Type of support: General support; Capital campaigns.
Limitations: Applications not accepted. No grants to individuals.
Application information: Contributes only to pre-selected organizations.
Officers and Directors: Mark Rauenhorst, Pres. and Director; Paul Lewis, V.P. and Director; Karen Rauenhorst, Secy.-Treas. and Director.
EIN: 411925821

4768
The Harold and Kate Reed Family Foundation
P.O. Box 5628
Minneapolis, MN 55440-5628

Donors: Harold S. Reed; Kate M. Reed.
Foundation type: Independent foundation.
Financial data (yr. ended 12/31/13): Assets, $4,502,196 (M); expenditures, $247,124; qualifying distributions, $195,774; giving activities include $195,000 for 32 grants (high: $20,000; low: $1,000).
Fields of interest: Elementary and secondary education; Undergraduate education; Domesticated animals.
Limitations: Applications not accepted. Giving primarily in FL and OR.
Application information: Unsolicited requests for funds not accepted.
Officers and Directors: Harold S. Reed, Pres. and Director; Kate M. Reed, V.P. and Director; Michella L. Johnson, Secy.-Treas.
EIN: 203982052

4769
Michael and Brittany Reger Family Foundation
3565 Frederick St.
Orono, MN 55391-9732

Donors: Michael Reger; Brittany Reger; Williston Reger; John M. Reger.
Foundation type: Independent foundation.
Financial data (yr. ended 12/31/14): Assets, $3,341,972; expenditures, $329,735; qualifying distributions, $327,700.
Fields of interest: Arts and culture; Religion; Youth development.
Type of support: Research.
Limitations: Applications not accepted. Giving primarily in CO and MN.
Application information: Unsolicited requests for funds not accepted.
Officer: Michael Reger, Pres.
Directors: Brittany Reger; Joseph Reger.
EIN: 274434063

4770
Regis Foundation
7201 Metro Blvd.
Minneapolis, MN 55439-2103 (952) 947-7777
Contact: Eric Bakken, Secy.
Main URL: http://www.regiscorp.com

Established in 1981 in Minnesota.
Donors: Regis Corp.; Regis, Inc.
Foundation type: Company-sponsored foundation.
Financial data (yr. ended 06/30/14): Assets, $76,160 (M); expenditures, $172,034; qualifying distributions, $172,034; giving activities include $171,000 for 2 grants (high: $170,000; low: $1,000).
Purpose and activities: The foundation supports organizations involved with arts and culture, education, human services, and Judaism.
Fields of interest: Arts and culture; Education; Elementary and secondary education; Higher education; Nonprofits; Public libraries; Judaism; Human services.

Type of support: Annual campaigns; Capital campaigns; General support; Capital and infrastructure; Scholarships; Regranting.
Limitations: Applications accepted. Giving primarily in the Minneapolis, MN, area.
Application information: Application form required.
 Initial approach: Letter
 Deadline(s): None
Officers: Dan Hanrahan, Pres.; Eric A. Bakken, Secy.; Steven Spiegel, Treas.
EIN: 411410790

4771
Reimer Foundation
8310 Creekside Cir., Ste. 820
Bloomington, MN 55437-3838

Established in 1985 in Minnesota.
Donor: William Reimer.
Foundation type: Independent foundation.
Financial data (yr. ended 11/30/13): Assets, $691,783 (M); expenditures, $263,677; qualifying distributions, $263,495; giving activities include $263,495 for 48 grants (high: $62,500; low: $20).
Fields of interest: Christianity; Human services.
Limitations: Applications accepted. Giving in the U.S., with emphasis on MN.
Application information: Application form required.
 Initial approach: Proposal
 Deadline(s): None
Officers: Dolores Reimer, Co-Chair.; William Reimer, Co-Chair.
Board Members: Barb Olson; Lynn Reimer; Michelle Vock.
EIN: 411557662

4772
Donald F. Reiner Educational Trust
P.O. Box 126
Springfield, MN 56087-0126
Application address: c/o Paul Pieschel, 101 N. Marshall, Springfield, MN 56087 tel.: (507) 723-4234

Donor: Springfield Lodging, LLC.
Foundation type: Independent foundation.
Financial data (yr. ended 12/31/13): Assets, $2,111,766 (M); expenditures, $228,484; qualifying distributions, $214,178; giving activities include $204,728 for 71 grants (high: $44,478; low: $250).
Fields of interest: Education.
Limitations: Applications accepted. Giving primarily in MN.
Application information: Application form required.
 Initial approach: Proposal
 Deadline(s): None
Trustees: Keith Kottke; Fr. Labat; Tucker Loomis; Paul Pieschel; Paul Tauer.
EIN: 264020412

4773
Robert & Helen Remick Charitable Foundation
P. O. Box 123
Lakefield, MN 56150-0123

Established in 1998 in Minnesota.
Donor: Robert Remick†.
Foundation type: Independent foundation.

Financial data (yr. ended 12/31/14): Assets, $11,554,065 (M); expenditures, $589,963; qualifying distributions, $467,104; giving activities include $440,985 for 33 grants (high: $57,000; low: $500).
Fields of interest: Arts and culture; Education; Environment; Foundations; Human services; Youth development.
Type of support: Equipment; Donated land.
Limitations: Applications not accepted. Giving primarily in MN, with emphasis on Windom. No grants to individuals.
Application information: Contributes only to pre-selected organizations.
Trustees: Howard C. Davis; Lynel Rae Nelson; John D. Remick; Cheryl Holthe Rients.
EIN: 411950527

4774
Autumn Rieks Foundation
4564 Kimbro Ave. N.
Lake Elmo, MN 55042-9508
Application address: c/o Lowell Rieks, 6550 Courtly Rd., Woodbury, MN 55125, tel.: (651) 738-6998

Established in 1995 in Minnesota.
Donors: Lowell Rieks; Beverly Rieks; Julie Landreville; Alan Landreville; Bob Reynolds.
Foundation type: Independent foundation.
Financial data (yr. ended 12/31/14): Assets, $431,582 (M); gifts received, $320,000; expenditures, $206,104; qualifying distributions, $205,850; giving activities include $205,850 for 13 grants (high: $151,500; low: $500).
Fields of interest: Education; Christianity; Human services; Child welfare.
Limitations: Applications accepted. Giving primarily in MN.
Application information: Application form required.
 Initial approach: Letter
 Deadline(s): None
Officers: Lowell Rieks, Pres.; Beverly Rieks, Secy.
EIN: 411832517

4775
Rising Sun Foundation
11126 Eastwood Ave., S.E.
Delano, MN 55328-8336

Donors: David J. Lubben; Nancy E. Kwam.
Foundation type: Independent foundation.
Financial data (yr. ended 12/31/14): Assets, $11,716 (M); gifts received, $201,927; expenditures, $252,498; qualifying distributions, $251,880; giving activities include $250,000 for 2 grants (high: $200,000; low: $50,000).
Fields of interest: Health; Diseases and conditions.
Type of support: Research.
Limitations: Applications not accepted. Giving primarily in CT and MN.
Application information: Unsolicited requests for funds not accepted.
Trustees: Nancy E. Kwam; David J. Lubben.
EIN: 271537557

4776
Riverway Foundation
8400 Normandale Lake Blvd., Ste. 920
Bloomington, MN 55437 (952) 921-3994
Contact: Terry R. Becker, Tr.

Established in 1995 in Minnesota.
Donors: Riverway Co.; H.M. Baskerville, Jr.; Terry R. Becker.
Foundation type: Company-sponsored foundation.
Financial data (yr. ended 12/31/13): Assets, $4,132,970 (M); expenditures, $217,237; qualifying distributions, $177,680; giving activities include $175,000 for 34 grants (high: $50,000; low: $1,200).
Purpose and activities: The foundation supports organizations involved with Alzheimer's disease, cancer research, domestic violence, housing, children and youth, family counseling, and senior citizens.
Fields of interest: Education; Community and economic development; Human services.
Type of support: General support; Pro bono consulting services; Matching grants; Continuing support; Annual campaigns; Capital campaigns; Capital and infrastructure; Equipment; Endowments; Debt reduction; Emergency funds; Program development; Program evaluations.
Application information: Application form required.
 Initial approach: Letter
 Copies of proposal: 1
 Deadline(s): None
Trustees: H.M. Baskerville, Jr.; Laura Lee Baskerville Becker; Terry R. Becker.
Number of staff: 1 part-time support.
EIN: 416406915

4777
RJW Foundation
20200 Lakeview Ave.
Excelsior, MN 55331-9358
Contact: Rodney M. Wilson

Established in 1996 in Minnesota.
Donors: Jenifer A. Wilson; Rodney M. Wilson.
Foundation type: Independent foundation.
Financial data (yr. ended 12/31/12): Assets, $3,296,429 (M); gifts received, $345,000; expenditures, $321,647; qualifying distributions, $148,413; giving activities include $148,413 for 23 grants (high: $35,000; low: $500).
Purpose and activities: Grant to provide affordable housing to women and children, support christian church and provide fund for college education.
Fields of interest: Education; Housing development; Religion.
Limitations: Applications not accepted. Giving primarily in MN. No grants to individuals.
Application information: Unsolicited requests for funds not accepted.
Officers: Jenifer A. Wilson, C.E.O. and Pres.; Rodney M. Wilson, Secy. and C.F.O.
EIN: 411858383

4778
Donald & Marie Roberts Charitable Foundation
22671 County Hwy. 10
Fergus Falls, MN 56537

Established in 1993 in Minnesota.
Donor: Donald Roberts.
Foundation type: Independent foundation.
Financial data (yr. ended 12/31/13): Assets, $3,375,591 (M); expenditures, $238,585; qualifying distributions, $197,574; giving activities

include $196,227 for 12 grants (high: $45,000; low: $1,409).

Fields of interest: Education; Health; Religion.

Type of support: General support; Annual campaigns; Research.

Limitations: Applications not accepted. Giving primarily in MN. No grants to individuals.

Application information: Contributes only to pre-selected organizations.

Officers: Shana Barry, Pres.; Steven Roberts, V.P. and Secy.-Treas.

EIN: 411765517

4779
Rodman Foundation
30 E. 7th St., Ste. 2000
Saint Paul, MN 55101-4930 (651) 228-0935
Contact: Frederick W. Titcomb, Pres. and Dir.

Established in 1969 in Minnesota.

Donors: Edward R. Titcomb†; Julie C. Titcomb†.

Foundation type: Independent foundation.

Financial data (yr. ended 12/31/13): Assets, $5,592,227 (M); expenditures, $229,468; qualifying distributions, $213,402; giving activities include $175,000 for 78 grants (high: $18,000; low: $200).

Fields of interest: Museums; Historical activities; Education; Elementary and secondary education; Environment; Domesticated animals; Science; Christianity; Reproductive rights; Human services; Youth services; Seniors.

Type of support: General support; Continuing support.

Limitations: Applications accepted. Giving primarily in MN and WA. No support for scientific research or religious organizations. No grants to individuals, or for capital campaigns, operating budgets, deficits or endowments.

Application information:
Initial approach: Letter
Deadline(s): None
Board meeting date(s): Oct.

Officers and Directors: Frederick W. Titcomb, Pres. and Director; Daniel C. Titcomb, V.P. and Director; Bruce L. Titcomb, Secy. and Director; E. Rodman Titcomb, Jr., Treas. and Director.

EIN: 237025570

4780
Roles Family Foundation
19500 Towering Oaks Tr.
Prior Lake, MN 55372-3446

Established in 2007 in Minnesota.

Donors: Thomas M. Roles; Kari L. Roles.

Foundation type: Independent foundation.

Financial data (yr. ended 12/31/12): Assets, $1,941,929 (M); gifts received, $255,884; expenditures, $141,838; qualifying distributions, $140,225; giving activities include $140,200 for 16 grants (high: $20,000; low: $2,500).

Fields of interest: Arts and culture; Community and economic development; Human services.

Limitations: Applications not accepted. Giving primarily in MN. No grants to individuals.

Application information: Unsolicited requests for funds not accepted.

Officers: Thomas M. Roles, Pres. and Treas.; Kari L. Roles, V.P.; Lisa M. Tonn, Secy.

Director: Kristi A. Blee.

EIN: 261584011

4781
Rose Francis Foundation
1010 W. Minnehaha Pwy.
Minneapolis, MN 55419

Donors: David Nassif; Monica Nassif.

Foundation type: Independent foundation.

Financial data (yr. ended 12/31/13): Assets, $4,002,309 (M); gifts received, $2,450; expenditures, $279,838; qualifying distributions, $255,946; giving activities include $254,696 for 15 grants (high: $50,000; low: $1,000).

Fields of interest: Education; Health; Agriculture.

Limitations: Applications not accepted.

Application information: Unsolicited requests for funds not accepted.

Officers and Directors: David Nassif, Pres. and Director; Monica Nassif, V.P. and Director; Calla Nassif, Secy. and Director; Aundrea Nassif, Treas. and Director.

EIN: 263074723

4782
The Rosen Family Foundation, Inc.
P.O. Box 933
Fairmont, MN 56031-0933

Established in 2002 in Minnesota.

Donors: Rosen's Diversified, Inc.; Roberta A. Rosen.

Foundation type: Company-sponsored foundation.

Financial data (yr. ended 12/31/13): Assets, $1,781,947 (M); gifts received, $254,375; expenditures, $187,810; qualifying distributions, $179,429; giving activities include $51,250 for 6 grants (high: $25,000; low: $1,000), and $128,000 for 123 grants to individuals (high: $1,250; low: $750).

Purpose and activities: The foundation supports organizations involved with education, grief counseling, agriculture, children and youth, senior citizens, and Christianity and awards college scholarships.

Fields of interest: Education; Early childhood education; Higher education; Bereavement counseling; Engineering; Mathematics; Agriculture; Christianity; Food aid; Child welfare; Senior services.

Type of support: General support; Program development; Student aid.

Limitations: Applications not accepted. Giving primarily in IA, NE, SD, and WI, with emphasis on MN.

Application information: Contributes only to pre-selected organizations and individuals.

Officers: Thomas J. Rosen, Pres. and Secy.; Dominick V. Driano, Jr., V.P.; Richard H. Rosen, Treas.

Director: Kann M. Rosen.

EIN: 412054672

4783
Sacred Portion Foundation
P.O. Box 268
Rockford, MN 55373-0268
Application address: c/o David Clark, 8150 20th St. S.E., Buffalo, MN 55313, tel.: (763) 477-6777

Established in 1996 in Minnesota.

Donors: John L. Clark; Nancy E. Clark; David A. Clark.

Foundation type: Operating foundation.

Financial data (yr. ended 12/31/13): Assets, $3,784,961 (M); gifts received, $143,900; expenditures, $279,789; qualifying distributions, $156,703; giving activities include $151,791 for 8 grants (high: $70,800; low: $2,400).

Purpose and activities: Giving for Christian organizations and activities. The grantmaker also maintains a farm and retreat center.

Fields of interest: Christianity; Adolescents.

Limitations: Applications accepted. Giving primarily in MN; some funding also in MO and TX.

Application information:
Initial approach: Proposal
Deadline(s): None

Officers: John L. Clark, Pres.; David A. Clark, Secy.-Treas.; Nancy E. Clark, Exec. Dir.

EIN: 411825330

4784
Samsara Foundation
2620 N. Glenhurst Pl.
Minneapolis, MN 55416-3957

Established in 1990 in Minnesota.

Donors: Wildwood Foundation; Tineka Kurth.

Foundation type: Independent foundation.

Financial data (yr. ended 12/31/13): Assets, $5,092,661 (M); expenditures, $235,296; qualifying distributions, $209,551; giving activities include $205,000 for 19 grants (high: $59,000; low: $1,000).

Fields of interest: Education; Science; Religion; Human services; Child welfare.

Type of support: General support.

Limitations: Applications not accepted. Giving primarily in MN and NY. No grants to individuals.

Application information: Contributes only to pre-selected organizations.

Officers: Tineka Kurth, Pres.; Kera Messinger, Secy.; William T. Messinger, Treas.

EIN: 411694707

4785
Sauer Children's Renew Foundation
P.O. Box 9088
North Saint Paul, MN 55109-0088 (651) 633-6165
Contact: Colleen O'Keefe, Exec. Dir.
Main URL: http://scrfmn.org/index.html
Grants List: http://scrfmn.org/2014grants.html
Grants List: http://scrfmn.org/2013grants.html
Grants List: http://scrfmn.org/2012grants.html
Grants List: http://scrfmn.org/2011grants.html

Established in 1997 in Minnesota.

Donors: Gary B. Sauer; Patricia A. Sauer; Spring Lake Park Lions Club; Barriere Construction Company.

Foundation type: Independent foundation.

Financial data (yr. ended 12/31/14): Assets, $5,430,319; gifts received, $1,045; expenditures, $488,793; qualifying distributions, $448,421.

Purpose and activities: Giving to improve the lives of disadvantaged children and their families.

Fields of interest: Child welfare; Adoption; Child care; Shelter and residential care.

Limitations: Applications accepted. Giving primarily in MN, with priority in the Twin Cities metro area. No support for political activities. No grants to individuals or for lobbying activities, endowments, deficit or debt reduction, fundraising activities or advertising.

Application information: See web site for additional policies and guidelines. Application form required.
>*Initial approach:* Cover letter including brief summary of the project or program
>*Deadline(s):* See web site
>*Final notification:* Grant proposals will be reviewed by the Charity Review Committee in Oct. and approved for funding by the Board of Trustees in late Nov.

Officers and Board Members: Patricia A. Sauer, Pres. and Director; Gary B. Sauer, Treas. and Director; Colleen O'Keefe, Exec. Dir.
EIN: 411859711

4786
The Sayer Charitable Foundation
1730 Meadow Woods Trail
Long Lake, MN 55356-9311
Contact: Michael Scott Sayer, Treas.

Established in 1994 in Minnesota.
Donors: George W. Sayer†; Evelyn W. Sayer†.
Foundation type: Independent foundation.
Financial data (yr. ended 12/31/13): Assets, $1,767,052 (M); gifts received, $185; expenditures, $245,059; qualifying distributions, $215,990; giving activities include $210,885 for 5 grants (high: $210,000; low: $100).
Purpose and activities: Giving for Catholic education and the economically disadvantaged.
Fields of interest: Education; Foundations; Catholicism; Low-income and poor people.
Type of support: Continuing support; Employee matching gifts; Endowments; Program development.
Limitations: Applications not accepted. Giving primarily in MN, with emphasis on the Twin Cities area.
Application information: Contributes only to pre-selected organizations.
>*Board meeting date(s):* Aug.

Officers: Patricia Sayer, Pres.; Michael Scott Sayer, Treas.
Directors: George Sayer III; John Sayer.
EIN: 411793832

4787
Schott Foundation
9350 Foxford Rd.
Chanhassen, MN 55317

Established in 1981 in Minnesota.
Donor: Schott Corp.
Foundation type: Company-sponsored foundation.
Financial data (yr. ended 03/31/14): Assets, $4,553,321 (M); expenditures, $263,516; qualifying distributions, $226,110; giving activities include $217,333 for 9 grants (high: $60,000; low: $2,500).
Purpose and activities: The foundation supports museums and organizations involved with education, the environment, and the humanities.
Fields of interest: Arts and culture; Humanities; Education; Environment; Natural resources; Health.
Type of support: General support; Scholarships.
Limitations: Applications accepted. Giving primarily in MN.
Application information: Application form required.

Initial approach: Letter of inquiry
>*Deadline(s):* None

Officers and Directors: Owen Schott, C.E.O. and Director; Wendell Schott, V.P. and Director.
EIN: 411392014

4788
The Schulze Family Foundation
14 Paddock Rd.
Edina, MN 55436-1346
Contact: Arthur R. Schulze Jr., Pres.

Established in 1996 in Minnesota.
Donors: Arthur R. Schulze, Jr.; Joan Schulze.
Foundation type: Independent foundation.
Financial data (yr. ended 11/30/13): Assets, $833,034 (M); gifts received, $1,600; expenditures, $341,962; qualifying distributions, $341,643; giving activities include $340,000 for 10 grants (high: $250,000; low: $500).
Fields of interest: Education; Health; Community and economic development.
Application information: Application form required.
>*Initial approach:* Letter
>*Deadline(s):* None

Officer: Arthur R. Schulze, Jr., Pres.
Director: Joan Schulze.
EIN: 411859038

4789
Seba Foundation
16523 Black Oaks Cir.
Wayzata, MN 55391-4515

Established in 2002 in Minnesota.
Donors: Steven King; Barbara King; Landscape Structures, Inc.
Foundation type: Independent foundation.
Financial data (yr. ended 12/31/13): Assets, $4,955,146 (M); gifts received, $171,552; expenditures, $308,076; qualifying distributions, $305,000; giving activities include $305,000 for 8 grants (high: $125,000; low: $5,000).
Fields of interest: Human services.
Limitations: Applications not accepted. Giving primarily in CA and MN. No grants to individuals.
Application information: Unsolicited requests for funds not accepted.
Officers: Steven King, Pres.; Adam King, V.P.; Erin King, Secy.
EIN: 550789357

4790
The William D. and Joyce E. Sexton Family Foundation
P.O. Box 296
Clara City, MN 56222-0296 (320) 847-3100
Contact: Kevin Noble, Secy.-Treas.

Established in 2003 in Delaware.
Donors: Joyce E. Sexton; William D. Sexton.
Foundation type: Independent foundation.
Financial data (yr. ended 12/31/13): Assets, $788,875 (M); gifts received, $250,000; expenditures, $277,700; qualifying distributions, $271,550; giving activities include $271,550 for 50 grants (high: $67,044; low: $100).
Fields of interest: Education; Diseases and conditions; Christianity.

Limitations: Applications not accepted. Giving primarily in MN.
Application information: Unsolicited requests for funds not accepted.
Officers: Joyce E. Sexton, Pres.; William D. Sexton, V.P.; Kevin Noble, Secy.-Treas.
Directors: Jennifer Ornburg; James Sexton; Mats Sexton; Thomas Sexton.
EIN: 680551421

4791
The Shared Fund
6550 York Ave. S., Ste. 402
Edina, MN 55435-2335 (952) 925-3411
Contact: Howard Weiner, Pres.

Established in 1994 in Minnesota.
Donors: Howard Weiner; Frederick Weiner.
Foundation type: Independent foundation.
Financial data (yr. ended 12/31/13): Assets, $1,951,539 (M); gifts received, $1,430; expenditures, $149,510; qualifying distributions, $149,510; giving activities include $147,950 for 37 grants (high: $37,500; low: $500).
Fields of interest: Arts and culture; Orchestral music; Natural history museums; Historic preservation; Nonprofits; Judaism.
Type of support: Regranting.
Application information: Application form required.
>*Initial approach:* Letter
>*Deadline(s):* None

Officers: Howard Weiner, Pres.; Frederick Weiner, V.P.
EIN: 411797725

4792
Soar Foundation
2708 Irving Ave. S.
Minneapolis, MN 55408-1049

Established in 1997 in Minnesota.
Donors: William E. Weisman Charitable Lead Annuity Trust; Wipfli, LLP; William E. Weisman.
Foundation type: Independent foundation.
Financial data (yr. ended 12/31/13): Assets, $1,446,345 (M); gifts received, $33,624; expenditures, $158,241; qualifying distributions, $150,349; giving activities include $147,588 for 23 grants (high: $30,388; low: $100).
Fields of interest: Diseases and conditions; Religion; Human services.
Limitations: Applications not accepted. Giving primarily in MN. No grants to individuals.
Application information: Unsolicited requests for funds not accepted.
Officers: William E. Weisman, Pres.; Alyn Marisa Weisman, Secy.; Charles Harris Weisman, Treas.
EIN: 411880574

4793
Squam Lake Foundation
c/o Fish Creek Ventures
1710 Douglas Drive N., No. 255
Golden Valley, MN 55422-4300

Established in 1987 in Minnesota.
Donor: Thirza Cleveland†.
Foundation type: Independent foundation.
Financial data (yr. ended 11/30/13): Assets, $2,853,349 (M); expenditures, $241,749;

qualifying distributions, $195,184; giving activities include $185,000 for 11 grants (high: $72,500; low: $500).

Purpose and activities: Giving for the arts, education, health, and Christian organizations.

Fields of interest: Arts and culture; Religion; Human services.

Type of support: Continuing support; Annual campaigns; Scholarships.

Limitations: Applications not accepted. Giving primarily in MN. No loans or program-related investments.

Application information: Unsolicited requests for funds not accepted.

Officers: C.H. Cleveland, Sr., Pres.; Pat Sligo, Secy.; Don Thorsett, Treas.

Directors: Charles A. Cleveland, Jr.; John Winston.

Number of staff: None.

EIN: 363492677

4794
St. Agnes Catholic Education Foundation
7040 Willow Creek Rd.
Eden Prairie, MN 55344-3224

Established in 2007 in Minnesota.

Donor: Mary Jo Feltl.

Foundation type: Independent foundation.

Financial data (yr. ended 12/31/14): Assets, $2,086,209 (M); gifts received, $79,170; expenditures, $280,553; qualifying distributions, $276,341; giving activities include $274,000 for 5 grants (high: $100,000; low: $14,000).

Fields of interest: Education.

Type of support: General support.

Limitations: Applications not accepted. Giving primarily in MN. No grants to individuals.

Application information: Contributes only to pre-selected organizations.

Officer: Mary Jo Feltl, Pres. and Secy.-Treas.

EIN: 260229866

4795
Gregg W. & Denise E. Steinhafel Family Foundation
2655 N. Shore Dr.
Wayzata, MN 55391-9347

Established in 2005 in Minnesota.

Donors: Gregg W. Steinhafel; Denise E. Steinhafel.

Foundation type: Independent foundation.

Financial data (yr. ended 12/31/14): Assets, $3,450,544; expenditures, $209,574; qualifying distributions, $176,000.

Fields of interest: Arts and culture; Education; Human services.

Limitations: Applications not accepted. Giving primarily in MN and WI. No grants to individuals.

Application information: Unsolicited requests for funds not accepted.

Officers: Gregg W. Steinhafel, Pres.; Denise E. Steinhafel, V.P.

Directors: David J. Steinhafel; Kevin M. Steinhafel; Kelly M. Sun.

EIN: 203613105

4796
Sundance Family Foundation
944 Grand Ave.
Saint Paul, MN 55105 (612) 822-8580
Contact: Jeneen Hartley Sago
FAX: (612) 822-8587;
E-mail: info@sundancefamilyfoundation.org; Main URL: http://www.sundancefamilyfoundation.org
Grants List: http://www.sundancefamilyfoundation.org/grantlists.html
YouTube: http://www.youtube.com/user/SundanceFamilyFdn

Established in 2003 in Minnesota.

Donors: Nancy Jacobs; Mark Sandercott.

Foundation type: Independent foundation.

Financial data (yr. ended 12/31/13): Assets, $4,315,919 (M); expenditures, $384,593; qualifying distributions, $358,181; giving activities include $235,377 for 32 grants (high: $25,000; low: $212).

Purpose and activities: Giving to support family stability worldwide.

Fields of interest: Housing development; Social enterprise; Human services; Family services; Adolescents.

International interests: Africa; Latin America; Russia.

Type of support: Program evaluations; Technical assistance; Program development.

Application information: See foundation web site for current application guidelines. Application form required.

Copies of proposal: 1

Officer and Trustees: Peg Thomas, Mgr. and Trustee; Yvonne Barrett; H. Yvonne Cheek; Nancy Jacobs; Mark Sandercott; John Savereide; Rob Scarlett; Segundo Velasquez.

EIN: 200685298

4797
Tamarack Foundation
1800 IDS Ctr.
80 S. 8th St., Ste. 1800
Minneapolis, MN 55402-2127

Established in 1995 in Minnesota.

Donor: Duncan N. Dayton.

Foundation type: Independent foundation.

Financial data (yr. ended 12/31/13): Assets, $3,907,414 (M); expenditures, $175,700; qualifying distributions, $133,150; giving activities include $129,860 for grants.

Purpose and activities: Giving primarily for higher education, family planning and women's services, and for environmental preservation.

Fields of interest: Arts and culture; Education; Undergraduate education; Natural resources; Nonprofits; Libraries; Females.

Type of support: Regranting.

Limitations: Applications not accepted. Giving primarily in CT. No grants to individuals.

Application information: Unsolicited requests for funds not accepted.

Officers: Duncan N. Dayton, Pres. and V.P.; James M. Karges, Secy.-Treas.

EIN: 411796504

4798
Tennant Foundation
(formerly Tennant Company Foundation)
701 N. Lilac Dr.
P.O. Box 1452
Minneapolis, MN 55440
Main URL: http://www.tennantco.com/am-en/Pages/SustainabilityDetails.aspx?itemid=9

Established in 1973 in Minnesota.

Donor: Tennant Co.

Foundation type: Company-sponsored foundation.

Financial data (yr. ended 12/31/13): Assets, $5,917 (M); gifts received, $395,000; expenditures, $402,547; qualifying distributions, $402,547; giving activities include $377,522 for 414 grants (high: $40,000; low: $10).

Purpose and activities: The foundation supports programs designed to improve the quality of life in communities through environmental initiatives and social services; promote workforce readiness through education, vocational rehabilitation and other related services; and contribute to cultural and arts organizations.

Fields of interest: Arts and culture; Performing arts; Theater; Orchestral music; Education; Higher education; Environment; Nonprofits; Hospital care; Employment; Job training; Job creation and workforce development; Housing development; Human services; Food banks.

Type of support: General support; Employee volunteer services; Employee matching gifts; Continuing support; Capital campaigns; Matching grants; Regranting.

Limitations: Applications accepted. Giving primarily in areas of company operations, with emphasis on the Minneapolis, MN, area and its western suburb. No support for United Way-supported organizations, umbrella organizations, lobbying or political organizations, national organizations without active local chapters, religious organizations not of direct benefit to the entire community, or elementary or secondary schools. No grants to individuals or for trips or tours, tickets, tables, advertising, or benefit purposes.

Publications: Application guidelines.

Application information:

Initial approach: Download application form and mail to foundation

Copies of proposal: 1

Deadline(s): None

Board meeting date(s): Biannually

Officers and Directors: Heidi M. Wilson, Pres.; Tyler Johnson, Treas.; Cheryl Timm, Admin.; Karen A. Durant; Thomas J. Dybsky; H. Chris Killingstad; Kathryn Lovik; Thomas J. Paulson.

Number of staff: 1 part-time professional; 1 part-time support.

EIN: 237297045

4799
Terhuly Foundation
c/o Hugh K. Schilling
2565 Walnut St.
Roseville, MN 55113-2522

Established in 1995 in Minnesota.

Donor: Hugh K. Schilling, Sr.

Foundation type: Independent foundation.

Financial data (yr. ended 12/31/14): Assets, $3,587,902; expenditures, $230,894; qualifying distributions, $187,263.

Fields of interest: Education; Zoos; Plant biodiversity; Foundations; Christianity; Human services.
Limitations: Applications not accepted. Giving primarily in MN; funding also in SD. No grants to individuals.
Application information: Unsolicited requests for funds not accepted.
Officers: Hugh K. Schilling, Sr., Pres.; Lynn M. Schilling Brown, V.P.; Terryl L. Schilling Gilberstadt, Secy.; Hugh K. Schilling, Jr., Treas.
Director: Margaret S. Schilling.
Number of staff: 1 part-time professional; 1 part-time support.
EIN: 411818562

4800
James R. Thorpe Foundation
4500 Chicago Ave. S., Ste. 101
Minneapolis, MN 55407-3981 (763) 250-9304
Contact: Kerrie Blevins
E-mail: info@jamesrthorpefoundation.org; Email for Kerrie Blevins: kerrieblevins@jamesthorpefoundation.org; Main URL: http://www.jamesrthorpefoundation.org Grants List: http://jamesrthorpefoundation.org/recent-grants

Established in 1974 in Minnesota.
Donor: James R. Thorpe†.
Foundation type: Independent foundation.
Financial data (yr. ended 11/30/13): Assets, $7,315,134 (M); expenditures, $346,415; qualifying distributions, $315,364; giving activities include $248,150 for 39 grants (high: $10,000; low: $500), and $10,000 for 1 foundation-administered program.
Purpose and activities: Primary areas of interest include the disadvantaged, youth, the elderly, education, and cultural programs. Giving for social service agencies and higher and secondary education; support also for community health care.
Fields of interest: Arts and culture; Performing arts; Dance; Ballet; Orchestral music; Education; Environment; Health; Mental health care; Housing development; Human services; Family services; Child welfare; Homeless services; Senior services; Low-income and poor people; People with disabilities.
Type of support: General support; Capital campaigns; Equipment; Program development; Internships; Scholarships.
Limitations: Applications accepted. Giving limited to Minneapolis, MN; funding to a lesser extent in the western metropolitan suburbs. No support for organizations in the greater MN area, the east metro area, or outside of MN. No grants to individuals, or for continuing support, emergency or endowment funds, deficit financing, land acquisition, matching gifts, publications, seminars, tours, benefits, multi-year commitments, or conferences; no loans.
Publications: Application guidelines; Annual report (including application guidelines).
Application information: See foundation web site for complete application guidelines.
   Initial approach: Foundation's online application system
   Copies of proposal: 1
   Deadline(s): Consult foundation web site for current deadlines
   Board meeting date(s): May and Nov.
Officers and Directors: Timothy Thorpe, Pres. and Director; Robert C. Cote, Treas. and Director; Kerrie

Blevins, Fdn. Mgr.; S. Ruggles Cote; Samuel A. Cote; Carolyn Jones; Margaret T. Richards; Richard Thorpe.
Number of staff: 1 part-time professional.
EIN: 416175293

4801
Trillium Family Foundation
2424 Territorial Rd.
Saint Paul, MN 55114-1506 6516420127

Established in 2001 in Minnesota.
Donors: Elmer L. & Eleanor J. Andersen Foundation; Anthony L. "Tony" Andersen†.
Foundation type: Independent foundation.
Financial data (yr. ended 12/31/14): Assets, $9,748,551; expenditures, $508,014; qualifying distributions, $464,751.
Fields of interest: Arts and culture; Education; Higher education; Community recreation.
Type of support: General support.
Limitations: Applications not accepted. Giving primarily in MN and WY. No grants to individuals.
Application information: Contributes only to pre-selected organizations.
Officers: Amy Anderson, Pres.; Fran Coyne, V.P.; Monroe Larson, Secy.; Jeff Peterson, Treas.
Director: Shelby Wilson.
EIN: 412009698

4802
Trust for the Meditation Process
2751 Hennepin Ave. S., No. 259
Minneapolis, MN 55408-1002 (612) 825-3116
Contact: Martha Bolinger, Dir.
E-mail: trustmed@bitstream.net; Main URL: http://www.trustformeditation.org

Established in 1986 in Minnesota.
Donor: Stephen M. Taylor.
Foundation type: Independent foundation.
Financial data (yr. ended 12/31/13): Assets, $4,783,019 (M); expenditures, $262,215; qualifying distributions, $213,236; giving activities include $175,378 for 24 grants (high: $15,000; low: $335).
Purpose and activities: Giving to organizations that reclaim and teach Christian contemplative traditions, that introduce meditation in the Christian community or that further understanding of contemplative practice in all spiritual traditions.
Fields of interest: Foundations; Rehabilitation of offenders; Religion; Spirituality; Human services; Youth development.
Type of support: Continuing support; Pro bono consulting services; Matching grants; Capital and infrastructure; Equipment; Program development; Convening; Publications; Seed money; Curriculum development; Scholarships; Research; Technical assistance.
Limitations: Giving on a national and international basis, primarily in the U.S.
Publications: Application guidelines.
Application information: See trust web site for application guidelines and requirements. Two copies are required: one submitted electronically as an email attachment and one submitted via surface mail. Application form required.
   Initial approach: Submit online inquiry form
   Copies of proposal: 2
   Board meeting date(s): Spring, Summer and Fall

Officer and Trustees: Deborah Chernick, Chair. and Trustee; Michael Lilja; Paul Taylor.
Director: Martha Bolinger.
EIN: 416286503

4803
J. S. Turner Family Foundation
c/o Tax Dept.
10350 Bren Rd., W.
Minnetonka, MN 55343-9014

Foundation type: Independent foundation.
Financial data (yr. ended 12/31/13): Assets, $3,873,650 (M); expenditures, $164,904; qualifying distributions, $163,650; giving activities include $159,000 for 38 grants (high: $35,000; low: $500).
Fields of interest: Arts and culture; Education; Christianity; Catholicism.
Limitations: Applications not accepted. Giving primarily in FL, MN and OH. No grants to individuals.
Application information: Contributes only to pre-selected organizations.
Officers: Susan R. Turner, Pres.; Jeffrey S. Turner, V.P.
EIN: 900298087

4804
Ross Wagner Foundation
103 Mensing Way
Cannon Falls, MN 55009-1143 (507) 263-3957
Contact: Nancy Vandergon, Secy.-Treas.
E-mail: info@rosswagnerfoundation.org; E-mail for Nancy Vandergon: nancyv@signletters.com; Main URL: http://www.rosswagnerfoundation.org

Established in 2006 in Minnesota.
Foundation type: Independent foundation.
Financial data (yr. ended 09/30/14): Assets, $1,203,097 (M); expenditures, $243,589; qualifying distributions, $233,489; giving activities include $232,216 for 12 grants to individuals (high: $28,412; low: $2,625).
Purpose and activities: Giving primarily for scholarships for students majoring in civil, aeronautical, mechanical, electrical, aerospace and chemical engineering. Students seeking degrees in chemistry and physics may also apply. It is open to students from United States and Canadian schools where Gemini, Inc. has plants: Cannon Falls, MN; Farmville, VA; Fallon, NV; Taylor, TX; Decorah, IA; Hanover, Ontario; and the hometowns of Geminis founders: Howard, SD and Randolph, MN. In addition, the student must be enrolled in one of the top engineering schools in the U.S. and Canada, as described on the Foundation's web site.
Fields of interest: University education; Graduate and professional education; Chemistry; Physics; Engineering.
International interests: Canada.
Type of support: Student aid.
Limitations: Applications accepted. Giving primarily to residents of Cannon Falls and Randolph, MN; Farmville, VA; Fallon, NV; Taylor, TX; Decorah, IA; Howard, SD; and Hanover, Ontario.
Application information: See foundation web site for complete application guidelines. Application form required.
   Initial approach: Proposal
   Copies of proposal: 1
   Deadline(s): Feb. 1

Officers and Directors: Frederick Oss, Pres. and Director; Nancy Vandergon, Secy.-Treas. and Director; David Schmitt; Larry Swanson.
EIN: 208983294

4805
Archie D. and Bertha H. Walker Foundation
23505 Smithtown Rd., No. 260
Excelsior, MN 55331-4548 (952) 380-1350
Contact: Jan DenBeste, Tr.

Established in 1953 in Minnesota.
Donors: Archie D. Walker†; Bertha H. Walker†.
Foundation type: Independent foundation.
Financial data (yr. ended 12/31/12): Assets, $6,257,857 (M); expenditures, $448,585; qualifying distributions, $381,307; giving activities include $246,475 for 101 grants (high: $12,825; low: $25), and $34,300 for 58 employee matching gifts.
Purpose and activities: Areas of major support include: 1) programs dealing with chemical dependency, chiefly alcoholism, and its effects on children and their development; 2) programs in the arts; and 3) programs addressing the treatment of racism, prejudice, and exclusivity. Within these 3 areas of primary interest, the foundation provides seed grants to pioneering programs. Also provides continued support of traditionally funded programs in conservation, education, and health. The foundation grants funds only to organizations that operate without prejudice.
Fields of interest: Arts and culture; Alcoholism; Diversity and intergroup relations.
Type of support: General support; Annual campaigns; Capital and infrastructure; Land acquisitions; Program development; Convening; Recordings; Publications; Seed money; Curriculum development; Scholarships; Research.
Limitations: Applications accepted. Giving primarily in the seven-county Minneapolis-St. Paul, MN, metropolitan area. No support for private foundations. No grants to individuals, or for endowment funds.
Publications: Application guidelines; Annual report (including application guidelines); Grants list.
Application information: Application form required.
 Initial approach: Letter or telephone
 Copies of proposal: 1
 Deadline(s): Feb. 2
 Board meeting date(s): Mar. and Oct.
Officers and Trustees: James H. Heron, Pres. and Trustee; Sally L. Walker, V.P. and Trustee; Molly G. Walker, Secy. and Trustee; Catherine L. Lamb, Treas. and Trustee; Janet DenBeste; Harriet W. Fitts; William S. Fitts; Julia W. Gilmore; Bronwyn A.E. Griffith; Dana D. McCannel; Louise W. McCannel; Herbert J. Motley, Jr.; Teri M. Motley; Joan Schoepke; Amy C. Walker; Berta B. Walker; Colin M. Walker; Alexa Griffith Winton.
Number of staff: 1 part-time professional.
EIN: 416022758

4806
Wallestad Foundation
730 Second Ave. S., Ste. 415
Minneapolis, MN 55402 (612) 288-2233

Established in 1986 in Minnesota.

Donors: Fluoroware, Inc.; Phadoris Wallestad†; Cary Humphries; Bev Geyer; Jay L. Bennett; Stan Geyer; Youthworks!; Entegris, Inc.; Harvest Foundation.
Foundation type: Independent foundation.
Financial data (yr. ended 12/31/13): Assets, $8,372,120; gifts received, $5,653; expenditures, $542,146; qualifying distributions, $351,030.
Purpose and activities: Giving primarily to Christian agencies and churches.
Fields of interest: Nonprofits; Christianity; Human services; Family services; Child welfare.
Type of support: Regranting; Program-related investments; Employee matching gifts.
Limitations: Applications accepted. Giving primarily in the Minneapolis, MN area.
Application information: Application form required.
 Initial approach: Letter
 Deadline(s): None
Officers: Jay L. Bennett, Chair.; Andy Bennett, Pres.; Sandra Byzewski, Secy.
EIN: 363485265

4807
The Walser Foundation
4401 American Blvd. W.
Bloomington, MN 55437-1122

Donor: Walser Holding Company, Inc.
Foundation type: Independent foundation.
Financial data (yr. ended 12/31/13): Assets, $292,955 (M); gifts received, $238,473; expenditures, $248,274; qualifying distributions, $247,274; giving activities include $246,249 for 22 grants (high: $35,000; low: $150).
Fields of interest: Education; Health.
Limitations: Applications not accepted. Giving primarily in MN.
Application information: Unsolicited requests for funds not accepted.
Officers: Paul M. Walser, Pres.; Andrew D. Walser, V.P.; Gelaine Halverson, Secy.-Treas.
EIN: 204968499

4808
Walsh-Brady Memorial Fund
c/o Trust Tax Services
P.O. Box 64713
Saint Paul, MN 55164-0713

Foundation type: Independent foundation.
Financial data (yr. ended 02/28/13): Assets, $3,772,832 (M); expenditures, $219,771; qualifying distributions, $174,230; giving activities include $174,230 for grants.
Fields of interest: Education; Christianity.
Type of support: General support.
Limitations: Applications not accepted. Giving primarily in NE.
Application information: Unsolicited requests for funds not accepted.
Trustee: US Bank, N.A.
EIN: 476117233

4809
B. & H. Way Foundation
721 E. Rice St.
Wayzata, MN 55391-1722

Established in 1999 in Minnesota.
Donor: John A. Berg.

Foundation type: Independent foundation.
Financial data (yr. ended 12/31/12): Assets, $3,551,085 (M); expenditures, $200,999; qualifying distributions, $180,110; giving activities include $180,110 for grants.
Fields of interest: Education; Human services; Child welfare.
Limitations: Applications not accepted. Giving primarily in MN. No grants to individuals.
Application information: Unsolicited requests for funds not accepted.
Officers and Directors: Kristen A. Berg, Pres. and Director; Megan E. Neisius, V.P. and Director; Nancy Berg, Secy. and Director; Mark Neisus, Treas. and Director; John A. Berg.
EIN: 411955405

4810
Frank L. Wedge Memorial Fund
c/o Trust Tax Services
P.O. Box 64713
Saint Paul, MN 55164-0713

Foundation type: Independent foundation.
Financial data (yr. ended 12/31/14): Assets, $4,455,422; expenditures, $280,685; qualifying distributions, $224,567.
Fields of interest: Health; Diseases and conditions.
Limitations: Applications not accepted. Giving primarily in ND.
Application information: Unsolicited requests for funds not accepted.
Trustee: US Bank, N.A.
EIN: 416189525

4811
Wells Family Foundation Trust
100 Federal Dr.
Saint Paul, MN 55111-4036

Established in 1992 in Minnesota.
Donor: Adele Roller.
Foundation type: Independent foundation.
Financial data (yr. ended 12/31/14): Assets, $5,008,176; expenditures, $213,362; qualifying distributions, $169,818.
Purpose and activities: Giving primarily for education and athletics, with emphasis on tennis; funding also for youth services and the arts.
Fields of interest: Arts and culture; Theater; Education; Higher education; Health; Racquet sports; Human services; Child welfare; Children and youth; Female young adults; Male young adults.
Type of support: General support; Continuing support; Annual campaigns; Capital campaigns; Endowments.
Limitations: Applications not accepted. Giving primarily in MN. No grants to individuals.
Application information: Unsolicited requests for funds not accepted.
 Board meeting date(s): Varies
Trustees: John J. Knip, Jr.; Lee Booth; Wendy Wells.
Number of staff: 1 part-time professional; 2 part-time support.
EIN: 411732561

4812
Wells Family Foundation, Inc.
c/o J.J. Knip, Jr.
100 Federal Dr.
Saint Paul, MN 55111-4036

Established in 1992 in Minnesota.
Foundation type: Independent foundation.
Financial data (yr. ended 12/31/14): Assets, $6,316,062; gifts received, $0; expenditures, $345,890; qualifying distributions, $305,569.
Fields of interest: Education; Protestantism; Human services.
Type of support: Annual campaigns.
Limitations: Applications not accepted. Giving primarily in FL and Minneapolis, MN. No grants to individuals.
Application information: Contributes only to pre-selected organizations.
Board meeting date(s): Quarterly
Officers: Adele S. Merck, Pres.; George G. Merck, V.P.; Kenneth S. Beall, Jr., Secy.; John J. Knip, Jr., Treas.
Number of staff: 1 part-time professional; 1 part-time support.
EIN: 411732563

4813
The Wendel Foundation
c/o Deborah Farley
7830 Main St., Ste. 215
Maple Grove, MN 55369-7068

Established in 1986 in Minnesota.
Donors: W. Hall Wendel, Jr.; Amy Wendel.
Foundation type: Independent foundation.
Financial data (yr. ended 12/31/13): Assets, $6,139,310 (M); expenditures, $309,655; qualifying distributions, $304,023; giving activities include $300,935 for 1 grant.
Fields of interest: Education.
Type of support: General support; Individual development; Program development; Seed money.
Limitations: Applications not accepted. Giving primarily in the Twin Cities, MN, metropolitan area. No grants to individuals.
Publications: Informational brochure.
Application information: Contributes only to pre-selected organizations.
Officers: Deborah A. Farley Cortez, Pres. and Secy.; W. Hall Wendel, Jr., V.P. and Treas.; William J. Berens, V.P.
EIN: 411584487

4814
Louis F. and Florence H. Weyand 1977
c/o Trust Tax Services
P.O. Box 64713
Saint Paul, MN 55164-0713
Application address: c/o Louis Weyand, 800 Nicollet Mall, Minneapolis, MN 55402, tel.: (612) 303-3205

Donors: Florence H. Weyand; Louis F. Weyand†.
Foundation type: Independent foundation.
Financial data (yr. ended 09/30/14): Assets, $3,763,977 (M); expenditures, $216,475; qualifying distributions, $158,686; giving activities include $144,711 for 30 grants (high: $25,460; low: $65).

Fields of interest: Arts and culture; Education; Health; Christianity; Human services; Youth development.
Type of support: General support.
Limitations: Applications accepted. Giving primarily in CA, FL, and MI. No grants to individuals.
Application information: Application form required.
Initial approach: Letter
Deadline(s): None
Trustees: Lois V. Bachman; Carolyn Yorston; U.S. Bank, N.A.
EIN: 942473421

4815
The Charles A. Weyerhaeuser Memorial Foundation
30 E. 7th St., Ste. 2000
Saint Paul, MN 55101-4930 (612) 228-0935
Contact: Lucy Rosenberry Jones, Pres.

Established in 1959 in Minnesota.
Donors: Carl A. Weyerhaeuser Trusts; Sarah-Maud W. Sivertsen Trusts; 1969 IRR Trust No. 2 SMWS; 1960 IRR Trust No. 3 SMWS; Rosenberry Charitable Term Trust; Sarah-Maud Sivertsen; Robert J. Sivertsen.
Foundation type: Independent foundation.
Financial data (yr. ended 02/28/13): Assets, $9,556,613 (M); gifts received, $38,213; expenditures, $444,140; qualifying distributions, $430,144; giving activities include $397,000 for 51 grants (high: $50,000; low: $500).
Purpose and activities: Giving primarily for the musical arts and a public radio station.
Fields of interest: Music; Historic preservation; Education; Radio; Shelter and residential care.
Type of support: Endowments; Continuing support; Annual campaigns.
Limitations: Applications accepted. Giving primarily in St. Paul, MN and NC. No grants to individuals.
Application information:
Initial approach: Proposal
Copies of proposal: 1
Deadline(s): None
Board meeting date(s): As required
Final notification: 3 months
Officers and Directors: Lucy Rosenberry Jones, Pres. and Director; Robert J. Sivertsen, V.P. and Director; Joseph S. Micallef, Secy.-Treas. and Director; Elise R. Donohue; Charles W. Rosenberry II.
EIN: 416012063

4816
Whaley Foundation
c/o John P. Whaley
1978 Summit Ave.
Saint Paul, MN 55105-1460

Established in 2000 in Minnesota.
Donor: John P. Whaley.
Foundation type: Independent foundation.
Financial data (yr. ended 12/31/13): Assets, $6,549,970 (M); gifts received, $353,920; expenditures, $468,792; qualifying distributions, $439,535; giving activities include $439,500 for 11 grants (high: $200,000; low: $1,000).
Fields of interest: Elementary and secondary education; Higher education; Christianity; Catholicism.

Limitations: Applications not accepted. Giving primarily in MN. No grants to individuals.
Application information: Contributes only to pre-selected organizations.
Directors: Annette M. Whaley; John P. Whaley.
EIN: 411988112

4817
Whitney Foundation
601 Carlson Pkwy., Ste. 800
Minnetonka, MN 55305-5229
Contact: Carol Vanornum
Application address: 730 2nd Ave. S., Ste. 425, Minneapolis, MN 55402

Established in 1959 in Minnesota.
Donors: Wheelock Whitney; Benson K. Whitney; Wheelock Whitney III; Joseph Whitney; Pennell Whitney.
Foundation type: Independent foundation.
Financial data (yr. ended 12/31/13): Assets, $1,205,226 (M); gifts received, $287,509; expenditures, $370,741; qualifying distributions, $359,946; giving activities include $351,660 for 220 grants (high: $80,000; low: $20).
Purpose and activities: Giving primarily for education, substance abuse programs, and human services.
Fields of interest: Arts and culture; Education; HIV/AIDS; Alcoholism; Human services; Child welfare.
Type of support: General support; Continuing support; Annual campaigns.
Limitations: Applications accepted. Giving limited to MN, with emphasis on Hennepin and Ramsey counties. No grants to individuals, or for publications, video productions, or trips.
Application information:
Initial approach: Proposal
Copies of proposal: 1
Deadline(s): None
Officers: Wheelock Whitney, Pres.; Pennell Whitney, V.P.; Joseph H. Whitney, Secy.-Treas.
Directors: Benson Whitney; Mary Whitney; Wheelock Whitney III.
Number of staff: 1 part-time support.
EIN: 416022514

4818
John and Margie Wiehoff Foundation
c/o Claire H. Topp
50 S. 6th St., Ste. 1500
Minneapolis, MN 55402-1498

Established in 2006 in Minnesota.
Donors: Margaret G. Wiehoff; John P. Wiefoff.
Foundation type: Independent foundation.
Financial data (yr. ended 12/31/13): Assets, $7,045,445 (M); gifts received, $599,200; expenditures, $241,841; qualifying distributions, $176,225; giving activities include $175,000 for 8 grants (high: $50,000; low: $5,000).
Fields of interest: University education; ALS.
Limitations: Applications not accepted. Giving primarily in MN. No grants to individuals.
Application information: Contributes only to pre-selected organizations.
Officers: Margaret G. Wiehoff, Pres.; John P. Wiehoff, Secy.-Treas.
Directors: Michelle A. Wiehoff; Theresa J. Wiehoff.
EIN: 205412977

4819
Virginia Wimmer Charitable Trust
c/o Trust Tax Services
P.O. Box 64713
Saint Paul, MN 55164-0713
Application address: c/o Sarah Godfrey, 800 Nicollet Mall, Minneapolis, MN 55402-7020, tel.: (612) 303-3208

Established in 1999 in Minnesota.
Foundation type: Independent foundation.
Financial data (yr. ended 06/30/13): Assets, $2,110,530 (M); expenditures, $182,182; qualifying distributions, $141,000; giving activities include $141,000 for 3 grants (high: $47,000; low: $47,000).
Purpose and activities: Giving for the support of educational programs for disadvantaged children.
Fields of interest: Education; Diseases and conditions.
Type of support: Research.
Limitations: Applications accepted. Giving primarily in MN.
Application information: Application form required.
Initial approach: Proposal
Deadline(s): None

Trustee: U.S. Bank, N.A.
EIN: 416465189

4820
Winds of Peace Foundation
(formerly Children's Haven, Inc.)
1104 Pearl Dr.
Faribault, MN 55021-3202 5077896418
E-mail: peacewinds@peacewinds.org; Main URL: http://www.peacewinds.org

Donors: Foldcraft, Inc.; Harold Nielsen; Harlo Investments, Inc.
Foundation type: Independent foundation.
Financial data (yr. ended 12/31/14): Assets, $7,444,505; expenditures, $670,960; qualifying distributions, $1,406,326.
Purpose and activities: The mission of the foundation is to contribute to global peace by promoting economic, social, and environmentally just relations.
Fields of interest: Economics; Economic development; Human rights; Basic and emergency aid; International development; International peace and security; Females; Indigenous peoples; Low-income and poor people.
International interests: Nicaragua.
Type of support: General support; Program-related investments; Matching grants; Capital campaigns; Program development; Convening; Seed money; Research; Technical assistance; Program evaluations.
Limitations: Applications not accepted. Giving primarily on an international basis, with an emphasis on Nicaragua. No support for children's organizations, religious organizations, and political groups. No grants to individuals.
Application information: Contributes only to pre-selected organizations.
Board meeting date(s): Mar. and Sept.
Officer and Directors: Stephen C. Sheppard, C.E.O. and Director; Annette Bjork; Silvia Conger; Donald J. Fleugel; Mark Lester; Harold Nielsen.
Number of staff: 1 full-time professional; 1 part-time professional; 1 full-time support.
EIN: 411343012

MISSISSIPPI

4821
Amory Outreach Foundation Inc.
P. O. Drawer 359
Amory, MS 38821-1951

Established in 1998 in Mississippi.
Donor: Richard Palmer.
Foundation type: Independent foundation.
Financial data (yr. ended 12/31/13): Assets, $5,408,628 (M); expenditures, $222,624; qualifying distributions, $222,597; giving activities include $219,302 for 32 grants (high: $55,000; low: $60).
Fields of interest: Community and economic development; Religion; Christianity; Human services.
Limitations: Applications not accepted. Giving primarily in MS. No grants to individuals.
Application information: Unsolicited requests for funds not accepted.
Officers: Lawrence R. Palmer, Jr., Pres. and Director; June Palmer, V.P.; Teresa Miley, Secy.-Treas.
EIN: 640900016

4822
William Robert Baird Charitable Trust
c/o Citizens National Bank
P.O. Box 911
Meridian, MS 39302-0911
Application address: c/o Citizens National Bank, Trust Department, 512 22nd Ave., Meridian, MS 39301, tel.: (601) 484-5221

Established in 1980 in Mississippi.
Donor: William Robert Baird†.
Foundation type: Independent foundation.
Financial data (yr. ended 03/31/13): Assets, $4,816,199 (M); expenditures, $231,801; qualifying distributions, $204,894; giving activities include $204,894 for 13 grants (high: $36,010; low: $3,557).
Purpose and activities: Giving primarily for human services.
Fields of interest: Human services; Food aid; Child welfare; Low-income and poor people.
Type of support: General support; Matching grants; Capital campaigns; Endowments; Emergency funds; Program development.
Limitations: Applications accepted. Giving limited to LA and MS. No grants to individuals.
Publications: Informational brochure.
Application information: Application form required.
    Initial approach: Proposal
    Deadline(s): None
    Board meeting date(s): Mar. and Nov.
Board Members: Donna Jill Johnson; Archie McDonnell, Jr.; Stephen Moore; Brian Ponder.
EIN: 646170042

4823
Barnett Foundation
P.O. Box 1071
Greenwood, MS 38935-1071

Established in 2000 in Unspecified.
Foundation type: Independent foundation.

Financial data (yr. ended 12/31/13): Assets, $1,553,507 (M); expenditures, $180,579; qualifying distributions, $151,300; giving activities include $151,300 for 5 grants (high: $100,000; low: $10,000).
Fields of interest: Arts and culture; Education; Higher education; Human services.
Limitations: Applications not accepted. Giving primarily in MS.
Application information: Unsolicited requests for funds not accepted.
Trustees: John M. Ford, Jr.; W.W. Gresham, Jr.; Richard G. Noble.
EIN: 631248965

4824
Biloxi Regional Medical Center, Inc.
P.O. Box 128
Biloxi, MS 39533-0128

Established in 2003 in Mississippi.
Foundation type: Operating foundation.
Financial data (yr. ended 09/30/14): Assets, $16,171,584 (M); expenditures, $385,647; qualifying distributions, $383,700; giving activities include $383,700 for 9 grants (high: $138,150; low: $5,400).
Fields of interest: Education; Graduate and professional education; Hospital care; Nursing care; Diseases and conditions.
Limitations: Applications not accepted. Giving primarily in MS. No grants to individuals.
Application information: Contributes only to pre-selected organizations.
Officers: Robert B. Briscoe, Chair.; Andy Carpenter, Vice-Chair.
Directors: Erroll Bradley; Larry Drawdy; Ann LaRosa; John McKee, MD; Alfred McNair, MD; Jeffrey O'Keefe; Edward Shumski, MD; Argile Smith.
EIN: 640657989

4825
The John Louis Black Family Foundation
(formerly The Lexington Foundation)
c/o John L. Black, Jr.
24 Provence Blvd.
Madison, MS 39110-8350

Established in 1994 in Mississippi.
Donor: John L. Black, Jr.
Foundation type: Independent foundation.
Financial data (yr. ended 12/31/13): Assets, $118,662 (M); expenditures, $301,128; qualifying distributions, $300,960; giving activities include $300,000 for 1 grant.
Fields of interest: Higher education; Human services.
Type of support: General support.
Limitations: Applications not accepted. Giving primarily in Jackson, MS. No grants to individuals.
Application information: Unsolicited requests for funds not accepted.
Trustees: John L. Black, Jr.; Sandra M. Black.
EIN: 646207058

4826
Brevard Family Foundation
P.O. Box 407
Tupelo, MS 38802-0407

Established in 1997 in Mississippi.
Donors: Henry C. Brevard, Jr.; Elizabeth B. Brevard.
Foundation type: Independent foundation.
Financial data (yr. ended 12/31/13): Assets, $2,543,213 (M); expenditures, $140,792; qualifying distributions, $140,167; giving activities include $140,167 for 11 grants (high: $100,000; low: $1,000).
Fields of interest: Education; Nonprofits; Health; Christianity; Human services.
Type of support: Regranting.
Limitations: Applications not accepted. Giving limited to MS. No grants to individuals.
Application information: Unsolicited requests for funds not accepted.
Directors: David E. Brevard; Elizabeth B. Brevard; Henry C. Brevard, Jr.; Marie E. Smith.
EIN: 640886776

4827
Carothers Construction Charitable Foundation
P.O. Box 189
Taylor, MS 38673-0189 (662) 473—2525
Contact: Sean B. Carothers, Pres. and Secy.-Treas.

Donors: Sean B. Carothers; Carothers Construction, Inc.
Foundation type: Operating foundation.
Financial data (yr. ended 12/31/13): Assets, $3,457,133 (M); gifts received, $200,000; expenditures, $293,812; qualifying distributions, $293,812; giving activities include $287,323 for 18 + grants (high: $60,000).
Fields of interest: Health care financing; Christianity.
Type of support: General support.
Limitations: Applications accepted. Giving primarily in MS. No grants to individuals.
Application information: Application form required.
    Initial approach: Letter
    Deadline(s): None
Officer: Sean B. Carothers, Pres. and Secy.-Treas.
EIN: 640892836

4828
Center for Mississippi Health Policy
120 N. Congress St., Ste. 700
Jackson, MS 39201-2615 (601) 709-2133
FAX: (601) 709-2134;
E-mail: info@mshealthpolicy.com; Main URL: http://www.mshealthpolicy.com
Twitter: https://twitter.com/mshealthpolicy

Established in 2005 in Mississippi.
Donors: The Bower Foundation; The Robert Wood Johnson Charitable Trust.
Foundation type: Operating foundation.
Financial data (yr. ended 12/31/13): Assets, $884,664 (M); gifts received, $18,088; expenditures, $1,219,642; qualifying distributions, $1,207,289; giving activities include $197,073 for 2 grants (high: $148,560; low: $48,513).
Purpose and activities: The mission of the Center for Mississippi Health Policy is to serve as a catalyst for health policy debate, providing information to policymakers and the general public and communicating research findings that will stimulate dialogue and inform decision-making.
Fields of interest: Diseases and conditions.
Type of support: Research.

Limitations: Applications not accepted. Giving primarily in MS. No grants to individuals.
Application information: Unsolicited requests for funds not accepted.
Officers: Anne B. Travis, Pres.; Ralph Didlake, MD, V.P.; John Sturdivant, Secy.-Treas.; Therese Hanna, Exec. Dir.
EIN: 203471008

4829
Colbert Foundation
P.O. Box 320849
Flowood, MS   39232-0849   (601) 919-4200
Contact: Thomas W. Colbert, Pres.

Established in 1986 in Mississippi.
Donor: Thomas W. Colbert, Sr.
Foundation type: Independent foundation.
Financial data (yr. ended 12/31/13): Assets, $339,440 (M); expenditures, $332,705; qualifying distributions, $147,149; giving activities include $147,149 for 4 grants (high: $65,693; low: $3,456).
Purpose and activities: Giving primarily for Christian and Protestant agencies and churches, and for higher education.
Fields of interest: Education; Disasters and emergency management; Religion; Theology.
Limitations: Applications accepted. Giving primarily in MS. No grants to individuals.
Application information: Application form required.
   Initial approach: Proposal
   Deadline(s): None
Officers: Thomas W. Colbert, Pres.; Thomas W. Colbert, Jr., V.P.; Ann B. Colbert, Secy.
Director: Willard G. Butler.
EIN: 640737344

4830
Community Foundation of East Mississippi
2212 B St.
P.O. Box 865
Meridian, MS   39302-0865   (601) 696-3035
Contact: Becky Glover, Exec. Dir.
FAX: (601) 696-3037; E-mail: office@cfem.org; Main URL: http://www.cfem.org
Facebook: https://www.facebook.com/cfeastmississippi
YouTube: http://www.youtube.com/user/cfem304

Established in 1984 in Mississippi.
Foundation type: Community foundation.
Financial data (yr. ended 12/31/12): Assets, $4,895,271 (M); gifts received, $614,749; expenditures, $749,161; giving activities include $388,593 for grants.
Purpose and activities: The foundation seeks to: 1) establish permanent charitable endowments; 2) promote philanthropy throughout East MS; 3) provide a vehicle for donors' charitable interests; and 4) provide leadership and resources in addressing ever changing challenges and opportunities.
Fields of interest: Crime prevention; Economic development; Community improvement; Child welfare.
Type of support: Curriculum development; Pro bono consulting services; Program-related investments; Matching grants.
Limitations: Applications accepted. Giving limited to eastern MS. No support for sectarian religious

purposes, state, regional, or national organizations, or veterans' or fraternal organizations. No grants for operating support for existing programs, endowment campaigns, conference attendance expenses, memberships or tickets to events, advertising and telephone solicitations, feasibility studies for capital campaigns, or fundraising expenses.
Publications: Annual report.
Application information: Visit foundation web site for application guidelines. Application form required.
   Initial approach: Telephone
   Board meeting date(s): Quarterly
Officer and Governances: Becky Glover, Exec. Dir.; John G. Compton; Michael Dudley; Clay Holladay; Melanie Mitchell; Pat Thomasson.
Number of staff: 1 full-time professional; 1 part-time support.
EIN: 640702225

4831
William B. & Saramel Crooks Foundation
c/o Kathryn Simmons, TrustMark National Bank
1701 Lakeland Ave., 2nd Fl.
Jackson, MS   39216-4884

Established in 1999 in Mississippi.
Donors: Saramel Repsher Crooks Evans; John A. Evans III; Saramel R. Evans.
Foundation type: Independent foundation.
Financial data (yr. ended 12/31/14): Assets, $3,933,702; gifts received, $59,612; expenditures, $194,013; qualifying distributions, $151,775.
Fields of interest: Education; Nonprofits; Communication media; Radio; Television; Human services; Child welfare.
Type of support: General support; Regranting.
Limitations: Applications not accepted. Giving primarily in MS. No grants to individuals.
Application information: Unsolicited requests for funds not accepted.
Officers and Directors: Saramel R. Evans, Pres. and Director; Saramel Repsher Crooks Evans II, Secy. and Director; John A. Evans III, Treas. and Director.
EIN: 640907797

4832
The Carl and Virginia Day Trust
P.O. Box 1018
Yazoo City, MS   39194-1018
Application address: c/o Rosemary Knox or Melba Mood, 104 S. Main, Yazoo City, MS 39194, tel.: (662) 746-4901

Established in 1948 in Mississippi.
Donor: Carl Day, MD†.
Foundation type: Independent foundation.
Financial data (yr. ended 12/31/13): Assets, $2,618,863 (M); expenditures, $65,637; qualifying distributions, $300,296; giving activities include $257,200 for 145 grants to individuals (high: $2,500; low: $900).
Purpose and activities: Provides interest-free loans to Mississippi residents under 25 years old who attend MS colleges.
Fields of interest: Higher education.
Type of support: Student aid; Loans to individuals.
Limitations: Applications accepted. Giving limited to residents of MS.
Publications: Annual report; Financial statement.
Application information: Application form required.

Initial approach: Letter
   Deadline(s): July 1 and Nov. 4
Trustees: Allen Bridgforth; Hugh Love, Jr.; Frank Patty, Jr.; Van Ray; Byron Seward.
Number of staff: 2 part-time professional.
EIN: 640386095

4833
Elizabeth McCarty Edwards Foundation
71 St. Andrews Dr.
Jackson, MS   39211-2468

Established in 1995 in Mississippi.
Foundation type: Independent foundation.
Financial data (yr. ended 12/31/13): Assets, $1,498,938 (M); expenditures, $214,892; qualifying distributions, $192,000; giving activities include $192,000 for 21 grants (high: $20,000; low: $1,000).
Fields of interest: Education; Health; Religion.
Limitations: Applications not accepted. Giving on a national basis. No grants to individuals.
Application information: Unsolicited requests for funds not accepted.
Officers: Elizabeth McCarty Edwards, Chair.; William Raynor Edwards, Vice-Chair.; Stephen McCarty Edwards, Secy.-Treas.
EIN: 640869104

4834
Family Care Foundation
(formerly Kittrell Family Foundation)
30 Darby Rd.
Hattiesburg, MS   39402   6012682068

Established in 1998 in Mississippi.
Donor: Kerry D. Kittrell.
Foundation type: Independent foundation.
Financial data (yr. ended 12/31/14): Assets, $0; gifts received, $225,000; expenditures, $205,244; qualifying distributions, $202,650.
Fields of interest: Christianity.
Type of support: General support.
Limitations: Applications accepted. Giving primarily in MS. No grants to individuals.
Application information: Application form required.
   Initial approach: Letter
   Deadline(s): None
Officers: Kerry D. Kittrell, Pres.; Lequita S. Kittrell, V.P.
Director: John David Kittrell.
EIN: 640893618

4835
Dr. and Mrs. R. Faser Triplett Foundation
124 One Madison Plz., Ste. 1500
Madison, MS   39110-2021

Donor: Rodney F. Triplett†.
Foundation type: Independent foundation.
Financial data (yr. ended 12/31/13): Assets, $5,542,530 (M); expenditures, $254,743; qualifying distributions, $201,318; giving activities include $201,318 for 1 grant.
Fields of interest: Education.
Limitations: Applications not accepted.
Application information: Unsolicited requests for funds not accepted.

Directors: Suzan T. Fuller; Diane T. Holloway; Rodney F. Triplett, Jr.; Jacqueline T. Walker; Lou Ann T. Woidtke.
EIN: 721361246

4836
The Florence Foundation
4519 McInnis Ave.
Moss Point, MS   39563-2815   (228) 474-0703
Contact: Dwain G. Luce Jr., Tr.

Established in 1984 in Alabama.
Donor: Florence Staples†.
Foundation type: Independent foundation.
Financial data (yr. ended 12/31/13): Assets, $3,975,243 (M); expenditures, $203,606; qualifying distributions, $181,600; giving activities include $156,000 for 23 grants (high: $25,000; low: $1,000).
Fields of interest: Education; Higher education; Graduate and professional education; Nursing care; Diseases and conditions; Respiratory system diseases; Human services.
Limitations: Applications accepted. Giving primarily in AL, with some emphasis on Mobile.
Application information:
  Initial approach: Proposal
  Deadline(s): None
  Board meeting date(s): Nov. or Dec., and as needed
Trustees: C. William Bodie, MD; Thomas F. Garth; Dwain G. Luce, Jr.
EIN: 630843906

4837
Fountain Family Foundation
(formerly D. G. & Margaret Fountain Charitable Foundation)
P.O. Box 10506
Jackson, MS   39289-0506

Established in 1997 in Mississippi.
Donors: D.G. Fountain; Margaret B. Fountain; Brad Fountain; Monica Fountain; Christopher G. Fountain; Lynette Fountain; James B. Fountain.
Foundation type: Independent foundation.
Financial data (yr. ended 12/31/14): Assets, $7,082,793 (M); gifts received, $10,000; expenditures, $403,255; qualifying distributions, $323,116; giving activities include $319,375 for 33 grants (high: $46,250; low: $500).
Fields of interest: Arts and culture; Higher education; Christianity; Human services; Child welfare.
Limitations: Applications not accepted. Giving primarily in MS. No grants to individuals.
Application information: Unsolicited requests for funds not accepted.
Directors: Christopher G. Fountain; James Bradley Fountain; Margaret B. Fountain.
EIN: 640885557

4838
Golding Foundation
101 Lee St.
Vicksburg, MS   39180-4992

Established in 1992 in Mississippi.
Donor: Stephen D. Golding.
Foundation type: Independent foundation.

Financial data (yr. ended 12/31/13): Assets, $9,448 (M); expenditures, $402,429; qualifying distributions, $396,890; giving activities include $396,890 for 2 grants (high: $226,890; low: $170,000).
Fields of interest: Education; Health; Human services.
Limitations: Applications not accepted. No grants to individuals.
Application information: Unsolicited requests for funds not accepted.
Officers: Stephen D. Golding, Pres.; Melody Golding, V.P.
Director: Joel Henderson.
EIN: 640820553

4839
Graeber Foundation
P.O. Box 40
Marks, MS   38646-0040

Established in 1955 in Mississippi.
Donors: James P. Graeber, Jr.; Lewis A. Graeber, Jr.
Foundation type: Independent foundation.
Financial data (yr. ended 12/31/13): Assets, $8,010,431 (M); gifts received, $5,000; expenditures, $435,798; qualifying distributions, $353,108; giving activities include $353,108 for 52 grants (high: $87,602; low: $100).
Purpose and activities: Giving primarily for education and to Presbyterian churches; funding also for health organizations and social services.
Fields of interest: Education; Higher education; Diseases and conditions; Protestantism; Human services.
Limitations: Applications not accepted. Giving primarily in MS. No grants to individuals.
Application information: Contributes only to pre-selected organizations.
Trustees: James P. Graeber, Jr.; John C. Graeber; William M. Graeber.
EIN: 646023660

4840
L. D. Hancock Foundation, Inc.
P.O. Box 2203
Tupelo, MS   38803-2203
Application address: c/o Billy H. Haygood, 316 South Thomas St., Tupelo, MS 38801, tel.: (662) 844-4080

Established in 1988 in Mississippi.
Donor: L.D. Hancock.
Foundation type: Operating foundation.
Financial data (yr. ended 12/31/13): Assets, $11,308,984 (M); gifts received, $539,904; expenditures, $401,202; qualifying distributions, $401,202; giving activities include $277,542 for 2 grants (high: $120,000; low: $100,000).
Fields of interest: Education services; Christianity; Human services; International relations.
Limitations: Applications accepted. Giving primarily in Tupelo, MS. No grants to individuals.
Application information:
  Initial approach: Letter
  Deadline(s): None
Officers and Directors: Elaine G. Hancock, Pres. and Director; Billy Haygood, V.P. and Director.
EIN: 640582491

4841
Beth M. Harris Foundation
1727 Renshaw Rd.
Yazoo City, MS   39194-8639

Established in 1996 in Mississippi.
Donors: Beth McCarty Harris; Ayres LP.
Foundation type: Independent foundation.
Financial data (yr. ended 06/30/13): Assets, $241,006 (M); gifts received, $100,000; expenditures, $243,544; qualifying distributions, $242,714; giving activities include $242,500 for 12 grants (high: $105,000; low: $5,000).
Fields of interest: Arts and culture; Theater; Christianity; Protestantism.
Limitations: Applications not accepted. No grants to individuals.
Application information: Contributes only to pre-selected organizations.
Officers and Directors: Beth McCarty Harris, Pres. and Director; Roy W. Harris, Secy.-Treas. and Director; Harrison Russel McCarty; W.B. McCarty III.
EIN: 640872809

4842
James W. Hood Family Foundation
c/o James W. Hood
P.O. Box 4931
Jackson, MS   39296   (601) 540-8600
Contact: James W. Hood, Pres.

Donor: James W. Hood.
Foundation type: Independent foundation.
Financial data (yr. ended 12/31/13): Assets, $12,724,664 (M); expenditures, $346,414; qualifying distributions, $239,300; giving activities include $239,300 for 11 grants (high: $100,000; low: $2,000).
Fields of interest: Education; University education.
Limitations: Applications accepted. Giving primarily in MS.
Application information:
  Initial approach: Proposal
  Deadline(s): None
Officers: James W. Hood, Pres.; Sylvia Napper, Secy.
Directors: J. Wilson Hood, Jr.; Paula J. Hood.
EIN: 202640916

4843
Warren A. Hood, Jr. Family Foundation
P.O. Box 682
Hattiesburg, MS   39403-0682   (601) 582-1545
Contact: Warren A. Hood Jr., Pres.

Established in 2006 in Mississippi.
Foundation type: Independent foundation.
Financial data (yr. ended 12/31/13): Assets, $10,115,315 (M); expenditures, $391,182; qualifying distributions, $320,000; giving activities include $320,000 for 1 grant.
Fields of interest: Protestantism.
Limitations: Applications accepted. Giving primarily in MS.
Application information:
  Initial approach: Proposal
  Deadline(s): None
Officer: Warren A. Hood, Jr., Pres.
EIN: 205928288

4844
Hope Foundation

1 Freedom Sq.
Laurel, MS 39440-3367

Established in 1997 in Wyoming.
Donors: Richard Headrick; Headrick Sign Company, Inc.; Headrick Companies, Inc.; Creative Sign Service.
Foundation type: Independent foundation.
Financial data (yr. ended 12/31/14): Assets, $382,255 (M); gifts received, $330,000; expenditures, $321,431; qualifying distributions, $320,970; giving activities include $170,370 for 8 grants (high: $170,370; low: $8,650).
Fields of interest: Religion; Christianity.
Limitations: Applications not accepted. Giving primarily in MS; some giving in GA and NC. No grants to individuals.
Application information: Contributes only to pre-selected organizations.
Officers: Richard Headrick, Pres.; Gina Headrick, V.P.; Burnice E. McCardle, Jr., Secy.-Treas.
Director: Brent Benson.
EIN: 721366054

4845
King's Daughters & Sons Circle No. 2

P.O. Box 932
Greenville, MS 38702-0932
Application address: c/o Becky Tindall, 244 Woodlawn, Greenville, MS 38701, tel.: (662) 335-4953

Foundation type: Independent foundation.
Financial data (yr. ended 09/30/13): Assets, $3,814,950 (M); expenditures, $225,357; qualifying distributions, $182,000; giving activities include $182,000 for 23 grants (high: $25,000; low: $1,000).
Purpose and activities: Giving primarily to attend the sick, help the poor and needy, and engage in any and all charitable works to benefit the community in the field of general welfare.
Fields of interest: Health; Community and economic development; Human services.
Limitations: Applications accepted. Giving primarily in MS.
Application information: Application form required.
  Initial approach: Request and complete application
  Deadline(s): Apr. 1
Officers: Pattye Wilson, Pres.; Brenda Kretchmar, V.P.; Betsy Dyer, Secy.; William F. Baird, Treas.
Directors: Katherine Crump; Kathy Bowman; Jan Engel; Lisa Percy.
EIN: 640303080

4846
The Lexington Foundation

P.O. Box 445
Lexington, MS 39095-0445
Application address: c/o Carolyn Mirick, 102 Andrews St., Lexington, MS 39095; tel.: (622) 834-2488

Donors: Nancy Barrett; Don Barrett.
Foundation type: Independent foundation.
Financial data (yr. ended 12/31/13): Assets, $2,400,236 (M); gifts received, $813,446; expenditures, $276,308; qualifying distributions, $185,063; giving activities include $174,563 for grants.
Fields of interest: Education; Christianity; Human services; Low-income and poor people.
Limitations: Applications accepted. Giving primarily in Lexington, MS.
Application information: Application form required.
  Initial approach: Letter
  Deadline(s): None
Officers: Richard Barrett, Pres.; S. Katherine Barrett, V.P.; Charles F. Barrett, Secy.; Carolyn S. Myrick, Mgr.
EIN: 640912814

4847
Lower Pearl River Valley Foundation

505 Williams Ave.
Picayune, MS 39466-3950 (601) 799-5353
Contact: A. Rachal, Admin. Asst.; Ted J. Alexander, C.E.O.
FAX: (601) 799-5116; E-mail: LPRVF@bellsouth.net

Established in 1998 in Mississippi.
Foundation type: Independent foundation.
Financial data (yr. ended 09/30/13): Assets, $0 (M); expenditures, $757,668; qualifying distributions, $642,886; giving activities include $371,793 for 10 grants (high: $174,245; low: $700).
Fields of interest: Education; Health; Community improvement; Children and youth.
Type of support: Program development; Matching grants; Seed money; Technical assistance.
Limitations: Applications accepted. Giving primarily in Pearl River County, MS. No support for religious, political or fraternal organizations, sectarian groups, and private schools. No grants to individuals or for scholarships, land acquisition, emergency funds, annual support campaigns, deficit financing, or production of films, books, and magazines; no loans.
Publications: Application guidelines; Biennial report (including application guidelines).
Application information: Application form required.
  Initial approach: Letter on applicant's organizational letterhead, to request an application
  Copies of proposal: 11
  Deadline(s): 2 months prior to board meeting
  Board meeting date(s): Quarterly
  Final notification: Within 2 weeks
Officers and Directors: Ted J. Alexander, Ed.D., C.E.O. and Director; Clyde Dease, Pres. and Director; Sidney Whitley, V.P. and Director; Pamela Thomas, Ed.D., Secy.; Rebecca Askew, Ph.D, Treas.; Tom Clark, Ed.D.; Martin Smith.
Number of staff: 2 full-time professional; 1 full-time support.
EIN: 640901092

4848
H. F. McCarty, Jr. Family Foundation

6360 I-55 N., Ste. 480
Jackson, MS 39211-2071

Established in 1995 in Mississippi.
Donors: Patti M. Sullivan; Marsha McCarty Wells; John R. McCarty; Katherine McCarty Flynt; Patti Stevens; H.F. McCarty, Jr.; Michael A. McCarty; Mary Helen McCarty Griffis; Mary Ann McCarty; Ashley Wells; Leslie Wells; Elizabeth Stevens; William A.

Stevens; Angela Flynt Little; Allen Flynt; Shellye S. McCarty; Terry B. Wells Trust; McCarty Enterprises, LLC; Elizabeth S. Buyan.
Foundation type: Independent foundation.
Financial data (yr. ended 12/31/13): Assets, $1,942 (M); gifts received, $188,980; expenditures, $189,485; qualifying distributions, $182,250; giving activities include $182,250 for 11 grants (high: $50,000; low: $6,250).
Fields of interest: Arts and culture; Art museums; Higher education; Hospital care; Diseases and conditions; Human services.
Limitations: Applications not accepted. Giving primarily in Jackson, MS.
Application information: Contributes only to pre-selected organizations.
Officers: John R. McCarty, Pres.; Ashley W. Hullender, V.P.; Katherine McCarty Flynt, Secy.; Patti M. Sullivan, Treas.
EIN: 640865125

4849
Mississippi Sports Medicine Foundation

1325 E. Fortification St.
Jackson, MS 39202-2442

Established in 1997 in Mississippi.
Donors: Felix H. Savoie, MD; Gene R. Barrett, MD; Larry D. Field, MD; Walter R. Shelton, MD.
Foundation type: Independent foundation.
Financial data (yr. ended 12/31/13): Assets, $1,646,208 (M); expenditures, $166,350; qualifying distributions, $160,338; giving activities include $157,000 for 10 grants (high: $32,000; low: $3,000).
Fields of interest: Education; Sports and recreation.
Type of support: General support; Scholarships.
Limitations: Applications not accepted. Giving primarily in Jackson, MS. No grants to individuals.
Application information: Unsolicited requests for funds not accepted.
Officers: Larry D. Field, Pres.; Chris P. Etheridge, V.P.; Robert R. Lodes, Secy.-Treas.
Board Members: Johnny Mims; Harry Walker.
EIN: 640869099

4850
Phillips Foundation

P.O. Box 471
Columbus, MS 39703-0471
Application address: c/o Betty Miller, 116 5th St. N., Columbus, MS 39701, tel.: (662) 327-8401

Established in 1941 in Mississippi.
Donor: Phillips Foundation Trust.
Foundation type: Operating foundation.
Financial data (yr. ended 12/31/13): Assets, $5,031,360 (M); expenditures, $202,938; qualifying distributions, $157,498; giving activities include $157,498 for grants.
Purpose and activities: Giving for the benefit of the indigent sick, in payment of expenses for medical, surgical, and hospital attention and services other than doctors' bills or surgical fees.
Fields of interest: Health; Diseases and conditions; Low-income and poor people.
Type of support: Grants to individuals.
Limitations: Applications accepted. Giving primarily to residents of Lowndes County, MS.
Application information: Application form required.

Initial approach: Proposal
Deadline(s): None
Officers: T.E. Lott, Jr., Pres.; George S. Hazard, Jr., Secy.
Trustees: John Davis; Alan Williams; James Woodard.
EIN: 646020136

4851
The Pruet Foundation
217 W. Capitol St.
Jackson, MS 39201-2004

Established in 1991 in Arkansas.
Donor: Chesley Pruet.
Foundation type: Independent foundation.
Financial data (yr. ended 12/31/13): Assets, $8,208,720 (M); expenditures, $479,917; qualifying distributions, $438,012; giving activities include $438,012 for 11 grants (high: $100,000; low: $2,350).
Fields of interest: Education; Cancers; Protestantism.
Limitations: Applications not accepted. Giving primarily in AR and MS. No grants to individuals.
Application information: Unsolicited requests for funds not accepted.
Officers: Paula James, Pres. and Treas.; Ann Calhoon, V.P. and Secy.
EIN: 710710627

4852
Jimmy & Hazel Sanders Charitable Trust I
P.O. Box 1169
Cleveland, MS 38732-1169

Established in 1997 in Mississippi.
Donor: James M. Sanders.
Foundation type: Independent foundation.
Financial data (yr. ended 12/31/13): Assets, $3,209,845 (M); expenditures, $276,484; qualifying distributions, $246,965; giving activities include $243,265 for grants (high: $125,000; low: $120).
Fields of interest: Higher education; Human services.
Type of support: General support.
Limitations: Applications not accepted. Giving primarily in MS. No grants to individuals.
Application information: Contributes only to pre-selected organizations.
Trustee: Michael W. Sanders.
EIN: 311570618

4853
Leo W. Seal, Jr. Family Foundation
P.O. Box 3720
Bay Saint Louis, MS 39521-3720
Contact: Leo W. Seal III, Pres.

Established in 1997 in Mississippi.
Donors: Leo W. Seal, Jr.; Schooler Family Foundation; Leo W. Seal Marital Trust.
Foundation type: Independent foundation.
Financial data (yr. ended 12/31/13): Assets, $12,720,850 (M); gifts received, $91,022; expenditures, $163,149; qualifying distributions, $148,735; giving activities include $148,735 for 51 grants (high: $15,000; low: $250).

Purpose and activities: Giving primarily for education, health organizations, and human services, and for religious purposes.
Fields of interest: Education; Diseases and conditions; Storms; Christianity; Protestantism; Catholicism; Human services; Child welfare; Shelter and residential care.
Limitations: Applications accepted. Giving primarily in MS. No grants to individuals.
Application information: Application form required.
Initial approach: Letter
Deadline(s): None
Officers: Leo W. Seal III, Pres.; John Baxter, V.P.; Jane P. Seal, V.P.; Clay Wagner, V.P.; Wallace Lee Seal, Secy.-Treas.
EIN: 721373522

4854
Homer Skelton Charitable Foundation
4555 Spring Meadow Way N.
Olive Branch, MS 38654-8133
Contact: Homer D. Skelton, Tr.

Donor: Homer D. Skelton.
Foundation type: Independent foundation.
Financial data (yr. ended 12/31/12): Assets, $3,336,886 (M); gifts received, $435,054; expenditures, $325,097; qualifying distributions, $323,122; giving activities include $323,122 for grants.
Purpose and activities: Giving primarily for education, children and family services, and social services; funding also for Christian schools and organizations.
Fields of interest: Elementary and secondary education; Higher education; Christianity; Human services; Family services; Child welfare.
Type of support: Student aid; Grants to individuals.
Limitations: Giving primarily to residents of TN; some giving also in MS.
Application information:
Initial approach: Letter or proposal
Deadline(s): None
Trustees: Catherine M. Skelton; Homer D. Skelton.
EIN: 621578268

4855
W. A. Taylor Foundation
650 N. Church Ave.
Louisville, MS 39339-2033

Donors: W.A. Taylor, Jr.; The Taylor Group, Inc.; TEMTCO.
Foundation type: Independent foundation.
Financial data (yr. ended 09/30/14): Assets, $2,029,418 (M); gifts received, $208,333; expenditures, $182,971; qualifying distributions, $182,531; giving activities include $165,000 for 14 grants (high: $126,000; low: $500).
Fields of interest: Education; Health; Camps; Youth development.
Limitations: Applications not accepted. Giving primarily in MS. No grants to individuals.
Application information: Contributes only to pre-selected organizations.
Trustees: Teresa Taylor Ktsanes; Gail G. Smith; Mitzi M. Taylor; Robert D. Taylor; William A. Taylor III.
EIN: 646028570

4856
Trehern Charitable Foundation
102 Doswell Ct.
Ocean Springs, MS 39564-5422 (228) 215-0457
Contact: Walter E. Trehern, Pres.

Established in 2006 in Mississippi.
Donors: Walter E. Trehern; Janet R. Trehern.
Foundation type: Independent foundation.
Financial data (yr. ended 12/31/13): Assets, $20,738 (M); gifts received, $260,000; expenditures, $258,157; qualifying distributions, $256,540; giving activities include $255,330 for 14 grants (high: $125,000; low: $50).
Fields of interest: Education; Undergraduate education.
Limitations: Applications accepted. Giving primarily in MS.
Application information: Application form required.
Initial approach: Proposal
Deadline(s): None
Officers: Walter E. Terhern, Pres.; Janet R. Trehern, Secy.; Walter E. Trehern, Treas.
EIN: 204832147

4857
Van Devender Family Foundation
(formerly Van Devender Foundation)
c/o William Van Devender
P.O. Box 5327
Jackson, MS 39296-5327

Established in 2002 in Michigan.
Donors: William J. Van Devender; Mollie M. Van Devender.
Foundation type: Operating foundation.
Financial data (yr. ended 09/30/13): Assets, $3,275 (M); gifts received, $432,560; expenditures, $431,202; qualifying distributions, $430,354; giving activities include $429,508 for 61 grants (high: $121,500; low: $40).
Fields of interest: Education; Religion; Youth development.
Limitations: Applications not accepted. Giving primarily in MS. No grants to individuals.
Application information: Contributes only to pre-selected organizations.
Trustees: Mollie M. Van Devender; William J. Van Devender.
EIN: 311480644

4858
Sam E. & Burnice C. Wittel Foundation
P.O. Box 1970
Jackson, MS 39215-1970

Established in 2006 in Mississippi.
Donor: Burnice Crosby Wittel†.
Foundation type: Independent foundation.
Financial data (yr. ended 12/31/13): Assets, $3,408,468 (M); gifts received, $1,556; expenditures, $219,047; qualifying distributions, $189,212; giving activities include $169,000 for 34 grants (high: $15,000; low: $500).
Fields of interest: Education; University education; Hospital care; Human services.
Limitations: Applications not accepted. Giving primarily in AL and MS. No grants to individuals.
Application information: Unsolicited requests for funds not accepted.

Director: T. Calvin Wells.
EIN: 204028699

MISSOURI

4859
Albers/Kuhn Family Foundation
555 N. New Ballas Rd., Ste. 130
Saint Louis, MO   63141-6884   (314) 997-4027;
2
Contact: James D. Eckhoff, Tr.
E-mail: jdeckhoff@earthlink.net

Established in 1999 in Missouri.
Donor: Hilda Albers Kuhn†.
Foundation type: Independent foundation.
Financial data (yr. ended 12/31/13): Assets,
$5,139,260 (M); expenditures, $219,477;
qualifying distributions, $202,500; giving activities
include $200,000 for 16 grants (high: $25,000;
low: $5,000).
Fields of interest: Science; Human services.
Limitations: Applications accepted. Giving limited to
St. Louis and Versailles, MO. No grants to
individuals.
Application information:
   Initial approach: Letter
   Copies of proposal: 1
   Deadline(s): None
Trustees: James D. Eckhoff; Lois Shuford; Robert
Thieme.
EIN: 436813186

4860
Andrews McMeel Universal Foundation
(formerly Andrews & McMeel Foundation)
1130 Walnut St.
Kansas City, MO   64106-2109

Established in 1991 in Missouri.
Donor: United Press Syndicate.
Foundation type: Company-sponsored foundation.
Financial data (yr. ended 12/31/13): Assets,
$2,966,502 (M); expenditures, $325,768;
qualifying distributions, $289,090; giving activities
include $289,090 for 224 grants (high: $55,000).
Purpose and activities: The foundation supports
organizations involved with arts and culture,
education, health, cancer, ALS, housing, human
services, and community development.
Fields of interest: Arts and culture; Education;
Human services.
Limitations: Applications not accepted. Giving
primarily in KS and MO, with emphasis on the
bi-state Kansas City area.
Application information: Unsolicited requests for
funds not accepted.
Officers: John P. McMeel, Pres.; Kathleen W.
Andrews, Secy.-Treas.
Directors: Hugh T. Andrews; James C. Andrews;
Suzanne M. Glynn; Maureen A. McMeel; Susan S.
McMeel; Bridget J. Rohmer.
EIN: 431570308

4861
Frederick Arnold Trust
P.O. Box 387
Saint Louis, MO   63166-0387   3144182643

Foundation type: Independent foundation.

Financial data (yr. ended 09/30/14): Assets,
$3,467,603; expenditures, $273,995; qualifying
distributions, $183,219 and $0 for set-asides.
Fields of interest: Nonprofits; Religion; Christianity;
Human services.
Type of support: Regranting.
Limitations: Applications not accepted. Giving
primarily in St. Louis, MO.
Application information: Unsolicited requests for
funds not accepted.
Trustee: U.S. Bank, N.A.
EIN: 436018119

4862
Arthur & Helen Baer Charitable Foundation
c/o UHY Advisors MO, Inc.
15 Sunnen Dr., Ste. 100
Saint Louis, MO   63143-3819

Established in 1984 in Missouri.
Donor: Helen K. Baer†.
Foundation type: Independent foundation.
Financial data (yr. ended 12/31/14): Assets,
$9,196,709 (M); expenditures, $623,284;
qualifying distributions, $453,618; giving activities
include $425,915 for 28 grants (high: $50,000;
low: $1,000).
Fields of interest: Arts and culture; Education;
Diseases and conditions.
Type of support: Capital and infrastructure;
Program-related investments; Equipment; Program
development; Scholarships.
Limitations: Applications not accepted. Giving
primarily in St. Louis, MO. No grants to individuals.
Application information: Contributes only to
pre-selected organizations.
Officers: Patrick E. Stark, Pres.; Philip N. Chilton,
Secy.
EIN: 431353474

4863
The Bakewell Foundation
(formerly The Edward L. Bakewell, Jr. Family
Foundation)
8820 Ladue Rd., Ste. 200
Saint Louis, MO   63124   (314) 862-5555
Contact: Richard W. Meier, Secy.

Established in 1987 in Missouri.
Donors: Bakewell Corp.; Edward L. Bakewell, Jr.;
Edward L. Bakewell III.
Foundation type: Company-sponsored foundation.
Financial data (yr. ended 12/31/13): Assets,
$7,714,770 (M); gifts received, $300,000;
expenditures, $403,629; qualifying distributions,
$383,114; giving activities include $358,600 for 7
grants (high: $200,000; low: $100).
Purpose and activities: The foundation supports
museums, hospitals, and health clinics and
organizations involved with higher education and
sustainability research.
Fields of interest: Arts and culture; Health; Religion.
Limitations: Applications accepted. Giving primarily
in CA, CO, FL, MO, and WY.
Application information: Application form required.
   Initial approach: Letter
   Deadline(s): None
Officers: Edward L. Bakewell III, Pres.; Richard W.
Meier, Secy.
EIN: 431434313

4864
Geraldine and R. A. Barrows Foundation
c/o UMB Bank, N.A.
P.O. Box 415044, M/S 1020307
Kansas City, MO   64141-6692   8168607711
Application address: c/o Jan Leonard, UMB Bank,
P.O. Box 41962, Kansas City, MO 64106, tel.: (816)
860-1933

Donor: G.M. Barrows†.
Foundation type: Independent foundation.
Financial data (yr. ended 12/31/14): Assets,
$7,981,632; expenditures, $471,088; qualifying
distributions, $425,614.
Fields of interest: Arts and culture; Orchestral
music; Education; Graduate and professional
education; Diseases and conditions; Cancers;
Television; Agriculture; Theology; Child welfare;
Youth development.
Limitations: Applications accepted. Giving limited to
the greater Kansas City, MO, area.
Application information:
   Initial approach: Proposal
   Deadline(s): None
Trustee: UMB Bank, N.A.
EIN: 431184875

4865
Bartlett and Company Grain Charitable Foundation
4900 Main St., Ste. 1200
Kansas City, MO   64112-2683

Established in 1986 in Missouri.
Donor: Bartlett and Co.
Foundation type: Company-sponsored foundation.
Financial data (yr. ended 04/30/14): Assets,
$3,857,891 (M); expenditures, $153,456;
qualifying distributions, $145,100; giving activities
include $145,100 for 27 grants (high: $50,000;
low: $250).
Purpose and activities: The foundation supports
organizations involved with arts and culture,
education, trichotillomania disorder, legal aid,
children services, and public policy.
Fields of interest: Health; Agriculture; Human
services.
Type of support: General support.
Limitations: Applications accepted. Giving primarily
in Washington, DC, Kansas City, MO, and VA. No
grants to individuals.
Application information:
   Initial approach: Proposal
   Deadline(s): None
Trustees: Paul D. Bartlett, Jr.; James B. Hebenstreit;
Marilyn B. Hebenstreit.
EIN: 436323269

4866
BEO Charitable Trust
7101 Westmoreland Dr.
Saint Louis, MO   63130-4424

Established in 2006 in Missouri.
Donor: Andrew O'Brien.
Foundation type: Independent foundation.
Financial data (yr. ended 12/31/13): Assets,
$5,680,501 (M); gifts received, $700,549;
expenditures, $323,236; qualifying distributions,
$275,840; giving activities include $275,840 for 21
grants (high: $62,500; low: $750).

Fields of interest: Arts and culture; Education; Human services.
Limitations: Applications not accepted. Giving primarily in St. Louis, MO.
Application information: Unsolicited requests for funds not accepted.
Officers: Andrew O'Brien, Pres.; Lori R. O'Brien, Treas.
EIN: 205580904

4867
BF Charitable Foundation
c/o US Bank, N.A.
P.O. Box 387
Saint Louis, MO   63166-0387   (314) 418-4948
Contact: Steven Bander, Tr.

Established in 2006 in Missouri.
Donors: Steven Joseph Bander; Patricia A. Bander.
Foundation type: Independent foundation.
Financial data (yr. ended 06/30/13): Assets, $2,586,124 (M); expenditures, $417,431; qualifying distributions, $385,410; giving activities include $380,000 for 5 grants (high: $300,000; low: $10,000).
Fields of interest: Higher education; Nonprofits; Human services.
Type of support: Regranting.
Limitations: Applications accepted. Giving primarily in MO, with emphasis on St. Louis.
Application information: Application form required.
  Initial approach: Letter of inquiry
  Deadline(s): None
Trustees: Patricia A. Bander; Steven Bander.
EIN: 206675392

4868
Bland Family Foundation
c/o Ryan Easley, Northern Trust
190 Carondelet Plz.
Saint Louis, MO   63105-3443

Established in 2002 in Missouri.
Foundation type: Independent foundation.
Financial data (yr. ended 11/30/13): Assets, $5,355,206 (M); expenditures, $377,033; qualifying distributions, $347,069; giving activities include $347,069 for 51 grants (high: $30,000; low: $500).
Fields of interest: Performing arts; Museums; Education; Natural resources; Human services.
Limitations: Applications not accepted. Giving primarily in CA, MO, and OR. No grants to individuals.
Application information: Unsolicited requests for funds not accepted.
Trustees: A. Stanley Bland III; Marian B. Langdon; Cynthia B. Medart; Gertrude B. Platt.
EIN: 300135800

4869
Ephraim Block Family Charitable Trust
(formerly Ephraim Block Family Foundation)
P.O. Box 387
Saint Louis, MO   63166-0387   (314) 505-8203
Contact: Angela Pearson, Trust Off., U.S. Bank, N.A.

Established in 1987 in Missouri.
Foundation type: Independent foundation.

Financial data (yr. ended 06/30/13): Assets, $4,448,502 (M); expenditures, $322,973; qualifying distributions, $256,267; giving activities include $238,500 for 2 grants (high: $155,025; low: $83,475).
Purpose and activities: Support for organizations providing aid to indigent Jewish people.
Fields of interest: Nonprofits; Human services; International development.
International interests: Israel.
Type of support: Regranting.
Limitations: Applications accepted. Giving primarily in MO and NY. No grants to individuals.
Application information: Application form required.
  Initial approach: Letter
  Deadline(s): None
Trustees: Sarah Rosenburg; U.S. Bank, N.A.
EIN: 436331011

4870
Abe & Anna Bograd Memorial Trust
c/o UMB Bank
P.O. Box 419692, M/S 102030
Kansas City, MO   64141-6692

Established in 1995 in Missouri.
Donor: Abe Bograd†.
Foundation type: Independent foundation.
Financial data (yr. ended 06/30/13): Assets, $5,881,355 (M); expenditures, $321,065; qualifying distributions, $262,600; giving activities include $215,000 for 8 grants (high: $37,000; low: $12,000).
Purpose and activities: Giving primarily to charitable organizations in the greater Kansas City area, specifically Jewish organizations.
Fields of interest: Orchestral music; Nonprofits; Judaism; Human services; Family services.
Type of support: Regranting.
Limitations: Applications not accepted. Giving primarily in the greater Kansas City area of KS and MO. No grants to individuals.
Application information: Unsolicited requests for funds not accepted.
Trustees: Wendy B. Martin; UMB Bank.
EIN: 436509121

4871
Milford and Lee Bohm Charitable Foundation
11502 New London Dr.
Creve Coeur, MO   63141-8345

Established in 1989 in Missouri.
Donors: Milford Bohm†; Leona Bohm.
Foundation type: Independent foundation.
Financial data (yr. ended 12/31/13): Assets, $6,476,096 (M); expenditures, $386,353; qualifying distributions, $359,150; giving activities include $359,150 for 117 grants (high: $60,000; low: $50).
Purpose and activities: Giving primarily to Jewish organizations, including welfare funds; support also for an affiliated fund for the elderly, a community fund, cultural organizations, the United Way, scholarship funds, and art and education funds.
Fields of interest: Dance; Theater; Orchestral music; Higher education; Environment; Nonprofits; Hospital care; Judaism; Human services; Senior services; Children; Adolescents; Seniors; Female children and youth; Indigenous peoples; Low-income

and poor people; People with disabilities; People with HIV/AIDS.
International interests: Israel.
Type of support: General support; Continuing support; Annual campaigns; Capital campaigns; Capital and infrastructure; Endowments; Emergency funds; Professorships; Fellowships; Internships; Scholarships; Research; Individual development; Regranting.
Limitations: Applications not accepted. Giving primarily in St. Louis, MO. No support for political or lobbying organizations. No grants to individuals, other than for scholarships.
Publications: Financial statement.
Application information: Unsolicited requests for funds not accepted.
Officer: Leona Lee Bohm, Mgr.
Number of staff: None.
EIN: 436355629

4872
The Boswell Foundation, Inc.
1078 S. Jefferson
Lebanon, MO   65536-3601   (417) 588-4151
Contact: John J. Boswell, Pres.

Established in 1985 in Missouri.
Donors: Johnathon Boswell Foundation; The Lois K. Boswell Charitable Lead Trust; Independent Stave Co., Inc.; Amie Boswell Foundation; Joe Boswell Foundation; Julie Boswell Foundation; LKB Investments, Inc.; ISCO Holding Co., Inc.
Foundation type: Company-sponsored foundation.
Financial data (yr. ended 11/30/13): Assets, $47,073 (M); gifts received, $195,000; expenditures, $190,107; qualifying distributions, $181,273; giving activities include $181,273 for 3 grants (high: $125,000; low: $20,000).
Purpose and activities: The foundation supports organizations involved with cancer research and Christianity. Special emphasis is directed toward programs designed to promote education.
Fields of interest: Education; Religion; Human services.
Type of support: General support.
Application information: Application form required.
  Initial approach: Letter
  Deadline(s): None
Officer: John J. Boswell, Pres.
Trustee: David Waugh.
EIN: 431409051

4873
Helen S. Boylan Foundation
P.O. Box 731
Carthage, MO   64836-0731   (417) 359-6558
Contact: Elizabeth S. Simmons, Pres.
E-mail: info@boylanfoundation.org; Main URL: http://www.boylanfoundation.org

Donors: Elbert Elwyn Boylan, Jr.; Helen S. Boylan Trust.
Foundation type: Independent foundation.
Financial data (yr. ended 09/30/13): Assets, $4,830,163 (M); expenditures, $374,358; qualifying distributions, $305,283; giving activities include $244,514 for 38 grants (high: $51,213; low: $500).
Fields of interest: Music; Elementary and secondary education; Higher education; Community and

economic development; Sports and recreation; Human services; Child welfare.

Type of support: Capital and infrastructure; Equipment; Land acquisitions; Program development; Curriculum development.

Limitations: Applications accepted. Giving primarily in MO and TX. No support for political organizations or religious activities. No grants to individuals, or for annual campaigns or endowments.

Publications: Application guidelines; Annual report; Financial statement.

Application information:

Initial approach: Proposal
Copies of proposal: 8
Deadline(s): None
Board meeting date(s): Quarterly: Feb., May, Aug., and Nov.

Officers and Directors: Elizabeth S. Simmons, Pres.; Jennifer A. Hering, V.P. and Director; Sally Spradling Stuart, Secy.-Treas.; James A. Deberry; Helen L. Duff; Eugene C. Hall; Ida S. Locarni; J. Shannon Spradling.

Number of staff: 1 part-time professional.

EIN: 431254043

4874
William J. Brace Charitable Trust
c/o Bank of America, N.A.
1200 Main St., 14th Fl.
Kansas City, MO 64121-9119 (816) 292-4301
Contact: Spence Heddens, Market President
E-mail: spence.heddens@ustrust.com; Main
URL: https://www.bankofamerica.com/
philanthropic/grantmaking.go

Established in 2002 in Missouri.

Donor: W.J. Brace Charitable Trust.

Foundation type: Independent foundation.

Financial data (yr. ended 02/28/14): Assets, $7,648,941 (M); expenditures, $391,816; qualifying distributions, $352,733; giving activities include $298,000 for 12 grants (high: $50,000; low: $10,000).

Purpose and activities: Giving primarily for the education and health of children, the health and care of aged persons and hospitals in Kansas City, MO.

Fields of interest: Arts and culture; Education; Nonprofits; Health; Hospital care; Human services; Child welfare.

Type of support: Regranting.

Limitations: Giving limited to MO, with emphasis on Kansas City. No grants for capital support.

Application information: Application form required.

Initial approach: Letter, no more than 3 pages
Copies of proposal: 2
Deadline(s): None

Trustee: Bank of America, N.A.

EIN: 597244050

4875
Willard J. and Mary G. Breidenthal Foundation
c/o UMB Bank, N.A.
P.O. Box 419226
Kansas City, MO 64141-6226 (913) 648-2800

Established in 1962 in Kansas.

Donors: Breidenthal Charitable Lead Trust; Willard J Breidenthal†.

Foundation type: Independent foundation.

Financial data (yr. ended 12/31/13): Assets, $3,957,586 (M); gifts received, $102,631; expenditures, $471,844; qualifying distributions, $432,811; giving activities include $429,250 for 23 grants (high: $250,000; low: $250).

Purpose and activities: Giving primarily for the arts, education, social services, and children and youth services, including programs for underprivileged children.

Fields of interest: Arts and culture; Museums; Education; Basketball; Human services; Child welfare; Youth services; Low-income and poor people.

Limitations: Applications accepted. Giving primarily in the bi-state Kansas City area. No grants to individuals.

Application information: Application form required.

Initial approach: Letter
Deadline(s): Nov. 1

Trustees: George Gray Breidenthal; McKenzie Breidenthal; UMB Bank.

EIN: 486103376

4876
The Brinklee Foundation
7733 Forsyth Blvd., Ste. 1375
Saint Louis, MO 63105-1834

Donors: Robert J. Trulaske, Sr.; Geraldine Trulaske.

Foundation type: Independent foundation.

Financial data (yr. ended 12/31/13): Assets, $340,317 (M); gifts received, $300,000; expenditures, $290,455; qualifying distributions, $290,455; giving activities include $290,100 for 9 grants (high: $125,000; low: $150).

Fields of interest: Education; Health; Children's hospital care; Children.

Limitations: Applications not accepted. Giving primarily in MO.

Application information: Unsolicited requests for funds not accepted.

Trustees: Michelle K. Trulaske; Steven L. Trulaske; Paul L. Vogel.

EIN: 454094220

4877
The Barbara and Helen Brown Family Foundation
c/o Eagle Bank
1052 S. Kirkwood Rd.
Saint Louis, MO 63122
Contact: Jim Hall
Main URL: http://www.brownsisters.org

Established in 2009 in Missouri.

Donors: Mary Helen Brown; Mary Helen Brown Revocable Living Trust.

Foundation type: Independent foundation.

Financial data (yr. ended 12/31/13): Assets, $5,407,886 (M); gifts received, $1,560,000; expenditures, $302,532; qualifying distributions, $231,243; giving activities include $178,001 for 9 grants (high: $50,000; low: $5,000).

Fields of interest: Health.

Limitations: Giving primarily in St. Louis, MO.

Application information: Full applications are by invitation only. See foundation web site for complete guidelines.

Initial approach: 2-page Letter of Intent form must be requested from the Executive Director

Officers and Directors: James N. Hall, Chair. and Pres.; Gregory Shepardson, Treas. and Director; Michelle O'Toole; Mike Sullivan.

EIN: 270167894

4878
Barbara Bryant Family Foundation
(doing business as Watermark Foundation)
204 N. Central Ave.
Clayton, MO 63105-3832

Established in 2007 in Missouri.

Donor: Barbara Murphy Bryant.

Foundation type: Independent foundation.

Financial data (yr. ended 12/31/13): Assets, $71,217 (M); gifts received, $400,000; expenditures, $435,765; qualifying distributions, $434,276; giving activities include $434,276 for 163 grants (high: $20,000; low: $250).

Fields of interest: Education; University education; Catholicism; Human services.

Type of support: General support.

Limitations: Applications not accepted. Giving primarily in DC, MO and VA. No grants to individuals.

Application information: Contributes only to pre-selected organizations.

Director: Barbara Murphy Bryant.

EIN: 261433726

4879
Build-A-Bear Workshop Bear Hugs Foundation
1954 Innerbelt Business Center Dr.
Saint Louis, MO 63114-5760 (314) 423-8000
E-mail: giving@buildabear.com; Main URL: http://
www.buildabear.com/shopping/contents/
content.jsp?catId=400002&id=700013
Children's Health and Wellness Grant
Recipients: http://www.buildabear.com/html/
en_US/aboutus/community/
2012ChampGrants.pdf
Domestic Pets Grant Recipients: http://
www.buildabear.com/html/en_US/aboutus/
community/2012BKPGrants.pdf
Literacy and Education Grant Recipients: http://
www.buildabear.com/html/en_US/aboutus/
community/2012LiteracyGrants.pdf

Established in 2006 in Missouri.

Donors: Build-A-Bear Workshop, Inc.; Build-A-Bear Workshop Canada Ltd.

Foundation type: Company-sponsored foundation.

Financial data (yr. ended 12/31/13): Assets, $830,320 (M); gifts received, $432,433; expenditures, $197,986; qualifying distributions, $165,781; giving activities include $165,781 for grants.

Purpose and activities: The foundation supports programs designed to promote health and wellness of children and families; care and welfare of animals; and literacy and education.

Fields of interest: Education; Early childhood education; Special needs education; Reading promotion; Domesticated animals; Animal rescue and rehabilitation; Humane education; Health; Animal therapy; Pediatrics; Diseases and conditions; Safety education; Child welfare; Children.

International interests: Canada.

Type of support: General support; Matching grants; Program development; Research; Public engagement and education.

Limitations: Applications accepted. Giving on a national basis primarily in areas of company operations in CA, CO, KY, MN, MO, NJ, PA, and WI, and in Canada. No support for private foundations, or for religious organizations not of direct benefit to the entire community, or political organizations. No grants for salaries for administrators, therapists, or medial personnel, professional development for staff, advertising, fuel for mobile clinics, research projects or experimental testing, capital campaigns, construction or "new facility" expense, fundraising or special events, or political activities; generally, no grants to individuals.

Publications: Application guidelines; Grants list.

Application information: Application form required.

Initial approach: Complete online application
Copies of proposal: 1
Deadline(s): Feb. 1 to Oct. 31; requests received after Sept. 1 will not be awarded until after Jan. 1

Officers and Directors: Dorrie Krueger, Pres. and Director; Jill Saunders, V.P.; Teresa Kroll, Secy. and Director; Jeff Fullmer, Treas. and Director; Heather Barksdale; Bob Buer; Mike Early; Jennifer Guinn; Michael Segura.

EIN: 204961009

4880
Butler Manufacturing Company Foundation

1540 Genessee St.
P.O. Box 419917
Kansas City, MO   64141-0917   (816) 968-3208

Established in 1952 in Missouri.

Donor: Butler Manufacturing Co.

Foundation type: Company-sponsored foundation.

Financial data (yr. ended 06/30/13): Assets, $6,181,903 (M); expenditures, $432,657; qualifying distributions, $356,375; giving activities include $344,000 for 120 grants (high: $10,000), and $8,150 for 40 employee matching gifts.

Purpose and activities: The foundation supports organizations involved with arts and culture, education, health, employment, housing, youth development, community development, disabled people, minorities, women, and economically disadvantaged people.

Fields of interest: Arts and culture; Education; Elementary and secondary education; Higher education; Nonprofits; Health; Hospital care; Community and economic development; Employment; Job training; Community improvement; Housing development; Youth development; Females; Ethnic and racial groups; Low-income and poor people; People with disabilities.

Type of support: General support; Grants to individuals; Employee volunteer services; Continuing support; Annual campaigns; Employee matching gifts; Capital campaigns; Seed money; Scholarships; Regranting.

Limitations: Applications accepted. Giving primarily in areas of company operations, with emphasis on the greater Kansas City, MO, area. No support for political organizations, religious organizations not of direct benefit to the entire community, pre-K-12 educational institutions, fraternal or veterans' organizations, national health organizations, local or regional chapters of national health organizations, or grantmaking foundations. No grants to individuals

(except for employee-related hardship grants and employee-related scholarships), or for tours, conferences, seminars, workshops, or similar events, fundraising, or endowments.

Publications: Application guidelines; Informational brochure (including application guidelines).

Application information:

Initial approach: Letter, E-mail or Telephone call
Copies of proposal: 1
Deadline(s): None
Board meeting date(s): Aug., Nov., Feb., and May
Final notification: Following board meetings

Officers: Harry Yeatman, Pres.; Dan Kumm, V.P. and Secy.; Natalie Treff, Treas.

Trustees: Barbara Bridger; Barbara Deloach.

Number of staff: 1 part-time support.

EIN: 440663648

4881
Ina Calkins Trust

1200 Main St., 14 Fl.
P.O. Box 219119
Kansas City, MO   64121-9119   8003577094
Main URL: http://www.calkinsboard.org

Established in 2000 in Missouri.

Foundation type: Independent foundation.

Financial data (yr. ended 12/31/14): Assets, $6,509,824; expenditures, $272,902; qualifying distributions, $232,684 and $0 for set-asides.

Purpose and activities: Giving to benefit the citizens of Kansas City, Missouri, in the areas of education and medical and welfare assistance.

Fields of interest: Higher education; Health; Human services; Seniors.

Type of support: General support; Grants to individuals; Student aid.

Limitations: Applications accepted. Giving limited to organizations and residents of Kansas City, MO.

Application information: Complete application guidelines available on Trust web site. Application form required.

Deadline(s): Oct. 1
Final notification: Nov.

Officers and Board Members: Linda B. Lyon, Pres.; Michael C. Kirk, V.P.; Spence Heddens, Secy. and Director; Lisa Jones Schellhorn; Robert N. Sawyer; Helen Emmott; Kevin Jones; Cappy Powell; Thomas J. Turner; Betsey R. Hughes.

Trustee: Bank of America, N.A.

EIN: 526994869

4882
Canfield Family Foundation

c/o Linda Currier Talx Corp.
9034 Sedgwick Pl. Dr.
Saint Louis, MO   63124-1891

Established in 2000 in Missouri.

Donor: William W. Canfield.

Foundation type: Independent foundation.

Financial data (yr. ended 06/30/13): Assets, $5,340,279 (M); gifts received, $502,780; expenditures, $379,030; qualifying distributions, $364,170; giving activities include $356,750 for 20 grants (high: $80,000; low: $500).

Fields of interest: Education; Christianity; Adolescents.

Type of support: General support.

Limitations: Applications not accepted. Giving primarily in MO. No grants to individuals.

Application information: Unsolicited requests for funds not accepted.

Officer: William W. Canfield, Pres.

EIN: 436854712

4883
The Capellupo Foundation Inc.

9839 Tesson Creek Estates Dr.
Saint Louis, MO   63123-6296
Application address: c/o Mona Sandroni, Secy., 3350 Greenwood Blvd., St. Louis, MO 63143, tel.: (314) 645-5900

Established in 2000 in Missouri.

Donors: John Capellupo; Mary Ann Capellupo.

Foundation type: Independent foundation.

Financial data (yr. ended 04/30/13): Assets, $725,930 (M); gifts received, $1,430; expenditures, $149,666; qualifying distributions, $146,866; giving activities include $146,866 for 23 grants (high: $100,000; low: $50).

Fields of interest: Education; University education; Religion; Human services.

Limitations: Applications accepted. Giving primarily in MO. No grants to individuals.

Officers and Directors: John Capellupo, Chair. and Pres.; Mona Sandroni, Secy. and Director; Mary Ann Capellupo; Mark Capellupo; Matthew Capellupo; Michael Capellupo; Kevin Capellupo.

EIN: 431888260

4884
Chapman Family Foundation

8020 Forsyth Blvd.
Saint Louis, MO   63105-1707

Donors: Robert H. Chapman; Cynthia M. Chapman.

Foundation type: Independent foundation.

Financial data (yr. ended 12/31/13): Assets, $12,365,511 (M); gifts received, $1,750,000; expenditures, $354,376; qualifying distributions, $352,406; giving activities include $346,400 for 24 grants (high: $115,000; low: $100).

Fields of interest: Education; Housing development; Human services.

Limitations: Applications not accepted.

Application information: Unsolicited requests for funds not accepted.

Officer: Susan Reynolds, Exec. Dir.

Trustees: Cynthia M. Chapman; Robert H. Chapman.

EIN: 266665176

4885
The Chod Family Foundation

18555 Booness Ln.
Glencoe, MO   63038-1732

Established in 1993 in Missouri.

Donor: Ronald Chod.

Foundation type: Independent foundation.

Financial data (yr. ended 12/31/13): Assets, $6,339,183 (M); gifts received, $90,074; expenditures, $354,591; qualifying distributions, $350,036; giving activities include $349,061 for 36 grants (high: $213,384; low: $350).

Fields of interest: Arts and culture; Education; Elementary education; University education; Nonprofits; Judaism; Human services; Food aid.

Type of support: Regranting.

Limitations: Applications not accepted. Giving primarily in St. Louis, MO. No grants to individuals.
Application information: Unsolicited requests for funds not accepted.
Officer: Ronald Chod, Pres.
EIN: 436475433

4886
Bernal T. Chomeau Private Foundation
10672 Country View Dr.
Creve Coeur, MO   63141-7819

Foundation type: Independent foundation.
Financial data (yr. ended 07/31/14): Assets, $2,800,009 (M); expenditures, $214,754; qualifying distributions, $204,880; giving activities include $201,000 for 22 grants (high: $20,000; low: $1,000).
Fields of interest: Environment; Sports and recreation; Human services.
Limitations: Applications not accepted. Giving primarily in MO and WI.
Application information: Unsolicited requests for funds not accepted.
Trustees: Kathleen C. Andrews; Douglas B. Chomeau; Stuart G. Chomeau.
EIN: 376475603

4887
Cinmar Family Foundation
6 Lon Cir.
Dearborn, MO   64439

Foundation type: Independent foundation.
Financial data (yr. ended 07/31/14): Assets, $5,158,723 (M); expenditures, $201,196; qualifying distributions, $167,954; giving activities include $166,000 for 5 grants (high: $50,000; low: $5,000).
Fields of interest: Health; Agriculture; Human services; Children.
Type of support: Research.
Limitations: Applications not accepted. Giving primarily in MO.
Application information: Unsolicited requests for funds not accepted.
Officers and Directors: Cindy L. Hill, Pres. and Director; Mark S. Hill, V.P. and Director; Jason S. Hill, Secy. and Director; Jared N. Pharis, Treas. and Director.
EIN: 461612312

4888
Copaken Family Foundation
1100 Walnut St., Ste. 2000
Kansas City, MO   64106-2126

Established in 1984 in Kansas.
Donors: Paul Copaken; Lois Copaken.
Foundation type: Independent foundation.
Financial data (yr. ended 09/30/13): Assets, $354,380 (M); expenditures, $190,124; qualifying distributions, $186,114; giving activities include $184,604 for 95 grants (high: $55,000; low: $50).
Fields of interest: Arts and culture; Performing arts; Higher education; Nonprofits; Diseases and conditions; Judaism; Child welfare; Females.
Type of support: General support; Regranting; Continuing support; Annual campaigns; Endowments; Program development; Seed money.

Limitations: Applications not accepted. Giving primarily in MO. No grants to individuals.
Application information: Unsolicited requests for funds not accepted.
Trustees: Jon Copaken; Keith Copaken; Lois Copaken; Paul Copaken.
EIN: 486264196

4889
The Floy L. and Paul F. Cornelsen Charitable Foundation
337 W. Lockwood Ave., Ste. D
Saint Louis, MO   63119-2952

Established in 1993 in Missouri.
Donors: Floy L. Cornelsen; Paul F. Cornelsen.
Foundation type: Independent foundation.
Financial data (yr. ended 06/30/13): Assets, $7,596,440 (M); gifts received, $2,000,000; expenditures, $313,822; qualifying distributions, $293,300; giving activities include $289,500 for 8 grants (high: $100,000; low: $1,500).
Purpose and activities: Giving primarily for Lutheran schools and services.
Fields of interest: Elementary and secondary education; Higher education; Graduate and professional education; Methodism; Theology; Family services; Child welfare.
Type of support: Capital and infrastructure; Matching grants; General support.
Limitations: Applications not accepted. Giving primarily in IL, St. Louis, MO, and Tacoma, WA. No grants to individuals.
Application information: Contributes only to pre-selected organizations.
Trustees: Kristina Cornelsen; Katherine St. John.
EIN: 431635732

4890
Evah C. Cray Residuary Charitable Trust
c/o UMB Bank
1010 Grand Blvd.
Kansas City, MO   64106-2202   (816) 860-7711
Contact: Kristen Comment

Established in 1992 in Kansas.
Foundation type: Independent foundation.
Financial data (yr. ended 06/30/13): Assets, $3,858,954 (M); expenditures, $204,991; qualifying distributions, $170,484; giving activities include $166,650 for 13 grants (high: $81,000; low: $2,000).
Fields of interest: Arts and culture; Historical activities; Education; Elementary and secondary education; Higher education; Animal welfare; Public administration; Religion; Human services.
Type of support: General support; Matching grants; Annual campaigns; Capital and infrastructure; Emergency funds; Program development; Curriculum development.
Limitations: Applications accepted. Giving limited to KS.
Application information: Application form required.
  Initial approach: Proposal
  Deadline(s): None
Trustees: Cloud L. Cray, Jr.; Jeri Kurth; June Lynn; UMB Bank, N.A.
EIN: 486320070

4891
Gladys K. Crown Foundation
101 S. Hanley Rd., Ste. 600
Saint Louis, MO   63105-3435
Contact: Randall Green, Pres.

Donor: Randall E. Green.
Foundation type: Independent foundation.
Financial data (yr. ended 12/31/13): Assets, $921,197; expenditures, $232,766; qualifying distributions, $224,617; giving activities include $224,617 for 21 grants (high: $64,217; low: $1,000).
Fields of interest: Nonprofits; Convalescent care; Judaism.
Type of support: Regranting.
Limitations: Applications not accepted. Giving primarily in MO. No grants to individuals.
Application information: Unsolicited requests for funds not accepted.
Officer: Randall E. Green, Pres.
EIN: 436849188

4892
The Curry Family Foundation
(formerly Mid-America Foundation)
4900 Main St., Ste. 210
Kansas City, MO   64112-1372
Contact: Lee Ellen Curry, Pres.; Steve O'Neill, V.P.
E-mail for Lee Ellen Curry:
lee@curryfoundationkc.org, tel.: (816) 931-2528;
E-mail for Steve
O'Neill: steve@curryfoundationkc.org, tel.: (816) 931-2529, Fax: (816) 931-2531; Main URL: http://www.curryfoundationkc.org
Grants List: http://www.curryfoundationkc.org/index.php?
option=com_content&view=category&layout=blog&id=11&Itemid=8
Grants List: http://www.curryfoundationkc.org/index.php?
option=com_content&view=category&layout=blog&id=12&Itemid=6

Established in 1986 in Missouri.
Donors: William H. Curry; Dorothy F. Curry.
Foundation type: Independent foundation.
Financial data (yr. ended 12/31/13): Assets, $12,453,159 (M); gifts received, $2,000; expenditures, $606,943; qualifying distributions, $501,863; giving activities include $340,000 for 36 grants (high: $20,000; low: $500).
Purpose and activities: Giving primarily for the arts and human services.
Fields of interest: Arts and culture; Orchestral music; Performing arts education; Education; Elementary education; Undergraduate education; School-based health care; Housing development; Human services; Food delivery.
Type of support: Scholarships; Matching grants; General support; Continuing support; Capital campaigns; Capital and infrastructure; Equipment; Endowments; Program development.
Limitations: Applications accepted. Giving primarily in Kansas City, MO. No grants to individuals.
Application information: Complete application guidelines available on foundation web site.
  Initial approach: Letter of Intent
  Deadline(s): Feb. 28 and Sep. 30
  Board meeting date(s): Jan., Apr., July and Oct.
Officers and Directors: Bill Curry, Chair.; Lee Curry, Pres. and Treas.; Steven O'Neill, V.P. and Secy.; Dorothy F. Curry; Doug Curry; Stanley Shaffer, MD.

Number of staff: 2 full-time professional.
EIN: 431428340

4893
Darr Family Foundation
2870-D S. Ingram Mill Rd.
Springfield, MO 65804-4127 (417) 888-1490
Contact: Thomas L. Slaight, Pres.
FAX: (417) 887-0283; *Main URL:* http://
www.darrff.org
Grants List: http://www.darrff.org/grants-made

Established in 2002 in Missouri.
Donors: Sheryl D. Hellweg; Marsha D. Slaight;
William N. Darr.
Foundation type: Independent foundation.
Financial data (yr. ended 06/30/13): Assets,
$5,292,284 (M); gifts received, $500,000;
expenditures, $329,625; qualifying distributions,
$294,433; giving activities include $243,350 for 7
grants (high: $200,000; low: $5,000).
Fields of interest: University education; Scouting
programs; Adult and child mentoring.
Limitations: Applications accepted. Giving primarily
in Springfield, MO. No grants to individuals.
Application information: Application form required.
Initial approach: Letter
Deadline(s): Feb. 28
Officers and Directors: Thomas L. Slaight, Pres. and
Director; Marsha D. Slaight, V.P. and Director; Erin
D. Danastasio, Secy. and Director; Zachary D.
Slaight, Treas. and Director; Cody Danastasio; Kurt
D. Hellweg; Sheryl D. Hellweg; Tyler D. Hellweg; Tara
L. Slaight.
EIN: 371439200

4894
Victor & Selene Deliniere Charitable
Foundation
P.O. Box 11356
Clayton, MO 63105-0156

Established in 2007 in Missouri.
Donors: Victor H. Deliniere Trust; Selene Deliniere
Trust.
Foundation type: Independent foundation.
Financial data (yr. ended 04/30/13): Assets,
$3,696,764 (M); expenditures, $213,864;
qualifying distributions, $179,720; giving activities
include $172,028 for 17 grants (high: $25,000;
low: $3,000).
Fields of interest: Environment; Animal welfare.
Limitations: Applications not accepted. Giving
primarily in St. Louis, MO. No grants to individuals.
Application information: Unsolicited requests for
funds not accepted.
Trustees: Arthur Rehm; Commerce Trust Co.
EIN: 436937088

4895
The Dierberg Foundation
c/o Tax Dept. - Mail Code 019
600 James S. McDonnell Blvd.
Hazelwood, MO 63042-2302

Established in 2003 in Missouri.
Donor: First Banks, Inc.
Foundation type: Company-sponsored foundation.
Financial data (yr. ended 12/31/13): Assets,
$12,252,587 (M); expenditures, $435,251;

qualifying distributions, $435,000; giving activities
include $435,000 for 17 grants (high: $282,000;
low: $500).
Purpose and activities: The foundation supports
museums and hospitals and organizations involved
with historic preservation, higher education, human
services, and Catholicism.
Fields of interest: Museums; Historic preservation;
Higher education; Nonprofits; Hospital care;
Catholicism; Human services; Youth services.
Type of support: General support; Annual
campaigns; Capital and infrastructure; Regranting.
Limitations: Applications not accepted. Giving
primarily in St. Louis, MO.
Application information: Contributes only to
pre-selected organizations.
Trustees: Ellen Dierberg; James F. Dierberg; James
F. Dierberg II; Mary W. Dierberg; Michael J. Dierberg.
EIN: 436897690

4896
John & Yvette Dubinsky Family Foundation
7777 Bonhomme
Saint Louis, MO 63105
Application address: c/o William H. Hobson, 8909
Ladue Rd., St. Louis, MO 63124, tel.: (314)
991-4999

Donor: John P. Dubinsky.
Foundation type: Independent foundation.
Financial data (yr. ended 12/31/13): Assets,
$231,087 (M); gifts received, $516,275;
expenditures, $303,978; qualifying distributions,
$302,539; giving activities include $302,513 for 95
grants (high: $50,000; low: $60).
Fields of interest: Arts and culture; Education;
Human services.
Application information:
Initial approach: Proposal
Deadline(s): None
Trustee: John P. Dubinsky.
EIN: 436786303

4897
Robert H. and Lorraine F. Duesenberg
Foundation
9026 Whitehaven Dr.
Saint Louis, MO 63123-2042

Established in 1994 in Missouri.
Donors: Robert H. Duesenberg; Lorraine F.
Duesenberg.
Foundation type: Independent foundation.
Financial data (yr. ended 01/31/15): Assets,
$6,064,628 (M); gifts received, $115,214;
expenditures, $303,523; qualifying distributions,
$301,350; giving activities include $301,350 for 29
grants (high: $80,000; low: $500).
Purpose and activities: Giving primarily for
education, and to Lutheran churches.
Fields of interest: Arts and culture; Education;
Higher education; Breast cancer; Methodism.
Type of support: Research.
Limitations: Applications not accepted. Giving
primarily in St. Louis, MO. No grants to individuals.
Application information: Contributes only to
pre-selected organizations.
Trustees: John R. Duesenberg; Robert H.
Duesenberg.
EIN: 436526262

4898
Dunn Family Foundation
1001 Locust St.
Kansas City, MO 64106-1904 (816) 391-2521
Contact: Robert P. Dunn, Pres.
Main URL: http://www.jedunn.com

Established in 1981 in Missouri.
Donors: J.E. Dunn Construction; William H. Dunn,
Sr.; Terrence P. Dunn; Steven D. Dunn; Robert P.
Dunn; Terry Dunn; William H. Dunn Family Trust;
Stephen D. Dunn Family Trust; Robert P. Dunn
Family Trust; Terry Dunn Family Trust.
Foundation type: Independent foundation.
Financial data (yr. ended 06/30/14): Assets,
$2,763,890 (M); gifts received, $108,643;
expenditures, $289,002; qualifying distributions,
$258,300; giving activities include $258,300 for
148 grants (high: $30,000; low: $100).
Purpose and activities: Giving primarily for: 1)
programs that help disabled youth and adults
overcome educational, mental and physical
challenges; 2) social service programs, health care
and emergency relief for seniors; 3) social welfare
services for ethnic minorities, especially programs
that enable them to gain education, employable
skills and economic advancement; 4) program
funding and capital support for construction,
renovation and equipment needs for academic
institutions; 5) support of faith-based institutions; 6)
health, with an emphasis on capital grants to
hospitals and other medical institutions; 7)
academic, counseling, health, job training,
mentoring, recreational, social services, and
tutoring programs that enrich children's lives; and 8)
civic programs that enhance economic
development .
Fields of interest: Education; Health; Community
and economic development; Religion; Human
services; Children; Adolescents; Seniors; Ethnic and
racial groups; People with disabilities.
Type of support: Debt reduction; General support;
Capital and infrastructure; Equipment.
Limitations: Applications accepted. Giving within a
75-mile radius of the greater metropolitan Kansas
City, MO, area. No support for the visual or
performing arts, other foundations, or organizations
without a phone book listing or ones with only a P.O.
Box and no street address or office location. No
grants to individuals, or for research, endowments,
travel, conferences, or telethons.
Application information: Application form required.
Initial approach: Letter
Deadline(s): None
Board meeting date(s): Quarterly
Officers and Directors: William H. Dunn, Sr., Chair.
and Director; Robert P. Dunn, Pres. and Director;
Kevin A. Dunn; Terrence P. Dunn, V.P. and Director;
William H. Dunn, Jr., V.P. and Director; Stephen D.
Dunn, V.P. , Treas. and Director.
EIN: 431244010

4899
William Edgar Charitable Foundation
P.O. Box 387
Saint Louis, MO 63166 (314) 505-8204
Contact: Carol Eaves

Established in 1998 in Missouri.
Foundation type: Independent foundation.
Financial data (yr. ended 06/30/13): Assets,
$3,691,602 (M); expenditures, $293,484;

qualifying distributions, $197,010; giving activities include $197,010 for grants.

Purpose and activities: Scholarships are awarded to graduates of public high schools in Ironton, MO. Funding also for the advancement of nonprofit scientific or technical projects of potential value and benefit to the development of Ironton and Iron County, MO. Funding as well for educational, literary, and nonprofit civic and secular charitable organizations.

Fields of interest: Education; Nonprofits; Community and economic development.

Type of support: Capital and infrastructure; Equipment; Emergency funds; Capacity-building and technical assistance; Program development; Seed money; Student aid.

Limitations: Applications accepted. Giving limited to Ironton and Iron County, MO. No support for churches and religious organizations, or for-profit entities. No grants to individuals (except for scholarships), or for regular operating costs, or fundraising dinners.

Publications: Application guidelines; Informational brochure (including application guidelines).

Application information: Application form required.
 Initial approach: Contact foundation for application form
 Copies of proposal: 5
 Deadline(s): Aug. 15

Trustee: U.S. Bank, N.A.

Number of staff: None.

EIN: 436829350

4900
Miriam Arnold Edmonston Charitable Foundation
P.O. Box 597
Mexico, MO 65265-0597

Established in 1993 in Missouri.

Donor: Miriam A. Edmonston†.

Foundation type: Independent foundation.

Financial data (yr. ended 12/31/14): Assets, $8,034,267; gifts received, $1,657; expenditures, $403,144; qualifying distributions, $343,680.

Fields of interest: Historic preservation; Education; Health; National defense; Sports and recreation.

Limitations: Applications not accepted. Giving primarily in MO. No grants to individuals.

Application information: Contributes only to pre-selected organizations.

Officers: Robert E. McIntosh, Pres.; Bradford A. Brett, V.P.; George Huffman, Secy.; Tim M. Williams, Treas.

Director: Kirk Ekern.

EIN: 431668568

4901
Estelle S. & Robert A. Long Ellis Foundation
4600 Madison Ave., Ste. 600
Kansas City, MO 64112-3031 (816) 410-4600
Contact: James H. Bernard Jr., Secy.-Treas.

Established in 2004 in Missouri.

Foundation type: Independent foundation.

Financial data (yr. ended 12/31/13): Assets, $6,258,268 (M); expenditures, $390,257; qualifying distributions, $335,000; giving activities include $335,000 for 12 grants (high: $60,000; low: $20,000).

Purpose and activities: Giving primarily for arts organizations.

Fields of interest: Arts and culture.

Limitations: Applications accepted. Giving primarily in the greater bi-state Kansas City area.

Application information:
 Initial approach: Letter or telephone
 Copies of proposal: 1
 Deadline(s): None
 Board meeting date(s): Varies
 Final notification: Varies

Officers and Directors: James H. Bernard, Pres. and Director; Jean Green, V.P. and Director; James H. Bernard, Jr., Secy.-Treas. and Director.

Number of staff: None.

EIN: 201034910

4902
Louise B. Empson Trust
c/o Commerce Trust Co.
P.O. Box 11356
Clayton, MO 63105-0156

Established in 2004 in Illinois.

Foundation type: Independent foundation.

Financial data (yr. ended 09/30/13): Assets, $5,416,764 (M); expenditures, $284,925; qualifying distributions, $253,082; giving activities include $245,280 for 2 grants (high: $122,640; low: $122,640).

Fields of interest: Higher education; Nonprofits; Health.

Type of support: General support; Regranting.

Limitations: Applications not accepted. Giving primarily in IL. No grants to individuals.

Application information: Contributes only to pre-selected organizations.

Trustee: Commerce Trust Co.

EIN: 376220876

4903
Enright Foundation Inc.
18513 E. 191st St.
Pleasant Hill, MO 64080-8485 (816) 540-2007
Contact: Margaret Huber, Pres.

Established in 1965 in Missouri.

Donor: Joseph J. Enright.

Foundation type: Independent foundation.

Financial data (yr. ended 03/31/13): Assets, $4,744,423 (M); expenditures, $253,999; qualifying distributions, $217,578; giving activities include $184,104 for 10 grants (high: $26,301; low: $300).

Fields of interest: Hospital care; Catholicism; Human services; Child welfare.

Type of support: General support.

Limitations: Applications accepted. Giving primarily in MO. No grants to individuals.

Application information: Application form required.
 Initial approach: Letter
 Deadline(s): None

Officers and Directors: Margaret L. Huber, Pres. and Director; Mary E. Westermayer, V.P. and Director; Mary Lou Cassidy, Secy. and Director; William L. Cassidy, Treas. and Director.

EIN: 436067639

4904
The Max and Melba Erlich Charitable Foundation
12 Radnor Rd.
Saint Louis, MO 63131-4829

Established in 2000 in Missouri.

Donors: Max Erlich; Melba Erlich.

Foundation type: Independent foundation.

Financial data (yr. ended 12/31/13): Assets, $2,447,129 (M); expenditures, $159,344; qualifying distributions, $123,000; giving activities include $123,000 for 22 grants (high: $50,000; low: $174).

Fields of interest: Education; Nonprofits; Judaism; Human services.

Type of support: General support; Regranting.

Limitations: Applications not accepted. Giving primarily in St. Louis, MO. No grants to individuals.

Application information: Unsolicited requests for funds not accepted.

Trustees: Max Erlich; Melba Erlich.

EIN: 431879298

4905
Essman Family Charitable Foundation
21 Somerset Downs
Saint Louis, MO 63124-1007

Established in 1999 in Missouri.

Donor: Alyn V. Essman.

Foundation type: Independent foundation.

Financial data (yr. ended 12/31/13): Assets, $648,750 (M); expenditures, $152,864; qualifying distributions, $144,175; giving activities include $144,175 for 49 grants (high: $21,550; low: $250).

Fields of interest: Arts and culture; Higher education; Nonprofits; Judaism; Human services.

Type of support: Regranting.

Limitations: Applications not accepted. Giving primarily in St. Louis, MO. No grants to individuals.

Application information: Contributes only to pre-selected organizations.

Trustees: Alyn V. Essman; Marlyn R. Essman; Sharyn M. Essman; Judy E. Taylor; Todd E. Taylor.

EIN: 436804331

4906
Ever and Anon Foundation
c/o UHY Advisors, Inc.
15 Sunnen Dr., Ste. 100
Saint Louis, MO 63143-3819 3146151200
Application address: 11 E Lincoln St., Belleville, IL 62220-2109 tel: (618) 233-1880

Established in 1998 in Missouri.

Donors: Elsie Kern; Fred J. Kern; Barbara M. Kern.

Foundation type: Independent foundation.

Financial data (yr. ended 12/31/14): Assets, $6,326,977; gifts received, $9,080; expenditures, $309,900; qualifying distributions, $308,924.

Fields of interest: Education; Community and economic development.

Limitations: Applications accepted. Giving limited to the Belleville, IL area.

Application information:
 Initial approach: Proposal
 Deadline(s): None

Trustees: Barbara M. Kern; Fred J. Kern.

EIN: 376350557

4907
Fabick Charitable Trust Inc.
1 Fabick Dr.
Fenton, MO 63026-2928   (636) 343-5900
Contact: David Kramer

Established in 1969 in Missouri.
Donor: John Fabick Tractor Co.
Foundation type: Company-sponsored foundation.
Financial data (yr. ended 12/31/13): Assets,
$9,900 (M); gifts received, $358,500;
expenditures, $355,000; qualifying distributions,
$355,000; giving activities include $355,000 for 28
grants (high: $50,000; low: $1,000).
Purpose and activities: The foundation supports
hospitals and organizations involved with education,
disaster relief, human services, and Christianity.
Fields of interest: Education; Graduate and
professional education; Hospital care; Disaster
relief; Christianity; Catholicism; Theology; Human
services; Child welfare; Scouting programs;
Homeless services; Victims of disaster.
Type of support: General support.
Limitations: Applications accepted. Giving primarily
in St. Louis, MO. No grants to individuals.
Application information: Application form required.
  Initial approach: Letter
  Copies of proposal: 1
  Deadline(s): Oct. 15
Officers: Harry Fabick, Pres.; Scott R. Borlinghaus,
Secy.
EIN: 237013262

4908
Kathryn G. Favre Charitable Foundation
10805 Sunset Office Dr., Ste. 100
Saint Louis, MO 63127-1028   (314) 966-8077

Established in 2006 in Missouri.
Donor: Kathryn G. Favre†.
Foundation type: Independent foundation.
Financial data (yr. ended 12/31/14): Assets,
$4,320,945; expenditures, $373,381; qualifying
distributions, $348,530.
Fields of interest: Zoos; Domesticated animals.
Type of support: General support.
Limitations: Applications accepted. Giving primarily
in St. Louis, MO. No grants to individuals.
Application information:
  Initial approach: Letter
  Deadline(s): None
Trustees: Charles A. Amen; Jerome Zitzmann.
EIN: 205137010

4909
The Steve and Linda Finerty Family Foundation
(formerly Finerty Family Foundation)
20 Algonquin Ln.
Saint Louis, MO 63119-3502

Established in 1999 in Missouri.
Donors: Steven L. Finerty; Linda M. Finerty.
Foundation type: Independent foundation.
Financial data (yr. ended 12/31/14): Assets,
$1,286,360 (M); gifts received, $364,592;
expenditures, $301,294; qualifying distributions,
$301,294; giving activities include $300,500 for 29
grants (high: $125,000; low: $500).
Purpose and activities: Giving primarily to improve
the quality of life in St. Louis, Missouri, with an

emphasis on the underprivileged, through support
for cultural institutions, youth programs, educational
services, and shelters and homes.
Fields of interest: Arts and culture; Education;
Domesticated animals.
Type of support: General support.
Limitations: Applications not accepted. Giving
limited to St. Louis, MO. No support for religious
programs. No grants to individuals, or for
scholarships or medical research.
Application information: Unsolicited requests for
funds not accepted.
Trustees: Linda Finerty; Steve Finerty.
EIN: 431867107

4910
Finley Charitable Foundation, Inc.
P.O. Box 242
Lamar, MO 64759-0242
Application address: c/o Robert Finlay, 446 N. Hwy.
W., Lamar, MO 64759, tel.: (417) 843-3370

Established in 1994 in Missouri.
Foundation type: Independent foundation.
Financial data (yr. ended 12/31/13): Assets,
$3,824,362 (M); expenditures, $198,220;
qualifying distributions, $197,837; giving activities
include $190,410 for 36 grants (high: $47,000;
low: $700).
Fields of interest: Education; Higher education;
Nonprofits; Diseases and conditions; Muscular
dystrophy; Community and economic development;
Religion; Protestantism; Scouting programs;
Seniors.
Type of support: Scholarships; Individual
development; Regranting.
Limitations: Applications accepted. Giving limited to
Barton County, MO.
Application information: Application form required.
  Initial approach: Proposal
  Deadline(s): None
Directors: Robert L. Finley; Kathryn M. Jenkins;
George D. Nichols.
EIN: 431660744

4911
Forster-Powers Charitable Trust
4635 Wyandotte St., Ste. 206
Kansas City, MO 64112-1537   (816) 753-7777
Contact: Robert E. Turgeon, Tr.

Established in 1968 in Missouri.
Foundation type: Independent foundation.
Financial data (yr. ended 12/31/13): Assets,
$8,637,852 (M); expenditures, $443,437;
qualifying distributions, $301,000; giving activities
include $301,000 for 20 grants (high: $50,000;
low: $2,000).
Purpose and activities: Giving primarily to
scholarship programs for higher and secondary
education; support also for Roman Catholic
churches and social services.
Fields of interest: Secondary education; Higher
education; Foundations; Nonprofits; Catholicism;
Human services.
Type of support: General support; Capital and
infrastructure; Scholarships; Regranting.
Limitations: Applications accepted. Giving primarily
in Kansas City, MO. No grants to individuals.
Application information:

Initial approach: Proposal
  Deadline(s): None
Trustees: Arnold W. Mears; Gerald Meiners; Robert
T. Schweiger; Robert E. Turgeon.
EIN: 436110478

4912
Milton Gaebler Charitable Foundation
P.O. Box 387
Saint Louis, MO 63166

Donor: Milton R. Geabler.
Foundation type: Independent foundation.
Financial data (yr. ended 07/31/13): Assets,
$7,413,872 (M); expenditures, $478,222;
qualifying distributions, $373,343; giving activities
include $354,600 for 5 grants (high: $70,920; low:
$70,920).
Fields of interest: Education; Religion.
Limitations: Applications not accepted.
Application information: Unsolicited requests for
funds not accepted.
Trustees: Raymond E. Gaebler; US Bank, N.A.
EIN: 276826858

4913
Edward Chase Garvey Memorial Foundation
P.O. Box 11356
Clayton, MO 63105-0156

Established in 1970 in Missouri.
Donor: Edward C. Garvey†.
Foundation type: Independent foundation.
Financial data (yr. ended 09/30/14): Assets,
$5,011,613 (M); expenditures, $373,459;
qualifying distributions, $329,604; giving activities
include $320,000 for 32 grants (high: $30,000;
low: $3,000).
Purpose and activities: Giving primarily for the arts,
higher education, natural resource conservation,
including a botanical garden, animal welfare, and
human services, including services for people who
are deaf.
Fields of interest: Arts and culture; Education;
Environment.
Type of support: General support; Annual
campaigns; Capital campaigns; Capital and
infrastructure; Program development; Curriculum
development; Scholarships.
Limitations: Applications accepted. Giving limited to
the greater St. Louis, MO area. No grants to
individuals.
Application information: Application form required.
  Initial approach: Letter
  Copies of proposal: 1
  Deadline(s): None
  Board meeting date(s): Aug.
Trustees: Bliss Shands; Lewis Shands; Commerce
Trust Company.
EIN: 436132744

4914
The Catherine Manley Gaylord Foundation
111 Westport Plz. Dr., Ste. 600
Saint Louis, MO 63146-3015

Established in 1959 in Missouri.
Donor: Catherine M. Gaylord†.
Foundation type: Independent foundation.

Financial data (yr. ended 06/30/14): Assets, $5,028,679; expenditures, $271,234; qualifying distributions, $220,418.
Fields of interest: Health; Human services; Youth development; Youth services.
Limitations: Applications not accepted. Giving primarily in the metropolitan St. Louis, MO, area. No support for private foundations. No grants to individuals; no loans.
Application information: Unsolicited requests for funds not accepted.
Officer and Trustees: Richard Fahey, Mgr. and Trustee; Thomas M. Fahey; Glenn K. Robbins II.
Number of staff: 1 full-time professional; 1 part-time support.
EIN: 436029174

4915
Clifford Willard Gaylord Foundation
702 Briarfarm Ln.
Kirkwood, MO   63122
Contact: Barbara P. Lawton, Tr.

Established in 1948 in Missouri.
Donor: Clifford W. Gaylord†.
Foundation type: Independent foundation.
Financial data (yr. ended 12/31/13): Assets, $8,593,013 (M); expenditures, $421,947; qualifying distributions, $394,000; giving activities include $394,000 for 66 grants (high: $25,000; low: $1,000).
Fields of interest: Arts and culture; Historic preservation; Education; Higher education; Environment; Health; Human services; Child welfare.
Type of support: General support; Continuing support; Annual campaigns; Capital campaigns; Capital and infrastructure.
Limitations: Applications not accepted. Giving primarily in MO. No grants to individuals or national charities.
Application information: Contributes only to pre-selected organizations.
Trustees: Daniel A. Graham; Herbert S. Jones; Barbara P. Lawton; Judy Moskoff; Dave White.
Number of staff: None.
EIN: 436027517

4916
Gershman Foundation
(formerly Gershman Charitable Trust)
150 Carondelet Plz., Ste. 2201
Saint Louis, MO   63105-3436

Established in 1986 in Missouri.
Donors: Gershman Investment Corp.; Bettie Gershman.
Foundation type: Independent foundation.
Financial data (yr. ended 11/30/13): Assets, $7,182,939 (M); expenditures, $253,507; qualifying distributions, $230,258; giving activities include $227,586 for 89 grants (high: $140,200; low: $50).
Purpose and activities: Giving primarily for Jewish federated giving programs, the arts, and health organizations.
Fields of interest: Health; Judaism; Human services.
Limitations: Applications not accepted. Giving primarily in St. Louis, MO. No grants to individuals.

Application information: Unsolicited requests for funds not accepted.
Trustees: Bettie Gershman; Diane L. Levine; Jeffrey S. Gershman; Karen G. Stern.
EIN: 431431049

4917
The Gilbert Foundation
(formerly The W. A. Gilbert Family Foundation)
609 S. Warson Rd.
Saint Louis, MO   63124-1254

Established in 1995 in Missouri.
Donors: William A. Gilbert; Helen A. Gilbert; Eric Gilbert; Sara Gilbert.
Foundation type: Independent foundation.
Financial data (yr. ended 12/31/13): Assets, $1,222,550 (M); gifts received, $66,605; expenditures, $223,615; qualifying distributions, $213,836; giving activities include $147,500 for 8 grants (high: $50,000; low: $1,500), and $64,000 for 6 grants to individuals (high: $15,000; low: $4,000).
Purpose and activities: Scholarship awards for educational advancement, including scholarships to dependent children of employees of Landscape Brands, Inc. and Upbeat, Inc.
Fields of interest: Arts and culture; Education.
Type of support: General support; Student aid.
Limitations: Applications accepted. Giving primarily in MN and MO.
Application information: Scholarship applications accepted from specific companies only. Application form required.
Initial approach: Proposal
Deadline(s): May
Trustees: Eric N. Gilbert; Helen A. Gilbert; Sara E. Gilbert; William A. Gilbert.
EIN: 431730251

4918
Elberth Reuben & Gladys Flora Grant Charitable Trust
c/o Commerce Trust Co.
8000 Forsyth Blvd.
P.O. Box 11356
Clayton, MO   63105-1707   (314) 746-7322
Contact: Cindy M. Lewis, V.P. and Trust Officer, Commerce Trust Co.

Established in 1987 in Missouri.
Donors: Gladys Flora Grant†; E. Reuben Grant†.
Foundation type: Independent foundation.
Financial data (yr. ended 07/31/13): Assets, $5,790,720 (M); expenditures, $351,523; qualifying distributions, $314,025; giving activities include $305,000 for 27 grants (high: $38,000; low: $3,000).
Purpose and activities: Giving primarily for higher education, human services, and the arts.
Fields of interest: Arts and culture; Education; Higher education; Environment; Protestantism; Human services; Youth development; People with disabilities.
Type of support: General support; Annual campaigns; Capital campaigns; Capital and infrastructure; Curriculum development.
Limitations: Applications accepted. Giving primarily in the greater St. Louis, MO area. No grants to individuals.

Application information: Guidelines will be faxed to applicants.
Initial approach: Letter
Deadline(s): July 31
Board meeting date(s): June and Nov.
Trustee: Commerce Trust Co.
EIN: 436332172

4919
Grassmere Foundation
801 W. 47th St., Ste. 400
Kansas City, MO   64112-1253   (816) 531-0708
Contact: Peter C. Brown, Pres. and Secy.-Treas.

Donors: Peter C. Brown; Kathleen T. Brown.
Foundation type: Independent foundation.
Financial data (yr. ended 12/31/13): Assets, $1,114,437 (M); expenditures, $196,583; qualifying distributions, $196,043; giving activities include $156,583 for 13 grants (high: $50,000; low: $1,000).
Fields of interest: Arts and culture; Education; Community and economic development.
Limitations: Applications accepted. Giving primarily in MO.
Application information: Application form required.
Initial approach: Proposal
Deadline(s): None
Officers and Directors: Peter C. Brown, Pres. and Secy.-Treas. and Director; Kathleen T. Brown, Exec. V.P. and Director; Peter C. Brown, Jr., V.P., Opers. and Director.
EIN: 270573550

4920
Green Family Foundation
9986 Manchester Rd.
Saint Louis, MO   63122-1934

Established in 2007 in Missouri.
Donor: Thomas Green.
Foundation type: Independent foundation.
Financial data (yr. ended 12/31/13): Assets, $8,222,451 (M); gifts received, $1,000,050; expenditures, $353,120; qualifying distributions, $275,050; giving activities include $274,500 for 24 grants (high: $50,000; low: $500).
Fields of interest: Higher education; Nonprofits; Judaism.
Type of support: General support; Regranting.
Limitations: Applications not accepted. Giving primarily in CA, FL and MO.
Application information: Unsolicited requests for funds not accepted.
Trustees: Thomas R. Green, Jr.; Linda R. Renner; Katherine A. Weber.
EIN: 326062139

4921
Griffin Family Foundation, Inc.
100 N. Jefferson St.
Mexico, MO   65265-3786   (573) 581-5280
Contact: Dan K. Erdel, Tr.

Established in 1998 in Missouri.
Donor: Anna Margaret Griffin.
Foundation type: Independent foundation.
Financial data (yr. ended 12/31/13): Assets, $5,623,471 (M); expenditures, $253,194; qualifying distributions, $238,108; giving activities

include $216,114 for 27 grants (high: $49,780; low: $464).
Fields of interest: Higher education.
Type of support: Student aid.
Limitations: Applications accepted. Giving primarily to residents of MO, with emphasis on Mexico, Moberly, and Springfield.
Application information: Application form required.
  Initial approach: Contact Foundation
  Deadline(s): None
Trustee: Dan K. Erdel.
Directors: Ruth Kent; Virginia Pehle; Ben Steinman; James Shemwell.
EIN: 431822804

4922
Anna M. Guilander Scholarship Trust
c/o First Bank Wealth Management
135 N. Meramec 3rd Fl.
Clayton, MO 63105-3751

Donor: Robert M. Guilander Trust.
Foundation type: Independent foundation.
Financial data (yr. ended 10/30/14): Assets, $5,749,722 (M); expenditures, $342,482; qualifying distributions, $238,015; giving activities include $238,015 for 49 grants to individuals (high: $15,000; low: $2,000).
Purpose and activities: Support for graduating seniors of Jersey Community Unit School District 100 H.S. who will be attending a college, university or trade school.
Fields of interest: Education.
Type of support: Student aid.
Limitations: Applications not accepted. Giving primarily in IL.
Application information: Contributes only to pre-selected organizations.
Trustees: Darlene Ward; Robert Guilander.
EIN: 271847433

4923
Lottie C. Hardy Trust
P.O. Box 387
Saint Louis, MO 63166-0387

Established in 1994 in Missouri.
Foundation type: Operating foundation.
Financial data (yr. ended 01/31/13): Assets, $3,211,768 (M); expenditures, $231,039; qualifying distributions, $167,758; giving activities include $157,700 for 3 grants (high: $101,735; low: $16,540).
Fields of interest: Medical education.
Limitations: Applications not accepted. Giving limited to MO. No grants to individuals.
Application information: Unsolicited requests for funds not accepted.
Trustee: U.S. Bank, N.A.
EIN: 436239401

4924
HB Oppenheimer Foundation
P.O. Box 946
Lee's Summit, MO 64063-0946

Foundation type: Independent foundation.
Financial data (yr. ended 12/31/13): Assets, $4,540,884 (M); expenditures, $342,199; qualifying distributions, $233,170; giving activities include $203,000 for 7 grants (high: $102,000; low: $2,000).
Fields of interest: Education; Religion; Human services.
Limitations: Applications not accepted. Giving primarily in MO.
Application information: Unsolicited requests for funds not accepted.
Officers: Hal Oppenheimer, Pres.; Alexis Oppenheimer, V.P.; Leo Oppenheimer, Treas.
EIN: 461474181

4925
HCG, Jr. Family Foundation
302 Hampshire Hill
Saint Louis, MO 63141-7207

Established in 2008 in Missouri.
Donors: Marilyn W. Griesedieck; Henry C. Griesedieck III; Paul H. Griesedieck; American Pulverizer, Inc.; Hustler Conveyor Company.
Foundation type: Independent foundation.
Financial data (yr. ended 12/31/13): Assets, $0 (M); gifts received, $881,103; expenditures, $388,342; qualifying distributions, $311,000; giving activities include $311,000 for 18 grants (high: $250,000; low: $1,000).
Fields of interest: Christianity.
Limitations: Applications not accepted. Giving primarily in MO.
Application information: Unsolicited requests for funds not accepted.
Officers: Marilyn W. Griesedieck, Pres.; Henry C. Griesedieck III, Secy.; Paul H. Griesedieck, Treas.
EIN: 263694769

4926
Florence Heiman Charitable Remainder Trust
(formerly Florence Heiman Private Foundation)
7409 Manchester Rd.
Saint Louis, MO 63143-3031

Established in 2002 in Missouri.
Donor: Florence Heiman Charitable Remainder Trust.
Foundation type: Independent foundation.
Financial data (yr. ended 12/31/14): Assets, $3,240,502; expenditures, $289,679; qualifying distributions, $253,557.
Fields of interest: Education; University education; Nonprofits; Judaism; Human services.
Type of support: Regranting.
Limitations: Applications not accepted. Giving primarily in MO. No grants to individuals.
Application information: Contributes only to pre-selected organizations.
Trustee: Isaac Young.
EIN: 900122117

4927
The Lilly Christy Busch Hermann Charitable Foundation
7701 Forsyth Blvd., 10th Fl.
Saint Louis, MO 63105-1818
Contact: Robert R. Hermann Jr., Tr.

Established in 1995 in Missouri.
Donor: Harbor Fund.
Foundation type: Independent foundation.

Financial data (yr. ended 12/31/13): Assets, $4,943,671 (M); expenditures, $320,602; qualifying distributions, $282,155; giving activities include $282,155 for 117 grants (high: $100,000; low: $50).
Purpose and activities: Giving for art and cultural programs, including theatres, museums, and orchestras; giving also for education, environmental conservation, and human services.
Fields of interest: Theater; Orchestral music; Museums; Elementary and secondary education; Higher education; Environment; Specialty hospital care; Protestantism; Special population support.
Limitations: Applications accepted. Giving primarily in St. Louis, MO. No support for political organizations. No grants to individuals.
Application information: Application form required.
  Initial approach: Letter
  Deadline(s): None
Trustees: Robert R. Hermann, Jr.; Carlota H. Holton.
EIN: 436543271

4928
Herschend Family Foundation
c/o Herschend Family Entertainment Corp.
100 Corporate Pl.
Branson, MO 65616-9100   (417) 334-0140
Contact: Austin Herschend

Established in 1985 in Missouri.
Donor: Jack R. Herschend.
Foundation type: Independent foundation.
Financial data (yr. ended 12/31/13): Assets, $3,345,687 (M); gifts received, $500; expenditures, $422,215; qualifying distributions, $405,008; giving activities include $402,506 for 65 grants (high: $168,756; low: $36).
Purpose and activities: Giving limited to Christian organizations, including churches and ministries to support family and social services, such as child welfare and development.
Fields of interest: Child educational development; Christianity; Protestantism; Human services; Family services; Child welfare; Child development; Low-income and poor people.
Limitations: Applications accepted. Giving limited to the Tri-Lakes area in southern MO, including Stone and Taney counties.
Application information: Application form required.
  Initial approach: Proposal
  Deadline(s): None
  Board meeting date(s): 3rd Tues. of Jan. and Sept.
Officers and Directors: Austin Herschend, Pres. and Director; James R. Herschend, V.P. and Director; Tiffany Herschend, Secy. and Director; Ronald Herschend, Treas. and Director.
Number of staff: None.
EIN: 431391940

4929
Hofheimer Charitable Trust
1 Ward Pkwy.
Kansas City, MO 64112 6606468500
Application address: Country Club Trust Co., P.O. Box 410889, Kansas City, MO 64141, tel.: (816) 279-6000

Established in 2001 in Missouri.
Foundation type: Independent foundation.

Financial data (yr. ended 12/31/14): Assets, $3,621,317; expenditures, $207,738; qualifying distributions, $176,000.
Fields of interest: Arts and culture; Nonprofits; Judaism; Interfaith; Human services; Food banks; Cemeteries and burial services.
Type of support: Regranting.
Limitations: Applications accepted. Giving primarily in Buchanan County, MO, and any adjacent county. No grants to individuals.
Application information:
  Initial approach: Proposal
  Deadline(s): None
Trustee: Country Club Trust Co.
EIN: 431935768

4930
Impact Group Charitable Foundation
12977 N. Outer 40 Dr., Ste. 300
Saint Louis, MO 63141-8656

Donor: Lauren Herring.
Foundation type: Independent foundation.
Financial data (yr. ended 12/31/13): Assets, $2,517,719 (M); expenditures, $168,791; qualifying distributions, $156,700; giving activities include $156,700 for 32 grants (high: $30,000; low: $100).
Fields of interest: Arts and culture; Education; Youth development.
Limitations: Applications not accepted. Giving primarily in MO.
Application information: Unsolicited requests for funds not accepted.
Officers: J. Michael Herring, Pres.; Laura Herring, Secy.; Lauren Herring, Treas.
EIN: 263602542

4931
Innovative Technology Education Fund
(formerly Humanities Instructional Television Educational Center)
7201 Delmar Blvd., Ste. 202
Saint Louis, MO 63130-4106 (314) 725-4833
E-mail: itef@innovteched.com; *Main URL:* http://innovteched.com
Grants List: http://innovteched.com/grants-we-give

Established in 1986 in Missouri.
Foundation type: Independent foundation.
Financial data (yr. ended 12/31/13): Assets, $6,588,897 (M); expenditures, $604,173; qualifying distributions, $529,842; giving activities include $301,811 for 5 grants (high: $108,723; low: $22,537).
Purpose and activities: The Innovative Technology Education Fund (ITEF) offers a competitive grant program for schools located within the Greater St. Louis area. It invites accredited K-12 educational institutions and their classroom educators to apply for a grant. Successful projects bring innovative learning to life through the integration of technology. ITEF supports leading edge, outside of the box ideas and models that positively impact student learning and support classroom educators by focusing on: (1) Student Achievement: Students reach new levels of educational success with the integration of technology to support a strong technology based curriculum, (2) Mobile / Extended Learning: Using technology to extend and enhance learning outside of the traditional classroom, and (3) Technology Skill

Development: Projects that support students and teachers in developing the skills and knowledge needed to function in and contribute to a technology-rich society.
Fields of interest: Education.
Limitations: Applications accepted. Giving limited to the bi-state St. Louis region.
Publications: Application guidelines.
Application information: Online application form required. See Fund web site for full application guidelines. Application form required.
  Initial approach: Use online application system on Fund web site
  Copies of proposal: 1
  Deadline(s): See Fund web site for specific dates
Officers and Directors: Tracy Toft Downing, Chair. and Director; Brenda Watt, Vice-Chair. and Director; Anne E. Dill, Secy. and Director; Joseph P. Komos, Treas. and Director; Beth Bender, Ph.D; Kathryn Kiefer.
Number of staff: 2
EIN: 431689900

4932
J. C. K. Family Foundation
4900 Main St., Ste. 700
Kansas City, MO 64112-1707

Donors: Curtis A. Krizek; Jennifer S. Krizek; Jas Trust.
Foundation type: Independent foundation.
Financial data (yr. ended 12/31/13): Assets, $854,980 (M); gifts received, $254,582; expenditures, $149,538; qualifying distributions, $140,560; giving activities include $140,560 for 13 grants (high: $25,000; low: $1,000).
Fields of interest: Education; Sports and recreation; Human services.
Limitations: Applications not accepted. Giving primarily in KS and MO. No grants to individuals.
Application information: Unsolicited requests for funds not accepted.
Trustees: Curtis A. Krizek; Jennifer S. Krizek.
EIN: 431533935

4933
JMG Foundation
P.O. Box 775280
Saint Louis, MO 63177-5280

Donors: John J. Hake; Matthew D. Hake; Gregory A. Hake; Gregory A. Have Irrevocable Trust.
Foundation type: Independent foundation.
Financial data (yr. ended 12/31/13): Assets, $11,100,030 (M); gifts received, $3,000,000; expenditures, $284,609; qualifying distributions, $250,000; giving activities include $250,000 for 3 grants (high: $150,000; low: $50,000).
Fields of interest: Religion.
Limitations: Applications not accepted. Giving primarily in IL and MO.
Application information: Unsolicited requests for funds not accepted.
Officer and Directors: John J. Hake, Pres. and Director; Gregory A. Hake; Matthew D. Hake; Mark Z. Schraier.
EIN: 273017668

4934
Gene Kauffman Scholarship Foundation, Inc.
P.O. Box 113
Princeton, MO 64673-0113
Contact: Angela Ormsby, Pres.

Established in 1998 in Missouri.
Donor: Gene Kauffman Scholarship Foundation Trust.
Foundation type: Independent foundation.
Financial data (yr. ended 06/30/13): Assets, $986 (M); gifts received, $229,283; expenditures, $231,555; qualifying distributions, $225,499; giving activities include $225,499 for grants.
Purpose and activities: Awards financial assistance for attendance at a Missouri college to unmarried female non-smokers who have graduated from a Mercer County, MO, high school.
Fields of interest: Education; Females.
Type of support: Student aid.
Limitations: Applications accepted. Giving limited to residents of Mercer County, MO. No support for home schooling.
Application information: Application form required.
  Initial approach: Proposal
  Deadline(s): None
  Board meeting date(s): Aug.
Officers: Angela Ormsby, Pres.; Ann Stanley, Secy.-Treas.
Directors: Wendel Myers; Kim Palmer; Betty Ann Shaffer.
Number of staff: 1 part-time support.
EIN: 431825689

4935
William T. Kemper II Charitable Trust
c/o Commerce Bank, N.A.
118 W. 47th St.
Kansas City, MO 64112-1601 (816) 234-2568
Contact: Christopher G. Blair

Established in 1988 in Missouri.
Foundation type: Independent foundation.
Financial data (yr. ended 03/31/13): Assets, $4,816,399 (M); expenditures, $267,981; qualifying distributions, $234,815; giving activities include $210,750 for 35 grants (high: $30,000; low: $1,000).
Purpose and activities: Giving primarily for education and human services.
Fields of interest: Arts and culture; Education; Elementary and secondary education; Hospital care; Human services; Adult and child mentoring.
Limitations: Applications accepted. Giving primarily in Kansas City, MO; some giving in KS. No grants to individuals.
Application information: Application form required.
  Initial approach: Telephone
  Deadline(s): None
Trustees: Robert W. Loyd; Commerce Bank, N.A.
EIN: 436337610

4936
Norma J. and William J. Kenney Charitable Foundation
P.O. Box 387
Saint Louis, MO 63166-0387

Foundation type: Independent foundation.

Financial data (yr. ended 12/31/14): Assets, $3,958,378; expenditures, $267,013; qualifying distributions, $211,241.
Fields of interest: Education; Housing development; Human services.
Limitations: Applications not accepted. Giving primarily in MO.
Application information: Unsolicited requests for funds not accepted.
Trustee: US Bank, N.A.
EIN: 204704256

4937
David G. and Karen H. Keske Charitable Trust
4387 N. Rider Trail
Earth City, MO   63045-1103

Donor: David G. Kerke.
Foundation type: Independent foundation.
Financial data (yr. ended 12/31/12): Assets, $222,699 (M); expenditures, $176,075; qualifying distributions, $176,075; giving activities include $176,075 for 3 grants (high: $100,000; low: $25,000).
Fields of interest: Education; Protestantism.
Limitations: Applications not accepted. Giving primarily in MO and OH.
Application information: Unsolicited requests for funds not accepted.
Officers: David G. Keske, Pres.; Karen A. Keske, Treas.
EIN: 204449820

4938
The Theodore A. Kienstra Foundation
c/o Theodore A. Kienstra, Jr
755 S. New Ballas Rd., Ste. 150
Saint Louis, MO   63141-8797

Donors: Theodore A. Kienstra, Jr.; Theodore A. Kienstra, Sr.; H. Diekemper Trust; Tony Soukenik.
Foundation type: Independent foundation.
Financial data (yr. ended 12/31/14): Assets, $6,898,244 (M); gifts received, $6,200; expenditures, $447,096; qualifying distributions, $419,860; giving activities include $419,350 for 65 grants (high: $102,500; low: $250).
Fields of interest: Elementary education; Catholicism.
Limitations: Applications not accepted. Giving primarily in MO. No grants to individuals.
Application information: Unsolicited requests for funds not accepted.
Officers: Theodore A. Kienstra, Jr., Pres.; Daniel Bruns, V.P.; Anthony J. Soukenik, Secy.; Patrick Wessels, Treas.
Board Members: Christina L. Kienstra; Faith Kienstra; Genevieve Casagrande; Kathleen Bruns; Kimberly McDonough.
EIN: 431727300

4939
William Toben King Educational Trust
320 Robidoux Ctr.
Saint Joseph, MO   64501-1736
Application address: c/o Commerce Trust Company, Att.: Lori Boyer, St. Joseph, MO 64501, tel.: (816) 236-5751

Established in 1991 in Missouri.
Donor: William Toben King.
Foundation type: Independent foundation.
Financial data (yr. ended 09/30/14): Assets, $8,323,434 (M); expenditures, $414,422; qualifying distributions, $340,878; giving activities include $330,150 for 37 grants (high: $134,575; low: $250).
Purpose and activities: Scholarships awarded to high school seniors of Buchanan and Andrew counties, Missouri, to obtain a college degree.
Fields of interest: Higher education.
Type of support: Student aid.
Limitations: Applications accepted. Giving limited to residents of Buchanan and Andrew counties, MO.
Application information:
   Initial approach: Letter
   Deadline(s): June 1
Trustees: James Counts; Pat Conway; Doug Flowers; Karen Woodbury.
EIN: 431582893

4940
Harvey Kornblum Foundation
190 Carondelet Plz., Ste. 600
Clayton, MO   63105-3433   (314) 480-1500

Donors: Harvey Kornblum; Michael J. Silver.
Foundation type: Independent foundation.
Financial data (yr. ended 12/31/14): Assets, $6,318,108; expenditures, $285,861; qualifying distributions, $231,277.
Fields of interest: Arts and culture; Education; Nonprofits.
Type of support: General support; Regranting.
Limitations: Applications accepted. Giving primarily in St. Louis, MO.
Application information:
   Initial approach: Proposal
   Deadline(s): None
Officers and Directors: Michael J. Silver, Chair. and Director; Kathy Kornblum, Pres. and Director; Gay Klearman Kornblum, V.P. and Director; Clare Tropp, V.P. and Director; Laura Klearman Silver, Secy.-Tres. and Director; Ann Mandelstamm.
EIN: 431697637

4941
Kuhn Foundation
4568 Meramec Bottom Rd., Ste. 6
Saint Louis, MO   63128   (314) 845-7700
Contact: Thomas E. Kuhn, Pres.

Established in 2005 in Missouri.
Foundation type: Independent foundation.
Financial data (yr. ended 05/31/13): Assets, $8,520,270 (M); expenditures, $437,247; qualifying distributions, $379,905; giving activities include $367,357 for 49 grants (high: $178,700; low: $50).
Fields of interest: Education; Zoos; Nonprofits; Judaism; Human services.
Type of support: Regranting.
Limitations: Applications accepted. Giving primarily in MO.
Application information: Application form required.
   Initial approach: Letter
   Deadline(s): None
Officer and Directors: Thomas E. Kuhn, Pres. and Director; Michael J. Kuhn; Steven L. Kuhn.
EIN: 203067498

4942
Joe and Lenore Lambert Foundation
P.O. Box 620
Chillicothe, MO   64601-0620

Established in 1991 in Missouri.
Donors: Lenore Lambert; Lenore Lambert Trust.
Foundation type: Independent foundation.
Financial data (yr. ended 12/31/13): Assets, $7,958,549 (M); gifts received, $153; expenditures, $316,020; qualifying distributions, $301,460; giving activities include $293,000 for 15 grants (high: $100,000; low: $2,500).
Fields of interest: Education; Specialty hospital care; Protestantism.
Limitations: Applications not accepted. Giving primarily in MO. No grants to individuals.
Application information: Contributes only to pre-selected organizations.
Officers: Michael F. Turner, Pres.; Thomas J. Ashbrook, V.P.; Laura Sue Daniels, Secy.-Treas.
EIN: 431578457

4943
Larson Financial Foundation
2501 S. Jefferson Ave.
Saint Louis, MO   63104-2307
E-mail: info@larson-foundation.com; Main
URL: http://www.larsonfinancialfoundation.com

Donors: Paul D. Larson; The Larson Financial Foundation.
Foundation type: Independent foundation.
Financial data (yr. ended 12/31/13): Assets, $2,472,068 (M); gifts received, $2,761,538; expenditures, $353,866; qualifying distributions, $342,039; giving activities include $205,000 for 2 grants (high: $175,000; low: $30,000).
Fields of interest: Economic development; Human services.
International interests: Mauritius.
Limitations: Applications not accepted. Giving primarily in TX; with some giving to Mauritius.
Application information: Unsolicited requests for funds not accepted.
Officer: John Peters, Exec. Dir.
Directors: Andy Kim; Paul D. Larson.
EIN: 383893553

4944
Edward & Thea Lawton Foundation
7215 Creveling Dr.
Saint Louis, MO   63130-4124

Established in 1991 in Missouri.
Foundation type: Independent foundation.
Financial data (yr. ended 03/31/13): Assets, $1,573,836 (M); expenditures, $183,319; qualifying distributions, $178,350; giving activities include $178,350 for 50 grants (high: $50,000; low: $50).
Fields of interest: Education; Religion; Judaism; Human services.
Limitations: Applications not accepted. Giving limited to MO. No grants to individuals.
Application information: Unsolicited requests for funds not accepted.
Trustees: Martha G. Aronson; Evelyn B. Goldberg; Miriam Wilhelm.
EIN: 431580512

4945
John and Mary Jane Lee Charitable Foundation
c/o U.S. Bank, N.A.
10 N. Hanley Rd.
Clayton, MO 63105 (314) 505-8204
Contact: Private Client Reserve

Foundation type: Independent foundation.
Financial data (yr. ended 10/31/13): Assets, $3,154,393 (M); expenditures, $384,421; qualifying distributions, $337,146; giving activities include $330,000 for 10 grants (high: $100,000; low: $5,000).
Purpose and activities: The purpose of the John & Mary Jane Lee Charitable Foundation is to award grants to Orthodox Catholic educational, charitable, and religious institutions that follow and preserve the traditional and orthodox teachings of the Roman Catholic Church.
Limitations: Applications accepted. Giving limited to organizations located in MO. No grants to individuals.
Application information: Application form required.
Trustee: U.S. Bank, N.A.
Committee Members: Donald Binz; James Hitchcock; Michael Houser; Gregory Kirsch.
EIN: 266700047

4946
Jerry Litton Family Memorial Foundation
P.O. Box 695
Chillicothe, MO 64601-0695

Donors: Mildred K. Litton; Mildred Litton Revocable Trust.
Foundation type: Independent foundation.
Financial data (yr. ended 07/31/14): Assets, $4,133,514 (M); expenditures, $459,121; qualifying distributions, $395,660; giving activities include $359,638 for 13 grants (high: $100,000; low: $1,000).
Fields of interest: Education; Higher education; Agriculture for youth.
Type of support: General support.
Limitations: Applications not accepted. Giving limited to Chillicothe, MO. No grants to individuals.
Application information: Contributes only to pre-selected organizations.
Officers: Lynn Hoover, Pres.; Edwin Turner, V.P.; Bonnie Mitchell, Secy.-Treas.
Directors: Rusty Black; Julie Bothwell; Don Chapman; Alvin Cohen; Merle Doughty; Laura Lee Gayfield; Bill Jackson; Lowell Mohler; E.L. Reed; Lauri Mitchell Shemwell; James Summerville; Eric Turner; James P. Valbracht; Larry Warren; Ron Wolf; Kristi Smith Wyatt.
EIN: 431092779

4947
John Sublett Logan Foundation Inc.
c/o Stephen Briggs
400 Jules St., Ste. 320
Saint Joseph, MO 64501-1736

Established in 1961 in Missouri.
Donors: Thomas A. Logan†; Sheridan A. Logan.
Foundation type: Independent foundation.
Financial data (yr. ended 12/31/13): Assets, $5,839,863 (M); expenditures, $403,815; qualifying distributions, $389,217; giving activities

include $333,000 for 6 grants (high: $90,000; low: $20,000).
Fields of interest: Higher education; Business education; Law education.
Type of support: Scholarships.
Limitations: Applications not accepted. Giving primarily in MO. No grants to individuals.
Application information: Contributes only to pre-selected organizations.
Directors: Stephen Briggs; William Carpenter, Jr.; Brian Dickens; William Mytton; E. Pat Speiser.
EIN: 436054176

4948
R. A. Long Foundation
600 Plaza W. Bldg.
4600 Madison Ave.
Kansas City, MO 64112-3012 (816) 410-4600
Contact: James H. Bernard Jr., Dir.

Established in 1958 in Missouri.
Donors: Loula Long Combs†; Sally Long Ellis†; R.A. Long Ellis†.
Foundation type: Independent foundation.
Financial data (yr. ended 11/30/13): Assets, $7,575,530 (M); expenditures, $478,315; qualifying distributions, $430,251; giving activities include $343,000 for 78 grants (high: $13,000; low: $1,500), and $1,000 for 2 employee matching gifts.
Purpose and activities: Giving limited to services for youth, including the areas of child welfare, recreation, rehabilitation, and education, all of which must be in the greater Kansas City, MO, area.
Fields of interest: Elementary and secondary education; Child welfare; Youth development; Youth services; Youth organizing.
Type of support: General support; Pro bono consulting services; Capital campaigns; Capital and infrastructure; Equipment; Program development; Seed money.
Limitations: Applications accepted. Giving limited to the greater Kansas City, MO, area. No grants to individuals, or for endowment funds, research programs, scholarships, or fellowships; no loans.
Publications: Application guidelines.
Application information:
Initial approach: Letter or telephone
Copies of proposal: 1
Deadline(s): Mar. 15 and Sept. 15
Board meeting date(s): Spring and fall
Final notification: Within 1 week of board meeting
Directors: James H. Bernard, Sr.; James H. Bernard, Jr.; Enid Chetham; Hayne Ellis III; Long Ellis, Jr.; Linna Place; James Pyle; Ann J. Thompson; Lois Uihlein.
Number of staff: None.
EIN: 446014081

4949
Longer Life Foundation
1370 Timberlake Manor Pkwy.
Chesterfield, MO 63017-6039
Contact: Philip S. Smalley MD, Managing Dir.
E-mail: psmalley@rgare.com; Application address: 161 Bay St., Ste. 4600, P.O. Box 620, Toronto, Ontario, Canada M5J 2S1, tel.: (416) 943-6797, fax: (416) 943-0880; Additional contact: Joan Heins, tel.: (314) 286-1912, e-mail:

jheins@dom.wustl.edu; Main URL: http://www.longerlife.org
Grants List: http://www.longerlife.org/current_research.htm

Established in 1998 in Missouri.
Donor: Reinsurance Group of America, Inc.
Foundation type: Company-sponsored foundation.
Financial data (yr. ended 12/31/13): Assets, $64,561 (M); gifts received, $400,000; expenditures, $401,671; qualifying distributions, $401,671; giving activities include $387,008 for 1 grant.
Purpose and activities: The foundation supports programs designed to study factors that assist in predicting mortality and morbidity of selected populations; and research methods to promote improvements in longevity and health by analyzing the effects of changes in medicine and advances in public health practices.
Fields of interest: Public health; Diseases and conditions.
Type of support: Research; Research and evaluation.
Limitations: Applications accepted. Giving primarily in St. Louis, MO.
Publications: Application guidelines; Grants list.
Application information: Letters of intent should be no longer than 1 to 2 pages. Applicants should also submit an NIH-format biographical sketch. A full application may be requested at a later date.
Initial approach: E-mail letter of intent
Deadline(s): Feb. 20
Final notification: Apr. 20
Officers and Directors: A. Greig Woodring, Chair. and Director; Larry Shapiro, MD, Vice-Chair. and Director; Sara McCarty, Secy.; Jeffrey Boyer, Treas.
EIN: 431819267

4950
The Lordi Marker Family Foundation
1216 W. 57th Terr.
Kansas City, MO 64113-1172 (816) 444-0330
Contact: Dennis C. Marker, Dir.

Established in 2005 in Missouri.
Donors: Susan Lordi Marker; Dennis C. Marker.
Foundation type: Independent foundation.
Financial data (yr. ended 12/31/13): Assets, $5,071,225 (M); gifts received, $500,000; expenditures, $202,590; qualifying distributions, $198,710; giving activities include $197,500 for 27 grants (high: $55,000; low: $2,500).
Fields of interest: Orchestral music; Specialty hospital care; Human services.
Type of support: Capital campaigns.
Limitations: Applications accepted. Giving primarily in MO.
Application information: Application form required.
Initial approach: Letter
Deadline(s): Jan. 1- Dec. 31
Directors: David Marker; Dennis C. Marker; Sara Lordi Marker; Susan Lordi Marker.
EIN: 203406848

4951
John Allan Love Charitable Foundation
c/o Brad Landsbaum
8000 Forsyth Blvd.
Saint Louis, MO   63105-1807
Application address: c/o John T. Saint, Jr., 7700
Forsyth Blvd., Ste. 1800, St. Louis, MO 63105,
tel.: (314) 621-5070

Established in 1966 in Missouri.
Donor: John Allan Love Trusts.
Foundation type: Independent foundation.
Financial data (yr. ended 12/31/13): Assets,
$3,369,554 (M); expenditures, $210,848;
qualifying distributions, $174,950; giving activities
include $174,950 for 20 grants (high: $20,000;
low: $5,000).
Fields of interest: Education; Zoos; Diseases and
conditions; Human services; Youth development;
People with disabilities.
Type of support: Research; Research and
evaluation.
Limitations: Applications accepted. Giving primarily
in St. Louis, MO.
Application information:
   Initial approach: Proposal
   Deadline(s): Aug. 31
Officers: Parker B. Condie, Pres.; Jack E. Thomas,
1st V.P.; Martin E. Galt III, 2nd V.P.; Robert H.
Quenon, Treas.
Director: John McKinney.
EIN: 436066121

4952
Maor Foundation
7701 Forsyth Blvd., Ste. 600
Clayton, MO   63105-1875   (314) 889-0890
Contact: Cheryl Ann Fox, Tr.
E-mail: maor@foxfamilyoffice.com

Established in 2004 in Missouri.
Donors: Sam Fox; Cheryl Ann Fox.
Foundation type: Independent foundation.
Financial data (yr. ended 12/31/13): Assets,
$9,505,937 (M); gifts received, $1,766,108;
expenditures, $312,700; qualifying distributions,
$307,700; giving activities include $307,700 for 12
grants (high: $76,300; low: $1,500).
Fields of interest: Education; Medical education;
Nonprofits; Hospital care; Judaism; Food banks;
International relations.
International interests: Israel.
Type of support: Policy, advocacy and systems
reform; Regranting.
Limitations: Applications not accepted. Giving
primarily in CA, Washington, DC, IL, NJ, and New
York, NY. No grants to individuals.
Application information: Contributes only to
pre-selected organizations.
Trustees: Cheryl Ann Fox; Avigail Goldgraber.
EIN: 421645906

4953
The Constance A. and Harry B. Mathews, Jr. Foundation
750 S. Hanley Rd., Apt. 54
Saint Louis, MO   63105-2695

Established in 1989 in Missouri.
Donors: Mathews Foundation; Margaret M. Jenks;
Harry B. Mathews.

Foundation type: Independent foundation.
Financial data (yr. ended 12/31/14): Assets,
$611,682 (M); expenditures, $203,701; qualifying
distributions, $201,800; giving activities include
$200,000 for 10 grants (high: $20,000; low:
$20,000).
Fields of interest: Christianity; Human services;
International relations.
Limitations: Applications not accepted. Giving
primarily in MO. No grants to individuals.
Application information: Unsolicited requests for
funds not accepted.
Trustees: Elizabeth Jenks Coggin; Margaret Jenks
Heckman; Margaret M. Jenks; Donald Smith.
EIN: 431509560

4954
Maxine Hillesland Charitable Foundation
P.O. Box 66916
Saint Louis, MO   63166-6916

Donor: Hillesland Charitable Trust.
Foundation type: Independent foundation.
Financial data (yr. ended 12/31/13): Assets,
$4,353,108 (M); expenditures, $202,449;
qualifying distributions, $165,600; giving activities
include $165,000 for 7 grants (high: $33,000; low:
$16,500).
Fields of interest: Education; Religion; Human
services.
Limitations: Applications not accepted. Giving
primarily in IA.
Application information: Unsolicited requests for
funds not accepted.
Trustee: Edward Jones Trust Company.
EIN: 376475504

4955
Louise D. McDonald Charitable Trust
P.O. Box 387
Saint Louis, MO   63166-0387
Application address: c/o Maria Stockton, 1615 S.
Glenstone Ave., Springfield, MO 65804-1505,
tel.: (417) 888-2207

Established in 1995 in Arkansas.
Foundation type: Independent foundation.
Financial data (yr. ended 08/31/13): Assets,
$283,997 (M); expenditures, $213,558; qualifying
distributions, $206,000; giving activities include
$205,000 for 2 grants (high: $200,000; low:
$5,000).
Fields of interest: Religion; Human services.
Type of support: General support.
Limitations: Applications accepted. Giving limited to
Little Rock, AR. No grants to individuals.
Application information: Application form required.
   Initial approach: Letter
   Deadline(s): None
Trustee: U.S. Bank, N.A.
EIN: 716163705

4956
Meda Scholarship Fund Trust
12555 Manchester Rd.
Saint Louis, MO   63131-3710

Donor: City of Mission.
Foundation type: Independent foundation.

Financial data (yr. ended 06/30/13): Assets,
$3,367,322 (M); gifts received, $3,321,935;
expenditures, $219,920; qualifying distributions,
$192,842; giving activities include $160,785 for 1
grant.
Fields of interest: Education.
Limitations: Applications not accepted. Giving
primarily in TX.
Application information: Unsolicited requests for
funds not accepted.
Trustee: Edward Jones Trust Co.
EIN: 376524304

4957
The Harold and Marilyn Melcher Foundation
800 W. 47th St., Ste. 720
Kansas City, MO   64112-1249

Donors: Marilyn B. Melcher; Harold S. Melcher;
Lynne F. Melcher; Richard A. Melcher; Laurie A.
Benjamin.
Foundation type: Independent foundation.
Financial data (yr. ended 12/31/13): Assets,
$729,394 (M); gifts received, $847,625;
expenditures, $358,560; qualifying distributions,
$352,681; giving activities include $352,681 for 24
grants (high: $251,300; low: $1,000).
Fields of interest: Animal welfare; Nonprofits;
Human services; Child welfare.
Type of support: Regranting.
Limitations: Applications not accepted. Giving
primarily in Kansas City, MO. No grants to
individuals.
Application information: Contributes only to
pre-selected organizations.
Officers and Directors: Harold Melcher, Fdn. Mgr.
and Director; Marilyn Melcher, Fdn. Mgr. and
Director; Randall D. Clark; Laurie Ann
Melcher-Benjamin; Lynne F. Melcher; Richard A.
Melcher; Steven N. Palmer.
EIN: 431671354

4958
Harry and Helena Messick Charitable Trust
P.O. Box 387
Saint Louis, MO   63166-0387

Donors: Helena Blanch Messick Charitable Trust;
Harry F. Messick Charitable Trust.
Foundation type: Independent foundation.
Financial data (yr. ended 12/31/13): Assets,
$4,018,805 (M); expenditures, $299,555;
qualifying distributions, $247,915; giving activities
include $240,583 for 38+ grants.
Fields of interest: Education; Human services.
Limitations: Applications not accepted. Giving
primarily in MO.
Application information: Unsolicited requests for
funds not accepted.
Trustee: US Bank, N.A.
EIN: 456676247

4959
Kenneth E. & Jane A. Meyer Foundation
3639 E. Kensington Way
Springfield, MO   65802-2470

Established in 1996 in Missouri.

Donors: Kenneth E. Meyer; Jane A. Meyer.
Foundation type: Independent foundation.
Financial data (yr. ended 12/31/12): Assets, $1,359,409 (M); gifts received, $120,000; expenditures, $313,118; qualifying distributions, $293,515; giving activities include $293,515 for grants.
Fields of interest: Education; University education; Christianity; Human services; Child welfare.
Limitations: Applications not accepted. Giving primarily in MO, with emphasis on Springfield. No grants to individuals.
Application information: Contributes only to pre-selected organizations.
 Board meeting date(s): Quarterly
Officers: Kenneth E. Meyer, Chair.; George C. Baldridge, Co-Vice-Chair.; Charles R. Meyer, Co-Vice-Chair.; Larry W. Meyer, Secy.; Curtis Graff, Treas.
EIN: 431771391

4960
MFA Oil Foundation

P.O. Box 519
Columbia, MO 65205-0519 (573) 876-0364
Application address: 201 Ray Young Dr., Columbia, MO 65201, tel.: (573) 876-0364

Donors: MFA Oil Co.; MFA Petroleum Company.
Foundation type: Company-sponsored foundation.
Financial data (yr. ended 08/31/14): Assets, $3,791,109 (M); gifts received, $400,637; expenditures, $193,047; qualifying distributions, $165,000; giving activities include $165,000 for 68 grants (high: $25,000; low: $800).
Purpose and activities: The foundation supports organizations involved with education, human services, civic affairs, and youth. Special emphasis is directed toward programs designed to build knowledge and leadership skills of rural youth; promote agricultural and cooperative education; and address and solve community problems and improve quality of life.
Fields of interest: Education; Public affairs; Human services; Adolescents.
Type of support: Scholarships; Building and renovations; Equipment; Program development.
Limitations: Applications accepted. Giving primarily in MO. No support for lobbying, political, or religious organizations, national organizations, or veterans', fraternal, or labor organizations. No grants to individuals, or for operating expenses, fundraising events, dinners, benefits, advertising, travel expenses, or sports sponsorships.
Publications: Application guidelines.
Application information: Application form required.
 Initial approach: Download application form and mail to foundation
 Deadline(s): None
Board Members: Kevin Bentley; Kevin Buckstead; Kenneth K. Caspall; Mark Fenner; Marion Kertz; Tom May; Clayton Uthe.
EIN: 431831800

4961
Mineral Area Osteopathic Foundation

c/o UMB Bank, N.A.
P.O. Box 415044, M/S 1020307
Kansas City, MO 64141-6692

Donor: Mineral Area Regional Medical Center.

Foundation type: Independent foundation.
Financial data (yr. ended 12/31/14): Assets, $7,289,407; expenditures, $435,483; qualifying distributions, $382,395.
Fields of interest: Education; University education; Medical education; Agriculture.
Limitations: Applications not accepted.
Application information: Unsolicited requests for funds not accepted.
Officer: Dwayne Damba, Pres.
Board Members: Victoria Damba; James Eaton; Lana L. Jinkerson; Marianne Klemm; James Moore; Richard Secor; Scott Vanness; Michael Zaricor.
EIN: 431535177

4962
Moneta Group Charitable Foundation

100 S. Brentwood Blvd., Ste. 500
Saint Louis, MO 63105 (314) 726-2300
Contact: Christie Schmuke
Main URL: http://www.monetagroup.com
Other: http://www.monetagroup.com/ Foundation.aspx

Established in 2000 in Missouri.
Donors: Peter G. Schick; Joe Sheehan; Joseph Sheehan; Donald T. Kula; Chandler Taylor; Daniel West; Tom O'Meara; Steve Finerty; Linda Pietroburgo; Don Kukla; Dave Sadler; Jim Blair; Michael Johnson; Tim Halls; Gene Diederich.
Foundation type: Company-sponsored foundation.
Financial data (yr. ended 12/31/13): Assets, $1,603,133 (M); gifts received, $181,631; expenditures, $259,189; qualifying distributions, $254,675; giving activities include $254,675 for 43 grants (high: $25,000; low: $1,000).
Purpose and activities: The foundation supports organizations involved with education, housing, human services, community development, senior citizens, economically disadvantaged people, and other areas.
Fields of interest: Education; Community and economic development; Housing development; Human services; Child welfare; Seniors; Low-income and poor people.
Limitations: Applications not accepted. Giving limited to St. Louis, MO, including the Metro East area. No support for churches or religious organizations not of direct benefit to the entire community, national organizations (except for local branches), or controversial organizations. No grants to individuals, or for fundraising events, endowments, debt reduction, general operating support for private or parochial schools, or start-up needs.
Application information: Contributes to organizations recommended by Moneta Group employees.
 Board meeting date(s): Feb., May, and Oct.
Officers: Chandler Taylor, Chair.; Daniel West, Treas.
Trustees: Gene Diederich; Donald T. Kukla; Doug Weber.
EIN: 431871586

4963
W. & E. Morgan Charitable Residual Trust

c/o CB& T
P.O. Box 70
Rock Port, MO 64482-0070 (660) 744-5333
Contact: Kymm Nuckolls; Jerry Moore

Established in 1988 in Missouri.
Donors: Warren Morgan†; Evalyn Morgan†.
Foundation type: Independent foundation.
Financial data (yr. ended 12/31/13): Assets, $6,501,251 (M); expenditures, $546,800; qualifying distributions, $310,038; giving activities include $280,925 for 77 grants (high: $34,500; low: $400), and $20,000 for 30 grants to individuals (high: $1,875; low: $625).
Purpose and activities: Support primarily to Atchison County, MO, non-profit organizations, including school districts, municipal agencies, churches, and community groups.
Fields of interest: Elementary and secondary education; Libraries; Fire prevention and control; Public affairs; Community and economic development; Protestantism; Cemeteries and burial services.
Type of support: General support; Capital campaigns; Program development.
Limitations: Applications accepted. Giving primarily in Atchison County, MO.
Application information:
 Initial approach: Letter
 Deadline(s): None
Trustees: Jody Ellison; Sharon Gaines; Kay Gibson; Tim Whelan; Citizens Bank & Trust.
EIN: 436347180

4964
Finis M. Moss Charitable Trust

108 W. Walnut St.
P.O. Box G
Nevada, MO 64772-2339 (417) 667-6616
Contact: Bryan Brekenridge, Tr.

Established in 1975 in Missouri.
Donor: Finis M. Moss†.
Foundation type: Independent foundation.
Financial data (yr. ended 12/31/13): Assets, $6,372,597 (M); expenditures, $412,056; qualifying distributions, $314,176; giving activities include $228,392 for 14 grants (high: $75,000; low: $1,500).
Purpose and activities: Giving primarily for education and community development.
Fields of interest: Education; Higher education; Cancers; Public libraries; Public administration; Community and economic development; Human services; Family services.
Type of support: General support; Capital campaigns.
Limitations: Applications accepted. Giving primarily in MO.
Application information: Application form required.
 Initial approach: Completed application Form
 Deadline(s): Jan. 31
Trustees: Bryan Breckenridge; Larry Forkner; Don Mills.
EIN: 237451729

4965
Judge C. F. Moulton Christmas Poor Fund

c/o Commerce Bank
118 W. 47th St.
Kansas City, MO 64112-1601

Established in 2008 in Missouri.
Foundation type: Independent foundation.

Financial data (yr. ended 03/31/13): Assets, $8,881,834 (M); expenditures, $560,861; qualifying distributions, $450,298; giving activities include $425,000 for 37 grants (high: $43,250; low: $2,500).
Fields of interest: Christianity; Human services.
Limitations: Applications not accepted. Giving primarily in MO.
Application information: Unsolicited requests for funds not accepted.
Trustee: Commerce Bank, N.A.
EIN: 436936927

4966
The David and Barbara Mungenast Foundation, Inc.

(formerly The Mungenast Foundation, Inc.)
5939 S. Lindbergh Blvd.
Saint Louis, MO 63123-7039
Main URL: http://www.mungenast.com/ Mungenast_Foundation.htm
Facebook: https://www.facebook.com/ MungenastAutomotiveFamily
Google Plus: https://plus.google.com/ 102879762827110904658/posts
Pinterest: http://www.pinterest.com/ mungenastauto
Twitter: https://twitter.com/MungenastAuto
YouTube: https://www.youtube.com/user/ MungenastAutomotive

Established in 1996 in Missouri.
Donors: David F. Mungenast; DDR Investment Co., Inc.; DRK Investment Co., Inc.; Capco Sales, Inc.; DFM Investment Co., Inc.; Mungenast Group Dealer Services; Barbara J. Mungenast; DAR, Inc.
Foundation type: Independent foundation.
Financial data (yr. ended 11/30/13): Assets, $4,399,465 (M); gifts received, $255,064; expenditures, $223,581; qualifying distributions, $218,124; giving activities include $216,700 for 10 grants (high: $74,000; low: $500), and $1,424 for 1 foundation-administered program.
Fields of interest: In-patient medical care; Hospice care; Human services; Food aid; Youth development.
Limitations: Applications not accepted. Giving primarily in St. Louis, MO. No grants to individuals.
Application information: Unsolicited requests for funds not accepted.
Officers: Raymond J. Mungenast, Secy.; David F. Mungenast, Jr., Treas.
Directors: Barbara J. Mungenast; Kurt A. Mungenast.
EIN: 431766152

4967
N.H. Corporation

211 N. Broadway, Ste. 3600
Saint Louis, MO 63102-2769

Donor: Laclede Gas Co.
Foundation type: Independent foundation.
Financial data (yr. ended 12/31/13): Assets, $484 (M); expenditures, $151,943; qualifying distributions, $150,000; giving activities include $150,000 for 1 grant.
Fields of interest: Education.
Limitations: Applications not accepted. Giving limited to St. Louis, MO. No grants to individuals.

Application information: Unsolicited requests for funds not accepted.
Officer and Directors: Walter L. Metcalfe, Jr., Pres and Director; Jim Hoagland.
EIN: 431395403

4968
The Neeb Family Foundation

1398 W. Adams Ave.
Saint Louis, MO 63122-3704

Established in 2004 in Missouri.
Donor: Larry W. Neeb.
Foundation type: Independent foundation.
Financial data (yr. ended 12/31/13): Assets, $4,953,907 (M); gifts received, $199,332; expenditures, $307,717; qualifying distributions, $278,445; giving activities include $278,445 for 41 grants (high: $47,765; low: $20).
Fields of interest: Education; Health; Christianity; Human services.
Limitations: Applications not accepted. Giving primarily in MO. No grants to individuals.
Application information: Contributes only to pre-selected organizations.
Officers: Larry W. Neeb, Pres. and Treas.; Kristina Williams, Secy.
Directors: Douglas M. Neeb; John M. Neeb; Martin J. Neeb.
EIN: 432067316

4969
Velma A. Neiman Charitable Foundation

c/o Walter Wittenberg
6434 Cecil Ave.
Clayton, MO 63105-2225

Established in 1988 in Missouri.
Donor: Velma A. Neiman†.
Foundation type: Independent foundation.
Financial data (yr. ended 12/31/13): Assets, $8,167,028 (M); expenditures, $357,147; qualifying distributions, $351,274; giving activities include $300,000 for 8 grants (high: $100,000; low: $25,000).
Fields of interest: Education; Secondary education; Catholicism; Human services.
Limitations: Applications not accepted. Giving primarily in MO. No grants to individuals.
Application information: Contributes only to pre-selected organizations.
EIN: 436362412

4970
Nichols Company Charitable Trust

4706 Broadway Ave., Ste. 260
Kansas City, MO 64112-1910 (816) 561-3456
Contact: Daniel Hollman, Treas.
Application address: 310 Ward Pkwy., Kansas City, MO 64112 Tel.: (816) 561-3456

Donors: J.C. Nichols Co.; Highwoods Realty L.P.
Foundation type: Company-sponsored foundation.
Financial data (yr. ended 12/31/13): Assets, $3,463,441 (M); expenditures, $163,335; qualifying distributions, $152,631; giving activities include $147,000 for 47 grants (high: $23,000; low: $500).
Purpose and activities: The foundation supports art museums and hospitals and organizations involved

with education, patient services, human services, and the real estate industry.
Fields of interest: Arts and culture; Community and economic development; Human services.
Type of support: General support.
Limitations: Applications accepted. Giving primarily in Kansas City, MO. No grants to individuals.
Application information:
  Initial approach: Letter
  Deadline(s): None
Officers: Barrett Brady, Pres.; Daniel Hollman, Treas.
EIN: 446015538

4971
The No Frills Foundation

c/o William Jochens
Greensfelder, Hemker & Gale, PC
10 S. Broadway, Ste. 2000
Saint Louis, MO 63102-1712

Established in 1998 in Missouri.
Donor: Paula Weil.
Foundation type: Independent foundation.
Financial data (yr. ended 12/31/13): Assets, $5,161,333 (M); expenditures, $270,666; qualifying distributions, $250,000; giving activities include $250,000 for 7 grants (high: $100,000; low: $10,000).
Purpose and activities: Giving primarily for higher education and the environment.
Fields of interest: Higher education; Natural resources; Infectious and parasitic diseases; Community beautification; Human services.
Limitations: Applications not accepted. Giving primarily in NY. No grants to individuals.
Application information: Contributes only to pre-selected organizations.
Trustee: Paula Weil.
Director: William Jochens.
EIN: 436801427

4972
George P. Obertate Trust

P.O. Box 387
Saint Louis, MO 63166-0387

Established in 2003 in Illinois.
Foundation type: Independent foundation.
Financial data (yr. ended 12/31/13): Assets, $3,065,092 (M); expenditures, $252,728; qualifying distributions, $160,237; giving activities include $155,705 for 1 grant.
Fields of interest: Protestantism; Human services.
Limitations: Applications not accepted. Giving primarily in Watertown, WI. No grants to individuals.
Application information: Contributes only to pre-selected organizations.
Trustee: U.S. Bank, N.A.
EIN: 376140950

4973
H. Tony & Marti Oppenheimer Foundation

132 Westwoods Dr.
Liberty, MO 64068-1181 8167214118

Foundation type: Independent foundation.
Financial data (yr. ended 12/31/14): Assets, $2,920,308 (M); expenditures, $781,612; qualifying distributions, $615,713.

Fields of interest: Arts and culture; Education; Foundations; Health.
Limitations: Applications not accepted. Giving primarily in CA and KS.
Application information: Unsolicited requests for funds not accepted.
Officers: Tony Oppenheimer, Chair. and C.E.O.; Marti Oppenheimer, Pres.; Jami Baron, Secy.; Brian Oppenheimer, Treas.
EIN: 461204810

4974
The Charlie & Mary Beth O'Reilly Family Foundation
1898 N. Monet Rd.
Nixa, MO   65714-7327

Established in 2000 in Missouri.
Donors: Charles H. O'Reilly, Jr.; Ryan O'Reilly; Patrick O'Reilly; Timothy O'Reilly; Mary Beth O'Reilly; Charlie O'Reilly.
Foundation type: Independent foundation.
Financial data (yr. ended 12/31/13): Assets, $6,718,041 (M); gifts received, $113,942; expenditures, $366,802; qualifying distributions, $338,290; giving activities include $335,800 for 87 grants (high: $32,000; low: $500).
Purpose and activities: Giving primarily for human services and to Roman Catholic agencies and churches.
Fields of interest: Arts and culture; Education; Nonprofits; Cancers; Breast cancer; Catholicism; Camps; Human services; Youth services.
Type of support: General support; Regranting.
Limitations: Applications not accepted. Giving primarily in MO. No grants to individuals.
Application information: Contributes only to pre-selected organizations.
Trustees: Charles H. O'Reilly, Jr.; Mary Beth O'Reilly; Patrick E. O'Reilly; Ryan C. O'Reilly; Timothy B. O'Reilly.
EIN: 436859254

4975
Larry & Nancy O'Reilly Family Foundation
2831 S. Ingram Mill Rd.
Springfield, MO   65804-4043

Established in 1999 in Missouri.
Donors: Leigh A. Flisher; Larry P. O'Reilly; Lauren P. O'Reilly; Ragan R. O'Reilly; Nancy D. O'Reillly; Mary Beth O'Reilly; Timothy B. O'Reilly; Ryan C. O'Reilly; Patrick E. O'Reilly; Charlie O'Reilly.
Foundation type: Independent foundation.
Financial data (yr. ended 12/31/13): Assets, $6,375,377 (M); expenditures, $255,382; qualifying distributions, $237,014; giving activities include $233,969 for 149 grants (high: $12,500; low: $25).
Purpose and activities: Giving primarily for human services, with a focus on children services.
Fields of interest: Cancers; Human services; Child welfare; Youth development; Youth services.
Type of support: General support; Capital and infrastructure; Equipment; Endowments.
Limitations: Applications not accepted. Giving primarily in MO, with some emphasis on Springfield. No grants to individuals.
Application information: Contributes only to pre-selected organizations.

Trustees: Leigh A. Flisher; Larry P. O'Reilly; Lauren P. O'Reilly; Nancy D. O'Reilly; Ragan R. O'Reilly.
EIN: 431872599

4976
Bee Payne-Stewart Foundation
4269 E. Berkley St.
Springfield, MO   65809-3521

Established in 1999 in Missouri.
Donor: Bee Payne-Stewart Trust.
Foundation type: Independent foundation.
Financial data (yr. ended 12/31/13): Assets, $3,593,721 (M); gifts received, $191,103; expenditures, $208,351; qualifying distributions, $208,351; giving activities include $195,640 for 28 grants (high: $30,000; low: $40).
Fields of interest: Health; Human services.
Limitations: Applications not accepted. Giving primarily in MO, with emphasis on Springfield. No grants to individuals.
Application information: Unsolicited requests for funds not accepted.
Officers: Susan Stewart-Daniel, Pres.; Julie Stewart, V.P.; Lora Stewart-Thomas, V.P.; J. Randolph Wilson, Treas.
EIN: 431863996

4977
The Pearl Foundation
P.O. Box 4572
Springfield, MO   65808-4572   4178870585
Application address: c/o Robert J. Helm, 1736 E. Sunshine, Ste. 913, Springfield, MO 65804, tel.: (417) 887-0585

Donor: Eddina F. Mackey.
Foundation type: Independent foundation.
Financial data (yr. ended 03/31/14): Assets, $7,294,948; expenditures, $390,593; qualifying distributions, $362,388.
Purpose and activities: Giving primarily for human services, and to Christian and Protestant churches.
Fields of interest: Arts and culture; Education; Nonprofits; Diseases and conditions; Christianity; Protestantism; Human services; Child welfare.
Type of support: Scholarships; General support; Regranting.
Limitations: Applications accepted. Giving primarily in MO.
Trustees: Robert J. Helm; Dayton Mackey; Eddina F. Mackey.
EIN: 431889713

4978
Peculiar Charitable Foundation
P.O. Box 331
Peculiar, MO   64078-0331
Application address: c/o Mary Catherine Dobson, P.O. Box 347, Raymore, MO 64083

Established in 1968 in Missouri.
Donor: E.P. Schug.
Foundation type: Independent foundation.
Financial data (yr. ended 12/31/13): Assets, $6,518,081 (M); expenditures, $306,432; qualifying distributions, $272,990; giving activities include $269,850 for grants.

Purpose and activities: Support for education, human services, Baptist and other Christian-based organizations, and health care.
Fields of interest: Education; Higher education; Nonprofits; Health; Christianity; Baptist; Human services.
Type of support: General support; Regranting; Program development; Scholarships; Student aid.
Limitations: Applications accepted. Giving primarily in Cass County, MO.
Application information: Application form required.
   Initial approach: Required applicaion form
   Deadline(s): May 1
Trustee: Sharon Shores.
Directors: Larry Dobson; Mary Catherine Dobson; Lauren C. Dobson Peter.
EIN: 436077697

4979
Pendergast-Weyer Foundation
9300 E. 155th St.
Kansas City, MO   64149-1161   (816) 322-0491

Established in 1976 in Missouri.
Donors: Mary Louise Weyer Pendergast†; Thomas J. Pendergast, Jr.†.
Foundation type: Independent foundation.
Financial data (yr. ended 06/30/13): Assets, $4,072,548 (M); gifts received, $58,949; expenditures, $625,447; qualifying distributions, $484,503; giving activities include $357,172 for 91 grants.
Purpose and activities: Giving primarily for Roman Catholic church-related pre-schools, elementary schools, high schools, and religious organizations. A minimum of 80 percent of all grants must go to Catholic institutions.
Fields of interest: Education; Diseases and conditions; Human services.
Type of support: Continuing support; Pro bono consulting services; Program development.
Limitations: Applications accepted. Giving limited to MO. No support for clergymen, chanceries, or church foundations. No grants to individuals, or for annual campaigns, seed money, building funds, land acquisition, endowment funds, matching gifts, research, publications, or conferences; no loans.
Publications: Application guidelines.
Application information: Application form required.
   Initial approach: Request application form
   Copies of proposal: 1
   Deadline(s): None
Officers: R. Kenneth Burnett, Pres.; Lynn Burnett, V.P.; Beverly J. Brayman, Secy.
Directors: Roger Brayman; Bernadette C. Cleary; Terry Dotson; Michael Heydon; Michael McGlenn; Mary Weir.
EIN: 431070676

4980
The Pillsbury Foundation
(formerly Fred Pillsbury Foundation)
10702 Manchester Rd., Ste. 10
Saint Louis, MO   63122-1321

Established in 1995 in Missouri.
Foundation type: Independent foundation.
Financial data (yr. ended 12/31/13): Assets, $9,749,583 (M); expenditures, $485,736; qualifying distributions, $411,423; giving activities

include $411,423 for 47 grants (high: $63,000; low: $50).
Fields of interest: Arts and culture; Education; Higher education; Christianity; Human services.
Limitations: Applications not accepted. Giving primarily in MO. No grants to individuals.
Application information: Contributes only to pre-selected organizations.
Officers: Linda J. Roos, Pres.; Cynthia Dickinson, V.P.; Elizabeth Hoffman, Secy.; Evelyn Kurtz, Treas.
EIN: 431699916

4981
Harry Portman Charitable Trust
c/o UMB Bank
P.O. Box 415044 M/S 1020307
Kansas City, MO 64141-6692

Established in 1991 in Missouri.
Donor: Harry Portman†.
Foundation type: Independent foundation.
Financial data (yr. ended 12/31/14): Assets, $3,708,997; expenditures, $212,030; qualifying distributions, $190,635.
Fields of interest: Arts and culture; Education; University education; Foundations; Nonprofits; Specialty hospital care; Judaism; Human services; Adult and child mentoring.
Type of support: General support; Capital and infrastructure; Equipment; Endowments; Individual development; Program development; Scholarships; Regranting.
Limitations: Applications not accepted. No grants to individuals.
Application information: Unsolicited requests for funds not accepted.
Trustees: Michael Schultz; UMB Bank, N.A.
EIN: 436406877

4982
Carol Swanson Price Foundation
6324 N. Chatham Ave., Ste. 101
Kansas City, MO 64151 8169315585

Established in 1969 in Missouri.
Foundation type: Independent foundation.
Financial data (yr. ended 12/31/14): Assets, $2,788,825; expenditures, $298,729; qualifying distributions, $282,151.
Fields of interest: Arts and culture; Education; Foundations; Hospital care; Diseases and conditions; Human services.
Type of support: General support; Research; Research and evaluation.
Limitations: Applications accepted. Giving primarily in CA.
Application information: Application form required.
  Initial approach: Letter
  Deadline(s): None
Trustee: Carol Swanson Price.
EIN: 431781880

4983
Prime Health Foundation
c/o UMB Bank
1010 Grand Blvd., 3rd Fl.
Kansas City, MO 64106-2220 8168607723
FAX: (816) 860-5080;
E-mail: director@primehealthfoundation.org;
Contact for logistical and technical questions:

Teesha Beeks, tel.: (816) 860-7131, e-mail: director@primehealthfoundation.org. Other questions can be directed to: Edna Rindner, tel.: (913) 484-5816, e-mail: Erindner22@gmail.com;
Main URL: http://www.primehealthfoundation.org
Grants List: http://www.primehealthfoundation.org/programs.htm

Established in 1978 in Missouri.
Foundation type: Independent foundation.
Financial data (yr. ended 12/31/13): Assets, $120,617 (M); expenditures, $485,261; qualifying distributions, $417,200; giving activities include $417,200 for 16 grants (high: $125,000).
Purpose and activities: The foundation enhances the development of healthcare delivery systems designed to provide appropriate health care services suitable for treatment. Areas of special interest include: disease prevention, including early detection of disease; improvement of conditions that contribute to morbidity and/or mortality (clinical, social or otherwise); improvements in quality of care and/or service delivery; promotion of wellness and healthy lifestyles; increased availability and accessibility of health care; consumer health education; health care provider education; appropriate use of health care resources; awareness about social issues affecting health, such as domestic violence, mental health, etc.; and other projects showing potential to improve community health.
Fields of interest: Health.
Limitations: Applications accepted. Giving primarily in the 7-county bi-state area of Cass, Clay, Jackson, Platte and Ray, MI, and Johnson and Wyandotte, KS. No grants for capital equipment.
Publications: Application guidelines.
Application information: See foundation web site for application requirements.
Directors: Robert Barrientos; Chito Belchez; Karin Chang, Ph.D; Mary Corcoran, Ph.D; Katie Cronin, JD, BSW; Clinton Fields; Mark Lovelace; Maria Alonso Luaces; Ryan Mize; James T. Nunnelly; Leo Prieto; Melissa Robinson; Tom Ryan; Susan Wilson, Ph.D.
EIN: 431057862

4984
George H. Riedel Foundation
c/o F&M Bank and Trust Co.
505 Broadway
P.O. Box 938
Hannibal, MO 63401-0938 (573) 221-6424

Established in 2001 in Missouri.
Donor: George H. Reidel Revocable Trust.
Foundation type: Independent foundation.
Financial data (yr. ended 12/31/13): Assets, $6,220,738 (M); expenditures, $330,069; qualifying distributions, $240,070; giving activities include $240,070 for 21 grants (high: $66,442; low: $1,000).
Purpose and activities: The purpose of the trust is to enhance the quality of life for the citizens of Hannibal, Missouri.
Fields of interest: Arts councils; Nonprofits; Human services; Child welfare.
Type of support: Program development; Matching grants; Regranting; Seed money.
Limitations: Applications accepted. Giving limited to Hannibal, MO. No grants to individuals or for capital improvements.
Application information:
  Initial approach: Proposal

Copies of proposal: 2
Deadline(s): None
Board meeting date(s): Feb., May, Aug., and Nov.
Trustee: FM Bank and Trust Co.
EIN: 431907873

4985
The Melvin F. & Adele S. Roman Foundation
c/o Sanford Spitzer
2217 Croydon Walk
Saint Louis, MO 63131-3253

Established in 2001 in Missouri.
Donors: Adele G. Roman; M&A Partnership.
Foundation type: Independent foundation.
Financial data (yr. ended 12/31/13): Assets, $1,835,672 (M); expenditures, $227,867; qualifying distributions, $195,750; giving activities include $195,000 for 14 grants (high: $75,000; low: $2,000).
Fields of interest: Arts and culture; Health; Judaism.
Limitations: Applications not accepted. Giving primarily in St. Louis, MO. No grants to individuals.
Application information: Unsolicited requests for funds not accepted.
Trustee: Sanford J. Spitzer.
EIN: 266003853

4986
John S. Ross Family Foundation
(formerly John S. & Jody J. Ross Foundation)
P.O. Box 11356
Clayton, MO 63105-0156

Established in 1992 in Missouri.
Donor: John S. Ross.
Foundation type: Independent foundation.
Financial data (yr. ended 12/31/14): Assets, $1,460,929; expenditures, $297,076; qualifying distributions, $286,005.
Fields of interest: Arts and culture; Art museums; Philanthropy; Religion.
Type of support: General support.
Limitations: Applications not accepted. Giving primarily in St. Louis, MO. No grants to individuals.
Application information: Unsolicited requests for funds not accepted.
Officers: John S. Ross, Pres.; Jody J. Ross, V.P.
EIN: 431544557

4987
The Rubin Family Foundation
c/o Matter Family Office
7711 Bonhomme Ave., Ste. 400
Clayton, MO 63105-1908

Established in 2001 in Missouri.
Donors: Pamela K. Rubin; Ronald T. Rubin; The Republic of Tea Inc; Ronald T. Rubin 1993 Trust.
Foundation type: Independent foundation.
Financial data (yr. ended 12/31/13): Assets, $6,360,501 (M); gifts received, $397,135; expenditures, $307,195; qualifying distributions, $303,029; giving activities include $303,029 for 46 grants (high: $114,494; low: $250).
Fields of interest: Education; Diseases and conditions; Judaism.
Limitations: Applications not accepted. Giving primarily in MO and TX. No grants to individuals.

Application information: Contributes only to pre-selected organizations.
Directors: Julie Liberman; Pamela K. Rubin; Ronald T. Rubin; Todd B. Rubin.
EIN: 371416413

4988
Harry L. Rust & Helen M. Rust Charitable Foundation
c/o A. Rust & Commerce Bank, N.A.
118 W. 47th St.
Kansas City, MO   64112
Application address: c/o Program Officer, 922 Walnut St., Ste. 200, Kansas City, MO 64106-1809, tel.: (816) 234-2577

Foundation type: Independent foundation.
Financial data (yr. ended 03/31/13): Assets, $4,960,567 (M); expenditures, $298,696; qualifying distributions, $261,777; giving activities include $229,150 for 22 grants (high: $15,000; low: $5,000).
Fields of interest: Education; Dental care; Christianity; Human services; Family services; Child welfare.
Limitations: Applications accepted. Giving primarily in CT, FL, MO, and NC.
Application information: Call for guidelines. Application form required.
   Initial approach: Letter
   Deadline(s): 1 month prior to foundation meeting
Trustees: Adam Rust; Commerce Bank.
EIN: 436929733

4989
Sachs Fund
400 Chesterfield Ctr., Ste. 600
Chesterfield, MO   63017-4890

Established in 1957 in Missouri.
Donors: Samuel C. Sachs; Sachs Electric Corp.; Sachs Holdings, Inc.; Mary L. Sachs; Louis Sachs†.
Foundation type: Company-sponsored foundation.
Financial data (yr. ended 04/30/14): Assets, $66,618 (M); gifts received, $250,000; expenditures, $256,145; qualifying distributions, $252,487; giving activities include $250,000 for 1 grant.
Purpose and activities: The fund supports hospitals and organizations involved with arts and culture, Parkinson's disease, and Judaism.
Fields of interest: Arts and culture; Nonprofits; Hospital care; Parkinson's disease; Judaism.
Type of support: General support; Regranting.
Limitations: Applications not accepted. Giving primarily in MO and NY. No grants to individuals.
Application information: Contributes only to pre-selected organizations.
Trustees: Mary L. Sachs; Stephen Sachs; Susan E. Sachs.
EIN: 436032385

4990
Ronald S. Saks Charitable Foundation Trust
6450 San Bonita Ave.
Saint Louis, MO   63105-3118

Donor: Ronald S. Saks.
Foundation type: Independent foundation.

Financial data (yr. ended 12/31/13): Assets, $232,930 (M); gifts received, $275,595; expenditures, $214,992; qualifying distributions, $213,767; giving activities include $212,830 for 16 grants (high: $55,000; low: $900).
Fields of interest: Education; Health; Diseases and conditions; Aerospace engineering.
Type of support: General support.
Limitations: Applications not accepted. Giving primarily in MO and WA.
Application information: Unsolicited requests for funds not accepted.
Trustees: Emily Saks Balestra; April Saks; Jocelin Saks Tindall.
EIN: 266167405

4991
Sander Foundation
524 High Hampton Rd.
Saint Louis, MO   63124-1014

Established in 2005 in Missouri.
Donors: Derick L. Driemeyer Trust; Derick L. Driemeyer.
Foundation type: Independent foundation.
Financial data (yr. ended 12/31/14): Assets, $3,537,831; gifts received, $0; expenditures, $352,616; qualifying distributions, $350,191.
Purpose and activities: Giving to organizations that assist challenged children, support selected education, or protect and improve our natural world environment. In addition, support is given to organizations that support wounded warriors. The foundation prefers to give to smaller organizations where the contribution can make a difference.
Fields of interest: Education; Environment; Child welfare; Children and youth; Low-income and poor people; Military personnel.
Type of support: General support; Matching grants; Land acquisitions; Endowments.
Limitations: Applications accepted. Giving primarily in MO. No support for political organizations. No grants to individuals.
Application information: Application form required.
   Initial approach: Letter
   Copies of proposal: 1
   Deadline(s): Varies
Trustees: Derick L. Driemeyer; Sally M. Driemeyer.
Number of staff: None.
EIN: 202007940

4992
Sappington House Foundation Library of Americana Trust
3 Balero Ct.
Ballwin, MO   63011-3419

Foundation type: Independent foundation.
Financial data (yr. ended 12/31/13): Assets, $187,496 (M); gifts received, $1,000; expenditures, $255,466; qualifying distributions, $253,274; giving activities include $236,949 for 2 grants (high: $168,843; low: $68,106).
Fields of interest: Education; Archives and special collections.
Limitations: Applications not accepted. Giving primarily in MO.
Application information: Unsolicited requests for funds not accepted.

Trustees: Dana E. Jones; William Randall McDonnell; Pam Walsh.
EIN: 901069707

4993
Sayler-Hawkins Foundation
8 Upper Price Rd.
Saint Louis, MO   63132

Established in 1984 in Missouri.
Donors: Marjorie Woods; John R. Woods, Sr.
Foundation type: Independent foundation.
Financial data (yr. ended 12/31/13): Assets, $2,636,630 (M); gifts received, $19,726; expenditures, $264,425; qualifying distributions, $145,000; giving activities include $145,000 for 23 grants (high: $40,000; low: $500).
Purpose and activities: Giving primarily to an advocacy group promoting firearms safety and for Protestant churches; some support also for museums.
Fields of interest: Museums; Education; Health; Protestantism; Fishing and hunting; Individual liberties; Unknown or not classified.
Limitations: Applications not accepted. Giving primarily in MO. No grants to individuals.
Application information: Unsolicited requests for funds not accepted.
   Board meeting date(s): Dec.
Officers and Directors: Judith H. Woods, Pres. and Director; Elizabeth Pollnow, Secy. and Director; John R. Woods, Jr., Treas. and Director.
EIN: 431347116

4994
Schneider Foundation
c/o U.S. Bank, N.A., Trust Dept.
1615 S. Glenstone Ave.
Springfield, MO   65808-3357

Established in 1990 in Missouri.
Donors: Henry Schneider; Jane Schneider.
Foundation type: Independent foundation.
Financial data (yr. ended 09/30/14): Assets, $8,768,726 (M); gifts received, $95,513; expenditures, $361,614; qualifying distributions, $288,887; giving activities include $285,000 for 7 grants (high: $125,000; low: $5,000).
Fields of interest: Education; Elementary and secondary education; Higher education; University education; Human services; Child welfare; Youth services.
Type of support: General support; Public engagement and education.
Limitations: Applications accepted. Giving limited to Springfield, MO.
Application information: Application form required.
   Initial approach: Letter
   Deadline(s): None
Officers: Henry Schneider, Pres.; R. Barnes Whitlock, Secy.
Directors: Susan Holliday; James Johnson; Douglas R. Nickell; Jane Schneider; Ross M. Schneider.
EIN: 431530098

4995
Victor E. & Caroline E. Schutte Foundation
1201 Walnut St., Ste. 2800
Kansas City, MO   64106-2159

Donor: Schutte Lumber Co.
Foundation type: Independent foundation.
Financial data (yr. ended 12/31/13): Assets, $4,276,478 (M); expenditures, $225,289; qualifying distributions, $187,535; giving activities include $186,000 for 11 grants (high: $50,000; low: $5,000).
Purpose and activities: Giving primarily for education.
Fields of interest: Arts and culture; Education; Higher education; Undergraduate education; Medical education; Hospital care; Diseases and conditions.
Type of support: General support; Matching grants; Capital campaigns; Endowments; Professorships; Curriculum development; Scholarships.
Limitations: Applications not accepted. Giving primarily in Kansas City, MO. No grants to individuals.
Application information: Contributes only to pre-selected organizations.
Trustees: John C. Aisenbrey; John C. Davis; David W. Frantze.
EIN: 436049974

4996
Schweinfurth Foundation
P.O. Box 387
Saint Louis, MO 63166-0387
Application address: c/o James Acton, U.S. Bank, N.A., 235 N. Elm, P.O. Box 709, Centralia, IL 62801, tel.: (618) 545-1217

Donor: Schweinfurth Trust.
Foundation type: Independent foundation.
Financial data (yr. ended 12/31/13): Assets, $4,099,712 (M); expenditures, $244,427; qualifying distributions, $193,610; giving activities include $190,100 for 14 grants (high: $68,808; low: $1,000).
Fields of interest: Arts and culture; Elementary and secondary education; Nonprofits; Community and economic development; Special Olympics; Human services.
Type of support: Regranting.
Application information: Application form required.
Initial approach: Contact Foundation
Deadline(s): May 1
Trustee: U.S. Bank, N.A.
EIN: 371331754

4997
Seiler Family Foundation
443 Hidden Lake Dr.
Saint Charles, MO 63304-8559

Established in 2006 in Missouri.
Donors: John Seiler; Edith Seiler.
Foundation type: Independent foundation.
Financial data (yr. ended 12/31/14): Assets, $1,761,086 (M); gifts received, $5,024; expenditures, $197,276; qualifying distributions, $174,977; giving activities include $139,300 for 8 grants (high: $26,000; low: $2,000).
Fields of interest: Health; Religion; Sports and recreation.
Limitations: Applications not accepted. Giving primarily in MO. No grants to individuals.
Application information: Unsolicited requests for funds not accepted.

Officers: Susette M. Martin, Pres.; Charles E. Martin, Jr., Secy.; David L. Jones, Treas.
EIN: 203553387

4998
Service Club for the Blind, Inc.
3719 Watson Rd.
Saint Louis, MO 63109-1236

Donors: Philip and Emma Craig Trust; The LCMS Foundation.
Foundation type: Independent foundation.
Financial data (yr. ended 09/30/14): Assets, $9,605,015 (M); gifts received, $64,070; expenditures, $654,037; qualifying distributions, $627,739; giving activities include $100 for grants, and $395,262 for grants to individuals.
Purpose and activities: Giving to provide educational, business, professional, and recreational opportunities for the blind community in the St. Louis, Missouri metropolitan area.
Fields of interest: People with vision impairments.
Type of support: General support; Student aid.
Limitations: Applications not accepted. Giving primarily in the St. Louis, MO metropolitan area.
Application information: Unsolicited requests for funds not accepted.
Officers: Kathleen Demskey, Pres.; Jack Lenk, 1st V.P.; Jusiata Tabor, 2nd V.P.; Anna Schell, Secy.; Celita White, Treas.
Directors: Bettina Vinson; Louis Wambler.
Trustee: Mark Detjen.
EIN: 430655872

4999
Shanahan Family Foundation
424 S. Woodsmill Rd., Ste. 325
Chesterfield, MO 63017-3479

Established in 2004 in Missouri.
Donor: Michael F. Shanahan, Sr.
Foundation type: Independent foundation.
Financial data (yr. ended 12/31/13): Assets, $192,851 (M); expenditures, $252,165; qualifying distributions, $221,971; giving activities include $221,971 for 47 grants (high: $27,500; low: $500).
Fields of interest: Education; Diseases and conditions; Human services.
Limitations: Applications not accepted. Giving primarily in St. Louis, MO. No grants to individuals.
Application information: Contributes only to pre-selected organizations.
Board meeting date(s): Varies
Trustees: Megan Mattern; Mary Ann Shanahan; Michael F. Shanahan, Sr.; Michael F. Shanahan, Jr.; Maureen Twardowski.
Number of staff: None.
EIN: 436911537

5000
Shawe Family Charitable Foundation
(formerly Earle & Annette Shawe Family Charitable Foundation, Inc.)
P.O. Box 387
Saint Louis, MO 63166-0387
Application address: 20 S. Charles St., Baltimore, MD 21201

Established in 1986 in Maryland.

Donors: Earle K. Shawe; Annette C. Shawe; Gail R. Shawe; Stephen D. Shawe; EKS Inv Ltd Partnership.
Foundation type: Independent foundation.
Financial data (yr. ended 06/30/14): Assets, $11,275,633; gifts received, $14,660; expenditures, $475,270; qualifying distributions, $407,107.
Purpose and activities: Giving primarily for education, Jewish agencies, and civic and cultural institutions.
Fields of interest: Arts and culture; Education; Nonprofits; Judaism; Children's rights; Human services.
Type of support: Advocacy; General support; Annual campaigns; Capital campaigns; Capital and infrastructure; Regranting; Endowments; Professorships; Scholarships.
Limitations: Applications accepted. Giving primarily in Palm Beach, FL, and Baltimore, MD. No grants to individuals.
Application information:
Initial approach: Proposal
Copies of proposal: 1
Deadline(s): None
Officers: Earle K. Shawe, Pres.; Annette C. Shawe, V.P.; Gail R. Shawe, Secy.; Stephen D. Shawe, Treas.
Number of staff: 1 part-time professional.
EIN: 521505784

5001
The Shepherd Foundation
222 S. Central Ave., Ste. 804
Saint Louis, MO 63105-3509 (314) 727-8677
Contact: Charles M.M. Shepherd, Chair.

Established in 1998 in Missouri.
Donor: Susan E. Shepherd†.
Foundation type: Independent foundation.
Financial data (yr. ended 12/31/13): Assets, $8,550,389 (M); expenditures, $232,890; qualifying distributions, $225,296; giving activities include $194,378 for 69 grants (high: $18,000; low: $25).
Fields of interest: Education; Health; Human services.
Application information:
Initial approach: Letter
Deadline(s): None
Officer: Charles M.M. Shepherd, Chair.
Directors: Sally S. Haimbaugh; Susan B. Ittner; Charles T. Shepherd; Susanne W. Shepherd; James M. Medart.
EIN: 911979191

5002
Clara L. Shumway Charitable Trust
c/o UMB Bank
P.O. Box 419692 M/S 1020305
Kansas City, MO 64141-6692

Foundation type: Independent foundation.
Financial data (yr. ended 09/30/13): Assets, $4,248,577 (M); expenditures, $207,017; qualifying distributions, $186,994; giving activities include $168,580 for 9 grants (high: $33,716; low: $16,858).
Fields of interest: Education; Health; Human services.
Limitations: Applications not accepted. Giving primarily in KS and Kansas City, MO.

Application information: Unsolicited requests for funds not accepted.
Trustee: UMB Bank, N.A.
EIN: 436743873

5003
Sigma-Aldrich Foundation
3050 Spruce St.
Saint Louis, MO 63103-2530
Contact: Kirk A. Richter, V.P.
Main URL: http://www.sigmaaldrich.com/customer-service/sigma-aldrich-foundation.html

Established in 2004 in Missouri.
Donor: Sigma-Aldrich Corp.
Foundation type: Company-sponsored foundation.
Financial data (yr. ended 12/31/13): Assets, $6,022,803 (M); expenditures, $336,761; qualifying distributions, $327,550; giving activities include $317,400 for 25 grants (high: $87,550; low: $1,500).
Purpose and activities: The foundation supports organizations involved with education, health, youth development, human services, and science.
Fields of interest: Education; Nonprofits; Health; Science; Human services; Family services; Youth development.
Type of support: Regranting; Employee volunteer services; General support; Continuing support; Annual campaigns; Scholarships; Research.
Limitations: Applications accepted. Giving primarily in areas of company operations in St. Louis, MO, and Milwaukee, WI. No support for discriminatory organizations, political candidates or organizations, athletic teams, or booster or social clubs. No grants to individuals, or for scholarships, supplies or materials for primary or secondary education facilities, political causes or campaigns, fundraising, athletic events, or extracurricular activities for educational institutions.
Publications: Application guidelines.
Application information: Multi-year funding is not automatic. Organizations receiving support are asked to provide status and evaluation reports. Application form required.
Initial approach: Complete online application form
Copies of proposal: 1
Deadline(s): None
Board meeting date(s): 2 or 3 times per year
Final notification: Following board meeting
Officers and Directors: Jai P. Nagarkatti, Pres.; Kirk A. Richter, V.P.; Barbara Branchfield, Secy.; Michael Hollenkemp, Treas.; Joseph D. Ackerman.
Number of staff: None.
EIN: 200884074

5004
The Silk Foundation
c/o Northern Trust Company
190 Carondelet Plz.
Saint Louis, MO 63105-3443

Foundation type: Independent foundation.
Financial data (yr. ended 11/30/13): Assets, $8,425,457 (M); expenditures, $468,107; qualifying distributions, $384,500; giving activities include $384,500 for 12 grants (high: $152,500; low: $5,000).
Fields of interest: Arts and culture; Nonprofits; Judaism.
Type of support: Regranting.

Limitations: Applications not accepted. Giving primarily in MO.
Application information: Contributes only to pre-selected organizations.
Officers: Gary Godwin, Pres.; Susan Godwin Kofkoff, Secy.; Richard Koskoff, Treas.
EIN: 261484066

5005
Simmons Charitable Foundation
c/o John Curby, Jr.
9808 Conway Rd.
Saint Louis, MO 63124

Established in 1994 in Missouri.
Donor: Edward C. Simmons III.
Foundation type: Independent foundation.
Financial data (yr. ended 12/31/14): Assets, $7,693,776; expenditures, $384,386; qualifying distributions, $288,806.
Purpose and activities: It is the intent of the foundation to support non-profit organizations that improve the health, education and well being of those individuals whom they serve. Through its gifts, the foundation hopes to have a meaningful impact on the organizations and their beneficiaries.
Fields of interest: Theater; Orchestral music; Secondary education; Natural resources; Alzheimer's disease.
Type of support: General support; Continuing support; Annual campaigns; Research; Capital campaigns; Capital and infrastructure; Endowments.
Limitations: Applications not accepted. Giving primarily in St. Louis, MO. No grants to individuals.
Application information: Unsolicited requests for funds not accepted.
Board meeting date(s): Varies
Trustees: C. Perry Bascom; John E. Curby, Jr.; Nancy S. Curby; Sally Curby Johnston; Elizabeth J. Parker; Edward C. Simmons III.
EIN: 436579684

5006
The Siteman Family Foundation
7701 Forsyth Blvd., Ste. 325
Saint Louis, MO 63105-1831

Established in 2000 in Missouri.
Donor: Alvin Siteman.
Foundation type: Independent foundation.
Financial data (yr. ended 12/31/13): Assets, $3,826,855 (M); expenditures, $185,075; qualifying distributions, $150,000; giving activities include $150,000 for 17 grants (high: $40,000; low: $5,000).
Fields of interest: Arts education; Performing arts; Education; Nonprofits; Health; Diseases and conditions; Judaism; Human services.
Type of support: Equipment; Regranting; Program development; Scholarships; Research.
Limitations: Applications not accepted. Giving primarily in St. Louis, MO. No grants to individuals.
Application information: Unsolicited requests for funds not accepted.
Trustee: Alvin Siteman.
EIN: 436855141

5007
Donald Slavik Family Foundation
9648 Olive Blvd., Ste. 103
Saint Louis, MO 63132-3002   (314) 991-8020
Contact: Susan Slavik Williams, Pres.

Donors: Ann A. Slavik; Donald S. Slavik; Susan Slavik Williams.
Foundation type: Independent foundation.
Financial data (yr. ended 12/31/13): Assets, $7,614,550 (M); expenditures, $461,799; qualifying distributions, $388,384; giving activities include $371,920 for 15 grants (high: $75,000; low: $10,000).
Purpose and activities: Giving primarily to U.S. charities involved in wildlife and nature conservation.
Fields of interest: Wildlife biodiversity.
Limitations: Applications accepted. Giving primarily in CA.
Application information:
Initial approach: Proposal
Deadline(s): None
Officers: Susan Slavik Williams, Pres.; Ann A. Slavik, Secy.-Treas.
Director: Felix Noble Williams.
EIN: 431778633

5008
Gene and Joan Slay Charitable Foundation
1441 Hampton Ave.
Saint Louis, MO 63139-3115

Established in 2005 in Missouri.
Donors: Gerald J. Zafft; Eugene P. Slay; Joan Slay; J.S. Leasing Company Inc. & Subsidiaries.
Foundation type: Independent foundation.
Financial data (yr. ended 12/31/13): Assets, $5,334,575 (M); gifts received, $10,000; expenditures, $235,758; qualifying distributions, $230,220; giving activities include $230,220 for 45 grants (high: $75,000; low: $75).
Fields of interest: Diseases and conditions; Catholicism; Human services; Youth development; Youth services.
Limitations: Applications not accepted. Giving primarily in MO. No grants to individuals.
Application information: Contributes only to pre-selected organizations.
Officers and Trustees: Joan E. Slay, Pres. and Trustee; Jill S. Garlich, V.P. and Trustee; Guy G. Slay, V.P. and Trustee; Jeffrey C. Slay, Secy. and Trustee; Gerald J. Zafft.
EIN: 436927039

5009
Roy W. Slusher Charitable Foundation
P.O. Box 387
Saint Louis, MO 63166-0387   3144182643

Established in 1988 in Missouri.
Donor: Roy W. Slusher Trust.
Foundation type: Independent foundation.
Financial data (yr. ended 02/28/15): Assets, $6,623,257; expenditures, $494,358; qualifying distributions, $152,402 and $0 for set-asides.
Purpose and activities: Funding to meet the needs of disadvantaged youth and their families and to increase the quality of life for the elderly through the following broad areas: educational scholarships, broad national health issues, youth camps and

programs, senior citizens programs, and public radio and television.

Fields of interest: Education; Undergraduate education; Nonprofits; Diseases and conditions; Communication media; Christianity; Human services; Basic and emergency aid; Food aid; Child welfare; Youth services; Homeless shelters; Senior services; International development.

Type of support: General support; Capital and infrastructure; Seed money; Regranting; Scholarships; Research; Research and evaluation.

Limitations: Applications not accepted. Giving primarily in Taney County, MO. No grants to individuals or for annual fundraising, endowments, or routine operating needs.

Publications: Informational brochure.

Application information: Contributes only to pre-selected organizations.

   Board meeting date(s): Mar. and Sept.

Officers: Charles A. Fuller, Jr., Fdn. Mgr.; Jerry Redfern, Fdn. Mgr.

Trustee: U.S. Bank, N.A.

Number of staff: 1 part-time professional.

EIN: 436339151

5010
Walter Sokoll Trust

111 E. Miller St.
Jefferson City, MO   65101-2915

Donor: Walter Sokoll†.

Foundation type: Independent foundation.

Financial data (yr. ended 12/31/13): Assets, $2,407,445 (M); gifts received, $3,096,738; expenditures, $278,090; qualifying distributions, $242,984; giving activities include $242,984 for 1 grant.

Fields of interest: Religion.

Limitations: Applications not accepted. Giving primarily in MO.

Application information: Unsolicited requests for funds not accepted.

Trustee: Central Trust and Investment Co.

EIN: 276454023

5011
South St. Joseph Progressive Association, Inc.

P.O. Box 4174
Saint Joseph, MO   64504-4174   (816) 364-7792
Contact: Danyle Morlock, Treas.

Donor: Julia A. Fisher Trust.

Foundation type: Independent foundation.

Financial data (yr. ended 12/31/13): Assets, $2,869,311 (M); gifts received, $275; expenditures, $199,779; qualifying distributions, $164,845; giving activities include $164,845 for 30 + grants (high: $30,000).

Fields of interest: Arts and culture; Foundations; Community and economic development; Human services.

Limitations: Applications accepted. Giving limited to South St. Joseph, MO.

Application information: Application form required.

   Initial approach: Proposal
   Deadline(s): None

Officers: John Boeh, Chair.; Jim Graves, Pres.; Darrell Grace, 1st V.P.; Robert Casebolt, 2nd V.P.;

Carolyn Sampson, Recording Secy.; Linda Blank, Corresponding Secy.; Danyle Morlock, Treas.

EIN: 431475002

5012
Greater St. Louis Health Foundation

(formerly Group Health Foundation of Greater St. Louis)
412 S. Clay Ave., Ste. 100
Kirkwood, MO   63122-5860   (314) 984-9829
Contact: Robert W. Swanson, Secy.
E-mail: info@gstlhf.com; Main URL: http://gstlhf.com

Established in 1986 in Missouri.

Foundation type: Independent foundation.

Financial data (yr. ended 12/31/13): Assets, $3,441,981 (M); expenditures, $325,075; qualifying distributions, $167,530; giving activities include $167,530 for 13 grants (high: $40,000; low: $5,000).

Purpose and activities: To promote health and prevent illness in the greater St. Louis, MO, area through support and financial aid to nonprofit organizations.

Fields of interest: Graduate and professional education; Medical education; Nursing care; Rehabilitation; Holistic medicine; Biomedicine; Diseases and conditions.

Type of support: Program development; Convening; Seed money; Curriculum development; Scholarships; Research; Research and evaluation.

Limitations: Applications accepted. Giving limited to the greater metropolitan St. Louis, MO, area. No grants to individuals, or for overhead costs or continuing support.

Application information: See foundation web site for guidelines.

   Initial approach: Letter
   Deadline(s): Feb 28, May 31, Aug 31, Nov 30
   Board meeting date(s): Feb., May, Aug., and Nov.

Officers and Directors: Richard Ellerbrake, Pres. and Director; Ralph L. Biddy, V.P. and Director; Robert W. Swanson, Exec. Secy. and Director; Taylor C. Scott, Treas.; Kenneth Guethle; Thomas H. Lake; Darwin W. Schlag.

EIN: 431141117

5013
Elaine Feld Stern Charitable Trust

c/o Blue Ridge Bank & Trust Co.
4200 Little Blue Pkwy.
Independence, MO   64057   (816) 358-5000
Contact: J. Bryan Allee

Established in 1989 in Missouri.

Donor: Elaine Feld Stern†.

Foundation type: Independent foundation.

Financial data (yr. ended 02/28/15): Assets, $3,373,053 (M); expenditures, $218,995; qualifying distributions, $191,179; giving activities include $169,000 for 46 grants (high: $20,000; low: $1,000).

Fields of interest: Diseases and conditions; Agriculture; Human services.

Limitations: Applications accepted. Giving primarily in Kansas City, MO. No support for tax-supported institutions. No grants to individuals, or for travel conferences or telethons.

Application information: Application form required.

   Initial approach: Letter
   Deadline(s): None

Trustees: Donald Kahan; Robert J. Margolin; Leslie Ann Strauss; Susan Feld Strauss.

EIN: 436354470

5014
Stifel Foundation, Inc.

501 N. Broadway
Saint Louis, MO   63102
Main URL: http://www.stifel.com

Donors: Stifel, Nicolaus & Co., Inc.; Stifel Financial Corporation.

Foundation type: Independent foundation.

Financial data (yr. ended 12/31/13): Assets, $4,956,230 (M); gifts received, $2,500,000; expenditures, $413,444; qualifying distributions, $413,444; giving activities include $412,700 for 35 grants (high: $50,000; low: $1,000).

Fields of interest: Health; Human services.

Limitations: Applications not accepted. Giving primarily in MO.

Application information: Unsolicited requests for funds not accepted.

Officers and Directors: James M. Zemlyak, Pres. and Director; John D. Haffenreffer, V.P. and Director; Catherine F. Kramer, V.P. and Director; David M. Minnick, Secy. and Director; James Laschober, Treas. and Director; Sharon A. Fleming.

EIN: 271439256

5015
Ruth M. & Francis A. Stroble Charitable Foundation

9880 Waterbury Dr.
Saint Louis, MO   63124-1067

Established in 1989 in Missouri.

Donors: Ruth M. Stroble; Francis A. Stroble.

Foundation type: Independent foundation.

Financial data (yr. ended 12/31/13): Assets, $2,032,663 (M); gifts received, $221,780; expenditures, $375,456; qualifying distributions, $370,882; giving activities include $369,572 for 45 grants (high: $50,500; low: $250).

Fields of interest: Education; Higher education; Nonprofits; Hospital care; Catholicism; Human services.

Type of support: Regranting.

Limitations: Applications not accepted. No grants to individuals.

Application information: Unsolicited requests for funds not accepted.

Trustees: Francis A. Stroble; Ruth M. Stroble.

EIN: 431532893

5016
Everett D. and Geneva V. Sugarbaker Foundation

2113 W. Main St.
Jefferson City, MO   65109-0912
Contact: Connie C. Moore, Treas.
Application address: 228 Papin Ave., Webster Grove, MO 63119-3716 tel.: (314) 231-2573

Established in 1997 in Missouri.

Donors: Geneva V. Sugarbaker; Everett V. Sugarbaker†.

Foundation type: Independent foundation.

Financial data (yr. ended 12/31/13): Assets, $8,249,136 (M); expenditures, $480,605; qualifying distributions, $427,000; giving activities include $427,000 for 37 grants (high: $72,500; low: $1,500).
Fields of interest: Education; Religion; Christianity.
Limitations: Applications accepted. Giving primarily in IL and TN. No grants to individuals.
Application information: Application form required.
   Initial approach: Proposal
   Deadline(s): Sept. 30
Officers: David J. Sugarbaker, Pres.; Evangeline Tolley, V.P.; Paul Sugarbaker, Secy.; Connie Moore, Treas.
Trustees: Elizabeth I. Akre; Katie Caliguri; Charles W. Digges IV; Rena Pedersen; Geneva V. Sugarbaker; Stephen P. Sugarbaker.
EIN: 431785474

5017
John J. Sullivan, Jr. Foundation
c/o J. Houlehan and M. Henke
11914 Summit
Kansas City, MO   64145-1035

Established in 1997 in Missouri.
Donor: John J. Sullivan, Jr.
Foundation type: Independent foundation.
Financial data (yr. ended 12/31/13): Assets, $6,304,996 (M); expenditures, $490,280; qualifying distributions, $420,945; giving activities include $380,579 for 85 grants (high: $40,750; low: $500).
Purpose and activities: Giving primarily to Roman Catholic agencies and churches and for education.
Fields of interest: Secondary education; Higher education; Catholicism.
Limitations: Applications not accepted. Giving primarily in KS and MO. No grants to individuals.
Application information: Contributes only to pre-selected organizations.
Trustees: Mark Henke; John Houlehan.
EIN: 742815203

5018
Sunnen Foundation
7910 Manchester Ave.
Saint Louis, MO   63143-2712
Contact: Kurt J. Kallaus, Pres.

Established in 1953 in Missouri.
Donors: Joseph Sunnen†; Helen Sly; Sunnen Products Co.
Foundation type: Independent foundation.
Financial data (yr. ended 12/31/13): Assets, $14,334,320 (M); gifts received, $20,000; expenditures, $543,437; qualifying distributions, $426,851; giving activities include $421,160 for 15 grants (high: $107,850; low: $700).
Purpose and activities: Specific goal-oriented projects for protection of reproductive and First Amendment rights, educational opportunities for the economically or physically disadvantaged and for youth and family services.
Fields of interest: Child educational development; Family planning; Reproductive rights; Family services; Child welfare; Child development; Children and youth; Low-income and poor people; People with disabilities.
Type of support: Capital campaigns; Matching grants; Program development.

Limitations: Applications accepted. Giving primarily in MO, with emphasis on the metropolitan St. Louis area. No support for educational institutions, environmental organizations, hospitals or medical charities, the arts or private day care centers. Generally no support for charities with broad-based public appeal, or religious bodies. No grants to individuals, or for scholarships, general operating costs, or research projects.
Publications: Informational brochure (including application guidelines).
Application information: Proposals submitted in notebooks, binders or plastic folders are not accepted.
   Initial approach: Proposal, not to exceed 10 pages
   Copies of proposal: 5
   Deadline(s): Proposal due June or July; final deadline is Aug. 1
   Board meeting date(s): Generally in Dec.
   Final notification: Jan.
Officers and Directors: Kurt J. Kallaus, Pres. and Director; Matthew S. Kreider, V.P. and Director; Ruth Cardinale, Secy. and Director; Susan S. Brasel, Treas. and Director; Helen S. Sly.
EIN: 436029156

5019
Tension Envelope Foundation
c/o ED Cockrell
819 E. 19th St.
Kansas City, MO   64108-1781   (816) 471-3800
Contact: William Berkley, Tr.

Established in 1954 in Missouri.
Donor: Tension Envelope Corp.
Foundation type: Company-sponsored foundation.
Financial data (yr. ended 11/30/14): Assets, $771,482 (M); expenditures, $285,002; qualifying distributions, $271,742; giving activities include $271,742 for grants.
Purpose and activities: The foundation supports organizations involved with arts and culture, education, human services, and community development.
Fields of interest: Higher education; Health; Community and economic development; Human services.
Type of support: General support; Student aid.
Application information: Application form required.
   Initial approach: Letter or Proposal
   Deadline(s): Feb. 15th for scholarships
Trustees: E. Bertram Berkley; Richard L. Berkley; William Berkley.
EIN: 446012554

5020
Richard H. and Viola B. Thorp Charitable Trust Foundation
P.O. Box 387
Saint Louis, MO   63166-0387

Established in 2004 in Missouri.
Donor: Richard & Viola Thorp Trust.
Foundation type: Independent foundation.
Financial data (yr. ended 12/31/14): Assets, $5,270,974 (M); expenditures, $350,186; qualifying distributions, $257,957; giving activities include $245,000 for 13 grants (high: $61,250; low: $6,125).

Fields of interest: Education; Specialty hospital care; Diseases and conditions; Christianity; Child welfare; People with vision impairments.
Type of support: General support.
Limitations: Applications not accepted. Giving primarily in FL and MO. No grants to individuals.
Application information: Unsolicited requests for funds not accepted.
Trustee: US Bank, N.A.
EIN: 206148240

5021
Bess Spiva Timmons Foundation, Inc.
c/o U.S. Bank, N.A., Trust Dept.
P.O. Box 8
Joplin, MO   64802-0008
E-mail: info@timmonsfoundation.org; Main
URL: http://www.timmonsfoundation.org

Established in 1967 in Missouri.
Donor: Bess Spiva Timmons†.
Foundation type: Independent foundation.
Financial data (yr. ended 12/31/14): Assets, $5,210,938 (M); expenditures, $320,212; qualifying distributions, $250,564; giving activities include $241,800 for 53 grants (high: $15,000; low: $1,000).
Purpose and activities: Primary area of interest is education programs for minorities; support also for health and medical research, the arts, social services, and ecology. Small, tax-exempt organizations, which have little or no federal, state, or local financial assistance, are favored for grants.
Fields of interest: Arts and culture; Higher education; Wildlife biodiversity; Health; Hospital care; Human services; Child welfare; Ethnic and racial groups.
Type of support: Equipment; Program development; Seed money; Scholarships.
Limitations: Applications accepted. Giving primarily in AZ, KS, MO and OR. No support for foreign organizations. No grants to individuals; or for operating funds, endowments, building projects, or major acquisitions.
Publications: Annual report.
Application information: See foundation web site for application policies and guidelines. Application form required.
   Initial approach: Letter with application information
   Copies of proposal: 1
   Deadline(s): 8/1
   Board meeting date(s): Oct.
Officers and Directors: Bryna Majidi, Pres.; Dana Whitby, V.P. and Director; Gregory G. Timmons, Secy. and Director; Tim Spears, Treas. and Director; Jennifer Svacina; Sarah Timmons; Catherine Weeks.
Trustee: U.S. Bank, N.A.
EIN: 436075014

5022
Ruth D. and Wylie Todd Charitable Foundation
307 Cabin Grove Ln.
Saint Louis, MO   63141-8171
Contact: Anna Polizzi-Keller, Tr.

Donors: Ruth Davis Todd Established Foundation; Oratory of St. Augustine and St. Gregory.
Foundation type: Independent foundation.

Financial data (yr. ended 12/31/13): Assets, $431,934 (M); gifts received, $250,000; expenditures, $440,256; qualifying distributions, $436,197; giving activities include $436,197 for 13 grants (high: $109,650; low: $9,682).
Fields of interest: Public affairs; Agriculture; Catholicism.
Limitations: Applications not accepted. Giving primarily in St. Louis, MO; some giving also in Alton, IL.
Application information: Contributes only to pre-selected organizations.
Trustees: Fr. Gregory Morhman; Anna Polizzi-Keller.
EIN: 263273942

5023
Earl C. & Elizabeth Toutz Charitable Trust
P.O. Box 387
Saint Louis, MO 63166-0387

Donor: Elizabeth Toutz.
Foundation type: Independent foundation.
Financial data (yr. ended 06/30/14): Assets, $6,062,927 (M); expenditures, $333,481; qualifying distributions, $282,500; giving activities include $280,000 for 12 grants (high: $42,000; low: $14,000).
Fields of interest: Undergraduate education; Specialty hospital care; Diseases and conditions; Arthritis; Muscular dystrophy; Cerebral palsy; Cancers; Protestantism; Youth development; Youth services; People with vision impairments.
Limitations: Applications not accepted. Giving primarily in FL and MO. No grants to individuals.
Application information: Contributes only to pre-selected organizations.
Trustee: U.S. Bank, N.A.
EIN: 436221144

5024
Steven L. Trulaske, Sr. Family Foundation
2001 E. Terra Ln.
O' Fallon, MO 63366-4434

Established in 2005 in Missouri.
Donor: R.J. Trulaske, Sr. and G.M. Trulaske Charitable Trust No. 2.
Foundation type: Independent foundation.
Financial data (yr. ended 12/31/12): Assets, $412,684 (M); gifts received, $321,155; expenditures, $305,400; qualifying distributions, $305,200; giving activities include $305,000 for 2 grants (high: $300,000; low: $5,000).
Fields of interest: Higher education; Specialty hospital care.
Limitations: Applications not accepted. Giving primarily in IN and St. Louis, MO.
Application information: Contributes only to pre-selected organizations.
Trustee: Steven L. Trulaske, Sr.
EIN: 203825998

5025
The Turner Family Foundation
c/o Julie Brown
4725 E. Royal Dr.
Springfield, MO 65809-2423

Established in 1997 in Missouri.

Donors: William V. Turner; Joseph W. Turner; Julie A. Brown; Al Turner.
Foundation type: Independent foundation.
Financial data (yr. ended 12/31/14): Assets, $4,757,597 (M); gifts received, $200,762; expenditures, $224,540; qualifying distributions, $208,258; giving activities include $199,750 for 41 grants (high: $12,500; low: $500).
Fields of interest: Arts and culture; Education; Foundations; Community and economic development.
Limitations: Applications not accepted. Giving primarily in MO, with emphasis on Springfield. No grants to individuals.
Application information: Unsolicited requests for funds not accepted.
Officers and Directors: Julie A. Brown, Pres. and Director; William V. Turner, V.P. and Director; Joseph W. Turner, Treas. and Director.
EIN: 431778211

5026
The UMB Financial Corporation Charitable Foundation
c/o UMB Bank, N.A.
P.O. Box 415044, M/S 1020307
Kansas City, MO 64141-6692
Application address: Scholarship Mgmt Services, Sholarship America, 1 Sholarship Way, P.O. Box 297

Established in 2007 in Missouri.
Donors: UMB Financial Corp.; UMB Bank, N.A.
Foundation type: Independent foundation.
Financial data (yr. ended 12/31/13): Assets, $4,591,229 (M); gifts received, $110,000; expenditures, $197,376; qualifying distributions, $193,600; giving activities include $190,500 for 22 grants (high: $25,000; low: $2,500).
Purpose and activities: Scholarship awards to dependents of associates of UMBF Corp., its affiliates and subsidiaries.
Fields of interest: Higher education.
Type of support: Scholarships; Student aid.
Application information: Application form required.
  Initial approach: Proposal
  Deadline(s): Jan. 25 for scholarships; none for grants
Officers and Directors: Mariner J. Kemper, Pres. and Director; Peter J. Desilva, V.P. and Director; Suan B. Teson, Secy.; Michael D. Hagedorn, Treas. and Director.
EIN: 205093263

5027
University Lane Foundation
c/o Greensfelder, Hemker & Gale, PC, William Jochens
10 S. Broadway, Ste. 2000
Saint Louis, MO 63102-1747

Established in 1998 in Missouri.
Donor: Mark S. Weil.
Foundation type: Independent foundation.
Financial data (yr. ended 12/31/13): Assets, $1,934,821 (M); expenditures, $345,682; qualifying distributions, $337,000; giving activities include $337,000 for 3 grants (high: $212,000; low: $25,000).
Fields of interest: Arts and culture; Performing arts; Art museums; Education; Higher education; Botanical gardens; Family planning; Maternal and

perinatal health; Learning disorders; Catholicism; Judaism; People with hearing impairments.
Limitations: Applications not accepted. Giving primarily in St. Louis, MO. No grants to individuals.
Application information: Contributes only to pre-selected organizations.
Trustees: John D. Weil; Mark S. Weil.
Director: William Jochens.
EIN: 436795986

5028
DeWitt & Caroline Van Evera Foundation
(formerly DeWitt Van Evera Foundation)
431D North Polo Dr.
Saint Louis, MO 63105-2652
Contact: Margretta Van Evera Forrester, Advisor
E-mail: grettaf@sw.bell.net

Established in 1959 in Utah.
Donors: Caroline Irene Van Evera†; DeWitt Van Evera†.
Foundation type: Independent foundation.
Financial data (yr. ended 12/31/13): Assets, $2,037,714 (M); expenditures, $282,299; qualifying distributions, $256,191; giving activities include $247,690 for 23 grants (high: $50,000; low: $1,000).
Purpose and activities: Grants primarily for education for at risk or underserved populations, including faculty development, arts education and programs for children.
Fields of interest: Education.
Type of support: General support; Continuing support; Capital and infrastructure; Endowments; Curriculum development; Scholarships.
Limitations: Applications not accepted. Giving primarily in MN and MO. No grants to individuals, or for matching gifts; no loans.
Application information: Unsolicited requests for funds not accepted. Almost all funding is distributed on a continuing basis to ongoing projects that have been selected by the foundation's advisors.
  Board meeting date(s): Late Apr. or early May
Trustee: U.S. Bank, N.A.
Advisors: Betsy Esber; Margretta V.E. Forrester; Stephen W. Van Evera.
Number of staff: None.
EIN: 876117907

5029
The Vassia Family Charitable Foundation
c/o Enterprise Trust
150 N. Meramec
Saint Louis, MO 63105-3779 (314) 889-2000
Contact: Victoria C. McCrea

Established in 2006 in Missouri.
Donors: Lucille A. Vassia; Mary Jane Vassia†.
Foundation type: Independent foundation.
Financial data (yr. ended 12/31/14): Assets, $1,588,301 (M); expenditures, $204,568; qualifying distributions, $173,000; giving activities include $173,000 for 11 grants (high: $60,000; low: $5,000).
Fields of interest: Education; Catholicism; Youth development.
Limitations: Applications accepted. Giving primarily in St. Louis, MO.
Application information: Application form required.
  Initial approach: Completed application form
  Deadline(s): Sept. 30

Trustee: Enterprise Bank & Trust Co.
EIN: 202533912

5030
Vatterott Foundation
10449 St. Charles Rock Rd.
Saint Ann, MO 63074-1825

Established in 1948 in Missouri.
Donors: Charles F. Vatterott, Jr.†; Joseph A.
Vatterott†; John Harvey Vatterott†; William H. Erker;
Mary Patricia Vatterott†; John C. Vatterott.
Foundation type: Independent foundation.
Financial data (yr. ended 05/31/13): Assets,
$2,711,765 (M); expenditures, $412,671;
qualifying distributions, $333,109; giving activities
include $333,109 for 55 grants (high: $55,000;
low: $500).
Purpose and activities: Giving primarily for
elementary and secondary education for
economically disadvantaged youngsters, programs
that serve minority populations and enhance racial
equality, and to Roman Catholic organizations and
human service agencies that serve the poor.
Fields of interest: Education; Elementary and
secondary education; Early childhood education;
Nonprofits; Religion; Christianity; Catholicism;
Human services; Ethnic and racial groups;
Low-income and poor people.
Type of support: General support; Regranting;
Continuing support; Capital campaigns; Seed
money.
Limitations: Applications not accepted. Giving
primarily in St. Louis, MO. No grants to individuals.
Application information: Unsolicited requests for
funds not accepted.
Trustees: Claire Vatterott Hundelt; Daniel Vatterott;
Frank J. Vatterott; Glennon R. Vatterott, Jr.; John C.
Vatterott; Madeleine Vatterott; Paul B. Vatterott, Jr.
Number of staff: 1 part-time professional.
EIN: 436031155

5031
VJS Charitable Private Foundation
21 River Trail Dr.
Saint Charles, MO 63303-6254

Established in 2006 in Missouri.
Donors: Carol Schulte Beck; Robert J. Beck; Vernon
J. Schulte.
Foundation type: Independent foundation.
Financial data (yr. ended 02/28/15): Assets,
$3,593,144 (M); gifts received, $500,000;
expenditures, $408,519; qualifying distributions,
$406,665; giving activities include $402,900 for 37
grants (high: $100,000; low: $1,000).
Fields of interest: Education; Higher education.
Limitations: Applications not accepted. Giving
primarily in MO.
Application information: Unsolicited requests for
funds not accepted.
Trustees: Carol Schulte Beck; Robert J. Beck.
EIN: 756743081

5032
Walter and Jean Voelkerding Charitable Trust
P.O. Box 81
Dutzow, MO 63342-0081

Established in 1968 in Missouri.
Donor: Walter J. Voelkerding†.
Foundation type: Independent foundation.
Financial data (yr. ended 02/28/13): Assets,
$3,600,017 (M); expenditures, $221,325;
qualifying distributions, $186,556; giving activities
include $186,556 for grants.
Purpose and activities: Giving primarily for Christian
organizations and churches.
Fields of interest: Christianity; Youth services.
Limitations: Applications accepted. Giving limited to
Warren County, MO. No grants to individuals.
Application information:
  Initial approach: Letter
  Deadline(s): None
  Board meeting date(s): Annually
Trustees: Aaron W. Marquart; William F. Marquart;
John J. Maune; David J. Voelkerding; Eric G.
Voelkerding; William J. Zollmann II.
EIN: 237015780

5033
George Von Hoffmann Foundation, Inc.
16751 Eagle Bluff Ct.
Chesterfield, MO 63005-4643

Donors: George Von Hoffmann; George Von
Hoffmann, Jr.; Von Hoffmann Press, Inc.; Von
Hoffmann Corp.
Foundation type: Independent foundation.
Financial data (yr. ended 10/31/13): Assets,
$5,709,646 (M); expenditures, $250,191;
qualifying distributions, $212,000; giving activities
include $212,000 for 43 grants (high: $55,000;
low: $1,500).
Fields of interest: Hospital care; Specialty hospital
care; Human services; Child welfare.
Limitations: Applications not accepted. Giving
primarily in St. Louis, MO. No grants to individuals.
Application information: Unsolicited requests for
funds not accepted.
Officers: Eric Von Hoffman, Pres.; Dale W. Von
Hoffmann, V.P. and Secy.; Bryan Lundstrom, V.P.;
George Von Hoffmann III, V.P.; Cindy Weis, V.P.
EIN: 436029902

5034
The Earl E. Walker and Myrtle E. Walker Foundation
120 W. Adams Ave., Ste. 306
Saint Louis, MO 63122-4084

Established in 1987 in Missouri.
Donors: CARR Lane Manufacturing; Walker Family
Trust; W & W, Inc.; Earl E. Walker; Myrtle E. Walker;
Home Towne Suites - Bowling Green LLC; Home
Towne Suites - Clarksville LLC; All American
Products.
Foundation type: Independent foundation.
Financial data (yr. ended 12/31/13): Assets,
$13,017,423 (M); expenditures, $176,923;
qualifying distributions, $116,008; giving activities
include $116,008 for 3 grants (high: $85,000; low:
$1,008).
Fields of interest: Arts and culture; Higher
education; Zoos.
Type of support: General support; Capital and
infrastructure; Endowments; Student aid.
Limitations: Applications not accepted. Giving
primarily in MO.

Application information: Unsolicited requests for
funds not accepted.
Trustees: Nancy E. Frost; Brian K. Humes; Peggy E.
Swisher; Mary E. Walker; Myrtle E. Walker; Thomas
E. Walker.
EIN: 431466121

5035
The George Herbert Walker Foundation
4549 Augusta Shores Ct.
Augusta, MO 63332-1575

Established in 1954 in New York.
Donors: G.H. Walker, Jr.†; George H. Walker III; Mary
Carter Walker†.
Foundation type: Independent foundation.
Financial data (yr. ended 12/31/13): Assets,
$1,744,001 (M); gifts received, $4,499;
expenditures, $241,233; qualifying distributions,
$201,150; giving activities include $201,150 for 25
grants (high: $100,000; low: $500).
Fields of interest: Science; Public affairs; Human
services.
Limitations: Applications not accepted. Giving
primarily in St. Louis, MO. No grants to individuals.
Application information: Contributes only to
pre-selected organizations.
Trustees: George H. Walker III; George H. Walker IV.
EIN: 136084806

5036
The Lloyd R. Wallace Charitable Foundation
217 Main St.
Braymer, MO 64624
Application address: c/o Michael R. Brown, 8976
N.E. Patton Rd., Hamilton, MO 64644, tel.: (816)
583-2185

Established in 2004 in Missouri.
Foundation type: Independent foundation.
Financial data (yr. ended 12/31/13): Assets,
$5,028,630 (M); expenditures, $287,132;
qualifying distributions, $240,594; giving activities
include $239,891 for 79 grants (high: $23,600;
low: $300).
Fields of interest: Hospital care.
Type of support: Student aid; General support.
Limitations: Applications accepted. Giving primarily
in MO.
Application information: Application form required.
  Initial approach: Request application form
  Deadline(s): None
Officers: Brian D. Prewitt, Pres.; James C. Jarrett,
V.P.; Michael R. Brown, Secy.
Directors: David Moore; Timothy L. Murray.
EIN: 412091015

5037
Audrey J. Walton and Ann Walton Kroenke Charitable Foundation
911 Crestland Ave.
Columbia, MO 65203-2311

Donors: Audrey J. Walton; Ann Walton Kroenke
Charitable Lead Trust.
Foundation type: Independent foundation.
Financial data (yr. ended 11/30/13): Assets,
$2,569,444 (M); gifts received, $388,793;
expenditures, $180,000; qualifying distributions,

$180,000; giving activities include $180,000 for 12 grants (high: $50,000; low: $5,000).
Fields of interest: Education; Higher education; Animal welfare; Human services; Child welfare.
Type of support: General support.
Limitations: Applications not accepted. Giving primarily in MO; funding also in CA. No grants to individuals.
Application information: Contributes only to pre-selected organizations.
Officers: Audrey J. Walton, Pres.; Ann Walton Kroene, V.P.; Henry T. Lowe, Secy.-Treas.
EIN: 431696655

5038
Welch Family Foundation
(formerly The Lantz Welch Charitable Foundation)
P.O. Box 14244
Kansas City, MO   64152-7244   (816) 741-7799

Established in 1985 in Missouri.
Donors: Lantz Welch; Timothy L. Brake.
Foundation type: Independent foundation.
Financial data (yr. ended 12/31/14): Assets, $2,227,333; expenditures, $398,455; qualifying distributions, $366,847.
Fields of interest: Arts and culture; Education; Health; Diseases and conditions; Legal services; Child welfare.
Type of support: General support; Program development.
Limitations: Applications accepted. Giving primarily in the metropolitan Kansas City, MO, area. No support for political campaigns. No grants to individuals.
Application information: Application form required.
   Initial approach: Proposal
   Deadline(s): Apr. 1 and Oct. 1
   Board meeting date(s): Twice a year
Officers and Directors: Lantz Welch, Chair. and Treas. and Director; Laura Welch, Pres. and Director; John W. Meara, Treas. and Director; Greg Welch.
EIN: 431388861

5039
John M. Wolff Foundation
P.O. Box 11356
Clayton, MO   63105-0156
*Application address:*c/o Brad Landsbaum The Commerce Trust Co., 8000 Forsyth Blvd., Clayton, MO 63105, tel.: (314) 746-5064

Established in 1956 in Missouri.
Donor: John M. Wolff†.
Foundation type: Independent foundation.
Financial data (yr. ended 12/31/14): Assets, $4,182,094 (M); expenditures, $205,552; qualifying distributions, $156,683; giving activities include $150,000 for 9 grants (high: $50,000; low: $5,000).
Fields of interest: Arts and culture; Hospital care; Hospice care; Astronomy; Human services; Food aid; Food banks.
Limitations: Applications accepted. Giving primarily in St. Louis, MO; some giving also in AZ. No grants to individuals.

Application information: Application form required.
   Initial approach: Letter
   Deadline(s): Oct. 1st
   Board meeting date(s): Oct.
Trustees: Michael R. Wolff; The Commerce Trust Co.
EIN: 436026247

5040
Wolff Shoe Foundation
1705 Larkin Williams Rd.
Fenton, MO   63026-2024

Established in 1984 in Missouri.
Donors: Wolff Shoe Co.; Elaine Wolff; William Wolff; William Wolff Trust; Sarah Wolff; Samuel Wolff.
Foundation type: Company-sponsored foundation.
Financial data (yr. ended 12/31/13): Assets, $31,121 (M); gifts received, $196,008; expenditures, $166,150; qualifying distributions, $166,150; giving activities include $166,150 for 12 grants (high: $50,000; low: $150).
Purpose and activities: The foundation supports organizations involved with education, health, and Judaism.
Fields of interest: Education; Elementary and secondary education; Higher education; Graduate and professional education; Nonprofits; Health; Hospital care; Judaism; Theology.
Type of support: General support; Scholarships; Regranting.
Limitations: Applications not accepted. Giving primarily in the St. Louis, MO, area. No grants to individuals.
Application information: Contributes only to pre-selected organizations.
Officers and Directors: Elaine Wolff, Mgr. and Director; Gary Wolff, Mgr. and Director; William Wolf, Mgr. and Director.
EIN: 431345719

5041
The Woodcock Foundation for the Appreciation of the Arts Inc.
9730 E. Watson Rd., Ste. 100
Saint Louis, MO   63126

Foundation type: Operating foundation.
Financial data (yr. ended 12/31/13): Assets, $2,262,449 (M); expenditures, $302,247; qualifying distributions, $282,405; giving activities include $282,405 for 1 grant.
Fields of interest: Arts and culture.
Limitations: Applications not accepted.
Application information: Unsolicited requests for funds not accepted.
Officers and Trustees: Lorrin S. Watson, Chair. and Trustee; Lynne M. Gale, Secy. and Trustee; Nick Gale; Barbara Hudock.
EIN: 263029895

5042
Herbert A. & Adrian W. Woods Foundation
c/o Bank of America, N.A.
100 North Broadway, MO2-100-07-15
Saint Louis, MO   63102-2728
Contact: Shanise Evans, V.P.
E-mail: shanise.evans@baml.com; Main URL: https://www.bankofamerica.com/philanthropic/grantmaking.go

Established in 1999 in Missouri.
Donor: Adrian W. Woods Trust.
Foundation type: Independent foundation.
Financial data (yr. ended 12/31/13): Assets, $7,470,883 (M); expenditures, $340,688; qualifying distributions, $271,744; giving activities include $248,000 for 20 grants (high: $30,000; low: $5,000).
Purpose and activities: The foundation is dedicated to the founders' interests in charitable organizations that serve abused, neglected, or troubled children; the poor; the Episcopal Church and its affiliates, including outreach programs; art and culture in the metropolitan St. Louis, Missouri area; animal welfare in Missouri; and victims of illness or disability, including research in this area.
Fields of interest: Specialty hospital care; Christianity; Human services; Child welfare; Youth development.
Limitations: Applications accepted. Giving primarily in St. Louis, MO. No grants to individuals.
Application information:
   Initial approach: Online approach via foundation web site
   Deadline(s): Sept. 1
Trustee: Bank of America, N.A.
EIN: 436826365

5043
Henry E. Wurst Family Foundation
1331 Saline St.
North Kansas City, MO   64116-4410   (816) 842-3113
Contact: Margaret S. Wurst, Secy.

Established in 1955 in Missouri.
Foundation type: Independent foundation.
Financial data (yr. ended 12/31/13): Assets, $3,548,476 (M); expenditures, $174,282; qualifying distributions, $166,928; giving activities include $166,500 for 90 grants (high: $9,000; low: $100).
Purpose and activities: Giving primarily to character building programs for youth. Some support also for welfare agencies, youth organizations, and higher education.
Fields of interest: Higher education; Human services; Child welfare.
Type of support: General support; Annual campaigns.
Application information:
   Initial approach: Proposal
   Copies of proposal: 1
   Deadline(s): None
Officers: John C. Wurst, Chair.; Michael S. Wurst, Vice-Chair.; Margaret S. Wurst, Secy.
Number of staff: None.
EIN: 486107464

MONTANA

5044
The Angora Ridge Foundation
c/o Daniel Weinberg
1524 W. Lakeshore Dr.
Whitefish, MT 59937

Established in 2004 in Montana.
Donors: Gayle Weinberg; Daniel Weinberg†; Lewis Weinberg.
Foundation type: Independent foundation.
Financial data (yr. ended 12/31/13): Assets, $6,760,516 (M); expenditures, $446,634; qualifying distributions, $412,752; giving activities include $412,752 for 45 grants (high: $150,000; low: $50).
Purpose and activities: Giving primarily for justice, recreation and healthy lifestyle, environmental education and conservation, marine ecology, the arts, and organizations in the foundation's local communities of the Oakland Bay Area, Whitefish, and Lake Tahoe.
Fields of interest: Arts and culture; Education; Environment; Services for offenders; Christianity; Sports and recreation; Human services.
Limitations: Applications not accepted. Giving primarily in MT. No grants to individuals.
Application information: Unsolicited request for funds not accepted.
Officers and Directors: Daniel C. Weinberg, Pres. and Director; Zachary Weinberg, Secy. and Director; Molly Jarmusz, Treas.; Abigail Weinberg.
EIN: 201674794

5045
Boe Brothers Foundation
(formerly The Lief Boe Charitable Trust)
c/o Davidson Trust Co.
P.O. Box 2309
Great Falls, MT 59403-2309 (406) 791-7324
Contact: Terri Bowers

Established in 1994 in Montana.
Foundation type: Independent foundation.
Financial data (yr. ended 12/31/13): Assets, $5,086,401 (M); expenditures, $295,954; qualifying distributions, $232,999; giving activities include $225,501 for 30 grants (high: $45,100; low: $337).
Fields of interest: Elementary and secondary education; Higher education; Public libraries; Protestantism; Human services; Child welfare.
Limitations: Applications accepted. Giving primarily in northern and central MT. No grants to individuals.
Application information: Application form required.
  Initial approach: Letter
  Deadline(s): None
Trustees: Al Faechner; Davidson Trust Co.
Number of staff: 1 part-time professional.
EIN: 841378691

5046
Broadbent Family Foundation, Inc.
P.O. Box 1019
Livingston, MT 59047-1019

Established in 1989 in Montana.

Donors: Robert R. Broadbent; William S. Broadbent; Camille W. Broadbent.
Foundation type: Independent foundation.
Financial data (yr. ended 12/31/13): Assets, $3,213,235 (M); gifts received, $15,500; expenditures, $230,008; qualifying distributions, $144,000; giving activities include $144,000 for 17 grants (high: $100,000; low: $500).
Purpose and activities: Giving primarily for education and wildlife preservation.
Fields of interest: Arts and culture; Education; Wildlife biodiversity; Protestantism; Child welfare.
Limitations: Applications not accepted. No grants to individuals.
Application information: Unsolicited requests for funds not accepted.
Officers and Directors: Robert R. Broadbent, Chair. and Director; William S. Broadbent, Pres. and Director; Mary K. Broadbent, V.P. and Director; James A. Posewitz, Secy. and Director; Camille W. Broadbent, Treas. and Director; John P. Bailey, Exec. Dir.
EIN: 810161642

5047
The Cinnabar Foundation
P.O. Box 7323
Missoula, MT 59807-7323 (406) 250-9810
Contact: Gary J. Wolfe, Exec. Dir.
E-mail for Gary J. Wolfe:
gwolfe@cinnabarfoundation.org; Main URL: http://www.cinnabarfoundation.org

Established in 1982 in Montana.
Donor: Leonard Sargent†.
Foundation type: Independent foundation.
Financial data (yr. ended 12/31/13): Assets, $9,865,800 (M); gifts received, $85,455; expenditures, $453,090; qualifying distributions, $439,348; giving activities include $370,000 for 110 grants (high: $10,000; low: $1,000).
Purpose and activities: Giving primarily to promote environmental protection and fish and wildlife conservation in MT and the greater Yellowstone ecosystem.
Fields of interest: Environment; Natural resources; Biodiversity; Wildlife biodiversity; Aquatic wildlife protection.
Type of support: General support; Matching grants; Land acquisitions; Convening; Capacity-building and technical assistance; Research; Student aid.
Limitations: Applications accepted. Giving limited to MT and the Yellowstone area.
Publications: Annual report; Annual report (including application guidelines); Multi-year report.
Application information: Complete application guidelines available on foundation web site. Application form required.
  Initial approach: Proposal (no more than 2 pages)
  Copies of proposal: 1
  Deadline(s): Generally, Mar. 31
  Board meeting date(s): Semiannually
  Final notification: May 31
Officers and Directors: Robin Tawney Nichols, Chair. and Director; Gordon "Corky" Brittan, Vice-Chair. and Director; Judi Stauffer, Secy. and Director; Ernest J. Turner, Treas. and Director; Gary J. Wolfe, Exec. Dir.; Grant Parker; James Posewitz.
Number of staff: 1 part-time professional.
EIN: 810415045

5048
Cora Foundation, Inc.
354 Brass Lantern Ct.
Bozeman, MT 59715-8619
Contact: Steven T. Ough, Pres.
E-mail: stough@corafoundation.org; Main URL: http://www.corafoundation.org

Established in 1997 in Texas.
Donors: Steven T. Ough; Linda R. Ough.
Foundation type: Independent foundation.
Financial data (yr. ended 12/31/13): Assets, $1,133,150 (M); gifts received, $255,613; expenditures, $180,243; qualifying distributions, $177,834; giving activities include $175,000 for 8 grants (high: $80,000; low: $5,000).
Purpose and activities: Giving primarily for Christian charities in the areas of education, spiritual development and human services.
Fields of interest: Christianity; Christians.
Type of support: Fundraising; Pro bono consulting services; Matching grants; Marketing; Capacity-building and technical assistance; Program development; Curriculum development; Technical assistance; Program evaluations.
Limitations: Applications not accepted. Giving limited to organizations in the U.S., with a preference for those in MT, ND, and TX. No support for non-Christian organizations. No grants to individuals, or for operating support.
Publications: Grants list.
Application information: Applications are only by invitation of the foundation's directors. The directors will initiate requests to apply based on their interests and research of organizations. Unknown people and organizations who contact the foundation requesting an invitation to apply will not be acknowledged.
  Board meeting date(s): Apr., Aug., Dec.
Officers: Steven T. Ough, Pres.; Linda R. Ough, Secy.-Treas.
Director: Bruce R. Ough.
EIN: 760528888

5049
Ila B. Dousman Fund Inc.
250 Wilderness Ln.
Whitefish, MT 59937-3230
Application address: 321 Fairway Dr., Whitefish, MT 59937, tel.: (406) 862-4487

Established in 1986 in Montana.
Foundation type: Independent foundation.
Financial data (yr. ended 12/31/13): Assets, $72,324 (M); expenditures, $222,852; qualifying distributions, $165,866; giving activities include $151,348 for 39 grants (high: $25,000; low: $500).
Fields of interest: Education; University education; Family planning; Human services; Child welfare; Adult and child mentoring.
Limitations: Applications accepted. Giving primarily in MT. No support for political purposes. No grants to individuals.
Application information: Application form required.
  Initial approach: Proposal
  Deadline(s): None
Officer: Kristin Tabor, Exec. Dir.
Directors: Carole I. Erickson; Leif B. Erickson.
EIN: 810417522

5050
Flathead Community Foundation
345 1st Ave. E.
Kalispell, MT 59903 (406) 756-9047
Contact: Lucy Smith, Exec. Dir.
FAX: (406) 758-2805;
E-mail: info@flatheadcommunityfoundation.org;
Mailing address: P.O. Box 1422, Kalispell, MT
59903; Main URL: http://
www.flatheadcommunityfoundation.org
Facebook: https://www.facebook.com/pages/
Flathead-Community-Foundation/
367840799997657?ref=hl

Established in 2005 in Montana.
Foundation type: Community foundation.
Financial data (yr. ended 12/31/12): Assets,
$748,718 (M); gifts received, $276,662;
expenditures, $192,209; giving activities include
$112,329 for 4+ grants (high: $27,500).
Purpose and activities: The foundation seeks to
enrich lives of present and future generations by
supporting philanthropy in the communities served.
Limitations: Applications accepted. Giving primarily
in Flathead, MT.
Application information: Visit foundation Web site
for application form and guidelines. Grants are
awarded from $100 -$1000. Application form
required.
  Initial approach: Submit application and
    attachments
  Copies of proposal: 6
  Deadline(s): Oct. 29
Officers and Directors: Lisa Schnee, Pres. and
Director; Mike Smith, V.P. and Director; Melinda
Morton, Secy. and Director; Ty Weber, Treas. and
Director; Heidi Escalante; Jeff Lewis; Laura Long;
Marc Lorenzen; John Michael Myers.
EIN: 203153511

5051
Foundation for Community Vitality
P.O. Box 7113
Billings, MT 59103-7113 4062481114
Contact: Lynda Bourque Moss, Exec. Dir.
E-mail: lynda@ffcv.net; Main URL: http://
www.ffcv.net/Foundation_for_Community_Vitality/
Contact_Us.html

Foundation type: Independent foundation.
Financial data (yr. ended 12/31/13): Assets,
$10,741,455 (M); gifts received, $51,786;
expenditures, $256,785; qualifying distributions,
$247,437; giving activities include $231,349 for 25
grants (high: $74,418; low: $100).
Purpose and activities: The organization aims to
work to enhance sustainable vitality of communities
in Montana and its surrounding region.
Fields of interest: Land resources; Community and
economic development; Sustainable development;
Economic development; American Indians.
Type of support: General support.
Limitations: Applications not accepted. Giving
primarily in MT and the surrounding region, with a
focus on the Yellowstone River region of MT and the
area around Sheridan, WY.
Application information: Proposals are by invitation
only.
Officers: Harvey Stewart, Pres.; James R. Scott,
V.P.; Michelle Sullivan, Secy.-Treas.
Director: Christine Scott; Courtney Scott.
EIN: 841376323

5052
Gallagher Western Montana Charitable Foundation
P.O. Box 4787
Missoula, MT 59806
Application address: c/o Carolyn Montgomery, P.O.
Box 3387, Missoula, MT 59806, tel.: (406)
240-6353

Established in 2001 in Montana.
Donor: W.J. & Rosemary Gallagher Foundation.
Foundation type: Independent foundation.
Financial data (yr. ended 12/31/13): Assets,
$6,272,681 (M); expenditures, $379,709;
qualifying distributions, $353,841; giving activities
include $316,600 for 28 grants (high: $55,000;
low: $2,000).
Fields of interest: Nonprofits; Health care clinics;
Human services; Food banks; Child welfare.
Type of support: General support; Regranting.
Limitations: Applications accepted. Giving limited to
MT, primarily in Missoula and western MT.
Application information: Application form required.
  Initial approach: Contact foundation for
    application form
  Deadline(s): Contact foundation for deadline
Trustee: US Bank.
Director: Carolyn Montgomery.
EIN: 912138399

5053
The Gerhart Foundation
P.O. Box 2286
Great Falls, MT 59403-2286 (406) 899-0277
Contact: William Beecher, Pres.

Established in 1995 in Montana.
Donor: Thomas L. Gerhart†.
Foundation type: Independent foundation.
Financial data (yr. ended 12/31/13): Assets,
$2,879,943 (M); expenditures, $162,715;
qualifying distributions, $148,800; giving activities
include $148,800 for 12 grants (high: $18,600;
low: $4,650).
Fields of interest: Education; Nonprofits; Human
services; Food banks; Youth services.
Type of support: Regranting.
Limitations: Applications accepted. Giving primarily
in Great Falls, MT.
Application information: Application form required.
  Initial approach: Letter
  Deadline(s): None
Officers: William Beecher, Pres.; Howard Noble,
V.P.; James Croff, Secy.
EIN: 810501137

5054
The Greater Montana Foundation
1038 Monroe Ave.
Helena, MT 59601-2661 (406) 443-5693
Contact: Sidney Armstrong, Exec. Dir.
E-mail: info@greatermontana.org; Application
address: c/o Robert Hoene, 281 Chapman Hill Rd.,
Ste. 1, Big Fork, MT 59911; Main URL: http://
www.greatermontana.org
Grants List: http://greatermontana.org/category/
awarded-grants-list
RSS feed: http://greatermontana.org/feed

Established in 1959 in Montana.
Foundation type: Independent foundation.

Financial data (yr. ended 12/31/13): Assets,
$9,756,437 (M); expenditures, $389,859;
qualifying distributions, $319,398; giving activities
include $288,800 for 21 grants (high: $48,000;
low: $200).
Fields of interest: Historic preservation; University
education; Communication media; Radio.
Limitations: Applications accepted. Giving primarily
in MT.
Application information: Application forms available
on foundation web site. Application form required.
  Initial approach: Proposal
  Deadline(s): Apr. 1
Officers: Randal Morger, Chair.; Sarah Etchart,
Co-Vice-Chair.; William Whitsitt, Co-Vice-Chair.;
Steve Browning, Secy.; Sidney O'Malley Armstrong,
Exec. Dir.
Trustees: Norma Ashby; Brody Craney; Darlene
Craney; Ronald Davis; Fred J. Flanders; Vic Miller;
Daniel Synder; Monty Wallis.
EIN: 816009847

5055
Hawkins Scholarship Foundation
c/o Davidson Trust Co.
P.O. Box 2309
Great Falls, MT 59403-2309 (406) 791-7325

Foundation type: Independent foundation.
Financial data (yr. ended 12/31/13): Assets,
$4,224,171 (M); expenditures, $219,673;
qualifying distributions, $177,350; giving activities
include $177,350 for 182 grants to individuals
(high: $2,000; low: $750).
Purpose and activities: The foundation awards
scholarships to high school graduates from Flathead
County, MT.
Fields of interest: Education.
Type of support: Student aid.
Limitations: Applications accepted. Giving limited to
residents of Flathead County, MT.
Application information: Application form required.
  Initial approach: Proposal
  Deadline(s): Prior to graduation
Trustee: Davidson Trust Co.
EIN: 816018444

5056
The Heisey Foundation
c/o U.S. Bank, N.A.
P.O. Box 5000
Great Falls, MT 59403-5000

Donor: Charles E. Heisey†.
Foundation type: Independent foundation.
Financial data (yr. ended 12/31/14): Assets,
$6,783,417 (M); expenditures, $329,728;
qualifying distributions, $296,511; giving activities
include $282,450 for 41 grants (high: $61,650;
low: $150).
Purpose and activities: Support for a high school
awards program for students attending specific
schools located in the foundation's trade area who
are making the most improvement in citizenship,
effort, and scholarship to the best of their ability,
and for scholarship funds at local colleges and
universities.
Fields of interest: Higher education.
Type of support: Scholarships; Student aid.
Limitations: Applications not accepted. Giving
limited to the Great Falls, MT, trade area.

Application information: Trustees designate eligible schools; students are recommended by their schools. Unsolicited requests for funds not accepted.

Board meeting date(s): Annually

Trustees: Daniel C. Ewen; C.R. Reiquam; Marilyn Rose; John D. Stephenson, Jr.; U.S. Bank, N.A.
EIN: 816009624

5057
The High Stakes Foundation
(formerly Montana Good Works Foundation)
P.O. Box 96
Arlee, MT 59821-0096 (406) 726-2030
Contact: Cherie Garcelon, Prog. Off.
Main URL: http://www.highstakesfoundation.org
Grants List: https://highstakesfoundation.wordpress.com/2014grants

Established in 2007 in Montana.
Donors: Mary Stranahan Trust; Mary Stranahan.
Foundation type: Independent foundation.
Financial data (yr. ended 12/31/13): Assets, $1,661,185 (M); expenditures, $292,809; qualifying distributions, $276,503; giving activities include $167,000 for 17 grants (high: $25,000; low: $2,500).
Fields of interest: Natural resources; Biodiversity; Wildlife biodiversity; Environmental education; Social sciences; Human services.
Type of support: Policy, advocacy and systems reform.
Limitations: Applications accepted. Giving primarily in MT.
Application information: See foundation web site for complete application guidelines. Application form required.
Initial approach: Completed application form
Deadline(s): Apr. 1 and Sept. 1
Officer: Dawn McGee, Pres. and Secy.; Cherie Garcelon, Mgr.
Directors: Joel Solomon; Mary Stranahan; Molly Stranahan.
EIN: 205815274

5058
Lippard-Clawiter Foundation
(formerly Charles W. & Gina S. Lippard Foundation)
P.O. Box 1605
Great Falls, MT 59403-1605
Contact: Pam Guschausky, Secy.-Treas.
FAX: (406) 727-0895; E-mail for Pam Guschausky: pamg@hamilton-misfeldt.com

Established in 1980 in Montana.
Foundation type: Independent foundation.
Financial data (yr. ended 12/31/13): Assets, $8,582,813 (M); expenditures, $430,198; qualifying distributions, $377,393; giving activities include $373,643 for grants.
Purpose and activities: Giving primarily for community development.
Fields of interest: Community and economic development; Sports and recreation; Human services; Youth organizing.
Type of support: General support; Equipment.
Limitations: Applications not accepted. Giving limited to Chouteau County, MT. No grants to individuals.

Application information: Unsolicited requests for funds not accepted.
Board meeting date(s): Nov. and May
Officers: Francis Engellant, Pres.; Allin Cheetham, V.P.; Pam Guschausky, Secy.-Treas.
Board Members: Ken Evans; Stan Klimas; Robert Quinn.
Number of staff: None.
EIN: 810394026

5059
Elizabeth A. Lynn Foundation
P.O. Box 439
Lakeside, MT 59922-0439
Contact: Diane Titch, Grant Admin.
Main URL: http://www.elizabethalynnfoundation.org

Established in 1981 in Washington.
Donor: Elizabeth A. Lynn†.
Foundation type: Independent foundation.
Financial data (yr. ended 11/30/14): Assets, $7,077,468 (M); expenditures, $411,273; qualifying distributions, $318,039; giving activities include $318,039 for 37 grants (high: $15,000; low: $5,000).
Purpose and activities: Elizabeth Lynn began the Elizabeth A. Lynn Foundation in 1984 to help strengthen the individuals and community that surrounded her and her family. Today, Elizabeth's children and grandchildren continue her legacy by giving back to the communities in which they reside (Puget Sound Corridor in WA; Blaine County, ID; Los Angeles, CA; and Portland, OR). The Foundation supports both academic and educational programs that promote all types of learning through tutoring, mentoring, career training, and enrichment programs for all ages.
Fields of interest: Education.
Type of support: General support; Capital campaigns; Capital and infrastructure; Equipment; Program development; Scholarships.
Limitations: Applications accepted. Giving limited to the following areas: Los Angeles, CA, Blaine County, ID, Portland, OR, and the Puget Sound Corridor, WA. No grants to individuals.
Publications: Application guidelines; Financial statement.
Application information: Letter of inquiry required; can be submitted between Dec. 1 and Jan. 31. Visit foundation web site for complete details, and for information on focus of foundation, guidelines, application format, deadlines, and all requirements and attachments.
Initial approach: Letter of inquiry between Dec. 1 - Jan. 31; see web site for instructions
Board meeting date(s): Once annually
Final notification: Foundation will respond to application by Nov.
Trustees: Traci Kennedy; Chloe Lynn; Elizabeth Lynn; Riley Lynn; Jody Moss.
EIN: 911156982

5060
Montana Mental Health Trust
P.O. Box 8666
Missoula, MT 59807-8666
Contact: E. Edwin Eck, Dir.
E-mail: montanamht@gmail.com; Main URL: http://www.mmht.org

Donor: Montana Mental Health Settlement Trust.

Foundation type: Independent foundation.
Financial data (yr. ended 06/30/13): Assets, $5,184,097 (M); gifts received, $5,642,594; expenditures, $386,159; qualifying distributions, $364,889; giving activities include $325,815 for 3 grants (high: $225,000; low: $8,749).
Fields of interest: Health; Human services.
Limitations: Applications accepted. Giving primarily in MT.
Publications: Application guidelines.
Application information: See foundation web site for complete application guidelines and application form. Application form required.
Initial approach: E-mail application
Deadline(s): See foundation web site for current deadlines
Trustees: Marcia Armstrong; William Docktor; Gary Mihelish; Robert Runkel; Sheriff Dan Tronrud; Pam Veis; John Warner.
Director: E. Edwin Eck.
EIN: 466395023

5061
Nance Family Foundation, Inc.
2924 Millennium Cir., Ste. A
Billings, MT 59102-7474
Application address: c/o Robert and Penelope Nance, 5033 Hwy. 3, Billings, MT 59106, tel.:(406) 245-2550

Established in 2007 in Montana.
Donors: Amy Nance-Cebull; Robert Nance; Penelope Nance.
Foundation type: Independent foundation.
Financial data (yr. ended 12/31/13): Assets, $4,915,482 (M); expenditures, $172,512; qualifying distributions, $161,000; giving activities include $161,000 for 6 grants (high: $95,000; low: $3,000).
Fields of interest: Education; Health.
Limitations: Applications accepted. Giving primarily in MT.
Application information:
Initial approach: Contact Foundation
Deadline(s): Contact Foundation
Officers: Penelope Nance, Pres.; Robert Nance, V.P.; Amy Nance-Cebull, Secy.-Treas.
EIN: 260469189

5062
The Sample Foundation, Inc.
P.O. Box 279
Billings, MT 59103 (406) 245-6342
Contact: Barbara Sample, Pres.
FAX: (406) 245-8303;
E-mail: applications@samplefoundation.org; Main URL: http://www.samplefoundation.org

Established in 1954 in Florida.
Donors: Helen S. Sample†; John Glen Sample†; Joseph S. Sample; Miriam T. Sample; Michael S. Sample; David F. Sample; Patrick G. Sample.
Foundation type: Independent foundation.
Financial data (yr. ended 10/31/13): Assets, $8,188,129 (M); gifts received, $176,225; expenditures, $407,198; qualifying distributions, $391,038; giving activities include $389,838 for 72 grants (high: $27,308; low: $100).
Purpose and activities: Giving primarily for health, social welfare, and services for the disadvantaged.

Grant support primarily for capital outlays or to assist in initiating a particular project.

Fields of interest: Human services.

Type of support: Capital campaigns; Equipment; Land acquisitions.

Limitations: Applications accepted. Giving primarily in Collier County, FL, and MT. No support for lobbying, or religious groups. No grants to individuals, or for scholarships, operating budgets, or duplication of services.

Publications: Application guidelines; Annual report; Grants list; Informational brochure (including application guidelines); Program policy statement.

Application information: Application information and form available on foundation web site. Application form required.

  Copies of proposal: 1
  Deadline(s): Aug. 1
  Board meeting date(s): Oct. 6th
  Final notification: Oct. 31

Officers and Trustees: Joseph S. Sample, Chair. and Trustee; Barbara Sample, Pres. & Exec. Dir.; Michael S. Sample, V.P. and Trustee; T.A. Cox, Treas. and Trustee; David F. Sample; Patrick G. Sample.

Number of staff: None.

EIN: 596138602

5063
Max & Betty Swanson Foundation

201 W. Main St., Ste. 201
Missoula, MT 59802-4326 (406) 728-0810
Contact: David B. Cotner, V.P.

Established in 2001 in Montana.

Donor: Max R. Swanson†.

Foundation type: Independent foundation.

Financial data (yr. ended 12/31/13): Assets, $3,663,291 (M); expenditures, $202,201;

qualifying distributions, $162,460; giving activities include $146,000 for 52 grants (high: $12,000; low: $200).

Fields of interest: Arts and culture; Education; Community and economic development; Human services.

Limitations: Applications accepted. Giving primarily in Missoula, MT.

Application information: Application form required.

  Deadline(s): None

Officers: Kurt Ingold, Pres.; David B. Cotner, V.P.; Clifford Gustafson, Secy.-Treas.

EIN: 810535708

5064
The Ruth and Vernon Taylor Foundation, Montana

1045 Reeves Rd. E., Ste. E
Bozeman, MT 59718-7701 (406) 587-5594

Established in 2004 in Montana.

Donor: James C. Taylor.

Foundation type: Independent foundation.

Financial data (yr. ended 12/31/14): Assets, $6,487,277; expenditures, $364,365; qualifying distributions, $350,169.

Fields of interest: Arts and culture; Museums; Planetariums; Foundations; Human services.

Type of support: Capital and infrastructure; Endowments.

Limitations: Applications accepted. Giving primarily in Bozeman, MT; some funding also in CA, Washington, DC and NC.

Application information:

  Initial approach: Proposal
  Deadline(s): None

Officers and Directors: James C. Taylor, Pres. and Director; Beatrice R. Taylor, V.P. and Director; Peggy L. Olson, Secy.-Treas.; Susan R. Taylor.

EIN: 201746884

5065
Wendy's of Montana Foundation Inc.

2906 2nd Ave. N., Ste. 212
Billings, MT 59101-2026 (406) 252-5125
Contact: Gregory C. McDonald, Pres.

Established in 1998 in Nevada.

Donors: Wendy's of Montana Inc.; Food Services of America; Sam E. McDonald, Jr.; Martin Family Foundation.

Foundation type: Company-sponsored foundation.

Financial data (yr. ended 12/31/13): Assets, $674,136 (M); gifts received, $131,920; expenditures, $236,793; qualifying distributions, $228,322; giving activities include $192,670 for 22 grants (high: $89,530; low: $250).

Purpose and activities: The foundation supports organizations involved with arts and culture, education, athletics, adoption, and community development.

Fields of interest: Arts and culture; Theater; Orchestral music; Art museums; Education; Higher education; Community and economic development; Baseball and softball; Track and field; Human services; Adoption; Youth services.

Type of support: General support; Program development; Sponsorships.

Limitations: Applications accepted. Giving primarily in Billings, MT.

Application information: Application form required.

  Initial approach: Proposal
  Deadline(s): Contact foundation for deadlines

Officers: Gregory C. McDonald, Pres.; John Wilcox, Secy.-Treas.

Director: John T. Jones.

EIN: 880393923

NEBRASKA

5066

America First Foundation

1004 Farnam St., Ste. 400
Omaha, NE 68102-1885 (402) 444-1630
Contact: Lisa Y. Roskens, Pres.
Main URL: http://www.am1stfoundation.org/
index.html

Established in 2002 in Nebraska.
Donors: America First Cos. L.L.C.; The Burlington
Capital Group LLC.
Foundation type: Operating foundation.
Financial data (yr. ended 12/31/12): Assets,
$1,249,541 (M); expenditures, $428,592;
qualifying distributions, $410,750; giving activities
include $410,750 for 39 grants (high: $50,000;
low: $1,000).
Purpose and activities: The foundation supports
programs designed to promote arts and culture,
education, senior care, and programs designed to
promote strong family values.
Fields of interest: Arts and culture; Education;
Higher education; Domesticated animals; Sports
and recreation; Sports; Family services; Senior
services.
Type of support: General support.
Limitations: Applications accepted. Giving primarily
in IA and NE; some giving to national organizations.
No support for national or religious organizations
(unless their programs address specific local
community needs), elementary or secondary
schools (except to provide special initiatives or
programs not covered by regular school budgets),
political action or advocacy groups, organizations
whose primary purpose is to support other non-profit
organizations, fraternal groups, athletic teams,
bands, veteran's organizations, volunteer
firefighters, or similar groups. No grants to
individuals, or for religious doctrines or tenets,
endowments, golf events or fundraisers, or tables at
fundraisers.
Publications: Application guidelines.
Application information: Application form required.
   Initial approach: Letter
   Deadline(s): None
   Board meeting date(s): Third Thurs. of Mar., June,
   Sept. and Dec.
Officers: Lisa Y. Roskens, Pres.; Michael J. Draper,
Secy.-Treas.
Directors: Mark A. Hiatt; Michael B. Yanney.
EIN: 010658759

5067

Ameritas Charitable Foundation

(formerly BLN Charitable Foundation)
5900 O St.
Lincoln, NE 68510-2234 (402) 325-4234
Contact: Sue Wilkinson, Secy. and Cont.

Established in 1985 in Nebraska.
Donor: Ameritas Life Insurance Corp.
Foundation type: Company-sponsored foundation.
Financial data (yr. ended 12/31/13): Assets,
$9,456,982 (M); expenditures, $425,963;
qualifying distributions, $419,662; giving activities
include $419,662 for 52 grants (high: $100,000;
low: $500).

Purpose and activities: The foundation has primary
interest in education programs, but will consider
civic, cultural, and health and welfare requests.
Fields of interest: Arts and culture; Children's
museums; Education; Secondary education; Higher
education; Animal welfare; Health; Hospital care;
Child abuse; Human services; Family services; Child
welfare; Scouting programs.
Type of support: General support; Continuing
support; Annual campaigns; Capital campaigns;
Equipment; Program development; Scholarships;
Sponsorships.
Limitations: Applications accepted. Giving primarily
in Lincoln, NE. No support for organizations that
utilize a major portion of their budget for
administration and solicitation. No grants to
individuals.
Publications: Application guidelines.
Application information: Application form required.
   Initial approach: Proposal
   Deadline(s): Apr. 1 and Nov. 1
   Board meeting date(s): May and Dec.
Officers and Directors: James P. Abel, Pres. and
Director; Sue Wilkinson, Secy. and Cont.; William W.
Lester, Treas. and Director; JoAnn M. Martin.
Number of staff: None.
EIN: 363428705

5068

Assurity Life Foundation

(formerly Security Financial Life Foundation)
2000 Q St.
Lincoln, NE 68503-3609 (402) 437-9504

Established in 1993 in Nebraska.
Donors: Security Mutual Life Insurance Co.; Security
Financial Life Insurance Co.; Assurity Life Insurance
Co.
Foundation type: Company-sponsored foundation.
Financial data (yr. ended 12/31/14): Assets,
$4,205,151; expenditures, $166,565; qualifying
distributions, $150,027.
Purpose and activities: The foundation supports
organizations involved with performing arts, higher
education, land conservation, health, heart disease,
human services, and economic development.
Fields of interest: Performing arts; Theater;
Orchestral music; Higher education; Land
resources; Nonprofits; Health; Health insurance;
Heart and circulatory system diseases; Sustainable
development; Human services.
Type of support: General support; Regranting.
Limitations: Applications accepted. Giving primarily
in Lincoln, NE. No grants to individuals.
Application information:
   Initial approach: Proposal
   Deadline(s): None
Officers and Directors: Thomas E. Henning, Pres.
and C.E.O. and Director; William R. Schmeeckle,
V.P.; Carol S. Watson, Secy.; Marvin P. Ehly, Treas.
and Director; Marc E. Lebaron; James E. McClerg;
David T. Wallman.
Number of staff: None.
EIN: 470775374

5069

Alan & Marcia Baer Foundation

1001 Fort Crook Rd. N., Ste. 140
Bellevue, NE 68005-4298 (402) 552-1001
Contact: Ted Baer, Pres.

Donor: E. John Brandeis†.
Foundation type: Independent foundation.
Financial data (yr. ended 06/30/13): Assets,
$4,390,387; expenditures, $378,411; qualifying
distributions, $235,716; giving activities include
$235,716 for 47 grants (high: $37,604; low: $250).
Fields of interest: Arts and culture; Education;
Higher education; Diseases and conditions;
Christianity; Judaism; Human services; Child
welfare.
Type of support: General support.
Limitations: Applications accepted. Giving primarily
in Omaha, NE. No grants to individuals.
Officers: Theodore Baer, Pres.; Kathy Baer, V.P. and
Secy.
Board Member: Zac Baer.
EIN: 476032560

5070

Hollis and Helen Baright Foundation

9290 W. Dodge Rd., Ste. 202
Omaha, NE 68114-3320
Application address: c/o Nick R. Taylor, Tr., 10050
Regency Cir., Ste. 200, Omaha, NE 68114-3794;
E-mail: ntaylor@fitzlaw.com

Established in 1995 in Nebraska.
Donor: Hollis I. Baright†.
Foundation type: Independent foundation.
Financial data (yr. ended 12/31/13): Assets,
$3,450,246 (M); expenditures, $246,678;
qualifying distributions, $204,000; giving activities
include $204,000 for 2 grants (high: $200,000;
low: $4,000).
Fields of interest: Education; Domesticated
animals.
Type of support: Capital and infrastructure; Student
aid.
Limitations: Applications accepted. Giving primarily
in the greater Omaha, NE, metropolitan area. No
grants for operating expenses.
Application information: Application form required.
   Initial approach: Contact foundation
   Deadline(s): None
Trustees: Ralph Palmer; Nick R. Taylor; Great
Western Bank.
EIN: 470789577

5071

**Oliver and Ferrol Barklage Foundation
Trust**

c/o Richard H. Sieling
2540 N. 55th St.
Omaha, NE 68104-4025

Established in 1989 in Nebraska.
Donors: Ferrol Barklage†; Oliver Barklage†.
Foundation type: Independent foundation.
Financial data (yr. ended 07/31/14): Assets,
$1,578,314; expenditures, $181,624; qualifying
distributions, $164,399.
Purpose and activities: Giving primarily for youth
programs, the visually impaired, and the disabled.
Fields of interest: Education; Health; Human
services.
Type of support: General support; Annual
campaigns; Capital campaigns; Capital and
infrastructure; Equipment; Land acquisitions;
Endowments; Emergency funds; Seed money;
Research; Program evaluations.

Limitations: Applications accepted. Giving primarily in Omaha, NE.
Publications: Application guidelines.
Application information:
  Initial approach: Letter
  Copies of proposal: 3
  Deadline(s): Mar. 31
  Board meeting date(s): June
Officers: Richard H. Sieling, Pres.; Mary Morinelli, V.P.; Richard D. Myers, Secy.
Number of staff: None.
EIN: 470729230

5072
Clifton B. & Anne S. Batchelder Foundation
409 S. 17th St., Ste. 500
Omaha, NE 68102-2603

Established in 2007 in Delaware.
Donors: Anne Stuart Batchelder; Anne Batchelder†; Anne Batchelder Interim Trust.
Foundation type: Independent foundation.
Financial data (yr. ended 12/31/14): Assets, $4,972,171 (M); expenditures, $338,273; qualifying distributions, $262,428; giving activities include $254,000 for 30 grants (high: $25,000; low: $1,000).
Fields of interest: Education; Health; Hospital care; Youth development.
Limitations: Applications not accepted. Giving primarily in NE. No grants to individuals.
Application information: Unsolicited requests for funds not accepted.
Officer: John K. Boyer, Secy.
Directors: Edward Batchelder; Mary Batchelder Bequette; Lucia Batchelder Pamp; Anne Batchelder Pratt.
EIN: 201162883

5073
Paul Beer Trust
c/o Wells Fargo Bank, N.A., Trust Tax Dept.
1919 Douglas St., 2nd Fl., MACN8000-027
Omaha, NE 68102-1317

Foundation type: Independent foundation.
Financial data (yr. ended 12/31/14): Assets, $14,748,333 (M); expenditures, $463,113; qualifying distributions, $391,488; giving activities include $366,056 for 7 grants (high: $174,028; low: $2,000).
Fields of interest: Education; Health; Protestantism.
Limitations: Applications not accepted. Giving primarily to Des Moines, IA; funding also in Troy, NY. No grants to individuals.
Application information: Contributes only to pre-selected organizations.
Trustee: Wells Fargo Bank, N.A.
EIN: 426215149

5074
Blair Area Community Foundation
1646 Washington St.
Blair, NE 68008 (402) 426-2810
Contact: Mary Jean Rahlfs, Secy.
E-mail: mjrahlfs@rvrco.net; Grant application address: P.O. Box 390, Blair, NE 68008; Main URL: http://
www.blairareacommunityfoundation.org

Established in 1998 in Nebraska.
Foundation type: Community foundation.
Financial data (yr. ended 06/30/14): Assets, $528,243 (M); gifts received, $430,631; expenditures, $362,512; giving activities include $336,282 for grants.
Purpose and activities: The foundation's mission is to support activities that enrich the community and support the values of the families that live in Washington County, Nebraska. Areas of support include education, fine arts, community betterment, parks and recreation, public facility development and improvements, health and welfare, and other charitable purposes.
Fields of interest: Arts and culture; Historic preservation; Education; Health; Community and economic development; Sports and recreation; Parks.
Type of support: Endowments; Program development.
Limitations: Applications accepted. Giving primarily in Washington County, NE. No grants to individuals (except for scholarships), or for annual appeals or regular operating expenses, supplies, annually recurring events or programs.
Publications: Application guidelines; Grants list.
Application information: Visit foundation web site for application form and guidelines. Application form required.
  Initial approach: Complete grant request form online or mail paper copy to foundation
  Copies of proposal: 1
  Deadline(s): Oct. 1
  Final notification: Dec. 1
Officers and Board Members: Mike Ferm, Pres. and Director; Sherman Berg, V.P. and Director; Mary Jean Rahlfs, Secy. and Director; Brian Brown, Treas. and Director; Vaughn Christensen; Keith Hartvigsen; Milt Heinrich; Darrell Logemann; Roger Olson; Emily Petersen; Ken Rhoades; Ray Russin; Dee Sylvis; Brad Taylor; Rachel Truhlsen; Dick Wardell.
EIN: 470825771

5075
Burnett Charitable Trust
1919 Douglas St., 2nd Fl., MAC N8000-027
Omaha, NE 68102-1310

Foundation type: Independent foundation.
Financial data (yr. ended 12/31/13): Assets, $6,295,272 (M); expenditures, $367,526; qualifying distributions, $297,527; giving activities include $276,619 for 5 grants (high: $61,471; low: $30,735).
Fields of interest: Elementary and secondary education; Christianity.
Limitations: Applications not accepted. Giving limited to IA.
Application information: Unsolicited requests for funds not accepted.
Trustees: John Thomas; Wells Fargo Bank, N.A.
EIN: 421253249

5076
Donald A. & Joan M. Cimpl Foundation
3626 S. 94th Ave.
Omaha, NE 68124-3817

Established in 1997 in Nebraska.
Donors: Donald A. Cimpl; Joan M. Cimpl.
Foundation type: Independent foundation.

Financial data (yr. ended 12/31/13): Assets, $2,343,173 (M); expenditures, $239,585; qualifying distributions, $238,760; giving activities include $238,760 for 11 grants (high: $150,000; low: $500).
Fields of interest: Secondary education; Undergraduate education; University education; Religion; Christianity.
Type of support: General support.
Limitations: Applications not accepted. Giving primarily in NE. No grants to individuals.
Application information: Contributes only to pre-selected organizations.
Officer: Donald A. Cimpl, Mgr.
EIN: 911804434

5077
Ron & Carol Cope Charitable Fund
P.O. Box 1746
Kearney, NE 68848-1746

Established in 2004 in Nebraska.
Donor: Carol Cope.
Foundation type: Independent foundation.
Financial data (yr. ended 12/31/13): Assets, $6,787,070 (M); gifts received, $804,882; expenditures, $295,974; qualifying distributions, $257,027; giving activities include $256,500 for 8 grants (high: $102,497; low: $12,517).
Fields of interest: Theater; Art museums; Higher education; Public libraries; Christianity; Catholicism.
Limitations: Applications not accepted. Giving primarily in NE. No grants to individuals.
Application information: Contributes only to pre-selected organizations.
Officers: Alan Oldfather, Pres.; William Oldfather, V.P.; Sherry Morrow, Secy.-Treas.
Director: Rachelle Bryant.
EIN: 200634714

5078
Frank M. and Alice M. Farr Trust
1101 12th St.
P.O. Box 329
Aurora, NE 68818-2005 (402) 694-3136
Contact: James E. Koepke, Tr.

Foundation type: Independent foundation.
Financial data (yr. ended 12/31/13): Assets, $5,440,680 (M); expenditures, $243,878; qualifying distributions, $243,878; giving activities include $205,427 for 10 grants (high: $135,185; low: $600).
Fields of interest: Arts and culture; Health; Community and economic development.
Limitations: Applications accepted. Giving limited to Hamilton County, NE.
Application information: Application form required.
  Deadline(s): Mar. 1
Trustees: Heritage Bank; James E. Koepke.
EIN: 466144457

5079
Frank M. and Alice M. Farr Trust
1101 12th St.
P.O. Box 329
Aurora, NE 68818-2005
Contact: James E. Koepke, Tr.

Established in 1985 in Nebraska.

Foundation type: Independent foundation.
Financial data (yr. ended 12/31/12): Assets, $4,976,949 (M); expenditures, $246,826; qualifying distributions, $246,826; giving activities include $211,122 for 14 grants (high: $89,259; low: $1,000).
Purpose and activities: Giving limited to governmental subdivisions or charities.
Fields of interest: Foundations; Public affairs; Community and economic development.
Type of support: General support; Capital and infrastructure.
Limitations: Applications accepted. Giving limited to Hamilton County, NE. No grants to individuals.
Application information: Application form required.
Initial approach: Completed application form
Deadline(s): Mar. 1
Trustees: James E. Koepke; Heritage Bank.
EIN: 476144457

5080
The Ferenc Family Charitable Foundation of Brooklyn

c/o Sidney Ferenc
P.O. Box 3067
Omaha, NE 68103-0067 (402) 330-6800
Contact: Amy Robb-Singleton

Donors: Sidney R. Ferenc; Rock Solid Gelt Ltd.
Foundation type: Independent foundation.
Financial data (yr. ended 11/30/13): Assets, $417 (M); gifts received, $100,000; expenditures, $202,693; qualifying distributions, $202,100; giving activities include $201,000 for 2 grants (high: $200,000; low: $1,000).
Fields of interest: Arts and culture; Museums; Health; Human services.
Type of support: Endowments.
Limitations: Applications accepted. Giving primarily in Washington, DC.
Application information:
Initial approach: Letter
Deadline(s): None
Officers and Directors: Sidney R. Ferenc, Pres. and Treas. and Director; Jeffrey A. Silver, Secy.
EIN: 208048908

5081
The Pearle Francis Finigan Foundation

6321 A St.
Lincoln, NE 68510-5010
Contact: Liana Sandin

Established in 2003 in Nebraska.
Donors: Pearle F. Finigan; William C. Finigan; Pearlie F. Finigan Estate.
Foundation type: Independent foundation.
Financial data (yr. ended 06/30/14): Assets, $15,993,734 (M); gifts received, $200,000; expenditures, $679,701; qualifying distributions, $459,091; giving activities include $434,862 for 44 grants (high: $85,000; low: $200).
Fields of interest: Education; Religion; Human services.
Limitations: Applications not accepted. Giving primarily in NE. No grants to individuals.
Application information: Unsolicited requests for funds not accepted.
Officers: Liana Sandin, Pres.; Kent Endacott, Secy.; Brian D. Runge, Treas.
EIN: 200432222

5082
Friedland Family Foundation

(formerly David & Nancy Friedland Foundation)
9959 Rockbrook Rd.
Omaha, NE 68124

Established in 1985 in Nebraska.
Donors: United Distillers Products Co.; Paula Friedland Boggust; David L. Friedland; Edward Friedland; Nancy B. Friedland; Melissa Friedland Steiner.
Foundation type: Independent foundation.
Financial data (yr. ended 12/31/13): Assets, $3,052,213 (M); expenditures, $242,012; qualifying distributions, $240,575; giving activities include $240,575 for 25 grants (high: $100,000; low: $150).
Purpose and activities: Giving primarily for Nebraska charities, with emphasis on medical needs for children.
Fields of interest: Arts and culture; Education; Higher education; Nonprofits; Health.
Type of support: General support; Capital campaigns; Capital and infrastructure; Endowments; Regranting.
Limitations: Applications not accepted. Giving primarily in Omaha, NE. No grants to individuals.
Application information: Unsolicited requests for funds not accepted.
Officers: Melissa Friedland Steiner, Pres.; Paula Friedland Boggust, V.P.; Edward Friedland, V.P.; Nancy B. Friedland, V.P.
EIN: 363354408

5083
Ike & Roz Friedman Foundation

22804 Hansen Ave.
Elkhorn, NE 68022 (402) 697-1111
Contact: Susan Cohn, Pres.

Established in 1989 in Nebraska.
Donors: Isadore Friedman‡; Rosalie Friedman.
Foundation type: Independent foundation.
Financial data (yr. ended 12/31/14): Assets, $6,924,517 (M); expenditures, $395,107; qualifying distributions, $344,585; giving activities include $344,585 for 38 grants (high: $130,000; low: $250).
Purpose and activities: Giving primarily to Jewish agencies and federated giving programs, health care, the arts, education, and human and children's services.
Fields of interest: Arts and culture; Museums; Higher education; Nonprofits; Diseases and conditions; Judaism; Human services; Child welfare.
Type of support: Regranting.
Limitations: Applications accepted. Giving primarily in NE.
Application information: Application form required.
Initial approach: Proposal
Deadline(s): None
Officer: Susie Cohn, Pres.
Directors: Arnold Joffe; Dana Wear.
EIN: 363687396

5084
The GFH & SAH Foundation

7411 Madison St.
Omaha, NE 68127-4352 (402) 505-6002
Contact: George F. Haddix, Chair.

Established in 1998 in Nebraska.
Donors: George F. Haddix; Sally A. Haddix.
Foundation type: Independent foundation.
Financial data (yr. ended 12/31/12): Assets, $120,089 (M); expenditures, $309,160; qualifying distributions, $305,900; giving activities include $305,900 for grants.
Fields of interest: Education; Higher education.
Limitations: Applications accepted. Giving primarily in Omaha, NE.
Application information:
Initial approach: Letter
Deadline(s): None
Officer and Trustee: George F. Haddix, Chair. and Trustee.
EIN: 470816444

5085
The Goldwin Foundation

121 S. 13th St., Ste. 800
Lincoln, NE 68508-1911
Application address: c/o Lawrence J. Chatters, 1540 S. 21st St., Lincoln, NE 68502, tel.: (402) 730-3437, email: lawrencechatters@gmail.com;
Main URL: http://goldwinfoundation.org

Donors: Drivemax Ltd.; Borgcamp Ltd.; Trans Invest Trade LLC; Sirus Products Ltd.; Synergy Sky Ltd.; Terama Products Ltd.; Exburg Group S A.
Foundation type: Independent foundation.
Financial data (yr. ended 12/31/13): Assets, $2,305,222 (M); gifts received, $2,750,000; expenditures, $444,778; qualifying distributions, $444,778; giving activities include $250,000 for 1 grant.
Fields of interest: Human services.
Type of support: General support.
Limitations: Applications accepted. Giving primarily in FL.
Application information: Application form required.
Initial approach: Proposal
Deadline(s): None
Officers and Directors: Lawrence J. Chatters, Pres. and Treas. and Director; Tarik Ghazy, V.P. and Director; Martin Cornelis Bobak; Peter Kosa; Sami A. Mekhemar.
EIN: 462386250

5086
Bruce E. & Debra K. Grewcock Foundation

13421 Hamilton St.
Omaha, NE 68154-5150

Established in 2002 in Nebraska.
Donors: Bruce E. Grewcock; Debra K. Grewcock.
Foundation type: Independent foundation.
Financial data (yr. ended 12/31/13): Assets, $3,028,100 (M); gifts received, $6,522; expenditures, $193,941; qualifying distributions, $171,650; giving activities include $171,650 for 10 grants (high: $52,150; low: $1,000).
Fields of interest: Arts and culture; Education; Zoos; Animal welfare; Nonprofits; Human services.
Type of support: Regranting.
Limitations: Applications not accepted. Giving primarily in NE. No grants to individuals.
Application information: Contributes only to pre-selected organizations.
Officers: Bruce E. Grewcock, Pres. and Treas.; Debra K. Grewcock, V.P. and Secy.

Director: William L. Grewcock.
EIN: 020573327

5087
Albert G. and Bernice F. Hansen Charitable Foundation

12165 W. Center Rd., Ste. 56
Omaha, NE 68144-3974
Contact: Robert Roh, Tr.

Established in 1993 in Nebraska.
Donor: Bernice F. Hansen.
Foundation type: Independent foundation.
Financial data (yr. ended 12/31/13): Assets, $5,626,145 (M); expenditures, $279,244; qualifying distributions, $199,100; giving activities include $113,564 for 10 grants (high: $31,200; low: $2,100), and $78,000 for 20 grants to individuals (high: $4,000; low: $2,000).
Purpose and activities: Giving primarily for education and for health care; scholarships are awarded to individuals who are graduating from high schools located in the counties of Chase, Dundy, Frontier, Hayes, Hitchcock, and Red Willow, NE.
Fields of interest: Elementary and secondary education; Higher education; Hospital care; Search and rescue; Community and economic development.
Type of support: Program development; Student aid.
Limitations: Applications accepted. Giving for scholarships limited to residents of Chase, Dundy, Frontier, Hayes, Hitchcock, and Red Willow counties, NE; giving for community development limited to the counties of Dundy and Hitchcock, NE.
Application information:
Initial approach: Letter
Deadline(s): None
Trustees: Jamey Hansen; William Plamer; Robert Roh.
EIN: 363847506

5088
The Harper Family Foundation

(formerly M & J Foundation)
6625 State St.
Omaha, NE 68152-1633
Contact: Mary Robbins, Pres.
FAX: (402) 571-2151; E-mail: robbins.mary@cox.net

Established in 1992 in Nebraska.
Foundation type: Independent foundation.
Financial data (yr. ended 12/31/13): Assets, $29,585,292 (M); expenditures, $816,644; qualifying distributions, $423,522; giving activities include $405,522 for 45 grants (high: $74,000; low: $1,000).
Purpose and activities: The overall objective of the foundation is to have an effect on the world around it, and to be able to make a difference, and to impact directly on people.
Fields of interest: Elementary and secondary education; Higher education; Nonprofits; Sports and recreation; Youth development.
Type of support: Regranting.
Limitations: Applications accepted. Giving primarily in NE. No grants to individuals.
Application information:
Initial approach: Proposal
Copies of proposal: 1
Deadline(s): None

Board meeting date(s): Fall
Final notification: 1 week from receipt
Officers and Directors: Halbert Wenngatz, Chair. and Director; Charles M. Harper, Jr., Vice-Chair. and Director; Mary Robbins, Interim Pres.; Carolyn J. Harper, Secy. and Director; Chris J. Murphy, Treas. and Director; Charles M. Harper, Sr., Chair. Emeritus and Director; Elizabeth Murphy; Kathleen S. Wenngatz.
Number of staff: 1 part-time support.
EIN: 470761456

5089
Hawkins Charitable Trust

2516 Deer Park Blvd.
Omaha, NE 68105-3771 (402) 342-1607
Contact: Kenneth Kim Hawkins

Established in 1964 in Nebraska.
Donor: Hawkins Construction Co.
Foundation type: Company-sponsored foundation.
Financial data (yr. ended 12/31/13): Assets, $5,403,463 (M); gifts received, $50,250; expenditures, $224,440; qualifying distributions, $223,215; giving activities include $223,215 for 19 grants (high: $34,160; low: $100).
Purpose and activities: The foundation supports organizations involved with education, health, baseball, human services, and business promotion.
Fields of interest: Education; Higher education; Nonprofits; Health; Specialty hospital care; Business promotion; Baseball and softball; Human services; Child welfare; Youth services; Scouting programs.
Type of support: General support; Annual campaigns; Capital and infrastructure; Scholarships; Regranting.
Limitations: Applications accepted. Giving primarily in NE. No grants to individuals.
Application information: Application form required.
Initial approach: Proposal
Deadline(s): None
Trustees: Chris Hawkins; Kim Hawkins; Fred Hawkins, Sr.; Fred Hawkins, Jr.
EIN: 476041927

5090
Herman Foundation

c/o Richard M. Herman
1302 S. 101 St., Ste. 201
Omaha, NE 68124-6012

Established in 2003 in Nebraska.
Donor: Richard L. Herman.
Foundation type: Independent foundation.
Financial data (yr. ended 12/31/13): Assets, $4,718,158 (M); expenditures, $321,425; qualifying distributions, $282,000; giving activities include $282,000 for 6 grants (high: $100,000; low: $10,000).
Fields of interest: Education; Religion; Youth development.
Limitations: Applications not accepted. Giving primarily in NE. No grants to individuals.
Application information: Unsolicited requests for funds not accepted.
Officers and Directors: Richard L. Herman, Pres. and Director; Richard M. Herman, V.P. and Treas. and Director; Richard Carstens.
EIN: 470896236

5091
Elmer E. Hester - Dundy County Public Schools Foundation

P.O. Box 33
Benkelman, NE 69021-0033 (308) 423-2214
Contact: Elmer Case, Pres.

Foundation type: Independent foundation.
Financial data (yr. ended 12/31/13): Assets, $4,939,635 (M); expenditures, $302,890; qualifying distributions, $200,563; giving activities include $200,563 for 6 grants (high: $126,000; low: $10,000).
Purpose and activities: Giving for youth development in Dundy County, Nebraska.
Fields of interest: Education; Sports and recreation; Youth development.
Type of support: General support; Grants to individuals; Student aid.
Limitations: Applications accepted. Giving limited to Dundy County, NE.
Application information:
Initial approach: Contact foundation
Deadline(s): July 31
Officers: Elmer Case, Pres.; Jon Tecker, V.P.; Dallas Watkins, Secy.; Stacey Waters, Treas.
Directors: Ron L. Jones; Jim Kent; John McDonald; John Metzger; Cheryl Gudden; Henry Krug, Jr.; Karen Harford; Keith Haskell; Scott Olson; Dan Parker; Tom Roundtree; Shad Stamm.
Number of staff: 1
EIN: 476026486

5092
B. Keith & Norma F. Heuermann Foundation

(formerly Bernard K. & Norma F. Heuermann Foundation)
c/o Union Bank and Trust Co., Custodian
2720 S. 177th St.
P.O. Box 542080
Omaha, NE 68154-8080
Contact: Timothy J. Otto, Secy.-Treas.

Established in 1991 in Nebraska.
Donors: B. Keith Heuermann; Norma F. Heuermann.
Foundation type: Independent foundation.
Financial data (yr. ended 07/31/13): Assets, $8,652,596 (M); expenditures, $460,047; qualifying distributions, $407,197; giving activities include $406,200 for 36 grants (high: $116,000; low: $250).
Purpose and activities: Giving primarily for children, education and for learning disabilities; funding also for hospitals, Christian schools, community foundations, and libraries.
Fields of interest: Education; Foundations; Hospital care; Christianity; Child welfare; Developmental disability services; Senior services.
Type of support: Program development; Matching grants; Land acquisitions; Capital campaigns; Annual campaigns; General support; Capital and infrastructure; Equipment; Endowments; Emergency funds; Fellowships; Research.
Limitations: Applications accepted. Giving primarily in NE, with emphasis on rural areas. No grants to individuals; no loans or non-monetary contributions.
Publications: Application guidelines.
Application information: If unfamiliar with the foundation, request guidelines.
Initial approach: 2-page proposal
Copies of proposal: 4

Deadline(s): None
Board meeting date(s): Summer, fall, and spring
Final notification: Varies
Officers and Directors: Bernard K. Heuermann, Pres. and Director; Norma F. Heuermann, V.P. and Director; Timothy J. Otto, Secy.-Treas. and Director; John B. Atkins; Scott P. Heuermann.
Number of staff: None.
EIN: 470748466

5093
Hickey Family Foundation
13310 I St.
Omaha, NE   68137-1111

Established in 1997 in Unspecified.
Donors: Bonnie Hickey; Bonnie Hickey Revocable Trust.
Foundation type: Independent foundation.
Financial data (yr. ended 05/31/13): Assets, $756,568 (M); expenditures, $175,997; qualifying distributions, $169,697; giving activities include $166,950 for 20 grants (high: $72,000; low: $1,000).
Fields of interest: Education; University education; Natural resources; Catholicism; Human services; Child welfare.
Limitations: Applications not accepted. No grants to individuals.
Application information: Contributes only to pre-selected organizations.
Officers: Bonnie Hickey, Pres.; Michael Kozlik, Secy.; Mary Jewell, Treas.
EIN: 396658959

5094
Home Instead Senior Care Foundation
13323 California St.
Omaha, NE   68154-5241   (402) 455-0883
Contact: Judith Sexton
E-mail: info@homeinsteadseniorcarefoundation.org;
Main URL: http://
www.homeinsteadseniorcarefoundation.org
Facebook: https://www.facebook.com/
HomeInsteadSeniorCareFoundation
Google Plus: https://plus.google.com/
115722471179213644955
Grants List: http://
www.homeinsteadseniorcarefoundation.org/
grant-awards

Established in 2003 in Nebraska.
Donors: Lori L. Hogan; Home Instead, Inc.; Paul R. Hogan; The Hundred Foundation.
Foundation type: Independent foundation.
Financial data (yr. ended 12/31/13): Assets, $136,727 (M); gifts received, $225,983; expenditures, $173,900; qualifying distributions, $173,353; giving activities include $171,000 for 14 grants (high: $20,000; low: $5,000).
Purpose and activities: Giving to support activities designed to improve the quality of life for seniors. Such opportunities may include research and development, education, scholarships, and/or advocacy for the health and well being of older adults.
Fields of interest: Human services; Senior services.
Application information: Letters of Inquiry must be submitted online through the Foundation web site. When all Letters of Inquiry have been reviewed, the Foundation will request full proposals from selected

organizations. See Foundation web site for complete application guidelines. Application form required.
Initial approach: Letter of Inquiry
Deadline(s): May 1 for Fall grants and Nov. 1 for Spring grants
Officers: Paul R. Hogan, Pres. and Treas.; Lori L. Hogan, V.P. and Secy.
Directors: Mary Alexander; April Cavanaugh; Kathy Curry; Joe Sanders; Patricia Wells.
EIN: 510457609

5095
The Hundred Foundation
24602 Jones Cir.
Waterloo, NE   68069

Donor: Paul R. Hogan.
Foundation type: Independent foundation.
Financial data (yr. ended 12/31/13): Assets, $5,157 (M); gifts received, $152,633; expenditures, $165,000; qualifying distributions, $163,500; giving activities include $162,000 for 12 grants (high: $50,000; low: $2,500).
Fields of interest: Arts and culture; Education; Human services.
Limitations: Applications not accepted. Giving primarily in NE.
Application information: Unsolicited requests for funds not accepted.
Officers: Paul R. Hogan, Pres. and Treas.; Lori L. Hogan, V.P. and Secy.
Director: Lakelyn K. Hogan.
EIN: 272075646

5096
Kaufmann-Cummings Foundation
P.O. Box 5792
Grand Island, NE   68802-1507
Contact: Richard K. Rabe, Tr.

Foundation type: Independent foundation.
Financial data (yr. ended 12/31/14): Assets, $2,787,307 (M); expenditures, $204,896; qualifying distributions, $182,000; giving activities include $180,000 for 26 grants (high: $34,000; low: $500).
Fields of interest: Higher education; Community and economic development; Human services; Child welfare.
Limitations: Applications not accepted. Giving primarily in Grand Island, NE. No grants to individuals.
Application information: Contributes only to pre-selected organizations.
Trustees: Richard K. Rabe; Gaylan Stehlik; Joel Wiegand.
EIN: 476205029

5097
E. H. Kilbourne Residuary Charitable Trust
c/o Wells Fargo Bank Indiana, N.A.
1919 Douglas St., 2nd Fl.
Omaha, NE   68102-1310
Application address: c/o Jennifer King, V.P., Wells Fargo Bank Indiana, N.A., P.O. Box 960, Fort Wayne, IN 46801, tel.: (260) 461-6458

Established in 1978 in Indiana.
Donor: Edgar Kilbourne†.
Foundation type: Independent foundation.

Financial data (yr. ended 11/30/13): Assets, $10,434,142 (M); expenditures, $523,155; qualifying distributions, $468,339; giving activities include $393,325 for 23 grants (high: $188,575; low: $2,559).
Purpose and activities: Giving primarily for higher education, including scholarships for graduating high school seniors in Allen County, IN, who are members of a church or synagogue. Support also for youth and social services.
Fields of interest: Education; Higher education; Protestantism; Human services; Child welfare.
Type of support: General support; Matching grants; Continuing support; Annual campaigns; Equipment; Scholarships.
Limitations: Applications accepted. Giving limited to Allen County, IN and MN. No grants to individuals (except for scholarships), or for endowment funds, research, publications, or conferences; no loans.
Application information: Scholarship awards paid directly to colleges; obtain applications from high schools. Application form required.
Initial approach: Letter
Deadline(s): Apr. 15 for scholarships
Board meeting date(s): May for scholarships; quarterly for other grants
Final notification: 6 weeks
Trustee: Wells Fargo Bank Indiana, N.A.
EIN: 356332820

5098
Kim Foundation
c/o Larry J. Courtnage
C&A Plaza
13609 California St., Ste. 500
Omaha, NE   68154-5245
E-mail: info@thekimfoundation.org; Main
URL: http://www.thekimfoundation.org
Blog: http://blog.thekimfoundation.org
E Newsletter: http://www.thekimfoundation.org/
html/mh_happenings/newsletter.html
Facebook: http://www.facebook.com/pages/
The-Kim-Foundation-Advocating-for-Mental-Health-S
ervices/120739160051
Twitter: https://twitter.com/kimfoundation

Established in 2000 in Nebraska.
Donors: Larry J. Courtnage; C&A Industries, Inc.; United Way of The Midlands.
Foundation type: Independent foundation.
Financial data (yr. ended 12/31/13): Assets, $6,270,872 (M); gifts received, $578,954; expenditures, $401,575; qualifying distributions, $378,779; giving activities include $264,390 for 16 grants (high: $25,150; low: $1,415).
Purpose and activities: Giving primarily to organizations that assist individuals with mental health difficulties.
Fields of interest: Mental health care; Diseases and conditions; Human services; Child welfare.
Limitations: Applications not accepted. Giving primarily in NE.
Application information: Unsolicited requests for funds not accepted.
Officers: Larry J. Courtnage, Pres.; Kathleen A. Courtnage, V.P. and Secy.; Vicki F. Witkovski, Treas.; Julia Hebenstreit, J.D., Exec. Dir.
EIN: 470837377

5099

Kinder Porter Scott Family Foundation

(formerly Anne K. and William L. Porter Foundation, Inc.)
c/o D.R. Stogsdill
233 S. 13th St., Ste. 1900
Lincoln, NE 68508-2095

Donors: Anne K. Porter; William L. Porter.
Foundation type: Independent foundation.
Financial data (yr. ended 12/31/13): Assets, $4,306,453 (M); expenditures, $271,159; qualifying distributions, $185,761; giving activities include $157,500 for 33 grants (high: $50,000; low: $100).
Fields of interest: Arts and culture; Children's museums; Education; Plant biodiversity; Public libraries; Human services.
Limitations: Applications not accepted. Giving primarily in NE. No grants to individuals.
Application information: Unsolicited requests for funds not accepted.
Officers: Jean Porter Jennings, Pres.; William D. Scott, V.P.; Robert Jennings, Secy.; Robert E. Scott, Treas.
EIN: 237052152

5100

Lienemann Charitable Foundation, Inc.

P.O. Box 81407
Lincoln, NE 68501-1407

Established in 1967 in Nebraska.
Donors: Del Lienemann, Sr.; Charlotte Lienemann; Douglas Lienemann.
Foundation type: Independent foundation.
Financial data (yr. ended 08/31/13): Assets, $1,164,280 (M); gifts received, $67,250; expenditures, $221,370; qualifying distributions, $221,370; giving activities include $203,458 for 7 grants (high: $107,200; low: $1,000).
Fields of interest: Orchestral music; Higher education; Foundations; Hospital care; Protestantism; Human services.
Limitations: Applications not accepted. Giving primarily in CO and NE. No grants to individuals.
Application information: Unsolicited requests for funds not accepted.
Officers: Del Lienemann, Sr., C.E.O. and Pres.; Douglas Lienemann, V.P.; Denise Scholz, Secy.; Del Lienemann, Jr., Treas.
Trustee: Dorothy Pflug.
EIN: 476044090

5101

Lothlorien Foundation

1325 Lynnwood Ln.
Omaha, NE 68152-5239 (402) 451-8051
Contact: Grace M. Longley, Secy.

Established in 1998 in Nebraska.
Donors: Michael C. Longley; Sally Freymark; Peter Freymark; Lothlorien Enterprises, LP.
Foundation type: Independent foundation.
Financial data (yr. ended 12/31/14): Assets, $1,147,128 (M); gifts received, $279,830; expenditures, $215,085; qualifying distributions, $200,956; giving activities include $200,956 for 27 grants (high: $53,500; low: $800).
Fields of interest: Education; Religion; Human services.

International interests: Africa.
Limitations: Applications accepted. Giving primarily in NE.
Application information: Application form required.
Initial approach: Contact foundation for application form
Deadline(s): None
Officers: Michael C. Longley, Pres.; Grace M. Longley, Secy.; Katharine Corbin, Treas.
EIN: 470816447

5102

Irene & Joseph Malek Charitable Trust

c/o Union Bank & Trust Co.
2720 S. 177th St.
Omaha, NE 68130-2898 4028276962
Application address: c/o Daniel Duffy, 10036 Fieldcrest Dr., Omaha, NE 68114, tel.: (402) 390-0300

Foundation type: Independent foundation.
Financial data (yr. ended 12/31/14): Assets, $3,261,705; expenditures, $195,313; qualifying distributions, $157,750.
Fields of interest: Education; Human services; Youth development.
Limitations: Applications accepted. Giving primarily in Omaha, NE.
Application information:
Initial approach: Proposal
Deadline(s): None
Trustees: Cassem, Tierney, Adams, Gotch; First National Bank of Omaha; Union Bank & Trust Co.
EIN: 527242731

5103

Mapes Charitable Trust

c/o Wells Fargo Bank Iowa, N.A.
1919 Douglas St., 2nd Fl., MAC N8000-0027
Omaha, NE 68102-1317

Established in 1996 in Iowa.
Donor: Mapes Charitable Trust.
Foundation type: Independent foundation.
Financial data (yr. ended 12/31/13): Assets, $7,366,084 (M); expenditures, $539,798; qualifying distributions, $451,560; giving activities include $430,000 for 9 grants (high: $125,000; low: $10,000).
Purpose and activities: Giving for education, as well as orphaned and injured wildlife.
Fields of interest: Higher education; Wildlife biodiversity; Animal welfare; Protestantism.
Limitations: Applications not accepted. Giving primarily in IA. No grants to individuals.
Application information: Contributes only to pre-selected organizations.
Trustees: Irving Stone; Wells Fargo Bank Iowa, N.A.
EIN: 426543426

5104

Midlands Community Foundation

217 N. Jefferson St.
Papillion, NE 68046-3111 (402) 991-8027
Contact: Tonee Gay, Exec. Dir.; Diane Knicky, Dir., Opers. and Public Rels.

FAX: (402) 991-8047;
E-mail: info@midlandscommunity.org; Main URL: http://www.midlandscommunity.org
Facebook: https://www.facebook.com/pages/Midlands-Community-Foundation/438124480396
Twitter: https://twitter.com/midlandscomfoun

Established in 1994 in Nebraska.
Foundation type: Community foundation.
Financial data (yr. ended 06/30/13): Assets, $5,846,105 (M); gifts received, $818,676; expenditures, $878,208; giving activities include $342,478 for 43+ grants (high: $65,000; low: $400).
Purpose and activities: Giving primarily for arts and culture, human services, community and economic development, health care and education.
Fields of interest: Arts and culture; Performing arts; Education; Higher education; Health; Hospital care; Mental health care; Cancers; Fire prevention and control; Community and economic development; Economic development; Sports and recreation; Human services; Child welfare; Infants and toddlers; Young adults; Female children and youth; Female infants and toddlers; Female adults; Male children and youth; Male infants and toddlers; Male adults; Single parents; Ethnic and racial groups; People of Latin American descent; Indigenous peoples; American Indians; Homeless people; Low-income and poor people; Victims of crime and abuse; People with disabilities; People with physical disabilities; People with vision impairments; People with hearing impairments; People with psychosocial disabilities; Terminally ill people; Substance abusers; Military personnel.
Type of support: Continuing support; Capital campaigns; Capital and infrastructure; Equipment; Land acquisitions; Convening; Seed money; Scholarships; Research; Technical assistance.
Limitations: Applications accepted. Giving limited to Sarpy and Cass counties, NE. No support for political organizations or political programs, or projects of religion-based organizations (unless the project is secular and does not give priority or preferential treatment to the religious organization or its members. No grants to individuals, or for routine general operating expenses, deficit reduction or general or administrative overhead expenses, or dinners, tickets, or conferences..
Publications: Application guidelines; Annual report; Informational brochure; Informational brochure (including application guidelines).
Application information: Visit the foundation's web site for application form and guidelines. Application form required.
Initial approach: Telephone
Copies of proposal: 10
Deadline(s): Feb. 1 and Aug. 1
Board meeting date(s): Second Tues. of every other month
Final notification: Within 60 days
Officers and Directors: Karla Rupiper, Pres. and Director; Terri Scholting, V.P. and Director; Randy Sump, V.P. and Director; Kevin Dasher, Secy.-Treas. and Director; Tonee Gay, Exec. Dir.; Tom Ackley; Janet Barna; Julie Bear; Brenda Carlson; Jan Davis; Bob Frederick; Mary Beth Harrold; Dr. Jim Langley; Bonnie Miller; Phil Pankonin; Lee Polikov; Jeff Rennter; Barb Slattery; Jim Thompson.
Number of staff: 1 full-time professional; 1 part-time professional.
EIN: 510191738

5105
Nebraska Community Foundation
3833 S. 14th St.
P.O. Box 83107
Lincoln, NE 68501-3107 (402) 323-7330
Contact: Jeffrey G. Yost, Pres. and C.E.O.
FAX: (402) 323-7349;
E-mail: info@nebcommfound.org; Main URL: http://
www.nebcommfound.org
Facebook: http://www.facebook.com/
nebraskacommunityfoundation
YouTube: http://www.youtube.com/user/
nebcommfound?feature=mhee

Established in 1993 in Nebraska.
Foundation type: Community foundation.
Financial data (yr. ended 06/30/14): Assets,
$98,799,218 (M); gifts received, $45,502,730;
expenditures, $36,897,190; giving activities
include $216,707 for 167 grants to individuals.
Purpose and activities: The Nebraska Community
Foundation uses the tools of philanthropy,
community development and economic
development to help communities help themselves.
NCF creates a path to greater prosperity for all by
helping communities: 1) envision a better future; 2)
develop local leadership and talent; 3) inspire
charitable giving and grow endowments; 4) fund
community needs and opportunities; 5) manage
financial resources; and 6) build and leverage every
local asset.
Fields of interest: Education; Community and
economic development.
Type of support: General support; Pro bono
consulting services; Leadership and professional
development; Employee matching gifts; Matching
grants; Endowments; Program development;
Convening; Publications; Student aid.
Limitations: Applications not accepted. Giving
primarily limited to Nebraska via Affiliated Fund
giving. No grants to individuals (except for
scholarships).
Publications: Annual report; Financial statement;
Informational brochure; Newsletter; Occasional
report; Program policy statement.
Application information: All grantmaking occurs
through the foundation's 227 affiliated funds.
Board meeting date(s): Quarterly
Officers and At Large Members: Dennis Stara,
Chair. and Director; Honorable Douglas Bereuter,
Chair., Communications Committee and Director;
Richard Walter, Chair., Fund Development
Committee and Director; Al Steuter, Vice-Chair. and
Director; Jeffrey G. Yost, Pres. and C.E.O. and
Director; Maxine Moul, Pres. Emeritus; Judy
Brockmeier, Secy. and Director; Lora Damme,
Treas. and Director; Diane M. Wilson, C.O.O. and
C.F.O. and Director; Les Lon, Cont. and Director;
K.C. Belitz; Steve Brewster; Joe Ferguson; Casey
Garrigan; Carol Lockwood; Lori Pankonin; Judy
Parks; Sara Coffee Radil; Lynn Roper; Greg Vasek;
Ray Welsh; Sandi Wendell.
Number of staff: 10 full-time professional; 3
part-time professional; 4 full-time support.
EIN: 470769903

5106
**Karl H. & Wealtha H. Nelson Family
  Foundation**
9290 W. Dodge Rd., Ste. 303
Omaha, NE 68114-4077 (402) 390-0390

Established in 1993 in Nebraska.

Donor: Wealtha H. Nelson†.
Foundation type: Independent foundation.
Financial data (yr. ended 12/31/14): Assets,
$4,187,530; gifts received, $0; expenditures,
$264,909; qualifying distributions, $185,500.
Fields of interest: Arts and culture; Museums;
Historic preservation; Education; Environment;
Foundations; Nonprofits; Health; Community and
economic development; Human services.
Type of support: Regranting.
Limitations: Applications accepted. Giving primarily
in Nebraska City, NE.
Application information: Application form required.
Initial approach: Proposal
Deadline(s): None
Officers: Ren Nelson, Pres.; Susan Wirth, V.P.;
George Blazek, Secy.; Andrew Grier, Treas.
Trustees: Sara B. Crook; Jason McNeely; Nicolas
Nelson.
Number of staff: 1 part-time support.
EIN: 363879767

5107
**Leland J. & Dorothy H. Olson Charitable
  Foundation**
c/o Hancock & Dana PC
1289 W. Dodge Rd., Ste. 100
Omaha, NE 68154-2188

Established in 1991 in Nebraska.
Donors: Leland Olson; Dorothy Olson.
Foundation type: Independent foundation.
Financial data (yr. ended 12/31/13): Assets,
$5,123,813 (M); expenditures, $265,762;
qualifying distributions, $225,000; giving activities
include $225,000 for 9 grants (high: $50,000; low:
$10,000).
Fields of interest: University education.
Limitations: Applications not accepted. Giving
primarily in NE.
Application information: Unsolicited requests for
funds not accepted.
Directors: David Olson; Karen Olson; Nancy Olson.
EIN: 470748772

5108
The Owen Foundation
P.O. Box 1085
Omaha, NE 68101-1085 (712) 347-5500
Contact: Robert E. Owen, Pres.

Established in 1959 in Nebraska.
Donors: Paxton & Vierling Steel Co.; Missouri Valley
Steel Co.; Northern Plains Steel Co.; Owen
Industries, Inc.
Foundation type: Company-sponsored foundation.
Financial data (yr. ended 11/30/14): Assets,
$1,510,849 (M); gifts received, $200,000;
expenditures, $177,179; qualifying distributions,
$167,650; giving activities include $164,484 for 21
grants (high: $50,000; low: $350).
Purpose and activities: The foundation supports
organizations involved with arts and culture, sports
and recreation, youth development, and Christianity.
Fields of interest: Arts and culture; Performing arts;
Opera; Christianity; Sports and recreation; Parks;
Festivals; Youth development.
Type of support: General support; Cash grants.
Limitations: Applications accepted. Giving primarily
in NE. No grants to individuals.
Application information:

Initial approach: Proposal
Deadline(s): None
Officers and Trustees: Robert E. Owen, Co-Pres. and
Trustee; Tyler R. Owen, Co-Pres. and Trustee; James
Pfeffer, Secy. and Trustee.
EIN: 476025298

5109
William R. Patrick Foundation
c/o Liakos & Matukewicz, LLP
11516 Nicholas St., Ste. 201
Omaha, NE 68154-4409

Established in 1989 in Nebraska.
Donor: Jean P. Bandler†.
Foundation type: Independent foundation.
Financial data (yr. ended 12/31/13): Assets,
$3,403,387 (M); expenditures, $232,094;
qualifying distributions, $145,644; giving activities
include $145,644 for 25 grants (high: $12,084;
low: $2,000).
Fields of interest: Arts and culture; Education;
Health; Addiction services; Religion; Human
services; Child welfare; Youth services; Scouting
programs; People with disabilities.
Limitations: Applications not accepted. Giving
primarily in Omaha, NE. No grants to individuals.
Application information: Unsolicited requests for
funds not accepted.
Officers and Directors: John G. Liakos, Pres. and
Treas. and Director; Elisabeth B. Liakos, Secy. and
Director; Michael J. Matukewicz.
EIN: 363712016

5110
Pegler Family Foundation
c/o First Nebraska Trust Co.
P.O. Box 81667
Lincoln, NE 68501-1667

Established in 1992 in Nebraska.
Donors: Donald H. Pegler, Jr.; Joann G. Pegler.
Foundation type: Independent foundation.
Financial data (yr. ended 12/31/14): Assets,
$3,289,024 (M); expenditures, $171,679;
qualifying distributions, $151,232; giving activities
include $120,600 for 24 grants (high: $25,000;
low: $100).
Purpose and activities: Giving primarily for youth
and community services.
Fields of interest: Arts and culture; Education;
Environment.
Type of support: General support; Continuing
support; Capital campaigns; Capital and
infrastructure; Equipment; Endowments; Program
development; Seed money; Student aid.
Limitations: Applications accepted. Giving primarily
in Lincoln, NE.
Application information: Application form required.
Initial approach: Letter
Deadline(s): None
Officers and Trustees: Donald H. Pegler III, Pres.
and Trustee; Leslie A. Pegler Deeter, V.P. and
Trustee; Susan L. Pegler Hoppe, V.P. and Trustee;
Jeff Semrad, Secy.-Treas.; Trent Deeter; Cary Kline;
Joann G. Pegler; Katey Pickel; Marian Pegler; Scott
Semrad.
EIN: 470762310

5111
Kitty M. Perkins Foundation
304 Nelson St.
P.O. Box 268
Cambridge, NE 69022-3592
Application address: c/o Kristina L. Witte, 70931
Drive 412, Wilsonville, NE 69046, tel.: (308)
697-3395; Main URL: http://
www.kmpfoundation.com

Established in 1966 in Illinois.
Donor: Kitty M. Perkins†.
Foundation type: Independent foundation.
Financial data (yr. ended 12/31/13): Assets,
$9,625,418 (M); expenditures, $481,900;
qualifying distributions, $417,750; giving activities
include $414,000 for 25 grants (high: $100,000;
low: $1,000).
Purpose and activities: Grants for higher
educational and medical purposes.
Fields of interest: Education; Health; Diseases and
conditions.
Type of support: General support; Research;
Continuing support; Annual campaigns; Capital
campaigns; Capital and infrastructure; Equipment;
Program development; Professorships.
Limitations: Applications accepted. Giving primarily
in NE; some funding also in Chicago, IL. No grants
to individuals, or for matching gifts; no loans.
Publications: Application guidelines.
Application information: Application guidelines and
form available on foundation web site. Application
form required.
  Initial approach: Proposal
  Copies of proposal: 2
  Deadline(s): None
  Board meeting date(s): As required
Officers and Directors: Kristina L. Witte, Pres. and
Director; J. August Shoemaker, V.P. and Director; D.
Charles Shoemaker, Secy. and Director; William E.
Shoemaker, Treas. and Director; Kathryn Heitmann.
EIN: 366154399

5112
**Physicians Mutual Insurance Company
Foundation**
2600 Dodge St.
Omaha, NE 68131
Contact: Debra L. Walton

Established in 1985 in Nebraska.
Donor: Physicians Mutual Insurance Co.
Foundation type: Company-sponsored foundation.
Financial data (yr. ended 12/31/13): Assets,
$707,480 (M); expenditures, $168,174; qualifying
distributions, $167,911; giving activities include
$167,911 for 16 grants (high: $65,000; low: $100).
Purpose and activities: The foundation supports
museums and botanical gardens and organizations
involved with higher education, youth development,
human services, and business and industry.
Fields of interest: Museums; Higher education;
Botanical gardens; Nonprofits; Business and
industry; Human services; Scouting programs;
Economics for youth; Senior services.
Type of support: General support; Continuing
support; Capital campaigns; Scholarships;
Regranting.
Limitations: Applications accepted. Giving primarily
in Omaha, NE. No grants to individuals.
Application information: Application form required.

Initial approach: Letter
  Deadline(s): None
Officers: Robert A. Reed, Pres.; Robert A. Reed, Jr.,
Secy.-Treas.
Director: William R. Hamsa, MD.
EIN: 363424068

5113
Quivey-Bay State Foundation
P.O. Box 2308
Scottsbluff, NE 69363-2757
Application Address: c/o Ted Cannon, 1515 E. 20th
St., Scottsbluff NE 69361, tel.: (308) 635-1153

Established in 1948 in Nebraska.
Donors: M.B. Quivey; Mrs. M.B. Quivey.
Foundation type: Independent foundation.
Financial data (yr. ended 01/31/15): Assets,
$5,608,246 (M); expenditures, $341,466;
qualifying distributions, $330,583; giving activities
include $330,583 for 51 grants (high: $40,000;
low: $150).
Fields of interest: Historic preservation; Higher
education; Animal welfare; Christianity; Human
services; Child welfare; Scouting programs.
Limitations: Applications accepted. Giving primarily
in western NE. No grants to individuals, or for
endowment funds.
Application information: Application form required.
  Initial approach: Letter
  Copies of proposal: 1
  Deadline(s): None
  Board meeting date(s): Oct. and Nov.
Officers: Gary Kelley, Pres.; Ted Cannon, Secy.; Zac
Karpf, Treas.
Directors: John Koenig; Steve Olsen; Charles
Richardson; Jerry Williams.
EIN: 476024159

5114
**Edgar & Frances Reynolds Foundation,
Inc.**
(formerly Edgar Reynolds Foundation, Inc.)
P.O. Box 1492
Grand Island, NE 68802-1492 (308) 380-0957

Established in 1977 in Nebraska.
Donors: Edgar Reynolds†; Frances Reynolds†.
Foundation type: Independent foundation.
Financial data (yr. ended 12/31/13): Assets,
$5,738,501 (M); expenditures, $417,020;
qualifying distributions, $311,868; giving activities
include $305,800 for 30 grants (high: $80,000;
low: $1,000).
Purpose and activities: Giving primarily for human
services and community development.
Fields of interest: Animal welfare; Community and
economic development; Human services.
Type of support: Capital and infrastructure;
Matching grants; Scholarships.
Limitations: Applications accepted. Giving primarily
in Grand Island, NE. No grants to individuals.
Publications: Application guidelines.
Application information: Application form required.
  Initial approach: Request application form
  Copies of proposal: 6
  Deadline(s): None
Officers: Fred Glade, Chair.; Gordon Glade,
Vice-Chair.

Trustees: Judy Brown; Kent Coen; Mike
Stoppkottee; Tim White.
EIN: 470589941

5115
Walter Scott, Jr. Foundation IV
409 S. 17th St., Ste. 500
Omaha, NE 68102-2609
Walter Scott, Jr.'s Giving Pledge Profile: http://
glasspockets.org/philanthropy-in-focus/
eye-on-the-giving-pledge/profiles/scott

Established in 2001 in Nebraska.
Donor: Walter Scott, Jr.
Foundation type: Independent foundation.
Financial data (yr. ended 12/31/13): Assets,
$5,431,166 (M); expenditures, $230,392;
qualifying distributions, $200,000; giving activities
include $200,000 for 1 grant.
Fields of interest: Human services.
Limitations: Applications not accepted. No grants to
individuals.
Application information: Unsolicited requests for
funds not accepted.
Officer: John K. Boyer, Genl. Counsel.
Trustee: Walter Scott, Jr.
EIN: 316648416

5116
A. J. & Lynda Scribante Family Foundation
(formerly Scribante Family Foundation)
6718 S. 93rd St.
Omaha, NE 68127-4454

Established in 1983 in Nebraska.
Donors: Adrian J. Scribante; Lynda Scribante.
Foundation type: Independent foundation.
Financial data (yr. ended 09/30/14): Assets,
$7,012,051; expenditures, $542,957; qualifying
distributions, $348,470.
Purpose and activities: Giving primarily to provide
opportunity, restore freedom, and enhance the
quality of life in America by supporting projects that
develop people into educated, responsible,
independent, and concerned members of society.
Projects focus on education, youth development,
and conservative values.
Fields of interest: Education; Higher education;
Veterinary medicine; Childbirth; Archives and special
collections; Leadership development; Christianity;
Youth development.
Type of support: General support; Matching grants;
Convening.
Limitations: Applications not accepted. Giving
primarily in CA, FL, KS, MN, NY, and TX. No grants
to individuals.
Application information: Contributes only to
pre-selected organizations.
Officers: A.J. Scribante, Pres. and Treas.; Lynda
Scribante, V.P.
Director: Dennis Blackman.
EIN: 363297872

5117
Barbara Udes Shaw Charitable Foundation
17007 Marcy St., Ste. 1
Omaha, NE 68118-3122

Established in 1997 in Nebraska.
Donor: Barbara Udes Shaw.

Foundation type: Independent foundation.
Financial data (yr. ended 12/31/14): Assets, $1,244,971; expenditures, $200,742; qualifying distributions, $193,905.
Fields of interest: Education; Christianity; Human services.
Limitations: Applications not accepted. Giving primarily in Omaha, NE. No grants to individuals.
Application information: Contributes only to pre-selected organizations.
Officers and Directors: Barbara Udes Shaw, Pres. and Director; Alden Awerkamp, V.P. and Director; Paula Provorse, Secy.-Treas. and Director.
EIN: 470804899

5118
Virginia Smith Charitable Trust
P.O. Box 525
Chappell, NE 69129 (308) 874-2929
Contact: Connie Loos

Donor: Virginia Smith Administrative Trust.
Foundation type: Independent foundation.
Financial data (yr. ended 12/31/13): Assets, $9,190,406 (M); expenditures, $461,446; qualifying distributions, $363,453; giving activities include $317,239 for 22 grants (high: $225,000; low: $750).
Fields of interest: Education; Child abuse; Human services; Youth development.
Limitations: Applications accepted. Giving primarily in Big Springs, Chappell and Lodgepole, NE.
Application information: Application form required.
    Initial approach: Completed application form
    Deadline(s): None
Officer: Leonard Littlejohn, Chair.
Trustees: Jerome E. Cabela; Merlyn Carlson; Janet Flohr; Kenneth Fornander.
EIN: 866348709

5119
Soli Deo Gloria Foundation
8929 N. 96th St.
Omaha, NE 68122-2321

Established in 2007 in Nebraska.
Donors: Brenda L. Whealy; Michael T. Whealy.
Foundation type: Independent foundation.
Financial data (yr. ended 12/31/14): Assets, $4,962,837; expenditures, $328,066; qualifying distributions, $280,000.
Fields of interest: Women's services.
Limitations: Applications not accepted. Giving primarily in Omaha, NE.
Application information: Contributes only to pre-selected organizations.
Officers and Directors: Michael T. Whealy, Pres. and Treas. and Director; Brenda L. Whealy, Secy. and Director.
EIN: 260286564

5120
Springer Family Charitable Trust
P.O. Box 82535
Lincoln, NE 68501-2535

Donor: William E. Springer†.
Foundation type: Independent foundation.
Financial data (yr. ended 12/31/14): Assets, $6,477,633 (M); expenditures, $340,005;

qualifying distributions, $316,259; giving activities include $289,104 for 2 grants (high: $218,287; low: $70,817).
Fields of interest: Animal welfare.
Limitations: Applications not accepted. Giving primarily in NE.
Application information: Contributes only to pre-selected organizations.
Trustee: Union Bank & Trust Co.
EIN: 266587018

5121
The Steinhart Foundation, Inc.
601 Central Ave., Ste. 105
Nebraska City, NE 68410-2468 (402) 873-3285
Contact: Keitha Thomson, Pres.

Established in 1954 in Nebraska.
Donors: Morton Steinhart†; Ella S. Steinhart†; Ella Steinhart Charitable Remainder Unitrust.
Foundation type: Independent foundation.
Financial data (yr. ended 12/31/14): Assets, $8,979,811 (M); expenditures, $545,027; qualifying distributions, $416,744; giving activities include $389,244 for 18 grants (high: $150,000; low: $500), and $27,500 for 11 grants to individuals (high: $2,500; low: $2,500).
Fields of interest: Higher education; Foundations; Human services.
Type of support: General support; Student aid.
Limitations: Giving primarily in Nebraska City, NE, and the immediate surrounding area.
Application information: Funds presently committed. Application form required.
    Initial approach: Proposal
    Copies of proposal: 1
    Deadline(s): None
    Board meeting date(s): Annually
Officers: Wende Schwake, Pres.; Dennis Marshall, V.P.; George T. Blazek, Secy.-Treas.
Trustees: Gary Ailes; Deroy Harshman; John James; Henry Schwake; Henry H. Schwake.
EIN: 476025185

5122
Robert Herman Storz Foundation
10050 Regency Cir., Ste. 101
Omaha, NE 68114-3721
Contact: Herbert A. Engdagl, Tr.

Donor: Robert Herman Storz†.
Foundation type: Independent foundation.
Financial data (yr. ended 12/31/14): Assets, $5,129,579 (M); expenditures, $416,650; qualifying distributions, $391,486; giving activities include $389,062 for 30 grants (high: $75,000; low: $1,000).
Fields of interest: Arts and culture; Human services.
Type of support: Annual campaigns; Matching grants; Capital campaigns; Capital and infrastructure.
Limitations: Applications accepted. Giving primarily in the Omaha, NE, area. No support for political organizations. No grants to individuals.
Application information:
    Initial approach: Letter
    Copies of proposal: 1
    Deadline(s): May 1, Sept. 1, Dec. 1
    Board meeting date(s): 2nd Mon. in May, Sept., and Dec.

Trustees: Susan Storz Butler; Herbert A. Engdahl; Diane Higgins; Robert S. Howard.
Number of staff: 1 full-time professional.
EIN: 476025980

5123
The Margaret & Martha Thomas Foundation
2205 N. 6th St., Ste. 10A
Beatrice, NE 68310-1264 (402) 228-3424
Contact: Michael Willet, Secy.-Treas.
E-mail: willetlaw@diodecom.net

Established in 2006 in Nebraska.
Donors: Margaret A. Thomas; Martha E. Thomas†.
Foundation type: Independent foundation.
Financial data (yr. ended 06/30/13): Assets, $4,634,305 (M); expenditures, $311,350; qualifying distributions, $240,826; giving activities include $240,826 for 10 grants (high: $35,000; low: $750).
Fields of interest: Education; Human services.
Type of support: General support.
Limitations: Applications accepted. Giving primarily in Wymore, NE.
Application information: Application form required.
    Initial approach: Completed application form
    Deadline(s): None
Officers: Dean Marples, Pres.; Jeffrey Nelson, V.P.; Michael Willet, Secy.-Treas.
EIN: 203652030

5124
Mary F. Tous Charitable Foundation
233 S. 13th St., Ste. 1900
Lincoln, NE 68508-2095
Contact: D.R. Stogsdill

Established in 2003 in Nebraska.
Donors: Mary F. Tous†; Fillmore County Foundation; Fillmore County Cinema Association.
Foundation type: Independent foundation.
Financial data (yr. ended 12/31/14): Assets, $3,804,642 (M); expenditures, $199,317; qualifying distributions, $178,794; giving activities include $128,976 for 28 grants (high: $21,976; low: $500), and $32,000 for 34 grants to individuals.
Fields of interest: Arts and culture; Education; Human services.
Type of support: General support.
Limitations: Applications not accepted. Giving primarily in NE. No grants to individuals.
Application information: Unsolicited requests for funds not accepted.
Trustee: Union Bank & Trust Co.
EIN: 206092468

5125
Milton G. & Miriam Waldbaum Family Foundation
(formerly Milton G. Waldbaum Family Foundation)
714 N. 158th St.
Omaha, NE 68118-2208 (402) 345-5866
Contact: John Waldbaum, Tr.

Established in 1988 in Nebraska.
Foundation type: Independent foundation.
Financial data (yr. ended 12/31/13): Assets, $6,669,309 (M); expenditures, $414,905;

qualifying distributions, $334,614; giving activities include $334,614 for 60 grants (high: $50,000; low: $100).

Fields of interest: Higher education; Nonprofits; Family planning; Human services; Child welfare.

Type of support: Regranting.

Limitations: Applications accepted. Giving on a national basis. No grants to individuals.

Application information: Application form required.

Initial approach: Proposal

Deadline(s): None

Trustees: Susan Hughson; Cheryl Waldbaum; Jerome Waldbaum; John Waldbaum; Natha Waldbaum.

Number of staff: None.

EIN: 363611254

5126
Lester A. Walker Foundation
(formerly The Walker Foundation)
P.O. Box 169
Fremont, NE 68026-0169

Donor: Lester A. Walker.

Foundation type: Independent foundation.

Financial data (yr. ended 12/31/14): Assets, $3,153,147 (M); expenditures, $168,824; qualifying distributions, $147,344; giving activities include $147,344 for 15 grants (high: $94,331; low: $1,179).

Fields of interest: Higher education; Foundations; Health; Hospital care; Community and economic development; Protestantism; Human services.

Limitations: Applications not accepted. Giving primarily in Fremont, NE; some funding in Phoenix, AZ. No grants to individuals.

Application information: Unsolicited requests for funds not accepted.

Trustees: Jane Walker; G. Michael Wiseman; Fremont National Bank & Trust Co.

EIN: 476022547

5127
The Weller Foundation, Inc.
P.O. Box 636
Atkinson, NE 68713-0636 (402) 925-2803

Established in 1979 in Nebraska.

Donors: E.C. Weller‡; Frances W. Weller‡.

Foundation type: Independent foundation.

Financial data (yr. ended 10/31/14): Assets, $8,491,227 (M); expenditures, $511,615; qualifying distributions, $411,152; giving activities include $373,775 for 158 grants to individuals (high: $6,250; low: $1,500).

Purpose and activities: Scholarships for students attending one of the technical community colleges in Nebraska or pursuing other vocational education, such as nursing.

Fields of interest: Vocational education; Nursing care.

Type of support: Student aid.

Limitations: Applications accepted. Giving limited to NE, with primary consideration for residents of Boyd, Brown, Garfield, Holt, Keya Paha, and Rock counties. No grants for scholarships for education toward a bachelor's degree.

Publications: Application guidelines.

Application information: Application form required.

Initial approach: Completed Application form

Deadline(s): For renewal applicants: June 1 for the fall semester and Nov. 1 for the spring semester. For new applicants: Apr. 1 for the fall semester and Nov. 1 for the spring semester

Final notification: Within 30 days of the deadlines

Officers: Dick Bilstein, Pres.; Bryan Rentschler, V.P.; Clark Gotschall, Secy.-Treas.

Directors: Jean Fleming; Dr. Robert Randall; Barb Shane.

Number of staff: 1 full-time support.

EIN: 470611350

5128
West Education Foundation
11808 Miracle Hills Dr.
Omaha, NE 68154-4403 (402) 963-1200

Established in 2006 in Nebraska.

Donor: West Corporation.

Foundation type: Company-sponsored foundation.

Financial data (yr. ended 12/31/14): Assets, $648,692 (M); gifts received, $200,004; expenditures, $167,856; qualifying distributions, $151,750; giving activities include $151,750 for grants.

Purpose and activities: The foundation provides scholarship awards to dependent children, under the age of 24, of employees of United States West Corporation, St. Peter, Minnesota. The program is administered by Scholarship America.

Fields of interest: Higher education.

Type of support: Student aid; Employee-related scholarships.

Limitations: Applications not accepted.

Application information: Contributes only through employee-related scholarships. Application form required.

Deadline(s): Mar. 15

Directors: Thomas B. Barker; Nancee Shannon R. Berger; Paul M. Mendlik.

EIN: 204763223

5129
York Community Foundation
603 N. Lincoln Ave.
York, NE 68467-4240 (402) 362-5531
Contact: Donna Bitner, Exec. Dir.
E-mail: ycf@yorkchamber.net; *Main URL:* http://www.yorkcommunityfoundation.org/index.html

Established in 1984 in Nebraska.

Foundation type: Community foundation.

Financial data (yr. ended 09/30/13): Assets, $7,050,617 (M); gifts received, $2,181,318; expenditures, $526,083; giving activities include $294,793 for 5+ grants (high: $95,341), $146,950 for 66 grants to individuals, and $6,624,320 for loans/program-related investments.

Purpose and activities: The foundation seeks to utilize charitable funds to strengthen and improve the community for the benefit of all its citizens.

Fields of interest: Arts and culture; Education; Health; Diseases and conditions; Community and economic development; Religion; Sports and recreation; Human services; Child welfare; Low-income and poor people.

Type of support: Program development; Student aid.

Limitations: Applications accepted. Giving limited to the York, NE, area. No support for religious purposes. No grants to individuals (except for scholarships), or for operating expenses, annual fund drives, endowment funds, or travel.

Application information: Visit foundation web site for application form and guidelines. Application form required.

Initial approach: Submit application form

Deadline(s): None

Officers and Directors: Kristie Holoch, Pres. and Director; Charles W. Harris, V.P. and Director; Donna Bitner, Exec. Dir.; Charles W. Campbell; Gordon B. Fillman; Richard Hankel; C.G. Holthus; Lawrence R. Kopsa; Garold Leggott; Donna Loschen; Judi Nordlund; Katie North; Kent Rauert; Sally Ruben; Cheryl Thomas-Miller.

EIN: 363324526

5130
C.W. Yount Foundation, Inc.
P.O. Box 441
Gering, NE 69341-0441

Donor: Charles W. Yount.

Foundation type: Independent foundation.

Financial data (yr. ended 12/31/13): Assets, $3,985,986 (M); expenditures, $467,234; qualifying distributions, $210,692; giving activities include $198,789 for 44 grants (high: $27,564; low: $500).

Purpose and activities: Scholarship awards paid directly to WNCC or UNCM for graduates of Gering High School or School District 60, Nebraska. Some giving to Christian faith based youth programs.

Fields of interest: Higher education; Community and economic development; Protestantism; Youth development.

Type of support: General support; Scholarships.

Limitations: Applications not accepted.

Application information: Unsolicited requests for funds not accepted.

Officers and Directors: Ernest Ouderkirk, Pres. and Director; Dale John, V.P. and Director; Thomas Holyoke, Secy. and Director; James A. Emery, Mgr. and Director.

EIN: 470600603

NEVADA

5131
A Charitable Foundation
2657 Windmill Pkwy., Ste. 220
Henderson, NV 89014-3384

Established in 1997 in Nevada.
Donor: Tactical Investment Management Corp.
Foundation type: Independent foundation.
Financial data (yr. ended 12/31/13): Assets, $5,574,175 (M); gifts received, $145,000; expenditures, $206,093; qualifying distributions, $185,483; giving activities include $121,135 for 32 grants (high: $35,000; low: $250), and $38,217 for 2 grants to individuals (high: $23,261; low: $14,956).
Fields of interest: Education; Environment; Christianity; Human services; Food banks; International development.
International interests: Brazil.
Type of support: Annual campaigns; Grants to individuals; Capital and infrastructure; Research and evaluation; Emergency funds; Research.
Limitations: Applications accepted. Giving primarily in California, Hawaii, and New York; some giving also in Brazil.
Application information: Application form required.
  Initial approach: Proposal
  Copies of proposal: 2
  Deadline(s): None
Officers and Directors: David S. Druz, Pres.; Colleen A. Haviland, Secy.-Treas.; Gregg Smith.
EIN: 880375802

5132
Andress Family Foundation
2300 W. Sahara Ave., Ste. 670
Las Vegas, NV 89102-4355
Contact: Madeleine Andress, Dir.; Don Andress, Dir.

Donors: Don Andress; Madeleine Andress.
Foundation type: Independent foundation.
Financial data (yr. ended 05/31/13): Assets, $20,383 (M); gifts received, $200,000; expenditures, $216,325; qualifying distributions, $216,200; giving activities include $216,200 for 7 grants (high: $200,000; low: $1,000).
Fields of interest: Performing arts; Education; Hospice care; Human services.
Type of support: General support.
Limitations: Applications accepted. Giving primarily in Las Vegas, NV.
Application information: Application form required.
  Initial approach: Letter
  Deadline(s): None
Directors: Don Andress; Louwanna Andress; Madeleine Andress; Melanie Tobiasson.
EIN: 880396633

5133
Patricia Miller and William Conrad Anton Foundation
(formerly Patricia Miller Anton and William Conrad Anton Foundation)
9 Avenida Fiori
Henderson, NV 89011-2401

Established in 2005 in Nevada.
Donors: William Anton; Patricia Anton.
Foundation type: Independent foundation.
Financial data (yr. ended 12/31/13): Assets, $4,688 (M); gifts received, $220,150; expenditures, $225,645; qualifying distributions, $217,954; giving activities include $217,954 for 35 grants (high: $50,000; low: $100).
Purpose and activities: The foundation is devoted to preserving the cultural character, built and natural settings and quality of life in selected small communities or institutions in the U.S. The foundation's focus is on cultural and historical preservation, land and water conservation, the decorative, fine and performing arts, and education.
Fields of interest: Education; Health; Religion.
Limitations: Applications not accepted. No grants to individuals.
Application information: Contributes only to pre-selected organizations.
Officers: William Anton, Chair.; Patricia Anton, Pres.; Christina Anton Hayes, Secy.; Peter Miller, Treas.
Trustees: Charles Burns; Paul Miller; Andrea Anton Weaver.
EIN: 206658967

5134
The Earl & Elizabeth Ash Foundation
c/o Scott Gunderson
18124 Wedge Pkwy., No. 542
Reno, NV 89511-8134

Established in 2002 in California.
Donors: Elizabeth Ash; Ash Family Trust.
Foundation type: Independent foundation.
Financial data (yr. ended 12/31/13): Assets, $4,613,850 (M); expenditures, $342,081; qualifying distributions, $315,500; giving activities include $249,500 for 4 grants (high: $115,000; low: $2,500).
Fields of interest: Museums; Specialty hospital care; Human services.
Limitations: Applications not accepted. Giving primarily in CA. No grants to individuals.
Application information: Unsolicited requests for funds not accepted.
Officers and Directors: David L. Peterson, Pres. and Director; Scott Gunderson, Secy.-Treas. and Director.
EIN: 141841243

5135
Robert R. Banks Foundation
P.O. Box 33361
Reno, NV 89533-3361
Application address: c/o Jeff Eckroth, Treas., 340 Cliff View Ct., Reno, NV 89523, tel.: (775) 827-3600

Established in 1995 in Nevada.
Foundation type: Independent foundation.
Financial data (yr. ended 04/30/13): Assets, $3,531,721 (M); expenditures, $250,105; qualifying distributions, $203,435; giving activities include $157,700 for 25 grants (high: $22,200; low: $2,500).
Purpose and activities: Giving primarily for children's services, including family, medical, and legal services.
Fields of interest: Family planning; Child welfare; Youth services; Scouting programs; Adult and child mentoring.

Limitations: Applications accepted. Giving primarily in NV. No grants to individuals.
Application information: Application form required.
  Initial approach: Proposal
  Copies of proposal: 6
  Deadline(s): Apr. 1
  Board meeting date(s): 3rd Wed. of each calendar quarter
Officers: Jack Harker, Chair.; Linda Horsey, Secy.; Jeff Eckroth, Treas.
Director: Steve Petersen.
EIN: 943221616

5136
The Brett and Deborah Barker Foundation
11440 Dixon Ln.
Reno, NV 89511-1529

Established in 2004 in Nevada.
Donors: Brett D. Barker; Deborah L. Barker.
Foundation type: Independent foundation.
Financial data (yr. ended 12/31/13): Assets, $4,167,145 (M); expenditures, $255,086; qualifying distributions, $250,000; giving activities include $250,000 for 11 grants (high: $50,000; low: $5,000).
Fields of interest: Education; Human services; Food banks; Family services; Child welfare; Youth services.
Limitations: Applications not accepted. Giving primarily in NV and NY. No grants to individuals.
Application information: Unsolicited requests for funds not accepted.
Trustees: Brett D. Barker; Deborah L. Barker.
EIN: 201186903

5137
Bendon Family Foundation
7881 W. Charleston Blvd., Ste. 250
Las Vegas, NV 89117-8327

Established in 1995 in Florida.
Donors: Dorothy Bendon; Bendon Clut.
Foundation type: Independent foundation.
Financial data (yr. ended 06/30/14): Assets, $10,487,153 (M); gifts received, $209,654; expenditures, $629,111; qualifying distributions, $573,232; giving activities include $440,400 for 71 grants (high: $100,000; low: $500).
Fields of interest: Arts and culture; Elementary and secondary education; Nonprofits; Human services; Family services; Child welfare.
Type of support: Regranting.
Limitations: Applications not accepted. Giving primarily in Maui, HI. No grants to individuals.
Application information: Unsolicited requests for funds not accepted.
Officers: James A. Bendon, Pres.; Susan Kaylor Bendon, V.P.
Director: John James Bendon.
EIN: 650631534

5138
Edna B. & Bruno Benna Foundation
8500 Dieringer Dr.
Reno, NV 89511-7555 (775) 853-4895
Contact: Edna B. Benna, Tr.

Donors: Edna B. Benna; Bruno Benna.
Foundation type: Independent foundation.

Financial data (yr. ended 12/31/13): Assets, $4,082,993 (M); expenditures, $224,212; qualifying distributions, $189,476; qualifying activities include $189,476 for 52 grants (high: $60,000; low: $40).
Fields of interest: Arts and culture; Art museums; Education; Medical specialties; Diseases and conditions; Religion; Catholicism; Human services.
Type of support: General support; Research.
Limitations: Applications accepted. Giving primarily in Reno, NV. No grants to individuals.
Application information: Application form required.
  Initial approach: Proposal
  Deadline(s): None
Trustee: Edna B. Benna.
EIN: 880367131

5139
Binion Family Foundation
3605 S. Town Center Dr., Ste. A
Las Vegas, NV 89135

Established in 2006 in Nevada.
Donors: Jack Binion; Phyllis Mae Cope.
Foundation type: Independent foundation.
Financial data (yr. ended 12/31/14): Assets, $3,426,838; gifts received, $50,491; expenditures, $173,090; qualifying distributions, $162,166.
Fields of interest: Education; Hospice care.
Limitations: Applications not accepted. Giving primarily in NV. No grants to individuals.
Application information: Unsolicited requests for funds not accepted.
Officers and Directors: Katie O'Neill, Pres. and Director; Dominic Polizzotto, Secy.; Chad Blackman, Treas.; Fancy Fechser; T.J. Fechser; Kellie O'Neill.
EIN: 208076667

5140
The Blue Oak Charitable Fund
P.O. Box 230579
Las Vegas, NV 89105-0579

Established in 1998 in California.
Donor: BFT Carriers, Inc.
Foundation type: Independent foundation.
Financial data (yr. ended 12/31/13): Assets, $6,921,070 (M); gifts received, $198,500; expenditures, $363,670; qualifying distributions, $330,000; giving activities include $330,000 for 24 grants (high: $119,275; low: $500).
Purpose and activities: The foundation supports organizations involved with medical research, animal welfare, and public policy.
Fields of interest: Domesticated animals; Diseases and conditions; Religion; Human services.
Type of support: General support; Research; Policy, advocacy and systems reform.
Limitations: Applications not accepted. Giving primarily in Washington, DC, NV. No grants to individuals.
Application information: Contributes only to pre-selected organizations.
Officers: Debra Middleton, Pres.; Dale Bottoms, Secy.-Treas.
Director: John Ciesielka.
EIN: 911897170

5141
Boyd Foundation
(doing business as The Boyd Family Foundation)
(also known as Boyd Foundation)
P.O. Box 4008
Incline Village, NV 89450-4008

Donor: Boyd Foundation.
Foundation type: Independent foundation.
Financial data (yr. ended 12/31/14): Assets, $3,952,087; expenditures, $278,691; qualifying distributions, $250,670.
Fields of interest: Higher education; Human services.
Type of support: Student aid; Scholarships; General support.
Limitations: Applications accepted. Giving on a national basis, with emphasis on CA.
Application information: Application form required.
  Initial approach: Proposal
  Deadline(s): None
Trustees: Denton L. Peoples; Mary Ann Zannon Peoples.
Number of staff: None.
EIN: 316668320

5142
C.A.N. Foundation
(formerly The Williams Foundation)
6817 S. Eastern Ave., Ste. 101
Las Vegas, NV 89119-4684   (702) 933-2213
Contact: Patricia Sanchez

Established in 1994 in Nevada.
Donor: Claudine B. Williams.
Foundation type: Independent foundation.
Financial data (yr. ended 10/31/14): Assets, $4,839,974 (M); expenditures, $243,863; qualifying distributions, $241,000; giving activities include $241,000 for 13 grants (high: $50,000; low: $6,000).
Purpose and activities: Giving primarily for education, children, youth, and social services; funding also for educational scholarships.
Fields of interest: Education; Human services; Child welfare; Youth organizing; Females.
Type of support: Scholarships.
Limitations: Applications accepted. Giving primarily in Las Vegas, NV. No grants to individuals.
Application information: Application form required.
  Initial approach: Proposal
  Deadline(s): None
Officer: Michael S. Williams, Pres. and Secy.-Treas.
Director: Theresa Williams.
EIN: 880329401

5143
Martin G. and Ruth A. Carver Foundation
9811 W. Charleston Blvd., Ste. 2-506
Las Vegas, NV 89117

Established in 2007 in Iowa.
Donors: Martin G. Carver; Ruth A. Carver.
Foundation type: Independent foundation.
Financial data (yr. ended 12/31/13): Assets, $9,470,845 (M); expenditures, $366,574; qualifying distributions, $398,355; giving activities include $298,355 for 31 grants (high: $55,000; low: $100).
Fields of interest: Arts and culture; Education; Protestantism.

Limitations: Applications not accepted. Giving primarily in CO and IA.
Application information: Contributes only to pre-selected organizations.
Officers: Martin G. Carver, Pres. and Treas.; Ruth A. Carver, V.P. and Secy.
EIN: 208571592

5144
The Castleman Family Foundation
917 Tahoe Blvd., Ste. 200
Incline Village, NV 89451-9422

Donor: Peter M. Castleman.
Foundation type: Independent foundation.
Financial data (yr. ended 12/31/13): Assets, $9,495,470 (M); expenditures, $461,893; qualifying distributions, $442,562; giving activities include $437,305 for 14 grants (high: $100,000; low: $1,000).
Fields of interest: Animal welfare; Health care clinics.
Limitations: Applications not accepted. Giving primarily in AZ. No grants to individuals.
Application information: Contributes only to pre-selected organizations.
Trustees: Peter M. Castleman; Sloane C. Castleman; Daniel J. O'Brien.
EIN: 205393405

5145
Center for the Encouragement of Self Reliance
8021 Golfers Oasis Dr.
Las Vegas, NV 89149-4616
Contact: Thu-Le Doan, Tr.
Application Address: 11 Brewster Ln., Oak Bridge, TN 37830, tel.: (702) 395-6680

Established in 1997 in Nevada.
Donors: Doan L. Phung; Thu-Le Doan; Vietnamese American Scholarship Fund; PAI Corporation.
Foundation type: Independent foundation.
Financial data (yr. ended 12/31/13): Assets, $7,439,547 (M); gifts received, $4,320; expenditures, $226,579; qualifying distributions, $196,820; giving activities include $196,820 for 29 grants (high: $18,820; low: $2,000).
Fields of interest: Education; Human rights; Immigrants and migrants.
International interests: Vietnam.
Limitations: Applications accepted. Giving in the U.S. and Vietnam.
Application information: Applicant must document financial need. Application form required.
  Initial approach: Letter
  Deadline(s): None
Trustees: Thu-Le Doan; Doan L. Phung.
EIN: 880378074

5146
Chami Family Foundation
2009 Eagle Trace Way
Las Vegas, NV 89117-5743
Application address: c/o Sandra Poiser, 1667 Lincoln Ave., Orange, CA 92865, tel.: (714) 283-5800,
email: sandra@investmentsconceptsinc.com

Donors: George Chami; Marcia Chami.

Foundation type: Independent foundation.
Financial data (yr. ended 12/31/13): Assets, $203,285 (M); gifts received, $175,000; expenditures, $151,394; qualifying distributions, $150,900; giving activities include $150,500 for 9 grants (high: $25,000; low: $1,500).
Fields of interest: Education; Health; Specialty hospital care; Human services.
Limitations: Applications accepted. Giving primarily in CA and MA.
Application information:
  Initial approach: Contact foundation
  Deadline(s): None
Directors: George Albert Chami II; George Chami; Marcia Chami; Mardah Chami; Sandra Poiser.
EIN: 456653445

5147
The Children of Light Foundation
(formerly The Omega Foundation)
P.O. Box 5667
Incline Village, NV 89450

Established in 1997 in Nevada.
Donors: Robert C. Elias; The Omega Foundation.
Foundation type: Independent foundation.
Financial data (yr. ended 12/31/13): Assets, $1,629,620 (M); expenditures, $216,196; qualifying distributions, $201,900; giving activities include $201,900 for 9 grants (high: $90,000; low: $2,000).
Purpose and activities: Giving primarily for education and human services.
Fields of interest: Education; Higher education; Human services.
Type of support: General support.
Limitations: Applications not accepted. Giving primarily in NV, with emphasis on Reno. No grants to individuals.
Application information: Contributes only to pre-selected organizations.
Officer and Trustee: Robert C. Elias, Pres. and Secy.-Treas. and Trustee.
EIN: 880379653

5148
Helen Close Charitable Foundation
c/o Barnard, Vogler & Co.
100 W. Liberty St., No. 1100
Reno, NV 89501-1959 (775) 786-6141
Contact: Kenneth E. Stieha Jr., Pres. and Tr.

Established in 1985 in Nevada.
Donor: Helen Close†.
Foundation type: Independent foundation.
Financial data (yr. ended 11/30/13): Assets, $6,336,894 (M); expenditures, $470,028; qualifying distributions, $394,423; giving activities include $371,938 for 29 grants (high: $48,400; low: $2,000).
Fields of interest: Higher education; Animal welfare; Fire prevention and control; Camps.
Type of support: Equipment; Seed money; Internships; Scholarships.
Limitations: Applications accepted. Giving primarily in northern NV. No support for religious organizations. No grants to individuals.
Application information: Application form required.
  Initial approach: Proposal
  Copies of proposal: 4
  Deadline(s): None

Officers and Trustees: Kenneth E. Stieha, Jr., Pres. and Trustee; David M. Quinn, V.P. and Trustee; Carole Mathisen, Secy. and Trustee; Betty Vogler, Treas. and Trustee.
EIN: 880214245

5149
Robert Cohen Private Foundation
c/o Solomon Dwiggins & Freer
9060 W. Cheyenne Ave.
Las Vegas, NV 89129-8911

Established in 2006 in Nevada.
Donor: Robert Cohen†.
Foundation type: Independent foundation.
Financial data (yr. ended 12/31/13): Assets, $2,812,501 (M); expenditures, $303,231; qualifying distributions, $234,531; giving activities include $138,200 for 15 grants (high: $77,000; low: $200).
Purpose and activities: Giving primarily for Jewish education.
Fields of interest: Judaism.
International interests: Israel.
Limitations: Applications not accepted. Giving primarily in Las Vegas, NV, and Israel. No grants to individuals.
Application information: Unsolicited requests for funds not accepted.
Officer: Asaf Ganot, Pres.
Trustee: Ruth Ganot.
EIN: 207196808

5150
The Brett and Karen Coleman Foundation
539 Riverside Dr.
Reno, NV 89503-5331

Established in 2004 in Nevada.
Donors: Karen Coleman; Brett Coleman.
Foundation type: Independent foundation.
Financial data (yr. ended 12/31/13): Assets, $2,298,652 (M); expenditures, $138,278; qualifying distributions, $119,167; giving activities include $119,167 for 8 grants (high: $25,000; low: $5,000).
Fields of interest: University education; Diabetes; Christianity; Judaism; Human services; Child welfare.
Type of support: Research.
Limitations: Applications not accepted. Giving primarily in NV. No grants to individuals.
Application information: Unsolicited requests for funds not accepted.
Trustees: Brett Coleman; Karen Coleman.
EIN: 201835821

5151
Crescere Foundation
c/o Beverly L. Ozmun
3259 E. Warm Springs Rd., Bldg. 27
Las Vegas, NV 89120-3157

Established in 1997 in Nevada.
Donors: Beverly O. Hamman; Stephen R. Hamman; Beverly L. Ozmun.
Foundation type: Independent foundation.
Financial data (yr. ended 12/31/14): Assets, $1,671,768 (M); gifts received, $275,000; expenditures, $289,103; qualifying distributions,

$281,068; giving activities include $280,000 for 8 grants (high: $150,000; low: $5,000).
Fields of interest: Christianity; Human services; Child welfare.
Limitations: Applications not accepted. Giving in the U.S., with emphasis on Henderson and Las Vegas, NV. No grants to individuals.
Application information: Contributes only to pre-selected organizations.
Officer: Beverly L. Ozmun, Pres.
EIN: 860877267

5152
Dermody Properties Foundation
5500 Equity Ave.
Reno, NV 89502-2343 (775) 858-8080
Contact: Carol Martin, Admin.
FAX: (775) 856-0831;
E-mail: cmartin@dermody.com; Main URL: http://www.dermody-properties.com/dp_foundation
Grants List: http://dermody.com/node/112

Established in 1987 in Nevada.
Donors: Dermody Properties, Inc.; DP Advisors LLC; DP Homes LLC; Michael C. Dermody; Tolles Trust DTD.
Foundation type: Company-sponsored foundation.
Financial data (yr. ended 12/31/13): Assets, $19,157 (M); gifts received, $150,000; expenditures, $145,735; qualifying distributions, $141,968; giving activities include $141,968 for grants.
Purpose and activities: The foundation supports organizations involved with arts and culture, education, and family services. Special emphasis is directed toward children and the elderly.
Fields of interest: Arts and culture; Education; Human services; Food aid; Food banks; Family services; Youth development; Children; Seniors.
Type of support: General support; Continuing support; Equipment; Program development; Convening; Scholarships; Sponsorships.
Limitations: Applications accepted. Giving primarily in Rochelle, IL, Las Vegas and Reno, NV, and Harrisburg, PA. No grants to individuals, or for endowments or capital campaigns.
Publications: Application guidelines; Grants list.
Application information: Grants range from $500 to $3,000. Application form required.
  Initial approach: Contact foundation for application form
  Copies of proposal: 1
  Deadline(s): Aug. 1
  Board meeting date(s): Quarterly
Officers: Michael C. Dermody, Co-Founder; Bruce Storey, Co-Founder.
Directors: James Mascaro; Sharon Mills; Becky Moody; Brian Quigley; Alice Swanson; Elizabeth Teske.
Number of staff: 1 part-time support.
EIN: 943086271

5153
Do Right Foundation
2540 S. Maryland Pkwy., Ste. 178
Las Vegas, NV 89109-1627
E-mail: dorightfdn@aol.com; Main URL: http://www.doright.org

Established in 1996 in Illinois.
Donor: James E. McCrink.

Foundation type: Independent foundation.
Financial data (yr. ended 12/31/13): Assets, $3,614,315 (M); gifts received, $1,000; expenditures, $298,513; qualifying distributions, $188,000; giving activities include $188,000 for 32 grants (high: $45,000; low: $3,000).
Purpose and activities: To help mankind create a more joyful society.
Fields of interest: Foundations; Safety education; Religion; Human rights; Family services; Parent education.
Type of support: General support.
Limitations: Applications not accepted. Giving on a national basis. No grants to individuals, or for general operating support.
Publications: Program policy statement.
Application information: Contributes only to pre-selected organizations.
Trustee: James E. McCrink.
Number of staff: 1 full-time professional.
EIN: 367160651

5154
EBV Foundation

(also known as Entrepreneur Bootcamp for Veterans with Disabilities)
38 Grand Corniche Dr.
Henderson, NV 89011-2004
E-mail: dani@ebvfoundation.org; Main URL: http://www.ebvfoundation.org

Donors: Theodore Lachowicz; Cheryl Lachowicz; Kevin Coyne; Sue Carusi; Cantor Fitzgerald; Bruce Carusi; Tom Foley; The Rumsfeld Foundation; Jeffrey Zander.
Foundation type: Independent foundation.
Financial data (yr. ended 12/31/13): Assets, $282,600 (M); gifts received, $94,222; expenditures, $165,266; qualifying distributions, $123,500; giving activities include $123,500 for grants.
Purpose and activities: Giving primarily to participating veterans to assist in the development of their business plans.
Fields of interest: Social enterprise; Veterans.
Limitations: Applications not accepted. Giving primarily in Syracuse, NY; some funding also in Henderson, NV.
Application information: Unsolicited requests for funds not accepted.
Officer: Theodore Lachowicz, Pres.
Board Members: George Bodine; Hon. John C. Cherundolo; Thomas C. Colella; Thomas Foley; Richard L. Haydon; Mark Larsen; Alex Panelli.
EIN: 263844672

5155
Edward Fein Foundation

(formerly Edward Feinstein Foundation)
P.O. Box 4057
Carson City, NV 89702-4057

Established in 1965 in New York.
Donor: Edward Fein.
Foundation type: Independent foundation.
Financial data (yr. ended 03/31/14): Assets, $8,997,548 (M); expenditures, $191,129; qualifying distributions, $189,717; giving activities include $185,000 for 4 grants (high: $100,000; low: $15,000).

Fields of interest: Education; Higher education; Nonprofits; Judaism; Human services.
International interests: Israel.
Type of support: Regranting.
Limitations: Applications not accepted. Giving primarily in AZ, CA, MA and PA. No grants to individuals.
Application information: Unsolicited requests for funds not accepted.
 Board meeting date(s): Jan.
Officer: Edward Fein, Pres.
EIN: 136220451

5156
Findlay Education Foundation

c/o Tyler Corder
310 N. Gibson
Henderson, NV 89014-6702

Established in 2006 in Nevada.
Donors: Clifford J. Findlay; Findlay Cadillac; Greg Heinrich; River City Petrolium; Findlay Shack Properties LLC; Findlay Management Group; Wiliiam Boyd; Al Clise; South Point Hotel Casino.
Foundation type: Independent foundation.
Financial data (yr. ended 12/31/13): Assets, $28,003 (M); gifts received, $413,300; expenditures, $424,000; qualifying distributions, $424,000; giving activities include $424,000 for 1 grant.
Fields of interest: Higher education.
Limitations: Applications not accepted. Giving primarily in NV.
Application information: Unsolicited requests for funds not accepted.
Officers and Trustees: Clifford J. Findlay, Pres. and Treas. and Trustee; Tyler Corder, Secy.; Bruce Becker; Jeffrey L. Burr.
EIN: 205109148

5157
Bruce Fishkin Scholarship Fund

5775 S. Fort Apache Rd., Ste. 120
Las Vegas, NV 89148-5627
Main URL: http://www.brucefishkinscholarshipfund.com
Facebook: https://www.facebook.com/brucefishkinscholarshipfund
Twitter: https://twitter.com/bfscholarship

Donors: Vince Gabor; Caleb Fishkin.
Foundation type: Independent foundation.
Financial data (yr. ended 12/31/13): Assets, $75,655 (M); gifts received, $428,508; expenditures, $499,494; qualifying distributions, $412,905; giving activities include $412,905 for 28 grants to individuals (high: $65,620; low: $1,000).
Purpose and activities: The fund awards scholarships to students enrolled at high schools in any of the following areas: Fairfield, Greens Farms, Redding, and Westport, Connecticut, and the cities and surrounding suburbs of Chicago, Illinois and Las Vegas, Nevada.
Fields of interest: Education.
Type of support: Student aid.
Application information: Online application process; see Fund web site for complete information. Application form required.
 Deadline(s): Dec. 15

Officer and Directors: Caleb Fishkin, Pres. and Secy. and Director; Eliot Bares; Vince Gabor; Cortney Fishkin; Joshua Fishkin.
EIN: 271647358

5158
The Foundation for the Cosmic Claimes & Consequences of Christ

6100 Neil Rd.
Reno, NV 89511-1132

Donor: Gary L. Grauberger.
Foundation type: Independent foundation.
Financial data (yr. ended 12/31/13): Assets, $823,004 (M); gifts received, $1,101,000; expenditures, $282,159; qualifying distributions, $279,450; giving activities include $279,000 for 13 grants (high: $50,000; low: $12,000).
Fields of interest: Christianity.
Limitations: Applications not accepted. Giving primarily in CA and CO.
Application information: Unsolicited requests for funds not accepted.
Officer: Gary L. Grauberger, Pres. and Treas.
Director: Linda K. Grauberger.
EIN: 454442942

5159
Fuserna Foundation

(formerly The Getty Family Foundation)
5390 Kietzke Ln., Ste. 202
Reno, NV 89511-3028 (775) 412-4322
Contact: Leah Langsdorf
FAX: (775) 786-5414;
E-mail: leah.langsdorf@suttonpl.com; UK address: 26 Curzon St., London, W1J7TQ, tel.: 020 7409 3900, fax: 020 7409 3901, e-mail: Katie.Morris@suttonpl.com; Main URL: http://fusernafoundation.org

Donors: John Paul Getty III; Ariadne Getty.
Foundation type: Independent foundation.
Financial data (yr. ended 12/31/13): Assets, $31,914 (M); gifts received, $351,952; expenditures, $322,722; qualifying distributions, $302,679; giving activities include $302,679 for 15 grants (high: $40,000; low: $10,000).
Fields of interest: Community and economic development; Human services; Youth development; LGBTQ people.
International interests: England; Wales.
Limitations: Applications accepted. Giving primarily in CA; some funding also in NY and in the Southern states; U.K. giving is primarily in England and Wales. No grants to individuals.
Publications: Application guidelines.
Application information: See foundation web site for applications procedures in both the U.S. and the U.K.
 Deadline(s): See foundation web site for current deadlines
 Final notification: 3-6 months
Officers and Directors: Ariadne Getty, Pres. and Exec. Dir.; Erin Otolski, V.P. and Director; John Ladner, Secy. and Director; Howard D. Reynolds, Treas. and Director.
Trustees: Louise Creasey; Patrick Maxwell.
EIN: 200461573

5160
Geomar Foundation
c/o Sourwine & Sloane, Ltd.
4950 Kietzke Ln., Ste. 302
Reno, NV 89504

Established in 1989 in New York.
Donors: George T. Scharffenberger; Marion A. Scharffenberger.
Foundation type: Independent foundation.
Financial data (yr. ended 12/31/13): Assets, $5,845,459 (M); expenditures, $254,041; qualifying distributions, $231,720; giving activities include $231,720 for 72 grants (high: $105,000; low: $100).
Fields of interest: Education; Higher education; Land resources; Health; Hospital care; Cancers; Libraries; Catholicism.
Type of support: Scholarships; Individual development; Policy, advocacy and systems reform.
Limitations: Applications not accepted. No grants to individuals.
Application information: Contributes only to pre-selected organizations.
Officer: Marion A. Scharffenberger, Pres.
EIN: 350677888

5161
William H. & Mattie W. Harris Foundation
6655 W. Sahara, Ste. B-118
Las Vegas, NV 89146 (702) 253-1317
FAX: (702) 253-0548;
E-mail: harrisfoundation@lvcoxmail.com; Main URL: http://harrisfoundation-nevada.com

Established in 2008 in Nevada.
Foundation type: Independent foundation.
Financial data (yr. ended 12/31/14): Assets, $9,032,900 (M); expenditures, $515,754; qualifying distributions, $413,325; giving activities include $354,660 for 96 grants (high: $37,625; low: $160).
Fields of interest: Arts and culture; Education; Domesticated animals; Community and economic development.
Limitations: Applications accepted. Giving primarily in AZ, CA, CO, NM, and NV. No grants to individuals.
Publications: Application guidelines.
Application information: The foundation requires a Letter of Inquiry prior to consideration of any proposal. See foundation web site for application guidelines. Application form required.
   Initial approach: Letter of Inquiry (max. 2 pgs.)
   Copies of proposal: 4
   Deadline(s): Mar. 1 for Letter of Inquiry; May 1 for application
Officers: RuthAnne Anderson, Pres.; Haydn Hite, Exec. V.P.; Jessica Hite, Secy.; Marilyn Hite, Treas.
Directors: Cassidy Harrison; Dustin Hite; Henry Hite.
EIN: 262841027

5162
Zhengxu & Ying He Foundation Inc.
5220 Belsera Ct.
Reno, NV 89519-6159 (776) 826-1079
Contact: Ying Fang, Secy.; Zhengxu He, Pres.

Established in 2007 in Nevada.
Foundation type: Independent foundation.

Financial data (yr. ended 12/31/14): Assets, $4,069,880 (M); expenditures, $333,118; qualifying distributions, $332,743.
Fields of interest: Education.
International interests: China.
Type of support: Scholarships.
Limitations: Applications accepted. Giving primarily in CT and China. No grants to individuals.
Application information:
   Initial approach: Letter
   Deadline(s): None
Officers: Zhengxu He, Pres.; Ying Fang, Secy.
Trustee: Qingdong He.
EIN: 260851791

5163
Houssels Family Foundation Corporation
1050 Indigo Dr., Ste. 120
Las Vegas, NV 89145

Established in 1998 in Nevada.
Donors: J.K. Houssels; Houssels FLP.
Foundation type: Independent foundation.
Financial data (yr. ended 12/31/13): Assets, $283 (M); gifts received, $404,360; expenditures, $406,635; qualifying distributions, $405,518; giving activities include $405,518 for 20 grants (high: $310,618; low: $100).
Purpose and activities: Giving primarily for the arts and human services.
Fields of interest: Arts and culture; Performing arts; Ballet; Education; Human services; Child welfare.
Limitations: Applications not accepted. Giving primarily in Las Vegas, NV. No grants to individuals.
Application information: Contributes only to pre-selected organizations.
Trustees: J.K. Houssels; Nancy C. Houssels.
EIN: 880411205

5164
Jansen Family Foundation
11351 Winter Cottage Pl.
Las Vegas, NV 89135-1705

Established in 2005 in Nevada.
Donors: Avis Jansen Charitable Remainder Trust; El Shaddai; Jansen Charitable Lead Annuity Trust; WJ Holding.
Foundation type: Independent foundation.
Financial data (yr. ended 06/30/14): Assets, $5,507,366; gifts received, $96,499; expenditures, $301,387; qualifying distributions, $244,664.
Fields of interest: Education; Christianity; Sports and recreation.
Limitations: Applications not accepted.
Application information: Unsolicited requests for funds not accepted.
Officer: Linda Tijerina, Pres.
EIN: 880432689

5165
The Jaquish & Kenninger Foundation
P.O. Box 129
Zephyr Cove, NV 89448-0129 (775) 588-4646
FAX: (775) 588-2272;
E-mail: info@jaquishkenningerfoundation.org; Main URL: http://www.jaquishkenningerfoundation.org

Established in 1997 in California.

Donors: Ruth L. Kenninger Trust; Gail A. Jaquish; Steven C. Kenninger.
Foundation type: Independent foundation.
Financial data (yr. ended 12/31/13): Assets, $8,267,341 (M); gifts received, $87,789; expenditures, $420,618; qualifying distributions, $197,000; giving activities include $197,000 for 8 grants (high: $100,000; low: $1,000).
Purpose and activities: Giving primarily for organizations who support developing excellence in leadership to strengthen Americans' personal and economic freedoms.
Fields of interest: Education; Higher education; Diseases and conditions; Human services.
Limitations: Applications accepted. Giving primarily in CA and IN. No grants to individuals.
Application information: Application form required.
   Initial approach: Completed application form
   Deadline(s): None
Officers: Gail A. Jaquish, Pres.; Steven C. Kenninger, Secy.-Treas.
Directors: R. Taylor Bennett; Stewart L. Hayes; Susan K. Kenninger; Dennis H. Vaughn.
EIN: 330759830

5166
The Joseph Family Foundation
3750 Las Vegas Blvd. S., Ste. 4306
Las Vegas, NV 89158-4376

Established in 1997 in California.
Donors: Janet Lynn Joseph; S. Michael Joseph.
Foundation type: Independent foundation.
Financial data (yr. ended 12/31/13): Assets, $4,497 (M); expenditures, $146,774; qualifying distributions, $145,833; giving activities include $145,800 for 17 grants (high: $50,000; low: $500).
Purpose and activities: Giving for Catholic education, youth services, and pro-life organizations.
Fields of interest: Elementary and secondary education; Higher education; Catholicism; Right to life; Minority rights; Child welfare.
Type of support: General support; Scholarships.
Limitations: Applications not accepted. Giving primarily in southern CA and PA. No grants for events, conferences and seminars, capital campaigns, equipment, building and renovation, or debt reduction.
Publications: Program policy statement.
Application information: Unsolicited requests for funds not accepted.
   Board meeting date(s): 3 times annually
Officers: S. Michael Joseph, Chair.; Stephen B. Colwell, C.F.O.; Janet Lynn Joseph, Exec. Dir.
Director: Clemenx Connoley.
Number of staff: None.
EIN: 911866055

5167
Joshua Foundation
471 Dart Brook Pl.
Henderson, NV 89012-4529 (928) 765-2201
Contact: Jan Marie Purdy, Fdn. Mgr.; Forrest Purdy Jr., Fdn. Mgr.

Established in 1996 in Nevada.
Donor: Cactus Family Trust.
Foundation type: Independent foundation.
Financial data (yr. ended 12/31/13): Assets, $9,231,141 (M); gifts received, $38,546;

expenditures, $658,031; qualifying distributions, $230,743; giving activities include $168,073 for 8 grants (high: $65,000; low: $1,000), and $1,000 for 1 grant to an individual.

Fields of interest: Agriculture; Community and economic development; Christianity; Human services.

Limitations: Applications accepted. Giving primarily in AZ, with emphasis on Williams.

Application Information: Application form required.

Initial approach: Proposal

Deadline(s): None

Officers: Forrest Purdy, Jr., Fdn. Mgr.; Jan Marie Purdy, Fdn. Mgr.

EIN: 880368741

5168
The Kara Foundation
11700 W. Charleston Blvd., Ste. 170-37
Las Vegas, NV   89135

Established in 1992 in Illinois.

Foundation type: Independent foundation.

Financial data (yr. ended 12/31/13): Assets, $9,720,595 (M); expenditures, $417,701; qualifying distributions, $379,990; giving activities include $237,100 for 56 grants (high: $15,000; low: $1,000).

Purpose and activities: Giving primarily for art and cultural programs, health care, education and the environment.

Fields of interest: Domesticated animals; Health; Human services.

Limitations: Applications not accepted. Giving primarily in IL. No grants to individuals.

Application information: Unsolicited requests for funds not accepted.

Officers: Patrick S. DeMoon, Pres. and Treas.; Judith A. DeMoon, Secy.

EIN: 363779796

5169
Kennedy Foundation
6502 S. Mccarran Blvd., Apt. D
Reno, NV   89509-6139
Application address: c/o Brian J. Kennedy, Pres., 4790 Caughlin Pkwy., No. 501, Reno, NV 89509, tel.: (775) 772-8488

Established in 2007 in Nevada.

Donor: Brian J. Kennedy.

Foundation type: Independent foundation.

Financial data (yr. ended 11/30/14): Assets, $750,134; expenditures, $125,475; qualifying distributions, $124,450.

Fields of interest: Arts and culture; Education; Community and economic development.

Limitations: Applications accepted. Giving primarily in Reno, NV.

Application information: Application form required.

Initial approach: Letter

Deadline(s): None

Officers and Trustees: Brian J. Kennedy, Pres. and Trustee; Nancy J. Kennedy, Secy. and Trustee; David W. Turner, Treas. and Trustee; David B. Thomas.

EIN: 205199307

5170
The Harold B. Larson Charitable and Testamentary Trust
1 W. Liberty St., 3rd Fl.
Reno, NV   89501-1913

Established in 2005 in Nevada.

Donor: Harold B. Larson†.

Foundation type: Independent foundation.

Financial data (yr. ended 12/31/13): Assets, $7,438,482 (M); expenditures, $381,488; qualifying distributions, $335,131; giving activities include $294,980 for 14 grants (high: $21,070; low: $21,070).

Fields of interest: Animal welfare.

Limitations: Applications not accepted. Giving primarily in CA, Washington, DC and NY. No grants to individuals.

Application information: Contributes only to pre-selected organizations.

Board meeting date(s): Annually in June

Trustees: Lenora Geenen; Western National Trust Co.

EIN: 206553630

5171
Theodore and Doris Lee Family Foundation
3271 S. Highland Dr., Ste. 704
Las Vegas, NV   89109-1051

Donors: Lee Charitable Lead Trust; Theodore B. Lee; Doris S. Lee.

Foundation type: Independent foundation.

Financial data (yr. ended 12/31/14): Assets, $1,159,517 (M); gifts received, $400,000; expenditures, $399,675; qualifying distributions, $399,650; giving activities include $399,650 for 28 grants (high: $200,000; low: $50).

Fields of interest: Arts and culture; Law education; Diseases and conditions; Human services.

Limitations: Applications not accepted. Giving primarily in CA and NV. No grants to individuals.

Application information: Unsolicited requests for funds not accepted.

Officers: Theodore B. Lee, Pres.; Doris S. Lee, Treas.

Directors: Ernest T.H. Lee; Gregory T.H. Lee.

EIN: 272531820

5172
Lemay Family Foundation
1555 Boulder Field Way
Reno, NV   89511-6570

Donor: Gene Lemay Family.

Foundation type: Independent foundation.

Financial data (yr. ended 12/31/13): Assets, $3,378,560 (M); expenditures, $182,727; qualifying distributions, $145,000; giving activities include $145,000 for 8 grants (high: $33,000; low: $5,000).

Fields of interest: Higher education; Christianity.

Limitations: Applications not accepted.

Application information: Unsolicited requests for funds not accepted.

Officers: H. Eugene LeMay, Jr., Pres.; Carla A. LeMay, Secy.

EIN: 263878466

5173
Lifestyle Homes Foundation
(formerly Pioneer Foundation)
P.O. Box 7548
Reno, NV   89510-7548

Established in 1987 in Nevada.

Donors: R.J. Lissner; Woodland Village North, LLC; Elaine Lissner; Project Solution.

Foundation type: Independent foundation.

Financial data (yr. ended 12/31/13): Assets, $6,109,153 (M); expenditures, $550,636; qualifying distributions, $327,806; giving activities include $316,905 for 10 grants (high: $134,541; low: $70).

Purpose and activities: Giving primarily for education, and children and youth services.

Fields of interest: Education; Domesticated animals; Child welfare.

Type of support: Research.

Limitations: Applications not accepted. Giving primarily in NV, with emphasis on Reno. No grants to individuals.

Application information: Contributes only to pre-selected organizations.

Director: R.J. Lissner.

EIN: 880230583

5174
Living Promise Foundation
2337 Dolphin Ct.
Las Vegas, NV   89074

Donor: The GKD Trust.

Foundation type: Independent foundation.

Financial data (yr. ended 12/31/13): Assets, $26,602 (M); gifts received, $235,171; expenditures, $362,384; qualifying distributions, $362,384; giving activities include $362,384 for 28 grants (high: $75,200; low: $200).

Fields of interest: Education; Religion; Christianity; Human services.

Limitations: Applications not accepted. Giving primarily in NV.

Application information: Unsolicited requests for funds not accepted.

Officers: Gregory A. Dean, Pres.; Kerry A.F. Dean, Secy.

Trustees: Aaron J. Dean; Emily R. Dean; Jared G. Dean; Lucas Dean.

EIN: 461156448

5175
Debra E. and Warner C. Lusardi Foundation
711 S. Caron St., Ste. 4
Carson City, NV   89701

Established in 2002 in California.

Donors: Warner C. Lusardi; Debra E. Lusardi.

Foundation type: Independent foundation.

Financial data (yr. ended 12/31/13): Assets, $3,113,540 (M); expenditures, $243,446; qualifying distributions, $241,600; giving activities include $241,600 for 11 grants (high: $100,000; low: $100).

Fields of interest: Education; Health; Religion.

Limitations: Applications not accepted. Giving primarily in CA and OH. No grants to individuals.

Application information: Unsolicited requests for funds not accepted.

Officers: Debra E. Lusardi, Pres.; Warner C. Lusardi, Secy.-Treas.
EIN: 300015380

5176
The Marshall R. Matley Foundation
c/o Wealth Management Dept.
P.O. Box 40430
Reno, NV   89504-4430   7756887995

Established in 1996 in Nevada.
Foundation type: Independent foundation.
Financial data (yr. ended 12/31/14): Assets, $4,160,288; expenditures, $333,038; qualifying distributions, $279,700.
Fields of interest: Elementary and secondary education; Higher education; Community health care; Children and youth; People with disabilities; People with physical disabilities; People with psychosocial disabilities.
Limitations: Applications not accepted. Giving primarily in NV.
Application information: Contributes only to pre-selected organizations.
Trustees: Daniel J. Klaich; Ernie Maupin; Western National Trust Co.
EIN: 880364211

5177
Paul E. & Helen S. Meyer Foundation
3315 E. Russell Rd., Ste. 199
Las Vegas, NV   89120-3459
E-mail: lvmeyerfndtn@aol.com

Established in 1994 in Nevada.
Donors: Paul E. Meyer†; Pauline Meyer†; Helen Meyer†; Paul Meyer Irrevocable Credit Trust; Paul Meyer Irrevocable Non Credit Trust; White Horse Youth Ranch.
Foundation type: Independent foundation.
Financial data (yr. ended 12/31/12): Assets, $9,376,676 (M); gifts received, $3,543,833; expenditures, $875,757; qualifying distributions, $563,114; giving activities include $144,022 for 15 grants (high: $39,500; low: $927).
Purpose and activities: Giving primarily to provide grants and scholarships for educational purposes.
Fields of interest: Higher education; Human services.
Type of support: General support; Program-related investments; Continuing support; Grants to individuals; Matching grants; Capital and infrastructure; Equipment; Endowments; Program development; Convening; Publications; Fellowships; Internships; Scholarships; Research; Technical assistance; Student aid.
Limitations: Applications not accepted. Giving primarily in Las Vegas, NV.
Application information: Unsolicited requests for funds not accepted.
   Board meeting date(s): Monthly
Officers and Directors: Amy Meyer, Pres. and Director; Laurie Howard Malm, V.P. and Director; Rebecca Mankiller, Secy. and Director; Carol Ann Flood, Treas. and Director.
Number of staff: 1 full-time professional; 4 part-time professional.
EIN: 880325604

5178
The Moran Foundation
2360 Corporate Cir., Ste. 400
Henderson, NV   89074

Established in 1997 in California.
Donors: Joseph P. Moran; Laurel A. Moran; Moran Charitable Remainder Net Income Unitrust.
Foundation type: Independent foundation.
Financial data (yr. ended 12/31/14): Assets, $4,790,821; expenditures, $247,388; qualifying distributions, $243,175.
Fields of interest: Education; Health; Catholicism; Right to life; Human services.
Limitations: Applications not accepted. No grants to individuals.
Application information: Unsolicited requests for funds not accepted.
Officers: Joseph P. Moran, Pres. and Treas.; Joshua P. Moran, Secy.
Directors: Laurel A. Moran; Lucille Ann Moran; Richard Jerome Moran.
EIN: 770455314

5179
L. M. Newman Family Foundation
601 Fairview Blvd.
Incline Village, NV   89451-8938

Established in 1994 in Nevada.
Donor: L. Mark Newman.
Foundation type: Independent foundation.
Financial data (yr. ended 11/30/13): Assets, $3,220,522 (M); gifts received, $50,000; expenditures, $232,586; qualifying distributions, $189,306; giving activities include $179,499 for 28 grants (high: $71,200; low: $35).
Fields of interest: Arts and culture; Education; Human services.
Type of support: General support.
Limitations: Applications not accepted. Giving primarily in CA and NV. No grants to individuals.
Application information: Unsolicited requests for funds not accepted.
Officer: L. Mark Newman, Mgr.
Directors: Darryl Newman; Denise Newman; Linda Newman; Paul Newman.
EIN: 943215798

5180
The Orchard House Foundation-A Nevada Non Profit Corporation
4795 Caughlin Pkwy., Ste. 100
Reno, NV   89519-1007

Established in 2000 in Nevada.
Donors: Maya P. Miller; Maya P. Miller Charitable Lead Annuity Trust 1; Maya P. Miller Charitable lead Annuity Trust 2.
Foundation type: Independent foundation.
Financial data (yr. ended 12/31/14): Assets, $9,005,959; gifts received, $852,148; expenditures, $593,500; qualifying distributions, $491,561.
Fields of interest: Human services.
Type of support: General support.
Limitations: Applications not accepted. Giving primarily in CA and NV. No grants to individuals.
Application information: Contributes only to pre-selected organizations.

Officer and Trustees: Carson A. Miller, Pres. and Trustee; Annika Christensen.
EIN: 880450156

5181
The Marguerite Petersen Foundation
4790 Caughlin Pkwy., Ste. 395
Reno, NV   89519-0907

Established in 2001 in Nevada.
Foundation type: Independent foundation.
Financial data (yr. ended 12/31/14): Assets, $4,099,329; expenditures, $241,143; qualifying distributions, $220,000.
Fields of interest: Arts and culture; University education; Foundations; Human services; Child welfare; Youth services; Scouting programs.
Limitations: Applications not accepted. Giving primarily in NV. No grants to individuals.
Application information: Unsolicited requests for funds not accepted.
Officers and Trustees: Kathleen P. Dees, Pres. and Secy. and Trustee; Steven K. Petersen, Treas. and Trustee; Robert E. Armstrong; Chris Askin; Douglas A. Petersen; David W. Turner.
EIN: 880460795

5182
Gregor G. Peterson Family Foundation
(formerly Dion Peterson Foundation, Inc.)
P.O. Box 4450
Incline Village, NV   89450-4450

Established in 1996 in Nevada.
Donors: Dion Z. Peterson; Gregor G. Peterson; Sybil Zaches Administrative Trust.
Foundation type: Independent foundation.
Financial data (yr. ended 12/31/13): Assets, $5,320,828 (M); expenditures, $327,611; qualifying distributions, $260,300; giving activities include $256,000 for 16 grants (high: $50,000; low: $1,500).
Fields of interest: Higher education; Foundations; Health; Human services.
Limitations: Applications not accepted. Giving primarily in CA, NJ and NV. No grants to individuals.
Application information: Contributes only to pre-selected organizations.
Officers and Trustees: Dion P. Russell, Pres.; Eric W. Peterson, Treas. and Trustee; Christopher J. Peterson.
EIN: 880374370

5183
The Pinnacle Entertainment Foundation
8918 Spanish Ridge Ave.
Las Vegas, NV   89148-1302   (702) 541-7777
Contact: Shelly Peterson
Main URL: https://www.pnkinc.com/pinnacle-entertainment-foundation

Donor: Pinnacle Entertainment, Inc.
Foundation type: Company-sponsored foundation.
Financial data (yr. ended 12/31/13): Assets, $874 (M); gifts received, $214,769; expenditures, $244,998; qualifying distributions, $244,998; giving activities include $243,700 for 27 grants (high: $50,000; low: $1,000).
Purpose and activities: The foundation supports community foundations and food banks and

organizations involved with arts and culture, higher education, and health.

Fields of interest: Higher education; Foundations; Patient social services; Hospital care; Sports and recreation; Food banks; Child welfare.

Type of support: General support; Program development; Scholarships; Sponsorships.

Limitations: Applications accepted. Giving primarily in LA and NV. No support for political candidates or organizations, discriminatory organizations or religious organizations, fraternal, alumni, trade, professional, or social organizations. No grants to individuals, or for administrative expenses, capital project funding, uniforms or trips for school-related organizations, booster clubs, youth athletics, or amateur sports teams, or study or travel grants.

Publications: Application guidelines.

Application information: Applications are limited to two per calendar year, per organization. Application form required.

   Initial approach: Complete online application

   Deadline(s): 90 days prior to need

Officers and Directors: Anthony M. Sanfillipo, Pres. and Director; John A. Godfrey, Secy. and Director; Stephen H. Capp, Treas.

EIN: 272612545

5184
The Pretti Foundation
1001 Tahoe Blvd.
Incline Village, NV 89451-9309

Established in 1997 in Nevada.

Donor: Gene T. Pretti.

Foundation type: Independent foundation.

Financial data (yr. ended 12/31/13): Assets, $2,520,115 (M); gifts received, $368,500; expenditures, $141,918; qualifying distributions, $141,595; giving activities include $141,595 for 5 grants (high: $110,000; low: $5,000).

Fields of interest: Education; Health; Human services.

Limitations: Applications not accepted. Giving primarily in NV. No grants to individuals.

Application information: Contributes only to pre-selected organizations.

Officers: Gene T. Pretti, Pres.; Steven M. Kleiman, Secy.

EIN: 860873397

5185
Shulman Family Foundation
(formerly Alex Shulman Family Foundation)
6940 O'Bannon Dr.
Las Vegas, NV 89117-2122

Established in 2001 in Washington.

Donor: Alex Shulman.

Foundation type: Independent foundation.

Financial data (yr. ended 12/31/13): Assets, $2,763,182 (M); expenditures, $271,405; qualifying distributions, $245,750; giving activities include $209,000 for 25 grants (high: $20,000; low: $2,000).

Purpose and activities: Giving primarily to Reform Jewish causes.

Fields of interest: Education; Nonprofits; Reform Judaism; Human services; Child welfare.

Type of support: Regranting.

Limitations: Applications not accepted. Giving primarily in Las Vegas, NV. No grants to individuals.

Application information: Contributes only to pre-selected organizations.

Officers: Barry Shulman, Pres.; Michael Shulman, V.P.; Jeff Shulman, Secy.

EIN: 912100817

5186
Marshall & Elaine Siegel Family Foundation
10609 Clarion Ln.
Las Vegas, NV 89134-5230

Established in 1998 in Minnesota.

Donors: Marshall Siegel; Elaine Siegel.

Foundation type: Independent foundation.

Financial data (yr. ended 12/31/13): Assets, $0 (M); expenditures, $147,764; qualifying distributions, $145,994; giving activities include $145,994 for 11 grants (high: $100,000; low: $25).

Fields of interest: Judaism; Developmental disability services.

Type of support: General support.

Limitations: Applications not accepted. Giving primarily in MN. No grants to individuals.

Application information: Unsolicited requests for funds not accepted.

Officers: Paul Siegel, Pres. and Treas.; Elaine Siegel, V.P. and Secy.

EIN: 880397249

5187
Smith Family Foundation
9601 Verlaine Ct.
Las Vegas, NV 89145-8694
Application address: c/o David J. Lyon, 11 Quietwood Ln., Sandy, UT 84092; tel.: (801) 523-0475

Donors: Edward D. Smith; Megan Smith; Shauna H. Smith; Brandon Smith.

Foundation type: Independent foundation.

Financial data (yr. ended 12/31/13): Assets, $123,572 (M); gifts received, $166,500; expenditures, $191,805; qualifying distributions, $191,805; giving activities include $60,455 for 4 grants (high: $50,000; low: $688), and $115,500 for 22 grants to individuals (high: $36,000; low: $500).

Fields of interest: Education; Higher education.

Limitations: Applications accepted. Giving primarily in NV and UT.

Application information: Application form required.

   Initial approach: Letter

   Deadline(s): None

Trustees: Edward D. Smith; Shauna H. Smith.

EIN: 274396874

5188
Special Assistance Fund for Energy
P.O. Box 10100
Reno, NV 89520-0024 (775) 834-5741

Donors: NV Energy; NV Energy Charitable Foundation.

Foundation type: Independent foundation.

Financial data (yr. ended 12/31/14): Assets, $90,461; gifts received, $308,060; expenditures, $307,726; qualifying distributions, $307,476.

Fields of interest: Human services; Family services; Senior services.

Limitations: Applications accepted. Giving primarily in CA and NV.

Application information:

   Initial approach: Proposal

   Deadline(s): None

Officers: Robert Jones, Pres.; Linda Ellsworth, Secy.; Karen C. Ross, Treas.

Directors: Carol Marin; Cloyd Phillips.

EIN: 880341058

5189
The Frieda & Leon Steinberg Charitable Foundation
8916 Players Club Dr.
Las Vegas, NV 89134-6353

Established in 2004 in Nevada.

Donors: Frieda Steinberg; Leon H. Steinberg; Frieda and Leon Steinberg Investment.

Foundation type: Independent foundation.

Financial data (yr. ended 12/31/13): Assets, $460,827 (L); gifts received, $452,950; expenditures, $205,700; qualifying distributions, $200,000; giving activities include $200,000 for 1 grant.

Fields of interest: Education; Judaism.

Limitations: Applications not accepted. Giving primarily in Las Vegas, NV. No grants to individuals.

Application information: Unsolicited requests for funds not accepted.

Officers: Leon H. Steinberg, Pres. and Treas.; Frieda Steinberg, V.P. and Secy.

EIN: 201986221

5190
The Charles H. Stout Foundation
1835 Wendy Way
Reno, NV 89509-8208
E-mail: richardmstout@earthlink.net; *Main URL:* http://www.chstoutfoundation.org

Established in 1982 in Nevada.

Foundation type: Independent foundation.

Financial data (yr. ended 06/30/13): Assets, $8,120,801 (M); expenditures, $390,640; qualifying distributions, $376,829; giving activities include $369,000 for 28 grants (high: $30,000; low: $2,000).

Fields of interest: Arts and culture; Education; Housing development.

Limitations: Applications accepted. Giving primarily in Siloam Springs, AR, Del Mar, CA, Reno, NV, New York, NY, or in communities where foundation trustees live or visit regularly. No grants to individuals; no loans.

Publications: Application guidelines; Informational brochure (including application guidelines).

Application information: Complete application guidelines available on foundation web site. Application form required.

   Initial approach: Use online application system on foundation web site

   Copies of proposal: 1

   Deadline(s): June 15

   Board meeting date(s): Sept. or Oct.

   Final notification: Within one month following board meeting

Officers and Trustees: Richard M. Stout, Pres. and Trustee; Martha Stout Gilweit, V.P. and Trustee; Katherine Gilweit Cartiglia, Secy. and Trustee; D.

Kent Clayburn, Treas.; Samantha Gilweit; Christopher H. Stout.
Members: Alexa Gilweit; Douglas B. McDonald.
EIN: 942797249

5191
Michael Sweig Foundation
1306 Hwy., Ste. 50
P.O. Box 10769
Zephyr Cove, NV   89448-2769

Established in 2000 in Illinois.
Donors: Michael Sweig; Morton Sweig†.
Foundation type: Independent foundation.
Financial data (yr. ended 12/31/14): Assets, $2,354,640 (M); gifts received, $250,000; expenditures, $292,885; qualifying distributions, $277,285; giving activities include $274,870 for 22 grants (high: $50,000; low: $500).
Fields of interest: Specialty hospital care; Diseases and conditions; Cancers; Human services.
Type of support: Research; Research and evaluation.
Limitations: Applications not accepted. Giving primarily in Chicago, IL; some funding also in CA and MA. No grants to individuals.
Application information: Contributes only to pre-selected organizations.
Trustee: Michael Sweig.
EIN: 367333404

5192
Timken-Sturgis Foundation
1525 Foothill Rd.
Gardnerville, NV   89460-6213   (775) 782-2445
Contact: Judy P. Sturgis, Secy.-Treas.

Established in 1949 in California.
Donors: Valerie Timken Whitney†; William T. Sturgis.
Foundation type: Independent foundation.
Financial data (yr. ended 11/30/13): Assets, $2,810,361 (M); expenditures, $168,974; qualifying distributions, $143,000; giving activities include $143,000 for 37 grants (high: $30,000; low: $500).
Fields of interest: Education; Higher education; Environment; Domesticated animals; Human services.
Type of support: Continuing support; Equipment; Land acquisitions; Scholarships; Research.
Limitations: Applications accepted. Giving primarily in southern CA and NV. No grants to individuals; no loans.
Application information:
    Initial approach: Letter
    Deadline(s): None
    Board meeting date(s): Nov.
Officers and Trustees: William T. Sturgis, Pres. and Trustee; Judy Pierce Sturgis, Secy.-Treas. and Trustee; Jason T. Sturgis.
Number of staff: 1 part-time support.
EIN: 943227435

5193
The Kilin and Cecilie To Foundation
2688 Olivia Heights Ave.
Henderson, NV   89052-6837
Contact: Cecilie To, Tr.; Kilin To, Tr.

Established in 1999 in New Jersey.

Donors: Cecilie To; Kilin To.
Foundation type: Independent foundation.
Financial data (yr. ended 05/31/14): Assets, $2,209,776 (M); gifts received, $2,000; expenditures, $139,612; qualifying distributions, $136,915; giving activities include $136,915 for 19 grants (high: $75,000; low: $100).
Purpose and activities: Giving primarily for education, human services, and health, including a healthcare foundation.
Fields of interest: Education; Foundations; Health; Religion.
Type of support: General support.
Limitations: Applications accepted. Giving primarily in Princeton, NJ.
Application information: Application form required.
    Initial approach: Letter requesting application format
    Deadline(s): None
Trustees: Cecilie To; Kilin To.
EIN: 226767675

5194
Vandevoort Family Foundation
2877 S. Paradise Rd., Ste. 302
Las Vegas, NV   89109-5239

Established in 1994 in Arizona.
Donors: Joel Vandevoort; Martha Vandevoort.
Foundation type: Independent foundation.
Financial data (yr. ended 12/31/14): Assets, $1,523,656 (M); gifts received, $199,875; expenditures, $166,214; qualifying distributions, $162,822; giving activities include $162,822 for 20 grants (high: $54,016; low: $100).
Fields of interest: Education; Nonprofits; Health; Christianity; Human services.
Type of support: General support; Regranting.
Limitations: Applications not accepted. Giving primarily in AZ. No grants to individuals.
Application information: Contributes only to pre-selected organizations.
Officers: Joel Vandevoort, Pres.; Martha Vandevoort, Secy.-Treas.
EIN: 363989526

5195
Harvey and Leslie Wagner Foundation
180 Village Blvd.
Incline Village, NV   89451-9450

Established in 2007 in Nevada.
Donors: Harvey E. Wagner; Leslie K. Wagner.
Foundation type: Independent foundation.
Financial data (yr. ended 12/31/13): Assets, $9,250,223 (M); expenditures, $455,388; qualifying distributions, $420,700; giving activities include $320,700 for 93 grants (high: $25,000; low: $200).
Fields of interest: Higher education.
Limitations: Applications not accepted. Giving primarily in CA, MA and NV.
Application information: Contributes only to pre-selected organizations.
Trustees: Andrea O'Riordan; Harvey E. Wagner; Leslie K. Wagner.
EIN: 260549401

5196
Webb Family Foundation, Inc.
7251 W. Lake Mead Blvd., Ste. 530
Las Vegas, NV   89128-8373
Contact: Lewis M. Webb, Pres.
Application address: 7 Journey, Ste. A, Aliso Viejo, CA 92656

Established in 1998 in Nevada.
Donors: Lewis M. Webb; Margaret A. Webb.
Foundation type: Independent foundation.
Financial data (yr. ended 06/30/13): Assets, $613,410 (M); expenditures, $175,960; qualifying distributions, $168,821; giving activities include $168,821 for 32 grants (high: $100,000; low: $25).
Fields of interest: Higher education; Hospital care; Christianity; Human services; Child welfare.
Limitations: Applications accepted. Giving primarily in CA and WV.
Application information: Application form required.
    Initial approach: Letter
    Copies of proposal: 1
    Deadline(s): None
Officers: Lewis M. Webb, Pres.; Margaret A. Webb, V.P.; Robert Underwood, Secy.
Directors: Karen Webb Armour; Jeremy L. Webb; Lewis M. Webb III.
EIN: 880381296

5197
West Star Foundation
14130 Saddlebow Dr.
Reno, NV   89511-6729

Established in 1954 in Minnesota.
Donors: Hazel P. Blume; Allen C. Blume; David J. Pugh; Lori E. Pugh; Marylyn H. Parmelee; Santoshi Wagner-Anue; William M. Pugh; James L. Pugh; Richard H. Pugh.
Foundation type: Independent foundation.
Financial data (yr. ended 12/31/13): Assets, $2,149,998 (M); expenditures, $264,986; qualifying distributions, $239,625; giving activities include $235,000 for 15 grants (high: $80,000; low: $2,500).
Fields of interest: Arts and culture; Environment; Philanthropy.
Type of support: General support; Capital and infrastructure; Endowments; Scholarships.
Limitations: Applications not accepted. No grants to individuals.
Application information: Unsolicited requests for funds not accepted.
Officers and Directors: David J. Pugh, Pres. and Director; William M. Pugh, Secy. and Director; James L. Pugh, Treas. and Director.
Board Members: Hazel Blume; Marylyn H. Parmelee; Richard H. Pugh; Lori E. Pugh; Santoshi Wagner-Anue.
EIN: 416020517

5198
Western Shoshone Scholarship Foundation
905 W. Main St.
Elko, NV   89803   (775) 748-1258
Contact: Katie Neddenriep

Donors: Barrick Cortez, Inc.; Barrick Gold Finance, Inc.
Foundation type: Independent foundation.

Financial data (yr. ended 12/31/13): Assets, $3,558,079 (M); gifts received, $1,304,710; expenditures, $378,430; qualifying distributions, $378,000; giving activities include $378,000 for 118 grants to individuals (high: $6,000; low: $1,500).
Purpose and activities: Scholarships to eligible students for university and college education, and vocational and technical training.
Fields of interest: Education.
Type of support: Student aid.
Application information: Application form required.
Initial approach: Completed application form
Deadline(s): July 5
Officers and Directors: Tim Buchanan, Pres. and Director; Jeff Zander, V.P. and Director; Rich Haddock, Genl. Counsel and Secy.; Mike Estes, Treas.; Sandra Barela; Patricia Knight; Gerald Tomoko; Rosalie Woods.
EIN: 364663132

5199
The Williams Family Foundation
59 Damonte Ranch Pkwy.
Reno, NV 89521

Donors: Stephen D. Williams; Lisa J. Williams.
Foundation type: Independent foundation.
Financial data (yr. ended 12/31/12): Assets, $3,956,743 (M); gifts received, $159,772; expenditures, $287,212; qualifying distributions, $269,000; giving activities include $269,000 for grants.
Fields of interest: Religion; Tribal and indigenous religions; Human services; Indigenous peoples.
Limitations: Applications not accepted. Giving primarily in CA and NV.
Application information: Unsolicited requests for funds not accepted.
Officers: Stephen D. Williams, Pres.; Lisa J. Williams, Secy.-Treas.
Trustee: Suzette M. Darney.
EIN: 261597598

5200
Wolzinger Family Foundation
c/o Mel Wolzinger
3100 Skipworth Dr.
Las Vegas, NV 89107-3242

Established in 2000 in Nevada.
Donors: Melvin B. Wolzinger; J.A. Johnson and C.W. Wolzinger Charitable Lead Annuity Trust.

Foundation type: Independent foundation.
Financial data (yr. ended 12/31/13): Assets, $5,209,054 (M); gifts received, $19,040; expenditures, $255,933; qualifying distributions, $240,188; giving activities include $240,188 for 47 grants (high: $35,000; low: $100).
Fields of interest: Arts and culture; Judaism; Child welfare; Youth services.
Limitations: Applications not accepted. Giving primarily in Las Vegas, NV, with some giving in New York, NY. No grants to individuals.
Application information: Contributes only to pre-selected organizations.
Officers: Melvin B. Wolzinger, Pres.; Jean Ann Johnson, Secy.; Constance Wolzinger, Treas.
EIN: 880468356

5201
Paul & Pamela Wood Foundation
c/o Ashley Quinn CPAS and Consultants
937 Tahoe Blvd., Ste. 200
Incline Village, NV 89451-7412

Established in 1999 in Nevada.
Donors: Paul A. Wood; Pamela R. Wood; Pamela A. Wood.
Foundation type: Independent foundation.
Financial data (yr. ended 12/31/13): Assets, $4,329,484 (M); expenditures, $206,565; qualifying distributions, $203,743; giving activities include $203,743 for 4 grants (high: $83,743; low: $40,000).
Fields of interest: Philosophy; Higher education; Nonprofits; Youth pregnancy prevention; Diseases and conditions; Food aid; Child welfare; International development.
International interests: Australia.
Type of support: Regranting.
Limitations: Applications not accepted. Giving primarily in CA, Washington, DC, NC, NY, and TX; giving internationally in Australia. No grants to individuals.
Application information: Contributes only to pre-selected organizations.
Officers: Pamela R. Wood, Pres.; Paul A. Wood, Secy.
EIN: 880444004

5202
Stephen A. Wynn and Elaine P. Wynn Foundation
3131 Las Vegas Blvd. S.
Las Vegas, NV 89109-1967 (702) 592-0058
Contact: Steve Dezii, Tr.

Established in 2000 in Nevada.
Donors: Solomon Kerzner; Beverly Rosenthal; Robert Arum 1988 Trust; Irwin A. Molasky Revocable Trust; The Lawrence Foundation; Marnell Foundation; Stephen A. Wynn; Elaine P. Wynn; Cydney Marsico; Bessemer Trust Company; Bob Tuttle; William Weidner; Bruce Rockowitz; Marc Schorr; Matt Maddox; Paiget.
Foundation type: Operating foundation.
Financial data (yr. ended 12/31/13): Assets, $518,978 (M); gifts received, $6,000; expenditures, $455,844; qualifying distributions, $455,844; giving activities include $350,000 for 2 grants (high: $250,000; low: $100,000).
Purpose and activities: Giving typically limited to the field of clinical human studies.
Fields of interest: Education; Human services.
Limitations: Applications accepted. Giving on a national basis, primarily in CA, IA, NV, NY and UT. No grants to individuals.
Application information: Application form required.
Initial approach: Letter
Deadline(s): None
Trustees: Steve Dezii; Stephen A. Wynn.
EIN: 943354332

5203
Yamagata Foundation
P.O. Box 400190
Las Vegas, NV 89140 (702) 451-1832
Contact: Merwin D. Grant, Secy.

Established in 2004 in Utah.
Donor: Gene H. Yamagata.
Foundation type: Independent foundation.
Financial data (yr. ended 12/31/13): Assets, $66,659 (M); gifts received, $358,516; expenditures, $334,936; qualifying distributions, $334,825; giving activities include $322,830 for 7 grants (high: $300,000; low: $1,500), and $5,000 for 1 grant to an individual.
Fields of interest: Higher education; Mormonism.
Limitations: Applications accepted. Giving primarily in HI and UT.
Application information:
Deadline(s): None
Officers: John Nitta, Pres.; Merwin D. Grant, Secy.
Director: Kent K. Nitta.
EIN: 201078807

NEW HAMPSHIRE

5204
The Barker Foundation Inc.
P.O. Box 328
Nashua, NH 03061-0328
Contact: Douglas M. Barker, Treas.

Established in 1954 in Maine.
Donors: Walter Barker†; Irene L. Barker†.
Foundation type: Independent foundation.
Financial data (yr. ended 12/31/13): Assets, $6,485,668 (M); expenditures, $279,964; qualifying distributions, $228,131; giving activities include $181,500 for 45 grants (high: $43,000; low: $200).
Purpose and activities: Giving primarily for health associations, social services and youth.
Fields of interest: Education; Hospital care; Diseases and conditions; Human services; Child welfare.
Type of support: General support; Continuing support; Annual campaigns; Capital campaigns; Capital and infrastructure; Equipment; Program development.
Limitations: Applications accepted. Giving primarily in NH. No grants to individuals.
Publications: Application guidelines.
Application information: Application form required.
  Initial approach: Proposal
  Deadline(s): None
  Board meeting date(s): Varies
Officers and Trustees: Elizabeth M. Bucknam, Pres. and Trustee; Susan B. Moran, V.P. and Trustee; Allan M. Barker, Secy. and Trustee; Douglas M. Barker, Treas.; Anne M. April; Dorothy A. Barker; Edward P. Moran, Jr.
EIN: 026005885

5205
John Bickford Foundation
P.O. Box 461
Portsmouth, NH 03802-0461
Contact: Charles G. Bickford, Pres.

Donor: John H. Bickford†.
Foundation type: Independent foundation.
Financial data (yr. ended 12/31/13): Assets, $4,637,583 (M); expenditures, $283,827; qualifying distributions, $197,500; giving activities include $197,500 for 47 grants (high: $22,500; low: $500).
Purpose and activities: Giving primarily for education, human services, and children's and family services.
Fields of interest: Arts and culture; Music; Museums; Education; Human services; Family services; Child welfare.
Type of support: General support; Matching grants; Continuing support; Annual campaigns; Equipment; Program development; Seed money; Curriculum development; Individual development.
Limitations: Applications accepted. Giving on a national basis, with emphasis on Morris County, NJ. No grants to individuals.
Application information: Grants are almost always made to charitable organizations already well known to the trustees.
  Initial approach: Letter

Copies of proposal: 1
Deadline(s): Mar. 1
Board meeting date(s): Spring
Final notification: Varies
Officers and Trustees: Charles G. Bickford, Pres. and Trustee; Marian Gerhart, V.P. and Trustee; Richard Kahn, Secy.-Treas. and Trustee; Andrew G. Bickford; Benjamin Bickford; John H. Bickford, Jr.; Lydia B. Bickford; Tatyana Bickford; Wilson Compton III; Frank L. Petrozzo, Jr.; Katrina Walsh.
Number of staff: 1 part-time support.
EIN: 237167663

5206
Charter Charitable Foundation
90 N. Main St.
Concord, NH 03301-4915 (603) 717-8452
E-mail: questions@charterfoundation.org;
Application address: c/o Heather A. Dockham, Asst. Secy., P.O. Box 245, Concord, NH 03302, tel.: (603) 545-8277; E-mail: heather@charterfoundation.org; Main URL: http://charterfoundation.org

Donors: K. Malcom Jones; Carol E. Koury; National Securities Corp.; Feminist Women's Health Center; The Butler Foundation.
Foundation type: Independent foundation.
Financial data (yr. ended 12/31/13): Assets, $8,280,987 (M); gifts received, $65,433; expenditures, $373,186; qualifying distributions, $350,018; giving activities include $340,523 for 32 grants (high: $100,000; low: $500).
Fields of interest: Education; Environment; Domesticated animals; Human services; Women's services.
Type of support: General support.
Limitations: Applications accepted. Giving in the U.S., with emphasis on MA and NH.
Application information: See foundation website for complete application guidelines. Application form required.
  Deadline(s): Mar. 15 and Oct. 15
Officers and Directors: Steven A. Albrecht, Chair. and Director; Christine Donovan, Secy. and Director; Kathryn Woodfin, Treas. and Director; Heather Dockham; Elizabeth R. Kapp; Cynthia Wentworth.
EIN: 200471816

5207
Taylor Christian Foundation
P.O. Box 457
Wolfeboro, NH 03894

Established in 2000 in New Hampshire.
Foundation type: Independent foundation.
Financial data (yr. ended 11/30/15): Assets, $5,285,914 (M); expenditures, $373,743; qualifying distributions, $306,981; giving activities include $304,200 for 19 grants (high: $139,000; low: $1,000).
Fields of interest: Christianity; Child welfare.
International interests: Honduras.
Limitations: Applications not accepted. Giving in the U.S., with emphasis on NH and WI; some funding also in Honduras. No grants to individuals.
Application information: Contributes only to pre-selected organizations.
Trustees: G. Robert Lockhart; Romona Lockhart.
EIN: 311745034

5208
Olin J. Cochran Trust
P.O. Box 477
Concord, NH 03302-0477

Foundation type: Independent foundation.
Financial data (yr. ended 12/31/13): Assets, $4,550,127 (M); expenditures, $219,556; qualifying distributions, $183,998; giving activities include $183,998 for 2 grants (high: $91,999; low: $91,999).
Fields of interest: Undergraduate education; People with disabilities; People with vision impairments.
Type of support: General support.
Limitations: Applications not accepted. Giving limited to Watertown and Boston, MA.
Application information: Contributes only to pre-selected organizations.
Trustee: TD Bank, N.A.
EIN: 026050390

5209
The Couch Family Foundation
P.O. Box 5010
Hanover, NH 03755-5010
Contact: Richard W. Couch

Established in 2001 in Massachusetts.
Donors: Richard W. Couch, Jr.; Barbara J. Couch.
Foundation type: Independent foundation.
Financial data (yr. ended 12/31/13): Assets, $38,200,101 (M); gifts received, $29,378,160; expenditures, $425,623; qualifying distributions, $248,870; giving activities include $212,925 for 45 grants (high: $20,500; low: $100).
Fields of interest: Opera; Higher education; Community and economic development; Christianity.
Limitations: Applications not accepted. Giving primarily in NH. No grants to individuals.
Application information: Unsolicited requests for funds not accepted.
Officer: Brooke Freeland, Mgr.
Trustees: Barbara J. Couch; Richard W. Couch.
EIN: 100000573

5210
The DEKA Foundation
340 Commercial St.
Manchester, NH 03101-1121

Donors: Dean Kamen; HHD, LLC.
Foundation type: Independent foundation.
Financial data (yr. ended 05/31/14): Assets, $10,548,648 (M); expenditures, $359,820; qualifying distributions, $325,000; giving activities include $325,000 for 3 grants (high: $275,000; low: $25,000).
Fields of interest: Science; Children.
Limitations: Applications not accepted. Giving primarily in NH. No grants to individuals.
Application information: Unsolicited requests for funds not accepted.
Directors: Stephen Hazard; Dean Kamen; Maureen Toohey; Robert Tuttle.
EIN: 271188399

5211
Dorr Foundation

84 Hillside Dr.
Portsmouth, NH 03801-5328 (603) 433-6438
Contact: Barbara McMillan, Chair.

Established in 1940 in Connecticut.
Donor: John Dorr‡.
Foundation type: Independent foundation.
Financial data (yr. ended 12/31/13): Assets, $7,307,672 (M); expenditures, $415,515; qualifying distributions, $346,682; giving activities include $335,958 for 19 grants (high: $30,000; low: $2,000).
Fields of interest: Science; Physical and earth sciences; Chemistry; Engineering; Biology.
Type of support: Equipment; Matching grants; Emergency funds; Program development; Seed money; Curriculum development; Scholarships; Research.
Limitations: Applications accepted. Giving primarily in CT, New York, NY, MA, ME, and NH. No grants to individuals, or for annual campaigns, conferences and seminars, or fellowships; no loans.
Application information:
  Deadline(s): None
Officer and Trustees: Barbara McMillan, Chair. and Trustee; Allen Hardon; Roger Hardon; Virginia Maxwell; Peter McMillan; Kenneth Punzelt; Shirley M. Punzelt; Virginia Sesler.
EIN: 136017294

5212
The Stannard & Dorothy Dunn Charitable Trust

7 Bliss Ln.
Lyme, NH 03768-3809 (603) 795-2080
Contact: Barbara D. Roby, Tr.

Established in 1991 in New Hampshire.
Donor: Dorothy O. Dunn‡.
Foundation type: Independent foundation.
Financial data (yr. ended 06/30/13): Assets, $5,588,898 (M); expenditures, $254,407; qualifying distributions, $223,658; giving activities include $219,895 for 74 grants (high: $16,250; low: $50).
Fields of interest: Performing arts; Museums; Historic preservation; Education; Natural resources; Domesticated animals; Health; Christianity; Human services.
Type of support: General support.
Limitations: Applications accepted. Giving primarily in NH. No grants to individuals.
Application information: Application form required.
  Initial approach: Letter
  Deadline(s): None
Trustee: Barbara D. Roby.
EIN: 026086871

5213
The Finlay Foundation

30 Temple St., Ste. 400
Nashua, NH 03060-3449
Main URL: http://www.thefinlayfoundation.org

Donors: Karin K. Finlay; Robert Finlay.
Foundation type: Independent foundation.
Financial data (yr. ended 12/31/13): Assets, $132,625 (M); gifts received, $249,000; expenditures, $257,078; qualifying distributions, $257,078; giving activities include $255,348 for 31 grants (high: $60,000; low: $500).
Purpose and activities: The Finlay Foundation improves the quality of life for Granite State residents by assisting children and families in need and promoting an array of forward-thinking cultural and educational initiatives.
Fields of interest: Education; Hospital care; Housing development; Human services; Children.
Type of support: Advocacy.
Limitations: Applications accepted. Giving primarily in NH.
Publications: Application guidelines.
Application information: Application form required.
  Initial approach: Online application form on foundation web site
  Deadline(s): None
Officer: Karin K. Finlay, Pres.
Trustee: Robert Finlay.
EIN: 262644613

5214
Samuel P. Hunt Foundation

555 Canal St., Ste. 710
Manchester, NH 03101-1517 (603) 622-4052
Contact: Douglas A. McIninch, Tr.
E-mail: fdtn555@aol.com

Established in 1951 in New Hampshire.
Donor: Samuel P. Hunt‡.
Foundation type: Independent foundation.
Financial data (yr. ended 12/31/14): Assets, $11,661,021 (M); expenditures, $625,611; qualifying distributions, $463,869; giving activities include $463,869 for 34 grants (high: $37,500; low: $75).
Fields of interest: Arts and culture; Education; Health; Christianity; Human services; Child welfare.
Type of support: General support; Matching grants; Continuing support; Capacity-building and technical assistance; Annual campaigns; Capital campaigns; Capital and infrastructure; Equipment; Land acquisitions; Emergency funds; Program development; Convening; Recordings; Publications; Seed money; Research.
Limitations: Applications accepted. Giving limited to NH. No support for public schools. No grants to individuals; no loans.
Publications: Application guidelines.
Application information: Videos, CDs, or documents or information in binders or notebooks are not accepted. Application form required.
  Initial approach: Completed application form
  Copies of proposal: 3
  Deadline(s): Mar. 15 and Sept. 15
Trustees: Douglas A. McIninch; James C. Tyrie.
Number of staff: 1 part-time support.
EIN: 026004471

5215
Oleonda Jameson Trust

c/o McLane Graf Raulerson & Middleton
11 S. Main St., Ste. 500
Concord, NH 03301 (603) 224-0600
Contact: Charles F. Leahy, Tr.

Established in 1977 in New Hampshire.
Donor: Oleonda Jameson‡.
Foundation type: Independent foundation.
Financial data (yr. ended 12/31/13): Assets, $5,937,464 (M); expenditures, $331,781; qualifying distributions, $296,803; giving activities include $290,836 for 21 grants (high: $50,000; low: $1,580).
Fields of interest: Arts and culture; Education; Secondary education; Foundations; Nonprofits; Health; Social sciences; Housing development; Human services; Family services; Child welfare; Low-income and poor people.
Type of support: Capital campaigns; Capital and infrastructure; Equipment; Emergency funds; Scholarships; Student aid; Regranting; Policy, advocacy and systems reform.
Limitations: Applications accepted. Giving limited to NH, with emphasis on the Concord area. No grants for endowment funds or general operating expenses.
Application information: Application form required.
  Initial approach: Letter
  Copies of proposal: 1
  Deadline(s): None
Trustee: Charles F. Leahy.
Number of staff: 1 part-time support.
EIN: 026048930

5216
Benjamin Kimball Trust

P.O. Box 477
Concord, NH 03302-0477

Foundation type: Independent foundation.
Financial data (yr. ended 12/31/13): Assets, $7,048,549 (M); expenditures, $357,046; qualifying distributions, $308,980; giving activities include $308,980 for 9 grants (high: $76,970; low: $150).
Fields of interest: Arts and culture; Historic preservation; Education; Health; Hospital care; Public libraries.
Limitations: Applications not accepted. Giving primarily in NH.
Application information: Unsolicited requests for funds not accepted.
Trustee: TD Bank, N.A.
EIN: 026004820

5217
Emily Landecker Foundation, Inc.

80 S. Main St., Ste. 202
Hanover, NH 03755-2053

Established in 2004 in New Hampshire.
Donors: Andrea Reimann-Ciardelli; Albert Reimann‡.
Foundation type: Independent foundation.
Financial data (yr. ended 12/31/13): Assets, $18,674,113 (M); gifts received, $2,200,000; expenditures, $334,589; qualifying distributions, $242,250; giving activities include $242,250 for 43 grants (high: $120,000; low: $250).
Fields of interest: Arts and culture; Higher education; Natural resources; Foundations; Human services.
Limitations: Applications not accepted. Giving primarily to NH, GA, and VT. No grants to individuals.
Application information: Contributes only to pre-selected organizations.
Officers and Directors: Andrea Reimann-Ciardelli, Pres.; Thomas L. Ciardelli, Secy.-Treas. and Director; Anthony Ciardelli; Lillian Ciardelli.
EIN: 201983521

5218
Caroline C. Levine Charitable Trust
20 Trafalgar Sq., Ste. 505
Nashua, NH 03063
Application address: 155 Lafayette Rd., Ste. 4, North Hampton, NH, Tel.: (603) 964-3922

Established in 1994 in New Hampshire.
Donor: Caroline C. Levine.
Foundation type: Independent foundation.
Financial data (yr. ended 12/31/13): Assets, $6,107,028 (M); expenditures, $456,151; qualifying distributions, $380,705; giving activities include $380,705 for 10 grants (high: $100,000; low: $500).
Fields of interest: Education; Christianity.
Limitations: Applications accepted. Giving primarily in NH. No grants to individuals.
Application information: Application form required.
 Initial approach: Letter
 Deadline(s): None
Trustees: Joseph W. Kenny; Caroline C. Levine.
EIN: 026101659

5219
The Linnell Foundation
39 Wentworth Rd.
P.O. Box 192
New Castle, NH 03854-0192

Established in 1977 in Massachusetts.
Donor: Robert C. Linnell†.
Foundation type: Independent foundation.
Financial data (yr. ended 12/31/13): Assets, $6,079,701 (M); expenditures, $344,758; qualifying distributions, $327,346; giving activities include $298,000 for 1 grant.
Fields of interest: Human services.
Type of support: Continuing support.
Limitations: Applications not accepted. Giving in the U.S., with emphasis on AR, NH and NY.
Application information: Unsolicited requests for funds not accepted.
 Board meeting date(s): Mar., June, Sept., and Dec.
Trustees: Elizabeth Ann Conner; Russell N. Cox; Charles R Hansen, Jr.; Renee Linnell; Robert J. Richards.
Number of staff: None.
EIN: 042625173

5220
Lion's Pride Foundation
115 Cottage Rd.
Moultonborough, NH 03254-4802

Established in 1976 in Minnesota.
Donor: Cathedral of St. John the Divine.
Foundation type: Independent foundation.
Financial data (yr. ended 12/31/14): Assets, $4,130,683 (M); gifts received, $160,000; expenditures, $190,483; qualifying distributions, $183,850; giving activities include $183,850 for 11 grants (high: $136,000; low: $500).
Fields of interest: Arts and culture; Art museums; Literature and writing; Education; University education; Protestantism; Winter sports.
Limitations: Applications not accepted. Giving primarily in MA, MN and New York, NY. No grants to individuals.

Application information: Unsolicited requests for funds not accepted.
Officers and Trustees: Louis F. Polk, Jr., Pres. and Trustee; Susan Bucknam, V.P. and Treas.; Richard N. Flint, Secy.; Christy P. Goldspink; Anna C. Polk; Kellyanna Polk.
EIN: 411289414

5221
The Lynch Family Charitable Foundation
c/o John H. Lynch
2 Watchtower Rd.
Hopkinton, NH 03229-2819

Established in 2001 in New Hampshire.
Donors: John H. Lynch; Susan E. Upton Lynch.
Foundation type: Independent foundation.
Financial data (yr. ended 12/31/13): Assets, $3,342,259 (M); expenditures, $245,023; qualifying distributions, $206,391; giving activities include $202,700 for 23 grants (high: $125,000; low: $200).
Fields of interest: Education; Foundations; Hospital care; Developmental disability services.
Type of support: General support.
Limitations: Applications not accepted. Giving primarily in NH. No grants to individuals.
Application information: Unsolicited requests for funds not accepted.
Officer: John H. Lynch, Chair.
EIN: 010561381

5222
James G. Martin Memorial Trust
20 Church Rd.
Rye Beach, NH 03871-9001
Contact: M. Martin

Donors: G. Martin; James G. Martin; Gerard M. Martin.
Foundation type: Independent foundation.
Financial data (yr. ended 03/31/14): Assets, $3,755,138 (M); gifts received, $1,000,000; expenditures, $599,311; qualifying distributions, $505,594; giving activities include $230,000 for 9 grants (high: $50,000; low: $5,000).
Purpose and activities: Giving primarily for education, health and human services.
Fields of interest: Education; Elementary education; Undergraduate education; Graduate and professional education; Hospital care; HIV/AIDS; Leukemia; Catholicism; Theology.
Type of support: Research.
Limitations: Applications accepted. Giving primarily in MA.
Application information: Application form required.
 Initial approach: Letter
 Deadline(s): None
Trustees: G. Martin; K. Martin; R. Solano.
EIN: 042613244

5223
Mascoma Savings Bank Foundation
67 N. Park St.
Lebanon, NH 03766-0435 (603) 443-8639
Contact: Anne D'Aveni
E-mail: Anne.Daveni@mascomabank.com;
Additional address: Kimberly Robinson, P.O. Box 435, Lebanon, NH 03766 tel.: (603) 448-3650;

Main URL: http://www.mascomabank.com/foundation
Grants List: http://www.mascomabank.com/stage/wp-content/uploads/Fnd-Awd-Granted-10-11.pdf

Established in 1988 in New Hampshire.
Donor: Mascoma Savings Bank.
Foundation type: Company-sponsored foundation.
Financial data (yr. ended 12/31/13): Assets, $5,667,750 (M); gifts received, $275,799; expenditures, $295,542; qualifying distributions, $261,823; giving activities include $261,823 for grants.
Purpose and activities: The foundation supports organizations involved with arts and culture, education, health, mental health, legal aid, hunger, sports, and human services.
Fields of interest: Education; Health; Religion.
Limitations: Applications accepted. Giving primarily in areas of company operations in central western NH and central eastern VT. No support for religious organizations not of direct benefit to the entire community. No grants to individuals or for major capital campaigns.
Publications: Application guidelines; Grants list.
Application information: The foundation considers requests for up to $7,500.
 Initial approach: Proposal
 Deadline(s): Apr. 1 and Oct. 1
 Final notification: 10 weeks
Officer and Trustees: Gretchen S. Taylor, Chair. and Trustee; Gretchen Cherington; Kathleen C. Hoyt; Nancy J. Reardon; Thomas F. Terry; Robert Resenblum.
EIN: 222816632

5224
The McIninch Foundation
555 Canal St., Ste. 710
Manchester, NH 03101-1517 (603) 622-4052

Donor: Ralph A. McIninch†.
Foundation type: Independent foundation.
Financial data (yr. ended 12/31/14): Assets, $6,154,803; expenditures, $407,765; qualifying distributions, $303,748.
Purpose and activities: Giving primarily for education, with emphasis on higher education; support also for the arts and cultural organizations, community funds, Protestant churches, environmental programs, and land acquisition and preservation.
Fields of interest: Arts and culture; Education; Higher education; Nonprofits; Protestantism; Human services.
Type of support: General support; Matching grants; Continuing support; Capacity-building and technical assistance; Annual campaigns; Capital campaigns; Regranting; Capital and infrastructure; Equipment; Land acquisitions; Program development; Recordings; Technical assistance; Program evaluations.
Limitations: Applications accepted. Giving limited to NH. No grants to individuals.
Publications: Application guidelines.
Application information: Guidelines and application form available via e-mail only. Applicants must be registered with the Director of Charitable Trusts, State of New Hampshire, Concord, New Hampshire. Application form required.
 Initial approach: Letter, e-mail or telephone
 Copies of proposal: 2

Deadline(s): Apr. 15 and Oct. 15
Board meeting date(s): June and Dec.
Final notification: 90 days after meeting
Officer and Trustees: Douglas McIninch, Pres. and Treas. and Trustee; Nancy M. McIninch, Secy. and Trustee; James A. Shanahan.
Number of staff: 1 part-time support.
EIN: 026006053

5225
Milford Educational Foundation
P.O. Box 483
Milford, NH   03055-0483   (603) 673-4778
Contact: Allen White

Foundation type: Independent foundation.
Financial data (yr. ended 12/31/12): Assets, $0 (M); expenditures, $289,799; qualifying distributions, $284,319; giving activities include $284,319 for 1 grant.
Purpose and activities: Student loans to residents of Milford, NH for higher education.
Fields of interest: Philanthropy.
Type of support: Student aid; Loans to individuals.
Limitations: Applications accepted. Giving limited to residents of Milford, NH.
Application information:
Initial approach: Contact foundation
Deadline(s): None
Officer: Allen White, Treas.
EIN: 237147469

5226
The Noah Foundation
18 Pickard Rd.
Canterbury, NH   03224-2315

Donor: Faith Berry.
Foundation type: Independent foundation.
Financial data (yr. ended 12/31/13): Assets, $1,255,247 (M); expenditures, $190,774; qualifying distributions, $159,228; giving activities include $156,706 for 14 grants (high: $50,000; low: $2,000).
Fields of interest: Environment; Domesticated animals; Agriculture.
Limitations: Applications not accepted. Giving primarily in NH.
Application information: Unsolicited requests for funds not accepted.
Trustee: Faith Berry.
EIN: 020522443

5227
The Olcott Family Foundation, Inc.
P.O. Box 1869
Wolfeboro, NH   03894
Application address: c/o Emery G. Olcott, 24 Dockside Ln., Ste. 111, Key Largo, FL 33037

Donor: Emery G. Olcott.
Foundation type: Independent foundation.
Financial data (yr. ended 12/31/14): Assets, $920,032 (M); expenditures, $201,770; qualifying distributions, $194,128; giving activities include $184,350 for 26 grants (high: $25,000; low: $200).
Fields of interest: Arts and culture; Education; Undergraduate education; Hospital care; Eye diseases.
Type of support: Endowments; Capital campaigns.

Application information: Application form required.
Initial approach: Letter
Deadline(s): None
Officers: Emery G. Olcott, Pres.; Barbara P. Olcott, 1st V.P. and Secy.; Charles W. Olcott, 2nd V.P.
EIN: 061468476

5228
The Oxford League, Inc.
1 Liberty Ln., E. Ste. 100
Hampton, NH   03842-1819

Donor: General Chemical.
Foundation type: Independent foundation.
Financial data (yr. ended 12/31/12): Assets, $2,662,448 (M); expenditures, $252,529; qualifying distributions, $195,162; giving activities include $195,162 for grants.
Fields of interest: Higher education; Philanthropy; Human services.
Limitations: Applications not accepted. Giving primarily in NY.
Application information: Unsolicited requests for funds not accepted.
Officers: Paul M. Meister, Pres.; Thomas L. Rea, V.P.; Paul M. Meister, Treas.
EIN: 020491795

5229
Robert and Sara Rothschild Family Foundation
P.O. Box 215
Holderness, NH   03245-0215

Established in 2003 in New Hampshire.
Donors: Robert Rothschild; Sara Rothschild.
Foundation type: Independent foundation.
Financial data (yr. ended 12/31/13): Assets, $4,446,093 (M); expenditures, $410,161; qualifying distributions, $334,601; giving activities include $334,601 for 2 grants (high: $332,101; low: $2,500).
Fields of interest: Education; Libraries.
International interests: Botswana; South Africa.
Limitations: Applications not accepted. Giving primarily in NH and southern Africa. No grants to individuals.
Application information: Unsolicited requests for funds not accepted.
Officer: Robert B. Rothschild, Pres.
Trustee: Sara L. Rothschild.
EIN: 522372404

5230
Salem Community Benefits, Inc.
3 S. Broadway
Salem, NH   03079-3005   (603) 898-2153
Contact: Ann R. Lally, Secy. and Treas.

Established in 1998 in New Hampshire.
Donor: Salem Co-operative Bank.
Foundation type: Company-sponsored foundation.
Financial data (yr. ended 03/31/14): Assets, $297,732 (M); gifts received, $200,000; expenditures, $144,685; qualifying distributions, $144,383; giving activities include $144,008 for 9 grants (high: $50,000; low: $2,500).
Purpose and activities: The foundation supports organizations involved with dental care and disability services.

Fields of interest: Education; Dental care; Mental health care; Human services; Developmental disability services.
Type of support: Equipment; Program development; Sponsorships.
Limitations: Applications accepted. Giving limited to the greater Salem, NH, area.
Application information: Application form required.
Initial approach: Letter
Deadline(s): None
Officers: Nadema Gemmell, Chair.; Ann R. Lally, Secy. and Treas.
Directors: David Beshara; John Korbey; James Rausch.
EIN: 020499456

5231
Fred A. and Donna P. Seigel Charitable Trust
33 Woodland Rd.
North Hampton, NH   03862-2333   (617) 457-0400
Contact: Fred A. Seigel, Tr.

Established in 2007 in New Hampshire.
Donors: Fred A. Seigel; Donna P. Seigel.
Foundation type: Independent foundation.
Financial data (yr. ended 12/31/13): Assets, $1,548,880 (M); expenditures, $386,010; qualifying distributions, $378,036; giving activities include $370,500 for 26 grants (high: $40,000; low: $2,500).
Fields of interest: Arts and culture; Performing arts; Education; Undergraduate education.
Limitations: Applications accepted. Giving primarily in MA, ME and NH.
Application information: Application form required.
Initial approach: Proposal
Deadline(s): None
Trustees: Donna P. Seigel; Fred A. Seigel; Julia P. Seigel.
EIN: 266158312

5232
Marion C. Smyth Trust
1001 Elm St.
Manchester, NH   03101-1828   (603) 623-3420
Contact: Charles S. Goodwin, Tr.

Established in 1946 in New Hampshire.
Donor: Marion C. Smyth†.
Foundation type: Independent foundation.
Financial data (yr. ended 12/31/12): Assets, $4,244,573 (M); expenditures, $355,192; qualifying distributions, $316,687; giving activities include $292,200 for 54 grants (high: $44,600; low: $750).
Purpose and activities: The purpose of the trust is to establish and maintain the Frederick Smyth Institute of Music, and to provide funding for musical education, including scholarships, in the city of Manchester, New Hampshire for the cultural benefit of its citizens and to expand their knowledge of the field of music.
Fields of interest: Arts and culture; Music; Opera; Orchestral music; Higher education.
Type of support: Continuing support; Equipment; Scholarships.
Limitations: Applications accepted. Giving primarily in NH.

Application information: Application form required for student scholarships.
Initial approach: Letter
Copies of proposal: 1
Deadline(s): June 1
Board meeting date(s): As required
Trustees: David H. Bellman; Charles S. Goodwin; Joseph E. Sheehan.
Number of staff: 1 part-time support.
EIN: 026005793

5233

The Daniel K. Thorne Foundation, Inc.

c/o Star Lake Farm
P.O. Box 308
Georges Mills, NH 03751
Contact: Daniel K. Thorne, Pres. and Dir.

Established in 1996 in New York.
Donor: Daniel K. Thorne.
Foundation type: Independent foundation.
Financial data (yr. ended 12/31/13): Assets, $6,903,843 (M); expenditures, $470,565; qualifying distributions, $344,206; giving activities include $329,000 for 10 grants (high: $75,000; low: $1,000).
Fields of interest: Natural resources; Biodiversity; Wildlife biodiversity.
Type of support: General support; Matching grants; Continuing support; Emergency funds.
Limitations: Applications accepted. Giving primarily in CO, Washington, DC, ME, MT, and NY.
Application information: Application form required.
Initial approach: Letter
Deadline(s): None
Board meeting date(s): Mar., June, Oct. and Dec. 15
Officers and Directors: Daniel K. Thorne, Pres. and Director; David W. Lowden, Secy.; Michael S. Forsman; Josiah Hornblower; Robert Lynch; Alexandra T. Thorne.
Number of staff: 1 part-time support.
EIN: 133857951

5234

Tillotson North Country Foundation, Inc.

111 Munn Rd.
Colebrook, NH 03576-3547   (603) 915-0018
Contact: Lori Morann

Established in 1996 in New Hampshire.
Foundation type: Independent foundation.
Financial data (yr. ended 12/31/13): Assets, $5,321,512 (M); expenditures, $297,769; qualifying distributions, $243,870; giving activities include $243,870 for 27 grants (high: $70,000; low: $1,000).
Fields of interest: Hospital care; Public libraries.
Type of support: General support.
Limitations: Applications accepted. Giving primarily in NH. No grants to individuals.
Application information: Application form required.
Initial approach: Letter
Deadline(s): None
Officers and Directors: Frederick E. Tillotson, Pres. and Director; Donald Dickson, V.P. and Director; Julie Riffon, Clerk and Director; Rosemary Mulliken, Treas.; Ron Massey; Diane Rioux; Ginette White.
EIN: 020494246

5235

Up The River Endeavors Inc.

90 N. Main St.
Concord, NH 03301-4915

Donors: Kenneth M. Jones; Charter Charitable Foundation.
Foundation type: Independent foundation.
Financial data (yr. ended 12/31/13): Assets, $68,549 (M); gifts received, $348,000; expenditures, $339,855; qualifying distributions, $338,921; giving activities include $291,000 for 13 grants (high: $36,000; low: $10,000).
Fields of interest: Education; Environment; Domesticated animals.
Limitations: Applications not accepted. Giving primarily in CA, CO, Washington, DC, GA, NY, and WI.
Application information: Unsolicited requests for funds not accepted.
Officer: Steve Albrecht, Exec. Dir.
Directors: David J. Andrews; Mona Cadena; Kenneth M. Jones; Carol E. Koury; Carina Koury-Jones; Amy Parish; Cindy Pearson.
EIN: 272593681

5236

Gilbert Verney Foundation

117 Antrim Rd.
Bennington, NH 03442-4205   (603) 588-3311

Established in 1947 in Massachusetts.
Donor: Monadnock Paper Mills, Inc.
Foundation type: Company-sponsored foundation.
Financial data (yr. ended 12/31/14): Assets, $2,263,882; gifts received, $150,000; expenditures, $313,940; qualifying distributions, $249,685.
Purpose and activities: The foundation supports hospitals and organizations involved with arts and culture, secondary education, conservation, human services, and Christianity.
Fields of interest: Arts and culture; Theater; Museums; Art museums; Secondary education; Natural resources; Land resources; Hospital care; Christianity; Human services; Family services; Child welfare; Developmental disability services.
Type of support: General support; Continuing support; Annual campaigns; Capital campaigns; Capital and infrastructure; Program development.
Limitations: Applications accepted. Giving primarily in NH and MA. No support for religious organizations or lobbying organizations. No grants to individuals.
Application information:
Initial approach: Proposal
Deadline(s): None
Officer: Richard G. Verney, Pres.
Trustees: Lumina V. Greenway; E. Geoffrey Verney.
EIN: 026007363

5237

Madelaine G. von Weber Trust

95 Market St.
Manchester, NH 03101-1933
Contact: William C. Tucker Esq.
Application address: c/o Todd C. Fahey, 20 Pepin Dr., Bow, NH 03304, tel.: (603) 738-0346

Established in 1990 in New Hampshire.
Donor: Madelaine G. von Weber‡.
Foundation type: Independent foundation.

Financial data (yr. ended 12/31/13): Assets, $8,356,631 (M); expenditures, $392,659; qualifying distributions, $362,552; giving activities include $334,054 for 25 grants (high: $75,000; low: $2,204).
Purpose and activities: Giving primarily for health, and children and social services.
Fields of interest: Health; Human services; Food banks; Child welfare.
Limitations: Applications accepted. Giving primarily in NH, with emphasis on Manchester. No grants to individuals.
Application information: Application form required.
Initial approach: Proposal
Deadline(s): None
Trustees: Todd C. Fahey; William Tucker.
EIN: 046055699

5238

Gibson Woodbury Charitable Foundation

P.O. Box 406
North Conway, NH 03860-0406   (603) 356-5315
Contact: Mark Butterfield, Exec. Dir.
E-mail: gwcf@gibsonwoodburyfoundation.org; Main URL: http://www.gibsonwoodburyfoundation.org

Established in 2010 in New Hampshire.
Donor: Evelyn Woodbury‡.
Foundation type: Operating foundation.
Financial data (yr. ended 06/30/13): Assets, $4,910,772 (M); gifts received, $561; expenditures, $293,985; qualifying distributions, $225,219; giving activities include $212,960 for 34 grants (high: $20,000; low: $700).
Purpose and activities: Giving primarily to enhance the vitality and wellness of organizations and residents of Mount Washington Valley, New Hampshire.
Fields of interest: Arts and culture; Performing arts; Education; Higher education; Diseases and conditions; Housing development; Human services; Food banks.
Type of support: Student aid; Research.
Limitations: Applications accepted. Giving primarily in the Mount Washington Valley in Carroll County, NH.
Application information: Application form available on foundation web site. Application form required.
Initial approach: Proposal
Deadline(s): May 15 and Nov. 15
Officer and Trustees: Mark Butterfield, Exec. Dir. and Trustee; Kenneth V. Cargill, Esq.
EIN: 272986345

5239

The Paul F. and Margaret M. Wutz Foundation

P.O. Box 2202
New London, NH 03257-2202

Established in 2000 in Ohio.
Donors: Paul F. Wutz; Margaret M. Wutz.
Foundation type: Independent foundation.
Financial data (yr. ended 12/31/14): Assets, $2,387,167; expenditures, $205,962; qualifying distributions, $184,478.
Purpose and activities: Support primarily for Suzuki-based music schools and programs.
Fields of interest: Music; Performing arts education; Education; Christianity.

Type of support: General support; Capital and infrastructure.
Limitations: Applications not accepted. No grants to individuals.

Application information: Unsolicited requests for funds not accepted.

NEW JERSEY

5240
A Friends' Foundation Trust
P.O. Box 1501, NJ2-130-03-31
Pennington, NJ 08534-1501
Application address: c/o L. Evans Hubbard, 9000
Hubbard Pl., Orlando, FL 32819

Established in 1959 in Florida.
Donors: Frank M. Hubbard; A Friends' Fund, Inc.
Foundation type: Independent foundation.
Financial data (yr. ended 12/31/13): Assets,
$9,700,814 (M); expenditures, $472,397;
qualifying distributions, $428,234; giving activities
include $338,500 for 53 grants (high: $39,000;
low: $1,000).
Purpose and activities: Support for private higher
education, civic affairs, the arts, youth activities,
religion, and health in central Florida.
Fields of interest: Arts and culture; Higher
education; Health; Diseases and conditions;
Disasters and emergency management; Religion;
Human services; Child welfare; Children; Adults;
Homeless people; Low-income and poor people;
People with disabilities.
Type of support: General support; Matching grants;
Continuing support; Annual campaigns; Capital
campaigns; Capital and infrastructure; Equipment;
Land acquisitions; Emergency funds; Program
development.
Limitations: Applications accepted. Giving primarily
in central FL. No grants for endowments.
Application information: Application form required.
  Initial approach: Letter
  Deadline(s): None
Trustee: Merrill Lynch Trust Co.
Board Members: Linda Hubbard; Michael E.
Hubbard; Connie H. Miller.
Number of staff: 1 part-time professional.
EIN: 596125247

5241
The Abrams Family Foundation
c/o Cohnreznick
23 Christopher Way
Eatontown, NJ 07724
Application address: c/o William Abrams, 975 Park
Ave., Apt. 16D, New York, NY 10028, tel.: (212)
583-4164

Established in 1993 in New York.
Donors: William H. Abrams; Vicki Abrams.
Foundation type: Independent foundation.
Financial data (yr. ended 12/31/13): Assets,
$3,656,677 (M); gifts received, $381,215;
expenditures, $295,276; qualifying distributions,
$215,830; giving activities include $210,000 for 5
grants (high: $85,000; low: $10,000).
Fields of interest: Higher education; Judaism.
Limitations: Applications accepted. Giving primarily
in NJ and NY. No grants to individuals or private
non-operating foundations.
Application information: Application form required.
  Initial approach: Letter
  Deadline(s): None
Trustees: David C. Abrams; Vicki S. Abrams; William
H. Abrams; Julie Abrams Leff.
EIN: 223272343

5242
The Myron and Elaine Adler Private Foundation, Inc.
c/o Elaine Adler, Myron Manufacturing Corp.
205 Maywood Ave.
Maywood, NJ 07607-1007

Established in 1997 in New Jersey.
Donors: Elaine Adler; Myron Adler.
Foundation type: Independent foundation.
Financial data (yr. ended 12/31/13): Assets,
$5,173,186 (M); gifts received, $500,000;
expenditures, $311,578; qualifying distributions,
$309,892; giving activities include $309,892 for 33
grants (high: $130,000; low: $20).
Purpose and activities: Giving primarily for Jewish
organizations.
Fields of interest: Education; Nonprofits; Speech
and hearing rehabilitation; Judaism; Human
services.
Type of support: General support; Regranting.
Limitations: Applications not accepted. Giving
primarily in NJ and NY. No grants to individuals.
Application information: Unsolicited requests for
funds not accepted.
Officers: Elaine Adler, Pres.; Myron Adler, V.P.;
Richard S. Adler, V.P.; William S. Adler, V.P.; Marie
Adler Kravecas, Secy.; Donald James Adler, Treas.
EIN: 223516532

5243
Akhoury Foundation Inc.
6 Pine Valley Way
Florham Park, NJ 07932

Established in 1995 in New Jersey.
Donor: Ravindranath Akhoury.
Foundation type: Independent foundation.
Financial data (yr. ended 12/31/13): Assets,
$205,704 (M); gifts received, $122,745;
expenditures, $162,385; qualifying distributions,
$160,442; giving activities include $159,495 for 48
grants (high: $21,445; low: $25).
Fields of interest: Elementary and secondary
education; Higher education; Nonprofits; Public
libraries; Catholicism; Human services.
International interests: India.
Type of support: Regranting.
Limitations: Applications not accepted. Giving
primarily in NJ and NY. No grants to individuals.
Application information: Contributes only to
pre-selected organizations.
Trustees: Priya Joy Akhoury; Ravindranath Akhoury;
Virginia Akhoury.
EIN: 223417520

5244
Alcon Cares, Inc.
c/o Tax Dept.
1 South Ridgedale Ave.
East Hanover, NJ 07936 (817) 293-0450
FAX: (800) 554-2660; Application Address: 6201 S.
Freeway, M.C. TC-39, Fort Worth, TX, 76134-2001,
Toll Free Number: (800) 222-8103; Main
URL: http://www.alcon.com/
corporate-responsibility/
patient-assistance-programs.aspx

Donor: Alcon Laboratories, Inc.
Foundation type: Operating foundation.

Financial data (yr. ended 12/31/13): Assets, $0
(M); gifts received, $248,849; expenditures,
$248,849; qualifying distributions, $248,849;
giving activities include $248,849 for 22,432
grants.
Purpose and activities: The foundation provides
medications to individuals who cannot afford their
medication and to those who lack prescription
insurance coverage; and provides access to eye
care medication for U.S. medical facilities serving
large numbers of Medicare and Medicaid patients.
Fields of interest: Health; Eye diseases;
Low-income and poor people.
Type of support: Grants to individuals; Donated
products; In-kind gifts.
Limitations: Applications accepted. Giving on a
national basis and to communities in which Alcon
has a facility. No support for religious, fraternal,
labor, political or veteran programs. No support for
non 501(c)(3) designated organizations, or for
individual or family requests for scholarships, or for
fellowship assistance, endowments, or capital and
building campaigns outside of community-aligned
grants, or for matching gifts, private schools K-12,
books, research papers, or articles in professional
journals, or for travel expenses.
Publications: Application guidelines.
Application information: Application form required.
  Initial approach: Download application form and
    mail or fax to foundation
  Deadline(s): None
Officers: Carol Duval, Treas.; Bettina Maunz, Pres.
Directors: David Malenfant; John Reding; Helen
Boudreau.
EIN: 204118713

5245
Allied Educational Foundation
82 N. Summit St.
Tenafly, NJ 07670-1016 (201) 569-8180
E-mail: info@AlliedEducationalFoundation.org; Main
URL: http://alliededucationalfoundation.org

Donors: New York Cardiac Ctr., Inc.; Allied Trades
Council; Barton, Babcock & Blair.
Foundation type: Independent foundation.
Financial data (yr. ended 12/31/12): Assets,
$6,495,247 (M); gifts received, $100,700;
expenditures, $686,228; qualifying distributions,
$414,528; giving activities include $300,091 for
grants, and $400,680 for 4
foundation-administered programs.
Purpose and activities: Giving primarily in the form
of educational seminars and training programs,
provision of publications for educational training,
and funds directly for education, study, and
research.
Fields of interest: Education.
Limitations: Applications not accepted.
Application information: Unsolicited requests for
funds not accepted.
Trustees: Benjamin Camadeco; James Crowley;
Bertram Gelfand; Herbert Pobiner; Theodore Turitz.
EIN: 136202432

5246
The Amboy Foundation, Inc.
c/o Amboy Bank
3590 U.S. Hwy. 9
Old Bridge, NJ 08857-2837
Contact: Karen Casey

Main URL: http://www.amboybank.com/home/about/amboy

Established in 1996 in New Jersey.
Donor: Amboy National Bank.
Foundation type: Company-sponsored foundation.
Financial data (yr. ended 12/31/13): Assets, $3,398,821 (M); expenditures, $188,533; qualifying distributions, $187,227; giving activities include $187,227 for 33 grants (high: $25,000; low: $1,500).
Purpose and activities: The foundation supports organizations involved with education, civic affairs, health, human services, social services, and culture. Special emphasis is directed toward programs designed to promote community development and social welfare, including local shelters and health and welfare clinics; benefit low to moderate income populations; provide educational initiatives to meet the housing needs of low to moderate income populations; and promote higher education, with a focus on business programs.
Fields of interest: Arts and culture; Education; Higher education; Business education; Health; Hospital care; Public affairs; Community and economic development; Housing development; Human services; Family services; Child welfare; Low-income and poor people.
Type of support: General support; Program development; Sponsorships.
Limitations: Applications accepted. Giving primarily in central NJ. No support for private clubs or fraternal organizations, labor groups, or pass-through organizations. No grants to individuals or for political causes.
Publications: Application guidelines.
Application information: Grants range from $1,000 to $10,000. Proposals should be no longer than 2 pages. Support is limited to 1 contribution per organization during any given year.
  Initial approach: Proposal
  Copies of proposal: 1
  Deadline(s): None
  Board meeting date(s): Quarterly
  Final notification: 30 days following board meetings
Officers and Trustees: Mary Kay Riccardi, V.P.; Patricia M. Keys, Secy. and Trustee; George G. Brennan, Treas. and Trustee; Marguerite DiSepio; George E. Scharpf.
EIN: 223484075

5247
American Friends of Even Yisroel Charitable Foundation
c/o Lisker
25 Dakota St.
Passaic, NJ 07055-3331

Established in 2000 in New York.
Donors: Sobel Family Trust; Edgar Billowitz; Ari Coopersmith; Chaim Friedman; Dobert Goodman; Edward Levy; Jacob Levy; Marvin Marmelstein; Jordan Most; Moshe Neurath; Aaron Stopper; Foundation Jewish Philanthropies of Buffalo; Eastern Union Funding; Stratford Ave. Trust; Agudath Israel of Long Island.
Foundation type: Independent foundation.
Financial data (yr. ended 12/31/13): Assets, $13,149 (M); gifts received, $262,212; expenditures, $251,635; qualifying distributions,

$200,219; giving activities include $200,219 for grants to individuals.
Fields of interest: Education; Judaism.
International interests: China; Netherlands.
Type of support: Grants to individuals.
Limitations: Applications not accepted. Giving primarily in CA, MA, OK, and PA.
Application information: Unsolicited requests for funds not accepted.
Trustees: Mitchell Lisker; Solomon Sobel.
EIN: 137173269

5248
American Water Charitable Foundation Inc.
1025 Laurel Oak Rd.
Voorhees, NJ 08043 (856) 309-4802
Contact: Carrie Necky, Secy.
E-mail: carrie.necky@amwater.com; Main URL: http://www.amwater.com/corporate-responsibility/Charitable-Foundation

Foundation type: Company-sponsored foundation.
Financial data (yr. ended 12/31/13): Assets, $13,139,644 (M); expenditures, $358,241; qualifying distributions, $310,520; giving activities include $310,520 for grants.
Purpose and activities: The foundation supports employee-identified nonprofit endeavors, in addition to targeted disaster relief efforts throughout the year. Support is primarily in areas of company operations.
Fields of interest: Environment; Water resources; Water pollution; Environmental education; Disaster relief; Unknown or not classified; Victims of disaster.
Type of support: Emergency funds; Employee volunteer services; Employee matching gifts.
Limitations: Applications not accepted. Giving primarily in area of company operations in CA, HI, IL, IN, IA, KY, MD, MI, MO, NJ, NY, PA, TN, VA, WV.
Application information: Contributes only to pre-selected organizations.
Officers and Board Members: Nick Rowe, Chair.; Debra D. Vernon, Pres.; Carrie Necky, Secy.; William D. Rogers, Treas. and Director; Jeffrey E. Sterba.
EIN: 274241172

5249
Anderson Foundation
c/o Thomas Anderson
31 Roebling Rd.
Bernardsville, NJ 07924-1409

Established in 1981 in New Jersey.
Donors: Thomas Anderson; Bear Stearns & Co.
Foundation type: Independent foundation.
Financial data (yr. ended 11/30/13): Assets, $12,081,200 (M); expenditures, $424,677; qualifying distributions, $412,435; giving activities include $352,683 for 13 grants (high: $110,000; low: $5,000).
Fields of interest: Christianity; Human services; Family services.
Limitations: Applications not accepted. Giving primarily in NJ; funding also in Garrison, NY. No grants to individuals.
Application information: Contributes only to pre-selected organizations.
Trustee: Thomas Anderson.
EIN: 222393971

5250
The Antz Foundation
P.O. Box 1501, NJ2-130-03-31
Pennington, NJ 08534-0671

Established in 1989 in New York.
Donor: John A. Thain.
Foundation type: Independent foundation.
Financial data (yr. ended 01/31/15): Assets, $434,464 (M); expenditures, $263,710; qualifying distributions, $259,426; giving activities include $255,900 for 9 grants (high: $100,000; low: $1,000).
Fields of interest: Higher education; Botanical gardens; Hospital care; Human services.
Type of support: General support.
Limitations: Applications not accepted. Giving primarily in NY; some funding also in MA. No grants to individuals, or scholarships; no loans.
Application information: Contributes only to pre-selected organizations.
Trustees: Carmen M. Thain; John Thain.
EIN: 133536523

5251
Armour-Lewis Family Foundation
c/o Mandel, Fekete & Bloom CPA
30 Montgomery St., Ste. 685
Jersey City, NJ 07302-3834

Established in 1998 in New Jersey.
Donor: Robert L. Armour Revocable Trust.
Foundation type: Independent foundation.
Financial data (yr. ended 12/31/14): Assets, $4,743,938 (M); expenditures, $444,727; qualifying distributions, $401,800; giving activities include $401,800 for 5 grants (high: $120,000; low: $60,000).
Fields of interest: Higher education; Graduate and professional education; Medical education; Veterinary medicine; Engineering; Theology; Senior assisted living.
Limitations: Applications not accepted. Giving primarily in NJ, NY, and PA. No grants to individuals.
Application information: Contributes only to pre-selected organizations.
Trustees: Tara L. Fallon; Warren Lloyd Lewis, Esq.; Louise Ouellette.
EIN: 223476006

5252
Ascena Foundation
(formerly The Dress Barn Fund)
933 Macarthur Blvd.
Mahwah, NJ 07430

Established in 1985 in Connecticut.
Donors: The Dress Barn Inc.; Maurices, Inc.; Ascena Retail Group, Inc.
Foundation type: Company-sponsored foundation.
Financial data (yr. ended 12/31/13): Assets, $54,360 (M); gifts received, $250,400; expenditures, $283,547; qualifying distributions, $283,517; giving activities include $283,517 for 71 grants (high: $58,088; low: $15).
Purpose and activities: The foundation supports organizations involved with higher education, health, employment services, human services, international relief and conflict resolution, business and industry, and women.

Fields of interest: Arts and culture; Diseases and conditions; Human services.
Type of support: General support; Employee matching gifts; Scholarships.
Limitations: Applications not accepted. Giving primarily in NY; giving also to national organizations.
Application information: Contributes only to pre-selected organizations.
Officer: Elliot S. Jaffe, Pres.
Trustee: Roslyn E. Jaffe.
EIN: 222731305

5253
Aufzien Foundation, Inc.
350 Passaic Ave.
Fairfield, NJ   07004-2025   (973) 575-5132
Contact: Alan Aufzien, Dir.

Established in 1987 in New Jersey.
Donors: Alan Aufzien; Norma Aufzien; Jonathan Aufzien; Leslie Levine; Lisa Aufzien.
Foundation type: Independent foundation.
Financial data (yr. ended 12/31/13): Assets, $6,121,059 (M); gifts received, $100,000; expenditures, $489,919; qualifying distributions, $374,350; giving activities include $374,350 for 32 grants (high: $111,200; low: $200).
Purpose and activities: Giving primarily to Jewish organizations and temples.
Fields of interest: Arts and culture; Higher education; Nonprofits; Diseases and conditions; Judaism; Human services; International relations.
Type of support: Annual campaigns; Capital campaigns; Emergency funds; Scholarships; Regranting.
Limitations: Applications accepted. Giving primarily in New York, NY; giving also in Washington, DC, FL, NJ, and PA. No grants to individuals.
Application information: Application form required.
   Initial approach: Letter
   Deadline(s): None
Directors: Alan Aufzien; Jonathan Aufzien; Lisa Aufzien; Norma Aufzien; Meredith Bauer; Leslie Levine.
EIN: 222838652

5254
The Avalo Foundation Inc.
c/o Merrill Lynch Trust Co.
100 Campus Dr., Ste. 350
Florham Park, NJ   07932-1052   (877) 331-8350
Contact: Matt Fountain; Donald Edmunds, Exec. Dir.

Donors: Christina Dennis; Merrill Lynch Trust Co.
Foundation type: Independent foundation.
Financial data (yr. ended 12/31/13): Assets, $4,861,020 (M); expenditures, $615,630; qualifying distributions, $529,747; giving activities include $355,900 for 8 grants (high: $125,000; low: $3,000).
Fields of interest: Agriculture; Religion; Human services; Food banks.
Type of support: General support.
Limitations: Applications accepted. Giving primarily in NJ.
Application information: Application form required.
   Initial approach: Proposal
   Deadline(s): None
Officers: Christina Dennis, Pres.; Donald Recchio, V.P.; Donald Edmunds, Exec. Dir.

Trustee: Aleta St. James.
EIN: 272446263

5255
The Avis Budget Charitable Foundation
(formerly The Cendant Charitable Foundation)
6 Sylvan Way
Parsippany, NJ   07054-4407   (973) 496-2579

Established in 2001 in Delaware.
Donors: Cendant Corp.; First American Real Estate Tax Svcs.
Foundation type: Company-sponsored foundation.
Financial data (yr. ended 12/31/14): Assets, $63,468; expenditures, $235,367; qualifying distributions, $235,367.
Purpose and activities: The foundation supports organizations involved with arts and culture, education, health, cancer, human services, community development, youth, and minorities.
Fields of interest: Arts and culture; Education; Health.
Type of support: General support; Scholarships.
Limitations: Applications accepted. Giving primarily in CA, NJ, and NY.
Application information:
   Initial approach: Proposal
   Deadline(s): None
Officers and Directors: David Wyshner, Pres., C.F.O., and Treas. and Director; Michael Tucker, Exec. V.P. and Genl. Counsel and Director; Jean Sera, V.P. and Secy.; Ned Linen, V.P. and Director.
EIN: 223758292

5256
Margaret and Marshall Bartlett Family Foundation, Inc.
Young's Rd.
P.O. Box 489
New Vernon, NJ   07976-0489

Established in 1997 in New Jersey.
Donors: Marshall P. Bartlett; Margaret W. Bartlett.
Foundation type: Independent foundation.
Financial data (yr. ended 12/31/14): Assets, $5,856,695 (M); expenditures, $348,379; qualifying distributions, $345,883; giving activities include $343,600 for 62 grants (high: $100,000; low: $50).
Purpose and activities: Giving primarily for higher education; some funding also for the arts and human services.
Fields of interest: Arts and culture; Education; Higher education; Human services.
Type of support: General support.
Limitations: Applications not accepted. No grants to individuals.
Application information: Unsolicited requests for funds not accepted.
Officers and Trustees: Marshall P. Bartlett, Pres. and Secy.-Treas. and Trustee; John P. Bartlett, V.P. and Trustee; Margaret W. Bartlett, V.P. and Trustee; Stephen W. Bartlett, V.P. and Trustee; David L. Scull.
EIN: 223512759

5257
The George W. Bauer Family Foundation
616 W. 1st Ave.
Roselle, NJ   07203-1005   (908) 241-2424

Established in 1965 in Unspecified.
Donor: C.H. Winans Company.
Foundation type: Independent foundation.
Financial data (yr. ended 06/30/14): Assets, $8,318,321 (M); expenditures, $459,160; qualifying distributions, $370,500; giving activities include $370,500 for 26 grants (high: $70,000; low: $5,000).
Fields of interest: Foundations; Health; Hospital care; Diseases and conditions; Christianity; Human services.
Limitations: Applications accepted. Giving primarily in NJ. No grants to individuals.
Application information: Application form required.
   Initial approach: Letter
   Deadline(s): Apr. 30
   Board meeting date(s): May or June
Officer: Carol A. Romano, Secy.
Trustees: Betsy Bauer; Thomas B. Boak; Donald B. Fedor; John W. Fedor; Nancy B. Howell.
EIN: 226069622

5258
David and Andrea Baum Family Foundation
(formerly David and Andrea Baum Foundation)
60 Woodcrest Ave.
Short Hills, NJ   07078-2124
Contact: David Baum, Tr.

Established in 2000 in New Jersey.
Donor: David M. Baum.
Foundation type: Independent foundation.
Financial data (yr. ended 11/30/14): Assets, $2,681,620 (M); expenditures, $186,511; qualifying distributions, $169,385; giving activities include $169,385 for 21 grants (high: $120,175; low: $100).
Fields of interest: Higher education; Diseases and conditions; Judaism.
Type of support: General support; Research.
Limitations: Applications not accepted. No grants to individuals; no loans or scholarships.
Application information: Contributes only to pre-selected organizations.
Trustees: Andrea Terzi Baum; David M. Baum.
EIN: 137178822

5259
Beane Family Foundation
P.O. Box 1501, NJ2-130-03-31
Pennington, NJ   08534-1501

Established in 1997 in New Jersey.
Donor: Silas Robert Beane, Jr.
Foundation type: Independent foundation.
Financial data (yr. ended 12/31/14): Assets, $3,628,216 (M); expenditures, $189,149; qualifying distributions, $164,322; giving activities include $148,000 for 39 grants (high: $10,000; low: $1,000).
Purpose and activities: Giving primarily for higher education and human services.
Fields of interest: Education; Human services; Youth development.
Limitations: Applications not accepted. Giving primarily in NJ, NY, and PA. No grants to individuals.
Application information: Unsolicited requests for funds not accepted.
Trustees: Rosa T. Beane; Silas Robert Beane, Jr.; Silas Robert Beane III; Maria E. Beane-Bonomet.
EIN: 311560574

5260
The Benaroya Charitable Foundation
(also known as The Jewish Help Fund Trust)
179 Lincoln St.
Englewood, NJ 07631-3120

Donors: The Wild Harp Co., Inc.; Raphael Benaroya; Linda Benaroya; Ezra & Renee Dabah Charitable Foundation Inc.; RB, Inc.
Foundation type: Independent foundation.
Financial data (yr. ended 12/31/13): Assets, $1,166,407 (M); expenditures, $250,939; qualifying distributions, $204,114; giving activities include $204,114 for grants.
Fields of interest: Nonprofits; Judaism.
Type of support: Regranting.
Limitations: Applications not accepted. No grants to individuals.
Application information: Contributes only to pre-selected organizations.
Trustees: Linda Benaroya; Raphael Benaroya; Shirley Benaroya.
EIN: 136873548

5261
Morris and Susan Benun Charitable Foundation, Inc.
1221 S. Elberon Sq.
Elberon, NJ 07740-4586

Donor: Morris C. Benun.
Foundation type: Independent foundation.
Financial data (yr. ended 12/31/13): Assets, $1,450,032 (M); gifts received, $485,000; expenditures, $197,852; qualifying distributions, $185,894; giving activities include $174,527 for 66 grants (high: $37,961; low: $18).
Fields of interest: Education; Diseases and conditions; Human services.
Limitations: Applications not accepted. Giving primarily in NJ and NY.
Application information: Unsolicited requests for funds not accepted.
Officers and Trustees: Morris C. Benun, Pres. and Treas. and Trustee; Susan Benun, Secy. and Trustee; Raymond M. Benun.
EIN: 273819206

5262
Susan V. Bershad Charitable Fund Inc.
28 South Mountain Ave.
Montclair, NJ 07042-1611

Foundation type: Independent foundation.
Financial data (yr. ended 11/30/13): Assets, $2,811,609 (M); expenditures, $344,533; qualifying distributions, $308,897; giving activities include $293,838 for 19 grants (high: $122,500; low: $1,000).
Fields of interest: Arts and culture; Education; Diseases and conditions.
Type of support: Research.
Limitations: Applications not accepted. Giving primarily in NJ and NY.
Application information: Unsolicited request for funds not accepted.
Officers: Susan V. Bershad, Pres. and Treas.; Bradley J. Bershad, V.P.; Elizabeth J. Bershad, Secy.
EIN: 364662468

5263
David Bershad Family Foundation Inc.
c/o David J. Bershad
402 Metzger Dr.
West Orange, NJ 07052

Established in 2009 in New Jersey.
Foundation type: Independent foundation.
Financial data (yr. ended 11/30/13): Assets, $4,108,832 (M); expenditures, $340,858; qualifying distributions, $334,107; giving activities include $334,107 for 48 grants (high: $116,757; low: $100).
Fields of interest: Arts and culture; Education; Legal services; Religion; Judaism; Human services.
Limitations: Applications not accepted. Giving primarily in NJ and NY.
Application information: Unsolicited requests for funds not accepted.
Officer: David J. Bershad, Pres.
Trustees: Jeffrey Bershad; William Bershad.
EIN: 800315868

5264
Joseph and Renee Bijou Family Foundation
2 Ethel Rd., Ste. 205A
Edison, NJ 08817-2839

Established in 1986 in New Jersey.
Donors: Joseph Bijou; Renee Bijou; Albert Bijou; York Preparatory School.
Foundation type: Independent foundation.
Financial data (yr. ended 06/30/13): Assets, $9,456,154 (M); gifts received, $21,000; expenditures, $190,042; qualifying distributions, $154,108; giving activities include $153,999 for 42 grants (high: $23,300; low: $100).
Purpose and activities: Giving primarily for Jewish organizations.
Fields of interest: Education; Nonprofits; Judaism; Human services.
Type of support: Regranting.
Limitations: Applications not accepted. Giving primarily in New York, NY. No grants to individuals.
Application information: Unsolicited requests for funds not accepted.
Officers: Joseph Bijou, Pres.; Renee Bijou, V.P.; Murray Dweck, V.P.
EIN: 222861787

5265
Billig Foundation
c/o Gail Billig
311 Walnut St.
Englewood, NJ 07631-3105

Established in 1954 in New York.
Donors: Sali Billig; Gail Billig.
Foundation type: Independent foundation.
Financial data (yr. ended 10/31/13): Assets, $2,879,876 (M); expenditures, $181,251; qualifying distributions, $154,120; giving activities include $150,620 for 46 grants (high: $28,700; low: $100).
Purpose and activities: Giving primarily to Jewish organizations and institutes.
Fields of interest: Arts and culture; Graduate and professional education; Nonprofits; Judaism; Theology; Human services.
International interests: Israel.
Type of support: Regranting.

Limitations: Applications not accepted. Giving primarily in New York, NY; some giving also in NJ. No grants to individuals.
Application information: Unsolicited requests for funds not accepted.
Trustees: Aaron Billig; Gail A. Billig; Evelyn Kenvin; Fred Kenvin.
EIN: 136147322

5266
Blessing for Life Foundation Inc.
1127 Somerset Ave.
Lakewood, NJ 08701-2139 (732) 886-1432
Contact: Daniel Lemberg, Pres.

Established in 2000 in New York.
Donor: Daniel Lemberg.
Foundation type: Independent foundation.
Financial data (yr. ended 12/31/13): Assets, $51,443 (M); gifts received, $362,000; expenditures, $323,511; qualifying distributions, $323,249; giving activities include $321,995 for 375 grants (high: $69,972; low: $10).
Purpose and activities: Giving primarily to Jewish agencies, temples, and schools.
Fields of interest: Elementary and secondary education; Judaism.
Limitations: Applications accepted. Giving primarily in NJ.
Application information: Application form required.
Initial approach: Letter
Deadline(s): None
Officers: Daniel Lemberg, Pres.; Blimy Lemberg, V.P.
EIN: 061602006

5267
Bloom Foundation
c/o Jamacha, LLC
161 Eagle Rock Ave.
Roseland, NJ 07068

Established in 2008 in New York.
Donors: David Bloom; Bloom Family 2009 Charitable Lead Trust.
Foundation type: Independent foundation.
Financial data (yr. ended 12/31/13): Assets, $5,418,497 (M); gifts received, $209,911; expenditures, $291,143; qualifying distributions, $269,785; giving activities include $269,535 for 19 grants (high: $152,025; low: $350).
Fields of interest: Education; Health; Human services.
Limitations: Applications not accepted.
Application information: Contributes only to pre-selected organizations.
Directors: David Bloom; Whitney Bloom; Philip S. Weber.
EIN: 262468318

5268
The Blue Foundation
P.O. Box 1501, NJ2-130-03-31
Pennington, NJ 08534-1501

Donor: Judith MacCready.
Foundation type: Independent foundation.
Financial data (yr. ended 12/31/14): Assets, $10,201,427 (M); gifts received, $932,340; expenditures, $446,884; qualifying distributions,

$357,086; giving activities include $322,000 for 10 grants (high: $150,000; low: $5,000).
Fields of interest: Arts and culture; Education; Foundations; Health; Human services.
Type of support: General support.
Limitations: Applications not accepted. Giving primarily in CA, MA, NY and WA.
Application information: Unsolicited requests for funds not accepted.
Officers: Martha Knox, Pres. and Treas.; Parker MacCready, V.P. and Secy.
EIN: 271579792

5269
Blue Oak Foundation
P.O. Box 1501, NJ2-130-03-31
Pennington, NJ 08534-1501

Established in 1994 in California.
Donors: E. Kirk Neely; Holly E. Myers.
Foundation type: Independent foundation.
Financial data (yr. ended 12/31/13): Assets, $4,069,323 (M); gifts received, $575,900; expenditures, $201,039; qualifying distributions, $172,168; giving activities include $158,000 for 30 grants (high: $20,000; low: $1,000).
Purpose and activities: Giving primarily for the support of children, youth, families and community development.
Fields of interest: Education; Environment; Health; Human services.
International interests: Central America.
Type of support: General support; Matching grants; Continuing support; Capital campaigns; Endowments; Program development; Seed money; Research.
Limitations: Applications not accepted. Giving primarily in Santa Clara and San Mateo counties, CA; some giving also in Central America. No support for religious or political organizations. No grants for conferences/seminars, debt reduction, travel expenses, or for scholarships.
Application information: Unsolicited requests for funds not accepted.
Officers: E. Kirk Neely, Pres.; Holly E. Myers, Secy.-Treas.
Number of staff: None.
EIN: 943214373

5270
BMI-Rupp Foundation
1200 Hendricks Causeway
Ridgefield, NJ 07657-2106 (201) 941-2121

Established in 2000 in New Jersey.
Donors: Alois J. Rupp; Alois K. Rupp.
Foundation type: Independent foundation.
Financial data (yr. ended 12/31/14): Assets, $5,189,528; gifts received, $1,000,000; expenditures, $437,324; qualifying distributions, $389,695.
Fields of interest: Diseases and conditions; Christianity; Human services.
Limitations: Applications accepted. Giving primarily in MD, NJ, and NY.
Application information: Application form required.
   Initial approach: Letter
   Deadline(s): None
Trustees: Alois J. Rupp; Alois K. Rupp; Christine Rupp.
EIN: 256722363

5271
Branfman Family Foundation
418 Queen Anne Rd.
Cherry Hill, NJ 08003-3300

Established in 2002 in New Jersey.
Donors: Alan R. Branfman; Mrs. Alan R. Branfman.
Foundation type: Independent foundation.
Financial data (yr. ended 12/31/13): Assets, $21,873 (M); gifts received, $176,564; expenditures, $216,647; qualifying distributions, $215,000; giving activities include $215,000 for 3 grants (high: $100,000; low: $40,000).
Purpose and activities: Giving for basic research into Parkinson's Disease.
Fields of interest: Musculoskeletal diseases; Brain and nervous system disorders.
Type of support: Research.
Limitations: Applications accepted. Giving primarily in CA, IL, and MA.
Application information: Application form required.
   Initial approach: Letter
   Deadline(s): None
Trustees: Alan R. Branfman; Joyce Branfman; Michael Wolk.
EIN: 020628229

5272
The Marilyn S. Broad Foundation, Inc.
7 Powell Dr.
West Orange, NJ 07052-1331 7328556011

Established in 2003 in District of Columbia.
Donors: Marilyn S. Broad; Exxon Mobil Corp.
Foundation type: Independent foundation.
Financial data (yr. ended 10/31/14): Assets, $2,412,369; expenditures, $302,222; qualifying distributions, $259,709.
Fields of interest: Education; Agriculture; Human services.
Limitations: Applications not accepted. Giving primarily in CA. No grants to individuals.
Application information: Unsolicited requests for funds not accepted.
Officers and Directors: Daniel Serviss, Pres. and Treas. and Director; Jonathan Serviss, Secy. and Director; Emily Serviss.
EIN: 522260304

5273
The Brook Fund, Inc.
182 W. Allendale Ave.
Allendale, NJ 07401-1723

Established in 1984 in New Jersey.
Donors: Barnett Rukin; Shortline Terminal Agency; Chenanar Valley Bus Lines; Julius Eisen; Susan Eisen; Donna Rukin.
Foundation type: Independent foundation.
Financial data (yr. ended 12/31/14): Assets, $2,473,350 (M); gifts received, $331,231; expenditures, $373,057; qualifying distributions, $333,345; giving activities include $333,345 for 109 grants (high: $69,525; low: $25).
Purpose and activities: Giving primarily for Jewish organizations; some funding also for higher education and social services.
Fields of interest: Higher education; Nonprofits; Hospital care; Diseases and conditions; Judaism; Human services.
Type of support: General support; Regranting.

Limitations: Applications not accepted. Giving primarily in NJ and NY.
Application information: Contributes only to pre-selected organizations.
Trustees: Julius Eisen; Barnett Rukin.
EIN: 222561995

5274
The Brooks Foundation
c/o Untracht Early
325 Columbia Tpke., Ste. 202
Florham Park, NJ 07932-1213

Established in 2000 in Wyoming.
Donors: T. Anthony Brooks; Linda Leith Brooks.
Foundation type: Independent foundation.
Financial data (yr. ended 12/31/13): Assets, $6,122,998 (M); gifts received, $5,500; expenditures, $273,745; qualifying distributions, $211,932; giving activities include $206,432 for 116 grants (high: $33,700; low: $70).
Purpose and activities: Giving primarily for education and to a community foundation; some funding also for the arts, the environment, health associations and human services.
Fields of interest: Arts and culture; Education; Higher education; Natural resources; Foundations; Diseases and conditions; Human services.
Limitations: Applications not accepted. Giving primarily in NY and WY. No grants to individuals.
Application information: Contributes only to pre-selected organizations.
Trustees: T. Anthony Brooks; Linda Leith Brooks.
EIN: 223761279

5275
The Elizabeth Broomfield Foundation Trust
P.O. Box 1501, NJ2-130-03-31
Pennington, NJ 08534-1501

Established in 2002 in New York.
Donor: Elizabeth Broomfield Trust.
Foundation type: Independent foundation.
Financial data (yr. ended 12/31/14): Assets, $5,721,534; expenditures, $360,483; qualifying distributions, $317,546.
Fields of interest: University education; Graduate and professional education; Health; Pharmacology.
Limitations: Applications not accepted. Giving primarily in Ann Arbor, MI. No grants to individuals.
Application information: Contributes only to pre-selected organizations.
Trustees: Kevin F. Hobbs; Merrill Lynch Trust Co.
EIN: 066514101

5276
The Brothers Ashkenazi Foundation, Inc.
759 Shrewsbury Ave.
Long Branch, NJ 07740-5027 (732) 574-9000

Donors: Isaac Ashkenazi; Ezra E. Ashkenazi; Ronald Ashkenazi; David E. Ashkenazi.
Foundation type: Independent foundation.
Financial data (yr. ended 02/28/14): Assets, $10,798,987 (M); gifts received, $49,692; expenditures, $385,431; qualifying distributions, $378,349; giving activities include $378,349 for 1,075 grants (high: $250,000; low: $70,000).

Purpose and activities: Giving primarily to Jewish agencies, temples, and schools, and to economically disadvantaged individuals.
Fields of interest: Education; Judaism; Economically disadvantaged people.
Type of support: Grants to individuals.
Application information:
Initial approach: Letter
Deadline(s): None
Trustees: Ezra E. Ashkenazi; Isaac Ashkenazi; Ronald Ashkenazi.
EIN: 223469592

5277
Browder Family Foundation
P.O. Box 1501, NJ2-130-03-31
Pennington, NJ 08534-1501

Established in 1999 in Florida.
Donors: Rhea Browder; Browder Trust; Browder Charitable Lead Annuity Trust.
Foundation type: Independent foundation.
Financial data (yr. ended 07/31/14): Assets, $1,571,929 (M); gifts received, $11,794; expenditures, $216,067; qualifying distributions, $211,907; giving activities include $206,550 for 21 grants (high: $128,200; low: $100).
Fields of interest: Protestantism; Human services; Youth development.
Limitations: Applications not accepted. Giving primarily in Ocala, FL. No grants to individuals.
Application information: Unsolicited requests for funds not accepted.
Trustees: William Browder; Bank of America, N.A.
EIN: 223682521

5278
Brown Foundation
545 Cedar Ln.
Teaneck, NJ 07666-1740

Established in 1985 in New Jersey.
Donor: David M. Brown.
Foundation type: Independent foundation.
Financial data (yr. ended 11/30/13): Assets, $3,937,006 (M); gifts received, $1,800,071; expenditures, $441,335; qualifying distributions, $413,000; giving activities include $413,000 for 12 grants (high: $115,000; low: $2,500).
Purpose and activities: Giving primarily to Jewish and human rights organizations; funding also for social services, and health organizations.
Fields of interest: Diseases and conditions; Cancers; Social sciences; Judaism; Human rights; Human services.
Type of support: Policy, advocacy and systems reform.
Limitations: Applications not accepted. Giving primarily in NJ and NY. No grants to individuals.
Application information: Contributes only to pre-selected organizations.
Officers and Trustees: David Brown, Pres. and Trustee; Adam R. Brown, Secy. and Trustee; Nikki Mintz Brown.
EIN: 222663141

5279
Brueckner Family Charitable Foundation
c/o Cappiccille & Co.
615 W. Mount Pleasant Ave.
Livingston, NJ 07039-1620

Established in 1999 in New Jersey.
Donors: Richard F. Brueckner; Laurie C. Brueckner.
Foundation type: Independent foundation.
Financial data (yr. ended 12/31/13): Assets, $1,614,936 (M); gifts received, $250,000; expenditures, $312,018; qualifying distributions, $296,650; giving activities include $296,650 for 12 grants (high: $186,000; low: $250).
Fields of interest: Arts and culture; Visual arts; Ballet; Orchestral music; Education; Higher education; Nonprofits; Christianity; Human services.
Type of support: General support; Regranting.
Limitations: Applications not accepted. Giving primarily in NJ, NY and PA. No grants to individuals.
Application information: Unsolicited requests for funds not accepted.
Advisory Committee: Laurie C. Brueckner; Richard F. Brueckner.
EIN: 134092823

5280
Charles E. and Edna T. Brundage Charitable, Scientific and Wildlife Conservation Foundation
c/o Mandel, Fekete & Bloom
30 Montgomery St., Ste. 685
Jersey City, NJ 07302-3834
Contact: Frank Fekete

Established in 1955 in New Jersey.
Donor: Edna T. Brundage†.
Foundation type: Independent foundation.
Financial data (yr. ended 12/31/13): Assets, $3,834,634 (M); expenditures, $201,692; qualifying distributions, $190,840; giving activities include $190,840 for 41 grants (high: $35,000; low: $500).
Fields of interest: Arts and culture; Orchestral music; Museums; Elementary and secondary education; Natural resources; Communication media; Community and economic development; Human services; Child welfare.
Type of support: General support; Capital campaigns; Equipment; Endowments; Program development; Scholarships.
Limitations: Applications accepted. Giving primarily in northern NJ; some giving also in MA, MN, NH, NY, and VT. No grants to individuals.
Application information: Unsolicited applications are not encouraged.
Initial approach: Proposal
Copies of proposal: 1
Deadline(s): Oct. 1
Board meeting date(s): Once annually in Oct. or Nov.
Final notification: Responses sent only to successful applications. Responses not sent to unsolicited applications
Officers and Trustees: William B. Cater, Jr., Pres. and Trustee; Charles B. Cater, V.P. and Treas. and Trustee; Annabel Cater, V.P.; June B. Cater, V.P. and Trustee; Kerry Cater, V.P. and Trustee; Joel Jukiro, V.P. and Trustee; James A. Jukosky, V.P. and Trustee; Susan Jukosky, V.P. and Trustee; Lorraine Garguilo, Secy.
EIN: 226050185

5281
The Brunetti Foundation
1655 U.S. Hwy. 9
Old Bridge, NJ 08857-2844 (732) 727-3300
Contact: John J. Brunetti, Pres.

Established in 1974 in New Jersey.
Donors: Aldercrest Development Corp.; John J. Brunetti; Stephen P. Brunetti; John J. Brunetti, Jr.; Joann H. Brunetti.
Foundation type: Independent foundation.
Financial data (yr. ended 12/31/13): Assets, $9,059,919 (M); gifts received, $160,000; expenditures, $428,921; qualifying distributions, $419,560; giving activities include $419,560 for 331 grants (high: $10,000; low: $200).
Purpose and activities: Support primarily for a military academy, higher education, medical research, and hospitals; funding also for Roman Catholic churches.
Fields of interest: Education; Higher education; Hospital care; Diseases and conditions; Catholicism; Human services.
Type of support: Endowments; Scholarships; Research; Research and evaluation.
Limitations: Applications accepted. Giving primarily in NJ. No grants to individuals.
Application information: Application form required.
Initial approach: Letter
Deadline(s): None
Officers: John J. Brunetti, Pres.; John J. Brunetti, Jr., V.P. and Secy.
EIN: 237346205

5282
Buddha Law Foundation Inc.
180 Tekening Dr.
Tenafly, NJ 07670-1219 (201) 568-2620
Contact: Alan Adler, Tr.

Established in 2000 in New York.
Donor: Alan Adler.
Foundation type: Independent foundation.
Financial data (yr. ended 07/31/13): Assets, $505,535 (M); gifts received, $125; expenditures, $371,363; qualifying distributions, $370,274; giving activities include $369,000 for 4 grants (high: $350,000; low: $5,000).
Fields of interest: Arts and culture; Buddhism; Human rights.
Limitations: Applications accepted. Giving in the U.S. and Moscow, Russia.
Application information: Application form required.
Initial approach: Letter
Deadline(s): None
Trustees: Alan Adler; Jordan Adler; Judith Adler.
EIN: 223762443

5283
John F. Byrne Family Foundation Inc.
53 Cardinal Dr.
P.O. Box 2369
Westfield, NJ 07091-2369 (908) 233-6800
Contact: Robert Schwartz Esq.

Donor: Doris M. Byrne Revocable Trust.
Foundation type: Independent foundation.
Financial data (yr. ended 01/31/14): Assets, $3,720,365 (M); expenditures, $224,383; qualifying distributions, $215,925; giving activities

include $169,900 for 3 grants (high: $100,000; low: $19,900).

Purpose and activities: Giving primarily for Roman Catholic organizations, churches, and schools.

Fields of interest: Elementary and secondary education; Catholicism.

Limitations: Applications accepted. Giving primarily in NJ. No grants to individuals or, generally, for operating funds.

Application information: Application form required.

   Initial approach: Letter

   Deadline(s): None

Trustees: Paul R. Barkus, Esq.; John R. Blasi; Michael C. Provine.

EIN: 043613397

5284
John J. & Rose Cali Family Foundation

c/o Cali Futures
11 Commerce Dr., Ste. 206
Cranford, NJ 07016-3501

Donors: John J. Cali; Rose C. Cali; Brant Cali.

Foundation type: Independent foundation.

Financial data (yr. ended 12/31/13): Assets, $2,949,957 (M); expenditures, $152,803; qualifying distributions, $150,225; giving activities include $150,225 for 19 grants (high: $40,000; low: $500).

Fields of interest: University education; Nonprofits.

Type of support: Regranting.

Limitations: Applications not accepted. Giving primarily in NJ. No grants to individuals.

Application information: Unsolicited requests for funds not accepted.

Officers: John Cali, Pres.; Rose Cali, Secy.-Treas.

Trustee: Brant Cali.

EIN: 222533638

5285
Cantor Foundation

c/o Nemiroff
611 Rte. 46
Hasbrouck Heights, NJ 07604

Established in 1995 in New York.

Donor: Richard Cantor.

Foundation type: Independent foundation.

Financial data (yr. ended 10/31/14): Assets, $844,313 (M); expenditures, $165,027; qualifying distributions, $131,250; giving activities include $131,250 for 23 grants (high: $75,000; low: $750).

Purpose and activities: Giving primarily for the arts, education, human services, health, and children's services, particularly a child development organization; funding also for a Jewish federated giving program.

Fields of interest: Performing arts; Education; Foundations; Nonprofits; Human services; Child welfare; Child development.

Type of support: Regranting.

Limitations: Applications not accepted. Giving primarily in NY; some funding also in CT. No grants to individuals.

Application information: Contributes only to pre-selected organizations.

Officer: Richard Cantor, Pres.

EIN: 133745664

5286
The Capebank Charitable Foundation

201 Shore Rd.
Linwood, NJ 08221

Foundation type: Independent foundation.

Financial data (yr. ended 12/31/13): Assets, $4,763,003 (M); expenditures, $298,385; qualifying distributions, $283,940; giving activities include $283,940 for 60 grants (high: $54,700; low: $40).

Fields of interest: Education; Human services.

Limitations: Applications not accepted.

Application information: Unsolicited requests for funds not accepted.

Officers: Robert F. Garrett III, Pres.; Guy Hackney, V.P.; Joan B. Ditmars, Secy.; Matthew Swift, Treas.

EIN: 261864694

5287
Nicholas H. and Margaret H. Carlozzi Charitable Foundation, Inc.

334 Crestmont Rd.
Cedar Grove, NJ 07009-1908 9738579028

Established in 1992 in New Jersey.

Donors: Nicholas H. Carlozzi†; Margaret H. Carlozzi†; Nicholas Carlozzi.

Foundation type: Independent foundation.

Financial data (yr. ended 12/31/14): Assets, $5,448,630; gifts received, $0; expenditures, $266,312; qualifying distributions, $260,000.

Fields of interest: Arts and culture; Arts education; Adult education; Basic and remedial instruction; Diseases and conditions; Human services; Family services; Child welfare; Youth development; Homeless services.

Type of support: General support; Continuing support; Public engagement and education; Capital campaigns; Capital and infrastructure; Seed money.

Limitations: Applications not accepted. No grants to individuals.

Application information: Unsolicited requests for funds not accepted.

Officers: Nicholas Carlozzi, Pres.; Robert Carlozzi, V.P. and Secy.; Beth Carlozzi, V.P. and Treas.; Mark Carlozzi, V.P.

Number of staff: None.

EIN: 223334346

5288
CBIS Foundation, Inc.

c/o Lonnie Wollin
124 Prospect St.
Ridgewood, NJ 07450-4406

Established in 2005 in Delaware.

Donors: Carol Collins; Budge Collins.

Foundation type: Independent foundation.

Financial data (yr. ended 06/30/13): Assets, $2,523,201 (M); expenditures, $234,014; qualifying distributions, $212,030; giving activities include $212,030 for grants.

Fields of interest: Education; Hospital care; Diseases and conditions; Christianity; Human services.

Limitations: Applications not accepted. Giving primarily in CA. No grants to individuals.

Application information: Contributes only to pre-selected organizations.

Officers and Directors: Budge Collins, Pres. and Director; Carol Collins, V.P. and Director; Lonnie Wollin, Secy.

EIN: 203362453

5289
Margaret and Peter Chang Foundation

P.O. Box 2189
Westfield, NJ 07091-2189 (908) 232-0292

Donor: Margaret S. Chang.

Foundation type: Independent foundation.

Financial data (yr. ended 12/31/13): Assets, $2,809,868; gifts received, $2,000,000; expenditures, $350,841; qualifying distributions, $324,773.

Fields of interest: Children's hospital care; Children.

Limitations: Applications accepted. Giving primarily in NJ.

Application information: Application form required.

   Initial approach: Request application form

   Deadline(s): None

Officers: Gwyneth B. McNabola, Pres.; David B. Foltz, V.P.; Dorothy M. Miller, Secy.; Cyrene M. Foltz, Treas.

EIN: 270765348

5290
Robert N. Chang Foundation

c/o Merrill Lynch Bank & Trust Co., FSB
P.O. Box 1501, NJ2-130-03-31
Pennington, NJ 08534-1501
Application address: c/o Allan Liu, Pres., 737 Rustic Ln., Mountain View, CA 94040

Established in 2000 in California.

Donor: Robert N. Chang†.

Foundation type: Independent foundation.

Financial data (yr. ended 08/31/13): Assets, $7,810,757 (M); expenditures, $504,735; qualifying distributions, $368,971; giving activities include $300,818 for 4 grants (high: $121,305; low: $45,500).

Purpose and activities: Giving primarily for higher education; funding also for an Asian philanthropic organization.

Fields of interest: Education; Higher education; People of Asian descent.

Type of support: General support.

Limitations: Applications accepted. Giving primarily in CA and WA.

Application information:

   Initial approach: Letter

   Deadline(s): None

Officers: Allan Liu, Pres.; Steven Liu, Secy.; Frank Zhoe Yu Tung, Treas.

EIN: 770550139

5291
Chanil Foundation

P.O. Box 1501, NJ2-130-03-31
Pennington, NJ 08534-1501

Established in 1993 in California.

Donors: Injoa Kim; Palmco Corp.

Foundation type: Independent foundation.

Financial data (yr. ended 12/31/13): Assets, $4,525,688 (M); expenditures, $178,493; qualifying distributions, $163,237; giving activities

include $153,000 for 10 grants (high: $30,000; low: $5,000).
Fields of interest: Arts and culture; Higher education; Human services.
Type of support: General support.
Limitations: Applications not accepted. Giving primarily in CA. No grants to individuals.
Application information: Unsolicited requests for funds not accepted.
Officers: Injoa Kim, Chair.; Sun Kee Kim, Pres.; Young J. Shin, C.F.O.
EIN: 330614959

5292
Chapman Family Charitable Trust
c/o Gardner Capital Management Corp.
66 E. Main St., Ste. 2
Little Falls, NJ 07424-5629

Established in 2006 in New York.
Foundation type: Independent foundation.
Financial data (yr. ended 12/31/13): Assets, $479,529 (M); expenditures, $203,214; qualifying distributions, $202,776; giving activities include $201,464 for 7 grants (high: $126,000; low: $100).
Fields of interest: Arts and culture; Education; Domesticated animals; Human services.
Limitations: Applications not accepted. Giving primarily in Washington, DC and NC. No grants to individuals.
Application information: Contributes only to pre-selected organizations.
Trustee: Max C. Chapman, Jr.
EIN: 205229189

5293
Chormann Family Foundation
P.O. Box 1501, NJ2-130-03-31
Pennington, NJ 08534-1501

Established in 1998 in Michigan.
Donors: Richard F. Chormann; Richard and Carolyn Chormann Charitable.
Foundation type: Independent foundation.
Financial data (yr. ended 07/31/13): Assets, $4,367,898 (M); gifts received, $245,676; expenditures, $219,190; qualifying distributions, $195,634; giving activities include $171,000 for 5 grants (high: $100,000; low: $10,000).
Fields of interest: Arts and culture; University education; Environment.
Type of support: General support.
Limitations: Applications not accepted. Giving primarily in MI. No grants to individuals.
Application information: Unsolicited requests for funds not accepted.
Officers: James Chormann, V.P.; Cynthia Hann, V.P.
Trustee: Merrill Lynch Trust Co.
EIN: 383439226

5294
Chu and Chan Foundation
P.O. Box 1501, NJ2-130-03-31
Pennington, NJ 08534-1501
Contact: Tony Chu, Pres.
Application address: 2705 Verdis Ln., Crofton, MD 21114

Established in 1998 in New York.
Donors: Lam Chu†; Emily Chu.

Foundation type: Independent foundation.
Financial data (yr. ended 04/30/13): Assets, $1,459,213 (M); expenditures, $191,438; qualifying distributions, $176,435; giving activities include $166,767 for 5 grants (high: $64,767; low: $5,000).
Fields of interest: Health; Diseases and conditions; Human services.
Type of support: General support.
Limitations: Applications accepted. Giving primarily in NY.
Application information: Application form required.
Initial approach: Letter
Deadline(s): None
Officers: Tony Chu, Co-Pres.; Jeff Sobel, Co-Pres.; Thomas Sobel, Secy.
Director: Emily Chu.
EIN: 113440906

5295
The Citta Foundation Inc.
201 Hooper Ave., Ste. 5A
Toms River, NJ 08753-7671 (732) 349-0200
Contact: Rosanne L. Citta, Pres.

Established in 1986 in Florida.
Donor: Citta Family Charitable Lead Trust.
Foundation type: Independent foundation.
Financial data (yr. ended 12/31/13): Assets, $5,734,217 (M); gifts received, $178,937; expenditures, $277,836; qualifying distributions, $197,450; giving activities include $197,450 for 29 grants (high: $83,000; low: $100).
Fields of interest: Education; Higher education; Health; Christianity; Human services; Child welfare.
Type of support: General support.
Limitations: Applications accepted. Giving primarily in Ocean County, NJ.
Application information:
Initial approach: Proposal
Deadline(s): None
Officers: Rosanne L. Citta, Pres.; Joseph A. Citta, Jr., V.P.; Marie Roselli, Secy.; Cheryl Zahn, Fdn. Mgr.
Trustees: Loriann Erbe; Kristin Farfalla.
EIN: 592635738

5296
Civitas Foundation
(formerly Quigley Family Foundation)
P.O. Box 1501, NJ2-130-03-31
Pennington, NJ 08534-1501

Established in 1998 in New Jersey.
Donors: John G. Quigley; Quigley Family Partners, LP; Kathryn Quigley.
Foundation type: Independent foundation.
Financial data (yr. ended 12/31/13): Assets, $564,006 (M); expenditures, $205,880; qualifying distributions, $201,902; giving activities include $182,850 for 17 grants (high: $59,000; low: $150).
Purpose and activities: Giving primarily for higher and other education.
Fields of interest: Education; Elementary and secondary education; Higher education.
Limitations: Applications not accepted. Giving primarily in Washington, DC, NJ, and NY. No grants to individuals.
Application information: Unsoliocited requests for funds not accepted.

Officers: Stanley L. Levin, Pres. and Treas.; David A. Handler, Secy.
EIN: 223594586

5297
CKT Foundation
P.O. Box 1501, NJ2-130-03-31
Pennington, NJ 08534-1501
Application address: c/o Ralph and Mary Stebbins, 3557 Kings Mill Rd., North Branch, MI 48461

Established in 2005 in Michigan.
Donors: Ralph S. Stebbins; Mary J. Stebbins.
Foundation type: Independent foundation.
Financial data (yr. ended 12/31/13): Assets, $9,522,152 (M); expenditures, $526,760; qualifying distributions, $433,076; giving activities include $314,910 for 1 grant.
Purpose and activities: Giving primarily through an affiliated family foundation for the betterment of Port Huron, Michigan.
Fields of interest: Foundations; Nonprofits; Community and economic development; Housing development; Human services.
Type of support: Regranting.
Limitations: Applications accepted. Giving primarily in the Port Huron, MI, area.
Application information:
Initial approach: Proposal
Deadline(s): None
Officers: Deborah Post, Pres.; Ralph Stebbins, V.P.; Mary J. Stebbins, Secy.
EIN: 203927820

5298
Clermont Foundation
P.O. Box 429
Summit, NJ 07902-0429
Contact: Gloria Choong

Established in 1992 in New Jersey.
Donors: Garnett L. Keith; Martha H. Keith.
Foundation type: Independent foundation.
Financial data (yr. ended 12/31/13): Assets, $6,063,080 (M); gifts received, $180,440; expenditures, $298,797; qualifying distributions, $287,706; giving activities include $281,850 for 51 grants (high: $50,000; low: $250).
Purpose and activities: Giving primarily to higher education and federated giving programs.
Fields of interest: Higher education; Nonprofits; Diseases and conditions; Community and economic development; Christianity; Human services.
Type of support: Annual campaigns; Matching grants; Capital campaigns; Scholarships; Regranting.
Limitations: Applications not accepted. Giving primarily in CA and MA. No grants to individuals.
Application information: Unsolicited requests for funds not accepted.
Officer: Gloria Choong, Secy.
Trustees: Garnett L. Keith; Martha H. Keith.
Number of staff: 1 part-time support.
EIN: 223177379

5299
The Manny and Ruthy Cohen Foundation
231 Chestnut Ave.
Marlton, NJ 08053-7147 (856) 795-2200
Contact: Stephen Morgan, Pres.

Established in 1986 in Connecticut.
Donor: Ruth Cohen†.
Foundation type: Independent foundation.
Financial data (yr. ended 12/31/13): Assets, $6,552,827 (M); expenditures, $327,996; qualifying distributions, $226,337; giving activities include $222,049 for 137 grants (high: $16,175; low: $100).
Fields of interest: Arts and culture; Performing arts; Higher education; Nonprofits; Diseases and conditions; Judaism; Human services.
Type of support: Regranting.
Limitations: Applications accepted. Giving primarily in Miami, FL, MD, NJ, and Philadelphia, PA. No grants to individuals.
Application information:
Initial approach: Proposal
Deadline(s): None
Officers: Stephen Morgan, Pres.; Keith B. Morgan, V.P.; Susan Heyman, Secy.-Treas.
EIN: 592744621

5300
The James and Loretta Colotto Foundation Inc.
c/o Bowen & Bowen
907 Main St.
Hackensack, NJ 07601-4914
Contact: Peter G. Bowen, Pres.

Donors: James V. Colotto; Loretta Colotto†.
Foundation type: Independent foundation.
Financial data (yr. ended 12/31/13): Assets, $4,079,733 (M); expenditures, $287,431; qualifying distributions, $240,690; giving activities include $196,500 for 28 grants (high: $20,000; low: $1,000).
Purpose and activities: Giving primarily for Roman Catholic organizations.
Fields of interest: Catholicism; Human services.
Limitations: Applications accepted. Giving primarily in MD.
Application information: Application form required.
Initial approach: Letter
Deadline(s): Sept. 30
Officers: Peter G. Bowen, Pres.; Michael Sciutella, V.P.; Eugene H. Gilmartin, Secy.
EIN: 223769926

5301
Columbia Bank Foundation
19-01 Rte. 208
Fair Lawn, NJ 07410-2832
Contact: Tony Rose, Sr. V.P.
FAX: (201) 794-5612; Main URL: https://www.columbiabankonline.com/home/about-us/columbia-bank-foundation
Columbia Bank Foundation Video: http://www.columbiabankonline.com/foundation/foundation_201-100191.html

Established in 2004 in New Jersey.
Donor: Columbia Financial Inc.
Foundation type: Company-sponsored foundation.
Financial data (yr. ended 12/31/13): Assets, $129,379 (M); gifts received, $293,260; expenditures, $180,033; qualifying distributions, $176,738; giving activities include $176,738 for 12 grants (high: $25,000; low: $5,000).
Purpose and activities: The foundation supports programs designed to promote health and human

services, affordable housing, community investment, economic development, and financial literacy. Special emphasis is directed toward organizations serving low- and moderate-income individuals and communities.
Fields of interest: Education; Early childhood education; Special needs education; Health; Community and economic development; Employment; Housing development; Home ownership; Financial counseling; Human services; Housing services; Low-income and poor people.
Type of support: Capital campaigns; Capital and infrastructure; Equipment; Program development.
Limitations: Applications accepted. Giving primarily in areas of company operations in NJ. No support for national health organizations, research/disease advocacy organizations, religious, political, labor, or fraternal organizations, or civic clubs. No grants to individuals, or for scholarships, general operating support, professional fees, employee compensation sports, athletic events or athletic programs, or travel-related events.
Publications: Application guidelines; Program policy statement.
Application information: Cover letters should be submitted using organization letterhead. Support is limited to 1 contribution per organization during any given year. Multi-year funding is not automatic. Application form required.
Initial approach: Download application form and mail proposal and application form to foundation
Copies of proposal: 1
Deadline(s): None
Board meeting date(s): Quarterly
Final notification: 3 months
Officers and Directors: Thomas J. Kemly, Pres.; Diane L. Weiss, Secy.; E. Thomas Allen, Treas. and Director; Eugene M. Schwartz, Genl. Counsel; Frank Czerwinski; Alex Grinewicz; Raymond G. Hallock; Noel R. Holland; Geri Kelly.
EIN: 201115566

5302
The S. Leigh Pierson & Douglas R. Conant Family Cookie Jar Foundation, Inc.
c/o Untracht Early
325 Columbia Tpke., Ste 202
Florham Park, NJ 07932-1212

Established in 2000 in New Jersey.
Donors: Leigh P. Pierson; Douglas R. Conant; Bruce J. Lipstein.
Foundation type: Independent foundation.
Financial data (yr. ended 12/31/14): Assets, $5,456,811; gifts received, $6,030; expenditures, $480,346; qualifying distributions, $444,515.
Fields of interest: Performing arts; Education; Higher education; Natural resources; Christianity; Human services; Food banks; Child welfare.
Limitations: Applications not accepted. Giving primarily in IL, NJ and RI. No grants to individuals.
Application information: Contributes only to pre-selected organizations.
Officers: Leigh P. Pierson, Pres.; Douglas R. Conant, Secy.; Jon Vegosen, Treas.
EIN: 223769553

5303
Conger Family Foundation, Inc.
31 E. Mountain Blvd.
P.O. Box 4470
Warren, NJ 07059-0470

Established in 2004 in New Jersey.
Foundation type: Independent foundation.
Financial data (yr. ended 12/31/13): Assets, $3,976,355 (M); expenditures, $242,334; qualifying distributions, $201,880; giving activities include $193,400 for 26 grants (high: $40,500; low: $150).
Fields of interest: Arts and culture; Higher education; Diseases and conditions; Human services.
Limitations: Applications not accepted. Giving primarily in MA. No grants to individuals.
Application information: Unsolicited requests for funds not accepted.
Officers and Trustees: William F. Conger, Pres. and Trustee; Ezra Jennings, V.P. and Trustee; Nancy P. Conger, Secy. and Trustee; Sean Devlin, Exec. Dir.
EIN: 223803069

5304
Cordover Family Foundation
(formerly The Ronald H. Cordover Family Foundation)
61 S. Paramus Rd., Ste. 278
Paramus, NJ 07652

Established in 1990 in Tennessee.
Donors: The Berkline Corp.; Ronald H. Cordover.
Foundation type: Independent foundation.
Financial data (yr. ended 12/31/13): Assets, $3,597,630 (M); expenditures, $275,879; qualifying distributions, $255,443; giving activities include $255,443 for 23 grants (high: $70,000; low: $52).
Purpose and activities: The foundation supports hospitals and organizations involved with arts and culture, education, and Judaism.
Fields of interest: Arts and culture; Visual arts; Museums; Art museums; Historic preservation; Education; Elementary education; Higher education; Hospital care; Judaism.
Type of support: General support.
Limitations: Applications not accepted. Giving primarily in Andover, Boston, and Cambridge, MA, Landover, MD, NJ, and New York, NY. No grants to individuals.
Application information: Contributes only to pre-selected organizations.
Trustees: Barbara A. Cordover; Jeffrey A. Cordover; Ronald H. Cordover; Valerie Katz.
EIN: 226498278

5305
Covance Charitable Foundation
210 Carnegie Ctr.
Princeton, NJ 08540-6233
Main URL: http://www.covance.com/about/corporate-responsibility/index.php

Donor: Covance Inc.
Foundation type: Company-sponsored foundation.
Financial data (yr. ended 12/31/13): Assets, $379,819 (M); gifts received, $385,362; expenditures, $300,398; qualifying distributions, $300,333; giving activities include $300,333 for 47 grants (high: $100,000; low: $100).

Purpose and activities: The foundation supports organizations involved with education, health, and medical research. Special emphasis is directed toward programs designed to deliver health education and medical treatment to patients around the globe.
Fields of interest: Education; Charter school education; Health; School-based health care; Biomedicine; Diseases and conditions; Genetic conditions and birth defects.
Type of support: General support; Research.
Limitations: Applications not accepted. Giving primarily in CA, GA, NJ, and VA.
Application information: Unsolicited requests for funds not accepted.
Officers: Joseph L. Herring, Pres.; Alison A. Cornell, V.P. and C.F.O.; James W. Lovett, V.P. and Secy.; Michele D. Peterson, V.P.; Robert S. Pringle, Treas.
EIN: 810587320

5306
Crane Foundation, Inc.
140 Sylvan Ave., Ste. 4
Englewood Cliffs, NJ   07632

Established in 1951 in Missouri.
Donor: Crane Co.
Foundation type: Company-sponsored foundation.
Financial data (yr. ended 12/31/13): Assets, $6,772,919 (M); expenditures, $282,746; qualifying distributions, $254,716; giving activities include $112,000 for 21 grants (high: $10,000; low: $1,000), and $72,270 for 85 employee matching gifts.
Purpose and activities: The foundation supports organizations involved with performing arts, K-12 and higher education, health, recreation, human services, philanthropy and voluntarism, and minorities.
Fields of interest: Arts and culture; Environment; Diseases and conditions.
International interests: Canada.
Type of support: General support; Employee matching gifts; Continuing support; Annual campaigns; Scholarships.
Limitations: Applications not accepted.
Application information: Unsolicited requests for funds not accepted.
Officers and Directors: Robert S. Evans, Chair and Director; Eric C. Fast, Pres. and C.E.O. and Director; Richard A. Maue, V.P. and C.F.O. and Director; Augustus I. DuPont, V.P., Secy., and Genl. Counsel and Director; Andrew L. Krawitt, V.P. and Co-Treas. and Director; Tazewell Rowe, V.P. and Co-Treas.; Elise M. Kopczick, V.P.
EIN: 436051752

5307
Edward L. Croman Foundation
395 Pleasant Valley Way
West Orange, NJ   07052-2998   (973) 736-4500
Contact: Edward L. Croman, Tr.

Established in 1989 in New Jersey.
Donors: Edward L. Croman; David Croman; Croman Equities Limited, LLC.
Foundation type: Independent foundation.
Financial data (yr. ended 12/31/13): Assets, $2,207,614 (M); gifts received, $215,583; expenditures, $357,676; qualifying distributions,

$351,394; giving activities include $351,394 for 57 grants (high: $77,667; low: $150).
Purpose and activities: Giving primarily to Jewish organizations, schools, and temples.
Fields of interest: Elementary and secondary education; Higher education; Nonprofits; Judaism.
Type of support: Regranting.
Limitations: Applications accepted. Giving primarily in NJ and NY; funding also in Cincinnati, OH. No grants to individuals.
Application information: Application form required.
  Initial approach: Proposal
  Deadline(s): None
Trustees: David Croman; Edward L. Croman; Steven Croman.
EIN: 223044476

5308
Ivon And Jane Culver Charitable Trust
P.O. Box 1501, NJ2-130-03-31
Pennington, NJ   08534-1501

Donor: Ivon and Jane Culver Irrevocable Trust.
Foundation type: Independent foundation.
Financial data (yr. ended 12/31/14): Assets, $12,789,374; expenditures, $619,742; qualifying distributions, $571,888.
Fields of interest: Arts and culture; Education; Human services.
Limitations: Applications not accepted.
Application information: Unsolicited requests for funds not accepted.
Trustees: Walter L. Schaefer, Jr.; Merrill Lynch Trust Company.
EIN: 452880898

5309
CYH Foundation
P.O. Box 517
Lakewood, NJ   08701-0517   (732) 886-1400
Contact: Jacob Halpern, Tr.

Established in 2003 in New Jersey.
Donors: Act Trust; Halpern Trust.
Foundation type: Independent foundation.
Financial data (yr. ended 12/31/12): Assets, $4,504,258 (M); gifts received, $275,000; expenditures, $352,005; qualifying distributions, $352,005; giving activities include $351,905 for grants.
Fields of interest: Judaism.
Limitations: Applications accepted. Giving primarily in NJ and NY. No grants to individuals.
Application information: Application form required.
  Initial approach: Proposal
  Deadline(s): None
Trustee: Jacob Halpern.
EIN: 593769177

5310
The Daft Family Foundation
c/o Hamel Assoc., Inc.
24 Washington Ave.
Chatham, NJ   07928-2101

Established in 1998 in Georgia.
Donors: Delphine H. Daft; Douglas N. Daft.
Foundation type: Independent foundation.
Financial data (yr. ended 12/31/14): Assets, $3,026,509 (M); expenditures, $289,147;

qualifying distributions, $282,500; giving activities include $282,500 for 12 grants (high: $70,000; low: $1,000).
Fields of interest: Arts and culture; Theater; Museums; Elementary and secondary education; Higher education; Hospital care; Goodwill promotion.
International interests: Australia.
Type of support: General support.
Limitations: Applications not accepted. Giving primarily in MA, with emphasis on Williamstown, and New York, NY. No grants to individuals.
Application information: Unsolicited requests for funds not accepted.
Trustee: Delphine H. Daft.
EIN: 586379765

5311
D'Aloia Family Foundation
c/o R.J. Diquollo
1 Giralda Farms., Ste. 130
Madison, NJ   07940-1027

Donors: G. Peter D'Aloia; Marguerite D'Aloia.
Foundation type: Independent foundation.
Financial data (yr. ended 12/31/13): Assets, $5,700,850 (M); gifts received, $4,644,234; expenditures, $222,674; qualifying distributions, $218,425; giving activities include $210,400 for 8 grants (high: $98,400; low: $500).
Fields of interest: Arts and culture; Education; Human services.
Limitations: Applications not accepted.
Application information: Unsolicited requests for funds not accepted.
Officers: G. Peter D'Aloia, Pres.; Marguerite D'Aloia, Secy.; Robert Diquollo, Treas.
EIN: 262453178

5312
The Dankis Christian Foundation, Inc.
143 High Oaks Dr.
Warren, NJ   07059-5464

Donor: Victor J. Dankis.
Foundation type: Independent foundation.
Financial data (yr. ended 12/31/12): Assets, $2,884,422 (M); gifts received, $482,760; expenditures, $168,038; qualifying distributions, $155,939; giving activities include $150,000 for 9 grants (high: $30,000; low: $10,000).
Fields of interest: Specialty hospital care; Christianity; Human services.
Limitations: Applications not accepted. Giving on a national basis. No grants to individuals.
Application information: Contributes only to pre-selected organizations.
Officers: Mark J. Dankis, Chair.; Brian K. Dankis, Secy.; Gary P. Dankis, Treas.
Trustees: Mildred L. Dankis; Victor J. Dankis.
EIN: 043700494

5313
The Davino Family Foundation Inc.
c/o Salvatore A. Davino
641 Shunpike Rd.
Chatham, NJ   07928-1567

Established in 2007 in New Jersey.
Donor: Salvatore A. Davino.

Foundation type: Independent foundation.
Financial data (yr. ended 12/31/13): Assets, $4,708 (M); gifts received, $235,000; expenditures, $232,331; qualifying distributions, $230,785; giving activities include $230,785 for 49 grants (high: $50,000; low: $200).
Fields of interest: Human services; Youth services.
Limitations: Applications not accepted. Giving primarily in NJ. No grants to individuals.
Application information: Contributes only to pre-selected organizations.
Officers: Salvatore A. Davino, Pres.; Frances Davino, V.P.; Anthony P. Davino, Secy.; Sandra Davino Niccolai, Treas.
EIN: 261591184

5314
Davis Charitable Foundation A New Jersey Non Profit Corporation
900 N., Kings Hwy., No. 100
Cherry Hill, NJ   08034-1516

Established in 2008 in New Jersey.
Donor: Jane C. Davis.
Foundation type: Independent foundation.
Financial data (yr. ended 12/31/13): Assets, $180,578 (M); gifts received, $250,000; expenditures, $148,372; qualifying distributions, $148,372; giving activities include $148,372 for 23 grants (high: $25,000; low: $500).
Fields of interest: Diseases and conditions; Sports and recreation; Human services.
Type of support: Research.
Limitations: Applications not accepted. Giving primarily in NJ.
Application information: Unsolicited requests for funds not accepted.
Officers: Jane C. Davis, Pres.; Mitchell R. Davis, Secy.; Patricia Davis Lahn, Treas.
EIN: 061831431

5315
The Degnan Family Foundation, Inc.
35 Beacon Hill Dr.
Chester, NJ   07930-3013

Donor: John J. Degnan 2011 Charitable Lead Annuity Trust.
Foundation type: Independent foundation.
Financial data (yr. ended 12/31/13): Assets, $1,340 (M); gifts received, $140,126; expenditures, $140,467; qualifying distributions, $139,000; giving activities include $139,000 for 26 grants (high: $75,000; low: $1,000).
Fields of interest: Education; Health; Agriculture.
Limitations: Applications not accepted. Giving primarily in NJ.
Application information: Unsolicited requests for funds not accepted.
Officer: Mary Degnan, Pres.
Trustees: Elena Brody; Cynthia Degnan; Philip Degnan.
EIN: 453326714

5316
Florence & Paul deRosa Memorial Fund for the Arts Inc.
71 Forest Rd.
Tenafly, NJ   07670-2230

Donor: Paul deRosa.
Foundation type: Independent foundation.
Financial data (yr. ended 12/31/13): Assets, $6,589,457 (M); expenditures, $328,495; qualifying distributions, $276,685; giving activities include $236,260 for 16 grants (high: $53,000; low: $960).
Fields of interest: Opera; Elementary and secondary education.
Limitations: Applications not accepted. Giving primarily in NJ, NY and PA. No grants to individuals.
Application information: Contributes only to pre-selected organizations.
Trustee: Paul deRosa.
EIN: 223113270

5317
Bonaventura Devine Foundation, Inc.
5 Pine Hollow
Bernardsville, NJ   07924-1623   (908) 204-0041
Contact: Mary Jane Kenny, Pres.

Established in 1991 in New Jersey.
Donor: Bonaventura Devine†.
Foundation type: Independent foundation.
Financial data (yr. ended 12/31/14): Assets, $4,335,316 (M); expenditures, $299,579; qualifying distributions, $234,500; giving activities include $234,500 for 22 grants (high: $50,000; low: $1,000).
Purpose and activities: Giving primarily for human services, education, health and childcare.
Fields of interest: Museums; Education; Hospital care; Home health care; Diseases and conditions; Human services; Food banks; Child welfare; Shelter and residential care; Senior services; Low-income and poor people.
Type of support: General support.
Limitations: Applications accepted. Giving primarily in FL and NJ. No grants to individuals.
Application information: Application form required.
   Initial approach: Letter
   Deadline(s): None
Officer: Mary Jane Kenny, Pres.
Trustees: Bonaventura Cooper; Christine Frisbee.
EIN: 223116667

5318
Diaco Family Foundation Inc
10 N. 7th St., No. 12
Belleville, NJ   07109-1116

Established in 2000 in New Jersey.
Donors: Joseph Diaco; Power Electric Co.
Foundation type: Independent foundation.
Financial data (yr. ended 09/30/13): Assets, $7,151,545 (M); gifts received, $150,000; expenditures, $439,245; qualifying distributions, $340,000; giving activities include $310,000 for 28 grants (high: $60,000; low: $5,000).
Fields of interest: Cancers; Religion; Human services.
Limitations: Applications not accepted. Giving primarily in NJ and NY. No grants to individuals.
Application information: Contributes only to pre-selected organizations.
Officers: Theodore F. Diaco, Pres.; Stephanie Emperio, V.P.; Joseph Manasia, V.P.; Valerie Silvestri, Secy.; Frank P. Diaco, Treas.
EIN: 223763549

5319
Dickinson Family Foundation Inc.
c/o Gramkow, Carnevale, Seifert & Co., LLC
2 Forest Ave.
Oradell, NJ   07649-1959   (201) 599-0008
Contact: Ann Dickinson, Secy.-Treas.
E-mail: Upchurchr@gcs-cpa.com

Established in 1998 in New Jersey.
Donors: Fairleigh S. Dickinson†; Elizabeth H. Dickinson; Fairleigh S. Dickson Charitable Marital Trust.
Foundation type: Independent foundation.
Financial data (yr. ended 12/31/13): Assets, $7,606,862 (M); gifts received, $73; expenditures, $576,416; qualifying distributions, $393,299; giving activities include $373,625 for 11 grants (high: $200,000; low: $1,000).
Fields of interest: Arts and culture; Historic preservation; Elementary and secondary education; Hospital care; Neurology; Human services; Child welfare.
Limitations: Applications accepted. Giving primarily in CT, MA, and NJ.
Application information: Application form required.
   Initial approach: Letter
   Deadline(s): None
Officer: Ann Dickinson, Secy.-Treas.
Trustees: Amanda Turner Phillips; Richard Purington; David D. Turner.
EIN: 911969396

5320
John A. & Joan M. Dietze Charitable Trust
P.O. Box 1501, NJ2-130-03-31
Pennington, NJ   08534-1501

Established in 2003 in Delaware.
Donors: Joan M. Dietze; United Way of Delaware; John A. Dietze.
Foundation type: Independent foundation.
Financial data (yr. ended 12/31/14): Assets, $6,602,248; expenditures, $359,950; qualifying distributions, $313,182.
Fields of interest: Education; Elementary and secondary education; Foundations; Diseases and conditions; Human services.
Limitations: Applications not accepted. No grants to individuals.
Application information: Unsolicited requests for funds not accepted.
Trustee: Merrill Lynch Trust Co.
Advisors: David L. Dietze; John A. Dietze, Jr.; Pamela Dietze Halbrook; Anna Dezeng Nelon; Valerie J. Tweiten.
EIN: 516523322

5321
The Doctor Family Foundation
P.O. Box 1501, NJ2-130-03-31
Pennington, NJ   08534-1501
Contact: Donald L. Doctor, Pres.

Established in 2004 in North Carolina.
Donors: Mary Doctor; Donald L. Doctor.
Foundation type: Independent foundation.
Financial data (yr. ended 11/30/14): Assets, $3,237,807 (M); expenditures, $206,747; qualifying distributions, $191,547; giving activities include $173,500 for 10 grants (high: $100,000; low: $1,000).

Fields of interest: Arts and culture; Education; Human services.

Type of support: General support.

Limitations: Applications accepted. Giving primarily in NC. No grants to individuals.

Application information: Application form required.

Initial approach: Proposal
Deadline(s): May 15

Officers: Donald L. Doctor, Pres.; Mary Doctor, Secy.-Treas.

Directors: Jordan Doctor; Landon Doctor.

EIN: 202047965

5322
Doll Family Foundation

c/o Robert C. Doll, Jr.
513 Christopher Dr.
Princeton, NJ 08540-2333

Donors: Robert C. Doll, Jr.; Leslie L. Doll.

Foundation type: Independent foundation.

Financial data (yr. ended 12/31/13): Assets, $35,276,953 (M); gifts received, $16,066,940; expenditures, $322,339; qualifying distributions, $246,950; giving activities include $246,950 for 19 grants (high: $200,000; low: $100).

Fields of interest: Education; Health; Christianity.

Limitations: Applications not accepted.

Application information: Unsolicited requests for funds not accepted.

Officers: Robert C. Doll, Jr., Pres. and Treas.; Leslie L. Doll, Secy.

Trustees: Brandon Hull; Donald Lough, Jr.; Marion Meeks; John Morrisey.

EIN: 522254198

5323
Domenica Foundation, Inc.

14 Sbar Blvd.
Moorestown, NJ 08057-1057
E-mail: info@domenicafoundation.org; Main URL: http://domenicafoundation.org

Established in 2006 in New Jersey.

Foundation type: Independent foundation.

Financial data (yr. ended 11/30/13): Assets, $7,074,408 (M); gifts received, $35,532; expenditures, $401,991; qualifying distributions, $304,000; giving activities include $304,000 for grants (high: $105,000; low: $2,000).

Fields of interest: Theater; Education; Nonprofits; Housing development; Catholicism; Shelter and residential care.

Type of support: Regranting.

Limitations: Applications not accepted. Giving primarily in NJ. No grants to individuals.

Application information: Contributes only to pre-selected organizations.

Officers: A. J. Piperno, Pres.; Elena Piperno, V.P.; Margaret Piperno, V.P.; Anthony Piperno, Secy.; Dominic Piperno, Treas.

EIN: 203904706

5324
The D'Onofrio Foundation

(formerly The D'Onofrio Charitable Foundation Trust)
124 N. Main St.
Forked River, NJ 08731-3634

Established in 2001 in New Jersey.

Donors: Donato D'Onofrio; Mary D'Onofrio.

Foundation type: Independent foundation.

Financial data (yr. ended 12/31/13): Assets, $1,728,936 (M); gifts received, $195,826; expenditures, $211,379; qualifying distributions, $207,825; giving activities include $207,825 for 36 grants (high: $152,375; low: $100).

Fields of interest: Health; Agriculture; Human services.

Limitations: Applications not accepted. Giving primarily in NJ.

Application information: Unsolicited requests for funds not accepted.

Trustees: Donato D'Onofrio; Linda D'Onofrio; Paul J. Dalton.

EIN: 912151046

5325
Dow Jones News Fund, Inc.

(formerly Dow Jones Newspaper Fund, Inc.)
P.O. Box 300
Princeton, NJ 08543-0300 (609) 452-2820
Contact: Linda Shockley, Managing Director
FAX: (609) 520-5804; E-mail: djnf@dowjones.com;
Main URL: https://www.newsfund.org
Facebook: http://www.facebook.com/pages/
Dow-Jones-News-Fund-Inc/102711476434184?
v=app_2373072738&ref=ts#!
Twitter: http://twitter.com/djnf

Established in 1958 in Delaware.

Donor: Dow Jones Foundation.

Foundation type: Independent foundation.

Financial data (yr. ended 12/31/13): Assets, $373,612 (M); gifts received, $886,900; expenditures, $557,049; qualifying distributions, $548,149; giving activities include $350,583 for 34 grants (high: $52,483; low: $3,000), and $55,000 for 56 grants to individuals (high: $1,000; low: $500).

Purpose and activities: Programs include editing internships (up to 100) for upper-level and graduate college students; reporting internships (up to 10) for sophomore and junior minority college students; grants to colleges and universities supporting workshops for high school minority students; grants to colleges and universities operating workshops for high school journalism teachers and publications advisers; selection of the National High School Journalism Teacher of the Year; and journalism career guides. See Fund web site for more information.

Fields of interest: Communication media; Ethnic and racial groups.

Type of support: Fellowships; Internships.

Limitations: Giving on a national basis. No grants for building or endowment funds, research, publications, or conferences and seminars; no loans.

Publications: Application guidelines; Annual report; Grants list.

Application information: Guidelines available for programs listed in the fund's annual report and on foundation web site. Unsolicited proposals are welcome as long as they directly relate to students' pursuit of careers in journalism. Application form required.

Initial approach: Letter and telephone
Copies of proposal: 1
Deadline(s): Submit proposal preferably in Sept.; deadline Oct. 1. See Web site for various program deadlines

Board meeting date(s): May and Nov.
Final notification: Dec. 1

Officers and Directors: Richard J. Levine, Pres. and Director; Robin Gibson Sawyer, Secy. and Director; Paul Schmidt, Treas. and Director; Don E. Carter, Dir. Emeritus; Ken Herts; Richard S. Holden; Thomas E. Engleman; Diana Mitsu Klos; Neal Lipschutz; Laurence J. O'Donnell; Dr. Reginald Owens; Dr. Russell G. Todd.

Number of staff: 3 full-time professional; 1 full-time support; 1 part-time support.

EIN: 136021439

5326
The Dreman Foundation Inc.

(formerly David Dreman Foundation)
c/o Contrarian Services Corp.
Harborside Financial Center Plz., Ste. 800-801
Jersey City, NJ 07311-4037

Established in 1986 in New Jersey.

Donor: David N. Dreman.

Foundation type: Independent foundation.

Financial data (yr. ended 11/30/13): Assets, $8,178,975 (M); expenditures, $327,255; qualifying distributions, $321,778; giving activities include $320,762 for 30 grants (high: $123,000; low: $500).

Purpose and activities: Giving primarily for the arts, education and health organizations.

Fields of interest: Arts and culture; Museums; Education; Higher education; Foundations; Diseases and conditions; Human services; Child welfare.

Type of support: General support; Convening; Publications; Fellowships; Research.

Limitations: Applications not accepted. No grants to individuals.

Application information: Unsolicited requests for funds not accepted.

Officers: David N. Dreman, Pres.; Holly Dreman, V.P.; Peter B. Neubauer, Secy.

Trustees: Solly Dreman; Sherrill Hershberg.

Number of staff: 1 full-time professional.

EIN: 222764782

5327
Murray & Florence Dweck Family Foundation

2 Ethel Rd., Ste. 205A
Edison, NJ 08817-2839

Established in 1986 in New Jersey.

Donors: Murray Dweck; Florence Dweck.

Foundation type: Independent foundation.

Financial data (yr. ended 06/30/14): Assets, $1,890,771; expenditures, $137,968; qualifying distributions, $134,095.

Fields of interest: Arts and culture; Judaism.

Limitations: Applications not accepted. Giving primarily in the greater New York, NY, area. No grants to individuals.

Application information: Unsolicited requests for funds not accepted.

Officers: Murray Dweck, Pres.; Joseph Bijou, V.P.; Florence Dweck, V.P.

EIN: 222796727

5328
Dexter & Carol Earle Foundation
c/o Citrin Cooperman & Co., LLP
290 W. Mount Pleasant Ave.
Livingston, NJ 07039

Established in 1989 in New York.
Donor: Dexter D. Earle.
Foundation type: Independent foundation.
Financial data (yr. ended 01/31/13): Assets, $166,067 (M); expenditures, $226,249; qualifying distributions, $220,450; giving activities include $220,450 for 17 grants (high: $100,000; low: $100).
Fields of interest: Elementary and secondary education; Higher education; Diseases and conditions; Human services.
Limitations: Applications not accepted. Giving primarily in NJ; some funding also in CT and VT. No grants to individuals.
Application information: Contributes only to pre-selected organizations.
Trustees: Carol A. Earle; Dexter D. Earle.
Number of staff: None.
EIN: 133532028

5329
The EBB Point Foundation
P.O. Box 1501, NJ2-130-03-31
Pennington, NJ 08534-1501

Established in 1999 in Maryland.
Donors: Katherine Borsecnik; Eugene S. Weil.
Foundation type: Independent foundation.
Financial data (yr. ended 06/30/13): Assets, $3,849,849 (M); gifts received, $1,737,253; expenditures, $205,610; qualifying distributions, $187,670; giving activities include $175,138 for 37 grants (high: $40,000; low: $64).
Fields of interest: Education; Nonprofits; Diseases and conditions; Human services.
Type of support: General support; Regranting.
Limitations: Applications not accepted. Giving primarily in Washington, DC and MA. No grants to individuals.
Application information: Unsolicited requests for funds not accepted.
Directors: Katherine Borsecnik; Eugene S. Weil.
EIN: 522207573

5330
Edison Properties Newark Foundation
(formerly Edison Properties Charitable Trust of Newark)
100 Washington St.
Newark, NJ 07102-3024
Contact: Margery Gottesman, Tr.

Donor: JWG Equipment Assocs.
Foundation type: Company-sponsored foundation.
Financial data (yr. ended 12/31/13): Assets, $6,949,323 (M); expenditures, $324,089; qualifying distributions, $320,783; giving activities include $317,435 for 56 grants (high: $48,000; low: $50).
Purpose and activities: The foundation supports organizations involved with arts and culture, education, human services, and community development. Special emphasis is directed toward programs designed to improve the quality of life in Newark, New Jersey.

Fields of interest: Arts and culture; Education.
Type of support: General support.
Limitations: Applications accepted. Giving primarily in Newark, NJ. No grants to individuals.
Application information: Application form required.
Initial approach: Proposal
Deadline(s): None
Trustees: Gary Debode; Jerome Gottesman; Margery Gottesman.
EIN: 226872667

5331
Martin & Rebecca Eisenberg Foundation
c/o Rockdale Capital
650 Liberty Ave.
Union, NJ 07083-8130

Established in 2003 in New York.
Donors: Martin Eisenberg; Warren Eisenberg.
Foundation type: Independent foundation.
Financial data (yr. ended 12/31/14): Assets, $1,558,946; gifts received, $1,445,200; expenditures, $216,824; qualifying distributions, $211,725 and $0 for set-asides.
Fields of interest: Visual arts; Education; Health; Judaism; Human services; Domestic violence shelters; Victims of crime and abuse.
Limitations: Applications not accepted. Giving primarily in NY. No grants to individuals.
Application information: Unsolicited requests for funds not accepted.
Officers: Martin Eisenberg, Pres. and Treas.; Rebecca Eisenberg, Secy.
Director: Ronald Eisenberg.
EIN: 800063656

5332
Elizabethtown Healthcare Foundation
P.O. Box 259
Elizabeth, NJ 07207-0259 (908) 994-8065
E-mail: dfletcher@trinitas.org

Established in 2002 in New Jersey.
Foundation type: Independent foundation.
Financial data (yr. ended 12/31/14): Assets, $11,447,777; expenditures, $718,649; qualifying distributions, $378,583.
Purpose and activities: Giving to strengthen existing and/or seed innovative initiatives that address health care and related needs in Elizabeth, NJ, and surrounding communities. Funding priorities include services for women and children, and mental health.
Fields of interest: Health.
Type of support: Program evaluations; Equipment; Program development; Seed money; Curriculum development.
Limitations: Applications accepted. Giving limited to Elizabeth, NJ, and surrounding communities. No support for lobbying activities or religious activities. No grants to individuals, or for budget deficits or general operating expenses, endowments, lending, research, annual appeals, fundraising dinners or journals, scholarships, attendance at workshops, or for conferences.
Publications: Application guidelines.
Application information: Application form required.
Initial approach: Proposal
Copies of proposal: 2
Deadline(s): Apr. 10 or Oct. 10
Board meeting date(s): May and Nov.

Officers: Mortimer Gershman, Chair.; Richard Width, Esq., Vice-Chair.; David A. Fletcher, Pres.; Alice A. Holzapfel, Secy.; David Gibbons, Treas.
Directors: John R. Blasi, Esq.; Richard Mackessey, MD; Victor Richel; Laurie Westra.
Number of staff: 1 part-time professional.
EIN: 222473474

5333
Joseph H. & Barbara I. Ellis Foundation
c/o Leo Group
1 Main St., Ste. 202
Chatham, NJ 07928-2426

Established in 1987 in New York.
Donor: Joseph H. Ellis.
Foundation type: Independent foundation.
Financial data (yr. ended 06/30/13): Assets, $1,868,699 (M); expenditures, $297,214; qualifying distributions, $297,214; giving activities include $297,214 for grants.
Purpose and activities: Giving primarily for environmental conservation, higher education, Jewish organizations, and community services.
Fields of interest: Education; Higher education; Environment; Wildlife biodiversity; Plant biodiversity; Nonprofits; Judaism; Human services.
Type of support: General support; Regranting.
Limitations: Applications not accepted. Giving primarily in New York, NY, Washington, DC and Arlington, VA. No grants to individuals.
Application information: Contributes only to pre-selected organizations.
Trustees: Barbara I. Ellis; Joseph H. Ellis.
EIN: 133437916

5334
Engel Family Foundation Inc.
48 Hook Rd.
Bayonne, NJ 07002-5007 (201) 339-0700

Established in 1985 in Delaware.
Donors: Tina Brachfeld; Andre S. Engel; Barry Engel; Blima Engel; Margaret I. Fishman; Rivky Paskesz; Tilly Roth; Miriam Stahl; Gel Spice Co., Inc.; Gershon Engel; Jacob Engel; Sherman Engel; Aaron Stahl; Philip Roth; Ary Engel.
Foundation type: Independent foundation.
Financial data (yr. ended 05/31/14): Assets, $756,615 (M); gifts received, $270,000; expenditures, $214,457; qualifying distributions, $213,926; giving activities include $213,926 for 34 grants (high: $50,600; low: $1,000).
Purpose and activities: Giving primarily to organizations that are engaged in Jewish religious education, including Jewish temples and yeshivas.
Fields of interest: Education; Nonprofits; Religion; Judaism; Human services.
Type of support: Regranting.
Limitations: Applications accepted. Giving primarily in Brooklyn, NY. No grants to individuals.
Application information: Application form required.
Initial approach: Letter
Deadline(s): None
Trustees: Andre S. Engel; Gershon Engel.
EIN: 133327931

5335

The Robert G. & Jane V. Engel Foundation, Inc.
80 Wearimus Rd.
P.O. Box 42
Ho-Ho-Kus, NJ   07423-0042

Established in 1986 in New Jersey.
Donors: Robert G. Engel; Jane V. Engel.
Foundation type: Independent foundation.
Financial data (yr. ended 09/30/14): Assets, $1,191,098 (M); gifts received, $260,236; expenditures, $309,045; qualifying distributions, $281,736; giving activities include $275,486 for 64 grants (high: $50,376; low: $100).
Purpose and activities: Giving for higher education, wildlife conservation, and health care.
Fields of interest: Museums; Higher education; Domesticated animals; Foundations; Health; Christianity.
Limitations: Applications accepted. Giving primarily in NJ and NY. No grants to individuals.
Application information:
  Initial approach: Letter
  Deadline(s): None
Officer: Jane V. Engel, Pres.
Trustees: Elizabeth Hunter Engel; Robert A. Engel; Jennifer E. Young.
EIN: 222764445

5336

The Lester M. and Sally Entin Foundation
c/o Marc J. Lenner
P.O. Box 2189
Clifton, NJ   07015-2189

Foundation type: Independent foundation.
Financial data (yr. ended 12/31/13): Assets, $8,826,242 (M); expenditures, $540,527; qualifying distributions, $348,850; giving activities include $348,850 for 37 grants (high: $115,000; low: $500).
Purpose and activities: Giving primarily to Jewish organizations; funding also for health organizations, education, and human services.
Fields of interest: Education; Nonprofits; Diseases and conditions; Breast cancer; Judaism; Human services.
Type of support: Regranting.
Limitations: Applications not accepted. Giving primarily in NJ, and NY. No grants to individuals.
Application information: Contributes only to pre-selected organizations.
Officers and Directors: Marc J. Lenner, Pres. and Treas. and Director; Robert A. Hoberman, V.P. and Secy. and Director.
EIN: 650758118

5337

Environmental Endowment for New Jersey, Inc.
P.O. Box 3446
Trenton, NJ   08619-0446   (609) 584-1593
Contact: Joan Burkholtz, Secy.
FAX: (609) 584-5341; *E-mail:* info@eenj.org; *Main URL:* http://www.eenj.org
Grants List: http://www.eenj.org/home/grant-list

Established in 1991 in New Jersey.
Foundation type: Independent foundation.

Financial data (yr. ended 04/30/13): Assets, $5,752,802 (M); expenditures, $331,478; qualifying distributions, $246,386; giving activities include $225,000 for 16 grants (high: $20,000; low: $5,000).
Purpose and activities: The endowment distributes funds from settlements of lawsuits brought to enforce compliance with the federal Clean Water Act. The projects funded must comply with the Court Orders entered in those cases and must have a clear and direct linkage to the waters impacted by the violations underlying the Clean Water Act enforcement cases.
Fields of interest: Environment.
Type of support: Program development; Seed money.
Limitations: Applications accepted. Giving primarily in NJ. No grants to individuals, endowments, or for general operating or capital expenditures.
Application information: Application guidelines available on foundation's web site. Application form required.
  Initial approach: Proposal
  Copies of proposal: 9
  Deadline(s): Dec. 15
Officers and Trustees: James F. Hall, Pres. and Trustee; Cindy Zipf, V.P. and Trustee; Joan Burkholtz, Secy.; Ronald Sprague, Treas. and Trustee; Sharon Finlayson; Nancy Hedinger; Doug O'Mally; Eric Stiles.
EIN: 223107878

5338

ESH Charitable Foundation
115 Christopher Columbus Dr., Ste. 400
Jersey City, NJ   07302-5526

Donors: 107 Kensington Partners, LLC; Ephraim Hasenfeld; Shoshana Hasenfeld; H.E. Northgate, Ltd.; New Hudson Partners, LLC; H.E. Sevilla, Inc.; Hasenfeld Stein, Inc.; 115 CCD Partners, LP.
Foundation type: Independent foundation.
Financial data (yr. ended 12/31/13): Assets, $0 (M); gifts received, $158,641; expenditures, $170,984; qualifying distributions, $170,984; giving activities include $170,984 for 822 grants (high: $4,000; low: $15).
Purpose and activities: Giving to Jewish faith based organizations.
Fields of interest: Nonprofits; Judaism.
Type of support: General support; Regranting.
Limitations: Applications not accepted.
Application information: Unsolicited requests for funds not accepted.
Trustees: Ephraim Hasenfeld; Shoshana Hasenfeld.
EIN: 113429423

5339

Essig Enright Family Foundation
66 Witherspoon St., Ste. 320
Princeton, NJ   08540

Established in 2003 in New Jersey.
Donors: Erin S. Enright; Stuart M. Essig.
Foundation type: Independent foundation.
Financial data (yr. ended 12/31/13): Assets, $9,919,834 (M); expenditures, $262,317; qualifying distributions, $256,588; giving activities include $256,588 for grants.

Fields of interest: Education; University education; Medical education; Diseases and conditions; Child welfare.
Type of support: General support; Scholarships.
Limitations: Applications not accepted. Giving primarily in NJ. No grants to individuals.
Application information: Unsolicited requests for funds not accepted.
Officers: Stuart M. Essig, Pres.; Erin S. Enright, Secy.-Treas.
Trustee: John Bell Henneman III.
EIN: 680533258

5340

The Heller Family Foundation, Inc.
c/o Ronald I. Heller
74 Farview Rd.
Tenafly, NJ   07670-2322
Contact: Ronald I. Heller

Foundation type: Independent foundation.
Financial data (yr. ended 11/30/13): Assets, $6,305,981 (M); expenditures, $272,861; qualifying distributions, $261,035; giving activities include $238,950 for 25 grants (high: $55,000; low: $100).
Fields of interest: Higher education; Human services.
Limitations: Applications not accepted. Giving primarily in NY and PA.
Application information: Unsolicited requests for funds not accepted.
Officers: Ronald Heller, Pres.; Joyce L. Heller, Treas.
Board Members: Lawrence Kupferberg; Rachel Scott.
EIN: 223556325

5341

Farrington Foundation
P.O. Box 1501, NJ2-130-03-31
Pennington, NJ   08534-1501

Established in 2000 in Florida.
Donor: Ethel Smith.
Foundation type: Independent foundation.
Financial data (yr. ended 02/28/13): Assets, $2,369,770 (M); expenditures, $373,298; qualifying distributions, $358,637; giving activities include $318,657 for 12 grants (high: $100,000; low: $2,057).
Fields of interest: Arts and culture; Domesticated animals.
Type of support: General support.
Limitations: Applications not accepted. Giving primarily in FL and MA. No grants to individuals.
Application information: Unsolicited requests for funds not accepted.
Trustees: E. N. Bagshawe; Merrill Lynch Trust Co.
EIN: 223741108

5342

The Farris Charitable Trust
71 Crest Dr.
Bernardsville, NJ   07924-1707
Contact: David Farris

Established in 1999 in New Jersey.
Donors: David J. Farris; Jill Farris.
Foundation type: Independent foundation.

Financial data (yr. ended 12/31/13): Assets,
$1,995,722 (M); gifts received, $1,780;
expenditures, $334,677; qualifying distributions,
$333,255; giving activities include $332,100 for 7
grants (high: $301,000; low: $100).
Fields of interest: Arts and culture; Health;
Diseases and conditions.
Limitations: Applications not accepted. Giving
primarily in NJ. No grants to individuals.
Application information: Unsolicited requests for
funds not accepted.
Trustees: David J. Farris; Jill Farris; Jennifer Louise
Moss; Julie Ellen Valentine.
EIN: 137148226

5343
Jeffrey & Debra Feinstein Foundation
c/o Linda Kao, Rockdale Capital
650 Liberty Ave.
Union, NJ   07083-8130

Established in 2003 in New York.
Donors: Jeffrey Feinstein; Leonard Feinstein.
Foundation type: Independent foundation.
Financial data (yr. ended 12/31/14): Assets,
$146,787 (M); expenditures, $221,450; qualifying
distributions, $217,575; giving activities include
$216,600 for 24 grants (high: $35,000; low: $500).
Fields of interest: Arts and culture; Education;
Nonprofits; Health; Diseases and conditions;
Judaism.
Type of support: Research; Regranting.
Limitations: Applications not accepted. Giving
primarily in NY. No grants to individuals.
Application information: Unsolicited requests for
funds not accepted.
Officers: Jeffrey Feinstein, Pres. and Treas.; Debra
Feinstein, Secy.
Director: Richard Feinstein.
EIN: 800063654

5344
Feldstein Medical Foundation, Inc.
c/o SMF
855 Valley Rd.
Clifton, NJ   07013-2441
E-mail: questions@feldsteinmedicalfoundation.org;
Main URL: http://
www.feldsteinmedicalfoundation.org
Grants List: http://
www.feldsteinmedicalfoundation.org/
PriorFunding.html

Established in 2007 in New Jersey.
Donors: Creston Electronics, Inc.; George Feldstein.
Foundation type: Independent foundation.
Financial data (yr. ended 05/31/13): Assets,
$5,535,029 (M); expenditures, $280,268;
qualifying distributions, $240,826; giving activities
include $239,592 for 4 grants (high: $60,000; low:
$59,592).
Purpose and activities: Giving primarily to fill a void
in the funding of medical research involving new
areas of research and smaller projects, especially
basic science, translation and implementation
studies, early clinical research and education.
Fields of interest: Medical education; Diseases and
conditions; Science.
Type of support: Research; Grants to individuals.
Limitations: Applications not accepted. Giving
primarily in NJ and NY.

Application information: Unsolicited requests for
funds not accepted.
Officers: David Feldstein, Pres.; Wendy King, V.P.;
Anne Baretz, Secy.; Daniel Feldstein, Treas.
EIN: 260349769

5345
Feline Friends Inc.
96 Oval Rd.
Essex Fells, NJ   07021-1521   (973) 228-2725
Contact: Sharon E. Schaedel, Tr.

Established in 2001 in New Jersey.
Donors: Gary Schaedel; Sharon E. Schaedel; Stacy
L. Frangella; Kimberly Hoover.
Foundation type: Operating foundation.
Financial data (yr. ended 12/31/13): Assets,
$10,002 (M); gifts received, $237,325;
expenditures, $253,575; qualifying distributions,
$250,553; giving activities include $250,553 for 5
grants (high: $188,660; low: $352).
Purpose and activities: Giving primarily for abused
and abandoned animals.
Fields of interest: Domesticated animals; Veterinary
medicine.
Limitations: Applications accepted. Giving primarily
in NJ.
Application information:
  Initial approach: Proposal
  Deadline(s): None
Trustees: Stacey L. Frangella; Kimberly Hoover;
Sharon E. Schaedel.
EIN: 223767315

5346
Fellstone Foundation, Inc.
c/o Porzio Bromberg and Newman, PC
100 Southgate Pkwy.
P.O. Box 1997
Morristown, NJ   07962-1997

Established in 1996 in New Jersey.
Donor: Francis H. Barker.
Foundation type: Independent foundation.
Financial data (yr. ended 10/31/14): Assets,
$979,465 (M); expenditures, $335,240; qualifying
distributions, $319,567; giving activities include
$319,000 for 13 grants (high: $100,000; low:
$1,000).
Fields of interest: Higher education; Diseases and
conditions; Sports and recreation.
Type of support: Research; Public engagement and
education.
Limitations: Applications not accepted. No grants to
individuals.
Application information: Unsolicited requests for
funds not accepted.
Officers and Trustees: Francis H. Barker, Pres. and
Trustee; Daryl S. Barker, Secy.-Treas. and Trustee;
Bruce S. Barker; Doane B. Weideman.
EIN: 311485263

5347
George & Patricia Ann Fisher Foundation
P.O. Box 1501, NJ2-130-03-31
Pennington, NJ   08534-1501

Established in 1995 in New York.
Donors: Ann Fisher; George Fisher.
Foundation type: Independent foundation.

Financial data (yr. ended 12/31/13): Assets,
$1,423,007 (M); expenditures, $227,573;
qualifying distributions, $215,849; giving activities
include $206,000 for 16 grants (high: $70,000;
low: $2,500).
Fields of interest: Higher education; Health; Human
services.
Limitations: Applications not accepted. Giving
primarily in Rochester, MN, NY, and Seattle, WA. No
grants to individuals.
Application information: Contributes only to
pre-selected organizations.
Trustees: Ann Fisher; George Fisher.
EIN: 161466669

5348
The Florin Family Foundation, Inc.
c/o Richard Florin
331 Changebridge Rd.
P.O. Box 189
Pine Brook, NJ   07058-9581

Established in 1995 in New Jersey.
Donor: Westport Corp.
Foundation type: Company-sponsored foundation.
Financial data (yr. ended 12/31/13): Assets,
$1,564,073 (M); gifts received, $500,000;
expenditures, $290,169; qualifying distributions,
$277,960; giving activities include $277,900 for 58
grants (high: $128,236; low: $36).
Purpose and activities: The foundation supports
community foundations and organizations involved
with higher education, domestic violence
prevention, family services, and Judaism.
Fields of interest: Community and economic
development; Religion; Human services.
Type of support: General support.
Limitations: Applications not accepted. Giving
primarily in MA, NJ, and NY. No grants to individuals.
Application information: Contributes only to
pre-selected organizations.
Officers: Richard Florin, Pres. and Treas.; Thelma
Florin, Secy.
Trustee: John Florin.
EIN: 223347455

5349
Fox Foundation
P.O. Box 753
Hammonton, NJ   08037-0753   (609) 561-8916

Established in 1956 in New Jersey.
Foundation type: Independent foundation.
Financial data (yr. ended 12/31/14): Assets,
$5,396,494; gifts received, $0; expenditures,
$280,809; qualifying distributions, $280,809.
Fields of interest: Arts and culture; Higher
education; Nonprofits; Hospital care; Diseases and
conditions; Christianity; Sports and recreation;
Human services; Child welfare.
Type of support: Annual campaigns; Endowments;
Scholarships; Research; Research and evaluation;
Regranting.
Limitations: Applications accepted. Giving primarily
in NJ. No grants to individuals.
Application information:
  Initial approach: Proposal
  Copies of proposal: 1
  Deadline(s): None
Trustees: Joy Fox Daly; Mark B. Fox; Holly Isenberg.
EIN: 226057667

5350
Frank Family Charity Fund Inc

(formerly Frank Charity Fund, Inc.)
c/o Milton Frank
2 Norfolk St.
Bergenfield, NJ   07621-3907

Established in 2002 in New Jersey.
Donors: Milton Frank; Stefan Frank.
Foundation type: Independent foundation.
Financial data (yr. ended 12/31/13): Assets,
$348,131 (M); gifts received, $136,000;
expenditures, $405,751; qualifying distributions,
$405,751; giving activities include $405,583 for 28
grants (high: $233,300; low: $1,000).
Fields of interest: Judaism.
Limitations: Applications not accepted. Giving
primarily in NJ and NY.
Application information: Unsolicited requests for
funds not accepted.
Officers: Milton Frank, Pres.; Stefan Frank, Treas.
EIN: 364516521

5351
The Anne & Gerald Freedman Charitable Foundation Inc

543 Riverside Dr. E.
Princeton, NJ   08540-4007

Established in 1997 in New Jersey.
Donors: Gerald H. Freedman; Anne L. Freedman.
Foundation type: Independent foundation.
Financial data (yr. ended 03/31/15): Assets,
$2,620,121 (M); gifts received, $119,433;
expenditures, $166,940; qualifying distributions,
$164,725; giving activities include $164,725 for 92
grants (high: $31,100; low: $125).
Purpose and activities: Giving primarily for Jewish
agencies; some giving also for arts and culture and
health care.
Fields of interest: Education; University education;
Health; Religion.
Type of support: General support.
Limitations: Applications not accepted. Giving
primarily in NJ. No grants to individuals.
Application information: Unsolicited requests for
funds not accepted.
Officers: Anne L. Freedman, Chair.; Deborah S.
Freedman, Exec. Secy.; Barry J. Freedman, Treas.
EIN: 223510720

5352
Twilight & Marc Freedman Foundation

P.O. Box 1501, NJ2-130-03-31
Pennington, NJ   08534-1501

Established in 2001 in Texas.
Donors: Marc Freedman; Twilight Freedman.
Foundation type: Independent foundation.
Financial data (yr. ended 12/31/13): Assets,
$2,058,229 (M); gifts received, $243,928;
expenditures, $265,335; qualifying distributions,
$254,210; giving activities include $247,500 for 21
grants (high: $75,000; low: $500).
Fields of interest: Higher education; Nonprofits;
Cancers; Protestantism; Human services; Child
welfare.
Type of support: Regranting.
Limitations: Applications not accepted. No grants to
individuals.

Application information: Unsolicited requests for
funds not accepted.
Officers: Marc Freedman, Pres. .; Twilight
Freedman, V.P.
Directors: Brian Anderson; Gary Anderson; Wendy
Freedman; Jennifer Lynn Holsombach; Monica
Freedman Snideman.
EIN: 760683871

5353
Freelander Family Charitable Trust

239 Greenway Rd.
Ridgewood, NJ   07450-4701

Established in 1994 in Massachusetts.
Foundation type: Independent foundation.
Financial data (yr. ended 12/31/14): Assets,
$4,967,051 (M); gifts received, $6,377;
expenditures, $219,906; qualifying distributions,
$177,630; giving activities include $177,630 for 29
grants (high: $35,000; low: $360).
Fields of interest: Arts and culture; Education;
Judaism; Adolescents; People with disabilities;
People with HIV/AIDS.
Limitations: Applications not accepted. Giving
primarily in Worcester, MA. No grants to individuals.
Application information: Contributes only to
pre-selected organizations.
   Board meeting date(s): Apr. 1 & Nov. 1
Trustees: Daniel H. Freelander; Michael S.
Freelander.
EIN: 043254349

5354
The Frelinghuysen Foundation

P.O. Box 729
Far Hills, NJ   07931-0729   (908) 439-3499

Established in 1950 in New Jersey.
Foundation type: Independent foundation.
Financial data (yr. ended 12/31/14): Assets,
$2,217,633; expenditures, $390,071; qualifying
distributions, $350,759.
Fields of interest: Arts and culture; Secondary
education; Higher education; Environment;
Nonprofits; Hospital care; Human services.
Type of support: General support; Regranting;
Capital campaigns; Equipment; Fellowships;
Internships.
Limitations: Applications accepted. Giving primarily
in NJ and NY. No grants to individuals.
Application information: Application form required.
   Initial approach: Typed letter
   Copies of proposal: 1
   Deadline(s): None
Officers: George L.K. Frelinghuysen, Pres. and
Treas.; Adaline H. Frelinghuysen, V.P. and Secy.;
Tina Marie Hinck, Compt.
Directors: Alice C. Frelinghuysen; Frederick
Frelinghuysen; Henry Frelinghuysen; Peter
Frelinghuysen; Virginia R. Frelinghuysen; Elizabeth
Ratiff; Beatrice van Roijen.
EIN: 221723755

5355
Carl & Sylvia Freyer Family Foundation Inc.

302 Fountain Rd.
Englewood, NJ   07631-4403

Established in 1989 in New Jersey.

Donors: Edco Supply Corp.; Carl J. Freyer; Sylvia
Freyer.
Foundation type: Independent foundation.
Financial data (yr. ended 03/31/13): Assets,
$748,050 (M); gifts received, $250,000;
expenditures, $319,689; qualifying distributions,
$316,984; giving activities include $316,984 for 21
grants (high: $90,000; low: $25).
Purpose and activities: Funding primarily for Jewish
temples and agencies.
Fields of interest: Nonprofits; Judaism; Human
services.
Type of support: Regranting.
Limitations: Applications not accepted. Giving
primarily in NJ and NY. No grants to individuals.
Application information: Contributes only to
pre-selected organizations.
Officer: Sylvia Freyer, Pres. and Treas.
Directors: Maura Ruskin; Louisa Susman.
EIN: 223000538

5356
Sid Friedman Charitable Support Organization

P.O. Box 1501, NJ2-130-03-31
Pennington, NJ   08534-1501

Donor: Sid Friedman Admin Trust.
Foundation type: Independent foundation.
Financial data (yr. ended 12/31/13): Assets,
$1,365,576 (M); gifts received, $1,499,778;
expenditures, $171,858; qualifying distributions,
$171,410; giving activities include $170,863 for
grants.
Limitations: Applications not accepted.
Application information: Unsolicited requests for
funds not accepted.
Trustee: Bank of America, N.A.
EIN: 463994326

5357
Frog Crossing Foundation Inc.

c/o Stephanie Fein
1 The Crossing
North Caldwell, NJ   07006-4414

Established in 2002 in New Jersey.
Donor: Stephanie Fein.
Foundation type: Independent foundation.
Financial data (yr. ended 12/31/13): Assets,
$4,763,089 (M); gifts received, $65,000;
expenditures, $266,699; qualifying distributions,
$224,860; giving activities include $224,860 for 17
grants (high: $23,480; low: $8,400).
Fields of interest: Visual arts; Elementary and
secondary education; Animal welfare; Sports and
recreation.
Limitations: Applications not accepted. No grants to
individuals.
Application information: Contributes only to
pre-selected organizations.
Officers and Trustees: Stephanie Fein, Pres. and
Trustee; Patricia Berlinger, V.P. and Trustee; Cecile
Fein, Co-Secy. and Trustee; Peter Hollander,
Co-Secy. and Trustee; Barbara Katz, Treas. and
Trustee.
EIN: 571142242

5358
Fund for Newark Abbey Inc.
520 Martin Luther King, Jr. Blvd.
Newark, NJ 07102-1314

Donor: Catholic Seminary Foundation of Indianapolis.
Foundation type: Independent foundation.
Financial data (yr. ended 12/31/14): Assets, $3,994,227; expenditures, $223,880; qualifying distributions, $200,000.
Fields of interest: Education; Catholicism.
Limitations: Applications not accepted. Giving primarily in Newark, NJ.
Application information: Unsolicited requests for funds not accepted.
Trustees: Elizabeth M. Durkin, Esq.; Eugene O'Hara; Melvin Valvano.
EIN: 223846806

5359
The Michael Fux Foundation, Inc.
187 State Rte. 36
West Long Branch, NJ 07764-1327

Established in 2006 in Unspecified.
Donors: John Rallis; The Peter Jay Sharp Foundation; Michael Fux; Gloria Rubin; Tom Kuhn; The Rallis Foundation.
Foundation type: Independent foundation.
Financial data (yr. ended 12/31/12): Assets, $308,622 (M); gifts received, $666,832; expenditures, $503,993; qualifying distributions, $211,500; giving activities include $211,500 for grants.
Fields of interest: Foundations; Nonprofits; Health; Specialty hospital care.
Type of support: Regranting.
Limitations: Applications not accepted. Giving primarily in FL. No grants to individuals.
Application information: Contributes only to pre-selected organizations.
Directors: Michael Fux; Michael C. Fux; Gloria Rubin.
EIN: 204210046

5360
Gabrellian Family Foundation Inc.
95 Rte. 17 N.
Paramus, NJ 07652 (201) 845-4100
Contact: Ani Gabrellian, V.P.

Donor: Mark Ani Gabrellian.
Foundation type: Independent foundation.
Financial data (yr. ended 12/31/13): Assets, $2,981,247 (M); gifts received, $1,000,000; expenditures, $387,432; qualifying distributions, $375,000; giving activities include $375,000 for 5 grants (high: $300,000; low: $5,000).
Fields of interest: Education; Human services.
Application information: Application form required.
Initial approach: Proposal
Deadline(s): None
Officers: Mark Gabrellian, Pres.; Ani Gabrellian, V.P.
Trustee: Joseph Scorese.
EIN: 223837793

5361
Albert and Janice Gamper Foundation
c/o Albert Gamper
475 Holland Rd.
Far Hills, NJ 07931-2642

Established in 2000 in New Jersey.
Donors: Albert Gamper; Janice Gamper.
Foundation type: Independent foundation.
Financial data (yr. ended 12/31/12): Assets, $565,550 (M); expenditures, $202,928; qualifying distributions, $200,000; giving activities include $200,000 for 1 grant.
Fields of interest: Performing arts; University education; Television.
Type of support: General support.
Limitations: Applications not accepted. Giving primarily in NJ. No grants to individuals.
Application information: Unsolicited requests for funds not accepted.
Trustees: Albert R. Gamper, Jr.; Christopher Gamper; Janice Gamper; Jennifer Gamper Meenan.
EIN: 223770735

5362
The Jose M. Garcia Foundation Inc.
851 Franklin Lakes Rd.
Franklin Lakes, NJ 07417-2242 (201) 891-2112
Contact: Donald H. Quinn, Pres.

Foundation type: Independent foundation.
Financial data (yr. ended 10/31/13): Assets, $8,155,144 (M); expenditures, $618,135; qualifying distributions, $389,628; giving activities include $343,500 for 9 grants (high: $160,000; low: $2,000).
Purpose and activities: Giving primarily to Christian and Lutheran churches and organizations, as well as to other religious organizations; funding also for children, youth and social services.
Fields of interest: Philanthropy; Religion; Christianity; Tribal and indigenous religions; Human services; Child welfare; People of Asian descent; Indigenous peoples; Homeless people.
International interests: Asia; Latin America.
Limitations: Applications accepted. Giving primarily in northern NJ; also giving on an international basis. No grants for administrative costs.
Application information: Application form required.
Initial approach: Letter
Deadline(s): Oct. 31
Officers: Donald H. Quinn, Pres.; Ella Glover, V.P.; Gordon D. Meyer, V.P.; Laura Figueroa, Secy.-Treas.
EIN: 223369956

5363
Gardinier Environmental Fund Inc.
300 High St.
Mount Holly, NJ 08060-1406

Foundation type: Independent foundation.
Financial data (yr. ended 12/31/12): Assets, $3,752,803 (M); expenditures, $218,197; qualifying distributions, $176,912; giving activities include $176,912 for grants.
Fields of interest: Arts and culture; Domesticated animals; Human services.
Limitations: Applications not accepted.
Application information: Unsolicited requests for funds not accepted.

Officers: Eugene Wentzel, Pres.; James Saxton, V.P.; Suzanne Kourlesis, Secy.
Trustee: Paul A. King.
EIN: 264786209

5364
Garfinkle Family Charitable Trust
c/o Weinberg Lieberman, C.P.A.s
155 Passaic Ave., Ste. 420
Fairfield, NJ 07004-3562

Established in 1987 in New York.
Donors: Sandor A. Garfinkle; Lorraine Garfinkle.
Foundation type: Independent foundation.
Financial data (yr. ended 12/31/13): Assets, $1,057,445 (M); gifts received, $30; expenditures, $163,274; qualifying distributions, $158,500; giving activities include $158,500 for 8 grants (high: $85,000; low: $500).
Fields of interest: Arts and culture; Judaism; Human services.
Limitations: Applications not accepted. Giving primarily in FL, NJ, and NY. No grants to individuals.
Application information: Unsolicited requests for funds not accepted.
Trustee: Lorraine Garfinkle.
EIN: 133411139

5365
Joanne W. Gauntt Charitable Foundation
P.O. Box 1501 NJ2-130-03-31
Pennington, NJ 08534-1501 (609) 274-6834

Established in 1999 in Florida.
Donors: Joanne W. Gauntt; Joanne W. Gauntt Trust.
Foundation type: Independent foundation.
Financial data (yr. ended 12/31/13): Assets, $4,729,161 (M); expenditures, $214,504; qualifying distributions, $190,936; giving activities include $172,072 for 5 grants (high: $85,348; low: $21,681).
Fields of interest: Higher education; Animal welfare.
Limitations: Applications accepted. Giving limited to KY, TN and TX. No grants to individuals.
Application information:
Initial approach: Proposal
Deadline(s): None
Trustee: Merrill Lynch Trust Co.
EIN: 527018780

5366
Genie Energy Charitable Foundation
550 Broad St.
Newark, NJ 07102-4531

Donor: Genie Energy Ltd.
Foundation type: Independent foundation.
Financial data (yr. ended 12/31/13): Assets, $1,600,488 (M); gifts received, $300,000; expenditures, $284,500; qualifying distributions, $284,500; giving activities include $284,500 for 25 grants (high: $100,000; low: $500).
Fields of interest: Education; Religion; Judaism; Human services.
Limitations: Applications not accepted.
Application information: Unsolicited requests for funds not accepted.
Director: Avi Golden.
EIN: 462343565

5367
Gestetner Family Charitable Foundation
c/o Gestetner
1472 Oakwood Ave.
Lakewood, NJ 08701-1737 (732) 901-1956
Contact: Marcel Gestetner, Tr.

Established in 2001 in New Jersey.
Donor: Bridgewater Crossing Developers, LLC.
Foundation type: Independent foundation.
Financial data (yr. ended 12/31/13): Assets,
$467,036 (M); expenditures, $219,112; qualifying
distributions, $217,448; giving activities include
$217,448 for 228 grants (high: $10,100; low: $10).
Fields of interest: Education; Judaism; Human
services.
Limitations: Applications accepted. Giving primarily
in NJ and NY. No grants to individuals.
Application information: Application form required.
Initial approach: Proposal
Deadline(s): None
Trustees: Hindy Gestetner; Marcel Gestetner.
EIN: 912169243

5368
The A. & S. Giancristofaro Family Foundation, Inc.
5 Quill Pen Way
Warren, NJ 07059-5517

Established in 2000 in New Jersey.
Donors: Anthony Giancristofaro; Suzan
Giancristofaro.
Foundation type: Independent foundation.
Financial data (yr. ended 12/31/13): Assets,
$10,156; gifts received, $283,977; expenditures,
$251,691; qualifying distributions, $250,000;
giving activities include $250,000 for 2 grants (high:
$200,000; low: $50,000).
Fields of interest: Nonprofits.
Type of support: Regranting.
Limitations: Applications not accepted. Giving
primarily in NJ. No grants to individuals.
Application information: Unsolicited requests for
funds not accepted.
Officers: Anthony Giancristofaro, Pres. and Secy.;
Suzan Giancristofaro, Treas.
Trustees: Diana Golden; Cheryl Haney.
EIN: 223761116

5369
The Giants Foundation, Inc.
Giants Stadium
50 Rte. 120
East Rutherford, NJ 07073-2131 (201)
935-8111
Contact: Allison Stangeby, Exec. Dir.
E-mail: Stangeby@giants.nfl.net; For GameOn! Grant
Program: c/o Allison Stangeby, Community Rels.
Dept., tel.: (201) 939-1673; Main URL: http://
www.giants.com/Community.asp

Established in 1992 in New Jersey.
Donors: New York Football Giants, Inc.; The National
Football League; The Quaker Oats Co.; New Jersey
Sports & Exposition Authority; Nelson Ferreira;
Michael Brennan; Anheuser Busch; JPMorgan
Chase; Tim Shinn; Dan Ward; Christie Family
Foundation; Paul Queally; Craig Martone; McLane
Securities.
Foundation type: Company-sponsored foundation.

Financial data (yr. ended 12/31/13): Assets,
$248,888 (M); gifts received, $387,531;
expenditures, $401,498; qualifying distributions,
$401,498; giving activities include $377,000 for 44
grants (high: $50,000; low: $1,000).
Purpose and activities: The foundation supports
organizations involved with education, health, youth,
and civic affairs. Special emphasis is directed
toward programs designed to support
disadvantaged youth and their families.
Fields of interest: Education; Health; Public affairs;
American football; Family services; Youth services;
Domestic violence shelters; Low-income and poor
people.
Type of support: General support; Annual
campaigns; Equipment; Program development;
Scholarships.
Limitations: Applications accepted. Giving primarily
in the metropolitan New York, NY, area, including NJ.
Publications: Application guidelines; Annual report.
Application information: Proposals for GameOn!
Grant Program should include coaching and high
school histories. Visit website for detailed proposal
requirements.
Initial approach: Proposal
Copies of proposal: 1
Deadline(s): Oct. 1 to Dec. 31
Board meeting date(s): Feb.
Final notification: Following board review; Mar. for
GameOn! Grant Program
Officers: Laurie Tisch, Chair. and Director; John K.
Mara, Pres.; Jonathan Tisch, V.P.; Francis X. Mara,
Secy.-Treas.; Alison Stangeby, Exec. Dir.
EIN: 223183916

5370
Gibson Family Foundation
3 Royal Oak Dr.
Far Hills, NJ 07931-2569

Established in 2008 in New York.
Donor: Peter Gibson.
Foundation type: Independent foundation.
Financial data (yr. ended 06/30/14): Assets,
$21,654 (M); gifts received, $209,500;
expenditures, $261,604; qualifying distributions,
$259,000; giving activities include $259,000 for 9
grants (high: $100,000; low: $1,000).
Fields of interest: Higher education; Human
services; Youth services.
Type of support: General support.
Limitations: Applications not accepted. Giving
primarily in NJ and NY.
Application information: Unsolicited requests for
funds not accepted.
Directors: Dana Gibson; Peter Gibson.
EIN: 261316921

5371
The Thomas Glasser Foundation, Inc.
P.O. Box 206
Garwood, NJ 07027-0206

Established in 2001 in New Jersey.
Donors: Marlene Glasser; Gerald Glasser; W.D.
Pearson; Mrs. W.D. Pearson; Paul Scherer; Mrs.
Paul Scherer.
Foundation type: Independent foundation.
Financial data (yr. ended 12/31/13): Assets,
$8,894,812 (M); expenditures, $383,544;
qualifying distributions, $379,675; giving activities

include $379,675 for 33 grants (high: $125,000;
low: $250).
Fields of interest: Undergraduate education;
Nonprofits; Hospital care; Judaism; Human
services.
Type of support: Regranting.
Limitations: Applications not accepted. Giving
primarily in NJ. No grants to individuals.
Application information: Unsolicited requests for
funds not accepted.
Officer: Marlene Glasser, Pres.
Directors: Laura Glasser-Baker; Meg Bloom
Glasser; Marjorie Ticknor.
EIN: 223838044

5372
Edward & Marjorie Goldberger Foundation
c/o Kinzel & Co.
195 Fairfield Ave., Ste. 1D
West Caldwell, NJ 07006-6419

Established in 1957 in New York.
Donor: Marjorie Goldberger.
Foundation type: Independent foundation.
Financial data (yr. ended 12/31/13): Assets,
$2,673,535 (M); expenditures, $192,229;
qualifying distributions, $178,618; giving activities
include $160,000 for 75 grants (high: $8,000; low:
$106).
Fields of interest: Arts and culture; Art museums;
Higher education; Nonprofits; Health; Hospital care;
Diseases and conditions; Judaism; Human services.
Type of support: Regranting.
Limitations: Applications not accepted. Giving
primarily in NY. No grants to individuals.
Application information: Contributes only to
pre-selected organizations.
Officers: Ann Jurdem, Chair. and V.P.; Susan
Jacoby, Pres. and Secy.
EIN: 136084528

5373
Goldstein Charity Fund Inc.
1423 Cedar Row
Lakewood, NJ 08701-1515 (732) 370-1141
Contact: Joshua Goldstein, Tr.

Established in 2000 in New Jersey.
Donors: Joshua Goldstein; Marcel Gestetner.
Foundation type: Independent foundation.
Financial data (yr. ended 12/31/13): Assets,
$7,043,189 (M); gifts received, $1; expenditures,
$201,230; qualifying distributions, $197,985;
giving activities include $197,985 for 122 grants
(high: $18,000; low: $18).
Fields of interest: Judaism.
Application information: Application form required.
Initial approach: Proposal
Deadline(s): None
Trustees: Joshua Goldstein; Pearl Goldstein; Morris
Silberberg.
EIN: 223711451

5374
The Goodwin Foundation
P.O. Box 943
Atco, NJ 08004-2722

Established in 1987 in New Jersey.
Donor: Richard C. Goodwin.

Foundation type: Operating foundation.
Financial data (yr. ended 12/31/13): Assets, $3,692,875 (M); expenditures, $452,201; qualifying distributions, $255,050; giving activities include $255,050 for 31 grants (high: $110,000; low: $100).
Fields of interest: Higher education; Nonprofits; Human services.
Type of support: Regranting.
Limitations: Applications not accepted. Giving primarily in NJ.
Application information: Contributes only to pre-selected organizations.
Trustees: Joanna Goodwin; John Goodwin; Richard C. Goodwin; Robert Goodwin.
EIN: 222882244

5375
Grace Charity Foundation Inc.
11 Edgewood Terr.
Randolph, NJ   07869-2821
E-mail: jinsoo.kim@graceCfoundation.org; Main URL: http://www.gracecfoundation.org

Established in 2006 in New Jersey.
Foundation type: Independent foundation.
Financial data (yr. ended 12/31/13): Assets, $5,726,309 (M); expenditures, $223,237; qualifying distributions, $170,562; giving activities include $148,506 for 27 grants (high: $23,500; low: $1,000).
Fields of interest: Education.
Type of support: Individual development.
Limitations: Applications not accepted. Giving primarily in NJ and VA. No grants to individuals.
Application information: Contributes only to pre-selected organizations.
Directors: Jinsoo Kim; Seong Kim; Stephen Kim.
EIN: 208080868

5376
Burton G. and Anne C. Greenblatt Foundation, Inc.
111 Coolidge St.
South Plainfield, NJ   07080-3801
Contact: Anne C. Greenblatt, Tr.

Established in 1989 in New Jersey.
Donors: Anne C. Greenblatt; Burton G. Greenblatt; G & W Laboratories, Inc.
Foundation type: Independent foundation.
Financial data (yr. ended 03/31/13): Assets, $0 (M); gifts received, $275,865; expenditures, $195,723; qualifying distributions, $195,723; giving activities include $195,293 for 79+ grants (high: $44,018).
Purpose and activities: Giving only to cultural, educational, and religious organizations, with emphasis on Jewish organizations.
Fields of interest: Arts and culture; Museums; Education; University education; Graduate and professional education; Health; In-patient medical care; Judaism.
International interests: Israel.
Limitations: Applications accepted. Giving primarily in NJ. No grants to individuals.
Application information:
   Initial approach: Letter
   Deadline(s): None

Trustees: Anne C. Greenblatt; Burton G. Greenblatt; Ronald Greenblatt.
EIN: 521638050

5377
Paul & Beryl Greetin Foundation Inc.
10 Park Pl.
Morristown, NJ   07960-7120   (973) 455-1970
Contact: Martin Liberman Esq., Tr.

Established in 2000 in New Jersey.
Foundation type: Independent foundation.
Financial data (yr. ended 09/30/13): Assets, $8,270,961 (M); expenditures, $469,759; qualifying distributions, $384,000; giving activities include $314,000 for 29 grants (high: $30,000; low: $500).
Fields of interest: Education; Nonprofits; Health; Diseases and conditions; Diabetes; Cancers; Protestantism; Judaism; Human services; Females.
Type of support: Regranting; Research; Research and evaluation.
Limitations: Applications accepted. Giving primarily in NJ and NY.
Application information: Application form required.
   Initial approach: Letter
Trustees: Bruce E. Goldman; Eric Liberman; Martin Liberman.
EIN: 223684650

5378
Max & Helena Gurwicz Charitable Foundation
3430 Atlantic Ave.
Atlantic City, NJ   08401-6101   6096463345
Application address: c/o Herzel Gurwicz, Mgr., 331 Tilton Rd., Northfield, NJ 08225, tel.: (609) 646-0420

Donors: Helena Gurwicz; Herzel Gurwicz.
Foundation type: Independent foundation.
Financial data (yr. ended 12/31/14): Assets, $3,111,521; expenditures, $131,355; qualifying distributions, $130,940.
Fields of interest: Health; Judaism.
Limitations: Applications accepted. Giving primarily in NJ, and Brooklyn, NY. No grants to individuals.
Application information:
   Initial approach: Letter
   Deadline(s): None
Officers: Bonnie Gurwicz, Mgr.; Herzel Gurwicz, Mgr.
EIN: 226212405

5379
The HAIR Foundation
17 Avenue of Two Rivers S.
Rumson, NJ   07760-1812

Established in 2003 in New Jersey.
Foundation type: Independent foundation.
Financial data (yr. ended 12/31/13): Assets, $149,118 (M); expenditures, $198,568; qualifying distributions, $193,800; giving activities include $193,800 for 13 grants (high: $59,400; low: $1,800).
Fields of interest: Arts and culture; Religion.
Limitations: Applications not accepted. No grants to individuals.
Application information: Unsolicited requests for funds not accepted.

Trustees: Gerald Farber; Jonathan Herman; Russell Herman; Joel Markel.
EIN: 383694455

5380
Sam Halpern Family Foundation Inc.
200 Central Ave., Ste. 102
Mountainside, NJ   07092-2807

Established in 1986 in New Jersey.
Donors: Sam Halpern; Gladys Halpern.
Foundation type: Independent foundation.
Financial data (yr. ended 12/31/13): Assets, $7,283,282 (M); expenditures, $350,000; qualifying distributions, $343,700; giving activities include $343,700 for 13 grants (high: $100,000; low: $500).
Purpose and activities: Giving primarily to Jewish educational and family service organizations, and to Jewish federated giving programs.
Fields of interest: Education; Nonprofits; Judaism; Family services.
Type of support: General support; Regranting.
Limitations: Applications not accepted. Giving primarily in NJ; some giving in NY. No grants to individuals.
Application information: Contributes only to pre-selected organizations.
Trustees: Gladys Halpern; Sam Halpern.
EIN: 222707942

5381
The Hanafin Foundation, Inc.
P.O. Box 91
Annandale, NJ   08801   (908) 735-6389
Contact: Jeanette Frey, Tr.

Established in 1996 in New Jersey.
Donor: Marcella G. Hanafin.
Foundation type: Independent foundation.
Financial data (yr. ended 12/31/13): Assets, $4,028,041 (M); expenditures, $249,263; qualifying distributions, $207,515; giving activities include $203,360 for 8 grants (high: $55,000; low: $12,790).
Fields of interest: Higher education; Teacher education; Animal welfare; Human services.
Limitations: Applications accepted. Giving primarily in AZ, NJ and NY. No grants to individuals.
Application information:
   Initial approach: Proposal
   Deadline(s): None
Trustees: Edward Elliot; Jeanette Frey; Ellen Hanafin; Erika Hanafin; Elizabeth Kukla.
EIN: 223264870

5382
Abraham and Bessie Hann Charitable Foundation Inc.
401 N. 5th Ave.
Edison, NJ   08817-2920

Established in 2004 in New Jersey.
Foundation type: Independent foundation.
Financial data (yr. ended 12/31/12): Assets, $2,926,678 (M); expenditures, $299,569; qualifying distributions, $286,677.
Fields of interest: Education; Judaism; Human services.

Limitations: Applications not accepted. Giving primarily in NJ and NY.
Application information: Unsolicited requests for funds not accepted.
Trustees: David Mykoff; Rabbi Abraham Mykoff; Rabbi Ronald Schwarzberg.
EIN: 201322035

5383
Alex and Laura Hanson CGF, Inc.
1 Moorehead Dr.
Pennington, NJ 08534-1700

Established in 2001 in New Jersey.
Donor: Alexander D. Hanson.
Foundation type: Independent foundation.
Financial data (yr. ended 09/30/14): Assets, $5,874,602 (M); gifts received, $2,000,000; expenditures, $304,295; qualifying distributions, $290,000; giving activities include $290,000 for 8 grants (high: $200,000; low: $5,000).
Purpose and activities: Giving primarily for education.
Fields of interest: Education; Higher education; Environment; Human services.
Limitations: Applications not accepted. Giving primarily in CT, NJ, and NY. No grants to individuals.
Application information: Contributes only to pre-selected organizations.
Trustees: Abigail Hanson; Alexander D. Hanson; Eliza F. Hanson; Laura F. Hanson.
EIN: 223834524

5384
The Samuel Harbanoff Foundation, Inc.
c/o J.F. Anderson, CPA, PC
34 Bridge St.
Metuchen, NJ 08827-2276 7329066222

Foundation type: Independent foundation.
Financial data (yr. ended 12/31/14): Assets, $217,224; expenditures, $120,919; qualifying distributions, $120,058.
Fields of interest: Judaism.
Limitations: Applications not accepted. Giving primarily in Bronx, NY.
Application information: Unsolicited requests for funds not accepted.
Officers: Richard M. Lipkin, Pres. and Treas.; Douglas F. Allen, Jr., Secy.
Directors: Robert M. Feldman, Dr.; Rabbi Levi Shemtov; Sarah M. Shemtov.
EIN: 271163755

5385
George And Ruth Harms Foundation
(formerly The Harms Foundation, Inc.)
P.O. Box 817
Farmingdale, NJ 07727-0817 (732) 938-4004
Contact: Gary Abadrabo, Secy. and Tr.

Established in 1997 in New Jersey.
Donors: George Harms; Ruth Harms.
Foundation type: Independent foundation.
Financial data (yr. ended 12/31/13): Assets, $390,742 (M); gifts received, $305,121; expenditures, $243,642; qualifying distributions, $242,914; giving activities include $242,731 for 38 grants (high: $50,000; low: $500).

Fields of interest: Education; Cancers; Protestantism; Human services.
Type of support: General support.
Limitations: Applications accepted. Giving primarily in NJ. No grants to individuals.
Application information: Application form required.
Initial approach: Letter
Deadline(s): None
Officers and Trustees: George Harms, Pres. and Trustee; Ruth Harms, V.P. and Trustee; Gary Abadrabo, Secy. and Trustee; Kathy Duffe, Treas.; Kevin Harms; Robert Harms.
EIN: 223548916

5386
The Harmstieg Foundation Inc.
46 Hidden Ledge Rd.
Englewood, NJ 07631-5125

Established in 2003 in New Jersey.
Donor: Warren Stieglitz.
Foundation type: Independent foundation.
Financial data (yr. ended 12/31/12): Assets, $402,602 (M); expenditures, $149,683; qualifying distributions, $141,370; giving activities include $141,370 for 14 grants (high: $66,370; low: $500).
Fields of interest: Arts and culture; Nonprofits; Religion; Judaism; Human services.
Type of support: General support; Regranting.
Limitations: Applications not accepted. Giving primarily in NY. No grants to individuals.
Application information: Unsolicited requests for funds not accepted.
Officers: Warren Stieglitz, Pres.; Carla Harman, Secy.-Treas.
EIN: 550823083

5387
Hawthorne Charitable Foundation
c/o Essex Equity
7 Columbia Pike, Ste. 201
Florham Park, NJ 07932-2276 (908) 988-1090
FAX: (888) 253-4969;
E-mail: Fax@EssexEquity.com; Main URL: http://hawthornecharitablefoundation.org

Donor: Basil Maher.
Foundation type: Independent foundation.
Financial data (yr. ended 12/31/14): Assets, $8,588,030 (M); expenditures, $356,431; qualifying distributions, $2,295,754; giving activities include $335,000 for 4 grants (high: $170,000; low: $5,000), and $1,939,323 for 1 loan/program-related investment.
Fields of interest: Arts and culture; Human services; Youth development.
Limitations: Applications not accepted. Giving primarily in NJ.
Application information: Unsolicited requests for funds not accepted.
Officers and Directors: Basil Maher, Chair., Treas. and Director; Miriam Duffy Maher, Pres. and Director; Scott Schley, Secy., Genl. Counsel and Director.
EIN: 271447633

5388
Heart Institute of Southern New Jersey
1400 E. Rte. 70
Cherry Hill, NJ 08034-2230

Established in 1999 in New Jersey.
Foundation type: Independent foundation.
Financial data (yr. ended 06/30/14): Assets, $9,936,195 (M); expenditures, $797,927; qualifying distributions, $423,500; giving activities include $423,500 for 6 grants (high: $392,500; low: $1,000).
Fields of interest: Hospital care; Diseases and conditions; Heart and circulatory system diseases.
Type of support: Research.
Limitations: Applications not accepted. Giving primarily in PA. No grants to individuals.
Application information: Contributes only to pre-selected organizations.
Officers and Board Members: Harvey L. Waxman, MD, Pres., Treas. and Director; William J. Untereker, MD, V.P. and Director; Michael Sheerin.
EIN: 222574758

5389
Joann Heffernan Heisen Family Foundation
c/o Porzio, Bromberg & Newman, PC
100 Southgate Pkwy.
P.O. Box 1997
Morristown, NJ 07962-1997

Donor: Joann Heffernan Heisen.
Foundation type: Independent foundation.
Financial data (yr. ended 11/30/13): Assets, $839,940 (M); expenditures, $377,879; qualifying distributions, $377,361; giving activities include $377,278 for 2 grants (high: $261,462; low: $115,816).
Fields of interest: Education; Health.
Limitations: Applications not accepted.
Application information: Unsolicited requests for funds not accepted.
Officers: Joann Heffernan Heisen, Pres.; David J. Lenihan, Secy.-Treas.
Trustee: Philip J. Siana.
EIN: 266678210

5390
Robert S. & Mary Jane Hekemian Family Foundation, Inc.
(formerly Robert S. Hekemian Family Foundation)
505 Main St.
P.O. Box 667
Hackensack, NJ 07602-0667 (201) 487-1500
Contact: Robert S. Hekemian, Pres.

Established in 1990 in New Jersey.
Donors: Robert S. Hekemian, Sr.; Hekemian Foundation.
Foundation type: Independent foundation.
Financial data (yr. ended 08/31/13): Assets, $3,503,951 (M); gifts received, $2,000; expenditures, $332,157; qualifying distributions, $306,997; giving activities include $306,997 for 14 grants (high: $237,500; low: $27).
Fields of interest: Arts and culture; Education; Religion.
Application information:
Initial approach: Letter
Deadline(s): None
Officers: Robert S. Hekemian, Pres.; Mary Jane Hekemian, V.P.; David B. Hekemian, Secy.
EIN: 223087695

5391
Robert & Esther Heller Foundation, Inc.
1 Paragon Dr., Ste. 145
Montvale, NJ 07645-1728

Established in 1998 in New Jersey.
Donors: Esther Heller; Robert Heller.
Foundation type: Independent foundation.
Financial data (yr. ended 12/31/13): Assets,
$646,580 (M); expenditures, $305,045; qualifying
distributions, $304,683; giving activities include
$303,953 for 33 grants (high: $170,000; low: $15).
Fields of interest: Nonprofits; Judaism.
Type of support: Regranting.
Limitations: Applications not accepted. Giving
primarily in CA and FL. No grants to individuals.
Application information: Contributes only to
pre-selected organizations.
Officers: Robert Heller, Pres.; Esther Heller, V.P. and
Secy.-Treas.
Trustees: Gary Heller; Paula Yormak.
EIN: 223585312

5392
The Hill Family Foundation, Inc.
c/o Vernon W. Hill, II
262 E. Main St.
Moorestown, NJ 08057-2931

Established in 1999 in New Jersey.
Donors: Vernon W. Hill II; Shirley Hill.
Foundation type: Independent foundation.
Financial data (yr. ended 09/30/13): Assets,
$10,213,741 (M); expenditures, $162,486;
qualifying distributions, $162,486; giving activities
include $160,000 for 4 grants (high: $100,000;
low: $5,000).
Fields of interest: Veterinary medicine.
Limitations: Applications not accepted. Giving
primarily in Philadelphia, PA. No grants to
individuals.
Application information: Contributes only to
pre-selected organizations.
Officers: Vernon W. Hill II, Pres.; Shirley Hill,
Secy.-Treas.
EIN: 223714460

5393
Sally Foss & James Scott Hill Foundation
c/o DB&F
5 Independence Way, Ste. 320
Princeton, NJ 08540-6627

Established in 1997 in New Jersey.
Donors: James Scott Hill†; Hill Charitable Trusts.
Foundation type: Independent foundation.
Financial data (yr. ended 12/31/13): Assets,
$7,954,531 (M); expenditures, $471,653;
qualifying distributions, $424,932; giving activities
include $343,917 for 24 grants (high: $82,708;
low: $1,000).
Fields of interest: Education; Housing development;
Human services.
Limitations: Applications not accepted. Giving
primarily in NJ. No grants to individuals.
Application information: Unsolicited requests for
funds not accepted.
Officers and Trustees: Michael Hill, Pres. and
Trustee; Richard Hill, V.P. and Trustee; Chessye
Moseley, Secy. and Trustee; Dorothy J. Frank, Treas.

and Trustee; John W. Chandler; Ann McClellan;
Cynthia Hill Dopp.
EIN: 223487949

5394
Hillswood Foundation
P.O. Box 1501, NJ2-130-03-31
Pennington, NJ 08534-1501

Established in 1999 in Minnesota.
Donor: James W. Emison†.
Foundation type: Independent foundation.
Financial data (yr. ended 12/31/14): Assets,
$3,773,747 (M); expenditures, $351,746;
qualifying distributions, $320,407; giving activities
include $300,000 for 10 grants (high: $150,000;
low: $5,000).
Fields of interest: Arts and culture; Education;
Higher education; Human services.
Limitations: Applications not accepted. Giving
primarily in IN and MN. No grants to individuals.
Application information: Unsolicited requests for
funds not accepted.
Officers: Jane B. Larson Emison, Pres.; Thomas W.
Emison, Secy.; William A. Emison, Treas.
Directors: Elizabeth A. Emison; Catherine Emison
Stoick.
Number of staff: None.
EIN: 411948564

5395
His Vision Inc.
P.O. Box 1463
Morristown, NJ 07962-1463

Donor: Sandi McNeil.
Foundation type: Independent foundation.
Financial data (yr. ended 12/31/13): Assets,
$2,304,919 (M); expenditures, $418,896;
qualifying distributions, $418,600; giving activities
include $418,600 for 8 grants (high: $225,000;
low: $100).
Fields of interest: Health; Christianity; Child welfare.
Limitations: Applications not accepted. Giving
primarily in NJ and NY.
Application information: Unsolicited requests for
funds not accepted.
Officers: Sandra McNeil-Rogers, Pres. and Treas.;
Shauna Wright, V.P. and Secy.; Michael La Motta,
V.P.; Robert Rogers, V.P.; Jaraun Wright, V.P.
EIN: 274384630

5396
Richard H. Holzer Memorial Foundation
25 Rockwood Pl., Ste. 335
Englewood, NJ 07631-4959 (201) 871-8810
Contact: Vivian Holzer, Pres.

Established in 1969 in New Jersey.
Donor: Erich Holzer†.
Foundation type: Independent foundation.
Financial data (yr. ended 12/31/13): Assets,
$7,424,306 (M); expenditures, $386,960;
qualifying distributions, $326,652; giving activities
include $320,750 for 58 grants (high: $50,000;
low: $250).
Purpose and activities: Giving primarily for the arts.
Fields of interest: Arts and culture; Performing arts;
Music; Higher education; Judaism.

Type of support: Continuing support; Annual
campaigns; Endowments.
Limitations: Applications accepted. Giving primarily
in northern NJ.
Application information: Application form required.
   Initial approach: Letter
   Deadline(s): None
   Board meeting date(s): Biannually
Officers: Vivian Holzer, Pres.; Robert Holzer, V.P.
and Treas.; Robin Greenbaum, Secy.; Eva Holzer,
Mgr.
Number of staff: 2 part-time professional.
EIN: 237014880

5397
Huffhines Trust
P.O. Box 1501, NJ2-130-03-31
Pennington, NJ 08534-1501

Established in 2007 in New Jersey.
Donor: Richard Nance.
Foundation type: Independent foundation.
Financial data (yr. ended 12/31/13): Assets,
$1,967,294 (M); gifts received, $598;
expenditures, $213,978; qualifying distributions,
$199,456; giving activities include $180,000 for 1
grant.
Fields of interest: Protestantism.
Limitations: Applications not accepted. No grants to
individuals.
Application information: Unsolicited requests for
funds not accepted.
Trustees: Richard Nance; MLTC.
EIN: 227007570

5398
Icap Foundation Inc
Harborside Financial Ctr., 1100 Plz. 5
Jersey City, NJ 07311 (212) 341-9732
Contact: Lynn Lax, V.P. and Dir.
E-mail: lynn.laxf@us icap.con

Donors: Dan Flannery; John Nixon; Glenn Jackson;
Dennis Crum; ICAP Holdings(USA) Inc.; ICAP
Services North America LLC.
Foundation type: Independent foundation.
Financial data (yr. ended 12/31/13): Assets,
$21,170 (M); gifts received, $46,858;
expenditures, $143,659; qualifying distributions,
$142,559; giving activities include $50,000 for 2
grants (high: $25,000; low: $25,000), and $92,559
for 8 grants to individuals (high: $30,000; low:
$5,000).
Fields of interest: Religion; Human services.
Limitations: Applications accepted. Giving primarily
in NJ.
Application information: Application form required.
   Initial approach: Proposal
   Deadline(s): None
Officers and Trustees: Dan Flannery, Chair. and
Pres. and Trustee; Daniel Cleaves, V.P. and Trustee;
John Nixon, V.P. and Trustee; Ken Pigaga, V.P.; Lynn
Lax, V.P. and Trustee; Rich Kaltenbach, V.P.; Stuart
Wexler, Secy. and Trustee; Glenn Worman, Treas.
EIN: 352459021

5399

Infinity Group Inc.

245 Hutchinson Rd.
Englewood, NJ   07631-4406   (201) 871-2048
Contact: Benjamin Chouake, Pres.

Established in 1995 in New Jersey.
Donors: Bejtra LLC; Benjamin Chouake.
Foundation type: Independent foundation.
Financial data (yr. ended 10/31/13): Assets,
$4,177,322 (M); expenditures, $213,810;
qualifying distributions, $213,660; giving activities
include $213,660 for 7 grants (high: $200,000;
low: $110).
Purpose and activities: Giving primarily for the
promotion of Jewish culture.
Fields of interest: Education; Judaism; Human
services.
Type of support: General support.
Limitations: Applications accepted. Giving primarily
in NY. No grants to individuals.
Application information: Application form required.
   Initial approach: Letter
   Deadline(s): None
Officer: Benjamin Chouake, Pres.
EIN: 223410823

5400

The Integra Foundation, Inc.

311 Enterprise Dr.
Plainsboro, NJ   08536-3344   (609) 775-8553
Contact: Gianna Sabella, Exec. Dir.
FAX: (949) 595-8703;
E-mail: gianna.sabella@integralife.com; Application
address: 2 Goodyear #A, Irvine, CA 92618; Main
URL: http://www.integra-foundation.org
Grants List: http://www.integra-foundation.org/
gh.asp

Established in 2002 in New Jersey.
Donor: Integra LifeSciences Corp.
Foundation type: Company-sponsored foundation.
Financial data (yr. ended 12/31/14): Assets,
$469,793 (M); gifts received, $562,500;
expenditures, $388,775; qualifying distributions,
$388,750; giving activities include $388,750 for
grants.
Purpose and activities: The foundation supports
programs designed to advance innovative medical
and health care research and education, primarily in
the areas of neurosurgery, reconstructive surgery,
and general surgery, to improve the outcome and
quality of life for patients and their communities.
Fields of interest: Medical education; Health;
Hospital care; Health care clinics; Neurology;
Reconstructive surgery; Diseases and conditions.
International interests: Canada.
Type of support: Sponsorships; Convening;
Equipment; Scholarships; General support;
Research; Program development.
Limitations: Applications accepted. Giving primarily
in areas of company operations, with emphasis on
MA, NJ, PA, and U. No support for political, fraternal,
social, veterans', or religious organizations. No
grants to individuals, or for programs that directly
support marketing or sales objectives of Integra
LifeSciences.
Publications: Application guidelines; Grants list;
Newsletter.
Application information: Application form required.
   Initial approach: Download application form and
      mail or fax to foundation
   Copies of proposal: 1

Deadline(s): None
   Board meeting date(s): Feb., May, Aug., and Nov.
Officers and Trustees: Gianna Sabella, Exec. Dir.;
Linda Littlejohns, Pres.; Simon Archibald, V.P.;
JoAnne Harla, V.P.; Karen March, V.P.; Nora
Brennan, Treas.; Stuart Essig; Jack Henneman;
Judith O'Grady.
Number of staff: 1 part-time professional.
EIN: 522388679

5401

The IV Fund

(formerly The Imada Foundation)
66 Witherspoon St., Ste. 303
Princeton, NJ   08542-3226

Established in 2004 in New Jersey.
Donor: Ivy B. Lewis.
Foundation type: Independent foundation.
Financial data (yr. ended 12/31/13): Assets,
$5,220,621 (M); expenditures, $230,639;
qualifying distributions, $223,475; giving activities
include $220,650 for 18 grants (high: $60,000;
low: $450).
Fields of interest: Education; Higher education;
Health; Judaism.
Limitations: Applications not accepted. Giving
primarily in IL and NJ. No grants to individuals.
Application information: Unsolicited requests for
funds not accepted.
Officer and Director: Ivy B. Lewis, Pres. and
Director.
EIN: 201422978

5402

Mark Jacobson Charitable Foundation

581 Main St., 5th Fl.
Woodbridge, NJ   07095

Donor: Mark Jacobson.
Foundation type: Independent foundation.
Financial data (yr. ended 12/31/13): Assets,
$10,666 (M); gifts received, $334,500;
expenditures, $327,908; qualifying distributions,
$327,400; giving activities include $327,400 for 2
grants (high: $317,400; low: $10,000).
Fields of interest: Education; Diabetes; Human
services.
Type of support: Research.
Limitations: Applications not accepted. Giving
primarily in NY.
Application information: Unsolicited requests for
funds not accepted.
Directors: Eden Jacobson; Mark Jacobson; Peri De
Grazia.
EIN: 464140893

5403

Jamacha Bloom Family Foundation

c/o Jamacha, LLC
161 Eagle Rock Ave.
Roseland, NJ   07068-1354

Established in 2007 in New Jersey.
Donors: William Bloom; Jamacha Bloom Charitable
Lead Annuity Trust.
Foundation type: Independent foundation.
Financial data (yr. ended 12/31/13): Assets,
$3,424,280 (M); gifts received, $41,285;
expenditures, $414,969; qualifying distributions,

$393,987; giving activities include $373,350 for 14
grants (high: $200,000; low: $100).
Fields of interest: Education; Human services.
Limitations: Applications not accepted. No grants to
individuals.
Application information: Unsolicited requests for
funds not accepted.
Trustees: Ruth Bloom; William Bloom.
EIN: 261614525

5404

Jensam Foundation, Inc.

c/o Michael Schwartzbard
100 Eagle Rock, Ste. 200
East Hanover, NJ   07936

Established in 1997 in New Jersey.
Donors: Herbert Kayden‡; Gabrielle Reem Kayden.
Foundation type: Independent foundation.
Financial data (yr. ended 12/31/13): Assets,
$5,313,880 (M); expenditures, $224,262;
qualifying distributions, $222,000; giving activities
include $222,000 for 3 grants (high: $121,000;
low: $1,000).
Fields of interest: University education; Science.
Limitations: Applications not accepted. No grants to
individuals.
Application information: Contributes only to
pre-selected organizations.
Officers: Joelle Kayden-Killian, Secy.; Michael
Schwartzbard, Treas.
EIN: 223523249

5405

JFI Charitable Trust

555 Madison Ave.
Lakewood, NJ   08701

Established in 1998 in New Jersey.
Donor: Joseph Iny.
Foundation type: Independent foundation.
Financial data (yr. ended 12/31/13): Assets,
$11,008,975 (M); gifts received, $2,000;
expenditures, $440,993; qualifying distributions,
$430,287; giving activities include $423,327 for 38
+ grants (high: $200,822).
Fields of interest: Nonprofits; Judaism.
Type of support: Regranting.
Limitations: Applications not accepted. Giving
primarily in MD, NJ and NY. No grants to individuals.
Application information: Contributes only to
pre-selected organizations.
Trustees: Joseph Iny; David Wilschanski; Naava
Zafrani.
EIN: 226766865

5406

The Joyce and Seward Johnson Foundation
Inc.

P.O. Box 369
Hopewell, NJ   08525-0369
Application address: 270 Madison Ave., 16th Fl.,
New York, NY 10016, tel.: (212) 293-5100

Established in 1990 in New Jersey.
Donors: J. Seward Johnson, Jr. Trust; J. Seward
Johnson, Jr.; Johnson 1998 Charitable Lead Tr. # 1;
Johnson 1998 Charitable Lead Tr. # 2.
Foundation type: Independent foundation.

Financial data (yr. ended 12/31/13): Assets, $3,375,926 (M); gifts received, $182,264; expenditures, $330,281; qualifying distributions, $313,910; giving activities include $311,830 for 31 grants (high: $50,000; low: $100).

Purpose and activities: Giving primarily for education and the arts; some funding for health care, including hospitals, children, youth, and social services.

Fields of interest: Arts and culture; Sculpture; Theater; Education; Higher education; Hospital care; Libraries; Buddhism; Human services; Child welfare.

Type of support: Research.

Limitations: Applications accepted. Giving primarily in NJ, and the metropolitan New York, NY, area, including Long Island and Westchester. No grants to individuals.

Application information:
  Initial approach: Proposal
  Deadline(s): None

Officers: J. Seward Johnson, Jr., Pres. and Treas.; Joyce H. Johnson, V.P. and Secy.

Trustee: Robert S. Matthews.

EIN: 223048720

5407
The Robert K. Johnson Foundation
c/o Cappiccille
615 W. Mt. Pleasant Ave.
Livingston, NJ   07039

Established in 2006 in New Jersey.

Donor: Robert K. Johnson.

Foundation type: Independent foundation.

Financial data (yr. ended 12/31/13): Assets, $5,494,600 (M); expenditures, $192,557; qualifying distributions, $181,258; giving activities include $181,258 for 14 grants (high: $25,000; low: $1,000).

Fields of interest: Arts and culture; Opera; Education; Higher education; Undergraduate education; University education; Natural resources; Land resources.

Limitations: Applications not accepted. No grants to individuals.

Application information: Contributes only to pre-selected organizations.

Trustee: Robert K. Johnson.

EIN: 206981384

5408
Blanche & George Jones Fund
c/o Bressler, Amery & Ross, P.C.
325 Columbia Tpke.
Florham Park, NJ   07932-1213   (973) 660-4474
Contact: Mary A. Powers Esq.

Established in 1981 in New Jersey.

Foundation type: Independent foundation.

Financial data (yr. ended 02/28/15): Assets, $3,413,579 (M); expenditures, $184,609; qualifying distributions, $151,441; giving activities include $151,441 for 34 grants (high: $10,000; low: $1,000).

Purpose and activities: Giving primarily for education, health care, and to Christian churches.

Fields of interest: Arts and culture; Education; Secondary education; Higher education; Nonprofits; Hospital care; Mental health care; Cancers; Buddhism; Christianity; Human services; Youth services.

Type of support: Regranting.

Limitations: Applications not accepted. Giving primarily in CA and FL. No grants to individuals.

Application information: Contributes only to pre-selected organizations.
  Board meeting date(s): Nov.

Officers: Barbara J. Foreman, Pres.; Gay Osborn, V.P.; Mary A. Powers, Secy.; Peter W. Roome, Treas.

Board Member: Christian Foreman Ellis.

EIN: 136028786

5409
William Jones Private Foundation Trust
P.O. Box 1501, NJ2-130-03-31
Pennington, NJ   08534-1501

Established in 2005 in Georgia.

Donor: William F. Jones Trust.

Foundation type: Independent foundation.

Financial data (yr. ended 05/31/13): Assets, $990,906 (M); expenditures, $241,762; qualifying distributions, $234,696; giving activities include $225,000 for 5 grants (high: $100,000; low: $10,000).

Fields of interest: Education; Undergraduate education; Specialty hospital care; Pediatrics.

Type of support: General support.

Limitations: Applications not accepted. Giving primarily in NJ and PA. No grants to individuals.

Application information: Unsolicited requests for funds not accepted.

Trustees: Linda Blackwell; Douglas Watson; Merrill Lynch Trust Co.

EIN: 586466949

5410
David M. C. Ju Foundation
435 Bernardsville Rd.
Mendham, NJ   07945-2927   (908) 766-1704
Contact: William Ju MD, Tr.

Established in 1964 in New York.

Donor: David M.C. Ju, MD†.

Foundation type: Independent foundation.

Financial data (yr. ended 08/31/13): Assets, $2,029,185 (M); expenditures, $331,476; qualifying distributions, $317,456; giving activities include $302,850 for 13 grants (high: $100,000; low: $100).

Fields of interest: Arts and culture; Theater; Children's museums; Education; Higher education; Medical education; Television; Protestantism.

International interests: Canada.

Limitations: Applications accepted. Giving primarily in NJ and Canada.

Application information: Direct applications from individuals not accepted. Recipient must be recommended by the original sponsor organization. Short term grants given only. Application form required.
  Initial approach: Letter
  Deadline(s): Between Sept. 1 and Dec. 1

Trustees: Doris Ju; William Ju, MD.

EIN: 136165238

5411
Judson Family Foundation, Inc.
124 Prospect St.
Ridgewood, NJ   07450-4406   2127852610

Established in 2002 in Delaware.

Donors: Erna Judson; Sundel Judson.

Foundation type: Independent foundation.

Financial data (yr. ended 09/30/14): Assets, $153,322; gifts received, $200,000; expenditures, $114,175; qualifying distributions, $114,175.

Fields of interest: Education; Diseases and conditions; Religion.

Type of support: Research.

Limitations: Applications not accepted. No grants to individuals.

Application information: Unsolicited requests for funds not accepted.

Officers and Directors: Sundel Judson, Pres. and Director; Lonnie Wollin, Secy. and Director.

EIN: 030485661

5412
Kalkin Family Foundation, Inc.
c/o Kalkin & Co., Inc.
40 Quimby Ln., 2nd Fl.
Bernardsville, NJ   07924-2279   (908) 696-1999
Contact: Eugene Kalkin, Tr.

Established in 1983 in New Jersey.

Donor: Eugene Kalkin.

Foundation type: Independent foundation.

Financial data (yr. ended 12/31/13): Assets, $3,498,042 (M); expenditures, $175,006; qualifying distributions, $146,031; giving activities include $146,031 for 73 grants (high: $20,000; low: $36).

Purpose and activities: Giving primarily for the arts, education, and Jewish organizations.

Fields of interest: University education.

Limitations: Applications accepted. Giving primarily in NJ and NY. No grants to individuals.

Application information: Application form required.
  Initial approach: Letter
  Deadline(s): None

Trustees: Eugene Kalkin; Joan Kalkin.

EIN: 133185333

5413
The Emerson & Barbara Kampen Foundation
(formerly The Emerson Kampen Foundation)
35 Nocentiono Dr.
Woolwich, NJ   08085-1813

Established in 1986 in Indiana.

Donor: Emerson Kampen.

Foundation type: Independent foundation.

Financial data (yr. ended 07/31/13): Assets, $8,360,038 (L); gifts received, $402,428; expenditures, $372,300; qualifying distributions, $339,238; giving activities include $339,238 for 8 grants (high: $169,238; low: $12,500).

Fields of interest: Undergraduate education; Foundations; Christianity; Human services; Youth services; Scouting programs.

Type of support: Equipment.

Limitations: Applications not accepted. Giving primarily in IN. No grants to individuals.

Application information: Contributes only to pre-selected organizations.

Trustees: Deborah Kampen Bigler; Joanie Dunham; Douglas S. Kampen; Pamela E. Mayes; Laura L. Shiver; Deborah L. Smith; Cynthia S. Van Zelst.

EIN: 351694614

5414
The Drew A. Katz Foundation, Inc.

(formerly Infinite Possibilities Foundation, Inc.)
905 N. Kings Hwy.
Cherry Hill, NJ 08034-1514
Main URL: http://drewakatzfoundation.org

Donors: Drew A. Katz; Urban Youth Golf &
Academics Programs; Vincent Curran; Herskowitz &
Hampton, LLC; Christine Leverence; Paul Meyer;
David Leof, MD; World Wide Rush, LLC; Carol Meyer;
Jeremy Koster; Mibo Construction Co., Inc.; Victoria
Logvinsky; Celebrity Bowling Classic.
Foundation type: Independent foundation.
Financial data (yr. ended 12/31/13): Assets,
$806,796 (M); gifts received, $392,037;
expenditures, $230,298; qualifying distributions,
$216,195; giving activities include $216,195 for 78
grants (high: $20,000; low: $100).
Fields of interest: Theater; Historic preservation;
Education; Law education; Medical education;
Foundations; Cancers; Christianity; Human
services; Child welfare.
Limitations: Applications not accepted. No grants to
individuals.
Application information: Unsolicited requests for
funds not accepted.
Director: Drew A. Katz.
EIN: 141862146

5415
The Harold & Yenny Kaufman Charitable
Foundation

125 Long Ave.
Hillside, NJ 07205-2350
Contact: Harold Kaufman

Established in 2000 in New York.
Donors: A. & E. Kaufman Family Partnership, L.P.;
Harold Kaufman; Yenny Kaufman.
Foundation type: Independent foundation.
Financial data (yr. ended 12/31/13): Assets,
$5,150,009 (M); gifts received, $10,000;
expenditures, $382,391; qualifying distributions,
$381,500; giving activities include $380,750 for 60
grants (high: $46,000; low: $250).
Fields of interest: Nonprofits; Judaism.
Type of support: General support; Regranting.
Limitations: Applications not accepted. Giving
primarily in Brooklyn, NY. No grants to individuals.
Application information: Unsolicited requests for
funds not accepted.
Directors: Harold Kaufman; Yenny Kaufman.
EIN: 912146031

5416
KDK Charitable Trust

c/o Untracht Early & Assocs., LLC
325 Columbia Tpke., No. 202
Florham Park, NJ 07932-1213

Established in 1997 in Connecticut.
Donor: Dennis J. Keegan.
Foundation type: Independent foundation.
Financial data (yr. ended 12/31/13): Assets,
$4,749,981 (M); expenditures, $201,780;
qualifying distributions, $174,831; giving activities
include $168,831 for 22 grants (high: $50,021;
low: $100).

Fields of interest: Education; Secondary education;
Higher education; Community and economic
development; Human services.
Limitations: Applications not accepted. Giving
primarily in CA, CT, Washington, DC and NH. No
grants to individuals.
Application information: Unsolicited requests for
funds not accepted.
Trustees: Dennis J. Keegan; Karen S. Keegan.
EIN: 066455317

5417
The Kean Foundation, Inc.

c/o Rothstein Kass
4 Becker Farm Rd.
Roseland, NJ 07068

Established in 1999 in New Jersey.
Donor: Thomas H. Kean.
Foundation type: Independent foundation.
Financial data (yr. ended 12/31/13): Assets,
$4,584,582 (M); gifts received, $1,011,533;
expenditures, $214,270; qualifying distributions,
$179,170; giving activities include $179,170 for 62
grants (high: $25,000; low: $100).
Fields of interest: Arts and culture; Higher
education; Environment; Human services; Youth
development.
Limitations: Applications not accepted. Giving
primarily on the East Coast, with emphasis on
Washington, DC, MA, NJ, and NY. No grants to
individuals.
Application information: Unsolicited requests for
funds not accepted.
Officers and Trustees: Thomas H. Kean, Pres. and
Trustee; Reed Kean, V.P. and Trustee; Thomas H.
Kean, Jr., V.P. and Trustee; Alexandra Kean-Strong,
Secy.-Treas. and Trustee.
EIN: 223697400

5418
Keller Family Foundation

P.O. Box 1501, NJ2-130-03-31
Pennington, NJ 08534-1501

Donors: Christoph Keller III; Julie Keller.
Foundation type: Independent foundation.
Financial data (yr. ended 12/31/14): Assets,
$4,608,164; expenditures, $263,672; qualifying
distributions, $220,603.
Fields of interest: Higher education; Protestantism.
Limitations: Applications not accepted. Giving
primarily in AR, with some giving in TN.
Application information: Contributes only to
pre-selected organizations.
Officers and Directors: Christoph Keller III, Pres.;
Julie Keller, V.P. and Secy.-Treas. and Director;
Thomas Christopher Keller.
EIN: 134333550

5419
The James Kerney Foundation

P.O. Box 6698
Trenton, NJ 08648-0698

Established in 1934 in New Jersey.
Foundation type: Independent foundation.
Financial data (yr. ended 12/31/14): Assets,
$3,357,916; expenditures, $235,025; qualifying
distributions, $196,398.

Purpose and activities: Giving primarily for
education, and Trenton, New Jersey based capital
programs.
Fields of interest: Arts and culture; Museums;
Education; Community and economic development;
Catholicism; Family services; Child welfare;
Adolescents; Single parents; Homeless people;
Low-income and poor people.
Type of support: Capital and infrastructure;
Matching grants; Equipment.
Limitations: Applications accepted. Giving limited to
Trenton, NJ, and its surrounding area. No support for
political organizations or national organizations. No
grants to individuals, or for operating budgets,
architectural drawings or conceptual plans.
Application information: Application form required.
Initial approach: Proposal
Copies of proposal: 1
Deadline(s): None
Board meeting date(s): July and Nov.
Officers: Judith M. Persichilli, Pres.; John E. Kerney,
Jr., V.P.; Sheila McNeil Welch, Secy.; T. Lincoln
Kerney II, Treas.
Trustees: Joseph P. Comly III; J. Regan Kerney;
Edward F. Meara.
EIN: 226055884

5420
George Kessel Foundation, Inc.

75 Portland Ave.
Bergenfield, NJ 07621-2306

Established in 1992 in New York.
Donor: George Kessel.
Foundation type: Independent foundation.
Financial data (yr. ended 12/31/13): Assets,
$188,641 (M); expenditures, $165,475; qualifying
distributions, $153,575; giving activities include
$153,545 for 11 grants (high: $75,000; low: $500).
Fields of interest: Education; Religion; Judaism;
Human rights.
Limitations: Applications not accepted. Giving
primarily in Washington, DC, NJ and NY. No grants
to individuals.
Application information: Unsolicited requests for
funds not accepted.
Trustees: George Kessel; Jeffrey Kessel; Steven
Kessel.
EIN: 222348710

5421
The Kingsberg Foundation

c/o Withumsmith & Brown
5 Vaughn Dr.
Princeton, NJ 08540

Established in 1954 in New York.
Foundation type: Independent foundation.
Financial data (yr. ended 12/31/13): Assets,
$7,042,918 (M); expenditures, $352,323;
qualifying distributions, $329,089; giving activities
include $325,892 for 54 grants (high: $75,000;
low: $95).
Purpose and activities: Giving primarily for Jewish
organizations, as well as for the arts and education;
funding also for health associations.
Fields of interest: Arts and culture; Theater;
Museums; Art museums; Education; Higher
education; Nonprofits; Diseases and conditions;
Judaism.

Type of support: Research; Research and evaluation; Regranting.
Limitations: Applications not accepted. Giving primarily in New York, NY, with some giving in MA. No grants to individuals.
Application information: Contributes only to pre-selected organizations.
Trustees: Alan D. Kingsberg; Harold J. Kingsberg; Ruth J. Kingsberg; Sally Anne Keller.
EIN: 136151289

5422
Kirby Foundation
P.O. Box 1501, NJ2-130-03-31
Pennington, NJ 08534-1501

Established in 1999 in Pennsylvania.
Donors: G. Michael Kirby; Deborah Kirby.
Foundation type: Independent foundation.
Financial data (yr. ended 07/31/12): Assets, $3,350,125 (M); expenditures, $232,191; qualifying distributions, $206,456; giving activities include $191,400 for 18 grants (high: $60,000; low: $1,200).
Fields of interest: Education; Health; Human services.
Limitations: Applications not accepted. Giving primarily in PA. No grants to individuals.
Application information: Unsolicited requests for funds not accepted.
Trustees: Deborah Kirby; Michael Kirby.
EIN: 256681647

5423
The Charles and Lynne Klatskin Family Charitable Trust
400 Hollister Rd.
Teterboro, NJ 07608-1147

Donor: Charles Klatskin.
Foundation type: Independent foundation.
Financial data (yr. ended 06/30/14): Assets, $2,375,751; gifts received, $150,000; expenditures, $187,273; qualifying distributions, $185,923.
Fields of interest: Education; Judaism; Human services.
Limitations: Applications not accepted. Giving primarily in NJ and NY. No grants to individuals.
Application information: Unsolicited requests for funds not accepted.
Trustees: Charles Klatskin; Deborah Klatskin; Lynne Klatskin; Samuel Klatskin.
EIN: 226831861

5424
The Walter C. Klein Foundation, Inc.
c/o McCabe Heidrich & Wong
4 Gatehall Dr.
Parsippany, NJ 07054-4518

Established in 1990 in New Jersey.
Donors: Walter C. Klein; Mary Eddy Klein; Margaret K. Klein.
Foundation type: Independent foundation.
Financial data (yr. ended 06/30/14): Assets, $4,765,580; gifts received, $5,061; expenditures, $289,685; qualifying distributions, $257,015.
Purpose and activities: Giving primarily for the arts.

Fields of interest: Arts and culture; Natural history museums; Higher education; Wildlife biodiversity; Reproductive health care; Human services; Child welfare.
Limitations: Applications not accepted. Giving primarily in NY. No grants to individuals.
Application information: Contributes only to pre-selected organizations.
Officers and Trustees: Margaret K. Klein, Pres. and Treas. and Trustee; Antoinette Geyelin Hoar, V.P. and Trustee; Robert Wong, Secy.; Walter C. Klein.
EIN: 521705026

5425
Faith & James Knight Foundation, Inc.
c/o R.J. Gaughran
P.O. Box 143
Middletown, NJ 07748-0143

Established in 1999 in New Jersey.
Donor: J.A. Knight†.
Foundation type: Independent foundation.
Financial data (yr. ended 06/30/13): Assets, $4,446,511 (M); gifts received, $305,456; expenditures, $475,089; qualifying distributions, $409,615; giving activities include $372,500 for 38 grants (high: $50,000; low: $1,000).
Purpose and activities: Giving primarily for women's issues, as well as for animal issues, education, and health care.
Fields of interest: Education; Animal welfare; Health; Women's services; Females.
Limitations: Applications not accepted. Giving primarily in NJ. No grants to individuals.
Application information: Contributes only to pre-selected organizations.
Trustees: Donna Balon; Cheryl Bliss; Robert J. Gaughran; Lisa Knight; Frances Lobl; Margot R. McCord.
Number of staff: None.
EIN: 223656542

5426
Fanny & Svante Knistrom Foundation
c/o Stickel, Frahn, & Lloyd
229 Main St.
Chatham, NJ 07928-2408 (973) 635-5200
Contact: David Lloyd

Established in 1972 in New Jersey.
Donors: Svante Knistrom†; Fanny Knistrom†.
Foundation type: Independent foundation.
Financial data (yr. ended 05/31/13): Assets, $8,775,393 (M); expenditures, $461,486; qualifying distributions, $395,139; giving activities include $366,900 for 36 grants (high: $25,000; low: $1,400).
Purpose and activities: Emphasis on health, education, and human rights, especially of marginal groups such as battered women, homeless families, and disabled persons.
Fields of interest: Education; Health; Youth pregnancy prevention; Abuse prevention; Human rights; Child welfare; Ethnic and racial groups; People with disabilities.
International interests: Mexico.
Type of support: General support; Matching grants; Capital campaigns; Seed money.
Limitations: Applications accepted. Giving primarily in CA, NH, NJ, and SC. No support for political or religious purposes. No grants to individuals.

Application information: Application form required.
Initial approach: Letter
Deadline(s): None
Officers: Virginia Kreuzberger, Pres.; Gregory P. Buesing, V.P. and Treas.; Douglas Kreuzberger, Secy.
Trustees: Donna Barrett; Eric Buesing; Guy K. Buesing; Jean Buesing; Donald Kreuzberger; Kurt Kreuzberger; Scott Kreuzberger; Karen Turner.
EIN: 222011417

5427
The Knowlton Foundation, Inc.
104 Hastings Pl.
Cinnaminson, NJ 08077-4526
Contact: Rex Knowlton

Established in 2006 in New Jersey.
Donors: Stephanie A. Zarus; Calvin H. Knowlton.
Foundation type: Independent foundation.
Financial data (yr. ended 06/30/13): Assets, $681,515 (M); gifts received, $23,500; expenditures, $181,076; qualifying distributions, $172,020; giving activities include $172,020 for 3 grants (high: $77,020; low: $35,000).
Fields of interest: Education; Health; Religion.
Limitations: Applications not accepted. Giving primarily in Washington, DC, NJ, and PA. No grants to individuals.
Application information: Contributes only to pre-selected organizations.
Officer and Trustees: Calvin H. Knowlton, Pres. and Trustee; Reginald K. Knowlton; Heather K. Omlor; Stephanie A. Zarus.
EIN: 203484102

5428
Arnold & Irene Kocurek Family Foundation 1986 Trust
P.O. Box 1501, NJ2-130-03-31
Pennington, NJ 08534-1501
Application address: c/o Jon Haffner, P.O. Box 75000, M/C 6596, Detroit, MI 48275-6596, tel.: (214) 890-4344

Established in 1986 in Texas.
Donors: Arnold J. Kocurek†; Irene B. Kocurek.
Foundation type: Independent foundation.
Financial data (yr. ended 02/28/13): Assets, $2,015,981 (M); expenditures, $420,343; qualifying distributions, $402,948; giving activities include $377,500 for 20 grants (high: $40,000; low: $7,500).
Fields of interest: Education; Specialty hospital care; Catholicism; Human services.
Type of support: General support.
Limitations: Applications accepted. Giving limited to TX, with emphasis on San Antonio. No grants to individuals.
Application information: Application form required.
Initial approach: Letter
Deadline(s): None
Officers: Irene B. Kocurek, Fdn. Mgr.; Karen Kocurek, Fdn. Mgr.; Suzanne Kocurek, Fdn. Mgr.
Trustee: Merrill Lynch Trust Co.
EIN: 746345100

5429
The Kolber Family Foundation
884 Navesink River Rd.
Locust, NJ 07760-2328

Donor: George Kolber.
Foundation type: Independent foundation.
Financial data (yr. ended 12/31/14): Assets, $26,331; expenditures, $170,715; qualifying distributions, $168,783.
Fields of interest: Higher education; Health care clinics; Human services.
Limitations: Applications not accepted. No grants to individuals.
Application information: Unsolicited requests for funds not accepted.
Trustees: Lisa Hutchings; George Kolber; Richard Kolber; Vita Kolber.
EIN: 223694860

5430
The Arthur Kontos Foundation Inc.
c/o Arthur Kontos
1 Channel Club Dr., Ste. 1703
Monmouth Beach, NJ 07750-1343

Donor: Arthur Kontos.
Foundation type: Independent foundation.
Financial data (yr. ended 11/30/13): Assets, $6,635,490 (M); expenditures, $354,385; qualifying distributions, $345,352; giving activities include $340,851 for 37 grants (high: $31,000; low: $1,000).
Purpose and activities: Giving primarily for the arts, including a college of art and design, as well as for health organizations, children, youth, and social services, and for charitable foundations.
Fields of interest: Arts and culture; Arts education; Foundations; Diseases and conditions; Human services; Child welfare.
Limitations: Applications not accepted. Giving primarily in NJ and NY. No grants to individuals.
Application information: Contributes only to pre-selected organizations.
Officers: James Kontos, Pres.; Arthur Kontos, V.P. and Secy.; Michael Kontos, V.P. and Treas.
EIN: 133339956

5431
Korean American Buddhist Foundation Inc.
380 North St.
Teterboro, NJ 07608-1204 (201) 468-3403
Contact: Soon Ja Cho, Secy.
E-mail: hopecho@gmail.com

Donor: Il Hwan Cho.
Foundation type: Independent foundation.
Financial data (yr. ended 12/31/13): Assets, $1,454,746 (M); expenditures, $210,817; qualifying distributions, $191,654; giving activities include $174,597 for 10 grants (high: $57,597; low: $2,000).
Fields of interest: Education; Religion; Buddhism; Human services.
Limitations: Applications accepted. Giving primarily in NY.
Application information: Application form required.
Initial approach: Letter
Deadline(s): None

Officers: IL Hwan Cho, Pres.; Soon Ja Cho, Secy.
EIN: 223386949

5432
Kresa Family Foundation
P.O. Box 1501, NJ2-130-03-31
Pennington, NJ 08534-1501

Established in 2005 in New Jersey.
Donors: Kent Kresa; Joyce Kresa.
Foundation type: Independent foundation.
Financial data (yr. ended 12/31/14): Assets, $13,166,162 (M); gifts received, $5,000; expenditures, $299,559; qualifying distributions, $192,341; giving activities include $134,000 for 14 grants (high: $50,000; low: $500).
Fields of interest: Orchestral music; Education; Nonprofits; Hospital care; Diseases and conditions; Human services; Child welfare.
Type of support: Research; Regranting.
Limitations: Applications not accepted. Giving primarily in CA; funding also in OR. No grants to individuals.
Application information: Contributes only to pre-selected organizations.
Officers: Kent Kresa, Pres.; Kiren Kresa-Reahl, MD, Secy.
EIN: 202890253

5433
The Kroon Foundation Inc.
c/o Cappiccille
615 W. Mount Pleasant Ave., Ste. 2
Livingston, NJ 07039-1672

Established in 1993 in New Jersey.
Donor: Richard E. Kroon.
Foundation type: Independent foundation.
Financial data (yr. ended 12/31/13): Assets, $4,177,448 (M); expenditures, $192,721; qualifying distributions, $183,500; giving activities include $183,500 for 34 grants (high: $50,000; low: $500).
Purpose and activities: Giving for education, human services, and religious organizations.
Fields of interest: Education; Higher education; Foundations; Religion; Human services; Child welfare.
Type of support: General support.
Limitations: Applications not accepted. Giving primarily in CT, MA and NJ. No grants to individuals.
Application information: Contributes only to pre-selected organizations.
Officers: Richard E. Kroon, Pres. and Treas.; Mary Jane Sheehan Kroon, Secy.
Trustee: David Fleming Kroon.
EIN: 223299243

5434
The John and Margaret A. Krupa Charitable Foundation
P.O. Box 1501, NJ2-130-03-31
Pennington, NJ 08534-1501

Established in 1997 in Florida.
Donors: John Krupa; Margaret A. Krupa.
Foundation type: Independent foundation.
Financial data (yr. ended 12/31/14): Assets, $4,536,662 (M); expenditures, $252,886; qualifying distributions, $210,994; giving activities

include $159,879 for 16 grants (high: $20,000; low: $5,000).
Fields of interest: Education; Domesticated animals; Health.
Limitations: Applications not accepted. Giving primarily in FL. No grants to individuals.
Application information: Unsolicited requests for funds not accepted.
Trustees: Margaret A. Krupa; Merrill Lynch Trust Co.
EIN: 656223528

5435
The Kurr Foundation
P.O. Box 143
Middletown, NJ 07748-0143

Established in 1992 in New Jersey.
Donor: Sara Zock.
Foundation type: Independent foundation.
Financial data (yr. ended 12/31/13): Assets, $8,247,363 (M); expenditures, $799,980; qualifying distributions, $615,388; giving activities include $397,940 for grants.
Purpose and activities: Giving primarily for education, health organizations, and children, youth and social services.
Fields of interest: Elementary and secondary education; Higher education; Hospital care; Diseases and conditions; Cancers; Christianity; Protestantism; Human services; Family services; Child welfare.
Limitations: Applications not accepted. Giving primarily in NJ and NY; some funding also in PA. No grants to individuals.
Application information: Contributes only to pre-selected organizations.
Officers and Trustees: John H. Rogicki, Pres. and Trustee; Robert J. Gaughran, Secy. and Trustee; Norma R. Pane, Treas. and Trustee.
EIN: 223176150

5436
The Kurtz Family Foundation, Inc.
271 Next Day Hill Ct.
Englewood, NJ 07631-1920

Established in 1996 in New Jersey.
Donors: Ronald Kurtz; Carol Kurtz; Steven Levitt.
Foundation type: Independent foundation.
Financial data (yr. ended 12/31/13): Assets, $4,508,083 (M); expenditures, $421,310; qualifying distributions, $359,750; giving activities include $356,000 for 53 grants (high: $107,500; low: $500).
Fields of interest: Museums; Education; Higher education; Business education; Environment; Nonprofits; Diseases and conditions; Human services; Ethnic and racial groups.
Type of support: Regranting.
Limitations: Applications not accepted. Giving primarily in MA. No grants to individuals.
Application information: Contributes only to pre-selected organizations.
Officers: Ronald Kurtz, Pres.; Carol Kurtz, Secy.
EIN: 223479749

5437
The Dale Kutnick & Laura Gordon Kutnick Foundation, Inc.
P.O. Box 1525, NJ2-130-03-31
Pennington, NJ 08534-1501

Established in 1996 in Connecticut.
Donor: Dale Kutnick.
Foundation type: Independent foundation.
Financial data (yr. ended 06/30/14): Assets, $6,926,673; gifts received, $1,388,275; expenditures, $340,611; qualifying distributions, $304,512.
Fields of interest: Education; Philanthropy; Human services.
Limitations: Applications not accepted. Giving primarily in CT and NY. No grants to individuals.
Application information: Unsolicited requests for funds not accepted.
Officers: Laura Gordon Kutnick, Pres.; Dale Kutnick, Secy.-Treas.
Trustee: Herbert Gordon.
EIN: 061469212

5438
The Carl and Gloria LaGrassa Family Foundation
4 Paisley Ln.
Basking Ridge, NJ 07920-3501

Established in 1998 in New Jersey.
Donors: Carl LaGrassa; Gloria LaGrassa.
Foundation type: Independent foundation.
Financial data (yr. ended 12/31/12): Assets, $1,083,395 (M); expenditures, $181,290; qualifying distributions, $165,775; giving activities include $165,775 for grants.
Fields of interest: Education; Religion; Human services.
Limitations: Applications not accepted. Giving primarily in PA. No grants to individuals.
Application information: Contributes only to pre-selected organizations.
Trustees: John Austin Gaines; Carl G. LaGrassa; Carla LaGrassa; Gloria LaGrassa.
EIN: 113439450

5439
Eugene W. & Gloria Landy Family Foundation
3499 Rte. 9 N., Ste. 3-C
Freehold, NJ 07728-3277
Contact: Eugene W. Landy, Tr.

Established in 2001 in New Jersey.
Donors: Eugene W. Landy; Gloria Landy.
Foundation type: Independent foundation.
Financial data (yr. ended 12/31/13): Assets, $2,146,624 (M); gifts received, $11,000; expenditures, $152,993; qualifying distributions, $149,743; giving activities include $149,743 for 44 grants (high: $40,000; low: $150).
Fields of interest: Education; Catholicism; Judaism; Human services.
Application information:
Initial approach: Proposal
Deadline(s): None
Trustees: Eugene W. Landy; Gloria Landy; Michael Landy; Samuel Landy.
EIN: 226903439

5440
Larson Family Foundation, Inc.
P.O. Box 1997
Morristown, NJ 07962-1997
Contact: P. Siana Porzio

Established in 1996 in Illinois.
Donors: Peter N. Larson; Maryle A. Larson.
Foundation type: Independent foundation.
Financial data (yr. ended 11/30/13): Assets, $4,837,144 (M); expenditures, $213,209; qualifying distributions, $191,566; giving activities include $160,500 for 9 grants (high: $105,000; low: $2,000).
Fields of interest: Arts and culture; Maritime museums; War memorials; Human services.
Type of support: General support.
Limitations: Applications not accepted. No grants to individuals.
Application information: Unsolicited requests for funds not accepted.
Officers and Trustees: Maryle A. Larson, Pres. and Trustee; Dana Larson Boote, Secy.-Treas. and Trustee; Peter N. Larson.
EIN: 311494115

5441
Lavery Foundation
15 Madison Ave.
Spring Lake, NJ 07762-1409

Established in 2001 in New Jersey.
Donors: Charlotte D. Lavery; John W. Lavery.
Foundation type: Independent foundation.
Financial data (yr. ended 06/30/13): Assets, $2,034,399 (M); gifts received, $300,000; expenditures, $204,394; qualifying distributions, $199,300; giving activities include $199,300 for 8 grants (high: $100,000; low: $1,000).
Fields of interest: University education; Diseases and conditions; Immune system diseases.
Type of support: Research.
Limitations: Applications not accepted. No grants to individuals.
Application information: Unsolicited requests for funds not accepted.
Trustees: Charlotte D. Lavery; John W. Lavery.
EIN: 226907824

5442
The Lazarus Charitable Trust
(formerly The Helen and Charles Lazarus Charitable Trust)
c/o Charles Lazarus, Toys R US
1 Geoffrey Way
Wayne, NJ 07470-2030

Established in 1986 in New Jersey.
Donor: Charles Lazarus.
Foundation type: Independent foundation.
Financial data (yr. ended 05/31/14): Assets, $4,000,904 (M); expenditures, $394,586; qualifying distributions, $348,575; giving activities include $348,575 for 43 grants (high: $120,000; low: $100).
Purpose and activities: Giving primarily to museums, as well as for health organizations, social services and Jewish agencies.
Fields of interest: Museums; Diseases and conditions; Judaism; Human services.

Limitations: Applications not accepted. Giving primarily in FL, New York, NY, and PA.
Application information: Contributes only to pre-selected organizations.
Officer: Charles Lazarus, Pres.
EIN: 133360876

5443
Bais Vaad Lchachomim Charitable Foundation
936 W. Kennedy Blvd.
Lakewood, NJ 08701-1258

Donors: Joseph Schonberger; Mosdos Gur; Madison Title Agency; Weiss Mayer; JJSP LLC; PSJJ; New Future Dreams; Pams Lunchroom.
Foundation type: Independent foundation.
Financial data (yr. ended 12/31/13): Assets, $41,705 (M); gifts received, $408,602; expenditures, $368,422; qualifying distributions, $368,278; giving activities include $368,278 for 9 grants.
Fields of interest: Judaism; Human services.
Limitations: Applications not accepted. Giving primarily in Lakewood, NJ, and Brooklyn, NY.
Application information: Unsolicited requests for funds not accepted.
Trustee: Joseph Schonberger.
EIN: 260299337

5444
The Leavens Foundation, Inc.
P.O. Box 673
Long Valley, NJ 07853 9738089500
Contact: Nancy Leavens, Pres.; Bill Leavens, Secy.
E-mail: leavensfoundation@gmail.com

Established in 1991 in New Jersey.
Foundation type: Independent foundation.
Financial data (yr. ended 12/31/14): Assets, $2,325,299; expenditures, $315,699; qualifying distributions, $288,422.
Purpose and activities: Giving primarily in the areas of water quality, open space, urban gardening, and family planning and services.
Fields of interest: Environment; Human services; Youth development.
Type of support: Capital and infrastructure; Matching grants; Equipment; Program development; Seed money.
Limitations: Applications not accepted. Giving primarily in Morris and Essex counties, NJ, and in areas where trustees live. No support for religious organizations (unless a board member has a direct affiliation). No grants to individuals.
Application information: Unsolicited requests for funds not accepted.
Board meeting date(s): May and Nov.
Officers: Nancy Leavens, Pres.; Bill Leavens, Secy.; William B. Leavens III, Treas.
Number of staff: None.
EIN: 521754606

5445
N. R. Leavitt Foundation
P.O. Box 4470
Warren, NJ 07059-0470 (908) 753-2440

Established in 1958 in New Jersey.
Donor: Nathan R. Leavitt†.

Foundation type: Independent foundation.
Financial data (yr. ended 12/31/14): Assets, $6,198,537; expenditures, $344,841; qualifying distributions, $341,414.
Fields of interest: Education; Health; Catholicism; Judaism; Human services.
Type of support: General support; Regranting; Fundraising.
Limitations: Applications accepted. Giving limited to the Elizabeth, NJ, area. No grants to individuals.
Application information: Grants generally awarded to the same six pre-selected organizations designated by the foundation's donor. Application form required.
  Initial approach: Proposal
  Deadline(s): Nov. 15
  Final notification: Dec.
Officers: Lawrence B. Diener, Pres.; William V. Engel, V.P.; R. Sean Devlin, Secy.; Martin B. O'Connor II, Treas.
EIN: 226034106

5446
The A. L. Levine Foundation, Inc.
(formerly Blanche & A. L. Levine Foundation, Inc.)
c/o Taxpayer
1 Wayne Hills Mall
Wayne, NJ   07470-3228

Established in 1996 in Florida.
Donor: A.L. Levine.
Foundation type: Independent foundation.
Financial data (yr. ended 09/30/13): Assets, $8,928,745 (M); expenditures, $513,116; qualifying distributions, $376,686; giving activities include $367,210 for 71 grants (high: $120,000; low: $100).
Fields of interest: Art museums; Foundations; Diseases and conditions; Judaism; Human services; Senior assisted living.
Limitations: Applications not accepted. Giving primarily in NJ and NY.
Application information: Contributes only to pre-selected organizations.
  Board meeting date(s): Yearly
Directors: Arthur L. Levine; Peter L. Levine; Adam J. Steiger; Andrew R. Steiger; Carole Ann Steiger; David L. Steiger; Joel J. Steiger.
EIN: 650554692

5447
The Lewis Foundation Inc.
c/o Kenneth R. Cohen, Davidson, Sochor, Ragsdale and Cohen, LLC
619 River Dr., Ste. 200
Elmwood Park, NJ   07407

Established in 1952 in New York.
Donors: Barbara Lewis; Salim B. Lewis†; Diana B. Lewis.
Foundation type: Independent foundation.
Financial data (yr. ended 08/31/13): Assets, $1,479,794 (M); expenditures, $409,250; qualifying distributions, $406,000; giving activities include $406,000 for 4 grants (high: $350,000; low: $1,000).
Fields of interest: Education; Higher education.
Limitations: Applications not accepted. Giving primarily in the New York metropolitan area. No grants to individuals.

Application information: Unsolicited requests for funds not accepted.
Officers: Salim B. Lewis, Pres.; Barbara Lewis, V.P.
EIN: 136062713

5448
The Judith & Lester Lieberman Foundation
685 Spring Valley Rd.
Morristown, NJ   07960-4454
Application address: c/o Judith Lieberman, 25 Lindsley Dr., Morristown, NJ, 07960 Tel: (973) 401-0050

Established in 1998 in New Jersey.
Donor: Lester Lieberman.
Foundation type: Independent foundation.
Financial data (yr. ended 12/31/13): Assets, $556,376 (M); gifts received, $373,984; expenditures, $177,007; qualifying distributions, $174,150; giving activities include $174,150 for 85 grants (high: $35,000; low: $10).
Purpose and activities: Giving primarily to Jewish organizations.
Fields of interest: Arts and culture; Education; Nonprofits; Hospital care; Judaism.
Type of support: Regranting.
Application information: Application form required.
  Initial approach: Letter
  Deadline(s): None
Officers: Judith Lieberman, Pres.; Jane Lieberman, V.P.; Susan Lieberman, Treas.
EIN: 223584229

5449
The Light Foundation, Inc.
429 15th St.
Lakewood, NJ   08701-1763

Established in 2006 in New Jersey.
Donors: David Gelley; Richard Roberts; Meir Gelley.
Foundation type: Independent foundation.
Financial data (yr. ended 12/31/13): Assets, $56,432 (M); gifts received, $185,600; expenditures, $198,761; qualifying distributions, $196,904; giving activities include $196,904 for 315 grants (high: $29,765; low: $18).
Fields of interest: Education; Judaism.
Limitations: Applications not accepted.
Application information: Contributes only to pre-selected organizations.
Officer: Meir Gelley, Pres.
EIN: 208111464

5450
The Lipper Family Charitable Foundation
c/o A. Michael Lipper
85 Hobart Ave.
Summit, NJ   07901-2808

Established in 1999 in New Jersey.
Donors: A. Michael Lipper; Ruth C. Lipper.
Foundation type: Independent foundation.
Financial data (yr. ended 11/30/13): Assets, $327,111 (M); expenditures, $188,679; qualifying distributions, $188,450; giving activities include $188,450 for 25 grants (high: $116,250; low: $100).
Purpose and activities: Giving primarily for the arts, particularly the symphony, as well as for education,

human services, health associations, and Episcopal churches.
Fields of interest: Arts and culture; Education; Human services.
Limitations: Applications not accepted. Giving primarily in NJ. No grants to individuals.
Application information: Unsolicited requests for funds not accepted.
Trustees: A. Michael Lipper; Ruth C. Lipper.
EIN: 137152755

5451
Harold I. & Faye B. Liss Foundation, Inc.
c/o Berkowitz Licht
75 Livingston Ave.
Roseland, NJ   07068-3093

Foundation type: Independent foundation.
Financial data (yr. ended 12/31/13): Assets, $4,785,417 (M); expenditures, $322,973; qualifying distributions, $249,500; giving activities include $227,500 for 16 grants (high: $50,000; low: $5,000).
Fields of interest: Higher education; Hospital care; Judaism.
Limitations: Applications not accepted. Giving primarily in NJ and NY. No grants to individuals.
Application information: Contributes only to pre-selected organizations.
Officers: Bernard S. Berkowitz, Chair.; Sandra Sussman, Secy.; Edward Haiken, Treas.
Trustees: Robert Sobel; Howard Sussman.
EIN: 223367243

5452
M/S Family Foundation
641 5th St.
Lakewood, NJ   08701-3227

Established in 2000 in New Jersey.
Donors: Moshe Mueller; Mueller and Co., Inc.; Harry Adler; Merit Consulting LLC; Cashmere Capital; Shlansky Free Loan Fund of BMG; Valcent Products Inc.; Global Green Solutions; Igor Chesnomzav Trust; Joseph Teichman.
Foundation type: Company-sponsored foundation.
Financial data (yr. ended 05/31/13): Assets, $2,574,221 (M); gifts received, $12,312; expenditures, $156,919; qualifying distributions, $144,105; giving activities include $144,105 for 121 grants (high: $29,000; low: $18).
Purpose and activities: The foundation supports organizations involved with education and Judaism.
Fields of interest: Arts and culture; Education; Human services.
Limitations: Applications not accepted. Giving primarily in NJ. No grants to individuals.
Application information: Contributes only to pre-selected organizations.
Trustees: Moshe Mueller; Shoshana Mueller.
EIN: 316642915

5453
The Bradley T. MacDonald Family Foundation, Inc.
(formerly The MacDonald Family Foundation, Inc.)
P.O. Box 1501, NJ2-130-03-31
Pennington, NJ   08534-1501

Established in 2004 in Delaware.

Donors: Brad MacDonald; Shirley MacDonald; Margaret MacDonald.
Foundation type: Independent foundation.
Financial data (yr. ended 12/31/13): Assets, $3,786,530 (M); expenditures, $185,459; qualifying distributions, $171,265; giving activities include $160,250 for 20 grants (high: $30,000; low: $750).
Fields of interest: Diseases and conditions; Human services.
Type of support: Research.
Limitations: Applications not accepted. Giving primarily in FL, MD, OH, PA and TN. No grants to individuals.
Application information: Unsolicited requests for funds not accepted.
Officers and Directors: Brad MacDonald, Pres. and Director; Kellie MacDonald Pizzico, V.P. and Fdn. Admin.; Margaret MacDonald, V.P.; Shirley MacDonald, V.P. and Director.
EIN: 200767790

5454
The John Victor Machuga Foundation Inc.
P.O. Box 738
Totowa, NJ 07511-0738

Established in 1994 in New Jersey.
Donor: John Victor Machuga†.
Foundation type: Independent foundation.
Financial data (yr. ended 12/31/14): Assets, $2,686,640; expenditures, $355,986; qualifying distributions, $315,250.
Purpose and activities: Giving primarily for higher education and hospitals.
Fields of interest: Higher education; Hospital care; Human services.
Type of support: Capital campaigns; Matching grants; Equipment; Program development.
Limitations: Applications not accepted. Giving primarily in northern NJ. No grants to individuals, or for salaries or construction.
Application information: Contributes only to pre-selected organizations.
Trustees: Albert V. Dahab; Joseph M. Makoujy; Stacy Waldman.
EIN: 223162765

5455
The Ingrid Mahan Foundation
P.O. Box 367
Millington, NJ 07946-0367 (908) 542-0055
Contact: Robert Goldstein, Tr.

Established in 2004 in New Jersey.
Donors: Ingrid T. Mahan; Wayne C. Stansill; Marvin Mahan.
Foundation type: Independent foundation.
Financial data (yr. ended 12/31/13): Assets, $4,618,863 (M); gifts received, $300,000; expenditures, $208,961; qualifying distributions, $178,013; giving activities include $161,985 for grants.
Purpose and activities: Giving primarily for cancer and heart disease.
Fields of interest: Education; Health; Science.
Application information: Application form required.
  Initial approach: Letter
  Deadline(s): None

Trustees: Nancy M. Ernst; Robert Goldstein; Ingrid T. Mahan.
EIN: 202033950

5456
The Mamiye Foundation, Inc.
180 Raritan Center Pkwy.
Edison, NJ 08837-3646

Established in 1982 in New Jersey.
Donors: Mamiye Brothers, Inc.; MB Kids Clothes LLC; Hyman M. Mamiye; Mamiye Sales.
Foundation type: Company-sponsored foundation.
Financial data (yr. ended 12/31/14): Assets, $110,495; gifts received, $204,796; expenditures, $256,920; qualifying distributions, $256,890.
Purpose and activities: The foundation supports hospitals and organizations involved with education, children and youth, disability services, and Judaism.
Fields of interest: Education; Elementary and secondary education; Nonprofits; Hospital care; Judaism; Child welfare; Developmental disability services.
Type of support: Annual campaigns; Capital and infrastructure; Program development; Scholarships; Sponsorships; Regranting.
Limitations: Applications accepted. Giving primarily in Deal and Ocean, NJ and Brooklyn and New York, NY. No grants to individuals.
Application information: Application form required.
  Initial approach: Letter
  Deadline(s): None
Trustees: Abraham Mamiye; Charles D. Mamiye; Charles M. Mamiye; Hyman M. Mamiye.
EIN: 222471712

5457
Joseph and Cheryl Marino Family Foundation, Inc.
70 Grand Ave., Ste. 109
River Edge, NJ 07661-1936

Established in 2007 in New Jersey.
Donor: Joseph Marino.
Foundation type: Independent foundation.
Financial data (yr. ended 12/31/13): Assets, $119,247 (M); gifts received, $100,000; expenditures, $270,334; qualifying distributions, $266,464; giving activities include $266,464 for 26 grants (high: $30,000; low: $500).
Fields of interest: Education; Health; Christianity; Judaism; Human services.
Limitations: Applications not accepted. Giving primarily in NJ. No grants to individuals.
Application information: Unsolicited requests for funds not accepted.
Officers: Joseph Marino, Pres.; Cheryl Marino, V.P.
EIN: 261604015

5458
Paula and William J. Marino Family Foundation
P.O. Box 1501, NJ2-130-03-31
Pennington, NJ 08534-1501

Donors: William J. Marino; Paula Marino.
Foundation type: Independent foundation.
Financial data (yr. ended 12/31/13): Assets, $3,458,332 (M); expenditures, $388,160;

qualifying distributions, $351,714; giving activities include $339,378 for grants.
Type of support: General support.
Limitations: Applications not accepted.
Application information: Unsolicited request for funds not accepted.
Officers and Trustees: William J. Marino, Pres. and Treas. and Trustee; Paula Marino, V.P. and Secy.; Douglas W. Marino; Gregory S. Marino; Lauren M. Marino; Megan M. Marino.
EIN: 453967497

5459
Markey Family Foundation, Inc.
c/o P. Siana Porzio Bromberg & Newman
P.O. Box 1997
Morristown, NJ 07962-1997

Established in 2002 in New Jersey.
Donors: Andrew J. Markey; Elizabeth M. Markey.
Foundation type: Independent foundation.
Financial data (yr. ended 12/31/13): Assets, $893,947 (M); gifts received, $217,882; expenditures, $224,194; qualifying distributions, $215,235; giving activities include $208,625 for 25 grants (high: $75,000; low: $50).
Fields of interest: Education; Catholicism; Human services.
Limitations: Applications not accepted. No grants to individuals.
Application information: Unsolicited requests for funds not accepted.
Officers and Trustees: Andrew J. Markey, Pres. and Trustee; Elizabeth M. Markey, Secy.-Treas. and Trustee; Jean M. Finsen; Kevin A. Markey; Michael G. Markey; Timothy P. Markey; Mary Ellen Mayer.
EIN: 300072584

5460
Markowitz Family Foundation
c/o Goldmark Group
1155 Bloomfield Ave.
Clifton, NJ 07012-2308

Established in 1999 in New York.
Donors: Eugene Markowitz; The Goldmark Group, Inc.; Mark Gold L.P.; Renee Markowitz.
Foundation type: Company-sponsored foundation.
Financial data (yr. ended 06/30/12): Assets, $277,207 (M); gifts received, $251,546; expenditures, $178,442; qualifying distributions, $178,442; giving activities include $178,442 for 31 + grants (high: $87,500).
Purpose and activities: The foundation supports organizations involved with Judaism.
Fields of interest: Diseases and conditions; Religion; Human services.
Limitations: Applications not accepted. No grants to individuals.
Application information: Unsolicited requests for funds not accepted.
EIN: 134035030

5461
The Marron Foundation, Inc.
118 State Rt. 17 N.
Upper Saddle River, NJ 07458-2354

Established in 2006 in New Jersey.
Donor: Dorothy Marron†.

Foundation type: Independent foundation.
Financial data (yr. ended 12/31/13): Assets, $4,624,030 (M); expenditures, $276,023; qualifying distributions, $225,723; giving activities include $202,023 for 21 grants (high: $109,873; low: $200).
Fields of interest: Education; Hospital care; Christianity; Human services; Family services; Child welfare.
Limitations: Applications not accepted. Giving primarily in NJ and NY. No grants to individuals.
Application information: Unsolicited requests for funds not accepted.
Trustees: Frank Centrella; Martha Marron; Peter Marron.
EIN: 208081437

5462
The Maschler Family Foudation
(formerly The Manor Charitable Fund)
110 Fieldcrest Ave.
Edison, NJ 08837-3626
Application address: c/o Matthew Maschler, 2255 Glades Rd., Ste. 324A, Boca Raton, FL 33431, tel.: (561) 208-3334

Established in 2001 in New York.
Foundation type: Independent foundation.
Financial data (yr. ended 12/31/13): Assets, $3,288,786 (M); expenditures, $165,146; qualifying distributions, $160,063; giving activities include $160,063 for 24 grants (high: $85,000; low: $18).
Fields of interest: Nonprofits; Diseases and conditions; Judaism.
Type of support: General support; Regranting; Research.
Limitations: Applications accepted. Giving primarily in FL. No grants to individuals.
Application information: Application form required.
  Initial approach: Letterhead
  Deadline(s): None
Directors: Erik Maschler; Matthew Maschler; Sheldon Maschler.
EIN: 137268385

5463
Robert Earl McConnell Foundation
P.O. Box 1501, NJ2-130-03-31
Pennington, NJ 08534-1501

Established in 1936 in Florida.
Foundation type: Independent foundation.
Financial data (yr. ended 12/31/14): Assets, $2,234,255; expenditures, $204,849; qualifying distributions, $175,192.
Purpose and activities: Giving for education, environmental organizations, community and youth services, and for health services.
Fields of interest: Secondary education; Higher education; Hospital care; Diseases and conditions; Human services; Child welfare.
Limitations: Applications not accepted. Giving primarily in FL, MA, NY, and VA. No grants to individuals.
Application information: Contributes only to pre-selected organizations.
Officer: James S. Kelly, Exec. V.P.
Trustees: Jennifer Arndt; Cameron Brooks; Polly McConnell; Andrew Pott; Tony Wagner.
EIN: 596153509

5464
McCrane Foundation, Inc.
P.O. Box 1501, NJ2-130-03-31
Pennington, NJ 08534-1501

Established in 1992 in New Jersey.
Donors: John A. McCrane; Margit McCrane.
Foundation type: Independent foundation.
Financial data (yr. ended 12/31/14): Assets, $2,462,392; expenditures, $369,155; qualifying distributions, $344,983.
Fields of interest: Arts and culture; Performing arts; Orchestral music; Higher education; Human services.
Type of support: General support.
Limitations: Applications not accepted. Giving primarily in NJ and PA. No grants to individuals.
Application information: Contributes only to pre-selected organizations.
Trustees: John A. McCrane; Margit McCrane.
EIN: 223170915

5465
McDowell Foundation
c/o GLC
1 International Blvd., Ste. 700
Mahwah, NJ 07495-0019

Donors: Laura McCurdy; Linn Feidelson; Fletcher H. McDowell; Electra V. McDowell; Robert Feidelson.
Foundation type: Independent foundation.
Financial data (yr. ended 12/31/13): Assets, $1,990,874 (M); gifts received, $424,158; expenditures, $263,547; qualifying distributions, $239,790; giving activities include $239,790 for 27 grants (high: $100,000; low: $150).
Fields of interest: Education; Diseases and conditions.
Type of support: General support; Research.
Limitations: Applications not accepted. Giving primarily in New York, NY. No grants to individuals.
Application information: Unsolicited requests for funds not accepted.
Trustees: Linn Feidelson; Robert Feidelson; Electra V. Lang; Laura McCurdy; Fletcher H. McDowell.
EIN: 136172492

5466
Milano Foundation, Inc.
c/o Robert J. DiQuollo
One Giralda Farms, Ste. 130
Madison, NJ 07940-1027

Donors: Robert J. Milano; Sidonia Milano Charitable Lead Trust.
Foundation type: Independent foundation.
Financial data (yr. ended 12/31/13): Assets, $2,196,383 (M); gifts received, $105,000; expenditures, $460,348; qualifying distributions, $444,325; giving activities include $437,025 for 26 grants (high: $112,500; low: $1,500).
Fields of interest: Arts and culture; Education; Higher education; Health; Judaism; Child welfare.
Limitations: Applications not accepted. Giving primarily in CA, NJ and NY. No grants to individuals.
Application information: Contributes only to pre-selected organizations.
Officers and Trustees: Robert J. DiQuollo, Pres.; Colleen Betzler, V.P. and Trustee.
EIN: 132620691

5467
The Miller Family Endowment, Inc.
3 Wilshire Terr.
Livingston, NJ 07039-6214 2122970400

Established in 2000 in Delaware.
Donors: Carol Miller; Paul Miller.
Foundation type: Independent foundation.
Financial data (yr. ended 12/31/13): Assets, $3,383,153; expenditures, $183,081; qualifying distributions, $152,436.
Fields of interest: Education; Judaism; Human services.
Limitations: Applications not accepted. No grants to individuals.
Application information: Unsolicited requests for funds not accepted.
Officers: Paul S. Miller, Chair.; Carol P. Miller, Co-Pres.; Margo H. Weill, Co-Pres.; Jason Miller, V.P. and Secy.; Nicole F. Gould, V.P. and Treas.
EIN: 223761835

5468
Steve J. Miller Foundation
P.O. Box 1501, NJ2-130-03-31
Pennington, NJ 08534-1501 (609) 274-1979
Contact: Michael Fox

Established in 1946 in Wisconsin.
Donors: Central Cheese Co., Inc.; Steve J. Miller†.
Foundation type: Independent foundation.
Financial data (yr. ended 12/31/13): Assets, $3,010,297 (M); expenditures, $213,299; qualifying distributions, $186,942; giving activities include $170,500 for 24 grants (high: $31,000; low: $1,000).
Purpose and activities: Funding primarily for education and children's services.
Fields of interest: Arts and culture; Education; Environment; Health; Human services; Child welfare.
Type of support: General support; Pro bono consulting services; Matching grants; Continuing support; Financial sustainability; Annual campaigns; Capital campaigns; Capital and infrastructure; Equipment; Endowments; Debt reduction; Emergency funds; Program development; Convening; Curriculum development; Fellowships; Scholarships; Research.
Limitations: Applications accepted. Giving primarily in AZ.
Publications: Application guidelines.
Application information: Application form required.
  Initial approach: Letter
  Copies of proposal: 1
  Deadline(s): None
  Board meeting date(s): June
Officers: Norman C. Miller, Chair.; Paulina Miller, Vice-Chair.; James Holcomb, Secy.-Treas.
Trustees: Theodore W. Miller; Kurt Spreyer.
Number of staff: None.
EIN: 396051879

5469
Minerva Foundation
P.O. Box 1501, NJ2-130-03-31
Pennington, NJ 08534-1501

Established in 2003 in Virginia.
Donors: Kristie Miller; Kristie Miller Charitable Annuity Trust.

Foundation type: Independent foundation.
Financial data (yr. ended 10/31/14): Assets, $7,884,733 (M); gifts received, $300,000; expenditures, $381,513; qualifying distributions, $322,684; giving activities include $301,678 for 9 grants (high: $100,000; low: $1,678).
Fields of interest: Arts and culture; History museums; Education; Undergraduate education; Family services; Scouting programs.
Limitations: Applications not accepted. Giving primarily in Washington, DC, IL and NY. No grants to individuals.
Application information: Contributes only to pre-selected organizations.
Officers: Kristie Miller, Pres.; William S. Twaddell, V.P.; Ellen Johnson Twaddell, Secy.
EIN: 201836334

5470
The Minio Family Foundation Inc.
26 Rancho Polo
Colts Neck, NJ   07722-2506   7323801522

Established in 1998 in New Jersey.
Donor: John Minio.
Foundation type: Independent foundation.
Financial data (yr. ended 09/30/14): Assets, $1,944,744; gifts received, $0; expenditures, $177,336; qualifying distributions, $144,995 and $0 for set-asides.
Fields of interest: Education; Undergraduate education; Health; Diseases and conditions.
Type of support: General support.
Limitations: Applications not accepted. No grants to individuals.
Application information: Unsolicited requests for funds not accepted.
Officers: John Minio, Pres. and Treas.; Loraine Minio, V.P. and Secy.; Anthony Minio, V.P.
EIN: 223621436

5471
Jacques H. & Selma Mitrani Foundation
(formerly Jacques H. Mitrani Foundation)
125 Dunnell Rd., Apt. 304
Maplewood, NJ   07040-2682

Established in 1969 in Pennsylvania.
Donor: Selma T. Mitrani†.
Foundation type: Independent foundation.
Financial data (yr. ended 07/31/14): Assets, $5,678,141 (M); gifts received, $32,150; expenditures, $355,295; qualifying distributions, $290,157; giving activities include $275,400 for 7 grants (high: $150,000; low: $2,900).
Fields of interest: Education; Judaism.
Type of support: General support.
Limitations: Applications not accepted. No grants to individuals.
Application information: Unsolicited requests for funds not accepted.
Trustees: Jill Comerchero; Leonard Comerchero; Matthew Comerchero; Melissa Comerchero; Myrna Comerchero.
EIN: 237103779

5472
MNS Foundation
29 Chicanos Dr.
Lakewood, NJ   08701-1520   (732) 905-8449
Contact: Mordechai Schon, Tr.

Donor: Mordechai Schon.
Foundation type: Independent foundation.
Financial data (yr. ended 12/31/13): Assets, $1,083,339 (M); gifts received, $300,000; expenditures, $179,854; qualifying distributions, $179,830; giving activities include $178,775 for 54 grants (high: $32,300; low: $125).
Fields of interest: Religion.
Limitations: Applications accepted. Giving primarily in NJ.
Application information: Application form required.
  Initial approach: Letter
  Deadline(s): None
Trustees: Mordechai Schon; Nissele Schon.
EIN: 263738591

5473
Edmond N. & Virginia H. Moriarty Charitable Foundation, Inc.
c/o C.P. Abraham
1 Jefferson Rd.
Parsippany, NJ   07054-2891

Established in 1997 in New Jersey.
Donor: Virginia H. Moriarty.
Foundation type: Independent foundation.
Financial data (yr. ended 12/31/14): Assets, $2,404,467; gifts received, $1,375; expenditures, $326,881; qualifying distributions, $318,000.
Purpose and activities: Giving primarily for education.
Fields of interest: Education; Human services; Youth development.
Limitations: Applications not accepted. Giving primarily in NJ, NY and PA. No grants to individuals.
Application information: Contributes only to pre-selected organizations.
Officers and Directors: Virginia H. Moriarty, Pres. and Director; Edmond N. Moriarty III, V.P. and Treas. and Director; Elizabeth N. Moriarty, Secy. and Director; Susan M. Gallagher; John D. Moriarty; Mary Ellen Moriarty; Patricia M. Parisi; Kathleen M. Skiff.
EIN: 223666468

5474
MTB Charitable Foundation Ltd.
105 Harbor Dr.
Jersey City, NJ   07305-4505

Established in 2001 in New Jersey.
Donors: Mendel Brachfeld; Tina Brachfeld; Star Snacks Co., LLC.
Foundation type: Independent foundation.
Financial data (yr. ended 11/30/13): Assets, $797,761 (M); gifts received, $535,403; expenditures, $364,890; qualifying distributions, $364,890; giving activities include $364,321 for 186 grants (high: $100,000; low: $36).
Fields of interest: Nonprofits; Judaism.
Type of support: Regranting.
Limitations: Applications not accepted. Giving primarily in NJ and NY. No grants to individuals.
Application information: Contributes only to pre-selected organizations.

Trustees: Jacob Brachfeld; Mendel Brachfeld; Tina Brachfeld.
EIN: 300084835

5475
Boyd and Evelyn Mullen Charitable Foundation
P.O. Box 1501, NJ2-130-03-31
Pennington, NJ   08534-0671
Application address: c/o Merrill Lynch, Div. of Bank of America, Attn.: Becky Buschkel, 1221 McKinney St., Ste. 3800, Houston, TX 77010, tel.: (713) 422-8321

Donors: Evelyn Z. Mullen†; Boyd Mullen Estate Trust.
Foundation type: Independent foundation.
Financial data (yr. ended 12/31/13): Assets, $6,308,493 (M); expenditures, $256,013; qualifying distributions, $210,483; giving activities include $171,000 for 13 grants (high: $30,000; low: $2,500).
Fields of interest: Education; Diseases and conditions; Housing development.
Type of support: Research.
Limitations: Applications accepted. Giving primarily in TX.
Application information: Application form required.
  Initial approach: Contact foundation for application form
  Deadline(s): Sept. 30
Trustees: Barton Bentley; Amanda Gyeszly; Bank of America.
EIN: 452235211

5476
H. Herbert Myers Memorial Foundation
c/o McCabe Heidrich & Wong, P.C.
4 Gatehall Dr.
Parsippany, NJ   07054-4518

Established in 1964 in New York.
Foundation type: Independent foundation.
Financial data (yr. ended 12/31/13): Assets, $5,139,145 (M); expenditures, $277,838; qualifying distributions, $221,560; giving activities include $206,435 for 70 grants (high: $82,835; low: $25).
Purpose and activities: Giving primarily to Jewish agencies and temples.
Fields of interest: Higher education; Nonprofits; Diseases and conditions; Judaism.
Type of support: Regranting.
Limitations: Applications not accepted. No grants to individuals.
Application information: Unsolicited requests for funds not accepted.
Trustees: Philip Berman; Martin Myers.
EIN: 116044697

5477
The Navesink Foundation
c/o Tripar, J. Hugh Devlin
47 W. River Rd., Ste. A
Rumson, NJ   07760-1311

Established in 1998 in New Jersey.
Donor: J. Hugh Devlin.
Foundation type: Independent foundation.

Financial data (yr. ended 12/31/13): Assets, $5,158,131 (M); gifts received, $20,620; expenditures, $299,587; qualifying distributions, $250,664; giving activities include $230,044 for 59 grants (high: $50,000; low: $1).
Purpose and activities: Giving primarily to education and social services.
Fields of interest: Arts and culture; Education; Higher education; Water resources; Nonprofits; Health; Catholicism; Human services.
Type of support: Regranting.
Limitations: Applications not accepted. Giving primarily in CA, NJ and PA.
Application information: Contributes only to pre-selected organizations.
Trustees: J. Hugh Devlin; Nancy Devlin.
EIN: 137154218

5478
Levon & Claudia Nazarian Foundation, Inc.
21 Cameo Ct.
Cherry Hill, NJ   08003-5124

Established in 2001 in New Jersey.
Donors: Levon Nazarian; Nazar Nazarian; Artemis Nazarian; Nazarian Family Foundation.
Foundation type: Independent foundation.
Financial data (yr. ended 12/31/13): Assets, $5,963,615 (M); gifts received, $25,000; expenditures, $221,149; qualifying distributions, $221,700; giving activities include $221,700 for 30 grants (high: $140,200; low: $500).
Fields of interest: Education; Human services.
International interests: Armenia.
Limitations: Applications not accepted. Giving primarily in NY and PA. No grants to individuals.
Application information: Unsolicited requests for funds not accepted.
Directors: Claudia Nazarian; Levon Nazarian; Nazar Nazarian.
EIN: 113587458

5479
Nitzavim Trust
P.O. Box 703
Edison, NJ   08818-0703

Donors: Herschel Parnes; The Herschel Parnes 2008 Grandchildren; E. H. Parnes Foundation.
Foundation type: Independent foundation.
Financial data (yr. ended 12/31/13): Assets, $4,531,909 (M); gifts received, $572,533; expenditures, $264,423; qualifying distributions, $264,423; giving activities include $255,761 for 28 grants (high: $50,000; low: $50).
Fields of interest: Religion.
Limitations: Applications not accepted. Giving primarily in NJ and NY.
Application information: Unsolicited requests for funds not accepted.
Officer: Herschel Parnes, Mgr.
EIN: 263819354

5480
The Olsen Foundation, a New Jersey Nonprofit Corporation
66 Witherspoon, Ste. 272
Princeton, NJ   08542-3226   (609) 466-4661
Contact: Gregory H. Olsen, Tr.

Donor: Gregory H. Olsen.
Foundation type: Independent foundation.
Financial data (yr. ended 12/31/13): Assets, $23,387 (M); gifts received, $188,855; expenditures, $230,052; qualifying distributions, $229,362; giving activities include $223,950 for 19 grants (high: $50,000; low: $450).
Purpose and activities: Giving primarily for higher education, as well as for youth development, and social services.
Fields of interest: Education; Higher education; Human services; Youth development; Youth services; Adult and child mentoring.
Limitations: Applications accepted. Giving primarily in NJ.
Application information: Application form required.
  Initial approach: Letter
  Deadline(s): None
Trustees: Krista J. Dibsie; Kimberly A. Lapadula; Gregory H. Olsen.
EIN: 260029441

5481
The O'Neal Foundation, Inc.
c/o Merrill Lynch Trust Co.
P.O. Box 1560
Pennington, NJ   08534-0746

Established in 2000 in New York.
Donors: E. Stanley O'Neal; Nancy A. Garvey.
Foundation type: Independent foundation.
Financial data (yr. ended 09/30/13): Assets, $2,258,187 (M); gifts received, $7,500; expenditures, $321,038; qualifying distributions, $265,000; giving activities include $265,000 for 9 grants (high: $100,000; low: $5,000).
Fields of interest: Performing arts; Education; Health; Specialty hospital care; Cancers; Child welfare.
Limitations: Applications not accepted. Giving primarily in NJ and NY. No grants to individuals.
Application information: Contributes only to pre-selected organizations.
Officers: E. Stanley O'Neal, Pres.; Jerome L. Levine, Secy.; Nancy A. Garvey, Treas.
EIN: 134122557

5482
Onyx and Breezy Foundation
160 Summit Ave.
Montvale, NJ   07645-1750
Application address: c/o Mark Shefts, P.O. Box 656, Tuxedo Park, NY 10987, tel.: (201) 782-7400

Established in 2005 in New York.
Donors: Mark Shefts; Rothstein Rosenfeldt Adler; Penson Financial Services; LMB Funding; Assents LLC; The NIR Group.
Foundation type: Independent foundation.
Financial data (yr. ended 12/31/12): Assets, $394,045 (M); gifts received, $358,194; expenditures, $399,284; qualifying distributions, $383,503; giving activities include $271,766 for 48 + grants (high: $34,407).
Fields of interest: Animal welfare.
Type of support: General support.
Limitations: Applications accepted. Giving primarily in CA, FL and NJ. No grants to individuals.
Application information: Application form required.
  Initial approach: Proposal
  Deadline(s): None

Trustees: Mark Shefts; Wanda Shefts.
EIN: 137437754

5483
The Ostberg Foundation, Inc.
87 Ruckman Rd.
P.O. Box 1098
Alpine, NJ   07620-1098
Contact: Christine Dineen

Established in 1980 in New York.
Donor: Henry D. Ostberg.
Foundation type: Independent foundation.
Financial data (yr. ended 11/30/13): Assets, $679,773 (M); gifts received, $552,215; expenditures, $159,013; qualifying distributions, $149,477; giving activities include $84,303 for grants, and $65,174 for 23 grants to individuals (high: $22,932; low: $250).
Purpose and activities: Provides assistance to the elderly and ill.
Fields of interest: Senior services; Seniors; Homeless people; Low-income and poor people; People with disabilities.
International interests: Africa; Europe; Haiti.
Type of support: General support; Grants to individuals; Matching grants.
Limitations: Applications accepted. Giving on a national and international basis. No grants for educational purposes.
Application information: Grants to individuals made by referral from social service agencies. Application form required.
  Initial approach: Letter
  Copies of proposal: 1
  Deadline(s): None
  Board meeting date(s): Quarterly
Officers and Directors: Henry D. Ostberg, Pres. and Director; Neal Ostberg, V.P. and Director; Sydelle Ostberg, Secy. and Director; Brent Burns; Christine Dineen.
EIN: 132963335

5484
Oster Family Foundation, Inc.
429 Sylvan Ave.
Englewood Cliffs, NJ   07632-2703

Established in 1992 in New Jersey.
Donors: Commercial Realty; Bernard Oster, Inc.; Oster Realty; ABA Realty; Interstate Realty; Miriam Oster†; Oster Finance; Oster Properties LLP.
Foundation type: Operating foundation.
Financial data (yr. ended 04/30/14): Assets, $6,452,165 (M); expenditures, $456,685; qualifying distributions, $441,740.
Purpose and activities: Giving for Jewish organizations, including to a museum of Jewish heritage.
Fields of interest: Museums; Education; Nonprofits; Diseases and conditions; Judaism; Human services.
Type of support: Regranting.
Limitations: Applications not accepted. Giving primarily in NJ and NY. No grants to individuals.
Application information: Contributes only to pre-selected organizations.
Officers: Ann Oster, Pres.; Avi Oster, V.P.; Dan Oster, V.P.
EIN: 223188305

5485
The Pacific Foundation, Inc.
(formerly The John S. Johnson III Foundation, Inc.)
P.O. Box 369
Hopewell, NJ   08525-0369
Main URL: http://www.thepacificfoundation.org

Established in 1998 in New Jersey.
Donors: Johnson 1998 Charitable Trust No. 1;
Johnson 1998 Charitable Trust No. 2; John S.
Johnson III; Atlantic Foundation; India Blake
Foundation; Joyce & Stuart Johnson Foundation.
Foundation type: Independent foundation.
Financial data (yr. ended 12/31/13): Assets,
$398,540 (M); gifts received, $646,866;
expenditures, $647,231; qualifying distributions,
$531,843; giving activities include $409,026 for 16
grants (high: $280,000; low: $576).
Fields of interest: Arts and culture; Education;
Psychology and behavioral science; Communication
media.
Type of support: General support.
Limitations: Applications not accepted. Giving
primarily in NY. No grants to individuals.
Application information: Contributes only to
pre-selected organizations.
Officers: John S. Johnson III, Pres.; Susan Short,
V.P.; Michael Greenleaf, Secy.; Lakshman Acuthan,
Treas.
EIN: 223606109

5486
Palmer Walbridge Foundation
P.O. Box 1501, NJ2-130-03-31
Pennington, NJ   08534-1501

Established in 2002 in Florida.
Donor: Kenneth Walbridge.
Foundation type: Independent foundation.
Financial data (yr. ended 12/31/13): Assets,
$3,502,077 (M); expenditures, $209,882;
qualifying distributions, $199,055; giving activities
include $180,000 for 21 grants (high: $52,000;
low: $1,000).
Fields of interest: Education; Environment;
Botanical gardens; Human services.
Type of support: General support.
Limitations: Applications not accepted. Giving
primarily in ME. No grants to individuals.
Application information: Unsolicited requests for
funds not accepted.
Trustee: Merrill Lynch Trust Co.
EIN: 016174485

5487
The Larry and Nancy Pantirer Family Foundation, Inc.
60 E. Hartshorn Dr.
Short Hills, NJ   07078-1630   (973) 992-2443
Contact: Nancy Pantirer, Tr.; Larry Pantirer, Tr.

Established in 1999 in New Jersey.
Donors: Larry Pantirer; Nancy Pantirer.
Foundation type: Independent foundation.
Financial data (yr. ended 10/31/13): Assets,
$51,430 (M); gifts received, $219,690;
expenditures, $177,699; qualifying distributions,
$176,759; giving activities include $175,820 for 27
grants (high: $51,000; low: $100).

Fields of interest: Education; Higher education;
Nonprofits; Cancers; Judaism; Human services;
People with vision impairments.
Type of support: Regranting.
Limitations: Applications accepted. Giving primarily
in MD, NJ and NY.
Application information: Application form required.
  Initial approach: Letter
  Deadline(s): None
Trustees: David Pantirer; Larry Pantirer; Nancy
Pantirer.
EIN: 223693281

5488
Paragano Family Foundation, Inc.
222 Mt. Airy Rd., Ste. 203
Basking Ridge, NJ   07920-2336
Contact: Nazario Paragano, Tr.

Established in 1983 in New Jersey.
Donor: Nazario Paragano.
Foundation type: Independent foundation.
Financial data (yr. ended 12/31/13): Assets,
$7,561,418 (M); gifts received, $263,300;
expenditures, $376,431; qualifying distributions,
$350,750; giving activities include $340,800 for 60
grants (high: $25,000; low: $300).
Purpose and activities: Giving primarily for Roman
Catholic churches, religious orders and agencies,
including youth services; support also for health and
education.
Fields of interest: Education; Health; Hospital care;
Alzheimer's disease; Cancers; Catholicism; Human
services; Youth services.
Type of support: General support.
Limitations: Applications accepted. Giving primarily
in CT, NJ, and NY. No grants to individuals.
Application information: Application form required.
  Initial approach: Letter
  Copies of proposal: 1
  Board meeting date(s): Sept.
Trustees: Eileen Paragano; Nazario Paragano.
EIN: 222483286

5489
Parnassus Foundation
25 N. Murray Ave.
Ridgewood, NJ   07450-3008

Established in 1986 in Delaware.
Donor: Raphael Bernstein.
Foundation type: Independent foundation.
Financial data (yr. ended 11/30/13): Assets,
$131,322 (M); gifts received, $48,672;
expenditures, $250,577; qualifying distributions,
$243,742; giving activities include $237,065 for 9
grants (high: $125,000; low: $250).
Purpose and activities: Giving primarily for museum
exhibitions, related catalogues, and educational
programs; funding also for higher education.
Fields of interest: Arts and culture; Art museums;
Education; Higher education.
International interests: Canada.
Type of support: General support.
Limitations: Applications not accepted. Giving
primarily in Washington, DC, and New York, NY;
giving also in Canada. No grants to individuals.
Application information: Unsolicited requests for
funds not accepted.

Officers: Raphael Bernstein, Pres.; Jane Bernstein,
V.P.; Carol Boulanger, Secy.
EIN: 521491214

5490
Pasternak Family Foundation
c/o Chestnut Ridge Capital, LLC
85 Challenger Rd., Ste. 501
Ridgefield Park, NJ   07660-2112

Established in 2004 in New Jersey.
Donor: Kenneth Pasternak.
Foundation type: Independent foundation.
Financial data (yr. ended 06/30/13): Assets,
$4,018,881 (M); expenditures, $223,055;
qualifying distributions, $217,919; giving activities
include $201,765 for 22 grants (high: $70,500;
low: $100).
Fields of interest: Higher education; Foundations;
Nonprofits; Community and economic development;
Judaism; Human services.
Type of support: Regranting.
Limitations: Applications not accepted. Giving
primarily in NJ and NY. No grants to individuals.
Application information: Unsolicited requests for
funds not accepted.
Trustee: Kenneth Pasternak.
EIN: 550887890

5491
Kamlaben and Raojibhai Patel Family Foundation, Inc.
273 Chestnut Ridge Rd.
Woodcliff Lake, NJ   07677-7738

Established in 1999 in New Jersey.
Donors: Ashokkumar Patel; Nehat Patel; Nimeet
Patel; Ashok Patel Charitable Lead Annuity Trust.
Foundation type: Independent foundation.
Financial data (yr. ended 12/31/13): Assets,
$3,257,931 (M); expenditures, $194,096;
qualifying distributions, $163,202; giving activities
include $163,202 for 18 grants (high: $50,000;
low: $500).
Fields of interest: Education; Human services.
International interests: India.
Limitations: Applications not accepted. Giving
primarily in NJ and in India. No grants to individuals.
Application information: Unsolicited requests for
funds not accepted.
Trustees: Mahendra Patel; Nimeet Patel; Yashvant
Patel.
EIN: 223696766

5492
Vallavbhai and Savitaben Patel Foundation Inc.
101 Chestnut Ridge Rd., Ste 2A
Montvale, NJ   07645-1801

Established in 1999 in New Jersey.
Donors: Kiran V. Patel; Paresh V. Patel; Yashvant V.
Patel.
Foundation type: Independent foundation.
Financial data (yr. ended 12/31/14): Assets,
$6,943,413; expenditures, $395,287; qualifying
distributions, $337,000.
Fields of interest: Cultural awareness; Education;
Hospital care; Diseases and conditions; Eye
diseases; Housing development; Religion; Human

services; Child welfare; People with vision impairments.
International interests: India.
Type of support: Research.
Limitations: Applications not accepted. Giving primarily in CA, CT, NJ, and NY; giving also in India. No grants to individuals.
Application information: Contributes only to pre-selected organizations.
Trustees: Kiran V. Patel; Paresh V. Patel; Yashvant V. Patel.
EIN: 223696763

5493
Paterson Childrens' Foundation
570 Park Ave.
Paterson, NJ   07504-1009
Application Address: c/o David J. Van Lenten, Pres., 185 Buena Vista Ave., Hawthorne, NJ 07506, tel.: (973) 427-0079

Foundation type: Independent foundation.
Financial data (yr. ended 06/30/13): Assets, $2,115,470 (M); expenditures, $151,743; qualifying distributions, $143,750; giving activities include $143,750 for 7 grants (high: $45,000; low: $250).
Fields of interest: Education; Christianity.
Limitations: Applications accepted. Giving primarily in NJ. No grants to individuals.
Application information: Application form required.
Initial approach: Request application form
Deadline(s): None
Officers: David J. Van Lenten, Pres.; Cynthia Czesak, Secy.; James R. Suessmann, Treas.
Trustees: John H. Fairclough; Fred Giannetto; Donald B. Steen.
EIN: 221487292

5494
Joseph A. Patrick Foundation, Inc.
(formerly Jonathan S. Patrick Foundation, Inc.)
305 Harborside Plz., Ste. 10
Jersey City, NJ   07311-4012

Established in 1966 in New York.
Donors: Joseph A. Patrick; Sean M. Patrick; Shelly K. Patrick; Scott R. Patrick; Shannon C. Bell; Timothy A. Patrick, Jr.; Stuart K. Patrick; Jill C. Castro.
Foundation type: Independent foundation.
Financial data (yr. ended 12/31/13): Assets, $5,113,455 (M); expenditures, $324,028; qualifying distributions, $253,589; giving activities include $253,570 for 40 grants (high: $160,000; low: $100).
Fields of interest: Higher education; Hospital care; Diseases and conditions; Christianity; Human services.
Type of support: General support.
Limitations: Applications not accepted. Giving primarily in the NY-NJ-CT Tri-state area. No grants to individuals.
Application information: Unsolicited requests for funds not accepted.
Officers: Stuart K. Patrick, Pres.; John J. Glynn, Treas.
Director: Kate Patrick.
EIN: 136208825

5495
Joan Whitney and Charles Shipman Payson Foundation
c/o GLC
1 International Blvd., Ste. 700
Mahwah, NJ   07495-0019

Established in 1987 in Maine.
Donor: John W. Payson.
Foundation type: Independent foundation.
Financial data (yr. ended 10/31/13): Assets, $2,881 (M); expenditures, $359,154; qualifying distributions, $350,000; giving activities include $350,000 for 1 grant.
Fields of interest: Education; University education.
Type of support: General support.
Limitations: Applications not accepted. Giving primarily in CT and ME. No grants to individuals.
Application information: Unsolicited requests for funds not accepted.
Trustee: John W. Payson.
EIN: 010430129

5496
The Robert S. & Star Pepper Foundation Inc.
c/o Robert J. Diquollo
1 Giralda Farms, Ste. 130
Madison, NJ   07940-1027

Established in 2002 in New Jersey.
Donors: Robert S. Pepper; Star Pepper.
Foundation type: Independent foundation.
Financial data (yr. ended 12/31/13): Assets, $4,589,941 (M); expenditures, $435,324; qualifying distributions, $395,120; giving activities include $389,120 for 17 grants (high: $100,000; low: $500).
Fields of interest: Arts and culture; Higher education; Diseases and conditions; Christianity; Human services.
Limitations: Applications not accepted. Giving primarily in CA; some funding also in Washington, DC, and Ashland, OR. No grants to individuals.
Application information: Contributes only to pre-selected organizations.
Officers: Robert S. Pepper, Chair.; Star Pepper, Pres.; Robert J. Diquollo, Treas.
EIN: 753034316

5497
The Perricone Family Charitable Trust
120 Eagle Rock Dr., Ste. 330
East Hanover, NJ   07936-3158

Established in 2002 in New Jersey.
Donors: Marilyn Perricone; Philip Perricone.
Foundation type: Independent foundation.
Financial data (yr. ended 12/31/14): Assets, $529,754; gifts received, $0; expenditures, $153,353; qualifying distributions, $153,296.
Fields of interest: Philanthropy; Agriculture; Human services.
Limitations: Applications not accepted. Giving primarily in NJ. No grants to individuals.
Application information: Unsolicited requests for funds not accepted.
Trustees: Marilyn Perricone; Philip Perricone.
EIN: 226921200

5498
Petrucci Family Foundation, Inc.
171 Rte. 173, Ste. 201
Asbury, NJ   08802-9801

Established in 2004 in New Jersey.
Donors: James G. Petrucci; J.G. Petrucci Co., Inc.
Foundation type: Operating foundation.
Financial data (yr. ended 12/31/13): Assets, $6,342,466 (M); expenditures, $236,646; qualifying distributions, $192,815; giving activities include $192,815 for 21 grants (high: $83,333; low: $1,000).
Fields of interest: Elementary and secondary education; University education; Catholicism.
Limitations: Applications not accepted. Giving primarily in NJ and NY. No grants to individuals.
Application information: Contributes only to pre-selected organizations.
Trustees: Bruno N. Dori; James G. Petrucci; Jeanne Petrucci.
EIN: 201601999

5499
Pheasant Hill Foundation, Inc.
c/o Porzio, Bromberg & Newman P.C.
100 Southgate Pkwy.
P.O. Box 1997
Morristown, NJ   07962-1997

Established in 1996 in New Jersey.
Donor: Robert N. Wilson.
Foundation type: Independent foundation.
Financial data (yr. ended 08/31/13): Assets, $8,305,699 (M); gifts received, $70,000; expenditures, $321,881; qualifying distributions, $317,150; giving activities include $317,150 for 53 grants (high: $85,500; low: $500).
Purpose and activities: Giving primarily for education, the environment and federated giving programs.
Fields of interest: Arts and culture; Museums; Historical activities; Historic preservation; Higher education; Undergraduate education; Environment; Wildlife biodiversity; Aquatic wildlife protection; Nonprofits; Television.
Type of support: General support; Regranting.
Limitations: Applications not accepted. No grants to individuals.
Application information: Contributes only to pre-selected organizations.
Officers and Trustees: Robert N. Wilson, Pres. and Trustee; Jonathan R. Wilson, Secy.-Treas. and Trustee; Eileen H. Roan.
EIN: 311481806

5500
Pierson Family Foundation, Inc.
(formerly James and Nancy Pierson Foundation)
111 Northfield Ave., Ste. 206
West Orange, NJ   07052-4703
Application address: c/o James Pierson, 89 Dodd St., East Orange, NJ 07019, tel.: (973) 673-5000

Donors: A & A Fuel Oil Co.; Harry Charlton Co., Inc.; Dixon Bros., Inc.; J.W. Pierson Co.; James W. Pierson.
Foundation type: Operating foundation.
Financial data (yr. ended 06/30/14): Assets, $7,677,691; gifts received, $150,000;

expenditures, $253,997; qualifying distributions, $207,304.
Fields of interest: Education; Hospital care; Diseases and conditions; Religion; Human services.
Limitations: Applications accepted. Giving primarily in NJ.
Application information:
Initial approach: Proposal
Deadline(s): None
Officers: James W. Pierson, Pres.; Jennifer Pierson, V.P.; Sally Pierson, Secy.; Nancy H. Pierson, Treas.
Trustees: Phoebe Pierson; Gerald Platter.
EIN: 222770138

5501
The Alan and Elisa Pines Family Foundation, Inc.
16 Mountain Ridge Dr.
Livingston, NJ   07039-3407
Contact: Elisa Pines, Tr.; Alan Pines, Tr.

Established in 1999 in New Jersey.
Donors: Alan Pines; Elisa Pines.
Foundation type: Independent foundation.
Financial data (yr. ended 10/31/13): Assets, $80,624 (M); gifts received, $132,286; expenditures, $197,044; qualifying distributions, $195,369; giving activities include $195,369 for 23 grants (high: $42,600; low: $720).
Fields of interest: Education; Nonprofits; Judaism.
Type of support: Regranting.
Limitations: Applications accepted. Giving primarily in Washington, DC, NJ and NY.
Application information: Application form required.
Initial approach: Letter
Deadline(s): None
Trustees: Alan Pines; Elisa Pines; Seymour Pinewski.
EIN: 223693306

5502
Pinkin Foundation Inc
c/o James E. Pinkin
14 Henderson Dr.
West Caldwell, NJ   07006-6608

Donors: James E. Pinkin; Lois M. Pinkin.
Foundation type: Independent foundation.
Financial data (yr. ended 12/31/13): Assets, $101,369 (M); gifts received, $186,000; expenditures, $189,194; qualifying distributions, $188,990; giving activities include $188,990 for 10 grants (high: $71,000; low: $1,000).
Fields of interest: Education; Philanthropy; Health.
Limitations: Applications not accepted. Giving primarily in MD and NJ. No grants to individuals.
Application information: Unsolicited requests for funds not accepted.
Officers: James E. Pinkin, Pres.; Jeffrey S. Pinkin, V.P.; Steven J. Pinkin, V.P.; Lois M. Pinkin, Secy.
EIN: 223596871

5503
Plafsky Family Foundation
c/o HMK Associates
31 Dehart St.
Morristown, NJ   07960

Established in 2006 in New Jersey.
Donor: Nathan Plafsky.

Foundation type: Independent foundation.
Financial data (yr. ended 05/31/13): Assets, $129,834 (M); expenditures, $223,177; qualifying distributions, $223,075; giving activities include $223,075 for grants.
Fields of interest: Nonprofits; Judaism; Human services.
Type of support: Regranting.
Limitations: Applications not accepted. Giving primarily in NJ and NY. No grants to individuals.
Application information: Contributes only to pre-selected organizations.
Officers and Trustees: Joan Plafsky, Secy. and Trustee; Robert A. Plafsky, Treas. and Trustee.
EIN: 202992265

5504
The Poole Family Foundation Inc.
18 Lenox Rd.
Summit, NJ   07901-3733

Donors: John Poole; Sharon Poole.
Foundation type: Independent foundation.
Financial data (yr. ended 12/31/14): Assets, $12,521,352 (M); expenditures, $420,199; qualifying distributions, $401,758; giving activities include $395,755 for 25 grants (high: $140,295; low: $500).
Fields of interest: Arts and culture; Religion; Human services.
Limitations: Applications not accepted. Giving primarily in NJ. No grants to individuals.
Application information: Unsolicited requests for funds not accepted.
Officers: John N. Poole, Pres.; Sharon T. Poole, V.P.; Amanda G. Poole, Secy.
Board Member: Jennie E. Poole.
EIN: 223480365

5505
Glen and Cynthia Post Foundation
(formerly Post Family Foundation)
P.O. Box 1501, NJ2-130-03-31
Pennington, NJ   08534-1501

Established in 2003 in Florida.
Donor: Glen F. Post III.
Foundation type: Independent foundation.
Financial data (yr. ended 05/31/13): Assets, $3,454,177 (M); expenditures, $242,539; qualifying distributions, $219,050; giving activities include $205,523 for 6 grants (high: $100,000; low: $15,000).
Fields of interest: Higher education; Christianity.
Type of support: General support.
Limitations: Applications not accepted. Giving primarily in LA, TN and TX. No grants to individuals.
Application information: Unsolicited requests for funds not accepted.
Trustees: Cynthia S. Post; Glen F. Post III.
EIN: 586463580

5506
The Lucille Previti Lupton Foundation, Inc.
2020 New Rd., Apt. 2A
Linwood, NJ   08221-1039

Established in 2009 in New Jersey.
Foundation type: Independent foundation.

Financial data (yr. ended 12/31/14): Assets, $6,918,836; expenditures, $420,535; qualifying distributions, $350,000.
Fields of interest: Higher education; Foundations.
Limitations: Applications not accepted. Giving primarily in D.C. and NJ. No grants to individuals.
Application information: Unsolicited requests for funds not accepted.
Officers: Andrew H. Previti, Pres.; Frank Previti, V.P.; Maureen Previti, Secy.-Treas.
EIN: 271301607

5507
Florence Bullock Ragan Family Foundation
P.O. Box 1501, NJ2-130-03-31
Pennington, NJ   08534-1501

Donors: Florence Ragan Clat†; Florence Ragan Charity Lead Annuity Trust.
Foundation type: Independent foundation.
Financial data (yr. ended 12/31/13): Assets, $1,136,490 (M); gifts received, $146,000; expenditures, $219,334; qualifying distributions, $212,255; giving activities include $205,500 for 12 grants (high: $30,000; low: $1,000).
Fields of interest: Health; Community and economic development; Religion; Food banks; Scouting programs.
Type of support: General support.
Limitations: Applications not accepted. Giving primarily in MT and UT. No grants to individuals.
Application information: Contributes only to pre-selected organizations.
Directors: Joann Bullock Lossee; Nicolas A. Alord; Michael W. Stratton; Warren B. Stratton.
EIN: 870903217

5508
The Daniel J. Ragone Family Foundation, Inc.
617 Centre St.
Haddonfield, NJ   08033-2208   8564296188

Donor: David J. Ragone.
Foundation type: Independent foundation.
Financial data (yr. ended 12/31/14): Assets, $756,072; expenditures, $220,286; qualifying distributions, $214,000.
Fields of interest: Education.
Limitations: Applications not accepted. Giving primarily in NJ. No grants to individuals.
Application information: Unsolicited requests for funds not accepted.
Officers and Trustees: Lillian Ragone, Chair. and Trustee; Daniel J. Ragone, Pres. and Trustee; Daniel J. Ragone, Jr., V.P. and Trustee; David N. Ragone, Secy. and Trustee; Dean A. Ragone, Treas. and Trustee.
EIN: 205490137

5509
Research Fund for Cystic Fibrosis Inc.
62 S. Woodland St.
Englewood, NJ   07631-3723

Foundation type: Independent foundation.
Financial data (yr. ended 12/31/14): Assets, $3,481,883; expenditures, $210,231; qualifying distributions, $151,870.

Purpose and activities: The organization supports education, research, care and assistance for cystic fibrosis.

Fields of interest: Cystic fibrosis.

Type of support: Research.

Limitations: Applications not accepted. Giving limited to NJ and NY.

Application information: Unsolicited requests for funds not accepted.

Officers: Carolyn Denning, Pres. and Treas.; John E. Scaglione, V.P. and Secy.

EIN: 222545566

5510
Fannie E. Rippel Foundation

14 Maple Ave., Ste. 200
Morristown, NJ 07960-5451   (973) 540-0101
Contact: Patricia MacBain, Office Mgr.
FAX: (973) 540-0404;
E-mail: info@rippelfoundation.org; Main URL: http://www.rippelfoundation.org
Facebook: https://www.facebook.com/RippelFoundation

Established in 1953 in New Jersey.

Donor: Julius S. Rippel†.

Foundation type: Independent foundation.

Financial data (yr. ended 04/30/13): Assets, $81,335,353 (M); gifts received, $23,000; expenditures, $5,400,368; qualifying distributions, $4,320,551; giving activities include $317,519 for 17 grants (high: $121,864; low: $150), and $3,221,052 for foundation-administered programs.

Purpose and activities: The core purposes of the foundation are research and treatment related to cancer and heart disease, the health of women and the elderly, and the quality of our nations hospitals. In todays health environment, the trustees have determined that major advances in these areas will come from substantially new ways of thinking about how we maintain our health, as well as how we define, structure, and deliver healthcare. New paradigms are needed that embrace the wholeness of the individual, the power of science, the globalization of medicine, and the challenging dynamics of our healthcare system. Knowing that purposeful actions can produce significant results, the mission of the foundation is to strategically invest its limited resources to seed innovation, catalyze change, and create model processes that will lead to improvements in health. The goal is to achieve better health, better care and lower costs for all.

Fields of interest: Health; Health care access; Community health care; Hospital care; Specialty hospital care; Out-patient medical care; Geriatrics; Heart and circulatory system diseases; Cancers; Gerontology; Spirituality; Seniors; Females.

Type of support: System and operational improvements; Ethics and accountability; Program development; Research.

Limitations: Applications not accepted. Giving on a national basis. No grants to individuals, or for general purposes, operating budgets, continuing support, annual campaigns, deficit financing, scholarships, indirect costs, or building funds, no loans.

Publications: Financial statement; Grants list.

Application information: Unsolicited requests for funds not accepted. Check foundation web site periodically for information.

Board meeting date(s): Approximately 4 times a year

Officers and Trustees: John D. Campbell, Chair. and Trustee; Laura K. Landy, C.E.O. and Pres. and Trustee; Chana Fitton, C.O.O.; Elizabeth G. Christopherson, Secy.; Edward W. Ahart; Elliott S. Fisher; David S. Surrenda.

Number of staff: 4 full-time professional; 2 part-time professional.

EIN: 221559427

5511
Philip W. Riskin Charitable Foundation

c/o SGA Group
100 Walnut Ave., Ste. 103
Clark, NJ 07066-1256

Established in 1993 in New Jersey.

Donor: Philip W. Riskin.

Foundation type: Operating foundation.

Financial data (yr. ended 12/31/14): Assets, $5,090,029; expenditures, $230,465; qualifying distributions, $230,465.

Purpose and activities: Giving primarily for the arts, health and medical research, social services, and to Jewish organizations.

Fields of interest: Arts and culture; Performing arts; Art museums; Nonprofits; Hospital care; Family planning; Diseases and conditions; Judaism; Human services; Child welfare.

Type of support: Regranting.

Limitations: Applications not accepted. Giving primarily in NJ, and New York, NY. No grants to individuals.

Application information: Contributes only to pre-selected organizations.

Officers: Jane Riskin Bean, Pres.; Francesca Liechenstein, Secy.

Trustees: George Bean; Michael Liechenstein.

EIN: 223265173

5512
The Kenneth & Hazel Roe Foundation, Inc.

700 Kinderkamack Rd.
Oradell, NJ 07649-1533   (201) 986-4649

Established in 1997 in Florida.

Donor: Hazel T. Roe.

Foundation type: Independent foundation.

Financial data (yr. ended 12/31/13): Assets, $3,440,755 (M); expenditures, $181,345; qualifying distributions, $174,100; giving activities include $174,100 for 24 grants (high: $17,100; low: $1,000).

Fields of interest: Museums; Higher education; Developmental disability services.

Type of support: Scholarships.

Limitations: Applications not accepted. Giving primarily in MA, NJ and NY. No grants to individuals.

Application information: Unsolicited requests for funds not accepted.

Officers: Hollace Lindsay Roe, Pres.; Ralph C. Roe II, V.P.; Randell B. Roe, V.P.; William Edwards, Secy.

Director: Alan Lindsay.

EIN: 582305353

5513
Roma Bank Community Foundation, Inc.

2300 Rte. 33
Robbinsville, NJ 08691-1411
Contact: Emma Cartier, Secy. and Tr.

Established in 2006 in New Jersey.

Donor: Roma Bank.

Foundation type: Operating foundation.

Financial data (yr. ended 12/31/13): Assets, $5,376,358 (M); expenditures, $259,048; qualifying distributions, $257,599; giving activities include $256,150 for 30 grants (high: $20,000; low: $2,500).

Fields of interest: Museums; Education; Housing development; Christianity; Human services.

Limitations: Applications accepted. Giving primarily in NJ.

Application information:
Initial approach: Proposal
Deadline(s): None

Officers: Nicholas Carnivale, Chair.; Peter A. Inverso, Pres.; Sharon L. Lamont, Treas.

Trustees: Robert Cashill; Kevin Cummings; Alfred DeBlasio, Jr.; James Kilgore; Eric Lear; Michele N. Siekerka, Esq.; William Walsh, Jr.

EIN: 562582815

5514
Rsfzmkh Foundation

99 Caven Point Rd.
Jersey City, NJ 07305-4605

Donor: Moshe Chaim Panzer.

Foundation type: Independent foundation.

Financial data (yr. ended 11/30/13): Assets, $379,283 (M); gifts received, $225,000; expenditures, $266,000; qualifying distributions, $266,000; giving activities include $266,000 for 6 grants to individuals (high: $125,000; low: $5,000).

Fields of interest: Judaism.

Limitations: Applications not accepted. Giving primarily in NY.

Application information: Unsolicited requests for funds not accepted.

Officers: Moshe Chaim Panzer, Pres.; Mark Posner, V.P.; Judith Panzer, Secy.

EIN: 261633369

5515
Rukh Family Foundation Inc.

28 Ambrose Valley Ln.
Piscataway, NJ 08854-4242

Established in 2006 in New Jersey.

Donor: Rupen Patel.

Foundation type: Independent foundation.

Financial data (yr. ended 12/31/13): Assets, $387,706 (M); gifts received, $231,500; expenditures, $219,399; qualifying distributions, $204,112; giving activities include $204,112 for 6 grants (high: $150,000; low: $1,000).

Fields of interest: Health; Religion; Human services.

Limitations: Applications not accepted. Giving primarily in NJ.

Application information: Unsolicited requests for funds not accepted.

Officers: Rupen Patel, Pres.; Hina Patel, V.P.

Trustee: Gautam Patel.

EIN: 208098164

5516
David and Eleanore Rukin Philanthropic Foundation

182 W. Allendale Ave.
Allendale, NJ 07401-1723   2017858881

Established in 1951 in New Jersey.
Donors: David Rukin; Eleanore Rukin; Barnett Rukin; Susan Eisen.
Foundation type: Independent foundation.
Financial data (yr. ended 12/31/14): Assets, $6,623,788; expenditures, $524,553; qualifying distributions, $348,180.
Fields of interest: Arts and culture; Elementary and secondary education; Higher education; Nonprofits; Diseases and conditions; Judaism; Human services; Youth services.
Type of support: Regranting.
Limitations: Applications accepted. Giving primarily in MA, ME, NJ, and NY.
Application information:
  Initial approach: Proposal
  Deadline(s): None
Trustees: Julius Eisen; Susan Eisen; Barnett Rukin.
EIN: 221715380

5517
Peter & Mary Russo Family Foundation Inc.
c/o Peter J. Russo, Jr.
42 E. 5th St.
Surf City, NJ   08008-5276

Established in 2004 in New Jersey.
Foundation type: Independent foundation.
Financial data (yr. ended 12/31/13): Assets, $5,395,393 (M); gifts received, $977,180; expenditures, $216,671; qualifying distributions, $216,671; giving activities include $190,000 for 16 grants (high: $40,000; low: $1,925).
Fields of interest: Health; Diseases and conditions; Human services.
Limitations: Applications not accepted.
Application information: Unsolicited requests for funds not accepted.
Officers: Peter J. Russo, Jr., Pres. and Treas.; Marianne Nahin, V.P. and Secy.; Nancy McDevitt, V.P.
EIN: 030422500

5518
Sanders Family Foundation
P.O. Box 1501, NJ2-130-03-31
Pennington, NJ   08534-1501

Donor: Harvey Sanders.
Foundation type: Independent foundation.
Financial data (yr. ended 08/31/14): Assets, $2,873,212; gifts received, $338,500; expenditures, $235,996; qualifying distributions, $223,352.
Fields of interest: Education; Nonprofits; Cystic fibrosis; Judaism; Human services; Child welfare.
Type of support: General support; Research; Regranting.
Limitations: Applications not accepted. Giving primarily in MD and New York, NY. No grants to individuals.
Application information: Contributes only to pre-selected organizations.
Trustees: Ellen G. Sanders; Harvey L. Sanders; Samuel Sultanik.
EIN: 206038266

5519
Sastaunik Charitable Remainder Trust
P.O. Box 1501, NJ2-130-03-31
Pennington, NJ   08534-1501

Donor: Patricia J. Sastaunik Admin Tr.
Foundation type: Independent foundation.
Financial data (yr. ended 12/31/13): Assets, $3,131,594 (M); expenditures, $283,894; qualifying distributions, $263,166; giving activities include $240,685 for 1 grant.
Fields of interest: Higher education.
Limitations: Applications not accepted. Giving primarily in Las Vegas, NV.
Application information: Unsolicited requests for funds not accepted.
Trustee: Merrill Lynch Trust Co.
EIN: 860847336

5520
Rueben & Muriel Savin Foundation
P.O. Box 1501, NJ2-130-03-31
Pennington, NJ   08534-1501

Established in 2001 in California.
Donors: Nathan Savin; Muriel Savin Charitable Lead Trust; Muriel Savin†.
Foundation type: Independent foundation.
Financial data (yr. ended 03/31/13): Assets, $4,803,401 (M); expenditures, $417,985; qualifying distributions, $397,978; giving activities include $324,000 for 23 grants (high: $100,000; low: $1,000).
Fields of interest: Arts and culture; Museums; University education; Nonprofits; Public libraries.
Type of support: General support; Regranting.
Limitations: Applications not accepted. Giving primarily in CA and IA. No grants to individuals.
Application information: Contributes only to pre-selected organizations.
Directors: Susan Enzle; Linda Paul; David L. Peterson; Nathan E. Savin.
EIN: 943399358

5521
John H. Schimmel Charitable Trust
P.O. Box 1501, NJ2-130-03-31
Pennington, NJ   08534-1501

Donor: John H. Schimmel.
Foundation type: Independent foundation.
Financial data (yr. ended 12/31/14): Assets, $4,577,971; expenditures, $252,189; qualifying distributions, $221,787.
Fields of interest: Health; Diseases and conditions; Human services.
Limitations: Applications not accepted.
Application information: Unsolicited requests for funds not accepted.
Trustees: Henry P. Hart; Merrill Lynch Trust Co.
EIN: 906168507

5522
The Helen Schlaffer Foundation Trust
P.O. Box 1501, NJ2-130-03-31
Pennington, NJ   08534-1501

Foundation type: Independent foundation.

Financial data (yr. ended 12/31/14): Assets, $5,520,054; expenditures, $278,784; qualifying distributions, $249,174.
Fields of interest: Wildlife biodiversity; Domesticated animals; Animal welfare; Christianity; Human services; Child care.
Type of support: Regranting.
Limitations: Applications not accepted. Giving primarily in Washington, DC and NY. No grants to individuals.
Application information: Contributes only to pre-selected organizations.
Trustees: Joan Mahony; Mary A. Pohli; Merrill Lynch Trust Co.
EIN: 207019957

5523
The Peter G. Schlotterer & Elizabeth M. Zipf Charitable Trust
420 Benigno Blvd., 1st Fl., Unit A
Bellmawr, NJ   08031   (856) 933-2225
Contact: Kathleen E. Schroeder, Tr.

Foundation type: Independent foundation.
Financial data (yr. ended 06/30/13): Assets, $5,964,451 (M); expenditures, $296,031; qualifying distributions, $296,031; giving activities include $187,000 for 3 grants (high: $82,000; low: $25,000).
Fields of interest: Education; Domesticated animals.
Application information:
  Initial approach: Proposal
  Deadline(s): None
Trustees: Kathleen E. Schroeder; Elizabeth M. Zipf.
EIN: 266500892

5524
Schwartz Family Foundation
20 Greenbriar Rd.
Oakhurst, NJ   07755-1648

Established in 1994 in New Jersey.
Donors: Moshe Isaac Foundation; Sondra Schwartz; Allen Schwartz; Nicholas Schwartz; Jeffrey Schwartz.
Foundation type: Independent foundation.
Financial data (yr. ended 12/31/14): Assets, $1,144,434; gifts received, $67,000; expenditures, $374,950; qualifying distributions, $373,350 and $0 for set-asides.
Fields of interest: Judaism.
Limitations: Applications not accepted. Giving primarily in NJ and NY. No grants to individuals.
Application information: Unsolicited requests for funds not accepted.
Trustees: Allan Schwartz; Jeffrey Schwartz; Sondra Schwartz.
EIN: 223339658

5525
The Arnold A. Schwartz Foundation
c/o Difrancesco & Kunzman
15 Mountain Blvd.
Warren, NJ   07059-6327   (908) 757-7800
Contact: Steven Kunzman, V.P.

Established in 1953 in New Jersey.
Donor: Arnold A. Schwartz†.
Foundation type: Independent foundation.

Financial data (yr. ended 11/30/13): Assets, $4,822,772 (M); expenditures, $304,672; qualifying distributions, $246,953; giving activities include $231,000 for 45 grants (high: $15,000; low: $1,000).
Purpose and activities: Giving primarily for health and human services.
Fields of interest: Arts education; Education; Hospital care; Libraries; Judaism; Human services; Basic and emergency aid; Family services; Child welfare; Child development; Housing for the homeless; Seniors; Homeless people.
Type of support: General support; Matching grants; Continuing support; Annual campaigns; Capital campaigns; Capital and infrastructure; Equipment; Program development; Scholarships; Research.
Limitations: Applications accepted. Giving primarily in Middlesex, Somerset, and Union counties, NJ. No grants to individuals, or for endowment funds; no loans.
Application information: Application form required.
Initial approach: Letter
Deadline(s): Aug. 31
Board meeting date(s): Feb., June, Sept., and Nov.
Officers: Edwin A. Kunzman, Pres.; Steven Kunzman, V.P.; Louis Harding, Secy.; Kenneth Turnbull, Treas.
Trustees: Victor DiLeo; Thomas Hyland; David Lackland; Michael Lackland; Robert Shapiro.
EIN: 226034152

5526
The Scire Family Foundation Inc.
c/o Patrick Scire
868 Navesink River Rd.
Locust, NJ 07760-2328

Established in 1998 in New Jersey.
Donor: Patrick Scire.
Foundation type: Independent foundation.
Financial data (yr. ended 09/30/14): Assets, $1,005,988; gifts received, $2,200; expenditures, $131,225; qualifying distributions, $128,725 and $0 for set-asides.
Fields of interest: Arts and culture; Theater; Education; University education; Environment; Nonprofits; Health; Film and video; Youth development.
Type of support: Individual development; Regranting.
Limitations: Applications not accepted. No grants to individuals.
Application information: Unsolicited requests for funds not accepted.
Officers: Patrick Scire, Pres. and Treas.; Jennifer Scire, V.P. and Secy.; Salvatore Scire, V.P.
EIN: 223650428

5527
Gay D. & William F. Scott Family Foundation
P.O. Box 1501, NJ2-130-03-31
Pennington, NJ 08534-1501

Established in 2006 in New Jersey.
Donors: Gay Scott; William Scott.
Foundation type: Independent foundation.
Financial data (yr. ended 10/31/14): Assets, $3,257,704 (M); expenditures, $363,211; qualifying distributions, $343,157; giving activities

include $330,220 for 33 grants (high: $50,000; low: $200).
Fields of interest: Arts and culture; University education; Catholicism; Judaism; Human services; Family services; Scouting programs.
Type of support: General support.
Limitations: Applications not accepted. Giving primarily in TX. No grants to individuals.
Application information: Contributes only to pre-selected organizations.
Officers: William Scott, Pres.; James Scott, V.P.; William Scott II, V.P.; Gay Scott, Secy.-Treas.
EIN: 203797595

5528
The Selective Group Foundation
40 Wantage Ave.
Branchville, NJ 07826-5640
FAX: (973) 948-0282;
E-mail: foundation@selective.com; Main URL: http://www.selective.com

Established in 2005 in New Jersey.
Donors: Selective Insurance Group, Inc.; Selective insurance Company of America.
Foundation type: Company-sponsored foundation.
Financial data (yr. ended 12/31/13): Assets, $90,159 (M); gifts received, $400,000; expenditures, $399,941; qualifying distributions, $396,283; giving activities include $396,283 for 69 grants (high: $50,000; low: $100).
Purpose and activities: The foundation supports programs designed to provide health and human services; promote civic responsibility; and support home, auto, and business safety.
Fields of interest: Education; Nonprofits; Health; Hospital care; Disasters and emergency management; Fire prevention and control; Automotive safety; Public affairs; Housing development; Business and industry; Human services; Family services; Child welfare; Low-income and poor people.
Type of support: General support; Employee volunteer services; Employee matching gifts; Capital campaigns; Capital and infrastructure; Equipment; Program development; Scholarships; Regranting.
Limitations: Applications not accepted. Giving primarily in areas of company operations, with emphasis on NJ. No support for religious organizations, international organizations, state or federal agencies, discriminatory organizations, political organizations, or animal organizations. No grants to individuals, or for arts or entertainment, advertising, or sponsorships.
Application information: Contributes only to pre-selected organizations.
Officers: Gail L. Peterson, Pres.; Michael H. Lanza, Secy. and Director; Dale A. Thatcher, Treas. and Director.
EIN: 203539039

5529
The Sella Foundation Trust
P.O. Box 397
Newton, NJ 07860-0397

Established in 1994 in New Jersey.
Donor: George J. Sella, Jr.
Foundation type: Independent foundation.
Financial data (yr. ended 12/31/13): Assets, $4,381,158 (M); expenditures, $171,679;

qualifying distributions, $170,200; giving activities include $170,200 for 36 grants (high: $20,000; low: $500).
Purpose and activities: Giving primarily for services for children and/or the disabled.
Fields of interest: Education; Human services.
Limitations: Applications not accepted. Giving primarily in NJ. No grants to individuals.
Application information: Unsolicited requests for funds not accepted.
Trustee: George J. Sella, Jr.
EIN: 226638737

5530
Seven Oaks Foundation Inc.
95 Treadwell Ave.
Madison, NJ 07940-1020 (973) 377-4627
Contact: Andrew J. O'Keefe, Tr.

Established in 2005 in New Jersey.
Donors: Anne G. O'Keefe; Andrew J. O'Keefe.
Foundation type: Independent foundation.
Financial data (yr. ended 12/31/13): Assets, $301,630 (M); expenditures, $179,573; qualifying distributions, $176,573; giving activities include $172,478 for 16 grants (high: $50,000; low: $100).
Fields of interest: University education.
Type of support: General support.
Limitations: Applications accepted. Giving primarily in NJ and VA.
Application information: Application form required.
Initial approach: Letter
Deadline(s): None
Trustees: Andrew J. O'Keefe; Anne G. O'Keefe; Catherine O'Keefe.
EIN: 203554578

5531
The Eliahou Joseph and David Shamah Foundation Inc.
P.O. Box 627
Princeton, NJ 08542-0627

Established in 2007 in New Jersey.
Donor: Eliahou Joseph Shamah†.
Foundation type: Independent foundation.
Financial data (yr. ended 12/31/13): Assets, $6,930,357 (M); gifts received, $1,804,554; expenditures, $261,959; qualifying distributions, $204,286; giving activities include $200,711 for 20 grants (high: $70,000; low: $360).
Purpose and activities: Giving primarily to yeshivas; support also for Jewish organizations.
Fields of interest: Elementary and secondary education; Judaism.
Limitations: Applications not accepted. Giving primarily in Brooklyn, NY.
Application information: Contributes only to pre-selected organizations.
Officers: James E. Sitt, Pres.; Beth Sitt, Secy.-Treas.
Trustee: Anita Sitt.
EIN: 260837643

5532
The Shapiro Family Foundation
252 Highwood Ave.
Tenafly, NJ 07670-1208

Established in 1998 in New Jersey.

Donors: Harris Shapiro†; Shirley Shapiro; Elaine Appellof; Diane Shamas.
Foundation type: Independent foundation.
Financial data (yr. ended 12/31/13): Assets, $1,108,671 (M); gifts received, $1,228,101; expenditures, $312,083; qualifying distributions, $306,930; giving activities include $306,930 for 76 grants (high: $50,000; low: $25).
Fields of interest: Arts and culture; Education; Diseases and conditions; Judaism; Human services; Child welfare.
Type of support: General support; Research.
Limitations: Applications not accepted. Giving primarily in NJ and NY. No grants to individuals.
Application information: Unsolicited requests for funds not accepted.
Officer: Diane Shamas, Fdn. Mgr.
Trustee: Shirley Shapiro.
EIN: 226767630

5533
Dr. Howard and Brenda Sheridan Family Foundation

P.O. Box 1501, NJ2-130-03-31
Pennington, NJ 08534-1501 6092746834

Donors: Howard Sheridan; Brenda Sheridan.
Foundation type: Independent foundation.
Financial data (yr. ended 12/31/14): Assets, $2,295,754; expenditures, $388,942; qualifying distributions, $375,339.
Fields of interest: Education; University education; Domesticated animals; Health.
Type of support: General support.
Limitations: Applications not accepted. Giving primarily in FL and LA. No grants to individuals.
Application information: Unsolicited requests for funds not accepted.
Trustees: Brenda Sheridan; Howard Sheridan.
EIN: 466879829

5534
The Shilling Family Foundation

500 Morris Ave.
Springfield, NJ 07081-1020 (973) 467-0070
Contact: A. Gary Shilling, Chair.

Established in 1993 in New Jersey.
Donor: A. Gary Shilling.
Foundation type: Independent foundation.
Financial data (yr. ended 11/30/14): Assets, $5,968,518 (M); gifts received, $576,207; expenditures, $324,090; qualifying distributions, $300,100; giving activities include $300,100 for 51 grants (high: $40,000; low: $100).
Purpose and activities: Giving primarily for education and Christian organizations.
Fields of interest: Arts and culture; Education; Nonprofits; Health; Christianity.
Type of support: General support; Annual campaigns; Endowments; Regranting.
Limitations: Applications accepted. Giving primarily in MA, NJ, and NY. No grants to individuals.
Application information:
Initial approach: Proposal
Deadline(s): None
Officers: A. Gary Shilling, Chair.; Margaret B. Shilling, Secy.-Treas.
Trustees: Andrew J. Shilling; Geoffrey B. Shilling; Jennifer E. Shilling; Stephen E. Shilling.
EIN: 223270538

5535
George, Jack, and Joan Shuster Foundation

(formerly George Shuster Foundation)
c/o Jacob Shuster
1840 Frontage Rd., Apt. 1006
Cherry Hill, NJ 08034-2204

Donor: George Shuster†.
Foundation type: Operating foundation.
Financial data (yr. ended 12/31/13): Assets, $3,178,097 (M); expenditures, $258,328; qualifying distributions, $252,655; giving activities include $252,655 for 43 grants (high: $48,860; low: $18).
Fields of interest: Education; Judaism.
Limitations: Applications not accepted. Giving primarily in NJ and PA. No grants to individuals.
Application information: Contributes only to pre-selected organizations.
Directors: Elliot Norry; Gail Norry; Jacob Shuster.
EIN: 010636574

5536
The Silverman Family Charitable Foundation, Inc.

(formerly Elizabeth S. & Stephen I. Silverman Foundation, Inc.)
144 N. Main St.
Cranbury, NJ 08512-3310

Established in 2001 in New Jersey.
Donors: Elizabeth S. Silverman; Stephen I. Silverman.
Foundation type: Independent foundation.
Financial data (yr. ended 12/31/14): Assets, $3,420,462 (M); gifts received, $257,723; expenditures, $211,620; qualifying distributions, $204,000; giving activities include $204,000 for 2 grants (high: $104,000; low: $100,000).
Fields of interest: Education; Higher education; Medical education; Protestantism; Judaism.
Limitations: Applications not accepted. Giving primarily in NJ and NY. No grants to individuals.
Application information: Unsolicited requests for funds not accepted.
Officers and Directors: Stephen I. Silverman, Pres. and Treas. and Director; Elizabeth S. Silverman, Secy. and Director; Elinor W. Silverman; Mary R. Silverman; Susannah L. Silverman.
EIN: 223658069

5537
The Cynthia L. & William E. Simon, Jr. Foundation

310 South St.
P.O. Box 1913
Morristown, NJ 07962-1913
Application address: William E. Simon Jr., c/o William E. Simon & Sons, 11100 Santa Monica Blvd., Ste. 1910, Los Angeles, CA 90025-3335

Established in 1994 in New Jersey.
Donors: William E. Simon Foundation, Inc.; William E. Simon, Jr.; U.S. Dept. of Education - Carol M. White Physical Ed. Program; Cynthia L. Simon.
Foundation type: Independent foundation.
Financial data (yr. ended 12/31/14): Assets, $303,989 (M); gifts received, $390,000; expenditures, $152,611; giving activities include $143,155 for 55 grants (high: $46,000; low: $25).

Purpose and activities: Giving primarily for education; funding also for children, youth and social services, and health care.
Fields of interest: Education; Secondary education; Nonprofits; Health; Human services; Child welfare.
Type of support: Regranting.
Limitations: Applications accepted. Giving primarily in CA and MA.
Application information: Application form required.
Initial approach: Letter
Deadline(s): None
Officer and Trustees: Cynthia L. Simon, Pres. and Trustee; William E. Simon, Jr.
EIN: 133799555

5538
Herbert Smilowitz Private Foundation

P.O. Box 511
East Rutherford, NJ 07073-0511

Established in 1998 in New Jersey.
Donors: Herbert Smilowitz; Marilyn Smilowitz.
Foundation type: Independent foundation.
Financial data (yr. ended 12/31/13): Assets, $3,875,825 (M); gifts received, $453,680; expenditures, $387,843; qualifying distributions, $338,836; giving activities include $338,836 for 147 grants (high: $50,000; low: $25).
Fields of interest: Education; Nonprofits; Judaism; Human services.
Type of support: General support; Regranting.
Limitations: Applications not accepted. No grants to individuals.
Application information: Unsolicited requests for funds not accepted.
Trustees: Herbert Smilowitz; Marilyn Smilowitz.
EIN: 137171363

5539
George Graham and Elizabeth Galloway Smith Foundation, Inc.

P.O. Box 202
Hopewell, NJ 08525 (609) 466-2210
Contact: Ellen S. Morehouse, Pres. and Secy.

Donors: Elizabeth G. Smith Charitable Lead Unitrust; Elizabeth G. Smith†; Beatrice Erlin†; George G. Smith†.
Foundation type: Independent foundation.
Financial data (yr. ended 05/31/15): Assets, $8,986,496 (M); gifts received, $452,983; expenditures, $200; qualifying distributions, $430,365; giving activities include $427,500 for 14 grants (high: $225,000; low: $2,500).
Purpose and activities: Funding primarily for an arts center and other music and arts organizations; funding also for education and human services.
Fields of interest: Performing arts; Orchestral music; Science museums; Education; Higher education; Land resources; Animal rescue and rehabilitation; Nonprofits; Human services.
Type of support: Capital and infrastructure; Equipment; Program development; Regranting.
Limitations: Applications accepted. Giving primarily in western NY, with emphasis on Buffalo and Orchard Park; funding also in NJ and PA. No grants to individuals.
Application information: Application form required.
Initial approach: Letter

Deadline(s): June 15 for requests above $1,000; none for requests below that amount
Board meeting date(s): July
Officers: Ellen S. Morehouse, Pres. and Secy.; George G. Smith III, V.P. and Treas.
Directors: C. Schuyler Morehouse; Janet Smith.
EIN: 166031530

5540
G. Whitney Snyder Charitable Fund
61 Hodge Rd.
Princeton, NJ   08540-3075   (412) 471-1331
Contact: Linda S. Hayes, Pres.
E-mail: lshayes61@gmail.com

Foundation type: Independent foundation.
Financial data (yr. ended 12/31/13): Assets, $4,275,503 (M); expenditures, $271,933; qualifying distributions, $262,900; giving activities include $253,750 for 40 grants (high: $51,000; low: $500).
Purpose and activities: Giving primarily for education.
Fields of interest: Secondary education; Higher education; Health; Diseases and conditions; Protestantism; Human services; Child welfare.
Type of support: General support; Annual campaigns.
Limitations: Applications accepted. Giving primarily in PA.
Application information:
Initial approach: Letter
Deadline(s): None
Officers: Linda Snyder Hayes, Pres.; Carolyn Snyder Miltenberger, Secy.
Trustees: G. Whitney Snyder, Jr.; Nina Snyder.
EIN: 251611761

5541
The Harold B. and Dorothy A. Snyder Foundation
331 Newman Springs Rd., Bldg. 1, No. 143
Red Bank, NJ   07701-5688
Application address: P.O. Box 671, Moorestown, NJ 08057-0671
E Newsletter: http://snyderfoundation.com/page.php?id=10

Established in 1971 in New Jersey.
Donor: Harold B. Snyder, Sr.†.
Foundation type: Independent foundation.
Financial data (yr. ended 09/30/14): Assets, $10,722,832 (M); expenditures, $602,117; qualifying distributions, $445,198; giving activities include $192,500 for 6 grants (high: $150,000; low: $500).
Purpose and activities: Support for programs in Union County, NJ, and scholarships to either residents of Union County, NJ, or applicants attending a college or university in Union County, who are high school or college graduates with a cumulative GPA of 3.2 or above, or who are an undergraduate in their junior or senior year, pursuing a degree in nursing, special education, or construction management, or a graduate pursuing a degree/vocation in the ministry an accredited educational institution.
Fields of interest: Nursing care; Rehabilitation; Heart and circulatory system diseases; Human services.

Type of support: Capital campaigns; Matching grants; Building and renovations; Equipment; Seed money.
Limitations: Giving primarily in the Union County, NJ, area. No support for colleges. No grants to individuals directly.
Application information: Application form required.
Officers: Laura Stammel, Chair.; J. Vernon Whittenburg, Secy.; Shannon Cortese, Treas.; John Nolan, Exec. Dir.
Trustees: Paul Cortese; Arline S. Cortez.
Number of staff: 1 full-time professional; 1 part-time support.
EIN: 222316043

5542
The Helen M. Snyder Foundation
3163 Kennedy Blvd.
North Bergen, NJ   07047

Donor: Richard Snyder.
Foundation type: Independent foundation.
Financial data (yr. ended 06/30/13): Assets, $4,410,226 (M); gifts received, $2,550,465; expenditures, $331,286; qualifying distributions, $246,700; giving activities include $246,700 for 19 grants (high: $100,000; low: $1,000).
Fields of interest: Education; Diseases and conditions; Christianity; Protestantism; Human services.
Limitations: Applications not accepted. Giving primarily in NJ. No grants to individuals.
Application information: Unsolicited requests for funds not accepted.
Directors: Joseph Farrell; Catherine Keens; Edward M. Lombard.
EIN: 223036062

5543
Michele Snyder Foundation, Inc.
c/o PGB Trust & Investments
500 Hills Dr., Ste. 300
Bedminster, NJ   07921-1538

Established in 2000 in Maryland.
Donor: Michele Snyder.
Foundation type: Independent foundation.
Financial data (yr. ended 12/31/14): Assets, $373,626; expenditures, $355,041; qualifying distributions, $346,300.
Fields of interest: University education; Judaism.
Type of support: General support.
Limitations: Applications not accepted. Giving primarily in MD. No grants to individuals.
Application information: Unsolicited requests for funds not accepted.
Director: Michele Snyder.
EIN: 522272965

5544
The Sorala Foundation
617 Caranetta Dr.
Lakewood, NJ   08701-3119

Established in 2005 in New Jersey.
Donors: Ezrial Munk; Yaffa Munk; Judah Munk; Leo Mallah; National Society for Hebrew Day Schools; Eli Esptein; Keren Avreichim; Steve Solinga; Avi Weinstiock; United Congregrations Mesorah; Lillian Zeides Foundation; Camp Chaviva; Asher Kohn;

Nathan Munk; Aaron Munk; Congregation Shaare Tefila; Young Israel of New Rochelle; Yesodei HaTorah; Chessed Congregations of America.
Foundation type: Independent foundation.
Financial data (yr. ended 03/31/14): Assets, $1,851,296 (M); gifts received, $779,902; expenditures, $358,305; qualifying distributions, $340,124; giving activities include $338,149 for 204 grants (high: $38,450; low: $18), and $1,975 for foundation-administered programs.
Fields of interest: Education; Judaism.
Limitations: Applications not accepted. Giving primarily in NJ and NY.
Application information: Unsolicited requests for funds not accepted.
Officer: Ezrial Munk, Pres.
Trustee: Yaffa Munk.
EIN: 206186035

5545
Southpole Foundation Inc.
222 Bridge Plz. S.
Fort Lee, NJ   07024-5712
Main URL: http://www.southpolefoundation.org

Donors: Against All Odds U.S.A., Inc.; Daewon Khym.
Foundation type: Independent foundation.
Financial data (yr. ended 12/31/13): Assets, $4,886,120 (M); expenditures, $288,460; qualifying distributions, $240,488; giving activities include $228,100 for 15 grants (high: $25,600; low: $500).
Purpose and activities: Giving for the welfare of the community by providing economic assistance and leadership in socially meaningful ways, including funding scholarships, giving grants to organizations servicing the community and promoting community services.
Fields of interest: Education; Higher education; Health; Community and economic development.
Type of support: General support; Grants to individuals; Scholarships; Individual development.
Limitations: Applications not accepted. Giving primarily in NJ and NY.
Application information: Contributes only to pre-selected organizations.
Officers: Daewon Khym, Pres.; Kwangwon Khym, Secy.; Esther Khym, Treas.
EIN: 200471235

5546
The Donald W. Spiro Foundation
c/o Donald W. Spiro
399 Ski Trail
Kinnelon, NJ   07405-2247

Established in 1986 in New Jersey.
Donors: Donald W. Spiro; Evelyn Spiro.
Foundation type: Independent foundation.
Financial data (yr. ended 06/30/15): Assets, $6,442,810 (M); expenditures, $310,115; qualifying distributions, $302,500; giving activities include $300,000 for 1 grant (high: $300,000; low: $300,000).
Fields of interest: Education; Undergraduate education; Hospital care; Diseases and conditions; Cancers; Christianity; Human services.
Limitations: Applications not accepted. Giving primarily in NY. No grants to individuals.

Application information: Contributes only to pre-selected organizations.
Trustees: Donald W. Spiro; Evelyn Spiro.
EIN: 222770724

5547
Spohler Foundation, Inc.
c/o John Spohler
Windy Hill Farm
P.O. Box 444
Bedminster, NJ 07921-0444

Established in 1997 in New Jersey.
Donor: John Spohler.
Foundation type: Independent foundation.
Financial data (yr. ended 12/31/13): Assets, $5,412,212 (M); gifts received, $61,685; expenditures, $240,655; qualifying distributions, $212,000; giving activities include $212,000 for 16 grants (high: $20,000; low: $5,000).
Fields of interest: Undergraduate education; Females.
Limitations: Applications not accepted. Giving primarily in NY, with some giving in CA.
Application information: Contributes only to pre-selected organizations.
Officers: Linda Spohler, Pres.; Jana Herndon, V.P.; Bruce Spholer, V.P.; Brenda Spohler-Benoit, V.P.
Trustee: John Spohler.
EIN: 223510898

5548
Spruce Street Foundation
47 Hulfish St., Ste. 305
Princeton, NJ 08542-3706

Established in 1994 in New Jersey.
Donor: David W. Mills.
Foundation type: Independent foundation.
Financial data (yr. ended 11/30/13): Assets, $3,922,387 (M); gifts received, $1,100; expenditures, $198,818; qualifying distributions, $150,000; giving activities include $150,000 for 2 grants (high: $100,000; low: $50,000).
Fields of interest: Higher education; Foundations; Legal services; Religion.
Limitations: Applications not accepted. Giving primarily in Santa Cruz, CA, Princeton, NJ, and New York, NY. No grants to individuals.
Application information: Contributes only to pre-selected organizations.
Officers: David W. Mills, Pres.; Kenneth J. Slutsky, V.P.; Allen B. Levithan, Secy.; Steven B. Smotrich, Treas.
EIN: 223343609

5549
Norman E. and Gwyneth L. Staats Foundation
1017 Grove Ave.
Thorofare, NJ 08086-3061 (858) 848-7664
Contact: Jean Smith, Pres.

Foundation type: Independent foundation.
Financial data (yr. ended 12/31/13): Assets, $1,926,484 (M); expenditures, $349,691; qualifying distributions, $348,459; giving activities include $345,000 for 13 grants (high: $150,000; low: $2,500).

Fields of interest: Wildlife biodiversity; Animal welfare.
Limitations: Applications accepted. Giving primarily in NJ.
Application information: Application form required.
Initial approach: Proposal
Deadline(s): Sept. 30
Officers: Jean Smith, Pres.; Gail Bancroft, V.P.; Kay Tombleson, Secy.; Diana Kane, Treas.
EIN: 200790484

5550
Stanley's Garden Foundation
47 Essex Dr.
Tenafly, NJ 07670-2303 (201) 568-1488
Contact: Kathy Leventhal, Tr.

Donors: Neisloss Family Foundation, Inc.; Richard Leventhal.
Foundation type: Independent foundation.
Financial data (yr. ended 12/31/13): Assets, $3,673,298 (M); gifts received, $1,261,100; expenditures, $418,919; qualifying distributions, $390,134; giving activities include $389,754 for 7 grants (high: $200,000; low: $250).
Fields of interest: Education; Health; Diseases and conditions; Judaism.
Limitations: Applications accepted. Giving primarily in CA.
Application information:
Initial approach: Proposal
Deadline(s): None
Trustees: Kathy Leventhal; Richard Leventhal.
EIN: 266138709

5551
Jane and Frances Stein Foundation
c/o Friedman, LLP
100 Eagle Rock Ave., Ste. 200
East Hanover, NJ 07936-3149

Donors: Thomas & Lonnie Schwartz Foundation; Alvin Schwartz Charitable Lead Trust.
Foundation type: Independent foundation.
Financial data (yr. ended 12/31/13): Assets, $1,842,789 (M); gifts received, $527,169; expenditures, $339,852; qualifying distributions, $320,350; giving activities include $320,350 for 39 grants (high: $12,750; low: $250).
Fields of interest: Domesticated animals; Diseases and conditions; Religion.
Limitations: Applications not accepted. Giving primarily in NY.
Application information: Unsolicited requests for funds not accepted.
Officers: Frances Stein, Pres.; Claire F. Dickinson, V.P.; Michael Goldman, Secy.
EIN: 274830712

5552
Stern Family Foundation
514 Maitland Ave.
Teaneck, NJ 07666-2918
Contact: Ronald Stern, Tr.; Beth Stern, Tr.

Established in 1999 in New Jersey.
Donors: Henry Stern; Beth Stern; Ronald Stern.
Foundation type: Independent foundation.
Financial data (yr. ended 12/31/13): Assets, $116,446 (M); gifts received, $270,000;

expenditures, $323,124; qualifying distributions, $323,124; giving activities include $322,938 for 28 grants (high: $75,560; low: $800).
Fields of interest: Education; Judaism.
Limitations: Applications accepted. Giving primarily in NJ and NY.
Application information:
Initial approach: Proposal
Deadline(s): None
Trustees: Beth Stern; Henry Stern; Ronald Stern.
EIN: 223697066

5553
The Stone Foundation of New Jersey
179 Ave. of the Commons, Ste. 2
Shrewsbury, NJ 07702-4558
Contact: Caroline P. Huber, Pres.

Established in 1997 in Delaware.
Donor: Caroline Huber.
Foundation type: Independent foundation.
Financial data (yr. ended 06/30/13): Assets, $3,170,592 (M); gifts received, $300,000; expenditures, $442,209; qualifying distributions, $394,808; giving activities include $394,808 for 25 grants (high: $30,000; low: $6,308).
Fields of interest: Theater; Education; Environment; Human services; Women's services.
Type of support: General support; Capital campaigns; Program development.
Limitations: Applications accepted. Giving primarily in Monmouth, NJ, and in areas where board members reside.
Application information:
Initial approach: E-mail (preferred) or letter
Copies of proposal: 3
Deadline(s): Feb. 1
Board meeting date(s): Apr.
Final notification: June 1
Officers: Caroline P. Huber, Pres. and Treas.; Eleanor H. Huber, V.P.; Samuel G. Huber, Secy.
Directors: Joseph W. Huber; Martha Huber.
EIN: 133947516

5554
Altoon Sutton Memorial Fund
c/o Elie Sutton
77 Brighton Ave.
Deal, NJ 07723-1121

Established in 1998 in New Jersey.
Donors: Sutton Investments, Inc.; J.S. Shamohs.
Foundation type: Independent foundation.
Financial data (yr. ended 12/31/13): Assets, $1,093,536 (M); expenditures, $238,404; qualifying distributions, $237,980; giving activities include $237,980 for 277 grants (high: $10,000; low: $25).
Fields of interest: Judaism.
Type of support: General support.
Limitations: Applications not accepted. No grants to individuals.
Application information: Unsolicited requests for funds not accepted.
Officers: Elie Sutton, Pres.; Samuel Sutton, V.P.; Abraham M. Sutton, Secy.
EIN: 223606267

5555
The Take Shape for Life Charitable Foundation, Inc.
P.O. Box 1501, NJ2-130-03-31
Pennington, NJ 08534-1501

Established in 2004 in Delaware.
Donor: Medifast, Inc.
Foundation type: Independent foundation.
Financial data (yr. ended 12/31/13): Assets, $319,460 (M); gifts received, $215,000; expenditures, $218,700; qualifying distributions, $217,722; giving activities include $215,000 for 1 grant.
Fields of interest: Higher education; Diseases and conditions; National defense; Christianity.
Type of support: General support.
Limitations: Applications not accepted. Giving primarily in MD and PA. No grants to individuals.
Application information: Contributes only to pre-selected organizations.
Officers and Directors: Kellie T. MacDonald-Pizzico, V.P. and Fdn. Admin.; Margaret MacDonald-Sheetz, V.P.; Shirley D. MacDonald, V.P. and Director.
EIN: 200983877

5556
Tamarin Foundation Inc.
c/o Untracht Early
325 Columbia Tpke., Ste. 202
Florham Park, NJ 07932-1212

Donor: Laura Ulrich.
Foundation type: Independent foundation.
Financial data (yr. ended 12/31/13): Assets, $2,171,008 (M); expenditures, $331,024; qualifying distributions, $330,670; giving activities include $325,405 for 2 grants (high: $244,405; low: $81,000).
Fields of interest: Human services.
Limitations: Applications not accepted.
Application information: Unsolicited requests for funds not accepted.
Officers: Laura Ulrich, Pres.; Ilana Levine, Secy.
Director: Anthony Davis.
EIN: 208367754

5557
Tedesco Family Private Foundation
111 Paterson Ave.
Hoboken, NJ 07030-6012

Established in 2005 in New Jersey.
Donors: Mark Tedesco; Francis Tedesco; Josephine Tedesco†; Tedesco Family Partnership.
Foundation type: Independent foundation.
Financial data (yr. ended 12/31/13): Assets, $5,577,577 (M); expenditures, $257,506; qualifying distributions, $240,000; giving activities include $240,000 for 5 grants (high: $150,000; low: $5,000).
Fields of interest: Elementary and secondary education.
Type of support: General support.
Limitations: Applications not accepted. Giving primarily in NJ. No grants to individuals.
Application information: Unsolicited requests for funds not accepted.
Trustees: Joseph F. Ferrara; Harris Kantor; Mark Tedesco; Thomas Santucci.
EIN: 203483267

5558
Teiger Foundation
c/o Sabal & Associates
293 Eisenhower Pkwy., Ste. 140
Livingston, NJ 07039-1716

Donor: David Teiger.
Foundation type: Independent foundation.
Financial data (yr. ended 06/30/13): Assets, $2,340 (M); gifts received, $419,500; expenditures, $418,739; qualifying distributions, $400,000; giving activities include $400,000 for 1 grant.
Fields of interest: Arts and culture.
Type of support: General support.
Limitations: Applications not accepted. Giving primarily in MN and NY.
Application information: Unsolicited requests for funds not accepted.
Officers: David Teiger, Pres.; John Silberman, Secy.-Treas.
Directors: Gary Garrels; Kati Lovaas; Joel Wachs.
EIN: 263533921

5559
Thomas and Mary Ann Tizzio Foundation
10 Deepdale Dr.
Middletown, NJ 07748

Established in 2006 in New Jersey.
Donors: Thomas R. Tizzio; Mary Ann Tizzio.
Foundation type: Independent foundation.
Financial data (yr. ended 12/31/13): Assets, $3,948,088 (M); expenditures, $181,883; qualifying distributions, $142,289; giving activities include $127,000 for 21 grants (high: $35,000; low: $1,500).
Fields of interest: Health; Diseases and conditions.
Limitations: Applications not accepted. No grants to individuals.
Application information: Contributes only to pre-selected organizations.
Trustees: Mary Ann Tizzio; Thomas R. Tizzio.
EIN: 208076647

5560
W. Parsons Todd Foundation, Inc.
c/o Drinker Biddle & Shanley LLP
500 Campus Dr.
Florham Park, NJ 07932-1047

Donor: W. Parsons Todd.
Foundation type: Operating foundation.
Financial data (yr. ended 12/31/13): Assets, $5,131,680 (M); expenditures, $201,294; qualifying distributions, $192,294; giving activities include $188,321 for 5 grants (high: $183,703; low: $500).
Fields of interest: History museums; Christianity.
Type of support: General support.
Limitations: Applications not accepted. Giving primarily in NJ. No grants to individuals.
Application information: Contributes only to pre-selected organizations.
Trustees: Melvin S. Heller; Douglas A. Propp; Rodney Propp.
EIN: 136116488

5561
The Tuchman Foundation
P.O. Box 582
Kingston, NJ 08528-0582

Established in 1996 in New Jersey.
Donors: Martin Tuchman; Warren Serenbetz; Garden State Chassis.
Foundation type: Independent foundation.
Financial data (yr. ended 12/31/13): Assets, $5,596,854 (M); gifts received, $1,025,000; expenditures, $300,893; qualifying distributions, $294,511; giving activities include $284,704 for 25 grants (high: $80,467; low: $50).
Fields of interest: Diseases and conditions; Parkinson's disease; Human services.
Type of support: General support; Research; Research and evaluation.
Limitations: Applications not accepted. Giving primarily in NJ. No grants to individuals.
Application information: Contributes only to pre-selected organizations.
Officers: Martin Tuchman, Chair. and Pres.; William Geoghan, V.P. and Secy.; Richard Gross, V.P. and Treas.
Trustees: Arieh Feigenbaum; Margaret Tuchman.
EIN: 226682754

5562
The Tufenkian Foundation
c/o John Antranig Kasbarian
20 Capitol Dr.
Moonachie, NJ 07074-1407 (201) 221-1055; 367
FAX: (201) 221-1070;
E-mail: akasbarian@tufenkian.com; Main
URL: http://www.tufenkianfoundation.org
Facebook: https://www.facebook.com/TufenkianFoundation

Donors: James Tufenkian; Westpac Banking Corp.; Vahe Nahabetian; Sara Anjargolian; Kirakos Vapurciyan; George M. Aghjayan; Onnik Keshishian; Anahid Mardirosian; Itsmyseat.com; Kpaa-Kaiser Permanente; United Way of NYC; Virginia L. Davies; Adrienne V. Tashjian; Alber K. Karamanoukian; Alex Sarafian; Tufenkian Import/Export Ventures; John Kasbarian; K. George Najarian.
Foundation type: Operating foundation.
Financial data (yr. ended 11/30/13): Assets, $11,405,144 (M); gifts received, $180,915; expenditures, $440,524; qualifying distributions, $440,524; giving activities include $370,595 for 25 grants (high: $100,016; low: $75), and $413,956 for foundation-administered programs.
Purpose and activities: Giving primarily for the benefit of Armenian society.
Fields of interest: Education; Human services; Child welfare.
International interests: Armenia.
Limitations: Applications not accepted. No grants to individuals.
Application information: Unsolicited requests for funds not accepted.
Officers: James Tufenkian, Chair.; John Antranig Kasbarian, Exec. Dir.
EIN: 133976159

5563
Twin Chimney Inc.
234 W. Delaware Ave.
Pennington, NJ 08534-1603

Established in 1986 in New Jersey.
Donors: F. Helmut Weymar; Caroline Weymar.
Foundation type: Independent foundation.
Financial data (yr. ended 11/30/13): Assets, $3,550,220 (M); expenditures, $238,229; qualifying distributions, $235,463; giving activities include $234,641 for 103 grants (high: $25,000; low: $100).
Purpose and activities: Giving primarily for education.
Fields of interest: Arts and culture; Elementary and secondary education; Higher education; Domesticated animals; Foundations; Diseases and conditions; Protestantism; Human services.
Type of support: General support.
Limitations: Applications not accepted. Giving primarily in MA, NJ, NY, and PA. No grants to individuals.
Application information: Contributes only to pre-selected organizations.
Officers: F. Helmut Weymar, Pres.; Caroline S. Weymar, Secy.
Trustees: Emily B. Weymar Van Dixhoorn; Matthew D. Weymar.
EIN: 222787076

5564
The Ullmann Family Foundation, Inc.
2107 Arbor Way
Martinsville, NJ 08836-2216

Established in 1990 in Florida.
Donors: Irma Ullmann†; Leonard Ullmann.
Foundation type: Independent foundation.
Financial data (yr. ended 08/31/13): Assets, $3,535,248 (M); gifts received, $54; expenditures, $215,727; qualifying distributions, $212,245; giving activities include $210,025 for 22 grants (high: $34,000; low: $1,000).
Fields of interest: Vocational post-secondary education; Higher education; Cystic fibrosis; Community organizing; Judaism.
Limitations: Applications not accepted. Giving primarily in FL and NY. No grants to individuals.
Application information: Contributes only to pre-selected organizations.
Officers: Jeremy Michael Ullmann, Pres.; Steven D. Schneider, V.P.; Nancy Ullmann-Schneider, Secy.-Treas.
EIN: 650252674

5565
United Vision Foundation
24 Link Dr.
Rockleigh, NJ 07647-2504

Established in 1998 in New York.
Donor: Yann Sandt.
Foundation type: Independent foundation.
Financial data (yr. ended 07/31/13): Assets, $18,640,014 (M); expenditures, $466,202; qualifying distributions, $397,268; giving activities include $287,000 for 3 grants (high: $132,000; low: $45,000), and $390,412 for foundation-administered programs.
Fields of interest: International peace and security.

Type of support: General support; Grants to individuals.
Limitations: Applications not accepted. Giving in the U.S., with some emphasis on Washington, DC, NJ and OH.
Application information: Contributes only to pre-selected organizations.
Officers and Directors: Michael Sommer, Pres. and Director; Mark Sano, Secy.-Treas. and Director.
EIN: 911924248

5566
The Lucy and Eleanor S. Upton Charitable Foundation
30 Montgomery St., Ste. 685
Jersey City, NJ 07302-3834

Established in 1965 in New Jersey.
Donor: Eleanor S. Upton†.
Foundation type: Independent foundation.
Financial data (yr. ended 12/31/13): Assets, $7,117,095 (M); expenditures, $381,555; qualifying distributions, $357,000; giving activities include $357,000 for 26 grants (high: $75,000; low: $5,000).
Purpose and activities: Giving primarily for the arts, education, hospitals, including a children's hospital, and social services.
Fields of interest: Arts and culture; Orchestral music; Education; Elementary and secondary education; Specialty hospital care; Human services; Child welfare.
Type of support: General support; Fellowships; Research.
Limitations: Applications accepted. Giving primarily in NJ. No grants to individuals.
Application information:
  Initial approach: Proposal
  Copies of proposal: 1
  Deadline(s): Oct. 1
  Board meeting date(s): Oct. or Nov., annually
  Final notification: Successful applicants will be notified in the Nov.-Dec. timeframe
Trustees: William B. Cater, Jr.; Frank L. Fekete; Susan Jukosky; Francis X. O'Brien.
EIN: 226074947

5567
Vaughn-Jordan Foundation
P.O. Box 1501, NJ2-130-03-31
Pennington, NJ 08534-1501

Established in 1988 in Florida.
Foundation type: Independent foundation.
Financial data (yr. ended 12/31/14): Assets, $4,447,679 (M); expenditures, $229,466; qualifying distributions, $198,080; giving activities include $137,600 for 8 grants (high: $40,000; low: $5,000).
Fields of interest: Education; University education; Environment; Sports and recreation.
Type of support: General support.
Limitations: Applications not accepted. Giving primarily in FL. No grants to individuals.
Publications: Annual report.
Application information: Unsolicited requests for funds not accepted.
Trustees: Katherine Hetzel; Alvin H. Vaughn; C. Roland Vaughn III; James A. Vaughn, Jr.; James P. Vaughn; James L. Watt.
EIN: 650362992

5568
The James P. Verhalen Family Foundation, Inc.
c/o M. Geltman Nisivoccia LLP
200 Valley Rd., Ste. 300
Mount Arlington, NJ 07856-1320

Established in 1999 in New Jersey.
Donors: James P. Verhalen; Joyce Pandolfi.
Foundation type: Independent foundation.
Financial data (yr. ended 12/31/13): Assets, $5,969,894 (M); expenditures, $344,304; qualifying distributions, $278,780; giving activities include $278,780 for 34 grants (high: $25,000; low: $1,000).
Purpose and activities: Giving for the furtherance of the Jesuit faith.
Fields of interest: Higher education; Graduate and professional education; Theology.
Type of support: General support.
Limitations: Applications not accepted. Giving primarily in NJ and MD. No grants to individuals.
Application information: Contributes only to pre-selected organizations.
Officers: Joyce Pandolfi, Pres.; Florence W. Verhalen, V.P.; James P. Verhalen, Jr., Secy.; Phillip William Verhalen, Treas.
EIN: 223694939

5569
Waldis Family Foundation Inc.
c/o John Methfessel, Esq.
3 Ethel Rd., Ste. 300
Edison, NJ 08818-3012

Established in 2007 in New Jersey.
Donors: Anastasia Waldis; Stephen Waldis.
Foundation type: Independent foundation.
Financial data (yr. ended 12/31/14): Assets, $1,464,043 (M); gifts received, $2,100; expenditures, $124,281; qualifying distributions, $124,281 and $0 for set-asides.
Fields of interest: Education; Adolescents.
Limitations: Applications not accepted. Giving primarily in NJ.
Application information: Unsolicited requests for funds not accepted.
Directors: John Methfessel; Thomas Miller; Joel Werbel.
EIN: 208490871

5570
Waterfowl Research Foundation, Inc.
1128 Campus Dr. W.
Morganville, NJ 07751 7323720202

Foundation type: Independent foundation.
Financial data (yr. ended 12/31/14): Assets, $8,991,673 (M); expenditures, $485,617; qualifying distributions, $380,390.
Purpose and activities: Giving to support waterfowl preservation programs.
Fields of interest: Wildlife biodiversity.
Type of support: Research; Research and evaluation.
Limitations: Applications not accepted. Giving primarily in the U.S. and Canada. No grants to individuals.
Application information: Contributes only to pre-selected organizations.
  Board meeting date(s): Apr. and Dec.

Officers: Arthur C. Romaine, Chair.; E. Coe. Kerr, Treas.
Number of staff: 1 part-time support.
EIN: 136122167

5571

The Thomas P. Waters Foundation

c/o Christina G. Alt
605 Main St., Ste. 212
Riverton, NJ 08077-1440

Foundation type: Independent foundation.
Financial data (yr. ended 08/31/13): Assets, $4,579,418 (M); expenditures, $249,447; qualifying distributions, $225,953; giving activities include $206,000 for 49 grants (high: $15,000; low: $400).
Purpose and activities: Giving primarily for education, Christian organizations and ministries, and environmental protection and conservation; some funding for children, youth, women, and social services.
Fields of interest: Education; Higher education; Diseases and conditions; Housing development; Christianity; Human services; Child welfare; Females; American Indians.
Type of support: Research.
Limitations: Applications not accepted. Giving primarily in GA and TX; some giving also in PA and VA. No grants to individuals.
Application information: Contributes only to pre-selected organizations.
Trustees: Christina G. Alt; Damon C. Waters; James A. Waters; Kenneth M. Waters; Robert T. Waters; T. Patrick Waters III.
EIN: 237836361

5572

The Waterview Foundation Inc.

234 W. Delaware Ave.
Pennington, NJ 08534-1603

Donors: James L. Mersfelder; Sandra L. Stark.
Foundation type: Independent foundation.
Financial data (yr. ended 08/31/14): Assets, $4,562,691; gifts received, $200,000; expenditures, $205,035; qualifying distributions, $200,000.
Fields of interest: Education; Hospital care; Human services; Basic and emergency aid; International development.
Limitations: Applications not accepted. Giving primarily in NJ and NY. No grants to individuals.
Application information: Contributes only to pre-selected organizations.
Officers: James L. Mersfelder, Mgr.; Sandra L. Stark, Mgr.
EIN: 223825678

5573

Blanche M. and George L. Watts Mountainside Community Foundation

210 Orchard St.
Westfield, NJ 07090-3134
Contact: Thomas C. Phelan
Main URL: http://www.wattsmountainside.org

Established in 2005 in New Jersey.
Donors: Mary Patricia Komich†; George L. Watts†; Blanche M. Watts†.

Foundation type: Independent foundation.
Financial data (yr. ended 12/31/13): Assets, $4,584,061 (M); expenditures, $273,002; qualifying distributions, $240,554; giving activities include $148,079 for 12 grants (high: $40,000; low: $750), and $70,750 for 9 grants to individuals (high: $15,000; low: $5,250).
Fields of interest: Higher education; Human services.
Type of support: Student aid; General support.
Limitations: Applications accepted. Giving limited to organizations benefiting the citizens of Mountainside, NJ. No support for political organizations.
Application information: Application form required.
    Initial approach: See website
    Deadline(s): Mar. and Sept. 15th
Officers: Nicholas Bradshaw, Pres.; John Clifford, V.P.; Bart A. Barre, Secy.; G. Dewey Moser, Treas.
Directors: John Amalse; Christopher Belden; Patricia Connelly; Sue Winans; Tricia Yurochko.
Number of staff: None.
EIN: 202942228

5574

We Live To Give Foundation, Inc.

(formerly Gala Organization Foundation, Inc.)
P.O. Box 6282
Freehold, NJ 07728-6282

Foundation type: Independent foundation.
Financial data (yr. ended 06/30/13): Assets, $641,375 (M); gifts received, $5,177; expenditures, $215,367; qualifying distributions, $210,000; giving activities include $210,000 for 3 grants (high: $110,000; low: $25,000).
Fields of interest: Education; Human services.
Limitations: Applications not accepted. Giving in the U.S., with emphasis on NY, OH, and TX.
Application information: Unsolicited requests for funds not accepted.
Officers and Directors: Kanti Gala, Pres. and Director; Kulin S. Desai; Shivaram Kumar; Manipal Reddy; Rajesh Shah.
EIN: 223566308

5575

Wei Family Private Foundation

359 Centre St., Ste. 2
Nutley, NJ 07110-2791
E-mail: info@wfpf888.org; *Main URL:* http://wfpf888.org
Application address: P.O. Box 14, Glen Rock, NJ 07452-0014, e-mail: admin@wfpf888.org

Donors: Chung KI Wei†; Wei Charitable Remainder Unitrust.
Foundation type: Independent foundation.
Financial data (yr. ended 12/31/13): Assets, $4,015,828 (M); expenditures, $239,925; qualifying distributions, $213,231; giving activities include $213,231 for 34 grants to individuals (high: $43,333; low: $2,000).
Purpose and activities: Scholarships for students of Chinese heritage pursuing an electrical engineering graduate degree at Columbia University or a science, engineering, or mathematics degree at Oregon State University.
Fields of interest: Higher education.
Limitations: Applications accepted. Giving primarily in NY and OR.

Application information: Application guidelines available on foundation web site. Application form required.
Officers: John W. Donnelly, Pres.; Janet Chen, V.P.; Edward Chen, Secy.-Treas.
EIN: 264525149

5576

The Irving Weinstein Foundation Inc.

c/o J.F. Anderson, CPA, PC
34 Bridge St.
Metuchen, NJ 08840-2276

Donors: Steven Lipkin; Millbrook Partners LLC; Irving Weinstein†.
Foundation type: Independent foundation.
Financial data (yr. ended 03/31/15): Assets, $7,319,390 (M); expenditures, $456,895; qualifying distributions, $400,533; giving activities include $272,134 for 6 grants (high: $135,000; low: $414).
Fields of interest: Higher education; Medical education; Hospital care.
Type of support: Research.
Limitations: Applications not accepted. Giving primarily in NY. No grants to individuals.
Application information: Contributes only to pre-selected organizations.
Officers and Directors: Joan Lipkin, Vice-Chair. and Director; Richard Lipkin, Secy. and Director; Steven M. Lipkin, Treas. and Director.
EIN: 136093068

5577

Weintraub Family Foundation

14 Grasmere Ct.
Livingston, NJ 07039-3406

Established in 2003 in New Jersey.
Donor: Joshua B. Weintraub.
Foundation type: Independent foundation.
Financial data (yr. ended 06/30/13): Assets, $565,416 (M); gifts received, $719,459; expenditures, $268,288; qualifying distributions, $251,038; giving activities include $251,038 for 44 grants (high: $43,000; low: $100).
Fields of interest: Education; Health; Human services.
Limitations: Applications not accepted.
Application information: Unsolicited requests for funds not accepted.
Officers: Joshua B. Weintraub, Pres.; Sharon R. Weintraub, Secy.-Treas.; Daniel Weintraub, Mgr.
EIN: 141878788

5578

Jack Weisberg Charitable Foundation Inc.

c/o SJM, C.P.A., PC
17 Nokomis Ave.
Rockaway, NJ 07866 (201) 207-8282

Established in 2000 in New York.
Donor: Jack Weisberg.
Foundation type: Independent foundation.
Financial data (yr. ended 12/31/13): Assets, $5,785,534 (M); gifts received, $1,000,000; expenditures, $194,243; qualifying distributions, $162,000; giving activities include $162,000 for 1 grant.

Purpose and activities: Giving primarily to an organization which provides performance space and assists artists for presentation of music and art; funding also for international medical relief.

Fields of interest: Arts and culture; International relations.

Limitations: Applications not accepted. Giving primarily in New York, NY.

Application information: Unsolicited requests for funds not accepted.

Officers: Jack Weisberg, Pres.; Stanley J. Morin, Secy.

EIN: 223771411

5579

James & Virginia Welch Foundation

c/o McCabe, Heidrich & Wong
4 Gatehall Dr.
Parsippany, NJ 07054-4518

Established in 1964 in New Jersey.

Donors: James O. Welch, Jr.; Virginia B. Welch.

Foundation type: Independent foundation.

Financial data (yr. ended 12/31/13): Assets, $4,500,167 (M); expenditures, $198,523; qualifying distributions, $174,566; giving activities include $171,150 for 58 grants (high: $50,000; low: $200).

Fields of interest: Education; University education; Nonprofits; Addiction services; Diseases and conditions; Human services.

Type of support: Research; Research and evaluation; Regranting.

Limitations: Applications not accepted. Giving primarily in MA, NJ and NY. No grants to individuals.

Application information: Contributes only to pre-selected organizations.

Officers: James O. Welch, Jr., Pres.; Virginia B. Welch, V.P.; Robert Wong, Secy.-Treas.

EIN: 223504396

5580

Lisa Wendel Memorial Foundation

c/o Dorfman, Mizrach & Thaler, LLP
555 Rte. 1 S.
Iselin, NJ 08830

Established in 1990 in Florida.

Donors: Gerald Wendel; Joshua Wendel.

Foundation type: Independent foundation.

Financial data (yr. ended 12/31/14): Assets, $3,641,883 (M); expenditures, $188,852; qualifying distributions, $182,426; giving activities include $169,183 for 49 grants (high: $25,200; low: $100).

Fields of interest: Education; Health; Human services.

Type of support: General support.

Limitations: Applications not accepted. Giving primarily in NV.

Application information: Unsolicited requests for funds not accepted.

Officers: Gerald Wendel, Pres.; Thomas Bergman, V.P.; David Dorfman, Secy.; Michael Wendel, Treas.

Directors: Diane Mason; Brian Wendel.

EIN: 133217479

5581

Frank X. Weny & Mary Ethel Weny Charitable Trust

2035 E. Hamburg Tpke., Ste. E
Wayne, NJ 07470-6251 (973) 831-8700
Contact: William C. Hanse, Tr.

Established in 2000 in New Jersey.

Donor: Frank X. Weny†.

Foundation type: Independent foundation.

Financial data (yr. ended 12/31/13): Assets, $11,249,490 (M); expenditures, $412,498; qualifying distributions, $310,000; giving activities include $310,000 for 22 grants (high: $55,000; low: $1,000).

Purpose and activities: Giving primarily for a museum of fine art, as well as for health care, human services, Christian organizations, and YMCAs.

Fields of interest: Art museums; Health; Christianity; Human services.

Limitations: Applications accepted. Giving primarily in MA and NJ. No grants to individuals.

Application information: Application form required.

Initial approach: Proposal
Deadline(s): None

Trustees: William C. Hanse; Roger W. Ludwig.

EIN: 316636669

5582

The Westfield Foundation

301 N. Ave. W.
P.O. Box 2295
Westfield, NJ 07091 (908) 233-9787
Contact: Elizabeth B. Chance, Exec. Dir.
FAX: (908) 233-2177;
E-mail: foundation@westfieldnj.com; Main
URL: http://www.thewestfieldfoundation.com
RSS feed: http://thewestfieldfoundation.com/feed

Established in 1975 in New Jersey.

Foundation type: Community foundation.

Financial data (yr. ended 12/31/13): Assets, $14,292,935 (M); gifts received, $155,026; expenditures, $478,450; giving activities include $414,838 for 18+ grants (high: $40,000).

Purpose and activities: The foundation's mission is to enhance and support the quality of life of the citizens of Westfield, NJ.

Fields of interest: Arts and culture; Historic preservation; Education; Health; Community and economic development; Human services.

Type of support: Capacity-building and technical assistance; Matching grants; Capital and infrastructure; Equipment; Emergency funds; Program development; Convening; Publications; Seed money; Curriculum development; Research; Technical assistance.

Limitations: Applications accepted. Giving limited to the Westfield, NJ, area. No support for churches, hospitals (except for programs with a strong Westfield orientation), religious organizations for religious activities, or private or parochial schools. No grants to individuals (except for scholarships), or for annual giving, operating expenses, deficit financing, travel, retro-funding, or endowments, unless suggested by the donor of a particular fund.

Publications: Application guidelines; Annual report; Financial statement; Informational brochure; Newsletter.

Application information: Visit foundation web site for application form and guidelines. Application form required.

Initial approach: Submit application form and attachments
Copies of proposal: 1
Deadline(s): Jan. 1, Apr. 1, Aug. 1, and Oct. 1
Board meeting date(s): Feb., May, Sept., and Nov.
Final notification: 1 week after board meeting

Officers and Trustees: Russell Finestein, Pres. and Trustee; Beth Cassie, V.P. and Trustee; Howard Cohen, Secy. and Trustee; Alice Fertig, Treas. and Trustee; Elizabeth B. Chance, Exec. Dir.; Gerard Abbattista; Claudia Andreski; Jay Boyle; Sal Caruana; Karen Fountain; Robert Gorelick; Ray Kostyack; Michelle Mattessich; Janet Sarkos; Mark Swingle; Darielle Walsh.

Number of staff: 1 part-time professional.

EIN: 222155896

5583

The Harold Wetterberg Foundation

89 Headquarters Plz.
Morristown, NJ 07960 9739931743
Application address for veterinary graduate education scholarships: Academic and Student Affairs Program Specialist, Association of American Veterinary Medical Colleges, 1101 Vermont Ave., NW, Ste. 301, Washington, DC 20005-3539

Established in 1961 in New Jersey.

Donor: Harold Wetterberg†.

Foundation type: Independent foundation.

Financial data (yr. ended 12/31/14): Assets, $2,075,365; expenditures, $267,804; qualifying distributions, $238,336.

Fields of interest: Arts and culture; Education; Higher education; Animal welfare; Veterinary medicine; Biology; Livestock and ranching; Community service.

Type of support: General support; Capital campaigns; Research and evaluation; Scholarships.

Limitations: Applications accepted. Giving primarily in NJ and NY.

Application information: Application form required.

Initial approach: Letter or Proposal or Completed application form
Copies of proposal: 1
Deadline(s): For vetenary medical colleges by Mar. 31 for Scholarships; None for other requests
Board meeting date(s): Varies

Officers and Trustees: Albert G. Besser, Pres. and Trustee; Gene R. Korf, Secy. and Trustee; Samuel R. Hoffer, Treas. and Trustee.

Number of staff: None.

EIN: 226042915

5584

Wicks Chapin Inc

855 Centennial Ave.
Piscataway, NJ 08855

Established in 1985 in New Jersey.

Donors: John C. Foley; Edward J. Foley III; Joan Foley†; Foley Inc.; E.J. Foley Inc.

Foundation type: Independent foundation.

Financial data (yr. ended 12/31/13): Assets, $3,112,890; gifts received, $100,000; expenditures, $259,416; qualifying distributions, $224,333.

Fields of interest: Elementary and secondary education; Health; Diseases and conditions; Human services; Family services.
Type of support: Research; Research and evaluation.
Limitations: Applications not accepted. Giving primarily in NJ. No grants to individuals.
Application information: Contributes only to pre-selected organizations.
Officers and Trustees: Edward J. Foley III, Co-Pres. and Trustee; John C. Foley, Co-Pres. and Trustee.
EIN: 222691706

5585
The Gregory and Claire Wilcox Family Foundation
P.O. Box 1501, NJ2-130-03-31
Pennington, NJ 08534-1501
Application address: c/o Claire or Gregory Wilcox, P.O. Box 654, Saunderstown, RI 02874, tel.: (609) 274-6834

Donors: Gregory Wilcox; Claire Wilcox.
Foundation type: Independent foundation.
Financial data (yr. ended 12/31/13): Assets, $1,856,524 (M); gifts received, $200,000; expenditures, $243,753; qualifying distributions, $226,309; giving activities include $214,000 for 5 grants (high: $80,000; low: $8,000).
Fields of interest: Education; Health; Human services.
Limitations: Applications accepted. Giving primarily in RI.
Application information: Application form required.
Initial approach: Letter
Deadline(s): None
Trustees: Claire Wilcox; Greg Wilcox.
EIN: 800326194

5586
The Wildwood Foundation
144 Hillcrest Ave.
Summit, NJ 07902
Application address: Wildwood Foundation, 469 Morris Ave., 3rd Fl., Summit, NJ 07901

Donor: Elaine B. Burnett.
Foundation type: Independent foundation.
Financial data (yr. ended 12/31/13): Assets, $5,888,379 (M); expenditures, $397,064; qualifying distributions, $292,950; giving activities include $260,000 for 8 grants (high: $75,000; low: $5,000).
Fields of interest: Education; Domesticated animals; Health; Human services.
Type of support: Research.
Limitations: Applications accepted. Giving primarily in NJ.
Application information: Application form required.
Initial approach: Letter
Deadline(s): None
Directors: Daniel P. Dougherty; Peter W. Ulicny; Walter P. Ulicny.
EIN: 061519655

5587
The Wilf Family Education Foundation Inc.
200 Central Ave., Ste. 102
Mountainside, NJ 07092-1961

Established in 1995 in New Jersey.
Donors: Leonard Wilf; Zygmunt Wilf; Mark Wilf; Judith Wilf†.
Foundation type: Independent foundation.
Financial data (yr. ended 12/31/13): Assets, $4,984,938 (M); expenditures, $187,661; qualifying distributions, $183,000; giving activities include $183,000 for 8 grants (high: $50,000; low: $500).
Fields of interest: Arts and culture; Art museums; Education; Religion; Judaism.
Type of support: General support.
Limitations: Applications not accepted. Giving primarily in NJ and NY. No grants to individuals.
Application information: Unsolicited requests for funds not accepted.
Trustees: Elizabeth Wilf; Jason Wilf; Jeffrey Wilf; Jonathan Wilf; Joseph Wilf; Leonard Wilf; Mark Wilf; Orin Wilf; Zygmunt Wilf.
EIN: 223411571

5588
The Wilf Family Hospital & Medical Research Foundation Inc.
200 Central Ave.
Mountainside, NJ 07092

Established in 1995 in New Jersey.
Donors: Leonard Wilf; Zygmunt Wilf; Mark Wilf; Judith Wilf†.
Foundation type: Independent foundation.
Financial data (yr. ended 12/31/13): Assets, $5,025,501 (M); expenditures, $166,897; qualifying distributions, $160,500; giving activities include $160,500 for 9 grants (high: $110,000; low: $500).
Fields of interest: Hospital care; Health care clinics; Cancers; Judaism.
Type of support: Research.
Limitations: Applications not accepted. Giving primarily in NJ and NY. No grants to individuals.
Application information: Unsolicited requests for funds not accepted.
Trustees: Elizabeth Wilf; Jason Wilf; Jeffrey Wilf; Jonathan Wilf; Joseph Wilf; Leonard Wilf; Mark Wilf; Orin Wilf; Zygmunt Wilf.
EIN: 223411572

5589
Willingham Foundation
P.O. Box 1501, NJ2-130-03-31
Pennington, NJ 08534-1501
Contact: Rebecca Bushkuhl

Established in 1961 in Texas.
Foundation type: Independent foundation.
Financial data (yr. ended 12/31/14): Assets, $2,175,112 (M); expenditures, $185,233; qualifying distributions, $162,183; giving activities include $143,778 for 16 grants (high: $20,000; low: $4,778).
Fields of interest: Education; Elementary and secondary education; University education; Community recreation; Human services.
Limitations: Applications accepted. Giving limited to TX, with an emphasis on Smith County.
Application information: Application form required.
Initial approach: Letter
Deadline(s): May 31

Officers: C. Harold Willingham, Pres.; Larry Willingham, V.P.; Nancy Willingham, V.P.; Sara Willingham Bowyer, Secy.
EIN: 756035231

5590
Elizabeth Ruthruff Wilson Foundation
P.O. Box 1501, NJ2-130-03-31
Pennington, NJ 08534-1501 (517) 423-4148
Contact: Theresa Powers
Application address: P.O. Box 27, Tecumseh, MI 49286

Established in 1997 in Michigan.
Donor: Mary Elizabeth Wilson†.
Foundation type: Independent foundation.
Financial data (yr. ended 12/31/14): Assets, $4,239,106 (M); expenditures, $233,177; qualifying distributions, $198,153; giving activities include $152,945 for 17 grants (high: $39,250; low: $650).
Purpose and activities: Giving for the promotion of music and the performing arts in Lenawee County, Michigan.
Fields of interest: Arts and culture; Education; Community and economic development.
Type of support: Program development; Matching grants; Scholarships; Student aid.
Limitations: Applications accepted. Giving primarily in Lenawee County, MI. No support for political or religious organizations, or athletic and recreational facilities. No grants for endowments, salaries, travel expenses, loans or debt retirement, or emergency funding.
Publications: Application guidelines.
Application information:
Initial approach: Proposal
Copies of proposal: 1
Deadline(s): None
Officers: John Waltman, V.P.; Sheri Powers, Secy.; Theresa Powers, Exec. Dir.
Trustee: Marilyn Mason.
Number of staff: 1 part-time support.
EIN: 383372941

5591
The Alan and Hope Winters Family Foundation
c/o L. Borenstein, C.P.A.
P.O. Box 570
Ridgefield, NJ 07657-0570

Established in 1995 in New Jersey.
Donors: Alan Winters; Hope Winters.
Foundation type: Independent foundation.
Financial data (yr. ended 12/31/14): Assets, $5,940,536 (M); gifts received, $384,600; expenditures, $290,587; qualifying distributions, $290,587; giving activities include $265,790 for 25 grants (high: $99,600; low: $200).
Fields of interest: Education; Human services; Child welfare.
Type of support: Professorships; Seed money; Curriculum development.
Limitations: Applications not accepted. Giving primarily in New York, NY. No grants to individuals.
Application information: Contributes only to pre-selected organizations.
Trustees: Alan Winters; Hope Winters.
Number of staff: 1 part-time professional.
EIN: 526775755

5592
WKBJ Partnership Foundation
(formerly The Made in Dover Foundation)
50 Smith Rd.
Denville, NJ 07834-9405 (973) 328-0303
Contact: Bob Howitt, Pres.

Established in 1990 in New Jersey.
Donors: Joan S. Howitt; Robert M. Howitt; Family Development Ctr.; Jody Summerhays.
Foundation type: Operating foundation.
Financial data (yr. ended 12/31/13): Assets, $1,145,985 (M); expenditures, $504,889; qualifying distributions, $491,697.
Purpose and activities: Giving primarily for education, particularly financially disadvantaged students.
Fields of interest: Education.
Type of support: General support; Capital campaigns; Convening; Seed money; Curriculum development; Scholarships; Technical assistance.
Limitations: Applications accepted. No support for religious or political organizations.
Application information: Application form required.
Initial approach: Letter, Email
Deadline(s): None
Trustee: Bob Howitt.
Number of staff: 1 full-time professional.
EIN: 223000244

5593
Mel Wolf Foundation
P.O. Box 1501, NJ2-130-03-31
Pennington, NJ 08534-1501

Established in 2005 in Nevada.
Donor: Mel Wolf†.
Foundation type: Independent foundation.
Financial data (yr. ended 12/31/14): Assets, $4,370,708; expenditures, $289,036; qualifying distributions, $251,354.
Fields of interest: Community and economic development; Human services.
Limitations: Applications not accepted. Giving primarily in CO, Washington, DC, and WV. No grants to individuals.
Application information: Contributes only to pre-selected organizations.
Trustees: George Castelle; Susan Giullian; Susan-Louise Fessend.
EIN: 201270730

5594
The Woolley-Clifford Foundation
c/o Krinitz, Sperber
580 Sylvan Ave., Ste. 1C
Englewood Cliffs, NJ 07632-3105

Established in 1953 in Delaware.
Donors: Stewart B. Clifford; Cornelia W. Clifford; Stewart B. Clifford Charitable Lead Annuity Trust.
Foundation type: Independent foundation.
Financial data (yr. ended 12/31/13): Assets, $1,644,102 (M); gifts received, $269,771; expenditures, $334,057; qualifying distributions, $327,969; giving activities include $316,550 for 66 grants (high: $55,000; low: $100).
Purpose and activities: Giving primarily for the arts and education.
Fields of interest: Arts and culture; Elementary and secondary education; Higher education; Graduate and professional education; Theology; Human services.
Limitations: Applications not accepted. Giving primarily in NY. No grants to individuals.
Application information: Unsolicited requests for funds not accepted.
Officers and Trustees: Stewart B. Clifford, Pres. and Trustee; Cornelia W. Clifford, V.P. and Trustee; J.C. Danner, Secy. and Trustee; C.C. Wareham, Treas. and Trustee.
EIN: 136100412

5595
The Yates Family Charitable Foundation
43 Baileys Mill Rd.
Basking Ridge, NJ 07920-4020

Foundation type: Independent foundation.
Financial data (yr. ended 12/31/13): Assets, $717,722 (M); gifts received, $116,677; expenditures, $218,120; qualifying distributions, $218,120; giving activities include $217,565 for 7 grants (high: $201,000; low: $500).
Fields of interest: Education; Environment; Housing development; Human services.
Limitations: Applications not accepted. Giving primarily in CA.
Application information: Unsolicited requests for funds not accepted.
Officers: Christopher M. Yates, C.E.O.; Matthew Fleissig, C.F.O.
Trustee: Marc J. Dearth.
EIN: 454782317

5596
Yin-Shun Foundation
67 Lawrence Rd.
Lafayette, NJ 07848-3018

Established in 1996 in New Jersey.
Donors: Eva Lin; Ray Jui Chuang Chung; Tai Hwa Yen.
Foundation type: Independent foundation.
Financial data (yr. ended 12/31/13): Assets, $8,945,362 (M); gifts received, $123,918; expenditures, $746,240; qualifying distributions, $561,135; giving activities include $414,704 for 13 grants (high: $120,000; low: $393).
Fields of interest: Education; Religion; Buddhism; Human services.
International interests: Taiwan.
Type of support: Continuing support.
Limitations: Applications not accepted. Giving primarily in Lafayette, NJ, and Taiwan. No grants to individuals.
Application information: Unsolicited requests for funds not accepted.
Officers and Trustees: Ven Bhikkhu Bodhi, Chair. and Trustee; Juichang Chuang, Secy. and Trustee; Hueyling Wu, Treas. and Trustee; Ven Bhikkhu Chang-Tzu; Wan-Ju Chen; Tsuku Lee; Taihua Kathy Wu.
EIN: 223458312

5597
The Yoh Foundation
c/o Peter Digiovanni
3122 Fire Rd., Ste. 200
Egg Harbor Township, NJ 08234-5859

Established in 2006 in Pennsylvania.
Donors: James W. Yoh; H. Julie Yoh.
Foundation type: Independent foundation.
Financial data (yr. ended 12/31/12): Assets, $486,378 (M); expenditures, $357,199; qualifying distributions, $351,500; giving activities include $351,500 for grants.
Fields of interest: Education; Foundations.
Type of support: Individual development.
Limitations: Applications not accepted. Giving primarily in CA and NJ. No grants to individuals.
Application information: Contributes only to pre-selected organizations.
Directors: H. Julie Yoh; James Yoh.
EIN: 203811596

5598
Zakaria Family Foundation
2330 Plz., 5 Harborside
Jersey City, NJ 07311-4017

Established in 2007 in New Jersey.
Donor: Arshad Zakaria.
Foundation type: Independent foundation.
Financial data (yr. ended 12/31/13): Assets, $6,610,111 (M); gifts received, $396,659; expenditures, $216,466; qualifying distributions, $174,874; giving activities include $174,874 for 8 grants (high: $72,300; low: $4,824).
Fields of interest: University education.
Limitations: Applications not accepted. Giving primarily in MA. No grants to individuals.
Application information: Unsolicited requests for funds not accepted.
Officer: Arshad Zakaria, Chair.
EIN: 261607321

5599
The Nochim & Rivka Zeldes Foundation
131 Village Path
Lakewood, NJ 08701-2578

Established in 1984 in Unspecified.
Donor: Nochim Zeldes.
Foundation type: Independent foundation.
Financial data (yr. ended 11/30/13): Assets, $2,742,880 (M); expenditures, $226,355; qualifying distributions, $220,755; giving activities include $220,755 for 36 grants (high: $28,000; low: $180).
Purpose and activities: Giving primarily for education and Jewish organizations.
Fields of interest: Education; Religion; Human services.
Limitations: Applications not accepted. Giving primarily in Lakewood, NJ, and Brooklyn, NY. No grants to individuals.
Application information: Contributes only to pre-selected organizations.
Directors: Abraham Brudny; Rywa Zeldes; Shimon Zeldes.
EIN: 112724793

5600
Zichron Yehoshua Vasher Foundation
751 Winthrop Ave.
Teaneck, NJ 07666-2266
Contact: Ofra Weinberger, Tr.

Established in 1999 in New York.

Donor: Judah Weinberger.
Foundation type: Independent foundation.
Financial data (yr. ended 11/30/14): Assets, $799,119 (M); gifts received, $39,761; expenditures, $284,270; qualifying distributions, $284,270; giving activities include $283,647 for 3 grants (high: $278,495; low: $2,200).
Fields of interest: Human services.
Type of support: General support; Scholarships.
Limitations: Applications accepted. Giving primarily in NJ, NY and OH.
Application information: Application form required.
  Initial approach: Letter
  Deadline(s): None
Trustee: Ofra Weinberger.
EIN: 223692106

5601
The Zimmer Family Foundation Inc.
c/o Jennifer Zimmer
145 E. Saddle River Rd.
Saddle River, NJ   07458-3033

Donors: Stuart Zimmer; Jennifer Zimmer.
Foundation type: Independent foundation.
Financial data (yr. ended 12/31/13): Assets, $8,861,245 (M); gifts received, $5,600; expenditures, $402,659; qualifying distributions, $398,680; giving activities include $387,800 for 10 grants (high: $190,000; low: $500).
Fields of interest: Education; Diseases and conditions; Judaism; Human services.
Limitations: Applications not accepted. Giving primarily in NJ; some funding in NY. No grants to individuals.

Application information: Contributes only to pre-selected organizations.
Officers and Directors: Stuart Zimmer, Chair. and Director; Jennifer Zimmer, Pres. and Director; Mendy Herson.
EIN: 810586837

5602
Zissu Family Foundation
145 Forest Dr.
Short Hills, NJ   07078-3205

Established in 1993 in New Jersey.
Donor: Frederick Zissu†.
Foundation type: Independent foundation.
Financial data (yr. ended 12/31/14): Assets, $6,662,824; expenditures, $252,721; qualifying distributions, $249,330.
Fields of interest: Nonprofits; Health; Judaism; Human services.
Type of support: Regranting.
Limitations: Applications not accepted. No grants to individuals.
Application information: Unsolicited requests for funds not accepted.
Trustees: Barbara Kushnick; Sandra Rosenbaum; Jeffrey A. Zissu.
EIN: 226612155

5603
Zobel Foundation, Inc.
c/o Zager Fuchs, PC
268 Broad St.
P.O. Box 489
Red Bank, NJ   07701

Established in 2000 in New Jersey.
Donor: Franklyn Ellis.
Foundation type: Independent foundation.
Financial data (yr. ended 10/31/14): Assets, $230,586 (M); gifts received, $230,150; expenditures, $261,569; qualifying distributions, $234,780; giving activities include $234,780 for 59 grants (high: $25,000; low: $100).
Purpose and activities: To provide aid to worthy and deserving educational, religious, medical and community projects and charities.
Fields of interest: Education; Religion; Human services.
Type of support: General support; Continuing support; Program development; Fellowships; Scholarships; Research.
Limitations: Applications not accepted. No grants to individuals.
Application information: Unsolicited requests for funds not accepted.
Officers: Lawrence M. Fuchs, Pres. and CEO; Franklyn R. Ellis, V.P.; Lavina O. Ellis, V.P.; Madeline R. Ottino, Secy.
Number of staff: 3 part-time professional; 3 part-time support.
EIN: 223764673

NEW MEXICO

5604
Akerson Family Foundation
54 Rock Pt.
Albuquerque, NM   87122-0000

Established in 1994 in New Mexico.
Donors: Warren Akerson; Loretta D. Akerson.
Foundation type: Independent foundation.
Financial data (yr. ended 12/31/14): Assets, $4,867,095; gifts received, $333,217; expenditures, $233,644; qualifying distributions, $233,644.
Purpose and activities: Giving primarily for education and Catholic organizations.
Fields of interest: Philanthropy; Religion; Human services.
Type of support: General support.
Limitations: Applications not accepted. Giving primarily in NM. No grants to individuals.
Application information: Unsolicited request for funds not accepted.
Officer: Warren Akerson, Mgr.
Number of staff: None.
EIN: 850427304

5605
Angelica Foundation
1688 Cerro Gordo Rd.
Santa Fe, NM   87501-6175
E-mail: info@angelicafoundation.org; Main
URL: http://angelicafoundation.org
Blog: http://angelicafoundation.org/blog.html

Established in 1994 in California.
Donors: Sigrid Rausing Trust; Open Society Institute; The Keller Group Investment; Ruben and Elizabeth Ransing Trust.
Foundation type: Independent foundation.
Financial data (yr. ended 12/31/13): Assets, $3,659,690 (M); gifts received, $354,430; expenditures, $754,738; qualifying distributions, $592,581; giving activities include $324,465 for 13 + grants (high: $227,500).
Purpose and activities: The foundation supports progressive organizations and programs in the United States and Latin America that empower communities to become more economically, socially and environmentally just.
Fields of interest: Environment; Foundations; Human rights; Human services; Females; Indigenous peoples.
International interests: Latin America; Mexico.
Type of support: Annual campaigns.
Limitations: Applications not accepted. No support for public education, political organizations, or programs promoting religious doctrines . No grants to individuals, or for academic scholarships, conferences, or fundraising events.
Publications: Annual report.
Application information: Contributes only to pre-selected organizations.
Officers and Directors: Suzanne D. Gollin, Pres. and Director; James D. Gollin, Secy.-Treas. and Director; Christopher Brown; Nancy Harris Campbell; Nina Royal; Gladys Schmidt.

Number of staff: 1 part-time professional; 2 part-time support.
EIN: 330632647

5606
B.F. Foundation
766 Calle del Resplandor
Santa Fe, NM   87505-5988

Established in 1965 in Arizona.
Donors: Harvey W. Branigar, Jr.†; Sarah L. Branigar; Sarah L. Branigar Charitable Lead Annuity Trust.
Foundation type: Independent foundation.
Financial data (yr. ended 12/31/13): Assets, $4,447,091 (M); gifts received, $131,758; expenditures, $264,418; qualifying distributions, $192,653; giving activities include $159,050 for 30 grants (high: $26,500; low: $50).
Purpose and activities: Giving primarily for education and conservation.
Fields of interest: Arts and culture; Museums; Education; Higher education; Environment; Botanical gardens.
Type of support: General support; Internships; Scholarships.
Limitations: Applications not accepted. Giving primarily in AZ, CO, and NM. No grants or scholarships to individuals directly.
Application information: Unsolicited requests for funds not accepted.
Officers: David D. Chase, Chair.; Katherin Lee Chase, Pres. and Exec. Dir.; Sara Chase Shaw, Secy.; Richard W. Shaw, Treas.
Number of staff: 1 full-time professional; 1 part-time professional.
EIN: 366141070

5607
Zane Bennett Family Foundation
c/o Ned W. Bennett
51 Ranch Estates Rd.
Santa Fe, NM   87506-2149

Established in 2005 in Texas.
Donor: Ned W. Bennett.
Foundation type: Independent foundation.
Financial data (yr. ended 12/31/13): Assets, $1,468,749 (M); expenditures, $209,309; qualifying distributions, $200,000; giving activities include $200,000 for 1 grant.
Fields of interest: Museums; Diseases and conditions; Alzheimer's disease.
Limitations: Applications not accepted. Giving primarily in TX and NM.
Application information: Unsolicited requests for funds not accepted.
Officers and Directors: Ned W. Bennett, Pres. and Treas. and Director; Sandra G. Zane, V.P. and Secy. and Director; Glen Philip Bennett; Cathy Lee Galleher; Christopher A. Galleher; Ian R. Galleher; Amy B. Kaser; Jeremy R. Zane.
EIN: 203636308

5608
Carlsbad Foundation, Inc.
114 S. Canyon St.
Carlsbad, NM   88220-5733   (505) 887-1131
Contact: Jim Harrison, Exec. Dir.

Established in 1977 in New Mexico.

Foundation type: Community foundation.
Financial data (yr. ended 06/30/14): Assets, $25,561,218 (M); gifts received, $248,583; expenditures, $1,603,754; giving activities include $278,625 for 1+ grant, and $83,091 for 166 grants to individuals.
Purpose and activities: The foundation exists to improve the quality of life for the people of Carlsbad and South Eddy County, NM. The foundation provides leadership for local charitable organizations by building and preserving permanent funds for the support of arts and humanities, community development, education, environmental needs, health and human services, and law and protection.
Fields of interest: Arts and culture; Education; Environment; Health; Mental health care; Diseases and conditions; Community and economic development; Human services; Food aid; Unknown or not classified.
Type of support: General support; Pro bono consulting services; Program-related investments; Continuing support; Building and renovations; Matching grants; Loans to individuals; Equipment; Emergency funds; Program development; Convening; Publications; Seed money; Scholarships; Technical assistance; Student aid.
Limitations: Applications accepted. Giving limited to South Eddy County, NM, with emphasis on Carlsbad. No grants for annual campaigns.
Publications: Annual report (including application guidelines); Newsletter.
Application information: Grants to individuals are by nomination only.
  Initial approach: Letter
  Copies of proposal: 1
  Deadline(s): 1 week in advance of board meetings for organizations; nominations for individuals accepted throughout the year
  Board meeting date(s): Monthly
  Final notification: Individual recipients announced at Sept. meeting
Officers and Directors: Craig Stephens, Pres. and Director; Larry Henderson, V.P. and Director; Richard J. Forrest, Jr., Secy. and Director; Amy Power, Treas. and Director; Jim Harrison, Exec. Dir.; Wanda Durham; Neal Dungan; Judy Lunardon; Vicki Moutray; Mary Waterscheid.
Number of staff: 1 full-time professional; 1 full-time support; 1 part-time support.
EIN: 850206472

5609
Chamiza Foundation
1919 5th St., Ste. C
Santa Fe, NM   87505-6012   (505) 216-2140
Contact: Donna Vogel, Exec. Dir.
E-mail: donna@chamiza.org; Main URL: http://www.chamiza.org

Established in 1989 in New Mexico.
Donors: Gifford Phillips; Mia Toya.
Foundation type: Independent foundation.
Financial data (yr. ended 12/31/12): Assets, $2,582,401 (M); expenditures, $287,214; qualifying distributions, $257,167; giving activities include $127,034 for 16 grants (high: $20,000; low: $700).
Purpose and activities: Generally only funds programs initiated by Pueblo Indians that enhance the cultural preservation of language, art, lifeways, and creativity in Pueblo culture; giving limited to the New Mexico Pueblo Indians.

Fields of interest: Arts and culture; Cultural awareness; Linguistics; Agriculture; American Indians.
Type of support: General support; Program development; Convening; Publications; Seed money; Curriculum development; Internships.
Limitations: Applications accepted. Giving limited to the Pueblo Indian tribes of NM. No support for programs originated by organizations other than Pueblo entities who apply without written request. No grants to individuals.
Publications: Application guidelines; Grants list; Multi-year report.
Application information:
  Initial approach: Letter
  Copies of proposal: 15
  Deadline(s): Mar. and June
  Board meeting date(s): Mar. and June
  Final notification: 5 weeks
Officers and Directors: Marjorie Phillips Elliott, Chair. and Director; Alice Phillips Swistel, Vice-Chair. and Director; Diane Reyna, Pres. and Director; Beverly R. Singer, V.P. and Director; Joann Kocher Phillips, Secy. and Director; Hayes Lewis, Treas. and Director; Donna Vogel, Exec. Dir.; Carnell Chosa; Ted Jojola; Cynthia Chavez Lamar; James L. Phillips; Deborah Flynn Post; Mia Toya; Brian Vallo.
Number of staff: 1 full-time professional.
EIN: 850373197

5610
Community Foundation of Southern New Mexico

301 S. Church St., Ste. H
Las Cruces, NM   88001   (575) 521-4794
Contact: Luan Wagner Burn Ph.D, Exec. Dir.
E-mail: luan@cfsnm.org; Main URL: http://www.cfsnm.org
Facebook: https://www.facebook.com/The-Community-Foundation-of-Southern-New-Mexico-222851104402713/

Established in 1999 in New Mexico.
Foundation type: Community foundation.
Financial data (yr. ended 12/31/13): Assets, $15,627,021 (M); gifts received, $1,461,428; expenditures, $1,333,152; giving activities include $379,885 for 2+ grants (high: $12,139), and $25,386 for 38 grants to individuals.
Purpose and activities: The foundation serves as a charitable resource linking donors with community needs.
Limitations: Applications accepted. Giving primarily in Dona Ana, Grant, Hidalgo, Lincoln, Luna, Otero and Sierra counties, NM.
Publications: Annual report; Financial statement.
Application information: Visit foundation for information.
Officers and Directors: Jeremy Settles, Pres. and Director; Richard Williams, V.P. and Director; Diana Seward, Secy. and Director; Beth Fant, Treas. and Director; Luan Wagner Burn, Ph.D, Exec. Dir.; Mellow Honek, At-Large; Ken Binkley; Barrett Brewer; Jennifer Cervantes; Abel Covarrubias; Many Leatherwood; Denten Park.
EIN: 850455682

5611
Con Alma Health Foundation, Inc.

144 Park Ave.
Santa Fe, NM   87501-1833   (505) 438-0776
FAX: (505) 438-6223; E-mail: staff@conalma.org;
Main URL: http://www.conalma.org
Con Alma Health Foundation's Philanthropy Promise: http://www.ncrp.org/philanthropys-promise/who
Facebook: http://www.facebook.com/pages/Con-Alma-Health-Foundation/97700599976
Online Application Powerpoint: http://conalma.org/resources_list/online-application-powerpoint
Online Application Video: http://conalma.org/resources_list/cahf-online-grant-application-introduction-video
RebelMouse: https://www.rebelmouse.com/ConAlmaHealthFoundation
Twitter: https://twitter.com/NMhealth
YouTube: http://www.youtube.com/user/ConAlmaNM

Established in 2001 in New Mexico.
Donors: Kellogg Foundation; Robert Wood Johnson Foundation; McCune Foundation; Grantmakers in Health.
Foundation type: Independent foundation.
Financial data (yr. ended 12/31/13): Assets, $26,999,029 (M); gifts received, $355,100; expenditures, $1,401,052; qualifying distributions, $1,096,455; giving activities include $366,600 for 56 grants (high: $13,500; low: $250).
Purpose and activities: The foundation is organized to be aware of and respond to the health rights and needs of culturally and demographically diverse peoples and communities of New Mexico. The foundation seeks to address the health needs of underserved populations, to support and strengthen nonprofits that seek to improve the health of the underserved, to encourage leaders in the field, and to inform the development of public policies that promote wellness and access to preventive health care.
Fields of interest: Health; Children and youth; Infants and toddlers; Adolescents; Seniors; Females; Ethnic and racial groups; People of Latin American descent; Indigenous peoples; American Indians; Immigrants and migrants; Homeless people; People with HIV/AIDS.
Type of support: General support; Capacity-building and technical assistance; Program development; Convening; Seed money; Research; Technical assistance; Program evaluations.
Limitations: Applications accepted. Giving limited to NM. No support for lobbying. No grants to individuals, for scholarships/fellowships, or for bricks, mortar, or property.
Publications: Application guidelines; Annual report; Grants list; Informational brochure.
Application information: Application form available on foundation web site. See foundation web site for guidelines and requirements.
  Initial approach: See online application process on foundation web site
  Deadline(s): Varies according to grant cycle
  Board meeting date(s): Jan., Apr., July and Oct.
  Final notification: Varies
Officers and Trustees: Louis Luna, V.P.; Alfredo Vigil, MD, Secy. and Trustee; Richard Tyner, Treas.; Yvette Kaufman-Bell; Ardena Orosco; Sherrick Roanhorse; Valerie Romero-Leggott, MD; Twila Rutter; Benny Shendo, Jr.

Number of staff: 3 full-time professional; 3 part-time professional; 1 full-time support.
EIN: 850484396

5612
Continental Divide Electric Education Foundation

P.O. Box 1087
Grants, NM   87020-1087
Contact: Corina Sandoval
Main URL: http://www.cdec.coop

Established in 1988 in New Mexico.
Donor: Continental Divide Electric Cooperative, Inc.
Foundation type: Company-sponsored foundation.
Financial data (yr. ended 12/31/13): Assets, $4,591,462 (M); gifts received, $4,474; expenditures, $269,141; qualifying distributions, $225,875; giving activities include $225,875 for 144 grants to individuals (high: $1,625; low: $1,500).
Purpose and activities: The foundation awards college scholarships to active members and the immediate family members of active members of Continental Divide Electric Cooperative, Inc. attending an institution in Arizona or New Mexico.
Fields of interest: Education.
Type of support: Student aid; Individual development.
Limitations: Applications accepted. Giving primarily in AZ and NM.
Publications: Application guidelines.
Application information: Grants of up to $3,000 are awarded each year. Application form required.
  Initial approach: Completed application form
  Deadline(s): May 1
  Board meeting date(s): 2nd Thurs. of each month
  Final notification: Within 30 days
Officers: Lynn Head, Pres.; Keith Gottlieb, V.P.; Arsenio Salazar, Secy.-Treas.
EIN: 850365720

5613
The Edgar Foster Daniels Foundation

450 Circle Dr.
Santa Fe, NM   87501-8882

Established in 1995 in New Mexico.
Donor: Edgar Foster Daniels.
Foundation type: Independent foundation.
Financial data (yr. ended 12/31/13): Assets, $11,125 (M); gifts received, $341,000; expenditures, $336,362; qualifying distributions, $336,362; giving activities include $190,000 for 3 grants (high: $135,000; low: $20,000).
Purpose and activities: Giving primarily for major operas; some support also for a hospital foundation.
Fields of interest: Opera; Health.
Limitations: Applications not accepted. Giving on a national basis. No grants to individuals.
Application information: Contributes only to pre-selected organizations. Unsolicited requests for funds not accepted.
Officers: Edgar Foster Daniels, Pres.; Kurt Sommer, V.P.; Barbara Yost, Secy.
Number of staff: 1 full-time professional.
EIN: 850435024

5614
The Forrest Family Foundation
112 Dickson Ln.
Carlsbad, NM 88220-8800

Established in 1998 in New Mexico.
Donors: Barbara J. Forrest; Richard J. Forrest; Robert H. Forrest; Betty J. Forrest.
Foundation type: Independent foundation.
Financial data (yr. ended 12/31/13): Assets, $1,035,709 (M); gifts received, $250,000; expenditures, $183,233; qualifying distributions, $177,000; giving activities include $177,000 for 8 grants (high: $50,000; low: $500).
Fields of interest: Community and economic development; Protestantism; Human services.
Type of support: General support.
Limitations: Applications not accepted. Giving primarily in NM, with emphasis on Carlsbad. No grants to individuals.
Application information: Contributes only to pre-selected organizations.
Officers: Richard J. Forrest, Pres.; Robert J. Forrest, V.P.; Barbara J. Forrest, Secy.; Betty J. Forrest, Treas.
EIN: 850456721

5615
Joseph C. and Esther Foster Foundation, Inc.
7 Avenida Vista Grande, Ste. 160
Santa Fe, NM 87508-9198

Established in 1961 in Massachusetts.
Donors: Joseph C. Foster†; Esther J. Foster†.
Foundation type: Independent foundation.
Financial data (yr. ended 12/31/14): Assets, $3,615,330 (M); expenditures, $278,473; qualifying distributions, $190,500; giving activities include $190,500 for 34 grants (high: $20,000; low: $1,000).
Fields of interest: Education; Judaism; Human services.
Type of support: Annual campaigns; Program-related investments; Matching grants.
Limitations: Applications not accepted. Giving primarily in NM and NY. No grants to individuals.
Application information: Unsolicited requests for funds not accepted.
Officers and Directors: Daniel Foster Haft, Pres. and Treas. and Director; Roger Scoviller, Clerk; Burt Haft; Nicole Werkmeister, Esq.
EIN: 046114436

5616
Garfield Street Foundation
330 Garfield St.
Santa Fe, NM 87501-2612 (505) 992-5100

Established in 1999 in New Mexico.
Donors: BGK Equities II, LLC; Edward M. Gilbert; BGKP Properties, Inc.; BGK Property Mgmt. LLC; Fresno Clinton Operating Assoc., LP.
Foundation type: Independent foundation.
Financial data (yr. ended 06/30/14): Assets, $226,612; gifts received, $365,900; expenditures, $440,109; qualifying distributions, $358,924.
Fields of interest: Arts and culture; Orchestral music; Education; Human services.
Limitations: Applications accepted. Giving primarily in NM, with emphasis on Santa Fe.

Application information: Application form required.
Initial approach: Letter from an agency on behalf of their client
Deadline(s): None
Officer: Robin Smith, V.P.
Directors: Ian Brownlow; Eileen Gabaldon; Steve Love.
EIN: 752830956

5617
The Gumbo Foundation
347 E. Palace Ave.
Santa Fe, NM 87501-2275

Established in 2002 in New Mexico.
Donors: Mary Emily Hogan; Tracey Elise Hogan; William Hobson Hogan; Elise W. Schmidt.
Foundation type: Independent foundation.
Financial data (yr. ended 11/30/13): Assets, $5,175,712 (M); expenditures, $250,325; qualifying distributions, $213,370; giving activities include $209,000 for 45 grants (high: $10,000; low: $1,000).
Fields of interest: University education; Graduate and professional education; Domesticated animals; Health; Diseases and conditions; Storms; Human services.
Type of support: General support; Fellowships; Research.
Limitations: Applications not accepted. Giving primarily in NM. No grants to individuals.
Application information: Unsolicited requests for funds not accepted.
Officers: Elise W. Schmidt, Pres.; Mary Emily Hogan, V.P.; Tracey Elise Hogan, V.P.; William Hobson Hogan, V.P.; Paul B. Schmidt, Secy.-Treas.
EIN: 043727883

5618
The H. B. and Lucille Horn Foundation
634 Graceland Dr. S.E.
Albuquerque, NM 87108-3335 (505) 265-3553

Established in 1961 in New Mexico.
Donors: H.B. Horn; Lucille L. Horn.
Foundation type: Independent foundation.
Financial data (yr. ended 09/30/14): Assets, $1,606,391 (M); expenditures, $144,501; qualifying distributions, $139,850; giving activities include $139,850 for 8 grants (high: $109,500; low: $1,000).
Fields of interest: Arts and culture; Nonprofits; Human rights; Human services.
Type of support: Regranting.
Limitations: Applications accepted. Giving primarily in Albuquerque, NM. No grants to individuals.
Application information:
Initial approach: Proposal
Deadline(s): None
Officers: Thomas E. Horn, Pres.; Edward T. Peter, V.P.; Ruthie Horn Robbins, Secy.-Treas.
EIN: 856011264

5619
King-Carpenter Foundation
P.O. Box 10850
Albuquerque, NM 87184-0850

Donors: Ellen J. King; James N. King.
Foundation type: Independent foundation.

Financial data (yr. ended 12/31/13): Assets, $2,498,189 (M); gifts received, $200,000; expenditures, $222,283; qualifying distributions, $200,000; giving activities include $200,000 for 1 grant.
Fields of interest: Nonprofits.
Type of support: Regranting.
Limitations: Applications not accepted.
Application information: Unsolicited requests for funds not accepted.
Officers and Directors: James N. King, Pres. and Director; Ellen J. King, V.P. and Director; Cynthia K. Schultz, Secy. and Director; Michelle E. King, Treas. and Director.
EIN: 270244287

5620
Lea County Electric Education Foundation
P.O. Box 1447
Lovington, NM 88260-1447 (575) 396-3631
Main URL: http://www.lcecnet.com

Established in 1986 in New Mexico.
Donor: Lea County Electric Cooperative, Inc.
Foundation type: Company-sponsored foundation.
Financial data (yr. ended 12/31/13): Assets, $1,175,512 (M); gifts received, $87,404; expenditures, $221,234; qualifying distributions, $145,253; giving activities include $143,500 for 96 grants to individuals (high: $2,000; low: $750).
Purpose and activities: The foundation awards college scholarships to active members and children of active members of Lea County Electric Cooperative who are attending institutions of higher education in New Mexico or Texas.
Type of support: Scholarships.
Limitations: Applications accepted. Giving limited to NM and TX.
Publications: Application guidelines.
Application information: Application form required.
Initial approach: Completed application form
Deadline(s): Jan. 10
Final notification: May 1
Officers: John Ingle, Pres.; Dean Kinsolving, V.P.; Dan Hardin, Secy.-Treas.
Trustees: Robert Caudle; John Graham; Terry Davis; Ray Hilburn; Wade Roberts; Kenny Wallace.
EIN: 850351147

5621
Nirvana Manana Institute
(also known as NMI Foundation)
8234 Raintree N.E.
Albuquerque, NM 87122-1333 (505) 275-1827
Contact: Carol Tucker Trelease, Secy.

Established in 1996 in New Mexico.
Donor: David C. Rigsby.
Foundation type: Independent foundation.
Financial data (yr. ended 12/31/13): Assets, $16,554 (M); gifts received, $194,000; expenditures, $189,062; qualifying distributions, $181,940; giving activities include $181,940 for 19 grants (high: $35,000; low: $1,000).
Purpose and activities: Giving limited to the area of family planning and overpopulation awareness.
Fields of interest: Community and economic development; Human rights; Human services.
Type of support: General support; Matching grants; Continuing support.

Limitations: Applications accepted. Giving primarily in NM. No grants to individuals, or for land or building acquisitions.

Application information:
Initial approach: Letter
Deadline(s): None

Officers: David Rigsby, Pres.; Pamela Ray, V.P.; Carol Tucker Trelease, Secy.

Directors: Ethan Gutierrez; Ginger Jaschke; John McMullin; Chuck Scott.

Number of staff: None.

EIN: 850437479

5622

Quail Roost Foundation

P.O. Box 2035
El Prado, NM 87529-2035

Established in 2004 in New Mexico.

Donors: Kerry Heubeck; Jack Dreyfus.

Foundation type: Independent foundation.

Financial data (yr. ended 12/31/13): Assets, $5,010,069 (M); gifts received, $10,750; expenditures, $288,387; qualifying distributions, $233,108; giving activities include $173,500 for 53 grants (high: $12,000; low: $750).

Fields of interest: Education; Health; Interfaith; Basic and emergency aid; International development.

Limitations: Applications not accepted. No grants to individuals.

Application information: Contributes only to pre-selected organizations.

Officers and Trustees: Ha White, Chair. and Trustee; Carol White, Vice-Chair. and Trustee; Jeff Sanders, Secy. and Trustee; Sanjay Poovandan, Treas. and Trustee; Fred Doerr; Loretta Ortizy Pino; H'Krih Shelhamer; Mehdi Shelhamer.

EIN: 760754268

5623

The Schnieders Family Foundation

P.O. Box 31278
Santa Fe, NM 87594-1278

Donor: Richard J. Schnieders.

Foundation type: Independent foundation.

Financial data (yr. ended 12/31/14): Assets, $4,652,677; expenditures, $362,437; qualifying distributions, $317,628.

Fields of interest: Education; Agriculture; Human services; Children.

Type of support: General support.

Limitations: Applications not accepted. Giving primarily in CT and MD.

Application information: Unsolicited requests for funds not accepted.

Officers and Directors: Elizabeth Schnieders, Pres. and Director; Richard J. Schnieders, Secy. and Director; Margaret H. Marshall; Caroline A. Schnieders.

EIN: 271439586

5624

The Simon Charitable Foundation

524 Don Gaspar Ave.
Santa Fe, NM 87505-2626   (505) 982-0733; 5
FAX: (505) 212-0101; E-mail: susan@simoncf.org;
Main URL: http://simoncf.org
YouTube: http://www.youtube.com/channel/
UC1x2k2mxkngDfoB-IOKosuw

Established in 2009 in New Mexico.

Donor: Ronald M. Simon Trust.

Foundation type: Independent foundation.

Financial data (yr. ended 06/30/13): Assets, $525,147 (M); gifts received, $1,809,000; expenditures, $1,638,101; qualifying distributions, $1,637,015; giving activities include $170,000 for 20 grants (high: $25,000; low: $5,000), $221,303 for 90 grants to individuals (high: $6,000; low: $250), and $1,419,322 for 4 foundation-administered programs.

Purpose and activities: Scholarship awards and stipends to students of the University of New Mexico, Albuquerque, and Santa Fe public schools.

Fields of interest: Arts and culture; Education; Secondary education; University education; Human services.

Type of support: Student aid.

Limitations: Applications not accepted.

Application information: Unsolicited requests for funds not accepted.

Officers and Directors: Steven Simon, Chair. and Director; Steven McCarl, V.P. and Director; J. Alan Marks, Secy. and Director; Ben Benjamin, Treas. and Director; Glen Newkirk.

EIN: 273309123

5625

Clark L. Tanner Foundation

745 Calle del Resplandor
Santa Fe, NM 87505-5978

Established in 2003 in New Mexico.

Donor: Deon T. Hilger.

Foundation type: Independent foundation.

Financial data (yr. ended 12/31/14): Assets, $3,190,402 (M); expenditures, $159,054; qualifying distributions, $148,700; giving activities include $148,700 for 10 grants (high: $40,000; low: $5,000).

Purpose and activities: Giving primarily to universities for schizophrenic research.

Fields of interest: University education; Diseases and conditions; Sports and recreation.

Type of support: Research.

Limitations: Applications not accepted. Giving primarily in UT. No grants to individuals.

Application information: Unsolicited requests for funds not accepted.

Board Members: Jona Nusink Curry; Susan Dickinson; Alison Hilger; Deon T. Hilger; Kristin Hilger.

EIN: 816116761

5626

Taos Community Foundation

114 Des Georges Ln.
P.O. Box 1925
Taos, NM 87571-1925   (575) 737-9300
Contact: Elizabeth Crittenden-Palacios, Foundation Dir.

FAX: (575) 751-7130; E-mail: info@taoscf.org;
Additional e-mail: grantsofficer@taoscf.org; Main
URL: http://www.taoscf.org
Facebook: http://www.facebook.com/pages/
Taos-Community-Foundation/118285861519436
LinkedIn: http://www.linkedin.com/pub/
taos-community-foundation/33/bb0/87b

Established in 1994 in New Mexico.

Foundation type: Community foundation.

Financial data (yr. ended 06/30/13): Assets, $7,142,696 (M); gifts received, $874,581; expenditures, $927,926; giving activities include $382,455 for grants.

Purpose and activities: The mission of the foundation is to enhance the quality of life in the communities served by encouraging permanent charitable giving for present and future generations. Giving primarily in the areas of health and human services; education and activities for youth; visual, literary, and performing arts; community and economic development; natural environment; and historic preservation.

Fields of interest: Arts and culture; Visual arts; Music; Historic preservation; Education; Environment; Natural resources; Health; Community and economic development; Sustainable development; Human services; Family services; Child welfare.

Type of support: General support; Program-related investments; Continuing support; In-kind gifts; Matching grants; Leadership and professional development; Annual campaigns; Loans to individuals; Capital campaigns; Building and renovations; Equipment; Land acquisitions; Endowments; Emergency funds; Grantee relations; Publications; Seed money; Curriculum development; Scholarships; Program evaluations; Student aid.

Limitations: Applications accepted. Giving limited to Taos and western Colfax counties, NM. No support for religious purposes, or government agencies. No grants to individuals (except for scholarships).

Publications: Annual report; Financial statement; Grants list; Informational brochure; Newsletter.

Application information: Visit foundation web site for application guidelines. Based on letter of inquiries, selected LOI applicants may receive a formal invitation to submit further information, if needed. Application form required.
Initial approach: E-mail letter of inquiry
Copies of proposal: 1
Deadline(s): See web site
Board meeting date(s): Feb., Apr., June, Aug., Oct. and Dec.

Directors: Laurie Mitchell Dunn; John Hamilton; Bill Hudson; George R. Jaramillo; William J. Knight; Dave Lambert; Wanda Lucero; Vernon Lujan; Ben Maddox; Scott McAdams; Robert Shaw; Andrea Szekeres.

Number of staff: 2 full-time professional; 1 part-time professional; 1 full-time support; 1 part-time support.

EIN: 850425147

5627

Doris Goodwin Walbridge Foundation

P.O. Box 32196
Santa Fe, NM 87594-2196   (505) 983-0536

Established in 2001 in Wisconsin.

Foundation type: Independent foundation.

Financial data (yr. ended 12/31/14): Assets, $7,714,789; expenditures, $449,157; qualifying distributions, $356,988.

Fields of interest: Human services.
Limitations: Applications accepted. Giving primarily in NM; some funding also in IL and WI.
Application information: Application form required.
  Initial approach: Email
  Deadline(s): None
Officers and Directors: Stephen Gaber, Pres. and Director; Ryann Whalen, Secy. and Director; Barry Herskowitz, Treas. and Director; David Gaber.
EIN: 391999473

5628
Watersheds Foundation
302 E. Coronado Rd.
Santa Fe, NM 87505-2606

Established in 1999 in New Mexico.
Donor: David W. Douglas.
Foundation type: Independent foundation.
Financial data (yr. ended 12/31/14): Assets, $3,032,883; expenditures, $186,734; qualifying distributions, $186,299.
Fields of interest: Environment; Protestantism; Catholicism; Human services.
International interests: Developing Countries.
Type of support: Equipment; Seed money; Technical assistance.
Limitations: Applications not accepted. No grants to individuals.
Application information: Unsolicited requests for funds not accepted.

Officers: David W. Douglas, Pres.; Bob Morneau, V.P.; Dick Rowe, V.P.; Deborah S. Douglas, Recording Secy.; Erik Mason, Treas.
Director: Jim Brown.
EIN: 850466068

NEW YORK

5629
1848 Foundation
c/o Marks, Paneth & Shron, LLP
660 White Plains Rd., Ste. 450
Tarrytown, NY 10591-5173

Established in 1986 in Connecticut.
Donor: Alan Ritter.
Foundation type: Independent foundation.
Financial data (yr. ended 03/31/14): Assets,
$8,078,966 (M); expenditures, $404,362;
qualifying distributions, $342,890; giving activities
include $316,750 for 23 grants (high: $50,000;
low: $250).
Purpose and activities: Giving primarily to civil rights
advocacy groups.
Fields of interest: Child abuse; Human rights;
Individual liberties; Antidiscrimination; Child
welfare.
Type of support: Advocacy; General support.
Limitations: Applications not accepted. Giving
primarily in New York, NY; giving also in CT and GA.
No grants to individuals.
Application information: Unsolicited requests for
funds not accepted.
Officers: Alan I. Ritter, Pres.; Jonathan Ritter, V.P.;
Eileen S. Silverstein, Secy.; Becky Hubbert, Treas.
EIN: 066302129

5630
21st Century ILGWU Heritage Fund
275 7th Ave., 18th Fl.
New York City, NY 10001-6708 (212) 645-2740
Contact: Muzaffar Chishti, Exec. Dir.

Established in 1999 in New York.
Donor: International Ladies Garment Workers Union.
Foundation type: Independent foundation.
Financial data (yr. ended 12/31/13): Assets,
$4,795,144 (M); expenditures, $603,994;
qualifying distributions, $566,170; giving activities
include $393,800 for 31 grants (high: $68,000;
low: $500).
Fields of interest: Equal opportunity in education;
Law education; Employment; Human services;
Immigrants and migrants.
Type of support: Program development; Research;
Equal access; Program evaluations.
Limitations: Applications accepted. Giving primarily
in NY. No grants to individuals; or for general
operating support.
Application information: Application form required.
Initial approach: Proposal
Copies of proposal: 1
Deadline(s): Apr. 30 and Oct. 31
Officers and Directors: Jay Mazur, Chair. and Pres.
and Director; Irwin Solomon, Secy. and Director;
Lloyd Goldenberg, Treas.; Muzaffar Chishti, Exec.
Dir.; Nina Bernstein; David Dinkins; Roy Godson.
Number of staff: 2 part-time professional.
EIN: 311593055

5631
The 5 51 5 Foundation, Inc.
755 Park Ave., Apt 12B
New York City, NY 10021-4283

Established in 2007 in New York.
Donor: David C. Hodgson.
Foundation type: Independent foundation.
Financial data (yr. ended 12/31/14): Assets,
$178,656 (M); expenditures, $378,399; qualifying
distributions, $378,399; giving activities include
$378,100 for 16 grants (high: $250,000; low:
$500).
Fields of interest: Education; Higher education.
Limitations: Applications not accepted. Giving
primarily in CA, MD, NH, NY, and OH. No grants to
individuals.
Application information: Contributes only to
pre-selected organizations.
Officers: Laurie B. Hodgson, Pres.; Richard Gold,
Secy.; David C. Hodgson, Treas.
EIN: 208844111

5632
A.B. Reins Foundation
c/o Douglas Boustead
540 N. State Rd.
Briarcliff Manor, NY 10510

Donor: Bart D. Reiss.
Foundation type: Independent foundation.
Financial data (yr. ended 12/31/13): Assets,
$1,846,443 (M); gifts received, $865,673;
expenditures, $310,196; qualifying distributions,
$285,000; giving activities include $285,000 for 6
grants (high: $200,000; low: $5,000).
Fields of interest: Health; Vision care; Human
services.
Limitations: Applications not accepted. Giving
primarily in CA.
Application information: Unsolicited requests for
funds not accepted.
Officers: Bart D. Reiss, Pres.; Douglas Boustead,
Secy.-Treas.
EIN: 450678213

5633
A.P.W. Foundation Inc.
1415 52nd St.
Brooklyn, NY 11219-3920

Established in 1994 in New York.
Donors: Abraham Weiss; Regina Weiss; A & RW
Properties LLC; Moshe Weiss.
Foundation type: Independent foundation.
Financial data (yr. ended 12/31/14): Assets,
$4,309,958; expenditures, $319,015; qualifying
distributions, $269,548.
Purpose and activities: Giving primarily to Jewish
agencies, temples, and schools.
Fields of interest: Elementary and secondary
education; Judaism.
Limitations: Applications not accepted. Giving
primarily in NY. No grants to individuals.
Application information: Unsolicited requests for
funds not accepted.
Officer: Regina Weiss, Pres.
Trustee: Moshe Weiss.
EIN: 113242355

5634
Abba's Ambassadors, Inc.
P.O. Box 165
South Salem, NY 10590-0165
E-mail: info@abbasambassadors.org; Main
URL: http://www.abbasambassadors.org
Facebook: https://www.facebook.com/
AbbasAmbassadors

Established in 2006 in Georgia.
Donors: John F. Gibson; Cynthia D. Gibson; Jennifer
Gibson; Daniel Gibson.
Foundation type: Independent foundation.
Financial data (yr. ended 12/31/13): Assets,
$357,840 (M); gifts received, $292,572;
expenditures, $345,571; qualifying distributions,
$342,686; giving activities include $233,920 for 8
grants (high: $70,870; low: $12,226), and $94,525
for 8 grants to individuals (high: $21,052; low:
$2,500).
Purpose and activities: The purpose of Abba's
Ambassadors is to bring together people who have
a heart for missions with those missionaries in the
field who need support. Abba's Ambassadors aim to
bring the gospel to as many people as possible.
Fields of interest: Diseases and conditions;
Housing development; Religion.
International interests: Israel.
Type of support: General support; Grants to
individuals.
Limitations: Giving primarily in WA; with some giving
in Israel.
Officers: John F. Gibson, Pres.; Daniel F. Gibson,
V.P. and C.F.O.; Cynthia D. Gibson, Secy.
Directors: Elizabeth A. Gibson; Janell M. Gibson;
Jennifer L. Gibson; Joel T. Gibson.
EIN: 208043230

5635
The Abelard Foundation Inc.
250 Park Ave., 7th Fl.
New York, NY 10177-0799
Contact: Patricia Hewitt
*Application address for organizations located in the
eastern U.S. (east of the Mississippi River):* The
Abelard Foundation-East, Att.: Susan Collins, P.O.
Box 148, Lincoln, MA 01773, URL: http://
www.fdnweb.org/abelardeast; application address
for organizations located in the western U.S. (west
of the Mississippi River): Common Counsel
Foundation, Att.: Grants Administrator, 405 14th
St., Ste. 809, Oakland, CA 94612, URL: http://
www.commoncounsel.org/Abelard+Foundation
+West; Main URL: http://fdnweb.org/abelardeast/
Abelard Foundation's Philanthropy Promise: http://
www.ncrp.org/philanthropys-promise/who
Grants List: http://fdnweb.org/abelardeast/
grants-approved

Established in 1950 in New York.
Donor: Ethel B. Wells Trust.
Foundation type: Independent foundation.
Financial data (yr. ended 12/31/13): Assets,
$7,955,806 (M); gifts received, $111,000;
expenditures, $525,047; qualifying distributions,
$434,024; giving activities include $326,000 for 32
grants (high: $10,000; low: $9,000).
Purpose and activities: Giving especially for seed
money to new organizations and model projects,
with emphasis on protection of civil rights and civil
liberties; support for programs designed to achieve
social, political, and economic equality for urban and

rural poor, including giving them a voice in decisions about their environment.

Fields of interest: Natural resources; Public affairs; Urban development; Organized labor; Antidiscrimination; Human services.

Type of support: General support; Matching grants; Program development; Publications; Seed money; Technical assistance.

Limitations: Applications accepted. No support for medical, educational, cultural institutions, or government sponsored programs . No grants to individuals, or for building or endowment funds, continuing support, annual campaigns, emergency funds, scholarships, fellowships, research, or video or film production; no loans.

Publications: Grants list; Informational brochure (including application guidelines).

Application information: See foundation websites for complete application guidelines. Application form required.

> Initial approach: Letter
> Copies of proposal: 1
> Deadline(s): None
> Board meeting date(s): May and Nov.

Officers: Travis W. Buck, Pres.; Adele Bernhard, V.P.; Haleryn A. Buck, V.P.; Brian Collins, V.P.; Susan B. Collins, V.P.; Patricia Hewitt, Secy.; Mason T. Schreck, Treas.

Board Members: Anna Wells Bernhard; Jessica W. Bernhard; Michael Bernhard; Steven Bernhard; Melissa W. Blessing; Shea Breaux-Wells; Nancy Doll; Frances W. Magee; Lena Neufeld; Peter Neufeld; Shane Neufeld; Albert R. Schreck; Celeste W. Schreck; Charles R. Schreck; Christine Schreck; Teresa Juarez Schreck; Thomas A. Schreck; Albert B. Wells II; George B. Wells II; Kristen Wells; Susan M. Wells.

Number of staff: 1 part-time professional; 2 part-time support.

EIN: 136064580

5636
The Jayne and Leonard Abess Foundation Inc.

c/o Fiduciary Trust Company Int'l.
600 5th Ave.
New York City, NY   10020-2302
Application address: c/o Leonard L. Abess, 100 S.E. 32nd Rd., Miami, FL 33129

Established in 2004 in Florida.
Donors: Jayne Harris Abess; Leonard L. Abess.
Foundation type: Independent foundation.
Financial data (yr. ended 12/31/13): Assets, $8,713,918 (M); gifts received, $750,000; expenditures, $364,621; qualifying distributions, $330,870; giving activities include $323,700 for 22 grants (high: $104,000; low: $100).
Fields of interest: Arts education; Higher education; Nonprofits; Job training; Judaism; Vocational rehabilitation.
Type of support: General support; Regranting.
Limitations: Applications accepted. Giving primarily in FL.
Application information: Application form required.

> Initial approach: Letter
> Deadline(s): None

Officers and Directors: Jayne Harris Abess, Vice-Chair. and Director; Leonard L. Abess, Pres. and Director; Ashley Abess, Secy. and Director; Brett U. Abess; Mathew U. Abess.
EIN: 200052304

5637
Leonard L. and Bertha U. Abess Foundation Inc.

c/o Fiduciary Trust Company Int'l.
600 5th Ave.
New York City, NY   10020-2302   2126323000
Application address: c/o Leonard L. Abess, 100 S.E. 32nd Rd., Miami, FL 33129, tel.: (305) 577-7333

Established in 1989 in Florida.
Donor: Leonard L. Abess, Sr.
Foundation type: Independent foundation.
Financial data (yr. ended 12/31/14): Assets, $5,193,080; expenditures, $262,548; qualifying distributions, $233,537.
Fields of interest: Education; University education; Nonprofits; Judaism.
Type of support: General support; Regranting.
Limitations: Applications accepted. Giving primarily in Miami, FL. No grants to individuals.
Application information: Application form required.

> Initial approach: Letter
> Deadline(s): None

Officers and Directors: Leonard L. Abess, Jr., Pres. and Director; Jayne Harris Abess, V.P. and Director; Ashley Abess; Brett U. Abess; Matthew U. Abess.
EIN: 650151462

5638
Abettor Foundation

135 Central Park W.
New York City, NY   10023-2465

Established in 1998 in New York.
Donor: Bernice Manocherian.
Foundation type: Independent foundation.
Financial data (yr. ended 12/31/13): Assets, $1,621,745 (M); expenditures, $313,803; qualifying distributions, $295,750; giving activities include $295,750 for 33 grants (high: $73,434; low: $1,000).
Fields of interest: Arts and culture; Education; Nonprofits; Judaism; Human services.
Type of support: Regranting.
Limitations: Applications not accepted. Giving primarily in NY. No grants to individuals.
Application information: Unsolicited requests for funds not accepted.
Officer: Darel Banaim, Treas.
Trustee: Bernice Manocherian.
EIN: 137151571

5639
Abrahamson Family Foundation

16 Sutton Pl., No. 14A
New York City, NY   10022-3180

Donor: Ernest Abrahamson.
Foundation type: Independent foundation.
Financial data (yr. ended 12/31/13): Assets, $2,161,321 (M); gifts received, $100,000; expenditures, $217,472; qualifying distributions, $190,857; giving activities include $190,351 for 25 grants (high: $70,000; low: $250).
Fields of interest: Arts and culture; Education; Human services.
Limitations: Applications not accepted.
Application information: Unsolicited requests for funds not accepted.
Officers: Ernest Abrahamson, Pres.; Kathleen Abrahamson, V.P.; Kim Mellin, Secy.-Treas.

Trustees: Kurt Abrahamson; Mark Abrahamson.
EIN: 371612730

5640
Abramson Family Foundation Inc.

355 Meadowview Ave.
Hewlett Bay Park, NY   11557-1701

Established in 1997 in New York.
Donors: Richard Abramson; Lorraine Abramson.
Foundation type: Independent foundation.
Financial data (yr. ended 04/30/13): Assets, $1,271,572 (M); gifts received, $299,900; expenditures, $307,244; qualifying distributions, $307,100; giving activities include $307,100 for 17 grants (high: $150,000; low: $500).
Fields of interest: Nonprofits; Health; Judaism.
Type of support: Regranting.
Limitations: Applications not accepted. Giving primarily in Washington, DC and NY. No grants to individuals.
Application information: Contributes only to pre-selected organizations.
Officers: Richard Abramson, Pres.; Gregg Abramson, V.P. and Treas.; Jill Abramson, V.P.; Lorraine Abramson, V.P.
Director: Lauren Abramson.
EIN: 113374949

5641
Achilles Foundation

c/o Anchin
1375 Broadway
New York City, NY   10018-7001

Established in 2005 in New York.
Donor: William J. Murray.
Foundation type: Independent foundation.
Financial data (yr. ended 12/31/14): Assets, $3,492,067 (M); expenditures, $206,318; qualifying distributions, $150,750; giving activities include $150,500 for 7 grants (high: $40,000; low: $10,000).
Fields of interest: Arts and culture; Education; Foundations; Human services.
Limitations: Applications not accepted. Giving primarily in CA and NY. No grants to individuals.
Application information: Unsolicited requests for funds not accepted.
Trustee: William J. Murray.
EIN: 203849784

5642
Acworth Foundation

775 Park Ave., Ste. 255
Huntington, NY   11743-3976

Donor: Huntington Atrium Development.
Foundation type: Independent foundation.
Financial data (yr. ended 04/30/12): Assets, $65,524 (M); gifts received, $236,040; expenditures, $244,827; giving activities include $225,000 for 24 grants to individuals (high: $10,000; low: $500).
Fields of interest: Education.
Limitations: Applications not accepted.
Application information: Unsolicited requests for funds not accepted.
Officer: Brian Acworth, Fdn. Mgr.

Directors: Pattijo Alesci; Michael Januzzi.
EIN: 260292873

5643
Barry A. Adelman Family Foundation
48 Hampton Rd.
Scarsdale, NY 10583-3025
Contact: Barry A. Adelman

Established in 2001 in New York.
Donor: Barry A. Adelman.
Foundation type: Independent foundation.
Financial data (yr. ended 09/30/12): Assets, $2,078 (M); expenditures, $208,204; qualifying distributions, $204,876; giving activities include $204,876 for 14 grants (high: $152,976; low: $200).
Fields of interest: Education; Law education; Community and economic development; Religion; Judaism.
Limitations: Applications not accepted. Giving primarily in Ann Arbor, MI and New York, NY. No grants to individuals.
Application information: Unsolicited requests for funds not accepted.
Officers: Barry A. Adelman, Pres. and Treas.; Robin Adelman, V.P. and Secy.; Lauren B. Adelman, V.P.; Todd M. Adelman, V.P.
EIN: 134199594

5644
The Richard and Pamela Ader Foundation
820 Park Ave.
New York City, NY 10021

Donor: Richard Ader.
Foundation type: Independent foundation.
Financial data (yr. ended 12/31/14): Assets, $1,901; gifts received, $188,500; expenditures, $194,325; qualifying distributions, $194,325.
Fields of interest: Arts and culture; Education; Judaism; Youth development.
Limitations: Applications not accepted.
Application information: Unsolicited requests for funds not accepted.
Officers and Directors: Richard Ader, Pres. and Director; Paul J. Konigsberg, V.P. and Director; Pamela Ader, Secy.-Treas. and Director.
EIN: 260726465

5645
Joan & Alan Ades-Taub Foundation Inc.
575 Madison Ave., Ste. 1006
New York City, NY 10022-2511 (212) 605-0333
Contact: John Ades, Pres.

Established in 1997 in New York.
Donor: Alan M. Ades.
Foundation type: Independent foundation.
Financial data (yr. ended 12/31/13): Assets, $3,154,057 (M); expenditures, $176,466; qualifying distributions, $160,196; giving activities include $160,196 for 49 grants (high: $34,500; low: $10).
Purpose and activities: Giving for the arts, health, and religious organizations.
Fields of interest: Arts and culture; Opera; Health; In-patient medical care; Religion; Christianity; Judaism.

Limitations: Applications accepted. Giving on a national basis, with emphasis on NY.
Application information:
 Initial approach: Proposal
 Deadline(s): None
Officers: Joan Ades, Pres.; Alan M. Ades, V.P.; Jane Ades, Secy.
EIN: 113293314

5646
The Adikes Family Foundation
c/o Brosnan & Hegler, LLP
1325 Franklin Ave., No. 335
Garden City, NY 11530-1631

Established in 2001 in New York.
Donors: Park T. Adikes; Maryedith Adikes.
Foundation type: Independent foundation.
Financial data (yr. ended 12/31/13): Assets, $7,059,338 (M); gifts received, $253,505; expenditures, $424,020; qualifying distributions, $306,632; giving activities include $249,815 for 41 grants (high: $50,000; low: $600).
Fields of interest: Education; Nonprofits; Diseases and conditions; Çancers; Sports and recreation; Human services; Child welfare.
Type of support: Regranting.
Limitations: Applications not accepted. Giving primarily in NY. No grants to individuals.
Application information: Contributes only to pre-selected organizations.
Officer: Patricia Adikes-Hill, Exec. Dir.
Trustees: Maryedith Adikes; Park T. Adikes.
EIN: 116560827

5647
The Aeroflex Foundation
c/o Hecht & Assocs.
60 Cuttermill Rd., Ste. 512
Great Neck, NY 11021-3104

Established in 1964 in New York.
Foundation type: Independent foundation.
Financial data (yr. ended 09/30/14): Assets, $4,283,086 (M); expenditures, $414,118; qualifying distributions, $322,254; giving activities include $288,500 for 32 grants (high: $25,000; low: $1,000).
Purpose and activities: Giving primarily for the arts, health care and education.
Fields of interest: Arts and culture; Performing arts; University education; Specialty hospital care.
Limitations: Applications not accepted. Giving primarily in NY. No grants to individuals.
Application information: Contributes only to pre-selected organizations.
Trustees: Kay Knight Clarke; Derrick M. Hussey; William A. Perlmuth.
EIN: 136168635

5648
AFAR Foundation Inc.
c/o Bessemer Trust
630 Fifth Ave.
New York City, NY 10111

Donors: Gregory B. Sullivan; Wimmer Solutions; Pearson Charitablr Foundation; Elite Self Park Services, LLC.
Foundation type: Independent foundation.

Financial data (yr. ended 12/31/13): Assets, $6,840 (M); gifts received, $180,764; expenditures, $176,608; qualifying distributions, $176,593; giving activities include $167,609 for 1 grant.
Fields of interest: Education.
Limitations: Applications not accepted. Giving limited in Fort Collins, CO.
Application information: Unsolicited requests for funds not accepted.
Officers and Directors: Gregory B. Sullivan, Pres. and Treas. and Director; Joseph Diaz, V.P. and Secy.
EIN: 270181444

5649
S. & A. Agate Foundation, Inc.
c/o Anchin, Block & Anchin LLP
1375 Broadway
New York City, NY 10018-7001

Donors: Anita Agate; Anita Dann Friedman; Constance A. Austin.
Foundation type: Independent foundation.
Financial data (yr. ended 12/31/14): Assets, $5,582,485 (M); expenditures, $367,568; qualifying distributions, $285,100; giving activities include $282,515 for 27 grants (high: $150,125; low: $50).
Purpose and activities: Giving primarily for the arts, education, and Jewish organizations.
Fields of interest: Arts and culture; Education; Health; Hospital care; Diseases and conditions; Judaism; Human services; Females.
Type of support: Research.
Limitations: Applications not accepted. No grants to individuals.
Application information: Unsolicited requests for funds not accepted.
Officers: Anita Dann Friedman, Pres. and Treas.; Adam B. Friedman, Secy.
EIN: 136109670

5650
AGB Fund, Inc.
c/o CPI Associates Inc.
32 E. 57th St., 14th Fl.
New York City, NY 10022-2513 (212) 421-6600

Established in 1992 in New York.
Foundation type: Independent foundation.
Financial data (yr. ended 12/31/14): Assets, $3,583,577; expenditures, $260,134; qualifying distributions, $208,661.
Fields of interest: Arts and culture; Education; Environment; Hospital care; Science; Public affairs; Religion; Human services; Basic and emergency aid; Food aid; Child welfare; International development.
Limitations: Applications accepted. Giving primarily in NY. No grants to individuals.
Application information: Application form required.
 Initial approach: Letter
 Deadline(s): None
Officers: Elizabeth B. Nevin, Pres.; Stephen C. Nevin, V.P. and Secy.; Lee R. Robins, Treas.
EIN: 133632843

5651
AKC Fund, Inc.
c/o GHS Philanthropy Mgmt.
275 Madison Ave., Ste. 401
New York City, NY 10016 (212) 812-4362

Established in 1955 in New York.
Foundation type: Independent foundation.
Financial data (yr. ended 12/31/14): Assets, $6,534,435; expenditures, $314,569; qualifying distributions, $280,023.
Purpose and activities: Grants generally for education, conservation, health services, and the arts.
Fields of interest: Arts and culture; Secondary education; Higher education; Natural resources; Health; Human services.
Type of support: Continuing support; Annual campaigns; Capital campaigns.
Limitations: Applications not accepted. Giving primarily in the Northeast, with emphasis on CT and MA. No grants to individuals.
Application information: The Fund does not accept unsolicited applications.
Officers: Elizabeth R. Garside, Pres.; Elisabeth C. Gill, V.P.; Willard Wood, Secy.; Kathryn H. Childs, Treas.
Directors: Samuel A. Anderson; Ann Childs Collins; J. Vinton Lawrence; Peter Lawrence; Zoe Spring.
Number of staff: None.
EIN: 136091321

5652
Alex and Zoli Foundation
6 Ash St.
Monsey, NY 10952-1619 (646) 201-9286
Contact: Carol Ungar, Pres.

Established in 2006 in Ohio.
Donor: Carol Ungar.
Foundation type: Independent foundation.
Financial data (yr. ended 10/31/14): Assets, $67,849 (M); gifts received, $155,957; expenditures, $125,950; qualifying distributions, $124,500; giving activities include $124,500 for 19 grants (high: $62,500; low: $500).
Fields of interest: Religion; Judaism.
Limitations: Applications accepted. Giving primarily in NY. No grants to individuals.
Application information: Application form required.
  Initial approach: Letter
  Deadline(s): None
Officers: Carol Ungar, Pres.; Kenneth Marsh, Secy.; Eugene David Ungar, Treas.
EIN: 204856691

5653
Alexander Charitable Foundation
c/o PWA C.P.As.
1908 Ave. O
Brooklyn, NY 11230-6721

Established in 2000 in New York.
Donor: J. Kobi Alexander.
Foundation type: Independent foundation.
Financial data (yr. ended 12/31/13): Assets, $2,078,827 (M); expenditures, $180,620; qualifying distributions, $180,620; giving activities include $176,000 for 5 grants (high: $150,000; low: $1,000).

Fields of interest: Philanthropy; Diseases and conditions; Sports and recreation.
International interests: Israel.
Limitations: Applications not accepted. Giving primarily in NY. No grants to individuals.
Application information: Unsolicited requests for funds not accepted.
Trustees: Hana Basal Alexander; J. Kobi Alexander.
EIN: 137263003

5654
The Shana Alexander Charitable Foundation
c/o CHS Business
50 Montrose Rd.
Yonkers, NY 10710-2802

Established in 2006 in New York.
Donor: Shana Alexander†.
Foundation type: Independent foundation.
Financial data (yr. ended 12/31/13): Assets, $4,024,562 (L); expenditures, $413,431; qualifying distributions, $354,626; giving activities include $328,900 for 43 grants (high: $35,000; low: $1,000).
Fields of interest: Arts and culture; Performing arts education; Education; Environment; Breast cancer; Television; Women's rights; Women's services; Females.
Type of support: Research.
Limitations: Applications not accepted. Giving primarily in NY. No grants to individuals.
Application information: Contributes only to pre-selected organizations.
Officers: Lisa Alter, Pres.; Michael Feinstein, V.P.; Eleanora Kennedy, Secy.
EIN: 204227171

5655
Norman E. Alexander Family G Foundation Inc.
99 Park Ave., Ste. 1530
New York City, NY 10016-1601

Foundation type: Independent foundation.
Financial data (yr. ended 12/31/13): Assets, $6,047,517 (M); expenditures, $387,202; qualifying distributions, $387,102; giving activities include $380,000 for 11 grants (high: $125,000; low: $5,000).
Fields of interest: Judaism.
Type of support: General support.
Limitations: Applications not accepted. Giving primarily in New York, NY.
Application information: Unsolicited requests for funds not accepted.
Officers and Directors: Marjorie Alexander, Pres. and Director; Gail Binderman, Exec. V.P. and Treas. and Director; Daniel Binderman, V.P. and Secy. and Director.
EIN: 264413332

5656
The Frances Alexander Foundation
(formerly The Ann F. Kaplan & Robert Fippinger Foundation)
c/o WTAS
1177 Avenue of the Americas, 18th Fl.
New York City, NY 10036-2714

Established in 1991 in New York.
Donors: Ann F. Kaplan; Robert A. Fippinger.
Foundation type: Independent foundation.
Financial data (yr. ended 04/30/13): Assets, $605,249 (M); gifts received, $403,711; expenditures, $402,200; qualifying distributions, $402,200; giving activities include $402,100 for 48 grants (high: $100,000; low: $100).
Fields of interest: Art museums; Higher education; Public libraries; Human services; Women's services.
Type of support: General support; Scholarships.
Limitations: Applications not accepted. Giving primarily in NY, with emphasis on New York City. No grants to individuals.
Application information: Contributes only to pre-selected organizations.
Trustees: Robert A. Fippinger; Ann F. Kaplan.
EIN: 133638507

5657
Alff Aid, Inc.
1402 59th St.
Brooklyn, NY 11219-5016

Established in 1999 in New York.
Donors: Mayer Laufer; Fagenson & Co.; Robert Fagenson.
Foundation type: Independent foundation.
Financial data (yr. ended 12/31/12): Assets, $3,314,881 (M); gifts received, $1,500,020; expenditures, $187,172; qualifying distributions, $186,000; giving activities include $186,000 for grants.
Fields of interest: Judaism.
Limitations: Applications not accepted. Giving primarily in NY; funding also in NJ. No grants to individuals.
Application information: Contributes only to pre-selected organizations.
Officers: Mayer Laufer, Pres.; Doris Laufer, V.P.
EIN: 113145407

5658
ALG Family Foundation
c/o Peyser & Alexander Mgmt., Inc.
500 5th Ave., Ste. 2700
New York City, NY 10110-2799 (212) 764-6455
Contact: Anne Gilchrist, Pres.

Established in 2007 in New York.
Donor: Anne Gilchrist.
Foundation type: Independent foundation.
Financial data (yr. ended 12/31/13): Assets, $2,579,304 (M); expenditures, $374,716; qualifying distributions, $373,000; giving activities include $373,000 for 20 grants (high: $155,000; low: $1,000).
Fields of interest: Arts and culture; Gifted education.
Limitations: Applications accepted. Giving primarily in New York, NY.
Application information:
  Initial approach: Proposal
  Deadline(s): None
Officer: Anne Gilchrist, Pres.
EIN: 208623369

5659
Peter and Nancy Allatt Family Foundation II

(formerly The Tai-Ping II Foundation)
c/o Market St. Trust Co.
80 E. Market St., Ste. 300
Corning, NY 14830-2722

Established in 2005 in Massachusetts.
Donor: Gratia R. Montgomery Trust.
Foundation type: Independent foundation.
Financial data (yr. ended 12/31/14): Assets, $3,680,312; gifts received, $0; expenditures, $235,338; qualifying distributions, $203,500 and $0 for set-asides.
Purpose and activities: Giving primarily to a pre-school; support also for youth, conservation, and historical activities.
Fields of interest: Environment; Health; Human services.
Type of support: General support.
Limitations: Applications not accepted. Giving primarily in Cos Cob and Greenwich, CT; some giving in NY and Washington, DC. No grants to individuals.
Application information: Contributes only to pre-selected organizations.
Trustees: Nancy C. Allatt; Peter J.D. Allatt, Jr.; Lauren Walsh.
EIN: 202515474

5660
Allegany County Area Foundation, Inc.

6807 Route 19 N., Ste. 180
Crossroads Center
Belmont, NY 14813 (585) 808-8444
Contact: Patricia Oliver, Scholarship Coord.
E-mail: director@alleganycountyareafoundation.org;
Additional tel.: (585) 365-2319; Additional e-mail: oliverpa@yahoo.com; Main URL: http://www.alleganycountyareafoundation.org
Facebook: https://www.facebook.com/pages/Allegany-County-Area-Foundation/406523526079186

Established in 1983 in New York.
Foundation type: Community foundation.
Financial data (yr. ended 04/30/14): Assets, $8,311,035 (M); gifts received, $176,265; expenditures, $324,684; giving activities include $195,039 for grants to individuals.
Purpose and activities: The foundation provides community service grants for educational, social, cultural and civic projects benefiting Allegany County, NY.
Fields of interest: Arts and culture; Education; Health; Community improvement; Human services.
Limitations: Applications accepted. Giving limited to Allegany County, NY. No support for religious organizations for primarily religious purposes. No grants for building programs.
Publications: Application guidelines; Annual report; Informational brochure.
Application information: Visit foundation web site for grant information and application form. Application form required.
  Initial approach: Submit application form and attachments
  Copies of proposal: 1
  Deadline(s): June 30, Sept. 30, Dec. 31 and Mar. 15
  Board meeting date(s): Monthly

Officers and Directors: Carolyn J. Miller, Pres. and Director; Rodney K. Bennett, V.P., Admin. and Director; Richard A. Haberg, V.P., Finance and Director; Denis Dahlgren, Exec. Dir.; Evelyn Alessi; Thomas P. Brown; Lori Dzielski; Warren Emerson; Carrie E. Flanagan-Watson; Jane Foster; Leslie J. Haggstrom; John Morris; Dawn A. Wildrick-Cole, Esq.; Karen Williams.
Number of staff: 1 part-time professional; 1 part-time support.
EIN: 222506596

5661
Alternative Energy Foundation

1225 39th St.
Brooklyn, NY 11218

Foundation type: Independent foundation.
Financial data (yr. ended 12/31/12): Assets, $2,607,361 (M); gifts received, $225,000; expenditures, $158,573; qualifying distributions, $157,700; giving activities include $157,700 for grants.
Fields of interest: Judaism.
Limitations: Applications not accepted. Giving primarily in Brooklyn, NY.
Application information: Unsolicited requests for funds not accepted.
Trustees: David Landau; Rivka Landau; Sara Mayteles.
EIN: 261392098

5662
American Conservation Association, Inc.

30 Rockefeller Plz., Ste. 5600
New York City, NY 10112-0015
Contact: Carmen Reyes, Treas.

Established in 1958 in New York.
Donors: Laurance S. Rockefeller†; Laurance S. "Larry" Rockefeller, Jr.; Rockefeller Brothers Fund; Jackson Hole Preserve, Inc.; LSR Fund.
Foundation type: Operating foundation.
Financial data (yr. ended 12/31/13): Assets, $11,882 (M); gifts received, $652,040; expenditures, $857,845; qualifying distributions, $326,415; giving activities include $299,000 for 17 grants (high: $200,000; low: $1,000).
Purpose and activities: A private operating foundation organized to advance knowledge and understanding of conservation; to preserve the beauty of the landscape and the natural and living resources in areas of the U.S. and elsewhere; and to educate the public in the proper use of such areas.
Fields of interest: Natural resources.
Type of support: General support; Pro bono consulting services; Program-related investments; Continuing support; Public engagement and education; Convening; Publications; Technical assistance.
Limitations: Giving primarily to national organizations in Washington, DC and New York, NY. No grants to individuals, or for building funds, endowments, scholarships, or fellowships.
Application information:
  Initial approach: Letter or proposal
  Copies of proposal: 1
  Deadline(s): None

Board meeting date(s): Sept. or Oct.; Executive Committee meets as necessary
Final notification: Varies
Officers and Trustees: Laurance S. "Larry" Rockefeller, Jr., Pres. and Trustee; R. Scott Greathead, Secy. and Trustee; Carmen Reyes, Treas.; Charles M. Clusen, Exec. Dir.; John H. Adams; Frances G. Beinecke; Dr. William G. Conway; Henry L. Diamond; Fred I. Kent III; William B. McHenry; Patrick F. Noonan; Story Clark Resor; David S. Sampson; Cathleen Douglas Stone.
Number of staff: 2 part-time professional; 2 part-time support.
EIN: 131874023

5663
American Dream Foundation, Inc.

c/o Meltzer, Lippe, Goldstein & Breitstone, LLP
190 Willis Ave.
Mineola, NY 11501

Established in 2003 in New York.
Donor: Richard A. Grasso.
Foundation type: Independent foundation.
Financial data (yr. ended 12/31/13): Assets, $301,725 (M); expenditures, $358,030; qualifying distributions, $345,500; giving activities include $345,500 for 29 grants (high: $60,000; low: $1,000).
Purpose and activities: Giving primarily for higher education, human services, firefighter organizations, and citizenship programs.
Fields of interest: Higher education; Foundations; Fire prevention and control; Public affairs; Human services.
Limitations: Applications not accepted. Giving primarily in MT and NY.
Application information: Contributes only to pre-selected organizations.
Officers and Directors: Richard A. Grasso, Pres. and Director; Scott Newman, Secy. and Director; Lorraine P. Grasso, Treas. and Director.
EIN: 200363876

5664
American Express Charitable Fund

200 Vesey St., 48th Fl.
New York City, NY 10285-1000
Application address for organizations located outside of Phoenix, AZ, south FL, and Salt Lake City, UT: 3 World Financial Ctr., M.C. 01-48-04, New York, NY 10285-4804; E-mail for Phoenix, AZ: American Express Co., c/o Community Affairs, PhoenixLOIs@aexp.com; E-mail for south Florida: American Express Co., c/o Community Affairs, FtLauderdaleLOIs@aexp.com; E-mail for Salt Lake City, UT: American Express Co., c/o Community Affairs, SaltLakeCityLOIs@aexp.com; Main URL: http://about.americanexpress.com/csr/e-driven.aspx

Established in 2007 in New York.
Donor: American Express.
Foundation type: Company-sponsored foundation.
Financial data (yr. ended 12/31/14): Assets, $83,644 (M); expenditures, $373,330; qualifying distributions, $373,280; giving activities include $347,866 for grants.
Purpose and activities: The fund supports programs designed to promote historic preservation; leadership; and community service.

Fields of interest: Arts and culture; Cultural awareness; Performing arts; Museums; Historic preservation; Education; Higher education; Foundations; Nonprofits; Disasters and emergency management; Public affairs; Leadership development; Community and economic development; Human services; Food aid.
Type of support: General support; Employee volunteer services; Annual campaigns; Employee matching gifts; Capital and infrastructure; Program development; Sponsorships; Scholarships; Regranting.
Limitations: Applications not accepted. Giving primarily on a national basis in areas of company operations, with emphasis on Phoenix, AZ, Los Angeles and San Francisco, CA, Washington, DC, southern FL, Atlanta, GA, Chicago, IL, Boston, MA, New York, NY, Philadelphia, PA, Dallas and Houston, TX, and Salt Lake City, UT. No support for discriminatory organizations, religious organizations not of direct benefit to the entire community, or political organizations. No grants to individuals (except for employee-related scholarships), or for fundraising, goodwill advertising, souvenir journals, or dinner programs, travel, books, magazines, or articles in professional journals, endowments or capital campaigns, traveling exhibitions, or sports sponsorships.
Application information: The foundation is in the process of merging with the American Express Foundation.
Officers and Trustees: Timothy J. McClimon, Pres. and Trustee; Mary Ellen Craig, Secy.; David L. Yowan, Treas.; Tammy D. Fried, Counsel; Vernon E. Jordan, Jr.; Frank P. Popoff.
EIN: 261607898

5665
American Friends of Baruch Umarpeh Corp.
1274 49th St.
Brooklyn, NY   11219-3011
Application Address: c/o Pinchas Friedman, 1417 48th St., Brooklyn, NY 11219 tel.: (718) 437-7184

Donors: Jeffrey Eisner; The Norman and Joan Ciment Foundation; Marshall Gloria Mauer; Hollander Family Foundation; Oscar Bernice Novick; Leonard A. Wien; Harold Schacter; FJC Philanthropic Funds; William Moskovits; Martin Schwartz; Eli Almo.
Foundation type: Independent foundation.
Financial data (yr. ended 10/31/12): Assets, $6,064 (M); gifts received, $180,593; expenditures, $201,699; qualifying distributions, $199,950; giving activities include $199,950 for 3 grants (high: $157,050; low: $16,900).
Fields of interest: Religion; Human services.
Limitations: Applications accepted. Giving primarily in New York.
Application information: Application form required.
  Initial approach: Proposal
  Deadline(s): None
Officers: Dov Menzer, Secy.; David Schlessinger, Treas.
Director: Pinchas Friedman.
EIN: 331190140

5666
American Friends of Merkaz Chasidei Viznitz Inc.
285 Lee Ave.
Brooklyn, NY   11206-5498

Donors: Meir Baal Hanes; Joseph Stern; The Raab Foundation; Frankel Trading Corp; David Fuld; Chaim Simkowitz.
Foundation type: Independent foundation.
Financial data (yr. ended 12/31/12): Assets, $51,055 (M); gifts received, $242,918; expenditures, $172,050; qualifying distributions, $164,980; giving activities include $164,980 for 6 grants (high: $52,000; low: $17,700).
Fields of interest: Judaism.
Limitations: Applications not accepted. Giving primarily in Brooklyn, NY.
Application information: Unsolicited request for funds not accepted.
Officers: Chaim Stern, Pres.; Yehoshua Wertzberger, V.P.; Benjamin Schwartz, Treas.
Director: Chaim Meir Adler.
EIN: 270328382

5667
American Friends of Mosdos Hakerem, Inc.
c/o Jacob Kreitman
4 Treetop Ln.
Monsey, NY   10952-3611

Established in 1994 in New York.
Donors: Jack Rechnitz; Yisroel Tzvi Jacobs; Sol Marco; Roman Russ; Ida Russ; Harry Jacobs; Shlomo Rechnitz; Tara Rechnitz; Daniel Wexler; Genesis Info Security; Lazard; Michael Cholobel; Shlomo and Tamar Rechnitz Charity Foundation.
Foundation type: Operating foundation.
Financial data (yr. ended 08/31/14): Assets, $942,287 (M); gifts received, $285,530; expenditures, $312,513; qualifying distributions, $312,010; giving activities include $311,775 for 1 grant.
Purpose and activities: Giving primarily for yeshivas in Israel.
Fields of interest: Education; Judaism.
International interests: Israel.
Type of support: Scholarships.
Limitations: Applications not accepted. Giving limited to Israel.
Application information: Contributes only to pre-selected organizations.
Directors: Jacob Kreitman; Rivkah Kreitman.
EIN: 133047558

5668
American Friends of the Hebrew University Charitable Common Fund, Inc.
1 Battery Park Plz., 25th Fl.
New York City, NY   10004-1405
Main URL: http://www.afhu.org
Facebook: https://www.facebook.com/AmFriendsHU
Twitter: https://twitter.com/AmFriendsHU
YouTube: http://www.youtube.com/user/AmFriendsHU

Established in 1989 in New York.
Donors: Stanley Bogen; Ernest Bogan; Robert Savin; John Steinhardt; Fred S. Lafer; Edward Fein; Jane

Zimmerman; Ron Zimmerman; Richard Karp; Jane Karp; American Friends of Hebrew University.
Foundation type: Independent foundation.
Financial data (yr. ended 09/30/13): Assets, $2,066,568 (M); expenditures, $171,074; qualifying distributions, $166,414; giving activities include $166,414 for 31 grants (high: $113,564; low: $100).
Purpose and activities: Support for Jewish agencies, temples, and federated giving programs, the arts, education, and health.
Fields of interest: Arts and culture; Education; Nonprofits; Diseases and conditions; Judaism.
Type of support: General support; Continuing support; Research; Research and evaluation; Regranting.
Limitations: Applications not accepted. Giving primarily in New York, NY. No grants to individuals.
Application information: Unsolicited requests for funds not accepted.
Trustees: Stanley Bogen; Keith Sachs; Ira Lee Sorkin; Peter Willner.
EIN: 133525587

5669
American Society of the French Legion of Honor, Inc.
19 E. 64th St.
New York City, NY   10065-7002   (212) 439-0205
Contact: Elodie Massaro

Established in 1949 in New York.
Donors: Guy N. Wildenstein; Michel David-Weill.
Foundation type: Independent foundation.
Financial data (yr. ended 08/31/13): Assets, $4,417,265 (M); gifts received, $31,680; expenditures, $520,460; qualifying distributions, $445,318; giving activities include $394,900 for 28 grants (high: $40,000; low: $4,500).
Purpose and activities: Grants to promote friendship between France and the U.S. through education and literature. The society also publishes a newsletter and a magazine, and it holds a reception to promote an appreciation of French-American culture.
Fields of interest: Arts and culture; Literature and writing; Education; Higher education; International relations; Goodwill promotion.
International interests: France.
Type of support: Individual development.
Limitations: Applications accepted. Giving primarily in New York, NY, and Paris, France.
Application information:
  Initial approach: Proposal
  Deadline(s): None
Officers and Board Members: Guy N. Wildenstein, Pres. and Director; Bruno Bich, V.P. and Director; Walter J.P. Curley, V.P. and Director; Joseph Verner Reed, V.P. and Director; Nicole Hirsh, Secy. and Director; Ezra K. Zilkha, Treas. and Director; Francoise Cestac; Anne Cox Chambers; Michael Perez; Jean-Paul Picot; Antoine Treuille; Daniele Thomas-Easton.
EIN: 130434237

5670
The Amnon Foundation, Inc.
7281 Royce Pl.
Brooklyn, NY   11234-5814   (718) 851-1759
Contact: Amnon Levy

Established in 2004 in New York.
Donors: Amnon Levy; AKP Gourmet Inc.
Foundation type: Independent foundation.
Financial data (yr. ended 12/31/12): Assets, $0 (M); gifts received, $141,154; expenditures, $140,378; qualifying distributions, $140,344; giving activities include $140,344 for 5 grants (high: $94,500; low: $280).
Fields of interest: Religion.
Limitations: Applications accepted. Giving primarily in NY. No grants to individuals.
Application information:
   Initial approach: Letter
   Deadline(s): None
Trustee: Amnon Levy.
EIN: 202048991

5671
The Amphion Foundation
254 W. 31st St., 15th Fl.
New York City, NY   10001-2813   (212) 461-6956
Contact: James M. Kendrick, Secy.
FAX: (212) 810-4567;
E-mail: info@amphionfoundation.org; E-mail for grants inquiries: grantsmanager@amphionfoundation.org; Main URL: http://www.amphionfoundation.org
Grants List: https://amphionfoundation.org/news

Established in 1988 in New York.
Donor: Elliott C. Carter, Jr.
Foundation type: Independent foundation.
Financial data (yr. ended 12/31/13): Assets, $14,280,083 (M); gifts received, $3,530,600; expenditures, $467,431; qualifying distributions, $415,227; giving activities include $308,020 for 87 grants (high: $32,020; low: $1,000).
Purpose and activities: The foundation was established to encourage the performance of contemporary concert music, particularly by American composers, through support to performing and presenting organizations that have demonstrated sustained artistic excellence; support also to service organizations.
Fields of interest: Performing arts; Music; Education.
Limitations: Applications accepted. Giving primarily in NY. No support for recording projects, or for projects that are part of the curriculum of an educational institution. No grants for commissions for composers, or for endowments.
Application information: Application forms available on foundation web site. All applications must be typed and contain a working e-mail address. Application form required.
   Initial approach: Check guidelines on foundation web site prior to applying
   Copies of proposal: 1
   Deadline(s): See foundation web site for current deadlines
Officers: Virgil Blackwell, Pres.; John Link, Senior V.P.; Susan Feder, V.P.; James M. Kendrick, Secy.; Anthony Schmidt, Treas.
Directors: David Fulmer; Ara Guzelimian; Ursula Oppens; Fred Sherry.
EIN: 133438528

5672
The Jack and Mimi Leviton Amsterdam Foundation
71 Broad Brook Rd.
Bedford Hills, NY   10507-2207

Established in 1977 in Delaware.
Donors: Jack Amsterdam†; Dasha Epstein.
Foundation type: Independent foundation.
Financial data (yr. ended 12/31/14): Assets, $1,743,327 (M); gifts received, $132; expenditures, $256,535; qualifying distributions, $249,815; giving activities include $242,390 for 40 grants (high: $100,000; low: $100).
Purpose and activities: Giving primarily for the performing arts, education, and medical research.
Fields of interest: Arts and culture; Education; Human services.
Type of support: General support; Research.
Limitations: Applications not accepted. Giving primarily in the New York, NY, area. No grants to individuals.
Application information: Contributes only to pre-selected organizations.
Officers: Dasha Epstein, Pres.; Danielle Epstein, V.P.
EIN: 510220854

5673
Anderson Family Charitable Fund
c/o Bessemer Trust
630 5th Ave.
New York City, NY   10111-0100

Established in 2005 in Delaware.
Donor: Marjorie A. Matheson.
Foundation type: Independent foundation.
Financial data (yr. ended 12/31/14): Assets, $11,278,934; expenditures, $142,520; qualifying distributions, $118,255.
Fields of interest: Health care clinics; Diseases and conditions; Human services; Family services.
Type of support: General support.
Limitations: Applications not accepted. Giving primarily in FL and NY. No grants to individuals.
Application information: Contributes only to pre-selected organizations.
Officers and Directors: Marjorie A. Matheson, Pres. and Treas. and Director; Holly Hewitt Bard, Secy. and Director.
EIN: 204125250

5674
The Anderson Foundation Inc.
P.O. Box 1522
Elmira, NY   14902-1522   (607) 734—2271
Contact: Jane G. Joralemon, Pres. and Trustee

Established in 1960 in New York.
Donors: Jane G. Anderson; Douglas G. Anderson†.
Foundation type: Independent foundation.
Financial data (yr. ended 04/30/15): Assets, $3,659,837 (M); expenditures, $212,826; qualifying distributions, $187,500; giving activities include $187,500 for 21 grants (high: $18,600; low: $2,000).
Fields of interest: Arts and culture; Performing arts; Foundations; Hospital care; Public libraries; Human services; Food aid; Economics for youth; Children and youth.

Type of support: General support; Equipment; Debt reduction; Scholarships.
Limitations: Applications accepted. Giving primarily in Elmira, NY. No grants to individuals.
Application information: Application form required.
   Initial approach: Contact foundation for application
   Deadline(s): Mar. 1, Sept. 1 and Dec. 1
Officers and Trustees: Jane G. Joralemon, Pres. and Trustee; Paul Greenlee, Jr., V.P. and Trustee; Clover M. Drinkwater, Secy. and Trustee; E. William Whittaker, Treas. and Trustee; Elizabeth T. Dalrymple; Edwin P. Marosek; Margaret B. Streeter; Jeanne Whittaker Ward, Pres.
EIN: 166024689

5675
The William B. & Juliet J. Anderson Rosch Charitable Foundation
P.O. Box 116
Jamestown, NY   14702-0068

Established in 2005 in New York.
Foundation type: Independent foundation.
Financial data (yr. ended 12/31/14): Assets, $7,919,046 (M); expenditures, $429,439; qualifying distributions, $348,236; giving activities include $345,000 for 8 grants (high: $241,500; low: $10,000).
Fields of interest: Protestantism; Human services.
Limitations: Applications not accepted. No grants to individuals.
Application information: Contributes only to pre-selected organizations.
Trustee and Advisory Committee Members: Edith T. Bensink; Patricia Berg.
EIN: 816117173

5676
Anderson-Rogers Foundation, Inc.
(formerly Environmental Data Research Institute)
327 W. 19th St.
New York City, NY   10011-3901   (212) 989-9331
Contact: Sarah A. Pope, Pres.
E-mail: andersonrogersfoundation@gmail.com; Main URL: http://foundationcenter.org/grantmaker/arfdn

Established in 2000 in New York.
Donor: Porter W. Anderson.
Foundation type: Independent foundation.
Financial data (yr. ended 12/31/13): Assets, $10,143,173 (M); expenditures, $430,413; qualifying distributions, $359,500; giving activities include $359,500 for 36 grants (high: $25,000; low: $500).
Purpose and activities: Giving for the support of environmental education and activism, sustainable agriculture, family planning, abortion rights, sex education, the promotion of the separation of church and state, and the dissemination of humanist values.
Fields of interest: Natural resources; Water resources; Water pollution; Land resources; Biodiversity; Wildlife biodiversity; Endangered species protection; Domesticated animals; Animal welfare; Family planning; Abortion; Youth pregnancy prevention; Sexual education; Sustainable agriculture; Freedom of religion; Reproductive rights.
Type of support: General support; Capital and infrastructure; Equipment; Emergency funds;

Program development; Publications; Seed money; Curriculum development; Program evaluations.
Limitations: Applications accepted. Giving primarily in No giving limitations within the U.S. but giving primarily in NY state. No support for religious organizations. No grants to individuals, or for scholarships.
Publications: Application guidelines; Grants list.
Application information: Until further notice, the foundation is not accepting applications. See foundation web site for complete information.
  Initial approach: Brief letter of inquiry (not more than 2 pages)
  Copies of proposal: 1
  Board meeting date(s): Annual meeting Oct. 1st. Special meetings 4-6 times a year
  Final notification: Within 2 months
Officers and Trustees: Sarah A. Pope, Pres. and Treas. and Trustee; Porter W. Anderson, Jr., V.P. and Secy. and Trustee; Juliette R. Pope; Charles H. Rogers.
Number of staff: 2 part-time professional.
EIN: 223052390

5677
Joan and Peter Andrews Family Foundation
374 Delaware Ave., Ste. 209
Buffalo, NY 14202-1611

Donors: Peter C. Andrews; Joan K. Andrews.
Foundation type: Independent foundation.
Financial data (yr. ended 09/30/14): Assets, $359,180 (M); gifts received, $406,597; expenditures, $154,866; qualifying distributions, $148,835; giving activities include $144,500 for 17 grants (high: $20,000; low: $500).
Fields of interest: Arts and culture; Education; Domesticated animals.
Type of support: General support.
Limitations: Applications not accepted. Giving primarily in Washington, DC, and NY. No grants to individuals.
Application information: Unsolicited requests for funds not accepted.
Trustees: Joan K. Andrews; Peter C. Andrews; Dale B. Demyanick.
EIN: 166443273

5678
The Angel Foundation
c/o The Ayco Company, L.P.
P.O. Box 15014
Albany, NY 12212-5014

Established in 2008 in Connecticut.
Donors: Stephen F. Angel; Dolores W. Angel.
Foundation type: Independent foundation.
Financial data (yr. ended 12/31/13): Assets, $2,624,671 (M); expenditures, $336,200; qualifying distributions, $335,800; giving activities include $335,800 for 69 grants (high: $100,000; low: $100).
Fields of interest: Christianity; Human services.
Limitations: Applications not accepted. Giving primarily in CT. No grants to individuals.
Application information: Unsolicited requests for funds not accepted.
Trustees: Dolores W. Angel; Stephen F. Angel.
EIN: 262816498

5679
The Angelson Family Foundation
876 Park Ave.
New York City, NY 10075-1843

Established in 2007 in New York.
Donors: Mark Angelson; Marilyn Angelson.
Foundation type: Independent foundation.
Financial data (yr. ended 12/31/12): Assets, $8,612,457 (M); expenditures, $451,568; qualifying distributions, $416,640; giving activities include $416,640 for 28 grants (high: $100,000; low: $250).
Fields of interest: Arts and culture; Education; University education; Medical education; Human rights; International relations.
Limitations: Applications not accepted. Giving primarily in IL and NY. No grants to individuals.
Application information: Contributes only to pre-selected organizations.
Officers and Trustees: Marilyn Angelson, Chair. and Trustee; Mark Angelson, Pres. and Trustee; Genevieve Angelson; Jessica Angelson; Meredith Angelson.
EIN: 566683185

5680
Animal Welfare Trust
141 Halstead Ave., Ste. 301
Mamaroneck, NY 10543-2652 (914) 381-6177
Contact: Brad Goldberg, Pres.
FAX: (914) 381-6176;
E-mail: email@animalwelfaretrust.org; Mailing and application address: P.O. Box 737, Mamaroneck, NY 10543; Main URL: http://fdnweb.org/awt
Grants List: http://fdnweb.org/awt/grants/year/ 2013
E-mail for internships: ali@animalwelfaretrust.org

Established in 2001 in New York.
Donors: Bradley Goldberg; Eileen Kay Sterioff†.
Foundation type: Operating foundation.
Financial data (yr. ended 12/31/14): Assets, $3,970,474; expenditures, $495,572; qualifying distributions, $489,987.
Purpose and activities: The purpose of the trust is to make a difference in the welfare of animals. Its grants program has a particular focus on helping grassroots efforts that have a compelling vision as to how they can make a unique contribution to the animal welfare cause.
Fields of interest: Humane education; Vegetarianism.
Type of support: General support; Grants to individuals.
Limitations: Applications accepted. Giving on a national basis, with some emphasis in Mamaroneck, NY. Generally no support for local animal rescue/shelter and spay/neuter programs, or for wildlife management and conservation projects.
Publications: Application guidelines; Grants list.
Application information: See Trust web site for full application guidelines.
  Initial approach: Letter of inquiry by e-mail is encouraged
  Deadline(s): See Trust web site for deadlines
  Board meeting date(s): Quarterly
Officers and Directors: Bradley Goldberg, Pres. and Director; Mariann Sullivan, Esq., Secy. and Director; Lilli Lawner, C.S.W.; Amy Trakinski, Esq.; David Wolfson, Esq.

Number of staff: 1 full-time professional; 1 part-time professional; 3 part-time support.
EIN: 134131408

5681
The Frank J. Antun Foundation
100 Crossways Park W., Ste. 205
Woodbury, NY 11797-2012
Contact: Josephine Alex, Mgr.

Established in 1986 in New York.
Donor: Frank J. Antun†.
Foundation type: Independent foundation.
Financial data (yr. ended 08/31/13): Assets, $11,300,068 (M); expenditures, $612,030; qualifying distributions, $510,142; giving activities include $383,000 for 33 grants (high: $35,000; low: $2,000).
Purpose and activities: Giving primarily for health organizations, particularly for cancer; funding also for children, youth, and social services, and to services for people who are blind or hearing impaired.
Fields of interest: Health; Diseases and conditions; Cancers; Human services; Child welfare; Children and youth; People with disabilities; People with vision impairments; People with hearing impairments.
Limitations: Giving primarily in the greater New York, NY, area. No grants to individuals.
Application information: Application form required.
  Initial approach: Request application form
  Deadline(s): None
  Board meeting date(s): Varies
Officer: Josephine Alex, Mgr.
Trustees: Patricia Colgan; John Cremins; Joseph P. Scanlon.
Number of staff: 2 full-time professional; 1 part-time support.
EIN: 112822395

5682
The Apple Lane Foundation, Inc.
(formerly De Sieyes Family Foundation)
c/o Fiduciary Trust Company International
600 5th Ave.
New York City, NY 10020

Established in 1998 in Connecticut.
Donors: Virginia De Sieyes; Charles J. De Sieyes.
Foundation type: Independent foundation.
Financial data (yr. ended 12/31/13): Assets, $8,838,801 (M); expenditures, $422,952; qualifying distributions, $388,771; giving activities include $382,219 for 206 grants (high: $10,000; low: $100).
Purpose and activities: Giving to an art museum and a children's hospital.
Fields of interest: Museums; Hospital care.
Limitations: Applications not accepted. No grants to individuals.
Application information: Unsolicited requests for funds not accepted.
Officers and Directors: Charles J. De Sieyes, Pres. and Director; David C. De Sieyes, V.P. and Director; J.C. David Hadden.
EIN: 061501640

5683
Stuart S. Applebaum Giving Foundation
c/o S. Applebaum
145 E. 92nd St.
New York City, NY   10128-2431

Donor: Stuart S. Applebaum.
Foundation type: Independent foundation.
Financial data (yr. ended 12/31/14): Assets, $642,065; gifts received, $270,000; expenditures, $237,637; qualifying distributions, $232,231.
Fields of interest: Education; Nonprofits.
Type of support: General support; Regranting.
Limitations: Applications not accepted. No grants to individuals.
Application information: Contributes only to pre-selected organizations.
Officer: Stuart S. Applebaum, Pres., V.P., and Secy.-Treas.
Director: Irwyn Applebaum.
EIN: 371420725

5684
Arcadia Foundation
(formerly John B. Ryan Foundation, Inc.)
c/o Marcum LLP
10 Melville Park Rd.
Melville, NY   11747-3146

Donor: John B. Ryan.
Foundation type: Independent foundation.
Financial data (yr. ended 12/31/13): Assets, $1,391,642 (M); expenditures, $131,865; qualifying distributions, $129,335; giving activities include $126,700 for 7 grants (high: $35,000; low: $1,000).
Fields of interest: Arts and culture; Education; Health.
Type of support: General support.
Limitations: Applications not accepted. Giving primarily in New York, NY. No grants to individuals.
Application information: Unsolicited requests for funds not accepted.
Directors: John B. Ryan; Thomas Ryan.
EIN: 133398050

5685
Archangel Michael Foundation
c/o Bessemer Trust Co.
630 5th Ave.
New York City, NY   10111-0100

Established in 1998 in California.
Donor: Michael Huffington.
Foundation type: Independent foundation.
Financial data (yr. ended 09/30/14): Assets, $8,699,633 (M); expenditures, $461,327; qualifying distributions, $408,121; giving activities include $400,007 for 2+ grants (high: $250,000).
Fields of interest: Education; Medical education; Foundations.
Limitations: Applications not accepted. Giving primarily in CA and IN. No grants to individuals.
Application information: Contributes only to pre-selected organizations.
Trustee: Michael Huffington.
EIN: 957059949

5686
Peter & Rosanne Aresty Foundation
c/o Alfred Dunner, Inc.
1411 Broadway
New York City, NY   10018-3496

Established in 2001 in New York.
Donors: Joseph Aresty; Rosanne Aresty; Peter Aresty.
Foundation type: Independent foundation.
Financial data (yr. ended 12/31/13): Assets, $4,192,888 (M); expenditures, $227,350; qualifying distributions, $227,350; giving activities include $227,100 for 25 grants (high: $125,000; low: $250).
Fields of interest: Education; Land resources; Hospital care; Protestantism; Human services.
Limitations: Applications not accepted. No grants to individuals.
Application information: Unsolicited requests for funds not accepted.
Trustees: Peter Aresty; Rosanne Aresty.
EIN: 316666451

5687
Steven and Sheila Aresty Foundation
c/o Alfred Dunner, Inc.
1411 Broadway
New York City, NY   10018-3496

Established in 2001 in New York.
Donors: Joseph Aresty; Sheila Aresty; Steven Aresty.
Foundation type: Independent foundation.
Financial data (yr. ended 12/31/13): Assets, $5,070,637 (M); expenditures, $245,718; qualifying distributions, $223,224; giving activities include $207,017 for grants.
Fields of interest: Performing arts; Art museums; Higher education; Child welfare.
Limitations: Applications not accepted. Giving primarily in NY. No grants to individuals.
Application information: Unsolicited requests for funds not accepted.
Trustees: Sheila Aresty; Steven Aresty.
EIN: 316666392

5688
Armonia Foundation Inc.
c/o Sheldon M. Goldman
825 3rd Ave., 34th Fl.
New York City, NY   10022

Established in 2007 in Delaware.
Donors: Sheldon M. Goldman; Robert Feig; Dinah Pardasani; Gerald Jaeger.
Foundation type: Independent foundation.
Financial data (yr. ended 12/31/13): Assets, $375,365 (M); expenditures, $145,191; qualifying distributions, $139,000; giving activities include $139,000 for 3 grants (high: $74,000; low: $29,000).
Fields of interest: Education; Religion; Human services.
Limitations: Applications not accepted. Giving primarily in MA and NY. No grants to individuals.
Application information: Unsolicited requests for funds not accepte.
Officer: Sheldon M. Goldman, Pres.
EIN: 260714605

5689
Aronson Foundation
35 E. 20th St.
New York City, NY   10003-1320
E-mail: JA31628@aol.com

Established in 1992 in Missouri.
Donors: Adam Aronson†; Judith Aronson; Jonathan Aronson; Joshua Aronson; James Aronson.
Foundation type: Independent foundation.
Financial data (yr. ended 12/31/13): Assets, $3,750,444 (M); expenditures, $356,133; qualifying distributions, $329,641; giving activities include $327,048 for 2 grants (high: $326,048; low: $1,000).
Purpose and activities: Giving primarily for the arts, art education, and to cultural institutes.
Fields of interest: Arts and culture; Arts education; Young adults.
Type of support: Program development; Curriculum development; Fellowships; Internships; Scholarships.
Limitations: Applications not accepted. Giving primarily in the St. Louis, MO, metropolitan area. No support for political programs. No grants to individuals, or for "bricks and mortar" or buildings; grants rarely made to capital campaigns.
Application information: Contributes only to pre-selected organizations.
Board meeting date(s): Annually
Trustee: Jonathan Aronson; Joshua Aronson.
Number of staff: None.
EIN: 431616967

5690
Clement and Karen Arrison Family Charitable Foundation
35 Lincoln Pkwy.
Buffalo, NY   14222-1229   (716) 881-0760
Contact: Karen Arrison, Pres. and Treas.

Established in 2005 in New York.
Donors: Clement R. Arrison; Karen Arrison; Arrison Family Foundation.
Foundation type: Independent foundation.
Financial data (yr. ended 12/31/13): Assets, $4,969,148 (M); gifts received, $500,000; expenditures, $250,774; qualifying distributions, $231,195; giving activities include $231,195 for 44 grants (high: $52,300; low: $50).
Fields of interest: Performing arts; Radio.
Application information:
Initial approach: Proposal
Deadline(s): None
Officer: Karen Arrison, Pres. and Treas.
EIN: 203116729

5691
Art Matters, Inc.
P.O. Box 311
Prince St. Sta.
New York City, NY   10012-0006
Contact: Sacha Yanow, Prog. Dir.
E-mail: info@artmattersfoundation.org; Main URL: http://www.artmattersfoundation.org
Facebook: https://www.facebook.com/pages/Art-Matters-Foundation/539352129419101

Established in 1985 in New York.
Donors: Good Works Foundation; Laura Donnelley Charitable Lead Trust.

Foundation type: Independent foundation.
Financial data (yr. ended 12/31/13): Assets, $79,727 (M); gifts received, $311,357; expenditures, $310,930; qualifying distributions, $294,230; giving activities include $7,000 for 1 grant, and $179,650 for 39 grants to individuals (high: $10,000; low: $3,000).
Purpose and activities: Giving is provided to encourage exploration of issues and ideas; experimentation in visual arts, media, and performance; and presentation of new art.
Fields of interest: Visual arts.
Type of support: Fellowships; Grants to individuals.
Limitations: Applications not accepted. Giving limited to NY. No support for organizations or individuals working in dance or music, or for individual art studies. No grants for publications.
Application information: The grantmaker considers applications by invitation only. See web site for additional information.
Officers: Laura Donnelley, Chair.; Linda Earle, Pres.; Cee Brown, V.P.; Alexander Grey, Secy.; Catherine Gund, Treas.
Directors: Regine Basha; Mary L. Beebe; Gai Gherardi; David Mendoza; Laurence Miller; Lowery Sims; Marianne Weems; Philip Yenawine; Bruce Yonemoto.
EIN: 133271577

5692
Artists Fellowship Inc.

c/o Salmagundi Club
47 5th Ave.
New York City, NY 10003-4303 (212) 255-7740; 216
E-mail: info@Artistsfellowship.org; Main URL: http://artistsfellowship.org

Donor: J. B. Lankes†.
Foundation type: Independent foundation.
Financial data (yr. ended 10/31/13): Assets, $4,883,603 (M); gifts received, $76,600; expenditures, $300,738; qualifying distributions, $283,547; giving activities include $234,303 for 66 grants to individuals (high: $23,500; low: $500).
Purpose and activities: Grants for emergency aid to professional fine artists (painters, graphic artists, printmakers, and sculptors), and their families in times of emergency, disability or bereavement. One does not need to be a member of the fellowship to receive assistance, nor does membership in the fellowship entitle one to assistance.
Fields of interest: Printmaking; Senior services; Seniors; People with disabilities.
Type of support: Grants to individuals.
Application information: See Fellowship web site for complete application guidelines.
Officers: Wende Caporale, Pres.; Charles Yoder, V.P.; Priscilla McCarthy, Recording Secy.; Joyce Zeller, Corresponding Secy.; Pamela Singleton, Treas.
Trustees: Edith Rae Brown; Terry Brown; Fran Dembitzer; Franklin Feldman; Ira Goldberg; Richard Heinrich; Morton Kaish; Tim Newton; David B. Pena; Claudia Seymour; Sharon Sprung.
EIN: 136122134

5693
Arts and Letters Foundation, Inc.

230 E. 50th St., Ste. 3B
New York City, NY 10022-7702

Established in 1997 in New York.
Donor: Janice Gerton.
Foundation type: Independent foundation.
Financial data (yr. ended 12/31/13): Assets, $1,370,955 (M); gifts received, $100,000; expenditures, $156,405; qualifying distributions, $150,051; giving activities include $150,051 for 33 grants (high: $50,000; low: $50).
Fields of interest: Arts and culture; Music; Education; University education; Human services.
Limitations: Applications not accepted. Giving primarily in NY.
Application information: Unsolicited requests for funds not accepted.
Officers: Janice Gerton, Pres.; Elizabeth Griffin, Secy.
EIN: 522069719

5694
The Asen Foundation

c/o Robert Scott Asen
224 E. 49th St.
New York City, NY 10017-1554

Donor: Robert Scott Asen.
Foundation type: Independent foundation.
Financial data (yr. ended 12/31/13): Assets, $2,292,953 (M); expenditures, $272,154; qualifying distributions, $262,543; giving activities include $262,543 for 57 grants (high: $75,793; low: $100).
Fields of interest: Arts and culture; Education; Environment.
Limitations: Applications not accepted. Giving primarily in Washington, DC. No grants to individuals.
Application information: Unsolicited requests for funds not accepted.
Trustee: Robert Scott Asen.
EIN: 207361210

5695
Asher Foundation

(formerly Marco Foundation)
c/o Kestenbaum
18 Clover Dr.
Great Neck, NY 11021-1819 (516) 487-3565
Contact: Alan Kestenbaum, Tr.

Established in 2002 in New York.
Donors: Deborah Kestenbaum; Alan Kestenbaum; Michael Barenholtz.
Foundation type: Independent foundation.
Financial data (yr. ended 06/30/13): Assets, $187,299 (M); gifts received, $100,000; expenditures, $219,199; qualifying distributions, $215,691; giving activities include $215,691 for 36 grants (high: $75,000; low: $100).
Fields of interest: Higher education; Nonprofits; Judaism.
Type of support: Regranting.
Limitations: Applications accepted. Giving primarily in NY. No grants to individuals.
Application information:
  Initial approach: Proposal
  Deadline(s): None
Trustees: Alan Kestenbaum; Deborah Kestenbaum.
EIN: 820551097

5696
Athens Community Foundation

c/o Eugene Hatton
409 Howard Hall Rd.
Catskill, NY 12414-6025 (518) 945-2574

Foundation type: Independent foundation.
Financial data (yr. ended 12/31/14): Assets, $4,492,755; gifts received, $3,500; expenditures, $214,552; qualifying distributions, $190,971 and $0 for set-asides.
Fields of interest: Performing arts; Education; Community and economic development; Housing development.
Limitations: Applications accepted. Giving primarily in NY.
Application information: Application form required.
  Initial approach: Proposal
  Deadline(s): End of October
Trustees: Daniel DeVinney; Eugene Hatton; Leo Palmateer.
EIN: 371419086

5697
Atlantic Charitable Foundation

(formerly Jewish Education Research & Development Foundation)
456A Central Ave., Ste. 149
Cedarhurst, NY 11516-1907

Established in 2006 in New York.
Donors: Gary Gettenberg; Lynn Gettenberg; Brooklyn Endoscopy and Surgery Center; The Diskin Trust; Lynn Gettenberg Irrevocable Trust; Gary Gettenberg Irrevocable Trust; Gotlieb Family Trust; Kenridge, LLC; Neve Shaanan Irrevocable Trust.
Foundation type: Independent foundation.
Financial data (yr. ended 11/30/14): Assets, $2,695,098 (M); gifts received, $825,000; expenditures, $239,829; qualifying distributions, $239,829; giving activities include $239,579 for 21 grants (high: $65,000; low: $1,275).
Purpose and activities: Giving primarily to Jewish educational institutions and yeshivas.
Fields of interest: Education; Judaism.
Limitations: Applications accepted. Giving primarily in New York, NY.
Application information: Application form required.
  Initial approach: Letter
  Deadline(s): None
Trustees: Gary Gettenberg; Lynn Gettenberg.
EIN: 203992879

5698
Charles J. & Burton S. August Family Foundation

240 Sandringham Rd.
Rochester, NY 14610-3458 (585) 381-4615
Contact: Robert August, Tr.

Established in 1989 in New York.
Donors: Burton S. August; Charles J. August†; Karpus Investment Management.
Foundation type: Independent foundation.
Financial data (yr. ended 06/30/14): Assets, $7,154,674 (M); expenditures, $376,499; qualifying distributions, $320,095; giving activities include $318,195 for 20 grants (high: $54,000; low: $400).
Purpose and activities: Giving primarily for health and human services, and for education.

Fields of interest: Higher education; Health; Human services; Child welfare; Children and youth; Seniors; Homeless people; Low-income and poor people; People with disabilities; People with physical disabilities; People with vision impairments; People with hearing impairments; People with psychosocial disabilities; Substance abusers.

Type of support: General support; Matching grants; Capital campaigns; Capital and infrastructure; Equipment; Emergency funds; Program development; Seed money; Scholarships.

Limitations: Applications accepted. Giving primarily in Rochester and Monroe County, NY. No support for political organizations. No grants to individuals, or for continuing support.

Application information:
Initial approach: Proposal
Copies of proposal: 1
Deadline(s): None
Board meeting date(s): Approximately June 15

Trustees: Andrew August; Burton S. August, Jr.; Burton Stuart August; Jan August; Jean B. August; Joan August; John August; Robert August; Susan Eastwood; Elizabeth August Mafrici; David C. Mitchell; Michael Telesca.

Number of staff: None.

EIN: 161355601

5699

The Abraham Ausch Charity Foundation, Inc.

12 Herschel Terr.
Monsey, NY 10952-2915

Established in 2004 in New York.

Donor: Abraham Ausch.

Foundation type: Independent foundation.

Financial data (yr. ended 12/31/14): Assets, $13,098 (M); gifts received, $55,000; expenditures, $133,400; qualifying distributions, $133,400; giving activities include $133,400 for 1 grant.

Fields of interest: Judaism.

Limitations: Applications not accepted.

Application information: Unsolicited requests for funds not accepted.

Officer: Abraham Ausch, Pres.

EIN: 800115033

5700

The Authors League Fund

31 E. 32nd St., 7th Fl.
New York City, NY 10016-5509 (212) 268-1208
Contact: Isabel A. Howe, Exec. Dir.
FAX: (212) 564-5363;
E-mail: staff@authorsleaguefund.org; Main URL: www.authorsleaguefund.org

Donors: Joanne Leedom-Ackerman; Priscilla McMillian; Nathan & Dorothy Shainberg Endowment; Winchell Smith†; The Herman Lissner Foundation; Spencer Johnson; Garrison Keillor; Jenny Lind Nillson.

Foundation type: Independent foundation.

Financial data (yr. ended 12/31/13): Assets, $7,212,619 (M); gifts received, $160,150; expenditures, $378,505; qualifying distributions, $343,926; giving activities include $234,424 for 1 grant.

Purpose and activities: The Authors League Fund helps professional writers and dramatists who find

themselves in financial need because of medical or health-related problems, temporary loss of income or other misfortune. The fund gives open-ended, interest-free, no-strings-attached loans. These loans are not grants or scholarships meant to subsidize personal writing projects.

Fields of interest: Arts and culture.

Type of support: Loans to individuals.

Limitations: Applications accepted. Giving primarily in New York, NY.

Publications: Application guidelines.

Application information: See fund web site for complete application procedures and guidelines. Application form required.
Initial approach: Application available on fund web site
Deadline(s): None

Officers: Pat Cummings, Pres.; Sidney Offit, V.P.; Marian Seldes, Secy.; James Stewart, Treas.; Isabel Howe, Exec. Dir.

Directors: Peter Blauner; Georges Borchardt; Gretchen Cryer; Karen Swenson; Jennifer Egan; Molly Haskell; Paula Giddings.

EIN: 131966496

5701

The Avanessians Foundation

Bowling Green Sta.
P.O. Box 73
New York City, NY 10274-0073

Donor: Armen A. Avanessians.

Foundation type: Independent foundation.

Financial data (yr. ended 12/31/13): Assets, $28,070,629 (M); gifts received, $1,671,270; expenditures, $322,762; qualifying distributions, $231,000; giving activities include $231,000 for 8 grants (high: $100,000; low: $5,000).

Purpose and activities: Giving primarily for higher education; some funding also for human services, including an Armenian organization.

Fields of interest: Higher education; Community and economic development; Human services.

Limitations: Applications not accepted. Giving primarily in New York, NY.

Application information: Contributes only to pre-selected organizations.

Trustee: Armen A. Avanessians.

EIN: 266671956

5702

Milton and Sally Avery Arts Foundation

300 Central Park W., Ste. 16J
New York City, NY 10024 (212) 595-7338

Established in 1983 in New York.

Donor: Sally M. Avery†.

Foundation type: Independent foundation.

Financial data (yr. ended 12/31/13): Assets, $62,950,583 (M); gifts received, $60,646,741; expenditures, $511,772; qualifying distributions, $415,750 and $0 for set-asides.

Purpose and activities: Awards restricted to art education, with emphasis on the visual arts, and to further the development of artists through nonprofit institutions, and to artists' communities and residency programs.

Fields of interest: Arts and culture; Arts education; Painting; Sculpture; Elementary and secondary education; Higher education.

Type of support: Professorships; Fellowships; Internships; Scholarships.

Limitations: Applications accepted. Giving primarily in NY. No support for religious or political organizations. No grants to individuals.

Publications: Annual report.

Application information: Application form required.
Initial approach: Letter
Copies of proposal: 1
Deadline(s): None

Trustees: March A. Cavanaugh; Philip G. Cavanaugh; Sean A. Cavanaugh; Harvey Shipley Miller.

EIN: 133093638

5703

AYN Foundation

c/o Sacks Press & Lacher, PC
600 3rd Ave.
New York City, NY 10016-1901
E-mail: info@aynfoundation.com; Main URL: http://www.aynfoundation.com

Established in 1992 in New York.

Donors: Philippa de Menil Friedrich; Heiner Friedrich.

Foundation type: Operating foundation.

Financial data (yr. ended 06/30/13): Assets, $2,731,370 (M); expenditures, $550,451; qualifying distributions, $236,000; giving activities include $232,000 for 1 grant, and $4,000 for 1 grant to an individual.

Fields of interest: Arts and culture.

Type of support: General support.

Limitations: Applications not accepted. Giving primarily in New York, NY.

Application information: Unsolicited requests for funds not accepted.

Officers: Heiner Friedrich, Pres.; Fariha Friedrich, Secy.

EIN: 133692868

5704

Eddie & Shawna Azar Charitable Foundation

1060 E. 8th St.
Brooklyn, NY 11230-4102 (212) 391-1080
Contact: Eddie Azar, Tr.

Established in 1998 in New York.

Donor: Eddie Azar.

Foundation type: Independent foundation.

Financial data (yr. ended 05/31/14): Assets, $43,088 (M); gifts received, $210,000; expenditures, $168,628; qualifying distributions, $168,628; giving activities include $167,563 for 24 grants (high: $35,900; low: $1,000).

Purpose and activities: Giving for Jewish organizations that provide aid to the sick and needy.

Fields of interest: Judaism.

Type of support: General support.

Limitations: Applications accepted. Giving primarily in Brooklyn and New York, NY; some funding also in NJ.

Application information:
Initial approach: Letter
Deadline(s): None

Trustees: Eddie Azar; Shawna Azar.

EIN: 311567610

5705
The B Z Foundation
1455 E. 15th St.
Brooklyn, NY 11230-6601

Donors: Chaim Foundation; Ben Epstein; Global Charitable Foundation; Susi Austein Trust; Chaim Foundation; SA 1-10 Trust; Ben Epstein & Assocs.; Joe Mosseri; Austein Trust; Reuven Epstein; Diane Azrak; David Leiner; Congregation Avreichim; Seforim Bookstore; Bluerock Capital; NYS Tax Credit.
Foundation type: Independent foundation.
Financial data (yr. ended 11/30/13): Assets, $12,332 (M); gifts received, $244,125; expenditures, $147,960; qualifying distributions, $147,515; giving activities include $147,515 for 94 grants (high: $21,600; low: $16).
Purpose and activities: Giving primarily to Jewish agencies, temples and yeshivas.
Fields of interest: Education; Judaism.
Type of support: General support.
Limitations: Applications not accepted. No grants to individuals.
Application information: Unsolicited requests for funds not accepted.
Trustee: Ben Epstein.
EIN: 010566453

5706
T. Backer Fund, Inc.
P.O. Box 364
Chatham, NY 12037-0364

Donors: Judith B. Grunberg; Daniel Grunberg.
Foundation type: Operating foundation.
Financial data (yr. ended 12/31/13): Assets, $6,819,048 (M); expenditures, $338,431; qualifying distributions, $278,734; giving activities include $274,500 for 29 grants (high: $40,000; low: $200).
Purpose and activities: Giving primarily for conservation, medical research, the arts, and education.
Fields of interest: Arts and culture; Education; Human services.
Type of support: General support.
Limitations: Applications not accepted. Giving primarily in NY. No grants to individuals.
Application information: Contributes only to pre-selected organizations.
Officers: Judith B. Grunberg, Pres.; Daniel Grunberg, V.P.
Director: David Grunberg.
EIN: 141640994

5707
Balbach Family Foundation
7811 E. Quaker Rd.
Orchard Park, NY 14127-2061

Established in 1998 in New York.
Donors: Charles E. Balbach; Margaret C. Balbach†; Carl T. Balbach; Melissa T. Balbach; Harvard University.
Foundation type: Independent foundation.
Financial data (yr. ended 06/30/13): Assets, $1,018,501 (M); gifts received, $211,000; expenditures, $251,339; qualifying distributions, $246,769; giving activities include $244,522 for 69 grants (high: $26,250; low: $100).

Purpose and activities: The foundation is a family-oriented charitable organization. The family members (trustees of the foundation) are interested in supporting the established arts, cultural, educational, and social service organizations in their local communities of western New York. The trustees prefer to support organizations in which family members have direct interest or involvement. Supported organizations should have a balanced budget and an established record of consistent quality delivery of services.
Fields of interest: Arts and culture; Art museums; Education; Foundations; Human services; Food banks; Child welfare.
Type of support: General support; Matching grants; Capital campaigns; Equipment; Endowments; Program development; Seed money; Research.
Limitations: Applications not accepted. Giving primarily in western NY. No support for religious or political organizations. No grants to individuals.
Application information: Contributes only to pre-selected organizations.
Board meeting date(s): Varies
Trustees: Carl T. Balbach; Charles E. Balbach; Melissa T. Balbach.
Number of staff: 1 part-time professional.
EIN: 161542054

5708
The Balm Foundation, Inc.
c/o Jeanne Anselmo
P.O. Box 600
Sea Cliff, NY 11579-0600

Established in 1993 in New York.
Donors: Howard Stein; Janet Stein.
Foundation type: Independent foundation.
Financial data (yr. ended 11/30/13): Assets, $4,416,133 (M); expenditures, $555,946; qualifying distributions, $547,736; giving activities include $419,530 for 12 grants (high: $120,000; low: $250).
Purpose and activities: Giving primarily to health organizations.
Fields of interest: Medical education; Hospital care; Diseases and conditions; Human services.
Limitations: Applications not accepted. Giving primarily in CA and NY. No grants to individuals.
Application information: Contributes only to pre-selected organizations.
Officer: Janet Stein, Pres.
Directors: Peggy Davis; Vincent McGee.
Number of staff: 1 part-time professional.
EIN: 133746421

5709
The Bandier Family Foundation Inc.
Gin Ln.
P.O. Box 2190
Southampton, NY 11969-2190 (646) 254-7435
Contact: Martin Bandier, Pres.

Established in 1994 in New York.
Donor: Martin Bandier.
Foundation type: Independent foundation.
Financial data (yr. ended 11/30/13): Assets, $33,449 (M); gifts received, $150,000; expenditures, $190,526; qualifying distributions, $190,526; giving activities include $189,724 for 36 grants (high: $55,000; low: $85).

Purpose and activities: Giving primarily for higher education, health care, and animal welfare.
Fields of interest: Education; University education; Religion; Human services.
Limitations: Applications accepted. Giving primarily in NY and PA. No grants to individuals.
Application information:
Initial approach: Proposal
Deadline(s): None
Officers and Directors: Martin Bandier, Pres. and Director; Dorothy Bandier, Secy.-Treas. and Director.
EIN: 133803092

5710
Bank of Utica Foundation Inc.
c/o M&H
P.O. Box 477
Utica, NY 13503-0477

Established in 1992 in New York.
Donor: Bank of Utica.
Foundation type: Company-sponsored foundation.
Financial data (yr. ended 12/31/13): Assets, $3,285,261 (M); gifts received, $666,110; expenditures, $183,587; qualifying distributions, $182,610; giving activities include $182,610 for 57 grants (high: $25,000; low: $200).
Purpose and activities: The foundation supports health centers and organizations involved with arts and culture, education, housing, golf, human services, and community economic development.
Fields of interest: Arts and culture; Arts councils; Performing arts; Education; Higher education; Nonprofits; Health care clinics; Public libraries; Community and economic development; Housing development; Golf.
Type of support: General support; Program development; Individual development; Regranting.
Limitations: Applications not accepted. Giving limited to Utica, NY. No grants to individuals.
Application information: Unsolicited requests for funds not accepted.
Officers: Tom E. Sinnott, Chair.; Barry J. Sinnott, Pres.; Brian R. Loughlin, V.P.
EIN: 161423958

5711
The Baobab Fund
200 Madison Ave., 5th Fl.
New York City, NY 10016-3912

Established in 2002 in Delaware.
Donor: Gideon G. Rose.
Foundation type: Independent foundation.
Financial data (yr. ended 12/31/13): Assets, $1,800,595 (M); gifts received, $225,000; expenditures, $285,244; qualifying distributions, $283,275; giving activities include $283,275 for 66 grants (high: $35,000; low: $50).
Fields of interest: University education; Animal welfare; Human rights.
Limitations: Applications not accepted. Giving primarily in CT, MA and NY. No grants to individuals.
Application information: Unsolicited requests for funds not accepted.
Officers: Gideon G. Rose, Pres. and Treas.; Sheri Berman, V.P. and Secy.
EIN: 331007796

5712
Bar Chuma Foundation, Inc.
128 Middleton St., Ste. 3
Brooklyn, NY 11206-8039

Donor: David Inzlicht.
Foundation type: Independent foundation.
Financial data (yr. ended 12/31/13): Assets, $3,484,624 (M); gifts received, $711,290; expenditures, $240,015; qualifying distributions, $236,980; giving activities include $236,980 for 19 grants (high: $39,980; low: $1,800).
Fields of interest: Judaism.
Officers: David Inzlicht, Pres.; Esther Inzlicht, V.P.; Daniel Inzlicht, Secy.-Treas.
EIN: 260291189

5713
Barbara Hope Foundation
c/o BCRS Associates, LLC
77 Water St., 9th Fl.
New York City, NY 10005-3701

Established in 2006 in New York.
Donors: Roy J. Zuckerberg; Samson Advisors, Inc.; Barbara Zuckerberg.
Foundation type: Independent foundation.
Financial data (yr. ended 12/31/13): Assets, $265,347 (M); gifts received, $84,240; expenditures, $155,972; qualifying distributions, $155,072; giving activities include $153,667 for 20 grants (high: $75,000; low: $54).
Fields of interest: Arts and culture; Health; Human services.
Limitations: Applications not accepted. Giving primarily in NY. No grants to individuals.
Application information: Unsolicited requests for funds not accepted.
Directors: Barbara Zuckerberg; Dina Zuckerberg; Lloyd Zuckerberg.
EIN: 208275334

5714
Barbash Family Fund Inc.
265 W. Main St.
Babylon, NY 11702-3419

Established in 1993 in New York.
Donors: Maurice Barbash; Lillian Barbash; Cathy Barbash.
Foundation type: Independent foundation.
Financial data (yr. ended 12/31/13): Assets, $1,881,980 (M); gifts received, $864,492; expenditures, $217,040; qualifying distributions, $215,090; giving activities include $215,090 for 97 grants (high: $25,000; low: $100).
Purpose and activities: Giving primarily for arts and culture and education.
Fields of interest: Music; Opera; Education; Elementary and secondary education; Undergraduate education; Animal welfare; Hospital care.
Limitations: Applications not accepted. Giving primarily in NY. No grants to individuals.
Application information: Unsolicited requests for funds not accepted.
Officers: Lillian Barbash, Pres.; Susan Barbash, V.P.; Cathy Barbash, Secy.; Shepard Barbash, Treas.
EIN: 113184479

5715
Carole A. and Norman Barham Family Foundation
c/o Ayco Co., L.P. - NTG
P.O. Box 15014
Albany, NY 12212-5014

Established in 1997 in New Jersey.
Donors: Carole A. Barham; Norman Barham.
Foundation type: Independent foundation.
Financial data (yr. ended 12/31/13): Assets, $3,977,090 (L); gifts received, $116,965; expenditures, $282,153; qualifying distributions, $274,750; giving activities include $274,750 for 33 grants (high: $50,000; low: $500).
Purpose and activities: Giving for education, recreation, family and youth services, and health and social services.
Fields of interest: Education; Higher education; Health; Human services; Youth organizing.
Type of support: General support; Capital campaigns; Scholarships.
Limitations: Applications not accepted. Giving primarily in NJ and NY. No grants to individuals.
Application information: Contributes only to pre-selected organizations.
Trustees: Carole A. Barham; Norman Barham.
EIN: 223546954

5716
Peter K. Barker Foundation
c/o BCRS Associates, LLC
77 Water St., 9th Fl.
New York City, NY 10005-3701

Established in 1983 in California.
Donor: Peter K. Barker.
Foundation type: Independent foundation.
Financial data (yr. ended 12/31/13): Assets, $4,059,974 (M); expenditures, $187,138; qualifying distributions, $155,490; giving activities include $152,900 for 18 grants (high: $30,000; low: $500).
Fields of interest: Education; Diseases and conditions; Religion.
Type of support: General support.
Limitations: Applications not accepted. Giving primarily in Los Angeles and Pasadena, CA. No grants to individuals.
Application information: Unsolicited requests for funds not accepted.
Trustees: Peter K. Barker; Robin B. Barker.
EIN: 133198247

5717
Barney II Foundation
125 Summerhaven Dr. S.
East Syracuse, NY 13057-3111

Established in 1987 in Illinois.
Donors: William Reichardt, Sr.; William Reichardt, Jr.
Foundation type: Independent foundation.
Financial data (yr. ended 12/31/13): Assets, $1,355,689 (M); gifts received, $26,960; expenditures, $475,496; qualifying distributions, $342,670; giving activities include $342,670 for 100 grants (high: $50,000; low: $60).
Purpose and activities: Giving primarily to Christian churches and charities.
Fields of interest: Higher education; Philanthropy; Christianity; Human services.

Limitations: Applications not accepted. Giving primarily in IL. No grants to individuals.
Application information: Contributes only to pre-selected organizations.
Officer: William Reichardt, Jr., Pres.
Director: Sabra Reichardt.
EIN: 363434490

5718
The Barnwood Foundation
c/o Lisa A. Underwood
525 W. 22nd St., Apt. 2F
New York City, NY 10011-1115

Established in 2007 in New York.
Donors: Michael G. Barnes; Lisa A. Underwood.
Foundation type: Independent foundation.
Financial data (yr. ended 12/31/13): Assets, $7,711,931 (M); gifts received, $1,000,000; expenditures, $347,129; qualifying distributions, $320,796; giving activities include $315,500 for 30 grants (high: $35,000; low: $1,000).
Fields of interest: Higher education; Land resources; Food banks.
Limitations: Applications not accepted. Giving primarily in CT and NY. No grants to individuals.
Application information: Contributes only to pre-selected organizations.
Trustees: Michael G. Barnes; Lisa A. Underwood.
EIN: 207409517

5719
Jeannette Barron Charitable Trust
4 New King St.
P.O. Box 339
White Plains, NY 10604

Established in 2002 in New York.
Foundation type: Independent foundation.
Financial data (yr. ended 02/28/13): Assets, $2,524,644 (M); expenditures, $407,983; qualifying distributions, $390,800; giving activities include $390,800 for 35 grants (high: $68,000; low: $500).
Fields of interest: Dance; Education; Higher education; Nonprofits; Judaism; Human services.
Type of support: Regranting.
Limitations: Applications not accepted. Giving primarily in NY. No grants to individuals.
Application information: Contributes only to pre-selected organizations.
Trustee: Froma Benerofe.
EIN: 137275387

5720
The Matan Baseser Foundation
40 Rodney St.
Brooklyn, NY 11211-7526
Contact: Moshe Kestenbaum

Established in 2006 in New York.
Donors: Gitty Kestenbaum; Kollel Damesek Eliezer; United Talmudic Seminary.
Foundation type: Independent foundation.
Financial data (yr. ended 05/31/14): Assets, $0 (M); gifts received, $225,100; expenditures, $178,419; qualifying distributions, $177,841; giving activities include $177,766 for 7+ grants (high: $29,200).

Fields of interest: Education; Nonprofits; Religion; Judaism.
Type of support: Regranting.
Limitations: Applications not accepted. Giving primarily in Brooklyn, NY. No grants to individuals.
Application information: Unsolicited requests for funds not accepted.
Officer: Gitty Kestenbaum, Mgr.
EIN: 205125738

5721
The Bassman Family Charitable Trust
522 W. End Ave., Apt. 12-A
New York City, NY   10024-3211

Donors: Lori Bassman; Harley Bassman.
Foundation type: Independent foundation.
Financial data (yr. ended 12/31/13): Assets, $295,375 (M); gifts received, $100,867; expenditures, $221,051; qualifying distributions, $197,526; giving activities include $197,526 for 74 grants (high: $66,600; low: $10).
Fields of interest: Arts and culture; Education; Religion; Judaism.
Type of support: General support.
Limitations: Applications not accepted. Giving primarily in NY.
Application information: Unsolicited requests for funds not accepted.
Trustees: Harley Bassman; Lori Bassman.
EIN: 453191770

5722
Theodore & Ruth Baum Charitable Foundation
(formerly Theodore B. Family Baum Foundation)
1 Penn Plz., Ste. 2620
New York City, NY   10119-0002

Established in 1967 in New Jersey.
Donors: Elizabeth Baum; Theodore B. Baum; Dana Baum Hopper; Ruth Baum.
Foundation type: Independent foundation.
Financial data (yr. ended 12/31/13): Assets, $1,683,423 (M); gifts received, $50,000; expenditures, $225,197; qualifying distributions, $225,198; giving activities include $222,284 for 84 grants (high: $119,522; low: $36).
Purpose and activities: Giving primarily for the arts, health, higher education, human services, and Jewish organizations.
Fields of interest: Arts and culture; Museums; Higher education; Health; Diseases and conditions; Community and economic development; Judaism; Human services.
Type of support: General support.
Limitations: Applications not accepted. Giving primarily in New York, NY. No grants to individuals.
Application information: Unsolicited requests for funds not accepted.
Officers: Ruth Baum, Pres.; Theodore B. Baum, V.P. and Treas.; Dana Baum Hopper, Secy.
EIN: 226088058

5723
The Baumann Family Foundation
(formerly The Hirschhorn/Baumann Family Foundation)
c/o Bank of America, N.A.
114 W. 47th St.
New York City, NY   10036-1510

Established in 1993 in New York.
Donors: Hannah H. Baumann†; Hannah H. Baumann Charitable Lead Trust; James S. Baumann.
Foundation type: Independent foundation.
Financial data (yr. ended 12/31/14): Assets, $3,536,565 (M); gifts received, $321,200; expenditures, $201,143; qualifying distributions, $180,453; giving activities include $176,603 for 33 grants (high: $59,000; low: $250).
Fields of interest: Art museums; Higher education; Nonprofits; Judaism.
Type of support: Regranting.
Limitations: Applications not accepted. Giving primarily in New York, NY. No grants to individuals.
Application information: Unsolicited requests for funds not accepted.
Trustee: James S. Baumann.
EIN: 137020953

5724
BBL Charitable Foundation, Inc.
P.O. Box 12789
Albany, NY   12212-2789

Established in 1999 in New York.
Donors: Donald Led Duke; BBL Construction Services, LLC; BBL Carlton, LLC; Richard J. Fasenmyer Foundation; SWF LP; BBL Equinox At Tradition.
Foundation type: Independent foundation.
Financial data (yr. ended 12/31/13): Assets, $293,877 (M); gifts received, $611,946; expenditures, $362,525; qualifying distributions, $362,500; giving activities include $362,500 for 92 grants (high: $50,000; low: $150).
Fields of interest: Education; Higher education; Nonprofits; Hospital care; Health care clinics; Family services.
Type of support: General support; Regranting.
Limitations: Applications not accepted. Giving primarily in NY. No grants to individuals.
Application information: Contributes only to pre-selected organizations.
Directors: Kevin Gleason; Stephen Obermayer.
EIN: 141810413

5725
Leo Cox Beach Philanthropic Foundation
P.O. Box 2218
Glens Falls, NY   12801-6218   (518) 792-3146
Contact: Deborah Burnham, Dir.

Established in 1989 in New York.
Donor: Thomas C. Beach, Jr.
Foundation type: Independent foundation.
Financial data (yr. ended 07/31/14): Assets, $3,076,610 (M); expenditures, $228,222; qualifying distributions, $192,000; giving activities include $192,000 for 13 grants (high: $48,800; low: $2,100).

Fields of interest: Arts and culture; Museums; Education; Hospital care; Communication media; Human services.
Type of support: Equipment.
Limitations: Applications accepted. Giving primarily in NY. No grants to individuals.
Application information: A major portion of funding (90 percent) is committed; the remainder of giving is limited to Washington County, NY. Application form required.
  Initial approach: Letter or phone
  Deadline(s): None
Directors: Deborah Burnham; Dorothy Jackson; Michael F. Massiano; Pauline E. Palmer; John T. Snell, Esq.; Barbara Velsini.
EIN: 141732259

5726
Beacon of Learning Foundation
c/o Sacks Press & Lacher
600 3rd Ave., 18th Fl.
New York City, NY   10016
Application address: c/o Karin J. Barkhorn, Esq., Bryan Cave, 1290 Ave. of Americas, New York, NY 10104

Donors: John K. Menoudakos; Chryssanthy Menoudakos.
Foundation type: Independent foundation.
Financial data (yr. ended 12/31/14): Assets, $159,355 (M); gifts received, $388,972; expenditures, $321,738; qualifying distributions, $302,730; giving activities include $302,730 for 7 grants (high: $60,000; low: $11,790).
Purpose and activities: Scholarships to individuals for higher education.
Fields of interest: Education.
Type of support: Student aid.
Limitations: Applications accepted. Giving primarily in PA.
Application information: Application form required.
  Initial approach: Letter
  Deadline(s): None
Officers: Chryssanthy Menoudakos, Pres.; John K. Menoudakos, Exec. V.P. and Secy.
EIN: 272520016

5727
Nancy Jones Beard Foundation
c/o Brown Brothers Harriman Trust Co., N.A.
140 Broadway
New York City, NY   10005-1108

Established in 2004 in Connecticut.
Donors: Eugene P. Beard; Nancy J. Beard.
Foundation type: Independent foundation.
Financial data (yr. ended 12/31/13): Assets, $5,673,293 (M); gifts received, $261,809; expenditures, $240,355; qualifying distributions, $196,359; giving activities include $191,250 for 18 grants (high: $70,000; low: $250).
Fields of interest: Education; Health; Religion.
Limitations: Applications not accepted. No grants to individuals.
Application information: Unsolicited requests for funds not accepted.
Trustees: Eugene P. Beard; Gregory Scott Beard; Nancy Jones Beard.
EIN: 020735167

5728
Beck Foundation
c/o Beck, Mack & Oliver, LLC
360 Madison Ave., 18th Fl.
New York City, NY 10017-5001
Contact: T. Edmund Beck Jr.

Established in 1954 in New York.
Donor: T. Edmund Beck†.
Foundation type: Independent foundation.
Financial data (yr. ended 12/31/13): Assets,
$4,819,666 (M); gifts received, $555,300;
expenditures, $178,364; qualifying distributions,
$168,550; giving activities include $166,000 for 30
grants (high: $17,000; low: $1,000).
Purpose and activities: Grants primarily for higher
and other education.
Fields of interest: Elementary and secondary
education; Higher education; Health; Christianity.
Limitations: Applications not accepted. Giving
primarily in NJ and NY. No grants to individuals, or
for program-related investments, or in-kind gifts; no
loans.
Application information: Contributes only to
pre-selected organizations.
Directors: John C. Beck; T. Edmund Beck, Jr.
EIN: 136082501

5729
The Beckman Family Foundation
75 Garden Rd.
Scarsdale, NY 10583-2107

Established in 1993 in New York.
Donors: Shari L. Beckman; Joel S. Beckman.
Foundation type: Independent foundation.
Financial data (yr. ended 10/31/14): Assets,
$781,004 (M); gifts received, $984,117;
expenditures, $289,446; qualifying distributions,
$285,686; giving activities include $284,536 for 22
grants (high: $125,000; low: $100).
Fields of interest: Higher education; Nonprofits;
Diseases and conditions; Judaism.
Type of support: General support; Regranting.
Limitations: Applications not accepted. Giving
primarily in NY. No grants to individuals.
Application information: Unsolicited requests for
funds not accepted.
Trustees: Jacob Beckman; Joel S. Beckman; Shari
L. Beckman; Steven B. Beckman.
EIN: 137034350

5730
Beckwith Family Foundation
c/o Bessemer Trust
630 5th Ave., 34th Fl.
New York City, NY 10111
Application address: c/o John Trabucco, 2790
Mosside Blvd., Ste. 610, Monroeville, PA
15146-2743, tel.: (412) 374-1023

Established in 1999 in Pennsylvania.
Donor: Virginia P. Beckwith†.
Foundation type: Independent foundation.
Financial data (yr. ended 09/30/14): Assets,
$7,861,009 (M); expenditures, $437,412;
qualifying distributions, $385,751; giving activities
include $379,500 for 26 grants (high: $80,000; low:
low: $1,500).
Fields of interest: Arts and culture; Art museums;
Education; Diseases and conditions.

Limitations: Applications accepted. Giving primarily
in FL and PA. No grants to individuals.
Application information:
Initial approach: Proposal
Deadline(s): None
Trustee: G. Nicholas Beckwith III.
EIN: 311607888

5731
The Mary Taylor and Christopher C. Behrens Foundation, Inc.
303 Pondfield Rd.
Bronxville, NY 10708-4936

Established in 2005 in New York.
Donors: Mary Taylor Behrens; Christopher C.
Behrens.
Foundation type: Independent foundation.
Financial data (yr. ended 06/30/14): Assets,
$1,976,888 (M); gifts received, $1,201,901;
expenditures, $183,569; qualifying distributions,
$177,116; giving activities include $174,450 for 16
grants (high: $100,000; low: $50).
Fields of interest: Education; University education;
Diseases and conditions; Human services.
Type of support: Research.
Limitations: Applications not accepted. Giving
primarily in NY. No grants to individuals.
Application information: Unsolicited requests for
funds not accepted.
Officers and Directors: Mary Taylor Behrens, Pres.
and Director; Christopher C. Behrens, V.P. and
Treas. and Director; John D. Dadakis, Esq., Secy.
and Director.
EIN: 202271170

5732
The Beir Foundation
110 E. 59th St.
New York City, NY 10022-1306

Established in 1944 in New York.
Donor: Robert L. Beir.
Foundation type: Independent foundation.
Financial data (yr. ended 12/31/13): Assets,
$8,773,757 (M); expenditures, $313,310;
qualifying distributions, $229,706; giving activities
include $229,706 for 49 grants (high: $35,000;
low: $100).
Fields of interest: Education; Elementary and
secondary education; Higher education; Judaism;
Human services.
Limitations: Applications not accepted. Giving
primarily in the New York, NY, area. No grants to
individuals.
Application information: Contributes only to
pre-selected organizations.
Officers: Joan S. Beir, Pres.; Michael Katz, Secy.
Number of staff: 1 part-time professional.
EIN: 136084093

5733
Beitar Illit Advanced Talmud Project
17 Copperbeech Ln.
Lawrence, NY 11559-2628

Donors: Barry Simon; CSU Industries, Inc.; Jeffrey
Stewart; Rabbi and Mrs Oldak; Jeffrey Weissman.
Foundation type: Independent foundation.

Financial data (yr. ended 12/31/13): Assets,
$9,041 (M); gifts received, $158,448;
expenditures, $149,839; qualifying distributions,
$147,690; giving activities include $147,690 for 3
grants (high: $87,590; low: $11,950).
Fields of interest: Judaism.
International interests: Israel.
Limitations: Applications not accepted. Giving
primarily in Israel; some funding also in NY.
Application information: Unsolicited requests for
funds not accepted.
Trustees: Carol Weissman; Jeffrey Weissman;
Mordecai Weissman.
EIN: 113618915

5734
Jennifer & Thomas Bell Family Foundation
c/o Thomas Davidson, The Ayco Co. LP
321 Broadway
P.O. Box 860
Saratoga Springs, NY 12866-0860

Established in 2000 in Connecticut.
Donors: Thomas Bell; Jennifer Bell.
Foundation type: Independent foundation.
Financial data (yr. ended 12/31/13): Assets,
$1,668,836 (M); expenditures, $272,610;
qualifying distributions, $259,140; giving activities
include $259,140 for 24 grants (high: $60,000;
low: $100).
Fields of interest: Arts and culture; Education;
Elementary and secondary education; Christianity;
Human services.
Limitations: Applications not accepted. Giving
primarily in GA. No grants to individuals.
Application information: Unsolicited requests for
funds not accepted.
Directors: Jennifer Bell; Thomas Bell.
EIN: 061600450

5735
The Bender Family Foundation
111 Washington Ave.
Albany, NY 12210-2214 (518) 446-9638
FAX: (518) 446-9708; E-mail: jmahoney@cfcr.org;
Main URL: http://www.cfgcr.org/benderff
Grants List: http://www.cfgcr.org/benderff/
grantmaking.html

Established in 1997 in New York.
Donors: Matthew Bender IV; Matthew Bender
Charitable Lead Trust IV.
Foundation type: Independent foundation.
Financial data (yr. ended 12/31/13): Assets,
$2,376,899 (M); gifts received, $67,570;
expenditures, $216,280; qualifying distributions,
$178,500; giving activities include $178,500 for 36
grants (high: $20,000; low: $250).
Purpose and activities: Funding primarily to foster,
preserve, and fund the arts, culture, education,
history and environment of the New York State
Capital Region.
Fields of interest: Arts and culture; History;
Education; Environment; Natural resources; Youth
development.
Type of support: Capital campaigns; Capital and
infrastructure; Equipment; Program development;
Seed money.
Limitations: Applications accepted. Giving primarily
in Albany County, NY. No support for annual fund
drives. No grants to individuals.

Application information: See foundation web site for complete application guidelines.
Officers: Matthew Bender IV, Pres.; Phoebe P. Bender, V.P.
Board Members: M. Christian Bender; Jeffrey P. Bender.
EIN: 161526228

5736
The Bendit Family Foundation
111 8th Ave.
New York City, NY 10011

Established in 2007 in New York.
Donors: Charles R. Bendit; Karyn K. Bendit.
Foundation type: Independent foundation.
Financial data (yr. ended 12/31/13): Assets, $593,615 (M); expenditures, $347,960; qualifying distributions, $342,050; giving activities include $342,050 for 21 grants (high: $67,000; low: $500).
Fields of interest: Nonprofits; Judaism.
Type of support: Regranting.
Limitations: Applications not accepted. Giving primarily in NY. No grants to individuals.
Application information: Unsolicited requests for funds not accepted.
Trustees: Charles R. Bendit; Karyn K. Bendit.
EIN: 261576412

5737
The James Gordon Bennett Memorial Corporation
c/o Pamela Gubitosi
620 8th Ave.
New York City, NY 10018-1618

Established in 1919 in New York.
Foundation type: Independent foundation.
Financial data (yr. ended 12/31/13): Assets, $5,955,104 (M); expenditures, $286,589; qualifying distributions, $286,589; giving activities include $166,125 for grants, and $94,900 for 13 grants to individuals (high: $12,350; low: $2,750).
Purpose and activities: Direct aid limited to employees for ten years or more of a daily newspaper published in New York City, together with their immediate families; any surplus funds to be applied to scholarship aid to children of these persons.
Fields of interest: Higher education; Publishing.
Type of support: Student aid; Grants to individuals.
Limitations: Applications not accepted. Giving limited to employees (and their immediate families) of New York City daily newspapers. No grants for building or endowment funds, operating budgets, or special projects.
Application information: Unsolicited requests for funds not accepted.
Officers and Directors: Carolyn Lee, Chair.; Michael Ragano, Pres.; Pam Gupitosi, Secy.-Treas. and Director.
EIN: 136150414

5738
The Stefany and Simon Bergson Foundation
P.O. Box 695
Palisades, NY 10964-0695

Established in 1999 in New York.

Donors: Stefany Bergson; Simon Bergson; Manhattan Beer Distributors, LLC.
Foundation type: Independent foundation.
Financial data (yr. ended 12/31/13): Assets, $430,507 (M); gifts received, $234,780; expenditures, $346,468; qualifying distributions, $345,937; giving activities include $334,235 for 55 grants (high: $130,500; low: $10).
Purpose and activities: Giving primarily for the arts, education, Jewish organizations and temples, and human services.
Fields of interest: Arts and culture; Performing arts; Elementary and secondary education; Higher education; Nonprofits; Diseases and conditions; Judaism; Human services.
Type of support: Regranting.
Limitations: Applications not accepted. Giving primarily in NY. No grants to individuals.
Application information: Unsolicited requests for funds not accepted.
Trustees: Simon Bergson; Stefany Bergson.
EIN: 134077237

5739
Louis Berkowitz Family Foundation, Inc.
P.O. Box 840
East Setauket, NY 11733-1809 (631) 689-5985
Contact: Gail Hoefener, Pres. and Treas.

Established in 1983 in New York.
Donor: Louis Berkowitz†.
Foundation type: Independent foundation.
Financial data (yr. ended 12/31/13): Assets, $3,676,362 (M); expenditures, $187,036; qualifying distributions, $181,477; giving activities include $180,000 for 33 grants (high: $30,000; low: $250).
Purpose and activities: Giving primarily for hospitals and education; support also for Jewish organizations.
Fields of interest: Education; Health; Hospital care; Diseases and conditions; Cancers; Judaism.
Type of support: Equipment; Program development; Research.
Limitations: Applications accepted. Giving primarily in the metropolitan New York, NY, area. No grants to individuals.
Application information: Application form required.
  Initial approach: Request application form
  Copies of proposal: 1
  Deadline(s): None
Officers: Gail Hoeffner, Pres. and Treas.; Laurie Chaplin, V.P.; Karen Hoefener, V.P.; Lynn Schor, V.P.; Frederick Siegmund, Secy.
Number of staff: None.
EIN: 133190334

5740
The Bernheim Foundation Inc.
c/o Charles Bernheim
33 E. 70th St., Ste. 5E
New York City, NY 10021-4985

Established in 1955 in New York.
Donors: Charles A. Bernheim; Elinor K. Bernheim†; Leonard H. Bernheim, Jr.†; Stephanie H. Bernheim; Rachel O. Bernheim.
Foundation type: Independent foundation.
Financial data (yr. ended 12/31/13): Assets, $2,860,285 (M); gifts received, $326,172;

expenditures, $175,903; qualifying distributions, $173,159; giving activities include $171,422 for 95 grants (high: $10,000; low: $100).
Fields of interest: Arts and culture; Religion; Human services.
Type of support: General support; Continuing support; Capital campaigns.
Limitations: Applications not accepted. Giving primarily in New York, NY. No grants to individuals.
Application information: Unsolicited requests for funds not accepted.
Officers: Charles A. Bernheim, Pres.; Joshua Rubenstein, V.P. and Secy.; Stephanie H. Bernheim, V.P.
EIN: 136084144

5741
The Bernhill Fund
c/o Sacks Press & Lacher, PC
600 3rd Ave.
New York City, NY 10017-1901

Established in 1977 in New York.
Donor: The Bernhard Foundation, Inc.
Foundation type: Independent foundation.
Financial data (yr. ended 10/31/13): Assets, $1,216,877 (M); expenditures, $337,714; qualifying distributions, $325,580; giving activities include $325,580 for grants.
Purpose and activities: Grants to urban community organizations and service delivery projects; support also for institutions of particular interest to the trustees, including the fine and performing arts, higher and other education, the environment and ecology, wildlife and animal welfare, the homeless, hospices, and AIDS programs.
Fields of interest: Arts and culture; Performing arts; Museums; Education; Higher education; Natural resources; Domesticated animals; HIV/AIDS; Communication media; Public affairs; Human services.
Type of support: General support; Continuing support; Program development; Seed money.
Limitations: Applications not accepted. Giving primarily in New York, NY; some giving in CT and FL. No grants to individuals, or for annual campaigns, emergency funds, deficit financing, matching gifts, scholarships, fellowships, demonstration projects, publications, or conferences; no loans.
Application information: Contributes only to pre-selected organizations.
Officers: William L. Bernhard, Pres.; Catherine G. Cahill, V.P.
EIN: 132988599

5742
Bet Lev Foundation
c/o Baker Tilly Virchow Krause, LLP
1 Penn Plz.
New York City, NY 10119

Established in 2004 in Texas.
Donors: Holly B. Lev; Ann L. Bronfman†; Presence Marketing.
Foundation type: Independent foundation.
Financial data (yr. ended 12/31/13): Assets, $10,617,670 (M); gifts received, $1,089,939; expenditures, $611,431; qualifying distributions, $518,416; giving activities include $442,431 for 16 + grants (high: $113,000).

Fields of interest: Education; Community and economic development; Human services.
Type of support: General support.
Limitations: Applications not accepted. Giving in the U.S., with some emphasis on CA and CO. No grants to individuals.
Application information: Unsolicited requests for funds not accepted.
Directors: Steven Bookoff; Holly Lev; Yoav Lev.
EIN: 251905937

5743
Sol E. Betesh & Sons Foundation, Inc.
c/o Mitzi International
1 E. 33rd St., 10th Fl.
New York City, NY   10016-5011

Established in 1988 in New York.
Donors: Sol E. Betesh; Norma Betesh; Elliot Betesh; Michael Betesh; Steven Betesh; Baby Boom Consumer; Betgold; Steven's Baby Boom, Ltd.; Betgold International; Mitzi International.
Foundation type: Independent foundation.
Financial data (yr. ended 12/31/12): Assets, $29,515 (M); gifts received, $355,513; expenditures, $376,234; qualifying distributions, $376,020; giving activities include $376,020 for grants.
Purpose and activities: Giving primarily to yeshivas and other Jewish agencies and temples.
Fields of interest: Nonprofits; Judaism; Human services.
Type of support: Regranting.
Limitations: Applications not accepted. Giving primarily in New York City, with emphasis on Brooklyn, NY. No grants to individuals.
Application information: Contributes only to pre-selected organizations.
Officers: Sol E. Betesh, Pres.; Elliot Betesh, V.P.; Michael Betesh, V.P.; Norma Betesh, Secy.
EIN: 133479984

5744
Betts Family Foundation
313 W. 102nd St.
New York City, NY   10025-4942

Established in 1998 in New York.
Donor: Roland W. Betts.
Foundation type: Independent foundation.
Financial data (yr. ended 12/31/13): Assets, $267,768 (M); expenditures, $135,134; qualifying distributions, $126,865; giving activities include $115,590 for 10 grants (high: $45,000; low: $250).
Fields of interest: Arts and culture; Education; Human services.
Limitations: Applications not accepted. Giving primarily in CT, NY and TX. No grants to individuals.
Application information: Contributes only to pre-selected organizations.
Trustees: Jessica E. Betts; Lois P. Betts; Margaret W. Betts; Roland W. Betts.
EIN: 137152740

5745
The Big Wood Foundation
c/o Anchin
1375 Broadway
New York City, NY   10018-7001

Established in 1987 in Delaware.
Donors: Marjorie Stern; Michael Stern; Milton & Bernice Stern Foundation; The Stern Family 1997 Trust.
Foundation type: Independent foundation.
Financial data (yr. ended 12/31/13): Assets, $6,363,544 (M); gifts received, $278,468; expenditures, $797,707; qualifying distributions, $475,741; giving activities include $279,620 for 64 grants (high: $35,000; low: $100).
Fields of interest: Arts and culture; Education; Higher education; Human services; Child welfare.
Limitations: Applications not accepted. Giving in the U.S., with emphasis on New York, NY. No grants to individuals.
Application information: Contributes only to pre-selected organizations.
Officers: Michael Stern, Pres. and Treas.; Marjorie Stern, Secy.
Directors: Mark Stern; Ricki Stern.
EIN: 133440362

5746
The Bikuben Foundation New York, Inc.
36 W. 74th St.
New York City, NY   10023-2411
Contact: Irene Krarup
E-mail: bg@bikubenfonden.dk; Application address: c/o Matti Bekkevold, Bikuben Fonden, Fiolstraede 44, 1171 Kobenhaun K, Copenhagen, Denmark, tel.: (453) 377-9385; Danish language URL: http://www.bikubenfonden.dk

Established in 2003 in Unspecified.
Donor: Bikubenfonden.
Foundation type: Independent foundation.
Financial data (yr. ended 12/31/13): Assets, $17,592,717 (M); expenditures, $789,669; qualifying distributions, $180,208; giving activities include $175,050 for 38 grants (high: $7,150; low: $2,600).
Purpose and activities: Giving primarily to individuals involved in the arts to enable them to improve or enhance a literary, artistic, musical, scientific, or teaching skill or talent. The foundation also makes a condominium in New York City available to artists, writers, scholars, and researchers in connection with specific projects requiring the presence of the grantee in New York City.
Fields of interest: Arts and culture; Housing development.
Type of support: Student aid.
Limitations: Applications accepted. Giving primarily in NY.
Application information:
Initial approach: Letter
Deadline(s): June 15
Officers and Directors: Soeren Kaare-Andersen, Pres. and Director; Irene Krarup, V.P. and Treas. and Director; Peter Hoejland, Secy. and Director.
EIN: 582680849

5747
The W. Richard Bingham and Winifred W. Bingham Foundation
c/o The Ayco Co., LP
P.O. Box 860
Saratoga Springs, NY   12866-0860

Established in 1999 in California.

Donors: Winifred W. Bingham; W. Richard Bingham.
Foundation type: Independent foundation.
Financial data (yr. ended 12/31/13): Assets, $3,059,033 (M); gifts received, $101,935; expenditures, $237,586; qualifying distributions, $224,177; giving activities include $224,177 for 14 grants (high: $100,000; low: $250).
Fields of interest: Ballet; Education; Science; Community and economic development; Human services.
Limitations: Applications not accepted. Giving primarily in CA. No grants to individuals.
Application information: Unsolicited requests for funds not accepted.
Trustee: Winifred W. Bingham.
EIN: 943346733

5748
Birchas Mordechai Charitable Foundation
c/o Bracha Weits
614 Ave. J
Brooklyn, NY   11230-3504

Established in 2008 in New York.
Donors: Abraham Klein; Smithtown Healthcare; Bracha Weits; Sara Dina Klein.
Foundation type: Independent foundation.
Financial data (yr. ended 12/31/13): Assets, $1,549,150 (M); gifts received, $250,000; expenditures, $295,860; qualifying distributions, $292,210; giving activities include $289,360 for 33 grants (high: $160,000; low: $100).
Fields of interest: Judaism.
Limitations: Applications not accepted. Giving primarily in Brooklyn, NY. No grants to individuals.
Application information: Contributes only to pre-selected organizations.
Trustees: Bracha Weits; Mordechai Weits.
EIN: 262294829

5749
The Birchrock Foundation
c/o The Ayco Co., LP - NTG
P.O. Box 15014
Albany, NY   12212-5014
Application address: c/o Rebecca Maxwell, 899 N. Nobleboro Rd., Waldoboro, ME 04572

Established in 1998 in Massachusetts.
Donor: Lawrence J. Lasser.
Foundation type: Independent foundation.
Financial data (yr. ended 12/31/13): Assets, $4,754,012 (M); expenditures, $429,698; qualifying distributions, $368,983; giving activities include $368,983 for 45 grants (high: $50,000; low: $5).
Purpose and activities: Giving for art museums, and private foundations, as well as aid to indigent persons who are receiving less than $500 per person through the "In a Pinch Fund" program.
Fields of interest: Art museums; Foundations; Low-income and poor people.
Type of support: General support; Grants to individuals.
Limitations: Applications accepted. Giving primarily in MA and ME.
Application information: Application form required.
Initial approach: Completed application form
Deadline(s): None

Officers: Ethan Lasser, Mgr.; Lawrence J. Lasser, Mgr.; Michelle Lasser, Mgr.
EIN: 043424527

5750
Adelaide C. Bird University of Maine Trust
Church St. Sta.
P.O. Box 1297
New York City, NY   10008-1297

Foundation type: Independent foundation.
Financial data (yr. ended 12/31/14): Assets, $4,609,137 (M); expenditures, $278,542; qualifying distributions, $244,597; giving activities include $218,259 for 4 grants (high: $109,130; low: $36,376).
Fields of interest: Education; Higher education.
Limitations: Applications not accepted. Giving primarily in ME.
Application information: Unsolicited requests for funds not accepted.
Trustee: Deutsche Bank Trust Co., N.A.
EIN: 136579662

5751
Egon & Telsi Birnbaum Foundation
1721 50th St.
Brooklyn, NY   11204-1259

Donors: Egon Birnbaum; Telsi Birnbaum.
Foundation type: Independent foundation.
Financial data (yr. ended 09/30/13): Assets, $17,857 (M); gifts received, $278,382; expenditures, $266,761; qualifying distributions, $266,761; giving activities include $266,673 for 21 + grants (high: $78,580).
Fields of interest: Judaism.
Limitations: Applications not accepted. Giving primarily in Lakewood, NJ, and Brooklyn, NY. No grants to individuals.
Application information: Unsolicited requests for funds not accepted.
Officers: Egon Birnbaum, Mgr.; Telsi Birnbaum, Mgr.
EIN: 112678412

5752
Milton and Sylvia Birnbaum Foundation
1429 54th St.
Brooklyn, NY   11219-4228

Established in 2002 in New York.
Donors: Milton Birnbaum; Sylvia Birnbaum.
Foundation type: Independent foundation.
Financial data (yr. ended 03/31/13): Assets, $125,935 (M); expenditures, $192,370; qualifying distributions, $192,370; giving activities include $190,960 for 15 grants (high: $100,000; low: $100).
Fields of interest: Judaism.
Limitations: Applications not accepted. Giving primarily in Brooklyn, NY. No grants to individuals.
Application information: Contributes only to pre-selected organizations.
Trustee: Irwin Birnbaum.
Directors: Milton Birnbaum; Sylvia Birnbaum.
EIN: 306026229

5753
Laszlo Bito and Olivia Carino Foundation Inc.
c/o Israeloff Trattner
450 7th Ave., Ste. 2701
New York City, NY   10123

Established in 2002 in New York.
Donors: Olivia Carino; Laszlo Bito.
Foundation type: Independent foundation.
Financial data (yr. ended 12/31/13): Assets, $4,743,944 (M); expenditures, $380,037; qualifying distributions, $368,700; giving activities include $368,700 for 6 grants (high: $125,000; low: $500).
Fields of interest: Human services.
International interests: Hungary.
Limitations: Applications not accepted. Giving primarily in New York, NY, and Budapest, Hungary. No grants to individuals.
Application information: Contributes only to pre-selected organizations.
Officer and Directors: Laszlo Bito, Pres. and Director; Olivia Carino.
EIN: 223863244

5754
Harry S. Black & Allon Fuller Fund
c/o U.S. Trust
1 Bryant Park, NY1-100-28-05
New York City, NY   10036-6715   (646) 855-1011
Contact: Christine O'Donnell
Main URL: https://www.bankofamerica.com/philanthropic/grantmaking.go

Established in 1930 in New York.
Donor: Harry S. Black.
Foundation type: Independent foundation.
Financial data (yr. ended 12/31/14): Assets, $4,776,529; expenditures, $261,442; qualifying distributions, $218,905.
Purpose and activities: Grantmaking is focused on the following areas: 1) Health Care: The Fund supports access to health care, health education, and health policy analysis and advocacy; emphasis will be placed on programs serving low-income communities, and 2) Physical Disabilities: The Fund supports access programs for physically disabled individuals, disability policy analysis and advocacy, workforce development programs, and programs that improve quality of life for the disabled.
Fields of interest: Health; Diseases and conditions; People with physical disabilities.
Type of support: General support; Program development.
Limitations: Giving limited to organizations located in and serving Chicago, IL, and New York, NY. No grants to individuals, or for endowment funds, capital campaigns or research.
Publications: Application guidelines.
Application information: Application guidelines available on Fund web site.
   Initial approach: Online via Fund web site
   Deadline(s): July 31
   Final notification: Dec. 31
Trustee: Bank of America, N.A.
Number of staff: 1 part-time professional; 1 part-time support.
EIN: 136072632

5755
John N. Blackman, Sr. Foundation
c/o Schain Leifer Guralnick
10 E. 40th St., Ste. 2710
New York City, NY   10016-0348   (212) 679-0380
Contact: Howard Schain, Pres.

Established in 1988 in New York.
Donors: Mutual Marine Office, Inc.; John Blackman; Mark Blackman.
Foundation type: Independent foundation.
Financial data (yr. ended 08/31/13): Assets, $1,536,199 (M); gifts received, $200,000; expenditures, $276,056; qualifying distributions, $212,500; giving activities include $212,500 for 51 grants (high: $10,000; low: $2,000).
Purpose and activities: Giving primarily for health and human services.
Fields of interest: Arts and culture; Domesticated animals; Diseases and conditions; Religion; Human services; Youth development.
Limitations: Applications accepted. Giving primarily in NY. No grants to individuals.
Application information: Application form required.
   Initial approach: Letter
   Deadline(s): None
Officer: Howard Schain, Pres.
Trustees: John N. Blackman, Jr.; Mark W. Blackman.
EIN: 222938619

5756
Nancy & Robert S. Blank Foundation
c/o Whitcom Partners
712 5th Ave., 45th Fl.
New York City, NY   10019-4108

Established in 1993 in Pennsylvania.
Donors: Robert S. Blank; Nancy L. Blank; Matthew S. Blank; Samuel A. Blank; Wendy Blank Chaikin.
Foundation type: Independent foundation.
Financial data (yr. ended 08/31/14): Assets, $2,045,856 (M); gifts received, $100,000; expenditures, $315,137; qualifying distributions, $313,310; giving activities include $313,310 for 51 grants (high: $60,500; low: $100).
Purpose and activities: Giving primarily for Jewish federated giving programs and education.
Fields of interest: Higher education; University education; Nonprofits; Judaism; Human services; Jewish people.
Type of support: General support; Regranting.
Limitations: Applications not accepted. Giving primarily in NY. No grants to individuals.
Application information: Unsolicited requests for funds not accepted.
Officers: Robert S. Blank, Pres.; Nancy L. Blank, V.P.
EIN: 232738179

5757
The Blinken Foundation Inc.
c/o Allison Blinken
630 Park Ave., Apt. 11B
New York City, NY   10065

Established in 1965 in New York.
Donors: Alan J. Blinken; Donald M. Blinken; Milt Blinken†; Robert J. Blinken; Blinken Joint Account.
Foundation type: Independent foundation.
Financial data (yr. ended 12/31/13): Assets, $507,005 (M); expenditures, $376,582; qualifying

distributions, $371,900; giving activities include $368,900 for 47 grants (high: $56,000; low: $250).
Fields of interest: Arts and culture; Performing arts; Theater; Orchestral music; Education; Hospital care; Family planning; Biology; Judaism.
International interests: Hungary.
Type of support: General support; Annual campaigns; Fellowships.
Limitations: Applications not accepted. Giving primarily in New York, NY. No grants to individuals.
Application information: Unsolicited requests for funds not accepted.
Officer: Donald M. Blinken, Pres. and Treas.
Directors: Alan J. Blinken; Allison Blinken.
EIN: 136190153

5758
Freya & Richard Block Family Foundation
c/o Richard Block
111 Central Park N., Apt. PHA
New York City, NY 10026-4281

Established in 1999 in New York.
Donors: Richard H. Block; Freya Block.
Foundation type: Independent foundation.
Financial data (yr. ended 07/31/14): Assets, $1,701,362; expenditures, $298,019; qualifying distributions, $279,714.
Fields of interest: Education; Community and economic development; Human services.
Limitations: Applications not accepted. Giving primarily in NY. No grants to individuals.
Application information: Unsolicited requests for funds not accepted.
Officer: Nadia Block, Mgr.
Directors: Freya Block; Richard H. Block.
EIN: 134092442

5759
The Block Family Foundation, Inc.
c/o Anchin, Block and Anchin, LLP
1375 Broadway
New York City, NY 10018
Contact: James A. Block, Pres.

Established in 1975 in New Jersey.
Donors: Barbara Block; James A. Block.
Foundation type: Independent foundation.
Financial data (yr. ended 06/30/14): Assets, $19,628 (M); gifts received, $195,000; expenditures, $182,807; qualifying distributions, $180,903; giving activities include $179,000 for 6 grants (high: $60,000; low: $1,000).
Purpose and activities: Giving primarily for higher education and cultural programs; support also for a Jewish welfare fund.
Fields of interest: Performing arts; Art museums; University education; Nonprofits; Hospital care; Camps.
Type of support: Regranting.
Limitations: Applications accepted. Giving primarily in New York, NY.
Application information:
Initial approach: Letter
Deadline(s): None
Officers: James A. Block, Pres.; Barbara Block, Exec. V.P.; Peter M. Block, V.P.; Valerie M. Block, V.P.; Alexis Romay, V.P.; William Bush, Secy.-Treas.
EIN: 510138517

5760
Margaret Kendrick Blodgett Foundation
c/o Fiduciary Trust Co. International
600 5th Ave.
New York City, NY 10020-2302

Established in 1964 in New York.
Donor: Mrs. Thomas H. Blodgett‡.
Foundation type: Independent foundation.
Financial data (yr. ended 12/31/14): Assets, $956,698 (M); expenditures, $222,798; qualifying distributions, $215,799; giving activities include $213,000 for 8 grants (high: $100,000; low: $3,000).
Fields of interest: Education; Higher education; Domesticated animals; Philanthropy.
Type of support: General support.
Limitations: Applications not accepted. Giving limited to MA. No grants to individuals.
Application information: Unsolicited requests for funds not accepted.
Officers and Directors: Elizabeth H. Richardson, Chair.; Dr. Thomas L. Hall, Vice-Chair. and Director; Dr. John K. Hall; Adam A. Reeves; Anne K. Richardson; Margaret H. Whitfield.
EIN: 136144050

5761
The Bloomberg Sisters Foundation
c/o Geller & Co., LLC
909 3rd Ave., 16th Fl.
New York City, NY 10022-4797
Michael R. Bloomberg's Giving Pledge
Profile: http://glasspockets.org/
philanthropy-in-focus/eye-on-the-giving-pledge/
profiles/bloomberg

Established in 1998 in New York.
Donor: Michael R. Bloomberg.
Foundation type: Independent foundation.
Financial data (yr. ended 12/31/13): Assets, $4,490,497 (M); expenditures, $346,829; qualifying distributions, $330,520; giving activities include $330,000 for 25 grants (high: $30,000; low: $5,000).
Fields of interest: Animal welfare; Human services; Child welfare.
Type of support: General support.
Limitations: Applications not accepted. Giving primarily in NY; with some giving in OR. No grants to individuals.
Application information: Contributes only to pre-selected organizations.
Trustees: Emma Bloomberg; Georgina Bloomberg; Susan E.B. Bloomberg; Patricia Harris.
EIN: 137151342

5762
Blue Hill Road Foundation Inc.
c/o Leshkowitz Co.
270 Madison Ave.
New York City, NY 10016-0602

Established in 1994 in New York.
Donors: Fred Lee Barber Co., Inc.; Fred Lee Barber‡; David Barber.
Foundation type: Company-sponsored foundation.
Financial data (yr. ended 12/31/13): Assets, $5,389,698 (M); gifts received, $1,786,572; expenditures, $284,482; qualifying distributions,

$279,478; giving activities include $279,000 for grants.
Purpose and activities: Giving primarily for education and hospitals.
Limitations: Applications not accepted. Giving primarily in NY. No grants to individuals.
Application information: Unsolicited requests for funds not accepted.
Officers: David Barber, Secy.; Daniel Barber, Treas.
EIN: 133799422

5763
Blue Ridge Foundation, Inc.
c/o BCRS Associates LLC
77 Water St, 9th Fl.
New York City, NY 10005-4414

Established in 1985 in New York.
Donors: Walter Scheuer; Marcelle Halpern; Susan Scheuer 1993 Charitable Trust; David Scheuer 1993 Charitable Trust; Judith Scheuer 1993 Charitable Trust.
Foundation type: Independent foundation.
Financial data (yr. ended 10/31/13): Assets, $542,202 (M); expenditures, $272,205; qualifying distributions, $262,902; giving activities include $259,100 for 8 grants (high: $100,000; low: $6,600).
Purpose and activities: Giving primarily for arts and culture, and for charitable endowment and gift funds.
Fields of interest: Arts and culture; Performing arts; Dance; Education; Higher education; Child welfare.
Limitations: Applications not accepted. Giving primarily in New York, NY; some giving in MA and Swarthmore, PA. No grants to individuals.
Application information: Contributes only to pre-selected organizations.
Officers and Directors: Marge Scheuer, Pres. and Director; Judith Scheuer, Secy. and Director; Jeffrey J. Scheuer, Treas. and Director; Susan Scheuer.
EIN: 133282554

5764
Blue Star Foundation, Inc.
c/o Cronin, CPA
401 Columbus Ave., Ste. 100
Valhalla, NY 10595-1349

Established in 2005 in New York.
Donor: David Grin.
Foundation type: Operating foundation.
Financial data (yr. ended 06/30/13): Assets, $0 (M); gifts received, $37,000; expenditures, $210,923; qualifying distributions, $210,000; giving activities include $210,000 for 2 grants (high: $190,000; low: $20,000).
Fields of interest: Elementary and secondary education; Judaism.
Limitations: Applications not accepted. Giving primarily in NY.
Application information: Contributes only to pre-selected organizations.
Officers: David Grin, Pres.; Eugene Grin, Secy.
EIN: 201450579

5765
The Norman and Julia Bobrow Family Foundation
c/o Weisberg, Mole, Krantz & Goldfarb, LLP
185 Crossways Park Dr.
Woodbury, NY 11797-2040

Established in 1997 in New York.
Donors: Julia Bobrow; Norman Bobrow.
Foundation type: Independent foundation.
Financial data (yr. ended 12/31/13): Assets,
$2,110,108 (M); gifts received, $600,745;
expenditures, $400,588; qualifying distributions,
$398,763; giving activities include $398,763 for 45
grants (high: $100,018; low: $338).
Purpose and activities: Giving primarily for Jewish
organizations.
Fields of interest: Judaism; Human services; Child
welfare.
Type of support: Capital campaigns; Emergency
funds; Scholarships.
Limitations: Applications not accepted. Giving
primarily in New York, NY. No grants to individuals.
Application information: Contributes only to
pre-selected organizations.
Trustees: Julia Bobrow; Norman Bobrow.
Number of staff: None.
EIN: 137111547

5766
The Paul and Irene Bogoni Operating Foundation
340 Riverside Dr.
New York City, NY 10025-3423

Donors: Paul Bogoni; Irene Bogoni.
Foundation type: Operating foundation.
Financial data (yr. ended 12/31/13): Assets,
$288,161 (M); gifts received, $60,000;
expenditures, $216,578; qualifying distributions,
$216,578; giving activities include $157,217 for 7
grants (high: $100,000; low: $300).
Fields of interest: Education; Health; Catholicism.
Limitations: Applications not accepted. No grants to
individuals.
Application information: Unsolicited requests for
funds not accepted.
Officers and Directors: Paul Bogoni, Pres.; Irene
Bogoni, V.P. and Secy.; Joan M. Fisher, Treas. and
Director; Michael Cohen, Esq.
EIN: 161635037

5767
Albert C. Bostwick Foundation
c/o Bessemer Trust
630 5th Ave., 34th Fl.
New York City, NY 10111-0100 (516) 508-9623
Contact: Albert C. Bostwick Jr., Tr.

Established in 1958 in New York.
Donor: Albert C. Bostwick†.
Foundation type: Independent foundation.
Financial data (yr. ended 12/31/14): Assets,
$3,835,320 (M); expenditures, $192,910;
qualifying distributions, $184,504; giving activities
include $176,000 for 9 grants (high: $43,000; low:
$5,000).
Fields of interest: University education; Veterinary
medicine; Health; Hospital care; Diseases and
conditions; Human services.

Type of support: Research; Research and
evaluation.
Limitations: Applications accepted. Giving primarily
in NY. No grants to individuals.
Application information: Application form required.
Initial approach: Letter
Deadline(s): None
Board meeting date(s): Annually
Trustees: Albert C. Bostwick, Jr.; Andrew G.C. Sage
II; Michael R. Parker.
EIN: 116003740

5768
Leona Bothmer Foundation
c/o Sullivan & Worcester, LLP
1633 Broadway
New York City, NY 10019

Established in 2007 in Connecticut.
Donor: Leona Bothmer†.
Foundation type: Independent foundation.
Financial data (yr. ended 12/31/14): Assets,
$5,482,376 (M); expenditures, $416,687;
qualifying distributions, $277,500; giving activities
include $277,500 for 13 grants (high: $30,000;
low: $2,500).
Fields of interest: Animal welfare; Human services.
Limitations: Applications not accepted. Giving
primarily in CT, Washington, D.C., and NY. No grants
to individuals.
Application information: Contributes only to
pre-selected organizations.
Trustee: Constantine P. Ralli.
EIN: 061816606

5769
The Boustead Family Foundation Inc.
540 N. State Rd.
Briarcliff Manor, NY 10510-1598

Established in 1998 in New Jersey.
Foundation type: Independent foundation.
Financial data (yr. ended 12/31/13): Assets,
$3,933,742 (M); expenditures, $226,850;
qualifying distributions, $171,247; giving activities
include $171,000 for 23 grants (high: $28,000;
low: $1,000).
Fields of interest: Higher education; Diseases and
conditions; Fire prevention and control;
Protestantism.
Type of support: General support.
Limitations: Applications not accepted. Giving
primarily in NJ, NY, and PA. No grants to individuals.
Application information: Contributes only to
pre-selected organizations.
Officers: Douglas Boustead, Pres.; Michael
Boustead, Secy.-Treas.
EIN: 522097838

5770
The Bovin Family Foundation
c/o Clearly, Gottlieb, Steen & Hamilton
1 Liberty Plz.
New York City, NY 10006-1404

Established in 2000 in New York.
Donors: Denis A. Bovin; Steven M. Loeb.
Foundation type: Independent foundation.
Financial data (yr. ended 12/31/13): Assets,
$7,106 (M); gifts received, $264,525;

expenditures, $293,958; qualifying distributions,
$293,946; giving activities include $289,433 for 49
grants (high: $100,000; low: $25).
Fields of interest: Museums; Higher education;
Foundations; Hospital care; Judaism; Human
services.
Type of support: Research.
Limitations: Applications not accepted. Giving
primarily in MA and NY; some funding also in NJ. No
grants to individuals.
Application information: Contributes only to
pre-selected organizations.
Trustees: Denis A. Bovin; Steven M. Loeb.
EIN: 134107990

5771
The Box of Rain Foundation
c/o Amiel Peretz
17 Mallard Lake Rd.
Pound Ridge, NY 10576-2020

Established in 2001 in New York.
Donor: Amiel M. Peretz.
Foundation type: Independent foundation.
Financial data (yr. ended 11/30/14): Assets,
$1,397,797; expenditures, $180,829; qualifying
distributions, $171,988.
Fields of interest: Education; Higher education;
Hospital care; Human services; Child welfare.
Type of support: General support.
Limitations: Applications not accepted. Giving
primarily in NY. No grants to individuals.
Application information: Unsolicited requests for
funds not accepted.
Trustees: Amiel M. Peretz; Dylan M. Peretz; Michelle
Young Peretz; Taylor M. Peretz.
EIN: 134157443

5772
The Boxer Foundation
66 Commack Rd., Ste. 201
Commack, NY 11725-3489

Established in 1985 in New York.
Donor: Leonard Boxer.
Foundation type: Independent foundation.
Financial data (yr. ended 11/30/14): Assets,
$6,672,782 (M); expenditures, $286,453;
qualifying distributions, $234,129; giving activities
include $206,742 for 57 grants (high: $30,000;
low: $50).
Purpose and activities: Funding primarily for
hospitals and health care, and for Jewish agencies
and temples.
Fields of interest: Arts and culture; Education;
Higher education; Hospital care; Diseases and
conditions; Alzheimer's disease; Judaism; Human
services.
Type of support: General support.
Limitations: Applications not accepted. Giving
primarily in the greater metropolitan New York, NY,
area, including Long Island. No grants to individuals.
Application information: Contributes only to
pre-selected organizations.
Officer: Steven Boxer, Mgr.
EIN: 133345823

5773
The Boyer-Snyder Family Foundation
c/o Phoebe C. Boyer
333 Central Park W., Ste. 86
New York City, NY 10025-7105

Donors: Todd R. Snyder 2010 Charitable Lead; Todd R. Snyder; Todd R. Snyder 2013 Charitable Lead; Todd R. Snyder 2011 Charitable Lead.
Foundation type: Independent foundation.
Financial data (yr. ended 12/31/13): Assets, $1,879,962 (M); gifts received, $310,422; expenditures, $275,732; qualifying distributions, $275,732; giving activities include $260,574 for 19 grants (high: $130,000; low: $100).
Fields of interest: Education; Community and economic development; Human services.
Limitations: Applications not accepted. Giving primarily in CT and New York, NY.
Application information: Unsolicited requests for funds not accepted.
Officers: Phoebe C. Boyer, Pres.; Todd R. Snyder, Secy.-Treas.
EIN: 274218205

5774
The John Brademas Foundation
53 Washington Sq. S., 3rd Fl.
New York City, NY 10012-1098

Established in 1993 in New York.
Donor: John Brademas.
Foundation type: Independent foundation.
Financial data (yr. ended 12/31/13): Assets, $2,635,432 (M); expenditures, $275,000; qualifying distributions, $275,000; giving activities include $275,000 for 3 grants (high: $200,000; low: $25,000).
Fields of interest: Education; University education; Human services.
Type of support: General support; Scholarships.
Limitations: Applications not accepted. Giving primarily in NY. No grants to individuals.
Application information: Unsolicited requests for funds not accepted.
Trustees: David A. Berenson; John Brademas; Michelle O'Connor.
EIN: 133708587

5775
Bradley Family Charitable Foundation Trust
107 Brewery Rd.
New City, NY 10956-6115

Established in 2006 in New York.
Donors: Camille Cosby; William Cosby, Jr.; Edward R. Bradley, Jr.†
Foundation type: Independent foundation.
Financial data (yr. ended 12/31/13): Assets, $4,084,391 (M); expenditures, $217,596; qualifying distributions, $185,385; giving activities include $185,000 for 13 grants (high: $35,000; low: $1,000).
Fields of interest: Arts and culture.
Limitations: Applications not accepted. Giving primarily in NY.
Application information: Unsolicited requests for funds not accepted.

Trustees: Patricia Blanchet; Ronald Gault; Gary A. Jakalow.
EIN: 137489040

5776
The Brand Foundation of New York, Inc.
(formerly The Martha and Regina Brand Foundation, Inc.)
c/o Mel Ginsberg, CPA
747 3rd Ave., 3rd Fl.
New York City, NY 10017-2810

Established in 1962 in New York.
Donors: Martha Brand†; Marjorie D. Kogan.
Foundation type: Independent foundation.
Financial data (yr. ended 12/31/13): Assets, $1,073,209 (M); expenditures, $202,313; qualifying distributions, $193,532; giving activities include $184,210 for 24 grants (high: $25,600; low: $500).
Purpose and activities: Giving primarily for arts and culture, higher education, human services, Jewish agencies and temples, as well as for other religious purposes.
Fields of interest: Arts and culture; Theater; Higher education; Animal welfare; Nonprofits; Judaism; Human services.
Type of support: Regranting.
Limitations: Applications not accepted. Giving primarily in CA, Washington, DC, NY, and SC. No grants to individuals.
Application information: Contributes only to pre-selected organizations.
Officers: Barton H. Kogan, Pres. and Secy.; Michael S. Kogan, V.P. and Treas.
Director: Fr. Vincent Rigdon.
EIN: 136159106

5777
Barbara & Gary Brandt Family Foundation
529 5th Ave.
New York City, NY 10017
Contact: Citrin Cooperman

Foundation type: Independent foundation.
Financial data (yr. ended 12/31/13): Assets, $4,070,184 (M); expenditures, $227,747; qualifying distributions, $169,042; giving activities include $156,575 for 34 grants (high: $30,000; low: $200).
Fields of interest: Arts and culture; Education; Nonprofits; Public affairs; Judaism; Youth development.
Type of support: General support; Regranting.
Limitations: Applications not accepted. Giving primarily in New York, NY.
Application information: Unsolicited requests for funds not accepted.
Trustees: Barbara Brandt; Gary Brandt.
EIN: 261396548

5778
Norbert & Henry Bratt Charitable Trust
4309 Broadway
New York City, NY 10033-3729

Established in 2007 in New York.
Donor: Henry Bratt Trust.
Foundation type: Independent foundation.

Financial data (yr. ended 12/31/12): Assets, $4,709,185 (M); expenditures, $391,463; qualifying distributions, $374,850; giving activities include $347,100 for 36 grants (high: $62,300; low: $500).
Fields of interest: Education; Nonprofits; Judaism; Child welfare.
Type of support: Regranting.
Limitations: Applications not accepted. Giving primarily in NY. No grants to individuals.
Application information: Contributes only to pre-selected organizations.
Trustees: Bruce Miller; Fred Zilker.
EIN: 016253830

5779
Simon Dina & Henry Bratt Charitable Trust
P.O. Box 9364
Bardonia, NY 10954-9364
Contact: David Smith

Established in 2006 in New York.
Donor: Ralph Shoiock, CPA.
Foundation type: Operating foundation.
Financial data (yr. ended 12/31/13): Assets, $4,584,268 (M); expenditures, $733,211; qualifying distributions, $345,000; giving activities include $345,000 for 3 grants (high: $250,000; low: $20,000).
Fields of interest: Judaism; People with disabilities.
Limitations: Applications accepted. Giving primarily in NY. No grants to individuals.
Application information:
Initial approach: Proposal
Deadline(s): None
EIN: 207162614

5780
Henry & Wendy Breck Foundation
c/o CBIZ
1065 Avenue of the Americas, 10th Fl.
New York City, NY 10018-0772

Established in 1993 in New York.
Donor: Henry Breck.
Foundation type: Independent foundation.
Financial data (yr. ended 12/31/14): Assets, $822,702; expenditures, $261,671; qualifying distributions, $257,040.
Fields of interest: Education; Religion; Human services.
Limitations: Applications not accepted. Giving primarily in New York, NY. No grants to individuals.
Application information: Unsolicited requests for funds not accepted.
Officers: Henry Breck, Pres. and Treas.; Wendy Breck, V.P. and Secy.
Director: Christopher Breck.
EIN: 133669369

5781
The Brenner Family Foundation
919 3rd Ave., 24th Fl.
New York City, NY 10022-3902

Established in 2005 in New York.
Foundation type: Independent foundation.
Financial data (yr. ended 12/31/13): Assets, $3,925,762 (M); expenditures, $545,559; qualifying distributions, $480,844; giving activities

include $411,661 for 36 grants (high: $89,280; low: $1,000).
Fields of interest: Arts and culture; Education; Human rights; Human services.
Limitations: Applications not accepted. No grants to individuals.
Application information: Unsolicited requests for funds not accepted.
Officers: Kim E. Baptiste, Pres. and Secy.; Michele C. Tocci, V.P.; Leslie J. Fishman, Treas.; Pamela Baptiste, Exec. Dir.
EIN: 571217214

5782
The Briar Foundation
32 Bonnie Briar Ln.
Larchmont, NY 10538-1349

Established in 2010 in New York.
Donor: Carol J. Loomis.
Foundation type: Independent foundation.
Financial data (yr. ended 12/31/13): Assets, $6,114,072 (M); expenditures, $350,238; qualifying distributions, $350,238; giving activities include $350,092 for 56 grants (high: $20,000; low: $100).
Fields of interest: Health; Human services.
Limitations: Applications not accepted. Giving primarily in NY.
Application information: Unsolicited requests for funds not accepted.
Trustees: Barbara Loomis Liptack; Thomas Liptack; Carol Loomis; John Loomis; Mark Loomis; Stephanie Loomis.
EIN: 356829452

5783
The Bridgewater Fund, Inc.
40 5th Ave.
New York City, NY 10011-8843
Contact: Paul Kaplan

Donors: Ursula Lerse; Reginald Fullerton; Charles A. Rivkin; Paul J. Sperry; Paul D. Kaplan; Karl Zerfoss.
Foundation type: Independent foundation.
Financial data (yr. ended 11/30/14): Assets, $897,147 (M); gifts received, $130,628; expenditures, $193,798; qualifying distributions, $197,000; giving activities include $197,000 for 81 grants (high: $30,000; low: $100).
Fields of interest: Arts and culture; Education; Human services.
Type of support: General support.
Limitations: Applications not accepted. Giving primarily in NY. No grants to individuals.
Application information: Contributes only to pre-selected organizations.
Officers: Paul D. Kaplan, Pres.; David Kaplan, V.P.; Katherine Kaplan, V.P.
EIN: 237442465

5784
The Peter and Devon Briger Foundation II
c/o BCRS Associates, LLC
77 Water St., 9th Fl.
New York City, NY 10005-4414

Established in 2007 in Delaware.
Donor: Peter L. Briger.
Foundation type: Independent foundation.

Financial data (yr. ended 12/31/13): Assets, $4,103,984 (M); gifts received, $389,210; expenditures, $256,121; qualifying distributions, $253,921; giving activities include $225,000 for 2 grants (high: $200,000; low: $25,000).
Fields of interest: Arts and culture; Museums; Education; Specialty hospital care; Diseases and conditions; Child welfare.
Type of support: Research; Research and evaluation.
Limitations: Applications not accepted. Giving primarily in NJ and New York, NY. No grants to individuals.
Application information: Contributes only to pre-selected organizations.
Directors: Devon Briger; Peter L. Briger.
EIN: 261586986

5785
Brillo-Sonnino Family Foundation
350 West Broadway
New York City, NY 10013
Contact: Mark D. Sonnino, Tr.

Established in 2006 in New York.
Donors: Mark D. Sonnino; Lyn Brillo.
Foundation type: Operating foundation.
Financial data (yr. ended 02/28/15): Assets, $6,303,462 (M); expenditures, $415,190; qualifying distributions, $333,026; giving activities include $332,776 for 27 grants (high: $200,000; low: $100).
Fields of interest: Education; Undergraduate education; Christianity; Human services; Family services.
Limitations: Applications not accepted. Giving primarily in CA and NY. No grants to individuals.
Application information: Contributes only to pre-selected organizations.
Trustee: Lyn Brillo; Mark D. Sonnino; Nicholas Mamary.
EIN: 204463571

5786
Earl W. & Hildagunda A. Brinkman Private Charitable Foundation
3392 Buffalo Rd.
Rochester, NY 14624-1121   (585) 247-1911

Foundation type: Independent foundation.
Financial data (yr. ended 09/30/14): Assets, $3,928,234; expenditures, $239,801; qualifying distributions, $180,511.
Fields of interest: Education; University education; Hospital care; Human services.
Limitations: Applications accepted. Giving primarily in NY, with some giving in CT.
Application information: Application form required.
  Initial approach: Letter
  Deadline(s): None
Trustees: Christina Rae Brinkman; Robert J. Brinkman; Michelle J. Carlquist; Danielle K. Hawthorne; Eleanor Hawthorne; Kevin S. Hawthorne; Andrew J. Laniak.
EIN: 223038088

5787
Carolyn S. Brody Family Foundation
c/o BCRS Associates, LLC
77 Water St., 9th Fl.
New York City, NY 10005-3701

Established in 2007 in New York.
Donor: Carolyn Schwenker Brody.
Foundation type: Independent foundation.
Financial data (yr. ended 12/31/14): Assets, $18,590 (M); gifts received, $135,000; expenditures, $144,000; qualifying distributions, $144,000; giving activities include $143,050 for 14 grants (high: $50,000; low: $250).
Fields of interest: Arts and culture; Education; Human services.
Limitations: Applications not accepted. Giving primarily in Washington, DC; some giving in New York, OH and VA. No grants to individuals.
Application information: Unsolicited requests for funds not accepted.
Trustee: Carolyn Schwenker Brody.
EIN: 651320240

5788
Brooklyn Benevolent Society
57 Willoughby St.
Brooklyn, NY 11201-5290
Contact: Cornelius A. Heaney, Secy.

Established in 1845 in New York.
Donor: Cornelius Heaney‡.
Foundation type: Independent foundation.
Financial data (yr. ended 12/31/14): Assets, $5,357,923 (M); expenditures, $368,833; qualifying distributions, $300,870; giving activities include $253,500 for 38 grants (high: $15,000; low: $500).
Fields of interest: Education; Secondary education; Higher education; Nonprofits; Catholicism; Human services; Child welfare.
Type of support: General support; Scholarships; Regranting.
Limitations: Applications accepted. Giving limited to New York, NY, with emphasis on the borough of Brooklyn. No grants to individuals.
Application information: Application form required.
  Initial approach: Proposal
  Deadline(s): Oct. 30
Officers: Richard H. Freeman, Pres.; James J. Daly, V.P.; Cornelius A. Heaney, Secy.; Thomas E. Powers, Treas.
Trustees: Peter M. Altman; William B. Bice; Colin P. Crowley; Brian C. Deane; David V. Farrell; Duncan A. Fraser; John G. Ingram; Arnold Ring.
Number of staff: 2 part-time support.
EIN: 111661344

5789
Frank and Deenie Brosens Foundation
c/o BCRS Associates, LLC
77 Water St., 9th Fl.
New York City, NY 10005-3701

Established in 1989 in New York.
Donors: Frank P. Brosens; Deenie M. Brosens.
Foundation type: Independent foundation.
Financial data (yr. ended 01/31/13): Assets, $21,135 (M); gifts received, $330,000; expenditures, $359,481; qualifying distributions,

$359,481; giving activities include $359,481 for 37 grants (high: $100,000; low: $10).

Purpose and activities: Giving primarily for education and hospitals; some funding for the environment, health foundations, children, youth, and social services.

Fields of interest: Elementary and secondary education; Undergraduate education; Natural resources; Hospital care; Diseases and conditions; Human services; Child welfare; Youth organizing.

Type of support: General support.

Limitations: Applications not accepted. Giving primarily in CT, NJ, and NY. No grants to individuals.

Application information: Contributes only to pre-selected organizations.

Trustees: Deenie M. Brosens; Frank P. Brosens.

EIN: 133532018

5790
William Gundry Broughton Charitable Private Foundation, Inc.
133 Saratoga Rd., Ste. 6
Glenville, NY   12302-4108
Contact: Shirley M. Vogt, Pres.

Established in 1995 in New York.

Donor: William Broughton Charitable Remainder Unitrust.

Foundation type: Independent foundation.

Financial data (yr. ended 12/31/13): Assets, $9,913,556 (M); expenditures, $463,165; qualifying distributions, $397,971; giving activities include $375,000 for 40 grants (high: $30,000; low: $1,000).

Fields of interest: Education; Human services; Youth development.

Limitations: Applications not accepted. Giving primarily in Schenectady County, NY. No support for non 501(c)(3) organizations. No grants to individuals.

Application information: Contributes only to pre-selected organizations.

Board meeting date(s): 5 times per year

Officers: Shirley M. Vogt, Pres.; Ronald L. Lagasse, V.P.; Grace E. Golden, Secy.; Jean M. Duxbury, Treas.

Directors: John DeleDonne; Howard I. Mack; Phyllis J. Mrozkowski.

EIN: 223122633

5791
The William Brown Foundation, Inc.
c/o Morrison Cohen LLP
909 3rd Ave.
New York City, NY   10022-4731

Established in 1986 in New York.

Donor: William Brown Charitbale Rem Unitrust.

Foundation type: Independent foundation.

Financial data (yr. ended 12/31/13): Assets, $6,087,876 (M); gifts received, $94,889; expenditures, $539,975; qualifying distributions, $362,995; giving activities include $298,000 for 44 grants (high: $25,000; low: $250).

Purpose and activities: Giving primarily for health and human services, religion, and scholarship funds.

Fields of interest: Education; Higher education; Hospital care; Christianity; Judaism; Human services; Child welfare.

Type of support: Individual development.

Limitations: Applications not accepted. Giving primarily in NY. No grants to individuals.

Application information: Contributes only to pre-selected organizations.

Directors: Geoffrey Barefoot; Michael Fleischer; Jerome Tarnoff; Mark Weingarten.

EIN: 133307838

5792
The Jean I. & Charles H. Brunie Foundation
c/o Wolf Maryles & Associates, LLC
220 E. 42nd St., Ste. 2201
New York City, NY   10017

Established in 1986 in New York.

Donors: Charles H. Brunie; Jean I. Brunie.

Foundation type: Independent foundation.

Financial data (yr. ended 02/28/13): Assets, $0 (M); expenditures, $152,931; qualifying distributions, $147,988; giving activities include $141,679 for 1 grant.

Fields of interest: Health.

Limitations: Applications not accepted. Giving primarily in NY, with some giving in Washington, DC. No grants to individuals.

Application information: Unsolicited requests for funds not accepted.

Trustees: Charles H. Brunie; Jean I. Brunie.

EIN: 133384777

5793
BSD Endowment Foundation
c/o Daniel Baumann, CPA
1132 E. 12th St.
Brooklyn, NY   11230-4812

Donors: Abraham Muller; Stellar Capital Consulting, LLC; Jacob Muller.

Foundation type: Independent foundation.

Financial data (yr. ended 10/31/13): Assets, $570,997 (M); gifts received, $461,000; expenditures, $132,601; qualifying distributions, $132,601; giving activities include $132,601 for 82 grants (high: $45,000; low: $10).

Fields of interest: Judaism.

Limitations: Applications not accepted.

Application information: Unsolicited requests for funds not accepted.

Officer: Abraham Muller, Pres.

EIN: 261393485

5794
BSR Memorial Trust
1068 54th St.
Brooklyn, NY   11219-4042   (212) 561-5743

Donors: Norman Rafalowitz; Gail Rafalowitz; Jonathan Melohn; Gary Barnett; Schron Family Charity Fund LLC; Beth Oloth.

Foundation type: Operating foundation.

Financial data (yr. ended 12/31/14): Assets, $0; gifts received, $209,579; expenditures, $416,038; qualifying distributions, $406,124.

Fields of interest: Nonprofits; Judaism.

Type of support: Regranting.

Limitations: Applications accepted. Giving primarily in NY.

Application information: Application form required.

Initial approach: Letter
Deadline(s): None

Officers: Norman Rafalowitz, Pres.; Chaim Rafalowitz, Secy.; Issachar Brinbaum, Treas.

EIN: 137153239

5795
The BTMU Foundation, Inc.
(formerly The BTM Foundation, Inc.)
1251 Ave. of the Americas, 37th Fl.
New York City, NY   10020-1104   (212) 782-4627
Contact: Beth Gilroy, V.P.

Established in 1997 in New York.

Donors: The Bank of Tokyo, Mitsubishi Trust Co.; The Bank of Tokyo, Mitsubishi UFJ Trust Co.; Union Bank, N.A.

Foundation type: Company-sponsored foundation.

Financial data (yr. ended 12/31/13): Assets, $5,216,874 (M); gifts received, $5,000; expenditures, $426,781; qualifying distributions, $420,250; giving activities include $420,000 for 60 grants (high: $50,000; low: $500).

Purpose and activities: The foundation supports nonprofit organizations involved with education, community development, and human services. Special emphasis is directed toward programs serving low and moderate income people and neighborhoods.

Fields of interest: Arts education; Reading promotion; Health; Community and economic development; Sustainable development; Urban development; Housing development; Food aid; Senior services; Low-income and poor people; People with physical disabilities; People with psychosocial disabilities.

Type of support: General support; Program development.

Limitations: Applications accepted. Giving primarily in New York, NY. No support for political, religious, sectarian, fraternal, veterans, labor, or lobbying organizations. No grants to individuals, or for advertising, fundraising, capital campaigns, tickets or memberships, or debt reduction.

Publications: Application guidelines; Grants list.

Application information: Application form required.

Initial approach: Complete application form
Copies of proposal: 1
Deadline(s): Apr. 30 for Community Dev Financial Institutions, June 30 for non CDFI organizations
Board meeting date(s): 4th quarter

Officers and Directors: Katsumi Hatao, Chair. and Director; Johannes Worsoe, Pres. and Director; Elizabeth Lyman, Sr. V.P.; Beth Gilroy, V.P.; J.J. Ko, V.P.; Andrew Rasanen, V.P.; Thomas Pennington, Secy.; Thomas Greene, Treas.; Noriaki Goto; David Gruppo; Keiichi Hotta; Anthony Marino; Toshihide Motoshita; Isaac Shapiro.

EIN: 133916201

5796
The Buchalter Foundation
c/o FLSV LLP
1475 Franklin Ave.
Garden City, NY   11530-1662

Established in 1996 in New Jersey.

Donor: Lawrence R. Buchalter.

Foundation type: Independent foundation.

Financial data (yr. ended 08/31/13): Assets, $1,644,868 (M); expenditures, $369,899; qualifying distributions, $365,750; giving activities include $364,000 for 11 grants (high: $250,000; low: $1,000).
Fields of interest: Education; Agriculture; Human services.
Type of support: General support.
Limitations: Applications not accepted. Giving primarily in CA, NJ, and NY. No grants to individuals; no loans or scholarships.
Application information: Contributes only to pre-selected organizations.
Trustee: Lawrence R. Buchalter.
EIN: 137109408

5797
The Don and Maggie Buchwald Foundation
10 E. 44th St.
New York City, NY 10017

Donors: Donald Buchwald; Margaret Buchwald.
Foundation type: Independent foundation.
Financial data (yr. ended 06/30/13): Assets, $4,872,162 (M); gifts received, $75,559; expenditures, $217,601; qualifying distributions, $206,250; giving activities include $206,250 for 23 grants (high: $100,000; low: $250).
Fields of interest: Arts and culture; Education; Human services.
Limitations: Applications not accepted. Giving primarily in MA and NY.
Application information: Unsolicited requests for funds not accepted.
Officers and Directors: Margaret Buchwald, Pres. and Director; Donald Buchwald, V.P. and Secy.-Treas. and Director.
EIN: 454059273

5798
The William and Mary Buckley Foundation
c/o BCRS Associates, LLC
77 Water St., 9th Fl.
New York City, NY 10005-3701

Established in 1993 in New York.
Donor: William J. Buckley.
Foundation type: Independent foundation.
Financial data (yr. ended 01/31/13): Assets, $5,053,779 (M); gifts received, $587,650; expenditures, $224,695; qualifying distributions, $224,095; giving activities include $223,685 for 98 grants (high: $49,500; low: $50).
Fields of interest: Education; Christianity; Human services.
Limitations: Applications not accepted. Giving primarily in CT, NY and SC. No grants to individuals; no loans or scholarships.
Application information: Contributes only to pre-selected organizations.
Trustees: Mary K. Buckley; William J. Buckley.
EIN: 133748080

5799
Buffalo Sabres Alumni Association
c/o Robert Travis
45 Bryant Woods N.
Amherst, NY 14228-3600 (716) 630-2400
Contact: Robert Travis, Treas. and Dir.

Main URL: http://www.sabresalumni.com
Flickr: https://www.flickr.com/photos/84418649@N04
Scholarship address: The Buffalo Sabres Alumni Scholarship Program, c/o Buffalo Sabres Alumni Assoc., First Niagara Ctr., 1 Seymour H. Knox III Plz., Buffalo, NY 14203

Established in 1989 in New York.
Foundation type: Independent foundation.
Financial data (yr. ended 12/31/13): Assets, $519,036 (M); gifts received, $185,309; expenditures, $370,893; qualifying distributions, $140,570; giving activities include $140,570 for 26 grants (high: $30,000; low: $70), and $229,597 for foundation-administered programs.
Fields of interest: Education; Diseases and conditions.
International interests: Canada.
Type of support: Student aid; Individual development; General support; Scholarships.
Limitations: Applications accepted. Giving limited to western NY; scholarships funding includes Southern Ontario, Canada.
Application information: See foundation web site for scholarship application form. Application form required.
  Initial approach: Letter on organization's letterhead
  Deadline(s): None, for grants; July 1, for scholarships
Officers and Directors: Rob Ray, Pres. and Director; Derek Smith, V.P. and Director; David Elibol, Secy.; Robert Travis, Treas. and Director; Cliff Benson; Jay McKee; Craig Muni; Michael Peca; Andrew Peters; Larry Playfair; Ric Seiling; Darryl Shannon.
EIN: 161356116

5800
Buller Family Foundation
c/o KGS, LLP
125 Jericho Tpke., No. 300
Jericho, NY 11753-1016 (516) 997-7500
Contact: Mitchell G. Kahn, Tr.

Established in 2004 in New York.
Donors: James Buller; Mark Buller.
Foundation type: Independent foundation.
Financial data (yr. ended 12/31/13): Assets, $4,032,515 (M); expenditures, $298,713; qualifying distributions, $280,985; giving activities include $280,985 for 52 grants (high: $35,000; low: $200).
Fields of interest: Nonprofits; Judaism; Human services; Child welfare.
Type of support: Regranting.
Limitations: Applications accepted. Giving primarily in New York, NY.
Application information: Application form required.
  Initial approach: E-mail
  Deadline(s): None
Trustees: Sarah Beatty-Buller; Cheryl Buller; James Buller; Mark Buller; Mitchell Kahn.
EIN: 116598655

5801
The Walter J. & Anna H. Burchan Charitable Trust
6 Ford Ave.
Oneonta, NY 13820-1818 (607) 432-6720
Contact: Ronald R. Haus Esq., Mgr. and Tr.

Established in 1980 in New York.
Donor: Anna H. Burchan.
Foundation type: Independent foundation.
Financial data (yr. ended 12/31/14): Assets, $3,995,370 (M); expenditures, $274,208; qualifying distributions, $237,000; giving activities include $237,000 for 10 grants (high: $100,000; low: $2,000).
Purpose and activities: Giving primarily for youth and local charities.
Fields of interest: Education; Health; Hospital care; Community and economic development; European football; Human services; Youth development.
Limitations: Applications accepted. Giving primarily in Delaware and Otsego counties, NY. No grants to individuals.
Application information:
  Initial approach: Letter
  Copies of proposal: 1
  Deadline(s): None
Officer and Trustees: Ronald R. Haus, Mgr. and Trustee; Elsie I. Haus; Karen A. Moran.
Number of staff: 1 part-time professional.
EIN: 222294069

5802
The Burpee Foundation
c/o Windels Marx Lane & Mittendorf, LLP
156 W. 56th St.
New York City, NY 10019-3800 (212) 237-1000
Contact: Mel P. Barkan, V.P.

Established in 2002 in New York.
Donor: George C. Ball, Jr.
Foundation type: Independent foundation.
Financial data (yr. ended 12/31/13): Assets, $9,348,137 (M); expenditures, $357,816; qualifying distributions, $269,003; giving activities include $209,000 for 7 grants (high: $63,500; low: $7,500).
Fields of interest: Education; Environment; Convalescent care; Gardening.
Limitations: Applications accepted. Giving on a national basis. No grants to individuals.
Application information: Application form required.
  Initial approach: Contact foundation for current application information
  Deadline(s): None
Officers and Trustees: George C. Ball, Jr., Pres. and Treas. and Trustee; Mel P. Barkan, V.P. and Trustee; David A. Brauner, Secy. and Trustee.
EIN: 743047509

5803
The Burrows Little Falls Foundation
501 W. Main St.
Little Falls, NY 13365-1829 (315) 823-2300
Contact: Carolyn Zaklukiewicz, Tr.

Established in 1990 in New York.
Donors: Burrows Paper Corp.; Gladys A. Burrows; R.W. Burrows, Jr.
Foundation type: Operating foundation.
Financial data (yr. ended 12/31/13): Assets, $3,296,049 (M); gifts received, $222,000; expenditures, $288,155; qualifying distributions, $273,618; giving activities include $272,647 for 60 grants (high: $67,400; low: $90).
Purpose and activities: Giving to education, community services, health and hospitals, and youth services.

Fields of interest: Education; Hospital care; Diseases and conditions; Public administration; Sports and recreation; Youth services.
Type of support: General support; Grants to individuals; Student aid.
Limitations: Applications accepted. Giving primarily in Little Falls, NY.
Application information: Application form required.
Initial approach: Proposal
Deadline(s): None
Trustees: R.W. Burrows; Margaret B. Goldman; Carolyn Zaklukiewicz.
EIN: 223059155

5804
The Burton Foundation
c/o Dorian Alex Vergos & Co., LLC
352 7th Ave.
New York City, NY   10001

Donor: Burton B. Staniar.
Foundation type: Independent foundation.
Financial data (yr. ended 12/31/13): Assets, $1,754,834 (M); gifts received, $284,703; expenditures, $190,263; qualifying distributions, $173,317; giving activities include $166,567 for 47 grants (high: $15,000; low: $50).
Fields of interest: Arts and culture; Higher education; Hospital care.
Limitations: Applications not accepted. Giving primarily in NY and VA. No grants to individuals.
Application information: Contributes only to pre-selected organizations.
Trustee: Burton B. Staniar.
EIN: 133975899

5805
The Irving T. Bush Foundation, Inc.
c/o Edward J. Walsh, Jr.
100 N. Village Ave., Ste. 35
Rockville Center, NY   11570

Foundation type: Independent foundation.
Financial data (yr. ended 07/31/14): Assets, $2,425,255 (M); expenditures, $209,350; qualifying distributions, $172,000; giving activities include $164,500 for 32 grants (high: $15,000; low: $1,000).
Fields of interest: Education; University education; Hospital care; Cancers; Libraries; Christianity; Judaism; Camps; Human services.
Limitations: Applications not accepted. Giving primarily in NY. No grants to individuals.
Application information: Unsolicited requests for funds not accepted.
Officers and Directors: Thomas F. Walsh, Pres. and Director; Edward J. Walsh, Jr., Esq., V.P. and Secy. and Director; Louella Silberberg.
EIN: 136043483

5806
The Buster Foundation
c/o Robin H. Moss
1530 Broadway
New York City, NY   10036-4048

Established in 2003 in New York.
Donors: Robin H. Moss; Charles B. Moss III; Elizabeth H. Moss; Charles B. Moss, Jr.
Foundation type: Independent foundation.

Financial data (yr. ended 09/30/13): Assets, $5,159,728 (M); gifts received, $1,974,491; expenditures, $409,644; qualifying distributions, $384,439; giving activities include $384,189 for 33 grants (high: $125,000; low: $100).
Purpose and activities: Giving primarily for medical research, health, and the arts and education.
Fields of interest: Arts and culture; Education; Health; Neurology; Diseases and conditions.
International interests: United Kingdom of Great Britain and Northern Ireland.
Type of support: Professorships; Research; Endowments; Continuing support; General support; Equipment; Fellowships; Scholarships.
Limitations: Applications not accepted. Giving primarily in the U.S., with limited giving in the United Kingdom. No support for political or religious organizations. No grants to individuals.
Application information: Contributes only to pre-selected organizations.
Trustees: Charles B. Moss III; Elizabeth H. Moss; Robin H. Moss.
EIN: 510494444

5807
The Andrew Cader Foundation Inc.
c/o Trisha Morena-Santiago
35 Ricky Rd.
Ronkonkoma, NY   11779-5017

Established in 2002 in New York.
Donor: Andrew Cader.
Foundation type: Independent foundation.
Financial data (yr. ended 11/30/13): Assets, $10,988,320 (M); expenditures, $403,633; qualifying distributions, $388,992; giving activities include $383,500 for 15 grants (high: $125,000; low: $1,000).
Fields of interest: Arts and culture; Education; Health; Public affairs; Winter sports; Human services; Child welfare.
Limitations: Applications not accepted. Giving primarily in CO and NY. No grants to individuals.
Application information: Contributes only to pre-selected organizations.
Officers and Directors: Andrew Cader, Pres. and Director; Michael Cader, V.P. and Secy. and Director; Seth J. Lapidow, Treas. and Director; Richard Hogan; Nina Kaminer.
EIN: 030497916

5808
CAL Foundation Inc.
c/o Sacks Press Lacher
600 3rd Ave.
New York City, NY   10016-1901

Established in 1957 in New York.
Donor: Linda L. Hackett.
Foundation type: Independent foundation.
Financial data (yr. ended 12/31/13): Assets, $4,407,029 (M); expenditures, $220,546; qualifying distributions, $190,500; giving activities include $190,500 for 47 grants (high: $25,000; low: $500).
Fields of interest: Arts and culture; Education; Environment; Animal welfare; Religion; Human services.
Limitations: Applications not accepted. Giving primarily in the metropolitan New York, NY, area. No grants to individuals.

Application information: Contributes only to pre-selected organizations.
Officers: Linda Hackett, Pres.; Melinda Hackett, V.P.; Montague H. Hackett, Jr., Secy.
EIN: 136083347

5809
The Calamus Foundation
c/o Myer, Greene & Degge
P.O. Box 930
Pearl River, NY   10965-0930

Donors: Loring R. McAlpin; David H. McAlpin, Jr.; Joan R. McAlpin Charitable Lead Trust.
Foundation type: Independent foundation.
Financial data (yr. ended 11/30/14): Assets, $4,543,220 (M); gifts received, $177,153; expenditures, $253,287; qualifying distributions, $186,056; giving activities include $183,500 for 16 grants (high: $50,000; low: $2,500).
Fields of interest: Religion; Human rights; Human services.
Type of support: General support.
Limitations: Applications not accepted. Giving primarily in CA, MA, NY, and PA. No grants to individuals.
Application information: Unsolicited requests for funds not accepted.
Officers: Loring McAlpin, Pres.; Daniel Wolfe, Secy.
Director: Gary Schwartz.
EIN: 133922034

5810
Donald Grant and Ann Martin Calder Foundation
164 E. 72nd St.
New York City, NY   10021-4363

Established in 1996 in Delaware.
Donors: Ann Martin Calder; Donald Calder.
Foundation type: Independent foundation.
Financial data (yr. ended 12/31/13): Assets, $2,697,922 (M); expenditures, $176,135; qualifying distributions, $174,710; giving activities include $172,900 for 25 grants (high: $30,000; low: $100).
Fields of interest: Education; Health; Diseases and conditions.
Limitations: Applications not accepted. No grants to individuals.
Application information: Unsolicited requests for funds not accepted.
Directors: Ann Martin Calder; Cornelia Martin Calder; Donald Grant Calder; Donald Grant Calder, Jr.; Isabella Swift Calder.
EIN: 133917776

5811
Len Camber Charitable Trust
c/o Manger and Beller
295 Madison Ave., Ste. 901
New York City, NY   10017-7755   (212) 986-3025
Contact: Robert Manger, Tr.

Established in 2006 in New York.
Foundation type: Independent foundation.
Financial data (yr. ended 12/31/13): Assets, $433,035 (M); expenditures, $216,973; qualifying distributions, $211,353; giving activities include $200,615 for 48 grants (high: $55,000; low: $150).

Fields of interest: Theater; Education.
Type of support: Research.
Limitations: Applications accepted. Giving primarily in NY and TX, with some giving in FL. No grants to individuals.
Application information: Application form required.
   Initial approach: Letter
   Deadline(s): None
Trustees: Sanford Goldstein; Robert Manger.
EIN: 656444559

5812
The Vincent Camuto Charitable Trust
(formerly The Kristen & Vincent Camuto Charitable Trust)
c/o BDO USA, LLP
100 Park Ave.
New York City, NY   10017-5516

Foundation type: Independent foundation.
Financial data (yr. ended 12/31/13): Assets, $4,485,239 (M); expenditures, $226,604; qualifying distributions, $149,000; giving activities include $149,000 for 6 grants (high: $100,000; low: $1,500).
Purpose and activities: Giving primarily for children's services.
Fields of interest: Education; Specialty hospital care; Diseases and conditions; Religion; Human services; Child welfare.
Type of support: Research.
Limitations: Applications not accepted. Giving primarily in CT and NY. No grants to individuals.
Application information: Unsolicited requests for funds not accepted.
Trustees: Robert Camuto; David J. Sweet, Esq.
EIN: 137051137

5813
John R. & Dorothy D. Caples Fund
c/o Deutsche Bank Trust Co., N.A.
P.O. Box 1297, Church St. Sta.
New York City, NY   10008-1297

Established in 1994 in New York.
Foundation type: Independent foundation.
Financial data (yr. ended 12/31/14): Assets, $3,399,732; expenditures, $234,781; qualifying distributions, $207,901.
Fields of interest: Arts and culture; Education; Religion; Human services.
Limitations: Applications not accepted. Giving primarily in NJ and NY. No grants to individuals.
Application information: Contributes only to pre-selected organizations.
Trustees: Urban S. Mulvehill; Deutsche Bank Trust Co., N.A.
EIN: 311441038

5814
The Richard E. Capri Foundation
330 Motor Pky., Ste. 202
Hauppauge, NY   11788-5118   (631) 273-4429

Established in 2008 in New York.
Foundation type: Independent foundation.
Financial data (yr. ended 06/30/13): Assets, $12,364,836 (M); expenditures, $389,958; qualifying distributions, $389,958; giving activities

include $323,600 for 27 grants (high: $55,000; low: $1,000).
Purpose and activities: The foundation provides funding to organizations researching prevention for chronic diseases and efforts to assist sufferers of cancer, leukemia, and other debilitating diseases.
Fields of interest: Diseases and conditions; Leukemia.
Type of support: Program development; Research.
Limitations: Applications accepted. Giving primarily in NY.
Application information: Application form required.
   Initial approach: Letter
   Deadline(s): None
Officers: Edward L. Wolf, Pres.; Steven Wolf, V.P.; Ellen Wolf, Secy.; Jeffrey Wolf, Treas.
EIN: 266445474

5815
The Carnegie Foundation
545 Broadway
Brooklyn, NY   11206-2962

Donors: Isaac Jacobowitz; Sim Sholen Realty, Inc.
Foundation type: Operating foundation.
Financial data (yr. ended 11/30/13): Assets, $0 (M); gifts received, $110,000; expenditures, $202,461; qualifying distributions, $202,461; giving activities include $175,153 for grants.
Fields of interest: Judaism.
Limitations: Applications not accepted. No grants to individuals.
Application information: Contributes only to pre-selected organizations.
Trustees: Isaac Jacobs; Rachel Jacobs.
EIN: 510439076

5816
The P. and C. Carroll Foundation
c/o The Ayco Co., LP - National Tax Group
P.O. Box 15014
Albany, NY   12212-5014

Donors: Philip J. Carroll, Jr.; Charlene P. Carroll.
Foundation type: Independent foundation.
Financial data (yr. ended 12/31/13): Assets, $4,674,880 (M); expenditures, $421,688; qualifying distributions, $358,300; giving activities include $358,300 for 43 grants (high: $60,000; low: $250).
Fields of interest: Arts and culture; Education; Zoos; Human services; Youth development.
Limitations: Applications not accepted. Giving primarily in Birmingham, AL, Washington, DC, Atlanta, GA, New Orleans, LA, and Houston, TX. No grants to individuals.
Application information: Contributes only to pre-selected organizations.
Officers: Philip J. Carroll, Jr., Pres.; Charlene P. Carroll, Secy.
EIN: 450529796

5817
Frank & Ruth E. Caruso Foundation
P.O. Box 399
New York City, NY   10040-0399
Contact: Lisa Turngren, Pres.
E-mail: laturngren@netscape.net

Established in 2002 in New Jersey.

Donors: Ruth Caruso†; Frank Caruso†.
Foundation type: Independent foundation.
Financial data (yr. ended 12/31/14): Assets, $5,036,209 (M); expenditures, $277,689; qualifying distributions, $241,538; giving activities include $165,000 for 9 grants (high: $33,500; low: $2,000).
Purpose and activities: Grants for calendar years 2013-2015 are devoted to the area of sexual violence prevention, funding small (under $1 million operating budget) grassroots community-based organizations in NYC.
Fields of interest: Sexual abuse.
Type of support: General support; Program development.
Limitations: Applications not accepted. Giving primarily in the New York City, New York area. No support for public or private schools, colleges, universities, hospitals, or religious or political organizations. No grants to individuals.
Application information: Does not accept unsolicited proposals, applications, or telephone calls.
Officer: Lisa Turngren, Pres.
EIN: 820581784

5818
The Carwill Foundation
c/o BCRS Assocs., LLC
77 Water St., 9th Fl.
New York City, NY   10005-4414

Established in 1985 in New York.
Donor: William C. Stutt.
Foundation type: Independent foundation.
Financial data (yr. ended 08/31/13): Assets, $474,652 (M); gifts received, $554,004; expenditures, $302,982; qualifying distributions, $297,021; giving activities include $290,100 for 105 grants (high: $100,000; low: $100).
Purpose and activities: Giving primarily for the arts, education, health and medical research, and children and social services.
Fields of interest: Arts and culture; Elementary and secondary education; Higher education; Environment; Diseases and conditions; Cancers; Human services; Child welfare.
Type of support: Annual campaigns; Capital campaigns; Endowments; Professorships; Scholarships; Research; Research and evaluation.
Limitations: Applications not accepted. Giving primarily in FL. No grants to individuals.
Application information: Unsolicited requests for funds not accepted.
Trustees: Carolyn Stutt; David S. Stutt; William C. Stutt.
EIN: 133318130

5819
Sophia & William Casey Foundation
c/o Grant Thornton, LLP
445 Broadhollow Rd.
Melville, NY   11747
Application address: c/o Bernadette Casey-Smith, 12 Glenwood Rd., Roslyn Harbor, NY 11576, tel.: (516) 621-9332

Established in 1974 in New York.
Donors: William J. Casey†; Sophia B. Casey†.
Foundation type: Independent foundation.

Financial data (yr. ended 11/30/13): Assets, $8,411,506 (M); expenditures, $464,359; qualifying distributions, $395,600; giving activities include $384,100 for 18 grants (high: $75,000; low: $500).
Fields of interest: Education; Higher education; Nonprofits; International studies; Public affairs; National security; Catholicism; Human services.
Type of support: Regranting.
Limitations: Applications accepted. Giving primarily in Washington, DC and NY. No grants to individuals.
Application information: Application form required.
   Initial approach: Letter
   Deadline(s): None
Officer: Bernadette Casey-Smith, Pres.
EIN: 510153218

5820
Castle Foundation
440 Mamaroneck Ave.
Harrison, NY   10528-1633

Established in 1989 in New York.
Donors: Castle Oil Corp.; Rom Terminals, Ltd.
Foundation type: Independent foundation.
Financial data (yr. ended 12/31/13): Assets, $89,247 (M); gifts received, $100,000; expenditures, $162,588; qualifying distributions, $162,500; giving activities include $162,500 for 16 grants (high: $41,000; low: $500).
Fields of interest: Education; Law education; Catholicism.
Limitations: Applications not accepted. Giving primarily in NY. No grants to individuals.
Application information: Contributes only to pre-selected organizations.
Trustees: Camille Romita; Mauro C. Romita; Michael Romita.
EIN: 133490144

5821
Catalyst Foundation
c/o Epoch Microelectronics, Inc.
420 Columbus Ave., Ste. 204
Valhalla, NY   10595-1382   (914) 332-8570
FAX: (914) 332-8576;
E-mail: catalysis@catalyst-foundation.org; Main URL: http://www.catalyst-foundation.org

Established in 1992 in Texas.
Foundation type: Independent foundation.
Financial data (yr. ended 12/31/14): Assets, $4,606,244; expenditures, $348,659; qualifying distributions, $277,400.
Purpose and activities: The goal of the foundation is to contribute to the fusion of scientific and engineering research. To provide a concrete paradigm, it fosters university cross-disciplinary research projects in which at least one discipline is related to analog or mixed analog-digital integrated circuit design and analysis. Preference is given to projects that help diffuse such work geographically. The research support provided by the foundation is in the form of grants.
Fields of interest: Education; University education; Science.
Limitations: Applications accepted. Giving primarily in NY and OR. No grants to individuals.
Application information: Check foundation web site for updates regarding new funding opportunities. Application form required.

Initial approach: See foundation web site
Deadline(s): None
Officers: Ken Suyama, Pres.; Yoshihiko Horio, V.P.; William H. Caudill, Secy.; Hatsumi Suyama, Treas.
Director: Shigeko Woolfalk.
EIN: 760383386

5822
Cathedral Fund
c/o Perelson Weiner, LLP
1 Dag Hammarskjold Plz., 42nd Fl.
New York City, NY   10017-2286

Established in 1995 in Massachusetts.
Donors: Frances P. Caille; Branta Foundation; Harvey Picker†; Frances Hamill.
Foundation type: Independent foundation.
Financial data (yr. ended 12/31/13): Assets, $4,202,058 (M); expenditures, $295,533; qualifying distributions, $275,500; giving activities include $270,000 for 3 grants (high: $250,000; low: $10,000).
Fields of interest: Higher education; Foundations; Specialty hospital care; Human services; Family services; Women's services.
Limitations: Applications not accepted. Giving primarily in Boston, MA. No grants to individuals.
Application information: Contributes only to pre-selected organizations.
Trustee: Frances Hamill.
EIN: 133843243

5823
John and Margo Catsimatidis Foundation, Inc.
823 11th Ave.
New York City, NY   10019

Donors: John Catsimatidis; 1790 Building Corp.; United Refining, Inc.
Foundation type: Independent foundation.
Financial data (yr. ended 12/31/13): Assets, $13,184 (M); gifts received, $25,000; expenditures, $161,169; qualifying distributions, $160,641; giving activities include $160,641 for 48 grants (high: $25,000; low: $52).
Fields of interest: Education; Diseases and conditions; Diabetes.
Limitations: Applications not accepted. Giving primarily in NY. No grants to individuals.
Application information: Contributes only to pre-selected organizations.
Officers: John Catsimatidis, Pres.; Margo Catsimatidis, Secy.-Treas.
EIN: 134090349

5824
CDL Foundation Inc.
7 Rolling Hill Ln.
Lawrence, NY   11559-1507

Established in 1997 in New York.
Donors: Steven Krausman; Lisa Krausman; Menachem Lipshutz.
Foundation type: Independent foundation.
Financial data (yr. ended 12/31/12): Assets, $1,317,105 (M); gifts received, $1,621,000; expenditures, $396,174; qualifying distributions, $396,000; giving activities include $396,000 for grants.

Fields of interest: Judaism.
Limitations: Applications not accepted. Giving primarily in NY. No grants to individuals.
Application information: Contributes only to pre-selected organizations.
Directors: Lisa Krausman; Steven Krausman; Jonathan Scheiner.
EIN: 061492452

5825
CDVSJ Foundation
880 3rd Ave., Ste. 1206
New York City, NY   10022

Donor: Zaber Corporation Inc.
Foundation type: Independent foundation.
Financial data (yr. ended 12/31/13): Assets, $2,125,411 (M); gifts received, $500,000; expenditures, $230,045; qualifying distributions, $224,750; giving activities include $224,750 for 11 grants (high: $128,000; low: $1,000).
Fields of interest: Education; Higher education.
Limitations: Applications not accepted. Giving primarily in PA.
Application information: Unsolicited requests for funds not accepted.
Officers: Stephen T. Mong, Pres.; Viola Meehan, Secy.
Directors: David Mong; Josephine Mong; Cynthia Sun.
EIN: 453846013

5826
Centennial Foundation
c/o Joel E. Sammet & Co., LLP
15 Maiden Ln., No. 500
New York City, NY   10038

Established in 1965 in New York.
Donors: Henry H. Arnhold; Arnhold Ceramics, Inc.; A.M. & S.M. Kellen Foundation; Arnhold Foundation; A. Bleichroeder; S. Bleichroeder; Stephen M. Kellen; A & S Bleichroeder Holdings.
Foundation type: Independent foundation.
Financial data (yr. ended 12/31/13): Assets, $2,825,610 (M); gifts received, $20,000; expenditures, $314,726; qualifying distributions, $294,375; giving activities include $283,250 for 13 grants (high: $80,000; low: $2,500).
Purpose and activities: Giving primarily for the arts, particularly art museums, higher education, social services, and to Jewish and other federated giving programs.
Fields of interest: Arts and culture; Art museums; Education; Higher education; Business education; Nonprofits; Human services.
Type of support: Regranting.
Limitations: Applications not accepted. Giving primarily in New York, NY. No grants to individuals.
Application information: Contributes only to pre-selected organizations.
Officers: Henry H. Arnhold, Chair.; John P. Arnhold, Pres.; Michael M. Kellen, Secy.-Treas.
Number of staff: 1 part-time support.
EIN: 136189397

5827
Century Arts Foundation
P.O. Box 1989
Sag Harbor, NY   11963-0069

Foundation type: Independent foundation.
Financial data (yr. ended 12/31/13): Assets, $9,553,108 (M); expenditures, $626,889; qualifying distributions, $563,311; giving activities include $400,000 for 9 grants (high: $100,000; low: $2,000).
Fields of interest: Arts and culture; Education.
Limitations: Applications not accepted. Giving primarily in AZ, NM and NY.
Application information: Contributes only to pre-selected organizations.
Officers: Justine Compton, Pres.; Nicholas Wentworth, Secy.
EIN: 800293886

5828
The John and Melissa Ceriale Foundation Inc.
c/o Geoffrey Berger, Ayco Company, L.P.
321 Broadway.
P.O. Box 860
Saratoga Springs, NY 12866—0860

Donor: John V. Ceriale.
Foundation type: Independent foundation.
Financial data (yr. ended 12/31/13): Assets, $5,080,112 (M); gifts received, $11; expenditures, $404,657; qualifying distributions, $362,500; giving activities include $362,500 for 11 grants (high: $200,000; low: $3,000).
Fields of interest: Arts and culture; Education; Human services.
Limitations: Applications not accepted. Giving primarily in PA.
Application information: Unsolicited requests for funds not accepted.
Officers and Directors: John V. Ceriale, Pres. and Director; Melissa Ceriale, V.P. and Secy. and Director; Robert Tomasello, Treas. and Director.
EIN: 271262041

5829
Cerullo Family Foundation
c/o The Ayco Company, LP
P.O. Box 860
Saratoga Springs, NY 12866-0860

Established in 2007 in New Hampshire.
Donors: John J. Cerullo III; Geraldine F. Cerullo.
Foundation type: Independent foundation.
Financial data (yr. ended 12/31/13): Assets, $7,226,382 (M); gifts received, $10,463; expenditures, $273,122; qualifying distributions, $261,000; giving activities include $261,000 for 3 grants (high: $100,000; low: $61,000).
Fields of interest: Education; Higher education.
Limitations: Applications not accepted. Giving primarily in MA and NH. No grants to individuals.
Application information: Contributes only to pre-selected organizations.
Trustees: John J. Cerullo III; Geraldine F. Cerullo.
EIN: 261615106

5830
Chada Foundation, Inc.
c/o A. Scherzer
4 Executive Blvd., Ste. 202
Suffern, NY 10901-4190

Established in 1991 in New York.

Donors: Esther Reichman; David Scharf Family Trust; Asher Scharf; So Charitable Trust; Chesed Global Foundation.
Foundation type: Independent foundation.
Financial data (yr. ended 11/30/13): Assets, $1,449,965 (L); gifts received, $166,500; expenditures, $520,828; qualifying distributions, $441,419; giving activities include $441,110 for grants.
Fields of interest: Judaism.
Limitations: Applications not accepted. Giving primarily in NY. No grants to individuals.
Application information: Unsolicited requests for funds not accepted.
Officers: Esther Reichman, Pres.; Asher Scharf, V.P. and Secy.
Directors: Moses Scharf; Helene Teitelbaum.
EIN: 133650373

5831
The Chaim Hatzlacha Foundation
21 Walton St.
Brooklyn, NY 11206-5051

Foundation type: Independent foundation.
Financial data (yr. ended 12/31/12): Assets, $0 (M); expenditures, $250,000; qualifying distributions, $250,000; giving activities include $250,000 for 1 grant.
Fields of interest: Human services.
Limitations: Applications not accepted.
Application information: Unsolicited requests for funds not accepted.
EIN: 260206652

5832
The Chapman Perelman Foundation
35 E. 62nd St.
New York City, NY 10065-8014

Donor: Ronald O. Perelman.
Foundation type: Independent foundation.
Financial data (yr. ended 12/31/13): Assets, $0 (M); gifts received, $250,941; expenditures, $250,941; qualifying distributions, $250,941; giving activities include $235,698 for 33 grants (high: $50,000; low: $168), and $15,000 for 1 grant to an individual.
Fields of interest: Education; Health; Human services.
Limitations: Applications not accepted.
Application information: Unsolicited requests for funds not accepted.
Officers and Directors: Anna Chapman, MD, Co-Chair. and Secy.-Treas. and Director; Ronald O. Perelman, Co-Chair. and Director.
EIN: 271862853

5833
Chasanoff Foundation, Inc.
2 Jericho Plz.
Jericho, NY 11753-1658
Contact: Robert W. Chasanoff

Established in 1989 in New York.
Donors: Chasco Co.; Hubspot Co.; Allan Chasanoff; Michael J. Chasanoff; Nancy Chasanoff; Robert Chasanoff; Judith Chasanoff; Stephen Chasanoff.
Foundation type: Independent foundation.

Financial data (yr. ended 06/30/14): Assets, $0 (M); gifts received, $171,000; expenditures, $170,885; qualifying distributions, $171,000; giving activities include $171,000 for 10 grants (high: $100,000; low: $1,000).
Fields of interest: Arts and culture; Performing arts; Higher education; Hospital care; Cancers; Judaism.
Limitations: Applications not accepted. Giving primarily in NY. No grants to individuals.
Application information: Unsolicited requests for funds not accepted.
Officers and Directors: Allan Chasanoff, Pres.; Nancy Chasanoff Butler, V.P. and Mgr. and Director; Robert Chasanoff, V.P. and Director; Stephen Chasanoff, V.P. and Director; Judith Chasanoff, Secy.
EIN: 112978524

5834
Chasdei Y.D.K.E., Inc.
79 Lorimer St.
Brooklyn, NY 11206-4888

Established in 2006 in New York.
Donors: Yeshiva Tiferes Bunim; Jacob Hoffman; Congregation Bais Mordechai; Bais Yaakov Faigeh Schonberger Ofadas Ye; Reb Meir Baal Hanes Kolel Munkasch; Kollel Kol Yakov; Yeshiva Ohel Simon.
Foundation type: Independent foundation.
Financial data (yr. ended 12/31/12): Assets, $3,666,234 (M); gifts received, $391,000; expenditures, $269,424; qualifying distributions, $231,800; giving activities include $231,800 for grants.
Purpose and activities: Giving primarily to Jewish agencies, temples, and schools.
Fields of interest: Elementary and secondary education; Judaism.
Limitations: Applications not accepted. Giving primarily in Brooklyn, NY.
Application information: Unsolicited requests for funds not accepted.
Officer: Jacob Hoffman, Pres.
EIN: 204261948

5835
Chasdei Yakov Foundation Inc.
56 Main St.
Monsey, NY 10952-3011

Donor: Sholem Potash.
Foundation type: Independent foundation.
Financial data (yr. ended 12/31/13): Assets, $0 (M); gifts received, $311,172; expenditures, $303,322; qualifying distributions, $303,248; giving activities include $303,248 for 32 grants (high: $105,592; low: $36).
Fields of interest: Education; Judaism; Human services.
Limitations: Applications not accepted. Giving primarily in Brooklyn, NY.
Application information: Unsolicited requests for funds not accepted.
Directors: Moishe Lichter; Sholem Potash; Riva Zucker.
EIN: 274764203

5836
Owen Cheatham Foundation
40 Sutton Pl., Ste. 6A
New York City, NY   10022-2305
Contact: Kenneth Kennerly, Pres. and Dir.
E-mail: ocfound@aol.com

Donors: Owen Robertson Cheatham†; Celeste W.
Cheatham; Celeste Cheatham O'Neil.
Foundation type: Independent foundation.
Financial data (yr. ended 12/31/13): Assets,
$4,916,467 (M); expenditures, $413,824;
qualifying distributions, $343,755; giving activities
include $237,868 for 21 grants (high: $99,240;
low: $200).
Fields of interest: Arts and culture; Vocal music;
Education; Health; Diseases and conditions;
Christianity; Human services.
Type of support: Research; Research and
evaluation.
Limitations: Applications accepted. Giving primarily
in NY. No grants to individuals.
Application information: Application form required.
Initial approach: Proposal
Deadline(s): None
Board meeting date(s): July
Officers and Directors: Kenneth R. Kennerly, Pres.
and Director; Owen C. Kennerly, V.P. and Director;
McDonald Budd, Secy. and Director; Stephen O'Neil,
Treas. and Director.
Number of staff: 1 full-time professional.
EIN: 136097798

5837
Marc and Elka Chemtob Charitable Foundation
1946 Coney Island Ave.
Brooklyn, NY   11223-2329   (718) 376-5400
Contact: Marc Chemtob, Tr.

Donor: Marc Chemtob.
Foundation type: Independent foundation.
Financial data (yr. ended 12/31/13): Assets,
$1,124,521 (M); gifts received, $247,377;
expenditures, $433,808; qualifying distributions,
$418,977; giving activities include $376,813 for 4
grants (high: $231,000; low: $10,100).
Fields of interest: Judaism.
Limitations: Applications accepted. Giving primarily
in Brooklyn and New York, NY.
Application information: Application form required.
Initial approach: Contact foundation for
application form
Deadline(s): None
Trustees: Elka Chemtob; Marc Chemtob.
EIN: 326070477

5838
The Patricia Chernoff Charitable Trust
c/o WithumSmithBrown, PC
1411 Broadway, 9th Fl.
New York City, NY   10018-3496   (212) 751-9100
Contact: Karen Heath, Tr.

Established in 1991 in New York.
Foundation type: Independent foundation.
Financial data (yr. ended 12/31/13): Assets,
$705,177 (M); expenditures, $227,307; qualifying
distributions, $220,866; giving activities include
$220,000 for 1 grant.
Fields of interest: Philanthropy.

Type of support: Research.
Limitations: Applications accepted. Giving primarily
in New York, NY. No grants to individuals.
Application information:
Initial approach: Letter
Deadline(s): None
Trustees: Karen Heath; Richard L. Ottinger.
EIN: 136971188

5839
The Chervenak-Nunnalle Foundation, Inc.
105 W. 55th St., Ste. 6A
New York City, NY   10019-5336

Donor: James Chervenak.
Foundation type: Independent foundation.
Financial data (yr. ended 12/31/13): Assets,
$3,965,998 (M); expenditures, $348,354;
qualifying distributions, $307,500; giving activities
include $307,500 for 26 grants (high: $25,000;
low: $5,000).
Fields of interest: Arts and culture; Health; Human
services.
Limitations: Applications not accepted. Giving
primarily in MA and NY.
Application information: Unsolicited requests for
funds not accepted .
Officers: James Chervenak, Pres. and Treas.; R.
Edward Townsend, Jr., Secy.
Directors: Gerard I. Borod; Thomas W. Vail.
EIN: 262414940

5840
Chesed Foundation
3920 Cypress Ave.
Brooklyn, NY   11224-1119

Established in 1997 in New York.
Donors: Michael Weiss; Michael Weiss Trust;
Pelstate Trust; Idy Weiss Irrevocable Trust.
Foundation type: Independent foundation.
Financial data (yr. ended 12/31/13): Assets,
$4,495,187 (M); gifts received, $186,083;
expenditures, $440,433; qualifying distributions,
$436,465; giving activities include $264,303 for 12
grants (high: $59,675; low: $3,700).
Fields of interest: Judaism.
Limitations: Applications not accepted. Giving
primarily in Brooklyn, NY. No grants to individuals.
Application information: Contributes only to
pre-selected organizations.
Trustee: Michael Weiss.
EIN: 113364001

5841
Chess Foundation
c/o CNG
3 Manhattanville Rd.
Purchase, NY   10577

Foundation type: Independent foundation.
Financial data (yr. ended 12/31/13): Assets,
$5,308,159 (M); expenditures, $257,350;
qualifying distributions, $244,919; giving activities
include $240,000 for 20 grants (high: $50,000;
low: $1,000).
Fields of interest: Education; Health; Human
services.
Limitations: Applications not accepted.

Application information: Unsolicited requests for
funds not accepted.
Trustees: Caroline Wallach; Scott Wallach.
EIN: 300782279

5842
Children's Foundation of Erie County, Inc.
P.O. Box 560
Kenmore, NY   14217-0560   (716) 877-0418

Established in 1836 in New York.
Donor: Hilary Bradford.
Foundation type: Independent foundation.
Financial data (yr. ended 12/31/14): Assets,
$5,653,414; expenditures, $227,175; qualifying
distributions, $217,659.
Purpose and activities: Giving for organizations
serving needy children in Erie County, New York.
Fields of interest: Education; Health; Human
services; Child welfare; Youth development.
Application information: Application form required.
Initial approach: Proposal
Deadline(s): Jan. 15
Officers: Betsy Mitchell, Pres. and Director;
Elizabeth S. Gurney, V.P. and Director; Ted Walsh,
Secy. and Director; Anne M. Denman, Treas.
Trustees: Bonnie G. Flickinger, Ph.D; Charles J.
Hahn, Esq.; David Edmunds, Esq.; W. Lawrence
Buck; Mary Gresham, Ph.D; Richard W. Cutting;
Rosa Gonzalez, Ph.D; Warren E. Emblidge, Jr.
EIN: 166000171

5843
Lois Chiles Foundation
c/o Anchin
1375 Broadway
New York City, NY   10018-7001

Established in 2004 in New York.
Donors: Great Circle Trust; Lois Chiles; Richard
Gilder.
Foundation type: Independent foundation.
Financial data (yr. ended 12/31/14): Assets,
$1,450,102; expenditures, $169,841; qualifying
distributions, $161,750.
Fields of interest: Arts and culture; Education;
Human services.
Type of support: General support.
Limitations: Applications not accepted. Giving in the
U.S., primarily in New York, NY, and TX. No grants to
individuals.
Application information: Unsolicited requests for
funds not accepted.
Officers: Lois Chiles, Pres.; Sue Kiel, V.P.; Gary S.
Castle, Secy.
EIN: 201673659

5844
Chinook Charitable Trust
c/o BCRS Associates, LLC
77 Water St., 9th Fl.
New York City, NY   10005-4414

Foundation type: Independent foundation.
Financial data (yr. ended 11/30/13): Assets,
$1,201,792 (M); expenditures, $168,955;
qualifying distributions, $165,830; giving activities
include $165,000 for 8 grants (high: $50,000; low:
$5,000).

Fields of interest: Disasters and emergency management; Human services.
International interests: Canada; England.
Limitations: Applications not accepted. Giving primarily in NY, with some giving in Canada and England. No grants to individuals.
Application information: Unsolicited requests for funds not accepted.
Trustee: Wesley R. Edens.
EIN: 137391437

5845
Dominick & Rose Ciampa Foundation Inc.
c/o Dominick Ciampa, Gibgot Willenbacher & Co.
100 Hilton Ave., Ste. PH8
Garden City, NY 11530-1564

Established in 1999 in New York.
Donors: Dominick Ciampa; Rose Ciampa.
Foundation type: Independent foundation.
Financial data (yr. ended 12/31/13): Assets, $5,492,654 (M); expenditures, $212,410; qualifying distributions, $211,323; giving activities include $190,976 for 35 grants (high: $26,800; low: $500).
Fields of interest: Arts and culture; Education; Environment; Foundations; Catholicism; Human services.
Limitations: Applications not accepted. Giving primarily in NY. No grants to individuals.
Application information: Unsolicited requests for funds not accepted.
Officers: Dominick Ciampa, Pres.; Rose Ciampa, V.P.; Christine Ciampa, Mgr.
EIN: 113466090

5846
Herbert M. Citrin Charitable Foundation Inc.
1 Penn Plz., Ste. 3100
New York City, NY 10119-3100 (212) 695-8100
Contact: Howard M. Rubin Esq., Pres.

Established in 2004 in New York.
Foundation type: Independent foundation.
Financial data (yr. ended 12/31/13): Assets, $5,237,443 (M); expenditures, $298,218; qualifying distributions, $250,000; giving activities include $250,000 for 6 grants (high: $100,000; low: $12,500).
Fields of interest: Nonprofits; Human services; Child development.
Type of support: Regranting.
Limitations: Applications accepted. Giving primarily in NY.
Application information: Application form required.
Initial approach: Letter
Deadline(s): None
Officers: Howard M. Rubin, Pres.; Jane McGimsey, V.P.; Brian Zimmerman, Secy.
EIN: 260095080

5847
The Ulrika and Joel Citron Family Foundation
c/o Joel Citron
271 Central Park W.
New York City, NY 10024

Established in 2006 in New York.

Donor: Joel-Tomas Citron.
Foundation type: Independent foundation.
Financial data (yr. ended 12/31/13): Assets, $425,068 (M); gifts received, $55,000; expenditures, $326,844; qualifying distributions, $326,000; giving activities include $326,000 for 6 grants (high: $105,000; low: $6,000).
Fields of interest: Arts and culture; Education; Human services.
Limitations: Applications not accepted. Giving primarily in NY.
Application information: Unsolicited requests for funds not accepted.
Trustees: Joel-Tomas Citron; Ulrika Citron.
EIN: 208049477

5848
Frank E. Clark Charitable Trust
(formerly Clark Charitable Fund)
c/o JPMorgan Chase Bank, Philanthropic Svcs.
270 Park Ave., 16th Fl.
New York City, NY 10017-2014
Contact: Jonathan G. Horowitz, Prog. Off.
FAX: (212) 464-2304;
E-mail: Jonathan.g.horowitz@jpmchase.com; Main URL: http://fdnweb.org/feclark
Grants List: http://fdnweb.org/feclark/grants/year/contributions

Established in 1936 in New York.
Donor: Frank E. Clark†.
Foundation type: Independent foundation.
Financial data (yr. ended 12/31/13): Assets, $5,719,019 (M); expenditures, $332,795; qualifying distributions, $274,233; giving activities include $255,000 for 6 grants (high: $90,000; low: $30,000).
Purpose and activities: Giving primarily (through regional and national denominational bodies) for small churches and services for very low-income adults, including people who are homeless.
Fields of interest: Religion; Homeless people; Low-income and poor people.
Type of support: Program development; Capital campaigns.
Limitations: Applications accepted. Giving limited to New York, NY, for programs serving homeless adults; giving on a national basis for small churches. No support for private foundations. No grants to individuals or private foundations; no matching gifts or loans.
Publications: Application guidelines; Grants list.
Application information: With respect to grants to churches, only solicited proposals are accepted. Complete guidelines available on Trust web site.
Initial approach: Proposal
Copies of proposal: 1
Deadline(s): July 31
Board meeting date(s): Oct.
Final notification: Dec. 31
Trustee: JPMorgan Chase Bank, N.A.
Number of staff: None.
EIN: 136049032

5849
Clarkson Family Foundation
45 Sutton Pl. S.
New York City, NY 10022-2444

Established in 1996 in New York.
Donor: Bayard D. Clarkson, MD.

Foundation type: Independent foundation.
Financial data (yr. ended 12/31/13): Assets, $2,735,721 (M); expenditures, $165,508; qualifying distributions, $147,555; giving activities include $145,500 for 15 grants (high: $45,000; low: $1,000).
Fields of interest: Education; Domesticated animals; Diseases and conditions.
Type of support: Research.
Limitations: Applications not accepted. No grants to individuals.
Application information: Unsolicited requests for funds not accepted.
Trustees: Bayard D. Clarkson; Virginia C. Clarkson.
EIN: 137088453

5850
Louis & Virginia Clemente Foundation Inc.
c/o C. Caufield, Kelley Drye Warren LLP
101 Park Ave.
New York City, NY 10178-0001

Established in 1975 in New York.
Foundation type: Independent foundation.
Financial data (yr. ended 12/31/13): Assets, $4,484,916 (M); expenditures, $221,275; qualifying distributions, $213,588; giving activities include $211,000 for grants.
Fields of interest: Arts and culture; Museums; Art museums; Natural history museums; Education; Environment; Health; Diseases and conditions; Parkinson's disease; Human services; Food banks; Women's services.
Type of support: Scholarships.
Limitations: Applications not accepted. Giving primarily in NY. No grants to individuals.
Application information: Unsolicited requests for funds not accepted.
Officers: Harry A. LeBien, Pres.; Mary Ellen LeBien, Secy.
Directors: Laurent C. LeBien; Thomas E. LeBien; Michele LeBien Maxwell.
EIN: 510163549

5851
Cline Foundation
c/o BCRS Assocs., LLC
77 Water St., 9th Fl.
New York City, NY 10005-3701

Donors: J. Michael Cline; Fraydun Foundation.
Foundation type: Independent foundation.
Financial data (yr. ended 12/31/13): Assets, $300,633 (M); gifts received, $1,818,500; expenditures, $287,642; qualifying distributions, $283,810; giving activities include $180,451 for 6 grants (high: $50,000; low: $150).
Fields of interest: Natural history museums; Elementary and secondary education; Higher education; Domesticated animals.
Limitations: Applications not accepted. Giving primarily in CT, DC, MA, and NY. No grants to individuals.
Application information: Contributes only to pre-selected organizations.
Trustee: J. Michael Cline.
EIN: 223650542

5852
The Coby Foundation, Ltd.
511 Avenue of the Americas, No. 387
New York City, NY   10011-8436   (212) 741-7022
Contact: Ward L.E. Mintz, Exec. Dir.
FAX: (212) 741-6236;
E-mail: cobyfound@nyc.rr.com; Main URL: http://
www.cobyfoundation.org

Donor: Irene Zambelli Silverman†.
Foundation type: Independent foundation.
Financial data (yr. ended 12/31/14): Assets,
$13,194,096 (M); expenditures, $571,543;
qualifying distributions, $465,024; giving activities
include $369,500 for 15 grants (high: $50,000;
low: $1,000).
Purpose and activities: The foundation funds
projects in the textile and needle arts field. Its
funding is limited to non-profit organizations in the
Mid-Atlantic and New England.
Fields of interest: Arts and culture; Visual arts; Art
conservation; Design.
Type of support: Program development.
Application information: For complete application
information see foundation web site:
www.cobyfoundation.org. Application form required.
  Initial approach: Letter of inquiry
  Copies of proposal: 7
  Deadline(s): Six weeks before Jan., May, and
    Sept. quarterly meetings. Contact Exec. Dir. for
    exact dates
  Board meeting date(s): 3 times per year: Jan.,
    May, Sept.
  Final notification: Within 2 months of application
Officers and Directors: Leslie Shanken, Chair. and
Director; Rosemarie Garipoli, Vice-Chair. and
Director; Lucille A. Roussin, Secy. and Director; Lea
Paine Highet, Treas. and Director; Ward L.E. Mintz,
Exec. Dir.; Scott L. Fulmer; Martha C. Howell.
Number of staff: 1 part-time professional.
EIN: 133781874

5853
The Robert and Suzanne Cochran Family Foundation
145 Hudson St., Ste. 14A
New York City, NY   10013-2151

Established in 2000 in New York.
Donor: Robert P. Cochran.
Foundation type: Independent foundation.
Financial data (yr. ended 12/31/13): Assets,
$137,205 (M); gifts received, $75,000;
expenditures, $259,427; qualifying distributions,
$259,192; giving activities include $253,842 for 38
grants (high: $50,000; low: $60).
Fields of interest: Arts and culture; Art museums;
Education; Higher education; Environment;
Diseases and conditions.
Type of support: Research.
Limitations: Applications not accepted. Giving
primarily in NC and NY. No grants to individuals.
Application information: Contributes only to
pre-selected organizations.
Trustees: Robert P. Cochran; Suzanne H. Cochran.
EIN: 134118739

5854
Code Blue Charitable Foundation, Inc.
c/o Ashford Advisors, LLC
30B Grove St.
Pittsford, NY   14534-1334
Contact: P. Martin

Established in 2006 in Delaware.
Foundation type: Independent foundation.
Financial data (yr. ended 12/31/13): Assets,
$3,952,177 (M); gifts received, $1,008,996;
expenditures, $544,180; qualifying distributions,
$518,788; giving activities include $415,500 for 41
grants (high: $35,000; low: $250).
Fields of interest: Environment; Domesticated
animals; Human services.
Limitations: Applications not accepted. Giving
primarily in CA, Washington, DC and NY. No grants
to individuals.
Application information: Contributes only to
pre-selected organizations.
Officers and Directors: Shari Sant Plummer, Pres.
and Treas. and Director; Daniel Lee Plummer, Secy.
and Director.
EIN: 421718790

5855
The Cogitare Foundation
(formerly The Leonard & Charlotte Cooper
Foundation)
9 Waccabuc River Ln.
South Salem, NY   10590-1117
E-mail: info@cogitarefoundation.org; Main
URL: http://cogitarefoundation.org

Established in 1998 in Delaware.
Donors: Peter D. Cooper; Elaine Scialo; Joe
Scarpinito; S & C Investors, LLC; Weitz & Luxenberg;
Sloan Cooper; Mary Cooper.
Foundation type: Independent foundation.
Financial data (yr. ended 03/31/13): Assets,
$1,556,114 (M); gifts received, $83,511;
expenditures, $259,944; qualifying distributions,
$257,693; giving activities include $236,704 for 4
grants (high: $131,689; low: $17,830).
Purpose and activities: Giving primarily for the
improvement of people's lives in Africa by funding
programs that directly develop African communities,
including building houses, providing educational
opportunities, improving health care, and any other
creative approach to the problems faced by the poor.
Fields of interest: Higher education; Health;
Economic development; Housing development.
International interests: Africa.
Type of support: Continuing support; Pro bono
consulting services; Grants to individuals; Building
and renovations; Equipment; Internships;
Scholarships; Technical assistance.
Limitations: Applications not accepted. Giving
primarily in CA. No support for religious
organizations.
Application information: Unsolicited requests for
funds not accepted.
  Board meeting date(s): Apr. 27, Aug. 21
Officers: Randall Cooper, Chair.; Elaine Scialo,
Pres.; Peter D. Cooper, V.P.
EIN: 133998983

5856
The Craig & Deborah Cogut Foundation, Inc.
c/o L.H. Frishkoff & Co. LLP
529 5th Ave., 9th Fl.
New York City, NY   10017-4608

Donors: Craig Cogut; Deborah Cogut.
Foundation type: Independent foundation.
Financial data (yr. ended 12/31/13): Assets,
$284,424 (M); gifts received, $200,000;
expenditures, $200,432; qualifying distributions,
$200,432; giving activities include $200,000 for 1
grant.
Purpose and activities: Giving primarily for music
education.
Fields of interest: Music; Museums; Education;
Higher education.
Limitations: Applications not accepted. Giving
primarily in CT. No grants to individuals.
Application information: Contributes only to
pre-selected organizations.
Officers: Craig Cogut, Pres.; Deborah Cogut,
Secy.-Treas.
EIN: 133746440

5857
The Abby and David Cohen Family Foundation
Bowling Green Station
P.O. Box 73
New York City, NY   10274-0073

Established in 1999 in New York.
Donor: Abby J. Cohen.
Foundation type: Independent foundation.
Financial data (yr. ended 03/31/14): Assets,
$7,352,097 (M); gifts received, $598,766;
expenditures, $421,030; qualifying distributions,
$412,645; giving activities include $412,645 for 33
grants (high: $100,000; low: $1,000).
Purpose and activities: Giving primarily to Jewish
organizations; funding also for higher education,
health care, and the arts.
Fields of interest: Museums; Education; Higher
education; Graduate and professional education;
Nonprofits; Health; Judaism; Theology; Human
services.
Type of support: Regranting.
Limitations: Applications not accepted. Giving
primarily in New York, NY; funding also in Ithaca. No
grants to individuals.
Application information: Contributes only to
pre-selected organizations.
Trustees: Abby J. Cohen; David M. Cohen; Ellen M.
Cohen; Lauren G. Cohen.
EIN: 134090442

5858
Cohen Family Foundation, Inc.
The Ayco Co., LP
P.O. Box 860
Saratoga Springs, NY   12866-0860
Contact: Matthew Moore

Established in 1986 in New York.
Donors: Peter A. Cohen; Florence Cohen†; William
L. Cohen.
Foundation type: Independent foundation.
Financial data (yr. ended 12/31/13): Assets,
$202,833 (M); gifts received, $301,000;

expenditures, $139,700; qualifying distributions, $134,007; giving activities include $130,027 for 36 grants (high: $25,000; low: $100).
Purpose and activities: Giving primarily for Jewish institutions, higher education, and hospitals.
Fields of interest: Education; Health; Human services.
Limitations: Applications not accepted. Giving primarily in New York, NY; some giving in OH. No grants to individuals.
Application information: Contributes only to pre-selected organizations.
Officers: Peter A. Cohen, Pres.; William L. Cohen, V.P.; Lauren Cohen, Secy.; Andrew Cohen, Treas.
Director: Michele Cohen.
EIN: 133183001

5859
Joseph M. & Barbara Cohen Foundation, Inc.
410 E. 57th St.
New York City, NY   10022-3059

Established in 1990 in New York.
Donor: Joseph M. Cohen.
Foundation type: Independent foundation.
Financial data (yr. ended 10/31/13): Assets, $17,485 (M); gifts received, $119,806; expenditures, $285,101; qualifying distributions, $279,135; giving activities include $277,750 for 20 grants (high: $25,000; low: $1,000).
Purpose and activities: Giving primarily for art and cultural programs, medical research, social services, and Jewish organizations.
Fields of interest: Arts and culture; Diseases and conditions; Judaism; Human services; Food delivery.
Type of support: Research; Research and evaluation.
Limitations: Applications not accepted. Giving primarily in New York, NY. No grants to individuals.
Application information: Contributes only to pre-selected organizations.
Officers: Joseph M. Cohen, Pres.; Jarrod Cohen, Secy.; Raymond Merritt, Esq., Treas.
EIN: 133636511

5860
Karen B. Cohen Foundation, Inc.
c/o Stanley Garber
515 Madison Ave., 29th Fl.
New York City, NY   10022-5420

Donor: Karen B. Cohen.
Foundation type: Independent foundation.
Financial data (yr. ended 12/31/13): Assets, $2,870 (M); gifts received, $212,000; expenditures, $216,369; qualifying distributions, $216,369; giving activities include $216,275 for 25 grants (high: $50,000; low: $25).
Fields of interest: Arts and culture; Opera; Art museums; Education; Diseases and conditions; Libraries; Judaism.
Limitations: Applications not accepted. Giving primarily in New York, NY. No grants to individuals.
Application information: Contributes only to pre-selected organizations.
Officer: Karen B. Cohen, Pres.
EIN: 133833164

5861
Jacques & Emy Cohenca Foundation Inc.
550 Park Ave.
New York City, NY   10021-7369

Established in 1979 in New York.
Donors: Emy Cohenca; Jacques Cohenca†; Jason Industrial, Inc.; Jason of Illinois, Inc.; TBMC, Inc.
Foundation type: Independent foundation.
Financial data (yr. ended 12/31/13): Assets, $2,307,771 (M); gifts received, $100,000; expenditures, $395,643; qualifying distributions, $374,650; giving activities include $370,665 for 48 grants (high: $80,000; low: $250).
Fields of interest: Arts and culture; Museums; University education; Nonprofits; Hospital care; Diseases and conditions; Judaism; Human services.
Type of support: Regranting.
Limitations: Applications not accepted. Giving primarily in the greater metropolitan New York, NY, area. No grants to individuals.
Application information: Unsolicited requests for funds not accepted.
Officers: Emy Cohenca, Pres.; Philip Cohenca, Treas.
Director: Nevine Michaan.
EIN: 133022911

5862
Charles Cohn Foundation Inc.
c/o Marc S. Cohn
53 N. Park Ave., Ste. 302
Rockville Centre, NY   11570-4111

Donor: Marc S. Cohn.
Foundation type: Independent foundation.
Financial data (yr. ended 11/30/14): Assets, $5,344,186; expenditures, $258,156; qualifying distributions, $256,389.
Purpose and activities: The foundation provides donations to charitable organizations with a focus on medical care and research, and religious, educational, and cultural purposes.
Fields of interest: Arts and culture; Museums; Education; Specialty hospital care; Diseases and conditions; Religion; Judaism.
Type of support: Research.
Limitations: Applications not accepted. Giving primarily in NY. No grants to individuals.
Application information: Contributes only to pre-selected organizations.
Officers: Marc S. Cohn, Pres.; Daniel Cohn, V.P. and Treas.; Ellen Menscher, V.P.
EIN: 136129449

5863
Peter A. and Elizabeth S. Cohn Foundation, Inc.
1700 Broadway, No. 41
New York City, NY   10019-4613
Contact: John P. Engel, V.P. and Secy.

Established in 1955 in New York.
Donors: Peter A. Cohn†; Elizabeth S. Cohn†; John M. Angelo.
Foundation type: Independent foundation.
Financial data (yr. ended 06/30/15): Assets, $3,814,802 (M); expenditures, $328,332; qualifying distributions, $264,080; giving activities include $255,000 for 26 grants (high: $105,000; low: $500).

Fields of interest: Arts and culture; Higher education; Hospital care.
Application information: Application form required.
   Initial approach: Letter
   Deadline(s): None
Officers and Directors: John M. Angelo, Pres. and Director; John P. Engel, V.P. and Secy. and Director; Richard L. Grossman, V.P. and Treas. and Director.
EIN: 136117647

5864
Sol Cohn Foundation
c/o Zapken & Loeb, LLP
99 Woodbury Rd.
Hicksville, NY   11801   (516) 822-5000
Contact: Paul Cohn, Pres. and Director
Application address: c/o Seymour Cohn, 3687 Dijon Way, Palm Beach Gardens, FL 33410, tel.: (516) 482-3907

Established in 1952 in New York.
Foundation type: Independent foundation.
Financial data (yr. ended 04/30/14): Assets, $3,503,121 (M); expenditures, $176,948; qualifying distributions, $173,241; giving activities include $160,000 for 56 grants (high: $10,000; low: $500).
Fields of interest: Arts and culture; Education; Nonprofits; Religion; Judaism.
Type of support: General support; Regranting.
Limitations: Applications accepted. Giving primarily in NY. No grants to individuals.
Application information:
   Initial approach: Proposal
   Deadline(s): None
Officers and Directors: Paul Cohn, Pres. and Director; Marshall S. Cohn, V.P. and Director; Harold Cohn, Secy. and Director; Martin Cohn, Treas. and Director; Doris Cohn; Seymour Cohn.
EIN: 116005703

5865
Cohoes Savings Foundation
60 Remsen St.
P.O. Box 230
Cohoes, NY   12047-2833
E-mail: brennaja@nycap.rr.com; Main URL: http://www.cohoessavingsfoundation.org

Donors: Cohoes Savings Bank; Hudson River Bank & Trust Co.
Foundation type: Company-sponsored foundation.
Financial data (yr. ended 12/31/14): Assets, $4,354,380; expenditures, $315,413; qualifying distributions, $275,332.
Purpose and activities: The foundation supports organizations involved with arts and culture, health, human services, community development, and religion. Special emphasis is directed toward programs designed to promote self-help and self-sufficiency.
Fields of interest: Arts and culture; Health; Community and economic development; Human services; Developmental disability services; Unknown or not classified.
Type of support: Program development; Curriculum development; Scholarships; Research; Sponsorships.
Limitations: Applications accepted. Giving primarily in Albany, Rensselaer, Saratoga, Schenectady, and

Warren counties, NY. No support for religious organizations. No grants to individuals.
Publications: Application guidelines.
Application information: Application form required.
Initial approach: Request application form
Copies of proposal: 1
Deadline(s): None
Board meeting date(s): Quarterly
Officers and Directors: Harry L. Robinson, Chair. and Director; Frank D. Colarutolo, Secy. and Director; Chester C. DeLaMater, Treas. and Director; Jacqueline E. Brennan, Exec. Dir.; Albert Pasinella.
Number of staff: 1 full-time professional.
EIN: 141809837

5866
Deo B. Colburn Education Foundation
P.O. Box 824
Lake Placid, NY 12946-0824
Contact: Margaret E. Doran, Treas.

Established in 1987 in New York.
Donor: Deo B. Colburn.
Foundation type: Independent foundation.
Financial data (yr. ended 06/30/14): Assets, $6,561,337 (M); gifts received, $2,865; expenditures, $319,805; qualifying distributions, $285,441; giving activities include $252,750 for 277 grants to individuals (high: $1,500; low: $500).
Purpose and activities: Scholarship awards for post-secondary education to residents of the northeast portions of the Adirondack Park in northern NY.
Fields of interest: Higher education.
Type of support: Student aid.
Limitations: Applications accepted. Giving limited to the Adirondack region of northern NY.
Application information: Application can be obtained by contacting foundation or from guidance officer at qualifying high school. Application form required.
Initial approach: Proposal
Copies of proposal: 5
Deadline(s): Apr. 15
Officers and Directors: Craig Randall, Pres. and Director; John Lansing, V.P. and Director; Stephen Reed, Secy. and Director; Margaret E. Doran, Treas. and Director.
EIN: 222777121

5867
Robert & Patricia Colby Foundation
1100 Wehrle Dr., 2nd Fl.
Buffalo, NY 14221

Established in 1989 in New York.
Donors: Patricia Colby; P. Colby Unitrust.
Foundation type: Independent foundation.
Financial data (yr. ended 12/31/13): Assets, $4,136,079 (M); expenditures, $384,314; qualifying distributions, $335,000; giving activities include $335,000 for 31 grants (high: $45,000; low: $1,000).
Fields of interest: Orchestral music; Elementary and secondary education; Cancers; Religion; Sports and recreation.
Type of support: Advocacy.
Limitations: Applications not accepted. Giving primarily in Buffalo, NY. No grants to individuals.
Application information: Contributes only to pre-selected organizations.

Trustees: James M. Wadsworth; Michael Wadsworth; Manufacturers and Traders Trust Co.
EIN: 161315877

5868
Kenneth Cole Foundation
c/o TAG Assocs.
810 7th Ave.. 7th Fl.
New York City, NY 10019-5818

Established in 1994 in New York.
Donors: Kenneth D. Cole; The Wagner Family Foundation; The Harry Walker Agency, Inc.
Foundation type: Independent foundation.
Financial data (yr. ended 04/30/14): Assets, $13,507,900 (M); expenditures, $327,178; qualifying distributions, $289,550; giving activities include $289,500 for 23 grants (high: $100,000; low: $500).
Purpose and activities: Giving primarily for AIDS research; funding also for higher education, as well as for health associations.
Fields of interest: Arts and culture; Education; Higher education; Philanthropy; Foundations; Diseases and conditions; HIV/AIDS; Human services; Family services; Child welfare.
Type of support: Research.
Limitations: Applications not accepted. Giving primarily in NY; some giving also in Providence, RI. No grants to individuals.
Application information: Contributes only to pre-selected organizations.
Trustees: Kenneth D. Cole; Maria Cuomo Cole.
EIN: 133799161

5869
Roger V. Coleman Family Foundation Inc.
6 Brookside Dr.
Plandome, NY 11030-1405 (212) 935-1555
Contact: Roger V. Coleman, Pres.

Donor: Roger V. Coleman.
Foundation type: Independent foundation.
Financial data (yr. ended 12/31/13): Assets, $1,279,269 (M); gifts received, $650,000; expenditures, $342,915; qualifying distributions, $341,575; giving activities include $341,575 for 31 grants (high: $125,000; low: $25).
Fields of interest: Health care clinics; Diseases and conditions; Family services.
Type of support: Research.
Application information: Application form required.
Initial approach: Letter
Deadline(s): None
Officers: Roger V. Coleman, Pres.; Magaret M. Coleman, Secy.
Director: Joseph B. Sprung.
EIN: 271536756

5870
The Coleman Foundation
c/o Montrose Accounting
505 Park Ave., 20th Fl.
New York City, NY 10022-9306

Established in 1962 in New York.
Donors: Janet M. Coleman; Martin S. Coleman†; James Coleman.
Foundation type: Independent foundation.

Financial data (yr. ended 11/30/14): Assets, $4,640,524 (M); expenditures, $340,549; qualifying distributions, $288,604; giving activities include $276,900 for 26 grants (high: $54,000; low: $1,000).
Purpose and activities: Giving primarily for Jewish organizations, including welfare funds and temple support; giving also for health and human services.
Fields of interest: Education; Nonprofits; Health; Hospital care; Judaism; Human services.
Type of support: General support; Regranting.
Limitations: Applications not accepted. Giving primarily in AZ, Los Angeles, CA and New York, NY. No grants to individuals, or for endowment funds.
Application information: Contributes only to pre-selected organizations.
Trustee: John Coleman.
EIN: 136126040

5871
The Coles Family Foundation
c/o Wiener Frushtick & Straub PC
500 5th Ave., Ste. 2610
New York City, NY 10110-2699

Established in 1980 in New York.
Donors: Michael H. Coles; Joan C. Coles†.
Foundation type: Independent foundation.
Financial data (yr. ended 03/31/13): Assets, $436,708 (M); gifts received, $349,193; expenditures, $184,011; qualifying distributions, $173,212; giving activities include $173,212 for 79 grants (high: $15,000; low: $100).
Purpose and activities: Giving primarily for the arts, education, youth and social services, hospitals, particularly a cancer center, and to Roman Catholic and Protestant churches.
Fields of interest: Arts and culture; Theater; Elementary and secondary education; Medical education; Hospital care; Specialty hospital care; Protestantism; Catholicism; Human services; Child welfare.
Type of support: General support; Endowments.
Limitations: Applications not accepted. Giving primarily in the greater metropolitan New York, NY, area, as well as Long Island, particularly Shelter Island. No grants to individuals.
Application information: Contributes only to pre-selected organizations.
Trustees: Alison Aldredge; Isobel Coleman; Douglas Coles; Michael H. Coles; Richard Coles; Caroline Scudder; Roy C. Smith.
Number of staff: 1 part-time support.
EIN: 133050747

5872
Community Foundation of Orange County, Inc.
(also known as Community Foundation of Orange and Sullivan County)
(formerly Community Foundation of Orange and Sullivan, Inc.)
30 Scott's Corner Dr., Ste. 202
Montgomery, NY 12549-2262 (845) 769-9393
Contact: Karen VanHouten Minogue, Pres. and C.E.O.

FAX: (845) 769-9391; E-mail: admin@cfosny.org;
Additional e-mail: vanhouten@cfo-ny.org; Main
URL: http://www.cfoc-ny.org
Facebook: http://www.facebook.com/pages/
The-Community-Foundation-of-Orange-and-Sullivan/
120738087979457
LinkedIn: https://www.linkedin.com/pub/
community-foundation-of-orange-sullivan/
67/263/797
RSS feed: http://
www.yourcommunityfoundations.org/feed
Twitter: https://www.twitter.com/CFOCny

Established in 1999 in New York.
Donors: James Ottaway Jr. Trust; Provident Bank
Charitable Foundation; Mr. R.J. Smith; Mrs. R.J.
Smith; Gerry Foundation.
Foundation type: Community foundation.
Financial data (yr. ended 06/30/14): Assets,
$12,318,758 (M); gifts received, $1,783,766;
expenditures, $992,250; giving activities include
$337,774 for 7+ grants (high: $31,750), and
$99,550 for 91 grants to individuals.
Purpose and activities: The foundation, through
effective use of its endowment, seeks to enhance
the quality of life for those who live and work within
Orange County by encouraging the growth of a
permanent charitable endowment to meet the
community's immediate and emerging needs, and
by providing vehicles for donors with diverse
philanthropic interests in a way that makes giving
easy, personally satisfying, effective, and lasting.
Fields of interest: Health; Senior services.
Type of support: Student aid; Loans to individuals;
Scholarships; Endowments.
Limitations: Applications accepted. Giving primarily
in Orange County and Sullivan County, NY.
Publications: Annual report; Financial statement;
Grants list; Informational brochure; Newsletter.
Application information:
  Initial approach: Contact foundation
  Copies of proposal: 1
  Deadline(s): None
  Board meeting date(s): Every other month
Officers and Directors: Derrik Wynkoop, Chair. and
Director; Josh Sommers, Chair. Elect. and Director;
Tim McCausland, 1st Vice-Chair. and Director;
Michael Bonura, 2nd Vice-Chair. and Director;
William Bratton, 3rd Vice-Chair. and Director;
Katharine Fitzgerald, Secy. and Director; Jack
Berkowitz, Treas. and Director; Christopher Corallo,
Asst. Treas. and Director; Karen VanHouten
Minogue, Exec. Dir.; Anne Palmer Moss, Founding
Exec. Dir.; David Cocks, Emeritus; Ruth Kassel,
Emeritus; James H. Ottaway, Jr., Emeritus; John
Davies; Eric Fuentes; Philip Guarnieri; Gerald N.
Jacobowitz; Dr. Michelle A. Koury; Wayne Martin;
Susan Najork; Bonnie Orr; Andrew Pavloff; Raymond
J. Quattrini; Richard Shapiro, Esq.; Gerald J. Skoda;
Maggie Smith; R.J. Smith; Joe Vanderhoof; Amanda
Ward; Todd Whitney; Dr. Michele Winchester-Vega;
Wayne Zanetti.
Number of staff: 1 full-time professional; 1 full-time
support; 1 part-time support.
EIN: 061551843

5873
Companions in Courage Foundation
(formerly The LaFontaine Foundation)
325 Essjay Rd., Ste. 405
Williamsville, NY   14221-8214
Contact: Roger Simon

Main URL: http://www.CiC16.org
Facebook: http://www.facebook.com/pages/
Capanions-in-Courage-Foundation/125570560360
Twitter: https://twitter.com/CiC16foundation

Established in 1999 in New York.
Donors: Patrick "Pat" LaFontaine; Bill Isenberg;
Craig Hetherington; National Hockey League.
Foundation type: Independent foundation.
Financial data (yr. ended 12/31/13): Assets,
$494,390 (M); gifts received, $283,283;
expenditures, $417,361; qualifying distributions,
$408,568; giving activities include $215,974 for 2
+ grants (high: $215,050).
Purpose and activities: Giving primarily for the
installation of playrooms for children's hospitals.
Fields of interest: Children's hospital care; Children.
International interests: Canada.
Limitations: Applications not accepted. Giving
primarily in NY; with some funding also in Ottawa,
Canada. No grants to individuals.
Application information: Unsolicited requests for
funds not accepted.
Officers: Patrick "Pat" LaFontaine, Pres.; James
Johnson, Secy.; Roger Simon, Treas.
Directors: Marybeth LaFontaine; Dr. Sean Levchuck;
Rich Pluta; George Ross; Jerome Wood.
EIN: 161493691

5874
The John Conley Foundation for Ethics and Philosophy in Medicine
c/o James McGarry
25 Coolidge St., Ste. 1511
Larchmont, NY   10538
Contact: Monika Conley, Pres.

Established in 1991 in New York.
Donor: John Conley.
Foundation type: Independent foundation.
Financial data (yr. ended 12/31/13): Assets,
$4,321,277 (M); expenditures, $283,237;
qualifying distributions, $243,465; giving activities
include $214,360 for 4 grants (high: $110,000;
low: $5,000).
Fields of interest: Medical education; Health;
Hospital care.
Limitations: Applications accepted. Giving primarily
in New York, NY.
Application information:
  Initial approach: Proposal
  Deadline(s): None
Officers: Monika Conley, Pres.; Thomas Forlenza,
Treas.
Directors: Charles Cummings; Ivo P. Janecka.
EIN: 133626727

5875
Coremet Charitable Foundation
160 Broadway
New York City, NY   10038-4201

Donors: Elliot Czermak; Warren Katzman; Leo
Horowitz.
Foundation type: Independent foundation.
Financial data (yr. ended 12/31/14): Assets,
$190,580; gifts received, $150,000; expenditures,
$305,515; qualifying distributions, $305,410.
Fields of interest: Judaism.
Limitations: Applications not accepted. Giving
primarily in Brooklyn, NY. No grants to individuals.

Application information: Contributes only to
pre-selected organizations.
Officers: Leo Horowitz, Pres.; Elliot Czermak, V.P.;
Warren Katzman, V.P.
EIN: 208016257

5876
The Cornell Family Foundation
(formerly The Henry Cornell Foundation)
P.O. Box 73
Bowling Green Sta.
New York City, NY   10274-0073

Established in 1996 in New York.
Donors: Henry Cornell; Sotheby's; Sotheby's
Auction House.
Foundation type: Independent foundation.
Financial data (yr. ended 08/31/13): Assets,
$2,172,409 (M); gifts received, $90,000;
expenditures, $356,446; qualifying distributions,
$356,016; giving activities include $356,016 for 16
grants (high: $66,016; low: $1,000).
Fields of interest: Arts and culture; Art museums;
Higher education.
Limitations: Applications not accepted. Giving
primarily in New York, NY; some funding also in CA.
No grants to individuals.
Application information: Contributes only to
pre-selected organizations.
Trustees: Henry Cornell; Vanessa Cornell.
EIN: 133921374

5877
Cornell/Weinstein Family Foundation
39 Tobey Brook
Pittsford, NY   14534

Established in 1985 in New York.
Foundation type: Independent foundation.
Financial data (yr. ended 12/31/13): Assets,
$4,197,282 (M); expenditures, $272,968;
qualifying distributions, $234,000; giving activities
include $234,000 for 21 grants (high: $60,000;
low: $500).
Fields of interest: Arts and culture; Education;
Nonprofits; Judaism; Human services; Unknown or
not classified.
Type of support: Regranting.
Limitations: Applications not accepted. Giving
primarily in NY. No grants to individuals.
Application information: Contributes only to
pre-selected organizations.
Officers: Sherwin Weinstein, Secy.; Linda Cornell
Weinstein, Exec. Dir.
Directors: David Cornell; Michael Cornell; Olivia
Cornell; Joshua Weinstein; Rachel Weinstein.
EIN: 161264534

5878
The Cornerstone Foundation
6 D.A. Wieder Blvd., Ste. 201
Monroe, NY   10950-9111   (718) 302-3800
Contact: Rafael Ekstein, Tr.

Established in 2006 in New York.
Donors: Rafael Eckstein; Devorah Eckstein; Chana
Sasha Foundation Inc.
Foundation type: Independent foundation.
Financial data (yr. ended 12/31/13):
Assets, -$10,703 (M); gifts received, $200,000;

expenditures, $156,028; qualifying distributions, $153,933; giving activities include $153,933 for 28 grants (high: $22,600; low: $1,000).
Fields of interest: Religion.
Application information:
Initial approach: Proposal
Deadline(s): None
Trustees: Gittel Eckstein; Rafael Eckstein.
EIN: 204814176

5879
The Correspondents Fund
c/o The New York Times
620 8th Ave.
New York City, NY   10018
Contact: Barbara Baumgarten
Main URL: http://correspondentsfund.org

Foundation type: Independent foundation.
Financial data (yr. ended 04/30/14): Assets, $497,747 (M); expenditures, $162,308; qualifying distributions, $154,451; giving activities include $150,500 for 10 grants (high: $30,000; low: $2,500).
Purpose and activities: Provides temporary emergency relief and aid to men and women who have served in the U.S. press (television, radio, news, film or other U.S. organization) or abroad. Giving also for foreign press or other news organizations assistance to their spouse and children.
Fields of interest: Education; Human services.
Type of support: Emergency funds; Grants to individuals.
Application information:
Initial approach: Letter
Deadline(s): None
Officers: Ann Cooper, Pres.; Craig Whitney, Secy.; Richard C. Wald, Treas.
Trustees: Bonnie Angelo; Carrol Bogert; James L. Greenfield; Michael Oreskes; Ralph R. Schulz; Stephen B. Shepard.
EIN: 136100568

5880
Cortland Community Foundation
(formerly Cortland Savings Foundation)
P.O. Box 466
Cortland, NY   13045-0466
Main URL: http://www.cortlandcommunityfoundation.org

Established in 1998 in New York.
Donors: Nicholas Agnes Renzi; Martha W. Gutchess; Homer C. Gutchess; Jason Reed; Donald S. Ames.
Foundation type: Independent foundation.
Financial data (yr. ended 12/31/13): Assets, $1,523,872 (M); gifts received, $266,887; expenditures, $377,239; qualifying distributions, $357,316; giving activities include $357,316 for 52 grants (high: $52,660; low: $70).
Fields of interest: Education; Religion; Human services.
Limitations: Applications accepted. Giving primarily in Cortland, NY.
Application information: Application form required.
Initial approach: Proposal
Deadline(s): None
Officers: Thomas E. Gallagher, Pres.; Donald S. Ames, V.P.; Don Reed, Secy.; F. Michael Stapleton, Treas.

Director: Donald Armstrong.
EIN: 161561037

5881
Berthe M. Cote Foundation Inc.
c/o Fiduciary Trust Company International
600 5th Ave.
New York City, NY   10020

Foundation type: Independent foundation.
Financial data (yr. ended 10/31/14): Assets, $3,408,762 (M); expenditures, $205,763; qualifying distributions, $163,075; giving activities include $147,153 for 2 grants (high: $97,153; low: $50,000).
Fields of interest: Nonprofits; Health.
International interests: Israel.
Type of support: Regranting.
Limitations: Applications not accepted. Giving primarily in NY. No grants to individuals.
Application information: Unsolicited requests for funds not accepted.
Officers: E. Michael Difabio, Pres.; Michael D. Difabio, V.P.; Linda R. Franciscovich, V.P.
EIN: 141681452

5882
Randolph L. Cowen & Phyllis Green Foundation
Bowling Green Sta.
P.O. Box 73
New York City, NY   10274-0073

Established in 1996 in New York.
Donor: Randolph L. Cowen.
Foundation type: Independent foundation.
Financial data (yr. ended 05/31/13): Assets, $9,566,462 (M); expenditures, $222,388; qualifying distributions, $166,200; giving activities include $166,200 for 7 grants (high: $97,200; low: $1,000).
Fields of interest: Education; Philanthropy; Human services.
Type of support: General support.
Limitations: Applications not accepted. Giving primarily in New York, NY. No grants to individuals.
Application information: Unsolicited requests for funds not accepted.
Trustees: Randolph L. Cowen; Phyllis Green.
EIN: 137109419

5883
The Donald and Maria Cox Trust
c/o Fiduciary Trust
600 5th Ave.
New York City, NY   10020-2302

Established in 1985 in New York.
Donor: Donald M. Cox†.
Foundation type: Independent foundation.
Financial data (yr. ended 12/31/13): Assets, $199,938 (M); expenditures, $198,032; qualifying distributions, $192,748; giving activities include $191,295 for 31 grants (high: $40,000; low: $100).
Purpose and activities: Giving primarily for the arts, particularly art museums, education, health associations, social services, and Roman Catholic churches.

Fields of interest: Arts and culture; Art museums; Humanities; Education; Higher education; Diseases and conditions; Catholicism; Human services.
Limitations: Applications not accepted. Giving primarily in New York, NY. No grants to individuals.
Application information: Unsolicited requests for funds not accepted.
Trustee: Maria R. Cox.
EIN: 136864749

5884
Crane Family Foundation
c/o Todd M. Joseph
The Guaranty Bldg.
140 Pearl St., Ste. 100
Buffalo, NY   14202-4004

Established in 2007 in New York.
Donors: James D. Crane 2007 Chairtable Lead Trust; Carole E. Saffrin 2007 Charitable Lead Trust; Colleen A. Crane 2007 Chairtable Lead Trust; James D. Crane Trust; Carole E. Saffrin Trust; Colleen A. Crane Trust.
Foundation type: Independent foundation.
Financial data (yr. ended 12/31/13): Assets, $7,633,365 (M); gifts received, $957,842; expenditures, $294,003; qualifying distributions, $254,250; giving activities include $254,000 for 5 grants (high: $84,000; low: $30,000).
Fields of interest: Protestantism.
International interests: Belize.
Limitations: Applications not accepted. Giving primarily in Buffalo, NY, and Santa Cruz, Belize. No grants to individuals.
Application information: Unsolicited requests for funds not accepted.
Trustees: J.D. Crane; Todd M. Joseph; Mary Crane Kot; Paul R. Saffrin.
EIN: 208313839

5885
Cranshaw Corporation
c/o Edward F. Rover
1111 Park Ave., Ste. 13E
New York City, NY   10128-1234

Established in 1954 in Delaware.
Donor: Helen Babbott Sanders†.
Foundation type: Independent foundation.
Financial data (yr. ended 12/31/14): Expenditures, $414,668; qualifying distributions, $378,000.
Purpose and activities: Giving primarily for education and health care.
Fields of interest: Arts and culture; Education; Higher education; Natural resources; Hospital care; Non-natural disasters; Human services; Child welfare.
Limitations: Applications not accepted. Giving primarily in NY and VA. No grants to individuals.
Application information: Contributes only to pre-selected organizations.
Officers: Robert I. MacDonald, Pres.; Edward F. Rover, V.P.
EIN: 136110555

5886
Joseph & Joan Cullman Conservation Foundation, Inc.
c/o Citrin Cooperman
529 5th Ave.
New York City, NY 10017-4667

Established in 2006 in District of Columbia.
Donor: Joseph F. Cullman Trust.
Foundation type: Independent foundation.
Financial data (yr. ended 02/28/14): Assets, $5,283,413 (M); expenditures, $252,995; qualifying distributions, $182,000; giving activities include $182,000 for 10 grants (high: $29,000; low: $5,000).
Fields of interest: Natural history museums; Land resources; Wildlife biodiversity.
Limitations: Applications not accepted. Giving primarily in Washington, DC, and NY. No grants to individuals.
Application information: Unsolicited requests for funds not accepted.
Officers: Dorothy Treisman, Pres.†; Michael Cardozo, V.P. and Secy.-Treas.; Joel H. Treisman, Pres. and V.P.
EIN: 201499645

5887
Joseph & Joan Cullman Foundation for the Arts, Inc.
c/o Citrin Cooperman
529 5th Ave.
New York City, NY 10017-4608

Established in 2006 in District of Columbia.
Donor: Joseph F. Cullman Trust.
Foundation type: Independent foundation.
Financial data (yr. ended 02/28/13): Assets, $4,458,487 (M); expenditures, $291,162; qualifying distributions, $235,000; giving activities include $235,000 for 33 grants (high: $25,000; low: $6,000).
Purpose and activities: Giving primarily for the fine and performing arts.
Fields of interest: Performing arts; Dance; Theater; Art museums; Archives and special collections; Communication media.
Limitations: Applications not accepted. Giving primarily in New York, NY. No grants to individuals.
Application information: Contributes only to pre-selected organizations.
Officers: Dorothy Treisman, Pres.; Michael H. Cardozo, V, V.P. and Secy.-Treas.; Joel H. Treisman, V.P.
EIN: 201499861

5888
Barbara Bell Cumming Foundation
c/o Kelley Drye & Warren LLP
101 Park Ave.
New York City, NY 10178-0001 (212) 808-7800
Contact: Michael S. Insel, Tr.

Established in 1992 in New York.
Donor: Barbara Bell Cumming†.
Foundation type: Independent foundation.
Financial data (yr. ended 09/30/14): Assets, $2,917,421 (M); expenditures, $187,419; qualifying distributions, $153,909; giving activities include $149,000 for 40 grants (high: $25,000; low: $500).

Fields of interest: Arts and culture.
Type of support: General support.
Limitations: Applications accepted. Giving primarily in New York, NY. No grants to individuals.
Application information: Application form required.
Initial approach: Proposal
Deadline(s): Sept. 1
Trustee: Michael S. Insel.
EIN: 136999946

5889
Curtis Family Foundation
c/o Barry M. Strauss Assocs., Ltd.
307 5th Ave., 8th Fl.
New York City, NY 10016-6517

Donors: Alan Curtis; Curtis Partnership.
Foundation type: Independent foundation.
Financial data (yr. ended 10/31/14): Assets, $1,159,146; expenditures, $358,252; qualifying distributions, $341,569.
Fields of interest: Education; Nonprofits; Health; Diseases and conditions; Judaism; Human services.
Type of support: Regranting.
Limitations: Applications not accepted. Giving primarily in Palm Beach, FL. No grants to individuals.
Application information: Contributes only to pre-selected organizations.
Officers: Alan Curtis, Pres.; Christine W. Curtis, Secy.-Treas.
Directors: Bryan Curtis; Linda Curtis; Roberta Curtis; Mark Ginsberg.
EIN: 650441571

5890
Cutco Foundation Inc.
1116 E. State St.
Olean, NY 14760-3814
Contact: James M. Stitt Jr., Treas.

Established in 1995 in New York.
Donors: Cutco Cutlery Corp.; Alcas Corp.; Vector Marketing Corp.; Cutco Cutlery; Mike Lancellot; Cutco Corporation; Cutco Cutlery.
Foundation type: Company-sponsored foundation.
Financial data (yr. ended 12/31/13): Assets, $4,277,709 (M); gifts received, $48,829; expenditures, $360,343; qualifying distributions, $358,140; giving activities include $358,140 for 58 grants (high: $50,000; low: $200).
Purpose and activities: The foundation supports hospitals and community foundations and organizations involved with higher education.
Fields of interest: Higher education; Foundations; Hospital care.
Type of support: Capital campaigns; Matching grants; Capital and infrastructure; Endowments; Scholarships.
Limitations: Applications accepted. Giving primarily in Olean, NY. No grants to individuals.
Application information: Application form required.
Initial approach: Letter
Deadline(s): None
Officers: James E. Stitt, Pres.; John Whelpley, Secy.; James Stitt, Jr., Treas.
Directors: Brent Driscoll; Erick Laine; John Stitt.
Number of staff: None.
EIN: 161491450

5891
Carolyne E. and Eugene A. Czap Charitable Foundation
3001 Ave. M
Brooklyn, NY 11229-3201 (718) 692-1212
E-mail: grantapplication@czapfoundation.org; Main URL: http://czapfoundation.org

Established in 2010 in New York.
Donor: Eugene A. Czap.
Foundation type: Independent foundation.
Financial data (yr. ended 12/31/13): Assets, $6,338,376 (M); expenditures, $401,339; qualifying distributions, $313,162; giving activities include $235,025 for 3 grants (high: $135,000; low: $25).
Fields of interest: Diseases and conditions; Alzheimer's disease.
Type of support: Research.
Limitations: Applications accepted. Giving primarily in NJ and NY.
Application information: See foundation web site for guidelines. Application form required.
Initial approach: Letter
Deadline(s): Varies
Officers: Jeffrey Zell, Pres.; Mark I. Ettinger, V.P.; Benjamin Epstein, Treas.
EIN: 264709613

5892
Barbara & Haim Dabah Family Foundation, Inc.
180 E. 64th St.
New York City, NY 10065-7478

Donors: Haim Dabah; Barbara Dabah.
Foundation type: Independent foundation.
Financial data (yr. ended 12/31/12): Assets, $82,950 (M); gifts received, $228,500; expenditures, $411,140; qualifying distributions, $407,840; giving activities include $407,840 for grants.
Purpose and activities: Giving primarily for Jewish organizations, temples, and schools.
Fields of interest: Education; Diseases and conditions; Judaism; Human services; Child welfare.
Type of support: Research.
Limitations: Applications not accepted. Giving primarily in the metropolitan New York, NY, area.
Application information: Unsolicited requests for funds not accepted.
Officers: Haim Dabah, Pres.; Barbara Dabah, Secy.-Treas.
Director: Morris Dabah, Jr.
EIN: 300138485

5893
The Dabah Family Foundation, Inc.
29 W. 56th St.
New York City, NY 10019-3902

Established in 2005 in New York.
Donors: Victor H. Dabah; Solomon Dabah; Michael Silverman.
Foundation type: Independent foundation.
Financial data (yr. ended 12/31/13): Assets, $37,810 (M); gifts received, $325,900; expenditures, $298,943; qualifying distributions, $298,772; giving activities include $298,747 for grants.
Fields of interest: Judaism.

Limitations: Applications not accepted. Giving primarily in NY.
Application information: Contributes only to pre-selected organizations.
Officers: Victor H. Dabah, Pres.; Raquel Dabah, V.P.
Directors: Solomon Dabah; Sarah Harary; Joyce Silverman.
EIN: 550883176

5894
John & Joan D'Addario Foundation, Inc.
19 Danton Ln. N.
Lattingtown, NY 11560-1122

Established in 1998 in New York.
Donors: John D'Addario, Jr.; Joan D'Addario.
Foundation type: Independent foundation.
Financial data (yr. ended 05/31/14): Assets, $1,712,936 (M); gifts received, $208,940; expenditures, $202,005; qualifying distributions, $196,200; giving activities include $196,200 for 37 grants (high: $61,000; low: $200).
Fields of interest: Arts and culture; Music; Musical ensembles and groups; Orchestral music; Museums; Higher education; Specialty hospital care; Human services; Child welfare.
Limitations: Applications not accepted. Giving primarily in NY. No grants to individuals.
Application information: Contributes only to pre-selected organizations.
Officers: John D'Addario, Jr., Pres.; Joan D'Addario, Secy.-Treas.
Directors: John D'Addario III; Laura D'Addario; Michael D'Addario; Suzanne D'Addario.
EIN: 113440873

5895
The D'Addario Music Foundation Inc.
595 Smith St.
Farmingdale, NY 11735-1116 (631) 439-3300
Contact: John D'Addario Jr., Dir.
E-mail: foundation@daddario.com; Main
URL: http://www.daddariofoundation.org

Donor: D'Addario Co. Inc.
Foundation type: Independent foundation.
Financial data (yr. ended 05/31/13): Assets, $15,130 (M); gifts received, $385,121; expenditures, $377,848; qualifying distributions, $280,020; giving activities include $280,020 for 136 grants (high: $10,000; low: $750).
Fields of interest: Arts and culture; Education; Human services.
Application information: All organizations that have not been funded by the foundation in the last two years must submit a letter of inquiry to the foundation by email before being invited to submit a grant application. If an organization is reapplying for support, it may proceed directly to the application process on the foundation's web site. See foundation web site for complete application guidelines. Application form required.
Deadline(s): Letter of Inquiry deadlines: July 31 & Jan. 31; Grant application deadlines: Sep. 15 & Mar. 15
Trustees: Jim Bailey; John D'Addario III; Lyris Hung; Robert Polan.
Directors: Suzanne D'Addario Brouder; John D'Addario, Jr.
EIN: 112637844

5896
The Dalton Family Foundation
1044 Franklin Ave., Ste. 206
Garden City, NY 11530

Established in 2002 in New York.
Donor: Mark F. Dalton.
Foundation type: Independent foundation.
Financial data (yr. ended 12/31/13): Assets, $76,065 (M); gifts received, $200,000; expenditures, $203,185; qualifying distributions, $202,435; giving activities include $201,500 for 39 grants (high: $25,000; low: $1,000).
Fields of interest: Arts and culture; Education; Environment; Winter sports.
Type of support: General support.
Limitations: Applications not accepted. Giving primarily in Telluride, CO. No grants to individuals.
Application information: Unsolicited requests for funds not accepted.
Trustees: Mark F. Dalton; Susan K. Dalton.
EIN: 300133600

5897
The Dammann Fund, Inc.
1700 Broadway, 41st Fl.
New York City, NY 10019-4613 (212) 956-4118
Contact: Penelope Johnston, Pres.
FAX: (212) 262-9321;
E-mail: df@engelanddavis.com; Main URL: http://www.thedammannfund.com
Grants List: http://www.thedammannfund.com/jga.html

Established in 1946 in New York.
Foundation type: Independent foundation.
Financial data (yr. ended 11/30/13): Assets, $7,779,491 (M); expenditures, $518,856; qualifying distributions, $455,917; giving activities include $411,375 for 172 grants (high: $30,000; low: $125).
Purpose and activities: Giving primarily for teen parenthood programs and programs to foster independent living skills for the mentally ill.
Fields of interest: Mental health care; Family services; Child welfare.
Type of support: General support; Continuing support; Program development; Seed money.
Limitations: Applications accepted. Giving primarily in the greater metropolitan New York, NY, area, including southern Fairfield County, CT; giving also in Charlottesville, VA. No grants to individuals, or for scholarships, fellowships, or matching gifts; no loans.
Publications: Application guidelines.
Application information: A sample Application Form and an application Checklist along with complete application guidelines are available on fund web site. Applicants are encouraged, although not required, to submit simultaneously, by e-mail, the "project description/funding request" portion of their application package. Application form required.
Initial approach: Submit application
Copies of proposal: 1
Deadline(s): June 30 for Joint Gifts program
Board meeting date(s): May/June and Oct./Nov.
Final notification: Dec. 1
Officers and Directors: Penelope Johnston, Pres. and Director; Christopher M. Kramer, V.P. and Director; Daniel R. Kramer, V.P.; John P. Engel, Secy.; Lorraine M. Callaghan, Treas.; Katherine S. Penna.
EIN: 136089896

5898
Danzi Family Foundation Inc
45A King Arthurs Ct.
Saint James, NY 11780-3160

Established in 1998 in New York.
Donors: John A. Danzi; John A. Danzi LLC.
Foundation type: Independent foundation.
Financial data (yr. ended 12/31/13): Assets, $109,528 (M); gifts received, $145,000; expenditures, $148,785; qualifying distributions, $148,600; giving activities include $148,600 for grants.
Limitations: Applications not accepted. No grants to individuals.
Application information: Unsolicited requests for funds not accepted.
Officer and Director: John A. Danzi, Pres. and Director.
EIN: 113428923

5899
The Gloria & Sidney Danziger Foundation
c/o Cozen O'Conner
277 Park Ave., 20th Fl.
New York City, NY 10172

Established in 1959 in New York.
Donors: Sidney Danziger†; Robert E. Fischer; Rabbi B. Kreitman; Stanley T. Miller; Rabbi J. Kreitman.
Foundation type: Independent foundation.
Financial data (yr. ended 12/31/13): Assets, $1,877,401 (M); expenditures, $332,568; qualifying distributions, $295,645; giving activities include $244,206 for 73 grants (high: $61,000; low: $20).
Purpose and activities: Giving primarily to Jewish agencies, temples, schools, and Jewish federated giving programs; funding also for the arts, education, health care, and for medical research, particularly lymphoma.
Fields of interest: Arts and culture; Art museums; Ethnic museums; Education; Higher education; Nonprofits; Diseases and conditions; Judaism; Human services; Child welfare.
Type of support: Regranting.
Limitations: Applications not accepted. Giving primarily in NY. No grants to individuals; no loans.
Application information: Contributes only to pre-selected organizations.
Directors: Robert E. Fischer; Rabbi J. Kreitman; Stanley T. Miller.
EIN: 136124448

5900
Jessie Smith Darrah Charitable Trust
1 Court Sq., 19th Fl.
Long Island City, NY 11120-0001

Donor: Jessie S. Darrah†.
Foundation type: Independent foundation.
Financial data (yr. ended 12/31/14): Assets, $5,626,333; expenditures, $243,196; qualifying distributions, $207,429.
Fields of interest: Arts and culture; Education; Higher education; Environment; Nonprofits; Libraries; Community improvement; Protestantism; Human services; Family services; Women's services.
Type of support: Regranting; Fundraising.

Limitations: Applications not accepted. Giving primarily in Chautauqua County, NY. No grants to individuals.
Application information: Contributes only to pre-selected organizations.
Trustees: Samuel Price, Jr.; James M. Smith; Charles Ulrich III; Citibank, N.A.
EIN: 136129875

5901
The Scott & Susan Davidson Foundation Inc.
c/o M.H. Davidson & Co.
65 E. 55th St., 19th Fl.
New York City, NY 10022-3355

Established in 1999 in New York.
Donors: Scott E. Davidson; Susan Davidson; Marvin H. Davidson Foundation.
Foundation type: Independent foundation.
Financial data (yr. ended 12/31/13): Assets, $3,992,661 (M); gifts received, $221,730; expenditures, $158,087; qualifying distributions, $155,350; giving activities include $152,850 for 14 grants (high: $25,000; low: $2,500).
Fields of interest: Elementary and secondary education; Higher education; Diseases and conditions; Judaism; Human services.
Type of support: Research.
Limitations: Applications not accepted. Giving primarily in NY. No grants to individuals.
Application information: Unsolicited requests for funds not accepted.
Officers and Directors: Scott E. Davidson, Pres. and Director; Susan Davidson, Co-Secy. and Director; Stephen Dowicz, Co-Secy. and Director.
EIN: 134088730

5902
Kevin & Susie Davis Family Foundation
50 Hook Rd.
Bedford, NY 10506-1112

Established in 2007 in New York.
Donor: Kevin R. Davis.
Foundation type: Independent foundation.
Financial data (yr. ended 12/31/13): Assets, $545,716 (M); gifts received, $10,062; expenditures, $167,996; qualifying distributions, $155,981; giving activities include $148,500 for 11 grants (high: $75,000; low: $1,000).
Fields of interest: Education; University education; Medical education; Nonprofits; Diseases and conditions.
Type of support: General support; Research; Regranting.
Limitations: Applications not accepted. No grants to individuals.
Application information: Unsolicited requests for funds not accepted.
Officers and Directors: Kevin Davis, Pres. and Director; John J. Pomerantz, V.P. and Director; Susan Pomerantz-Davis, Secy.-Treas. and Director.
EIN: 260552012

5903
The D-B Trust
The Guaranty Bldg.
140 Pearl St., Ste. 100
Buffalo, NY 14202-4004

Established in 1984 in New York.
Foundation type: Independent foundation.
Financial data (yr. ended 12/31/13): Assets, $4,466,779 (M); expenditures, $214,552; qualifying distributions, $185,330; giving activities include $184,000 for 30 grants (high: $25,000; low: $1,000).
Fields of interest: Elementary and secondary education; Hospice care; Community and economic development; Human services.
Type of support: Continuing support; Capital campaigns; Capital and infrastructure; Endowments.
Limitations: Applications not accepted. No grants to individuals.
Application information: Unsolicited requests for funds not accepted.
Trustees: Elizabeth S. Mitchell; Anne H. Swift; Douglas G. Swift; Harlan J. Swift, Jr.
EIN: 222589701

5904
De La Cour Family Foundation
P.O. Box 94
Glen Cove, NY 11542-0094

Established in 1999 in Delaware.
Donor: Willis S. De La Cour‡.
Foundation type: Independent foundation.
Financial data (yr. ended 12/31/13): Assets, $9,736,156 (M); expenditures, $435,640; qualifying distributions, $371,774; giving activities include $369,100 for 107 grants (high: $35,000; low: $100).
Fields of interest: Education; Foundations; Housing development; Human services.
Limitations: Applications not accepted. Giving primarily in MA and NY. No grants to individuals.
Application information: Contributes only to pre-selected organizations.
Directors: Edmund P. De La Cour; Lea De La Cour; Willis S. De La Cour, Jr.
EIN: 233025610

5905
Dears Foundation, Inc.
c/o BCRS Associates, LLC
77 Water St., 9th Fl.
New York City, NY 10005-3701

Established in 1953 in New York.
Foundation type: Independent foundation.
Financial data (yr. ended 11/30/13): Assets, $4,332,263 (M); expenditures, $229,948; qualifying distributions, $218,590; giving activities include $218,205 for 24 grants (high: $25,000; low: $1,000).
Purpose and activities: Giving for higher education, health associations, and Jewish organizations.
Fields of interest: Higher education; Medical education; Nonprofits; Diseases and conditions; Parkinson's disease; Science; Judaism; Human services.
Type of support: Research; Regranting.
Limitations: Applications not accepted. Giving primarily in NY. No grants to individuals.
Application information: Contributes only to pre-selected organizations.
Officers and Directors: David A. Abramson, Pres. and Director; Daniel Abramson, V.P. and Director; Marc A. Abramson, Secy.-Treas. and Director.

Board Members: Ellen M. Abramson; Harriet A. Abramson; Deborah Y. Kirby.
EIN: 136160958

5906
The Deeds Foundation
c/o Wilson & Cowgill
666 Greenwich St., Ste. 704
New York City, NY 10014-6334

Established in 1994 in New York.
Donor: Nan Allen Nixon 1982 Trust.
Foundation type: Independent foundation.
Financial data (yr. ended 12/31/13): Assets, $6,567,488 (M); expenditures, $335,666; qualifying distributions, $301,309; giving activities include $284,875 for 35 grants (high: $50,000; low: $1,000).
Purpose and activities: Giving primarily for arts and culture.
Fields of interest: Arts and culture; Education; Higher education; Human services.
Limitations: Applications not accepted. Giving primarily in MD. No grants to individuals.
Application information: Unsolicited requests for funds not accepted.
Officers and Directors: Diane A. Nixon, Pres. and Director; Alexander M. Laughlin, V.P. and Secy. and Director; Robert L. Cahill, Jr., V.P. and Treas. and Director; Laura S. Bennett.
EIN: 133752427

5907
The Deegan Foundation
P.O. Box 110484
Brooklyn, NY 11211-0484

Donor: Berl Jacobowitz.
Foundation type: Operating foundation.
Financial data (yr. ended 11/30/13): Assets, $0 (M); gifts received, $513,600; expenditures, $504,269; qualifying distributions, $504,269; giving activities include $243,791 for grants.
Fields of interest: Judaism.
Limitations: Applications not accepted. No grants to individuals.
Application information: Contributes only to pre-selected organizations.
Trustee: Berl Jacobowitz.
EIN: 522388402

5908
The Michael & Dudley Del Balso Charitable Trust
115 Central Park W., Ste. 8D
New York City, NY 10023-4198

Established in 1986 in New York.
Donors: Jennison Assocs. Capital Corp.; Michael Del Balso.
Foundation type: Independent foundation.
Financial data (yr. ended 12/31/13): Assets, $5,572,040 (M); gifts received, $15,403; expenditures, $261,599; qualifying distributions, $250,500; giving activities include $250,500 for 37 grants (high: $97,500; low: $500).
Fields of interest: Arts and culture; Education; Environment.
Limitations: Applications not accepted. Giving primarily in CT and NY. No grants to individuals.

Application information: Unsolicited requests for funds not accepted.
Trustees: Dudley Del Balso; Michael Del Balso.
EIN: 136878848

5909
The Helen Matchett DeMario Foundation Inc.
c/o Windels Marx
156 W. 56th St.
New York City, NY   10019-3800   (212) 237-1197
Contact: David A. Brauner, V.P. and Treas.

Established in 1984 in New Jersey.
Foundation type: Independent foundation.
Financial data (yr. ended 12/31/13): Assets, $22,427,147 (M); expenditures, $211,707; qualifying distributions, $198,585; giving activities include $194,100 for 46 grants (high: $27,000; low: $500).
Purpose and activities: Giving for Jewish organizations, higher and legal education, and for human and women's services.
Fields of interest: Higher education; Hospital care; Diseases and conditions; Judaism; Human services; Women's services.
Limitations: Applications accepted. Giving primarily in NY. No grants to individuals.
Application information:
  Initial approach: Proposal
  Deadline(s): None
Officers and Directors: Michael L. Goldstein, Pres. and Director; Roy Sparber, V.P. and Secy. and Director; David Brauner, V.P. and Treas. and Director; David R. Kay; Mel Barkan.
EIN: 133213185

5910
Rohit & Katharine Desai Family Foundation
505 Park Ave., 12th Fl.
New York City, NY   10022

Established in 1984 in New York.
Donors: Rohit M. Desai; Katharine Desai.
Foundation type: Independent foundation.
Financial data (yr. ended 12/31/13): Assets, $4,517,930 (M); gifts received, $100,000; expenditures, $254,476; qualifying distributions, $233,592; giving activities include $213,500 for 25 grants (high: $58,000; low: $500).
Purpose and activities: Giving primarily for education, horticultural services, and Christian organizations.
Fields of interest: Museums; Art museums; Education; Higher education; Nonprofits; Community beautification; Christianity.
Type of support: Regranting.
Limitations: Applications not accepted. Giving primarily in MA and New York City. No grants to individuals.
Application information: Contributes only to pre-selected organizations.
Trustees: Katharine Desai; Rohit M. Desai; Vanessa Desai.
EIN: 133260252

5911
A. L. Desanctis, M.D. Foundation
c/o Morgan Stanley Trust, N.A
1 New York Plz., 7th Fl.
New York City, NY   10004-1913   2122767988
Application address: 2036 Vinette Pl., Massillon, OH 44646 tel.:(330) 832-1595

Established in 2002 in Ohio.
Donors: Donn Goodman; Alfred Desanctis Trust.
Foundation type: Independent foundation.
Financial data (yr. ended 12/31/14): Assets, $5,386,987; expenditures, $350,570; qualifying distributions, $251,053.
Purpose and activities: Scholarship awards to medical students attending either Hamilton College, New York, or Johns Hopkins University, Maryland.
Fields of interest: Education.
Type of support: General support; Student aid.
Limitations: Applications accepted. Giving primarily in MD and NY.
Application information: Application form required.
  Initial approach: Proposal
  Deadline(s): None
Trustee: Morgan Stanley Trust, N.A.
EIN: 050544325

5912
Deutsch Family Foundation
1163 E. 27th St.
Brooklyn, NY   11210

Donors: Robert Deutsch; David Deutsch; Isaac Deutsch.
Foundation type: Independent foundation.
Financial data (yr. ended 12/31/13): Assets, $1,148,986 (M); gifts received, $845,000; expenditures, $217,430; qualifying distributions, $208,853; giving activities include $207,555 for 38 grants (high: $36,000; low: $100).
Fields of interest: Judaism.
Limitations: Applications not accepted. Giving primarily in NY.
Application information: Contributes only to pre-selected organizations.
Officers: David Deutsch, Pres.; Robert Deutsch, Secy.; Isaac Deutsch, Treas.
EIN: 261619724

5913
Devine-Majors Foundation
c/o Genspring Family Offices
13-15 W. 54th St.
New York City, NY   10019-5422

Established in 2009 in New York.
Donor: William F. Majors.
Foundation type: Independent foundation.
Financial data (yr. ended 12/31/13): Assets, $5,757,885 (M); gifts received, $1,956,356; expenditures, $242,791; qualifying distributions, $225,820; giving activities include $225,820 for 5 grants (high: $210,380; low: $250).
Fields of interest: Education; Health; Human services.
Limitations: Applications not accepted.
Application information: Unsolicited requests for funds not accepted.
Officers: William F. Majors, Pres.; Robert I. Majors, Secy.; Maxine E. Devine Majors, Treas.
EIN: 271405032

5914
Diamondston Foundation, Inc.
2 Wyckoff Pl.
Woodmere, NY   11598-2130   (212) 697-2310
Contact: Jesse Margolin, Pres.

Established in 2000 in New York.
Foundation type: Independent foundation.
Financial data (yr. ended 12/31/13): Assets, $2,522,133 (M); expenditures, $217,712; qualifying distributions, $206,150; giving activities include $191,750 for 70 grants (high: $25,000; low: $500).
Fields of interest: University education; Health; Geriatrics; Diseases and conditions; Judaism; Human services.
Type of support: General support.
Limitations: Applications accepted. Giving primarily in MA and NY. No grants to individuals.
Application information:
  Initial approach: Letter
  Deadline(s): None
Officers: Jesse Margolin, Pres. and Treas.; David Margolin, V.P.; Michael Margolin, V.P.; Susan Smith, V.P.; Barbara Margolin, Secy.
EIN: 134112479

5915
The Winifred Crawford Dibert Foundation, Inc.
c/o Edward Wright
525 Fairmount Ave.
Jamestown, NY   14701-2750   (716) 665-4876
Contact: Jon A. Saff, Treas.

Established in 2000 in New York.
Donors: Winifred S. Dibert; Winifred Crawford Dibert†.
Foundation type: Independent foundation.
Financial data (yr. ended 12/31/13): Assets, $2,646,625 (M); expenditures, $175,356; qualifying distributions, $147,000; giving activities include $147,000 for 10 grants (high: $37,500; low: $1,000).
Fields of interest: Arts and culture; Health; Human services.
Type of support: General support.
Limitations: Applications accepted. Giving primarily in NY. No grants to individuals.
Application information: Application form required.
  Initial approach: Letter
  Deadline(s): None
Officers: Robert Ostrom, Pres.; Edward P. Wright, Secy.; Jon A. Saff, Treas.
Board Member: Jane Cleaver Becker.
EIN: 161589819

5916
The Dillard Foundation
(formerly Anna Karin J. & David B. Dillard Foundation)
c/o Seeta Ross
45 Rockefeller Plz., Ste. 1919
New York City, NY   10111-1995   (212) 632-1308
Contact: Christopher Dillard

Established in 1985 in New York.
Donors: David B. Dillard; Christopher Dillard.
Foundation type: Independent foundation.
Financial data (yr. ended 12/31/13): Assets, $4,672,490 (M); gifts received, $443,229;

expenditures, $236,829; qualifying distributions, $205,735; giving activities include $203,200 for 19 grants (high: $40,000; low: $300).

Fields of interest: Arts and culture; Theater; Music; Higher education; Environment.

Limitations: Applications accepted. Giving primarily in AK. No grants to individuals.

Application information: Application form required.

Initial approach: Letter

Deadline(s): None

Officers: David B. Dillard, Pres.; Anna Karin J. Dillard, V.P. and Secy.

Board Members: Christopher Dillard; James Dillard; Elizabeth Lewis.

EIN: 133318226

5917
Diogenes Charitable Foundation

c/o Kenneth Kuchin
123 Main St.
East Hampton, NY   11937-2714

Established in 1997 in New Jersey.

Donor: Kenneth Kuchin.

Foundation type: Independent foundation.

Financial data (yr. ended 12/31/13): Assets, $1,112,137 (M); gifts received, $240,000; expenditures, $305,715; qualifying distributions, $234,015; giving activities include $234,015 for 5 grants (high: $117,650; low: $5).

Fields of interest: Arts and culture; Art museums; Human services.

Limitations: Applications not accepted.

Application information: Unsolicited requests for funds not accepted.

Trustee: Kenneth Kuchin.

EIN: 133969938

5918
Distracted Globe Foundation

c/o Anchin
1375 Broadway
New York City, NY   10018

Donor: Wendy Vanden Heuvel.

Foundation type: Independent foundation.

Financial data (yr. ended 12/31/13): Assets, $261,473 (M); gifts received, $331,976; expenditures, $334,515; qualifying distributions, $329,032; giving activities include $317,000 for 46 grants (high: $30,000; low: $1,000).

Fields of interest: Arts and culture.

Limitations: Applications not accepted. Giving primarily in NY.

Application information: Unsolicited requests for funds not accepted.

Officers and Directors: Wendy Vanden Heuvel, Pres. and Director; Philippe Goldin, V.P. and Director; Etta Brandman, Esq., Treas. and Director.

EIN: 364667713

5919
The T. F. Dixon Family Foundation, Inc.

c/o Brown Brothers Harriman Trust Co. LLP
140 Broadway, 4th Fl.
New York City, NY   10005-1108   (212) 493-8000
Contact: Barbara O'Connell, Secy.

Established in 2000 in New York.

Donor: Thomas F. Dixon.

Foundation type: Independent foundation.

Financial data (yr. ended 12/31/13): Assets, $4,400,919 (M); gifts received, $458; expenditures, $272,657; qualifying distributions, $236,819; giving activities include $227,000 for 34 grants (high: $50,000; low: $500).

Fields of interest: Arts and culture; Performing arts; Museums; Education; Catholicism; Human services.

Limitations: Applications accepted. Giving in the U.S., primarily in ID, with emphasis on Boise. No grants to individuals.

Application information:

Initial approach: Letter

Board meeting date(s): Nov.

Officers and Directors: Thomas F. Dixon, Pres. and Director; Adam H. Dixon, V.P. and Director; Hillary A. Dixon, V.P. and Director; Linda F. Dixon, V.P. and Director; Barbara O'Connell, Secy.; Anna T. Korniczky, Treas.

Number of staff: 2 full-time professional.

EIN: 134118192

5920
DJ Charitable Foundation

98 Cuttermill Rd., Ste. 249S
Great Neck, NY   11021-3046

Donors: David Jacobowitz; David Jacobowitz Jadabe Trust; D.J. Grantor Trust.

Foundation type: Independent foundation.

Financial data (yr. ended 12/31/13): Assets, $14,357 (M); gifts received, $374,400; expenditures, $360,043; qualifying distributions, $357,993; giving activities include $357,993 for 176 grants (high: $50,000; low: $50).

Fields of interest: Education; Judaism.

Limitations: Applications not accepted.

Application information: Unsolicited requests for funds not accepted.

Trustee: David Jacobowitz.

EIN: 462570498

5921
The Dobson Foundation Inc.

3 W. 35th St., 9th Fl.
New York City, NY   10001-2204

Established in 1961 in New York.

Donor: Walter M. Jeffords, Jr.†.

Foundation type: Independent foundation.

Financial data (yr. ended 12/31/14): Assets, $5,579,174; expenditures, $164,705; qualifying distributions, $152,948.

Fields of interest: Arts and culture; Performing arts; Museums; Education; University education; Fire prevention and control; Equestrianism.

Limitations: Applications not accepted. Giving primarily on the East Coast, with emphasis on New York and Saratoga Springs, NY. No grants to individuals.

Application information: Contributes only to pre-selected organizations.

Officer: Sarah Jeffords Radcliffe, Pres.

EIN: 136168259

5922
Jonathan and Susan Dolgen Family Foundation Inc.

c/o Esanu
605 3rd Ave., 16th Fl.
New York City, NY   10158-1699

Established in 1997 in California.

Donors: Jonathan Dolgen; Susan Dolgen.

Foundation type: Independent foundation.

Financial data (yr. ended 12/31/13): Assets, $3,240,385 (M); gifts received, $490,125; expenditures, $389,660; qualifying distributions, $376,862; giving activities include $376,862 for 31 grants (high: $200,000; low: $90).

Fields of interest: Higher education; Nonprofits; Judaism.

Type of support: Regranting.

Limitations: Applications not accepted. No grants to individuals.

Application information: Contributes only to pre-selected organizations.

Officers: Susan Dolgen, Pres. and Treas.; Jonathan Dolgen, V.P. and Secy.

EIN: 133993946

5923
Doovin Trust

5223 15th Ave.
Brooklyn, NY   11219-3908   (718) 851-4811
Contact: Chaim Landau, Tr.

Established in 1999 in New York.

Donors: Ephraim Landau; A & E Trust; Triangle Trust; Concord Trust; Abland Family Partnership.

Foundation type: Independent foundation.

Financial data (yr. ended 11/30/13): Assets, $4,305,614 (M); gifts received, $30,000; expenditures, $250,695; qualifying distributions, $246,850; giving activities include $243,100 for 28 grants (high: $68,000; low: $50).

Fields of interest: Education; Nonprofits; Religion; Judaism; Human services.

Type of support: Regranting.

Application information: Application form required.

Initial approach: Letter

Deadline(s): None

Trustees: Chaim Landau; David Landau.

EIN: 116532369

5924
The Dorsky Foundation, Inc.

(formerly Samuel Dorsky Foundation, Inc.)
11-03 45th Ave.
Long Island City, NY   11101-5109
Contact: Karen A. Dorsky, Dir.

Donors: Samuel Dorsky; Karen A. Dorsky; Noah P. Dorsky.

Foundation type: Independent foundation.

Financial data (yr. ended 10/31/13): Assets, $360,336 (M); gifts received, $393,606; expenditures, $174,551; qualifying distributions, $169,666; giving activities include $166,250 for 5 grants (high: $140,000; low: $250).

Purpose and activities: Giving primarily for the arts and education.

Fields of interest: Arts and culture; Museums; Education; Hospital care; Diseases and conditions; Human services.

Type of support: Research; Research and evaluation.

Limitations: Applications not accepted. Giving primarily in Long Island City, NY. No grants to individuals.

Application information: Contributes only to pre-selected organizations.

Directors: David A. Dorsky; Karen A. Dorsky; Noah P. Dorsky.

EIN: 136121016

5925
The Doscas Family Foundation

11 Sterling Ln.
Sands Point, NY   11050-1201

Established in 2006 in New York.

Donors: Anne Doscas; John Doscas; Manhattan Charitable Foundation.

Foundation type: Independent foundation.

Financial data (yr. ended 12/31/13): Assets, $174,115 (M); expenditures, $222,336; qualifying distributions, $217,135; giving activities include $214,900 for 13 grants (high: $138,250; low: $200).

Fields of interest: University education; Diseases and conditions.

Type of support: Research; General support.

Limitations: Applications not accepted. No grants to individuals.

Application information: Unsolicited requests for funds not accepted.

Officers: John Doscas, Pres.; Anne Doscas, V.P.; Christopher Doscas, Secy.

EIN: 861176440

5926
Doshi Family Foundation, Inc.

560 S. Broadway
Hicksville, NY   11801-5013   (516) 393-6101
Contact: Ajit Shah CPA

Established in 1991 in New York.

Donors: Leena N. Doshi; Nitin V. Doshi; Doshi Trust FBO Neely Doshi-Cather; The Doshi Trust FBO Nishat Doshi.

Foundation type: Independent foundation.

Financial data (yr. ended 12/31/13): Assets, $4,027,785 (M); gifts received, $50,000; expenditures, $708,490; qualifying distributions, $287,153; giving activities include $287,153 for 12 grants (high: $150,000; low: $500).

Fields of interest: Education services; Human services.

Limitations: Applications accepted. Giving primarily in NJ.

Application information:
   Initial approach: Proposal
   Deadline(s): None

Directors: Anish Berry; Leena N. Doshi; Neely Doshi-Cather; Nishat Doshi; Nitin V. Doshi.

EIN: 113088579

5927
The Double-R Foundation

P.O. Box 2050
New York City, NY   10158-2050
E-mail: info@double-r-foundation.org; Application address: c/o Hugo Barreca, 69 8th Ave., Brooklyn, NY 11217, tel.: (212) 627-1430; e-mail:
hbarreca@double-r-foundation.org; Main URL: http://www.double-r-foundation.org

Established in 2003 in New York.

Donor: Frederick A. Jambes Trust.

Foundation type: Independent foundation.

Financial data (yr. ended 08/31/13): Assets, $8,203,572 (M); expenditures, $543,956; qualifying distributions, $422,708; giving activities include $355,025 for 68 grants (high: $50,000; low: $90).

Purpose and activities: The foundation focuses its efforts on the enrichment of life in New York City by supporting volunteer-based organizations that provide services.

Fields of interest: Arts and culture; Law education; Animal welfare; Nonprofits; Community and economic development; Human services.

Type of support: Regranting.

Limitations: Applications accepted. Giving limited for the benefit of New York City organizations. No grants to individuals.

Application information:
   Deadline(s): None

Officers and Directors: Hugo Barreca II, Pres. and Treas. and Director; Anne Barreca, V.P. and Director; Laura Barreca, Secy. and Director.

EIN: 432029214

5928
Julien T. Dougherty Memorial Trust

9 Hayrake Ln.
Chappaqua, NY   10514-2508

Donor: Marie-France Dougherty-Manners†.

Foundation type: Independent foundation.

Financial data (yr. ended 12/31/13): Assets, $30 (M); gifts received, $250,000; expenditures, $250,000; qualifying distributions, $250,000; giving activities include $250,000 for 1 grant.

Fields of interest: Food aid.

Limitations: Applications not accepted. Giving primarily in New York, NY.

Application information: Contributes only to pre-selected organizations.

Trustees: Patricia K. Richter; Vincent C. Travagliato.

EIN: 455094419

5929
Charles H. Douglas Charitable Trust

c/o TrustCo Bank
3 Sarnowski Dr.
Glenville, NY   12302-3503

Donor: Stephanie Bugden.

Foundation type: Independent foundation.

Financial data (yr. ended 12/31/14): Assets, $7,908,690; expenditures, $412,763; qualifying distributions, $362,338.

Fields of interest: Natural resources; Domesticated animals; Diseases and conditions; Cancers.

Limitations: Applications not accepted. Giving primarily in Washington, DC, and NY. No grants to individuals.

Application information: Contributes only to pre-selected organizations.

Trustees: John Van Norden, Esq.; TrustCo Bank.

EIN: 141814550

5930
Robert N. & Nancy A. Downey Foundation

c/o BCRS Associates., LLC
77 Water St., 9th Fl.
New York City, NY   10005-4414

Established in 1982 in New York.

Donor: Robert N. Downey.

Foundation type: Independent foundation.

Financial data (yr. ended 01/31/13): Assets, $523,778 (M); gifts received, $409,241; expenditures, $184,706; qualifying distributions, $180,706; giving activities include $178,356 for 81 grants (high: $40,012; low: $100).

Purpose and activities: Giving primarily for higher education, and to hospitals and health organizations; funding also for the arts, and human services.

Fields of interest: Arts and culture; Theater; Education; Higher education; Hospital care; Diseases and conditions; Human services.

Limitations: Applications not accepted. Giving primarily in NH and NY. No grants to individuals; no loans or program-related investments.

Application information: Unsolicited requests for funds not accepted.

Trustees: Nancy A. Downey; Robert N. Downey.

EIN: 133103213

5931
Doreen Downs Miller Foundation, Inc.

c/o BCRS Associates, LLC
77 Water St., 9th Fl.
New York City, NY   10005-4414
Contact: Doreen D. Miller, Pres., Treas. and Director

Donors: Doreen D. Miller; John D. and Doreen Miller Foundation; Doreen D. Miller 2013 Trust.

Foundation type: Independent foundation.

Financial data (yr. ended 06/30/14): Assets, $7,963,674 (M); gifts received, $1,287,587; expenditures, $463,466; qualifying distributions, $400,952; giving activities include $384,150 for 35 grants (high: $175,000; low: $300).

Fields of interest: Higher education; Human services; Child welfare; Parent education.

Limitations: Giving primarily in New York, NY; some funding also in CA. No grants to individuals; no loans.

Application information:
   Deadline(s): None

Officer and Director: Doreen D. Miller, Pres., Treas. and Director.

EIN: 743116739

5932
The Druskin Family Foundation, Inc.

c/o Ayco Company, L.P. - National Tax Group
P.O. Box 15014
Albany, NY   12212-5014

Established in 1997 in New Jersey.

Donors: Robert A. Druskin; Harriett A. Druskin.

Foundation type: Independent foundation.

Financial data (yr. ended 12/31/13): Assets, $218,822 (M); gifts received, $387,629; expenditures, $214,410; qualifying distributions, $214,410; giving activities include $214,410 for 40 grants (high: $50,000; low: $250).

Fields of interest: Education; Diseases and conditions; Cancers; Judaism; Human services.

Type of support: Research.
Limitations: Applications not accepted. Giving primarily in NJ. No grants to individuals.
Application information: Contributes only to pre-selected organizations.
Officers: Robert A. Druskin, Pres.; Harriett A. Druskin, V.P.
Trustees: Ben Druskin; Melissa Druskin.
EIN: 223512395

5933
DTS Foundation Inc.
c/o Coal Capital Group LLC
1377 E. 4th St., 4th Fl.
Brooklyn, NY   11230-4688
Application address: c/o David Silberstein, 1078 E. 27th St., Brooklyn, NY 11210, tel.: (718) 682-2600

Donor: David Silberstein.
Foundation type: Independent foundation.
Financial data (yr. ended 03/31/14): Assets, $46,494 (M); gifts received, $200,000; expenditures, $192,206; qualifying distributions, $192,206; giving activities include $191,036 for grants.
Limitations: Applications accepted. Giving primarily in NY.
Application information: Application form required.
  Initial approach: Letter
  Deadline(s): None
Officer and Directors: David Silberstein, Pres. and Director; Eli M. Silberstein; Tsirl Silberstein.
EIN: 461602363

5934
The Duke of Omnium Fund
c/o Sullivan & Cromwell, LLP
125 Broad St.
New York City, NY   10004-2498   (212) 558-4000

Established in 1993 in New York.
Donor: Albert H. Gordon.
Foundation type: Independent foundation.
Financial data (yr. ended 12/31/13): Assets, $1,578,478 (M); gifts received, $383,628; expenditures, $212,547; qualifying distributions, $202,335; giving activities include $201,950 for 40 grants (high: $46,000; low: $100).
Fields of interest: Elementary and secondary education; Higher education; Business education.
Limitations: Applications accepted. Giving primarily in MA and NH. No grants to individuals.
Application information: Application form required.
  Initial approach: Proposal
  Deadline(s): None
Trustee: Peter Coolidge.
EIN: 133740798

5935
Dungannon Foundation, Inc.
c/o CPI Assocs., Inc.
32 E. 57th St., 14th Fl.
New York City, NY   10022-2513   (212) 421-6600
Contact: Elizabeth R. Rea, Pres.

Established in 1985 in New York.
Donors: Michael Moorhead Rea†; Rossco of Palm Beach, Inc.; Rives R. Yost; Harlan R. Giles; Homer J. Rose; Mrs. Henry Chalfant; Cynthia C. Giles; Elizabeth Rea.

Foundation type: Operating foundation.
Financial data (yr. ended 12/31/13): Assets, $5,526 (M); gifts received, $197,800; expenditures, $213,822; qualifying distributions, $210,905; giving activities include $153,500 for 31 grants (high: $55,000; low: $500), and $30,000 for 1 grant to an individual.
Fields of interest: Arts and culture; Education; Human services.
Type of support: Grants to individuals.
Limitations: Applications accepted. Giving on a national and international basis.
Application information: Application form required.
  Initial approach: Letter
  Deadline(s): None
Officers: Elizabeth Richebourg Rea, Pres.; Gary Millman, V.P.; Arthur Potts, Jr., Secy.
EIN: 133312300

5936
The Dunn Family Foundation
(formerly Edward B. Dunn Foundation)
4 Pine Island, Ste. R
Rye, NY   10580-3111
Contact: Edward B. Dunn

Established in 1989 in New York.
Donor: Edward B. Dunn.
Foundation type: Independent foundation.
Financial data (yr. ended 12/31/13): Assets, $2,566,711 (M); gifts received, $25; expenditures, $148,628; qualifying distributions, $133,690; giving activities include $126,750 for 15 grants (high: $50,000; low: $250).
Purpose and activities: Giving for higher education, art and cultural institutes, and health and children, youth, and social services.
Fields of interest: Education.
Limitations: Applications not accepted. Giving primarily in MD and in the metropolitan New York, NY, area. No grants to individuals.
Application information: Unsolicited requests for funds not accepted.
Officer: Giovannella Dunn, Secy.
Director: Edward Dunn.
EIN: 133525637

5937
Dvaykus Fondation Inc.
45 Harborview W.
Lawrence, NY   11559-1911   (516) 239-8134
Contact: Roy S. Neuberger, Dir.

Donor: Neuberger Foundation.
Foundation type: Independent foundation.
Financial data (yr. ended 12/31/13): Assets, $4,610,971 (M); expenditures, $326,946; qualifying distributions, $317,130; giving activities include $314,600 for 6 grants (high: $100,000).
Fields of interest: Education; Judaism.
Limitations: Applications accepted. Giving primarily in NY.
Application information: Application form required.
  Initial approach: Letter
  Deadline(s): None
Directors: Linda Neuberger; Roy S. Neuberger.
EIN: 202070556

5938
Dworman Foundation, Inc.
c/o McGladrey, LLP
1185 Ave. of the Americas, 7th Fl.
New York City, NY   10036-2601
Other: https://secure.opentable.com

Donor: Alvin Dworman.
Foundation type: Independent foundation.
Financial data (yr. ended 09/30/13): Assets, $10,994 (M); gifts received, $155,000; expenditures, $144,618; qualifying distributions, $144,618; giving activities include $144,000 for 8 grants (high: $50,000; low: $1,000).
Fields of interest: Domesticated animals; Health; Human services.
Type of support: General support; Capital and infrastructure; Equipment.
Limitations: Applications not accepted. Giving primarily in Santa Barbara, CA, and New York, NY. No grants to individuals.
Application information: Contributes only to pre-selected organizations.
Officer: Alvin Dworman, Pres.
EIN: 116035630

5939
E.R.G. Foundation
c/o Raymond Gindi, Century 21
22 Cortlandt St.
New York City, NY   10007-3107

Established in 2001 in New York.
Donors: Raymond Gindi; Elizabeth Gindi; Isaac Gindi.
Foundation type: Independent foundation.
Financial data (yr. ended 12/31/13): Assets, $3,080,684 (M); gifts received, $372,000; expenditures, $204,441; qualifying distributions, $203,703; giving activities include $203,453 for 33 grants (high: $37,007; low: $1,000).
Purpose and activities: Giving primarily to Jewish agencies, temples, and schools.
Fields of interest: Education; Religion.
Limitations: Applications not accepted. Giving primarily in New York, NY. No grants to individuals.
Application information: Contributes only to pre-selected organizations.
Directors: Elizabeth Gindi; Raymond Gindi; Ezra Sultan.
EIN: 134171703

5940
Lucius & Eva Eastman Fund, Inc.
c/o John Eastman
43-07 42nd St., Apt. 5C
Sunnyside, NY   11104-2853   6314380315

Established in 1946 in New York.
Foundation type: Independent foundation.
Financial data (yr. ended 12/31/14): Assets, $3,603,309; gifts received, $135; expenditures, $189,826; qualifying distributions, $169,926.
Fields of interest: Arts and culture; Theater; Education; Communication media; Film and video; Community and economic development; Antidiscrimination; Senior services; Women's services; Arms control; Seniors; Females.
International interests: Vietnam.
Type of support: Seed money; Matching grants.

Limitations: Applications not accepted. Giving primarily in NY. No grants to individuals.
Application information: Contributes only to pre-selected organizations.
  Board meeting date(s): Three times per year
Officers and Directors: John Eastman, Pres. and Director; Benjamin Eastman, V.P. and Director; Terrell Wilson, Secy.-Treas. and Director; Selma Burkom; Jennifer Eastman; Carlos Hernandez; Merble Reagon.
EIN: 131958483

5941
EBA Foundation
545 Madison Ave., Ste. 600
New York City, NY   10022

Established in 2000 in New York.
Donors: Seymour Milstein; Abigail Black Elbaum; Vivian Milstein.
Foundation type: Independent foundation.
Financial data (yr. ended 12/31/13): Assets, $3,077,101 (M); expenditures, $203,891; qualifying distributions, $178,453; giving activities include $178,068 for 25 grants (high: $25,000; low: $500).
Purpose and activities: Giving primarily for higher education.
Fields of interest: Education; Health; Housing development; Religion; Judaism.
Limitations: Applications not accepted. Giving primarily in NY. No grants to individuals.
Application information: Unsolicited requests for funds not accepted.
Trustees: Abigail Black Elbaum; Constance Milstein.
EIN: 134098940

5942
David F. and Frances A. Eberhart Foundation
305 E. 87th St.
New York City, NY   10128-4801

Established in 1998 in New York.
Donors: David F. Eberhart; Frances A. Eberhart.
Foundation type: Independent foundation.
Financial data (yr. ended 12/31/13): Assets, $6,299,845 (M); gifts received, $10,000; expenditures, $260,329; qualifying distributions, $231,135; giving activities include $225,750 for 28 grants (high: $25,000; low: $1,000).
Fields of interest: Arts and culture; Education; Philanthropy.
Limitations: Applications not accepted. Giving primarily in NY. No grants to individuals.
Application information: Unsolicited requests for funds not accepted.
Officers: David F. Eberhart, Pres.; Frances A. Eberhart, V.P.; Wendy F. Eberhart, Secy.; Tracy A. Eberhart, Treas.
EIN: 133958121

5943
The Thomas J. Edelman Family Foundation
49 Lawrence Ave.
Lawrence, NY   11559-1446

Donors: Alex Edelman; Susan Edelman.
Foundation type: Independent foundation.

Financial data (yr. ended 12/31/14): Assets, $255,520 (M); gifts received, $330,000; expenditures, $311,072; qualifying distributions, $311,072; giving activities include $309,217 for 57 grants (high: $54,000; low: $200).
Purpose and activities: Giving primarily for Jewish education.
Fields of interest: Education; Judaism.
Limitations: Applications not accepted. Giving primarily in NY. No grants to individuals.
Application information: Contributes only to pre-selected organizations.
Officers: Alex Edelman, Pres.; Jeffrey Edelman, V.P.; Fay Greenberg, V.P.; Susan Edelman, Treas.
EIN: 113455820

5944
Edelweiss Foundation
c/o Veneruso, Curto, Schwartz & Curto, LLP
35 Grassy Sprain Rd., No. 400
Yonkers, NY   10710-4516

Established in 1999 in New York.
Donors: Robert H. Abplanalp; Josephine Abplanalp.
Foundation type: Independent foundation.
Financial data (yr. ended 12/31/13): Assets, $2,143,529 (M); gifts received, $15,000; expenditures, $141,922; qualifying distributions, $141,459; giving activities include $134,675 for 8 grants (high: $60,000; low: $250).
Purpose and activities: Giving primarily to Roman Catholic organizations and churches; funding also for hospitals.
Fields of interest: Nonprofits; Hospital care; Catholicism.
Type of support: Regranting.
Limitations: Applications not accepted. Giving primarily in NY. No grants to individuals.
Application information: Contributes only to pre-selected organizations.
Directors: Josephine Abplanalp; Marie Holcombe.
EIN: 134090193

5945
Educational Projects Foundation Inc.
2 Johns Rd.
Setauket, NY   11733-3020

Established in 1998 in New York.
Donor: Peter Cohn.
Foundation type: Independent foundation.
Financial data (yr. ended 08/31/14): Assets, $5,228,297 (M); gifts received, $365,963; expenditures, $325,614; qualifying distributions, $255,203; giving activities include $206,500 for 10 grants (high: $50,000; low: $5,000).
Fields of interest: Environment; Science; Human services.
Limitations: Applications not accepted. Giving primarily in New York, NY. No grants to individuals.
Application information: Unsolicited requests for funds not acceptedb.
Officers: David Cohn, Pres.; Carmela Taliercio-Cohn, V.P.; Bernice Cohn, Secy.
EIN: 134027467

5946
The Eggleston Foundation
c/o Levene, Gouldin & Thompson, LLP
P.O. Box F1706
Binghamton, NY   13902-0106   (607) 763-9200
Contact: Michael H. Zuckerman Esq.

Established in 1984 in New York.
Donor: Edith E. Lewis.
Foundation type: Independent foundation.
Financial data (yr. ended 12/31/13): Assets, $2,066,003 (M); expenditures, $182,960; qualifying distributions, $158,500; giving activities include $158,500 for 61 grants (high: $15,000; low: $500).
Fields of interest: Arts and culture; Performing arts; Higher education; Nonprofits; Community and economic development; Human services.
Type of support: Regranting.
Limitations: Applications accepted. Giving primarily in upstate NY. No grants to individuals.
Application information: Application form required.
  Initial approach: Letter
  Deadline(s): None
Trustees: Mary L. Meltzer; William E. Lewis.
EIN: 133216256

5947
Jonas Ehrlich Charitable Foundation II, Inc.
565 Montgomery St.
Brooklyn, NY   11225-3009

Established in 2001 in New York.
Donors: Jonas Ehrlich†; L'Yeladim Be'Ramatahava.
Foundation type: Independent foundation.
Financial data (yr. ended 12/31/13): Assets, $3,099,329 (M); expenditures, $207,090; qualifying distributions, $192,549; giving activities include $192,549 for 49 grants (high: $75,000; low: $18).
Purpose and activities: Giving primarily for Jewish education, temples and organizations.
Fields of interest: Judaism.
Limitations: Applications not accepted. No grants to individuals.
Application information: Unsolicited requests for funds not accepted.
Officers: Asher Lieblich, Pres.; Abraham Lieblich, Secy.; Chaya Lieblich, Treas.
EIN: 113621521

5948
Jonas Ehrlich Charitable Foundation
98 Cutter Mill Rd., Ste. 263S
Great Neck, NY   11021-3036

Foundation type: Operating foundation.
Financial data (yr. ended 09/30/13): Assets, $2,643,454 (M); expenditures, $287,030; qualifying distributions, $241,660; giving activities include $241,660 for 19 grants (high: $55,000; low: $180).
Fields of interest: Arts and culture; Education; Medical education; Judaism.
Limitations: Applications not accepted. Giving primarily in NY. No grants to individuals.
Application information: Contributes only to pre-selected organizations.
Officer: Karen Spitalnick, Exec. Dir.

Directors: Elliot Steigman; Gisela Steigman.
EIN: 113541255

5949

The Fred & Suzan Ehrman Foundation
115 Central Park W., Ste. 6A
New York City, NY 10023-4198

Established in 1968 in New York.
Donors: Fred Ehrman; Suzan Ehrman; Jack Schenker.
Foundation type: Independent foundation.
Financial data (yr. ended 12/31/13): Assets, $4,475,347 (M); gifts received, $26,000; expenditures, $359,175; qualifying distributions, $358,400; giving activities include $358,150 for 143 grants (high: $40,000; low: $50).
Fields of interest: Education; Nonprofits; Judaism; Human services.
Type of support: Regranting.
Limitations: Applications not accepted. Giving primarily in NY. No grants to individuals.
Application information: Contributes only to pre-selected organizations.
Officers and Directors: Fred Ehrman, Pres. and Treas. and Director; Suzan Ehrman, V.P. and Treas. and Director; Alyssa Ehrman, Secy. and Director; Eric Ehrman.
EIN: 136271584

5950

The Jeffrey & Lauren Eisenberger Foundation
c/o Jeffrey Eisenberger
1334 E. 27th St.
Brooklyn, NY 11210-5307

Established in 2006 in New York.
Donors: Jeffrey Eisenberger; Lauren Eisenberger.
Foundation type: Independent foundation.
Financial data (yr. ended 12/31/13): Assets, $244,494 (M); gifts received, $110,000; expenditures, $229,124; qualifying distributions, $228,020; giving activities include $228,020 for grants.
Fields of interest: Judaism; Human services.
Limitations: Applications not accepted. No grants to individuals.
Application information: Unsolicited requests for funds not accepted.
Trustees: Jeffrey Eisenberger; Lauren Eisenberger.
EIN: 204303299

5951

The Karen & David Eisner Foundation
165 West End Ave., Ste. 7D
New York City, NY 10023-5506

Established in 1997 in New York.
Donors: David Eisner; Karen Eisner.
Foundation type: Independent foundation.
Financial data (yr. ended 06/30/13): Assets, $2,428,431 (M); expenditures, $285,787; qualifying distributions, $229,758; giving activities include $229,758 for 15 grants (high: $50,000; low: $2,500).
Fields of interest: Judaism.
Type of support: General support.
Limitations: Applications not accepted. No grants to individuals.

Application information: Unsolicited requests for funds not accepted.
Officers and Directors: David Eisner, Pres. and Director; Karen Eisner, V.P. and Secy. and Director.
EIN: 133979797

5952

The Abraham & Raizel Ekstein Charitable Foundation
56 Francis Pl.
Monsey, NY 10952-2616 (718) 302-8600
Contact: Abraham Ekstein, Tr.; Raizel Ekstein, Tr.

Established in 2002 in New York.
Donors: Abraham Ekstein; Raizel Ekstein.
Foundation type: Independent foundation.
Financial data (yr. ended 12/31/13): Assets, $177,897 (M); gifts received, $267,637; expenditures, $206,419; qualifying distributions, $206,419; giving activities include $206,220 for 23 grants (high: $93,305; low: $1,000).
Fields of interest: Judaism.
Limitations: Applications accepted. Giving primarily in NY. No grants to individuals.
Application information:
Initial approach: Proposal
Deadline(s): None
Trustees: Abraham Ekstein; Raizel Ekstein.
EIN: 020665786

5953

Yalket Elazar Fund
28 Van Buren Dr.
Monroe, NY 10950

Donors: Madison Holding Trust; C. A. Marketing Inc.
Foundation type: Independent foundation.
Financial data (yr. ended 12/31/13): Assets, $0 (M); gifts received, $159,080; expenditures, $146,210; qualifying distributions, $146,210; giving activities include $144,600 for 17+ grants (high: $36,000).
Fields of interest: Religion.
Limitations: Applications not accepted.
Application information: Unsolicited requests for funds not accepted.
Director: Jacob Sofer.
EIN: 274314708

5954

The Electrical Industry Scholarship Fund, Inc.
158-11 Harry Van Arsdale Jr. Ave.
Flushing, NY 11365
Main URL: http://www.jibei.org

Donor: GHO Venturer-Olsen Foundation.
Foundation type: Independent foundation.
Financial data (yr. ended 09/30/13): Assets, $337,664 (M); gifts received, $146,440; expenditures, $140,382; qualifying distributions, $140,382; giving activities include $140,000 for 20 grants to individuals (high: $7,000; low: $7,000).
Limitations: Applications not accepted.
Application information: Unsolicited requests for funds not accepted.
Officers: Gerald Finkel, Chair.; Christopher Erikson, Vice-Chair.; John Marchell, Secy.
Director: Michael Yee.

Trustees: Gina Addeo; John Baker; Howard Baldinger; Joseph Barbaro; Lola Barton; Edward Cleary; Leon Conn; Daniel Hernandez; Harvey Lifton; Edwin Lopez; John Mannino; Raymond Melville; Lance van Arsdale; Thomas van Arsdale; Walter Whitelaw.
EIN: 061687979

5955

Deborah Elkins Foundation
35 Sutton Pl.
New York City, NY 10022-2464 (917) 885-1256
Contact: Karen Davis, Tr.

Established in 2004 in New York.
Foundation type: Independent foundation.
Financial data (yr. ended 05/31/13): Assets, $1,277,940 (M); expenditures, $248,828; qualifying distributions, $245,500; giving activities include $245,500 for 19 grants (high: $45,000; low: $500).
Fields of interest: Higher education; Hospital care; Diseases and conditions.
Type of support: Research.
Limitations: Applications accepted. Giving primarily in New York, NY.
Application information: Application form required.
Initial approach: Letter
Deadline(s): Mar. 15
Trustee: Karen Davis.
EIN: 206213194

5956

Ellman Foundation
c/o Marks Paneth & Shron LLP
685 3rd Ave., 5th Fl.
New York City, NY 10017-8401

Established in 1999 in New York.
Donors: Lee E. Ellman; Esther Ellman.
Foundation type: Independent foundation.
Financial data (yr. ended 11/30/14): Assets, $2,244,653; expenditures, $153,971; qualifying distributions, $119,878.
Fields of interest: Education; Health; Judaism.
Limitations: Applications not accepted.
Application information: Unsolicited requests for funds not accepted.
Officers: Esther Ellman, Pres.; Jan Ellman, Treas.
EIN: 136160971

5957

The Lincoln Ellsworth Foundation
c/o Morris & McVeigh, LLP
767 3rd Ave.
New York City, NY 10017-2023

Established in 1943 in New York.
Foundation type: Independent foundation.
Financial data (yr. ended 12/31/14): Assets, $4,280,067; expenditures, $247,975; qualifying distributions, $229,237.
Fields of interest: Natural history museums; Higher education; Domesticated animals; Animal welfare; Veterinary medicine; Human services.
Limitations: Applications not accepted. No grants to individuals.
Application information: Unsolicited requests for funds not accepted.

Officers: MacDonald Budd, Esq., Pres. and Secy.;
Richard J. Miller, Jr., V.P.
EIN: 136022017

5958
Bais Eluzer Fund
30 Van Buren Dr., Ste. 201
Monroe, NY 10950-5816

Foundation type: Independent foundation.
Financial data (yr. ended 12/31/12): Assets,
$1,850,327 (M); expenditures, $131,406;
qualifying distributions, $122,020; giving activities
include $122,020 for grants.
EIN: 262720026

5959
Elyachar Welfare Corp.
8 E. 48th St.,Ste. 3E
New York City, NY 10017-1005

Established in 1951 in New York.
Donors: Gerel Corp.; Timston Corp.; Ruradan Corp.;
Daniel Elyachar; Jonathan Elyachar.
Foundation type: Company-sponsored foundation.
Financial data (yr. ended 12/31/13): Assets,
$1,847,474 (M); expenditures, $178,734;
qualifying distributions, $161,963; giving activities
include $159,193 for 20 grants (high: $51,000;
low: $100).
Purpose and activities: The foundation supports
general charitable giving.
Fields of interest: Education; Religion; Human
services.
Type of support: General support.
Limitations: Applications not accepted. Giving
primarily in New York, NY.
Application information: Unsolicited requests for
funds not accepted.
Officers: Jonathan Elyachar, Pres.; Richard Katz,
V.P.
EIN: 136161372

5960
EMB Foundation, Ltd.
2621 Ave. N
Brooklyn, NY 11210-5228
Contact: Alex Gonter, Mgr.

Established in 1997 in New York.
Donors: Alex Gonter; Shlomo Gonter; Sam Tropper;
Neil Gonter; Joel Gonter; Mark Gonter; Steven
Oppenheimer; Mark Steiger.
Foundation type: Independent foundation.
Financial data (yr. ended 12/31/14): Assets,
$22,090 (M); gifts received, $164,010;
expenditures, $170,005; qualifying distributions,
$169,980; giving activities include $169,980 for
grants.
Application information:
  Initial approach: Proposal
  Deadline(s): None
Officer: Alex Gonter, Mgr.
EIN: 113393489

5961
EMSA Fund, Inc.
c/o Norman Foundation Inc.
147 E. 48th St.
New York City, NY 10017-1223
Contact: Alice Franklin, Pres.

Established in 1962 in Georgia.
Donors: Phoebe Weil Lundeen†; Samuel Franklin;
Emily Calvanese; Andrew Franklin; Audrey F.
Franklin; Andrew D. Franklin.
Foundation type: Independent foundation.
Financial data (yr. ended 12/31/13): Assets,
$6,070,858 (M); gifts received, $40,558;
expenditures, $344,963; qualifying distributions,
$279,817; giving activities include $273,957 for
109 grants (high: $40,250; low: $50).
Purpose and activities: Giving primarily for culture,
public policy, race relations, rural development, civil
rights, community development, and women's
programs, particularly for those who have been
neglected or hard to reach in the provision of such
programs; support also for environmental programs
and educational programs for minorities.
Fields of interest: Arts and culture; Museums;
Education; Natural resources; Nonprofits; Hospital
care; Community improvement; Judaism; Child
welfare.
Type of support: General support; Continuing
support; Annual campaigns; Capital campaigns;
Endowments; Emergency funds; Program
development; Seed money; Regranting.
Limitations: Applications accepted. Giving primarily
in CO. No grants to individuals; no loans.
Publications: Grants list.
Application information: Application form required.
  Initial approach: Letter
  Deadline(s): None
  Board meeting date(s): Annually
Officers: Alice Franklin, Pres.; Audrey Franklin, V.P.;
Andrew D. Franklin, Secy.
EIN: 586043282

5962
Emwiga Foundation
(formerly Overlock Family Foundation)
c/o BCRS Associates, LLC
77 Water St., 9th Fl.
New York City, NY 10005-4414

Established in 1984 in New York.
Donor: Willard J. Overlock, Jr.
Foundation type: Independent foundation.
Financial data (yr. ended 02/28/14): Assets,
$8,759,507 (M); expenditures, $303,901;
qualifying distributions, $188,990; giving activities
include $185,900 for 63 grants (high: $25,000;
low: $150).
Fields of interest: Education; Higher education;
Business education; Diseases and conditions;
Diabetes; Human services.
Type of support: Research.
Limitations: Applications not accepted. Giving
primarily in New York, NY. No grants to individuals,
or for scholarships; no loans.
Application information: Unsolicited requests for
funds not accepted.
Trustees: James G. Kenan III; Emily Phelps
Overlock; Katharine Overlock; Willard J. Overlock,
Jr.; Willard J. Overlock III.
EIN: 133247601

5963
Blanche T. Enders Charitable Trust
c/o JPMorgan Private Bank, Philanthropic Svcs.
270 Park Ave., 16th Fl.
New York City, NY 10017
Contact: Jonathan Horowitz, Prog. Off.
E-mail: jonathan.g.horowitz@jpmchase.com

Foundation type: Independent foundation.
Financial data (yr. ended 12/31/13): Assets,
$6,137,426 (M); expenditures, $348,775;
qualifying distributions, $286,518; giving activities
include $266,000 for 7 grants (high: $50,000; low:
$10,000).
Purpose and activities: Funding interests include
K-12 education, animal welfare, and care for the
blind, elderly, or disabled. Education grants are
made primarily to groups working in the New York
City public school system. The trust also provides
annual grants to four organizations named in the
trust instrument.
Fields of interest: Education; Animal welfare; Senior
services; Seniors; People with disabilities.
Limitations: Applications not accepted. Giving
primarily in New York, NY. No support for
organizations lacking 501(c)(3) status. No grants to
individuals.
Application information: Proposals accepted by
invitation only. Unsolicited proposals will not be
accepted.
  Board meeting date(s): Nov.
Trustee: JPMorgan Chase Bank, N.A.
EIN: 136164229

5964
Engineering Information Foundation
(also known as EiF)
180 W. 80th St., Ste. 207
New York City, NY 10024-6301   (212) 579-7596
Contact: Hans Rutimann, Pres.; Ruth Miller, Exec.
Dir.
FAX: (212) 579-7517; *E-mail:* info@eifgrants.org;
Main URL: http://www.eifgrants.org

Foundation type: Independent foundation.
Financial data (yr. ended 12/31/13): Assets,
$6,681,780 (M); expenditures, $447,059;
qualifying distributions, $378,012; giving activities
include $258,731 for 11 grants (high: $41,000;
low: $12,940).
Purpose and activities: Support for educational
research programs that advance the availability and
use of information related to engineering and
applied technologies, programs conducted by
engineering educators that encourage women to
undertake careers in engineering, and projects to
improve access to engineering information for
students and faculty of educational institutions in
developing countries.
Fields of interest: Science; Technology;
Engineering; Women's services; Females.
International interests: Developing Countries.
Type of support: Program development; Matching
grants; Research; Research and evaluation;
Information and Referral.
Limitations: Applications accepted. Giving on a
national and international basis. No grants to
individuals, or for general operating expenses, or for
equipment, general overhead, capital campaigns,
conferences, scholarships, assistantships, doctoral
candidates, or fellowships; no loans.

Publications: Application guidelines; Annual report (including application guidelines); Financial statement; Grants list.
Application information: Initial applications are not accepted online. Non-U.S. institutions are required to submit an affidavit of equivalency, and/or name of intermediary organization. Application guidelines available on foundation web site.
Initial approach: Proposal via surface mail
Copies of proposal: 5
Deadline(s): Feb. 28 and Aug. 31
Board meeting date(s): Apr. and Oct.
Final notification: Within 30 days of board meeting
Officers and Directors: Hans Rutimann, Pres. and Director; John J. Regazzi, V.P. and Director; Julie A. Shimer, Secy. and Director; Ruth A. Miller, Exec. Dir.; Eisen Jo Casaclang.
Number of staff: 1 part-time professional.
EIN: 131679606

5965
Bonnie S. Englebardt Family Charitable Trust
521 5th Ave., Ste. 1804
New York City, NY 10175-0003

Established in 2002 in New York.
Donor: Bonnie S. Englebardt.
Foundation type: Independent foundation.
Financial data (yr. ended 12/31/13): Assets, $763,944 (M); expenditures, $224,725; qualifying distributions, $221,066; giving activities include $221,066 for 52 grants (high: $37,406; low: $150).
Fields of interest: Photography; Education; Nonprofits; Judaism; Human services.
Type of support: Regranting.
Limitations: Applications not accepted. Giving primarily in NY. No grants to individuals.
Application information: Contributes only to pre-selected organizations.
Trustee: Bonnie S. Englebardt.
EIN: 367391092

5966
The Enkess Charitable Foundation Trust
1748 49th St.
Brooklyn, NY 11204-1218

Established in 2003 in New York.
Foundation type: Independent foundation.
Financial data (yr. ended 12/31/13): Assets, $1,617,910 (M); gifts received, $86,000; expenditures, $165,089; qualifying distributions, $140,415; giving activities include $140,415 for 20 grants (high: $29,000; low: $1,000).
Fields of interest: Judaism.
Limitations: Applications not accepted. Giving primarily in Brooklyn, NY.
Application information: Contributes only to pre-selected organizations.
Trustees: Andre Engel; Toby Engel.
EIN: 116573719

5967
The Eppley Foundation for Research, Inc.
Box 359
244 Madison Ave.
New York City, NY 10016 2127343771
Contact: Ingrid Eisenstadter, Dir. of Grants

Main URL: http://fdnweb.org/eppley

Established in 1947 in Rhode Island.
Donor: Marion Eppley†.
Foundation type: Independent foundation.
Financial data (yr. ended 12/31/14): Assets, $2,785,985; gifts received, $204,049; expenditures, $287,255; qualifying distributions, $274,913.
Purpose and activities: Giving focuses on the following areas of interest: innovative medical investigations, endangered animals and ecosystems, and climate change.
Fields of interest: Environment; Wildlife biodiversity; Endangered species protection; Biomedicine; Diseases and conditions; Physical and earth sciences; Chemistry; Ecology.
Type of support: Research.
Limitations: Applications accepted. Giving primarily in the United States and internationally. No support for social sciences, computer sciences, educational programs, or for research involving AIDS, cancer or heart disease.
Publications: Application guidelines; Informational brochure.
Application information: Please go to the foundation web site and read the information there before applying. All submissions must start with an e-mailed Letter of Inquiry, not to exceed 1,000 words, describing the project and qualifications, goals, novelty, and the broader ramifications of the work once completed. It is preferred that the LOI is in the body of the e-mail, but it may also be a Word doc attachment (not docx, or .pdf). Full proposals must be accompanied by the foundation's application form and at least 2 letters of reference from qualified individuals who are familiar with the work proposed. Mail two printed copies of the proposal and all attachments to Ingrid Eisenstadter at the foundation address above. Simultaneously, e-mail the proposal, application form and all attachments to Ingrid Eisenstadter at the e-mail address on the foundation web page, at the URL above. Send the proposal and application form as Word docs, not docx or .pdf (attachments may be any format). Grants are made only to nonprofit education and research organizations with a U.S. base to receive the funds. Application form required.
Initial approach: Letter of inquiry
Copies of proposal: 2
Deadline(s): Letters of Inquiry must be received by Mar. 15 or Sept. 15. If a full proposal is invited, deadlines for receipt are Apr. 15 and Oct. 15
Board meeting date(s): June and Dec.
Final notification: Within two weeks of board meetings
Officers: Joan Winant, Pres.; Amy S. Saar, Secy.
Director: John Winant, MD.
Number of staff: 1 part-time professional; 1 part-time support.
EIN: 050258857

5968
The Armand G. Erpf Fund, Inc.
c/o Condon, O'Meara, McGinty, and Donnelly, LLP
1 Battery Park Plz., 7th Fl.
New York City, NY 10004-1405
Application address: c/o Grant Admin., Armand G. Erpf Fund, 640 Park Ave., New York, NY 10065, tel.: (212) 535-6678

Established in 1951 in New York.
Donors: Armand G. Erpf†; Erpf Charitable Trust.

Foundation type: Independent foundation.
Financial data (yr. ended 11/30/13): Assets, $9,286,742 (M); expenditures, $549,407; qualifying distributions, $505,631; giving activities include $301,673 for 51 grants (high: $50,000; low: $75).
Purpose and activities: Giving primarily for conservation and the environment, arts and culture, education, and human services.
Fields of interest: Arts and culture; Performing arts; Museums; Education; Elementary and secondary education; Higher education; Natural resources; Human services.
Type of support: General support.
Limitations: Applications accepted. Giving primarily in NY. No grants to individuals, or for endowment funds.
Application information:
Initial approach: Proposal
Copies of proposal: 1
Deadline(s): None
Board meeting date(s): Quarterly
Officers and Trustees: Sue Erpf Van de Bovenkamp, Pres. and Trustee; Cornelia A. Erpf-Forsman, Exec. V.P. and Trustee; Roger D. Stone, V.P. and Trustee; Gina Caimi, Secy.; Jamie A. Halegoua, Treas. and Trustee; Robert B. Oxnam.
EIN: 136085594

5969
ESL Charitable Foundation
225 Chestnut St.
Rochester, NY 14604-2424 (585) 336-1000
Contact: Francine Patella-Ryan

Established in 2004 in New York.
Donor: ESL Federal Credit Union.
Foundation type: Company-sponsored foundation.
Financial data (yr. ended 12/31/13): Assets, $0 (M); gifts received, $438,275; expenditures, $438,275; qualifying distributions, $438,250; giving activities include $438,250 for 46 grants (high: $105,000; low: $150).
Fields of interest: Arts and culture; Nonprofits; Diseases and conditions; Community and economic development; Human services.
Type of support: General support; Regranting.
Limitations: Applications accepted. Giving primarily in Rochester, NY. No grants to individuals.
Application information: Application form required.
Initial approach: Letter
Deadline(s): None
Officers: David Fiedler, Pres.; William Freeman, V.P.; Faheem A. Masood, 1st V.P.; Arline Santiago, V.P. and Secy.; Marueen Wolfe, V.P. and Treas.
EIN: 820548352

5970
Alex J. Ettl Foundation
55 Remsen St.
Brooklyn, NY 11201-4112

Established in 1989 in New York.
Donor: Alex J. Ettl†.
Foundation type: Independent foundation.
Financial data (yr. ended 12/31/14): Assets, $4,244,161; expenditures, $249,344; qualifying distributions, $213,000.
Purpose and activities: Giving primarily for arts and culture and education.

Fields of interest: Performing arts; Ballet; Museums; Education; Environment.
Limitations: Applications not accepted. Giving primarily in NY. No grants to individuals.
Application information: Contributes only to pre-selected organizations.
Trustees: Cordelia E. Clement; Judith E. Hazen.
EIN: 226503965

5971
Eule Charitable Foundation
14 Hampton Rd.
Port Washington, NY   11050-3009

Established in 2003 in New York.
Donors: Daniel Eule; Soros Fund Charitable Foundation.
Foundation type: Independent foundation.
Financial data (yr. ended 11/30/13): Assets, $4,629,009 (M); gifts received, $400,000; expenditures, $213,166; qualifying distributions, $212,916; giving activities include $212,916 for 19 grants (high: $32,500; low: $500).
Fields of interest: Nonprofits; Diseases and conditions; Human services; Child welfare; International relations.
Type of support: Regranting.
Limitations: Applications not accepted. Giving primarily in Maplewood, NJ and NY. No grants to individuals.
Application information: Contributes only to pre-selected organizations.
Trustees: Beth Eule; Daniel Eule.
EIN: 137390001

5972
Evans Family Charitable Foundation
c/o Rogoff & Company PC
355 Lexington Ave., 6th Fl.
New York City, NY   10017-6603

Donors: Devorah Faiga Evans; Eric D. Evans.
Foundation type: Independent foundation.
Financial data (yr. ended 12/31/13): Assets, $978,887 (M); gifts received, $750,000; expenditures, $198,158; qualifying distributions, $197,099; giving activities include $197,099 for 10 + grants (high: $55,000).
Fields of interest: Judaism; Human services.
Limitations: Applications not accepted.
Application information: Unsolicited requests for funds not accepted.
Trustees: Devorah Faiga Evans; Eric D. Evans.
EIN: 276343134

5973
R. S. Evans Foundation
(formerly Evans Family Foundation, Inc.)
c/o Deutsche Bank Trust Co., N.A.
P.O. Box 1297
Church St. Sta.
New York City, NY   10008-1297

Established in 1997 in Connecticut.
Donor: Robert S. Evans.
Foundation type: Independent foundation.
Financial data (yr. ended 12/31/13): Assets, $14,465,579 (M); gifts received, $3,979,545; expenditures, $480,780; qualifying distributions,

$421,000; giving activities include $408,500 for 34 grants (high: $35,000; low: $1,000).
Purpose and activities: Giving primarily for education and health care.
Fields of interest: Education; Higher education; Business education; Environment; Hospital care; Cancers.
Limitations: Applications not accepted. Giving in the U.S., with some emphasis on the northeast, particularly CT, MA and ME. No grants to individuals.
Application information: Contributes only to pre-selected organizations.
Officers: Robert S. Evans, Pres.; Susan C. Evans, Secy.
Directors: Ashley Reid Evans; Jonathan Perry Evans; Michael Robinson.
Trustee: Deutsche Bank Trust Co., N.A.
EIN: 061480414

5974
Ezer Foundation
1302 46th St.
Brooklyn, NY   11219-2139
Contact: Aviezer Cohen

Established in 2000 in New York.
Donor: Aviezer Cohen.
Foundation type: Independent foundation.
Financial data (yr. ended 11/30/13): Assets, $408,931 (M); gifts received, $150,000; expenditures, $155,800; qualifying distributions, $153,500; giving activities include $153,500 for 11 + grants (high: $50,000).
Fields of interest: Education; Religion.
Limitations: Applications not accepted. No grants to individuals.
Application information: Unsolicited requests for funds not accepted.
Trustees: Aviezer Cohen; Elaine Cohen.
EIN: 137262821

5975
The Ezra Charitable Trust
25 Rosalind Pl.
Lawrence, NY   11559-1522

Established in 1998 in New York.
Donor: Ezra Birnbaum.
Foundation type: Independent foundation.
Financial data (yr. ended 12/31/13): Assets, $4,301,750 (M); expenditures, $224,046; qualifying distributions, $197,178; giving activities include $197,178 for 60 grants (high: $26,000; low: $54).
Fields of interest: Judaism.
Limitations: Applications not accepted. Giving primarily in Brooklyn, NY. No grants to individuals.
Application information: Unsolicited requests for funds not accepted.
Trustees: Caroline Birnbaum; Ezra Birnbaum; Moshe Birnbaum.
EIN: 116487876

5976
Magen Ezra Foundation
c/o Jack Cattan
37 W. 37th St.
New York City, NY   10018-6225

Established in 1998 in New York.

Donors: Judah Cattan; Ezra Jack Cattan; Jack Cattan; Ezrasons, Inc.; Keter Torah Synagogue Sephardic Community; Balanced Tech. Corp.; Embassy Apparel, Inc.
Foundation type: Independent foundation.
Financial data (yr. ended 11/30/13): Assets, $176,358 (M); gifts received, $271,000; expenditures, $327,296; qualifying distributions, $322,450; giving activities include $322,450 for 221 grants (high: $25,000; low: $18).
Purpose and activities: Giving primarily for Jewish organizations, temples, and schools.
Fields of interest: Education; Religion; Human services.
Limitations: Applications not accepted. Giving primarily in the metropolitan New York, NY, area. No grants to individuals.
Application information: Contributes only to pre-selected organizations.
Trustees: Ezra Jack Cattan; Judah Cattan.
EIN: 133980258

5977
The F. & J.S. Fund Inc.
c/o B. Mac Corkindale
3960 Merrick Rd.
Seaford, NY   11783-2826   (516) 783-1794

Donors: David W. and Sadie Klau Foundation; Irving Kriesberg.
Foundation type: Independent foundation.
Financial data (yr. ended 12/31/13): Assets, $11,142,625 (M); expenditures, $519,061; qualifying distributions, $403,900; giving activities include $400,239 for grants.
Purpose and activities: Giving primarily for education, health care, and human services.
Fields of interest: Museums; Higher education; Law education; Environment; Domesticated animals; Hospital care; Human services.
Limitations: Applications accepted. Giving primarily in NY. No grants to individuals.
Application information:
   Initial approach: Proposal
   Deadline(s): None
Officers: Felice K. Shea, Pres. and Treas.; Andrew B. Shea, V.P.; Katherine D. Shea, V.P.; Steven J.C. Shea, Secy.
EIN: 237042425

5978
The Fagin Family Foundation
c/o Allen I. Fagin
607 West End Ave., Ste. 5A
New York City, NY   10024-1606

Established in 1999 in New York.
Donors: Allen I. Fagin; Judith H. Fagin.
Foundation type: Independent foundation.
Financial data (yr. ended 12/31/13): Assets, $235,090 (M); gifts received, $175,138; expenditures, $192,198; qualifying distributions, $192,030; giving activities include $191,850 for 20 grants (high: $50,000; low: $1,000).
Fields of interest: Education; Philanthropy; Religion; Judaism.
Limitations: Applications not accepted. Giving primarily in NY. No grants to individuals.
Application information: Unsolicited requests for funds not accepted.

Officers: Allen I. Fagin, Pres.; Judith H. Fagin, V.P. and Treas.
Directors: Charles G. Fagin; Miriam Fagin; Robert B. Fagin.
EIN: 113493014

5979
Faith Home Foundation
77 Carmen Pl.
Amityville, NY 11701-3603 (631) 264-7161
Contact: Martha L. Peterson, Tr.

Established in 1878 in New York.
Foundation type: Independent foundation.
Financial data (yr. ended 11/30/13): Assets, $3,466,424 (M); expenditures, $244,448; qualifying distributions, $206,323; giving activities include $176,000 for 15 grants (high: $20,000; low: $10,000).
Purpose and activities: Giving primarily to institutions which provide medical assistance to the elderly in New York.
Fields of interest: Diseases and conditions; Human services; Nursing homes; Senior services; Seniors.
Limitations: Applications accepted. Giving primarily in the metropolitan New York, NY, area, with emphasis on Brooklyn and Staten Island. No grants to individuals.
Application information: Application form required.
Initial approach: Completed application form
Deadline(s): None
Officers: Henry A. Braun, Pres.; William P. Tucker, Secy.; Kevin P. Foley, Treas.
Trustees: Richard T. Arkwright; Owen E. Brooks; Allan Larsen; Martha L. Peterson.
EIN: 111776032

5980
Falconhead Foundation
c/o Brown Brothers Harriman Trust Co., LLC
140 Broadway, 5th Fl.
New York City, NY 10005-1108

Established in 1997 in Delaware.
Donor: Rodney and Evelyn Day Trust.
Foundation type: Independent foundation.
Financial data (yr. ended 12/31/13): Assets, $4,016,016 (M); expenditures, $208,864; qualifying distributions, $178,000; giving activities include $175,000 for 15 grants (high: $25,000; low: $5,000).
Purpose and activities: Giving primarily for housing and homeless services, religious organizations, and education.
Fields of interest: Education; Housing development; Religion; Child welfare; Homeless people.
Limitations: Applications not accepted. Giving primarily in NY and PA. No grants to individuals.
Application information: Contributes only to pre-selected organizations.
Officers: Rodney D. Day III, Pres. and C.E.O.; Allison Day Lanni, V.P.; Evelyn Day Lasry, V.P.; Hilary Day Maner, V.P.; Evelyn S. Day, Secy.
EIN: 133946281

5981
Maurice & Judi Falk Charitable Foundation
477 Madison Ave., Ste. 707
New York City, NY 10022-5844
Application address: c/o Maurice B. Falk, 17161 Northway Cir., Boca Raton, FL 33496;
E-mail: mbfalk43@gmail.com

Established in 1994 in New York.
Donors: Maurice B. Falk; Judi L. Falk.
Foundation type: Independent foundation.
Financial data (yr. ended 12/31/13): Assets, $3,361,321 (M); gifts received, $208,750; expenditures, $184,134; qualifying distributions, $168,000; giving activities include $168,000 for 5 grants (high: $100,000; low: $500).
Fields of interest: Education; Judaism.
Type of support: General support.
Limitations: Applications accepted. Giving primarily in New York, NY. No grants to individuals.
Application information:
Initial approach: Contact foundation
Deadline(s): None
Officer: Maurice B. Falk, Mgr.
EIN: 113239050

5982
The Nagle Family Foundation
19 Garden Ave.
Bronxville, NY 10708-3007
Contact: Arthur J. Nagle, Chair.

Established in 1987 in New York.
Donor: Arthur J. Nagle.
Foundation type: Independent foundation.
Financial data (yr. ended 12/31/13): Assets, $389,474 (M); gifts received, $27,450; expenditures, $280,667; qualifying distributions, $273,296; giving activities include $273,296 for 56 grants (high: $131,800; low: $25).
Purpose and activities: Giving primarily for education, social services, and to Protestant churches; funding also for a wrestling club.
Fields of interest: Education; Higher education; Protestantism; Human services.
Limitations: Applications not accepted. Giving primarily in NY. No grants to individuals.
Application information: Contributes only to pre-selected organizations.
Officer: Arthur J. Nagle, Chair.
Director: Paige L. Nagle.
EIN: 133453422

5983
The Vanderbilt Family Foundation
(formerly The William H. & Helen C. Vanderbilt Foundation)
c/o Fiduciary Trust Company Intl.
600 5th Ave.
New York City, NY 10020-2302

Donor: William H. Vanderbilt Charitable Trust.
Foundation type: Independent foundation.
Financial data (yr. ended 02/28/15): Assets, $5,988,373 (M); expenditures, $436,369; qualifying distributions, $394,161; giving activities include $385,500 for 25 grants (high: $70,000; low: $1,000).
Purpose and activities: Giving primarily for education, employment services, parks, and international development.

Fields of interest: Arts and culture; Elementary and secondary education; Environment; Environmental education; Health; Science; Economic development; Job training; Housing development; Parks; Human services; Basic and emergency aid; International development.
International interests: Caribbean; Honduras.
Limitations: Applications not accepted. Giving primarily in Washington, DC, New York, NY, Boston, MA and VT; giving also on an international basis, primarily in the Caribbean and Honduras. No grants to individuals.
Application information: Contributes only to pre-selected organizations.
Trustees: Ellen F. Vanderbilt Aidnoff; Anne C. Vanderbilt Hartwell; William Henry Vanderbilt, Jr.; Emily Vanderbilt Wade.
EIN: 042743143

5984
Zaleski Family Foundation
300 Central Park West, Ste. 29D
New York City, NY 10024-1595 (212) 579-4216
Contact: Michel Zaleski, Pres. and Secy.

Donor: Michel Zaleski.
Foundation type: Independent foundation.
Financial data (yr. ended 06/30/13): Assets, $6,210,254 (M); gifts received, $117,222; expenditures, $436,705; qualifying distributions, $279,250; giving activities include $279,250 for 13 grants (high: $200,000; low: $250).
Fields of interest: Arts and culture; Performing arts education; Historic preservation; Education; Graduate and professional education; Engineering; Neighborhood associations.
Limitations: Applications accepted. Giving primarily in MO and VT. No grants to individuals.
Application information: Application form required.
Initial approach: Proposal
Deadline(s): None
Officers: Michel Zaleski, Pres. and Secy.; Caroline Rob Zaleski, V.P. and Treas.
EIN: 133911432

5985
Katherine & George Fan Foundation
163 Cedar Ln.
Ossining, NY 10562-2405 (212) 757-4760

Established in 1994 in Delaware.
Donors: George Fan; Katherine Fan.
Foundation type: Independent foundation.
Financial data (yr. ended 08/31/14): Assets, $241,042; gifts received, $163,210; expenditures, $119,284; qualifying distributions, $117,500.
Purpose and activities: Support for education, primarily through scholarships to students of Chinese heritage; support also for museums.
Fields of interest: Arts and culture; Education; Diseases and conditions.
Type of support: General support; Student aid.
Limitations: Applications accepted. Giving primarily in New York, NY.
Application information: Application form required.
Initial approach: Letter
Deadline(s): None
Officer: George Fan, Pres. and Secy.
EIN: 133784702

5986
The Gloria and Hilliard Farber Foundation
980 5th Ave., Apt. 17B
New York City, NY   10075-0191

Established in 2000 in New York.
Donors: Gloria Farber; Hilliard Farber; Hilliard Farber & Co., Inc.
Foundation type: Independent foundation.
Financial data (yr. ended 05/31/14): Assets, $1,293,582 (M); gifts received, $500,000; expenditures, $426,095; qualifying distributions, $420,770; giving activities include $418,520 for 12 grants (high: $185,000; low: $1,000).
Fields of interest: Education; Child educational development; Human services; Youth services.
Limitations: Applications not accepted. Giving primarily in New York, NY. No grants to individuals.
Application information: Unsolicited requests for funds not accepted.
Directors: Gloria Farber; Hilliard Farber; Jennifer Farber; Melissa Farber.
EIN: 134132864

5987
Charles D. Farber Memorial Foundation, Inc.
200 E. 61st St., Ste. 34A
New York City, NY   10065-8575   (212) 371-5683

Established in 1969 in New York.
Donors: Jack Farber†; Lafayette College.
Foundation type: Independent foundation.
Financial data (yr. ended 12/31/13): Assets, $2,661,677 (M); expenditures, $186,892; qualifying distributions, $183,360; giving activities include $183,360 for 27 grants (high: $59,000; low: $40).
Fields of interest: Education; Higher education; Diseases and conditions; Judaism; Human services.
Type of support: Research; Research and evaluation.
Limitations: Applications accepted. Giving primarily in FL and NY.
Application information: Must demonstrate financial need. Application form required.
  Initial approach: Letter
  Deadline(s): None
Directors: Gail Farber; Corey Gelman.
EIN: 237017599

5988
Howard and Barbara Farkas Foundation
106-19 Metropolitan Ave.
Forest Hills, NY   11375-6739

Donor: Barbara Farkas†.
Foundation type: Independent foundation.
Financial data (yr. ended 12/31/13): Assets, $6,387,159 (M); expenditures, $288,800; qualifying distributions, $280,725; giving activities include $279,000 for 33 grants (high: $50,000; low: $1,000).
Fields of interest: Education; HIV/AIDS; Christianity; Human services; Food banks; Homeless services; Low-income and poor people; People with HIV/AIDS.
International interests: Africa.
Limitations: Applications not accepted. Giving primarily in NY. No grants to individuals.

Application information: Contributes only to pre-selected organizations.
Officers: John C. Crabill, Pres. and Treas.; James A. Beha, V.P.; Macy Ann Beha, Secy.
EIN: 133107852

5989
Morgan Le Fay Dreams Foundation
c/o Ayco Co. - NTG
P.O. Box 15014
Albany, NY   12212-5014

Established in 2006 in California.
Donor: Paul A. McCulley.
Foundation type: Independent foundation.
Financial data (yr. ended 12/31/13): Assets, $2,589,108 (M); expenditures, $188,355; qualifying distributions, $185,862; giving activities include $185,862 for 8 grants (high: $50,000; low: $1,000).
Fields of interest: Higher education; Child welfare; Youth development.
Limitations: Applications not accepted. Giving primarily in PA and CA. No grants to individuals.
Application information: Contributes only to pre-selected organizations.
Officer: Paul A. McCulley, C.E.O. and Pres.
Director: Robert D. Renn.
EIN: 208083502

5990
Frank J. Fee Foundation, Inc.
103 Fairview Park Dr.
Elmsford, NY   10523-1544   (914) 829-2000
Contact: Frank J. Fee III, Pres.

Donor: The Reliable Automatic Sprinkler Co., Inc.
Foundation type: Independent foundation.
Financial data (yr. ended 08/31/13): Assets, $56,535 (M); gifts received, $275,000; expenditures, $230,065; qualifying distributions, $230,000; giving activities include $230,000 for 4 grants (high: $75,000; low: $25,000).
Fields of interest: Education; Higher education; Christianity.
Type of support: Scholarships; Individual development.
Limitations: Applications accepted. Giving primarily in MA and NY.
Application information:
  Deadline(s): None
Officers: Frank J. Fee III, Pres. and Treas.; Kevin T. Fee, V.P. and Secy.
EIN: 136130510

5991
The Lee and Jeffrey Feil Family Foundation Inc.
c/o Jeffrey J. Feil
7 Penn Plz., Ste. 618
New York City, NY   10001-0016

Established in 2004 in New York.
Donor: Jeffrey J. Feil.
Foundation type: Independent foundation.
Financial data (yr. ended 12/31/13): Assets, $11,903 (M); gifts received, $225,000; expenditures, $234,935; qualifying distributions, $234,500; giving activities include $234,500 for 11 grants (high: $100,000; low: $1,000).

Fields of interest: University education; Law education; Nonprofits; Judaism; Human services.
Type of support: Regranting.
Limitations: Applications not accepted. Giving primarily in New York City and Long Island, NY. No grants to individuals.
Application information: Contributes only to pre-selected organizations.
Officers: Jeffrey J. Feil, Chair and Secy.-Treas.; Lee Feil, Pres.; Brian Feil, V.P.; Erika Feil, V.P.; Joshua Feil, V.P.
EIN: 432051211

5992
Fein Foundation
P.O. Box 173
Purchase, NY   10577

Established in 1954 in New York.
Donors: Bernard Fein†; Elaine Fein; Lawrence Fein; Kathy Fein Bierman; Susan Zawel; Adam Fein; David Fein.
Foundation type: Independent foundation.
Financial data (yr. ended 12/31/14): Assets, $4,411,573; expenditures, $237,089; qualifying distributions, $225,472.
Fields of interest: Arts and culture; Museums; Literature and writing; Education; Animal welfare; Nonprofits; Health; Diseases and conditions; Science; Human services; Child welfare.
Type of support: Regranting.
Limitations: Applications not accepted. No support for political organizations or political campaigns . No grants to individuals.
Publications: Grants list.
Application information: Unsolicited requests for funds not accepted.
Officer: Elaine Fein, Pres.
Trustees: Kathy Bierman; Adam Fein; David Fein; Susan Zawel.
Number of staff: 1 part-time professional.
EIN: 136161610

5993
Maurice & Carol Feinberg Family Foundation
c/o Marcum LLLP
750 3rd. Ave., 11th Fl.
New York City, NY   10021-2716

Established in 1993 in New York.
Donors: Carol J. Feinberg; Maurice Feinberg†.
Foundation type: Independent foundation.
Financial data (yr. ended 11/30/13): Assets, $3,318,046 (M); expenditures, $461,239; qualifying distributions, $377,936; giving activities include $362,083 for 55 grants (high: $75,000; low: $100).
Purpose and activities: Giving for higher and other education.
Fields of interest: Education; Elementary and secondary education; University education; Hospital care; Judaism; Human services.
Limitations: Applications not accepted. Giving primarily in MA and NY. No grants to individuals.
Application information: Contributes only to pre-selected organizations.
Officers and Directors: Carol J. Feinberg, Pres.; Hope Feinberg Schroy, V.P. and Director; Nancy

Feinberg Tobin, V.P. and Director; David Feinberg, Secy.-Treas.
EIN: 133746078

5994
Alfred and Harriet Feinman Foundation
c/o A. Feinman
134 Lincoln Ave.
Purchase, NY   10577-2311

Established in 1968 in New York.
Donor: Alfred Feinman.
Foundation type: Independent foundation.
Financial data (yr. ended 11/30/14): Assets, $2,081,884 (L); gifts received, $58,920; expenditures, $280,355; qualifying distributions, $276,552; giving activities include $227,300 for 45 grants (high: $50,000; low: $250).
Fields of interest: Education; Health; Christianity.
Limitations: Applications not accepted. Giving primarily in the greater New York, NY, area.
Application information: Unsolicited requests for funds not accepted.
Officers: Alfred Feinman, Pres.; Andrew Feinman, Secy.-Treas.
Directors: Martin Feinman; Robert Feinman.
EIN: 237007870

5995
The Steven and Marcy Feldman Family Foundation
1922 E. 3rd St.
Brooklyn, NY   11223-2832   (212) 683-6677
Contact: Steven Feldman, Dir.

Foundation type: Independent foundation.
Financial data (yr. ended 12/31/13): Assets, $19,856 (M); gifts received, $260,100; expenditures, $424,158; qualifying distributions, $424,093; giving activities include $424,093 for grants.
Application information:
  Initial approach: Proposal
  Deadline(s): None
Director: Steven Feldman.
EIN: 364692233

5996
Seymour Feldman Foundation Inc.
277 Broadway, Ste. 601
New York City, NY   10007-2029   (212) 233-5688

Established in 2005 in New York.
Donor: Seymour Feldman†.
Foundation type: Independent foundation.
Financial data (yr. ended 05/31/14): Assets, $4,648,176; expenditures, $402,119; qualifying distributions, $364,154.
Fields of interest: Museums; University education; Medical education; Hospital care; Judaism; International relations.
Type of support: General support; Policy, advocacy and systems reform.
Application information: Application form required.
  Initial approach: Proposal
  Deadline(s): None
Officers: Leslie C. Feldman, Pres. and Treas.; Jeffrey Feldman, V.P. and Secy.
EIN: 203555993

5997
Feldstein Family Charitable Foundation Inc.
1350 Avenue of the Americas, 3rd Fl.
New York City, NY   10019

Established in 1987 in New York.
Foundation type: Independent foundation.
Financial data (yr. ended 12/31/14): Assets, $3,723,908; expenditures, $186,200; qualifying distributions, $185,950.
Fields of interest: Arts and culture; Education; Natural resources; Nonprofits; Hospital care; Diabetes; Cancers; Judaism.
Type of support: Research; Regranting.
Limitations: Applications not accepted. No grants to individuals.
Application information: Unsolicited requests for funds not accepted.
Officers: Richard Feldstein, Pres. and Treas.; Judith Feldstein, V.P. and Secy.
EIN: 133412554

5998
The Fenton Family Foundation
c/o U.S. Trust
114 W. 47th St.
New York City, NY   10036-1510

Established in 2000 in California.
Donors: Noel Fenton; Sarah Fenton.
Foundation type: Independent foundation.
Financial data (yr. ended 12/31/13): Assets, $7,091,463 (M); gifts received, $267,500; expenditures, $344,837; qualifying distributions, $278,930; giving activities include $275,485 for 27 grants (high: $125,000; low: $500).
Fields of interest: Arts and culture; Education; University education; Environment; Diseases and conditions; Christianity; Sports training.
Limitations: Applications not accepted. Giving primarily in CA. No grants to individuals.
Application information: Unsolicited requests for funds not accepted.
Officers: Noel Fenton, Pres.; Wendy Fenton, Secy.; Sarah Fenton, C.F.O.
Directors: Devon Fenton; Lance Fenton; Peter Fenton.
EIN: 943380876

5999
The Whitworth and Dorothy Ferguson Foundation
(formerly Ferguson Family Foundation, Inc.)
48 Huntington Ct.
Williamsville, NY   14221-5310   (716) 632-6104
Contact: Dorothy T. Ferguson, Pres.

Established in 1954 in New York.
Donor: Ferguson Construction Co.
Foundation type: Independent foundation.
Financial data (yr. ended 12/31/13): Assets, $852,630 (M); expenditures, $218,103; qualifying distributions, $204,280; giving activities include $192,000 for 8 grants (high: $101,000; low: $500).
Fields of interest: Arts and culture; Performing arts; Planetariums; Education; Graduate and professional education; Natural resources; Zoos; Health; Hospital care; Diseases and conditions; Theology; Human services.

Type of support: General support; Annual campaigns; Capital campaigns; Endowments; Research; Research and evaluation.
Limitations: Applications accepted. Giving primarily in Buffalo, NY.
Application information: Application form required.
  Initial approach: Letter
  Copies of proposal: 1
  Deadline(s): None
  Board meeting date(s): Quarterly
Officers: Dorothy T. Ferguson, Pres.; Donald R. Ferguson, V.P.; Dale B. Demyanick, Secy.-Treas.
Director: Philip C. Kadet.
Number of staff: 1 part-time support.
EIN: 166043861

6000
The Ferriday Fund Charitable Trust
c/o BNY Mellon Wealth Mgmt.
1001 Franklin Ave.
Garden City, NY   11530-2901

Established in 1991 in New York.
Donor: Carolyn Ferriday†.
Foundation type: Independent foundation.
Financial data (yr. ended 07/31/13): Assets, $9,231,026 (M); expenditures, $423,136; qualifying distributions, $385,451; giving activities include $363,000 for 56 grants (high: $127,500; low: $500).
Purpose and activities: Giving primarily for education and historic preservation; funding also for health care, arts and culture, and human services.
Fields of interest: Historic preservation; Education; Higher education; Health; Hospital care; Human services.
Limitations: Applications not accepted. Giving primarily in CT, and New York, NY. No grants to individuals.
Application information: Contributes only to pre-selected organizations.
Trustees: Richard J. Carter, Jr.; BNY Mellon, N.A.
EIN: 136967609

6001
The Feuerring Foundation
138 Havilands Ln.
White Plains, NY   10605-3026
Contact: Denise Weiner

Donors: Gertrude Feuerring†; Ralph Feuerring†.
Foundation type: Independent foundation.
Financial data (yr. ended 12/31/14): Assets, $4,173,425 (M); expenditures, $245,487; qualifying distributions, $196,345; giving activities include $172,345 for 85 grants (high: $36,000; low: $200).
Fields of interest: Diseases and conditions; Housing development; Religion; Judaism.
Type of support: General support; Research.
Limitations: Applications not accepted. Giving primarily in New York, NY. No grants to individuals.
Application information: Unsolicited requests for funds not accepted.
Officers: Denise Weiner, Pres.; Nicole Hill, Secy.
EIN: 136221072

6002
Ficalora Family Foundation
173 Aldershot Ln.
Manhasset, NY 11030-3705

Established in 1998 in New York.
Donors: Joseph R. Ficalora; Alice B. Ficalora.
Foundation type: Independent foundation.
Financial data (yr. ended 12/31/14): Assets, $5,496,611; gifts received, $0; expenditures, $198,750; qualifying distributions, $192,500 and $0 for set-asides.
Fields of interest: Arts and culture; Education; Hospital care; Protestantism.
Type of support: General support.
Limitations: Applications not accepted. Giving primarily in NY. No grants to individuals.
Application information: Contributes only to pre-selected organizations.
Officers and Directors: Alice B. Ficalora, Pres. and Director; Joseph R. Ficalora, V.P. and Secy. and Director; John J. Ficalora, V.P. and Treas. and Director.
EIN: 113441781

6003
Fields Family Foundation
c/o Cary Fields
495 Broadway, 7th Fl.
New York City, NY 10012-0000

Established in 2007 in New York.
Donors: Cary Fields; Research and Planning LLC.
Foundation type: Independent foundation.
Financial data (yr. ended 12/31/13): Assets, $6,020,871 (M); expenditures, $266,358; qualifying distributions, $249,715; giving activities include $242,000 for 8 grants (high: $125,000; low: $5,000).
Fields of interest: Education; Higher education; Nonprofits; Judaism.
Type of support: Regranting.
Limitations: Applications not accepted.
Application information: Unsolicited requests for funds not accepted.
Trustees: Cary Fields; J. Alexander Fields; Kathleen Fields; Samantha Fields; Julian W. Friedman.
EIN: 386850467

6004
Fieldstone Foundation, Inc.
(formerly Meetinghouse Foundation, Inc.)
c/o Ayco Co., L.P. - National Tax Group
P.O. Box 15014
Albany, NY 12212-5014

Established in 1990 in Massachusetts.
Donor: Thomas R. Shepherd.
Foundation type: Independent foundation.
Financial data (yr. ended 12/31/13): Assets, $3,508,472 (M); expenditures, $267,829; qualifying distributions, $182,731; giving activities include $182,731 for 78 grants (high: $14,640; low: $100).
Fields of interest: Elementary and secondary education; Higher education; Environment; Religion; Human services.
Limitations: Applications not accepted. Giving primarily in GA and MA. No grants to individuals.
Application information: Unsolicited requests for funds not accepted.

Officers and Directors: Nancy Shepherd, Pres. and Director; Katharine S. Furney, Clerk and Director; Thomas R. Shepherd, Treas. and Director; Elizabeth R. Beneche; Ruth H. Shepherd; T. Nathanael Shepherd.
EIN: 223111728

6005
The Lori & Mark Fife Foundation, Inc.
126 E. 56th St., 22nd Fl.
New York City, NY 10022-3055

Established in 1996 in New York.
Donors: Mark Fife; Lori Fife.
Foundation type: Independent foundation.
Financial data (yr. ended 06/30/13): Assets, $1,613,424 (M); gifts received, $943,357; expenditures, $351,528; qualifying distributions, $351,128; giving activities include $349,738 for 29 grants (high: $200,000; low: $75).
Purpose and activities: Giving primarily for education and Jewish organizations, as well as to a theater company.
Fields of interest: Theater; Elementary and secondary education; Higher education; Nonprofits; Judaism.
Type of support: General support; Scholarships; Regranting.
Limitations: Applications not accepted. No grants to individuals.
Application information: Unsolicited requests for funds not accepted.
Officers: Lori Fife, Pres.; Howard Ruthman, V.P.; Mark Fife, Secy.-Treas.
EIN: 522026744

6006
The Fink Family Foundation
c/o Brain Cuneo, The Ayco Co.
321 Broadway
P.O. Box 860
Saratoga Springs, NY 12866-0860

Donors: Laurence D. Fink; Lori Fink.
Foundation type: Independent foundation.
Financial data (yr. ended 12/31/13): Assets, $8,464,179 (M); gifts received, $4,500,288; expenditures, $171,300; qualifying distributions, $150,000; giving activities include $150,000 for 3 grants (high: $100,000; low: $25,000).
Fields of interest: Orchestral music; Health.
Limitations: Applications not accepted. Giving primarily in New York, NY.
Application information: Unsolicited requests for funds not accepted.
Trustees: Laurence D. Fink; Lori W. Fink.
EIN: 262421487

6007
Howard Finkelstein Foundation, Inc.
(formerly Howard and Susan Finkelstein Foundation, Inc.)
c/o Israeloff Trattner & Co.
450 7th Ave., Ste. 2701
New York City, NY 10123-2701
Application address: 23 Carrington Dr., Greenwich, CT 06831, tel.: (212) 239-3300

Established in 2000 in New York.
Donors: Howard Finkelstein; Susan Finkelstein.

Foundation type: Independent foundation.
Financial data (yr. ended 11/30/13): Assets, $4,179,514 (M); expenditures, $222,550; qualifying distributions, $206,600; giving activities include $206,600 for 25 grants (high: $50,000; low: $100).
Fields of interest: Higher education; Nonprofits; Health; Judaism.
Type of support: Regranting.
Application information:
Initial approach: Letter
Deadline(s): None
Officer and Directors: Howard Finkelstein, Pres. and Director; Amy Cole; David Finkelstein; Stan Finkelstein; Lauren Finkelstein.
EIN: 134092400

6008
David & Laura Finn Family Foundation, Inc.
90 Wellington Ave.
New Rochelle, NY 10804-3708

Donors: David Finn; Laura Finn.
Foundation type: Independent foundation.
Financial data (yr. ended 03/31/13): Assets, $90,411 (M); gifts received, $11,976; expenditures, $167,845; qualifying distributions, $166,526; giving activities include $166,526 for 11 grants (high: $165,276; low: $40).
Fields of interest: University education; Nonprofits; Judaism.
Type of support: General support; Regranting.
Limitations: Applications not accepted. Giving primarily in RI. No grants to individuals.
Application information: Unsolicited requests for funds not accepted.
Officers: David Finn, Pres. and Treas.; Laura Finn, V.P.
EIN: 136179414

6009
Harry and Jane Fischel Foundation
875 Avenue of the Americas, Ste. 1701
New York City, NY 10001-3507 (212) 599-2828
FAX: (212) 867-8512;
E-mail: info@fischelfoundation.org; Application e-mail: grants@fischelfoundation.org; Main URL: http://fischelfoundation.org

Established in 1932 in New York.
Donor: Harry Fischel†.
Foundation type: Independent foundation.
Financial data (yr. ended 12/31/13): Assets, $13,774,680 (M); expenditures, $1,133,993; qualifying distributions, $659,765; giving activities include $425,470 for 15 grants (high: $377,000; low: $50).
Purpose and activities: Organized to develop Talmudic research to aid Jewish knowledge and to present the Orthodox Jewish contributions to civilization. Funding also to an institute which includes a school for training judges for religious courts, publishes tracts in the field of religious law, and researches and republishes Talmudic commentary in new editions utilizing heretofore unknown manuscripts; some giving also for Jewish education and temples.
Fields of interest: Education; Orthodox Judaism.
International interests: Israel.
Type of support: General support.

Limitations: Giving primarily in NY; some giving also in Israel. No grants to individuals.
Publications: Application guidelines.
Application information: Complete application guidelines available on foundation website. Application form required.

> *Initial approach:* E-mail grant application form on foundation web site to specific application e-mail address

Officers and Directors: Chief Rabbi Shear-Yashuv Cohen, Chair. and Director; Seth M. Goldstein, Pres. and Director; Rabbi Hillel Reichel, 1st V.P. and Director; Chaim Stepelman, 2nd V.P. and Director; Rabbi Aaron I. Reichel, Esq., Secy. and Director; Avishai Kraus, Esq.; David S. Locker; Donald Moses; Stuart Shor; Deborah Stepelman.
Number of staff: 1 part-time professional; 2 part-time support.
EIN: 135677832

6010
Lawton W. Fitt and James I. McLaren Foundation
Bowling Green Sta.
P.O. Box 73
New York City, NY   10274-0073

Established in 1996 in New York.
Donors: Lawton W. Fitt; James McLaren.
Foundation type: Independent foundation.
Financial data (yr. ended 09/30/14): Assets, $7,926,220 (M); gifts received, $772,570; expenditures, $317,043; qualifying distributions, $277,750; giving activities include $277,750 for 16 grants (high: $50,000; low: $200).
Purpose and activities: Giving primarily for international relations and education; some giving also for the arts and social services.
Fields of interest: Arts and culture; Performing arts; Education; Higher education; Nonprofits; Health; Diseases and conditions; Human services; Youth development; International development.
Type of support: Regranting.
Limitations: Applications not accepted. Giving primarily in NY and VA. No grants to individuals, or for scholarships; no loans.
Application information: Contributes only to pre-selected organizations.
Trustees: Lawton W. Fitt; James I. McLaren.
EIN: 133919763

6011
The John & Christine Fitzgibbons Foundation
405 Lexington Ave., 71st Fl.
New York City, NY   10174-0002

Established in 2007 in New York.
Donors: John B. Fitzgibbons; Christine Fitzgibbons.
Foundation type: Independent foundation.
Financial data (yr. ended 06/30/13): Assets, $2,005,987 (M); gifts received, $375,000; expenditures, $404,587; qualifying distributions, $401,660; giving activities include $401,660 for 18 grants (high: $100,000; low: $500).
Fields of interest: Education; Secondary education; Higher education; Environment; Health.
International interests: Africa.
Limitations: Applications not accepted. Giving primarily in MA, NH and NY. No grants to individuals.

Application information: Unsolicited requests for funds not accepted.
Trustees: Christine Fitzgibbons; John B. Fitzgibbons.
EIN: 137548509

6012
The Flaherty Family Foundation
130 E. 95th St.
New York City, NY   10128-1705

Donors: Peter A. Flaherty; Pamela Flaherty.
Foundation type: Independent foundation.
Financial data (yr. ended 10/31/13): Assets, $528,297 (M); gifts received, $856,456; expenditures, $433,482; qualifying distributions, $431,209; giving activities include $428,650 for 34 grants (high: $200,000; low: $100).
Fields of interest: Higher education; Human services.
Type of support: General support.
Limitations: Applications not accepted. Giving primarily in NY and OH. No grants to individuals.
Application information: Contributes only to pre-selected organizations.
Officers: Peter A. Flaherty, Pres.; Jonathan P. Flaherty, Treas.
Trustee: Pamela P. Flaherty.
EIN: 133919502

6013
Shirley & William R. Fleischer Foundation, Inc.
7 Penn Plz., Ste. 810
New York City, NY   10001-0011

Established in 1967 in New York.
Donors: Shirley Fleischer; William R. Fleischer†.
Foundation type: Independent foundation.
Financial data (yr. ended 12/31/13): Assets, $5,722,295 (M); expenditures, $264,427; qualifying distributions, $249,535; giving activities include $246,620 for 12 grants (high: $117,500; low: $20).
Purpose and activities: Giving to Jewish agencies and for human services.
Fields of interest: Education; Higher education; Nonprofits; Diseases and conditions; Judaism; Human services.
Type of support: Regranting.
Limitations: Applications not accepted. No grants to individuals.
Application information: Unsolicited requests for funds not accepted.
Officers and Trustees: Carl Fleischer, V.P. and Trustee; Donald Fleischer, V.P. and Trustee; Steven Fleischer, V.P. and Trustee.
EIN: 116048777

6014
Ruby B. Fleming Trust
1 Court Sq., 19th Fl.
Long Island City, NY   11120-4356

Foundation type: Independent foundation.
Financial data (yr. ended 12/31/14): Assets, $10,172,697; expenditures, $500,972; qualifying distributions, $459,617.
Fields of interest: Education; Nursing care; Public libraries; Housing development; Christianity; Human

services; Youth services; People with hearing impairments.
Limitations: Applications not accepted. Giving primarily in NY.
Application information: Unsolicited requests for funds not accepted.
Trustee: CitiBank, N.A.
EIN: 136644818

6015
Flowering Tree
225 E. 57th St., Apt. 18D
New York City, NY   10022-2861
E-mail: contactus@floweringtreeinc.org; Additional e-mail: floweringtreeinc@gmail.com; Main URL: http://www.floweringtreeinc.org
Facebook: https://www.facebook.com/pages/Flowering-Tree-Inc/195773717159535?fref=ts

Donors: Sumita Ambasta; Rajesh Ambasta; Sansar Capital Foundation.
Foundation type: Operating foundation.
Financial data (yr. ended 12/31/13): Assets, $6,246,895 (M); gifts received, $280,000; expenditures, $245,268; qualifying distributions, $245,106; giving activities include $210,000 for 3 grants (high: $90,000; low: $35,000).
Purpose and activities: The foundation's organization's mission is to support womens development and childrens education.
Fields of interest: Education; Children; Females.
International interests: India; Singapore.
Limitations: Applications accepted. Giving primarily in India. No grants to individuals.
Application information: Full proposals accepted by invitation only.

> *Initial approach:* Letter of inquiry
> *Deadline(s):* None

Board Members: Sumita Ambasta; Alice Fricke; Aditi Goswami; Christopher McLeod.
EIN: 352278100

6016
The Roger W. Follett Foundation, Inc.
c/o Lee & Emerson
35 W. Main St.
Norwich, NY   13815-1632   (607) 334-2247
Contact: Lee Emerson

Established in 1995 in New York.
Donor: Roger Follet†.
Foundation type: Independent foundation.
Financial data (yr. ended 12/31/13): Assets, $4,945,576 (M); expenditures, $294,786; qualifying distributions, $264,974; giving activities include $250,150 for 21 grants (high: $70,000; low: $1,000).
Purpose and activities: Giving primarily for a YMCA, a hospital, and a classic car museum; funding also for education, animal welfare, social services, and religion.
Fields of interest: Museums; Education; Animal welfare; Hospital care; Protestantism; Catholicism; Human services.
Application information: Application form required.

> *Initial approach:* Proposal
> *Deadline(s):* None

Officers: Peter V. Smith, Pres.; Thomas C. Emerson, V.P.; James I. Dunne, Secy.-Treas.
EIN: 223270901

6017
Fondation Femme Debut
50 Gramercy Park N., Ste. 5B
New York City, NY 10010-6320

Established in 2007 in New York.
Foundation type: Independent foundation.
Financial data (yr. ended 12/31/13): Assets, $3,991,525 (M); gifts received, $6,095; expenditures, $236,542; qualifying distributions, $200,000; giving activities include $200,000 for 14 grants (high: $166,000; low: $1,000).
Fields of interest: Arts education; Education; Health; Human services.
Limitations: Applications not accepted. Giving primarily in New York, NY.
Application information: Unsolicited requests for funds not accepted.
Trustees: Erick Konczyk; Anne T. Pelletier.
EIN: 261869586

6018
S. Forest Company, Inc.
1540 Broadway, 24th Fl.
New York City, NY 10036-4039

Established in 1952 in New York.
Donors: BNY Mellon, N.A.; Sidney Roffman; Dean W. Mathey.
Foundation type: Independent foundation.
Financial data (yr. ended 12/31/13): Assets, $6,578 (M); gifts received, $200,000; expenditures, $21,604; qualifying distributions, $178,800; giving activities include $178,800 for 30 grants (high: $30,000; low: $50).
Purpose and activities: Giving primarily to organizations providing assistance to girls and youth programs.
Fields of interest: Elementary and secondary education; Higher education; Christianity; Human services; Child welfare.
Type of support: General support.
Limitations: Applications not accepted. Giving primarily in NJ and New York, NY.
Application information: Unsolicited requests for funds not accepted.
Officers: Paul M. Frank, Pres. and Treas.; Darcy M. Katris, Secy.
EIN: 136069185

6019
Foundation "Q"
1750 44th St.
Brooklyn, NY 11204-1050
Contact: Arye Ringel

Established in 1990 in New York.
Donor: Stuart V. Rubinfeld.
Foundation type: Independent foundation.
Financial data (yr. ended 05/31/13): Assets, $617,288 (M); gifts received, $200,000; expenditures, $250,534; qualifying distributions, $245,826; giving activities include $244,726 for 31 grants (high: $131,010; low: $36).
Fields of interest: Education; Nonprofits; Religion; Judaism; Human services.
Type of support: Regranting.
Limitations: Applications not accepted. Giving primarily in the New York, NY, area. No grants to individuals.

Application information: Unsolicited requests for funds not accepted.
Trustees: Stuart V. Rubinfeld; Teena C. Rubinfeld.
EIN: 113014673

6020
The Foundation-to-Life, Inc.
c/o Popper & Company LLP
192 Lexington Ave.
New York City, NY 10016-6823

Established in 1990 in Unspecified.
Donors: Arthur A. Goldberg; Carol Goldberg.
Foundation type: Independent foundation.
Financial data (yr. ended 06/30/14): Assets, $1,237,888 (M); expenditures, $179,882; qualifying distributions, $166,117; giving activities include $162,675 for 37 grants (high: $96,500; low: $200).
Fields of interest: Arts and culture; Education.
Limitations: Applications not accepted. Giving limited to New York, NY. No grants to individuals.
Application information: Unsolicited requests for funds not accepted.
Officers: Carol Goldberg, Chair. - Secy. and Director; Arthur A. Goldberg, Pres. - Treas. and Director.
Director: Henry A. Lowet.
EIN: 133549650

6021
Fowey Light Fund, Inc.
c/o Hobish/Wiener
30 Scarsdale Farm Rd.
Scarsdale, NY 10583-1919

Established in 1989 in Florida.
Donors: Earl L. Wiener; S.G. & M.P. Wiener Fund.
Foundation type: Independent foundation.
Financial data (yr. ended 12/31/13): Assets, $2,413,900 (M); expenditures, $238,758; qualifying distributions, $223,000; giving activities include $223,000 for 57 grants (high: $10,000; low: $500).
Purpose and activities: Giving primarily to Jewish organizations, and for human services and the arts.
Fields of interest: Arts and culture; Nonprofits; Community and economic development; Judaism; Human rights; Human services.
Type of support: General support; Regranting.
Limitations: Applications not accepted. Giving primarily in FL. No grants to individuals.
Application information: Contributes only to pre-selected organizations.
Directors: Richard Hobish; JoAnn Kukulus; Florence Wiener; Fred Wiener.
EIN: 650060405

6022
The Wallace Fox Foundation
c/o Davidson Dawson
60 E. 42nd St., 38th Fl.
New York City, NY 10165-3802

Established in 2010 in New York.
Donor: Wallace Fox†.
Foundation type: Independent foundation.
Financial data (yr. ended 12/31/13): Assets, $3,587,682 (M); expenditures, $215,145; qualifying distributions, $170,000; giving activities

include $170,000 for 14 grants (high: $40,000; low: $500).
Fields of interest: Arts and culture; Health; Human services.
Limitations: Applications not accepted.
Application information: Unsolicited requests for funds not accepted.
Trustees: Gloria S. Neuwirth; Gail H. Roman.
EIN: 271136617

6023
Chaim & Rose Fraiman Foundation, Inc.
247 Seeley St.
Brooklyn, NY 11218-1207 (718) 965-1500

Established in 1983 in New York.
Donors: Chaim Fraiman; Rose Fraiman; John Bartley; Ted Weinberger; Steve Adelsberg.
Foundation type: Independent foundation.
Financial data (yr. ended 11/30/13): Assets, $2,030,889 (M); gifts received, $276,905; expenditures, $356,037; qualifying distributions, $348,645; giving activities include $348,645 for 41 grants (high: $125,000; low: $5).
Purpose and activities: Giving primarily to Jewish agencies, temples, and schools.
Fields of interest: Education; Hospital care; Religion.
Type of support: General support.
Limitations: Applications accepted. Giving primarily in the greater New York, NY, area.
Application information:
Initial approach: Letter
Deadline(s): None
Officers: Chaim Fraiman, Co-Pres. and V.P.; Rose Fraiman, Co-Pres. and V.P.; Steven Adelsberg, Secy.; Theodore Weinberger, Treas.
EIN: 112689575

6024
The Maj Franco Family Charitable Foundation
295 5th Ave., Ste. 312
New York City, NY 10016-7106

Donors: Joseph A. Franco; Marc Franco; Joseph N. Franco.
Foundation type: Independent foundation.
Financial data (yr. ended 06/30/13): Assets, $15,262 (M); gifts received, $296,000; expenditures, $290,998; qualifying distributions, $290,533; giving activities include $290,533 for 244 grants (high: $36,000; low: $36).
Fields of interest: Education; Philanthropy; Nonprofits; Judaism.
Type of support: Regranting.
Limitations: Applications not accepted.
Application information: Unsolicited requests for funds not accepted.
Officers: Joseph A. Franco, Pres.; Marc Franco, V.P.
Trustee: Joseph N. Franco.
EIN: 276370187

6025
Isaac S. Franco Family Foundation
350 5th Ave., Ste. 5001
New York City, NY 10118-5091

Donors: Isaac S. Franco; Fine Sheer Industries, Inc.
Foundation type: Independent foundation.

Financial data (yr. ended 12/31/14): Assets, $64 (M); gifts received, $199,500; expenditures, $199,412; qualifying distributions, $199,187; giving activities include $199,187 for 92 grants (high: $18,000; low: $36).
Fields of interest: Education; Judaism.
Limitations: Applications not accepted. Giving primarily in NY. No grants to individuals.
Application information: Contributes only to pre-selected organizations.
Officer: Isaac S. Franco, Pres.
EIN: 133759142

6026
Ernst & Elfriede Frank Foundation, Inc
112-01 Queens Blvd., Apt. 11C
Forest Hills, NY 11375-5589

Donor: Ernst L. Frank.
Foundation type: Independent foundation.
Financial data (yr. ended 08/31/13): Assets, $8,421,295 (M); expenditures, $405,521; qualifying distributions, $385,368; giving activities include $375,185 for 199 grants (high: $29,000; low: $100).
Purpose and activities: Giving primarily for the arts, health, and human services.
Fields of interest: Arts and culture; Education; Health; Hospital care; Diseases and conditions; Religion; Human services; Child welfare.
International interests: Canada; South America.
Limitations: Applications not accepted. Giving primarily in MA and NY. No grants to individuals.
Application information: Contributes only to pre-selected organizations.
Officers: Sybil Ann Brennan, V.P.; Ernest H. Frank, V.P.; Jephtha Tausig Edwards, V.P.; Kasara Gage, V.P.; Samantha Starr, V.P.; Eva-Maria Tausig, V.P.
EIN: 136106471

6027
D. W. Frankel Foundation, Inc.
160 E. 65th St.
New York City, NY 10021-6654

Established in 1976 in New York.
Donors: David F. Frankel; Diane F. Sherman; Eliza Howard; Jessa Sherman; Esme Howard; Gregory Frankel; David W. Frankel, Jr.
Foundation type: Independent foundation.
Financial data (yr. ended 12/31/13): Assets, $3,852,366 (M); gifts received, $15,000; expenditures, $328,847; qualifying distributions, $308,053; giving activities include $281,610 for 1 grant.
Purpose and activities: Giving primarily for the arts and education.
Fields of interest: Arts and culture; Education; Higher education; Judaism; Human services.
Type of support: General support.
Limitations: Applications not accepted. Giving primarily in CO, CT and NY. No grants to individuals.
Application information: Unsolicited requests for funds not accepted.
Officer: David F. Frankel, Pres.
Trustees: Linda Frankel; Diane F. Sherman.
EIN: 132874447

6028
The Franklin Fund
c/o Farkouh, Furman and Faccio, LLP
460 Park Ave., 12th Fl.
New York City, NY 10022-1906 2122455900

Established in 1958 in New York.
Donor: The Helena Franklin.
Foundation type: Independent foundation.
Financial data (yr. ended 06/30/13): Assets, $2,309,812 (M); expenditures, $203,233; qualifying distributions, $191,945; giving activities include $182,000 for 14 grants (high: $97,000; low: $500).
Fields of interest: Environment; Philanthropy; Religion.
Limitations: Applications not accepted. Giving primarily in NY. No grants to individuals.
Application information: Unsolicited requests for funds not accepted.
Trustees: Cynthia F. Franklin; George S. Franklin III; Sheila F. Lieber; Helena F. Rozier.
EIN: 136160092

6029
Fraydun Foundation Inc.
c/o Pan Am Equities Inc.
18 E. 50th St.
New York City, NY 10022-6817

Established in 1981 in New York.
Donors: Fraydun Manocherian; Pamela Equities Corp.; Fred Manocherian.
Foundation type: Independent foundation.
Financial data (yr. ended 12/31/13): Assets, $8,631,658 (M); gifts received, $555,350; expenditures, $339,611; qualifying distributions, $311,085; giving activities include $304,900 for 21 grants (high: $100,000; low: $5,000).
Fields of interest: Theater; Education; Mental health care; Diseases and conditions; Diabetes; Cancers; Film and video; People with vision impairments.
Limitations: Applications not accepted. No grants to individuals.
Application information: Unsolicited requests for funds not accepted.
Directors: Fraydun Manocherian; Jennifer Manocherian; Kimberly Manocherian.
EIN: 133185696

6030
Freedom For All
(formerly Katie Ford Foundation Inc.)
59 Wooster St., 5th Fl.
New York City, NY 10012-4399
Main URL: http://www.katieford.org

Donors: Katie Ford; Tom Roush.
Foundation type: Independent foundation.
Financial data (yr. ended 12/31/13): Assets, $512,051 (M); gifts received, $369,097; expenditures, $355,523; qualifying distributions, $351,441; giving activities include $212,202 for 13 grants (high: $60,814; low: $200).
Fields of interest: Religion; Human services.
International interests: India.
Type of support: Advocacy.
Limitations: Applications not accepted. Giving primarily in New York, NY and India.
Application information: Unsolicited requests for funds not accepted.

Officers: Katie Ford, Pres.; Lauren Lanier, V.P.; Adam Peltz, Treas.
EIN: 274874257

6031
Stephen C. Freidheim Foundation, Inc.
c/o Bessemer Trust
630 5th Ave., Ste. 3425
New York City, NY 10111-0100

Established in 2004 in New York.
Donor: Stephen C. Freidheim.
Foundation type: Independent foundation.
Financial data (yr. ended 12/31/13): Assets, $9,054,091 (M); gifts received, $13,757; expenditures, $289,426; qualifying distributions, $288,555; giving activities include $273,487 for 11 grants (high: $100,000; low: $5,000).
Fields of interest: Education; Higher education; Human services; Child welfare.
Limitations: Applications not accepted. Giving primarily in New Haven, CT, Washington, DC, IL, and New York, NY. No grants to individuals.
Application information: Unsolicited requests for funds not accepted.
Officers: Stephen C. Freidheim, Chair.; Marguerite Freidheim, Pres.; Cyrus Freidheim, C.I.O.; Lynn Waunford-Brown, Secy.
Board Members: Amandine Freidheim; Scott Freidheim.
EIN: 800116118

6032
D. E. French Foundation, Inc.
120 Genesee St., Rm. 503
Auburn, NY 13021-3620

Established in 1955 in New York.
Donors: Clara M. French†; D.E. French†.
Foundation type: Independent foundation.
Financial data (yr. ended 12/31/14): Assets, $5,028,299; expenditures, $267,795; qualifying distributions, $230,160.
Fields of interest: Arts and culture; Education; Graduate and professional education; Nonprofits; Health; Nursing care; Protestantism; Catholicism; Family services; Youth services; Cemeteries and burial services; Senior services; Children and youth; Seniors; People with disabilities; People with physical disabilities; People with psychosocial disabilities.
Type of support: General support; Matching grants; Continuing support; Annual campaigns; Capital campaigns; Capital and infrastructure; Equipment; Endowments; Scholarships; Regranting.
Limitations: Applications accepted. Giving primarily in the Cayuga County, NY, area. No support for political organizations. No grants to individuals.
Application information:
  Initial approach: Letter
  Copies of proposal: 1
  Deadline(s): None
  Board meeting date(s): Jan., Apr., July, and Oct.
  Final notification: Within reasonable time after quarterly board meeting
Officers and Directors: Ronald D. West, Pres. and Director; Caryl W. Adams, Secy.; Walter M. Lowe, Exec. Dir.; Frederick J. Atkins; James P. Costello; John P. McLane.

Number of staff: 1 part-time professional; 1 part-time support.
EIN: 166052246

6033
Fresh Direct Employee Foundation
23-30 Borden Ave.
Long Island City, NY   11101-4515

Donor: Fresh Direct, LLC.
Foundation type: Independent foundation.
Financial data (yr. ended 12/31/13): Assets, $64,303 (M); gifts received, $215,275; expenditures, $208,800; qualifying distributions, $264,102.
Type of support: Grants to individuals.
Limitations: Applications not accepted.
Application information: Unsolicited requests for funds not accepted.
Trustee: Gerald Bennett.
EIN: 456226628

6034
The Freund Family Foundation
1382 E. 23rd St.
Brooklyn, NY   11210-5113   (212) 962-3362

Established in 2002 in New York.
Donors: Bella Freund; Meir Freund.
Foundation type: Independent foundation.
Financial data (yr. ended 12/31/13): Assets, $3,277,086; gifts received, $355,000; expenditures, $127,751; qualifying distributions, $113,515.
Fields of interest: Judaism.
Type of support: General support.
Limitations: Applications accepted. Giving primarily in Brooklyn, NY. No grants to individuals.
Application information:
  Initial approach: Proposal
  Deadline(s): None
Trustees: Bella Freund; Meir Freund.
EIN: 200000450

6035
Anne and Natalio Fridman Foundation
993 Park Ave., Ste. 10-S
New York City, NY   10028-0809

Donors: David Fridman; Natalio Fridman; Anne Fridman.
Foundation type: Independent foundation.
Financial data (yr. ended 05/31/13): Assets, $11,280,404 (M); expenditures, $224,715; qualifying distributions, $182,171; giving activities include $182,171 for 32 grants (high: $45,000; low: $100).
Fields of interest: Higher education; Judaism.
Limitations: Applications not accepted. Giving primarily in NY. No grants to individuals.
Application information: Contributes only to pre-selected organizations.
Officers: Natalio S. Fridman, Pres. and Treas.; Anne H. Fridman, Secy.
Director: David M. Fridman.
EIN: 522357309

6036
Fried Family Foundation
645 Madison Ave., 5th Fl.
New York City, NY   10022-1010

Established in 1995 in New York.
Donor: J. Michael Fried.
Foundation type: Independent foundation.
Financial data (yr. ended 12/31/13): Assets, $1,689,104 (M); expenditures, $194,686; qualifying distributions, $176,325; giving activities include $176,325 for 16 grants (high: $35,000; low: $100).
Fields of interest: Arts and culture; Education; Judaism.
Limitations: Applications not accepted. Giving primarily in NY. No grants to individuals.
Application information: Unsolicited requests for funds not accepted.
Directors: J. Michael Fried; Janet C. Fried; Alan Hirmes.
EIN: 133807053

6037
Bob & Sheila Friedland Foundation
656 Central Park Ave.
Yonkers, NY   10704-2019

Donors: Friedland Realty, Inc.; Robert Friedland; Sheila G. Freidland.
Foundation type: Company-sponsored foundation.
Financial data (yr. ended 11/30/14): Assets, $23,618; gifts received, $125,000; expenditures, $125,988; qualifying distributions, $125,224.
Purpose and activities: The foundation supports organizations involved with education, women's services, international peace, leadership development, and Judaism.
Fields of interest: Education; Religion; Human services.
Type of support: General support; Program development.
Limitations: Applications not accepted. Giving primarily in Rockville, MD and New York, NY. No grants to individuals.
Application information: Contributes only to pre-selected organizations.
Officers: Robert Friedland, Pres. and Treas.; Sheila G. Friedland, Secy.
EIN: 133442016

6038
Lee and Maria Friedlander Family Foundation
52 S. Mountain Rd.
New City, NY   10956-2315

Established in 2006 in New York.
Donors: Maria Friedlander; Lee Friedlander.
Foundation type: Independent foundation.
Financial data (yr. ended 12/31/13): Assets, $3,512,304 (M); gifts received, $140,750; expenditures, $254,554; qualifying distributions, $254,554; giving activities include $233,500 for 27 grants (high: $35,000; low: $500).
Purpose and activities:
Fields of interest: Education; Housing development; Religion.
Limitations: Applications not accepted. Giving primarily in New York, NY.

Application information: Unsolicited requests for funds not accepted.
Officers: Lee Friedlander, Pres.; Maria Friedlander, Secy.
EIN: 205599631

6039
M. and E. Friedman Charitable Foundation
1630 53rd St.
Brooklyn, NY   11204-1420
Contact: Robert Friedman, Tr.

Established in 2007 in New York.
Donors: Corner Riverdale Trust; J. Friedman Family Trust; Sarah Friedman; Robert Friedman; Esther Friedman; Bernard Friedman; Chaim Friedman.
Foundation type: Independent foundation.
Financial data (yr. ended 05/31/13): Assets, $260,163 (M); gifts received, $245,903; expenditures, $173,894; qualifying distributions, $173,894; giving activities include $172,740 for 24 grants (high: $30,000; low: $1,000).
Fields of interest: Education; Religion; Human services.
Limitations: Applications accepted. Giving primarily in NJ and NY.
Application information: Application form required.
  Initial approach: Letter
  Deadline(s): None
Trustees: Esther Friedman; Robert Friedman.
EIN: 208863647

6040
Friedman Family Foundation
1134 E. 23rd St.
Brooklyn, NY   11210-4521

Established in 2001 in New York.
Donors: Michael Friedman; The MLF Charitable Lead Trust; Invicta Watch Company; Sterling Time LLC.
Foundation type: Independent foundation.
Financial data (yr. ended 11/30/13): Assets, $5,434 (M); gifts received, $180,000; expenditures, $219,318; qualifying distributions, $219,092; giving activities include $219,092 for 26 grants (high: $44,327; low: $1,100).
Fields of interest: Nonprofits; Judaism.
Type of support: Regranting.
Limitations: Applications not accepted.
Application information: Contributes only to pre-selected organizations.
Trustees: Leah Friedman; Michael Friedman.
EIN: 113636950

6041
The Frieman Foundation
c/o Rivka Frieman
1175 Park Ave., Ste. 10C
New York City, NY   10128-1211

Established in 1989 in New York.
Donors: Rivka Frieman; Teri-Jon Sports, Inc.; Pincus Platt; Morris Platt; Rifka Platt.
Foundation type: Independent foundation.
Financial data (yr. ended 11/30/13): Assets, $52,384 (M); gifts received, $176,628; expenditures, $167,320; qualifying distributions, $167,236; giving activities include $167,236 for 128 grants (high: $25,000; low: $25).
Fields of interest: Nonprofits; Judaism.

Type of support: Regranting.
Limitations: Applications not accepted. No grants to individuals.
Application information: Unsolicited requests for funds not accepted.
Officers: Rivka Frieman, Pres.; Morris Platt, Treas.
EIN: 133549076

6042
Friends of the Guiomar Smeets Foundation Inc.

90 Park Ave., 15th Fl.
New York City, NY   10016-1301
Contact: Edward Tanenbaum

Donors: Citco Fund Services USA Inc.; Citco Technology Management Inc.
Foundation type: Independent foundation.
Financial data (yr. ended 12/31/13): Assets, $453,079 (M); gifts received, $100,000; expenditures, $199,480; qualifying distributions, $199,390; giving activities include $199,280 for 1 grant.
Fields of interest: Human services.
Type of support: Scholarships.
Limitations: Applications not accepted. Giving primarily in NY.
Application information: Unsolicited requests for funds not accepted.
Officers: Marcia Seibald, Pres.; Charles Rund, Secy.; Ben Jansen, Co-Treas.; Jay Peller, Co-Treas.
EIN: 260260044

6043
Shmuel & Serena Fuchs Foundation

101 Fulton St.
Lawrence, NY   11559

Established in 2009 in New York.
Donor: Bernard Fuchs.
Foundation type: Operating foundation.
Financial data (yr. ended 12/31/13): Assets, $1,015,190 (M); expenditures, $148,336; qualifying distributions, $148,336; giving activities include $142,475 for 57 grants (high: $36,000; low: $75).
Fields of interest: Judaism.
Limitations: Applications not accepted. Giving primarily in NY. No grants to individuals.
Application information: Unsolicited requests for funds not accepted.
Trustees: Bernard Fuchs; Hannah Fuchs.
EIN: 450581746

6044
Abraham Fuchsberg Family Foundation, Inc.

529 W. 42nd St.
New York City, NY   10036   (212) 480-4240
Contact: Jonathan Minkoff, Pres.

Donors: Abraham Fuchsberg; Fuchsberg & Fuchsberg; Fuchsberg Family Foundation; Seymour Fuchsberg†; Ira Kessler; Ronnie Kessler.
Foundation type: Independent foundation.
Financial data (yr. ended 10/31/14): Assets, $4,684,550 (M); gifts received, $65,947; expenditures, $357,557; qualifying distributions, $299,000; giving activities include $299,000 for 25 grants (high: $30,000; low: $1,000).

Purpose and activities: Giving primarily for public interest groups and legal services; support also for Jewish welfare funds.
Fields of interest: Ballet; Nonprofits; Diseases and conditions; Courts; Legal services; Public affairs; Judaism; Human rights; Human services.
Type of support: Research; Research and evaluation; Regranting.
Limitations: Applications accepted. Giving on a national basis, with emphasis on New York, NY. No grants to individuals.
Application information:
  Initial approach: Proposal
  Copies of proposal: 1
  Deadline(s): None
  Board meeting date(s): Dec.
Officers: Jonathan Minkoff, Pres.; Irene Minkoff, V.P. and Co. Secy.; Rita Fuchsberg, Treas.-Co. Secy.
Number of staff: None.
EIN: 132966385

6045
Furman Foundation, Inc.

151 E. 83rd St., Ste. 1A
New York City, NY   10028-1907   (212) 288-1832
Contact: Gail Furman, Pres.

Established in 2000 in New York.
Donors: Jason Furman; Gail Ann Furman; Jay Furman.
Foundation type: Independent foundation.
Financial data (yr. ended 12/31/13): Assets, $340,833 (M); expenditures, $202,179; qualifying distributions, $200,900; giving activities include $200,900 for 16 grants (high: $50,000; low: $150).
Fields of interest: Arts and culture; Performing arts; Theater; Human rights; Human services; Child welfare.
Limitations: Applications accepted. Giving primarily in NY.
Application information:
  Initial approach: Proposal
  Deadline(s): None
Officer: Gail Furman, Pres.
Director: Loren Skeist.
EIN: 134094739

6046
Morris & Gertrude Furman Foundation

810 7th Ave., 10th Fl.
New York City, NY   10019-9000

Established in 1992 in New York.
Donor: Jay Furman.
Foundation type: Independent foundation.
Financial data (yr. ended 06/30/13): Assets, $964,502 (M); expenditures, $367,553; qualifying distributions, $365,384; giving activities include $365,384 for 63 grants (high: $100,000; low: $18).
Fields of interest: Education; Health; Religion.
Type of support: General support.
Limitations: Applications not accepted. Giving primarily in New York, NY. No grants to individuals.
Application information: Contributes only to pre-selected organizations.
Officer: Robert Murray, Mgr.
EIN: 136178557

6047
The Furth Family Foundation

35 Platt Pl.
White Plains, NY   10605

Established in 1986 in New York.
Donor: John L. Furth.
Foundation type: Independent foundation.
Financial data (yr. ended 11/30/13): Assets, $2,398,518 (M); expenditures, $326,403; qualifying distributions, $292,621; giving activities include $285,710 for 48 grants (high: $100,000; low: $500).
Purpose and activities: Giving primarily for the arts and education, as well as to health organizations and hospitals, including a children's hospital; funding also for other children and social services.
Fields of interest: Arts and culture; Education; Health.
Limitations: Applications not accepted. Giving primarily in CT and New York, NY. No grants to individuals.
Application information: Unsolicited requests for funds not accepted.
Trustees: Hope L. Furth; John L. Furth.
EIN: 133401839

6048
The G&A Foundation, Inc.

(formerly The Evelyn Paige Foundation, Inc.)
c/o Muchnick, Golieb & Golieb, PC
200 Park Ave., Ste. 1700
New York City, NY   10003-1531   (212) 315-5575
Contact: Margaret G. Axelrod, Pres.

Established in 1987 in New York.
Donor: Evelyn Paige†.
Foundation type: Independent foundation.
Financial data (yr. ended 12/31/14): Assets, $2,996,717 (M); gifts received, $30,000; expenditures, $221,604; qualifying distributions, $177,556; giving activities include $157,250 for 25 grants (high: $30,000; low: $1,000).
Fields of interest: Education; Agriculture; Judaism.
Type of support: General support; Continuing support; Annual campaigns; Emergency funds; Scholarships.
Limitations: Applications accepted. Giving limited to New York, NY. No grants to individuals.
Publications: Annual report.
Application information:
  Initial approach: Proposal
  Copies of proposal: 1
  Deadline(s): None
Officers: Margaret G. Axelrod, Pres.; John A. Golieb, Secy.-Treas.
Director: Abner J. Golieb.
EIN: 133435542

6049
Miller S. & Adelaide S. Gaffney Foundation

c/o Chemung Canal Trust Co., Trust Tax Dept.
P.O. Box 1522
Elmira, NY   14902-1522

Established in 1968 in New York.
Donor: Miller S. Gaffney.
Foundation type: Independent foundation.
Financial data (yr. ended 12/31/14): Assets, $6,681,718 (M); expenditures, $333,561; qualifying distributions, $311,561; giving activities

include $308,800 for 56 grants (high: $30,000; low: $1,000).

Purpose and activities: Giving primarily for education and health and human services.

Fields of interest: Arts and culture; Museums; Elementary and secondary education; Higher education; Foundations; Nonprofits; Health; Hospital care; Christianity; Human services; Youth development; Seniors.

Type of support: General support; Matching grants; Capital campaigns; Equipment; Endowments; Scholarships; Student aid; Regranting.

Limitations: Applications not accepted. Giving primarily in Broome County, NY.

Application information: Contributes only to pre-selected organizations.

Board meeting date(s): Nov.

Officers: Philip W. Gaffney, Chair.; David M. Gouldin, Vice-Chair.; Lawrence C. Anderson, Secy.

Trustees: David Miller Gaffney; James T. Gaffney; Jeffrey T. Gaffney; Douglas R. Johnson; Jennifer G. Oken; Brooke C. Redmond; Kent Turner.

EIN: 166101748

6050

The Gage Fund

P.O. Box 371
Pound Ridge, NY   10576-0371

Donor: Robert T. Gage†.

Foundation type: Independent foundation.

Financial data (yr. ended 11/30/13): Assets, $3,872,324 (M); expenditures, $234,826; qualifying distributions, $225,770; giving activities include $208,500 for grants (high: $35,000; low: $1,000).

Fields of interest: Arts and culture; Education; Environment; Community and economic development; Unknown or not classified.

Type of support: General support; Matching grants; Continuing support; Capital campaigns; Program development; Curriculum development.

Limitations: Applications not accepted. Giving primarily in NY. No grants to individuals.

Application information: Unsolicited requests for funds not accepted.

Officers: Thomas C. Gage, Pres.; Alan Kroll, Secy.; Michele L. Gage, Treas.

EIN: 136197404

6051

Thomas E. and Mary K. Gallagher Foundation

(formerly The Greylock Foundation)
c/o Bruce H. Sobel
270 Madison Ave. S., Ste. 1500
New York City, NY   10016-0601

Established in 1994 in New York.

Donor: Thomas E. Gallagher.

Foundation type: Independent foundation.

Financial data (yr. ended 11/30/13): Assets, $5,391,366 (M); expenditures, $160,597; qualifying distributions, $144,240; giving activities include $144,240 for 10 grants (high: $46,840; low: $2,500).

Fields of interest: Education; Foundations; Health; Catholicism; Human services.

Limitations: Applications not accepted. Giving primarily in CA and NV. No grants to individuals.

Application information: Unsolicited requests for funds not accepted.

Trustees: Mary K. Gallagher; Thomas E. Gallagher.

EIN: 956982534

6052

Marc Galler Research Foundation Inc.

115 Central Park W., Ste. 7-E
New York City, NY   10023-2005   (212) 877-3326

Donor: Beatrice Galler†.

Foundation type: Independent foundation.

Financial data (yr. ended 10/31/14): Assets, $10,868,193; expenditures, $300,407; qualifying distributions, $231,340.

Fields of interest: Arts and culture; Religion.

Application information: Application form required.

Initial approach: Letter

Deadline(s): None

Officers: Lynne Galler, Pres.; Hezzy Dattner, Secy.-Treas.

EIN: 237013433

6053

Galvan Foundation Charitable Trust

42 W. 39th St., 14th Fl.
New York City, NY   10018-2082

Donor: Henry Van Ameringen.

Foundation type: Independent foundation.

Financial data (yr. ended 12/31/13): Assets, $102,106 (M); gifts received, $275,000; expenditures, $228,026; qualifying distributions, $226,700; giving activities include $226,700 for 25 grants (high: $20,000; low: $2,500).

Fields of interest: Education; Health; Agriculture.

Limitations: Applications not accepted. Giving primarily in NY.

Application information: Unsolicited requests for funds not accepted.

Trustees: Henry Van Ameringen; T. Eric Galloway.

EIN: 454110126

6054

The Gant Family Foundation

(formerly Donald R. & Jane T. Gant Foundation)
c/o Raich, Ende, Malter & Co., LLP
475 Park Ave. S., 31st Fl.
New York City, NY   10016-6902

Established in 1968 in New York.

Donors: Donald R. Gant; Alison A. Grant.

Foundation type: Independent foundation.

Financial data (yr. ended 05/31/13): Assets, $9,018,742 (M); expenditures, $399,944; qualifying distributions, $390,625; giving activities include $388,500 for 91 grants (high: $75,000; low: $500).

Purpose and activities: Giving primarily for education and human services.

Fields of interest: Arts and culture; Education; Elementary and secondary education; Higher education; Business education; Hospital care; Protestantism; Human services.

Limitations: Applications not accepted. Giving primarily in CA, MA, NJ, NY and PA. No grants to individuals.

Application information: Contributes only to pre-selected organizations.

Trustees: Alison A. Gant; Christopher T. Gant; Donald R. Gant; Laura G. Lilienfield; Sarah G. Mandanis.

EIN: 237015091

6055

Gantcher Family Foundation

c/o Wolf Maryles & Associates LLC
220 E. 42nd St., Ste. 2201
New York City, NY   10017-5822

Donor: Nathan Gantcher.

Foundation type: Independent foundation.

Financial data (yr. ended 06/30/13): Assets, $8,959,886 (M); gifts received, $499,450; expenditures, $419,031; qualifying distributions, $404,375; giving activities include $395,125 for 20 grants (high: $306,000; low: $150).

Fields of interest: Education; Medical education; Nonprofits; Diseases and conditions; Religion; Judaism.

Type of support: Regranting; Research.

Limitations: Applications not accepted. Giving primarily in New York, NY.

Application information: Unsolicited requests for funds not accepted.

Trustee: Nathan Gantcher.

Directors: Alice Gantcher; Joel Gantcher; Michael Gantcher; Kimberly Gantcher Spodek.

EIN: 450948720

6056

The Jack Gantz Foundation Inc.

c/o Citrin Cooperman
709 Westchester Ave.
White Plains, NY   10605-1500

Established in 1985 in New York.

Donors: The Gantz Investment Co.; Empire Brushes, Inc.; Sarita Gantz; Elaine Gantz Berman; Joseph Gantz.

Foundation type: Independent foundation.

Financial data (yr. ended 10/31/13): Assets, $4,941,383 (M); expenditures, $388,400; qualifying distributions, $344,790; giving activities include $344,790 for 97 grants (high: $100,000; low: $30).

Fields of interest: Arts and culture; Higher education; Nonprofits; Judaism; Human services.

Type of support: Regranting.

Limitations: Applications not accepted. Giving primarily in CO and NY. No grants to individuals.

Application information: Contributes only to pre-selected organizations.

Officers: Sarita Gantz, Pres.; Joseph Gantz, Secy.-Treas.

Director: Elaine Gantz Berman.

EIN: 133352396

6057

The Garber Family Foundation

P.O. Box 997
Nyack, NY   10960-0997

Established in 1999 in Texas.

Donors: Ross B. Garber; Laurie A. Garber.

Foundation type: Independent foundation.

Financial data (yr. ended 12/31/13): Assets, $5,029,015 (M); expenditures, $284,808; qualifying distributions, $211,761; giving activities

include $193,748 for 12 grants (high: $147,667; low: $2,500).
Fields of interest: Arts and culture; Education; Health; Judaism.
Limitations: Applications not accepted. Giving primarily in Austin, TX. No grants to individuals.
Application information: Unsolicited requests for funds not accepted.
Officers: Ross B. Garber, Pres.; Laurie A. Garber, V.P.
Trustee: Adele Garber.
EIN: 742940367

6058
Garman Family Foundation
3556 Lakeshore Rd., Ste. 620
Buffalo, NY   14219-1460   (716) 822-4966

Established in 2000 in New York.
Donor: Richard E. Garman.
Foundation type: Independent foundation.
Financial data (yr. ended 12/31/14): Assets, $10,170,037; expenditures, $532,982; qualifying distributions, $431,516.
Fields of interest: Arts and culture; Education; Environment; Agriculture; Sports and recreation; Human services.
Limitations: Applications accepted. Giving limited to western NY. No grants to individuals.
Application information: Application form required.
   Initial approach: Letter of inquiry not more than 3 pages
   Deadline(s): None
Officers: Richard E. Garman, Pres.; Melissa G. Baumgart, Secy.-Treas.
Directors: Kathleen Gleason; Michelle Parrish; Jason K. Ziccarelli.
EIN: 161592064

6059
The Joseph and Anna Gartner Foundation
163 Hidden Ridge Common
Williamsville, NY   14221-5765

Established in 1981 in New York.
Donors: Carol N. Hirsh; Sanford M. Nobel.
Foundation type: Independent foundation.
Financial data (yr. ended 01/31/15): Assets, $4,191,144; gifts received, $170,360; expenditures, $215,971; qualifying distributions, $214,000.
Purpose and activities: Giving primarily for Jewish organizations, arts organizations, and social service agencies.
Fields of interest: Arts and culture; Science museums; Higher education; Nonprofits; Judaism; Human services.
Type of support: Regranting.
Limitations: Applications not accepted. Giving primarily in NY. No grants to individuals.
Application information: Unsolicited requests for funds not accepted.
Trustees: Carol N. Hirsh; Michael G. Hirsh; Margery S. Nobel; Sanford M. Nobel.
EIN: 222400456

6060
Gary Winick Memorial Fund, Inc.
c/o TAG Associates
75 Rockefeller Plz.
New York City, NY   10019

Donor: Gary Winick†.
Foundation type: Independent foundation.
Financial data (yr. ended 02/28/13): Assets, $20,373 (M); gifts received, $200,000; expenditures, $285,119; qualifying distributions, $285,119; giving activities include $285,000 for 2 grants (high: $250,000; low: $35,000).
Fields of interest: Education; Health; Film and video.
Limitations: Applications not accepted. Giving primarily in CA.
Application information: Unsolicited requests for funds not accepted.
Officer and Director: Mark Ross, Pres. and Director.
EIN: 451020762

6061
The Joseph and Susan Gatto Foundation
c/o Marcum LLP
10 Melville Park Rd.
Melville, NY   11747-3146

Established in 1996 in Connecticut.
Donor: Joseph D. Gatto.
Foundation type: Independent foundation.
Financial data (yr. ended 09/30/13): Assets, $7,214,808 (M); expenditures, $336,430; qualifying distributions, $333,840; giving activities include $331,750 for 10 grants (high: $176,000; low: $100).
Fields of interest: Education; Higher education; Law education; Human services.
Limitations: Applications not accepted. Giving primarily in NJ, NY and PA. No grants to individuals; no loans or scholarships.
Application information: Contributes only to pre-selected organizations.
Trustees: Joseph D. Gatto; Susan Gatto.
EIN: 133921102

6062
The Geduld/Cougar Foundation, Inc.
c/o Cougar Trading
1370 Ave. of the Americas
New York City, NY   10019-4602

Established in 2007 in New York.
Donor: Emanuel E. Geduld.
Foundation type: Independent foundation.
Financial data (yr. ended 12/31/13): Assets, $127,432 (M); gifts received, $600,000; expenditures, $401,588; qualifying distributions, $398,481; giving activities include $398,481 for 33 grants (high: $143,000; low: $45).
Purpose and activities: Giving primarily for education, health organizations and Jewish agencies and temples; some funding also for the arts.
Fields of interest: Arts and culture; Education; Diseases and conditions; Judaism.
Limitations: Applications not accepted. Giving primarily in NY. No grants to individuals.
Application information: Contributes only to pre-selected organizations.

Officers: Emanuel E. Geduld, Pres. and Treas.; Carl J. Bennett, V.P.; Arthur A. Feder, Secy.
EIN: 331153178

6063
The Geier Foundation
50 Jericho Quadrangle, Ste. 220
Jericho, NY   11753-2726

Foundation type: Independent foundation.
Financial data (yr. ended 03/31/13): Assets, $6,535,701 (M); expenditures, $354,492; qualifying distributions, $296,916; giving activities include $240,000 for 12 grants (high: $52,500; low: $5,000).
Fields of interest: Education; Diseases and conditions; Autism; Human services.
Type of support: General support.
Limitations: Applications not accepted. Giving primarily in CT, NY and VA.
Application information: Unsolicited requests for funds not accepted.
Officers: Hope Geier Smith, Pres.; Johanna Geier Howard, V.P.; Briell Smith, Secy.
EIN: 454700219

6064
The Geier Foundation
c/o DDK Co., LLP
50 Jericho Quadrangle
Jericho, NY   11753

Established in 1997 in New York.
Donor: Philip H. Geier, Jr.
Foundation type: Independent foundation.
Financial data (yr. ended 03/31/12): Assets, $6,252,554 (M); expenditures, $448,413; qualifying distributions, $448,413; giving activities include $340,000 for 11 grants (high: $115,000; low: $5,000).
Fields of interest: Performing arts; Art museums; Business education; Diseases and conditions; Autism; Child welfare.
Type of support: Research.
Limitations: Applications not accepted. Giving primarily in the metropolitan New York, NY, area. No grants to individuals.
Application information: Contributes only to pre-selected organizations.
Trustees: Johanna Geier Howard; Hope Smith; Theodore B. Smith III.
EIN: 227311735

6065
The Gela Foundation Inc.
42 W. 38th St., Ste. 901
New York City, NY   10018-6209

Established in 2006 in New York.
Donor: Joseph Greenfeld.
Foundation type: Independent foundation.
Financial data (yr. ended 12/31/13): Assets, $1,158,978 (M); gifts received, $200,000; expenditures, $323,423; qualifying distributions, $321,890; giving activities include $321,890 for 24 grants (high: $200,000; low: $500).
Fields of interest: Education; Religion.
Limitations: Applications not accepted. Giving primarily in NY. No grants to individuals.

Application information: Unsolicited requests for funds not accepted.
Directors: Jacob Greenfeld; Joseph Greenfeld; Baila Wald.
EIN: 208096298

6066
Geller Family Religious Foundation
57 Wesley Chapel Rd.
Suffern, NY 10901-2603 8456414747

Established in 1998 in New York.
Donor: Moshe Geller.
Foundation type: Independent foundation.
Financial data (yr. ended 05/31/14): Assets, $36; gifts received, $419,450; expenditures, $422,273; qualifying distributions, $422,035.
Fields of interest: Education; Religion; Human services.
Limitations: Applications not accepted. Giving primarily in NY; some giving in NJ and Israel. No grants to individuals.
Application information: Unsolicited requests for funds not accepted.
Trustees: Judith Geller; Moshe Geller; Shirley Preis.
EIN: 134029849

6067
Gelley Family Foundation
3101 Bedford Ave.
Brooklyn, NY 11210-3713

Established in 2007 in New York.
Donors: Solomon Heisler; Chanie Schon; Henry Schon; David Gelley; Clara Heisler; Heidi S. Gelley.
Foundation type: Independent foundation.
Financial data (yr. ended 12/31/14): Assets, $757,835; expenditures, $121,441; qualifying distributions, $115,320.
Fields of interest: Education; Judaism; Human services.
Limitations: Applications not accepted. Giving primarily in Brooklyn, NY. No grants to individuals.
Application information: Unsolicited requests for funds not accepted.
Officers: David Gelley, Pres.; Heidi Gelley, C.F.O.
Director: Baron M. Schon.
EIN: 208251000

6068
Gemiluth Chessed of Greater New York Inc.
c/o Wiss
14 Penn Plz., Ste. 1010
New York City, NY 10122

Foundation type: Operating foundation.
Financial data (yr. ended 10/31/13): Assets, $11,491,399 (M); gifts received, $2,050; expenditures, $498,374; qualifying distributions, $394,276; giving activities include $261,277 for 11 grants (high: $155,500; low: $2,000).
Purpose and activities: Giving primarily for Jewish human service programs, particularly for the elderly.
Fields of interest: Health; Judaism; Human services; Seniors.
Limitations: Applications not accepted. Giving primarily in NY.
Application information: Unsolicited requests for funds not accepted.

Officers: Peter A. Kahn, Co-Pres.; Vivian Niess, Co-Pres.; Gunther Weiskopf, V.P. and Treas.; Rabbi Manferd Gans, V.P.; David Stadtmauer, V.P.
EIN: 131915123

6069
Gemj Chehebar Foundation
1407 Broadway, Ste. 503
New York City, NY 10018-5151
FAX: 917-591-7008;
E-mail: donations@gemjchehebar.com; Main URL: http://www.gemjchehebar.com/foundation

Donors: Ezra A. Chehebar; Gabriel A. Chehebar; Rainbow USA, Inc.; Skiva International, Inc.
Foundation type: Independent foundation.
Financial data (yr. ended 12/31/13): Assets, $162,688 (M); gifts received, $320,000; expenditures, $386,959; qualifying distributions, $386,959; giving activities include $386,629 for 217 grants (high: $26,000; low: $36).
Fields of interest: Nonprofits; Judaism.
Type of support: Regranting.
Limitations: Applications not accepted.
Application information: Unsolicited requests for funds not accepted.
Directors: Ezra A. Chehebar; Gabriel A. Chehebar; Josef A. Chehebar; Michael A. Chehebar.
EIN: 263683879

6070
Grace George and Judith Silverburgh Foundation Inc.
c/o Lewis Braff
60 E. 42nd St.
New York City, NY 10165-0006

Established in 1990 in New York.
Donor: George Silverburgh†.
Foundation type: Independent foundation.
Financial data (yr. ended 08/31/13): Assets, $24,982 (M); expenditures, $354,868; qualifying distributions, $313,500; giving activities include $313,500 for grants.
Fields of interest: Education; Health; Diseases and conditions.
Limitations: Applications not accepted. Giving primarily in New York, NY; some giving also in the Bronx and Port Washington, NY and in Bridgeport, CT and Hoboken, NJ. No grants to individuals.
Application information: Contributes only to pre-selected organizations.
Officers: Roger C. Wollen, Pres.; Dori Wollen, V.P. and Secy.; Malcolm J. Hartman, Treas.
Director: Anne L. Manz.
EIN: 133585189

6071
Georgia G. Hiden Charitable Foundation
c/o Raphael P. Greenspan
Macri Greenspan & Moramarco
393 Old Country Rd., Ste. 300
Carle Place, NY 11514-2131

Donor: Georgia G. Hiden†.
Foundation type: Independent foundation.
Financial data (yr. ended 08/31/13): Assets, $7,086,495 (M); expenditures, $524,436; qualifying distributions, $368,537; giving activities

include $340,573 for 6 grants (high: $145,573; low: $15,000).
Fields of interest: Education; Public affairs; Youth development.
Limitations: Applications not accepted. Giving primarily in NY.
Application information: Unsolicited requests for funds not accepted.
Trustees: Sylvie C. Gaeckler; Raphael P. Greenspan, Esq., C.P.A.; Michael J. Lawler, CPA.
EIN: 261591874

6072
The Peter and Kristen Gerhard Foundation
Bowling Green Sta.
P.O. Box 73
New York City, NY 10274-0073

Donor: Peter C. Gerhard.
Foundation type: Independent foundation.
Financial data (yr. ended 08/31/13): Assets, $1,787,640 (M); expenditures, $178,182; qualifying distributions, $176,107; giving activities include $176,107 for 38 grants (high: $50,000; low: $18).
Purpose and activities: Giving primarily for education and the arts; funding also for health and human services.
Fields of interest: Arts and culture; Education; Elementary and secondary education; Higher education; Hospital care; Diseases and conditions; Human services.
Limitations: Applications not accepted. Giving primarily in NJ, with some emphasis on Hackensack and Tinton Falls. No grants to individuals, or for scholarships; no loans.
Application information: Contributes only to pre-selected organizations.
Trustees: Kristen Gerhard; Peter C. Gerhard.
EIN: 133921375

6073
Daniel & Flavia Gernatt Family Foundation
2698 Gowanda Zoar Rd.
Gowanda, NY 14070

Established in 1988 in New York.
Donor: Daniel Gernatt, Sr.
Foundation type: Independent foundation.
Financial data (yr. ended 12/31/13): Assets, $3,122,834 (M); gifts received, $50; expenditures, $184,739; qualifying distributions, $157,790; giving activities include $156,075 for 22 grants (high: $25,000; low: $250).
Fields of interest: Education; Religion; Human services.
Limitations: Applications not accepted. Giving primarily in the Collins and Gowanda, NY, areas. No grants to individuals.
Application information: Contributes only to pre-selected organizations.
Trustees: Daniel Gernatt, Sr.; Daniel Gernatt, Jr.; Cynthia Peglowski; Patricia Rebman; Phyllis Ulmer.
EIN: 222914177

6074
Lisa Beth Gerstman Foundation
439 Oak St.
Garden City, NY   11530-6419   (516) 594-4400
FAX: (516) 594-7085;
E-mail: info@lisabethgerstman.org; Main
URL: http://www.lisabethgerstman.org
Facebook: https://www.facebook.com/
LisaBethGerstmanFoundation
YouTube: http://youtube.com/user/
LISABETHGERSTMAN

Established in 2003 in New York.
Donors: Harvey Gerstman; Harvey Gerstman
Associates, Inc.; Christopher Reeves Foundation;
Daniel Gerstman; Gerstman LLC; Linda Gerstman;
Carolyn Gerstman.
Foundation type: Independent foundation.
Financial data (yr. ended 08/31/13): Assets,
$297,022 (M); gifts received, $79,377;
expenditures, $307,086; qualifying distributions,
$228,944; giving activities include $224,834 for 19
grants (high: $44,000; low: $200).
Purpose and activities: To afford children with
physical disabilities the opportunity to attend
summer day and sleep-away camps in an integrated
setting.
Fields of interest: Camps; Children and youth;
People with physical disabilities.
Limitations: Applications accepted. Giving limited to
the New York, NY, area, including Long Island and
Westchester, and the Northeast. No support for
political, social, fraternal, or arts organizations,
sectarian religious activities, political lobbying or
legislative activities, medical research
organizations, or for-profit enterprises. No grants to
individuals, or for capital campaigns or construction
projects, fund endowments, special events or
international programs, or start-up expenses or
seed capital funding for private businesses; no
loans.
Application information: See foundation web site
for application guidelines, including downloadable
application form. Application form required.
   Deadline(s): None
Officer and Directors: Carolyn Gerstman, Treas. and
Director; Bradley Gerstman; Cheryl Gerstman;
Daniel Gerstman; Harvey Gerstman; Linda
Gerstman; Pamela Gerstman.
EIN: 200704257

6075
Gesso Foundation
P.O. Box 1562
New York City, NY   10013-0869

Established in 2002 in New York.
Foundation type: Independent foundation.
Financial data (yr. ended 06/30/13): Assets,
$629,927 (M); expenditures, $388,563; qualifying
distributions, $278,625; giving activities include
$278,625 for 28 grants (high: $18,000; low:
$5,000).
Purpose and activities: Giving primarily for AIDS, the
environment, the arts, and social justice.
Fields of interest: Visual arts; Toxic substance
control; Water resources; Health; Suicide crisis
intervention; Film and video; Human services; Child
welfare; LGBTQ people.
Limitations: Applications accepted. Giving primarily
in NY. No grants to individuals.
Application information:

Initial approach: Letter
   Deadline(s): None
Officer: Joy Episalla, Treas.
Trustees: Michael Boodro; David Leiber; Loring
McAlpin; Kynaston McShine; Patrick Moore;
Rebecca Moore.
EIN: 137331662

6076
The Gettinger Family Foundation
1407 Broadway, Ste. 3310
New York City, NY   10018-5133   (212) 944-6093
Contact: Clark Gettinger, Pres.

Donor: Robert Gettinger.
Foundation type: Independent foundation.
Financial data (yr. ended 10/31/12): Assets,
$4,765,315 (M); expenditures, $234,225;
qualifying distributions, $207,000; giving activities
include $207,000 for grants.
Fields of interest: Health; Human services; Youth
development; Youth services.
Application information: Application form required.
   Initial approach: Letter
   Deadline(s): None
Officers: Clark Gettinger, Pres.; Carol Edelson,
Secy.-Treas.
EIN: 270581206

6077
The Giant Steps Foundation
c/o Weisermazars, LLP
135 W. 50th St.
New York City, NY   10020
E-mail: wendy@giantsteps.org; Main URL: http://
www.giantsteps.org

Donors: Tides Foundation; Jennifer Leeds; Liselotte
Gerard Leeds.
Foundation type: Independent foundation.
Financial data (yr. ended 11/30/14): Assets,
$13,022,925 (M); gifts received, $45,000;
expenditures, $572,057; qualifying distributions,
$505,930; giving activities include $433,580 for 24
grants (high: $100,000; low: $250).
Purpose and activities: The foundation was created
with a desire to spark others to pursue their dreams
and to create a kinder, gentler, and healthier world
for all living creatures. It does this via three avenues:
environmental preservation and education; wildlife
advocacy and domestic animal rescue; and human
health, fitness, and empowerment activities (with a
focus on underserved populations). The foundation
strongly encourages those it supports to engage in
sustainable, humane, and caring practices.
Fields of interest: Environment; Animal welfare;
Animal rescue and rehabilitation; Human services.
Type of support: General support.
Limitations: Applications not accepted. Giving in the
U.S., with emphasis on CA, MN and VA. No grants
to individuals.
Application information: Contributes only to
pre-selected organizations.
Officers and Directors: Jennifer Leeds, Pres. and
Director; Richard L. Braunstein, Secy.; Jeffrey J.
Sundheim, Treas. and Director; Lilo J. Leeds.
EIN: 522069841

6078
The Deane A. and John D. Gilliam Foundation
(formerly John D. Gilliam Foundation)
c/o BCRS Associates, LLC
77 Water St., 9th Fl.
New York City, NY   10005-4414

Established in 1978 in New York.
Donors: John D. Gilliam; Deane A. Gilliam.
Foundation type: Independent foundation.
Financial data (yr. ended 03/31/13): Assets,
$7,959,304 (M); gifts received, $305,785;
expenditures, $376,839; qualifying distributions,
$257,159; giving activities include $253,944 for 74
grants (high: $50,000; low: $50).
Purpose and activities: Giving primarily for health
care, human services, and arts and culture, with
emphasis on a New York theater.
Fields of interest: Arts and culture; Theater; Music;
Education; Nonprofits; Health; Hospital care;
Protestantism; Human services.
Type of support: Annual campaigns; Capital
campaigns; Endowments; Professorships;
Fellowships; Regranting.
Limitations: Applications not accepted. Giving
primarily in NY. No grants to individuals or for
scholarships; no loans.
Application information: Contributes only to
pre-selected organizations.
Trustees: Peter M. Fahey; Deane A. Gilliam; John D.
Gilliam; Donald R. Grant; Stephanae D. Lariviere.
EIN: 132967490

6079
Peter R. Gimbel & Elga Andersen-Gimbel Memorial Trust
c/o Marks Paneth & Shron, LLP
685 3rd Ave.
New York City, NY   10017-6701

Established in 1996 in New York.
Foundation type: Independent foundation.
Financial data (yr. ended 12/31/14): Assets,
$2,577,513 (M); expenditures, $179,227;
qualifying distributions, $129,579; giving activities
include $125,000 for 6 grants (high: $50,000; low:
$10,000).
Purpose and activities: Giving primarily for health
and environment.
Fields of interest: Environment; Domesticated
animals; Health.
Limitations: Applications not accepted. Giving
primarily in New York, NY, with some giving in
Washington, DC, and Boston, MA. No grants to
individuals.
Application information: Unsolicited requests for
funds not accepted.
Trustees: Bailey Gimbel; Leslie Gimbel; Thomas
S.T. Gimbel; Russell Kagen.
EIN: 137055292

6080
Gimprich Family Foundation, Inc.
c/o Hebrew Union College
1 W. 4th St.
New York City, NY   10012-1105
Contact: Zelda Goldsmith, Exec. Admin.

Donor: Marvin Gimprich†.
Foundation type: Independent foundation.

Financial data (yr. ended 05/31/13): Assets, $6,833,070 (M); expenditures, $558,885; qualifying distributions, $558,885; giving activities include $405,000 for 43 grants (high: $20,000; low: $4,000).
Fields of interest: Judaism; Individual liberties; Human services; Child welfare.
International interests: Israel.
Type of support: Seed money.
Limitations: Applications accepted. Giving in the U.S. and internationally, primarily in Israel. No grants to individuals, or for building.
Application information: Application form required.
  Initial approach: Letter
  Copies of proposal: 1
  Deadline(s): None
Officers: David M. Fishman, Pres.; Lila Gimprich d'Adolf, V.P.; Rosalie Dolmatch, Recording Secy.; Eric S. Wittstein, Treas.
Director: Leora Fishman.
Number of staff: 1 part-time professional.
EIN: 510147095

6081
Ned J. Giordano Foundation, Inc.
P.O. Box 409
Old Westbury, NY 11568-0409

Established in 2000 in New York.
Donor: Catherine Giordano.
Foundation type: Independent foundation.
Financial data (yr. ended 09/30/14): Assets, $1,008,237 (M); gifts received, $155,969; expenditures, $179,965; qualifying distributions, $177,660; giving activities include $177,660 for 3 grants (high: $91,736; low: $1,000).
Fields of interest: Disasters and emergency management; Human services; Youth development.
Type of support: General support.
Limitations: Applications not accepted. Giving primarily in Brookville and Mill Neck, NY. No grants to individuals.
Application information: Contributes only to pre-selected organizations.
Officers: Elizabeth Donnelly, Pres.; Marie Katherine Greco, Treas.
EIN: 113570016

6082
The Glens Falls Foundation
237 Glen St.
Glens Falls, NY 12801   (518) 761-7350
Contact: D. Michael Niles, Business Admin.
FAX: (518) 798-8620;
E-mail: administrator@glensfallsfoundation.org;
Main URL: http://www.glensfallsfoundation.org
Facebook: https://www.facebook.com/glensfallsfoundation
Twitter: https://twitter.com/thegffoundation

Established in 1939 in New York.
Foundation type: Community foundation.
Financial data (yr. ended 12/31/13): Assets, $15,140,899 (M); gifts received, $29,832; expenditures, $523,330; giving activities include $283,448 for 13+ grants (high: $65,000), and $147,225 for 85 grants to individuals.
Purpose and activities: Giving solely to promote the mental, moral, and physical improvement of the people of Glens Falls and environs. Direct financial aid to individuals limited to scholarships to medical students and to students at Dartmouth and Harvard colleges. All other scholarships are awarded through area institutions.
Fields of interest: Community and economic development; Human services.
Type of support: Capital campaigns; Matching grants; Capital and infrastructure; Equipment; Land acquisitions; Emergency funds; Program development; Convening; Seed money; Research; Student aid.
Limitations: Applications accepted. Giving limited to Warren, Washington, and northern Saratoga counties, NY. No grants for annual campaigns, continuing support, or endowment funds; no loans; no direct scholarship grants (except for medical students and students at Dartmouth and Harvard colleges).
Publications: Application guidelines; Annual report; Informational brochure.
Application information: Visit foundation web site for application form and guidelines. Application form required.
  Initial approach: Submit application
  Copies of proposal: 2
  Deadline(s): Mar. 20, June 20, Sept. 20, and Dec. 20
  Board meeting date(s): 2nd Wed. in Jan., Apr., July, and Oct.
  Final notification: Applicants will receive a written notice of the Committees Decision within ten (10) business days of the meeting.
Officers and Distribution Committee: Donna Metivier Perkett, Chair. and Director; Mark L. Behan, Vice-Chair. and Director; Elizabeth Barton-Navitsky; Cheryl Hogan; Stacey Mandelbaum, MD; Paul R. McPhillips; Kathryn O'Keeffe, MD.
Trustee: TD Bank, N.A.
EIN: 146036390

6083
The Fred C. Gloeckner Foundation, Inc.
550 Mamaroneck Ave., Ste. 510
Harrison, NY 10528-1609   (914) 698-2300
Contact: Joseph A. Simone, Secy.
FAX: (914) 698-0848; *Main URL:* http://gloecknerfoundation.org
Grants List: http://gloecknerfoundation.org/projects.htm

Established in 1960 in New York.
Donors: Frederick C. Gloeckner†; Raymond N. Zimmerman; Gatti Nursery; Bruce P. Geary.
Foundation type: Independent foundation.
Financial data (yr. ended 10/31/14): Assets, $2,892,473 (M); gifts received, $1,600; expenditures, $180,773; qualifying distributions, $147,702; giving activities include $147,702 for 16 grants (high: $15,000; low: $1,500).
Purpose and activities: To further research in floriculture and related fields through grants to higher educational and federal research institutions.
Fields of interest: Education.
Type of support: Equipment; Research.
Limitations: Applications accepted. Giving primarily in FL and NY. No grants to individuals.
Publications: Annual report.
Application information: Requests for only equipment are considered when supported by a research project outline. Grants, although approved for funding for only one year at a time, will be evaluated and considered for renewal upon receipt of a progress report, plans for the coming year, and a written request for continuation of funding. Application form required.
  Initial approach: Request application and/or download application from foundation web site
  Copies of proposal: 10
  Deadline(s): Apr. 1
  Board meeting date(s): Annually in June; grants paid in Aug.
Officers and Directors: Paul L. Daum, Pres. and Director; Richard Craig, V.P. and Director; Joseph A. Simone, Secy. and Director; Martin D. Kortjohn, Treas. and Director; Margery Daughtrey; Paul Allen Hammer; J. Michael Klesa; Andrew J. Lee; Jay Sheely.
EIN: 136124190

6084
Corlette Glorney Foundation, Inc.
c/o Kirkpatrick & Lockhart, LLP
599 Lexington Ave., 31st Fl.
New York City, NY 10022-6030
Application address: c/o The New York Academy of Medicine, Attn.: Anna Pomykala, 2 E. 103rd St., New York, NY 10029-5291, tel.: (212) 322-3645

Foundation type: Independent foundation.
Financial data (yr. ended 12/31/12): Assets, $2,512,931 (M); expenditures, $227,749; qualifying distributions, $193,231; giving activities include $170,000 for 1 grant.
Fields of interest: Biomedicine; Diseases and conditions.
Type of support: Fellowships; Research; Research and evaluation.
Limitations: Applications accepted. Giving limited to New York, NY. No grants to individuals.
Application information:
  Initial approach: Letter
  Deadline(s): None
Officers and Directors: Jeffrey Borer, Pres. and Director; Pascal Wirz, Secy. and Director; Robert F. Ambrose, Treas. and Director; William H. Bienfield, Pres. Emeritus and Director; Dr. Gary D. Jaworski; Peter Lawson-Johnston.
EIN: 136104151

6085
The Goddard Family Charitable Foundation
c/o Horowitz & Ullmann
275 Madison Ave., Ste. 902
New York City, NY 10016-1111
Application address: c/o Colin and Amanda Goddard, 30 Allenby Dr. Northport, NY 11768, tel.: (212) 532-3736

Donors: Amanda Goddard; Colin Goddard.
Foundation type: Independent foundation.
Financial data (yr. ended 12/31/13): Assets, $2,262,448 (M); expenditures, $134,603; qualifying distributions, $130,435; giving activities include $130,435 for 14 grants (high: $37,575; low: $500).
Fields of interest: Education; Sports and recreation; Human services.
Limitations: Applications accepted. Giving primarily in NY.
Application information:
  Initial approach: Contact foundation
  Deadline(s): None

Officers: Colin Goddard, Pres.; Amanda Goddard, V.P. and Secy.-Treas.
EIN: 271238428

6086

The Godinger Lefkowitz Memorial Foundation, Inc.

63-15 Traffic Ave.
Ridgewood, NY   11385-2629   (718) 418-1000
Contact: William Lefkowitz, V.P.

Donors: Arnold Godinger; William Lefkowitz; Godindger Silver Art Ltd.
Foundation type: Independent foundation.
Financial data (yr. ended 11/30/13): Assets, $25,179 (M); gifts received, $270,000; expenditures, $255,567; qualifying distributions, $254,497; giving activities include $254,497 for grants.
Purpose and activities: Giving primarily to Jewish agencies, temples, and schools.
Fields of interest: Education; Nonprofits; Judaism.
Type of support: Regranting.
Limitations: Applications accepted. Giving primarily in NY.
Application information: Application form required.
Initial approach: Letter
Deadline(s): None
Officers: Arnold Godinger, Pres.; William Lefkowitz, V.P.; Rita Godinger, Secy.
EIN: 133800381

6087

The Gogel Family Foundation

c/o Donald J. Gogel
31 Masterton Rd.
Bronxville, NY   10708

Established in 1997 in New York.
Donors: Jeffrey Bagatin; Donald J. Gogel.
Foundation type: Independent foundation.
Financial data (yr. ended 12/31/13): Assets, $7,346,915 (M); expenditures, $267,537; qualifying distributions, $235,250; giving activities include $230,000 for 3 grants (high: $200,000; low: $10,000).
Fields of interest: Education.
Limitations: Applications not accepted. Giving primarily in, New York, NY. No grants to individuals.
Application information: Contributes only to pre-selected organizations.
Trustees: Donald J. Gogel; Leah G. Gogel; Rebecca Gogel; Georgia Wall.
EIN: 137119435

6088

The Bradd J. Gold Family Foundation

4525 Livingston Ave.
The Bronx, NY   10471-3911

Established in 2004 in New York.
Donor: Bradd J. Gold.
Foundation type: Independent foundation.
Financial data (yr. ended 12/31/12): Assets, $130,693 (M); gifts received, $152,403; expenditures, $177,560; qualifying distributions, $177,560; giving activities include $177,560 for grants.
Fields of interest: Arts and culture; Nonprofits; Religion; Human services.

Type of support: General support; Regranting.
Limitations: Applications not accepted. Giving primarily in NY. No grants to individuals.
Application information: Unsolicited requests for funds not accepted.
Officers: Bradd J. Gold, Pres.; Patricia Khouri, V.P.; Paul Cuomo, Secy.-Treas.
EIN: 593790425

6089

The Gold Foundation

1750 44th St.
Brooklyn, NY   11204-1050
Contact: A. Ringel

Established in 2007 in New York.
Donor: Asher Graus.
Foundation type: Independent foundation.
Financial data (yr. ended 06/30/13): Assets, $1,792 (M); gifts received, $70,388; expenditures, $230,833; qualifying distributions, $230,833; giving activities include $230,779 for 8 grants (high: $114,000; low: $54).
Fields of interest: Religion; Judaism.
Limitations: Applications not accepted.
Application information: Unsolicited requests for funds not accepted.
Trustees: Asher Graus; Samuel Graus.
EIN: 261467138

6090

Samuel Goldberg & Sons Foundation Inc.

c/o D. Wechsler
400 Garden City Plz., Ste. 202
Garden City, NY   11530-3336

Established in 1943 in New York.
Foundation type: Independent foundation.
Financial data (yr. ended 12/31/13): Assets, $1,015,862 (M); expenditures, $412,968; qualifying distributions, $385,600; giving activities include $385,600 for 54 grants (high: $50,000; low: $500).
Purpose and activities: Giving primarily for Jewish agencies and synagogues and human services.
Fields of interest: Education; Higher education; Medical education; Animal welfare; Judaism; Human services.
Limitations: Applications not accepted. Giving primarily in NY; some funding in CA. No grants to individuals.
Application information: Contributes only to pre-selected organizations.
Directors: Amy Eller; Robert Goldberg; Donna Kenton; Michael Levine; Harvey M. Stone.
EIN: 136111269

6091

Golden Fleece Foundation Charity

346 Madison Ave.
New York City, NY   10017-3703

Established in 2007 in New York.
Donor: Retail Brand Alliance, Inc.
Foundation type: Independent foundation.
Financial data (yr. ended 12/31/13): Assets, $221,028 (M); gifts received, $407,800; expenditures, $452,170; qualifying distributions, $452,170; giving activities include $434,736 for 15 grants (high: $186,193; low: $978).

Fields of interest: Specialty hospital care; Cancers; Human services; Child welfare.
Limitations: Applications not accepted. Giving primarily in AZ and TN. No grants to individuals.
Application information: Contributes only to pre-selected organizations.
Officers: Claudio Del Vecchio, Chair. and Pres.; Debra Del Vecchio, V.P.; Emilie Antonetti, Secy.-Treas.
EIN: 261393747

6092

Jeffrey and Susan Goldenberg Foundation

Bowling Green Sta.
P.O. Box 73
New York City, NY   10274-0073

Established in 1999 in New York.
Donor: Jeffrey Goldenberg.
Foundation type: Independent foundation.
Financial data (yr. ended 09/30/13): Assets, $1,625,762 (M); expenditures, $169,544; qualifying distributions, $167,691; giving activities include $167,691 for 53 grants (high: $50,000; low: $36).
Fields of interest: Education; Early childhood education; Higher education; Undergraduate education; Nonprofits; Hospital care; Diseases and conditions; Judaism; Human services; Child welfare.
Type of support: Regranting.
Limitations: Applications not accepted. Giving primarily in ME and New York, NY and PA. No grants to individuals.
Application information: Contributes only to pre-selected organizations.
Trustees: Jeffrey Goldenberg; Susan Goldenberg.
EIN: 134050662

6093

The Goldenberg Foundation

2600 Nostrand Ave.
Brooklyn, NY   11210-4642

Established in 1993 in New York.
Donors: Harold Goldenberg; Leon Goldenberg.
Foundation type: Independent foundation.
Financial data (yr. ended 09/30/13): Assets, $2,645,089 (M); gifts received, $97,672; expenditures, $271,692; qualifying distributions, $271,692; giving activities include $266,500 for 8 + grants (high: $100,000).
Fields of interest: Nonprofits; Religion; Judaism.
Type of support: Regranting.
Limitations: Applications not accepted. Giving primarily in Brooklyn, NY. No grants to individuals.
Application information: Unsolicited requests for funds not accepted.
Officer: Harold Goldenberg, Pres.
Trustees: M. Bakst; A. Goldenberg; M. Goldenberg.
EIN: 113182539

6094

The Goldenson-Arbus Foundation, Inc.

(formerly The Isabelle and Leonard Goldenson Association, Inc.)
19 Mountain Ave.
Mount Kisco, NY   10549-1321

Established in 1946 in New York.
Foundation type: Independent foundation.

Financial data (yr. ended 12/31/13): Assets, $7,278,605 (M); expenditures, $464,816; qualifying distributions, $365,385; giving activities include $360,000 for 1 grant.
Fields of interest: Arts and culture; Foundations.
Limitations: Applications not accepted. No grants to individuals.
Application information: Contributes only to pre-selected organizations.
Officers: Martin Pompadur, Chair.; Loreen J. Arbus, Pres.; Maxine W. Goldenson, V.P.; Maryellen Mastrogiorgio, Secy.-Treas.
EIN: 136115597

6095
The Robert D. Goldfarb Foundation
80 Columbus Cir., PH 79
New York City, NY   10023-5800

Established in 1996 in New Jersey.
Donor: Robert D. Goldfarb.
Foundation type: Independent foundation.
Financial data (yr. ended 12/31/14): Assets, $23,438,278 (M); gifts received, $11,875,786; expenditures, $432,891; qualifying distributions, $382,543; giving activities include $378,944 for 12 grants (high: $100,000; low: $1,000).
Fields of interest: Arts and culture; Opera; University education; Heart and circulatory system diseases.
Type of support: Research.
Limitations: Applications not accepted. Giving primarily in NY. No grants to individuals.
Application information: Contributes only to pre-selected organizations.
Trustee: Robert D. Goldfarb.
EIN: 223478123

6096
Stanley F. Goldfein Foundation, Inc.
60 E. 42nd St., Ste. 2015
New York City, NY   10165-6210

Established in 1967 in New York.
Donor: Stanley F. Goldfein.
Foundation type: Independent foundation.
Financial data (yr. ended 05/31/13): Assets, $2,444,558 (M); expenditures, $211,432; qualifying distributions, $211,295; giving activities include $211,045 for grants.
Fields of interest: Orchestral music; Education; Environment; Diseases and conditions; Judaism; Human services; People with vision impairments.
Type of support: Research.
Limitations: Applications not accepted. Giving on a national basis. No grants to individuals.
Application information: Unsolicited requests for funds not accepted.
Officers: Stanley F. Goldfein, Pres.; Roanne Goldfein, Secy.; Myles S. Goldfein, Treas.
EIN: 237444440

6097
The Faith Golding Foundation, Inc.
1650 Broadway
New York City, NY   10019-6958
Contact: Faith Golding

Established in 1984 in New York.
Donors: First Sterling Corp.; Modern Properties, Inc.; Faith Golding.
Foundation type: Independent foundation.
Financial data (yr. ended 11/30/13): Assets, $4,850,540 (M); expenditures, $249,717; qualifying distributions, $228,392; giving activities include $218,000 for 6 grants (high: $100,000; low: $500).
Fields of interest: Opera; Museums; Education; Specialty hospital care.
Limitations: Applications not accepted. Giving primarily in New York, NY. No support for foundations. No grants to individuals.
Application information: Contributes only to pre-selected organizations.
Officers: Faith Golding, Pres.; Debra Perelman, V.P.; Terry Havel, Secy.-Treas.
EIN: 133260491

6098
Neal and Marlene Goldman Foundation
c/o Neal I. Goldman
767 3rd. Ave., 25th Fl.
New York City, NY   10017-2023

Established in 2007 in New York.
Donors: Neal I. Goldman; Marlene Mieske Goldman; Goldman Capital Management, Inc.
Foundation type: Independent foundation.
Financial data (yr. ended 12/31/13): Assets, $926,611 (M); gifts received, $104,343; expenditures, $157,853; qualifying distributions, $156,600; giving activities include $155,100 for 19 grants (high: $30,000; low: $500).
Fields of interest: Education; Diseases and conditions; Human services.
Type of support: Research.
Limitations: Applications not accepted. Giving primarily in CA and NY. No grants to individuals.
Application information: Unsolicited requests for funds not accepted.
Trustees: Benjamin Berg; Daniel Berg; Daniela Goldman; Jacob Goldman; Marlene Mieske Goldman; Neal I. Goldman; Alexandra Goldman Morrill.
EIN: 266091059

6099
Goldmann Family Foundation
(formerly Stephen and Joyce Goldmann Foundation)
c/o Ayco Co., LP
P.O. Box 15014
Albany, NY   12212-5014

Donor: Stephen F. Goldmann.
Foundation type: Independent foundation.
Financial data (yr. ended 12/31/14): Assets, $97,512 (M); gifts received, $52,067; expenditures, $219,199; qualifying distributions, $215,699; giving activities include $215,669 for 23 grants (high: $43,500; low: $1,000).
Fields of interest: Christianity; Human services.
Type of support: General support.
Limitations: Applications not accepted. Giving primarily in TX.
Application information: Unsolicited requests for funds not accepted.
Directors: Laura G. Benedict; Stephen C. Goldmann; Stephen F. Goldmann.
EIN: 453445601

6100
The Benjy & Adina Goldstein Charitable Foundation Inc.
1 Rewe St.
Brooklyn, NY   11211-1707

Established in 2000 in New York.
Donors: Benjamin Goldstein; David Goldstein; Foto Electronic Supply Co. Inc.; The Goldstein Family Charitable Foundation; Emerich Goldstein.
Foundation type: Independent foundation.
Financial data (yr. ended 12/31/13): Assets, $606,159 (M); gifts received, $300,000; expenditures, $355,986; qualifying distributions, $355,692; giving activities include $355,692 for grants.
Fields of interest: Nonprofits; Judaism; Child welfare.
Type of support: Regranting.
Limitations: Applications not accepted. No grants to individuals.
Application information: Contributes only to pre-selected organizations.
Trustees: Benjamin Goldstein; Emerich Goldstein.
EIN: 522264340

6101
The David and Esther Goldstein Charitable Trust
c/o David Goldstein
1644 51st St.
Brooklyn, NY   11204-1416

Established in 1999 in New York.
Donors: Esther Goldstein; A & E Family Partnership; A & E Kaufman Family Trust.
Foundation type: Independent foundation.
Financial data (yr. ended 12/31/13): Assets, $1,404,918 (M); expenditures, $117,397; qualifying distributions, $117,130; giving activities include $116,630 for 24 grants (high: $39,600; low: $360).
Fields of interest: Philanthropy; Judaism.
Limitations: Applications not accepted. Giving primarily in Brooklyn, NY. No grants to individuals.
Application information: Unsolicited requests for funds not accepted.
Trustees: David Goldstein; Armin Kaufman.
EIN: 116519669

6102
Goldstone Fund, Inc.
c/o Tanton Co., LLP
37 W. 57th St., 5th Fl.
New York City, NY   10019-3411
Contact: Janet L. Mulligan

Established in 1959 in New York.
Donor: Herbert A. Goldstone†.
Foundation type: Independent foundation.
Financial data (yr. ended 05/31/14): Assets, $7,381,438 (M); expenditures, $363,352; qualifying distributions, $300,612; giving activities include $291,175 for 49 grants (high: $30,000; low: $500).
Purpose and activities: Giving primarily for health care.
Fields of interest: Education; University education; Natural resources; Health; Diseases and conditions; Judaism; People with vision impairments.

Type of support: General support; Research.
Limitations: Applications not accepted. Giving primarily in NY. No grants to individuals.
Application information: Contributes only to pre-selected organizations.
Officers: Arthur H. Goldstone, Pres.; Jane G. Rittmaster, V.P.; Janet L. Mulligan, Secy.-Treas.
EIN: 136028782

6103
The Jonathan Plutzik & Lesley Goldwasser Family Foundation
1841 Broadway, Rm. 809
New York City, NY   10023-7603   (212) 957-4979
Contact: Jonathan Plutznik, Pres.

Established in 2003 in New York.
Donors: Johnathan Plutzik; Lesley Goldwasser Plutzik.
Foundation type: Independent foundation.
Financial data (yr. ended 11/30/13): Assets, $88,682 (M); expenditures, $519,887; qualifying distributions, $519,887; giving activities include $266,270 for 17+ grants (high: $146,165).
Fields of interest: Arts and culture; Higher education; Nonprofits.
Type of support: Regranting.
Limitations: Giving primarily in the New York, NY area.
Application information:
    Initial approach: Letter
Officer: Johnathan Plutzik, Pres. and Treas.
Directors: Deborah Plutzik Briggs; Lesley Goldwasser Plutzik.
EIN: 710927327

6104
Morrie & Susan Golick Family Foundation, Inc.
50 E. 79th St.
New York City, NY   10021-0231
Contact: Susan Golick

Established in 1997 in Florida.
Donor: Morrie Golick.
Foundation type: Independent foundation.
Financial data (yr. ended 09/30/13): Assets, $921,806 (M); gifts received, $200,000; expenditures, $249,515; qualifying distributions, $238,243; giving activities include $203,500 for 1 grant.
Fields of interest: Diseases and conditions; Immune system diseases.
Type of support: General support.
Limitations: Applications not accepted. Giving primarily in New York, NY. No grants to individuals.
Application information: Unsolicited requests for funds not accepted.
Officers: Susan Golick, Secy.-Treas.
EIN: 650798174

6105
Golub Charitable Foundation
c/o Citibank, N.A., Citicorp Trust Bank, FSB
1 Court Sq., 19th Fl.
Long Island City, NY   11120-0001

Established in 1992 in New York.
Donor: Herman B. Golub†.
Foundation type: Independent foundation.

Financial data (yr. ended 12/31/14): Assets, $4,186,518; expenditures, $215,990; qualifying distributions, $194,947.
Fields of interest: Higher education; Diseases and conditions; Parkinson's disease; Catholicism; Judaism; Human services.
Type of support: Research.
Limitations: Applications not accepted. Giving primarily in New York, NY. No grants to individuals.
Application information: Unsolicited requests for funds not accepted.
Trustee: Citibank, N.A.
EIN: 136327952

6106
The Goodman Family Foundation
134 E. 70th St.
New York City, NY   10021-5035

Established in 2003 in New York.
Donor: J. Josephson, Inc.
Foundation type: Company-sponsored foundation.
Financial data (yr. ended 12/31/13): Assets, $1,164,950 (M); gifts received, $150,000; expenditures, $299,733; qualifying distributions, $291,869; giving activities include $288,760 for 19 grants (high: $76,722; low: $250).
Purpose and activities: The foundation supports hospitals and organizations involved with education and Judaism.
Fields of interest: Arts and culture; Education; Religion.
Type of support: General support.
Limitations: Applications not accepted. Giving primarily in NY. No grants to individuals.
Application information: Contributes only to pre-selected organizations.
Officers and Directors: Mark Goodman, Pres. and Director; Judith Goodman, Secy. and Director; Gilbert Goodman.
EIN: 510486580

6107
The Goodman Family Foundation
1035 5th Ave.
New York City, NY   10028-0135   (212) 288-9067

Established in 1970 in New York.
Donor: Israel Matz†.
Foundation type: Independent foundation.
Financial data (yr. ended 06/30/14): Assets, $3,756,033; expenditures, $416,370; qualifying distributions, $314,829.
Purpose and activities: Giving primarily for education, the arts, and Jewish agencies and temples; funding also for health and human services.
Fields of interest: Arts and culture; Performing arts; Museums; Education; Higher education; Diseases and conditions; Judaism; Human services.
Type of support: Research; Research and evaluation.
Limitations: Applications accepted. Giving primarily in New York, NY. No grants to individuals.
Application information: Application form required.
    Initial approach: Letter
    Deadline(s): None
    Final notification: Within 6 months of application

Trustees: Claire Goodman Pellegrini Cloud; Leslie Ann Goodman; Randolph B. Goodman; Roy M. Goodman.
EIN: 136355553

6108
Goodman-Lipman Family Foundation Inc.
c/o Deer Management
1865 Palmer Ave.
Larchmont, NY   10538-3048

Established in 1999 in New York.
Donors: Robert P. Goodman; Jane Sarah Lipman.
Foundation type: Independent foundation.
Financial data (yr. ended 12/31/13): Assets, $9,631,456 (L); gifts received, $6,548,746; expenditures, $229,270; qualifying distributions, $166,478; giving activities include $160,103 for 46 grants (high: $50,000; low: $40).
Fields of interest: Education; Nonprofits; Diseases and conditions; Human services.
Type of support: General support; Regranting.
Limitations: Applications not accepted. Giving primarily in MA, New York, NY, and RI. No grants to individuals.
Application information: Unsolicited requests for funds not accepted.
Directors: James S. Goodman; Robert P. Goodman; Jane Sarah Lipman.
EIN: 134052449

6109
The William J. J. Gordon Family Foundation
c/o G. David Phelps Hamar
300 Park Ave., 19th Fl.
New York City, NY   10022

Established in 2003 in Massachusetts.
Donors: Nathan H. Gordon Corporation; William J.J. Gordon.
Foundation type: Independent foundation.
Financial data (yr. ended 12/31/13): Assets, $8,126,618 (M); expenditures, $520,602; qualifying distributions, $449,078; giving activities include $392,000 for 95 grants (high: $23,000; low: $500).
Purpose and activities: Giving primarily for education, the environment, animal organizations, and children, youth, and social services.
Fields of interest: Education; Higher education; Environment; Natural resources; Domesticated animals; Human services; Child welfare.
Type of support: Grants to individuals.
Limitations: Applications not accepted. Giving primarily in MA, ME, and TX, with emphasis on Austin.
Application information: Unsolicited requests for funds not accepted.
Trustees: Elizabeth Gordon; G. David Phelps Hamar.
EIN: 416517207

6110
The Allan S. Gordon Foundation
441 Lexington Ave.
New York City, NY   10017

Established in 1997 in Connecticut.
Donor: Laura Gordon.
Foundation type: Independent foundation.

Financial data (yr. ended 12/31/14): Assets, $5,388,811; expenditures, $219,849; qualifying distributions, $219,849.
Fields of interest: Performing arts; Education; Health; Reproductive health care; Childbirth; Judaism; Human services.
Type of support: General support; Annual campaigns; Emergency funds; Program development; Seed money.
Limitations: Applications not accepted. Giving primarily in NY. No grants to individuals.
Application information: Contributes only to pre-selected organizations.
Directors: Allan S. Gordon; Timothy C. Gordon.
Number of staff: 1 part-time professional.
EIN: 137107377

6111
The Kathy and Al Gordon Fund
570 Park Ave., No. 7B
New York City, NY   10021

Established in 2004 in New York.
Foundation type: Independent foundation.
Financial data (yr. ended 12/31/14): Assets, $321,007 (M); expenditures, $511,500; qualifying distributions, $382,733; giving activities include $382,733 for 9 grants (high: $270,000; low: $1,000).
Fields of interest: Education; Higher education; Catholicism; Racquet sports.
Limitations: Applications not accepted. Giving primarily in NY; funding also in NH. No grants to individuals.
Application information: Contributes only to pre-selected organizations.
Trustees: Kathleen Gordon; Nancy Mulligan; William A. Oates.
EIN: 306073441

6112
The Gordon Fund
(formerly The Gordon/Rousmaniere/Roberts Fund)
c/o Bessemer Trust
630 5th Ave.
New York City, NY   10111-0100

Established in 1985 in New York.
Donor: Albert H. Gordon.
Foundation type: Independent foundation.
Financial data (yr. ended 12/31/14): Assets, $5,447,806; expenditures, $221,973; qualifying distributions, $208,178.
Fields of interest: Arts and culture; Education; Hospital care; Catholicism.
Limitations: Applications not accepted. Giving primarily in CA, CT, MA, and NY. No grants to individuals.
Application information: Unsolicited requests for funds not accepted.
Trustees: John A. Roberts; Martha G. Roberts.
EIN: 133257793

6113
Gotham Charitable Foundation Trust
c/o CWC
7 Penn Plz.
New York City, NY   10001

Established in 2003 in New York.

Donor: Michael L. Moskowitz.
Foundation type: Independent foundation.
Financial data (yr. ended 12/31/13): Assets, $7,237,681 (M); expenditures, $325,514; qualifying distributions, $308,000; giving activities include $308,000 for 5 grants (high: $183,000; low: $20,000).
Fields of interest: Judaism.
Limitations: Applications not accepted. Giving primarily in CA, Washington, DC, NY and MA.
Application information: Contributes only to pre-selected organizations.
Trustee: Michael L. Moskowitz.
EIN: 116594112

6114
Adolph and Esther Gottlieb Foundation, Inc.
380 West Broadway
New York City, NY   10012-5115   (212) 226-0581
Contact: Sanford Hirsch, Exec. Dir.
FAX: (212) 274-1476;
E-mail: shirsch@gottliebfoundation.org; Main URL: http://www.gottliebfoundation.org

Established in 1976 in New York.
Donors: Adolph Gottlieb†; Esther Gottlieb†; Alice Yamin†; Ann Cooper†.
Foundation type: Independent foundation.
Financial data (yr. ended 06/30/14): Assets, $32,839,287 (M); expenditures, $1,080,488; qualifying distributions, $972,532; giving activities include $442,150 for grants to individuals.
Purpose and activities: The foundation maintains two separate grant programs: 1) Individual support program for painters, sculptors, and printmakers who have worked at least 20 years in a mature phase of their art, and are in current financial need; and 2) Emergency assistance program for painters, sculptors, and printmakers who have worked at least 10 years in a mature phase of their art and are in current financial need in excess of and unrelated to their normal economic situation, and which is the result of a recent emergency occurrence such as a fire, flood or medical emergency.
Fields of interest: Painting; Printmaking; Sculpture; Low-income and poor people.
Type of support: Emergency funds; Grants to individuals.
Limitations: Giving on a national and international basis. No support for charitable organizations, educational institutions or projects, artists working in crafts, or for dental work, or chronic situations. No grants for capital improvements, or for debt.
Publications: Application guidelines; Informational brochure.
Application information: Application information available on foundation web site. Application form required.
  Initial approach: Letter only, requesting application form for Individual Support program; letter or telephone for Emergency Assistance program
  Copies of proposal: 1
  Deadline(s): Dec. 15 for Individual Support Program grants; none for Emergency Assistance Program
  Board meeting date(s): Annually
  Final notification: Mar.
Officers and Directors: Robert Mangold, Pres.; Charlotta Kotik, V.P. and Director; Gordon Marsh, V.P. and Director; Sanford Hirsch, Secy.-Treas. and

Exec. Dir.; Sheila Ross, Mgr., Grants; Nancy Litwin, Mgr., Art Collection; Lynda Benglis.
Number of staff: 3 full-time professional; 1 part-time professional; 1 part-time support.
EIN: 132853957

6115
Gottlieb-Schwartz Family Foundation
724 Collfield Ave.
Staten Island, NY   10314-4253

Established in 1994 in New York.
Donors: Steven Schwartz; Michael Schwartz; Martin Gottlieb; Michael Gottlieb.
Foundation type: Independent foundation.
Financial data (yr. ended 12/31/13): Assets, $93,565 (M); gifts received, $135,003; expenditures, $178,832; qualifying distributions, $178,680; giving activities include $178,680 for 22 grants (high: $80,000; low: $300).
Fields of interest: Education; Religion.
Limitations: Applications not accepted. Giving primarily in Brooklyn and New York, NY. No grants to individuals.
Application information: Unsolicited requests for funds not accepted.
Officers: Michael Gottlieb, Pres.; Steven Schwartz, Treas.
EIN: 133794021

6116
The Stuart S. and Byrdie Gould Foundation
c/o Jay Gould
363 E. 76th St.
New York City, NY   10021-2421

Donor: Stuart S. Gould.
Foundation type: Independent foundation.
Financial data (yr. ended 12/31/13): Assets, $7,182,816 (M); expenditures, $399,489; qualifying distributions, $368,488; giving activities include $356,801 for 12 grants (high: $158,801; low: $1,000).
Fields of interest: Education; University education; Nonprofits.
Type of support: Regranting.
Limitations: Applications not accepted. Giving primarily in NC and NY. No grants to individuals.
Application information: Contributes only to pre-selected organizations.
Trustee: N. Jay Gould.
EIN: 650350361

6117
GP Family Foundation
810 Seventh Ave., 28th Fl.
New York City, NY   10019-9000
Contact: Aaron Cohen, Tr.

Established in 2008 in New York.
Donors: Louis Glick; LG & SG NY 1987 Trust; LG & SP NY 1987 Trust; Louis Glick Diamond Corporation.
Foundation type: Independent foundation.
Financial data (yr. ended 06/30/14): Assets, $6,472,372 (M); expenditures, $254,390; qualifying distributions, $248,890; giving activities include $243,000 for 7 grants (high: $120,000; low: $5,000).
Purpose and activities: Giving primarily to Jewish agencies, synagogues, and schools.

Fields of interest: Education; Judaism; Human services.

Limitations: Applications accepted. Giving primarily in NJ and NY.

Application information: Application form required.

Initial approach: Letter

Deadline(s): None

Officer: Simon Glick, C.I.O.

Trustees: Aaron Cohen; Shmuel Levinson.

EIN: 137568187

6118
Grace Family Foundation

(formerly The Tom and Bonnie Grace Family Foundation)
230 North St.
Rye, NY   10580-1520

Established in 2005 in New York.

Donor: Thomas G. Grace.

Foundation type: Independent foundation.

Financial data (yr. ended 12/31/13): Assets, $2,694,687 (M); expenditures, $164,776; qualifying distributions, $159,030; giving activities include $157,965 for 18 grants (high: $52,865; low: $500).

Fields of interest: Education; Catholicism; Human services.

Limitations: Applications not accepted. Giving primarily in NY. No grants to individuals.

Application information: Unsolicited requests for funds not accepted.

Officers: Anne E. Grace, Pres.; Thomas G. Grace, V.P.; Thomas G. Grace, Jr., Treas.

EIN: 593807866

6119
Helen I. Graham Charitable Foundation

9 Hunts Ln.
P.O. Box 320
Chappaqua, NY   10514-2631

Established in 1999 in New York.

Donor: Helen I. Graham Trust.

Foundation type: Independent foundation.

Financial data (yr. ended 12/31/13): Assets, $3,940,160 (M); expenditures, $194,257; qualifying distributions, $158,500; giving activities include $158,500 for 17 grants (high: $50,000; low: $500).

Fields of interest: Arts and culture; Education; Higher education; University education; Diseases and conditions; Human services. .

Type of support: Research.

Limitations: Applications not accepted. Giving primarily in CT, MT, NY, PA, and VA, with some giving in CA. No grants to individuals.

Application information: Contributes only to pre-selected organizations.

Trustees: Harvey Dann IV; Tyler Dann.

EIN: 134070185

6120
Graham Family Charitable Foundation

21 Inkberry St.
East Hampton, NY   11937-2243
Application address: c/o Graham Partners, Attn.: Monica Graham, 237 Park Ave., Ste. 900, New York, NY 10017, tel.: (212) 808-7430

Established in 1999 in New York.

Donor: Monica Graham.

Foundation type: Independent foundation.

Financial data (yr. ended 12/31/12): Assets, $7,638,590 (M); expenditures, $523,834; qualifying distributions, $389,400; giving activities include $389,400 for grants.

Fields of interest: Education; Catholicism; Human services; Child welfare.

Application information: Application form required.

Initial approach: Proposal

Deadline(s): None

Trustees: Monica Graham; Shirin Kermanshachi.

EIN: 134021970

6121
Gralnick Foundation

c/o Housman & Bloch, LLP
399 Knollwood Rd., Ste. 311
White Plains, NY   10603-1900

Donors: High Point Hospital; William Gralnick.

Foundation type: Independent foundation.

Financial data (yr. ended 03/31/13): Assets, $2,635,553 (M); expenditures, $165,784; qualifying distributions, $135,700; giving activities include $135,700 for 5 grants (high: $100,000; low: $200).

Fields of interest: Education; Undergraduate education; Health; Mental health care.

Limitations: Applications not accepted. Giving primarily in NY. No grants to individuals.

Application information: Unsolicited requests for funds not accepted.

Trustee: William Gralnick.

EIN: 136153757

6122
Gramercy Park Foundation Inc.

c/o Marks Paneth & Shron LLP
685 3rd Ave., 4th Fl.
New York City, NY   10017-6707

Established in 1952 in New York.

Donors: Benjamin Sonnenberg; Helen Sonnenberg Tucker.

Foundation type: Independent foundation.

Financial data (yr. ended 12/31/14): Assets, $4,592,003 (M); gifts received, $316; expenditures, $284,725; qualifying distributions, $248,926.

Purpose and activities: Giving primarily for the arts; funding also for health care and medical research organizations.

Fields of interest: Arts and culture; Performing arts; Theater; Museums; Health; Diseases and conditions; Human services.

Type of support: Research.

Limitations: Applications not accepted. Giving primarily in the metropolitan New York, NY, area. No grants to individuals.

Application information: Unsolicited requests for funds not accepted.

Officers: Helen Sonnenberg Tucker, Pres.; Steven Tucker, Secy.; William Spears, Co-Treas.; Barbara Tucker-Cardinal, Co-Treas.; Susan Tucker, Co-Treas.

Number of staff: 1 part-time support.

EIN: 132507282

6123
The Grand Marnier Foundation

183 Madison Ave. 15th Fl., Ste. 1504
New York City, NY   10016   (212) 323-3085
Contact: Elise Aubespin-Seignolle

Established in 1985 in New York.

Donor: Carillon Importers, Ltd.

Foundation type: Company-sponsored foundation.

Financial data (yr. ended 12/31/13): Assets, $6,195,785 (M); expenditures, $295,077; qualifying distributions, $213,419; giving activities include $195,000 for 10 grants (high: $25,000; low: $5,000).

Purpose and activities: The foundation supports organizations involved with arts and culture, French culture, and education and awards fellowships to students at select schools to study French civilization and culture.

Fields of interest: Arts and culture; Environment; Human services.

Type of support: General support; Capital and infrastructure; Program development; Fellowships; Scholarships; Sponsorships.

Limitations: Applications accepted. Giving primarily in New York, NY.

Application information: Application form required.

Initial approach: Proposal

Deadline(s): None

Officers and Directors: Scott Green, Pres. and Director; Hattie K. Jutagir, Secy. and Director; Francois Lecatonnoux, Treas. and Director; Kristell Belloir-Fairgrieve.

EIN: 133258414

6124
Grandison Foundation

1 N. Broadway, Ste. 1004
White Plains, NY   10601-2317
Contact: Garry B. Trudeau, Pres., Treas., and Dir.; Jane P. Trudeau, Chair., Secy., and Dir.

Established in 1996 in New York.

Donors: Garry B. Trudeau; Jane P. Trudeau; Trudeau Charitable Lead Trust.

Foundation type: Independent foundation.

Financial data (yr. ended 12/31/13): Assets, $3,623,159 (M); gifts received, $402,918; expenditures, $433,000; qualifying distributions, $380,675; giving activities include $378,175 for 28 grants (high: $225,000; low: $100).

Purpose and activities: Giving primarily for health care, including children's health, and for human services; funding also for the arts, community development, and federated giving programs.

Fields of interest: Arts and culture; Education; Nonprofits; Health; Diseases and conditions; Community and economic development; Human services; Child welfare.

Type of support: Regranting.

Limitations: Applications accepted. Giving primarily in NY. No grants to individuals.

Application information:

Initial approach: Proposal

Deadline(s): None

Board meeting date(s): Annually, usually in Dec.

Officers and Directors: Jane P. Trudeau, Chair. and Secy. and Director; Garry B. Trudeau, Pres. and Treas. and Director; Ann Pauley.

EIN: 133883296

6125
Grandview-Steers Foundation
c/o Robert Steers
15 Hilltop Pl.
Rye, NY   10580-1805

Established in 2001 in New York.
Donors: Lauren J. Steers; Robert H. Steers.
Foundation type: Independent foundation.
Financial data (yr. ended 12/31/12): Assets, $12,235,505 (M); gifts received, $5,660,000; expenditures, $282,887; qualifying distributions, $253,000; giving activities include $253,000 for grants.
Fields of interest: Education; University education; Specialty hospital care.
Limitations: Applications not accepted. Giving primarily in CT, DC and NY. No grants to individuals.
Application information: Contributes only to pre-selected organizations.
Trustees: Lauren J. Steers; Robert H. Steers.
EIN: 137297946

6126
Granit Foundation
c/o Arye Ringel
1750 44th St.
Brooklyn, NY   11204-1050

Established in 2002 in New Jersey.
Donor: Mark Wertenteil.
Foundation type: Independent foundation.
Financial data (yr. ended 06/30/13): Assets, $205,593 (M); gifts received, $265,000; expenditures, $143,394; qualifying distributions, $143,394; giving activities include $143,364 for 73 grants (high: $51,800; low: $1).
Fields of interest: Education; Judaism; Human services.
Limitations: Applications not accepted. No grants to individuals.
Application information: Contributes only to pre-selected organizations.
Trustees: Ilana Wertenteil; Mark Wertenteil.
EIN: 522366802

6127
Granny B & P Foundation
555 Madison Ave., Ste. 1302
New York City, NY   10022-3406

Foundation type: Independent foundation.
Financial data (yr. ended 12/31/13): Assets, $2,670,773 (M); expenditures, $271,195; qualifying distributions, $258,325; giving activities include $258,075 for 15 grants (high: $50,000; low: $2,500).
Fields of interest: Human services.
Limitations: Applications not accepted.
Application information: Unsolicited requests for funds not accepted.
Trustee: Brian S. Snyder.
EIN: 272621507

6128
Grano Family Foundation
c/o Joseph J. Grano, Centurion Holdings
1185 Ave. of the Americas, Ste. 1750
New York City, NY   10036-2604

Established in 2000 in New Jersey.
Donor: Joseph J. Grano, Jr.
Foundation type: Independent foundation.
Financial data (yr. ended 12/31/13): Assets, $1,326,868 (M); gifts received, $30; expenditures, $132,743; qualifying distributions, $122,215; giving activities include $120,000 for 10 grants (high: $25,000; low: $1,000).
Fields of interest: Diseases and conditions; Human services; Youth services.
Limitations: Applications not accepted. Giving primarily in CA, FL, NC and NY. No grants to individuals.
Application information: Contributes only to pre-selected organizations.
Trustees: Andrea J. Grano; Angela L. Grano; Joseph C. Grano; Joseph J. Grano, Jr.; Kathleen J. Grano.
EIN: 134150690

6129
Charles M. & Mary D. Grant Foundation
c/o JPMorgan Chase Bank, Philanthropic Svcs.
270 Park Ave., 16th Fl.
New York City, NY   10017-2014
Contact: Carolyn O'Brien, Grants Mgr.
FAX: (212) 464-2304;
E-mail: carolyn.r.obrien@jpmorgan.com; Main URL: http://fdnweb.org/grant
Grants List: http://fdnweb.org/grant/grants/category/contributions

Established in 1967 in New York.
Donor: Mary D. Grant†.
Foundation type: Independent foundation.
Financial data (yr. ended 12/31/13): Assets, $8,323,728 (M); expenditures, $464,250; qualifying distributions, $386,164; giving activities include $360,000 for 13 grants (high: $45,000; low: $20,000).
Purpose and activities: Support for organizations involved with community and economic development, health and human services, environment, and education.
Fields of interest: Education; Basic and remedial instruction; Environment; Health; Community and economic development; Economic development; Housing development; Human services; Child welfare.
Type of support: General support; Program development.
Limitations: Applications accepted. No support for organizations lacking 501(c)(3) status. No grants to individuals, or for research, endowment funds, or matching gifts; generally no scholarships or fellowships; no loans.
Publications: Application guidelines; Grants list.
Application information: All application materials must be submitted online. See foundation web site for complete application guidelines and requirements.
Copies of proposal: 1
Deadline(s): Apr. 30
Board meeting date(s): Aug.
Trustee: JPMorgan Chase Bank, N.A.
EIN: 136264329

6130
The Sarah E. Grant Foundation
c/o The Ayco Co.
P.O. Box 15014
Albany, NY   12212-5014

Established in 1997 in New York.
Donor: Geoffrey T. Grant.
Foundation type: Independent foundation.
Financial data (yr. ended 05/31/13): Assets, $21,511 (M); expenditures, $150,000; qualifying distributions, $150,000; giving activities include $150,000 for 1 grant.
Fields of interest: Education.
Limitations: Applications not accepted. Giving primarily in New York, NY. No grants to individuals; no loans or scholarships.
Application information: Unsolicited request for funds not accepted.
Trustees: Peter C. Gerhard; Annette M. Grant; Geoffrey T. Grant.
EIN: 133931292

6131
Grateful Foundation Inc.
411 Theodore Fremd Ave.
New York City, NY   10177-0073

Established in 1987 in Delaware.
Donor: Jordan Seaman.
Foundation type: Independent foundation.
Financial data (yr. ended 10/31/13): Assets, $9,658,089 (M); expenditures, $513,674; qualifying distributions, $440,250; giving activities include $440,250 for grants.
Purpose and activities: Giving primarily for the arts, health, and children, youth and social services.
Fields of interest: Arts and culture; Hospital care; Diseases and conditions; Human services; Child welfare.
Type of support: Research.
Limitations: Applications not accepted. Giving primarily in NY. No grants to individuals.
Application information: Contributes only to pre-selected organizations.
Officers: Jordan Seaman, Pres.; Alan Ast, Treas.
EIN: 112897411

6132
The Maurice R. & Corinne P. Greenberg Foundation, Inc.
c/o Marks Paneth
685 3rd Ave., 5th Fl.
New York City, NY   10017-4024

Established in 1984 in New York.
Donors: Greenberg Charitable Trust No. 1; Maurice R. "Hank" Greenberg; Corinne P. Greenberg; C.V. Starr & Co., Inc.
Foundation type: Independent foundation.
Financial data (yr. ended 09/30/14): Assets, $3,433,018 (M); gifts received, $1,550,000; expenditures, $301,879; qualifying distributions, $280,728; giving activities include $270,450 for 14 grants (high: $75,000; low: $1,000).
Fields of interest: Arts and culture; Higher education; Nonprofits; Diseases and conditions; Judaism; Human services.
Type of support: General support; Regranting.
Limitations: Applications not accepted. Giving primarily in the metropolitan New York, NY, area. No grants to individuals.
Application information: Contributes only to pre-selected organizations.
Officers and Directors: Maurice R. Greenberg, Chair. and Director; Corinne P. Greenberg, Pres. and Director; Evan G. Greenberg, V.P. and Director;

Jeffrey W. Greenberg, V.P. and Director; Lawrence S. Greenberg, V.P. and Director.
EIN: 133208725

6133
The Greenblatt Family Charitable Trust
c/o William Greenblatt
1 State St., 24th Fl.
New York City, NY 10004

Donor: William M. Greenblatt.
Foundation type: Independent foundation.
Financial data (yr. ended 12/31/13): Assets, $2,471,630 (M); expenditures, $173,221; qualifying distributions, $169,900; giving activities include $169,900 for 20 grants (high: $51,000; low: $50).
Fields of interest: Education; Religion; Human services.
Limitations: Applications not accepted. Giving primarily in NJ.
Application information: Unsolicited requests for funds not accepted.
Trustees: Judith S. Greenblatt; Steven Jacob Greenblatt; William M. Greenblatt.
EIN: 276946683

6134
Louis Greenspan Charitable Trust
12 Raymond Ave.
Poughkeepsie, NY 12603-2354 (845) 483-7745

Established in 1998 in New York.
Donor: Louis Greenspan†.
Foundation type: Independent foundation.
Financial data (yr. ended 12/31/13): Assets, $3,909,297 (M); expenditures, $218,365; qualifying distributions, $164,373; giving activities include $154,500 for 13 grants (high: $40,000; low: $1,500).
Fields of interest: Orchestral music; Secondary education; Higher education; Adult education; Hospital care; Public libraries; Senior services.
Limitations: Applications accepted. Giving primarily in Poughkeepsie, NY. No grants to individuals.
Application information:
    Initial approach: Letter
    Deadline(s): None
Trustees: Daniel F. Curtin; Gary Koch.
EIN: 146185658

6135
Greentree Foundation
220 Community Dr.
Manhasset, NY 11030-3814

Established in 1982 in New York.
Donor: Betsey C. Whitney†.
Foundation type: Operating foundation.
Financial data (yr. ended 12/31/14): Assets, $282,801,977 (M); expenditures, $12,280,793; qualifying distributions, $9,668,366; giving activities include $374,000 for 4 grants (high: $185,000; low: $2,000), and $9,294,366 for foundation-administered programs.
Purpose and activities: The foundation supports focused projects initiated by local community groups that provide clearly defined participatory roles for schools, parents, children and community-based

organizations in order to enhance educational achievements and lessen social and cultural tensions.
Fields of interest: Education; Foundations.
Type of support: Program development.
Limitations: Applications not accepted. Giving primarily in New York, NY. No grants to individuals.
Application information: Contributes only to pre-selected organizations.
    Board meeting date(s): Mar., June, Sept., and Dec.
Officers and Trustees: Richard Schaffer, Pres.; Kate R. Whitney, V.P. and Trustee; Sara R. Wilford, V.P. and Trustee; Laura E. Butzel, Esq., Secy.; Robert Carswell, Esq., Treas.; Franklin A. Thomas; Ronald A. Wilford.
Number of staff: 6 full-time professional; 24 full-time support; 2 part-time support.
EIN: 133132117

6136
The Dorothy and Harold Greenwald Foundation
c/o Holland Knight
31 W. 52nd St.
New York City, NY 10019

Foundation type: Independent foundation.
Financial data (yr. ended 12/31/13): Assets, $33,554 (M); expenditures, $309,017; qualifying distributions, $307,219; giving activities include $300,000 for 1 grant.
Fields of interest: Higher education; Judaism.
International interests: Israel.
Limitations: Applications not accepted. Giving primarily in CA and NY.
Application information: Unsolicited requests for funds not accepted.
Trustees: Frank H. Klein; Susan B. Rapp; Stewart Simon; Jacques Torczyner.
EIN: 846395329

6137
The Greenwich Collection, Ltd.
637 Greenwich St.
New York City, NY 10014-3306
E-mail: thegreenwichcollectionltd@charter.net

Established in 1987 in New York.
Donors: Merrill W. Ryman; Merrill Foundation; Robert Ryman.
Foundation type: Independent foundation.
Financial data (yr. ended 12/31/14): Assets, $39,814,516 (M); expenditures, $454,044; qualifying distributions, $416,496; giving activities include $187,000 for 20 grants (high: $15,000; low: $5,000).
Purpose and activities: Promotion of the public understanding of abstract art through ongoing work on various publications.
Fields of interest: Arts and culture.
Type of support: General support.
Limitations: Applications not accepted. Giving primarily in New York, NY. No grants to individuals.
Application information: Unsolicited requests for funds not accepted.
Officers: Robert Storr, Pres.; Naomi Spector, V.P.; Julia Brown, V.P.; Beverly M. Wolff, V.P.; Charles B. Wright III, Treas.; David Gray, Exec. Dir.

Directors: Ethan Ryman; George Ryman; William Ryman.
EIN: 133354167

6138
Dorothy G. Griffin Charitable Foundation
512 W. Court St.
Rome, NY 13440-4010 (315) 336-4400
Contact: Charles J. Schoff, Tr.

Established in 1995 in New York.
Donors: Dorothy G. Griffin; William L. Griffin; William F. Locke.
Foundation type: Independent foundation.
Financial data (yr. ended 12/31/13): Assets, $3,394,304 (M); gifts received, $500,000; expenditures, $381,239; qualifying distributions, $376,000; giving activities include $376,000 for 39 grants (high: $100,000; low: $1,000).
Fields of interest: Education; Community and economic development; Human services; Family services.
Type of support: General support.
Limitations: Applications accepted. Giving restricted to Rome, NY, and neighboring communities. No grants to individuals.
Application information:
    Initial approach: Proposal
    Deadline(s): None
Trustees: Dorothy G. Griffin; William L. Griffin; Charles J. Schoff.
EIN: 161541273

6139
The Grinberg Family Foundation
(formerly The Grinberg Foundation)
c/o Baker Tilly Virchow Krause,LLP
1 Penn Plz., Ste. 3000
New York City, NY 10119-0032

Established in 1982 in District of Columbia.
Donors: Miriam Grinberg Phalen; Alexander Grinberg; Efraim Grinberg.
Foundation type: Independent foundation.
Financial data (yr. ended 11/30/13): Assets, $6,125,882 (M); expenditures, $252,984; qualifying distributions, $240,266; giving activities include $239,929 for 15 grants (high: $125,000; low: $250).
Fields of interest: Arts and culture; Health; Cancers; Judaism; Human services.
Limitations: Applications not accepted. Giving primarily in FL and New York, NY. No grants to individuals.
Application information: Unsolicited requests for funds not accepted.
Officers: Miriam Grinberg Phalen, Pres.; Alexander Grinberg, Secy.; Efraim Grinberg, Treas.
EIN: 521233811

6140
Frank & Roslyn Grobman Foundation
c/o Dans Supreme Supermarkets, Inc.
474 Fulton Ave.
Hempstead, NY 11550-4133

Established in 1994 in New York.
Donor: Frank Grobman.
Foundation type: Independent foundation.

Financial data (yr. ended 12/31/13): Assets, $3,937,932 (M); expenditures, $186,198; qualifying distributions, $179,976; giving activities include $179,976 for 45 grants (high: $50,000; low: $5).
Fields of interest: Arts and culture; Community and economic development; Judaism; Human services.
Limitations: Applications not accepted. Giving primarily in NY.
Application information: Unsolicited requests for funds not accepted.
Directors: Frank Grobman; Richard Grobman.
EIN: 113241420

6141
The Grodzins Fund
155 E. 77th St., Ste. 3F
New York City, NY   10075-1915

Established in 1998 in New York.
Foundation type: Independent foundation.
Financial data (yr. ended 06/30/13): Assets, $3,830,989 (M); expenditures, $224,784; qualifying distributions, $190,494; giving activities include $184,500 for 54 grants (high: $20,000; low: $500).
Purpose and activities: Giving primarily for the arts and for children's services.
Fields of interest: Arts and culture; Education; Antidiscrimination; Child welfare.
Limitations: Applications not accepted. Giving primarily in NY. No grants to individuals.
Application information: Contributes only to pre-selected organizations.
Officer: Louis Slesin, Pres.
Directors: Muffie Meyer; Lesli Rice.
EIN: 134022751

6142
Allen I. Gross Charitable Foundation
50 Broadway, 3rd Fl.
New York City, NY   10004-1607

Established in 1987 in New York.
Donors: Allen I. Gross; AIG 2001 Trust; Brian Gross.
Foundation type: Independent foundation.
Financial data (yr. ended 11/30/13): Assets, $13,484,119 (M); gifts received, $250,000; expenditures, $472,930; qualifying distributions, $412,746; giving activities include $409,228 for 176 grants (high: $42,000; low: $18).
Purpose and activities: Giving primarily to Jewish agencies, temples, and schools.
Fields of interest: Elementary and secondary education; Nonprofits; Judaism.
Type of support: General support; Regranting.
Limitations: Applications not accepted. Giving primarily in NY. No grants to individuals.
Application information: Contributes only to pre-selected organizations.
Officer: Allen I. Gross, Pres.
Trustees: Brian Gross; Edie Gross; Jonathan Gross; Zahava Hurwitz; Carolyn Weiser.
EIN: 112906887

6143
J. & H. Gross Family Foundation
1224 E. 24th St.
Brooklyn, NY   11210-4533   (845) 362-2006

Established in 1996 in New York.
Donor: Jonathan Gross.
Foundation type: Independent foundation.
Financial data (yr. ended 06/30/13): Assets, $257,510 (M); gifts received, $2,999; expenditures, $214,387; qualifying distributions, $195,970; giving activities include $161,553 for grants.
Purpose and activities: Giving primarily to Jewish organizations, temples, and yeshivas.
Fields of interest: Education; Judaism.
Limitations: Applications accepted. Giving primarily in NY. No grants to individuals.
Application information: Application form required.
  Initial approach: Letter
  Copies of proposal: 1
  Deadline(s): None
Trustees: Heddy Gross; Jonathan Gross.
EIN: 113344451

6144
Grossman Family Foundation
1461 53rd St.
Brooklyn, NY   11219

Established in 1989 in New York.
Donors: Marton B. Grossman; Mindy Weiss; Sym Holding Corp.; Shaindy Steinberger; Isaac Grossman; Mindy Weiss Grantor Trust.
Foundation type: Independent foundation.
Financial data (yr. ended 11/30/13): Assets, $2,430,915 (M); gifts received, $75,000; expenditures, $291,067; qualifying distributions, $290,650; giving activities include $290,122 for 258 grants (high: $25,000; low: $25).
Purpose and activities: Giving primarily to Jewish organizations, temples and schools.
Fields of interest: Education; Judaism; Human services.
Type of support: General support; Capital and infrastructure.
Limitations: Applications not accepted. Giving primarily in Brooklyn, NY. No grants to individuals.
Application information: Contributes only to pre-selected organizations.
Officers: Marton B. Grossman, Pres.; Sheila Grossman, V.P.; Isaac Grossman, Secy.
EIN: 112994863

6145
The Stanley & Nancy Grossman Family Foundation
c/o Stanley Grossman, Pomerantz et al., LLP
600 3rd Ave.
New York City, NY   10016

Established in 1994 in New York.
Donors: Stanley Grossman; Nancy Grossman.
Foundation type: Independent foundation.
Financial data (yr. ended 12/31/13): Assets, $593,861 (M); expenditures, $136,098; qualifying distributions, $128,705; giving activities include $126,980 for 58 grants (high: $16,000; low: $100).
Fields of interest: Arts and culture; Religion; Sports and recreation.
Limitations: Applications not accepted. Giving primarily in New York, NY. No grants to individuals.
Application information: Unsolicited requests for funds not accepted.
Officers: Stanley Grossman, Pres. and Secy.; Nancy Grossman, V.P. and Treas.

Directors: Judd B. Grossman; Jillian Hirsch.
EIN: 133800204

6146
The Grossman Family Philanthropic Foundation
c/o Ronald Grossman
860 5th Ave., Ste. 6K
New York City, NY   10021-5856

Established in 2006 in New York.
Foundation type: Independent foundation.
Financial data (yr. ended 12/31/14): Assets, $8,883,228 (M); gifts received, $0; expenditures, $444,307; qualifying distributions, $399,021.
Fields of interest: Children and youth; Children; Adolescents; Low-income and poor people.
International interests: Israel.
Type of support: Seed money; Scholarships; Program development; Continuing support.
Limitations: Applications not accepted. Giving primarily in New York, NY. No support for religious, political and civic organizations, or for universities and art and cultural programs. No grants to individuals.
Application information: Unsolicited requests for funds not accepted.
Officers and Directors: Ronald Grossman, Chair. and Director; Bruce D. Grossman, Vice-Chair. and Director; Marilynn P. Grossman, Secy. and Director; Dianne M. Grossman, Treas. and Director.
Number of staff: None.
EIN: 205147463

6147
The Grubman Compton Foundation
(formerly Eric P. Grubman Foundation)
c/o BCRS Associates, LLC
77 Water St., 9th Fl.
New York City, NY   10005-4414

Established in 1996 in New Jersey.
Donor: Eric P. Grubman.
Foundation type: Independent foundation.
Financial data (yr. ended 07/31/14): Assets, $2,335,777 (M); gifts received, $884,500; expenditures, $231,570; qualifying distributions, $212,250; giving activities include $210,500 for 15 grants (high: $80,000; low: $1,000).
Fields of interest: Education; Elementary and secondary education; Foundations; Protestantism; Human services.
Limitations: Applications not accepted. Giving primarily in MA, MD, NJ and NY. No grants to individuals.
Application information: Contributes only to pre-selected organizations.
Trustees: Elizabeth K. Compton; Eric P. Grubman.
EIN: 133936474

6148
Stanley and Kathleen Grumbacher Foundation Inc.
70 E. 77th St., Ste. 2C
New York City, NY   10021-1811

Established in 1951 in New York.
Donors: Edythe Roland Grodnick; Gary Churgin; Stanley Grumbacher†; Alex Silberstein†.
Foundation type: Independent foundation.

Financial data (yr. ended 04/30/15): Assets, $3,159,600 (M); gifts received, $98,678; expenditures, $171,669; qualifying distributions, $171,669; giving activities include $130,100 for 12 grants (high: $85,000; low: $150).
Purpose and activities: Giving primarily to Jewish agencies and temples, for the arts, and for women's health issues and cancer.
Fields of interest: Arts and culture; Education; Judaism.
Type of support: General support; Continuing support; Annual campaigns; Capital campaigns; Capital and infrastructure; Emergency funds; Program development; Seed money.
Limitations: Applications not accepted. Giving primarily in the metropolitan New York, NY, area. No grants to individuals; no loans or program-related investments.
Application information: Unsolicited requests for funds not accepted.
Officers: Gary Churgin, V.P.; Jill Roland Butler, Secy.; Amy Churgin, Pres. and C.E.O.
EIN: 136161277

6149
Grunberg Family Foundation
c/o Philip Hyland
928 Broadway, Ste. 200
New York City, NY 10010-8111

Donor: Fanny Grunberg.
Foundation type: Independent foundation.
Financial data (yr. ended 12/31/14): Assets, $3,786,266; gifts received, $0; expenditures, $185,750; qualifying distributions, $179,130 and $0 for set-asides.
Fields of interest: Arts and culture; Museums; Judaism.
Type of support: General support.
Limitations: Applications not accepted. Giving primarily in CT, Washington, DC and NY. No grants to individuals.
Application information: Contributes only to pre-selected organizations.
Trustees: Mark Altschul; Ariel Grunberg; Michael Grunberg.
EIN: 208096860

6150
The Carol Martin Gruodis Memorial Education Fund
c/o Marks, Paneth & Shron, LLP
685 3rd Ave.
New York City, NY 10017-6701

Established in 2001 in New York.
Donor: Victor G. Gruodis.
Foundation type: Independent foundation.
Financial data (yr. ended 12/31/13): Assets, $820,201 (M); gifts received, $1,768; expenditures, $183,328; qualifying distributions, $179,560; giving activities include $177,560 for 21 grants (high: $49,960; low: $700).
Fields of interest: Arts and culture; Education; Higher education.
International interests: Lithuania.
Limitations: Applications not accepted. Giving primarily in Vilnius, Lithuania.
Application information: Unsolicited requests for funds not accepted.

Officers: Victor G. Groudis, Pres.; Ausra Groudis, Secy.; Vidamantas Venckaunas, Treas.
EIN: 134197176

6151
The Guela Charitable Trust
1700 Broadway, Ste. 2000
New York City, NY 10019-2300

Established in 2005 in New York.
Donors: Estanne Abraham Fawer; Chai X Four Charitable Trust; Martin Fawer; Simona A. Ganz.
Foundation type: Independent foundation.
Financial data (yr. ended 12/31/13): Assets, $190,488 (M); gifts received, $498,400; expenditures, $362,990; qualifying distributions, $362,502; giving activities include $324,340 for 2 + grants.
Fields of interest: Nonprofits; Judaism; Human services.
Type of support: Regranting.
Limitations: Applications not accepted. Giving primarily in New York, NY. No grants to individuals.
Application information: Contributes only to pre-selected organizations.
Trustees: Estanne Abraham Fawer; Martin Fawer; Simona A. Ganz.
EIN: 206468959

6152
Edna and Monroe C. Gutman Foundation, Inc.
477 Madison Ave., 10th Fl.
New York City, NY 10022-5841

Established in 1947 in New York.
Donors: Edna C. Gutman†; Monroe C. Gutman†; Cyrus H. Nathan; Robert Nathan.
Foundation type: Independent foundation.
Financial data (yr. ended 06/30/13): Assets, $6,850,252 (M); expenditures, $287,525; qualifying distributions, $251,417; giving activities include $249,000 for 15 grants (high: $200,000; low: $1,000).
Purpose and activities: Giving primarily for hospitals, and higher and other education.
Fields of interest: Education; Elementary and secondary education; Higher education; Hospital care.
Limitations: Applications not accepted. Giving primarily in MA, NY, and PA. No grants to individuals.
Application information: Contributes only to pre-selected organizations.
Officers: Margaret S. Nathan, Pres. and Secy.; Robert Nathan, V.P.; Michael T. Incantalupo, Treas.
EIN: 136094013

6153
H. & H. Charitable Trust
1 Lincoln Plz., Ste. 41-P
New York City, NY 10023-7141

Donor: Harriett B. Kravitz.
Foundation type: Independent foundation.
Financial data (yr. ended 12/31/14): Assets, $1,847,028; expenditures, $126,772; qualifying distributions, $119,443.
Fields of interest: Arts and culture; Ballet; Higher education; Land resources; Nonprofits; Hospital care; Christianity.

Type of support: Regranting.
Limitations: Applications not accepted. Giving primarily in NY. No grants to individuals.
Application information: Unsolicited requests for funds not accepted.
Trustee: Barbara Kravitz.
EIN: 222924281

6154
The Richard and Mica Hadar Foundation
(formerly The Hadar Foundation)
400 E. 84th St.
New York City, NY 10028-5606 (212) 832-9797
Contact: Richard Hadar, Co-Chair.
Main URL: http://www.hadarfoundation.org

Established in 1993 in Florida.
Donors: Richard Hadar; The Hadar Charitable Lead Trust.
Foundation type: Operating foundation.
Financial data (yr. ended 12/31/12): Assets, $3,444,519 (M); expenditures, $353,946; qualifying distributions, $176,510; giving activities include $163,450 for 39 grants (high: $28,500; low: $500), and $13,060 for 6 grants to individuals (high: $7,500; low: $40).
Purpose and activities: Giving in support of young artists and scholars, by providing academic scholarships, mentoring, and career guidance.
Fields of interest: Arts and culture; Arts education; Undergraduate education; University education.
Type of support: General support; Student aid.
Limitations: Giving primarily in NY.
Application information: Application form required.
 Deadline(s): Jan. 15
Officers: Richard Hadar, Co-Chair.; Mica B. Hadar, Co-Chair.; Beth Rosenberg, Exec. Dir.
Director: Ann Feminella.
EIN: 133721350

6155
W.W. & Lucretia Hafer Scholarship Trust
1100 Wehrle Dr., 2nd Fl.
Buffalo, NY 14221-7748

Foundation type: Independent foundation.
Financial data (yr. ended 08/31/14): Assets, $6,595,355 (M); expenditures, $246,240; qualifying distributions, $164,161; giving activities include $164,161 for 13 grants (high: $26,000; low: $4,000).
Fields of interest: Education; Higher education.
Limitations: Applications not accepted. Giving primarily in PA.
Application information: Unsolicited requests for funds not accepted.
Trustee: M&T Trust Co.
EIN: 466303496

6156
Hahn Family Foundation
1807 Elmwood Ave., Ste. 287
Buffalo, NY 14207-2434 (716) 447-7828
Contact: Charles D. Hahn, Tr.

Established in 1965 in New York.
Donors: Charles Hahn†; Charles J. Hahn.
Foundation type: Independent foundation.

Financial data (yr. ended 12/31/13): Assets, $7,824,477 (M); gifts received, $58,000; expenditures, $352,438; qualifying distributions, $343,270; giving activities include $247,150 for 132 grants (high: $30,000; low: $100).

Purpose and activities: Emphasis on ecology, particularly in the areas of renewable energy sources, farmland, waste management, and organic farming and integrated pest management; support also for organizations addressing local problems of Buffalo and Erie County, NY.

Fields of interest: Arts and culture; Education; Environment; Natural resources; Renewable energy; Animal welfare; Nonprofits; Organic farming; Human services; Food aid.

Type of support: General support; Matching grants; Program development; Seed money; Regranting.

Limitations: Applications accepted. Giving primarily in Buffalo and Erie County, NY. No support for organizations eligible for membership in, but not belonging to, the United Way. No grants to individuals or for overhead expenses.

Publications: Application guidelines.

Application information: Recommendations by college or university department heads or other similarly situated individuals are encouraged. Application form required.

Initial approach: Letter
Copies of proposal: 1
Deadline(s): None

Trustees: Charles D. Hahn; Charles J. Hahn; Eric S. Hahn; Anne H. Hahn-Baker.

Number of staff: 1 part-time support.

EIN: 166128499

6157
The Stephen & Carla Hahn Foundation
(formerly The Stephen Hahn Foundation)
c/o Israeloff Trattner and Co.
450 7th Ave., Ste 2701
New York City, NY 10123-2701

Established in 1991 in Connecticut.

Donors: Stephen R. Hahn†; The Mater Trust.

Foundation type: Independent foundation.

Financial data (yr. ended 12/31/13): Assets, $3,879,530 (M); expenditures, $209,428; qualifying distributions, $161,365; giving activities include $161,365 for 16 grants (high: $35,000; low: $355).

Purpose and activities: Giving primarily for the arts.

Fields of interest: Performing arts; Performing arts education; Human services.

Limitations: Applications not accepted. Giving primarily in CA. No grants to individuals.

Application information: Contributes only to pre-selected organizations.

Trustee: Carla Brasseur Hahn.

EIN: 066356055

6158
The Hajim Family Foundation
c/o CBIZ MHM
1065 Ave. of Americas, Fl. 10
New York City, NY 10018-2506

Established in 1987 in New York.

Donor: Edmund A. Hajim.

Foundation type: Independent foundation.

Financial data (yr. ended 12/31/13): Assets, $2,490,620 (M); gifts received, $4,900;

expenditures, $370,304; qualifying distributions, $364,584; giving activities include $361,749 for 45 grants (high: $100,000; low: $100).

Purpose and activities: Giving to higher education, hospitals, health associations, and Jewish agencies; some funding also to community funds and the arts.

Fields of interest: Arts and culture; Performing arts; Art museums; Historic preservation; Education; Elementary and secondary education; Higher education; Business education; Environment; Hospital care; Community and economic development; Human services; Child welfare.

Limitations: Applications not accepted. Giving primarily in FL, MA and NY. No grants to individuals.

Application information: Unsolicited requests for funds not accepted.

Trustees: Barbara Hajim; Edmund A. Hajim.

EIN: 136893956

6159
The Hales Family Foundation, Inc.
66 Brookwood Dr.
Briarcliff Manor, NY 10510-2041

Established in 1994 in New York.

Donor: Thomas E. Hales.

Foundation type: Independent foundation.

Financial data (yr. ended 12/31/13): Assets, $7,064,888 (M); gifts received, $300,000; expenditures, $320,386; qualifying distributions, $284,415; giving activities include $281,650 for 13 grants (high: $100,000; low: $1,000).

Fields of interest: Education; Religion; Human services.

Limitations: Applications not accepted. Giving primarily in NY. No grants to individuals.

Application information: Unsolicited requests for funds not accepted.

Directors: Alice Hales; Terence Hales; Thomas E. Hales.

EIN: 133801701

6160
The Hallingby Family Foundation, Inc.
7 Gracie Sq., Ste. 10A
New York City, NY 10028-8001
Contact: Paul L. Hallingby

Established in 1998 in Connecticut.

Donor: Paul L. Hallingby.

Foundation type: Operating foundation.

Financial data (yr. ended 04/30/13): Assets, $1,462,732 (M); expenditures, $150,626; qualifying distributions, $149,388; giving activities include $148,300 for 47 grants (high: $50,000; low: $100).

Fields of interest: Higher education; Environment; Animal welfare; Hospital care; Genetic conditions and birth defects; Libraries; Community and economic development; Reproductive rights; Human services.

Type of support: General support; Capital campaigns.

Limitations: Applications not accepted. Giving primarily in MA and New York, NY. No grants to individuals.

Application information: Contributes only to pre-selected organizations.

Officers: Paul L. Hallingby, Pres.; Julia H. Hallingby, V.P.; Thomas P. Spellane, Secy.-Treas.

EIN: 061516271

6161
The Handler Family Foundation
c/o Berdon LLP
1 Jericho Plz.
Jericho, NY 11753

Established in 2001 in New York.

Donors: Martha Handler; Richard Handler.

Foundation type: Independent foundation.

Financial data (yr. ended 11/30/13): Assets, $1,050,211 (M); expenditures, $187,847; qualifying distributions, $176,950; giving activities include $176,950 for 23 grants (high: $53,350; low: $50).

Fields of interest: Education; Higher education; Hospital care; Child welfare.

Limitations: Applications not accepted. Giving primarily in NY. No grants to individuals.

Application information: Contributes only to pre-selected organizations.

Officers: Richard Handler, Pres.; Martha Handler, V.P.

EIN: 137314630

6162
Milton & Miriam Handler Foundation
225 Broadway, Ste. 1806
New York City, NY 10007-3751 (212) 964-5485
Contact: Albert Kalter, Secy.

Donor: Milton Handler†.

Foundation type: Independent foundation.

Financial data (yr. ended 12/31/13): Assets, $8,692,331 (M); expenditures, $517,021; qualifying distributions, $475,988; giving activities include $385,000 for 13 grants (high: $50,000; low: $5,000).

Purpose and activities: Giving primarily for higher education; funding also for health care.

Fields of interest: Education; Higher education; Law education; Health.

Limitations: Applications accepted. Giving primarily in NY. No grants to individuals.

Application information: Application form required.

Initial approach: Letter
Deadline(s): Oct. 31

Officers: Lawrence Newman, Esq., Pres.; Albert Kalter, Secy.

Director: Dahlia Kalter.

EIN: 136136957

6163
The Stephen P. Hanson Family Foundation, Inc.
2109 Broadway Ste. 1518
New York City, NY 10023-2151

Donor: Stephen P. Hanson.

Foundation type: Independent foundation.

Financial data (yr. ended 12/31/13): Assets, $5,690,697 (M); gifts received, $325,000; expenditures, $325,841; qualifying distributions, $307,136; giving activities include $307,136 for 36 grants (high: $63,110; low: $16).

Fields of interest: Education; Diseases and conditions; Catholicism.

Limitations: Applications not accepted. Giving primarily in New York, NY.
Application information: Contributes only to pre-selected organizations.
Officer: Stephen P. Hanson, Mgr.
Directors: Stacy L. Gilbert; Howard W. Muchnick.
EIN: 263899785

6164
The Hap Foundation
c/o The Ayco Company, LP
P.O. Box 860
Saratoga Springs, NY 12866-0860

Donor: Wooden Nickel Foundation.
Foundation type: Independent foundation.
Financial data (yr. ended 12/31/13): Assets, $10,742,460 (M); expenditures, $247,734; qualifying distributions, $212,500; giving activities include $212,500 for 7 grants (high: $100,000; low: $2,500).
Fields of interest: Education; Human rights; Human services.
Limitations: Applications not accepted. Giving primarily in NY.
Application information: Unsolicited requests for funds not accepted.
Trustees: Ana Pincus; Henry A. Pincus.
EIN: 271699379

6165
The Happy Elephant Foundation
c/o Caryn Seidman-Becker
66 E. 93rd St.
New York City, NY 10128

Established in 2005 in New York.
Donors: Caryn Seidman-Becker; Marc Becker.
Foundation type: Independent foundation.
Financial data (yr. ended 10/31/13): Assets, $1,786,420 (M); gifts received, $1,000,000; expenditures, $350,291; qualifying distributions, $349,065; giving activities include $347,600 for 29 grants (high: $75,000; low: $100).
Fields of interest: Early childhood education; Human services; Child welfare; Females.
Limitations: Applications not accepted. Giving primarily in New York, NY. No grants to individuals.
Application information: Contributes only to pre-selected organizations.
Directors: Marc Becker; Kenneth Cornick; Caryn Seidman-Becker.
EIN: 593788470

6166
The Jerry and Janet Harary Family Foundation
1904 E. 2nd St.
Brooklyn, NY 11223-2830

Established in 2004 in New York.
Donors: Michael Harary; Jerry Harary.
Foundation type: Independent foundation.
Financial data (yr. ended 12/31/13): Assets, $0 (M); gifts received, $253,000; expenditures, $255,468; qualifying distributions, $255,468; giving activities include $255,177 for 51 grants (high: $100,000; low: $90).
Fields of interest: Judaism.

Limitations: Applications not accepted. Giving primarily in NY, with emphasis on the metropolitan New York area.
Application information: Unsolicited requests for funds not accepted.
Officers and Directors: Jerry Harary, Pres. and Director; Janet Harary, V.P.; Michael Harary, Secy. and Director; Leon J. Harary, Treas. and Director.
EIN: 562444173

6167
The Harjen Charitable Foundation
115 Central Park W., Apt. 11E
New York City, NY 10023-4212
Contact: Alice Shuchman

Established in 2008 in New York.
Foundation type: Independent foundation.
Financial data (yr. ended 12/31/13): Assets, $5,156,912 (M); expenditures, $258,674; qualifying distributions, $243,255; giving activities include $210,000 for 14 grants (high: $27,000; low: $4,000).
Fields of interest: Performing arts; Education; Diseases and conditions; Judaism; Human services.
Limitations: Applications not accepted. Giving primarily in NY. No grants to individuals.
Application information: Contributes only to pre-selected organizations.
Directors: Nina Roth; Alice Shuchman; Daniel Shuchman.
EIN: 260276553

6168
Harmon Foundation Inc.
30 Jericho Exec. Plz., Ste. 200W
Jericho, NY 11753-1028

Established in 1988 in New York.
Donors: William E. Harmon Trust, Inc.; Harmon Trust Foundation.
Foundation type: Independent foundation.
Financial data (yr. ended 12/31/13): Assets, $561,193 (M); gifts received, $276,000; expenditures, $311,838; qualifying distributions, $304,903; giving activities include $267,500 for grants.
Purpose and activities: Giving primarily for education and health.
Fields of interest: Education; Higher education; Medical education; Health; Hospital care; Cancers; Human services; Child welfare.
Type of support: Research.
Limitations: Applications not accepted. Giving primarily in CT. No grants to individuals.
Application information: Contributes only to pre-selected organizations.
Board meeting date(s): Oct.
Officers: Gregory N. Smith, Chair.; Mary H. Persson, Pres.; Michael B. Hollyday, V.P.; James Hollyday, Jr., Secy.; A.C. Barnes McNevin III, Treas.
EIN: 135562236

6169
The Harmon Foundation
c/o Tanton Co. LLP, Janet L. Mulligan
37 W. 57th St., 5th Fl.
New York City, NY 10019-3411

Established in 1988 in Delaware.

Donor: James A. Harmon.
Foundation type: Independent foundation.
Financial data (yr. ended 08/31/13): Assets, $5,166,346 (M); expenditures, $264,510; qualifying distributions, $217,588; giving activities include $213,726 for 31 grants (high: $75,000; low: $25).
Fields of interest: Arts and culture; Theater; Education; Higher education; Nonprofits; International relations.
Type of support: Regranting.
Limitations: Applications not accepted. Giving primarily in New York, NY. No grants to individuals.
Application information: Contributes only to pre-selected organizations.
Officers: James Harmon, Pres.; Leonard Leiman, Secy.; Jane Harmon, Treas.
EIN: 061180560

6170
Mary and Kathleen Harriman Foundation
(formerly W. Averell and Pamela C. Harriman Foundation)
c/o Brown Brothers Harriman Trust Co., N.A.
140 Broadway, 11th Fl.
New York City, NY 10005-1108
Contact: Barbara O'Connell, Asst. Secy.

Established in 1969 in New York.
Donor: W. Averell Harriman†.
Foundation type: Independent foundation.
Financial data (yr. ended 12/31/13): Assets, $4,890,906 (M); expenditures, $279,254; qualifying distributions, $223,460; giving activities include $179,500 for 38 grants (high: $17,500; low: $500).
Purpose and activities: Support primarily for the study of international affairs.
Fields of interest: Education; Higher education; Domesticated animals; International relations.
Type of support: General support; Annual campaigns; Capital campaigns.
Limitations: Applications not accepted. Giving on a national basis, with some emphasis on the East Coast. No grants to individuals.
Application information: Contributes only to pre-selected organizations.
Board meeting date(s): May
Officers and Directors: Kathleen L. Ames, Pres. and Director; Robert C. Fisk, V.P. and Director; Kathleen L. Mortimer, Secy. and Director; Averell H. Mortimer, Treas. and Director; Anna Korniczky; Barbara O'Connell.
Number of staff: 2 full-time professional.
EIN: 510193921

6171
Matthew and Jennifer Harris Family Foundation
12 E. 49th St., 38th Fl.
New York City, NY 10017-8220

Donors: Matthew Harris; Jennifer Harris.
Foundation type: Independent foundation.
Financial data (yr. ended 12/31/14): Assets, $0 (M); gifts received, $225,025; expenditures, $225,025; qualifying distributions, $225,000.
Fields of interest: Domesticated animals.
Limitations: Applications not accepted. Giving primarily in Washington, DC.

Application information: Unsolicited requests for funds not accepted.
Trustees: Jennifer Harris; Matthew C. Harris.
EIN: 456661063

6172
Jonathan M. Harris Foundation, Inc.
c/o BCRS Associates, LLC
77 Wall St., 9th Fl.
New York City, NY   10005-4414

Established in 2007 in Florida.
Donors: Jonathan M. Harris; Jonathan M. Harris Revocable Trust; Maize and Blue Charitable Trust.
Foundation type: Independent foundation.
Financial data (yr. ended 03/31/13): Assets, $1,031,501 (M); gifts received, $151,875; expenditures, $192,795; qualifying distributions, $182,555; giving activities include $177,500 for 8 grants (high: $75,000; low: $2,500).
Fields of interest: Education; Foundations; Nonprofits; Hospital care; Childbirth; Human services.
Type of support: Regranting.
Limitations: Applications not accepted. Giving primarily in New York, NY; some funding also in CT. No grants to individuals.
Application information: Unsolicited requests for funds not accepted.
Officers and Directors: Jonathan M. Harris, Pres. and Treas. and Director; Nicki Harris, V.P. and Director; Jennifer Lynn Harris, Secy. and Director; James R. Taylor.
EIN: 208613426

6173
The Hart Charitable Trust
c/o Gurnee F. Hart
133 E. 64th St.
New York City, NY   10065

Established in 1998 in New York.
Donor: Gurnee F. Hart.
Foundation type: Independent foundation.
Financial data (yr. ended 12/31/13): Assets, $1,216,538 (M); gifts received, $1,168; expenditures, $241,451; qualifying distributions, $240,283; giving activities include $240,283 for 14 grants (high: $71,000; low: $833).
Fields of interest: Orchestral music; Undergraduate education.
Type of support: General support.
Limitations: Applications not accepted. Giving primarily in CA and NY. No grants to individuals.
Application information: Unsolicited requests for funds not accepted.
Trustees: Gurnee F. Hart; Marjorie Hart.
EIN: 137129721

6174
A. & Z. Hasenfeld Foundation, Inc.
580 5th Ave.
New York City, NY   10036-4704
Contact: Alexander Hasenfeld

Donors: Alexander Hasenfeld; Zissy Hasenfeld; Hasenfeld-Stein Inc.; Zissel Hasenfeld.
Foundation type: Independent foundation.
Financial data (yr. ended 03/31/14): Assets, $1,984,784 (M); gifts received, $2,210,200;

expenditures, $286,080; qualifying distributions, $285,982; giving activities include $285,982 for 86 grants (high: $50,000; low: $100).
Purpose and activities: Giving primarily to Jewish organizations.
Fields of interest: Education; Nonprofits; Judaism; Human services.
Type of support: Regranting.
Application information: Application form required.
  Initial approach: Proposal
  Deadline(s): None
Officer and Trustee: Zissy Hasenfeld, Treas. and Trustee.
EIN: 237017589

6175
The Jock Hatfield Memorial Fund
c/o RR Advisory
1500 Broadway, 28th Fl.
New York City, NY   10036-4052

Donor: Jay Hatfield.
Foundation type: Independent foundation.
Financial data (yr. ended 12/31/13): Assets, $1,401,026 (M); gifts received, $631,400; expenditures, $297,034; qualifying distributions, $280,000; giving activities include $280,000 for 13 grants (high: $50,000; low: $500).
Fields of interest: Education; Human services; Youth development.
Limitations: Applications not accepted. Giving primarily in NY. No grants to individuals.
Application information: Contributes only to pre-selected organizations.
Officers: Jay Hatfield, Pres.; Eileen Hatfield, Treas.
EIN: 770126226

6176
Hathaway Family Foundation
889 Tower Hill Rd.
Millbrook, NY   12545-5430

Established in 2000 in New York.
Donor: David Hathaway.
Foundation type: Independent foundation.
Financial data (yr. ended 12/31/13): Assets, $7,253,603 (M); expenditures, $339,113; qualifying distributions, $321,500; giving activities include $321,500 for 66 grants (high: $40,000; low: $500).
Fields of interest: Elementary education; University education; Land resources.
Limitations: Applications not accepted. Giving primarily in CT, MD and NY. No grants to individuals.
Application information: Unsolicited requests for funds not accepted.
Officer: David Hathaway, Pres.
EIN: 223696161

6177
The Robert V. Hauff & John F. Dreeland Foundation
c/o Paul Wood
44 Wall St., Rm. 19th
New York City, NY   10005-2407

Established in 2001 in New York.
Donor: Robert V. Hauff†.
Foundation type: Independent foundation.

Financial data (yr. ended 12/31/13): Assets, $1,385,622 (M); expenditures, $199,065; qualifying distributions, $180,000; giving activities include $180,000 for 6 grants (high: $50,000; low: $5,000).
Fields of interest: Diseases and conditions; HIV/AIDS; Agriculture; Human services.
Limitations: Applications not accepted. Giving primarily in CO and the New York, NY metropolitan area. No grants to individuals.
Application information: Unsolicited requests for funds not accepted.
Trustees: Robert E. Burke; Milton Gordon; Paul G. Wood.
EIN: 134168109

6178
The Haven Foundation
c/o Marks Paneth & Shron
685 3rd Ave., 5th Fl.
New York City, NY   10017-8401   (212) 503-8800
Contact: Robert Lyons
Main URL: http://www.thehavenfdn.org

Established in 2006 in New York.
Donor: Stephen King.
Foundation type: Independent foundation.
Financial data (yr. ended 12/31/12): Assets, $12,983,347 (M); gifts received, $8,261,814; expenditures, $322,939; qualifying distributions, $310,999; giving activities include $280,793 for 33 grants to individuals (high: $25,000; low: $500).
Purpose and activities: The mission of the foundation is to strengthen and sustain the careers of freelance professional writers, artists and others connected with the entertainment industry across the U.S. The foundation accomplishes its mission through direct financial assistance to qualified persons, including emergency relief assistance and financial support. The foundation provides grants, renewable for up to five years, to freelance artists and writers experiencing career-threatening illness, accidents, natural disasters, or other emergency or personal catastrophes. Eligible applicants must be freelance-qualified persons (defined to include all persons connected with the artistic or entertainment industries including, but not limited to authors, actors, singers, dancers, directors, producers, choreographers, musicians, artists, screenwriters, technical support professionals, or other performers working in the book, movie, music, theater, dance, and television industries) who have derived at least one-third of his/her income over the past three years from his/her personal production, performance, or other work in their industry.
Fields of interest: Artist's services; Human services; Free goods distribution; People with disabilities.
Type of support: Grants to individuals.
Limitations: Applications accepted. Giving on a national basis. No support for commercial artists, bloggers, crafters, hobbyists, medical writers, or any artist whose work did not constitute the primary source of their income for several years. No grants for scholarships or fellowships, or for study, schooling, travel, or writing.
Publications: Application guidelines.
Application information: Application forms cannot be submitted through foundation web site or via e-mail. If applicants need their submitted material returned, they should include a self-addressed, stamped envelope. Application form required.

Initial approach: Download application form from foundation web site then submit via USPS, UPS, FedEx, or a similar private mail delivery service

Deadline(s): See foundation web site for current deadline

Officers and Directors: Arthur B. Greene, Pres. and Director; Susan Greene, Secy.-Treas. and Director; Frederic M. Sanders, Secy.; Marsha Defilippo; Stephen E. King; John McElroy; David Rapkin; Chuck Verrill.

EIN: 204356938

6179
R. & H. Healy Foundation
799 Park Ave., Ste. 17-A
New York City, NY 10021-3543

Established in 2006 in New York.
Donor: Daniel M. Healy.
Foundation type: Independent foundation.
Financial data (yr. ended 12/31/13): Assets, $0 (M); expenditures, $170,305; qualifying distributions, $142,305; giving activities include $142,305 for 21 grants (high: $52,500; low: $500).
Fields of interest: Arts and culture; Education; Philanthropy.
Application information:
Initial approach: Contact foundation
Deadline(s): None
Officers: Daniel M. Healy, Pres.; Patricia Hemm, V.P.; Raymond Kelly, Treas.
EIN: 205477954

6180
The Heffer Family Foundation, Inc.
c/o Lenat Co.
315 Westchester Ave.
Port Chester, NY 10573-3807

Established in 1997 in New York.
Donor: John Heffer.
Foundation type: Independent foundation.
Financial data (yr. ended 12/31/13): Assets, $1,547,791 (M); gifts received, $88,569; expenditures, $258,856; qualifying distributions, $242,412; giving activities include $242,412 for 36 grants (high: $138,000; low: $100).
Fields of interest: Higher education; Hospital care; Human services.
Limitations: Applications not accepted. Giving primarily in NY. No grants to individuals.
Application information: Contributes only to pre-selected organizations.
Trustees: Alison Heffer; Barbara Heffer; Douglas Heffer; John Heffer.
EIN: 133989464

6181
Hefta Foundation, Inc.
c/o Cromwell Leather
147 Palmer Ave.
Mamaroneck, NY 10543-3632

Established in 1994 in New York.
Donors: Harry M. Fleisch; Eleanor C. Fleisch.
Foundation type: Independent foundation.
Financial data (yr. ended 10/31/13): Assets, $1,645,480 (M); expenditures, $188,774; qualifying distributions, $180,997; giving activities

include $179,122 for 41 grants (high: $25,000; low: $250).
Purpose and activities: Giving primarily for Jewish organizations.
Fields of interest: Undergraduate education; Nonprofits; Diseases and conditions; Judaism; Human services.
Type of support: Regranting.
Limitations: Applications not accepted. Giving primarily in New York, NY. No grants to individuals.
Application information: Contributes only to pre-selected organizations.
Officers: Harry M. Fleisch, Pres.; Andrew P. Fleisch, V.P.; Thomas Fleisch, Secy.; Eleanor C. Fleisch, Treas.
EIN: 133796996

6182
Hegarty Family Foundation
P.O. Box 837
Southold, NY 11971-0837
Application address: c/o Michael Hegarty, Pres., 177 Old Briar, Briarcliff Mano, NY 10510, tel.: (914) 762-5147

Established in 1998 in New York.
Donors: Anita Lise-Ingrid Hegarty; Michael Hegarty.
Foundation type: Independent foundation.
Financial data (yr. ended 06/30/14): Assets, $2,616,896 (M); expenditures, $349,673; qualifying distributions, $275,000; giving activities include $275,000 for 6 grants (high: $100,000; low: $10,000).
Purpose and activities: Giving primarily for higher education.
Fields of interest: Arts and culture; Education; Human services.
Limitations: Applications accepted. Giving primarily in NY and VA. No grants to individuals.
Application information: Application form required.
Initial approach: Letter
Deadline(s): None
Officers: Michael Hegarty, Pres.; Anita Hegarty, Secy.
EIN: 061532648

6183
C.J. Heilig Foundation Inc.
c/o Dr. William Lecates
87 Chestnut St.
Cooperstown, NY 13326-1418

Established in 1997 in Connecticut.
Donor: Clifford J. Heilig.
Foundation type: Independent foundation.
Financial data (yr. ended 03/31/13): Assets, $11,018,121 (M); gifts received, $1,852,619; expenditures, $411,968; qualifying distributions, $384,699; giving activities include $384,699 for grants.
Fields of interest: Historic preservation; Education; Land resources; Health; Public affairs.
Type of support: Research.
Limitations: Applications not accepted. No grants to individuals.
Application information: Contributes only to pre-selected organizations.
Officer: William Lecates, Pres.
Directors: Dennis P. Clark; Deborah Lecates.
EIN: 061483018

6184
William and Diane Hein Foundation
(formerly William S. Hein Foundation)
6500 Main St., Ste. 5
Williamsville, NY 14221-5854
Application address: c/o William S. Hein, 2350 N. Forest R, Getzville, NY 14068, tel.:(716) 882-2600

Established in 1995 in New York.
Donors: William S. Hein; 2012 Hein Foundation Trust.
Foundation type: Independent foundation.
Financial data (yr. ended 12/31/13): Assets, $8,005,756 (M); gifts received, $579,000; expenditures, $438,777; qualifying distributions, $210,597; giving activities include $200,000 for 40 grants (high: $40,000; low: $1,000).
Fields of interest: Secondary education; Higher education; Christianity; Human services.
Limitations: Applications accepted. Giving primarily in NY. No grants to individuals.
Application information: Application form required.
Initial approach: Letter
Deadline(s): Oct. 15
Directors: Diane S. Hein; William S. Hein; Jamey Moran; William C. Moran.
EIN: 161484562

6185
Solomon & Clara Heisler Family Foundation
1661 53rd St.
Brooklyn, NY 11204-1421

Established in 1992 in New York.
Donors: Solomon Heisler; Clara Heisler.
Foundation type: Independent foundation.
Financial data (yr. ended 12/31/13): Assets, $9,406,474 (M); gifts received, $600,000; expenditures, $469,023; qualifying distributions, $375,611; giving activities include $373,226 for 37 grants (high: $40,000; low: $20).
Purpose and activities: Giving primarily to Jewish agencies, temples, and schools.
Fields of interest: Education; Graduate and professional education; Judaism; Theology; Human services.
Limitations: Applications not accepted. Giving primarily in Brooklyn, NY.
Application information: Contributes only to pre-selected organizations.
Officers: Solomon Heisler, Pres.; Clara Heisler, V.P.; Rosemarie Weingarten, Secy.; Anna Schon, Treas.
EIN: 113133210

6186
Heller Family Foundation
1437 59th St.
Brooklyn, NY 11219-5017

Established in 2004 in New York.
Donor: Leibel Rubin.
Foundation type: Independent foundation.
Financial data (yr. ended 12/31/12): Assets, $176,378 (M); gifts received, $130,000; expenditures, $196,632; qualifying distributions, $190,899; giving activities include $190,899 for grants.
Fields of interest: Judaism.
Limitations: Applications not accepted. Giving primarily in Brooklyn, NY. No grants to individuals.

Application information: Contributes only to pre-selected organizations.
Trustees: Moishe Heller; Sarah Heller.
EIN: 202055940

6187
The Hermine and David Heller Foundation
(formerly The David B. Heller Foundation)
Bowling Green Sta.
P.O. Box 73
New York City, NY   10274-0073

Donor: David B. Heller.
Foundation type: Independent foundation.
Financial data (yr. ended 02/28/13): Assets, $19,369,964 (M); expenditures, $339,079; qualifying distributions, $225,500; giving activities include $225,500 for 5 grants (high: $100,000; low: $500).
Purpose and activities: Giving primarily for higher education, human services, and community development.
Fields of interest: Arts and culture; Higher education; Foundations; Diseases and conditions; Community and economic development; Human services.
Limitations: Applications not accepted. Giving primarily in New York. No grants to individuals.
Application information: Contributes only to pre-selected organizations.
Trustees: David B. Heller; Hermine Riegerl Heller; Robert M. Heller.
EIN: 133936476

6188
Hemitt Foundation Inc.
1219 56th St.
Brooklyn, NY   11219

Donor: Hershey Mittleman.
Foundation type: Independent foundation.
Financial data (yr. ended 12/31/14): Assets, $9,983,252 (M); gifts received, $304,000; expenditures, $322,000; giving activities include $322,000 for 5 grants (high: $225,500; low: $1,500).
Fields of interest: Education; Religion; Human services.
Limitations: Applications not accepted. Giving primarily in Brooklyn, NY.
Application information: Unsolicited requests for funds not accepted.
Directors: Esther Mittleman; Hershey Mittleman; Joel Mittleman.
EIN: 263907114

6189
Elizabeth Wakeman Henderson Charitable
Foundation
c/o Fiduciary Trust Co. International
600 5th Ave.
New York City, NY   10020-2302

Established in 1997 in Ohio.
Donors: William H. Eshbaugh; E.W. Henderson†.
Foundation type: Independent foundation.
Financial data (yr. ended 12/31/14): Assets, $3,103,532; expenditures, $230,464; qualifying distributions, $210,525.

Purpose and activities: Giving primarily for the environment and wildlife.
Fields of interest: Elementary and secondary education; Higher education; Natural resources; Biodiversity; Wildlife biodiversity; Aquatic wildlife protection; Environmental education; Nonprofits.
Type of support: Regranting.
Limitations: Applications not accepted.
Application information: Unsolicited requests for funds not accepted.
Officers: W. Hardy Eshbaugh, Pres.; David C. Eshbaugh, Secy.
Trustees: E. Wendy Brown; Alan Van Coller; Ian Van Coller; Margaret C. Van Coller.
EIN: 656234202

6190
The Henkind Foundation
2 Westchester Park Dr.
White Plains, NY   10604   (914) 694-1533
Contact: Lewis Henkind, Pres.

Donor: Sol Henkind†.
Foundation type: Independent foundation.
Financial data (yr. ended 12/31/13): Assets, $2,769,590 (M); expenditures, $157,857; qualifying distributions, $155,974; giving activities include $148,474 for 8 grants (high: $89,474; low: $1,500).
Fields of interest: Domesticated animals; Health; Human services.
Limitations: Applications accepted. Giving primarily in New York, NY.
Application information: Application form required.
    Initial approach: Letter
    Deadline(s): None
Officer: Lewis Henkind, Pres.
Trustee: Elie Henkind-Katz.
EIN: 136165710

6191
Hennessy Foundation
c/o GDS Financial
295 Madison Ave.
New York City, NY   10017   (212) 599-8160
Contact: John F. Hennessy III, Pres.

Established in 1953 in New York.
Donor: Hensey Properties, Inc.
Foundation type: Independent foundation.
Financial data (yr. ended 12/31/13): Assets, $3,042,105 (M); expenditures, $174,186; qualifying distributions, $174,186; giving activities include $162,500 for 13 grants (high: $40,000; low: $500).
Fields of interest: Education; Graduate and professional education; Theology; Human services; Child welfare.
Type of support: Program development; Program-related investments; Seed money; Scholarships.
Limitations: Applications accepted. Giving primarily in NY.
Application information: Application form required.
    Initial approach: Letter
    Copies of proposal: 1
    Deadline(s): None
    Board meeting date(s): Quarterly
    Final notification: 3 months
Officers: John F. Hennessy, Pres.; David B. Hennessy, V.P.; Kathleen Hennessy, V.P.

Number of staff: 1 part-time support.
EIN: 136153737

6192
The Henshel Foundation
c/o Joy A. Henshel
24 Murray Hill Rd.
Scarsdale, NY   10583-2828

Established in 1986 in New York.
Donors: Emily B. Henshel†; Harry B. Henshel†; Joy A. Henshel; Dayle Henshel; Patti Henshel.
Foundation type: Independent foundation.
Financial data (yr. ended 05/31/13): Assets, $4,975,812 (M); expenditures, $286,172; qualifying distributions, $244,108; giving activities include $242,847 for 141 grants (high: $50,000; low: $25).
Purpose and activities: Giving primarily for Jewish organizations, health, education, human services, and the arts.
Fields of interest: Arts and culture; Theater; Orchestral music; Museums; Higher education; Nonprofits; Hospital care; Diseases and conditions; Judaism; Human services; Senior services; Children and youth; Adolescents; Females; Female children and youth; American Indians; Low-income and poor people; People with physical disabilities.
Type of support: Student aid; Scholarships; Research; Professorships; Emergency funds; Continuing support; Capital and infrastructure; Research and evaluation; Regranting.
Limitations: Applications not accepted. Giving primarily in NY.
Application information: Contributes only to pre-selected organizations.
    Board meeting date(s): Nov. and Apr.
Officers: Joy A. Henshel, Pres.; Patti J. Henshel, V.P.; Dayle Henshel, Secy.
Number of staff: None.
EIN: 136094082

6193
The Jane Henson Foundation
c/o Prager Metis CPAS LLC
675 3rd Ave., 3rd Fl.
New York City, NY   10017-5707

Established in 2000 in Connecticut.
Donors: Jane Henson; Cheryl Henson; Brian Henson; Heather Henson; Lisa Henson; John P. Henson.
Foundation type: Independent foundation.
Financial data (yr. ended 12/31/13): Assets, $6,493,919 (M); expenditures, $320,376; qualifying distributions, $273,126; giving activities include $270,000 for 7 grants (high: $100,000; low: $10,000).
Fields of interest: Arts and culture; Education; Human services.
Limitations: Applications not accepted. Giving primarily in CT, MD, and NY. No grants to individuals.
Application information: Contributes only to pre-selected organizations.
Officer: Heather Henson, Pres.
EIN: 061573700

6194

The Jim Henson Foundation
(formerly The Henson Foundation)
37-18 Northern Blvd., Ste. 400
Long Island City, NY   11101-1636   (212)
439-7504
E-mail: info@hensonfoundation.org; Main
URL: http://www.hensonfoundation.org
Grants List: http://www.hensonfoundation.org/
index.php/grant-awards/2010s/2012
Grants List: http://www.hensonfoundation.org/
index.php/grant-awards/2010s/2014-grants
Grants List: http://www.hensonfoundation.org/
index.php/grant-awards/2010s/2013-grants
Grants List: http://www.hensonfoundation.org/
index.php/grant-awards/2010s/2015
Grants List: http://www.hensonfoundation.org/
index.php/grant-awards/2010s/2011

Established in 1982 in New York.
Donors: James Maury "Jim" Henson†; Jane Henson
Foundation; Cheryl Henson; Jane Henson; Heather
Henson.
Foundation type: Independent foundation.
Financial data (yr. ended 12/31/13): Assets,
$3,447,486 (M); gifts received, $541,043;
expenditures, $324,378; qualifying distributions,
$313,514; giving activities include $197,000 for 43
grants (high: $20,000; low: $2,000).
Purpose and activities: The mission of the
foundation is to develop and encourage the creative
art of puppetry in the United States. Emphasis is on
contemporary puppet theater for adults, with some
focus on new works suitable for family audiences.
Grants are awarded for the development of
innovative puppet theater by American artists, for
American audiences.
Fields of interest: Performing arts.
Type of support: General support; Grants to
individuals.
Limitations: Applications accepted. Giving on a
national basis. No grants for publications, parades,
exhibitions, film or television projects.
Publications: Application guidelines; Grants list.
Application information: Grants only available to
American artists. Guidelines and application form
are available on foundation web site. Grant
awardees will not be allowed to receive new grants
the following year. Full proposals will only be
accepted by invitation. Application form required.
   Initial approach: 1-page letter of intent
   Copies of proposal: 1
   Deadline(s): See foundation web site for current
      deadlines
   Board meeting date(s): June and Nov.
   Final notification: No later than Dec. 7
Officers and Directors: Cheryl Henson, Pres. and
Director; Richard Termine, V.P.; Pam Arciero, Secy.;
Louis Borodinsky, Treas.; Leslee Asch; John Farrell;
Martin Robinson; Hanne Tierney.
Number of staff: 1 part-time support.
EIN: 133133702

6195

Herbst Family Foundation Inc.
301 Flurry Ln.
West Babylon, NY   11704-8044

Foundation type: Independent foundation.
Financial data (yr. ended 12/31/13): Assets, $0
(M); expenditures, $210,942; qualifying
distributions, $204,859; giving activities include
$201,000 for 6 grants (high: $75,000; low: $200).

Fields of interest: Nonprofits.
Type of support: General support; Regranting.
Limitations: Applications not accepted. Giving
primarily in NY. No grants to individuals.
Application information: Contributes only to
pre-selected organizations.
Trustee: Janice Herbst.
EIN: 113405415

6196

The Herringer Family Foundation
c/o The Ayco Co.
P.O. Box 15014
Albany, NY   12212-5014

Established in 1999 in California.
Donors: Maryellen C. Herringer; Frank C. Herringer.
Foundation type: Independent foundation.
Financial data (yr. ended 12/31/13): Assets,
$999,549 (M); expenditures, $249,778; qualifying
distributions, $232,500; giving activities include
$232,500 for 7 grants (high: $100,000; low:
$2,500).
Purpose and activities: Giving primarily for higher
education; support also for health organizations.
Fields of interest: Education; Higher education;
Health; Diseases and conditions.
Limitations: Applications not accepted. Giving
primarily in CA and NH. No grants to individuals.
Application information: Contributes only to
pre-selected organizations.
Officers: Maryellen C. Herringer, Pres.; Frank C.
Herringer, Secy. and C.F.O.
EIN: 943349884

6197

Arthur N. Hershaft Foundation
c/o Levene, Gouldin & Thompson, LLP
450 Plaza Dr.
Vestal, NY   13850-3657

Established in 1988 in New York.
Donors: Arthur N. Hershaft; Carol H. Hershaft†.
Foundation type: Independent foundation.
Financial data (yr. ended 12/31/14): Assets,
$2,664,750 (M); expenditures, $367,547;
qualifying distributions, $363,755; giving activities
include $339,874 for 64 grants (high: $100,000;
low: $80).
Purpose and activities: Giving primarily for human
services and Jewish organizations.
Fields of interest: Nonprofits; Diseases and
conditions; Judaism; Human services.
Type of support: Regranting.
Limitations: Applications not accepted. Giving
primarily in CT and NY. No grants to individuals.
Application information: Contributes only to
pre-selected organizations.
Trustees: Arthur N. Hershaft; Janet Hershaft;
Michael H. Zuckerman, Esq.
EIN: 226462965

6198

Hershman Family Foundation Inc.
43 Willow Rd.
Woodsburgh, NY   11598-2228   (516) 869-5400
Contact: Ronnie A. Hershman, Pres.; Hannah
Hershman, V.P.

Established in 1993 in New York.

Donors: Ronnie A. Hershman; Hannah Hershman.
Foundation type: Independent foundation.
Financial data (yr. ended 08/31/13): Assets,
$277,924 (M); gifts received, $393,000;
expenditures, $425,550; qualifying distributions,
$420,828; giving activities include $420,828 for 38
grants (high: $160,000; low: $200).
Purpose and activities: Giving primarily for Jewish
organizations.
Fields of interest: Nonprofits; Judaism.
Type of support: Regranting.
Limitations: Applications accepted. Giving primarily
in NY. No grants to individuals.
Application information: Application form required.
   Initial approach: Letter
   Deadline(s): None
Officers: Ronnie A. Hershman, Pres.; Hannah
Hershman, V.P.
EIN: 113178650

6199

**Gabriel and Sara Bildirici Hesed
Foundation**
12 E. 37th St.
New York City, NY   10016-2823

Donors: Line N Bath Creation; David Bildirichi;
Concepts in Time, LLC; E 14 Realty.
Foundation type: Independent foundation.
Financial data (yr. ended 12/31/14): Assets,
$96,209 (M); gifts received, $288,418;
expenditures, $312,951; qualifying distributions,
$308,439; giving activities include $308,439 for
148 grants (high: $15,000; low: $18).
Fields of interest: Judaism.
Limitations: Applications not accepted. Giving
primarily in NY.
Application information: Unsolicited requests for
funds not accepted.
Officers: Moris Antebi, Pres.; Albert Antebi, Secy.;
Sam Massry, Treas.
EIN: 134149144

6200

The Carl & Marsha Hewitt Foundation, Inc.
c/o JAD Consulting, LLC, Joseph De Maio Su
61 Broadway
New York City, NY   10006

Established in 1994 in New York.
Donors: Carl N. Hewitt; Education For Youth Society.
Foundation type: Independent foundation.
Financial data (yr. ended 10/31/13): Assets,
$1,571,014 (M); expenditures, $202,733;
qualifying distributions, $186,635; giving activities
include $181,450 for 52 grants (high: $25,000;
low: $50).
Purpose and activities: Giving primarily for the arts,
education, and community services.
Fields of interest: Arts and culture; Ballet;
Environment; Philanthropy.
Limitations: Applications not accepted. Giving
primarily in the greater metropolitan New York, NY
area. No grants to individuals.
Application information: Unsolicited requests for
funds not accepted.
Officers: Carl H. Hewitt, Pres. and Treas.; Marsha A.
Hewitt, V.P. and Secy.
EIN: 133798937

6201
Annette Heyman Foundation, Inc.
c/o 40 North Svcs. LLC
9 W. 57th St., 30th Fl.
New York City, NY   10019-2701

Donors: Annette Heyman; Samuel J. Heyman;
Annette Heyman Family LLC; Ronnie F. Heyman;
Jennifer H. Millstone; Larry S. Heyman; Eleanor H.
Propp; Elizabeth H. Winter.
Foundation type: Independent foundation.
Financial data (yr. ended 09/30/13): Assets,
$2,624,970 (M); gifts received, $575,000;
expenditures, $251,712; qualifying distributions,
$216,750; giving activities include $181,737 for 29
grants (high: $20,000; low: $250).
Purpose and activities: Giving primarily for the arts,
higher education, hospitals and health
organizations, social services, and Jewish
organizations, including a Jewish museum.
Fields of interest: Arts and culture; Performing arts;
Ethnic museums; Education; Higher education; Law
education; Nonprofits; Hospital care; Diseases and
conditions; Judaism; Human services.
Type of support: Annual campaigns; Capital
campaigns; Endowments; Professorships;
Research; Regranting.
Limitations: Applications not accepted. Giving
primarily in CT and NY, some giving also in FL and
MA. No grants to individuals.
Application information: Contributes only to
pre-selected organizations.
Officers and Directors: Ronnie F. Heyman, Pres. and
Director; Lazarus S. Heyman, V.P. and Secy. and
Director; Donald Spiegelman, Treas.; Annette
Heyman.
EIN: 066035519

6202
The DuBose and Dorothy Heyward
Memorial Fund
c/o BNY Mellon Wealth Mgmt.
1001 Franklin Ave.
Garden City, NY   11530-2901

Established in 1985 in New York.
Donor: Jenifer Heyward†.
Foundation type: Independent foundation.
Financial data (yr. ended 12/31/14): Assets,
$14,471,970 (M); expenditures, $714,269;
qualifying distributions, $507,218; giving activities
include $384,777 for 40 grants (high: $70,000;
low: $2,000).
Purpose and activities: Giving primarily for theater
and music programs.
Fields of interest: Performing arts; Theater; Music.
Type of support: General support; Grants to
individuals; Research.
Limitations: Applications not accepted. Giving
primarily in New York, NY. No grants to individuals.
Application information: Unsolicited requests for
funds not accepted.
Trustees: Albert J. Cardinali, Esq.; BNY Mellon, N.A.
EIN: 136840999

6203
HF Foundation
1936 54th St.
Brooklyn, NY   11204-1745   (347) 770-9634
Contact: Jacob Haas, Tr.

Donor: 20/20 Inspections, Inc.
Foundation type: Independent foundation.
Financial data (yr. ended 06/30/13): Assets,
$4,076 (M); gifts received, $305,101;
expenditures, $301,025; qualifying distributions,
$301,025; giving activities include $301,025 for 41
grants (high: $100,000; low: $100).
Fields of interest: Graduate and professional
education; Judaism; Theology.
Limitations: Applications accepted. Giving primarily
in Brooklyn, NY.
Application information:
  Initial approach: Proposal
  Deadline(s): None
Trustees: Jacob Haas; Raizy Haas.
EIN: 461621902

6204
Hickrill Foundation, Inc.
c/o Norman Foundation Inc.
147 E. 48th St.
New York City, NY   10017-1223
Contact: Denie S. Weil, V.P. and Secy.

Established in 1946 in New York.
Donors: The Norman Foundation; Frank A. Weil;
Samuel P. Harrington; William S. Weil; Debbie Weil
Harrington; Denie S. Weil; Amanda E. Weil;
Sandison E. Weil; John Timothy W. Harrington; Eliza
H. Myers; Samuel P. Harrington; Deborah W.
Harrington.
Foundation type: Independent foundation.
Financial data (yr. ended 12/31/13): Assets,
$7,087,948 (M); gifts received, $202,149;
expenditures, $516,183; qualifying distributions,
$445,771; giving activities include $438,747 for
128 grants (high: $300,000; low: $100).
Purpose and activities: The foundation primarily
supports a selected few community organizations in
the communities of the members of the foundation,
and a very few special projects of particular interest
to members of the foundation.
Fields of interest: Community and economic
development.
Limitations: Applications accepted. Giving on a
national basis. No grants to individuals.
Application information: Application form required.
  Initial approach: Letter
  Deadline(s): None
Officers: Frank A. Weil, Pres.; Denie S. Weil, V.P. and
Secy.
EIN: 136002949

6205
The Grace Hidary Foundation Inc.
65 W. 36th St., Ste. 1200
New York City, NY   10018-7902
Contact: Jack A. Hidary

Established in 1994 in New York.
Donors: Abraham J. Hidary, Jr.; Jack A. Hidary;
Morris Hidary; M. Hidary & Co., Inc.; Steven J.
Hidary; Abraham M. Hidary; Abraham J. Hidary, Sr.;
Eddie Hidary; Fred M. Hidary.
Foundation type: Independent foundation.
Financial data (yr. ended 12/31/14): Assets,
$166,763 (M); gifts received, $363,540;
expenditures, $366,401; qualifying distributions,
$365,635; giving activities include $364,835 for
124 grants (high: $114,453; low: $50).

Fields of interest: Elementary and secondary
education; Nonprofits; Judaism.
Type of support: Regranting.
Limitations: Applications not accepted. Giving
primarily in NY. No grants to individuals.
Application information: Contributes only to
pre-selected organizations.
Officers: Abraham J. Hidary, Pres.; Jack A. Hidary,
V.P.; Morris Hidary, Secy.-Treas.
EIN: 133785660

6206
High Five Foundation
c/o Gerald Kaminsky
605 3rd Ave., 43rd Fl.
New York City, NY   10158

Established in 1996 in New York.
Donor: Gerald P. Kaminsky.
Foundation type: Independent foundation.
Financial data (yr. ended 10/31/13): Assets,
$6,487,306 (M); expenditures, $323,490;
qualifying distributions, $311,021; giving activities
include $308,181 for 136 grants (high: $25,000;
low: $50).
Purpose and activities: Giving primarily for Jewish
organizations, health and medical services, and
higher education.
Fields of interest: Arts and culture; Museums;
Higher education; Health; Hospice care; Judaism.
Type of support: General support; Annual
campaigns; Capital campaigns; Capital and
infrastructure; Information and Referral;
Endowments; Emergency funds; Curriculum
development; Fellowships; Internships;
Scholarships.
Limitations: Applications not accepted. No grants to
individuals.
Publications: Annual report.
Application information: Contributes only to
pre-selected organizations.
Officers: Gerald P. Kaminsky, Pres.; Gary J.
Kaminsky, V.P. and Treas.; Jaclyn Kaminsky, Secy.
EIN: 113358107

6207
Robert Hiler Family Foundation
c/o Morgan Stanley Private Bank, N.A.
1 New York Plz., 7th Fl.
New York City, NY   10004

Established in 1984 in Indiana.
Donors: Charles D. Hiler & Son, Inc.; Accurate
Castings; Kingsbury Castings; Robert J. Hiler†;
Margaret F. Hiler.
Foundation type: Independent foundation.
Financial data (yr. ended 12/31/13): Assets,
$4,682,000 (M); expenditures, $226,211;
qualifying distributions, $198,615; giving activities
include $189,000 for 21 grants (high: $25,000;
low: $1,000).
Purpose and activities: Giving for religion, the arts,
and relief and community services.
Fields of interest: Performing arts; Orchestral
music; Undergraduate education; Foundations;
Hospice care; Religion; Protestantism; European
football; Human services.
Limitations: Applications not accepted. Giving
primarily in IN. No grants to individuals.

Application information: Contributes only to pre-selected organizations.
EIN: 316265093

6208
The Hilliard Foundation
100 W. 4th St.
Elmira, NY 14901-2190
Contact: Jan van den Blink, Pres. and Tr.

Donor: The Hilliard Corp.
Foundation type: Company-sponsored foundation.
Financial data (yr. ended 04/30/14): Assets, $1,006,360 (M); gifts received, $163,050; expenditures, $166,945; qualifying distributions, $163,248; giving activities include $163,050 for 22 grants (high: $20,000; low: $1,000).
Purpose and activities: The foundation supports history museums and organizations involved with secondary and higher education, health, and community economic development.
Fields of interest: Health; Community and economic development; Youth development.
Type of support: Capital campaigns.
Limitations: Applications accepted. Giving primarily in Elmira, NY. No grants to individuals.
Application information: Application form required.
   Initial approach: Letter
   Deadline(s): None
Officers and Trustees: Jan Van den Blink, Pres. and Trustee; Mary Welles Mooers Smith, V.P. and Trustee; John Alexander, Secy. and Trustee; Gordon Webster, Treas. and Trustee; George L. Howell; Gerald F. Schichtel; Paul H. Schweizer; Allen C. Smith; Richard W. Swan; Nelson Mooers van den Blink; Paul Webb.
EIN: 161176159

6209
The John S. Hilson Family Fund
(formerly Sonhil Fund, Inc.)
c/o Tanton and Co., LLP, Janet Mulligan
37 W. 57th St., 5th Fl.
New York City, NY 10019-3411

Established in 1963 in New York.
Donor: John S. Hilson†.
Foundation type: Independent foundation.
Financial data (yr. ended 06/30/13): Assets, $5,817,834 (M); expenditures, $284,591; qualifying distributions, $228,502; giving activities include $224,690 for 53 grants (high: $25,000; low: $100).
Purpose and activities: Giving primarily for education, health, and human services.
Fields of interest: Arts and culture; Education; Diseases and conditions; Human services; Child welfare.
Type of support: General support; Research; Research and evaluation.
Limitations: Applications not accepted. Giving primarily in the tri-state CT, NJ, and NY, area. No grants to individuals.
Application information: Contributes only to pre-selected organizations.
Officers: William E. Hilson, Pres.; Dwight Hilson, V.P.
EIN: 136135887

6210
David Himelberg Foundation
c/o Barry M. Strauss Assoc., Ltd.
307 5th Ave., 8th Fl.
New York City, NY 10016-6517

Established in 1998 in New York.
Donor: David Himelberg†.
Foundation type: Independent foundation.
Financial data (yr. ended 08/31/14): Assets, $10,269,498 (M); gifts received, $984,534; expenditures, $402,873; qualifying distributions, $341,015; giving activities include $272,915 for 45 grants (high: $29,500; low: $75).
Fields of interest: University education; Graduate and professional education; Medical education; Judaism; Theology.
Type of support: General support; Scholarships.
Limitations: Applications not accepted. Giving primarily in NY. No grants to individuals.
Application information: Contributes only to pre-selected organizations.
Trustee: Norman Himelberg.
EIN: 137200887

6211
Douglas A. Hirsch & Holly S. Andersen Family Foundation, Inc.
c/o BCRS Assocs., LLC
77 Water St., 9th Fl.
New York City, NY 10005-4401

Donor: Douglas A. Hirsch.
Foundation type: Independent foundation.
Financial data (yr. ended 12/31/13): Assets, $286,706 (M); gifts received, $203,935; expenditures, $190,990; qualifying distributions, $189,090; giving activities include $183,750 for 17 grants (high: $100,000; low: $250).
Purpose and activities: Giving primarily for education, health organizations and medical research, Jewish agencies and temples, and social services.
Fields of interest: Education; Foundations; Nonprofits; Diseases and conditions; Judaism; Human services.
Type of support: Research; Research and evaluation; Regranting.
Limitations: Applications not accepted. Giving primarily in New York, NY. No grants to individuals, or for scholarships; no loans.
Application information: Contributes only to pre-selected organizations.
Officers: Douglas A. Hirsch, Pres.; Barry S. Berger, Secy.; Holly S. Andersen, Treas.
EIN: 300218948

6212
Henry & Myrtle Hirsch Foundation
(formerly Louis Hirsch Foundation)
c/o Lawrence Gross
25 Chapel Pl., No. 2J
Great Neck, NY 11021-1407

Established in 1947 in New York.
Donors: Carole Friedman; S. Minotto; Henry Hirsch†; Myrtle G. Hirsch†.
Foundation type: Independent foundation.
Financial data (yr. ended 12/31/14): Assets, $4,416,643; expenditures, $298,147; qualifying distributions, $258,570.

Purpose and activities: Giving primarily to Jewish agencies, temples, and schools.
Fields of interest: Education; Nonprofits; Judaism; Human services.
Type of support: General support; Regranting.
Limitations: Applications not accepted. Giving primarily in NY. No grants to individuals.
Application information: Contributes only to pre-selected organizations.
Officers: Richard Hirsh, Pres.; David Hirsch, V.P.
EIN: 116035655

6213
The Hite Foundation, Inc.
c/o Nussbaum Yates Berg Klein & Wolpow, LLP
445 Broadhollow Rd., Ste. 319
Melville, NY 11747-3601
Contact: Arlene Ward
E-mail: atward165@gmail.com; Main URL: http://fdnweb.org/hite

Established in 1987 in New Jersey.
Donor: Lawrence Hite.
Foundation type: Independent foundation.
Financial data (yr. ended 06/30/13): Assets, $5,968,613 (M); gifts received, $100,000; expenditures, $719,213; qualifying distributions, $337,895; giving activities include $325,300 for 22 grants (high: $50,000; low: $500).
Purpose and activities: The foundation has two primary grant making focus areas: child welfare policy, with special interest in permanency planning, and 19th century British photography.
Fields of interest: Photography; Child welfare.
Type of support: Program development; Research.
Limitations: Applications not accepted. Giving primarily in the metropolitan New York, NY, area. No grants to individuals.
Application information: Proposals considered by invitation only. Unsolicited proposals not accepted.
Officers: Lawrence D. Hite, Pres.; Simon Levin, Secy.-Treas.
EIN: 222856867

6214
Hochman Family Foundation
1100 Park Ave.
New York City, NY 10128-1202

Established in 1998 in New York.
Donors: Richard Hochman; Carol Hochman; The Hochman Family 2003 Trust.
Foundation type: Operating foundation.
Financial data (yr. ended 12/31/13): Assets, $0 (M); gifts received, $181,200; expenditures, $151,053; qualifying distributions, $151,053; giving activities include $151,018 for 42 grants (high: $40,000; low: $50).
Purpose and activities: Giving primarily for education, health and Jewish organizations.
Fields of interest: Arts and culture; University education; Nonprofits; Diseases and conditions; Judaism; Human services.
Type of support: Regranting.
Limitations: Applications not accepted. Giving primarily in NY. No grants to individuals.
Application information: Unsolicited requests for funds not accepted.
Officers: Carol J. Hochman, Pres.; Richard H. Hochman, Secy.-Treas.

Director: Matthew Sirovich.
EIN: 134010994

6215
Hoffen Family Foundation
c/o Sandra Hoffen
27 W. 60th St.
P.O. Box 20891
New York City, NY 10023-0010

Established in 2007 in Unspecified.
Donors: Howard I. Hoffen; Sandra Hoffen.
Foundation type: Independent foundation.
Financial data (yr. ended 12/31/13): Assets,
$16,515,003 (M); gifts received, $1,231,533;
expenditures, $265,834; qualifying distributions,
$237,181; giving activities include $230,211 for 57
grants (high: $50,000; low: $150).
Fields of interest: Arts and culture; Education;
Judaism.
Limitations: Applications not accepted. Giving
primarily in NJ and NY.
Application information: Contributes only to
pre-selected organizations.
Officers: Sandra Hoffen, Chair.; Howard I. Hoffen,
Treas.
EIN: 261598880

6216
The Howard Hoffman & Sons Foundation, Inc.
1407 Broadway, Ste. 1201
New York City, NY 10018-2849 (212) 719-1070

Established in 2003 in New York.
Donors: Howard Hoffman; Jason Hoffman; Nathan
Hoffman; 618 Main Clothing Corp.; Madison
Brands, Inc.
Foundation type: Independent foundation.
Financial data (yr. ended 12/31/12): Assets,
$6,242 (M); gifts received, $286,466;
expenditures, $280,964; qualifying distributions,
$280,004; giving activities include $280,004 for
grants.
Fields of interest: Nonprofits; Judaism.
International interests: Israel.
Type of support: Regranting.
Limitations: Applications accepted. Giving primarily
in NJ and NY.
Application information:
 Initial approach: proposal
 Copies of proposal: 1
 Deadline(s): None
Officers: Howard Hoffman, Pres.; Nathan Hoffman,
Secy.; Jason Hoffman, Treas.
Trustee: David Hoffman.
EIN: 200089283

6217
The Richard Hogan & Carron Sherry Foundation, Inc.
353 Central Park West, Apt. 8
New York City, NY 10025-6597

Established in 1995 in New York.
Donors: Education for Youth Society; Richard Hogan.
Foundation type: Independent foundation.
Financial data (yr. ended 09/30/13): Assets,
$3,343,168 (M); expenditures, $201,273;
qualifying distributions, $187,265; giving activities

include $184,385 for 24 grants (high: $115,135;
low: $100).
Fields of interest: Education; Foundations;
Agriculture; Community and economic development.
Type of support: Scholarships.
Limitations: Applications not accepted. No grants to
individuals.
Application information: Contributes only
pre-selected organizations.
Officers and Directors: Richard Hogan, Pres. and
Treas. and Director; Carron Sherry, V.P. and Secy.
and Director; Nancy Oetinger; Maureen Sherry.
EIN: 133860420

6218
The Hohmann Foundation
11 E. 77th St.
New York City, NY 10075 (212) 861-6101

Established in 1993 in New York.
Donors: Frank L. Hohmann; Kristin Hohmann.
Foundation type: Independent foundation.
Financial data (yr. ended 12/31/14): Assets,
$2,985,245; expenditures, $204,150; qualifying
distributions, $204,150.
Fields of interest: Architecture; Museums; Art
museums; Natural history museums; Science
museums; Education; Higher education; Botanical
gardens; Protestantism.
Limitations: Applications accepted. Giving primarily
in DE, New York, NY; some giving also in
Washington, DC.
Application information:
 Initial approach: Proposal
 Deadline(s): None
Officer: Kristin Hohmann, C.F.O.
Trustee: Frank L. Hohmann.
EIN: 137010080

6219
The Helen and Claus Hoie Charitable Foundation
P.O. Box 1323
East Hampton, NY 11937-0703 (631)
907-4663
Contact: Judith Sneddon, C.O.O. and Dir.

Established in 2009 in New York.
Donor: Claus Hoie Revocable Trust.
Foundation type: Independent foundation.
Financial data (yr. ended 12/31/13): Assets,
$6,652,928 (M); gifts received, $126,600;
expenditures, $459,171; qualifying distributions,
$436,485; giving activities include $381,350 for 15
grants (high: $137,000; low: $500).
Purpose and activities: The purpose of the
foundation is to distribute artwork by Helen and
Claus Hoie to not-for-profit organizations where it will
serve a broad audience.
Fields of interest: Arts and culture.
Application information: Application form required.
 Initial approach: Letter
 Deadline(s): None
Officers and Directors: Alex Sneddon, Pres. and
Director; Judith Sneddon, C.O.O. and Director;
Phyllis Braff, Secy. and Director; Kenneth Lipper,
Treas. and Director.
EIN: 263285804

6220
The Holborn Foundation
c/o Bank of America
1 Bryant Park
New York City, NY 10036-6728

Established in 1998 in Unspecified.
Donors: Gillett A. Gilbert, Jr.; John N. Gilbert, Jr.;
John H. Hilbert, Jr.
Foundation type: Independent foundation.
Financial data (yr. ended 11/30/14): Assets,
$7,007,810; expenditures, $296,874; qualifying
distributions, $284,931.
Fields of interest: Arts and culture; Education;
Environment.
Limitations: Applications not accepted. Giving
primarily in MA, NY, OR, PA, and VT. No grants to
individuals.
Application information: Contributes only to
pre-selected organizations.
Trustees: Gillett A. Gilbert; John N. Gilbert, Jr.
EIN: 367213630

6221
Holmberg Foundation, Inc.
519 Washington St.
Jamestown, NY 14701-4925 (716) 483-0735
Contact: David W. Shepherd, Pres.

Established in 1992 in New York.
Donors: Mr. Holmberg; Mrs. Bessemer; Mary Tilley
Bessemer Charitable Reminder Unitrust.
Foundation type: Independent foundation.
Financial data (yr. ended 07/31/13): Assets,
$4,974,716 (M); expenditures, $252,711;
qualifying distributions, $203,922; giving activities
include $201,800 for 16 grants (high: $75,000;
low: $1,000).
Purpose and activities: Giving primarily for higher
education and youth service programs.
Fields of interest: Higher education; Youth
development; Children and youth; Low-income and
poor people.
Limitations: Applications accepted. Giving limited to
Southern Chautauqua County, NY. No grants to
individuals.
Publications: Application guidelines; Financial
statement; Program policy statement (including
application guidelines).
Application information: Application form required.
 Initial approach: Use application form at http://
  www.chautauquagrants.org
 Copies of proposal: 5
 Deadline(s): Apr. 15
 Board meeting date(s): May and June
Officers: David W. Shepherd, Pres.; Matthew W.
Moore, V.P.; Sandra M. Snabl, V.P.; Leslie A.
Johnson, Secy.; Joseph C. Johnson, Treas.
Number of staff: None.
EIN: 161426226

6222
Holocaust Memorial Study Center Inc.
4611 12th Ave., 1st Fl.
Brooklyn, NY 11219

Foundation type: Independent foundation.
Financial data (yr. ended 12/31/13): Assets,
$2,492,325 (M); expenditures, $211,588;
qualifying distributions, $205,250; giving activities

include $205,000 for 2 grants (high: $155,000; low: $50,000).
Fields of interest: Religion; Judaism.
Limitations: Applications not accepted. Giving primarily in NJ and NY.
Application information: Unsolicited requests for funds not accepted.
Trustees: David Bistricer; Shmuel Levinson.
EIN: 223654080

6223
Holtzman Family Foundation Inc.
28 E. 73rd St., Ste. 12B
New York City, NY 10021-4143

Donor: Samuel J. Holtzman.
Foundation type: Independent foundation.
Financial data (yr. ended 12/31/13): Assets, $4,855,110 (M); expenditures, $277,141; qualifying distributions, $236,500; giving activities include $236,500 for 28 grants (high: $60,000; low: $1,000).
Fields of interest: Art museums; Education; Nonprofits; Judaism; Human services.
Type of support: Regranting.
Limitations: Applications not accepted. Giving primarily in West Palm Beach, FL, Baltimore, MD and New York, NY. No grants to individuals.
Application information: Unsolicited requests for funds not accepted.
Officer: Carl Skoggard, Pres.
EIN: 526036091

6224
Josephine Lawrence Hopkins Foundation
c/o Cullen and Dykman, LLP
100 Quentin Roosevelt Blvd., Ste. 402
Garden City, NY 11530-4843   5163573815

Established in 1968 in New York.
Donor: Josephine H. Graeber†.
Foundation type: Independent foundation.
Financial data (yr. ended 12/31/14): Assets, $6,606,533; expenditures, $417,389; qualifying distributions, $348,851.
Purpose and activities: Giving primarily for human services.
Fields of interest: Arts and culture; Performing arts; Education; Catholicism; Human services; Child welfare.
Limitations: Applications not accepted. Giving primarily in New York, NY. No grants to individuals; no loans.
Application information: Contributes only to pre-selected organizations.
   Board meeting date(s): Annually, usually in Oct.
Officers and Directors: Ivan Obolensky, Pres. and Treas. and Director; Vera L. Colage, V.P. and Director; Allison A. F. Chase; Lee Harrison Corbin; Kathleen M. McCormack.
EIN: 136277593

6225
The G. & B. Horowitz Family Foundation, Inc.
(formerly Gedale B. and Barbara S. Horowitz Foundation)
c/o Cleary Gottlieb
1 Liberty Plz.
New York City, NY 10006-1404

Established in 1970 in New York.
Donors: Gedale B. Horowitz; Barbara S. Horowitz; Gedale B. Horowitz Charitable Lead Trust; Gedale B. & Barbara S. Horowitz March 31, 1994 Charitable Lead Annuity Trust.
Foundation type: Independent foundation.
Financial data (yr. ended 06/30/14): Assets, $3,712,892 (M); gifts received; $350,000; expenditures, $439,458; qualifying distributions, $437,575; giving activities include $434,650 for 16 grants (high: $250,000; low: $500).
Purpose and activities: Grants primarily for higher education, including a Conservative Jewish rabbinical seminary, as well as for the arts, particularly museums; funding also for Jewish organizations and temples.
Fields of interest: Art museums; Higher education; Graduate and professional education; Nonprofits; Hospital care; Diseases and conditions; Conservative Judaism; Theology; Human services.
Type of support: General support; Regranting.
Limitations: Applications not accepted. Giving primarily in New York, NY. No grants to individuals.
Application information: Contributes only to pre-selected organizations.
Officers: Gedale B. Horowitz, Pres.; Ruth Horowitz, V.P.; Seth Horowitz, V.P.; Steven M. Loeb, Secy.
EIN: 237101730

6226
Alice and Jaclyn Houseknecht Foundation
P.O. Box 2037
Montauk, NY 11954-0902

Donor: Alice G. Houseknecht.
Foundation type: Independent foundation.
Financial data (yr. ended 12/31/13): Assets, $1,785,971 (M); gifts received, $2,000,000; expenditures, $214,114; qualifying distributions, $212,057; giving activities include $210,000 for 3 grants (high: $100,000; low: $10,000).
Fields of interest: Arts and culture; Health; Human services.
Limitations: Applications not accepted.
Application information: Unsolicited requests for funds not accepted.
Officers and Directors: Alice G. Houseknecht, Pres. and Director; Roger Feit, V.P. and Director; Jaclyn Y. Houseknecht, Secy.-Treas. and Director.
EIN: 464144136

6227
The Houser Foundation Inc.
70 Willow St.
Brooklyn, NY 11201-1616

Donor: Daniel Houser.
Foundation type: Independent foundation.
Financial data (yr. ended 12/31/13): Assets, $4,419,206 (M); gifts received, $4,040,540; expenditures, $156,541; qualifying distributions, $156,541; giving activities include $153,000 for 23 grants (high: $25,000; low: $1,000).
Fields of interest: Environment; Diseases and conditions; Human services.
Limitations: Applications not accepted. Giving primarily in Jericho, NY.
Application information: Unsolicited requests for funds not accepted.

Directors: Anouchka Houser; Daniel Houser; Samuel Houser; Krystyna Jakubiak.
EIN: 263047089

6228
Houston Family Foundation
3 Pheasant Dr.
Armonk, NY 10504-1321

Established in 2004 in New York.
Donor: Anne Houston Charitable Lead Annuity Trust.
Foundation type: Independent foundation.
Financial data (yr. ended 12/31/14): Assets, $6,306,452 (M); expenditures, $397,346; qualifying distributions, $306,000; giving activities include $306,000 for 39 grants (high: $50,000; low: $500).
Fields of interest: Education; Environment; Diseases and conditions; Christianity; Human services; Family services.
Limitations: Applications not accepted. Giving primarily in IN. No grants to individuals.
Application information: Unsolicited requests for funds not accepted.
Directors: Anne H. Bentzen; Andrew G. Houston; Cynthia A. Houston.
EIN: 571133811

6229
The Alexander and Marjorie Hover Foundation
P.O. Box 524
Germantown, NY 12526-0524   (518) 537-6718
Contact: J. Nadine Rumke, Exec. Dir.

Established in 2009 in New York.
Foundation type: Independent foundation.
Financial data (yr. ended 12/31/13): Assets, $4,500,912 (M); expenditures, $294,906; qualifying distributions, $205,283; giving activities include $205,283 for 32 grants (high: $17,500; low: $500).
Fields of interest: Education; Religion; Human services.
Application information: Application form required.
   Initial approach: Letter
   Deadline(s): None
Officers: Lali Rumke, Pres.and Treas.; Carise M. Himelright, V.P.; John H. Rumke, Secy.; J. Nadine Rumke, Exec. Dir.
Directors: Nadea R. Archbold; William J. Archbold; Thomas Fucito; James H. Himelright III.
EIN: 263994213

6230
Stewart W. & Willma C. Hoyt Foundation, Inc.
70 Front St.
Binghamton, NY 13905-4722   (607) 772-0780
Contact: Catherine Schwoeffermann, Exec. Dir.
FAX: (607) 722-0747;
E-mail: hoytfoundation@stny.rr.com; Main URL: http://www.hoytfoundation.org
Grants List: http://www.hoytfoundation.org/grants_13.htm

Established in 1993 in New York.
Donor: Willma C. Hoyt†.
Foundation type: Independent foundation.

Financial data (yr. ended 12/31/13): Assets, $22,808,610 (M); expenditures, $719,296; qualifying distributions, $559,893; giving activities include $348,831 for 18 grants (high: $100,000; low: $2,500).

Purpose and activities: The foundation aims to use its resources to enhance the quality of life of the people of Broome County, NY, primarily through judicious grantmaking. The foundation focuses broadly on the areas of the arts, humanities, education, health and human services. The foundation is particularly interested in assisting programs that meet an urgent community need, that do not unnecessarily duplicate the work of other organizations, that have explored alternative funding sources, and that have some reasonable assurance of ongoing support.

Fields of interest: Arts and culture; Humanities; Education; Health; Human services.

Type of support: Capital campaigns; Pro bono consulting services; Matching grants; Capital and infrastructure; Equipment; Program development; Curriculum development; Technical assistance.

Limitations: Applications accepted. Giving limited to Broome County, NY. No support for religious purposes, or for economic development projects. No grants to individuals, or for annual campaigns of local chapters of national organizations, deficit financing, general operating, endowments, research, publications, or ongoing maintenance projects.

Publications: Annual report; Financial statement; Grants list.

Application information: A meeting with the Exec. Dir. and approval to submit submission of a full proposal to the foundation. Application form required.
  Initial approach: Telephone
  Copies of proposal: 1
  Deadline(s): Apr. 1 and Sept. 2
  Board meeting date(s): Quarterly; grantmaking meetings in June and Nov.
  Final notification: 1 to 3 days following board meetings

Officers and Directors: Marena Gonz, Chair. and Director; Gary D. Rein, Vice-Chair. and Director; Jeffery T. Smith, Secy.-Treas. and Director; Catherine Schwoeffermann, Exec. Dir.; Aubrey Clark; Louise Donohue; Michael J. Gavin.

Number of staff: 1 full-time professional; 1 part-time professional; 1 part-time support.

EIN: 223209342

6231
The Huber Family Foundation Inc
139 W. 78th St.
New York City, NY   10024-6702

Established in 1997 in Connecticut.
Donor: Richard L. Huber.
Foundation type: Independent foundation.
Financial data (yr. ended 12/31/14): Assets, $2,715,219; expenditures, $187,533; qualifying distributions, $160,850.
Fields of interest: Arts and culture; Art museums; Environment; Human services.
Limitations: Applications not accepted. Giving primarily in NY, with some giving in MA and VA. No grants to individuals.
Application information: Contributes only to pre-selected organizations.
Officers and Directors: Roberta P. Huber, Pres. and Director; Richard L. Huber, V.P. and Director; M.

Sebastian Huber, Secy.-Treas.; Alexander L. Huber; Benjamin P. Huber.
EIN: 061484291

6232
Nila B. Hulbert Foundation
6 Ford Ave.
Oneonta, NY   13820-1898   (607) 432-6724
Contact: William H. Hulbert, Mgr.

Donor: Nila B. Hulbert.
Foundation type: Independent foundation.
Financial data (yr. ended 12/31/13): Assets, $7,869,226 (M); expenditures, $418,294; qualifying distributions, $407,756; giving activities include $303,500 for 34 grants (high: $25,000; low: $1,000).
Fields of interest: Museums; Higher education; Hospital care; Community and economic development; Human services.
Limitations: Applications accepted. Giving primarily in Oneonta, NY.
Application information: Application form required.
  Initial approach: Letter
  Deadline(s): Sept. 30
Officer: William H. Hulbert, Fdn. Mgr.
Trustees: Carolyn H. Hulbert; Christopher W. Hulbert.
EIN: 237039996

6233
The Hurlburt Foundation, Inc.
c/o SP Cooper and Co., LLP
1 Executive Blvd., 4th Fl.
Yonkers, NY   10701-6822
Application address: c/o Wilbur F. Hurlburt III, 3030 Beneva Oaks Dr., Sarasota, FL 34238, tel.: (941) 924-9243

Established in 1998 in Florida.
Donors: Jean L. Hurlburt; Michael H. Kline, Sr.; Wilbur F. Hurlburt III.
Foundation type: Independent foundation.
Financial data (yr. ended 12/31/13): Assets, $7,636,900 (M); expenditures, $410,864; qualifying distributions, $297,300; giving activities include $225,000 for 26 grants (high: $25,000; low: $500).
Purpose and activities: Giving primarily for aid to children.
Fields of interest: Education; Diseases and conditions; Human services.
Type of support: General support.
Limitations: Applications accepted. Giving primarily in CO, FL, NC, NJ, NY and WA. No support for religious organizations, or to individuals other than children.
Application information: Application form required.
  Initial approach: Letter
  Copies of proposal: 1
  Deadline(s): Aug. 31
Officers and Directors: Michael H. Kline, Sr., Pres. and Director; Wilbur F. Hurlburt III, V.P. and Director; Jean L. Hurlburt, Secy. and Director; Herbert G. Kanarick, Treas. and Director; John S. Bohatch; Christina Colletti; Sunshine Hurlburt; Michael Kline, Jr.
Number of staff: 3 full-time support.
EIN: 650795533

6234
The Hymowitz Family Foundation Trust
c/o Entrust
375 Park Ave., 24th Fl.
New York City, NY   10152-3599

Established in 1999 in New York.
Donor: Gregg S. Hymowitz.
Foundation type: Independent foundation.
Financial data (yr. ended 06/30/13): Assets, $736,090 (M); gifts received, $160,300; expenditures, $160,259; qualifying distributions, $160,259; giving activities include $160,159 for 3 grants (high: $130,159; low: $5,000).
Fields of interest: Arts and culture; Education; Human services.
Limitations: Applications not accepted. Giving primarily in New York, NY. No grants to individuals.
Application information: Contributes only to pre-selected organizations.
Trustee: Gregg S. Hymowitz.
EIN: 134089721

6235
I Dream a World Foundation, Inc.
c/o Suzanne Lehmann
101 Central Park West, Ste. 18-F
New York City, NY   10023-4250

Established in 1997 in New York.
Donor: Suzanne Lehmann.
Foundation type: Independent foundation.
Financial data (yr. ended 12/31/13): Assets, $2,263,698 (M); gifts received, $1,218,169; expenditures, $186,084; qualifying distributions, $174,220; giving activities include $163,237 for 12 grants (high: $60,000; low: $1,000).
Purpose and activities: Grant for general purpose.
Fields of interest: Education.
Limitations: Applications not accepted. Giving primarily in New York, NY. No grants to individuals.
Application information: Unsolicited requests for funds not accepted.
Officers and Directors: Suzanne Lehmann, Pres.; Daniel Lehmann, V.P. and Secy.; Fred Gluck, V.P. and Director; Lisa Gluck, V.P. and Director; Susan Gluck, V.P. and Director.
EIN: 133942097

6236
I.W. Foundation, Inc.
630 W. 246th St., Ste. 323
Riverdale, NY   10471-3633

Established in 1997 in New York.
Foundation type: Independent foundation.
Financial data (yr. ended 12/31/14): Assets, $7,526,268; expenditures, $415,399; qualifying distributions, $320,504.
Purpose and activities: Giving primarily for higher education; some support also for health care.
Fields of interest: Arts and culture; Higher education; In-patient medical care; Human services.
Limitations: Applications not accepted. No grants to individuals.
Application information: Unsolicited requests for funds not accepted.
Officers: Peter Seiden, Chair.; Judith Levi, Pres.; Mark Levi, V.P.; Joan Seiden, Secy.; Harold Seiden, Treas.
EIN: 133924347

6237
IF Hummingbird Foundation, Inc.
(formerly The Iscol Family Foundation, Inc.)
63 Lyndel Rd.
Pound Ridge, NY 10576-1204 (914) 764-8479
Contact: Jill Iscol, Pres.

Established in 1990 in New York.
Donors: Kenneth Iscol; Jill Iscol.
Foundation type: Independent foundation.
Financial data (yr. ended 06/30/13): Assets, $965,899 (M); expenditures, $481,191; qualifying distributions, $325,410; giving activities include $325,410 for 107 grants (high: $70,000; low: $50).
Fields of interest: Arts and culture; Performing arts; Museums; Elementary and secondary education; Higher education; Natural resources; Specialty hospital care; Diseases and conditions; Public affairs; Individual liberties; Human services; Child welfare.
Type of support: General support; Matching grants; Continuing support; Annual campaigns; Endowments; Convening; Curriculum development; Scholarships.
Limitations: Applications accepted. Giving primarily in the metropolitan New York, NY, area, including Long Island and Westchester; some funding nationally. No grants to individuals.
Application information: Application form required.
  Initial approach: Letter
  Deadline(s): None
Officers and Directors: Jill Iscol, Pres. and Treas. and Director; Kenneth Iscol, V.P. and Secy. and Director.
Number of staff: 1 part-time professional; 2 part-time support.
EIN: 061314468

6238
The Ilsababy Foundation
P.O. Box 757
Caroga Lake, NY 12032

Donor: Bradford G. Dake.
Foundation type: Independent foundation.
Financial data (yr. ended 12/31/13): Assets, $46,348 (M); gifts received, $475,000; expenditures, $428,652; qualifying distributions, $428,366; giving activities include $428,366 for 43 grants (high: $33,210; low: $1,000).
Fields of interest: Arts and culture; Education; Environment.
Limitations: Applications not accepted. Giving primarily in NY.
Application information: Unsolicited requests for funds not accepted.
Trustees: Bradford G. Dake; Darla Oathout.
EIN: 454633586

6239
Imago Dei Foundation, Inc.
c/o Emil Woods
140 E. 45th St., Ste. 17C
New York City, NY 10017

Donor: Emil Woods.
Foundation type: Independent foundation.
Financial data (yr. ended 06/30/14): Assets, $246,221 (M); expenditures, $392,975; qualifying distributions, $392,000; giving activities include

$392,000 for 4 grants (high: $281,000; low: $1,000).
Fields of interest: Higher education; Foundations.
Limitations: Applications not accepted. Giving in the U.S., with some emphasis on NY.
Application information: Unsolicited requests for funds not accepted.
Trustees: Charles Cascarilla; Emil Woods.
EIN: 263868853

6240
IMS Foundation
506 Quentin Rd.
Brooklyn, NY 11223-2006

Established in 1999 in New York.
Donors: Raymond Salem; Ikeddi Imports, LLC; Ikeddi Enterprises Inc.
Foundation type: Independent foundation.
Financial data (yr. ended 12/31/13): Assets, $3,174 (M); gifts received, $340,000; expenditures, $361,078; qualifying distributions, $359,822; giving activities include $359,822 for 93 grants (high: $95,670; low: $18).
Fields of interest: Judaism.
Limitations: Applications not accepted.
Application information: Contributes only to pre-selected organizations.
Officer: Raymond J. Salem, Pres.
EIN: 134026345

6241
The Independent Foundation
30 Broad St., 24th Fl.
New York City, NY 10004-2961 (212) 584-2740

Established in 2002 in New York.
Donors: Levi & Korsinsky LLP; Eduard Korsinsky; Joseph E. Levi.
Foundation type: Independent foundation.
Financial data (yr. ended 12/31/13): Assets, $1,464,382 (M); gifts received, $976,493; expenditures, $218,414; qualifying distributions, $217,798; giving activities include $217,798 for 149 grants (high: $60,000; low: $18).
Purpose and activities: Giving primarily to Jewish agencies, temples, and schools.
Fields of interest: Education; Judaism.
Application information: Application form required.
  Initial approach: Letter
  Deadline(s): None
Officers: Eduard Korsinsky, Pres.; Joseph E. Levi, Secy.
EIN: 116526222

6242
The Indira Foundation
c/o BCRS Associates., LLC
77 Water St., 9th Fl.
New York City, NY 10005-4414

Established in 1999 in Connecticut.
Donors: Avi Nash; Sandra Nash.
Foundation type: Independent foundation.
Financial data (yr. ended 08/31/13): Assets, $8,527,938 (M); gifts received, $109,436; expenditures, $378,585; qualifying distributions, $365,370; giving activities include $360,520 for 25 grants (high: $50,000; low: $1).

Fields of interest: Education; Elementary and secondary education; Higher education; Diseases and conditions; Communication media; Hinduism; Human services.
International interests: India.
Limitations: Applications not accepted. Giving primarily in IL and NY. No grants, gifts, scholarships, or loans to individuals.
Application information: Contributes only to pre-selected organizations.
Trustees: Avi Nash; Sandra Nash.
EIN: 134051213

6243
Indus Charitable Foundation Inc.
c/o Indus Capital Partners, LLC
888 7th Ave.
New York City, NY 10019-3386

Established in 2007 in New York.
Donor: Indus Capital Partners, LLC.
Foundation type: Company-sponsored foundation.
Financial data (yr. ended 12/31/13): Assets, $1,216,573 (M); gifts received, $190,800; expenditures, $182,663; qualifying distributions, $180,563; giving activities include $176,300 for 11 grants (high: $25,000; low: $900).
Purpose and activities: The foundation supports organizations involved with Japanese culture, education, the environment, baseball, and human services.
Fields of interest: Cultural awareness; Education; Higher education; Air quality; Water resources; Water pollution; Baseball and softball; Human services; Child welfare.
Type of support: General support.
Limitations: Applications not accepted. Giving primarily in NY.
Application information: Unsolicted requests for funds not accepted.
Officers: Brian Guzman, Secy.; James Weiner, Treas.
Director: Matthew Sippel.
EIN: 261496848

6244
Elizabeth & Frank Ingrassia Foundation
c/o The Ayco Co., L.P.
P.O. Box 15014
Albany, NY 12212-5014

Established in 1994 in New York.
Donor: Francis J. Ingrassia.
Foundation type: Independent foundation.
Financial data (yr. ended 09/30/14): Assets, $3,546,098 (M); expenditures, $357,575; qualifying distributions, $325,000; giving activities include $325,000 for 2 grants (high: $200,000; low: $125,000).
Purpose and activities: Giving primarily for education, juvenile diabetes research, and to Catholic churches.
Fields of interest: Education; Higher education; Diabetes; Catholicism.
Type of support: Research.
Limitations: Applications not accepted. Giving primarily in NY; some giving also in PA. No grants to individuals, or for scholarships; no loans.
Application information: Contributes only to pre-selected organizations.

Trustees: Francis J. Ingrassia; Elizabeth McCaul.
EIN: 133801229

6245
Initial Teaching Alphabet Foundation
P.O. Box 11355
Hauppauge, NY 11788-0991 (631) 813-2991
Contact: Keith Bub, Pres.
Main URL: http://www.ita-foundation.org

Established in 1965 in New York.
Donors: Eugene Kelly†; Eugene Kelly Trust.
Foundation type: Operating foundation.
Financial data (yr. ended 12/31/13): Assets,
$453,472 (M); gifts received, $300,000;
expenditures, $555,479; qualifying distributions,
$555,391; giving activities include $318,363 for 9
grants (high: $87,218; low: $21,501).
Purpose and activities: Giving primarily to promote,
maintain, and advance education, in all its fields,
and in particular, but without limiting the generality
of the foregoing, by the development,
standardization, propagation, dissemination,
teaching, and use of the Initial Teaching Alphabet,
with the aim of improving reading and writing skills.
Fields of interest: Education; Early childhood
education; Elementary education; Secondary
education; University education; Adult education.
Type of support: Program development; Pro bono
consulting services; Research and evaluation;
Convening; Publications; Research; Technical
assistance.
Limitations: Applications accepted. Giving primarily
in CA, IL, MN, NY, and TX. No grants to individuals,
or for building or endowment funds, general support,
scholarships, fellowships, or matching gifts; no
loans.
Publications: Application guidelines; Informational
brochure; Occasional report; Program policy
statement.
Application information: Complete application
guidelines available on foundation web site.
Application form required.
    Copies of proposal: 2
    Board meeting date(s): May or June
Officers: Keith Bub, Pres. and Treas.; Shelly Jerviss,
V.P.; Maurice S. Spanbock, Secy.; Carol McKay.
Directors: Betty E. Thompson, Exec. Dir.; Martha
Bogart; Dr. Max Bogart; Frank G. Jennings.
Number of staff: 2 full-time professional.
EIN: 112074243

6246
John N. Insall Foundation for Orthopaedics Inc.
270 Madison Ave., 17th Fl.
New York City, NY 10016-0601
Application address: c/o Kathy Lenhardt, Insall Scott
Kelly Institute, 210 E. 64th St., 4th Fl., New York,
NY 10065-7471, tel.: (212) 434-4340,
e-mail: klenhardt@iskinstitute.com

Established in 2001 in New York.
Donors: Mary V. Insall Foundation; Mary V. Insall.
Foundation type: Independent foundation.
Financial data (yr. ended 06/30/13): Assets,
$2,559,563 (M); expenditures, $226,208;
qualifying distributions, $217,757; giving activities
include $217,336 for 5 grants (high: $123,336;
low: $5,000).

Purpose and activities: Grants to practicing
orthopedic surgeons who are within five years of
completing fellowships in either adult knee
reconstruction or sports medicine.
Fields of interest: Orthopedics.
Type of support: Fellowships.
Limitations: Applications accepted. Giving primarily
in Chicago, IL, and New York, NY.
Application information: Candidates for the Insall
Travelling Fellowship are required to fill out the
fellowship's application form. Application form
required.
    Initial approach: Proposal
    Deadline(s): Varies
Directors: John S. Erwin; Mary V. Insall; Joseph
Leshkowitz.
EIN: 134167179

6247
Mary V. Insall Foundation
c/o Leshkowitz Co.
270 Madison Ave., Ste. 17
New York City, NY 10016-0601 (212) 532-5550
Contact: Mark V. Insall, Dir.
Application address: 400 E. 51st St., New York, NY
10022

Donors: Mary V. Insall; Naftali Zvi Leshkowitz
Memorial Foundation.
Foundation type: Independent foundation.
Financial data (yr. ended 05/31/14): Assets,
$3,036,550 (M); gifts received, $1,505,781;
expenditures, $141,206; qualifying distributions,
$133,250; giving activities include $133,000 for
grants.
Fields of interest: Human services.
Application information: Application form required.
    Initial approach: Letter
    Deadline(s): None
Directors: John S. Erwin; Mary V. Insall; Joseph
Leshkowitz.
EIN: 570547714

6248
Institute for Depression Studies and Treatment
c/o B. Strauss Assoc. Ltd.
307 5th Ave., 8th Fl.
New York City, NY 10016-6517

Donors: Trygve Myrhen; Frampton Family Charitable
Foundation; George A. Wiegers; George Wood; Beth
Wood; Brenton Durham; Lori Durham; Lydia Harvey;
Cannon Harvey; Lydia McKee; Reiman Foundation;
His Global Inc.; Wiegers Family Foundation; The
Hicks Charitable Foundation.
Foundation type: Independent foundation.
Financial data (yr. ended 06/30/13): Assets,
$418,606 (M); gifts received, $167,108;
expenditures, $432,481; qualifying distributions,
$432,481; giving activities include $223,123 for 4
grants (high: $190,123; low: $1,000).
Fields of interest: Education.
Limitations: Applications not accepted.
Application information: Unsolicited requests for
funds not accepted.
Officers and Directors: George A. Wiegers, Chair.
and Director; Heather Mulvihill, Vice-Chair. and
Director; Peyton F. Perry, Treas. and Director; Ann
Ayers; Susan Drumm; Jack Eck, MD; Susan Milhoan;

Ann Benson Reidy; Jeannie Ritter; Beth Slifer; Beth
Wood.
EIN: 262755241

6249
International Shinto Foundation, Inc.
245 E. 58 St., Ste. 8D
New York City, NY 10022-1340

Donors: International Shinto Foundation Tokyo;
World Mate; World Mate Japan.
Foundation type: Operating foundation.
Financial data (yr. ended 06/30/13): Assets,
$142,982 (M); gifts received, $447,084;
expenditures, $377,477; qualifying distributions,
$376,085; giving activities include $144,638 for 3
+ grants (high: $100,000).
Purpose and activities: Giving primarily to spread
the knowledge and understanding of the Shinto
religion and its culture.
Fields of interest: Higher education; Religion;
Shintoism; Human services.
Limitations: Applications not accepted. Giving
primarily in CA, Washington, DC, and New York, NY.
No grants to individuals.
Application information: Contributes only to
pre-selected organizations.
Officers: Toshu Fukami, Pres.; Toyokatsu Habata,
Secy.
Directors: Katherine Marshall; Midori Miyazaki;
Ishmael Noko.
EIN: 133903933

6250
Iroquois Avenue Foundation
c/o Sheehan & Co.
437 Madison Ave., 29th Fl.
New York City, NY 10022-7035

Established in 1989 in Delaware.
Donor: Lydia B. Mann†.
Foundation type: Independent foundation.
Financial data (yr. ended 12/31/14): Assets,
$4,182,267; expenditures, $270,666; qualifying
distributions, $211,346.
Purpose and activities: Giving primarily for
education, health, and human services; support
also for the arts.
Fields of interest: Arts and culture; Education;
University education; Diseases and conditions;
Public libraries; Human services; Child welfare.
Type of support: General support.
Limitations: Applications not accepted. Giving
primarily in CT, MA, NY and RI. No grants to
individuals.
Application information: Contributes only to
pre-selected organizations.
Officers and Directors: Peter A.B. Melhado, Pres.
and Director; Michael Kavoukjian, Secy. and
Director; Peter M. Schulte, Treas. and Director.
EIN: 133562887

6251
Issroff Family Foundation
111 Broadway, Ste. 1
Trinity Bldg.
New York City, NY 10006

Established in 2006 in New York.
Donor: David Issroff.

Foundation type: Independent foundation.
Financial data (yr. ended 12/31/13): Assets, $9,569,549 (M); expenditures, $498,133; qualifying distributions, $387,138; giving activities include $378,550 for 32 grants (high: $50,000; low: $250).
Fields of interest: Foundations; Nonprofits.
Type of support: Regranting.
Limitations: Applications not accepted. Giving primarily in New York, NY. No grants to individuals.
Application information: Unsolicited requests for funds not accepted.
Trustees: David Issroff; Lisa Issroff.
EIN: 760849175

6252
Ivorybill Foundation, Inc.
c/o P. Martin, Ashford Advisors, LLC
30B Grove St.
Pittsford, NY   14534-1334
Roger and Victoria Sant's Giving Pledge Profile: http://glasspockets.org/philanthropy-in-focus/eye-on-the-giving-pledge/profiles/sant

Established in 2006 in Delaware.
Donors: Roger W. Sant; Victoria P. Sant.
Foundation type: Independent foundation.
Financial data (yr. ended 12/31/13): Assets, $5,149,809 (M); gifts received, $1,000,000; expenditures, $398,799; qualifying distributions, $368,800; giving activities include $366,500 for 15 grants (high: $250,000; low: $1,000).
Fields of interest: Arts and culture; Education; Environment.
Limitations: Applications not accepted. No grants to individuals.
Application information: Unsolicited requests for funds not accepted.
Officers and Directors: Alexis G. Sant, Pres. and Treas. and Director; Christine D. Sant, Secy. and Director.
EIN: 743195386

6253
J.A.T. Foundation
c/o Joseph Templer
149 Heyward St.
Brooklyn, NY   11206-4804

Established in 1995 in New York.
Donors: Joseph Templer; Julius Templer; Elegant Headwear Co., Inc.
Foundation type: Independent foundation.
Financial data (yr. ended 12/31/13): Assets, $1,243,347 (M); gifts received, $389,160; expenditures, $167,810; qualifying distributions, $166,710; giving activities include $166,710 for 15 grants (high: $35,000; low: $2,000).
Fields of interest: Judaism.
Limitations: Applications not accepted. No grants to individuals.
Application information: Contributes only to pre-selected organizations.
Trustees: Joseph Templer; Rosa Templer.
EIN: 113303849

6254
The Violet Jabara Charitable Trust
c/o Steven J. Wohl, Esq.
445 Hamilton Ave., Ste. 1102
White Plains, NY   10601-1832
E-mail: info@jabaratrust.org; Main URL: http://jabaratrust.org
Grants List: http://jabaratrust.org/grants.html

Established in 2007 in New York.
Donor: Linda K. Jacobs.
Foundation type: Independent foundation.
Financial data (yr. ended 12/31/13): Assets, $1,309,962 (M); expenditures, $178,031; qualifying distributions, $154,686; giving activities include $146,967 for 13 grants (high: $25,000; low: $1,000).
Purpose and activities: The mission of the Trust is two-fold: to help improve the lives of the people in developing countries of the Middle East and to foster greater understanding of Middle Eastern culture in the United States. Consideration will also be given to United States organizations whose purpose is to enhance understanding of Middle Eastern culture and issues.
Fields of interest: Cultural awareness; Health; Agriculture; Economic development; Islam; Women's rights; Women's services; International development; International exchange.
International interests: Egypt; Iran; Iraq; Jordan; Lebanon; Northern Africa; Syria; West Bank/Gaza (Palestinian Territories); Yemen.
Type of support: General support; Program-related investments.
Limitations: Applications accepted. Giving primarily in the Middle East, with emphasis on Lebanon, Jordan, Syria, Iraq, Iran, Palestine, Yemen, Egypt and North Africa; U.S. organizations, whose purpose is to enhance understanding of Middle Eastern culture and issues will also be considered. No grants to individuals.
Application information: Unsolicited full proposals not accepted. If interested after review of letter of inquiry, the Trust will respond with full proposal guidelines.
   Initial approach: Letter of inquiry
Trustee: Linda K. Jacobs.
EIN: 137560427

6255
The Joan L. & Julius H. Jacobson II Foundation Inc.
c/o Baker Tilly
1 Penn Plz., Ste. 3000
New York City, NY   10119-0032

Established in 1997 in New York.
Donors: Julius H. Jacobson II; Joan L. Jacobson.
Foundation type: Independent foundation.
Financial data (yr. ended 12/31/13): Assets, $3,957,709 (M); expenditures, $247,480; qualifying distributions, $187,593; giving activities include $187,486 for 6 grants (high: $50,000; low: $2,486).
Fields of interest: Arts and culture; Higher education; Medical education; Hospital care; Diseases and conditions; Public affairs.
Type of support: Research.
Limitations: Applications not accepted. Giving primarily in MA and New York, NY. No grants to individuals.
Application information: Contributes only to pre-selected organizations.

Officers: Julius H. Jacobson II, Pres. and Treas.; Joan L. Jacobson, V.P. and Secy.
EIN: 133938814

6256
The Jamakepe Foundation
(formerly Matthew J. Edmonds and Julie Anne Quay Foundation)
767 5th Ave., 12th Fl.
New York City, NY   10153-0099

Established in 2007 in New York.
Donors: Matthew J. Edmonds; Ainyff; Jamakepe Investments LLC; Cowles Charitable Trust.
Foundation type: Independent foundation.
Financial data (yr. ended 12/31/13): Assets, $928,644 (M); gifts received, $35,000; expenditures, $164,682; qualifying distributions, $162,457; giving activities include $146,886 for 17 grants (high: $35,000; low: $241).
Fields of interest: Education; Health; Hospital care; Human services.
Limitations: Applications not accepted. No grants to individuals.
Application information: Unsolicited requests for funds not accepted.
Trustees: Matthew J. Edmonds; Julie Anne Quay.
EIN: 261605129

6257
Janklow Foundation
445 Park Ave.
New York City, NY   10022-2606

Established in 1986 in New York.
Donor: Morton L. Janklow.
Foundation type: Independent foundation.
Financial data (yr. ended 06/30/13): Assets, $2,693,137 (M); expenditures, $348,931; qualifying distributions, $333,461; giving activities include $330,040 for 122 grants (high: $50,000; low: $50).
Purpose and activities: Giving primarily for arts and cultural institutions, higher education and human services.
Fields of interest: Arts and culture; Education; Higher education; Law education; Hospital care; Human services; International relations.
Limitations: Applications not accepted. Giving primarily in New York, NY. No grants to individuals.
Application information: Contributes only to pre-selected organizations.
Trustees: Linda LeRoy Janklow; Lucas Janklow; Morton L. Janklow; Angela Stein.
EIN: 133357111

6258
The Jarx Foundation Inc.
c/o Janet Moses
P.O. Box 407
Harrison, NY   10528-0407

Established in 1997 in New York.
Donors: Ellen M. Capra; James R. Capra; Fiona Druckenmiller; Stanley F. Druckenmiller.
Foundation type: Independent foundation.
Financial data (yr. ended 12/31/13): Assets, $1,689,112 (M); gifts received, $370,000; expenditures, $390,663; qualifying distributions,

$390,663; giving activities include $389,737 for 9 grants (high: $152,428; low: $5,000).
Fields of interest: Secondary education; Catholicism; Human services.
Limitations: Applications not accepted. Giving primarily in New York, NY; some funding also in CO. No grants to individuals.
Application information: Contributes only to pre-selected organizations.
Officers and Directors: James R. Capra, Pres. and Director; Ellen M. Capra, V.P. and Director; Janet Moses, Secy. and Director; Elliot H. Levine, Treas.
EIN: 133946523

6259
The Peter Jennings Foundation Inc.
c/o Mark J. Weinstein, Hogan Lovells U.S. LLP
875 3rd Ave.
New York City, NY   10022-6225

Donor: Peter Jennings†.
Foundation type: Independent foundation.
Financial data (yr. ended 12/31/13): Assets, $2,793,469 (M); gifts received, $276; expenditures, $278,825; qualifying distributions, $225,000; giving activities include $225,000 for 18 grants (high: $40,000; low: $5,000).   .
Purpose and activities: Giving for education, social and human services, and for the freedom of the press.
Fields of interest: Education; Higher education; Freedom of association and expression; Freedom of information; Human services; Homeless shelters.
Limitations: Applications not accepted. Giving primarily in NY. No grants to individuals.
Application information: Contributes only to pre-selected organizations.
Officers and Directors: Kayce Freed Jennings, Pres. and Director; Mark J. Weinstein, Treas.; Christopher Jennings; Elizabeth Jennings.
EIN: 134033625

6260
JI Foundation, Inc.
c/o Patterson, Belknap, Webb & Tyler, LLP
1133 Ave. of the Americas, Ste. 2200
New York City, NY   10036-6710

Established in 1954 in New York.
Donor: Jane W.I. Droppa.
Foundation type: Independent foundation.
Financial data (yr. ended 12/31/13): Assets, $6,556,765 (M); expenditures, $382,311; qualifying distributions, $332,084; giving activities include $319,000 for 23 grants (high: $75,000; low: $500).
Purpose and activities: Giving primarily to fish/wildlife organizations, education, the arts, and human services.
Fields of interest: Arts and culture; Natural history museums; Education; Graduate and professional education; Law education; Wildlife biodiversity; Aquariums; Nonprofits; Diseases and conditions; Protestantism; Theology; Human services; Child welfare.
Type of support: General support; Capital campaigns; Research; Regranting.
Limitations: Applications not accepted. Giving primarily in Washington, DC, Baltimore, MD, and New York, NY; funding also in NJ. No grants to individuals.

Application information: Contributes only to pre-selected organizations.
Officers and Trustees: Jane W.I. Droppa, Pres.; Larry D. Droppa, V.P. and Trustee; Antonia M. Grumbach, Secy. and Trustee; Daniel Watson Droppa; Jack J. Droppa; Dana W. Hiscock.
EIN: 136149199

6261
JIA Charitable Foundation
2722 Ave. K
Brooklyn, NY   11210-3722

Established in 1999 in New York.
Donors: George Grossberger; GPM 48th St. LLC.
Foundation type: Independent foundation.
Financial data (yr. ended 12/31/13): Assets, $110,460 (M); gifts received, $195,254; expenditures, $172,186; qualifying distributions, $171,883; giving activities include $171,883 for grants.
Fields of interest: Nonprofits; Judaism; Human services.
Type of support: Regranting.
Limitations: Applications not accepted. Giving primarily in Brooklyn, NY. No grants to individuals.
Application information: Unsolicited requests for funds not accepted.
Trustees: George Grossberger; Vickie Grossberger.
EIN: 113522310

6262
JJC Foundation, Inc.
114 E. 30th St.
New York City, NY   10016-7303

Established in 1997 in Delaware.
Donor: John Peter Clay.
Foundation type: Independent foundation.
Financial data (yr. ended 10/31/13): Assets, $7,420,313 (M); expenditures, $479,354; qualifying distributions, $366,369; giving activities include $322,500 for 7 grants (high: $110,000; low: $7,500).
Fields of interest: Education; Heart and circulatory system diseases.
Type of support: Research.
Limitations: Applications not accepted. Giving primarily in NY. No grants to individuals.
Application information: Contributes only to pre-selected organizations.
Officer: Jennifer Mary Ellen Clay, Pres.
EIN: 133922180

6263
JKW Foundation
c/o Jean Stein
10 Gracie Sq.
New York City, NY   10028-8031

Established in 1997 in New York.
Donor: Doris Jones Stein Charitable Lead Trust.
Foundation type: Independent foundation.
Financial data (yr. ended 12/31/13): Assets, $13,030,461 (M); expenditures, $333,451; qualifying distributions, $280,260; giving activities include $269,700 for 43 grants (high: $55,000; low: $100).
Purpose and activities: Giving for art and cultural programs, education, and social services.

Fields of interest: Arts and culture; Education; Higher education; Communication media; Public affairs; Human rights; Human services.
Limitations: Applications not accepted. Giving in the U.S., with strong emphasis in New York, NY. No grants to individuals.
Application information: Contributes only to pre-selected organizations.
Trustee: Jean Stein.
EIN: 137127165

6264
The JLK Foundation, Inc.
437 Madison Ave., 36th Fl.
New York City, NY   10022-7001

Established in 2007 in New York.
Donor: Jeffrey L. Kenner.
Foundation type: Independent foundation.
Financial data (yr. ended 12/31/13): Assets, $43,190 (M); gifts received, $164,435; expenditures, $318,215; qualifying distributions, $314,500; giving activities include $314,500 for 13 grants (high: $175,000; low: $1,000).
Fields of interest: Vocational secondary education; Undergraduate education; Domesticated animals; Communication media; Radio.
Type of support: General support.
Limitations: Applications not accepted. Giving primarily in CO, Washington, DC, OR and PA. No grants to individuals.
Application information: Contributes only to pre-selected organizations.
Director: Jeffrey L. Kenner.
EIN: 841655914

6265
The Jockey Club Foundation
40 E. 52nd St., 15th Fl.
New York City, NY   10022-5911
Contact: Nancy Kelly, Secy.
E-mail: contactus@tjcfoundation.org; Main
URL: http://www.tjcfoundation.org

Established in 1943 in New York.
Donors: New York Racing Assn.; Clark Foundation; The John C. Cavanagh Trust; Edith Allen Clark Trust; Cedar Hill Foundation; Hettinger Foundation; NYRA Charities; Thoroughbred Racing Associations of America.
Foundation type: Independent foundation.
Financial data (yr. ended 12/31/13): Assets, $9,208,211 (M); gifts received, $245,295; expenditures, $553,672; qualifying distributions, $526,991; giving activities include $72,182 for 17 grants (high: $25,700; low: $341), and $327,273 for 73 grants to individuals (high: $17,184; low: $300).
Purpose and activities: The foundation's mission is to assist needy individuals in the thoroughbred racing industry.
Fields of interest: Low-income and poor people.
Type of support: General support; Grants to individuals.
Limitations: Applications not accepted. Giving on a national basis.
Application information: Unsolicited requests for funds not accepted.
Officers: Nancy Kelly, Secy.; Laura Barillaro, Treas.

Trustees: John Hettinger, Managing Tr.; C. Steven Duncker; Daniel G. VanClief.
EIN: 136124094

6266
The 1994 Christopher W. Johnson Charitable Trust No. 33

(formerly The Christopher W. Johnson Charitable Trust)
c/o The Johnson Co., Inc.
610 5th Ave., 2nd Fl.
New York City, NY 10020-0100

Established in 1994 in New York.
Donors: Betty W. Johnson; Christopher W. Johnson.
Foundation type: Independent foundation.
Financial data (yr. ended 12/31/13): Assets, $11,912,684 (M); expenditures, $461,670; qualifying distributions, $441,450; giving activities include $440,000 for 2 grants (high: $250,000; low: $190,000).
Fields of interest: Child welfare.
Limitations: Applications not accepted. Giving primarily in Austin, TX; some funding also in New York, NY. No grants to individuals.
Application information: Unsolicited requests for funds not accepted.
Trustees: Betty W. Johnson; Christopher W. Johnson.
EIN: 137046311

6267
J. Howard & Brenda LaGrange Johnson Family Foundation

19 E. 72nd St., Ste. 9D
New York City, NY 10021-4193 (212) 249-3660
Contact: J. Howard Johnson, Admin.

Established in 1997 in New York.
Foundation type: Independent foundation.
Financial data (yr. ended 12/31/13): Assets, $364,015 (M); gifts received, $300,000; expenditures, $304,381; qualifying distributions, $304,381; giving activities include $302,581 for 33 grants (high: $100,000; low: $100).
Purpose and activities: Giving primarily for education, hospitals, and health associations; support also for churches of various denominations, and for a performing arts center.
Fields of interest: Performing arts; Education; Hospital care; Diseases and conditions; Christianity; Youth development.
Application information:
    Initial approach: Proposal
    Deadline(s): None
Officer: J. Howard Johnson, Admin.
Director: Brenda LaGrange Johnson.
EIN: 133952877

6268
Johnson Foundation

(formerly John Alfred & Oscar Johnson Memorial Trust)
c/o Bessemer Trust Co., N.A.
630 5th Ave., Ste. 3425
New York City, NY 10111-0100

Established in 1996 in New York.
Foundation type: Independent foundation.

Financial data (yr. ended 01/31/13): Assets, $5,133,929 (M); expenditures, $326,501; qualifying distributions, $297,490; giving activities include $232,965 for 25 grants (high: $100,000; low: $100).
Fields of interest: Education; Natural resources; Diseases and conditions; Community and economic development; Human services; Child welfare; Youth development.
Type of support: Research; Research and evaluation.
Limitations: Giving primarily in Jamestown, NY. No grants to individuals.
Officer: Carol W. Sellstrom, Exec. Dir.
Trustees: John L. Sellstrom; Bessemer Trust Co., N.A.
EIN: 166438291

6269
The Johnson Foundation

17 Christopher St.
New York City, NY 10014-3518

Donors: Peter James Johnson, Sr.; Aaron Seligson; Peter James Johnson, Jr.
Foundation type: Independent foundation.
Financial data (yr. ended 06/30/14): Assets, $6,607,032 (M); gifts received, $8,120; expenditures, $342,270; qualifying distributions, $298,569; giving activities include $294,860 for 19 grants (high: $110,000; low: $60).
Fields of interest: Education; Catholicism; Human services.
Type of support: General support; Continuing support; Research.
Limitations: Applications not accepted. Giving primarily in NY. No grants to individuals.
Application information: Unsolicited requests for funds not accepted.
Officers and Directors: Christopher Johnson, Chair. and Pres. and Director; Peter James Johnson, Jr., V.P. and Secy. and Director; Veronica Johnson, Treas. and Director; Blanche A. Johnson; Veronica F. Johnson.
EIN: 133696561

6270
The 1994 Robert W. Johnson IV Charitable Trust

c/o The Johnson Co. Inc.
630 5th Ave., 2nd Fl.
New York City, NY 10020

Established in 1994 in New York.
Donor: Betty W. Johnson.
Foundation type: Independent foundation.
Financial data (yr. ended 12/31/13): Assets, $9,104,933 (M); expenditures, $263,455; qualifying distributions, $245,250; giving activities include $245,000 for 26 grants (high: $50,000; low: $1,000).
Fields of interest: Arts and culture; Orchestral music; Museums; Foundations; Diseases and conditions; Diabetes; Immune system diseases; Human services; Child welfare.
Type of support: Research.
Limitations: Applications not accepted. Giving primarily in NY. No grants to individuals.
Application information: Contributes only to pre-selected organizations.

Trustees: Betty W. Johnson; Robert W. Johnson IV.
EIN: 137046310

6271
Johnson-Stillman Family Foundation

c/o Bauer & Keller
21 W. 38th St.
New York City, NY 10018

Donor: Frances D. Spier†.
Foundation type: Independent foundation.
Financial data (yr. ended 12/31/13): Assets, $9,195,015 (M); expenditures, $368,761; qualifying distributions, $364,274; giving activities include $354,000 for 23 grants (high: $144,500; low: $1,000).
Fields of interest: Education; Plant biodiversity; Philanthropy; Christianity.
Limitations: Applications not accepted. Giving primarily in New York, NY; some giving also in CT and WA. No grants to individuals.
Application information: Unsolicited requests for funds not accepted.
Trustees: Lewis E. Lehrman; Louise S. Lehrman; Stanley W. Stillman.
EIN: 137097866

6272
The Paolo Pellegrini and Henrietta Jones Foundation

c/o Flynn Family Office
135 W. 50th St.
New York City, NY 10020

Donors: Paolo Pellegrini; Henrietta Jones.
Foundation type: Independent foundation.
Financial data (yr. ended 12/31/13): Assets, $4,038,573 (M); expenditures, $300,478; qualifying distributions, $299,877; giving activities include $291,992 for 5 grants (high: $233,192; low: $300).
Fields of interest: Education.
International interests: England.
Limitations: Applications not accepted. Giving primarily in London, England and in New York, NY.
Application information: Contributes only to pre-selected organizations.
Trustees: Henrietta Jones; Paolo Pellegrini.
EIN: 263948210

6273
The Peter T. Joseph Foundation

c/o Wendy Evans Joseph
500 Park Ave.
New York City, NY 10022-1611 2123542000

Established in 1990 in New York.
Donor: Peter T. Joseph.
Foundation type: Independent foundation.
Financial data (yr. ended 12/31/14): Assets, $3,575,816; expenditures, $346,616; qualifying distributions, $330,276.
Purpose and activities: Giving primarily for ballet, art museums, education, health, and human services.
Fields of interest: Ballet; Art museums; Education; Diseases and conditions; Human services.
Type of support: Continuing support.
Limitations: Applications not accepted. Giving primarily in NJ, NY, and OH. No grants to individuals.

Application information: Contributes only to pre-selected organizations.
Officers and Directors: Wendy Evans Joseph, Pres. and Director; John A. Silberman, V.P. and Director; Kathleen Joseph Reinhart, Secy. and Director; Evelyn C. Joseph, Treas. and Director; Danielle Joseph.
EIN: 133562511

6274
Joukowsky Family Foundation
620 Park Ave., 5th Fl.
New York City, NY   10065-6561   (212) 355-3151
Contact: Nina J. Koprulu, Pres. and Dir.
FAX: (212) 355-3147; Main URL: http://
www.joukowsky.org

Established in 1981 in New York.
Donor: Artemis A.W. Joukowsky.
Foundation type: Independent foundation.
Financial data (yr. ended 10/31/13): Assets, $17,762,237 (M); expenditures, $809,466; qualifying distributions, $741,135; giving activities include $325,000 for 23 grants (high: $100,000; low: $1,000).
Purpose and activities: Giving primarily for higher and secondary education; support also for a wide range of cultural, social, archaeological and historical activities.
Fields of interest: Education.
Type of support: Scholarships; Fellowships; Capital campaigns; General support; Continuing support; Endowments.
Limitations: Applications not accepted.
Publications: Grants list.
Application information: Contributes only to pre-selected organizations.
Officers and Directors: Nina J. Koprulu, Pres. and Director; Vivien M. Bailey-Barnum, C.O.O.; Emily R. Kessler, Secy. and Exec. Dir.; Henry Christensen III; Artemis A.W. Joukowsky; Martha S. Joukowsky.
Number of staff: 3 full-time professional; 1 part-time professional.
EIN: 133242753

6275
The Joyce Charitable Fund
37 Seminary Rd.
Bedford, NY   10506-1227

Established in 2005 in Delaware.
Foundation type: Independent foundation.
Financial data (yr. ended 12/31/13): Assets, $2,074,899 (M); expenditures, $220,720; qualifying distributions, $192,813; giving activities include $186,440 for 51 grants (high: $25,715; low: $35).
Fields of interest: Education; Higher education; Nonprofits; Diseases and conditions; Christianity; Human services.
Type of support: General support; Regranting.
Limitations: Applications not accepted. Giving primarily in Washington, DC and NY. No grants to individuals.
Application information: Contributes only to pre-selected organizations.
Officers: Timothy J. Joyce, Pres.; Nancy D. Joyce, Secy.-Treas.
EIN: 651259920

6276
Aaron & Ruth Jungreis Foundation
(formerly The Jungreis Foundation)
515 Ocean Ave.
Lawrence, NY   11559-2813

Established in 1999 in New York.
Donors: Aaron Jungreis; Ruth Jungreis.
Foundation type: Independent foundation.
Financial data (yr. ended 12/31/13): Assets, $1,468,801 (M); gifts received, $575,000; expenditures, $242,161; qualifying distributions, $206,318; giving activities include $201,138 for 52 grants (high: $90,000; low: $72).
Fields of interest: Education; Religion; Judaism; Human services.
Limitations: Applications not accepted. Giving primarily in NJ and NY. No grants to individuals.
Application information: Unsolicited requests for funds not accepted.
Officers: Aaron Jungreis, Pres.; Ruth Jungreis, V.P.
EIN: 113466420

6277
The JVZ Foundation
c/o James C. Zelter
45 E. 82nd St., Ste. 8E
New York City, NY   10028

Established in 2007 in New York.
Donors: James C. Zelter; Vivian Zelter.
Foundation type: Independent foundation.
Financial data (yr. ended 12/31/14): Assets, $1,438,757 (M); gifts received, $693,885; expenditures, $405,437; qualifying distributions, $404,887; giving activities include $403,637 for 17 grants (high: $8,222; low: $45).
Fields of interest: Elementary and secondary education; Higher education.
Limitations: Applications not accepted. No grants to individuals.
Application information: Unsolicited requests for funds not accepted.
Trustees: James C. Zelter; Vivian Zelter.
EIN: 208042292

6278
The Kahan Family Foundation
15 Satmar Dr.
Monroe, NY   10950-6056

Established in 2005 in New York.
Donor: Yudel Kahan.
Foundation type: Independent foundation.
Financial data (yr. ended 11/30/13): Assets, $306,278 (M); gifts received, $47,000; expenditures, $159,330; qualifying distributions, $159,330; giving activities include $159,100 for 13 grants (high: $70,000; low: $1,000).
Fields of interest: Judaism.
Limitations: Applications not accepted. Giving primarily in NY. No grants to individuals.
Application information: Unsolicited requests for funds not accepted.
Trustees: Lea Kahan; Yudel Kahan.
EIN: 203986883

6279
Michele & Thomas Kahn Foundation Inc.
25 Central Park W., Apt. 16J
New York City, NY   10023-7209

Established in 1999 in New York.
Donor: Irving Kahn.
Foundation type: Independent foundation.
Financial data (yr. ended 03/31/13): Assets, $1,099,702 (M); expenditures, $157,338; qualifying distributions, $155,538; giving activities include $153,738 for 37 grants (high: $56,000; low: $83).
Fields of interest: Education; University education; Religion; Human services.
Type of support: General support.
Limitations: Applications not accepted. Giving primarily in NY. No grants to individuals.
Application information: Contributes only to pre-selected organizations.
Officers: Thomas Kahn, Pres.; Irving Kahn, V.P.
EIN: 134049922

6280
The Kallinikeion Foundation
c/o Bessemer Trust Co., N.A.
630 5th Ave.
New York City, NY   10111-0001

Established in 1994 in Delaware.
Donors: Alexandra Kallin†; Alexandra Kallin Terminating Trust.
Foundation type: Independent foundation.
Financial data (yr. ended 12/31/14): Assets, $5,663,212; expenditures, $232,009; qualifying distributions, $215,595.
Purpose and activities: Giving to promote the Greek Orthodox Church, the study of the Greek language (both ancient and modern) and the study of Greek culture.
Fields of interest: Arts and culture; Higher education.
Type of support: General support.
Limitations: Applications not accepted. Giving primarily in MA and NY. No grants to individuals.
Application information: Contributes only to pre-selected organizations.
Officers: Emanuel G. Demos, Pres.; Helen Moneo, V.P.; Helen Hadjiyannakis Bender, Secy.; George Tsandikos, Treas.
Directors: Froso Beys; Robert G. Stephanopoulos.
EIN: 133752109

6281
Abraham Kamber Foundation
551 5th Ave., Ste. 2210
New York City, NY   10176
Contact: Steven M. Levy

Established in 1950 in New York.
Donors: Steven M. Levy; Peter B. Levy; Gloria K. Levy; Stanley H. Levy.
Foundation type: Independent foundation.
Financial data (yr. ended 12/31/13): Assets, $5,586,940 (M); expenditures, $311,483; qualifying distributions, $228,065; giving activities include $204,990 for 23 grants (high: $87,000; low: $25).
Purpose and activities: Giving primarily to Jewish institutions and synagogues.

Fields of interest: Education; Nonprofits; Emergency medical services; Judaism; Human services.
Type of support: General support; Regranting.
Limitations: Applications not accepted. No grants to individuals.
Application information: Unsolicited requests for funds not accepted.
Trustees: Peter B. Levy; Steven M. Levy.
EIN: 136102029

6282
Kaminer Foundation
95 Charles St., Ste. 5
New York City, NY 10014-2621 (212) 255-2339
Contact: Henry Kaminer, Tr.

Established in 1985 in New Jersey.
Donors: Henry Kaminer; Phyllis Kaminer†; Kaminer Partners.
Foundation type: Independent foundation.
Financial data (yr. ended 12/31/13): Assets, $756,631 (M); expenditures, $424,146; qualifying distributions, $396,126; giving activities include $394,650 for 20 grants (high: $263,000; low: $100).
Purpose and activities: Giving primarily for Jewish organizations; funding also for education, health and human services.
Fields of interest: Education; Nonprofits; Diseases and conditions; Judaism; Human services.
Type of support: Regranting.
Limitations: Giving primarily in NY. No grants to individuals.
Application information:
  Initial approach: Letter
  Deadline(s): None
  Board meeting date(s): Nov.
Trustees: Ariel Kaminer; Henry Kaminer; Martin Kaminer.
EIN: 222595518

6283
The Kandell Fund
59 E. 54th St.
New York City, NY 10022-4211

Established in 1952 in New York.
Donors: Leonard Kandell†; Florence Kandell†; Alice Joseph; Leslie Friedberg; Cynthia Marvell Brown; Elinor Friedberg; Andrew Joseph†; Benjamin Joseph; Alice Kandell; Leslie Kandell.
Foundation type: Independent foundation.
Financial data (yr. ended 12/31/13): Assets, $124,309 (M); gifts received, $220,000; expenditures, $284,585; qualifying distributions, $284,085; giving activities include $282,400 for 165 grants (high: $10,000; low: $100).
Fields of interest: Arts and culture; Museums; Natural resources; Nonprofits; Hospital care; Human services.
Type of support: Regranting.
Limitations: Applications not accepted. No support for political organizations . No grants to individuals.
Application information: Contributes only to pre-selected organizations.
Officers: Donald Gordon, Pres. and Treas.; Debra Fechter, Secy.
Directors: Alice Kandell; Leslie Kandell.
EIN: 136117648

6284
The Naomi Kaplan Family Foundation
82 Magnolia Ave.
Larchmont, NY 10538-4010

Established in 2002 in New York.
Donor: Naomi Kaplan.
Foundation type: Independent foundation.
Financial data (yr. ended 12/31/13): Assets, $433,709 (M); expenditures, $202,738; qualifying distributions, $191,163; giving activities include $183,500 for 4 grants (high: $100,000; low: $8,500).
Fields of interest: Higher education; Judaism; Religion for youth.
Limitations: Applications not accepted. Giving primarily in NJ and NY. No grants to individuals.
Application information: Contributes only to pre-selected organizations.
Trustees: John Ferguson; Naomi Kaplan; James O'Connor.
EIN: 030452265

6285
Kasowitz Family Foundation, Inc.
40 Bond St., Ste. TH2
New York City, NY 10012-2497

Donor: Sheldon Kasowitz.
Foundation type: Independent foundation.
Financial data (yr. ended 12/31/14): Assets, $1,202,585; expenditures, $171,825; qualifying distributions, $169,756.
Fields of interest: Arts and culture; Education; Human services.
Limitations: Applications not accepted.
Application information: Unsolicited requests for funds not accepted.
Officers: Sheldon Kasowitz, Pres.; Samantha Kasowitz, V.P.
EIN: 264807628

6286
Irfan Kathwari Foundation Inc.
1875 Palmer Ave.
Larchmont, NY 10538-3053 (203) 743-8438
E-mail: kathwarifoundation@gmail.com

Established in 1992 in New York.
Donors: IFO Enterprises, Ltd.; M. Farooq Kathwari.
Foundation type: Independent foundation.
Financial data (yr. ended 06/30/13): Assets, $6,931,366 (M); expenditures, $268,455; qualifying distributions, $247,905; giving activities include $209,000 for 23 grants (high: $35,000; low: $1,000), and $35,250 for 61 grants to individuals.
Purpose and activities: The foundation supports organizations involved with education, minority enrollment, humanitarian assistance, and conflict resolution, and grants scholarships to children of employees of Ethan Allen Interiors, Inc. The foundation also supports special projects focused on Kashmir.
Fields of interest: Education; Right to free movement and asylum; Females; Female children and youth.
International interests: India; Pakistan; Southeastern Asia.

Type of support: General support; Annual campaigns; Equipment; Program development; Scholarships.
Limitations: Applications accepted. Giving primarily in Washington, DC and New York, NY.
Application information: Application form required.
  Initial approach: Letter
  Copies of proposal: 1
  Deadline(s): None
Officers: M. Farooq Kathwari, Pres.; Farah Kathwari, V.P.; Omar Kathwari, Secy.; Farida Kathwari, Treas.
EIN: 133681135

6287
The Rosalie Katz Family Foundation, Inc.
360 Hamilton Ave., Ste. 1110
White Plains, NY 10601-1811

Established in 2001 in New York.
Donor: Rosalie Katz†.
Foundation type: Independent foundation.
Financial data (yr. ended 12/31/13): Assets, $3,661,644 (M); gifts received, $382,260; expenditures, $223,945; qualifying distributions, $204,104; giving activities include $204,104 for grants (high: $43,500; low: $250).
Fields of interest: Education; Religion; Human services.
Limitations: Applications not accepted. Giving primarily in Houston, TX. No grants to individuals.
Application information: Unsolicited requests for funds not accepted.
Officers: Meredith Gantcher, Pres.; Gary Katz, V.P.; Wendy Waxman, Secy.
EIN: 311757404

6288
The Katzin Foundation
110 Riverside Dr., Ste. 16F
New York City, NY 10024-3734

Established in 1995 in California.
Donors: Jerome S. Katzin; David Katzin.
Foundation type: Independent foundation.
Financial data (yr. ended 12/31/13): Assets, $2,768,841 (M); expenditures, $170,640; qualifying distributions, $160,500; giving activities include $160,500 for 18 grants (high: $40,000; low: $2,500).
Fields of interest: Nonprofits; Judaism; Human services; Child welfare; Unknown or not classified.
International interests: Israel.
Type of support: Regranting.
Limitations: Applications not accepted. Giving primarily in CA, NY and Israel. No grants to individuals, or for projects or research.
Application information: Contributes only to pre-selected organizations.
  Board meeting date(s): Semi-annually
Officers: Jerome S. Katzin, Pres.; Daniel Katzin, Treas.; Diane Katzin, Exec. Dir.
Directors: Dr. David Katzin.
Number of staff: 1 full-time professional.
EIN: 330680076

6289
Richard and Jane Katzman Foundation
15 W. 81st St., Ste. 12C
New York City, NY 10024-6022

Donor: Richard Katzman.
Foundation type: Independent foundation.
Financial data (yr. ended 12/31/13): Assets, $715,177 (M); gifts received, $81,100; expenditures, $149,243; qualifying distributions, $145,000; giving activities include $145,000 for 4 grants (high: $100,000; low: $5,000).
Fields of interest: Education; Health; Human services.
Limitations: Applications not accepted. Giving primarily in NY.
Application information: Unsolicited requests for funds not accepted.
Officers and Directors: Jane Dray Katzman, Pres. and Director; Richard Katzman, V.P. and Secy.-Treas.
EIN: 274266074

6290
Charles and Pauline Kautz Foundation
c/o Rouis and Co., LLP
P.O. Box 209
Wurtsboro, NY   12790-0209
Application address: c/o Robert Curtis, Tr., P.O. Box 18, Obernberg, NY 12767, tel.: (845) 482-6064

Established in 1976 in New York.
Donor: Charles P. Kautz‡.
Foundation type: Independent foundation.
Financial data (yr. ended 12/31/13): Assets, $6,194,613 (M); expenditures, $297,993; qualifying distributions, $252,490; giving activities include $232,840 for grants to individuals.
Purpose and activities: Scholarships only to graduates of Delaware Valley High School continuing their education at a higher institution.
Fields of interest: Education.
Type of support: Student aid; Individual development.
Limitations: Applications accepted. Giving limited to the Delaware Valley, NY, area.
Application information: Applications available at Guidance Dept. of Delaware Valley High School, NY. Application form required.
   Deadline(s): May 1
Trustees: Ruth Burstman; Robert Curtis; Debra Reimer; Thomas Roche; Fred Stabberd.
EIN: 141579429

6291
The KCEG Foundation
27 Robert Pitt Dr.
Monsey, NY   10952-3332

Established in 1997 in New York.
Donors: Ephraim Grossman; The Wechsler Group.
Foundation type: Independent foundation.
Financial data (yr. ended 12/31/13): Assets, $835,624 (M); gifts received, $500,000; expenditures, $208,931; qualifying distributions, $208,787; giving activities include $208,012 for 8 + grants (high: $80,830).
Purpose and activities: Giving primarily to Jewish organizations.
Fields of interest: Education; Judaism.
Type of support: General support.
Limitations: Applications not accepted. Giving primarily in NY. No grants to individuals.
Application information: Contributes only to pre-selected organizations.

Trustees: Ephraim Grossman; Hendel Grossman.
EIN: 137103161

6292
Keeler Motor Car Company Charitable Foundation
P.O. Box 11002
Loudonville, NY   12211

Donor: Keeler Motor Car Co., Inc.
Foundation type: Company-sponsored foundation.
Financial data (yr. ended 06/30/14): Assets, $1,610,213 (M); gifts received, $250,000; expenditures, $338,684; qualifying distributions, $317,850; giving activities include $317,850 for 80 grants (high: $50,000; low: $250).
Fields of interest: Arts and culture; Education; Higher education; Health.
Limitations: Applications not accepted.
Application information: Contributes only to pre-selected organizations.
Trustee: Alexander Keeler.
EIN: 461612917

6293
Charles S. Keene Foundation
1 Court Sq., 19th Fl.
Long Island City, NY   11120

Foundation type: Independent foundation.
Financial data (yr. ended 12/31/14): Assets, $9,828,547; expenditures, $459,049; qualifying distributions, $444,556.
Fields of interest: Arts and culture; Religion; Human services.
Limitations: Applications not accepted. Giving primarily in New York, NY.
Application information: Unsolicited requests for funds not accepted.
Trustee: CitiBank, N.A.
EIN: 136053173

6294
James Keene Foundation
340 West End Ave., Rm. 1A
New York City, NY   10023-8148

Established in 1998 in New York.
Donors: Betty Wendriner Trust; Norma Reid; David Backman; Sherrie Backman; James Garfinkel; Daniel V. Klein.
Foundation type: Independent foundation.
Financial data (yr. ended 12/31/13): Assets, $2,935,303 (M); expenditures, $284,557; qualifying distributions, $209,740; giving activities include $209,740 for 16 grants (high: $86,580; low: $250).
Fields of interest: Judaism.
Limitations: Applications not accepted. Giving primarily in NY. No grants to individuals.
Application information: Contributes only to pre-selected organizations.
Directors: Avrohom Kirschenbaum; Maurice Kirschenbaum; Mordechai Kirschenbaum; Bella Pliskin.
EIN: 133377892

6295
The Denis P. and Carol A. Kelleher Charitable Foundation
17 Battery Pl., 11th Fl.
New York City, NY   10004-1101

Established in 2000 in New York.
Donor: Denis P. Kelleher.
Foundation type: Independent foundation.
Financial data (yr. ended 10/31/13): Assets, $3,916,836 (M); gifts received, $811,778; expenditures, $414,123; qualifying distributions, $400,883; giving activities include $397,144 for 58 grants (high: $85,000; low: $100).
Purpose and activities: Giving primarily for higher education, Roman Catholic organizations and churches, and social services, including Irish organizations.
Fields of interest: Historic preservation; Higher education; Nonprofits; Catholicism; Human services.
Type of support: Regranting.
Limitations: Applications not accepted. Giving primarily in New York, NY. No grants to individuals.
Application information: Contributes only to pre-selected organizations.
Directors: Carol A. Kelleher; Denis P. Kelleher; Denis P. Kelleher, Jr.; Sean M. Kelleher; Colleen P. Sorrentino.
EIN: 134149751

6296
The Keller Family Charitable Trust
c/o The Ayco Co., Tax Dept.
P.O. Box 15014
Albany, NY   12212-5014

Donors: Craig P. Keller; C. Joyce Keller.
Foundation type: Independent foundation.
Financial data (yr. ended 12/31/13): Assets, $754,126 (M); gifts received, $198,325; expenditures, $187,944; qualifying distributions, $186,450; giving activities include $186,450 for 36 grants (high: $40,000; low: $750).
Fields of interest: Arts and culture; Education; Religion.
Limitations: Applications not accepted. Giving primarily in PA.
Application information: Unsolicited requests for funds not accepted.
Trustees: C. Joyce Keller; Craig P. Keller.
EIN: 386858805

6297
Keller-Shatanoff Foundation
c/o Irving Gluck
5314 18th Ave.
Brooklyn, NY   11204-1522

Established in 1993 in New York.
Donor: Betty S. Keller‡.
Foundation type: Independent foundation.
Financial data (yr. ended 12/31/13): Assets, $4,129,627 (M); expenditures, $270,227; qualifying distributions, $203,556; giving activities include $197,000 for 12 grants (high: $25,000; low: $2,000).
Fields of interest: Arts education; Opera; Art museums; Graduate and professional education; Nonprofits; Dental care; Diseases and conditions; Judaism.

Type of support: Regranting.
Limitations: Applications not accepted. Giving primarily in NY. No grants to individuals.
Application information: Contributes only to pre-selected organizations.
Trustees: Irving Gluck; Steve Israel; Helaine Solc.
EIN: 133699801

6298
The Kelsey Family Foundation
c/o J. Velten
33 White Cliff Ln.
Nesconset, NY 11767-1625

Established in 1997 in New Jersey.
Donor: John L. Kelsey.
Foundation type: Independent foundation.
Financial data (yr. ended 12/31/13): Assets, $3,602,311 (M); expenditures, $163,890; qualifying distributions, $160,450; giving activities include $158,000 for 36 grants (high: $40,000; low: $100).
Fields of interest: University education; Hospital care; Child welfare.
Limitations: Applications not accepted. Giving primarily in FL. No grants to individuals.
Application information: Unsolicited requests for funds not accepted.
Trustees: Grayson Kelsey Hardman; Anne H.P. Kelsey; John L. Kelsey; Jonathan C. Kelsey.
EIN: 137107820

6299
The Kenlou Foundation Inc.
P.O. Box 25300
Rochester, NY 14625-0300

Established in 2000 in New York.
Donors: Richard E. Williams; Mary E. Swierkos; John K. Williams; Robert M. Williams.
Foundation type: Independent foundation.
Financial data (yr. ended 12/31/13): Assets, $3,379,054 (M); gifts received, $90; expenditures, $175,748; qualifying distributions, $150,400; giving activities include $150,400 for 22 grants (high: $25,000; low: $1,000).
Fields of interest: Arts and culture; Maritime museums; Water resources; Domesticated animals; Hospice care; Cancers; Human services.
Limitations: Applications not accepted. Giving primarily in Rochester, NY. No grants to individuals.
Application information: Contributes only to pre-selected organizations.
Officers: Richard E. Williams, Pres.; John K. Williams, V.P.; Robert M. Williams, Secy.; Mary E. Swierkos, Treas.
EIN: 161596738

6300
Marion E. Kenworthy - Sarah H. Swift Foundation, Inc.
NY 10065-6136 (212) 988-0473
Contact: Rosalind W. Harris, Admin.
FAX: (212) 988-2483; E-mail: ksfdtn@aol.com; Main URL: http://www.kenworthyswiftfoundation.org

Established in 1962 in New York.
Donors: Marion E. Kenworthy†; Mary L. Bonnell.
Foundation type: Independent foundation.

Financial data (yr. ended 12/31/13): Assets, $10,194,287 (M); expenditures, $480,641; qualifying distributions, $438,026; giving activities include $399,500 for 36 grants (high: $15,000; low: $4,500).
Purpose and activities: Giving primarily to promote and advance the mental and emotional health and well being of children and young persons under 21 years of age, through the development and improvement of understanding and practice in the fields of adoption, guidance, preventive psychiatry and in other fields of child welfare.
Fields of interest: Early childhood education; Mental health care; Crime prevention; Human services; Family services; Child welfare; Child development; Children and youth; Adolescents.
Type of support: General support; Continuing support; Program development; Publications; Seed money; Research; Program evaluations; Research and evaluation.
Limitations: Applications accepted. Giving primarily in New York City and the surrounding tri-state area. No support for political organizations, or for narcotics addiction treatment or autism. No grants to individuals, or for building or capital funds or for bricks and mortar projects.
Publications: Application guidelines; Informational brochure (including application guidelines).
Application information: Application guidelines available on foundation web site.
  Initial approach: Proposal
  Copies of proposal: 3
  Deadline(s): Mar. 31 and Oct. 31
  Board meeting date(s): May and Dec.
  Final notification: 1 month after board meeting
Officers and Directors: Trudy Festinger, Pres. and Director; Dr. Alice P. Lin, V.P. and Director; Stephen Wise Tulin, Esq., Secy.-Treas. and Director.
Number of staff: 1 part-time support.
EIN: 136140940

6301
Kenyon Charitable Foundation
1 Hemlock Hollow
Chappaqua, NY 10514-1923 (914) 238-8098

Established in 2007 in New York.
Donors: Mark J. Kenyon; Ann M. Kenyon.
Foundation type: Independent foundation.
Financial data (yr. ended 12/31/13): Assets, $603,292 (M); expenditures, $210,038; qualifying distributions, $191,513; giving activities include $191,513 for 24 grants (high: $100,000; low: $250).
Fields of interest: University education.
Type of support: General support.
Limitations: Applications accepted. Giving primarily in ME and NC. No grants to individuals.
Application information: Application form required.
  Initial approach: Letter
  Deadline(s): None
Trustees: Ann M. Kenyon; Mark J. Kenyon.
EIN: 207535967

6302
Keren Eliyahu, Inc.
c/o Alexander Scharf
305 West End Ave.
New York City, NY 10023-8157

Donors: Senior Home Care, Inc.; Solomon T. Scharf; Zakain Assocs., LP; White Plains Hotel Limited Partnership; The Esplanade Venture Partnership LP; David Scharf; Alexander Scharf.
Foundation type: Independent foundation.
Financial data (yr. ended 12/31/12): Assets, $443,781 (M); gifts received, $25,500; expenditures, $339,338; qualifying distributions, $334,578; giving activities include $334,578 for grants.
Purpose and activities: Giving primarily to Jewish agencies, temples, and schools.
Fields of interest: Elementary and secondary education; Judaism.
Limitations: Applications not accepted. Giving primarily in New York, NY. No grants to individuals.
Application information: Contributes only to pre-selected organizations.
Officers: Alexander Scharf, Pres. and Treas.; Susan Diamond, Secy.
Director: David Scharf.
EIN: 133978200

6303
The Jeff and Erica Keswin Family Foundation
405 Park Ave., 6th Fl.
New York City, NY 10022-9422

Established in 2002 in New York.
Donors: Erica Keswin; Jeffrey Keswin.
Foundation type: Independent foundation.
Financial data (yr. ended 12/31/13): Assets, $2,471,975 (M); gifts received, $583,430; expenditures, $395,115; qualifying distributions, $385,820; giving activities include $381,525 for 27 grants (high: $145,000; low: $50).
Fields of interest: Education; Nonprofits; Diseases and conditions; Libraries; Judaism.
Type of support: Regranting.
Limitations: Applications not accepted. Giving primarily in New York, NY. No grants to individuals.
Application information: Contributes only to pre-selected organizations.
Trustees: Erica Keswin; Jeffrey Keswin.
EIN: 134193962

6304
The Hagop Kevorkian Fund
1025 Northern Blvd., Ste. 209
Roslyn, NY 11576-1506

Donor: Hagop Kevorkian†.
Foundation type: Independent foundation.
Financial data (yr. ended 12/31/13): Assets, $4,279,708 (M); expenditures, $514,942; qualifying distributions, $451,847; giving activities include $411,000 for 5 grants (high: $140,000; low: $27,000).
Purpose and activities: Giving to promote interest in Near and Middle Eastern art through exhibitions and fellowships administered by the recipient institutions for research and study in this field.
Fields of interest: Art museums; Higher education.
International interests: Middle East.
Type of support: Professorships; Curriculum development; Fellowships; Internships; Research.
Limitations: Applications not accepted. Giving primarily in NY. No grants to individuals.

Application information: Unsolicited requests for funds not accepted.

Board meeting date(s): Spring and fall

Officers: Ralph Minasian, Pres. and Treas.; Martin D. Polevoy, V.P. and Secy.

Directors: Ralph S. Hattox; Michele C. Tocci.

EIN: 131839686

6305
Key & Candle Foundation
P.O. Box 307
Scarsdale, NY 10583-0307

Established in 2006 in New York.

Donors: John Manley; Marguerite Manley†; Christopher Manley; Frances Manley; Robert Orens; Sarah Orens; Edward Manley.

Foundation type: Independent foundation.

Financial data (yr. ended 12/31/12): Assets, $51,171 (M); gifts received, $119,663; expenditures, $147,443; qualifying distributions, $134,911; giving activities include $134,911 for 3 grants (high: $96,803; low: $11,808).

Fields of interest: Mental health care; Human services.

Limitations: Applications not accepted. Giving primarily in NY.

Application information: Unsolicited requests for funds not accepted.

Officers: Susanne Manley, Pres.; John Manley, Secy.-Treas.

Director: Daniel Martin.

EIN: 342054306

6306
The Peter and Eaddo Kiernan Foundation
c/o BCRS Assoc., LLC
77 Water St., 9th Fl.
New York City, NY 10005-4414

Established in 1991 in New York.

Donor: Peter D. Kiernan.

Foundation type: Independent foundation.

Financial data (yr. ended 05/31/14): Assets, $207,426 (M); gifts received, $358,100; expenditures, $338,134; qualifying distributions, $331,784; giving activities include $329,884 for 12 grants (high: $100,000; low: $1,000).

Fields of interest: Education; Higher education; Foundations.

Limitations: Applications not accepted. Giving primarily in New York, NY; funding also in NJ, and Charlottesville, VA. No grants to individuals or for scholarships; no loans.

Application information: Contributes only to pre-selected organizations.

Trustees: Eaddo H. Kiernan; Peter D. Kiernan.

EIN: 133637705

6307
The David M. Kies Family Foundation
c/o Sullivan & Cromwell LLP
125 Broad St.
New York City, NY 10004-2498

Established in 2001 in New York.

Donor: David M. Kies.

Foundation type: Independent foundation.

Financial data (yr. ended 11/30/14): Assets, $1,435,154 (M); expenditures, $152,797; qualifying distributions, $151,940; giving activities include $151,550 for 22 grants (high: $100,000; low: $100).

Fields of interest: Education; Higher education; Health; Community and economic development.

Limitations: Applications not accepted. Giving primarily in PA; with some giving in NY. No grants to individuals.

Application information: Unsolicited requests for funds not accepted.

Trustees: Laura Kies Gever; David M. Kies; Kathryn L. Kies.

EIN: 134199760

6308
David Kimmel Foundation
c/o Harry Wendroff, BT & Co., LLP
1 Penn Plz., Ste. 5335
New York City, NY 10119-0219 2126955003
Application address: c/o Stephen Mason Esq., 7737 La Mirada Dr., Boca Raton, FL 33433

Established in 2000 in New York.

Donor: David Kimmel†.

Foundation type: Independent foundation.

Financial data (yr. ended 12/31/14): Assets, $7,787,992; expenditures, $510,552; qualifying distributions, $460,963.

Fields of interest: Health; Judaism; Human services.

Limitations: Applications accepted. Giving primarily in NY. No grants to individuals.

Application information: Application form required.

Initial approach: Letter

Deadline(s): None

Directors: Harry Wendroff; Stephen Mason; Shirley Bernstein-Mason; Nancy Viola; Susan Wendroff; Diane Kimmel Dalsimer.

EIN: 134110021

6309
The Elbrun & Peter Kimmelman Family Foundation, Inc.
800 3rd Ave., Ste. 3100
New York City, NY 10022-7667

Established in 1979 in New York.

Donor: Peter Kimmelman.

Foundation type: Independent foundation.

Financial data (yr. ended 11/30/14): Assets, $4,196; gifts received, $219,348; expenditures, $220,241; qualifying distributions, $219,902.

Purpose and activities: Giving primarily for the arts and education.

Fields of interest: Arts and culture; Education; Human services.

Type of support: General support; Annual campaigns.

Limitations: Applications not accepted. Giving primarily in Washington, DC and New York, NY. No grants to individuals.

Application information: Contributes only to pre-selected organizations.

Officers: Peter Kimmelman, Pres.; Elbrun Kimmelman, Treas.

Directors: E. Kweilen Hatleskog; P. Damian Kimmelman.

EIN: 132967083

6310
Rattray Kimura Foundation
c/o Carol Rattray
923 5th Ave., Ste. 8A
New York City, NY 10021-2649

Established in 2001 in New York.

Donors: Carol Rattray; Timothy S. Rattray.

Foundation type: Independent foundation.

Financial data (yr. ended 12/31/13): Assets, $201,708 (M); gifts received, $269,885; expenditures, $220,254; qualifying distributions, $204,905; giving activities include $204,905 for 19 grants (high: $53,000; low: $25).

Fields of interest: Higher education; Natural resources; Disasters and emergency management.

Type of support: General support.

Limitations: Applications not accepted. Giving primarily in New York, NY.

Application information: Unsolicited requests for funds not accepted.

Officers: Carol Rattray, Pres.; Timothy S. Rattray, Secy.

EIN: 134110129

6311
Charles & Lucille King Family Foundation, Inc.
1212 Avenue of the Americas, 7th Fl.
New York City, NY 10036-1600 (212) 682-2913
Contact: Michael Donovan, Educational Dir.; Karen E. Kennedy, Asst. Educational Dir.
E-mail: kingscholarships@aol.com; Main URL: http://www.kingfoundation.org
Grants List: http://www.kingfoundation.org/winners.html

Established in 1988 in New Jersey.

Donors: Diana King; Karen Rabe.

Foundation type: Independent foundation.

Financial data (yr. ended 12/31/13): Assets, $1,560,182 (M); gifts received, $5,950; expenditures, $371,675; qualifying distributions, $299,147; giving activities include $226,360 for 73 grants (high: $73,500; low: $100).

Purpose and activities: Giving primarily for scholarship awards available to junior and senior undergraduate college students of film and television currently attending a four year accredited university in the United States.

Fields of interest: Higher education; Communication media; Human services.

Type of support: General support; Student aid.

Limitations: Giving on a national basis.

Publications: Application guidelines; Informational brochure (including application guidelines).

Application information: See foundation web site for application guidelines and procedures. Scholarship application forms can only be downloaded from foundation web site between Sept. and Mar. Also, grant guidelines for various programs available on web site.

Initial approach: Letter, telephone, e-mail to request application

Deadline(s): Mar. 15 for the following academic year

Board meeting date(s): Annually

Officers and Directors: Diana King, Chair. and Pres. and Director; Charles J. Brucia, V.P. and Treas. and Director; Eugene V. Kokot, Secy. and Director; M. Graham Coleman.

Number of staff: None.
EIN: 133489257

6312
Kingjay Foundation Trust
c/o Steven Stern
760 Park Ave.
New York City, NY 10021-4152

Established in 2006 in New York.
Donors: Judith Stern; Roy H. Stern.
Foundation type: Independent foundation.
Financial data (yr. ended 12/31/13): Assets, $4,915,517 (M); expenditures, $334,750; qualifying distributions, $334,750; giving activities include $334,750 for 47 grants (high: $244,800; low: $180).
Fields of interest: Judaism.
Limitations: Applications not accepted. No grants to individuals.
Application information: Contributes only to pre-selected organizations.
Officers: Roy H. Stern, Pres.; Judith Stern, Treas.
EIN: 116605083

6313
The Kirby Family Foundation
c/o The Ayco Company, LP
P.O. Box 860
Saratoga Springs, NY 12866-0860
Contact: Shelly Stone

Established in 1985 in Pennsylvania.
Donors: Robert E. Kirby†; Robert Kirby Charitable Lead Annuity Trust; Robert Kirby Clat Distribution.
Foundation type: Independent foundation.
Financial data (yr. ended 12/31/14): Assets, $4,940,124 (M); gifts received, $243,915; expenditures, $510,555; qualifying distributions, $269,500; giving activities include $269,500 for 69 grants (high: $20,000; low: $1,000).
Fields of interest: Arts and culture; Theater; Orchestral music; Elementary and secondary education; Higher education; Film and video; Human services.
Type of support: General support; Scholarships.
Limitations: Applications not accepted. Giving primarily in CA, FL, and NY. No grants to individuals.
Application information: Contributes only to pre-selected organizations.
Officers and Directors: Linda K. Mewshaw, Chair. and Pres.; Michael F. Mewshaw, V.P. and Director; Sean K. Mewshaw, Secy.-Treas. and Director; Marc P. Mewshaw.
EIN: 251513507

6314
Maimon and Ruth Kirschenbaum Foundation Inc.
510 Crown St., Rm. 510
Brooklyn, NY 11213-5137

Donors: D. Maimon Kirschenbaum; Ruth Kirschenbaum.
Foundation type: Independent foundation.
Financial data (yr. ended 12/31/13): Assets, $36 (M); gifts received, $110,927; expenditures, $124,861; qualifying distributions, $124,715; giving activities include $124,715 for 29 grants (high: $28,050; low: $18).

Fields of interest: Education; Religion.
Limitations: Applications not accepted. Giving primarily in Brooklyn, NY.
Application information: Unsolicited requests for funds not accepted.
Directors: D. Maimon Kirschenbaum; Ruth Kirschenbaum; Bella Pliskin.
EIN: 461164297

6315
Martin Kirzner Family Foundation
1082 E. 23rd St.
Brooklyn, NY 11210-4513

Established in 2003 in Unspecified.
Donor: Martin Kirzner.
Foundation type: Independent foundation.
Financial data (yr. ended 12/31/13): Assets, $241,926 (M); gifts received, $253,600; expenditures, $195,547; qualifying distributions, $195,547; giving activities include $194,497 for grants.
Fields of interest: Judaism.
Limitations: Applications not accepted. No grants to individuals.
Application information: Unsolicited requests for funds not accepted.
Trustee: Martin Kirzner.
EIN: 200401597

6316
The William Kistler Charitable Fund
c/o Anchin, Block & Anchin, LLP
1375 Broadway
New York City, NY 10018-7086

Established in 2007 in New York.
Donor: William L. Kistler III.
Foundation type: Independent foundation.
Financial data (yr. ended 12/31/13): Assets, $247 (M); gifts received, $359,000; expenditures, $358,776; qualifying distributions, $357,356; giving activities include $356,000 for 23 grants (high: $40,000; low: $500).
Fields of interest: Natural resources; Religion; Human services.
Limitations: Applications not accepted. Giving primarily in NY. No grants to individuals.
Application information: Contributes only to pre-selected organizations.
Officers and Directors: William L. Kistler III, Pres. and Director; David S. Barr, Secy.-Treas.; Brian G. Kistler; Eileen K. Kistler; Robert A.F. Thurman.
EIN: 261606967

6317
Kitov Foundation
c/o BCRS Associates, LLC
77 Water St., 9th Fl.
New York City, NY 10005-3701

Established in 1987 in New York.
Donor: Jacob Z. Schuster.
Foundation type: Independent foundation.
Financial data (yr. ended 06/30/14): Assets, $3,255,768 (M); gifts received, $50,000; expenditures, $233,801; qualifying distributions, $227,251; giving activities include $224,042 for 184 grants (high: $15,000; low: $12).

Purpose and activities: Giving primarily for Jewish organizations, temples, and yeshivas.
Fields of interest: Elementary and secondary education; Judaism.
International interests: Israel.
Limitations: Applications not accepted. Giving primarily in NY; some funding also in Israel. No grants to individuals.
Application information: Contributes only to pre-selected organizations.
Trustees: Diane T. Schuster; Jacob Z. Schuster.
EIN: 133437905

6318
Samuel & Francine Klagsbrun Foundation
c/o Traust Sollus CPA's
70 E. 55th St., Ste. 12th Fl.
New York City, NY 10022

Established in 1987 in New York.
Donors: Samuel C. Klagsbrun; Francine Klagsbrun.
Foundation type: Independent foundation.
Financial data (yr. ended 12/31/13): Assets, $370,602 (M); expenditures, $242,729; qualifying distributions, $240,204; giving activities include $240,204 for 124 grants (high: $46,250; low: $15).
Fields of interest: Arts and culture; Museums; Higher education; Graduate and professional education; Nonprofits; Mental health care; Judaism; Theology; Human services.
International interests: Israel.
Type of support: General support; Continuing support; Capital campaigns; Regranting.
Limitations: Applications not accepted. No grants to individuals.
Application information: Contributes only to pre-selected organizations.
Directors: Francine Klagsbrun; Samuel C. Klagsbrun.
EIN: 133452159

6319
The Arthur Klaus Family Foundation
(also known as AK Foundation)
21-09 Borden Ave.
Long Island City, NY 11101-4531

Established in 2006 in Delaware.
Donor: Burma Bibas, Inc.
Foundation type: Independent foundation.
Financial data (yr. ended 11/30/14): Assets, $3,203,977 (M); expenditures, $169,580; qualifying distributions, $156,700; giving activities include $156,700 for 27 grants (high: $75,000; low: $250).
Fields of interest: Education; Judaism.
Limitations: Applications not accepted. No grants to individuals.
Application information: Unsolicited requests for funds not accepted.
Officers: Arthur Klaus, Pres.; Vivian Klaus, V.P. and Secy.; Ryan Klaus, V.P.
EIN: 205792833

6320
The Lester & Esther Klaus Family Foundation
(formerly The Lester Klaus Family Foundation)
21-09 Borden Ave.
Long Island City, NY 11101-4531

Established in 2006 in Delaware.
Donor: Burma Bibas, Inc.
Foundation type: Independent foundation.
Financial data (yr. ended 11/30/14): Assets, $3,034,421 (M); expenditures, $270,464; qualifying distributions, $258,250; giving activities include $258,250 for 36 grants (high: $97,500; low: $500).
Fields of interest: Nonprofits; Judaism.
Type of support: Regranting.
Limitations: Applications not accepted. No grants to individuals.
Application information: Unsolicited requests for funds not accepted.
Officers: Lester Klaus, Pres.; Esther Klaus, V.P. and Secy.; Fraddie Rapp, V.P.; Jeffrey Klaus, V.P.; Michael Klaus, V.P.; Steven Klaus, V.P.
EIN: 205793010

6321
The Mortimer & Barbara Klaus Family Foundation

21-09 Borden Ave.
Long Island City, NY   11101-4531

Established in 2006 in Delaware.
Donor: Burma Bibas, Inc.
Foundation type: Independent foundation.
Financial data (yr. ended 11/30/13): Assets, $3,602,534 (M); expenditures, $186,087; qualifying distributions, $172,048; giving activities include $172,048 for 32 grants (high: $52,000; low: $500).
Fields of interest: Arts and culture; Education; Health.
Limitations: Applications not accepted. No grants to individuals.
Application information: Unsolicited requests for funds not accepted.
Officers: Mortimer Klaus, Pres.; Barbara Klaus, V.P. and Secy.; Anne Klaus, V.P.; Barry Klaus, V.P.
EIN: 205747828

6322
Harry S. Klavan Memorial Foundation

(formerly Rabbi Joshua & Fannie D. Klavan Memorial Foundation)
137-16 72nd Rd.
Flushing, NY   11367-2317

Donors: Harry S. Klavan†; Rena S. Klavan.
Foundation type: Independent foundation.
Financial data (yr. ended 12/31/13): Assets, $595,550 (M); gifts received, $240,000; expenditures, $221,760; qualifying distributions, $216,622; giving activities include $216,622 for 6 + grants.
Fields of interest: Education; Judaism; Human services.
Limitations: Applications not accepted. Giving primarily in New York, NY. No grants to individuals.
Application information: Unsolicited requests for funds not accepted.
Director: Shulamith K. Goldstein.
EIN: 526054006

6323
The Kleban Foundation, Inc.

c/o Marks Paneth & Shron, LLP
685 3rd Ave.
New York City, NY   10017
Main URL: http://www.newdramatists.org/kleban_award.htm

Established in 1988 in New York.
Donor: Edward L. Kleban†.
Foundation type: Independent foundation.
Financial data (yr. ended 06/30/15): Assets, $2,908,058 (M); expenditures, $309,150; qualifying distributions, $271,155; giving activities include $200,000 for 4 grants to individuals (high: $50,000; low: $50,000).
Purpose and activities: Support for individual theatrical lyricists and librettists.
Fields of interest: Theater; Education.
Type of support: Individual development; Grants to individuals.
Limitations: Applications accepted. Giving primarily in New York, NY.
Publications: Application guidelines.
Application information: See foundation web site for complete application information. Application form required.
    Initial approach: Written application
    Deadline(s): Sept. 15
Officers: Richard Maltby, Jr., Pres. and Director; Sheldon Harnick, V.P. and Director; Sarah Douglas, Secy.; Richard Terrano, Treas. and Director.
Directors: Andre Bishop; Elliot H. Brown, Dir.; Jonathan Weidman; Maury Yeston.
Number of staff: 1 part-time professional.
EIN: 133490882

6324
George & Adele Klein Foundation

535 Madison Ave., 35th Fl.
New York City, NY   10022-1240

Established in 1968 in New York.
Donors: George Klein; Adele Klein†.
Foundation type: Independent foundation.
Financial data (yr. ended 03/31/13): Assets, $876,708 (M); gifts received, $803,500; expenditures, $359,700; qualifying distributions, $359,600; giving activities include $359,600 for 3 grants (high: $250,000; low: $9,600).
Purpose and activities: Giving primarily to Jewish organizations, temples, and schools.
Fields of interest: Education; Medical education; Diseases and conditions.
Type of support: Research.
Limitations: Applications not accepted. No grants to individuals.
Application information: Unsolicited requests for funds not accepted.
Officer: George Klein, Pres.
EIN: 136279924

6325
Ruth and Seymour Klein Foundation, Inc.

c/o Barbara G. Klein
16 Tallwoods Rd.
Armonk, NY   10504-1035

Donors: Seymour M. Klein†; Ruth L. Klein†.
Foundation type: Independent foundation.

Financial data (yr. ended 04/30/13): Assets, $5,478,048 (M); expenditures, $317,384; qualifying distributions, $307,300; giving activities include $304,000 for 44 grants (high: $55,000; low: $1,000).
Purpose and activities: Giving primarily for health care and the arts.
Fields of interest: Arts and culture; Museums; Education; Health; Hospital care; Human services.
Type of support: General support; Annual campaigns; Capital campaigns; Endowments; Scholarships.
Limitations: Applications not accepted. Giving primarily in NY. No grants to individuals.
Application information: Unsolicited requests for funds not accepted.
Officers and Directors: Barbara G. Klein, Pres. and Director; Zoe S. Klein, V.P. and Secy. and Director; Jason A. Klein, V.P. and Treas. and Director; Kathleen Kheel.
Number of staff: None.
EIN: 136114763

6326
The Kleinschmidt Family Foundation

730 Columbus Ave., Apt. 16I
New York City, NY   10025-6687   (212) 698-0800
Contact: Robert W. Kleinschmidt, Pres., Treas., and Dir.

Established in 2004 in New York.
Donors: Robert W. Kleinschmidt; Paul Kleinschmidt; Alexander Kleinschmidt.
Foundation type: Independent foundation.
Financial data (yr. ended 12/31/13): Assets, $7,983,258 (M); gifts received, $460,000; expenditures, $351,237; qualifying distributions, $344,801; giving activities include $344,185 for 55 grants (high: $50,000; low: $100).
Fields of interest: Education; Aquatic wildlife protection; Nonprofits; Protestantism.
Type of support: Regranting.
Limitations: Applications accepted. Giving primarily in NY.
Application information:
    Initial approach: Proposal
    Deadline(s): None
Officers and Directors: Robert W. Kleinschmidt, Pres. and Treas. and Director; Nell F. Kleinschmidt, V.P. and Secy. and Director; Alexander Kleinschmidt; Lara Kleinschmidt; Paul Kleinschmidt.
EIN: 270112179

6327
Klingenstein Fund

(formerly Clara Buttenwieser Unger Memorial Foundation)
c/o Lee P. Klingenstein
31 Oxford Rd.
Scarsdale, NY   10583-2145

Established in 1940 in New York.
Donors: Lee Paul Klingenstein; Paul H. Klingenstein; Alan Klingenstein; Joanne K. Ziesing; Frances S. Klingenstein.
Foundation type: Independent foundation.
Financial data (yr. ended 12/31/13): Assets, $3,576,319 (M); gifts received, $158,900; expenditures, $384,649; qualifying distributions,

$370,638; giving activities include $360,974 for 78 grants (high: $118,267; low: $50).

Fields of interest: Education; Higher education; Diseases and conditions; Judaism; Human services.

Limitations: Applications not accepted. No grants to individuals.

Application information: Contributes only to pre-selected organizations.

Officers: Lee Paul Klingenstein, Pres.; Paul H. Klingenstein, V.P.; Joanne K. Ziesing, Secy.; Alan L. Klingenstein, Treas.

EIN: 136077894

6328
The Klingenstein Third Generation Foundation

c/o Tanton & Co., LLP
125 Park Ave., Ste. 1700
New York City, NY 10017-5529
Contact: Sally Klingenstein Martell, Exec. Dir.
E-mail: info@ktgf.org; E-mail and telephone for Sally Klingenstein Martell: sally@ktgf.org; (212) 492-6179; Main URL: http://www.ktgf.org

Established in 1993 in New York.

Donors: Esther A. and Joseph Klingenstein Fund; Andrew Klingenstein; Nancy Simpkins; Thomas Klingenstein; Sarah Martell; Amy Pollinger; Andrew Julie Klingenstein Family.

Foundation type: Independent foundation.

Financial data (yr. ended 09/30/13): Assets, $7,901,635 (M); gifts received, $39,000; expenditures, $390,935; qualifying distributions, $344,777; giving activities include $229,790 for 18 grants (high: $30,000; low: $1,000).

Purpose and activities: Support for programs that strive to improve the lives of families afflicted by depression, with a focus on those that address child and adolescent depression and Attention Deficit Hyperactivity Disorder (ADHD). The foundation operates three funding programs. Two are post-doctoral fellowship programs to fund clinical or basic research. One of these programs supports researchers investigating childhood and adolescent depression. The other supports researchers investigating ADHD in children. Investigators must hold a Ph.D. and/or an M.D. degree, and have completed all research training, including post-doctoral training. The foundation's third funding program supports medical student training programs at a number of institutions. These programs increase students' exposure to the field of child psychiatry. The foundation no longer funds outside the three fellowship programs.

Fields of interest: Medical education; Depression.

Type of support: General support; Fellowships.

Limitations: Applications accepted. Giving on a national basis. No support for direct service programs.

Application information: Complete application guidelines available on foundation web site.

Officers: Andrew Klingenstein, Pres.; Susan Klingenstein, V.P.; Nancy Simpkins, Secy.; Thomas Klingenstein, Treas.; Sally Klingenstein Martell, Exec. Dir.

Directors: Kathy Klingenstein; Amy Pollinger.

Number of staff: 2 part-time professional.

EIN: 133732439

6329
The Klingenstein-Martell Foundation

(formerly The Sarah D. Klingenstein Foundation)
c/o Tanton and Co.
37 W. 57th St., 5th Fl.
New York City, NY 10019

Established in 1999 in Delaware.

Donors: Sarah Klingenstein Martell; John Klingenstein.

Foundation type: Independent foundation.

Financial data (yr. ended 12/31/13): Assets, $5,603,086 (M); expenditures, $253,205; qualifying distributions, $230,121; giving activities include $223,750 for 8 grants (high: $115,000; low: $1,250).

Fields of interest: Elementary and secondary education; Judaism; Human services; Youth services.

Limitations: Applications not accepted. No grants to individuals.

Application information: Contributes only to pre-selected organizations.

Officers and Trustees: Sarah Klingenstein Martell, Pres. and Trustee; Robin Krause, Secy.; Lauren Hammer Breslow, Treas.; Christopher Michael Martell.

EIN: 134078024

6330
Knafel Family Foundation

885 3rd Ave., Ste. 2640
New York City, NY 10022-5086

Established in 1994 in New York.

Donors: Sidney R. Knafel; Andrew G. Knafel.

Foundation type: Independent foundation.

Financial data (yr. ended 12/31/13): Assets, $20,000,736 (M); expenditures, $523,317; qualifying distributions, $355,966; giving activities include $355,000 for 33 grants (high: $100,000; low: $500).

Fields of interest: Arts and culture; Education; Secondary education; Higher education; Diseases and conditions; Judaism; Human services.

Type of support: Research; Research and evaluation.

Limitations: Applications not accepted. Giving primarily in MA and NY. No grants to individuals.

Application information: Contributes only to pre-selected organizations.

Officers: Sidney R. Knafel, Pres.; Andrew G. Knafel, Treas.

Director: Douglas R. Knafel.

EIN: 133779562

6331
The Knapp Fund

c/o Silvercrest Asset Mgmt.
1330 Ave. of the Americas
New York City, NY 10019-5434

Established in 1917 in New York.

Donor: George O. Knapp†.

Foundation type: Independent foundation.

Financial data (yr. ended 08/31/13): Assets, $3,944,927 (M); expenditures, $201,765; qualifying distributions, $170,500; giving activities include $170,500 for 20 grants (high: $50,000; low: $2,000).

Fields of interest: Education; Elementary and secondary education; Environment; Diseases and conditions; Human services.

Type of support: Endowments; General support; Individual development; Continuing support; Annual campaigns; Capital and infrastructure; Research; Research and evaluation; Program development; Scholarships.

Limitations: Applications not accepted. Giving primarily in CT, FL, NY and PA. No grants to individuals, or for matching gifts; no loans.

Application information: Unsolicited requests for funds not accepted.

Officers: George O. Knapp III, Pres.; Anne S. Mauk, V.P. and Treas.; Bart A. Johnston, V.P.; Amber Waugaman, Secy.

Directors: W. Jared Knapp III; Sarah S. Obregon; Louise Knapp Page; F. Russell Sprole.

EIN: 136068384

6332
Nat R. & Martha M. Knaster Charitable Trust

c/o Schulman Lobel
1001 6th Ave., 10 Fl.
New York City, NY 10018-5587 (212) 768-0300

Established in 2006 in New York.

Donor: Martha Knaster.

Foundation type: Independent foundation.

Financial data (yr. ended 05/31/14): Assets, $4,075,954; expenditures, $314,805; qualifying distributions, $253,438.

Fields of interest: Education; Judaism; Human services.

Limitations: Applications accepted. Giving primarily in Great Neck and New York, NY.

Application information: Application form required.
Initial approach: Letter
Deadline(s): None

Trustees: Michael A. Lobel; Richard Shapiro; Bruce Wolfson.

EIN: 206617134

6333
Kochov Foundation

4515 18th Ave.
Brooklyn, NY 11204-1292

Established in 2002 in New York.

Donors: Moses Eilenberg; Leah Goldberger; Abraham Stern; Yud, Inc.

Foundation type: Independent foundation.

Financial data (yr. ended 12/31/13): Assets, $3,610,707 (M); expenditures, $393,891; qualifying distributions, $158,286; giving activities include $156,536 for 4 grants (high: $108,036; low: $500).

Fields of interest: Judaism.

Limitations: Applications not accepted. Giving primarily in NY. No grants to individuals.

Application information: Unsolicited requests for funds not accepted.

Trustees: Leah Goldberger; Joseph Leff.

EIN: 300128032

6334
Kenneth L. and Katherine G. Koessler Family Foundation, Inc.
c/o Paul Wachter
21 Meadow Dr.
Buffalo, NY   14216   (716) 871-1669

Established in 1991 in New York.
Donors: Anne Laura K. Brosnahan; Katherine K. Juhasz; Kenneth L. Koessler, Jr.
Foundation type: Independent foundation.
Financial data (yr. ended 12/31/13): Assets, $3,987,960 (M); expenditures, $210,714; qualifying distributions, $155,150; giving activities include $155,150 for 30 grants (high: $56,500; low: $250).
Fields of interest: Education; Undergraduate education; Hospital care; Catholicism.
Type of support: General support; Capital and infrastructure.
Limitations: Applications accepted. Giving generally limited to the western NY area.
Application information: Application form required.
  Initial approach: Letter
  Deadline(s): Nov. 30th
Officers: Katherine K. Juhasz, Pres.; Mary Wachter, V.P.; Anne Laura Brosnahan, Secy.; Paul Wachter, Treas.
EIN: 223137752

6335
The Paul J. Koessler Foundation Inc.
100 Corporate Pkwy., Ste. 410
Amherst, NY   14226-1200   (716) 831-9044
Contact: William C. Hilbert
E-mail: bill@onyxadvisors.com

Donors: Paul J. Koessler†; John W. Koessler, Jr.; Mary R. Koessler†.
Foundation type: Independent foundation.
Financial data (yr. ended 12/31/13): Assets, $4,688,514 (M); expenditures, $327,055; qualifying distributions, $292,500; giving activities include $292,500 for 22 grants (high: $85,000; low: $1,000).
Purpose and activities: Funding primarily for education.
Fields of interest: Orchestral music; Education; Secondary education; Hospital care; Catholicism; Human development; Youth development.
Type of support: General support; Program-related investments; Annual campaigns; Capital campaigns; Capital and infrastructure; Scholarships.
Limitations: Applications accepted. Giving primarily in Buffalo, NY. No grants to individuals.
Application information:
  Initial approach: Proposal
  Deadline(s): None
Officers and Directors: Eric Koessler, V.P. and Director; Paul J. Koessler, Jr., V.P. and Director; Paul C. Hilbert, Secy.-Treas. and Director; Gretchen White.
EIN: 161406642

6336
The John W. & Mary M. Koessler Foundation
100 Corporate Pkwy., Ste. 410
Amherst, NY   14226-1200   (716) 831-9044
E-mail: bill@onyxadvisors.com

Donor: Mary M. Koessler.
Foundation type: Independent foundation.
Financial data (yr. ended 12/31/13): Assets, $179,841 (M); expenditures, $172,812; qualifying distributions, $162,450; giving activities include $162,450 for 78 grants (high: $30,000; low: $200).
Fields of interest: Arts and culture; Education; Religion; Sports and recreation.
Limitations: Applications accepted. Giving primarily in NY. No grants to individuals.
Application information:
  Initial approach: Proposal
  Deadline(s): None
Officers and Directors: Mary M. Koessler, Pres. and Director; Mary C. Smith, V.P. and Director; Paul C. Hilbert, Secy.
EIN: 161406643

6337
Koha Foundation, Inc.
c/o Mac Corkindale
3960 Merrick Rd.
Seaford, NY   11783-2826

Established in 2005 in Connecticut.
Donor: Craig Nevill-Manning.
Foundation type: Independent foundation.
Financial data (yr. ended 12/31/13): Assets, $4,000,778 (M); expenditures, $295,402; qualifying distributions, $268,168; giving activities include $264,665 for 9 grants (high: $127,065; low: $100).
Fields of interest: Education; Nonprofits; Health; Community and economic development; Human rights; Human services.
Limitations: Applications not accepted. No grants to individuals.
Application information: Unsolicited requests for funds not accepted.
Officers: Kirsten Nevill-Manning, Pres.; Craig Nevill-Manning, V.P.
EIN: 202462647

6338
Leizer Kohn and Ruth Kerman Foundation
c/o Neil Kerman
1401 Ocean Ave.
Brooklyn, NY   11230-3971

Established in 2001 in New York.
Donor: Neil Kerman.
Foundation type: Independent foundation.
Financial data (yr. ended 12/31/13): Assets, $400,276 (M); gifts received, $412,327; expenditures, $119,905; qualifying distributions, $119,700; giving activities include $119,650 for 18 grants (high: $33,000; low: $1,000).
Fields of interest: Nonprofits; Judaism.
Type of support: Regranting.
Limitations: Applications not accepted. Giving primarily in NY. No grants to individuals.
Application information: Contributes only to pre-selected organizations.
Officers: Neil Kerman, Pres.; Barbara Kerman, Secy.
Director: Asher Wagh.
EIN: 113640747

6339
Zichron Moshe Vesther Kohn Foundation
768 Bedford Ave.
Brooklyn, NY   11205-1508

Donors: Kohn Family Trust; New Century Mgmt. Svcs. LLC; Blum Foundation; Nachum Sherman.
Foundation type: Independent foundation.
Financial data (yr. ended 12/31/13): Assets, $426; gifts received, $338,954; expenditures, $386,581; qualifying distributions, $384,832.
Fields of interest: Judaism.
Limitations: Applications not accepted. Giving primarily in NY. No grants to individuals.
Application information: Contributes only to pre-selected organizations.
Trustees: Herb Kohn; Sara Kohn.
EIN: 113435079

6340
William & Sheila Konar Foundation
75 Thruway Park Dr.
West Henrietta, NY   14586-9795   (585) 334-4110
Contact: William B. Konar, Dir.

Established in 1982 in New York.
Donors: Sheila Konar; William B. Konar.
Foundation type: Independent foundation.
Financial data (yr. ended 12/31/13): Assets, $7,233,844 (M); gifts received, $1,012,492; expenditures, $478,658; qualifying distributions, $415,000; giving activities include $415,000 for 42 grants (high: $200,000; low: $1,000).
Fields of interest: Nonprofits; Diseases and conditions; Judaism; Human services.
Type of support: Regranting.
Limitations: Applications accepted. Giving primarily in NY and CA. No grants to individuals.
Application information: Application form required.
  Initial approach: Letter
  Deadline(s): None
Directors: Howard E. Konar; Rachael K. Guttenberg; Sheila Konar; William B. Konar.
EIN: 222434846

6341
John and Janet Kornreich Charitable Foundation Ltd.
4 Saddle Ridge Rd.
Old Westbury, NY   11568-1150
Contact: John Kornreich, Mgr.

Established in 1999 in New York.
Donors: John Kornreich; Janet Kornreich.
Foundation type: Operating foundation.
Financial data (yr. ended 12/31/13): Assets, $3,077,464 (M); gifts received, $60,000; expenditures, $377,410; qualifying distributions, $376,385; giving activities include $376,385 for 25 grants (high: $100,000; low: $150).
Fields of interest: Education; Philanthropy; Human services; Family services; Developmental disability services.
Limitations: Applications accepted. Giving primarily in Nassau County, NY. No grants to individuals.
Application information: Application form required.
  Initial approach: Letter
  Deadline(s): None
Officer: John Kornreich, Mgr.

Directors: Myron Bloom; Janet Kornreich.
EIN: 133974159

6342
Stuart and Nicole Kovensky Family Foundation
18 Long Pond Rd.
Armonk, NY 10504-2625

Donors: Stuart R. Kovensky; Nicole Greene Kovensky.
Foundation type: Independent foundation.
Financial data (yr. ended 12/31/13): Assets, $1,574,940 (M); gifts received, $50,000; expenditures, $189,662; qualifying distributions, $167,698; giving activities include $163,813 for 50 grants (high: $50,000; low: $20).
Fields of interest: Arts and culture; Education; Cystic fibrosis; Human services.
Type of support: General support.
Limitations: Applications not accepted. Giving primarily in NY.
Application information: Unsolicited requests for funds not accepted.
Officers and Directors: Nicole Greene Kovensky, Chair. and Secy. and Director; Stuart R. Kovensky, Pres. and Treas. and Director.
EIN: 383859398

6343
The David Kozicki Memorial Foundation
c/o Marcel Gross
691 Dahill Rd.
Brooklyn, NY 11218-5571

Established in 1995 in New York.
Donors: Zvi Kozicki; Aaron Wachspress.
Foundation type: Independent foundation.
Financial data (yr. ended 12/31/13): Assets, $2,919,417 (M); gifts received, $39,525; expenditures, $229,818; qualifying distributions, $219,658; giving activities include $218,158 for 25 + grants (high: $55,025; low: $720).
Purpose and activities: Giving primarily to yeshivas and Jewish temples.
Fields of interest: Education; Judaism.
Limitations: Applications not accepted. No grants to individuals.
Application information: Contributes only to pre-selected organizations.
Officer: Zvi Kozicki, Pres.
Director: Judy Kozicki.
EIN: 113208317

6344
Abraham Krasne Foundation
65 W. Red Oak Ln.
White Plains, NY 10604-3616

Established in 1989 in New York.
Donors: Krasdale Foods Inc.; Alpha I Marketing Corp.; Beta II Marketing Corp.; Consolidated Supermarket Supply LLC.
Foundation type: Company-sponsored foundation.
Financial data (yr. ended 12/31/13): Assets, $2,609,308 (M); gifts received, $260,000; expenditures, $270,306; qualifying distributions, $270,125; giving activities include $270,000 for 13 grants (high: $50,000; low: $1,000).

Purpose and activities: Giving primarily for Jewish federated giving programs, health and medical services, and higher education.
Fields of interest: Education; Health; Religion.
Limitations: Applications not accepted. Giving primarily in CT and NY. No grants to individuals.
Application information: Contributes only to pre-selected organizations.
Officers: Charles A. Krasne, Pres.; Kenneth Krasne, V.P. and Secy.; Thatcher Krasne, Treas.
Directors: Kim Krasne Bacon; Steven Loeb, Esq.
EIN: 136112855

6345
The Krauss Charitable Foundation
c/o Joseph B. Sprung
575 Madison Ave., 10th Fl.
New York City, NY 10022-6903
Contact: Melvyn Krauss, Pres.
Application address: 43 Los Charros Ln., Portola Valley, CA 94028

Donors: Melvyn Krauss; Irene Krauss.
Foundation type: Independent foundation.
Financial data (yr. ended 12/31/12): Assets, $7,205,871 (M); expenditures, $148,500; qualifying distributions, $148,500; giving activities include $148,500 for 26 grants (high: $30,000; low: $1,000).
Fields of interest: Arts and culture; Health; Diseases and conditions.
Limitations: Applications accepted. Giving primarily in NY. No grants to individuals.
Application information: Application form required.
  Initial approach: Letter
  Deadline(s): None
Officer: Melvyn Krauss, Pres.
EIN: 113183212

6346
The Krimendahl/Saint-Amand Foundation
(formerly The H. Frederick Krimendahl II Foundation)
c/o BCRS Assocs., LLC
77 Water St., 9th Fl.
New York City, NY 10005-4414

Established in 1968 in New York.
Donors: H. Frederick Krimendahl II; Elizabeth K. Krimendahl.
Foundation type: Independent foundation.
Financial data (yr. ended 05/31/13): Assets, $9,972,577 (M); gifts received, $40,000; expenditures, $349,199; qualifying distributions, $338,197; giving activities include $337,342 for 65 grants (high: $48,500; low: $150).
Purpose and activities: Giving primarily for education, the arts, and animal welfare.
Fields of interest: Arts and culture; Performing arts; Education; Higher education; Animal welfare; Veterinary medicine; Diseases and conditions; Human services.
Limitations: Applications not accepted. No grants to individuals.
Application information: Contributes only to pre-selected organizations.
Trustees: James S. Marcus; Emilia A. Saint-Amand.
EIN: 237000391

6347
David B. Kriser Foundation Inc.
888 Park Ave.
New York City, NY 10075-0235

Established in 1977 in New York.
Donor: David B. Kriser†.
Foundation type: Independent foundation.
Financial data (yr. ended 12/31/13): Assets, $8,008,906 (M); expenditures, $295,036; qualifying distributions, $242,685; giving activities include $242,685 for 44 grants (high: $77,500; low: $150).
Fields of interest: Orchestral music; Education; Health; Hospital care.
Limitations: Applications not accepted. Giving primarily in New York, NY. No grants to individuals.
Application information: Contributes only to pre-selected organizations.
Officer: Alice Netter, Pres.
Director: Laurie Sprayregen.
EIN: 132932531

6348
The Lynn and Jules Kroll Family Foundation, Inc.
(formerly The Herman Kroll Memorial Foundation, Inc.)
845 3rd Ave., 4th Fl.
New York City, NY 10022-6647 (646) 708-7580
Contact: Jules B. Kroll, Pres.

Donor: Jules B. Kroll.
Foundation type: Independent foundation.
Financial data (yr. ended 12/31/13): Assets, $454,853 (M); expenditures, $373,359; qualifying distributions, $362,989; giving activities include $356,760 for 13 grants (high: $100,000; low: $750).
Fields of interest: Arts and culture; Education; Law education; Human services.
Type of support: General support.
Limitations: Applications accepted. Giving primarily in Washington, DC and New York, NY.
Application information: Application form required.
  Initial approach: Letter
  Deadline(s): None
Officers and Directors: Jules B. Kroll, Pres.; Lynn Korda Kroll, Secy. and Director.
Board Members: Dana Kroll; Jeremy Kroll; Nicholas Kroll; Vanessa Kroll.
EIN: 133346838

6349
Elroy and Terry Krumholz Foundation, Inc.
c/o BFFA
1430 Broadway, No. 1208
New York City, NY 10018-3384

Established in 1992 in New York.
Donors: Terry Krumholz†; Roy Krumholz†.
Foundation type: Independent foundation.
Financial data (yr. ended 12/31/13): Assets, $3,271,783 (M); gifts received, $3,271,783; expenditures, $252,573; qualifying distributions, $252,323; giving activities include $171,550 for 31 grants (high: $70,000; low: $1,000).
Purpose and activities: Primary areas of interest include animal welfare, the arts, community services, education, cancer patient/family support services, social services, including special camping

and community services, and Jewish community programs.

Fields of interest: Arts and culture; Arts education; Education; Animal welfare; Nonprofits; Judaism; Human services.

Type of support: Equipment; Seed money; Internships; Scholarships; Regranting.

Limitations: Applications not accepted. Giving primarily in NY. No support for political or fraternal organizations. No grants to individuals, or for endowment funds, private foundations, publications, or conferences; no giving for salaries, operating support, deficit financing, capital financing, or non-humane organizations; no loans.

Application information: Unsolicited requests for funds not accepted.

> *Board meeting date(s):* 3 to 4 times per year, as needed

Trustees: Harriet Krantz; Diane Razzano; Rosalind Sackoff.

Number of staff: None.

EIN: 133641606

6350
Alice L. Kulick Foundation, Inc.
150 E. 58th St., 16th Fl.
New York City, NY   10155-0002

Established in 1998 in New York.

Donor: Alice L. Kulick.

Foundation type: Independent foundation.

Financial data (yr. ended 12/31/13): Assets, $24,592 (M); gifts received, $200,000; expenditures, $213,740; qualifying distributions, $213,740; giving activities include $211,947 for 10 grants (high: $135,000; low: $294).

Fields of interest: Nonprofits; Judaism.

Type of support: Regranting.

Limitations: Applications not accepted. Giving primarily in NY. No grants to individuals.

Application information: Contributes only to pre-selected organizations.

Officers and Directors: Alice L. Kulick, Pres. and Treas.; Renee Brodie, Secy. and Director; Eugene Wallach.

EIN: 134036648

6351
Jack and Dorothy Kupferberg Family Foundation
c/o Seth Kupferberg
131-38 Sanford Ave.
Flushing, NY   11355-4231

Established in 2001 in New York.

Donors: Dorothy Kupferberg; Jack Kupferberg‡.

Foundation type: Independent foundation.

Financial data (yr. ended 11/30/14): Assets, $6,231,656; gifts received, $0; expenditures, $399,138; qualifying distributions, $309,326 and $0 for set-asides.

Fields of interest: Education; Undergraduate education; Health; Diabetes; Cancers; Youth services.

Type of support: Research; Research and evaluation.

Limitations: Applications not accepted. No grants to individuals.

Application information: Unsolicited requests for funds not accepted.

Trustees: Lenn Kupferberg; Marcia Kupferberg; Seth Kupferberg.

EIN: 061636083

6352
The Stanford L. & Sheila Kurland Family Foundation
c/o Ayco Co., LP
P.O. Box 15014
Albany, NY   12212-1504

Established in 1997 in California.

Donors: Stanford L. Kurland; Sheila Kurland.

Foundation type: Independent foundation.

Financial data (yr. ended 12/31/13): Assets, $3,916,816 (M); expenditures, $184,145; qualifying distributions, $184,000; giving activities include $184,000 for 12 grants (high: $100,000; low: $1,000).

Fields of interest: Education; Judaism.

Type of support: General support.

Limitations: Applications not accepted. No grants to individuals.

Application information: Contributes only to pre-selected organizations.

Officers: Sheila Kurland, Pres.; Stanford L. Kurland, C.F.O.

EIN: 954606475

6353
L & L Foundation
570 Park Ave.
New York City, NY   10065
Contact: Mildred C. Brinn, Pres., Treas. and Dir.

Established in 1963 in New York.

Foundation type: Independent foundation.

Financial data (yr. ended 12/31/13): Assets, $7,905,860 (M); expenditures, $354,128; qualifying distributions, $273,342; giving activities include $197,700 for 22 grants (high: $90,000; low: $350).

Purpose and activities: Giving primarily for the arts, health care, and human services.

Fields of interest: Arts and culture; Arts education; Visual arts; Performing arts; Art museums; Health; Hospital care; Protestantism; Human services; Child welfare.

Limitations: Applications accepted. Giving primarily in NY. No grants to individuals.

Application information: Application form required.

> *Initial approach:* Letter
> *Deadline(s):* None

Officers and Directors: Mildred C. Brinn, Pres. and Treas. and Director; Peter F. De Gaetano, Secy. and Director.

EIN: 136155758

6354
L. J. Charitable Foundation
98 Cuttermill Rd., Ste. 249S
Great Neck, NY   11021-3046

Donors: David Jacobowitz; DJ Jadabe Trust; DJ Grantor Trust; DJ Davbel Trust.

Foundation type: Independent foundation.

Financial data (yr. ended 12/31/13): Assets, -$6,358 (M); gifts received, $154,025; expenditures, $146,636; qualifying distributions, $144,896; giving activities include $135,996 for

106 grants (high: $12,250; low: $67), and $8,900 for 23 grants to individuals (high: $1,000; low: $100).

Fields of interest: Education; Diseases and conditions; Human services.

Limitations: Applications not accepted.

Application information: Unsolicited requests for funds not accepted.

Trustee: David Jacobwitz.

EIN: 261231085

6355
La Fondation Cuvelier
30 E. 71st St., Apt. 7A
New York City, NY   10021-4965

Established in 2007 in New York.

Donors: Guillaume Cuvelier; Andrea Cuvelier.

Foundation type: Independent foundation.

Financial data (yr. ended 12/31/13): Assets, $3,613,285 (M); expenditures, $172,156; qualifying distributions, $144,350; giving activities include $144,350 for 13 grants (high: $40,000; low: $400).

Fields of interest: Elementary and secondary education.

Limitations: Applications not accepted.

Application information: Unsolicited requests for funds not accepted.

Trustees: Andrea Cuvelier; Guillaume Cuvelier.

EIN: 266157257

6356
The Lachman Family Foundation Inc.
c/o David B. Petshaft PC
138 Rolling Hill Rd.
Manhasset, NY   11030-2517

Established in 2002 in New York.

Donor: Leon Lachman.

Foundation type: Independent foundation.

Financial data (yr. ended 12/31/12): Assets, $11,119,593 (M); gifts received, $1,000,505; expenditures, $446,164; qualifying distributions, $442,000; giving activities include $442,000 for grants.

Fields of interest: Orchestral music; Education; Higher education; Graduate and professional education; Health; Wildfires; International development.

Type of support: Individual development.

Limitations: Applications not accepted. Giving primarily in MD, NY and WI. No grants to individuals.

Application information: Contributes only to pre-selected organizations.

Officers and Directors: Leon Lachman, Pres. and Treas. and Director; Joan Lachman, V.P. and Secy. and Director; Julie Lachman, V.P. and Director; Lawrence Lachman, V.P. and Director; David B. Petshaft, V.P. and Director.

EIN: 320033014

6357
Ladenburg Foundation
c/o Anchin Block & Anchin, LLP
1375 Broadway
New York City, NY   10018-7001

Established in 2001 in New York.

Donors: Claudia Bussmann; Dr. Martin Bussmann; Margaret Bussmann; Richard Bussmann; Courtney Bussman; Margaret Blades.
Foundation type: Independent foundation.
Financial data (yr. ended 12/31/14): Assets, $4,364 (M); gifts received, $144,001; expenditures, $143,500; qualifying distributions, $140,910; giving activities include $137,000 for 3 grants (high: $106,000; low: $15,000).
Purpose and activities: Giving primarily for higher education, including journalism scholarships, a German center for American studies, and a student exchange program, as well as for human rights and the Special Olympics.
Fields of interest: Arts and culture; Education; Religion.
International interests: Germany; Israel.
Limitations: Applications not accepted. Giving primarily in NY; some funding in Heidelberg, Germany and Jerusalem, Israel. No grants to individuals.
Application information: Unsolicited requests for funds not accepted.
Officers and Directors: Claudia Engelhorn, Chair. and Director; Martin Bussmann, Pres. and Treas. and Director; Henry Christensen III, Esq.
EIN: 134156286

6358
Asmund S. Laerdal Foundation, Inc.
167 Myers Corners Rd.
Wappingers Falls, NY   12590-3869
E-mail: brenda.barnes@laerdal.com

Established in 1977 in Delaware.
Donor: Laerdal Medical Corp.
Foundation type: Independent foundation.
Financial data (yr. ended 12/31/14): Assets, $6,932,692; expenditures, $330,050; qualifying distributions, $252,050.
Purpose and activities: The purpose of the foundation is to provide financial support for research or development in the field of acute medicine. Funding priorities include the diagnosis, treatment, and transport of patients with an acute, life-threatening disease or injury. The term encompasses all phases of life support, from the onset of symptoms or the infliction of injury until the patient is stabilized in a non-critical condition. Suitable projects may include experimental or clinical studies, development of teaching and training procedures, improvements of patient transport, and publication of clinical data. Special consideration is given to projects related to pre-hospital emergency care.
Fields of interest: Graduate and professional education; Diseases and conditions.
Type of support: Convening; Program development; Research; Publications; Research and evaluation; Curriculum development.
Limitations: Applications accepted. Giving on a national basis. No grants to individuals directly, or for overhead costs for institutions and universities, general operating expenses or reduction of deficits. No support for travel expenses in connection with conferences, symposia, and scientific meetings, unless they are related to the grantmaker's objectives or an outgrowth of one of its grant programs.
Publications: Informational brochure (including application guidelines).
Application information:

Initial approach: Proposal of no more than 4 double-spaced pages on organization's letterhead
Copies of proposal: 2
Deadline(s): Apr. 15 and Oct. 15
Final notification: 3-4 months
Officers and Board Member: Tore Laerdal, Chair.; Patricia Goodwin, V.P. and Director.
EIN: 132885659

6359
Lainoff Family Foundation Inc.
477 Madison Ave., 10th Fl.
New York City, NY   10022-5841

Established in 1997 in New York.
Donors: Irwin Lainoff; Carole Lainoff.
Foundation type: Independent foundation.
Financial data (yr. ended 12/31/13): Assets, $3,938,176 (M); expenditures, $219,607; qualifying distributions, $200,048; giving activities include $200,000 for 42 grants (high: $25,000; low: $1,000).
Fields of interest: Arts and culture; Higher education; Health care clinics; Human services; Child welfare.
Type of support: General support.
Limitations: Applications not accepted. Giving primarily in Washington, DC, and VA. No grants to individuals.
Application information: Contributes only to pre-selected organizations.
Officers and Directors: Carole Lainoff, Pres. and Director; Michael Lainoff, Co-Treas. and Director; Steven Lainoff, Co-Treas. and Director.
EIN: 133949510

6360
Lake Placid Education Foundation
1992 Saranac Ave.
Crestview Plz., Ste. 3
Lake Placid, NY   12946-1173   (518) 523-4433
Contact: John Lansing

Established in 1922 in New York.
Donor: Melvil Dewey†.
Foundation type: Independent foundation.
Financial data (yr. ended 06/30/13): Assets, $6,097,624 (M); expenditures, $331,194; qualifying distributions, $268,858; giving activities include $240,800 for 33 grants (high: $45,000; low: $500).
Purpose and activities: Giving for public and private schools, the arts, and libraries.
Fields of interest: Arts and culture; Education; Elementary and secondary education; Higher education; Libraries.
Type of support: General support; Program-related investments; Matching grants; Continuing support; Equipment; Program development; Convening; Seed money; Scholarships; Student aid.
Limitations: Applications accepted. Giving primarily in the northern Adirondack region of NY. No support for political organizations.
Application information: Application form required.
Initial approach: Letter
Copies of proposal: 1
Deadline(s): May 1
Board meeting date(s): June, Dec., and Sept.
Final notification: Two months

Officers: Frederick C. Calder, Pres.; Catherine I. Johnston, V.P.; John Rosenthal, Secy.; Lisa Weibrecht, Treas.; John S. Lansing, Exec. Dir.
Directors: Adele Connors; W. John Friedlander; Sara Kelly Jones; Hilary McDonald; John McMillin; Greg Peacock; Meredith M. Prime.
Number of staff: 1 part-time professional; 1 part-time support.
EIN: 510243919

6361
Lamaj Foundation
c/o Vera Aryeh
435 E. 52nd St., Ste. 1D
New York City, NY   10022-6445

Established in 2003 in New York.
Donors: Jalaa Equities, LP; Richard Morawczyk; Laura Aryeh Morawczyk.
Foundation type: Independent foundation.
Financial data (yr. ended 12/31/13): Assets, $443,767 (M); gifts received, $5,221; expenditures, $119,307; qualifying distributions, $114,781; giving activities include $113,000 for 6 grants (high: $70,000; low: $500).
Fields of interest: Education; Higher education; Religion; Human services.
International interests: Mexico.
Type of support: General support.
Limitations: Applications not accepted. Giving primarily in New York, NY and Albuquerque, NM. No grants to individuals.
Application information: Unsolicited requests for funds not accepted.
Trustees: Jason M. Aryeh; Vera Aryeh; Laura Aryeh Murawczyk; Richard Murawczyk.
EIN: 562417932

6362
Pinches & Chanie Landau Foundation
1164 44th St.
Brooklyn, NY   11219-1833

Donor: Pinches Landau.
Foundation type: Independent foundation.
Financial data (yr. ended 12/31/13): Assets, $194,300 (M); gifts received, $480,000; expenditures, $285,700; qualifying distributions, $285,700; giving activities include $285,700 for 5 grants (high: $270,000; low: $200).
Fields of interest: Education; Judaism; Human services.
Limitations: Applications not accepted. Giving primarily in Brooklyn, NY.
Application information: Unsolicited requests for funds not accepted.
Directors: Chanie Landau; Pinches Landau; Solomon Landau.
EIN: 461665626

6363
Jeffrey and Nancy Lane Foundation
c/o John Justice, The Ayco Co., LP
P.O. Box 860
Saratoga Springs, NY   12866-0860

Established in 1987 in New York.
Donor: Jeffrey B. Lane.
Foundation type: Independent foundation.

Financial data (yr. ended 12/31/13): Assets, $398,639 (M); gifts received, $298,045; expenditures, $170,934; qualifying distributions, $170,869; giving activities include $170,869 for 52 grants (high: $29,994; low: $50).
Purpose and activities: Giving primarily to Jewish agencies, as well as for education.
Fields of interest: Arts and culture; Health; Human services.
Type of support: General support.
Limitations: Applications not accepted. Giving primarily in FL and NY. No grants to individuals.
Application information: Unsolicited requests for funds not accepted.
Officers: Jeffrey B. Lane, Pres. and Treas.; Nancy Z. Lane, Secy.
EIN: 112842376

6364
The Lanie & Ethel Foundation
250 W. 57th St., Ste. 1928
New York City, NY 10107-0011

Established in 2001 in New York.
Donors: J. Thurmond Smithgall; James T. Smithgall; Lessie Smithgall.
Foundation type: Independent foundation.
Financial data (yr. ended 12/31/13): Assets, $1,632,396 (M); gifts received, $64,455; expenditures, $211,123; qualifying distributions, $162,252; giving activities include $148,785 for 11 grants (high: $64,585; low: $2,500).
Fields of interest: Arts and culture; Orchestral music.
International interests: Germany.
Type of support: General support.
Limitations: Applications not accepted. Giving primarily in NY and Germany. No grants to individuals.
Application information: Unsolicited requests for funds not accepted.
Trustees: Katherine Gill; Alfred F. Hubay; John Roberts; Thurmond J. Smithgall; Daniel Tucker.
EIN: 134133103

6365
W. & J. Larson Family Foundation
726 Exchange St., Ste. 800
Buffalo, NY 14210-1484

Established in 1985 in New York.
Donors: Joan J. Larson; Wilfred J. Larson.
Foundation type: Independent foundation.
Financial data (yr. ended 10/31/13): Assets, $5,351,383 (M); expenditures, $369,446; qualifying distributions, $358,541; giving activities include $354,825 for 34 grants (high: $100,000; low: $500).
Fields of interest: Historic preservation; Education; Human services.
Limitations: Applications not accepted. Giving on a national basis. No grants to individuals.
Application information: Contributes only to pre-selected organizations.
Trustees: Brian D. Baird; Joan J. Larson; Wilfred J. Larson; Joseph D. Mitchell; Larry J. Nelson.
EIN: 166281709

6366
Lassalle Fund, Inc.
c/o Norman Foundation
147 E. 48th St.
New York City, NY 10017-1223
Contact: Nancy N. Lassalle

Established in 1966 in New York.
Donors: The Norman Foundation; Nancy N. Lassalle.
Foundation type: Independent foundation.
Financial data (yr. ended 12/31/13): Assets, $4,681,348 (M); expenditures, $256,326; qualifying distributions, $203,854; giving activities include $199,052 for 17 grants (high: $30,000; low: $100).
Purpose and activities: Giving primarily for ballet, education, and the performing arts.
Fields of interest: Arts and culture; Performing arts; Ballet; Theater; Music; Opera; Performing arts education; Art museums.
Limitations: Applications accepted. Giving primarily in NY. No grants to individuals.
Application information:
 Initial approach: Letter
 Deadline(s): None
Officer: Nancy N. Lassalle, Pres.
EIN: 136213551

6367
Aaron Laub Memorial Foundation
30-50 Whitestone Expwy., Ste. 300
Flushing, NY 11354-1995

Established in 1988 in New York.
Donors: Perry Chemical Corp.; Norman A. Septimies; Daniel Lerer; Jack Eizikovitz.
Foundation type: Independent foundation.
Financial data (yr. ended 11/30/13): Assets, $1,416,945 (M); gifts received, $321,534; expenditures, $416,265; qualifying distributions, $416,265; giving activities include $406,000 for 15 + grants (high: $192,000).
Fields of interest: Elementary and secondary education; Higher education; Hospital care; Judaism.
International interests: Israel.
Limitations: Applications not accepted. Giving primarily in NY, especially in Brooklyn and Queens, and NJ; some giving also in Israel. No grants to individuals.
Application information: Contributes only to pre-selected organizations.
Trustee: Irving Laub.
EIN: 113018695

6368
The Bernard & Muriel Lauren Foundation
c/o Cassin & Cassin LLP
2900 Westchester Ave., Ste. 402
New York City, NY 10017-5947

Established in 2006 in New York.
Donor: Muriel Lauren†.
Foundation type: Independent foundation.
Financial data (yr. ended 12/31/13): Assets, $4,627,383 (M); expenditures, $278,591; qualifying distributions, $211,500; giving activities include $211,500 for 48 grants (high: $15,000; low: $1,500).
Fields of interest: University education; Law education; Homeless people.

Limitations: Applications not accepted. Giving primarily in NY and VA. No grants to individuals.
Application information: Contributes only to pre-selected organizations.
Trustees: David Baum; Joseph M. Cassin; Keelin C. Pye.
EIN: 205741250

6369
John S. & Florence G. Lawrence Foundation, Inc.
275 Madison Ave., 2nd Fl.
New York City, NY 10016

Established in 1955 in New York.
Donor: John S. Lawrence.
Foundation type: Independent foundation.
Financial data (yr. ended 04/30/13): Assets, $5,263,209 (M); expenditures, $233,870; qualifying distributions, $216,952; giving activities include $170,050 for 48 grants (high: $20,000; low: $500).
Purpose and activities: Giving primarily for Jewish welfare organizations and religious activities; support also for education, hospitals, and the arts.
Fields of interest: Arts and culture; Education; Nonprofits; Health; Diseases and conditions; Religion.
Type of support: Regranting; Research.
Limitations: Applications not accepted.
Application information: Unsolicited requests for funds not accepted.
Officers and Directors: James G. Lawrence, Pres. and Treas. and Director; Betsy P. Schiff, Exec. V.P. and Secy. and Director; Robert J. Peyser.
Number of staff: 1 part-time support.
EIN: 136099026

6370
Bernard and Dorothy Layton Foundation
c/o Theodore J. Vittoria Jr., Vittoria & Purdy
1 Rockefeller Plz., Ste. 321
New York City, NY 10020-2134

Established in 2002 in New York.
Donor: Bernard Layton Trust.
Foundation type: Independent foundation.
Financial data (yr. ended 12/31/14): Assets, $3,213,802 (M); expenditures, $208,998; qualifying distributions, $162,290; giving activities include $158,400 for 6 grants (high: $50,000; low: $12,500).
Fields of interest: Higher education; Medical education.
Limitations: Applications not accepted. Giving primarily in NY. No grants to individuals.
Application information: Unsolicited requests for funds not accepted.
Trustees: Edmond V. Ledonne; Theodore J. Vittoria, Jr.
EIN: 146222827

6371
Lazbridge Foundation
c/o Chadbourne & Park
1301 Ave. of the Americas
New York City, NY 10019-6022

Foundation type: Independent foundation.

Financial data (yr. ended 12/31/13): Assets, $1,552,037 (M); expenditures, $336,932; qualifying distributions, $336,299; giving activities include $336,000 for 4 grants (high: $300,000; low: $5,000).
Limitations: Applications not accepted.
Application information: Unsolicited requests for funds not accepted.
Officers: Ilene Sackler Lefcourt, Pres.; Jeffrey Lefcourt, V.P. and Secy.; Karen Lefcourt-Taylor, V.P. and Treas.
EIN: 611707183

6372
James T. Lee Foundation Inc.
FDR Station
P.O. Box 606
New York City, NY   10150-0606

Established in 1958 in New York.
Donor: James T. Lee†.
Foundation type: Independent foundation.
Financial data (yr. ended 11/30/14): Assets, $2,972,551 (M); expenditures, $328,889; qualifying distributions, $294,794; giving activities include $280,000 for 24 grants (high: $20,000; low: $1,000).
Purpose and activities: Giving primarily for higher and other education, as well as for the arts, health organizations and specialized hospitals, and children, youth, and social services, including a guide dog program for the blind.
Fields of interest: Arts and culture; Education; Human services.
Type of support: Continuing support; Annual campaigns; Debt reduction; Emergency funds; Program development; Scholarships; Research.
Limitations: Applications not accepted. Giving primarily in the New York, NY, metropolitan area, including Westchester County. No grants to individuals, or for operating budgets, seed money, capital or endowment funds, publications, or conferences; no loans.
Application information: Contributes only to pre-selected organizations.
Officers and Directors: Raymond O'Keefe, Pres. and Director; Delcour S. Potter, V.P. and Director; Richard W. Wheeless, Secy.-Treas. and Director; Verne S. Atwater; Leelee Brown; Paul Duffy; Stephen Siegel; Vincent Ziccolella.
EIN: 131878496

6373
Legacy Foundation of Tompkins County
(formerly Tompkins County Foundation, Inc.)
P.O. Box 97
Ithaca, NY   14851-0097
Contact: Janet Hewitt, Rec. Secy.
E-mail: jhewitt@tompkinsfinancial.com; Main URL: http://www.tclegacy.org
Grants List: http://www.tclegacy.org/grants.htm

Established in 1945 in New York.
Foundation type: Independent foundation.
Financial data (yr. ended 12/31/14): Assets, $2,910,542 (M); gifts received, $224,328; expenditures, $232,259; qualifying distributions, $183,399; giving activities include $183,399 for 44 grants (high: $12,700; low: $250).
Purpose and activities: Giving for the arts, education, environment, and human services.

Fields of interest: Arts and culture; Humanities; Education; Environment; Health; Mental health care; Community and economic development; Housing development; Human services; Child welfare.
Type of support: Capital campaigns; Matching grants; Capital and infrastructure; Equipment; Program development; Seed money.
Limitations: Applications accepted. Giving limited to the Tompkins County, NY, area. No support for sectarian organizations or to other foundations. No grants for operating expenses.
Publications: Application guidelines; Annual report; Informational brochure; Newsletter.
Application information: Grant applications are now submitted online. See foundation web site for complete application information.
 Copies of proposal: 1
 Deadline(s): Apr. 15 and Sept. 15
 Board meeting date(s): May and Oct.
 Final notification: June 15 and Nov. 15
Officers and Directors: James Brown, Pres. and Director; Anne DiGiacomo, V.P. and Director; Mary Kane, Secy.-Treas. and Director; Larry Baum; Greg Hartz; Mary Opperman; Sean Whittaker.
Number of staff: 1 part-time support.
EIN: 156018481

6374
Legacy Heritage Fund Limited
(formerly KBRK, Inc.)
477 Madison Ave., 10th Fl.
New York City, NY   10022-5841   (212) 686-7160
Main URL: http://www.legacyheritage.org/index.html

Donors: VHIV, Inc.; IIMI, Inc.; JLRJ, Inc.; MRHM, Inc.; Susan Wexner Revocable Trust; LMCL, Inc.
Foundation type: Independent foundation.
Financial data (yr. ended 06/30/13): Assets, $37,968,081 (M); expenditures, $1,380,473; qualifying distributions, $1,125,248; giving activities include $213,187 for 27 grants (high: $48,500; low: $250).
Fields of interest: Education; Nonprofits; Judaism.
International interests: Israel.
Type of support: Regranting.
Limitations: Applications not accepted. Giving primarily in the U.S., with emphasis on New York, NY; funding also in Israel. No grants to individuals (except for Legacy Heritage fellowships).
Application information: Unsolicited requests for funds not accepted.
Officers and Directors: Susan Wexner, Pres. and Secy.-Treas. and Director; Mark Saks, Esq., V.P. and General Counsel; Saul G. Argus; Raymond Kanner; Gregg H. Levy, Esq.; Michael S. Oberman, Esq.; Walter Stern.
EIN: 134077801

6375
Jane A. and Alan G. Lehman Foundation
(formerly John A. Lehman and Alan G. Lehman Foundation)
c/o Andrew P. Segal, CPA
777 3rd Ave., 38th Fl.
New York City, NY   10017

Established in 2004 in Pennsylvania.
Donor: Allan G. Lehman.
Foundation type: Independent foundation.

Financial data (yr. ended 12/31/14): Assets, $7,819,348; expenditures, $352,697; qualifying distributions, $308,000.
Fields of interest: Art museums; Undergraduate education; Aquariums.
Limitations: Applications not accepted. Giving primarily in AZ and NY. No grants to individuals.
Application information: Unsolicited requests for funds not accepted.
Trustee: Joanne L. Brandt.
EIN: 256818502

6376
The Reuben and Jane Leibowitz Foundation, Inc.
c/o Jen Partners LLC
680 5th Ave., 25th Fl.
New York City, NY   10019
Contact: Reuben Leibowitz

Established in 1986 in New York.
Donor: Reuben S. Leibowitz.
Foundation type: Independent foundation.
Financial data (yr. ended 11/30/13): Assets, $2,759,060 (M); gifts received, $176,003; expenditures, $241,313; qualifying distributions, $225,110; giving activities include $217,965 for 33 grants (high: $40,000; low: $210).
Purpose and activities: Giving primarily for education and Jewish organizations.
Fields of interest: Education; Nonprofits; Judaism.
Type of support: Regranting.
Limitations: Applications not accepted. Giving primarily in NY; some funding also in Washington, DC. No grants to individuals.
Application information: Contributes only to pre-selected organizations.
Trustees: Jane Leibowitz; Reuben S. Leibowitz; David Warmflash.
EIN: 133382812

6377
Laura Lemle Family Foundation
c/o Laura C. Lemle
317 E. 84th St.
New York City, NY   10028-2903

Donor: Gertrude Lemle.
Foundation type: Independent foundation.
Financial data (yr. ended 12/31/12): Assets, $4,323,747 (M); expenditures, $231,526; qualifying distributions, $201,070; giving activities include $201,070 for grants.
Fields of interest: Education; Nonprofits; Hospital care; Children.
Type of support: Regranting.
Limitations: Applications not accepted. Giving primarily in NY. No grants to individuals.
Application information: Contributes only to pre-selected organizations.
Trustee: Laura C. Lemle.
EIN: 516576020

6378
Leo & Trude Lemle Family Foundation
(formerly Lemle Family Foundation)
c/o Robert S. Lemle
317 E. 84th St.- Storefront
New York City, NY   10028-2903

Established in 1994 in New York.
Donors: Leo K. Lemle; Gertrude B. Lemle; Laura C. Lemle.
Foundation type: Independent foundation.
Financial data (yr. ended 11/30/13): Assets, $3,674,992 (M); expenditures, $194,927; qualifying distributions, $169,763; giving activities include $169,570 for 5 grants (high: $100,000; low: $4,570).
Purpose and activities: Giving primarily for Jewish federated giving programs and other various Jewish organizations, art and cultural programs, and for education.
Fields of interest: Arts and culture; Museums; Education; Nonprofits; Judaism.
Type of support: Regranting.
Limitations: Applications not accepted. Giving primarily in New York, NY; some funding also in Oberlin, OH. No grants to individuals.
Application information: Unsolicited requests for funds not accepted.
Trustees: Gertrude B. Lemle; Robert S. Lemle.
EIN: 137053800

6379
Emes V'Shalom Lenetzach Foundation
c/o Kalmanowitz & Lee
575 8th Ave., Ste. 1706
New York City, NY 10018-3067

Donors: Zolton Weinberger; Lillian Weinberger.
Foundation type: Independent foundation.
Financial data (yr. ended 12/31/13): Assets, $962,156 (M); gifts received, $500,000; expenditures, $228,010; qualifying distributions, $228,010; giving activities include $226,410 for 17 grants (high: $95,000; low: $360).
Fields of interest: Judaism.
Limitations: Applications not accepted. No grants to individuals.
Application information: Contributes only to pre-selected organizations.
Officers: Zolton Weinberger, Pres.; Lillian Weinberger, Treas.
EIN: 204880802

6380
The Lenox Foundation
20 Corporate Woods Blvd.
Albany, NY 12211-2396

Established in 1997 in Ohio.
Foundation type: Independent foundation.
Financial data (yr. ended 12/31/14): Assets, $9,263,371 (M); expenditures, $478,770; qualifying distributions, $415,814; giving activities include $368,230 for 43 grants (high: $50,000; low: $500).
Fields of interest: Education; Diseases and conditions; Religion; Human services; Youth development.
Type of support: Research.
Limitations: Applications not accepted. Giving primarily in OH and NY. No grants to individuals.
Application information: Contributes only to pre-selected organizations.
Officers: Marcia P. Floyd, Pres. and Treas.; Frederick P. Floyd, V.P. and Secy.
Directors: Charles B. Floyd; Frederick P. Floyd, Jr.; Kathleen E. Floyd.
EIN: 311532337

6381
The Dorothea L. Leonhardt Foundation, Inc.
169 W. End Ave.
Brooklyn, NY 11235

Established in 1988 in New York.
Donor: Frederick H. Leonhardt†.
Foundation type: Independent foundation.
Financial data (yr. ended 07/31/13): Assets, $13,826,529 (M); expenditures, $675,409; qualifying distributions, $473,686; giving activities include $366,850 for 44 grants (high: $114,000; low: $100).
Fields of interest: Arts and culture; Performing arts; Museums; Education; Diseases and conditions; Legal services; Human services; Child welfare.
Type of support: General support; Continuing support; Capital and infrastructure; Endowments; Professorships; Research.
Limitations: Applications not accepted. Giving primarily in NY. No grants to individuals.
Application information: Unsolicited requests for funds not accepted.
Officers: Joanne Leonhardt Cassullo, Pres.; Alexander D. Forger, V.P.; Richard A. Stark, V.P.; Guilford W. Gaylord, Secy.-Treas.
Number of staff: 1 full-time professional.
EIN: 133420520

6382
The Lerer Family Charitable Foundation Inc.
c/o Tag Assocs., LLC
75 Rockefeller Plz., Ste. 900
New York City, NY 10019-6908

Established in 2000 in New York.
Donor: Kenneth B. Lerer.
Foundation type: Independent foundation.
Financial data (yr. ended 08/31/13): Assets, $3,586,374 (M); gifts received, $532,660; expenditures, $243,368; qualifying distributions, $221,993; giving activities include $221,993 for 7 grants (high: $86,993; low: $10,000).
Fields of interest: Arts and culture; Education; Human services; Children.
Limitations: Applications not accepted. Giving primarily in New York, NY. No grants to individuals.
Application information: Unsolicited requests for funds not accepted.
Officers: Kenneth B. Lerer, Pres.; Katherine R. Sailer, V.P.
EIN: 311753295

6383
Saul & Eleanor Lerner Foundation
1705 Broadway
Hewlett, NY 11557-1634

Established in 1965 in New York.
Donors: Saul Lerner; Eleanor Lerner†.
Foundation type: Independent foundation.
Financial data (yr. ended 12/31/14): Assets, $3,597,300; expenditures, $277,821; qualifying distributions, $264,400.
Purpose and activities: Giving primarily for education, health associations, and Jewish organizations.
Fields of interest: Education; Diseases and conditions; Judaism; Human services.

Limitations: Applications not accepted. Giving primarily in NY. No grants to individuals.
Application information: Unsolicited requests for funds not accepted.
Trustee: Stephen Lerner.
EIN: 116042721

6384
David M. Leuschen Foundation
c/o BCRS Assocs., LLC
77 Water St., 9th Fl.
New York City, NY 10005-4401

Established in 1988 in Connecticut.
Donor: David M. Leuschen.
Foundation type: Independent foundation.
Financial data (yr. ended 04/30/13): Assets, $1,577 (M); gifts received, $216,350; expenditures, $215,925; qualifying distributions, $214,675; giving activities include $213,250 for 6 grants (high: $100,000; low: $8,250).
Fields of interest: Historical activities; Education; Land resources; Human services.
Limitations: Applications not accepted. Giving in the U.S., with some emphasis on MT and VA. No grants to individuals or for scholarships; no loans.
Application information: Unsolicited requests for funds not accepted.
Trustees: Jonathan L. Cohen; David M. Leuschen; Patricia A. Napoli.
EIN: 133501179

6385
Edgar M. Leventritt Foundation, Inc.
P.O. Box 125
Cold Spring, NY 10516-0125

Established in 1939 in New York.
Donor: Curtiss Wright Corp.
Foundation type: Independent foundation.
Financial data (yr. ended 12/31/13): Assets, $7,500,550 (M); expenditures, $540,079; qualifying distributions, $351,270; giving activities include $348,261 for 130 grants (high: $100,317; low: $100).
Purpose and activities: Giving primarily for education and youth programs.
Fields of interest: Education; Nonprofits; Family services; Child welfare.
Type of support: Regranting.
Limitations: Applications not accepted. Giving primarily in MA and NY. No grants to individuals or for scholarships; no loans.
Application information: Contributes only to pre-selected organizations.
Officers: Anthony Berner, Pres.; Rosalie L. Loewen, V.P. and Treas.; Katherine P. Socarras, Secy.
EIN: 136111037

6386
The Sharon Levine Foundation
c/o BCRS Associates, LLC
77 Water St., 9th Fl.
New York City, NY 10005-4401

Established in 2006 in New York.
Donor: Sharon M. Elghanayan.
Foundation type: Independent foundation.
Financial data (yr. ended 12/31/13): Assets, $8,878,548 (M); expenditures, $437,625;

qualifying distributions, $399,185; giving activities include $390,000 for 24 grants (high: $200,000; low: $500).
Purpose and activities: Giving primarily for education, children and social services, Jewish federated giving programs, and to a cancer hospital.
Fields of interest: Education; Law education; Animal welfare; Nonprofits; Specialty hospital care; Cancers; Human services; Child welfare.
Type of support: Regranting.
Limitations: Applications not accepted. Giving primarily in New York, NY. No grants to individuals.
Application information: Contributes only to pre-selected organizations.
Trustee: Sharon M. Elghanayan.
EIN: 205390754

6387
Morris Levine Key Food Stores Foundation, Inc.
(formerly Key Food Stores Foundation, Inc.)
1200 South Ave.
Staten Island, NY 10314-3413

Established in 1962 in New York.
Donors: Allen Newman; Man-Dell Food Stores, Inc.; Pick Quickfoods, Inc.; Dan's Supreme Supermarkets, Inc.; Key Food Stores Cooperative, Inc.; Donald & Linda Gross Foundation; Frank & Roslyn Grobman Foundation.
Foundation type: Company-sponsored foundation.
Financial data (yr. ended 08/31/13): Assets, $208,022 (M); gifts received, $139,000; expenditures, $528,756; qualifying distributions, $339,436; giving activities include $337,802 for 18 grants (high: $147,902; low: $250).
Purpose and activities: The foundation supports organizations involved with education, health, cancer, human services, the supermarket industry, and Judaism.
Fields of interest: Education; Health; Cancers; Breast cancer; Business and industry; Judaism; Human services; Homeless services.
Type of support: Scholarships; General support.
Limitations: Applications not accepted. Giving primarily in NY. No grants to individuals.
Application information: Unsolicited requests for funds not accepted.
Officers and Directors: Dean Janeway, Pres. and Director; George Knobloch, Secy.-Treas. and Director; Lawrence Mandel.
EIN: 116035538

6388
The Levitin Family Charitable Trust
1222 E. 22nd St.
Brooklyn, NY 11210-4515

Established in 1998 in New York.
Foundation type: Independent foundation.
Financial data (yr. ended 12/31/13): Assets, $1,948,039 (M); gifts received, $384,000; expenditures, $180,431; qualifying distributions, $167,199; giving activities include $167,199 for 80 grants (high: $20,000; low: $100).
Purpose and activities: Giving primarily for Jewish organizations, temples, and schools.
Fields of interest: Education; Nonprofits; Judaism.
Type of support: Regranting.
Limitations: Applications not accepted. Giving primarily in Brooklyn, NY. No grants to individuals.

Application information: Contributes only to pre-selected organizations.
Trustees: Eli Levitin; Raizy Levitin.
EIN: 116496569

6389
Edwin A. and Carolyne Levy Charitable Foundation, Inc.
366 Madison Ave.
New York City, NY 10017

Established in 2001 in New York.
Donors: Edwin A. Levy; Edwin Carolyn Levy.
Foundation type: Independent foundation.
Financial data (yr. ended 03/31/13): Assets, $445,852 (M); gifts received, $216,600; expenditures, $176,141; qualifying distributions, $174,201; giving activities include $174,201 for grants.
Fields of interest: Diseases and conditions.
Limitations: Applications not accepted. Giving primarily in Healdburg, CA and New York, NY. No grants to individuals.
Application information: Unsolicited requests for funds not accepted.
Officers: Edwin A. Levy, C.E.O. and Pres.; Carolyne Levy, Secy.
Director: Robert Greenberg.
EIN: 134171755

6390
The Norman S. Levy Family Foundation Inc.
c/o Global Imports
140 58th St., Bldg. B, Ste. 5F
Brooklyn, NY 11220

Established in 1994 in New York.
Donors: Global Imports, Inc.; Norman S. Levy.
Foundation type: Independent foundation.
Financial data (yr. ended 12/31/13): Assets, $109,249 (M); gifts received, $99,000; expenditures, $232,612; qualifying distributions, $232,562; giving activities include $232,562 for 38 grants (high: $36,000; low: $500).
Purpose and activities: Giving primarily for Jewish organizations.
Fields of interest: Nonprofits; Judaism.
Type of support: Regranting.
Limitations: Applications not accepted. No grants to individuals.
Application information: Unsolicited requests for funds not accepted.
Officers: Norman S. Levy, Pres.; Jeffrey Sitt, V.P.; Morris Sitt, Secy.
EIN: 133773989

6391
Frances and Jack Levy Foundation
820 5th Ave., 8th Fl.
New York City, NY 10065

Established in 2001 in New York.
Donors: Frances Levy; Jack Levy.
Foundation type: Independent foundation.
Financial data (yr. ended 06/30/14): Assets, $1,815,462 (M); gifts received, $10,005; expenditures, $276,956; qualifying distributions, $265,102; giving activities include $265,102 for 51 grants (high: $60,000; low: $100).

Purpose and activities: Giving primarily for Jewish organizations, as well as for social services, and education.
Fields of interest: Art museums; Education; Higher education; Nonprofits; Health; Hospital care; Judaism; Human services; Child welfare; Females.
Type of support: General support; Regranting.
Limitations: Applications not accepted. Giving primarily in NY. No grants to individuals.
Application information: Unsolicited requests for funds not accepted.
Trustees: Frances Levy; Jack Levy.
EIN: 137279189

6392
Andrew and Marina Lewin Family Foundation, Inc.
515 West End Ave., Apt. 11D
New York City, NY 10024-4345
Contact: Andrew Lewin, Pres.

Established in 2004 in New York.
Foundation type: Independent foundation.
Financial data (yr. ended 12/31/13): Assets, $8,374,327 (M); expenditures, $481,196; qualifying distributions, $347,452; giving activities include $314,144 for 13 grants (high: $101,644; low: $2,500).
Fields of interest: Arts and culture; Higher education.
Type of support: General support.
Limitations: Applications accepted. Giving primarily in NH and NY.
Application information: The foundation considers grant requests from organizations in the fields of art and education.
  Initial approach: Letter of inquiry (2 pages)
  Deadline(s): None
  Board meeting date(s): June and Dec.
Officers and Directors: Andrew Lewin, Pres. and Director; Marina Lewin, Secy.-Treas. and Director; Ian Schwieger.
EIN: 061685933

6393
The Lewy Family Foundation
c/o R. Stein
29 W. 38th St., 14th Fl.
New York City, NY 10018-5504

Established in 1996 in New York.
Donors: Glen S. Lewy; Zachary Lewy.
Foundation type: Independent foundation.
Financial data (yr. ended 12/31/13): Assets, $3,520,267 (M); expenditures, $203,216; qualifying distributions, $189,096; giving activities include $187,250 for 13 grants (high: $60,000; low: $200).
Fields of interest: Historic preservation; Elementary and secondary education; Higher education; Education services; Educational exchanges; Nonprofits; Cerebral palsy; Judaism.
Type of support: Regranting; Research.
Limitations: Applications not accepted. Giving primarily in Washington, DC, New York, NY, and Brattleboro, VT. No grants to individuals.
Application information: Contributes only to pre-selected organizations.
Officer: Glen S. Lewy, Chair.

Directors: Brooke Lewy; Cheryl Winter Lewy; Marshall Lewy; Zachary Jason Lewy.
EIN: 133907886

6394
Li Foundation, Inc.
57 Glen St.
Glen Cove, NY 11542-2771
E-mail: admin@lifoundation.org

Established in 1944 in New York.
Foundation type: Independent foundation.
Financial data (yr. ended 12/31/13): Assets, $7,602,090 (M); expenditures, $452,040; qualifying distributions, $346,133; giving activities include $301,994 for 8 grants (high: $52,000; low: $5,000).
Purpose and activities: Scholarship and fellowship awards paid directly to colleges or universities for Chinese students to study in the U.S.
Fields of interest: Higher education.
International interests: China.
Type of support: Fellowships; Scholarships.
Limitations: Applications not accepted.
Application information: Unsolicited requests for funds not accepted.
Officers and Directors: Taie Li, Pres. and Director; Marie Chun, V.P. and Director; Gail Chun-Deduonni, Secy. and Director; Ling Li, Treas. and Director; Minfong Ho Dennis; Carlos Chang Koo; Anna Li; Edward Leong Way; Eric Leong Way.
Number of staff: 3
EIN: 136098783

6395
The Kenneth & Jane S. Libby Foundation, Inc.
c/o Leicht & Rein Tax Assocs.
570 7th Ave., Ste. 1804
New York City, NY 10018-1623

Established in 2001 in Connecticut.
Donor: Kenneth Libby.
Foundation type: Independent foundation.
Financial data (yr. ended 06/30/13): Assets, $1,810 (M); expenditures, $188,151; qualifying distributions, $185,858; giving activities include $185,041 for 6 grants (high: $90,000; low: $10,000).
Fields of interest: Arts and culture; Diseases and conditions; ALS; Human services.
Limitations: Applications not accepted. Giving primarily in CA and OR. No grants to individuals.
Application information: Unsolicited requests for funds not accepted.
Officers and Directors: Linda Libby Rind, Pres. and Director; Louis S. Libby, MD, V.P.; Jocelyn Libby, Secy.-Treas.
EIN: 061563725

6396
Bertha & Isaac Liberman Foundation, Inc.
c/o Jerome Tarnoff, Morrison Cohen LLP
909 3rd Ave.
New York City, NY 10022-4731 (212) 735-8632
Contact: Jerome Tarnoff, Pres.

Established in 1947 in New York.
Donor: Isaac Liberman†.
Foundation type: Independent foundation.

Financial data (yr. ended 06/30/13): Assets, $9,317,311 (M); expenditures, $460,246; qualifying distributions, $433,026; giving activities include $392,000 for 22 grants (high: $70,000; low: $500).
Purpose and activities: Giving primarily for the arts, particularly art museums, as well as for education, social services, and Jewish organizations.
Fields of interest: Arts and culture; Performing arts; Art museums; Higher education; Hospital care; Judaism; Human services.
Type of support: General support; Capital campaigns; Capital and infrastructure; Program development.
Limitations: Applications accepted. Giving primarily in New York, NY. No grants to individuals.
Application information:
Deadline(s): None
Officers and Directors: Jerome Tarnoff, Pres. and Director; Michele Gerber Klein, V.P. and Director; Karin J. Lundell, Secy. and Director; David B. Forer, Treas. and Director; John Moscow.
EIN: 136119056

6397
The Lichtenstein Foundation Inc.
350 5th Ave.
New York City, NY 10118-0100 (212) 563-2000
Contact: Seymour Lichtenstein, Pres. and Dir.

Donor: Seymour Lichtenstein.
Foundation type: Independent foundation.
Financial data (yr. ended 11/30/13): Assets, $1,843,161 (M); gifts received, $200,250; expenditures, $218,334; qualifying distributions, $217,717; giving activities include $217,467 for 35 grants (high: $105,371; low: $100).
Fields of interest: Arts and culture; Education; University education; Human services.
Type of support: General support.
Limitations: Applications accepted. Giving primarily in MD and New York, NY. No grants to individuals.
Application information: Application form required.
Initial approach: Letter
Deadline(s): None
Officers and Directors: Seymour Lichtenstein, Pres. and Director; Marvin Robinson, Secy. and Director; Marita Lichtenstein, Treas. and Director.
EIN: 136121017

6398
David L. Lieb Foundation, Inc.
c/o David Graber
150 E. 58th St., 20th Fl.
New York City, NY 10155-0002

Donor: David L. Lieb†.
Foundation type: Independent foundation.
Financial data (yr. ended 12/31/13): Assets, $6,881,008 (M); expenditures, $370,515; qualifying distributions, $290,361; giving activities include $162,933 for 103 grants (high: $15,000; low: $25).
Purpose and activities: Giving primarily for a Jewish welfare fund and other Jewish organizations; support also for higher education, health care, the arts, and human services.
Fields of interest: Health; Diseases and conditions; Religion.
Type of support: Research.

Limitations: Applications not accepted. Giving primarily in NY. No grants to individuals.
Application information: Contributes only to pre-selected organizations.
Officers: Barbara Lieb Baumstein, Pres.; Sam Lieb, V.P.; Toby Lieb, Secy.; Jeffrey Baumstein, Treas.
EIN: 136077728

6399
Avi Lieberman Foundation
1272 E. 10th St.
Brooklyn, NY 11230-4719

Donor: Gloria Lieberman.
Foundation type: Independent foundation.
Financial data (yr. ended 12/31/14): Assets, $389,544 (M); gifts received, $18,000; expenditures, $163,532; qualifying distributions, $162,572; giving activities include $162,572 for 7 + grants (high: $40,000).
Fields of interest: Education; Religion; Judaism; Human services.
Trustees: Gloria Lieberman; Moshe Lieberman.
EIN: 270659721

6400
D. A. Liebowitz Family Foundation
c/o Weber Moses & Co.
225 Broadway, Ste. 2420
New York City, NY 10007-3711

Established in 2004 in New York.
Donor: David A. Liebowitz.
Foundation type: Independent foundation.
Financial data (yr. ended 12/31/13): Assets, $144,672 (M); gifts received, $100; expenditures, $345,859; qualifying distributions, $338,935; giving activities include $338,935 for 25 grants (high: $110,000; low: $1,000).
Purpose and activities: Giving primarily for the arts, education, and Jewish organizations; funding also for social services.
Fields of interest: Arts and culture; Education; Nonprofits; Judaism; Human services.
Type of support: Regranting.
Limitations: Applications not accepted. Giving primarily in New York, NY. No grants to individuals.
Application information: Unsolicited requests for funds not accepted.
Officer: David A. Liebowitz, Pres.
EIN: 201917490

6401
Lippes Family Charitable Foundation
c/o Gerald S. Lippes
665 Main St., Ste. 300
Buffalo, NY 14203-1425 (716) 853-5100
Contact: Gerald S. Lippes, Chair.

Established in 1989 in New York.
Donor: Gerald S. Lippes.
Foundation type: Independent foundation.
Financial data (yr. ended 12/31/13): Assets, $1,306,493 (M); expenditures, $215,569; qualifying distributions, $206,927; giving activities include $206,927 for 45 grants (high: $30,000; low: $250).
Fields of interest: Arts and culture; Higher education; Environment; Nonprofits; Diseases and conditions; Judaism; Human services.

Type of support: Regranting.
Limitations: Applications accepted. Giving primarily in Buffalo and New York, NY. No grants to individuals.
Application information: Application form required.
  Initial approach: Letter
  Deadline(s): None
Officers: Gerald L. Lippes, Chair.; Tracy G. Lippes, V.P. and Secy.; Adam S. Lippes, V.P.; David F. Lippes, V.P.
EIN: 223019880

6402
C. & Y. Lipschitz Family Foundation
1615 48th St.
Brooklyn, NY   11204-1155

Donors: Chaim Lipschitz; Yocheved Lipschitz.
Foundation type: Independent foundation.
Financial data (yr. ended 12/31/13): Assets, $1,151,645 (M); gifts received, $226,000; expenditures, $188,663; qualifying distributions, $152,415; giving activities include $152,415 for 11 grants (high: $50,000; low: $1,800).
Fields of interest: Education; Religion.
Limitations: Applications not accepted. Giving primarily in Brooklyn, NY.
Application information: Unsolicited requests for funds not accepted.
Directors: Chaim Lipschitz; Fishel Lipschitz; Yocheved Lipschitz.
EIN: 260848399

6403
Marc and Jennifer Lipschultz Family Foundation
c/o KKR Financial Services Company LLC
730 5th Ave., 8th Fl.
New York City, NY   10019-4105

Donor: Marc Lipschultz.
Foundation type: Independent foundation.
Financial data (yr. ended 12/31/13): Assets, $1,602,012 (M); gifts received, $512,722; expenditures, $335,795; qualifying distributions, $318,295; giving activities include $311,043 for grants.
Fields of interest: Education; Religion; Sports and recreation.
Limitations: Applications not accepted.
Application information: Unsolicited requests for funds not accepted.
Officers and Directors: Marc S. Lipschultz, Pres. and Director; Jennifer S. Lipschultz, V.P. and Director; Jessica Phillips, Secy.; James M. Goldrick, Treas.
EIN: 452258060

6404
The Lipton Foundation
51 W. 52nd St.
New York City, NY   10019-6119

Established in 2001 in New York.
Donor: Wachtell, Lipton, Rosen & Katz.
Foundation type: Company-sponsored foundation.
Financial data (yr. ended 12/31/13): Assets, $9,265,168 (M); expenditures, $405,635; qualifying distributions, $405,635; giving activities include $405,000 for 25 grants (high: $55,000; low: $5,000).
Purpose and activities: The foundation supports museums and food banks and organizations involved with higher and law education, wildlife preservation, human services, and Judaism.
Fields of interest: Education; Religion; Human services.
Type of support: General support; Program development.
Limitations: Applications not accepted. Giving primarily in NY. No grants to individuals.
Application information: Contributes only to pre-selected organizations.
Officers: Susan L. Lipton, Pres.; Martin Lipton, V.P. and Secy.; Katherine B. Lipton, V.P.; Samantha D. Lipton, V.P.; Constance Monte, Treas.
EIN: 582629617

6405
Gerda Lissner Foundation, Inc.
15 E. 65th St., 4th Fl.
New York City, NY   10065-6501   (212) 826-6100
Contact: Stephen DeMaio, Pres.
FAX: (212) 826-0366;
E-mail: mail@gerdalissner.com; Main URL: http://www.gerdalissner.org
Grants List: http://www.gerdalissner.org/awards.html

Established in 1994 in New York.
Donor: Gerda Lissner†.
Foundation type: Independent foundation.
Financial data (yr. ended 12/31/13): Assets, $9,400,962 (M); gifts received, $200; expenditures, $909,114; qualifying distributions, $813,625; giving activities include $104,500 for 15 grants (high: $20,000; low: $500), and $226,000 for 43 grants to individuals (high: $15,000; low: $2,000).
Purpose and activities: Giving primarily for awards to assist in the development of world class opera singers.
Fields of interest: Opera.
Type of support: General support; Grants to individuals.
Publications: Application guidelines.
Application information: See grantmaker web site for application information and form. Application form required.
  Initial approach: Telephone or e-mail
  Deadline(s): Mar. 1
Officers: Stephen DeMaio, Pres.; Michael Fornabaro, V.P. and Treas.; Rev. John A. Kamas, Secy.
Trustees: Dorothy Moore; Barbara Ann Testa.
Number of staff: 1 full-time support; 1 part-time support.
EIN: 133566516

6406
The Litterman Family Foundation
(formerly The Robert & Mary Litterman Foundation)
Bowling Green Sta.
P.O. Box 73
New York City, NY   10274-0073

Established in 1994 in New Jersey.
Donor: Robert B. Litterman.
Foundation type: Independent foundation.
Financial data (yr. ended 09/30/13): Assets, $8,405,718 (M); gifts received, $300,000; expenditures, $351,049; qualifying distributions, $351,000; giving activities include $351,000 for 38 grants (high: $100,000; low: $1,000).
Purpose and activities: Giving primarily for health associations, human services, federated giving programs, and to a YMCA.
Fields of interest: Nonprofits; Diseases and conditions; Human services.
Type of support: General support; Regranting.
Limitations: Applications not accepted. Giving primarily in CO, NJ and New York, NY. No grants to individuals.
Application information: Contributes only to pre-selected organizations.
Trustees: Adam J. Litterman; Mary Litterman; Nadia K. Litterman; Robert Litterman.
EIN: 133805239

6407
The Little One Foundation
c/o Bessemer Trust Company
630 5th Ave.
New York City, NY   10111-0100

Donor: Stephen Hahn†.
Foundation type: Independent foundation.
Financial data (yr. ended 12/31/13): Assets, $4,539,996 (M); expenditures, $266,170; qualifying distributions, $262,459; giving activities include $262,000 for 14 grants (high: $50,000; low: $2,000).
Fields of interest: Arts and culture; Education; Human services.
Limitations: Applications not accepted.
Application information: Unsolicited requests for funds not accepted.
Trustees: Isabelle Hahn Cohen; Kenneth N. Musen; Beth D. Tractenberg.
EIN: 456398647

6408
Victoria Loconsolo Foundation, Inc.
2660 Coney Island Ave.
Brooklyn, NY   11223-5504
E-mail: jaloconsolo@thepaintstoreny.com

Established in 1981 in New York.
Donor: John A. Loconsolo.
Foundation type: Independent foundation.
Financial data (yr. ended 12/31/13): Assets, $4,314,239 (M); gifts received, $91,680; expenditures, $222,776; qualifying distributions, $184,500; giving activities include $184,500 for 17 grants (high: $131,500; low: $500).
Purpose and activities: Giving primarily for education and children's services.
Fields of interest: Education.
Type of support: General support; Individual development; Continuing support; Endowments; Scholarships.
Limitations: Applications not accepted. Giving primarily in New York, NY. No grants to individuals.
Application information: Unsolicited requests for funds not accepted.
Officers and Directors: John A. Loconsolo, Chair. and Director; Regina Dedick, Pres. and Director; Jonathan Chiaro, V.P. and Director; Elizabeth Loconsolo, Secy.-Treas. and Director; Maria Caccese; Antoinette Chiaro; Janet D'Auria; Paul

D'Auria; Jacqueline Loconsolo; William M. Petrella; Rose Marie Rizzo.
EIN: 112577394

6409
Loewy Family Foundation Inc.
80 Wall St., No. 1018
New York City, NY   10005-3601   (212) 269-2466
Contact: John P. Reiner, Secy.-Treas.

Established in 1966 in New York.
Donors: Alfred Loewy†; Edna Loewy Butler†.
Foundation type: Independent foundation.
Financial data (yr. ended 06/30/14): Assets, $10,385,848 (M); expenditures, $509,119; qualifying distributions, $462,461; giving activities include $433,834 for 7 grants (high: $256,667; low: $14,500).
Purpose and activities: Giving primarily for higher education.
Fields of interest: Elementary and secondary education; Higher education.
Type of support: Equipment; Program development; Fellowships; Scholarships; Research.
Limitations: Applications accepted. Giving primarily in CA, NM, NY, PA, and VA. No grants to individuals.
Application information: Application form required.
  Initial approach: Proposal in letter form
  Copies of proposal: 1
  Deadline(s): None
Officers and Directors: Brigitte Loewy Linz, Chair. and Pres.; Erik A. Hanson, CPA, V.P. and Director; Peter Erwin Linz, V.P. and Director; Edward B. Pennfield, V.P. and Director; Mischa A. Zabotin, V.P. and Director; John P. Reiner, Secy.-Treas. and Director.
EIN: 136225288

6410
Long Cove Foundation, Inc.
c/o P. Martin, Ashford Advisors, LLC
30B Grove St.
Pittsford, NY   14534-1334

Established in 2006 in Delaware.
Donors: Roger W. Sant; Victoria p. Sant.
Foundation type: Independent foundation.
Financial data (yr. ended 12/31/13): Assets, $5,147,543 (M); gifts received, $1,000,000; expenditures, $292,993; qualifying distributions, $261,906; giving activities include $259,598 for 25 grants (high: $80,000; low: $500).
Fields of interest: Education; Environment; Human services.
Limitations: Applications not accepted. Giving primarily in CA, ME and MT. No grants to individuals.
Application information: Unsolicited requests for funds not accepted.
Officers and Directors: Michael J. Sant, Pres. and Treas. and Director; Kristin W. Sant, Secy. and Director.
EIN: 412217896

6411
The Longhill Charitable Foundation
c/o Weisermazars, LLP
135 W. 50th St.
New York City, NY   10020-1201

Established in 1971 in New York.

Donor: Wilbur A. Cowett†.
Foundation type: Independent foundation.
Financial data (yr. ended 06/30/14): Assets, $19,417,672 (M); gifts received, $15,000,000; expenditures, $203,831; qualifying distributions, $185,760; giving activities include $166,750 for 64 grants (high: $25,000; low: $250).
Fields of interest: Health; Judaism; Human services.
Limitations: Applications not accepted. Giving primarily in New York, NY. No grants to individuals.
Application information: Unsolicited requests for funds not accepted.
Officers: Fred Cowett, Pres.; Anne F. Cowett, V.P.; Peter Nussbaum, Treas.
EIN: 237149847

6412
The Lopatin Family Foundation
c/o BCRS Assocs., LLC
77 Water St., 9th Fl.
New York City, NY   10005-3701

Established in 1994 in New York.
Donors: Jonathan M. Lopatin; Brenda Lopatin.
Foundation type: Independent foundation.
Financial data (yr. ended 08/31/13): Assets, $13,221,044 (M); expenditures, $603,432; qualifying distributions, $514,547; giving activities include $424,850 for 29 grants (high: $200,000; low: $200).
Purpose and activities: Giving primarily for Jewish organizations.
Fields of interest: Education; Graduate and professional education; Nonprofits; Mental health care; Judaism; Theology; Human services.
Type of support: Regranting.
Limitations: Applications not accepted. Giving primarily in the greater metropolitan New York, NY, area. No grants to individuals, or for scholarships; no loans.
Application information: Contributes only to pre-selected organizations.
Trustee: Jonathan M. Lopatin.
EIN: 133797381

6413
Lorber Charitable Fund
125 Jericho Turnpike, Ste. 501
Jericho, NY   11753   (516) 882-2060
Contact: Brian Lorber, Pres.

Established in 1997 in New York.
Donors: Howard M. Lorber; Lorber 2000 Charitable Lead Trust; Lorber 2002 Charitable Lead Trust; Lorber 2001 Charitable Lead Trust.
Foundation type: Independent foundation.
Financial data (yr. ended 12/31/12): Assets, $831,949 (M); gifts received, $274,511; expenditures, $288,778; qualifying distributions, $280,049; giving activities include $280,049 for grants.
Fields of interest: Health; Religion; Human services.
Limitations: Applications accepted. Giving primarily in NY. No grants to individuals.
Application information: Application form required.
  Initial approach: Letter
  Deadline(s): None
Officers: Brian Lorber, Pres.; Michael Lorber, Treas.
Director: Ira Stechel.
EIN: 113375574

6414
Lowenbraun Family Foundation
1259 E. 31st St.
Brooklyn, NY   11210-4740

Donors: Chaim Lowenbraun; Miriam Lowenbraun.
Foundation type: Independent foundation.
Financial data (yr. ended 06/30/13): Assets, $687,282 (M); expenditures, $180,165; qualifying distributions, $176,249; giving activities include $170,340 for 5+ grants.
Fields of interest: Education; Religion; Judaism; Human services.
Limitations: Applications not accepted. Giving primarily in NY.
Application information: Unsolicited requests for funds not accepted.
Trustees: Chaim Lowenbraun; Miriam Lowenbraun.
EIN: 456655433

6415
LSK Foundation
c/o Audrey Binkhorst
P.O. Box 181
Point Lookout, NY   11569-0181

Established in 1987 in New York.
Donor: Sonja K. Binkhorst.
Foundation type: Independent foundation.
Financial data (yr. ended 12/31/13): Assets, $234,870 (M); gifts received, $300,000; expenditures, $244,915; qualifying distributions, $242,950; giving activities include $237,050 for 10 grants (high: $200,000; low: $1,000).
Fields of interest: Hospital care; Judaism.
Type of support: General support.
Limitations: Applications not accepted. Giving primarily in NY. No grants to individuals.
Application information: Unsolicited requests for funds not accepted.
Trustees: Audrey Binkhorst; Gordon Binkhorst; Mark Binkhorst.
EIN: 133427131

6416
Lubin Family Foundation
c/o DDK & Co., LLP
1 Penn Plz., 4th Fl.
New York City, NY   10119-0002
Contact: Sara L. Schupf.

Established in 1993 in New York.
Donor: Tillie K. Lubin†.
Foundation type: Independent foundation.
Financial data (yr. ended 12/31/13): Assets, $8,470,749 (M); gifts received, $1,335,147; expenditures, $326,083; qualifying distributions, $286,532; giving activities include $279,750 for 23 grants (high: $124,500; low: $250).
Fields of interest: Science museums; Elementary and secondary education; Higher education; University education; Environment; Science.
Type of support: General support.
Limitations: Applications not accepted. Giving primarily in CT and New York, NY. No grants to individuals.
Application information: Contributes only to pre-selected organizations.
Trustee: Sara L. Schupf.
EIN: 136991626

6417
Lubo Fund, Inc.
c/o Norman Foundation Inc.
147 E. 48th St.
New York City, NY 10017-1223
Contact: Lucinda W. Bunnen, Pres.

Established in 1958 in Georgia.
Donors: Belinda Reusch; Robert L. Bunnen, Jr.;
Lucinda W. Bunnen; Melissa Bunnen Jernigan;
Robert L. Bunnen.
Foundation type: Independent foundation.
Financial data (yr. ended 12/31/13): Assets,
$10,248,407 (M); gifts received, $69,294;
expenditures, $536,027; qualifying distributions,
$430,381; giving activities include $420,354 for
135 grants (high: $75,000; low: $75).
Purpose and activities: Giving primarily for the arts,
education and human services.
Fields of interest: Arts and culture; Photography;
Performing arts; Education; Environment; Diseases
and conditions; Judaism; Human services.
Type of support: General support; Matching grants;
Continuing support; Annual campaigns; Emergency
funds; Program development; Publications; Seed
money.
Limitations: Giving primarily in GA, with emphasis on
Atlanta. No grants to individuals, or for land
acquisition, renovation projects, endowment funds,
scholarships, fellowships, research, or
conferences; no loans.
Application information:
  Initial approach: Letter
  Deadline(s): None
  Board meeting date(s): July
Officer: Lucinda W. Bunnen, Pres.
EIN: 586043631

6418
The Lucelia Foundation Inc.
625 Clinton Sq.
Rochester, NY 14604

Established in 1998 in New York.
Donor: Elizabeth G. Miller.
Foundation type: Independent foundation.
Financial data (yr. ended 12/31/13): Assets,
$4,189,910 (M); expenditures, $391,949;
qualifying distributions, $380,544; giving activities
include $380,544 for 31 grants (high: $200,000;
low: $150).
Purpose and activities: Giving primarily for the arts,
with an emphasis on American and contemporary
art.
Fields of interest: Arts education; Visual arts;
Museums.
Type of support: General support; Program-related
investments; Continuing support; Annual
campaigns; Capital campaigns; Capital and
infrastructure; Equipment; Program development;
Publications; Seed money; Curriculum development;
Fellowships; Internships; Research.
Limitations: Applications not accepted. No grants to
individuals.
Application information: Contributes only to
pre-selected organizations.
Officers and Directors: Elizabeth G. Gosnell, Pres.
and Director; Richard A. Miller, Treas.
EIN: 134009608

6419
The Lucky One Foundation
(formerly The Lillian Sara Hahn Foundation)
c/o Bessemer Trust
630 5th Ave.
New York City, NY 10111-0100

Donor: Stephen Hahn Estate.
Foundation type: Independent foundation.
Financial data (yr. ended 12/31/14): Assets,
$7,259,801; expenditures, $356,077; qualifying
distributions, $346,089.
Fields of interest: Arts and culture; Environment;
Sports and recreation.
Limitations: Applications not accepted.
Application information: Unsolicited requests for
funds not accepted.
Trustees: Lillian Sara Hahn; Kenneth N. Musen;
Michael Ward Stout.
EIN: 456398630

6420
Lucky Star Foundation
c/o Anchin Block & Anchin LLP
1375 Broadway
New York City, NY 10018-7001

Donors: Judith O'Connor Gluckstern; Steven M.
Gluckstern; One Heart, Inc.; Judith Gluckstern.
Foundation type: Independent foundation.
Financial data (yr. ended 12/31/13): Assets,
$2,748 (M); gifts received, $170,000;
expenditures, $170,772; qualifying distributions,
$169,505; giving activities include $166,500 for 13
grants (high: $50,000; low: $1,000).
Fields of interest: Arts and culture; Performing arts;
Education.
Limitations: Applications not accepted. No grants to
individuals.
Application information: Contributes only to
pre-selected organizations.
Officers: Judith O'Connor Gluckstern, Pres.; Steven
M. Gluckstern, V.P.; Steve Germain, Secy.
EIN: 133710572

6421
The Lufkin Family Foundation
(formerly The Dan W. Lufkin Foundation)
c/o Radinglass & Co., LLP, Dan W. Lufkin
711 5th Ave., 10th Fl.
New York City, NY 10022-3111

Established in 1998 in New York.
Donor: Dan W. Lufkin.
Foundation type: Independent foundation.
Financial data (yr. ended 12/31/13): Assets,
$2,541,555 (M); expenditures, $149,793;
qualifying distributions, $141,067; giving activities
include $139,650 for 7 grants (high: $50,000; low:
$2,650).
Purpose and activities: Giving primarily for
children's causes and services, the environment, as
well as environmental health, and to health
organizations focusing on the health of humans and
animals.
Fields of interest: Environment; Animal welfare;
Nonprofits; Housing development; Child welfare.
Type of support: Regranting.
Limitations: Applications not accepted. Giving
primarily in CA, CT, MD and NY. No grants to
individuals.

Application information: Contributes only to
pre-selected organizations.
Trustees: Margaret L. Bishop; Alison W. Lufkin
Faber; Hugh J. Freund; Abigail F. Lufkin; Dan W.
Lufkin; Elise G.B. Lufkin.
EIN: 133999095

6422
The Lux Foundation
P.O. Box 73
Bowling Green Sta.
New York City, NY 10274-0073

Established in 2005 in Delaware.
Donors: Deborah M. Lehr; John F.W. Rogers.
Foundation type: Independent foundation.
Financial data (yr. ended 12/31/13): Assets,
$3,312,649 (M); expenditures, $200,737;
qualifying distributions, $180,000; giving activities
include $180,000 for 4 grants (high: $100,000;
low: $5,000).
Fields of interest: Museums; Elementary and
secondary education; Social sciences.
Type of support: Capital campaigns; Policy,
advocacy and systems reform; Program
development.
Limitations: Applications not accepted. Giving
primarily in Washington, DC. No grants to
individuals.
Application information: Contributes only to
pre-selected organizations.
Officer: John F.W. Rogers, Pres.
EIN: 203979808

6423
M & M Family Foundation
783 Bedford Ave., Apt. 1A
Brooklyn, NY 11205-1567 (917) 807-0138
Contact: Meilech Levy, Tr.

Donors: Meilech Levy; Malky Levy.
Foundation type: Independent foundation.
Financial data (yr. ended 03/31/13): Assets,
$1,749,951 (M); expenditures, $148,389;
qualifying distributions, $144,903; giving activities
include $144,903 for grants.
Type of support: General support.
Limitations: Applications accepted. Giving primarily
in NY.
Application information: Application form required.
  Initial approach: Proposal
  Deadline(s): None
Trustees: Malky Levy; Meilech Levy.
EIN: 263747928

6424
M Y B Foundation
1327H 46th St.
Brooklyn, NY 11219-2140

Established in 2000 in New York.
Donor: Elizabeth Jakabovits.
Foundation type: Independent foundation.
Financial data (yr. ended 12/31/13): Assets,
$93,751 (M); gifts received, $300,000;
expenditures, $253,249; qualifying distributions,
$253,249; giving activities include $252,619 for
grants.
Fields of interest: Judaism.

Limitations: Applications not accepted. Giving primarily in NY. No grants to individuals.
Application information: Contributes only to pre-selected organizations.
Trustee: Ann Kahn.
EIN: 116472759

6425
The M&E Foundation
(formerly Moric & Elsa Bistricer Foundation)
c/o Moric Bistricer
4611 12th Ave.
Brooklyn, NY   11219-2539

Established in 1988 in New York.
Donors: Moric Bistricer; Elsa Bistricer; Eliza Bistricer; 1999 Bistricer Family Trust; MB 2006 Lead Trust.
Foundation type: Independent foundation.
Financial data (yr. ended 04/30/14): Assets, $15,985,020 (M); gifts received, $286,250; expenditures, $134,086; qualifying distributions, $128,053; giving activities include $126,594 for 63 grants (high: $33,200; low: $18).
Purpose and activities: Giving primarily to Jewish organizations for the purpose of advancing education and assisting the needy.
Fields of interest: Judaism; Human services; Jewish people.
Limitations: Applications not accepted. Giving primarily in Brooklyn, NY. No grants to individuals.
Application information: Unsolicited requests for funds not accepted.
Officer: Moric Bistricer, Fdn. Mgr.
Director: Eliza Bisticer.
EIN: 112914881

6426
M.F.K. Foundation
25 Locust Hollow Dr.
Monsey, NY   10952-2410

Established in 2006 in New York.
Donor: Mendel Klein.
Foundation type: Independent foundation.
Financial data (yr. ended 12/31/13): Assets, $0 (M); gifts received, $274,061; expenditures, $220,943; qualifying distributions, $217,434; giving activities include $217,434 for 221 grants (high: $37,500; low: $5).
Purpose and activities: Giving primarily to Jewish agencies, temples, and schools.
Fields of interest: Elementary and secondary education; Judaism.
Limitations: Applications not accepted. Giving primarily in NY. No grants to individuals.
Application information: Contributes only to pre-selected organizations.
Trustees: Chaim S. Klein; Feigie Klein; Mendel Klein.
EIN: 208118161

6427
The M66 Foundation Inc.
101 Central Park West, Apt. 2C
New York City, NY   10023-4250

Donor: Jose Serpieri, Jr.
Foundation type: Independent foundation.

Financial data (yr. ended 12/31/12): Assets, $1,379,326 (M); expenditures, $340,874; qualifying distributions, $336,357; giving activities include $336,357 for grants.
Fields of interest: Education; Environment; Human services.
Limitations: Applications not accepted.
Application information: Unsolicited requests for funds not accepted.
Directors: Richard Gold; Jonathan Korngold; Kristen Korngold.
EIN: 274378922

6428
Georges & Claire Mabardi Foundation
45 Combes Dr.
Manhasset, NY   11030-2204

Established in 1998 in New York.
Foundation type: Independent foundation.
Financial data (yr. ended 12/31/13): Assets, $3,827,752 (M); expenditures, $221,862; qualifying distributions, $208,885; giving activities include $196,500 for 14 grants (high: $60,000; low: $1,500).
Purpose and activities: Giving primarily for education and human services.
Fields of interest: Elementary education; Public transportation; Christianity; Human services; People with disabilities.
Type of support: General support.
Limitations: Applications not accepted. Giving primarily in the greater metropolitan New York, NY, area, including Long Island. No grants to individuals.
Application information: Contributes only to pre-selected organizations.
Officers and Directors: Marc Devenoge, Pres. and Director; Burt Lewis, Secy. and Director; Mary Louise Devenoge, Treas. and Director.
EIN: 132918244

6429
MacArthur Family Charitable Foundation
c/o The Ayco Co., L.P.
P.O. Box 860
Saratoga Springs, NY   12866-0860
Contact: Heather Hudson

Donors: C.J. MacArthur; Gina G. MacArthur.
Foundation type: Independent foundation.
Financial data (yr. ended 06/30/14): Assets, $4,634,568 (M); expenditures, $288,120; qualifying distributions, $269,000; giving activities include $269,000 for 6 grants (high: $200,000; low: $1,500).
Fields of interest: Education; Higher education; Graduate and professional education; Theology.
Type of support: General support.
Limitations: Applications not accepted. Giving primarily in CA and New York, NY.
Application information: Unsolicited requests for funds not accepted.
Officers: Gina G. MacArthur, Chair.; Alan Halperin, Secy.-Treas.
EIN: 273141382

6430
Stephen Mack and Kelly Mack Family Foundation, Inc.
c/o Solon Mack Capital, LLC
110 E. 59th St., 22nd Fl.
New York City, NY   10022-1304

Established in 2006 in New York.
Donor: Stephen Mack.
Foundation type: Independent foundation.
Financial data (yr. ended 12/31/12): Assets, $170,092 (M); gifts received, $222,600; expenditures, $230,630; qualifying distributions, $230,600; giving activities include $230,600 for 13 grants (high: $190,000; low: $600).
Fields of interest: Education; Health; Housing development.
Limitations: Applications not accepted. Giving primarily in NY. No grants to individuals.
Application information: Unsolicited request for funds not accepted.
Officers: Stephen Mack, Pres.; Kerry Kennedy, V.P.; Kelly Mack, V.P.; Richard Mack, V.P.
EIN: 203901963

6431
Ian & Arrielle Tepper Madover Family Foundation, Inc.
(formerly Arielle Tepper Charitable Foundation, Inc.)
c/o Janover, LLC
100 Quentin Roosevelt Blvd., Ste. 516
Garden City, NY   11530-4843

Donors: Susan J. Tepper Charitable Trust; Arielle Tepper Madover.
Foundation type: Independent foundation.
Financial data (yr. ended 11/30/12): Assets, $2,389,194 (M); gifts received, $1,069,558; expenditures, $339,597; qualifying distributions, $327,500; giving activities include $327,500 for grants.
Fields of interest: Arts and culture; Theater; Education; Human services; Child welfare.
Limitations: Applications not accepted. Giving primarily in NY. No grants to individuals.
Application information: Unsolicited requests for funds not accepted.
Officers: Arielle Tepper Madover, Pres. and Treas.; Ian Madover, V.P. and Secy.
Director: Martin Wasser.
EIN: 650454051

6432
Timothy Maguire Foundation
c/o The Ayco Company, L.P. - NTG
P.O. Box 15014
Albany, NY   12212

Donors: Timothy Maguire; James J. Maguire Revocable Trust.
Foundation type: Independent foundation.
Financial data (yr. ended 12/31/13): Assets, $469,901 (M); gifts received, $125,000; expenditures, $352,723; qualifying distributions, $344,907; giving activities include $344,907 for 16 grants (high: $100,000; low: $1,000).
Fields of interest: Education; Catholicism; Human services.
Limitations: Applications not accepted. Giving primarily in CA; some giving also in PA.

Application information: Unsolicited requests for funds not accepted.
Officers and Directors: Timothy Maguire, Pres. and Director; Franny Glomb, C.F.O.; Sue Maguire, Secy.
EIN: 270870730

6433
Maher Family Foundation
c/o Blackrock Kelso Capital
40 E. 52nd St., Ste. 21
New York City, NY 10022-5911

Donor: James Maher.
Foundation type: Independent foundation.
Financial data (yr. ended 12/31/13): Assets, $1,090,735 (M); gifts received, $419,389; expenditures, $200,662; qualifying distributions, $189,902; giving activities include $189,902 for 19 grants (high: $62,500; low: $1,000).
Purpose and activities: Giving primarily for education, health organizations, and youth, family, and social services.
Fields of interest: Arts and culture; Education; Elementary and secondary education; Higher education; Business education; Environment; Addiction services; Diseases and conditions; Winter sports; Human services; Family services; Child welfare; Developmental disability services.
Limitations: Applications not accepted. Giving primarily in NY, with some emphasis on New York; some giving also in MA and UT. No grants to individuals.
Application information: Contributes only to pre-selected organizations.
Trustee: James Maher.
EIN: 134082818

6434
John F. Maher Family Foundation
c/o Bessemer Trust
630 5th Ave., 34th Fl.
New York City, NY 10111-0100

Established in 1998 in California.
Donor: John F. Maher†.
Foundation type: Independent foundation.
Financial data (yr. ended 06/30/13): Assets, $1,883,064 (M); expenditures, $178,141; qualifying distributions, $173,042; giving activities include $167,750 for 24 grants (high: $50,000; low: $250).
Fields of interest: Arts and culture; Education; Higher education; Wildlife biodiversity; Aquatic wildlife protection; Health.
Limitations: Applications not accepted. Giving primarily in CT. No grants to individuals.
Application information: Unsolicited requests for funds not accepted.
Officer: Helen S. Maher, Secy.-Treas.
EIN: 954650932

6435
Iris and Shalom Maidenbaum Foundation, Inc.
(formerly Esther & Nathan Maidenbaum Foundation, Inc.)
132 Spruce St.
Cedarhurst, NY 11516-1915

Donors: Esther Maidenbaum; David Schreiber; The Heller Foundation; Shalom Maidenbaum.
Foundation type: Independent foundation.
Financial data (yr. ended 12/31/13): Assets, $129,318 (M); gifts received, $225,000; expenditures, $317,581; qualifying distributions, $312,506; giving activities include $312,506 for 93 grants (high: $57,980; low: $18).
Fields of interest: Arts and culture; Education; Law education; Religion; Judaism.
Type of support: General support.
Limitations: Applications not accepted. No grants to individuals.
Application information: Unsolicited requests for funds not accepted.
Officers: Shalom Maidenbaum, Pres.; Iris Maidenbaum, V.P.; Nathan Maidenbaum, Secy.
EIN: 237055848

6436
Makioka Foundation
c/o BCRS Associates, LLC
77 Water St., 9th Fl.
New York City, NY 10005-3701

Established in 1993 in New York.
Donors: Jun Makihara; Megumi Oka.
Foundation type: Independent foundation.
Financial data (yr. ended 02/28/14): Assets, $4,571,369 (M); expenditures, $160,072; qualifying distributions, $135,530; giving activities include $132,650 for 36 grants (high: $50,000; low: $250).
Fields of interest: Arts and culture; Education; Community and economic development; Protestantism.
Limitations: Applications not accepted. Giving primarily in Boston, MA. No grants to individuals; no loans or scholarships.
Application information: Unsolicited requests for funds not accepted.
Trustees: Jun Makihara; Megumi Oka.
EIN: 133748081

6437
The James Hilton and Emma Austin Manning Foundation, Inc.
c/o C. O'Donnell, US Trust/Bank of America, N.A.
114 W. 47th St.
New York City, NY 10036-1510

Established in 1958 in New York.
Donors: Beatrice Austin Manning†; Alfred M. Hoelzer†; J.H. Manning Trust.
Foundation type: Independent foundation.
Financial data (yr. ended 07/31/14): Assets, $7,610,840 (M); expenditures, $359,115; qualifying distributions, $300,000; giving activities include $300,000 for 3 grants (high: $100,000; low: $100,000).
Purpose and activities: Giving primarily for higher education; some giving also for sports medicine research.
Fields of interest: University education; Medical specialties; Diseases and conditions.
Type of support: Research; Research and evaluation.
Limitations: Applications not accepted. Giving primarily in San Francisco, CA, Milwaukee, WI and New York, NY. No grants to individuals, or for student aid, general support, capital or endowment

funds, scholarships, fellowships, or matching gifts; no loans.
Application information: Unsolicited requests for funds not accepted.
Officers and Directors: John H. Bell, Jr., Pres. and Director; Juliet Alexander, Secy. and Director; Susan Porter; Martin R. Post, MD; Gillian Shepherd.
Number of staff: None.
EIN: 136123540

6438
Amir and Rosita Manocherian Family Foundation
150 E. 58th St.
New York City, NY 10155-0001

Donors: Amir Manocherian; Rosita Manocherian; Robert Manocherian; Mireille Manocherian; Fameco, LLC; Jed Manocherian.
Foundation type: Company-sponsored foundation.
Financial data (yr. ended 12/31/13): Assets, $1,550,735 (M); gifts received, $646,684; expenditures, $321,473; qualifying distributions, $317,851; giving activities include $317,851 for 27 grants (high: $50,000; low: $1,000).
Purpose and activities: The foundation supports hospitals and organizations involved with theater, education, cancer, diabetes, medical research, hunger, automotive safety, and Judaism.
Fields of interest: Arts and culture; Education; Health.
Type of support: General support; Program development.
Limitations: Applications not accepted. Giving primarily in NY. No grants to individuals.
Application information: Unsolicited requests for funds not accepted.
Trustees: Alan Manocherian; Rosita Manocherian.
EIN: 137335693

6439
The Manzanita Foundation
(formerly The Tanya & Charles Brandes Foundation)
c/o SKP, LLP
1745 Broadway, 18th Fl.
New York City, NY 10019-4640

Established in 1996 in California.
Donors: Charles H. Brandes; Linda Brandes; Tanya Brandes.
Foundation type: Independent foundation.
Financial data (yr. ended 12/31/13): Assets, $9,955,188 (M); expenditures, $386,102; qualifying distributions, $278,343; giving activities include $278,343 for 1 grant.
Fields of interest: Education; Diseases and conditions; HIV/AIDS.
Type of support: Research; Research and evaluation.
Limitations: Applications accepted. Giving primarily in CA, with emphasis on Beverly Hills and San Diego and VA. No grants to individuals.
Application information:
   Initial approach: Letter
   Deadline(s): None
Officer: Tanya M. Johnson, Pres.
EIN: 330709977

6440
Marbeh Shalom Foundation, Inc.
c/o E. S. Originals
440 9th Ave.
New York City, NY 10001

Donors: Morris Shalom; Ezra Shalom; Milton Shalom.
Foundation type: Independent foundation.
Financial data (yr. ended 12/31/13): Assets, $30,032 (M); gifts received, $215,000; expenditures, $258,622; qualifying distributions, $258,437; giving activities include $258,437 for 274 grants (high: $47,030; low: $18).
Fields of interest: Religion; Judaism.
Limitations: Applications not accepted. Giving primarily in Brooklyn, NY.
Application information: Unsolicited requests for funds not accepted.
Officers: Morris Shalom, Pres.; Ezra Shalom, Treas.
EIN: 452818049

6441
Marble Fund Inc.
c/o Marcum & Kliegman, LLP
750 Third Ave., 11th Fl.
New York City, NY 10017-2716
Contact: Marion H. Levy, Pres.

Established in 1952 in New York.
Donors: M. William Levy†; Marion H. Levy; Caryn L. Magid; William Guy Levy.
Foundation type: Independent foundation.
Financial data (yr. ended 12/31/13): Assets, $655,685 (M); expenditures, $245,016; qualifying distributions, $238,570; giving activities include $236,470 for 78 grants (high: $35,000; low: $50).
Fields of interest: Arts and culture; Education; Higher education; Domesticated animals; Hospital care; Specialty hospital care; Human services.
Type of support: General support; Annual campaigns; Capital campaigns; Capital and infrastructure; Seed money; Research; Technical assistance.
Limitations: Applications accepted. Giving primarily in NY. No grants to individuals.
Application information: Application form required.
Initial approach: Letter
Deadline(s): None
Officers: Marion H. Levy, Pres.; Caryn L. Magid, Secy.; William Guy Levy, Treas.
EIN: 136084387

6442
The Marine Society of the City of New York
17 Battery Pl., Ste. 714
New York City, NY 10004-1207 (212) 425-0448
FAX: (212) 425-1117;
E-mail: info@marinesocietyny.org; Main URL: http://www.marinesocietyny.org

Established in 1770 in New York.
Foundation type: Independent foundation.
Financial data (yr. ended 12/31/12): Assets, $2,774,277 (M); gifts received, $2; expenditures, $334,027; qualifying distributions, $171,430; giving activities include $171,430 for grants.
Purpose and activities: Giving to improve maritime knowledge and for the needs of distressed shipmasters and their widows and orphans.

Fields of interest: Education; Marine science; Christianity; Human services.
Type of support: General support; Grants to individuals.
Limitations: Applications not accepted. Giving primarily on the East Coast, with emphasis on NY.
Application information: Unsolicited requests for funds not accepted.
Officers: Timothy Ferrie, Pres.; James McNamara, V.P.; Robert H. Pouch, V.P.; Cynthia J. Roboson, Secy.; Thomas F. Fox, Treas.
EIN: 135643623

6443
The Jacob Marley Foundation, Inc.
47 Guilford Rd.
Port Washington, NY 11050-4426 (516) 767-9235
Main URL: http://www.jacobmarley.org

Established in 1993 in New York.
Donors: Christopher Quackenbush†; Traci Quackenbush.
Foundation type: Independent foundation.
Financial data (yr. ended 12/31/13): Assets, $4,770,084 (M); gifts received, $16,450; expenditures, $220,853; qualifying distributions, $157,500; giving activities include $157,500 for 7 grants (high: $65,000; low: $2,500).
Purpose and activities: Giving primarily for education.
Fields of interest: Education; Camps; Child welfare.
Limitations: Applications not accepted. Giving primarily in New York, NY. No grants to individuals.
Application information: Unsolicited requests for funds not accepted.
Officers and Directors: Carlton D. Brown, Pres. and Director; Traci L. Vicklund, V.P. and Director; Thomas M. O'Brien, Secy. and Director; James J. Dunne III; William F. Hickey; Gail Quackenbush; Michael A. Quackenbush; Mark Viklund.
EIN: 113165445

6444
Mars Foundation
38 Olympia Ln.
Monsey, NY 10952-2843

Established in 2000 in New York.
Donors: Aryeh Goldstein; Sarah Goldstein; Cong TA of KJ.
Foundation type: Independent foundation.
Financial data (yr. ended 12/31/13): Assets, $96,285 (M); gifts received, $203,600; expenditures, $169,450; qualifying distributions, $166,617; giving activities include $165,430 for 10 grants (high: $109,894; low: $3,036).
Fields of interest: Religion.
Type of support: General support.
Limitations: Applications not accepted. Giving primarily in NY. No grants to individuals.
Application information: Unsolicited requests for funds not accepted.
Officer: Aryeh Goldstein, Pres.
Trustee: Sarah Goldstein.
EIN: 311743263

6445
Marshall Family Foundation
5810 Lake Bluff Rd.
North Rose, NY 14516-9727 (585) 423-1860

Established in 1995 in New York.
Donors: W. Gilman Marshall†; Ina Marshall.
Foundation type: Independent foundation.
Financial data (yr. ended 12/31/14): Assets, $6,571,060; expenditures, $333,156; qualifying distributions, $322,500.
Fields of interest: Historic preservation; Education; Foundations; Hospital care; Diseases and conditions; HIV/AIDS; Community and economic development; Human services; Community service for youth; Multilateral cooperation.
Limitations: Applications accepted. Giving primarily in NY. No grants to individuals.
Application information:
Initial approach: Letter
Deadline(s): None
Trustees: Gary Marshall; Kent Marshall.
EIN: 166430502

6446
The Marshall Family Foundation Inc.
(formerly The James Harper Marshall Foundation, Inc.)
c/o Coopersmith Simon & Vogel PC
50 Charles Lindbergh Blvd., Ste. 605
Uniondale, NY 11553-3600

Donors: James Harper Marshall; John H. Peace.
Foundation type: Independent foundation.
Financial data (yr. ended 12/31/13): Assets, $7,372,279 (M); expenditures, $306,655; qualifying distributions, $262,601; giving activities include $237,000 for 38 grants (high: $25,000; low: $500).
Fields of interest: Arts and culture; Dance; Education; University education; Natural resources; Biodiversity; Wildlife biodiversity; Foundations; Nonprofits; Hospital care; Golf; Youth development; Youth services.
Type of support: General support; Scholarships; Advocacy; Regranting.
Limitations: Applications not accepted. Giving primarily in NY. No grants to individuals.
Application information: Unsolicited requests for funds not accepted.
Officers and Directors: Lee Harper Marshall, Pres. and Director; Edward G. Beimfohr, Esq., Secy.; Donna Ensign Marshall, Treas.
EIN: 133157280

6447
Martini Family Foundation
c/o Proskauer Rose, LLP
11 Times Sq.
New York City, NY 10036-8299

Established in 2007 in New York.
Donors: Samuel Martini; ECT Holdings, LLC; ECI Opportunities LLC.
Foundation type: Independent foundation.
Financial data (yr. ended 12/31/13): Assets, $427,707 (M); gifts received, $175,210; expenditures, $269,711; qualifying distributions, $255,605; giving activities include $255,605 for 31 grants (high: $45,801; low: $100).

Fields of interest: Education; Sports and recreation; Human services.
Limitations: Applications not accepted. Giving primarily in NY. No grants to individuals.
Application information: Contributes only to pre-selected organizations.
Trustee: ECI Opportunities LLC.
EIN: 656469293

6448
The Lucille and Paul Maslin Foundation Inc.
600 Mamaroneck Ave., Ste. 400
Harrison, NY 10528-1635

Established in 2000 in New York.
Donor: Lucille Maslin 2000 Charitable Lead Trust.
Foundation type: Independent foundation.
Financial data (yr. ended 12/31/13): Assets, $185,966 (M); gifts received, $274,893; expenditures, $251,680; qualifying distributions, $251,380; giving activities include $251,000 for 20 grants (high: $10,000; low: $1,000).
Fields of interest: Higher education; Nonprofits; Hospital care; Cancers; Film and video; Non-natural disasters; Judaism; Human services; Food delivery.
Type of support: Regranting.
Limitations: Applications not accepted. No grants to individuals.
Application information: Contributes only to pre-selected organizations.
Officers and Directors: Janet Cheever, Pres. and Director; Benjamin Cheever, V.P. and Director; Stephen Katz, Treas. and Director; Andrew Cheever; John Cheever.
EIN: 137230954

6449
The David J. Mastrocola Foundation
c/o MJSM
P.O. Box 331
Plainview, NY 11803-0331

Established in 1998 in New York.
Donor: David J. Mastrocola.
Foundation type: Independent foundation.
Financial data (yr. ended 12/31/14): Assets, $687,242; expenditures, $200,026; qualifying distributions, $199,786.
Fields of interest: Philanthropy; Health; Religion; Children.
Type of support: General support.
Limitations: Applications not accepted. Giving primarily in Westport, CT and Boston, MA. No grants to individuals.
Application information: Unsolicited requests for funds not accepted.
Trustees: David J. Mastrocola; Steven C. Mero.
EIN: 134036266

6450
The MAT Charitable Foundation Inc.
c/o William T. McCallum, CPA, P.C.
780 3rd Ave., Ste. 2805
New York City, NY 10017-2024 (212) 644-6464
Contact: William T. McCallum

Established in 1992 in New York.
Donor: Ruth Uris†.
Foundation type: Independent foundation.

Financial data (yr. ended 12/31/13): Assets, $8,115,248 (M); expenditures, $457,058; qualifying distributions, $392,359; giving activities include $371,725 for 34 grants (high: $80,250; low: $250).
Purpose and activities: Giving primarily for the fostering of and developing interest in modern and contemporary art; funding also for children's education.
Fields of interest: Visual arts; Performing arts; Education; Elementary and secondary education; Higher education; Environment; Human services; Child welfare.
Type of support: General support.
Limitations: Applications accepted. Giving primarily in New York, NY. No grants to individuals.
Application information: Application form required.
  Initial approach: Letter
  Deadline(s): None
Officers: Jane U. Bayard, Pres.; Amy Wolf, V.P. and Treas.
Number of staff: 1 part-time professional.
EIN: 136991067

6451
Mathis-Pfohl Foundation
5-46 46th Ave.
Long Island City, NY 11101-5215 (718) 784-4800
Contact: Matthew Quigley

Established in 1947 in Iowa.
Donors: James M. Pfohl; Ann Kirby; Lynn Quigley.
Foundation type: Independent foundation.
Financial data (yr. ended 12/31/13): Assets, $5,272,908 (M); expenditures, $375,125; qualifying distributions, $337,687; giving activities include $336,627 for 286 grants (high: $60,000; low: $100).
Purpose and activities: Giving primarily for education, human services, and the arts.
Fields of interest: Arts and culture; Education; Higher education; Catholicism; Human services.
Limitations: Applications accepted. Giving primarily in the New York, NY, area. No grants to individuals.
Application information: Application form required.
  Initial approach: Letter
  Deadline(s): None
  Board meeting date(s): As required
Directors: Paula C. Kirby; Louis Anthony Pfohl; Leonard Matthew Quigley.
EIN: 116013764

6452
Stella Matutina Foundation
1300 Clinton Sq.
Rochester, NY 14604-1730
Contact: J. Garrett

Established in 1992 in New York.
Donors: John H. Dessauer Charitable Lead Unitrust; John H. Dessauer†; Margaret Lee Dessauer†.
Foundation type: Independent foundation.
Financial data (yr. ended 09/30/14): Assets, $2,850,106 (M); gifts received, $71,304; expenditures, $229,324; qualifying distributions, $195,379; giving activities include $195,000 for 6 grants (high: $100,000; low: $5,000).
Fields of interest: Education; Human services.
Type of support: Scholarships.

Limitations: Applications not accepted. Giving primarily in Rochester, NY. No grants to individuals.
Application information: Contributes only to pre-selected organizations.
Officers and Directors: Kathleen Whelehan, Pres. and Director; Louis A. Langie, Jr., V.P. and Director; John L. Garrett, Secy.-Treas. and Director; Matthew H. Clark.
EIN: 161399369

6453
The Maurer Family Foundation
c/o Christine O'Donnell, Bank of America, N.A.
1 Bryant Park
NY1-100-28-05
New York City, NY 10036-6715
Main URL: http://maurerfamilyfoundation.org

Established in 1996 in Florida.
Donors: Gilbert C. Maurer; Ann E. Maurer.
Foundation type: Independent foundation.
Financial data (yr. ended 12/31/13): Assets, $3,034,993 (M); expenditures, $401,008; qualifying distributions, $400,405; giving activities include $369,500 for 19 grants (high: $250,000; low: $2,500).
Purpose and activities: Giving for programs designed to broaden access to the arts and for programs directed toward raising artistic standards.
Fields of interest: Arts and culture; Art museums; Higher education.
Limitations: Applications not accepted. Giving primarily in NY. No grants to individuals.
Application information: Contributes only to pre-selected organizations.
Officers and Directors: Gilbert C. Maurer, Chair.; Ann Maurer, Pres.; Merideth M. Hutchinson, V.P. and Director; Christopher C. Maurer, V.P. and Director; David W. Maurer, V.P. and Director; Jonathan G. Maurer, V.P. and Director; Peter J. Maurer, V.P. and Director.
EIN: 311469474

6454
The MBS Family Foundation Inc.
c/o Marcum & Kliegman, LLP
750 3rd Ave., 11th Fl.
New York City, NY 10017-9113

Donor: Michelle B. Stein.
Foundation type: Independent foundation.
Financial data (yr. ended 12/31/13): Assets, $111,517 (M); gifts received, $73,000; expenditures, $185,082; qualifying distributions, $177,753; giving activities include $175,959 for 26 grants (high: $50,000; low: $154).
Fields of interest: Nonprofits; Judaism; Human services.
Type of support: Regranting.
Limitations: Applications not accepted. No grants to individuals.
Application information: Contributes only to pre-selected organizations.
Officer: Michelle B. Stein, Pres.
EIN: 201865079

6455
The McCaddin-McQuirk Foundation, Inc.
c/o O'Connor Davies, LLP
665 5th Ave.
New York City, NY 10022-5342
Application address: c/o Julien N. Vachon, P.O. Box 5001, New York, NY 10185; tel.: (212) 935-8619

Established in 1902 in New York.
Donors: Rt. Rev. John McQuirk†; Ann Eliza McCaddin Walsh†.
Foundation type: Independent foundation.
Financial data (yr. ended 12/31/14): Assets, $5,576,618 (M); expenditures, $191,743; qualifying distributions, $166,431; giving activities include $156,300 for 68 grants (high: $9,000; low: $300).
Purpose and activities: Giving to foster educational opportunities for poorer students to be priests, deacons, catechists or lay teachers of the Roman Catholic Church in the U.S. or elsewhere.
Fields of interest: Education; Religion; Human services.
International interests: Africa; Asia; Canada; Europe; India; South America.
Type of support: Scholarships.
Limitations: Applications accepted. Giving in the U.S. and internationally.
Application information: Applications must be made through a bishop, rector, or head of a seminary.
  Initial approach: Proposal
  Deadline(s): Dec. 1
Officers: John Caffrey, Secy.; John Cullinane, Pres.; David C. Muccia, V.P.; Thomas F. Blaney, Treas.
Trustees: Julien N. Vachon; John J. Eager; Frank J. Hardart III; Rev. Thomas A. Modungo; Charles E. F. Millard; Victor Ziminsky III; Carrol A. Muccia, Jr.; Martin W. Ronan, Jr., Esq.
EIN: 136134444

6456
The Mary A. and John M. McCarthy Foundation
c/o KCG Capital Advisors
800 3rd Ave., 12th Fl.
New York City, NY 10022-7649

Established in 1985 in New York.
Donors: Mary A. McCarthy; John M. McCarthy.
Foundation type: Independent foundation.
Financial data (yr. ended 11/30/12): Assets, $3,827,439 (M); expenditures, $228,421; qualifying distributions, $174,987; giving activities include $162,600 for 14 grants (high: $25,000; low: $600).
Fields of interest: Arts and culture; Theater; Historic preservation; Education; Animal welfare; Specialty hospital care; Human services; Child welfare.
Type of support: General support; Capital and infrastructure; Scholarships.
Limitations: Applications not accepted. Giving primarily in CT, IN, MA, and NY. No grants to individuals.
Publications: Multi-year report.
Application information: Contributes only to pre-selected organizations.
  Board meeting date(s): Semiannually
Trustees: John M. McCarthy; Laurette E. McCarthy; Mary A. McCarthy; Neil M. McCarthy; Stephen J. McCarthy; Tara A. McCarthy.

Number of staff: 1 part-time professional.
EIN: 136863980

6457
The McCooey Charitable Foundation
c/o O'Connor Davies Munns & Dobbins, LLP
665 5th Ave.
New York City, NY 10022-5305

Established in 2005 in New York.
Donor: John M. & Mary A. Joyce Foundation.
Foundation type: Independent foundation.
Financial data (yr. ended 12/31/13): Assets, $1,447,993 (M); expenditures, $156,685; qualifying distributions, $148,943; giving activities include $144,725 for 28 grants (high: $27,000; low: $50).
Fields of interest: Education; Catholicism; Human services.
Limitations: Applications not accepted. Giving primarily in NY. No grants to individuals.
Application information: Unsolicited requests for funds not accepted.
Officers: Mary C. McCooey, Pres. and Treas.; Michael P. McCooey, V.P.; Mary Catherine Dodman, Secy.
EIN: 651260666

6458
Margaret Ogilvie McCormick Charitable Trust
1100 Wehrle Dr., 2nd Fl.
Buffalo, NY 14221 7168425506
Application address: c/o Larry Hartman, M&T Bank, 21 E. Market St., York, PA 17401, tel.: (717) 255-2045

Established in 1991 in Pennsylvania.
Foundation type: Independent foundation.
Financial data (yr. ended 12/31/14): Assets, $3,531,467; expenditures, $220,193; qualifying distributions, $184,300 and $0 for set-asides.
Fields of interest: Community and economic development.
Limitations: Applications accepted. Giving limited to the Harrisburg, PA, area.
Application information: Application form required.
  Initial approach: Letter
  Deadline(s): None
Trustee: M&T Trust Co.
EIN: 236216167

6459
The McCormick Family Foundation
130 Shore Rd., Ste. 352
Port Washington, NY 11050-2205

Established in 2000 in New York.
Donors: Michael McCormick; Genine McCormick.
Foundation type: Independent foundation.
Financial data (yr. ended 11/30/13): Assets, $4,015,812 (M); gifts received, $99,609; expenditures, $363,836; qualifying distributions, $352,562; giving activities include $319,105 for 14 grants (high: $200,000; low: $1,000).
Fields of interest: Education; Philanthropy; Human services.
Limitations: Applications not accepted. No grants to individuals.

Application information: Unsolicited requests for funds not accepted.
Officer: Genine R. McCormick, Secy.
Director: Michael P. McCormick.
EIN: 113532010

6460
Anne McCormick Trust
1100 Wehrle Dr., 2nd Fl.
Buffalo, NY 14221 7168425506
Application address: C/O Larry Hartman, M&T Bank, 21 E. Market St., York, PA 17401, tel.: (717) 852-3011

Donors: Anne McCormick†; McCormick Family Foundation.
Foundation type: Independent foundation.
Financial data (yr. ended 12/31/14): Assets, $7,962,986; expenditures, $471,530; qualifying distributions, $398,030.
Fields of interest: Foundations.
Limitations: Applications accepted. Giving limited to Cumberland, Dauphin, Franklin, and Perry counties, PA. No grants to individuals.
Application information: Application form required.
  Initial approach: Proposal
  Deadline(s): None
Trustee: M&T Bank.
EIN: 236471389

6461
The McDade Family Foundation
c/o CBIZ MHM LLC
1065 Ave. of the Americas
New York City, NY 10018-1878

Established in 2007 in New York.
Donors: Herbert H. McDade III; Martha Monserrate-McDade.
Foundation type: Independent foundation.
Financial data (yr. ended 12/31/14): Assets, $6,726,275; gifts received, $2,800; expenditures, $430,794; qualifying distributions, $423,540.
Fields of interest: Education.
Limitations: Applications not accepted. Giving primarily in CT and NY. No grants to individuals.
Application information: Contributes only to pre-selected organizations.
Trustees: Herbert H. McDade III; Martha Monserrate-McDade.
EIN: 260800085

6462
Ruth McDayton Foundation
494 Eighth Ave., 7th Fl.
New York City, NY 10001-2519 (212) 267-5353
Contact: Richard A. Watson, Tr.

Foundation type: Independent foundation.
Financial data (yr. ended 05/31/15): Assets, $4,697,815 (M); gifts received, $172; expenditures, $188,559; qualifying distributions, $188,559; giving activities include $160,000 for 4 grants (high: $50,000; low: $35,000).
Fields of interest: Arts and culture; Museums.
Type of support: General support.
Limitations: Applications accepted. Giving primarily in CT, NJ, and NY.
Application information: Application form required.

Initial approach: Proposal
Deadline(s): None
Trustees: Robert D. Oucherloney; Richard A. Watson.
EIN: 133788809

6463
The John and Patty McEnroe Foundation

(formerly John McEnroe Foundation)
c/o L.H. Frishkoff & Co.
529 5th Ave., 9th Fl.
New York City, NY 10017-4608

Established in 1986 in New York.
Donors: John McEnroe; Btig, LLC; Michael Kazarnowicz; Sport Time Team Tennis LLC; Cantor Fitzgerald Relief Fund Admin; Bjorn Borg; The Laurie M. Tisch Foundation; The Lizzie and Jonathan Tisch Found; Eastern Regional Medical Center; National Tennis Foundation; Remington Reynolds, LLC; Dunlop Slazenger International; The Steve Tisch Family Foundation.
Foundation type: Independent foundation.
Financial data (yr. ended 12/31/13): Assets, $407,755 (M); gifts received, $60,308; expenditures, $138,393; qualifying distributions, $136,730; giving activities include $135,450 for 12 grants (high: $32,000; low: $1,000).
Purpose and activities: Giving for the arts, medicine, environmental concerns and human services.
Fields of interest: Education; Environment; Sports and recreation.
Limitations: Applications not accepted. Giving primarily in NY. No grants to individuals.
Application information: Unsolicited requests for funds not accepted.
Officers: John McEnroe, Pres. and Treas.; Mark T. McEnroe, V.P. and Secy.; John P. McEnroe, V.P.
EIN: 133389114

6464
The Lisa McGraw Figure Skating Foundation Inc.

c/o Rockefeller Co.
30 Rockefeller Plz., Ste. 5600
New York City, NY 10112

Established in 1997 in New Jersey.
Donor: Elizabeth McGraw Webster.
Foundation type: Independent foundation.
Financial data (yr. ended 12/31/13): Assets, $6,246,489 (M); expenditures, $253,322; qualifying distributions, $197,383; giving activities include $192,500 for 9 grants (high: $60,000; low: $5,000).
Purpose and activities: Giving primarily for sports and athletics, particularly ice-skating.
Fields of interest: Sports and recreation.
Limitations: Applications not accepted. Giving on a national basis. No grants to individuals.
Application information: Unsolicited requests for funds not accepted.
Officers and Trustees: Elizabeth McGraw Webster, Pres. and Trustee; Curtis M. Webster, V.P. and Trustee; Samuel W. Lambert III, Secy.; Theo M. Webster, Treas.; Paul Wylie.
EIN: 223473319

6465
The John P. McNulty Scholarship Fund

c/o BCRS Associates, LLC
77 Water St., 9th Fl.
New York City, NY 10005-3701

Established in 2005 in Florida.
Donor: Anne Welsh McNulty.
Foundation type: Independent foundation.
Financial data (yr. ended 12/31/13): Assets, $759,830 (M); expenditures, $375,148; qualifying distributions, $372,183; giving activities include $368,958 for 5 grants (high: $129,000; low: $22,530).
Fields of interest: Education; Undergraduate education; University education.
Limitations: Applications not accepted. Giving primarily in NY and PA. No grants to individuals.
Application information: Unsolicited requests for funds not accepted.
Trustee: Anne Welsh McNulty.
EIN: 203833675

6466
Elisabeth and George Mead Charitable Foundation

c/o R. Runyon
185 N. Broad St.
Norwich, NY 13815-1019 (607) 798-1001

Established in 1988 in New York.
Donor: Elizabeth Mead†.
Foundation type: Independent foundation.
Financial data (yr. ended 12/31/13): Assets, $2,393,123 (M); expenditures, $136,962; qualifying distributions, $132,596; giving activities include $127,304 for 24 grants (high: $86,441; low: $100).
Fields of interest: Education; Higher education; University education; Hospital care; Community and economic development.
Type of support: Individual development.
Limitations: Applications accepted. Giving primarily in NY. No grants for operating expenses, or for trips or continuing support.
Application information: Application form required.
Initial approach: Proposal
Copies of proposal: 2
Deadline(s): None
Board meeting date(s): Jan., Mar., June and Sept.
Trustee: Richard M. Runyon.
EIN: 222864944

6467
Meade Foundation, Inc.

15 Wheeler Ave.
Hammondsport, NY 14840-9566 (607) 569-4200
Contact: J.F. Meade III, Pres. and Tr.

Established in 1989 in New York.
Donor: Joseph F. Meade, Jr.†.
Foundation type: Independent foundation.
Financial data (yr. ended 12/31/13): Assets, $10,419,104 (M); expenditures, $452,451; qualifying distributions, $419,100.
Fields of interest: Museums; Nonprofits; Public libraries; Religion; Human services.
Type of support: Regranting.
Limitations: Applications accepted. Giving primarily in Hammondsport, NY. No grants to individuals.

Application information:
Initial approach: Proposal
Deadline(s): None
Officers and Trustees: Joseph F. Meade III, Pres. and Trustee; D.C. Meade, V.P. and Trustee; J.F. Meade IV, Secy. and Trustee; Greg J.T Hintz, Treas. and Trustee.
EIN: 161339424

6468
The Meadowlark Foundation

c/o Amy Seagroatt, The Ayco Company, LP
321 Broadway
P.O. Box 860
Saratoga Springs, NY 12866-0860

Donors: Garrett M. Moran; Mary J. Penniman.
Foundation type: Independent foundation.
Financial data (yr. ended 12/31/13): Assets, $7,719,072 (M); expenditures, $400,337; qualifying distributions, $358,496; giving activities include $350,000 for 3 grants (high: $200,000; low: $50,000).
Fields of interest: Human services.
Limitations: Applications not accepted. Giving primarily in MA.
Application information: Unsolicited requests for funds not accepted.
Trustees: Garrett M. Moran; Mary J. Penniman.
EIN: 274327976

6469
Medarchei Hayehudi Charitable Foundation

c/o Mordechai Klein
614 Ave. J
Brooklyn, NY 11230-3504

Donors: Medford Multicare; Nursing Care Center at Medford; Mordechai Klein; Abraham Klein; Dinah Klein.
Foundation type: Independent foundation.
Financial data (yr. ended 12/31/13): Assets, $2,861,114 (M); gifts received, $938,839; expenditures, $171,117; qualifying distributions, $170,095; giving activities include $169,545 for 25 grants (high: $60,000; low: $35).
Fields of interest: Religion; Judaism.
Limitations: Applications not accepted. Giving primarily in NY.
Application information: Unsolicited requests for funds not accepted.
Trustees: Mordechai Klein; Rivka Klein.
EIN: 262294489

6470
The Richard Meier Foundation

475 10th Ave., 6th Fl.
New York City, NY 10018-9721 (212) 967-6060
Contact: Richard Meier, Tr.

Established in 1997 in New York.
Donor: Richard Meier.
Foundation type: Independent foundation.
Financial data (yr. ended 12/31/13): Assets, $8,013,752 (M); expenditures, $338,939; qualifying distributions, $221,058; giving activities include $220,808 for 19 grants (high: $200,000; low: $412).

Fields of interest: Museums; Art museums; Education; Higher education; Animal welfare; Judaism.

Limitations: Applications accepted. Giving primarily in NY. No grants to individuals.

Application information: Application form required.

  Initial approach: Proposal

  Deadline(s): None

Trustees: Sanford B. Ehrenkranz; Ana Meier; Richard Meier.

EIN: 133978415

6471
D. B. Melville Trust

Church St. Sta.
P.O. Box 1297
New York City, NY   10008-1297

Foundation type: Independent foundation.

Financial data (yr. ended 12/31/14): Assets, $6,463,696 (M); expenditures, $378,312; qualifying distributions, $333,506; giving activities include $304,000 for 1 grant.

Fields of interest: Art museums.

Limitations: Applications not accepted. Giving limited to Stony Brook, NY.

Application information: Unsolicited requests for funds not accepted.

Trustee: Deutsche Bank Trust Co., N.A.

EIN: 136919198

6472
The Mendell Family Fund Inc.

(formerly The Ira L. & Margaret P. Mendell Fund, Inc.)
c/o MBAF CPAS LLC
440 Park Ave. South, FL 3
New York City, NY   10016-8012

Established in 1954 in New York.

Donors: Ira L. Mendell; Thomas G. Mendell.

Foundation type: Independent foundation.

Financial data (yr. ended 11/30/14): Assets, $3,461,706 (M); expenditures, $203,202; qualifying distributions, $153,090; giving activities include $150,000 for 19 grants (high: $25,000; low: $500).

Fields of interest: Arts and culture; Higher education; Community recreation; Human rights; Human services; Youth development.

Type of support: Annual campaigns; Endowments; Scholarships.

Limitations: Applications not accepted. Giving primarily in Washington, DC, NY, VA, and VT. No grants to individuals.

Application information: Contributes only to pre-selected organizations.

Officers: Thomas G. Mendell, Pres.; James Mendell, V.P. and Secy.; Alice M. Starr, V.P. and Treas.

EIN: 136159009

6473
The Menezes Foundation, Inc.

c/o U.S. Trust, Bank of America
114 W. 47th St.
New York City, NY   10036-1510

Established in 2000 in New York.

Donors: Tara A. Menezes; Victor J. Menezes.

Foundation type: Independent foundation.

Financial data (yr. ended 09/30/14): Assets, $4,520,368 (M); gifts received, $250,000; expenditures, $315,973; qualifying distributions, $292,420; giving activities include $288,370 for 33 grants (high: $25,000; low: $250).

Fields of interest: Higher education; Nonprofits; Catholicism; Human services.

Type of support: Regranting.

Limitations: Applications not accepted. Giving primarily in NY. No grants to individuals.

Application information: Contributes only to pre-selected organizations.

Officers and Directors: Victor J. Menezes, Pres. and Director; Tara A. Menezes, Secy. and Director; Pia A. Menezes, Treas. and Director; M. Alia Menezes; Mita N. Menezes.

EIN: 134147704

6474
The Menges Family Foundation

c/o Cordelia S. Menges
215 E. 72nd St.
New York City, NY   10021-4576

Established in 1997 in New York.

Donor: Carl B. Menges.

Foundation type: Independent foundation.

Financial data (yr. ended 12/31/13): Assets, $1,872,461 (M); gifts received, $101,385; expenditures, $312,316; qualifying distributions, $295,350; giving activities include $295,350 for 12 grants (high: $125,000; low: $2,000).

Fields of interest: Historic preservation; Education; Elementary and secondary education; Human services.

Limitations: Applications not accepted. Giving primarily in NY. No grants to individuals.

Application information: Contributes only to pre-selected organizations.

Committee Members: Benjamin Menges; Carl B. Menges; Cordelia S. Menges; James Menges; Samuel Menges.

EIN: 311588765

6475
Janis and Alan Menken Foundation, Inc.

P.O. Box 443
North Salem, NY   10560-0443   (914) 669-6770
Contact: Janis Menken, Pres. and Dir.

Established in 1996 in New York.

Donor: Alan Menken.

Foundation type: Independent foundation.

Financial data (yr. ended 12/31/13): Assets, $51,880 (M); gifts received, $200,000; expenditures, $168,586; qualifying distributions, $168,482; giving activities include $168,351 for 200 grants (high: $15,000; low: $100).

Fields of interest: Education; Environment; Human services.

Limitations: Applications accepted. Giving primarily in NY. No grants to individuals.

Application information:

  Initial approach: Proposal

  Deadline(s): None

Officers and Directors: Janis Menken, Pres. and Director; Alan Menken, V.P. and Director; Eric Kunis, Secy.

EIN: 133920424

6476
The Mere Foundation

10 Melville Park Rd.
Melville, NY   11747-3146

Foundation type: Independent foundation.

Financial data (yr. ended 12/31/14): Assets, $3,344,724; expenditures, $385,749; qualifying distributions, $216,027.

Fields of interest: Diseases and conditions; Agriculture; Judaism.

Type of support: Research.

Limitations: Applications accepted. Giving primarily in FL and NY.

Application information:

  Initial approach: Letter

  Deadline(s): None

Officer and Directors: Robert Spielman, Pres. and Director; Mark M. O'Connell; Morton Wiggins.

EIN: 271154389

6477
The Meredith Family Foundation

c/o Waldman, Hirsch & Co.
1 Penn Plz., Ste. 2620
New York City, NY   10119-2699

Donors: Gregory Meredith; Audrey Meredith.

Foundation type: Independent foundation.

Financial data (yr. ended 12/31/13): Assets, $901,856 (M); gifts received, $7,500; expenditures, $283,743; qualifying distributions, $283,442; giving activities include $283,442 for 29 grants (high: $160,000; low: $108).

Fields of interest: Education; Higher education; Diseases and conditions; Child welfare.

Type of support: Research; Research and evaluation.

Limitations: Applications not accepted.

Application information: Unsolicited requests for funds not accepted.

Trustees: Thomas Duffey; Audrey Meredith; Gregory Meredith; Bradford Yates.

EIN: 137094993

6478
Meridian Capital Foundation

1 Battery Park Plz., 26th Fl.
New York City, NY   10004-1432

Donors: Beech Street Holdings LLC; Meridian Capital Group LLC.

Foundation type: Independent foundation.

Financial data (yr. ended 12/31/13): Assets, $13,344,508 (M); gifts received, $7,500,000; expenditures, $302,161; qualifying distributions, $300,000; giving activities include $300,000 for 6 grants (high: $75,000; low: $25,000).

Fields of interest: Health; Religion; Human services.

Limitations: Applications not accepted. Giving primarily in NY; with some giving to NJ.

Application information: Unsolicited requests for funds not accepted.

Officer: Jay Lobell, Treas.

Trustee: Ralph Herzka.

EIN: 356943076

6479
Pearl Welinsky Merlo Foundation
150 E. 69th St., Ste. 4B
New York City, NY 10021-5704 2128610925

Established in 2003 in Delaware.
Donor: Ellen Merlo.
Foundation type: Independent foundation.
Financial data (yr. ended 06/30/14): Assets, $556,145; gifts received, $100,331; expenditures, $135,935; qualifying distributions, $134,354.
Fields of interest: Education; Health; Human services.
Type of support: Research.
Limitations: Applications not accepted. Giving primarily in New York, NY.
Application information: Contributes only to pre-selected organizations.
Officers and Directors: Ellen Merlo, Pres. and Director; Phyllis Kornbluth, V.P.
EIN: 200645981

6480
Julia & Gilbert Merrill Foundation, Inc.
c/o Abigail Merrill
850 Park Ave., Rm. 6A
New York City, NY 10021

Established in 1990 in New York.
Donors: Gilbert Merrill; Julia Merrill.
Foundation type: Independent foundation.
Financial data (yr. ended 12/31/13): Assets, $3,591,557 (M); expenditures, $187,661; qualifying distributions, $165,713; giving activities include $152,741 for 17 grants (high: $70,000; low: $16).
Purpose and activities: Giving primarily for the arts, education, and health organizations.
Fields of interest: Arts and culture; Education; Diseases and conditions.
Limitations: Applications not accepted. Giving primarily in FL and NY. No grants to individuals.
Application information: Unsolicited requests for funds not accepted.
Officers: Julia Merrill, Pres.; Abigail Merrill, V.P.
EIN: 521711329

6481
Martha Mertz Foundation, Inc.
60 E. 42nd St., Ste. 1540
New York City, NY 10165-6210

Established in 1939 in New York.
Donor: DeWitt W. Mertz‡.
Foundation type: Independent foundation.
Financial data (yr. ended 12/31/14): Assets, $7,378,895 (M); expenditures, $497,358; qualifying distributions, $400,449; giving activities include $259,500 for 11 grants (high: $49,000; low: $1,000).
Purpose and activities: Giving primarily for unwed mothers.
Fields of interest: Human services; Adolescent parenting; Child welfare; Single parent support; Women's services; Females; Single parents.
Limitations: Applications not accepted. Giving primarily in New York, NY. No grants to individuals.
Application information: Contributes only to pre-selected organizations.

Officers: Jonathan B. Reilly, Pres.; Robert A.N. Cudd, V.P. and Treas.; Nancy H. Cudd, Secy.
EIN: 136129085

6482
Messinger Family Foundation, Inc.
140 Osborn Rd.
Harrison, NY 10528-1018

Established in 1998 in New York.
Donor: Martin Messinger.
Foundation type: Independent foundation.
Financial data (yr. ended 11/30/13): Assets, $4,401,116 (M); expenditures, $150,945; qualifying distributions, $149,317; giving activities include $149,000 for 56 grants (high: $10,000; low: $500).
Purpose and activities: Giving primarily for Jewish organizations, higher education and health and medical services.
Fields of interest: Orchestral music; Higher education; Health; Judaism.
Type of support: General support; Program-related investments; Matching grants; Continuing support; Financial sustainability; Capacity-building and technical assistance; Annual campaigns; Capital campaigns; Capital and infrastructure; Equipment; Land acquisitions; Endowments; Debt reduction; Emergency funds; Program development; Professorships; Curriculum development; Fellowships; Scholarships; Program evaluations.
Limitations: Applications not accepted. No grants to individuals.
Application information: Contributes only to pre-selected organizations.
 Board meeting date(s): Periodically
Directors: Daryl Messinger; Lisa Messinger; Martin Messinger; Sarah Messinger; Alice Messinger Rosenblatt.
Number of staff: None.
EIN: 133979672

6483
Metzger-Price Fund, Inc.
437 Madison Ave., 29th Fl.
New York City, NY 10022
Contact: Isaac A. Saufer Esq., Secy.-Treas.

Established in 1970 in New York.
Donors: Estelle Metzger‡; Leonard Metzger‡.
Foundation type: Independent foundation.
Financial data (yr. ended 06/30/13): Assets, $1,001,290 (M); gifts received, $223,959; expenditures, $237,257; qualifying distributions, $233,619; giving activities include $214,800 for 159 grants (high: $4,500; low: $1,000).
Purpose and activities: Giving to aid the handicapped and for health services; support also for child welfare and social service agencies, recreation, and the elderly.
Fields of interest: Education; Health; Community and economic development; Human services; Family services; Child welfare; Senior services; Seniors; Females; Ethnic and racial groups; Homeless people; Low-income and poor people; People with disabilities.
Type of support: General support; Continuing support; Program development.
Limitations: Applications accepted. Giving primarily in the New York City metropolitan area. No grants to individuals, or for capital campaigns or building

funds; one issuance of grant in single calendar year to same organization; grants awards range from $1000-$5000.
Publications: Financial statement.
Application information:
 Initial approach: Proposal
 Copies of proposal: 1
 Deadline(s): Submit proposal preferably two
   months prior to board meetings, end of month
 Board meeting date(s): Jan., Apr., July, and Oct.,
   end of month (25th-30th)
 Final notification: Positive responses only
Officers: Ronald B. Sobel, Pres.; Don Robert Johnson, V.P.; Isaac A. Saufer, Secy.-Treas.
Number of staff: None.
EIN: 237072764

6484
The Margaret and Leo Meyer and Hans M. Hirsch Foundation, Inc.
82 Ross Ave.
P.O. Box 61240
Staten Island, NY 10306-7240

Foundation type: Independent foundation.
Financial data (yr. ended 12/31/14): Assets, $4,799,091 (M); gifts received, $100,000; expenditures, $290,503; qualifying distributions, $212,100; giving activities include $212,100 for 6 grants (high: $100,000; low: $2,100).
Fields of interest: Science; Judaism; Human services.
Limitations: Applications not accepted. Giving primarily in NY.
Application information: Unsolicited requests for funds not accepted.
Officers: Paul Forster, Pres.; David Forster, V.P. and Treas.
EIN: 262982246

6485
Anthony E. Meyer Family Foundation Inc.
c/o Ocean Road Advisors
767 5th Ave., 18th Fl.
New York City, NY 10153

Established in 2005 in New York.
Donor: Edward H. Meyer.
Foundation type: Independent foundation.
Financial data (yr. ended 12/31/13): Assets, $3,251,768 (M); expenditures, $326,358; qualifying distributions, $310,728; giving activities include $298,854 for 33 grants (high: $75,000; low: $25).
Fields of interest: Higher education; Communication media; Judaism; Human services; Child welfare.
Limitations: Applications not accepted. Giving primarily in New York, NY. No grants to individuals.
Application information: Unsolicited requests for funds not accepted.
Officers and Directors: Anthony E. Meyer, Pres. and Director; Sandra R. Meyer, Secy. and Director; Edward H. Meyer, Treas. and Director.
EIN: 203982790

6486
Margaret A. Meyer Family Foundation, Inc.

c/o Ocean Road Advisors, Inc.
767 5th Ave., 18th Fl.
New York City, NY 10153-0033

Established in 2005 in New York.
Donor: Edward H. Meyer.
Foundation type: Independent foundation.
Financial data (yr. ended 12/31/13): Assets,
$4,390,146 (M); expenditures, $231,926;
qualifying distributions, $213,804; giving activities
include $205,000 for 11 grants (high: $25,000;
low: $10,000).
Fields of interest: Education; Environment;
Judaism; Human services; International relations.
Limitations: Applications not accepted. Giving
primarily in CA, Washington, DC, MA, and NY. No
grants to individuals.
Application information: Unsolicited requests for
funds not accepted.
Officers and Directors: Anthony E. Meyer, Pres. and
Director; Margaret A. Meyer, Secy. and Director;
Edward H. Meyer, Treas. and Director.
EIN: 203983138

6487
Roslyn Milstein Meyer and Jerome Meyer Foundation

(formerly Roslyn Milstein Meyer Foundation)
c/o Eric Kaplan, R&J Meyer
335 Madison Ave., 15th Fl.
New York City, NY 10017-4631

Established in 1996 in New York.
Donors: Irma Milstein; Paul Milstein†; Roslyn Meyer;
Jerome Meyer; Milstein Family Foundation.
Foundation type: Independent foundation.
Financial data (yr. ended 12/31/13): Assets,
$108,365 (M); gifts received, $300,000;
expenditures, $323,338; qualifying distributions,
$322,950; giving activities include $322,950 for 27
grants (high: $55,000; low: $500).
Purpose and activities: Giving primarily for health
organizations, education, and social services.
Fields of interest: Arts and culture; Performing arts;
Education; Diseases and conditions; Judaism;
Camps; Human services.
Limitations: Applications not accepted. Giving
primarily in New Haven, CT, and New York, NY. No
grants to individuals.
Application information: Contributes only to
pre-selected organizations.
Trustees: Jerome Meyer; Roslyn Meyer; Irma
Milstein.
EIN: 133921828

6488
Roger & Barbara Michaels Family Fund Inc.

c/o Tarlow & Co., C.P.A.'s
7 Penn Plz., Ste. 210
New York City, NY 10001-0012 (212) 697-8540

Foundation type: Independent foundation.
Financial data (yr. ended 12/31/13): Assets,
$4,864,395 (M); expenditures, $226,375;
qualifying distributions, $175,300; giving activities
include $173,160 for grants.

Fields of interest: Arts and culture; Education;
Higher education; Environment; Foundations;
Hospital care; Diseases and conditions; Community
and economic development; Human services.
Limitations: Applications accepted. Giving primarily
in NY.
Application information: Application form required.
Initial approach: Letter
Deadline(s): None
Directors: Alice M. Ginandes; Barbara R. Michaels;
Roger A. Michaels.
EIN: 133022845

6489
Janice Michelle Foundation Inc.

c/o JAD Consulting LLC
61 Broadway, Ste. 512
New York City, NY 10006-2711

Established in 1998 in New York.
Donor: George Varsam.
Foundation type: Independent foundation.
Financial data (yr. ended 09/30/13): Assets,
$1,255,805 (M); gifts received, $254,935;
expenditures, $398,994; qualifying distributions,
$395,994; giving activities include $393,468 for 47
grants (high: $150,000; low: $100).
Purpose and activities: Giving primarily for Greek
Orthodox agencies and churches, and human and
community services.
Fields of interest: Education; Diseases and
conditions; Orthodox Christianity.
Limitations: Applications not accepted. No grants to
individuals.
Application information: Contributes only to
pre-selected organizations.
Officers: George Varsam, Pres. and Treas.; Lori
Varsam, V.P. and Secy.; Fotios Varsam, V.P.; Alex
Zawoloka, V.P.
EIN: 113458719

6490
Milbank Memorial Fund

645 Madison Ave., 15th Fl.
New York City, NY 10022-1095 (212) 355-8400
Contact: Carmen Hooker Odom, Pres.
FAX: (212) 355-8599; E-mail: info@milbank.org;
Main URL: http://www.milbank.org
Facebook: https://www.facebook.com/
MilbankMemorialFund
Twitter: https://twitter.com/milbankfund

Established in 1905 in New York.
Donor: Elizabeth Milbank Anderson†.
Foundation type: Operating foundation.
Financial data (yr. ended 12/31/13): Assets,
$85,827,207 (M); expenditures, $4,096,193;
qualifying distributions, $3,471,868; giving
activities include $289,500 for 59 grants (high:
$50,500; low: $1,000).
Purpose and activities: The fund is an endowed
national foundation that supports nonpartisan
analysis, study, and research of significant issues
in health policy.
Fields of interest: Health; Diseases and conditions;
Public affairs; Human services.
Type of support: Research.
Limitations: Applications not accepted. Giving on a
national basis.
Publications: Informational brochure; Newsletter;
Occasional report.

Officers and Directors: Samuel L. Milbank, Chair.
and Director; Peter M. Gottsegen, Vice-Chair. and
Director; Carmen Hooker Odom, Pres. and Director;
Kathleen S. Andersen, V.P. and Secy.; Byron L.
Knief, Treas. and Director; John R. Ball; Carolyn C.
Clark; Thomas E. Harvey; Robert F. Hoerle; Clarion
E. Johnson; Harry A. Nurkin; Louisa J. Palmer;
Rosemary A. Stevens; Joseph M. Sullivan; Carll
Tucker.
Number of staff: 6 full-time professional; 4 part-time
professional; 3 full-time support.
EIN: 135562282

6491
The Harvey R. & Ruth Miller Charitable Fund

1060 5th Ave.
New York City, NY 10128-0104

Established in 2007 in New York.
Donor: Harvey R. Miller.
Foundation type: Independent foundation.
Financial data (yr. ended 04/30/13): Assets,
$1,036,571 (M); gifts received, $150,000;
expenditures, $417,225; qualifying distributions,
$400,717; giving activities include $396,500 for 24
grants (high: $202,000; low: $250).
Purpose and activities: Giving primarily for the arts,
particularly the opera and television, law school, and
to Jewish organizations.
Fields of interest: Opera; Education; Law education;
Nonprofits; Television.
Type of support: Regranting.
Limitations: Applications not accepted. Giving
primarily in New York, NY. No grants to individuals.
Application information: Unsolicited requests for
funds not accepted.
Trustees: Harvey R. Miller; Ruth Miller.
EIN: 204827716

6492
Morgan & Marjorie L. Miller Charitable Trust

11 Normandy Ln.
Scarsdale, NY 10583-7620

Established in 1987 in New York.
Donors: Marjorie Miller; Eleanor Leff; Morgan Miller.
Foundation type: Independent foundation.
Financial data (yr. ended 12/31/13): Assets,
$308,879 (M); gifts received, $70,114;
expenditures, $167,560; qualifying distributions,
$166,350; giving activities include $166,350 for 71
grants (high: $34,000; low: $60).
Fields of interest: Education; Health; Judaism.
Type of support: General support.
Limitations: Applications not accepted. Giving
primarily in NY. No grants to individuals.
Application information: Contributes only to
pre-selected organizations.
Trustees: Marjorie Miller; Morgan Miller.
EIN: 061187583

6493
Charles Lawrence Keith and Clara Miller Foundation

217 Thompson St.
New York City, NY 10012-1327

Established in 1976 in New York.

Donor: Charles L. Keith†.
Foundation type: Independent foundation.
Financial data (yr. ended 01/31/13): Assets, $7,853,507 (M); expenditures, $464,190; qualifying distributions, $360,399; giving activities include $305,200 for 28 grants (high: $20,000; low: $5,000).
Purpose and activities: Support for institutions involved in the preservation of human rights and the elimination of human suffering.
Fields of interest: Higher education; Human rights; Human services.
Type of support: Continuing support; Annual campaigns; Convening; Curriculum development.
Limitations: Applications not accepted. Giving limited to the greater metropolitan New York, NY, area. No grants for scholarships, fellowships, or prizes; no loans.
Application information: Contributes only to pre-selected organizations.
Directors: Linda Fisher; Brian O'Dwyer; Susan Ould; Honie Ann Peacock.
EIN: 132918230

6494
Miller-Sweezy Charitable Trust

c/o Levine & Seltzer
150 E. 52nd St., Ste. 21st Fl.
New York City, NY   10011-5515

Established in 1986 in New York.
Donors: Kenneth H. Miller; Elizabeth Sweezy; Josh Fergenbaum.
Foundation type: Independent foundation.
Financial data (yr. ended 11/30/13): Assets, $319,928 (M); gifts received, $81,253; expenditures, $310,010; qualifying distributions, $308,700; giving activities include $308,700 for 49 grants (high: $100,000; low: $60).
Fields of interest: Human services; Youth development; International relations.
Limitations: Applications not accepted. Giving primarily in New York, NY. No grants to individuals.
Application information: Unsolicited requests for funds not accepted.
Trustees: Kenneth H. Miller; Elizabeth Sweezy.
EIN: 133395958

6495
Steven A. and Marianne M. Mills Charitable Foundation

16 Prescott Ave.
Bronxville, NY   10708-3013

Established in 2001 in New York.
Donor: Steven A. Mills.
Foundation type: Independent foundation.
Financial data (yr. ended 12/31/13): Assets, $52,744 (M); gifts received, $158,300; expenditures, $179,125; qualifying distributions, $177,100; giving activities include $175,200 for 41 grants (high: $36,300; low: $225).
Fields of interest: Theater.
Limitations: Applications not accepted. Giving primarily in NY. No grants to individuals.
Application information: Unsolicited requests for funds not accepted.
Officers: Steven A. Mills, Pres.; Marianne M. Mills, V.P. and Treas.; John Clark Mills, Secy.
EIN: 311764912

6496
Edward L. Milstein Foundation

c/o Edward L. Milstein
335 Madison Ave., Ste. 1500
New York City, NY   10017-4611

Established in 1996 in New York.
Donors: Irma Milstein; Paul Milstein†; Edward L. Milstein; Milstein Family Foundation; Joseph B. Rose; Wendi and Joseph B. Rose Foundation.
Foundation type: Independent foundation.
Financial data (yr. ended 12/31/13): Assets, $319,657 (M); gifts received, $322,808; expenditures, $281,106; qualifying distributions, $281,106; giving activities include $276,050 for 12 grants (high: $135,000; low: $150).
Purpose and activities: Giving for Jewish education.
Fields of interest: Arts and culture; Cultural awareness; Education; Diseases and conditions; Judaism.
Limitations: Applications not accepted. Giving primarily in CT and NY. No grants to individuals.
Application information: Contributes only to pre-selected organizations.
Trustees: Edward L. Milstein; Irma Milstein.
EIN: 133921821

6497
The Arthur and Phyllis Milton Foundation, Inc.

425 E. 58th St., Ste. 43A
New York City, NY   10022-2300   (212) 355-7770

Established in 1996 in New York.
Donors: Arthur Milton†; Phyllis Milton.
Foundation type: Independent foundation.
Financial data (yr. ended 12/31/14): Assets, $1,497,057 (M); expenditures, $240,721; qualifying distributions, $215,018.
Fields of interest: Secondary education; Medical education; Convalescent care; Food delivery; Special population support; People with vision impairments.
Type of support: General support.
Limitations: Applications accepted. Giving primarily in CA and NY.
Application information:
  Initial approach: Proposal
  Deadline(s): None
Officers: Phyllis Milton, Pres.; David Gotterer, V.P. and Treas.; James Purdy, Secy.
EIN: 133922759

6498
The Mindel Foundation

c/o Morris Tuchman, Esq.
134 Lexington Ave.
New York City, NY   10016-8107

Established in 1998 in New York.
Donors: Morris Tuchman; Nelson Tuchman; Mitchell Adler.
Foundation type: Independent foundation.
Financial data (yr. ended 12/31/13): Assets, $1,111,790 (M); gifts received, $1,250,000; expenditures, $272,112; qualifying distributions, $271,645; giving activities include $271,595 for 33 grants (high: $51,700; low: $10).
Purpose and activities: Giving primarily for Jewish organizations, temples, and schools.
Fields of interest: Education; Nonprofits; Judaism.

Type of support: Regranting.
Limitations: Applications not accepted. Giving primarily in NY. No grants to individuals.
Application information: Contributes only to pre-selected organizations.
Trustees: Mitchell Adler; Morris Tuchman, Esq.; Nelson Tuchman.
EIN: 066462625

6499
Samuel & Rose Mitchell Foundation

c/o Estral Assocs.
3 E. 69th St., Ste. M-1
New York City, NY   10021-4943

Established in 1954 in Delaware.
Donor: Estelle M. Konheim.
Foundation type: Independent foundation.
Financial data (yr. ended 12/31/14): Assets, $859,043 (M); expenditures, $168,201; qualifying distributions, $136,634; giving activities include $118,677 for 42 grants (high: $21,920; low: $596).
Fields of interest: Arts and culture; Health; Religion.
Type of support: Research.
Limitations: Applications not accepted. Giving primarily in the greater New York, NY, area.
Application information: Unsolicited requests for funds not accepted.
Officers: Patricia Heffron, Pres.; Ann Polansky, Secy.; Nancy K. Greene, Treas.
Number of staff: 1 part-time professional.
EIN: 136128527

6500
The Mittlemann Family Foundation

c/o Spritzer, Kaufman, LLP
19 W. 44th St., Ste. 1703
New York City, NY   10036-6101

Foundation type: Independent foundation.
Financial data (yr. ended 12/31/13): Assets, $3,732,383 (M); expenditures, $267,583; qualifying distributions, $200,259; giving activities include $151,709 for 34 grants (high: $100,000; low: $50).
Fields of interest: Arts and culture; Higher education; Human services; Youth development.
Limitations: Applications not accepted. Giving primarily in Providence, RI.
Application information: Unsolicited requests for funds not accepted.
Officers: Josef Mittlemann, Pres.; Marsy Mittlemann, Secy.
EIN: 133158539

6501
Moach Charitable Foundation

1375 E. 23rd St.
Brooklyn, NY   11210-5112
Contact: Michael Steinberger, Tr.

Established in 2006 in New York.
Donors: Martin Zonenshayn; Pitya Yakobovich.
Foundation type: Independent foundation.
Financial data (yr. ended 10/31/12): Assets, $0 (M); gifts received, $146,866; expenditures, $147,098; qualifying distributions, $147,062; giving activities include $147,062 for 3 grants (high: $50,000; low: $47,062).
Fields of interest: Education; Human services.

Limitations: Applications accepted. Giving primarily in Brooklyn and New York, NY.
Application information: Application form required.
Initial approach: Letter
Deadline(s): None
Trustee: Michael Steinberger.
EIN: 205616628

6502
The Richard A. & Helene M. Monaghan Family Foundation
c/o The Ayco Co., L.P.-NTG
P.O. Box 15014
Albany, NY 12212-5014

Established in 1999 in Massachusetts.
Donors: Richard A. Monaghan; Helene Monaghan.
Foundation type: Independent foundation.
Financial data (yr. ended 12/31/13): Assets, $1,321,995 (M); expenditures, $405,789; qualifying distributions, $389,650; giving activities include $389,650 for 48 grants (high: $100,000; low: $100).
Fields of interest: Secondary education; University education; Foundations; Christianity; Human services.
Limitations: Applications not accepted. Giving primarily in Washington, DC, MA and NJ. No grants to individuals.
Application information: Contributes only to pre-selected organizations.
Directors: Helene M. Monaghan; Richard A. Monaghan.
EIN: 046907347

6503
Monderer Foundation, Inc.
(formerly Monderer Family Foundation, Inc.)
140 West End Ave., Apt. 29B
New York City, NY 10023-6149

Established in 2004 in Unspecified.
Donors: Carol B. Turchin; Benjamin Monderer.
Foundation type: Independent foundation.
Financial data (yr. ended 12/31/13): Assets, $4,413,675 (M); gifts received, $314,653; expenditures, $222,170; qualifying distributions, $179,200; giving activities include $179,200 for 12 grants (high: $105,000; low: $200).
Fields of interest: Arts and culture; Education; Human services.
Limitations: Applications not accepted. Giving primarily in NY. No grants to individuals.
Application information: Contributes only to pre-selected organizations.
Officers: Carol B. Turchin, Pres. and Treas.; Benjamin Monderer, V.P. and Secy.
EIN: 201842981

6504
Earle K. and Katherine F. Moore Foundation
c/o Citrin Cooperman
529 5th Ave.
New York City, NY 10017-4667

Established in 2007 in New York.
Donor: Katherine F. Moore.
Foundation type: Independent foundation.

Financial data (yr. ended 04/30/15): Assets, $3,096,427 (M); expenditures, $208,543; qualifying distributions, $193,555; giving activities include $190,000 for 5 grants (high: $75,000; low: $15,000).
Fields of interest: Arts and culture; Nonprofits; Communication media; Human services; Homeless services.
Type of support: General support; Regranting.
Limitations: Applications not accepted. Giving primarily in Washington, DC and New York, NY. No grants to individuals.
Application information: Contributes only to pre-selected organizations.
Trustees: Lucilla Tayama; Janis Weiss.
EIN: 166562816

6505
The Robert & Mary Lou Morgado Charitable Trust
(formerly The I'll Be There Foundation)
c/o Tag Assocs., LLC
75 Rockefeller Plz., Ste. 900
New York City, NY 10019

Established in 1995 in New York.
Donors: Mary Lou Morgado; Robert J. Morgado.
Foundation type: Independent foundation.
Financial data (yr. ended 11/30/13): Assets, $6,343,561 (M); gifts received, $404,894; expenditures, $264,138; qualifying distributions, $217,791; giving activities include $217,791 for 30 grants (high: $78,000; low: $10).
Purpose and activities: Giving primarily for higher education.
Fields of interest: Arts and culture; Higher education; Law education; Diseases and conditions; Human services.
Type of support: Research.
Limitations: Applications not accepted. Giving primarily in HI. No grants to individuals.
Application information: Contributes only to pre-selected organizations.
Trustees: Mary Lou Morgado; Robert J. Morgado.
EIN: 137072672

6506
Louis Morin Charitable Trust
140 Broadway, 4th Fl.
New York City, NY 10005-1101

Established in 2000 in New York.
Donor: Lily Lewis†.
Foundation type: Independent foundation.
Financial data (yr. ended 12/31/14): Assets, $5,353,094 (M); expenditures, $308,255; qualifying distributions, $259,757.
Fields of interest: Education; Science.
Type of support: Fellowships.
Limitations: Applications not accepted. Giving primarily in NY. No grants to individuals.
Application information: Contributes only to pre-selected organizations.
Trustee: Brown Brothers Harriman.
EIN: 137216266

6507
Flora F. Morrell Charitable Trust
271 Madison Ave., Ste. 905
New York City, NY 10016-1001

Foundation type: Independent foundation.
Financial data (yr. ended 12/31/13): Assets, $4,157,531 (M); expenditures, $203,704; qualifying distributions, $158,460.
Fields of interest: Judaism.
Limitations: Applications not accepted.
Application information: Unsolicited requests for funds not accepted.
Trustees: Isabell Coffey; Charles Shabsels.
EIN: 207220914

6508
Norman M. Morris Foundation, Inc.
26 Legendary Cir.
Rye Brook, NY 10573-1815 (914) 934-9229
Contact: Deborah Daum, Secy.-Treas.

Established in 1947 in New York.
Donor: Norman M. Morris†.
Foundation type: Independent foundation.
Financial data (yr. ended 12/31/13): Assets, $4,115,220 (M); expenditures, $306,550; qualifying distributions, $283,700; giving activities include $283,700 for 25 grants (high: $70,000; low: $500).
Purpose and activities: Giving primarily for health care and social services.
Fields of interest: Elementary and secondary education; Higher education; Nonprofits; Hospital care; Diseases and conditions; Judaism; Human services.
Type of support: Regranting.
Limitations: Applications accepted. Giving in the U.S., with emphasis on NY. No grants to individuals.
Application information:
Initial approach: Proposal
Deadline(s): None
Officers: Robert Morris, Pres.; Sandi Morris, V.P.; Deborah Daum, Secy.-Treas.
Trustees: John Daum; Jeffery Morris; Lauren Morris.
EIN: 136119134

6509
The David & Mildred Morse Charitable Trust
222 E. 41st St.
New York City, NY 10017-6739 (212) 326-3939
Contact: John J. Hyland, Tr.; Jones Day

Established in 1995 in New York.
Donor: Mildred H. Morse†.
Foundation type: Independent foundation.
Financial data (yr. ended 12/31/13): Assets, $3,569,126 (M); expenditures, $317,189; qualifying distributions, $283,135; giving activities include $267,750 for 22 grants (high: $50,000; low: $1,000).
Fields of interest: Education; Christianity; Judaism; Human services.
Type of support: General support.
Limitations: Applications accepted. Giving primarily in NY. No grants to individuals or for loans.
Application information: Application form required.
Initial approach: Letter
Deadline(s): None
Trustees: John J. Hyland; Joan Straus.
EIN: 137063711

6510
The Stacey C. & Robert R. Morse Family Foundation
1000 Park Ave., Ste. 3A
New York City, NY 10028-0934

Established in 2000 in New York.
Donors: Robert R. Morse; Stacey C. Morse.
Foundation type: Independent foundation.
Financial data (yr. ended 12/31/13): Assets, $36,346 (M); gifts received, $149,711; expenditures, $204,042; qualifying distributions, $200,894; giving activities include $200,042 for 15 grants (high: $120,000; low: $17).
Fields of interest: Museums; Elementary and secondary education; Higher education; Nonprofits; Human services.
Type of support: General support; Regranting.
Limitations: Applications not accepted. Giving primarily in New York, NY. No grants to individuals.
Application information: Unsolicited requests for funds not accepted.
Trustees: Robert R. Morse; Stacey C. Morse.
EIN: 134142518

6511
The Henry & Rose Moskowitz 1999 Family Foundation
50 W. 17th St.
New York City, NY 10011-5702

Established in 2000 in New York.
Donors: Henry Moskowitz‡; Rose Moskowitz.
Foundation type: Independent foundation.
Financial data (yr. ended 12/31/13): Assets, $1,592,589 (M); gifts received, $119,340; expenditures, $294,669; qualifying distributions, $292,769; giving activities include $290,869 for grants.
Fields of interest: Judaism.
Limitations: Applications not accepted. No grants to individuals.
Application information: Unsolicited requests for funds not accepted.
Officers: Rose Moskowitz, Pres.; Mark Moskowitz, Secy.
EIN: 116537576

6512
Mozel Charitable Trust
c/o Kenneth Weissbrot
972 Park Ln.
Valley Stream, NY 11581-2742

Established in 2001 in New York.
Donor: Claire A. Mozel‡.
Foundation type: Independent foundation.
Financial data (yr. ended 12/31/13): Assets, $6,293,666 (M); expenditures, $361,407; qualifying distributions, $254,139; giving activities include $225,035 for 17 grants (high: $100,000; low: $1,500).
Fields of interest: Museums; Education; Higher education; Health; Judaism.
Limitations: Applications not accepted. Giving primarily in NY. No grants to individuals.
Application information: Contributes only to pre-selected organizations.
Trustees: Nicholas Petras; Kenneth Weissbrot.
EIN: 116534643

6513
MRA Foundation
1943 E. 3rd St.
Brooklyn, NY 11223-2831

Donor: Diana Azrack.
Foundation type: Independent foundation.
Financial data (yr. ended 11/30/13): Assets, $61,332 (M); expenditures, $314,576; qualifying distributions, $314,576; giving activities include $314,576 for 4 grants (high: $160,000; low: $31,074).
Fields of interest: Housing development; Judaism.
Limitations: Applications not accepted. Giving primarily in Brooklyn, NY.
Application information: Unsolicited requests for funds not accepted.
Officers: Raymond Azrak, Pres.; Albert Azrak, V.P.; David Nakash, Secy.
EIN: 266673761

6514
MSG Charitable Foundation Trust
c/o Kalmanowitz & Lee, CPA's, PLLC
575 8th Ave., Ste. 1706
New York City, NY 10018-3067
E-mail: ikcpa@hotmail.com

Established in 2005 in New York.
Donors: Marton Guttman; Sara Guttman.
Foundation type: Independent foundation.
Financial data (yr. ended 12/31/14): Assets, $1,006,872 (M); gifts received, $500,000; expenditures, $284,773; qualifying distributions, $284,773; giving activities include $283,113 for 24 grants (high: $100,000; low: $18).
Fields of interest: Judaism; Jewish people.
Limitations: Applications not accepted. No grants to individuals.
Application information: Contributes only to pre-selected organizations.
Officers: Marton Guttman, Pres.; Moishe Guttman, V.P.; Sara Guttman, Treas.
EIN: 204756751

6515
Mule Family Foundation
c/o BCRS Associates, LLC
77 Water St., 9th Fl.
New York City, NY 10005-3801

Established in 1994 in New York.
Donor: Edward A. Mule.
Foundation type: Independent foundation.
Financial data (yr. ended 08/31/14): Assets, $18,955,996 (M); expenditures, $355,048; qualifying distributions, $339,190; giving activities include $333,550 for 37 grants (high: $200,000; low: $250).
Fields of interest: Education; Higher education; University education; Health; Hospital care; Alzheimer's disease; Presbyterianism; Human services; Youth services.
Type of support: General support.
Limitations: Applications not accepted. Giving primarily in Greenwich, CT, New York, NY, and Philadelphia, PA. No grants to individuals.
Application information: Unsolicited requests for funds not accepted.
Trustee: Edward A. Mule.
EIN: 133801234

6516
Mulroy Family Foundation
c/o The Guaranty Building
140 Pearl St., Ste. 100
Buffalo, NY 14202-4040 7168564000

Established in 1989 in New York.
Foundation type: Independent foundation.
Financial data (yr. ended 12/31/14): Assets, $2,827,042; expenditures, $141,750; qualifying distributions, $132,657.
Fields of interest: Arts and culture; Sports and recreation; Human services.
Type of support: General support.
Limitations: Applications not accepted. Giving primarily in Buffalo, NY. No grants to individuals.
Application information: Unsolicited requests for funds not accepted.
Trustee: James M. Wadsworth.
EIN: 161314725

6517
The MW Charitable Foundation
4706 18th Ave.
Brooklyn, NY 11204-1260
Contact: Maurice Wolf

Donor: Maurice Wolf.
Foundation type: Independent foundation.
Financial data (yr. ended 11/30/13): Assets, $983,779 (M); gifts received, $169,000; expenditures, $169,403; qualifying distributions, $168,003; giving activities include $168,003 for 28 grants.
Fields of interest: Religion; Human services; International relations.
Type of support: General support.
Limitations: Applications not accepted. Giving primarily in NY. No grants to individuals.
Application information: Unsolicited requests for funds not accepted.
Trustees: Esther Wolf; Maurice Wolf.
EIN: 203985529

6518
MZL 40 Foundation
40 Maple Ave.
Cedarhurst, NY 11516-2222

Donors: Leo Zisman; Ohrot Shel Tzion.
Foundation type: Independent foundation.
Financial data (yr. ended 12/31/13): Assets, $1,858,153 (M); gifts received, $200,000; expenditures, $444,760; qualifying distributions, $413,140; giving activities include $412,890 for 70 grants (high: $200,000; low: $180).
Fields of interest: Education; Public affairs; Judaism.
Limitations: Applications not accepted.
Application information: Unsolicited requests for funds not accepted.
Trustee: Myrna Zisman.
EIN: 421687141

6519
Nassimi Family Foundation, Inc.
370 7th Ave., Ste. 1600
New York City, NY 10001-3901

Established in 1994 in New York.

Donors: N-Alpha Holdings; Edward Nassimi; Mike Nassimi; Winbrook Management, Inc.; Mouris Nassimi; Oliver Nassimi; Iwan Nassimi.
Foundation type: Independent foundation.
Financial data (yr. ended 02/28/13): Assets, $2,644 (M); gifts received, $322,960; expenditures, $324,989; qualifying distributions, $324,794; giving activities include $324,794 for grants.
Fields of interest: Judaism.
Limitations: Applications not accepted.
Application information: Unsolicited requests for funds not accepted.
Officers: Edward Nassimi, Mgr.; Mike M. Nassimi, Mgr.
EIN: 133781329

6520
National Mah Jongg League Foundation, Inc.

c/o Samuel Greenberg & Co.
1430 Broadway, No. 1615
New York City, NY   10018-3356

Established in 1995 in New York.
Donor: National Mah Jongg League, Inc.
Foundation type: Independent foundation.
Financial data (yr. ended 02/28/15): Assets, $7,135,601 (M); gifts received, $1,825,000; expenditures, $393,772; qualifying distributions, $375,000; giving activities include $375,000 for 18 grants (high: $150,000; low: $1,000).
Purpose and activities: Giving primarily for health organizations, particularly a children's hospital.
Fields of interest: Specialty hospital care; Children's hospital care; Diseases and conditions; Cancers; Child welfare; Children.
Type of support: Research.
Limitations: Applications not accepted. Giving in the U.S. with emphasis on FL and NY. No grants to individuals.
Application information: Unsolicited requests for funds not accepted.
Officers: David Unger, Pres.; Larry Unger, V.P.; Ruth Unger, V.P.; Marilyn Starr, Secy.; Norman Greenberg, Treas.
EIN: 133791092

6521
M. & H. Neiman Foundation, Inc.

39 Broadway, Rm. No. 2510
New York City, NY   10006-3003

Established in 1972 in New York.
Donors: Marvin Neiman; Solomon Neiman; Perl Foundation.
Foundation type: Independent foundation.
Financial data (yr. ended 10/31/13): Assets, $57,010 (M); gifts received, $174,000; expenditures, $144,966; qualifying distributions, $144,800; giving activities include $144,800 for 14 grants (high: $47,500; low: $500).
Purpose and activities: Giving primarily to yeshivas.
Fields of interest: Judaism.
Limitations: Applications not accepted. Giving primarily in NY. No grants to individuals.
Application information: Unsolicited requests for funds not accepted.
Officers: Marvin Neiman, Pres.; Helen Neiman, V.P.; Louis Neiman, Secy.
EIN: 237042788

6522
Nelco Foundation Inc

164 W. 25th St.
New York City, NY   10001-7400

Established in 1953 in New York.
Donors: Leon Jolson; Nelco Sewing Machine Sales Corp.; Nelco Foundation UWO Leon Jolson Tr.
Foundation type: Independent foundation.
Financial data (yr. ended 05/31/14): Assets, $5,856,385 (M); gifts received, $375,000; expenditures, $388,705; qualifying distributions, $313,955; giving activities include $313,955 for 78 grants (high: $30,000; low: $180).
Purpose and activities: The foundation supports Jewish agencies and temples, museums, and organizations involved with education, medical research, and human services.
Fields of interest: Education; Judaism; Human services.
Limitations: Applications not accepted. Giving primarily in the greater metropolitan New York, NY, area. No grants to individuals.
Application information: Contributes only to pre-selected organizations.
Officers and Trustees: Barbara Blumenthal, Pres. and Trustee; David Blumenthal, V.P.
EIN: 136089850

6523
Neporent Family Foundation

c/o Popper
192 Lexington Ave.
New York City, NY   10016

Donors: Mark A. Neporent; Lisa King Neporent.
Foundation type: Independent foundation.
Financial data (yr. ended 12/31/13): Assets, $648,766 (M); gifts received, $105,804; expenditures, $192,412; qualifying distributions, $186,433; giving activities include $186,433 for 15 grants (high: $128,000; low: $250).
Fields of interest: Arts and culture; Education; University education; Health.
Limitations: Applications not accepted. Giving primarily in NY.
Application information: Unsolicited requests for funds not accepted.
Trustees: Lisa King Neporent; Mark A. Neporent.
EIN: 453565015

6524
The Nets Foundation, Inc.

c/o Brooklyn Nets
15 Metrotech Ctr., 11th Fl.
Brooklyn, NY   11201

Established in 2007 in New Jersey.
Donors: Barclays Capital; Forest City Ratner Companies; Forest City Ratner Companies Foundation; New Jersey Basketball, LLC.
Foundation type: Company-sponsored foundation.
Financial data (yr. ended 06/30/13): Assets, $285,584 (M); gifts received, $169,369; expenditures, $370,626; qualifying distributions, $348,500; giving activities include $348,500 for 23 grants (high: $75,000; low: $1,000).
Purpose and activities: The foundation supports programs designed to promote youth; foster education; and strengthen communities.

Fields of interest: Arts and culture; Historic preservation; Education; Higher education; Community and economic development; Sports; Basketball; Human services; Child welfare; Youth services; Adult and child mentoring; Adolescents.
Type of support: General support; Program development.
Limitations: Applications not accepted. Giving primarily in NJ and NY.
Application information: Contributes only to pre-selected organizations.
Officers and Directors: Brett Yormark, Pres. and Director; Leo Ehrline, V.P. and Secy. and Director; Charlie Mierswa, V.P. and Treas. and Director; Bruce Ratner.
EIN: 205370246

6525
The Netter Foundation, Inc.

(formerly Alice & Fred Netter Foundation)
411 Theodore Fremd Ave., Ste. 206S
Rye, NY   10580-1411

Established in 1965 in New York.
Donors: K. Fred Netter; Alice D. Netter.
Foundation type: Independent foundation.
Financial data (yr. ended 12/31/13): Assets, $4,928,502 (M); expenditures, $315,113; qualifying distributions, $244,860; giving activities include $240,000 for 115 grants (high: $15,000; low: $100).
Purpose and activities: Giving primarily for the arts, cancer research, education, and senior citizens services.
Fields of interest: Performing arts; Music; Education; Nonprofits; Diseases and conditions; Social sciences; Human services; Seniors; Ethnic and racial groups.
Type of support: General support; Continuing support; Annual campaigns; Capital campaigns; Capital and infrastructure; Endowments; Research; Research and evaluation; Regranting.
Limitations: Applications not accepted. No grants to individuals.
Application information: Contributes only to pre-selected organizations.
Officers: Ronald A. Netter, Pres. and Treas.; Nadine Levy, V.P.; Alfred E. Netter, Secy.
EIN: 136176542

6526
I. & B. Neuman Foundation, Inc.

122 E. 42nd St.
New York City, NY   10168-0002

Established in 1956 in New York.
Donors: Irving Neuman†; Herbert Neuman; Marvin Herbert.
Foundation type: Independent foundation.
Financial data (yr. ended 12/31/13): Assets, $530,456 (M); gifts received, $200,000; expenditures, $233,657; qualifying distributions, $228,924; giving activities include $225,290 for 99 grants (high: $50,000; low: $50).
Purpose and activities: Giving primarily for education and Jewish organizations.
Fields of interest: Education; Nonprofits; Judaism; Human services.
International interests: Israel.
Type of support: Regranting.

Limitations: Applications not accepted. Giving primarily in NY. No grants to individuals.
Application information: Unsolicited requests for funds not accepted.
Officers: Herbert Neuman, Pres.; Marvin Neuman, Secy.-Treas.
Number of staff: None.
EIN: 136161492

6527
New Tamarind Foundation, Inc.
c/o O'Connor Davies Munns and Dobbins
665 5th Ave.
New York City, NY 10022-5305
Main URL: www.newtamarindfoundation.org

Donors: Helaine Lerner; Harriet Heilbrunn†; Robert Heilbrunn Trust; Harriet Heilbrunn Trust; Marital Trust.
Foundation type: Independent foundation.
Financial data (yr. ended 06/30/14): Assets, $87,002,616; expenditures, $228,012; qualifying distributions, $218,012.
Fields of interest: Theater; Higher education; Nonprofits.
Type of support: Regranting.
Limitations: Applications not accepted. Giving primarily in NY.
Application information: Unsolicited requests for funds not accepted.
Officers and Directors: Helaine Lerner, Pres. and Director; Joan Rechnitz, Secy.-Treas.
EIN: 263324875

6528
Newcastle Foundation Trust
c/o Brown Brothers Harriman Trust Co., N.A.
140 Broadway, 5th Fl.
New York City, NY 10005-1101

Established in 2000 in Massachusetts.
Foundation type: Independent foundation.
Financial data (yr. ended 12/31/14): Assets, $5,208,518 (M); expenditures, $349,122; qualifying distributions, $300,533; giving activities include $289,000 for 23 grants (high: $50,000; low: $500).
Fields of interest: Historical activities; Education; Hospital care; Diseases and conditions; Human services.
Type of support: General support.
Limitations: Applications not accepted. No grants to individuals.
Application information: Unsolicited requests for funds not accepted.
Trustees: Timothy J. Barberich; Eileen P. Gebrian; Brown Brothers Harriman Trust Co.
EIN: 522283813

6529
The Newcomb-Hargraves Foundation
c/o Newcomb & Hargraves
7 W. 81st St., Ste. 11B
New York City, NY 10024-6049

Established in 2000 in New York.
Donors: Nancy S. Newcomb; John A. Hargraves.
Foundation type: Independent foundation.

Financial data (yr. ended 12/31/14): Assets, $2,103,546; expenditures, $185,028; qualifying distributions, $180,895.
Fields of interest: Arts and culture; Historic preservation; University education; Environment.
Limitations: Applications not accepted. No grants to individuals.
Application information: Unsolicited requests for funds not accepted.
Trustees: John A. Hargraves; Nancy S. Newcomb.
EIN: 316650840

6530
Jerome A. and Estelle R. Newman Assistance Fund Inc.
43 Appletree Ln.
Carle Place, NY 11514-1320 (516) 279-4900
Contact: Michael Greenberg, Treas.

Established in 1954 in New York.
Donors: Howard A. Newman†; Jerome A. Newman†.
Foundation type: Independent foundation.
Financial data (yr. ended 06/30/14): Assets, $9,800,456 (M); expenditures, $491,602; qualifying distributions, $419,000; giving activities include $419,000 for 16 grants (high: $133,500; low: $2,500).
Purpose and activities: Giving primarily to Jewish education and welfare organizations, including a guild for the blind; support also for higher education.
Fields of interest: Arts and culture; Theater; Higher education; Foundations; Nonprofits; Communication media; Judaism; Human services; Basic and emergency aid; International development.
Type of support: Regranting.
Limitations: Applications accepted. Giving primarily in NY. No loans or grants to individuals.
Application information: Application form required.
  Initial approach: Letter
  Deadline(s): None
  Board meeting date(s): Sept.
Officers and Directors: William C. Newman, Pres. and Director; Robert H. Haines, Secy. and Director; Victoria Woolner Samuels, V.P. and Director; Michael Greenberg, Treas. and Director; Andrew H. Levy; Jeffrey A. Newman; William C. Scott; Catherine N. Woolner.
EIN: 136096241

6531
The Lizbeth & Frank Newman Charitable Foundation
40 E. 61st St., No. 15B
New York City, NY 10065-8033
Contact: Mary Reen, Treas.

Established in 1999 in New York.
Donors: Frank N. Newman; Lizebeth Newman.
Foundation type: Independent foundation.
Financial data (yr. ended 12/31/13): Assets, $17,978 (M); gifts received, $460,000; expenditures, $490,231; qualifying distributions, $470,956; giving activities include $434,250 for 6 grants (high: $108,000; low: $1,250).
Purpose and activities: Giving primarily to performing arts and cultural institutions.
Fields of interest: Arts and culture; Performing arts; Museums; Education; Higher education.
Limitations: Applications not accepted. Giving primarily in NY. No grants to individuals.

Application information: Contributes only to pre-selected organizations.
Officers: Frank Newman, Pres.; Lizabeth Newman, V.P. and Secy.; Mary Reen, Treas.
EIN: 134067790

6532
The Carol & Melvin Newman Family Foundation, Inc.
(formerly The Morris & Ida Newman Family Foundation, Inc.)
c/o Melvin D. Newman
145 Central Park W.
New York City, NY 10023-2004

Established in 1955 in New York.
Donors: Melvin D. Newman; Carol Newman.
Foundation type: Independent foundation.
Financial data (yr. ended 12/31/13): Assets, $2,099,360 (M); expenditures, $163,604; qualifying distributions, $154,244; giving activities include $154,244 for 89 grants (high: $25,000; low: $1).
Purpose and activities: Giving primarily for Jewish temples, education, and organizations, and Jewish federated giving programs; some funding for the arts, education, and human services.
Fields of interest: Arts and culture; Performing arts; Education; Higher education; Nonprofits; Hospital care; Judaism; Human services.
Type of support: General support; Scholarships; Regranting.
Limitations: Applications not accepted. Giving primarily in NY. No grants to individuals.
Application information: Unsolicited requests for funds not accepted.
Officers: Melvin D. Newman, Pres.; Carol Newman, V.P. and Treas.
Director: Joshua Newman.
EIN: 136162759

6533
Newman Family Foundation, Inc.
c/o The Ayco Co., LP-NTG
P.O. Box 15014
Albany, NY 12212-5014

Established in 2007 in New York.
Donor: Mark S. Newman.
Foundation type: Independent foundation.
Financial data (yr. ended 12/31/14): Assets, $2,129,848 (M); expenditures, $328,630; qualifying distributions, $299,500; giving activities include $299,500 for 25 grants (high: $75,000; low: $500).
Fields of interest: University education; National security; Religion.
Limitations: Applications not accepted. Giving primarily in Washington, DC, FL, NY. No grants to individuals.
Application information: Unsolicited requests for funds not accepted.
Officers: Mark S. Newman, Pres.; Sharon M. Newman, Secy.-Treas.
Director: Alison Newman.
EIN: 260298188

6534
Amy Klette Newman Foundation
473 West End Ave., Apt. 10C
New York City, NY 10024-4978

Established in 2000 in Florida.
Donor: Amelia G. Newman†.
Foundation type: Independent foundation.
Financial data (yr. ended 12/31/13): Assets,
$4,359,490 (M); expenditures, $253,913;
qualifying distributions, $246,627; giving activities
include $217,500 for 21 grants (high: $25,000;
low: $500).
Fields of interest: Higher education; Health;
Hospital care; Cancers; Judaism; Human services.
Limitations: Applications not accepted. Giving
primarily in NJ and NY. No grants to individuals.
Application information: Contributes only to
pre-selected organizations.
Trustees: Carol Joseph; Marc Joseph.
EIN: 582524051

6535
The Niemiec Family Fund
c/o Barry M. Strauss Assocs., Ltd.
307 5th Ave., 8th Fl.
New York City, NY 10016-6517

Established in 1992 in New York.
Donor: David W. Niemiec.
Foundation type: Independent foundation.
Financial data (yr. ended 03/31/13): Assets,
$1,476,306 (M); gifts received, $424,780;
expenditures, $204,986; qualifying distributions,
$204,175; giving activities include $202,450 for 15
grants (high: $85,000; low: $500).
Fields of interest: Arts education; Music; Education;
Higher education; Business education; Christianity.
Limitations: Applications not accepted. Giving
primarily in NY. No grants to individuals.
Application information: Contributes only to
pre-selected organizations.
Trustees: David W. Niemiec; Melanie M. Niemiec.
EIN: 133689379

6536
NM Morris Family Foundation
9 Rustling Ln.
Bedford, NY 10506-1815 (914) 234-0511
Contact: Wendy Aglietti, Secy.-Treas.

Foundation type: Independent foundation.
Financial data (yr. ended 12/31/14): Assets,
$6,602,412 (M); expenditures, $377,865;
qualifying distributions, $340,828; giving activities
include $340,828 for 93 grants (high: $50,000;
low: $91).
Fields of interest: Education; Domesticated
animals; Diseases and conditions.
Application information:
  Initial approach: Proposal
  Deadline(s): None
Officers and Directors: Kenneth Lubin, Pres. and
Director; Carol Hundert, V.P. and Director; Wendy
Aglietti, Secy.-Treas. and Director.
EIN: 274723253

6537
Nok Charitable Organization, Inc.
(also known as NOK Foundation, Inc.)
c/o Quest Partners LLC
126 E. 56th St., 19th Fl.
New York City, NY 10022-3613 (212) 838-7222
Contact: Nigol Koulajian
E-mail: info@nokfoundation.com; Main URL: http://
www.nokfoundation.com

Established in 2002 in New York.
Foundation type: Independent foundation.
Financial data (yr. ended 12/31/13): Assets, $0
(M); gifts received, $4,990; expenditures,
$455,546; qualifying distributions, $368,488;
giving activities include $269,709 for 31 grants
(high: $120,000; low: $108).
Purpose and activities: The foundation was created
in order to cultivate and promote the study of
Eastern philosophy and religion, as well as yoga.
Fields of interest: Buddhism; Hinduism.
International interests: India.
Type of support: General support; Grants to
individuals; In-kind gifts; Continuing support;
Financial sustainability; Loans to individuals; Capital
and infrastructure; Endowments; Emergency funds;
Program development; Convening; Publications;
Seed money; Curriculum development; Fellowships;
Internships; Scholarships; Research; Program
evaluations; Student aid.
Limitations: Applications accepted. Giving primarily
in NY and India.
Publications: Informational brochure.
Application information: The grantmaker is currently
focusing on a large scale internal project and will not
be accepting applications for scholarships until
further notice. Application form required.
  Initial approach: E-mail or letter
  Copies of proposal: 1
  Deadline(s): None
  Final notification: 4 weeks
Officer and Directors: Nigol Koulajian, Pres. and
Director; Carla Koulajian; Laura Koulajian; Paula
Tursi.
EIN: 020654795

6538
Nonna's Garden
17-20 Whitestone Expwy., Ste. 501
Whitestone, NY 11357-3000

Established in 2007 in New York.
Donors: Michael Repole; Peaceworks Holdings, LLC.
Foundation type: Independent foundation.
Financial data (yr. ended 12/31/13): Assets,
$9,313,051 (M); gifts received, $10,750;
expenditures, $528,966; qualifying distributions,
$435,000; giving activities include $435,000 for 13
grants (high: $140,000; low: $2,500).
Fields of interest: University education; Specialty
hospital care; Diseases and conditions; Skin
conditions; Cancers.
Limitations: Applications not accepted. Giving
primarily in New York, NY. No grants to individuals.
Application information: Contributes only to
pre-selected organizations.
Trustees: Maria A. Repole; Michael Repole.
EIN: 137548350

6539
North America LAPB Inc.
c/o Louis Pizzarello
137 Hampton Rd.
Southampton, NY 11968-4923

Donors: Shreveport Sees Russia LLC; Lavelle Fund
for the Blind Inc.; Highland Clinic; The Alcon
Foundation Inc.
Foundation type: Independent foundation.
Financial data (yr. ended 12/31/13): Assets,
$9,950 (M); gifts received, $154,290;
expenditures, $167,275; qualifying distributions,
$167,275; giving activities include $163,190 for 1
grant.
Fields of interest: Diseases and conditions.
Limitations: Applications not accepted.
Application information: Unsolicited requests for
funds not accepted.
Officers: Louis Pizarello, Pres.; Kathy Spahn, Secy.;
Kristin Gamble, Treas.
EIN: 043796216

6540
Northern Chautauqua Community
Foundation, Inc.
212 Lake Shore Dr. W.
Dunkirk, NY 14048-1436 (716) 366-4892
Contact: Diane Hannum, Exec. Dir.
FAX: (716) 366-3905;
E-mail: info@nccfoundation.org; Grant application
e-mail: grants@nccfoundation.org; Additional e-mail:
dhannum@nccfoundation.org; Main URL: http://
www.nccfoundation.org
Facebook: https://www.facebook.com/
NCCFoundation
Twitter: https://twitter.com/NCCFoundation

Established in 1987 in New York.
Foundation type: Community foundation.
Financial data (yr. ended 12/31/13): Assets,
$22,816,608 (M); gifts received, $591,031;
expenditures, $582,806; giving activities include
$190,723 for 10+ grants (high: $20,000), and
$144,148 for 268 grants to individuals.
Purpose and activities: The foundation seeks to
enrich the area in which the community lives and
works. Primary areas of interest include education,
family services, community funds, cultural
programs, and other general charitable activities.
Fields of interest: Arts and culture; Education;
Higher education; Basic and remedial instruction;
Reading promotion; Environment; Rivers and lakes;
Animal welfare; Voluntarism; Hospital care; Hospice
care; Addiction services; Libraries; Community and
economic development; Sustainable development;
Sports and recreation; Parks; Family services; Youth
development; Senior services; Seniors.
Type of support: Capital and infrastructure;
Matching grants; Equipment; Program development;
Seed money; Scholarships; Student aid; Public
engagement and education.
Limitations: Applications accepted. Giving limited to
northern Chautauqua County, NY. No support for
religious organizations. No grants to individuals
(except for designated scholarship funds), or for
capital campaigns, general operating budgets,
publication of books, conferences, or annual
fundraising campaigns.
Publications: Application guidelines; Annual report
(including application guidelines); Financial
statement; Newsletter.

Application information: Visit foundation web site for application form and guidelines. Application form required.

 Initial approach: E-mail letter of interest (not to exceed 2 pages)
 Copies of proposal: 1
 Deadline(s): Community Grants Program: Mar. 1 and Sept. 1 for letter of interest; Mar. 19 and Sept. 24 for full proposal
 Board meeting date(s): Quarterly
 Final notification: Community Grants Program: Mar. 6 and Sept. 11 for letter of interest determination; Early May and Early Nov. for grant notification

Officers and Directors: Peter Clark, Pres. and Director; Elizabeth Booth, V.P. and Director; John D'Agostino, Secy. and Director; Kathy Kaus, Treas. and Director; Diane Hannum, Exec. Dir.; Helen Baran; Jerry Hall; Jim Holton; Priscilla Koch; Blair Koss; Ryan Mourer; Gina Paradis; Pete Ryan; Richard Ryan; Susan L. Wells; Monica White.
Number of staff: 3 full-time professional; 2 part-time professional.
EIN: 161271663

6541
The Norwegian Children's Home Association of New York, Inc.
P.O. Box 280104
Brooklyn, NY 11228-0104 (718) 238-4326

Established in 2000 in New York.
Foundation type: Independent foundation.
Financial data (yr. ended 12/31/14): Assets, $3,466,671; gifts received, $150; expenditures, $219,649; qualifying distributions, $180,299.
Purpose and activities: Scholarship awards to students who are at least 25 percent Norwegian ancestry or with a significant Norwegian affiliation.
Fields of interest: Higher education.
Type of support: Student aid.
Application information: Application form required.
 Initial approach: Letter
 Deadline(s): Mar. 16
Officers: Hans Ternsten, Pres.; Kjell Kittillsen, V.P.; Sonia Nerjes, Secy.; Barbara Kristiansen, Corresponding Secy.; Lillian Eidhammer, Treas.
EIN: 111666853

6542
The Greater Norwich Foundation
c/o NBT Bank, N.A.
52 S. Broad St.
Norwich, NY 13815-1646 (607) 337-6193

Established in 1965 in New York.
Donors: Ivory Residual Estate; Kent Barbara Turner; Fred Miers; Charles Burr Charitable Trust; Raymond & Alma Willard Charitable Trust; James Sue Hoy; Peter Smith Laurel Wilt Bank; James Dunne; Weinman Family Foundation; Particia & William Smith Foundation; Thomas Bonie Emerson; Community Foundation of Sarasota; Curran Foundation; W.E. Eaton Charitable Trust; Mary Cattan; Thomas & Esther Flanagan Charitable Trust.
Foundation type: Independent foundation.
Financial data (yr. ended 03/31/13): Assets, $7,244,834 (M); gifts received, $30,285; expenditures, $380,552; qualifying distributions, $350,071; giving activities include $301,879 for 22 grants (high: $60,000; low: $250), $45,250 for 32

grants to individuals (high: $3,000; low: $500) and $0 for set-asides.
Fields of interest: Arts and culture; Historic preservation; Education; Higher education; Animal welfare; Hospital care; Human services; Child welfare.
Type of support: Annual campaigns; Capital campaigns; Capital and infrastructure; Equipment; Program development; Scholarships; Student aid.
Limitations: Applications accepted. Giving primarily in the Norwich, NY, area.
Publications: Informational brochure.
Application information: Application form required.
 Initial approach: Letter or grant application
 Copies of proposal: 1
 Deadline(s): Apr. 15 and Oct. 15
 Board meeting date(s): May and Nov.
Trustees: James I. Dunne; Jane E. Eaton; Thomas C. Emerson, Esq.; Esther C. Flanagan; Patrick Flanagan; James A. Hoy; Frederic B. Miers; H. William Smith, Jr.; Peter V. Smith; NBT Bank, N.A.
EIN: 166064927

6543
Agnus Noster Foundation
27-28 Thomson Ave., No. 441
Long Island City, NY 11101-2938

Established in 1997 in Delaware.
Foundation type: Independent foundation.
Financial data (yr. ended 02/28/13): Assets, $2,542,429 (M); expenditures, $204,991; qualifying distributions, $175,821; giving activities include $175,821 for 8 grants (high: $131,321; low: $1,500).
Fields of interest: Arts and culture; Education; Religion.
Limitations: Applications not accepted. Giving primarily in NY. No grants to individuals.
Application information: Unsolicited requests for funds not accepted.
Officers: Gayle Susan Marra, Pres.; Vincenzo R. Marra, Secy.
EIN: 133936959

6544
Jane W. Nuhn Charitable Trust
c/o Van DeWater & Van DeWater
P.O. Box 112
Poughkeepsie, NY 12602-0112
Contact: Michael De Cordova, Tr.

Established in 1988 in New York.
Foundation type: Independent foundation.
Financial data (yr. ended 12/31/13): Assets, $11,136,732 (M); expenditures, $583,584; qualifying distributions, $477,131; giving activities include $431,225 for 17 grants (high: $60,000; low: $1,500).
Purpose and activities: Giving primarily for the arts, higher education, and human services.
Fields of interest: Arts and culture; Higher education; Protestantism; Human services.
Type of support: General support; Matching grants; Capital and infrastructure; Equipment; Endowments.
Limitations: Applications accepted. Giving primarily in Dutchess County, NY, with some emphasis on Poughkeepsie. No grants to individuals.
Publications: Annual report.
Application information:

 Initial approach: Letter
 Deadline(s): None
 Board meeting date(s): Quarterly
Trustees: Edward V.K. Cunningham, Jr.; Michael De Cordova; Noel De Cordova, Jr.
EIN: 146134057

6545
The Bernard W. Nussbaum Family Foundation
(formerly The Bernard and Toby Nussbaum Family Foundation)
c/o Wachtell, Lipton, Rosen & Katz
51 W. 52nd St.
New York City, NY 10019-6119

Established in 1986 in New York.
Donor: Bernard W. Nussbaum.
Foundation type: Independent foundation.
Financial data (yr. ended 04/30/14): Assets, $596,782; gifts received, $100,711; expenditures, $177,085; qualifying distributions, $175,085.
Purpose and activities: Giving primarily for Jewish organizations and education.
Fields of interest: Arts and culture; Higher education; Graduate and professional education; Law education; Nonprofits; Judaism; Theology; Child welfare.
Type of support: Regranting.
Limitations: Applications not accepted. Giving primarily in New York, NY. No grants to individuals.
Application information: Contributes only to pre-selected organizations.
Officers: Bernard W. Nussbaum, Pres.; Martin Nussbaum, V.P. and Treas.; Constance Monte, Secy.
EIN: 133374849

6546
NYBDC Charitable Foundation Inc.
50 Beaver Street
Albany, NY 12207-1511

Established in 2000 in New York.
Donors: New York Business Development Corp.; Empire State Certified Development Corporation; New York Business Development Corporation.
Foundation type: Company-sponsored foundation.
Financial data (yr. ended 09/30/13): Assets, $1,588,194 (M); gifts received, $391,955; expenditures, $190,604; qualifying distributions, $171,550; giving activities include $171,550 for 8 grants (high: $95,550; low: $5,000).
Purpose and activities: The foundation supports fire departments and organizations involved with secondary and higher education and community economic development.
Type of support: General support; Continuing support.
Limitations: Applications not accepted.
Application information: Contributes only to pre-selected organizations.
Officer: Patrick J. Mackrell, Pres.
Directors: James J. Byrnes; Herbert G. Chorbajian; Thomas F. Goldrick, Jr.; Jeffrey M. Levy; Robert W. Lazar.
EIN: 141834499

6547
The Oberoi Family Foundation
c/o BCRS Associates, LLC
77 Water St., 9th Fl.
New York City, NY   10005-3701

Established in 1997 in New York.
Donor: Alok Oberoi.
Foundation type: Independent foundation.
Financial data (yr. ended 05/31/13): Assets,
$2,420,616 (M); expenditures, $244,161;
qualifying distributions, $240,121; giving activities
include $239,736 for 17 grants (high: $100,000;
low: $406).
Fields of interest: Education; Higher education;
Human services; Youth development.
Limitations: Applications not accepted. Giving
primarily in NY. No grants to individuals.
Application information: Unsolicited requests for
funds not accepted.
Trustees: Alok Oberoi; Majini Oberoi.
EIN: 133932623

6548
Odyssey Partners Foundation, Inc.
1 Rockefeller Plz., 20th Fl.
New York City, NY   10020

Established in 1965 in New York.
Donor: Odyssey Investment Partners, LLC.
Foundation type: Company-sponsored foundation.
Financial data (yr. ended 01/31/13): Assets, $6
(M); expenditures, $260,080; qualifying
distributions, $255,780; giving activities include
$251,250 for 13 grants (high: $125,000; low:
$1,000).
Purpose and activities: The foundation supports
organizations involved with arts and culture,
education, health, and human services.
Fields of interest: Arts and culture; Religion; Human
services.
Limitations: Applications not accepted. Giving
primarily in New York, NY. No grants to individuals.
Application information: Unsolicited requests for
funds not accepted.
Officer: Joshua Nash, Pres.
Trustee: Morris Rosenthal.
EIN: 136186566

6549
Sylvan and Ann Oestreicher Foundation, Inc.
c/o Marks Paneth & Shron, LLP
685 3rd Ave.
New York City, NY   10017-4024

Established in 1948 in New York.
Donor: Sylvan Oestreicher†.
Foundation type: Independent foundation.
Financial data (yr. ended 04/30/13): Assets,
$4,099 (M); gifts received, $21,271; expenditures,
$409,657; qualifying distributions, $381,889;
giving activities include $303,000 for 9 grants (high:
$100,000; low: $13,000).
Fields of interest: Education; Hospital care;
Catholicism; Human services.
Limitations: Applications not accepted. Giving
primarily in New York, NY; funding also in Los
Angeles, CA.
Application information: Contributes only to
pre-selected organizations.

Officers: Joseph Teklits, Pres.; Annabel Santana,
Secy.
EIN: 136085974

6550
The Offensend Family Foundation
1 Main St., Ste. 5D
Brooklyn, NY   11201-1148

Established in 1998 in New York.
Donors: David Offensend; Janet Offensend.
Foundation type: Independent foundation.
Financial data (yr. ended 12/31/13): Assets,
$480,975 (M); gifts received, $19,708;
expenditures, $316,553; qualifying distributions,
$309,597; giving activities include $301,800 for 47
grants (high: $100,000; low: $250).
Purpose and activities: Giving for education, parks,
children's art and cultural institutes, public
institutes and services.
Fields of interest: Arts and culture; Performing arts;
Museums; Education; Higher education; Business
education; Family planning; Public libraries;
Protestantism; Parks; Child welfare.
Type of support: General support; Annual
campaigns; Capital campaigns; Capital and
infrastructure; Endowments; Curriculum
development.
Limitations: Applications not accepted. Giving
primarily in Brooklyn and New York, NY; some
funding also in CT and Boston, MA. No grants to
individuals.
Application information: Contributes only to
pre-selected organizations.
Trustees: David G. Offensend; Janet M. Offensend.
Number of staff: None.
EIN: 134011882

6551
O'Grady Foundation
140 E. 81st St., Ste. 5C
New York City, NY   10028-1807   (212) 744-2713
Contact: Kathleen C. O'Grady, Pres.
E-mail: info@theogradyfoundation.org; Main
URL: http://www.theogradyfoundation.org
Grants List: http://www.theogradyfoundation.org/
grant-portfolio.html

Established in 1993 in Connecticut.
Donors: Thomas B. O'Grady†; Kathleen O'Grady.
Foundation type: Independent foundation.
Financial data (yr. ended 12/31/14): Assets,
$5,243,426; expenditures, $310,357; qualifying
distributions, $243,121.
Purpose and activities: Giving primarily for technical
assistance for arts and cultural organizations with
budgets of less than $4 million; also supports
arts-in-education programs targeting primary and
middle school age children.
Fields of interest: Arts and culture; Arts education.
Type of support: General support; Pro bono
consulting services; Matching grants; Continuing
support; Seed money; Internships; Technical
assistance; Program evaluations.
Limitations: Applications accepted. Giving primarily
in New York, NY. No support for political
organizations and religious institutions. No grants to
individuals.

Application information: See foundation web site
for complete application guidelines. Application
form required.
  Board meeting date(s): Aug.
Officers and Directors: Kathleen C. O'Grady, Pres.
and Director; Anne E. Lupica, Secy.-Treas. and
Director.
Trustee: Jacqueline P. Beckley.
Number of staff: None.
EIN: 061383651

6552
Ohel Harav Yehoshua Boruch Foundation, Inc.
1315 Elm Ave.
Brooklyn, NY   11230-5915

Established in 1994 in New York.
Donors: Ben Landa; Josh Farkovits; Esther
Farkovits; Meir Fischil; Teddy Pollack.
Foundation type: Independent foundation.
Financial data (yr. ended 12/31/13): Assets,
$17,042,260 (M); gifts received, $950,000;
expenditures, $262,639; qualifying distributions,
$255,000; giving activities include $255,000 for 7
grants (high: $100,000; low: $2,500).
Purpose and activities: Giving primarily to Jewish
temples and schools.
Fields of interest: Education; Judaism.
Limitations: Applications not accepted. Giving
primarily in NY. No grants to individuals.
Application information: Contributes only to
pre-selected organizations.
Officers: Ben Landa, Pres.; Esther Farkovitz, V.P.
and Treas.; Dena Hersh, Secy.
EIN: 113201774

6553
Ohel Rachel Ve Leah Foundation, Inc.
28 W. 36th St., Ste. 305
New York City, NY   10018-8013

Established in 2009 in New York.
Donors: E.L.I.S., LLC; Isaac Hadriye; Common
Sense Fund.
Foundation type: Independent foundation.
Financial data (yr. ended 12/31/13): Assets,
$22,049 (M); gifts received, $386,318;
expenditures, $371,036; qualifying distributions,
$371,036; giving activities include $369,734 for
164 grants (high: $50,000; low: $36).
Fields of interest: Arts and culture; Judaism; Human
services.
Limitations: Applications not accepted. No grants to
individuals.
Application information: Contributes only to
pre-selected organizations.
Trustees: Elliot Romano; Isaac Hadriye; Lillian
Romano; Shelly Hadriye.
EIN: 271394375

6554
Old York Foundation
1 Bryant Park
New York City, NY   10036-2711

Established in 1987 in Unspecified.
Donor: Seymour Durst.
Foundation type: Operating foundation.

Financial data (yr. ended 12/31/13): Assets, $1,707,838 (M); expenditures, $333,350; qualifying distributions, $333,350; giving activities include $300,000 for 1 grant.
Fields of interest: Higher education.
Limitations: Applications not accepted. Giving primarily in NY. No grants to individuals.
Application information: Contributes only to pre-selected organizations.
Officers: Wendy Durst Kreeger, Pres. and Director; Alexander Durst, V.P.; Anita Durst, V.P.; Helena Durst, V.P.; Evan Kreeger, V.P.; Keith Kreeger, V.P.; Laura Kreeger Neil, V.P.; Douglas Kreeger, Secy.; Douglas Durst, Treas.
EIN: 133387401

6555
Vivian and Paul Olum Charitable Foundation

c/o Levene, Gouldin & Thompson, LLP
450 Plaza Dr.
Vestal, NY 13850-3657

Established in 1984 in New York.
Donor: Paul Olum†.
Foundation type: Independent foundation.
Financial data (yr. ended 12/31/13): Assets, $5,392,844 (M); gifts received, $5,052; expenditures, $174,619; qualifying distributions, $153,041; giving activities include $143,275 for 52 grants (high: $15,000; low: $50).
Fields of interest: Education; Diseases and conditions; Sports and recreation; Human rights; Human services; International peace and security.
Limitations: Applications not accepted. Giving primarily in CA, MA and NY. No grants to individuals.
Application information: Contributes only to pre-selected organizations.
Trustees: Joyce Olum-Galaski; Kenneth Olum; Michael H. Zuckerman.
EIN: 222559174

6556
One Million Years Foundation, Inc.

134 Greene St., Ste. 3F
New York City, NY 10012-3296

Donors: On Kawahara; Hiroko Kawahara.
Foundation type: Independent foundation.
Financial data (yr. ended 12/31/13): Assets, $3,901,015 (M); gifts received, $800,000; expenditures, $362,376; qualifying distributions, $353,178; giving activities include $300,000 for 1 grant.
Fields of interest: Museums.
Limitations: Applications not accepted. Giving primarily in Beacon, NY. No grants to individuals.
Application information: Contributes only to pre-selected organizations.
Directors: Akito Kawahara; Hiroko Kawahara; On Kawahara; Sahe Kawahara; Kasper Konig.
EIN: 134177993

6557
Cyril F. & Marie E. O'Neil Foundation

c/o Sacks Press Lacher
600 3rd Ave., 18th Fl.
New York City, NY 10016-1901

Established in 1957 in Ohio.

Foundation type: Independent foundation.
Financial data (yr. ended 12/31/14): Assets, $7,132,329; expenditures, $355,623; qualifying distributions, $284,608.
Purpose and activities: Giving primarily for education, health care, and to Roman Catholic agencies and churches.
Fields of interest: Secondary education; Higher education; Health; Catholicism.
Limitations: Applications not accepted. No grants to individuals.
Application information: Contributes only to pre-selected organizations.
Officer: Ralph M. O'Neil, Pres.
Directors: Anne O'Neil; Karen O'Neil; Maria O'Neil; Mark O'Neil; Monica O'Neil; Peter O'Neil; Stephen O'Neil.
EIN: 346523819

6558
The Ong Family Foundation

c/o Law Office of Deborah Chan, P.C.
401 Broadway, Ste. 1100
New York City, NY 10013-3024 (212) 226-8698
Contact for questions regarding the foundation or the application process: Nelson Louis, mobile tel.: (917) 596-3378, e-mail: nlouis@ongfamilyfoundation.org;
Main URL: http://www.ongfamilyfoundation.org/home.html
Grants List: http://www.ongfamilyfoundation.org/past.html

Established in 1997 in New York.
Donors: Danny O. Yee; Bank of China.
Foundation type: Independent foundation.
Financial data (yr. ended 01/31/14): Assets, $3,676,406 (M); expenditures, $452,160; qualifying distributions, $444,201; giving activities include $431,026 for 25 grants (high: $100,000; low: $250).
Purpose and activities: The foundation seeks to fund programs that are comprehensive, community-based and preventive in nature.
Fields of interest: Arts and culture; Education; Human services; People of Asian descent.
Type of support: General support; Matching grants; Capacity-building and technical assistance; Capital campaigns; Capital and infrastructure; Equipment; Convening; Scholarships; Technical assistance.
Limitations: Applications accepted. Giving primarily in the Greater NY Metropolitan Area. No support for non-501c(3) organizations, or for foundations or political activities. No grants to individuals or for debt reduction.
Application information: See foundation guidelines for further information.
   Initial approach: Letter of Inquiry (1-page preferred, but 2 pages maximum)
   Copies of proposal: 1
   Deadline(s): Deadlines are set in the 1st quarter of the year
Officer: Nelson Louis, Exec. Dir.
Trustees: Danny O. Yee; Donald Ong Yee; Larry Ong Yee; Stephanie L. Yee.
EIN: 133986239

6559
Ontario Children's Foundation

(formerly Ontario Children's Home)
P.O. Box 82
Canandaigua, NY 14424-0082
Application address for education assistance: c/o Jane Wheeler, 4160 W. Lake Rd., Canadaigua, NY 14424, e-mail: jwheele4@rochester.rr.com

Established in 1863 in New York.
Foundation type: Independent foundation.
Financial data (yr. ended 09/30/14): Assets, $4,183,313 (M); gifts received, $37,909; expenditures, $205,914; qualifying distributions, $181,659; giving activities include $180,294 for grants.
Purpose and activities: Giving primarily for child welfare including programs for eyeglasses, general dental work and medications, and recreation; support also for student loans. Recipients must be under 21 years of age, reside in Ontario County, New York, and need financial help.
Fields of interest: Education; Dental care; Vision care; Sports and recreation; Child welfare.
Type of support: Emergency funds; Loans to individuals; Student aid.
Limitations: Giving limited to children in Ontario County, NY.
Application information: Contact high school guidance counselors or school nurses in Ontario County, NY, for application. Application form required.
   Initial approach: Letter
   Copies of proposal: 1
   Deadline(s): None
   Board meeting date(s): 2nd Tues. in Oct.
Officers: Richard Hawks, Pres.; Bruce Kennedy, V.P.; Paul Hudson, Secy.; Richard Appel, Treas.
Board of Managers: Jayne Baker; Karen Blazey; Mary Brady; Cynthia Fackler; Nancy Finkle; Linda Marsh; Caroline C. Shipley.
Trustees: Geoffrey Astles; Randall Farnsworth; Deborah Wilbur.
EIN: 166028318

6560
Osceola Foundation, Inc.

3000 Marcus Ave., No. 2E4
New Hyde Park, NY 11042-1005
Contact: Sosin Kriegel

Established in 1963 in New York.
Foundation type: Independent foundation.
Financial data (yr. ended 12/31/13): Assets, $4,475,682 (M); expenditures, $276,903; qualifying distributions, $190,600; giving activities include $190,600 for 28 grants (high: $28,600; low: $100).
Purpose and activities: Giving primarily for education, the arts, and social services.
Fields of interest: Music; Historic preservation; Education; Higher education; Natural resources; Human services.
Type of support: General support; Capital campaigns; Program development.
Limitations: Applications not accepted. Giving primarily in FL, MA, NY, OH, and SC. No grants to individuals.
Application information: Contributes only to pre-selected organizations.
Officers: Ann B. Oliver, Pres.; Deborah B. Beale, Secy.; Barbara B. Spitler, Treas.

Director: Walter Beinecke III.
EIN: 136094234

6561
The Ostgrodd Foundation, Inc.
c/o McGladrey, LLP
1185 Avenue of the Americas
New York City, NY 10036
Contact: Barbara Grodd, Pres. and Treas.

Established in 1995 in New York.
Donor: Barbara Grodd.
Foundation type: Independent foundation.
Financial data (yr. ended 12/31/13): Assets, $1,916,949 (M); gifts received, $2,479; expenditures, $241,524; qualifying distributions, $233,539; giving activities include $233,154 for 30 grants (high: $100,000; low: $500).
Purpose and activities: Giving for a range of interests, but there is a focus on small, established community-based organizations that work in challenging neighborhoods, often (but not exclusively) with ex-offender populations.
Fields of interest: Arts and culture; Museums; Higher education; Environment; Family planning; Diseases and conditions; Cancers; Services for offenders; Adolescents; Females; Males; Low-income and poor people; Offenders; Ex-offenders.
Type of support: General support; Continuing support; Program development; Research; Research and evaluation.
Limitations: Applications not accepted. Giving primarily in New York, NY. No support for religious or political organizations. No grants to individuals.
Application information: Contributes only to pre-selected organizations.
Officers and Directors: Barbara Grodd, Pres. and Treas. and Director; Patricia Grodd Stone, Secy. and Director; James Grodd.
Number of staff: None.
EIN: 133826884

6562
Harry & Helen Ostreicher Family Foundation
c/o Wasser Brettler, CPA
132 Nassau St., Ste. 300
New York City, NY 10038-2435

Established in 1996 in Delaware.
Donors: Harry Ostreicher; Helen Ostreicher.
Foundation type: Independent foundation.
Financial data (yr. ended 07/31/13): Assets, $1,991,525 (M); expenditures, $199,413; qualifying distributions, $196,491; giving activities include $196,361 for 17 grants (high: $50,000; low: $1,000).
Purpose and activities: Giving primarily for Jewish education and organizations.
Fields of interest: Education; Judaism.
Type of support: General support.
Limitations: Applications not accepted. Giving primarily in NY. No grants to individuals.
Application information: Contributes only to pre-selected organizations.
Officer: Helen Ostreicher, V.P.
EIN: 113241598

6563
Marvin & Susan Ostreicher Family Foundation
46 Stauderman Ave.
Lynbrook, NY 11563

Established in 1994 in New York.
Donors: Marvin Ostreicher; Susan Ostreicher; Barry Bokow.
Foundation type: Independent foundation.
Financial data (yr. ended 11/30/13): Assets, $512,145 (M); gifts received, $30,000; expenditures, $348,567; qualifying distributions, $348,186; giving activities include $345,722 for 11 + grants (high: $200,000).
Purpose and activities: Giving primarily to Jewish agencies, temples, and schools.
Fields of interest: Elementary and secondary education; Nonprofits; Judaism.
Type of support: Regranting.
Limitations: Applications not accepted.
Application information: Contributes only to pre-selected organizations.
Officers: Marvin Ostreicher, Pres.; Susan Ostreicher, Secy.
EIN: 113241597

6564
Chaim and Dvora Ostreicher Foundation
67-42 180th St.
Fresh Meadows, NY 11365-3516

Established in 2001 in New York.
Donor: Robert Ostreicher.
Foundation type: Independent foundation.
Financial data (yr. ended 12/31/13): Assets, $128,882 (M); gifts received, $334,050; expenditures, $340,960; qualifying distributions, $340,660; giving activities include $337,000 for 22 grants (high: $50,000; low: $1,000).
Fields of interest: Judaism.
Limitations: Applications not accepted. No grants to individuals.
Application information: Unsolicited requests for funds not accepted.
Officers and Directors: Robert Ostreicher, Pres. and Treas. and Director; Dvora Ostreicher, Secy. and Director; David Ostreicher; Michael Ostreicher.
EIN: 113637425

6565
The O'Sullivan Children Foundation, Inc.
c/o Carole O'Sullivan
4 Bridle Path Dr.
Old Westbury, NY 11568-1608

Established in 1981 in New York.
Donors: Kevin P. O'Sullivan†; Carole O'Sullivan; Charles Dolan.
Foundation type: Independent foundation.
Financial data (yr. ended 09/30/14): Assets, $1,508,960 (M); gifts received, $500; expenditures, $486,642; qualifying distributions, $470,976; giving activities include $394,357 for 16 grants (high: $332,575; low: $200).
Purpose and activities: Giving primarily for education, health associations and hospitals, and children, youth, and social services.
Fields of interest: Education; Hospital care; Diseases and conditions; Human services; Child welfare.
Type of support: Capital campaigns; Endowments.
Limitations: Applications not accepted. Giving primarily in the greater metropolitan New York, NY, area, with some emphasis on Long Island.
Application information: Contributes only to pre-selected organizations.
Officers: Carole O'Sullivan, Pres.; Joseph W. Muldoon, V.P. and Secy.; Erin A. O'Sullivan McKenna, Secy.
Director: James McKenna.
Number of staff: 1 full-time professional.
EIN: 133126389

6566
Packin Family Foundation, Inc.
110 Varick Ave.
Brooklyn, NY 11237-1217
Application address: c/o Joseph Packin, 48 Suffolk Blvd., Atlantic Beach, NY 11509, tel.: (718) 366-1484

Established in 2000 in New York.
Donors: David Packin; Joseph H. Packin; Eugene Packin; D & M Lumber Products Co., Inc.; Steven Packin.
Foundation type: Independent foundation.
Financial data (yr. ended 12/31/13): Assets, $409,819 (M); gifts received, $19,840; expenditures, $150,746; qualifying distributions, $150,746; giving activities include $150,500 for 1 grant.
Fields of interest: Disasters and emergency management.
Type of support: General support.
Limitations: Applications accepted. Giving primarily in Brooklyn, NY. No grants to individuals.
Application information: Application form required.
Initial approach: Proposal
Deadline(s): None
Officer: Joseph Packin, Pres.
EIN: 113550180

6567
The Paiken Foundation
11 Paiken Dr.
Spring Valley, NY 10977-3842 (917) 771-3140
Contact: Shmyer Breuer, Dir.

Donor: Shmyer Breuer.
Foundation type: Independent foundation.
Financial data (yr. ended 12/31/13): Assets, $311,117 (M); gifts received, $150,200; expenditures, $220,541; qualifying distributions, $219,006; giving activities include $219,006 for 118 grants (high: $114,000; low: $20).
Fields of interest: Judaism.
Application information:
Initial approach: Telephone of letter
Deadline(s): None
Directors: Shmyer Breuer; Chana Breuer; Moses Fischman.
EIN: 611583593

6568
Pajwell Foundation
c/o Wolf Maryles & Assocs., LLC
220 E. 42nd St., Ste. 2201
New York City, NY 10017-5822

Established in 1999 in Colorado.

Donor: Pamela Joseph.
Foundation type: Independent foundation.
Financial data (yr. ended 12/31/13): Assets, $1,208,730 (M); expenditures, $192,410; qualifying distributions, $179,999; giving activities include $179,999 for 57 grants (high: $58,000; low: $100).
Fields of interest: Arts and culture; Art museums; University education; Environment; Diseases and conditions; Human services; Family services; Child welfare.
Type of support: Research.
Limitations: Applications not accepted. Giving primarily in CO. No grants to individuals.
Application information: Contributes only to pre-selected organizations.
Officer: Pamela Joseph, Pres.
EIN: 522192469

6569
The Palisades Educational Foundation, Inc.

(formerly The Pren-Hall Foundation, Inc.)
665 5th Ave., 11th Fl.
New York City, NY   10022-5305   (212) 688-5151
Contact: Gerald J. Dunworth, Treas. and Dir.; Gibney Anthony

Established in 1949 in Delaware.
Donor: Prentice-Hall, Inc.
Foundation type: Independent foundation.
Financial data (yr. ended 12/31/13): Assets, $3,721,605 (M); expenditures, $184,985; qualifying distributions, $144,230; giving activities include $117,500 for 19 grants (high: $15,000; low: $1,000).
Purpose and activities: Giving primarily to health associations and hospitals, as well as for education, children, youth and social services.
Fields of interest: Arts and culture; Higher education; Law education; Philanthropy; Hospital care; Diseases and conditions; Cancers; Human services; Child welfare.
Type of support: General support; Continuing support; Program development; Scholarships; Research.
Limitations: Applications accepted. Giving primarily in CT, NJ, and NY. No grants to individuals, or for fellowships or pledges; no loans.
Application information: Application form required.
  Initial approach: Letter
  Deadline(s): Sept. 30
  Board meeting date(s): Nov. or Dec.
Officers and Directors: Donald A. Schaefer, Pres. and Director; Frederick W. Anthony, Secy.; Gerald J. Dunworth, Treas. and Director.
EIN: 516015053

6570
The Vincent and Harriet Palisano Foundation

P.O. Box 1133
Buffalo, NY   14205-1133   (716) 882-3488

Established in 1962 in New York.
Donors: Vincent H. Palisano†; Harriet A. Palisano†.
Foundation type: Independent foundation.
Financial data (yr. ended 05/31/13): Assets, $3,285,714 (M); expenditures, $327,305; qualifying distributions, $303,724; giving activities

include $287,161 for 34 grants (high: $100,000; low: $1,000).
Purpose and activities: Emphasis on higher and secondary education, including scholarship funds for selected colleges and high schools in western NY; also giving for cancer research.
Fields of interest: Secondary education; Higher education.
Type of support: General support; Equipment; Scholarships; Research.
Limitations: Applications accepted. Giving primarily in the Buffalo, NY, area. No grants to individuals.
Application information:
  Initial approach: Proposal
  Deadline(s): None
Trustees: James M. Beardsley; Sharon S. Heseltine; Beverly A. Leek.
EIN: 166052186

6571
The Palm Foundation

Bowling Green Sta.
P.O. Box 73
New York City, NY   10274-0073

Established in 1993 in New York.
Donor: Gregory K. Palm.
Foundation type: Independent foundation.
Financial data (yr. ended 04/30/14): Assets, $11,660,506 (M); expenditures, $390,263; qualifying distributions, $367,991; giving activities include $367,991 for 9 grants (high: $328,741; low: $1,000).
Purpose and activities: Giving primarily for the arts and to a charitable gift fund.
Fields of interest: Arts and culture; Education; Philanthropy.
Limitations: Applications not accepted. Giving primarily in New York, NY and Cincinnati, OH. No grants to individuals; no loans or scholarships.
Application information: Contributes only to pre-selected organizations.
Trustees: Gregory K. Palm; Jennifer Palm; Katherine Palm; Susan Rose Palm.
EIN: 133748059

6572
The Francis Asbury Palmer Foundation

c/o The Solaris Group, LLC
598 Madison Ave.
New York City, NY   10022-1610

Established in 1897 in New York.
Donor: Francis Asbury Palmer†.
Foundation type: Independent foundation.
Financial data (yr. ended 04/30/14): Assets, $5,756,768 (M); expenditures, $404,008; qualifying distributions, $377,342; giving activities include $340,000 for 10 grants (high: $65,000; low: $5,000).
Purpose and activities: Support for Christian theological seminaries and other higher education organizations.
Fields of interest: Higher education; Graduate and professional education; Christianity; Theology.
Limitations: Applications not accepted. Giving primarily in CT, IL, MD, NY, PA and TN. No grants to individuals.
Application information: Contributes only to pre-selected organizations. Unsolicited requests for funds not accepted.

Officer: Diana L. Reed, Pres.
Directors: Allison C. Hansen; E. Gayle McGuigan, Jr.; Phillip P. McGuigan; Susan K. Reed.
EIN: 136400635

6573
Pat Palmer Foundation, Inc.

P.O. Box 751149
Forest Hills, NY   11375-8749
Contact: Mark Finkelstein, Pres.

Donor: Pat Palmer Bernard†.
Foundation type: Independent foundation.
Financial data (yr. ended 06/30/14): Assets, $3,283,270 (M); expenditures, $281,485; qualifying distributions, $171,000; giving activities include $171,000 for 6 grants (high: $45,000; low: $10,000).
Fields of interest: Domesticated animals.
Limitations: Applications accepted. Giving primarily in AZ, MA and TX.
Application information: Application form required.
  Initial approach: Letter
  Deadline(s): None
Officers: Mark Finkelstein, Pres.; David Walsh, Treas.
Director: Brian Gibson.
EIN: 208559990

6574
The Paneth Family Charitable Trust

3900 Shore Pkwy.
Brooklyn, NY   11235-1130

Established in 1992 in New York.
Donors: Morton Paneth; Samuel Paneth; Leah Werner; Thomas Paneth; Meir Grunwald.
Foundation type: Independent foundation.
Financial data (yr. ended 12/31/12): Assets, $7,182,006 (M); gifts received, $10,000; expenditures, $583,331; qualifying distributions, $388,985; giving activities include $388,985 for grants.
Purpose and activities: Giving primarily to Jewish agencies, temples, and schools.
Fields of interest: Elementary and secondary education; Judaism.
Limitations: Applications not accepted. Giving primarily in NY. No grants to individuals.
Application information: Contributes only to pre-selected organizations.
Trustees: Morton Paneth; Samuel Paneth; Thomas Paneth; Leah Werner.
EIN: 116415770

6575
Park Charitable Trust

(formerly Park Foundation)
5223 15th Ave.
Brooklyn, NY   11219-3908   (718) 851-5333
Contact: Efraim Landau, Dir.

Donors: Ephraim Landau; A. Landau Trust; Triangle Trust; A & E Trust; Ephraim Family TSG II Trust.
Foundation type: Operating foundation.
Financial data (yr. ended 12/31/13): Assets, $7,437,582 (M); gifts received, $515,000; expenditures, $432,603; qualifying distributions, $412,710; giving activities include $408,160 for 16 grants (high: $100,000; low: $360).

Purpose and activities: Giving primarily for Jewish education.
Fields of interest: Education; Judaism.
Type of support: General support.
Limitations: Applications accepted. Giving primarily in NY. No grants to individuals.
Application information: Application form required.
  Initial approach: Letter
  Deadline(s): None
Directors: Efraim Landau; Goldy Landau.
EIN: 116450788

6576
Jim and Shirley Parke Foundation
c/o The Ayco Co., LP - NTG
P.O. Box 15014
Albany, NY 12212-5014

Established in 2001 in Connecticut.
Donors: Jim A. Parke; Shirley Parke.
Foundation type: Independent foundation.
Financial data (yr. ended 12/31/14): Assets, $3,752,752 (M); gifts received, $1,527,120; expenditures, $214,935; qualifying distributions, $210,000; giving activities include $210,000 for 3 grants (high: $200,000; low: $5,000).
Fields of interest: Foundations; Human services; Youth development.
Limitations: Applications not accepted. Giving primarily in CT. No grants to individuals.
Application information: Unsolicited requests for funds not accepted.
Directors: Jim A. Parke; Shirley Parke.
EIN: 061603828

6577
The Gary W. Parr Family Foundation, Inc.
174 E. Lake Rd.
Tuxedo Park, NY 10987-4243
Contact: Gary W. Parr, Chair.

Established in 1996 in North Carolina.
Donors: Gary W. Parr; Wilton Parr.
Foundation type: Independent foundation.
Financial data (yr. ended 12/31/13): Assets, $3,865,411 (M); gifts received, $1,256,448; expenditures, $172,325; qualifying distributions, $172,325; giving activities include $172,325 for 4 grants (high: $125,000; low: $175).
Fields of interest: Arts and culture; Education; Human services.
Limitations: Applications accepted. Giving primarily in NC. No grants to individuals.
Application information: Application form required.
  Initial approach: Letter
  Deadline(s): None
Officer: Gary W. Parr, Chair.
EIN: 562003520

6578
Moses L. Parshelsky Foundation
Old Chelsea Sta.
P.O. Box 1203
New York City, NY 10011-1203 (646) 638-4700

Established in 1949 in New York.
Donor: Moses L. Parshelsky†.
Foundation type: Independent foundation.

Financial data (yr. ended 12/31/14): Assets, $8,695,441; expenditures, $540,560; qualifying distributions, $455,573.
Purpose and activities: Emphasis on the aged, the handicapped, and hospitals; support also for higher and secondary education, temple support and religious activities, youth agencies, mental health, and Jewish welfare funds.
Fields of interest: Arts and culture; Dance; Secondary education; Higher education; Nonprofits; Hospital care; Mental health care; Cancers; Judaism; Human services; Child welfare; Senior services; Seniors; People with disabilities.
Type of support: Regranting.
Limitations: Applications accepted. Giving limited to the five boroughs of New York City, NY. No grants to individuals, or for building or endowment funds, or operating budgets.
Application information: Application form required.
  Initial approach: Proposal
  Copies of proposal: 1
  Deadline(s): Nov. 1
Trustees: Tony B. Berk; John Krinsky; Robert D. Krinsky.
Number of staff: 1 part-time professional.
EIN: 111848260

6579
Patrina Foundation
901 Pelhamdale Ave.
Pelham, NY 10803-2928 (212) 233-1559
Contact: Kara D'Angelo, Exec. Dir.
E-mail: karadangelo@patrinafoundation.org;
Additional tel.: (914) 886-5390; Main URL: http://www.patrinafoundation.org/index.php
Grant Database: http://www.patrinafoundation.org/grants.php

Established in 1990 in New York.
Donor: Lorinda P. de Roulet.
Foundation type: Independent foundation.
Financial data (yr. ended 12/31/13): Assets, $8,924,705 (M); expenditures, $621,194; qualifying distributions, $518,786; giving activities include $412,675 for 59 grants (high: $35,000; low: $75).
Purpose and activities: Giving primarily to improve the lives of girls and women by supporting social and educational nonprofit programming designed to meet the unique needs of girls and women in the greater New York, NY metropolitan area.
Fields of interest: Elementary and secondary education; Women's services; Females; Female children and youth; Female infants and toddlers; Female young adults.
Type of support: Continuing support; Program development; Seed money; Curriculum development; Internships; Scholarships.
Limitations: Applications accepted. Giving primarily in the greater New York, NY, metropolitan area. No grants to individuals, or for advocacy.
Publications: Application guidelines.
Application information: Application form required.
  Initial approach: E-mail or telephone, followed by proposal and cover letter
  Copies of proposal: 6
  Deadline(s): See foundation web site for current deadlines
  Board meeting date(s): Mar., June, and Nov.
  Final notification: Within 4 months
Officers and Trustees: Lorinda P. de Roulet, Pres. and Trustee; Whitney Bullock, Secy. and Trustee; Daniel C. de Roulet, Treas. and Trustee; Kara

D'Angelo, Exec. Dir.; Alexandra Bullock; Daniel C. de Roulet, Jr.; Mary Jo McLoughlin; Elizabeth Rainoff.
Number of staff: 1 part-time professional.
EIN: 113035018

6580
Andrew M. Paul Family Foundation
283 Pondfield Rd.
Bronxville, NY 10708-4936

Established in 1997 in New York.
Donor: Andrew M. Paul.
Foundation type: Independent foundation.
Financial data (yr. ended 08/31/14): Assets, $384,408; gifts received, $0; expenditures, $280,286; qualifying distributions, $277,713.
Fields of interest: Education; Higher education; Human services.
Limitations: Applications not accepted. Giving in the U.S., with emphasis on NY.
Application information: Contributes only to pre-selected organizations.
Officer: Andrew M. Paul, Pres.
Trustee: Margaret B. Paul.
EIN: 137143442

6581
Alice A. Paxton Charitable Trust
1100 Wehrle Dr., 2nd Fl.
Buffalo, NY 14221

Established in 2001 in Maryland.
Donor: Alice A. Paxton Trust.
Foundation type: Independent foundation.
Financial data (yr. ended 11/30/14): Assets, $3,705,921 (M); expenditures, $222,931; qualifying distributions, $170,000; giving activities include $170,000 for 9 grants (high: $50,000; low: $10,000).
Purpose and activities: Giving for the prevention of cruelty to animals and wildlife preservation.
Fields of interest: Wildlife biodiversity.
Type of support: General support; Advocacy.
Limitations: Applications not accepted. Giving primarily in MD and PA. No grants to individuals.
Application information: Contributes only to pre-selected organizations.
Trustee: M&T Bank.
EIN: 016180869

6582
Peale Foundation, Inc.
c/o Elizabeth Allen
665 Old Quaker Hill Rd.
Pawling, NY 12564-3452

Donors: JME II Charitable Lead Trust; JME Charitable Lead Trust; Ruth S. Peale Trust; Schiff, Hardin & Waite; Pawling Charitable Lead Annuity Trust.
Foundation type: Independent foundation.
Financial data (yr. ended 09/30/13): Assets, $6,867,891 (M); expenditures, $567,070; qualifying distributions, $422,293; giving activities include $368,680 for 23 grants (high: $85,000; low: $300).
Purpose and activities: Giving primarily for religion, community and educational programs.
Fields of interest: Education; Community and economic development; Protestantism.

Limitations: Applications not accepted. Giving primarily in NY.
Application information: Unsolicited requests for funds not accepted.
Officers and Directors: Margaret P. Everett, Pres. and Director; John S. Peale, V.P. and Director; Elizabeth Peale Allen, Secy.-Treas. and Director.
EIN: 141746478

6583
Peckham Family Foundation
c/o John R. Peckham
29 Old Aspetong Rd.
Katonah, NY   10536

Established in 1999 in New York.
Donors: Amy K. Peckham; John R. Peckham; Peckham Industries, Inc.
Foundation type: Independent foundation.
Financial data (yr. ended 12/31/13): Assets, $2,489,745 (M); gifts received, $240,000; expenditures, $360,346; qualifying distributions, $350,587; giving activities include $350,587 for 92 grants (high: $30,000; low: $100).
Fields of interest: Arts and culture; Arts councils; Performing arts; Museums; Elementary and secondary education; Higher education; Natural resources; Health; Hospital care; Diseases and conditions; Human services; Child welfare; Youth organizing.
Limitations: Applications not accepted. Giving primarily in NY. No grants to individuals.
Application information: Unsolicited requests for funds not accepted.
Trustees: Amy Peckham; John R. Peckham.
EIN: 141814765

6584
The Peek Family Foundation, Inc.
c/o WTAS LLC
1177 Ave. of the Americas, 18th Fl.
New York City, NY   10036

Established in 1999 in New York.
Donors: Elizabeth Peek; Jeffrey Peek.
Foundation type: Independent foundation.
Financial data (yr. ended 12/31/13): Assets, $8,934,125 (M); expenditures, $362,661; qualifying distributions, $320,635; giving activities include $305,200 for 85 grants (high: $50,000; low: $150).
Fields of interest: Arts and culture; Ballet; Historic preservation; Higher education; Nonprofits; Christianity; Human services; Child welfare.
Type of support: Regranting.
Limitations: Applications not accepted. Giving primarily in NY. No grants to individuals.
Application information: Unsolicited requests for funds not accepted.
Officers: Jeffrey Peek, Pres.; Elizabeth Peek, V.P.
Director: Andrew Peek.
EIN: 134087127

6585
The Laura Pels International Foundation
for Theater
429 E. 52nd St., No. 5F
New York City, NY   10022
Contact: Laura Pels, Pres. and Exec. Dir.
E-mail: ccinerar@laurapels.com

Established in 2002 in New York.
Donor: Laura J. Pels.
Foundation type: Independent foundation.
Financial data (yr. ended 12/31/13): Assets, $5,998,964 (M); expenditures, $603,382; qualifying distributions, $545,891; giving activities include $247,600 for 12 grants (high: $60,000; low: $1,100).
Purpose and activities: The foundation is committed to the support of outstanding theatrical productions (excluding musicals, dance and performance art), not bricks and mortar nor the support of endowment or extra curriculum activities, apart from support of educational and cross-cultural opportunities for students, awards for playwrights, actors or directors, and playwrights interested in learning English and management of theaters in Anglo-Saxon countries, as well as American actors or any other nationality wishing to learn French.
Fields of interest: Theater.
International interests: England.
Limitations: Applications not accepted. Giving primarily in NY, DC and London. No support for religious or political organizations. No grants to individuals.
Application information: Contributes only to pre-selected organizations.
Officers: Laura J. Pels, Pres. and Exec. Dir.; Janet Dunham, V.P.; Christine Cinerar, Secy.-Treas.
Directors: Jean Audouze; Eileen Best; Paul Epstein; Todd Haimes; Christian Keutgen; Elliott Mottley; Bill Zabel.
EIN: 161632202

6586
Performing Arts Foundation
c/o Spitz & Greenstein C.P.A.'s
494 8th Ave., Ste. 806
New York City, NY   10001-2542

Donor: Herman Rottenberg.
Foundation type: Independent foundation.
Financial data (yr. ended 08/31/13): Assets, $4,429,723 (M); expenditures, $332,152; qualifying distributions, $270,766; giving activities include $250,450 for 13 grants (high: $150,400; low: $750).
Fields of interest: Performing arts; Music; Art museums; Education; Foundations; Judaism.
Type of support: General support.
Limitations: Applications not accepted. Giving primarily in New York, NY and PA. No grants to individuals.
Application information: Contributes only to pre-selected organizations.
Officers: Daniel Rottenberg, Pres.; Sharon Trulock, Secy.; Melvin Spitz, CPA, Treas.
EIN: 136149781

6587
The Perlman Family Foundation Inc.
c/o Compass
655 Madison Ave., 23rd. Fl.
New York City, NY   10065

Established in 2003 in Georgia.
Donors: Richard Perlman; Ellen Hanson.
Foundation type: Independent foundation.
Financial data (yr. ended 03/31/13): Assets, $229,345 (M); gifts received, $301,500; expenditures, $269,811; qualifying distributions,

$269,669; giving activities include $269,669 for 37 grants (high: $168,500; low: $100).
Fields of interest: Education; Environment; Health.
Limitations: Applications not accepted. No grants to individuals.
Application information: Contributes only to pre-selected organizations.
Directors: Ellen Hanson; Andrew Perlman; Richard Perlman.
EIN: 200255205

6588
The William S. Perper Foundation
One Rockefeller Plz., No. 321
New York City, NY   10020-2134
Contact: J. Purdy

Donor: William Perper†.
Foundation type: Independent foundation.
Financial data (yr. ended 12/31/13): Assets, $3,334,835 (M); expenditures, $309,433; qualifying distributions, $282,145; giving activities include $280,000 for 8 grants (high: $100,000; low: $10,000).
Fields of interest: Education; Health; Religion.
Type of support: General support.
Limitations: Applications not accepted. Giving primarily in New York, NY; with some giving in MD.
Application information: Unsolicited requests for funds not accepted.
Trustees: James Coleman; James A. Purdy; Kevin C. Sunkel.
EIN: 456337299

6589
Persian Heritage Foundation
450 Riverside Dr., Ste. 24
New York City, NY   10027-6820   (212) 851-5723
Contact: Ehsan Yarshater

Established in 1985 in Delaware.
Donor: Ehsan Yarshater.
Foundation type: Independent foundation.
Financial data (yr. ended 06/30/13): Assets, $12,306,408 (M); gifts received, $20,000; expenditures, $286,504; qualifying distributions, $201,565; giving activities include $175,550 for 16 grants (high: $100,000; low: $200).
Purpose and activities: Grants for publications about Iran.
Fields of interest: Arts and culture; History; Linguistics; Literature and writing; Anthropology; Archaeology; Religion; Human services.
Type of support: Publications.
Application information:
   Initial approach: Proposal
   Deadline(s): None
Officers: Ehsan Yarshater, Pres.; Farhad Kazemi, V.P. and Secy.; Vahid Noshirvani, V.P. and Treas.
EIN: 133201819

6590
The Leslie Peter Foundation
115 Broadway, 15th Fl.
New York City, NY   10006-1604

Established in 2000 in Delaware.
Donor: Edward L. Peter.
Foundation type: Independent foundation.

Financial data (yr. ended 12/31/13): Assets, $7,513,621 (M); expenditures, $368,539; qualifying distributions, $331,550; giving activities include $331,550 for 29 grants (high: $30,000; low: $5,000).
Fields of interest: Education; Health; Cancers; Human services; Child welfare.
Limitations: Applications not accepted. Giving primarily in FL, MA and NJ. No grants to individuals.
Application information: Contributes only to pre-selected organizations.
Directors: E. Boyd Clarke; Jacqueline Gero; Ruth Peter; David Warmflash.
EIN: 134147292

6591
David B. Peterson Foundation
712 5th Ave., 47th Fl.
New York City, NY 10019-4108
Givesmart: http://www.givesmart.org/Stories/Donors/Pete-Peterson
Peter G. Peterson's Giving Pledge Profile: http://glasspockets.org/philanthropy-in-focus/eye-on-the-giving-pledge/profiles/peterson

Donor: Peter G. Peterson.
Foundation type: Independent foundation.
Financial data (yr. ended 11/30/13): Assets, $4,555,289 (M); expenditures, $256,530; qualifying distributions, $227,777; giving activities include $227,502 for 16 grants (high: $141,000; low: $2).
Fields of interest: Education; Land resources; Animal welfare.
Limitations: Applications not accepted. No grants to individuals.
Application information: Unsolicited requests for funds not accepted.
Officers: Peter G. Peterson, Chair.; David B. Peterson, Pres.; Michael A. Peterson, Secy.-Treas.
EIN: 261606939

6592
Holly Peterson Foundation
712 5th Ave., 47th Fl.
New York City, NY 10019-4108
Givesmart: http://www.givesmart.org/Stories/Donors/Pete-Peterson
Peter G. Peterson's Giving Pledge Profile: http://glasspockets.org/philanthropy-in-focus/eye-on-the-giving-pledge/profiles/peterson

Donor: Peter G. Peterson.
Foundation type: Independent foundation.
Financial data (yr. ended 11/30/13): Assets, $3,885,024 (M); expenditures, $304,870; qualifying distributions, $303,350; giving activities include $303,075 for 20 grants (high: $100,000; low: $1,000).
Fields of interest: Higher education; Foundations; Human services; Child welfare.
Limitations: Applications not accepted. Giving primarily in NY.
Application information: Unsolicited requests for funds not accepted.
Officers: Peter G. Peterson, Chair.; Holly Peterson, Pres.; Michael A. Peterson, Secy.-Treas.
EIN: 261607014

6593
James S. Peterson Foundation
712 5th Ave., 47th Fl.
New York City, NY 10019-4108
Givesmart: http://www.givesmart.org/Stories/Donors/Pete-Peterson
Peter G. Peterson's Giving Pledge Profile: http://glasspockets.org/philanthropy-in-focus/eye-on-the-giving-pledge/profiles/peterson

Donor: Peter G. Peterson.
Foundation type: Independent foundation.
Financial data (yr. ended 11/30/13): Assets, $4,568,173 (M); expenditures, $231,208; qualifying distributions, $229,775; giving activities include $229,500 for 20 grants (high: $70,000; low: $1,000).
Fields of interest: Education; Elementary and secondary education; Foundations; Judaism.
Limitations: Applications not accepted.
Application information: Unsolicited requests for funds not accepted.
Officers: Peter G. Peterson, Chair.; James S. Peterson, Pres.; Michael A. Peterson, Secy.-Treas.
EIN: 261607047

6594
Michael A. Peterson Foundation
712 5th Ave., 47th Fl.
New York City, NY 10019-4108
Peter G. Peterson's Giving Pledge Profile: http://glasspockets.org/philanthropy-in-focus/eye-on-the-giving-pledge/profiles/peterson

Donor: Peter G. Peterson.
Foundation type: Independent foundation.
Financial data (yr. ended 11/30/13): Assets, $4,123,476 (M); expenditures, $252,202; qualifying distributions, $251,218; giving activities include $229,500 for 18 grants (high: $50,000; low: $500).
Fields of interest: Education; Higher education; Diseases and conditions; International relations.
Limitations: Applications not accepted. Giving primarily in NY.
Application information: Unsolicited requests for funds not accepted.
Officers: Peter G. Peterson, Chair.; Michael A. Peterson, Pres. and Secy.-Treas.
EIN: 261607103

6595
Attilio & Beverly Petrocelli Foundation
9 Park Pl., 4th Fl.
Great Neck, NY 11021-5030

Established in 2004 in New York.
Donors: Attilio Petrocelli; Beverly Petrocelli.
Foundation type: Independent foundation.
Financial data (yr. ended 12/31/12): Assets, $8,200,799 (M); gifts received, $1,000,000; expenditures, $368,630; qualifying distributions, $344,180; giving activities include $331,530 for 40 grants (high: $100,000; low: $250).
Fields of interest: Higher education; Diseases and conditions; Cancers; Catholicism; Judaism.
Type of support: Research; Research and evaluation.
Limitations: Applications not accepted. Giving primarily in NH and NY. No grants to individuals.

Application information: Contributes only to pre-selected organizations.
Directors: Jill Lamoretti; Michael Lamoretti; Attilio Petrocelli; Beverly Petrocelli; Melissa Weinbaum; Michael J. Weinbaum.
EIN: 201690418

6596
Lydia & Rob Petty Family Foundation
c/o B Strauss Association, Ltd.
307 5th Ave., 8th Fl.
New York City, NY 10016-6517

Established in 2007 in Delaware.
Donor: Robert Petty.
Foundation type: Independent foundation.
Financial data (yr. ended 11/30/14): Assets, $489,634; gifts received, $230,000; expenditures, $383,534; qualifying distributions, $374,236.
Fields of interest: Education; Environment; Diseases and conditions.
Limitations: Applications not accepted.
Application information: Contributes only to pre-selected organizations.
Trustees: Lydia Petty; Robert Petty.
EIN: 208411971

6597
The Ralph A. Pfeiffer and Jane C. Pfeiffer Foundation, Inc.
1 Rockefeller Plz., Ste. 2321
New York City, NY 10020-2026

Established in 1997 in Connecticut.
Donor: Jane C. Pfeiffer.
Foundation type: Independent foundation.
Financial data (yr. ended 12/31/13): Assets, $158,121 (M); expenditures, $194,328; qualifying distributions, $165,000; giving activities include $165,000 for 4 grants (high: $50,000; low: $15,000).
Fields of interest: Education; University education; Human services.
Type of support: General support.
Limitations: Applications not accepted. Giving primarily in IN, MD, MI and OH. No grants to individuals.
Application information: Contributes only to pre-selected organizations.
Officers and Directors: Jane C. Pfeiffer, Pres. and Director; Jonathan Smith, Secy.-Treas.; Susan L. Sanders.
EIN: 061480028

6598
Phaedrus Foundation
500 5th Ave., Ste. 2700
New York City, NY 10110-2799 (212) 764-6455
Contact: Peyser Alexander; Thomas Buckner, Pres. and Dir.

Established in 1991 in New York.
Donor: Foundation for the Needs of Others, Inc.
Foundation type: Independent foundation.
Financial data (yr. ended 12/31/13): Assets, $973,119 (M); expenditures, $235,003; qualifying distributions, $229,715; giving activities include $229,715 for 51 grants (high: $57,500; low: $50).

Purpose and activities: Giving primarily for the arts; funding also for education, and children and youth services.

Fields of interest: Arts and culture; Performing arts; Music; Performing arts education; Higher education; Human services; Child welfare.

Limitations: Applications accepted. Giving primarily in New York, NY. No grants to individuals.

Application information:
   Initial approach: Proposal
   Deadline(s): None

Officers and Directors: Thomas W. Buckner, Pres. and Director; Kamala Buckner, Secy.

Number of staff: 1 full-time support; 2 part-time support.

EIN: 223120375

6599
Phalarope Foundation

(formerly Raval Charitable Foundation)
c/o Rockefeller & Co. Inc.
30 Rockefeller Plz., Ste. 5600
New York City, NY 10112-0002

Established in 1992 in Massachusetts.
Foundation type: Independent foundation.
Financial data (yr. ended 12/31/13): Assets, $4,100,295 (M); expenditures, $322,823; qualifying distributions, $240,000; giving activities include $240,000 for 2 grants (high: $170,000; low: $70,000).
Fields of interest: Film and video; Human services.
Limitations: Applications not accepted. Giving primarily in CA and New York, NY. No grants to individuals.
Application information: Unsolicited requests for funds not accepted.
Trustees: Rebecca Dent; Winthrop Rutherfurd, Jr.
EIN: 046729068

6600
Charles Phillips Foundation

105 W. 86th St., Ste. 303
New York City, NY 10024-3412
E-mail: info@phillipscharitable.org

Donors: Charles Phillips; Karen Phillips.
Foundation type: Independent foundation.
Financial data (yr. ended 12/31/13): Assets, $56,806 (M); gifts received, $10,250; expenditures, $182,992; qualifying distributions, $181,795; giving activities include $104,950 for 4 grants (high: $75,000; low: $4,950), and $57,210 for 18 grants to individuals (high: $7,000; low: $1,170).
Fields of interest: Education; Graduate and professional education; Engineering; Human services; Single parent support; Military personnel.
Limitations: Applications accepted. Giving primarily in NY, NY.
Application information:
   Initial approach: Proposal
   Deadline(s): None
Officers and Directors: Charles Phillips, Chair. and Director; Karen Phillips, Secy. and Director; Eric Garvin; Young Huh.
EIN: 272854481

6601
The Ha Phuong Foundation

c/o The Ayco Company, L.P.
321 Broadway
P.O. Box 860
Saratoga Springs, NY 12866-0860

Donor: Chinh E. Chu.
Foundation type: Independent foundation.
Financial data (yr. ended 12/31/13): Assets, $227,875 (M); expenditures, $150,111; qualifying distributions, $150,000; giving activities include $150,000 for 1 grant.
Fields of interest: Education; Human rights; Human services.
Limitations: Applications not accepted.
Application information: Unsolicited requests for funds not accepted.
Trustees: Chinh E. Chu; Ha Phuong Chu.
EIN: 270389020

6602
Pickman Foundation Inc.

118-21 Queens Blvd., Ste. 316
Forest Hills, NY 11375-7209

Established in 1959 in New York.
Donor: Morton Pickman.
Foundation type: Independent foundation.
Financial data (yr. ended 05/31/13): Assets, $4,243,703 (M); expenditures, $232,780; qualifying distributions, $196,930; giving activities include $192,600 for 10 grants (high: $70,600; low: $1,000).
Fields of interest: Ethnic museums; Higher education; Nonprofits; Community improvement; Judaism; Human services; Child welfare.
Type of support: Regranting.
Limitations: Applications not accepted. Giving primarily in FL and the greater New York, NY, area. No grants to individuals.
Application information: Contributes only to pre-selected organizations.
Officers: Gladys Pickman, Pres.; Teresa Pickman, Secy.-Treas.
EIN: 116036666

6603
Picotte Family Foundation Trust

20 Corporate Woods Blvd., Ste. 600
Albany, NY 12211-2370

Established in 1987 in New York.
Donors: Kathleen M. Picotte; Picotte Charitable Lead Trusts.
Foundation type: Independent foundation.
Financial data (yr. ended 12/31/14): Assets, $4,535,077 (M); expenditures, $248,732; qualifying distributions, $210,492; giving activities include $177,500 for 8 grants (high: $100,000; low: $2,500).
Purpose and activities: Giving primarily to Roman Catholic churches, schools, and organizations.
Fields of interest: Arts and culture; Higher education; Catholicism; Human services; Child welfare; People with disabilities.
Limitations: Applications not accepted. Giving primarily in the Albany, NY, area. No grants to individuals.
Application information: Unsolicited requests for funds not accepted.

Trustees: Rhea P. Clark; Marcia P. Floyd; John D. Picotte; Michael B. Picotte.
EIN: 141699412

6604
The Hargrove Pierce Foundation

c/o L.H. Frishkoff & Co., LLP
529 5th Ave., 9th Fl.
New York City, NY 10017

Donors: David Hyde Pierce; Brian Hargrove.
Foundation type: Independent foundation.
Financial data (yr. ended 12/31/13): Assets, $5,026,686 (M); gifts received, $304,960; expenditures, $231,191; qualifying distributions, $204,480; giving activities include $193,960 for 13 grants (high: $100,000; low: $500).
Fields of interest: Education; Health; Religion.
Limitations: Applications not accepted. Giving primarily in CA. No grants to individuals.
Application information: Unsolicited requests for funds not accepted.
Officers: David Hyde Pierce, Pres.; David Brian Hargrove, C.F.O. and Secy.
Trustee: Candace Burnett.
EIN: 920183406

6605
Lev Pinchas Foundation, Inc.

175 Grandview Ave.
Monsey, NY 10952-1421

Donor: Dare Msy Charitable Foundation.
Foundation type: Independent foundation.
Financial data (yr. ended 12/31/13): Assets, $1,680,132 (M); expenditures, $177,301; qualifying distributions, $162,487; giving activities include $162,487 for 1+ grant.
Fields of interest: Religion.
Limitations: Applications not accepted. Giving primarily in Monsey, NY.
Application information: Unsolicited requests for funds not accepted.
Officers: Haym D. Rosenberg, Pres. and Treas.; Joy G. Rosenberg, Secy.
EIN: 611630697

6606
The Pincus Family Fund

450 Lexington Ave., 32nd Fl.
New York City, NY 10017-3140
E-mail: elipori@warburgpincus.com

Established in 1961 in New York.
Donors: Lionel I. Pincus†; Suzanne Pincus†.
Foundation type: Independent foundation.
Financial data (yr. ended 12/31/13): Assets, $26,248,371 (M); gifts received, $573,822; expenditures, $330,788; qualifying distributions, $309,885; giving activities include $300,000 for 2 grants (high: $200,000; low: $100,000).
Fields of interest: Education; Nonprofits.
Type of support: Program development; Regranting.
Limitations: Applications not accepted. No loans or grants to individuals, or for capital funds, construction and equipment, scholarships, or fellowships.
Application information: Contributes only to pre-selected organizations.

Officers: Henry Pincus, Co-Pres.; Matthew Pincus, Co-Pres.; Edwin Gustafson, Jr., Secy.-Treas.
EIN: 136089184

6607
The Pinkus Foundation
(formerly The Scott and Linda Pinkus Foundation)
c/o BCRS Associates, LLC
77 Water St., 9th Fl.
New York City, NY 10005-3701

Established in 1999 in New Jersey.
Donor: Scott M. Pinkus.
Foundation type: Independent foundation.
Financial data (yr. ended 10/31/14): Assets, $1,860,415 (M); expenditures, $179,909; qualifying distributions, $170,308; giving activities include $168,685 for 28 grants (high: $40,000; low: $200).
Fields of interest: Education; Health; Human services.
Type of support: General support.
Limitations: Applications not accepted. Giving primarily in NY. No grants to individuals; no loans or scholarships.
Application information: Unsolicited requests for funds not accepted.
Trustee: Scott M. Pinkus.
EIN: 134051212

6608
The Pittman Family Foundation
c/o TAG Assocs.
75 Rockefeller Plz.
New York City, NY 10019-6907

Established in 1997 in Colorado.
Donor: Robert W. Pittman.
Foundation type: Independent foundation.
Financial data (yr. ended 04/30/13): Assets, $1,959,036 (M); gifts received, $860,059; expenditures, $449,699; qualifying distributions, $392,703; giving activities include $392,703 for 68 grants (high: $90,000; low: $50).
Purpose and activities: Giving primarily for arts and culture, education, health associations, and human services.
Fields of interest: Arts and culture; Ballet; Museums; Education; Elementary and secondary education; Higher education; Foundations; Diseases and conditions; Human services; Child welfare.
Limitations: Applications not accepted. Giving on a national basis, with emphasis on New York, NY. No grants to individuals.
Application information: Contributes only to pre-selected organizations.
Trustees: Robert W. Pittman; Veronique Choa Pittman.
EIN: 541876548

6609
The Planalp-Trevor Charitable Trust
48 W. 88th St.
New York City, NY 10024-2502

Established in 2007 in New York.
Donors: Stephen Trevor; Ronnie Planalp.
Foundation type: Independent foundation.

Financial data (yr. ended 11/30/13): Assets, $24,753 (M); gifts received, $200,000; expenditures, $289,290; qualifying distributions, $289,290; giving activities include $269,830 for 28 grants (high: $152,425; low: $50).
Fields of interest: Education; Business education; Film and video.
Limitations: Applications not accepted. Giving primarily in NY. No grants to individuals.
Application information: Contributes only to pre-selected organizations.
Trustees: Ronnie Planalp; Stephen Trevor.
EIN: 208682483

6610
The Kronhill Pletka Foundation
123A W. 69th St.
New York City, NY 10023-5127
E-mail: info@kronhillpletkafoundation.org;
Application email:
LOI@kronhillpletkafoundation.org; Main
URL: http://www.kronhillpletkafoundation.org/index.html

Established in 2007 in New York.
Foundation type: Independent foundation.
Financial data (yr. ended 12/31/14): Assets, $5,920,886; expenditures, $528,716; qualifying distributions, $485,911.
Fields of interest: Higher education; Judaism.
Limitations: Applications accepted. Giving primarily in New York, NY. No grants to individuals.
Publications: Application guidelines.
Application information: The specific project proposal should not exceed 1,000 words. See foundation web site for specific application guidelines.
Initial approach: Letter of intent via e-mail
Deadline(s): 1st Fri. of Feb., May, Aug. and Nov.
Officer and Trustee: Irene Pletka, Chair. and Pres. and Trustee.
EIN: 261466252

6611
Therese Plunkett Foundation
c/o Citigroup Trust Delaware, N.A.
2 Court Sq., 8th Fl.
Long Island City, NY 11120-4356

Established in 2003 in California.
Donor: Therese M. Plunkett Trust.
Foundation type: Independent foundation.
Financial data (yr. ended 03/31/13): Assets, $3,464,451 (M); expenditures, $186,301; qualifying distributions, $165,288; giving activities include $148,418 for 13 grants (high: $40,000; low: $2,000).
Fields of interest: Education; Public libraries; Judaism; Human services; Youth services.
Type of support: General support.
Limitations: Applications not accepted. Giving primarily in CA. No grants to individuals.
Application information: Unsolicited requests for funds not accepted.
Trustee: Citigroup Trust, N.A.
EIN: 201078653

6612
Plymouth Hill Foundation
P.O. Box 687
Millbrook, NY 12545-0687

Established in 1993 in New York.
Foundation type: Independent foundation.
Financial data (yr. ended 09/30/13): Assets, $4,062,968 (M); expenditures, $205,979; qualifying distributions, $196,169; giving activities include $194,000 for 35 grants (high: $20,000; low: $500).
Purpose and activities: Giving primarily for education and for medical and community services.
Fields of interest: Natural history museums; Education; Environment; Health; Science; Housing development.
Type of support: General support; Continuing support; Annual campaigns; Research and evaluation; Capital campaigns; Capital and infrastructure; Equipment; Land acquisitions; Endowments; Program development; Seed money; Research.
Limitations: Applications not accepted. Giving primarily in Dutchess County, NY. No support for political or fraternal organizations. No grants to individuals.
Application information: Unsolicited requests for funds not accepted.
Officers and Directors: Robert Goodstein, Pres. and Director; Jeanne Goodwin, V.P. and Director; Gillian Goodwin, Secy. and Director; Andrew Goodwin, Treas. and Director.
Number of staff: None.
EIN: 223136685

6613
Pohly-Turaj Family Foundation Inc.
c/o WTAS, LLC
1177 Ave. of the Americas, Ste. 18
New York City, NY 10036-2714

Established in 2003 in New York.
Donors: Julie Pohly; Robert Pohly; Samlyn Capital.
Foundation type: Independent foundation.
Financial data (yr. ended 12/31/12): Assets, $28,799 (M); gifts received, $249,799; expenditures, $240,459; qualifying distributions, $233,254; giving activities include $233,254 for grants.
Fields of interest: Ballet; Orchestral music; Elementary and secondary education; Alumni relations; Nonprofits; Human services.
Type of support: Regranting.
Limitations: Applications not accepted. Giving primarily in NY. No grants to individuals.
Application information: Contributes only to pre-selected organizations.
Officers: Julie Turaj Pohly, Pres.; Robert Pohly, Treas.
EIN: 900113039

6614
Yvonne & Leslie Pollack Family Foundation Inc.
8 Long Meadow Rd.
Bedford, NY 10506-1120 (914) 234-7096

Established in 1998 in New York.
Donors: Leslie Pollack; Rae Pollack†.
Foundation type: Independent foundation.

Financial data (yr. ended 12/31/14): Assets, $6,887,265; expenditures, $390,462; qualifying distributions, $370,970.

Purpose and activities: Giving primarily for the arts, health, human services, and to Jewish organizations.

Fields of interest: Arts and culture; Education; Nonprofits; Diseases and conditions; Judaism; Human services.

Type of support: Regranting.

Limitations: Applications accepted. Giving primarily in New York, NY. No grants to individuals.

Application information:
 Initial approach: Proposal
 Deadline(s): None

Officers and Directors: Leslie Pollack, Pres. and Director; Yvonne Pollack, Secy. and Director; Fredrica Pollack Ford; Jonathan Pollack; Jennifer Pollack Reiner.

EIN: 133985619

6615
The Geri & Lester Pollack Family Foundation, Inc.

(formerly The Pollack Family Foundation, Inc.)
c/o Centre Partners
825 3rd Ave., 40th Fl.
New York City, NY 10022-7592 (212) 332-5851
Contact: Lester Pollack, Pres.

Established in 1986 in New York.
Donors: Lester Pollack; Bruce Pollack.
Foundation type: Independent foundation.
Financial data (yr. ended 09/30/13): Assets, $564,596 (M); expenditures, $392,861; qualifying distributions, $389,261; giving activities include $389,026 for 19 grants (high: $75,000; low: $150).
Purpose and activities: Giving primarily for social services and to Jewish agencies and temples.
Fields of interest: Education; Nonprofits; Diseases and conditions; Judaism; Human services; Child welfare.
Type of support: General support; Capital campaigns; Scholarships; Regranting.
Limitations: Applications accepted. Giving primarily in New York, NY. No grants to individuals.
Application information: Application form required.
 Initial approach: Letter
 Deadline(s): None
Officers and Directors: Lester Pollack, Pres. and Director; Geri Pollack, V.P. and Director; Bruce Pollack, Secy.-Treas. and Director.
EIN: 133384943

6616
Pollock Foundation

(formerly S. Wilson & Grace M. Pollock Foundation)
1100 Wehrle Dr., 2nd Fl.
Amherst, NY 14221-7748

Established in 1997 in Pennsylvania.
Donors: Grace Pollock; S. Wilson Pollock.
Foundation type: Independent foundation.
Financial data (yr. ended 04/30/13): Assets, $8,661,164 (M); gifts received, $35; expenditures, $414,482; qualifying distributions, $375,000; giving activities include $375,000 for 3 grants (high: $250,000; low: $25,000).
Fields of interest: Arts and culture; Hospital care; Libraries; Human services; People with vision impairments.

Limitations: Applications not accepted. Giving primarily in PA. No grants to individuals.
Application information: Contributes only to pre-selected organizations.
Trustee: M&T Bank.
Directors: Lauren P. Cacciamani; Paul A. Cacciamani, Esq.; Courtney P. Gordon; David H. McLane, Ph.D; Lindsay Kathryn Pollock.
EIN: 237889770

6617
The Pollock Foundation

61 Broadway
New York City, NY 10006-2701
Contact: Oscar Pollock

Established in 1983 in New York.
Donor: Oscar S. Pollock.
Foundation type: Independent foundation.
Financial data (yr. ended 11/30/13): Assets, $935,046 (M); gifts received, $50,000; expenditures, $218,896; qualifying distributions, $195,066; giving activities include $180,000 for 8 grants (high: $108,000; low: $1,000).
Fields of interest: Arts and culture; Community and economic development; Housing development.
Limitations: Applications not accepted. Giving primarily in MA and NY. No grants to individuals.
Application information: Unsolicited requests for funds not accepted.
Officers: Oscar S. Pollock, Pres.; Mary Nan Pollock, V.P.
EIN: 133195928

6618
The Hazen Polsky Foundation, Inc.

(formerly The Polsky Foundation, Inc.)
667 Madison Ave.
New York City, NY 10021-8029

Donors: Alexander Polsky; Cynthia H. Polsky; Leon B. Polsky.
Foundation type: Independent foundation.
Financial data (yr. ended 12/31/13): Assets, $10,154,037 (M); expenditures, $593,200; qualifying distributions, $533,361; giving activities include $312,192 for 17 grants (high: $50,000; low: $250).
Purpose and activities: Giving primarily for the arts, education, and to hospitals, particularly a cancer hospital.
Fields of interest: Arts and culture; Education; Health; Hospital care; Specialty hospital care.
Limitations: Applications not accepted. Giving primarily in NY, with emphasis on the metropolitan New York City area. No grants to individuals.
Application information: Contributes only to pre-selected organizations.
Officers: Cynthia H. Polsky, Chair.; Leon Polsky, Pres.; Nicholas Polsky, V.P. and Secy.; Alexander Polsky, V.P. and Treas.
EIN: 510245812

6619
Jay & Hadasa Pomrenze Foundation

c/o Cohnreznick LLP
1212 6th Ave.
New York City, NY 10036-1602

Established in 1986 in Delaware.

Donors: Hadasa Pomrenze; Jay Pomrenze; Shusterman Family Foundation.
Foundation type: Independent foundation.
Financial data (yr. ended 12/31/13): Assets, $42,433 (M); gifts received, $212,958; expenditures, $182,596; qualifying distributions, $178,119; giving activities include $176,700 for 33 grants (high: $37,750; low: $180).
Fields of interest: Education; Judaism; Human services.
Limitations: Applications not accepted. Giving primarily in NJ and NY. No grants to individuals.
Application information: Contributes only to pre-selected organizations.
Officers: Jay Pomrenze, Pres.; Hadasa Pomrenze, V.P.
EIN: 222905892

6620
Doyle S. & Helen Poorman Foundation

c/o M&T Bank
1100 Wehrle Dr., 2nd Fl.
Buffalo, NY 14221

Established in 1999 in Pennsylvania.
Foundation type: Independent foundation.
Financial data (yr. ended 12/31/14): Expenditures, $153,332; qualifying distributions, $128,958 and $0 for set-asides.
Purpose and activities: Giving primarily for education, Protestant agencies and churches.
Fields of interest: Education; Religion; Human services.
Limitations: Applications not accepted. Giving primarily in PA. No grants to individuals.
Application information: Unsolicited requests for funds not accepted.
Trustee: M&T Trust Co.
EIN: 256582756

6621
Posner-Wallace Foundation

(formerly Lillian & Stanley Posner Foundation)
c/o James R. Posner
P.O. Box 1585, Cathedral Station
New York, NY 10025-1585
E-mail: Posnerplus@aol.com

Established in 1957 in District of Columbia.
Donors: Irving Wallace†; Stanley Posner†; Lillian Posner Wallace†.
Foundation type: Independent foundation.
Financial data (yr. ended 12/31/13): Assets, $5,211,935 (M); expenditures, $306,985; qualifying distributions, $286,105; giving activities include $229,990 for 243 grants (high: $25,000; low: $100).
Fields of interest: Arts and culture; Education; Elementary and secondary education; Higher education; Technology; Disasters and emergency management; Judaism; Food aid.
International interests: Israel.
Type of support: General support; Pro bono consulting services; Continuing support; Program-related investments; Mission-related investments; Annual campaigns; Emergency funds; Program development; Scholarships; Technical assistance.
Limitations: Applications not accepted. Giving primarily in the greater metropolitan Washington,

DC, area; giving also in Israel. No grants to individuals.

Application information: Contributes only to pre-selected organizations.

Officers and Trustees: James R. Posner, Chair. and Trustee; Rachel C. Smith, Secy. and Trustee; Elisabeth Posner Schouten, Treas. and Gen. Mgr. and Trustee; Diana L. Erbsen; Lawrence D. Posner; Nicolas D. Posner; Jill J. Prosky.

Number of staff: 1 part-time professional.

EIN: 526037555

6622
Ralph B. Post Trust

c/o NBT Bank, N.A.
52 S. Broad St.
Norwich, NY 13815
Application address: c/o Post Memorial Scholarship Fund, NBT Bank, N.A., 241 Main St., Ste. 200, Buffalo, NY 14203, tel.: (716) 566-3032

Established in 1985 in New York.

Foundation type: Independent foundation.

Financial data (yr. ended 09/30/13): Assets, $2,128,388 (M); expenditures, $207,403; qualifying distributions, $191,149; giving activities include $184,274 for 33 grants to individuals (high: $21,323; low: $625).

Purpose and activities: Awards scholarships to female residents of specified geographic areas who are majoring in nursing.

Fields of interest: Graduate and professional education; Nursing care.

Type of support: Student aid.

Limitations: Applications accepted. Giving limited to residents of the town of Ballston Spa, the village of Ballston Spa, and the town of Milton, who are majoring in nursing.

Application information:
Deadline(s): None

Trustee: NBT Bank, N.A.

EIN: 146052967

6623
The Philip E. Potter Foundation

6 Ford Ave.
Oneonta, NY 13820-1818 (607) 432-6724
Contact: Anne T. Wolek, Fdn. Mgr.

Donors: Philip E. Potter; Mrs. Philip E. Potter; Lillian W. Potter†.

Foundation type: Independent foundation.

Financial data (yr. ended 10/31/14): Assets, $12,354,223 (M); expenditures, $532,558; qualifying distributions, $400,562; giving activities include $366,305 for grants to individuals.

Purpose and activities: Awards scholarships mostly to Oneonta High School graduates in Oneonta, NY.

Fields of interest: Higher education.

Type of support: Student aid; Scholarships.

Limitations: Applications accepted. Giving limited to residents of Otsego and Delaware counties, NY, with emphasis on residents of Oneonta.

Application information: Application form required.
Initial approach: Standard application form available at area high school and the foundation office
Deadline(s): 5

Officer: Anne T. Wolek, Mgr.

Trustees: Sue Anne De Dergh; Sally Anne Dunleary; Maureen P. Hulbert; Robert W. Moyer.

EIN: 166169167

6624
The Potts Memorial Foundation

P.O. Box 1015
Hudson, NY 12534-9015 (518) 828-6983
Contact: Sidney Richter

Established in 1922 in New York.

Foundation type: Independent foundation.

Financial data (yr. ended 12/31/13): Assets, $5,303,594 (M); expenditures, $285,641; qualifying distributions, $238,206; giving activities include $235,000 for 9 grants (high: $45,000; low: $15,000).

Purpose and activities: A private foundation established to provide for the care, treatment, and rehabilitation of persons afflicted with tuberculosis; also supports efforts to eradicate tuberculosis, including fellowship programs for physicians.

Fields of interest: Medical education; Health; Rehabilitation; Diseases and conditions.

Type of support: Capital and infrastructure; Equipment; Program development; Research; Convening; Research and evaluation; Publications; Seed money; Fellowships; Internships; Scholarships.

Limitations: Applications accepted. Giving on a national and international basis. No grants to individuals, or for endowment funds or matching gifts; no loans.

Application information:
Initial approach: Proposal via mail
Deadline(s): None
Board meeting date(s): May and Oct.

Officers: Brian Daggett, Pres.; Kathleen A. McDonough, Ph.D, V.P.; Donna D. Klose, Secy.; Sid Richter, Treas.

Trustees: John Chan, MD; Joseph J. Fusco, MD; Richard Gullot, MD; Anthony Malanga, MD; Donna O'Hare, MD.

EIN: 141347714

6625
The Pratt-Northam Foundation

P.O. Box 104
Lowville, NY 13367-0104 (315) 771-9889
Contact: Thomas Yousey II, Exec. Dir.
E-mail: prattnortham@frontier.com; Main
URL: http://www.prattnortham.org
Grants List: http://www.prattnortham.org/grants.html

Established in 1962 in New York.

Donor: Hazel Northam†.

Foundation type: Independent foundation.

Financial data (yr. ended 12/31/13): Assets, $5,647,439 (M); expenditures, $252,077; qualifying distributions, $206,625; giving activities include $183,278 for 61 grants (high: $11,710; low: $700).

Purpose and activities: The foundation's mission is to improve the quality of life in the communities of the Black River Valley, New York.

Fields of interest: Arts and culture; Education; Public administration.

Type of support: Capital campaigns; Matching grants; Program development.

Limitations: Applications accepted. Giving limited to the Black River Valley region of NY. No grants to individuals.

Application information: Application form required.
Initial approach: Contact foundation for application or download application from foundation web site
Copies of proposal: 1
Deadline(s): None
Board meeting date(s): Bimonthly

Officers and Directors: Randall Schell, Pres. and Director; Donna Loucks, V.P.; James Randall, Secy.; Thomas Sauter, Treas.; Thomas Yousey II, Exec. Dir.; Gordon Allen; Roy Hammecker; Sally Jackson; Katie Liendecker; Chris Lorence; Randolph Myers; Tina Schneider; Jo Ann Ventura.

Number of staff: 1 part-time professional.

EIN: 166088207

6626
Mary Hicks Preston Historical Improvement & Betterment Foundation Inc.

P.O. Box 21
Phelps, NY 14532-0021 (315) 548-8631
Main URL: http://www.phelpsny.com/business/preston-foundation

Donor: Mary Hicks Preston†.

Foundation type: Independent foundation.

Financial data (yr. ended 12/31/13): Assets, $7,770,482; expenditures, $470,094; qualifying distributions, $526,238.

Purpose and activities: Giving primarily to preserve historical buildings and artifacts in Phelps, New York, in order to increase recreational, educational, and cultural opportunities.

Fields of interest: Arts and culture; Historic preservation; Economic development; Community improvement.

Type of support: General support.

Limitations: Applications accepted. Giving primarily in Phelps, NY, and surrounding areas. No grants to individuals.

Application information: Application form required.
Initial approach: See foundation web site for application form
Deadline(s): None

Officers: Floyd A. Ridley, Pres.; Frank Murphy, V.P.; Robert F. Spink, Secy.; James E. Cheney, Treas.

Director: Aleta Williamson.

EIN: 203986225

6627
Price Family Foundation

450 E. 83rd St., PH1A
New York City, NY 10028-6299

Established in 1997 in New Jersey.

Donor: Michael Price.

Foundation type: Independent foundation.

Financial data (yr. ended 12/31/14): Assets, $2,122,129 (M); gifts received, $2,045,555; expenditures, $347,319; qualifying distributions, $335,875; giving activities include $335,875 for 31 grants (high: $200,000; low: $100).

Fields of interest: Education; Higher education; Foundations; Specialty hospital care; Religion; Human services.

Limitations: Applications not accepted. No grants to individuals.

Application information: Unsolicited requests for funds not accepted.

Trustees: Michael Price; Vikki Price; Howard Sontag.

EIN: 137137846

6628
The Price Family Foundation, Inc.
25 E. 86th St.
New York City, NY   10028-0553
Contact: Robert Price, Dir.

Established in 1998 in New York.
Donors: Robert Price; Price Communications.
Foundation type: Independent foundation.
Financial data (yr. ended 12/31/13): Assets, $114,274 (M); gifts received, $272,917; expenditures, $231,218; qualifying distributions, $231,105; giving activities include $231,105 for 21 grants (high: $60,000; low: $100).
Purpose and activities: Giving primarily to health organizations and Jewish organizations and temples; funding also for social services.
Fields of interest: Higher education; Medical education; Hospital care; Specialty hospital care; Diseases and conditions; Judaism; Human services.
Limitations: Applications accepted. Giving in the U.S. with emphasis on New York, NY.
Application information:
   Initial approach: Letter
   Deadline(s): None
Directors: Eileen Farbman; Robert Price; Steve Price.
EIN: 134003955

6629
The Prince Family Foundation
c/o BCRS Assocs., LLC
77 Wall St., 9th Fl.
New York City, NY   10005-3701

Established in 1999 in New York.
Donor: Scott Prince.
Foundation type: Independent foundation.
Financial data (yr. ended 05/31/13): Assets, $4,204,500 (M); expenditures, $201,449; qualifying distributions, $197,449; giving activities include $193,000 for 8 grants (high: $50,000; low: $5,000).
Fields of interest: Higher education; Cancers; Judaism; Human services.
Limitations: Applications not accepted. Giving primarily in NY and PA. No grants to individuals or for scholarships; no loans.
Application information: Contributes only to pre-selected organizations.
Trustees: Daniel Och; Scott Prince; Sharon Prince.
EIN: 134088759

6630
The Probitas Foundation Ltd.
229 Berkeley Pl.
Brooklyn, NY   11217-3801

Donor: Alain Bourgeois.
Foundation type: Independent foundation.
Financial data (yr. ended 10/31/13): Assets, $19,840 (M); gifts received, $182,660; expenditures, $185,438; qualifying distributions, $185,410; giving activities include $182,660 for 2 grants (high: $157,660; low: $25,000).

Limitations: Applications not accepted. Giving primarily in New York, NY.
Application information: Unsolicited requests for funds not accepted.
Officers and Directors: Alain Bourgeois, Pres. and Director; Claire Bourgeois, V.P. and Director; Alexander Bourgeois, Treas. and Director.
EIN: 453804704

6631
The Project for Life Inc.
270 S. Service Rd., Ste. 45
Melville, NY   11747-2339   (631) 622-9401
Contact: Christine Tourtoulis
Main URL: http://projectforlife.org

Donor: Christopher S. Pascucci.
Foundation type: Independent foundation.
Financial data (yr. ended 09/30/13): Assets, $1,834,390 (M); gifts received, $2,000,050; expenditures, $168,786; qualifying distributions, $167,438; giving activities include $162,322 for 6 grants (high: $82,500; low: $1,000).
Fields of interest: Religion; Human services; Children.
Limitations: Applications accepted. Giving primarily in NY.
Application information: Application form required.
   Initial approach: Completed application form
   Deadline(s): None
Officers and Directors: Christopher S. Pascucci, Pres. and Director; Silvana B. Pascucci, V.P. and Director; Peter I. Cavallaro, Secy.; Charles E. Becker, Treas.; Michael C. Pascucci.
EIN: 460817618

6632
Provident Bank Charitable Foundation
400 Rella Blvd.
Montebello, NY   10901   (845) 359-8478
Main URL: http://www.providentbanking.com

Foundation type: Independent foundation.
Financial data (yr. ended 12/31/13): Assets, $4,139,035 (M); expenditures, $137,686; qualifying distributions, $121,850; giving activities include $121,417 for 11 grants (high: $50,000; low: $1,000).
Fields of interest: Education; Health; Human rights.
Limitations: Applications accepted. Giving primarily in NY.
Application information: Application form required.
   Initial approach: Completed application form
   Deadline(s): Mar. 31, June 30, Sept. 30 and Dec. 31
Officers: Stephanie Yaniga, Pres. and Exec. Dir.; David Bagatelle, Exec. V.P.; Jack Kopnisky, Exec. V.P.; Jim Peoples, Exec. V.P.; Dan Rothstein, Exec. V.P.; Rodney Whitwell, Exec. V.P.; Katharine Brown, V.P. and Secy.; Lynne Tracey, V.P. and Treas.; Gerry Filandro, V.P.; Harold Peterson, V.P.; Ben Hirsh, C.A.O. and Cont.
Director: Thomas F. Jauntig, Jr.
EIN: 320103899

6633
Psalm 11612 Foundation
13389 Rt 39 Rice Ln., Lot 2
Chaffee, NY   14030-9770

Established in 2002 in New York.
Donors: Mark S. Balus; Kathleen M. Balus.
Foundation type: Independent foundation.
Financial data (yr. ended 12/31/13): Assets, $1,942,506 (M); expenditures, $186,686; qualifying distributions, $167,500; giving activities include $167,500 for 4 grants (high: $130,000; low: $1,500).
Fields of interest: Arts and culture; Community and economic development; Christianity; Protestantism; Human services.
Limitations: Applications not accepted. Giving primarily in NY. No grants to individuals.
Application information: Unsolicited requests for funds not accepted.
Directors: Kathleen M. Balus; Mark S. Balus; Cameron McCarty; Marshall McCarty; Thomas R. Zugger.
EIN: 026151036

6634
Purple Plume Foundation
(formerly The Whitman-Carlyon Foundation)
240 West End Ave., Apt. 13CD
New York City, NY   10023-3602
Contact: Barbara Whitman

Donors: David Carlyon; Barbara Whitman; Lois Whitman; Martin J. Whitman.
Foundation type: Independent foundation.
Financial data (yr. ended 12/31/13): Assets, $4,841,561 (M); expenditures, $339,534; qualifying distributions, $334,739; giving activities include $330,804 for 19 grants (high: $133,500; low: $500).
Fields of interest: Arts and culture; Education; University education; Human rights.
Limitations: Applications not accepted. Giving primarily in IL, MI and New York, NY. No grants to individuals.
Application information: Unsolicited requests for funds not accepted.
Trustee: Barbara Whitman.
EIN: 571144326

6635
Pyewacket Foundation
8 E. 80th St.
New York City, NY   10075-0110

Established in 1997 in New York.
Donors: William H. Janeway; Janeway 1999 Charitable Remainder Unitrust No. 1; Weslie R. Janeway; Janeway 1999 Charitable Remainder Unitrust No. 2.
Foundation type: Independent foundation.
Financial data (yr. ended 12/31/13): Assets, $35,011,075 (M); expenditures, $517,588; qualifying distributions, $275,000; giving activities include $275,000 for 2 grants (high: $250,000; low: $25,000).
Fields of interest: Higher education; Social sciences.
Limitations: Applications not accepted. Giving primarily in Princeton, NJ and Brooklyn, NY; funding also in Bar Harbor, ME. No grants to individuals.
Application information: Contributes only to pre-selected organizations.
Officer: William H. Janeway, Pres.
Trustee: Weslie R. Janeway.
EIN: 137051522

6636
QIBQ Foundation
(also known as Susan Wexner Charitable
Foundation)
c/o Hertz, Herson & Co., LLP
477 Madison Ave., 10th Fl.
New York City, NY 10022-5802

Established in 1986 in New York.
Donor: Susan R. Wexner.
Foundation type: Independent foundation.
Financial data (yr. ended 12/31/13): Assets,
$4,920,594 (M); expenditures, $257,360;
qualifying distributions, $255,588; giving activities
include $255,565 for 6 grants (high: $250,000;
low: $730).
Fields of interest: Education; Human services.
International interests: Israel.
Limitations: Applications not accepted. Giving in
New Haven, CT. No grants to individuals.
Application information: Contributes only to
pre-selected organizations.
Trustees: Michael S. Oberman; Mark W. Saks;
Susan R. Wexner.
EIN: 133424462

6637
The Quinn Family Foundation
6 Pond View Dr.
Upper Brookville, NY 11771-2816
Contact: William John Quinn, Tr.

Donors: William Quinn; Joanne Quinn.
Foundation type: Independent foundation.
Financial data (yr. ended 06/30/14): Assets,
$1,357,161 (M); expenditures, $198,910;
qualifying distributions, $182,269; giving activities
include $182,269 for 39 grants (high: $48,350;
low: $90).
Fields of interest: Education; Specialty hospital
care; Diseases and conditions; Religion;
Catholicism; Human services; Youth development;
Youth services.
Type of support: Research and evaluation.
Limitations: Applications not accepted. Giving
primarily in NY. No grants to individuals.
Application information: Contributes only to
pre-selected organizations.
Board meeting date(s): May
Trustee: William John Quinn.
Number of staff: None.
EIN: 113520444

6638
Doris G. Quinn Foundation
P.O. Box 478
Crown Point, NY 12928-0478
Main URL: http://www.dorisgquinnfoundation.org/

Established in 1986 in New York.
Donor: Doris G. Quinn.
Foundation type: Independent foundation.
Financial data (yr. ended 12/31/14): Assets,
$3,845,558 (M); expenditures, $192,124; giving
activities include $158,494 for 16 grants (high:
$12,668; low: $4,500).
Purpose and activities: Giving primarily for
education.
Fields of interest: Education; University education;
Health.

Limitations: Applications not accepted. Giving
primarily in CA, NC, NJ, NY, PA and WI. No grants to
individuals.
Application information: Contributes only to
pre-selected organizations.
Officers and Trustees: David A. Barnebl, Pres. and
Trustee; Linda G. Grandey; Eugene J. Callahan;
Richard P. Terbrusch, Treas. and Trustee.
EIN: 133406777

6639
The Stephen D. Quinn Foundation
c/o Marks Paneth and Shron LLP
685 3rd Ave., 4th Fl.
New York City, NY 10017-6701

Established in 1993 in Connecticut.
Donor: Stephen D. Quinn.
Foundation type: Independent foundation.
Financial data (yr. ended 07/31/13): Assets,
$5,918,992 (M); gifts received, $7,213;
expenditures, $319,635; qualifying distributions,
$314,103; giving activities include $312,330 for 8
grants (high: $286,610; low: $500).
Purpose and activities: Giving primarily to The
Church of Jesus Christ of Latter-day Saints; funding
also for education and community development.
Fields of interest: Education; Community and
economic development; Mormonism.
Limitations: Applications not accepted. Giving
primarily in UT. No grants to individuals.
Application information: Contributes only to
pre-selected organizations.
Trustees: Cydney P. Quinn; Stephen D. Quinn.
EIN: 133789066

6640
The R & S Family Foundation, Inc.
1372 Coney Island Ave.
Brooklyn, NY 11230-4120

Donors: Steven Unger; The Steven Unger Family
Trust; The Steven Unger 2011 Family Trust.
Foundation type: Independent foundation.
Financial data (yr. ended 12/31/13): Assets,
$81,670 (M); gifts received, $210,000;
expenditures, $188,816; qualifying distributions,
$188,614; giving activities include $188,614 for 20
grants (high: $53,785; low: $564).
Fields of interest: Education; Nonprofits; Judaism;
Human services.
Type of support: Regranting.
Limitations: Applications not accepted. No grants to
individuals.
Application information: Unsolicited requests for
funds not accepted.
Officers: Steven Unger, Pres.; Judah Unger, V.P.;
Rivkah Unger, V.P.
EIN: 010722832

6641
The Rachel Foundation
1846 50th St.
Brooklyn, NY 11204-1252
Contact: Jacob Rieger

Donors: Triangle Trust; Landau Trust; Jacob Rieger;
Rachel Rieger.
Foundation type: Independent foundation.

Financial data (yr. ended 11/30/13): Assets,
$3,721,747 (M); gifts received, $730,000;
expenditures, $155,479; qualifying distributions,
$153,100; giving activities include $153,100 for 14
grants (high: $100,000; low: $1,500).
Fields of interest: Education; Religion; Judaism;
Human services.
Limitations: Applications not accepted. Giving
primarily in NY.
Application information: Contributes only to
pre-selected organizations.
Directors: Abraham Rieger; Rachel Rieger.
EIN: 204057294

6642
Jill and Mark Rachesky Charitable Foundation
40 W. 57th St., 24th Fl.
New York City, NY 10019-4001 (212) 262-0005
Contact: Jill Rachesky, Tr.

Established in 2001 in New York.
Donors: Mark H. Rachesky; Jill Rachesky.
Foundation type: Independent foundation.
Financial data (yr. ended 12/31/13): Assets,
$8,303 (M); gifts received, $228,052;
expenditures, $350,239; qualifying distributions,
$350,100; giving activities include $350,100 for 32
grants (high: $120,000; low: $100).
Fields of interest: Theater; Higher education;
Nonprofits; Hospital care; Diseases and conditions;
Judaism; Human services.
Type of support: Research; Regranting.
Limitations: Applications accepted. Giving primarily
in New York, NY and in Philadelphia, PA. No grants
to individuals.
Application information: Application form required.
Initial approach: Letter
Deadline(s): None
Trustees: Jill Rachesky; Mark H. Rachesky.
EIN: 137313091

6643
Radio Drama Network, Inc.
c/o Pryor Cashman LLP
7 Times Sq.
New York City, NY 10036-6569
Contact: Richard Kay, Pres.

Established in 1990 in New York.
Donor: Himan Brown†.
Foundation type: Independent foundation.
Financial data (yr. ended 06/30/15): Assets,
$16,620,723 (M); expenditures, $390,806;
qualifying distributions, $214,750; giving activities
include $214,000 for 7 grants (high: $162,000;
low: $8,500).
Fields of interest: Higher education; Television.
Limitations: Applications accepted. Giving primarily
in New York, NY. No grants to individuals.
Application information: Unsolicited requests for
funds not accepted.
Initial approach: Letter
Board meeting date(s): June and Dec.
Officers and Directors: Melina Brown, Pres. and
Director; Richard Kay, Secy.; Mrs. Barrie Brown,
V.P.; Eli Kopelman, Treas.
Number of staff: 2 part-time support.
EIN: 133253712

6644
Tony Randall Theatrical Fund, Inc.
Ansonia Sta.
P.O. Box 230460
New York City, NY 10023-0008
Contact: Heather Randall, Pres.
E-mail: tonyrandallfund@gmail.com; Main
URL: http://www.TonyRandallTheatricalFund.org
Blog: http://www.tonyrandalltheatricalfund.org/news-and-updates
Facebook: https://www.facebook.com/tonyrandallfund
Grants List: http://www.tonyrandalltheatricalfund.org/grant-recipients

Established in 1981 in New York.
Donor: Anthony L. Randall†.
Foundation type: Independent foundation.
Financial data (yr. ended 06/30/14): Assets, $3,787,810 (M); expenditures, $542,994; qualifying distributions, $356,604; giving activities include $284,750 for 34 grants (high: $71,500; low: $500).
Purpose and activities: Giving primarily to professional non-profit theater organizations in the tri-state area.
Fields of interest: Arts and culture; Theater.
Limitations: Applications not accepted. Giving primarily in the CT, NJ, NY tri-state area. No grants to individuals.
Publications: Grants list.
Application information: Contributes only to pre-selected organizations. Applications are currently by invitation only. Check fund web site for latest information.
Officers: Heather Randall, Chair. and Exec. Dir.; Kristie Ashton, V.P.; Scott Gildea, Treas.
Director: Leslie A. Newson.
EIN: 133082489

6645
Neena Rao Charitable Corporation
369 Guy Park Ave.
Amsterdam, NY 12010-1030

Established in 1999 in New York.
Donors: C.K.G. Rao; Jyoti Rao; C.P. Rao.
Foundation type: Independent foundation.
Financial data (yr. ended 12/31/13): Assets, $2,274,541 (M); gifts received, $240,000; expenditures, $285,027; qualifying distributions, $280,648; giving activities include $280,648 for 25 grants (high: $158,000; low: $50).
Purpose and activities: Giving primarily to improve education and healthcare for women and children in the U.S. and in India.
Fields of interest: Education; Children's hospital care; Hinduism; Human services; Children; Females.
International interests: India.
Limitations: Applications not accepted. Giving in the U.S., with emphasis on Amsterdam, NY, and Cincinnati, OH; funding also in India. No grants to individuals.
Application information: Unsolicited requests for funds not accepted.
EIN: 141816910

6646
Rapaport Family Charitable Trust
c/o Rita Barrison
1000 Park Blvd., Ste. 212
Massapequa Park, NY 11762-2740

Established in 1993 in New York.
Donors: Elisa Peter Rapaport; Jessica F. Shapiro.
Foundation type: Independent foundation.
Financial data (yr. ended 12/31/13): Assets, $8,973,858 (M); gifts received, $16,220; expenditures, $274,046; qualifying distributions, $266,195; giving activities include $266,195 for 10 grants (high: $100,000; low: $1,300).
Fields of interest: Environment; Hospital care; Diseases and conditions; Cancers; Human services.
Limitations: Applications not accepted. Giving primarily in New York, NY. No grants to individuals.
Application information: Contributes only to pre-selected organizations.
Trustees: Elisa Rapaport; Peter Rapaport.
Number of staff: 1 part-time professional.
EIN: 137029273

6647
Rapaport Shallat Foundation
Bay Place Forest Ct.
Huntington, NY 11743-0000

Foundation type: Independent foundation.
Financial data (yr. ended 12/31/13): Assets, $4,699,762 (M); expenditures, $211,895; qualifying distributions, $205,904; giving activities include $202,156 for 63 grants (high: $25,000; low: $200).
Purpose and activities: Giving primarily for Jewish organizations, schools, and federated giving programs, and for the arts.
Fields of interest: Arts and culture; Education; Nonprofits; Judaism.
Type of support: Regranting.
Limitations: Applications not accepted. Giving primarily in New York, NY. No grants to individuals.
Application information: Contributes only to pre-selected organizations.
Directors: Barton A. Shallat; Jane A. Shallat.
EIN: 137027583

6648
Raphael Foundation, Inc.
c/o Babyfair, Inc.
34 W. 33rd St., Ste. 818
New York City, NY 10001-3304

Established in 1962 in New York.
Donors: Maurice Shamah; Steven Shamah; Ecolo Ltd.
Foundation type: Independent foundation.
Financial data (yr. ended 12/31/13): Assets, $1,061,838 (M); gifts received, $190,000; expenditures, $358,079; qualifying distributions, $353,011; giving activities include $350,664 for 110 grants (high: $50,000; low: $50).
Purpose and activities: Giving primarily to Jewish agencies, temples, federated giving programs, and yeshivas.
Fields of interest: Elementary and secondary education; Nonprofits; Religion; Judaism; Human services.
Type of support: General support; Capital and infrastructure; Regranting.

Limitations: Applications not accepted. Giving primarily in NY. No grants to individuals.
Application information: Unsolicited requests for funds not accepted.
Officers: Maurice Shamah, Mgr.; Steven Shamah, Mgr.
EIN: 237185539

6649
Rasba Charitable Foundation
52 Washington Ave.
Brooklyn, NY 11215-1202

Donor: Bella Ausch.
Foundation type: Independent foundation.
Financial data (yr. ended 12/31/13): Assets, $2,613 (M); gifts received, $197,156; expenditures, $215,258; qualifying distributions, $203,776; giving activities include $203,776 for 81 grants (high: $57,830; low: $50).
Fields of interest: Religion; Judaism.
Limitations: Applications not accepted.
Application information: Unsolicited requests for funds not accepted.
EIN: 206877634

6650
Rattie Family Foundation
c/o The Ayco Company - NTG
P.O. Box 15014
Albany, NY 12212-5014

Donors: Keith O. Rattie; Nancy E. Rattie.
Foundation type: Independent foundation.
Financial data (yr. ended 12/31/13): Assets, $387,771 (M); gifts received, $58,731; expenditures, $146,085; qualifying distributions, $144,160; giving activities include $144,160 for 13 grants (high: $100,000; low: $200).
Fields of interest: Arts and culture; Education; Human services.
Limitations: Applications not accepted. Giving primarily in UT.
Application information: Unsolicited requests for funds not accepted.
Trustees: Keith Rattie; Nancy E. Rattie.
EIN: 276999375

6651
Richard Ravitch Foundation, Inc.
c/o Richard Ravitch
1115 5th Ave.
New York City, NY 10128-0100

Established in 1949 in New York.
Donor: Richard Ravitch.
Foundation type: Independent foundation.
Financial data (yr. ended 11/30/13): Assets, $2,765,789 (M); gifts received, $1,093,481; expenditures, $210,055; qualifying distributions, $189,767; giving activities include $189,350 for 19 grants (high: $50,000; low: $100).
Purpose and activities: Giving primarily for education, hospitals, and public affairs.
Fields of interest: Education; Health; Public affairs.
Limitations: Applications not accepted. Giving primarily in NY. No grants to individuals.
Application information: Unsolicited requests for funds not accepted.

Officers and Directors: Richard Ravitch, Pres. and Director; Judah Gribetz, V.P. and Director; Joseph Ravitch, V.P. and Director; Michael Ravitch, Treas. and Director.
EIN: 136093139

6652
Raymond Foundation Inc.
P.O. Box 518
Greene, NY 13778 (607) 656-2481
Contact: Linda Raymond, Pres.

Established in 1964 in New York.
Donors: George G. Raymond‡; The Raymond Corp.; Madeline Young.
Foundation type: Company-sponsored foundation.
Financial data (yr. ended 12/31/13): Assets, $6,644,027 (M); gifts received, $54,100; expenditures, $376,694; qualifying distributions, $348,192; giving activities include $348,192 for 101 grants (high: $200,000; low: $50).
Purpose and activities: The foundation supports fire departments and organizations involved with theater, education, health, housing development, human services, and community economic development.
Fields of interest: Arts and culture; Education; Environment.
Type of support: Annual campaigns; Matching grants; Capital campaigns; Capital and infrastructure; Program development; Scholarships; Sponsorships.
Limitations: Applications accepted. Giving primarily in areas of company operations in CA and NY. No grants to individuals, or for endowments or general operating support; no loans.
Publications: Application guidelines; Annual report; Program policy statement.
Application information: Application form required.
 Initial approach: Proposal
 Deadline(s): None
Officers: James F. Barton, Chair.; Pete Raymond, Vice-Chair.; Terri Brant, Exec. Secy.; Patrick J. McManus, Treas.
Trustees: Richard Najarian; John Pilkington; Jean C. Raymond; Karen Raymond; Stephen S. Raymond; Steve Vannostrand; Jeanette L. Williamson.
EIN: 166047847

6653
The RDM Foundation
2329 Nostrand Ave., Ste. 500
Brooklyn, NY 11210-3948

Established in 1996 in New York.
Donors: Rosenthal Family Trust; Tomas Rosenthal.
Foundation type: Independent foundation.
Financial data (yr. ended 12/31/13): Assets, $446,153 (M); gifts received, $200,000; expenditures, $142,087; qualifying distributions, $142,087; giving activities include $141,950 for grants.
Purpose and activities: Giving for Jewish learning institutions.
Fields of interest: Education; Religion; Human services.
Type of support: General support.
Limitations: Applications not accepted. No grants to individuals.
Application information: Contributes only to pre-selected organizations.

Trustee: Judy Rosenthal.
EIN: 116472758

6654
Realex Charitable Fund Inc.
c/o Realex Capital Corp.
444 Madison Ave., 18th Fl.
New York City, NY 10022-6903

Donors: Henry Gross; Mahiz Reiss; H. Gross Family, LP; Madison Title Agency; Geneva Partners; Westborough Executive Park; The Reiss Foundation.
Foundation type: Independent foundation.
Financial data (yr. ended 12/31/13): Assets, $225 (M); gifts received, $188,500; expenditures, $188,500; qualifying distributions, $188,500; giving activities include $188,500 for 1 grant.
Fields of interest: Judaism.
Limitations: Applications not accepted. Giving primarily in MD and NY. No grants to individuals.
Application information: Contributes only to pre-selected organizations.
Officers: Henry Gross, Pres.; Helene Reiss, V.P.; Mark Gross, Secy.-Treas.
EIN: 311646865

6655
Realty Foundation of New York
551 5th Ave., Ste. 415
New York City, NY 10176-0415
FAX: (212) 949-9319; E-mail: pfrfny@aol.com

Established in 1956 in New York.
Donors: Benenson Capital Funding; Williams Real Estate Co. Inc.; Eugene M. Grant & Co. LLC.; Newmark & Co.; Jack Resnick & Sons Inc. Mgmt; Colliers ABR; Rose Associates; Shneider/Helmsley-Spear, Inc.; Silverstein Properties, Inc.; Tishman Speyer Properties; ABS Partners Real Estate, LLC; Urstadt Property Company-Inc.; RFR Holding LLC; George S. Kaufman; Wells Fargo; Eugene and Emily Grant Family Foundation; Lawrence Ruben Company, Inc.; The Trump Organization; Urstadt Biddle Properties; Time Equities, Inc.; The Durst Organization; Sterling Equities, Inc.; Silverstein Properties, Inc.; Rose Associates, Inc.; Pershing Square Capital Management, LP; Newmark Knight Frank; Jones Lang LaSalle; Jack Resnick & Sons, Inc.; Solow Building Company, LLC; George Company & Sons, Inc.; Fried Frank; Fred F. French Investing; First Service Williams; Estreich & Co., Inc.; Eastdil Secured; Durst Fetner Residential; Digby Management, Co. LLC; Cassidy Turley; Capital One Bank; Brown Harris Stevens; Brause Realty Inc.; Bank of New York Mellon; Related Properties; Atco Properties & Management; Benenson Capital Partners; Brookfield Financial Properties; Rittenhouse; C.B. Richard Ellis; Cushman & Wakefield, Inc.; Donald Zucker Company; Rockefeller Development Corp.; Eastern Consolidated Properties; Eugene M. Grant & Co.; Fisher Brothers; Gotham Organization, Inc.; H.J. Kalikow, LLC; Jeffries Morris, Inc.; L&L Holding Co.; Maurray Hill Properties; Minskoff Equities; Paramount Group, Inc.; RFR Realty; Schneider & Schneider; SR Capital, LLC; Studley, Inc.; The Feil Organization; Tishman Speyer Properties; Weiler Arnow Managment Co, Inc.; Working Realty; Malkin Holdings; Larka Family Properties.
Foundation type: Independent foundation.

Financial data (yr. ended 06/30/13): Assets, $2,300,263 (M); gifts received, $890,250; expenditures, $581,994; qualifying distributions, $665,620; giving activities include $321,350 for 121 grants to individuals (high: $30,000; low: $300).
Purpose and activities: Provides assistance to financially needy employees, and awards scholarships to employees and children of employees of the real estate industry in New York City.
Fields of interest: Education; Human services.
Type of support: Student aid; Grants to individuals.
Publications: Informational brochure.
Application information: Application form required.
 Initial approach: Proposal
 Deadline(s): None
Officers: Patricia Frank, Exec. Dir.
Directors: Lawrence Ackman; Earle S. Altman; David Arena; John Avlon; Albert P. Behler; Jerome Belson; Lawrence Benenson; Mark P. Boisi; Luis Brause; Maureen Clancy.
EIN: 136016622

6656
The REBNY Foundation Inc.
570 Lexington Ave.
New York City, NY 10022-6837 (212) 532-3100
Contact: Angela Pinsky, Exec. Dir.

Established in 1985 in New York.
Donors: The Real Estate Board of New York, Inc.; Morgan Guaranty Trust Co. of New York; Daniel Brodsky; Anthony Colletti; H. Henry Eighanayan; Kamran Eighanayan; Frederick Eighanayan; Susan Hendik; Lawrence Feiner; George Kaufman; Leonard Litwin; Carole Pittelman; Ira Pittelman; Andrea Resnick; Jonathan Resnick; Peter Resnick; Scott Resnick; Eugene & Emily Grant Family; Steven Rotter; Bell Marc Admin. Corp.; Brown Harris Stevens Residential, Inc.; Century 21 William B. May; Citi Habits, Inc.; The Clarett Group; Corcoran Group Real Estate; D.J. Knight & Co Ltd.; D.Q. Acquisition LLC; Durst Organization L.P.; Fox Residential Group Inc.; George Comfort & Sons Inc.; Glenwood Management Group; Jack Halstead Property LLC; Jack Resnick & Sons Inc.; Jack Resnick & Sons Inc. Mgmt.; JPMorgan Chase Bank, N.A.; The Kandell Fund; LKBOC LLC; The Malkin Fund; Manhattan Mortgage; Montgageit Inc.; NYT Capital Inc.; One Canal Place LLC; Preferred Empire Mortgage Co.; Reckson Associate Realty Corp.; Related Residential Sales LLC; The Sheldon Sotow Foundation; Stribling & Associates, Ltd.; Sothebys International Realty; The Sunshine Group, Ltd.; Trump Mortgage LLC; Warburg Realty Partnership; Veronica Hackett The Clarett Group; Warburg Realty Partnership, Ltd.; Douglas Elliman; Stanley Stahl Management Inc.; Newark & Co. Real Estate, Inc.; The Helena Assoc., LLC; Ogden Cap Properties, Inc.; Silverstein Property, Inc.; Riverplace 1 Holding, Inc.; William B. May Co.; Wells Fargo Home Mortgage; Tishman Speyer Property; Parish of Trinity Church; Related Partners Inc.
Foundation type: Independent foundation.
Financial data (yr. ended 06/30/13): Assets, $867,395 (M); gifts received, $623,430; expenditures, $623,850; qualifying distributions, $673,850; giving activities include $230,091 for 30 grants (high: $78,802; low: $500).
Purpose and activities: Giving primarily for projects concerning housing and social services.

Fields of interest: Foundations; Human services; Housing services.
Limitations: Applications accepted. Giving primarily in the metropolitan New York, NY, area.
Application information:
 Initial approach: Letter
 Deadline(s): None
Officers: Mary Ann Tighe, Pres.; William Auerbach, C.F.O.; Leonard Boxer, V.P.; Daniel Brodsky, V.P.; Robert Knakal, V.P.; Samuel Lindenbaum, V.P.; Frederick Peters, V.P.; Adam Rose, V.P.; William Rudin, V.P.; Steven Spinola, V.P.; Alan Wiener, V.P.; Donald Zucker, V.P.; Leonard Litwin, Secy.; Joel Picket, Treas.; Angela Pinsky, Exec. Dir.
EIN: 133317104

6657
The Judith and Donald Rechler Foundation, Inc.
c/o Donald Rechler
85 S. Service Rd.
Plainview, NY 11803

Established in 1998 in New York.
Donors: Donald Rechler; Judith Rechler.
Foundation type: Independent foundation.
Financial data (yr. ended 12/31/13): Assets, $3,827,196 (M); expenditures, $257,870; qualifying distributions, $246,700; giving activities include $246,450 for 54 grants (high: $51,000; low: $40).
Fields of interest: Art museums; University education; Diseases and conditions; Judaism.
Type of support: Research.
Limitations: Applications not accepted. Giving primarily in NY.
Application information: Unsolicited requests for funds not accepted.
Directors: Donald Rechler; Judith Rechler; Mitchell Rechler.
EIN: 113430161

6658
The Reich Family Charitable Trust
131 Dover St.
Brooklyn, NY 11235-3719

Established in 1993 in New York.
Donors: Raymond Reich; Sue Reich; Steven Adelsberg.
Foundation type: Independent foundation.
Financial data (yr. ended 12/31/13): Assets, $342,654 (M); gifts received, $268,553; expenditures, $147,260; qualifying distributions, $145,634; giving activities include $145,584 for 56 grants (high: $54,070; low: $36).
Purpose and activities: Giving to Jewish organizations, including temples, yeshivas, and funds.
Fields of interest: Philanthropy; Health; Judaism.
Limitations: Applications not accepted. Giving primarily in Brooklyn, NY. No grants to individuals.
Application information: Unsolicited requests for funds not accepted.
Trustees: Raymond Reich; Sue Reich.
EIN: 137029481

6659
The Reich Fund
c/o Seymour Reich
640 Park Ave.
New York City, NY 10065

Established in 1975 in New York.
Donor: Seymour Reich.
Foundation type: Independent foundation.
Financial data (yr. ended 10/31/14): Assets, $6,417,353 (M); expenditures, $335,313; qualifying distributions, $274,130; giving activities include $274,130 for 32 grants (high: $140,000; low: $100).
Purpose and activities: Giving primarily to Jewish agencies and temples; also support for educational institutions.
Fields of interest: Higher education; Nonprofits; Judaism; Human services.
Type of support: Regranting.
Limitations: Applications not accepted. Giving primarily in NY. No grants to individuals.
Application information: Unsolicited requests for funds not accepted.
Trustees: Elizabeth Brimberg; Stanlee Brimberg; Lilian Reich; Seymour Reich.
EIN: 510166322

6660
Charles and Helen Reichert Family Foundation Inc.
7 Concord Dr. S.
Fort Salonga, NY 11768 (631) 261-7541
Contact: Charles Reichert, Pres.

Donors: Charles Reichert; Helen Reichert.
Foundation type: Independent foundation.
Financial data (yr. ended 12/31/13): Assets, $48,600 (M); gifts received, $400,000; expenditures, $351,500; qualifying distributions, $351,500; giving activities include $351,500 for 6 grants (high: $200,000; low: $1,000).
Fields of interest: Arts and culture; Health; Cancers; Human services.
Limitations: Applications accepted. Giving primarily in NY.
Application information: Application form required.
 Initial approach: Letter
 Deadline(s): None
Officers: Charles Reichert, Pres.; Helen Reichert, V.P.; Ann Reichert, Secy.; Tami Lee Beirele, Treas.
EIN: 462873807

6661
Reidy Family Foundation
c/o Bessemer Trust
630 5th Ave.
New York City, NY 10111-0100

Donors: Francis J. Reidy, Jr.; Juliette T. Reidy; James W. Reidy; Pieter H. Reidy; Michael L. Reidy.
Foundation type: Independent foundation.
Financial data (yr. ended 12/31/14): Assets, $277,969; expenditures, $210,781; qualifying distributions, $209,500.
Fields of interest: Education; Diseases and conditions; Religion.
Limitations: Applications not accepted. Giving primarily in VA.
Application information: Unsolicited requests for funds not accepted.

Trustees: Francis J. Reidy, Jr.; James W. Reidy; Juliette T. Reidy; Michael L. Reidy; Pieter H. Reidy.
EIN: 806051204

6662
Reiss Family Foundation
c/o Georgica Advisors, LLC
152 W. 57th St., 46th Fl.
New York City, NY 10019-3310 (212) 277-5600
Contact: Richard Reiss Jr., Tr.

Established in 1987 in New York.
Donor: Richard Reiss.
Foundation type: Independent foundation.
Financial data (yr. ended 12/31/13): Assets, $2,987,610 (M); expenditures, $389,225; qualifying distributions, $379,550; giving activities include $376,550 for 76 grants (high: $50,000; low: $250).
Fields of interest: Arts and culture; Performing arts; Art museums; Education; Elementary and secondary education; Higher education; Natural resources; Diseases and conditions; Parkinson's disease; Judaism; Human services; Child welfare.
Type of support: Research.
Application information:
 Initial approach: Proposal
 Deadline(s): None
Trustees: Bonnie Reiss; Richard Reiss, Jr.
EIN: 133383095

6663
The Jack and Pearl Resnick Foundation
c/o Jack Resnick & Sons Inc.
110 E. 59th St., 37th Fl.
New York City, NY 10022-1308

Established in 1989 in New York.
Donors: Jack Resnick; Pearl Resnick†.
Foundation type: Independent foundation.
Financial data (yr. ended 03/31/13): Assets, $5,594,166 (M); expenditures, $247,878; qualifying distributions, $242,500; giving activities include $239,000 for 12 grants (high: $50,000; low: $10,000).
Purpose and activities: Giving primarily for higher education, including medical education and theology; support also for Jewish agencies.
Fields of interest: Orchestral music; Graduate and professional education; Medical education; Film and video; Judaism; Theology.
Limitations: Applications not accepted. Giving primarily in Palm Beach, FL and New York, NY. No grants to individuals.
Application information: Unsolicited requests for funds not accepted.
Officers and Directors: Burton P. Resnick, Pres. and Director; Marilyn Katz, V.P. and Secy. and Director; Ira Resnick, V.P. and Director; Steven J. Rotter.
EIN: 133579145

6664
Rexford Fund Inc.
350 5th Ave., Ste. 6730
New York City, NY 10118

Established in 1967 in New York.
Donors: Marcus Schloss & Co., Inc.; Rexford Offshore, LLC; Rexford Management, Inc.; Irwin Schloss.

Foundation type: Company-sponsored foundation.
Financial data (yr. ended 12/31/13): Assets, $7,352,297 (M); gifts received, $300,000; expenditures, $324,646; qualifying distributions, $310,422; giving activities include $310,172 for 66 grants (high: $200,000; low: $40).
Purpose and activities: The foundation supports organizations involved with arts and culture, education, the environment, health, human services, and Judaism.
Fields of interest: Arts and culture; Education; Human services.
Type of support: General support; Capital campaigns.
Limitations: Applications not accepted. Giving primarily in CT and New York, NY. No grants to individuals.
Application information: Contributes only to pre-selected organizations.
Officers and Directors: Douglas Schloss, Pres. and Director; Richard Schloss, Secy. and Director; Irwin Schloss.
EIN: 136222049

6665
Rheinstrom Hill Community Foundation

502 Union St.
Hudson, NY 12534-2816 (518) 828-1565

Established in 1986 in New York.
Donors: Carroll Rheinstrom; Marjorie Rheinstrom; Irene and Carroll Rheinstrom Trust; Rheinstrom Fund.
Foundation type: Independent foundation.
Financial data (yr. ended 05/31/14): Assets, $1,690,772; gifts received, $0; expenditures, $341,757; qualifying distributions, $321,154 and $0 for set-asides.
Purpose and activities: Giving primarily for education, community development, and human services, including fire control and rescue services.
Fields of interest: Arts and culture; Education; Elementary and secondary education; Higher education; Wildlife biodiversity; Wildlife rehabilitation; Health; Hospice care; Libraries; Search and rescue; Fire prevention and control; Community improvement; Christianity; Human services; Food aid; Child welfare; Youth services.
Limitations: Applications accepted. Giving primarily in Columbia County, NY. No grants to individuals.
Application information: Application form required.
Initial approach: Letter
Deadline(s): None
Officers: Richard Koskey, Pres.; Ed Herrington, V.P.; Jean Howe Lossi, Secy.
EIN: 141683989

6666
Lawrence I. & Blanche H. Rhodes Memorial Fund

P.O. Box 7
Wynantskill, NY 12198-0007

Established in 1994 in New York.
Foundation type: Independent foundation.
Financial data (yr. ended 07/31/14): Assets, $1,877,922 (M); expenditures, $213,403; qualifying distributions, $167,675; giving activities include $150,000 for 47 grants (high: $15,000; low: $750).

Purpose and activities: Giving primarily for education and religious organizations.
Fields of interest: Historical activities; Education; Higher education; Graduate and professional education; Dental care; Diseases and conditions; Christianity.
Type of support: Individual development.
Limitations: Applications not accepted. Giving primarily in NY and PA. No grants to individuals.
Application information: Contributes only to pre-selected organizations.
Officers: William J. Dwyer, Pres.; Peter Loomis, Exec. V.P.; John Smirich, V.P.; Fred Eckel, Secy.; Barbara Egnot, Treas.; Dennis Marr, Exec. Dir.
EIN: 222159155

6667
The RHR Family Foundation Inc.

c/o Stanley Marks and Company LLP
32 Fostertown Rd.
Newburgh, NY 12550-1279

Established in 2000 in New York.
Donors: Richard O. Rieger; Heidi G.C. Rieger.
Foundation type: Independent foundation.
Financial data (yr. ended 09/30/14): Assets, $2,662,643 (M); gifts received, $2,225; expenditures, $143,474; qualifying distributions, $143,474; giving activities include $140,000 for 5 grants (high: $50,000; low: $15,000).
Fields of interest: Education; Early childhood education; Health; Community and economic development; Human services.
Limitations: Applications not accepted. Giving primarily in NY. No grants to individuals.
Application information: Contributes only to pre-selected organizations.
Officers: Heidi G.C. Rieger, Pres.; Richard O. Rieger, V.P. and Secy.-Treas.
Director: Jerome L. Levin.
EIN: 134093927

6668
The William L. Richter Family Foundation

(formerly Richter Family Foundation)
c/o Richter Investment Corp.
875 Third Ave., 11th Fl.
New York City, NY 10022
Application address: William L. Richter, c/o Richter Inv. Corp., 299 Park Ave., New York, NY 10171
Tel.: (212) 891-2109

Established in 2005 in New York.
Donors: William L. Richter; Richter Investment Corp.
Foundation type: Independent foundation.
Financial data (yr. ended 12/31/13): Assets, $6,544,168 (M); gifts received, $1,000,000; expenditures, $264,166; qualifying distributions, $219,183; giving activities include $215,183 for 36 grants (high: $100,000; low: $25).
Fields of interest: Arts and culture; Higher education; Economic development; Judaism; Human services; International development.
Limitations: Applications accepted. Giving primarily in CT and NY.
Application information: Application form required.
Initial approach: Contact foundation for application form
Deadline(s): Contact foundation for deadline
Trustees: Ari Richter; William L. Richter.
EIN: 203467361

6669
Ridgewood Foundation

71-02 Forest Ave.
Ridgewood, NY 11385

Donor: Ridgewood Savings Bank.
Foundation type: Company-sponsored foundation.
Financial data (yr. ended 12/31/13): Assets, $4,188,670 (M); gifts received, $750,000; expenditures, $200,640; qualifying distributions, $200,000; giving activities include $200,000 for 2 grants (high: $100,000; low: $100,000).
Purpose and activities: The foundation supports organizations involved with Alzheimer's disease, hunger, housing, human services, and Catholicism.
Fields of interest: Religion; Human services.
Type of support: General support.
Limitations: Applications not accepted.
Application information: Contributes only to pre-selected organizations.
Officers: Peter M. Boger, Pres.; Norman L. McNamme, V.P.; Anthony J. Simeone, V.P.; Laura Camelo, Secy.; Leonard Stekol, Treas.
Trustees: Michael A. Agnes; Henry A. Braun; James J. Dixon; Robert W. Donohue; Margart Mary Fitzpatrick; Paul C. Fitzpatrick; Mary A. Ledermann.
EIN: 050584005

6670
The Robert S. Rifkind Charitable Foundation

825 8th Ave.
New York City, NY 10019-7416

Established in 1986 in New York.
Donors: Robert S. Rifkind; Arleen Rifkind.
Foundation type: Independent foundation.
Financial data (yr. ended 12/31/13): Assets, $665,187 (M); gifts received, $82,976; expenditures, $201,184; qualifying distributions, $195,000; giving activities include $195,000 for 7 grants (high: $70,000; low: $5,000).
Purpose and activities: Giving primarily for Jewish higher education and to Jewish organizations.
Fields of interest: Higher education; Graduate and professional education; Judaism; Theology.
Type of support: General support.
Limitations: Applications not accepted. Giving primarily in New York, NY. No grants to individuals.
Application information: Unsolicited requests for funds not accepted.
Trustee: Robert S. Rifkind.
EIN: 133374924

6671
The Ring Foundation, Inc.

212 5th Ave.
New York City, NY 10010-2103

Established in 1979 in New York.
Donors: Leo Ring; Michael Ring; Frank Ring; Freda Ring.
Foundation type: Independent foundation.
Financial data (yr. ended 05/31/13): Assets, $4,979,210 (M); gifts received, $9,000; expenditures, $329,763; qualifying distributions, $322,454; giving activities include $322,454 for 24 grants (high: $201,250; low: $50).
Purpose and activities: Support for Jewish religious, cultural, and educational institutions.

Fields of interest: Elementary and secondary education; Higher education; Nonprofits; Hospital care; Judaism; Human services.
Type of support: Capital and infrastructure; Regranting.
Limitations: Applications not accepted. Giving primarily in NY. No grants to individuals.
Application information: Unsolicited requests for funds not considered.
Officers: Frank Ring, Pres.; Michael Ring, Secy.; Louise Ring, Treas.
EIN: 133015418

6672
Risen Son Foundation, Inc.
4476 Main St., Ste. 106
Amherst, NY 14226-4463   (716) 839-1292
Contact: Paula Laughlin

Donor: David A. Rich, Sr.
Foundation type: Independent foundation.
Financial data (yr. ended 12/31/13): Assets, $6,147,188 (M); gifts received, $165,000; expenditures, $563,157; qualifying distributions, $460,701; giving activities include $387,350 for 26 grants (high: $75,000; low: $150).
Fields of interest: Arts and culture; Human services; Youth development.
Type of support: General support.
Limitations: Applications accepted. Giving primarily in MS.
Application information:
   Initial approach: Proposal
   Deadline(s): None
Officers: David A. Rich, Sr., Pres.; Grace E. Rich, V.P. and Secy.; David A. Rich, Jr., Treas.
EIN: 204446969

6673
The Toby and Nataly Ritter Family Foundation
c/o Toby G. Ritter
1450 Flagler Dr.
Mamaroneck, NY   10543-4605

Established in 2005 in New York.
Donors: Nataly Ritter; Toby G. Ritter; Ritter Foundation, Inc.
Foundation type: Independent foundation.
Financial data (yr. ended 12/31/13): Assets, $4,470,506 (M); expenditures, $255,038; qualifying distributions, $191,359; giving activities include $186,650 for 48 grants (high: $32,600; low: $100).
Fields of interest: Arts and culture; Museums; University education; Hospital care; Judaism.
Limitations: Applications not accepted. Giving primarily in PA. No grants to individuals.
Application information: Contributes only to pre-selected organizations.
Trustees: Nataly Ritter; Toby G. Ritter.
Number of staff: None.
EIN: 562475574

6674
Irene Ritter Foundation
45 E. 89th St.
New York City, NY   10128

Established in 1999 in New York.

Donors: David Ritter; Ritter Foundation, Inc.
Foundation type: Independent foundation.
Financial data (yr. ended 11/30/13): Assets, $7,008,401 (M); expenditures, $353,351; qualifying distributions, $270,083; giving activities include $241,050 for 33 grants (high: $100,000; low: $250).
Fields of interest: Education; Higher education; Hospital care.
Type of support: Research.
Limitations: Applications not accepted. Giving primarily in New York, NY. No grants to individuals.
Application information: Contributes only to pre-selected organizations.
Officer and Directors: David Ritter, Pres. and Director; Jennifer Ritter; Michael Ritter.
EIN: 134090839

6675
RJL Charitable Foundation
c/o Michael Kessler
42-09 235th St.
Douglaston, NY   11363-1526

Established in 1999 in New York.
Donors: Jeffrey Levine; Randi Levine; Douglas Development; Levine Builders; New Cassel Construction; Darjess LLC; Levine Builders; Jel Family LP; Clinton Management.
Foundation type: Independent foundation.
Financial data (yr. ended 12/31/13): Assets, $14,834 (M); gifts received, $265,000; expenditures, $314,845; qualifying distributions, $305,400; giving activities include $305,400 for 32 grants (high: $45,000; low: $100).
Fields of interest: Performing arts; Museums; Education; Nonprofits; Diseases and conditions; Cancers; Judaism; Youth development.
Type of support: Regranting; Research; Research and evaluation.
Limitations: Applications not accepted. Giving primarily in NY and PA. No grants to individuals.
Application information: Contributes only to pre-selected organizations.
Directors: Michael Kessler; Jeffrey Levine; Randi Levine.
EIN: 113508299

6676
David and Lucille Robbins Foundation, Inc.
c/o Larry Katz
66 S. Tyson Ave.
Floral Park, NY   11001-1805

Donor: David Robbins†.
Foundation type: Independent foundation.
Financial data (yr. ended 12/31/13): Assets, $2,202,336 (M); gifts received, $200,000; expenditures, $163,383; qualifying distributions, $155,000; giving activities include $155,000 for 3 grants (high: $70,000; low: $30,000).
Fields of interest: Nonprofits; Religion; Human services.
Type of support: Regranting.
Limitations: Applications not accepted. Giving primarily in FL, MD and NY.
Application information: Unsolicited requests for funds not accepted.
Officers: Larry Katz, Pres.; Arthur H. Brown, V.P. and Treas.; Janet V. Callea, V.P.; Lauren Cramer, Secy.
EIN: 271536886

6677
Roche Foundation Inc.
c/o Robert G. Wilmers
350 Park Ave., 6th Fl.
New York City, NY   10022-6081

Established in 1997 in New York.
Donor: Robert G. Wilmers.
Foundation type: Independent foundation.
Financial data (yr. ended 11/30/13): Assets, $9,110,923 (M); expenditures, $344,408; qualifying distributions, $337,345; giving activities include $334,145 for 6 grants (high: $120,000; low: $1,000).
Fields of interest: Arts exchange; Art museums; Languages; Botanical gardens.
Limitations: Applications not accepted. Giving primarily in MA and NY. No grants to individuals.
Application information: Contributes only to pre-selected organizations.
Officers: Robert G. Wilmers, Pres.; Elisabeth Roche Wilmers, Treas.
EIN: 161543635

6678
Edward & Ellen Roche Relief Foundation
c/o U.S. Trust, Philanthropic Solutions
1 Bryant Park, NY1-100-28-05
New York City, NY   10036-6715   (646) 743-0425
Contact: Sara Rosen, V.P.
E-mail: sara.rosen@ustrust.com; Main URL: https://www.bankofamerica.com/philanthropic/grantmaking.go

Established in 1930 in New York.
Donor: Edward Roche†.
Foundation type: Independent foundation.
Financial data (yr. ended 12/31/13): Assets, $5,653,735 (M); expenditures, $290,442; qualifying distributions, $247,622; giving activities include $210,000 for grants.
Purpose and activities: The Foundation funds organizations that have a proven track record serving disadvantaged women and youth. Recognizing the diverse array of programs that serve disadvantaged women and youth, the Foundation has chosen to focus its limited resources on projects that address one or more of the following (in no particular order): 1) housing needs of women and families, 2) economic security of low-income women, 3) violence against women, and 4) child welfare.
Fields of interest: Early childhood education; Elementary education; Child educational development; Health; Human services; Child welfare; Child development; Women's services; Females; Ethnic and racial groups; Low-income and poor people.
Type of support: General support; Program development; Seed money.
Limitations: Giving limited to New York City. Generally, no support for individual schools, after-school programs or childcare centers, organizations with annual budgets in excess of $10 million, or organizations that receive more than 75% of annual revenue from government contracts. Generally, no support for health care or disabilities, for endowment campaigns, capital projects, or research.
Publications: Application guidelines; Financial statement; Program policy statement.
Application information: Complete application guidelines are available on foundation web site.

Initial approach: Online through foundation web site

Deadline(s): July 31

Final notification: Dec. 31

Trustee: Bank of America, N.A.

EIN: 135622067

6679

Rock Foundation, Inc.

222 Central Park South

New York City, NY   10019-1408   (212) 765-5399

Contact: Adelaide de Menil, Pres.

Donors: Adelaide de Menil; Arnold D. Friedman; George de Menil; Adelaide de Menil Foundation; ADM Charitable Lead Annuity Trust.

Foundation type: Operating foundation.

Financial data (yr. ended 05/31/12): Assets, $5,362,155 (M); gifts received, $568,211; expenditures, $1,628,989; qualifying distributions, $1,400,892; giving activities include $200,000 for 1 grant.

Fields of interest: Museums; Nonprofits; Child welfare.

International interests: Denmark; Russia.

Type of support: General support; Regranting.

Limitations: Applications accepted. Giving primarily in upstate NY, Houston, TX, Copenhagen, Denmark, and St. Petersburg, Russia.

Application information:

Initial approach: Letter

Deadline(s): Apr. 1

Officers and Directors: Adelaide de Menil, Pres. and Director; Arnold D. Friedman, Secy.-Treas.; James M. Carolan, Secy.; Victoria de Menil; John Doar.

EIN: 060944728

6680

The Rodgers Family Foundation, Inc.

(formerly Richard and Dorothy Rodgers Foundation)

c/o c/o J. Rubenstein Esq.

575 Madison Ave.

New York City, NY   10022-2585

Established in 1952 in New York.

Donors: Richard Rodgers†; Dorothy F. Rodgers†.

Foundation type: Independent foundation.

Financial data (yr. ended 12/31/14): Assets, $10,516,515 (M); expenditures, $462,960; qualifying distributions, $369,548; giving activities include $350,000 for 41 grants (high: $60,000; low: $150).

Purpose and activities: Giving primarily to arts and cultural organizations, as well as a parks organization.

Fields of interest: Arts and culture; Theater; Ethnic museums; Education; Parks; Human services.

Limitations: Applications not accepted. Giving primarily in New York, NY. No grants to individuals.

Application information: Contributes only to pre-selected organizations.

Officers: Linda Rodgers Emory, Pres.; Jasmine M. Campirides Hanif, Esq., Secy.; Joshua S. Rubenstein, Esq., Treas.

EIN: 136062852

6681

The Roe Foundation, Inc.

(formerly G.R.M. Foundation, Inc.)

c/o Pan Am Equities, Inc.

18 E. 50th St.

New York City, NY   10022-6817

Donors: Greg Manocherian; Jed Manocherian; Fraydun Foundation; Domestic Air Conditioning Services, Inc.; John Manocherian; Morris & Gertrude Furman Foundation.

Foundation type: Operating foundation.

Financial data (yr. ended 12/31/13): Assets, $186,250 (M); gifts received, $96,000; expenditures, $216,892; qualifying distributions, $216,892; giving activities include $194,975 for 38 grants (high: $57,200; low: $125).

Fields of interest: Wildlife biodiversity; Hospital care; Human services.

Limitations: Applications not accepted. Giving primarily in NY. No grants to individuals.

Application information: Contributes only to pre-selected organizations.

Officers and Directors: Greg Manocherian, Pres. and Director; John Manocherian, V.P.; Jed Manocherian, Secy. and Director; Edward Ackerman, Treas.

EIN: 133840700

6682

The Roothbert Fund Inc.

475 Riverside Dr., Rm. 1622

New York City, NY   10115-0107   (212) 870-3116

E-mail: mail@roothbertfund.org; *Main URL:* http://www.roothbertfund.org

Established in 1958 in New York.

Donors: Albert Roothbert†; Toni Roothbert†.

Foundation type: Independent foundation.

Financial data (yr. ended 12/31/13): Assets, $4,882,770 (M); gifts received, $26,800; expenditures, $234,103; qualifying distributions, $215,742; giving activities include $148,500 for 52 grants to individuals (high: $4,000; low: $1,500).

Purpose and activities: To assist college or university students who are motivated by spiritual values and have shown distinguished academic achievement, with preference to those considering teaching as a vocation.

Fields of interest: Education; Teacher education.

Type of support: Scholarships; Individual development.

Limitations: Applications accepted. Giving primarily in the ME to NC corridor, with emphasis on those areas in reasonable commutation distances of New Haven, CT, Washington, DC, New York, NY, and Philadelphia, PA. No grants to individuals directly, or for capital funds, endowment funds, operating budgets, general support, special projects, or matching gifts; no loans.

Publications: Application guidelines; Annual report; Informational brochure.

Application information: Interview with Scholarship Committee is a requirement in the application process; interviews take place in Mar., normally in New York, NY, Washington, DC, Philadelphia, PA, and New Haven, CT. Application form required.

Initial approach: Letter with SASE requesting application after Nov. 1

Copies of proposal: 1

Deadline(s): Submit fund form between Nov. 1 and Jan. 31; deadline Feb. 1

Board meeting date(s): Apr. and Oct.; awards grants annually in Apr.

Final notification: Apr.

Officers and Directors: Blake T. Newton III, Pres. and Director; Charles Van Horne, V.P. and Treas. and Director; Jane Friedman Century, V.P. and Director; Leonisa Ardizzone; John P. Devlin; Barbara A. Edwards; James G. Heinegg; Donna M. Johnson; Mark Overmyer-Velazquez; Jeffrey K. Pegram; James A. Rosengarten; Vijay R. Varma; Nathalis W. Wamba; Stephen F. Wilder.

Number of staff: 1 part-time professional.

EIN: 136162570

6683

Rose & Kiernan Charitable Foundation, Inc.

99 Troy Rd.

East Greenbush, NY   12061-1027   (518) 244-4245

Contact: Joseph F. Vitale, Dir.

Main URL: http://www.rkinsurance.com/Site/384000384/531283200.asp

Established in 2001 in New York.

Donor: Rose & Kiernan, Inc.

Foundation type: Company-sponsored foundation.

Financial data (yr. ended 12/31/14): Assets, $2,811,763; gifts received, $256,685; expenditures, $123,492; qualifying distributions, $120,430.

Purpose and activities: The foundation supports organizations involved with higher education, health, cerebral palsy, and human services.

Fields of interest: Higher education; Nonprofits; Health; Hospital care; Health care clinics; Cerebral palsy; Human services; Family services; Child welfare; Developmental disability services.

Type of support: Program development; Scholarships; General support; Regranting.

Limitations: Applications accepted. Giving primarily in areas of company operations in upstate NY.

Application information: Application form required.

Initial approach: Letter

Deadline(s): None

Directors: Charles R. Daniels III; John F. Murray, Jr.; Mark C. Nickel; Joseph F. Vitale.

EIN: 141831866

6684

Marshall Rose Family Foundation, Inc.

(formerly Jill & Marshall Rose Foundation, Inc.)

c/o Georgetown GP

667 Madison Ave.

New York City, NY   10065-8029

Donors: Marshall Rose; Alan R. Grossman.

Foundation type: Independent foundation.

Financial data (yr. ended 11/30/14): Assets, $4,771,174 (M); gifts received, $75,000; expenditures, $427,719; qualifying distributions, $418,915; giving activities include $418,665 for 55 grants (high: $75,000; low: $250).

Fields of interest: Arts and culture; Education; Higher education; Graduate and professional education; Nonprofits; Judaism; Theology; Human services.

Type of support: General support; Annual campaigns; Endowments; Curriculum development; Regranting.

Limitations: Applications not accepted. No grants to individuals.
Application information: Contributes only to pre-selected organizations.
Directors: Simeon Brinberg; Marshall Rose.
EIN: 133036439

6685
The Isabel Rose Foundation
(formerly Jonathan & Isabel Ezrow Foundation)
90 Franklin St., 11th Fl.
New York City, NY 10013-3415
Contact: Peter Lev

Donors: Susan and Elihu Rose Foundation, Inc.; Rose Elihu; Isabel Rose.
Foundation type: Independent foundation.
Financial data (yr. ended 12/31/13): Assets, $1,757,999 (M); gifts received, $159,960; expenditures, $178,302; qualifying distributions, $178,290; giving activities include $178,265 for 39 grants (high: $25,000; low: $125).
Fields of interest: Arts and culture; Education; Judaism.
Limitations: Applications not accepted. Giving primarily in New Haven, CT, and New York, NY. No grants to individuals.
Application information: Unsolicited requests for funds not accepted.
Officer and Director: Isabel Rose, Pres. and Director.
EIN: 134066366

6686
The Wendi and Joseph B. Rose Foundation
200 Madison Ave., 5th Fl.
New York City, NY 10016-3912

Established in 2001 in Delaware.
Donors: Joseph B. Rose; Marshall & Jill Rose Foundation.
Foundation type: Independent foundation.
Financial data (yr. ended 12/31/13): Assets, $1,471,873 (M); expenditures, $311,469; qualifying distributions, $308,050; giving activities include $308,050 for 12 grants (high: $200,000; low: $250).
Fields of interest: Education; University education; Human services.
Limitations: Applications not accepted. Giving primarily in CT and NY. No grants to individuals.
Application information: Unsolicited requests for funds not accepted.
Officers and Directors: Joseph B. Rose, Pres. and Treas. and Director; Wendi Rose, V.P. and Secy. and Director.
EIN: 134168730

6687
The Rose Marrow Fund
200 Madison Ave., 5th Fl.
New York City, NY 10016-3998

Established in 2002 in Delaware.
Donor: Emily Rose.
Foundation type: Independent foundation.
Financial data (yr. ended 12/31/13): Assets, $34,203 (M); gifts received, $183,579; expenditures, $191,870; qualifying distributions,

$190,345; giving activities include $190,345 for 65 grants (high: $15,000; low: $25).
Fields of interest: Higher education; Community and economic development; Judaism.
Limitations: Applications not accepted. Giving primarily in NY. No grants to individuals.
Application information: Contributes only to pre-selected organizations.
Officers: Emily Rose, Pres.; James H. Marrow, V.P.
EIN: 431982037

6688
Rosedorf Foundation
1139 57th St.
Brooklyn, NY 11219-4522
Contact: David Weisz, Pres.

Established in 1999 in New York.
Donors: David Weisz; David Weisz and Sons Inc.
Foundation type: Independent foundation.
Financial data (yr. ended 12/31/13): Assets, $1,509,128 (M); expenditures, $440,920; qualifying distributions, $433,665; giving activities include $433,665 for 63 grants (high: $105,300; low: $100).
Fields of interest: Judaism.
Application information: Application form required.
Initial approach: Letter
Deadline(s): None
Officers: David Weisz, Pres.; Rachelle Weisz, V.P.
EIN: 113523188

6689
Florence & Robert A. Rosen Family Foundation
33 S. Service Rd.
Jericho, NY 11753-1006

Established in 2004 in New York.
Donors: Florence Rosen; Robert A. Rosen.
Foundation type: Independent foundation.
Financial data (yr. ended 12/31/13): Assets, $1,785,693 (M); gifts received, $254,119; expenditures, $270,708; qualifying distributions, $257,730; giving activities include $257,730 for 46 grants (high: $75,000; low: $50).
Fields of interest: Education; Health care clinics; National defense; Judaism; Human services.
Limitations: Applications not accepted. Giving primarily in Jericho, NY. No grants to individuals.
Application information: Contributes only to pre-selected organizations.
Trustees: Florence Rosen; Robert A. Rosen.
EIN: 830411921

6690
The Jack & Mae Rosenberg Charitable Trust
c/o Curtis Mallet
101 Park Ave., Ste. 3500
New York City, NY 10178-0061

Established in 1995 in New York.
Donor: Herbert Stoller.
Foundation type: Independent foundation.
Financial data (yr. ended 12/31/14): Assets, $4,058,124 (M); expenditures, $206,196; qualifying distributions, $163,990; giving activities include $153,000 for 3 grants (high: $105,000; low: $20,000).

Fields of interest: Education; University education; Specialty hospital care; Autism.
Type of support: Public engagement and education.
Limitations: Applications not accepted. Giving primarily in CT, MA, Baltimore, MD and NY. No grants to individuals.
Application information: Unsolicited requests for funds not accepted.
Trustee: Herbert Stoller.
EIN: 137050361

6691
Thomas Jefferson Rosenberg Foundation Inc.
5 Hanover Sq., 23rd Fl.
New York City, NY 10004-2614   (212) 869-1490

Established in 1989 in New York.
Donor: Henry Rosenberg.
Foundation type: Independent foundation.
Financial data (yr. ended 12/31/13): Assets, $1,372,488 (M); gifts received, $344,725; expenditures, $370,776; qualifying distributions, $359,863; giving activities include $353,370 for 26 grants (high: $100,000; low: $50).
Purpose and activities: Giving for higher education, Jewish agencies, and human service organizations.
Fields of interest: Arts and culture; Undergraduate education; Diseases and conditions; Judaism; Human services.
Limitations: Applications accepted. Giving primarily in NY.
Application information: Application form required.
Initial approach: Proposal
Deadline(s): None
Officers: Henry Rosenberg, Pres.; Carol Rosner, Secy.
EIN: 133436858

6692
The Jonathan & Lisa Rosenstein Charitable Foundation
53 Park Dr. S.
Rye, NY 10580-1826

Donors: Jonathan Rosenstein; Lisa Rosenstein.
Foundation type: Independent foundation.
Financial data (yr. ended 06/30/13): Assets, $2,025 (M); gifts received, $342,000; expenditures, $340,180; qualifying distributions, $340,180; giving activities include $340,000 for 3 grants.
Fields of interest: Education; Higher education; Diseases and conditions; Human services.
Type of support: General support.
Limitations: Applications not accepted. Giving primarily in PA.
Application information: Unsolicited requests for funds not accepted.
Trustees: Jonathan Rosenstein; Lisa Rosenstein.
EIN: 273212846

6693
Barbara & William Rosenthal Family Foundation
1 Court Sq., 19th Fl.
Long Island City, NY 11120

Established in 1998 in New York.

Donors: Dr. William Rosenthal; Mrs. William Rosenthal; Edward Morris Bakwin; Barbara Bakwin Rosenthal Trust.
Foundation type: Independent foundation.
Financial data (yr. ended 06/30/14): Assets, $7,922,331 (M); gifts received, $116,816; expenditures, $366,988; qualifying distributions, $332,994; giving activities include $300,000 for 11 grants (high: $50,000; low: $10,000).
Fields of interest: Education; Hospital care; Autism; National defense; Sports and recreation; Women's services.
Limitations: Applications not accepted. Giving primarily in New York, NY. No grants to individuals.
Application information: Unsolicited requests for funds not accepted.
Trustee: Citibank, N.A.
EIN: 226753977

6694
Robert and Jodi Rosenthal Family Foundation

c/o First Long Island Investors, Inc.
1 Jericho Plz., Ste. 201
Jericho, NY 11753—1656 (516) 935-1200
Contact: Robert D. Rosenthal, Tr.
E-mail: robert@fliinvestors.com

Established in 1996 in New York.
Donors: Robert D. Rosenthal; Jodi Rosenthal.
Foundation type: Independent foundation.
Financial data (yr. ended 12/31/13): Assets, $123,288 (M); gifts received, $90,556; expenditures, $170,110; qualifying distributions, $169,925; giving activities include $169,925 for 25 grants (high: $71,400; low: $100).
Purpose and activities: Giving primarily for education, Jewish organizations, and medical centers.
Fields of interest: Health; Religion; Human services.
Limitations: Applications accepted. Giving primarily in NY.
Application information:
  Initial approach: Proposal
  Deadline(s): Oct. 31
Trustees: Jodi Rosenthal; Robert D. Rosenthal.
EIN: 113357219

6695
Harry and Andrew H. Rosenthal Foundation, Inc.

c/o Maxwell Shmerler & Co.
11 Martine Ave., Ste. 970
White Plains, NY 10606-4027

Donor: Andrew H. Rosenthal.
Foundation type: Independent foundation.
Financial data (yr. ended 02/28/14): Assets, $1,725,552 (M); gifts received, $150,000; expenditures, $193,276; qualifying distributions, $192,500; giving activities include $192,500 for 21 grants (high: $35,000; low: $4,000).
Fields of interest: Education; Health; Hospital care; Human services.
Limitations: Applications not accepted. Giving primarily in NY. No grants to individuals.
Application information: Unsolicited requests for funds not accepted.

Officers: Andrew H. Rosenthal, Pres.; Katherine Edersheim Tuckman, V.P.; William A. Shmerler, Secy.; Bruce A. Tuckman, Treas.
EIN: 132631210

6696
The Ida and William Rosenthal Foundation

131 E. 66th St., Apt. 10C
New York City, NY 10065 (212) 879-9353

Established in 1953 in New York.
Donors: Ida Rosenthal†; William Rosenthal†.
Foundation type: Independent foundation.
Financial data (yr. ended 08/31/14): Assets, $3,367,285 (M); expenditures, $177,796; qualifying distributions, $149,614; giving activities include $144,250 for 20 grants (high: $20,000; low: $200).
Purpose and activities: Grants are awarded to selected educational institutions primarily for scholarships, and to arts organizations mainly for educational outreach programs and museum publications.
Fields of interest: Arts and culture; Education; Human services.
Limitations: Applications accepted. Giving primarily in the New York City metropolitan area. No grants to individuals, or for matching gifts or capital campaigns; no loans.
Publications: Grants list.
Application information: Application form required.
  Initial approach: Proposal
  Deadline(s): Aug. 31
Officers and Directors: Catherine Coleman Brawer, Pres. and Director; Robert A. Brawer, Secy. and Director; Christopher P. Brawer, Treas. and Director; Nicholas A. Brawer; Wendy H. Brawer.
Number of staff: 1 part-time professional.
EIN: 136141274

6697
Birkas Rosh Foundation Inc.

1570 46th St.
Brooklyn, NY 11219-2725 2127680151
Application address: Usher Brecher, 14 Maple Leaf Rd., Monsey, NY 10952, tel.: (845) 426-3147

Established in 2000 in New York.
Donors: Judah Brecher; Joel Brecher; Michael Brecher; Bernat Steinmetz; Elky Spiegel; Feigie Spiegel; Amy Steinmetz; Michael Steinmetz; Yechiel Spiegel.
Foundation type: Independent foundation.
Financial data (yr. ended 06/30/14): Assets, $4,202,076; gifts received, $135,637; expenditures, $124,215; qualifying distributions, $116,950.
Fields of interest: Judaism.
Limitations: Applications accepted. Giving primarily in NY. No grants to individuals.
Application information:
  Initial approach: Proposal
  Deadline(s): None
Officers: Usher Brecher, Pres.; Helen Brecher, V.P.; Michael Steinmetz, Secy.-Treas.
EIN: 311732874

6698
Leo Rosner Foundation, Inc.

6 Westway
White Plains, NY 10605-3523 (914) 682-2800
Contact: William D. Robbins, Pres.

Established in 1960 in New York.
Foundation type: Independent foundation.
Financial data (yr. ended 10/31/13): Assets, $11,377,250 (M); expenditures, $621,992; qualifying distributions, $530,268; giving activities include $422,100 for 31 grants (high: $50,000; low: $5,000).
Fields of interest: Arts and culture; Museums; Education; Higher education; Nonprofits; Hospital care; Community and economic development; Judaism; Human services.
Type of support: Program development; Convening; Scholarships; Regranting.
Limitations: Applications accepted. Giving primarily in CT and NY.
Application information:
  Initial approach: Proposal
  Deadline(s): None
  Board meeting date(s): Mid-Oct.
Officers and Directors: William D. Robbins, Pres. and Director; Mildred R. Caplow, V.P. and Director; June Rosner, V.P. and Director; Marcy Wachtel, V.P. and Director; Amy H. Caplow Chan, Secy.-Treas. and Director.
Number of staff: 1 part-time professional.
EIN: 136161637

6699
Waldo T. & Ruth S. Ross Charitable Trust Foundation

c/o Glens Falls National Bank Trust
P.O. Box 216
Glens Falls, NY 12801-3505

Established in 2009 in New York.
Donor: Ruth S. Ross†.
Foundation type: Independent foundation.
Financial data (yr. ended 12/31/14): Assets, $6,179,755; expenditures, $282,508; qualifying distributions, $252,436 and $0 for set-asides.
Fields of interest: Arts and culture; Religion; Human services.
Limitations: Applications not accepted. Giving primarily in NY. No grants to individuals.
Application information: Unsolicited requests for funds not accepted.
Trustees: Robert Hafner; Kevin O'Brien; Glens Falls National Bank & Trust Co.
EIN: 276594166

6700
Roth Family Foundation Inc.

(formerly White-Roth Family Foundation, Inc.)
c/o Nancy Roth
14 Foxwood Rd.
Great Neck, NY 11024-1202

Established in 2000 in Florida.
Donor: Ruth G. White†.
Foundation type: Independent foundation.
Financial data (yr. ended 12/31/12): Assets, $2,904,087 (M); expenditures, $242,720; qualifying distributions, $222,500; giving activities include $222,500 for grants.
Fields of interest: Nonprofits.

Type of support: Regranting.
Limitations: Applications accepted. Giving primarily in NY.
Application information:
 Initial approach: Proposal
 Deadline(s): None
Officer: Larry Roth, Pres.
Director: Nancy A. Roth.
EIN: 650917154

6701

Marcia and Phillip Rothblum Foundation
(formerly David Rothblum Foundation, Inc.)
c/o Rothblum
575 Madison Ave., Ste. 1000
New York City, NY 10017

Established in 1998 in New York.
Donors: Philip Rothblum; Marcia Rothblum.
Foundation type: Independent foundation.
Financial data (yr. ended 12/31/13): Assets, $978,436 (M); gifts received, $325,000; expenditures, $172,189; qualifying distributions, $167,649; giving activities include $165,500 for 35 grants (high: $25,000; low: $500).
Fields of interest: Foundations; Family planning; Abortion; Judaism.
Limitations: Applications not accepted. Giving primarily in NY and PA. No grants to individuals.
Application information: Unsolicited requests for funds not accepted.
Officers: Philip Rothblum, Pres.; Joyce R. Weidenaar, Secy.; Lisa Rothblum, Treas.
EIN: 112125721

6702

Pamela and Stuart Rothenberg Foundation
Bowling Green Sta.
P.O. Box 73
New York City, NY 10274-0073

Established in 1996 in New York.
Donors: Stuart M. Rothenberg; Pamela Rothenberg.
Foundation type: Independent foundation.
Financial data (yr. ended 07/31/14): Assets, $4,506,617 (M); expenditures, $175,144; qualifying distributions, $171,300; giving activities include $171,300 for 11 grants (high: $50,000; low: $2,500).
Fields of interest: Education; Foundations; Health; Human services; Child welfare; Children.
Limitations: Applications not accepted. Giving primarily in New York, NY. No grants to individuals; no loans or scholarships.
Application information: Contributes only to pre-selected organizations.
Trustees: Pamela Rothenberg; Stuart M. Rothenberg.
EIN: 137109412

6703

Henry and Gertrude Rothschild Foundation Inc.
162 E. 80th St.
New York City, NY 10075-0426
Contact: Diana Parker

Established in 1986 in New York.
Donors: Henry Rothschild; Gertrude Rothschild.
Foundation type: Independent foundation.

Financial data (yr. ended 08/31/13): Assets, $0 (M); expenditures, $285,867; qualifying distributions, $257,455; giving activities include $257,455 for 1 grant.
Purpose and activities: Giving for nature conservation and health and medical services.
Fields of interest: Domesticated animals.
Limitations: Applications not accepted. Giving primarily in Washington, DC and FL. No grants to individuals.
Application information: Unsolicited requests for funds not accepted.
Officer: Diana Parker, Pres.
EIN: 133370395

6704

The Maks & Lea Rothstein Charitable Youth Trust
535 W. 110th St.
New York City, NY 10025-2086 (212) 222-0309
Contact: Yehoshua Berinstein
Main URL: http://www.rothsteintrust.org

Donor: Maks Rothstein†.
Foundation type: Operating foundation.
Financial data (yr. ended 12/31/13): Assets, $23,589,759 (M); gifts received, $15,979; expenditures, $634,196; qualifying distributions, $586,001; giving activities include $395,952 for 49 grants (high: $104,392; low: $800).
Fields of interest: Education; University education; Judaism; Child welfare.
Type of support: General support.
Limitations: Applications not accepted. No grants to individuals.
Application information: Contributes only to pre-selected organizations.
Officer: Sergio Rothstein, Chair.
Board of Directors: Michael Gewirtz; Meir Hertz; Robert Katz; Gary Litke; Seth Ottensosser; Joe Paul; Daniel Victor.
EIN: 316652819

6705

John W. and Jeanne M. Rowe Foundation
c/o The Ayco Company-NTG
P.O. Box 15014
Albany, NY 12212-5014

Donors: Jeanne M. Rowe; John W. Rowe.
Foundation type: Independent foundation.
Financial data (yr. ended 12/31/13): Assets, $11,148,782 (M); gifts received, $1,018,337; expenditures, $279,726; qualifying distributions, $229,566; giving activities include $229,566 for 10 grants (high: $50,000; low: $2,500).
Fields of interest: Arts and culture; Diseases and conditions; Community and economic development.
Limitations: Applications not accepted. Giving primarily in Chicago, IL.
Application information: Unsolicited requests for funds not accepted.
Trustees: Jeanne M. Rowe; John W. Rowe.
EIN: 453694862

6706

The Roxe Foundation
c/o Bessemer Trust
630 5th Ave.
New York City, NY 10111-0001

Established in 1997 in Connecticut.
Donors: Joseph D. Roxe; Maureen L. Roxe.
Foundation type: Independent foundation.
Financial data (yr. ended 12/31/14): Assets, $3,481,950; expenditures, $343,646; qualifying distributions, $319,917.
Purpose and activities: Giving to support education, the performing arts, health care, and medical research.
Fields of interest: Arts and culture; Orchestral music; Education; Secondary education; Higher education; Medical education; Diseases and conditions; Cancers; Libraries; Religion; Christianity.
Type of support: Research; Research and evaluation.
Limitations: Applications not accepted. Giving primarily in CT and NY. No grants to individuals.
Application information: Contributes only to pre-selected organizations.
Officer and Trustee: Joseph D. Roxe, Chair. and Trustee.
Number of staff: 1 part-time support.
EIN: 061480884

6707

The Nancy & Miles Rubin Foundation
(formerly The Jacob & Mae D. Rubin Foundation)
c/o Citrin Cooperman & Co. LLP
529 5th Ave.
New York City, NY 10017

Established in 1961 in Connecticut.
Donors: Miles Rubin; Andrew Rosen; Nancy Rubin.
Foundation type: Independent foundation.
Financial data (yr. ended 10/31/14): Assets, $700,031 (M); gifts received, $871; expenditures, $291,005; qualifying distributions, $285,800; giving activities include $285,800 for 32 grants (high: $50,000; low: $1,000).
Fields of interest: Education; Philanthropy; Human services; Females.
Type of support: General support.
Limitations: Applications not accepted. Giving primarily in CA, NY and Washington, DC. No grants to individuals.
Application information: Unsolicited requests for funds not accepted.
Trustees: Miles Rubin; Nancy Rubin.
EIN: 136092976

6708

Nathan Rudy & Sons Foundation, Inc.
711 Ave. R
Brooklyn, NY 11223-2211

Established in 1989 in New York.
Donors: Edward M. Rudy; Isaac Rudy.
Foundation type: Independent foundation.
Financial data (yr. ended 12/31/13): Assets, $0 (M); gifts received, $169,041; expenditures, $170,748; qualifying distributions, $169,560; giving activities include $169,560 for grants.
Purpose and activities: Giving primarily to Orthodox Jewish organizations.
Fields of interest: Education; Nonprofits; Orthodox Judaism; Human services.
Type of support: General support; Regranting.
Limitations: Applications not accepted. Giving primarily in Brooklyn, NY.

Application information: Contributes only to pre-selected organizations.
Trustees: Edward M. Rudy; Isaac Rudy.
EIN: 112943196

6709
The Rum Fund
200 Madison Ave., 5th Fl.
New York City, NY   10016-3903
Contact: Michael Blum

Established in 1998 in Delaware.
Donor: Susan and Elihu Rose Foundation, Inc.
Foundation type: Independent foundation.
Financial data (yr. ended 12/31/13): Assets, $5,040,557 (M); gifts received, $500,000; expenditures, $231,204; qualifying distributions, $142,933; giving activities include $142,933 for 72 grants (high: $9,000; low: $29).
Fields of interest: Arts and culture; Education; Religion.
Type of support: General support.
Limitations: Applications not accepted. Giving primarily in MN and NY. No grants to individuals.
Application information: Contributes only to pre-selected organizations.
Officers: Abigail Rose, Pres.; Michael Blum, V.P.
EIN: 134022921

6710
The Richard W. Rupp Foundation
1806 Liberty Bldg.
Buffalo, NY   14202-3618

Established in 1998 in New York.
Donor: Richard W. Rupp.
Foundation type: Independent foundation.
Financial data (yr. ended 12/31/13): Assets, $10,318,059 (M); expenditures, $567,265; qualifying distributions, $468,508; giving activities include $420,000 for 47 grants (high: $40,000; low: $1,000).
Fields of interest: Human services.
Type of support: General support.
Limitations: Applications not accepted. Giving primarily in Buffalo, NY. No grants to individuals.
Application information: Contributes only to pre-selected organizations.
Directors: Chester E. Borczynski; Peter J. Brevorka; Christina D. Rupp; Susan S. Rupp; William R. Rupp.
EIN: 161551594

6711
Russo Family Charitable Foundation Inc.
3710 Milestrip Rd.
Blasdell, NY   14219-1527

Established in 1988 in New York.
Donors: Celia Russo; John A. Russo; Joseph L. Russo.
Foundation type: Independent foundation.
Financial data (yr. ended 12/31/13): Assets, $5,433,537 (M); expenditures, $336,320; qualifying distributions, $260,800; giving activities include $260,800 for 29 grants (high: $27,000; low: $200).
Fields of interest: Arts and culture; Education; Higher education; Nonprofits; Health; Hospital care; Hospice care; Catholicism; Camps; Human services.

Type of support: Regranting.
Limitations: Applications not accepted. Giving primarily in NY. No grants to individuals.
Application information: Contributes only to pre-selected organizations.
Officers: Joseph L. Russo, Pres.; Celia Russo, V.P.; John A. Russo, Secy.-Treas.
EIN: 161339086

6712
The Russo Family Foundation
1170 5th Ave., Ste 12B
New York City, NY   10029-6527

Established in 2006 in New York.
Donor: Thomas A. Russo.
Foundation type: Independent foundation.
Financial data (yr. ended 06/30/13): Assets, $1,429,357 (M); gifts received, $160,797; expenditures, $151,745; qualifying distributions, $151,745; giving activities include $148,939 for 26 grants (high: $90,000; low: $39).
Fields of interest: Education; Health; Community and economic development.
Limitations: Applications not accepted. Giving primarily in NY. No grants to individuals.
Application information: Unsolicited requests for funds not accepted.
Officers and Directors: Thomas Russo, Pres. and Director; Marcy Russo, Secy.-Treas. and Director.
EIN: 203950808

6713
The Ruth Foundation
136-20 38th Ave., Ste. 11D
Flushing, NY   11354-4232

Established in 1999 in New York.
Donors: Eglisau Estates Ltd.; Alison G. Fung; Eglisau Estate Family, LP.
Foundation type: Independent foundation.
Financial data (yr. ended 12/31/13): Assets, $21,654 (M); gifts received, $296,000; expenditures, $311,345; qualifying distributions, $310,431; giving activities include $306,775 for 14 grants (high: $100,475; low: $500).
Fields of interest: Health; Diseases and conditions; Religion.
Limitations: Applications not accepted. Giving primarily in NY.
Application information: Contributes only to pre-selected organizations.
Officers: Lai Wah Fung, Pres.; Alison G. Fung, V.P. and Secy.-Treas.
Directors: Stephen G. Fung; Robert C. Lee.
EIN: 113507688

6714
Betty and Irving Ruthen Private Foundation Inc.
1217 E. 27th St.
Brooklyn, NY   11210-4622   (917) 913-1452

Foundation type: Independent foundation.
Financial data (yr. ended 12/31/13): Assets, $92,582 (M); gifts received, $358,000; expenditures, $352,222; qualifying distributions, $351,337; giving activities include $351,337 for 1 + grant.
Fields of interest: Education; Human services.

Application information: Application form required.
Initial approach: Letter
Deadline(s): None
Directors: Ephraim Zagelbaum; Pincus D. Zagelbaum; Yechiel Zagelbaum; Yoel Zagelbaum.
EIN: 800590280

6715
The Derald H. Ruttenberg Foundation
800 3rd Ave., 40th Fl.
New York City, NY   10022-7604

Established in 1985 in New York.
Donors: Derald H. Ruttenberg; Rutco, Inc.; Tinicum Investors; Eric M. Ruttenberg; Hattie Ruttenberg.
Foundation type: Independent foundation.
Financial data (yr. ended 03/31/13): Assets, $211,698 (M); gifts received, $452,096; expenditures, $281,757; qualifying distributions, $280,644; giving activities include $280,644 for 58 grants (high: $96,613; low: $100).
Fields of interest: Arts and culture; Ballet; Art museums; Education; Medical education; Hospital care; Racquet sports; Children.
Limitations: Applications not accepted. Giving primarily in DC, MA and NY. No grants to individuals.
Application information: Unsolicited requests for funds not accepted.
Directors: Eric M. Ruttenberg; John C. Ruttenberg.
EIN: 133317499

6716
Raymond and Beverly Sackler Foundation, Inc.
17 E. 62nd St.
New York City, NY   10065-7204

Established in 1967 in New York.
Donors: Richard S. Sackler, MD; Jonathan D. Sackler; Raymond R. Sackler, MD; Beverly Sackler.
Foundation type: Operating foundation.
Financial data (yr. ended 12/31/14): Assets, $7,838,246 (M); expenditures, $1,814,879; qualifying distributions, $1,744,997; giving activities include $401,136 for 4 grants (high: $200,000; low: $25,000), and $1,351,741 for foundation-administered programs.
Fields of interest: Medical education; Diseases and conditions.
Type of support: General support; Research.
Limitations: Applications not accepted. Giving primarily in Washington, DC and New York, NY. No grants to individuals.
Application information: Contributes only to pre-selected organizations.
Officers and Directors: Jonathan D. Sackler, C.E.O. and Pres. and Director; Raymond R. Sackler, MD, V.P.; Richard S. Sackler, MD, V.P. and Director; Beverly Sackler, Secy.-Treas. and Director; Evan Vosburgh, Exec. Dir.
Number of staff: 7 full-time professional; 5 part-time professional.
EIN: 237022467

6717
Raymond & Beverly Sackler Fund for the Arts & Sciences
17 E. 62nd St.
New York City, NY   10021

Established in 2001 in Delaware.
Donors: Raymond R. Sackler, MD; Jonathan D. Sackler; Beverly Sackler; Richard S. Sackler, MD; Purdue Pharma, Inc.; PLP Associates Holdings, Inc.
Foundation type: Independent foundation.
Financial data (yr. ended 12/31/13): Assets, $6,996,161 (M); expenditures, $306,907; qualifying distributions, $281,056; giving activities include $281,056 for 9 grants (high: $125,000; low: $5,000).
Purpose and activities: Giving primarily for the arts, higher education, medical research, and to a hospital.
Fields of interest: Arts and culture; Ballet; Opera; Higher education; Hospital care; Diseases and conditions.
Type of support: Research; Research and evaluation.
Limitations: Applications not accepted. Giving primarily in CT, MA, and NY. No grants to individuals.
Application information: Contributes only to pre-selected organizations.
Officers and Directors: Beverly Sackler, Chair. and Secy.-Treas.; Jonathan D. Sackler, Pres. and C.E.O. and Director; Raymond R. Sackler, MD, V.P.; Richard S. Sackler, MD, V.P. and Director.
EIN: 134085037

6718
The Sakhai Family Foundation, Inc.
c/o Lisa Sakhai
5 The Drawbridge
Woodbury, NY   11797-1013

Donors: Lisa A. Sakhai; Sakhai Family Philanthrophy Trust; David K. Sakhai Charitable Lead Trust; Lisa A. Sakhai Charitable Lead Trust.
Foundation type: Independent foundation.
Financial data (yr. ended 12/31/13): Assets, $330,572 (M); gifts received, $240,000; expenditures, $176,514; qualifying distributions, $162,014; giving activities include $162,014 for 66 grants (high: $50,155; low: $150).
Fields of interest: Diseases and conditions; Religion; Human services.
Limitations: Applications not accepted. Giving primarily in NY.
Application information: Unsolicited requests for funds not accepted.
Officers and Directors: William Ahdout, Pres. and Director; Kenneth Grossman, V.P. and Director; Lisa A. Sakhai, Secy.-Treas. and Director.
EIN: 264728895

6719
The Katherine M. and Richard J. Salisbury 54 Endowment Fund
c/o Christina T. Seagroatt
79 N. Pearl St.
Albany, NY   12207

Foundation type: Independent foundation.
Financial data (yr. ended 06/30/13): Assets, $1,327,846 (M); expenditures, $186,529; qualifying distributions, $162,860; giving activities include $162,860 for 1 grant.
Fields of interest: Christianity.
Limitations: Applications not accepted. Giving primarily in NY.
Application information: Unsolicited requests for funds not accepted.

Trustee: Christina L. Tangredi Seagroatt.
EIN: 546460461

6720
The Sallie Foundation, Inc.
c/o Brahman Capital Corp.
655 3rd Ave., 11th Fl.
New York City, NY   10017-9119

Established in 1995 in New York.
Donors: Braham Securities, Inc.; Gary Gladstein; Jordan Seaman; Mitchell A. Kuflik; Robert L. Goldstein; BTIG, LLC; A. Alex Porter; Bruce Richards; Avis Richards; Chip Kaye; Sheryl Kaye; Dan Kilmurray; Eagle Capital; George Weiss; Greenlight Capital; Paul Orlin; Victoria Orlin; Penza Family Foundation; Seth Rosen; Libby Rosen; The Starker Family Foundation; Tom Facciola; The Grateful Foundation; Marilyn Sultz; Faythe K. Kurtz; Irving Sultz; Rachel Rader; Julie and Martin Franklin Charitable Foundation; Kenneth Rader; Meryl & Charles Witmer Charitable Foundation; Robert Rubenstein; Alan Matson; E. Katia Rubenstein; David P. Larkin; Bill D'Eredita; The Roskind Family Foundation; Wendy Kerdell; David Kerdell; Josh Slan; Stacy Hochfelder; Peter Hochfelder; Stacey Cohn; Emile Lester; Diane Monaco; Kinha Lester; Loren Katzovitz; Michael Dubin; Elizabeth Landau; Victoria Dubin; Kim Katzovitz; Melissa Saperstein; Lisa Cummins; Susan Bender; Terri Wein; Evan Wein; Howard Bender; Robert Saperstein.
Foundation type: Independent foundation.
Financial data (yr. ended 12/31/13): Assets, $495,947 (M); gifts received, $125,948; expenditures, $340,129; qualifying distributions, $339,600; giving activities include $339,600 for 5 grants (high: $260,000; low: $1,000).
Fields of interest: Education; Disasters and emergency management; Human services.
Limitations: Applications not accepted. Giving primarily in NY. No grants to individuals.
Application information: Unsolicited requests for funds not accepted.
Officers: Mitchell A. Kuflik, Pres.; Robert J. Sobel, V.P.; Peter A. Hochfelder, Secy.
Director: Alan Eisenberg.
EIN: 133842759

6721
The William R. and Virginia F. Salomon Family Foundation, Inc.
c/o Baker Tilly
1 Penn Plz., Ste. 3000
New York City, NY   10119-0032

Established in 1954 in New York.
Donor: William R. Salomon.
Foundation type: Independent foundation.
Financial data (yr. ended 12/31/13): Assets, $1,277,962 (M); expenditures, $184,855; qualifying distributions, $172,183; giving activities include $168,100 for 19 grants (high: $100,000; low: $100).
Fields of interest: Arts and culture; Education; Health.
Type of support: General support; Annual campaigns; Capital and infrastructure; Research.
Limitations: Applications not accepted. Giving primarily in New York, NY. No grants to individuals.
Application information: Unsolicited requests for funds not accepted.

Officer and Directors: William R. Salomon, Pres. and Treas. and Director; Susan S. Neiman; Peter F. Salomon.
EIN: 136088823

6722
Richard and Bette Saltzman Foundation
262 Central Park W., Apt. 9A
New York City, NY   10024-3512

Established in 2001 in New York.
Donors: Richard Saltzman; Bette Saltzman.
Foundation type: Independent foundation.
Financial data (yr. ended 12/31/13): Assets, $2,810,486 (M); expenditures, $302,748; qualifying distributions, $300,090; giving activities include $300,090 for 43 grants (high: $72,000; low: $100).
Fields of interest: Elementary and secondary education; Immune system diseases; Judaism.
Limitations: Applications not accepted. Giving primarily in NY. No grants to individuals.
Application information: Unsolicited requests for funds not accepted.
Officers: Richard B. Saltzman, Pres. and Treas.; Bette A. Saltzman, V.P. and Secy.
EIN: 522361828

6723
The Joe & Sandy Samberg Foundation, Inc.
4 Ann Ln.
Rye, NY   10580-4102

Established in 2007 in New York.
Donors: Joseph Samberg; Sandra Samberg.
Foundation type: Independent foundation.
Financial data (yr. ended 06/30/14): Assets, $1,548,642 (M); expenditures, $165,648; qualifying distributions, $157,041; giving activities include $157,041 for 57 grants (high: $60,000; low: $50).
Fields of interest: Human services; Youth services.
Limitations: Applications not accepted. Giving primarily in NY. No grants to individuals.
Application information: Contributes only to pre-selected organizations.
Officers: Sandra Samberg, Pres.; Joseph Samberg, V.P.
Director: Robert Michaelson.
EIN: 260469459

6724
The Rebecca and Arthur Samberg Foundation
c/o Arthur Samberg
77 Bedford Rd.
Katonah, NY   10536-2141

Foundation type: Independent foundation.
Financial data (yr. ended 11/30/13): Assets, $826,256 (M); expenditures, $421,712; qualifying distributions, $419,056; giving activities include $416,306 for 17 grants (high: $151,586; low: $1,000).
Fields of interest: Arts and culture; Human services; Child welfare.
Limitations: Applications not accepted. Giving primarily in Westchester County, NY.
Application information: Contributes only to pre-selected organizations.

Officers: Rebecca Samberg, Pres. and Treas.; Laura Samberg, V.P. and Secy.
EIN: 542113024

6725
Ernest & Rose Samuels Foundation Inc.
c/o Feldheim
8 Hillcrest Ln.
Woodbury, NY   11797-1102

Established in 1977 in Florida.
Donor: Ernest Samuels.
Foundation type: Independent foundation.
Financial data (yr. ended 12/31/13): Assets, $3,890,689 (M); expenditures, $248,278; qualifying distributions, $178,528; giving activities include $146,528 for 29 grants (high: $7,500; low: $2,264).
Fields of interest: Museums; Natural resources; Housing development; Judaism; Human services; Food aid.
Limitations: Applications not accepted. Giving primarily in NY. No grants to individuals.
Application information: Unsolicited requests for funds not accepted.
Officers: Herbert D. Feldheim, Pres.; Deborah Feldheim, Secy.
EIN: 591733119

6726
Sani Family Foundation Inc.
34-09 Queens Blvd.
Long Island City, NY   11101

Established in 1965 in New York.
Donors: CGS Industries, Inc.; Lal C. Sani; Ashok Sani; Triple SSS Partnership L.P.
Foundation type: Independent foundation.
Financial data (yr. ended 01/31/14): Assets, $5,385,892; gifts received, $414,360; expenditures, $224,486; qualifying distributions, $224,486.
Purpose and activities: Giving primarily for higher education, health organizations, social services, and to Hindu organizations.
Fields of interest: Higher education; Diseases and conditions; Hinduism; Human services.
Limitations: Applications not accepted. Giving primarily in NY. No grants to individuals.
Application information: Contributes only to pre-selected organizations.
Officers and Directors: Sham G. Sani, Pres.; Lal C. Sani, V.P. and Secy. and Director.
Trustees: Sunil Sani; Suresh Sani.
EIN: 136201183

6727
The Peg Santvoord Foundation Inc.
c/o Meyer Handelman Co., LLC
P.O. Box 817
Purchase, NY   10577-0817   9149394060
Application address: c/o Donn Russell, Dir., 200 Waverly Pl., New York, NY 10014, tel.: (212) 242-5249

Established in 1966 in New York.
Foundation type: Independent foundation.
Financial data (yr. ended 06/30/14): Assets, $803,281; expenditures, $169,704; qualifying distributions, $165,121.

Purpose and activities: The foundation makes grants only to theater venues. Eligible venues must be open all year, have a box office where tickets may be purchased, and must advertise as such.
Fields of interest: Performing arts.
Type of support: Program development.
Limitations: Applications accepted. Giving limited to New York, NY. No support for theater groups. No grants to individuals.
Application information: Application form required.
   Initial approach: Letter
   Deadline(s): None
Officers and Directors: William R. Handelman, Pres. and Treas. and Director; Russell J. Handelman, V.P. and Secy. and Director; Joseph W. Handelman; Donn Russell.
EIN: 136183822

6728
Sargol Charitable Trust
412 Ave. C
Brooklyn, NY   11218-4518   (212) 603-6141
Contact: Asher Goodman

Donor: Asher Goodman.
Foundation type: Independent foundation.
Financial data (yr. ended 12/31/13): Assets, $7,627,752 (M); gifts received, $281,368; expenditures, $204,112; qualifying distributions, $204,112; giving activities include $203,237 for 2 + grants (high: $200,000).
Fields of interest: Religion; Human services.
Type of support: General support; Scholarships.
Limitations: Applications accepted. Giving primarily in Brooklyn, NY. No grants to individuals directly.
Application information: Application form required.
   Initial approach: Letter
   Deadline(s): None
Trustees: Rachel Goodman; Yitzchok Goodman; Raphael Grossman.
EIN: 116478559

6729
Ann and Richard Sarnoff Family Foundation
15 W. 81st St., 14th Fl.
New York City, NY   10024-6022

Donors: Ann Sarnoff; Richard Sarnoff.
Foundation type: Independent foundation.
Financial data (yr. ended 12/31/13): Assets, $270,632 (M); gifts received, $100,000; expenditures, $214,908; qualifying distributions, $214,255; giving activities include $214,255 for 47 grants (high: $50,000; low: $100).
Fields of interest: Arts and culture; Education; Religion.
Limitations: Applications not accepted.
Application information: Unsolicited requests for funds not accepted.
Trustees: Ann Sarnoff; Richard Sarnoff.
EIN: 206673225

6730
Abdul Satar & Family Foundation
57-07 31st Ave.
Woodside, NY   11377-1210

Donor: Shock Coffee LLC.
Foundation type: Independent foundation.

Financial data (yr. ended 12/31/13): Assets, $525,245 (M); gifts received, $250,000; expenditures, $395,450; qualifying distributions, $393,000; giving activities include $393,000 for 29 grants (high: $49,000; low: $2,000).
Fields of interest: Religion.
Limitations: Applications not accepted. Giving primarily in NY.
Application information: Unsolicited requests for funds not accepted.
Officers: Hakim Najmi, Pres.; Ghulam Ali Najimi, V.P.; Solyman Najimi, Secy.
EIN: 454046375

6731
The Sato Family Foundation, Inc
c/o Colibri
237 W. 37th St., 10th Fl.
New York City, NY   10018-5704

Established in 2001 in New York.
Donors: Joseph Wechsler; Samuel Wechsler; MTS Assocs. LLC.
Foundation type: Independent foundation.
Financial data (yr. ended 12/31/13): Assets, $6,041,896 (M); expenditures, $460,452; qualifying distributions, $444,479; giving activities include $441,200 for 15 grants (high: $145,000; low: $200).
Purpose and activities: Giving primarily to Jewish agencies and federated giving programs.
Fields of interest: Nonprofits; Judaism; Human services.
International interests: Belgium.
Type of support: Regranting.
Limitations: Applications not accepted. Giving on a national and international basis, with emphasis on Brooklyn, NY, and Antwerp, Belgium.
Application information: Unsolicited requests for funds not accepted.
Directors: Joseph Wechsler; Samuel Wechsler.
EIN: 134140924

6732
Jed David Satow Family Foundation, Inc.
c/o Phillip M.Satow
583 Broadway
New York City, NY   10012-3211

Established in 1999 in New York.
Donors: Phillip M. Satow; Donna Satow.
Foundation type: Independent foundation.
Financial data (yr. ended 12/31/13): Assets, $1,150,105 (M); expenditures, $292,290; qualifying distributions, $289,190; giving activities include $288,545 for 1 grant.
Fields of interest: Higher education; Judaism.
Type of support: General support; Continuing support; Endowments; Scholarships.
Limitations: Applications not accepted. No grants to individuals.
Application information: Contributes only to pre-selected organizations.
Officers and Directors: Donna Satow, Pres. and Director; Julie Satow, Secy.-Treas.; Michael Satow; Phillip M. Satow.
EIN: 134067343

6733
Saunders Foundation
762 Brooks Ave.
Rochester, NY 14619-2234

Established in 1986 in New York.
Donors: Lewis Tree; Carl Myers; Ann Myers.
Foundation type: Independent foundation.
Financial data (yr. ended 12/31/13): Assets,
$1,168,767 (M); gifts received, $540;
expenditures, $216,501; qualifying distributions,
$206,454; giving activities include $206,164 for 31
grants (high: $74,656; low: $100).
Fields of interest: Undergraduate education;
Medical education; Nonprofits; Hospital care;
Protestantism; Human services.
Type of support: Regranting.
Limitations: Applications not accepted. Giving
primarily in upstate NY. No grants to individuals.
Application information: Contributes only to
pre-selected organizations.
Officers: Carole M. Saunders, Pres.; Patricia
Redding, V.P.; Robert Sant, Jr., Secy.-Treas.
EIN: 161289330

6734
The Alisa and Peter Savitz Foundation
(formerly HPS Foundation)
c/o BCRS Assocs., LLC
77 Water St., 9th Fl.
New York City, NY 10005-3701

Established in 1993 in New York.
Donor: Peter Savitz.
Foundation type: Independent foundation.
Financial data (yr. ended 05/31/14): Assets,
$4,731,557 (M); expenditures, $312,453;
qualifying distributions, $270,953; giving activities
include $265,453 for 40 grants (high: $50,000;
low: $5).
Fields of interest: Theater; Elementary and
secondary education; Foundations; Judaism;
Human services.
Limitations: Applications not accepted. No grants to
individuals; no loans or scholarships.
Application information: Unsolicited requests for
funds not accepted.
Trustees: Alisa B. Savitz; Peter Savitz.
EIN: 133748074

6735
Roberta Schaefer Family Foundation
3 Colonial Dr.
Upper Brookville, NY 11545-2811
Contact: Roberta Waller

Foundation type: Independent foundation.
Financial data (yr. ended 05/31/13): Assets,
$7,391,076 (M); expenditures, $391,743;
qualifying distributions, $329,552; giving activities
include $329,552 for 10 grants (high: $111,302;
low: $500).
Fields of interest: Health; Hospital care; Diseases
and conditions; Diabetes; Religion; Judaism.
Type of support: General support; Research.
Limitations: Applications not accepted. Giving
primarily in NY.
Application information: Unsolicited requests for
funds not accepted.

Officers and Directors: Roberta Waller, Pres. and
Director; Bruce Waller, V.P. and Secy. and Director.
EIN: 452036152

6736
H. Schaffer Foundation Inc.
2 Claire Pass
Saratoga Springs, NY 12866 (802) 438-2676
Contact: Sonya A. Stall, Pres.

Established in 1982 in New York.
Donor: Henry Schaffer†.
Foundation type: Independent foundation.
Financial data (yr. ended 10/31/14): Assets,
$3,088,248 (M); expenditures, $163,451;
qualifying distributions, $156,623; giving activities
include $154,500 for 5 grants (high: $100,000;
low: $1,000).
Fields of interest: Arts and culture; Education;
Human services.
Limitations: Applications accepted. Giving primarily
in NY. No support for political organizations.
Application information:
Initial approach: Letter of request
Copies of proposal: 1
Deadline(s): None
Board meeting date(s): Annually
Officers: Sonya A. Stall, Pres.; Andrea B. Shay, V.P.;
Jeffrey R. Stall, MD, Secy.-Treas.
Number of staff: 3 part-time support.
EIN: 222325485

6737
The Irving and Geraldine Schaffer
Foundation, Inc.
165 Underhill Rd.
Scarsdale, NY 10583-1006 (914) 899-3500
Contact: Robin Schaffer, Pres. and Treas.

Established in 1968 in New York.
Donors: Irving Schaffer†; Geraldine Schaffer†.
Foundation type: Independent foundation.
Financial data (yr. ended 12/31/14): Assets,
$6,083,387 (M); expenditures, $364,181;
qualifying distributions, $288,649; giving activities
include $288,649 for 35 grants (high: $25,000;
low: $250).
Purpose and activities: Giving primarily for Jewish
institutions and for higher education.
Fields of interest: Higher education; Graduate and
professional education; Medical education;
Nonprofits; Judaism; Theology; Human services.
Type of support: Regranting.
Application information: Application form required.
Initial approach: Letter
Deadline(s): None
Officers: Robin Schaffer, Pres. and Treas.; Peter
Schaffer, V.P. and Secy.
Directors: Frederick P. Schaffer; S. Andrew Schaffer.
EIN: 132626706

6738
Morris & Dvora Scharf Foundation, Inc.
c/o Robins and Assocs., LLP
247 W. 35th St., 14th Fl.
New York City, NY 10001-1908

Established in 2000 in New York.
Donors: Morris Scharf; Dvora Scharf.
Foundation type: Independent foundation.

Financial data (yr. ended 12/31/12): Assets,
$9,186,826 (M); expenditures, $365,200;
qualifying distributions, $363,300; giving activities
include $362,700 for grants.
Fields of interest: Judaism.
Limitations: Applications not accepted. No grants to
individuals.
Application information: Contributes only to
pre-selected organizations.
Officers and Directors: Tsvi Scharf, V.P. and
Director; Dvora Scharf, Secy. and Director; Lipa
Scharf, Treas. and Director; Morris Scharf, Mgr. and
Director.
EIN: 134115138

6739
Leopold Schepp Foundation
551 5th Ave., Ste. 3000
New York City, NY 10176-3201 (212) 692-0191
Main URL: http://www.scheppfoundation.org

Established in 1925 in New York.
Donors: Leopold Schepp†; Florence L. Schepp†.
Foundation type: Independent foundation.
Financial data (yr. ended 02/28/13): Assets,
$10,125,550 (M); gifts received, $141,597;
expenditures, $862,772; qualifying distributions,
$778,534; giving activities include $344,500 for 57
grants to individuals (high: $8,500; low: $1,000).
Purpose and activities: Giving primarily to assist
young men and women of character and ability who
have insufficient means to complete their vocational
or professional education. Undergraduate
scholarships to individuals under 30 years of age;
graduate scholarships to individuals under 40 years
of age; a small number of fellowships for
independent study and research to individuals in the
arts and literature, medicine, and oceanography.
Fields of interest: Education; Higher education.
Type of support: Fellowships; Grants to individuals;
Student aid.
Limitations: Applications accepted. Giving to
students on a national basis. No grants for already
incurred debt.
Application information: See foundation web site
for current information and deadlines.
Board meeting date(s): May and Oct.
Officers and Trustees: Barbara McLendon, Pres.
and Trustee; William L.D. Barrett, V.P. and Trustee;
Kathryn Batchelder Cashman, V.P. and Trustee; Sue
Ann Dawson, V.P. and Trustee; James G. Turino,
Treas.; SuzanneClair Guard, Exec. Dir.; Edythe
Bobrow; Louise M. Bozorth; Susan Brenner; Anne
Coffin; Emily Crawford; Betty David; William G.
Gridley, Jr.; Nancy Grossman; Diana P. Hermann;
Michele A. Paige; Elizabeth Stone Potter; Bruno A.
Quinson; Robert F. Reder, MD; Banning Repplier.
Number of staff: 1 full-time professional; 1 full-time
support; 2 part-time support.
EIN: 135562353

6740
The Howard and Debbie Schiller
Foundation
P.O. Box 73
Bowling Green Sta.
New York City, NY 10274-0073

Established in 1996 in New York.
Donor: Howard B. Schiller.
Foundation type: Independent foundation.

Financial data (yr. ended 06/30/13): Assets, $8,450,358 (M); gifts received, $1,094,558; expenditures, $373,125; qualifying distributions, $317,933; giving activities include $317,933 for 8 grants (high: $100,000; low: $2,500).
Fields of interest: Education; University education; Religion; Human services.
Limitations: Applications not accepted. Giving primarily in MI, NJ and New York, NY. No grants to individuals.
Application information: Contributes only to pre-selected organizations.
Trustees: Debbie Schiller; Howard B. Schiller.
EIN: 133933626

6741
Schiro Family Foundation
c/o The Ayco Co., LP-NTG
P.O. Box 15014
Albany, NY   12212-5014

Established in 1999 in New Jersey.
Donors: James Schiro; CVC Capital Partners.
Foundation type: Independent foundation.
Financial data (yr. ended 12/31/12): Assets, $2,096,473 (M); gifts received, $40,000; expenditures, $212,980; qualifying distributions, $201,000; giving activities include $201,000 for 2 grants (high: $200,000; low: $1,000).
Fields of interest: Education; Sports and recreation.
Type of support: General support.
Limitations: Applications not accepted. Giving primarily in NJ and NY. No grants to individuals.
Application information: Unsolicited requests for funds not accepted.
Trustees: James Schiro; Tomasina Schiro.
EIN: 226825661

6742
Priscilla & Richard J. Schmeelk Foundation Inc.
c/o J. Anderson
1003 Park Blvd., Ste. 4
Massapequa Park, NY   11762-2741

Established in 1983 in New York.
Donor: Richard J. Schmeelk.
Foundation type: Independent foundation.
Financial data (yr. ended 12/31/13): Assets, $1,717,170 (M); gifts received, $142,187; expenditures, $415,961; qualifying distributions, $401,925; giving activities include $401,925 for 24 grants (high: $15,000; low: $1,000).
Fields of interest: Education; Health; Hospital care; Catholicism; Judaism; Child welfare; Children; Adolescents.
International interests: Canada.
Type of support: Continuing support; Annual campaigns; Endowments; Scholarships.
Limitations: Applications not accepted. Giving primarily in New York, NY. No grants to individuals.
Publications: Annual report.
Application information: Contributes only to pre-selected organizations.
Officers: Richard J. Schmeelk, Pres. and Treas.; Priscilla M. Schmeelk, V.P. and Secy.
Directors: Andrew C. Schmeelk; Matthew R. Schmeelk.
EIN: 133126387

6743
Helen & Irving Schneider Foundation
1125 5th Ave.
New York City, NY   10128-0143

Donors: Irving Schneider; Helen Schneider; Is Revocable Trust.
Foundation type: Independent foundation.
Financial data (yr. ended 12/31/13): Assets, $3,079,111 (M); gifts received, $34,600; expenditures, $171,001; qualifying distributions, $167,636; giving activities include $165,000 for 5 grants (high: $50,000; low: $25,000).
Fields of interest: Arts and culture; Education; Judaism.
Limitations: Applications not accepted. Giving primarily in New York, NY. No grants to individuals.
Application information: Unsolicited requests for funds not accepted.
Officers: Lynn C. Schneider, V.P. and Secy.; Mindy Schneider, V.P. and Secy.
EIN: 136165503

6744
Schonberger Family Foundation
166 Hillair Cir.
White Plains, NY   10605-4506

Established in 1987 in New York.
Donors: Elias Schonberger; David Schonberger; Mark Schonberger; Stuart Schonberger; Nadine Shaoul.
Foundation type: Independent foundation.
Financial data (yr. ended 12/31/13): Assets, $4,805,188 (M); gifts received, $268,879; expenditures, $208,413; qualifying distributions, $183,579; giving activities include $175,979 for 101 grants (high: $75,000; low: $15).
Fields of interest: Arts and culture; Undergraduate education; Religion; Human services.
Limitations: Applications not accepted. Giving primarily in New York, NY. No grants to individuals.
Application information: Unsolicited requests for funds not accepted.
Officers: Elias Schonberger, Pres. and Treas.; David Schonberger, V.P.; Mark Schonberger, V.P.; Stuart Schonberger, V.P.
EIN: 133314123

6745
Schonfeld Family Foundation
57 W. 57th St., Ste. 512
New York City, NY   10019-2802   (212) 319-9393
Contact: Arnold Schonfeld, Tr.

Established in 1971 in New York.
Donors: Arnold Schonfeld; Sidney Schonfeld.
Foundation type: Independent foundation.
Financial data (yr. ended 12/31/13): Assets, $5,933,190 (M); gifts received, $210,000; expenditures, $275,826; qualifying distributions, $275,049; giving activities include $275,049 for 27 grants (high: $34,250; low: $500).
Purpose and activities: Giving primarily for Jewish organizations.
Fields of interest: Education; Judaism.
Limitations: Applications accepted. Giving primarily in NY. No grants to individuals.
Application information: Application form required.
Initial approach: Letter
Deadline(s): None

Trustee: Arnold Schonfeld.
EIN: 237113225

6746
The Steven B. Schonfeld Foundation, Inc.
1 Jericho Plz.
Jericho, NY   11753-1680

Established in 2001 in Delaware.
Donor: Steven B. Schonfeld.
Foundation type: Independent foundation.
Financial data (yr. ended 12/31/13): Assets, $1,015,736 (M); gifts received, $175,000; expenditures, $175,402; qualifying distributions, $175,212; giving activities include $174,750 for 20 grants (high: $110,500; low: $25).
Fields of interest: Education; Philanthropy; Health.
Limitations: Applications not accepted. Giving primarily in New York, NY. No grants to individuals.
Application information: Unsolicited requests for funds not accepted.
Officers: Steven B. Schonfeld, Pres.; Kathryn Licursi, V.P.; Harriet Sue Schonfeld, V.P.
EIN: 134166757

6747
Schonkopf Family Foundation
466 Central Ave.
Cedarhurst, NY   11516-2007

Established in 1997 in New York.
Donors: Albert Schonkopf; Esplain Associates Three, LLC.
Foundation type: Independent foundation.
Financial data (yr. ended 12/31/13): Assets, $901,688 (M); gifts received, $118,000; expenditures, $243,071; qualifying distributions, $241,299; giving activities include $241,051 for 263 grants (high: $20,000; low: $15).
Fields of interest: Judaism; Human services.
Limitations: Applications not accepted. No grants to individuals.
Application information: Contributes only to pre-selected organizations.
Trustees: Albert Schonkopf; Tova Schonkopf.
EIN: 133935025

6748
The School of Dreams, Inc.
148 Lafayette St., 3rd Fl.
New York City, NY   10013-3115

Donors: Lafayette 148, Inc.; Harvey Lok; Cindy Yang; Eric Sit; Kevin Bauer; Yuk Chun Lok; Deirdre Quinn; Ida Siu.
Foundation type: Independent foundation.
Financial data (yr. ended 12/31/13): Assets, $109,623 (M); gifts received, $201,293; expenditures, $201,293; qualifying distributions, $201,293; giving activities include $200,974 for 1 grant.
Fields of interest: Education.
International interests: China.
Limitations: Applications not accepted. Giving primarily in China.
Application information: Unsolicited requests for funds not accepted.

Officers: Ida Siu, Chair.; Charles P. Wang, Secy.; Harvey Lok, Treas.
EIN: 320280578

6749
The Lewis Schott Foundation
c/o A. Kozak and Co.
192 Lexington Ave., Ste. 1100
New York City, NY   10016-6823

Donor: Lewis M. Schott.
Foundation type: Independent foundation.
Financial data (yr. ended 12/31/13): Assets, $313,926 (M); gifts received, $376,100; expenditures, $233,723; qualifying distributions, $229,889; giving activities include $227,250 for 12 grants (high: $100,000; low: $250).
Purpose and activities: Giving primarily for health and human services, and to a Jewish federated giving program.
Fields of interest: Arts and culture; Education; Nonprofits; Family planning; Diseases and conditions; Racquet sports; Human services.
Type of support: Regranting.
Limitations: Applications not accepted. No grants to individuals.
Application information: Contributes only to pre-selected organizations.
Officers: Lewis M. Schott, Pres.; Nash W. Schott, Secy.
Directors: Victoria de Rothschild; Steven G. Schott.
EIN: 581969908

6750
E. & M. Schreiber Family Foundation
180 Riverside Dr.
New York City, NY   10024-1021
Application address: c/o Morris Schreiber, 1715 44th St., Brooklyn, N.Y. 11204, tel.: (718) 972-9692

Established in 1988 in New York.
Donors: Emanuel Schreiber; Mary Schreiber; Morris Schreiber.
Foundation type: Independent foundation.
Financial data (yr. ended 06/30/13): Assets, $1,503,168 (M); gifts received, $15,000; expenditures, $197,209; qualifying distributions, $197,209; giving activities include $197,115 for 10 grants (high: $50,000; low: $215).
Fields of interest: Education; Judaism.
Limitations: Applications accepted. Giving primarily in NY. No grants to individuals.
Application information:
   Initial approach: Letter
   Deadline(s): 30 days before end of fiscal year
Directors: Mary Schreiber; Morris Schreiber.
EIN: 133475648

6751
Schwalbe Brothers Foundation Inc.
185 Madison Ave., Ste. 1700
New York City, NY   10016-4325

Established in 1945 in New York.
Foundation type: Independent foundation.
Financial data (yr. ended 12/31/12): Assets, $1,381,883 (M); expenditures, $323,573; qualifying distributions, $312,900; giving activities include $312,900 for grants.

Purpose and activities: Giving primarily to Jewish temples and organizations, and for Jewish education.
Fields of interest: Education; Graduate and professional education; Judaism; Theology.
Limitations: Applications not accepted. Giving primarily in New York, NY. No grants to individuals.
Application information: Unsolicited requests for funds not accepted.
Officer: Peter Schwalbe, Secy.-Treas.
Directors: James Schwalbe; Jeremy Schwalbe; Robert Schwalbe.
EIN: 136162779

6752
Barry K. Schwartz Family Foundation
159 Mahopac Ave.
Granite Springs, NY   10527-1127

Established in 1987 in Delaware.
Donor: Barry K. Schwartz.
Foundation type: Independent foundation.
Financial data (yr. ended 10/31/13): Assets, $57,891 (M); gifts received, $326,480; expenditures, $338,956; qualifying distributions, $336,450; giving activities include $336,450 for 35 grants (high: $154,000; low: $20).
Fields of interest: Diseases and conditions; Judaism; Human services; Family services; Child welfare.
Limitations: Applications not accepted. Giving primarily in NY and Providence, RI. No grants to individuals.
Application information: Contributes only to pre-selected organizations.
Officers: Barry K. Schwartz, Pres.; Sheryl R. Schwartz, V.P.
EIN: 133472786

6753
The Schwartz Family Foundation
(formerly Samuel & Bertha Schwartz Foundation)
c/o CSSC
65A Monroe Ave.
Pittsford, NY   14534-1318   (585) 248-0960

Established in 1951 in New York.
Donor: Herman H. Schwartz‡.
Foundation type: Independent foundation.
Financial data (yr. ended 12/31/13): Assets, $11,240,922 (M); expenditures, $343,075; qualifying distributions, $385,100; giving activities include $385,100 for 28 grants (high: $243,500; low: $250).
Purpose and activities: Giving primarily for Jewish welfare and temple support, as well as to a musical theater festival, and for education.
Fields of interest: Theater; Education; Higher education; Judaism; Human services.
Type of support: Annual campaigns; Capital and infrastructure; Equipment; Scholarships.
Limitations: Applications accepted. Giving primarily in Auburn and New York, NY. No grants to individuals.
Application information: Application form required.
   Initial approach: Letter
   Deadline(s): None
Officers and Trustees: Lois Ellenoff, Chair. and Trustee; Bradley W. Schwartz, Pres. and Trustee; Gregory Ellenoff, Treas. and Trustee; Debra S. Ellenoff; Douglas Ellenoff; Margery Schwartz.

Number of staff: 1 part-time support.
EIN: 156017667

6754
David Schwartz Foundation, Inc.
c/o Sacks Co.
600 3rd Ave., Rm. 1801
New York City, NY   10016-1918

Established in 1945 in New York.
Donors: Jonathan Logan, Inc.; David Schwartz.
Foundation type: Independent foundation.
Financial data (yr. ended 05/31/13): Assets, $9,594,570 (M); expenditures, $479,061; qualifying distributions, $315,796; giving activities include $315,796 for grants.
Fields of interest: Arts and culture; Theater; Higher education; Nonprofits.
Type of support: General support; Regranting.
Limitations: Applications not accepted. Giving primarily in NY, with emphasis on the metropolitan New York area. No grants to individuals.
Application information: Unsolicited requests for funds not accepted.
   Board meeting date(s): Annually, usually in May or June
Officers and Directors: Richard J. Schwartz, Pres. and Director; John Schwartz, V.P. and Director; Sheila Schwartz, V.P. and Director; Jenny Schwartz Stone, V.P. and Director; Stephen D. Gardner, Treas. and Director.
EIN: 226075974

6755
Arnold & Marie Schwartz Fund for Education and Health Research
465 Park Ave.
New York City, NY   10022-1919

Established in 1971 in Delaware.
Donor: Arnold Schwartz Charitable Trust.
Foundation type: Independent foundation.
Financial data (yr. ended 03/31/13): Assets, $1,451,157 (M); expenditures, $371,442; qualifying distributions, $255,080; giving activities include $255,080 for grants.
Purpose and activities: Giving primarily for the arts, higher education, particularly a college of pharmacy, environmental education, and health organizations.
Fields of interest: Opera; Art museums; Higher education; Environmental studies; Diseases and conditions; Community and economic development.
Type of support: General support; Capital and infrastructure; Scholarships.
Limitations: Applications not accepted. Giving primarily in New York, NY.
Application information: Unsolicited requests for funds not accepted.
Officer and Directors: Ruth Kerstein, Secy. and Director; Sylvia Kossel.
Trustee: Marie D. Schwartz.
EIN: 237115019

6756
The Steven Schwartzberg Foundation, Inc.
12 Wrights Mill Rd.
Armonk, NY   10504-1142

Donors: Harris Schwartzberg; Judy Starer; Al Schwartzberg; Nicole Schwartzberg; Florence Schwartzberg.
Foundation type: Independent foundation.
Financial data (yr. ended 12/31/13): Assets, $1,300,202 (M); expenditures, $322,270; qualifying distributions, $320,065; giving activities include $315,000 for 2 grants (high: $300,000; low: $15,000).
Fields of interest: Higher education.
Type of support: Scholarships.
Limitations: Applications not accepted. Giving primarily in Ann Arbor, MI.
Application information: Unsolicited requests for funds not accepted.
Officers: Harris Schwartzberg, Pres.; Nicole Schwartzberg, Secy.; Al Schwartzberg, Treas.
EIN: 262415050

6757
Schwarz Family Foundation
211 E. 70th St., Ste. 23A
New York City, NY 10021-5208

Established in 1998 in New York.
Donor: Jeffrey E. Schwarz.
Foundation type: Independent foundation.
Financial data (yr. ended 12/31/13): Assets, $232,644 (M); gifts received, $296,636; expenditures, $219,987; qualifying distributions, $219,930; giving activities include $219,930 for 30 grants (high: $26,000; low: $100).
Purpose and activities: Giving primarily for Jewish organizations and education.
Fields of interest: Education; Judaism.
Limitations: Applications not accepted. Giving primarily in New York, NY. No grants to individuals.
Application information: Contributes only to pre-selected organizations.
Trustees: Joel Greenblatt; Rabbi Irwin Kula; Jeffrey E. Schwarz; Sherwood Schwarz.
EIN: 226743828

6758
Edith M. Schweckendieck Trust
1 Court Sq., 19th Fl.
Long Island City, NY 11120

Established in 1922 in New York.
Donor: Edith M. Schweckendieck†.
Foundation type: Independent foundation.
Financial data (yr. ended 12/31/14): Assets, $4,458,045; expenditures, $208,807; qualifying distributions, $203,259.
Fields of interest: Cancers; Child welfare; Senior services; Seniors; People with disabilities.
Type of support: General support; Capital and infrastructure; Endowments.
Limitations: Applications not accepted. Giving primarily in NY. No grants to individuals.
Application information: Contributes only to pre-selected organizations.
Trustee: Citibank, N.A.
EIN: 136055135

6759
William P. & Gertrude Schweitzer Foundation, Inc.
317 Madison Ave., Ste. 614
New York City, NY 10017-5225

Established in 1961 in New York.
Donor: Gertrude Schweitzer†.
Foundation type: Independent foundation.
Financial data (yr. ended 12/31/13): Assets, $3,170,372 (M); expenditures, $140,859; qualifying distributions, $130,000; giving activities include $130,000 for 17 grants (high: $25,000; low: $1,000).
Fields of interest: Arts and culture; Orchestral music; Museums; Animal welfare; Judaism.
Limitations: Applications not accepted. Giving primarily in New York, NY. No grants to individuals.
Application information: Unsolicited requests for funds not accepted.
Officers: Peter Schweitzer, C.E.O. and Pres. and Director; Penelope Ayers, Secy.
EIN: 136160772

6760
C. Schwimmer Charity Foundation
211 Wallabout St.
Brooklyn, NY 11206-4926

Foundation type: Independent foundation.
Financial data (yr. ended 11/30/13): Assets, $0 (M); gifts received, $437,500; expenditures, $434,553; qualifying distributions, $423,553; giving activities include $423,553 for 54+ grants (high: $86,300).
Fields of interest: Religion; Judaism.
Limitations: Applications not accepted.
Application information: Unsolicited requests for funds not accepted.
Trustee: Cheskel Schwimmer.
EIN: 461556476

6761
The Elizabeth and Stanley D. Scott Foundation Inc.
145 Hudson St., Ste. 10B
New York City, NY 10013-2103

Established in 2000 in New York.
Donors: Stanley D. Scott; Elizabeth Scott.
Foundation type: Independent foundation.
Financial data (yr. ended 06/30/13): Assets, $4,446,431 (M); gifts received, $1,424,029; expenditures, $220,888; qualifying distributions, $186,463; giving activities include $186,463 for 89 grants (high: $10,000; low: $100).
Fields of interest: Arts and culture; Historical activities; Genealogy; Historic preservation; Education; Protestantism; Human services; Females.
Limitations: Applications not accepted. Giving primarily in NY. No grants to individuals.
Application information: Contributes only to pre-selected organizations.
Directors: Peter Kimmelman; Elizabeth Scott; Stanley D. Scott.
EIN: 134144166

6762
The William C. and Cindy L. Scott Foundation
445 Park Ave., Ste. 1905
New York City, NY 10022-8617

Established in 1997 in Delaware.
Donor: William C. Scott.

Foundation type: Independent foundation.
Financial data (yr. ended 04/30/14): Assets, $1,953,039; expenditures, $191,363; qualifying distributions, $137,450.
Fields of interest: Arts and culture; Education; Health.
Limitations: Applications accepted. Giving primarily in NY.
Application information: Application form required.
  Initial approach: Letter
  Deadline(s): None
Officers: William C. Scott, Pres.; Cindy L. Scott, Secy.
EIN: 133999250

6763
The Joseph C. and Judith A. Scully Foundation
204 Montery Ave.
Pelham, NY 10803-2310
Application address: c/o Joseph C. Scully, Tr., 15202 Lakeshore Rd., Lakeside, MI 49116

Established in 1999 in Illinois.
Donors: Joseph Scully; Judith Scully.
Foundation type: Independent foundation.
Financial data (yr. ended 12/31/13): Assets, $511,974 (M); gifts received, $212,425; expenditures, $238,742; qualifying distributions, $187,600; giving activities include $187,600 for 15 grants (high: $125,000; low: $100).
Fields of interest: Education; University education; Employment; Sports and recreation.
Limitations: Applications accepted. Giving primarily in Chicago, IL. No grants to individuals.
Application information:
  Initial approach: Letter
  Deadline(s): None
Trustees: Joseph C. Scully; Judith A. Scully.
EIN: 367295474

6764
Sdei Israel Foundation, Inc.
1570 46th St.
Brooklyn, NY 11219-2725 (718) 436-1353
Contact: Abraham Weingarten

Established in 2000 in New York.
Donors: Netherland Mgmt. Co.; Joel Spiegel; Park Mgmt.; Sutton Mgmt.; Minam Spiegel; Amy Steinmetz; Pessie Richard; Feiga Spiegel; Bernat Steinmetz; Abraham Weingarten; Elka Spiegel; Michael Steinmetz; Yechiel Spiegel; Lee Cohen; Sara Spiegel; Isreal Spiegel.
Foundation type: Independent foundation.
Financial data (yr. ended 06/30/14): Assets, $4,449,813 (M); gifts received, $457,011; expenditures, $207,430; qualifying distributions, $199,817; giving activities include $199,817 for 40 grants (high: $30,000; low: $250).
Fields of interest: Education; Religion; Judaism; Human services.
Limitations: Applications accepted. Giving primarily in NY.
Application information:
  Initial approach: Proposal
  Deadline(s): None
Officers: Michael Steinmetz, Pres.; Sarah Spiegel, V.P. and Secy.; Joel David Spiegel, V.P.
EIN: 311732886

6765
SDF Family Foundation
1442 51st St.
Brooklyn, NY 11219-3605

Established in 1997 in New York.
Donor: Samuel D. Friedman.
Foundation type: Independent foundation.
Financial data (yr. ended 12/31/13): Assets, $0 (M); gifts received, $356,334; expenditures, $323,537; qualifying distributions, $294,521; giving activities include $294,521 for 20+ grants.
Fields of interest: Religion; Judaism; Human services.
Limitations: Applications not accepted. No grants to individuals.
Application information: Unsolicited requests for funds not accepted.
Directors: Chaya V. Friedman; Samuel D. Friedman.
EIN: 113347643

6766
Seacoast Foundation
c/o Gelfand Rennert & Feldman, LLP
360 Hamilton Ave., Ste. 100
White Plains, NY 10601-1847 (212) 307-8000
Contact: Jeffrey Rosen, Mgr.

Established in 1969 in New York.
Donor: Robert Dylan.
Foundation type: Operating foundation.
Financial data (yr. ended 12/31/13): Assets, $448 (M); gifts received, $107,000; expenditures, $137,985; qualifying distributions, $137,960; giving activities include $137,960 for 37 grants (high: $110,000; low: $100).
Fields of interest: Arts and culture; Health; Diseases and conditions; Television; Judaism; Human services; Child welfare; Senior services; Seniors.
Type of support: Research; Research and evaluation.
Limitations: Applications accepted. Giving primarily in NY. No grants to individuals.
Application information: Application form required.
Initial approach: Letter
Deadline(s): None
Officers: Robert Dylan, Mgr.; Jeffery Rosen, Mgr.; Mario Testani, Mgr.
EIN: 237034949

6767
Seaman Family Foundation
500 N. Broadway, Ste. 238
Jericho, NY 11753-2128

Established in 1987 in New York.
Donor: Morton Seaman.
Foundation type: Independent foundation.
Financial data (yr. ended 10/31/14): Assets, $1,125,075 (M); expenditures, $270,776; qualifying distributions, $229,401; giving activities include $211,455 for 19 grants (high: $78,200; low: $25).
Purpose and activities: Giving primarily to Jewish organizations.
Fields of interest: University education; Nonprofits; Orthopedics; Diseases and conditions; Heart and circulatory system diseases; Kidney diseases; Legal services; Disasters and emergency management; Judaism.

Type of support: Regranting.
Limitations: Applications not accepted. Giving primarily in NY.
Application information: Contributes only to pre-selected organizations.
Officers: Morton Seaman, Pres.; Lois Seaman, Treas.
EIN: 112951057

6768
The Securitas Foundation
284 W. 11th St.
New York City, NY 10014-2202

Established in 1998 in New York.
Donors: Securitas Partners; Sara Hendrickson; John Hendrickson.
Foundation type: Independent foundation.
Financial data (yr. ended 12/31/13): Assets, $651,598 (M); gifts received, $50,000; expenditures, $314,281; qualifying distributions, $311,929; giving activities include $309,944 for 28 grants (high: $41,000; low: $50).
Fields of interest: Dance; Music; Opera; Orchestral music; Art museums; Education.
Type of support: General support.
Limitations: Applications not accepted. Giving primarily in CA. No grants to individuals.
Application information: Contributes only to pre-selected organizations.
Officers: John Hendrickson, Pres.; Sara Hendrickson, V.P. and Secy.-Treas.
Trustees: Jung Lee; Elizabeth Turner.
EIN: 223624166

6769
Seelig Charitable Foundation Trust
1 The Poplars
Roslyn, NY 11576-1816

Established in 2003 in New York.
Foundation type: Independent foundation.
Financial data (yr. ended 12/31/13): Assets, $4,157,697 (M); expenditures, $232,148; qualifying distributions, $201,047; giving activities include $192,551 for 53 grants (high: $30,797; low: $30).
Fields of interest: Hospital care; Diseases and conditions; Judaism; Child welfare.
Type of support: Research.
Limitations: Applications not accepted. Giving primarily in NY. No grants to individuals.
Application information: Contributes only to pre-selected organizations.
Trustees: Henry Klosowski; Bari Pelton; Brett Pelton.
EIN: 116506325

6770
Sefn Trust
13 Lorimer St.
Brooklyn, NY 11206-4880

Donors: Samuel J. Nojovits; Esther F. Nojovits.
Foundation type: Independent foundation.
Financial data (yr. ended 11/30/13): Assets, $1,808 (M); gifts received, $85,000; expenditures, $160,907; qualifying distributions, $160,000; giving activities include $160,000 for 2 grants (high: $150,000; low: $10,000).

Fields of interest: Judaism.
Limitations: Applications not accepted. Giving primarily in Brooklyn, NY.
Application information: Unsolicited requests for funds not accepted.
Trustees: Esther F. Nojovits; Samuel Nojovits.
EIN: 906192179

6771
The SEG Foundation
982 E. 17th St.
Brooklyn, NY 11230-3710

Established in 2006 in New York.
Donors: Saul Elliot Goldbaum; Moshe Katlowitz; Chaim Electronic Corp.; Jacob Rosenberg.
Foundation type: Independent foundation.
Financial data (yr. ended 04/30/13): Assets, $1,912,131 (M); gifts received, $455,750; expenditures, $246,702; giving activities include $232,800 for 17+ grants (high: $68,050).
Fields of interest: Judaism.
Type of support: General support.
Limitations: Applications not accepted. Giving primarily in Brooklyn, NY. No grants to individuals.
Application information: Unsolicited requests for funds not accepted.
Trustees: Chana Goldbaum; Saul Elliot Goldbaum.
EIN: 204909577

6772
The Seligman Foundation
900 5th Ave., Apt. 9B
New York City, NY 10021-4141 (212) 879-6767
Contact: Florence Seligman, Tr.

Donors: Benjamin Seligman†; Florence Seligman.
Foundation type: Independent foundation.
Financial data (yr. ended 12/31/14): Assets, $898,189 (M); expenditures, $229,978; qualifying distributions, $218,913; giving activities include $218,913 for 23 grants (high: $25,000; low: $500).
Fields of interest: Education; Judaism; Human services.
Limitations: Applications accepted. Giving primarily in New York, NY. No grants to individuals.
Application information: Application form required.
Initial approach: Letter
Deadline(s): None
Trustees: Rachel Odo; Florence Seligman; Nicole Seligman.
EIN: 136092864

6773
The Seligsohn Family Foundation, Inc.
10 Hillview Dr.
Scarsdale, NY 10583-7532

Established in 1992 in New York.
Donor: Gerald Seligsohn.
Foundation type: Independent foundation.
Financial data (yr. ended 12/31/12): Assets, $272,905 (M); expenditures, $267,964; qualifying distributions, $264,406; giving activities include $264,406 for grants.
Purpose and activities: Giving primarily to Jewish institutes.
Fields of interest: Education; Nonprofits; Judaism.
Type of support: Regranting.

Limitations: Applications not accepted. Giving primarily in NY. No grants to individuals.
Application information: Contributes only to pre-selected organizations.
Directors: Joseph Leshkowitz; Gerald Seligsohn; Sandra Seligsohn.
EIN: 133683755

6774
Irving and Sara Selis Foundation, Inc.
40 E. 88th St., Ste. 3A
New York City, NY   10128-1176   (212) 722-7447
Contact: Michael D. Robbins, Pres.
FAX: (212) 369-3050; E-mail: LOR.MDR@verizon.net

Established in 2006 in New York.
Donors: Sara Selis Article Fourth Trust; Sara Selis†.
Foundation type: Independent foundation.
Financial data (yr. ended 12/31/13): Assets, $2,386,185 (M); expenditures, $152,542; qualifying distributions, $149,501; giving activities include $146,750 for 25 grants (high: $25,000; low: $500).
Fields of interest: Public libraries; People with vision impairments.
Application information:
   Initial approach: Letter
   Copies of proposal: 1
Officers: Michael D. Robbins, Pres.; Lois O. Robbins, V.P.; Carol Joy Heller, Secy.-Treas.
EIN: 270066678

6775
The Senator Foundation
510 Madison Ave., 28th Fl.
New York City, NY   10022

Donors: Alexander Klabin; Douglas Silverman.
Foundation type: Independent foundation.
Financial data (yr. ended 12/31/13): Assets, $2,785,809 (M); gifts received, $925,000; expenditures, $150,087; qualifying distributions, $150,000; giving activities include $150,000 for 8 grants (high: $25,000; low: $10,000).
Fields of interest: Education; University education; Housing development.
Limitations: Applications not accepted. Giving primarily in NJ, NY and FL.
Application information: Unsolicited requests for funds not accepted.
Officers: Jessica Harris, Pres.; Edward Larmann, Treas.
Directors: George Aitken Davies; Alexander Klabin; Kristen Klabin; Douglas Silverman.
EIN: 271986635

6776
The Serenbetz Family Foundation, Inc.
695 West St.
Harrison, NY   10528-2508

Established in 1998 in New Jersey.
Donors: Warren L. Serenbetz; Jean Serenbetz; Thelma Serenbetz; Paul H. Serenbetz; Stuart W. Serenbetz; Warren L. Serenbetz, Jr.; Martin Tuchman; Clay R. Serenbetz.
Foundation type: Independent foundation.
Financial data (yr. ended 12/31/13): Assets, $7,946,581 (M); gifts received, $220,000; expenditures, $377,385; qualifying distributions,

$366,505; giving activities include $360,000 for 8 grants (high: $80,000; low: $5,000).
Fields of interest: Orchestral music; Education; Child welfare.
Type of support: General support.
Limitations: Applications not accepted. Giving primarily in CT and NY. No grants to individuals.
Application information: Contributes only to pre-selected organizations.
Officers and Trustees: Thelma R. Serenbetz, Pres. and Trustee; Cynthia L. Serenbetz, V.P. and Trustee; Jean B. Serenbetz, Secy.-Treas. and Trustee; Clay R. Serenbetz; Paul H. Serenbetz; Stuart W. Serenbetz; Warren L. Serenbetz; Warren L. Serenbetz, Jr.
EIN: 133993644

6777
Seven Turns Fund, Inc.
(formerly Rizavi Friedland Foundation, Inc.)
c/o BNLY Group LLC
2150 Broadway, PH2A
New York City, NY   10023-3801

Established in 2006 in New York.
Donors: Shaiza Rizavi; Jonathan Friedland.
Foundation type: Independent foundation.
Financial data (yr. ended 11/30/14): Assets, $3,445,420 (M); gifts received, $498,956; expenditures, $373,970; qualifying distributions, $369,268; giving activities include $365,317 for 26 grants (high: $100,000; low: $259).
Fields of interest: Music; Natural history museums; Education; Higher education; Business education; Natural resources; Christianity.
Limitations: Applications not accepted. No grants to individuals.
Application information: Contributes only to pre-selected organizations.
Directors: Jonathan Friedland; Dara Metz; Shaiza Rizavi.
EIN: 203992304

6778
The SGMG Foundation
1045 Channel Dr.
Hewlett Harbor, NY   11557-2616
Contact: Peter Grossman, Pres.

Established in 2004 in Delaware.
Donors: Peter Grossman; Vivian Milstein.
Foundation type: Independent foundation.
Financial data (yr. ended 12/31/13): Assets, $2,379,150 (M); gifts received, $150,000; expenditures, $246,894; qualifying distributions, $243,450; giving activities include $243,450 for 17 grants (high: $100,425; low: $500).
Fields of interest: Undergraduate education; Human services.
Type of support: Scholarships.
Limitations: Applications accepted. Giving primarily in New York, NY. No grants to individuals.
Application information: Application form required.
   Initial approach: Letter
   Deadline(s): None
Officer: Peter Grossman, Pres.
Trustees: Geoffrey Grossman; Matthew Grossman; Sharon Grossman.
EIN: 810650429

6779
The Shachar Foundation
215 W. 88th St., Ste. 8F
New York City, NY   10024

Donor: Lawrence H. Schwartz.
Foundation type: Independent foundation.
Financial data (yr. ended 12/31/13): Assets, $3,435,245 (M); gifts received, $1,800; expenditures, $262,281; qualifying distributions, $216,565; giving activities include $216,205 for 23 grants (high: $200,000; low: $75).
Fields of interest: Education; Diseases and conditions; Judaism.
Limitations: Applications not accepted. Giving primarily in NJ and NY.
Application information: Unsolicited requests for funds not accepted.
Trustees: Shelley Levine; Lawrence H. Schwartz.
EIN: 137486623

6780
The Shack Sackler Foundation
c/o Chadbourne & Park
1301 Ave. of the Americas
New York City, NY   10019

Donor: Kathe A. Sackler, MD.
Foundation type: Independent foundation.
Financial data (yr. ended 12/31/13): Assets, $6,995,077 (M); gifts received, $1,200,000; expenditures, $263,846; qualifying distributions, $263,089; giving activities include $262,800 for 34 grants (high: $100,000; low: $300).
Fields of interest: Education; University education; Religion; Human services.
Limitations: Applications not accepted. Giving primarily in NY and RI.
Application information: Unsolicited requests for funds not accepted.
Officers and Directors: Kathe A. Sackler, MD, Pres. and Director; Susan A. Shack, MD, V.P. and Director; Lauren D. Kelly, Secy.; Leslie J. Schreyer.
EIN: 134043144

6781
The Shackouls Family Foundation
c/o The Ayco Company, L.P.
P.O. Box 860
Saratoga Springs, NY   12866-0860

Established in 2006 in Texas.
Donors: Bobby S. Shackouls; David Anderson Shackouls.
Foundation type: Independent foundation.
Financial data (yr. ended 02/28/13): Assets, $1,708,489 (M); gifts received, $403,732; expenditures, $243,249; qualifying distributions, $228,000; giving activities include $228,000 for 25 grants (high: $50,000; low: $1,500).
Fields of interest: Higher education; Nonprofits; Diseases and conditions; Scouting programs.
Type of support: Regranting.
Limitations: Applications not accepted. Giving primarily in MS and TX. No grants to individuals.
Application information: Contributes only to pre-selected organizations.
Trustees: Bobby S. Shackouls; David Anderson Shackouls; Judith Ann Shackouls.
EIN: 204495741

6782
Mel & Pamela Shaftel Foundation, Inc.
c/o The Ayco Co. L.P.
P.O. Box 15014
Albany, NY 12212-5014

Established in 1994 in New York.
Donors: Mel Shaftel; Pamela Shaftel.
Foundation type: Independent foundation.
Financial data (yr. ended 07/31/13): Assets,
$608,714 (M); gifts received, $286,543;
expenditures, $182,530; qualifying distributions,
$179,056; giving activities include $179,056 for 50
grants (high: $50,689; low: $100).
Fields of interest: Education; Environment; Youth
development.
Limitations: Applications not accepted. No grants to
individuals.
Application information: Unsolicited requests for
funds not accepted.
Officers: Mel Shaftel, Pres. and Treas.; Pamela
Shaftel, V.P. and Secy.
Trustee: Lauren Shaftel.
EIN: 223342427

6783
Sarah and Sasson Shalam Foundation
1538 Ocean Pkwy.
Brooklyn, NY 11230-7004

Established in 1993 in New York.
Donors: Sonny Shalam; Sasson Shalam.
Foundation type: Independent foundation.
Financial data (yr. ended 12/31/13): Assets,
$160,287 (M); gifts received, $5,110;
expenditures, $197,050; qualifying distributions,
$193,766; giving activities include $193,036 for 9
grants (high: $80,000; low: $5,800).
Fields of interest: Education; Religion.
Limitations: Applications not accepted. Giving
primarily in NY. No grants to individuals.
Application information: Unsolicited requests for
funds not accepted.
Officers: Sasson Shalam, Pres.; Abraham Shalam,
Treas.
EIN: 133731350

6784
The Shalom Ish Foundation
1333 60th St.
Brooklyn, NY 11219-5019

Established in 1998 in New York.
Donors: Ish Shalom†; Saul N. Friedman; Ish Shalom
Trust; Maison Grande Assocs.; Morris Friedman;
Benjamin Friedman; Alexander Orenstein; Eva
Friedman; Simeon Friedman; JREZ LLC; Pinnacle
Realty of New York LLC.
Foundation type: Independent foundation.
Financial data (yr. ended 09/30/14): Assets,
$3,205,470 (M); gifts received, $31,400;
expenditures, $465,862; qualifying distributions,
$436,100; giving activities include $436,100 for 19
grants (high: $97,000; low: $1,800).
Purpose and activities: Giving primarily for Jewish
synagogues and yeshivas.
Fields of interest: Education; Judaism; Human
services.
Limitations: Applications not accepted. Giving
primarily in NY. No grants to individuals.

Application information: Contributes only to
pre-selected organizations.
Trustee: Morris Friedman.
EIN: 113405442

6785
Shanken Family Foundation
387 Park Ave. S.
New York City, NY 10016-8810 (212) 684-4884
Contact: Marvin R. Shanken, Dir.

Established in 1999 in New York.
Donor: M. Shanken Communications, Inc.
Foundation type: Company-sponsored foundation.
Financial data (yr. ended 12/31/13): Assets,
$3,373,546 (M); gifts received, $300,000;
expenditures, $428,340; qualifying distributions,
$420,500; giving activities include $420,500 for
grants.
Purpose and activities: The foundation supports
medical centers and organizations involved with
education, Autism, diabetes research, disability
services, civil and human rights, and Judaism.
Fields of interest: Education; Diseases and
conditions; Human services.
Type of support: General support; Program
development; Research.
Limitations: Applications accepted. Giving primarily
in CT, FL, and New York, NY. No grants to
individuals.
Application information: Application form required.
Initial approach: Proposal
Deadline(s): None
Final notification: Within 2 months
Officer: Mel Manion, Treas.
Director: Marvin R. Shanken.
EIN: 134027049

6786
The Robert F. & Anna Marie Shapiro Family Foundation Inc.
c/o Janet L. Mulligan, Tanton & Co., LLP
37 W. 57th St., 5th Fl.
New York City, NY 10019-3411

Donors: Robert F. Shapiro; Anna Marie Shapiro.
Foundation type: Independent foundation.
Financial data (yr. ended 11/30/13): Assets,
$4,449,431 (M); expenditures, $400,437;
qualifying distributions, $316,071; giving activities
include $312,600 for 26 grants (high: $200,000;
low: $250).
Fields of interest: Arts education; Art museums;
Hospital care.
Type of support: General support.
Limitations: Applications not accepted. Giving
primarily in New York, NY. No grants to individuals.
Application information: Unsolicited requests for
funds not accepted.
Officers: Robert F. Shapiro, Pres.; Anna Marie
Shapiro, V.P. and Secy.; Janet L. Mulligan, Treas.
EIN: 133140202

6787
Sharon Steel Foundation
c/o Arthur Y. Fox, C.P.A.
420 Lexington Ave., Ste. 1733
New York City, NY 10170
Contact: Malvin Sander

Application address: 115 Maid Marion Ln.,
McMurray, PA 15317

Established in 1953 in Pennsylvania.
Donor: Sharon Steel Corp.
Foundation type: Company-sponsored foundation.
Financial data (yr. ended 12/31/13): Assets,
$1,559,552 (M); expenditures, $167,656;
qualifying distributions, $161,693; giving activities
include $158,022 for 10 grants (high: $48,022;
low: $5,000).
Purpose and activities: The foundation supports
organizations involved with education and human
services.
Fields of interest: Education; Secondary education;
Higher education; Nonprofits; Human services; Child
welfare; Foster care.
Type of support: General support; Program
development; Scholarships; Regranting.
Limitations: Applications accepted. Giving primarily
in CT, NH, NY, OH, PA, and RI. No grants to
individuals.
Application information:
Initial approach: Proposal
Deadline(s): None
Trustees: Christian L. Oberbeck; Malvin G. Sandler;
Hume R. Steyer.
EIN: 256063133

6788
J. D. Shatford Memorial Trust
c/o JPMorgan Chase Bank, N.A.
270 Park Ave., 16th Fl.
New York City, NY 10017-2014
E-mail: connie.a.brandeis@JPMorgan.com;
Application address: c/o Advisory Committee, P.O.
Box 192, Hubbards, Nova Scotia B0J 1T0; e-mail:
info@jdshatfordmemorialtrust.org; Main
URL: http://fdnweb.org/shatford
Grants List: http://fdnweb.org/shatford/recipients

Established in 1955 in New York.
Foundation type: Independent foundation.
Financial data (yr. ended 12/31/14): Assets,
$7,452,116 (M); expenditures, $431,214;
qualifying distributions, $350,574; giving activities
include $326,675 for 20 grants (high: $111,000;
low: $1,750).
Purpose and activities: Emphasis on scholarship
aid, secondary and higher education, and charities
limited to Hubbards, Nova Scotia, Canada,
organizations and residents.
Fields of interest: Secondary education;
Protestantism.
International interests: Canada.
Type of support: General support; Student aid.
Limitations: Applications accepted. Giving limited to
Hubbards, Nova Scotia, Canada.
Publications: Grants list; Informational brochure.
Application information: Complete application
guidelines available on Trust web site. Application
form required.
Deadline(s): None
Trustee: JPMorgan Chase Bank, N.A.
EIN: 136029993

6789
Emma A. Sheafer Charitable Trust
c/o JPMorgan Chase Bank, N.A. Private Foundation
Services
270 Park Ave., 16th Fl.
New York City, NY   10017-2014
Contact: Jonathan Horowitz, Prog. Officer
FAX: (212) 464-2304;
E-mail: jonathan.g.horowitz@jpmchase.com;
Application Phone: (212) 464-1477; Main
URL: http://fdnweb.org/sheafer
Grants List: http://fdnweb.org/sheafer/grants/
category/contributions

Established in 1975 in New York.
Donor: Emma A. Sheafer†.
Foundation type: Independent foundation.
Financial data (yr. ended 12/31/14): Assets,
$6,353,597 (M); expenditures, $361,842;
qualifying distributions, $295,146; giving activities
include $275,000 for 11 grants (high: $25,000;
low: $25,000).
Purpose and activities: Giving primarily for the
performing arts in New York City.
Fields of interest: Performing arts.
Type of support: Capital campaigns;
Capacity-building and technical assistance; Program
development.
Limitations: Applications accepted. Giving limited to
New York, NY. No grants to individuals, or for
research, scholarships, matching gifts or
fellowships; no loans.
Publications: Application guidelines; Grants list;
Informational brochure.
Application information: Organizations may not
receive more than 1 grant every 3 years. See
foundation web site for full application
requirements.
   Initial approach: Use online application system on
     trust web site
   Copies of proposal: 1
   Deadline(s): April 1 and Oct. 1
   Board meeting date(s): June and Dec.
   Final notification: June and Dec.
Trustees: John C. Russell; JPMorgan Chase Bank,
N.A.
Number of staff: None.
EIN: 510186114

6790
Frances D. Sheetz Charitable Trust
1100 Wehrle Dr., 2nd Fl.
Buffalo, NY   14221

Foundation type: Independent foundation.
Financial data (yr. ended 12/31/13): Assets,
$2,961,087 (M); expenditures, $181,260;
qualifying distributions, $127,530; giving activities
include $127,530 for 2 grants (high: $63,765; low:
$63,765).
Fields of interest: Housing development; Religion.
Limitations: Applications not accepted. Giving
primarily in NJ and PA.
Application information: Unsolicited requests for
funds not accepted.
Trustees: Douglas E. Cook; Manufacturers and
Traders Bank.
EIN: 166537295

6791
SHEL Foundation, Inc.
1632 42nd St.
Brooklyn, NY   11204-1026

Donors: Shea Grosman; Michael Herzog; Yochanan
Herzog; Benjamin Klein.
Foundation type: Independent foundation.
Financial data (yr. ended 06/30/14): Assets,
$140,541; gifts received, $195,485; expenditures,
$202,934; qualifying distributions, $202,077.
Fields of interest: Nonprofits; Judaism.
Type of support: General support; Regranting.
Limitations: Applications not accepted.
Application information: Unsolicited requests for
funds not accepted.
Directors: Shea Grosman; Yehuda Gutwein; Michael
Herzog.
EIN: 201437417

6792
Murray G. & Beatrice H. Sherman Foundation
115 Central Park West, Apt. 29F
New York City, NY   10023-4198

Established in 1999 in New York.
Foundation type: Independent foundation.
Financial data (yr. ended 12/31/14): Assets,
$5,924,361 (M); expenditures, $361,709;
qualifying distributions, $306,404; giving activities
include $280,809 for 18 grants (high: $50,000;
low: $1,000).
Fields of interest: Arts and culture; Education;
Nonprofits; Hospital care; Public libraries;
Community and economic development; Right to
free movement and asylum; Human services; Basic
and emergency aid; Youth services; International
development.
Type of support: Regranting.
Limitations: Applications not accepted. Giving
primarily in New York, NY. No grants to individuals.
Application information: Contributes only to
pre-selected organizations.
Trustees: William S. Sherman; CitiBank, N.A.
EIN: 311623371

6793
The Romita Shetty and Nasser Ahmad Foundation Inc.
c/o Da Capital
24 W. 40th St., 2nd Fl.
New York City, NY   10018-1898

Foundation type: Independent foundation.
Financial data (yr. ended 12/31/13): Assets, $0
(M); expenditures, $248,535; qualifying
distributions, $209,350; giving activities include
$209,350 for 15 grants (high: $52,000; low:
$1,000).
Fields of interest: Education; Foundations.
Limitations: Applications not accepted. Giving
primarily in New York, NY.
Application information: Unsolicited requests for
funds not accepted.
Officers: Nasser Ahmed, Pres.; Ayesha Ahmed, V.P.;
Romita Shetty, Secy.
EIN: 271428517

6794
Rachel Bat Shulamit Foundation
c/o Fleet Street, Ltd.
512 7th Ave.
New York City, NY   10018

Established in 2000 in New York.
Donors: Fleet Street Ltd.; Jolie Intimates.
Foundation type: Independent foundation.
Financial data (yr. ended 04/30/14): Assets,
$759,945 (M); expenditures, $270,361; qualifying
distributions, $270,361; giving activities include
$269,111 for 14 grants (high: $133,532; low:
$2,600).
Purpose and activities: Giving primarily to Jewish
agencies, temples, and schools.
Fields of interest: Religion.
International interests: Israel.
Limitations: Applications not accepted. Giving
primarily in NJ and NY; giving also in Israel. No grants
to individuals.
Application information: Unsolicited requests for
funds not accepted.
Officers: Manny Haber, Pres.; Raymond Haber,
Treas.; Stephen Haber, Secy.
EIN: 134122676

6795
The Stanley S. Shuman Family Foundation
711 5th Ave., 9th Fl.
New York City, NY   10022-3111

Established in 1966 in New York.
Donor: Stanley S. Shuman.
Foundation type: Independent foundation.
Financial data (yr. ended 12/31/14): Assets,
$1,762,973; expenditures, $376,233; qualifying
distributions, $365,102.
Fields of interest: Education; Elementary and
secondary education; Higher education; Law
education; Child welfare.
Type of support: General support.
Limitations: Applications not accepted. Giving
primarily in MA, and New York, NY. No grants to
individuals.
Application information: Contributes only to
pre-selected organizations.
Trustees: David Shuman; Michael Shuman; Stanley
S. Shuman.
EIN: 136216917

6796
Sidewalk Angels Foundation
P.O. Box 356
Bedford Hills, NY   10507-0356   2125572727
E-mail: info@sidewalkangelsfoundation.org; Main
URL: http://www.sidewalkangelsfoundation.org
Facebook: https://www.facebook.com/
sidewalkangels
Twitter: http://twitter.com/sidewalkangels

Established in 2004 in New York.
Donors: Rob Thomas; Marisol Thomas; New Bidnis
Inc.; Music Mastermind Inc.
Foundation type: Operating foundation.
Financial data (yr. ended 12/31/13): Assets,
$40,062 (M); gifts received, $393,782;
expenditures, $464,398; qualifying distributions,
$435,000; giving activities include $435,000 for 18
grants (high: $230,000; low: $5,000).

Purpose and activities: The foundation seeks through its efforts to encourage people to locally address problems such as animals that have been abandoned and abused as well as people who are destitute, homeless, or cannot afford proper medical care.
Fields of interest: Animal welfare; Homeless services; Homeless people; Low-income and poor people.
Limitations: Applications not accepted. Giving in the U.S., with emphasis on NY.
Application information: Unsolicited requests for funds not accepted.
Officers: Marisol Thomas, Pres.; Robert Thomas, V.P.; Maria Maldonado, Secy.; Greg Prato, Treas.
Directors: Michael Lippman; Jeff Maldonado; Melissa Lopez Maldonado.
EIN: 200285336

6797
Ruth and Jerome A. Siegel Foundation
1175 Old White Plains Rd.
Mamaroneck, NY 10543-1018

Established in 1951 in New York.
Donors: Jerome Siegel; Ruth Siegel; Titan Industrial Corp.
Foundation type: Company-sponsored foundation.
Financial data (yr. ended 11/30/13): Assets, $683,356 (M); gifts received, $500,720; expenditures, $195,046; qualifying distributions, $186,732; giving activities include $183,997 for 70 grants (high: $50,000; low: $35).
Purpose and activities: The foundation supports museums and organizations involved with performing arts, education, health, human services, and Judaism.
Fields of interest: Performing arts; Museums; Education; Higher education; Medical education; Nonprofits; Health; Hospital care; Judaism; Human services; Child welfare; Adult and child mentoring.
Type of support: General support; Program development; Regranting.
Limitations: Applications not accepted. Giving limited to New York, NY. No grants to individuals.
Application information: Contributes only to pre-selected organizations.
Officer and Directors: Jerome A. Siegel, Pres. and Treas. and Director; Henry Siegel.
EIN: 136066216

6798
The Nathan and Marilyn Silberman Foundation
c/o Nathan and Marilyn Silberman
1388 E. 24th St.
Brooklyn, NY 11210-5143

Established in 2000 in New York.
Donors: Marilyn Silberman; Nathan Silberman.
Foundation type: Independent foundation.
Financial data (yr. ended 12/31/13): Assets, $58,096 (M); gifts received, $125,000; expenditures, $125,220; qualifying distributions, $125,220; giving activities include $125,030 for 160 grants (high: $16,720; low: $18).
Fields of interest: Judaism.
Limitations: Applications not accepted. No grants to individuals.
Application information: Unsolicited requests for funds not accepted.

Trustees: Marilyn Silberman; Nathan Silberman.
EIN: 116534409

6799
The Robert Sillins Family Foundation Inc.
224 W. 49th St., Ste. 411
New York City, NY 10019-7405 (212) 262-6622
Contact: Susan Sillins, Pres.

Donors: R. Sillins Charitable Lead Trust III; R. Sillins Charitable Lead Trust IV.
Foundation type: Independent foundation.
Financial data (yr. ended 12/31/13): Assets, $8,120,562 (M); gifts received, $181,695; expenditures, $466,625; qualifying distributions, $389,350; giving activities include $389,350 for 48 grants (high: $50,000; low: $850).
Purpose and activities: Giving primarily for Jewish agencies and temples, as well as for Jewish education.
Fields of interest: Education; Philanthropy; Judaism.
Limitations: Applications accepted. Giving primarily in NY.
Application information: Application form required.
Initial approach: Letter
Deadline(s): Aug. 15
Officers: Susan Sillins, Pres.; Benjamin Sillins, V.P.; Bernard Sillins, Secy.
EIN: 521756848

6800
Louis & Martha Silver Foundation, Inc.
2975 Westchester Ave., Ste. 100
Purchase, NY 10577-2500 (914) 285-1430
Contact: Steven Gelles, Treas.

Established in 1964 in New York.
Donors: Louis Silver†; Martha Silver†.
Foundation type: Independent foundation.
Financial data (yr. ended 12/31/13): Assets, $4,322,388 (M); expenditures, $220,332; qualifying distributions, $210,470; giving activities include $210,470 for 73 grants (high: $36,000; low: $250).
Purpose and activities: Emphasis on Jewish giving, including temple support, welfare funds, hospitals, and yeshivas; funding also for education, hospitals, and social services.
Fields of interest: Education; Nonprofits; Hospital care; Judaism; Human services.
Type of support: Regranting.
Limitations: Applications accepted. Giving primarily in NY; giving also in CT and NJ. No grants to individuals.
Application information: Application form required.
Initial approach: Letter
Deadline(s): None
Officers: Phyllis Gelles, Pres.; Steven Gelles, Treas.
Directors: Martin Silver; Robert Silver.
EIN: 136165326

6801
The Harvey Silverman Foundation, Inc.
c/o Harvey Silverman
111 Beach Ln.
Wainscott, NY 11975-2708

Donor: Harvey Silverman.
Foundation type: Independent foundation.

Financial data (yr. ended 11/30/13): Assets, $5,602,904 (M); expenditures, $378,430; qualifying distributions, $354,460; giving activities include $203,845 for 45 grants (high: $55,000; low: $25).
Purpose and activities: Giving primarily for health care, medical research, and to Jewish agencies and temples.
Fields of interest: Education; Nonprofits; Health; Diseases and conditions; Judaism; Human services.
Type of support: Research; Research and evaluation; Regranting.
Limitations: Applications not accepted. Giving primarily in NJ, and New York, NY. No grants to individuals.
Application information: Contributes only to pre-selected organizations.
Officers: Harvey Silverman, Pres.; Stanley Silverman, V.P.; Karen Silverman, Secy.-Treas.
EIN: 133343289

6802
The Raine & Stanley Silverstein Family Foundation, Inc.
c/o Krusch & Modell
10 Rockefeller Plz., Ste. 710
New York City, NY 10020-1966

Established in 1996 in New York.
Donors: Raine Silverstein; Stanley Silverstein.
Foundation type: Independent foundation.
Financial data (yr. ended 11/30/14): Assets, $270,781 (M); gifts received, $310,707; expenditures, $327,042; qualifying distributions, $309,088; giving activities include $309,088 for 77 grants (high: $53,490; low: $250).
Purpose and activities: Giving primarily for Jewish higher education, human services, and to Jewish agencies and temples.
Fields of interest: Higher education; Judaism; Human services.
Limitations: Applications not accepted. Giving primarily in NY. No grants to individuals.
Application information: Unsolicited requests for funds not accepted.
Officers: Stanley Silverstein, Pres.; Raine Silverstein, V.P. and Treas.; Nina Miner, V.P.; Flori Silverstein, V.P.
EIN: 113353084

6803
Howard A. Silverstein Foundation
c/o BCRS Assocs., LLC
77 Water St., 9th Fl.
New York City, NY 10005-4401

Established in 1986 in New York.
Donor: Howard A. Silverstein.
Foundation type: Independent foundation.
Financial data (yr. ended 07/31/13): Assets, $6,062,320 (M); gifts received, $493,147; expenditures, $319,645; qualifying distributions, $317,395; giving activities include $314,765 for 10 grants (high: $144,965; low: $5,000).
Purpose and activities: Giving primarily for education, health, and Jewish organizations.
Fields of interest: Arts and culture; Photography; Art museums; Elementary and secondary education; Higher education; Nonprofits; Health; Hospital care; Judaism; Human services.
Type of support: Regranting.

Limitations: Applications not accepted. Giving primarily in New York, NY and Philadelphia, PA. No grants to individuals.
Application information: Contributes only to pre-selected organizations.
Trustees: Howard A. Silverstein; Patricia B. Silverstein.
EIN: 133385065

6804
Zichorn Simcha D'Sassov Foundation
86 Rte., Ste. 59
Spring Valley, NY 10977

Donor: Schmuel Horowitz.
Foundation type: Independent foundation.
Financial data (yr. ended 02/28/13): Assets, $7,693 (M); gifts received, $151,369; expenditures, $144,719; qualifying distributions, $143,803; giving activities include $143,803 for 153 grants (high: $19,833; low: $18).
Fields of interest: Education; Religion; Human services.
Limitations: Applications not accepted. Giving primarily in NY.
Application information: Unsolicited requests for funds not accepted.
Trustees: Schmuel Horowitz; Rachel Horowitz.
EIN: 450673679

6805
Joseph T. & Helen M. Simpson Foundation
1100 Wehrle Dr., 2nd Fl.
Buffalo, NY 14221

Established in 1954 in Pennsylvania.
Foundation type: Independent foundation.
Financial data (yr. ended 12/31/13): Assets, $4,609,342 (M); expenditures, $421,776; qualifying distributions, $286,625; giving activities include $286,625 for 105 grants (high: $120,500; low: $200).
Purpose and activities: Giving primarily for the arts, education, health organizations, and children, youth and social services.
Fields of interest: Arts and culture; Education; Higher education; Diseases and conditions; Human services; Child welfare.
Limitations: Applications not accepted. Giving primarily in Harrisburg, PA. No grants to individuals.
Application information: Contributes only to pre-selected organizations.
Officer: Hugh J.T. Simpson, Exec. Dir.
Trustee: M and T Trust Co.
EIN: 236242538

6806
Louis P. Singer Fund Inc.
c/o Kresch & Gerbasi, LLP
250 W. 57th St., Ste. 1723
New York City, NY 10107-1708

Established in 1961 in New York.
Donors: Berkshire Hathaway Inc.; Midge A. Korczak.
Foundation type: Independent foundation.
Financial data (yr. ended 08/31/14): Assets, $1,862,363 (M); expenditures, $338,502; qualifying distributions, $307,843; giving activities include $307,843 for 102 grants (high: $88,000; low: $100).

Purpose and activities: Giving for Jewish organizations, foundations supporting primary and college education, and for youth and human services.
Fields of interest: Art museums; Education; Foundations; Judaism; Human services.
Limitations: Applications not accepted. Giving primarily in NY. No grants to individuals.
Application information: Unsolicited requests for funds not accepted.
Officers: Midge A. Korczak, Pres.; Leslie S. Lomas, V.P.; John D. Viener, Secy.-Treas.
EIN: 136077788

6807
Joseph & Irene Skalny Charitable Trust
95 Washington St., Atrium 1 N.
Buffalo, NY 14203-2885

Foundation type: Independent foundation.
Financial data (yr. ended 11/30/14): Assets, $6,006,301 (M); expenditures, $365,419; qualifying distributions, $303,240; giving activities include $296,775 for 21 grants (high: $133,000; low: $275).
Fields of interest: Education; Domesticated animals; Health.
Type of support: Advocacy.
Limitations: Applications not accepted. Giving primarily in Rochester, NY.
Application information: Unsolicited requests for funds not accepted.
Trustee: HSBC Bank USA.
EIN: 263876922

6808
The SKL Foundation
935 E. 23 St.
Brooklyn, NY 11210-3621

Donor: Sandy Liebhard.
Foundation type: Independent foundation.
Financial data (yr. ended 12/31/12): Assets, $3,058,029 (M); gifts received, $2,800,000; expenditures, $221,094; qualifying distributions, $189,100; giving activities include $189,100 for 14 grants (high: $100,000; low: $500).
Fields of interest: Nonprofits; Judaism.
Type of support: Regranting.
Limitations: Applications not accepted. Giving primarily in NY. No grants to individuals.
Application information: Contributes only to pre-selected organizations.
Trustees: Kranie Liebhard; Sandy Liebhard.
EIN: 542100045

6809
The C. F. Roe Slade Foundation
c/o Bank of America, N.A.
114 W. 47th St.
New York City, NY 10036-1510

Established in 1969 in New York.
Donor: Marie-Antoinette Slade†.
Foundation type: Independent foundation.
Financial data (yr. ended 06/30/13): Assets, $3,591,948 (M); expenditures, $205,264; qualifying distributions, $185,000; giving activities include $185,000 for grants.

Purpose and activities: Giving for cultural institutes and arts.
Fields of interest: Arts and culture; Orchestral music; Higher education; Botanical gardens; Hospital care; Public affairs.
Type of support: General support; Capital and infrastructure; Research.
Limitations: Applications not accepted. Giving primarily in CT and NY. No grants to individuals.
Application information: Contributes only to pre-selected organizations.
Trustees: John H. Bell, Jr.; W. Macy Johnson; Susan Porter.
EIN: 136205873

6810
Michael & Ruth Slade Foundation
114 Piping Rock Rd.
Locust Valley, NY 11560-2507

Established in 2000 in New York.
Donors: Michael Slade; Ruth Slade.
Foundation type: Independent foundation.
Financial data (yr. ended 12/31/13): Assets, $754,958 (M); expenditures, $233,425; qualifying distributions, $228,652; giving activities include $228,652 for 33 grants (high: $60,000; low: $18).
Fields of interest: Education; Nonprofits; Hospital care; Diseases and conditions; Judaism; Human services.
Type of support: Research; Regranting.
Limitations: Applications not accepted. Giving primarily in NY.
Application information: Unsolicited requests for funds not accepted.
Trustees: Michael Slade; Ruth Slade.
EIN: 113478088

6811
Slovin Foundation
111 E. 61st St.
New York City, NY 10065-8101
Contact: Bruce Slovin

Established in 1988 in New York.
Donor: Bruce Slovin.
Foundation type: Independent foundation.
Financial data (yr. ended 02/28/13): Assets, $19,450 (M); gifts received, $396,540; expenditures, $376,615; qualifying distributions, $223,215; giving activities include $223,215 for grants.
Purpose and activities: Giving primarily to Jewish organizations, including organizations for research in Jewish history and culture; funding also for the arts, education, and social services.
Fields of interest: Arts and culture; Education; Nonprofits; Judaism; Human services.
Type of support: Regranting.
Limitations: Applications not accepted. Giving primarily in Los Angeles, CA and New York, NY. No grants to individuals.
Application information: Unsolicited requests for funds not accepted.
Officer: Bruce Slovin, Pres.
EIN: 236912396

6812
Bailey Smith Charitable Trust
640 5th Ave., 9th Fl.
New York City, NY 10019

Foundation type: Independent foundation.
Financial data (yr. ended 12/31/14): Assets, $5,823,494 (M); expenditures, $323,693; qualifying distributions, $275,143; giving activities include $260,000 for 1 grant.
Fields of interest: Catholicism.
Limitations: Applications not accepted. Giving primarily in Sayville, NY.
Application information: Unsolicited requests for funds not accepted.
Trustees: Sean J. McDonough; Barbara Spare; Elizabeth Walton.
EIN: 266130281

6813
George V. and Jean A. Smith Charitable Trust
P.O. Box 6437
Ithaca, NY 14851-6437

Foundation type: Independent foundation.
Financial data (yr. ended 12/31/13): Assets, $11,859,753 (M); expenditures, $360,223; qualifying distributions, $258,995; giving activities include $251,227 for 22 grants (high: $77,699; low: $1,295).
Fields of interest: Education; Environment; Human services.
Limitations: Applications not accepted.
Application information: Unsolicited requests for funds not accepted.
Trustee: Tompkins Trust Company.
EIN: 166484804

6814
Byron & Beth Smith Family Foundation
c/o The Ayco Co.-NTG
P.O. Box 15014
Albany, NY 12212-5014

Donors: Byron Smith; Beth Smith.
Foundation type: Independent foundation.
Financial data (yr. ended 12/31/12): Assets, $1,852,176 (M); gifts received, $1,749; expenditures, $131,785; qualifying distributions, $130,120; giving activities include $130,120 for 2 grants (high: $110,120; low: $20,000).
Fields of interest: Business education; Christianity.
Limitations: Applications not accepted. No grants to individuals.
Application information: Unsolicited requests for funds not accepted.
Trustees: Byron Smith; Beth Smith.
EIN: 261436074

6815
Roy & Marianne Smith Foundation
c/o BCRS Assocs., LLC
77 Water St., 9th Fl.
New York City, NY 10005-4414

Established in 1980 in New Jersey.
Donors: Roy C. Smith; Marianne F. Smith.
Foundation type: Independent foundation.

Financial data (yr. ended 03/31/13): Assets, $915,943 (M); expenditures, $370,957; qualifying distributions, $361,984; giving activities include $361,984 for 14 grants (high: $200,000; low: $5).
Purpose and activities: Giving for juvenile diabetes research, the arts, education, and health and social services.
Fields of interest: Arts and culture; Museums; Higher education; Business education; Nonprofits; Hospital care; Diseases and conditions; Diabetes; Human services; Scouting programs; Special population support.
Type of support: Research; Regranting.
Limitations: Applications not accepted. Giving primarily in NJ and NY. No grants to individuals, or for scholarships; no loans.
Application information: Unsolicited requests for funds not accepted.
Trustees: Michael Coles; Marianne F. Smith; Roy C. Smith.
EIN: 133050754

6816
Malcolm E. Smith, Jr. Foundation, Inc.
30 Smith Ln.
P.O. Box 452
Saint James, NY 11780-3810

Established in 1996 in Maine.
Foundation type: Independent foundation.
Financial data (yr. ended 12/31/13): Assets, $2,770,233 (M); expenditures, $177,305; qualifying distributions, $166,250; giving activities include $166,000 for 7 grants (high: $40,000; low: $1,000).
Fields of interest: University education; Gardening.
Type of support: General support.
Limitations: Applications not accepted. Giving primarily in CA and VA. No grants to individuals.
Application information: Unsolicited requests for funds not accepted.
Officers and Directors: Malcolm E. Smith Jr., Pres. and Director; Jennifer Huntley, V.P. and Director; Helen L. Brosseau, Secy. and Director.
EIN: 113344933

6817
Harry E. and Florence W. Snayberger Memorial Foundation
(also known as Snayberger Memorial Foundation)
c/o M&T Bank
1100 Wehrle Dr., 2nd Fl.
Amherst, NY 14221-7748 (716) 842-5506
Contact: Carolyn Bernatonis, Trust Dept.
E-mail: cbernatonis@mtb.com

Established in 1976 in Pennsylvania.
Donor: Harry E. Snayberger†.
Foundation type: Independent foundation.
Financial data (yr. ended 03/31/13): Assets, $4,259,364 (M); expenditures, $225,626; qualifying distributions, $187,800; giving activities include $35,900 for 47 grants (high: $3,000; low: $400), and $151,900 for 92 grants to individuals (high: $1,700; low: $200).
Purpose and activities: Giving primarily for youth program organizations that benefit the youth of Schuylkill County, PA. Also awards scholarships for higher education, exclusively to Schuylkill County, PA, residents.

Fields of interest: Higher education; Child welfare; Scouting programs.
Type of support: General support; Student aid.
Limitations: Applications accepted. Giving limited to residents of Schuylkill County, PA.
Application information: Scholarship applicants must be no older than 25 years of age. Application form required.
  Initial approach: Pick up application at any of the M&T Bank offices located in Schuylkill County, PA, between mid-Dec. and the end of Feb.
  Copies of proposal: 1
  Deadline(s): Last work day in Feb.
  Board meeting date(s): Yearly, or as required
  Final notification: Approximately mid-Oct. for scholarships and May for organizations
Trustee: M&T Bank.
Number of staff: None.
EIN: 232056361

6818
The John Ben Snow Foundation, Inc.
50 Presidential Plz., Ste. 106
Syracuse, NY 13202-2279 (315) 471-5256
Contact: Jonathan L. Snow, Pres.
E-mail: johnbensnow@verizon.net; Main
URL: http://www.johnbensnow.com/jbsf

Established in 1948 in New York.
Donor: John Ben Snow†.
Foundation type: Independent foundation.
Financial data (yr. ended 12/31/13): Assets, $8,627,634 (M); expenditures, $475,773; qualifying distributions, $390,577; giving activities include $292,300 for 38 grants (high: $40,000; low: $800).
Purpose and activities: The mission of the foundation is to make grants within specific focus areas to enhance the quality of life in central and northern New York state. The focus areas are: arts and culture, community, education, journalism, disabilities, and the environment.
Fields of interest: Arts and culture; Historic preservation; Education; Higher education; Environment; Natural resources; Libraries; Publishing; Community and economic development; Child welfare; Children and youth; People with disabilities.
Type of support: Capital and infrastructure; Matching grants; Equipment; Program development; Publications; Seed money; Fellowships; Scholarships.
Limitations: Applications accepted. Giving limited to central NY, with emphasis on Onondaga and Oswego counties. No support for religious organizations or for-profit groups. No grants to individuals, endowment funds, or contingency financing.
Publications: Annual report (including application guidelines); Financial statement.
Application information: Applicants should also include a 1-page executive summary. All inquiries should be made by mail only.
  Initial approach: Letter of inquiry
  Copies of proposal: 1
  Deadline(s): Jan. 1 for letters of inquiry; submit inquiry preferably from July through Dec.; submit application by Apr. 1; submit either a final report after project is completed by Mar. 1 or a progress report by Mar. 1
  Board meeting date(s): June
  Final notification: July 1

Officers and Directors: Jonathan L. Snow, Pres. and Director; David H. Snow, V.P. and Treas. and Director; Emelie Melton Williams, Secy. and Director; Angus M. Burton; Valerie A. MacFie.
Number of staff: 1 part-time support.
EIN: 136112704

6819
Valentine Perry Snyder Fund

c/o JPMorgan Chase Pank, N.A. Private Foundation Svcs.
270 Park Ave., 16th Fl.
New York City, NY 10017-2014 8668885157
Contact: Casey Castaneda, Prog. Off.
FAX: (212) 464-2304;
E-mail: casey.b.castaneda@jpmorgan.com; Main URL: http://fdnweb.org/snyder
Grants List: http://fdnweb.org/snyder/grants/category/contributions

Established in 1942 in New York.
Donor: Sheba Torbert Snyder†.
Foundation type: Independent foundation.
Financial data (yr. ended 12/31/14): Assets, $8,916,030; expenditures, $517,943; qualifying distributions, $424,618.
Purpose and activities: Giving primarily for youth and other human services, community workforce development programs, and public affairs.
Fields of interest: Public affairs; Job training; Human services; Child welfare.
Type of support: General support; Program development.
Limitations: Applications accepted. Giving limited to New York, NY. No support for organizations lacking 501(c)(3) status. No grants to individuals, or for research-related programs, scholarships, fellowships, or matching gifts; no loans.
Publications: Application guidelines; Grants list.
Application information: Organizations must have an annual budget of under $1.5 million to be eligible. See foundation web site for application guidelines and requirements.
> *Initial approach:* Proposal via online application on foundation web site
> *Copies of proposal:* 1
> *Deadline(s):* Sept. 1
> *Board meeting date(s):* Dec.
> *Final notification:* Dec.

Trustee: JPMorgan Chase Bank, N.A.
EIN: 136036765

6820
Societe des Professeurs Francais en Amerique

(formerly Societe des Professeurs Francais en Amerique)
1001 Avenue of the Americas, 11th Fl.
New York City, NY 10018
Application address: Marandon Scholarships, SPFFA

Established in 1904 in New York.
Donors: Louise Dufrenoy†; Jeanne Marandon†.
Foundation type: Independent foundation.
Financial data (yr. ended 12/31/13): Assets, $3,726,365 (M); gifts received, $14,835; expenditures, $273,072; qualifying distributions, $246,620.
Purpose and activities: Scholarship awards for U.S. researchers, undergraduates and graduate

students, and high school students studying French in the U.S., France, or Quebec, Canada.
Fields of interest: Education.
International interests: Africa; Belgium; Canada; Caribbean; Europe; France; Haiti.
Type of support: Student aid.
Limitations: Applications accepted. Giving limited to U.S. citizens.
Publications: Grants list; Informational brochure.
Application information: Application form required.
> *Initial approach:* Letter
> *Copies of proposal:* 1
> *Deadline(s):* Dec. 15

Officers: Anne Berthelot, Pres.; Anne Mullen-Hohl, 1st V.P.; Frantz-Antoine Leconte, 2nd V.P.; Hugues St. Fort, Secy.; Diane Paravazian, Treas.
Directors: Cecile Ackapo-Satchiavi; Andre Benhaim; Maxine Blanchard; Roger Celestin; Nora Cottille-Foley; Carmen Coll; Brigitte Lane; Brigitte Mahuzier; Robert Pine; Peter Schulman.
Number of staff: 1 part-time support.
EIN: 133150248

6821
The Society of the Friendly Sons of Saint Patrick in the City of New York

3 W. 51st St., Rm. 604
New York City, NY 10019-6909 (212) 269-1770
Contact: Jacqueline M. McCarthy
Main URL: http://www.friendlysonsnyc.com
Facebook: https://www.facebook.com/pages/The-Society-of-the-Friendly-Sons-of-Saint-Patrick-in-the-City-of-New-York/137611946293243

Established in 1945 in New York.
Foundation type: Independent foundation.
Financial data (yr. ended 03/31/13): Assets, $3,208,256 (M); gifts received, $246,490; expenditures, $1,059,026; qualifying distributions, $909,093; giving activities include $300,000 for 42 grants (high: $30,000; low: $2,500).
Purpose and activities: Giving primarily to Roman Catholic agencies and services.
Fields of interest: Education; Hospital care; Catholicism; Sports and recreation; Human services; People with disabilities.
Type of support: Individual development.
Limitations: Applications accepted. Giving primarily in NY. No grants to individuals.
Application information:
> *Initial approach:* Letter

Officers: John C. Walton, Pres.; Matthew T. McLaughlin, 1st V.P.; Kevin J. Rooney, 2nd V.P.; John A. Coleman III, Secy.; Thomas H. Sullivan, Treas.
Number of staff: 1 full-time professional; 1 part-time professional.
EIN: 136164757

6822
Sokol Family Foundation

1074 Broadway
Woodmere, NY 11598-1235

Donors: Adam Sokol; David Sokol; Mendy Sokol.
Foundation type: Independent foundation.
Financial data (yr. ended 11/30/13): Assets, $11,376 (M); expenditures, $177,616; qualifying distributions, $177,616; giving activities include $177,616 for 29 grants (high: $25,000; low: $250).
Fields of interest: Judaism.

Limitations: Applications not accepted. Giving primarily in NY. No grants to individuals.
Application information: Unsolicited requests for funds not accepted.
Trustees: Steven Adelsberg; Adam Sokol; David Sokol; Mendy Sokol; Susan Sokol.
EIN: 616293034

6823
The Sokoloff Foundation, Inc.

200 E. 78th St., Ste. 16D
New York City, NY 10075-2017 (212) 744-5337
Contact: Stephen Sokoloff, Mgr.

Established in 1960 in New York.
Donors: Gertrude Sokoloff†; Stephen Sokoloff.
Foundation type: Independent foundation.
Financial data (yr. ended 12/31/13): Assets, $9,479,068 (M); gifts received, $209,273; expenditures, $404,903; qualifying distributions, $390,876; giving activities include $383,345 for 53 grants (high: $80,000; low: $100).
Fields of interest: Arts and culture; Judaism.
Limitations: Applications accepted. Giving primarily in New York, NY.
Application information:
> *Initial approach:* Letter
> *Deadline(s):* None

Officer and Trustee: Stephen Sokoloff, Mgr. and Trustee.
EIN: 136155196

6824
Some Voices Foundation

c/o Jeremy M. Booth, WTAS LLC
1177 Ave. of the Americas, 18th Fl.
New York City, NY 10036-2714

Donor: Daniel A. Michalow.
Foundation type: Independent foundation.
Financial data (yr. ended 12/31/13): Assets, $3,337,221 (M); gifts received, $122,980; expenditures, $291,420; qualifying distributions, $277,482; giving activities include $266,610 for 12 grants (high: $150,000; low: $500).
Fields of interest: Education; Diseases and conditions; Human services.
Limitations: Applications not accepted. Giving primarily in New York.
Application information: Unsolicited requests for funds not accepted.
Trustee: Daniel A. Michalow.
EIN: 357013701

6825
The Abraham & Beverly Sommer Foundation

810 7th Ave., 29th Fl.
New York City, NY 10019-5871

Established in 1977 in New York.
Donor: Beverly Sommer.
Foundation type: Independent foundation.
Financial data (yr. ended 12/31/13): Assets, $4,118,240 (M); expenditures, $259,705; qualifying distributions, $239,875; giving activities include $239,875 for 33 grants (high: $50,000; low: $2,500).

Purpose and activities: Giving primarily to health organizations, human services, and Jewish organizations.
Fields of interest: Arts and culture; Performing arts; Nonprofits; Health; Eye diseases; Judaism; Human rights; Child welfare.
Type of support: Regranting.
Limitations: Applications not accepted. Giving primarily in FL and NY. No grants to individuals.
Application information: Unsolicited requests for funds not accepted.
Officers: Beverly Sommer, Pres.; Amy Sommer, V.P.; Frank Stella, Secy.-Treas.
EIN: 132960992

6826
The Elizabeth & Michel Sorel Charitable Organization, Inc.
25 W. 45th St., Ste. 504
New York City, NY 10036-4902 (212) 730-3552
Contact: Judy Cope, Exec. Dir.
E-mail for Judy Cope: Judy@Sorelmusic.org; Main URL: http://www.sorelmusic.org

Donors: Claudette Sorel†; Ellen Rosenberg.
Foundation type: Independent foundation.
Financial data (yr. ended 12/31/13): Assets, $5,191,638 (M); expenditures, $526,605; qualifying distributions, $414,902; giving activities include $158,400 for 12 grants (high: $65,000; low: $500), $14,000 for 5 grants to individuals (high: $5,000; low: $1,000), and $139,000 for foundation-administered programs.
Purpose and activities: The organization intends to create opportunities for women in composition, conducting, piano, voice and film scoring.
Fields of interest: Arts and culture; Music; Orchestral music; Education; Religion; Females.
Limitations: Giving primarily in NY.
Officers and Directors: Berge Avedisian, Pres. and Treas. and Director; Walter J. Killmer, Jr., V.P. and Secy. and Director; Judy Cope, Exec. Dir.
EIN: 133918852

6827
The Jeanne Sorensen-Siegel Foundation Inc.
(formerly The Joel and Jeanne Leff Foundation, Inc.)
781 5th Ave., Ste. 605
New York City, NY 10022-1012

Donors: Joel B. Leff; Jeanne Sorensen-Leff; Herbert J. Siegel.
Foundation type: Independent foundation.
Financial data (yr. ended 11/30/13): Assets, $1,066,628 (M); expenditures, $210,480; qualifying distributions, $182,534; giving activities include $176,000 for 12 grants (high: $75,000; low: $200).
Fields of interest: Arts and culture; Education; Health.
Limitations: Applications not accepted. Giving primarily in the greater New York, NY, area. No grants to individuals.
Application information: Contributes only to pre-selected organizations.
Officer: Jeanne Sorensen Siegel, Pres.
EIN: 133192850

6828
Sorgente Group Foundation
c/o Sorgente Group
805 3rd Ave., 18th Fl.
New York City, NY 10022-7546

Foundation type: Independent foundation.
Financial data (yr. ended 12/31/13): Assets, $369,496 (M); expenditures, $167,361; qualifying distributions, $117,500; giving activities include $117,500 for 7 grants (high: $37,750; low: $3,000).
Fields of interest: Human services.
Limitations: Applications not accepted.
Application information: Unsolicited requests for funds not accepted.
Officers: Valter Mainetti, Pres.; Veronica Mainetti, V.P. and Secy.; Stefano Cervone, V.P. and Treas.
EIN: 263903732

6829
Carol & Charles Spaeth Memorial Fund
1 Court Sq., 19th Fl.
Long Island City, NY 11120-0001

Foundation type: Independent foundation.
Financial data (yr. ended 12/31/14): Assets, $4,992,283; expenditures, $249,270; qualifying distributions, $223,304.
Fields of interest: Domesticated animals; Human services.
Limitations: Applications not accepted.
Application information: Unsolicited requests for funds not accepted.
Trustee: CitiBank, N.A.
EIN: 136883977

6830
The Sparkplug Foundation
Park West Finance Station
P.O. Box 20956
New York City, NY 10025-0016
E-mail: info@sparkplugfoundation.org; Tel./Fax: (877) 866-8285; Main URL: http://sparkplugfoundation.org
Grant Database: http://sparkplugfoundation.org/past-grants

Established in 2003 in New York.
Donors: Felice Gelman; Yoram Gelman; Emmaia Gelman.
Foundation type: Independent foundation.
Financial data (yr. ended 12/31/13): Assets, $5,846,258 (M); expenditures, $582,222; qualifying distributions, $440,665; giving activities include $439,480 for 55 grants (high: $10,100; low: $4,000).
Purpose and activities: Giving is focused on providing seed money for new organizations, projects or ideas. The foundation makes one-time grants for activities which create sustainable organizing and communities, while recognizing the importance of developing individual cultures by favoring projects that promote diversity. The main areas of focus are music, education, and grassroots organizations, as well as exploring funding projects in the area of alternative and sustainable energies.
Fields of interest: Musical ensembles and groups; Education; Environment; Science; Community and economic development; Human rights; Right to free movement and asylum; International relations;

Young adults; Female adults; LGBTQ people; Ethnic and racial groups; People of Asian descent; People of African descent; People of Latin American descent; Indigenous peoples; American Indians; Immigrants and migrants; People with HIV/AIDS.
International interests: Israel; West Bank/Gaza (Palestinian Territories).
Type of support: Capacity-building and technical assistance; Grants to individuals; Program development; Convening; Publications; Seed money; Curriculum development; Research; Technical assistance; Program evaluations.
Limitations: Applications accepted. Giving to every state in the USA. Some giving in Israel for projects that involve Palestinian communities. No support for university-based projects, or for non-secular activities. No grants to non-501(c)(3) organizations unless they have a fiscal sponsor. No grants for performances, tickets or tuitions, equipment, computers or for operating support.
Application information: Complete application guidelines and deadlines available on foundation web site. Application form required.
  Initial approach: Submit preliminary questionnaire on foundation web site
  Copies of proposal: 1
  Deadline(s): See foundation web site for current deadlines
  Board meeting date(s): Within 4 weeks of deadline dates
  Final notification: Usually within 1 month
Trustees: Felice Gelman; Yoram Gelman; Emmaia Gelman.
Number of staff: 1 part-time professional.
EIN: 331033952

6831
Helen and Irving Spatz Foundation
c/o Buchbinder Tunick & Co., LLP
1 Penn Plz., Ste. 5335
New York City, NY 10119-5335

Donor: Irving Spatz†.
Foundation type: Independent foundation.
Financial data (yr. ended 12/31/13): Assets, $8,574,954 (M); expenditures, $440,386; qualifying distributions, $380,865; giving activities include $336,000 for 15 grants (high: $200,000; low: $250).
Purpose and activities: Giving primarily for higher education, including a medical school; funding also for Jewish organizations.
Fields of interest: Higher education; Medical education; Diseases and conditions; Judaism.
Type of support: General support.
Limitations: Applications not accepted. Giving primarily in NY. No grants to individuals.
Application information: Contributes only to pre-selected organizations.
Directors: Marc Niederhoffer; Richard Niederhoffer; Janet Spatz; Martin Spatz.
EIN: 136816200

6832
Charles Spear Charitable Trust
P.O. Box 1527
New York City, NY 10268-1521

Donor: Charles Spielberger†.
Foundation type: Independent foundation.

Financial data (yr. ended 12/31/13): Assets, $10,905,158 (M); expenditures, $289,228; qualifying distributions, $221,000; giving activities include $221,000 for 17 grants (high: $35,000; low: $5,000).
Fields of interest: Domesticated animals; Diseases and conditions; Human services; Child welfare.
Type of support: Research; Research and evaluation.
Limitations: Applications not accepted. No grants to individuals.
Application information: Contributes only to pre-selected organizations.
Trustee: Caroline Barrett.
EIN: 112113021

6833
Spektor Family Foundation, Inc.
262 Central Park West, Apt. 14E
New York City, NY   10024-3512   (212) 790-5700
Contact: Mira Spektor, Pres.
Application address: c/o Mira Spektor, 262 Central Park West, Apt. 14E, New York, NY 10024, tel.: (212) 790-5700

Established in 1968 in New York.
Donor: Eryk Spektor†.
Foundation type: Independent foundation.
Financial data (yr. ended 07/01/14): Assets, $3,123,464 (M); expenditures, $259,373; qualifying distributions, $252,805; giving activities include $248,805 for 40 grants (high: $50,000; low: $250).
Purpose and activities: Support primarily for Jewish organizations, arts, community services and education.
Fields of interest: Museums; Higher education; University education; Maternal and perinatal health; Judaism; Human services.
Type of support: General support; Scholarships.
Limitations: Applications accepted. Giving primarily in NY. No grants to individuals.
Application information: Application form required.
  Initial approach: Letter
  Deadline(s): None
Officer: Mira Spektor, Pres.
EIN: 136277982

6834
Spencer Charitable Fund
P.O. Box 197
Larchmont, NY   10538-0197   (914) 834-1900
Contact: Gordon S. Oppenheimer Esq., Tr.

Established in 1985 in New York.
Foundation type: Independent foundation.
Financial data (yr. ended 07/31/14): Assets, $3,072,478 (M); expenditures, $148,168; qualifying distributions, $139,872; giving activities include $130,500 for 9 grants (high: $25,000; low: $5,000).
Purpose and activities: Giving primarily for higher education.
Fields of interest: Education; Health; Diseases and conditions.
Limitations: Applications accepted. Giving primarily in NY. No grants to individuals.
Application information: Application form required.
  Initial approach: Proposal
  Deadline(s): None

Trustees: Alexander Oppenheimer; Gordon S. Oppenheimer; Jason Oppenheimer.
EIN: 136855911

6835
Sperandio Family Foundation
c/o Bessemer Trust, Tax Dept.
630 5th Ave., 34th Fl.
New York City, NY   10111-0100   5165089623

Established in 1995 in New York.
Donors: Robert V. Sperandio; Jacqueline Sperandio; Elizabeth F. Sperandio; Mark C. Sperandio.
Foundation type: Independent foundation.
Financial data (yr. ended 12/31/14): Assets, $210,281; expenditures, $269,161; qualifying distributions, $268,240.
Purpose and activities: Giving primarily for women and children.
Fields of interest: Education; Health; Domestic violence; Community and economic development; Children; Females.
Limitations: Applications accepted. Giving primarily in NY, with some giving in FL and WA.
Application information: Application form required.
  Initial approach: Letter
  Deadline(s): None
Officers: Jacqueline Sperandio, Pres.; Robert V. Sperandio, Secy.-Treas.
Trustees: Elizabeth F. Sperandio; Mark C. Sperandio.
EIN: 161490918

6836
The Speranza Foundation
302 A W. 12th St., Ste. 103
New York City, NY   10014-7906   (212) 206-6314
Contact: Kathleen Treat, Pres.
E-mail: info@speranzafoundation.com; Main URL: http://www.speranzafoundation.com
Facebook: https://www.facebook.com/pages/Speranza-Foundation/1463747300580682?ref=hl
Twitter: https://twitter.com/SperanzaFdn

Donor: Kathleen Treat.
Foundation type: Independent foundation.
Financial data (yr. ended 12/31/13): Assets, $45,206 (M); gifts received, $350,000; expenditures, $345,356; qualifying distributions, $303,500; giving activities include $250,000 for 2 grants (high: $200,000; low: $50,000), and $53,500 for 5 grants to individuals (high: $21,500; low: $1,000).
Purpose and activities: Giving primarily for the arts; grants also to individuals in order to: 1) provide funds for future projects in the arts; or 2) recognize excellence and outstanding achievement in the arts.
Fields of interest: Arts and culture; Film and video; Human services; Females; Female children and youth.
Type of support: Grants to individuals.
Application information: Unsolicited applications are not accepted. After review of initial paragraph, If there is interest in more information, an application will be sent. Only submissions which generate interest will receive a response and application. Application form required.
  Initial approach: Submit a paragraph of no more than 500 words

Officers: Kathleen Treat, Pres.; Carolyn Ebner, V.P.; Jay Gordon, Treas.
EIN: 263213052

6837
Jerry and Emily Spiegel Family Foundation, Inc.
(formerly Jerry Spiegel Foundation, Inc.)
P.O. Box 6
Hicksville, NY   11802-0006

Established in 1958 in New York.
Donors: Jerry Spiegel†; Emily Spiegel†.
Foundation type: Independent foundation.
Financial data (yr. ended 03/31/13): Assets, $34,055 (M); expenditures, $214,452; qualifying distributions, $200,000; giving activities include $200,000 for 1 grant.
Purpose and activities: Giving primarily for higher education, the arts, health associations, and to Jewish organizations and temples.
Fields of interest: Education; Diseases and conditions; Judaism; Human services.
Type of support: General support; Scholarships; Research.
Limitations: Applications not accepted. Giving primarily in NY and PA. No grants to individuals.
Application information: Contributes only to pre-selected organizations. Unsolicited requests for funds not accepted.
Officers: Pamela Sanders, Secy.; Lise Wilks, Treas.
EIN: 116006020

6838
The Spiegel Foundation
(formerly The Edward and Deanne Spiegel Foundation)
c/o BCRS Associates, LLC
77 Water St., 9th Fl.
New York City, NY   10005-4414

Established in 1985 in New York.
Donor: Edward P. Spiegel.
Foundation type: Independent foundation.
Financial data (yr. ended 09/30/13): Assets, $8,328,087 (M); expenditures, $459,631; qualifying distributions, $361,983; giving activities include $283,418 for 23 grants (high: $55,000; low: $50).
Fields of interest: Elementary and secondary education; Business education; Nonprofits; Diseases and conditions; Cancers; Judaism; Human services; Child welfare.
Type of support: Regranting.
Limitations: Applications not accepted. Giving primarily in New York, NY. No grants to individuals.
Application information: Unsolicited requests for funds not accepted.
Trustees: Elana B. Siegel; Bradley C. Spiegel; Deanne Spiegel.
EIN: 133318169

6839
Spirit Foundations, Inc.
c/o Sexter & Warmflash
115 Broadway
New York City, NY   10006-1602

Established in 1978 in New York.

Donors: John Ono Lennon†; Yoko Ono Lennon; Bag One Arts, Inc.; Fuji Films, Japan; Nike, Inc.; Together Magazine; Das Ventures Ltd.; LSL Productions, Inc.; Rock Annex NY LLC; Mark Lapidos Productions LTD.
Foundation type: Independent foundation.
Financial data (yr. ended 11/30/13): Assets, $1,090,663 (M); gifts received, $6,066; expenditures, $169,542; qualifying distributions, $169,527; giving activities include $169,527 for 3 grants (high: $107,527; low: $15,000).
Purpose and activities: Giving primarily for human services, international affairs, and women's causes.
Fields of interest: Early childhood education; Diseases and conditions; Community and economic development; Human services; Child welfare; Females.
International interests: England; Japan.
Type of support: General support; Research.
Limitations: Applications not accepted. Giving primarily in Tokyo, Japan and Liverpool, England; some giving also in New York, NY.
Application information: Contributes only to pre-selected organizations.
Officers: Yoko Ono Lennon, Pres.; David Warmflash, Secy.-Treas.
Director: Jonas Herbsman.
EIN: 132971714

6840
The Spiritus Gladius Foundation
(formerly D.C. Foundation, Inc.)
c/o Meyer Handelman Co.
P.O. Box 817
Purchase, NY   10577-0817

Established in 1959 in New York.
Donor: Nedenia H. Hartley.
Foundation type: Independent foundation.
Financial data (yr. ended 08/31/14): Assets, $6,182,455 (M); expenditures, $309,628; qualifying distributions, $278,271; giving activities include $278,000 for 6 grants (high: $100,000; low: $500).
Purpose and activities: Giving primarily for health care, education, health associations and the arts and culture, particularly to a theater center in Connecticut.
Fields of interest: Arts and culture; Theater; Education; Health; Diseases and conditions; Diabetes; Human services; Child welfare.
Type of support: Research; Research and evaluation.
Limitations: Applications not accepted. Giving primarily in CT and NY. No grants to individuals.
Application information: Contributes only to pre-selected organizations.
Officers and Trustees: Nedenia H. Hartley, Pres. and Trustee; Donald E. Handelman, V.P. and Treas. and Trustee; William R. Handelman, Secy. and Trustee; Joseph W. Handelman; Nedenia C. Rumbough; Stanley H. Rumbough.
EIN: 136113272

6841
The Spitzer Trust
c/o Abe Fish, C.P.A.
14 Waverly Pl.
Monsey, NY   10952-2537

Established in 1976 in New York.
Donors: Albert Spitzer; Erika Spitzer.

Foundation type: Independent foundation.
Financial data (yr. ended 10/31/13): Assets, $4,897,905 (M); expenditures, $272,963; qualifying distributions, $189,948; giving activities include $189,948 for 92 grants.
Purpose and activities: Support primarily for Jewish giving, including congregations and yeshivas.
Fields of interest: Judaism.
Limitations: Applications not accepted. Giving primarily in Brooklyn, NY. No grants to individuals.
Application information: Unsolicited requests for funds not accepted.
Trustees: Albert Spitzer; Eli Spitzer; Erika Spitzer; Michael Spitzer.
EIN: 112419181

6842
Margaret W. Spofford Foundation
c/o O'Connor Davies, LLP
665 5th Ave.
New York City, NY   10022

Established in 1994 in Delaware.
Donors: Margaret W. Spofford; L.C. and Margaret Walker Foundation.
Foundation type: Independent foundation.
Financial data (yr. ended 12/31/14): Assets, $7,346,569 (M); expenditures, $440,288; qualifying distributions, $356,246; giving activities include $329,394 for 39 grants (high: $78,000; low: $1,000).
Fields of interest: Arts and culture; Literature and writing; Education; Family planning; Community improvement; Christianity.
Type of support: General support.
Limitations: Applications not accepted. Giving primarily in NY and UT. No grants to individuals.
Application information: Contributes only to pre-selected organizations.
Officers and Directors: C. Nicholas Spofford, Pres.; John S.W. Spofford, V.P. and Treas. and Director.
EIN: 133803322

6843
Squier Family Foundation
c/o The Ayco Co., L.P. NTG
P.O. Box 15014
Albany, NY   12212-5014

Established in 2000 in Connecticut.
Donors: David L. Squier; Sue Squier.
Foundation type: Independent foundation.
Financial data (yr. ended 12/31/13): Assets, $2,565,400 (M); gifts received, $405,418; expenditures, $159,391; qualifying distributions, $153,850; giving activities include $153,850 for 30 grants (high: $30,000; low: $500).
Fields of interest: Education; Religion; Human services.
Limitations: Applications not accepted. Giving primarily in CT and ID. No grants to individuals.
Application information: Unsolicited requests for funds not accepted.
Trustees: David L. Squier; Sue Squier.
EIN: 061577514

6844
Mary Reinhart Stackhouse Foundation
c/o U.S. Trust, Philanthropic Solutions
1 Bryant Park, NY1-100-28-05
New York City, NY   10036-6715   (646) 855-0956
Contact: Ken Goody, Senior Vice President
E-mail: kenneth.l.goody@ustrust.com; Main
URL: https://www.bankofamerica.com/
philanthropic/grantmaking.go

Established in 1999 in New Jersey.
Donor: Mary Stackhouse Trust.
Foundation type: Independent foundation.
Financial data (yr. ended 12/31/14): Assets, $8,667,382; expenditures, $414,247; qualifying distributions, $375,703.
Purpose and activities: Giving for environmental and conservation organizations, and to support further education of needy caddies.
Fields of interest: Education; Environment; Sports and recreation.
Limitations: Giving primarily in FL and NJ. No grants to individuals.
Application information: Complete application guidelines available on foundation web site.
Initial approach: Online
Deadline(s): Sept. 15
Trustees: Bob McCurdy; Bank of America, N.A.
EIN: 527077828

6845
The Stanton Family Foundation
c/o BCRS Associates., LLC
77 Water St., 9th Fl.
New York City, NY   10005-4414

Established in 1996 in New Jersey.
Donor: Daniel W. Stanton.
Foundation type: Independent foundation.
Financial data (yr. ended 09/30/13): Assets, $3,549,071 (M); expenditures, $445,743; qualifying distributions, $344,622; giving activities include $338,622 for 36 grants (high: $250,000; low: $2).
Purpose and activities: Giving primarily for education and health and human services.
Fields of interest: Education; Elementary and secondary education; Higher education; Business education; Hospital care; Diseases and conditions; Human services; Child welfare.
Limitations: Applications not accepted. Giving primarily in FL, MA, and NY. No grants to individuals, or for scholarships; no loans.
Application information: Contributes only to pre-selected organizations.
Trustees: Daniel W. Stanton; Mary B. Stanton.
EIN: 137103245

6846
Howard E. Stark Charitable Foundation
53 N. Park Ave., Ste. 50
Rockville Centre, NY   11570-4111   (516) 678-1927

Foundation type: Independent foundation.
Financial data (yr. ended 05/31/13): Assets, $5,282,839 (M); expenditures, $299,956; qualifying distributions, $250,809; giving activities include $215,264 for 17 grants (high: $30,000; low: $224).

Fields of interest: Housing development; Food aid; Homeless services.
Limitations: Applications accepted. Giving primarily in MA and NY.
Application information: Application form required.
 Initial approach: Request formal grant application from foundation
 Deadline(s): None
Officer: Jennifer A. Franz, Exec. Dir.
Trustee: Michael T. Pagano.
EIN: 260270223

6847
The Starker Family Foundation Inc.
c/o JAD Consulting LLC
61 Broadway, Ste. 512
New York City, NY 10006-2744

Donor: Steven Starker.
Foundation type: Independent foundation.
Financial data (yr. ended 09/30/14): Assets, $478,106 (M); expenditures, $475,838; qualifying distributions, $471,288; giving activities include $391,232 for 125 grants (high: $50,000; low: $36).
Fields of interest: Education; Nonprofits; Health; Diseases and conditions; Judaism; Human services; Child welfare; Jewish people.
Type of support: Regranting; Research; Research and evaluation.
Limitations: Applications not accepted. No grants to individuals.
Application information: Contributes only to pre-selected organizations.
Officers: Steven Starker, Pres. and Treas.; Farrel Starker, V.P. and Secy.; Stuart Dix, V.P.; Ray Starker, V.P.
EIN: 133986718

6848
Starmar Foundation
c/o Bettina Finn
38 Evans Dr.
Brookville, NY 11545-3146

Donors: Brian Finn; Bettina Finn.
Foundation type: Independent foundation.
Financial data (yr. ended 12/31/13): Assets, $2,502,524 (M); expenditures, $208,841; qualifying distributions, $205,526; giving activities include $201,549 for 36 grants (high: $29,000; low: $400).
Fields of interest: Arts and culture; Education; Human services.
Limitations: Applications not accepted. Giving primarily in New York, NY.
Application information: Unsolicited requests for funds not accepted.
Officers: Bettina Finn, Pres.; Arden Finn, V.P.; Brian Finn, V.P.; Marissa Finn, Secy.; Steven Finn, Treas.
EIN: 274208964

6849
The Statue Foundation, Inc.
c/o Barbara K. Eisold
353 Central Park W.
New York City, NY 10025-6597
E-mail: beisold0@gmail.com

Established in 1997 in New York.
Donors: Barbara K. Eisold; Katz Family Trust.

Foundation type: Independent foundation.
Financial data (yr. ended 12/31/13): Assets, $2,441,347 (M); gifts received, $103,713; expenditures, $198,625; qualifying distributions, $158,467; giving activities include $158,467 for 25 grants (high: $30,000; low: $135).
Fields of interest: Education; Human services; International relations.
Limitations: Applications not accepted. Giving primarily in New York, NY. No grants to individuals.
Application information: Unsolicited requests for funds not accepted.
Officer: Barbara K. Eisold, Pres.
Directors: Elizabeth Eisold Blaylock; Kenneth Eisold; Katherine Eisold Miller.
EIN: 133947134

6850
The Stebbins Fund Inc.
c/o Sacks Press
600 3rd Ave., 18th Fl.
New York City, NY 10016-1901

Established in 1947 in New York.
Donor: Bruce Balding.
Foundation type: Independent foundation.
Financial data (yr. ended 12/31/13): Assets, $3,401,254 (M); gifts received, $50,000; expenditures, $198,776; qualifying distributions, $154,300; giving activities include $154,300 for 50 grants (high: $25,000; low: $500).
Purpose and activities: Giving primarily for education, including higher education and art education; support also for museums and historical preservation.
Fields of interest: Arts and culture; Museums; Historic preservation; Education; Higher education; Environment; Animal welfare; Hospital care; Libraries; Christianity.
Type of support: General support; Annual campaigns; Capital campaigns.
Limitations: Applications not accepted. Giving primarily in NY. No grants to individuals, or for endowment funds; no loans.
Application information: Unsolicited requests for funds not accepted.
Officers: James F. Stebbins, Pres.; Jane S. Greenleaf, V.P.; Theodore E. Stebbins, Jr., V.P.
Directors: Victoria Stebbins Greenleaf; J. Wright Rumbough, Jr.; Edwin E.F. Stebbins; Michael Morgan Stebbins.
EIN: 116021709

6851
The Stecher Family Foundation
(formerly The Esta and Jamie Stecher Foundation)
c/o The Ayco Co., L.P.
P.O. Box 15014
Albany, NY 12212-5014

Donors: Esta Eiger Stecher; Goldman Sachs Family Office; Jamie B.W. Stecher.
Foundation type: Independent foundation.
Financial data (yr. ended 07/31/13): Assets, $3,927,782 (M); expenditures, $239,096; qualifying distributions, $220,520; giving activities include $220,520 for 54 grants (high: $50,000; low: $50).
Purpose and activities: Giving primarily for Jewish organizations, including Jewish theological seminaries.

Fields of interest: Judaism; Youth development.
Limitations: Applications not accepted. Giving primarily in New York, NY. No grants to individuals, or for scholarships; no loans.
Application information: Unsolicited requests for funds not accepted.
Trustee: Jamie B.W. Stecher.
EIN: 133918278

6852
The Fredric E. Steck Family Foundation
c/o BCRS Associates, LLC
77 Water St., 9th Fl.
New York City, NY 10005-4414

Established in 1999 in New York.
Donor: Fredric E. Steck.
Foundation type: Independent foundation.
Financial data (yr. ended 05/31/13): Assets, $2,440,086 (M); expenditures, $390,104; qualifying distributions, $382,885; giving activities include $379,850 for 29 grants (high: $100,000; low: $500).
Fields of interest: Education; Domesticated animals; Human services.
Limitations: Applications not accepted. Giving primarily in CA. No grants to individuals, or for scholarships; no loans.
Application information: Unsolicited requests for funds not accepted.
Trustee: Fredric E. Steck.
EIN: 134073097

6853
Steckler Family Foundation, Inc.
(formerly Philip H. & Lois R. Steckler Foundation)
c/o Weisermazars, LLP
135 W. 50th St.
New York City, NY 10020-1299

Established in 1969 in New York.
Donor: Philip H. Steckler, Jr.†
Foundation type: Independent foundation.
Financial data (yr. ended 07/31/13): Assets, $1,301,346 (M); expenditures, $334,842; qualifying distributions, $302,550; giving activities include $294,800 for 10 grants (high: $100,000; low: $300).
Purpose and activities: Giving primarily for hospitals and health services, especially cancer-related organizations and higher and secondary education; some support for churches, youth services, and cultural activities.
Fields of interest: Education; Religion; Youth development.
Type of support: Capital campaigns; Endowments; Seed money; Scholarships; Research.
Limitations: Applications not accepted. Giving primarily in NY. No grants to individuals.
Application information: Unsolicited requests for funds not accepted.
Officers: Philip H. Steckler III, Pres.; Alan Steckler, Secy.; Donald H. Steckler, Treas.
EIN: 132621420

6854
The Meir and Ruth Stefansky Charitable Trust
3 Roman Blvd.
Monsey, NY 10952-3105

Established in 2005 in New York.
Donor: Meir Stefansky.
Foundation type: Operating foundation.
Financial data (yr. ended 01/31/13): Assets, $108,168 (M); gifts received, $410,000; expenditures, $439,136; qualifying distributions, $430,961; giving activities include $32,900 for grants, and $47,100 for 2 grants to individuals (high: $40,000; low: $7,100).
Purpose and activities: Giving to Jewish scholars who shed insight into complex areas of Jewish law.
Fields of interest: Judaism.
International interests: Israel.
Type of support: Grants to individuals.
Limitations: Applications not accepted. Giving primarily in Israel.
Application information: Unsolicited requests for funds not accepted.
Officer: N.B. Spitzer, Admin.
Trustees: Meir Stefansky; Ruth Stefansky.
EIN: 200699712

6855
Allen A. Stein Family Foundation, Inc.

c/o Davidson, Dawson & Clark LLP
60 E. 42nd St., 38th Fl.
New York City, NY 10165-0006
E-mail: cakehoe@davidsondavidson.com

Established in 2002 in New York.
Donor: Allen A. Stein†.
Foundation type: Independent foundation.
Financial data (yr. ended 12/31/13): Assets, $8,837,630 (M); expenditures, $511,500; qualifying distributions, $405,766; giving activities include $399,200 for 98 grants (high: $30,000; low: $250).
Purpose and activities: Giving primarily for Jewish education, organizations and temples.
Fields of interest: Graduate and professional education; Nonprofits; Judaism; Theology.
International interests: Israel.
Type of support: General support; Continuing support; Regranting; Annual campaigns; Capital campaigns; Capital and infrastructure; Equipment; Program development; Research.
Limitations: Applications not accepted.
Application information: Contributes only to pre-selected organizations.
  Board meeting date(s): Quarterly
Officers and Directors: Elaine Stein Roberts, Pres. and Director; Margot Stein, V.P. and Secy. and Director; Bernard Roberts, V.P. and Treas. and Director; Eric Stein, V.P. and Director; Sharon Stein, V.P. and Director.
Number of staff: 1 part-time professional.
EIN: 134153383

6856
The Nachum & Feige Stein Foundation

1675 52nd St.
Brooklyn, NY 11204-1419
Contact: Nachum Stein, Pres.

Established in 1975 in New York.
Donors: Nachum Stein; Feige Stein; Chaim Perlow; Hasenfeld-Stein Inc.
Foundation type: Independent foundation.
Financial data (yr. ended 06/30/13): Assets, $624,302 (M); gifts received, $146,250; expenditures, $164,298; qualifying distributions,

$162,910; giving activities include $160,810 for 206 grants (high: $14,900; low: $18).
Fields of interest: Nonprofits; Judaism; Human services.
Type of support: Regranting.
Limitations: Applications accepted. Giving primarily in NY. No grants to individuals.
Application information:
  Initial approach: Proposal
  Deadline(s): None
Officers and Trustees: Nachum Stein, Pres. and Trustee; Feige Stein, Secy. and Trustee.
EIN: 510142287

6857
Meyer & Jean Steinberg Family Foundation, Inc.

(formerly Meyer Steinberg Foundation, Inc.)
521 5th Ave., Ste. 1804
New York City, NY 10175-1804 (212) 824-1100
Contact: Susan Green, Pres.

Established in 1965 in New York.
Donors: Meyer Steinberg†; Bonnie Englebardt; Susan Zizesgreen; Carol Weisman; Lois Zaro; Jean Steinberg.
Foundation type: Independent foundation.
Financial data (yr. ended 12/31/13): Assets, $438,179 (M); expenditures, $151,269; qualifying distributions, $143,340; giving activities include $143,240 for 22 grants (high: $50,000; low: $490).
Fields of interest: Public affairs; Human services.
Application information:
  Initial approach: Letter
  Deadline(s): None
Officers: Susan Green, Pres.; Justin Green, Treas.
EIN: 136199973

6858
B. & M. Steinmetz Foundation

c/o David Soifer, C.P.A.
24 Jackson Ave.
Spring Valley, NY 10977-1908
Application address: c/o Bernat Steinmetz, Pres., 18 W. 33rd St., Brooklyn, NY 10005; tel.: (212) 563-5733

Established in 1969 in New York.
Donors: Bernat Steinmetz; Michael Steinmetz; Shraga Brecher; LSM Mgmt. Co.; Shoretown Management Co.; Fort Management; Town Management; Sara Spiegel; Margit Steinmetz†; Bernat Steinmatz Trust; 10 East Side LLC; Pessie Richard; Shraga Brecher; Leah Cohen.
Foundation type: Independent foundation.
Financial data (yr. ended 05/31/13): Assets, $20,662,606 (M); gifts received, $7,000; expenditures, $340,655; qualifying distributions, $323,541; giving activities include $323,541 for 50 grants (high: $100,000; low: $148).
Purpose and activities: Giving primarily to Jewish organizations, temples, and yeshivas. The foundation gives to religious organizations or to those with a letter of recommendation from a religious organization.
Fields of interest: Judaism.
Limitations: Applications accepted. Giving primarily in New York, NY.
Application information:
  Initial approach: Proposal
  Deadline(s): None

Officers: Bernat Steinmetz, Pres.; Michael Steinmetz, V.P.; Fay Weingarten, V.P.; Helen Brecher, Secy.; Abraham Weingarten, Treas.
EIN: 237048163

6859
S. & E. Steinmetz Foundation

352 Marcy Ave.
Brooklyn, NY 11206-4854 (718) 782-5769
Contact: Solomon Steinmetz, Tr.

Established in 1999 in New York.
Donors: Chaim Babab; Joseph Babab; Riviera Mgmt.; Ridge Mgmt.; Bay Mgmt.; Park Mgmt.; E & C Trust; Solomon Steinmetz.
Foundation type: Independent foundation.
Financial data (yr. ended 06/30/14): Assets, $2,799,767 (M); gifts received, $16,770; expenditures, $209,607; qualifying distributions, $207,531; giving activities include $207,531 for 98 grants (high: $28,000; low: $250).
Fields of interest: Judaism.
Limitations: Applications accepted. Giving primarily in Brooklyn and New York, NY.
Application information:
  Initial approach: Proposal
  Deadline(s): None
Trustees: Esther Steinmetz; Solomon Steinmetz.
EIN: 113481171

6860
Jerome L. Stern Family Foundation, Inc.

(formerly Jerome L. and Jane Stern Foundation, Inc.)
270 Madison Ave., 16 Fl.
New York City, NY 10016-0601 2129728165

Established in 1944 in New York.
Donors: Jerome L. Stern; Ronald A. Stern.
Foundation type: Independent foundation.
Financial data (yr. ended 02/28/15): Assets, $9,630,349; expenditures, $527,171; qualifying distributions, $418,985.
Purpose and activities: Giving primarily for Jewish higher education, temples and agencies; funding also for art museums.
Fields of interest: Art museums; Higher education; Judaism; Human services.
Limitations: Applications not accepted. Giving primarily in New York, NY. No grants to individuals.
Application information: Contributes only to pre-selected organizations.
Officers and Directors: Jerome L. Stern, Pres. and Secy.; Geoffrey S. Stern, Treas. and Director; Ellen L. Stern; Ronald A. Stern.
EIN: 136127063

6861
The Dianne & David Stern Foundation

c/o Raich, Ende, Malter & Co. LLP
475 Park Ave. S., 31st Fl.
New York City, NY 10016-6901

Established in 2008 in New York.
Donors: David J. Stern; Dianne B. Stern.
Foundation type: Independent foundation.
Financial data (yr. ended 02/28/13): Assets, $9,341,314 (M); gifts received, $375,000; expenditures, $396,903; qualifying distributions, $375,000; giving activities include $375,000 for grants.

Fields of interest: Natural resources.
Limitations: Applications not accepted. Giving primarily in CA. No grants to individuals.
Application information: Contributes only to pre-selected organizations.
Trustees: David J. Stern; Dianne B. Stern; Eric A. Stern.
EIN: 261598679

6862
Walter P. & Elizabeth M. Stern Foundation, Inc.
450 Fort Hill Rd.
Scarsdale, NY   10583-2413
Contact: Walter P. Stern, Pres.
FAX: (212) 649-1533; E-mail: wps@capgroup.com

Established in 1963 in New York.
Donors: Elizabeth M. Stern; Walter P. Stern.
Foundation type: Independent foundation.
Financial data (yr. ended 12/31/13): Assets, $7,291,277 (M); gifts received, $1,489,941; expenditures, $449,029; qualifying distributions, $420,291; giving activities include $412,584 for 43 grants (high: $100,000; low: $12).
Fields of interest: Higher education; Nonprofits; Public policy; National security; Judaism; International relations.
International interests: Israel.
Type of support: General support; Continuing support; Endowments; Scholarships; Regranting; Policy, advocacy and systems reform.
Limitations: Applications not accepted. Giving primarily in Washington, DC, and New York and Westchester counties, NY. No grants to individuals.
Application information: Unsolicited requests for funds not accepted.
Board meeting date(s): Varies annually
Officers and Directors: Walter P. Stern, Pres. and Director; Elizabeth M. Stern, Secy. and Director; David M.C. Stern; Sarah M. Stern; William M. Stern.
Number of staff: None.
EIN: 136111129

6863
Sternberg Charitable Trust
85 Bellevue Ave.
Rye, NY   10580-1840

Established in 1994 in New York.
Donor: Stuart L. Sternberg.
Foundation type: Independent foundation.
Financial data (yr. ended 12/31/14): Assets, $9,721,736 (M); gifts received, $900; expenditures, $314,000; qualifying distributions, $281,500; giving activities include $278,110 for 17 grants (high: $150,000; low: $200).
Purpose and activities: Giving primarily for the arts, education, health organizations, social services, the environment, religion, and the arts.
Fields of interest: Arts and culture; Elementary and secondary education; Natural resources; Foundations; Health; Diseases and conditions; Human services.
Limitations: Applications not accepted. Giving primarily in NY. No grants to individuals.
Application information: Contributes only to pre-selected organizations.
Trustees: Lisa Sternberg; Stuart L. Sternberg.
EIN: 137046097

6864
Sternklar Family Foundation, Inc.
(formerly Bezalel Art Foundation)
80 Maiden Ln., Ste. 2204
New York City, NY   10038-5326

Donors: Jack Sternklar; Lila Sternklar.
Foundation type: Independent foundation.
Financial data (yr. ended 06/30/13): Assets, $1,838,517 (M); expenditures, $289,638; qualifying distributions, $289,638; giving activities include $242,198 for 58 grants (high: $115,000; low: $18).
Purpose and activities: Giving primarily to Jewish organizations.
Fields of interest: Education; Religion; Human services.
Limitations: Applications not accepted. Giving primarily in the metropolitan New York, NY, area. No grants to individuals.
Application information: Unsolicited requests for funds not accepted.
Officers: Jack Sternklar, Pres.; Lila Sternklar, V.P.
EIN: 133041079

6865
Charlotte and Henry G. Stifel Foundation
c/o McGrath, Doyle & Phair
150 Broadway, Ste. 1212
New York City, NY   10038-4361

Established in 2001 in New Jersey.
Donor: Henry G. Stifel.
Foundation type: Independent foundation.
Financial data (yr. ended 04/30/14): Assets, $54,813 (M); gifts received, $222,937; expenditures, $223,408; qualifying distributions, $223,258; giving activities include $223,258 for 53 grants (high: $35,000; low: $47).
Fields of interest: Arts and culture; Art museums; Land resources; Spinal cord injuries and diseases; Christianity; Human services.
Type of support: Research.
Limitations: Applications not accepted. Giving primarily in NJ and WY. No grants to individuals.
Application information: Unsolicited requests for funds not accepted.
Officers and Directors: Henry G. Stifel, Pres. and Director; Charlotte Stifel, Secy. and Director.
EIN: 226877261

6866
Still Point Fund
c/o Eisenberg
150 Broadway, Ste. 1102
New York City, NY   10038

Established in 1997 in Vermont.
Donor: Brenda Ross Winter Charitable Lead Annuity Trust.
Foundation type: Independent foundation.
Financial data (yr. ended 12/31/13): Assets, $8,658,899 (M); gifts received, $500,000; expenditures, $549,560; qualifying distributions, $439,953; giving activities include $407,546 for 48 grants (high: $60,000; low: $46).
Purpose and activities: Giving primarily for conservation and organic farming research.
Fields of interest: Arts and culture; Education; Natural resources; Family planning; Organic farming;

Housing development; Human services; Food banks; Child welfare.
Type of support: General support.
Limitations: Applications not accepted. Giving primarily in PA and VA. No grants to individuals.
Application information: Contributes only to pre-selected organizations.
Officer and Directors: Guy N. Lancaster, Secy. and Director; Bettina Jane Lancaster; Christa Lancaster; Timothy Lancaster.
EIN: 043370051

6867
Stires-Stark Family Foundation
c/o Matthew Moore, The Ayco Co., L.P.
P.O. Box 860
Saratoga Springs, NY   12866-0860

Established in 2005 in New York.
Donors: Sidney Stark; Morgan Stark.
Foundation type: Independent foundation.
Financial data (yr. ended 12/31/13): Assets, $81,672 (M); gifts received, $101,295; expenditures, $139,999; qualifying distributions, $139,814; giving activities include $139,814 for 13 grants (high: $33,452; low: $50).
Fields of interest: Music; Education.
Limitations: Applications not accepted. Giving primarily in NY. No grants to individuals.
Application information: Unsolicited requests for funds not accepted.
Trustees: Mason V.C. Stark; Morgan B. Stark; Nicholas M. Stark; Sidney S. Stark.
EIN: 206772741

6868
Stony Wold-Herbert Fund, Inc.
136 E. 57th St., Rm. 1705
New York City, NY   10022-2924   (212) 753-6565
Contact: Cheryl S. Friedman, Exec. Dir.
FAX: (212) 753-6053;
E-mail: director@stonywold-herbertfund.com; Main URL: http://www.stonywoldherbertfund.com

Established in 1974 in New York.
Foundation type: Independent foundation.
Financial data (yr. ended 12/31/13): Assets, $6,569,298 (M); gifts received, $3,782; expenditures, $458,899; qualifying distributions, $434,337; giving activities include $311,600 for 11 grants (high: $71,600; low: $1,000), and $33,325 for 14 grants to individuals (high: $3,025; low: $625).
Purpose and activities: Support for four programs: 1) research grants to doctors within the greater New York, NY, area involved in studying respiratory diseases; 2) pulmonary fellowships to doctors in the greater New York, NY, area training in the respiratory field; 3) grants for New York City community service projects in the pulmonary field; and 4) supplementary grants for college undergraduates or vocational school students, 16 years or older, living in the greater New York City area only, with respiratory illnesses.
Fields of interest: University education; Health; Diseases and conditions.
Type of support: Convening; Grants to individuals; Research; Seed money; Fellowships; Scholarships; Student aid.
Limitations: Giving limited to New York, NY, area. No grants for capital or endowment funds, operating

budgets, annual campaigns, seed money, emergency funds, or matching gifts; no loans.
Publications: Application guidelines; Annual report; Informational brochure; Newsletter.
Application information: Grant guidelines for various programs are available on the fund web site. Application form required.
> *Initial approach:* Letter, telephone, or e-mail
> *Copies of proposal:* 8
> *Deadline(s):* Oct. 15 for research and fellowship grants; Mar. 1 for community service proposals
> *Board meeting date(s):* Mar., May and Nov.
> *Final notification:* 2 to 3 weeks

Officers and Board Members: H. Kent Atkins, Pres.; Mrs. Ronald Carr, V.P. and Director; Nicholas Moore, Secy.; Alan Breed, Treas.; Cheryl S. Friedman, Exec. Dir.; Ashton Harvey; Mrs. James L. German III; Mrs. George C. Moore; Joan Reibman; Lawrence L. Scharer, MD; Neil Schluger; Henry M. Thomas III, MD.
Number of staff: 2 part-time professional.
EIN: 132784124

6869
Stowe Family Foundation
912 5th Ave., Ste. 6B
New York City, NY   10021-4159
Contact: Richard H. Stowe, Tr.

Established in 1996 in New York.
Donors: Richard H. Stowe; Virginia K. Stowe.
Foundation type: Independent foundation.
Financial data (yr. ended 09/30/13): Assets, $832,202 (M); expenditures, $249,541; qualifying distributions, $231,305; giving activities include $231,305 for 26 grants (high: $40,775; low: $200).
Fields of interest: Arts and culture; Higher education; Natural resources; Mental health care; Community and economic development; Christianity; Human services; Child welfare.
Limitations: Applications accepted. Giving primarily in Brunswick, ME, New York, NY, and PA.
Application information: Application form required.
> *Initial approach:* Letter
> *Deadline(s):* None

Trustee: Richard H. Stowe.
EIN: 137104307

6870
The Strauss Foundation Inc.
c/o Sacks
600 3rd Ave.
New York City, NY   10016-1901

Established in 2005 in New York.
Donors: Sylvie Strauss Trust; Renato Strauss Trust; Noemi Strauss; Strauss Family Trust; Roberto Strauss Trust; Noemi Strauss Trust.
Foundation type: Independent foundation.
Financial data (yr. ended 12/31/13): Assets, $531,498 (M); gifts received, $15,000; expenditures, $174,924; qualifying distributions, $173,789; giving activities include $173,789 for 13 grants (high: $100,000; low: $400).
Fields of interest: Higher education; Judaism.
International interests: Israel.
Limitations: Applications not accepted. No grants to individuals.
Application information: Unsolicited requests for funds not accepted.

Directors: Warren Gleicher; Ernst Strauss; Renato Strauss.
EIN: 202357393

6871
The Peter & Caroline Striano Foundation
65-45 Fresh Meadow Ln.
Flushing, NY   11365-2011

Established in 1991 in New York.
Donors: Peter J. Striano; Unity Electric Co., Inc.; Caroline Striano.
Foundation type: Independent foundation.
Financial data (yr. ended 12/31/12): Assets, $30,085 (M); expenditures, $311,445; qualifying distributions, $311,049; giving activities include $310,699 for 51 grants (high: $45,100; low: $25).
Purpose and activities: Giving primarily for education and health associations.
Fields of interest: Arts and culture; Education; Higher education; Nonprofits; Health; Catholicism; Human services.
Type of support: Regranting.
Limitations: Applications not accepted. No grants to individuals.
Application information: Unsolicited requests for funds not accepted.
Officers: Peter Striano, Pres.; Caroline Striano, V.P.; Christine Arella, Secy.; Marisa Striano, Treas.
EIN: 113078596

6872
Strong Foundation of New York
c/o Roger Strong
30 E. 71st St., Ste. 9A
New York City, NY   10021-4956
E-mail: rogerstrong71@verizon.net

Established in 1961 in New York.
Donors: Roger L. Strong; Marguerite Strong†; Lee Strong; Roger L. Strong, Jr.; Jeffrey Strong; Thomas Strong; Julia Ernst†.
Foundation type: Independent foundation.
Financial data (yr. ended 03/31/13): Assets, $7,544,618 (M); gifts received, $148,266; expenditures, $269,367; qualifying distributions, $186,400; giving activities include $186,400 for grants.
Purpose and activities: Giving primarily for primary and secondary education and the arts, and to Jewish agencies.
Fields of interest: Arts and culture; Education; Higher education; Natural resources; Libraries; Judaism; Young adults.
Type of support: General support; Matching grants; Continuing support; Regranting; Annual campaigns; Fundraising; Capital campaigns; Capital and infrastructure; Land acquisitions; Endowments; Emergency funds; Program development; Internships.
Limitations: Applications not accepted. Giving primarily in New York, NY and Phoenix, AZ. No grants to individuals.
Publications: Annual report.
Application information: Contributes only to pre-selected organizations.
> *Board meeting date(s):* Quarterly

Officers: Roger L. Strong, Pres.; Roger L. Strong, Jr., V.P.; Lee Strong, Secy.
Trustees: Jeffrey Strong; Thomas Strong.

Number of staff: None.
EIN: 136093147

6873
Mark Stuart, Jr. Foundation
20 Broad St.
New York City, NY   10005

Donor: Mark J. Stuart, Jr.
Foundation type: Independent foundation.
Financial data (yr. ended 02/28/13): Assets, $46,293 (M); gifts received, $180,000; expenditures, $164,432; qualifying distributions, $163,616; giving activities include $162,801 for 16 grants (high: $100,000; low: $501).
Fields of interest: Education; University education; Health.
Limitations: Applications not accepted. Giving primarily in NY. No grants to individuals.
Application information: Unsolicited requests for funds not accepted.
Officer: Mark J. Stuart, Jr.
EIN: 237008867

6874
Stuntz Family Foundation
c/o Eisneramper LLP
750 3rd Ave., 16th Fl.
New York City, NY   10017-2716

Established in 1997 in New York.
Donors: Mayo Stuntz; Elizabeth Stuntz; Mayo S. Stuntz, Jr.
Foundation type: Independent foundation.
Financial data (yr. ended 11/30/13): Assets, $9,235,889 (M); gifts received, $38,585; expenditures, $524,827; qualifying distributions, $444,580; giving activities include $433,860 for 33 grants (high: $75,000; low: $500).
Purpose and activities: Giving primarily for education and human services, as well as for Jewish organizations.
Fields of interest: Education; Judaism; Human services.
Limitations: Applications not accepted. Giving primarily in NY. No grants to individuals.
Application information: Contributes only to pre-selected organizations.
Officer: Mayo S. Stuntz, Jr., Pres.
Director: Elizabeth Stuntz.
EIN: 133979253

6875
The Geraldine Stutz Trust
156 W. 56th St., Ste. 900
New York City, NY   10019-3927   (212) 755-8686
Contact: Allen Greenberg, Dir.

Established in 1997 in Connecticut.
Donor: Geraldine Stutz†.
Foundation type: Independent foundation.
Financial data (yr. ended 12/31/13): Assets, $5,887,348 (M); expenditures, $407,652; qualifying distributions, $342,460; giving activities include $312,300 for 24 grants (high: $85,000; low: $1,000).
Purpose and activities: Giving primarily for the arts.
Fields of interest: Arts and culture; Arts education; Design; Theater; Radio; Human services.
Type of support: Individual development.

Limitations: Applications accepted. Giving primarily in NY.
Application information: Application form required.
Initial approach: Proposal
Deadline(s): None
Directors: Eileen White Dillon; Allen Greenberg; Emma Turner.
EIN: 061484214

6876
Sumitomo Corporation of America Foundation
600 3rd Ave.
New York City, NY   10016-2001
Main URL: http://www.sumitomocorp.com/about/community.html

Established in 2004 in New York.
Donor: Sumitomo Corporation of America "SCOA".
Foundation type: Company-sponsored foundation.
Financial data (yr. ended 03/31/14): Assets, $9,172,979 (M); expenditures, $487,183; qualifying distributions, $448,755; giving activities include $441,000 for 21 grants (high: $150,000; low: $1,000).
Purpose and activities: The foundation supports organizations involved with arts and culture, education, relief assistance, and social services. Special emphasis is directed toward programs designed to enhance understanding in the United States of Japan, its people, culture, and society through research, education, and cultural initiatives.
Fields of interest: Arts and culture; Cultural awareness; Performing arts; Museums; Education; Higher education; Disaster relief; Community and economic development; Human services; Child welfare.
Type of support: Sponsorships; Cash grants; General support; Research.
Limitations: Applications not accepted. Giving primarily in areas of company operations, with emphasis on NY. No grants to individuals.
Application information: Contributes only to pre-selected organizations.
Officers and Directors: Hideki Iwasawa, Pres. and Dir.; Elizabeth Peters, Secy. and Dir.; Masao Hirota, Treas. and Dir.; William Kane; Shinichi Watabe.
EIN: 202103634

6877
Summit Foundation
c/o Marcum LLP
750 3rd Ave., 11th Fl.
New York City, NY   10017-9113

Established in 1994 in New York.
Donor: Cody J. Smith.
Foundation type: Independent foundation.
Financial data (yr. ended 09/30/13): Assets, $3,316,819 (M); gifts received, $1,707,646; expenditures, $398,103; qualifying distributions, $389,115; giving activities include $385,380 for 18 grants (high: $130,300; low: $280).
Fields of interest: Higher education; Undergraduate education; Philanthropy; Human services; Youth services.
Limitations: Applications not accepted. Giving primarily in CA, MA, MN and NY. No grants to individuals; no loans or scholarships.
Application information: Contributes only to pre-selected organizations.

Trustee: Cody J. Smith.
EIN: 133805672

6878
Sunrise Charitable Foundation Inc.
c/o Sunrise Securities
600 Lexington Ave., 23rd Fl.
New York City, NY   10022-4503

Established in 2006 in New York.
Donors: Lisa Low; Nathan A. Low; Sunrise Securities Inc.
Foundation type: Company-sponsored foundation.
Financial data (yr. ended 12/31/13): Assets, $1,625,413 (M); gifts received, $234,725; expenditures, $368,410; qualifying distributions, $366,861; giving activities include $365,293 for 30 grants (high: $96,735; low: $140).
Purpose and activities: The foundation supports nonprofit organizations involved with Judaism and Israel.
Fields of interest: Education; Religion; Human services.
Type of support: General support.
Limitations: Applications not accepted. Giving primarily in New York, NY.
Application information: Contributes only to pre-selected organizations.
Officer and Director: Nathan A. Low, Pres. and Director.
EIN: 510568537

6879
Edna Bailey Sussman Fund
c/o Boyce Etal
30 Jericho Executive Plz., Ste. 200W
Jericho, NY   11753-1028   (516) 282-7070

Established in 1984 in New York.
Donors: Arthur H. Dean†; Edward S. Miller.
Foundation type: Independent foundation.
Financial data (yr. ended 04/30/13): Assets, $7,444,909 (M); expenditures, $330,118; qualifying distributions, $322,072; giving activities include $304,508 for 10 grants (high: $63,700; low: $4,085).
Purpose and activities: Giving to further the preservation of wildlife, the control of pollution, and the preservation of natural land and resources by funding internships for individuals in a field of study at an institution of higher learning in an area that significantly impacts the environment.
Fields of interest: Higher education; Environment.
Type of support: Internships.
Limitations: Applications accepted. Giving primarily in CA, CO, CT, MI, NC, NY and VA. No grants to individuals directly.
Application information: The fund only accepts applications from colleges and universities with which it has established relationships. It does not accept applications from individuals. Stipends are disbursed to institution on behalf of intern selected by fund trustees. Application form required.
Initial approach: Request application form
Deadline(s): None
Trustees: Robert H. Frey; Edward S. Miller.
EIN: 133187064

6880
Otto Sussman Trust
c/o Boyce
30 Jericho Executive Plz., Ste. 200 W
Jericho, NY   11753-1028
Application address: c/o M. Fleming, P.O. Box 53446, Temple Heights Post Office, Washington, DC 20009

Established in 1947 in New York.
Donor: Otto Sussman†.
Foundation type: Independent foundation.
Financial data (yr. ended 12/31/14): Assets, $7,002,252 (M); expenditures, $268,669; qualifying distributions, $310,278; giving activities include $268,669 for 120 grants to individuals (high: $7,500; low: $353).
Purpose and activities: Giving to residents of NJ, NY, PA and OK who, in the opinion of the trustees, are in need of financial assistance due to death or illness in their immediate families or some other unusual or unfortunate circumstance.
Fields of interest: Low-income and poor people.
Type of support: Grants to individuals.
Limitations: Applications accepted. Giving limited to residents of NJ, NY, OK and PA.
Application information: Application form required.
Initial approach: Proposal
Deadline(s): None
Trustees: Martita Fleming; Catherine B. Glennon; Edward S. Miller.
EIN: 136075849

6881
Abe & Yvette Sutton Family Foundation Inc.
1 E. 33rd St., 6th Fl.
New York City, NY   10016-5011

Established in 1996 in New York.
Donors: Bag Bazaar, Ltd.; Accessory Exchange, LLC.
Foundation type: Independent foundation.
Financial data (yr. ended 02/28/14): Assets, $143,050 (M); expenditures, $167,338; qualifying distributions, $166,405; giving activities include $166,405 for grants.
Type of support: General support.
Limitations: Applications not accepted. Giving primarily in New York, NY. No grants to individuals.
Application information: Unsolicited requests for funds not accepted.
Officers: Solomon Sutton, Pres.; Alan Haber, V.P.; Jacob Sutton, Secy.
EIN: 133882767

6882
Ruth & David Sutton Family Foundation
1 E. 33rd St., 7th Fl.
New York City, NY   10016-2831

Established in 1993 in New York.
Donors: David Sutton; Paul Sutton; Ruth Sutton; Steven Sutton; Cudlie Accessories, LLC; DS Associates; David Sutton Ira First Clearing Corp.; Ruth Sutton National Financial Services; Sutton Holdings GP.
Foundation type: Independent foundation.
Financial data (yr. ended 05/31/14): Assets, $43,849 (M); gifts received, $214,980; expenditures, $354,048; qualifying distributions,

$353,818; giving activities include $353,818 for grants.
Fields of interest: Education; Judaism.
Type of support: General support.
Limitations: Applications not accepted. No grants to individuals.
Application information: Contributes only to pre-selected organizations.
Trustees: Paul Sutton; Steven Sutton.
EIN: 137014537

6883
Mary & Abe Sutton Foundation
c/o Sutton Investment
291 Broadway, 19th Fl.
New York City, NY   10007-1814

Established in 2003 in New York.
Donors: Esther Sutton; Elie A. Sutton; Shirley Sutton; Abraham Sutton.
Foundation type: Independent foundation.
Financial data (yr. ended 12/31/13): Assets, $272,303 (M); gifts received, $246,000; expenditures, $243,509; qualifying distributions, $242,947; giving activities include $242,947 for 96 grants (high: $90,000; low: $52).
Purpose and activities: Giving primarily for Jewish educational organizations.
Fields of interest: Judaism.
Limitations: Applications not accepted. Giving primarily in NY. No grants to individuals.
Application information: Unsolicited requests for funds not accepted.
Directors: David Hirsh; Abraham Sutton; Mary Sutton.
EIN: 830346075

6884
The Sutton Trust Foundation
c/o Wiggin and Dana
450 Lexington Ave., Ste. 3800
New York City, NY   10017-3913

Established in 2005 in New York.
Donors: Richard Perry; Rebecca C. Byrne; James R. Byrne; Michael Carpenter; Mrs. Michael Carpenter; Sir Peter Lampl; D.F.K. Finlay; Martin J. Sullivan; Christopher Wright; Auda Advisor Associates; Scott Lampl Trust; Perry Capital; Geoffrey Scott Walker; Chatterjee Charitable Foundation; EMG Madonna Educational Foundation; Perry Partners.
Foundation type: Independent foundation.
Financial data (yr. ended 12/31/13): Assets, $446,246 (M); gifts received, $385,882; expenditures, $458,186; qualifying distributions, $439,773; giving activities include $437,732 for 9 grants (high: $139,065; low: $3,750).
Fields of interest: Higher education.
International interests: England.
Limitations: Applications not accepted. Giving primarily in England. No grants to individuals.
Application information: Unsolicited requests for funds not accepted.
Trustees: Bruce Hood; Sir Peter Lampl; Erica Walker.
EIN: 201886191

6885
The Suwinski Family Foundation Inc.
(formerly The Sheffield Foundation, Inc.)
451 Sheffield Rd.
Ithaca, NY   14850-9246

Established in 2000 in New York.
Donors: Jan H. Suwinski; Susan J. Suwinski.
Foundation type: Independent foundation.
Financial data (yr. ended 12/31/14): Assets, $4,074,577 (M); gifts received, $592,766; expenditures, $193,570; qualifying distributions, $177,567; giving activities include $176,000 for 73 grants (high: $12,500; low: $500).
Fields of interest: Environment; Health; Agriculture.
Limitations: Applications not accepted. Giving primarily in NY, OR and the Washington, DC area. No grants to individuals.
Application information: Unsolicited requests for funds not accepted.
Officers and Directors: Jan Suwinski, Pres. and Treas. and Director; Susan Suwinski, Secy. and Director; Karen Suwinski.
EIN: 161587911

6886
SVM Foundation
c/o Philip L. Milstein
545 Madison Ave., 6th Fl., Ste. 600
New York City, NY   10022-4608

Established in 1996 in New York.
Donors: Seymour Milstein†; Vivian Milstein.
Foundation type: Independent foundation.
Financial data (yr. ended 12/31/14): Assets, $3,123,097 (M); expenditures, $353,211; qualifying distributions, $342,750; giving activities include $342,500 for 8 grants (high: $135,000; low: $4,000).
Fields of interest: Arts and culture; Higher education; Foundations; Nonprofits; Judaism.
Type of support: Regranting; Grants to individuals.
Limitations: Applications not accepted. Giving primarily in NY.
Application information: Unsolicited requests for funds not accepted.
Trustees: Constance J. Milstein; Philip L. Milstein; Vivian Milstein.
EIN: 137105557

6887
Sweeney Family Foundation
c/o The Ayco Company, L.P. - NTG
P.O. Box 15014
Albany, NY   12212-5014

Donors: Sean S. Sweeney; Caroline Sweeney.
Foundation type: Independent foundation.
Financial data (yr. ended 12/31/13): Assets, $1,518,178 (M); gifts received, $368,270; expenditures, $402,810; qualifying distributions, $397,830; giving activities include $397,830 for 8 grants (high: $200,000; low: $1,000).
Fields of interest: Undergraduate education; Cancers.
Limitations: Applications not accepted.
Application information: Unsolicited requests for funds not accepted.
Trustees: Caroline Sweeney; Sean S. Sweeney.
EIN: 266527053

6888
The Holly and Bradford Swett Charitable Trust
1536 3rd Ave., 3rd Fl.
New York City, NY   10028-2167

Established in 2003 in New York.
Donors: Robert Wilmers; Holly McAllister; Bradford N. Swett†.
Foundation type: Independent foundation.
Financial data (yr. ended 09/30/14): Assets, $1,763,705 (M); expenditures, $126,303; qualifying distributions, $125,843; giving activities include $125,843 for 6 grants (high: $50,096; low: $7,921).
Fields of interest: Education; Land resources; Foundations; Brain and nervous system disorders; Community and economic development.
Limitations: Applications not accepted. Giving primarily in NY and WY. No grants to individuals.
Application information: Unsolicited requests for funds not accepted.
Trustee: Holly McAllister.
EIN: 116589503

6889
Switzer Foundation
112 W. 34th S., 18th Fl.
New York City, NY   10120-0001
Contact: Frank Dougan, Pres.

Donors: Margaret Switzer†; Sarah Switzer†.
Foundation type: Independent foundation.
Financial data (yr. ended 12/31/13): Assets, $6,488,942 (M); expenditures, $385,780; qualifying distributions, $344,390; giving activities include $311,000 for 28 grants (high: $21,000; low: $6,000).
Purpose and activities: Giving primarily for young women in the metropolitan New York, New York, area for medical education; funding particularly for schools of nursing.
Fields of interest: Higher education; Graduate and professional education; Hospital care; Nursing care; Human services.
Type of support: Scholarships.
Limitations: Applications accepted. Giving primarily in the metropolitan New York, NY, area, including NJ. No grants to individuals, or for building or endowment funds, operating budgets, or special projects.
Publications: Informational brochure.
Application information: Application form required.
   Initial approach: Letter
   Copies of proposal: 1
   Deadline(s): None
   Board meeting date(s): Apr. and Oct.
Officers: Frank Dougan, Pres.; Dolores Ross, V.P.; Margaret Warren, Secy.; Michael Glen, Treas.
Number of staff: 1 full-time professional.
EIN: 135596831

6890
The Tahari Family Foundation
c/o Marcum LLP
10 Melville Park Rd.
Melville, NY   11747-3146   (631) 414-4000
Contact: Elie Tahari, Pres.

Established in 2005 in New York.
Donors: Elie Tahari; Husein Jafferjee; Elie Tahari Ltd.

Foundation type: Independent foundation.
Financial data (yr. ended 12/31/14): Assets, $6,416 (M); gifts received, $360,990; expenditures, $356,454; qualifying distributions, $355,182; giving activities include $354,000 for 9 grants (high: $172,000; low: $3,000).
Fields of interest: Arts and culture; Foundations; Judaism; Human services.
Limitations: Applications accepted. Giving primarily in CA and NY.
Application information:
  Initial approach: Letter
  Deadline(s): None
Officer: Elie Tahari, Pres.
EIN: 206739119

6891
The Tang Fund
c/o Oscar Tang
551 5th Ave., Fl. 33
New York City, NY   10176-0959

Established in 1984 in New York.
Donors: Oscar L. Tang; Reich & Tang; Robert F. Hoerle.
Foundation type: Independent foundation.
Financial data (yr. ended 11/30/13): Assets, $67,417,275 (M); gifts received, $140,400; expenditures, $540,322; qualifying distributions, $169,175; giving activities include $169,175 for 38 grants (high: $25,000; low: $19).
Purpose and activities: Giving primarily for higher and secondary education; support also for cultural programs and community development.
Fields of interest: Arts and culture; Secondary education; Higher education; Community and economic development; Goodwill promotion.
International interests: China.
Limitations: Applications not accepted. Giving primarily in NY. No grants to individuals.
Application information: Contributes only to pre-selected organizations.
Officers: Oscar L. Tang, Pres. and Treas.; Gwenn S. Winkhaus, Secy.
Director: Tracy L. Tang.
EIN: 133256295

6892
Paul P. Tanico Foundation Inc.
101 Park Ave., 23rd Fl.
New York City, NY   10178-2399   (212) 251-3300
Contact: Paul P. Tanico, Pres.

Established in 2009 in New York.
Donor: Paul P. Tanico.
Foundation type: Independent foundation.
Financial data (yr. ended 12/31/13): Assets, $167,984 (M); expenditures, $294,749; qualifying distributions, $291,023; giving activities include $279,850 for 15 grants (high: $60,000; low: $5,000).
Fields of interest: Education.
Application information: Application form required.
  Initial approach: Letter
  Deadline(s): None
Officers: Paul P. Tanico, Pres.; Eugene Massamillo, V.P.; Anthony Federici, Secy.-Treas.
EIN: 271511143

6893
The Tanner-Frank Foundation
c/o Barry M. Strauss Assocs., Ltd.
307 5th Ave., 8th Fl.
New York City, NY   10016-6517

Established in 2000 in New York.
Donor: Frederick Frank.
Foundation type: Independent foundation.
Financial data (yr. ended 12/31/13): Assets, $10,363,938 (M); gifts received, $250; expenditures, $224,894; qualifying distributions, $127,750; giving activities include $127,500 for 7 grants (high: $98,500; low: $1,000).
Fields of interest: Higher education; Philanthropy; Nonprofits; Judaism.
Type of support: Regranting.
Limitations: Applications not accepted. Giving primarily in New Haven, CT. No grants to individuals.
Application information: Contributes only to pre-selected organizations.
Trustees: Frederick Frank; Mary Tanner.
EIN: 137102288

6894
The Kenneth J. Tedaldi Foundation, Inc.
P.O. Box 815
Quogue, NY   11959-0815   (631) 653-5549
Contact: Kenneth J. Tedaldi, Pres.

Established in 1993 in New York.
Donor: Kenneth J. Tedaldi.
Foundation type: Independent foundation.
Financial data (yr. ended 12/31/13): Assets, $2,042,330 (M); gifts received, $100,000; expenditures, $165,718; qualifying distributions, $154,150; giving activities include $154,150 for 24 grants (high: $36,000; low: $300).
Fields of interest: Education; Diseases and conditions; Religion.
Type of support: Research.
Application information:
  Initial approach: Proposal
  Deadline(s): None
Officers: Kenneth J. Tedaldi, Pres.; Kathie Wolland, Secy.
EIN: 113190508

6895
Judy & Warren Tenney Foundation
845 Forest Ave.
Rye, NY   10580-3103   (212) 371-4446
Contact: Judy E. Tenney, Pres.

Established in 1989 in New York.
Donors: Warren Tenney†; Judy E. Tenney.
Foundation type: Independent foundation.
Financial data (yr. ended 12/31/13): Assets, $5,320,340 (M); expenditures, $228,889; qualifying distributions, $162,340; giving activities include $162,340 for 50 grants (high: $52,200; low: $8).
Purpose and activities: Giving primarily for the arts and Jewish organizations.
Fields of interest: Arts and culture; Higher education; Nonprofits; Judaism.
Type of support: Regranting.
Limitations: Applications accepted. Giving primarily in New York, NY. No grants to individuals.
Application information:

Initial approach: Proposal
  Deadline(s): None
Officers: Judy E. Tenney, Pres.; Amy T. Levere, V.P.; Alice J. Tenney, V.P.; Laura E. Tenney, V.P.; Lester C. Migdal, Secy.-Treas.
EIN: 133482305

6896
Tensor Foundation
P.O. Box 149
Dobbs Ferry, NY   10522-0149

Established in 1993 in New York.
Donors: Archie C. McKellar; Marie T. McKellar.
Foundation type: Independent foundation.
Financial data (yr. ended 12/31/14): Assets, $4,186,799 (M); gifts received, $25,313; expenditures, $255,441; qualifying distributions, $226,333.
Fields of interest: Water resources; Mathematics.
Limitations: Applications not accepted. Giving primarily in Dobbs Ferry, NY; support also in Washington, DC. No grants to individuals.
Application information: Contributes only to pre-selected organizations.
Trustees: Archie C. McKellar; Marie T. McKellar.
EIN: 137017367

6897
Thanksgiving Foundation
c/o Bessemer Trust Co., N.A.
630 5th Ave.
New York City, NY   10111-0001

Established in 1985 in New Jersey.
Donors: Thomas M. Peters; Marion Post Peters.
Foundation type: Independent foundation.
Financial data (yr. ended 07/31/13): Assets, $7,790,195 (M); gifts received, $1,050; expenditures, $376,541; qualifying distributions, $322,351; giving activities include $197,000 for 101 grants (high: $10,000; low: $500).
Fields of interest: Arts and culture; Museums; Elementary and secondary education; Higher education; Environment; Wildlife biodiversity; Hospital care; Christianity; Human services; Child welfare.
Limitations: Applications not accepted. Giving primarily in NJ, NY, VA, and WY. No grants to individuals.
Application information: Contributes only to pre-selected organizations.
Officers: Mark C. Winmill, Chair.; Thomas H. Stine, Pres.
Trustee: Bessemer Trust Co., N.A.
EIN: 136861874

6898
Alvin F. and Ruth K. Thiem Charitable Foundation
19 Prince St.
Rochester, NY   14607

Established in 1992 in New York.
Donor: Alvin F. Thiem†.
Foundation type: Independent foundation.
Financial data (yr. ended 12/31/13): Assets, $6,176,498 (M); expenditures, $370,090; qualifying distributions, $318,754; giving activities

include $314,000 for 20 grants (high: $78,000; low: $1,000).
Fields of interest: Performing arts; Elementary and secondary education; Higher education; Christianity.
Limitations: Applications not accepted. Giving primarily in NY. No grants to individuals.
Application information: Contributes only to pre-selected organizations.
Officers: Richard F. O'Connor, Esq., Pres.; Louis Lococo, Secy.; Don O'Neill, Treas.
Board Member: Joan Klafehn.
EIN: 161419723

6899
The Three Chicks Charitable Trust
c/o Baker Nye
477 Madison Ave., Ste. 1600
New York City, NY 10022-5834   (212) 826-3030
Contact: Richard Nye, Tr.

Established in 2006 in New York.
Foundation type: Independent foundation.
Financial data (yr. ended 12/31/12): Assets, $1,394,523 (M); expenditures, $286,233; qualifying distributions, $280,000; giving activities include $280,000 for grants.
Fields of interest: Education; Undergraduate education; Christianity; Human services.
Limitations: Applications accepted. Giving primarily in CO.
Application information:
  Initial approach: Letter
  Deadline(s): None
Trustee: Richard Nye.
EIN: 204427115

6900
The Lizzie & Jonathan Tisch Foundation, Inc.
655 Madison Ave., 11th Fl.
New York City, NY 10065-8043

Established in 1995 in New York.
Donors: Joan H. Tisch; Greater Talent Network, Inc.
Foundation type: Independent foundation.
Financial data (yr. ended 12/31/13): Assets, $17,800,346 (M); gifts received, $4,305,475; expenditures, $955,020; qualifying distributions, $850,264; giving activities include $194,660 for 21 grants (high: $49,500; low: $500).
Fields of interest: Arts and culture; Performing arts; Art museums; Education; Secondary education; Higher education; Health; Judaism; Human services.
Limitations: Applications not accepted. Giving primarily in New York, NY. No grants to individuals.
Application information: Contributes only to pre-selected organizations.
Officers and Directors: Jonathan M. Tisch, Pres. and Director; Elizabeth S. Tisch, Sr. V.P.; Barry L. Bloom, Secy.-Treas.
EIN: 311641042

6901
Sarah Tod Fund
c/o Withumsmith and Brown PC
1411 Broadway, 9th Fl.
New York City, NY 10018

Foundation type: Independent foundation.

Financial data (yr. ended 12/31/13): Assets, $5,596,217 (M); expenditures, $287,833; qualifying distributions, $250,750; giving activities include $248,000 for 50 grants (high: $75,000; low: $250).
Fields of interest: Education; Higher education; Health; Hospital care; Community improvement; Human services.
Type of support: Scholarships.
Limitations: Applications not accepted. No grants to individuals.
Application information: Unsolicited requests for funds not accepted.
Trustee: Catherine M. Randolph.
EIN: 131963936

6902
Carl E. Touhey Foundation
Pine W. Plz. Bldg., 2 Washington Ave.
Albany, NY 12205-5522

Established in 1989 in New York.
Donors: Carl E. Touhey; Charles L. Touhey.
Foundation type: Independent foundation.
Financial data (yr. ended 12/31/13): Assets, $2,576,620 (M); gifts received, $2,928; expenditures, $353,384; qualifying distributions, $350,973; giving activities include $333,200 for 11 grants (high: $200,000; low: $1,000).
Fields of interest: Arts and culture; Orchestral music; Higher education.
Limitations: Applications not accepted. Giving primarily in NY. No grants to individuals.
Application information: Unsolicited requests for funds not accepted.
Officers and Trustees: Carl E. Touhey, Pres. and Trustee; Charles L. Touhey, V.P. and Secy. and Trustee; Paul G. Glotzbecker, Treas. and Trustee; John J. Touhey; Lila M. Touhey; Virginia E. Touhey.
EIN: 223016226

6903
Touradji Family Foundation
P.O. Box 728
Sagaponack, NY 11962-0728

Donors: Pejman Touradji; Shannon Touradji.
Foundation type: Independent foundation.
Financial data (yr. ended 12/31/12): Assets, $26,590,452 (M); gifts received, $5,000,000; expenditures, $301,141; qualifying distributions, $300,600; giving activities include $300,000 for 2 grants (high: $250,000; low: $50,000).
Fields of interest: Foundations; Diseases and conditions; Human services.
Limitations: Applications not accepted. Giving primarily in New York, NY.
Application information: Contributes only to pre-selected organizations.
Trustees: Pejman Touradji; Shannon Touradji.
EIN: 271533902

6904
Tov V Chesed Foundation
4515 18th Ave.
Brooklyn, NY 11204-1292

Donors: Itzhak Toub; Jacob Stern; Abraham Stern; USI; Moses Eilenberg.
Foundation type: Operating foundation.

Financial data (yr. ended 12/31/13): Assets, $4,918,262 (M); expenditures, $254,714; qualifying distributions, $150,540; giving activities include $148,540 for 5 grants (high: $132,000; low: $180).
Purpose and activities: Giving primarily to Jewish agencies, temples, and schools.
Fields of interest: Education; Judaism.
Limitations: Applications not accepted. Giving primarily in Brooklyn, Queens, and Monroe, NY; some giving also in Lakewood, NJ. No grants to individuals.
Application information: Contributes only to pre-selected organizations.
Officers: Jacob Stern, Pres.; Abraham Stern, V.P.
EIN: 113407656

6905
Tradition Foundation
c/o Martin Vegh
121 Joseph Ave.
Staten Island, NY 10314-5054

Donors: Martin Vegh; Robert Fagenson; J. Fagenson; Spencer St Realty, LLC; Steven Gottlieb.
Foundation type: Independent foundation.
Financial data (yr. ended 12/31/13): Assets, $7,265,911 (M); expenditures, $326,121; qualifying distributions, $324,409; giving activities include $323,659 for 16 grants (high: $89,300; low: $720).
Purpose and activities: Giving primarily to Jewish agencies, temples, and schools.
Fields of interest: Education; Judaism.
Limitations: Applications not accepted. Giving primarily in NY. No grants to individuals.
Application information: Contributes only to pre-selected organizations.
Trustees: Martin Vegh; Susan Vegh.
EIN: 137112949

6906
The Treetops Foundation
c/o Baker Tilly
1 Penn Plz., Ste. 3000
New York City, NY 10119

Established in 1999 in New York.
Donors: Lisa Belzberg; Matthew Bronfman; Stacey K. Bronfman; Ann Bronfman†; Ann Bronfman Foundation; Enchanted Candle Inc.
Foundation type: Independent foundation.
Financial data (yr. ended 12/31/13): Assets, $13,902,987 (M); gifts received, $1,079,939; expenditures, $469,953; qualifying distributions, $423,507; giving activities include $420,643 for 24 + grants (high: $150,080).
Fields of interest: Arts and culture; Education; Judaism; Human services.
Limitations: Applications not accepted. Giving primarily in New York, NY. No grants to individuals.
Application information: Contributes only to pre-selected organizations.
Trustees: Matthew Bronfman; Stacey K. Bronfman.
EIN: 134093466

6907
The Treiber Family Foundation Inc.
377 Oak St., Ste. 405-7
Garden City, NY 11530-6553

Foundation type: Independent foundation.
Financial data (yr. ended 12/31/13): Assets, $157,008 (M); expenditures, $321,021; qualifying distributions, $290,900; giving activities include $290,900 for 35 grants (high: $76,100; low: $100).
Purpose and activities: Giving for building funds to educational, religious, and youth services organizations; giving also for human services.
Fields of interest: Education; University education; Hospital care; Religion; Human services; Family services; Child welfare.
Limitations: Applications not accepted. Giving primarily in NY. No grants to individuals.
Application information: Contributes only to pre-selected organizations.
Officers: H. Craig Treiber, Pres.; John H. Treiber, V.P.; Peter S. Treiber, Secy.; Scott R. Treiber, Treas.
EIN: 113440919

6908
The Triangle Fund
c/o Rachel Sherman
80 E. Market St., Ste. 202
Corning, NY 14830-2722 (607) 962-0189
Contact: Chris Sproule

Established in 1997 in New York.
Donors: Robert W. Houghton; Amory Houghton, Jr.; Peter Page; Adelaide Griswold; Mark Keaton; Hope Newell; Brian G. Ooten; Alanson B. Houghton III; William Hallenbeck, Jr.; Gratia H. Lassalle; Nina B. Houghton; James D. Houghton; Alanson B. Houghton II; Eleanor Hallenbeck; Brian G. Ooten; James R. Houghton; Wilson R. Page III.
Foundation type: Independent foundation.
Financial data (yr. ended 12/31/13): Assets, $4,824,523 (M); gifts received, $326,241; expenditures, $311,636; qualifying distributions, $265,959; giving activities include $218,226 for 24 grants (high: $25,945; low: $1,017).
Purpose and activities: Giving primarily for programs that support meaningful relationships among school, community, and family to positively affect at-risk children and youth.
Fields of interest: Arts and culture; Education; Child welfare; Youth development.
Type of support: General support; Program development.
Limitations: Applications accepted. Giving primarily in Chemung, Schoyler, and Steuben counties, NY. No grants to individuals.
Application information: Application form required.
Initial approach: Proposal
Deadline(s): May 8
Officers: Nina B. Houghton, Pres.; Robert W. Houghton, V.P.; Rachel J. Sherman, Secy.; James D. Houghton, Treas.
Directors: Amory Houghton III; Christina F. Houghton; Joanne Houghton; Gratia H. Lassalle; Macy H. Allatt McGinness; Megan H. Mowbray; Tessa E. Mowbray.
EIN: 311591261

6909
Tribune New York Foundation
220 E. 42nd St.
New York City, NY 10017-5836 (212) 210-2634

Established in 1958 in New York.
Donors: WPIX, Inc.; Daily News, LP.
Foundation type: Independent foundation.

Financial data (yr. ended 12/31/13): Assets, $6,935,586 (M); expenditures, $203,470; qualifying distributions, $171,000; giving activities include $171,000 for 14 grants (high: $30,000; low: $2,500).
Purpose and activities: Giving to improve the vitality of cultural offerings in the community and to enhance broadcasting and journalism throughout the CT, NJ, and NY tri-state area.
Fields of interest: Arts and culture; Education; Health; Diseases and conditions; Communication media; Publishing; Human services; Child welfare.
Type of support: General support; Employee matching gifts; Research; Research and evaluation.
Limitations: Applications accepted. Giving limited to the tri-state CT, NJ, and NY area, with emphasis on the five boroughs of New York. No support for religious organizations. No grants to individuals, or for fundraising dinners.
Publications: Application guidelines.
Application information: Application form required.
Initial approach: Contact foundation
Deadline(s): None
Board meeting date(s): June and Dec.
Officers and Directors: Julio Marenghi, V.P. and Director; Catherine Davis, Secy.-Treas. and Director.
EIN: 136161525

6910
The Robert Mize & Isa White Trimble Family Foundation, Inc.
c/o Allen and Brown
60 E. 42nd St., Ste. 1741
New York City, NY 10165-6210

Established in 1978 in New York.
Donors: Mary Ray Finneran†; Gerard Finneran†.
Foundation type: Independent foundation.
Financial data (yr. ended 06/30/13): Assets, $5,680,331 (M); expenditures, $381,702; qualifying distributions, $217,250; giving activities include $217,250 for grants.
Purpose and activities: Giving primarily for hospitals; support also for social services, including child welfare programs, and Roman Catholic religious and welfare organizations.
Fields of interest: Education; Nonprofits; Hospital care; Diseases and conditions; Catholicism; Human services; Child welfare; People with vision impairments.
Type of support: Research; Individual development; Regranting.
Limitations: Applications not accepted. Giving primarily in NY. No grants to individuals; no loans.
Application information: Contributes only to pre-selected organizations.
Officers and Directors: Daniel J. Ashley, Pres. and Director; Rita H. Rowan, V.P., and Treas. and Director; Thomas J. Rowan, V.P. and Director; Daniel C. Ashley, Secy. and Director.
EIN: 132972532

6911
Jean L. & Raymond S. Troubh Fund
c/o LCS Tax LLC
595 Madison Ave., 16th Fl.
New York City, NY 10022-1907

Established in 1964 in New York.
Donors: Jean L. Troubh; Jean S. Troubh.
Foundation type: Independent foundation.

Financial data (yr. ended 05/31/14): Assets, $477,045 (M); gifts received, $500; expenditures, $209,513; qualifying distributions, $197,855; giving activities include $197,855 for 30 grants (high: $88,500; low: $50).
Purpose and activities: Giving to city parks, public services and human services; giving also to Jewish agencies.
Fields of interest: Arts and culture; Philanthropy; Sports and recreation.
Limitations: Applications not accepted. Giving primarily in New York, NY. No grants to individuals.
Application information: Unsolicited requests for funds not accepted.
Officers: Jean L. Troubh, Pres.; Raymond S. Troubh, V.P. and Secy.
EIN: 136178229

6912
Mildred Faulkner Truman Foundation
P.O. Box 89
Owego, NY 13827-0089 (607) 687-0225
Contact: Stephanie Carrigg, Grant Exec.
E-mail: info@mftf.net; Main URL: http://www.mftf.net

Established in 1985 in New York.
Donor: Mildred Faulkner Truman†.
Foundation type: Independent foundation.
Financial data (yr. ended 08/31/14): Assets, $7,359,220 (M); expenditures, $436,184; qualifying distributions, $350,237; giving activities include $350,237 for 39 grants (high: $36,204; low: $1,000).
Purpose and activities: Giving primarily to organizations which enhance the benefit and residents of Tioga County, NY. The foundation wishes to accomplish this mission by encouraging grant requests for critical needs, capital projects, and seed money for new and special projects or programs.
Fields of interest: Historic preservation; Education; Higher education; Community college education; Public libraries; Community improvement; Sports; Human services.
Type of support: Capital campaigns; Matching grants; Capital and infrastructure; Equipment; Emergency funds; Program development; Seed money; Scholarships.
Limitations: Applications accepted. Giving primarily in Owego and Tioga counties, NY. No grants to individuals.
Publications: Annual report (including application guidelines).
Application information: All files must be in one of the following formats: Word, Excel, PDF or Plain Text Document. Application form required.
Initial approach: Use application form on foundation web site
Board meeting date(s): Jan., Apr., June, Sept.
Officers and Advisory Board Members: Dean L. Smith, Chair.; Irene C. Graven, Vice-Chair. and Director; Robert Williams, Secy.; Jarvis Edson, Treas.; Edwin B. Bartow; Ronald Dougherty; Carole LaPlante; Tina Lounsbury; Hope VanScoy.
Trustee: M&T Investment Group, Inc.
Number of staff: 1 part-time professional.
EIN: 166271201

6913
TSP Foundation
524 Clubhouse Rd.
Woodmere, NY 11598 (516) 398-1064
Contact: Joshua Schein, Pres.

Donors: Joshua Schein; Eileen Schein.
Foundation type: Independent foundation.
Financial data (yr. ended 12/31/13): Assets, $7,063,494 (M); expenditures, $360,020; qualifying distributions, $275,000; giving activities include $275,000 for 1 grant.
Fields of interest: Nonprofits.
Type of support: Regranting.
Limitations: Applications accepted. Giving primarily in NY.
Application information:
  Initial approach: Proposal
  Deadline(s): None
Officers: Joshua Schein, Pres.; Eileen Schein, Treas.
EIN: 263148603

6914
The Tsvi-Ora Foundation
73 Wortman Ave.
Brooklyn, NY 11207-8326

Established in 1997 in New York.
Donors: TSVI-ORA & Sons Corp.; 1804 76th Street LLC; 1903-1909 Broadway LLC; DCD Marketing LTD; 1219 Avenue J LLC; Mitchell Vilinsky; Ruvane Vilinsky; Edward Vilinsky; 107 Northern Boulevard Realty LLC.
Foundation type: Independent foundation.
Financial data (yr. ended 12/31/13): Assets, $293,029 (M); gifts received, $444,000; expenditures, $391,066; qualifying distributions, $391,066; giving activities include $390,716 for grants.
Fields of interest: Religion.
Limitations: Applications not accepted. No grants to individuals.
Application information: Contributes only to pre-selected organizations.
Officers: Mitchell Vilinsky, Pres.; Ruvane Vilinsky, V.P.; Edward Vilinsky, Secy.-Treas.
EIN: 113433976

6915
Michael Tuch Foundation, Inc.
122 E. 42nd St., Ste. 1501
New York City, NY 10168-1503 (212) 943-9082
Contact: Martha Tuck Rozett, Pres.

Established in 1946 in New York.
Donor: Michael Tuch†.
Foundation type: Independent foundation.
Financial data (yr. ended 12/31/13): Assets, $6,200,912 (M); gifts received, $83,503; expenditures, $425,274; qualifying distributions, $392,845; giving activities include $362,000 for 76 grants (high: $15,000; low: $1,000).
Purpose and activities: Giving primarily for the arts, including museums, and for educational institutions and programs.
Fields of interest: Arts and culture; Performing arts; Theater; Music; Museums; Education; Libraries; Community and economic development; Employment; Human services; Food aid; Child

welfare; Senior services; Low-income and poor people.
Type of support: General support; Continuing support; Program development; Curriculum development; Internships.
Limitations: Applications accepted. Giving primarily in New York, NY. No support for religion or health organizations. No grants to individuals.
Application information: Application form required.
  Initial approach: Letter
  Copies of proposal: 1
  Deadline(s): None
  Board meeting date(s): May
Officers: Martha Tuck Rozett, Pres.; Jonathan S. Tuck, V.P.; Joshua S. Rozett, Secy.-Treas.
Directors: Daniel H. Tuck; David A. Tuck.
Number of staff: 1 part-time professional; 1 part-time support.
EIN: 136002848

6916
Ruth Turner Fund, Inc.
c/o Gloria S. Neuwirth, Davidson, Dawson & Clark LLP
60 E. 42nd St., 38th Fl.
New York City, NY 10165-3897

Established in 1973 in New York.
Donor: Ruth Turner†.
Foundation type: Independent foundation.
Financial data (yr. ended 12/31/13): Assets, $4,501,380 (M); expenditures, $414,731; qualifying distributions, $385,937; giving activities include $357,500 for 18 grants (high: $55,000; low: $5,000).
Purpose and activities: Support for medical research and programs for the visually impaired; grants also for youth and social services, and primary and secondary education, as well as human rights.
Fields of interest: Early childhood education; Secondary education; Diseases and conditions; Human rights; Human services; Child welfare; Homeless services; Homeless people; People with disabilities.
Type of support: General support; Continuing support; Research; Program development; Research and evaluation; Seed money.
Limitations: Applications not accepted. Giving primarily in New York, NY. No grants to individuals.
Application information: Contributes only to pre-selected organizations.
  Board meeting date(s): June
Officers: Gloria S. Neuwirth, Esq., Pres.; Jessica Neuwirth, Esq., Secy.; Stephanie P. Mermin, Treas.
Directors: Chris Avery, Esq.; Suzanne Black; Chris Sorensen, Esq.
EIN: 237240889

6917
The Sandra and Howard Tytel Family Charitable Foundation Inc.
c/o Howard Tytel
100 Oyster Bay Rd.
Mill Neck, NY 11765-1310

Donors: Howard Tytel; Sandra Tytel.
Foundation type: Independent foundation.
Financial data (yr. ended 12/31/13): Assets, $475,206 (M); expenditures, $124,841; qualifying

distributions, $120,098; giving activities include $115,365 for 12 grants (high: $35,000; low: $400).
Fields of interest: Education; Higher education; Law education; Health; Hospital care; Human services.
Limitations: Applications not accepted. Giving primarily in NY. No grants to individuals.
Application information: Contributes only to pre-selected organizations.
Officers: Howard Tytel, Pres.; Sandra Tytel, Secy.
EIN: 113551535

6918
U & Y Family Foundation
140 Broadway, 38th Fl.
New York City, NY 10005-1117 (212) 532-5550
Contact: Meilech Levy, Tr.

Donors: Uriel Cohen; Yael Cohen.
Foundation type: Independent foundation.
Financial data (yr. ended 03/31/14): Assets, $1,408,208 (M); expenditures, $172,140; qualifying distributions, $168,599; giving activities include $168,599 for grants.
Purpose and activities: Giving to further Orthodox Jewish religious purposes, particularly public Jewish charities, educational organizations, and places of worship.
Fields of interest: Orthodox Judaism; Jewish people.
Application information:
  Initial approach: Proposal
  Deadline(s): None
Trustees: Malka Levy; Meilech Levy.
EIN: 263868269

6919
Henry Uihlein II and Mildred A. Uihlein Foundation
c/o Heaven Hill Farm
302 Bear Cub Ln.
Lake Placid, NY 12946-3117

Established in 1979 in Wisconsin.
Donors: Henry Uihlein II†; Suzanne M. Uihlein 1997 Charitable Trust.
Foundation type: Independent foundation.
Financial data (yr. ended 12/31/13): Assets, $21,868,003 (M); expenditures, $954,340; qualifying distributions, $985,905; giving activities include $372,660 for 28 grants (high: $102,000; low: $2,500).
Purpose and activities: Giving primarily for education, funding also for the arts, and human services.
Fields of interest: Arts and culture; Historic preservation; Education; Higher education; Foundations; Human services.
Limitations: Applications not accepted. Giving primarily in NY. No grants to individuals.
Application information: Contributes only to pre-selected organizations.
Officer: John D. Leekley, Jr., Chair.
Trustees: James McKenna; Eleonore Wotherspoon.
EIN: 391322495

6920
The United Elenar Foundation
5223 15th Ave.
Brooklyn, NY 11219-3908 (718) 851-5333
Contact: Efraim Landau, Dir.

Established in 1997 in New York.
Donors: Chaim Landau; A & E Trust; Triangle Trust; Sib Chai Inc.
Foundation type: Independent foundation.
Financial data (yr. ended 11/30/13): Assets, $5,295,449 (M); gifts received, $35,000; expenditures, $327,172; qualifying distributions, $290,260; giving activities include $285,310 for 8 grants (high: $195,500; low: $5,000).
Purpose and activities: Giving primarily to Jewish agencies and temples and for Jewish education; funding also for educational opportunities for indigent youth.
Fields of interest: Education; Judaism; Child welfare.
Limitations: Applications accepted. Giving primarily in Brooklyn, New York.
Application information: Application form required.
  Initial approach: Letter
  Deadline(s): Oct. 15
Directors: Chaim Landau; Efraim Landau; Naomi Rabinowicz.
EIN: 116496241

6921
Haji Usman & Hazarbai Mundia Foundation

159 Locust Ave.
Garden City, NY   11530-6533   (516) 763-1962
Contact: Abdul Mundia MD, Dir.

Established in 1994 in New York.
Donors: Abdul Mundia, MD; Munib Mundia, MD; Mubasir Mundia, MD.
Foundation type: Independent foundation.
Financial data (yr. ended 12/31/13): Assets, $496,197 (M); gifts received, $249,611; expenditures, $212,362; qualifying distributions, $211,368; giving activities include $5,400 for 6 grants (high: $2,500; low: $50), and $205,968 for 25 grants to individuals (high: $25,862; low: $862).
Purpose and activities: Giving for health, education, and the welfare of East Indian people.
Fields of interest: Arts services; Higher education; Health; Islam; Human services.
International interests: India.
Type of support: General support; Equipment; Scholarships.
Limitations: Applications accepted. Giving primarily in NY and India.
Application information: Application form required.
  Initial approach: Letter
  Deadline(s): None
Directors: Abdul Mundia, MD; Mubasir Mundia, MD; Munib Mundia, MD; Roshanara Mundia.
EIN: 113236306

6922
Utica National Group Foundation Inc.

P.O. Box 530
Utica, NY   13503-0530   (315) 734-2000
Contact: Bernard Turi
Main URL: http://www.uticanational.com

Established in 1987 in New York.
Donor: Utica Mutual Insurance Co.
Foundation type: Company-sponsored foundation.
Financial data (yr. ended 12/31/13): Assets, $6,339,877 (M); expenditures, $311,735; qualifying distributions, $292,819; giving activities include $292,819 for 57 grants (high: $80,000; low: $25).

Purpose and activities: The foundation supports organizations involved with education, substance abuse treatment, human services, and community development. Special emphasis is directed toward programs that support the healthy development of children and families; and that address the root causes of social problems.
Fields of interest: Education; Higher education; Nonprofits; Health; Substance abuse treatment; Community and economic development; Human services; Family services; Child welfare.
Type of support: Annual campaigns; Employee matching gifts; Matching grants; General support; Capital and infrastructure; Equipment; Program development; Seed money; Scholarships; Regranting.
Limitations: Applications accepted. Giving primarily in the greater Utica, NY, area, with emphasis on Herkimer, Madison, and Oneida counties. No grants for political activities or voter registration activity.
Publications: Application guidelines; Annual report (including application guidelines).
Application information: Application form required.
  Initial approach: E-mail the completed application form
  Copies of proposal: 10
  Deadline(s): Jan. 15, Apr. 15, July 15, and Oct. 15
  Board meeting date(s): Quarterly
Officers: J. Douglas Robinson, Pres.; Kristen H. Martin III, Secy.; Brain W. Miller, Treas.
Directors: Russell A. Aceveda; C. William Bachman; Alfred B. Calligaris; Richard Creedon; Paul A. Hagstrom; Gregory M. Harden; Jerry J. Hartman; Zelda J. Holcomb; Nicholas O. Matt; Peter O'Neill; Alan J. Pope; Timothy R. Reed; Linda E. Romano; Eric Scholl.
EIN: 161313450

6923
Utopia Fund

c/o Withusmith and Brown PC
1411 Broadway, 9th Fl.
New York City, NY   10018-3496

Established in 1952 in New York.
Foundation type: Independent foundation.
Financial data (yr. ended 12/31/13): Assets, $3,785,215 (M); expenditures, $173,408; qualifying distributions, $154,500; giving activities include $151,750 for 8 grants (high: $100,000; low: $250).
Purpose and activities: Giving primarily for education and hospitals, including medical research.
Fields of interest: Arts and culture; Performing arts; Historic preservation; Education; Elementary and secondary education; Higher education; Hospital care; Diseases and conditions; Heart and circulatory system diseases; Human services.
Type of support: Scholarships; General support; Research.
Limitations: Applications not accepted. Giving primarily in CT, MA, and NY. No grants to individuals.
Application information: Contributes only to pre-selected organizations.
Trustee: Catherine M. Randolph.
EIN: 131963929

6924
Vaad Haartzy Inc.

1454 49th St.
Brooklyn, NY   11219-3201

Donors: Nathan Retek; Eli Retek.
Foundation type: Independent foundation.
Financial data (yr. ended 12/31/13): Assets, $223,303 (M); gifts received, $5,460; expenditures, $166,956; qualifying distributions, $162,592; giving activities include $153,161 for 156 grants (high: $21,590; low: $20), and $9,431 for 16 grants to individuals (high: $5,000; low: $25).
Fields of interest: Education; Nonprofits; Religion; Judaism; Human services.
Type of support: Regranting; Grants to individuals; General support.
Limitations: Applications not accepted.
Application information: Unsolicited requests for funds not accepted.
Officer: Nathan Retek, Pres.
Directors: Malkie Greenfield; Naftali Tyberg.
EIN: 202408780

6925
The C. George Van Kampen Foundation

c/o Sungeun Han Andersen
1050 5th Ave., Apt. 8-F
New York City, NY   10028-0140

Established in 2004 in New York.
Donors: C. George Van Kampen†; Sung Han-Andersen.
Foundation type: Independent foundation.
Financial data (yr. ended 12/31/13): Assets, $999,536 (M); expenditures, $199,709; qualifying distributions, $152,214; giving activities include $134,000 for 3 grants (high: $100,000; low: $9,000).
Fields of interest: Arts education; Higher education; Diseases and conditions; Human services.
Type of support: Research; Research and evaluation.
Limitations: Applications not accepted. Giving in the U.S., with emphasis on New York, NY. No grants to individuals.
Application information: Contributes only to pre-selected organizations.
Officers: Sung Han-Andersen, Pres.; G. Chris Andersen, V.P.
EIN: 161686511

6926
Lee and Cynthia Vance Foundation

c/o BCRS Assocs., LLC
77 Water St., 9th Fl.
New York City, NY   10005-4414

Established in 1993 in New York.
Donors: Lee G. Vance; Jonathan Leroy King; Jacqueline E. King; Ashley Dartnell.
Foundation type: Independent foundation.
Financial data (yr. ended 06/30/13): Assets, $8,163,007 (M); gifts received, $12,200; expenditures, $411,349; qualifying distributions, $351,828; giving activities include $316,577 for 92 grants (high: $40,000; low: $2).
Fields of interest: Arts and culture; Education; Higher education; Foundations; Radio; Human services.

Limitations: Applications not accepted. Giving primarily in New York, NY. No grants to individuals.
Application information: Contributes only to pre-selected organizations.
Trustees: Cynthia King Vance; Lee G. Vance.
EIN: 133789060

6927
The Melinda & William J. Vanden Heuvel Foundation Inc.
711 5th Ave., Ste. 900
New York City, NY 10022-3111

Established in 1997 in New York.
Donors: William J. Vanden Heuvel; Melinda Vanden Heuvel.
Foundation type: Independent foundation.
Financial data (yr. ended 09/30/14): Assets, $179,543 (M); gifts received, $235,115; expenditures, $271,287; qualifying distributions, $271,210; giving activities include $266,550 for 81 grants (high: $25,000; low: $250).
Fields of interest: Arts and culture; Higher education; Diseases and conditions; Catholicism; Human services; Child welfare.
Limitations: Applications not accepted. Giving primarily in NY. No grants to individuals.
Application information: Unsolicited requests for funds not accepted.
Officers: Melinda F. Vanden Heuvel, Chair.; William J. Vanden Heuvel, Pres.; Ashley Von Perfall, Secy.; John C. Pierce, Treas.
EIN: 133980534

6928
Lillian Vernon Foundation
c/o MGI Repetti LLP
500 5th Ave., 5th Fl.
New York City, NY 10110

Established in 1993 in Connecticut.
Donor: Lillian Vernon.
Foundation type: Independent foundation.
Financial data (yr. ended 06/30/13): Assets, $3,699,357 (M); expenditures, $349,910; qualifying distributions, $325,492; giving activities include $315,341 for 19+ grants (high: $100,000).
Fields of interest: Performing arts; Museums; Higher education; Libraries; Human services.
Limitations: Applications not accepted. Giving primarily in NY. No grants to individuals.
Application information: Contributes only to pre-selected organizations.
Trustees: David Hochberg; Fred Hochberg; Lillian Vernon.
EIN: 223390451

6929
Villchur Foundation
P.O. Box 306
Woodstock, NY 12498-0306

Established in 1993 in New York.
Donor: Edgar Villchur.
Foundation type: Independent foundation.
Financial data (yr. ended 12/31/13): Assets, $4,533,770 (M); gifts received, $675; expenditures, $189,103; qualifying distributions, $150,200; giving activities include $150,200 for 58 grants (high: $60,000; low: $100).

Purpose and activities: Giving for international family planning.
Fields of interest: Arts and culture; Disasters and emergency management; Human services.
Type of support: General support.
Limitations: Applications not accepted. No grants to individuals.
Application information: Unsolicited requests for funds not accepted.
Officers: Miriam Berg, Pres.; Nancy Summer, V.P; Gloria Buley, Secy.
EIN: 141764435

6930
The Viola Foundation
c/o Bernath & Rosenberg, P.C.
1430 Broadway, Ste. 702
New York City, NY 10018-3308

Established in 1997 in New York.
Donors: James H. Bernath; Bernath & Rosenberg PC.
Foundation type: Independent foundation.
Financial data (yr. ended 12/31/13): Assets, $120,800 (M); gifts received, $235,000; expenditures, $223,857; qualifying distributions, $223,587; giving activities include $223,509 for 137 grants (high: $60,000; low: $36).
Fields of interest: Graduate and professional education; Judaism; Theology.
Type of support: General support.
Limitations: Applications not accepted. Giving primarily in NY. No grants to individuals.
Application information: Unsolicited requests for funds not accepted.
Trustees: James H. Bernath; Susi Bernath.
EIN: 133915359

6931
Moses & Miriam Vogel Foundation
1130 E. 22nd St.
Brooklyn, NY 11210-3620

Established in 1992 in New York.
Donors: Moses Vogel; Miriam Vogel; Sara Gross; Aviva Kiffel; Karen Gross; Peter Gross.
Foundation type: Independent foundation.
Financial data (yr. ended 12/31/13): Assets, $3,487,290 (M); gifts received, $20,656; expenditures, $287,517; qualifying distributions, $265,562; giving activities include $248,062 for 336 grants (high: $25,000; low: $18).
Purpose and activities: Giving primarily for Jewish organizations.
Fields of interest: Nonprofits; Judaism.
Type of support: Regranting.
Limitations: Applications not accepted. No grants to individuals.
Application information: Contributes only to pre-selected organizations.
Trustees: Sara Gross; Miriam Vogel; Solomon Vogel.
Director: Moses Vogel.
EIN: 136991651

6932
The Laura B. Vogler Foundation, Inc.
51 Division St., Box 501
Sag Harbor, NY 11963-3162
E-mail: voglerfound@gmail.com; Application address: P.O. Box 610508, Bayside, N.Y. 11361-0508; Main URL: https://sites.google.com/site/voglerfoundation

Established in 1959 in New York.
Donors: Laura B. Vogler†; John J. Vogler†.
Foundation type: Independent foundation.
Financial data (yr. ended 10/31/13): Assets, $5,352,284 (M); expenditures, $273,325; qualifying distributions, $246,015; giving activities include $196,770 for 82 grants (high: $3,000; low: $1,500).
Purpose and activities: Awards one-time non-renewable grants for new programs in the areas of health, youth, child welfare, the disadvantaged, the elderly, and other related services.
Fields of interest: Health; Religion; Human services.
Type of support: Program development; Seed money; Research.
Limitations: Applications accepted. Giving limited to New York City and Long Island, NY. No grants to individuals, or for building or endowment funds, annual fundraising campaigns, or matching gifts; no loans.
Application information: Complete application guidelines available on foundation web site. Application form required.
 Initial approach: Proposal
 Copies of proposal: 1
 Deadline(s): Jan. 1, Apr. 1, July 1 and Oct. 1
Officers and Directors: Lawrence L. D'Amato, Pres. and Director; Laraine Diamond, Secy.-Treas.; June D'Amato; Max L. Kupferberg; Stephen S. Schwander; Karen M. Yost.
Number of staff: 2 part-time professional.
EIN: 116022241

6933
Vogt Family Foundation, Inc.
443 Delaware Ave.
Buffalo, NY 14202-1524

Donors: Mary Lou Vogt†; Peter A. Vogt; Mary R. Koessler†.
Foundation type: Independent foundation.
Financial data (yr. ended 12/31/13): Assets, $6,552,094 (M); expenditures, $437,706; qualifying distributions, $373,000; giving activities include $373,000 for 39 grants (high: $100,000; low: $500).
Fields of interest: Arts and culture; Orchestral music; Education; Zoos; Hospital care; Catholicism.
Type of support: Endowments; Scholarships.
Limitations: Applications not accepted. Giving primarily in FL, NY, and WA. No grants to individuals.
Application information: Contributes only to pre-selected organizations.
 Board meeting date(s): Nov.
Officers and Trustees: Mary Kathryn Schneider, Chair. and Trustee; Anne E. McCune, Vice-Chair.; Jean Tracy Tremblay; Peter J. Vogt; Peter J. Vogt.
EIN: 061333037

6934
Keren Nachmen Vyeshaya Foundation
c/o A. Ringel
307 5th Ave., 8th Fl.
New York City, NY   10016-6517

Established in 2007 in New York.
Donor: Jacob Kahan.
Foundation type: Independent foundation.
Financial data (yr. ended 06/30/14): Assets, $330,803 (M); gifts received, $100,000; expenditures, $239,066; qualifying distributions, $239,066; giving activities include $238,950 for 7 grants (high: $195,000; low: $250).
Fields of interest: Education; Philanthropy; Judaism.
Limitations: Applications not accepted. No grants to individuals.
Application information: Unsolicited requests for funds not accepted.
Trustees: Gita Kahan; Jacob Kahan.
EIN: 205941886

6935
The Lance R. Wachenheim Foundation
3 Manhattanville Rd.
Purchase, NY   10577

Established in 2007 in New York.
Donors: Lance R. Wachenheim; Edgar Wechenheim III.
Foundation type: Independent foundation.
Financial data (yr. ended 12/31/13): Assets, $6,891,141 (M); gifts received, $603,720; expenditures, $258,850; qualifying distributions, $257,050; giving activities include $255,000 for 6 grants (high: $128,000; low: $3,000).
Fields of interest: Children's hospital care; Food banks; Children.
Type of support: General support.
Limitations: Applications not accepted. Giving primarily in NY. No grants to individuals.
Application information: Unsolicited requests for funds not accepted.
Trustees: Edgar Wachenheim III; Lance R. Wachenheim.
EIN: 261497632

6936
Svetlana and Herbert M. Wachtell Foundation
c/o Wachtell, Lipton, Rosen, & Katz
51 W. 52nd St.
New York City, NY   10019-6119

Established in 2001 in New York.
Donors: Herbert M. Wachtell; Svetlana Stone Wachtell.
Foundation type: Independent foundation.
Financial data (yr. ended 10/31/13): Assets, $5,121,493 (M); expenditures, $282,346; qualifying distributions, $255,202; giving activities include $254,801 for grants.
Fields of interest: Arts and culture; Education; Law education; Social sciences; Judaism; Human services.
Limitations: Applications not accepted. Giving primarily in NY. No grants to individuals.
Application information: Contributes only to pre-selected organizations.

Officers and Directors: Herbert M. Wachtell, Pres. and Treas. and Director; Svetlana Stone Wachtell, V.P. and Secy. and Director; Laura Murphy.
EIN: 134197999

6937
The Kim and David Wagman Foundation
3 Manhattanville Rd.
Purchase, NY   10577-2116

Established in 2005 in New York.
Donors: Edgar Wachenheim III; Kim W. Wagman.
Foundation type: Independent foundation.
Financial data (yr. ended 12/31/13): Assets, $6,817,278 (M); gifts received, $603,720; expenditures, $237,850; qualifying distributions, $236,050; giving activities include $234,000 for 14 grants (high: $105,000; low: $1,000).
Fields of interest: Education; Child care.
Limitations: Applications not accepted. Giving primarily in NY. No grants to individuals.
Application information: Contributes only to pre-selected organizations.
Trustees: David A. Wagman; Kim W. Wagman.
EIN: 202578755

6938
Rose and Sherle Wagner Foundation
c/o Scialo & Co., C.P.A., PC
4 Executive Blvd., No. 304
Suffern, NY   10901-4173

Established in 1994 in New York.
Donors: Rose Wagner; Sherle Wagner†; Wagner Charitable Lead Trust.
Foundation type: Independent foundation.
Financial data (yr. ended 12/31/12): Assets, $8,688,638 (M); gifts received, $100,000; expenditures, $418,446; qualifying distributions, $395,553; giving activities include $237,500 for 17 grants (high: $20,000; low: $2,500).
Purpose and activities: Giving primarily for grassroots organizing for social and economic justice.
Fields of interest: Education; Student services; Community improvement; Human rights; Immigrant rights; Minority rights; Human services; Youth services; Females; Ethnic and racial groups; Low-income and poor people.
Type of support: General support.
Limitations: Applications not accepted. Giving primarily in NY. No grants to individuals.
Application information: Contributes only to pre-selected organizations.
Trustee: Rose Wagner.
Director: Amy Wagner.
Number of staff: 1 full-time professional; 6 part-time support.
EIN: 133738106

6939
Waldron Rise Foundation Inc.
4 Scr Ln.
Victor, NY   14564-9631
Application address: P.O. Box 1734, Fairport, NY 14450, tel.: (585) 421-9824

Established in 2009 in Delaware.
Donor: Catherine Whitman Charitable Trust.
Foundation type: Independent foundation.

Financial data (yr. ended 09/30/13): Assets, $7,253,032 (M); gifts received, $344,466; expenditures, $374,540; qualifying distributions, $325,335; giving activities include $322,794 for 17 grants (high: $87,569; low: $1,000).
Fields of interest: Education; Domesticated animals; Human services.
Limitations: Applications accepted. Giving primarily in Rochester, NY.
Application information:
Initial approach: Proposal
Deadline(s): None
Officers and Directors: Bradley R. Whitman, Pres.; Michelle Whitman, V.P.; Daniel M. Meyers, Secy. and Director; Renier F. Chaintreuil, Treas. and Director; Christine B. Whitman.
EIN: 264794724

6940
Kohanim Wallerstein Foundation Inc.
1373 E. 13th St.
Brooklyn, NY   11230-5957   (718) 627-4467
Contact: Shmuel Wallerstein, Dir.

Donors: Lou Wallerstein; Charlotte Wallerstein; Shmuel Wallerstein; Seasonal Packaging, Inc.
Foundation type: Independent foundation.
Financial data (yr. ended 09/30/13): Assets, $1,433,091 (M); gifts received, $75,000; expenditures, $152,522; qualifying distributions, $152,522; giving activities include $150,000 for 2 grants (high: $100,000; low: $50,000).
Fields of interest: Judaism.
Type of support: General support.
Limitations: Applications accepted. Giving primarily in Brooklyn, NY. No grants to individuals.
Application information: Application form required.
Initial approach: Letter
Deadline(s): None
Directors: Chaya Wallerstein; Raphael Wallerstein; Shmuel Wallerstein.
EIN: 132895298

6941
The Walrath Family Foundation
c/o Torella & Associates, LLC
165 Madison Ave., Ste. 502
New York City, NY   10016-5431

Established in 2007 in New York.
Donor: Michael Walrath.
Foundation type: Independent foundation.
Financial data (yr. ended 12/31/13): Assets, $5,647,594 (M); gifts received, $35,091; expenditures, $300,276; qualifying distributions, $260,300; giving activities include $258,000 for 20 grants (high: $75,000; low: $1,000).
Fields of interest: Environmental studies; Catholicism.
Type of support: Individual development.
Limitations: Applications not accepted. No grants to individuals.
Application information: Contributes only to pre-selected organizations.
Trustees: Michael Walrath; Michelle Walrath.
EIN: 261317389

6942
Leo S. Walsh Foundation
P.O. Box 222
Westhampton Beach, NY   11978

Established in 2004 in New York.
Donor: Sandra Walsh.
Foundation type: Independent foundation.
Financial data (yr. ended 12/31/14): Assets, $7,705,909 (M); expenditures, $374,286; qualifying distributions, $346,096; giving activities include $265,000 for 76 grants (high: $7,000; low: $500).
Fields of interest: Domesticated animals; Hospice care; Public libraries; Human services; Women's services.
Limitations: Applications not accepted.
Application information: Unsolicited requests for funds not accepted.
Trustees: Devon Walsh; Sandra Walsh.
EIN: 201301554

6943
Richard F. Walsh/Alfred W. Ditolla/Harold Spivak Foundation
(formerly Richard F. Walsh Foundation)
c/o I.A.T.S.E.
207 W. 25th St., 4th Fl.
New York City, NY   10001

Donors: IATSE; Spivak Lipton, LLP.
Foundation type: Independent foundation.
Financial data (yr. ended 09/30/13): Assets, $312,645 (M); gifts received, $204,803; expenditures, $259,511; qualifying distributions, $259,067; giving activities include $45,000 for 20 grants (high: $5,000; low: $500), and $209,500 for 84 grants to individuals (high: $3,000; low: $1,000).
Fields of interest: Arts and culture; Diseases and conditions; Floods; Human services.
International interests: Canada.
Type of support: Research; Grants to individuals.
Limitations: Applications not accepted. Giving primarily in NY; some giving in Canada.
Application information: Unsolicited requests for funds not accepted.
Trustees: Daniel Ditolla; Matthew Loeb; James B. Wood.
EIN: 136208834

6944
Walther Family Foundation
c/o BCRS Associates, LLC
77 Water St., 9th Fl.
New York City, NY   10005

Donor: Artur Walther.
Foundation type: Independent foundation.
Financial data (yr. ended 04/30/14): Assets, $1,547,545 (M); gifts received, $386,130; expenditures, $604,401; qualifying distributions, $576,126; giving activities include $331,507 for 18 grants (high: $138,000; low: $780).
Purpose and activities: The foundation is dedicated to collecting and promoting contemporary photographic art across recent historical periods and diverse geographic regions. Its mission is to present to the public, through in-depth annual exhibitions and a program of publishing, works of historical and contemporary significance from artists working in Africa, Asia, and other parts of the world whose enduring contributions to photography significantly expand the understanding, conception, and history of the medium. The foundation is expected to collect and exhibit a segment of modern and contemporary European and American photography, uniting the various focuses of the collection in lively, rigorous curatorial dialogue through thematic and conceptual relationships.
Fields of interest: Arts and culture.
Limitations: Applications not accepted.
Application information: Unsolicited requests for funds not accepted.
Officer and Director: Artur Walther, Pres. and Director.
EIN: 271125212

6945
Warwick Savings Foundation
c/o Alario & Associates CPA's PLLC
28 Railroad Ave.
Warwick, NY   10990-1525   (845) 986-8717
Contact: Louis Ulatowski, Secy.
Application address: 39 Washington, Rd., Monroe, NY 10950

Established in 1997 in New York.
Donor: Warwick Community Bancorp, Inc.
Foundation type: Company-sponsored foundation.
Financial data (yr. ended 12/31/13): Assets, $5,998,004 (M); expenditures, $303,803; qualifying distributions, $293,971; giving activities include $283,200 for 32 grants (high: $50,000; low: $1,500).
Purpose and activities: The foundation supports historical societies and organizations involved with education, health, housing development, therapeutic riding, and human services.
Fields of interest: Historic preservation; Education; Secondary education; Higher education; Health; Hospital care; School-based health care; Hospice care; Housing development; Equestrianism; Human services; Child welfare; Developmental disability services.
Type of support: General support.
Limitations: Applications accepted. Giving limited to NY. No grants to individuals.
Application information: Application form required.
  Initial approach: Letter
  Deadline(s): Sept. 30
Officers and Directors: John McDermott III, Pres. and Director; Lois E. Ulatowski, Secy.; R. Michael Kennedy, Treas. and Director; Frances M. Gorish; Ann Sakac; Mary Smith; Thomas Sullivan.
EIN: 061504632

6946
Washington Square Fund
FDR Station
P.O. Box 7938
New York City, NY   10150-7938
Contact: Louise Chinn, Pres.

Established in 1969 in New York.
Foundation type: Independent foundation.
Financial data (yr. ended 06/30/13): Assets, $3,486,920 (M); expenditures, $275,426; qualifying distributions, $229,157; giving activities include $215,000 for 10 grants (high: $25,000; low: $10,000).
Purpose and activities: Grants for child welfare, youth agencies, families, welfare and social programs, education about health, teenage pregnancy prevention, guidance of troubled teenagers, and family planning and counseling. Preference is for pilot and special projects, usually of 2 to 3 years duration; emergency funding provided for ongoing programs.
Fields of interest: Education; Family planning; Human services; Family services; Child welfare; Adolescents; Young adults; Female children and youth; Female young adults; Male young adults.
Type of support: Emergency funds; Program development; Seed money.
Limitations: Applications accepted. Giving limited to New York City. No grants to individuals, or for unrestricted operating funds.
Application information:
  Initial approach: Letter or proposal
  Copies of proposal: 1
  Deadline(s): None
  Board meeting date(s): Quarterly
  Final notification: 1-4 months
Officers and Directors: Louise Chinn, Pres. and Director; Neil E. Botwinoff, V.P. and Director; Carolyn Crippen, Secy. and Director; Charles W. Kraushaar, Treas. and Director; Katie Palmer; Suzanne Randolph; Theresa Thompson; Mary-Ellen Weinrib; Cornelia Whiting; Gilbert Zalman.
Number of staff: 1 part-time support.
EIN: 131624213

6947
The Watts Family Foundation
c/o Bessemer Trust
630 5th Ave., Ste. 3425
New York City, NY   10111-0100

Established in 1997 in Massachusetts.
Donors: Beverly Watts; David B. Watts; Scudder Charitable Foundation.
Foundation type: Independent foundation.
Financial data (yr. ended 06/30/13): Assets, $7,379,124 (M); expenditures, $366,219; qualifying distributions, $351,982; giving activities include $330,029 for 17 grants (high: $152,529; low: $1,000).
Purpose and activities: Giving primarily for higher and other education; funding also for human services, and an Episcopal church.
Fields of interest: Elementary and secondary education; Higher education; Natural resources; Episcopalianism and Anglicanism; Lutheranism; Human services.
Limitations: Applications not accepted. Giving primarily in MA. No grants to individuals.
Application information: Contributes only to pre-selected organizations.
Trustees: Beverly Watts; David B. Watts.
EIN: 043402936

6948
The Lorne Weil Charitable Foundation
c/o Scientific Games
750 Lexington Ave., 25th Flr.
New York City, NY   10022-9813

Established in 2000 in New York.
Foundation type: Independent foundation.
Financial data (yr. ended 12/31/13): Assets, $207,737 (M); gifts received, $2,880;

expenditures, $151,574; qualifying distributions, $145,700; giving activities include $145,700 for 18 grants (high: $35,000; low: $500).

Fields of interest: Arts and culture; Education; Higher education; Judaism; Human services.

Limitations: Applications not accepted. No grants to individuals.

Application information: Contributes only to pre-selected organizations.

Officers and Directors: A. Lorne Weil, Pres. and Treas. and Director; Richard M. Weil, V.P. and Director; John C. Novogrod, Secy. and Director.

EIN: 134078531

6949
The Weill Family Foundation

(formerly Sanford I. Weill Charitable Foundation, Inc.)
P.O. Box 3977
Albany, NY 12203-0977
Sanford Weill's Giving Pledge Profile: http://glasspockets.org/philanthropy-in-focus/eye-on-the-giving-pledge/profiles/weill

Established in 1967 in New York.

Donors: Joan H. Weill; Sanford I. Weill.

Foundation type: Independent foundation.

Financial data (yr. ended 12/31/12): Assets, $61,162,769 (M); gifts received, $10,015,250; expenditures, $1,141,124; qualifying distributions, $442,500; giving activities include $442,500 for 4 grants (high: $150,000; low: $67,500).

Fields of interest: Arts and culture; Education; Health.

Type of support: Program development.

Limitations: Applications not accepted. Giving primarily in the metropolitan New York, NY, area. No grants to individuals.

Application information: Contributes only to pre-selected organizations.

Officers and Directors: Sanford I. Weill, Chair. and Treas. and Director; Joan H. Weill, Pres. and Director; Michael T. Masin, Secy. and Director; Kenneth J. Bialkin; Jessica Bibliowicz; Tommy Bibliowicz; Arthur Mahon.

EIN: 136223609

6950
Kurt Weill Foundation for Music, Inc.

7 E. 20th St., 3rd Fl.
New York City, NY 10003-1106 (212) 505-5240
FAX: (212) 353-9663; E-mail: kwfinfo@kwf.org; Main
URL: http://www.kwf.org
Grants List: http://www.kwf.org/grants-a-prizes/grant-program/23-kw/88-grants-awarded-1984-2008

Donor: Lotte Lenya†.

Foundation type: Operating foundation.

Financial data (yr. ended 12/31/14): Assets, $30,187,500; gifts received, $724; expenditures, $1,559,372; qualifying distributions, $1,224,456.

Purpose and activities: Awards grants to organizations and individuals for projects directly related to Kurt Weill and Lotte Lenya. Applications are accepted in the following categories: Research and Travel, Kurt Weill Dissertation Fellowships, Publication Assistance, Educational Outreach, College/University Performance, Professional Performance, and Broadcasts. In addition, foundation programs include maintenance of a

research center and archives, publication of a newsletter and critical editions of Weill's musical works, and production consultation.

Fields of interest: Theater; Musical theater; Music; Opera.

International interests: Germany; Scotland.

Limitations: Applications accepted. Giving primarily in NY and PA, Germany, and Scotland.

Publications: Application guidelines; Informational brochure; Newsletter.

Application information: Application form and guidelines available on foundation web site. For acceptable languages, contact foundation. Application form required.

Initial approach: Application forms on foundation web site
Copies of proposal: 1
Deadline(s): Nov. 1; June 1 exclusively for College/University Performance grants
Final notification: Feb. 1

Officers and Trustees: Ed Harsh, Chair. and Trustee; Kim H. Kowalke, C.E.O. and Pres. and Trustee; Philip Getter, Sr. V.P. and Trustee; Guy Stern, V.P. and Trustee; Susan Feder, Secy. and Trustee; Milton Coleman, Emeritus; Paul Epstein, Emeritus; Walter Hinderer, Emeritus; Joanne Hubbard Cossa; Welz Kauffman.

Number of staff: 6 full-time professional; 1 full-time support.

EIN: 136139518

6951
John S. and Amy S. Weinberg Foundation

Bowling Green Sta.
P.O. Box 73
New York City, NY 10274-0073

Established in 1993 in New York.

Donor: John S. Weinberg.

Foundation type: Independent foundation.

Financial data (yr. ended 07/31/13): Assets, $23,187,944 (M); gifts received, $51,988; expenditures, $436,635; qualifying distributions, $377,750; giving activities include $377,750 for 62 grants (high: $100,000; low: $250).

Fields of interest: Arts and culture; Education; Higher education; Diseases and conditions; Cystic fibrosis; Human services; Child welfare.

Type of support: Research; Research and evaluation.

Limitations: Applications not accepted. Giving primarily in MA, and the metropolitan New York, NY, area; funding also in CT, with emphasis on Greenwich. No grants to individuals; no loans or scholarships.

Application information: Contributes only to pre-selected organizations.

Trustees: Robert S. Kaplan; Amy S. Weinberg; John S. Weinberg.

EIN: 133749671

6952
Weingarten Family Foundation

1661 53rd St.
Brooklyn, NY 11204-1421

Established in 1992 in New York.

Donor: Otto I. Weingarten.

Foundation type: Independent foundation.

Financial data (yr. ended 12/31/13): Assets, $6,595,570 (M); expenditures, $370,088;

qualifying distributions, $296,159; giving activities include $288,900 for 11 grants (high: $113,500; low: $1,000).

Purpose and activities: Giving primarily for Jewish organizations and yeshivas.

Fields of interest: Elementary and secondary education; Judaism; Human services.

International interests: Israel.

Limitations: Applications not accepted. Giving primarily in NJ and Brooklyn, NY. No grants to individuals.

Application information: Contributes only to pre-selected organizations.

Officers: Otto I. Weingarten, Pres.; Rosemarie Weingarten, V.P.; Simone Krause, Secy.; Hershie Weingarten, Treas.

EIN: 113133160

6953
Jeffrey and Susan Weingarten Foundation

c/o BCRS Assocs., LLC
77 Water St., 9th Fl.
New York City, NY 10005-4414

Established in 1991 in New York.

Donors: Jeffrey M. Weingarten; Susan Weingarten.

Foundation type: Independent foundation.

Financial data (yr. ended 06/30/13): Assets, $409,115 (M); expenditures, $149,116; qualifying distributions, $147,866; giving activities include $146,601 for 9 grants (high: $100,000; low: $300).

Purpose and activities: Giving primarily to education; support also for Jewish agencies, the performing arts, and health and medicine.

Fields of interest: Performing arts; Education; Elementary and secondary education; Higher education; Judaism.

International interests: England.

Limitations: Applications not accepted. Giving primarily in London, England; some funding also in Philadelphia, PA. No grants to individuals.

Application information: Contributes only to pre-selected organizations.

Trustees: Michael R. Armellino; Jeffrey M. Weingarten; Amanda Weingarten.

EIN: 133639274

6954
The Weininger Foundation, Inc.

(formerly The Richard and Gertrude Weininger Foundation, Inc.)
c/o Stroock, Etta Brandman
180 Maiden Ln.
New York City, NY 10038-4925

Established in 1982 in New York.

Donor: Gertrude Weininger†.

Foundation type: Independent foundation.

Financial data (yr. ended 11/30/14): Assets, $5,578,039 (M); expenditures, $283,382; qualifying distributions, $199,695; giving activities include $187,500 for 30 grants (high: $22,500; low: $1,000).

Purpose and activities: Giving primarily for arts and culture, education and human services; some giving also for religious organizations.

Fields of interest: Arts and culture; Performing arts; Education; University education; Health; Specialty hospital care; Religion; Human services.

Limitations: Applications not accepted. Giving primarily in NY. No grants to individuals.

Application information: Contributes only to pre-selected organizations.
Officers and Directors: Peter Simon, Pres. and Director; William A. Perlmuth, V.P. and Director; Peter Simon, Jr., V.P. and Director; Etta Brandman, Esq., Secy.-Treas. and Director.
EIN: 133147339

6955
The Isak and Rose Weinman Foundation Inc.
c/o Brown Bros. Harriman Tr. Co., N.A.
140 Broadway, 5th Fl.
New York City, NY 10005-1101

Donor: Lilliana Teruzzi†.
Foundation type: Independent foundation.
Financial data (yr. ended 12/31/13): Assets, $14,903,294 (M); expenditures, $529,050; qualifying distributions, $416,935; giving activities include $411,000 for 32 grants (high: $50,000; low: $1,000).
Purpose and activities: Giving primarily for the arts, hospitals and health associations, Jewish organizations, and social services.
Fields of interest: Arts and culture; Performing arts; Theater; Opera; Orchestral music; Art museums; Education; Hospital care; Diseases and conditions; Judaism; Human services; Child welfare.
Limitations: Applications not accepted. Giving primarily in New York, NY. No grants to individuals.
Application information: Contributes only to pre-selected organizations.
Officers: Donna Landau Hardiman, Pres. and Secy.; Blair Landau Trippe, V.P. and Treas.
Directors: Barbara Landau; W. Loeber Landau; Frederick A. Terry, Jr.
EIN: 136110132

6956
J. Weinstein Foundation Inc.
c/o Rockridge Farm
961 Rte. 52
Carmel, NY 10512-4733 (845) 225-7647
Contact: Salvatore Cappuzzo, Secy.-Treas.

Established in 1948 in New York.
Donors: Joe Weinstein†; J.W. Mays, Inc.
Foundation type: Independent foundation.
Financial data (yr. ended 12/31/13): Assets, $7,573,198 (M); expenditures, $256,836; qualifying distributions, $250,750; giving activities include $250,750 for 37 grants (high: $100,000; low: $500).
Purpose and activities: Support for higher education in the U.S. and Israel, temple support, hospitals, and Jewish welfare funds.
Fields of interest: Museums; Higher education; Nonprofits; Hospital care; Judaism; Human services.
International interests: Israel.
Type of support: General support; Continuing support; Endowments; Research; Regranting.
Limitations: Applications accepted. Giving primarily in NY.
Application information: Application form required.
Initial approach: Proposal
Deadline(s): None

Officers and Directors: Lloyd J. Shulman, Pres. and Director; Gail Koster, V.P. and Director; Salvatore Cappuzzo, Secy.-Treas.
EIN: 116003595

6957
Weintraub Family Foundation
20 Morris Ln.
Scarsdale, NY 10583-4402

Donor: Testamentary Trust Paragraph 6.
Foundation type: Independent foundation.
Financial data (yr. ended 12/31/13): Assets, $2,326,906 (M); gifts received, $380,700; expenditures, $595,673; qualifying distributions, $290,721; giving activities include $290,721 for 12 grants (high: $126,720; low: $218).
Fields of interest: Judaism.
Limitations: Applications not accepted. Giving primarily in NY.
Application information: Unsolicited requests for funds not accepted.
Directors: David Weintraub; Ellen Weintraub; Peter Weintraub.
EIN: 204336659

6958
The Weiser Philanthropic Fund
135 W. 50th St.
New York City, NY 10020-1201 2128127000

Established in 2003 in New York.
Donors: Weiser LLP; Weisermazars, LLP.
Foundation type: Independent foundation.
Financial data (yr. ended 12/31/14): Assets, $13,549; gifts received, $225,000; expenditures, $216,297; qualifying distributions, $216,297.
Fields of interest: Arts and culture; Education; Nonprofits; Diseases and conditions; Judaism.
Type of support: Regranting.
Limitations: Applications not accepted. Giving primarily in NY. No grants to individuals.
Application information: Contributes only to pre-selected organizations.
Directors: Andrew M. Cohen; Douglas A. Phillips; Harry C. Steinmetz.
EIN: 200294869

6959
The Carol and Michael Weisman Family Charitable Trust
521 Fifth Ave., No. 1804
New York City, NY 10175-1804

Donors: Carol Weisman; Michael Weisman.
Foundation type: Independent foundation.
Financial data (yr. ended 12/31/13): Assets, $48,328 (M); gifts received, $275,541; expenditures, $370,579; qualifying distributions, $368,497; giving activities include $368,447 for 23 grants (high: $100,000; low: $500).
Fields of interest: Nonprofits; Diseases and conditions; Immune system diseases.
Type of support: Regranting.
Limitations: Applications not accepted. Giving primarily in NY. No grants to individuals.
Application information: Contributes only to pre-selected organizations.
Trustee: Carol Weisman.
EIN: 386804476

6960
The Philippa V. Weismann Family Foundation
115 Central Park West, Apt. 8FE
New York City, NY 10023

Foundation type: Independent foundation.
Financial data (yr. ended 12/31/12): Assets, $2,438,378 (M); gifts received, $150,000; expenditures, $164,492; qualifying distributions, $140,300; giving activities include $140,300 for 14 grants (high: $35,000; low: $300).
Fields of interest: Arts and culture; Environment; Housing development.
Limitations: Applications not accepted.
Application information: Unsolicited requests for funds not accepted.
Trustee: Philippa V. Weismann.
EIN: 266668048

6961
The Weiss Family Chesed Foundation
44 Olympia Ln.
Monsey, NY 10952-2836

Established in 2005 in New York.
Donors: Prospect Park Realty; Prospect Realty LP; G & M Capital Inc.
Foundation type: Independent foundation.
Financial data (yr. ended 04/30/13): Assets, $558,218 (M); expenditures, $313,868; qualifying distributions, $302,857; giving activities include $302,857 for 19+ grants (high: $72,000).
Purpose and activities: Giving primarily to Jewish agencies, temples, and schools. The foundation also awards grants to individuals in need and to individuals who have expertise in religious matters and special social skills, and who have the ability to bring people closer to the Orthodox Jewish faith.
Fields of interest: Nonprofits; Orthodox Judaism; Human services.
Type of support: Regranting.
Limitations: Applications not accepted. Giving primarily in CT, NJ, and NY.
Application information: Unsolicited requests for funds not accepted.
Trustees: Mark Weiss; Susan Weiss; Yehuda Zakatinsky.
EIN: 201161965

6962
The Joseph H. & Miriam F. Weiss Foundation, Inc.
1500 Broadway, Ste. 1600
New York City, NY 10036-4055

Established in 1995 in New York.
Donors: Joseph H. Weiss; Miriam F. Weiss.
Foundation type: Independent foundation.
Financial data (yr. ended 12/31/13): Assets, $680,815 (M); gifts received, $40,000; expenditures, $241,053; qualifying distributions, $238,785; giving activities include $238,785 for 48 grants (high: $25,135; low: $1,000).
Purpose and activities: Giving primarily to Jewish temples, organizations, and schools.
Fields of interest: Education; Nonprofits; Judaism.
Type of support: Regranting.
Limitations: Applications not accepted. Giving primarily in Brooklyn, NY. No grants to individuals.

Application information: Unsolicited requests for funds not accepted.
Officers: Joseph H. Weiss, Pres.; Miriam F. Weiss, V.P.; Harold Weiser, Secy.
EIN: 133800609

6963
Mor & Eva Weiss Foundation
1651 50th St.
Brooklyn, NY 11204-1154

Donor: FNW Realty Corp.
Foundation type: Independent foundation.
Financial data (yr. ended 12/31/13): Assets, $5,874 (M); gifts received, $111,000; expenditures, $205,200; qualifying distributions, $205,200; giving activities include $205,200 for grants.
Limitations: Applications not accepted. Giving primarily in NY.
Application information: Unsolicited requests for funds not accepted.
Trustee: Eva Weiss.
EIN: 461526621

6964
Franklin H. & Ruth L. Wells Foundation
1100 Wehrle Dr., 2nd Fl.
Buffalo, NY 14221-7748
Contact: Miles J. Gibbons Jr., Exec. Dir.
E-mail for Miles J. Gibbons, Jr.:
mgibbons989@earthlink.net

Established in 1983 in Pennsylvania.
Donors: Ruth L. Wells Annuity Trust; Frank Wells Marital Trust.
Foundation type: Independent foundation.
Financial data (yr. ended 05/31/14): Assets, $5,389,212 (M); expenditures, $257,350; qualifying distributions, $249,377; giving activities include $185,500 for 16 grants (high: $50,000; low: $500).
Purpose and activities: Startup funding for new programs in education, human services, community development, health care, and cultural arts.
Fields of interest: Arts and culture; Education; Higher education; Health; Community and economic development; Human services; Youth services; Scouting programs.
Type of support: Equipment; Emergency funds; Program development; Seed money.
Limitations: Applications accepted. Giving primarily in Dauphin, Cumberland, and Perry counties, PA. No support for religious activities. No grants to individuals, or for endowments, debts, or capital campaigns.
Application information:
Initial approach: Letter
Copies of proposal: 1
Board meeting date(s): Apr. and Oct.
Officer: Miles J. Gibbons, Jr., Exec. Dir.
Trustee: M & T Trust Co.
Number of staff: 1 full-time professional.
EIN: 222541749

6965
Westlawn Foundation
5223 15th Ave.
Brooklyn, NY 11219-3908 (718) 851-4811
Contact: Ephraim Landau, Dir.

Established in 2006 in New York.
Donors: Ephraim Landau; Triangle Trust; A&E Trust; Concord Trust; Deland Turst II; Deland Turst I; Ephraim Family TSG Trust II.
Foundation type: Independent foundation.
Financial data (yr. ended 11/30/13): Assets, $6,032,674 (M); gifts received, $175,000; expenditures, $381,121; qualifying distributions, $381,121; giving activities include $369,300 for 34 + grants (high: $10,000).
Fields of interest: Diseases and conditions; Religion; Human services.
Limitations: Applications not accepted. Giving primarily in NY.
Application information: Unsolicited requests for funds not accepted.
Directors: Ephraim Landau; Goldy Landau.
EIN: 204057446

6966
The John, Marie and Joseph Whalen Foundation Inc.
385 Watervliet Shaker Rd.
Latham, NY 12208

Established in 2000 in Maryland.
Donors: Fr. John P. Whalen; Whalen Lead Trust.
Foundation type: Independent foundation.
Financial data (yr. ended 05/31/13): Assets, $5,394,074 (M); gifts received, $376,107; expenditures, $249,567; qualifying distributions, $180,000; giving activities include $180,000 for grants.
Fields of interest: Education; Catholicism; Human services.
Limitations: Applications not accepted. Giving primarily in NY. No grants to individuals.
Application information: Contributes only to pre-selected organizations.
Officers: Philip J. Whalen, Jr., Chair.; Fr. Kenneth Doyle, Vice-Chair.; Serena Thompson, Secy.- Treas.
Directors: Sr. Patricia Houlihan; Howard Hubbard; Elizabeth Simcoe; Lauren Van Denmark; Joseph P. Whalen, Sr.; Mary P. Whalen.
EIN: 522256192

6967
Whalesback Foundation
1 Pierrepont St.
Brooklyn, NY 11201-3302

Established in 1996 in Pennsylvania.
Donors: Theodore Roosevelt III; Theodore Roosevelt IV.
Foundation type: Independent foundation.
Financial data (yr. ended 12/31/13): Assets, $5,265,059 (M); expenditures, $233,681; qualifying distributions, $183,000; giving activities include $183,000 for 17 grants (high: $50,000; low: $500).
Fields of interest: Art museums; Natural history museums; Business education; Domesticated animals; International relations.
Limitations: Applications not accepted. Giving primarily in NY. No grants to individuals.
Application information: Contributes only to pre-selected organizations.
Officer and Trustees: Theodore Roosevelt IV, Pres. and Secy.-Treas. and Trustee; Constance Roosevelt.
EIN: 311478498

6968
Naida S. Wharton Foundation
c/o PSR LLP
500 Bi-County Blvd., Ste. 201
Farmingdale, NY 11735-3931

Established in 1999 in New Jersey.
Donor: Naida S. Wharton.
Foundation type: Independent foundation.
Financial data (yr. ended 12/31/13): Assets, $8,163,763 (M); expenditures, $322,438; qualifying distributions, $293,600; giving activities include $293,600 for 42 grants (high: $80,000; low: $200).
Fields of interest: Education; Higher education; Family planning; Community and economic development; Human services.
Limitations: Applications not accepted. Giving primarily in NY. No grants to individuals.
Application information: Unsolicited requests for funds not accepted.
Trustee: Naida S. Wharton.
EIN: 223692830

6969
Charlotte & Edward K. Wheeler Foundation
c/o Bessemer Trust
630 5th Ave.
New York City, NY 10111-0100 5165089623
Application address: c/o Ripplewood Holdings, Attn.: Ian L. Snow, Secy.-Treas., 1 Rockefeller Plz., 32nd Fl., New York, NY 10020

Established in 1987 in District of Columbia.
Donor: Edward K. Wheeler.
Foundation type: Independent foundation.
Financial data (yr. ended 12/31/14): Assets, $2,471,461; expenditures, $151,631; qualifying distributions, $144,350.
Fields of interest: Arts and culture; Education; Human services.
Limitations: Applications accepted. Giving on a national basis, with some emphasis on the greater metropolitan Washington, DC, area, including MD and VA, and in New York, NY, and MT.
Application information: Application form required.
Initial approach: Letter
Deadline(s): None
Officers: Frederica Wheeler Johnson, Chair.; Kendall Wheeler, Pres.; Ian K. Snow, Secy.- Treas.
EIN: 521503237

6970
Whispering Bells Foundation
c/o McGladrey LLP
1185 Ave. of the Americas
New York City, NY 10036-2601

Established in 1990 in New York.
Donors: Workman Publishing Co.; Peter Workman; Carolan Workman.
Foundation type: Independent foundation.
Financial data (yr. ended 12/31/12): Assets, $1,398,200 (M); gifts received, $550,000; expenditures, $263,430; qualifying distributions, $260,050; giving activities include $260,050 for grants.
Fields of interest: Education; Nonprofits; Human rights; Human services; Low-income and poor people.

Type of support: Regranting.
Limitations: Applications not accepted. Giving primarily in NY. No grants to individuals.
Application information: Contributes only to pre-selected organizations.
Officer and Trustees: Peter Workman, Pres. and Trustee; Edward Klagsbrun; Carolan Workman.
EIN: 136962126

6971
The White Cedar Fund

(formerly Nolen-Bradley Family Fund)
162 Clinton St.
Brooklyn, NY   11201-4618

Established in 2006 in New York.
Donors: Eliot Nolen; Tim Bradley.
Foundation type: Independent foundation.
Financial data (yr. ended 12/31/13): Assets, $2,323,064 (M); expenditures, $343,284; qualifying distributions, $338,783; giving activities include $338,783 for 16 grants (high: $53,200; low: $1,000).
Fields of interest: Arts and culture; Environment; Catholicism.
Limitations: Applications not accepted. Giving primarily in NY. No grants to individuals.
Application information: Contributes only to pre-selected organizations.
Directors: Timothy Bradley; Eliot Nolen.
EIN: 205717546

6972
The Judith C. White Foundation Inc.

225 W. 34th St., Ste. 1313
New York City, NY   10122-1313   (212) 736-8255
Contact: Jeffrey Kovner, Pres. and Dir.

Established in 2000 in New York.
Donor: Judith C. White.
Foundation type: Independent foundation.
Financial data (yr. ended 12/31/13): Assets, $6,187,464 (M); expenditures, $441,324; qualifying distributions, $382,693; giving activities include $354,033 for 39 grants (high: $50,000; low: $100).
Purpose and activities: Giving primarily to organizations for the support of children, the needy, orphans, and homeless people.
Fields of interest: Higher education; Hospital care; Legal services; Human services; Child welfare; Adoption; Homeless services.
Type of support: General support.
Limitations: Applications accepted. Giving primarily in the metropolitan New York, NY, area.
Application information:
 Initial approach: Proposal
 Deadline(s): None
Officer and Directors: Jeffrey Kovner, Pres. and Director; Amy Kovner; Kristin Kovner; Nicholas Kovner.
EIN: 113548952

6973
Rodney L. White Foundation, Inc.

c/o N. Rifkin, McGladrey & Pullen, LLP
1185 Avenue of the Americas, 19th Fl.
New York City, NY   10036-2602

Established in 1965 in New York.

Donors: Shelby White; Tracy White; Jerome Levy Foundation.
Foundation type: Independent foundation.
Financial data (yr. ended 06/30/13): Assets, $812,738 (M); expenditures, $293,633; qualifying distributions, $293,633; giving activities include $293,533 for 15 grants (high: $60,000; low: $5,000).
Purpose and activities: Giving primarily for the arts.
Fields of interest: Ballet; Art museums; Historic preservation; Cancers.
Type of support: General support; Capital campaigns.
Limitations: Applications not accepted. Giving primarily in New York, NY. No grants to individuals.
Application information: Unsolicited requests for funds not accepted.
Officers: Shelby White, Pres.; Tracy White, Secy.
EIN: 136182934

6974
The Whitehead Foundation, Inc.

c/o BCRS Assocs.
77 Water St., 9th Fl.
New York City, NY   10005-4414
Givesmart: http://www.givesmart.org/Stories/Donors/John-Whitehead

Established in 2007 in New York.
Donors: John C. Whitehead; Paul B. Kazarian Family Charitable Foundation.
Foundation type: Independent foundation.
Financial data (yr. ended 06/30/13): Assets, $7,435,833 (M); gifts received, $400,000; expenditures, $410,374; qualifying distributions, $405,624; giving activities include $399,565 for 102 grants (high: $100,000; low: $100).
Fields of interest: Arts and culture; Education; Human services.
Limitations: Applications not accepted. Giving primarily in CA, Washington, DC, MA, NJ, and NY. No grants to individuals.
Application information: Contributes only to pre-selected organizations.
Officers and Directors: John C. Whitehead, Pres. and Director; Wade Greene, Secy. and Director; John G. Whitehead, Treas. and Director; Susan Ginsburg; Timothy P. Maloney.
EIN: 205605569

6975
The Whittemore Foundation

1221 Ave. of the Americas, 5th Fl.
New York City, NY   10020-1001

Established in 1988 in New York.
Donors: Frederick B. Whittemore; Laurence F. Whittemore.
Foundation type: Independent foundation.
Financial data (yr. ended 12/31/13): Assets, $2,940,608 (M); expenditures, $277,110; qualifying distributions, $200,607; giving activities include $200,607 for 54 grants (high: $30,000; low: $250).
Fields of interest: Theater; Elementary and secondary education; Higher education; Libraries.
Limitations: Applications not accepted. Giving primarily in CT and NH. No grants to individuals.
Application information: Contributes only to pre-selected organizations.

Officers: Frederick B. Whittemore, Pres.; Edward B. Whittemore, V.P.; Laurence F. Whittemore, V.P.
EIN: 133527578

6976
Zichron Alter Meir Wilamowsky Foundation

49 Sealy Dr.
Lawrence, NY   11559-2419

Established in 2001 in New York.
Donors: David Rybak; Eli Wilamowsky.
Foundation type: Independent foundation.
Financial data (yr. ended 12/31/13): Assets, $10,219,200 (M); expenditures, $460,432; qualifying distributions, $266,588; giving activities include $266,588 for grants.
Fields of interest: Judaism.
Limitations: Applications not accepted. Giving primarily in NY. No grants to individuals.
Application information: Contributes only to pre-selected organizations.
Directors: Eli Wilamowsky; Rhona Wilamowsky; Steven Wilamowsky.
EIN: 311795391

6977
Lise and Jeffrey Wilks Family Foundation

P.O. Box 6
Hicksville, NY   11802-0006

Foundation type: Independent foundation.
Financial data (yr. ended 07/31/13): Assets, $1,814,332 (M); expenditures, $243,674; qualifying distributions, $243,225; giving activities include $243,225 for 36 grants (high: $50,000; low: $250).
Fields of interest: Education; Judaism; Human services.
Limitations: Applications not accepted.
Application information: Unsolicited requests for funds not accepted.
Officer: Jeffrey Wilks, V.P.
EIN: 274318322

6978
Fred and Floy Willmott Foundation

95 Washington St., Atrium 1N
Buffalo, NY   14203-2885

Established in 1984 in New York.
Foundation type: Independent foundation.
Financial data (yr. ended 12/31/14): Assets, $5,750,796 (M); expenditures, $406,215; qualifying distributions, $325,269; giving activities include $293,335 for 55 grants (high: $35,000; low: $1,000).
Purpose and activities: Giving primarily for Methodist churches and other religious organizations; support also for aging, education, including higher education, and social services.
Fields of interest: Theater; Elementary and secondary education; Child educational development; Vocational post-secondary education; Higher education; Diseases and conditions; Community and economic development; Christianity; Presbyterianism; Human services; Seniors.
Type of support: Systems reform; Research; Research and evaluation.

Limitations: Applications not accepted. Giving primarily in Monroe County, NY. No grants to individuals.
Application information: Contributes only to pre-selected organizations.
Trustees: John D. Cooke; Luther Miller; HSBC Bank USA.
EIN: 222587484

6979
Elaine P. & Richard U. Wilson Foundation
(also known as Wilson Foundation)
1501 Pittsford-Victor Rd., Ste. 101
Victor, NY 14564-9645

Established in 1963 in New York.
Donor: Katherine M. Wilson†.
Foundation type: Independent foundation.
Financial data (yr. ended 12/31/14): Assets, $3,512,388; gifts received, $0; expenditures, $412,812; qualifying distributions, $340,580.
Fields of interest: Arts and culture; Orchestral music; Science museums; Human services.
Type of support: Annual campaigns; Capital campaigns; Capital and infrastructure; Scholarships.
Limitations: Applications not accepted. Giving primarily in upstate, NY, with emphasis on Rochester.
Application information: Unsolicited requests for funds not accepted.
Trustees: Kim Budd; Charles Sahler; Jason Sahler; David Wilson; Deborah Wilson.
EIN: 166042023

6980
Windy River Foundation
c/o Patterson, Belnap, Webb & Tyler et al
1133 Avenue of the Americas, Ste. 2200
New York City, NY 10036-6710

Established in 1987 in New York.
Donor: Rosalie Coe Weir.
Foundation type: Independent foundation.
Financial data (yr. ended 12/31/13): Assets, $16,230 (M); gifts received, $207,417; expenditures, $213,364; qualifying distributions, $210,650; giving activities include $210,650 for 17 grants (high: $27,500; low: $500).
Fields of interest: Education; Nonprofits; Human services.
Type of support: Regranting; Individual development.
Limitations: Applications not accepted. Giving Primarily in NY. No grants to individuals.
Application information: Unsolicited requests for funds not accepted.
Trustees: Dana W. Hiscock; Rosalie Coe Weir.
EIN: 133402438

6981
Barry Wish Family Foundation, Inc.
c/o Myer, Greene & Degge
P.O. Box 930
Pearl River, NY 10965-0930

Established in 1996 in Florida.
Donors: Barry N. Wish; Jonathan Adess Wish; Stacey Adess Silverstein; Wishco, Inc.
Foundation type: Independent foundation.

Financial data (yr. ended 12/31/13): Assets, $5,699,268 (M); expenditures, $218,127; qualifying distributions, $200,735; giving activities include $200,735 for 34 grants (high: $100,000; low: $100).
Fields of interest: Arts and culture; Education; Human services.
Limitations: Applications not accepted. Giving primarily in FL. No grants to individuals.
Application information: Unsolicited requests for funds not accepted.
Officers: Barry N. Wish, Pres.; Lindsey Wish, V.P.; Oblio Wish, V.P.; Jonathan A. Wish, Secy.; Stacey A. Silverstein, Treas.
EIN: 650720792

6982
WLC and SBC Family Foundation
c/o Brown Rudnick
7 Times Sq., 47th Fl.
New York City, NY 10036-6536

Established in 2007 in Connecticut.
Donor: Peter R. Chapman.
Foundation type: Independent foundation.
Financial data (yr. ended 12/31/14): Assets, $1,271,298 (M); expenditures, $412,171; qualifying distributions, $388,500; giving activities include $388,500 for 10 grants (high: $260,000; low: $1,000).
Fields of interest: Education; Human services; Youth development.
Limitations: Applications not accepted. No grants to individuals.
Application information: Unsolicited requests for funds not accepted.
Officer: Kenneth R. Asher, Secy.
Trustees: Peter R. Chapman; Susan Chapman.
EIN: 261291625

6983
The WOH Foundation
1309 Ave. U
Brooklyn, NY 11229-3305

Established in 1997 in New York.
Donors: Edward Friedman; Jacob Friedman.
Foundation type: Independent foundation.
Financial data (yr. ended 11/30/14): Assets, $34,487 (M); gifts received, $185,275; expenditures, $172,410; qualifying distributions, $172,406; giving activities include $172,406 for grants.
Limitations: Applications not accepted. Giving primarily in Brooklyn, NY. No grants to individuals.
Application information: Unsolicited requests for funds not accepted.
Directors: Edward Friedman; Jacob Friedman.
EIN: 137103155

6984
The Esther & Morton Wohlgemuth Foundation
447 7th St.
Brooklyn, NY 11215-3614
Contact: Melissa Wohlgemuth

Established in 1956 in New York.
Donors: Morton Wohlgemuth†; Esther Wohlgemuth; Alexander Wohlgemuth; Robert Wohlgemuth.

Foundation type: Independent foundation.
Financial data (yr. ended 12/31/13): Assets, $3,592,286 (M); expenditures, $189,015; qualifying distributions, $170,275; giving activities include $170,275 for 127 grants (high: $12,000; low: $25).
Fields of interest: Arts and culture; Art museums; Higher education; Nonprofits; Health; Family planning; Diseases and conditions; Judaism; Human services.
Type of support: Regranting.
Limitations: Applications not accepted. Giving primarily in NY. No grants to individuals.
Application information: Unsolicited requests for funds not accepted.
Officers: Melissa Wohlgemuth, V.P.; Robert Wohlgemuth, V.P.
EIN: 136086849

6985
The Edwin & Shirley Woldar Family Foundation, Inc.
5 Woodbury Farms Dr.
Woodbury, NY 11797-1242
Contact: Paul Woldar, Pres.; Jay Woldar, Secy.-Treas.
E-mail: paul.woldar@woldarfamilyfoundation.org;
Main URL: http://www.woldarfamilyfoundation.org
Grants List: http://www.woldarfamilyfoundation.org/charities.html

Established in 2001 in Delaware.
Donors: Edwin Woldar†; Shirley Woldar†.
Foundation type: Independent foundation.
Financial data (yr. ended 12/31/13): Assets, $3,155,711 (M); expenditures, $230,600; qualifying distributions, $192,414; giving activities include $154,325 for 19 grants (high: $25,000; low: $500).
Purpose and activities: Giving with emphasis on helping children, funding research for medical advancement, educational institutions and the care for the less fortunate. Also to support the Jewish ideals of Tzedukah.
Fields of interest: Education; Diseases and conditions; Judaism; Human services; Child welfare.
Type of support: Research.
Limitations: Applications not accepted. Giving in the U.S., primarily in NY. No grants to individuals.
Application information: Unsolicited requests for funds not accepted.
Officers: Paul Woldar, Pres.; Jay Woldar, Secy.-Treas.
EIN: 223819532

6986
The Wolf Family Foundation
1637 60th St.
Brooklyn, NY 11204-5016

Established in 2005 in New York.
Donor: Leibel Rubin.
Foundation type: Independent foundation.
Financial data (yr. ended 12/31/13): Assets, $1,693,817 (M); gifts received, $310,000; expenditures, $431,904; qualifying distributions, $419,615; giving activities include $419,615 for 34 grants (high: $190,000; low: $50).
Fields of interest: Philanthropy; Religion; Judaism; Human services.
Limitations: Applications not accepted. Giving primarily in Brooklyn, NY. No grants to individuals.

Application information: Unsolicited requests for funds not accepted.

Trustees: Chaim Zvi Wolf; Rachel Wolf.

EIN: 203990564

6987
Elliot K. Wolk Family Foundation, Inc.

c/o Elliot K. Wolk
11 Morris Ln.
Scarsdale, NY 10583-4401

Established in 1983 in New York.

Donors: Elliot K. Wolk; Nancy Wolk.

Foundation type: Independent foundation.

Financial data (yr. ended 11/30/13): Assets, $2,228,379 (M); gifts received, $134,580; expenditures, $279,164; qualifying distributions, $274,314; giving activities include $272,275 for 25 grants (high: $100,000; low: $75).

Fields of interest: Arts and culture; Museums; Higher education; Medical education; Nonprofits; Health; Diseases and conditions; Judaism.

Type of support: General support; Regranting; Annual campaigns; Capital campaigns; Research.

Limitations: Applications not accepted. Giving primarily in New York and Westchester County, NY. No grants to individuals.

Application information: Unsolicited requests for funds not accepted.

Officers: Elliot K. Wolk, Pres. and Treas.; Nancy Wolk, V.P. and Secy.

Director: Andrew Wolk.

EIN: 133221847

6988
Wong Family Foundation

c/o Shulman, Jones & Co.
287 Bowman Ave.
Purchase, NY 10577-2568 (914) 251-9200

Established in 2007 in Delaware.

Donors: Stephen R. Wong; Nathalie Wong.

Foundation type: Independent foundation.

Financial data (yr. ended 12/31/14): Assets, $2,362,637; expenditures, $123,450; qualifying distributions, $120,000.

Fields of interest: Education; Health; Diseases and conditions.

Type of support: General support; Research.

Limitations: Applications accepted. Giving primarily in MA and NY.

Application information:
Initial approach: Proposal
Deadline(s): None

Officers and Directors: Stephen R. Wong, Pres. and Director; Arthur Brill, Secy.; Nathalie Wong, Treas. and Director.

EIN: 208574331

6989
Woodland Foundation

c/o Jeremiah Bogert, Silvercrest Asset Mgmt.
1330 Ave. of the Americas
New York City, NY 10019-5400

Established in 1950 in Delaware.

Donor: William Durant Campbell†.

Foundation type: Independent foundation.

Financial data (yr. ended 12/31/13): Assets, $2,691,329 (M); expenditures, $294,885;

qualifying distributions, $251,500; giving activities include $251,500 for 20 grants (high: $130,000; low: $500).

Purpose and activities: Giving primarily for the arts, education, and Christian and Episcopal organizations and churches.

Fields of interest: Arts and culture; Performing arts; Education; Higher education; Hospital care; Christianity; Episcopalianism and Anglicanism; Lutheranism; Scouting programs.

Type of support: Annual campaigns; Capital campaigns; Capital and infrastructure; Endowments.

Limitations: Applications not accepted. Giving on a national basis, with emphasis on New York and Westchester County, NY. No grants to individuals.

Application information: Contributes only to pre-selected organizations.
Board meeting date(s): Dec.

Officers and Trustees: Margot C. Bogert, Pres. and Trustee; Jeremiah M. Bogert, V.P. and Treas. and Trustee; Winthrop Rutherfurd, Jr., Secy. and Trustee; Jeremiah M. Bogert, Jr.; Millicent D. Bogert; Rev. Terence L. Elsberry; Stowe Tattersall.

EIN: 136018244

6990
Woodmere Foundation

c/o Ayco Co., Jerry Delsordo
P.O. Box 860
Saratoga Springs, NY 12866-0860

Established in 1993 in Pennsylvania.

Donor: Robert B. Knutson.

Foundation type: Independent foundation.

Financial data (yr. ended 12/31/13): Assets, $3,363,586 (M); expenditures, $294,928; qualifying distributions, $250,286; giving activities include $221,391 for 42 grants (high: $20,000; low: $200).

Purpose and activities: Giving for the arts, human services, conservation, education, and medical services and research.

Fields of interest: Arts and culture; Performing arts; Opera; Museums; Education; Natural resources; Diseases and conditions; Human services.

Limitations: Applications not accepted. Giving in the U.S., with some emphasis on NM and PA. No grants to individuals.

Application information: Contributes only to pre-selected organizations.

Officer: Robert B. Knutson, Pres.

EIN: 251705913

6991
The A. Woodner Fund Inc.

35 W. 9th St., Ste. 8A
New York City, NY 10011-8945

Established in 2000 in New York.

Donors: Ian Woodner Family Collection, Inc.; Andrea Woodner.

Foundation type: Independent foundation.

Financial data (yr. ended 12/31/13): Assets, $1,094 (M); gifts received, $340,000; expenditures, $345,300; qualifying distributions, $344,100; giving activities include $344,100 for 35 grants (high: $167,500; low: $100).

Fields of interest: Arts and culture; Drawing; Education.

Limitations: Applications not accepted. Giving primarily in NY. No grants to individuals.

Application information: Contributes only to pre-selected organizations.
Board meeting date(s): Annually

Officer and Director: Andrea Woodner, Pres. and Director.

EIN: 134092338

6992
The Woods Foundation

(formerly The Ward W. Woods Foundation)
c/o Bessemer Trust Co., N.A.
630 5th Ave., Ste. 3425
New York City, NY 10111-0001

Established in 1985 in New York.

Donors: Ward W. Woods, Jr.; Priscilla B. Woods; Katherine Weld Bacon; Nebris Corporation; North Hailey Corporation; S. Ranch.

Foundation type: Independent foundation.

Financial data (yr. ended 09/30/13): Assets, $1,230,364 (M); gifts received, $346,385; expenditures, $268,215; qualifying distributions, $267,938; giving activities include $265,888 for 39 grants (high: $26,428; low: $100).

Purpose and activities: Giving primarily for wildlife conservation and the environment; funding also for the arts, education, recreation, and international affairs.

Fields of interest: Arts and culture; Higher education; Natural resources; Biodiversity; Wildlife biodiversity; Sports; Multilateral cooperation.

Limitations: Applications accepted. Giving primarily in CA, and New York, NY. No grants to individuals.

Application information: Application form required.
Initial approach: Letter
Deadline(s): None

Officers and Directors: Ward W. Woods, Jr., Pres. and Director; Priscilla B. Woods, V.P. and Director; Robert Roriston, Secy.-Treas.; Katherine Woods Emerick; Alexandra Woods.

EIN: 133314966

6993
Ann Eden Woodward Foundation

P.O. Box 4287
Huntington, NY 11743-0777

Established in 1963 in New York.

Donor: Ann Eden Woodward†.

Foundation type: Independent foundation.

Financial data (yr. ended 05/31/13): Assets, $3,819,115 (M); expenditures, $240,151; qualifying distributions, $180,017; giving activities include $179,799 for 24 grants (high: $25,000; low: $850).

Purpose and activities: Giving for the arts, including museums, and for hospitals, environmental and wildlife preservation, and public libraries.

Fields of interest: Arts and culture; Museums; Education; Natural resources; Biodiversity; Wildlife biodiversity; Hospital care; Diseases and conditions; Public libraries; Human services.

Limitations: Applications not accepted. Giving primarily in the metropolitan New York, NY, area, including Long Island. No grants to individuals.

Application information: Contributes only to pre-selected organizations.

Trustees: J.A. Wood; Judy S. Woods.

EIN: 136126021

6994
The World Society Of Czestochowa Jews and Their Descendants, Inc
c/o Funaro & Co., P.C.
350 5th Ave., 41st Fl.
New York City, NY 10118-4100

Donors: Sigmund Rolat; Rubein Margules.
Foundation type: Independent foundation.
Financial data (yr. ended 12/31/13): Assets, $22,880 (M); gifts received, $374,000; expenditures, $368,288; qualifying distributions, $241,540; giving activities include $241,540 for 16 grants (high: $31,350; low: $3,000).
Fields of interest: Film and video.
International interests: Belgium.
Limitations: Applications not accepted. Giving primarily in NE and NY; with some giving in Belgium.
Application information: Unsolicited requests for funds not accepted.
Officer: Sigmund Rolat, Pres.
EIN: 205101779

6995
Victor R. Wright Foundation
c/o BCRS Assocs., LLC
77 Water St., 9th Fl.
New York City, NY 10005-3701

Established in 1985 in New York.
Donor: Victor R. Wright.
Foundation type: Independent foundation.
Financial data (yr. ended 07/31/13): Assets, $1,809,303 (M); expenditures, $263,053; qualifying distributions, $246,199; giving activities include $243,354 for 26 grants (high: $50,000; low: $250).
Fields of interest: Elementary and secondary education; Higher education; Hospital care; Diseases and conditions; Human services; Child welfare.
Type of support: General support.
Limitations: Applications not accepted. No grants to individuals; no loans or scholarships.
Application information: Unsolicited requests for funds not accepted.
Trustees: Raymond E. Worsdale; Joann Wright; Victor R. Wright.
EIN: 133318173

6996
Wunsch Foundation, Inc.
902 Broadway, Ste. 1603
New York City, NY 10010-6029

Established in 1943 in New York.
Donors: WEA Enterprises Co., Inc.; Joseph W. Wunsch; Eric M. Wunsch; Samuel Wunsch; 9th Avenue Equities; 63rd Street Equities.
Foundation type: Independent foundation.
Financial data (yr. ended 12/31/12): Assets, $9,541,875 (M); gifts received, $212,940; expenditures, $459,256; qualifying distributions, $433,345; giving activities include $433,345 for 53 grants (high: $160,000; low: $200).
Purpose and activities: Funding primarily for higher education and for museums.
Fields of interest: Arts and culture; Visual arts; Museums; Art museums; Education; Nonprofits; Health.
Type of support: Regranting.

Limitations: Applications not accepted. Giving primarily in NY. No grants to individuals.
Application information: Contributes only to pre-selected organizations.
Officers: Eric M. Wunsch, Pres.; Ethel Wunsch, Secy.; Peter Wunsch, Treas.
EIN: 116006013

6997
Wurtele Foundation Inc.
1 W. Church St.
Elmira, NY 14901-2741 6077342271

Established in 1981 in New York.
Donor: Joanna Wurtele.
Foundation type: Independent foundation.
Financial data (yr. ended 12/31/14): Assets, $4,602,861; expenditures, $232,051; qualifying distributions, $200,000.
Fields of interest: Educational management; Nonprofits.
Type of support: General support; Capacity-building and technical assistance.
Limitations: Applications not accepted. Giving primarily in LA, with emphasis on Baton Rouge. No grants to individuals.
Application information: Contributes only to pre-selected organizations.
Officers and Trustees: Joanna Wurtele, Pres. and Trustee; Clover M. Drinkwater, Secy. and Trustee; Elizabeth Lowman McCullough.
EIN: 133098760

6998
The Wyckoff Family Foundation, Inc.
159 Maxwell Ave.
Geneva, NY 14456-1538

Established in 2001 in New York.
Donors: Margaret H. Wyckoff†; Janet R. Wyckoff.
Foundation type: Independent foundation.
Financial data (yr. ended 12/31/14): Assets, $7,667,943 (M); expenditures, $425,615; qualifying distributions, $334,180; giving activities include $327,019 for 28 grants (high: $61,904; low: $1,400).
Fields of interest: Arts and culture; Education; University education; Child welfare; Family counseling; Youth services.
Limitations: Applications not accepted. Giving primarily in NY and VA. No grants to individuals.
Application information: Contributes only to pre-selected organizations.
Officers and Directors: Stephen G. Wyckoff, Pres. and Director; Katie Flowers, V.P. and Director; Janet R. Wyckoff, Secy.-Treas.; Ned Clark; Robert McFadden.
EIN: 100001401

6999
The Y & M Charity Foundation, Inc.
149 Heyward St.
Brooklyn, NY 11206-4804

Established in 2004 in New York.
Donor: Templer Family Trust.
Foundation type: Independent foundation.
Financial data (yr. ended 12/31/13): Assets, $31,275 (M); gifts received, $93,644; expenditures, $241,617; qualifying distributions,

$240,935; giving activities include $240,935 for 25 grants (high: $150,000; low: $100).
Fields of interest: Judaism.
Limitations: Applications not accepted. No grants to individuals.
Application information: Unsolicited requests for funds not accepted.
Officer: Joseph Templer, Pres.
EIN: 770641473

7000
Yad Leazor Torah Vochesed Fund
22 W. 38th St., 12th Fl.
New York City, NY 10018-6269 (212) 302-3400
Contact: Ben Fruchtzweig, Tr.

Donors: Zicron Elimelech Foundation; Rabbi Chaim Berlin; David Cohen; Ezra Trust Foundation; Ezra Beyman; Debbie Beyman; Congregation Bais Yisroel; Jacob Weinreb; Deborah Weinreb; Shimon Brecher; Diamond Foundation; Israel Lieber; Yair Ben Moshe.
Foundation type: Independent foundation.
Financial data (yr. ended 12/31/12): Assets, $28,310 (M); gifts received, $162,165; expenditures, $169,907; qualifying distributions, $169,907; giving activities include $169,907 for 1 grant.
Fields of interest: Judaism.
Limitations: Giving in New York, NY. No grants to individuals.
Application information:
 Deadline(s): None
Trustee: Ben Fruchtzweig.
EIN: 204309873

7001
Eva & Jason Yagoda Charitable Foundation
c/o Weiss Co., LLP
22 W. 38th St.
New York City, NY 10018-6269 (212) 302-3400
Contact: Jason Yagoda, Secy.

Established in 2000 in New York.
Donors: Eva Yagoda; Jason Yagoda; Dabha Children Charitable Foundation.
Foundation type: Independent foundation.
Financial data (yr. ended 06/30/13): Assets, $192,918 (M); gifts received, $306,000; expenditures, $270,955; qualifying distributions, $270,955; giving activities include $270,030 for 22 grants (high: $101,600; low: $500).
Fields of interest: Education; Judaism.
Type of support: General support.
Limitations: Applications accepted. Giving primarily in Brooklyn and New York, NY. No grants to individuals.
Application information:
 Deadline(s): None
Officers: Eve Yagoda, Pres.; Jason Yagoda, Secy.
EIN: 113531503

7002
Yahad Foundation, Inc.
c/o Zell & Ettinger
3001 Ave. M
Brooklyn, NY 11210-4744

Established in 1996 in New York.

Donors: Barry Webster; Helen Webster; Ben Webster.

Foundation type: Independent foundation.

Financial data (yr. ended 12/31/13): Assets, $965,823 (M); gifts received, $223,866; expenditures, $226,308; qualifying distributions, $213,487; giving activities include $199,902 for grants (high: $37,500; low: $42).

Purpose and activities: Giving primarily to yeshivas and to Jewish temples.

Fields of interest: Elementary and secondary education; Judaism.

Limitations: Applications not accepted. Giving primarily in NY. No grants to individuals.

Application information: Unsolicited requests for funds not accepted.

Officers: Barry Webster, Pres.; Helen Webster, V.P.; Mark Ettinger, Secy.

EIN: 113136436

7003
The Yaspan-Unterberg Foundation, Inc.

c/o Robert Yaspan
36 Pembroke Dr.
Glen Cove, NY 11542

Established in 1991 in New York.

Donors: Barbara Yaspan; Richard Yaspan; Robert Yaspan; David Yaspan; Janet Meltzer; Peggy Shapiro.

Foundation type: Independent foundation.

Financial data (yr. ended 12/31/14): Assets, $2,970,382; expenditures, $296,372; qualifying distributions, $251,993.

Purpose and activities: Giving primarily to Jewish agencies.

Fields of interest: Natural history museums; Education; Nonprofits; Diseases and conditions; Judaism; Human services.

Type of support: Regranting.

Limitations: Applications not accepted. Giving primarily in New York, NY. No grants to individuals.

Application information: Contributes only to pre-selected organizations.

Officers: Richard Yaspan, Pres.; David Yaspan, Secy.-Treas.

Directors: Janet Meltzer; Peggy Shapiro.

EIN: 133608916

7004
George M. Yeager Family Foundation

(formerly The Yeager-Wood Foundation)
c/o Hymes, C.P.A.
55 Pondfield Rd.
Bronxville, NY 10708-4904

Established in 1985 in New York.

Donor: George M. Yeager.

Foundation type: Independent foundation.

Financial data (yr. ended 12/31/13): Assets, $1,414,640 (M); expenditures, $174,770; qualifying distributions, $171,300; giving activities include $171,300 for 22 grants (high: $52,100; low: $100).

Fields of interest: Museums; Public libraries; Political organizations; Christianity.

Limitations: Applications not accepted. Giving primarily in NY. No grants to individuals.

Application information: Contributes only to pre-selected organizations.

Officers: George M. Yeager, Pres. and Secy.; Kerry Yeager Stevens, V.P.; Scott Alden Yeager, V.P.

EIN: 133314441

7005
Yearley Family Foundation

c/o Ayco Company, LP - NTG
P.O. Box 15014
Albany, NY 12212-5014 (914) 874-6998
Contact: Andrew Yearley, Tr.
FAX: (212) 332-1748;
E-mail: Andrewyearley18@gmail.com; Mailing address: 1 Richbell Rd., Scarsdale, N.Y. 10583

Established in 2000 in Massachusetts.

Donors: Douglas C. Yearley; Anne D. Yearley; Peter Yearley; Andrew Yearley.

Foundation type: Independent foundation.

Financial data (yr. ended 12/31/13): Assets, $4,558,999 (M); expenditures, $248,925; qualifying distributions, $210,000; giving activities include $210,000 for 9 grants (high: $75,000; low: $5,000).

Purpose and activities: Giving primarily to non-profit institutions dedicated to improving the lives of young people from underprivileged circumstances for education, health and well being, and assistance to their families. Primary fields of interest include educational scholarships and early education programs targeting inner-city youth who are disadvantaged by income, health, and inadequate public services. The foundation seeks to target small to medium-size organizations where its contribution can have an impact and where it can engage with program directors on a personal level.

Fields of interest: Child welfare; Children and youth; Low-income and poor people; Slum youth.

Limitations: Applications accepted. Giving limited to organizations serving populations in MA, NJ, NY, and PA. No grants to individuals.

Application information: One electronic copy of proposal should be submitted by email to andrewyearley18@gmail.com. Common Grant Application Form plus Common Grant Application Cover Sheet should be utilized. Proposals are accepted from organizations serving populations in PA, NJ, NY, and MA only. The foundation extends grants on an annual basis with the objective to support worthy organizations for a maximum of three years. First year grants are typically more modest with the objective to gain familiarity with program and organization. Grants have been as large as $75,000 to $100,000 per year in the third year of a grant.

> *Deadline(s):* June 15th
> *Board meeting date(s):* July and Nov.
> *Final notification:* Dec. 15th

Trustees: Andrew Yearley; Anne D. Yearley; Douglas C. Yearley, Jr.; Peter B. Yearley; Sandra D. Yearley.

EIN: 043540667

7006
YGBL Foundation, Inc.

2327 E. 2nd St.
Brooklyn, NY 11223-5345

Donor: Kennedy International Inc.

Foundation type: Independent foundation.

Financial data (yr. ended 12/31/13): Assets, $1,713,592 (M); gifts received, $830,000; expenditures, $584,298; qualifying distributions,

$403,982; giving activities include $403,982 for 18 + grants.

Fields of interest: Education; Human services.

Limitations: Applications not accepted. Giving primarily in Brooklyn, NY.

Application information: Unsolicited requests for funds not accepted.

Directors: Helen Guindi; Henry J. Guindi.

EIN: 274183703

7007
Divrei Yitzchok Foundation

1165 E. 24th St.
Brooklyn, NY 11210-4506

Established in 2001 in New York.

Donor: Marvin Beinhorn.

Foundation type: Independent foundation.

Financial data (yr. ended 12/31/14): Assets, $540,467; gifts received, $106,000; expenditures, $137,522; qualifying distributions, $130,930.

Fields of interest: Education; Judaism; Human services.

Type of support: General support.

Limitations: Applications not accepted. Giving primarily in Brooklyn, NY. No grants to individuals.

Application information: Contributes only to pre-selected organizations.

Trustees: Esther Beinhorn; Marvin Beinhorn.

EIN: 113603802

7008
Yms Foundation Inc.

1570 46th St.
Brooklyn, NY 11219-2725 (212) 563-5733
Contact: Michael Steinmetz, V.P. and Secy.
Application address: 900 E. 19 St., Brooklyn, NY 11230, tel.: (212) 563-5733

Donors: Town Mgmt. Co.; Michael Steinmetz; Bernat Steinmetz; Growth Trust Fund; Park Mgmt.; 36 Plaza Corp.; Sutton Place Mgmt. Co.; Battery Park Mgmt.; Pessie Richard; Cindy Steinmetz; Israel Steinmetz; Tammi Steinmetz; LSM Mgmt.; Lea Cohen; Amy Steinmetz; Erica Steinmetz; Yechiel Spiegal; Feiga Spiegal; Sharge Brecher.

Foundation type: Independent foundation.

Financial data (yr. ended 06/30/13): Assets, $2,267,534 (M); gifts received, $75,000; expenditures, $241,655; qualifying distributions, $241,335; giving activities include $241,335 for grants.

Purpose and activities: Giving primarily to Jewish agencies, temples, and schools.

Fields of interest: Elementary and secondary education; Judaism.

Limitations: Applications accepted. Giving primarily in Brooklyn, NY.

Application information:
> *Initial approach:* Proposal
> *Deadline(s):* None

Officers: Bernat Steinmetz, Pres.; Michael Steinmetz, V.P. and Secy.; Ruth Steinmetz, V.P.; Abraham Weingarten, Treas.

EIN: 311732873

7009
The Christine and Jaime Yordan Foundation

c/o BCRS Associates, LLC
77 Water St., 9th Fl.
New York City, NY 10005-3701

Established in 1993 in Connecticut.
Donor: Jaime E. Yordan.
Foundation type: Independent foundation.
Financial data (yr. ended 07/31/14): Assets, $2,894,935 (M); expenditures, $162,588; qualifying distributions, $155,588; giving activities include $155,588 for 19 grants (high: $30,588; low: $250).
Fields of interest: Education; University education; Environment; Community and economic development; Human services.
Limitations: Applications not accepted. No grants to individuals, or for scholarships; no loans.
Application information: Contributes only to pre-selected organizations.
Trustees: Isabel C. Yordan; Jaime E. Yordan; Peter D. Yordan.
EIN: 133755228

7010
The Yoreinu Foundation

443 N. Franklin St., Ste. 210
Syracuse, NY 13204-5426
Contact: David Roth, Exec. Dir.
E-mail: dtroth@gmail.com; Mailing address: c/o David Roth, Exec. Dir., 24 Derech Beit Lechem, Apt. 25, Jerusalem 9310927, Israel; Israel tel.: 011-972-50-538-2353

Established in 1991 in New York.
Donors: Laurence Roth†; Marsha Roth.
Foundation type: Independent foundation.
Financial data (yr. ended 12/31/14): Assets, $4,399,782 (M); gifts received, $600,000; expenditures, $393,595; qualifying distributions, $256,350; giving activities include $255,500 for 19 grants (high: $25,000; low: $5,000).
Purpose and activities: The Yoreinu Foundation's mission is to promote the ideology of Modern-Orthodox Judaism that supports the synthesis of Jewish values and the observance of Jewish law with the secular, modern world, amidst the religious Zionist sector in Israel that has a significant role to play in fostering Jewish unity, a shared Jewish identity, and ethical social values; ultimately resulting in enhanced Jewish pride and the sanctification of G-d's name (Kiddush Hashem). The Foundation's primary target population is the religious Zionist sector in Israel, followed by the general (secular) Jewish sector. The Foundation's focus is the synthesis of Torah and democracy, social justice, the status of women, Jewish unity, and world culture, as reflected in the Foundation's values statement and ideological platform.
Fields of interest: Orthodox Judaism.
International interests: Israel.
Type of support: General support; Program development; Seed money; Technical assistance.
Limitations: Applications not accepted. Giving limited to Israel. No grants to individuals or for capital projects; no loans.
Application information: The foundation does not accept unsolicited applications.
    Board meeting date(s): Twice a year, or when necessary
Officer: David Roth, Exec. Dir.

Trustees: Alexander S. Pasquale; Marsha Roth.
EIN: 161404154

7011
Chaim Yehoshua Yosef Charitable Foundation

c/o Ken Grossman
31 Deerwood Rd.
Suffern, NY 10901-3231

Established in 2003 in New York.
Donors: Kenneth Grossman; William Ahdout.
Foundation type: Independent foundation.
Financial data (yr. ended 03/31/15): Assets, $293,829 (M); gifts received, $169,900; expenditures, $316,385; qualifying distributions, $316,385; giving activities include $314,950 for grants.
Purpose and activities: Giving primarily to Jewish organizations and temples.
Fields of interest: Graduate and professional education; Nonprofits; Judaism; Theology; Human services.
Type of support: Regranting.
Limitations: Applications not accepted. Giving primarily in NY.
Application information: Contributes only to pre-selected organizations.
Officer and Trustees: Kenneth Grossman, Chair. and Trustee; William Ahdout; Devorah Grossman.
EIN: 200051840

7012
The Young Family Foundation

(formerly Bracebridge & Yuriko Young Family Foundation)
c/o BCRS Associates, LLC
77 Water St., 9th Fl.
New York City, NY 10005-4414

Donor: Bracebridge H. Young, Jr.
Foundation type: Independent foundation.
Financial data (yr. ended 05/31/13): Assets, $487,144 (M); gifts received, $235; expenditures, $214,773; qualifying distributions, $203,835; giving activities include $200,000 for 4 grants (high: $50,000; low: $50,000).
Purpose and activities: Giving primarily for education, with some giving to hospitals and for children's services.
Fields of interest: Arts and culture; Education; Elementary and secondary education; Aquariums; Hospital care; Human services; Child welfare.
Limitations: Applications not accepted. Giving primarily in MA. No grants to individuals; no loans or scholarships.
Application information: Contributes only to pre-selected organizations.
Trustee: Bracebridge H. Young, Jr.
EIN: 133531986

7013
Youth Foundation, Inc.

370 Lexington Ave., Ste. 1206
New York City, NY 10017-6584
Contact: Johanna M. Lee
Main URL: http://fdnweb.org/youthfdn

Established in 1940 in New York.

Donors: Alexander M. Hadden†; Mrs. Alexander M. Hadden†.
Foundation type: Independent foundation.
Financial data (yr. ended 12/31/13): Assets, $11,834,808 (M); gifts received, $9,021; expenditures, $596,912; qualifying distributions, $500,415; giving activities include $10,000 for grants, and $334,715 for grants to individuals.
Purpose and activities: Giving primarily for scholarships to exceptionally worthy, financially needy, secondary school seniors for their undergraduate college education.
Fields of interest: Education.
Type of support: General support; Student aid.
Limitations: Applications accepted. Giving on a national basis.
Publications: Application guidelines; Informational brochure; Program policy statement.
Application information: Complete application guidelines are available on foundation web site. Application form required.
    Initial approach: Letter requesting application (include SASE). No emails or telephone calls accepted
    Copies of proposal: 1
    Deadline(s): Feb. 28
    Board meeting date(s): 2nd Tues. of every month (except Apr., July, Aug., Oct. and Dec.)
    Final notification: May
Officers and Directors: Pamela S. Fulweiler, Pres. and Director; Margaret C. Cushing, V.P. and Director; Mrs. Robert B. Stockman, V.P. and Director; Guy N. Robinson, Secy. and Director; S. Scott Nicholls, Jr., Treas. and Director; Charles E. Baskett; Enrico de Allesandrini; Sven E. Hsia; Mrs. James C. Larmett; E. Timothy McAuliffe; Elizabeth Ann Stribling-Kivlan; Mrs. Vincent S. Villard, Jr.
Number of staff: 1 full-time professional.
EIN: 136093036

7014
Zafirovski Family Foundation

c/o The Ayco Co., L.P. - NTG
P.O. Box 15014
Albany, NY 12212-5014

Established in 2005 in Illinois.
Donor: Mike Zafirovski.
Foundation type: Independent foundation.
Financial data (yr. ended 12/31/14): Assets, $3,392,912 (M); expenditures, $195,552; qualifying distributions, $147,500; giving activities include $147,500 for 3 grants (high: $80,000; low: $15,000).
Fields of interest: Education; Christianity.
Limitations: Applications not accepted. Giving primarily in IL, NC, and PA. No grants to individuals.
Application information: Contributes only to pre-selected organizations.
Officers and Directors: Mike S. Zafirovski, Pres. and Director; Kirk M. Zafirovski, V.P. and Director; Matthew D. Zafirovski, V.P. and Director; Todd A. Zafirovski, V.P.; Robin G. Zafirovski, Secy. and Treas. and Director.
EIN: 203610677

7015
Chasdei Zahavi Foundation

1574 Carroll St.
Brooklyn, NY 11213-5330

Established in 2000 in New York.
Donors: Tzirel Goldman; Shmuel Goldman.
Foundation type: Independent foundation.
Financial data (yr. ended 09/30/13): Assets, $695,769 (M); expenditures, $244,185; qualifying distributions, $243,228; giving activities include $243,228 for 62 grants (high: $76,706; low: $36).
Fields of interest: Education; Religion; Human services.
Limitations: Applications not accepted. Giving primarily in Brooklyn, NY.
Application information: Unsolicited requests for funds not accepted.
Trustees: Shmuel Goldman; Tzirel Goldman; Aliza Scheinfeld.
EIN: 113527951

7016
The Zamir Family Foundation
587 5th Ave., 10th Fl.
New York City, NY 10017-8835
Application address: c/o Asher Roshanzamir, 303 E. 57th St., Apt. 14L, New York, NY 10022-2947, tel.: (212) 832-3334

Established in 2007 in New York.
Donors: Asher Roshanzamir; Michael L. Roshanzamir.
Foundation type: Independent foundation.
Financial data (yr. ended 12/31/13): Assets, $16 (M); gifts received, $134,300; expenditures, $137,098; qualifying distributions, $136,858; giving activities include $133,405 for 132 grants (high: $31,750; low: $36).
Fields of interest: Education; Judaism; Human services.
Application information: Application form required.
  Initial approach: Proposal
  Deadline(s): None
Trustees: Asher Roshanzamir; Michael L. Roshanzamir.
EIN: 261541647

7017
Zarin-Rosenfeld Family Foundation
212 W. 18th St., Ste. 11A
New York City, NY 10011-9109

Established in 2000 in New York.
Donors: Gerald Rosenfeld; Judith Zarin.
Foundation type: Independent foundation.
Financial data (yr. ended 12/31/13): Assets, $277,362 (M); gifts received, $374,836; expenditures, $293,642; qualifying distributions, $288,752; giving activities include $286,000 for 9 grants (high: $70,000; low: $10,000).
Fields of interest: Education; Judaism.
Limitations: Applications not accepted. Giving primarily in NY. No grants to individuals.
Application information: Contributes only to pre-selected organizations.
Trustees: Gerald Rosenfeld; Judith Zarin.
EIN: 134116103

7018
The Zarrella Family Foundation, Inc.
c/o Ashford Advisors, LLC
30B Grove St.
Pittsford, NY 14534-1334   5856970362

Donor: Ronald L. Zarrella.
Foundation type: Independent foundation.
Financial data (yr. ended 12/31/14): Assets, $3,178,074; expenditures, $305,039; qualifying distributions, $301,325.
Fields of interest: Education.
Limitations: Applications not accepted. Giving primarily in NY.
Application information: Unsolicited requests for funds not accepted.
Officers: Ronald L. Zarrella, Pres.; Linda J. Zarrella, V.P.; Katharine K. Zarrella, Secy.; Lily E. Zarrella, Treas.
EIN: 364719352

7019
S. Z. & P. R. Zedakah Fund
c/o J. Furst
1244 49th St.
Brooklyn, NY 11219-3009

Established in 1995 in New York.
Donor: S. Gutfruend.
Foundation type: Independent foundation.
Financial data (yr. ended 11/30/13): Assets, $103,470 (M); gifts received, $284,669; expenditures, $231,743; qualifying distributions, $231,743; giving activities include $231,743 for 256 grants (high: $25,000; low: $25).
Fields of interest: Judaism.
Limitations: Applications not accepted. No grants to individuals.
Application information: Unsolicited requests for funds not accepted.
Trustees: Pauline Gutfruend; S. Gutfruend.
EIN: 113335250

7020
Zedukah Vechesed Foundation Inc.
c/o David Soifer
24 Jackson Ave.
Spring Valley, NY 10977-1908
Application address: c/o Naftali Steinmetz, 356 Marcy Ave., Brooklyn, NY 11211, tel.: (718) 599-7177

Established in 1967 in New York.
Donors: Steinmetz Bros., Inc.; Emanuel Steinmetz; Yitzchak Steinmetz; Rita Wagshall; Solomon Steinmetz; Jrr Mgmt.; Shoretown Mgmt.; Sherman Mgmt.; Clara Steinmetz; Moffat Realty.
Foundation type: Independent foundation.
Financial data (yr. ended 05/31/13): Assets, $6,937,213 (M); gifts received, $15,000; expenditures, $320,019; qualifying distributions, $312,280; giving activities include $312,280 for 14 + grants (high: $76,000).
Fields of interest: Judaism.
Limitations: Applications accepted. Giving primarily in Brooklyn, NY. No grants to individuals.
Application information:
  Initial approach: Proposal
  Deadline(s): None
Trustee: Naftali Steinmetz.
EIN: 237057565

7021
Zeitz Foundation
67 Radnor Rd.
Great Neck, NY 11023-1451
Contact: Joseph Rosenthal

Established in 1943 in Florida.
Foundation type: Independent foundation.
Financial data (yr. ended 06/30/13): Assets, $3,479,124 (M); expenditures, $204,443; qualifying distributions, $166,020; giving activities include $166,020 for grants.
Fields of interest: Arts and culture; Early childhood education; Higher education; Health; Judaism.
Type of support: General support.
Limitations: Applications not accepted.
Application information: Unsolicited requests for funds not accepted.
Officers: Joseph Rosenthal, Pres.; Peter Levin, Secy.; Emme Deland, Treas.
EIN: 116037021

7022
Zemsky Family Foundation
(formerly Russer Foods/Zemsky Family Trust)
c/o Taurus Partners
726 Exchange St., Ste. 412
Buffalo, NY 14210-1484
Application address: c/o Sam Zemsky, 6420 S.E. Harbor Cir., Stuart, FL 34996-1958; tel.: (716) 566-2911

Established in 1987 in New York.
Donors: Zemco Industries, Inc.; Sam Zemsky; Mrs. Sam Zemsky; Shirley Zemsky.
Foundation type: Independent foundation.
Financial data (yr. ended 12/31/13): Assets, $903,985 (M); gifts received, $250,000; expenditures, $158,102; qualifying distributions, $154,950; giving activities include $154,950 for 13 grants (high: $50,000; low: $500).
Purpose and activities: Giving primarily for the arts, education, medical research and human services.
Fields of interest: Arts and culture; Education; Diseases and conditions; Human services.
Type of support: Student aid; Research; Research and evaluation.
Limitations: Applications accepted. Giving primarily in FL, western MA, and NY, with emphasis on Buffalo.
Application information:
  Initial approach: Proposal
  Deadline(s): None
Trustees: Howard Zemsky; Sam Zemsky.
EIN: 112867625

7023
Zenkel Foundation
15 W. 53rd St.
New York City, NY 10019-5410

Established in 1987 in New York.
Donor: Lois Zenkel.
Foundation type: Independent foundation.
Financial data (yr. ended 12/31/13): Assets, $2,283,799 (M); gifts received, $27,500; expenditures, $203,114; qualifying distributions, $170,769; giving activities include $164,000 for 21 grants (high: $45,000; low: $500).

Purpose and activities: Giving primarily for Jewish welfare, the arts, higher education, the environment, and human rights.

Fields of interest: Arts and culture; Photography; Art museums; Higher education; Environment; Nonprofits; Hospital care; Diseases and conditions; Community and economic development; Judaism; Human rights; Diversity and intergroup relations; Human services.

Type of support: General support; Annual campaigns; Capital campaigns; Capital and infrastructure; Professorships; Scholarships; Research; Research and evaluation; Regranting.

Limitations: Applications not accepted. Giving primarily in CT and NY. No grants to individuals.

Application information: Contributes only to pre-selected organizations.

  Board meeting date(s): Apr.

Officers and Directors: Lois S. Zenkel, Pres. and Director; Daniel R. Zenkel, Secy.-Treas. and Director; Lisa Z. Sheldon; Bruce Zenkel; Gary B. Zenkel.

EIN: 133380631

7024
The Zichron Shimon Foundation
10 Yale Dr.
Monsey, NY   10952-2629

Donors: Samuel Lefkovits; Leib Lefkowitz.
Foundation type: Independent foundation.
Financial data (yr. ended 12/31/13): Assets, $5,879 (M); gifts received, $362,900; expenditures, $357,515; qualifying distributions, $357,016; giving activities include $357,016 for 85 grants (high: $151,120; low: $100).
Fields of interest: Religion; Judaism.
Limitations: Applications not accepted.
Application information: Unsolicited requests for funds not accepted.
Trustees: Leib Lefkowitz; Samuel Lefkowitz; Sarah Lefkowitz.
EIN: 274387209

7025
Zichron Yonason Foundation
39 Mariner Way
Monsey, NY   10952-1656

Established in 2002 in New York.
Donors: Michael Steif; Efraim Steif.
Foundation type: Independent foundation.
Financial data (yr. ended 12/31/12): Assets, $279,096 (M); gifts received, $168,500; expenditures, $167,512; qualifying distributions, $163,807; giving activities include $163,807 for grants.
Fields of interest: Judaism.
Limitations: Applications not accepted. No grants to individuals.
Application information: Unsolicited requests for funds not accepted.
Trustees: Efraim Steif; Michael Steif.
EIN: 364516001

7026
Zichron Yosef Chesed Foundation
1342 E. 5th St.
Brooklyn, NY   11230-4626   (718) 758-9424
Contact: Raphael Grossman

Established in 1998 in New York.
Donors: Zev Pollack Co.; Yedida Pollak Irrevocable Trust; Zev Pollak Irrevocable Trust; Max Knoph Foundation; Rika Knoph Foundation; David Pollak Family Trust.
Foundation type: Independent foundation.
Financial data (yr. ended 11/30/14): Assets, $471,690 (M); gifts received, $210,725; expenditures, $200,504; qualifying distributions, $200,504; giving activities include $200,404 for 11 + grants (high: $69,000).
Purpose and activities: Giving primarily for scholarships for Jewish students.
Fields of interest: Arts and culture; Judaism; Human services.
Type of support: General support; Scholarships.
Limitations: Applications accepted. Giving primarily in New York, NY; some giving also in Israel.
Application information: Application form required.
  Initial approach: Letter
  Deadline(s): None
Trustee: Zev Pollack.
EIN: 113483759

7027
The Robert D. Ziff Foundation
c/o ZBI, LLC
350 Park Ave., 4th Fl.
New York City, NY   10022-6022

Established in 2000 in Delaware.
Donors: Ziff Investment Partnership LP II; Robert D. Ziff.
Foundation type: Independent foundation.
Financial data (yr. ended 12/31/14): Assets, $7,801,291; expenditures, $285,217; qualifying distributions, $279,025.
Fields of interest: Arts and culture; Education; Higher education; Nonprofits; Hospital care; Diseases and conditions; Human services.
Type of support: Regranting.
Limitations: Applications not accepted. Giving primarily in New York, NY; some funding also in FL. No grants to individuals.
Application information: Contributes only to pre-selected organizations.
Officers and Directors: Robert D. Ziff, Pres. and Director; David Gray, V.P. and Secy.; Spencer Lehv, V.P. and Treas.; Michelle Locher.
EIN: 134083712

7028
Marie and John Zimmermann Fund, Inc.
c/o Withumsmith Brown, PC
1411 Broadway, 9th Fl.
New York City, NY   10018-3496

Established in 1942 in New York.
Donor: Marie Zimmermann†.
Foundation type: Independent foundation.
Financial data (yr. ended 12/31/13): Assets, $8,479,353 (M); expenditures, $443,426; qualifying distributions, $389,442; giving activities include $310,000 for 14+ grants (high: $75,000).
Fields of interest: Higher education.
Type of support: General support; Program-related investments.
Limitations: Applications not accepted. Giving primarily in CT and NY. No grants to individuals.

Application information: Unsolicited requests for funds not accepted.
  Board meeting date(s): June
Officers: John C. Zimmermann III, Pres.; Kristin Z. Miskavage, V.P.; J. Dail Zimmermann, Treas.
Directors: Kenneth L. Goody; Kate J. Schneider.
EIN: 136158767

7029
Susan Zirkl Z L Memorial Charitable Foundation Trust
250 W. 57th St., Ste. 615
New York City, NY   10107-0605

Foundation type: Independent foundation.
Financial data (yr. ended 12/31/13): Assets, $9,970,801 (M); expenditures, $457,352; qualifying distributions, $324,847; giving activities include $250,000 for 9 grants (high: $75,000; low: $5,000).
Fields of interest: Diseases and conditions; Judaism; Human services.
Type of support: Research.
Limitations: Applications not accepted. Giving primarily in NJ and New York, NY.
Application information: Unsolicited requests for funds not accepted.
Trustees: Michael D. Lissner; Harry Rosenberg.
EIN: 453005204

7030
Ziv Israel Association
c/o Kamerman
156 Fifth Ave., 10th Fl.
New York City, NY   10010-7751

Established in 1989 in New York.
Donors: Emanuel Toporowitz; Marc L. Geraldine Schottenstein; Imra Reich Foundation; Louis Altman; Olga Kuchevsky; Steven Weiss; Naomi Weiss; Vaad Mishmeres ML; David Altman; Suzan Z. Glenn Prise; Mark Blisko; Sport/Ellie Inc.; Dan Stchel; Elain Blisko; Markc L. Hurwitz; Nachlat Halvim; Mayer Blisko; Shari Stchel.
Foundation type: Independent foundation.
Financial data (yr. ended 12/31/13): Assets, $8,659 (M); gifts received, $498,937; expenditures, $433,073; qualifying distributions, $431,000; giving activities include $431,000 for 5 grants (high: $242,000; low: $7,500).
Purpose and activities: Giving for rabbinical education.
Fields of interest: Graduate and professional education; Judaism; Theology.
International interests: Israel.
Limitations: Applications not accepted. Giving primarily in Israel.
Application information: Unsolicited requests for funds not accepted.
Trustees: Aric Bodenstein; Emanuel Toporowitz.
EIN: 237321981

7031
Sergei S. Zlinkoff Fund for Medical Research & Education, Inc.
622 3rd Ave., 32nd Fl.
New York City, NY   10017

Established in 1956 in New York.
Donor: Sergei S. Zlinkoff†.

Foundation type: Independent foundation.
Financial data (yr. ended 10/31/14): Assets, $3,032,791; expenditures, $243,941; qualifying distributions, $202,050.
Fields of interest: Higher education; Medical education.
Type of support: General support.
Limitations: Applications not accepted. Giving primarily in New York, NY. No grants to individuals.
Application information: Unsolicited requests for funds not accepted.
Officers: Mack Lipkin, Jr., MD, Pres.; William M. Kelly, V.P. and Treas.; Marion Anderson, V.P.; Dennis W. Cope, MD, V.P.; Henry Chung, MD, V.P.; Deborah L. Goldsmith, V.P.; Ralph E. Hansmann, V.P.; Barbara Lipkin, V.P.; John O. Lipkin, MD, V.P.; Ellen Parker, V.P.; Kay Williams, V.P.; Jerome J. Cohen, Secy.
EIN: 136094651

7032
The Zukerman Charitable Trust
555 Madison Ave., 12th Fl.
New York City, NY   10022

Foundation type: Independent foundation.
Financial data (yr. ended 12/31/13): Assets, $3,921,380 (M); gifts received, $92,504; expenditures, $311,675; qualifying distributions, $302,605; giving activities include $300,000 for 4 grants (high: $125,000; low: $50,000).
Fields of interest: Secondary education; University education.
Type of support: Fellowships; Endowments.
Limitations: Applications not accepted. Giving primarily in CA, MA and NY. No grants to individuals.
Application information: Contributes only to pre-selected organizations.
Trustees: Karen D. Zukerman; Morris E. Zukerman.
EIN: 137213846

7033
The Mark Zurack & Kathy Ferguson Foundation
c/o BCRS Assocs., LLC
77 Water St., 9th Fl.
New York City, NY   10005-4414

Established in 1996 in New York.
Donors: Mark A. Zurack; Kathy L. Ferguson.
Foundation type: Independent foundation.
Financial data (yr. ended 10/31/13): Assets, $7,543,620 (M); expenditures, $322,856; qualifying distributions, $302,884; giving activities include $301,840 for 15 grants (high: $75,000; low: $995).
Fields of interest: Education; Religion; Human services.
Limitations: Applications not accepted. Giving primarily in New York, NY. No grants to individuals.
Application information: Unsolicited requests for funds not accepted.
Trustees: Kathy Ferguson; Mark Zurack.
EIN: 133926309

7034
Zwerling Family Foundation
c/o BCRS Assocs., LLC
77 Water St., 9th Fl.
New York City, NY   10005-4414

Established in 1989 in New Jersey.
Donor: Gary L. Zwerling.
Foundation type: Independent foundation.
Financial data (yr. ended 06/30/14): Assets, $21,933 (M); gifts received, $167,958; expenditures, $271,950; qualifying distributions, $269,575; giving activities include $268,200 for 35 grants (high: $114,000; low: $100).
Fields of interest: Arts and culture; Museums; Education; Higher education; Nonprofits; Diseases and conditions; Judaism; Human services.
Type of support: Regranting.
Limitations: Applications not accepted. No grants to individuals; no loans or scholarships.
Application information: Unsolicited requests for funds not accepted.
Trustees: Gary L. Zwerling; Marie Rose Zwerling.
EIN: 133532036

7035
Daniel B. Zwirn Foundation
c/o BCRS Associates, LLC
77 Water St., 9th Fl.
New York City, NY   10005-4414

Donor: Daniel B. Zwirn.
Foundation type: Independent foundation.
Financial data (yr. ended 12/31/13): Assets, $20,000 (M); gifts received, $173,808; expenditures, $173,809; qualifying distributions, $173,809; giving activities include $172,500 for 7 grants (high: $50,000; low: $500).
Fields of interest: Education; Higher education; Youth development.
Limitations: Applications not accepted. Giving primarily in New York, NY and Washington, DC.
Application information: Unsolicited requests for funds not accepted.
Officers: Daniel B. Zwirn, Pres.; Thomas G. Amon, Secy.
EIN: 454845155

7036
The Zyman Foundation, Inc.
c/o The Ayco Co., L.P.
321 Broadway
P.O. Box 860
Saratoga Springs, NY   12866-4110

Established in 2005 in Florida.
Donors: Sylvia Zyman; Sergio Zyman.
Foundation type: Independent foundation.
Financial data (yr. ended 06/30/14): Assets, $3,343,603 (M); expenditures, $207,017; qualifying distributions, $171,750; giving activities include $171,750 for 8 grants (high: $51,000; low: $250).
Fields of interest: Child advocacy; Christianity; Adoption; Foster care; International development.
Limitations: Applications not accepted. Giving primarily in FL. No grants to individuals.
Application information: Unsolicited requests for funds not accepted.
Officers and Directors: Sergio Zyman, Chair. and Director; Sylvia Zyman, Pres. and Secy.; Jennifer Zyman, V.P.; Jessica Zyman, V.P.
EIN: 203624795

NORTH CAROLINA

7037
The Claude S. Jr. and Raenelle B. Abernethy Testamentary Charitable Trust
417 6th St. N.W.
Hickory, NC 28601-3501

Established in 2010 in North Carolina.
Donor: Claude Abernethy†.
Foundation type: Independent foundation.
Financial data (yr. ended 12/31/13): Assets, $5,045,497 (M); expenditures, $349,317; qualifying distributions, $257,000; giving activities include $257,000 for 20 grants (high: $35,000; low: $500).
Fields of interest: Arts and culture; Education; Human services.
Limitations: Applications not accepted. Giving primarily in Hickory and Newton, NC.
Application information: Unsolicited requests for funds not accepted.
Trustees: Claude S. Abernethy III; Martha A. Sowers; Anne A. Wepner.
EIN: 276561536

7038
Norman G. Aehle Charitable Trust
c/o Wells Fargo Bank, N.A., Trust Dept.
1 W 4th St. 4th Fl. MAC D4000-041
Winston-Salem, NC 27101-3818

Donor: Aehle Living Trust.
Foundation type: Independent foundation.
Financial data (yr. ended 12/31/14): Assets, $23,360 (M); expenditures, $225,813; qualifying distributions, $224,755; giving activities include $223,500 for 11 grants (high: $53,500; low: $17,000).
Fields of interest: Diseases and conditions; Human services; Youth development.
Limitations: Applications not accepted.
Application information: Unsolicited requests for funds not accepted.
Trustee: Wells Fargo Bank, N.A.
EIN: 376492891

7039
The Agarwal Foundation
1330 Sunday Dr., Ste. 105
Raleigh, NC 27607-5196

Established in 2007 in North Carolina.
Donors: Sajjan Kumar Agarwal; Asha R. Agarwal; Agarwal Charitable Lead Annuity Trust.
Foundation type: Independent foundation.
Financial data (yr. ended 12/31/13): Assets, $9,406,405 (M); gifts received, $3,201,548; expenditures, $266,062; qualifying distributions, $157,550; giving activities include $157,550 for 17 grants (high: $40,000; low: $1,000).
Fields of interest: Education; Health; Autism; Human services; International relations.
Limitations: Applications not accepted. Giving primarily in GA, NC and NJ. No grants to individuals.
Application information: Contributes only to pre-selected organizations.

Directors: Asha R. Agarwal; Ankit K. Agarwal; Rohit K. Agarwal; Linwood A. Jackson.
EIN: 421747195

7040
The Arcadia Foundation
1525 W. WT Harris Blvd.
Charlotte, NC 28262-8522
Contact: F.B. Dent, Pres.

Established in 1950 in South Carolina.
Foundation type: Independent foundation.
Financial data (yr. ended 12/31/14): Assets, $2,717,863 (M); expenditures, $199,925; qualifying distributions, $168,700; giving activities include $167,700 for 15 grants (high: $30,000; low: $1,500).
Purpose and activities: Giving primarily for higher education, medical facilities, the arts and civic organizations.
Fields of interest: Education; Protestantism; Human services.
Type of support: Annual campaigns; Capital campaigns; Endowments.
Limitations: Applications not accepted. Giving primarily in SC.
Application information: Unsolicited requests for funds not accepted.
Officers and Trustees: F.B. Dent, Pres. and Trustee; F.B. Dent, Jr., V.P. and Treas.; Magruder H. Dent, Secy.
Number of staff: None.
EIN: 570298275

7041
Stanley & Marty Arkwright Conservation Trust
c/o Wells Fargo Bank, N.A., Trust Tax. Dept.
1 W. 4th St., 4th Fl., MAC D4000-041
Winston-Salem, NC 27101-3818

Established in 2003 in Montana.
Foundation type: Independent foundation.
Financial data (yr. ended 12/31/14): Assets, $4,370,149; expenditures, $265,924; qualifying distributions, $217,423.
Fields of interest: University education.
Limitations: Applications not accepted. Giving primarily in MT. No grants to individuals.
Application information: Unsolicited requests for funds not accepted.
Trustee: Wells Fargo Bank, N.A.
EIN: 816088061

7042
Hildegard Balin Charitable Trust
c/o Wells Fargo Bank, N.A.
1 W. 4th St., 4th Fl., MAC D4000-041
Winston-Salem, NC 27101-3818
E-mail: grantadministration@wellsfargo.com; *Main URL:* https://www.wellsfargo.com/privatefoundationgrants/balin

Established in 1996 in California.
Foundation type: Independent foundation.
Financial data (yr. ended 12/31/13): Assets, $6,037,590 (M); expenditures, $432,013; qualifying distributions, $258,987; giving activities include $242,000 for grants.

Purpose and activities: Support for human services, especially for services benefiting the elderly and the disadvantaged; giving also for animal welfare and health.
Fields of interest: Domesticated animals; Animal welfare; Health; Human services; Food aid; Child welfare; Senior assisted living; Senior services; Seniors; Low-income and poor people.
Limitations: Applications accepted. Giving primarily in CA, with emphasis on Santa Barbara County. No grants to individuals.
Application information: See foundation website for complete application guidelines. Application form required.
Deadline(s): July 31
Trustees: David F. Horton; Wells Fargo Bank, N.A.
EIN: 776132316

7043
Bane Charitable Foundation
(also known as E. M. Ich Bane Trust)
1525 W. WT Harris Blvd., D1114-044
Charlotte, NC 28262

Established in 1990 in Virginia.
Donor: Eugene M. Bane†.
Foundation type: Independent foundation.
Financial data (yr. ended 12/31/13): Assets, $4,319,395 (M); expenditures, $234,089; qualifying distributions, $194,252; giving activities include $181,000 for 26 grants (high: $36,200; low: $1,810).
Purpose and activities: Giving primarily for education, medical research, community relief, and child care.
Fields of interest: Education; Hospital care; Diseases and conditions; Human services; Child welfare.
Type of support: Research.
Limitations: Applications not accepted. Giving primarily in VA. No grants to individuals.
Application information: Unsolicited requests for funds not accepted.
Trustee: Wells Fargo Bank, N.A.
EIN: 546293471

7044
Bob Barker Company Foundation, Inc.
(formerly The Robert Barker Foundation, Inc.)
134 N. Main St.
Fuquay Varina, NC 27526-1920

Established in 2004 in North Carolina.
Donors: Robert J. Barker, Jr.; Bob Barker Inc.
Foundation type: Operating foundation.
Financial data (yr. ended 12/31/13): Assets, $4,405,549 (M); gifts received, $688,550; expenditures, $291,942; qualifying distributions, $290,263; giving activities include $218,600 for 16 grants (high: $50,000; low: $600).
Fields of interest: Protestantism; Human services.
Limitations: Applications not accepted. Giving primarily in NC; funding also in UT. No grants to individuals.
Application information: Unsolicited requests for funds not accepted.
Directors: Patricia M. Barker; Robert J. Barker; Robert J. Barker, Jr.; Nancy B. Johns.
EIN: 201276455

7045
BB&T Charitable Foundation
c/o Branch Banking & Trust, Trust Tax Dept.
P.O. Box 2907
Wilson, NC 27894-2907

Established in 1998 in North Carolina.
Donors: BB&T Corp.; First Virginia Bank.
Foundation type: Company-sponsored foundation.
Financial data (yr. ended 12/31/14): Assets, $28,637 (M); expenditures, $198,390; qualifying distributions, $197,458; giving activities include $196,458 for 10 grants (high: $50,000; low: $3,125).
Purpose and activities: The foundation supports organizations involved with arts and culture, education, the environment, health, human services, and community development.
Fields of interest: Arts and culture; Museums; Education; Higher education; Environment; Nonprofits; Health; Community and economic development; Economic development; Housing development; Human services.
Type of support: General support; Matching grants; Regranting; Annual campaigns; Capital campaigns; Capital and infrastructure; Endowments; Emergency funds; Program development; Professorships; Publications; Curriculum development; Scholarships.
Limitations: Applications not accepted. Giving primarily in areas of company operations in NC. No grants to individuals.
Application information: Contributes only to pre-selected organizations.
 Board meeting date(s): Bi-monthly
Trustee: Branch Banking &Trust Co.
Number of staff: None.
EIN: 562093089

7046
The Irwin Belk Educational Foundation
1525 W. WT Harris Blvd., D1114-044
Charlotte, NC 28262

Donors: Carl G. Belk; Irwin Belk; Irwin Belk Charitable Lead Trusts; Irwin Belk Charitable Lead Unitrust CW; Irwin Belk Charitable Lead Unitrust PB; Irwin Belk Charitable Lead Unitrust MM; Irwin Belk Charitable Lead Unitrust SB; Irwin Belk Charitable Lead Unitrust IB; Irwin Belk Charitable Lead Unitrust DB; Irwin Belk Charitable Lead Unitrust JW.
Foundation type: Independent foundation.
Financial data (yr. ended 12/31/13): Assets, $557,342 (M); gifts received, $208,492; expenditures, $254,211; qualifying distributions, $243,150; giving activities include $242,150 for 51 grants (high: $20,000; low: $2,000).
Purpose and activities: Giving primarily for arts and culture, libraries, and to religious organizations.
Fields of interest: Arts and culture; Science museums; Public libraries; Protestantism.
Type of support: General support.
Limitations: Applications not accepted. Giving primarily in NC. No grants to individuals.
Application information: Unsolicited requests for funds not accepted.
Directors: Bill Belk; Carl G. Belk; Irene Belk Miltimore; Marilyn Belk Wallis.
EIN: 561783301

7047
Victor E., Jr. & Jane McNair Bell Family Foundation
P.O. Box 17274
Raleigh, NC 27619-7274

Established in 1997 in North Carolina.
Donors: Jane McNair Bell; Victor E. Bell, Jr.; Bell Investments Limited Partnership; Daniel L. Cook; Laura Schaefer Bell; Fairley Bell Cook; John McNair Bell; Mary Grady Koonce Bell; Victor E. Bell III.
Foundation type: Independent foundation.
Financial data (yr. ended 12/31/14): Assets, $5,023,778; expenditures, $261,515; qualifying distributions, $235,842.
Fields of interest: Arts and culture; Education; Nonprofits; Diseases and conditions; Christianity; Human services.
Type of support: Regranting.
Limitations: Applications not accepted. Giving primarily in NC. No grants to individuals.
Application information: Contributes only to pre-selected organizations.
Officers: Victor E. Bell III, Chair.; Fairley Bell Cook, Pres. and Treas.; John McNair Bell, V.P. and Secy.
EIN: 562019191

7048
Bell Foundation
P.O. Box 3288
Greensboro, NC 27402-3288

Established in 2005 in North Carolina.
Donors: Steven D. Bell; Jonathan D. Bell; Evan D. Bell.
Foundation type: Independent foundation.
Financial data (yr. ended 12/31/13): Assets, $4,690,444 (M); gifts received, $332,500; expenditures, $236,260; qualifying distributions, $192,000; giving activities include $192,000 for 7 grants (high: $125,000; low: $5,000).
Fields of interest: Education; Environment; Foundations; Nonprofits.
Type of support: General support; Regranting.
Limitations: Applications not accepted. Giving primarily in Greensboro, NC. No grants to individuals.
Application information: Unsolicited requests for funds not accepted.
Officers: Steven D. Bell, Pres.; Jonathan D. Bell, Secy.-Treas.
EIN: 203954920

7049
The Donald H. & Barbara K. Bernstein Family Foundation
1525 W. W.T. Harris Blvd., D1114-044
Charlotte, NC 28262
Application address: c/o Donald Bernstein, 482 Fenton Pl., Charlotte, NC 27211, tel.: (704) 332-8880

Established in 1988 in North Carolina.
Donors: Donald H. Bernstein; Barbara K. Bernstein.
Foundation type: Independent foundation.
Financial data (yr. ended 12/31/14): Assets, $393,268 (M); gifts received, $200,053; expenditures, $230,287; qualifying distributions, $226,773; giving activities include $224,530 for 37 grants (high: $40,000; low: $50).

Purpose and activities: Giving for arts and culture, education and public welfare, with an emphasis on Jewish institutes.
Fields of interest: Arts and culture; Education; Nonprofits; Judaism.
Type of support: Regranting.
Limitations: Applications accepted. Giving primarily in Sarasota, FL and Charlotte, NC. No grants to individuals.
Officers: Donald H. Bernstein, Pres. and Treas.
EIN: 581804268

7050
Bertsch Family Charitable Foundation Inc
6625 Creek Wood Dr.
Chapel Hill, NC 27514-7443   (919) 967-2580

Donor: Bertsch Charitable Trust.
Foundation type: Independent foundation.
Financial data (yr. ended 12/31/14): Assets, $6,377,756; expenditures, $364,120; qualifying distributions, $314,000.
Fields of interest: Education; Basic and remedial instruction; Health; Christianity; Adoption; Special population support.
Limitations: Applications accepted. Giving primarily in NC and IN. No grants to individuals.
Application information: Application form required.
 Initial approach: Letter
 Deadline(s): None
Officers: Diane Bertsch, Pres.; Jordan Shamp, V.P. and Secy.
EIN: 352057621

7051
Francis & Monte Bettman Foundation
c/o Wells Fargo Bank N.A., Trust Tax Dept.
1 W. 4th St., 4th Fl., MAC D4000-041
Winston-Salem, NC 27101-3818

Foundation type: Independent foundation.
Financial data (yr. ended 12/31/13): Assets, $3,873,414 (M); expenditures, $220,688; qualifying distributions, $179,548; giving activities include $165,963 for 7 grants (high: $23,709; low: $23,709).
Fields of interest: Health; Judaism; Human services; Youth development.
Type of support: General support.
Limitations: Applications not accepted. Giving primarily in CA, FL, and OR.
Application information: Unsolicited requests for funds not accepted.
Trustee: Wells Fargo Bank, N.A.
EIN: 936033920

7052
Charle & Ruth Billingsley Foundation
c/o Wells Fargo Bank, N.A., Trust Tax. Dept.
1 W. 4th St., 4th Fl., MAC D4000-041
Winston-Salem, NC 27101-3818
E-mail: grantadministration@wellsfargo.com; Main URL: https://www.wellsfargo.com/privatefoundationgrants/billingsley

Established in 1989 in California.
Donor: U.S. Trust Co.
Foundation type: Independent foundation.

Financial data (yr. ended 12/31/14): Assets, $4,427,869; expenditures, $262,529; qualifying distributions, $211,645.
Fields of interest: Performing arts; Museums; Environment; Health; Human services; Child welfare; Youth development.
Type of support: General support.
Limitations: Applications accepted. Giving primarily in CA. No grants to individuals.
Application information: See foundation website for complete application guidelines. Application form required.
   Deadline(s): Apr. 30 and Aug. 31
Trustee: Wells Fargo Bank, N.A.
EIN: 336047988

7053
Blue Bell Foundation
c/o Wells Fargo Bank, N.A.
1 W. 4th St., 4th Fl., D4000-041
Winston-Salem, NC   27101-3818   (910) 373-3412
Application address: P.O. Box 21488, Greensboro, NC 27420, tel.: (910) 373-3412

Established in 1944 in North Carolina.
Donors: Blue Bell, Inc.; Wrangler Apparel Corp.
Foundation type: Company-sponsored foundation.
Financial data (yr. ended 12/31/14): Assets, $5,797,584; expenditures, $427,703; qualifying distributions, $386,111.
Purpose and activities: The foundation supports organizations involved with arts and culture, education, health, athletics, human services, and community development.
Fields of interest: Arts and culture; Education; Religion.
Limitations: Applications accepted. Giving primarily in areas of company operations, with emphasis on NC. No grants to individuals.
Application information: Application form required.
   Initial approach: Letter
   Deadline(s): None
Trustee: Wells Fargo Bank, N.A.
EIN: 566041057

7054
Nickolas Bunn Boddie, Sr. and Lucy Mayo Boddie Foundation
c/o Tax & Risk Mgmt.
P.O. Box 1908
Rocky Mount, NC   27802-1908

Established in 1996 in North Carolina.
Donor: B. Mayo Boddie.
Foundation type: Independent foundation.
Financial data (yr. ended 12/31/14): Assets, $5,416,632; expenditures, $334,515; qualifying distributions, $289,075.
Purpose and activities: Giving primarily for education and social services.
Fields of interest: Higher education; Diseases and conditions; Protestantism; Human services.
Limitations: Applications not accepted. Giving primarily in NC. No grants to individuals.
Application information: Contributes only to pre-selected organizations.
Officers: B. Mayo Boddie, Pres.; William L. Boddie, V.P.; Michael W. Boddie, Secy.; B. Mayo Boddie, Jr., Treas.
EIN: 561678893

7055
Boddie Noell Foundation
c/o Tax and Risk Mgmt.
P.O. Box 1908
Rocky Mount, NC   27802-1908

Established in 2004 in North Carolina.
Donor: Boddie Noell Enterprises Inc.
Foundation type: Independent foundation.
Financial data (yr. ended 12/31/13): Assets, $3,843,101 (M); expenditures, $232,119; qualifying distributions, $198,580; giving activities include $197,480 for 43 grants (high: $23,500; low: $500).
Fields of interest: Education; Hospital care; Economic development; Human services.
Limitations: Applications not accepted. Giving primarily in NC. No grants for individuals.
Application information: Contributes only to pre-selected organizations.
Officers and Directors: William L. Boddie, Pres. and Director; Michael H. Hancock, V.P. and Director; Pamela Larimer, Secy.-Treas.; Douglas E. Anderson; Mayo Boddie, Sr.
EIN: 201897695

7056
The Bolick Foundation
P.O. Box 307
Conover, NC   28613-0307

Established in 1967 in North Carolina.
Donor: Southern Furniture Co. of Conover, Inc.
Foundation type: Company-sponsored foundation.
Financial data (yr. ended 06/30/14): Assets, $11,438,594 (M); expenditures, $549,457; qualifying distributions, $429,750; giving activities include $429,750 for 67 grants (high: $100,000; low: $250).
Purpose and activities: The foundation supports organizations involved with historical activities, education, health, human services, international relief, and Christianity.
Fields of interest: Historical activities; Education; Elementary and secondary education; Higher education; Graduate and professional education; Health; Hospice care; Christianity; Theology; Human services; Basic and emergency aid; Scouting programs; International development.
Type of support: General support; Annual campaigns; Capital campaigns; Capital and infrastructure.
Limitations: Applications not accepted. Giving primarily in NC. No grants to individuals.
Application information: Contributes only to pre-selected organizations.
Trustees: Jerome W. Bolick; Judith L. Bolick; Linda B. Bolick.
EIN: 566086348

7057
Harry H. and Anna Borun Foundation
c/o Wells Fargo Bank, N.A. Trust Tax Dept.
1 W. 4th St., 4th Fl., MAC D4000-041
Winston-Salem, NC   27101-3818
Application address: c/o Executive Committe, 1530 3rd Ave., Birmingham, AL 35294

Established in 1957 in California.
Donors: Anna Borun†; Harry Borun†.
Foundation type: Independent foundation.

Financial data (yr. ended 12/31/13): Assets, $7,747,580 (M); expenditures, $366,687; qualifying distributions, $345,115; giving activities include $339,000 for grants.
Fields of interest: University education; Natural resources; Nonprofits; Human services.
Type of support: Regranting.
Limitations: Applications accepted. Giving primarily in CA; some giving also in NY. No grants to individuals.
Application information: Application form required.
   Initial approach: Proposal
   Deadline(s): May 15
EIN: 956150362

7058
The A. Pat and Kathryne L. Brown Foundation, Inc.
c/o Thomas F. Foster
P.O. Box 1550
High Point, NC   27261-1550

Established in 1991 in North Carolina.
Donor: Kathryne L. Brown†.
Foundation type: Independent foundation.
Financial data (yr. ended 12/31/13): Assets, $4,323,712 (M); expenditures, $377,398; qualifying distributions, $350,516; giving activities include $340,000 for 15 grants (high: $85,000; low: $5,000).
Purpose and activities: Giving for education, hospitals, and human services.
Fields of interest: Education; Higher education; Hospital care; Christianity; Human services.
Limitations: Applications not accepted. Giving primarily in NC. No grants to individuals.
Application information: Contributes only to pre-selected organizations.
   Board meeting date(s): May and Nov.
Officers and Directors: Ann Busby, Pres. and Director; W. Calvin Reynolds, V.P. and Director; Jeff Horney, Secy. and Director; Thomas F. Foster, Treas. and Director; Tom Blount; Meredith Eanes; David L. Maynard.
EIN: 561761750

7059
Harry G. & Mary Lore Flowe Brown Trust
c/o Wells Fargo Bank, N.A.
1 W. 4th St., 4th Fl., MAC D4000-041
Winston-Salem, NC   27101-3818

Established in 2004 in North Carolina.
Donor: Mary Lore F. Brown Trust.
Foundation type: Independent foundation.
Financial data (yr. ended 12/31/13): Assets, $8,230,814 (M); gifts received, $140,500; expenditures, $434,747; qualifying distributions, $370,775; giving activities include $349,068 for 14 grants (high: $34,907; low: $8,726).
Fields of interest: Higher education; Health; Protestantism.
Limitations: Applications not accepted. No grants to individuals.
Application information: Contributes only to pre-selected organizations.
Trustee: Wells Fargo Bank, N.A.
EIN: 256857069

7060
Bryan Foundation, Inc.
(formerly James E. and Mary Z. Bryan Foundation, Inc.)
c/o First Citizens Bank, Trust Dept.
P.O. Box 29522
Raleigh, NC 27626-0522 (919) 755-7422
Contact: William H. Bryan, Pres.

Established in 1954 in North Carolina.
Donors: James E. Bryan†; Mary Z. Bryan†.
Foundation type: Independent foundation.
Financial data (yr. ended 06/30/13): Assets, $6,866,990 (M); expenditures, $217,141; qualifying distributions, $182,550; giving activities include $175,000 for grants.
Purpose and activities: To aid needy and worthy students who are residents of North Carolina through grants to trade schools, colleges, or universities; support also for secondary schools.
Fields of interest: Education; Secondary education; Vocational education; Higher education.
Type of support: Scholarships; Loans to individuals; Individual development.
Limitations: Applications accepted. Giving limited to NC. No grants directly to individuals, or for general support.
Publications: Financial statement.
Application information: Application form required.
  Initial approach: Letter
  Deadline(s): Jan. 31
  Board meeting date(s): Mar.
Officers: William H. Bryan, Pres.; James M. "Kee" Zealy, Jr., V.P.; Frank Holding, Jr., Secy.
Number of staff: 1 part-time support.
EIN: 566034567

7061
F. L. R. and Adelaide G. Burks Charitable Trust
c/o Wells Fargo Bank, N.A.
1 W. 4th St., 4th Fl., MAC D4000-041
Winston-Salem, NC 27101-3818

Foundation type: Independent foundation.
Financial data (yr. ended 06/30/14): Assets, $3,197,778 (M); expenditures, $187,111; qualifying distributions, $158,418; giving activities include $153,582 for 12 grants (high: $16,202; low: $7,632).
Fields of interest: University education; Medical education; Children's hospital care; Christianity; Human services; Youth services; Scouting programs; Children.
Type of support: General support.
Limitations: Applications not accepted. Giving limited to CA, FL, and PA.
Application information: Unsolicited requests for funds not accepted.
Trustee: Wells Fargo Bank, N.A.
EIN: 946347864

7062
Burlington Industries Foundation
P.O. Box 26540
Greensboro, NC 27415-6540 (336) 379-2903
Contact: Delores C. Sides, Exec. Dir.

Established in 1943 in North Carolina.
Donors: Burlington Industries, Inc.; Burlington Industries LLC.

Foundation type: Company-sponsored foundation.
Financial data (yr. ended 09/30/13): Assets, $1,054,195 (M); expenditures, $266,232; qualifying distributions, $262,075; giving activities include $259,075 for 52 grants (high: $50,000; low: $25).
Purpose and activities: The foundation supports art councils and organizations involved with education, multiple sclerosis, youth development, and business promotion.
Fields of interest: Community and economic development; Human services; Youth development.
Type of support: Annual campaigns; Grants to individuals; Employee volunteer services; Capital campaigns; Capital and infrastructure; Employee matching gifts; Program development; Scholarships.
Limitations: Applications accepted. Giving primarily in areas of company operations in NC, SC, and VA. Generally, no support for sectarian or denominational religious organizations, national organizations, private secondary schools, or historic preservation organizations. No grants to individuals (except for employees in distress), or for conferences, seminars, workshops, endowments, outdoor dramas, films, or documentaries, or medical research; no loans.
Publications: Application guidelines.
Application information:
  Initial approach: Proposal
  Copies of proposal: 1
  Deadline(s): None
  Board meeting date(s): Annually
Officer: Delores C. Sides, Exec. Dir.
Trustees: Park R. Davidson; Joseph L. Gorga; George W. Henderson III.
EIN: 566043142

7063
Anne Klinger Burns Memorial Fund
1525 W. W.T. Harris Blvd.
Charlotte, NC 28288-1161
Application address: Center for Scholarship Administration, 4320-G Wade Hampton Blvd., Taylors, SC 29687, tel.: (866) 601-0001, URL: http://www.csacholars.org

Donors: Thomas J. Burke; Anne Klinger Burns†.
Foundation type: Independent foundation.
Financial data (yr. ended 12/31/14): Assets, $3,120,950 (M); expenditures, $206,317; qualifying distributions, $175,812; giving activities include $100,000 for 2 grants (high: $50,000; low: $50,000), and $50,000 for 5 grants to individuals (high: $15,000; low: $5,000).
Purpose and activities: Students who are graduates of Academy Park H.S. and who are attending and matriculating in a 4 year college program.
Fields of interest: Higher education; Diseases and conditions; Religion.
Type of support: Research; Scholarships.
Limitations: Applications accepted. Giving primarily in PA, SC and TN.
Application information: Application form required.
  Initial approach: Email
  Deadline(s): Mar. 28
Trustees: Thomas J. Burke, Jr., Esq.; Wells Fargo Bank, N.A.
EIN: 906108387

7064
C3 Foundation, Inc.
3301 Benson Dr., Ste. 601
Raleigh, NC 27609-7331

Established in 2008 in North Carolina.
Donor: Lonnie C. Poole III.
Foundation type: Independent foundation.
Financial data (yr. ended 12/31/13): Assets, $1,195,398 (M); expenditures, $244,658; qualifying distributions, $244,658; giving activities include $229,334 for 3 grants (high: $220,000; low: $1,000).
Fields of interest: Education.
Limitations: Applications not accepted. Giving primarily in Raleigh, NC.
Application information: Unsolicited requests for funds not accepted.
Officers and Directors: Lisa R. Poole, Pres. and Director; Lonnie C. Poole III, V.P. and Director; Joseph P. Davis III, Secy.-Treas. and Director; Todd Saieed.
EIN: 262511733

7065
Dan Cameron Family Foundation, Inc.
P.O. Box 3649
Wilmington, NC 28406-0649 (910) 762-2676
Contact: William H. Cameron, Dir.

Established in 1998 in North Carolina.
Donors: Daniel D. Cameron; Elizabeth H. Cameron.
Foundation type: Operating foundation.
Financial data (yr. ended 12/31/13): Assets, $8,357,814 (M); expenditures, $454,725; qualifying distributions, $390,310; giving activities include $390,310 for 116 grants (high: $45,000; low: $100).
Fields of interest: Arts and culture; Art museums; Education; Higher education; Human services; Youth services.
Limitations: Applications accepted. Giving primarily in MI and NC. No grants to individuals.
Application information:
  Initial approach: Proposal
  Deadline(s): None
Directors: Charlotte Cameron; Daniel D. Cameron, Jr.; William H. Cameron; Hilda C. Dill; Swanna C. Saltiel.
EIN: 562087335

7066
Harry E. Canaday Fund
2615 Churchill Rd.
Raleigh, NC 27608-1947

Foundation type: Independent foundation.
Financial data (yr. ended 12/31/13): Assets, $3,610,500 (M); expenditures, $210,748; qualifying distributions, $181,133; giving activities include $181,133 for 4 grants (high: $90,566; low: $9,057).
Fields of interest: Arts and culture; Education; Religion.
Limitations: Applications not accepted. Giving primarily in Benson, NC.
Application information: Unsolicited requests for funds not accepted.
Trustee: Catherine Canaday McLamb.
EIN: 276097607

7067
William Coltrane & Norma Craft Cannon Charitable Trust
1525 W. W.T. Harris Blvd., D1114-044
Charlotte, NC 28288-0001

Donor: William C. Cannon Marital Trust.
Foundation type: Independent foundation.
Financial data (yr. ended 12/31/14): Assets, $10,501,988; expenditures, $525,239; qualifying distributions, $450,030.
Fields of interest: Museums; Graduate and professional education; Health; Hospice care; Christianity; Youth services; Scouting programs.
Limitations: Applications not accepted. Giving primarily in NC. No grants to individuals.
Application information: Contributes only to pre-selected organizations.
Trustee: William C. Cannon, Jr.; Wells Fargo Bank, N.A.
EIN: 256893619

7068
Carroll Family Foundation, Inc.
201 N. Elm St., Ste. 201
Greensboro, NC 27401-2447

Donors: Roy E. Carroll II; Vanessa Y. Carroll; Patsy R. Carroll.
Foundation type: Independent foundation.
Financial data (yr. ended 12/31/13): Assets, $166,673 (M); gifts received, $150,000; expenditures, $138,373; qualifying distributions, $137,773; giving activities include $137,773 for 9 grants (high: $75,000; low: $500).
Fields of interest: Undergraduate education; Health; Religion; Human services.
Limitations: Applications not accepted. Giving primarily in Greensboro, NC. No grants to individuals.
Application information: Unsolicited requests for funds not accepted.
Officer: Curtis L. Nichols, Secy.
Directors: Patsy R. Carroll; Roy E. Carroll II; Vanessa Y. Carroll.
EIN: 550852518

7069
The Cary Foundation Inc.
(formerly The Bray Cary Foundation, Inc.)
c/o Tinsley & Terry, CPA's
6700 Fairview Rd., Ste. 350
Charlotte, NC 28210-3324
Application address: c/o A. Bray Cary, Jr., P.O. Box 11848, Charleston, WV 25339-1848, tel.: (304) 345-7711

Donors: A. Bray Cary, Jr.; Ripley Athletic Boosters.
Foundation type: Independent foundation.
Financial data (yr. ended 12/31/13): Assets, $3,327,265 (M); expenditures, $286,448; qualifying distributions, $266,732; giving activities include $265,893 for 22 grants (high: $62,965; low: $500).
Purpose and activities: Giving primarily for higher education and Christian churches, and to human service organizations.
Fields of interest: Higher education; Hospital care; Diseases and conditions; Public libraries; Christianity; Human services.

Type of support: Research; Research and evaluation.
Limitations: Applications accepted. Giving primarily in WV. No grants to individuals.
Application information: Application form required.
Initial approach: Letter
Deadline(s): None
Officer: A. Bray Cary, Jr., Pres.
EIN: 562002202

7070
Cary Oil Foundation Inc.
110 Mackenan Dr., Ste. 300
Cary, NC 27511 (919) 460-3197
Contact: Anthony Craig Stephenson, Secy.-Treas. and Dir.

Established in 1996 in North Carolina.
Donors: Cary Oil Co. Inc.; Stanly Lorren.
Foundation type: Company-sponsored foundation.
Financial data (yr. ended 12/31/13): Assets, $3,559,167 (M); gifts received, $200,000; expenditures, $231,592; qualifying distributions, $172,195; giving activities include $170,197 for 23 grants (high: $45,000; low: $200).
Purpose and activities: The foundation supports organizations involved with education, health, hunger, human services, international relief, and Christianity.
Fields of interest: Religion; Human services; Youth development.
Type of support: General support.
Limitations: Applications accepted. Giving primarily in NC. No grants to individuals.
Application information: Application form required.
Initial approach: Letter
Deadline(s): None
Officers and Directors: Harry D. Stephenson, Pres. and Director; Thomas C. Stephenson, V.P. and Director; Anthony Craig Stephenson, Secy.-Treas. and Director.
EIN: 561950150

7071
Wayland H. Cato, Jr. Foundation, Inc.
13777 Ballantyne Corporate Pl., Ste. 300
Charlotte, NC 28277-3422

Established in 1997 in South Carolina.
Donors: Wayland H. Cato; Wayland H. Cato, Jr.
Foundation type: Independent foundation.
Financial data (yr. ended 12/31/13): Assets, $2,807,572 (M); expenditures, $193,336; qualifying distributions, $174,605; giving activities include $174,605 for 24 grants (high: $100,000; low: $100).
Purpose and activities: Giving primarily for education; funding also for health organizations and community foundations.
Fields of interest: Higher education; Foundations; Diseases and conditions.
Limitations: Applications not accepted. Giving primarily in SC, with emphasis on Charleston; some funding also in Charlotte, NC. No grants to individuals.
Application information: Unsolicited requests for funds not accepted.
Officers and Directors: Wayland H. Cato, Jr., Pres. and Director; Clarice Cato Goodyear, V.P. and Director; Theresa Gebhardt, Secy.-Treas. and

Director; John P.D. Cato; Thomas E. Cato; Harold Pratt-Thomas.
EIN: 570988435

7072
Myrtle C. Chaley Trust
1525 W. W.T. Harris Blvd., D1114-044
Charlotte, NC 28262

Foundation type: Independent foundation.
Financial data (yr. ended 12/31/13): Assets, $3,611,993 (M); expenditures, $201,110; qualifying distributions, $157,762; giving activities include $145,330 for 6 grants (high: $38,750; low: $3,228).
Purpose and activities: Giving for higher education and Protestant churches and agencies.
Fields of interest: Undergraduate education; Protestantism; Human services; Retirement housing.
Limitations: Applications not accepted. Giving primarily in SC. No grants to individuals.
Application information: Unsolicited requests for funds not accepted.
Trustee: Wells Fargo Bank, N.A.
EIN: 586325609

7073
Robert Lee & Thomas M. Chastain Charitable Foundation
c/o Wells Fargo Bank N.A., Trust Tax Dept.
1 W. 4th St., 4th Fl., MAC D4000-041
Winston-Salem, NC 27101-3818

Established in 1966 in Florida.
Donor: Robert Lee Chastain†.
Foundation type: Independent foundation.
Financial data (yr. ended 12/31/14): Assets, $3,828,444; expenditures, $205,638; qualifying distributions, $172,376.
Purpose and activities: Grants policy confined to community and publicly-managed agencies with emphasis given to public higher education, programs in the humanities, arts, and sciences, and environmental resource management projects offering benefits to the general population. A few trustee-initiated contributions may exceed these limits.
Fields of interest: Arts and culture; Humanities; Higher education; Environment.
Limitations: Applications not accepted. No support for church-related groups or national charities . No grants to individuals.
Application information: Unsolicited requests for funds not accepted.
Trustee: Wells Fargo Bank, N.A.
EIN: 596171294

7074
Chatham Foundation, Inc.
c/o First Citizens Bank
P.O. Box 29522
Raleigh, NC 27626-0522 9197167347
Application address: c/o First Citizens Bank, Att.: Kirsten H. Janko, 4300 Six Forks Rd., Raleigh, NC 27609, tel.: (919) 716-7576

Established in 1943 in North Carolina.
Foundation type: Independent foundation.

Financial data (yr. ended 12/31/14): Assets, $4,645,529; expenditures, $271,126; qualifying distributions, $250,023.
Purpose and activities: The foundation supports parks, playgrounds, and libraries and organizations involved with arts and culture and Christianity.
Fields of interest: Visual arts; Planetariums; Higher education; Health; Economic development; Christianity; Human services.
Type of support: General support; Capital and infrastructure; Scholarships.
Limitations: Applications accepted. Giving primarily in NC. No grants to individuals (except for employee-related scholarships), or for endowments or research; no loans; no matching gifts.
Application information: Application form required.
  Initial approach: Letter
  Deadline(s): Sept. 1st
  Board meeting date(s): As required
Trustee: First Citizens Bank.
EIN: 560771852

7075
Childtrust Foundation
5151 Glenwood Ave., Ste. 300
Raleigh, NC 27612-3267

Established in 2003 in North Carolina.
Donors: James H. Maynard; Investors Management Corp.
Foundation type: Independent foundation.
Financial data (yr. ended 12/31/14): Assets, $11,265,948; expenditures, $732,568; qualifying distributions, $435,000.
Fields of interest: Arts and culture; Education; Community and economic development.
Limitations: Applications not accepted. Giving primarily in NC. No grants to individuals.
Application information: Unsolicited requests for funds not accepted.
Officers and Directors: James H. Maynard, Pres. and Director; Easter A. Maynard, V.P. and Director; Ronald M. Barbee, Secy.; Richard A. Urquhart III, Treas. and Director; Theodore M. Fowler.
EIN: 200477249

7076
The CJB Foundation Inc.
2502 Gillette Dr.
Wilmington, NC 28403-4862

Established in 1998 in North Carolina.
Donor: Janice Brown Charitable Lead.
Foundation type: Independent foundation.
Financial data (yr. ended 12/31/13): Assets, $5,760,576 (M); gifts received, $407,611; expenditures, $312,390; qualifying distributions, $270,000; giving activities include $270,000 for 15 grants (high: $25,000; low: $5,000).
Fields of interest: Community college education; Foundations; Hospital care; Human services.
Type of support: General support.
Limitations: Applications not accepted. Giving primarily in NC. No grants to individuals.
Application information: Unsolicited requests for funds not accepted.
Officers: Deborah B. Rudisill, Pres.; Amy Brown North, V.P.; Pamela B. Vinson, V.P.
EIN: 562114277

7077
Elmira D. Coate Trust
c/o Wells Fargo Bank, N.A., Trust Tax Dept.
1 W. 4th St., 4th Fl., MAC D4000-041
Winston-Salem, NC 27101-3818

Foundation type: Independent foundation.
Financial data (yr. ended 12/31/14): Assets, $8,159,251; expenditures, $389,239; qualifying distributions, $316,041.
Fields of interest: Health.
Limitations: Applications not accepted. Giving primarily in NJ.
Application information: Unsolicited requests for funds not accepted.
Trustee: Wells Fargo Bank, N.A.
EIN: 226287603

7078
The Coffey Foundation, Inc.
P.O. Box 1161
Lenoir, NC 28645-1170
Contact: Harriet Hailey

Established in 1979 in North Carolina.
Donor: Harold F. Coffey Trust.
Foundation type: Independent foundation.
Financial data (yr. ended 11/30/13): Assets, $8,122,752 (M); expenditures, $525,484; qualifying distributions, $424,683; giving activities include $123,000 for 21 grants (high: $30,000; low: $1,250), and $288,000 for 43 grants to individuals (high: $8,000; low: $1,000).
Purpose and activities: Giving for higher education, youth, and social services; support also for individual scholarships.
Fields of interest: Education; Higher education; Nonprofits; Health; Human services; Food aid; Child welfare.
Type of support: General support; Student aid; Regranting.
Limitations: Giving primarily in Caldwell County, NC; scholarships limited to high school seniors of Caldwell County. No grants to individuals (except for educational scholarships).
Application information: Application forms for student grants available at high schools in Caldwell County, NC. Application form required. Application form required.
  Deadline(s): Apr. 15 for scholarships
Trustees: Rahn Chase; Jennie Goodman Deal; Robert O. Floyd; Leslie D. Hines, Jr.; Betty Lou Miller; Deborah Ashley Smith; Bruce Vanderbloemen.
EIN: 566047501

7079
V. V. Cooke Foundation Corporation
P.O. Box 369
Benson, NC 27504-0202   (919) 207-2841
Contact: David B. Cook
E-mail: merhoff@bellsouth.net

Established in 1947 in Kentucky.
Donors: V.V. Cooke†; Mrs. V.V. Cooke†.
Foundation type: Independent foundation.
Financial data (yr. ended 08/31/13): Assets, $5,460,266 (M); gifts received, $1,000; expenditures, $290,194; qualifying distributions, $214,520; giving activities include $171,000 for 72 grants (high: $19,500; low: $100).

Purpose and activities: Emphasis on religious (primarily Baptist), educational, civic and humanitarian organizations.
Fields of interest: Higher education; Religion; Christianity; Child welfare.
Type of support: Scholarships; Program development; Professorships; Land acquisitions; General support; Equipment; Endowments; Emergency funds; Continuing support; Capital campaigns; Capital and infrastructure; Annual campaigns.
Limitations: Applications accepted. Giving primarily in Louisville, KY. No support for 509(a)(3) organizations.
Application information: Personal interviews not granted.
  Initial approach: Proposal
  Copies of proposal: 8
  Deadline(s): Mid. Jan., Apr., July and Oct.
  Board meeting date(s): Quarterly
  Final notification: Following board meeting
Officers and Directors: Robert L. Hook, Jr., Pres. and Director; Joe D. Cross, Jr., V.P. and Director; Frank P. Hillard, Secy.-Treas. and Director; Theodore L. Merhoff, Exec. Dir.; Trudi C. Cooke; V.V. Cooke, Jr.; Jane C. Cross; June C. Hook.
Number of staff: 1 part-time professional.
EIN: 616033714

7080
The Donald & Elizabeth Cooke Foundation
P.O. Box 1940
Southern Pines, NC 28388-1940

Established in 1980 in North Carolina.
Donor: Elizabeth G. Cooke†.
Foundation type: Independent foundation.
Financial data (yr. ended 12/31/13): Assets, $4,692,821 (M); expenditures, $213,740; qualifying distributions, $199,555; giving activities include $170,500 for 17 grants (high: $70,000; low: $1,000).
Purpose and activities: Giving primarily for education.
Fields of interest: Education; Higher education; Law education; Human services.
Limitations: Applications not accepted. Giving primarily in NC. No grants to individuals.
Application information: Contributes only to pre-selected organizations.
Officers: Sandy G. Patterson, Pres.; Mary MacLauchlin Pope, V.P.; Carol M. White, Secy.
Director: Debbie Riley Hobbs.
EIN: 581408721

7081
The Marion Stedman Covington
Foundation
P.O. Box 29304
Greensboro, NC 27429-9304   (336) 282-0480
Contact: Alexa S. Aycock, Grants Coord.
E-mail: info@mscovingtonfoundation.org; Main URL: http://www.mscovingtonfoundation.org
Grants List: http://
www.mscovingtonfoundation.org/grantees.php

Established in 1986 in North Carolina.
Donor: Marion Stedman Covington†.
Foundation type: Independent foundation.

Financial data (yr. ended 12/31/14): Assets, $8,204,892; expenditures, $400,967; qualifying distributions, $358,397.

Purpose and activities: Giving for the field of historic preservation through financial support and leadership.

Fields of interest: Historic preservation.

Type of support: General support; Matching grants; Continuing support; Capital campaigns; Capital and infrastructure; Equipment; Program development; Convening; Professorships; Publications; Seed money; Fellowships; Scholarships.

Limitations: Applications accepted. Giving primarily in NC. No grants to individuals, or for annual campaigns.

Publications: Annual report (including application guidelines); Grants list; Program policy statement.

Application information: Stapled material or material placed in a bound book will not be accepted. Application form required.

   Initial approach: Submit application form via foundation web site
   Copies of proposal: 1
   Deadline(s): Mar. 1 and Sept. 1
   Board meeting date(s): Fall and spring
   Final notification: June and Nov.

Trustees: Kathleen H. Crockett; Steven J. Frost; Jane C. Hilderbrand; Jo Ramsey Leimanstoll; Steven D. Schuster; Ann C. Sylvia.

Number of staff: 1 part-time professional.

EIN: 566286555

7082
Ethel W. Crawley Memorial Educational Fund

c/o Trust Tax Dept.
P.O. Box 2907
Wilson, NC 27894-2907
Application address: c/o Will Crews, 223 W. Nash St., Wilson, NC 27893-3801, tel.: (252) 246-4935

Established in 2001 in North Carolina.

Donor: Ethel W. Crawley†.

Foundation type: Independent foundation.

Financial data (yr. ended 12/31/13): Assets, $3,517,790 (M); gifts received, $4,208; expenditures, $337,641; qualifying distributions, $280,774; giving activities include $266,274 for 19 grants to individuals (high: $51,160; low: $182).

Purpose and activities: Scholarship awards to individuals who are residents of Halifax County, North Carolina, for at least two years prior to graduation.

Fields of interest: Higher education.

Type of support: Student aid.

Limitations: Applications accepted. Giving primarily in Halifax County, NC.

Application information: Application form required.

   Initial approach: Proposal
   Deadline(s): Mar. 15

Trustee: Branch Banking & Trust Co.

EIN: 566534286

7083
David Boyd Davis Charitable Trust

P.O. Box 184
Spencer, NC 28159-0184

Donor: David Davis†.

Foundation type: Independent foundation.

Financial data (yr. ended 12/31/13): Assets, $1,157,966 (M); expenditures, $263,623; qualifying distributions, $255,189; giving activities include $255,000 for 6 grants (high: $100,000; low: $10,000).

Fields of interest: Community and economic development; Housing development; Human services.

Type of support: General support; Capital campaigns.

Limitations: Applications not accepted. Giving primarily in NC.

Application information: Unsolicited requests for funds not accepted.

Trustee: David B. Jordan.

EIN: 516546438

7084
Tom Davis Fund

P.O. Box 25864
Winston-Salem, NC 27114-5864 (336) 765-4363
Contact: Cheryl Hartman, Exec. Dir.
FAX: (336) 765-1248;
E-mail: cherrylhartman@triad.rr.com

Established in 1988 in North Carolina.

Donor: Thomas H. Davis†.

Foundation type: Independent foundation.

Financial data (yr. ended 12/31/13): Assets, $7,603,796 (M); expenditures, $462,532; qualifying distributions, $355,270; giving activities include $331,020 for 45 grants (high: $50,000; low: $100).

Purpose and activities: The family of the late Thomas H. Davis is committed to furthering his dedication and leadership in support of education, medical education and research, promoting the values and development of youth, especially in aviation, and the advancement of aviation safety.

Fields of interest: Museums; Education; Aerospace engineering; Youth development.

Type of support: Research and evaluation.

Limitations: Applications accepted. Giving primarily in NC; also giving in FL. No grants to individuals.

Application information: Application form required.

   Initial approach: Letter
   Copies of proposal: 8
   Deadline(s): None

Officers: G. Franklin T. Davis, Pres.; Thomas H. Davis, Jr., V.P. and Treas.; Nancy D. McGlothlin, V.P.; Winifred Davis Pierce, V.P.; Juliana D. West, V.P.; Cherryl L. Hartman, Secy. and Exec. Dir.

EIN: 581813100

7085
The Deal Foundation

1525 W. W.T. Harris Blvd.
Charlotte, NC 28262
Application Address: P.O. Drawer G, High Point, NC, 27261, Application Phone: (336) 887-7300

Established in 1989 in North Carolina.

Foundation type: Independent foundation.

Financial data (yr. ended 12/31/14): Assets, $2,847,349 (M); expenditures, $249,984; qualifying distributions, $146,000; giving activities include $145,000 for 20 grants (high: $29,000; low: $1,000).

Fields of interest: Education; Environment; Human services.

Limitations: Applications accepted. Giving primarily in NC.

Application information: Application form required.

   Initial approach: Letter
   Deadline(s): None

Officers: Doris P. Deal, Secy.; R.L. Deal, Treas.

EIN: 581842530

7086
John G. Duncan Trust

c/o Wells Fargo Bank, N.A.
1 W. 4th St., 4th Fl., MAC D4000-041
Winston-Salem, NC 27101-3818
Contact: Jim Luensmann; Colleen Lynch
Application address: c/o Wells Fargo Bank, N.A., 1740 Broadway, MAC C7300-483, Denver, CO 80274, tel.: (720) 947-6732; E-mail for Colleen Lynch: colleen.f.lynch@wellsfargo.com; Main URL: https://www.wellsfargo.com/privatefoundationgrants/duncan

Established in 1955 in Colorado.

Donor: John G. Duncan†.

Foundation type: Independent foundation.

Financial data (yr. ended 12/31/13): Assets, $7,110,264 (M); expenditures, $411,192; qualifying distributions, $341,442; giving activities include $317,500 for 146 grants (high: $5,000; low: $500).

Fields of interest: Arts and culture; Education; Health; Religion; Human services.

Type of support: Capital campaigns; Capital and infrastructure; Equipment; Emergency funds; Program development; Seed money; Research.

Limitations: Applications accepted. Giving limited to CO. No support for other grantmaking organizations. No grants to individuals, or for general operating expenses or endowments.

Publications: Application guidelines.

Application information: See trust web site for complete application guidelines and procedures. Application form required.

   Initial approach: Submit online application via trust web site
   Copies of proposal: 1
   Deadline(s): Jan. 31, Apr. 30, July 31, and Oct. 31
   Board meeting date(s): Feb., May, Aug. and Nov.
   Final notification: Generally within 60 days of each deadline

Trustee: Wells Fargo Bank, N.A.

Number of staff: None.

EIN: 846016555

7087
Eddy Foundation

(formerly Eddy Foundation Charitable Trust)
c/o Wells Fargo Bank, N.A.
1 W. 4th St., 4th Fl., MAC D4000-041
Winston-Salem, NC 27101-3818
Application addresses: For University of Minnesota-Duluth students: Dept. of Communication Sciences and Disorders, University of Minnesota, 221 Bohannon Hall, 10 University Dr., Duluth, MN 55812-2496; For non-University students and special situations: Edwin H. Eddy Foundation Scholarship, Northwest Bank Minnesota North, N.A., Trust Dept., P.O. Box 488, Duluth, MN 55801-0488

Established in 1982 in Minnesota.

Donor: Edwin H. Eddy, Jr.†.

Foundation type: Independent foundation.
Financial data (yr. ended 06/30/13): Assets, $3,228,582 (M); expenditures, $218,513; qualifying distributions, $179,886; giving activities include $164,631 for 2 grants (high: $160,131; low: $4,500).
Purpose and activities: Grants for research into and treatment of individuals with speech or hearing disorders. Also awards scholarships for students studying in the field of communication disorders: 1st priority for Duluth, MN, area residents at the University of Minnesota, Duluth; 2nd priority for area residents at other institutions; and 3rd priority for non-residents at the University of Minnesota, Duluth.
Fields of interest: Special needs education; Speech and hearing rehabilitation; Diseases and conditions; People with disabilities.
Type of support: Continuing support; Grants to individuals; Matching grants; Convening; Research; Professorships; Research and evaluation; Curriculum development; Internships; Scholarships; Technical assistance; Student aid.
Limitations: Applications accepted. Giving limited to the Duluth, MN, area. No grants for capital improvements or salaries.
Publications: Application guidelines; Informational brochure (including application guidelines); Program policy statement.
Application information: Application form required for scholarships.
  Initial approach: Proposal
  Copies of proposal: 8
  Deadline(s): July 10 for scholarships
Trustees: Rodney Edwards; Elizabeth Simonson; Barbara A. Spencer; Wells Fargo Bank, N.A.
EIN: 416242226

7088
Harold T. Edgar Charitable Trust
1525 W. W.T. Harris Blvd. D1114-044
Charlotte, NC   28262

Foundation type: Independent foundation.
Financial data (yr. ended 12/31/13): Assets, $7,035,701 (M); expenditures, $198,177; qualifying distributions, $138,725; giving activities include $120,000 for 6 grants (high: $32,000; low: $14,000).
Fields of interest: Graduate and professional education; Protestantism; Theology; Human services; Youth services; Scouting programs.
Limitations: Applications not accepted. Giving primarily in NJ. No grants to individuals.
Application information: Contributes only to pre-selected organizations.
Trustee: Wells Fargo Bank, N.A.
EIN: 226023917

7089
Elks of Los Angeles Foundation
c/o Wells Fargo Bank, N.A., Trust Tax Dept.
1 W. 4th St., 4th Fl., MAC D4000-041
Winston-Salem, NC   27101-3818

Established in 1929 in California.
Donors: Louis J. Christopher Trust; Fred and Lucille Hirsch Foundation.
Foundation type: Independent foundation.
Financial data (yr. ended 12/31/13): Assets, $4,673,061 (M); gifts received, $123,856; expenditures, $407,530; qualifying distributions, $355,126; giving activities include $332,600 for 34 grants (high: $16,700; low: $9,200).
Purpose and activities: Giving limited to community-based charities in the greater Los Angeles, CA, area.
Fields of interest: Diseases and conditions; Food aid; Family services; Child welfare; Youth services; Homeless services.
Type of support: Research; Research and evaluation.
Limitations: Applications not accepted. Giving primarily in CA. No grants to individuals.
Application information: Contributions limited to local charities already known to the foundation; requests for funds from ineligible organizations not considered.
Trustee: Wells Fargo Bank, N.A.
EIN: 956019849

7090
The John G. B., Jr. and Jane R. Ellison Family Foundation, Inc.
P.O. Box 29027
Greensboro, NC   27429-9027

Established in 1996 in North Carolina.
Donors: Elizabeth M. Ellison; John G.B. Ellison, Jr.; The Ellison Company, Inc.
Foundation type: Independent foundation.
Financial data (yr. ended 12/31/13): Assets, $14,146,605 (M); expenditures, $178,317; qualifying distributions, $178,119; giving activities include $160,450 for 13 grants (high: $66,500; low: $200).
Fields of interest: Arts education; Art museums; Education; Higher education; Nonprofits; Protestantism; Human services; Child welfare; Low-income and poor people.
Type of support: Regranting.
Limitations: Applications not accepted. Giving primarily in NC. No grants to individuals.
Application information: Contributes only to pre-selected organizations.
Officers: John G.B. Ellison, Jr., Pres. and Treas.; Jane R. Ellison, Secy.; Elizabeth M. Ellison, Exec. Dir.
EIN: 561981120

7091
Emma Barnsley Foundation
c/o Wells Fargo Bank, N.A., Trust Tax Dept.
1 W. 4th St., 4th Fl., MAC D4000-041
Winston-Salem, NC   27101-3818
E-mail: grantadministration@wellsfargo.com;
Application Address: c/o Wells Fargo Bank, N.A., 4101 JBS Pkwy., Odessa, TX, 79762-8131, Application Phone: (432) 498-4400; Main
URL: https://www.wellsfargo.com/privatefoundationgrants/barnsley

Donor: Emma Barnsley†.
Foundation type: Independent foundation.
Financial data (yr. ended 12/31/14): Assets, $3,353,812 (M); expenditures, $191,868; qualifying distributions, $147,803; giving activities include $140,000 for 14 grants (high: $30,000; low: $3,000).
Purpose and activities: To promote the prevention of cruelty to animals and for the study, care, protection, and preservation of animals, both domestic and wild, and their environment.
Fields of interest: Education; Environment; Animal welfare.
Limitations: Applications accepted. Giving primarily in TX.
Application information: See foundation website for complete application guidelines. Application form required.
  Initial approach: Proposal
  Deadline(s): Aug. 31
Trustee: Wells Fargo Bank, N.A.
EIN: 264785578

7092
The Eplee Foundation, Inc.
9059 Walkers Ferry Rd.
Charlotte, NC   28214-3339

Established in 1991 in North Carolina.
Donors: Herbert W. Eplee, Sr.; Shirley J. Eplee.
Foundation type: Independent foundation.
Financial data (yr. ended 12/31/13): Assets, $4,225,556 (M); expenditures, $160,907; qualifying distributions, $117,500; giving activities include $117,500 for 15 grants (high: $20,000; low: $1,000).
Purpose and activities: Giving primarily for Christian evangelism.
Fields of interest: Education; Religion; Human services.
Limitations: Applications not accepted. Giving primarily in NC. No grants to individuals.
Application information: Unsolicited requests for funds not accepted.
Officers: Herbert W. Eplee, Sr., Pres.; Shirley J. Eplee, Secy.
Directors: Gordon Kelly Eplee; Herbert W. Eplee, Jr.; Melvin Glen Eplee.
EIN: 561761082

7093
Herschel H. & Cornelia N. Everett Foundation
c/o Wells Fargo Bank N.A., Trust Tax Dept.
1 W. 4th St., 4th Fl., MAC D4000-041
Winston-Salem, NC   27101-3818

Established in 2001 in North Carolina.
Foundation type: Independent foundation.
Financial data (yr. ended 06/30/14): Assets, $4,943,953 (M); expenditures, $207,114; qualifying distributions, $164,558; giving activities include $148,000 for 8 grants (high: $33,000; low: $2,000).
Fields of interest: Education; Graduate and professional education; Christianity; Theology.
Type of support: General support.
Limitations: Applications not accepted. Giving primarily in NC; some funding also in VA. No grants to individuals.
Application information: Contributes only to pre-selected organizations.
Trustees: Paul B. Wyche; Wells Fargo Bank, N.A.
EIN: 566093697

7094
Evernham Family-Racing for a Reason
(formerly Racing for a Reason)
130 Infield Ct.
Mooresville, NC 28117-8026

Established in 1997 in North Carolina.
Donors: Jeffrey M. Gordon; Evernham Motorsports, LLC; Freightliner, LLC; Daimler Trucks North America, LLC; Phillips Motorsports Marketing; Raymond D. Evernham, Jr.; True Speed Enterprises, Inc.; MSC Industrial; Mary Evernham; Ron Pratte; Ingersoll Racing Co.; Ryan Newman Motorsports, Inc.
Foundation type: Independent foundation.
Financial data (yr. ended 12/31/13): Assets, $21,573 (M); gifts received, $375,090; expenditures, $381,630; qualifying distributions, $349,043; giving activities include $349,043 for 15 grants (high: $205,268; low: $100).
Fields of interest: Arts and culture; Health; Autism; Human services; Children.
Type of support: General support.
Limitations: Applications not accepted. Giving primarily in NC. No grants to individuals.
Application information: Contributes only to pre-selected organizations.
Officer: Raymond D. Evernham, Jr., Pres.
Directors: Ann Eaton; Raymond J. Evernham; William Evernham.
EIN: 562053289

7095
Freeman E. Fairfield - Meeker Charitable Trust
c/o Wells Fargo Bank, N.A.
1 W. 4th Fl., 4th Fl., MAC D4000-041
Winston-Salem, NC 27101-3818
Application address: c/o Diane Dunham, P.O. Box 2302, Meeker, CO 81641-2302, tel.: (702) 878-4466

Established in 1969 in Colorado.
Donor: Freeman E. Fairfield†.
Foundation type: Independent foundation.
Financial data (yr. ended 11/30/13): Assets, $4,397,241 (M); expenditures, $222,417; qualifying distributions, $187,348; giving activities include $158,642 for 31 grants (high: $50,000; low: $800).
Purpose and activities: Support for programs within Meeker and Rio Blanco County, Colorado, and scholarships for graduates of Meeker High School.
Fields of interest: Historic preservation; Education; Public administration; Judaism; Human services.
Type of support: General support; Student aid.
Limitations: Applications accepted. Giving limited to Meeker and Rio Blanco County, CO.
Application information: Scholarship application form available from the Trust and from the Meeker High School guidance counselor. Scholarships are available only to graduates of Meeker High School. Application form required.
  Initial approach: Letter
  Copies of proposal: 6
  Deadline(s): For grants more than $1500: Oct. 1 and Apr. 1
  Board meeting date(s): As necessary
Trustee: Wells Fargo Bank, N.A.
EIN: 846068906

7096
Smith Family Foundation
(formerly Liberty Hosiery Mills Foundation)
c/o Trust Company of the South
P.O. Box 1898
Burlington, NC 27216-1898

Established in 1952 in North Carolina.
Donors: A.S. Cooper Charitable Lead Unitrust; William H. Smith.
Foundation type: Independent foundation.
Financial data (yr. ended 06/30/13): Assets, $4,714,533 (M); expenditures, $256,459; qualifying distributions, $215,441; giving activities include $206,654 for 47 grants (high: $25,000; low: $577).
Fields of interest: Arts and culture; Education; Higher education; Health; Diseases and conditions; Christianity.
Type of support: General support.
Limitations: Applications not accepted. Giving limited to Alamance, Orange, Guilford, Durham, Caswell, Chatham, Randolph, Montgomery, and Moore counties, NC. No grants to individuals.
Application information: Contributes only to pre-selected organizations.
Officer: James H. Smith, Jr., Exec. Dir.
Trustees: J. Harold Smith; The Trust Co. of the South.
EIN: 566040787

7097
First Gaston Foundation, Inc.
(formerly Myers-Ti-Caro Foundation, Inc.)
P.O. Box 2696
Gastonia, NC 28053-2696 (704) 864-9242
Contact: B. Frank Matthews II, Chair.

Established in 1950 in North Carolina.
Donors: Textiles, Inc.; Threads, Inc.
Foundation type: Independent foundation.
Financial data (yr. ended 09/30/14): Assets, $10,277,864 (M); expenditures, $576,296; qualifying distributions, $492,386; giving activities include $226,377 for 33 grants (high: $63,800; low: $300), and $193,530 for 35 grants to individuals (high: $16,000; low: $429).
Purpose and activities: Grants for higher and secondary education, including scholarships to high school seniors in Gaston County, North Carolina; support also for social services and youth, religious welfare, health and hospitals, and arts and culture.
Fields of interest: Arts and culture; Secondary education; Higher education; Nonprofits; Health; Hospital care; Diseases and conditions; Human services; Child welfare.
Type of support: Capital campaigns; Capital and infrastructure; Scholarships; Student aid; Regranting.
Limitations: Giving limited to Gaston County, NC.
Application information: Application form required for Gaston County high school senior scholarships.
  Initial approach: Letter
  Copies of proposal: 1
  Deadline(s): Mar. 1 and Oct. 1
  Board meeting date(s): May and Dec.
  Final notification: May 31 and Dec. 31
Officers and Trustees: B. Frank Matthews II, Chair. and Trustee; Tom D. Efird, Vice-Chair. and Trustee; Robert P. Caldwell, Jr., Secy.; Charlton K. Torrence, Jr., Treas.; Mary Adams; Barbara Myers Cozort; Albert G. Myers, Jr.; Albert G. Myers III; James C. Windham, Jr.

Number of staff: 1 full-time support.
EIN: 560770083

7098
Clara Helen Firth Charitable Trust
(formerly Clara Helen Firth Testamentary Trust)
c/o Wells Fargo Bank, N.A.
1 W. 4th St., 4th Fl., Mac D4000-041
Winston-Salem, NC 27101-3818

Foundation type: Independent foundation.
Financial data (yr. ended 02/28/15): Assets, $6,349,265 (M); expenditures, $380,491; qualifying distributions, $314,678; giving activities include $295,967 for 5 grants (high: $207,177; low: $14,798).
Fields of interest: Animal welfare; Human services.
Limitations: Applications not accepted. Giving on a national basis.
Application information: Unsolicited requests for funds not accepted.
Trustee: Wells Fargo Bank, N.A.
EIN: 956698210

7099
Flowers Charitable Foundation
1525 W. WT Harris Blvd., D1114-044
Charlotte, NC 28262
E-mail: grantsadministration@wellsfargo.com;
Application address: c/o Andrea Duggins, 1 W. 4th St., 2nd Fl., Winston-Salem, NC 27101, tel.: (855) 241-6645

Established in 1982 in New Jersey.
Donor: Frank S. Flowers†.
Foundation type: Independent foundation.
Financial data (yr. ended 12/31/13): Assets, $3,456,866 (M); expenditures, $203,132; qualifying distributions, $165,720; giving activities include $152,000 for 28 grants (high: $15,000; low: $2,500).
Purpose and activities: Support for nonprofit hospitals, Protestant churches, youth groups, and clubs in Gloucester and/or Salem counties, NJ; support also for Gloucester County, NJ public high schools, in the form of scholarship funds for college or vocational/technical studies, with preference given to Paulsboro High School graduates.
Fields of interest: Education; Health; Hospital care; Protestantism; Child welfare; Child development; People with disabilities.
Type of support: General support; Capital and infrastructure; Equipment; Scholarships.
Limitations: Applications accepted. Giving primarily in NJ, with emphasis on Gloucester and Salem counties and the boroughs of Paulsboro and Wenonah; some giving also in Philadelphia, PA. No grants to individuals.
Application information: Application form required.
  Initial approach: E-mail
  Deadline(s): Mar. 15
  Board meeting date(s): May
Trustee: Wells Fargo Bank, N.A.
EIN: 226318172

7100
Ed & Claude Fortson Charitable Trust
c/o Wells Fargo Bank, N.A.
1525 W. WT Harris Blvd., D1114-044
Charlotte, NC 28262

Established in 1987 in Georgia.
Donor: Edred Fortson†.
Foundation type: Independent foundation.
Financial data (yr. ended 12/31/13): Assets, $8,081,905 (M); expenditures, $365,791; qualifying distributions, $259,030; giving activities include $228,500 for 12 grants (high: $42,000; low: $5,000).
Purpose and activities: Giving primarily for education, health care, health associations, and human services.
Fields of interest: Education; Health; Diseases and conditions; Cancers; Christianity; Camps; Human services.
Type of support: General support; Research.
Limitations: Applications not accepted. Giving primarily in Henry County, GA. No grants to individuals.
Application information: Unsolicited requests for funds not accepted.
Trustee: Wells Fargo Bank, N.A.
Advisory Committee: James L. Henderson, Jr.; J.W. Martin; Keith McBrayer.
EIN: 586201850

7101
F. Gordon Foster Charitable Trust
1 W. 4th St., D4000-041
Winston-Salem, NC 27101

Foundation type: Independent foundation.
Financial data (yr. ended 12/31/14): Assets, $4,023,874 (M); expenditures, $227,359; qualifying distributions, $183,339; giving activities include $168,700 for 5 grants (high: $44,300; low: $31,100).
Fields of interest: Health; Religion; Human services.
Limitations: Applications not accepted.
Application information: Unsolicited requests for funds not accepted.
Trustees: Malcolm B. Wernik; Wells Fargo Bank, N.A.
EIN: 237848106

7102
The Foundation for Christian Arts, Pastoral Development and the Poor, Inc.
1320A Airlie Rd.
Wilmington, NC 28403-3727

Established in 2003 in North Carolina.
Donor: Michael E. Lopez.
Foundation type: Independent foundation.
Financial data (yr. ended 12/31/13): Assets, $697,663 (M); gifts received, $170,000; expenditures, $150,525; qualifying distributions, $150,350; giving activities include $109,500 for 6 grants (high: $44,500; low: $3,000), and $40,850 for 5 grants to individuals (high: $20,000; low: $850).
Fields of interest: Religion.
Type of support: Grants to individuals.
Limitations: Applications not accepted. Giving primarily in NC.
Application information: Unsolicited requests for funds not accepted.
Officers: Michael E. Lopez, Pres.; Kent Henry, V.P.; Julie Lopez, Secy.-Treas.
EIN: 050593068

7103
Fox Family Foundation, Inc.
2451 Croasdaile Farm Pkwy., Ste. 101
Durham, NC 27705-1466 (919) 383-5575
Contact: David D. Beischer, Exec. Dir.
FAX: (919) 383-5577;
E-mail: dbeischer@foxfoundation.org

Established in 1991 in North Carolina.
Donors: Frances Hill Fox†; Fox Charitable Lead Unitrust.
Foundation type: Independent foundation.
Financial data (yr. ended 12/31/13): Assets, $10,777,386 (M); gifts received, $330,560; expenditures, $532,918; qualifying distributions, $417,318; giving activities include $409,521 for 45 + grants (high: $35,000).
Purpose and activities: Giving for health care, family and youth services, the arts, human services, and education.
Fields of interest: Arts and culture; Education; Pharmacies; Mental health care; Diseases and conditions; Agriculture; Housing development; Human services; Youth development.
Type of support: General support; Pro bono consulting services; Matching grants; Continuing support; Capacity-building and technical assistance; Annual campaigns; Capital campaigns; Capital and infrastructure; Equipment; Endowments; Internships; Scholarships.
Limitations: Applications accepted. Giving limited to organizations that are headquartered in Durham, Orange, and Wake counties, NC. No support for religious or political organizations. No grants to individuals or for expenditure responsibility.
Publications: Application guidelines; Grants list.
Application information: Application form required.
   Initial approach: Letter of inquiry or telephone
   Copies of proposal: 1
   Deadline(s): Sept. 1
   Board meeting date(s): 2nd Wed. in May and Nov.
   Final notification: Dec. 1
Officer and Directors: David D. Beischer, Exec. Dir.; Susan Fox Beischer; John W. Mallard; A. William Kennon; J. David Ross.
Number of staff: 1 full-time professional; 1 part-time support.
EIN: 561756144

7104
Peter & Mildred Galanti Foundation
c/o Wells Fargo Bank, N.A.
1 W. 4th St., 4th Fl., MAC D4000-041
Winston-Salem, NC 27101-3818

Foundation type: Independent foundation.
Financial data (yr. ended 06/30/14): Assets, $3,387,731 (M); expenditures, $178,606; qualifying distributions, $146,728; giving activities include $135,836 for 11 grants (high: $73,352; low: $1,358).
Fields of interest: Education; Catholicism; Youth development.
Limitations: Applications not accepted. Giving primarily in NJ and RI. No grants to individuals.
Application information: Unsolicited requests for funds not accepted.
Trustee: Wells Fargo Bank, N.A.
EIN: 237981682

7105
Gambrell Family Foundation
6100 Fairview Rd., Ste. 640
Charlotte, NC 28210-4267 (704) 553-8296
Contact: Sarah Belk Gambrell, Pres.

Established in 1998 in North Carolina.
Donor: Sarah Belk Gambrell.
Foundation type: Independent foundation.
Financial data (yr. ended 12/31/14): Assets, $1,158,103 (M); expenditures, $248,257; qualifying distributions, $246,879; giving activities include $245,500 for 13 grants (high: $40,000; low: $500).
Fields of interest: Education; Protestantism; Youth development.
Type of support: General support; Scholarships.
Limitations: Applications accepted. Giving primarily in NC and VA; some giving in NY and SC.
Application information: Application form required.
   Initial approach: Letter
   Deadline(s): None
Officers: Sarah Belk Gambrell, Pres.; Sally Gambrell, V.P.; Larry Estridge, Secy.
EIN: 562120679

7106
Gambrill Foundation
1525 W. WT Harris Blvd., D1114-044
Charlotte, NC 28262-8522 (336) 747-8002
E-mail: grantadministration@wellsfargo.com; Main URL: https://www.wellsfargo.com/privatefoundationgrants/gambrill

Donor: Anne J. Gambrill†.
Foundation type: Independent foundation.
Financial data (yr. ended 12/31/13): Assets, $4,769,242 (M); expenditures, $235,905; qualifying distributions, $204,458; giving activities include $176,500 for 21 grants (high: $25,000; low: $2,000).
Fields of interest: Music; Historic preservation; Education; Higher education; Graduate and professional education; Nonprofits; Health; Hospice care; Pediatrics; Engineering; Libraries; Interfaith; Human services; Food aid.
Type of support: Regranting.
Limitations: Applications accepted. Giving primarily in SC. No grants to individuals.
Application information: See foundation website for complete application guidelines. Application form required.
   Initial approach: Proposal
   Deadline(s): Apr. 1 and Sept. 15
Trustees: Lia F. Albergotti; Fred L. Foster, Jr.; Ann D. Herbert; Robert M. Rainey; F. McKinnon Wilkinson; Wells Fargo Bank, N.A.
EIN: 576029520

7107
Edwin B. Garrigues Trust
c/o Wells Fargo Bank, N.A.
1525 W. WT Harris Blvd., D1114-044
Charlotte, NC 28288-1161 8003523705
Application address: c/o Duane Morris, LLP, 30 S. 17th St., Philadelphia, PA 19103-4196, tel.: (215) 979-1927

Established in 1922 in Pennsylvania.
Foundation type: Independent foundation.

Financial data (yr. ended 12/31/14): Assets, $4,116,587; expenditures, $236,355; qualifying distributions, $180,037.
Purpose and activities: Giving primarily for music scholarship assistance.
Fields of interest: Music.
Type of support: Scholarships.
Limitations: Applications accepted. Giving primarily in the Philadelphia, PA, area. No grants to individuals.
Application information: Application form required.
  Deadline(s): Feb. 15
Trustees: Frank G. Cooper; Wells Fargo Bank, N.A.
EIN: 236220616

7108
Garrow Family Charitable Foundation

c/o Wells Fargo Bank, N.A., Trust Tax Dept.
1 W. 4th St., 4th Fl., MAC D4000-041
Winston-Salem, NC 27101-3818

Established in 2009 in Oregon.
Foundation type: Independent foundation.
Financial data (yr. ended 12/31/14): Assets, $1,555,710 (M); expenditures, $193,582; qualifying distributions, $173,473; giving activities include $166,431 for 6 grants (high: $27,739; low: $27,738).
Fields of interest: Education; Diseases and conditions; Religion.
Limitations: Applications not accepted.
Application information: Unsolicited requests for funds not accepted.
Trustee: Wells Fargo Bank, N.A.
EIN: 326099554

7109
Mary W. Geschick Charitable Trust

1525 W. WT Harris Blvd., D1114-044
Charlotte, NC 28262-8522

Donor: Mary W. Geschick Res. Trust.
Foundation type: Independent foundation.
Financial data (yr. ended 12/31/14): Assets, $8,161,275; expenditures, $415,951; qualifying distributions, $322,158.
Fields of interest: Health; Religion; Human services.
Limitations: Applications not accepted. Giving primarily in Philadelphia, PA.
Application information: Unsolicited requests for funds not accepted.
Trustee: Wells Fargo Bank, N.A.
EIN: 464254341

7110
Marguerite L. Gilmore Charitable Foundation

c/o Wells Fargo Bank, N.A., Trust Tax
! W. 4th St., 4th Fl.MAC D4000-041
Winston-Salem, NC 27101-3818

Donor: Marguerite L. Gilmore.
Foundation type: Independent foundation.
Financial data (yr. ended 12/31/14): Assets, $4,048,663; expenditures, $416,563; qualifying distributions, $372,104.
Fields of interest: Arts education; Education.
Limitations: Applications not accepted. Giving primarily in MN.

Application information: Unsolicited requests for funds not accepted.
Trustee: Wells Fargo Bank, N.A.
EIN: 262313618

7111
The Carrie E. and Lena V. Glenn Foundation, Inc.

1552 Union Rd., Ste. D
Gastonia, NC 28054-5582   (704) 867-0296
Contact: Barbara H. Vourhees
FAX: (704) 867-4496;
E-mail: glennfnd@bellsouth.net; Main URL: http://www.theglennfoundation.org

Established in 1971 in North Carolina.
Donors: Carrie Eugenia Glenn†; Lena Viola Glenn†.
Foundation type: Independent foundation.
Financial data (yr. ended 06/30/13): Assets, $6,797,001 (M); expenditures, $427,522; qualifying distributions, $384,170; giving activities include $315,000 for 28 grants (high: $65,000; low: $2,450).
Purpose and activities: To promote and support the charitable spirit of the Glenn sisters by helping people in need through grants for religious, health, educational and community needs.
Fields of interest: Arts and culture; Elementary and secondary education; Environment; Christianity; Human services; Child welfare; Children and youth; Infants and toddlers; Children; Adolescents; Adults; Young adults; Seniors; Females; Female children and youth; Female infants and toddlers; Female adults; Males; Male children and youth; Male infants and toddlers; Male adults; Single parents; Ethnic and racial groups; People of African descent; People of Latin American descent; Homeless people; Low-income and poor people; Victims of crime and abuse; People with disabilities; People with physical disabilities; People with psychosocial disabilities; People with HIV/AIDS; Terminally ill people; Substance abusers.
Type of support: General support; Matching grants; Capital and infrastructure; Equipment; Program development; Seed money.
Limitations: Applications accepted. Giving only to Gaston County, NC, or to out-of-county organizations whose programs benefit citizens of Gaston County, NC. No multi-year grants, planning grants, or fund-raising campaigns; no grants to individuals; no grants for scholarships.
Application information: Complete application guidelines available on foundation web site.
  Initial approach: Request application form by using form on foundation web site
  Board meeting date(s): Quarterly
Officers and Directors: Julia M. Shovelin, Chair. and Director; H. Timothy Efird II, Vice-Chair. and Director; Emily C. Craig, Secy. and Director; Charles W. Gallman, Treas. and Director; Robert H. Collis; John L. Frye; Laura G. Lineberger.
Number of staff: 1 part-time professional.
EIN: 201808211

7112
Daniel Gordon Family Foundation

151 Easton Dr.
Mooresville, NC 28117-6012

Established in 1996 in Colorado.
Donor: Edward Gordon Charitable Lead Trust.

Foundation type: Independent foundation.
Financial data (yr. ended 12/31/13): Assets, $2,462,132 (M); gifts received, $231,623; expenditures, $162,951; qualifying distributions, $156,935; giving activities include $156,935 for 51 grants (high: $25,250; low: $150).
Fields of interest: Education; Philanthropy; Health.
Type of support: General support.
Limitations: Applications not accepted. Giving primarily in NC. No grants to individuals.
Application information: Unsolicited requests for funds not accepted.
Officers: Daniel Gordon, Pres. and Treas.; Linda Gordon, Secy.
EIN: 841333330

7113
The Griffin Endowment

1850 E. Third St., Ste. 205
Charlotte, NC 28204-3297
Contact: Haynes G. Griffin, Secy.-Treas.

Established in 1990 in North Carolina.
Donors: Clarence A. Griffin†; Elizabeth S. Griffin.
Foundation type: Independent foundation.
Financial data (yr. ended 06/30/13): Assets, $3,505,099 (M); expenditures, $200,664; qualifying distributions, $166,112; giving activities include $166,112 for 13 grants (high: $40,000; low: $200).
Purpose and activities: Giving primarily for education and human services.
Fields of interest: Elementary education; Secondary education; Nursing care; Family planning; Agriculture; Protestantism; Human services; Food aid.
Type of support: General support.
Limitations: Applications accepted. Giving primarily in Charlotte, NC. No grants to individuals.
Application information:
  Initial approach: Letter
  Deadline(s): None
  Board meeting date(s): Quarterly
Officers and Directors: Clarence A. Griffin III, Pres. and Director; Jeffrey Griffin, V.P.; Haynes G. Griffin, Secy.-Treas.
Number of staff: 1 part-time support.
EIN: 561687879

7114
James and Pauline Hackbarth Foundation, Inc.

6654 Castlebrook Way
Ocean Isle Beach, NC 28469-5620

Established in 2005 in New Jersey.
Donor: James P. Hackbarth†.
Foundation type: Independent foundation.
Financial data (yr. ended 06/30/14): Assets, $5,421,386 (M); expenditures, $576,512; qualifying distributions, $518,407; giving activities include $441,110 for 5 grants (high: $408,610; low: $2,500).
Fields of interest: Education; Public libraries.
Limitations: Applications not accepted. Giving primarily in NJ. No grants to individuals.
Application information: Contributes only to pre-selected organizations.
Officers: James Hackbarth, Chair. and Pres.; Leonard Lesniak, Vice-Chair. and Treas.; Marc Keane, Secy.; Joe Englert, Treas.

Trustee: Mona Rodriguez.
EIN: 200521089

7115
Joseph A. & Edith D. Hamill Fund
c/o Wells Fargo Bank, N.A. - Trust Tax Dept.
1 W. 4th St., 4th Fl., MAC D4000-041
Winston-Salem, NC 27101-3818

Foundation type: Independent foundation.
Financial data (yr. ended 12/31/13): Assets, $5,457,782 (M); expenditures, $289,734; qualifying distributions, $241,642; giving activities include $224,759 for 4 grants (high: $89,903; low: $44,952).
Fields of interest: Wildlife biodiversity; Cancers; Human services; People with vision impairments.
Limitations: Applications not accepted. No grants to individuals.
Application information: Contributes only to pre-selected organizations.
Trustee: Wells Fargo Bank, N.A.
EIN: 236283449

7116
Haney Foundation Trust
1525 W. WT Harris Blvd., D1114-044
Charlotte, NC 28262

Established in 2012 in Pennsylvania.
Donor: Haney Foundation Trust.
Foundation type: Independent foundation.
Financial data (yr. ended 12/31/13): Assets, $6,934,681 (M); expenditures, $406,453; qualifying distributions, $335,660; giving activities include $316,681 for 22 grants (high: $219,243; low: $658).
Fields of interest: Education; Protestantism; Human services.
Limitations: Applications not accepted. Giving primarily in Philadelphia, PA. No grants to individuals.
Application information: Contributes only to pre-selected organizations.
Trustee: Wells Fargo Bank, N.A.
EIN: 462078386

7117
Gibson T. Harrison Trust
c/o Wells Fargo Bank, N.A., Trust Tax Dept.
1 W. 4th St., 4th Fl., MAC D4000-041
Winston-Salem, NC 27101-3818

Foundation type: Independent foundation.
Financial data (yr. ended 12/31/14): Assets, $4,864,511; expenditures, $273,696; qualifying distributions, $232,002.
Fields of interest: Community service; Human services.
Limitations: Applications not accepted. Giving primarily in PA. No grants to individuals.
Application information: Contributes only to pre-selected organizations.
Trustee: Wells Fargo Bank, N.A.
EIN: 236211568

7118
Harvest Time Foundation
806 N. Post Rd.
Shelby, NC 28150-4247 (704) 482-3456

Donors: Herman D. Mims Living Trust; Machine Builders & Design, Inc.
Foundation type: Independent foundation.
Financial data (yr. ended 12/31/13): Assets, $4,464,008 (M); gifts received, $416,000; expenditures, $1,346,756; qualifying distributions, $267,800; giving activities include $267,800 for 11 grants (high: $248,000; low: $600).
Fields of interest: Christianity.
Type of support: General support.
Limitations: Applications accepted. Giving primarily in NC.
Application information: Application form required.
 Initial approach: Proposal
 Deadline(s): None
Trustee: Bank of the Ozarks.
Board Members: Steve Hyde; Douglas King; David Mims; Darryl Mims; Teresa McFarland; Charlie Marshall; Barry Shearer.
EIN: 061700689

7119
The Harvey-McNairy Foundation Inc.
P.O. Box 189
Kinston, NC 28502-0189

Established in 2007 in North Carolina.
Donors: Harvey Enterprises Inc.; Tidewater Transit Co.; Mallard Oil Company.
Foundation type: Company-sponsored foundation.
Financial data (yr. ended 12/31/13): Assets, $3,898,624 (M); gifts received, $275,000; expenditures, $204,178; qualifying distributions, $168,500; giving activities include $168,500 for 15 grants (high: $75,000; low: $1,000).
Purpose and activities: The foundation supports nonprofit organizations involved with religion.
Fields of interest: Religion; Christianity.
Type of support: General support.
Limitations: Applications not accepted.
Application information: Unsolicited requests for funds not accepted.
Officers: Leigh H. McNairy, Pres.; John O. McNairy, Secy.-Treas.
EIN: 208686982

7120
Hayden-Harman Foundation
c/o J. Patrick Harman
P.O. Box 1762
Burlington, NC 27216-1762 3362288138

Established in 2000 in North Carolina.
Foundation type: Independent foundation.
Financial data (yr. ended 12/31/14): Assets, $8,610,689; expenditures, $547,713; qualifying distributions, $347,907.
Purpose and activities: Giving primarily for the arts, education, health, and youth and social services.
Fields of interest: Arts and culture; Education; Higher education; Breast cancer; Community and economic development; Human services; Youth development.
Type of support: Individual development.
Limitations: Applications not accepted. Giving primarily in NC. No grants to individuals.

Application information: Unsolicited requests for funds not accepted.
 Board meeting date(s): Varies
Officers: J. Patrick Harman, Pres.; David L. Harman, V.P.; Patrick H. Harman, V.P.; Susan S. Harman, Secy.; Phoebe N. Harman, Treas.
Number of staff: 2 full-time support.
EIN: 562180022

7121
The Hayes Family Charitable Trust
c/o Foundation of the Carolinas
220 N. Tryon St.
Charlotte, NC 28202

Donor: Mariam Cannon Hayes Living Trust.
Foundation type: Independent foundation.
Financial data (yr. ended 12/31/13): Assets, $9,404,433 (M); expenditures, $366,808; qualifying distributions, $354,473; giving activities include $285,000 for 27 grants (high: $20,000; low: $5,000).
Fields of interest: Christianity; Human services.
Limitations: Applications not accepted. Giving primarily in NC.
Application information: Unsolicited requests for funds not accepted.
Officers and Trustees: Robert C. Hayes, Jr., Pres. and Trustee; Winslow Hayes Galloway, Secy.-Treas. and Trustee; Barbara W. Hayes; Robert C. Hayes.
EIN: 266155281

7122
H. T. Helb Trust
c/o Wells Fargo Bank, N.A.
1 W. 4th St., 4th Fl., MAC D4000-041
Winston-Salem, NC 27101-3818

Established in 2004 in Pennsylvania.
Foundation type: Independent foundation.
Financial data (yr. ended 10/31/14): Assets, $4,377,922 (M); expenditures, $251,032; qualifying distributions, $210,397; giving activities include $196,463 for 4 grants (high: $78,585; low: $29,468).
Fields of interest: Nonprofits; Hospital care; Diseases and conditions; Protestantism; Human services.
Type of support: General support; Regranting.
Limitations: Applications not accepted. Giving primarily in PA. No grants to individuals.
Application information: Contributes only to pre-selected organizations.
Trustee: Wells Fargo Bank, N.A.
EIN: 236278588

7123
The Helton Family Foundation
2236 Coley Forest Pl.
Raleigh, NC 27607-3124

Established in 1998 in North Carolina.
Donor: W. Charles Helton.
Foundation type: Independent foundation.
Financial data (yr. ended 06/30/13): Assets, $1,529,030 (M); expenditures, $312,769; qualifying distributions, $312,525; giving activities include $310,025 for 3 grants (high: $200,025; low: $10,000).

Fields of interest: Arts and culture; Health; Human services.
Limitations: Applications not accepted. Giving primarily in Raleigh, NC. No grants to individuals.
Application Information: Contributes only to pre-selected organizations.
Officers: W. Charles Helton, Pres.; Thomas Dale Helton, V.P.; Barbara S. Helton, Secy.; Laura Elaine Helton, Treas.
EIN: 562094702

7124
Henderson & Harriet Welfare Association
1496 Carey Chapel Rd.
Henderson, NC   27537-9779

Foundation type: Independent foundation.
Financial data (yr. ended 12/31/13): Assets, $296,741 (M); expenditures, $255,036; qualifying distributions, $255,000; giving activities include $255,000 for 2 grants (high: $250,000; low: $5,000).
Fields of interest: Arts and culture; Education.
Limitations: Applications not accepted.
Application information: Unsolicited requests for funds not accepted.
Officers: My Cooper, Pres.; V.L. Cook, Secy.; Janet Slaughter, Treas.
EIN: 560503963

7125
The C. M. Herndon Foundation
6606 Barbee Rd.
Durham, NC   27713-8538

Established in 1992 in North Carolina.
Donor: C. M. Herndon†.
Foundation type: Independent foundation.
Financial data (yr. ended 12/31/14): Assets, $4,475,736; expenditures, $279,408; qualifying distributions, $241,571.
Fields of interest: Science museums; Higher education; Veterinary medicine; Public libraries; Human services; Food delivery; Senior services.
Limitations: Applications not accepted. Giving primarily in Durham, NC. No grants to individuals.
Application information: Contributes only to pre-selected organizations.
Trustees: Robert F. Bailey; Gus T. Godwin; Edwin J. Walker.
EIN: 582018112

7126
Efrid L. & Marie Hine Charitable Trust
c/o First Citizens Bank, N.A.
P.O. Box 29522
Raleigh, NC   27626-0522

Foundation type: Independent foundation.
Financial data (yr. ended 12/31/14): Assets, $4,165,723; expenditures, $237,359; qualifying distributions, $202,008.
Purpose and activities: Support only for Augsburg Lutheran Church, Winston-Salem, North Carolina.
Fields of interest: Methodism.
Limitations: Applications not accepted. Giving limited to Winston-Salem, NC.
Application information: Contributes only to a pre-selected organization; unsolicited requests for funds not considered or acknowledged.

Trustee: First Citizens Bank.
EIN: 510191041

7127
The Robert B. & Janet A. Hoffman Foundation, Inc.
c/o Eton Advisors LP
5915 Farrington Rd., Ste. 202
Chapel Hill, NC   27517

Established in 2004 in Delaware.
Donors: Double V Growth, LLC; Janet Hoffman; Robert Jane Hoffman.
Foundation type: Independent foundation.
Financial data (yr. ended 12/31/13): Assets, $1,692,408 (M); expenditures, $178,334; qualifying distributions, $165,017; giving activities include $165,017 for 18 grants (high: $56,000; low: $50).
Fields of interest: Arts and culture; Art museums; Education; Higher education; Environment.
Limitations: Applications not accepted. No grants to individuals.
Application information: Contributes only to pre-selected organizations.
Directors: Janet A. Hoffman; Robert B. Hoffman.
EIN: 201798512

7128
William G. & Helen C. Hoffman Foundation
1525 W. WT Harris Blvd., D1114-044
Charlotte, NC   28288   (888) 234-1999
E-mail: grantadministration@wellsfargo.com; Main URL: https://www.wellsfargo.com/privatefoundationgrants/hoffman

Established in 1998 in New Jersey.
Foundation type: Independent foundation.
Financial data (yr. ended 12/31/13): Assets, $5,830,665 (M); expenditures, $203,033; qualifying distributions, $157,751; giving activities include $150,000 for 10 grants (high: $25,000; low: $5,000).
Purpose and activities: Giving primarily for the blind and medical research for the prevention of blindness.
Fields of interest: Education; Elementary and secondary education; Hospital care; Eye diseases; Public libraries; Christianity; Child welfare; Low-income and poor people; People with vision impairments.
Type of support: Research.
Limitations: Applications accepted. Giving primarily in NJ and NY. No grants to individuals.
Application information: See foundation website for complete application guidelines. Application form required.
     Deadline(s): Jan. 15 and Aug. 22
     Board meeting date(s): Mar. and Oct.
Trustee: Wells Fargo Bank, N.A.
EIN: 237981677

7129
Roy & Marian Holleman Foundation Trust
c/o Wells Fargo Bank, N.A.
1 W. 4th St., 4th Fl., MAC D4000-041
Winston-Salem, NC   27101-3818

Foundation type: Independent foundation.

Financial data (yr. ended 12/31/14): Assets, $4,258,443 (M); expenditures, $286,997; qualifying distributions, $232,738; giving activities include $215,000 for 6 grants (high: $90,000; low: $10,000).
Fields of interest: Education; Human services.
Limitations: Applications not accepted. Giving primarily in CA.
Application information: Unsolicited requests for funds not accepted.
Trustee: Wells Fargo Bank, N.A.
EIN: 273867635

7130
Dr. Arthur J. & Helen M. Horvat Foundation
1525 W. WT Harris Blvd., D1114-044
Charlotte, NC   28262   8003523705
Application address: 4320-G Wade Hampton Blvd., Taylors, SC 29687, tel.: (866) 608-0001.

Established in 1987 in Pennsylvania.
Foundation type: Independent foundation.
Financial data (yr. ended 12/31/14): Assets, $5,569,472; expenditures, $372,901; qualifying distributions, $320,892.
Purpose and activities: Giving limited to scholarships for local area residents who are enrolled in a high school or college, and studying chemistry, physics, biology, life sciences, or another major leading to a career in the medical or health professions.
Fields of interest: Dental care; Biomedicine; Diseases and conditions; Physical and earth sciences; Biology; Biochemistry.
Type of support: Scholarships; Student aid; Research; Research and evaluation.
Limitations: Applications accepted. Giving limited to residents of Duryea, PA, and surrounding areas.
Publications: Informational brochure (including application guidelines).
Application information: Complete application information available at http://www.csascholars.org . Application form required.
     Initial approach: See website http://www.csascholars.org
     Copies of proposal: 1
     Deadline(s): Apr. 15
Trustees: John R. Saurman; Nicholas D. Tellie, Esq.; Wells Fargo Bank, N.A.
EIN: 236846849

7131
Winnifred C. Howard Trust
Wells Fargo Bank, N.A., Trust Tax Dept.
1 W. 4th St., 4th Fl., MAC D4000-041
Winston-Salem, NC   27101-3818

Established in 2007 in North Carolina.
Donor: Winnifred C. Howard†.
Foundation type: Independent foundation.
Financial data (yr. ended 12/31/14): Assets, $3,670,211 (M); expenditures, $198,604; qualifying distributions, $162,724; giving activities include $150,800 for 8 grants (high: $18,850; low: $18,850).
Fields of interest: Arts and culture; Religion; Human services.
Limitations: Applications not accepted. No grants to individuals.
Application information: Contributes only to pre-selected organizations.

Trustee: Wells Fargo Bank, N.A.
EIN: 256910655

7132

The Howe Foundation, Inc.
P.O. Box 227
Belmont, NC   28012-0227   (704) 825-5372
Contact: Henry Howe, Dir.

Established in 1966 in North Carolina.
Donors: Beltax Corp.; Knitcraft, Inc.
Foundation type: Company-sponsored foundation.
Financial data (yr. ended 10/31/13): Assets,
$2,493,862 (M); expenditures, $298,547;
qualifying distributions, $268,450; giving activities
include $268,450 for 45 grants (high: $200,000;
low: $200).
Purpose and activities: The foundation supports
organizations involved with arts and culture,
education, human services, Christianity, and people
with mental disabilities.
Fields of interest: Arts and culture; Education;
Elementary and secondary education; Higher
education; Christianity; Human services; People
with psychosocial disabilities; People with
intellectual disabilities.
Type of support: General support.
Limitations: Applications accepted. Giving limited to
the Belmont, NC, area. No grants to individuals.
Application information: Application form required.
  Initial approach: Letter
  Deadline(s): None
Officer: H.T. Howe, Treas.
Directors: Dave Hall; Dave Howe; H.R. Howe.
EIN: 566070727

7133

The Hudson Foundation
c/o Thomas Hudson, Jr.
1450 Raleigh Rd., 3rd Fl.
Chapel Hill, NC   27517-8833

Established in 2002 in North Carolina.
Donors: Thomas W. Hudson, Jr.; The Hudson
Foundation.
Foundation type: Independent foundation.
Financial data (yr. ended 12/31/14): Assets,
$4,558,283; expenditures, $283,895; qualifying
distributions, $266,645.
Fields of interest: Business education; Nonprofits;
Diseases and conditions; Protestantism.
Type of support: Regranting.
Limitations: Applications not accepted. Giving
primarily in NC.
Application information: Unsolicited requests for
funds not accepted.
Trustees: Kenneth D. Hudson; Mary J. Hudson; T.
Warner Hudson III; Thomas W. Hudson, Jr.
EIN: 226932710

7134

C. Giles Hunt Charitable Trust
c/o Wells Fargo Bank N.A.
1 W. 4th St., 4th Fl., MAC D4000-41
Winston-Salem, NC   27101-3818
Contact: David A. Frosaker, V.P. and Trust Off., Wells
Fargo Bank Northwest, N.A.
Grant request e-mail address:
pcsgrantrequest@wellsfargo.com; Main

URL: https://www.wellsfargo.com/
privatefoundationgrants/hunt

Established in 1974 in Oregon.
Donor: C. Giles Hunt†.
Foundation type: Independent foundation.
Financial data (yr. ended 12/31/13): Assets,
$6,105,045 (M); expenditures, $334,051;
qualifying distributions, $268,799; giving activities
include $249,672 for 41 grants (high: $20,000;
low: $1,498).
Purpose and activities: Giving primarily for
education, including for public libraries.
Fields of interest: Secondary education; Libraries;
Public administration; Human services; Child
welfare.
Type of support: General support; Capital
campaigns; Capital and infrastructure; Equipment.
Limitations: Giving primarily in Douglas County, OR.
No grants to individuals.
Publications: Application guidelines.
Application information: Application form required.
  Initial approach: Online application only. E-mail to
    request the link to the application. Hard copy
    not accepted.
  Copies of proposal: 1
  Deadline(s): Submit proposal in Jan. or Feb.;
    deadline Feb. 28
  Board meeting date(s): Mar. and Apr.
  Final notification: June or July
Trustee: Wells Fargo Bank Northwest, N.A.
EIN: 237428278

7135

Vicky and Sam Hunt Foundation
P.O. Drawer 2440
Burlington, NC   27216

Established in 1998 in North Carolina.
Donors: R. Samuel Hunt III; Victoria S. Hunt; Hunt
Electric Supply; Atlas Lighting Products Inc.
Foundation type: Operating foundation.
Financial data (yr. ended 12/31/13): Assets,
$494,656 (M); gifts received, $255,000;
expenditures, $428,739; qualifying distributions,
$425,600; giving activities include $425,600 for 18
grants (high: $300,000; low: $500).
Fields of interest: Education; Higher education;
Domesticated animals.
Limitations: Applications not accepted. Giving
primarily in FL and NC. No grants to individuals.
Application information: Unsolicited requests for
funds not accepted.
Trustees: R. Samuel Hunt III; R. Samuel Hunt IV;
Victoria S. Hunt.
EIN: 562115931

7136

Estelle Hunter Charitable Trust
c/o Wells Fargo Bank, N.A., Trust Tax Dept.
1 W. 4th St., 4th Fl., MAC D4000-041
Winston-Salem, NC   27101-3818

Foundation type: Independent foundation.
Financial data (yr. ended 12/31/14): Assets,
$11,788,340 (M); expenditures, $483,825;
qualifying distributions, $376,189; giving activities
include $345,844 for grants (high: $129,691; low:
$43,231).

Purpose and activities: Giving primarily for higher
education, and for human services, including a
children's home.
Fields of interest: Higher education; Human
services; Shelter and residential care; Children.
Limitations: Applications not accepted. Giving
primarily in Denver, CO.
Application information: Unsolicited requests for
funds not accepted.
Trustee: Wells Fargo Bank, N.A.
EIN: 846016605

7137

Charles R. Jelm Charitable Foundation
1525 W. WT Harris Blvd.
Charlotte, NC   28288-5709

Established in 1990 in Florida.
Donor: Charles R. Jelm Trust.
Foundation type: Independent foundation.
Financial data (yr. ended 01/31/15): Assets,
$9,296,550; expenditures, $501,975; qualifying
distributions, $393,943.
Fields of interest: Education; Health; Specialty
hospital care; Eye diseases; National defense;
Christianity; Human services.
Type of support: General support.
Limitations: Applications not accepted. Giving
primarily in CO, FL and OH. No grants to individuals.
Application information: Unsolicited requests for
funds not accepted.
Trustees: Robert J. Cicek; Camilla Glenn; Charles L.
Jelm; Cheryl A. Jelm; Lisa Petrosky.
EIN: 650122428

7138

**Wayne and Carolyn Jones Charitable
Foundation**
3620 Cape Center Dr.
Fayetteville, NC   28304-4405
Contact: Wayne Jones, Pres.; Carolyn Jones,
Secy.-Treas.
Application Address: 63 East Bay St., Charleston, SC
29401.

Established in 2000 in North Carolina.
Donors: Carolyn Jones; Wayne Jones.
Foundation type: Independent foundation.
Financial data (yr. ended 12/31/14): Assets,
$2,518,027 (M); expenditures, $304,525;
qualifying distributions, $284,380; giving activities
include $284,380 for 11 grants (high: $225,000;
low: $50).
Purpose and activities: Giving primarily to an art
museum.
Fields of interest: Arts and culture; Education;
Sports and recreation.
Limitations: Applications accepted. Giving primarily
in Charleston, SC. No grants to individuals.
Application information: Application form required.
  Initial approach: Letter
  Deadline(s): None
Officers: Wayne Jones, Pres.; Carolyn Jones,
Secy.-Treas.
EIN: 311738970

7139

M.H. Judd Charitable Trust
c/o Wells Fargo Bank, N.A.
1 W. 4th st., 4th Fl.
Winston-Salem, NC 27101-3818

Foundation type: Independent foundation.
Financial data (yr. ended 03/31/14): Assets,
$3,634,643 (M); expenditures, $192,938;
qualifying distributions, $160,868; giving activities
include $150,884 for 6 grants (high: $52,809; low:
$3,772).
Fields of interest: Education; Health; Religion.
Type of support: General support.
Limitations: Applications not accepted. Giving
primarily in GA.
Application information: Unsolicited requests for
funds not accepted.
Trustee: Wells Fargo Bank, N.A.
EIN: 586118252

7140

Louis J. & Golda I. Kanitz Scholarship
Memorial Fund
c/o Wells Fargo Bank, N.A., Trust Tax Dept.
1 W. 4th St., 4th Fl., MAC D4000-041
Winston-Salem, NC 27101-3818

Established in 1994 in California.
Foundation type: Independent foundation.
Financial data (yr. ended 12/31/14): Assets,
$5,654,949 (M); expenditures, $326,228;
qualifying distributions, $282,682; giving activities
include $182,139 for 10 grants (high: $52,267;
low: $3,853), and $88,450 for 78 grants to
individuals (high: $2,000; low: $500).
Purpose and activities: Giving primarily for
education and Roman Catholic churches.
Fields of interest: Education; Secondary education;
Higher education; Catholicism.
Type of support: Individual development.
Limitations: Applications not accepted. Giving
primarily in CA and MI.
Application information: Unsolicited requests for
funds not accepted.
Trustee: Wells Fargo Bank, N.A.
EIN: 946665743

7141

Fred E. Kassner Family Foundation
(formerly Kassner Family Foundation)
1525 W. WT Harris Blvd., D1114-044
Charlotte, NC 28262-8522

Established in 1998 in Pennsylvania.
Donors: Fred Kassner†; Sanford C. Bernstein & Co.
Foundation type: Independent foundation.
Financial data (yr. ended 12/31/13): Assets,
$3,182,568 (M); gifts received, $157,091;
expenditures, $204,459; qualifying distributions,
$177,000; giving activities include $176,000 for 13
grants (high: $50,000; low: $5,000).
Fields of interest: Education; Health; Human
services.
Type of support: General support.
Limitations: Applications not accepted. No grants to
individuals.
Application information: Unsolicited requests for
funds not accepted.

Trustees: Gerda Kassner; Michelle Kassner; Ellen
Teitelbaum.
EIN: 223594386

7142

H.L. Katz Foundation
(formerly Harry Katz Memorial Fund)
c/o Wells Fargo Bank, N.A.
1 W. 4th St., 4th Fl., MAC D4000-041
Winston-Salem, NC 27101-3818
E-mail: reginald.middleton@wachovia.com; Main
URL: https://www.wellsfargo.com/
privatefoundationgrants/katz

Established in 1955 in New Jersey.
Foundation type: Independent foundation.
Financial data (yr. ended 12/31/14): Assets,
$3,894,384; expenditures, $195,107; qualifying
distributions, $146,170.
Purpose and activities: Support primarily for Jewish
organizations, including education and community
and family services.
Fields of interest: Education; Judaism; Family
services.
Type of support: General support; Capital
campaigns; Equipment; Program development.
Limitations: Applications accepted. Giving primarily
in Atlantic County, NJ. No grants to individuals.
Application information: See foundation website for
complete application guidelines. Application form
required.
Deadline(s): Oct. 1
Trustee: Wells Fargo Bank, N.A.
Number of staff: 1 full-time professional; 1 full-time
support.
EIN: 510171174

7143

The Kenan Family Foundation
P.O. Box 4150
Chapel Hill, NC 27515-4150

Established in 1984 in North Carolina.
Donor: Frank H. Kenan†.
Foundation type: Independent foundation.
Financial data (yr. ended 12/31/14): Assets,
$6,328,278; expenditures, $308,177; qualifying
distributions, $278,433.
Purpose and activities: Giving primarily for
education.
Fields of interest: Humanities; Education;
Economics.
Type of support: Continuing support; Endowments.
Limitations: Applications not accepted. Giving
primarily in NC. No grants to individuals.
Application information: Unsolicited requests for
funds not accepted.
Officers and Directors: Elizabeth Kenan Howell,
Pres. and Director; Thomas S. Kenan III, V.P. and
Treas. and Director; Annice Hawkins Kenan, V.P.
and Director; Owen Gwyn, Jr.; Elizabeth Price Kenan;
Roberta Sterling Kenan.
EIN: 581587972

7144

The Thomas S. Kenan III Foundation
P.O. Box 4150
Chapel Hill, NC 27515-4150

Established in 1993 in North Carolina.

Donor: Thomas S. Kenan III.
Foundation type: Independent foundation.
Financial data (yr. ended 06/30/14): Assets,
$4,100,955 (M); expenditures, $220,352;
qualifying distributions, $174,358; giving activities
include $168,260 for 30 grants (high: $20,000;
low: $1,000).
Purpose and activities: Giving to higher education,
cultural and environmental institutes, and to
education foundations.
Fields of interest: Arts and culture; Education;
Higher education; Natural resources.
Type of support: General support; Continuing
support; Endowments.
Limitations: Applications not accepted. Giving
primarily in NC. No grants to individuals.
Application information: Unsolicited requests for
funds not accepted.
Officers and Directors: Thomas S. Kenan III, Pres.
and Director; Steven R. Armstrong, Secy.-Treas. and
Director; Christopher A. Shuping.
EIN: 561816652

7145

Catherine Kennedy Home Foundation
P.O. Box 4782
Wilmington, NC 28406-1782

Established in 2001 in North Carolina.
Donors: The Catherine Kennedy Home, Inc.; Allie
Morriss Fetchig Charitable Remainder Unitrust.
Foundation type: Independent foundation.
Financial data (yr. ended 06/30/13): Assets,
$3,608,483 (M); expenditures, $191,231;
qualifying distributions, $179,178; giving activities
include $177,500 for 23 grants (high: $15,000;
low: $1,500).
Fields of interest: Hospice care; Christianity;
Human services; Food delivery; Domestic violence
shelters; Developmental disability services; Senior
services; Seniors.
Limitations: Applications accepted. Giving primarily
in Wilmington, NC.
Application information: Application form required.
Initial approach: Written application
Deadline(s): Feb. 28
Officers and Directors: Ann Parker, Chair.; Anita
Liebscher, Secy.; Anna P. Erwin, Treas.; Martha
Clark; Garry A. Garris; Linda Hundley; Mrs. Chris
Johnson; Besty Leonard; Jane Maloy; Ned Marable;
Anne Murchison.
EIN: 522282843

7146

Ketchum Foundation
c/o Wells Fargo Bank, N.A.
1 W. 4th St., 4th Fl
Winston-Salem, NC 27101-3818

Foundation type: Independent foundation.
Financial data (yr. ended 12/31/14): Assets,
$3,954,341 (M); expenditures, $196,482;
qualifying distributions, $156,144; giving activities
include $142,938 for 3 grants (high: $71,469; low:
$14,294).
Fields of interest: Protestantism; Shelter and
residential care; Female children and youth; Male
children and youth.
Type of support: General support.

Limitations: Applications not accepted. Giving limited to Crossnore, Jacksonville, and Lake Waccamaw, NC.
Application information: Unsolicited requests for funds not accepted.
Trustee: Wells Fargo Bank, N.A.
EIN: 581475963

7147
Mary C. Kistler Trust
c/o Wells Fargo Bank, N.A.
1 W. 4th St., 4th Fl., MAC D4000-041
Winston-Salem, NC   27101-3818

Donor: Wachovia Bank, N.A.
Foundation type: Independent foundation.
Financial data (yr. ended 09/30/13): Assets, $10,240,727 (M); expenditures, $478,806; qualifying distributions, $407,759; giving activities include $381,967 for 5 grants (high: $152,787; low: $57,295).
Fields of interest: Elementary and secondary education; Hospital care; Family services; Child welfare.
Type of support: General support.
Limitations: Applications not accepted. Giving primarily in NC.
Application information: Contributes only to pre-selected organizations.
Trustee: Wells Fargo Bank, N.A.
EIN: 566049771

7148
M.R. Koons Charitable Trust
1525 W. WT Harris Blvd., D1114-044
Charlotte, NC   28262

Foundation type: Independent foundation.
Financial data (yr. ended 12/31/13): Assets, $8,797,593 (M); expenditures, $471,731; qualifying distributions, $412,235; giving activities include $394,125 for 9 grants (high: $114,125; low: $9,542).
Fields of interest: Higher education; University education; Health; Hospital care; Christianity; Human services.
Type of support: General support.
Limitations: Applications not accepted. Giving primarily in PA. No grants to individuals.
Application information: Contributes only to pre-selected organizations.
Trustee: Wells Fargo Bank, N.A.
EIN: 236752597

7149
Michael J. Kosloski Foundation
1525 W. W.T. Harris Blvd., D1114-044
Charlotte, NC   28262

Established in 2000 in North Carolina.
Foundation type: Independent foundation.
Financial data (yr. ended 12/31/13): Assets, $6,134,237 (M); expenditures, $332,709; qualifying distributions, $315,464; giving activities include $312,825 for 7 grants (high: $190,000; low: $10,000).
Purpose and activities: Giving primarily for health care and community services, including a rescue squad.

Fields of interest: Higher education; Medical education; Health; Hospital care; Community and economic development; Child welfare.
Type of support: General support.
Limitations: Applications not accepted. Giving primarily in NJ.
Application information: Unsolicited requests for funds not accepted.
Trustee: Wells Fargo Bank, N.A.
EIN: 226800804

7150
The Maurice J. Koury Foundation Inc.
P.O. Box 850
Burlington, NC   27216-0850

Established in 1991 in North Carolina.
Donor: Maurice J. Koury.
Foundation type: Independent foundation.
Financial data (yr. ended 09/30/13): Assets, $2,511,340 (M); gifts received, $223,749; expenditures, $161,574; qualifying distributions, $158,800; giving activities include $158,800 for 2 grants (high: $150,000; low: $8,800).
Fields of interest: Education.
Type of support: Capital and infrastructure.
Limitations: Applications not accepted. Giving primarily in NC. No grants to individuals.
Application information: Unsolicited requests for funds not accepted.
Officers and Directors: Maurice J. Koury, Chair. and Pres.; Anne Kirkpatrick Koury, Secy. and Director; Miltom E. Petty, Treas. and Director; Ernest A. Koury, Jr.
EIN: 561781568

7151
KPB Corporation
P.O. Box 11797
Charlotte, NC   28220-1797

Donor: Julian Price Family Foundation.
Foundation type: Independent foundation.
Financial data (yr. ended 12/31/13): Assets, $1,882,861 (M); expenditures, $402,615; qualifying distributions, $333,003; giving activities include $325,542 for 43 grants (high: $48,500; low: $250).
Purpose and activities: Giving primarily for higher education, health associations, and social services.
Fields of interest: Education; Higher education; Foundations; Diseases and conditions; Human services; Child welfare.
Limitations: Applications not accepted. Giving primarily in NC and VA. No grants to individuals.
Application information: Contributes only to pre-selected organizations.
Trustees: Carolyn Taylor; J.M. Bryan Taylor; John Taylor; Shawn Taylor.
EIN: 943418538

7152
Harry Kramer Memorial Fund
1 W. 4th St., D4000-041
Winston-Salem, NC   27101-3818
E-mail: grantadministration@wellsfargo.com; Main URL: https://www.wellsfargo.com/privatefoundationgrants/kramer

Established in 1982 in Florida.

Foundation type: Independent foundation.
Financial data (yr. ended 12/31/14): Assets, $6,140,636 (M); gifts received, $344; expenditures, $317,580; qualifying distributions, $209,690; giving activities include $160,000 for 14 grants (high: $45,000; low: $5,000).
Purpose and activities: To provide support for the general welfare of the people of Israel, the care of the sick or the aged, the education of individuals in the South Florida area, and to assist religious organizations.
Fields of interest: Education; Nonprofits; Health; Judaism; Human services; International relations.
International interests: Israel.
Type of support: Capital campaigns; Capital and infrastructure; Program development; Seed money; Scholarships; Regranting.
Limitations: Applications accepted. Giving primarily in FL and NY. No grants to individuals or for operating budgets or continuing support.
Application information: See foundation website for complete application guidelines. Application form required.
   Deadline(s): June 30
Trustees: Leslie J. August; Wells Fargo Bank, N.A.
EIN: 596644290

7153
Jenny H. & Otto F. Krauss Charitable Foundation
900 Stonecutter Ct.
Raleigh, NC   27614-9060

Donor: Otto F. Krauss.
Foundation type: Independent foundation.
Financial data (yr. ended 12/31/13): Assets, $7,517,011 (M); expenditures, $425,942; qualifying distributions, $335,233; giving activities include $334,000 for 22 grants (high: $40,000; low: $3,000).
Purpose and activities: Giving primarily for education and Christian and Protestant churches; funding also for social services.
Fields of interest: Education; Higher education; Christianity; Protestantism; Human services.
Type of support: General support.
Limitations: Applications not accepted. Giving primarily in MI. No grants to individuals.
Application information: Contributes only to pre-selected organizations.
Trustees: Alan F. Krauss; Frederick G. Krauss; Virginia Krauss.
EIN: 382837174

7154
Anna Pitzl and J. Fred Krost Charitable Trust No. 2
c/o Wells Fargo Bank, N.A.
1 W. 4th St., 4th Fl., MAC D4000-041
Winston-Salem, NC   27101-3818

Foundation type: Independent foundation.
Financial data (yr. ended 04/30/13): Assets, $4,088,425 (M); expenditures, $246,050; qualifying distributions, $200,925; giving activities include $187,226 for 10 grants (high: $36,844; low: $12,287).
Fields of interest: Education; Health; Religion.
Limitations: Applications not accepted. Giving primarily in MN. No grants to individuals.

Application information: Unsolicited requests for funds not accepted.
Trustee: Wells Fargo Bank, N.A.
EIN: 416268462

7155
The Ladane Foundation
11 Causeway Dr.
Ocean Isle Beach, NC 28469-7505
9105797300

Established in 2000 in North Carolina.
Donor: Ladane Williamson.
Foundation type: Independent foundation.
Financial data (yr. ended 12/31/13): Assets, $4,338,422; expenditures, $262,472; qualifying distributions, $236,263.
Fields of interest: Education; Health; Religion.
Limitations: Applications not accepted. Giving primarily in PA and TN. No grants to individuals.
Application information: Unsolicited requests for funds not accepted.
Officers: Ladane Williamson, Pres.; Paula Buis, Secy.-Treas.
Directors: Kendra Ladane Bullington; Mitchell Grant Bullington; Odell Frasier Bullington.
EIN: 134105176

7156
James B. Ladd Trust
c/o Wells Fargo Bank, N.A., Trust Tax Dept.
1 W. 4th St., 4th Fl., MAC D4000-041
Winston-Salem, NC 27101-3818

Established in 1994 in Minnesota.
Foundation type: Independent foundation.
Financial data (yr. ended 12/31/13): Assets, $8,944,383 (M); expenditures, $543,707; qualifying distributions, $419,087; giving activities include $394,793 for 8 grants (high: $234,290; low: $50).
Purpose and activities: Giving primarily for Masonic agencies.
Fields of interest: Religion; Human services.
Type of support: General support.
Limitations: Applications not accepted. Giving primarily in MN. No grants to individuals.
Application information: Unsolicited requests for funds not accepted.
Trustee: Wells Fargo Bank, N.A.
EIN: 416045879

7157
John and Maria Laffin Trust
c/o Wells Fargo Bank, N.A., Trust Tax Dept.
1 W. 4th St., 4th Fl., MAC D4000-041
Winston-Salem, NC 27101-3818
Main URL: https://www.wellsfargo.com/privatefoundationgrants/laffin

Foundation type: Independent foundation.
Financial data (yr. ended 12/31/13): Assets, $4,988,613 (M); expenditures, $275,246; qualifying distributions, $215,988; giving activities include $200,000 for 29 grants (high: $28,000; low: $2,000).
Purpose and activities: The foundation priorities are as follows: 30 percent of any periodic distribution amount shall be granted to animal welfare organizations or foundations within Los Angeles City

and County that are demonstrably dedicated to the preservation and humane placement of abandoned and/or homeless small domesticated animals even when no homes for such animals are readily or immediately available; 25 percent of any periodic distribution amount shall be granted to medical research organizations that do not arbitrarily exclude from consideration any alternative or seemingly radical and/or controversial treatment that the American Medical Association may currently oppose; 25 percent of any periodic distribution amount shall be granted to humanitarian organizations that establish, to the trustee's satisfaction, that 80 percent or more of their proceeds are in fact used to alleviate human misery, suffering, and starvation, whenever and wherever these may occur in any part of the world; 20 percent of any periodic distribution amount shall be granted to educational institutions at the college and university level in the Los Angeles City and County areas that are dedicated to maintaining and raising the standards of scholastic excellence rather than to the proliferation of mediocrity.
Fields of interest: Education; Animal welfare; Diseases and conditions; Human services.
Type of support: General support; Scholarships; Research.
Limitations: Applications accepted. Giving primarily in CA for education and animal welfare; worldwide giving for humanitarian and medical research. No grants to individuals.
Application information: See foundation website for complete application guidelines. Application form required.
    Deadline(s): May 31 and Oct. 31
    Board meeting date(s): June 30 and Dec. 31
Trustee: Wells Fargo Bank, N.A.
EIN: 946609731

7158
J. C. Landon Testamentary Trust
c/o Wells Fargo Bank, N.A.
1 W. 4th St., 4th Fl., MAC D4000-041
Winston-Salem, NC 27101-3818
Application address: c/o Wells Fargo Bank, N.A., Trust Dept., P.O. Box 2088, San Angelo, TX 76902-2088

Donor: JC Landon, Jr. Estate.
Foundation type: Independent foundation.
Financial data (yr. ended 12/31/14): Assets, $3,438,160 (M); expenditures, $249,530; qualifying distributions, $187,139; giving activities include $174,367 for 1 grant.
Purpose and activities: Scholarship awards to students of Texas A&M University, College Station.
Fields of interest: Education.
Type of support: Scholarships.
Limitations: Applications accepted. Giving limited to College Station, TX.
Application information: Application form required.
    Initial approach: Letter
    Deadline(s): Apr. 1
Trustee: Wells Fargo Bank Texas, N.A.
EIN: 756522984

7159
Landry's Helping Heart Foundation
1525 W. WT Harris Blvd., D1114-044
Charlotte, NC 28262

Established in 2008 in Georgia.
Donors: William J. Albertson; Crista Albertson.
Foundation type: Independent foundation.
Financial data (yr. ended 12/31/13): Assets, $5,471,718 (M); expenditures, $280,216; qualifying distributions, $237,208; giving activities include $230,208 for 2 grants (high: $226,708; low: $3,500).
Fields of interest: Human services.
Limitations: Applications not accepted. Giving primarily in OH.
Application information: Unsolicited requests for funds not accepted.
Trustees: Crista Albertson; William J. Albertson.
EIN: 261631464

7160
Lerner Family Foundation, Inc.
524 W. Innes St.
Salisbury, NC 28144-2826

Established in 1990 in North Carolina.
Donors: Bernice L. Lerner; Morton S. Lerner; Bernice L. Lerner Irrevocable Trust.
Foundation type: Independent foundation.
Financial data (yr. ended 09/30/14): Assets, $6,023,774; expenditures, $338,471; qualifying distributions, $267,498.
Fields of interest: Higher education; Foundations; Nonprofits; Diseases and conditions; Judaism; Human services; Victim aid; Women's services.
Type of support: General support; Scholarships; Regranting.
Limitations: Applications not accepted. Giving primarily in NC. No grants to individuals.
Application information: Unsolicited requests for funds not accepted.
Officer and Directors: Mark Lerner, MD, Pres. and Director; Amanda R. Lerner, Secy. and Director; Richard I. Lerner, Treas. and Director; Dena P. Lerner.
EIN: 561720870

7161
The Levine-Sklut Family Foundation
(formerly The Lori L. Sklut Foundation)
c/o Jonathan Shumate, Genspring
4064 Colony Rd., Ste. 195
Charlotte, NC 28211-5033

Established in 1995 in Unspecified.
Donors: Lori Levine Sklut; Eric Sklut.
Foundation type: Independent foundation.
Financial data (yr. ended 12/31/13): Assets, $20,645,115 (M); gifts received, $1,503,491; expenditures, $296,556; qualifying distributions, $150,907; giving activities include $149,519 for 8 grants (high: $68,500; low: $1,000).
Purpose and activities: Giving primarily for Jewish organizations, as well as for social services, and to a children's hospital.
Fields of interest: Nonprofits; Specialty hospital care; Judaism; Human services.
Type of support: General support; Regranting.
Limitations: Applications not accepted. Giving primarily in Charlotte, NC. No grants to individuals.
Application information: Contributes only to pre-selected organizations.
Directors: Eric R. Sklut; Lori Levine Sklut.
EIN: 561904190

7162
Solon E. & Espie Watts Little Scholarship Loan Fund, Inc.
43 Union St. S.
Concord, NC 28025-5009 (704) 786-8173
Contact: Steve L. Medlin, Pres. and Secy.,-Treas.

Established in 1982 in North Carolina.
Donor: Espie Watts Little†.
Foundation type: Independent foundation.
Financial data (yr. ended 12/31/13): Assets, $2,525,233 (M); expenditures, $390,960; qualifying distributions, $367,891; giving activities include $214,700 for 67 grants to individuals (high: $19,400; low: $1,400).
Purpose and activities: Loans only to graduates of Alexander County Central High School, North Carolina.
Fields of interest: Higher education.
Type of support: Student aid; Loans to individuals.
Limitations: Applications accepted. Giving limited to Alexander County, NC high school graduates.
Application information: Application form required.
 Initial approach: Proposal
 Deadline(s): None
Officer: Steve L. Medlin, Pres. and Secy.-Treas.
Number of staff: 1 full-time professional; 1 part-time professional.
EIN: 581491453

7163
Live Oak Foundation
1525 W. WT Harris Blvd.
Charlotte, NC 28262

Established in 1966 in Pennsylvania.
Donor: Charlotte C. Weber.
Foundation type: Independent foundation.
Financial data (yr. ended 08/31/14): Assets, $24,873 (M); gifts received, $162,250; expenditures, $159,335; qualifying distributions, $154,335; giving activities include $154,325 for 36 grants (high: $55,000; low: $25).
Fields of interest: Arts and culture; Education; Health; Hospital care.
Limitations: Applications accepted. Giving primarily in FL.
Application information:
 Initial approach: Proposal
 Copies of proposal: 1
 Deadline(s): None
Trustees: Juliet W. Reid; Charlotte C. Weber; Chester C. Weber; John C. Weber, Jr.; Christina W. Whitney.
EIN: 236424637

7164
George and Frances London Educational Foundation
P.O. Box 20389
Raleigh, NC 27619-0389 (919) 787-8880
Contact: David D. Dahl, Tr.

Established in 1996 in North Carolina.
Donor: Frances P. London.
Foundation type: Independent foundation.
Financial data (yr. ended 12/31/13): Assets, $6,784,586 (M); expenditures, $408,002; qualifying distributions, $352,500; giving activities include $352,500 for 49 grants to individuals (high: $11,250; low: $3,750).

Purpose and activities: Scholarship awards to high school seniors in North Carolina counties.
Fields of interest: University education.
Type of support: Student aid.
Limitations: Applications accepted. Giving limited to residents NC.
Application information: Nominations shall be solicited from guidance counselors of high schools selected by the trustees. In addition, any interested high school senior from high schools in North Carolina counties may apply on his/her own initiative. Application form required.
 Initial approach: Guidance counselor recommendation or letter from individual students
 Deadline(s): Spring of senior year
 Board meeting date(s): Mar. 31
Trustees: Sandra Martin Clark; David D. Dahl; Matthew C. Dahl.
EIN: 582233144

7165
Edith H. Lynum Trust
c/o Wells Fargo Bank, N.A., Trust Tax Dept.
1 W. 4th St., 4th Fl., MAC D4000-041
Winston-Salem, NC 27101-3818 8887304933

Foundation type: Independent foundation.
Financial data (yr. ended 12/31/14): Assets, $2,371,343; expenditures, $159,808; qualifying distributions, $130,526.
Fields of interest: Education; Higher education; Health; Diseases and conditions.
Type of support: General support; Research.
Limitations: Applications not accepted. Giving primarily in MN and WI. No grants to individuals.
Application information: Unsolicited requests for funds not accepted.
Trustee: Wells Fargo Bank, N.A.
EIN: 416013654

7166
John R. & Carolyn J. Maness Family Foundation
c/o Eton Advisors LP
5915 Farrington Rd., No. 202
Chapel Hill, NC 27517-9900

Established in 1995 in North Carolina.
Donors: Carolyn J. Maness Living Trust; John R. Maness; Carolyn J. Maness.
Foundation type: Independent foundation.
Financial data (yr. ended 12/31/13): Assets, $3,081,584 (M); expenditures, $151,266; qualifying distributions, $136,500; giving activities include $136,500 for 31 grants (high: $26,000; low: $500).
Fields of interest: Arts and culture; Education; Religion.
Type of support: General support.
Limitations: Applications not accepted. Giving primarily in NC. No grants to individuals.
Application information: Unsolicited requests for funds not accepted.
Officer: Carolyn J. Maness, Pres. and Secy.
EIN: 561949954

7167
Marietta College Trust LD Ryan-Main
1525 W. W. T. Harris Blvd., D1114-044
Charlotte, NC 28262
Contact: Ryan Main

Donor: Marietta college Trust.
Foundation type: Independent foundation.
Financial data (yr. ended 12/31/13): Assets, $13,118,701 (M); gifts received, $11,772,331; expenditures, $326,579; qualifying distributions, $209,036; giving activities include $167,527 for 1 grant.
Fields of interest: Education; Higher education.
Type of support: General support.
Limitations: Applications not accepted. Giving primarily in OH.
Application information: Unsolicited requests for funds not accepted.
Trustee: Wells Fargo Bank.
EIN: 756355551

7168
John C. Markey Charitable Fund
1227 Princeton Ave.
Charlotte, NC 28209-1429
Contact: John C. Markey II, Treas.
Application address: 1800 Camden Rd., Charlotte, NC 28203

Established in 1966 in Ohio.
Donor: John C. Markey†.
Foundation type: Independent foundation.
Financial data (yr. ended 06/30/13): Assets, $3,280,447 (M); expenditures, $240,106; qualifying distributions, $215,020; giving activities include $211,000 for 20 grants (high: $75,000; low: $1,000).
Purpose and activities: Giving primarily for cultural and educational institutions, and religion.
Fields of interest: Arts and culture; Education; Religion; Human services.
Limitations: Applications accepted. Giving primarily in Wallingford, CT, and OH. No grants to individuals.
Application information: Application form required.
 Initial approach: Letter
 Deadline(s): None
Officers: Carl T. Anderson, Pres. and Secy.; Philip Lisle, V.P.; John Clifton Markey II, Treas.
EIN: 346572724

7169
Marlboro County General Hospital Charity Trust
c/o Trust Tax Dept
P.O. Box 2907
Wilson, NC 27894-2907

Established in 1983 in South Carolina.
Foundation type: Independent foundation.
Financial data (yr. ended 12/31/13): Assets, $7,128,697 (M); expenditures, $330,704; qualifying distributions, $289,215; giving activities include $233,790 for 4 grants (high: $118,790; low: $5,000).
Purpose and activities: Giving primarily for health care.
Fields of interest: Graduate and professional education; Health; Hospital care; Emergency care; Nursing care; Diseases and conditions; Low-income and poor people.

Type of support: General support.
Limitations: Applications not accepted. Giving primarily in Marlboro County, SC. No grants to individuals.
Application information: Contributes only to pre-selected organizations.
Trustee: Branch Banking &Trust Co.
EIN: 570737029

7170
Edward N. and Margaret G. Marsh Foundation

c/o Wells Fargo Bank N.A., Trust Tax Dept.
1 W. 4th St., 4th Fl., MAC D4000-041
Winston-Salem, NC   27101-3818   8887304933
Application address: c/o Wells Fargo Bank, N.A., Attn.: Linda Jex, Trust Off., P.O. Box 9502, Las Vegas, NV 89102, tel.: (902) 765-3967; Main URL: https://www.wellsfargo.com/privatefoundationgrants/marsh

Foundation type: Independent foundation.
Financial data (yr. ended 12/31/14): Assets, $5,117,033; expenditures, $275,492; qualifying distributions, $222,302.
Fields of interest: Education; Domesticated animals; Health.
Application information: Application form required.
Initial approach: Letter
Deadline(s): June 30th
Trustee: Wells Fargo Bank, N.A.
EIN: 270974165

7171
The Marsh Foundation, Inc.

c/o U.S. Trust, Bank of America, N.A.
P.O. Box 26262
Greensboro, NC   27402-6262
Contact: Gretchen M. Johnston, Pres.
Application address: P.O. Box 35329, Charlotte, NC 28235

Donors: Marsh Realty Co.; Marsh Assocs.; Marsh Mortgage Co.
Foundation type: Company-sponsored foundation.
Financial data (yr. ended 12/31/13): Assets, $3,354,330 (M); gifts received, $313,896; expenditures, $170,965; qualifying distributions, $142,500; giving activities include $142,500 for 16 grants (high: $70,450; low: $550).
Purpose and activities: The foundation supports museums and organizations involved with K-12 education, health, human services, and Christianity.
Fields of interest: Education; Health; Religion.
Type of support: General support; Scholarships.
Limitations: Applications accepted. Giving primarily in NC. No support for political organizations. No grants to individuals.
Application information: Application form required.
Initial approach: Letter
Deadline(s): None
Officers: Gretchen M. Johnston, Pres.; G. Alex Marsh III, V.P.; Hunter Johnston McLawhorn, V.P.; James H. McLawhorn, Secy.
EIN: 566056515

7172
Maurice J. Masserini Charitable Trust

c/o Wells Fargo Bank, N.A., Trust Tax Dept.
1 W. 4th St., 4th Fl., MAC D4000-041
Winston-Salem, NC   27101-3818

Foundation type: Independent foundation.
Financial data (yr. ended 12/31/14): Assets, $3,827,338; expenditures, $227,530; qualifying distributions, $184,820.
Purpose and activities: Support for a hospital, health organizations, child welfare and youth services, and the elderly.
Fields of interest: Arts and culture; Domesticated animals; Disasters and emergency management.
Type of support: Capital and infrastructure; Matching grants; Equipment; Program development; Convening; Scholarships; Research.
Limitations: Applications not accepted. Giving primarily in CA. No grants to individuals or for salaries.
Application information: Unsolicited requests for funds not accepted.
Trustee: Wells Fargo Bank, N.A.
Number of staff: 1 full-time professional.
EIN: 956812685

7173
Mattei Foundation

(formerly The Mattei Casey Foundation Trust)
1 Morrocroft Ctr.
6805 Morrison Blvd., Ste. 370
Charlotte, NC   28211-3564

Established in 2004 in North Carolina.
Donor: J. Scott Mattei.
Foundation type: Independent foundation.
Financial data (yr. ended 11/30/13): Assets, $6,163,917 (M); expenditures, $341,124; qualifying distributions, $291,171; giving activities include $284,205 for 24 grants (high: $200,000; low: $100).
Fields of interest: Nonprofits; Diseases and conditions.
Type of support: Research; Regranting.
Limitations: Applications not accepted. Giving primarily in NC. No grants to individuals.
Application information: Contributes only to pre-selected organizations.
Trustee: J. Scott Mattei.
EIN: 206376517

7174
Ron and Sharon Matthews Family Foundation

609 Executive Pl.
Fayetteville, NC   28305-5712
Contact: Ron Matthews, Secy.; Sharon Matthews, Pres.

Donors: Sharon Matthews; Family Foods, Inc.
Foundation type: Independent foundation.
Financial data (yr. ended 12/31/14): Assets, $2,148,642 (M); gifts received, $25,000; expenditures, $141,982; qualifying distributions, $141,500; giving activities include $141,500 for 13 grants (high: $50,000; low: $100).
Fields of interest: Education; Diseases and conditions; Protestantism.
Type of support: Research.

Limitations: Applications accepted. Giving primarily in NC.
Application information: Application form required.
Initial approach: Letter
Deadline(s): None
Officers: Sharon Matthews, Pres.; Ron Matthews, Secy.
EIN: 263549628

7175
Inez T. Mattison Trust

c/o Wells Fargo Bank,N. A.
1 W. 4th St., 4th Fl., MAC D4000-041
Winston-Salem, NC   27101-3818

Foundation type: Independent foundation.
Financial data (yr. ended 12/31/13): Assets, $4,904,845 (M); expenditures, $276,355; qualifying distributions, $224,045; giving activities include $208,769 for 6 grants (high: $49,871; low: $9,284).
Fields of interest: University education; Animal welfare; Hospital care; Christianity; Females.
Type of support: General support.
Limitations: Applications not accepted. Giving limited to Tacoma and Seattle, WA. No grants to individuals.
Application information: Unsolicited requests for funds not accepted.
Trustee: Wells Fargo Bank, N.A.
EIN: 237212646

7176
The John P. McConnell Foundation

1 W. 4th St., D4000-041
Winston-Salem, NC   27101-3818

Established in 1997 in North Carolina.
Donors: John McConnell; Green Spring Foundation; Allscripts Healthcare Solutions Inc.
Foundation type: Independent foundation.
Financial data (yr. ended 12/31/13): Assets, $3,637,970 (M); expenditures, $274,146; qualifying distributions, $249,789; giving activities include $243,350 for 28 grants (high: $100,000; low: $350).
Fields of interest: Education; Patient social services; Substance abuse treatment; Diseases and conditions; Cancers; Christianity; Human services; Child welfare.
Limitations: Applications not accepted. Giving primarily in NC. No grants to individuals.
Application information: Unsolicited requests for funds not accepted.
Trustee: Wells Fargo Bank, N.A.
EIN: 562051268

7177
William B. McGuire, Jr. Family Foundation

c/o William B. McGuire
309 E. Morehead St., Ste. 275
Charlotte, NC   28202-2301

Established in 1996 in North Carolina.
Donor: William B. McGuire, Jr.
Foundation type: Independent foundation.
Financial data (yr. ended 12/31/14): Assets, $5,925,953; gifts received, $0; expenditures, $347,186; qualifying distributions, $296,700 and $0 for set-asides.

Fields of interest: Arts and culture; Art museums; Education; Protestantism; Human services.
Limitations: Applications not accepted. Giving primarily in NC and SC. No grants to individuals.
Application information: Contributes only to pre-selected organizations.
Officers and Directors: William B. McGuire, Jr., Chair. and Director; Susanne H. McGuire, Pres. and Director; Caroline R. McGuire, V.P. and Director; William H. McGuire, V.P. and Director; Molly L. McGuire, Secy. and Director.
EIN: 561988052

7178
John Luther & Isabelle Gray McLean Trust
(formerly Almena C. & Malcolm P. McLean Trust)
P.O. Box 1368
Lumberton, NC   28359-1368

Established in 1964 in North Carolina.
Donors: Protective Agency Inc.; John L. McLean; John P. McLean.
Foundation type: Independent foundation.
Financial data (yr. ended 12/31/13): Assets, $4,180,163 (M); gifts received, $35,000; expenditures, $199,761; qualifying distributions, $171,880; giving activities include $171,880 for 18 + grants (high: $93,330).
Fields of interest: Higher education; Nonprofits; Protestantism; Human services.
Type of support: General support; Scholarships; Regranting.
Limitations: Applications not accepted. Giving primarily in NC.
Application information: Unsolicited requests for funds not accepted.
Trustees: Isabelle G. McLean; John P. McLean.
EIN: 566065281

7179
Violet H. McLendon Educational Trust
c/o Wells Fargo Bank N.A., Trust Tax Dept.
1 W. 4th Fl., 4th Fl., MAC D4000-041
Winston-Salem, NC   27101-3818

Established in 1989 in Alabama.
Foundation type: Independent foundation.
Financial data (yr. ended 12/31/14): Assets, $6,711,103 (M); expenditures, $359,812; qualifying distributions, $314,855; giving activities include $305,000 for 3 grants (high: $243,500; low: $15,250).
Purpose and activities: Support primarily for college scholarship funds.
Fields of interest: Community college education; Protestantism.
Type of support: Scholarships.
Limitations: Applications not accepted. Giving primarily FL, with some giving also in AL and GA. No grants to individuals.
Application information: Contributes only to pre-selected organizations.
Trustee: Wells Fargo Bank, N.A.
EIN: 636160114

7180
Erwin Bellamy McMerty Foundation
3048 River Rd. S.E., Ste. 1200
Winnabow, NC   28479-5248

Foundation type: Independent foundation.
Financial data (yr. ended 12/31/13): Assets, $3,520,937 (M); expenditures, $193,254; qualifying distributions, $180,750; giving activities include $180,000 for 31 grants (high: $20,000; low: $1,000).
Fields of interest: Education; Housing development; Religion.
Limitations: Applications not accepted. Giving primarily in Wilmington, NC.
Application information: Unsolicited requests for funds not accepted.
Directors: Brian J. McMerty; Sarah Lyell Bellamy McMerty.
EIN: 263497338

7181
John N. McNeil and Stella McNeil Scholarship Trust
c/o Wells Fargo Bank, N.A., Trust Tax Dept.
1 W. 4th St., 4th Fl., MAC D4000-041
Winston-Salem, NC   27101-3818
Application address: c/o Kingsford High School, Att.: Rita Edberg, 431 Hamilton Ave., Kingsford, MI 49802, tel.: (906) 776-2670

Foundation type: Independent foundation.
Financial data (yr. ended 12/31/13): Assets, $4,913,026 (M); expenditures, $247,005; qualifying distributions, $191,552; giving activities include $177,000 for 43 grants (high: $28,500; low: $1,500).
Purpose and activities: The organization provides scholarships to graduating seniors of Kingsford High School.
Fields of interest: Higher education.
Type of support: Student aid.
Limitations: Applications accepted. Giving primarily in MI.
Application information:
  Initial approach: Proposal
  Deadline(s): Mar.
Trustee: Wells Fargo Bank, N.A.
EIN: 386788691

7182
Albert & Helen C. Meserve Memorial Fund
c/o Wells Fargo Bank, N.A.
1 W. 4th St., 4th Fl., MAC D4000-041
Winston-Salem, NC   27101-3818
Application address: c/o Fairfield County FDN, 523 Danbury Rd., Wilton, CT 06897; tel.: 203-834-9393; Main URL: https://www.wellsfargo.com/privatefoundationgrants/meserve

Established in 1983 in Connecticut.
Donors: Albert W. Meserve†; Helen C. Meserve†.
Foundation type: Independent foundation.
Financial data (yr. ended 08/31/14): Assets, $4,099,614 (M); expenditures, $245,778; qualifying distributions, $190,149; giving activities include $169,800 for 30 grants (high: $8,000; low: $1,000).
Fields of interest: Arts and culture; Historic preservation; Education; Higher education; Philanthropy; Sustainable development; Urban development; Human services; Child welfare; Senior services.
Type of support: Program development; Pro bono consulting services; Matching grants; Convening;

Seed money; Scholarships; Individual development; Technical assistance.
Limitations: Applications accepted. Giving primarily in Bethel, Bridgewater, Brookfield, Danbury, New Fairfield, New Milford, Newton, Redding, Ridgefield, and Sherman, CT. No support for religious or sectarian organizations, political activities, or groups desiring to benefit their own membership. No grants to individuals directly, or endowment or general fund drives, operating budgets of United Way agencies, or deficit financing.
Application information:
  Initial approach: Proposal
  Deadline(s): Apr. 1st for June and Oct. 1st for Dec.
Trustees: David C. Murphy; Wells Fargo Bank, N.A.
Number of staff: 2 part-time professional; 1 part-time support.
EIN: 066254956

7183
Melba Bayers Meyer Charitable Trust
1525 W. WT Harris Blvd., D1114-044
Charlotte, NC   28288-5709
Application address: c/o Wells Fargo Bank Philanthropic Service, 1 W. 4th St., 6th Fl., Winston Salem, NC 27101-3818, tel.: (336) 747-8184; Main URL: https://www.wellsfargo.com/privatefoundationgrants/meyer2

Established in 1995 in Pennsylvania.
Donor: Melba Bayers Meyer†.
Foundation type: Independent foundation.
Financial data (yr. ended 05/31/13): Assets, $6,768,031 (M); expenditures, $393,959; qualifying distributions, $332,013; giving activities include $312,821 for 16 grants (high: $100,000; low: $7,500).
Fields of interest: Animal welfare; Health; Human services; Child welfare; American Indians.
Limitations: Applications accepted. Giving primarily in AL, and Pensacola, FL. No grants to individuals.
Application information: See foundation website for complete application guidelines. Application form required.
  Initial approach: Proposal
  Deadline(s): May 1
Trustee: Wells Fargo Bank, N.A.
EIN: 656192782

7184
Milton and Sophie Meyer Fund
c/o Wells Fargo Bank, N.A., Trust Tax Dept.
1 W. 4th St., 4th Fl., MAC D4000-041
Winston-Salem, NC   27101-3818
E-mail: grantadministration@wellsfargo.com; Main URL: https://www.wellsfargo.com/privatefoundationgrants/meyer3

Established in 1980 in California.
Donor: Milton Meyer†.
Foundation type: Independent foundation.
Financial data (yr. ended 12/31/14): Assets, $3,590,397 (M); expenditures, $216,415; qualifying distributions, $184,117; giving activities include $158,500 for 29 grants (high: $15,000; low: $1,500).
Purpose and activities: Giving limited to Jewish charities.
Fields of interest: Education; Nonprofits; Judaism.
Type of support: General support; Continuing support; Regranting; Annual campaigns; Capital

campaigns; Capital and infrastructure; Endowments; Emergency funds; Seed money; Scholarships; Research.

Limitations: Applications accepted. Giving primarily in the San Francisco Bay Area, CA. No grants to individuals.

Application information: See foundation website for complete application guidelines. Application form required.

    Deadline(s): Jan. 31, May 31, Sept. 30, and Nov. 30

Trustee: Wells Fargo Bank, N.A.

Directors: Norman Plotkin; Sander Stadtler.

EIN: 946480997

7185
The B. W. and Barbara Miller Foundation
309 S. Laurel Ave.
Charlotte, NC 28207-1503

Established in 2002 in North Carolina.

Donors: B. Miller Crat; Bank of America, N.A.

Foundation type: Independent foundation.

Financial data (yr. ended 06/30/13): Assets, $89,666 (M); gifts received, $142,028; expenditures, $173,787; qualifying distributions, $172,725; giving activities include $172,725 for 28 grants (high: $65,000; low: $500).

Fields of interest: Education; Higher education; Agriculture; Human services.

Limitations: Applications not accepted. Giving primarily in NC. No grants to individuals.

Application information: Unsolicited requests for funds not accepted.

Trustee: Barbara A. Whitton.

EIN: 546504825

7186
K Josh & Wynona Owen Mize Charitable Trust
P.O. Box 2907, Trust Tax Dept.
Wilson, NC 27894-2907

Donors: Transamerica Life Insurance; Jose and Wynona Mize Trust; King Joshua Mize†; King Joshua Mize Estate.

Foundation type: Independent foundation.

Financial data (yr. ended 12/31/13): Assets, $6,614,129 (M); gifts received, $2,791; expenditures, $184,188; qualifying distributions, $116,330; giving activities include $116,330 for 7 grants (high: $25,593; low: $12,796).

Fields of interest: Housing development; Religion; International relations.

Limitations: Applications not accepted. Giving primarily in KY and TN.

Application information: Unsolicted requests for funds not accepted.

Trustee: Branch Banking & Trust Co.

EIN: 274879791

7187
Jack Moon Scholarship Foundation
c/o Wells Fargo Bank, N.A. Trust Tax Dept.
1 W. 4th St., 4th Fl., MAC D4000-041
Winston-Salem, NC 27101-3818

Established in 2005 in Minnesota.

Donor: Jack Moon†.

Foundation type: Independent foundation.

Financial data (yr. ended 12/31/13): Assets, $4,862,501 (M); expenditures, $580,556; qualifying distributions, $390,880; giving activities include $369,405 for 1 grant.

Purpose and activities: Scholarship awards to graduates of Duluth Denfeld High School, Minnesota, planning to attend an accredited vocational or trade school in Minnesota, Wisconsin or Michigan.

Fields of interest: Higher education.

Type of support: Student aid.

Limitations: Applications not accepted. Giving primarily in Duluth, MN.

Application information: Unsolicited requests for funds not accepted.

Trustee: Wells Fargo Bank, N.A.

EIN: 202403787

7188
J. Leonard & Dorothy B. Moore Foundation
c/o Wells Fargo Bank, N.A., Trust Tax Dept.
1 W. 4th St., 4th Fl., MAC D4000-041
Winston-Salem, NC 27101-3818

Established in 2000 in North Carolina.

Foundation type: Independent foundation.

Financial data (yr. ended 12/31/14): Assets, $5,894,649 (M); expenditures, $357,751; qualifying distributions, $272,567; giving activities include $256,345 for 3 grants (high: $128,635; low: $25,635).

Fields of interest: Foundations; Christianity.

Limitations: Applications not accepted. Giving primarily in Richmond, VA. No grants to individuals.

Application information: Unsolicited requests for funds not accepted.

Trustee: Wells Fargo Bank, N.A.

EIN: 566558952

7189
O. Leonard Moretz Foundation Trust, Inc.
c/o Wells Fargo Bank, N.A., Trust Tax Dept.
1 W. 4th Fl., MAC D4000-041
Winston-Salem, NC 27101-3818

Established in 1980 in North Carolina.

Foundation type: Independent foundation.

Financial data (yr. ended 07/31/14): Assets, $3,264,476 (M); expenditures, $190,215; qualifying distributions, $164,203; giving activities include $157,500 for 15 grants (high: $65,000; low: $1,000).

Fields of interest: Education; Undergraduate education; Hospice care; Science; Christianity; Human services; Family services; Child welfare; Scouting programs.

Limitations: Applications not accepted. Giving primarily in NC. No grants to individuals.

Application information: Contributes only to pre-selected organizations.

Trustee: Wells Fargo Bank, N.A.

EIN: 580012117

7190
Morgan Creek Foundation
301 W. Barbee Chapel Rd., Ste. 100
Chapel Hill, NC 27517-8834
FAX: (919) 933-4048;
E-mail: info@morgancreekfoundation.org; Main

URL: http://www.morgancreekfoundation.org/index.html

Established in 2005 in North Carolina.

Donor: Mark W. Yusko.

Foundation type: Independent foundation.

Financial data (yr. ended 12/31/13): Assets, $3,327,844 (M); gifts received, $250; expenditures, $242,008; qualifying distributions, $235,313; giving activities include $232,000 for 30 grants (high: $25,000; low: $1,000).

Purpose and activities: The foundation's mission is to help educate disadvantaged children and youth and give them the opportunity to develop the skills necessary to become successful.

Fields of interest: Reading promotion; Human services; Child welfare.

Limitations: Applications not accepted. Giving primarily in NC. No grants to individuals.

Application information: Contributes only to pre-selected organizations.

Officers and Directors: Mark W. Yusko, Pres. and Director; Stacey Yusko, V.P. and Director; Wendy L. Ruggiero, Treas.; Michael P. Hennessy; Andrea Szigethy; Joshua Tilley.

EIN: 203999739

7191
John and Frances Morisey Trust Account
3601 Williamsborough Ct.
Raleigh, NC 27609-6355

Donors: John C. Morisey, Jr.; Frances D. Morisey.

Foundation type: Independent foundation.

Financial data (yr. ended 12/31/13): Assets, $1,173,646 (M); gifts received, $99,560; expenditures, $228,356; qualifying distributions, $213,900; giving activities include $212,700 for 45 grants (high: $61,750; low: $100).

Purpose and activities: Giving primarily for Christian organizations; funding also for health associations, and human services.

Fields of interest: Patient social services; Diseases and conditions; Christianity; Protestantism; Human services; Youth development.

Type of support: General support.

Limitations: Applications not accepted. Giving primarily in NC. No grants to individuals.

Application information: Contributes only to pre-selected organizations.

Trustees: Frances D. Morisey; John C. Morisey, Jr.; John C. Morisey III.

EIN: 566419428

7192
The Moritz Foundation
1525 W. WT Harris Blvd.
Charlotte, NC 28288-5709 3367478186

Established in 2000 in Connecticut.

Donor: Kenneth N. Musen.

Foundation type: Independent foundation.

Financial data (yr. ended 12/31/14): Assets, $2,868,925 (M); expenditures, $230,559; qualifying distributions, $196,500.

Fields of interest: Environment; Domesticated animals.

Type of support: General support.

Limitations: Applications not accepted. Giving primarily in NY and WI. No grants to individuals.

Application information: Unsolicited requests for funds not accepted.
Trustees: Andrea Marie Lieselotte Goelkel; Carl-Heinz Heuer; Ester Mazzarelli; Kenneth N. Musen; David A. Ringold.
EIN: 066504115

7193
Robert Haywood Morrison Foundation
c/o Dr. Cynthia Haldenby Tyson
1409 E. Boulevard, Ste. 3C
Charlotte, NC 28203-5817
FAX: (704) 343-9039;
E-mail: haldenbytyson@aol.com

Established in 2001 in North Carolina.
Donors: Robert H. Morrison†; Cynthia H. Tyson.
Foundation type: Independent foundation.
Financial data (yr. ended 11/30/13): Assets, $18,953,752 (M); expenditures, $1,177,311; qualifying distributions, $627,399; giving activities include $392,620 for 16 grants (high: $200,000; low: $20).
Purpose and activities: Giving primarily to support higher education, the arts and culture, and the natural environment.
Fields of interest: Arts and culture; Museums; Art museums; Higher education; Natural resources.
Type of support: Endowments; Capital campaigns; Capital and infrastructure.
Limitations: Applications not accepted. Giving primarily in NC, SC, and VA. No grants to individuals.
Application information: Contributes only to pre-selected organizations.
Board meeting date(s): 1st Thurs. of Mar. and Sept.
Officers: Cynthia H. Tyson, Pres.; Barbara Scruggs, Secy.
Trustee: Bank of America, N.A.
Number of staff: 1 full-time professional.
EIN: 010561393

7194
Christopher L. Moseley Foundation
1525 W. W.T. Harris Blvd.
Charlotte, NC 28288-5709

Established in 2007 in North Carolina.
Donor: Lisa Dean Moseley.
Foundation type: Independent foundation.
Financial data (yr. ended 09/30/14): Assets, $2,967,770 (M); expenditures, $226,460; qualifying distributions, $192,085; giving activities include $179,597 for 7 grants (high: $39,643; low: $15,000).
Fields of interest: Education; Medical education; Health; Children's hospital care; Children.
Type of support: General support.
Limitations: Applications not accepted. Giving primarily in New York, NY and PA. No grants to individuals.
Application information: Contributes only to pre-selected organizations.
Officers and Board Members: Lisa Dean Moseley, Pres. and Director; William J. Martin, Esq., Secy.-Treas.; Owen Brett Jones; Maruna Kaiser; David K. Solacoff, MD.
EIN: 260144456

7195
Mosser Memorial Trust
(formerly Robert K. Mosser Trust)
c/o Wells Fargo Bank, N.A., Trust Tax Dept.
1 W. 4th St., 4th Fl. MAC D4000-041
Winston-Salem, NC 27101-3818

Foundation type: Independent foundation.
Financial data (yr. ended 12/31/13): Assets, $5,616,306 (M); expenditures, $249,331; qualifying distributions, $192,011; giving activities include $179,033 for 5 grants (high: $35,807; low: $35,806).
Fields of interest: Education; Health; Hospital care; Christianity.
Limitations: Applications not accepted.
Application information: Unsolicited requests for funds not accepted.
Trustee: Wells Fargo Bank, N.A.
EIN: 236951735

7196
Mount Olive Pickle Company Foundation
812 N. Chestnut St.
Mount Olive, NC 28365-1218

Established in 1994 in North Carolina.
Donor: Mount Olive Pickle Co., Inc.
Foundation type: Company-sponsored foundation.
Financial data (yr. ended 04/30/14): Assets, $2,678,836 (M); gifts received, $225,000; expenditures, $208,574; qualifying distributions, $206,900; giving activities include $206,900 for 15 grants (high: $171,000; low: $250).
Purpose and activities: The foundation supports organizations involved with theater, education, housing development, youth development, and community development.
Fields of interest: Arts and culture; Education; Community and economic development.
Type of support: General support; Capital campaigns.
Limitations: Applications not accepted. Giving primarily in Mount Olive and Wayne County, NC. No grants to individuals.
Application information: Unsolicited requests for funds not accepted.
Officers: R. Faison Hester, Pres.; William H. Bryan, Secy.
Directors: Margaret Ann P. Parvin; Emmett Judson Pope III.
EIN: 561888088

7197
Eleanor R. Nalle Trust
c/o Wells Fargo Bank, N.A., Trust Tax Dept.
1 W. 4th St., 4th Fl., MAC D4000-041
Winston-Salem, NC 27101-3818

Foundation type: Independent foundation.
Financial data (yr. ended 12/31/14): Assets, $6,297,123; expenditures, $277,726; qualifying distributions, $242,556.
Fields of interest: Religion; Human services; Youth development.
Limitations: Applications not accepted. Giving primarily in Virginia.
Application information: Unsolicited requests for funds not accepted.
Trustee: Wells Fargo Bank, N.A.
EIN: 237349235

7198
Charles & Irene Nanney Foundation
c/o David Powell Nanney Jr.
P.O. Box 19763
Raleigh, NC 27619-9766

Established in 1961 in North Carolina.
Donors: Charles P. Nanney†; Irene B. Nanney†.
Foundation type: Independent foundation.
Financial data (yr. ended 12/31/14): Assets, $3,526,250; expenditures, $173,473; qualifying distributions, $170,957.
Fields of interest: Higher education; Law education; Nonprofits; Protestantism; Human services; Youth services.
Type of support: Regranting.
Limitations: Applications not accepted. Giving primarily in NC. No grants to individuals.
Application information: Contributes only to pre-selected organizations.
Trustees: Charles D. Gray III; Mary Ellen Jennings; David P. Nanney, Jr.
EIN: 566046763

7199
Robert Sidney Needham Foundation
1525 W. W.T. Harris Blvd., D1114-044
Charlotte, NC 28288-1161 (855) 739-2920
E-mail: grantadministration@wellsfargo.com; Main URL: https://www.wellsfargo.com/privatefoundationgrants/needham

Donor: Dorothy E. Needham†.
Foundation type: Independent foundation.
Financial data (yr. ended 12/31/14): Assets, $7,788,332; expenditures, $449,309; qualifying distributions, $379,422 and $0 for set-asides.
Purpose and activities: Grant awards to individuals through New Jersey colleges and universities supporting the Robert Sydney Needham Memorial Scholarship Program.
Fields of interest: Undergraduate education; University education.
Type of support: Scholarships.
Limitations: Applications accepted. Giving limited to NJ. No grants to individuals (directly).
Application information: See foundation website for complete application guidelines. Application form required.
Initial approach: Email
Deadline(s): Apr. 1
Trustees: John B. Newman, Esq.; Nina Stack; Wells Fargo Bank, N.A.
EIN: 300562220

7200
Leo Niessen, Jr. Charitable Trust
c/o Wells Fargo Bank, N.A., Trust Tax Dept.
1 W. 4th St., 4th Fl., MAC D4000-041
Winston-Salem, NC 27101-3818
1-888-234-1999
FAX: 1-877-746-5889;
E-mail: grantadministration@wellsfargo.com; Main URL: https://www.wellsfargo.com/privatefoundationgrants/niessen

Established in 1994 in Pennsylvania.
Donor: Leo Niessen, Jr.†.
Foundation type: Independent foundation.
Financial data (yr. ended 06/30/13): Assets, $3,559,856 (M); expenditures, $236,691;

qualifying distributions, $205,989; giving activities include $192,000 for 19 grants (high: $35,000; low: $2,000).
Fields of interest: Arts and culture; Education; Secondary education; Higher education; Religion; Human services; Child welfare; Females.
Type of support: General support; Scholarships.
Limitations: Applications accepted. Giving primarily in NJ and PA.
Application information: Applications must be submitted through the online grant application form or alternative accessible application designed for assistive technology users. See Trust web site for complete application information. Application form required.
 Initial approach: Complete online application form on trust web site
 Deadline(s): Apr. 30
Trustees: William R. Sasso, Esq.; Wells Fargo Bank, N.A.
EIN: 227723097

7201
The Nivison Family Foundation
c/o Arthur E. Nivison
4104 Atlantic Ave., Ste. 140
Raleigh, NC 27604-1803

Established in 2004 in North Carolina.
Donors: W.B. Nivison; WBN LLC.
Foundation type: Operating foundation.
Financial data (yr. ended 12/31/13): Assets, $2,087,830 (M); expenditures, $283,276; qualifying distributions, $253,134; giving activities include $253,134 for 40 grants (high: $101,384; low: $500).
Fields of interest: Education; Graduate and professional education; Community and economic development; Protestantism; Theology.
Type of support: Regranting; Fundraising.
Limitations: Applications not accepted. Giving primarily in VA and NC. No grants to individuals.
Application information: Contributes only to pre-selected organizations.
Officer: Arthur E. Nivison, Mgr.
EIN: 810657168

7202
North Carolina Foam Industries/Barnhardt Foundation
(formerly North Carolina Foam Foundation)
P.O. Box 34276
Charlotte, NC 28234-4276

Donors: North Carolina Foam Industries, Inc.; Thomas Barnhardt; NCFI Banhardt Foundation; Banhardt Manufacturigng Co.
Foundation type: Company-sponsored foundation.
Financial data (yr. ended 12/31/13): Assets, $7,236,392 (M); gifts received, $267,380; expenditures, $281,885; qualifying distributions, $245,600; giving activities include $245,600 for 71 grants (high: $25,000; low: $100).
Purpose and activities: The foundation supports arts councils and organizations involved with education, health, and human services.
Fields of interest: Education; Health; Religion.
Limitations: Applications not accepted. Giving primarily in Charlotte, NC. No grants to individuals.
Application information: Contributes only to pre-selected organizations.

Trustee: Ralph Falero.
EIN: 566068247

7203
Anna Oschwald Trust
c/o Wells Fargo Bank, N.A., Trust Tax Dept.
1 W. 4th St., 4th Fl., MAC D4000-041
Winston-Salem, NC 27101-3818

Established in 2000 in New Jersey.
Donor: Anna Oschwald†.
Foundation type: Independent foundation.
Financial data (yr. ended 12/31/14): Assets, $8,462,000 (M); expenditures, $471,746; qualifying distributions, $379,818; giving activities include $353,187 for 13 grants (high: $28,587; low: $10,149).
Fields of interest: Higher education; Animal welfare; Hospital care; Diseases and conditions; Human services; Child welfare.
Type of support: Research.
Limitations: Applications not accepted. Giving primarily in Red Bank, NJ, and NY, with emphasis on New York City and Port Washington; funding also in Washington, DC and Philadelphia, PA. No grants to individuals.
Application information: Contributes only to pre-selected organizations.
Trustee: Stephen J. Oppenheim; Wells Fargo Bank, N.A.
EIN: 256626923

7204
Outer Banks Community Foundation, Inc.
13 Skyline Rd.
Southern Shores, NC 27949 (252) 261-8839
Contact: Lorelei Costa, Exec. Dir.
FAX: (252) 261-0371; E-mail: info@obcf.org; Main URL: http://www.obcf.org
E Newsletter: http://www.obcf.org/news-updates/e-newsletter
Facebook: https://www.facebook.com/pages/Outer-Banks-Community-Foundation/131828147548
YouTube: http://www.youtube.com/channel/UCy8W-OVykhp_jyMPQOOwpug

Established in 1982 in North Carolina.
Foundation type: Community foundation.
Financial data (yr. ended 12/31/13): Assets, $12,020,686 (M); gifts received, $774,648; expenditures, $540,648; giving activities include $204,754 for 12+ grants (high: $19,300), and $111,687 for 4 grants to individuals (high: $7,000).
Purpose and activities: The foundation seeks to enhance the quality of life in the Outer Banks community by providing leadership and opportunities through the development and utilization of donor funds.
Fields of interest: Arts and culture; Historic preservation; Education; Environment; Health; Disasters and emergency management; Community and economic development; Human services; Youth development.
Type of support: Capital and infrastructure; Pro bono consulting services; Matching grants; Equipment; Endowments; Emergency funds; Program development; Convening; Recordings; Publications; Seed money; Scholarships; Technical assistance; Student aid.

Limitations: Applications accepted. Giving limited to the Outer Banks, NC, area. No grants to individuals (except through designated scholarship funds), or for annual operating expenses.
Publications: Application guidelines; Annual report; Financial statement; Grants list; Informational brochure; Newsletter.
Application information: Visit foundation web site for online application and guidelines. Application form required.
 Initial approach: Contact foundation
 Deadline(s): Feb. 6, May 1, July 31, Oct. 30
 Board meeting date(s): First Thurs. of Mar., June, Sept., and Dec.
Officers and Directors: Sharon Elliott, Pres. and Director; Ed Olsen, V.P. and Director; Avery Harrison, Secy. and Director; Bob Muller, Treas. and Director; Lorelei Costa, Exec. Dir.; John Graham; Deloris Harrell; Mike Kelly; Dorothy Killingsworth; Scott Leggat; Loretta Michael; Teresa Osbourn; Chris Seawell.
Number of staff: 1 full-time professional; 1 full-time support.
EIN: 581516313

7205
P & B Foundation
1025 Holleybank Dr.
Matthews, NC 28105-6531 (704) 821-3200
Contact: Larry C. Pratt, Pres. and Secy.

Established in 1970 in Michigan.
Donors: Kurt Cunningham; Pam Cunningham; C. Wilbur Peters; Eli Scholarship Fund; Grace Baptist Church; International Bible College; Providence Development Partners, LLC.
Foundation type: Independent foundation.
Financial data (yr. ended 08/31/14): Assets, $16,552,308 (M); expenditures, $663,106; qualifying distributions, $551,339; giving activities include $431,556 for 31 grants (high: $91,868; low: $1,250).
Purpose and activities: Giving primarily for Baptist church-related educational and religious institutions.
Fields of interest: Christianity; Baptist.
Type of support: General support; Program-related investments.
Limitations: Applications accepted. Giving primarily in AL, NC, MO, OH and VA. No grants to individuals.
Application information: Application form required.
 Initial approach: Letter
 Deadline(s): None
Officers: Larry C. Pratt, Pres. and Secy.; C. Wilbur Peters, V.P. and Treas.
Directors: Roger Peterson; Barry Shearer.
EIN: 237083912

7206
Jerome & Mildred Paddock Foundation
c/o Wells Fargo Bank, N.A.
1 W. 4th St., D4000-041
Winston-Salem, NC 27101
E-mail: grantadministration@wellsfargo.com; Wells Fargo Philanthropic Services: Toll-free tel.: 1-(888) 234-1999; tel. for technical questions about online application: 1-(888) 235-4351; fax: 1-(877) 746-5889; Application address: Paddock Foundation, 1819 Main St., No. 230, Sarasota, FL 34236, tel.: (941) 361-5803; Main URL: https://

www.wellsfargo.com/privatefoundationgrants/
paddock

Foundation type: Independent foundation.
Financial data (yr. ended 05/31/13): Assets,
$4,819,344 (M); expenditures, $238,470;
qualifying distributions, $183,158; giving activities
include $165,500 for 25 grants (high: $15,000;
low: $2,000).
Purpose and activities: Giving primarily for
disadvantaged children and the elderly.
Fields of interest: Health; Human services; Child
welfare; Seniors; Low-income and poor people.
Limitations: Applications accepted. Giving primarily
in Sarasota County, FL. No grants to individuals, or
for endowments, debt reduction, operating
expenses, conferences or seminars, workshops,
travel, surveys, advertising, research, fund raising or
for annual campaigns or capital campaigns.
Publications: Grants list.
Application information: Application guidelines and
form available on foundation web site. Application
form required.
  Copies of proposal: 6
  Deadline(s): Jan. 15
  Final notification: Mar. 15
Trustee: Wells Fargo Bank, N.A.
Number of staff: None.
EIN: 596200844

7207
Clifford A. and Lillian C. Peeler Family Foundation, Inc.
1816 E. Innes St.
Salisbury, NC 28145-2153

Established in 1997 in North Carolina.
Donor: Clifford Peeler†.
Foundation type: Independent foundation.
Financial data (yr. ended 06/30/14): Assets,
$3,256,587; expenditures, $205,347; qualifying
distributions, $170,008.
Fields of interest: Education services;
Protestantism; Human services; Child welfare;
Seniors; Females.
Limitations: Applications not accepted. Giving
primarily in NC. No grants to individuals.
Application information: Unsolicited requests for
funds not accepted.
Officers: Larry Peeler, Pres. and Treas.; Shirley
Ritchie, Secy.
EIN: 562060988

7208
Sylvia Perkin Perpetual Charitable Trust
c/o Wells Fargo IM&T Fid. Tax, SVCMAC D4000-04
1 W. 4th St., 4th Fl.
Winston-Salem, NC 27101
Main URL: https://www.wellsfargo.com/
privatefoundationgrants/perkin

Established in 1986 in Pennsylvania.
Donor: Sylvia Perkin†.
Foundation type: Independent foundation.
Financial data (yr. ended 04/30/13): Assets,
$7,087,157 (M); expenditures, $381,587;
qualifying distributions, $336,679; giving activities
include $324,500 for 39 grants (high: $60,000;
low: $1,000).

Purpose and activities: Giving primarily for Jewish
agencies and federated giving programs, education,
human services, and arts and culture.
Fields of interest: Arts and culture; Historic
preservation; Education; Higher education;
Nonprofits; Judaism; Human services; Child welfare.
Type of support: General support; Scholarships;
Regranting.
Limitations: Applications accepted. Giving limited to
Lehigh Valley, Allentown, PA. No grants to
individuals.
Application information: See foundation website for
complete application guidelines.
  Initial approach: Proposal
  Deadline(s): Feb. 1
Trustees: James D. Christie; Jed Rapoport; Wells
Fargo Bank, N.A.
EIN: 236792999

7209
Piedmont Triad Charitable Foundation, Inc.
(doing business as Wyndham Championship)
(formerly Greensboro Jaycees Charitable
Foundation)
416 Galimore Dairy Rd., Ste. M
Greensboro, NC 27409-9528
Main URL: http://
www.wyndhamchampionship.com/

Established in 1967 in North Carolina.
Donors: SETRAC; The Haley Foundation; Robert
Long; Greensboro Junior Chamber of Commerce;
The PGA Tour; Guilford County; ALS Therapy
Development Foundation; Foundation Fighting
Blindness; Texas Children's Hospital; Acushnet
Company; MBNA Mastercard, Inc.; DaimlerChrysler
Corp.; Granville Capital, Inc.; Multiple Sclerosis
Society; Muscular Dystrophy Association; Weaver
Foundation; Robert E., Jr. and Kathryn Scott Long
Family Foundation; The John McConnell Foundation;
Wishes By Wyndham Foundation; The Joseph M.
Bryan Foundation of Greater GSO, Inc.; John
McConnnell; Robert E. Long, Jr.
Foundation type: Operating foundation.
Financial data (yr. ended 12/31/13): Assets,
$1,360,762 (M); gifts received, $777,110;
expenditures, $11,983,134; qualifying
distributions, $521,350; giving activities include
$345,098 for 44 grants (high: $53,000; low: $30).
Fields of interest: Arts and culture; Foundations;
Diseases and conditions; Economic development;
Protestantism; Golf; Human services; Food banks;
Child welfare.
Limitations: Applications not accepted. Giving
primarily in GA and NC. No grants to individuals.
Application information: Contributes only to
pre-selected organizations.
Officers and Board Members: Robert E. Long, Jr.,
Chair. and Director; J.B. Davis, Vice-Chair. and
Director; Mike Bumpass, Treas.; Steve Bowden;
Carole Bruce; James B. Crouch, Jr.; Louis Dejoy;
Paul Fulton; Allen E. Gant, Jr.; Mike Haley; George
House; Bill Johnson; Harold L. Martin, Sr.; John
McConnell; Mackey McDonald; Walter McDowell;
Bonnie McElveen-Hunter; Jim Melvin; T. David Neill;
Tom Nolan; Carl Pettersson; William H. Smith; Rob
Spilman, Jr.; Fred Starr; John Swofford; Thomas C.
Watkins; Dunlop White III; Steven B. Wiggs.
EIN: 566085407

7210
The Pillmore Family Foundation
1709 Shadow Forest Dr.
Matthews, NC 28105-7225

Established in 2000 in Pennsylvania.
Donors: Eric Pillmore; Pamela Pillmore.
Foundation type: Independent foundation.
Financial data (yr. ended 12/31/14): Assets,
$4,847,449; gifts received, $552,720;
expenditures, $401,879; qualifying distributions,
$374,737.
Fields of interest: Education; Christianity; Human
services.
Limitations: Applications not accepted. Giving in the
U.S., with emphasis on CO, PA and VA. No grants to
individuals.
Application information: Contributes only to
pre-selected organizations.
Officers: Eric Pillmore, Pres.; Pam Pillmore, V.P.
EIN: 233064365

7211
John W. Plansoen Trust
1525 W. WT Harris Blvd., D1114-044
Charlotte, NC 28262

Foundation type: Independent foundation.
Financial data (yr. ended 12/31/13): Assets,
$4,707,819 (M); expenditures, $238,104;
qualifying distributions, $226,249; giving activities
include $216,199 for 12 grants (high: $75,670;
low: $10,000).
Fields of interest: Hospital care; Protestantism;
Human services.
Limitations: Applications not accepted. Giving
primarily in FL and MA. No grants to individuals.
Application information: Contributes only to
pre-selected organizations.
Trustees: Hector L. Plansoen; Helen Post; Johanna
Young; Wells Fargo Bank, N.A.
EIN: 226020281

7212
Lawrence E. Pope Foundation
1349-C South Park Dr.
Kernersville, NC 27284-3887

Donor: Lawrence E. Pope.
Foundation type: Independent foundation.
Financial data (yr. ended 12/31/13): Assets,
$2,695,564 (M); expenditures, $206,363;
qualifying distributions, $160,780; giving activities
include $156,200 for 10 grants (high: $30,000;
low: $2,000).
Fields of interest: Education; Christianity; Human
services.
Limitations: Applications not accepted.
Application information: Unsolicited requests for
funds not accepted.
Officers and Directors: Scott L. Pope, Pres. and
Director; Amy P. Stinnett, V.P. and Director; Jeffrey
B. Taylor, Secy.-Treas. and Director; Robert Hunter;
George Thomas.
EIN: 263532956

7213

The Marjorie Merriweather Post Foundation

c/o Eton Advisors, LP
5915 Farrington Rd., Ste. 202
Chapel Hill, NC 27517-9900   (919) 442-1545
Contact: W. Jackson Parham

Established in 1956 in District of Columbia.
Donor: Marjorie Merriweather Post‡.
Foundation type: Independent foundation.
Financial data (yr. ended 12/31/13): Assets, $6,739,848 (M); expenditures, $414,750; qualifying distributions, $343,480; giving activities include $315,000 for 18 grants (high: $68,000; low: $2,500).
Fields of interest: Arts and culture; Performing arts; Orchestral music; Natural history museums; Historical activities; Elementary education; Higher education; Natural resources; Forest preservation; Hospital care; Catholicism; Human services.
Limitations: Giving primarily on the East Coast, with emphasis on Washington, DC. No grants to individuals.
Publications: Application guidelines.
Application information: All grant monies must be used within the territorial U.S.
   Initial approach: Proposal
   Copies of proposal: 1
   Deadline(s): Mar. 1 and Sept. 1
   Board meeting date(s): Spring and fall
   Final notification: Notification sent only to those organizations which are approved for grants
Officers: Nina Craig Rumbough, Chair.; Spotswood P. Dudley, Vice-Chair.; Henry A. Dudley, Jr., Vice-Chair.; Pattie J. Hebert, Secy.; Leonard L. Silverstein, Treas.
Trustees: Ellen Macneille Charles; George D. Iverson.
EIN: 526054705

7214

The Pratt Family Foundation, Inc.

8505 Case Ridge Dr.
Oak Ridge, NC 27310-9684
E-mail: Jpratt1011@aol.com; Application address: c/o Craven Shelton & Gann, Attn.: Sandy Shelton, 445 Dolley Madison Rd., Ste. 110, Greensboro, NC 27410, tel.: (336) 299-6061; Main URL: http://prattfoundation.org

Established in 1999 in North Carolina.
Donors: William J. Pratt; Jeanne M. Pratt.
Foundation type: Independent foundation.
Financial data (yr. ended 12/31/13): Assets, $3,433,741 (M); expenditures, $256,012; qualifying distributions, $192,500; giving activities include $192,500 for 16 grants (high: $40,000; low: $2,500).
Purpose and activities: Giving primarily to organizations promoting excellence in schools as well as advancements in healthcare and medical technology. Also gives to agencies addressing such issues as domestic violence, poverty, youth at-risk, and homelessness in the Greater Greensboro/Piedmont Triad community.
Fields of interest: Elementary education; Higher education; Graduate and professional education; Hospital care; Theology; Human services; Child development.
Type of support: General support.

Limitations: Applications accepted. Giving primarily in NC. No grants to individuals.
Application information: Application form available on foundation web site. Application form required.
   Deadline(s): None
Officers: William J. Pratt, Pres.; Ryan M. Pratt, V.P.; Desiree Pratt, Secy.; William H. Pratt, Treas.
Board Members: Ana Carmina McCoy; Donna Pratt; Jeanne Anne Pratt; Mandy Sloan.
EIN: 311677890

7215

Rusty Pulliam Foundation, Inc.

2 Walden Ridge Dr.
Asheville, NC 28803

Donors: Winston W. Pulliam, Jr.; Pulliam Properties; Rusty Pulliam.
Foundation type: Independent foundation.
Financial data (yr. ended 12/31/13): Assets, $1,860 (M); gifts received, $169,000; expenditures, $177,788; qualifying distributions, $175,450; giving activities include $175,450 for 18 grants (high: $74,200; low: $200).
Fields of interest: Education; Higher education; Religion; Human services.
Limitations: Applications not accepted. Giving primarily in NC.
Application information: Unsolicited requests for funds not accepted.
Officers: Winston W. Pulliam, Jr., Pres.; John G. Kelso, Secy.; Lawrence C. Pulliam, Treas.
Directors: James Hardy Johnson, Jr.; Scott Rogers.
EIN: 460796397

7216

Trent Ragland, Jr. Trust

1525 W. WT Harris Blvd., D1114-044
Charlotte, NC 28262

Established in 1959 in North Carolina.
Donor: W. Trent Ragland, Jr.
Foundation type: Independent foundation.
Financial data (yr. ended 12/31/13): Assets, $6,074,349 (M); expenditures, $330,036; qualifying distributions, $278,670; giving activities include $268,062 for 77 grants (high: $107,500; low: $100).
Purpose and activities: Support primarily for higher education and human services, including community funds; support also for health and cultural programs, including historic preservation.
Fields of interest: Arts and culture; Historic preservation; Higher education; Nonprofits; Health; Diseases and conditions; Public libraries; Christianity; Human services.
Type of support: Regranting.
Limitations: Applications not accepted. Giving primarily in FL, NC, and VA. No grants to individuals.
Application information: Contributes only to pre-selected organizations.
Trustee: Wells Fargo Bank, N.A.
Number of staff: 1 part-time support.
EIN: 566035980

7217

O'H. Rankin Foundation, Inc.

601 Colville Rd.
Charlotte, NC 28207-2307

Established in 1976 in Unspecified.
Donors: Nancy Rankin; David Rankin; Samuel B. Rankin.
Foundation type: Independent foundation.
Financial data (yr. ended 05/31/13): Assets, $4,204,979 (M); gifts received, $35,759; expenditures, $249,240; qualifying distributions, $182,420; giving activities include $182,420 for 45 grants (high: $34,500; low: $500).
Fields of interest: Orchestral music; Museums; Elementary and secondary education; Higher education; Health; Diseases and conditions; Human services.
Type of support: General support; Continuing support; Research; Annual campaigns; Capital campaigns; Capital and infrastructure; Emergency funds.
Limitations: Applications accepted. Giving primarily in the Charlotte, NC, area. No grants to individuals.
Application information:
   Initial approach: Proposal
   Deadline(s): None
Officers: David H. Rankin, Chair.; Samuel B. Rankin, Pres.; Nancy O'H. Rankin, V.P.; Betty R. Hechenbleikner, Secy.-Treas.
EIN: 237005335

7218

The Redwoods Group Foundation Inc.

2801 Slater Rd., Ste. 220
Morrisville, NC 27560-8477   (919) 462-9759
Contact: Laurel Vadala, Grants Facilitator; Dan Baum, Exec. Dir.
FAX: (919) 481-6462;
E-mail: LVadala@RedwoodsGroup.comDBaum@RedwoodsGroupFoundation.org; Alternate Phone: (919) 469-7369; Main URL: http://redwoodsgroupfoundation.org

Established in 2007 in North Carolina.
Donors: The Redwoods Group, Inc.; The Columbia Foundation.
Foundation type: Operating foundation.
Financial data (yr. ended 12/31/13): Assets, $65,923 (M); gifts received, $89,674; expenditures, $691,242; qualifying distributions, $615,823; giving activities include $195,070 for 81 grants (high: $3,250; low: $50), and $370,106 for 3 foundation-administered programs.
Purpose and activities: The foundation supports programs designed to promote child sexual abuse prevention, drowning prevention, and growing in the field of social entrepreneurship.
Fields of interest: Education; Child abuse; Sexual abuse; Safety education; Public policy; Business and industry; Entrepreneurship; Swimming; Human rights; Human services; Children.
Type of support: General support; Employee volunteer services; Annual campaigns; Employee matching gifts; Equal access; Pro bono board services; Pro bono human resources services; Policy, advocacy and systems reform.
Limitations: Applications accepted. No support for labor organizations, religious organizations for religious purposes or fraternal or social organizations. No grants to individuals, or for arts for the general public or aid to domestic animals.
Publications: Newsletter.
Application information: Application form required.
   Initial approach: Contact foundation for deadlines and application form
   Deadline(s): Varies

Officers and Directors: Kevin A. Trapani, Pres.; Mac Kendall; Jennifer A. Trapani, V.P. and Secy.; William C. Mecklenburg, Jr., V.P.; Brian Keel, Treas.; Dan Baum, Exec. Dir.
EIN: 770698917

7219
Paul, Jr. and Martha N. Rees Charitable Trust

c/o Trust Tax Dept.
P.O. Box 2907
Wilson, NC   27894-2907

Established in 2006 in Virginia.
Donor: Martha Rees.
Foundation type: Independent foundation.
Financial data (yr. ended 12/31/13): Assets, $9,199,033 (M); gifts received, $851; expenditures, $484,167; qualifying distributions, $389,180; giving activities include $389,180 for 17 grants (high: $63,929; low: $11,188).
Fields of interest: Higher education; Catholicism.
Limitations: Applications not accepted. Giving primarily in MI, NY, PA, and VA. No grants to individuals.
Application information: Contributes only to pre-selected organizations.
Trustee: Branch Banking & Trust Co.
EIN: 206740669

7220
Dorothy N. Ribenack Charitable Trust

c/o Wells Fargo Bank, N.A.
1 W. 4th St., 4th Fl., MAC D4000-041
Winston-Salem, NC   27101-3818

Foundation type: Independent foundation.
Financial data (yr. ended 10/31/14): Assets, $8,079,351 (M); expenditures, $410,581; qualifying distributions, $339,399; giving activities include $316,822 for 6 grants (high: $63,092; low: $1,362).
Fields of interest: Nursing care; Rehabilitation; Human services.
Type of support: General support.
Limitations: Applications not accepted. Giving primarily in Duluth, MN.
Application information: Unsolicited requests for funds not accepted.
Trustee: Wells Fargo Bank, N.A.
EIN: 416054248

7221
The Mary Lynn Richardson Fund

c/o Piedmont Trust Co.
P.O. Box 20124
Greensboro, NC   27420-0124   (336) 274-5471

Established in 1940 in North Carolina.
Donor: Mary Lynn Richardson†.
Foundation type: Independent foundation.
Financial data (yr. ended 12/31/13): Assets, $6,980,831 (M); expenditures, $350,815; qualifying distributions, $313,349; giving activities include $293,388 for 40 grants (high: $25,000; low: $2,000).
Purpose and activities: Though the foundation is not a bricks and mortar fund, the foundation does make grants for basic needs funding (health,

education and shelter). The foundation also dispenses half its monies to foreign missions.
Fields of interest: Higher education; Health; Christianity; Human services; Child welfare; Senior services; International relations; Seniors; Low-income and poor people.
Type of support: General support; Grants to individuals; Seed money; Research; Volunteer development.
Limitations: Applications accepted. Giving primarily in NC, with an emphasis on Guilford County; giving internationally also to 501(c)(3) foreign organizations. No grants for building funds.
Publications: Application guidelines.
Application information: Application form required.
  Initial approach: Letter
  Copies of proposal: 1
  Deadline(s): Aug. 31
  Board meeting date(s): Nov.
  Final notification: Dec. 31
Trustees: Patricia S. Agnew; Eric R. Calhoun; Matthew Lem; Betsy Boney Mead; Britt A. Preyer.
Number of staff: None.
EIN: 066025946

7222
Hubert A. Ritchie Foundation

38 W. 1st Ave.
Lexington, NC   27292

Established in 2000 in North Carolina.
Foundation type: Independent foundation.
Financial data (yr. ended 12/31/14): Assets, $4,589,155; expenditures, $273,511; qualifying distributions, $242,600.
Fields of interest: Education; Elementary education; Secondary education; University education; Christianity.
Type of support: General support.
Limitations: Applications not accepted. Giving primarily in Salisbury, NC. No grants to individuals.
Application information: Unsolicited requests for funds not accepted.
Trustees: Barbara Brown; Timmy L. Ervin; Donald Menius; Newbridge Bank.
EIN: 546481375

7223
Oscar C. Rixson Foundation, Inc.

P.O. Box 19255
Asheville, NC   28815-1255   8282741121
E-mail: mojo@asheville.com

Established in 1925 in New York.
Donors: Oscar C. Rixson†; Mary Rixson†; Eleanor Rixon Cannon†; Ulrika Rixon Booth†.
Foundation type: Independent foundation.
Financial data (yr. ended 12/31/14): Assets, $3,233,975; gifts received, $84,358; expenditures, $363,076; qualifying distributions, $287,625.
Purpose and activities: Grants only to evangelical churches, missions, and organizations in support of missionaries. Grant requests for non-Protestant, non-evangelical purposes will not be considered. Since grants originate within the Rixson Board, requests for grants are neither solicited nor desired.
Fields of interest: Protestantism.
International interests: Africa; Canada; Europe; South America.

Type of support: General support; Grants to individuals; Continuing support.
Limitations: Applications not accepted. Giving throughout the U.S., Canada, Africa, Europe, South America, and the Far East. No support for welfare programs, or for non-Protestant evangelical programs.
Application information: General applications for grants are not solicited.
  Board meeting date(s): Last Sat. of Apr.
Officers and Directors: Alan L. Mojonnier, Pres. and Director; James M. Gilbert, V.P. and Director; Richard Yeskoo, Secy. and Director; Timothy VanWyck, Treas. and Director; Donald Dunkerton; Thomas J. Elliott, Sr.; RADM. Thomas J. Elliot, Jr.; Sajan Joseph; Raul Sanchez.
Number of staff: 2 part-time support.
EIN: 136129767

7224
C.L. Robbins Trust

c/o Wells Fargo Bank, N.A., Trust Tax Dept.
1 W. 4th St, 4th Fl. MAC D4000-041
Winston-Salem, NC   27101-3818

Foundation type: Independent foundation.
Financial data (yr. ended 12/31/14): Assets, $6,318,382 (M); expenditures, $331,549; qualifying distributions, $274,252; giving activities include $252,307 for 27 grants (high: $59,713; low: $750).
Fields of interest: Health; Christianity.
Limitations: Applications not accepted. Giving primarily in NC.
Application information: Contributes only to pre-selected organizations.
Trustee: Wells Fargo Bank, N.A.
EIN: 566077467

7225
H. English and Ermine Carter Robinson Foundation

1525 W. WT Harris Blvd., D1114-044
Charlotte, NC   28262
Application address: Wells Fargo Bank, N.A., 3280 Peachtree Rd. N.E., Atlanta GA 30305, tel.: (336) 747-8185

Established in 1991 in North Carolina.
Donor: Harry English Robinson, Jr.
Foundation type: Independent foundation.
Financial data (yr. ended 12/31/13): Assets, $4,125,137 (M); expenditures, $220,683; qualifying distributions, $174,245; giving activities include $156,750 for 26 grants (high: $62,000; low: $500).
Fields of interest: Arts and culture; Historical activities; Education; Foundations; Health; Christianity; Human services; Youth services.
Limitations: Applications accepted. Giving primarily in Atlanta, GA. No grants to individuals.
Application information:
  Initial approach: Proposal
  Deadline(s): None
Trustee: Wells Fargo Bank, N.A.
EIN: 581981556

7226
Henry J. Robitaille Trust
1525 W. WT Harris Blvd. D1114-044
Charlotte, NC   28288-0001

Foundation type: Independent foundation.
Financial data (yr. ended 12/31/14): Assets,
$3,646,718; expenditures, $221,664; qualifying
distributions, $184,161.
Fields of interest: Health; Religion; Christianity;
Human services.
Limitations: Applications not accepted. Giving
primarily in Washington, DC and RI.
Application information: Unsolicited requests for
funds not accepted.
Trustee: Wells Fargo Bank, N.A.
EIN: 056066742

7227
Rocky Mount Community Foundation, Inc.
P.O. Box 1898
Burlington, NC   27216-1898   2524430551
Application address: c/o J. Buckley Strandberg, P.O.
Box 8105, Rocky Mount, NC 27804-1105,
tel.: (252) 446-6131

Established in 1997 in North Carolina.
Donor: Rocky Mount Merchants Association.
Foundation type: Independent foundation.
Financial data (yr. ended 12/31/14): Assets,
$4,171,974; expenditures, $238,905; qualifying
distributions, $202,276.
Fields of interest: Arts and culture; Historic
preservation; Higher education; Archives and
special collections; Community and economic
development; Christianity; Human services; Youth
services.
Limitations: Applications accepted. Giving limited to
the Rocky Mount, NC, area.
Application information: Application form required.
   Initial approach: Letter
   Deadline(s): None
Officer: J. Buckley Strandberg, Pres. and Secy.
Directors: Bill Daughtridge; Eugene F. Holland, Jr.;
John B. Kincheloe, Jr.; Charles Penny; Cindy
Stewart.
Trustee: Trust Co. of the South.
EIN: 562055212

7228
Florence Rogers Charitable Trust
P.O. Box 36006
Fayetteville, NC   28303   (910) 484-2033

Established in 1961 in North Carolina.
Donor: Florence L. Rogers†.
Foundation type: Independent foundation.
Financial data (yr. ended 03/31/15): Assets,
$6,005,975; expenditures, $508,011; qualifying
distributions, $310,124.
Purpose and activities: Support for music and the
arts, education, recreation, hunger programs, youth
and child welfare, nursing and hospices, wildlife,
and the general quality of life in the area. Preference
is given to seed money for new ideas.
Fields of interest: Arts and culture; Museums;
Elementary and secondary education; Higher
education; Graduate and professional education;
Botanical gardens; Nursing care; Protestantism;
Special population support.

Type of support: General support; Matching grants;
Equipment; Emergency funds; Program
development; Convening; Publications; Seed
money; Scholarships; Research.
Limitations: Applications accepted. Giving primarily
in Cumberland County, Fayetteville, and
southeastern NC. No grants to individuals, or for
building or endowment funds, scholarships, or
fellowships; no loans.
Publications: Informational brochure (including
application guidelines).
Application information: Application form required.
   Initial approach: Grant application form
   Copies of proposal: 1
   Deadline(s): None
   Board meeting date(s): Monthly
Trustees: J. William Lambert; Jessie Tally.
Number of staff: 2 full-time professional; 1 part-time
professional; 2 full-time support; 1 part-time
support.
EIN: 566074515

7229
The Rolander Family Foundation
2724 Snowy Meadow Ct.
Raleigh, NC   27614-7586   (919) 876-0838
Contact: Stephen B. Rolander, Pres.

Established in 2000 in Pennsylvania.
Foundation type: Independent foundation.
Financial data (yr. ended 12/31/13): Assets,
$6,325,886 (M); expenditures, $332,325;
qualifying distributions, $317,260; giving activities
include $317,260 for 50 grants (high: $35,000;
low: $500).
Purpose and activities: Giving primarily for the arts,
public broadcasting, medical research, programs
and facilities for children with special needs,
religion, and housing development.
Fields of interest: Orchestral music; Museums;
Historic preservation; Diseases and conditions;
Communication media; Housing development;
Religion; Human services; Child welfare.
International interests: Africa; Central America;
Haiti; South America.
Type of support: General support; Annual
campaigns; Capital campaigns; Capital and
infrastructure; Research; Equipment; Research and
evaluation; Program development.
Limitations: Applications accepted. Giving on a
national basis, particularly to areas where members
of the board or family reside.
Publications: Application guidelines.
Application information: Application form required.
   Initial approach: Letter
   Copies of proposal: 1
   Deadline(s): None
   Board meeting date(s): Twice yearly
Officers: Stephen B. Rolander, Pres.; Nancy R.
Leroy, V.P.; Stephen C. Leroy, Secy.
Directors: W. Scott Leroy; William B. Leroy; C. Arthur
Rolander III; C. Arthur Rolander, Jr.; Mildred D.
Rolander.
Number of staff: 2 part-time professional.
EIN: 912080946

7230
Smith Rolla Trust f/b/o Charities
c/o Wells Fargo Bank, N.A. Trust Tax Dept.
1 W. 4th St., 4th Fl., MAC D4000-041
Winston-Salem, NC   27101-3818

Foundation type: Independent foundation.
Financial data (yr. ended 12/31/13): Assets,
$5,766,009 (M); expenditures, $280,793;
qualifying distributions, $265,651; giving activities
include $239,000 for 3 grants (high: $133,340;
low: $39,000).
Fields of interest: Domesticated animals; Animal
welfare; Religion.
Type of support: General support.
Limitations: Applications not accepted. Giving
primarily in PA.
Application information: Unsolicited requests for
funds not accepted.
Trustee: Wells Fargo Bank, N.A.
EIN: 236212351

7231
**The E. T. Rollins, Jr. and Frances P. Rollins
Foundation**
3511 Shannon Rd., Ste. 140
Durham, NC   27707-6340

Established in 2005 in North Carolina.
Donors: E.T. Rollins, Jr.; Frances P. Rollins.
Foundation type: Independent foundation.
Financial data (yr. ended 12/31/13): Assets,
$5,262,956 (M); expenditures, $250,560;
qualifying distributions, $203,187; giving activities
include $203,187 for 20 grants (high: $100,000;
low: $1,000).
Fields of interest: Ballet; Orchestral music; Science
museums; Education; University education; Human
services.
Limitations: Applications not accepted. Giving
primarily in NC. No grants to individuals.
Application information: Unsolicited requests for
funds not accepted.
Trustee: Frances P. Rollins.
EIN: 204802775

7232
Rostan Family Foundation
P.O. Box 970
Valdese, NC   28690-0970

Established in 1995 in North Carolina.
Donors: John P. Rostan, Jr.†; Naomi B. Rostan.
Foundation type: Independent foundation.
Financial data (yr. ended 12/31/13): Assets,
$7,145,587 (M); expenditures, $375,802;
qualifying distributions, $308,050; giving activities
include $308,050 for 24 grants (high: $167,050;
low: $1,500).
Fields of interest: University education;
Foundations; Health; Hospice care; Public libraries;
Christianity; Human services; Scouting programs.
Limitations: Applications not accepted. Giving
limited to NC, with emphasis on Burke County. No
grants to individuals.
Application information: Contributes only to
pre-selected organizations. Unsolicited requests for
funds not accepted.
Officers and Trustees: Mrs. John P. Rostan, Jr.,
C.E.O. and Pres. and Trustee; John P. Rostan III, V.P.
and Secy. and Trustee; James H. Rostan, V.P. and
Treas. and Trustee.
Number of staff: None.
EIN: 561901626

7233
S.D.R. Foundation, Inc.
8704 Highhill Rd.
Raleigh, NC   27615-2038

Established in 1999 in North Carolina.
Donors: David S. Rendall; Suganthi E. Rendall; Shalini Bennett.
Foundation type: Independent foundation.
Financial data (yr. ended 12/31/13): Assets, $824,779 (M); gifts received, $909,905; expenditures, $222,009; qualifying distributions, $217,315; giving activities include $217,000 for 4 grants (high: $194,000; low: $2,000).
Fields of interest: Education; Religion; Human services.
Limitations: Applications not accepted. Giving primarily in PA and NC, with some giving in VA. No grants to individuals.
Application information: Unsolicited requests for funds not accepted.
Officers: David S. Rendall, Pres.; Suganthi E. Rendall, V.P.; Shalini R. Bennett, Secy.; Vaneetha R. Demski, Treas.
Board Member: Robert E. Monroe.
EIN: 562170889

7234
Caroline J. S. Sanders Charitable Trust No. II
c/o Wells Fargo Bank, N.A.
1 W. 4th St., 4th Fl., MAC D4000-041
Winston-Salem, NC   27101-3818

Established in 1990 in Pennsylvania.
Donor: Caroline J.S. Sanders†.
Foundation type: Independent foundation.
Financial data (yr. ended 09/30/14): Assets, $3,652,896 (M); expenditures, $227,470; qualifying distributions, $183,715; giving activities include $162,000 for 49 grants (high: $12,000; low: $2,000).
Fields of interest: Arts and culture; Education; Health; Human services; Children and youth.
Type of support: General support; Equipment; Program development; Scholarships.
Limitations: Applications accepted. Giving primarily in NJ and PA. No support for churches or athletic events. No grants to individuals, or for fundraising, or endowment or general operating funds; no loans.
Application information: Application form required.
Initial approach: Online grant application
Deadline(s): Applications must be submitted by Mar. 1 and/or Sept. 1 to be reviewed at the semi-annual grant meetings
Board meeting date(s): Apr. and Oct.
Trustee: Wells Fargo Bank, N.A.
EIN: 232676889

7235
Kurt Sandt Trust
c/o Wells Fargo Bank, N.A., Trust Tax Dept.
1 W. 4th St., 4th Fl., MAC D4000-041
Winston-Salem, NC   27101-3818

Foundation type: Independent foundation.
Financial data (yr. ended 12/31/14): Assets, $11,576,098; expenditures, $292,415; qualifying distributions, $230,353.
Fields of interest: Higher education.

Limitations: Applications not accepted. Giving primarily in MN.
Application information: Unsolicited requests for funds not accepted.
Trustee: Wells Fargo Bank, N.A.
EIN: 466088034

7236
L. Florence Schmidt Foundation
c/o Wells Fargo Bank, N. A., Trust Tax Dept.
1 W. 4th St., 4th Fl. MAC D4000-041
Winston-Salem, NC   27101-3818

Established in 2007 in North Carolina.
Donor: L. Florence Schmidt Trust.
Foundation type: Independent foundation.
Financial data (yr. ended 12/31/13): Assets, $3,495,830 (M); expenditures, $396,553; qualifying distributions, $359,523; giving activities include $348,065 for 5 grants (high: $69,613; low: $69,613).
Fields of interest: Animal welfare; Health; Specialty hospital care; Alzheimer's disease; Youth services; Senior assisted living.
Limitations: Applications not accepted. Giving primarily in FL, with some giving in PA and TN. No grants to individuals.
Application information: Contributes only to pre-selected organizations.
Trustee: Wells Fargo Bank, N.A.
EIN: 510644401

7237
Schug Foundation
c/o Peggy Cobb Schug
7013 Erin Ct.
Charlotte, NC   28210-4906
Application address: c/o Phillips M. Bragg, 1031 S. Caldwell St., Ste. 200, Charlotte, NC, 28203; tel.: (704) 377-0261.

Established in 2001 in North Carolina.
Donor: Peggy C. Schug.
Foundation type: Independent foundation.
Financial data (yr. ended 12/31/14): Assets, $1,133,857 (M); expenditures, $216,025; qualifying distributions, $195,905; giving activities include $195,905 for 77 grants to individuals (high: $5,000; low: $137).
Purpose and activities: Scholarship awards to residents of Mecklenburg, Haywood or Jackson counties, North Carolina.
Fields of interest: Higher education.
Type of support: Student aid.
Limitations: Applications accepted. Giving primarily to residents of Mecklenburg, Haywood and Jackson counties, NC.
Application information: Application form required.
Initial approach: Contact foundation
Deadline(s): Apr. 30
Trustees: John B. Schug; Peggy C. Schug.
EIN: 566583795

7238
The Sara Smith Self Foundation, Inc.
1001 W. 4th St.
Winston-Salem, NC   27101-2410   (336) 607-7314
Contact: Robert L. Edwards, Secy.-Treas. and Dir.

Established in 2005 in North Carolina.
Donor: Sara Smith Self.
Foundation type: Independent foundation.
Financial data (yr. ended 12/31/13): Assets, $3,830,438 (M); expenditures, $229,553; qualifying distributions, $184,000; giving activities include $184,000 for 32 grants (high: $25,000; low: $500).
Fields of interest: Education; Diseases and conditions; Religion; Human services.
Type of support: General support; Student aid.
Limitations: Applications accepted. Giving primarily in NC.
Application information: Application form required.
Initial approach: Letter
Deadline(s): None
Officers and Directors: Smith Winborne Self, V.P. and Director; Robert L. Edwards, Secy.-Treas. and Director; Robert Sheldon.
EIN: 203631059

7239
Gerald & Olivia Shapiro Family Foundation
1525 W. WT Harris Blvd., D1114-044
Charlotte, NC   28288-5709

Foundation type: Independent foundation.
Financial data (yr. ended 12/31/14): Assets, $2,424,471 (M); expenditures, $214,645; qualifying distributions, $191,800; giving activities include $190,800 for 9 grants (high: $100,000; low: $1,500).
Fields of interest: Education; Judaism; Human services.
Limitations: Applications not accepted. Giving primarily in FL and IL.
Application information: Unsolicited requests for funds not accepted.
Trustees: Gerald M. Shapiro; Olivia S. Shapiro.
EIN: 271521392

7240
The Bill & Susan Sherrard Foundation
c/o Wells Fargo Bank, N.A.
1 W. 4th St., 4th Fl., MAC D4000-041
Winston-Salem, NC   27101-3818
E-mail: grantadministration@wellsfargo.com; Main URL: https://www.wellsfargo.com/privatefoundationgrants/sherrard

Established in 1993 in Illinois.
Donor: William Sherrard†.
Foundation type: Independent foundation.
Financial data (yr. ended 06/30/13): Assets, $5,673,321 (M); expenditures, $223,654; qualifying distributions, $177,246; giving activities include $165,832 for 9 grants (high: $74,500; low: $832).
Purpose and activities: Giving primarily to organizations benefiting residents of Henry County, Illinois, in the areas of education, historic preservation and nursing care.
Fields of interest: Education; Foundations; Protestantism.
Type of support: General support.
Limitations: Applications accepted. Giving primarily in IA and Henry County, IL. No grants to individuals.
Application information: See foundation website for complete application guidelines. Application form required.
Deadline(s): Oct. 15

Trustee: Wells Fargo Bank, N.A.
EIN: 363918216

7241
Newton B. Shingleton Trust
1525 W. WT Harris Blvd., D1114-044
Charlotte, NC 28288-1161
Application address: c/o Kevin Grogan, 1 W. 4th St.,
2nd Fl., Winston-Salem, NC 27101, tel.: (855)
739-2920; Main URL: https://
www.wellsfargo.com/privatefoundationgrants/
shingleton

Established in 1990 in Virginia.
Foundation type: Independent foundation.
Financial data (yr. ended 04/30/13): Assets,
$4,609,099 (M); expenditures, $267,857;
qualifying distributions, $223,379; giving activities
include $205,821 for 76 grants (high: $60,000;
low: $264).
Purpose and activities: Giving primarily to Christian
churches and for education.
Fields of interest: Education; Higher education;
Libraries; Fire prevention and control; Christianity;
Human services; People with vision impairments.
Type of support: General support.
Limitations: Applications accepted. Giving primarily
in VA. No grants to individuals.
Application information: Application form required.
Initial approach: Contact Trust for application
Deadline(s): Dec. 31
Trustee: Wells Fargo Bank, N.A.
EIN: 546329857

7242
Shugart Family Foundation
4004 Long Meadow Ln.
Winston-Salem, NC 27106-6315

Established in 2000 in North Carolina.
Donors: Shugart Enterprises, LLC; Shugart
Management Inc.; Grover F. Shugart, Jr.
Foundation type: Company-sponsored foundation.
Financial data (yr. ended 04/30/14): Assets,
$548,690 (M); expenditures, $175,402; qualifying
distributions, $167,200; giving activities include
$167,200 for 89 grants (high: $12,000; low: $100).
Purpose and activities: The foundation supports
organizations involved with education, health,
hunger, human services, business, and Christianity.
Fields of interest: Education; Nonprofits; Health;
Business and industry; Christianity; Human
services; Food banks; Food delivery; Child welfare;
Youth services; Developmental disability services.
Type of support: General support; Regranting.
Limitations: Applications not accepted. Giving
primarily in NC; giving also to national organizations.
No grants to individuals.
Application information: Contributes only to
pre-selected organizations.
Directors: Grover F. Shugart, Jr.; Kay W. Shugart.
EIN: 562230054

7243
Silverback Foundation, Inc.
1414 Raleigh Rd., Ste. 250
Chapel Hill, NC 27517-8834 (919) 969-9300
Contact: Elliot G. Bossen, V.P.

Established in 2004 in Unspecified.

Donors: Elliott G. Bossen; Connie Nickell Bossen.
Foundation type: Independent foundation.
Financial data (yr. ended 12/31/13): Assets,
$4,650,739 (M); gifts received, $500,000;
expenditures, $236,698; qualifying distributions,
$234,300; giving activities include $234,300 for 13
grants (high: $46,500; low: $600).
Fields of interest: Arts and culture; Education;
Higher education.
Application information:
Initial approach: Proposal
Deadline(s): None
Officers: Connie Nickell Bossen, Pres.; Elliott G.
Bossen, V.P.
EIN: 830380210

7244
The Marc and Mattye Silverman Family Foundation
(formerly The Silverman Foundation)
c/o Mattye B. Silverman
6707-C Fairview Rd.
Charlotte, NC 28210-3660

Established in 1989 in North Carolina.
Donors: Marc H. Silverman; Mattye B. Silverman.
Foundation type: Independent foundation.
Financial data (yr. ended 03/31/13): Assets,
$2,496,020 (M); gifts received, $11,010;
expenditures, $188,382; qualifying distributions,
$176,793; giving activities include $172,099 for 73
grants (high: $38,058; low: $18).
Fields of interest: Performing arts; Museums;
Higher education; Nonprofits; Diseases and
conditions; Judaism; Human services.
Type of support: Annual campaigns; Capital
campaigns; Fellowships; Regranting.
Limitations: Applications not accepted. Giving
primarily in Charlotte, NC. No grants to individuals.
Application information: Contributes only to
pre-selected organizations.
Officers and Directors: Mattye B. Silverman, Pres.
and Director; Debra L. Foster, V.P.; Shara K.
Silverman, V.P.; Lorin S. Stiefel, Secy.; Marc W.
Silverman, Treas.
Number of staff: None.
EIN: 561678118

7245
Sites Designated Charities Trust
(formerly Venette and Mabel Sites Foundation)
c/o Wells Fargo Bank, N.A., Trust Tax Dept.
1 W. 4th St., 4th Fl., MAC D4000-041
Winston-Salem, NC 27101-3818

Foundation type: Independent foundation.
Financial data (yr. ended 12/31/14): Assets,
$6,158,437; expenditures, $375,524; qualifying
distributions, $314,636.
Fields of interest: Education; Christianity;
Protestantism; Human services.
Type of support: General support.
Limitations: Applications not accepted. Giving
primarily in IL, IN, NY and VA.
Application information: Unsolicited requests for
funds not accepted.
Trustee: Wells Fargo Bank, N.A.
EIN: 356018382

7246
C. Hamilton Sloan Foundation
4900 Falls of Neuse, Ste. 150
Raleigh, NC 27609
Application address: c/o Ann C. Sloan, P.O. Box
29636, Raleigh, NC 27626, tel.: (919) 573-3211

Established in 1994 in North Carolina.
Donor: C. Hamilton Sloan Charitable Lead Trust.
Foundation type: Independent foundation.
Financial data (yr. ended 12/31/13): Assets,
$129,852 (M); gifts received, $252,053;
expenditures, $264,281; qualifying distributions,
$261,200; giving activities include $261,200 for 44
grants (high: $61,500; low: $200).
Fields of interest: Dance; Museums; Higher
education; Zoos; Multiple sclerosis; Cancers;
Protestantism; Human services; Food delivery;
Youth services; Scouting programs.
Type of support: Research.
Application information: Application form required.
Initial approach: Proposal
Deadline(s): None
Trustees: Ann C. Sloan; O. Temple Sloan, Jr.; W.
Gerald Thornton.
EIN: 561870847

7247
William Harold Smith Charitable Trust
1105 Airport Rd.
Marion, NC 28752-5633 (828) 652-9443
Contact: Matt Smith, Tr.

Established in 1998 in North Carolina.
Foundation type: Independent foundation.
Financial data (yr. ended 12/31/13): Assets,
$4,950,243 (M); expenditures, $308,746;
qualifying distributions, $292,599; giving activities
include $247,214 for grants to individuals.
Purpose and activities: Awards scholarships to
graduates of McDowell High School, Marion, North
Carolina.
Fields of interest: Education.
Type of support: Scholarships; Individual
development; Student aid.
Limitations: Applications accepted. Giving primarily
in McDowell County, NC.
Application information: Applications are available
in McDowell High School guidance office.
Application form required.
Initial approach: Completed application with
personal essay and 2 recommendations
returned to guidance office
Deadline(s): Apr. 2
Final notification: Within 60 days after deadline
Trustee: Matt Smith.
EIN: 566526359

7248
The Wilson L. Smith Family Foundation
113 Canterberry Dr.
Salisbury, NC 28144-9459

Established in 1989 in North Carolina.
Donors: Ronald L. Smith; Wilson L. Smith.
Foundation type: Independent foundation.
Financial data (yr. ended 12/31/13): Assets,
$20,299,458 (M); gifts received, $310,708;
expenditures, $481,919; qualifying distributions,
$327,345; giving activities include $327,345 for 20
grants (high: $150,000; low: $1,000).

Purpose and activities: Giving primarily for education, human services and to a Lutheran church.
Fields of interest: Higher education; Graduate and professional education; Methodism; Theology; Human services; Scouting programs.
Limitations: Applications not accepted. Giving primarily in Salisbury, NC. No grants to individuals.
Application information: Unsolicited requests for funds not accepted.
Officers: Ronald L. Smith, Pres.; Timothy Smith, Treas.
EIN: 561658247

7249
The General William A. Smith Trust
c/o Trust Tax Dept.
P.O. Box 2907
Wilson, NC   27894-2907

Established in 1940 in North Carolina.
Donors: Genl. William A. Smith; William Smith Trust; William Smith XXI Trust.
Foundation type: Independent foundation.
Financial data (yr. ended 12/31/14): Assets, $5,620,825 (M); gifts received, $52,212; expenditures, $399,545; qualifying distributions, $333,018; giving activities include $325,935 for 16 grants (high: $124,085; low: $500).
Fields of interest: Education; Higher education; Community and economic development; Protestantism; Human services.
Type of support: General support; Continuing support; Annual campaigns; Capital campaigns; Capital and infrastructure; Equipment; Endowments; Emergency funds; Program development; Professorships; Scholarships.
Limitations: Applications accepted. Giving primarily in Anson County, NC. No grants to individuals.
Application information:
  Initial approach: Proposal
  Deadline(s): Dec. 31
Trustee: Branch Banking & Trust Co.
Directors: Joe E. Gaddy; Joanne Huntley; Frank F. Mills.
EIN: 566042630

7250
Snyder's-Lance Foundation
P.O. Box 32368
Charlotte, NC   28232-2368   (704) 554-1421

Established in 1956 in North Carolina.
Donor: Lance, Inc.
Foundation type: Company-sponsored foundation.
Financial data (yr. ended 12/31/14): Assets, $7,491; expenditures, $406,754; qualifying distributions, $404,232.
Purpose and activities: The foundation supports hospices and organizations involved with arts and culture, education, hunger, youth development, and business.
Fields of interest: Arts and culture; Education; Human services.
Type of support: General support; Scholarships.
Limitations: Applications accepted. Giving primarily in Charlotte, NC. No grants to individuals, or for scholarships or fellowships; no loans.
Application information:
  Initial approach: Proposal
  Copies of proposal: 1

Deadline(s): None
  Board meeting date(s): As required
Officer: Sid Levy, Exec. Dir.
Director: Rick D. Puckett.
Trustee: Bank of America, N.A.
Number of staff: 1
EIN: 566039487

7251
Spring Charitable Trust
1525 W. WT Harris Blvd., D1114-044
Charlotte, NC   28288-5709

Established in 1998 in Pennsylvania.
Foundation type: Independent foundation.
Financial data (yr. ended 01/31/15): Assets, $13,554,859; expenditures, $588,436; qualifying distributions, $449,372.
Purpose and activities: Giving primarily for health care, including a children's hospital, and social services.
Fields of interest: Specialty hospital care; Human services.
Limitations: Applications not accepted. Giving primarily in Tampa, FL and PA. No grants to individuals.
Application information: Contributes only to pre-selected organizations.
Trustees: Dianne L. Semingson; Wells Fargo Bank, N.A.
EIN: 236290545

7252
SPX Foundation
(formerly Sealed Power Foundation)
13320 Ballantyne Corporate Pl.
Charlotte, NC   28277   (704) 752-4400
Contact: Jennifer Epstein
Application address: 13515 Ballantyne Corporate Pl., Charlotte, NC 28277; Main URL: http://www.spx.com

Established in 1982 in Michigan.
Donors: SPX Corp.; O-Z Gedney Co., LLC; EGS Electrical Group, LLC; Flair Corp.
Foundation type: Company-sponsored foundation.
Financial data (yr. ended 07/31/14): Assets, $799 (M); gifts received, $170,000; expenditures, $171,235; qualifying distributions, $169,218; giving activities include $169,218 for 183 employee matching gifts.
Purpose and activities: The foundation supports organizations involved with arts and culture, education, health, human services, and civic affairs.
Type of support: General support; Employee matching gifts; Capital campaigns.
Limitations: Applications accepted. Giving primarily in Charlotte, NC.
Publications: Informational brochure (including application guidelines).
Application information: Application form required.
  Initial approach: Proposal
  Copies of proposal: 1
  Deadline(s): None
Officers and Trustees: Robert B. Foreman, V.P. and Trustee; Jeremy Smeltser, Secy.-Treas. and Trustee; Christopher J. Kearney; Kevin Lilly.
EIN: 386058308

7253
J. and V. Stapleton Charitable Trust
c/o Wells Fargo Bank, N.A. Trust Tax Dept.
1 W. 4th St., 4th Fl., MAC D4000-041
Winston-Salem, NC   27101-3818

Donor: John and Vilma Stapleton Family Trust.
Foundation type: Independent foundation.
Financial data (yr. ended 12/31/13): Assets, $6,856,188 (M); gifts received, $7,984; expenditures, $308,831; qualifying distributions, $238,294; giving activities include $215,059 for 1 grant.
Fields of interest: Religion.
Limitations: Applications not accepted. Giving primarily in NY.
Application information: Unsolicited requests for funds not accepted.
Trustee: Wells Fargo Bank, N.A.
EIN: 356967993

7254
Charles & Lynn Steinmetz Family Foundation
1525 W. WT Harris Blvd., D1114-044
Charlotte, NC   28262

Established in 2000 in Florida.
Donors: Charles P. Steinmetz; Lynn L. Steinmetz.
Foundation type: Independent foundation.
Financial data (yr. ended 12/31/13): Assets, $217,266 (M); expenditures, $180,000; qualifying distributions, $176,236; giving activities include $175,000 for 8 grants (high: $100,000; low: $5,000).
Fields of interest: Arts and culture; Orchestral music; Education; Human services.
Limitations: Applications not accepted. Giving primarily in Orlando, FL. No grants to individuals.
Application information: Unsolicited requests for funds not accepted.
Officer: Matthew A. Steinmetz, Secy.-Treas.
EIN: 593591506

7255
Stonecutter Foundation, Inc.
230 Spindale St.
Spindale, NC   28160-1604
Contact: Terri C. Barringer, Secy.-Treas.

Established in 1944 in North Carolina.
Donors: Stonecutter Mills Corp.; Ivy Cowan; Myra Cowan; James Cowan.
Foundation type: Company-sponsored foundation.
Financial data (yr. ended 03/31/14): Assets, $9,550,327 (M); gifts received, $5,500; expenditures, $572,204; qualifying distributions, $377,450; giving activities include $377,450 for 44 grants (high: $50,000; low: $200).
Purpose and activities: The foundation supports organizations involved with arts and culture, higher education, community and economic development, and religion and awards student loans.
Fields of interest: Arts and culture; Arts councils; Museums; Education; Higher education; Religion; Christianity.
Type of support: General support; Loans to individuals; Capital and infrastructure; Student aid.
Limitations: Applications accepted. Giving primarily in NC; giving in Rutherford and Polk County, NC, for student loans.

Application information: Application form required.
Initial approach: Contact foundation for application
Deadline(s): None
Officers: D. Daniel Briscoe, Pres.; C. Ray Bridges, V.P.; James R. Cowan, V.P.; Terri C. Barringer, Secy.-Treas.
Directors: Carolyn Keever; Dillard Morrow.
EIN: 566044820

7256
The Stowe Foundation, Inc.
(formerly Robert Lee Stowe, Jr. Foundation, Inc.)
P.O. Box 351
Belmont, NC   28012-0351
Contact: Robert L. Stowe III, Pres.; Daniel Harding Stowe, V.P.

Established in 1945 in North Carolina.
Donors: R.L. Stowe Mills, Inc.; Robert Lee Stowe, Jr.†; Robert Lee Stowe III.
Foundation type: Independent foundation.
Financial data (yr. ended 12/31/13): Assets, $2,592,279 (M); expenditures, $164,940; qualifying distributions, $161,407; giving activities include $156,500 for 14 grants (high: $100,000; low: $1,000).
Fields of interest: Arts and culture; Education; Botanical gardens; Christianity; Human services.
Limitations: Applications not accepted. Giving primarily in NC, with emphasis on the Charlotte area. No grants to individuals.
Application information: Contributes only to pre-selected organizations.
Officers: Robert Lee Stowe III, Pres.; Daniel Harding Stowe, V.P.; Richmond H. Stowe, Secy.; Jean H. Gibson, Treas.
EIN: 566034773

7257
Strickland Family Foundation
2000 W. 1st St., Ste. 604
Winston-Salem, NC   27104-4225
Contact: Cynthia S. Graham, V.P.

Established in 1995 in North Carolina.
Donor: Robert L. Strickland.
Foundation type: Independent foundation.
Financial data (yr. ended 07/31/13): Assets, $11,505,641 (M); gifts received, $5,000,000; expenditures, $392,371; qualifying distributions, $245,225; giving activities include $245,225 for grants.
Purpose and activities: Giving primarily for the arts, higher education, health, and Protestant organizations.
Fields of interest: Education; Religion; Human services.
Limitations: Applications accepted. Giving primarily in NC. No grants to individuals.
Application information:
Initial approach: Proposal
Deadline(s): None
Board meeting date(s): May or June
Officers: Elizabeth M. Strickland, Pres.; Robert E.M. Strickland, V.P; Cynthia S. Graham, V.P.; Robert L. Strickland, Secy.
Number of staff: 1 full-time support.
EIN: 561900147

7258
Strowd Roses, Inc.
P.O. Box 3558
Chapel Hill, NC   27515-3558   (919) 245-1716
Contact: Jennifer B. Boger
FAX: (919) 929-1990;
E-mail: executivedirector@strowdroses.org; Contact for applicants affiliated with the Chapel Hill-Carrboro City Schools: Exec. Dir., Public School Foundation, P.O. Box 877, Carrboro, NC 27510, tel.: (919) 968-8819, e-mail: psf@chccs.k12.nc.us; Main URL: http://www.strowdroses.org
Facebook: https://www.facebook.com/StrowdRoses
Grants List: http://strowdroses.org/PastGrantRecipList.html
Instagram: https://instagram.com/strowd_roses
Twitter: https://twitter.com/strowdroses

Established in 2001 in North Carolina.
Donors: Irene H. Strowd†; Gladis H. Adams Charitable Trust; Community Action Network.
Foundation type: Independent foundation.
Financial data (yr. ended 12/31/13): Assets, $7,418,852 (M); gifts received, $100; expenditures, $340,115; qualifying distributions, $313,932; giving activities include $303,430 for 56 grants (high: $33,000; low: $811).
Purpose and activities: Giving to support programs and projects which improve the quality of life for citizens of Chapel Hill and Carrboro, North Carolina. The foundation also makes an annual bloc grant to cover funding requests from programs operating under the auspices of the Chapel Hill-Carrboro City Schools. This grant is administered by the Public School Foundation of Chapel-Hill Carrboro.
Fields of interest: Arts and culture; Elementary and secondary education; Environment; Health; Sports and recreation; Child welfare; Children and youth; Adolescents; Seniors; Females; Female children and youth; People of African descent; People of Latin American descent; Immigrants and migrants; Homeless people; Low-income and poor people; People with physical disabilities; People with psychosocial disabilities.
Type of support: General support; Grants to individuals; Matching grants; Continuing support; Capacity-building and technical assistance; Capital campaigns; Capital and infrastructure; Equipment; Endowments; Debt reduction; Program development; Convening; Seed money; Internships; Program evaluations.
Limitations: Applications accepted. Giving limited to Chapel Hill and Carrboro, NC.
Publications: Application guidelines; Grants list; Informational brochure.
Application information: Application guidelines and form available on foundation web site. Application form required.
Initial approach: Letter requesting application
Copies of proposal: 1
Deadline(s): Jan. 31, Apr. 30, and July 31
Board meeting date(s): Mid-Mar., mid-June, and mid-Sept.
Final notification: Four weeks following board meeting
Officers and Directors: Edward A. Norfleet, Pres. and Director; Sydenham B. Alexander, V.P. and Director; Stephen B. Miller, Secy. and Director.
Board Members: Frederick H. Black; Jennifer B. Boger; Rosemary Waldorf.
Number of staff: None.
EIN: 562241874

7259
Stuart George and Jeanette Charitable Trust
c/o Wells Fargo Bank N.A., Trust Tax Dept.
1 W. 4th St., 4th Fl., MAC D4000-041
Winston-Salem, NC   27101-3818

Foundation type: Independent foundation.
Financial data (yr. ended 12/31/14): Assets, $9,364,578; expenditures, $633,154; qualifying distributions, $468,994.
Fields of interest: Arts and culture; Music; Health; Human services; Children.
Type of support: General support.
Limitations: Applications not accepted.
Application information: Unsolicited requests for funds not accepted.
Trustee: Wells Fargo Bank, N.A.
EIN: 270522116

7260
The Stubblefield Foundation, Inc.
8508 Park Rd., 123
Charlotte, NC   28210-5803
Contact: Fred Stubblefield Jr., Pres.

Established in 1991 in North Carolina.
Donor: Fred Stubblefield III.
Foundation type: Independent foundation.
Financial data (yr. ended 12/31/13): Assets, $3,293,200 (M); gifts received, $180,140; expenditures, $252,336; qualifying distributions, $218,870; giving activities include $218,870 for 24 grants (high: $125,000; low: $250).
Fields of interest: Education; Religion; Human services.
Limitations: Applications not accepted. Giving primarily in NC. No grants to individuals.
Application information: Unsolicited requests for funds not accepted.
Officer and Directors: Fred Stubblefield, Jr., Pres. and Director; Lisa S. Ballard; Fred Stubblefield III; Nancy K. Stubblefield.
EIN: 561760217

7261
Summer Rest Foundation
P.O. Box 1330
Wrightsville Beach, NC   28480-1330

Established in 1998 in North Carolina.
Donors: George C. Turner; Sue M. Turner; George Todd Turner; Tisha Turner.
Foundation type: Independent foundation.
Financial data (yr. ended 12/31/13): Assets, $7,033,945 (M); expenditures, $450,042; qualifying distributions, $362,063; giving activities include $360,813 for 24 grants (high: $77,500; low: $2,000).
Fields of interest: Higher education; Nonprofits; National defense; Protestantism; Human services; Youth services.
Type of support: General support; Regranting.
Limitations: Applications not accepted. Giving primarily in NC and VA.
Application information: Contributes only to pre-selected organizations.
Trustees: Jay G. Loftin, Jr.; Sue M. Turner.
EIN: 566534008

7262
Walter and Louise Sutcliffe Foundation
1 W. 4th St., 2nd Fl.
Winston-Salem, NC 27101-3818 336 747-8203
E-mail: grantadministration@wellsfargo.com; Main
URL: https://www.wellsfargo.com/
privatefoundationgrants/sutcliffe

Established in 1990 in New Jersey.
Donor: Louise Sutcliffe†.
Foundation type: Independent foundation.
Financial data (yr. ended 12/31/14): Assets,
$4,976,158; expenditures, $291,298; qualifying
distributions, $241,227.
Purpose and activities: The foundation provides
grants to institutions for nursing education and
cancer research.
Fields of interest: Graduate and professional
education; Nursing care; Diseases and conditions;
Cancers.
Type of support: Program development;
Scholarships; Research; Research and evaluation.
Limitations: Applications accepted. Giving primarily
in NJ. No grants to individuals, or for endowments,
general operating support, or fundraising events,
including dinners, benefits, or athletic events; no
loans.
Publications: Application guidelines.
Application information: See foundation website for
complete application guidelines. Application form
required.
  Initial approach: Use online application system on
    foundation web site
  Copies of proposal: 1
  Deadline(s): Feb. 15th and Sept. 1st
  Board meeting date(s): Apr. and Nov.
Trustee: Wells Fargo Bank, N.A.
EIN: 521720225

7263
Sarah H. Sutherland Charitable Trust
c/o BB&T, Trust Tax
P.O. Box 2907
Wilson, NC 27894-2907

Foundation type: Independent foundation.
Financial data (yr. ended 12/31/13): Assets,
$4,558,354 (M); expenditures, $251,712;
qualifying distributions, $193,357; giving activities
include $193,357 for 4 grants (high: $95,427; low:
$2,500).
Fields of interest: Undergraduate education;
Catholicism.
Limitations: Applications not accepted. Giving
primarily in NC. No grants to individuals.
Application information: Contributes only to
pre-selected organizations.
Trustee: Branch Banking & Trust Co.
EIN: 566456377

7264
Szulik Family Foundation
3717 William J. Cowan Wynd
Raleigh, NC 27612-5399

Donors: Matthew J. Szulik; Kyle Szulik.
Foundation type: Independent foundation.
Financial data (yr. ended 12/31/13): Assets,
$8,822,401 (M); expenditures, $392,673;
qualifying distributions, $411,789; giving activities

include $380,250 for 20 grants (high: $50,000;
low: $250).
Fields of interest: Education; Human services.
Limitations: Applications not accepted.
Application information: Unsolicited requests for
funds not accepted.
Trustees: Kyle Szulik; Matthew J. Szulik.
EIN: 276979466

7265
S.E.H. Tabitha Foundation, Inc.
128 S. Tryon St., Ste. 1580
Charlotte, NC 28202

Established in 2006 in North Carolina.
Donor: Ruth P. Heinemann Irrevocable Trust.
Foundation type: Independent foundation.
Financial data (yr. ended 12/31/14): Assets,
$6,079,305; expenditures, $356,558; qualifying
distributions, $309,513.
Fields of interest: International relations.
Limitations: Applications not accepted. Giving
primarily in Palmer Lake, CO.
Application information: Unsolicited requests for
funds not accepted.
Director: Susan E. Heinemann.
EIN: 300411158

7266
TerKeurst Foundation
1109 Cuthbertson Rd.
Waxhaw, NC 28173-7798

Foundation type: Independent foundation.
Financial data (yr. ended 12/31/14): Assets,
$64,821 (M); expenditures, $219,801; qualifying
distributions, $216,056; giving activities include
$204,782 for 16 grants (high: $75,150; low: $100).
Fields of interest: Religion.
Limitations: Applications not accepted. Giving
primarily in NC. No grants to individuals.
Application information: Unsolicited requests for
funds not accepted.
Officers and Trustees: Lysa TerKeurst, Pres. and
Trustee; Hope TerKeurst, Secy. and Trustee; Arthur
TerKeurst III, Treas. and Trustee.
EIN: 466425149

7267
Thomasville Furniture Industries
Foundation
c/o Wells Fargo Bank, N.A., Trust Tax Dept.
1 W. 4th St., 4th Fl., D4000-041
Winston-Salem, NC 27101-3818

Established in 1960 in North Carolina.
Donors: Thomasville Furniture Industries, Inc.;
Interco.
Foundation type: Company-sponsored foundation.
Financial data (yr. ended 12/31/14): Assets,
$9,776,889; expenditures, $463,849; qualifying
distributions, $392,739.
Purpose and activities: The foundation supports
hospices and organizations involved with education,
health, cancer, youth development, child welfare,
and community economic development.
Fields of interest: Education; Diseases and
conditions; Human services.
Type of support: General support; Matching grants;
Program development; Scholarships.

Limitations: Applications not accepted. Giving
primarily in NC. No grants to individuals (except for
employee-related scholarships).
Application information: Contributes only to
pre-selected organizations and individuals.
Trustee: Wells Fargo Bank, N.A.
EIN: 566047870

7268
C. E. Towne Scholarship Fund
c/o Wells Fargo Bank, N.A.
1 W. 4th St., 4th Fl., MAC D4000-041
Winston-Salem, NC 27101-3818
Application address: c/o California Masonic
Foundation, 111 California St., San Francisco, CA
94108-2284, tel.: (414) 292-9196

Foundation type: Independent foundation.
Financial data (yr. ended 06/30/14): Assets,
$6,387,249 (M); expenditures, $261,512;
qualifying distributions, $197,777; giving activities
include $170,500 for 47 grants to individuals (high:
$10,000; low: $1,000).
Purpose and activities: Scholarship awards
primarily to children of Masonic families.
Fields of interest: Higher education.
Type of support: Student aid.
Application information: Applications are to be
requested from the California Masonic Foundation.
Application form required.
  Deadline(s): Feb. 28
Trustee: Wells Fargo Bank, N.A.
EIN: 946700587

7269
The Trexler Foundation
P.O. Box 32486
Charlotte, NC 28232-2486

Established in 1986 in North Carolina.
Donors: Charles B. Trexler†; Mary Margaret Trexler;
Alice E. Trexler; C. Brent Trexler, Jr.; James Henry
Trexler; John F. Trexler.
Foundation type: Independent foundation.
Financial data (yr. ended 12/31/13): Assets,
$9,230,037 (M); gifts received, $3,500,000;
expenditures, $277,759; qualifying distributions,
$245,500; giving activities include $245,500 for 18
grants (high: $128,000; low: $1,000).
Fields of interest: Arts and culture; Orchestral
music; Higher education; Christianity; Human
services.
Type of support: General support; Capital
campaigns; Scholarships.
Limitations: Applications not accepted. Giving
primarily in Charlotte, NC. No grants to individuals.
Application information: Unsolicited requests for
funds not accepted.
  Board meeting date(s): Varies
Directors: Alice E. Trexler; C. Brent Trexler, Jr.;
Charles B. Trexler; James Henry Trexler; Mary
Margaret Trexler.
EIN: 561546464

7270
The Peggy Ann Triplett Foundation
2512 Independence Blvd., Ste. 100
Wilmington, NC 28412

Foundation type: Independent foundation.

Financial data (yr. ended 12/31/13): Assets, $4,495,602 (M); expenditures, $2,062,526; qualifying distributions, $279,779; giving activities include $279,779 for 1 grant.
Fields of interest: Hospice care.
Limitations: Applications not accepted. Giving primarily in NC.
Application information: Contributes only to pre-selected organizations.
Trustees: Michael C. Smith; William A. Vestal.
EIN: 266276685

7271
TSH Charitable Foundation
2425 N. Center St., Ste. 362
Hickory, NC   28601-1320

Donors: Patricia A. Anderson; Particia A. Anderson Irrevocable Trust CLAT.
Foundation type: Independent foundation.
Financial data (yr. ended 04/30/14): Assets, $5,191,957 (M); gifts received, $486,978; expenditures, $218,320; qualifying distributions, $199,531; giving activities include $136,525 for 26 grants (high: $25,920; low: $350).
Fields of interest: Education; Human services.
Limitations: Applications not accepted. Giving primarily in NC.
Application information: Unsolicited requests for funds not accepted.
Officers: Deborah Beaver Looper, Pres.; Donna Beaver Fleming, Secy.-Treas.
Director: Angela Beaver Simmons.
EIN: 264731530

7272
The UAI Foundation
P.O. Box 13628
Research Triangle Park, NC   27709-3628

Established in 2007 in North Carolina.
Donor: UAI Technology, Inc.
Foundation type: Independent foundation.
Financial data (yr. ended 11/30/13): Assets, $4,013,748 (M); expenditures, $169,689; qualifying distributions, $165,000; giving activities include $165,000 for 2 grants (high: $155,000; low: $10,000).
Fields of interest: University education.
Limitations: Applications not accepted. Giving primarily in NC. No grants to individuals.
Application information: Contributes only to pre-selected organizations.
Officers: Steven F. Maier, Pres.; Laura L. Maier, V.P.; Mark E. Friedman, Secy.-Treas.
EIN: 261159753

7273
R. T. Vanderbilt Trust
1525 W. WT Harris Blvd.
Charlotte, NC   28288-1114

Established in 1951 in Connecticut.
Foundation type: Independent foundation.
Financial data (yr. ended 12/31/14): Assets, $10,206,220 (M); expenditures, $506,931; qualifying distributions, $430,975; giving activities include $414,975 for 77 grants (high: $105,000; low: $200).

Purpose and activities: Giving primarily for education and conservation; support also for health care, and cultural programs.
Fields of interest: Arts and culture; Historic preservation; Education; Higher education; Natural resources; Health; Hospital care; Human services.
Type of support: General support; Capital and infrastructure; Endowments; Program development.
Limitations: Applications not accepted. Giving in the U.S., with emphasis on CT. No grants to individuals.
Application information: Contributes only to pre-selected organizations.
   Board meeting date(s): Apr., June, Sept., and Dec.
Trustees: Hugh B. Vanderbilt, Jr.; Paul Vanderbilt.
Number of staff: 2 part-time support.
EIN: 066040981

7274
David Von Drehle Corporation Private Foundation
612 3rd Ave. N.E.
Hickory, NC   28601

Donors: David Von Drehle Corporation; Steve Von Drehle; Raymond Von Drehle.
Foundation type: Independent foundation.
Financial data (yr. ended 12/31/13): Assets, $2,114 (M); gifts received, $180,000; expenditures, $183,332; qualifying distributions, $183,300; giving activities include $183,300 for 48 grants (high: $30,000; low: $100).
Fields of interest: Arts and culture; Human services; Youth development.
Limitations: Applications not accepted.
Application information: Unsolicited requests for funds not accepted.
Trustees: Steve Von Drehle; Raymond Von Drehle.
EIN: 262942513

7275
Wagner Agape Foundation
c/o Terence B. Stanaland
101 S. Elm St.
Greensboro, NC   27401-2698

Established in 2002 in North Carolina.
Donor: R. Donald Wagner.
Foundation type: Independent foundation.
Financial data (yr. ended 06/30/14): Assets, $1,833,156 (M); expenditures, $223,128; qualifying distributions, $204,100; giving activities include $201,950 for 12 grants (high: $60,000; low: $1,000).
Purpose and activities: Giving to Baptist faith cooperative fellowships.
Fields of interest: Philanthropy; Religion.
Type of support: Program development.
Limitations: Applications not accepted. Giving primarily in NC. No grants to individuals.
Application information: Unsolicited requests for funds not accepted.
Officers: Rev. R. Donald Wagner, Chair.; Terence B. Stanaland, Secy.
Directors: Rebecca W. Quate; Steven W. Wagner.
EIN: 030469046

7276
Wake Electric Care, Inc.
414 E. Wait St.
Wake Forest, NC   27588-1229
Contact: Fred Keller
Application address: P.O. Box 1229, Wake Forest, NC 27588

Established in 2002 in North Carolina.
Foundation type: Company-sponsored foundation.
Financial data (yr. ended 12/31/13): Assets, $201,000 (M); gifts received, $143,924; expenditures, $143,274; qualifying distributions, $143,239; giving activities include $143,239 for 54 grants (high: $19,000; low: $400).
Purpose and activities: The foundation supports organizations involved with education, recreation, and human services.
Fields of interest: Education; Secondary education; Higher education; Sports and recreation; Human services; Youth services.
Type of support: General support; Equipment; Program development; Scholarships.
Limitations: Applications accepted. Giving primarily in areas of company operations in Durham, Franklin, Granville, Johnston, Nash, Wake, and Vance, NC.
Application information: Application form required.
   Initial approach: Proposal
   Deadline(s): Mar., June, Sept. & Dec.
Directors: Carolyn Barnes; Molly Bostic; Hubert L. Gooch, Jr.; Jan Hopkins; Cedric Jones; Robert Lanier; Michelle McGhee; Frances McIver; Frank Pearce.
EIN: 561938901

7277
A. W. Wallace Charitable Trust
c/o Wells Fargo Bank N.A., Trust Tax Dept.
1 W. 4th St., 4th Fl., MAC D4000-041
Winston-Salem, NC   27101-3818

Established in 2004 in Texas.
Donor: Adrian W. Wallace†.
Foundation type: Independent foundation.
Financial data (yr. ended 12/31/14): Assets, $6,831,020 (M); expenditures, $395,590; qualifying distributions, $315,949; giving activities include $297,094 for 2 grants (high: $207,966; low: $89,128).
Fields of interest: Education; Higher education.
Type of support: Scholarships; Individual development.
Limitations: Applications not accepted. Giving primarily in KS and TX. No grants to individuals.
Application information: Unsolicited requests for funds not accepted.
Trustee: Wells Fargo Bank, N.A.
EIN: 436907367

7278
Albert A. Walters Foundation
c/o Wells Fargo Bank, N.A., Trust Tax Dept.
1 W. 4th St., 4th Fl. MAC D4000-041
Winston-Salem, NC   27101-3818

Established in 2010 in New Jersey.
Donor: Albert A. Walters†.
Foundation type: Independent foundation.
Financial data (yr. ended 12/31/14): Assets, $4,999,050 (M); expenditures, $285,219; qualifying distributions, $234,061; giving activities

include $217,735 for 11 grants (high: $22,625; low: $19,511).
Fields of interest: Domesticated animals; Health; Youth development.
Limitations: Applications not accepted. Giving primarily in NJ and NY. No grants to individuals.
Application information: Unsolicited requests for funds not accepted.
Trustee: Wells Fargo Bank, N.A.
EIN: 546916455

7279
Ralph J. Wann Foundation
c/o Wells Fargo Bank N.A., Trust Tax Dept.
1 W. 4th St., 4th Fl., MAC D4000-041
Winston-Salem, NC 27101-3818

Foundation type: Independent foundation.
Financial data (yr. ended 12/31/14): Assets, $4,734,821; expenditures, $268,523; qualifying distributions, $227,299.
Purpose and activities: Giving primarily to support a humane society.
Fields of interest: Animal welfare; Human services; People with disabilities.
Type of support: General support.
Limitations: Applications not accepted. Giving primarily in CO.
Application information: Unsolicited requests for funds not accepted.
Trustee: Wells Fargo Bank, N.A.
EIN: 846022561

7280
Paul R. & Alma M. Waters Foundation
c/o Wells Fargo Bank, N.A., Trust Tax Dept.
1 W. 4th St., 4th Fl., MAC D4000-041
Winston-Salem, NC 27101-3818

Established in 2001 in North Carolina.
Foundation type: Independent foundation.
Financial data (yr. ended 12/31/14): Assets, $8,817,995; expenditures, $386,159; qualifying distributions, $300,279.
Purpose and activities: Giving primarily for Baptist churches and organizations.
Fields of interest: Baptist.
Type of support: General support.
Limitations: Applications not accepted. Giving primarily in NC. No grants to individuals.
Application information: Contributes only to pre-selected organizations.
Trustee: Wells Fargo Bank, N.A.
EIN: 566587332

7281
The Way Foundation
P.O. Box 4107
Wilmington, NC 28406-1107 (910) 799-1815
Contact: John D. Gillilan Jr.

Established in 2007 in North Carolina.
Donor: Neuwirth Motors, Inc.
Foundation type: Company-sponsored foundation.
Financial data (yr. ended 12/31/13): Assets, $45,720 (M); gifts received, $199,453; expenditures, $174,125; qualifying distributions, $173,900; giving activities include $173,900 for 22 grants (high: $19,500; low: $1,000).

Purpose and activities: The foundation supports secondary and higher education, human services, and religion.
Fields of interest: Health; Religion; Human services.
Type of support: General support.
Limitations: Applications accepted. Giving primarily in NC. No grants to individuals.
Application information: Application form required.
　Initial approach: Proposal
　　Deadline(s): None
Officers: John S. Gillilan, Jr., Chair.; John C. Martin, Jr., Vice-Chair.; Armied A. Godwin III, Pres.; Jackie Martin, Secy.; Cindy P. Godwin, Treas.
EIN: 450572015

7282
The Weatherspoon Foundation
135 Perrin Pl.
Charlotte, NC 28207-2257

Established in 1999 in North Carolina.
Donors: Van L. Weatherspoon; Mrs. G. Scott Francis; G. Scott Francis.
Foundation type: Independent foundation.
Financial data (yr. ended 12/31/14): Assets, $5,350,968; expenditures, $167,646; qualifying distributions, $167,600.
Fields of interest: Arts and culture; History museums; Religion.
Type of support: General support.
Limitations: Applications not accepted. Giving primarily in NC. No grants to individuals.
Application information: Unsolicited requests for funds not accepted.
Board Members: Martha Kay Massey Weatherspoon; Van L. Weatherspoon.
EIN: 562154056

7283
Mildred Sheffield Wells Charitable Trust
c/o Bank of America, N.A.
1 Hanover Sq., 3rd Fl.
Raleigh, NC 27601-1754
Application address: c/o Distribution Committee, 1100 Conference Dr., Greenville, NC 27858, tel.: (252) 756-8888

Established in 1997 in North Carolina.
Foundation type: Independent foundation.
Financial data (yr. ended 09/30/13): Assets, $6,542,026 (M); expenditures, $351,028; qualifying distributions, $299,012; giving activities include $245,346 for 14 grants (high: $38,000; low: $2,000).
Purpose and activities: Giving primarily for organizations engaged in cancer and arthritis research.
Fields of interest: Music; Parent-teacher involvement; Hospital care; Arthritis; Fire prevention and control; Community and economic development; Protestantism; Human services; Food banks; Youth services; Seniors.
Type of support: Research.
Limitations: Applications accepted. Giving primarily in Pitt County, NC; giving nationally to organizations engaged in arthritis or cancer research.
Application information: Application form required.
　Deadline(s): None
Officer: James G. Sullivan, Chair.
Members: Robert Hudak; Danny D. McNally.

Trustee: Bank of America, N.A.
EIN: 566505336

7284
Vivian S. West-West Memorial Fund
c/o Bank of America, N.A.
1 Hanover Sq., 3rd Fl.
Raleigh, NC 27601-1754
Application address: c/o James G. Sullivan, 1100 Conference Dr., Greenville, NC 27858-5974, tel.: (252) 756-8888

Established in 1998 in North Carolina.
Foundation type: Independent foundation.
Financial data (yr. ended 03/31/15): Assets, $7,340,375 (M); expenditures, $445,652; qualifying distributions, $352,098; giving activities include $295,000 for 8 grants (high: $60,000; low: $5,000).
Fields of interest: Arts and culture; Education; Higher education; Christianity; Human services.
Limitations: Applications accepted. Giving primarily in Greenville, NC. No grants to individuals.
Application information: Application form required.
　Initial approach: Request application form
　　Deadline(s): None
Officer and Trustees: James G. Sullivan, Chair. and Trustee; Bank of America, N.A.
Committee Member: David Emswiler.
Director: Danny D. McNally.
EIN: 566520255

7285
Frank L. Weyenberg Charitable Trust
c/o Wells Fargo Bank N.A.
1 W. 4th St., 4th Fl., MAC D4000-041
Winston-Salem, NC 27101-3818

Established in 1983 in Florida.
Foundation type: Independent foundation.
Financial data (yr. ended 07/31/14): Assets, $6,097,963 (M); expenditures, $307,689; qualifying distributions, $255,447; giving activities include $238,500 for 20 grants (high: $25,000; low: $3,000).
Purpose and activities: Giving primarily for education, health, and the arts.
Fields of interest: Philanthropy; Social sciences; Human services.
Limitations: Applications not accepted. Giving on a national basis. No grants to individuals.
Application information: Unsolicited requests for funds not accepted.
Trustee: Wells Fargo Bank, N.A.
EIN: 391461670

7286
Whitener Foundation
P.O. Box 1856
High Point, NC 27261-1856

Foundation type: Independent foundation.
Financial data (yr. ended 12/31/14): Assets, $3,752,914 (M); expenditures, $232,655; qualifying distributions, $142,688; giving activities include $141,887 for 71 grants (high: $7,500; low: $100).
Fields of interest: Arts and culture; Theater; Orchestral music; Education; Higher education;

Diseases and conditions; Protestantism; Human services; Child welfare.
Limitations: Applications not accepted. Giving primarily in NC. No grants to individuals.
Application information: Unsolicited requests for funds not accepted.
Officers and Directors: Edgar Whitener, Pres. and Director; Marshall Pittman, V.P. and Director; Lorene Ward, Secy.-Treas.
EIN: 521467548

7287
Ada L. & Albert M. Wibel Foundation
c/o Trust Tax Dept
P.O. Box 2907
Wilson, NC 27894-2907
Application address: c/o Branch Banking & Trust Company, 6400 Arlington Blvd., Falls Church, VA 22042, tel.: (703) 241-3168

Donor: Mary E. Wibel Interim Trust.
Foundation type: Independent foundation.
Financial data (yr. ended 12/31/13): Assets, $7,255,314 (M); expenditures, $426,606; qualifying distributions, $323,000; giving activities include $323,000 for 28 grants (high: $12,000; low: $11,000).
Purpose and activities: Giving to organizations that provide care and aid, deliver meals, visiting nurse organizations, and that provide routine or special transportation for the elderly; provide food, shelter, medical care, and housing to disadvantaged children; to organizations that provide hospice care for terminally ill patients, and for the support of caregivers' organizations.
Fields of interest: Nursing care; Home health care; Food delivery; Child welfare; Senior services.
Limitations: Applications accepted. Giving limited to the Washington, DC metropolitan area.
Application information: Application form required.
  Initial approach: Letter
  Deadline(s): None
Trustees: Karen N. Conrad; Branch Banking & Trust Co.
EIN: 206966139

7288
James and Mildred Wilkinson Charitable Trust
928 Harvest St.
Durham, NC 27704-5216

Established in 2009 in North Carolina.
Donor: James B. Wilkinson†.
Foundation type: Independent foundation.
Financial data (yr. ended 12/31/13): Assets, $4,960,724 (M); gifts received, $430,000; expenditures, $366,801; qualifying distributions, $222,741; giving activities include $222,741 for 65 grants (high: $15,000; low: $500).
Fields of interest: Education; Housing development; Religion.
Limitations: Applications not accepted. Giving primarily in NC.

Application information: Unsolicited requests for funds not accepted.
Trustees: H. Connor Kennett; Charles T. Wilkinson.
EIN: 271102300

7289
Walter & Marie Williams Foundation
207 Crown Point Rd.
Greenville, NC 27858 (252) 752-4366
Contact: Walter Williams, Pres.

Established in 2006 in North Carolina.
Donors: Walter L. Williams; Marie S. Williams.
Foundation type: Independent foundation.
Financial data (yr. ended 12/31/12): Assets, $6,145,905 (M); expenditures, $204,145; qualifying distributions, $165,649; giving activities include $165,649 for grants.
Purpose and activities: Giving primarily for education, human services, and to Baptist churches.
Fields of interest: Education; Health; Religion.
Limitations: Applications accepted. Giving primarily in NC.
Application information:
  Initial approach: Contact foundation
  Deadline(s): None
Trustees: Marie S. Williams; Walter L. Williams.
EIN: 205940392

7290
Wise Family Charitable Trust
118 Spring Creek Ln.
Wilmington, NC 28411-7647
Contact: Margaret Hunter, Tr.

Foundation type: Independent foundation.
Financial data (yr. ended 12/31/13): Assets, $2,310,437 (M); expenditures, $147,500; qualifying distributions, $147,500; giving activities include $147,500 for 3 grants (high: $67,500; low: $40,000).
Fields of interest: Arts and culture; Education.
Limitations: Applications not accepted. Giving primarily in CA.
Application information: Contributes only to pre-selected organizations.
Trustee: Margaret Hunter.
EIN: 205242708

7291
Elizabeth Burns Yost Trust
c/o Trust Tax Dept.
P.O. Box 2907
Wilson, NC 27894-2907 9106932733
Application address: c/o Branch Banking Trust Company, 130 Applecross Rd. Pinehurst, NC 28374-8520; tel.: (910) 693-2733

Established in 1989 in North Carolina.
Donor: Elizabeth Burns Yost†.
Foundation type: Independent foundation.

Financial data (yr. ended 12/31/13): Assets, $3,005,824 (M); expenditures, $182,668; qualifying distributions, $140,587 and $0 for set-asides.
Fields of interest: Arts and culture; Education; Health.
Type of support: Capital and infrastructure; Equipment; Program development.
Limitations: Applications accepted. Giving limited to Anson County, NC.
Application information: Application form required.
  Initial approach: Letter
  Deadline(s): None
  Board meeting date(s): Mar., June, Sept., and Dec.
Trustee: Branch Banking & Trust Co.
EIN: 566355993

7292
The Yount Foundation, Inc.
1234 S. Center St.
Hickory, NC 28601-5042

Established in 2006 in North Carolina.
Donors: Benny Yount; Paramount Ford, LLC; Paraount Kia of Asheville; BCL, LLC; Paramount Motor Sales, LLC; JCMC Custom Solutions.
Foundation type: Independent foundation.
Financial data (yr. ended 12/31/13): Assets, $454,995 (M); gifts received, $725,000; expenditures, $369,707; qualifying distributions, $349,050; giving activities include $349,050 for 26 grants (high: $130,200; low: $100).
Fields of interest: Higher education; Christianity; Protestantism.
Limitations: Applications not accepted. Giving primarily in MO and NC.
Application information: Contributes only to pre-selected organizations.
Officers: Benny Yount, Pres.; Cherrie Yount, V.P.; Nick Kincaid, Secy.; Lisa Yount, Treas.
EIN: 205240159

7293
The Zelnak Private Foundation
c/o PNC Bank, N.A.
409 Drummond Dr.
Raleigh, NC 27609-7033

Established in 1998 in North Carolina.
Donor: Stephen P. Zelnak, Jr.
Foundation type: Independent foundation.
Financial data (yr. ended 12/31/13): Assets, $2,815,092 (M); expenditures, $317,193; qualifying distributions, $300,000; giving activities include $300,000 for 1 grant.
Purpose and activities: Giving primarily for education and religious organizations.
Fields of interest: Human services.
Type of support: General support.
Limitations: Applications not accepted. Giving primarily in NC. No grants to individuals.
Application information: Contributes only to pre-selected organizations.
Trustees: Judy D. Zelnak; Stephen P. Zelnak, Jr.
EIN: 562115096

NORTH DAKOTA

7294
Vern and Ruth Berge Scholarship Foundation
606 W. Pine Cir.
Bottineau, ND   58318-1507

Foundation type: Independent foundation.
Financial data (yr. ended 12/31/13): Assets, $1,167,602 (M); expenditures, $226,374; qualifying distributions, $190,000; giving activities include $190,000 for 1 grant.
Fields of interest: Education.
Limitations: Applications not accepted. Giving primarily in ND.
Application information: Unsolicited requests for funds not accepted.
Officers: Donald Indvik, Chair.; Mae Streich, Secy.-Treas.
Directors: David Berge; Howard Beyer.
EIN: 462066496

7295
Community Foundation of Grand Forks, East Grand Forks and Region
(also known as Greater Grand Forks Community Foundation)
(formerly Greater Grand Forks Community Foundation)
620 DeMers Ave.
Grand Forks, ND   58201-4531   (701) 746-0668
Contact: Kristi Mishler, Exec. Dir.
FAX: (701) 772-3018;
E-mail: communityfoundation@gofoundation.org;
Main URL: http://www.gofoundation.org
Blog: http://gofoundation.org/blog
Facebook: http://www.facebook.com/pages/Community-Foundation-of-Grand-Forks-East-Grand-Forks-Region/301984133722
YouTube: http://www.youtube.com/user/CommunityFoundationG

Established in 1997 in North Dakota.
Foundation type: Community foundation.
Financial data (yr. ended 12/31/13): Assets, $8,333,107 (M); gifts received, $1,127,685; expenditures, $623,484; giving activities include $340,475 for 18+ grants (high: $30,750).
Purpose and activities: The foundation seeks to manage and develop diverse endowments that generate funding to address the quality of life in the Grand Forks, ND, area.
Fields of interest: Arts and culture; Education; Community and economic development; Human services; Child welfare.
Type of support: Endowments; Convening; Publications; Curriculum development; Scholarships; Research.

Limitations: Applications accepted. Giving limited to northwest MN and northeast ND. No support for religious organizations for religious purposes. No grants to individuals, or for non-program operating expenses, annual appeals or capital campaigns.
Publications: Annual report; Informational brochure (including application guidelines).
Application information: Visit foundation web site for application form and guidelines. Application form required.
   Initial approach: Contact foundation
   Board meeting date(s): Quarterly in Mar., June, Sept., and Dec.
   Final notification: Quarterly
Officers and Directors: Kristin Shea, Pres. and Director; Jim Satrom, V.P. and Director; Marilynn Ogden, Secy.-Treas. and Director; Kristi Mishler, Exec. Dir.; Sandy Crary; David Evenson; Cathi Feeley; Mary Dale Hansen; Joan Hawthorne; Derrick Johnson; Curt Kreun; Bill Lee; Dr. Lee Lipp; John Marchell; Gerard Neil; Margaret Tweten; Barry Wilfahrt.
Number of staff: 2 full-time professional; 1 full-time support.
EIN: 450448088

7296
Noel & Judith Fedje Foundation
2429 E. Country Club Dr.
Fargo, ND   58103-5730

Donors: Noel I. Fedje; Judith A. Fedje.
Foundation type: Independent foundation.
Financial data (yr. ended 12/31/13): Assets, $5,186,346 (M); gifts received, $233,318; expenditures, $221,313; qualifying distributions, $216,200; giving activities include $216,200 for 57 grants (high: $26,000; low: $100).
Fields of interest: Arts and culture; Education; Nonprofits; Hospital care; Diseases and conditions; Protestantism; Human services; Child welfare.
Type of support: Regranting.
Limitations: Applications not accepted.
Application information: Unsolicited requests for funds not accepted.
Officers and Trustees: Noel I. Fedje, Pres. and Trustee; Judith A. Fedje, V.P. and Trustee; Jill Fedje Johnson; Julie Fedje Johnston; Lori Fedje Paulson; Kari Fedje Rasmus.
EIN: 450418868

7297
Myra Foundation
P.O. Box 13536
Grand Forks, ND   58208-3536   (701) 795-3414
Contact: John V. Botsford, Pres.
E-mail: jbotsford@myrafoundation.org; Main URL: http://myrafoundation.org/index.html
Grants List: http://myrafoundation.org/current_receipients.html

Established in 1941 in North Dakota.
Donor: John E. Myra†.
Foundation type: Independent foundation.
Financial data (yr. ended 12/31/14): Assets, $7,447,228 (M); expenditures, $471,646; qualifying distributions, $351,660; giving activities include $351,660 for 47 grants (high: $36,000; low: $100).
Fields of interest: Education; Agriculture; Human services.
Type of support: General support; Capital and infrastructure; Equipment; Scholarships.
Limitations: Applications accepted. Giving primarily in Grand Forks County, ND. No grants to individuals, or for endowment funds, research, or matching gifts; no loans.
Publications: Informational brochure (including application guidelines).
Application information: See foundation web site for complete application guidelines.
   Initial approach: Proposal
   Copies of proposal: 1
   Deadline(s): Nov. 1
   Board meeting date(s): Quarterly
Officers: John Botsford, Pres.; Donna J. Gillig, Secy.-Treas.
Director: Kent Cronquist.
EIN: 450215088

7298
Arthur H. Pearson Testamentary Charitable Remainder Unitrust
Box 305
Westhope, ND   58793-0305
Application address: c/o Margo Helgerson, 225 5th Ave., Westhope, ND 58793, tel.: (701) 263-7717

Foundation type: Independent foundation.
Financial data (yr. ended 12/31/13): Assets, $8,262,285 (M); expenditures, $489,658; qualifying distributions, $373,980; giving activities include $373,980 for 11 grants (high: $110,116; low: $5,000).
Fields of interest: Education; Community and economic development; Sports and recreation; Human services.
Limitations: Applications accepted. Giving primarily in ND.
Application information: Application form required.
   Initial approach: Proposal
   Deadline(s): None
Trust Committee: Margo Helgerson; Don Clement; John Showronik.
EIN: 450451872

OHIO

7299
A Good Day Foundation
414 Walnut St., Ste. 1014
Cincinnati, OH 45202-3913 (513) 651-9333
Contact: T. Hunley

Established in 2002 in Ohio.
Donors: Gloria J. Fehr†; A Good Neighbor
Foundation.
Foundation type: Operating foundation.
Financial data (yr. ended 06/30/13): Assets,
$84,221 (M); gifts received, $400,000;
expenditures, $433,513; qualifying distributions,
$410,837; giving activities include $354,001 for
338 grants to individuals.
Purpose and activities: Giving primarily to
individuals and families that are in need of
immediate aid and services.
Fields of interest: Cancers; Basic and emergency
aid; Child welfare; Children.
Type of support: General support; Grants to
individuals.
Limitations: Giving primarily in KY and OH; some
funding also in TX.
Application information:
Initial approach: Letter or telephone
Deadline(s): None
Officers and Directors: James Minutolo, Pres. and
Director; Betty Bassett, V.P. and Director; Donald
Feldman, Treas. and Director; Gary Sallquist; Emily
K. Uhl.
EIN: 223885978

7300
Abrams Family Foundation
c/o Marlyon E. Abrams
3710 State Rte. 133 S.
Williamsburg, OH 45176-9798 (513) 724-6101

Donors: Marlyon E. Abrams; Jessie H. Abrams Rev.
Trust; Marlyon E. Abrams Rev. Trust; Jessie H.
Abrams.
Foundation type: Independent foundation.
Financial data (yr. ended 12/31/13): Assets,
$8,354,867 (M); gifts received, $2,876,147;
expenditures, $359,739; qualifying distributions,
$300,000; giving activities include $300,000 for 1
grant.
Fields of interest: Education.
Limitations: Applications accepted. Giving primarily
in Williamsburg, OH.
Application information: Application form required.
Initial approach: Proposal
Deadline(s): Apr. 1
Officers: Marlyon E. Abrams, Pres. and Treas.;
Jessie H. Abrams, Secy.
Board Member: Brian Abrams.
EIN: 271665086

7301
F.W. Albrecht Family Foundation
2700 Gilchrist Rd.
Akron, OH 44305-4433 (330) 733-2861
Contact: Sue Guthier

Established in 1990 in Ohio.

Donors: Fred W. Albrecht Grocery Co.; Albrecht Inc.
Foundation type: Company-sponsored foundation.
Financial data (yr. ended 12/31/14): Assets,
$3,254,076 (M); gifts received, $831,860;
expenditures, $229,702; qualifying distributions,
$217,694; giving activities include $217,694 for
grants.
Purpose and activities: The foundation supports
organizations involved with education, animals and
wildlife, and human services.
Fields of interest: Education; Human services;
Youth development.
Type of support: General support; Scholarships.
Limitations: Applications accepted. Giving limited to
areas of company operations in OH. No grants to
individuals.
Application information: Application form required.
Initial approach: Letter
Deadline(s): None
Directors: F. Steven Albrecht; Douglas A. Flinn;
Daniel J. McPeek; Katie Albrecht Swartz; James H.
Trout.
EIN: 341663626

7302
The Alpaugh Foundation
525 Vine St., Ste. 1925
Cincinnati, OH 45202-3121 (513) 621-1826

Established in 1986 in Ohio.
Donors: Peter A. Alpaugh; The Alpaugh Family 20
Year Charitable Lead Trust; The Alpaugh Family 15
Year Charitable Lead Trust.
Foundation type: Independent foundation.
Financial data (yr. ended 06/30/14): Assets,
$3,472,363 (M); gifts received, $326,280;
expenditures, $390,592; qualifying distributions,
$363,637; giving activities include $360,380 for
116 grants (high: $100,000; low: $25).
Fields of interest: Arts and culture; Performing arts;
Education; Higher education; Animal welfare;
Abortion; Diseases and conditions; Human services;
Family services; Child welfare; Parent education.
Limitations: Applications accepted. Giving primarily
in OH, with emphasis on Cincinnati. No grants to
individuals.
Application information:
Initial approach: Proposal
Deadline(s): None
Officer: Peter A. Alpaugh, Mgr.
EIN: 316314074

7303
The American Electric Power System Educational Trust Fund
c/o AEP Tax Dept.
1 Riverside Plz.
Columbus, OH 43215-2373 (614) 716-1000
Scholarship address: AEP, Human Resources, 1
Riverside Plaza, Columbus, OH 43215

Donors: American Electric Power Co., Inc.;
Columbus Southern Power Co.; Ohio Power Co.;
CSW Foundation.
Foundation type: Company-sponsored foundation.
Financial data (yr. ended 02/28/14): Assets,
$5,816,511 (M); expenditures, $307,305;
qualifying distributions, $300,162; giving activities
include $295,000 for 125 grants to individuals
(high: $2,500; low: $2,000).

Purpose and activities: The foundation awards
college scholarships to children of AEP employees.
Fields of interest: Higher education.
Type of support: Scholarships.
Limitations: Applications not accepted. Giving
primarily in areas of company operations, including
IN, OH, and VA.
Publications: Program policy statement.
Application information: Contributes only through
employee-related scholarships.
Trustees: Joe Cisneros; Venita McCellon-Allen;
Robert P. Powers.
EIN: 237418083

7304
Elizabeth Mendenhall Anderson Foundation
c/o U.S. Bank, N.A.
P.O. Box 1118, ML-CN-OH-W10X
Cincinnati, OH 45201-1118

Established in 1998 in Ohio.
Donor: Annie W. Anderson.
Foundation type: Independent foundation.
Financial data (yr. ended 12/31/12): Assets,
$1,160,166 (M); expenditures, $230,059;
qualifying distributions, $210,000; giving activities
include $210,000 for grants.
Fields of interest: Diseases and conditions;
Catholicism.
Type of support: General support.
Limitations: Applications not accepted. Giving
primarily in OH. No grants to individuals.
Application information: Unsolicited requests for
funds not accepted.
Officer: Joseph Krabbe, Pres.
Trustees: Christine Buttress; James Wellinghoff.
EIN: 311608634

7305
William P. Anderson Foundation
c/o PNC Advisors, Ohio
P.O. Box 1198
Cincinnati, OH 45273-9631
Contact: Phyllis Wahl

Foundation type: Independent foundation.
Financial data (yr. ended 10/31/13): Assets,
$6,443,262 (M); expenditures, $357,783;
qualifying distributions, $308,492; giving activities
include $291,425 for 60 grants (high: $12,000;
low: $1,000).
Purpose and activities: Giving primarily for the arts,
health care and for AIDS research.
Fields of interest: Arts and culture; Visual arts;
Performing arts; Education; Natural resources;
Nonprofits; Health; Hospital care; HIV/AIDS; Crime
prevention; Child welfare.
Type of support: Annual campaigns; Capital
campaigns; Capital and infrastructure; Equipment;
Seed money; Research; Regranting.
Limitations: Applications accepted. Giving primarily
in Cincinnati, OH. No grants to individuals.
Application information: Application form required.
Initial approach: Letter
Copies of proposal: 1
Deadline(s): Oct. 1
Board meeting date(s): Nov.
Officers and Trustees: William P. Anderson, V, Pres.
and Trustee; Michael A. Coombe, V.P. and Trustee;
Harry W. Whittaker, V.P. and Trustee; Phyllis C.

Wahl, Secy. and Trustee; Grenville Anderson, Treas. and Trustee; Nicholas R. Anderson; John L. Campbell; Will Claflin; Tucker J. Coombe; James A. Myers; David Whittaker; Polly W. Whittaker.
EIN: 316034059

7306
Anderton Bentley Fund
P.O. Box 630858
Cincinnati, OH 45263-0858
Application address: c/o Advisory Committee, Attn.: Anderton Bentley, P.O. Box 1868, Toledo, OH 43603

Foundation type: Independent foundation.
Financial data (yr. ended 09/30/13): Assets, $0 (M); expenditures, $175,724; qualifying distributions, $173,919; giving activities include $173,159 for 1 grant.
Fields of interest: Arts and culture; Art museums.
Limitations: Applications accepted. Giving primarily in Toledo, OH. No grants to individuals.
Application information: Application form required.
   Initial approach: Proposal
   Deadline(s): None
Trustee: Fifth Third Bank.
EIN: 346509881

7307
The Andrews Foundation
3401 Enterprise Pkwy., Ste. 340
Beachwood, OH 44122-7340 (440) 449-8910
Contact: Laura Baxter-Heuer, Pres.
E-mail: andrewsfdn@aol.com

Established in 1951 in Ohio.
Donor: Mrs. Matthew Andrews†.
Foundation type: Independent foundation.
Financial data (yr. ended 12/31/13): Assets, $8,663,307 (M); expenditures, $485,016; qualifying distributions, $357,121; giving activities include $321,000 for 13 grants (high: $50,000; low: $5,000).
Purpose and activities: Giving primarily for education.
Fields of interest: Performing arts; Secondary education; Higher education; Specialty hospital care; Alcoholism; Cancers.
Type of support: General support; Annual campaigns; Capital campaigns; Endowments.
Limitations: Applications accepted. Giving limited to OH. No grants to individuals.
Application information:
   Initial approach: Letter
   Copies of proposal: 1
   Deadline(s): None
   Board meeting date(s): Spring and fall
Officers and Trustees: Laura Baxter-Heuer, Pres. and Trustee; Michael A. Heuer, V.P. and Trustee.
Number of staff: 1 full-time professional.
EIN: 346515110

7308
The Angels on Track Foundation
8286 Clover Rd. N.E.
Salineville, OH 43945-9418 (330) 738-3197
FAX: (330) 738-3198;
E-mail: info@angelsontrack.org; Main URL: http://www.angelsontrack.org
E Newsletter: http://www.angelsontrack.org/newsletter.html

Established in 1997 in Ohio.
Foundation type: Independent foundation.
Financial data (yr. ended 12/31/13): Assets, $3,599,032 (M); gifts received, $125; expenditures, $193,840; qualifying distributions, $145,560; giving activities include $144,120 for 1 grant.
Purpose and activities: The foundation's mission is to provide the financial backing needed to improve railroad crossing safety throughout Ohio, and to educate local highway authorities on the various programs available through state and federal funding.
Fields of interest: Safety education.
Type of support: General support.
Limitations: Giving limited to OH.
Trustees: Dennis F. Moore; Vicky L. Moore.
EIN: 311549790

7309
The Evenor Armington Fund
P.O. Box 1558, Dept. EA4E86
Columbus, OH 43216-1558

Established in 1954 in Ohio.
Donor: Everett Armington.
Foundation type: Independent foundation.
Financial data (yr. ended 06/30/13): Assets, $1,863,663 (M); expenditures, $354,658; qualifying distributions, $332,893; giving activities include $325,000 for 25 grants (high: $25,000; low: $3,000).
Purpose and activities: Grants primarily for special projects, usually short-term, in education, child welfare, medical research, health, the arts, the environment, and public policy organizations, including human rights, peace and justice, and the struggle against poverty.
Fields of interest: Arts and culture; Education; Environment; Natural resources; Health; Diseases and conditions; Public policy; Human rights; Human services; Child welfare; International peace and security.
Type of support: General support; Pro bono consulting services; Continuing support; Annual campaigns; Emergency funds; Program development; Research; Publications; Research and evaluation; Policy, advocacy and systems reform.
Limitations: Applications not accepted. Giving primarily in CA, NH, NY and OH. No grants to individuals.
Application information: Contributes only to pre-selected organizations.
   Board meeting date(s): Summer
Trustee: Huntington National Bank.
EIN: 346525508

7310
David Tod Arrel Trust
c/o PNC Bank, N.A.
P.O. Box 94651
Cleveland, OH 44101-4651

Foundation type: Independent foundation.
Financial data (yr. ended 12/31/14): Assets, $9,383,886; expenditures, $419,887; qualifying distributions, $359,613 and $0 for set-asides.
Fields of interest: Family services.
Type of support: General support.
Limitations: Applications not accepted. Giving limited to Youngstown, OH.
Application information: Contributes only to pre-selected organizations; unsolicited requests for funds not considered or acknowledged.
Trustee: PNC Bank, N.A.
EIN: 346515526

7311
Athens Foundation
2 S. Court St., 2nd Fl.
P.O. Box 366
Athens, OH 45701-0366 (740) 594-6061
Contact: Susan Urano, Exec. Dir.
FAX: (740) 594-6061;
E-mail: susan@athensfoundation.org; Main URL: http://www.athensfoundation.org
Blog: http://www.athensfoundation.blogspot.in
Facebook: https://www.facebook.com/pages/The-Athens-Foundation/312616252558
Twitter: http://twitter.com/AthensFDN

Established in 1980 in Ohio.
Donors: Thelma Sheridan†; Deluxe Corp.
Foundation type: Community foundation.
Financial data (yr. ended 09/30/13): Assets, $4,333,317 (M); gifts received, $321,769; expenditures, $418,967; giving activities include $195,847 for 9+ grants (high: $15,000).
Purpose and activities: The foundation's mission is to enhance the quality of life for the people of the Athens region through building endowments, awarding grants, and providing leadership on key community issues now and for generations to come.
Fields of interest: Arts and culture; Humanities; Education; Environment; Natural resources; Animal welfare; Health; Hospital care; Mental health care; Public affairs; Sports and recreation; Human services; Children; People with disabilities.
Type of support: Continuing support; Pro bono consulting services; Leadership and professional development; Capital campaigns; Program development; Convening; Curriculum development; Research; Technical assistance.
Limitations: Applications accepted. Giving limited to Athens County, OH. No support for religious or political purposes, or for legislative action groups. No grants to individuals, or for endowments, budget deficits, scholarships, or annual fund raising drives.
Publications: Application guidelines; Annual report; Financial statement; Grants list; Informational brochure; Newsletter; Program policy statement.
Application information: Visit foundation web site for grant guidelines, pre-eligibility screening questions, and online application. Application form required.
   Initial approach: Contact foundation
   Deadline(s): Mar. 15 For Spring Grant., Sept. 15 For Fall Grant.
   Board meeting date(s): Last Tues. of every month
   Final notification: May

Officers and Board Members: Judith Millesen, Chair., Devel. and Director; Paul Wiehl, Chair., Grants Comm. and Director; Michael Carpenter, Pres. and Director; Dr. Tom Davis, V.P. and Director; Kerry Pigman, Secy. and Director; Scott Robe, Treas. and Director; Susan Urano, Exec. Dir.; Ann Fox; Rev. Peter Galbraith; John Haseley; Wendy Jakmas; Dr. Vipin Koshal; Thomas Kostohryz; Jim McDonald; Andrea Reik; Wendy Weiser.
Number of staff: 1 full-time professional; 2 part-time professional.
EIN: 311040215

7312
Austin-Bailey Health and Wellness Foundation
2719 Fulton Dr. N.W., Ste. D
Canton, OH 44718-3519 (330) 580-2380
Contact: Don A. Sultzbach, Exec. Dir.
FAX: (330) 580-2381; E-mail: abfdn@sbcglobal.net;
Main URL: http://fdnweb.org/austinbailey
Grants List: http://fdnweb.org/austinbailey/grant-awards

Established in 1996 in Ohio.
Foundation type: Independent foundation.
Financial data (yr. ended 06/30/13): Assets, $7,410,543 (M); gifts received, $1,475; expenditures, $493,186; qualifying distributions, $324,058; giving activities include $324,058 for 30 grants (high: $30,000; low: $1,479).
Purpose and activities: The purpose of the foundation is to support programs that promote the physical and mental well-being of citizens of Holmes, Stark, Tuscarawas and Wayne counties, OH. The foundation emphasizes healthcare affordability concerns of people who are uninsured and underinsured, economically disadvantaged, children, single parents and the aging. The foundation also advocates programs that speak to the mental health needs of individuals and families.
Fields of interest: Health; Health insurance; Dental care; Mental health care; Public health; Human services; Family services.
Type of support: General support; Employee matching gifts; Matching grants; Continuing support; Equipment; Emergency funds; Program development; Convening; Seed money; Curriculum development; Scholarships.
Limitations: Applications accepted. Giving limited to Holmes, Stark, Tuscarawas, and Wayne counties, OH. No support for religious organizations for overtly religious purposes. No grants to annual and capital campaigns, membership drives, fundraising, advertising, or endowment funds.
Publications: Application guidelines; Financial statement; Grants list; Informational brochure; Informational brochure (including application guidelines).
Application information: Application form required.
Initial approach: Telephone call to request grant guidelines
Copies of proposal: 6
Deadline(s): See foundation web site for current deadlines
Board meeting date(s): 2nd Thurs. in Jan., Mar., June, and Sept.
Final notification: 14 days after board meeting in Mar. and Sept.
Officers and Trustees: Frederick W. Rohrig, Chair. and Trustee; Charles R. Conklin, DO, Vice-Chair. and Trustee; Virginia Neutzling, RN, BS, M.Ed, Secy. and Trustee; Peter Kopko, Treas. and Trustee; Don A.

Sultzbach, Exec. Dir.; Daniel J. Fuline; Diane K. Jarrett; Elton D. Lehman, DO; David A. Miller; Daniel N. Moretta, DO; John L. Muhlbach, Jr.; Scott P. Sandrock; Eugene A. Thorn III; Thomas F. Turner.
Number of staff: 2 part-time professional; 1 part-time support.
EIN: 341845584

7313
Bahmann Foundation
(formerly Emma and Laura Bahmann Family Foundation)
8041 Hosbrook Rd., Ste. 210
Cincinnati, OH 45236-2907
Contact: John T. Gatch, Exec. Dir.
FAX: (513) 891-3722; E-mail: info@bahmann.org;
Main URL: http://www.bahmann.org

Established in 1984 in Ohio.
Donors: Emma Leah Bahmann†; Laura Belle Bahmann†.
Foundation type: Independent foundation.
Financial data (yr. ended 12/31/13): Assets, $8,688,172 (M); expenditures, $630,032; qualifying distributions, $502,949; giving activities include $223,373 for 30+ grants (high: $47,000).
Purpose and activities: The mission of the Bahmann Foundation is to reduce isolation of low-income older adults through technology. This is accomplished by granting funds to nonprofit charitable organizations that provide applicable services. Foundation grants help fund services and purchase equipment that stimulate mental and physical activity in elderly adults. Giving also to benefit the hearing or communication-disorder impaired elderly who live in nonprofit institutions.
Fields of interest: Speech and hearing rehabilitation; Ear, nose and throat diseases; Adults; Seniors.
Type of support: Equipment; Employee matching gifts; In-kind gifts; Fellowships; Scholarships; Matching grants; Technical assistance; Student aid.
Limitations: Applications not accepted. Giving limited to the greater Cincinnati, OH, area, and northern KY region.
Publications: Informational brochure; Newsletter.
Application information: Unsolicited requests for funds not accepted.
Board meeting date(s): Quarterly
Officer: John T. Gatch, Exec. Dir.
Trustee: Lewis G. Gatch.
Number of staff: 1 full-time professional; 1 part-time professional.
EIN: 316369498

7314
Baird Brothers Company Foundation
P.O. Box 1558, Dept. EA4E86
Columbus, OH 43216-1558

Established in 1977 in Ohio.
Donor: Baird Brothers Co.
Foundation type: Independent foundation.
Financial data (yr. ended 06/30/13): Assets, $3,751,405 (M); expenditures, $258,234; qualifying distributions, $232,613; giving activities include $205,916 for 11 grants (high: $59,197; low: $1,500).
Purpose and activities: Giving primarily to Presbyterian churches, local community improvement, and educational programs.

Fields of interest: Museums; Historical activities; Education; Undergraduate education; Public administration; Community and economic development; Protestantism.
Type of support: General support.
Limitations: Applications not accepted. Giving limited to Nelsonville, OH. No grants to individuals.
Application information: Unsolicited requests for funds not accepted.
Board meeting date(s): Monthly
Trustee: The Huntington National Bank.
Directors: Steven E. Cox; Jane E. Harmony; Wilbert W. Warren, Jr.
EIN: 316194844

7315
C. Glenn Barber Foundation
P.O. Box 94651
Cleveland, OH 44101-4651

Established in 1978 in Ohio.
Foundation type: Independent foundation.
Financial data (yr. ended 12/31/13): Assets, $3,608,500 (M); expenditures, $156,169; qualifying distributions, $151,894; giving activities include $150,444 for 1 grant.
Purpose and activities: Support for higher education, primarily through an annual grant to Ohio State University in Columbus, and through scholarships and scholarship funds.
Fields of interest: Higher education.
Type of support: Scholarships; Research.
Limitations: Applications not accepted. Giving limited to OH.
Application information: Unsolicited requests for funds not accepted.
Trustee: PNC Bank, N.A.
EIN: 346765153

7316
David & Rebecca Barron Foundation Trust
(formerly David & Carole Barron Foundation)
P.O. Box 1118, ML CN-OH-W10X
Cincinnati, OH 45201-1118

Established in 1997 in Ohio.
Donor: David R. Barron.
Foundation type: Independent foundation.
Financial data (yr. ended 12/31/13): Assets, $1,144,572 (M); expenditures, $199,388; qualifying distributions, $190,637; giving activities include $189,500 for 11 grants (high: $75,000; low: $250).
Fields of interest: Elementary and secondary education; Higher education; Human services; Food aid; Adolescents; Homeless people.
Type of support: General support.
Limitations: Applications not accepted. Giving primarily in Cincinnati, OH. No grants to individuals.
Application information: Unsolicited requests for funds not accepted.
Trustees: David R. Barron; Dennis L. Manes, Esq.
EIN: 311521552

7317
The John C. Bates Foundation
2401 Front St.
Toledo, OH 43605-1145

Established in 1993 in Ohio.

Donors: Heidtman Steel Products, Inc.; Centaur, Inc.; HS Processing, LP.
Foundation type: Company-sponsored foundation.
Financial data (yr. ended 03/31/13): Assets, $1,376,365 (M); gifts received, $158,100; expenditures, $157,491; qualifying distributions, $156,740; giving activities include $153,558 for 22 grants (high: $33,333; low: $75).
Purpose and activities: The foundation supports zoological societies, community foundations, and organizations involved with education, health, human services, and Christianity.
Fields of interest: Education; Elementary and secondary education; Higher education; Zoos; Foundations; Health; Cancers; Christianity; Human services; Family services.
Type of support: Capital campaigns; Program development; Scholarships.
Limitations: Applications not accepted. Giving primarily in IN, MI, and OH. No grants to individuals.
Application information: Contributes only to pre-selected organizations.
Officers and Trustees: Darlene B. Dotson, Pres. and Trustee; John M. Carey, Secy. and Trustee; Mark E. Ridenour, Treas. and Trustee; John C. Bates; John C. Bates, Jr.; Sarah J. Bates; Debra A. Shinkle.
EIN: 341749094

7318
Waite M. B-Brand Foundation
c/o KeyBank N.A.
P.O. Box 10099
Dayton, OH 45402
Application address: c/o Gregory Alexander, 1000 Jackson, Toledo, OH 43624

Established in 1965 in Ohio.
Foundation type: Independent foundation.
Financial data (yr. ended 02/28/14): Assets, $2,740,583 (M); expenditures, $174,395; qualifying distributions, $158,027; giving activities include $151,500 for 28 grants (high: $20,000; low: $500).
Purpose and activities: Giving primarily for the arts, health care, and human services.
Fields of interest: Arts and culture; Education; Natural resources; Health; Diseases and conditions; Human services; Youth services.
Type of support: General support; Matching grants; Capital campaigns; Capital and infrastructure; Program development; Seed money.
Limitations: Applications accepted. Giving primarily in the Toledo, OH, area. No grants to individuals.
Application information:
Initial approach: Proposal
Deadline(s): None
Trustees: Gregory G. Alexander; Gregory S. Shumaker; Hope J. Welles; KeyBank, N.A.; Phil H. Wolf.
EIN: 346563471

7319
Beck Family Foundation
8534 E. Kemper Rd.
Cincinnati, OH 45249 (513) 489-1955

Established in 2002 in Ohio.
Donor: Louis S. Beck.
Foundation type: Independent foundation.
Financial data (yr. ended 09/30/14): Assets, $1,043,580; gifts received, $302,500;

expenditures, $353,748; qualifying distributions, $341,145.
Fields of interest: Judaism; Youth development.
Limitations: Applications accepted. Giving primarily in FL and OH.
Application information: Application form required.
Initial approach: E-mail
Deadline(s): None
Officers: Louis S. Beck, Pres. and Treas.; Ryan Beck, V.P.; Steven Beck, V.P.; Staci Graef, V.P.; Patty S. Beck, Secy.
EIN: 850487227

7320
Florence Simon Beecher Foundation
P.O. Box 1558, Dept EA4E86
Columbus, OH 43216

Established in 1969 in Ohio.
Donor: Florence Simon Beecher.
Foundation type: Independent foundation.
Financial data (yr. ended 12/31/14): Assets, $8,391,310; expenditures, $449,141; qualifying distributions, $398,470.
Fields of interest: Orchestral music; Community and economic development; Child welfare.
Type of support: Capital campaigns; Capital and infrastructure; Equipment; Program development.
Limitations: Applications not accepted. Giving limited to Youngstown and Mahoning County, OH.
Application information: Unsolicited request for funds not accepted.
Trustee: Huntington National Bank.
EIN: 346613413

7321
Ward Beecher Foundation
P.O. Box 1558, Dept. EA4E86
Columbus, OH 43216-1558

Established in 1958 in Ohio.
Donor: Ward Beecher†.
Foundation type: Independent foundation.
Financial data (yr. ended 12/31/14): Assets, $4,405,365 (M); expenditures, $245,868; qualifying distributions, $197,045; giving activities include $177,500 for 12 grants (high: $37,500; low: $5,000).
Purpose and activities: Support for capital building drives for hospitals, community funds, and youth agencies.
Fields of interest: Arts and culture; Philanthropy; Human services.
Type of support: General support; Annual campaigns; Capital campaigns; Building and renovations; Equipment.
Limitations: Applications not accepted. Giving limited to Mahoning County OH. No grants to individuals, or for scholarships, fellowships, matching gifts, endowment funds, or research; no loans.
Application information: Unsolicited requests for funds not accepted.
Board meeting date(s): As required
Trustee: Huntington National Bank.
EIN: 346516441

7322
John and Susan Berding Family Foundation
6753 Rapid Run Rd.
Cincinnati, OH 45233-1425

Donor: John Berding.
Foundation type: Independent foundation.
Financial data (yr. ended 12/31/14): Assets, $7,252,736; gifts received, $0; expenditures, $321,149; qualifying distributions, $296,231.
Fields of interest: Education.
Limitations: Applications not accepted. Giving primarily in IL and OH. No grants for Grants will be awarded to individuals or organizations for charitable, religious or educational purposes.
Application information: Unsolicited requests for funds not accepted.
Officers and Trustees: John Berding, Pres. and Trustee; Susan Berding, V.P. and Trustee.
EIN: 205909751

7323
Lenore and Norman Berke Charitable Foundation, Inc.
c/o Jerome Spevack
7 Hampshire Ct.
Beachwood, OH 44122-2205

Established in 1994 in Unspecified.
Foundation type: Independent foundation.
Financial data (yr. ended 12/31/12): Assets, $36,297 (M); gifts received, $202,236; expenditures, $166,070; qualifying distributions, $166,070; giving activities include $163,000 for 4 grants (high: $70,000; low: $3,000).
Fields of interest: Nonprofits; Health; Judaism.
Type of support: Regranting.
Limitations: Applications not accepted. No grants to individuals.
Application information: Unsolicited requests for funds not accepted.
Officers and Directors: Jerome Spevack, Pres. and Director; Sheldon M. Lewin, Secy.-Treas. and Director; Ivan J. Mervis; Faye Sholiton.
EIN: 650529667

7324
The Marshall L. and Deborah L. Berkman Family Charitable Trust
c/o J. Talbot Young
925 Euclid Ave., Ste. 2000
Cleveland, OH 44115-1407

Established in 1996 in Ohio.
Donors: Deborah L. Berkman; Louis Berkman Investment Company; Ellen F. Berkman; Laura B. Coleman; Martha B. Winfield.
Foundation type: Independent foundation.
Financial data (yr. ended 12/31/13): Assets, $3,866,259 (M); gifts received, $32,470; expenditures, $182,197; qualifying distributions, $162,000; giving activities include $162,000 for 28 grants (high: $25,000; low: $500).
Purpose and activities: Giving for music and higher education.
Fields of interest: Arts and culture; Education; Human services.
Limitations: Applications not accepted. No grants to individuals.
Application information: Unsolicited requests for funds not accepted.

Trustees: Ellen F. Berkman; Laura B. Coleman; Martha B. Winfield.
EIN: 341845200

7325
Ralph L. & Florence A. Bernard Foundation
1735 S. Hawkins, Ste. 3
Akron, OH   44320
Application address: c/o Ralph L. Bernard, Jr., P.O. Box 8176, Akron, OH 44320-0176, tel.: (330) 836-9306

Established in 1998 in Ohio.
Donor: Ralph L. Bernard.
Foundation type: Independent foundation.
Financial data (yr. ended 04/30/13): Assets, $4,686,746 (M); expenditures, $297,460; qualifying distributions, $195,650; giving activities include $195,650 for 10 grants (high: $50,750; low: $250).
Fields of interest: Education; Health; Catholicism; Human services.
Limitations: Applications accepted. Giving primarily in OH. No grants to individuals.
Application information:
   Initial approach: Proposal
   Deadline(s): None
Trustees: Ralph L. Bernard, Jr.; Regina A. Dain.
EIN: 341867382

7326
Lester J. Besl Family Foundation
3660 Dixie Hwy.
Fairfield, OH   45014-1105
Application Address: c/o Dennis Doyle, 7757 Hopper Rd., Cincinnati, OH 45230, tel.: (513) 784-8012

Established in 1981 in Ohio.
Donors: Force Control Industries, Inc.; Lester J. Besl; James C. Besl.
Foundation type: Independent foundation.
Financial data (yr. ended 12/31/13): Assets, $2,563,472 (M); expenditures, $212,036; qualifying distributions, $195,000; giving activities include $195,000 for 5 grants (high: $80,000; low: $25,000).
Purpose and activities: Awards grants and interest-free loans to organizations engaged in the support and education of disadvantaged children and young adults.
Fields of interest: Higher education; Hospital care; Christianity.
Type of support: General support; Program-related investments; Scholarships.
Limitations: Applications not accepted. Giving primarily in OH. No grants to individuals.
Application information: Contributes only to pre-selected organizations.
Officers: James C. Besl, Pres.; Dennis M. Doyle, Secy.; Michael L. Besl, Treas.
Trustees: Joseph E. Besl; Karen M. Murrell.
EIN: 311016859

7327
Bicknell Fund
1111 Superior Ave., Ste. 700
Cleveland, OH   44114-2540   (216) 363-6382
Contact: Marianne Grega, Secy.-Treas.
FAX: (216) 363-6488; Main URL: http://fdnweb.org/bicknellfund/

Established in 1949 in Ohio.
Donors: Kate H. Bicknell†; Warren Bicknell, Jr.†; Warren Bicknell III; Kate B. Kirkham.
Foundation type: Independent foundation.
Financial data (yr. ended 12/31/13): Assets, $7,262,407 (M); expenditures, $426,422; qualifying distributions, $337,402; giving activities include $318,937 for 42 grants (high: $35,000; low: $437).
Purpose and activities: The Bicknell Fund was formed for the purpose of promoting the well-being of mankind, and to that end to engage in such forms of charitable, benevolent, educational, scientific and research work as from time to time shall seem expedient to the trustees. Main areas of focus include social and human services to help the needy and homeless in the Cleveland, Ohio, area, and education.
Fields of interest: Elementary and secondary education; Secondary education; Special needs education; Higher education; Health; Mental health care; Human services; Family services; Child welfare; Child development; Youth mentoring.
Type of support: Annual campaigns; Capital campaigns; Capital and infrastructure; Program development; Scholarships.
Limitations: Applications accepted. Giving primarily in the greater Cleveland, OH, area. No grants to individuals; or for endowments, or multi-year pledges; no loans.
Publications: Application guidelines.
Application information: Multi-year grants not awarded. Application guidelines are available on foundation web site.
   Initial approach: Proposal; questionnaire available on foundation web site. Proposals sent by fax or e-mail will not be accepted
   Copies of proposal: 1
   Deadline(s): Submit proposal prior to Apr. 1 or Sept. 1
   Board meeting date(s): June and Nov.
   Final notification: 4 weeks following board meeting
Officers and Trustees: Samantha K. Crowley, Pres. and Trustee; Warren Bicknell III, V.P. and Trustee; Marianne Grega, Secy.-Treas.; Wendy H. Bicknell; W. Gates Kirkham; Henry L. Meyer III; Kate B. Luzius; Henry E. Siebert; Alexander S. Taylor II.
Number of staff: None.
EIN: 346513799

7328
Ann D. Black Charitable Trust
c/o KeyBank
4900 Tiedeman Rd., OH-01-49-0150
Brooklyn, OH   44144-2302

Foundation type: Independent foundation.
Financial data (yr. ended 12/31/14): Assets, $3,648,991 (M); expenditures, $214,728; qualifying distributions, $183,415; giving activities include $170,104 for 10 grants (high: $26,043; low: $5,205).
Fields of interest: Undergraduate education; University education; Hospital care; Human services; Scouting programs.
Limitations: Applications not accepted. Giving limited to OH. No grants to individuals.
Application information: Unsolicited requests for funds not accepted.
Trustee: KeyBank, N.A.
EIN: 346741740

7329
The Sam and Rachel Boymel Foundation
5200 Camelot Dr.
Fairfield, OH   45014-4009
Application address: c/o Nancy Wenning, High St., Journal Sq., Hamilton, OH 45011; tel.: (513) 867-5133

Established in 1997 in Ohio.
Donors: Rachel Boymel; Samuel Boymel; Suncoke Energy Inc.
Foundation type: Independent foundation.
Financial data (yr. ended 12/31/13): Assets, $3,900,146 (M); gifts received, $100,000; expenditures, $215,843; qualifying distributions, $177,886; giving activities include $177,886 for 18 grants (high: $44,250; low: $1,000).
Purpose and activities: Giving primarily to Jewish agencies, temples, and schools.
Fields of interest: Education; Religion; Human services.
Limitations: Applications accepted. Giving primarily in New York, NY and Cincinnati, OH.
Application information: Application form required.
   Initial approach: Proposal
   Deadline(s): None
Trustees: Rachel Boymel; Sam Boymel; Steve Boymel; Gidon Eldad; Fay Sosna.
EIN: 311578615

7330
Brentwood Foundation
30799 Pinetree Rd., Ste. 274
Cleveland, OH   44124-5903   (216) 328-9294
Contact: Christine Gibbons, Dir.
FAX: (216) 328-9219;
E-mail: brentfoundation@sbcglobal.net; Tel. for information regarding South Pointe Hospital grant application process: (216) 491-7234 or (216) 491-7461; Main URL: http://www.brentwood-foundation.org

Established in 1994 in Ohio.
Foundation type: Independent foundation.
Financial data (yr. ended 12/31/13): Assets, $24,111,962 (M); expenditures, $590,279; qualifying distributions, $533,811; giving activities include $409,648 for 1 grant.
Purpose and activities: Giving to enhance osteopathic medicine, research and patient care by: 1) providing educational opportunities designed to strengthen the capabilities of students and practitioners, (including interns and residents), 2) supporting research efforts which focus upon the acquisition, advancement, and dissemination of knowledge in this field, 3) educating the public about osteopathic services and trends, and 4) initiating activities designed to advance and improve patient care in osteopathic hospitals and in the community.
Fields of interest: Medical education; Hospital care.
Type of support: General support; Pro bono consulting services; Matching grants; Continuing support; Equipment; Program development; Convening; Curriculum development; Research.
Limitations: Applications accepted. Giving primarily in OH, particularly Northeast OH. The foundation will consider funding requests outside of OH if they directly impact OH or Northeast OH. No support for activities which are in direct competition with the osteopathic education and medical activities being conducted within the Cleveland Clinic Health System. No grants to individuals.

Publications: Application guidelines; Annual report; Annual report (including application guidelines); Financial statement; Grants list; Informational brochure (including application guidelines).
Application information: Grant requests submitted from South Pointe Hospital and other hospitals or programs within the Cleveland Clinic Health System must follow South Pointe Hospital's grant application procedures. See web site for application guidelines and Grant Cover Sheet.

Initial approach: Letter of inquiry
Copies of proposal: 2
Deadline(s): Apr. 1 or Sept. 1 (If a deadline date falls on a weekend or a holiday, the following Mon. will be considered the deadline date)
Board meeting date(s): June and Nov.

Officers and Trustees: Roger F. Classen, Chair. and Trustee; Raymond J. Grabow, Vice-Chair.; Michael F. Killeen, Secy. and Trustee; George Kappos, Jr., Treas. and Trustee; Richard Barone; Vincent F. DeCrane; David Krahe, DO; Gregory P. Kurtz; Michael McClain, DO; Michael Merriman; Brenda R. Saridakis; Jeffrey A. Stanley, DO.
Director: Christine Gibbons.
Number of staff: 1 full-time professional.
EIN: 341783117

7331
The Robert H. Brethen Foundation
40 N. Main St., Ste. 2560
Dayton, OH 45423-1730 (937) 224-1730

Established in 1988 in Ohio.
Donors: Robert H. Brethen; Celstar Group, Inc.
Foundation type: Independent foundation.
Financial data (yr. ended 10/31/14): Assets, $4,877,876; gifts received, $313,259; expenditures, $231,307; qualifying distributions, $203,245.
Fields of interest: Health; Hospice care; Christianity; Human services; Homeless services; Adolescents.
Type of support: General support.
Limitations: Applications accepted. Giving primarily in the greater Dayton, OH, area. No grants to individuals.
Application information:
Initial approach: Letter
Deadline(s): None
Officers and Trustees: Robert H. Brethen, Pres. and Treas.; David M. Brethen, Secy. and Trustee; Karen B. Johns.
EIN: 311213173

7332
Douglas & Janet Brews Foundation
c/o KeyBank N.A.
4900 Tiedeman Rd., OH-01-49-0150
Brooklyn, OH 44144-2302

Foundation type: Independent foundation.
Financial data (yr. ended 12/31/14): Assets, $3,535,521 (M); expenditures, $190,113; qualifying distributions, $169,741; giving activities include $165,590 for 5 grants (high: $33,118; low: $33,118).
Fields of interest: Specialty hospital care; Human services; People with vision impairments.
Limitations: Applications not accepted. Giving limited to Cleveland, OH. No grants to individuals.

Application information: Unsolicited requests for funds not accepted.
Trustee: KeyBank N.A.
EIN: 346508419

7333
Brinck Family Foundation, Inc.
(doing business as Sanctity of Life Foundation)
P.O. Box 53295
Cincinnati, OH 45253-0295

Established in 2000 in Ohio.
Donors: Joseph A. Brinck II; Cynthia A. Brinck; JTL Consulting, Inc.; Kentucky Christian Foundation; J. Cortell; Mrs. J. Cortell; American Microproducts; JTM Provisions, Inc.; Stetler and Brinck, Inc.; United Trust Group, Inc.; Christian Community Foundation; Louisville Christian Foundation; National Christian Foundation; Universal Guarantee Life Insurance Co.; Joseph Brinck; River Foundation; Duncan Taylor; Blue Grass Comm. Foundation; Mashni.
Foundation type: Independent foundation.
Financial data (yr. ended 09/30/13): Assets, $62,477 (M); gifts received, $409,424; expenditures, $381,965; qualifying distributions, $381,965; giving activities include $344,898 for 9 grants (high: $149,723; low: $700).
Purpose and activities: Giving primarily to pro-life activities and programs.
Fields of interest: Christianity; Right to life.
Limitations: Applications not accepted. Giving in the U.S., with some emphasis on CA, GA, and OH. No grants to individuals.
Application information: Contributes only to pre-selected organizations.
Officer: Joseph A. Brinck, Pres.
EIN: 311774144

7334
The Brocker Foundation Inc.
6075 Silica Rd.
Austintown, OH 44515-1081

Donor: Bruce E. Brocker.
Foundation type: Independent foundation.
Financial data (yr. ended 12/31/13): Assets, $6,836,349 (M); expenditures, $290,344; qualifying distributions, $254,000; giving activities include $254,000 for 21 grants (high: $30,000; low: $4,000).
Fields of interest: Religion; Youth development; International relations.
Limitations: Applications not accepted.
Application information: Unsolicited requests for funds not accepted.
Officers: Bruce E. Brocker, Pres.; Deborah J. Brocker, Secy.-Treas.
Trustee: Matthew C. Brocker.
EIN: 274347700

7335
Mary Jane Brooks Charitable Trust
P.O. Box 39
Steubenville, OH 43952-5039

Foundation type: Independent foundation.
Financial data (yr. ended 12/31/13): Assets, $9,369,220 (M); gifts received, $71,795; expenditures, $443,147; qualifying distributions,

$396,500; giving activities include $396,500 for 3 grants (high: $355,000; low: $18,500).
Fields of interest: Health.
Limitations: Applications not accepted. Giving primarily in Steubenville, OH.
Application information: Unsolicited requests for funds not accepted.
Trustees: R. Peterson Chalfant; David E. D'Anniballe; Edward M. George.
EIN: 271018187

7336
Warren Brown Family Foundation
6475 Perimeter Dr.
P.O. Box 163
Dublin, OH 43016-8459
Contact: Jan Brown, Pres.
E-mail: wbff@bellsouth.net

Established in 1996 in Ohio.
Donor: D. Warren Brown†.
Foundation type: Independent foundation.
Financial data (yr. ended 12/31/13): Assets, $3,172,661 (M); expenditures, $219,878; qualifying distributions, $202,100; giving activities include $202,100 for 28 grants (high: $80,000; low: $500).
Purpose and activities: Giving primarily for youth, education, church/ministry, health, and the Marion, Ohio, community.
Fields of interest: Arts and culture; Education; Nonprofits; Child welfare.
Type of support: General support; Continuing support; Annual campaigns; Capital campaigns; Regranting; Capital and infrastructure; Equipment; Emergency funds; Professorships; Scholarships; Research.
Limitations: Applications accepted. Giving primarily in Marion, OH. No grants to individuals.
Application information: Application form required.
Initial approach: Letter (no more than 3 pages)
Copies of proposal: 5
Deadline(s): Sept. 1
Board meeting date(s): Bi-annually
Final notification: Dec. 31
Officers: Janice J. Brown, Pres.; Douglas W. Brown, Secy.; Joe D. Donithen, Treas.
Trustees: Katherine B. Shepherd; James H. Wyland.
EIN: 341811779

7337
The Charles M. and Helen M. Brown Memorial Foundation
c/o KeyBank N.A.
4900 Tiedeman Rd., OH-01-49-0150
Brooklyn, OH 44144-2302

Established in 1999 in Ohio.
Donors: Helen M. Brown Trust; Helen Brown†.
Foundation type: Independent foundation.
Financial data (yr. ended 12/31/13): Assets, $5,042,584 (M); expenditures, $264,123; qualifying distributions, $221,003; giving activities include $209,500 for 29 grants (high: $50,000; low: $1,000).
Fields of interest: Human services.
Limitations: Applications not accepted. Giving primarily in Cleveland, OH. No grants to individuals.
Application information: Contributes only to pre-selected organizations.

Trustees: Raymond L. Pianka; KeyBank N.A.
EIN: 347104901

7338
Brush Foundation

25350 Rockside Rd., 3rd Fl.
Bedford Heights, OH 44146-3704 (216) 961-8804; 1250
Contact: Kate Ingersoll, Prog. Off.
E-mail: brushfoundation@hotmail.com; Main URL: http://fdnweb.org/brush
Grants List: http://fdnweb.org/brush/project-grants

Established in 1928 in Ohio.
Donors: Charles F. Brush†; Maurice Perkins†; Rufus S. Day, Jr. Trust.
Foundation type: Independent foundation.
Financial data (yr. ended 12/31/14): Assets, $6,913,855; gifts received, $554; expenditures, $376,970; qualifying distributions, $357,394.
Purpose and activities: To ensure that family planning worldwide becomes acceptable, available, accessible, affordable, effective and safe. Funding is focused, nationally and internationally, on those organizations with innovative projects which will: 1) Protect and enhance people's ability to manage their reproductive health; 2) Carry out public policy analysis and/or public education in areas related to reproductive behavior and its social implications; and 3) Advance the knowledge and purposeful behavior of young people regarding sexuality within both a social and health context. The current major interests of the foundation are adolescent sexuality and the control of adolescent pregnancy, preservation of the freedom of choice of women to plan the spacing and number of children, how laws and regulations may control population growth, and pilot family planning programs in Third World countries. Grants range from $5,000 to $25,000.
Fields of interest: Family planning; Reproductive rights; Adolescents; Adults; Young adults; Females; Female children and youth; Female adults; Female young adults; Male young adults.
International interests: Developing Countries.
Type of support: Student aid; General support; Public engagement and education.
Limitations: Applications accepted. Giving in the U.S., with some emphasis on northeast OH; giving also on an international basis. No grants for capital endowment funds, operating support, or fellowships; no loans.
Publications: Application guidelines.
Application information: See foundation website for complete application guidelines. Application form required.
Officers and Board of Managers: Abigail English, Pres. and Director; Henry C. Doll, Secy. and Director; Ellen Rome, MD, Treas. and Director; Daphne Byers; Cindie Carroll-Pankhurst, Ph.D; Jacqueline Darroch, Ph.D; Stacey Easterling; Gita P. Gidwani, MD; Elizabeth Stites; Dan Pellegrom.
Trustee: KeyBank N.A.
Number of staff: 1 part-time professional.
EIN: 346000445

7339
Bryan Area Foundation, Inc.

110 S. Walnut St., Ste. C
P.O. Box 651
Bryan, OH 43506-1316 (419) 633-1156
Contact: Jack E. Brace, Pres. and C.E.O.
FAX: (419) 633-9262;
E-mail: foundation@bryanareafoundation.org; Main URL: http://www.bryanareafoundation.org

Established in 1969 in Ohio.
Foundation type: Community foundation.
Financial data (yr. ended 06/30/14): Assets, $19,750,852 (M); gifts received, $875,325; expenditures, $547,483; giving activities include $123,234 for 2+ grants (high: $75,000), and $110,610 for 95 grants to individuals.
Purpose and activities: The foundation seeks to enhance the quality of life for all citizens of the Bryan, OH area, now and for generations to come by building community endowment, addressing needs through grantmaking, and serving as a leader, catalyst and resource for charitable giving. Focus areas include historic preservation, higher education, health care, agriculture, recreation, children and youth services, community development and religion.
Fields of interest: Arts and culture; Historic preservation; Education; Higher education; Environment; Health; Agriculture; Community and economic development; Community beautification; Religion; Sports and recreation; Scouting programs; Youth mentoring; Agriculture for youth; Senior services.
Type of support: Capital campaigns; Matching grants; Building and renovations; Equipment; Program development; Curriculum development; Research; Technical assistance; Student aid.
Limitations: Applications accepted. Giving limited to the Bryan, OH, area. No support for religious or sectarian purposes. No grants to individuals (except for scholarships), or for endowments, make-up of operating deficits, post-event, or after-the-fact situations.
Publications: Application guidelines; Newsletter; Occasional report.
Application information: Visit foundation web site for application form and guidelines. All applicants must schedule a meeting with the Exec. Dir. at least 30 days in advance of the grant deadline. Application form required.
    Initial approach: Contact foundation
    Copies of proposal: 10
    Deadline(s): Mar. 31, June 30, Sept. 30, and Dec. 29
    Board meeting date(s): Quarterly
    Final notification: Mar., June, Sept., and Dec.
Officers and Trustees: James C. Wood III, Chair. and Trustee; William G. Martin, Vice-Chair. and Trustee; Jack E. Brace, C.E.O. and Pres. and Trustee; Michael A. Shaffer, Secy. and Trustee; George H. Gardner, Treas. and Trustee; Christopher Cullis; Laura Eckhardt; Beth Hollabaugh; Mark Miller; Glen L. Newcomer; E. Clifford Oberlin III; Pamela B. Steel; Constance M. Tipton.
Members: James R. Bard; Jason Beals; Bruce O. Benedict; George Brown; Julie A. Brown; Wayne Carlin; Michael Culler; Emily Ebaugh; Philip L. Ennen; Diana Moore Eschhofen; Betty Franks; Karen K. Gallagher; Ralph W. Gallagher; David Gorzelanczyk; Thomas M. Herman; Stephen Hess; Albert Horn, Jr.; Jason Kunsman; Bruce Manett; Nancy Merillat; David C. Newcomer; William Pepple; Diana Savage; David Schumm; Carolyn Sharrock-Dorsten; C.

Gregory Spangler; Dean L. Spangler; William Steel; George E. Stockman; Mary Thaman; John G. Toner; Tom Turnbull; Kirkland Vashaw; Ann Vreeland.
Number of staff: 1 full-time professional; 2 part-time professional.
EIN: 237041310

7340
Building Healthy Lives Foundation

625 Eden Park Dr., Ste. 200
Cincinnati, OH 45202-6057 (513) 419-6587
Contact: Dianne Dunkelman, Pres.
FAX: (513) 241-2888;
E-mail: kclark@clevercrazes.com; Main URL: http://www.clevercrazes.com

Donors: National Speaking of Women's Health; Duke Energy; The Kurzrok Foundation; Carol Ann and Ralph V. Haile Jr. Foundation; The Selz Foundation, Inc.; JRO Charitable Lead Annuity Trust; Jodi Geiser.
Foundation type: Independent foundation.
Financial data (yr. ended 12/31/12): Assets, $43,945,859 (M); gifts received, $341,883; expenditures, $3,107,664; qualifying distributions, $430,425; giving activities include $430,425 for grants.
Fields of interest: Health; Human services; Youth development.
Limitations: Applications accepted. Giving primarily in Cincinnati, OH.
Application information: Application form required.
    Initial approach: Proposal
    Deadline(s): None
Officers: Dianne Dunkelmann, Pres.; Lorrence Kellar, Secy.
Directors: Guy M. Hild; Sandra Lobert; Patricia Smitson.
EIN: 300214078

7341
Anthony D. Bullock III Foundation

3074 Madison Rd.
Cincinnati, OH 45209-1723 (513) 721-1350
Contact: Kyle C. Brooks, Dir.

Established in 1997 in Ohio.
Donors: Eleine H. Brooks; Kyle C. Brooks.
Foundation type: Independent foundation.
Financial data (yr. ended 05/31/13): Assets, $577,901 (M); gifts received, $2,066; expenditures, $156,688; qualifying distributions, $150,620; giving activities include $150,020 for 2 grants (high: $100,000; low: $50,020).
Fields of interest: Education.
Limitations: Applications accepted. Giving primarily in OH and IL. No grants to individuals.
Application information: Application form required.
    Initial approach: 1 page letter
    Deadline(s): None
Officers: Eleine H. Brooks; Kyle C. Brooks.
EIN: 311580767

7342
The Richard A. Busemeyer Atheist Foundation

440 Hidden Valley Ln.
Cincinnati, OH 45215-2542 5139488955

Established in 1992 in Florida.
Donor: Richard A. Busemeyer†.

Foundation type: Independent foundation.
Financial data (yr. ended 12/31/14): Assets, $3,893,016; expenditures, $302,636; qualifying distributions, $300,000.
Fields of interest: Diseases and conditions; Human rights; Human services.
Application information: Application form required.
Initial approach: Proposal
Deadline(s): None
Officers and Directors: Daniel Busemeyer, Pres. and Treas.; Michael Busemeyer, V.P. and Director; Steven Busumeyer, Secy. and Director.
EIN: 650317422

7343
Thomas Busse Charitable Successor Trust
c/o KeyBank N.A.
10 W. 2nd St., 26th Fl.
Dayton, OH 45402-1791

Established in 2000 in Ohio.
Donor: Thomas W. Busse.
Foundation type: Independent foundation.
Financial data (yr. ended 11/30/13): Assets, $4,037,098 (M); expenditures, $217,191; qualifying distributions, $189,534; giving activities include $179,555 for 9 grants (high: $24,240; low: $6,464).
Fields of interest: Music; Opera; Orchestral music; Art museums; Education; Religion.
Limitations: Applications not accepted. Giving primarily in Cincinnati, OH. No grants to individuals.
Application information: Unsolicited requests for funds not accepted.
Trustee: KeyBank, N.A.
EIN: 527136713

7344
Kenneth L. Calhoun Charitable Trust
4900 Tiedeman Rd., OH-01-49-0150
Brooklyn, OH 44144-2302
Application address: c/o Brian L. Cherkala, 219 S. Main St., Akron, OH 44308, tel.: (330) 258-4044

Established in 1982 in Ohio.
Donor: Kenneth Calhoun†.
Foundation type: Independent foundation.
Financial data (yr. ended 07/31/14): Assets, $6,427,419 (M); expenditures, $317,796; qualifying distributions, $279,126; giving activities include $266,749 for 60 grants (high: $13,000; low: $500).
Purpose and activities: Giving primarily for the arts; as well as education, health organizations, and human services.
Fields of interest: Arts and culture; Education; Higher education; Diseases and conditions; Community and economic development; Human services; Child welfare.
Limitations: Applications accepted. Giving primarily in the greater Akron, OH, area with emphasis on Summit County. No grants to individuals.
Application information: Application form required.
Initial approach: Letter
Deadline(s): June 30
Trustee: KeyBank N.A.
EIN: 341370330

7345
M. E. & F. J. Callahan Foundation
4760 Richmond Rd., Ste. 400
Warrensville Heights, OH 44128-5656

Established in 1975 in Ohio.
Donors: F.J. Callahan; Timothy J. Callahan; Cornelia S. Richards.
Foundation type: Independent foundation.
Financial data (yr. ended 12/31/13): Assets, $441,962 (M); gifts received, $100,125; expenditures, $235,610; qualifying distributions, $227,345; giving activities include $225,000 for 1 grant.
Fields of interest: Arts and culture; Arts education; Music; Art museums; Elementary and secondary education; Higher education.
Type of support: General support.
Limitations: Applications not accepted. Giving primarily in Cleveland, OH. No grants to individuals.
Application information: Unsolicited requests for funds not accepted.
Officers: Timothy J. Callahan, Pres.; Connie Richards, Secy.; Nancy Callahan, Treas.
EIN: 510164320

7346
The Callahan Memorial Award Commission, Inc.
2775 Bishop Rd.
Wickliffe, OH 44092-2272
Contact: Ronald P. Lemmo

Established in 1997 in Ohio.
Foundation type: Independent foundation.
Financial data (yr. ended 12/31/13): Assets, $0 (M); gifts received, $500; expenditures, $212,689; qualifying distributions, $211,303; giving activities include $203,193 for 1 grant, and $2,000 for 2 grants to individuals (high: $1,000; low: $1,000).
Purpose and activities: Scholarship awards to 2 graduating students of Case Western Reserve School of Dentistry or Ohio State United School of Dentistry.
Fields of interest: Education; Philanthropy.
Type of support: Student aid.
Limitations: Applications accepted. Giving limited to residents of OH.
Application information: Application form required.
Initial approach: Letter
Deadline(s): None
Officers: Dr. Joseph T. Mellion, Chair.; Dr. Joseph Crowley, Vice Chair.; Dr. Ronald Lemmo, Secy.-Treas.
Trustees: Dr. James T. Fanno; Dr. Jed J. Jacobson; Dr. John N. Kramer; Dr. Kevin Laing; Dr. Marsha Pyle; Dr. David G. Rummel.
EIN: 311334266

7347
The Cardinal Foundation
3055 Kettering Blvd., Ste. 200
Dayton, OH 45439-1996

Established in 1998 in Ohio.
Donors: Thomas D. MacLeod; Barbara B. MacLeod.
Foundation type: Independent foundation.
Financial data (yr. ended 11/30/14): Assets, $225,157; gifts received, $249,827; expenditures, $359,656; qualifying distributions, $356,000.

Purpose and activities: Giving primarily for education, health, human services, and services to children who are blind.
Fields of interest: Arts and culture; Education; Human services.
Limitations: Applications not accepted. Giving in the U.S., with emphasis on MO, NY and OH. No grants to individuals.
Application information: Unsolicited requests for funds not accepted.
Officer: Thomas D. MacLeod, Pres.
Trustees: William J. Leibold, Esq.; Barbara B. MacLeod.
EIN: 311681353

7348
The Cassner Foundation
835 S. High St.
Hillsboro, OH 45133-9602

Donors: Rotary Forms Press, Inc.; Computer Stock Forms, Inc.; Unit Sets; Alvin Cassner†; Carl Cassner†.
Foundation type: Independent foundation.
Financial data (yr. ended 03/31/14): Assets, $3,911,391 (M); expenditures, $276,859; qualifying distributions, $274,300; giving activities include $186,000 for 20 grants (high: $67,300; low: $200), and $87,500 for 25 grants to individuals (high: $3,500; low: $3,500).
Purpose and activities: Giving primarily for education and human services; also awards four-year scholarships for room and board or tuition at a university or college within a 500-mile radius of Highland County, Ohio.
Fields of interest: Higher education; Diseases and conditions; Community and economic development; Christianity; Human services; Child welfare; People with disabilities.
Type of support: General support; Student aid; Research; Research and evaluation.
Limitations: Applications not accepted. Giving primarily in OH.
Application information: Unsolicited requests for funds not accepted.
Officers: Jon Cassner, Pres.; Brian Cassner, Treas.
EIN: 386090665

7349
Chaney Family Foundation
1837 Winchester Rd.
Lyndhurst, OH 44124-3710

Donor: Cleveland Syrup Corp.
Foundation type: Independent foundation.
Financial data (yr. ended 12/31/13): Assets, $8,756,052 (M); gifts received, $2,972,648; expenditures, $433,307; qualifying distributions, $343,822; giving activities include $343,822 for 2 grants (high: $171,911; low: $171,911).
Fields of interest: Education; Foundations; Health.
Limitations: Applications not accepted. Giving primarily in IN and OH.
Application information: Unsolicited requests for funds not accepted.
Officer: James B. Chaney, Pres.
EIN: 461186115

7350
Chemed Foundation
255 E. 5th St., Ste. 2600
Cincinnati, OH 45202-4726 (513) 762-6870

Established in 1991 in Ohio.
Donors: Chemed Corp.; Roto-Rooter, Inc.
Foundation type: Company-sponsored foundation.
Financial data (yr. ended 12/31/14): Assets, $9,537,221; expenditures, $483,985; qualifying distributions, $471,900.
Purpose and activities: The foundation supports organizations involved with arts and culture, education, housing, and human services.
Fields of interest: Arts and culture; Education; Elementary and secondary education; Higher education; Nonprofits; Housing development; Human services.
Type of support: Annual campaigns; General support; Capital campaigns; Scholarships; Regranting.
Limitations: Applications accepted. Giving primarily in OH. No grants to individuals.
Publications: Annual report.
Application information: Application form required.
  Initial approach: Letter
  Copies of proposal: 1
  Deadline(s): None
  Board meeting date(s): Mar., June, Sept., and Dec.
Officers and Directors: Sandra E. Laney, Pres. and Director; Kevin J. McNamara, Secy.; David J. Lohbeck, Treas.; Thomas C. Hutton.
EIN: 311326421

7351
The Stanley & Susan Chesley Foundation
c/o Fifth Third Bank
P.O. Box 630858
Cincinnati, OH 45263-0858
Application address: c/o Fifth Third Bank, Attn.: Carol Schneider, 38 Fountain Sq. Plz., MD 1090 HB, Cincinnati, OH 45263-0001, tel.: (513) 534-7240

Established in 1996 in Ohio.
Donor: Stanley M. Chesley.
Foundation type: Independent foundation.
Financial data (yr. ended 12/31/14): Assets, $163,624 (M); expenditures, $248,162; qualifying distributions, $242,225; giving activities include $241,712 for 26 grants (high: $25,000; low: $750).
Purpose and activities: Giving primarily for Jewish organizations, as well as for education and social services.
Fields of interest: Education; Higher education; Nonprofits; Judaism; Human services.
Type of support: Regranting.
Limitations: Applications accepted. Giving primarily in the greater Cincinnati, OH, area. No grants to individuals.
Application information: Application form required.
  Initial approach: Letter
  Deadline(s): None
Trustees: Richard A. Chesley; Stanley M. Chesley; Lauren Chesley Cohen.
EIN: 311490928

7352
Christ Foundation
P.O. Box 1180
Hartville, OH 44632-1180
Contact: Patricia P. Moore, Secy.
E-mail: christfoundation@neo.rr.com

Established in 1971 in Ohio.
Donors: Jerry Moore; Sara C. Gibbs; Gerald H. Moore; Patricia P. Moore.
Foundation type: Independent foundation.
Financial data (yr. ended 12/31/14): Assets, $4,964,049 (M); expenditures, $140,674; qualifying distributions, $133,360; giving activities include $121,731 for 35 grants (high: $20,000; low: $100).
Purpose and activities: Giving limited to persons, projects, programs, and institutions affiliated with the Church of Christ.
Fields of interest: Higher education; Christianity; Human services.
Type of support: General support; Capital and infrastructure.
Limitations: Applications accepted. Giving primarily in OH.
Application information: Application form required.
  Initial approach: Proposal
  Deadline(s): None
Officers: Jerry Moore, Pres.; Patricia Moore, Secy.; Lewis Yoder, Treas.
EIN: 237121546

7353
Walter H. Christen Charitable Trust
P.O. Box 94651
Cleveland, OH 44101-4651

Foundation type: Independent foundation.
Financial data (yr. ended 04/30/15): Assets, $1,977,374 (M); expenditures, $347,734; qualifying distributions, $310,493; giving activities include $280,000 for 13 grants (high: $28,000; low: $14,000).
Fields of interest: Art museums; Hospital care; Cancers; Public libraries; Human services; Youth services.
Limitations: Applications not accepted. Giving limited to OH, primarily in Toledo. No grants to individuals.
Application information: Contributes only to pre-selected organizations; unsolicited requests for funds not considered or acknowledged.
Trustee: PNC Bank, N.A.
EIN: 346757371

7354
Cleveland Indians Charities, Inc.
c/o Progressive Field
2401 Ontario St.
Cleveland, OH 44115-4003 (216) 420-4400
E-mail: cic@indians.com; Additional tel.: (216) 420-HITS; Main URL: http://cleveland.indians.mlb.com/NASApp/mlb/cle/community/cic.jsp

Established in 1989 in Ohio.
Donors: Huntington Bancshares Inc.; McDonald Investments, Inc.; Cleveland Indians Baseball Co., Inc.; Jim Thome; Ellis Burks; Travis Hafner; CC Sabathia; Medical Mutual of Ohio.
Foundation type: Company-sponsored foundation.

Financial data (yr. ended 12/31/13): Assets, $1,310,505 (M); gifts received, $170,955; expenditures, $1,021,810; qualifying distributions, $1,021,810; giving activities include $392,815 for grants, and $559,416 for 4 foundation-administered programs.
Purpose and activities: The foundation support programs designed to promote youth education and recreation.
Fields of interest: Education; Sports and recreation; Baseball and softball; Youth services; Adolescents.
Type of support: General support; In-kind gifts; Scholarships.
Limitations: Applications not accepted. Giving limited to Cleveland, OH. No grants to individuals.
Application information: Contributes only to pre-selected organizations.
Officers and Trustees: Paul J. Dolan, Chair. and Trustee; Robert A. DiBiasio, Pres. and Trustee; Sarah Taylor, Treas.; Chris Antonetti; Rick Manning.
Number of staff: 2 full-time professional; 12 part-time support.
EIN: 341618536

7355
CLH Foundation
1991 Madison Rd.
Cincinnati, OH 45208-3216
Application address: c/o Christine H. Heekin, 301 E. 4th St., Ste. 3300, Cincinnati, OH 45202, tel.: (513) 651-6832

Established in 1998 in Ohio.
Donor: Charles L. Heekin Trust.
Foundation type: Independent foundation.
Financial data (yr. ended 12/31/13): Assets, $8,815,110 (M); gifts received, $614,099; expenditures, $355,760; qualifying distributions, $330,300; giving activities include $330,300 for 35 grants (high: $106,000; low: $225).
Fields of interest: Elementary education; Nonprofits; Health; Community and economic development; Youth development.
Type of support: Regranting.
Limitations: Applications accepted. Giving primarily in Cincinnati, OH.
Application information: Application form required.
  Initial approach: Letter (not exceeding 3 pages)
  Deadline(s): None
Officers and Trustees: Christine H. Heekin, Pres. and Trustee; Christopher J. Heekin, V.P. and Trustee; James K. Heekin, Secy. and Trustee; Albert E. Heekin IV, Treas. and Trustee.
EIN: 311346007

7356
Community Foundation for Crawford County
(formerly Bucyrus Area Community Foundation)
254 E. Mansfield St.
Bucyrus, OH 44820 (419) 562-3958
FAX: (419) 617-7308; E-mail: info@cfcrawford.org; Main URL: http://cfcrawford.org
E Newsletter: http://cfcrawford.org/newsletter
Facebook: https://www.facebook.com/bacfoundation
Twitter: http://twitter.com/bacfoundation
YouTube: http://www.youtube.com/user/bucyrusfoundation

Established in 1985 in Ohio.

Foundation type: Community foundation.
Financial data (yr. ended 12/31/13): Assets, $14,597,874 (M); gifts received, $290,687; expenditures, $606,372; giving activities include $394,950 for 20+ grants (high: $62,168), and $6,800 for 6 grants to individuals.
Purpose and activities: As a catalyst, the foundation works to enhance the quality of life for all residents of Crawford County by: 1) offering a flexible vehicle that assures donors' charitable interests and goals are realized; 2) offering support (financial, expert/technical assistance) in response to emerging community needs; and 3) standing ready to partner with community organizations and collaboratives in support of promising innovations.
Fields of interest: Arts and culture; Education; Environment; Health; Hospice care; Computer science; Community and economic development; Sports and recreation; Human services; Family services; Adolescents.
Type of support: Annual campaigns; Matching grants; Capital and infrastructure; Equipment; Emergency funds; Program development; Scholarships; Student aid.
Limitations: Applications accepted. Giving limited to the Crawford County, OH, area (except for the Galion area including Polk Township). No support for sectarian religious purposes (except for designated grants). No grants to individuals (including graduate fellowships and travel grants to individuals, except for designated grants), or for operating funds, annual campaigns, research, or endowment programs; no loans.
Publications: Annual report; Financial statement; Grants list; Informational brochure (including application guidelines); Multi-year report.
Application information: Applications also available in Word format to be downloaded and e-mailed to foundation; visit foundation web site for application and guidelines. Application form required.
> *Initial approach:* Complete online grant application
> *Deadline(s):* Dec. 31 and Apr. 24 and Aug. 21
> *Board meeting date(s):* 6 times a year
> *Final notification:* Mar. and June and Oct.
Officers and Trustees: Tim Stenson, Chair. and Trustee; Lisa D. Workman, Pres. and Trustee; Valerie Sanderson, V.P. and Trustee; Michael Dostal, Secy. and Trustee; Roger Miller, Treas. and Trustee; Janet P. Pry, Exec. Dir.; Jessoca Berger; Annie Carter; Bob Hiltbrand; Janel Hord; Justin McMullen; Rick Niese; Mike Romanoff; Brad Starkey.
Number of staff: 1 part-time professional; 1 part-time support.
EIN: 341465822

7357
Community Foundation of Union County, Inc.

(also known as Union County Foundation)
126 N. Main St.
P.O. Box 608
Marysville, OH   43040-0608   (937) 642-9618
Contact: David A. Vollrath, Exec. Dir.
FAX: (937) 642-7376;
E-mail: info@unioncountyfoundation.org; Main URL: http://www.unioncountyfoundation.org
Facebook: http://www.facebook.com/pages/Union-County-Foundation/138721636147097?sk=wall

Established in 1993 in Ohio.
Foundation type: Community foundation.
Financial data (yr. ended 12/31/13): Assets, $7,630,805 (M); gifts received, $420,578; expenditures, $640,306; giving activities include $306,093 for 7+ grants (high: $73,386), and $119,272 for 108 grants to individuals.
Purpose and activities: The foundation seeks to enhance the quality of life for all the citizens of Union County, and to provide a vehicle whereby gifts of any size might be invested and used in perpetuity to that end.
Fields of interest: Arts and culture; Education; Higher education; Environment; Health; Religion; Sports and recreation; Children and youth; Adolescents; Seniors; Military personnel.
Type of support: General support; In-kind gifts; Continuing support; Program development; Curriculum development; Student aid.
Limitations: Applications accepted. Giving limited to Union County, OH. No support for sectarian religious programs. No grants to individuals (except from designated funds), or for buildings or equipment, endowments, fundraising campaigns, conferences, or annual meetings.
Publications: Application guidelines; Annual report; Grants list; Informational brochure.
Application information: Visit foundation web site for application form and guidelines. Application form required.
> *Initial approach:* Phone or personal contact with Director
> *Copies of proposal:* 1
> *Deadline(s):* First business day of Jan., Apr., July, and Oct.
> *Board meeting date(s):* 3rd Thurs. of Feb., May, Aug., and Nov.
> *Final notification:* Quarterly
Officers and Trustees: Jim Cox, Chair. and Trustee; Chad Hoffman, Vice-Chair. and Trustee; Dr. Victor Trianfo, Secy. and Trustee; David F. Allen, Treas. and Trustee; David A. Vollrath, Exec. Dir.; Steve Yurasek, Legal Counsel; Brian Ravencraft, C.P.A.; Dr. Charlotte Agnone; Ken Boehm; Jerry Born, Ph.D; Bruce Daniels; Dick Douglass; Mardy Hanlon-Stolte; Eugene Mayer; Joseph Mitchell; Carroll Ormeroid; Alan Seymour; Dr. Carol Young.
Number of staff: 2 part-time professional.
EIN: 310628641

7358
The Stephen A. Comunale, Jr. Charitable Foundation

2300 Sourek Trail
Akron, OH   44313-4758

Established in 2006 in Ohio.
Donors: Stephen A. Comunale; Gary Edwards; Steve Jane Comunale; S.A. Comunale Co., Inc.
Foundation type: Independent foundation.
Financial data (yr. ended 12/31/12): Assets, $1,687,608 (M); gifts received, $518,686; expenditures, $476,654; qualifying distributions, $165,943; giving activities include $165,943 for grants.
Fields of interest: Hospital care; Cancers.
Limitations: Applications not accepted. Giving primarily in OH. No grants to individuals.
Application information: Unsolicited requests for funds not accepted.
Officers: John Comunale, Pres.; Rennick Andreoli, Chair.; Amanda Comunale, Vice-Chair.; Monica Stevens, Secy.; Dale Ruther, Treas.

Directors: Heather Caristo; Jane Comunale; Steve Comunale; Julie Deane; Kevin Fink; Nick George; Ruthie George; Dennis McCluskey; Susie Schoellkoph.
EIN: 204345267

7359
Virginia Conlogue Foundation

6610 Golf Green Dr.
Centerville, OH   45459-5804   (937) 435-9666
Contact: Daniel T. Johns, Tr.

Established in 2001 in Ohio.
Donor: Virginia Conlogue†.
Foundation type: Independent foundation.
Financial data (yr. ended 12/31/13): Assets, $5,781,886 (M); expenditures, $308,307; qualifying distributions, $234,658; giving activities include $225,389 for 13 grants (high: $40,000; low: $2,389).
Purpose and activities: Giving primarily to benefit social programs.
Fields of interest: Education; Health; Eye diseases; Christianity; Human services; Food banks.
Limitations: Applications accepted. Giving primarily in Dayton and Montgomery counties, OH. No grants to individuals.
Application information: Application form required.
> *Initial approach:* Letter
> *Deadline(s):* None
Trustee: Daniel T. Johns.
EIN: 311807237

7360
The Conn Family Foundation

11160 Kenwood Rd., Ste. 220
Cincinnati, OH   45242-1818

Established in 2001 in Ohio.
Donors: Raymond A. Conn; Joan D. Conn; Olivia D. Conn; Andrew D. Conn; Nicolette Conn.
Foundation type: Independent foundation.
Financial data (yr. ended 12/31/14): Assets, $1,191,368; expenditures, $259,069; qualifying distributions, $255,608.
Fields of interest: Higher education; Foundations; Christianity.
Limitations: Applications not accepted. No grants to individuals.
Application information: Contributes only to pre-selected organizations.
Officers: Raymond A. Conn, Pres.; Joan D. Conn, V.P.; Alan R. Trenz, Secy.-Treas.
EIN: 311784407

7361
The Connor Group Foundation

c/o Larry Connor
10510 Springboro Pike
Miamisburg, OH   45342

Established in 2007 in Ohio.
Donors: Larry Connor; Lawrence S. Connor.
Foundation type: Independent foundation.
Financial data (yr. ended 11/30/13): Assets, $633,182 (M); gifts received, $701,060; expenditures, $173,701; qualifying distributions, $168,681; giving activities include $168,681 for 12 grants (high: $71,396; low: $200).

Fields of interest: Education; Diseases and conditions; Human services.
Limitations: Applications not accepted. Giving primarily in MN and OH.
Application information: Unsolicited requests for funds not accepted.
Officers: Larry Connor, Pres.; Bob Holzapfel, Treas.
EIN: 208499807

7362
Cooper Tire & Rubber Foundation
701 Lima Ave.
Findlay, OH   45840-2315   (419) 423-1321
Contact: Bradley E. Hughes, Tr.

Established in 1953 in Ohio.
Donor: Cooper Tire & Rubber Co.
Foundation type: Company-sponsored foundation.
Financial data (yr. ended 12/31/13): Assets, $18,430 (M); gifts received, $400,000; expenditures, $389,714; qualifying distributions, $389,644; giving activities include $389,644 for 95 grants (high: $75,000; low: $22).
Purpose and activities: The foundation supports organizations involved with arts and culture, education, health, and youth development.
Fields of interest: Education; Health; Human services.
Type of support: General support; Employee matching gifts; Capital campaigns.
Limitations: Applications accepted. Giving primarily in areas of company operations in IN, OH, and TX.
Application information: Application form required.
  Initial approach: Letter
  Deadline(s): None
Trustees: Susan DeVene; Bradley E. Hughes; Thomas N. Lause.
EIN: 237025013

7363
The Corbett Foundation
127 W. 9th St., Ste. 3
Cincinnati, OH   45202-6103   (513) 241-3320
Contact: Karen P. McKim, Exec. Dir.

Established in 1958 in Ohio.
Donors: J. Ralph Corbett†; Patricia A. Corbett†.
Foundation type: Independent foundation.
Financial data (yr. ended 04/30/13): Assets, $12,782,602 (M); expenditures, $606,774; qualifying distributions, $537,294; giving activities include $398,280 for 15 grants (high: $250,000; low: $2,500).
Purpose and activities: Giving primarily for arts and cultural organizations, education, and community projects.
Fields of interest: Arts and culture; Arts education; Performing arts; Theater; Opera; Orchestral music; Art museums; Education.
Type of support: General support; Matching grants; Capital campaigns; Equipment; Program development.
Limitations: Giving primarily in the greater Cincinnati, OH, area. No grants to individuals.
Application information:
  Initial approach: Proposal
  Deadline(s): None
  Final notification: Within 2 months
Officers: James A. Markely, Jr., V.P. and Treas.; Karen P. McKim, Exec. Dir.

Trustees: Joyce J. Salinger; Nancy F. Walker.
EIN: 316050360

7364
Justin F. Coressel Charitable Trust
101 Clinton St., Ste. 2000
Defiance, OH   43512-2172   (419) 782-2000
Contact: Terry L. Melton, Tr.

Donor: Justin F. Coressel.
Foundation type: Independent foundation.
Financial data (yr. ended 12/31/13): Assets, $3,939,244 (M); expenditures, $180,408; qualifying distributions, $173,620; giving activities include $173,620 for 25 grants (high: $25,000; low: $20).
Purpose and activities: Giving primarily for higher education and Roman Catholic churches.
Fields of interest: Elementary and secondary education; Higher education; Health; Community and economic development; Catholicism; Human services; Child welfare.
Type of support: Capital and infrastructure.
Limitations: Applications accepted. Giving primarily in Defiance, OH. No grants to individuals.
Application information:
  Initial approach: Proposal
  Deadline(s): None
Trustees: Mark Hench; Terry L. Melton; Paul E. Moser.
EIN: 237022234

7365
The Albert M. Covelli Foundation
3900 E. Market St.
Warren, OH   44484-4723

Donors: Albert M. Covelli; Sam A. Covelli; Alcadan, LLC; Sylcon, LLC; Covelli Family Limited Partnership II; Covelli Family Limited Partnership; Dalcan, LLC; Cadle, LLC; Cad Capital, LLC; Flapan, LLC; Covelli Enterprises.
Foundation type: Independent foundation.
Financial data (yr. ended 12/31/13): Assets, $5,868,701 (M); gifts received, $234,459; expenditures, $265,370; qualifying distributions, $259,625; giving activities include $259,625 for 24 grants (high: $95,425; low: $500).
Fields of interest: Foundations; Catholicism; Human services; Child welfare.
Limitations: Applications not accepted. Giving primarily in FL and Warren, OH. No grants to individuals.
Application information: Unsolicited requests for funds not accepted.
Trustee: Albert M. Covelli; Josephine Covelli; Sam Covelli; Annette Ford.
EIN: 341383117

7366
J. Ford Crandall Depository Foundation
P.O. Box 1558, Dept. EA4E86
Columbus, OH   43216

Established in 1975 in Ohio.
Donors: J. Ford Crandall†; Interfaith Hope Maintenance.
Foundation type: Independent foundation.
Financial data (yr. ended 12/31/13): Assets, $5,567,502 (M); gifts received, $8,617;

expenditures, $275,393; qualifying distributions, $243,289; giving activities include $214,237 for 16 grants (high: $50,000; low: $4,700).
Fields of interest: Arts and culture; Education; Higher education; Nonprofits; Hospital care; Civic participation; Human services; Family services; Civics for youth.
Type of support: General support; Capital campaigns; Capital and infrastructure; Equipment; Endowments; Scholarships; Regranting.
Limitations: Applications not accepted.
Application information: Unsolicited requests for funds not accepted.
Trustees: Andrew G. Bresko; Brad Allen Calhoun; Socrates Kolitsos; Michael Ray, Jr.; Bruce E. Sherman; The Huntington National Bank.
EIN: 346513634

7367
Crossroads Foundation
1111 Superior Ave. E., Ste. 700
Cleveland, OH   44114   (216) 363-6489

Established in 1995 in Ohio.
Foundation type: Independent foundation.
Financial data (yr. ended 12/31/13): Assets, $6,794,947 (M); expenditures, $367,576; qualifying distributions, $317,361; giving activities include $311,500 for 14 grants (high: $100,000; low: $4,000).
Purpose and activities: Giving primarily for Christian education and youth services.
Fields of interest: Elementary and secondary education; Higher education; Christianity; Youth services.
Type of support: General support; Capital and infrastructure.
Limitations: Applications accepted. Giving primarily in OH. No grants to individuals.
Application information: Application form required.
  Initial approach: Letter (no more than 2 pages, without attachments or enclosures)
  Deadline(s): None
Officers: Dudley S. Blossom, Pres.; Kathryn F. Blossom, V.P.; Daniel L. Horn, Secy.; Kirk A. Linn, Treas.
Trustee: Donald T. Moore.
EIN: 341811495

7368
Cure Tay-Sachs Foundation
12730 Triskett Rd.
Cleveland, OH   44111-2529
FAX: (216) 251-6728;
E-mail: questions@curetay-sachs.org; Application address: c/o Kenneth Bihn, Pres., 7291 Chestnut Ct., Olmsted Falls, OH 44138, tel.: (216) 251-9070; Main URL: http://www.curetay-sachs.org

Established in 2007 in Ohio.
Donors: Kenneth Bihn; Ranch Foundations; ABB Foundation; Timothy Bihn; Carl Hopf; Rick Steiger; Desiree Hopf; Bruce Steiger; Richard Karl; Robert Bihn; Fosbel, Inc.; Nu-Di Corp.; Alan Shonberg.
Foundation type: Independent foundation.
Financial data (yr. ended 12/31/13): Assets, $1,584,853 (M); gifts received, $478,617; expenditures, $286,301; qualifying distributions, $201,220; giving activities include $201,220 for 5 grants (high: $73,638; low: $4,530).

Purpose and activities: Giving primarily for the research and development of treatment for Tay-Sachs disease.

Fields of interest: Education; Diseases and conditions.

Type of support: Research.

Limitations: Applications accepted. Giving primarily in MA.

Application information:
Initial approach: Letter
Deadline(s): None

Officers: Kenneth Bihn, Pres.; Timothy Bihn, V.P.; Robert Bihn, Treas.

EIN: 260256621

7369
The Daberko Charitable Foundation
6120 Parkland Blvd., Ste. 303
Mayfield Heights, OH 44124-6129
Contact: Ronald E. Bates

Established in 2001 in Ohio.

Donor: David A. Daberko.

Foundation type: Independent foundation.

Financial data (yr. ended 12/31/13): Assets, $741,504 (M); expenditures, $122,766; qualifying distributions, $121,446; giving activities include $120,000 for 3 grants (high: $50,000; low: $25,000).

Fields of interest: Art museums; Education; Speech and hearing rehabilitation.

Limitations: Applications not accepted. Giving primarily in OH. No grants to individuals.

Application information: Unsolicited requests for funds not accepted.

Trustees: David A. Daberko; Deborah L. Daberko.

EIN: 020533614

7370
Damico Family Foundation
c/o HPM Partners LLC
600 Superior Ave., Ste. 1000
Cleveland, OH 44114-1291

Established in 2002 in Ohio.

Donors: Joseph F. Damico, Jr.; Pamela C Damico Declaration Of Trust; Joseph Bianco; Joseph D. Damico; Lauren C. Damico; Lindsay Bianco.

Foundation type: Independent foundation.

Financial data (yr. ended 12/31/13): Assets, $4,444,127 (M); gifts received, $2,500; expenditures, $235,637; qualifying distributions, $227,100; giving activities include $227,100 for 19 grants (high: $50,000; low: $1,500).

Fields of interest: Higher education; Nonprofits; Hospital care; Christianity.

Type of support: Regranting.

Limitations: Applications not accepted. Giving primarily in IL. No grants to individuals.

Application information: Unsolicited requests for funds not accepted.

Officers: Joseph F. Damico, Jr., Pres.; Anthony D. DeCello, Secy.; Pamela C. Damico, Treas.

EIN: 010702653

7371
The Danis Foundation Inc.
3233 Newmark Dr.
Miamisburg, OH 45342-5422 (937) 228-1225
Contact: Karen Applegarth

Established in 1957 in Ohio.

Donor: Danis Building Construction Co.

Foundation type: Company-sponsored foundation.

Financial data (yr. ended 12/31/13): Assets, $409,374 (M); expenditures, $135,424; qualifying distributions, $132,865; giving activities include $132,864 for 26 grants (high: $32,312; low: $340).

Purpose and activities: The foundation supports food banks and organizations involved with education, health, heart disease, and human services.

Fields of interest: Education; Higher education; Health care clinics; Heart and circulatory system diseases; Human services; Food banks.

Type of support: General support; Capital campaigns; Capital and infrastructure; Program development; Scholarships.

Limitations: Applications accepted. Giving primarily in the Dayton, OH, area.

Application information: Application form required.
Initial approach: Request application form
Deadline(s): May 31

Officers: John Danis, Pres. and Secy.-Treas.; Thomas P. Hammelrath, V.P.

Number of staff: 1 part-time professional.

EIN: 316041012

7372
William Dauch Foundation
(formerly Believers Foundation)
1570 Dutch Hollow Rd.
Elida, OH 45807-1803 (419) 339-4441
Contact: Thomas E. Brown, Treas.

Established in 1986 in Ohio.

Donors: Gladys Dauch; Thomas E. Brown; Marilyn Brown; Brown Supply Co.; Debra Grant; Bible Believers of Lima; True Word Tabernacle.

Foundation type: Independent foundation.

Financial data (yr. ended 12/31/13): Assets, $5,064,497 (M); gifts received, $70,872; expenditures, $578,662; qualifying distributions, $551,734; giving activities include $123,890 for 8 grants (high: $48,000; low: $195).

Purpose and activities: Support to organizations that promote Christian knowledge and dissemination of the Gospel.

Fields of interest: Christianity.

International interests: Canada; India; Philippines; South Africa.

Limitations: Applications accepted. Giving primarily in OH and WA; giving internationally in South Africa. No grants to individuals.

Application information: Application form required.
Initial approach: Letter
Deadline(s): None

Officers and Trustees: Debra Grant, Pres. and Trustee; Marilyn Brown, Secy. and Trustee; Thomas E. Brown, Treas. and Trustee; Tamara Brown LeRoux.

EIN: 341516486

7373
Davey Company Foundation
1500 N. Mantua St.
P.O. Box 5193
Kent, OH 44240-5193 (330) 673-9511
Contact: Marjorie L. Conner, Secy.

Established in 1957 in Ohio.

Donor: The Davey Tree Expert Co.

Foundation type: Company-sponsored foundation.

Financial data (yr. ended 12/31/13): Assets, $1,124,813 (M); gifts received, $150,000; expenditures, $190,920; qualifying distributions, $187,507; giving activities include $48,250 for 42 + grants (high: $3,000; low: $500), and $138,667 for 16 grants to individuals (high: $47,000).

Purpose and activities: The foundation supports organizations involved with higher education, health, and arboriculture.

Fields of interest: Higher education; Forest preservation; Health; Hospital care.

Type of support: General support; Employee matching gifts; Research; Scholarships.

Limitations: Applications accepted. Giving primarily in CA and OH. No grants to individuals (except for employee-related scholarships).

Application information: Application form required.
Initial approach: Letter
Copies of proposal: 1
Deadline(s): None

Officers: Karl J. Warnke, Pres.; Patrick M. Covey, V.P.; Steven A. Marshal, V.P.; Joseph R. Paul, V.P.; Marjorie L. Conner, Secy.; Christopher Basy, Treas.

Trustees: R. Douglas Cowan; J. Dawson Cunningham; William J. Ginn; Douglas K. Hall; Sandra W. Harbrecht; John E. Warfel.

EIN: 346555132

7374
Carleton F. and Ruth T. Davidson Trust
c/o Norma Dillon
285 Ridge Mall
Springfield, OH 45504-1329

Established in 1987 in Ohio.

Donor: Carleton F. Davidson.

Foundation type: Independent foundation.

Financial data (yr. ended 12/31/13): Assets, $8,119,574 (M); expenditures, $379,500; qualifying distributions, $374,944; giving activities include $327,500 for 8 grants (high: $202,000; low: $1,000).

Fields of interest: Art museums; Higher education; Christianity; Sports and recreation; Housing services.

Limitations: Applications not accepted. Giving primarily in Springfield, and Clark County, OH. No grants to individuals.

Application information: Contributes only to pre-selected organizations.

Trustees: Norma Dillon; Douglas Rice.

EIN: 316328010

7375
Defiance Area Foundation, Inc.
507 5th St.
Defiance, OH 43512 (419) 782-3130
Contact: Christine R. Yoder, Exec. Dir.
E-mail: defoundation@defnet.com; Main URL: http://www.defianceareafoundation.org

Established in 1979 in Ohio.

Foundation type: Community foundation.

Financial data (yr. ended 06/30/13): Assets, $5,369,802 (M); gifts received, $855,303; expenditures, $450,410; giving activities include $350,213 for 10+ grants (high: $153,000); and $14,970 for 24 grants to individuals.

Purpose and activities: The foundation exists to fund charitable activities in Defiance County, OH.

Fields of interest: Arts and culture; Education; Health; Community and economic development; Sports and recreation; Senior services.

Type of support: Emergency funds; Matching grants; Capital campaigns; Capital and infrastructure; Equipment; Program development; Convening; Publications; Seed money; Curriculum development; Research; Technical assistance; Student aid.

Limitations: Applications accepted. Giving limited to the Defiance County, OH. No support for sectarian religious purposes. No grants to individuals (except for scholarships), or for debt reduction, fundraising, operating expenses of well established organizations, or endowment funds (except in unusual circumstances).

Publications: Application guidelines; Annual report; Annual report (including application guidelines); Financial statement; Grants list; Informational brochure; Informational brochure (including application guidelines); Newsletter; Newsletter (including application guidelines); Occasional report; Occasional report (including application guidelines); Quarterly report; Quarterly report (including application guidelines).

Application information: Visit foundation web site for application guidelines and grant request form. Application form required.

   Initial approach: Letter, telephone, or personal contact
   Deadline(s): Mar. 31, Sept. 30
   Board meeting date(s): Jan., Apr., July, and Oct.
   Final notification: After quarterly board meeting

Officers and Trustees: Mike Steyer, Pres. and Trustee; Mike Klein, V.P. and Trustee; Terry Melton, Secy. and Trustee; William Koester, Treas. and Trustee; Christine Yoder, Exec. Dir.; Sharon Farrell; Amy Galbraith; Todd Harpest; Deb Hench; Joe Howard; John Jacob; Rita Kissner; Gary Konst; Glen Kuhn; Anne Murray; Doug Shindler; Sam Strausbaugh; Mike Wolfe.

Number of staff: 1 part-time professional; 1 part-time support.

EIN: 341278087

7376
The DeHoff Family Foundation

821 S. Main St.
North Canton, OH   44720-3156   (330) 499-8153
Contact: Robert J. DeHoff, Dir.

Established in 2004 in Ohio.
Donors: Linda M. DeHoff; Robert J. DeHoff.
Foundation type: Independent foundation.
Financial data (yr. ended 12/31/13): Assets, $139,848 (M); expenditures, $200,000; qualifying distributions, $200,000; giving activities include $200,000 for 1 grant.
Fields of interest: Philanthropy; Foundations.
Limitations: Applications accepted. Giving primarily in OH. No grants to individuals.
Application information: Application form required.
   Initial approach: Request application form
   Deadline(s): None
Directors: Daniel J. DeHoff; Linda M. DeHoff; Robert J. DeHoff; Molly M. Holtzer.
EIN: 161695116

7377
The Mary and Dr. George L. Demetros Charitable Trust

106 S. Main St., Ste. 500
Akron, OH   44308-1445

Established in 2002 in Ohio.
Donor: Mary Demetros†.
Foundation type: Independent foundation.
Financial data (yr. ended 12/31/14): Assets, $5,670,086; expenditures, $317,103; qualifying distributions, $274,818.
Fields of interest: Arts and culture; Music; Art museums; Education; Zoos; Human services.
Limitations: Applications not accepted. Giving primarily in Akron, OH. No grants to individuals.
Application information: Unsolicited requests for funds not accepted.
Trustee: FirstMerit Trust Co.
Trust Advisors: Richard H. Harris; Philip A. Lloyd; Michael A. Sweeney.
EIN: 352168489

7378
Jeanette Dermitt Hospital

c/o KeyBank N.A.
4900 Tiedeman Rd., OH-01-49-0
Brooklyn, OH   44144-2302

Foundation type: Independent foundation.
Financial data (yr. ended 12/31/14): Assets, $5,485,854; expenditures, $384,765; qualifying distributions, $334,809.
Fields of interest: Health; Hospital care.
Limitations: Applications not accepted.
Application information: Unsolicited requests for funds not accepted.
Trustee: KeyBank N.A.
EIN: 166110717

7379
Arnold C. Dienstberger Foundation

P.O. Box 223
Delphos, OH   45833-0223   (419) 692-1321

Established in 1999 in Ohio.
Donors: Donald Elizabeth Helmkamp Trust; Albert Etzkorn Trust.
Foundation type: Independent foundation.
Financial data (yr. ended 12/31/14): Assets, $6,080,214; expenditures, $318,146; qualifying distributions, $310,000.
Purpose and activities: Giving primarily for education and community development.
Fields of interest: Elementary and secondary education; Public libraries; Disasters and emergency management; Community and economic development; Sports.
Type of support: General support; Capital and infrastructure; Equipment.
Limitations: Applications accepted. Giving limited to the Delphos, OH, area school district. No grants to individuals.
Application information: Application form required.
   Initial approach: Proposal
   Deadline(s): Nov. 1
Officers: Rick Miller, Pres.; Nicholas J. Clark, V.P.; Jerry Gilden, Secy.; Douglas Harter, Treas.
Trustees: William Massa; Doris Neumeier; John Nomina.
EIN: 346539337

7380
Frederick W. and Janet P. Dorn Foundation

1111 Superior Ave.
Cleveland, OH   44114-2507

Established in 1990 in Ohio.
Donors: Janet D. Heil†; Janet Heil Charitable Lead Unitrust.
Foundation type: Independent foundation.
Financial data (yr. ended 12/31/14): Assets, $4,260,639; gifts received, $72,089; expenditures, $206,761; qualifying distributions, $186,730.
Fields of interest: Arts and culture; Health; Christianity; Human services.
Type of support: General support.
Limitations: Applications not accepted. Giving primarily in the Cleveland, OH, area. No grants to individuals.
Application information: Unsolicited requests for funds not accepted.
Officers: Robert F. Dorn, Pres.; Deborah K. Dorn, V.P.; Phillip A. Ranney, Secy.-Treas.
Trustees: Philip R. Dorn; Elizabeth Mather.
EIN: 341653306

7381
Downing Foundation

7 Grandin Ln.
Cincinnati, OH   45208-3363   (513) 321-2230
Contact: W. Charles Blum, Secy.

Established in 1994 in Ohio.
Donor: Jack G. Downing.
Foundation type: Independent foundation.
Financial data (yr. ended 05/31/14): Assets, $4,443,723 (M); expenditures, $301,994; qualifying distributions, $236,000; giving activities include $236,000 for 14 grants (high: $43,000; low: $1,000).
Purpose and activities: Giving primarily for Roman Catholic agencies, churches, and schools.
Fields of interest: Education; Catholicism; Human services.
Type of support: General support.
Limitations: Applications accepted. Giving primarily in KY and OH. No grants to individuals.
Application information: Application form required.
   Initial approach: Proposal
   Deadline(s): None
Officers: Mary J. Blum, Chair.; W. Charles Blum, Secy.
Trustees: Christine L. Blum; Tracy A. Blum.
EIN: 311416687

7382
Jose G. Duarte Foundation

c/o Richard F. Carlile
10050 Innovation Dr., Ste. 400
Dayton, OH   45342-4934

Established in 2007 in Ohio.
Donor: Jose G. Duarte Trust.
Foundation type: Independent foundation.
Financial data (yr. ended 12/31/14): Assets, $7,724,746; expenditures, $446,835; qualifying distributions, $357,550.
Fields of interest: Catholicism.
Limitations: Applications not accepted.

Application information: Unsolicited requests for funds not accepted.
Directors: Alberto Eduardo Duarte Fernandez; Roberto Duarte Fernandez; Martha Romero Ibarra.
EIN: 261222662

7383
The Cyrus Eaton Foundation
The Heights Rockefeller Bldg.
2475 Lee Blvd., Ste. 2H
Cleveland Heights, OH 44118-1227   (216) 320-2285
FAX: (216) 320-2287;
E-mail: cyrus.eaton.foundation@deepcove.org; Main URL: http://www.deepcove.org
Grants List: http://www.deepcove.org/Grants/pastyeargrants.html

Established in 1955 in Delaware.
Foundation type: Independent foundation.
Financial data (yr. ended 12/31/13): Assets, $3,355,785 (M); expenditures, $203,643; qualifying distributions, $175,569; giving activities include $148,600 for 50 grants (high: $15,000; low: $1,000).
Purpose and activities: Giving primarily to support non-profit organizations in Cleveland and northeast Ohio whose programs enhance the quality of life in the area, and whose aims are in accord with Cyrus Eaton, the founder of the foundation.
Fields of interest: Arts and culture; Education; Environment; Natural resources; Public affairs; Community and economic development; Human services; International peace and security.
International interests: Canada.
Type of support: General support; Endowments; Program development; Seed money.
Limitations: Applications accepted. Giving primarily in OH, with emphasis on Cleveland. No support for municipalities or organizations lacking 501(c)(3) status. No grants to individuals, or for tickets or tables for events.
Publications: Application guidelines.
Application information: See foundation web site for complete guidelines. The completed application may be mailed by U.S. mail, faxed or e-mailed. Application form required.
  Initial approach: See foundation web site for Required Information Sheet
  Copies of proposal: 1
  Deadline(s): May 1st for June meeting; Oct. 1st for Nov. meeting
  Board meeting date(s): June and Nov.
  Final notification: Following board meeting
Officers and Board Members: Catherine L. Eaton, Pres. and Director; Ralph Higgins, Jr., V.P. and Director; Alice J. Gulick, Secy. and Director; Henry W. Gulick, Treas. and Director; Pamela Niedes; Raymond Szabo.
Number of staff: 1 part-time support.
EIN: 237440277

7384
The Ebenezer Charitable Trust
76 N. Mulberry St.
Mansfield, OH 44902-1241

Donors: John E. Bevier; Carol E. Bevier.
Foundation type: Independent foundation.
Financial data (yr. ended 12/31/13): Assets, $2,659,824 (M); gifts received, $76,564; expenditures, $234,234; qualifying distributions, $200,600; giving activities include $200,600 for 9 grants (high: $60,000; low: $2,000).
Fields of interest: Education; Community and economic development; Human services.
Limitations: Applications not accepted. Giving primarily in OH.
Application information: Unsolicited requests for funds not accepted.
Trustee: Jerod Them.
EIN: 276932920

7385
David W. Edward Charitable Fund
c/o Farmers Trust Co.
42 McClurg Rd.
Youngstown, OH 44512-6700

Foundation type: Independent foundation.
Financial data (yr. ended 12/31/13): Assets, $4,178,831 (M); expenditures, $213,554; qualifying distributions, $196,616; giving activities include $190,104 for 3 grants (high: $63,368; low: $63,368).
Fields of interest: Education; Undergraduate education; Human services.
Limitations: Applications not accepted. Giving primarily in OH and PA.
Application information: Unsolicited requests for funds not accepted.
Trustee: Farmers Trust Company.
EIN: 341863585

7386
The Edwards Foundation
(formerly J. T. Edwards Company Foundation)
495 S. High St., Ste. 150
Columbus, OH 43215-5695

Established in 1964 in Ohio.
Donors: Edwards Industries, Inc.; Ross Willoughby Co.; Edwards Insulation; Duffy Homes; Swan Manufacturing Co.; Mooney and Moses of Ohio, Inc.; Jeffrey W. Edwards; Multicon Builders, Inc.; F.A. Kohler, Inc.; Peter H. Edwards.
Foundation type: Company-sponsored foundation.
Financial data (yr. ended 06/30/14): Assets, $4,936 (M); gifts received, $145,000; expenditures, $168,630; qualifying distributions, $168,500; giving activities include $168,500 for 10 grants (high: $50,000; low: $1,000).
Purpose and activities: The foundation supports organizations involved with arts and culture, education, and human services.
Fields of interest: Education.
Type of support: General support.
Limitations: Applications not accepted. No grants to individuals; no loans or program-related investments.
Application information: Unsolicited requests for funds not accepted.
Officer: John A. Leibold, Treas.
Trustees: Paula Cochran; Jeffrey W. Edwards; Peter H. Edwards; Judith Sandbo.
EIN: 237447588

7387
Elisha-Bolton Foundation
1111 Superior Ave., E. Ste. 700
Cleveland, OH 44114-2540   (216) 363-6481
E-mail: j.sekerak@advsrv.com

Donors: Betsy Bolton Schafer; Julian B. Schafer; Gilbert P. Schafer III.
Foundation type: Independent foundation.
Financial data (yr. ended 12/31/13): Assets, $5,080,124 (M); expenditures, $293,082; qualifying distributions, $254,536; giving activities include $234,500 for 56 grants (high: $20,000; low: $1,000).
Purpose and activities: Emphasis on health, higher education, and Christian religious organizations; support also for disaster relief.
Fields of interest: Visual arts; Performing arts; Elementary and secondary education; Higher education; Environment; Natural resources; Nonprofits; Health; Diseases and conditions; Religion; Christianity.
Type of support: General support; Continuing support; Annual campaigns; Program development; Scholarships; Regranting.
Limitations: Applications accepted. Giving on a national basis. No grants to individuals.
Application information: Application form required.
  Initial approach: Letter
  Copies of proposal: 1
  Deadline(s): None
  Board meeting date(s): Sept.
Officers: Gilbert P. Schafer III, Co-Pres.; Julian B. Schafer, Co-Pres.; James C. Sekerak, Secy.-Treas.
Trustee: Kenneth G. Hochman.
Number of staff: None.
EIN: 341500135

7388
Endowment for Biblical Research
c/o Charles Stocking
9736 Carnoustie Rd.
Perrysburg, OH 43551-3505

Established in 1920 in Massachusetts.
Donors: Mary Beecher Longyear†; Charles Stocking.
Foundation type: Independent foundation.
Financial data (yr. ended 12/31/13): Assets, $175,972 (M); gifts received, $173,444; expenditures, $210,018; qualifying distributions, $209,670; giving activities include $206,301 for 1 grant.
Purpose and activities: Giving to facilitate and advance research on the Bible and to increase public understanding of the Bible, its application to human needs, and biblically related religious history.
Fields of interest: History; Theology.
Type of support: Research.
Limitations: Applications not accepted. Giving primarily in Cambridge, MA. No support for denominational and non-biblical education.
Application information: Contributes only to pre-selected organizations.
Officers and Trustees: Lance Carden, Chair. and Trustee; Charles A. Stocking, Treas. and Trustee; Bruce Butterfield; Stephen R. Howard; Virginia B. Stopfel.
Number of staff: 1 part-time professional.
EIN: 042104439

7389
Entelco Foundation
132 W. 2nd St., Ste. B
Perrysburg, OH 43551-7632

Established in 1979 in Ohio.
Donors: Stephen Stranahan; Entelco Corp.; Ann A. Stranahan.
Foundation type: Company-sponsored foundation.
Financial data (yr. ended 12/31/13): Assets, $4,722,605 (M); expenditures, $225,076; qualifying distributions, $157,111; giving activities include $156,400 for 58 grants (high: $20,000; low: $100).
Purpose and activities: The foundation supports organizations involved with arts and culture, education, human services, community development, and other areas.
Fields of interest: Education; Religion; Human services.
Type of support: General support; Employee volunteer services; Capital campaigns; Program development.
Limitations: Applications accepted. Giving primarily in the Toledo and northwestern OH area, and areas where Entelco Corporation, its founders and stockholders have charitable interests. No grants to individuals, or for endowments, publications, debt reduction, film or video production, or land acquisition.
Publications: Application guidelines.
Application information: Application form required.
 Initial approach: Letter
 Copies of proposal: 1
 Deadline(s): None
 Board meeting date(s): May and Nov.
Trustees: Ann A. Stranahan; Stephen Stranahan.
Director: Louise Jackson.
Number of staff: 1 part-time support.
EIN: 341288595

7390
Isaac Ettlinger Trust
P.O. Box 630858
Cincinnati, OH 45263-0858

Foundation type: Independent foundation.
Financial data (yr. ended 12/31/14): Assets, $8,240,160; expenditures, $414,643; qualifying distributions, $314,983.
Fields of interest: Nonprofits.
Type of support: Regranting.
Limitations: Applications not accepted. Giving primarily in Cincinnati, OH.
Application information: Contributes only to pre-selected organizations.
Trustee: Fifth Third Bank.
EIN: 316019860

7391
Jesse Eyman Trust
c/o Robert Herron
132 1/2 E. Ct. St.
Washington Court House, OH 43160-1375

Established in 1924 in Ohio.
Foundation type: Independent foundation.
Financial data (yr. ended 12/31/13): Assets, $7,092,739 (M); expenditures, $288,642; qualifying distributions, $288,642; giving activities

include $220,632 for 26 grants (high: $40,000; low: $450).
Purpose and activities: Emphasis on medical and dental payments to organizations on behalf of needy persons; some support for social service and health agencies.
Fields of interest: Education; Health; Christianity; Human services; Low-income and poor people.
Limitations: Applications accepted. Giving limited to Fayette County, OH. No grants to individuals (except through intermediary businesses providing services to the indigent); no loans.
Application information: Application form required.
 Initial approach: Proposal
 Deadline(s): None
Trustees: Robert Herron; Jessee Persinger.
EIN: 316040007

7392
Clara Faber Foundation
1872 Front St.
Cuyahoga Falls, OH 44221-3912 (330) 867-8422
Contact: Guy Klapp, Tr.

Established in 2003 in Ohio.
Donor: Clara Faber.
Foundation type: Independent foundation.
Financial data (yr. ended 12/31/13): Assets, $3,644,460 (M); expenditures, $230,396; qualifying distributions, $210,430; giving activities include $210,430 for 29 grants (high: $40,000; low: $60).
Fields of interest: Education; Foundations; Human services.
Limitations: Applications accepted. Giving primarily in OH.
Application information: Application form required.
 Initial approach: Letter
 Deadline(s): None
Trustees: James C. Dunn; John Kane; Guy Klapp.
EIN: 383672582

7393
The Fedeli Family Charitable Foundation
P.O. Box 318003
Independence, OH 44131-8003

Established in 2000 in Ohio.
Donor: Umberto Fedeli, Jr.
Foundation type: Independent foundation.
Financial data (yr. ended 12/31/13): Assets, $3,766,909 (M); gifts received, $650,553; expenditures, $161,090; qualifying distributions, $143,250; giving activities include $143,025 for 78 grants (high: $15,000; low: $100).
Fields of interest: Education; Nonprofits; Hospital care; Diseases and conditions; Religion; Human services.
Type of support: Regranting.
Limitations: Applications not accepted. Giving primarily in Cleveland, OH. No grants to individuals.
Application information: Contributes only to pre-selected organizations.
Trustees: Umberto Fedeli, Jr.; MaryEllen Trails.
EIN: 311740537

7394
Mark S. Feldstein Private Foundation
P.O. Box 10099
Toledo, OH 43699-0099 4192594736
Application address: Mark Feldstein, 405 Madison Ave., Toledo, OH 43604; tel.: (419) 259-6529

Established in 2003 in Ohio.
Donor: Mark S. Feldstein.
Foundation type: Independent foundation.
Financial data (yr. ended 12/31/14): Assets, $511,446; gifts received, $25,000; expenditures, $127,098; qualifying distributions, $120,957.
Fields of interest: Education; Diseases and conditions; Religion; Human services; Youth organizing.
Limitations: Applications accepted. Giving primarily in OH.
Application information: Application form required.
 Initial approach: Letter
 Deadline(s): None
Trustees: KeyBank, N.A.; PNC Bank, N.A.
EIN: 576202955

7395
Judge and Mrs. Carl B. Felger Memorial Trust
P.O. Box 910
Piqua, OH 45356-0910

Donor: Edith M. Felger†.
Foundation type: Operating foundation.
Financial data (yr. ended 12/31/13): Assets, $4,956,184 (M); expenditures, $274,940; qualifying distributions, $274,940.
Limitations: Applications not accepted.
Application information: Unsolicited requests for funds not accepted.
Trustees: Paul P. Gutmann; William B. McNeil; Jack L. Neuenschwander.
EIN: 316539962

7396
The Ferry Family Foundation
1422 Euclid Ave., Ste. 1030
Cleveland, OH 44115-2001

Established in 2002 in Ohio.
Foundation type: Independent foundation.
Financial data (yr. ended 12/31/14): Assets, $3,972,334 (M); expenditures, $488,999; qualifying distributions, $421,423; giving activities include $410,000 for 21 grants (high: $80,000; low: $500).
Fields of interest: Arts and culture; Higher education; Law education; Botanical gardens; Human services; Food banks.
Limitations: Applications not accepted. Giving primarily in OH, with emphasis on Cleveland. No grants to individuals.
Application information: Contributes only to pre-selected organizations.
Trustees: Carol Colangelo; William Culbertson; Carolyn P. Ferry.
EIN: 326000096

7397
The Feth Family Foundation
3604 W. Glencoe Rd.
Richfield, OH 44286-9335

Donors: William R. Feth; Karen W. Feth.
Foundation type: Independent foundation.
Financial data (yr. ended 12/31/13): Assets,
$2,391,715 (M); gifts received, $500,000;
expenditures, $161,862; qualifying distributions,
$150,650; giving activities include $150,650 for 66
grants (high: $35,000; low: $150).
Fields of interest: Education; Religion; Human
services.
Limitations: Applications not accepted.
Application information: Unsolicited requests for
funds not accepted.
Officers: William R. Feth, Pres.; Michael W.
Sweeney, Secy.; Karen W. Feth, Treas.
EIN: 454039737

7398
Fibus Family Foundation
P.O. Box 470
Niles, OH   44446-0470

Established in 1982 in Ohio.
Donors: C. Kenneth Fibus; Steel City Corp.; M.
Fibus†; Dinesol Plastics, Inc.; Fibus Family
Properties, LLC.
Foundation type: Independent foundation.
Financial data (yr. ended 05/31/13): Assets,
$2,213,921 (M); gifts received, $250,000;
expenditures, $217,115; qualifying distributions,
$201,328; giving activities include $201,328 for 51
grants (high: $126,000; low: $100).
Purpose and activities: Giving primarily for health
organizations and Jewish agencies.
Fields of interest: University education; Nonprofits;
Multiple sclerosis; Diabetes; Cancers; Judaism;
Human services.
Type of support: Regranting.
Limitations: Applications not accepted. No grants to
individuals.
Application information: Unsolicited requests for
funds not accepted.
Trustee: C. Kenneth Fibus.
EIN: 341340458

7399
John D. Finnegan Foundation
P.O. Box 1558, Dept. EA4E86
Columbus, OH   43216-1558   (330) 742-7021
Application address: c/o Huntington National Bank,
30050 Chagrin Blvd., Pepper Pike, OH 44124,
tel.: (330) 742-7021

Donor: John D. Finnegan†.
Foundation type: Independent foundation.
Financial data (yr. ended 12/31/14): Assets,
$5,695,465 (M); expenditures, $236,146;
qualifying distributions, $196,795; giving activities
include $173,500 for 11 grants (high: $50,000;
low: $1,000).
Fields of interest: Higher education; Nonprofits;
Catholicism; Human services; Senior services;
Seniors.
Type of support: General support; Capital
campaigns; Capital and infrastructure; Equipment;
Regranting.
Limitations: Applications accepted. Giving primarily
in Youngstown, OH. No grants to individuals, or for
operating budgets, scholarships, fellowships, or
matching gifts; no loans.
Application information: Application form required.
Initial approach: Letter

Copies of proposal: 1
Deadline(s): None
Board meeting date(s): Apr., Oct., and Dec.
Final notification: Varies
Trustee: Huntington National Bank.
EIN: 346516439

7400
Firman Fund
1422 Euclid Ave., Ste. 1150
Cleveland, OH   44115-2063

Established in 1951 in Ohio.
Donor: Pamela H. Firman†.
Foundation type: Independent foundation.
Financial data (yr. ended 12/31/14): Assets,
$9,174,021 (M); expenditures, $419,509;
qualifying distributions, $364,401; giving activities
include $351,000 for 25 grants (high: $145,000;
low: $500).
Fields of interest: Arts and culture; Natural history
museums; Education; Environment; Health; Human
services.
Type of support: General support; Annual
campaigns; Capital campaigns; Capital and
infrastructure; Scholarships.
Limitations: Applications not accepted. Giving
primarily in Denver, CO, Tallahassee, FL,
Thomasville, GA, and Cleveland, OH. No grants to
individuals, or for research; no loans.
Application information: Unsolicited requests for
funds not accepted.
Board meeting date(s): Apr. and Nov.
Officers: Neil A. Brown, Secy.; Carole M. Nowak,
Treas.
Trustees: Royal Firman III; Stephanie Firman;
Cynthia F. Webster.
EIN: 346513655

7401
Fishel Foundation
1366 Dublin Rd.
Columbus, OH   43215-1093

Established in 1993 in Ohio.
Donors: Fishel Co.; Diane L. Keeler.
Foundation type: Company-sponsored foundation.
Financial data (yr. ended 02/28/14): Assets,
$2,331,573 (M); gifts received, $512,227;
expenditures, $210,924; qualifying distributions,
$201,967; giving activities include $201,967 for 19
grants (high: $61,000; low: $200).
Purpose and activities: The foundation supports
organizations involved with higher education, health,
children, Christianity, and refugees.
Fields of interest: Health; Religion; Human services.
Type of support: General support.
Limitations: Applications not accepted. Giving
primarily in Columbus, OH. No grants to individuals.
Application information: Unsolicited requests for
funds not accepted.
Officer: Kathy C. Blackstone, Treas.
Trustee: Diane L. Keeler.
EIN: 316063414

7402
The Richard J. Fitton Family Foundation
219 High St.
Hamilton, OH   45011-6017

Established in 1999 in Ohio.
Donor: Richard J. Fitton.
Foundation type: Independent foundation.
Financial data (yr. ended 12/31/13): Assets,
$4,208,017 (M); expenditures, $249,415;
qualifying distributions, $220,814; giving activities
include $219,334 for 8 grants (high: $100,000;
low: $1,500).
Fields of interest: Arts and culture; Higher
education; Foundations.
Type of support: General support.
Limitations: Applications not accepted. Giving
primarily in OH. No grants to individuals.
Application information: Unsolicited requests for
funds not accepted.
Trustee: First Financial Bank.
EIN: 311653186

7403
Fleck Scholarship Fund
P.O. Box 59
Lebanon, OH   45036-0059

Foundation type: Independent foundation.
Financial data (yr. ended 12/31/14): Assets,
$4,918,851; expenditures, $353,119; qualifying
distributions, $303,576.
Fields of interest: Education.
Type of support: Scholarships.
Limitations: Applications not accepted. Giving
primarily in OH.
Application information: Unsolicited requests for
funds not accepted.
Trustee: LCNB National Bank.
EIN: 208934863

7404
Fleischmann Foundation
7811 Laurel Ave., Ste. B
Cincinnati, OH   45243   (513) 621-1384

Established in 1931 in Ohio.
Donors: Julius Fleischmann†; Charles Fleischmann
III†.
Foundation type: Independent foundation.
Financial data (yr. ended 12/31/14): Assets,
$8,286,908; expenditures, $260,619; qualifying
distributions, $219,367.
Fields of interest: Arts and culture; Art museums;
History; Historic preservation; Education;
Environment; Foundations; Archaeology.
Type of support: General support.
Limitations: Applications accepted. Giving primarily
in OH. No grants to individuals.
Application information: Application form required.
Initial approach: Proposal
Deadline(s): None
Officers and Trustees: Noah Fleischmann, Pres. and
Trustee; Blair S. Fleischmann, Secy. and Trustee;
Charles Fleischmann IV; Louisa Fleischmann; Burd
B. Schlessinger.
EIN: 316025516

7405
Louise & Leonard Fletcher Foundation
c/o PNC Bank, N.A.
P.O. Box 94651
Cleveland, OH   44101-4651

Established in 1991 in Ohio.

Donors: Leonard H. Fletcher; Louise A. Fletcher.
Foundation type: Independent foundation.
Financial data (yr. ended 11/30/14): Assets, $1,728,642 (M); expenditures, $161,131; qualifying distributions, $150,366; giving activities include $142,500 for 4 grants (high: $62,500; low: $20,000).
Fields of interest: Education; Health; Human services.
Limitations: Applications not accepted. Giving primarily in OH. No grants to individuals.
Application information: Unsolicited requests for funds not accepted.
Trustee: PNC Bank, N.A.
EIN: 341694479

7406
The Fortney Foundation
31269 Bradley Rd.
North Olmsted, OH 44070-3875

Established in 2006 in Ohio.
Foundation type: Independent foundation.
Financial data (yr. ended 12/31/13): Assets, $3,440,321 (M); expenditures, $185,138; qualifying distributions, $171,000; giving activities include $171,000 for 33 grants (high: $18,000; low: $1,000).
Fields of interest: Education; Agriculture; Human services; Children.
Type of support: General support.
Limitations: Applications not accepted. Giving primarily in OH.
Application information: Unsolicited requests for funds not accepted.
Trustees: Robert L. Fortney; Ruth A. Fortney.
EIN: 208082606

7407
Donald J. Foss Memorial Employees Trust
604 Madison Ave.
Wooster, OH 44691-4764 (330) 264-4440
Contact: Allan K. Rodd, Tr.

Established in 1956 in Ohio.
Donors: Donald J. Foss†; Mrs. Donald J. Foss†; Walter R. Foss†.
Foundation type: Independent foundation.
Financial data (yr. ended 04/30/13): Assets, $7,159,613 (M); expenditures, $358,215; qualifying distributions, $357,766; giving activities include $145,000 for 2 grants (high: $125,000; low: $20,000), and $212,766 for 28 grants to individuals (high: $8,300; low: $120).
Purpose and activities: Grants awarded primarily to employees of the Wooster Brush Co. or members of their immediate families in time of sickness, death, or other unfortunate circumstances; some additional charitable giving.
Fields of interest: Higher education; Nonprofits; Human services; Low-income and poor people.
Type of support: General support; Grants to individuals; Regranting.
Limitations: Applications accepted. Giving primarily in Wooster, OH.
Application information: Application form required.
Deadline(s): None
Trustees: William Fagert; Allan K. Rodd; Thomas W. Zook.
EIN: 346517801

7408
The Foundation for Appalachian Ohio
36 Public Square
P.O. Box 456
Nelsonville, OH 45764-1133 (740) 753-1111
Contact: Cara Dingus Brook, Pres. and C.E.O.
FAX: (740) 753-3333; E-mail: info@ffao.org;
Additional e-mail: cbrook@ffao.org; Main
URL: http://www.appalachianohio.org
Facebook: https://www.facebook.com/foundationforappalachianohio

Established in 1998 in Ohio.
Foundation type: Community foundation.
Financial data (yr. ended 12/31/12): Assets, $12,140,667 (M); gifts received, $2,517,485; expenditures, $1,296,084; giving activities include $152,235 for 111+ grants, and $173,186 for 53 grants to individuals.
Purpose and activities: Enriches the current and future quality of life in the 32 counties of Appalachian Ohio by fostering access to opportunity.
Fields of interest: Education; Leadership development; Community and economic development; Economic development; Family services; Child welfare.
Type of support: General support; Pro bono consulting services; Individual development; Continuing support; Financial sustainability; Endowments; Emergency funds; Program development; Convening; Publications; Curriculum development; Scholarships; Technical assistance.
Limitations: Applications accepted. Giving limited to 32 county Appalachian Ohio region, including Adams, Ashtabula, Athens, Belmont, Brown, Carroll, Clermont, Columbiana, Coshocton, Gallia, Guernsey, Harrison, Highland, Hocking, Holmes, Jackson, Jefferson, Lawrence, Mahoning, Meigs, Monroe, Morgan, Muskingum, Noble, Perry, Pike, Ross, Scioto, Trumbull, Tuscarawas, Vinton and Washington. No grant for capital requests for buildings or renovations.
Publications: Informational brochure.
Application information: Visit foundation's website for current grant opportunities.
Deadline(s): Varies
Officers and Trustees: Ronald Strickmaker, Chair. and Trustee; Christiane W. Schmenk, Vice-Chair. and Trustee; Cara Dingus Brook, Pres. and C.E.O. and Trustee; Holly Shelton, V.P., Donor Srvs. and Admin. and Trustee; Megan Wanczyk, V.P., Annual Fund and Comm. and Trustee; Ron Cremeans, Secy. and Trustee; T.J. Conger, Treas. and Trustee; David Gruber, C.F.O. and Trustee; Phyllis Moody, Cont. and Trustee; Mike Brooks; Jeffery Chaddock; Matt Elli; Terry P. Fleming; Barbara Hansen; Belinda Jones; Mike Moore; B.J. Smith; Alan Stockmeister; David Wilhelm.
EIN: 311620483

7409
Harry K. Fox and Emma R. Fox Charitable Foundation
c/o PNC Bank, N.A.
P.O. Box 94651
Cleveland, OH 44101-4651
Application address for grant applications and related materials and requests for information: Harry K. Fox and Emma R. Fox Charitable Foundation, Att.: Harold E. Friedman, Secy., Skylight Office Tower, 1660 W. 2nd St., Ste. 1100, Cleveland, OH 44113-1448, tel.: (216) 583-7000 or direct dial (216) 583-7130.

Also send copies of grant applications (cover letter and summarized proposal) to the other trustees: Nancy S. Friedman, 23149 Laureldale Rd., Shaker Heights, OH 44122 and Stephen L. Strayer, PNC Bank, PNC Institutional Investments, 1 Cascade Pl., 6th Fl., Akron, OH 44308

Established in 1959 in Ohio.
Donor: Emma R. Fox†.
Foundation type: Independent foundation.
Financial data (yr. ended 12/31/13): Assets, $9,341,696 (M); expenditures, $417,262; qualifying distributions, $399,511; giving activities include $351,000 for 89 grants (high: $26,500; low: $1,000).
Fields of interest: Arts and culture; Education; Hospital care; Human services; Child welfare.
Type of support: General support; Continuing support; Annual campaigns; Capital campaigns; Capital and infrastructure; Equipment; Program development; Seed money; Scholarships.
Limitations: Applications accepted. Giving primarily in northeastern OH, including Cuyahoga and adjacent counties, with emphasis on the greater Cleveland area. No support for religious organizations (though the foundation may provide support for non-sectarian programs), or political organizations. No grants to individuals, or for multi-year grants; no loans.
Publications: Application guidelines.
Application information:
Initial approach: Letter
Copies of proposal: 3
Deadline(s): May 15 for June meeting and Nov. 15 for Dec. meeting
Board meeting date(s): June and Dec.
Officer and Trustees: Harold E. Friedman, Secy. and Trustee; Nancy S. Friedman; PNC Bank, N.A.
Number of staff: 1 part-time professional.
EIN: 346511198

7410
Walter Henry Freygang Foundation
2794 Forestview Dr.
Akron, OH 44333-2785

Established in 1949 in New Jersey.
Donors: Walter Henry Freygang†; Marie A. Freygang†.
Foundation type: Independent foundation.
Financial data (yr. ended 08/31/14): Assets, $9,967,892; expenditures, $475,452; qualifying distributions, $407,025.
Fields of interest: Education; Higher education; Specialty hospital care; Diseases and conditions; Human services; Food delivery; Child welfare.
Limitations: Applications not accepted. Giving primarily in NJ, NY, OH and MA. No grants to individuals.
Application information: Contributes only to pre-selected organizations.
Board meeting date(s): Oct.
Officers: Dale G. Freygang, Pres. and Treas.; James Drennan, V.P.; Katherine A. Freygang, Secy.
Trustees: Joseph A. Drennan; Antje Freygang; David B. Freygang; W. Nicholas F. Freygang.
EIN: 226027952

7411
Sidney Frohman Foundation
c/o Flynn, Py, & Kruse
165 E. Washington Row
Sandusky, OH 44870-2610

Established in 1952 in Ohio.
Donors: Sidney Frohman†; Blanche P. Frohman†.
Foundation type: Independent foundation.
Financial data (yr. ended 12/31/14): Assets, $8,996,808; expenditures, $488,297; qualifying distributions, $426,960.
Purpose and activities: Giving primarily for human services, as well as community development, the United Way, the arts, and health.
Fields of interest: Performing arts; Education; Nonprofits; Health; Community and economic development; Human services; People with vision impairments.
Type of support: General support; Capital campaigns; Capital and infrastructure; Equipment; Endowments; Program development; Regranting.
Limitations: Applications not accepted. Giving primarily in OH, with emphasis on Sandusky. No grants to individuals.
Application information: Contributes only to pre-selected organizations.
Trustees: Daniel C. Frohman; Donald G. Koch; Donald J. Mazza.
EIN: 346517809

7412
Meshech Frost Testamentary Trust
c/o PNC Bank, N.A.
P.O. Box 94651
Cleveland, OH 44101-4651

Established in 1922 in Ohio.
Donor: Meshech Frost†.
Foundation type: Independent foundation.
Financial data (yr. ended 12/31/14): Assets, $4,987,996; expenditures, $238,677; qualifying distributions, $213,691 and $0 for set-asides.
Purpose and activities: Fifty-percent of giving is for civic improvement or beautification and fifty-percent for organizations that give aid to the needy poor, including support for local colleges, a rehabilitation center and a community fund.
Fields of interest: Performing arts; Higher education; Nonprofits; Hospital care; Rehabilitation; Public administration; Human services.
Type of support: General support; Regranting.
Limitations: Applications not accepted. Giving limited to Tiffin, OH.
Application information: Unsolicited requests for funds not accepted.
Trustee: PNC Bank, N.A.
EIN: 316019431

7413
The Frost-Parker Foundation
165 E. Washington Row
Sandusky, OH 44870-2610 (419) 625-8324
Contact: Melvyn J. Stauffer, Secy.

Established in 1986 in Ohio.
Donors: Ruth F. Parker; Ruth F. Parker Trust.
Foundation type: Independent foundation.
Financial data (yr. ended 04/30/14): Assets, $176,044 (M); gifts received, $411,921; expenditures, $346,913; qualifying distributions,

$346,354; giving activities include $322,850 for 24 grants (high: $90,000; low: $250).
Purpose and activities: Giving primarily for higher education and the arts.
Fields of interest: Arts and culture; Performing arts; Education; Higher education; Community and economic development; Human services.
Type of support: General support; Capital campaigns; Capital and infrastructure; Equipment; Scholarships.
Limitations: Giving primarily in northern OH, with emphasis on Sandusky. No grants to individuals.
Application information:
Deadline(s): None
Officers and Trustees: Ruth F. Parker, Pres. and Treas. and Trustee; Mary Jane S. Hill, V.P. and Trustee; Melvyn J. Stauffer, Secy. and Trustee.
EIN: 341515319

7414
The Gale Foundation
1111 Superior Ave., Ste. 700
Cleveland, OH 44114

Established in 1995 in Ohio.
Donors: The William Bingham Foundation; Elizabeth B. Blossom.
Foundation type: Independent foundation.
Financial data (yr. ended 12/31/13): Assets, $9,280,877 (M); expenditures, $471,620; qualifying distributions, $408,715; giving activities include $396,328 for 23 grants (high: $100,000; low: $2,000).
Fields of interest: Secondary education; Natural resources; Nonprofits; Health; Prenatal care; Christianity; Human services.
Type of support: General support; Regranting; Capital campaigns; Capital and infrastructure; Land acquisitions.
Limitations: Applications not accepted. Giving primarily in Brunswick, GA, and VA; some funding also in Augusta, ME. No grants to individuals.
Application information: Unsolicited requests for funds not accepted.
Officers: Benjamin Gale, Pres.; Deborah B. Gale, V.P.; Daniel L. Horn, Secy.; Kirk A. Linn, Treas.
Trustees: Charles L. Freer; Deborah G. Freer; Mary B. Gale; Thomas V. Gale.
EIN: 341812999

7415
Thomas H. and Barbara W. Gale Foundation
1111 Superior Ave., Ste. 700
Cleveland, OH 44114

Established in 1995 in Ohio.
Donors: The William Bingham Foundation; Elizabeth B. Blossom.
Foundation type: Independent foundation.
Financial data (yr. ended 12/31/13): Assets, $8,234,457 (M); expenditures, $362,522; qualifying distributions, $334,915; giving activities include $327,000 for 22 grants (high: $45,000; low: $2,000).
Fields of interest: Arts and culture; Music; Higher education; Environment; Diseases and conditions; Cancers.
Type of support: General support; Matching grants; Capital campaigns; Capital and infrastructure; Endowments.

Limitations: Applications not accepted. No grants to individuals.
Application information: Unsolicited requests for funds not accepted.
Officers: Barbara W. Gale, Pres.; Thomas H. Gale, V.P.; Alicia W. Gale, 2nd V.P.; Jennifer G. Mantzaris, Secy.; Elizabeth A. Gale, Treas.
EIN: 341813012

7416
Garcia Family Charitable Foundation Trust
10 W. 2nd St., 26th Fl.
Dayton, OH 45402

Established in 1998 in Indiana.
Donors: Juan C. Garcia, MD; Maria N. Garcia.
Foundation type: Independent foundation.
Financial data (yr. ended 12/31/13): Assets, $71,015 (M); gifts received, $250,000; expenditures, $208,951; qualifying distributions, $208,246; giving activities include $207,200 for 8 grants (high: $192,000; low: $500).
Purpose and activities: Giving for education, health organizations and human services.
Fields of interest: Education; Higher education; Nonprofits; Health; Hospital care; Diseases and conditions; Cancers; Catholicism.
Type of support: Regranting.
Limitations: Applications not accepted. Giving primarily in CT and IN. No grants to individuals.
Application information: Contributes only to pre-selected organizations.
Trustee: KeyBank, N.A.
EIN: 356664933

7417
Gardner Foundation
10 W. 2nd St., 26th Fl.
Dayton, OH 45402-1971
Application address: c/o Eugenie Campbell, 1424 Black Horse Run, Lebanon, OH 45036

Established in 1952 in Ohio.
Foundation type: Independent foundation.
Financial data (yr. ended 05/31/13): Assets, $4,456,589 (M); expenditures, $237,573; qualifying distributions, $209,000; giving activities include $209,000 for grants.
Purpose and activities: Giving to organizations that disburse scholarships to Middletown and Cincinnati, Ohio, students.
Fields of interest: Education; Foundations.
Type of support: General support; Student aid.
Limitations: Applications accepted. Giving limited to Middletown and Cincinnati, OH. No grants to individuals (except for limited scholarship program).
Publications: Application guidelines; Program policy statement.
Application information: Application form required.
Initial approach: Proposal
Deadline(s): None
Board meeting date(s): June 18 and 19
Officers and Trustees: Lee H. Gardner, Pres. and Trustee; Eugenie Campbell, V.P., Opers. and Trustee; Edward T. Gardner III, Co-V.P., Finance and Trustee; Robert Gardner III, Co-V.P., Finance and Trustee; Tina Evans, Secy. and Trustee; Susanah A. Gardner, Treas. and Trustee; Mimi Gardner Gates.
EIN: 316050604

7418
Virginia Gay Fund
c/o PNC Bank, N.A.
P.O. Box 94651
Cleveland, OH 44101-4651

Established in 1914 in Ohio.
Foundation type: Independent foundation.
Financial data (yr. ended 12/31/13): Assets, $859,037; expenditures, $155,421; qualifying distributions, $149,416.
Purpose and activities: Primarily provides relief assistance to retired teachers, ages 55 and over, who served a minimum of 20 years teaching in the public schools of Ohio.
Fields of interest: Senior services; Women's services; Seniors; Females; Low-income and poor people; Retired people.
Type of support: Grants to individuals.
Limitations: Applications not accepted. Giving limited to OH.
Application information: Unsolicited requests for funds not accepted.
Trustee: PNC Bank, N.A.
Number of staff: 1 part-time professional.
EIN: 314379588

7419
Henry H. Geary, Jr. Memorial Foundation
c/o KeyBank, N.A.
4900 Tiedeman Rd., OH-01-49-0150
Brooklyn, OH 44144-2302

Established in 1995 in Ohio.
Donor: H.H. Geary, Jr. Irrevocable Trust.
Foundation type: Independent foundation.
Financial data (yr. ended 12/31/14): Assets, $7,425,785; expenditures, $384,919; qualifying distributions, $330,021.
Fields of interest: Education; Nonprofits; Protestantism; Human services.
Type of support: Regranting.
Limitations: Applications not accepted. Giving primarily in Findlay and Fostoria, OH. No grants to individuals.
Application information: Contributes only to pre-selected organizations.
Trustee: KeyBank, N.A.
EIN: 341594662

7420
Frank & Pearl E. Gelbman Charitable Trust
P.O. Box 1558, Dept. EA4E86
Columbus, OH 43216-1558

Established in 2005 in Ohio.
Donors: Pearl Gelbman Trust; Frank Gelbman Trust; Gelbman Charitable Trust.
Foundation type: Independent foundation.
Financial data (yr. ended 12/31/14): Assets, $10,379,243 (M); expenditures, $508,050; qualifying distributions, $453,785; giving activities include $415,150 for 39 grants (high: $100,000; low: $500).
Fields of interest: Arts and culture; Historic preservation; Higher education; Nonprofits; Human services.
Type of support: Regranting.

Limitations: Applications not accepted. Giving primarily in Youngstown, OH. No grants to individuals.
Application information: Contributes only to pre-selected organizations.
Trustee: Huntington National Bank.
EIN: 206609204

7421
The George Foundation
P.O. Box 21609
Columbus, OH 43221-0609 (614) 451-5468

Established in 1982 in Ohio.
Donors: Kaplan Trucking Co.; Noel George Trust; Jack M. George Family Charitable Lead Unitrust.
Foundation type: Independent foundation.
Financial data (yr. ended 12/31/14): Assets, $7,545,964; expenditures, $417,268; qualifying distributions, $408,715.
Fields of interest: Arts and culture; Ballet; Orchestral music; Museums; Education; Environment.
Limitations: Applications accepted. Giving primarily in Columbus, OH.
Application information: Application form required.
  Initial approach: Letter
  Deadline(s): None
Officers: Jack George, Pres.; Joan George, Secy.-Treas.
Trustees: Carol George; Sarah George.
EIN: 311030194

7422
Geotrac Charitable Foundation
257 Benedict Ave., Bldg. D
Norwalk, OH 44857-2715 (419) 668-2552
Contact: John D. Payne, Treas. and Tr.

Established in 2004 in Ohio.
Donors: Sandra A. White; Daniel J. White.
Foundation type: Independent foundation.
Financial data (yr. ended 12/31/13): Assets, $3,282,235 (M); expenditures, $170,842; qualifying distributions, $163,758; giving activities include $160,033 for 16 grants (high: $50,000; low: $200).
Fields of interest: Education; Agriculture; Religion; Human services.
Limitations: Applications accepted. Giving primarily in OH.
Application information: Application form required.
  Initial approach: Letter
  Deadline(s): Mar. 31 and Sept. 30
Officers and Trustees: Brad L. Mason, Pres. and Trustee; Daniel J. White, Secy. and Trustee; John D. Payne, Treas. and Trustee; Samantha Ludwig; Mary Tester; Wesley W. White.
EIN: 206377323

7423
Allene N. Gilman Charitable Trust
c/o Neil M. Moss
4608 Sawmill Rd.
Columbus, OH 43220-2247

Donor: Allene N. Gilman†.
Foundation type: Independent foundation.
Financial data (yr. ended 12/31/13): Assets, $4,792,816 (M); expenditures, $272,207;

qualifying distributions, $223,400; giving activities include $223,400 for 38 grants (high: $29,000; low: $1,000).
Fields of interest: Education; Nonprofits; Homeless services.
Type of support: Regranting.
Limitations: Applications not accepted.
Application information: Unsolicited requests for funds not accepted.
Trustee: Neil M. Moss.
EIN: 266375848

7424
Russell and Mary Gimbel Foundation
P.O. Box 1223
Mansfield, OH 44901-1223 (419) 342-6301

Established in 1989 in Ohio.
Donors: Russell Gimbel†; Mary Gimbel.
Foundation type: Independent foundation.
Financial data (yr. ended 12/31/13): Assets, $4,038,391 (M); expenditures, $187,100; qualifying distributions, $172,422; giving activities include $172,422 for grants.
Fields of interest: Arts and culture; Education; Higher education; Graduate and professional education; Animal welfare; Nursing care; Diseases and conditions; Human services.
Type of support: General support.
Limitations: Applications accepted. Giving primarily in Mansfield, OH.
Application information: Application form required.
  Initial approach: Request application form
  Deadline(s): None
Trustees: Donald L. Dewald; John Hancock; Robert Kerst; Nelson Whisler; Jay Wineland.
EIN: 341626310

7425
The Frank Hadley Ginn and Cornelia Root Ginn Charitable Trust
(also known as The Ginn Foundation)
13940 Cedar Road
Box 239
University Heights, OH 44118
Contact: Walter Ginn, Pres. and Trustee
E-mail: info@ginnfoundation.org; Main URL: http://www.ginnfoundation.org
Grants List: http://www.ginnfoundation.org/grants2012.html
Grants List: http://www.ginnfoundation.org/grants2013.html
Grants List: http://www.ginnfoundation.org/grants2011.html

Established in 1991 in Ohio.
Donor: Alexander Ginn†.
Foundation type: Independent foundation.
Financial data (yr. ended 12/31/13): Assets, $3,202,000 (M); expenditures, $181,000; qualifying distributions, $170,000; giving activities include $170,000 for 27 grants (high: $15,000; low: $2,500).
Purpose and activities: The foundation seeks to address education and community-based health care needs of low-income individuals through supporting effective programs and services that bring about long-term solutions for individuals and the community, principally in Cuyahoga County, OH. The foundation will also consider assisting nonprofits in building internal capacity to meet their

goals in areas such as fundraising, technology, infrastructure, and staff development.

Fields of interest: Arts education; Education; Health; Community health care; Public health.

Type of support: General support; Fundraising; Capacity-building and technical assistance; Program development; Program evaluations.

Limitations: Applications accepted. Giving primarily in Cuyahoga County, OH; support also for trustee-sponsored proposals for organizations in Washington, DC, Chicago, IL, and the metropolitan Minneapolis-St. Paul, MN, area. No grants to individuals, or for endowment, capital, or annual fund campaigns, or special events or attendance at conferences or symposia.

Application information: Applications submitted by fax not considered.
Initial approach: Proposal
Copies of proposal: 1
Deadline(s): Mar. 15 and Sept. 15
Board meeting date(s): Early May and Nov.
Final notification: Immediately following Board meetings

Trustees: Meredith G. Carr; Patricia G. Feeney; Ann L. Ginn; Mary C. Ginn; Walter P. Ginn; Tara F. VanWynkel.

EIN: 346953379

7426
Jerome S. Glazer Foundation, Inc.
9200 Floral Ave.
Cincinnati, OH 45242-6954

Established in 2002 in Ohio.

Donor: Bradford A. Glazer.

Foundation type: Independent foundation.

Financial data (yr. ended 12/31/13): Assets, $4,360,004 (M); expenditures, $186,244; qualifying distributions, $164,554; giving activities include $155,675 for 34 grants (high: $45,000; low: $100).

Fields of interest: Arts and culture; Education; Nonprofits; Religion; Judaism.

Type of support: Regranting.

Limitations: Applications not accepted. Giving primarily in OH. No grants to individuals.

Application information: Unsolicited requests for funds not accepted.

Officers: Alfred H. Moses, Chair.; Bradford A. Glazer, Pres. and Treas.; David H. Glazer, V.P.

Directors: Jill N. Glazer; Melissa A. Glazer; Michelle B. Glazer; Susan F. Glazer.

EIN: 311787788

7427
J. Harrington & Marie E. Glidden Foundation
c/o KeyBank
10 W. 2nd St., 26th Fl.
Dayton, OH 45402-1791

Established in 1998 in Ohio.

Donor: Marie E. Glidden†.

Foundation type: Independent foundation.

Financial data (yr. ended 12/31/14): Assets, $4,213,010; expenditures, $302,987; qualifying distributions, $265,544.

Fields of interest: Secondary education; Graduate and professional education; Catholicism; Theology.

Type of support: General support; Continuing support.

Limitations: Applications not accepted. Giving primarily in Cleveland, OH. No grants to individuals.

Application information: Unsolicited requests for funds not accepted.

Officers: Timothy Cleary, Pres. and Treas.; John M. Cleary, V.P. and Secy.; Anne C. Grevey, V.P.

Trustee: KeyBank, N.A.

EIN: 341881366

7428
Goerlich Family Foundation, Inc.
405 Madison Ave., Ste. 2250
Toledo, OH 43604-1207

Established in 1965 in Ohio.

Donors: John Goerlich†; Selma E. Goerlich†; Selma Goerlich Putman; Paul Putnam; Sandrea Sue Goerlich Alexander.

Foundation type: Independent foundation.

Financial data (yr. ended 12/31/13): Assets, $3,149,865 (M); expenditures, $176,762; qualifying distributions, $171,886; giving activities include $152,465 for 111 grants (high: $19,500; low: $25).

Fields of interest: Education; Health; Human services.

Type of support: General support; Capital campaigns; Scholarships.

Limitations: Applications not accepted. Giving primarily in MI and OH. No grants to individuals.

Application information: Unsolicited requests for funds not accepted.

Officers and Trustees: William F. Bates, Pres. and Treas. and Trustee; Selma Goerlich Putman, V.P. and Trustee; Sandrea Sue Goerlich Alexander, Secy. and Trustee.

EIN: 340970919

7429
Gosiger Foundation
108 McDonough St.
Dayton, OH 45402-2246

Established in 1992 in Ohio.

Donors: Gosiger, Inc.; Jane Haley Trust.

Foundation type: Company-sponsored foundation.

Financial data (yr. ended 12/31/13): Assets, $4,146,129 (M); gifts received, $162,500; expenditures, $465,829; qualifying distributions, $415,367; giving activities include $415,367 for 40 grants (high: $100,000; low: $300).

Purpose and activities: The foundation supports organizations involved with arts and culture, education, conservation, human services, and Catholicism.

Fields of interest: Arts and culture; Education; Health.

Type of support: General support; Scholarships.

Limitations: Applications not accepted. Giving primarily in Dayton, OH. No grants to individuals.

Application information: Contributes only to pre-selected organizations.

Officers and Trustees: Jane Gosiger Haley, Pres. and Trustee; John R. Haley, V.P. and Trustee; Peter G. Haley, V.P. and Trustee; Hugh E. Wall III, Secy.; Jerry R. Pressel, Treas.

EIN: 311365457

7430
Robert Gould Foundation Inc.
P.O. Box 225
Milford, OH 45150-0225 (513) 831-8077
Contact: Laura Beckman Sheldon, Tr.

Donor: Robert Gould†.

Foundation type: Independent foundation.

Financial data (yr. ended 12/31/13): Assets, $8,543,112 (M); expenditures, $396,433; qualifying distributions, $375,018; giving activities include $183,300 for 17 grants (high: $40,000; low: $2,500).

Fields of interest: Arts and culture; Education; Elementary and secondary education; Winter sports; Human services.

Type of support: General support.

Limitations: Applications accepted. Giving primarily in CO, NY, and OH. No grants to individuals.

Application information: Application form required.
Initial approach: Letter
Deadline(s): None

Trustees: Susan Beckman; Laura Beckman Sheldon.

EIN: 316064275

7431
Gries Family Foundation
1801 E. 9th St., Ste. 1600
Cleveland, OH 44114-3100 (216) 861-1148

Established in 1986 in Ohio.

Donors: Robert D. Gries; Ellen G. Cole; Sarah Gries.

Foundation type: Independent foundation.

Financial data (yr. ended 12/31/14): Assets, $3,619,259; expenditures, $296,646; qualifying distributions, $239,977.

Purpose and activities: The foundation's main focus is on general philanthropic activities in the greater Cleveland, Ohio area.

Type of support: General support.

Limitations: Applications accepted. Giving primarily in the greater Cleveland, OH, area. No grants to individuals.

Application information: Contributes primarily to charities in which family members have been involved.
Initial approach: Letter
Copies of proposal: 1
Board meeting date(s): 4 to 6 times a year

Officers and Trustees: Robert D. Gries, Pres. and Trustee; David G. Cole, V.P. and Trustee; Sally P. Gries, Secy.-Treas. and Trustee.

EIN: 341536795

7432
Thomas R. Gross Family Foundation
1241 Gibbard Ave.
Columbus, OH 43219-2438 (513) 721-5086
Contact: Thomas R. Gross, Tr.

Established in 1997 in Ohio.

Foundation type: Independent foundation.

Financial data (yr. ended 12/31/13): Assets, $3,483,479 (M); expenditures, $156,688; qualifying distributions, $141,200; giving activities include $141,000 for 19 grants (high: $25,000; low: $1,000).

Fields of interest: Arts and culture; Higher education; Nonprofits; Health; Christianity; Human services.

Type of support: General support; Regranting.
Limitations: Applications accepted. Giving primarily in the greater Columbus, OH area. No grants to individuals.
Application information: Application form required.
    Initial approach: Letter
    Deadline(s): None
Trustees: David B. Gross; Michael L. Gross; Thomas R. Gross; Thomas R. Gross, Jr.
EIN: 311529104

7433
The Gross/Hutton Family Foundation
9435 Waterstone Blvd., No. 390
Cincinnati, OH   45249-8226
Application address: c/o Sandra L. Gross, Pres., 4985 Walnut Woods Ln., Cincinnati, OH 45243-4063, tel.: (513) 241-3111

Established in 2007 in Ohio.
Donors: John S. Hutton; Sandra L. Gross.
Foundation type: Independent foundation.
Financial data (yr. ended 12/31/13): Assets, $799,783 (M); gifts received, $402,284; expenditures, $189,395; qualifying distributions, $185,600; giving activities include $185,500 for 6 grants (high: $95,000; low: $500).
Fields of interest: Arts and culture; Environment.
Limitations: Applications accepted. Giving primarily in Cincinnati, OH. No grants to individuals.
Application information: Application form required.
    Initial approach: Letter
    Deadline(s): None
Officers: Sandra L. Gross, Pres.; John S. Hutton, V.P.; Michael Schwartz, Secy.; Anthony Schweier, Treas.
EIN: 208419458

7434
H and B Family Foundation
P. O. Box 298
Lima, OH   45802-0298
Application address: 225 North West St., Lima, OH 45801, tel.: (419) 229-3060

Established in 2005 in Ohio.
Donors: Beverly A. Hawk Trust; Henry Hawk Revocable Trust; Beverly A. Hawk.
Foundation type: Independent foundation.
Financial data (yr. ended 12/31/13): Assets, $3,155,235 (M); expenditures, $245,889; qualifying distributions, $220,000; giving activities include $220,000 for 6 grants (high: $75,000; low: $15,000).
Fields of interest: Arts and culture; Historic preservation; Education; Housing development; Catholicism.
Limitations: Applications accepted. Giving primarily in Lima, OH.
Application information: Application form required.
    Initial approach: Contact foundation for application form
    Deadline(s): None
Officers: Beverly A. Hawk, Pres.; David C. Krock, Secy.; Daniel F. Clifford, Treas.
EIN: 203508196

7435
The Jacqueline and Willis Hamilton Foundation
c/o Charitable Trust Administration Co.
Plaza S. Two
7261 Engle Rd., Ste. 202
Cleveland, OH   44130

Established in 1994 in California.
Donor: Jacqueline Hamilton.
Foundation type: Independent foundation.
Financial data (yr. ended 12/31/13): Assets, $6,415,941 (M); expenditures, $291,172; qualifying distributions, $265,000; giving activities include $265,000 for 9 grants (high: $45,000; low: $20,000).
Fields of interest: Education; Public affairs; Human services; Family services.
Limitations: Applications not accepted.
Application information: Unsolicited requests for funds not accepted.
Officer: Jacqueline Hamilton, Pres.
Trustees: Laurie Hasson; Karen Schiefelbein.
EIN: 330643046

7436
The Hampson Family Foundation
40835 Webster Rd.
Lagrange, OH   44050-9418

Established in 2006 in Ohio.
Donor: Lois J. Hampson Estate.
Foundation type: Independent foundation.
Financial data (yr. ended 12/31/13): Assets, $5,783,438 (M); expenditures, $392,645; qualifying distributions, $310,478; giving activities include $310,478 for 4 grants (high: $138,000; low: $15,000).
Fields of interest: Education; Housing development; Human services; Food banks.
Limitations: Applications not accepted. Giving primarily in OH. No grants to individuals.
Application information: Unsolicited requests for funds not accepted.
Officer and Trustees: Karen L. Mole, Pres. and Trustee; Daniel Lent; Jerry Pearl; Robert Yost.
EIN: 341949208

7437
The Hankins Foundation
c/o C.J. D'Ambrosia, C.P.A.
1900 E. 9th St., Ste. 3200
Cleveland, OH   44114-3485

Established in 1952 in Ohio.
Donors: Edward R. Hankins†; Ann H. Long†; Jane H. Lockwood†; Ruth Leale Hankins.
Foundation type: Independent foundation.
Financial data (yr. ended 12/31/13): Assets, $5,505,750 (M); expenditures, $227,920; qualifying distributions, $207,200; giving activities include $207,000 for 37 grants (high: $22,500; low: $1,000).
Fields of interest: Arts and culture; Education; Nonprofits; Health; Diseases and conditions; Human services; Child welfare.
Type of support: General support; Regranting.
Limitations: Applications not accepted. Giving primarily in AZ and OH. No grants to individuals; no loans.

Application information: Contributes only to pre-selected organizations.
    Board meeting date(s): As required
Trustees: Janet L. Harbour; Richard R. Hollington, Jr.; Gordon Long.
Number of staff: 1 full-time professional; 4 part-time support.
EIN: 346565426

7438
John & Virginia Hankison Foundation
1000 Jackson St.
Toledo, OH   43604-5573   (419) 241-9000
Contact: John H. Burson, Secy.

Established in 2003 in Ohio.
Donor: John E. Hankison.
Foundation type: Independent foundation.
Financial data (yr. ended 12/31/14): Assets, $3,629,790 (M); expenditures, $187,075; qualifying distributions, $157,847; giving activities include $138,000 for 20 grants (high: $20,000; low: $100).
Fields of interest: Arts and culture; Education; Domesticated animals.
Limitations: Applications not accepted. Giving primarily in OH.
Application information: Unsolicited requests for funds not accepted.
Officers: Thomas H. Criqui, Pres.; John H. Burson, Secy.; Nancy Lee Ligibel, Treas.
EIN: 352218778

7439
Haskell Fund
1111 Superior Ave., Ste. 700
Cleveland, OH   44114-2540   (216) 363-6481
Contact: James C. Sekerak, Treas.

Donors: Melville H. Haskell†; Coburn Haskell; Melville H. Haskell, Jr.†; Mark Haskell.
Foundation type: Independent foundation.
Financial data (yr. ended 12/31/13): Assets, $4,949,082 (M); expenditures, $291,597; qualifying distributions, $237,758; giving activities include $227,500 for 94 grants (high: $12,000; low: $500).
Purpose and activities: Giving locally for community services; national support for education, including building funds, hospitals and health agencies, community funds and social services, and the environment.
Fields of interest: History; Education; Environment; Natural resources; Biodiversity; Wildlife biodiversity; Animal welfare; Nonprofits; Health; Hospital care; HIV/AIDS; Marine science; Archaeology; Human rights; Human services.
Type of support: General support; Regranting; Continuing support; Fundraising; Annual campaigns; Building and renovations; Endowments; Program development; Scholarships; Research.
Limitations: Applications accepted. Giving on a national basis, with emphasis on AZ, CA, and Cleveland, OH. No grants to individuals.
Application information: Application form required.
    Initial approach: Letter
    Copies of proposal: 1
    Deadline(s): None
    Board meeting date(s): Early fall
Officers and Trustees: Schuyler A. Haskell, Co-Chair. and Trustee; Mary Haskell Walker,

Co-Chair.; Coburn T. Haskell, Co-Pres. and Trustee; Eric T. Haskell, Co-Pres. and Trustee; Mark Haskell, V.P. and Trustee; Paulette Kitko, Secy.; James C. Sekerak, Treas.; Sarah Haskell Greene; Olivia A. Kazanjian; Justyn Haskell Manley; Katherine H. Starbuck.
Number of staff: None.
EIN: 346513797

7440
John Hauck Foundation
c/o Fifth Third Bank N.A.
P.O. Box 630858
Cincinnati, OH   45263-0858

Established in 1989 in Ohio.
Donor: Frederick Hauck.
Foundation type: Independent foundation.
Financial data (yr. ended 09/30/13): Assets, $12,740,566 (M); expenditures, $442,794; qualifying distributions, $347,380; giving activities include $345,900 for 19 grants (high: $75,000; low: $5,000).
Purpose and activities: Giving primarily for education, museums and historical societies, and children and youth services,.
Fields of interest: Museums; Historic preservation; Education; Higher education; Specialty hospital care; Human services; Child welfare.
Type of support: Capital campaigns; Capital and infrastructure; Program development; Research.
Limitations: Applications not accepted. Giving primarily in Cincinnati, OH. No grants to individuals.
Application information: Contributes only to pre-selected organizations.
Trustees: E. Allen Elliott; Narley L. Harley; John W. Hauck; Fifth Third Bank, N.A.
EIN: 316366846

7441
Hazelbaker Foundation
1661 Old Henderson Rd.
Columbus, OH   43220-3644

Established in 1985 in Ohio.
Donors: Ralph E. Hazelbaker; Billie E. Hazelbaker.
Foundation type: Independent foundation.
Financial data (yr. ended 02/28/15): Assets, $1,561,537 (M); gifts received, $200,000; expenditures, $230,304; qualifying distributions, $178,617; giving activities include $178,392 for 11 grants (high: $58,692; low: $100).
Fields of interest: Arts and culture; Theater; Higher education; Health; Diseases and conditions; Special Olympics; Youth services; Homeless services; International development.
Limitations: Applications not accepted. Giving primarily in IN and OH.
Application information: Unsolicited requests for funds not accepted.
Board meeting date(s): Quarterly
Officers: Ralph E. Hazelbaker, Pres.; Billie E. Hazelbaker, Secy.; R. Brian Hazelbaker, Treas.
EIN: 311131197

7442
Health Foundation of Greater Massillon
(formerly The Community Health Foundation)
1237 Lincoln Way E.
Massillon, OH   44646-6992   (330) 837-6864
Contact: John J. McGrath, Pres.
FAX: (330) 837-3639;
E-mail: john@healthfoundation-massillon.org; Main URL: http://www.healthfoundation-massillon.org

Established in 1997 in Ohio.
Foundation type: Independent foundation.
Financial data (yr. ended 12/31/13): Assets, $7,833,779 (M); gifts received, $23,696; expenditures, $403,101; qualifying distributions, $338,799; giving activities include $222,811 for 32 + grants (high: $45,000).
Purpose and activities: Giving primarily to enhance the quality of life by collaborating with and supporting qualified wellness organizations and innovation in health programs and initiatives.
Fields of interest: Health; Public health.
Type of support: Program development; Equipment; Continuing support.
Limitations: Applications accepted. Giving limited to Western Stark, Eastern Wayne, and Northern Tuscarawas counties, OH. No support for religious organizations for religious purposes. No grants to individuals, or for annual appeals, or membership drives, fundraising projects, capital campaigns, or endowment funds.
Publications: Application guidelines; Annual report (including application guidelines); Grants list; Informational brochure; Informational brochure (including application guidelines).
Application information: See foundation web site for full application requirements and guidelines.
Initial approach: Proposal
Copies of proposal: 2
Deadline(s): Feb. 28 and Aug. 31
Board meeting date(s): 4th Fri. of each month
Final notification: June and Dec.
Officers and Board Members: Lynn Hamilton, Chair. and Director; John J. McGrath, Pres.; Robert Gessner, Secy.; Ted Miller, Treas. and Director; Fred Blosser; Katy Catazaro-Perry; Mark Christine; John Ferrero, Jr.; Chris Goff; Susan Koosh; William Leffler, D.D.S.; Judith Paquelet; Melissa Shearer; James Snivley; Vanessa Stergios; Marion "Stu" Stewart.
Number of staff: 1 part-time professional; 1 full-time support.
EIN: 311516370

7443
The Heffner Fund
2300 Brown Rd.
Grove City, OH   43123
Contact: William G. Heffner, Tr.

Established in 1965 in Ohio.
Donors: Agg Rok Materials Co.; Trigon Investments, Ltd.
Foundation type: Independent foundation.
Financial data (yr. ended 12/31/13): Assets, $2,759,460 (M); gifts received, $75,000; expenditures, $171,500; qualifying distributions, $171,500; giving activities include $171,500 for 54 grants (high: $10,000; low: $500).
Fields of interest: Higher education; Environment; Nonprofits; Christianity; Human services; Child welfare.
Type of support: General support; Regranting.

Limitations: Applications accepted. Giving primarily in OH.
Application information: Application form required.
Initial approach: Letter
Deadline(s): None
Trustee: William G. Heffner.
EIN: 346568632

7444
The Heimann Family Foundation
9000 Kugler Mill Rd.
Cincinnati, OH   45243-1524   (513) 831-2161
Contact: Robert A. Heimann, Pres.

Established in 1986 in Ohio.
Foundation type: Independent foundation.
Financial data (yr. ended 05/30/15): Assets, $2,861,236 (M); expenditures, $142,219; qualifying distributions, $141,500; giving activities include $141,500 for 22 grants (high: $20,000; low: $500).
Fields of interest: Education; Higher education; Christianity.
Limitations: Applications accepted. Giving primarily in Cincinnati, OH. No grants to individuals.
Application information: Application form required.
Initial approach: Typewritten letter
Deadline(s): None
Officers and Trustees: Robert A. Heimann, Pres. and Trustee; Sandra Heimann, V.P. and Trustee; Paige DeBuys, V.P. and Trustee; Robert Heimann, Jr., V.P. and Trustee.
EIN: 311197600

7445
Heimbinder Family Foundation
c/o William E. Reichard
1991 Crocker Rd., Ste. 550
Westlake, OH   44145-1998

Established in 1989 in Ohio.
Donors: Isaac Heimbinder; Sheila Heimbinder.
Foundation type: Independent foundation.
Financial data (yr. ended 12/31/13): Assets, $6,765,027 (M); expenditures, $472,563; qualifying distributions, $433,777; giving activities include $433,415 for 128 grants (high: $56,000; low: $100).
Fields of interest: Theater; University education; Hospice care; Catholicism.
Type of support: Program-related investments.
Limitations: Applications not accepted. Giving primarily in TX. No grants to individuals.
Application information: Contributes only to pre-selected organizations.
Trustees: Isaac Heimbinder; Sheila Heimbinder; William E. Reichard.
EIN: 346921501

7446
Heinrich Family Foundation
228 Candlewood Pl.
Saint Mary's, OH   45885-9660
E-mail: jheinr1097@aol.com

Established in 2000 in Ohio.
Donors: The Alfred D. Heinrich Charitable Lead Trust; The Gladys L. Heinrich Charitable Lead Trust.
Foundation type: Independent foundation.

Financial data (yr. ended 12/31/13): Assets, $1,364,578 (M); gifts received, $100,464; expenditures, $147,049; qualifying distributions, $135,800; giving activities include $135,800 for 12 grants (high: $78,500; low: $300).
Fields of interest: Education; Community and economic development; Human services.
Limitations: Applications not accepted. Giving primarily in IL and OH. No grants to individuals.
Application information: Contributes only to pre-selected organizations.
Board meeting date(s): Dec. 31
Officers: James R. Heinrich, Pres. and Treas.; Janice E. Heinrich, V.P.; Sharon L. Heinrich, Secy.
EIN: 341929479

7447
Daisy Hickok Trust

P.O. Box 630858
Cincinnati, OH   45263-0858

Foundation type: Independent foundation.
Financial data (yr. ended 12/31/13): Assets, $3,344,022 (M); expenditures, $192,826; qualifying distributions, $144,464; giving activities include $143,934 for 3 grants (high: $47,978; low: $47,978).
Fields of interest: Religion; Human services; Youth development.
Limitations: Applications not accepted. Giving primarily in Toledo, OH.
Application information: Unsolicited requests for funds not accepted.
Trustee: Fifth Third Bank.
EIN: 346580634

7448
Hieronymus Family Fund Inc.

1278 Maue Rd.
Miamisburg, OH   45342-3475

Established in 1993 in Ohio.
Donor: Harriet Hieronymus.
Foundation type: Independent foundation.
Financial data (yr. ended 12/31/14): Assets, $3,535,773; expenditures, $230,404; qualifying distributions, $230,404.
Purpose and activities: Giving primarily for the arts, education, and Christian churches.
Fields of interest: Performing arts; Historic preservation; Education; Christianity.
Type of support: Scholarships.
Limitations: Applications not accepted. Giving primarily in OH. No grants to individuals.
Application information: Contributes only to pre-selected organizations.
Trustees: Bryan Hieronymus; Lee Hieronymus; Paul Hieronymus; Theodore Hieronymus.
EIN: 311381301

7449
Charles F. High Foundation

1232 State Rte. 4 S.
Bucyrus, OH   44820-9589   (419) 562-2074
Contact: John R. Clime, Admin.

Established in 1939 in Ohio.
Donor: Charles F. High†.
Foundation type: Independent foundation.

Financial data (yr. ended 12/31/13): Assets, $8,065,466 (M); expenditures, $382,713; qualifying distributions, $361,556; giving activities include $346,482 for 58 grants to individuals (high: $8,370; low: $2,748).
Purpose and activities: Scholarships awarded only to male residents of Ohio to attend Ohio State University.
Fields of interest: University education.
Type of support: Student aid.
Limitations: Applications accepted. Giving limited to residents of OH.
Application information: Application form required.
Initial approach: Letter
Deadline(s): Mar. 1
Trustees: S. Bowman; J.R. Clime; F.J. Farmer; J.R. Miller II; D.J. Wingate.
EIN: 346527860

7450
Highfield Foundation

c/o Fifth Third Bank
38 Fountain Sq., 1090CA
Cincinnati, OH   45263-0001

Established in 1990 in Ohio.
Donor: Samuel Benedict.
Foundation type: Independent foundation.
Financial data (yr. ended 09/30/13): Assets, $4,133,951 (M); expenditures, $247,011; qualifying distributions, $200,530; giving activities include $200,000 for 39 grants (high: $24,000; low: $1,000).
Fields of interest: Arts and culture; Education; Higher education; Natural resources; Health; Protestantism.
Type of support: General support; Capital and infrastructure; Endowments; Scholarships.
Limitations: Applications not accepted. Giving on a national basis. No grants to individuals.
Application information: Unsolicited requests for funds not accepted.
Trustee: Fifth Third Bank.
EIN: 316391904

7451
Homan Foundation

974 Pavillion St.
Cincinnati, OH   45202-1725   8593416450

Established in 1969 in Ohio.
Donors: Auto Vehicle Parts Co.; Frank X. Homan.
Foundation type: Independent foundation.
Financial data (yr. ended 12/31/14): Assets, $2,263,358; expenditures, $355,273; qualifying distributions, $333,350.
Fields of interest: Education; Hospital care; Christianity; Catholicism; Human services.
Type of support: General support; Continuing support; Annual campaigns; Capital campaigns; Capital and infrastructure; Equipment; Endowments; Emergency funds; Program development; Seed money; Fellowships; Scholarships; Research; Technical assistance.
Limitations: Applications accepted. Giving primarily in Naples, FL and Cincinnati, OH. No grants to individuals.
Application information: Application form required.
Initial approach: Letter
Copies of proposal: 1
Deadline(s): Nov. 15

Trustees: Frank X. Homan; Walter E. Homan; Ronald L. Lusby.
EIN: 237038734

7452
Home is the Foundation

1751 N. Barron St.
Eaton, OH   45320-9277   (937) 472-0500
Contact: Bill Hutton
FAX: (937) 472-0501; Main URL: http://www.hitfoundation.org
Facebook: https://www.facebook.com/HITFoundation

Established in 2003 in Ohio.
Donors: Franklin Steet; Mary Bullen.
Foundation type: Operating foundation.
Financial data (yr. ended 12/31/13): Assets, $1,813,816 (M); gifts received, $912,642; expenditures, $635,654; qualifying distributions, $474,316; giving activities include $125,000 for grants.
Fields of interest: Housing development.
Application information: Application form required.
Initial approach: Apply in person or contact foundation for application form
Deadline(s): None
Officers: Mary Bullen, Pres.; Chip Christman, Treas.; Billy J. Hutton, Jr., Exec. Dir.
Directors: Bruce Barnes; Jessica Johnson; JoAn Kreitzer; Lisa Noble; Sharon Shute; Mike Simpson.
EIN: 421580792

7453
The W. Henry Hoover Fund

4900 Tiedeman Rd., OH-01-49-0150
Brooklyn, OH   44144-2302
Application address: c/o KeyBank N.A., Attn.: James Baker, 4495 Everhard Rd., N.W., Canton, OH 44718, tel.: (330) 497-3614

Established in 1945 in Ohio.
Donor: W. Henry Hoover†.
Foundation type: Independent foundation.
Financial data (yr. ended 12/31/14): Assets, $5,696,912 (M); expenditures, $310,951; qualifying distributions, $277,213; giving activities include $271,000 for 27 grants (high: $50,000; low: $2,000).
Fields of interest: Arts and culture; Higher education; Environmental education; Nonprofits; Diseases and conditions; Human services; Child welfare.
Type of support: Regranting.
Limitations: Applications accepted. Giving primarily in OH, with emphasis on Canton.
Application information: Application form required.
Initial approach: Letter
Deadline(s): None
Trustee: KeyBank, N.A.
Grant Committee Members: Charles H. Hoover; Lawrence R. Hoover; Timothy Hoover.
EIN: 346573738

7454
The Jeffrey Horvitz Foundation

6095 Parkland Blvd., Ste. 300
Mayfield Heights, OH   44124-6140

Established in 1995 in Ohio.

Donors: Jeffrey E. Horvitz; Samuel Horvitz.
Foundation type: Independent foundation.
Financial data (yr. ended 12/31/13): Assets, $67,864 (M); expenditures, $208,507; qualifying distributions, $207,195; giving activities include $206,100 for 6 grants (high: $150,000; low: $1,000).
Fields of interest: Museums; Art museums; Education; Higher education; Diseases and conditions.
Type of support: Research; Research and evaluation.
Limitations: Applications not accepted. Giving primarily in MA. No grants to individuals.
Application information: Contributes only to pre-selected organizations.
Officers and Trustees: Jeffrey E. Horvitz, Pres. and Trustee; Richard A. Horvitz, Secy.-Treas. and Trustee; Carol Horvitz.
EIN: 341817950

7455
Howe Family Foundation
c/o Roger L. Howe, Tr.
1 W. 4th St., Ste. 2222
Cincinnati, OH 45202-3628

Established in 1991 in Ohio.
Donors: Roger L. Howe; Karen C. Howe; R. Edwin Howe; Mary H. Davis; Joyce L. Howe; Roger L. Howe Charitable Lead Trust.
Foundation type: Independent foundation.
Financial data (yr. ended 12/31/13): Assets, $6,766,117 (M); gifts received, $338,161; expenditures, $388,679; qualifying distributions, $327,950; giving activities include $327,750 for 36 grants (high: $155,000; low: $200).
Fields of interest: Arts and culture; Education; Higher education; Natural resources; Nonprofits; Health care clinics.
Type of support: General support; Regranting.
Limitations: Applications not accepted. Giving primarily in FL and OH. No grants to individuals.
Application information: Contributes only to pre-selected organizations.
Officers: Karen C. Howe, Pres.; Mary H. Davis, Secy.; R. Edwin Howe, Treas.
Trustees: Joyce L. Howe; Roger L. Howe.
EIN: 311339302

7456
George J. Hubert Jr. Foundation Inc.
5603 Boomer Rd.
Cincinnati, OH 45247

Donors: Amanda Hubert; Anthony Hubert; Benjamin G. Hubert; Christopher Hubert; Cynthia Hubert; Robert Hubert; Scott Hubert; Tiffany Hubert; Joshua A. Hubert; Zachary Hubert; Daniel Klare; Karen Klare; Kathleen Smith; Matthew Smith; Bank of America; George Hubert Family LLC; Edward Isakson; Kimberly Isakson; Michael Hengehold; Mary Anne Hengehold; Karen Hubert; George J. Hubert; St. Ignatius of Loyola; Paul Ruffing; St. Rose Church; Michael Mary Anne Hengehold; St. Jude Parish; St. Peter Claver latin School for Boys; Our lady of Visitation; St. James Church.
Foundation type: Independent foundation.
Financial data (yr. ended 12/31/13): Assets, $11,026,459 (M); gifts received, $586,390; expenditures, $456,768; qualifying distributions,

$381,899; giving activities include $323,170 for 30 grants (high: $15,250; low: $500).
Purpose and activities: Giving primarily for Roman Catholic organizations, missions, education, particularly secondary schools, and churches; some funding for community and social services.
Fields of interest: Education; Elementary and secondary education; Higher education; Community and economic development; Catholicism; Human services; Child welfare.
Limitations: Applications not accepted. Giving in the U.S., with emphasis on OH.
Application information: Contributes only to pre-selected organizations.
Officers: George J. Hubert, Jr., Pres.; Kathleen Smith, Secy.; Anthony Hubert, Treas.
EIN: 223882420

7457
Hueneke Foundation Trust
P.O. Box 1558, Dept. EA4E86
Columbus, OH 43216-1558

Established in 2002 in Ohio.
Foundation type: Independent foundation.
Financial data (yr. ended 12/31/14): Assets, $3,485,102 (M); expenditures, $184,567; qualifying distributions, $165,158; giving activities include $148,300 for 14 grants (high: $30,000; low: $1,500).
Fields of interest: Education; Human services; Youth development.
Limitations: Applications not accepted. Giving primarily in OH.
Application information: Contributions only to pre-selected organizations.
Trustee: The Huntington National Bank.
EIN: 347147551

7458
Ruth M. Hughes Scholarship Trust
P.O. Box 1558, DEPT EA4E86
Columbus, OH 43216-2307 (740) 455-7060

Established in 1995 in Ohio.
Foundation type: Independent foundation.
Financial data (yr. ended 12/31/13): Assets, $6,080,705 (M); expenditures, $340,193; qualifying distributions, $308,309; giving activities include $284,000 for 22 grants (high: $82,500; low: $2,500).
Purpose and activities: Scholarship awards to graduates of Muskingum County high schools, Ohio.
Fields of interest: Higher education.
Type of support: Student aid.
Limitations: Applications accepted. Giving limited to Muskingum County, OH.
Publications: Annual report.
Application information: Application form required.
 Initial approach: Completed Application form
 Deadline(s): May 1
Trustee: Huntington National Bank.
Committee Members: Wayne Phillips II; Thomas Seiber; Charles Walker.
EIN: 316442501

7459
Hummer Family Foundation
2000 Auburn Dr., Ste. 330
Cleveland, OH 44122-4327

Donor: James Hummer.
Foundation type: Independent foundation.
Financial data (yr. ended 12/31/13): Assets, $2,487,309 (M); expenditures, $225,149; qualifying distributions, $212,000; giving activities include $212,000 for 7 grants (high: $110,000; low: $2,000).
Fields of interest: Education; Diseases and conditions; Human services.
Limitations: Applications not accepted. Giving primarily in OH.
Application information: Unsolicited requests for funds not accepted.
Officers: James J. Hummer, Pres. and Secy.; Terrance P. Fergus, V.P. and Treas.
EIN: 262448401

7460
Mariett L. Huntington Residue Fund
c/o KeyBank, N.A.
4900 Tiedeman, OH-01-49-0150
Brooklyn, OH 44144-2302

Foundation type: Independent foundation.
Financial data (yr. ended 12/31/14): Assets, $5,117,227; expenditures, $298,528; qualifying distributions, $251,739.
Fields of interest: Health; Hospital care; Mental health care; Religion; Family services.
Type of support: General support.
Limitations: Applications not accepted. Giving primarily in OH.
Application information: Unsolicited requests for funds not accepted.
Trustee: KeyBank, N.A.
EIN: 346500660

7461
John C. Hutchins Endowment Fund
c/o Keybank
4900 Tiedeman Rd., OH-01-49-0150
Brooklyn, OH 44144-2302

Foundation type: Independent foundation.
Financial data (yr. ended 12/31/13): Assets, $4,103,760 (M); expenditures, $223,027; qualifying distributions, $196,274; giving activities include $188,382 for 1 grant.
Fields of interest: Education.
Limitations: Applications not accepted.
Application information: Unsolicited requests for funds not accepted.
Trustee: Keybank, N.A.
EIN: 346536918

7462
Tom & Evelyn Ingle Charitable Trust
P.O. Box 630858
Cincinnati, OH 45263-0858

Established in 1999 in Indiana.
Donor: Tom Ingle†.
Foundation type: Independent foundation.
Financial data (yr. ended 12/31/14): Assets, $2,783,295 (M); expenditures, $168,075; qualifying distributions, $133,400; giving activities include $133,070 for 28 grants (high: $22,944; low: $2,294).
Fields of interest: Domesticated animals; Protestantism; Human services.

Limitations: Applications not accepted. Giving primarily in Evansville, IN. No grants to individuals.
Application information: Unsolicited requests for funds not accepted.
Trustee: Fifth Third Bank.
EIN: 356683779

7463
The Iott Family Foundation
5245 Keener Rd.
Monclova, OH 43542-9707

Established in 1991 in Ohio.
Donor: W.D. Iott.
Foundation type: Independent foundation.
Financial data (yr. ended 12/31/12): Assets, $2,642,331 (M); expenditures, $251,575; qualifying distributions, $210,000; giving activities include $210,000 for grants.
Purpose and activities: Giving primarily for Roman Catholic organizations, education, and human services.
Fields of interest: Secondary education; Undergraduate education; Nonprofits; Catholicism; Human services.
Type of support: General support; Regranting.
Limitations: Applications not accepted. Giving primarily in Toledo, OH. No grants to individuals.
Application information: Contributes only to pre-selected organizations.
Officers and Directors: Richard B. Iott, Chair., Pres. and Treas. and Director; Constance J. Iott, V.P. and Secy.; Devon E. Iott; Ian W. Iott.
EIN: 341695607

7464
Jane L. Jenkins Charitable Fund
c/o PNC Bank, N.A.
P.O. Box 94651
Cleveland, OH 44101-4651

Foundation type: Independent foundation.
Financial data (yr. ended 05/31/13): Assets, $4,149,286 (M); expenditures, $199,848; qualifying distributions, $193,641; giving activities include $188,034 for 3 grants (high: $62,678; low: $62,678).
Fields of interest: Domesticated animals; Health; Human services; People with vision impairments.
Type of support: General support.
Limitations: Applications not accepted. Giving primarily in OH.
Application information: Unsolicited requests for funds not accepted.
Trustee: PNC Bank, N.A.
EIN: 346512109

7465
The Tom H. and Anne H. Jenkins Charitable Trust
26228 Lake Rd.
Bay Village, OH 44140-2567
Contact: Stephen H. Jenkins, Tr.

Donors: Tom H. Jenkins; Anne H. Jenkins.
Foundation type: Independent foundation.
Financial data (yr. ended 12/31/14): Assets, $1,501,440 (M); expenditures, $357,299; qualifying distributions, $355,000; giving activities

include $355,000 for 4 grants (high: $175,000; low: $1,000).
Purpose and activities: Giving primarily for medical care for economically disadvantaged people, and for training skills for people who are either unemployed or disabled.
Fields of interest: Education; Health; Specialty hospital care; Human services; Economically disadvantaged people; People with disabilities; Unemployed people.
Limitations: Applications accepted. Giving primarily in northeast OH.
Application information: Application form required.
  Initial approach: Proposal sent 120 days before funds are needed
  Deadline(s): None
Trustees: Stephen H. Jenkins; Timothy J. Jenkins.
EIN: 456545911

7466
Jennings Memorial Foundation
160 S. Main St., 16th Fl.
Akron, OH 44308 8103427089
Application address: c/o Donald A. Snide, 8316 S. Maple St., Zeeland, MI 49464

Established in 1997 in Michigan.
Donors: Edith Jennings Trust; Wyman Jennings Trust.
Foundation type: Independent foundation.
Financial data (yr. ended 12/31/14): Assets, $4,199,078 (M); expenditures, $346,230; qualifying distributions, $284,428.
Purpose and activities: The foundation supports charities primarily in the area of Montrose, Michigan, with emphasis on public education, Protestant churches, and municipal agencies.
Fields of interest: Elementary and secondary education; Fire prevention and control; Public administration; Protestantism; Human services.
Type of support: General support; Equipment.
Limitations: Applications accepted. Giving primarily in Montrose, MI, and surrounding areas. No support for political organizations.
Publications: Application guidelines.
Application information: Application form required.
  Initial approach: Proposal
  Copies of proposal: 1
  Deadline(s): None
  Board meeting date(s): 3rd Thurs. in Feb., Apr., June, Oct., and Dec.
Officers and Directors: Donald A. Snide, Pres. and Director; James McCartney, Treas. and Director; Gwen Kelley; Donald W. Snide; John C. Wendling.
Trustee: FirstMerit Bank, N.A.
EIN: 386684041

7467
Joffe Foundation
4400 Drake Rd.
Cincinnati, OH 45243-4114
Application address: c/o Sandra Joffe, 7840 Montgomery Rd., Cincinnati, OH 45236, tel.:(513) 792-9292

Donors: Sandra Joffe; Stephen Joffe; Heidi Joffe.
Foundation type: Independent foundation.
Financial data (yr. ended 12/31/13): Assets, $6,605 (M); gifts received, $150,038; expenditures, $442,029; qualifying distributions,

$296,275; giving activities include $296,275 for 10 grants (high: $259,668; low: $500).
Fields of interest: Arts and culture; Education; Nonprofits; Human services.
Type of support: Regranting.
Limitations: Applications accepted. Giving primarily in CA and OH.
Application information: Application form required.
  Initial approach: Letter
  Deadline(s): None
Officers and Directors: Stephen Joffe, Pres. and Director; Sandra Joffe, Treas. and Director.
EIN: 200080918

7468
Johnson Family Foundation
c/o U.S. Bank, N.A.
P.O. Box 1118, ML CN-OH-W10X
Cincinnati, OH 45201-1118

Established in 1997 in Ohio.
Donors: Arlyn T. Johnson; Samuel J. Johnson IV.
Foundation type: Independent foundation.
Financial data (yr. ended 04/30/14): Assets, $13,565,594 (M); gifts received, $5,100,000; expenditures, $457,037; qualifying distributions, $374,011; giving activities include $361,800 for 17 grants (high: $45,000; low: $7,500).
Purpose and activities: Giving primarily for education and human services.
Fields of interest: Education; Hospice care; Human services; Child welfare; Homeless people; People with disabilities.
Limitations: Applications not accepted. Giving primarily in KY, MA, and OH; some giving in New York, NY. No grants to individuals.
Application information: Contributes only to pre-selected organizations.
Directors: Terry K. Crilley; Lauren Lipcon Dale; David B. Hamilton; Gwendolyn Kess Johnson; Johanna Johnson; Zachary Johnson; Charlotte Johnson Lilly; Jesse Lipcon; Patricia L. Johnson Lipcon; Scott Lipcon; Todd Lipcon; Crosley Johnson Sigmon.
EIN: 311542859

7469
The Raymond C. and Anna T. Johnson Foundation, Inc.
407 Vine St., No. 218
Cincinnati, OH 45202-2521   (513) 800-2056
Contact: Amy Goodwin, Pres. and Exec. Dir.

Donor: Raymond C. Johnson Charitable Lead UniTrust.
Foundation type: Independent foundation.
Financial data (yr. ended 12/31/13): Assets, $5,152,989 (M); gifts received, $455,663; expenditures, $500,216; qualifying distributions, $436,512; giving activities include $374,680 for 36 grants (high: $28,300; low: $500).
Fields of interest: Diseases and conditions; Human services.
Limitations: Applications not accepted. Giving primarily in OH and VA.
Application information: Unsolicited requests for funds not accepted.
Officers: Alan S. Threlkeld, Pres. and Exec. Dir.; Deborah J. Case, V.P.; Robert T. Threlkeld, Secy.-Treas.
EIN: 261548389

7470
Ralph R. and Grace B. Jones Foundation
419 S. Market St.
Wooster, OH 44691-4727
Application address: c/o Douglas Drushal, 225 N.
Market St., Wooster, OH 44691, tel.: (330)
264-4444

Established in 1997 in Ohio.
Donors: Kathryn G. Long; Ralph Jones Charitable.
Foundation type: Independent foundation.
Financial data (yr. ended 12/31/13): Assets,
$5,754,099 (M); gifts received, $8,500;
expenditures, $274,574; qualifying distributions,
$270,545; giving activities include $228,045 for 27
grants (high: $34,333; low: $500), $5,000 for 1
grant to an individual, and $25,000 for 1 loan/
program-related investment.
Fields of interest: Education; Philanthropy; Religion.
Limitations: Applications accepted. Giving primarily
in OH.
Application information:
  Initial approach: Contact foundation
  Deadline(s): None
Trustees: J. Douglas Drushal; Kathryn G. Long;
Matthew A. Long.
EIN: 311508706

7471
The Kim Jordan Foundation
20820 Chagrin Blvd., Ste. 300
Shaker Heights, OH 44122-5323

Donor: Kathryn H. Jordan.
Foundation type: Independent foundation.
Financial data (yr. ended 12/31/13): Assets,
$9,752,951 (M); gifts received, $400,000;
expenditures, $461,600; qualifying distributions,
$342,522; giving activities include $342,522 for 15
grants (high: $140,100; low: $3).
Fields of interest: Higher education; Health;
Protestantism; Human services.
Limitations: Applications not accepted. Giving
primarily in TX and WI.
Application information: Unsolicited requests for
funds not accepted.
Trustee: Kathryn H. Jordan.
EIN: 266579229

7472
Juniper Tree Foundation
(formerly Morelock Family Foundation)
P.O. Box 37429
Cincinnati, OH 45222-0429

Established in 2004 in Ohio.
Donor: John P. Morelock, Jr.
Foundation type: Operating foundation.
Financial data (yr. ended 12/31/13): Assets,
$599,340 (M); gifts received, $349,000;
expenditures, $268,314; qualifying distributions,
$267,813; giving activities include $267,813 for 23
grants (high: $147,751; low: $250).
Fields of interest: Christianity; Human services.
Limitations: Applications not accepted. No grants to
individuals.
Application information: Contributes only to
pre-selected organizations.
Trustees: John P. Morelock, Jr.; Jeffrey C. Paas; Paul
R. Stanken.
EIN: 200749868

7473
Kamm Foundation
25642 Lake Rd.
Bay Village, OH 44140

Donors: J.O. Kamm; J.S. Kamm; Electric Furnace
Foundation.
Foundation type: Independent foundation.
Financial data (yr. ended 12/31/14): Assets,
$3,786,345; expenditures, $209,667; qualifying
distributions, $195,500.
Fields of interest: Education; Publishing;
Christianity.
Type of support: General support; Scholarships.
Limitations: Applications not accepted. Giving
primarily in MA and OH. No grants to individuals.
Application information: Unsolicited requests for
funds not accepted.
Officers and Trustees: J.S. Kamm, Pres. and
Trustee; J.O. Kamm II, V.P. and Secy. and Trustee;
C.P. Kamm, V.P. and Treas. and Trustee.
EIN: 346533601

7474
The Kangesser Foundation
(formerly The Robert E., Harry A., and M. Sylvia
Kangesser Foundation)
10 Daisy Ln.
Pepper Pike, OH 44124

Established in 1947 in Ohio.
Donors: Robert E. Kangesser†; Harry A.
Kangesser†; M. Sylvia Kangesser†.
Foundation type: Independent foundation.
Financial data (yr. ended 12/31/14): Assets,
$3,163,082; expenditures, $291,066; qualifying
distributions, $249,250.
Purpose and activities: Giving primarily for Jewish
organizations, including welfare funds and yeshivas.
Fields of interest: Education; Religion; Sports and
recreation.
Type of support: General support; Continuing
support; Annual campaigns; Capital campaigns;
Capital and infrastructure.
Limitations: Applications not accepted. Giving
primarily in the greater Cleveland, OH, area. No
grants to individuals.
Application information: Contributes only to
pre-selected organizations.
  Board meeting date(s): Usually in Sept. or Oct.
Officers: Hedy Kangesser Adler, Pres. and Treas.;
David F. Adler, Secy.
EIN: 346529478

7475
Avrum Katz Foundation
c/o Taft Law
200 Public Sq.
Cleveland, OH 44114-2302

Established in 1993 in Ohio.
Donor: Avrum S. Katz†.
Foundation type: Independent foundation.
Financial data (yr. ended 12/31/13): Assets,
$2,417,201 (M); expenditures, $286,195;
qualifying distributions, $130,000; giving activities
include $130,000 for 2 grants (high: $80,000; low:
$50,000).
Purpose and activities: Support primarily for the
benefit of children, the elderly, animals and
healthcare related research.

Fields of interest: Animal welfare; Diseases and
conditions; Judaism; Family services; Child welfare;
Senior services; Children and youth; Adults.
Type of support: General support; Employee
matching gifts; Matching grants; Continuing
support; Annual campaigns; Emergency funds;
Program development; Research.
Limitations: Applications not accepted. Giving on a
national basis. No support for arts, sciences
programs, or political organizations. No grants to
individuals.
Publications: Grants list.
Application information: Contributes only to
pre-selected organizations.
  Board meeting date(s): Varies
Officer: Missia H. Vaselaney, Pres.
Trustees: Kerry Chelm; Michael R. Donaldson; Mark
R. Stornes.
Number of staff: 1 full-time professional.
EIN: 341471066

7476
The James Lehr Kennedy Foundation
6265 Riverside Dr., Ste. B
Dublin, OH 43017-5401   (614) 734-1976
Contact: James Lehr Kennedy, Pres.

Established in 2006 in Ohio.
Donor: James Lehr Kennedy.
Foundation type: Independent foundation.
Financial data (yr. ended 12/31/13): Assets,
$1,111,915 (M); expenditures, $418,185;
qualifying distributions, $418,185; giving activities
include $414,550 for 19 grants (high: $21,050;
low: $100).
Fields of interest: Higher education; Human
services.
Type of support: Scholarships.
Application information: Application form required.
  Initial approach: Completed application form
  Deadline(s): None
Officers: James Lehr Kennedy, Pres.; Thomas J.
Byrne, Secy.; Gerald L. Robertson, Treas.
EIN: 204513432

7477
William Kilworth Charitable Foundation
c/o KeyBank N.A.
10 W. 2nd St., 26th Fl.
Dayton, OH 45402
Application Address: c/o KeyBank Trust Department,
WA-31-01-0210, , 1101 Pacific Ave 2nd Floor,
Tacoma, WA, 98402

Established in 1968 in Washington.
Foundation type: Independent foundation.
Financial data (yr. ended 12/31/13): Assets,
$4,886,140 (M); expenditures, $228,480;
qualifying distributions, $187,759; giving activities
include $176,000 for 37 grants (high: $15,000;
low: $1,000).
Purpose and activities: Giving for education, the
arts, and human services.
Fields of interest: Arts and culture; Education;
Higher education; Human services; Child welfare.
Type of support: General support; Annual
campaigns; Capital campaigns; Capital and
infrastructure; Equipment; Seed money.
Limitations: Applications accepted. Giving limited to
Tacoma and the Pierce County area WA. No grants
to individuals.

Application information: Scholarship program administered by colleges; standard form available from each school. Application form required.

Initial approach: Letter requesting application guidelines

Copies of proposal: 1

Deadline(s): Nov. 15

Board meeting date(s): Dec.

Final notification: Dec. 31

Trustee: KeyBank N.A.

EIN: 916072527

7478
J. Donald and Julianne Kincaid Educational Trust

14 S. 5th St.

Zanesville, OH 43701-3517 7404557252

Application address: c/o Scott D. Eickelberger of Kincaid, Taylor & Geyer, 50 North 4th St., Zanesville, OH 43701, tel.: (740) 454-2591

Foundation type: Independent foundation.

Financial data (yr. ended 06/30/14): Assets, $9,254,432; expenditures, $459,216; qualifying distributions, $459,216.

Fields of interest: Education.

Type of support: Student aid.

Application information: Application form required.

Initial approach: Proposal

Deadline(s): May 1

Trustee: Jody Spencer.

EIN: 451429722

7479
Patricia Kisker Foundation

P.O. Box 630858

Cincinnati, OH 45263-0858 5135345310

Application address: c/o Fifth Third Bank, Attn.: P. Wharton, 38 Fountain Square Plz., Cincinnati, OH 45263, tel.: (513) 579-5498

Established in 2004 in Ohio.

Donor: Patricia Kisker Court.

Foundation type: Independent foundation.

Financial data (yr. ended 12/31/14): Assets, $7,423,061; expenditures, $411,671; qualifying distributions, $300,530.

Fields of interest: Art museums; Higher education; Diseases and conditions; Cancers; Religion; Human services; Food banks.

Type of support: General support.

Limitations: Applications accepted. Giving primarily in Cincinnati, OH. No grants to individuals.

Application information: Application form required.

Initial approach: Letter

Deadline(s): None

Trustee: Fifth Third Bank.

EIN: 306081757

7480
Klock Kingston Foundation

(formerly Jay E. Klock and Lucia De L. Klock Kingston Foundation)

c/o KeyBank N.A.

4900 Tiedeman Rd., OH-01-49-0150

Brooklyn, OH 44144-2302

Established in 1966 in New York.

Foundation type: Independent foundation.

Financial data (yr. ended 12/31/14): Assets, $5,161,669; expenditures, $294,876; qualifying distributions, $251,444.

Fields of interest: Arts and culture; Elementary and secondary education; Nonprofits; Hospital care; Diseases and conditions; Community and economic development; Catholicism; Human services; Adult day care; Child welfare; Youth services.

Type of support: Regranting.

Limitations: Applications not accepted. Giving primarily in NY. No grants to individuals.

Application information: Unsolicited requests for funds not accepted.

Trustee: KeyBank N.A.

EIN: 146038479

7481
The F. & J. Kloenne Foundation

P.O. Box 630858

Cincinnati, OH 45263-0858

Application address: Fifth Third Bank c/o Paula Wharton, 38 Fountain Square Plz., Cincinnati, OH 45263, tel.: (513) 579-5498

Established in 1999 in Ohio.

Foundation type: Independent foundation.

Financial data (yr. ended 12/31/14): Assets, $3,767,613 (M); expenditures, $218,100; qualifying distributions, $184,403; giving activities include $180,000 for 17 grants (high: $25,000; low: $5,000).

Purpose and activities: Giving primarily for human services and children's health care.

Fields of interest: Arts and culture; University education; Hospital care; Human services.

Limitations: Applications accepted. Giving primarily in OH. No grants to individuals.

Application information: Application form required.

Initial approach: Letter

Deadline(s): None

Trustees: Narley L. Harley; Fifth Third Bank.

EIN: 311629017

7482
The Knight Family Foundation

c/o HPM Partners, LLC

600 Superior Ave., Ste. 1000

Cleveland, OH 44114-2619

Donors: The Rebecca W. Knight 2000 Revocable Trust; Lester B. Knight; James Knight; Amelia Knight; Charles Knight; Jessica Knight.

Foundation type: Independent foundation.

Financial data (yr. ended 12/31/13): Assets, $8,110,614 (M); gifts received, $2,561,024; expenditures, $379,166; qualifying distributions, $330,652; giving activities include $330,652 for 8 grants (high: $89,652; low: $5,000).

Fields of interest: Education; Health; Human services.

Type of support: General support.

Limitations: Applications not accepted. Giving primarily in IL and MN.

Application information: Unsolicited requests for funds not accepted.

Trustees: Lester B. Knight; Rebecca W. Knight.

EIN: 276566394

7483
Miriam G. Knoll Charitable Foundation

300 High St.

Hamilton, OH 45011-6078 5134257576

Application address: c/o First Financial Bank-WRG, 815 S. Breiel Blvd., Middletown, OH 45042, tel.: (513) 425-7532

Established in 1985 in Ohio.

Foundation type: Independent foundation.

Financial data (yr. ended 10/31/14): Assets, $6,783,358; expenditures, $393,719; qualifying distributions, $365,712.

Purpose and activities: Giving primarily to Ohio community foundations; support also for the arts and human services, including services for people with disabilities.

Fields of interest: Arts and culture; Performing arts; Higher education; Foundations; Community and economic development; Housing development; Protestantism; Human services; Youth development.

Type of support: General support; Capital and infrastructure; Scholarships.

Limitations: Applications accepted. Giving limited to OH, primarily in Middletown. No grants to individuals.

Application information:

Initial approach: Proposal

Deadline(s): None

Officer: John Peterson, Exec. Dir.

Advisors: Roland P. Ely, Jr.; Joseph Lyons; John D. Sawyer; William H. Shaefer.

Trustee: First Financial Bank.

EIN: 316282842

7484
Milton A. & Charlotte R. Kramer Charitable Foundation

c/o North Point Tower

1001 Lakeside Ave., Ste. 900

Cleveland, OH 44114-1177

Established in 1984 in Ohio.

Donor: Charlotte R. Kramer.

Foundation type: Independent foundation.

Financial data (yr. ended 12/31/14): Assets, $5,340,648 (M); expenditures, $302,372; qualifying distributions, $297,597; giving activities include $295,381 for 94 grants (high: $162,500; low: $127).

Purpose and activities: Giving for the arts, education, human services and Jewish agencies.

Fields of interest: Education; Health; Judaism.

Type of support: General support; Matching grants; Annual campaigns; Endowments; Program development; Scholarships; Program evaluations.

Limitations: Applications not accepted. Giving primarily in the Cleveland, OH, area; funding also in NY. No grants to individuals.

Application information: Contributes only to pre-selected organizations.

Board meeting date(s): Varies

Directors: Michael J. Horvitz; Elizabeth Kramer; Mark R. Kramer; Toby Kramer.

EIN: 341467089

7485
Louise Kramer Foundation
3055 Kettering Blvd., Ste. 418
Dayton, OH 45439 (937) 293-9193
Contact: William Lincoln, Tr.

Established in 1965 in Ohio.
Donor: Louise Kramer†.
Foundation type: Independent foundation.
Financial data (yr. ended 12/31/13): Assets,
$7,194,475 (M); expenditures, $373,533;
qualifying distributions, $313,126; giving activities
include $312,000 for 31 grants (high: $50,000;
low: $1,000).
Purpose and activities: Giving primarily for higher
education, health associations, youth development,
human services, and Christian schools and
churches.
Fields of interest: Higher education; Diseases and
conditions; Christianity; Human services; Youth
development; Youth services; Homeless shelters.
Type of support: General support; Continuing
support; Capital campaigns; Capital and
infrastructure.
Limitations: Applications accepted. Giving primarily
in Dayton, OH. No grants to individuals.
Application information:
Initial approach: Proposal
Deadline(s): None
Board meeting date(s): Varies
Trustees: Hugh E. Wall III; Peter H. Kuntz; William T.
Lincoln.
EIN: 316055729

7486
Robert A. Kutz Foundation
(formerly Robert Kutz Charitable Trust)
63 Corson Ave.
Akron, OH 44302-1201

Established in 1987 in Ohio.
Donor: Robert A. Kutz†.
Foundation type: Independent foundation.
Financial data (yr. ended 12/31/12): Assets, $0
(M); expenditures, $265,842; qualifying
distributions, $262,550; giving activities include
$262,550 for 16 grants (high: $58,000; low:
$1,250).
Purpose and activities: Funding primarily for local
youth-oriented programs.
Fields of interest: Education; Economics; Religion;
Human services.
Type of support: Equipment; Program development;
Scholarships.
Limitations: Applications not accepted. Giving
limited to Summit County, OH.
Application information: Unsolicited requests for
funds not accepted.
Board meeting date(s): Varies
Director: W. Paul Jeffery.
EIN: 346977068

7487
Jean Thomas Lambert Foundation
c/o Patrick J. Weschler
3800 Embassy Pkwy., Ste. 300
Akron, OH 44333-8332 (330) 376-5300

Established in 1999 in Ohio.
Donors: Jean Thomas Lambert Trust; Jean Thomas
Lambert Charitable Lead Annuity Trust.

Foundation type: Independent foundation.
Financial data (yr. ended 12/31/14): Assets,
$1,839,814; expenditures, $322,145; qualifying
distributions, $293,236.
Purpose and activities: Giving primarily for historical
preservation; support also for education and
conservation.
Fields of interest: Museums; Historic preservation;
Education; Natural resources.
Limitations: Applications accepted. Giving primarily
in OH; giving also in CT.
Application information:
Deadline(s): Mar. 15
Officers: Nancy Reymann, Pres. and C.E.O.; Patrick
J. Weschler, Secy.
Trustees: Thomas Lambert; Adam Reymann.
EIN: 341897221

7488
Richard I. and Arline J. Landers Foundation
590 Lexington Ave.
Mansfield, OH 44907-1505 (419) 756-3211

Established in 1989 in Ohio.
Donors: Arline J. Landers; Richard I. Landers†.
Foundation type: Independent foundation.
Financial data (yr. ended 12/31/13): Assets,
$3,902,014 (M); expenditures, $199,137;
qualifying distributions, $164,175; giving activities
include $164,175 for 19 grants (high: $30,000;
low: $500).
Purpose and activities: Giving primarily for the
preservation and promotion of the history of the
state of Ohio; support also for general charitable
giving.
Fields of interest: Historic preservation; Higher
education; Employment; Judaism; Human services.
Type of support: Seed money.
Limitations: Applications accepted. Giving primarily
in OH. No grants to individuals.
Application information: Application form required.
Initial approach: Letter
Deadline(s): None
Board meeting date(s): Monthly
Trustees: Richard M. Kleshinski; Larry A. Morrison;
Jason Murray.
Number of staff: None.
EIN: 341623986

7489
Rachel Boyce Lang Charitable Trust
16924 St. Clair Ave.
East Liverpool, OH 43920-4255

Established in 1998 in Ohio.
Donor: Rachel Boyce Lang†.
Foundation type: Independent foundation.
Financial data (yr. ended 12/31/13): Assets,
$6,875,361 (M); expenditures, $400,547;
qualifying distributions, $338,037; giving activities
include $337,487 for 6 grants (high: $93,065; low:
$14,422).
Purpose and activities: Giving primarily for higher
education and human services, including a
retirement community.
Fields of interest: Higher education; Health care
clinics; Christianity; Human services; Seniors;
Retired people.
Limitations: Applications not accepted. Giving
primarily in OH. No grants to individuals.

Application information: Contributes only to
pre-selected organizations.
Trustees: Charles B. Lang; James R. Lang; Mary Sue
Lang.
EIN: 311603385

7490
The Laub Foundation
19655 Parklane Dr.
Rocky River, OH 44116-4220

Established in 1958 in Ohio.
Donors: Herbert J. Laub†; Elsie K. Laub†.
Foundation type: Independent foundation.
Financial data (yr. ended 10/31/13): Assets,
$4,773,940 (M); expenditures, $314,551;
qualifying distributions, $243,818; giving activities
include $239,000 for 62 grants (high: $7,500; low:
$2,500).
Purpose and activities: Grants primarily for
scholarship programs of colleges and private
schools, cultural programs, and youth agencies.
Fields of interest: Arts and culture; Secondary
education; Higher education; Human services;
Youth development.
Type of support: General support; Matching grants;
Continuing support; Publications; Scholarships.
Limitations: Applications accepted. Giving primarily
in Cuyahoga County, OH, and adjacent counties. No
grants to individuals or for deficit financing or
endowment funds; no loans.
Publications: Annual report.
Application information: Distribution of grants
made at Aug. meeting.
Initial approach: Required application form
Copies of proposal: 2
Deadline(s): None
Board meeting date(s): Feb., May, Aug., and Nov.
Final notification: After Aug. meeting
Officer: Lisa Roberts-Mamone, Secy.
Trustees: Charles D. Berry; Laurence A. Bartell;
Tristy Berry; Jordan Westropp; Katherine C. Wolk;
Thomas C. Westropp.
Number of staff: 1 part-time professional.
EIN: 346526087

7491
Lawry Foundation
P.O. Box 94651
Cleveland, OH 44101-4651

Donor: Marion Schultz Lawry.
Foundation type: Independent foundation.
Financial data (yr. ended 12/31/13): Assets,
$10,082,130 (M); expenditures, $490,585;
qualifying distributions, $414,563; giving activities
include $374,508 for 6 grants (high: $62,418; low:
$62,418).
Fields of interest: Health; Diseases and conditions;
Human services.
Limitations: Applications not accepted. Giving
primarily in OH.
Application information: Unsolicited requests for
funds not accepted.
Trustee: PNC Bank, N.A.
EIN: 276707238

7492
Frank W. Lawson Charitable Trust
P.O. Box 630858
Cincinnati, OH   45263-0858

Established in 2007 in Ohio.
Donor: Katherine Lawson†.
Foundation type: Independent foundation.
Financial data (yr. ended 12/31/14): Assets, $4,140,923; expenditures, $232,537; qualifying distributions, $170,327.
Fields of interest: Christianity.
Limitations: Applications not accepted. No grants to individuals.
Application information: Unsolicited requests for funds not accepted.
Trustee: Fifth Third Bank.
EIN: 261094646

7493
The Gladys and Ralph Lazarus Foundation
(formerly Ralph Lazarus Foundation)
c/o Frost Brown Todd
3300 Great American Tower
301 E. 4th St.
Cincinnati, OH   45202

Established in 1994 in Ohio.
Donor: Gladys Lazarus.
Foundation type: Independent foundation.
Financial data (yr. ended 06/30/13): Assets, $1,876,094 (M); expenditures, $193,037; qualifying distributions, $190,386; giving activities include $185,000 for 22 grants (high: $35,000; low: $500).
Fields of interest: Art museums; Education; Higher education; Nonprofits; Health; Public libraries; Radio; Community and economic development; Child welfare.
Type of support: Regranting.
Limitations: Applications not accepted. Giving primarily in CA, NH, NY, OH, and TX. No grants to individuals.
Application information: Contributes only to pre-selected organizations.
Trustees: Kathryn Lazarus Baron; James Lazarus; John R. Lazarus.
EIN: 316018922

7494
Elizabeth Ann Leach Charitable Trust
c/o Keybank N.A.
4900 Tiedeman Rd., OH-01-49-0150
Brooklyn, OH   44144-2302
Application address: Seymour Epstein, P.O. Box 404, Wiscasset, ME 04578; Wiliam Logan, P.O. Box 250, Wiscasset, ME 04578

Donor: Elizabeth Leach†.
Foundation type: Independent foundation.
Financial data (yr. ended 12/31/13): Assets, $5,407,012 (M); gifts received, $50,294; expenditures, $318,312; qualifying distributions, $281,104; giving activities include $233,672 for 22 grants (high: $40,000; low: $1,681).
Fields of interest: Health; Sports and recreation; Youth development.
Limitations: Applications accepted. Giving primarily in ME.
Application information: Application form required.

Initial approach: Letter
Deadline(s): None
Trustees: Seymour Epstein; William W. Logan; KeyBank N.A.
EIN: 616386848

7495
William C. & Mildred K. Lehman Charitable Trust
3040 West Point Rd. S.E.
Lancaster, OH   43130-8640   (740) 569-3040
Contact: William J. Sitterley, Tr.
E-mail: info@sitterleyscholarshiptrusts.com; Main URL: http://www.fairfieldcountyscholarships.com

Established in 1998 in Ohio.
Donors: William C. Lehman†; Mildred K. Lehman.
Foundation type: Independent foundation.
Financial data (yr. ended 05/31/14): Assets, $3,890,651 (M); expenditures, $170,473; qualifying distributions, $158,361; giving activities include $137,600 for 24 grants to individuals (high: $8,600; low: $3,000), and $158,361 for foundation-administered programs.
Purpose and activities: Giving to promote the education and welfare of the residents of Hocking County to better enable them to contribute in a useful and worthwhile manner to their community.
Type of support: Student aid.
Limitations: Applications accepted. Giving to residents of Fairfield and Hocking counties, OH.
Application information: See Trust web site for complete application guidelines. Application form required.
Initial approach: Completed application form
Deadline(s): Mar. 15
Trustee: William J. Sitterley.
EIN: 311613162

7496
The G.R. Lincoln Family Foundation
30195 Chagrin Blvd., Ste. 250
Cleveland, OH   44124-5719

Donors: Constance P. Lincoln; G. Russell Lincoln; Laura Heath Irrevocable Trust.
Foundation type: Independent foundation.
Financial data (yr. ended 12/31/13): Assets, $7,093,977 (M); expenditures, $331,759; qualifying distributions, $291,275; giving activities include $291,075 for 23 grants (high: $53,375; low: $1,000).
Fields of interest: Arts and culture; Education; Higher education; Natural resources; Hospital care.
Limitations: Applications not accepted. Giving primarily in OH.
Application information: Unsolicited requests for funds not accepted.
Advisory Committee: G. Russell Lincoln, Pres.; Christopher Horsburgh; Brinton C. Lincoln; Constance P. Lincoln; James D. Lincoln.
EIN: 383471702

7497
The Carl H. and Edyth B. Lindner Foundation
(formerly Carl H. Lindner Foundation)
P.O. Box 358
Cincinnati, OH   45201

Established in 1993 in Ohio.
Donors: Carl H. Lindner, Jr.; Edyth B. Lindner; William Martin; Mrs. William Martin; Carl & Edyth Lindner 2008 Charitable Lead Trust.
Foundation type: Independent foundation.
Financial data (yr. ended 12/31/13): Assets, $23,611,030 (M); gifts received, $2,899,643; expenditures, $393,057; qualifying distributions, $382,970; giving activities include $379,783 for 11 grants (high: $250,000; low: $500).
Fields of interest: Community and economic development; Christianity; Protestantism; Human services.
Limitations: Applications not accepted. Giving primarily in Cincinnati, OH. No grants to individuals.
Application information: Contributes only to pre-selected organizations.
Officers and Trustees: Edyth B. Lindner, Pres. and Trustee; Lou Ann Flint, Secy.-Treas.; Carl H. Lindner III; Keith E. Lindner; S. Craig Lindner.
EIN: 310738034

7498
The Linnemann Family Foundation
5885 Graves Lake Dr.
Cincinnati, OH   45243   (513) 785-6060
Contact: Calvin C. Linnemann, Pres.

Established in 1995 in Ohio.
Donors: Patricia G. Linnemann; Calvin C. Linnemann.
Foundation type: Independent foundation.
Financial data (yr. ended 12/31/13): Assets, $4,592,155 (M); expenditures, $322,993; qualifying distributions, $304,700; giving activities include $304,500 for 23 grants (high: $60,000; low: $2,000).
Purpose and activities: Gives preference to organizations with activities in the greater Cincinnati, OH, area. Grants are generally restricted to the fields of religion, education, medical and community projects. However, to the extent funds are available, grants may be made for other projects.
Fields of interest: Arts and culture; Education; Natural resources; Biodiversity; Wildlife biodiversity; Zoos; Botanical gardens; Health; Population studies; Community and economic development; Religion; Christianity; Child welfare.
Limitations: Applications accepted. Giving in the U.S., with an emphasis on the greater Cincinnati, OH, area. No grants to individuals.
Application information: Application form required.
Initial approach: Letter
Deadline(s): None
Officers: Calvin C. Linnemann, Pres.; Patricia G. Linnemann, Secy.-Treas.
Trustees: Catherine A. Linnemann; Mark D. Linnemann.
EIN: 311394291

7499
Katherine K. Lippitt Foundation
c/o PNC Bank, N.A.
P.O. Box 94651
Cleveland, OH   44101-4651

Foundation type: Independent foundation.
Financial data (yr. ended 12/31/13): Assets, $3,202,651 (M); expenditures, $172,172; qualifying distributions, $167,059; giving activities

include $162,000 for 31 grants (high: $50,000; low: $500).
Fields of interest: Arts and culture; Education; Human services.
Limitations: Applications not accepted.
Application information: Unsolicited requests for funds not accepted.
Trustees: John B. Black; Peter M. Black; Kenneth G. Hochman; PNC Bank, N.A.
EIN: 616433804

7500
Arline & Clay Littick Charitable Trust
P.O. Box 94651
Cleveland, OH 44101-4651

Established in 1971 in Ohio.
Foundation type: Independent foundation.
Financial data (yr. ended 12/31/12): Assets, $3,039,502 (M); expenditures, $162,683; qualifying distributions, $142,744; giving activities include $142,744 for grants.
Purpose and activities: The trust supports the charitable and educational organizations of the community of Zanesville and Muskingum counties.
Fields of interest: Education; Human services.
Limitations: Applications not accepted. Giving primarily in Cleveland and Zanesville, OH.
Application information: Unsolicited requests for funds not accepted.
Trustee: PNC Bank, N.A.
EIN: 316103993

7501
LKC Foundation
3536 Edwards Rd., Ste. 201
Cincinnati, OH 45208-1368

Established in 1996 in Delaware.
Foundation type: Independent foundation.
Financial data (yr. ended 12/31/12): Assets, $8,587,999 (M); expenditures, $507,348; qualifying distributions, $419,255; giving activities include $419,255 for grants.
Fields of interest: Arts and culture; Performing arts; Theater; Education; Higher education; Nonprofits; Diseases and conditions; Judaism; Human services; Child welfare.
Type of support: General support; Regranting; Annual campaigns; Capital campaigns; Capital and infrastructure.
Limitations: Applications not accepted. Giving primarily in OH, with emphasis on Cincinnati; some funding nationally. No grants to individuals.
Application information: Unsolicited requests for funds not accepted.
Officers and Directors: Lucille K. Carothers, Pres. and Treas. and Director; Gabriel Stern, V.P. and Secy. and Director; Ellen Stern Kerr, V.P.
EIN: 311490185

7502
Bill and Jackie Lockwood Family Foundation
239 Spirea Dr.
Dayton, OH 45419-3540

Established in 2002 in Ohio.
Donor: Jackie Lockwood.
Foundation type: Independent foundation.

Financial data (yr. ended 12/31/13): Assets, $4,499,382 (M); expenditures, $224,680; qualifying distributions, $214,715; giving activities include $214,715 for 61+ grants (high: $24,000).
Fields of interest: Arts and culture; Health; Hospital care; Human services.
Limitations: Applications not accepted. Giving primarily in MA and OH. No grants to individuals.
Application information: Contributes only to pre-selected organizations.
Trustees: Jacquelyn E. Lockwood; William D. Lockwood.
EIN: 036100828

7503
Stella & Frederick Loeb Charitable Trust
106 S. Main St., 16 Fl.
Akron, OH 44308

Established in 1990 in Michigan.
Donor: Frederick Loeb†.
Foundation type: Independent foundation.
Financial data (yr. ended 08/31/14): Assets, $5,777,677 (M); gifts received, $1,831; expenditures, $372,262; qualifying distributions, $361,511; giving activities include $299,100 for 75 grants (high: $10,000; low: $250).
Fields of interest: Arts and culture; Performing arts; Education; Nonprofits; Human services; Child welfare; Youth development.
Type of support: Regranting.
Limitations: Applications accepted. Giving primarily in Flint, MI.
Publications: Application guidelines.
Application information: Application form required.
Initial approach: Letter
Deadline(s): None
Trustee: FirstMerit Bank, N.A.
EIN: 386571896

7504
Loeb Foundation
c/o LCNB National Bank
P.O. Box 59
Lebanon, OH 45036-0059 (513) 932-1414
Contact: B.H. Wright Jr., Tr.
FAX: (513) 932-1492; E-mail: bwright@lcnb.com

Established in 1992 in Ohio.
Donor: Justus H. Loeb†.
Foundation type: Independent foundation.
Financial data (yr. ended 09/30/14): Assets, $7,119,165 (M); expenditures, $444,495; qualifying distributions, $368,415; giving activities include $321,344 for 3 grants (high: $192,000; low: $53,000).
Purpose and activities: Giving primarily for fire and police protection.
Fields of interest: Police agencies; Fire prevention and control; Seniors.
Type of support: Equipment; Loans to individuals; Grants to individuals.
Limitations: Applications accepted. Giving limited to Warren County, OH.
Publications: Annual report.
Application information:
Initial approach: Letter
Copies of proposal: 3
Deadline(s): Aug. 30; None for Stay in Home program

Board meeting date(s): Early Sept.
Final notification: Late Sept.
Trustees: Michael E. Foley; LCNB National Bank.
Number of staff: None.
EIN: 316225986

7505
Lowe-Marshall Trust
c/o C. Marshall Lowe
5301 C. Huffman Ln.
Chesterhill, OH 43728-9021
E-mail: mblowe@morganco.net

Donors: James T. Lowe†; Constance M. Lowe†.
Foundation type: Independent foundation.
Financial data (yr. ended 12/31/13): Assets, $6,819,072 (M); expenditures, $350,200; qualifying distributions, $350,060; giving activities include $350,000 for 3 grants (high: $200,000; low: $50,000).
Purpose and activities: Primary areas of interest include peacemaking and conflict resolution projects, and sustainable development in Appalachia and other economically depressed rural areas. Funding also for environmental quality, protection and beautification, and community improvement and capacity building.
Fields of interest: Environment; Natural resources; Community and economic development; Sustainable development; International development.
International interests: Central America.
Type of support: General support; Program-related investments; Continuing support; Annual campaigns; Program development; Seed money.
Limitations: Applications not accepted. Giving primarily in OH. No grants to individuals.
Publications: Program policy statement.
Application information: Contributes only to pre-selected organizations.
Officer and Trustees: C. Marshall Lowe, Chair. and Trustee; Betty M. Lowe; Peter A. Lowe.
EIN: 316084154

7506
Otto Luedeking Trust
P.O. Box 630858
Cincinnati, OH 45263-0858

Foundation type: Independent foundation.
Financial data (yr. ended 12/31/14): Assets, $12,828,489; expenditures, $319,024; qualifying distributions, $243,315.
Fields of interest: Hospice care; Human services; Child welfare.
Limitations: Applications not accepted. Giving primarily in Cincinnati, OH.
Application information: Unsolicited requests for funds not accepted.
Trustee: Fifth Third Bank.
EIN: 316019731

7507
The Joe & Kim Lukens Family Foundation
6565 Ludlum Rd.
Morrow, OH 45152

Established in 1999 in Ohio.
Donors: Neace Lukens Holding Co.; Joseph T. Lukens.

Foundation type: Company-sponsored foundation.
Financial data (yr. ended 12/31/13): Assets, $1,776,801 (M); gifts received, $372,213; expenditures, $228,168; qualifying distributions, $228,018; giving activities include $220,000 for 2 grants (high: $200,000; low: $20,000).
Purpose and activities: The foundation supports organizations involved with education, health, grief counseling, sports, children services, and religion.
Fields of interest: Health; Religion; Human services.
Type of support: General support.
Limitations: Applications not accepted. Giving primarily in IN, KY, and OH. No grants to individuals.
Application information: Contributes only to pre-selected organizations.
Officers and Directors: Joseph T. Lukens, Pres. and Treas. and Director; H. Kimberly Lukesn, Secy. and Director; Ashley Lukens; Chelsey Lukens; Heidi Lukens.
EIN: 311642444

7508
Neils A. & Ruth Lundgard Foundation
P.O. Box 630858
Cincinnati, OH   45263-0858
*Application address:*c/o Joyce Kittel ,Fifth Third Bank, 123 Market St., Piqua, OH 45356, tel.: (937) 778-4408

Established in 1990 in Ohio.
Foundation type: Independent foundation.
Financial data (yr. ended 12/31/13): Assets, $5,070,489 (M); expenditures, $259,241; qualifying distributions, $225,848; giving activities include $225,318 for 20 grants (high: $45,000; low: $2,000).
Fields of interest: Education; Hospital care; Diseases and conditions; Public affairs; Christianity; Human services; Child welfare.
Type of support: General support; Capital campaigns; Capital and infrastructure; Seed money; Scholarships.
Limitations: Applications accepted. Giving primarily in Miami County, OH.
Application information: Application form required.
  Initial approach: Letter
  Copies of proposal: 1
  Deadline(s): None
Trustee: Fifth Third Bank.
EIN: 316375418

7509
The Niels A. and Ruth Lungard Charitable Trust
P.O. Box 630858
Cincinnati, OH   45263-0858   (937) 778-4408
Contact: Joyce Kittel
Application address: c/o, Fifth Third Bank, 123 Market St., 342511, Piqua, OH 45356, tel.: (937) 778-4408

Established in 2002 in Ohio.
Donor: Ruth Lundgard Trust.
Foundation type: Independent foundation.
Financial data (yr. ended 12/31/14): Assets, $3,352,487 (M); expenditures, $178,476; qualifying distributions, $156,400; giving activities include $155,870 for 22 grants (high: $25,000; low: $2,000).
Fields of interest: Education; Health; Human services.

Limitations: Applications accepted. Giving primarily in Piqua, OH.
Application information: Application form required.
  Initial approach: Letter
  Deadline(s): None
Trustee: Fifth Third Bank.
EIN: 316678858

7510
The M.L.M Charitable Foundation
3131 Executive Pkwy., No. 102
Toledo, OH   43606-1327

Established in 1967 in Ohio.
Donors: Mary L. McKenny; Charles A. McKenny†; Charles A. McKenny Charitable Lead Trust; Mary L. McKenny Charitable Lead Trust.
Foundation type: Independent foundation.
Financial data (yr. ended 12/31/13): Assets, $6,954,784 (M); expenditures, $366,259; qualifying distributions, $327,270; giving activities include $325,350 for 62 grants (high: $40,000; low: $100).
Fields of interest: Arts and culture; Education; Higher education; Nonprofits; Christianity; Human services; Independent living for people with disabilities.
Type of support: General support; Program development; Scholarships; Regranting.
Limitations: Applications not accepted. Giving primarily in IN, MI and OH. No grants to individuals.
Application information: Contributes only to pre-selected organizations.
Officers: Mary L. McKenny, Pres. and Treas.; Anne E. McKenny, V.P. and Secy.
Trustee: Arthur E. McKenny.
EIN: 341018519

7511
Frank Mangano Foundation
119 E. State St.
Alliance, OH   44601-4933

Established in 1988 in Ohio.
Donor: Frank J. Mangano†.
Foundation type: Independent foundation.
Financial data (yr. ended 12/31/13): Assets, $10,041,105 (M); expenditures, $365,327; qualifying distributions, $351,009; giving activities include $333,406 for 66 grants (high: $139,000; low: $100).
Purpose and activities: Giving primarily for education and human services.
Fields of interest: Education; Protestantism; Human services.
Type of support: General support; Capital campaigns.
Limitations: Applications not accepted. Giving primarily in OH and VA. No grants to individuals.
Application information: Contributes only to pre-selected organizations.
Trustee: Margaret E. Mangano.
EIN: 341600651

7512
F. T. & Anna C. Manley Memorial Fund
c/o Key Bank N.A.
4900 Tiedeman Rd., OH-01-49-0
Brooklyn, OH   44144-2302

Established in 1987 in New York.
Foundation type: Independent foundation.
Financial data (yr. ended 12/31/14): Assets, $3,369,891 (M); expenditures, $182,876; qualifying distributions, $145,941; giving activities include $136,291 for 19 grants (high: $10,000; low: $2,400).
Fields of interest: Education; Health; Agriculture.
Limitations: Applications not accepted. Giving primarily in NY. No grants to individuals.
Application information: Unsolicited requests for funds not accepted.
Trustee: KeyBank N.A.
EIN: 136905221

7513
Marafiki Global Aids Ministry
(formerly Rafiki Aids Ministry)
P.O. Box 4074
Dublin, OH   43016-0563
E-mail: marafikiglobalaidsministry@yahoo.com
Facebook: https://www.facebook.com/
Marafiki.Global

Established in 1996 in Ohio.
Donors: Robert Karaffa; Tracee Karaffa; St. Paul's Episcopal Church Outreach Grant Council; Betty Jane Ford; Barbara Davis; Rotary Club of Columbus; Upper Arlington Senior Fund; Pat Shuter; Barbara Galantowicz; Fee Mission Council; Mark Galantowicz; Jack Shuter; Newark Rotary Club; Rotary Club of Upper Arlington; Terry Davis.
Foundation type: Operating foundation.
Financial data (yr. ended 12/31/13): Assets, $11,032 (M); gifts received, $200,800; expenditures, $193,079; qualifying distributions, $193,079; giving activities include $160,186 for grants.
Purpose and activities: Giving to provide food, shelter, medical care, education, a safe Christian living environment, and loving support to children worldwide who have been orphaned by HIV/AIDS.
International interests: Bahamas; Kenya.
Limitations: Applications not accepted. Giving primarily in Kikuyu, Kenya and Nassau, Bahamas.
Application information: Contributes only to pre-selected organizations.
Officers: John Nganga, Chair. and C.E.O.; Susan Munga, Vice-Chair.; Patti Chapman, Secy.; Molapo Kgabo, Treas.
EIN: 311586466

7514
Jacob R. Marcus Trust
P.O. Box 1118, ML CN-OH-W10X
Cincinnati, OH   45201-1118

Foundation type: Independent foundation.
Financial data (yr. ended 12/31/13): Assets, $4,903,672 (M); expenditures, $309,966; qualifying distributions, $253,463; giving activities include $243,193 for 1 grant.
Fields of interest: Education.
Limitations: Applications not accepted. Giving primarily in Cincinnati, OH.
Application information: Unsolicited requests for funds not accepted.
Trustee: U.S. Bank, N.A.
EIN: 316540485

7515
Marnick Foundation
4550 Red Bank Expwy.
Cincinnati, OH 45227 (513) 651-8437

Established in 1996 in Ohio.
Donor: Martha H. Ragland.
Foundation type: Independent foundation.
Financial data (yr. ended 12/31/14): Assets, $4,754,190; expenditures, $277,410; qualifying distributions, $266,400.
Fields of interest: Art museums; Education; Catholicism; Human services.
Type of support: General support.
Limitations: Applications accepted. Giving primarily in Cincinnati, OH.
Application information: Application form required.
  Initial approach: Letter
  Deadline(s): None
Trustees: Eric W. Ragland; H. Nicholas Ragland III; H. Nicholas Ragland IV; John J. Ragland; Joseph A. Ragland; Martha H. Ragland; Peter D. Ragland.
EIN: 311493613

7516
The S. Livingston Mather Charitable Trust
1422 Euclid Ave., Ste. 1130
Cleveland, OH 44115-2065

Established in 1953 in Ohio.
Donor: S. Livingston Mather†.
Foundation type: Independent foundation.
Financial data (yr. ended 12/31/13): Assets, $7,001,817 (M); expenditures, $386,374; qualifying distributions, $345,729; giving activities include $312,633 for 36 grants (high: $75,000; low: $300).
Purpose and activities: Primary areas of interest include cultural programs, education, child welfare, and social services. Support also for youth programs and the environment and natural resources.
Fields of interest: Arts and culture; Education; Environment; Natural resources; Family planning; Family services; Child welfare.
Type of support: General support; Continuing support; Annual campaigns; Capital campaigns; Capital and infrastructure; Endowments; Emergency funds; Program development; Seed money; Scholarships.
Limitations: Applications not accepted. Giving primarily in northeastern OH. No support for science and medical research programs, or in areas appropriately supported by the government and/or the United Way. No grants to individuals, or for deficit financing or mass mailing solicitations; no loans.
Application information: Unsolicited requests for funds not accepted.
  Board meeting date(s): Quarterly, and as required
Trustee: The Glenmede Trust Co., N.A.
Number of staff: 1 part-time support.
EIN: 346505619

7517
George C. Matthes Trust
c/o KeyBank
4900 Tiedeman, OH-01-49-0150
Brooklyn, OH 44144-2302

Foundation type: Independent foundation.

Financial data (yr. ended 12/31/14): Assets, $9,427,238; expenditures, $507,557; qualifying distributions, $434,048.
Fields of interest: Hospital care; Diseases and conditions; Human services.
Type of support: General support.
Limitations: Applications not accepted. Giving primarily in OH.
Application information: Unsolicited requests for funds not accepted.
Trustee: KeyBank, N.A.
EIN: 346724395

7518
J. Bryan and Norma R. McCann Charitable and Educational Trust
14 S. 5th St.
Zanesville, OH 43701-3517 (740) 454-2591
Contact: Jody D. Spencer, Tr.

Foundation type: Independent foundation.
Financial data (yr. ended 06/30/14): Assets, $3,790,301 (M); expenditures, $179,170; qualifying distributions, $179,171; giving activities include $3,051 for 1 grant, and $112,072 for 213 grants to individuals (high: $1,000; low: $250).
Purpose and activities: Giving primarily to a Presbyterian church, with the remainder to be used for grants or loans for worthy graduates of high schools in Washington County, Ohio, with preference to eligible students from Fort Frye High School.
Fields of interest: Religion.
Type of support: Student aid.
Limitations: Applications accepted. Giving primarily in Beverly and Washington County, OH.
Application information: Application form required.
  Initial approach: Proposal
  Deadline(s): Apr. 25
Trustee: Century National Bank.
Committee Members: Rita Frum; Amanda Herb; Susan Rauch; Jason Turley.
EIN: 367425931

7519
Mary Sedate McCann Trust
P.O. Box 10032
Toledo, OH 43699-0032

Foundation type: Independent foundation.
Financial data (yr. ended 12/31/14): Assets, $3,682,086; expenditures, $232,689; qualifying distributions, $171,676.
Fields of interest: Health; Human services; Seniors.
Limitations: Applications not accepted. Giving primarily in OH.
Application information: Unsolicited requests for funds not accepted.
Trustees: Mark H. Boss; David W. Carter.
EIN: 346525695

7520
Mccarthy Family Foundation
c/o Fairport Asset
3636 Euclid Ave., Ste. 400
Cleveland, OH 44115 (216) 431-2748

Donors: Green Bay Packers; Deb Holly; Millercoors; Ariens Co.; Mike Holly.
Foundation type: Independent foundation.

Financial data (yr. ended 12/31/13): Assets, $789,940 (M); gifts received, $500,000; expenditures, $250,589; qualifying distributions, $240,600; giving activities include $240,600 for 7 grants (high: $100,000; low: $1,000).
Fields of interest: Education; Higher education; Religion; Human services.
Limitations: Applications accepted. Giving primarily in KS, PA and WI.
Application information: Application form required.
  Initial approach: Telephone Call
  Deadline(s): None
Trustees: Jessica A. McCarthy; Michael J. McCarthy.
EIN: 452784199

7521
Harold & Helen McMaster Foundation, Inc.
6711 Monroe St., Bldg. 4, Ste. A
Sylvania, OH 43560-1968 (419) 885-2626
Contact: Scott Savage

Established in 1988 in Ohio.
Donors: Harold A. McMaster; Helen E. McMaster.
Foundation type: Independent foundation.
Financial data (yr. ended 11/30/14): Assets, $9,643,207 (M); expenditures, $437,412; qualifying distributions, $300,600; giving activities include $300,600 for 12 grants (high: $100,000; low: $2,000).
Purpose and activities: Giving primarily for the arts and education.
Fields of interest: Arts and culture; Education; Human services.
Type of support: General support; Continuing support; Annual campaigns; Capital campaigns; Capital and infrastructure; Endowments; Debt reduction; Program development; Curriculum development; Research; Technical assistance.
Limitations: Applications accepted. Giving primarily in OH, with emphasis on Defiance and Toledo.
Application information: Application form required.
  Initial approach: Letter
  Copies of proposal: 1
  Deadline(s): None
Officers and Trustees: Helen E. McMaster, Pres. and Trustee; Frank D. Jacobs, Secy. and Trustee; Nancy L. Cobie, Treas. and Trustee; Jeanine E. Dunn; Alan J. McMaster; Ronald A. McMaster.
Number of staff: 1 full-time professional; 1 part-time professional.
EIN: 341576110

7522
The Mead Foundation
c/o KeyBank, N.A.
P.O. Box 10099
Dayton, OH 45402 (419) 259-6195
Contact: Eileen Sullivan

Established in 1998 in Ohio.
Donor: Elsie Hawkins†.
Foundation type: Independent foundation.
Financial data (yr. ended 03/31/13): Assets, $3,960,380 (M); expenditures, $240,597; qualifying distributions, $208,325; giving activities include $198,000 for 54 grants (high: $11,000; low: $500).
Fields of interest: Education; Health; Diseases and conditions; Human services.

Limitations: Applications accepted. Giving primarily in OH. No grants to individuals.
Application information:
Initial approach: Letter
Deadline(s): None
Board meeting date(s): Mar.
Trustee: KeyBank, N.A.
EIN: 341865129

7523
George and Deborah Mehl Family Foundation Inc.
c/o W. Stuart Dornette
425 Walnut St., Ste. 1800
Cincinnati, OH 45202-3948

Established in 1999 in Ohio.
Donor: George and Deborah Mehl Family Trust.
Foundation type: Independent foundation.
Financial data (yr. ended 12/31/13): Assets, $8,561,975 (M); expenditures, $439,250; qualifying distributions, $406,339; giving activities include $397,764 for 18 grants (high: $74,764; low: $1,000).
Purpose and activities: Giving primarily to Christian organizations.
Fields of interest: Education; Prenatal care; Christianity; Family services; Child welfare.
Limitations: Applications not accepted. Giving primarily in AZ, CO, and OH. No grants to individuals.
Application information: Contributes only to pre-selected organizations.
Officers and Trustees: W. Stuart Dornette, Pres. and Trustee; Bonnie Mehl, V.P. and Trustee; Martha Dornette, Secy. and Trustee; David Mehl, Treas. and Trustee.
EIN: 311679603

7524
Messer Construction Foundation
5158 Fishwick Dr.
Cincinnati, OH 45216-2216 (513) 482-5329
Contact: E. Paul Hitter Jr.
Main URL: http://www.messer.com

Established in 2003 in Ohio.
Donor: Messer Construction Co.
Foundation type: Company-sponsored foundation.
Financial data (yr. ended 09/30/13): Assets, $215,577 (M); gifts received, $250,000; expenditures, $196,773; qualifying distributions, $195,134; giving activities include $193,500 for 10 grants (high: $25,000; low: $3,750).
Purpose and activities: The foundation supports programs designed to promote economic inclusion, education, and workforce development.
Fields of interest: Education; Health; Human services.
Type of support: General support.
Limitations: Applications accepted. Giving primarily in areas of company operations in Indianapolis, IN, Knoxville, Lexington, and Louisville, KY, Cincinnati, Columbus, and Dayton, OH, and Nashville, TN. No grants to individuals.
Publications: Application guidelines; Grants list; Program policy statement.
Application information: Application form required.
Initial approach: See Website
Copies of proposal: 12
Deadline(s): Postmarked by Mar. 28

Officers and Directors: Andrew R. Lorenz, Pres. and Director; Stephen L. Keckeis, Secy. and Director; John Megibben, Treas. and Director.
EIN: 200262239

7525
The Mifsud Family Foundation
(formerly OJM Family Foundation)
P.O. Box 309
Wadsworth, OH 44282

Established in 1998 in Ohio.
Donor: Oscar J. Mifsud.
Foundation type: Independent foundation.
Financial data (yr. ended 12/31/13): Assets, $1,225,598 (M); gifts received, $11,377; expenditures, $297,907; qualifying distributions, $287,003; giving activities include $287,003 for 37 grants (high: $150,000; low: $250).
Fields of interest: Education; Diseases and conditions.
Type of support: Endowments; Research.
Limitations: Applications not accepted. Giving limited to OH. No grants to individuals.
Application information: Contributes only to pre-selected organizations.
Officers: Oscar J. Mifsud, Pres. and Treas.; Judith D. Mifsud, V.P. and Secy.
Trustees: Craig Kohrs; Shelly A. Mifsud Kohrs; Elizabeth Mifsud; Ryan S. Mifsud.
EIN: 341881436

7526
The Sydell & Arnold Miller Foundation
(formerly Arnold M. & Sydell L. Miller Foundation)
32333 Aurora Rd., Ste. 300
Solon, OH 44139-2851

Established in 1997 in Ohio.
Donors: Sydell L. Miller Charitable Lead Annuity Trust; Lauren Spilman Charitable Lead Annuity Trust; Stacie Halpern Charitable Lead Annuity Trust; Sydell L. Miller; Lauren Spilman 2007 Charitable Lead Annuity Trust; Stacie Halpern 2003 Charitable Lead Annuity Trust; Lauren Spilman 2003 Charitable Lead Annuity Trust; Stacie Halpern 2007 Charitable Lead Annuity Trust.
Foundation type: Independent foundation.
Financial data (yr. ended 12/31/13): Assets, $14,055,240 (M); gifts received, $852,320; expenditures, $196,874; qualifying distributions, $188,796; giving activities include $188,796 for 38 grants (high: $75,000; low: $50).
Fields of interest: Arts and culture; Higher education; Foundations; Diseases and conditions; Judaism.
Type of support: General support.
Limitations: Applications not accepted. Giving primarily in FL and OH.
Publications: Financial statement.
Application information: Contributes only to pre-selected organizations.
Officers: Sydell L. Miller, Pres. and Treas.; Lauren B. Spilman, V.P.; Stacie L. Halpern, Secy.
EIN: 341460324

7527
George Lee Miller Memorial Trust
c/o KeyBank
4900 Tiedeman Rd., OH-01-49-0150
Brooklyn, OH 44144-2302

Established in 1982 in Ohio.
Foundation type: Independent foundation.
Financial data (yr. ended 12/31/13): Assets, $4,061,970 (M); expenditures, $229,413; qualifying distributions, $199,274; giving activities include $189,417 for 8 grants (high: $30,307; low: $15,153).
Fields of interest: Historic preservation; Higher education; Hospital care; Protestantism; Human services.
Type of support: General support.
Limitations: Applications not accepted. Giving primarily in the Canton, OH, area. No grants to individuals.
Application information: Unsolicited requests for funds not accepted.
Trustee: KeyBank, N.A.
EIN: 346748261

7528
Emerson R. Miller Trust
c/o PNC Bank, N.A.
P.O. Box 94651
Cleveland, OH 44101-4651

Foundation type: Independent foundation.
Financial data (yr. ended 12/31/14): Assets, $3,783,477; expenditures, $338,289; qualifying distributions, $303,127 and $0 for set-asides.
Fields of interest: Education; Religion; Human services.
Type of support: General support.
Limitations: Applications not accepted. Giving primarily in OH.
Application information: Unsolicited requests for funds not accepted.
Trustee: PNC Bank, N.A.
EIN: 316064532

7529
The Milliron Foundation
P.O. Box 1026
Mansfield, OH 44901-1026

Established in 1997 in Ohio.
Donor: Grant Milliron.
Foundation type: Independent foundation.
Financial data (yr. ended 12/31/13): Assets, $2,006,043 (M); gifts received, $236,668; expenditures, $173,390; qualifying distributions, $167,190; giving activities include $165,000 for 8 grants (high: $33,000; low: $7,000).
Fields of interest: Foundations; Christianity; Human services.
Limitations: Applications not accepted. Giving primarily in Mansfield, OH. No grants to individuals.
Application information: Unsolicited requests for funds not accepted.
Officers and Trustees: Grant Milliron, Pres. and Trustee; Roger E. Shank, Treas. and Trustee.
EIN: 311541621

7530

A. Malachi & Barbara W. Mixon III, Foundation
Republic Bldg.
25 W. Prospect Ave., Ste.1400
Cleveland, OH 44115-1048

Established in 1991 in Ohio.
Donors: A. Malachi Mixon III; Barbara W. Mixon.
Foundation type: Independent foundation.
Financial data (yr. ended 11/30/14): Assets,
$92,648; expenditures, $220,779; qualifying
distributions, $211,800.
Fields of interest: Arts and culture; Education;
Human services.
Limitations: Applications not accepted. Giving
primarily in Cleveland, OH. No grants to individuals.
Application information: Contributes only to
pre-selected organizations.
Officer: A. Malachi Mixon III, Pres.
Trustees: Robert N. Gudbranson; Barbara W. Mixon.
EIN: 341692992

7531

Montauk Foundation
200 Market Ave. N., Ste. 210
Canton, OH 44702-1437 (330) 452-1144

Established in 1983 in Ohio.
Donors: Barbara C. Timken; Louise B. Timken.
Foundation type: Independent foundation.
Financial data (yr. ended 09/30/14): Assets,
$3,688,996; expenditures, $157,865; qualifying
distributions, $155,000.
Fields of interest: Architecture; Historic
preservation.
Type of support: Capital campaigns; Capital and
infrastructure; Program development; Convening.
Limitations: Applications accepted. Giving primarily
in MA. No grants to individuals.
Application information:
  Initial approach: Proposal
  Deadline(s): None
Officers and Trustees: Barbara C. Timken, Pres. and
Trustee; Polly M. Timken, V.P. and Trustee; Jeffrey
Halm, Secy.-Treas.
Number of staff: None.
EIN: 341411177

7532

John C. and Sally S. Morley Family Foundation
c/o Rebecca H. Dent
25201 Chagrin Blvd., Ste. 370
Beachwood, OH 44122-5637

Established in 1998 in Ohio.
Donors: John C. Morley; Sally S. Morley; John C. and
Sally S. Morley Charitable Lead Trust No. 2; John C.
and Sally S. Morley Charitable Lead Trust No. 1.
Foundation type: Independent foundation.
Financial data (yr. ended 12/31/13): Assets,
$20,280 (M); gifts received, $200,000;
expenditures, $314,443; qualifying distributions,
$310,303; giving activities include $308,333 for 4
grants (high: $100,000; low: $33,333).
Purpose and activities: Support primarily for the
arts and education.
Fields of interest: Performing arts; Art museums;
Education; Higher education.

Type of support: General support; Matching grants;
Annual campaigns; Capital and infrastructure;
Endowments; Professorships; Scholarships.
Limitations: Applications not accepted. Giving
primarily in OH. No grants to individuals.
Application information: Contributes only to
pre-selected organizations.
Trustee: Rebecca H. Dent.
EIN: 347065759

7533

T. R. Murphy Residuary Trust
422 Main St.
Zanesville, OH 43701-3515
Application address: c/o Scott D. Eickelberger, 50 N.
4th St., Zanesville, OH 43701, tel.: (750) 454-2591

Foundation type: Independent foundation.
Financial data (yr. ended 06/30/14): Assets,
$3,466,155 (M); expenditures, $184,649;
qualifying distributions, $184,649; giving activities
include $37,318 for grants, and $108,928 for 406
grants to individuals (high: $500; low: $200).
Purpose and activities: Awards scholarships to
worthy graduates of Muskingum County, OH, high
schools; also supports operating expenses of local
area Catholic schools.
Fields of interest: Education; Elementary and
secondary education; Catholicism.
Type of support: General support; Individual
development; Student aid.
Limitations: Applications accepted. Giving limited to
Muskingum County, OH.
Application information: Application form required
for scholarships.
  Deadline(s): May 1 for scholarships
Trustee: Huntington National Bank.
Committee Members: Scott D. Eickelberger;
Jennifer Mallett; Perry Robinson; Jeff Zellers; Mark
Ulbrich.
EIN: 316285970

7534

The R. C. and Katharine M. Musson Charitable Foundation
P.O. Box 7038
Akron, OH 44306-0038 (330) 773-7651

Established in 1984 in Ohio.
Donor: R.C. Musson†.
Foundation type: Independent foundation.
Financial data (yr. ended 12/31/13): Assets,
$3,657,055 (M); expenditures, $248,557;
qualifying distributions, $209,410; giving activities
include $118,960 for 63 grants (high: $25,000;
low: $600).
Purpose and activities: Giving primarily for human
services.
Fields of interest: Arts and culture; Higher
education; Basic and remedial instruction; Health;
Rehabilitation; Mental health care; Housing
development; Human services; People with
disabilities.
Type of support: Emergency funds; General support;
Continuing support; Annual campaigns; Capital and
infrastructure; Scholarships.
Limitations: Applications accepted. Giving primarily
in Summit County, OH. No grants to individuals.
Publications: Application guidelines.
Application information: Application form required.

Initial approach: Letter
Deadline(s): None
Trustees: Irvin J. Musson, Jr.; Irvin J. Musson III;
Bennie D. Segers; Robert S. Segers.
EIN: 341549070

7535

The Louis S. & Mary Myers Foundation
53 Aurora St.
Hudson, OH 44236-2902

Established in 1956 in Ohio.
Donors: Louis S. Myers; Myers Industries, Inc.; Mary
S. Myers; Stephen E. Myers.
Foundation type: Independent foundation.
Financial data (yr. ended 12/31/13): Assets,
$5,465,000 (M); expenditures, $259,862;
qualifying distributions, $250,000; giving activities
include $250,000 for 2 grants (high: $200,000;
low: $50,000).
Fields of interest: Arts and culture; Education;
Foundations; Health.
Type of support: General support; Capital and
infrastructure.
Limitations: Applications not accepted. Giving
primarily in Akron, OH. No grants to individuals.
Application information: Contributes only to
pre-selected organizations.
Officer: Stephen E. Myers, Pres.
EIN: 346555862

7536

Horace & Letitia Newton Scholarship Fund
10 W. 2nd St., 26th Fl.
Dayton, OH 45402-1791 4192598655
Application address: c/o Keybank N.A., Att.: Diane
Ohns, P.O. Box 10099, Toledo, OH 43699-0099.

Established in 1991 in Ohio.
Foundation type: Independent foundation.
Financial data (yr. ended 12/31/14): Assets,
$5,264,371; expenditures, $278,065; qualifying
distributions, $241,909.
Fields of interest: Higher education.
Type of support: Scholarships.
Application information: Application form required.
  Initial approach: Proposal
  Deadline(s): None
Trustee: KeyBank, N.A.
EIN: 346502592

7537

NLT Foundation, Inc.
c/o Ignite Philanthropy Advisors
1776 Mentor Ave., No. 260
Cincinnati, OH 45212-3661 (513) 351-1945
Contact: Michelle Jenney
E-mail: singmire@ignitephilanthropy.com
Grants List: http://
nltfoundation.grantsmanagement08.com/?
page_id=6

Established in 1997 in Massachusetts.
Donor: Nellie L. Taft.
Foundation type: Independent foundation.
Financial data (yr. ended 12/31/13): Assets,
$3,352,294 (M); expenditures, $151,484;
qualifying distributions, $132,193; giving activities
include $120,458 for 13 grants (high: $10,000;
low: $5,000).

Fields of interest: Arts and culture; Education; Environment.

Type of support: General support; Land acquisitions; Program development; Seed money.

Limitations: Applications accepted. Giving primarily in Boston, MA, mid-coast ME and Cincinnati, OH.

Publications: Application guidelines.

Application information: Application form required.

Initial approach: Telephone

Copies of proposal: 4

Deadline(s): Apr. 15, July 15

Officers: Dudley S. Taft, Pres.; Lucy Rosborough, Secy.

Trustees: Ken Mahler; Perin Mahler; Dudley S. Taft, Jr.; Thomas W. Taft.

Number of staff: None.

EIN: 043361704

7538
Hartzell Norris Charitable Trust

P.O. Box 630858

Cincinnati, OH   45263-0858

Main URL: http://www.hartzellindustries.com/careers/community.html

Established in 1943 in Ohio.

Donors: Hartzell Industries, Inc.; Melinda H. Grubbs.

Foundation type: Company-sponsored foundation.

Financial data (yr. ended 10/31/13): Assets, $5,223,868 (M); gifts received, $41,548; expenditures, $307,424; qualifying distributions, $264,047; giving activities include $263,847 for 67 grants (high: $19,762; low: $500).

Purpose and activities: The foundation supports organizations involved with arts and culture, education, health, cancer, housing development, human services, and Christianity.

Fields of interest: Arts and culture; Education; Elementary and secondary education; Higher education; Nonprofits; Health; Hospital care; Cancers; Housing development; Christianity; Human services; Scouting programs.

Type of support: General support; Regranting.

Limitations: Applications not accepted. Giving primarily in OH.

Application information: Unsolicited requests for funds not accepted.

Trustee: Fifth Third Bank of Western Ohio.

EIN: 316024521

7539
Norweb Foundation

c/o Keybank

4900 Tiedeman Rd., OH-01-49-0150

Brooklyn, OH   44144-2302

Established in 1952 in Ohio.

Donors: R. Henry Norweb, Jr.†; Elizabeth Norweb.

Foundation type: Independent foundation.

Financial data (yr. ended 12/31/14): Assets, $887,600 (M); expenditures, $166,125; qualifying distributions, $160,060; giving activities include $154,350 for 95 grants (high: $50,000; low: $50).

Fields of interest: Arts and culture; Secondary education; Natural resources; Nonprofits; Sports and recreation; Human services.

Type of support: General support; Annual campaigns; Capital campaigns; Regranting.

Limitations: Applications not accepted. Giving primarily in OH. No grants to individuals.

Application information: Contributes only to pre-selected organizations.

Trustees: Henry R. Norweb III; KeyBank N.A.

EIN: 346517914

7540
L. K. O'Donnell Family Charitable Trust

c/o KeyBank N.A.

4900 Tiedeman Rd., OH-01-49-0150

Brooklyn, OH   44144-2302

Foundation type: Independent foundation.

Financial data (yr. ended 12/31/13): Assets, $6,252,870 (M); expenditures, $332,008; qualifying distributions, $283,721; giving activities include $269,952 for 9 grants (high: $42,200; low: $28,133).

Fields of interest: Education; Catholicism.

Limitations: Applications not accepted. Giving primarily in OH.

Application information: Unsolicited requests for funds not accepted.

Trustee: KeyBank, N.A.

EIN: 347180756

7541
The Ohio Valley Foundation

c/o Fifth Third Bank

P.O. Box 630858

Cincinnati, OH   45263-0858

Contact: Heidi B. Jark, V.P. and Mgr., Fifth Third Bank

Application address: c/o Fifth Third Bank Foundation, 38 Fountain Sq. Plz. M/D 1090CA, Cincinnati, OH 45263, tel.: (513) 534-4397

Established in 1946 in Ohio.

Donors: John J. Rowe†; L. McGrath†; John W. Warrington†.

Foundation type: Independent foundation.

Financial data (yr. ended 09/30/13): Assets, $6,972,130 (M); expenditures, $384,232; qualifying distributions, $322,521; giving activities include $304,000 for 16 grants (high: $25,000; low: $4,000).

Fields of interest: Arts and culture; Museums; Education; Human services; Community service for youth.

Type of support: Capital campaigns; Capital and infrastructure.

Limitations: Applications accepted. Giving primarily in the greater Cincinnati, OH, area. No support for religious organizations. No grants to individuals, or for endowment funds or operating budgets.

Publications: Application guidelines; Annual report.

Application information: Organizations will be given an Ohio Common Grant Application Form by invitation from the foundation. Application form required.

Initial approach: Letter

Copies of proposal: 1

Deadline(s): None

Board meeting date(s): Jan., Mar., June, and Sept.

Final notification: Immediately after meeting

Officers and Board Members: Thomas Shiller, Chair. and Director; Phillip C. Long, Secy.-Treas.; Mitchel D. Livingston, Ph.D; Mike Michael; Carolyn McCoy; Leigh Prop; Jann Seidenfaden; Dudley S. Taft.

Number of staff: None.

EIN: 316008508

7542
The O'Neill Brothers Foundation

1406 W. 6th St., 3rd Fl.

Cleveland, OH   44113-1300

Application address: c/o Robert K. Healey, 30679 Bainbridge Rd., Ste. 1, Solon, OH 44139, tel.: (440) 248-5500

Established in 1953 in Michigan.

Donors: William J. O'Neill†; P.J. O'Neill†; H.M. O'Neill†; Francis J. O'Neill†; George C. Fortner†; Robert K. Healey; Mrs. Robert K. Healey.

Foundation type: Independent foundation.

Financial data (yr. ended 12/31/13): Assets, $6,923,242 (M); expenditures, $352,033; qualifying distributions, $286,612; giving activities include $251,808 for 55 grants (high: $50,000; low: $27).

Purpose and activities: Giving primarily to Roman Catholic agencies, churches, schools, and hospitals.

Fields of interest: Secondary education; Higher education; Natural resources; Animal welfare; Health; Diseases and conditions; Community and economic development; Catholicism; Child welfare; Youth services.

Type of support: General support.

Limitations: Applications accepted. Giving primarily in Cleveland, OH; giving also in FL. No grants to individuals.

Application information: Application form required.

Initial approach: Letter

Deadline(s): None

Board meeting date(s): Quarterly

Officers and Trustees: Robert K. Healey, Jr., Pres. and Trustee; Frances J. O'Neill III, V.P. and Treas. and Trustee; Daniel J. O'Neill, Secy.

EIN: 346545084

7543
Robert O. and AnnaMae Orr Family Foundation

1817 Brookwood Dr.

Akron, OH   44313-5061

Contact: Karen Murray, Exec. Dir.

E-mail: karenmurray45@yahoo.com; *Main URL:* http://www.orrfamilyfoundation.org

Established in 1998 in Ohio.

Donor: Robert O. Orr†.

Foundation type: Independent foundation.

Financial data (yr. ended 12/31/14): Assets, $8,347,246; expenditures, $666,593; qualifying distributions, $500,836.

Fields of interest: Arts and culture; Education; Community and economic development; Christianity; Human services; Youth development.

Type of support: General support; Equipment; Program development.

Limitations: Applications accepted. Giving limited to Summit and Stark counties, OH, with emphasis on Akron. No support for political organizations. No grants to individuals.

Publications: Application guidelines.

Application information: Application form required.

Initial approach: Complete application form on foundation web site or request form from foundation

Copies of proposal: 1

Deadline(s): None

Officer and Board Members: Karen Murray, Exec. Dir.; Kate Baker; Karen Stevens; Mary Stark; Michael Stark.
Number of staff: 1 part-time professional.
EIN: 341867983

7544
Oscar Cohrs Trust
P.O. Box 630858
Cincinnati, OH 45263-0858

Foundation type: Independent foundation.
Financial data (yr. ended 12/31/14): Assets, $5,581,139; expenditures, $357,421; qualifying distributions, $270,877.
Fields of interest: Human services; Seniors.
Limitations: Applications not accepted. Giving primarily in OH.
Application information: Unsolicited requests for funds not accepted.
Trustee: Fifth Third Bank.
EIN: 316019835

7545
Osteopathic Heritage Foundations
(formerly Doctors Hospital Development Foundation)
1500 Lake Shore Dr., Ste. 230
Columbus, OH 43204-3800 (614) 737-4370
Contact: Richard Vincent, Pres.
FAX: (614) 737-4371;
E-mail: heritage@ohf-ohio.org; Toll-free tel.: (866) 737-4370; Main URL: http://www.osteopathicheritage.org
E Newsletter: http://www.osteopathicheritage.org/News/eNewsletter.aspx
Grant Database: http://www.osteopathicheritage.org/FundingPriorities/fundingawards.aspx
Knowledge Center: http://www.osteopathicheritage.org/newsandreports.aspx

Established in 1998 in Ohio.
Donors: The Columbus Foundation and Affiliated Organizations; Doctors Hospital.
Foundation type: Independent foundation.
Financial data (yr. ended 12/31/12): Assets, $13,456,901 (M); expenditures, $428,340; qualifying distributions, $309,616; giving activities include $9,902,690 for 31 grants (high: $6,400,000).
Purpose and activities: Comprised of two private foundations that share a common mission and vision, while maintaining separate boards and funding concentration: 1) the Osteopathic Heritage Foundation supports community health and quality of life - primarily in central Ohio - as well as osteopathic medical education and research throughout the nation, and 2) the Osteopathic Heritage Foundation of Nelsonville directs its funding support primarily to improving community health and quality of life in southeastern Ohio. The foundations' focus on health and quality of life is broad and concentrated primarily on mission-related, target priorities, including the following: improving access to oral health care; reducing the prevalence of overweight/obesity in central Ohio; resolving healthcare workforce shortages; enhancing access to healthcare services; enhancing osteopathic medical education;

and medical research. In addition, the foundations have made reducing homelessness a recent funding priority.
Fields of interest: Health; Community health care; Public health; Homeless shelters; Homeless services; Homeless people.
Type of support: Capacity-building and technical assistance; Endowments; Program development; Information and Referral.
Limitations: Applications not accepted. Giving primarily in the following OH counties: Athens, Delaware, Fairfield, Fayette, Franklin, Hocking, Jackson, Knox, Licking, Madison, Meigs, Morgan, Perry, Pickaway, Ross, Union, Vinton, and Washington.
Publications: Informational brochure.
Application information: Unsolicited requests for funds generally not accepted. Grant requests are considered through a Request for Proposals (RFP) process. See foundation web site for RFP summary and application forms.
Officers and Directors: Robert A. Palma, DO, Chair., Osteopathic Heritage Fdn. and Director; Frederick L. Oremus, Chair., Osteopathic Heritage Fdn. of Nelsonville and Director; Jane W. Cunningham, Vice-Chair., Osteopathic Heritage Foundation and Director; Joseph A. Holtel, DO, Vice-Chair., Osteopathic Heritage Fdn. of Nelsonville and Director; Richard A. Vincent, C.E.O. and Pres. and Director; Terri Donlin Huesman, V.P., Progs.; George O. Faerber, DO, Secy., Osteopathic Heritage Fdn. and Director; Mark R. Seckinger, Secy., Osteopathic Heritage Fdn. of Nelsonville and Director; Richard A. Mitchell, Treas. and Director; Theodore M. Ofat, Cont.; Thomas M. Anderson, DO; J. Michael Brooks; Steven E. Cox; Rebecca deVillers, DO; Susan L. Hunter; Jeffrey Hutchison, DO; Peter E. Johnston, DO; Kathy Krendl, Ph.D; Edward Schreck, DO.
EIN: 316056252

7546
Peoples Bancorp Foundation Inc.
138 Putnam St.
P.O. Box 738
Marietta, OH 45750-2923 (740) 374-6172
Contact for Robert E. Evans Scholarship: Larry E. Holdren

Established in 2003 in Ohio.
Donor: Peoples Bank, N.A.
Foundation type: Company-sponsored foundation.
Financial data (yr. ended 12/31/14): Assets, $854,670; gifts received, $305,000; expenditures, $312,734; qualifying distributions, $302,225.
Purpose and activities: The foundation supports organizations involved with arts and culture, education, human services, youth, and community development. Special emphasis is directed toward programs designed to assist low- to moderate-income families.
Fields of interest: Arts and culture; Education; Health.
Type of support: General support; Program development; Student aid.
Limitations: Applications accepted. Giving primarily in areas of company operations in Athens, Belmont, Fairfield, Franklin, Gallia, Guernsey, Meigs, Morgan, Noble, and Washington counties, OH, Boyd and Greenup counties, KY, and Cabell, Mason, Wetzel, and Wood counties, WV.
Publications: Application guidelines.
Application information: Application form required.
Initial approach: Completed application form

Deadline(s): None
Board meeting date(s): Quarterly
Officers and Directors: Richard Stafford, Chair. and Pres. and Director; Larry E. Holdren, V.P. and Director; Ryan Kirkham, Secy.; Beth A. Worthington, Treas. and Director; George W. Broughton; Kristi A. Close; Theodore Pat Sauber; Charles W. Sulerzyski.
EIN: 300222364

7547
Edward V. & Jessie L. Peters Charitable Trust
P.O. Box 1558, Dept. EA4E86
Columbus, OH 43216
Application address: Stephen English, 650 Smithfield St., Ste. 1000, Pittsburgh, PA 15222, tel.: (412) 667-6439

Established in 1990 in Pennsylvania.
Donor: Jessie L. Peters.
Foundation type: Independent foundation.
Financial data (yr. ended 12/31/13): Assets, $7,129,847 (M); expenditures, $331,177; qualifying distributions, $313,602; giving activities include $300,000 for 18 grants (high: $50,500; low: $5,000).
Fields of interest: Arts and culture; Music; Education; Nonprofits; Community and economic development; Water sports; Human services.
Type of support: General support; Regranting.
Limitations: Applications accepted. Giving primarily in PA. No grants to individuals.
Application information: Application form required.
Initial approach: Letter
Deadline(s): Nov. 1
Trustee: Huntington National Bank, N.A.
EIN: 256358729

7548
The Philada Home Fund
1234 Inglenook Pl.
Cincinnati, OH 45208-2918
Contact: Ron Weitzenkorn, Tr.
E-mail: info@independentgov.com
Application address: c/o Amy Hirschman, 434 Springfield Pike, Cincinnati, OH 45215, tel.: (513) 761-1866

Foundation type: Operating foundation.
Financial data (yr. ended 12/31/13): Assets, $6,830,968 (M); expenditures, $283,479; qualifying distributions, $253,667; giving activities include $144,410 for 14 grants (high: $71,898; low: $2,846), and $23,370 for 5 grants to individuals (high: $7,164; low: $1,158).
Purpose and activities: The purpose of the foundation is to assist qualified low-income senior adults with rental subsidies in the Cincinnati, OH area.
Fields of interest: Rent and mortgage assistance; Adults; Seniors; Low-income and poor people.
Type of support: Continuing support; Pro bono consulting services; Endowments; Program development; Program evaluations.
Limitations: Giving primarily in Cincinnati, OH.
Publications: Informational brochure; Occasional report.
Application information: Application form required.
Initial approach: Letter
Deadline(s): None
Board meeting date(s): Quarterly

Officers: Donald J. Shuller, Pres.; Jon Hoffheimer, Secy.; Ronald J. Weitzenkorn, Treas.
Trustees: Ethan Boger; Linda Denham; Louis L. Rauh; Mark Sass.
Number of staff: 2 full-time professional; 1 part-time professional.
EIN: 310677810

7549
Robert and Elaine Pott Foundation

P.O. Box 630858
Cincinnati, OH   45263-0858
Application address: c/o Fifth Third Bank, Trust & Investment Mgmt., P.O. 719, Evansville, IN 47705, tel.: (812) 456-3215

Established in 1977 in Indiana.
Foundation type: Independent foundation.
Financial data (yr. ended 03/31/13): Assets, $5,177,292 (M); expenditures, $304,220; qualifying distributions, $232,754; giving activities include $232,424 for 4 grants (high: $83,799; low: $30,670).
Purpose and activities: Giving to institutions having schools or departments of engineering.
Fields of interest: Higher education; Graduate and professional education; Engineering.
Type of support: Scholarships.
Limitations: Applications accepted. Giving limited to educational institutions in IN and WI.
Application information:
   Initial approach: Proposal
   Deadline(s): Apr. 30
Trustee: Fifth Third Bank, N.A.
EIN: 356290997

7550
Edward W. Powers Charitable Fund

c/o PNC Bank, N.A.
P.O. Box 94651
Cleveland, OH   44101-4651

Established in 1966 in Ohio.
Donor: Edward W. Powers†.
Foundation type: Independent foundation.
Financial data (yr. ended 12/31/13): Assets, $1,718,491 (M); expenditures, $239,022; qualifying distributions, $229,698; giving activities include $221,174 for 9 grants (high: $50,000; low: $5,000).
Fields of interest: Arts and culture; Orchestral music; Nonprofits; Hospital care; Rehabilitation; Diseases and conditions; Community improvement; Human services; Youth services.
Type of support: General support; Regranting.
Limitations: Applications not accepted. Giving primarily in Youngstown, OH. No grants to individuals.
Application information: Contributes only to pre-selected organizations.
Trustee: PNC Bank, N.A.
EIN: 346577350

7551
Charles M. & Thelma M. Pugliese Charitable Foundation

P.O. Box 2620
Wintersville, OH   43953   (740) 264-5429

Established in 1998 in Ohio.

Donors: Charles M. Pugliese; Thelma M. Pugliese.
Foundation type: Independent foundation.
Financial data (yr. ended 12/31/14): Assets, $10,730,332; expenditures, $485,491; qualifying distributions, $473,471.
Fields of interest: Education; Elementary and secondary education.
Limitations: Applications accepted. Giving limited to within a 30-mile radius of Market St. and 4th St. in Steubenville, OH. No grants to individuals.
Application information:
   Initial approach: Proposal
   Deadline(s): None
Trustees: H. Lee Kinney; William McElwain; Thomas P. Timmons.
EIN: 341784660

7552
George B. Quatman Foundation

P.O. Box 630858
Cincinnati, OH   45263-0858   (937) 227-6447

Established in 1994 in Ohio.
Foundation type: Independent foundation.
Financial data (yr. ended 12/31/14): Assets, $5,420,140; expenditures, $314,429; qualifying distributions, $268,530.
Fields of interest: Education; Secondary education; Human services.
Type of support: Capital campaigns; Capital and infrastructure; Equipment; Seed money.
Limitations: Applications accepted. Giving primarily in OH, with emphasis on Dayton and Lima. No grants to individuals.
Application information: Application form required.
   Initial approach: Letter
   Copies of proposal: 2
   Deadline(s): None
   Board meeting date(s): Mar., June, Sept., and Dec.
   Final notification: 60 days
Trustee: Fifth Third Bank.
EIN: 316068296

7553
The Esther and Hyman Rapport Philanthropic Trust

c/o Richard C. Klein
33800 Jackson Rd.
Moreland Hills, OH   44022-1820

Established in 2005 in Ohio.
Donor: Esther Rapport†.
Foundation type: Independent foundation.
Financial data (yr. ended 12/31/13): Assets, $8,643,979 (M); expenditures, $475,210; qualifying distributions, $423,428; giving activities include $413,000 for 28 grants (high: $50,000; low: $2,000).
Fields of interest: Education; Judaism; Human services.
Limitations: Applications not accepted. Giving primarily in NY and OH. No grants for individuals.
Application information: Contributes only to pre-selected organizations.
Trustees: Richard C. Klein; Roger D. Klein; Dennis A. Linden.
EIN: 866338329

7554
Rayen School General Fund Irrevocable Trust

c/o PNC Bank, N.A.
P.O. Box 94651
Cleveland, OH   44101-4651

Foundation type: Independent foundation.
Financial data (yr. ended 12/31/14): Assets, $3,622,916; expenditures, $182,674; qualifying distributions, $170,824.
Fields of interest: Education.
Type of support: General support.
Limitations: Applications not accepted. Giving primarily in OH.
Application information: Unsolited requests for funds not accepted.
Trustee: PNC Bank, N.A.
EIN: 347151049

7555
John C. and Margaret Hanson Reed Fund

c/o KeyBank, N.A.
P.O. Box 10099
Toledo, OH   43699-0099

Established in 2007 in Ohio.
Donors: The Margaret H. Reed Trust; M.H. & J.C. Reed Trust.
Foundation type: Independent foundation.
Financial data (yr. ended 12/31/14): Assets, $3,090,564; expenditures, $228,028; qualifying distributions, $201,559.
Fields of interest: Undergraduate education; University education; Christianity.
Limitations: Applications not accepted. Giving primarily in OH. No grants to individuals.
Application information: Contributes only to pre-selected organizations.
Trustee: KeyBank, N.A.
EIN: 261117506

7556
Phyllis & Sidney Reisman Foundation

3201 Enterprise Pkwy, Ste. 320
Beachwood, OH   44122

Established in 1999 in Ohio.
Donor: Sidney Reisman.
Foundation type: Independent foundation.
Financial data (yr. ended 11/30/14): Assets, $4,349,895 (M); gifts received, $441,345; expenditures, $220,804; qualifying distributions, $200,022; giving activities include $200,022 for 19 grants (high: $72,000; low: $400).
Fields of interest: Education; Health; Judaism.
Limitations: Applications not accepted. Giving primarily in NY and Cleveland, OH. No grants to individuals.
Application information: Unsolicited requests for funds not accepted.
Trustees: Allen T. Reisman; Peter J. Reisman; Sidney Reisman.
EIN: 341881441

7557
Renner Foundation

1120 Chester Ave., Ste. 470
Cleveland, OH   44114-3521

Established in 1947 in Ohio.
Donor: R. Richard Renner, MD‡.
Foundation type: Independent foundation.
Financial data (yr. ended 05/31/13): Assets, $3,490,961 (M); expenditures, $209,728; qualifying distributions, $163,000; giving activities include $163,000 for 2 grants (high: $86,500; low: $76,500).
Fields of interest: Arts and culture; Higher education; Diseases and conditions; Religion.
Type of support: Endowments; Scholarships.
Limitations: Applications not accepted. Giving primarily in OH and WV. No grants to individuals.
Application information: Unsolicited requests for funds not accepted.
Officers: Karen Renner Sargent, Pres.; Debra Renner, V.P.; Jennie Renner-Yeomans, Secy.; Steven Renner, Treas.
Trustees: Brett Percy; David Percy; Jennifer Percy-Falls; Kevin Percy; Daniel S. Renner; John W. Renner; J. Robert Renner; Mary Renner; Reid Renner; Richard R. Renner; Robert Renner; Tamara Renner; Tara Renner; Ann Stillwater.
Number of staff: None.
EIN: 340684303

7558
The Reynolds and Reynolds Company Foundation

P.O. Box 2608
Dayton, OH 45401-2608 (937) 485-8138
E-mail: alice_davisson@revrey.com; *Main URL:* http://www.reyrey.com/company/community/company_foundation.asp
Address for Texas A&M Scholarship: Reynolds and Reynolds Open Undergraduate Scholarship Program, Scholarship Management Services, 1 Scholarship Way, P.O. Box 297, Saint Peter, MN 56082; Contact for Wright State Scholarship: Mary Hutcheson, Enrollment Advisor, Dept. of Computer Science and Engineering, Wright State University, 3640 Colonel Glenn Hwy., Dayton, OH 45435, e-mail: mary.hutcheson@wright.edu

Established in 1986 in Ohio.
Donor: The Reynolds and Reynolds Co.
Foundation type: Company-sponsored foundation.
Financial data (yr. ended 12/31/14): Assets, $4,334,837; expenditures, $251,933; qualifying distributions, $209,230.
Purpose and activities: The foundation supports higher education programs designed to prepare students for key roles in regional communities in which Reynolds has a significant presence; and community based programs that have exceptional benefits for the communities in which Reynolds operates.
Fields of interest: Higher education; Community and economic development.
Type of support: General support; Continuing support; Annual campaigns; Program development; Scholarships; Student aid.
Limitations: Applications accepted. Giving primarily in areas of company operations in Dayton, OH. No support for primary or secondary schools, sectarian organizations, political candidates, fraternal or veterans' organizations, or organizations without adequate accounting records or procedures. No grants to individuals (except for scholarships), or for political parties or offices, tax-supported universities or colleges for operating purposes, deficits or debt retirement, endowments, courtesy events, or capital campaigns.

Publications: Application guidelines.
Application information: All proposals must be submitted electronically. Support is limited to 1 contribution per organization during any given year. Multi-year funding is not automatic. Application form required.
   Initial approach: E-mail proposal
   Copies of proposal: 1
   Deadline(s): Feb. 10, May 11, Aug. 10, and Nov. 9
   Board meeting date(s): Mar. 1, June 7, Sept. 6, and Dec. 6
Officer and Trustees: Jim Penikas, Treas.; Dave Bates; Robert Burnett; Nicole Case; Willie Daughters; Jon Strawsburg.
EIN: 311168299

7559
The Frederic and Lundy Reynolds Family Foundation

(formerly The Reynolds Lajadesh Foundation)
c/o Chagrin Corporate Center
20820 Chagrin Blvd., Ste. 300
Shaker Heights, OH 44122-5323

Established in 2000 in Ohio.
Donor: Fredric G. Reynolds.
Foundation type: Independent foundation.
Financial data (yr. ended 12/31/14): Assets, $1,447,447; expenditures, $198,506; qualifying distributions, $179,750.
Fields of interest: Education; Agriculture; Human services.
Limitations: Applications not accepted. Giving primarily in CA. No grants to individuals.
Application information: Unsolicited requests for funds not accepted.
Trustees: Fredric G. Reynolds; Lundy E. Reynolds.
EIN: 341953315

7560
Ridgecliff Foundation Inc.

P.O. Box 26167
Fairview Park, OH 44126-0167
Contact: Michael A. Minelli, 2nd V.P.
E-mail: minelli.michael01@gmail.com; *Main URL:* http://www.ridgecliff.org

Established in 1991 in Ohio.
Donors: Mount Sinai Medical Center; Laurelwood Hospital.
Foundation type: Independent foundation.
Financial data (yr. ended 12/31/13): Assets, $8,862,511 (M); expenditures, $495,633; qualifying distributions, $453,763; giving activities include $438,313 for 33 grants (high: $35,000; low: $2,000).
Purpose and activities: Giving to promote research, patient care and charity care in the field of mental health and chemical dependency, and activities that promote health care generally.
Fields of interest: Health; Mental health care; Addiction services; Diseases and conditions; Psychology and behavioral science; Child welfare; Children and youth; Children; Adults; Young adults; Victims of crime and abuse; People with psychosocial disabilities; Substance abusers.
Type of support: Program development.
Limitations: Applications accepted. Giving primarily in Ashtabula, Cuyahoga, Geauga, Lake, Lorain, Mahoning, Medina, Portage, Summit, and Trumbull

counties, OH. No grants to individuals, or for construction projects, feasibility studies, ongoing projects beyond one year, or equipment which is not an integral part of a program.
Publications: Application guidelines; Grants list.
Application information: Awards limited to 1 grant per organization in a 12-month period.
   Copies of proposal: 9
   Deadline(s): Mar. 31 and Sept. 30 for funding in Feb. and Aug.
   Board meeting date(s): Jan., May, Aug., and Nov.
   Final notification: Jan. 31 and July 31
Officers and Trustees: Thomas TS Kaung, Pres. and Trustee; Gregory J. Malafarina, 1st V.P. and Treas.; Michael A. Minelli, 2nd V.P. and Grant Review Comm. Chair.; J. David Ingersoll, Secy.; Paul McHugh, Investment Comm. Chair. and Trustee; Donna Bonvissuto, Program Evaluator; Blanche Dortch; Hollie Gallagher; Elena Lidrbauch; Mary Therese Matousek; Roberta Taliaferro.
Number of staff: None.
EIN: 341671405

7561
The Charles E. and Mabel M. Ritchie Memorial Foundation

106 S. Main St., 16th Fl.
Akron, OH 44308-1417

Established in 1954 in Ohio.
Donor: Mabel M. Ritchie‡.
Foundation type: Independent foundation.
Financial data (yr. ended 12/31/14): Assets, $7,386,084 (M); expenditures, $396,355; qualifying distributions, $350,356; giving activities include $312,194 for 88 grants (high: $15,000; low: $1,000).
Purpose and activities: Giving primarily for social services, education, the arts, and children's and healthcare services.
Fields of interest: Arts and culture; Education; Higher education; Hospital care; Community and economic development; Child welfare.
Type of support: General support; Matching grants; Continuing support; Annual campaigns; Capital campaigns; Capital and infrastructure; Equipment; Endowments; Program development; Scholarships; Research.
Limitations: Applications not accepted. Giving limited to Summit County, OH. No grants to individuals.
Application information: Unsolicited requests for funds not accepted.
   Board meeting date(s): 3 or 4 times per year
Trustee: FirstMerit Bank, N.A.
EIN: 346500802

7562
Harold C. & Marjorie Q. Rosenberry Foundation

c/o Huntington National Bank
232 W. 3rd St., Ste. 322
Dover, OH 44622-2969 (330) 364-7421

Established in 1994 in Ohio.
Foundation type: Independent foundation.
Financial data (yr. ended 12/31/14): Assets, $7,195,529; expenditures, $373,432; qualifying distributions, $333,763.

Purpose and activities: Giving primarily for hospitals, the arts, education, and community development.
Fields of interest: Arts and culture; History museums; Elementary and secondary education; Higher education; Hospital care; Public libraries; Search and rescue; Community and economic development; Human services; Family services.
Type of support: Capital and infrastructure; Program-related investments; Land acquisitions; Debt reduction; Publications.
Limitations: Applications accepted. Giving limited to Tuscarawas County, OH. No grants to individuals.
Application information: Application form required.
  Initial approach: Request application form
  Deadline(s): None
Trustee: Huntington National Bank.
EIN: 341772635

7563
Leighton A. Rosenthal Family Foundation
c/o Parkland Mgmt. Co.
1001 Lakeside Ave., No. 900
Cleveland, OH   44114-1177   (216) 479-2200
Contact: Jane R. Horvitz, Tr.; Cynthia R. Boardman, Tr.

Established in 1986 in Ohio.
Donor: Leighton A. Rosenthal†.
Foundation type: Independent foundation.
Financial data (yr. ended 10/31/13): Assets, $3,551,159 (M); expenditures, $462,451; qualifying distributions, $448,206; giving activities include $435,150 for 11 grants (high: $187,500; low: $650).
Purpose and activities: Giving primarily for medical research and Jewish agencies and temples.
Fields of interest: Arts and culture; Philanthropy; Foundations; Diseases and conditions; Judaism.
Type of support: Research; Research and evaluation.
Limitations: Applications accepted. Giving primarily in OH, with some emphasis on Cleveland.
Application information: Application form required.
  Initial approach: Letter
  Deadline(s): None
Trustees: Cynthia R. Boardman; Jane R. Horvitz.
EIN: 136877098

7564
Helen L. & Marie F. Rotterman Trust
1900 Kettering Twr.
Dayton, OH   45423-1127
Contact: Jeffrey B. Shulman, Tr.

Established in 1982 in Ohio.
Foundation type: Independent foundation.
Financial data (yr. ended 07/31/13): Assets, $3,697,901 (M); expenditures, $208,527; qualifying distributions, $174,000; giving activities include $174,000 for grants.
Purpose and activities: Grants to Catholic colleges and missionary organizations, and scholarships to Catholic young women enrolled in Trinity College or who are in high school and plan to enroll there; preference is for students from the Dayton, OH, metropolitan area.
Fields of interest: Education; Catholicism; Females.
Type of support: Scholarships; General support; Student aid.

Limitations: Applications not accepted. Giving primarily in Washington DC, and to residents of Dayton, OH.
Application information: Unsolicited requests for funds not accepted.
Trustees: Mildred Hubler; Jan S. Scheid; Jeffrey B. Shulman.
EIN: 316236156

7565
Bill & Melinda Rupp Foundation Inc.
P.O. Box 26
Archbold, OH   43502-0026   (419) 445-4765
Contact: Claire R. Morton, Tr.
Application address: 113 Quail Run, Archbold, OH 43502

Donor: Melinda M. Rupp.
Foundation type: Independent foundation.
Financial data (yr. ended 12/31/13): Assets, $566,961 (M); gifts received, $445,132; expenditures, $206,018; qualifying distributions, $200,000; giving activities include $200,000 for 1 grant.
Application information: Application form required.
  Initial approach: Letter
  Deadline(s): Dec. 1
Trustees: Claire R. Morton; Emily J. Rupp; Melinda M. Rupp.
EIN: 274397392

7566
The Albert J. Ryan Foundation
225 W. Court St.
Cincinnati, OH   45202-1012   (513) 721-5525
Contact: Robert H. Mitchell Esq., Co-Trustee
FAX: (516) 721-4268; *E-mail for Robert H. Mitchell, Esq.:* rhm@manleyburke.com; *Main URL:* http://www.albertjryanfoundation.org
Grants List: http://www.albertjryanfoundation.org/fellows.cfm

Established in 1967 in Ohio.
Foundation type: Independent foundation.
Financial data (yr. ended 12/31/13): Assets, $2,590,503 (M); expenditures, $252,594; qualifying distributions, $213,093; giving activities include $190,000 for 3 grants (high: $65,000; low: $60,000).
Fields of interest: University education; Medical education.
Type of support: Scholarships; Research.
Limitations: Applications not accepted. Giving limited to MA, NH, and OH.
Application information: Contributes only to pre-selected organizations; participating colleges select scholars to receive scholarships from foundation.
Officer and Trustees: Michael J. Bohman, V.P. and Trustee; Robert H. Mitchell; Manley Burke, LPA; U.S. Bank, N.A.
EIN: 316066371

7567
S.E.C. Charitable Corp.
1041 Catawba Valley Dr.
Cincinnati, OH   45226-1701

Established in 1997 in Ohio.
Donor: Susan Castleberry.

Foundation type: Independent foundation.
Financial data (yr. ended 12/31/13): Assets, $4,460,162 (M); gifts received, $250,000; expenditures, $221,026; qualifying distributions, $216,800; giving activities include $213,700 for 44 grants (high: $30,000; low: $250).
Fields of interest: Arts and culture; Education; Youth development.
Type of support: General support.
Limitations: Applications not accepted. No grants to individuals.
Application information: Unsolicited requests for funds not accepted.
Trustees: Anne Pund Castleberry; Edward F. Castleberry; Kelly Castleberry; Susan Castleberry; Elizabeth Driscoll; Christine Castleberry Lippert.
EIN: 311529509

7568
The Sage Cleveland Foundation
(formerly The Standard Products Foundation)
c/o William J. Culbertson Esq.
1900 E. 9th St., Ste. 3200
Cleveland, OH   44114-3485

Established in 1953 in Ohio.
Donor: The Standard Products Co.
Foundation type: Company-sponsored foundation.
Financial data (yr. ended 12/31/14): Assets, $5,876,218; gifts received, $0; expenditures, $170,077; qualifying distributions, $145,539.
Purpose and activities: The foundation supports health clinics and organizations involved with arts and culture, higher education, and substance abuse.
Fields of interest: Arts and culture; Education; Human services.
Limitations: Applications not accepted. Giving primarily in Cleveland, OH. No grants to individuals.
Application information: Contributes only to pre-selected organizations.
Officers and Trustees: J. S. Reid, Jr., Pres. and Trustee; R. Steven Kestner, Secy. and Trustee; Edward B. Brandon; Sarah S. Cutler; John D. Sigel.
EIN: 346525047

7569
Sandfair Foundation
32400 Fairmount Blvd.
Pepper Pike, OH   44124   (216) 831-2400
Contact: William E. Conway, Pres. and Treas.

Established in 1995 in Ohio.
Donors: The William E. Conway Trust; Mary French Conway; Jane C. Barber; William T. Conway; Peter F. Conway; Anne Conway Juster.
Foundation type: Independent foundation.
Financial data (yr. ended 12/31/13): Assets, $2,059,564 (M); gifts received, $197,241; expenditures, $191,502; qualifying distributions, $181,025; giving activities include $181,025 for 6 grants (high: $40,400; low: $625).
Purpose and activities: The foundation supports children in education, including religious education, the arts, and health care.
Fields of interest: Arts and culture; Museums; Education; Elementary and secondary education; Health; Housing development; Human services; Children and youth; Infants and toddlers; Children; Adolescents; Female children and youth; Male children and youth; Low-income and poor people.

Type of support: General support; Matching grants; Annual campaigns; Capital campaigns; Capital and infrastructure; Land acquisitions; Endowments; Emergency funds; Professorships; Seed money; Curriculum development; Scholarships.
Limitations: Applications accepted. Giving primarily in CO, northern NM, northeastern OH, and SC. No grants to individuals.
Application information: Application form required.
  Initial approach: Letter
  Copies of proposal: 1
  Deadline(s): None
  Final notification: 1 month
Officers: William E. Conway, Pres. and Treas.; Anne Conway Juster, Secy.
Directors: Mary French Conway; Peter F. Conway.
Number of staff: 1 part-time professional; 1 part-time support.
EIN: 341815135

7570
Sauerland Foundation
600 Falls Rd.
Chagrin Falls, OH 44022-2561 4402472881

Established in 1994 in Ohio.
Donors: Franz Sauerland; Elizabeth Sauerland.
Foundation type: Independent foundation.
Financial data (yr. ended 12/31/14): Assets, $4,142,689; gifts received, $101,325; expenditures, $201,425; qualifying distributions, $201,425.
Fields of interest: Land resources; Nonprofits; Science; Crime prevention; Housing development; Human services.
Type of support: General support; Regranting.
Limitations: Applications accepted. Giving primarily in OH. No grants to individuals.
Application information: Application form required.
  Initial approach: Proposal
  Deadline(s): None
Trustees: Elizabeth Sauerland; Franz Sauerland.
EIN: 341787952

7571
Ralph and Lucille Schey Foundation
(formerly The Schey Foundation)
1139 W. Hill Dr.
Gates Mills, OH 44040-9667
Main URL: http://thescheyfoundation.org

Established in 1985 in Ohio.
Donors: Ralph E. Schey; Walter A. Rajki; Lucille L. Schey.
Foundation type: Independent foundation.
Financial data (yr. ended 06/30/14): Assets, $4,713,912; expenditures, $375,519; qualifying distributions, $354,325.
Purpose and activities: Giving primarily for arts and education.
Fields of interest: Arts and culture; Performing arts; Theater; Higher education; Business education; Human services.
Type of support: Scholarships; General support.
Limitations: Applications not accepted. Giving primarily in MA and Cleveland, OH. No grants to individuals.
Application information: Contributes only to pre-selected organizations.
Officer: Lucille L. Schey, Pres.

Trustee: David E. Cook.
EIN: 341502219

7572
Schooler Family Foundation
P.O. Box 6579
Columbus, OH 43206-0579
Contact: Heather L. Schooler, Mgr., Grants & Communications
E-mail: schoolerfamilyfoundation@gmail.com

Established in 1985 in Ohio.
Donors: Seward D. Schooler†; Edith Schooler†.
Foundation type: Independent foundation.
Financial data (yr. ended 12/31/14): Assets, $5,865,915 (M); expenditures, $362,602; qualifying distributions, $327,897; giving activities include $265,417 for 17 grants (high: $50,000; low: $500).
Purpose and activities: Support for a broad range of charitable programs.
Limitations: Applications not accepted. Giving primarily in Ohio, with emphasis on east central, and to a lesser extent central and southeastern, Ohio and elsewhere in the U.S. No support for research using, or conducted on, animals. No grants to individuals.
Application information: The Foundation welcomes interest or inquiries from two types of tax-exempt organizations - those which have received past funding from the Foundation and those located in or benefiting the residents and communities of Coshocton County, Frazeysburg and Perryton, Ohio. Organizations so qualifying are to, first, submit an initial letter of inquiry. Letters of inquiry are to be received by the Foundation on or before May 1 of each year. Following review and consideration of all letters of inquiry, the Schooler Family Foundation will, no later than July 1 each year, request formal proposals from selected organizations. Requested proposals are to be received on or before September 1 of each year.
  Board meeting date(s): As required or advised and in accord with grantmaking cycles
Officers and Trustees: David R. Schooler, Pres. and Trustee; Steven Barr, V.P. and Trustee; Heather L. Schooler, Secy. and Mgr., Grants and Communications and Trustee; Dean Schooler, Treas.; C. Fenning Pierce; Deana Schooler Puls; Matthew Schooler; Wesley Schooler.
Number of staff: 3 part-time professional.
EIN: 311157433

7573
Saul Schottenstein Foundation B
441 Vine St., Ste. 3700
Cincinnati, OH 45202-3009
Main URL: http://www.saulschottensteinfoundationb.org

Foundation type: Independent foundation.
Financial data (yr. ended 12/31/13): Assets, $6,912,409 (M); expenditures, $461,316; qualifying distributions, $436,471; giving activities include $355,713 for 39 grants (high: $170,382; low: $60).
Fields of interest: Education; Religion; Sports and recreation.
Limitations: Applications not accepted. Giving primarily in OH.

Application information: Unsolicited requests for funds not accepted.
Officer: Jeffrey P. Harris, Pres.
EIN: 270167751

7574
Saul Schottenstein Foundation D
c/o Arshot Investment Corporation
107 S. High St., 3rd Fl.
Columbus, OH 43215-3456

Foundation type: Independent foundation.
Financial data (yr. ended 12/31/13): Assets, $6,192,360 (M); gifts received, $447; expenditures, $974,295; qualifying distributions, $218,608; giving activities include $170,007 for 39 grants (high: $25,250; low: $20).
Fields of interest: Education; Health; Community and economic development; Religion; Human services.
Type of support: General support.
Limitations: Applications not accepted. Giving primarily in NY and OH.
Application information: Contributes only to pre-selected organizations.
Officer: William Schottenstein, Pres.
EIN: 270167675

7575
Lori Schottenstein Foundation
4300 E. 5th Ave.
Columbus, OH 43219-1816

Established in 1997 in Ohio.
Donor: Lori Schottenstein.
Foundation type: Independent foundation.
Financial data (yr. ended 12/31/13): Assets, $6,471,746 (M); gifts received, $100,000; expenditures, $205,827; qualifying distributions, $188,174; giving activities include $188,174 for 6 grants (high: $99,266; low: $500).
Purpose and activities: Giving primarily for Jewish agencies and temples; some funding also for education.
Fields of interest: Education; Nonprofits; Judaism.
Type of support: Regranting.
Limitations: Applications not accepted. Giving in OH, with an emphasis on New Albany. No grants to individuals.
Application information: Contributes only to pre-selected organizations.
Officers: Geraldine Schottenstein, Pres.; Jay Schottenstein, V.P.; Susan Diamond, Secy.
EIN: 311533377

7576
The Miriam & Stanley Schwartz, Jr. Philanthropic Foundation
268 N. Parkview Ave.
Columbus, OH 43209-1438
Contact: Robert Schwartz, V.P.
Main URL: http://www.escorpltd.com

Established in 1998 in Ohio.
Foundation type: Independent foundation.
Financial data (yr. ended 12/31/13): Assets, $8,590 (M); gifts received, $240,000; expenditures, $240,162; qualifying distributions, $240,162; giving activities include $240,000 for 44 grants (high: $27,500; low: $1,000).

Purpose and activities: Giving primarily for Jewish and other federated giving programs, education, health, particularly cancer research, and human services.

Fields of interest: Education; Higher education; Nonprofits; Hospital care; Judaism; Human services; Child welfare.

Type of support: Regranting.

Limitations: Applications not accepted. Giving primarily in FL and OH; giving also in MA and MO. No grants to individuals.

Application information: Contributes only to pre-selected organizations.

Officers: Bruce Schwartz, Chair.; James Schwartz, Pres.; Robert Schwartz, V.P. and Secy.-Treas.

EIN: 311577991

7577

The Schwebel Family Foundation

P.O. Box 6018
Youngstown, OH 44501-6018

Established in 1989 in Ohio.

Donors: Frances Solomon; Schwebel Baking Co.

Foundation type: Independent foundation.

Financial data (yr. ended 12/31/13): Assets, $3,474,273 (M); gifts received, $500,000; expenditures, $191,210; qualifying distributions, $170,708; giving activities include $170,708 for 96 grants (high: $30,000; low: $50).

Fields of interest: Music; Higher education; University education; Nonprofits; Diseases and conditions; Judaism; Youth services.

Type of support: General support; Regranting.

Limitations: Applications not accepted. Giving primarily in Youngstown, OH. No grants to individuals.

Application information: Contributes only to pre-selected organizations.

Board meeting date(s): Early Dec.

Trustees: David Alter; Barry Solomon; Alyson Winick.

EIN: 341600311

7578

Scion Farms Foundation

P.O. Box 2186
Zanesville, OH 43702-2186
Contact: Rachel Stukey, Pres.

Donor: The Longaberger Foundation.

Foundation type: Independent foundation.

Financial data (yr. ended 12/31/13): Assets, $2,406,093 (M); expenditures, $352,452; qualifying distributions, $346,404; giving activities include $250,000 for 1 grant.

Fields of interest: Education; Health; Hospital care; Children.

Limitations: Applications accepted. Giving primarily in OH.

Application information: Application form required.

Initial approach: Letter

Deadline(s): None

Officer: Rachel Stukey, Pres.

EIN: 272220666

7579

Scotford Foundation

211 S. Main St.
Poland, OH 44514-2026 (330) 757-3761

Established in 1978 in Ohio.

Donors: John P. Scotford; Judy Scotford; John Scotford, Jr.; Laura Scotford; Stephen L. Scotford.

Foundation type: Independent foundation.

Financial data (yr. ended 12/31/14): Assets, $4,416,336; expenditures, $219,823; qualifying distributions, $193,880.

Purpose and activities: Giving primarily to Protestant agencies and churches and for education.

Fields of interest: Elementary and secondary education; Higher education; Protestantism; Youth development.

Type of support: General support; Matching grants; Annual campaigns; Capital campaigns; Capital and infrastructure; Land acquisitions; Endowments.

Limitations: Applications accepted. Giving primarily in FL, OH and WA. No grants to individuals.

Application information: Application form required.

Initial approach: Letter

Deadline(s): None

Board meeting date(s): Varies

Trustees: John P. Scotford; John P. Scotford, Jr.; Laura L. Scotford; Stephen L. Scotford.

EIN: 341278622

7580

Seaman Family Foundation Trust

1000 Venture Blvd.
Wooster, OH 44691-9358

Established in 1993 in Ohio.

Donors: Richard N. Seaman; Judith Seaman; Seaman Corp.

Foundation type: Independent foundation.

Financial data (yr. ended 12/31/14): Assets, $2,404,710 (M); gifts received, $198,946; expenditures, $273,366; qualifying distributions, $260,100; giving activities include $259,900 for 31 grants (high: $102,000; low: $500).

Fields of interest: Higher education; Nonprofits; Cancers; Human services.

Type of support: Regranting.

Limitations: Applications not accepted. Giving primarily in the Wooster, OH. No grants to individuals.

Application information: Unsolicited requests for funds not accepted.

Trustees: Judith G. Seaman; Kimberly A. Seaman; Richard N. Seaman.

EIN: 341770650

7581

The Sears-Swetland Family Foundation

(formerly The Sears-Swetland Foundation)
13003 Lake Shore Blvd.
Bratenahl, OH 44108-1144
Contact: Ruth Swetland Eppig, Pres.
E-mail: sears.swetland.fdn@gmail.com; E-mail for Ruth Swetland Eppig: rseppig@aol.com; Main URL: http://www.searsswetlandfoundation.wordpress.com
Grants List: http://searsswetlandfoundation.wordpress.com/who-we-fund

Established in 1949 in Ohio.

Donors: Anna L. Sears†; Lester M. Sears†; Ruth P. Sears†; Mary Ann Swetland†; David W. Swetland†; David Sears Swetland; Ruth Swetland Eppig; Polly Swetland Jones.

Foundation type: Independent foundation.

Financial data (yr. ended 12/31/13): Assets, $4,751,614 (M); gifts received, $911,002; expenditures, $280,893; qualifying distributions, $313,930; giving activities include $198,000 for 27 grants (high: $50,000; low: $500), and $100,000 for 1 loan/program-related investment.

Purpose and activities: Support for smart growth, conservation, urban revitalization and fair access, education and environmental health in the greater Cleveland, Ohio, area.

Fields of interest: Arts and culture; Education; Environment; Philanthropy; Diseases and conditions; Community and economic development; Sustainable development; Economic development; Employment; Housing development; Human rights; Youth development.

Type of support: General support; Matching grants; Continuing support; Capacity-building and technical assistance; Annual campaigns; Capital campaigns; Capital and infrastructure; Research; Equipment; Land acquisitions; Program development; Seed money; Curriculum development; Internships; Scholarships.

Limitations: Applications accepted. Giving primarily in the Cleveland, OH, area. No grants to individuals.

Publications: Application guidelines; Grants list; Program policy statement.

Application information:

Initial approach: E-mail

Deadline(s): Submit proposal preferably before Nov.; annual fund proposals before June

Board meeting date(s): As needed

Final notification: 60 days

Officers: Ruth Swetland Eppig, Pres.; Marianne E. Eppig, Secy.

Trustees: Lydia L. Harrington; David Sears Swetland.

Number of staff: 1 part-time professional.

EIN: 346522143

7582

Murray and Agnes Seasongood Good Government Foundation

15 E. 8th St., Ste. 200W
Cincinnati, OH 45202-2087 (513) 721-2180
Contact: D. David Altman
FAX: (513) 721-2299;
E-mail: info@seasongoodfoundation.com; Main URL: http://www.seasongoodfoundation.com
Grants List: http://www.seasongoodfoundation.com/projects.html

Established in 1987 in Ohio.

Foundation type: Independent foundation.

Financial data (yr. ended 12/31/14): Assets, $6,820,726; expenditures, $378,170; qualifying distributions, $337,139.

Fields of interest: Education; University education; Environment; Foundations; Communication media; Legal services; Public administration; Community improvement; Community organizing; Human services.

Type of support: Program development; Internships; Research.

Limitations: Applications accepted. Giving primarily in Cincinnati, OH.

Publications: Application guidelines; Informational brochure.

Application information: See foundation web site for complete application guidelines. Application form required.

Copies of proposal: 15
Deadline(s): At least two weeks before a board meeting
Board meeting date(s): Feb., May, Aug. and Nov.
Trustees: D. David Altman; Mary Asbury; William T. Bahlman, Jr.; Elizabeth Blume; Jay Chatterjee; Marjorie Davies; David Mann; Melanie Moody; Jerry Newfarmer; Dr. Julie Olberding; Bruce Petrie, Sr.; Dr. Myrtis Powell; Hon. Fanon Rucker; Mary Schubauer-Berigan; David Singleton; Dr. Henry Winkler.
Number of staff: 1 part-time professional.
EIN: 311220827

7583
Ladislas & Vilma Segoe Family Foundation
8050 Hosbrook Rd., Ste. 102
Cincinnati, OH 45236-2907 (513) 984-3587
Contact: Lewis G. Gatch, Tr.

Established in 1991 in Ohio.
Donor: Vilma Segoe†.
Foundation type: Independent foundation.
Financial data (yr. ended 12/31/13): Assets, $3,235,284 (M); expenditures, $281,709; qualifying distributions, $214,346; giving activities include $207,628 for 33 grants (high: $26,328; low: $100).
Fields of interest: Arts and culture; Education; Human services.
Type of support: General support; Scholarships.
Limitations: Applications accepted. Giving limited to the greater Cincinnati, OH, area. No grants to individuals.
Application information: Application form required.
Initial approach: Letter
Deadline(s): Quarterly
Trustees: David W. Ellis III; Lewis G. Gatch.
EIN: 316369499

7584
Dorothy T. & Myron T. Seifert Charitable Trust
c/o PNC Bank, N.A.
P.O. Box 94651
Cleveland, OH 44101-4651

Established in 1996 in Ohio.
Foundation type: Independent foundation.
Financial data (yr. ended 12/31/13): Assets, $6,435,055 (M); expenditures, $266,961; qualifying distributions, $229,705; giving activities include $201,951 for 22 grants (high: $25,866; low: $3,601).
Fields of interest: Museums; Historic preservation; Higher education; Hospital care; Diseases and conditions; Libraries; Protestantism.
Type of support: General support.
Limitations: Applications not accepted. Giving primarily in OH. No grants to individuals.
Application information: Unsolicited requests for funds not accepted.
Trustee: PNC Bank, N.A.
EIN: 316535424

7585
Della Selsor Trust
P.O. Box 1488
Springfield, OH 45501-1488
Contact: Glenn W. Collier, Tr.; Walter A. Wildman, Tr.

Application address: 1 S. Limestone St., Springfield, OH 45502, tel.: (937) 324-5541

Established in 1966 in Ohio.
Donor: Della Selsor†.
Foundation type: Independent foundation.
Financial data (yr. ended 12/31/13): Assets, $4,886,869 (M); expenditures, $255,507; qualifying distributions, $232,017; giving activities include $161,548 for 67 grants (high: $13,250; low: $150).
Fields of interest: Arts and culture; Arts councils; Orchestral music; Art museums; Education; Higher education; Basic and remedial instruction.
Limitations: Applications accepted. Giving primarily in the Springfield, OH, area. No grants to individuals.
Application information: Application form required.
Initial approach: Letter or telephone
Deadline(s): None
Trustees: Glenn W. Collier; Walter A. Wildman.
EIN: 510163338

7586
Shannon Family Charitable Foundation
c/o Fifth Third Bank
P.O. Box 630858
Cincinnati, OH 45263-0858

Established in 2005 in Florida.
Donor: Bruce Shannon.
Foundation type: Independent foundation.
Financial data (yr. ended 12/31/14): Assets, $5,522,123; expenditures, $334,168; qualifying distributions, $267,862.
Fields of interest: Animal welfare; Specialty hospital care; Diseases and conditions; Housing development; Human services; Family services; Youth organizing.
Type of support: Research.
Limitations: Applications not accepted. Giving primarily in MI. No grants to individuals.
Application information: Unsolicited requests for funds not accepted.
Trustee: Fifth Third Bank.
EIN: 206669463

7587
D.C. Shaw Trust f/b/o Boys And Girls Clubs of Toledo
c/o PNC Bank, N.A.
P.O. Box 94651
Cleveland, OH 44101-4651

Foundation type: Independent foundation.
Financial data (yr. ended 12/31/13): Assets, $4,197,087 (M); expenditures, $227,482; qualifying distributions, $207,262; giving activities include $190,208 for 1 grant.
Fields of interest: Youth development; Youth services.
Type of support: General support.
Limitations: Applications not accepted. Giving primarily in Toledo, OH.
Application information: Unsolicited requests for funds not accepted.
Trustees: James C. Anderson, Esq.; Bryce Harrbaugh; PNC Bank, N.A.
EIN: 316636137

7588
Jasper H. Sheadle Trust
c/o KeyBank N.A.
4900 Tiedeman Rd., OH-01-49-0150
Brooklyn, OH 44144-2302

Established in 1917 in Ohio.
Donor: Jasper H. Sheadle†.
Foundation type: Independent foundation.
Financial data (yr. ended 12/31/14): Assets, $2,503,158; expenditures, $199,268; qualifying distributions, $175,705.
Purpose and activities: To provide pensions for elderly American-born women or couples (62 and over) only, who are residing in Cuyahoga or Mahoning counties, OH.
Fields of interest: Senior services; Seniors.
Type of support: Grants to individuals.
Limitations: Applications not accepted. Giving limited to residents of Cuyahoga and Mahoning counties, OH.
Application information: Unsolicited requests for funds not accepted.
Board meeting date(s): Varies
Trustee: KeyBank, N.A.
Managers: John J. Donnelly; Mark Hollingsworth, Jr.; Annette Mannion.
Number of staff: 1 part-time professional.
EIN: 346506457

7589
Kate B. Sheadle Trust
c/o KeyBank N.A.
4900 Tiedeman Rd., OH-01-49-0150
Brooklyn, OH 44144-2302

Foundation type: Independent foundation.
Financial data (yr. ended 12/31/13): Assets, $4,431,580 (M); expenditures, $204,115; qualifying distributions, $194,190; giving activities include $190,854 for 5 grants (high: $49,314; low: $23,595).
Fields of interest: Education; Domesticated animals.
Limitations: Applications not accepted.
Application information: Unsolicited requests for funds not accepted.
Trustee: KeyBank N.A.
EIN: 346508538

7590
Dale and Alyce Sheely Family Foundation
P.O. Box 1558, Dept. EA4E86
Columbus, OH 43216

Established in 1994 in Ohio.
Donors: Dale R. Sheely, Sr.; Carol I. Colkitt Trust; Cynthia Sheely Oliver; Dale & Alyce Sheely Family Foundation.
Foundation type: Independent foundation.
Financial data (yr. ended 12/31/13): Assets, $1,601,397 (M); gifts received, $234,038; expenditures, $195,599; qualifying distributions, $189,025; giving activities include $182,400 for 368 grants (high: $1,000; low: $400).
Purpose and activities: Support for churches, religious groups, education, and a relief program in Columbiana, Mahoning, and Trumbull counties, Ohio.

Fields of interest: Elementary and secondary education; Religion; Protestantism; Human services.
International interests: Scotland.
Type of support: Emergency funds.
Limitations: Applications not accepted. Giving limited to Mahoning Valley, OH.
Application information: Contributes only to pre-selected organizations.
Officer: Dale R. Sheely, Sr., Chair.
Director: Alyce Sheely.
Trustee: Huntington National Bank.
EIN: 347012061

7591
William M. Shinnick Educational Fund
3608 Maple Ave.
Zanesville, OH 43701-3771 (740) 452-2273
Contact: William M. Shinnick, Admin. Asst.

Established in 1923 in Ohio.
Donors: William M. Shinnick; Eunice Hale Buckingham.
Foundation type: Independent foundation.
Financial data (yr. ended 06/30/14): Assets, $5,148,805 (M); gifts received, $402,830; expenditures, $354,608; qualifying distributions, $302,236; giving activities include $261,000 for grants.
Purpose and activities: Scholarship awards and loans to students who are residents of Muskingum County, Ohio.
Fields of interest: Higher education.
Type of support: Student aid; Loans to individuals.
Limitations: Applications accepted. Giving limited to residents of Muskingum County, OH.
Publications: Application guidelines; Informational brochure.
Application information: Application form required.
Initial approach: Telephone
Deadline(s): June 30
Board meeting date(s): Varies
Officers: Thomas Price, Pres.; Jody Ballas; Barbara Cornell, Secy.
Trustees: William S. Barry; C. Trafford Dick; Mark Watson; Terry Martin; William D. Joseph.
Number of staff: 1 full-time professional.
EIN: 314394168

7592
The Jeff and Jennie Sidwell Family Foundation
5240 Wortman Rd.
Zanesville, OH 43701-9382 (740) 849-2422

Established in 2006 in Ohio.
Donor: Sidwell Materials, Inc.
Foundation type: Company-sponsored foundation.
Financial data (yr. ended 12/31/14): Assets, $399,673; gifts received, $250,000; expenditures, $271,500; qualifying distributions, $271,500.
Purpose and activities: The foundation supports nonprofit organizations involved with health care, health organizations, and youth development.
Fields of interest: Health; Diseases and conditions; Youth development.
Limitations: Applications accepted. Giving primarily in OH.
Application information:
Initial approach: Proposal
Deadline(s): None

Officers: Jeffrey Sidwell, Pres.; Jennie Sidwell, V.P.; Adam Sidwell, Secy.
EIN: 203991810

7593
Sinai Scholars Inc.
100 E. 3rd St., 5th Fl.
Dayton, OH 45402-2119

Established in 2009 in Ohio.
Donors: Joel Vandersluis; Adam Waldman; Lee Schear; Lee & Patti Schear Family Foundation; Ervin Pavlosky.
Foundation type: Independent foundation.
Financial data (yr. ended 12/31/12): Assets, $156,225 (M); gifts received, $372,800; expenditures, $342,192; qualifying distributions, $280,015; giving activities include $280,015 for grants.
Fields of interest: Education; Judaism.
Limitations: Applications not accepted.
Application information: Unsolicited requests for funds not accepted.
Officer: Lee Schear, Pres.
Directors: John M. Cloud; Patricia J. Schear.
EIN: 270550342

7594
Skestos Family Foundation
147 E. Deshler Ave.
Columbus, OH 43206-2623

Established in 2007 in Ohio.
Donor: George A. Skestos.
Foundation type: Independent foundation.
Financial data (yr. ended 12/31/13): Assets, $0 (M); gifts received, $300,000; expenditures, $305,170; qualifying distributions, $303,330; giving activities include $303,330 for 11 grants (high: $155,000; low: $500).
Fields of interest: Education; University education; Youth development; Domestic violence shelters.
Limitations: Applications not accepted. Giving primarily in OH. No grants to individuals.
Application information: Contributes only to pre-selected organizations.
Officers and Trustees: George A. Skestos, Pres. and Trustee; Terrie L. Rice, Secy.-Treas.; Stephanie K. Gabriele; Alexandra T. Holmes; Jason J. Skestos.
EIN: 260563890

7595
Skyler Foundation
P.O. Box 145496
Cincinnati, OH 45250-5496
Application address: c/o Charles Schiff, 3457 Observatory Pl., Cincinnati, OH 45208, tel.: (513) 870-2580

Established in 1994 in Ohio.
Donor: John J. Schiff, Jr.
Foundation type: Independent foundation.
Financial data (yr. ended 09/30/15): Assets, $9,883,993 (M); gifts received, $1,500,500; expenditures, $441,587; qualifying distributions, $409,275; giving activities include $409,000 for 16 grants (high: $75,000; low: $5,000).
Fields of interest: Arts and culture; Arts education; Education; Elementary and secondary education;

Higher education; Specialty hospital care; Dental care; Astronomy; Child welfare.
Type of support: General support; Program development.
Limitations: Applications accepted. Giving primarily in Cincinnati, OH. No grants to individuals.
Application information:
Initial approach: 1-page letter
Deadline(s): None
Board meeting date(s): Annually
Trustees: Marguerite Gieske; Charles O. Schiff; John J. Schiff III.
EIN: 311420623

7596
Slitzer Lapausky Foundation
1422 Euclid Ave., Ste. 1130
Cleveland, OH 44115-2065 2167716960

Donors: Bonnie Wade-Lapausky; Rodney M Bonnie.
Foundation type: Independent foundation.
Financial data (yr. ended 12/31/14): Assets, $2,378,314; expenditures, $201,235; qualifying distributions, $176,358.
Fields of interest: Health; Liver diseases.
Type of support: General support; Research.
Limitations: Applications not accepted. Giving primarily in Towson, MD.
Application information: Unsolicited requests for funds not accepted.
Trustee: The Private Trust Co.
EIN: 454924885

7597
The Smiley Family Charitable Foundation
6364 Pearl Rd., Ste. 301
Parma Heights, OH 44130

Established in 1997 in Ohio.
Donor: Raymond E. Smiley.
Foundation type: Independent foundation.
Financial data (yr. ended 12/31/13): Assets, $4,037,343 (M); gifts received, $5,000; expenditures, $119,531; qualifying distributions, $121,368; giving activities include $121,368 for 42 + grants (high: $21,810).
Fields of interest: Education; Religion; Human services.
Limitations: Applications not accepted. Giving primarily in OH. No grants to individuals.
Application information: Unsolicited requests for funds not accepted.
Officers: Raymond E. Smiley, Pres. and Treas.; Eleanor M. Smiley, Secy.
EIN: 311543239

7598
Lloyd L. and Louise K. Smith Foundation
106 S. Main St., 16th Fl.
Akron, OH 44308-1418 (330) 384-7301
E-mail: brenda.moubray@firstmerit.com

Established in 1992 in Ohio.
Donor: Lloyd L. Smith Trust.
Foundation type: Independent foundation.
Financial data (yr. ended 12/31/14): Assets, $5,725,046; expenditures, $277,898; qualifying distributions, $245,900.

Fields of interest: Arts and culture; Education; Nonprofits; Health; Human services; Food aid; Child welfare.

Type of support: General support; Matching grants; Regranting; Continuing support; Annual campaigns; Capital campaigns; Capital and infrastructure; Equipment; Endowments; Program development; Scholarships; Research.

Limitations: Applications accepted. Giving primarily in Summit County, OH. No grants to individuals.

Application information:

   Initial approach: Letter

   Deadline(s): None

   Board meeting date(s): As needed

Trustees: Allan Johnson, Esq.; Orville L. Reed III; FirstMerit Bank, N.A.

EIN: 341717038

7599

The Southard Foundation

10004 Tarrington Ct.

Powell, OH   43065-8498

Donors: Robert C. Southard; Dorothy P. Southard.

Foundation type: Independent foundation.

Financial data (yr. ended 12/31/13): Assets, $1,626,512 (M); expenditures, $203,490; qualifying distributions, $203,150; giving activities include $196,453 for 17 grants (high: $37,500; low: $1,500).

Fields of interest: Museums; Elementary and secondary education; Hospital care; Human services; Child welfare.

Type of support: General support.

Limitations: Applications not accepted. Giving primarily in Columbus, OH; some giving in FL. No grants to individuals.

Application information: Contributes only to pre-selected organizations.

Officers: Stephen Rowland Southard, Pres.; M. Martha Southard, V.P.

EIN: 311229974

7600

Stafast Foundation Inc.

(also known as Stay Fast Foundation Inc.)

505 Lake Shore Blvd.

Painesville, OH   44077-1121   (440) 479-8652

Contact: Joan M. Selle, Tr.

Application address: 7767 Litchfield, Mentor, OH 44060, tel.: (440) 479-8652

Established in 1985 in Ohio.

Donors: Stafast Products Inc.; Donald S. Selle; Joan M. Selle.

Foundation type: Company-sponsored foundation.

Financial data (yr. ended 12/31/13): Assets, $241,491 (M); gifts received, $234,800; expenditures, $197,557; qualifying distributions, $190,000; giving activities include $190,000 for 12 grants (high: $50,000; low: $2,000).

Purpose and activities: The foundation supports organizations involved with radio, human services, and Christianity.

Fields of interest: Religion; Human services; Youth development.

Type of support: General support.

Limitations: Applications accepted. Giving primarily in CO, FL, NC, and OH.

Application information: Application form required.

   Initial approach: Letter

   Deadline(s): June 30

Trustees: Donald S. Selle; Joan M. Selle.

EIN: 341485142

7601

Sam S. & Rose Stein Foundation

165 E. Washington Row

Sandusky, OH   44870-2610   (419) 625-8324

Contact: M.J. Stauffer, Secy.

Foundation type: Independent foundation.

Financial data (yr. ended 12/31/13): Assets, $4,042,973 (M); expenditures, $307,917; qualifying distributions, $262,160; giving activities include $244,138 for 28 grants (high: $40,000; low: $500).

Purpose and activities: Giving generally for organizations that will benefit ailing youth, ailing aged and medical research.

Fields of interest: Health; Human services; Child welfare.

Limitations: Giving primarily in northern OH, with emphasis on Erie County. No grants to individuals.

Application information:

   Deadline(s): None

Officers and Trustees: Marcia L. Goff, Pres. and Trustee; Martin E. Goff, V.P. and Trustee; M.J. Stauffer, Secy. and Trustee; David F. Goff, Treas. and Trustee.

EIN: 341406795

7602

Steiner-King Foundation

(formerly The Joseph L. Steiner and Marjorie S. Steiner Foundation)

7300 Wood Meadow Dr.

Cincinnati, OH   45243

Established in 1994 in Ohio.

Donor: Joseph Steiner.

Foundation type: Independent foundation.

Financial data (yr. ended 12/31/13): Assets, $4,386,946 (M); expenditures, $290,933; qualifying distributions, $288,801; giving activities include $209,255 for 62 grants (high: $30,000; low: $200).

Purpose and activities: Giving primarily for human services and religious organizations.

Fields of interest: Arts and culture; Education; Diseases and conditions; Religion; Human rights; Human services.

Limitations: Applications not accepted. Giving primarily in CA, CO, and NY. No grants to individuals.

Application information: Contributes only to pre-selected organizations.

Trustees: Elizabeth King; Margaret King; John A. Steiner; Michael Steiner.

EIN: 311420608

7603

Robert & Christine Steinmann Family

2011 Madison Rd.

Cincinnati, OH   45208

Contact: Hugh Campbell

E-mail: kfister@rocketmail.com; *Main URL:* http://www.steinmannfoundation.org

Established in 2003 in Ohio.

Donors: Robert P. Steinmann; Steinmann Pharmacy, Inc.

Foundation type: Independent foundation.

Financial data (yr. ended 12/31/13): Assets, $4,509,778 (M); expenditures, $230,514; qualifying distributions, $198,027; giving activities include $198,027 for grants.

Purpose and activities: Giving primarily for the support of Judeo/Christian organizations, educational scholarships in pharmacy and nursing, aid and medical care for the elderly and needy, and cancer research, with a focus in the greater Cincinnati, Ohio, area.

Fields of interest: Graduate and professional education; Nursing care; Geriatrics; Christianity; Senior services.

Type of support: Scholarships; Endowments.

Limitations: Applications accepted. Giving primarily in OH. No support for political or conduit or for-profit organizations. No grants for overhead operating needs, funds to service debt, travel or group trips or for video productions.

Application information: See foundation website for complete application guidelines. Application form required.

   Deadline(s): Varies

Directors: Bruce Fister; Kent D. Fister; Carolyn Rose; Robert Stretch.

EIN: 200166460

7604

Harry Stensen Memorial Trust Foundation

c/o KeyBank N.A.

P.O. Box 10099

Toledo, OH   43699-0099   (419) 259-8655

Contact: Diane H. Ohns

Established in 1986 in Ohio.

Foundation type: Independent foundation.

Financial data (yr. ended 05/31/13): Assets, $2,606,487 (M); expenditures, $254,448; qualifying distributions, $212,639; giving activities include $206,100 for 20 grants (high: $57,000; low: $1,300).

Fields of interest: Education; Nonprofits; Community and economic development; Human services.

Type of support: General support; Regranting; Capital and infrastructure; Equipment.

Limitations: Applications accepted. Giving limited to the Port Clinton, OH, area. No grants to individuals.

Application information: Application form required.

   Initial approach: Letter

   Deadline(s): Apr.

Trustee: KeyBank, N.A.

EIN: 346619471

7605

The STERIS Foundation

5960 Heisley Rd.

Mentor, OH   44060

Established in 1995 in Ohio.

Donor: STERIS Corp.

Foundation type: Company-sponsored foundation.

Financial data (yr. ended 03/31/14): Assets, $836,880 (M); gifts received, $1,005,211; expenditures, $236,094; qualifying distributions, $236,082; giving activities include $235,500 for 8 grants (high: $200,000; low: $500).

Purpose and activities: The foundation supports organizations involved with arts and culture, health, human services, heart disease, diabetes, and human services.

Fields of interest: Arts and culture; Theater; Nonprofits; Health; Hospital care; Nursing care; Diabetes; Heart and circulatory system diseases; Human services.

Type of support: General support; Regranting.

Limitations: Applications not accepted. Giving primarily in areas of company operations in OH. No grants to individuals.

Application information: Contributes only to pre-selected organizations.

Officers and Trustees: Gerard J. Reis, Pres.; Suzanne Forsythe, V.P.; Dennis Patton, Co-Secy.; Jane Steger, Co-Secy.; John R. Schloss, Treas. and Trustee; Walter Rosebrough; Michael Tokich; Les Vinney; Donald Whitehouse.

EIN: 341807803

7606
Sterling Family Foundation
2000 Beaver Pl. Ave., S.W.
Canton, OH 44706-1963

Established in 2002 in Ohio.

Donors: W. Donald Sterling; William D. Sterling†; The Beaver Excavating Co.

Foundation type: Independent foundation.

Financial data (yr. ended 12/31/13): Assets, $2,929,838 (M); gifts received, $150,000; expenditures, $203,705; qualifying distributions, $193,451; giving activities include $186,000 for 14 grants (high: $70,000; low: $2,000).

Fields of interest: Agriculture; Religion; Human services.

Limitations: Applications not accepted. Giving primarily in OH. No grants to individuals.

Application information: Unsolicited requests for funds not accepted.

Officers and Trustees: W. Mark Sterling, Pres. and Trustee; Jeffrey W. Sterling, V.P. and Trustee; Richard Williams, Secy.-Treas. and Trustee; Mary Lou Sterling.

EIN: 753088351

7607
Stillson Foundation
c/o Fifth Third Bank, Trust Dept.
P.O. Box 630858
Cincinnati, OH 45263-0858
Application address: c/o Fifth Third Bank Attn.: Keri Randall, 38 Fountain Square Plz., MD1090CA, Cincinnati, OH 45263, tel.: (513) 534-8786

Foundation type: Independent foundation.

Financial data (yr. ended 12/31/13): Assets, $7,655,887 (M); expenditures, $304,514; qualifying distributions, $227,982; giving activities include $205,000 for 8 grants (high: $100,000; low: $5,000).

Fields of interest: Arts and culture; Zoos; Botanical gardens; Nonprofits; Human services.

Type of support: General support; Capital campaigns; Program development; Regranting.

Limitations: Applications accepted. Giving primarily in the greater Cincinnati, OH area.

Application information: Application form required.
Initial approach: Request application form
Deadline(s): None

Trustee: Fifth Third Bank.

EIN: 311327107

7608
The Swagelok Foundation
6262 Cochran Rd.
Solon, OH 44139-3308

Established in 2000 in Ohio.

Donor: Swagelok Company.

Foundation type: Independent foundation.

Financial data (yr. ended 12/31/13): Assets, $3,400,259 (M); gifts received, $1,000,000; expenditures, $233,782; qualifying distributions, $233,782; giving activities include $232,975 for 41 grants (high: $25,000; low: $500).

Purpose and activities: Giving primarily for secondary education, as well as for health associations, children and social services, and federated giving programs.

Fields of interest: Arts and culture; Secondary education; Nonprofits; Diseases and conditions; Human services; Child welfare.

Type of support: Regranting.

Limitations: Applications not accepted. Giving primarily in OH. No grants to individuals.

Application information: Unsolicited requests for funds not accepted.

Officers and Trustees: Matt Lopiccolo, Pres. and Trustee; Anthony J. Coyne, Secy.; Douglas S. Spicer, Treas. and Trustee; Brooks Gerbitz; Edward A. Lozick; Greg Shaw; Sally Turner; Larry Vandendriessche.

EIN: 341923618

7609
Dudley Taft Charitable Foundation
c/o Fifth Third Bank
P.O. Box 630858
Cincinnati, OH 45263-0858
Application address: Dudley Taft Charitable Foundation, 312 Walnut St., Cincinnati, OH 45202, tel.: (513) 241-8880

Established in 1997 in Ohio.

Donor: Dudley Taft.

Foundation type: Independent foundation.

Financial data (yr. ended 12/31/13): Assets, $5,385,648 (M); expenditures, $266,344; qualifying distributions, $236,613; giving activities include $236,000 for 14 grants (high: $100,000; low: $1,000).

Fields of interest: Arts and culture; Museums; Education; Higher education; Nonprofits; Scouting programs.

Type of support: Regranting.

Limitations: Applications accepted. Giving primarily in the greater Cincinnati, OH, area. No grants to individuals.

Application information: Application form required.
Initial approach: Letter
Deadline(s): None

Officers: Dudley S. Taft, Pres.; David A. Kohnen, Secy.; Lee A. Carter, Treas.

EIN: 311532283

7610
Frank M. Tait Foundation
40 N. Main St., Ste. 1530
Dayton, OH 45423-1021 (937) 222-2401

Established in 1955 in Ohio.

Donors: Frank M. Tait†; Mrs. Frank M. Tait†.

Foundation type: Independent foundation.

Financial data (yr. ended 12/31/14): Assets, $7,818,153; expenditures, $435,697; qualifying distributions, $393,367.

Purpose and activities: Giving primarily for youth development.

Fields of interest: Arts and culture; Historical activities; Education; Science; Human services; Child development; Youth development.

Type of support: Annual campaigns; Matching grants; Capital and infrastructure; Equipment; Program development; Seed money.

Limitations: Applications accepted. Giving limited to Montgomery County, OH. No support for religious purposes. No grants to individuals, or for endowment funds, operating budgets, continuing support, emergency funds, deficit financing, research, publications, conferences, scholarships, fellowships or selective capital campaigns; no loans.

Publications: Grants list; Informational brochure (including application guidelines).

Application information: Application form required.
Initial approach: Contact foundation for the application form
Copies of proposal: 1
Deadline(s): Contact foundation for the deadline
Board meeting date(s): Quarterly
Final notification: 2 months

Officers: Irvin G. Bieser, Jr., Chair.; Allen M. Hill, Secy.-Treas.; Jennifer A. Roer, Exec. Dir.

Trustees: Thomas Breitenbach; R. Daniel Sadlier; James M. Woodhull II.

Number of staff: 1 part-time professional.

EIN: 316037499

7611
Taj Foundation
1174 E. Home Rd.
Springfield, OH 45503-6663 (937) 398-0054
Contact: Tajuddin Ahmed, Pres.

Established in 1987 in Ohio.

Donors: Tajuddin Ahmed; Shahana Ahmed; Satiad H. Siddiqi; Edith Siddiqi; Afshan Syed; Ashfaq Ahmed; Afshan Ahmed.

Foundation type: Independent foundation.

Financial data (yr. ended 12/31/13): Assets, $4,242,282 (M); gifts received, $125,207; expenditures, $259,851; qualifying distributions, $230,552; giving activities include $230,552 for 18 grants (high: $100,500; low: $500).

Purpose and activities: Giving primarily for education and Islamic associations.

Fields of interest: Arts and culture; Education; Health; Islam; Human services; International relations.

Type of support: General support; Scholarships.

Application information: Application form required.
Initial approach: Letter
Deadline(s): None

Officers: Tajuddin Ahmed, Pres.; Ashfaq Ahmed, V.P.; Afshan Syed, Secy.-Treas.

EIN: 311191104

7612
Nelson Talbott Foundation
37070 Shaker Blvd.
Chagrin Falls, OH 44022-6644

Established in 1947 in Ohio.
Donor: Nelson S. Talbott.
Foundation type: Independent foundation.
Financial data (yr. ended 09/30/13): Assets, $4,085,284 (M); expenditures, $242,848; qualifying distributions, $199,235; giving activities include $199,235 for 120 grants (high: $35,000; low: $50).
Purpose and activities: Giving primarily for conservation programs and local charities.
Fields of interest: Arts and culture; Higher education; Environment; Natural resources; Human services.
Limitations: Applications not accepted. Giving primarily in Washington, DC, and Cleveland, OH. No grants to individuals.
Application information: Contributes only to pre-selected organizations.
Trustees: A.L. Fabems; E. P. Talbott; Nelson S. Talbott.
EIN: 316039441

7613
Paul P. Tell Foundation, Inc.
195 S. Main St., Ste. 200
Akron, OH 44308-1314 3304348355

Established in 1952 in Ohio.
Donors: Anne P. Tell; David J. Schipper; Michael Tell†; Paul P. Tell Sr. Trust.
Foundation type: Independent foundation.
Financial data (yr. ended 12/31/14): Assets, $12,963,650; expenditures, $241,144; qualifying distributions, $215,300.
Purpose and activities: Giving for the furtherance of Evangelical Christianity; on-going grants primarily for foreign missions.
Fields of interest: Christianity.
Type of support: Continuing support.
Limitations: Applications accepted. Giving in the U.S. with emphasis on OH. No support for educational institutions. No grants to individuals, or for building, start-up, or endowment funds, scholarships, fellowships, or matching gifts; no loans.
Application information:
  Initial approach: Proposal
  Deadline(s): None
Officers: David J. Schipper, Pres.; Terry Hollister, V.P.; Jean Anne Schipper, Secy.-Treas.
Trustees: Mary Bloom; David Fair; Peter Keslar.
EIN: 346537201

7614
Walter E. Terhune Memorial Fund
4900 Tiedman Rd., OH-01-49-0150
Brooklyn, OH 44144-2032 (419) 259-8218

Donor: Walter E. Terhune Memorial Endowment Trust.
Foundation type: Independent foundation.
Financial data (yr. ended 12/31/13): Assets, $10,307,783 (M); expenditures, $317,011; qualifying distributions, $257,179; giving activities include $240,500 for 28 grants (high: $40,000; low: $1,000).
Fields of interest: Arts and culture; Education; Human services.
Limitations: Applications accepted. Giving primarily in OH.
Application information: Application form required.

Initial approach: Letter
Deadline(s): Mar. 31 and Sept. 30
Trustee: Keybank N.A.
EIN: 352446722

7615
The Tetlak Foundation
c/o CJ D'Ambrosia, CPA
1900 E. 9th St., Ste. 3200
Cleveland, OH 44114-3485

Established in 1998 in Ohio.
Donor: Joseph F. Tetlak.
Foundation type: Independent foundation.
Financial data (yr. ended 12/31/14): Assets, $1,748,932 (M); expenditures, $309,460; qualifying distributions, $298,261; giving activities include $298,261 for grants.
Purpose and activities: Giving primarily for Roman Catholic charities and schools, the arts, and higher education.
Fields of interest: Arts and culture; Education; University education; Religion.
Limitations: Applications not accepted. Giving primarily in OH; some funding also in IN.
Application information: Unsolicited requests for funds not accepted.
Officers and Trustees: Joseph F. Tetlak, Pres. and Trustee; Jane T. Haylor, Secy. and Trustee; Edward G. Ptaszek, Jr., Treas. and Trustee.
EIN: 341880531

7616
The Thendara Foundation, Inc.
425 Walnut St., Ste. 1800
Cincinnati, OH 45202-3948

Established in 1984 in Ohio.
Donors: C. Lawson Reed†; Dorothy W. Reed.
Foundation type: Independent foundation.
Financial data (yr. ended 12/31/13): Assets, $10,083,283 (M); expenditures, $506,317; qualifying distributions, $403,792; giving activities include $379,245 for 121 grants (high: $40,000; low: $500).
Purpose and activities: Giving primarily for the arts, and social services.
Fields of interest: Arts and culture; Education; Environment; Health; Social sciences; Film and video; Human services; Child welfare.
Type of support: General support; Policy, advocacy and systems reform.
Limitations: Applications not accepted. Giving primarily in CA and CO; some giving also in NY and OH. No grants to individuals.
Application information: Contributes only to pre-selected organizations.
Trustees: James M. Anderson; Janet Reed Goss; C.L. Reed III; Dorothy Foster Reed; Foster A. Reed.
EIN: 311126072

7617
H. L. Thompson, Jr. Family Foundation
c/o KeyBank N.A.
10 W. 2nd St., 26th Fl.
Dayton, OH 45402

Established in 2000 in Ohio.
Donor: Henry L. Thompson, Jr. Trust.
Foundation type: Independent foundation.

Financial data (yr. ended 12/31/14): Assets, $6,234,310 (M); expenditures, $295,794; qualifying distributions, $277,476; giving activities include $270,000 for 36 grants (high: $47,000; low: $1,000).
Purpose and activities: Giving primarily for education, particularly to an Episcopal school; funding also for museums, a community foundation, animal welfare, and for a center for abused children.
Fields of interest: Museums; Education; Land resources; Animal welfare; Foundations; Child abuse; Christianity.
Limitations: Applications not accepted. Giving primarily in CT, FL, MA, PA, and WV. No grants to individuals.
Application information: Unsolicited requests for funds not accepted.
Trustee: KeyBank, N.A.
EIN: 341912416

7618
The Throckmorton Foundation
39 E. Market St., Ste. 402
Akron, OH 44308-2032 (330) 258-2394
Contact: Mark A. Mosley, Trust Off., Huntington National Bank

Established in 2002 in Ohio.
Donor: The Morford C. Throckmorton Trust.
Foundation type: Independent foundation.
Financial data (yr. ended 06/30/13): Assets, $5,946,860 (M); gifts received, $5,196; expenditures, $356,145; qualifying distributions, $298,138; giving activities include $298,138 for grants to individuals.
Purpose and activities: Scholarships to individuals of Native American or African American descent who demonstrate economic need and who are attending Grove City College or other colleges or universities in eastern Ohio or western Pennsylvania. Giving also for general scholarship funds.
Fields of interest: Higher education.
Type of support: Scholarships; Student aid.
Limitations: Applications accepted. Giving limited to eastern OH and western PA.
Application information: The college, university, or institution of higher learning will present to the trustee a list of candidates who meet the criteria, and the trustee will determine the recipients and the amounts to be awarded.
Trustees: Neil A. Maly; John Rasnik; The Huntington National Bank.
EIN: 616288548

7619
The TKBW Private Foundation
8007 Airport Hwy., Ste. B
Holland, OH 43528 (419) 866-8190

Established in 1999 in Ohio.
Donors: Toy D. Keeble; Bruce W. Wetzel.
Foundation type: Independent foundation.
Financial data (yr. ended 12/31/14): Assets, $6,379,581 (M); expenditures, $326,933; qualifying distributions, $291,864.
Fields of interest: Education; Health; Human services.
Type of support: General support.
Limitations: Applications accepted. Giving primarily in OH.
Application information: Application form required.

Initial approach: Proposal
Deadline(s): None
Trustees: Amy C. Husted; Stacy L. Owen; Bruce W. Wetzel.
EIN: 341903674

7620
The Dennis and Sara Trachsel Foundation
P.O. Box 747
Marion, OH 43301-0747
Application address: c/o Kevin R. Hall, 355 E. Center St., Marion, OH 43302, tel.: (740) 383-6109

Established in 1997 in Ohio.
Donor: Dennis L. Trachsel.
Foundation type: Independent foundation.
Financial data (yr. ended 12/31/14): Assets, $6,207,927 (M); expenditures, $396,787; qualifying distributions, $286,349; giving activities include $60,000 for 2 grants (high: $30,000; low: $30,000), and $175,231 for 21 grants to individuals (high: $15,000; low: $4,080).
Purpose and activities: Scholarship awards to students attending any accredited college, university trade school or technical school.
Fields of interest: Higher education.
Type of support: Scholarships; Student aid.
Limitations: Applications accepted. Giving primarily in Marion, OH.
Application information: Application form required.
Initial approach: Proposal
Deadline(s): Apr. 4
Trustees: Kevin Hall; James Waddell; Jonathan Williamson.
EIN: 311472824

7621
Norman & Carol Traeger Foundation, Inc.
100 E. Campus View Blvd., Ste. 115
Columbus, OH 43235-4647 (614) 258-3191
Contact: Norman L. Traeger, Tr.

Established in 1980 in Ohio.
Donors: Carol Traeger; Norman L. Traeger.
Foundation type: Independent foundation.
Financial data (yr. ended 04/30/13): Assets, $3,589,866 (M); expenditures, $233,881; qualifying distributions, $196,310; giving activities include $196,310 for grants.
Purpose and activities: Giving primarily to Jewish schools, organizations, and temples.
Fields of interest: Education; Nonprofits; Judaism; Human services; Family services.
Type of support: General support; Annual campaigns; Program development; Scholarships; Regranting; Research.
Limitations: Applications accepted. Giving primarily in OH. No grants to individuals.
Application information: Application form required.
Initial approach: Letter
Deadline(s): None
Trustees: Carol Traeger; Norman L. Traeger; Alan Wassertrom.
EIN: 310988108

7622
Susan & John Turben Foundation
P.O. Box 22747
Beachwood, OH 44122-0747

Donors: John F. Turben; Dr. Susan H. Turben; John F. Turben Revocable Trust.
Foundation type: Independent foundation.
Financial data (yr. ended 12/31/13): Assets, $597,821; gifts received, $79,125; expenditures, $340,618; qualifying distributions, $305,479; giving activities include $305,479 for 64 grants (high: $30,270; low: $100).
Fields of interest: Education; Foundations; Specialty hospital care; Diseases and conditions; Protestantism; Catholicism.
Limitations: Applications not accepted. Giving primarily in OH.
Application information: Contributes only to pre-selected organizations.
Officers and Trustees: Dr. Susan H. Turben, Pres. and Trustee; John F. Turben, V.P. and Trustee; Thomas N. Littman, Secy.; Debra L. Bauman, Treas.; Sandra L. Keily-Kolb; James H. Kimberly; Newton S. Kimberly, Jr.; Mary S. Prien; Andrew Sikorovski; David C. Turben; Nicolas A. Turben.
EIN: 341725277

7623
Tuscarawas County Community Foundation
1323 4th St. NW
New Philadelphia, OH 44663-1205 (330) 602-6264
Contact: Scott Robinson, Exec. Dir.
E-mail: info@tuscfoundation.com; Main URL: http://tuscfoundation.com
Grant Awardees: http://tuscfoundation.com/grant-awardees
Scholarship Awardees: http://tuscfoundation.com/scholarship-awardees

Established in 2001 in Ohio.
Foundation type: Independent foundation.
Financial data (yr. ended 12/31/13): Assets, $9,071,905 (M); gifts received, $4,500; expenditures, $451,488; qualifying distributions, $374,941; giving activities include $325,192 for 32 grants (high: $55,000; low: $229).
Purpose and activities: The foundation's mission is to enhance the quality of life in the Tuscarawas County community through the strengthening of its educational, economic, social, and cultural fabrics by: 1) making charitable grants of investment income; 2) educating the community regarding the ways the needs of local citizens can be served; 3) attracting and investing endowment resources; and 4) being accountable for grantmaking and financial reporting to the community.
Fields of interest: Arts and culture; Humanities; Education; Environment; Health; Community and economic development; Human services.
Type of support: Continuing support; Grants to individuals; Capacity-building and technical assistance; Annual campaigns; Capital campaigns; Capital and infrastructure; Equipment; Scholarships; Student aid.
Limitations: Applications accepted. Giving primarily limited to Tuscarawas County, OH, area. No support for religious organizations. No grants to individuals (except through scholarship funds), operating expenses of well-established organizations, deficit financing, endowment funds, annual appeals, or conference or recognition events.
Publications: Application guidelines; Financial statement; Grants list; Informational brochure; Occasional report.
Application information: Application form required.

Initial approach: Personal contact by letter or telephone
Copies of proposal: 6
Deadline(s): June 15
Board meeting date(s): Every 3 months
Final notification: July
Officers and Directors: Robert R. Gerber, Pres. and Director; Karen Jenkins, V.P. and Director; Renee Brown Parker, Secy. and Director; Janine Garber, Treas.; Scott Robinson, Exec. Dir.; Alan Bambeck; John Beitzel; Blair A. Hillyer; John Maxwell; Kent Watson.
Number of staff: 1 part-time support.
EIN: 341930804

7624
Tuscora Park Health & Wellness Foundation
460 W. Paige Ave.
Barberton, OH 44203-2564 (330) 745-5995
Contact: Debora Rolland
FAX: (330) 745-3990;
E-mail: tuschealthfdn@yahoo.com; Main URL: http://www.barbertoncf.org/tphwf
Blog: http://www.barbertoncf.org/tphwf-news

Established in 1996 in Ohio.
Foundation type: Independent foundation.
Financial data (yr. ended 12/31/13): Assets, $4,839,104 (M); gifts received, $48; expenditures, $268,939; qualifying distributions, $210,500; giving activities include $177,000 for 28 grants (high: $25,000; low: $1,500), and $33,500 for 7 grants to individuals (high: $6,500; low: $2,000).
Purpose and activities: Giving primarily to charitable organizations that share the foundation's mission of providing health and wellness opportunities for the citizens of Barberton, Ohio, and surrounding communities. The foundation also provides nursing scholarships to residents of the historical service area of Barberton Citizens Hospital, now Summa Barberton, for the purpose of encouraging careers in nursing.
Fields of interest: Education; Graduate and professional education; Health; Nursing care; Human services.
Type of support: Equipment; Program development; Convening; Student aid.
Limitations: Applications accepted. Giving primarily for the benefit of residents of Barberton, OH, and surrounding communities. No support for religious organizations. No grants for membership drives, endowments, lobbying activities, deficits, or operating expenses.
Application information: See web site for application policies, guidelines and forms or contact the foundation for application guidelines and materials. Application form required.
Initial approach: Proposal
Copies of proposal: 6
Deadline(s): Jan. 2, Apr. 1, July 1, and Oct. 1
Board meeting date(s): Feb., May, Aug., and Nov.
Final notification: Within 1 week of board meeting
Officers and Governors: Pat Roberts, Pres. and Director; Aaron Lepp, Vice-Pres. and Director; Michael Moldvay, Treas. and Director; Patti Cleary; Leonard Foster; Douglas Gormley; Duane Isham; Kathy Jobe; Larry Lauter; Patrick McGrath; William Roderick.
Number of staff: 3 full-time professional.
EIN: 341193807

7625
I. J. Van Huffel Foundation
c/o Farmers Trust
1625 Niles Cortland Rd., Ste. 2
Warren, OH 44484-1165 (330) 609-5057

Established in 1951 in Ohio.
Donor: Van Huffel Tube Corp.
Foundation type: Independent foundation.
Financial data (yr. ended 12/31/14): Assets,
$3,789,607; expenditures, $199,900; qualifying
distributions, $166,414 and $0 for set-asides.
Purpose and activities: Giving primarily for human
services and to Roman Catholic organizations.
Fields of interest: Arts and culture; Education;
Higher education; Nonprofits; Hospital care;
Hospice care; Protestantism; Catholicism; Human
services; Child welfare.
Type of support: Continuing support; Regranting;
Capital and infrastructure; Fundraising;
Scholarships.
Limitations: Applications accepted. Giving primarily
in OH. No grants to individuals.
Application information: Application form required.
 Initial approach: Letter
 Deadline(s): None
Trustee: Farmers Trust Co.
Directors: Kareen Klier; Evelyn M. Lawlor; Cheryle
Remley; Ruth A. Van Huffel.
EIN: 346516726

7626
Van Meter/Barnhart Family Fund
(formerly John N. Browning Family Fund L, Inc.)
c/o U.S. Bank, N.A.
P.O. Box 1118, ML CN-OH-W10X
Cincinnati, OH 45201-1118

Foundation type: Independent foundation.
Financial data (yr. ended 04/30/13): Assets,
$4,314,629 (M); expenditures, $210,540;
qualifying distributions, $193,102; giving activities
include $191,500 for 32 grants (high: $29,000;
low: $500).
Fields of interest: Arts and culture; Theater;
Education; Higher education; Health; Diseases and
conditions; Cancers; Public libraries; Protestantism;
Human services; Youth services; Scouting
programs.
Limitations: Applications not accepted. Giving
primarily in KY. No grants to individuals.
Application information: Unsolicited requests for
funds not accepted.
Officers: Florence V.M. Barnhart, Pres.; John Van
Meter, Secy.
Trustee: Isaac C. Van Meter, Jr.
EIN: 311284451

7627
The Venner Family Foundation
507 Red Rock Dr.
Wadsworth, OH 44281-2210

Donors: James Venner; Linda Venner; Clampco
Products Inc.
Foundation type: Independent foundation.
Financial data (yr. ended 12/31/13): Assets,
$3,520,790 (M); gifts received, $1,000,000;
expenditures, $147,870; qualifying distributions,
$146,100; giving activities include $146,100 for 55
grants (high: $46,000; low: $250).

Fields of interest: Arts and culture; Education;
Religion.
Limitations: Applications not accepted. Giving
primarily in OH.
Application information: Unsolicited requests for
funds not accepted.
Trustees: James Venner; Linda Venner.
EIN: 271272999

7628
Vista Foundation
1991 Madison Rd.
Cincinnati, OH 45208-3216 (513) 488-0053
Contact: Helen K. Heekin, Pres. and Tr.

Established in 1998 in Ohio.
Donors: Charles L. Heekin II; Charles L. Heekin
Charitable Lead Annuity Trust II.
Foundation type: Independent foundation.
Financial data (yr. ended 12/31/13): Assets,
$6,858,632 (M); gifts received, $613,999;
expenditures, $262,442; qualifying distributions,
$236,150; giving activities include $236,150 for 34
grants (high: $101,550; low: $100).
Fields of interest: Arts and culture; Education;
Environment; Nonprofits; Human services.
Type of support: Regranting.
Limitations: Applications accepted. Giving primarily
in Cincinnati, OH.
Application information: Application form required.
 Initial approach: Letter, not to exceed 3 pages
 Deadline(s): None
Officers and Trustees: Helen K. Heekin, Pres. and
Trustee; Charles L. Heekin II, V.P. and Trustee; Peter
Heekin, V.P. and Trustee; R. McShane Heekin, Secy.
and Trustee; Micaela Heekin, Treas. and Trustee.
EIN: 311347794

7629
The Phil Wagler Charitable Foundation
3710 Tabs Dr.
Uniontown, OH 44685

Established in 1988 in Ohio.
Donors: Phil Wagler; Wagler Homes of Akron, Inc.;
Wagler Homes of Cleveland, Inc.
Foundation type: Independent foundation.
Financial data (yr. ended 12/31/12): Assets,
$7,762,576 (M); expenditures, $614,218;
qualifying distributions, $419,800; giving activities
include $419,800 for grants.
Purpose and activities: Giving primarily to Christian
organizations and for human services.
Fields of interest: Christianity; Human services;
Food aid; Homeless shelters.
Type of support: General support.
Limitations: Applications not accepted. Giving
primarily in OH; some funding also in FL and MD. No
grants to individuals.
Application information: Contributes only to
pre-selected organizations.
Trustee: Phil Wagler.
EIN: 346886145

7630
Margaret M. Walker Charitable Foundation
c/o Farmers Trust Company
42 McClurg Rd.
Youngstown, OH 44512 (330) 743-7000

Donor: Margaret M. Walker Charitable Lead Trust.
Foundation type: Independent foundation.
Financial data (yr. ended 12/31/13): Assets,
$3,926,775 (M); expenditures, $219,314;
qualifying distributions, $197,680; giving activities
include $188,500 for 13 grants (high: $60,000;
low: $2,000).
Purpose and activities: Giving for Christian
ministries, relief services organizations, children,
women and family services, and food services.
Fields of interest: Christianity; Human services;
Food delivery; Family services; Women's services;
Infants and toddlers; Children; Adolescents;
Females; Female young adults; Males; Male adults;
Male young adults; Single parents; Ethnic and racial
groups; Homeless people; Low-income and poor
people; People with disabilities; People with
physical disabilities; Substance abusers.
Type of support: Capital and infrastructure; Capital
campaigns; Equipment; General support; Program
development.
Limitations: Applications accepted. Giving primarily
in PA. No grants to individuals.
Application information: Application form required.
 Initial approach: Letter
 Deadline(s): None
Trustee: Farmers Trust Company.
Advisors: Richard Epstein; Joe Evans; David Levine.
Number of staff: None.
EIN: 251790413

7631
Fred & Alice Wallace Charitable Memorial Foundation, Inc.
130 W. 2nd St., Ste. 924
Dayton, OH 45402-1501 (937) 223-8194
Contact: Dennis Hanaghan, Exec. Dir.
FAX: (937) 223-6967;
E-mail: jucelenhochwalt@yahoo.com

Established in 1978 in Ohio.
Foundation type: Independent foundation.
Financial data (yr. ended 12/31/13): Assets,
$9,752,225 (M); expenditures, $553,893;
qualifying distributions, $468,229; giving activities
include $424,063 for 19 grants (high: $75,000;
low: $5,063).
Fields of interest: Education; Diseases and
conditions.
Type of support: Continuing support; Capital
campaigns; Equipment; Emergency funds;
Convening; Curriculum development.
Limitations: Applications accepted. Giving limited to
OH, with emphasis on the Miami Valley area. No
grants to individuals.
Publications: Financial statement; Informational
brochure (including application guidelines); Program
policy statement.
Application information: Application form required.
 Initial approach: Letter of intent
 Copies of proposal: 4
 Deadline(s): None
 Board meeting date(s): July and Dec.
 Final notification: As appropriate
Officers: Dennis Hanaghan, Pres. and Exec. Dir.;
Jacob Worner, V.P.; J.R. Hochwalt, Secy.-Treas.
Number of staff: 1 full-time professional; 3 part-time
professional.
EIN: 310944135

7632
Wasserstrom Foundation
477 S. Front St.
Columbus, OH 43215-5625 (614) 228-6525
Contact: Rodney Wasserstrom, Tr.

Established in 1963 in Ohio.
Donors: Rodney Wasserstrom; N. Wasserstrom & Sons; Quadra-Tech; The Wasserstrom Co.; Amtekco Industries.
Foundation type: Independent foundation.
Financial data (yr. ended 09/30/14): Assets, $4,926,821 (M); gifts received, $319,500; expenditures, $258,584; qualifying distributions, $230,669; giving activities include $229,100 for 19 grants (high: $100,000; low: $100).
Fields of interest: Education; Nonprofits; Hospital care; Diseases and conditions; Judaism; Human services.
Type of support: General support; Annual campaigns; Capital campaigns; Endowments; Regranting.
Limitations: Applications accepted. Giving limited to central OH. No grants to individuals.
Application information: Application form required.
Initial approach: Letter of request on letterhead
Deadline(s): None
Board meeting date(s): Sept.
Trustees: Alan Wasserstrom; Rodney Wasserstrom.
EIN: 316041116

7633
Walter E. and Caroline H. Watson Foundation
c/o PNC Bank, N.A.
P.O. Box 94651
Cleveland, OH 44101-4651

Established in 1964 in Ohio.
Donor: Walter E. Watson†.
Foundation type: Independent foundation.
Financial data (yr. ended 12/31/13): Assets, $7,772,435 (M); expenditures, $378,676; qualifying distributions, $357,535; giving activities include $336,020 for 48 grants (high: $37,000; low: $1,000).
Purpose and activities: Giving to support public institutions of learning in Ohio and public and charitable institutions in the Youngstown and Mahoning Valley, Ohio, area; emphasis on health and hospitals, child development and youth agencies, community development, health and family services, and arts and cultural programs.
Fields of interest: Arts and culture; Education; Higher education; Nonprofits; Health; Diseases and conditions; Community and economic development; Human services; Child welfare.
Type of support: General support; Continuing support; Annual campaigns; Capital campaigns; Capital and infrastructure; Equipment; Program development; Regranting.
Limitations: Applications not accepted. Giving primarily in OH, including the Youngstown and Mahoning Valley areas. No grants to individuals, or for endowment funds.
Application information: Contributes only to pre-selected organizations.
Board meeting date(s): 3 or 4 times per year
Trustee: PNC Bank, N.A.
EIN: 346547726

7634
William M. Weiss Foundation
7490 Hunters Hollow Trail
Novelty, OH 44072-9541

Established in 1994 in Ohio.
Donor: William M. Weiss.
Foundation type: Independent foundation.
Financial data (yr. ended 12/31/14): Assets, $5,467,752; expenditures, $323,462; qualifying distributions, $289,250.
Fields of interest: Mental health care; Christianity; Judaism; Human services.
Type of support: General support.
Limitations: Applications not accepted. Giving primarily in NJ, NY, OH, and TX. No grants to individuals.
Application information: Contributes only to pre-selected organizations.
Directors: David Weiss; Jeffrey Weiss.
EIN: 341787366

7635
The Welty Family Foundation
3595 N. Fork Dr.
Akron, OH 44333-2137

Established in 1999 in Ohio.
Donor: Jerry H. Welty.
Foundation type: Independent foundation.
Financial data (yr. ended 12/31/14): Assets, $9,066,338; gifts received, $0; expenditures, $732,366; qualifying distributions, $406,702.
Fields of interest: Art museums; Hospice care; Protestantism; Human services.
Limitations: Applications not accepted. Giving primarily in Akron, OH. No grants to individuals.
Application information: Unsolicited requests for funds not accepted.
Officers: Jerry H. Welty, Pres.; Emily C. Welty, V.P.; Richard C. Fedorovich, Treas.
Trustees: Monica Welty Brown; Ronald S. Kopp; Chad C. Welty.
EIN: 341908053

7636
Wightman-Wieber Foundation
(formerly The Michelle Wightman Charitable Foundation)
100 E. Water St.
Sandusky, OH 44870 (419) 625-8424
Contact: Marla Smith

Established in 1999 in Ohio.
Foundation type: Independent foundation.
Financial data (yr. ended 12/31/13): Assets, $6,081,750 (M); expenditures, $296,814; qualifying distributions, $264,427; giving activities include $252,453 for 62 grants (high: $25,000; low: $500).
Fields of interest: Education; Foundations; Disasters and emergency management; Human services; Family services.
Limitations: Applications accepted. Giving primarily in the Sandusky/Erie County, OH, community. No grants to individuals.
Application information: Application form required.
Initial approach: Request application form
Deadline(s): Applications accepted between Mar. 1 and Sep. 1 of each year

Officers and Trustees: Gene Kidwell, Pres. and Trustee; Kevin Lutz, Secy.-Treas.; Ann Murray; Darlene Lowery; George Mylander; Karleen Wieber; Rhonda Watt; KeyBank, N.A.
EIN: 341831533

7637
The E. F. Wildermuth Foundation
1014 Dublin Rd.
Columbus, OH 43215-1116 (614) 487-0040
Contact: Robert W. Lee, Treas.

Foundation type: Independent foundation.
Financial data (yr. ended 12/31/13): Assets, $4,070,682 (M); expenditures, $263,457; qualifying distributions, $194,392; giving activities include $168,000 for 13 grants (high: $42,500; low: $1,000).
Purpose and activities: Giving primarily for higher education, including optometry programs at colleges and universities; funding also for human services, as well as to a children's hospital.
Fields of interest: Ballet; Higher education; Specialty hospital care; Eye diseases; Protestantism; Human services.
Type of support: Research.
Limitations: Applications accepted. Giving primarily in OH and contiguous states. No grants to individuals.
Application information:
Initial approach: Proposal
Deadline(s): July 1
Officers: Chris Campbell, Chair.; John Campbell, Pres.; Elizabeth Patterson, Secy.; Robert W. Lee, Treas.
Trustees: Karl Borton; Thomas Borton; Patrick Campbell; Kathleen Glumac; David T. Patterson; Jonathon Slaughter.
EIN: 316050202

7638
Williams Foundation
P.O. Box 94651
Cleveland, OH 44101-4651

Established in 1938 in Ohio.
Donors: Harriette R. Downey; William J. Williams; Helen D. Williams; Mary Frances W. Clauder; Lawrence H. Kyte, Jr.; B.J. Development LLC.
Foundation type: Independent foundation.
Financial data (yr. ended 12/31/12): Assets, $8,258,293 (M); gifts received, $50,861; expenditures, $322,287; qualifying distributions, $284,000; giving activities include $284,000 for grants.
Purpose and activities: Giving primarily for education, health, human services, and to Roman Catholic churches.
Fields of interest: Art museums; Education; Higher education; Zoos; Health; Catholicism; Human services.
Type of support: General support.
Limitations: Applications not accepted. Giving primarily in Cincinnati, OH; some funding also in Cleveland. Generally no grants to individuals.
Application information: Contributes only to pre-selected organizations.
Trustees: Mary Frances W. Clauder; Sharon W. Frisbie; Carol W. Jodar; Lawrence H. Kyte, Jr.; Ryan

Kyte; Helen D. Williams; Richard F. Williams; Thomas L. Williams; W. Joseph Williams, Jr.
EIN: 316032504

7639
The Clyde Williams Foundation
345 Greenbriar Dr.
Avon Lake, OH 44012-2155

Established in 2002 in Ohio.
Donor: The Williams Family Foundation.
Foundation type: Independent foundation.
Financial data (yr. ended 12/31/14): Assets, $662,027 (M); expenditures, $211,584; qualifying distributions, $204,891; giving activities include $203,550 for 7 grants (high: $145,000; low: $1,050).
Fields of interest: Higher education; Eye diseases; Protestantism.
Limitations: Applications not accepted. Giving primarily in Cleveland, OH.
Application information: Unsolicited requests for funds not accepted.
Trustees: Karen A.P. Assink.
EIN: 010671468

7640
Williamson Family Foundation
8399 Tippecanoe Rd.
Canfield, OH 44406-8106

Donors: WKBN Broadcasting Corp.; Warren P. Williamson III; Lowry A. Stewart; Martha J. Stewart.
Foundation type: Company-sponsored foundation.
Financial data (yr. ended 12/31/13): Assets, $2,042,002 (M); gifts received, $200; expenditures, $301,021; qualifying distributions, $276,465; giving activities include $276,465 for 4 grants (high: $200,000; low: $250).
Purpose and activities: The foundation supports historical societies and hospitals and organizations involved with education, animals and wildlife, and Huntington's disease.
Fields of interest: Historic preservation; Education; Higher education; Aquariums; Domesticated animals; Nonprofits; Hospital care; Diseases and conditions.
Type of support: General support; Regranting.
Limitations: Applications not accepted. Giving primarily in CA and OH. No grants to individuals.
Application information: Unsolicited requests for funds not accepted.
Officers: Warren P. Williamson III, Chair.; John D. Williamson II, Vice-Chair.; Martha Stewart, Secy.-Treas.
Trustees: John Boydston; Susan Brownlee; Lowry Stewart; Joseph Bradley Williamson; Lynn Williamson; Warren P. Williamson IV.
EIN: 346568495

7641
J. B. & Garnet A. Wilson Charitable Trust
P.O. Box 686
Waverly, OH 45690-0686 (740) 947-2727

Donor: Garnet A. Wilson†.
Foundation type: Independent foundation.
Financial data (yr. ended 12/31/13): Assets, $2,087,744 (M); expenditures, $234,998;

qualifying distributions, $219,491; giving activities include $202,503 for grants.
Purpose and activities: Scholarships only to Pike County students attending a state-supported college or university in OH.
Fields of interest: Higher education.
Type of support: Student aid.
Limitations: Applications accepted. Giving limited to residents and graduates of Pike County, OH, schools.
Application information: Application form required.
Initial approach: Letter
Deadline(s): Prior to 1st year of college
Trustees: Blaine Beekman; Billy S. Moore; Glenda Williams.
EIN: 310983188

7642
Thomas A. Wilson Foundation
c/o PNC Bank N.A.
P.O. Box 94651
Cleveland, OH 44101-4651
Application address: John Montoya, PNC Bank, N.A.,, 2 PNC Plz., 7th Fl., 620 Liberty Ave., Pittsburgh, PA 15222, tel.: (412) 768-8538

Established in 1971 in Pennsylvania.
Foundation type: Independent foundation.
Financial data (yr. ended 12/31/13): Assets, $6,640,124 (M); expenditures, $445,401; qualifying distributions, $413,284; giving activities include $385,000 for 1 grant.
Purpose and activities: Giving primarily for Christian education and for health care programs.
Fields of interest: Health; Christianity.
Type of support: General support.
Limitations: Applications accepted. Giving primarily in McKeesport, PA. No grants to individuals.
Application information: Application form required.
Initial approach: Letter
Deadline(s): None
Trustee: PNC Bank, N.A.
EIN: 237358862

7643
Milton A. & Roslyn Z. Wolf Family Foundation
25700 Science Park Dr., Ste. 350
Beachwood, OH 44122-7326

Established in 2002 in Ohio.
Donors: Wolf Real Estate; Roslyn Z. Wolf; Milton Wolf†.
Foundation type: Independent foundation.
Financial data (yr. ended 12/31/13): Assets, $6,888,615 (M); expenditures, $454,974; qualifying distributions, $418,062; giving activities include $418,000 for 8 grants (high: $100,000; low: $20,000).
Fields of interest: Education; Nonprofits; Judaism.
Type of support: Regranting.
Limitations: Applications not accepted. Giving primarily in New York, NY, and Cleveland, OH.
Application information: Contributes only to pre-selected organizations.
Officers: Caryn Wolf Wechsler, Pres.; Nancy Wolf, V.P.; Sherri Wolf, V.P.; Michael A. Shemo, Secy.; Michael Holowaty, Treas.
EIN: 030485546

7644
The Wolfe Family Charitable Foundation
1 Seagate, Ste. 1960
Toledo, OH 43604-1522

Established in 1993 in Ohio.
Donors: Frederic D. Wolfe; Christine Wolfe Nichols; Mary T. Wolfe.
Foundation type: Independent foundation.
Financial data (yr. ended 12/31/13): Assets, $7,860,793 (M); gifts received, $8,977; expenditures, $354,781; qualifying distributions, $337,978; giving activities include $330,750 for 66 grants (high: $105,000; low: $50).
Fields of interest: Orchestral music; Education; Higher education; Human services.
Limitations: Applications not accepted. Giving primarily in OH. No grants to individuals.
Application information: Contributes only to pre-selected organizations.
Trustees: John Held; Christine W. Nichols; William A. Nichols; Elizabeth T. Wolfe; Frederic D. Wolfe; Frederica R. Wolfe; Mary T. Wolfe.
EIN: 341756997

7645
Woodruff Foundation
c/o Foundation Management Svcs.
1422 Euclid Ave., Ste. 966
Cleveland, OH 44115-2001 (216) 621-2901
Contact: Karen Thompson-Shaheen; Kara McCullough
FAX: (216) 621-8198;
E-mail: ktshaheen@fmscleveland.com; E-mail for Karen Thompson-Shaheen: ktshaheen@fmscleveland.com; e-mail for Kara McCullough: kmccullough@fmscleveland.com; Main URL: http://www.fmscleveland.com/woodruff Grants List: http://www.fmscleveland.com/woodruff/grants.cfm

Established in 1986 in Ohio.
Foundation type: Independent foundation.
Financial data (yr. ended 12/31/13): Assets, $11,934,797 (M); expenditures, $577,820; qualifying distributions, $708,141; giving activities include $432,450 for 25 grants (high: $68,000; low: $1,000).
Purpose and activities: Giving primarily to support the development and delivery of mental health services in Cuyahoga County, OH. Specifically, the foundation seeks to fund projects that will foster and enhance: the treatment of persons affected by mental disorders and chemical dependency; educational programs related to mental health, the coordination of mental health resources in the community; research into the causes, nature and recurrence of mental illness. High priority areas of interest include encouraging the implementation of innovative prevention and treatment programs and strengthening the effectiveness of existing service delivery systems.
Fields of interest: Mental health care; Addiction services; Alcoholism.
Type of support: Emergency funds; Program development; Seed money; Research.
Limitations: Applications accepted. Giving limited to Cuyahoga County, OH. No grants for scholarships or fellowships, operating expenses, endowments, or annual fundraising campaigns.
Publications: Application guidelines; Financial statement; Grants list.

Application information: Online applications are available 1 month prior to deadlines. See foundation web site for necessary application details. Mass mailings are not accepted. Application form required.

  Initial approach: Use online application process
  Deadline(s): Jan. 1, May 1, and Sept. 1
  Board meeting date(s): Feb., June, and Oct.
Officers and Trustees: Valerie Raines, Pres. and Trustee; Richard A. Paulson, V.P.; Valerie Bradley Hicks, Secy.-Treas.; Mark Bonhard; Lovell J. Custard; Maryellen Davis, MD; David Doll; Franklin J. Hickman; Nancy Lowery-Bregar; R. Jeffrey Pollock; Ella Holt Thomas.
Number of staff: None.
EIN: 237425631

7646
Woodward Family Charitable Foundation
3805 Edwards Rd., 3rd Fl.
Cincinnati, OH   45209-1900

Established in 1993 in Ohio.
Donors: Marianna M. Woodward; Huntington National Bank.
Foundation type: Independent foundation.
Financial data (yr. ended 12/31/13): Assets, $3,879,507 (M); gifts received, $137,295; expenditures, $172,510; qualifying distributions, $146,492; giving activities include $144,534 for 50 grants (high: $10,500; low: $500).
Fields of interest: Arts and culture; Environment; Domesticated animals.
Limitations: Applications not accepted. No grants to individuals.
Application information: Unsolicited requests for funds not accepted.
Trustees: Jeanette Bunn; Anthony Woodward; Huntington National Bank.
EIN: 367015446

7647
The Wyler Family Foundation
401 Milford Pkwy., Ste. A
Milford, OH   45150-9119   (513) 752-7450
Main URL: http://www.wylerfamilyfoundation.org

Donors: Agency Serv. Consolidated, Inc.; Jeff Wyler Eastgate, Inc.; Jeff Wyler Colerain, Inc.; Katz, Teller, Brant & Hild; Turnbull-wahlert Construction, Inc.; Jeff Wyler Florence, Inc.
Foundation type: Independent foundation.
Financial data (yr. ended 12/31/13): Assets, $2,117,783 (M); gifts received, $697,731; expenditures, $411,063; qualifying distributions, $411,063; giving activities include $407,401 for 56 grants (high: $62,500; low: $200), and $211,801 for 4 foundation-administered programs.
Fields of interest: Health; Community and economic development; Youth development.
Limitations: Applications accepted. Giving primarily in OH. No support for sports, athletic events, or athletic programs; travel-related events, including students trips or tours; development or production of books, films, videos, or television programs; memorial campaigns; individuals, including those seeking scholarship or fellowship assistance.
Publications: Application guidelines.
Application information: See foundation web site for complete application guidelines and procedures.

  Initial approach: Use online application on foundation web site
  Deadline(s): None
  Final notification: Up to 4 months
Officers: Jeffrey L. Wyler, C.E.O.; J. David Wyler, Pres.; W. Scott Bristow, V.P.; Linda Wyler, Secy.; Julie Bristow, Treas.
EIN: 264396121

7648
William & Dorothy Yeck Family Foundation
5222 Little Woods Ln.
Dayton, OH   45429-2124

Established in 1986 in Ohio.
Donors: YBG, Inc.; William S. Yeck†.
Foundation type: Independent foundation.
Financial data (yr. ended 11/30/13): Assets, $4,748,241 (M); expenditures, $269,134; qualifying distributions, $232,550; giving activities include $232,550 for 5 grants (high: $88,000; low: $250).
Fields of interest: Historic preservation; Higher education; Libraries.
Limitations: Applications not accepted. Giving primarily in Dayton and Centerville, OH. No grants to individuals.
Application information: Unsolicited requests for funds not accepted.
Trustee: Robert Yeck.
EIN: 311190146

7649
Eric B. Yeiser Family Foundation
7811 Laurel Ave., Ste. B
Cincinnati, OH   45243-2608   (513) 621-1384
Contact: Eric B. Yeiser, Tr.

Established in 1999 in Ohio.
Donor: Eric B. Yeiser.
Foundation type: Independent foundation.
Financial data (yr. ended 12/31/14): Assets, $3,805,377 (M); gifts received, $357,201; expenditures, $185,247; qualifying distributions, $166,000; giving activities include $166,000 for 14 grants (high: $30,000; low: $1,000).
Fields of interest: Education; Health; Diseases and conditions; Multiple sclerosis.
Type of support: General support.
Limitations: Applications accepted. Giving limited to the Cincinnati, OH, area.
Application information: Application form required.
  Initial approach: Letter
  Deadline(s): None
Trustees: James Brun; Joslin Coonan; Eric B. Yeiser.
EIN: 311646815

7650
The Abner and Esther Yoder Charitable Foundation
P.O. Box 80469
Canton, OH   44708-0469
Contact: Esther Yoder, Secy.

Established in 1991 in Ohio.
Donor: Stark Truss Co., Inc.
Foundation type: Independent foundation.
Financial data (yr. ended 12/31/13): Assets, $241,408 (M); gifts received, $267,500; expenditures, $206,272; qualifying distributions,

$206,150; giving activities include $206,150 for 48 grants (high: $65,000; low: $200).
Purpose and activities: Giving primarily to evangelical Christian organizations.
Fields of interest: Christianity.
Type of support: General support.
Limitations: Giving primarily in OH, OK and TX. No grants to individuals.
Application information:
  Deadline(s): None
Officers: Abner Yoder, Pres.; Esther Yoder, Secy.; Wendy Spillman, Treas.
EIN: 341677646

7651
The Craig Young Family Foundation
7104 Ravens Run
Cincinnati, OH   45244-3592

Established in 1994 in Ohio.
Donor: Craig S. Young.
Foundation type: Independent foundation.
Financial data (yr. ended 12/31/12): Assets, $5,837,737 (M); expenditures, $336,034; qualifying distributions, $277,050; giving activities include $277,050 for grants.
Fields of interest: Education; Zoos; Nonprofits; Diseases and conditions; Housing development; Human services; Child welfare; Youth development.
Type of support: Regranting.
Limitations: Applications not accepted. Giving primarily in Cincinnati, OH. No grants to individuals.
Application information: Contributes only to pre-selected organizations.
Officers: Craig S. Young, Pres.; Mary E. Young, Secy.
Trustees: Robert Buechner; Margaret S. Young.
EIN: 311423879

7652
The Hugo H. and Mabel B. Young Foundation
P.O. Box 63
Loudonville, OH   44842-0063
Application address: c/o Michael C. Bandy, P.O. Box 63, Loudonville, OH 44842,
email: hugomabelyoung@gmail.com

Established in 1963 in Ohio.
Foundation type: Independent foundation.
Financial data (yr. ended 04/30/14): Assets, $5,885,432 (M); expenditures, $320,757; qualifying distributions, $268,364; giving activities include $258,275 for 20 grants (high: $30,000; low: $2,500).
Fields of interest: Orchestral music; Education; Foundations; Public libraries; Community and economic development; Christianity; Sports and recreation; Human services.
Type of support: Capital campaigns; Matching grants; Capital and infrastructure; Equipment; Scholarships.
Limitations: Applications accepted. Giving primarily in Ashland and Holmes counties, OH. No grants to individuals, or for general purposes or matching gifts; no loans.
Publications: Application guidelines.
Application information: Application form required.
  Initial approach: Letter
  Copies of proposal: 7
  Deadline(s): Apr. 1

Board meeting date(s): 3rd Tues. in May
Final notification: Late May or early June
Officers and Trustees: Barb Burd, Pres.; Jon H. Cooperrider II, V.P.; Michael C. Bandy, Secy.-Treas. and Trustee; James J. Dudte; William B. LaPlace; Phillip A. Ranney.
EIN: 346560664

7653
Ruth C. Young Trust
P. O. Box 1558, Dept. EA4E86
Columbus, OH 43216-1558

Foundation type: Independent foundation.
Financial data (yr. ended 12/31/13): Assets, $4,410,914 (M); expenditures, $222,943; qualifying distributions, $199,547; giving activities include $182,684 for 10 grants (high: $27,403; low: $9,134).
Fields of interest: Arts and culture; Health; Religion.
Limitations: Applications not accepted. Giving primarily in OH.
Application information: Unsolicited request for funds not accepted.
Trustee: Huntington National Bank.
EIN: 316208204

OKLAHOMA

7654
Ad Astra Foundation
5653 N. Pennsylvania Ave.
Oklahoma City, OK   73112-7769

Established in 1986 in Oklahoma.
Donors: Richard L. Sias; Jeannette F. Sias.
Foundation type: Independent foundation.
Financial data (yr. ended 12/31/14): Assets, $6,064,837; expenditures, $390,747; qualifying distributions, $350,900.
Purpose and activities: Giving primarily for the performing arts and education.
Fields of interest: Arts and culture; Orchestral music; Higher education; Christianity.
Type of support: General support.
Limitations: Applications not accepted. Giving limited to Oklahoma City, OK. No grants to individuals.
Application information: Contributes only to pre-selected organizations.
  Board meeting date(s): Quarterly
Officers: Richard Sias, Chair.; Alice Pippin, Pres.; Jeannette F. Sias, V.P. and Secy.; Phil Pippin, Treas.
Board Members: Patrick Alexander; Eddie Walker.
EIN: 731278163

7655
Asbjornson Foundation
2202 S. Troost Ave.
Tulsa, OK   74114-1320   (918) 583-2266
Contact: Norman H. Asbjornson, Tr.

Established in 1999 in Oklahoma.
Donor: Norman H. Asbjornson.
Foundation type: Independent foundation.
Financial data (yr. ended 12/31/14): Assets, $11,337,688 (M); expenditures, $239,504; qualifying distributions, $208,868; giving activities include $205,000 for 2 grants (high: $165,000; low: $40,000).
Fields of interest: Education services; Community and economic development.
Type of support: General support.
Limitations: Applications accepted. Giving primarily in Winifred, MT. No grants to individuals.
Application information:
  Initial approach: Proposal
  Deadline(s): None
Trustee: Norman H. Asbjornson.
EIN: 731582633

7656
Mary K. Ashbrook Foundation for El Reno
P.O. Box 627
El Reno, OK   73036-0627   (405) 262-4684
Contact: Virginia Sue Douglas, Tr.

Established in 1978 in Oklahoma.
Donors: Mary K. Ashbrook†; El Reno Senior Citizens Center.
Foundation type: Independent foundation.
Financial data (yr. ended 06/30/14): Assets, $4,317,946 (M); expenditures, $370,973; qualifying distributions, $277,264; giving activities

include $184,866 for 18 grants (high: $37,458; low: $2,050).
Fields of interest: Arts and culture; Education; Human services.
Type of support: Continuing support; Matching grants; Capital and infrastructure; Equipment; Land acquisitions; Emergency funds; Program development; Seed money; Scholarships.
Limitations: Applications accepted. Giving limited to El Reno, OK. No grants to individuals, or for deficit financing, endowment funds, research, fellowships, demonstration projects, publications, or conferences; no loans.
Publications: Application guidelines.
Application information: Application form required.
  Initial approach: Completed application form
  Deadline(s): None
  Board meeting date(s): Monthly
  Final notification: 1 month
Trustees: Sherry Sue Davis; Virginia Sue Douglas; Gayle Meinberg.
EIN: 731049531

7657
William S. & Ann Atherton Foundation
1924 S. Utica Ave., Ste. 1018
Tulsa, OK   74104-6512
Contact: Jessica Ann Faubert, Pres.

Established in 1997 in Oklahoma.
Donor: William S. Atherton.
Foundation type: Independent foundation.
Financial data (yr. ended 12/31/13): Assets, $6,477,447 (M); expenditures, $375,970; qualifying distributions, $318,884; giving activities include $285,135 for 48 grants (high: $100,000; low: $250).
Fields of interest: Museums; Historic preservation; Higher education; Natural resources.
Type of support: Continuing support; Matching grants; Annual campaigns; Endowments; Program development; Research.
Limitations: Applications accepted. Giving primarily in MI and OK.
Application information: Application form required.
  Initial approach: Proposal
  Copies of proposal: 1
  Deadline(s): None
Officers: William S. Atherton, Chair.; Jessica Ann Faubert, Pres.; Preston B. Smith, Secy.; J. Thomas Atherton, Treas.
Directors: Delores Ann Atherton; Michael Dirk Atherton.
Number of staff: 1 full-time professional.
EIN: 731520309

7658
The Barnes Family Foundation
2431 E. 61st St., Ste. 720
Tulsa, OK   74136

Donor: William C. Barnes.
Foundation type: Independent foundation.
Financial data (yr. ended 12/31/14): Assets, $3,570,743; gifts received, $2,000; expenditures, $123,380; qualifying distributions, $118,380 and $0 for set-asides.
Fields of interest: Christianity; Human services.
Type of support: General support.
Limitations: Applications not accepted. Giving primarily in Tulsa, OK.

Application information: Contributes only to pre-selected organizations.
Trustees: Marsha K. Barnes; William C. Barnes.
EIN: 204643353

7659
James E. and Mary M. Barnes Foundation
(formerly J/MB Foundation)
9521-B Riverside Pkwy.
PMB 546
Tulsa, OK   74137
Application address: c/o Jim and Mary Barnes, 6 Wooded Gate Dr., Dallas, TX 75230, tel.: (918) 496-8650

Established in 1997 in Oklahoma.
Donors: James E. Barnes; Mary M. Barnes.
Foundation type: Independent foundation.
Financial data (yr. ended 12/31/13): Assets, $3,819,476 (M); expenditures, $182,098; qualifying distributions, $170,500; giving activities include $170,500 for 10 grants (high: $40,000; low: $3,500).
Purpose and activities: Funding primarily for the arts, community development, and education, with a focus on local charities of family members.
Fields of interest: Ballet; Art museums; Elementary and secondary education; Higher education; Community improvement; Christianity; Child welfare.
Type of support: General support; Annual campaigns; Capital campaigns; Endowments; Program development; Curriculum development; Scholarships.
Limitations: Applications accepted. Giving primarily in Enid, Stillwater and Tulsa, OK, and Jackson, WY. No grants to individuals.
Application information: Application form required.
  Initial approach: Letter or phone.
  Deadline(s): None
Trustees: Mary M. Barnes; Kristos P. Kever; Lori H. Markes.
Number of staff: None.
EIN: 311591203

7660
The Barnett Family Foundation, Inc.
(formerly Florence L.J. and Howard G. Barnett Foundation)
6742 S. Evanston Ave.
Tulsa, OK   74136-4509
Contact: Howard G. Barnett Jr., Tr.

Established in 1997 in Oklahoma.
Donors: Florence L.J. Barnett†; Howard G. Barnett.
Foundation type: Independent foundation.
Financial data (yr. ended 12/31/13): Assets, $7,813,965 (M); expenditures, $491,223; qualifying distributions, $355,047; giving activities include $350,227 for 38 grants (high: $50,000; low: $250).
Fields of interest: Arts and culture; Higher education; Diseases and conditions; Human services; Child welfare.
Limitations: Applications accepted. Giving primarily in Tulsa, OK.
Application information: Application form required.
  Initial approach: Proposal
  Deadline(s): None
Trustees: Billie Barnett; Howard G. Barnett, Jr.
EIN: 736295453

7661
The Albert and Hete Barthelmes Foundation, Inc.
401 S. Boston., Ste. 250
Mid-Continent Twr.
Tulsa, OK 74103-4039 (918) 392-0906
Contact: Arlene Bean
FAX: (918) 392-0908; E-mail: abean@ahbf.org

Established in 1993 in Oklahoma.
Donors: Albert J. Barthelmes†; Hedwig Barthelmes†.
Foundation type: Independent foundation.
Financial data (yr. ended 12/31/14): Assets, $8,805,294 (M); expenditures, $547,757; qualifying distributions, $355,955; giving activities include $309,285 for 30 grants (high: $60,000; low: $500).
Purpose and activities: Giving primarily to support Tulsa area programs that are collaborative in nature and offer significant impact in the fields of the arts and sciences.
Fields of interest: Arts and culture; Performing arts.
Type of support: General support; Matching grants; Capital campaigns; Scholarships.
Limitations: Applications accepted. Giving primarily in Tulsa, OK. No support for organizations whose administrative expenses, including fundraising, exceed 25% of its annual budget. No grants to individuals.
Publications: Application guidelines.
Application information: Application form required.
   Initial approach: As per grant guidelines for application
   Copies of proposal: 1
   Deadline(s): As per grant guidelines for deadline
Officer and Director: Theresa M. Collins, Pres.
Number of staff: 1 full-time professional; 2 part-time support.
EIN: 731423086

7662
Dan E. & Neva L. Brannin Foundation
3905 W. Roanoke St.
Broken Arrow, OK 74011-1281

Established in 1997 in Oklahoma.
Donor: Neva L. Brannin.
Foundation type: Independent foundation.
Financial data (yr. ended 12/31/13): Assets, $6,421,391 (M); expenditures, $385,726; qualifying distributions, $282,059; giving activities include $282,059 for 10 grants (high: $143,559; low: $1,000).
Fields of interest: Museums; Environment; Protestantism.
Type of support: General support.
Limitations: Applications not accepted. Giving primarily in OK. No grants to individuals.
Application information: Unsolicited requests for funds not accepted.
Trustees: Alder Brannin; Caroline Brannin; Clark Stewart Brannin; Dan Graham Brannin; Joe Brannin; Nancy Louise Brannin; Mary Catherine Brannin Elliott; Flint Whistler.
EIN: 731531791

7663
Broadhurst Foundation
1630 S. Boston Ave.
Tulsa, OK 74119-4416 (918) 294-9789
Contact: Ann S. Cassidy, Chair.

Established in 1951 in Oklahoma.
Donor: William Broadhurst†.
Foundation type: Independent foundation.
Financial data (yr. ended 12/31/13): Assets, $7,081,687 (M); expenditures, $581,779; qualifying distributions, $308,250; giving activities include $254,488 for 31 grants (high: $50,000; low: $500).
Purpose and activities: Support for scholarship funds for students training for the Christian ministry at institutions selected by the foundation; grants also for human services, youth services and for health care.
Fields of interest: Education; Religion; Human services.
Type of support: Continuing support; Capital campaigns; Capital and infrastructure; Equipment; Seed money; Fellowships; Scholarships.
Limitations: Applications accepted. Giving primarily in Tulsa, OK. No grants to individuals, or for scholarship funds, except at 31 schools the foundation currently supports.
Application information: Application form required.
   Initial approach: Proposal
   Copies of proposal: 1
   Deadline(s): None
   Board meeting date(s): Quarterly
   Final notification: 1 month
Officer: Ann S. Cassidy, Chair.
Trustees: Cadijah Frizzell; R. Patrick Gilmore.
Number of staff: 1 full-time professional; 1 part-time professional; 1 part-time support.
EIN: 736061115

7664
Harry and Louise Brown Foundation
6303 N. Portland Ste. 304
Oklahoma City, OK 73112-2202

Established in 1995 in Oklahoma.
Donor: David R. Brown.
Foundation type: Independent foundation.
Financial data (yr. ended 12/31/13): Assets, $4,514,107 (M); gifts received, $21,436; expenditures, $198,923; qualifying distributions, $189,346; giving activities include $188,000 for 30 grants (high: $105,000; low: $500).
Fields of interest: Education; Public affairs; Human services.
Type of support: General support; Continuing support; Annual campaigns; Capital campaigns; Program development; Research.
Limitations: Applications not accepted. Giving primarily in OK. No grants to individuals.
Application information: Contributes only to pre-selected organizations.
   Board meeting date(s): Apr. and Dec.
Officers: David R. Brown, Pres. and Treas.; Ann N. Brown, V.P.; Marianne B. Rooney, Secy.
Directors: D. Randolph Brown, Jr.; Susan Brown.
Number of staff: None.
EIN: 731485811

7665
Mike and Susan Burkhart Foundation
5387 S. Sheridan Rd.
Tulsa, OK 74145-7521

Established in 2005 in Oklahoma.
Donors: Susan Burkhart; Mike Burkhart.
Foundation type: Independent foundation.
Financial data (yr. ended 12/31/13): Assets, $2,992,886 (M); expenditures, $173,553; qualifying distributions, $157,000; giving activities include $157,000 for 16 grants (high: $25,000; low: $2,000).
Fields of interest: Education; Diseases and conditions; Christianity; Human services; Child welfare.
Limitations: Applications not accepted. Giving primarily in KY, OK and TN. No grants to individuals.
Application information: Contributes only to pre-selected organizations.
Officers: Mike Burkhart, Pres.; Susan Burkhart, Secy.; Mark Springer, Treas.
Directors: Bryan Burkhart; Matt Burkhart; Randy Cloud.
EIN: 202372810

7666
Cherokee Strip Community Foundation
(formerly Enid Community Foundation, Inc.)
114 S. Independence, Ste. 140
Enid, OK 73701 (580) 234-3988
Contact: Mary M. Stallings, Exec. Dir.
FAX: (580) 234-3311;
E-mail: mary@cherokeestripcf.com; Mailing address: P.O. Box 263, Enid, OK 73702; Main URL: http://www.cherokeestripcf.com
Facebook: https://www.facebook.com/pages/Cherokee-Strip-Community-Foundation/699700060052750

Established in 2000 in Oklahoma.
Donors: Harold Hamm; Sue Hamm; St. Mary's Hospital; Helen Garriott; Owen Garriott.
Foundation type: Community foundation.
Financial data (yr. ended 12/31/13): Assets, $14,753,301 (M); gifts received, $376,415; expenditures, $482,898; giving activities include $342,627 for 11+ grants (high: $36,557).
Purpose and activities: The foundation seeks to distribute resources to the community, particularly in the areas of arts and culture, health and human services, recreation and neighborhoods, economic development, and education and the environment.
Fields of interest: Arts and culture; Education; Environment; Health; Diseases and conditions; Community and economic development; Economic development; Sports and recreation; Human services.
Type of support: Capacity-building and technical assistance; Pro bono consulting services; Matching grants; Equipment; Endowments; Program development; Convening; Curriculum development; Technical assistance; Program evaluations.
Limitations: Applications accepted. Giving primarily in the Cherokee Strip Region, OK. No support for sectarian or religious purposes. No grants to individuals, or for operating or maintenance expenses, medical or scholarly research, membership fees, ticket sales for charitable fundraising events, travel for groups, or capital debt reductions.
Publications: Application guidelines; Annual report; Financial statement; Grants list; Informational

brochure (including application guidelines);
Newsletter.

Application information: Visit foundation web site for application form and guidelines. Before a grant proposal is requested by the foundation, a letter of intent must be submitted for consideration. Faxed letters of intent and proposals are not accepted. Application form required.

> *Initial approach:* Letter of Intent (no longer than 2 pages)
> *Copies of proposal:* 12
> *Deadline(s):* July 31 for Letter of Intent; Sept. 1 for grant proposal
> *Board meeting date(s):* Feb., May, Aug., and Nov.
> *Final notification:* Within 6 weeks for full grant proposal invitation; Nov. Board meeting for grants

Officers and Trustees: Richard DeVaughn, Pres. and Trustee; Tim Traynor, V.P. and Trustee; Amber Fitzgerald, Secy. and Trustee; Linda Record, Treas. and Trustee; Mary M. Stallings, Exec. Dir.; Pamela Ballard; Brad Boeckman; Cheryl Bryan; Mark Dick; Peter Dillingham; Todd Earl; Tom Evans; Willa Jo Fowler; Don Gaston; Steve Glasser; David Grissett; Aaron Harmon; Kaleb Hennigh; Chrystal Howard; Dr. Marcie Mack; George Milacek; Marcy Price; Dr. David Russell; Walter P. Scheffe; Bill Shewey; Steve Whitfill.

Number of staff: 1 full-time professional.

EIN: 731547637

7667
The Chilton Foundation

(formerly The Chilton Foundation Trust)
P.O. Box 1620
Tulsa, OK 74101-1620 9186191544
Application address: Patti Lu Bell Brown C/o Bokf , 5956 Sherry Ln., Ste. 700,

Established in 1945 in Texas.

Donors: Arthur L. Chilton†; Leonore Chilton†.

Foundation type: Independent foundation.

Financial data (yr. ended 12/31/14): Assets, $11,383,435; expenditures, $558,899; qualifying distributions, $490,450.

Purpose and activities: Giving for the assistance and promotion of the welfare of humanity.

Fields of interest: Medical education; Health; Hospital care; Religion; Human services; Child welfare.

Limitations: Applications accepted. Giving primarily in Dallas County, TX and in AR. No grants to individuals.

Application information: Application form required.

> *Initial approach:* Letter
> *Deadline(s):* None

Trustee: Bank of America, N.A.

EIN: 756006996

7668
The George and Jennie Collins Foundation

2627 E. 21st St., Ste. 200
Tulsa, OK 74114-1728
Contact: Roger B. Collins, Chair.

Established in 1943 in Oklahoma.

Donors: George F. Collins, Jr.†; Liberty Glass Co.; Roger B. Collins.

Foundation type: Independent foundation.

Financial data (yr. ended 12/31/13): Assets, $4,406,629 (M); expenditures, $288,083;

qualifying distributions, $264,250; giving activities include $259,000 for 12 grants (high: $150,000; low: $1,000).

Purpose and activities: Giving primarily for higher education.

Fields of interest: Higher education; Human services.

Type of support: General support; Capital and infrastructure; Equipment.

Limitations: Applications accepted. Giving primarily in the Tulsa, OK, area. No grants to individuals.

Application information: Application form required.

> *Initial approach:* Letter
> *Copies of proposal:* 1
> *Deadline(s):* None

Officer: Roger B. Collins, Chair.

Trustees: Andrew Collins; Frances R. Collins.

Number of staff: 1 full-time professional.

EIN: 736093053

7669
George F. Collins, Jr. Foundation

1924 S. Utica Ave., Ste. 800
Tulsa, OK 74104-6516 9187489860

Established in 1968 in Oklahoma.

Foundation type: Independent foundation.

Financial data (yr. ended 12/31/14): Assets, $4,165,830; expenditures, $229,147; qualifying distributions, $217,500.

Fields of interest: Business education.

Type of support: General support; Annual campaigns; Capital campaigns; Capital and infrastructure; Scholarships.

Limitations: Applications not accepted. Giving primarily in Sapulpa, OK. No grants to individuals.

Application information: Unsolicited requests for funds not accepted.

Trustees: George Fulton Collins IV; Roger B. Collins; Suzanne M. Collins.

EIN: 237008179

7670
Crio Ministries Evangelistic Association, Inc.

c/o Ronald N. Hesser
5905 Witteville Dr.
Poteau, OK 74953-1947
Main URL: http://www.crioministries.org
Twitter: https://twitter.com/Crio_Int

Donors: Linda Kanak; Ronald N. Hesser; George Ollie; Bob Kanak.

Foundation type: Operating foundation.

Financial data (yr. ended 12/31/13): Assets, $13,045 (M); gifts received, $271,194; expenditures, $272,568; qualifying distributions, $272,063; giving activities include $217,863 for grants.

Purpose and activities: Giving to support member evangelists, assist in planting churches (buying property, buildings, and sound equipment), provide leadership training and developmental resources, and provide social services to orphans, widows and the poor.

Fields of interest: Elementary and secondary education; Christianity.

International interests: Africa.

Type of support: Building and renovations; Land acquisitions; Scholarships.

Limitations: Applications not accepted. No grants to individuals.

Application information: Contributes only to pre-selected organizations.

Officers: Ronald N. Hesser, Pres.; Curtis B. Hesser, V.P.; Hillary Grantham, Secy.-Treas.

Board Members: Reggie Goodin; Glenn Quirk; Leanne Robertson.

EIN: 731579626

7671
Dill Foundation Inc.

300 Riverwalk Terr., Ste. 210
Jenks, OK 74037-5617

Established in 2000 in Oklahoma.

Donors: G. Michael Dill; Shelley M. Dill.

Foundation type: Independent foundation.

Financial data (yr. ended 12/31/13): Assets, $3,298,040 (M); gifts received, $49,979; expenditures, $185,115; qualifying distributions, $169,500; giving activities include $169,500 for 16 grants (high: $34,500; low: $1,000).

Fields of interest: Secondary education; Undergraduate education; Catholicism; Equestrianism; Youth services; Male children and youth.

Type of support: General support; Capital campaigns.

Limitations: Applications not accepted. No grants to individuals.

Application information: Unsolicited requests for funds not accepted.

Officers: G. Michael Dill, Chair. and Pres.; Shelley M. Dill, Secy.

EIN: 731593019

7672
Nellie Dobson Trust

c/o Bank of Oklahoma, N.A.
P.O. Box 1620
Tulsa, OK 74101-1620
Application Address: c/o V.P., Financial Affairs, Northeastern Oklahoma A&M College, 200 I St. NE, Miami, OK, 74354

Established in 1968 in Oklahoma.

Donor: Nellie Dobson†.

Foundation type: Independent foundation.

Financial data (yr. ended 01/31/15): Assets, $10,309,992 (M); expenditures, $649,158; qualifying distributions, $439,020; giving activities include $362,925 for 2 grants (high: $337,605; low: $25,320).

Purpose and activities: Giving to the Northeastern Oklahoma A&M College, Oklahoma, for its scholarship fund.

Fields of interest: Undergraduate education.

Type of support: Scholarships.

Limitations: Applications accepted. Giving primarily in Miami, OK.

Application information:

> *Initial approach:* Proposal
> *Deadline(s):* None

Trustee: Bank of Oklahoma, N.A.

EIN: 736131333

7673
Judith E. Drabek Foundation Trust
2601 N.W. Expwy., Ste. 601W
Oklahoma City, OK 73112-7217 (405)
848-2000
Contact: Patrick Donnelly, Pres.

Established in 2003 in Oklahoma.
Foundation type: Independent foundation.
Financial data (yr. ended 09/30/13): Assets,
$3,992,819 (M); expenditures, $299,471;
qualifying distributions, $212,213; giving activities
include $202,213 for 6 grants (high: $69,930; low:
$1,500).
Fields of interest: Philanthropy; Agriculture; Human
services; Food banks; Scouting programs.
Type of support: General support.
Limitations: Applications accepted. Giving primarily
in OK. No grants to individuals.
Application information: Application form required.
Initial approach: Proposal
Deadline(s): None
Officer and Trustee: Patrick Donnelly, Pres. and
Trustee.
EIN: 200493601

7674
Richard P. Dulaney Foundation, Inc.
P.O. Box 20705
Oklahoma City, OK 73156-0705 (405)
239-7961
Contact: Richard P. Dulaney, Dir.

Established in 2003 in Oklahoma.
Donor: Richard P. Dulaney.
Foundation type: Independent foundation.
Financial data (yr. ended 12/31/13): Assets,
$24,828 (M); gifts received, $121,612;
expenditures, $260,217; qualifying distributions,
$258,245; giving activities include $256,550 for 23
grants (high: $195,600; low: $50).
Fields of interest: Religion; Human services.
Limitations: Applications accepted. Giving primarily
in OK.
Application information: Application form required.
Initial approach: Letter
Deadline(s): None
Director: Richard P. Dulaney.
EIN: 311819479

7675
The Elpis Foundation
6625 S. Jamestown Ave.
Tulsa, OK 74136-2610

Established in 2005 in Oklahoma.
Donor: John G. Nikkel.
Foundation type: Independent foundation.
Financial data (yr. ended 12/31/13): Assets,
$3,995,286 (M); expenditures, $198,526;
qualifying distributions, $185,080; giving activities
include $185,080 for 11 grants (high: $77,500;
low: $80).
Fields of interest: Housing development; Religion.
Limitations: Applications not accepted. Giving
primarily in NH and OK. No grants to individuals.
Application information: Unsolicited requests for
funds not accepted.
Trustees: Melody A. McSparran; Carole A. Nikkel;
John G. Nikkel; Robert E. Nikkel.
EIN: 202033062

7676
Jean I. Everest Foundation
6305 Waterford Blvd., Ste. 305
Oklahoma City, OK 73118-1116 (405)
840-1575
Contact: James H. Everest, Pres.

Donors: Jean I. Everest; James H. Everest; Christine
G. Everest.
Foundation type: Independent foundation.
Financial data (yr. ended 09/30/13): Assets,
$4,810,250 (M); expenditures, $200,752;
qualifying distributions, $187,525; giving activities
include $187,525 for 20 grants (high: $50,000;
low: $1,000).
Purpose and activities: Giving primarily for
education, community work, and health and social
services.
Fields of interest: Education; Environment; Hospital
care; Diseases and conditions; Community and
economic development; Protestantism; Human
services; Child welfare.
Type of support: Research.
Limitations: Applications accepted. Giving primarily
in Oklahoma City, OK. No grants to individuals.
Application information:
Initial approach: Proposal
Deadline(s): None
Officers and Trustees: James H. Everest, Pres. and
Trustee; Christine G. Everest, V.P. and Treas. and
Trustee; Tricia L. Everest, Secy. and Trustee.
EIN: 736106627

7677
The Heyman Evergreen Foundation
15 E. 5th St., Ste. 3200
Tulsa, OK 74103-4340

Established in 1998 in Oklahoma.
Donors: Barbara G. Heyman; Stephen J. Heyman;
Herbert Gussman Trust.
Foundation type: Independent foundation.
Financial data (yr. ended 12/31/13): Assets,
$5,486,307 (M); expenditures, $261,899;
qualifying distributions, $239,525; giving activities
include $239,525 for 18 grants (high: $100,000;
low: $500).
Purpose and activities: Giving primarily for
healthcare, the arts, and education.
Fields of interest: Art museums; Education; Higher
education; Hospital care.
Limitations: Applications not accepted. Giving
primarily in New York, NY, and Tulsa, OK. No grants
to individuals.
Application information: Unsolicited requests for
funds not accepted.
Officers: Stephen J. Heyman, Pres. and Treas.;
Alexandra H. Nash, V.P. and Secy.
EIN: 731535560

7678
Charles C. Faranna Scholarship Trust
4008 S. Elm Pl., Ste. F
Broken Arrow, OK 74011-2021

Established in 1989 in Oklahoma.
Donor: Charles C. Faranna.
Foundation type: Independent foundation.
Financial data (yr. ended 06/30/13): Assets, $0
(M); expenditures, $468,490; qualifying
distributions, $173,471; giving activities include

$173,471 for 111 grants to individuals (high:
$36,206; low: $802).
Purpose and activities: Scholarship award to
graduates of Broken Arrow Senior High School,
Oklahoma, attending a state college or university.
Fields of interest: Higher education.
Type of support: Student aid.
Limitations: Applications not accepted. Giving
primarily to residents of Broken Arrow and Norman,
OK.
Application information: Unsolicited requests for
funds not accepted.
Trustees: Mark Harper; Elizabeth Pullum; JoAnn
Sanning.
EIN: 736251335

7679
The Fleischaker Family Foundation
100 N. Broadway, Ste. 2460
Oklahoma City, OK 73102-8868

Established in 2003 in Oklahoma.
Donors: David S. Fleischaker; Paula Anne
Fleischaker.
Foundation type: Independent foundation.
Financial data (yr. ended 12/31/13): Assets,
$4,037,619 (M); gifts received, $160,000;
expenditures, $220,041; qualifying distributions,
$164,069; giving activities include $160,060 for 6
grants (high: $100,000; low: $5,000).
Fields of interest: Education; Heart and circulatory
system diseases.
Type of support: Research.
Limitations: Applications not accepted. Giving
primarily in NY and OK. No grants to individuals.
Application information: Unsolicited requests for
funds not accepted.
Officers: Paula Anne Fleischaker, Pres.; David S.
Fleischaker, V.P.; Emily R. Fleischaker, Secy.;
Joseph L. Fleischaker, Treas.
EIN: 810627666

7680
French Family Charitable Foundation
P.O. Box 1265
Edmond, OK 73034-1265

Donor: Hal French.
Foundation type: Independent foundation.
Financial data (yr. ended 12/31/13): Assets,
$12,405,936 (M); expenditures, $398,844;
qualifying distributions, $368,350; giving activities
include $368,350 for 13 grants (high: $330,600;
low: $200).
Fields of interest: Child abuse; Human services;
Child welfare.
Limitations: Applications not accepted. Giving
primarily in OK. No grants to individuals.
Application information: Contributes only to
pre-selected organizations.
Directors: Gabe French; Hal French; Megan French.
EIN: 731546685

7681
The Fugitt Foundation
P.O. Box 1226
McAlester, OK 74502-1226

Established in 2004 in Oklahoma.
Donor: Gary Fugitt.

Foundation type: Independent foundation.
Financial data (yr. ended 12/31/13): Assets, $5,392,722 (M); expenditures, $178,592; qualifying distributions, $156,058; giving activities include $156,058 for 12 grants (high: $135,300; low: $200).
Fields of interest: Higher education; Religion; Christianity; Human services.
Limitations: Applications not accepted. Giving primarily in OK. No grants to individuals.
Application information: Contributes only to pre-selected organizations.
Trustee: Gary Fugitt.
EIN: 201189418

7682
The Lyle M. Gelvin Foundation, Inc.
(formerly Lyle M. Gelvin Foundation)
P.O. Box 837
Eufaula, OK 74432 (918) 452-3703

Established in 1992 in Oklahoma.
Donors: Lyle Pacific Corp.; Lyle M. Gelvin†.
Foundation type: Independent foundation.
Financial data (yr. ended 12/31/14): Assets, $9,546,089; expenditures, $465,328; qualifying distributions, $434,400.
Purpose and activities: Grants are primarily focused on charitable organizations located within a 30-mile radius of Tulsa or Eufaula, OK, whose programs primarily benefit the citizens of these areas in the fields of civic and cultural, education, family and community service, health care, and religion.
Fields of interest: Arts and culture; Education; Health; Hospital care; Religion; Human services.
Type of support: Capital campaigns; Matching grants; Capital and infrastructure; Equipment; Land acquisitions; Program development.
Limitations: Applications accepted. Giving primarily in OK, with emphasis within a 30-mile radius of Tulsa or Eufaula. No grants to individuals.
Publications: Application guidelines; Informational brochure (including application guidelines).
Application information: Application form required.
  Initial approach: Proposal
  Copies of proposal: 2
  Deadline(s): None
Officers: Therese Starr, Pres. and Treas.; Terry Doverspike, V.P. and Secy.
EIN: 731419663

7683
GKJ Foundation
8177 S. Harvard Ave., Ste. 538
Tulsa, OK 74137-1612
Contact: Glaudia K. Jacobson, Tr.; Theordore Jacobson, Tr.

Established in 2005 in Oklahoma.
Donors: Glaudia K. Jacobson; Theodore T. Jacobson; Claudia K. Jacobson Trust.
Foundation type: Independent foundation.
Financial data (yr. ended 12/31/12): Assets, $666,597 (M); gifts received, $275,000; expenditures, $288,441; qualifying distributions, $255,000; giving activities include $255,000 for grants.
Fields of interest: Higher education; Nonprofits.
Type of support: Regranting.
Limitations: Applications accepted. Giving primarily in OK.

Application information: Application form required.
  Initial approach: Letter
  Deadline(s): None
Trustees: Glaudia K. Jacobson; Theodore T. Jacobson.
EIN: 203947383

7684
The Charles B. Goddard Foundation Trust
P.O. Box 1485
Ardmore, OK 73401-1485 (580) 226-6040
Contact: William R. Goddard Jr., Tr.

Established in 1958 in Oklahoma.
Donor: Charles B. Goddard†.
Foundation type: Independent foundation.
Financial data (yr. ended 06/30/13): Assets, $7,895,936 (M); expenditures, $418,494; qualifying distributions, $399,100; giving activities include $399,100 for grants.
Purpose and activities: Giving primarily for health care, as well as for youth and social services, and to a performing arts center.
Fields of interest: Performing arts; Education; Foundations; Health; Hospital care; Cancers; Human services; Child welfare.
Type of support: General support; Continuing support; Annual campaigns; Capital and infrastructure; Equipment; Emergency funds; Seed money; Research.
Limitations: Applications accepted. Giving primarily in south central OK, and north TX. No grants to individuals; no loans.
Application information: Application form required.
  Initial approach: Letter of request
  Copies of proposal: 1
  Deadline(s): None
  Board meeting date(s): As required
Trustees: Garland Clay; Jennifer Goddard; Katherine Goddard; William R. Goddard, Jr.
EIN: 756005868

7685
Janet and Kenneth R. Goodin Family Foundation
14800 Dalea Dr.
Oklahoma City, OK 73142-1908 (405) 604-6944
Contact: Janet Goodin, Dir.; Kenneth R. Goodin, Dir.

Donors: Janet R. Goodin; Kenneth R. Goodin.
Foundation type: Independent foundation.
Financial data (yr. ended 12/31/13): Assets, $2,314,897 (M); gifts received, $100,000; expenditures, $174,749; qualifying distributions, $170,365; giving activities include $169,500 for 11 grants (high: $125,000; low: $1,000).
Fields of interest: Education; Christianity; Human services.
Limitations: Applications accepted. Giving primarily in OK.
Application information: Application form required.
  Initial approach: Letter
  Deadline(s): None
Directors: Janet Goodin; Kenneth R. Goodin.
EIN: 273667514

7686
Pearl M. & Julia J. Harmon Foundation
P.O. Box 52568
Tulsa, OK 74152-0568
Main URL: http://www.harmonfound.org

Established in 1962 in Oklahoma.
Donors: Julia J. Harmon†; Claude C. Harmon†.
Foundation type: Independent foundation.
Financial data (yr. ended 05/31/13): Assets, $60,561,534 (M); expenditures, $613,386; qualifying distributions, $3,319,574; giving activities include $173,779 for 38 grants (high: $20,000; low: $500), $128,043 for 2 foundation-administered programs and $3,000,000 for loans/program-related investments.
Purpose and activities: Giving primarily for low-interest loans to charitable organizations.
Fields of interest: Education; Christianity; Human services.
Type of support: General support; Program-related investments.
Limitations: Applications accepted. Giving limited to AR, KS, NM, OK and TX, with preference given to northeastern OK. No support for medical research or evangelical organizations. No grants or loans to individuals or for-profit businesses.
Publications: Application guidelines.
Application information: All available funds are being directed toward the foundation's operating program; the foundation does not expect to solicit proposals over the next several years. However, applications are being accepted for program-related investment loans. Application form available on foundation web site. Application form required.
  Deadline(s): None
  Board meeting date(s): As necessary
Officer and Trustees: George L. Hangs, Jr., Exec. Dir. and Trustee; Cathey Frederick; G. E. Holmes; Jean M. Kuntz; Mary Grant Wendl.
EIN: 736095893

7687
Joe & Jean Holliman Family Foundation
(formerly Howard E. Felt Foundation)
8118 E. 63rd St.
Tulsa, OK 74133-1901

Established in 1945 in Oklahoma.
Donors: Joe M. Holliman†; Jean F. Holliman.
Foundation type: Independent foundation.
Financial data (yr. ended 12/31/13): Assets, $5,294,517 (M); expenditures, $211,296; qualifying distributions, $200,000; giving activities include $200,000 for 2 grants (high: $100,000; low: $100,000).
Fields of interest: Health; Religion.
Type of support: General support; Capital campaigns; Capital and infrastructure; Program development.
Limitations: Applications not accepted. Giving primarily in Oklahoma City and Tulsa, OK. No grants to individuals.
Application information: Contributes only to pre-selected organizations.
Officers: Jean F. Holliman, Pres.; Joanna H. Potts, V.P. 1 and Secy.- Treas.; Janice H. Stanfield, V.P. 2.
Director: John H. Holliman.
EIN: 736092860

7688
Howard Family Charitable Foundation, Inc.
P.O. Box 2898
Oklahoma City, OK 73101-2898 (405)
488-6208
Contact: Mickey Clagg, V.P.
Application address: P.O. Box 61250, Okalahoma
City, OK 73146

Established in 2007 in Oklahoma.
Donors: Vicki P. Howard; Robert E. Howard II.
Foundation type: Independent foundation.
Financial data (yr. ended 12/31/13): Assets,
$6,082,836 (M); expenditures, $211,020;
qualifying distributions, $205,439; giving activities
include $180,500 for 32 grants (high: $57,500;
low: $500), and $24,939 for 1 grant to an individual.
Fields of interest: Food banks; Adult and child
mentoring; Domestic violence shelters.
Limitations: Applications accepted. Giving primarily
in OK.
Application information: Application form required.
  Initial approach: Letter
  Deadline(s): None
Officers: Robert E. Howard II, Pres.; Vicki P. Howard,
V.P. and Secy.; Mickey Clagg, V.P.
EIN: 208623940

7689
Howard Foundation
12301 N. Rockwell
Oklahoma City, OK 73142-2704 (405)
720-1570

Established in 2002 in Oklahoma.
Donors: William F. Howard; Judith S. Howard.
Foundation type: Independent foundation.
Financial data (yr. ended 12/31/14): Assets,
$1,416,325; gifts received, $200,000;
expenditures, $245,493; qualifying distributions,
$245,000.
Fields of interest: Protestantism; Human services.
Limitations: Applications accepted. Giving primarily
in OK.
Application information: Application form required.
  Initial approach: Letter
  Deadline(s): None
Trustees: Judith S. Howard; William F. Howard.
EIN: 522387154

7690
M. D. and Barbara Jirous Foundation, Inc.
(formerly M. D. Jirous Foundation Inc.)
2701 W. I-44 Service Rd.
Oklahoma City, OK 73112-3775

Established in 1995 in Oklahoma.
Donors: M.D. Jirous; Jay Jirous; Jeanette Jirous;
Marvin Jirous; Barbara Jirous.
Foundation type: Independent foundation.
Financial data (yr. ended 12/31/13): Assets,
$12,124,988 (M); gifts received, $404,900;
expenditures, $559,839; qualifying distributions,
$451,432; giving activities include $380,160 for 84
grants (high: $100,000; low: $200).
Purpose and activities: Giving primarily for
education.
Fields of interest: Historic preservation; Education;
Alumni relations; Catholicism.
Type of support: General support; Scholarships.

Limitations: Applications not accepted. Giving
primarily in OK. No grants to individuals.
Application information: Contributes only to
pre-selected organizations.
Officers and Directors: M.D. Jirous, Pres. and
Director; Barbara Jirous, V.P. and Director; William
E. Owen, Secy. and Director; Jay Jirous; Thomas
Collins.
EIN: 731483496

7691
The W. J. Jones Family Foundation
(formerly Catherine May Jones Foundation)
1433 Glenbrook Dr.
Oklahoma City, OK 73118-1025

Established in 1987 in Oklahoma.
Donor: W.J. Jones.
Foundation type: Independent foundation.
Financial data (yr. ended 12/31/13): Assets,
$3,718,430 (M); expenditures, $191,591;
qualifying distributions, $229,305; giving activities
include $172,000 for 11 grants (high: $25,000;
low: $5,000).
Fields of interest: Health; Diseases and conditions;
Cancers; Christianity; Human services; Child
welfare.
Type of support: Research and evaluation;
Research.
Limitations: Applications not accepted. Giving
primarily in OK. No grants to individuals.
Application information: Contributes only to
pre-selected organizations.
Trustees: Jerry Austin; Patricia G. Carey; Jack
Homra; Randall D. Mock; Jon C. Sawvell; Tami
Spaulding.
EIN: 731314764

7692
Montfort and Allie Brown Jones Foundation
P. O. Box 1234
Bristow, OK 74010-1234
Application address: 121 E. 6th Ave., Bristow, OK
74010-3038, tel.: (918) 367-5979

Established in 1960 in Oklahoma.
Donor: Allie B. Jones†.
Foundation type: Independent foundation.
Financial data (yr. ended 08/31/13): Assets,
$3,730,180 (M); expenditures, $220,796;
qualifying distributions, $211,472; giving activities
include $183,500 for 5 grants (high: $55,000; low:
$1,000).
Purpose and activities: Grants limited to
organizations operating within and benefiting the city
of Bristow, Oklahoma; some giving also for
scholarship funds for higher education in
Mississippi and Texas.
Fields of interest: Higher education; Sports and
recreation; Human services; Low-income and poor
people.
Limitations: Applications accepted. Giving primarily
in MS, OK, and TX. No grants to individuals directly.
Application information: Application form required.
  Deadline(s): Oct. 1
Officers: Roger Collins, Chair.; Stan Earnhardt,
Treas.
Trustees: James Bertelsmeyer; Hazel Earnhardt;
Robert Jackson.
EIN: 730721557

7693
The Kerr Foundation Inc.
12501 North May Ave.
Oklahoma City, OK 73120-1948 (405)
749-7991
Contact: Mrs. Robert S. Kerr Jr.
FAX: (405) 749-2877;
E-mail: ccastle@thekerrfoundation.org; Main
URL: http://www.thekerrfoundation.org

Established in 1963 in Oklahoma.
Donor: Grayce B. Kerr Flynn†.
Foundation type: Independent foundation.
Financial data (yr. ended 12/31/13): Assets,
$26,266,152 (M); expenditures, $1,540,703;
qualifying distributions, $1,041,870; giving
activities include $354,146 for 56 grants (high:
$50,000; low: $500).
Purpose and activities: Giving primarily for 1)
education, particularly higher learning and
pre-collegiate organizations, including health
science centers and medical research done by
educational institutions, 2) arts and culture,
particularly organizations in the visual and
performing arts areas, as well as museums and
libraries, 3) health, particularly institutions providing
health care, medical research, or outreach
organizations employing primarily professionals
from the allied health area, 4) human services,
particularly organizations providing services in
diverse areas to the public, and specifically to the
disadvantaged, people with special needs and the
elderly, and 5) public affairs-related programs.
Generally all grants are challenge grants.
Fields of interest: Arts and culture; Visual arts;
Performing arts; Museums; Education; Health;
Diseases and conditions; Public administration;
Human services; Youth services.
Type of support: Capital and infrastructure; In-kind
gifts; Matching grants; Equipment; Program
development; Professorships; Curriculum
development; Fellowships; Research; Internships;
Research and evaluation; Program evaluations.
Limitations: Applications accepted. Giving primarily
in AR, CO, Washington, DC, KS, MO, NM, OK, and
TX. No grants to individuals, or generally for
continuing support.
Publications: Application guidelines; Grants list.
Application information: See foundation web site
for full guidelines and downloadable application
form. Application form required.
  Initial approach: Application form on web site
  Copies of proposal: 3
  Deadline(s): See web site for current deadline
  Board meeting date(s): Quarterly
  Final notification: Next day following receipt of
    application
Officers and Trustees: Lou C. Kerr, Pres.; Laura Kerr
Ogle, V.P. and Secy. and Trustee; Steven. S. Kerr,
V.P. and Trustee; Cody T. Kerr; Ruth Leebron
Levenson.
Number of staff: 4 full-time professional; 1 part-time
professional.
EIN: 731256122

7694
Kimmell Family Foundation
52 N.W. 42nd St.
Oklahoma City, OK 73118-8505 (405)
525-6601
Contact: Thomas Hill, Pres.

Donors: Garman O. Kimmell; Tom Hill; Kay Hill; Kimray Inc.; Garman O. Kimmell 2001 Rev. Trust.
Foundation type: Independent foundation.
Financial data (yr. ended 12/31/13): Assets, $1,226,457 (M); gifts received, $55,503; expenditures, $302,086; qualifying distributions, $286,351; giving activities include $268,000 for 2 grants (high: $200,000; low: $68,000).
Purpose and activities: Giving primarily to Christian ministries.
Fields of interest: Christianity.
Limitations: Applications accepted. Giving in the U.S., with emphasis on OK.
Application information: Application form required.
  Initial approach: Letter
  Deadline(s): None
Officers: Thomas A. Hill, Pres.; Kay K. Hill, Secy.; David K. Hill, Sr., Treas.
Director: Thomas A. Hill III.
EIN: 731620045

7695
Krueger Charitable Foundation
6929 E. 62nd Pl.
Tulsa, OK 74133-4044

Established in 1994 in Oklahoma.
Donors: W.C. Krueger; Carol K. Krueger; Alma M. Krueger.
Foundation type: Independent foundation.
Financial data (yr. ended 12/31/13): Assets, $3,171,875 (M); expenditures, $185,010; qualifying distributions, $178,147; giving activities include $176,240 for 5 grants (high: $75,000; low: $1,700).
Purpose and activities: Giving for the arts, youth services, and libraries.
Fields of interest: Arts and culture; Theater; Education; Libraries; Radio; Child welfare.
Limitations: Applications not accepted. Giving primarily in CO, MA, NY, and OK. No grants to individuals.
Application information: Contributes only to pre-selected organizations.
Trustees: Angie Jackson; Amy E. Krueger; Carol K. Krueger; Gary Edward Morris; Mitchell Stein.
EIN: 731459816

7696
Kullgren Family Charitable Trust
P.O. Box 1620
Tulsa, OK 74101-1620

Foundation type: Independent foundation.
Financial data (yr. ended 12/31/13): Assets, $3,344,431 (M); expenditures, $207,266; qualifying distributions, $191,087; giving activities include $184,500 for 23 grants (high: $20,000; low: $500).
Fields of interest: Education; Health; Human services.
Limitations: Applications not accepted. Giving primarily in Denver, CO.
Application information: Unsolicited requests for funds not accepted.
Trustees: Sharon Wilkinson; BOKF, N.A.
EIN: 387003679

7697
Robert Clay Liddell Foundation
3000 Berry Rd.
Norman, OK 73072-7472   (405) 310-3103

Established in 2004 in Oklahoma.
Donors: Commercial Brick Corp.; Suzanne Rose; Kelly Rose; Richard D. Liddell; Doris Dahl.
Foundation type: Company-sponsored foundation.
Financial data (yr. ended 12/31/13): Assets, $0 (M); gifts received, $1,585,111; expenditures, $281,773; qualifying distributions, $273,088; giving activities include $273,088 for 10 grants (high: $131,220; low: $500).
Fields of interest: Addiction services; Christianity; Shelter and residential care.
Application information: Application form required.
  Initial approach: Letter
  Deadline(s): None
Officers: Richard D. Liddell, Pres.; Larry Pruitt, Secy.
Director: Kelly Rose.
EIN: 200420550

7698
Byrd Fielder Livengood Charitable Trust
P.O. Box 1620
Tulsa, OK 74101-1620
Application address: c/o Bank of Texas, Attn.: Melvin R. Camp, P.O. Box 1088, Sherman, TX 75091, tel.: (903) 813-5102

Established in 2005 in Texas.
Foundation type: Independent foundation.
Financial data (yr. ended 05/31/14): Assets, $7,106,075 (M); expenditures, $361,234; qualifying distributions, $310,367; giving activities include $292,500 for 5 grants (high: $145,000; low: $20,000).
Purpose and activities: Giving primarily for medical care, shelter, assistance and support for elderly persons.
Fields of interest: Health; Hospital care; Human services; Food delivery; Seniors; Indigenous peoples.
Limitations: Applications accepted. Giving primarily in the Sherman, TX, area.
Application information:
  Initial approach: Proposal
  Deadline(s): None
Trustees: Melvin R. Camp; C.H. Gillespie III; Jimmy Harrell; Ray Stephens; Dorothy Mckee; Bank of Texas, N.A.
EIN: 201409711

7699
Lockhart Foundation
P.O. Box 21708
Oklahoma City, OK 73156-1708   (405) 848-8899
Contact: Brian Hill, Tr.

Established in 2007 in Oklahoma.
Donors: Marion S. Lockhart; Lockhart Revocable Trust.
Foundation type: Independent foundation.
Financial data (yr. ended 12/31/13): Assets, $4,449,738 (M); expenditures, $305,520; qualifying distributions, $272,757; giving activities include $270,960 for 7 grants (high: $200,000; low: $960).
Fields of interest: Animal welfare.

Limitations: Applications accepted. Giving primarily in OK, with emphasis on Cleveland and Oklahoma County. No grants to individuals.
Application information: Application form required.
  Initial approach: Proposal
  Deadline(s): None
  Final notification: Approximately three months from the date of submission
Trustee: Brian Hill.
EIN: 262134446

7700
Robert C. and Mary E. Lolmaugh Trust Foundation
(formerly Lolmaugh Trust Foundation)
P.O. Box 1228
Guymon, OK 73942-1228

Established in 1998 in Oklahoma.
Foundation type: Independent foundation.
Financial data (yr. ended 06/30/13): Assets, $4,370,325 (M); expenditures, $231,799; qualifying distributions, $177,107; giving activities include $177,107 for 15 grants (high: $32,107; low: $5,000).
Purpose and activities: Giving for operating expenses for organizations that improve the quality of life for residents of OK.
Fields of interest: Arts and culture; Health; Hospital care; Emergency care; Community and economic development; Christianity; Human services; Child welfare.
Type of support: General support.
Limitations: Applications not accepted. Giving primarily in OK. No grants to individuals.
Application information: Unsolicited requests for funds not accepted.
Trustee: City National Bank.
EIN: 731516313

7701
Tom and Judy Love Foundation
10601 N. Pennsylvania Ave.
Oklahoma City, OK 73120-4108

Donors: Gemini Motor Transport, LP; Judith Judith; Thomas Love.
Foundation type: Independent foundation.
Financial data (yr. ended 12/31/13): Assets, $2,897,690 (M); gifts received, $3,052,572; expenditures, $160,923; qualifying distributions, $153,000; giving activities include $153,000 for 1 grant.
Fields of interest: Religion.
Limitations: Applications not accepted. Giving primarily in Oklahoma City, OK.
Application information: Unsolicited requests for funds not accepted.
Officers and Directors: Judith M. Love, Pres. and Director; Thomas E. Love, V.P. and Director; Kristine M. Rogers, Secy.; Douglas J. Stussi, Treas.; Frank C. Love IV; Gregory M. Love; Laura A. Love; Jennifer Love Meyer.
EIN: 463640241

7702
P. Vincent & Sally S. Lovoi Family Foundation
1246 Hazel Blvd.
Tulsa, OK 74114-3928
Contact: P. Vincent Lovoi, Tr.

Donors: P. Vincent Lovoi; Sally S. Lovoi.
Foundation type: Independent foundation.
Financial data (yr. ended 12/31/12): Assets, $2,574,768 (M); expenditures, $118,871; qualifying distributions, $114,700; giving activities include $114,700 for grants.
Fields of interest: Arts and culture; Religion; Human services.
Limitations: Applications accepted. Giving primarily in OK.
Application information: Application form required.
 Initial approach: Letter
 Deadline(s): None
Trustee: P. Vincent Lovoi.
EIN: 731602213

7703
John W. and Jerry E. Marshall Foundation
c/o Donald B. Atkins
1406 Terrace Dr.
Tulsa, OK 74104-4626

Established in 2002 in Oklahoma.
Donors: John W. Marshall; Jerry E. Marshall; Scot M. Marshall.
Foundation type: Independent foundation.
Financial data (yr. ended 12/31/12): Assets, $4,828,625 (M); gifts received, $448,785; expenditures, $263,028; qualifying distributions, $231,640; giving activities include $231,640 for grants.
Fields of interest: Higher education; Human services.
Limitations: Applications not accepted. Giving primarily in OK. No grants to individuals.
Application information: Contributes only to pre-selected organizations.
Trustees: Jerry E. Marshall; Scot M. Marshall.
EIN: 760716481

7704
Karl & Georgia Martin, Sr., Anna Belle Flynn, Karl & June Martin, Jr. Foundation
6307 Waterford Blvd., Ste. 160
Oklahoma City, OK 73118-1117 (405) 840-8401
Contact: Joe Womack, Tr.

Established in 1996 in Oklahoma.
Donor: Karl & June Martin Trust.
Foundation type: Independent foundation.
Financial data (yr. ended 12/31/13): Assets, $7,512,524 (M); expenditures, $534,939; qualifying distributions, $405,000; giving activities include $405,000 for 13 grants (high: $64,000; low: $10,000).
Purpose and activities: Awards limited to students enrolled in petroleum studies at the University of Oklahoma, University of Tulsa, and Oklahoma State University.
Fields of interest: University education.
Type of support: Scholarships; Student aid.
Limitations: Applications accepted. Giving primarily in OK.

Application information: Application form required.
 Initial approach: Request application form
 Deadline(s): April 30
Trustees: Richard A. Goranson; Edward J. Havrilla; Paul Kallenberger; Joe Womack.
EIN: 731504147

7705
Massey Family Foundation
1400 W. Main St.
Durant, OK 74701-4906

Established in 2004 in Oklahoma.
Donors: John L. Massey; John Michael Massey; Massey Investment.
Foundation type: Independent foundation.
Financial data (yr. ended 12/31/13): Assets, $6,208,167 (M); gifts received, $1,200,000; expenditures, $450,580; qualifying distributions, $336,160; giving activities include $336,160 for 31 grants (high: $100,000; low: $100).
Fields of interest: Higher education; Protestantism; Human services.
Limitations: Applications not accepted. Giving primarily in OK.
Application information: Contributes only to pre-selected organizations.
Officers: John L. Massey, Pres.; Gregory L. Massey, V.P.
Directors: Steve Burrage; Mary Frank.
EIN: 432065394

7706
Merkel Family Foundation
2431 E. 61st St., Ste. 600
Tulsa, OK 74136-1243 (918) 744-5222

Foundation type: Independent foundation.
Financial data (yr. ended 12/31/14): Assets, $4,777,896; expenditures, $548,326; qualifying distributions, $224,224.
Fields of interest: Museums; Education; Higher education; Alzheimer's disease; Human services; Scouting programs.
Limitations: Applications accepted. Giving primarily in OK. No grants to individuals.
Application information: Application form required.
 Initial approach: Letter
 Copies of proposal: 1
 Deadline(s): None
Trustees: Bryant J. Coffman; Jon R. Stuart; John B. Turner.
EIN: 736248411

7707
The Merrick Foundation
2932 N.W. 122nd St.
Bradley Sq., Ste. D
Oklahoma City, OK 73120-1955
E-mail: fwmerrick@foundationmanagementinc.com;
Main URL: http://www.foundationmanagementinc.com/foundations/merrick-foundation

Established in 1948 in Oklahoma.
Donor: Mrs. Frank W. Merrick‡.
Foundation type: Independent foundation.
Financial data (yr. ended 12/31/13): Assets, $10,367,269 (M); expenditures, $526,716; qualifying distributions, $443,717; giving activities

include $361,150 for 54 grants (high: $100,000; low: $100).
Purpose and activities: The mission of the foundation is to enhance the quality of life of Oklahomans and their communities with primary emphasis on South Central Oklahoma. With this goal in mind, the foundation trustees are committed to furthering the philanthropic vision of Ward S. Merrick, Sr. by awarding grants to charitable organizations that foster independence and achievement, and that stimulate educational, economic and cultural growth. The foundation's major areas of interest are education, health and medical research, arts and humanities, and social services.
Fields of interest: Arts and culture; Higher education; Diseases and conditions; Human services; Youth services.
Type of support: General support; Matching grants; Annual campaigns; Research; Capital campaigns; Research and evaluation; Capital and infrastructure; Program development; Seed money; Technical assistance; Program evaluations.
Limitations: Applications accepted. Giving primarily in OK, with emphasis on South Central OK. No grants to individuals, or for endowment funds.
Publications: Application guidelines; Annual report; Informational brochure.
Application information: Application guidelines available on foundation web site. Application form required.
 Initial approach: Online application process on foundation web site. All correspondence will be done through e-mail
 Copies of proposal: 1
 Deadline(s): See foundation web site for current deadlines
 Board meeting date(s): May and Nov.
Officers and Trustees: Frank W. Merrick, Pres. and Trustee; Will Merrick, Exec. V.P.; Robert Merrick, C.F.O. and Trustee; Randy Macon, Exec. Dir.; Valda M. Buchanan; Laura Clay; Charles R. Coe, Jr.; Ross M. "Rick" Coe; Ward I. Coe; Michael McCauley; Ward S. Merrick III; Jessie Nance.
Number of staff: None.
EIN: 736111622

7708
Lou and Connie Miller Charitable Foundation
4821 S. Sheridan Rd., Ste. 225
Tulsa, OK 74145-5716 (918) 236-3477
Contact: Max R. Vowel, Pres.

Established in 2005 in Oklahoma.
Donor: Louis H. Miller Trust.
Foundation type: Independent foundation.
Financial data (yr. ended 11/30/14): Assets, $8,619,708 (M); expenditures, $404,754; qualifying distributions, $346,815; giving activities include $346,815 for 39 grants (high: $62,500; low: $180).
Fields of interest: Ballet; Botanical gardens; Foundations; Human services.
Type of support: General support.
Limitations: Applications accepted. Giving primarily in Tulsa, OK. No grants to individuals.
Application information: Application form required.
 Initial approach: Letter
 Deadline(s): None

Officers: Max R. Vowel, Pres.; W. Kirk Clausing, V.P.; Madeline K. Gilmore, Secy.-Treas.
EIN: 134222602

7709
Jerome B. Miller Family Foundation
P.O. Box 278
Guthrie, OK   73044-0278

Established in 1993 in Oklahoma.
Donor: Jerome B. Miller.
Foundation type: Independent foundation.
Financial data (yr. ended 12/31/13): Assets, $1,967,679 (M); expenditures, $291,603; qualifying distributions, $277,800; giving activities include $277,800 for 8 grants (high: $200,000; low: $50).
Fields of interest: Education; Human services.
Type of support: General support.
Limitations: Applications not accepted. Giving primarily in Chicago, IL and OK. No grants to individuals.
Application information: Unsolicited requests for funds not accepted.
Officers and Directors: Jerome B. Miller, Pres. and Director; Julie P. Robinson, V.P. and Director.
EIN: 731438698

7710
James D. & Cathryn M. Moore Foundation
(formerly Ruth & Allen Mayo Charitable Foundation)
2200 S. Utica Pl.
Tulsa, OK   74114-7006

Established in 1999 in Oklahoma.
Donors: CMM Charitable Lead Trust I; CMM Charitable Lead Trust II.
Foundation type: Independent foundation.
Financial data (yr. ended 03/31/14): Assets, $6,400,483 (M); expenditures, $510,935; qualifying distributions, $315,387; giving activities include $315,387 for 35 grants (high: $30,000; low: $1,000).
Fields of interest: Arts and culture; Opera; Art museums; Higher education; Christianity; Youth development.
Type of support: General support.
Limitations: Applications not accepted. Giving primarily in Tulsa, OK. No grants to individuals.
Application information: Contributes only to pre-selected organizations.
Trustees: Cathryn Mayo Moore; James D. Moore.
EIN: 736315876

7711
Oklahoma Surgical Hospital Foundation, Inc.
2408 E. 81st St., No. 300
Tulsa, OK   74137-4230

Donor: Oklahoma Surgical Hospital, LLC.
Foundation type: Independent foundation.
Financial data (yr. ended 12/31/13): Assets, $359,923 (M); gifts received, $203,410; expenditures, $127,908; qualifying distributions, $127,908; giving activities include $125,000 for 6 grants (high: $40,000; low: $5,000).
Fields of interest: Education; Philanthropy; Health; Human services.

Limitations: Applications accepted. Giving primarily in OK.
Application information: Application form required.
Initial approach: Letter
Deadline(s): First come, First served
Officer: James D. Cash, MD, Chair.
Board Members: Craig Johnson, MD; Rodney L. Plaster, MD.
EIN: 203308716

7712
Owasso Outreach Foundation
9919 N. Cadbury Ridge St.
Owasso, OK   74055-7731   (918) 836-6317
Contact: Randolph S. Baskins, Tr.

Established in 2006 in Oklahoma.
Donors: Gary W. Johnson; Steven E. Baskins; William R. Thomas; Randolph S. Baskins.
Foundation type: Independent foundation.
Financial data (yr. ended 12/31/13): Assets, $3,845,804 (M); expenditures, $328,778; qualifying distributions, $296,500; giving activities include $296,500 for 11 grants (high: $100,000; low: $5,000).
Purpose and activities: Giving limited to Christian organizations.
Fields of interest: Christianity.
Limitations: Applications accepted. Giving primarily in MO. No grants to individuals.
Application information: Application form required.
Initial approach: Letter
Deadline(s): None
Trustees: Randolph S. Baskins; Steven E. Baskins; Gary W. Johnson; William R. Thomas.
EIN: 205853758

7713
Robert A. Parman Foundation
c/o Trust Company of Oklahoma
6307 Waterford Blvd., Ste. 215
Oklahoma City, OK   73118
Application address: c/o The Law Office of Tom A. Hemry, P.C., Att.: Jerry Hemry, P.O. Box 22486, Oklahoma City, OK, 73123, tel.: (405) 602-2053

Established in 1962 in Oklahoma.
Donor: Robert A. Parman‡.
Foundation type: Independent foundation.
Financial data (yr. ended 08/31/14): Assets, $4,507,260 (M); gifts received, $1,800; expenditures, $367,724; qualifying distributions, $241,281; giving activities include $218,500 for 14 grants (high: $60,000; low: $1,000).
Purpose and activities: Support primarily for higher education; grants also to social service organizations.
Fields of interest: Higher education; Diseases and conditions; Arthritis; Kidney diseases; Human services; Food banks.
Limitations: Applications accepted. Giving primarily in OK. No grants to individuals.
Application information:
Initial approach: Letter
Deadline(s): None
Trustees: J.W. Lanier; Richard Metheny; Jerry M. Thomason.
EIN: 736098053

7714
Glenn W. Peel Foundation
116 S. Main St.
Newkirk, OK   74647-4512   (580) 362-2583

Established in 1978 in Oklahoma.
Donor: Glenn W. Peel‡.
Foundation type: Independent foundation.
Financial data (yr. ended 09/30/14): Assets, $4,079,770; gifts received, $2,298; expenditures, $215,270; qualifying distributions, $199,435.
Purpose and activities: Giving primarily for education and human services.
Fields of interest: Arts and culture; Education; Hospice care; Diseases and conditions; Christianity; Youth development.
Type of support: Capital campaigns; Research.
Limitations: Applications accepted. Giving primarily in OK.
Publications: Application guidelines.
Application information:
Initial approach: Proposal
Copies of proposal: 1
Deadline(s): None
Board meeting date(s): 1st Fri. of Apr., July, Oct., and Dec.
Officers: Jack De McCarty, Pres.; Thomas M. Rigden, Secy.-Treas.
Directors: Marybeth Glass; Philip A. Ross; Betty J. Scott.
EIN: 731057392

7715
Pros For Africa Inc.
1 N.E. 2nd St., Ste. 201
Oklahoma City, OK   73104-2242
Main URL: http://prosforafrica.com/

Donors: Reggie N. Whitten; Guy Sperduto, CPA; Brenda Alexander; Mercy Shared Services; UBS Financial Services Inc.; Giant Experiences; Chris Carey Foundation; Whitten Newman Foundation; Michael Burrage; Amal E. Moorad; Brad Henry for Governor; Bobby Alexander; Roy Williams.
Foundation type: Independent foundation.
Financial data (yr. ended 12/31/13): Assets, $33,638 (M); gifts received, $430,515; expenditures, $466,484; qualifying distributions, $201,066; giving activities include $201,066 for 2 grants (high: $171,066; low: $30,000).
Fields of interest: Education; Health; Human services.
Limitations: Applications not accepted. Giving primarily in OK.
Application information: Unsolicited requests for funds not accepted.
Officers: Reggie N. Whitten, Pres.; Rachelle Newman Whitten, V.P.; Jeffrey Hargrave, Secy.
EIN: 271674673

7716
Rathburn Family Charitable Foundation
6010 E. 117th St.
Tulsa, OK   74137-8514

Donors: Gary J. Rathburn; Anita L. Rathburn.
Foundation type: Independent foundation.
Financial data (yr. ended 12/31/13): Assets, $4,931,113 (M); gifts received, $100,000; expenditures, $239,618; qualifying distributions,

$237,943; giving activities include $237,943 for 4 grants (high: $106,943; low: $20,000).

Fields of interest: Higher education; Health care administration and financing.

Limitations: Applications not accepted. Giving primarily in OK and PA.

Application information: Unsolicited requests for funds not accepted.

Trustees: Anita L. Rathburn; Gary J. Rathburn.

EIN: 456625820

7717

A. E. & Juanita Richardson Charitable Foundation

P.O. Box 679
Nowata, OK 74048
Application Address: c/o Arvest Trust Co., 100 S.E. Frank Phillips Blvd., Bartlesville, OK, 74003, Application Phone: (918) 337-4337

Foundation type: Independent foundation.

Financial data (yr. ended 12/31/14): Assets, $5,548,522 (M); expenditures, $338,332; qualifying distributions, $278,426; giving activities include $278,426 for 16 grants (high: $77,500; low: $2,500).

Purpose and activities: Giving primarily for medical, healthcare, education and spiritual objectives.

Fields of interest: Education; Elementary and secondary education; Higher education; Community and economic development; Christianity; Human services.

Type of support: Individual development.

Limitations: Applications not accepted. Giving primarily in MO and OK. No grants to individuals.

Application information: Contributes only to pre-selected organizations. Application form required.

Trustees: Jessie L. Blackwell; Todd Cone; Benjamin C. Killion; W.E. Maddux; Linda Mills; Sandra Moore; Phyllis Willis.

EIN: 911914497

7718

Steven Russell Smith Foundation

4141 S. Jackson
Tulsa, OK 74107-7017

Donors: Tamara Smith; Steve R. Smith.

Foundation type: Independent foundation.

Financial data (yr. ended 12/31/13): Assets, $8,351,686 (M); gifts received, $1,280,763; expenditures, $419,878; qualifying distributions, $213,945; giving activities include $158,200 for 11 grants (high: $45,000; low: $600).

Fields of interest: Domesticated animals; Community and economic development; Youth development.

Limitations: Applications not accepted. Giving primarily in OK.

Application information: Unsolicited requests for funds not accepted.

Trustees: Annette Hathcoat; Scott Haus; Brandon Smith; Steve R. Smith; Tamara Smith.

EIN: 450558764

7719

Paul L. & Helen I. Sisk Charitable Trust

5319 S. Lewis Ste. 110
Tulsa, OK 74105-6536

Established in 1989 in Oklahoma.

Foundation type: Independent foundation.

Financial data (yr. ended 12/31/13): Assets, $4,303,058 (M); expenditures, $317,613; qualifying distributions, $190,451; giving activities include $146,000 for 30 grants (high: $36,500; low: $500).

Purpose and activities: Giving primarily to Protestant churches, and for health and human services.

Fields of interest: Religion; Human rights; Human services.

Limitations: Applications accepted. Giving primarily in Tulsa, OK. No grants to individuals.

Application information:
Initial approach: Letter
Deadline(s): None
Board meeting date(s): Semianuualy

Trustees: Charles W. Harris; Ruth Sowards.

EIN: 736243607

7720

The Buel J. Staton Charitable Trust

324 S. Husband
Stillwater, OK 74074 (405) 880-2922

Established in 2005 in Oklahoma.

Donor: Buel J. Staton‡.

Foundation type: Independent foundation.

Financial data (yr. ended 12/31/14): Assets, $314,172; expenditures, $168,981; qualifying distributions, $164,281.

Fields of interest: Museums; Christianity; Seniors.

Limitations: Applications accepted. Giving primarily in Stillwater, OK.

Application information: Application form required.
Initial approach: Completed application form
Deadline(s): None

Trustee: Gerald E. Bradshaw.

EIN: 686249451

7721

Stone Family Foundation

320 S. Boston Ave., 19th Fl.
Tulsa, OK 74103-3706 (918) 583-1178
Contact: Samuel C. Stone, Pres.

Established in 1997 in Kansas.

Donor: Clifford W. Stone.

Foundation type: Independent foundation.

Financial data (yr. ended 12/31/13): Assets, $9,052,697 (M); expenditures, $480,962; qualifying distributions, $431,836; giving activities include $429,586 for 42 grants (high: $40,000; low: $2,000).

Purpose and activities: Giving primarily for the arts, particularly museums, education, hospitals, and to a rowing association.

Fields of interest: Arts and culture; Art museums; Education; Health; Hospital care; Protestantism; Sports and recreation.

Type of support: Continuing support; In-kind gifts; Matching grants; Annual campaigns; Equipment; Land acquisitions; Scholarships.

Limitations: Applications accepted. Giving primarily in KS, MO, and OK. No support for political organizations.

Application information:
Initial approach: Proposal
Deadline(s): None

Officers: Samuel C. Stone, Pres.; Sue Stone Hunter, V.P. and Secy.

Trustees: Britton Hunter; Sara Stone Laughren.

EIN: 431773536

7722

Dave & Barbara Sylvan Foundation

1 W. 3rd St., Ste. 918
Tulsa, OK 74103-3517 (918) 587-6756

Donors: Dave R. Sylvan; Barbara Sylvan.

Foundation type: Independent foundation.

Financial data (yr. ended 12/31/13): Assets, $4,868,057 (M); expenditures, $240,666; qualifying distributions, $215,245; giving activities include $215,245 for 49 grants (high: $100,000; low: $100).

Fields of interest: Arts and culture; Judaism; Human services.

Limitations: Applications accepted. Giving primarily in IL and OK. No grants to individuals.

Application information: Application form required.
Initial approach: Letter
Deadline(s): None

Directors: Debra Sylvan de Leeuw; James Framel; Barbara Sylvan; Dave R. Sylvan.

EIN: 731206320

7723

Carol Tandy Foundation

8177 S. Harvard Ave., No. 402
Tulsa, OK 74137-1600

Donor: Carol Tandy.

Foundation type: Independent foundation.

Financial data (yr. ended 12/31/13): Assets, $1,949,623 (M); gifts received, $260,000; expenditures, $269,932; qualifying distributions, $248,906; giving activities include $246,200 for 10 grants (high: $75,000; low: $350).

Fields of interest: Domesticated animals; Agriculture; Housing development.

Limitations: Applications not accepted. Giving primarily in Tulsa, OK.

Application information: Unsolicited requests for funds not accepted.

Trustees: Shawna Baker; Carol Tandy.

EIN: 274373617

7724

Thomas Educational Foundation Inc.

P.O. Box 231
Thomas, OK 73669-0231

Foundation type: Independent foundation.

Financial data (yr. ended 06/30/14): Assets, $2,874,722 (M); expenditures, $335,188; qualifying distributions, $293,016; giving activities include $134,398 for 1 grant, $158,618 for 53 grants to individuals (high: $7,695; low: $665), and $449,452 for foundation-administered programs.

Purpose and activities: The foundation provides scholarships to Thomas Fay Custer School graduates for the furtherance of their post secondary education. Teacher grants are also provided to the Thomas Fay Custer School System for the benefit of the students and teachers.

Fields of interest: Education; Teacher education.

Type of support: Student aid.

Limitations: Applications not accepted. Giving primarily in OK.
Application information: Unsolicited requests for funds not accepted.
Officers: Lu Ann Alexander, Pres.; Jim Litsch, V.P.; Ladonna Taylor, Secy.; Kari Didier, Treas.
Trustees: David Beck; Yvonne Covey; Duane Nicholas; Cody Parker; Mary Ann Sanders.
EIN: 731449664

7725
The Robert S. and Helen Grey Trippet Foundation, Inc.
P.O. Box 701775
Tulsa, OK   74170-1775
Contact: Robert C. Simpson, Pres.

Established in 1991 in Oklahoma.
Donors: Helen Grey Trippet†; Robert S. Trippet.
Foundation type: Independent foundation.
Financial data (yr. ended 07/31/14): Assets, $8,383,936 (M); expenditures, $445,490; qualifying distributions, $363,555; giving activities include $312,500 for 26 grants (high: $99,000; low: $250).
Fields of interest: Arts and culture; Higher education; Nonprofits; Diseases and conditions; Human services.
Type of support: Research; Research and evaluation; Regranting.
Limitations: Applications accepted. Giving primarily in OK. No grants to individuals.
Application information:
  Deadline(s): None
Officers: Robert C. Simpson, Pres.; J. W. Moore, Jr., V.P.; Willliam J. Rea, Jr., V.P.; Cory P. Simpson, V.P.; Barbara R. Kelley, Secy.-Treas.
EIN: 731390841

7726
Gregg Wadley Foundation Inc.
4812 Bocage Ln.
Oklahoma City, OK   73131-1842

Established in 2005 in Oklahoma.
Donor: Gregg A. Wadley.
Foundation type: Independent foundation.
Financial data (yr. ended 12/31/13): Assets, $4,301,231 (M); expenditures, $291,991; qualifying distributions, $262,683; giving activities include $262,683 for 16 grants (high: $100,000; low: $200).
Fields of interest: Cultural awareness; Ethnic museums; University education.
Limitations: Applications not accepted. Giving primarily in OK. No grants to individuals.
Application information: Contributes only to pre-selected organizations.
Directors: Susan E. Brackett; Gregg A. Wadley; Gregg A. Wadley II.
EIN: 203976660

7727
The Ben and Bonnie Walkingstick Foundation
1001 Manvel Ave.
Chandler, OK   74834-3853

Donors: Ben T. Walkingstick, Jr.; Bonnie J. Walkingstick.

Foundation type: Independent foundation.
Financial data (yr. ended 12/31/12): Assets, $313,405 (M); gifts received, $200,000; expenditures, $174,520; qualifying distributions, $172,500; giving activities include $172,500 for 8 grants (high: $100,000; low: $1,000).
Fields of interest: Education; Community and economic development.
Limitations: Applications not accepted. Giving primarily in IN and OK.
Application information: Unsolicited requests for funds not accepted.
Trustees: Ben T. Walkingstick, Jr.; Boonnie J. Walkingstick.
EIN: 273590081

7728
Tom L. Ward Foundation
P.O. Box 54525
Oklahoma City, OK   73154-1525

Established in 2006 in Oklahoma.
Donors: Tom L. Ward; Sch'ree D. Ward.
Foundation type: Independent foundation.
Financial data (yr. ended 12/31/13): Assets, $166,360 (M); gifts received, $350,000; expenditures, $200,219; qualifying distributions, $200,218; giving activities include $200,000 for 1 grant.
Fields of interest: Child welfare; Male children and youth.
Limitations: Applications not accepted. Giving primarily in Piedmont, OK. No grants to individuals.
Application information: Contributes only to pre-selected organizations.
Officers: Tom L. Ward, Chair.; Trent L. Ward, Pres.; Sch'ree D. Ward, V.P.; John D. Garrison, Secy.
EIN: 203160317

7729
Warren Charite' Foundation
P.O. Box 470372
Tulsa, OK   74147-0372   (918) 492-8100
Contact: Mark Ross

Established in 1968 in Oklahoma.
Donors: William K. Warren; Jean Warren; Elizabeth Warren Blankenship; Marilyn Vandever; EWB Charitable Trust; J.M. Warren Trust; Blankenship Trust; Patricia Warren Swindle; Dorothy Warren King†.
Foundation type: Independent foundation.
Financial data (yr. ended 12/31/13): Assets, $4,042,521 (M); expenditures, $159,750; qualifying distributions, $150,344; giving activities include $150,344 for 5 grants (high: $116,000; low: $1,000).
Purpose and activities: Giving primarily for education and human services, with a preference toward local Catholic health care facilities.
Fields of interest: Higher education; Health; Catholicism; Human services; Child welfare.
Type of support: General support.
Limitations: Applications accepted. Giving primarily in IN and Tulsa, OK; funding also in San Diego, CA. No grants to individuals.
Application information: Application form required.
  Initial approach: Letter
  Deadline(s): None

Officers and Directors: W.K. Warren, Jr., Pres. and Director; M.A. Buntz, V.P. and Treas. and Director; A.N. Warren, V.P. and Director; J.K. Morgan, Secy.
EIN: 730776064

7730
The Charles & Marion Weber Foundation
P.O. Box 14011
Tulsa, OK   74159-1011   (918) 583-8361
Contact: Gordon L. Nielsen, Pres.

Established in 2007 in Oklahoma.
Foundation type: Independent foundation.
Financial data (yr. ended 12/31/13): Assets, $3,638,094 (M); expenditures, $248,918; qualifying distributions, $176,500; giving activities include $176,500 for 30 grants (high: $15,000; low: $1,000).
Fields of interest: Arts and culture; Foundations; Human services.
Limitations: Applications accepted. Giving primarily in OK.
Application information: Application form required.
  Initial approach: Proposal
  Deadline(s): None
Officers: Gordon L. Nielsen, Pres.; Pamela Low, V.P.; Charles O. Meyers, Jr., Treas.
Board Members: Catherine G. Nielsen; Kathryn Burke.
EIN: 207338204

7731
Wegener Foundation, Inc.
(formerly The Herman and Mary Wegener Foundation, Inc.)
P.O. Box 18335
Oklahoma City, OK   73154-0335   (405) 235-8455
Contact: Lee Holmes, Pres.; Meredith Edmison, Exec. Dir.
FAX: (405) 235-8454; Additional tel.: (405) 208-8534

Established in 1954 in Oklahoma.
Donors: Herman H. Wegener†; Mary Wegener.
Foundation type: Independent foundation.
Financial data (yr. ended 12/31/13): Assets, $3,477,589 (M); gifts received, $895; expenditures, $357,943; qualifying distributions, $234,316; giving activities include $218,500 for 67 grants (high: $10,000; low: $1,000).
Purpose and activities: The foundation gives primarily to social service organizations and to those organizations focused on programs that serve at-risk children and youth.
Fields of interest: Education; Agriculture; Employment; Housing development; Youth development; Special population support.
Type of support: General support; Continuing support; Capital campaigns; Capital and infrastructure; Equipment; Land acquisitions; Endowments; Emergency funds; Program development; Seed money; Curriculum development; Scholarships.
Limitations: Applications accepted. Giving primarily in Oklahoma City, OK. No support for non-501 (c)(3) entities. No grants to individuals.
Publications: Application guidelines.
Application information: The foundation rarely accepts applications from outside OK.

Initial approach: Request copy of application guidelines
Copies of proposal: 1
Deadline(s): Oct. 31
Board meeting date(s): Annually in Nov.
Final notification: By the end of the year
Officers and Trustees: Lee Holmes, Pres. and Trustee; Jeff Wegener, V.P. and Treas. and Trustee; Rosemary Fields, V.P. and Trustee; Eugene C. Wegener, V.P. and Trustee; Mark Wegener, V.P.; Rodney Wegener; Kay Wolfard.
Number of staff: 1 part-time professional.
EIN: 736095407

7732
Welch Family Foundation, Inc.
1100 Oneok Plz.
100 W. 5th St.
Tulsa, OK 74103-4279

Established in 1997 in Oklahoma.
Donors: William J. Welch; William J. Welch Trust.
Foundation type: Independent foundation.
Financial data (yr. ended 12/31/14): Assets, $3,866,148; expenditures, $172,863; qualifying distributions, $168,908.
Fields of interest: Education; Protestantism; Human services.
Limitations: Applications not accepted. Giving primarily in Tulsa, OK. No grants to individuals.
Application information: Unsolicited requests for funds not accepted.
Officers and Directors: David McKinney, Pres. and Director; Peggy Welch, V.P. and Secy. and Director; Grace Sensintaffar; Douglas S. Welch; William J. Welch, Jr.
EIN: 731502461

7733
Harold A. and Edna L. White Foundation
P.O. Box 1620
Tulsa, OK 74101-1620

Established in 2000 in Oklahoma.
Donor: Harold A. White Trust.
Foundation type: Independent foundation.
Financial data (yr. ended 12/31/13): Assets, $6,488,727 (M); expenditures, $325,909; qualifying distributions, $279,025; giving activities include $259,450 for 6 grants (high: $155,250; low: $11,050).
Fields of interest: Religion; Sports and recreation; Human services.
Type of support: General support.
Limitations: Applications not accepted. Giving primarily in Tulsa, OK.
Application information: Unsolicited requests for funds not accepted.
Trustee: Bank of Oklahoma, N.A.
EIN: 731582836

7734
Stanley White Foundation
c/o Clyde Chrisman
2537 E. 46th Pl.
Tulsa, OK 74105-5148

Established in 2002 in Oklahoma.
Donor: Stanley White Trust.
Foundation type: Independent foundation.

Financial data (yr. ended 12/31/14): Assets, $3,025,910 (M); expenditures, $219,680; qualifying distributions, $190,834; giving activities include $155,000 for 2 grants (high: $150,000; low: $5,000).
Fields of interest: University education; Nonprofits; Entrepreneurship.
Type of support: General support; Regranting.
Limitations: Applications not accepted. Giving primarily in OK. No grants to individuals.
Application information: Unsolicited requests for funds not accepted.
Trustees: Clyde Chrisman; John B. Johnson; Michael Fretz.
EIN: 731519161

7735
The Whitwell-Meyer Foundation
11122 S. Yale Ave.
Tulsa, OK 74137-7620
Application address: c/o Thomas D. Whitwell, 5904 W. Orlando Cir., Broken Arrow, OK 74011, tel.: (918) 492-4209

Donors: Linda L. Meyer; Thomas D. Whitwell; Sara E. Whitwell; Robert D. Meyer.
Foundation type: Independent foundation.
Financial data (yr. ended 12/31/13): Assets, $127,469 (M); gifts received, $299,255; expenditures, $438,651; qualifying distributions, $436,785; giving activities include $436,785 for 5 grants (high: $311,785; low: $10,000).
Fields of interest: Religion.
Limitations: Applications accepted. Giving primarily in OK.
Application information: Application form required.
Initial approach: Letter
Deadline(s): None
Trustees: Linda L. Meyer; Robert D. Meyer; Sara E. Whitwell; Thomas D. Whitwell.
EIN: 272546121

7736
Patti Johnson Wilson Foundation
c/o The Trust Company of Oklahoma
1924 S. Utica Ave., Ste. 500
Tulsa, OK 74104-6540
Application address: c/o The Trust Company of Oklahoma, Attn.: Paul E. Kallenberger, P.O. Box 3348, Tulsa, OK 74101-3348, email: paul.kallenberger@trustok.com

Established in 1973 in Oklahoma.
Donor: Patti Johnson Wilson.
Foundation type: Independent foundation.
Financial data (yr. ended 08/31/13): Assets, $11,932,220 (M); gifts received, $33,171; expenditures, $983,235; qualifying distributions, $417,738; giving activities include $218,000 for 16 grants (high: $50,000; low: $500), and $176,000 for 53 grants to individuals (high: $4,000; low: $1,500).
Purpose and activities: Giving primarily for the arts and human services; also grants scholarships to students in the fields of music, engineering, and liberal arts at the University of Oklahoma, Oklahoma City University, Oklahoma State University, University of Kansas, Kansas State University, University of Tulsa, and University of Arkansas.
Fields of interest: Music; Opera; Art museums; Higher education; Human services.

Type of support: General support; Student aid.
Limitations: Applications accepted. Giving primarily in AR, KS, and OK.
Publications: Application guidelines.
Application information: Application form required.
Initial approach: Email or Letter
Deadline(s): Apr. 1 for scholarships; Oct. 1 for grants
Board meeting date(s): Nov.
Trustees: Kathleen L. Childs; Barbara Ann Glass; Frank X. Henke III; Paul Kallenberger; Frederick P. Koontz; Nancy Johnson Leake; Mary Ann Meckfessel; James M. Sturdivant; The Trust Co. of Oklahoma.
EIN: 736156280

7737
Donna Dantini Witt Foundation
3131 S. Columbia Cir.
Tulsa, OK 74105
Application address: c/o Donna C. Witt, 4127 Gulf of Mexico Dr., Ste. 101, Longboat Key, FL 34228, tel.: (918) 366-2840

Donor: Donna C. Witt.
Foundation type: Independent foundation.
Financial data (yr. ended 12/31/13): Assets, $5,650,117 (M); expenditures, $263,284; qualifying distributions, $255,047; giving activities include $255,047 for 12 grants (high: $90,850; low: $694).
Fields of interest: Arts and culture; Education; University education; Christianity; Family services; Domestic violence shelters.
Limitations: Applications accepted. Giving primarily in OK.
Application information: Application form required.
Initial approach: Letter
Deadline(s): None
Officer: Donna C. Witt, Pres.
EIN: 205975850

7738
Charles Wolff, Jr. & Jessica Short Wolff Foundation
P.O. Box 1620
Tulsa, OK 74101-1620

Foundation type: Independent foundation.
Financial data (yr. ended 10/31/13): Assets, $4,709,209 (M); expenditures, $337,144; qualifying distributions, $225,848; giving activities include $214,793 for 4 grants (high: $107,370; low: $21,479).
Fields of interest: Hospital care; Youth development.
Limitations: Applications not accepted. Giving limited to Topeka and Wichita, KS. No grants to individuals.
Application information: Unsolicited requests for funds not accepted.
Trustee: Bank of Oklahoma, N.A.
EIN: 486104050

7739
Young Family Foundation
P.O. Box 1267
Fort Gibson, OK   74434-1267
Application address: c/o Joseph P. Rigali, 62 Walnut
St., Wellesley, MA 02481-2109, tel.: (918)
458-9271

Established in 2000 in Massachusetts.

Donors: Tina B. Young; E. Ryker Young.
Foundation type: Independent foundation.
Financial data (yr. ended 11/30/14): Assets,
$6,706,385 (M); expenditures, $371,658;
qualifying distributions, $312,771; giving activities
include $312,701 for 8 grants (high: $80,000; low:
$9,600).
Fields of interest: Education; Christianity.

Limitations: Applications accepted. Giving primarily
in OK.
Application information:
   Initial approach: Proposal
   Deadline(s): None
Trustees: E. Ryker Young; Tina B. Young.
EIN: 043525914

OREGON

7740
Edward & Romell Ackley Foundation
P.O. Box 3168
Portland, OR   97208-3168   (503) 275-6564

Established in 2003 in Oregon.
Donor: R.V. Ackley Trust.
Foundation type: Independent foundation.
Financial data (yr. ended 12/31/14): Assets, $4,471,113; expenditures, $302,624; qualifying distributions, $249,706.
Fields of interest: Philanthropy; Specialty hospital care; Diseases and conditions; Human services; Child welfare; Adoption; Youth development.
Type of support: General support.
Limitations: Applications accepted. Giving primarily in Portland, OR.
Application information: Application form required.
   Initial approach: Contact foundation for application form
   Deadline(s): Contact foundation for deadline
Trustee: U.S. Bank, N.A.
EIN: 206014363

7741
John G. Atkins Foundation, Inc.
P.O. Box 1870
Brookings, OR   97415-0050   (541) 469-7741
Contact: Rory W. Smith, Pres. and Treas.

Established in 2005 in Oregon.
Donors: Jayne Gibney†; Carol Diaz; Bill Ryland; Patricia Ryland.
Foundation type: Independent foundation.
Financial data (yr. ended 12/31/13): Assets, $1,546,533 (M); expenditures, $293,884; qualifying distributions, $289,216; giving activities include $289,216 for 9 grants (high: $103,698; low: $1,300).
Fields of interest: Education; Community and economic development.
Limitations: Applications accepted. Giving limited to Curry County, OR.
Application information:
   Initial approach: Letter
   Deadline(s): None
   Final notification: Usually within 2 months
Officers: Rory W. Smith, Pres. and Treas.; Craig Friar, Secy.
Director: Christine Schabeck.
EIN: 203019932

7742
The Lamb Baldwin Foundation
1410 N.W. Kearney St., Ste. 1010
Portland, OR   97209-2771   5032245560
Application address: 805 S.W. Broadway, Ste. 1900, Portland, OR 97205, tel.: (503) 224-5560

Donor: Gregory S. Baldwin.
Foundation type: Independent foundation.
Financial data (yr. ended 12/31/14): Assets, $2,974,769; expenditures, $160,661; qualifying distributions, $146,350.
Fields of interest: Arts and culture; Education; Higher education; Environment.

Limitations: Applications accepted. Giving primarily in MA; with some giving in PA and OR.
Application information: Application form required.
   Initial approach: Letter
   Deadline(s): None
Officers and Trustees: Joan Lamb Baldwin, Pres. and Trustee; Steven Schell, Secy. and Trustee; Benjamin Baldwin, Treas. and Trustee; Chi Baldwin; Brain Kimura; Sera Baldwin Kimura.
EIN: 931236468

7743
Janet E. Bowen Foundation
1331 N.W. Lovejoy St., Ste. 775
Portland, OR   97209-2987

Donor: Walter C. Bowen.
Foundation type: Independent foundation.
Financial data (yr. ended 12/31/13): Assets, $530,959 (M); expenditures, $251,429; qualifying distributions, $251,429; giving activities include $250,000 for 1 grant.
Fields of interest: Education.
Type of support: Research.
Limitations: Applications not accepted. Giving primarily in OR.
Application information: Unsolicited requests for funds not accepted.
Officers: Walter C. Bowen, Pres.; Denise Lilley, Secy.
Director: Elizabeth J. Bowen.
EIN: 260544424

7744
The E. C. Brown Foundation
c/o Maurice R. Williams, C.P.A.
Otis Elevator Bldg.
230 N.W. 10th Ave.
Portland, OR   97209-3109   5032252903

Donor: Ellis C. Brown, MD†.
Foundation type: Independent foundation.
Financial data (yr. ended 12/31/13): Assets, $6,643,439 (M); gifts received, $143,000; expenditures, $419,084; qualifying distributions, $348,461; giving activities include $325,000 for 9 grants (high: $167,600; low: $6,300).
Purpose and activities: To promote and carry on the program of the foundation in instruction and education with respect to sex and marriage; to facilitate growth in understanding and practice of positive human relationships, with emphasis on the family and health. Produces educational films relating to sex education, the family, and health.
Fields of interest: Elementary education; Secondary education; Health; Diseases and conditions; Family services.
Type of support: Continuing support; Program-related investments.
Limitations: Applications not accepted. Giving primarily in OR.
Publications: Annual report.
Application information: Unsolicited requests for funds not accepted; grants are made only in support of foundation-initiated projects.
Administrator: Michael Gottfredson.
EIN: 930491026

7745
Castle Foundation
c/o U.S. Bank, N.A.
P.O. Box 3168
Portland, OR   97208-3168
Contact: Carolyn O'Malley
Application address: c/o U.S. Bank, N.A., Attn.: Michael I. Poulter or Songa Corbin, 170 S. Main St., Ste. 600, Salt Lake City, UT 84101, Portland, OR tel.: (503) 275-4327

Established in 1953 in Utah.
Foundation type: Independent foundation.
Financial data (yr. ended 06/30/13): Assets, $3,471,830 (M); expenditures, $228,338; qualifying distributions, $192,164; giving activities include $183,120 for 76 grants (high: $5,000; low: $1,000).
Fields of interest: Arts and culture; Elementary and secondary education; Higher education; Health; Human services; Child welfare.
Type of support: General support; Equipment; Program development; Scholarships.
Limitations: Applications accepted. Giving primarily in UT.
Publications: Application guidelines.
Application information: Application form required.
   Initial approach: Letter
   Copies of proposal: 4
   Deadline(s): None
   Board meeting date(s): May and Nov.
   Final notification: 3 weeks after board meeting
Trustee: U.S. Bank, N.A.
EIN: 876117177

7746
Harry Wilson and Clare Cayo Trust Fund
P.O. Box 3168
Portland, OR   97208-3168

Foundation type: Independent foundation.
Financial data (yr. ended 09/30/13): Assets, $10,800,445 (M); expenditures, $430,491; qualifying distributions, $341,626; giving activities include $331,000 for 6 grants (high: $75,000; low: $31,000).
Fields of interest: Education; Christianity; Catholicism; Human services.
Limitations: Applications not accepted. Giving primarily in Seattle, WA.
Application information: Contributes only to pre-selected organizations.
Trustee: U.S. Bank, N.A.
EIN: 916380315

7747
Robert and Frances Chaney Family Foundation
P.O. Box 840
Jacksonville, OR   97530-0840   (541) 899-9199
Contact: Carrie Hanson, Exec. Dir.
FAX: (541) 899-9679;
E-mail: chanson.familyfoundation@gmail.com; Main URL: http://www.familyfoundationchaney.org

Established in 2006 in Oregon.
Donors: Frances Chaney; Robert Chaney.
Foundation type: Independent foundation.
Financial data (yr. ended 05/31/13): Assets, $8,760,636 (M); expenditures, $497,619; qualifying distributions, $399,013; giving activities

include $327,464 for 69 grants (high: $15,000; low: $500).

Purpose and activities: Giving primarily to organizations to build a better future by granting funds for educational purposes, human services, charitable and faith-based groups, and other purposes focusing on benefiting children, families and public safety personnel.

Fields of interest: Higher education; Human services.

Limitations: Applications accepted. Giving limited to organizations whose projects or programs exclusively benefit the residents of Jackson & Josephine Counties, OR; Barry County, MO; and Cabell County, WV. No support for visual and performing arts programs. No grants to individuals or for endowments, annual fund drives, overhead expenses, fundraising events, or for property acquisition.

Application information: Application guidelines available on foundation web site. Application form required.

> *Initial approach:* Contact foundation website for application form
> *Deadline(s):* Jan 31 and July 31

Officers and Trustees: Frances Chaney, Pres.; Robin Whitzel, V.P. and Trustee; Susan Krammer, Secy.-Treas. and Trustee; Jason Anderson; Brenda Green; Cerise Stephens.

EIN: 205052365

7748
Charis Fund

P. O. Box 82270
Portland, OR 97282-0270

Established in 1938 in California.
Donors: Hugh Trowbridge Dobbins†; Roberta Lloyd Dobbins†.
Foundation type: Independent foundation.
Financial data (yr. ended 12/31/13): Assets, $5,121,570 (M); gifts received, $520; expenditures, $469,141; qualifying distributions, $415,079; giving activities include $408,785 for 78 grants (high: $10,000; low: $1,000).
Purpose and activities: Giving for small projects relating to social, health, educational, and some religious needs, normally based in areas in which the trustees reside.
Fields of interest: Education; Health; Human services; Food aid; Women's services; Low-income and poor people.
Type of support: Emergency funds; Program development; Seed money.
Limitations: Applications accepted. Giving primarily in CA, western OR, and western WA. No grants to individuals or for operating funds; no scholarships.
Publications: Informational brochure (including application guidelines); Newsletter.
Application information: Application form required.
> *Initial approach:* Letter
> *Copies of proposal:* 8
> *Deadline(s):* Mar. 31 and Sept. 30
> *Final notification:* Within 6 months

Officers: Roberta C. D'Anneo, Pres.; Peter T. Dobbins, V.P.; Susan C. Meland, Secy.; Deborah Dobbins Warner, Treas. and Director.
Trustees: Andrea J. D'Anneo; Allan C. D'Anneo; Lewis M. Dobbins; Janet Simmonds Pollack; Diana D. Seder.
EIN: 946077619

7749
Chiles Foundation

111 S.W. 5th Ave., Ste. 4050
Portland, OR 97204-3643   (503) 222-2143
E-mail: cf@uswest.net

Established in 1949 in Oregon.
Donors: Eva Chiles Meyer†; Earle A. Chiles†; Virginia H. Chiles†.
Foundation type: Independent foundation.
Financial data (yr. ended 12/31/14): Assets, $2,222,009; expenditures, $986,520; qualifying distributions, $776,865.
Purpose and activities: Primary focus is to assist and support educational and medical advancement.
Fields of interest: Arts and culture; Higher education; Diseases and conditions.
International interests: Germany.
Type of support: Scholarships; Research; Research and evaluation.
Limitations: Applications accepted. Giving primarily in OR and the Pacific Northwest; some funding also CA and Munich, Germany. No support for projects involving litigation. No grants to individuals, or for deficit financing, mortgage retirement, no loans.
Application information: Application form required.
> *Initial approach:* Contact foundation for application form
> *Deadline(s):* Between July 1 and July 15

Officers and Trustees: Earle M. Chiles, Pres. and Trustee; J. Kenneth Menges, Jr., Secy. and Trustee; Pedro Garcia.
Number of staff: 2 full-time professional; 2 part-time professional; 1 full-time support.
EIN: 936031125

7750
The Coffman Family Foundation

4902 McLoughlin Dr.
Central Point, OR 97502

Established in 1993 in California.
Donors: Ronnie D. Coffman; Adelia A. Coffman.
Foundation type: Independent foundation.
Financial data (yr. ended 12/31/13): Assets, $43,697 (M); gifts received, $50,470; expenditures, $277,388; qualifying distributions, $276,988; giving activities include $274,507 for 16 grants (high: $77,000; low: $552).
Purpose and activities: Giving primarily to Protestant organizations, ministries, schools, and Pentecostal churches.
Fields of interest: Education; Protestantism; Human services; Family services; Child welfare.
Limitations: Applications not accepted. Giving primarily in OR. No grants to individuals.
Application information: Unsolicited requests for funds not accepted.
Officer and Director: Adelia A. Coffman, Pres. and Director.
EIN: 330592687

7751
The Coit Family Foundation

111 S.W. 5th Ave., Ste. 1500
Portland, OR 97204-3619
Contact: Peter Duffy

Established in 1997 in Oregon.
Donor: Barbara E. Coit.
Foundation type: Independent foundation.

Financial data (yr. ended 12/31/13): Assets, $4,994,963 (M); gifts received, $603,564; expenditures, $239,237; qualifying distributions, $190,683; giving activities include $187,593 for 17 grants (high: $29,938; low: $2,000).
Fields of interest: Arts and culture; Education; Animal welfare; Communication media; Human services; Food banks.
Limitations: Applications not accepted. Giving primarily in Portland, OR. No grants to individuals.
Application information: Contributes only to pre-selected organizations.
Officers: Barbara Coit Yeager, Pres.; Ann Coit Goss, V.P.; Susan Coit, Secy.; William E. Coit, Treas.
EIN: 911806333

7752
Collins - McDonald Trust Fund

1618 S.W. 1st Ave., Ste. 500
Portland, OR 97201-5706
Contact: James C. Lynch, Tr.
Application address: 620 N. 1st Lakeview, OR 97630, tel.: (541) 947-2196

Established in 1940 in Oregon.
Foundation type: Independent foundation.
Financial data (yr. ended 12/31/13): Assets, $9,471,355 (M); expenditures, $317,818; qualifying distributions, $308,227; giving activities include $9,970 for 3 grants (high: $7,500; low: $1,000), and $294,400 for 46 grants to individuals (high: $12,300; low: $2,600).
Purpose and activities: The fund awards scholarships for higher education to graduates of local high schools only; grants also for social and health services.
Fields of interest: Hospital care; Disasters and emergency management; Human services.
Type of support: Capital and infrastructure; Equipment; Student aid.
Limitations: Applications accepted. Giving limited to Lake County, OR.
Application information: Application form required.
> *Initial approach:* Letter
> *Deadline(s):* None

Trustees: Timothy R. Bishop; Paul Harlan; James E. Lynch.
EIN: 936021894

7753
The Collins Companies Foundation

2910 S.W. Town Center Loop W, Ste. 300
Wilsonville, OR 97070-9315
Contact: Nancy L. Helseth, Secy.

Donors: Maribeth W. Collins; Collins Pine Company.
Foundation type: Independent foundation.
Financial data (yr. ended 12/31/14): Assets, $241,707 (M); gifts received, $373,602; expenditures, $241,707; qualifying distributions, $204,094; giving activities include $203,710 for 10 grants (high: $50,000; low: $3,648).
Fields of interest: Environment; Disasters and emergency management; Human services.
Limitations: Applications accepted. Giving primarily in Kane, PA.
Application information:
> *Initial approach:* Contact Foundation
> *Deadline(s):* None

Officers and Directors: Cherida C. Smith, Pres. and Director; Nancy L. Helseth, Secy. and Director;

Timothy R. Bishop, Treas.; Lee Diane Collins; Terry S. Collins; Truman W. Collins, Jr.; Eric Schooler.
EIN: 262768979

7754
Franklin Conklin Foundation
520 N.W. Oak Ave., Ste. C
Corvallis, OR 97330-9567

Established in 1997 in Oregon.
Foundation type: Independent foundation.
Financial data (yr. ended 12/31/13): Assets, $5,341,736 (M); expenditures, $311,726; qualifying distributions, $291,000; giving activities include $291,000 for 46 grants (high: $30,000; low: $500).
Fields of interest: Education; Public affairs; Antidiscrimination; Human services; International relations.
Limitations: Applications not accepted. Giving on a national basis, with some emphasis on Washington, DC, MA, NY, and OR. No grants to individuals.
Application information: Unsolicited requests for funds not accepted.
Officers: Harold H. Demarest, Jr., Pres.; David P. Demarest, V.P.; Frank C. Demarest, Secy.; Anne Demarest Taft, Treas.
EIN: 911844877

7755
The Curry Stone Foundation
985 S.W. Disk Dr., Ste. 110
Bend, OR 97702-1873   (541) 323-2299
E-mail: info@currystone.org; Main URL: http://www.currystone.org

Established in 2006 in Oregon.
Donors: Clifford Curry; Delight Stone.
Foundation type: Independent foundation.
Financial data (yr. ended 12/31/14): Assets, $13,576; gifts received, $160,000; expenditures, $417,498; qualifying distributions, $389,299.
Fields of interest: Higher education; Autism; Human services.
Type of support: Research.
Limitations: Applications accepted. Giving primarily in KY, OR and TX.
Application information: Application guidelines available on foundation web site.
   Board meeting date(s): Mar. and Oct.
Officers: Delight Stone, Pres.; Louisa Silva, V.P.; Clifford Curry, Secy.-Treas.
Director: Gary Feuerstein.
EIN: 208002857

7756
Bernard Daly Educational Fund
P.O. Box 351
Lakeview, OR 97630-0123   (541) 947-2196

Established in 1922 in Oregon.
Donors: Bernard Daly†; Jess and Alta Roberts Trust; Charles Bogner Trust.
Foundation type: Independent foundation.
Financial data (yr. ended 05/31/13): Assets, $5,719,677 (M); expenditures, $426,150; qualifying distributions, $381,633; giving activities include $377,000 for 51 grants to individuals (high: $7,800; low: $2,600).

Purpose and activities: Giving primarily for financial aid for study at technical schools and colleges in OR.
Fields of interest: Vocational education.
Type of support: Student aid.
Limitations: Applications accepted. Giving primarily in Lake County, OR.
Application information: Application form required.
   Initial approach: Contact Foundation
   Copies of proposal: 2
   Deadline(s): None
Officers: Alan Parks, Chair.; Melinda Howard, Vice-Chair.; Dave Vandenberg, Secy.-Treas.
Trustee: Mike Sabin.
EIN: 936025466

7757
Demorest Family Foundation
1581 S.W. Upper Hall St.
Portland, OR 97201-2562

Established in 2005 in Oregon.
Donor: Harry L. Demorest.
Foundation type: Independent foundation.
Financial data (yr. ended 12/31/14): Assets, $7,788,288 (M); expenditures, $344,482; qualifying distributions, $324,927; giving activities include $323,000 for 31 grants (high: $50,000; low: $1,000).
Fields of interest: Arts and culture; Science museums; Education; Nonprofits; Human services; Child welfare; Youth development.
Type of support: Regranting.
Limitations: Applications not accepted. Giving primarily in OR. No grants to individuals.
Application information: Contributes only to pre-selected organizations.
Officers and Directors: Harry L. Demorest, Pres. and Director; Kaaren M. Demorest, Secy. and Director; Christine Barbour; Scott E. Demorest.
EIN: 203399144

7758
Bob and Evelyn Dieringer Family Foundation
10505 S.E. 44th Ave.
Milwaukie, OR 97222-5202

Donor: Victoria Evelyn Dieringer Trust.
Foundation type: Independent foundation.
Financial data (yr. ended 12/31/13): Assets, $7,585,638 (M); expenditures, $464,473; qualifying distributions, $432,026; giving activities include $428,144 for 5+ grants (high: $240,000).
Fields of interest: Christianity; Human services.
Limitations: Applications not accepted. Giving primarily in Portland, OR. No grants to individuals.
Application information: Unsolicited requests for funds not accepted.
Trustee: Eugene Dieringer.
EIN: 273650979

7759
Pam and Mark Donegan Foundation
2130 Windham Oaks Ct.
West Linn, OR 97068-2446

Established in 2012 in Oregon.
Donors: Pamela Donegan; Mark Donegan.
Foundation type: Independent foundation.

Financial data (yr. ended 12/31/13): Assets, $312,223 (M); gifts received, $302,337; expenditures, $283,310; qualifying distributions, $275,000; giving activities include $275,000 for 3 grants (high: $250,000; low: $5,000).
Fields of interest: Education.
Limitations: Applications not accepted.
Application information: Unsolicited requests for funds not accepted.
Trustees: Mark Donegan; Pamela Donegan.
EIN: 455233697

7760
Arthur R. Dubs Foundation
3551 E. Barnett Rd., Ste. 105
Medford, OR 97504   (541) 773-9407

Established in 1997 in Oregon.
Donor: Arthur R. Dubs.
Foundation type: Independent foundation.
Financial data (yr. ended 12/31/13): Assets, $6,202,593 (M); gifts received, $1,643,368; expenditures, $375,488; qualifying distributions, $373,100; giving activities include $373,100 for 55 grants (high: $120,000; low: $200).
Fields of interest: Health; Diseases and conditions; Religion; Human services.
Application information: Application form required.
   Initial approach: Letter
   Copies of proposal: 3
   Deadline(s): None
Officers: David P. Hyatt, Pres.; Michele A. Pillon, Secy.
EIN: 931192741

7761
Gordon Elwood Foundation
670 Superior Ct., Ste. 108
Medford, OR 97504   (541) 282-0643
Contact: Rhonda Gressett, Off. Mgr.; Kathy Bryon, Exec. Dir.
FAX: (541) 282-0644;
E-mail: office@gordonelwoodfoundation.org; Main URL: http://www.gordonelwoodfoundation.org

Established in 1999 in Oregon.
Donors: Gordon Elwood†; Jefferson Regional Health Alliance; Start Making A Reader Today (SMART); Medford Schools Foundation; NetCorp; Literacy Council of Jackson County.
Foundation type: Independent foundation.
Financial data (yr. ended 06/30/14): Assets, $8,243,294 (M); gifts received, $28,134; expenditures, $498,715; qualifying distributions, $436,226; giving activities include $178,015 for 34 grants (high: $10,000; low: $1,000), and $145,342 for foundation-administered programs.
Purpose and activities: Investing in southern Oregon's youth, individuals, families and communities.
Fields of interest: Education; Vocational post-secondary education; Public/private ventures; Community organizing; Youth development; Children and youth; Infants and toddlers; Children; Adolescents; Adults; Young adults; Single parents; People of Latin American descent; Homeless people; Low-income and poor people; People with psychosocial disabilities.
Type of support: General support; Pro bono consulting services; In-kind gifts; Capacity-building and technical assistance; Equipment; Matching

grants; Program development; Seed money; Scholarships; Technical assistance.
Limitations: Applications accepted. Giving limited to Curry, Jackson, Josephine, and Klamath counties, OR. No grants to individuals or for projects seeking to influence elections, political candidates, or legislation.
Publications: Application guidelines; Financial statement; Grants list; Informational brochure (including application guidelines); Multi-year report (including application guidelines).
Application information: See foundation web site for application guidelines and procedures, and downloading of application form. Application form required.

> *Initial approach:* Telephone call
> *Deadline(s):* Mar. 1 and Sept. 1.
> *Board meeting date(s):* Quarterly
> *Final notification:* June 15 and Dec. 15

Officers and Trustees: Burke Raymond, Chair.; John Duke, V.P.; Stephanie Johnson, Secy. and Trustee; Annette Batzer, Treas.; Kathy Bryon, Exec. Dir.; Dan Kosmatka; Jan Murphy.
Number of staff: 1 full-time professional; 1 part-time support.
EIN: 931267972

7762
Erath Family Foundation
c/o Irvine & Company CPAS LLC
345 N.E. 102nd Ave.
Portland, OR 97220-4108   (503) 252-8449
Contact: John D. Irvine, Secy.

Established in 2006 in Oregon.
Donor: Richard C. Erath.
Foundation type: Independent foundation.
Financial data (yr. ended 12/31/13): Assets, $3,164,295 (M); expenditures, $199,153; qualifying distributions, $165,700; giving activities include $165,700 for 10 grants (high: $99,091; low: $1,000).
Purpose and activities: Giving only for projects that advance science and education in the fields of enology and viticulture.
Fields of interest: University education; Science.
Limitations: Applications accepted. Giving primarily in OR.
Application information:

> *Initial approach:* Proposal
> *Deadline(s):* None

Officers: Richard C. Erath, Pres.; John D. Irvine, Secy.
Directors: Lisa Shara Hall; John A. Hirschy; Gary Horner; Greg Jones, Ph.D.
EIN: 205237609

7763
Flowerree Foundation
P.O. Box 8098
Portland, OR 97207-8098

Established in 1961 in Oregon.
Donors: Robert E. Flowerree; Elaine D. Flowerree; Flowerree Residuary Marital Trust.
Foundation type: Independent foundation.
Financial data (yr. ended 12/31/13): Assets, $8,549,252 (M); gifts received, $500; expenditures, $405,216; qualifying distributions, $311,098; giving activities include $309,250 for 57 grants (high: $25,000; low: $250).

Fields of interest: Education; Higher education; Natural resources; Botanical gardens; Community and economic development; Religion; Christianity; Human services.
Type of support: Annual campaigns; Employee matching gifts; Capital campaigns; Seed money.
Limitations: Applications not accepted. Giving primarily in CA, LA, and OR. No grants to individuals.
Application information: Unsolicited requests for funds not accepted.
Officers and Directors: Ann D. Flowerree, Pres. and Director; David R. Flowerree, V.P. and Director; Elaine D. Flowerree, V.P. and Director; John H. Flowerree, V.P. and Director; David M. Munro, Secy. and Director.
EIN: 936034207

7764
Four Way Community Foundation
P.O. Box 652
Grants Pass, OR 97528   (541) 479-9775
Contact: Jann Taylor, Exec. Dir.
E-mail: fourway.murphy@gmail.com; Main
URL: http://fourwaycommunityfoundation.com

Established in 1975 in Oregon.
Foundation type: Community foundation.
Financial data (yr. ended 06/30/13): Assets, $4,398,117 (M); gifts received, $70,462; expenditures, $382,931; giving activities include $291,847 for 56 grants (high: $24,863; low: $180).
Purpose and activities: The foundation supports charitable organizations benefiting the residents of Josephine and Western Jackson counties in Oregon.
Fields of interest: Community and economic development; Human services.
Type of support: Capital campaigns; Capital and infrastructure; Equipment; Student aid.
Limitations: Applications accepted. Giving limited to Josephine and Western Jackson counties, OR. No support for sectarian religious purposes. No grants for emergency funding, debt retirement, annual fund drive contributions.
Publications: Application guidelines; Informational brochure (including application guidelines).
Application information: Application form required.

> *Initial approach:* Submit application
> *Copies of proposal:* 1
> *Deadline(s):* Apr. 1
> *Board meeting date(s):* 3rd Tues. of month
> *Final notification:* Late May

Officers and Directors: Richard Adams, Pres. and Director; Debbie Brownell, V.P. and Director; Margaret Bradford, Secy. and Director; Mike Peil, Treas. and Director; Jann Taylor, Exec. Dir.; Susan Cohen; Ranee Niedermeyer; Jennifer Krauss Phillippi; Chuck Potter; Midge Renton; Steve Roe; Jann Taylor; Todd Thompson.
Number of staff: 1 part-time professional.
EIN: 510173092

7765
A. J. Frank Family Foundation
P.O. Box 79
Mill City, OR 97360-0079
Contact: Ryan Banning

Established in 1959 in Oregon.
Donors: A.J. Frank; L.D. Frank; Frank Lumber Co., Inc.; Frank Timber Products, Inc.
Foundation type: Independent foundation.

Financial data (yr. ended 09/30/13): Assets, $7,272,794 (M); gifts received, $70,000; expenditures, $427,358; qualifying distributions, $368,926; giving activities include $368,926 for 46 grants (high: $65,100; low: $100).
Purpose and activities: Giving primarily to Roman Catholic organizations and schools, as well as for human services.
Fields of interest: Education; Elementary and secondary education; Higher education; Catholicism; Human services.
Limitations: Applications accepted. Giving primarily in OR. No grants to individuals.
Application information:

> *Initial approach:* Letter
> *Deadline(s):* Aug. 15 and Dec. 15
> *Final notification:* Jan. 15 and Sept. 15

Directors: C.M. Carey; D.D. Frank; J.T. Frank.
EIN: 930523395

7766
Frank and Mary Gill Foundation
(formerly Gill Family Foundation)
01740 S.W. Military Rd.
Portland, OR 97219-8384

Established in 2000 in Oregon.
Donors: Mary Kay Gill; Frank C. Gill.
Foundation type: Independent foundation.
Financial data (yr. ended 12/31/13): Assets, $1,898,551 (M); gifts received, $335,544; expenditures, $324,395; qualifying distributions, $311,500; giving activities include $311,500 for 16 grants (high: $70,000; low: $5,000).
Fields of interest: Education; Hospital care; Religion; Child welfare.
Limitations: Applications not accepted. Giving primarily in OR. No grants to individuals.
Application information: Unsolicited requests for funds not accepted.
Officers and Directors: Mary Kay Gill, Pres. and Secy. and Director; Frank C. Gill, V.P. and Treas. and Director; Katherine L. Gill; Megan K. Gill.
EIN: 931307026

7767
N. B. Giustina Foundation
P.O. Box 989
Eugene, OR 97440-0989
Contact: L.M. Giustina, Pres.

Established in 1994 in Oregon.
Donor: Natale B. Giustina†.
Foundation type: Independent foundation.
Financial data (yr. ended 09/30/14): Assets, $7,414,736 (M); expenditures, $348,058; qualifying distributions, $276,207; giving activities include $276,000 for 9 grants (high: $80,000; low: $5,000).
Fields of interest: Arts and culture; Education; Health; Hospital care; Scouting programs.
Limitations: Applications not accepted. Giving primarily in OR.
Application information: Contributes only to pre-selected organizations.
Officers: L.M. Giustina, Pres.; Irene Giustina Goldbeck, V.P.; Natalie Newlove, Secy.-Treas.
EIN: 931139522

7768
The Glennco Foundation
2626 Swan Lake Rd.
Klamath Falls, OR 97603-9674

Established in 1996 in Oregon.
Donors: Glenn J. Lorenz; Glenn T. Lorenz; Susan M. Lorenz.
Foundation type: Independent foundation.
Financial data (yr. ended 12/31/13): Assets, $6,556,419 (M); expenditures, $388,165; qualifying distributions, $276,990; giving activities include $265,000 for 8 grants (high: $100,000; low: $5,000).
Fields of interest: Catholicism; Human services.
Type of support: General support.
Limitations: Applications not accepted. Giving primarily in CA and OR. No grants to individuals.
Application information: Unsolicited requests for funds not accepted.
Officers: Glenn T. Lorenz, Pres. and Secy.-Treas.; Susan M. Lorenz, V.P.
Director: Richard Fairclo.
EIN: 931221596

7769
Harvest House Foundation
990 Owen Loop N.
Eugene, OR 97402-9173

Donor: Hawkins Charitable Lead Trust.
Foundation type: Independent foundation.
Financial data (yr. ended 12/31/13): Assets, $919,868 (M); gifts received, $90,000; expenditures, $173,778; qualifying distributions, $173,728; giving activities include $171,000 for 1 grant.
Fields of interest: Maternal and perinatal health; Christianity.
Type of support: General support.
Limitations: Applications not accepted. Giving primarily in GA and OR.
Application information: Contributes only to pre-selected organizations.
Trustees: Mary Cooper; Benjamin Hawkins; Beth Hawkins; Daniel Hawkins; Robert C. Hawkins; Shirley Jean Hawkins; Stephanie Hawkins; Steve Miller; Sandy Silverthorne.
EIN: 943381306

7770
Haskell Foundation
P.O. Box 3168
Portland, OR 97208-3168

Established in 1978 in Oregon.
Foundation type: Independent foundation.
Financial data (yr. ended 06/30/13): Assets, $2,258,814 (M); expenditures, $201,542; qualifying distributions, $163,281; giving activities include $157,867 for 5 grants (high: $39,467; low: $19,733).
Fields of interest: Education; Diseases and conditions; Human services.
Limitations: Applications not accepted. Giving limited to Aloha and Portland, OR.
Application information: Unsolicited requests for funds not accepted.
Trustee: U.S. Bank.
EIN: 930710980

7771
Ralph Haugse Memorial Trust
P.O. Box 3168
Portland, OR 97208-3168
Application address: c/o US Bank PCG, Attn.: Rebekah Fink, Trust Off., 302 N. Last Chance Gulch, Helena, MT 59601-5002, tel.: (406) 454-5004

Donor: Ralph A. Haugse QTP Trust.
Foundation type: Independent foundation.
Financial data (yr. ended 07/31/13): Assets, $6,031,693 (M); expenditures, $355,288; qualifying distributions, $320,898; giving activities include $315,644 for 9 grants (high: $133,267; low: $1,022).
Fields of interest: University education.
Type of support: Scholarships.
Limitations: Applications accepted. Giving primarily in MT.
Application information: Application form required.
Trustee: U.S. Bank, N.A.
EIN: 276400625

7772
The Heath Foundation
14845 S.W. Murray Scholls Dr., Ste. 110
Beaverton, OR 97007-9237

Donor: Donald Heath Revocable Living Trust.
Foundation type: Independent foundation.
Financial data (yr. ended 12/31/13): Assets, $962,884 (M); expenditures, $237,675; qualifying distributions, $153,675; giving activities include $153,675 for 2 grants (high: $103,675; low: $50,000).
Fields of interest: Cancers.
Type of support: Research.
Limitations: Applications not accepted. Giving primarily in Portland, OR, and SD. No grants to individuals.
Application information: Contributes only to pre-selected organizations.
Director: Linda Smiley.
EIN: 263845215

7773
Madrona Hill Foundation
P.O. Box 4514
Salem, OR 97302-8514 (503) 364-4910
Contact: Mark Burnham, Secy.-Treas.

Established in 2007 in Oregon.
Donors: Mark Burnham; Cheryl Burnham.
Foundation type: Independent foundation.
Financial data (yr. ended 12/31/13): Assets, $1,517,118 (M); gifts received, $750,000; expenditures, $126,348; qualifying distributions, $117,199; giving activities include $115,000 for 2 grants (high: $100,000; low: $15,000).
Fields of interest: Human services; Youth development.
Limitations: Applications accepted. Giving primarily in MT. No grants to individuals.
Application information: Application form required.
  Initial approach: Letter
  Deadline(s): Apr. 30 and Oct. 30
Officers: Cheryl Burnham, Pres.; Mark Burnham, Secy.-Treas.
Director: Charles Burnham.
EIN: 261478178

7774
Hitchman Foundation, Inc.
680 Hawthorne Ave. S.E., Ste. 140
Salem, OR 97301-1085 (503) 585-7774
Contact: Kent Aldrich, Pres.

Foundation type: Independent foundation.
Financial data (yr. ended 12/31/13): Assets, $2,504,501 (M); expenditures, $219,093; qualifying distributions, $139,000; giving activities include $139,000 for 6 grants (high: $45,000; low: $3,500).
Fields of interest: Arts and culture; Arts education; Education; Diseases and conditions; Housing development; Christianity; Human services; Child welfare; Youth services.
Type of support: General support; Capital and infrastructure.
Limitations: Applications accepted. Giving primarily in the greater Salem, OR, area. No grants to individuals.
Application information: Application form required.
  Initial approach: Letter
  Copies of proposal: 1
  Deadline(s): Oct. 15
  Board meeting date(s): Dec.
Officers: Kent Aldrich, Pres.; Pamela Scott, Secy.; Keith Bauer, Treas.
EIN: 930572469

7775
Holzman Foundation Inc.
P.O. Box 3168
Portland, OR 97208-3168

Established in 1990 in Oregon.
Donors: Irwin B. Holzman; Renee R. Holzman; Reliable Credit Assn.
Foundation type: Independent foundation.
Financial data (yr. ended 12/31/13): Assets, $6,224,610 (M); expenditures, $311,132; qualifying distributions, $306,764; giving activities include $266,710 for grants.
Purpose and activities: Giving primarily for health care and human services.
Fields of interest: Nonprofits; Hospital care; Judaism; Human services.
Type of support: Continuing support; Matching grants; Annual campaigns; Capital campaigns; Regranting; Capital and infrastructure; Equipment; Endowments; Emergency funds; Program development; Convening; Publications; Seed money; Curriculum development; Scholarships; Research; Technical assistance.
Limitations: Applications not accepted. No grants to individuals.
Application information: Unsolicited requests for funds not accepted.
  Board meeting date(s): Thanksgiving Day
Officers: Renee R. Holzman, Pres.; Irwin B. Holzman, Secy.
Directors: Becky Holzman; Jay L. Holzman; Lawrence J. Holzman; Lee M. Holzman.
Number of staff: 1 part-time support.
EIN: 931041588

7776
Huddart Family Foundation
109 S. 1st St.
Silverton, OR 97381

Established in 2007 in Oregon.
Donors: Huddart Family, LLC; Margaret M. Huddart; James L. Huddart; Peggy M. Huddart.
Foundation type: Independent foundation.
Financial data (yr. ended 12/31/13): Assets, $3,856,473 (M); gifts received, $15,500; expenditures, $375,424; qualifying distributions, $357,841; giving activities include $355,000 for 7 grants (high: $120,000; low: $5,000).
Fields of interest: Christianity; Child welfare; Housing services.
Limitations: Applications not accepted. Giving primarily in OR. No grants to individuals.
Application information: Contributes only to pre-selected organizations.
Officers: James L. Huddart, Pres.; Peggy M. Huddart, Secy.; Aaron L. Huddart, Treas.
Directors: Adam L. Huddart; Sarah Huddart; Brenda R. Massey.
EIN: 261469914

7777
Howard Wallis & Dorise Carlyon Irwin Foundation
P.O. Box 3168
Portland, OR   97208-3168   (503) 275-5923
Contact: Rebecca Bibleheimer

Established in 1991 in Oregon.
Donor: Dorise Carlyon Hinton-Irwin.
Foundation type: Independent foundation.
Financial data (yr. ended 06/30/14): Assets, $2,978,581 (M); expenditures, $222,077; qualifying distributions, $196,947; giving activities include $172,500 for 58 grants (high: $5,000; low: $1,000).
Fields of interest: Arts and culture; Education; Elementary and secondary education; Health; Human services; Child welfare.
Limitations: Applications accepted. Giving primarily in Portland, OR. No grants to individuals.
Application information: Application form required.
   Initial approach: Contact foundation for application form
   Deadline(s): Contact foundation for deadline
Officers: Eric H. I. Hoffman, Pres.; Kelsey Green Grout, Secy.
Directors: Alan Green, Jr.; Jean I. Hoffman; Sally H. Miller.
Trustee: U.S. Bank, N.A.
EIN: 931067941

7778
Jonas Family Foundation Trust
60355 Sunset View Dr.
Bend, OR   97702-8111
E-mail: barbnone@sonic.net; Application address: Barbara A. Doolittle, 5195 Corrick Rd., Santa Rosa, CA 94509

Established in 2000 in California.
Donors: William M. Jonas; Adele M. Jonas.
Foundation type: Independent foundation.
Financial data (yr. ended 12/31/13): Assets, $11,675,116 (L); expenditures, $507,409; qualifying distributions, $503,089; giving activities include $407,000 for 23 grants (high: $30,000; low: $1,500).
Fields of interest: Education; Philanthropy; Child welfare.

Limitations: Applications accepted. Giving primarily in CA. No grants to individuals.
Application information: Application form required.
   Initial approach: Request application form
   Deadline(s): None
Officers: Nicole Dunderdale, Pres.; Barbara A. Doolittle, Secy.; Beverly Dunderdale, Treas.
EIN: 946749856

7779
The Frederick D. & Gail Y. Jubitz Foundation
33 N.E. Middlefield Rd.
Portland, OR   97211-1233
Application address: 233 S.E. 2nd Ave

Established in 2001 in Oregon.
Donors: Fred Jubitz; Gail Jubitz.
Foundation type: Independent foundation.
Financial data (yr. ended 12/31/13): Assets, $2,760,537 (M); expenditures, $368,901; qualifying distributions, $340,375; giving activities include $340,375 for 9 grants (high: $214,287; low: $3).
Purpose and activities: Giving primarily for the arts and education.
Fields of interest: Art museums; Secondary education; Higher education; Human services.
Limitations: Applications accepted. Giving primarily in OR.
Application information: Application form required.
   Initial approach: Letter
   Deadline(s): None
Officers: Fred Jubitz, Pres. and Treas.; Gail Jubitz, Secy.
Director: Matthew Jubitz.
EIN: 931326797

7780
Jurrens Family Foundation
c/o Top Kohlbush Hoem
1201 S.W. 12th Ave.
Portland, OR   97205

Established in 2007 in Oregon.
Donor: Candace Jurrens.
Foundation type: Independent foundation.
Financial data (yr. ended 12/31/13): Assets, $2,284,234 (M); expenditures, $183,169; qualifying distributions, $164,613; giving activities include $158,099 for 4 grants (high: $131,900; low: $199).
Fields of interest: Philanthropy; Housing development; Youth development.
Limitations: Applications not accepted. Giving primarily in OR. No grants to individuals.
Application information: Unsolicited requests for funds not accepted.
Officers: Candace Jurrens, Pres.; Robert Damion Jurrens, V.P.; Sara Beth Jurrens, Secy.
Directors: Jaime Grady Jurrens; Joshua Martin Jurrens.
EIN: 260703347

7781
Karuna Foundation
3013 N.E. 9th Ave.
Portland, OR   97212-3150
Main URL: http://www.karunafoundation.us

Donor: Eric Lemelson.
Foundation type: Independent foundation.
Financial data (yr. ended 12/31/13): Assets, $5,575,725 (M); gifts received, $78,983; expenditures, $334,046; qualifying distributions, $328,287; giving activities include $275,274 for 5 grants (high: $200,000; low: $6,720).
Fields of interest: Environment.
Limitations: Applications not accepted. Giving primarily in Washington, DC.
Application information: Unsolicited requests for funds not accepted.
Officer: Eric Lemelson, Pres.
Directors: Elizabeth Kaufmann; Holly Pruett; Jennifer Bruml; Julia Novy-Hildesly; Lafcadio Cortese; Lisa Danzing; Patrick Maloney; Sybil Ackerman.
EIN: 272831197

7782
Kimmel Family Foundation
81 Pine Ct.
Eagle Point, OR   97524-9673

Established in 2000 in California.
Foundation type: Operating foundation.
Financial data (yr. ended 06/30/13): Assets, $21,478,100 (M); expenditures, $855,543; qualifying distributions, $201,125; giving activities include $201,125 for 28 grants (high: $42,330; low: $100).
Fields of interest: Wildlife biodiversity; Specialty hospital care; Child welfare; Youth services.
Type of support: Research.
Limitations: Applications not accepted. Giving primarily in OR. No grants to individuals.
Application information: Contributes only to pre-selected organizations.
Officers: Sandra F. Kimmel, Pres. and C.E.O.
Directors: Robert Crews; Howard J. Kimmel; James Rowe.
EIN: 330941520

7783
Kinnie Family Foundation
12915 N.W. Skyline Blvd.
Portland, OR   97231-2432

Established in 2001 in Oregon.
Donors: D. Craig Kinnie; Cynthia A. Kinnie.
Foundation type: Independent foundation.
Financial data (yr. ended 12/31/13): Assets, $4,694,243 (M); gifts received, $25,020; expenditures, $276,655; qualifying distributions, $243,545; giving activities include $242,000 for 21 grants (high: $28,000; low: $3,000).
Fields of interest: Health; Agriculture; Human services; Food banks.
Limitations: Applications not accepted. Giving primarily in OR.
Application information: Unsolicited requests for funds not accepted.
Officers: D. Craig Kinnie, Pres. and Treas.; Cynthia A. Kinnie, V.P. and Secy.
Directors: Kristin Kinnie; Ryan Kinnie.
EIN: 260015458

7784
Klamath Medical Service Bureau Foundation
11144 Siskin Ln.
Klamath Falls, OR 97601-8640 5418844164

Established in 1994 in Oregon.
Foundation type: Independent foundation.
Financial data (yr. ended 12/31/14): Assets, $3,563,931; expenditures, $236,085; qualifying distributions, $195,497.
Purpose and activities: Giving primarily for education and human services.
Fields of interest: Philanthropy; Health; Human services.
Type of support: Endowments.
Limitations: Applications not accepted. Giving primarily in Klamath Falls, OR.
Application information: Contributes only to pre-selected organizations.
Officers: Robert W. Graham, MD, Chair.; Don Crane, Vice-Chair.; Timothy A. Bailey, Pres.; Blake Berven, MD, Treas.
Number of staff: 1 part-time professional.
EIN: 931123593

7785
Barbara Emily Knudson Foundation
3637 N.E. Sandy Blvd., Ste. 206
Portland, OR 97232-1978 (503) 949-4218
E-mail: knudsonfoundation@gmail.com; Main
URL: http://www.gosw.org/sites/knudsonfoundation
Grants List: http://gosw.org/sites/knudsonfoundation/past-grants
Scholarships List: http://gosw.org/sites/knudsonfoundation/scholarships

Foundation type: Independent foundation.
Financial data (yr. ended 12/31/14): Assets, $5,070,875; gifts received, $26,933; expenditures, $290,249; qualifying distributions, $245,062.
Purpose and activities: Grants primarily for education, health, and social service programs within the state of Oregon.
Fields of interest: Education; Health; Housing development; Human services.
Limitations: Applications accepted. Giving primarily in OR.
Application information: See foundation website for complete application guidelines.
Officers: Emilee Provost, Exec. Dir and Secy.; Richard McGinty, Treas.; Lee Peterson, Exe. Dir.
Directors: Steve Blowers; Patrick Melius; Sharon Smith.
EIN: 272245059

7786
The James R. Kuse Family Foundation
(formerly The James R. Kuse Foundation)
P.O. Box 8989
Portland, OR 97207-8989 (503) 248-1141

Established in 1989 in Georgia.
Donors: James R. Kuse†; Shirley R. Kuse; Carol K. Ehlen.
Foundation type: Independent foundation.
Financial data (yr. ended 12/31/14): Assets, $3,662,921; expenditures, $244,293; qualifying distributions, $203,500.

Purpose and activities: Support for charities primarily in the metropolitan Portland, OR, area, with special emphasis on programs for student education, ill and handicapped children, and the fragile elderly.
Fields of interest: Child welfare; Seniors.
Type of support: General support; Matching grants; Continuing support; Annual campaigns; Capital campaigns; Capital and infrastructure; Equipment; Endowments; Emergency funds; Scholarships.
Limitations: Applications accepted. Giving primarily in the Portland, OR, and San Francisco, CA, areas. No support for religious or political organizations. No grants to individuals, or for memberships.
Application information:
  Initial approach: Proposal
  Deadline(s): None
  Board meeting date(s): Quarterly
Trustees: Carol K. Ehlen; Kate E. Ehlen; Lynn Kuse Ehret; MacGregor Ehlen; Nicholas R. Ehlen.
Number of staff: 1 part-time professional.
EIN: 581845413

7787
Lamb Foundation
P.O. Box 1705
Lake Oswego, OR 97035-0575 (503) 635-8010
FAX: (503) 635-6544;
E-mail: lambfdn@lambfoundation.org; Main
URL: http://www.lambfoundation.org
Grants List: http://www.lambfoundation.org/grants/2015
Grants List: http://www.lambfoundation.org/grants

Established in 1971 in Oregon.
Foundation type: Independent foundation.
Financial data (yr. ended 12/31/14): Assets, $6,694,918 (M); expenditures, $366,887; qualifying distributions, $318,483; giving activities include $253,385 for 44 grants (high: $30,000; low: $100).
Purpose and activities: Support for a wide range of creative programs to improve the quality of the human experience.
Fields of interest: Arts and culture; Environment; Child welfare; Children and youth.
Type of support: Program development; Matching grants; Seed money.
Limitations: Giving limited to the Pacific Northwest, with emphasis on OR and WA. No grants to individuals, or for scholarships or for proposals submitted to individual directors.
Publications: Financial statement; Grants list; Informational brochure; Program policy statement.
Application information: Grant proposals will be accepted only at the invitation of the Lamb Foundation; unsolicited applications will not be accepted. However, an organization may submit general organizational and contact information using the online contact form.
  Deadline(s): Instructions and deadlines are provided to those who are invited to apply
Officers and Directors: Barbara Lamb, Pres. and Director; Gayle Horton, V.P. and Director; Kari Anne McDonald, Secy. and Director; Carl Lamb, Treas. and Director; Kristin Bailey; Brenda Lamb; Margaret Minnick.
Administrator: Debra Iguchi.
Number of staff: 1 part-time professional.
EIN: 237120564

7788
The Larson Legacy
14404 S.E. Krause Ln.
Happy Valley, OR 97086-6534 (503) 593-5674
Contact: Leland E.G. Larson, Pres.

Established in 1997 in Oregon.
Donors: Leland E.G. Larson; Kathleen C. Larson; Hilda Larson Trust.
Foundation type: Independent foundation.
Financial data (yr. ended 12/31/13): Assets, $2,592,088 (M); gifts received, $200,000; expenditures, $297,013; qualifying distributions, $287,307; giving activities include $264,319 for 39 grants (high: $109,865; low: $250).
Purpose and activities: Giving for the environment, human rights, and civil liberties, thereby creating a more compassionate, kinder world.
Fields of interest: Education; Environment; Human rights; Individual liberties; Human services.
International interests: India.
Type of support: Annual campaigns.
Limitations: Applications accepted. Giving primarily on an international basis, with some emphasis on India, as well as in the northwestern U.S., with a focus on CA, OR, and WA. No support for religious organizations.
Publications: Multi-year report.
Application information: Application form required.
  Initial approach: Letter with cover sheet
  Copies of proposal: 6
  Deadline(s): None
  Board meeting date(s): Annually
Officers: Leland E.G. Larson, Pres.; Kathleen C. Larson, V.P.; David M. Larson, Secy.-Treas.
Number of staff: None.
EIN: 911859861

7789
Red and Gena Leonard Foundation
P.O. Box 1024
Hermiston, OR 97838-3024 (541) 564-9177
Contact: Tracy Gammell, Exec. Dir.
FAX: (541) 567-5358;
E-mail: rglfoundation@qwestoffice.net; Main
URL: http://www.leonardfoundation.org

Donor: Gena Leonard & Related Trusts.
Foundation type: Independent foundation.
Financial data (yr. ended 06/30/14): Assets, $6,059,267 (M); expenditures, $304,421; qualifying distributions, $254,878; giving activities include $15,000 for 2 grants (high: $14,000; low: $1,000), and $206,234 for grants to individuals.
Purpose and activities: Giving to improve the educational opportunities of average students of good character with poor financial circumstances who have a desire to seek further educational opportunities.
Fields of interest: Higher education; Community college education; Graduate and professional education; Nursing care.
Type of support: Student aid.
Limitations: Applications accepted. Giving limited to Gilliam, Grant, Morrow, Umatilla, and Wheeler counties, OR.
Application information: See web site for complete application policies, guidelines and application form. Students must complete the application form, provide official transcripts, a completed FAFSA form, a completed SAR form, and have two letters of recommendation. Application form required.
  Initial approach: Complete application form

Copies of proposal: 2
Deadline(s): Mar. 15
Officers: Glenn S. Chowning, Pres.; Larry Mills, V.P.; Ron Daniels, Secy.; Nellie Madison, Treas.; Tracy Gammell, Exec. Dir.
Director: Nancy Mabry.
EIN: 931232272

7790
Leupold & Stevens Foundation
3250 Wembley Park Rd.
Lake Oswego, OR   97034
Application Address: c/o Linda Neale, 6714 S.W. Burlingame Ave. Portland OR 97219 tel.: (503) 697-5089

Established in 2002 in Oregon.
Donor: Leupold & Stevens, Inc.
Foundation type: Independent foundation.
Financial data (yr. ended 12/31/13): Assets, $1,391,649 (M); gifts received, $167,221; expenditures, $209,784; qualifying distributions, $207,200; giving activities include $207,200 for 43 grants (high: $15,075; low: $800).
Fields of interest: Arts and culture; Museums; Education; Higher education; Undergraduate education; Environment; Natural resources; Mental health care; Human services; Youth development.
Limitations: Applications accepted. Giving primarily in Portland, OR. No grants to individuals.
Application information: Application form required.
Initial approach: Proposal
Deadline(s): Sept. 1
Officers: Linda Neale, Chair.; Jennifer L. Van Ditti, Secy.; Don Waggoner, Co-Treas.; Greg Waggoner, Co-Treas.
Trustees: Terry Clifford; Georgia Leupold Marshall; Michael Slack; Toni Stevens.
EIN: 680517512

7791
The Lindgren Foundation
4800 Meadows Rd., Ste. 200
Lake Oswego, OR   97035-4293

Established in 1992 in Oregon.
Donors: Ruby F. Lindgren Trust; Clarence R. Lindgren†.
Foundation type: Independent foundation.
Financial data (yr. ended 04/30/13): Assets, $2,735,322 (M); expenditures, $238,618; qualifying distributions, $192,825; giving activities include $192,350 for 9 grants (high: $115,000; low: $2,000).
Fields of interest: Higher education; Christianity.
Limitations: Applications not accepted. Giving primarily in NH, NY and WA. No grants to individuals.
Application information: Contributes only to pre-selected organizations.
Officers: Paul E. Lindgren, Pres.; Eric W. Lindgren, Secy.-Treas.
Trustees: Brooke E. Lindgren; Theodore A. Nedderman.
EIN: 931090831

7792
Living Water Foundation
(formerly WF Foundation)
1075 W. Historic Columbia River Hwy.
Troutdale, OR   97060-1348

Donors: Chris G. Wolcott; Guy R. Wolcott; First Babtist Church; April Wolcott; WPC Holding, Inc.; Crosswalk Ministry; Wolcott Family Living Trust; Guy R. Wolcott II; Guy R. Wolcott II Trust-Wolcott Living Trust.
Foundation type: Independent foundation.
Financial data (yr. ended 10/31/14): Assets, $251,798 (M); gifts received, $429,547; expenditures, $349,154; qualifying distributions, $349,154; giving activities include $348,158 for 2 grants (high: $343,558; low: $4,600).
Purpose and activities: Giving primarily to Christian ministries, education and orphanage housing.
Fields of interest: Education; Christianity; Orphanages.
International interests: India.
Limitations: Applications not accepted. Giving primarily in India; funding also in the U.S., with emphasis on OR. No grants to individuals.
Application information: Unsolicited requests for funds not accepted.
Officers: Guy R. Wolcott, Pres.; Chris G. Wolcott, Secy.
Director: Guy R. Wolcott II.
EIN: 931291150

7793
The Leightman Maxey Foundation
P.O. Box 907
Medford, OR   97501-0272   (541) 734-9322
Contact: Dee Ann Harris, Exec. Dir.
Email for Dee Ann Harris:
daharris@leightmanmaxeyfoundation.org; Main URL: http://www.leightmanmaxeyfoundation.org
Facebook: http://www.facebook.com/pages/Leightman-Maxey-Foundation/249161328490310
Grants List: http://www.leightmanmaxeyfoundation.org/?page_id=35

Established in 2003 in Oregon.
Foundation type: Independent foundation.
Financial data (yr. ended 12/31/14): Assets, $6,549,814; expenditures, $436,262; qualifying distributions, $337,260.
Purpose and activities: Giving to provide educational experiences related to careers, finance and nutrition for individuals to encourage and enable them to be self-reliant, productive members of society.
Fields of interest: Education.
Limitations: Applications accepted. Giving primarily in Jackson, Josephine, Klamath and Curry counties, OR. No support for projects seeking to influence elections or promote legislation. No grants to individuals or for political candidates.
Publications: Application guidelines.
Application information: See grantmaker web site for complete application policies, guidelines and application form. Application form required.
Initial approach: Follow link to application system on foundation web site
Copies of proposal: 1
Deadline(s): Mar. 1 and Sept. 1
Final notification: 10-12 weeks after each deadline
Officer and Trustee: Dee Ann Harris, Exec. Dir. and Trustee.
EIN: 476261291

7794
Anna May Family Foundation
1314-B Center Dr.
P.O. Box 264
Medford, OR   97501-7943   (541) 601-9915
Contact: Amy Belkin, Secy.
E-mail: anna.mayff@gmail.com; Main URL: http://www.annamay.org
Grants List: http://www.annamay.org/pastgrants.htm#2012
Grants List: http://www.annamay.org/pastgrants.htm#2011
Grants List: http://www.annamay.org/cycle.htm

Established in 1999 in Oregon.
Donor: Anna L. May.
Foundation type: Independent foundation.
Financial data (yr. ended 12/31/13): Assets, $3,351,990 (M); expenditures, $226,294; qualifying distributions, $174,907; giving activities include $147,970 for 35 grants (high: $10,000; low: $1,000).
Fields of interest: Arts and culture; Education; Human services.
Type of support: General support; Emergency funds.
Limitations: Applications accepted. Giving primarily in Jackson County, OR.
Publications: Application guidelines.
Application information: See foundation web site for complete application guidelines. Application form required.
Initial approach: Letter
Copies of proposal: 2
Deadline(s): Feb. 15
Board meeting date(s): May 1
Officers: Michael Lynch, Pres.; Steve Erb, V.P.; Amy Belkin, Secy. and Exec. Dir.; Douglass Schmor, Treas.
Directors: Karen Bartalini; Ralph Burelle; John Dailey; Jaymey Sweeney.
Number of staff: 1 full-time professional.
EIN: 931269424

7795
McKay Family Foundation
76 Centennial Loop, Ste. D
Eugene, OR   97401-7913   (541) 484-7102
Contact: Amy L. Romero, Tr.

Established in 1986 in Oregon.
Donors: Miles E. McKay†; Eleanor P. McKay†.
Foundation type: Independent foundation.
Financial data (yr. ended 12/31/13): Assets, $3,839,098 (M); expenditures, $198,083; qualifying distributions, $165,931; giving activities include $165,931 for 24 grants (high: $20,000; low: $2,000).
Purpose and activities: Giving primarily for human services.
Fields of interest: Education; Human services; Family services; Child welfare; Homeless services; Children and youth; Homeless people.
Type of support: Capital campaigns; Matching grants; Capital and infrastructure; Equipment.
Limitations: Applications accepted. Giving limited to OR charities serving Lane County. No support for religious denominations or political organizations. No support for church operations.
Application information: Application form required.
Initial approach: Proposal
Copies of proposal: 5

Deadline(s): None
Board meeting date(s): Varies
Trustees: Philip F. Baird, Jr.; C. Bruce Kilen; Amy L. Romero; Tracie McKay Shojai; Kelly L. Thakkar; Dale Williams.
Number of staff: None.
EIN: 930935036

7796
Mentor Graphics Foundation
8005 S.W. Boeckman Rd.
Wilsonville, OR 97070-7777 (503) 685-7000
Contact: Twiaa Bennett, Chair.
Main URL: http://www.mentor.com

Established in 1985 in Oregon.
Donor: Mentor Graphics Corp.
Foundation type: Company-sponsored foundation.
Financial data (yr. ended 12/31/13): Assets, $164,885 (M); gifts received, $403,750; expenditures, $354,363; qualifying distributions, $354,363; giving activities include $350,370 for 408 grants (high: $25,000; low: $100).
Purpose and activities: The foundation supports organizations involved with arts and culture, education, health, disaster relief, and human services.
Fields of interest: Arts and culture; Visual arts; Performing arts; Museums; Education; Health; Science; Engineering; Mathematics; Disaster relief; Human services; Victims of disaster.
Type of support: General support; Employee matching gifts; Program development.
Limitations: Applications accepted. Giving primarily in areas of major company operations, with emphasis on OR. No support for religious, political, or gender-based organizations, or for animal rights organizations. No grants to individuals, or for environmental causes, capital campaigns, building, political campaigns or ballots, sponsorships of dinners or social events, or fundraisers.
Publications: Application guidelines; Program policy statement.
Application information: Grants limited to $25,000; no grants less than $1,000; grants cannot represent more than 5% of organization's annual budget. Application form required.
Initial approach: Proposal
Copies of proposal: 1
Deadline(s): Mar. 1, June 1, Sept. 1 and Dec. 1
Board meeting date(s): Mar.
Final notification: 2 weeks following board meeting
Officers: Twila Bennett, Chair.; Dean Freed, Secy.
Directors: Diane Cain-Pozzo; Aj Jattuso; Rick Pier; Juan Rey; Steve Shively; Mike Vishy.
Number of staff: None.
EIN: 930870309

7797
Harry A. Merlo Foundation, Inc.
1001 S.E. Sandy Blvd.
Portland, OR 97214 (503) 963-9463
Contact: Harry A. Merlo, Pres.

Established in 1988 in Oregon.
Donor: Harry A. Melo.
Foundation type: Independent foundation.
Financial data (yr. ended 12/31/13): Assets, $8,183,330 (M); gifts received, $1,415; expenditures, $473,106; qualifying distributions,

$435,428; giving activities include $345,129 for 31 grants (high: $100,500; low: $200).
Fields of interest: Education; Higher education; Adult education; Nonprofits; Community and economic development; Catholicism; Human services; Child welfare.
Type of support: General support; Matching grants; Continuing support; Capital campaigns; Capital and infrastructure; Professorships; Regranting.
Limitations: Applications accepted. Giving primarily in Portland, OR. No grants to individuals.
Application information: Application form required.
Initial approach: Letter
Deadline(s): None
Officers: Harry A. Merlo, Pres.; Harry A. Merlo, Jr., V.P.
Number of staff: 1 part-time professional.
EIN: 943086742

7798
Metro Portland New Car Dealers Charitable Foundation
777 N.E. 7th Ave.
Portland, OR 97232-2101

Established in 2004 in Oregon.
Donors: Metro Portland New Car Dealers Association; The Oregonian.
Foundation type: Independent foundation.
Financial data (yr. ended 12/31/14): Assets, $16,664 (M); gifts received, $260,700; expenditures, $259,761; qualifying distributions, $259,469; giving activities include $255,000 for 5 grants (high: $97,500; low: $5,000).
Fields of interest: Health; Diseases and conditions; Youth development.
Limitations: Applications not accepted. Giving primarily in OR. No grants to individuals.
Application information: Unsolicited requests for funds not accepted.
Officer: Greg Remensberger, Exec. V.P.
Directors: Jim Fisher; Greg Goodwin; Russ Humberston, Jr.; Shannon Inukai-Coffee; Dave Jachter; Bob Lanphere, Jr.; Chris Meier; Erinn Sowle; Neil Shelton; Bob Wentworth.
EIN: 721579317

7799
Herbert I. and Elsa B. Michael Foundation
c/o U.S. Bank, N.A.
P.O. Box 3168
Portland, OR 97208
Application address: c/o U.S. Bank, N.A., Att.: Michael I. Polter/Songa Corbin, P.O. Box 3058, Portland, OR 97204, tel.: (801) 534-6045

Established in 1950 in Utah.
Donor: Elsa B. Michael†.
Foundation type: Independent foundation.
Financial data (yr. ended 09/30/13): Assets, $7,008,659 (M); expenditures, $374,455; qualifying distributions, $315,290; giving activities include $300,500 for 59 grants (high: $15,000; low: $2,000).
Purpose and activities: Giving primarily for cultural programs and higher and secondary education. Some giving for hospitals and social service agencies.
Fields of interest: Arts and culture; Education; Higher education; Hospital care; Human services; Child welfare.

Type of support: General support; Matching grants; Scholarships.
Limitations: Applications accepted. Giving primarily in the greater Salt Lake City, UT, area. No support for sectarian religious activities.
Publications: Application guidelines.
Application information:
Initial approach: Letter
Copies of proposal: 6
Deadline(s): None
Board meeting date(s): Apr. and Oct.
Trustee: U.S. Bank, N.A.
Advisory Committee: Christine M. Durham; Matthew Durrant; Keith Odendahl; Tracy D. Smith; Michael K. Young.
EIN: 876122556

7800
James E. & Lila G. Miller Charitable Trust
1805 NW. Glisan St.
Portland, OR 97209-2010
Contact: Ted Miller, Tr.

Established in 1985 in Oregon.
Donors: James E. Miller; Lila G. Miller.
Foundation type: Independent foundation.
Financial data (yr. ended 05/31/14): Assets, $6,426,214 (M); expenditures, $380,265; qualifying distributions, $294,620; giving activities include $294,620 for 12 grants (high: $72,000; low: $5,000).
Purpose and activities: Giving primarily for higher education and Christian organizations.
Fields of interest: Higher education; Christianity; Human services.
Type of support: General support; Capital and infrastructure; Scholarships.
Limitations: Applications not accepted. Giving primarily in CA and OR. No grants to individuals.
Application information: Contributes only to pre-selected organizations.
Deadline(s): None
Trustees: Lila G. Miller; Ted M. Miller.
EIN: 936174460

7801
The Morey Family Foundation
1536 S.W. Highland Pkwy.
Portland, OR 97221-2630 (503) 475-6423

Established in 2005 in Oregon.
Donors: Timothy Clark-Morey; Kifton Development, Inc.; Robert Timi Morey; Wellner Morey-Forest Grove I LLC.
Foundation type: Company-sponsored foundation.
Financial data (yr. ended 08/31/13): Assets, $80,604 (M); gifts received, $7,000; expenditures, $156,820; qualifying distributions, $154,210; giving activities include $154,210 for 1 grant.
Purpose and activities: The foundation awards college sholarships to individuals based on academic performance and financial need.
Fields of interest: Education; Foundations.
Type of support: Scholarships.
Application information: Application form required.
Initial approach: Scholarship application form
Deadline(s): Spring
Officers: Timothy Clark-Morey, Pres.; Robert Morey, V.P.; Jeannine L. McGowan, Secy.
Board Member: Kiffi Harris.
EIN: 202033108

7802
Morris Family Foundation
839 Alder Creek Dr.
Medford, OR 97504-8900
Application address: c/o Gary Rosenberger, Pres.,
437 De Barr Ave., Medford, OR 97501-1661,
tel.: (541) 779-1869

Established in 1998 in Oregon.
Donor: Earl W. Morris.
Foundation type: Independent foundation.
Financial data (yr. ended 06/30/14): Assets,
$9,148,045 (M); expenditures, $546,220;
qualifying distributions, $448,801; giving activities
include $412,441 for 3 grants (high: $277,217;
low: $3,600).
Purpose and activities: Scholarship awards to
students in Jackson County, Oregon, School
Districts No. 6, No. 35, No. 91 and No. 9, who are
enrolled at Rogue Community College, Oregon, and
are engaged in technical vocational education
programs; giving also for orphans and victims of
disasters.
Fields of interest: Education.
Type of support: General support; Scholarships.
Limitations: Applications accepted. Giving limited to
residents of Jackson County, OR.
Application information: Application form required.
Initial approach: Letter or scholarship application
form
Deadline(s): None
Officers: Gary Rosenberger, Pres.; Jean Miller, V.P.;
Erick Lieder, Secy.; Richard Entinger, Treas.; Pam
Murphy, Exec. Dir.
EIN: 931230039

7803
Samuel T. & Mary K. Naito Foundation
c/o Robert J. Preston, Esq.
707 S.W. Washington St., Ste. 1500
Portland, OR 97205 (503) 224-2223
Application address: Samuel T. Naito, Pres., 2225
N.W. Pinnacle Dr., Portland, OR 97229, tel.: (503)
517-4305

Established in 2004 in Oregon.
Donor: Samuel T. Naito.
Foundation type: Independent foundation.
Financial data (yr. ended 12/31/14): Assets,
$407,350 (M); gifts received, $100,000;
expenditures, $135,459; qualifying distributions,
$133,893; giving activities include $132,525 for 58
grants (high: $20,000; low: $500).
Fields of interest: Education; Religion; Sports and
recreation.
Limitations: Applications accepted. Giving primarily
in OR.
Application information: Application form required.
Initial approach: Letter
Deadline(s): None
Officers: Samuel T. Naito, Pres.; Robert J. Preston,
Secy.; Marsha Allen, Treas.
EIN: 202005571

7804
Joe & Frances Naumes Family Foundation
P.O. Box 996
Medford, OR 97501-0071

Established in 1994 in Oregon.
Donors: Frances A. Naumes†; Michael D. Naumes.

Foundation type: Independent foundation.
Financial data (yr. ended 12/31/13): Assets,
$2,167,989 (M); expenditures, $161,360;
qualifying distributions, $150,539; giving activities
include $148,700 for 34 grants (high: $20,500;
low: $250).
Purpose and activities: Giving primarily for arts and
culture, education, health care, and human
services.
Fields of interest: Arts and culture; Education;
Health.
Limitations: Applications not accepted. Giving
primarily in OR, with emphasis on Medford. No
grants to individuals.
Application information: Unsolicited requests for
funds not accepted.
Directors: Michael D. Naumes; Susan F. Naumes.
EIN: 931138741

7805
R. H. Parker/United Foundation
515 E. Burnside
P.O. Box 4487
Portland, OR 97208-4487 (503) 238-6464
Contact: R.H. Parker, Pres.

Established in 1994 in Oregon.
Donors: United Finance Co.; Richard H. Parker.
Foundation type: Company-sponsored foundation.
Financial data (yr. ended 12/31/13): Assets,
$6,473,928 (M); gifts received, $500,000;
expenditures, $231,006; qualifying distributions,
$226,824; giving activities include $221,750 for 46
grants (high: $60,000; low: $100).
Purpose and activities: The foundation supports
museums and organizations involved with higher
education, youth, and other areas.
Fields of interest: Arts and culture; Education;
Sports and recreation.
Type of support: General support; Capital and
infrastructure; Program development; Scholarships.
Limitations: Applications accepted. Giving primarily
in the Pacific Northwest, with emphasis on OR and
WA. No grants to individuals.
Publications: Grants list.
Application information: Application form required.
Initial approach: Letter
Copies of proposal: 1
Deadline(s): July 31
Officers: Richard H. Parker, Jr., Pres.; Roger Lloyd,
V.P.; Richard H. Parker III, V.P.; Lorine G. Cox, Secy.
Director: Judy Ann Parker.
EIN: 931155287

7806
William L. & Ruth L. Pendleton Memorial Fund
c/o U.S. Bank National Association
P.O. Box 3168
Portland, OR 97208-3168
Application Address: c/o William Dolan, U.S. Bank,
111 S.W. 5th Ave., Portland, OR 97204, tel.: (503)
275-5929

Established in 1987 in Arizona.
Donors: Ruth Pendleton†; William Pendleton†.
Foundation type: Independent foundation.
Financial data (yr. ended 12/31/13): Assets,
$3,836,465 (M); expenditures, $271,324;
qualifying distributions, $222,380; giving activities

include $215,444 for 45 grants (high: $36,344;
low: $1,000).
Purpose and activities: To provide services and
benefits for children and the elderly.
Fields of interest: Orchestral music; Education;
Child educational development; Diseases and
conditions; Christianity; Child welfare; Senior
services.
Type of support: General support; Matching grants;
Continuing support; Capital campaigns; Capital and
infrastructure; Equipment; Program development.
Limitations: Applications accepted. Giving limited to
AZ. No grants to individuals.
Application information: Application form required.
Initial approach: Proposal
Deadline(s): Sept. 30
Trustee: U.S. Bank, N.A.
Committee Members: Donna Burt; William A. Miller;
Don Prior; Janet Wilson.
EIN: 742475483

7807
Portland Women's Foundation
(also known as Battered Women's Foundation)
(formerly Portland Women's Union Foundation)
P.O. Box 4901
Portland, OR 97207-1032

Established in 1983 in Oregon.
Donors: Andy Bryant; Nancy Kay Bryant; Candace
Clark Beber; Clark Lewis Family Foundation.
Foundation type: Independent foundation.
Financial data (yr. ended 04/30/13): Assets,
$3,145,073 (M); gifts received, $40,505;
expenditures, $226,793; qualifying distributions,
$198,755; giving activities include $191,303 for 24
grants (high: $35,000; low: $5,000).
Purpose and activities: Giving primarily to benefit
women in the areas of housing and education for
self-sufficiency.
Fields of interest: Education; Housing development;
Human services; Women's services; Females;
Low-income and poor people.
Type of support: Annual campaigns; In-kind gifts;
Technical assistance.
Limitations: Applications accepted. Giving limited to
the Tri-County area of Multnomah, including
Clackamas and Washington counties, OR. No
support for research projects, or resource or data
banks, services that do not directly benefit women,
or for childcare. No grants to individuals, or for start
up costs.
Publications: Application guidelines.
Application information: Copies of financial
statements for the past two years are required.
Application form required.
Initial approach: Completed application form
Copies of proposal: 1
Deadline(s): Nov. 15
Board meeting date(s): Sept., Oct., Nov., Jan. and
Mar.
Officers: Mary Roberts, Pres.; Cynthia Griffin, Secy.
and Director; Marcella McGee, Treas.
Board Members: Verna Bailey; Lynne Bangsund;
Alice Bergman; Cobi Jackson; Martha Gazley; Nicole
Deering; Cathie Glennon; Gundrun Granholm;
Stephanie Knight; Karen Nelson; Anne Noell; Dana
Plautz; Dianne Redd; Kimberlee Sheng; Christy
Stockton; Jeanne Teisher; Megan Wentworth; Sonia
Worcel.
EIN: 930386905

7808
Robert B. & Pearl P. Richardson Trust
P.O. Box 3168
Portland, OR 97208-3168

Foundation type: Independent foundation.
Financial data (yr. ended 12/31/14): Assets, $5,431,942; expenditures, $338,126; qualifying distributions, $286,649 and $0 for set-asides.
Fields of interest: Education; Health; Religion.
Limitations: Applications not accepted. Giving primarily in MT.
Application information: Unsolicited requests for funds not accepted.
Trustee: US Bank.
EIN: 816010500

7809
Carl and Camilla Rietman Charitable Foundation
P.O. Box D
Lakeside, OR 97449-0803
Scholarship application address: c/o Alfred C. Walsh, Jr., 280 N. Collier, Coquille, OR 97423, tel.: (541) 396-2169

Established in 1996 in Oregon.
Donors: Albert Hadley; Camilla Rietman†.
Foundation type: Independent foundation.
Financial data (yr. ended 09/30/14): Assets, $6,341,257 (M); expenditures, $350,214; qualifying distributions, $304,021; giving activities include $279,231 for 85 grants to individuals (high: $69,808; low: $2,500).
Purpose and activities: College scholarships for students and graduates of Coquille High School in Coquille, Oregon, who will attend, or are attending, any fully accredited post-secondary institutions; giving also for Protestant churches and hospitals.
Fields of interest: Higher education; Hospital care; Protestantism.
Type of support: General support; Student aid.
Limitations: Applications accepted. Giving primarily in Coquille, OR; scholarships limited to students and graduates of Coquille High School, OR.
Application information: References must be attached to scholarship application form. Application form required.
 Deadline(s): Apr. 15
Trustees: John S. Burles; Michael Coen; Alfred C. Walsh, Jr.
EIN: 931221623

7810
The Roundhouse Foundation
P.O. Box 1784
Sisters, OR 97759-1784

Established in 2002 in Oregon.
Donors: Gertrude Boyle; Frank Deggendorfer; Kathy Deggendorfer.
Foundation type: Independent foundation.
Financial data (yr. ended 12/31/13): Assets, $7,734,559 (M); gifts received, $952,000; expenditures, $377,834; qualifying distributions, $314,950; giving activities include $314,950 for 43 grants (high: $40,500; low: $250).
Fields of interest: Arts and culture; Education; Land resources; Child welfare.
Type of support: General support.

Limitations: Applications not accepted. Giving primarily in OR. No grants to individuals.
Application information: Unsolicited requests for funds not accepted.
Trustee: Kathleen Deggendorfer.
EIN: 226930631

7811
Carol and Velma Saling Foundation
6500 S.W. Macadam Ave., Ste. 300
Portland, OR 97239-3569

Donors: Saling Marital Trust; Saling Family Revocable Living Trust.
Foundation type: Independent foundation.
Financial data (yr. ended 12/31/13): Assets, $4,549,954 (M); gifts received, $150,000; expenditures, $224,208; qualifying distributions, $220,000; giving activities include $220,000 for 14 grants (high: $20,000; low: $11,000).
Fields of interest: Environmental studies; Social sciences; Food banks; Low-income and poor people.
Type of support: Policy, advocacy and systems reform.
Limitations: Applications not accepted. Giving primarily in Portland, OR. No grants to individuals.
Application information: Contributes only to pre-selected organizations.
Officers: Tim Nay, Chair.; Adaire R. Miller, Secy.
Director: Richard Baroway.
EIN: 931260713

7812
Santos Family Foundation
4110 S.E. Hawthorne Blvd., No. 423
Portland, OR 97214 (202) 236-0174
FAX: (971) 255-0351; E-mail: santlen@aol.com;
Main URL: http://fdnweb.org/santos

Established in 2000 in Massachusetts.
Donor: Paul J. Santos, Jr.
Foundation type: Independent foundation.
Financial data (yr. ended 10/31/14): Assets, $3,390,342; expenditures, $333,315; qualifying distributions, $305,770.
Purpose and activities: Giving primarily to improve automobile safety, especially the crash-worthiness of passenger vehicles.
Fields of interest: Automotive safety.
Limitations: Applications accepted. Giving primarily in MA; funding also in VA. No grants to individuals.
Application information: Application form required.
 Initial approach: Letter
 Deadline(s): None
Trustees: Paul Santos, Jr.; Anne Stuart.
EIN: 043493830

7813
The J. Frank Schmidt Family Charitable Foundation
P.O. Box 189
Boring, OR 97009-0189

Established in 1986 in Oregon.
Donors: J. Frank Schmidt, Jr.; Evelyn Schmidt.
Foundation type: Independent foundation.
Financial data (yr. ended 09/30/13): Assets, $5,708,462 (M); expenditures, $297,684; qualifying distributions, $279,238; giving activities

include $275,045 for 103 grants (high: $41,000; low: $100).
Purpose and activities: Giving primarily to universities and botanical gardens for horticultural research, and to medical associations for medical research.
Fields of interest: Education; Higher education; Health; Hospital care; Diseases and conditions; Agriculture; Community beautification; Human services; Child welfare.
Type of support: General support; Matching grants; Research and evaluation; Continuing support; Annual campaigns; Endowments; Program development; Scholarships; Research.
Limitations: Applications not accepted. Giving primarily in OR. No grants to individuals.
Publications: Annual report.
Application information: Contributes only to pre-selected organizations.
Directors: Jan Schmidt Barkley; J. Frank Schmidt III; Jean Schmidt Webster.
Number of staff: None.
EIN: 931265440

7814
Anne & Eli Shapira Charitable Foundation
7327 S.W. Barnes Rd., No. 124
Portland, OR 97225-6119 (877) 586-9416
Contact: Robert Thompson, Exec. Dir.
FAX: (877) 586-9416;
E-mail: robbt@shapirafoundation.org; Main URL: http://www.shapirafoundation.org
Grants List: http://www.shapirafoundation.org/newsinfo.html

Established in 2000 in Oregon.
Donor: Elijahu Shapira.
Foundation type: Independent foundation.
Financial data (yr. ended 12/31/13): Assets, $2,192,855 (M); expenditures, $313,183; qualifying distributions, $302,743; giving activities include $236,894 for 23 grants (high: $50,000; low: $2,320).
Purpose and activities: The focus of the foundation is to provide strong family support including tutoring, mentoring and counseling services to disadvantaged families and individuals, to improve educational opportunities for disadvantaged and/or disabled individuals, and to enhance the healthy development of individuals faced with disadvantages or disabilities that may hinder their quality of life.
Fields of interest: Languages; Education; Special needs education; Human services; Youth services.
Type of support: Individual development.
Limitations: Giving primarily in OR. No support for athletic teams, or political or religious organizations. No grants to individuals, or for capital campaigns, fundraisers, debt reduction drives, or lobbying activities.
Application information: After letter of inquiry is reviewed, foundation will invite full applications. Unsolicited full applications will not be accepted. See foundation web site for additional policies and guidelines. Application form required.
 Initial approach: Letter of inquiry (1-2 pages)
 Copies of proposal: 1
Trustees: Anne L. Shapira; Elijahu Shapira.
EIN: 931306729

7815
Sharkey Family Charitable Foundation
1101 Siskiyou Blvd.
Ashland, OR 97520-2238

Established in 1994 in Oregon.
Donors: A. Sharkey Charitable Lead Trust; Patricia Wolfe.
Foundation type: Independent foundation.
Financial data (yr. ended 12/31/13): Assets, $4,090,523 (M); gifts received, $28,199; expenditures, $196,744; qualifying distributions, $160,794; giving activities include $150,000 for 14 grants (high: $15,000; low: $5,000).
Purpose and activities: Giving to organizations providing children's and family services.
Fields of interest: Arts and culture; Education; Diseases and conditions; Family services; Child welfare.
Type of support: Research.
Limitations: Applications not accepted. Giving primarily in FL, OR and WA. No support for organizations lacking 501(c)(3) status. No grants to individuals.
Application information: Contributes only to pre-selected organizations.
Officers: Linda Dunhill, Pres. and Secy.-Treas.; Carl W. Wolfe, V.P.
Director: Patricia Wolfe.
EIN: 931161303

7816
L. S. "Sam" Shoen Foundation
P.O. Box 3168
Portland, OR 97208-3168 5034643580
Application address: c/o Samuel W. Shoen, 1253 Umatilla St., Port Townsend, WA 98368, tel.: (206) 344-3689

Established in 2000 in Washington.
Donor: Katabasis Intl.
Foundation type: Independent foundation.
Financial data (yr. ended 12/31/14): Assets, $4,028,336; expenditures, $235,873; qualifying distributions, $201,901.
Fields of interest: Education; Higher education; School libraries and media centers; Religion; School athletics.
Type of support: General support; Endowments.
Limitations: Applications accepted. Giving primarily in OR and WA.
Application information: Application form required.
Initial approach: Contact foundation for application form
Deadline(s): Contact foundation for deadline
Trustees: Samuel W. Shoen; U.S. Bank, N.A.
EIN: 916508655

7817
Morris & Helen Silver Foundation
P.O. Box 18234
Portland, OR 97218-0234
Contact: Karrie Montgomery
E-mail: sara@silverfoundation.org; Main URL: http://www.silverfoundation.org
Grants List: http://www.silverfoundation.net/grantees

Established in 2001 in Montana.
Donor: F. Morris Silver‡.
Foundation type: Independent foundation.

Financial data (yr. ended 12/31/12): Assets, $4,562,895 (M); expenditures, $321,927; qualifying distributions, $148,120; giving activities include $148,120 for grants.
Fields of interest: Arts and culture; Theater; Elementary and secondary education; Foundations; Human services.
Type of support: Capital campaigns; Matching grants; Capital and infrastructure; Emergency funds; Program development; Curriculum development; Program evaluations.
Limitations: Applications accepted. Giving limited to Missoula, MT. No support for religious or political organizations.
Publications: Application guidelines; Informational brochure (including application guidelines).
Application information: Application form required.
Initial approach: Contact foundation for application form
Copies of proposal: 1
Deadline(s): Mar. 31 and Sept. 30
Board meeting date(s): Quarterly
Final notification: 2 months
Officers: Timothy J. Sather, Pres.; Carolyn R. Montgomery, V.P.; Thomas H. Boone, Secy.-Treas.
EIN: 841398903

7818
Simple Actions Family Foundation
P.O. Box 2736
Corvallis, OR 97339-2736
Main URL: http://simpleactionsfamilyfoundation.org
Grants List: http://www.simpleactionsfamilyfoundation.org/archive

Established in 2008 in Oregon.
Donors: Eric Helpenstell; Bonnie Helpenstell.
Foundation type: Independent foundation.
Financial data (yr. ended 12/31/13): Assets, $1,034,064 (M); gifts received, $480,000; expenditures, $444,226; qualifying distributions, $444,226; giving activities include $436,640 for 91 grants (high: $26,640; low: $500).
Fields of interest: Education; Mental health care; Housing development.
Limitations: Applications not accepted. Giving primarily in OR.
Application information: Unsolicited requests for funds not accepted.
Officers: Bonnie Helpenstell, Pres.; Lily Helpenstell, V.P.; Emily Helpenstell, Secy.; Eric Helpenstell, Treas.
EIN: 263209131

7819
The Singer Foundation
457 Spyglass Dr.
Eugene, OR 97401-2091 (541) 485-8444

Established in 1986 in Oregon.
Donor: Kenneth Singer.
Foundation type: Independent foundation.
Financial data (yr. ended 10/31/13): Assets, $2,495,999 (M); expenditures, $230,754; qualifying distributions, $218,648; giving activities include $216,335 for grants.
Purpose and activities: Giving to organizations that improve the quality of life for residents of Eugene, Oregon. Also provides scholarship awards to graduating seniors attending a college in Oregon.

Fields of interest: Education; Hospital care; Judaism.
Type of support: General support; Scholarships; Student aid.
Limitations: Applications accepted. Giving primarily in Eugene, OR.
Application information: Application form required.
Initial approach: Letter
Deadline(s): None
Officers: Roberta L. Singer, Chair.; Kenneth M. Singer, Pres.; Kenda H. Singer, V.P.; Carolyn Rubenstein, Secy.
EIN: 943027910

7820
Spencer Family Foundation
5665 S.W. Meadows Rd., Ste. 310
Lake Oswego, OR 97035-3192

Established in 2005 in Oregon.
Donors: Dental Components, Inc.; John Spencer; Christine Braet; Janelle Spencer; Joseph Braet.
Foundation type: Company-sponsored foundation.
Financial data (yr. ended 06/30/13): Assets, $3,555,685 (M); gifts received, $324,131; expenditures, $296,676; qualifying distributions, $289,147; giving activities include $196,315 for 7 grants (high: $75,000; low: $2,500).
Purpose and activities: The foundation supports camps and organizations involved with education, dental care, cystic fibrosis, child welfare, human services, and Christianity.
Fields of interest: Education; Secondary education; Dental care; Cystic fibrosis; Child abuse; Christianity; Camps; Human services; Developmental disability services; Women's services.
Type of support: General support.
Limitations: Applications not accepted. Giving primarily in OR; giving also to national organizations. No grants to individuals.
Application information: Contributes only to pre-selected organizations.
Officers: John Spencer, Pres.; Janelle Spencer, Secy.-Treas.
Directors: Amy Spencer; Jason Spencer; Laura Spencer.
EIN: 203401912

7821
Eminger Stewart Foundation
P.O. Box 3168
Portland, OR 97208-3168 5034643580
Application address: c/o US Bank, Attn.: Linda Thomas-Bush, 800 Willamette St., Eugene, OR 97401, tel.: (503) 465-4120

Donor: E. Stewart III.
Foundation type: Independent foundation.
Financial data (yr. ended 02/28/14): Assets, $4,416,292; expenditures, $228,088; qualifying distributions, $166,961 and $0 for set-asides.
Fields of interest: Education.
Limitations: Applications accepted. Giving primarily in Grant County, OR.
Application information: Application form required.
Initial approach: Request application form
Deadline(s): Contact US Bank for deadline
Trustee: US Bank.
EIN: 356797693

7822
Faye & Lucille Stewart Foundation
P.O. Box 11135
Eugene, OR 97440-3335 (541) 681-7228
E-mail: information@stewartlegacy.com; Main
URL: http://stewartlegacy.com

Donor: Faye H. Stewart†.
Foundation type: Independent foundation.
Financial data (yr. ended 09/30/13): Assets,
$8,013,475 (M); expenditures, $264,912;
qualifying distributions, $238,024; giving activities
include $210,060 for 23 grants (high: $72,500;
low: $500).
Fields of interest: Education; Foundations;
Christianity; Human services.
Limitations: Applications accepted. Giving primarily
in OR.
Application information: Application form required.
Initial approach: Contact foundation for
application form
Deadline(s): None
Officers and Directors: Michael Solomon, Pres. and
Secy. and Director; Rhett Carlile, V.P. and Director;
Robert Bronson, Treas. and Director; Ronald A.
Irvine; Faye Stewart II.
EIN: 930800814

7823
Wayne C. Stewart Foundation
P.O. Box 3168
Portland, OR 97208-3168
Application address: 1025 N.W. Bond St., Bend, OR
97701-2001, tel. (541) 465-4120

Established in 2007 in Oregon.
Donor: W. C. Stewart.
Foundation type: Independent foundation.
Financial data (yr. ended 02/28/15): Assets,
$7,170,177 (M); expenditures, $415,003;
qualifying distributions, $342,216; giving activities
include $333,516 for 27 grants (high: $117,600;
low: $4,400).
Fields of interest: Education; Higher education.
Type of support: Scholarships.
Limitations: Applications accepted. Giving primarily
in OR.
Application information: Contact foundation for
application information.
Trustee: U.S. Bank, N.A.
EIN: 916574050

7824
Charles D. Trover Family Foundation
16025 S.W. Roberts Rd.
Sherwood, OR 97140-5061

Established in 2008 in Oregon.
Donor: Charles D. Trover.
Foundation type: Independent foundation.
Financial data (yr. ended 06/30/14): Assets,
$6,614,804 (M); gifts received, $7,550;
expenditures, $338,794; qualifying distributions,
$284,906; giving activities include $284,906 for 16
grants (high: $35,000; low: $9,453).
Fields of interest: Education; Religion; Human
services.
Limitations: Applications not accepted. Giving
primarily in OR.
Application information: Contributes only to
pre-selected organizations.

Officers and Directors: Charles D. Trover, Pres. and
Director; Tami Lynn Trover Crosson, Secy. and
Director; Sara Lee Montag; Chad Charles Trover.
EIN: 208020190

7825
Watt Brothers Scholars Trust
P.O. Box 999
Tillamook, OR 97141-0999
Application address: c/o Phyllis Wustenberg, P.O.
Box 3312, Bay City, OR 97107-3312, tel.: (503)
377-2283

Donor: Margaret Watt Edwards.
Foundation type: Operating foundation.
Financial data (yr. ended 12/31/13): Assets,
$1,611,305 (M); expenditures, $141,258;
qualifying distributions, $129,252; giving activities
include $129,252 for 51 grants to individuals (high:
$5,333; low: $666).
Purpose and activities: Scholarship awards to high
school seniors of Tillamook County, Oregon, who are
in pursuit of a post high school education.
Fields of interest: Education.
Type of support: Student aid.
Limitations: Applications accepted. Giving limited to
Tillamook County, OR.
Application information: Application form required.
Initial approach: Letter
Deadline(s): June 11
Officers: Phyllis Wustenberg, Chair.; Mark
Wustenberg, Secy.
Director: Prudence Denny.
EIN: 931224469

7826
Wessinger Foundation
706 N.W. Culpepper Terr.
Portland, OR 97210-3123 (503) 227-2995
Contact: Lynne Siegel, Admin.

Donor: Paul Wessinger Trust.
Foundation type: Independent foundation.
Financial data (yr. ended 09/30/13): Assets,
$5,784,817 (M); expenditures, $373,121;
qualifying distributions, $324,610; giving activities
include $300,000 for 50 grants (high: $52,500;
low: $1,000).
Purpose and activities: Giving primarily for
education, particularly education foundations, arts
and culture, health care, including health services
for women, youth and social services, and
community development.
Fields of interest: Theater; Historic preservation;
Education; Health; Diseases and conditions;
Non-natural disasters; Community and economic
development; Human services; Youth services;
Children and youth; Adolescents; Seniors; Females;
Homeless people; Low-income and poor people;
People with disabilities; People with HIV/AIDS;
Substance abusers.
Type of support: General support; Matching grants;
Capital campaigns; Capital and infrastructure;
Equipment; Program development; Scholarships;
Research.
Limitations: Applications accepted. Giving limited to
the Pacific Northwest, with emphasis on Multuonah,
Clackamas, and Washington counties, OR. No
grants to individuals.
Publications: Application guidelines.
Application information:

Initial approach: Letter
Copies of proposal: 1
Board meeting date(s): Quarterly
Officers: Gainor Wessinger Arzt, Pres.; Robert D.
Geddes, Secy.; Henry W. Wessinger, Treas.
Directors: William W. Wessinger, Emeritus; Anna
Boggess; Nancy W. Kline; Barbara W. Newton; Julie
Vigeland; E. Charles Wessinger; Joseph M.
Wessinger; Kathryn W. Withers.
EIN: 930754224

7827
West Family Foundation
680 G St., Ste. B
Jacksonville, OR 97530-9876 (541) 899-9976
Contact: Carrie Hanson, Exec. Dir.
FAX: (541) 899-9679; E-mail for Carrie Hanson:
chanson.familyfoundation@gmail.com; Main
URL: http://www.familyfoundationwest.org
Grant Database: http://
www.familyfoundationwest.org/awards.htm

Established in 2007 in Oregon.
Foundation type: Independent foundation.
Financial data (yr. ended 05/31/14): Assets,
$9,192,941 (M); expenditures, $541,178;
qualifying distributions, $440,085; giving activities
include $369,771 for 66 grants (high: $10,000;
low: $500).
Purpose and activities: Giving to benefit children
and families who reside in southern Oregon by
providing grants for educational purposes, human
services and other charitable causes.
Fields of interest: Diseases and conditions; Human
services; Family services; Child welfare; Children
and youth.
Limitations: Applications accepted. Giving limited to
Curry, Jackson, Josephine, and Klamath counties in
southern OR. No support for projects that have a
specific religious purpose, or for visual and
performing arts programs. No grants for
endowments or annual fund drives, indirect or
overhead expenses, sponsorship of fundraising
events or for property acquisition or capital
campaigns.
Application information: See grantmaker web site
for guidelines and online application form.
Proposals requesting more than $20,000 or less
than $1,000 not accepted. Application form
required.
Initial approach: Online
Deadline(s): Feb. 28
Final notification: 9-12 weeks following deadlines.
Officers and Trustees: Steven F. West, Pres. and
Trustee; Carolyn S. West, V.P. and Treas. and
Trustee; Jason M. Anderson, Secy. and Trustee;
Carrie Hanson, Exec. Dir.; Chelsey West.
EIN: 204720365

7828
Merle S. & Emma J. West Scholarship Fund
(also known as West Scholarship Fund)
c/o U.S. Bank, N.A.
P.O. Box 3168
Portland, OR 97208-3168 (541) 883-3857
Contact: Rebecca Bibleheimer, Trust Off.
E-mail for Rebecca Bibleheimer:
rebecca.bibleheimer@usbank.com; Main
URL: http://www.merlewestscholarship.com

Established in 1984 in Oregon.
Foundation type: Independent foundation.
Financial data (yr. ended 12/31/13): Assets, $3,725,671 (M); gifts received, $100; expenditures, $245,626; qualifying distributions, $187,500; giving activities include $173,192 for 30 grants (high: $45,676; low: $667).
Purpose and activities: Giving primarily for scholarship funds available to graduates of Klamath County, Oregon, high schools.
Fields of interest: Education.
Type of support: Scholarships.
Limitations: Applications accepted. Giving limited to residents of Klamath County, OR.
Publications: Application guidelines.
Application information: Application form available on fund web site. See fund's web site for complete application guidelines.
Initial approach: Submit application online or by mail
Deadline(s): Varies
Trustee: U.S. Bank, N.A.
EIN: 936160221

7829
Western Lane Community Foundation
(formerly Western Lane County Foundation)
1525 W. 12th St., Ste. 18
P.O. Box 1589
Florence, OR 97439-8482 (541) 997-1274
Contact: Gayle Waiss, Exec. Dir.
FAX: (541) 997-1274; *E-mail:* wlcf@oregonfast.net;
Main URL: http://www.wlcfonline.org
E Newsletter: http://www.wlcfonline.org/newsletter.html

Established in 1974 in Oregon.
Foundation type: Community foundation.
Financial data (yr. ended 12/31/13): Assets, $5,389,073 (M); gifts received, $27,361; expenditures, $308,471; giving activities include $180,922 for grants, and $23,953 for grants to individuals.
Purpose and activities: The foundation seeks to improve life in Western Lane County, OR, and promote effective philanthropy.
Fields of interest: Arts and culture; Education; Health; Science; Community improvement.
Type of support: Capital and infrastructure; Equipment; Endowments; Program development; Seed money; Student aid.
Limitations: Applications accepted. Giving limited to Western Lane County, OR, defined as the Mapleton and Siuslaw school districts. No support for sectarian religious purposes. No grants to individuals (except for scholarships), or for emergency funding, travel to or in support of conferences, debt retirement or operational deficits, or annual fund drives or operation expenses (except during a start up period not to exceed three years).
Publications: Application guidelines; Annual report; Informational brochure; Newsletter; Program policy statement.

Application information: Visit foundation web site for application form and guidelines. Application form required.
Initial approach: Submit application
Copies of proposal: 11
Deadline(s): Jan. 15
Board meeting date(s): Monthly
Officers and Directors: Cindy Cable, Pres. and Director; Tom Bassett, V.P. and Director; Pat Stewart, Secy. and Director; Roger McCorkle, Treas. and Director; Gayle Waiss, Exec. Dir.; Lis Farm; Jim Grano; Dr. Ray Mans; Dee Osborne; Nancy Walker.
EIN: 237438503

7830
Paul R. and Anna Lee White Family Charitable Foundation
P.O. Box 3168
Portland, OR 97208-3168

Established in 1985 in Colorado.
Foundation type: Independent foundation.
Financial data (yr. ended 12/31/13): Assets, $4,017,903 (M); expenditures, $239,323; qualifying distributions, $181,675; giving activities include $173,353 for 16 grants (high: $17,000; low: $5,000).
Purpose and activities: Giving primarily for education, health, and youth organizations.
Fields of interest: Higher education; Health; Hospital care; Community mental health care; Libraries; Child welfare.
Limitations: Applications not accepted. Giving primarily in CO and Sheridan, WY. No grants to individuals.
Application information: Contributes only to pre-selected organizations.
Trustee: U.S. Bank.
EIN: 846191934

7831
The Woodard Family Foundation
(also known as Woodard Family Foundation)
P.O. Box 10666
Eugene, OR 97440-2666 (541) 343-9402
Contact: Tyson Woodard, Dir.
FAX: (541) 343-0122;
E-mail: infowff@woodardff.com; Main URL: http://www.woodardff.com

Established in 1952 in Oregon.
Donors: Walter A. Woodard‡; Carlton Woodard.
Foundation type: Independent foundation.
Financial data (yr. ended 06/30/14): Assets, $10,253,646 (M); expenditures, $530,914; qualifying distributions, $494,451; giving activities include $355,610 for 152 grants (high: $25,000; low: $100).
Purpose and activities: It is the desire of the foundation to assist charitable organizations in developing the internal capacity to meet present and

future needs; not to remove responsibilities from people.
Fields of interest: Arts and culture; Education; Higher education; Business education; Community and economic development; Human services.
Type of support: General support; Pro bono consulting services; Annual campaigns; Capital campaigns; Capital and infrastructure; Land acquisitions; Program development; Professorships; Seed money.
Limitations: Applications not accepted. Giving limited to local organizations in the greater Cottage Grove/Eugene, OR, area.
Application information: Unsolicited letters of inquiry and applications for grants are not accepted. Grant requests may only be submitted upon an invitation to apply and after the foundation has assigned the applicant an account name and password. See foundation web site for complete application guidelines.
Board meeting date(s): Quarterly
Officers and Directors: Tod Woodard, Pres. and Director; Andrew Woodard, V.P. and Treas. and Director; Pepper Woodard Bridgens, Secy. and Director; Dena Woodard McCoy; Carlton Woodard; Joy Woodard; Kim Woodard; Kristen A. Woodard; Tyson Woodard.
Number of staff: 1 part-time professional; 1 part-time support.
EIN: 936026550

7832
The Wyss Foundation
620 S.W. 5th Ave., Ste. 1010
Portland, OR 97204-1424
E-mail: lwyss@aol.com

Established in 1989 in Oregon.
Donors: Judith Wyss; Loren L. Wyss.
Foundation type: Independent foundation.
Financial data (yr. ended 04/30/13): Assets, $5,921,848 (M); expenditures, $198,462; qualifying distributions, $197,702; giving activities include $169,800 for 67 grants (high: $6,000; low: $1,000).
Fields of interest: Arts and culture; Education; Environment; Wildlife biodiversity; Human services.
International interests: United Kingdom of Great Britain and Northern Ireland.
Type of support: General support; Program development.
Limitations: Applications not accepted. Giving primarily in CA, and the Portland, OR, area. No support for political causes, medical research or for lobbying groups. No grants to individuals.
Application information: Unsolicited requests for funds not accepted.
Officer: Judith Wyss, Pres. and Treas.
Directors: James Damis; Edmund J. Wyss; Emily A. Wyss; Isabel J. Wyss; Jennifer A. Wyss-Jones.
Number of staff: None.
EIN: 931010019

PENNSYLVANIA

7833
100 Acre Wood Foundation
201 S. Hellertown Ave.
Quakertown, PA   18951-1768

Established in 2000 in Pennsylvania.
Donors: Kenneth F. Brown; Pamela H. Brown.
Foundation type: Independent foundation.
Financial data (yr. ended 04/30/13): Assets,
$789,719 (M); expenditures, $206,382; qualifying
distributions, $201,240; giving activities include
$201,240 for 7 grants (high: $126,870; low:
$1,250).
Purpose and activities: Giving primarily to a YMCA,
as well as for human services.
Fields of interest: Human services; Child
development.
Limitations: Applications not accepted. Giving
primarily in Quakertown, PA. No grants to
individuals.
Application information: Unsolicited requests for
funds not accepted.
Trustees: Kenneth F. Brown; Pamela H. Brown;
Shawn P. Brown.
EIN: 256714457

7834
The 1830 Family Foundation
c/o Glenmede Trust Co., N.A.
1650 Market St., Ste. 1200
Philadelphia, PA   19103-7391

Established in 2008 in Pennsylvania.
Foundation type: Independent foundation.
Financial data (yr. ended 06/30/14): Assets,
$8,288,284 (M); gifts received, $3,000,000;
expenditures, $273,518; qualifying distributions,
$230,500; giving activities include $224,500 for 72
grants (high: $10,000; low: $1,000).
Fields of interest: Child development.
Limitations: Applications not accepted. Giving
primarily in CT, FL and PA.
Application information: Unsolicited requests for
funds not accepted.
Officers and Trustees: Laura T. Buck, Chair. and
Trustee; Laura B. Marshall, Pres. and Trustee; Sarah
B. Schmader, V.P. and Trustee; Elizabeth B. King,
Secy.-Treas. and Trustee; Charles H. King III.
EIN: 261462775

7835
The Aaron Family Foundation
2401 Pennsylvania Ave., Apt. 5824
Philadelphia, PA   19130-3010

Established in 1998 in Pennsylvania.
Donors: Daniel Aaron; Geraldine Aaron.
Foundation type: Independent foundation.
Financial data (yr. ended 12/31/13): Assets,
$622,655 (M); gifts received, $250,682;
expenditures, $389,618; qualifying distributions,
$387,116; giving activities include $386,325 for 51
grants (high: $100,000; low: $100).
Purpose and activities: Giving primarily for the arts,
education, social services, and Jewish
organizations.

Fields of interest: Arts and culture; Education;
Nonprofits; Family planning; Diseases and
conditions; Judaism; Human services; Child welfare.
Type of support: Regranting.
Limitations: Applications not accepted. Giving
primarily in FL and PA. No grants to individuals.
Application information: Unsolicited requests for
funds not accepted.
Trustee: Geraldine Aaron.
EIN: 237996346

7836
Adams Foundation Inc.
200 Alpha Dr.
Pittsburgh, PA   15238-2929   (412) 963-1087
Contact: Shelley M. Taylor, V.P. and Secy.

Established in 1955 in Pennsylvania.
Donors: Rolland L. Adams†; ABARTA Inc.
Foundation type: Company-sponsored foundation.
Financial data (yr. ended 12/31/13): Assets,
$2,072,666 (M); expenditures, $132,181;
qualifying distributions, $131,015; giving activities
include $131,000 for 10 grants (high: $45,000;
low: $500).
Purpose and activities: The foundation supports
food banks and civic centers and organizations
involved with arts and culture, education, mental
health, and arthritis.
Fields of interest: Arts and culture; Ballet; Theater;
Education; Higher education; Mental health care;
Arthritis; Community improvement; Food banks.
Type of support: General support.
Limitations: Applications accepted. Giving primarily
in Ithaca, NY and Pittsburgh, PA. No grants to
individuals.
Application information: Application form required.
   Initial approach: Letter
   Copies of proposal: 1
   Deadline(s): None
Officers and Trustees: Mary R. Hudson, Pres. and
Trustee; Shelley M. Taylor, V.P. and Secy. and
Trustee; James A. Taylor, Treas. and Trustee;
Alexandra J. Taylor.
EIN: 240866511

7837
Albert A. Alley Family Foundation
1510 Cornwall Rd.
Lebanon, PA   17042-7479

Established in 1986 in Pennsylvania.
Donor: Albert A. Alley, MD.
Foundation type: Independent foundation.
Financial data (yr. ended 12/31/14): Assets,
$6,641 (M); gifts received, $150,847;
expenditures, $146,022; qualifying distributions,
$145,114; giving activities include $145,114 for 33
grants (high: $92,210; low: $100).
Fields of interest: Philanthropy; Human services;
Youth development; Youth services; Scouting
programs.
Type of support: Capital campaigns; Scholarships.
Limitations: Applications not accepted. Giving
limited to PA.
Application information: Unsolicited requests for
funds not accepted.
Trustees: Albert A. Alley, MD; Richard Alley, MD.
EIN: 236862791

7838
Amaranth Foundation
c/o Duane Morris LLP
30 S. 17th St.
Philadelphia, PA   19103-4196

Donor: Joan M. Moran.
Foundation type: Independent foundation.
Financial data (yr. ended 12/31/13): Assets,
$55,087 (M); gifts received, $309,104;
expenditures, $270,198; qualifying distributions,
$265,455; giving activities include $262,575 for 67
grants (high: $32,000; low: $100).
Purpose and activities: Giving for the arts, animal
welfare, and religion.
Fields of interest: Performing arts; Music;
Domesticated animals; Religion; Human services.
Limitations: Applications not accepted. Giving
primarily in PA, with emphasis on Allentown. No
grants to individuals.
Application information: Unsolicited requests for
funds not accepted.
Trustee: Joan M. Moran.
EIN: 237743235

7839
American Eagle Outfitters Foundation
77 Hot Metal St.
Pittsburgh, PA   15203-2382   (412) 432-4552
Main URL: http://www.ae.com

Established in 1999 in Pennsylvania.
Donor: American Eagle Outfitters, Inc.
Foundation type: Company-sponsored foundation.
Financial data (yr. ended 01/31/14): Assets,
$5,131,695 (M); gifts received, $336,327;
expenditures, $471,523; qualifying distributions,
$445,717; giving activities include $407,052 for 64
grants (high: $15,000; low: $1,000).
Purpose and activities: The foundation supports
programs designed to promote conservation and
youth development.
Fields of interest: Environment; Natural resources;
Youth development; Youth mentoring; Adult and
child mentoring.
Type of support: General support; Employee
volunteer services; Donated products; Program
development; Scholarships.
Limitations: Applications accepted. Giving primarily
in Ottawa, KS, New York, NY, and Pittsburgh, PA. No
support for organizations budgeting over 30 percent
of funds for fundraising purposes, discriminatory
organizations, individual religious organizations,
political organizations or candidates, lobbying
groups, or veterans' or fraternal organizations. No
grants to individuals, or for fashion shows, political
campaigns, medical or health-related causes,
goodwill advertising, or capital campaigns.
Application information:
   Initial approach: Proposal
   Copies of proposal: 1
   Deadline(s): None
Officers: Fred Grover, Pres.; Rick Milazzo, V.P.;
Michael Jennings, Secy.; Mary Roland, Treas.
Board Members: Michael Leedy; Lori Matthews;
Dave Reep; Laura Rowan; Helga Ying.
Director: Marcie Eberhart.
EIN: 251827476

7840
Harriett Ames Charitable Trust
c/o PNC Bank, N.A.
1600 Market St., 29th Fl.
Philadelphia, PA 19103-7240

Established in 1952 in New York.
Donor: Harriett Ames†.
Foundation type: Independent foundation.
Financial data (yr. ended 12/31/14): Assets, $2,118,186; expenditures, $237,588; qualifying distributions, $224,000 and $0 for set-asides.
Purpose and activities: Giving primarily for the arts, particularly to art museums, education, and health.
Fields of interest: Arts and culture; Museums; Art museums; Education; Higher education; Animal welfare; Hospital care; Diseases and conditions; Judaism; Human services.
Type of support: General support; Annual campaigns.
Limitations: Applications not accepted. Giving primarily in the metropolitan New York, NY, area and in Philadelphia, PA. No grants to individuals.
Application information: Contributes only to pre-selected organizations. Unsolicited requests for funds not considered.
  Board meeting date(s): Varies
Trustee: Steven Ames.
Number of staff: None.
EIN: 236286757

7841
Applestone Foundation
c/o BNY Mellon Trust of Delaware
P.O. Box 185
Pittsburgh, PA 15230-0185

Donor: 1957 Charity Foundation, Inc.
Foundation type: Independent foundation.
Financial data (yr. ended 06/30/13): Assets, $3,867,509 (M); expenditures, $216,531; qualifying distributions, $185,131; giving activities include $184,810 for 18 grants (high: $22,000; low: $3,000).
Fields of interest: Education; Environment; Youth services.
Type of support: Student aid; General support.
Limitations: Applications not accepted. Giving primarily in PA.
Application information: Unsolicited requests for funds not accepted.
Trustees: Michael Moran; BNY Mellon Trust of Delaware.
EIN: 841663629

7842
Arkema Inc. Foundation
(formerly Atofina Chemicals, Inc. Foundation)
900 First Ave.
King of Prussia, PA 19406-1308 (215) 419-7735
Contact: Diane Milici, Admin.
E-mail: diane.milici@arkema.com; Main URL: http://www.arkema-americas.com/en/social-responsibility/arkema-inc.-foundation/index.html

Established in 1957 in Pennsylvania.
Donors: Elf Atochem North America, Inc.; Atofina Chemicals, Inc.; Arkema Inc.
Foundation type: Company-sponsored foundation.

Financial data (yr. ended 12/31/13): Assets, $329,492 (M); gifts received, $380,000; expenditures, $327,325; qualifying distributions, $325,851; giving activities include $325,851 for 155 grants (high: $50,000; low: $250).
Purpose and activities: The foundation supports organizations involved with arts and culture, education, and civic affairs. Special emphasis is directed toward programs designed to advance elementary school science education.
Fields of interest: Arts and culture; Museums; Education; Elementary education; STEM education; Higher education; Nonprofits; Science; Communication media; Public affairs.
Type of support: General support; Employee matching gifts; Matching grants; Continuing support; Annual campaigns; Capital and infrastructure; Equipment; Emergency funds; Regranting; Scholarships.
Limitations: Applications accepted. Giving primarily in areas of company operations, with some emphasis on the Philadelphia, PA, area; giving in Axis, AL, Calvert City, Carrollton, and Louisville, KY, Blooming Prairie, MN, Geneseo, NY, Birdsboro, PA, Memphis, TN, and Beaumont, Crosby, and Houston, TX for the Science Teacher Program. No support for veterans', fraternal, labor, or sectarian religious organizations, or sports teams. No grants to individuals (except for employee-related scholarships), or for endowments, special projects, research, publications, conferences, courtesy advertising, entertainment promotions, event sponsorships, public education, athletic competitions, or political causes or campaigns; no loans.
Publications: Application guidelines.
Application information: Letters of inquiry should be no longer than 2 pages.
  Initial approach: Letter of inquiry; download application form and mail to nearest participating company facility for Science Teacher Program
  Copies of proposal: 1
  Deadline(s): None
  Board meeting date(s): Mar., June, Sept., and Dec.
  Final notification: 1 to 3 months
Trustees: Ryan Dirkx; Chris Giangrasso; Bernard Roche.
Number of staff: 1 part-time professional.
EIN: 236256818

7843
The Armstrong Foundation
(formerly John C. and Eve S. Bogle Foundation)
2 Penn Ctr. Plz., Ste. 803
Philadelphia, PA 19102-1721

Established in 1993 in Pennsylvania.
Donor: John C. Bogle.
Foundation type: Independent foundation.
Financial data (yr. ended 12/31/14): Assets, $8,248,441; expenditures, $390,406; qualifying distributions, $376,331.
Fields of interest: Historic preservation; Education; Higher education; Natural resources; Nonprofits; Heart and circulatory system diseases; Protestantism.
Type of support: Regranting.
Limitations: Applications not accepted. Giving primarily in NJ and PA. No grants to individuals.
Application information: Unsolicited requests for funds not accepted.

Trustees: Eve S. Bogle; John C. Bogle.
EIN: 232642354

7844
Arronson Foundation
1 S. Broad St., Ste. 2100
Philadelphia, PA 19107 (215) 238-1700
Contact: Joseph C. Kohn Esq., Pres. and Treas.

Established in 1957 in Delaware.
Donor: Gertrude Arronson†.
Foundation type: Independent foundation.
Financial data (yr. ended 10/31/14): Assets, $4,748,873 (M); expenditures, $245,667; qualifying distributions, $193,174; giving activities include $170,675 for 11 grants (high: $125,000; low: $675).
Purpose and activities: Emphasis on Jewish organizations and education, particularly higher education; support also for the performing arts and other cultural programs, hospitals and hospices, nursing and medical research, women's issues, and family planning.
Fields of interest: Arts and culture; Performing arts; Theater; Music; Education; Higher education; Nonprofits; Hospital care; Nursing care; Hospice care; Family planning; Diseases and conditions; Judaism; Women's services; Females.
International interests: Israel.
Type of support: Annual campaigns; Regranting; Capital campaigns; Capital and infrastructure; Endowments; Seed money; Scholarships; Research; Research and evaluation.
Limitations: Applications accepted. Giving primarily in Philadelphia, PA.
Application information: Application form required.
  Initial approach: Letter
  Copies of proposal: 1
  Deadline(s): None
Officers: Joseph C. Kohn, Esq., Pres. and Treas.; Amy Goldberg, V.P.; Ellen Kohn, V.P.
EIN: 236259604

7845
Ashland Foundation
96 Silver Birch Dr.
Lancaster, PA 17602-7014

Established in 1949 in Pennsylvania.
Foundation type: Independent foundation.
Financial data (yr. ended 10/31/14): Assets, $3,348,963 (M); expenditures, $179,665; qualifying distributions, $163,077; giving activities include $150,110 for 158 grants (high: $25,000; low: $100).
Purpose and activities: Giving primarily for health associations, education and human services.
Fields of interest: Education; Diseases and conditions; Human services; Youth development.
Type of support: General support; Matching grants; Continuing support; Annual campaigns; Endowments; Emergency funds; Fellowships; Scholarships; Research.
Limitations: Applications not accepted. Giving primarily in Lancaster and Schuylkill counties, PA. No grants to individuals.
Application information: Unsolicited requests for funds not accepted.
Officers: Diane K. Reidler, Pres.; Gail Mackey, V.P.; Helen Reidler, Secy.; Jessica Lupold, Treas.
Trustees: Chris Lupold; Keith Mackey.

Number of staff: 2 part-time professional.
EIN: 236245778

7846
The Auldridge Fund
c/o Roy S. Neff
1225 Farview Rd.
Villanova, PA   19085-2037

Established in 1998 in Pennsylvania.
Donors: Roy S. Neff; Rosalind S. Neff.
Foundation type: Independent foundation.
Financial data (yr. ended 12/31/13): Assets,
$2,133,420 (M); expenditures, $253,912;
qualifying distributions, $246,500; giving activities
include $246,500 for 1+ grant.
Fields of interest: Arts and culture; Education;
Nonprofits; Health.
Type of support: Regranting.
Limitations: Applications not accepted. Giving
primarily in PA. No grants to individuals.
Application information: Unsolicited requests for
funds not accepted.
Officers and Directors: Roy S. Neff, Pres. and
Director; Rosalind S. Neff, Secy. and Director.
EIN: 232900851

7847
Aventis Behring Foundation for Research and Advancement of Patient Health
(formerly ZLB Behring Foundation for Research and
Advancement of Patient Health)
c/o Jason Mugridge
1020 1st Ave.
P.O. Box 61501
King of Prussia, PA   19406-0901

Established in 2001 in Pennsylvania.
Donor: CSL Behring.
Foundation type: Company-sponsored foundation.
Financial data (yr. ended 09/30/13): Assets,
$328,868 (M); expenditures, $171,691; qualifying
distributions, $171,691; giving activities include
$168,493 for 4 grants (high: $74,978; low:
$29,271).
Purpose and activities: The foundation provides
funding for research projects and community
initiatives designed to advance the standard of care
for people with bleeding disorders.
Fields of interest: Education; Diseases and
conditions.
Type of support: Research.
Limitations: Applications not accepted. Giving
primarily in CA, IL, NY, PA, TX, and VA.
Application information: Unsolicited requests for
funds not accepted.
Officers: Greg Boss, Secy.; Jason Mugride, Treas.;
Garrett E. Bergman, Exec. Dir.
EIN: 311807278

7848
Ayers Foundation
c/o PNC Bank, N.A.
620 Liberty Ave., 30th Fl.
Pittsburgh, PA   15222-2722   (412) 762-3502
Contact: Bruce Bickel
FAX: (412) 762-4160;
E-mail: bruce.bickel@pnc.com

Established in 2005 in Pennsylvania.

Donors: Florence Ayers; Renee Ayers; James A.
Ayers II.
Foundation type: Independent foundation.
Financial data (yr. ended 12/31/13): Assets,
$7,237,983 (M); expenditures, $399,274;
qualifying distributions, $341,190; giving activities
include $322,255 for 19 grants (high: $30,900;
low: $1,200).
Purpose and activities: The focus of the foundation
is to support organizations that provide services to
poverty stricken underserved children.
Fields of interest: Education; Human services;
Children; Victims of crime and abuse.
Type of support: Public engagement and education.
Limitations: Applications accepted. Giving primarily
in Pittsburgh, PA. No grants to individuals.
Publications: Application guidelines.
Application information: Application form required.
   Initial approach: Letter
   Copies of proposal: 1
   Deadline(s): Contact foundation for current
      deadlines
   Final notification: 30 days
Officers: James A. Ayers II, Chair.; Florence Ayers,
Vice-Chair.; Renee Ayers, Pres.; Cynthia Hamorsky,
Secy.; Bruce Bickel, Exec. Dir.
Trustee: PNC Bank, N.A.
EIN: 203272241

7849
Charles Ayling Trust
(formerly Charles Lincoln Ayling Trust)
c/o BNY Mellon, N.A.
P.O. Box 185
Pittsburgh, PA   15230-0185

Foundation type: Independent foundation.
Financial data (yr. ended 12/31/14): Assets,
$7,487,420; expenditures, $409,196; qualifying
distributions, $362,481.
Fields of interest: Health; Hospital care.
Limitations: Applications not accepted. Giving
limited to Boston, MA.
Application information: Contributes only to
pre-selected organizations.
Trustee: BNY Mellon, N.A.
EIN: 046245939

7850
Barbara Bradley Baekgaard Family Foundation
c/o Joan Byrne Hall
7 Spring Mill Ln.
Haverford, PA   19041-1060

Donor: Barbara B. Baekgaard.
Foundation type: Independent foundation.
Financial data (yr. ended 12/31/13): Assets,
$4,368,157 (M); expenditures, $230,630;
qualifying distributions, $195,500; giving activities
include $195,500 for 18 grants (high: $50,000;
low: $500).
Fields of interest: Foundations; Seniors.
Limitations: Applications not accepted. Giving in the
U.S., with emphasis on IN.
Application information: Unsolicted requests for
funds not accepted.
Trustees: Barbara B. Baekgaard; James Byrne;
Thomas Byrne; Joan Byrne Hall; Anne-Marie Ray.
EIN: 800670424

7851
Michael Baker Corporation Foundation
100 Airside Dr.
Moon Township, PA   15108

Established in 2006 in Pennsylvania.
Donor: Michael Baker Corporation.
Foundation type: Company-sponsored foundation.
Financial data (yr. ended 12/31/13): Assets,
$322,015 (M); gifts received, $75,771;
expenditures, $455,113; qualifying distributions,
$455,113; giving activities include $441,242 for
193 grants (high: $52,400; low: $25).
Purpose and activities: The foundation supports
hospitals and organizations involved with education,
children services, community economic
development, and engineering.
Fields of interest: Education; Higher education;
Nonprofits; Health; Hospital care; Engineering;
Community and economic development; Human
services; Child welfare.
Type of support: General support; Employee
matching gifts; Continuing support; Program
development; Scholarships; Sponsorships;
Regranting.
Limitations: Applications not accepted. Giving
primarily in areas of company operations in PA. No
grants to individuals.
Application information: Contributes only to
pre-selected organizations.
Officers and Directors: David G. Higie, Pres. and
Exec. Dir.; H. James McKnight, Secy. and Director;
James M. Kempton, Treas. and Director; Jeffrey S.
Hill.
EIN: 830448116

7852
Summerfield Baldwin, Jr. Foundation
c/o PNC Bank, N.A.
620 Liberty Ave., 10th Fl.
Pittsburgh, PA   15222-2705

Established in 1946 in Maryland.
Foundation type: Independent foundation.
Financial data (yr. ended 12/31/14): Assets,
$6,396,794 (M); expenditures, $257,836;
qualifying distributions, $222,670; giving activities
include $213,274 for 9 grants (high: $50,000; low:
$5,000).
Fields of interest: Historic preservation; Education;
Higher education; Natural resources; Nonprofits;
Hospital care; Human services.
Type of support: General support; Regranting.
Limitations: Applications not accepted. Giving
primarily in MD and VA. No grants to individuals.
Application information: Contributes only to
pre-selected organizations.
Trustee: PNC Bank, N.A.
EIN: 526023112

7853
Leo C. Balzereit Trust
c/o Glenmede Trust Co., N.A.
1650 Market St., Ste. 1200
Philadelphia, PA   19103-7391   (215) 419-6000

Donor: Leo C. Balzereit Trust.
Foundation type: Independent foundation.
Financial data (yr. ended 12/31/14): Assets,
$8,627,964; expenditures, $478,961; qualifying
distributions, $453,075.

Fields of interest: Education; Housing development; Human services.
Limitations: Applications accepted. Giving primarily in NY and PA.
Application information:
  Initial approach: Proposal
  Deadline(s): None
Trustees: Leo G. Balzereit; Jane B. Gruson; The Glenmede Trust Co., N.A.
EIN: 236859847

7854
Bannerot-Lappe Foundation Charitable Trust

c/o BNY Mellon, N.A.
P.O. Box 185
Pittsburgh, PA 15230-0185
Contact: Laurie A. Moritz

Established in 1994 in Pennsylvania.
Donor: Joane Lappe Bowman†.
Foundation type: Independent foundation.
Financial data (yr. ended 05/31/13): Assets, $5,826,420 (M); expenditures, $364,398; qualifying distributions, $340,680; giving activities include $330,000 for 12 grants (high: $70,000; low: $5,000).
Fields of interest: Education; Animal welfare; Animal training; Human services; People with vision impairments.
Limitations: Applications not accepted. Giving primarily in NJ, NY and PA.
Application information: Contributes only to pre-selected organizations.
Trustee: BNY Mellon, N.A.
EIN: 256440597

7855
The Beach Foundation

300 Barr Harbor Dr., Ste. 220
West Conshohocken, PA 19428-3902

Established in 1997 in Pennsylvania.
Donor: Thomas E. Beach.
Foundation type: Independent foundation.
Financial data (yr. ended 12/31/13): Assets, $10,392,283 (M); expenditures, $419,843; qualifying distributions, $413,300; giving activities include $413,300 for 41 grants (high: $60,000; low: $50).
Fields of interest: Education; Natural resources; Nonprofits; Public affairs; Human services; International relations.
Type of support: Policy, advocacy and systems reform; Regranting.
Limitations: Applications not accepted. Giving primarily in CA, NH and PA. No grants to individuals.
Application information: Contributes only to pre-selected organizations.
Officers and Directors: Thomas E. Beach, Pres. and Director; Walter T. Beach, V.P. and Director; Jonathan T. Beach, Secy. and Director; Theodore T. Beach, Treas. and Director.
EIN: 232897351

7856
Beacon Foundation Inc.

(formerly The Giant Eagle Foundation)
c/o Giant Eagle, Inc.
101 Kappa Dr.
Pittsburgh, PA 15238-2809   (412) 963-6200
Contact: David S. Shapira, Dir.

Donor: Giant Eagle, Inc.
Foundation type: Company-sponsored foundation.
Financial data (yr. ended 06/30/13): Assets, $46,287,856 (M); expenditures, $517,074; qualifying distributions, $395,494; giving activities include $395,494 for 1 grant.
Purpose and activities: The foundation supports organizations involved with education and Judaism.
Fields of interest: Education; Higher education; Graduate and professional education; Nonprofits; Judaism; Theology.
Type of support: General support; Continuing support; Program development; Regranting.
Limitations: Applications accepted. Giving primarily in Pittsburgh, PA.
Application information:
  Initial approach: Letter of inquiry
  Deadline(s): None
Directors: Gerald Chait; Edward Moravitz; Louis Plung; Charles Porter; David S. Shapira; Norman Weizenbaum.
EIN: 202734721

7857
Frederick H.Jr. & Margaret S. Bedford Charitable Foundation

c/o Victaulic Co.
4901 Kesslersville Rd.
Easton, PA 18040-6714

Established in 1989 in Delaware.
Donor: Victaulic Co.
Foundation type: Company-sponsored foundation.
Financial data (yr. ended 12/31/13): Assets, $7,360,186 (M); gifts received, $1,000,000; expenditures, $356,166; qualifying distributions, $351,658; giving activities include $346,659 for 71 grants (high: $139,827; low: $300).
Purpose and activities: The foundation supports organizations involved with performing arts, education, the environment, health, human services, children, and women.
Fields of interest: Arts and culture; Education; Health.
Limitations: Applications not accepted. Giving on primarily in NC, NJ, NY, TX, with an emphasis on PA. No grants to individuals.
Application information: Contributes only to pre-selected organizations.
Officers: John F. Malloy, Pres.; Pierre D'Arenberg, V.P.; Mark Van De Voorde, Secy.; Muffie B. Murray, Treas.
EIN: 133544702

7858
Kenneth W. Beels Charitable Trust

c/o BNY Mellon, N.A.
P.O. Box 185
Pittsburgh, PA 15230-0185

Foundation type: Independent foundation.

Financial data (yr. ended 12/31/14): Assets, $5,726,561; expenditures, $365,782; qualifying distributions, $299,364.
Fields of interest: Education; Protestantism; Human services.
Limitations: Applications not accepted. Giving primarily in IL and PA. No grants to individuals.
Application information: Contributes only to pre-selected organizations.
Trustees: Robert W. McFate; BNY Mellon, N.A.
EIN: 256770248

7859
The Harriet & George Blank Bella Foundation

148A Old York Rd.
New Hope, PA 18938-1409   (908) 526-1297
Contact: George W. Blank, Tr.

Donors: George W. Blank; Harriet I. Blank.
Foundation type: Operating foundation.
Financial data (yr. ended 12/31/13): Assets, $2,333,974 (M); gifts received, $6,061; expenditures, $245,999; qualifying distributions, $208,340; giving activities include $208,340 for 20 grants (high: $50,000; low: $250).
Fields of interest: Arts and culture; Education; Judaism.
Application information: Application form required.
  Initial approach: Letter
  Deadline(s): None
Trustees: George W. Blank; Harriet I. Blank.
EIN: 376438089

7860
Bennett Family Foundation

(also known as Eleanore Bennett Charitable Trust 1)
161 Washington St., Ste. 1500
Conshohocken, PA 19428-2051
E-mail: trustees@bennettfoundation.org; Mailing address: P.O. Box 15017, Boston, MA 02215; Main URL: http://www.bennettfoundation.org

Donor: Eleanore Bennett†.
Foundation type: Independent foundation.
Financial data (yr. ended 05/31/14): Assets, $5,871,060 (M); expenditures, $341,983; qualifying distributions, $279,500; giving activities include $279,500 for 41 grants (high: $22,500; low: $250).
Fields of interest: Education; Higher education; Health; Mental health care; Residential mental health care; Nutrition; Youth development; Youth services.
Type of support: General support; Matching grants; Continuing support; Capital campaigns; Capital and infrastructure; Equipment; Program development; Internships; Research; Program evaluations.
Limitations: Applications accepted. Giving primarily in the greater Boston, MA metropolitan area and the greater Philadelphia, PA area. No grants to individuals.
Application information: Delaware Valley Grantmakers Common Grant Application Form accepted. Complete application guidelines available on foundation web site. Application form required.
  Initial approach: E-mail letter of inquiry to trustees, per guidelines on foundation web site
Trustees: Stewart B. Chapin; Thomas M. Chapin.
EIN: 306016982

7861
William L. & Margaret L. Benz Foundation
c/o BNY Mellon, N.A.
P.O. Box 185
Pittsburgh, PA 15230-0185
Contact: Laurie Moritz, Trust Off., BNY Mellon, N.A.

Established in 1987 in Pennsylvania.
Donor: Margaret L. Benz†.
Foundation type: Independent foundation.
Financial data (yr. ended 05/31/14): Assets,
$3,644,393 (M); expenditures, $191,133;
qualifying distributions, $171,534; giving activities
include $163,000 for 88 grants (high: $33,800;
low: $400).
Purpose and activities: Scholarship awards to
Blairsville, Pennsylvania, residents for higher
education; support also for the Blairsville public
library.
Fields of interest: Education; Higher education;
Libraries.
Type of support: General support; Student aid.
Limitations: Applications accepted. Giving limited to
residents of Blairsville, PA.
Application information: Application form required.
  Deadline(s): None
Trustee: BNY Mellon, N.A.
EIN: 256276186

7862
Harold and Renee Berger Foundation
605 Arbutus St.
Philadelphia, PA 19119-3505
Application address: c/o Judge Harold Berger, 1622
Locust St., Philadelphia, PA 19103, tel.: (215)
875-3000

Established in 1986 in Pennsylvania.
Donors: Harold Berger; Renee Berger.
Foundation type: Independent foundation.
Financial data (yr. ended 12/31/13): Assets,
$163,391 (M); gifts received, $25,000;
expenditures, $183,306; qualifying distributions,
$181,724; giving activities include $181,724 for 28
grants (high: $108,444; low: $20).
Fields of interest: Museums; Higher education;
Nonprofits; Judaism; Human services.
Type of support: Regranting.
Limitations: Applications accepted. Giving primarily
in Philadelphia, PA. No grants to individuals.
Application information: Application form required.
  Initial approach: Letter
  Deadline(s): None
Officer: Harold Berger, Pres.
EIN: 232439490

7863
The Bergman Foundation
400 3rd Ave.
Kingston, PA 18704-5816

Established in 1950 in Pennsylvania.
Donor: Justin Bergman, Jr.
Foundation type: Independent foundation.
Financial data (yr. ended 09/30/14): Assets,
$4,145,882; gifts received, $24,931;
expenditures, $261,272; qualifying distributions,
$261,272.
Fields of interest: Education; Nonprofits; Public
libraries; Community and economic development;
Judaism; Child welfare.

Type of support: General support; Annual
campaigns; Capital campaigns; Seed money;
Regranting.
Limitations: Applications not accepted. Giving
primarily in PA. No grants to individuals.
Application information: Unsolicited requests for
funds not accepted.
  Board meeting date(s): Quarterly
Trustees: Cordelia Bergman; Linda Harris; Harry
Hiscox; Cordelia Tallman.
EIN: 246014771

7864
Bergstrom Foundation
625 Liberty Ave.
Pittsburgh, PA 15222-3152
Contact: Christopher F. Farrell

Established in 1960 in Pennsylvania.
Donors: Henry A. Bergstrom†; Margaret A.
Bergstrom†.
Foundation type: Independent foundation.
Financial data (yr. ended 12/31/13): Assets,
$7,073,829 (M); expenditures, $343,561;
qualifying distributions, $341,497; giving activities
include $318,900 for 11 grants (high: $110,000;
low: $4,900).
Purpose and activities: The focus of the foundation
is youth, education, health and social sciences in
Pittsburgh.
Fields of interest: Arts and culture; Education;
Health; Human services; Youth development; Youth
services.
Type of support: Annual campaigns; Capital
campaigns; Public engagement and education.
Limitations: Applications not accepted. Giving
primarily in the Pittsburgh, PA, area. No grants to
individuals.
Application information: Unsolicited requests for
funds not accepted.
  Board meeting date(s): Contact foundation for
  dates
Officers: Ashley F. Bergstrom, Chair.; Henry A.
Bergstrom, Jr., Pres.; Larry E. Phillips, Esq., V.P.
Number of staff: None.
EIN: 251112093

7865
**The Edwin J. and Barbara R. Berkowitz
Family Foundation**
506 Oak Terr.
Merion Station, PA 19066-1341 (610)
664-8335
Contact: Edwin J. Berkowitz, Tr.

Donor: Edwin J. Berkowitz.
Foundation type: Independent foundation.
Financial data (yr. ended 12/31/13): Assets,
$9,925 (M); gifts received, $350,000;
expenditures, $341,070; qualifying distributions,
$340,900; giving activities include $340,900 for 43
grants (high: $50,000; low: $500).
Purpose and activities: Giving primarily for
education and to Jewish organizations.
Fields of interest: Education; University education;
Nonprofits; Judaism.
International interests: Israel.
Type of support: Regranting.
Limitations: Applications accepted. Giving primarily
in PA and NJ; some giving also in Israel.
Application information: Application form required.

Initial approach: Letter
Deadline(s): None
Trustees: Alan Berkowitz; Arthur M. Berkowitz;
Barbara R. Berkowitz; Daniel M. Berkowitz; Edwin J.
Berkowitz; Pnina B. Siegler.
EIN: 237978506

7866
Berkowitz II Foundation Inc.
c/o Michael Martin
140 Silver Springs Rd.
Milford, PA 18337-7774

Foundation type: Independent foundation.
Financial data (yr. ended 12/31/12): Assets,
$4,011,644 (M); expenditures, $231,221;
qualifying distributions, $179,530; giving activities
include $179,530 for 28 grants (high: $41,000;
low: $500).
Fields of interest: Education; Health; Human
services.
Limitations: Applications not accepted.
Application information: Unsolicited requests for
funds not accepted.
Officers: Michael Martin, Pres. and C.E.O.; Roberta
Martin, V.P.; Helen Sherman, Secy.-Treas.
EIN: 264464319

7867
Archie W. and Grace Berry Foundation
100 Four Falls Corporate Ctr., Ste. 202
West Conshohocken, PA 19428-2950

Established in 1988 in Pennsylvania.
Donor: Archie W. Berry, Sr.
Foundation type: Independent foundation.
Financial data (yr. ended 06/30/14): Assets,
$7,373,129 (M); expenditures, $367,741;
qualifying distributions, $316,400; giving activities
include $315,000 for 9 grants (high: $75,000; low:
$5,000).
Fields of interest: Arts and culture; Natural
resources.
Limitations: Applications not accepted. Giving
primarily in PA, VA, and WY; some funding also in
CA, ID and NY. No grants to individuals.
Application information: Unsolicited requests for
funds not accepted.
Trustees: Barbara Berry; Robert R. Berry; Susan
Berry Kohlhas.
EIN: 236951678

7868
Charles G. Berwind Foundation, Inc.
3000 Centre Sq. W.
1500 Market St.
Philadelphia, PA 19102-2100 2155632800

Donor: Berwind Corporation.
Foundation type: Independent foundation.
Financial data (yr. ended 09/30/14): Assets,
$7,639,078; expenditures, $437,027; qualifying
distributions, $363,891.
Purpose and activities: Scholarship awards to
students to attend accredited institutions of higher
learning in the U.S.
Fields of interest: Higher education.
Type of support: Student aid.
Limitations: Applications accepted. Giving primarily
to residents of PA.

Application information: Application form required.
Initial approach: Scholarship application
Deadline(s): Varies; contact foundation
Officers: C. Graham Berwind, Pres.; Joanna B. Creamer, V.P.; Eileen P. Moore, Secy.; Bruce J. McKenney, Treas.
Selection Committee: Walter Arader; Sandra Berwind; Michelle M. Mancini; Constance McSherry.
EIN: 203039970

7869
Betts Foundation
1800 Pennsylvania Ave. W.
Warren, PA 16365-1932 (814) 723-1250

Established in 1957 in Pennsylvania.
Donor: Betts Industries, Inc.
Foundation type: Company-sponsored foundation.
Financial data (yr. ended 12/31/13): Assets, $5,054,963 (M); gifts received, $125,000; expenditures, $215,697; qualifying distributions, $168,677; giving activities include $168,677 for 47 grants (high: $40,000; low: $336).
Purpose and activities: The foundation supports organizations involved with theater, higher education, animal welfare, legal aid, human services, and community development.
Fields of interest: Education; Health; Human services.
Limitations: Applications accepted. Giving primarily in Warren County, PA.
Application information: Application form required.
Initial approach: Letter or telephone call
Deadline(s): None
Trustees: C.R. Betts; M.J. Betts; R.E. Betts; Richard T. Betts; T.E. Betts; M.D. Hedges.
EIN: 256035169

7870
Theodora B. Betz Foundation
c/o Roy Ross
1600 Market St., Ste. 3600
Philadelphia, PA 19103-7212

Established in 1989 in Pennsylvania.
Foundation type: Independent foundation.
Financial data (yr. ended 04/30/14): Assets, $3,747,521 (M); expenditures, $269,532; qualifying distributions, $225,925; giving activities include $200,000 for 2 grants (high: $100,000; low: $100,000).
Fields of interest: Higher education; Hospital care; Diseases and conditions; ALS; Cancers.
Type of support: Research.
Limitations: Applications not accepted. Giving primarily in NH and PA. No grants to individuals.
Application information: Contributes only to pre-selected organizations.
Trustees: Henry Kwiecinski; George Nofer.
EIN: 236965187

7871
BGM Foundation
875 Parkway Rd.
Allentown, PA 18104-3398

Established in 2002 in Pennsylvania.
Donors: Brijbala Asnani; Gul Asnani.
Foundation type: Independent foundation.

Financial data (yr. ended 12/31/13): Assets, $4,088 (M); gifts received, $144,710; expenditures, $172,499; qualifying distributions, $171,000; giving activities include $171,000 for 2 grants (high: $170,000; low: $1,000).
Fields of interest: Diseases and conditions; Hinduism.
International interests: Canada; India.
Type of support: Research.
Limitations: Applications not accepted. Giving primarily in India and Alberta, Canada, with some giving in CA and IL. No grants to individuals.
Application information: Unsolicited requests for funds not accepted.
Officers: Gul Asnani, Pres. and Treas.; Brijbala Asnani, Secy.
EIN: 470880370

7872
Henry & Helen Bienenfeld Foundation
828 Red Lion Rd.
Philadelphia, PA 19115

Established in 2007 in Pennsylvania.
Donors: Henry Bienenfeld; Helen Bienenfeld.
Foundation type: Independent foundation.
Financial data (yr. ended 06/30/14): Assets, $3,728,861 (M); gifts received, $150,000; expenditures, $172,761; qualifying distributions, $170,500; giving activities include $170,500 for 20 grants (high: $20,000; low: $500).
Fields of interest: Health; Religion; Judaism; Human services.
Type of support: Research.
Limitations: Applications not accepted. Giving primarily in PA and NY. No grants to individuals.
Application information: Contributes only to pre-selected organizations.
Trustees: Helen Bienenfeld; Jack Bienenfeld; Michael Bienenfeld.
EIN: 261503146

7873
Marilyn and J. Robert Birnhak Foundation
P.O. Box 2300
Fort Washington, PA 19034-2300

Established in 1986 in Pennsylvania.
Donors: J. Robert Birnhak; Marilyn J. Birnhak; Weight Watchers of Philadelphia, Inc.
Foundation type: Independent foundation.
Financial data (yr. ended 06/30/13): Assets, $151,754 (M); gifts received, $200,000; expenditures, $210,144; qualifying distributions, $210,000; giving activities include $210,000 for 2 grants (high: $200,000; low: $10,000).
Fields of interest: Theater; Higher education; Judaism.
Type of support: General support.
Limitations: Applications not accepted. Giving primarily in PA. No grants to individuals.
Application information: Unsolicited requests for funds not accepted.
Trustees: J. Robert Birnhak; Marilyn J. Birnhak.
EIN: 222779210

7874
The Bishop Foundation
(also known as The Bishop Foundation)
1600 E. Cumberland St.
Lebanon, PA 17042-8323 (717) 273-1685
Contact: Katherine J. Bishop, Tr.

Established in 1957 in Pennsylvania.
Foundation type: Independent foundation.
Financial data (yr. ended 12/31/13): Assets, $3,377,971 (M); expenditures, $181,202; qualifying distributions, $153,898; giving activities include $153,898 for 17 grants (high: $100,000; low: $500).
Purpose and activities: Giving primarily for health services; some giving also for education, and Christian churches and ministries.
Fields of interest: Arts and culture; Education; Secondary education; Higher education; Nonprofits; Health; Christianity; Human services; Child welfare.
Type of support: General support; Regranting.
Limitations: Applications accepted. Giving primarily in Lebanon County, PA. No grants to individuals.
Application information: Application form required.
Initial approach: Letter
Deadline(s): None
Trustees: Katherine J. Bishop; Thomas C. Bishop; Trudie Bishop.
EIN: 236255835

7875
Elizabeth S. Black Charitable Trust
c/o PNC Bank, N.A.
P.O. Box 609
Pittsburgh, PA 15230-9738 4127625188
Application address: c/o PNC Bank, N.A., Att.: Brian Dornseif, 1900 E. 9th St., 13th Fl., Cleveland, OH 44114, tel.: (216) 222-2799

Foundation type: Independent foundation.
Financial data (yr. ended 10/31/14): Assets, $10,517,608; expenditures, $565,680; qualifying distributions, $504,388.
Fields of interest: Arts and culture; Elementary and secondary education; Higher education; Education services; Foundations; Protestantism; Human services; Child welfare; Youth organizing.
Type of support: General support.
Limitations: Applications accepted. Giving primarily in the Oil City, PA area. No grants to individuals.
Application information: Application form required.
Deadline(s): None
Trustee: PNC Bank, N.A.
EIN: 043731472

7876
Black Family Foundation
1540 E. Lake Rd., Ste. 300
Erie, PA 16511-1091

Established in 1993 in Pennsylvania.
Donors: 1998 Black Family Charitable Lead Annuity Trust; Erie Community Foundation; Samuel P. Black III.
Foundation type: Independent foundation.
Financial data (yr. ended 12/31/13): Assets, $2,840,406 (M); expenditures, $433,106; qualifying distributions, $316,466; giving activities include $300,000 for 10 grants (high: $40,000; low: $20,000).

Fields of interest: Environment; Domesticated animals; Human services.
Limitations: Applications accepted. Giving primarily in CA, Washington, DC, FL and SC. No grants to individuals.
Application information: Application form required.
   Initial approach: Completed application form
   Deadline(s): None
Officers: Samuel P. Black III, Pres.; John A. Lauer, V.P.; James D. Cullen, Secy.-Treas.
EIN: 251705824

7877

The Blackhorse Foundation
454 S. Main St.
Wilkes-Barre, PA 18701-2208

Established in 1993 in Pennsylvania.
Donors: A.L. Simms; Ronald W. Simms; Richard A. Rose; Rhea P. Simms; Virginia Rose; Emma Simms.
Foundation type: Independent foundation.
Financial data (yr. ended 12/31/13): Assets, $5,542,425 (M); gifts received, $31,146; expenditures, $254,265; qualifying distributions, $210,750; giving activities include $210,750 for 58 grants (high: $50,000; low: $100).
Fields of interest: Higher education; Health.
Limitations: Applications not accepted. Giving primarily in Wilkes-Barre, PA. No grants to individuals.
Application information: Unsolicited requests for funds not accepted.
Officers: Ronald W. Simms, Pres.; Rhea P. Simms, Secy.; Richard A. Rose, Treas.
EIN: 232725907

7878

The Raymond and Elizabeth Bloch Educational and Charitable Foundation
603 Frick Bldg.
Pittsburgh, PA 15219

Established in 1989 in Pennsylvania.
Donor: Raymond Bloch†.
Foundation type: Independent foundation.
Financial data (yr. ended 12/31/13): Assets, $3,176,026 (M); expenditures, $224,598; qualifying distributions, $158,246; giving activities include $152,000 for 8 grants (high: $75,000; low: $1,000).
Purpose and activities: Giving primarily for self-help projects for children in impoverished parts of the world and to organizations concerned with issues of world peace through international law and arms control; some support also for medical research to relieve pain caused primarily by headaches.
Fields of interest: Education; Religion; Human services.
Limitations: Applications not accepted. Giving primarily in PA. No grants to individuals.
Application information: Unsolicited request for funds not accepted.
Trustee: Bernard L. Bloch.
EIN: 251561204

7879

The Blue Ribbon Foundation of Blue Cross of Northeastern Pennsylvania
(formerly Hospital Service Association of Northeastern Pennsylvania Foundation)
19 N. Main St.
Wilkes-Barre, PA 18711-0300 (570) 200-6305
Contact: Cynthia A. Yevich, Exec. Dir.
FAX: (570) 200-6699;
E-mail: christine.zavaskas@bcnepa.com; Additional contact: Jennifer R. Deemer, Grant and Prog. Specialist, Jennifer.Deemer@bcnepa.com
Grants List: https://www.bcnepa.com/Community/BlueRibbon/Grants.aspx

Established in 2001 in Pennsylvania.
Donors: Blue Cross of Northeastern Pennsylvania; Hospital Service Assn. of N.E. PA.
Foundation type: Company-sponsored foundation.
Financial data (yr. ended 12/31/14): Assets, $9,344 (M); gifts received, $163,000; expenditures, $250,002; qualifying distributions, $251,519; giving activities include $236,796 for 28 grants (high: $35,796; low: $1,000).
Purpose and activities: The foundation supports programs designed improve the heath and wellness of residents in Pennsylvania communities. Special emphasis is directed toward programs designed to address critical health issues through creative, community-based, programmatic initiatives; produce measurable health and wellness results; foster collaboration and partnership among community organizations; and address the root causes of specific diseases and conditions to help moderate escalating healthcare costs.
Fields of interest: Child educational development; Medical education; Reading promotion; Nonprofits; Health; Health care access; Health insurance; Health care clinics; Dental care; Preventive care; Pharmacies; Mental health care; Addiction services; Substance abuse prevention; Substance abuse treatment; Exercise; Nutrition; Obesity; Diseases and conditions; Diabetes; Heart and circulatory system diseases; Cancers; Financial counseling; Human services; Family services; Children; Seniors; Females; Victims of crime and abuse; People with disabilities.
Type of support: Translation ; Equal access; Public engagement and education; Regranting.
Limitations: Applications accepted. Giving limited to areas of company operations in Bradford, Carbon, Clinton, Lackawanna, Luzerne, Lycoming, Monroe, Pike, Sullivan, Susquehanna, Tioga, Wayne, and Wyoming counties, PA. No support for schools, parent/teacher organizations, camps, organizations not of direct benefit to the entire community, camps of any kind, emergency response organizations, or political candidates or organizations. No grants to individuals, or for equipment or fixed assets, tours, trips, or conferences, capital campaigns or building, annual campaigns, general operating support, scholarships, endowments, debt reduction, or fundraising.
Publications: Application guidelines; Annual report; Grants list; Informational brochure; Program policy statement.
Application information: Grant requests should not exceed $15,000. Potential applicants are encouraged to contact the foundation to discuss proposals and/or projects. Support is limited to 1 contribution per organization during any given year. Organizations receiving support are asked to provide an interim report and a final report. Application form required.

Initial approach: Download application form and mail proposal and application form to foundation
Deadline(s): Mar. 8, June 7, and Oct. 4
Board meeting date(s): Apr. 16, July 11, and Nov. 12
Officers and Directors: John P. Moses, Esq., Chair. and Director; Denise S. Cesare, Pres. and Director; William J. Farrell, C.F.O. and Treas.; Gertude McGowan, Secy.; Cynthia A. Yevich, Exec. Dir.; Judith O. Graziano; Alan S. Hollander, Esq.; Sir. M. Martin de Porres Mc-Hale; John J. Menapace; Paul H. Rooney, Jr.; Bruce Sickel.
EIN: 233101673

7880

Blue Sky Family Foundation
c/o BNY Mellon, N.A.
P.O. Box 185
Pittsburgh, PA 15230-0185

Foundation type: Independent foundation.
Financial data (yr. ended 06/30/14): Assets, $3,577,671; expenditures, $211,371; qualifying distributions, $204,088.
Fields of interest: Education; Health; Agriculture.
Limitations: Applications not accepted. Giving primarily in PA. No grants to individuals.
Application information: Unsolicited requests for funds not accepted.
Trustee: Ranney R. Moran.
EIN: 300285433

7881

The Boardman Family Foundation
c/o BNY Mellon, N.A.
P.O. Box 185
Pittsburgh, PA 15230-0185

Established in 1998 in New Jersey.
Donors: Jean R. Boardman; Jean Boardman Charitable Lead Annuity.
Foundation type: Independent foundation.
Financial data (yr. ended 05/31/13): Assets, $5,349,899 (M); gifts received, $559,207; expenditures, $231,182; qualifying distributions, $196,598; giving activities include $188,500 for 10 grants (high: $75,000; low: $3,000).
Fields of interest: University education; Animal welfare; Foundations.
Type of support: General support.
Limitations: Applications not accepted.
Application information: Unsolicited requests for funds not accepted.
Trustee: BNY Mellon, N.A.
EIN: 137166339

7882

The Bolte Family Foundation
c/o BDP International
510 Walnut St., Fl. 14
Philadelphia, PA 19106-3619

Established in 2007 in Pennsylvania.
Donor: BDP International, Inc.
Foundation type: Company-sponsored foundation.
Financial data (yr. ended 12/31/13): Assets, $9,216 (M); gifts received, $235,000; expenditures, $267,791; qualifying distributions,

$267,080; giving activities include $267,080 for 13 grants (high: $160,000; low: $1,000).
Purpose and activities: The foundation supports children's hospitals and organizations involved with higher education, patient services, breast cancer, and chemistry.
Fields of interest: Higher education; Patient social services; Hospital care; Breast cancer; Chemistry; Human services; Child welfare.
Type of support: General support.
Limitations: Applications not accepted. Giving primarily in PA. No grants to individuals.
Application information: Contributes only to pre-selected organizations.
Officers: William Connors, Pres.; Thomas Kramer, V.P.; Midge Clark, Treas.
EIN: 412237563

7883
August & Minnie Bonomo Perpetual Charitable Trust
c/o PNC Bank
620 Liberty Ave.,10th Fl.
Pittsburgh, PA   15222-2705

Foundation type: Independent foundation.
Financial data (yr. ended 12/31/13): Assets, $5,861,071 (M); expenditures, $307,697; qualifying distributions, $261,561; giving activities include $259,200 for 3 grants (high: $86,400; low: $86,400).
Fields of interest: Education; Religion; Christianity; Human services.
Limitations: Applications not accepted. Giving primarily in NY and PA.
Application information: Unsolicited Requests for funds not accepted.
Trustee: PNC Bank, N.A.
EIN: 256378526

7884
The Bon-Ton Stores Foundation
(also known as The Bon-Ton Stores Foundation)
2801 E. Market St., Bldg. E
York, PA   17402-2420

Established in 1991 in Pennsylvania.
Donors: The Bon-Ton Department Stores, Inc.; Associates of the Bon-Ton Dept. Stores.
Foundation type: Company-sponsored foundation.
Financial data (yr. ended 01/31/14): Assets, $226,474 (M); gifts received, $200,000; expenditures, $186,657; qualifying distributions, $185,227; giving activities include $178,327 for 28 grants (high: $53,277; low: $100), and $6,900 for 5 grants to individuals (high: $2,000; low: $600).
Purpose and activities: The foundation supports organizations involved with arts and culture, education, water conservation, health, cancer, human services, and Judaism.
Fields of interest: Arts and culture; Performing arts; Education; Medical education; Water conservation; Health; Health care clinics; Diseases and conditions; Genetic conditions and birth defects; Cancers; Breast cancer; Community and economic development; Judaism; Human services; Child welfare.
Type of support: General support; Employee volunteer services; Employee matching gifts; Program development; Scholarships; Grants to individuals; Sponsorships; Research.

Limitations: Applications not accepted. Giving primarily in areas of store operations in PA. No grants to individuals (except for disaster grants).
Application information: Contributes only to pre-selected organizations and individuals.
  Board meeting date(s): Quarterly
Officers and Directors: Mary Kerr, Pres. and Director; Gregory Yawman, Secy. and Director; Michael Webb, Treas. and Director; Christine Hojnacki; Kimberly Krummerich; Pamela Pratt; Kathleen Weber.
EIN: 232656774

7885
The Ross J. Born Family Charitable Trust
c/o Ross J. Born
3571 Catherine Ave.
Allentown, PA   18103-5311

Established in 1991 in Pennsylvania.
Donors: Ross J. Born; Wendy Born.
Foundation type: Independent foundation.
Financial data (yr. ended 12/31/13): Assets, $1,944,080 (M); expenditures, $363,103; qualifying distributions, $342,860; giving activities include $342,860 for 74 grants (high: $206,800; low: $75).
Purpose and activities: Giving primarily to charities and agencies that provide services to the needy.
Fields of interest: Education; Nonprofits; Health; Judaism; Human services; Child welfare; Youth development.
Type of support: General support; Continuing support; Annual campaigns; Capital campaigns; Equipment; Emergency funds; Regranting; Program development; Seed money.
Limitations: Applications not accepted. Giving primarily in the Lehigh Valley, PA, area. No grants to individuals.
Application information: Unsolicited requests for funds not accepted.
Trustee: Ross J. Born.
EIN: 237653033

7886
Borowsky Family Foundation
220 Society Hill Towers, Ste. 31B
Philadelphia, PA   19106

Established in 1999 in Pennsylvania.
Donor: Irvin J. Borowsky.
Foundation type: Independent foundation.
Financial data (yr. ended 12/31/13): Assets, $4,556,141 (M); expenditures, $228,226; qualifying distributions, $204,475; giving activities include $204,475 for 65 grants (high: $28,850; low: $100).
Fields of interest: Arts and culture; Music; Education; Nonprofits; Human services.
Type of support: Regranting.
Limitations: Applications not accepted. Giving primarily in PA. No grants to individuals.
Application information: Contributes only to pre-selected organizations.
Officers: Irvin J. Borowsky, Chair. and Treas.; Laurie Wagman, Pres.; Gwen Borowsky Camp, V.P. and Secy.; Ned Borowsky, V.P.
EIN: 232949444

7887
Boscia Family Foundation
c/o Jon A. Boscia
150 Monument Rd., Ste. 403
Bala-Cynwyd, PA   19004

Established in 2004 in Pennsylvania.
Donors: Donna L. Boscia; Jon A. Boscia.
Foundation type: Independent foundation.
Financial data (yr. ended 12/31/13): Assets, $6,757,491 (M); gifts received, $250,000; expenditures, $187,988; qualifying distributions, $182,941; giving activities include $181,000 for 40 grants (high: $25,000; low: $500).
Fields of interest: Arts and culture; Performing arts education; Art museums; History museums; Education; University education; Zoos; Housing development; Human services; Youth services.
Limitations: Applications not accepted. Giving primarily in PA. No grants to individuals.
Application information: Contributes only to pre-selected organizations.
Officers: Jon A. Boscia, Pres.; Donna L. Boscia, V.P.; Brandon J. Boscia, Secy.; Nicole M. Boscia, Treas.
EIN: 200614587

7888
The Boudinot Foundation
c/o E.R. Boynton
30 Valley Stream Pkwy.
Malvern, PA   19355

Foundation type: Independent foundation.
Financial data (yr. ended 12/31/14): Assets, $6,594,665 (M); gifts received, $317,428; expenditures, $349,738; qualifying distributions, $295,000; giving activities include $295,000 for 15 grants (high: $50,000; low: $5,000).
Fields of interest: Education; Land resources; Animal welfare; Sports and recreation; Human services.
Limitations: Applications not accepted. Giving primarily in CA, ID, KY, MD, ME, NH, and PA.
Application information: Unsolicited requests for funds not accepted.
Officers and Directors: Carol A. Atterbury, Pres. and Director; Michael B. Atterbury, Secy.-Treas. and Director; Edwin R. Boynton.
EIN: 275271360

7889
Joseph G. Bradley Charitable Foundation
c/o Cozen O'Connor
1900 Market St.
Philadelphia, PA   19103

Established in 1990 in Pennsylvania.
Foundation type: Independent foundation.
Financial data (yr. ended 11/30/13): Assets, $6,767,845 (M); expenditures, $301,547; qualifying distributions, $291,361; giving activities include $285,000 for 5 grants (high: $75,000; low: $50,000).
Purpose and activities: The foundation awards grants to churches, museums, and other organizations for organ restoration.
Fields of interest: Music; Art museums; Protestantism; Catholicism.
Type of support: Equipment.
Application information:

Initial approach: Proposal
Deadline(s): None
Trustee: Andrew R. Nehrbas.
EIN: 237647762

7890
Howell A. & Ann M. Breedlove Charitable Foundation
2015 Blairmont Dr.
Pittsburgh, PA   15241-2202

Established in 1991 in Pennsylvania.
Donors: Howell A. Breedlove; Ann M. Breedlove.
Foundation type: Independent foundation.
Financial data (yr. ended 12/31/13): Assets, $230,732 (M); expenditures, $159,408; qualifying distributions, $155,250; giving activities include $155,250 for 23 grants (high: $51,000; low: $50).
Fields of interest: Arts and culture; Education; Environment; Foundations; Nonprofits; Christianity; Human services; Child welfare.
Type of support: Regranting.
Limitations: Applications not accepted. No grants to individuals.
Application information: Unsolicited requests for funds not accepted.
Trustees: Alan Merkle Breedlove; Ann M. Breedlove; Howell A. Breedlove; John Adams Breedlove; Mark Howell Breedlove; William Parker Breedlove; Ann Marie Garbin.
EIN: 251661386

7891
Bridge Builders Community Foundation
(formerly Venango Area Community Foundation)
206 Seneca St., National Transit Bldg. Annex, Ste. 10
P.O Box 374
Oil City, PA   16301-1367   (814) 677-8687
Contact: Jeanne Best, Opers. Dir.
FAX: (814) 677-0653;
E-mail: execdirbbcf@gmail.com; Main URL: http://www.bridgebuilderscommunityfoundations.org
Facebook: https://www.facebook.com/B.B.CommunityFoundations?ref=profile
Twitter: http://twitter.com/BBCF

Established in 1975 in Pennsylvania.
Foundation type: Community foundation.
Financial data (yr. ended 08/30/13): Assets, $5,876,108 (M); gifts received, $827,370; expenditures, $456,855; giving activities include $168,873 for 11+ grants (high: $35,595), and $155,945 for 261 grants to individuals.
Purpose and activities: The foundation seeks to contribute to the quality of life in the Venango, Clarion and Forest Counties, PA.
Fields of interest: Arts and culture; Education; Higher education; Community and economic development; Religion; Sports and recreation; Human services.
Type of support: Endowments; Scholarships; Student aid.
Limitations: Applications accepted. Giving limited to Clarion, Forest and Venango counties, PA.
Publications: Application guidelines; Annual report; Informational brochure.
Application information: Visit the foundation's web site for more information. Application form required.
  Copies of proposal: 1

Deadline(s): Late Summer
Board meeting date(s): Monthly
Officers and Trustees: Dr. Charles Marlin, Pres. and Trustee; Joe Keebler, Esq., V.P. and Trustee; Susan Williams, Secy. and Trustee; Rev. Jerry Belloit, Treas. and Trustee; Trenton Moulin, Exec. Dir.; Dorry Foster; Dr. William Kaufman; Lynn McCaslin; Norm Wimer.
Number of staff: 2 full-time professional.
EIN: 251292553

7892
Margaret Briggs Foundation
c/o PNC Bank, N.A.
620 Liberty Ave., 10th Fl.
Pittsburgh, PA   15222-2722
Application address: Margaret Briggs Foundation, c/o PNC Bank, P.O. Box 937, Scranton, PA 18501, tel.: (570) 961-7337

Established in 1969 in Pennsylvania.
Donor: Margaret Briggs†.
Foundation type: Independent foundation.
Financial data (yr. ended 12/31/13): Assets, $12,277,014 (M); expenditures, $513,466; qualifying distributions, $450,637; giving activities include $441,250 for 46 grants (high: $50,000; low: $750).
Fields of interest: Education; Medical education; Nonprofits; Rehabilitation; Diseases and conditions; Housing development; Human services; Youth development; Youth services.
Type of support: Regranting.
Limitations: Applications accepted. Giving limited to the greater Scranton/Lackawanna County, PA, area.
Publications: Application guidelines.
Application information:
  Initial approach: Proposal
  Copies of proposal: 6
  Deadline(s): None
  Board meeting date(s): Quarterly
Directors: William J. Calpin; James Fleming; Thomas G. Gallagher; Judith O. Graziano; Kevin E. Rogers.
EIN: 232719328

7893
Richard G. & Audrey A. Brinkman Foundation
c/o Glenmede Trust Co., N.A.
1650 Market St., Ste. 1200
Philadelphia, PA   19103-7391

Donor: Richard G. Brinkman Trust.
Foundation type: Independent foundation.
Financial data (yr. ended 12/31/14): Assets, $4,760,542; expenditures, $271,479; qualifying distributions, $245,936.
Fields of interest: Child welfare; Adolescents.
Limitations: Applications not accepted. Giving primarily in PA.
Application information: Unsolicited requests for funds not accepted.
Trustee: The Glenmede Trust Co., N.A.
EIN: 306170580

7894
The Britton Family Foundation
c/o J.E. Spoden
100 State St., Ste. 700
Erie, PA   16507-1459
Contact: Suzanne E. Britton, Pres.

Established in 1989 in Pennsylvania.
Donor: John E. Britton.
Foundation type: Independent foundation.
Financial data (yr. ended 12/31/13): Assets, $3,812,203 (M); expenditures, $209,061; qualifying distributions, $183,000; giving activities include $178,000 for 28 grants (high: $100,000; low: $500).
Fields of interest: Arts and culture; Health; Human services.
Type of support: General support.
Limitations: Applications accepted. Giving limited to the Lee County, FL area, and the Erie, PA area. No grants to individuals.
Application information: Application form required.
  Initial approach: Letter
  Copies of proposal: 3
  Deadline(s): Nov. 15
  Board meeting date(s): June and Dec.
Officers and Directors: Suzanne E. Britton, Pres. and Director; Judith B. Bonanno, V.P. and Secy. and Director; John W. Britton, V.P. and Treas. and Director; James E. Spoden, Esq., Treas. and Director.
EIN: 251618532

7895
The Broadbent Family Foundation
(formerly The Broadbent Foundation)
15 Chestnut Hill Dr.
Mohnton, PA   19540-9330   (610) 796-7682

Established in 1992 in Pennsylvania.
Donor: John H. Broadbent, Jr.
Foundation type: Independent foundation.
Financial data (yr. ended 06/30/14): Assets, $2,825,116; expenditures, $142,002; qualifying distributions, $129,852.
Purpose and activities: Scholarship awards for residents of Berk County and who are graduates of Governor Mifflin High School, Shillington, Pennsylvania.
Fields of interest: Education.
Type of support: Student aid.
Limitations: Applications accepted. Giving primarily to Berks County, PA.
Application information: Application form required.
  Initial approach: Completed application form
  Deadline(s): None
Trustees: John H. Broadbent, Jr.; Richard L. Broadbent; Dana L. Bunting.
EIN: 232703271

7896
The Solomon and Sylvia Bronstein Foundation
c/o Glenmeade Trust Co., N.A.
1650 Market St., Ste. 1200
Philadelphia, PA   19103-7391

Established in 1985 in Pennsylvania.
Donor: Solomon Bronstein†.
Foundation type: Independent foundation.

Financial data (yr. ended 06/30/14): Assets, $6,327,501 (M); expenditures, $359,259; qualifying distributions, $300,860; giving activities include $289,000 for 38 grants (high: $25,000; low: $2,500).
Purpose and activities: Giving primarily for Jewish organizations; funding also for education and the arts.
Fields of interest: Arts and culture; Education; Nonprofits; Judaism; Human services.
Type of support: Regranting.
Limitations: Applications not accepted. Giving primarily in Philadelphia, PA; some funding also in NY. No grants to individuals.
Application information: Unsolicited requests for funds not accepted.
Trustees: Gerald Broker; Joshua Broker; Matthew J. Comisky; Ian Comisky.
EIN: 222656339

7897
Brooks Family Foundation
3465 Treeline Dr.
Murrysville, PA   15668-1523   (724) 325-4490
Contact: Robert J. Brooks, Dir.

Established in 1995 in Pennsylvania.
Donor: Robert J. Brooks.
Foundation type: Independent foundation.
Financial data (yr. ended 12/31/13): Assets, $505,481 (M); expenditures, $356,151; qualifying distributions, $352,415; giving activities include $352,415 for 28 grants (high: $261,000; low: $20).
Fields of interest: Higher education; Health; Community and economic development; Human services; Senior services.
Limitations: Applications not accepted. No grants to individuals.
Application information: Unsolicited requests for funds not accepted.
Directors: Robert J. Brooks; Susan C. Brooks.
EIN: 251774477

7898
Brooks Foundation
c/o PNC Charitable Trusts
249 5th Ave.
1 PNC Plz., 20th Fl.
Pittsburgh, PA   15222   4127629161
E-mail: charitabletrusts@pnc.com; Application address: c/o PNC Bank, N.A., Charitable Trust Grant Review Comm., One PNC Plz., 20th Fl., 249 5th Ave., Pittsburgh, PA 15222, tel.: (412) 762-5157 or (513) 651-8463

Foundation type: Independent foundation.
Financial data (yr. ended 12/31/14): Assets, $4,988,634; expenditures, $286,075; qualifying distributions, $233,036 and $0 for set-asides.
Fields of interest: Arts and culture; Performing arts; Museums; Education; Higher education; Protestantism; Catholicism; Human services; Child welfare.
Type of support: General support.
Limitations: Applications accepted. Giving primarily in PA. No support for private foundations, or for fraternal, political, labor or advocacy groups. No grants to individuals, or for general operating costs or events.
Application information: Full proposals will not be accepted. Proposals will be invited upon review of

inquiry. See web site PNC.com, under "Corporate & Institutional", then under "Special Segments", click on "Non-profits and Government Institutions", and then "Charitable Trust Grants". Application form required.
Initial approach: Call or submit a letter of inquiry
Trustee: PNC Bank, N.A.
EIN: 256026627

7899
Cora L. Brooks Foundation
P.O. Box 399
Springtown, PA   18081   (610) 346-7158
Contact: Laura Herzog Kaplus, Dir.
E-mail: clbf@foundationoffices.org; Main URL: http://www.foundationoffices.org

Established in 1999 in Illinois.
Donor: Susan Hurd Cumings.
Foundation type: Independent foundation.
Financial data (yr. ended 12/31/14): Assets, $11,007,421; expenditures, $568,459; qualifying distributions, $516,191.
Purpose and activities: The foundation's primary interest is environmental conservation or restoration within the watersheds of the Delaware and Susquehanna Rivers, with particular emphasis on environmental protection issues relating to clean water and water related ecologies. The foundation prefers to support organizations whose annual revenue is $5 million or less.
Fields of interest: Environment; Natural resources; Toxic substance control; Rivers and lakes; Land resources; Biodiversity; Wildlife biodiversity; Aquatic wildlife protection; Bird preservation; Endangered species protection; Plant biodiversity; Forest preservation; Domesticated animals; Farmlands; Community beautification.
Type of support: Equipment; Matching grants; Emergency funds; Program development; Research; Capacity-building and technical assistance; Research and evaluation; Policy, advocacy and systems reform; Technical assistance.
Limitations: Applications not accepted. Giving within watersheds of the Delaware and Susquehanna Rivers, an area that includes 5 states. Please ensure that the project falls within this geographic area. No support for political organizations, or organizations whose revenue is greater than $5,000,000 (as shown on the organization's Form 990.). No grants to individuals, or for naming opportunities, multi-year pledges, school or public education programs or any education-related request, or for ongoing support.
Application information: The foundation will not be accepting grant proposals in 2015.
Board meeting date(s): Annual
Trustees: Elizabeth Bray; Susan Cumings; Douglas Law; Bank of America, N.A.
Director: Laura Herzog Kaplus.
Number of staff: 1 full-time professional; 1 part-time professional.
EIN: 367256643

7900
The Brossman Family Charitable Trust for Scholarships
c/o Ephrata National Bank
P.O. Box 457
Ephrata, PA   17522-0457
Application address: c/o ENB Money Mgmt. Group, 47 E. Main St., Ephrata, PA 17522-2713, tel.: (717) 733-6576

Established in 1986 in Pennsylvania.
Donor: William and Jemima Brossman Charitable Foundation.
Foundation type: Independent foundation.
Financial data (yr. ended 10/31/13): Assets, $0 (M); gifts received, $376,175; expenditures, $376,175; qualifying distributions, $376,175; giving activities include $354,500 for 120 grants to individuals (high: $3,000; low: $1,500).
Fields of interest: Higher education.
Type of support: Student aid.
Limitations: Applications accepted. Giving limited to residents of the Ephrata, PA, area.
Application information: Student must be a high school graduate and resident of Ephrata area school district, Ephrata, PA, or of a high school served by Denver & Ephrata Telephone & Telegraph Co. Application form required.
Initial approach: Application can be obtained from selection committee
Deadline(s): June 15
Trustee: The Ephrata National Bank.
EIN: 232860047

7901
James and Noel Browne Charitable Trust
36 Newgate Rd.
Pittsburgh, PA   15202-1002   (412) 367-3880
Contact: James J. Browne, Tr.

Donors: James J. Browne; Noel W. Browne.
Foundation type: Independent foundation.
Financial data (yr. ended 12/31/13): Assets, $2,498,067 (M); gifts received, $201,215; expenditures, $202,308; qualifying distributions, $200,000; giving activities include $200,000 for 1 grant.
Fields of interest: Higher education; Youth development.
Limitations: Applications accepted. Giving primarily in PA. No grants to individuals.
Application information:
Initial approach: Proposal
Deadline(s): None
Trustees: James J. Browne; Noel W. Browne.
EIN: 256797452

7902
Ben F. Bryer Foundation
c/o BNY Mellon, N.A.
P.O. Box 185
Pittsburgh, PA   15230-0185

Established in 2003 in New York.
Donor: Ben F. Bryer†.
Foundation type: Independent foundation.
Financial data (yr. ended 05/31/14): Assets, $5,882,046 (M); expenditures, $325,394; qualifying distributions, $287,321; giving activities include $270,000 for 4 grants (high: $125,000; low: $25,000).

Fields of interest: University education; Pediatrics; Libraries; Public libraries.

Type of support: General support; Research.

Limitations: Applications not accepted. Giving primarily in IL, IN, MI and NY. No grants to individuals.

Application information: Unsolicited requests for funds not accepted.

Trustee: BNY Mellon, N.A.

EIN: 137384132

7903
Caroline Alexander Buck Foundation

1600 Market St., Ste. 3600
Philadelphia, PA   19103-7212   (215) 751-2085
Contact: Bruce A. Rosenfield Esq., Dir.

Donors: Caroline A. Churchman†; W. Morgan Churchman.

Foundation type: Independent foundation.

Financial data (yr. ended 12/31/14): Assets, $11,466,688 (M); expenditures, $374,105; qualifying distributions, $529,073; giving activities include $320,731 for 13 grants (high: $257,837; low: $3,447), and $191,281 for 1 loan/ program-related investment.

Purpose and activities: Giving primarily for education and social services.

Fields of interest: Education; Elementary education; Protestantism; Human services.

Type of support: In-kind gifts.

Limitations: Applications accepted. Giving primarily in PA, with emphasis on the greater metropolitan Philadelphia area. No grants to individuals.

Application information: Application guidelines are available upon request.

Initial approach: Proposal
Deadline(s): None
Board meeting date(s): Spring and fall

Directors: J. Alexander Churchman; Lee Stirling Churchman; Leidy McIlvaine Churchman; W. Morgan Churchman; George Connell; Gordon L. Keen, Jr., Esq.; Wendy Mackey; Beverly Anne McConnell; Bruce A. Rosenfield, Esq.; Binney H.C. Wietlisbach.

EIN: 236257115

7904
The Helen R. Buck Foundation

c/o Glenmede Trust Co., N.A.
1650 Market St., Ste. 1200
Philadelphia, PA   19103-7391   (215) 419-6000

Established in 1992 in Pennsylvania.

Donor: Helen R. Buck†.

Foundation type: Independent foundation.

Financial data (yr. ended 12/31/14): Assets, $3,950,470; expenditures, $180,021; qualifying distributions, $171,201.

Fields of interest: Museums; Historic preservation; Education; Environment; Fire prevention and control; Christianity.

Application information:

Initial approach: Proposal
Deadline(s): None

Trustees: C. Austin Buck II; Martha B. Bartlett; Nancy B. Pyne; The Glenmede Trust Co.

EIN: 237693437

7905
Bucks County Foundation

60 E. Court St.
P.O. Box 2073
Doylestown, PA   18901   (215) 997-8566
Contact: Linda Goodwin, Exec. Dir.
FAX: (215) 997-8564;
E-mail: lg@buckscountyfoundation.org; Main
URL: http://www.buckscountyfoundation.org

Established in 1979 in Pennsylvania.

Foundation type: Community foundation.

Financial data (yr. ended 12/31/12): Assets, $11,313,113 (M); gifts received, $45,777; expenditures, $536,957; giving activities include $341,526 for 18+ grants (high: $34,000).

Purpose and activities: The foundation seeks to enhance the quality of life for residents of the county by stimulating philanthropic opportunity and developing long-term financial assets to meet a wide range of the community's charitable needs.

Fields of interest: Arts and culture; Higher education; Environment; Health; Community and economic development; Human services.

Type of support: Scholarships; Matching grants; Publications; Program development; Capacity-building and technical assistance; General support; Equipment; Endowments; Convening; Capital campaigns; Capital and infrastructure; Annual campaigns.

Limitations: Applications accepted. Giving limited to the Bucks County, PA area. No support for religious purposes. No grants for deficit financing, advertising publications, or research.

Publications: Application guidelines; Annual report; Financial statement; Informational brochure.

Application information: Delaware Valley Grantmakers Common Grant Application Form accepted. Visit foundation web site for application guidelines. Application form required.

Initial approach: Submit application form and attachments
Copies of proposal: 1
Deadline(s): Jan. 15 and July 15
Board meeting date(s): Mar., July, Sept., and Dec.
Final notification: 60 days

Officers and Distribution Committee Members: Grace Deon, Esq., Pres. and Director; Ron Bolig, Esq., Treas. and Director; Linda Goodwin, Exec. Dir.; Frederick Breitenfeld, Jr.; John Detweiler; Jere Hohmann; Lucy Steitz; Peter Van Dire, J.D.

Trustees: Bank of New York; First National Bank and Trust of Newtown; First Savings Bank of Perkasie; PNC; Univest; Wells Fargo.

EIN: 239031005

7906
Burket-Plack Foundation Inc.

c/o Glenmede Trust Co., N.A.
1650 Market St., Ste. 1200
Philadelphia, PA   19103-7391   (215) 419-6000
Contact: Nina Cohen

Established in 1993 in Pennsylvania.

Donor: Carmen W. Burket†.

Foundation type: Independent foundation.

Financial data (yr. ended 12/31/13): Assets, $7,794,874 (M); expenditures, $413,953; qualifying distributions, $343,976; giving activities include $333,000 for 35 grants (high: $40,000; low: $1,500).

Purpose and activities: Giving for the prevention of cruelty to animals and for the preservation of the environment.

Fields of interest: Environment; Animal welfare.

Type of support: General support.

Limitations: Applications accepted. Giving primarily in Philadelphia, PA. No grants to individuals.

Application information:

Initial approach: Proposal
Deadline(s): None

Directors: Barbara Reibman; Nancy C. Smith; Howard Wellens.

EIN: 232735643

7907
Burkholder Family Foundation

7615 Lancaster Ave.
P.O. Box 465
Myerstown, PA   17067

Established in 2009 in Pennsylvania.

Donors: Melvin S. Burkholder; Corby Burkholder; Matthew V. Burkholder; Dutch Valley Food Distributors Inc.; Lane Burkholder.

Foundation type: Independent foundation.

Financial data (yr. ended 12/31/13): Assets, $809,539 (M); gifts received, $403,890; expenditures, $389,637; qualifying distributions, $360,621; giving activities include $360,621 for 11 grants (high: $200,000; low: $5,250).

Fields of interest: Fire prevention and control.

Limitations: Applications not accepted. Giving primarily in PA.

Application information: Unsolicited requests for funds not accepted.

Officers: Melvin S. Burkholder, Pres.; Matthew V. Burkholder, V.P.; Lane Burkholder, Secy.; Corby Burkholder, Treas.

EIN: 262899494

7908
Butz Foundation

P.O. Box 509
Allentown, PA   18105-0509

Established in 1997 in Pennsylvania.

Donors: Lee A. Butz; Dolores A. Butz; Alvin H. Butz, Inc.

Foundation type: Independent foundation.

Financial data (yr. ended 06/30/13): Assets, $565,548 (M); gifts received, $750,000; expenditures, $344,181; qualifying distributions, $344,181; giving activities include $341,916 for 20 grants (high: $82,000; low: $1,000).

Fields of interest: Higher education; Nonprofits; Business promotion.

Type of support: Regranting.

Limitations: Applications not accepted. Giving primarily in PA. No grants to individuals.

Application information: Contributes only to pre-selected organizations.

Officers: Greg L. Butz, Pres.; Eric R. Butz, V.P.; Lee A. Butz, V.P.; Shari L. Butz, V.P.; Dolores A. Butz, Secy.

EIN: 232940646

7909
Calligan Family Foundation
P.O. Box 1873
Cranberry Township, PA   16066-0873   (412)
391-2920
Contact: Scott R. Calligan, Dir.

Established in 2003 in Pennsylvania.
Donors: Marian E. Calligan; Scott R. Calligan.
Foundation type: Independent foundation.
Financial data (yr. ended 07/31/13): Assets,
$3,533,576 (M); gifts received, $200,000;
expenditures, $331,644; qualifying distributions,
$307,500; giving activities include $307,500 for 6
grants (high: $250,000; low: $2,500).
Fields of interest: Education.
Type of support: Research.
Limitations: Applications accepted. Giving primarily
in PA.
Application information:
  Initial approach: Proposal
  Deadline(s): None
Directors: Marian E. Calligan; Scott R. Calligan.
EIN: 200224570

7910
Stephen G. Calvert Memorial Merit Scholarship Foundation
5 Tower Bridge, 300 Barr Harbor Dr., Ste. 600
West Conshohocken, PA   19428-2998

Established in 1996 in Pennsylvania.
Donors: Keystone Foods Corp.; Keystone Foods
LLC.
Foundation type: Company-sponsored foundation.
Financial data (yr. ended 10/31/14): Assets,
$5,530 (M); gifts received, $180,000;
expenditures, $190,797; giving activities include
$183,000 for grants to individuals.
Purpose and activities: The foundation awards
college scholarships to dependents of employees of
Keystone Foods.
Fields of interest: Higher education.
Type of support: Scholarships; Employee-related
scholarships.
Limitations: Applications not accepted. Giving
limited to areas of company operations in AL, GA,
KY, MI, NC, and PA.
Application information: Contributes only through
employee-related scholarships. Application form
required.
  Initial approach: Letter
  Deadline(s): None
Officers: Edward M. Delate, Pres.; Donna Curtis,
Secy.; Frank Pelone, Treas.
Director: Charles Wallace.
EIN: 232816413

7911
Alpin J. and Alpin W. Cameron Memorial Fund
c/o PNC Bank
620 Liberty Ave., 10th Fl.
Pittsburgh, PA   15222-2705   (412) 768-8192
Contact: Amy Rees

Established in 1957 in Pennsylvania.
Donors: Alpin W. Cameron†; Alpin J. Cameron†.
Foundation type: Independent foundation.
Financial data (yr. ended 09/30/13): Assets,
$4,404,508 (M); expenditures, $249,604;

qualifying distributions, $199,343; giving activities
include $192,000 for 89 grants (high: $10,000;
low: $500).
Purpose and activities: Primary areas of interest
include education, science, literary, and charitable
(aid to the needy).
Fields of interest: Arts and culture; Museums;
Humanities; Literature and writing; Education;
Higher education; Environment; Health; Hospital
care; Diseases and conditions; Libraries; Human
services; Youth services.
Limitations: Applications accepted. Giving primarily
in the Philadelphia, PA, area.
Application information: Application form required.
  Initial approach: Letter
  Deadline(s): None
  Board meeting date(s): 4 to 5 times per year
Trustee: PNC Bank, N.A.
Board Members: Jonathan H. Sprogell; Margaret
Anne Van Denbergh; Ross Van Denbergh; Margaret
Walton-Ralph.
EIN: 236213225

7912
Charles Talbot Campbell Charitable Foundation
c/o PNC Bank, N.A.
P.O. Box 609
Pittsburgh, PA   15230-9738

Established in 1975 in Pennsylvania.
Donor: Charles Talbot Campbell†.
Foundation type: Independent foundation.
Financial data (yr. ended 01/31/14): Assets,
$7,906,689 (M); expenditures, $371,157;
qualifying distributions, $351,035; giving activities
include $333,000 for 16 grants (high: $75,000;
low: $2,500).
Purpose and activities: Emphasis on agencies for
the handicapped, youth music programs, and
ophthalmological research.
Fields of interest: Arts and culture; Education; Youth
development.
Type of support: General support; Continuing
support; Research.
Limitations: Applications not accepted. Giving
primarily in western PA. No support for community
funds. No grants to individuals; no loans.
Application information: Unsolicited requests for
funds not accepted.
Trustee: PNC Bank, N.A.
EIN: 251287221

7913
Joseph H. Cannon Charitable Trust
c/o PNC Bank, N.A.
P.O. Box 609
Pittsburgh, PA   15230-9738

Foundation type: Independent foundation.
Financial data (yr. ended 10/31/13): Assets,
$4,601,262 (M); expenditures, $230,385;
qualifying distributions, $215,632; giving activities
include $203,364 for 3 grants (high: $67,788; low:
$67,788).
Fields of interest: Religion; Human services.
Type of support: General support.
Limitations: Applications not accepted. Giving
primarily in Champaign, IL.
Application information: Unsolicited requests for
funds not accepted.

Trustee: PNC Bank, N.A.
EIN: 376378428

7914
Cardinal O'Hara Scholarship Fund
c/o William R. Sasso
2005 Market St., Ste. 2600
Philadelphia, PA   19103-7018

Foundation type: Independent foundation.
Financial data (yr. ended 06/30/13): Assets,
$387,472 (M); expenditures, $156,952; qualifying
distributions, $152,101; giving activities include
$152,101 for 1 grant.
Fields of interest: Education.
Limitations: Applications not accepted.
Application information: Unsolicited requests for
funds not accepted.
Trustee: William R. Sasso.
EIN: 452754224

7915
Carita Foundation
c/o BNY Mellon, N.A
P.O. Box 185
Pittsburgh, PA   15230-0185

Foundation type: Independent foundation.
Financial data (yr. ended 06/30/14): Assets,
$4,650,698 (M); expenditures, $230,431;
qualifying distributions, $214,487; giving activities
include $208,600 for 32 grants (high: $30,000;
low: $1,000).
Fields of interest: Education; Environment; Animal
welfare; Health; Females; Female children and
youth.
Type of support: General support.
Limitations: Applications not accepted. Giving
primarily in PA. No grants to individuals.
Application information: Contributes only to
pre-selected organizations.
Trustees: Mr. Robert C. Legnini; Mrs. Robert C.
Legnini.
EIN: 020733877

7916
Gunard Berry Carlson Memorial Foundation, Inc.
350 Marshallton-Thorndale Rd.
Downingtown, PA   19335-2063

Established in 1957 in Pennsylvania.
Foundation type: Independent foundation.
Financial data (yr. ended 12/31/12): Assets,
$2,799,223 (M); expenditures, $216,543;
qualifying distributions, $114,450; giving activities
include $114,450 for 12 grants (high: $30,000;
low: $1,600).
Fields of interest: Secondary education; Higher
education; Health; Hospital care; Catholicism.
Type of support: Scholarships; Program
development; General support; Equipment; Capital
campaigns; Capital and infrastructure; Annual
campaigns.
Limitations: Applications not accepted. Giving
primarily in PA. No grants to individuals.
Application information: Contributes only to
pre-selected organizations.
  Board meeting date(s): May 15 & Nov. 15

Officers and Directors: Frederick C. Travaglini, Pres.; Gunard C. Travaglini, V.P.; Barbara Travaglini, Secy.-Treas.; A.F. Travaglini.
EIN: 236261693

7917
Carnahan-Jackson Foundation
c/o Northwest Savings Bank, N.A.
1030 State St., Ste. 1
Erie, PA 16501-1840
Application address: P.O. Box 3326, Jamestown, NY 14702-3326, tel.: (716) 483-1015

Established in 1972 in New York.
Donor: Katharine J. Carnahan†.
Foundation type: Independent foundation.
Financial data (yr. ended 07/31/13): Assets, $11,494,960 (M); expenditures, $580,445; qualifying distributions, $549,354; giving activities include $423,870 for 41 grants (high: $50,000; low: $1,000).
Purpose and activities: Primary areas of interest include higher and other education, libraries, hospitals, and youth; support also for the handicapped, drug abuse programs, ecology, housing, community development, dance and other performing arts groups, and church support; some support for certain prior interests of the donor.
Fields of interest: Performing arts; Education; Higher education; Hospital care; Christianity; Human services; Child welfare.
Type of support: General support; Matching grants; Continuing support; Capital campaigns; Capital and infrastructure; Equipment; Program development; Seed money; Curriculum development; Scholarships.
Limitations: Applications accepted. Giving primarily in Chautauqua County, NY, particularly in the Jamestown area. No grants to individuals.
Publications: Application guidelines; Grants list.
Application information:
  Initial approach: Letter
  Copies of proposal: 8
  Deadline(s): June and Sept.
  Board meeting date(s): June and Dec.
Trustee: Northwest Savings Bank, N.A.
Number of staff: 2 part-time professional; 1 part-time support.
EIN: 166151608

7918
James W. Case Trust
c/o BNY Mellon, N.A.
P.O. Box 185
Pittsburgh, PA 15230-0185

Foundation type: Independent foundation.
Financial data (yr. ended 06/30/13): Assets, $4,412,298 (M); expenditures, $241,311; qualifying distributions, $223,398; giving activities include $213,533 for 4 grants (high: $106,767; low: $21,353).
Fields of interest: Health; Children's hospital care; Human services; Children.
Limitations: Applications not accepted. Giving primarily in FL and PA.
Application information: Unsolicited requests for funds not accepted.
Trustee: BNY Mellon, N.A.
EIN: 256031784

7919
Lucy H. Casteel Foundation
c/o PNC Bank, N.A.
P.O. Box 609
Pittsburgh, PA 15230-9738

Foundation type: Independent foundation.
Financial data (yr. ended 12/31/14): Assets, $6,226,472; expenditures, $325,331; qualifying distributions, $278,243 and $0 for set-asides.
Fields of interest: Education; Higher education; Religion; Christianity; Human services.
Type of support: General support.
Limitations: Applications not accepted. Giving primarily in PA, TN and VA.
Application information: Unsolicited requests for funds not accepted.
Trustee: PNC Bank, N.A.
EIN: 251775628

7920
Julius & Ray Charlestein Foundation
1710 Romano Dr.
Plymouth Meeting, PA 19462-2822 (610) 239-6000
Contact: Ellyn Phillips, Exec. Dir.

Established in 1963 in Pennsylvania.
Donors: Premier Dental Products Co.; Premier Medical Co.; Morton L. Charlestein.
Foundation type: Company-sponsored foundation.
Financial data (yr. ended 06/30/14): Assets, $3,332,717 (M); gifts received, $390,000; expenditures, $444,396; qualifying distributions, $401,151; giving activities include $401,151 for grants.
Purpose and activities: The foundation supports organizations involved with education, ALS, human services, and Judaism.
Fields of interest: Education; Secondary education; Graduate and professional education; Nonprofits; ALS; Judaism; Theology; Human services.
Type of support: General support; Annual campaigns; Program development; Scholarships; Regranting.
Limitations: Applications accepted. Giving primarily in the Philadelphia, PA, area. No grants to individuals.
Application information:
  Initial approach: Proposal
  Deadline(s): None
Officers: Gary Charlestein, Secy.-Treas.; Ellyn Phillips, Exec. Dir.
EIN: 232310090

7921
Alice P. Chase Trust
c/o BNY Mellon, NA
P.O. Box 185
Pittsburgh, PA 15230-0185

Established in 1956 in Massachusetts.
Donor: Alice P. Chase†.
Foundation type: Independent foundation.
Financial data (yr. ended 08/31/14): Assets, $6,741,458 (M); expenditures, $302,638; qualifying distributions, $253,567; giving activities include $240,000 for 7 grants (high: $50,000; low: $20,000).
Purpose and activities: Giving primarily for education, youth services, and homeless support.

Fields of interest: Education; Community and economic development; Housing development; Human services; Youth services; Domestic violence shelters; People with disabilities; People with vision impairments.
Type of support: General support; Capital campaigns; Capital and infrastructure; Equipment; Program development; Technical assistance.
Limitations: Applications not accepted. Giving limited to the greater Boston, MA, area. No grants to individuals or for matching gifts; no loans.
Application information: Contributes only to pre-selected organizations.
Trustee: BNY Mellon, N.A.
EIN: 046093897

7922
C.C. Chenault, Jr. Agricultural Foundation
c/o PNC Bank, N.A.
P.O. Box 609
Pittsburgh, PA 15230-9738

Foundation type: Independent foundation.
Financial data (yr. ended 08/31/14): Assets, $3,675,434 (M); expenditures, $188,781; qualifying distributions, $168,368; giving activities include $155,395 for 1 grant.
Fields of interest: Education.
Type of support: General support.
Limitations: Applications not accepted. Giving limited to KY.
Application information: Contributes only to pre-selected organizations.
Trustee: PNC Bank, N.A.
EIN: 616102245

7923
Child Development Foundation
(also known as Child Development Foundation)
(formerly Child Development Center)
2500 DeKalb Pike, Ste. 100
Norristown, PA 19401-2007 (610) 277-4000
Contact: Trish Ewing, Exec. Asst.
E-mail: ewing@childdevelopmentfoundation.org;
Main URL: http://www.childdevelopmentfoundation.org

Established in 1987 in Pennsylvania.
Foundation type: Independent foundation.
Financial data (yr. ended 06/30/13): Assets, $7,706,939 (M); gifts received, $120; expenditures, $468,421; qualifying distributions, $372,592; giving activities include $350,985 for 39 grants (high: $35,000; low: $2,000).
Purpose and activities: Giving limited to organizations aiding disabled or handicapped children.
Fields of interest: Child educational development; Child welfare; Child development; Children and youth; Infants and toddlers; Adolescents; Female children and youth; Female infants and toddlers; Female young adults; Male children and youth; Male infants and toddlers; Male young adults; People with disabilities; People with physical disabilities; People with vision impairments; People with psychosocial disabilities.
Type of support: General support; Equipment; Program development.
Limitations: Applications accepted. Giving limited to Montgomery County, PA. No grants to individuals, or

for capital campaigns, debt service, or multi-year commitments.

Publications: Application guidelines; Financial statement; Informational brochure (including application guidelines).

Application information: Application form required.
Initial approach: Request application
Copies of proposal: 13
Deadline(s): Mar. 31
Board meeting date(s): Varies
Final notification: Mid-June

Officers and Directors: Joseph M. Dimino, Pres. and Director; R. Kurtz Holloway, Esq., V.P. and Director; Sandra Zuchero, Secy.-Treas. and Director; Joanne E. Bryers; Matthew Cappelletti, Jr.; Mark Constable; Wendy Davis; J. David Farrell, Esq.; Christine P. Wiegand, Esq.; Deborah Young, MD.

Number of staff: 1 part-time support.

EIN: 231539361

7924
The Clareth Fund: The Philadelphia Association of Zeta Psi Fraternity

30 S. 17th St.
Philadelphia, PA   19103-4196
Contact: Frank G. Cooper, Esq.

Foundation type: Independent foundation.

Financial data (yr. ended 12/31/13): Assets, $5,454,669 (M); expenditures, $300,114; qualifying distributions, $237,297; giving activities include $40,000 for 2 grants (high: $20,000; low: $20,000), and $183,250 for 39 grants for individuals (high: $7,000; low: $250).

Fields of interest: Graduate and professional education.

Type of support: General support; Loans to individuals; Student aid.

Limitations: Applications not accepted. Giving limited to PA.

Application information: Unsolicited requests for funds not accepted.

Officers and Directors: McBee Butcher, Pres. and Director; Peter B. Pakradooni, V.P.; Gregory E. McElroy, Secy. and Director; James P. Bodine, Treas.; Andrew Biros; R. Carter Caldwell; Richard L. Guest; Dr. Kenneth Kazahaya; Dr. Masayuki Kazahaya; David L. Sims; Jonathan R. Stott.

EIN: 232092500

7925
Clark Associates Charitable Foundation

c/o Fred E. Clark
2205 Old Philadelphia Pike
Lancaster, PA   17602-3416
Main URL: http://www.clarkassociatesinc.biz/charitablefoundation.html

Established in 2001 in Pennsylvania.

Donors: Fred E. Clark; Commercial Stainless, Inc.; Hawk Industries, Inc.; Calumet Enterprises Inc.; Clark Associates, Inc.; The Webstaurant Store Inc.; Noble Chemical Inc.; 11400, Inc.

Foundation type: Company-sponsored foundation.

Financial data (yr. ended 12/31/13): Assets, $2,429,847 (M); gifts received, $952,630; expenditures, $386,376; qualifying distributions, $386,017; giving activities include $386,017 for 93 grants (high: $50,000; low: $50).

Purpose and activities: The foundation supports fire departments and organizations involved with arts

and culture, education, health, human services, and Christianity.

Fields of interest: Arts and culture; Orchestral music; Education; Higher education; Health; Fire prevention and control; Christianity; Human services; Homeless services.

Type of support: General support.

Limitations: Applications not accepted. Giving primarily in Lancaster, PA.

Application information: Contributes only to pre-selected organizations.

Trustees: Elizabeth A. Clark; Fred E. Clark.

EIN: 256773373

7926
Andrew L. Clark Family Charitable Trust
(formerly Clark Family Charitable Trust)

c/o BNY Mellon, N.A.
P.O. Box 185
Pittsburgh, PA   15230-0185
Application address: c/o BNY Mellon, N.A., Attn.: Grace Allen, 200 Park Ave., New York, NY 10166, tel.: (212) 922-8143

Established in 1989 in New Jersey.

Donor: Andrew L. Clark.

Foundation type: Independent foundation.

Financial data (yr. ended 08/31/13): Assets, $4,423,830 (M); expenditures, $241,726; qualifying distributions, $225,168; giving activities include $215,000 for 3 grants (high: $72,000; low: $71,000).

Purpose and activities: Giving primarily for education and youth services.

Fields of interest: Education; Secondary education; Family services; Child welfare; Special population support.

Limitations: Applications accepted. Giving primarily in West Orange, NJ, and New York, NY. No grants to individuals.

Application information: Application form required.
Initial approach: Letter
Copies of proposal: 2
Deadline(s): None

Trustee: BNY Mellon, N.A.

EIN: 136948420

7927
The Clark Family Foundation

1475 River Rd.
P.O. Box 466
Marietta, PA   17547-9401   (717) 426-5200
Contact: Merrell F. Clark, Pres.

Established in 2004 in Pennsylvania.

Donor: Merrell F. Clark.

Foundation type: Independent foundation.

Financial data (yr. ended 12/31/13): Assets, $6,028,771 (M); gifts received, $618,000; expenditures, $459,062; qualifying distributions, $395,675; giving activities include $395,675 for 18 grants (high: $76,500; low: $300).

Fields of interest: Public libraries; Christianity; Human services; Child care.

Type of support: General support.

Limitations: Applications accepted. Giving primarily in PA. No grants to individuals.

Application information: Application form required.
Initial approach: Letter
Deadline(s): None

Officers: Merrell F. Clark, Pres.; Doris D. Clark, V.P.; Ann M. Clark, Secy.; Jennifer C. Hessinger, Treas.

EIN: 201658721

7928
Bryn Clovis Foundation, Inc.

c/o BNY Mellon, N.A.
P.O. Box 185
Pittsburgh, PA   15230-0185

Foundation type: Independent foundation.

Financial data (yr. ended 06/30/14): Assets, $3,273,406 (M); expenditures, $154,512; qualifying distributions, $147,446; giving activities include $143,905 for 16 grants (high: $25,000; low: $1,905).

Fields of interest: Education; Animal welfare; Health; Christianity.

Limitations: Applications not accepted. Giving primarily in PA. No grants to individuals.

Application information: Unsolicited requests for funds not accepted.

Trustee: Elizabeth Moran.

EIN: 830413632

7929
CNB Foundation Inc.

1 S. 2nd St.
P.O. Box 42
Clearfield, PA   16830-2355

Donors: CNB Financial Corp.; CNB Bank.

Foundation type: Independent foundation.

Financial data (yr. ended 12/31/13): Assets, $482,585 (M); gifts received, $309,917; expenditures, $221,190; qualifying distributions, $221,190; giving activities include $220,420 for 42 grants (high: $37,200; low: $500).

Fields of interest: Education; Nonprofits; Health; Hospital care; Disasters and emergency management; Adolescents.

Type of support: Capital campaigns; Annual campaigns; Regranting.

Limitations: Applications not accepted. Giving primarily in PA.

Application information: Unsolicited requests for funds not accepted.

Officers: Vincent C. Turiano, Chair. and C.E.O.; Mary Ann Conaway, Secy.; Brian W. Wingard, Treas.

Directors: Joseph B. Bower, Jr.; Mark D. Breakey; Richard L. Greslick, Jr.

EIN: 272417365

7930
George F. Coffin, Jr. & Claire E. Coffin Trust

P.O. Box 3215
Lancaster, PA   17604-3216

Established in 2007 in Pennsylvania.

Foundation type: Independent foundation.

Financial data (yr. ended 12/31/13): Assets, $2,964,166 (M); expenditures, $166,988; qualifying distributions, $138,185; giving activities include $138,185 for 5 grants (high: $27,637; low: $27,637).

Fields of interest: Animal welfare; Health care administration and financing; Children; Females.

Limitations: Applications not accepted. Giving primarily in PA. No grants to individuals.

Application information: Unsolicited requests for funds not accepted.
Trustee: Fulton Bank, N.A.
EIN: 266147530

7931
Hannah S. and Samuel A. Cohn Memorial Foundation
2 E. Broad St., 6th Fl.
Hazleton, PA 18201-6530
FAX: (570) 459-0729;
E-mail: mdcohn@lbec-law.com

Established in 1987 in Pennsylvania.
Foundation type: Independent foundation.
Financial data (yr. ended 03/31/13): Assets, $9,073,214 (M); gifts received, $10,300; expenditures, $481,339; qualifying distributions, $395,915; giving activities include $393,331 for 38 grants (high: $110,000; low: $695).
Purpose and activities: Giving primarily to Jewish organizations, human services, hospitals, and higher education.
Fields of interest: Education; Nonprofits; Hospital care; Judaism; Antidiscrimination.
International interests: Israel.
Type of support: Annual campaigns; Capital campaigns; Capital and infrastructure; Endowments; Regranting; Emergency funds.
Limitations: Applications not accepted. Giving on a national basis; some giving also in Israel. No grants to individuals.
Publications: Annual report.
Application information: Contributes only to pre-selected organizations.
Officers: Gerald L. Cohn, Pres.; Martin D. Cohn, Secy.
Number of staff: None.
EIN: 232500519

7932
Columbia Healthcare Foundation Inc.
15 N. 3rd St.
Columbia, PA 17512-1103 (717) 684-2077
Contact: C. Edwin Swisher III, Treas.

Established in 1999 in Pennsylvania.
Foundation type: Independent foundation.
Financial data (yr. ended 06/30/13): Assets, $2,277,026 (M); expenditures, $184,469; qualifying distributions, $165,536; giving activities include $165,536 for 9 grants (high: $40,000; low: $2,036).
Purpose and activities: Giving to medical and related fields.
Fields of interest: Hospital care; Emergency care; Fire prevention and control.
Type of support: Capital campaigns.
Limitations: Applications accepted. Giving limited to the Lancaster County, PA, area.
Application information: Application form required.
  Initial approach: Telephone or letter
  Deadline(s): None
Officers: Paul H. Dellinger, Chair.; Philip H. Glatfelter II, Pres.; Jacques M. Geisenberger, Jr., Secy.; C. Edwin Swisher III, Treas.
Trustees: Michael Gerfin; John M. Jensen; William H. Kloidt, Jr.; Kevin Kraft; Robert M. Kuhn; Kathleen Lutz; Donald Nikolaus; Roseann Nikolaus; Lynn Wonsick.
EIN: 220485650

7933
Community Foundation of Greene County, Pennsylvania
108 E. High St.
P.O. Box 768
Waynesburg, PA 15370 (724) 627-2010
Contact: Bettie B. Stammerjohn, Exec. Dir.; An'Etta Neff, Admin. Asst.
FAX: (724) 627-2011; E-mail: cfgcpa@gmail.com; Main URL: http://www.cfgcpa.org

Established in 2000 in Pennsylvania.
Foundation type: Community foundation.
Financial data (yr. ended 12/31/13): Assets, $3,699,806 (M); gifts received, $442,815; expenditures, $632,629; giving activities include $257,921 for 7+ grants (high: $73,908), and $107,000 for 150 grants to individuals.
Purpose and activities: The foundation seeks to strengthen Greene County, PA by building charitable endowments, maximizing benefits to donors, making effective grants, and providing leadership to address community needs.
Fields of interest: Arts and culture; Education; Environment; Nonprofits; Health; Sustainable development; Economic development; Community improvement; Sports and recreation; Human services; Food aid; Food banks; Child welfare; Women's services.
Type of support: Building and renovations; Matching grants; Capacity-building and technical assistance; Equipment; Program development; Convening; Publications; Seed money; Curriculum development; Research; Technical assistance; Program evaluations; Student aid.
Limitations: Applications accepted. Giving primarily in Greene County, PA. No support for political organizations. No grants to individuals (except for scholarships), or for debt reduction, or capital campaign funds; no multi-year grants.
Publications: Application guidelines; Annual report; Financial statement; Grants list; Informational brochure; Newsletter; Occasional report; Program policy statement.
Application information: See web site www.cfgcpa.org for additional information. Application form required.
  Initial approach: Telephone
  Copies of proposal: 1
  Deadline(s): Feb. 27 for Homeless Fund; June 15 and Oct. 1 for Discretionary Grants; year-round for EITC Innovation Curriculum Grants
  Board meeting date(s): 3rd Thurs. of alternating months, beginning in Jan.
  Final notification: 6 weeks to 2 months
Officers and Directors: Nancy I. Davis, Ed.D., Chair. and Director; Connie Grimes, Vice-Chair. and Director; Thelma Szarell, Secy. and Director; Thomas G. Milinovich, Treas. and Director; Jeffrey Widdup, Asst. Treas.; Bettie B. Stammerjohn, Exec. Dir.; Mark Carlson; Linda Cofront; Kim Grimes; Morris Harper, MD; Jessica Johnson; Goldie Saesan; Chad Sethman, Ph.D; Dolly Throckmorton; Jim Zalar.
Number of staff: 1 full-time professional; 1 full-time support.
EIN: 251881899

7934
The Conestoga Road Foundation
c/o E.R. Boynton
30 Valley Stream Pkwy.
Malvern, PA 19355

Foundation type: Independent foundation.
Financial data (yr. ended 12/31/13): Assets, $6,715,313 (M); expenditures, $413,618; qualifying distributions, $315,000; giving activities include $315,000 for 13 grants (high: $110,000; low: $3,000).
Fields of interest: Education; Housing development; Human services.
Limitations: Applications not accepted. Giving primarily in NY and PA.
Application information: Unsolicited request for funds not accepted.
Officers and Directors: George R. Atterbury, Jr., Pres. and Director; Darsie L. Atterbury, Secy.-Treas. and Director.
EIN: 275271188

7935
John F. Connelly Scholarship Fund
1 Crown Way, Tax Dept.
Philadelphia, PA 19154-4599

Established in 1991 in Pennsylvania.
Donor: The Conelly Foundation.
Foundation type: Independent foundation.
Financial data (yr. ended 12/31/13): Assets, $4,314,664 (M); gifts received, $160,000; expenditures, $164,283; qualifying distributions, $164,283; giving activities include $164,000 for 83 grants to individuals (high: $2,000; low: $2,000).
Purpose and activities: Awards undergraduate scholarships only to children of employees of Crown Cork & Seal Co., Inc.
Fields of interest: Education.
Type of support: Scholarships.
Limitations: Applications not accepted. Giving on a national and international basis.
Application information: Unsolicited requests for funds not accepted.
Officers and Trustees: Josephine C. Mandeville, Chair. and Trustee; John W. Conway, Pres. and Trustee; Timothy J. Donahue, Exec. V.P. and C.F.O. and Trustee; Thomas A. Kelly, Sr. V.P.; William T. Gallagher, V.P. and Secy.; Michael B. Burns, V.P. and Treas.; Joseph C. Pearce, V.P.; Emily C. Riley.
EIN: 232667541

7936
Cornerstone Foundation
(formerly GCP Foundation)
4020 Main St.
Elverson, PA 19520-9305

Established in 1989 in Pennsylvania.
Donors: Edward H. Cone; Frontline Placement Technologies, Inc.
Foundation type: Independent foundation.
Financial data (yr. ended 12/31/13): Assets, $13,276,088 (M); expenditures, $467,953; qualifying distributions, $372,890; giving activities include $372,890 for 9 grants (high: $148,550; low: $2,500).
Purpose and activities: Giving primarily to Baptist organizations, including churches, missions, Bible colleges, and a theological seminary; funding also

for other Protestant organizations, particularly faith-based Christian camps.
Fields of interest: Graduate and professional education; Baptist; Theology; Camps.
Type of support: General support; Program-related investments.
Limitations: Applications not accepted. Giving in the U.S., with emphasis on PA. No grants to individuals.
Application information: Contributes only to pre-selected organizations.
Officers: Edward H. Cone, Pres. and Treas.; Robert L. Cone, V.P. and Secy.
Directors: Philip J. Cone; Stephen E. Cone; Derial H. Sanders; Julie Cone Zuber.
EIN: 232593411

7937
Charles L. Cost Foundation
2400 Ardmore Blvd.
Pittsburgh, PA 15221-5299

Established in 1988 in Pennsylvania.
Donor: Charles L. Cost.
Foundation type: Independent foundation.
Financial data (yr. ended 12/31/14): Assets, $1,004 (M); gifts received, $242,000; expenditures, $241,000; qualifying distributions, $241,000; giving activities include $241,000 for 7 grants (high: $100,000; low: $1,000).
Purpose and activities: Giving primarily for higher education and to a children's hospital; funding also for human services.
Fields of interest: Higher education; Specialty hospital care; Human services; Child welfare.
Type of support: General support.
Limitations: Applications not accepted. Giving primarily in Pittsburgh, PA. No grants to individuals.
Application information: Unsolicted requests for funds not accepted.
Officer: Charles L. Cost, Pres.
EIN: 251588998

7938
The Cottage Bridge Foundation
60 Longuevue Dr.
Pittsburgh, PA 15228-1539

Established in 2007 in Pennsylvania.
Donors: David J. Blair; Marianne Bokan-Blair.
Foundation type: Independent foundation.
Financial data (yr. ended 12/31/14): Assets, $4,524,736 (M); gifts received, $555,242; expenditures, $285,717; qualifying distributions, $259,741; giving activities include $245,500 for 10 grants (high: $125,000; low: $3,000).
Fields of interest: Arts and culture; Higher education; Diseases and conditions; Human services.
Type of support: Research.
Limitations: Applications not accepted. Giving primarily in MA; funding also in PA. No grants to individuals.
Application information: Contributes only to pre-selected organizations.
Officers and Directors: David J. Blair, Chair., V.P. and Treas. and Director; Marianne Bokan-Blair, Vice-Chair. and Pres. and Director.
EIN: 208724288

7939
The Cove Charitable Trust
c/o BNY Mellon, N.A.
P.O. Box 185
Pittsburgh, PA 15230-0185

Established in 1964 in Massachusetts.
Donors: Aileen Kelly Pratt†; Edwin H.B. Pratt†.
Foundation type: Independent foundation.
Financial data (yr. ended 12/31/14): Assets, $4,875,507; expenditures, $281,890; qualifying distributions, $238,386.
Fields of interest: Education; Domesticated animals; Hospital care; Community and economic development; Christianity; Human services; Housing for the homeless; Homeless people.
Type of support: General support; Continuing support; Annual campaigns; Capital and infrastructure; Program development; Seed money.
Limitations: Applications not accepted. Giving primarily in MA. No grants to individuals, or for scholarships, fellowships, emergency funds, deficit financing, equipment and materials, land acquisition, renovation projects, endowments, research, publications, or conferences and seminars; no loans or program-related investments.
Application information: Unsolicited requests for funds not accepted.
Trustee: BNY Mellon, N.A.
EIN: 046118955

7940
Covenant Foundation
535 Gradyville Rd., Ste. 5127
Newtown Square, PA 19073

Established in 1990 in Pennsylvania.
Donors: Dorothy H. Schneider; Arnold Schneider, Jr.
Foundation type: Independent foundation.
Financial data (yr. ended 12/31/14): Assets, $6,022,014 (M); gifts received, $290,704; expenditures, $372,270; qualifying distributions, $370,740; giving activities include $370,740 for 4 grants (high: $350,000; low: $1,740).
Fields of interest: Christianity.
Limitations: Applications not accepted. Giving primarily in PA. No grants to individuals.
Application information: Unsolicited requests for funds not accepted.
Trustees: Arnold Schneider, Jr.; Dorothy H. Schneider.
EIN: 237451873

7941
Samuel D. Cozen Memorial Fund
1900 Market St.
Philadelphia, PA 19103-3527

Established in 1983 in Pennsylvania.
Donors: Carl Daikeler; Gamble Insurance Services; Cozen O'Connor Foundation; Stephen A. Cozen; Ross Family Fund; Julius and Ray Charlestein Foundation; Kenneth Gamble.
Foundation type: Independent foundation.
Financial data (yr. ended 09/30/14): Assets, $362,415 (M); expenditures, $150,845; qualifying distributions, $149,441; giving activities include $131,500 for 33 grants.
Fields of interest: Education; Health; Human services.

Limitations: Applications not accepted. Giving primarily in Philadelphia, PA. No grants to individuals.
Application information: Unsolicited requests for funds not accepted.
Trustees: Stephen A. Cozen; Ellen Scarcelle; Burton K. Stein; Harold D. Sukonik.
EIN: 232267009

7942
The Craig-Dalsimer Fund
1900 Market St.
Philadelphia, PA 19103-3508 2156653723

Established in 1987 in Pennsylvania.
Donor: Janet Craig Dalsimer†.
Foundation type: Independent foundation.
Financial data (yr. ended 02/28/15): Assets, $2,063,196; expenditures, $214,773; qualifying distributions, $206,255.
Fields of interest: Children's hospital care; Children.
Limitations: Applications accepted. Giving primarily in Philadelphia, PA. No grants to individuals.
Application information:
  Initial approach: Proposal
  Deadline(s): None
Officers: David Kaufman, Esq., Chair.; Lida Freeman, Secy.-Treas.
Director: David R. Glyn, Esq.
EIN: 232714023

7943
Gene Crary Trust
c/o PNC Bank, N.A.
620 Liberty Ave., 10th Fl.
Pittsburgh, PA 15222

Foundation type: Independent foundation.
Financial data (yr. ended 12/31/13): Assets, $4,233,653 (M); expenditures, $214,378; qualifying distributions, $170,777; giving activities include $168,768 for 1 grant.
Fields of interest: Religion.
Limitations: Applications not accepted. Giving primarily in PA.
Application information: Unsolicited requests for funds not accepted.
Trustee: PNC Bank, N.A.
EIN: 256281508

7944
Crawford Heritage Community Foundation
911 Diamond Park
P.O. Box 933
Meadville, PA 16335 (814) 336-5206
Contact: Christian Maher, Exec. Dir.
FAX: (814) 724-1407;
E-mail: executive@crawfordheritage.org; Additional Address: 415 Chestnut Street, Meadville, PA 16335; Main URL: http://www.crawfordheritage.org
Facebook: http://www.facebook.com/pages/Crawford-Heritage-Community-Foundation/147574338611417
YouTube: http://www.youtube.com/user/crawfordheritage?feature=watch

Established in 1998 in Pennsylvania.
Foundation type: Community foundation.

Financial data (yr. ended 12/31/12): Assets, $12,741,847 (M); gifts received, $1,340,275; expenditures, $578,532; giving activities include $303,700 for 22 grants (high: $19,197), and $135,484 for 120 grants to individuals.

Purpose and activities: The foundation awards discretionary grants twice yearly to assist nonprofit organizations meet the changing opportunities and needs in Crawford County, PA. Grants are made county-wide from the Crawford Heritage Community Foundation Unrestricted Fund and the Ben Franklin Trust, in the Titusville area from the Fred Lintner Fund and from the Bernadene R. and John B. Cooley Fund to benefit programs for children and youth.

Fields of interest: Arts and culture; Education; Environment; Health; Science; Film and video; Agriculture; Community and economic development; Community beautification.

Type of support: Capacity-building and technical assistance; Capital and infrastructure; Equipment; Program development; Convening; Publications; Curriculum development; Scholarships; Research; Program evaluations.

Limitations: Applications accepted. Giving limited to Crawford County, PA. No support for religious or political purposes. No grants to individuals (except for scholarships), or for annual campaigns or endowments, or for routine operating expenses (i.e., salaries, rent, and/or utilities); no loans.

Publications: Application guidelines; Annual report; Grants list; Informational brochure; Newsletter.

Application information: Visit foundation web site for online application and guidelines. Application form required.

   Initial approach: Complete online application

   Deadline(s): June 15 and Dec. 15

   Board meeting date(s): Jan. and July

   Final notification: Feb. and Aug.

Officers and Directors: Paul L. Huber, Pres. and Director; Rev. Barry Cressman, 1st V.P. and Director; Saundra Mook, 2nd V.P. and Director; Milosh Mamula, 3rd V.P. and Director; Carl E. Terry, Secy. and Director; John K. Hodges, Treas. and Director; Christian Maher, Exec. Dir.; Dwight Haas, Dir. Emeritus; Christopher A. Junker, Esq., Dir. Emeritus; Mary Alice Kirkpatrick, Dir. Emeritus; Christine B. Lang, Dir. Emeritus; Melissa Mencotti, Dir. Emeritus; Stephen P. Mizner, Dir. Emeritus; Ken Montag, Dir. Emeritus; John Nesbitt, MD, Dir. Emeritus; Rev. William A. Smith, Dir. Emeritus; Mark Strausbaugh, CPA, Dir. Emeritus; Earl Yingling, Dir. Emeritus; Robert S. Bailey; Greg Bush; Robin Ernst; Charlotte Foresther; David Gagnon; Judith Griffin; Nita Hughes; Todd Ishimaru; Jeffrey S. Lang; Ken Lindberg; Mathew L. Sampson, Esq.; Samuel Spencer; Lisa Pepicelli Youngs, Esq.

Number of staff: 5 full-time professional; 1 part-time professional; 2 part-time support.

EIN: 251813245

7945

E. R. Crawford Trust Fund "A"

4000 Crooked Run Rd.

North Versailles, PA 15137-2354 (412) 751-2770

Established in 1936 in Pennsylvania.

Donor: E.R. Crawford†.

Foundation type: Independent foundation.

Financial data (yr. ended 12/31/14): Assets, $8,760,767; expenditures, $421,407; qualifying distributions, $404,398.

Purpose and activities: Giving to deserving employees or former employees of McKeesport Tin Plate Company, who through illness, accident, other misfortune, or age, have been deprived of the power or opportunity to earn the livelihood formerly enjoyed by them.

Fields of interest: Arts and culture; Hospital care; Libraries; Christianity; Protestantism; Human services; Child welfare.

Type of support: General support; Grants to individuals; Scholarships.

Limitations: Applications accepted. Giving primarily in PA, with emphasis on Allegheny County.

Application information: Application form required for individuals. Application form required.

   Initial approach: Letter

   Deadline(s): None

Trustees: Bernadine H. Kovacs; Rebecca Shaw McHolme; Robert D. Johnson.

Number of staff: 4

EIN: 256031554

7946

The Crebilly Foundation

c/o Bruce A. Rosenfield

1600 Market St., Ste. 3600

Philadelphia, PA 19103-7286

Established in 2004 in Pennsylvania.

Donors: James K. Robinson, Jr.†; David M. Robinson.

Foundation type: Independent foundation.

Financial data (yr. ended 12/31/13): Assets, $830,934 (M); expenditures, $155,395; qualifying distributions, $149,028; giving activities include $147,510 for 29 grants (high: $50,000; low: $500).

Fields of interest: Education; Health; Religion.

Limitations: Applications not accepted. No grants to individuals.

Application information: Unsolicited requests for funds not accepted.

Trustees: David M. Robinson; Dawnee McEuen Robinson; James K. Robinson III; Laurie S. Robinson.

EIN: 680552977

7947

The Curaterra Foundation

c/o Carl A. Guarino

228 Mine Rd.

Malvern, PA 19355-9648

Established in 2004 in Delaware.

Donors: Alice B. Guarino; Carl A. Guarino.

Foundation type: Independent foundation.

Financial data (yr. ended 12/31/13): Assets, $10,926,920 (M); gifts received, $3,252,343; expenditures, $454,054; qualifying distributions, $444,211; giving activities include $416,025 for 12 grants (high: $100,000; low: $1,025).

Fields of interest: Human services; Homeless people; Low-income and poor people.

Limitations: Applications not accepted. Giving primarily in NY and PA. No grants to individuals.

Application information: Unsolicited requests for funds not accepted.

Officers: Carl A. Guarino, Chair.; Alice B. Guarino, Pres.; Doris Leisch, V.P.; Tiel Batters Guarino, Secy.; Eric Guarino, Treas.

Directors: Christopher Guarino; Karen Guarino.

EIN: 201909615

7948

The Carmen Danella Foundation

1105 Green Lane Rd.

Malvern, PA 19355-8626

Donor: Carmen Danella†.

Foundation type: Independent foundation.

Financial data (yr. ended 12/31/14): Assets, $2,599,275 (M); expenditures, $355,109; qualifying distributions, $331,915; giving activities include $331,915 for 18 grants (high: $84,000; low: $250).

Fields of interest: Arts and culture; Education; Zoos; Domesticated animals.

Limitations: Applications not accepted. Giving primarily in PA.

Application information: Unsolicited requests for funds not accepted.

Trustees: Sharon Danella; Richard Hevner.

Number of staff: None.

EIN: 251858500

7949

Eugenia B. Darnall Trust

c/o PNC Bank

620 Liberty Ave., 10th Fl.

Pittsburgh, PA 15222

Donor: Eugenia B. Darnall Cemetery Fund.

Foundation type: Independent foundation.

Financial data (yr. ended 12/31/13): Assets, $5,043,510 (M); gifts received, $13,028; expenditures, $248,362; qualifying distributions, $217,416; giving activities include $215,819 for 1 grant.

Fields of interest: Education.

Limitations: Applications not accepted. Giving primarily in MD.

Application information: Unsolicited requests for funds not accepted.

Trustee: PNC Bank, N.A.

EIN: 526060737

7950

The Marc David Foundation

c/o Marc Berman

P.O. Box 645

Spring House, PA 19477-0645 (877) 829-5500

Established in 1999 in Pennsylvania.

Donor: Marc H. Berman.

Foundation type: Independent foundation.

Financial data (yr. ended 12/31/13): Assets, $1,973,048 (M); gifts received, $251,141; expenditures, $203,477; qualifying distributions, $195,250; giving activities include $195,250 for 16 grants (high: $52,800; low: $500).

Fields of interest: Community and economic development; Religion; Human rights.

Type of support: General support.

Limitations: Applications accepted. Giving primarily in PA.

Application information: Application form required.

   Initial approach: Letter

   Deadline(s): None

Trustees: David I. Berman; Marc H. Berman.

EIN: 256627678

7951
Mirrel Davis Trust for Charity
c/o PNC Bank, N.A.
P.O. Box 609
Pittsburgh, PA 15230-9738

Foundation type: Independent foundation.
Financial data (yr. ended 12/31/13): Assets,
$11,032,158 (M); expenditures, $545,430;
qualifying distributions, $478,662; giving activities
include $434,728 for 11 grants (high: $65,209;
low: $13,042).
Fields of interest: Education; Health; Community
and economic development; Judaism.
Limitations: Applications not accepted.
Application information: Unsolicited requests for
funds not accepted.
Trustee: PNC Bank, N.A.
EIN: 256064855

7952
Deerfield Charitable Trust
P.O. Box 166
Knoxville, PA 16928-0166 (814) 326-4185

Established in 2010 in Pennsylvania.
Donor: Jane E. Glover†.
Foundation type: Independent foundation.
Financial data (yr. ended 12/31/13): Assets,
$6,484,262 (M); expenditures, $338,815;
qualifying distributions, $308,614; giving activities
include $304,290 for 35 grants (high: $82,000;
low: $740).
Fields of interest: Arts and culture; Education;
Disasters and emergency management.
Limitations: Applications accepted. Giving primarily
in Northern Tioga, PA.
Application information: Application form required.
    Initial approach: See website for application form
    Deadline(s): Apr. 1 and Oct. 1
Trustees: Hilma F. Cooper; Brian W. Edgcomb; John
C. Kenyon; David C. Murdock; Eugene Seelye.
EIN: 276341752

7953
Delaware County Community Foundation
102 Chesley Dr., Ste. 1A
Media, PA 19063 (610) 892-8620
Contact: Iris Mireya Leon, Exec. Dir.
FAX: (610) 540-0190; E-mail: info@delcocf.org;
Main URL: http://www.delcocf.org
RSS feed: http://delcocf.org/feed

Established in 2002 in Pennsylvania.
Foundation type: Community foundation.
Financial data (yr. ended 12/31/12): Assets,
$1,638,656 (M); gifts received, $246,491;
expenditures, $332,196; giving activities include
$215,932 for 6+ grants (high: $37,000).
Purpose and activities: The foundation aims to
encourage local philanthropy by assisting donors
with their charitable objectives through lasting
legacies that improve the quality of life for residents
of Delaware County.
Fields of interest: Arts and culture; Education;
Environment; Domesticated animals; Health;
Community and economic development; Human
services; Family services; Child welfare; Children
and youth.
Limitations: Applications accepted. Giving primarily
in Delaware County, VA.

Application information: Visit web site for
application and guidelines per grant type.
Application form required.
    Deadline(s): Varies
Officers and Directors: Grant Gegwich, Chair. and
Director; David A. Stitely, Chair. Emeritus and
Director; Joe Costigan, C.F.A., Vice-Chair. and
Director; David Kauffman, Secy. and Director; Marc
Simmons, CPA, Treas. and Director; Iris Mireya
Leon, Exec. Dir.; Joseph E. Lastowka, Jr., Esq.,
Emeritus; Carmen P. Belefonte, Esq.; Peter J. Berol;
Edward P. Caine, CPA; Stephen Carroll, Esq.;
Anthony J. Cavaliere; Barbara A. Denczi; Steven R.
Derby; Leo A. Hackett, Esq.; Lydia Holiat; James E.
Turner; Randolph B. Winton.
Board of Advisors: James C. Brennan, Esq.; Bruce
M. Brown; Fred Dewey; Brian T. Hannon; Jack
Holefelder, Jr.; Kim Landry; Robert E. Latshaw;
Hollie McDonald; Colleen P. Morrone; Laura Otten,
Ph.D; Joseph Pew; David L. Phillips, Ed.D.; Louis E.
Prevost; Gwendolyn A. Smith; Rev. Dr. Larry V.
Smoose; Laura Solomon, Esq.; Dennis Woody, Esq.;
Florence F. Wright, Esq.
EIN: 611419515

7954
DENTSPLY International Foundation
221 W. Philadelphia St., Ste. 60W
York, PA 17401-2991 (717) 845-7511

Established in 1955 in Pennsylvania.
Donor: DENTSPLY International Inc.
Foundation type: Company-sponsored foundation.
Financial data (yr. ended 12/31/14): Assets,
$8,753; gifts received, $75,000; expenditures,
$339,526; qualifying distributions, $349,492.
Purpose and activities: The foundation supports
organizations involved with higher education, health,
and human services.
Fields of interest: Education; Health; Human
services.
Type of support: General support; Scholarships.
Limitations: Applications accepted. Giving primarily
in DE and PA.
Application information:
    Initial approach: Proposal
    Copies of proposal: 1
    Deadline(s): None
Trustees: Teresa A. Dolan; William E. Reardon;
Leslie A. Satfin; Bret W. Wise.
Number of staff: None.
EIN: 236297307

7955
G. Fred & Sylvia Dibona Family Foundation
c/o Sylvia M. Dibona
915 Waverly Rd.
Bryn Mawr, PA 19010-1930

Donor: Sylvia M. DiBona.
Foundation type: Independent foundation.
Financial data (yr. ended 12/31/13): Assets,
$3,514,879 (M); gifts received, $118,997;
expenditures, $230,134; qualifying distributions,
$196,865; giving activities include $195,000 for 12
grants (high: $100,000; low: $200).
Fields of interest: Education; Diseases and
conditions; Youth development.
Type of support: General support.
Limitations: Applications not accepted. Giving
primarily in PA. No grants to individuals.

Application information: Unsolicited requests for
funds not accepted.
Officers: Sylvia M. Dibona, Pres.; Christine D.
Lobley, Secy.; G. Fred Dibona III, Treas.
EIN: 202771993

7956
The Dicerbo Foundation Inc.
c/o The PA Trust Co.
5 Radnor Corp. Ctr., Ste. 450
Radnor, PA 19087-4526

Established in 1994 in New York.
Donor: Louis P. Dicerbo II.
Foundation type: Independent foundation.
Financial data (yr. ended 12/31/13): Assets,
$1,847,951 (M); gifts received, $271,975;
expenditures, $288,638; qualifying distributions,
$264,217; giving activities include $262,717 for 13
grants (high: $200,000; low: $1,000).
Fields of interest: Higher education; Hospital care;
Catholicism.
Limitations: Applications not accepted. Giving
primarily in NY, PA, and TX. No grants to individuals.
Application information: Contributes only to
pre-selected organizations.
Officers: Louis P. Dicerbo II, Chair.; Eileen Patricia
Dicerbo, Vice-Chair.; Joy Bushwell, V.P.; Cheri
Dicerbo, V.P.; Cindy Silverstein, V.P.; Nancy Reddan,
Corp. Secy.
EIN: 113202308

7957
Conway Wing Dickson and Gertrude Finck Dickson Memorial Trust
c/o BNY Mellon, N.A.
P.O. Box 185
Pittsburgh, PA 15230-0185

Foundation type: Independent foundation.
Financial data (yr. ended 12/31/14): Assets,
$8,471,335 (M); expenditures, $441,943;
qualifying distributions, $387,613; giving activities
include $361,395 for 9 grants (high: $40,155; low:
$40,155).
Fields of interest: Education; Law education;
Health; Christianity; Human services.
Type of support: Research.
Limitations: Applications not accepted. Giving
primarily in PA. No grants to individuals.
Application information: Contributes only to
pre-selected organizations; unsolicited requests for
funds not considered or acknowledged.
Trustee: BNY Mellon, N.A.
EIN: 236992853

7958
The Dietrich Foundation, Inc.
P.O. Box 649
Gladwyne, PA 19035-0649 (215) 988-0778
Contact: Daniel W. Dietrich II, Pres., Treas., and Dir.

Established in 1953 in Delaware.
Donor: Dietrich American Foundation.
Foundation type: Independent foundation.
Financial data (yr. ended 12/31/13): Assets,
$3,576,196 (M); expenditures, $414,906;
qualifying distributions, $389,175; giving activities
include $385,733 for 16 grants (high: $55,000;
low: $7,500).

Purpose and activities: Giving primarily for higher education, as well as the arts, particularly the performing arts, music, visual arts, museums, and other cultural programs.
Fields of interest: Arts and culture; Performing arts; Music; Museums; Higher education.
Type of support: Continuing support; Program development; Publications.
Limitations: Applications not accepted. Giving primarily in Philadelphia, PA, and New York, NY. No grants to individuals.
Application information: Contributes only to pre-selected organizations.
Officers and Directors: Daniel W. Dietrich II, Pres. and Treas. and Director; Joseph G.J. Connolly, Secy. and Director.
Number of staff: None.
EIN: 236255134

7959
Dietz & Watson Foundation
c/o Glenmede Trust Co., N.A.
1650 Market St., Ste. 1200
Philadelphia, PA   19103-7391

Established in 2001 in Pennsylvania.
Donor: Dietz & Watson.
Foundation type: Company-sponsored foundation.
Financial data (yr. ended 12/31/13): Assets, $9,334,423 (M); expenditures, $423,381; qualifying distributions, $371,150; giving activities include $370,150 for 89 grants (high: $44,000; low: $100).
Purpose and activities: The foundation supports organizations involved with education, health, cancer, Tourette's syndrome, digestive diseases, sports, and human services.
Fields of interest: Education; Health; Diseases and conditions.
Type of support: General support; Scholarships.
Limitations: Applications not accepted. Giving primarily in MD, NJ, NY, and Philadelphia, PA. No grants to individuals.
Application information: Contributes only to pre-selected organizations.
Officers and Trustees: Cynthia Eni Yingling, Pres. and Trustee; Ruth Eni, Treas. and Trustee; Christopher W. Eni; Louis J. Eni, Jr.
EIN: 233028685

7960
Kathryn J. Dinardo Trust Fund
c/o Samuel J. Pasquarelli, Esq.
Two PNC Plz., 28th Fl.
620 Liberty Ave.
Pittsburgh, PA   15222-2705

Established in 2001 in Pennsylvania.
Foundation type: Independent foundation.
Financial data (yr. ended 12/31/13): Assets, $4,213,366 (M); expenditures, $374,524; qualifying distributions, $340,000; giving activities include $300,000 for 22 grants (high: $50,000; low: $500).
Fields of interest: Education; Graduate and professional education; Hospital care; Christianity; Theology; Human services; Child welfare; Youth services.
Type of support: Equipment.
Limitations: Applications not accepted. Giving primarily in PA. No grants to individuals.

Application information: Contributes only to pre-selected organizations.
Trustee: Samuel J. Pasquarelli, Esq.
EIN: 256494383

7961
K. H. Dominion Foundation
c/o Glenmede Trust Co., N.A.
1650 Market, Ste. 1200
Philadelphia, PA   19103-7391

Donors: Glenn O. Head; Kathryn S. Head; Carol A. Head.
Foundation type: Independent foundation.
Financial data (yr. ended 12/31/13): Assets, $11,267,252 (M); gifts received, $248,000; expenditures, $341,283; qualifying distributions, $328,443; giving activities include $321,000 for 15 grants (high: $150,000; low: $5,000).
Purpose and activities: Grant credit to animal, environment and farm foundation.
Fields of interest: Environment; Domesticated animals; Agriculture.
Limitations: Applications not accepted.
Application information: Unsolicited requests for funds not accepted.
Trustees: Linda A. Delma; Kathryn S. Head.
EIN: 276973048

7962
Ruth E Donnally Charitable Trust
c/o PNC Bank, N.A.
620 Liberty Ave., 10th Fl.
Pittsburgh, PA   15222-2705

Foundation type: Independent foundation.
Financial data (yr. ended 12/31/13): Assets, $5,379,986 (M); expenditures, $287,786; qualifying distributions, $242,256; giving activities include $236,030 for 11 grants (high: $21,458; low: $21,457).
Fields of interest: Education; Health; Human services.
Limitations: Applications not accepted. Giving primarily in PA.
Application information: Unsolicited Requests for funds not accepted.
Trustees: Robert B. Wolf; PNC Bank, N.A.
EIN: 256357829

7963
Mary J. Donnelly Foundation
4752 Bayard St.
Pittsburgh, PA   15213-1766   (412) 818-4626
Contact: Frederick N. Egler Jr., Tr.

Established in 1951 in Pennsylvania.
Donor: Mary J. Donnelly†.
Foundation type: Independent foundation.
Financial data (yr. ended 06/30/14): Assets, $3,695,080 (M); gifts received, $372; expenditures, $175,551; qualifying distributions, $161,250; giving activities include $159,000 for 26 grants (high: $15,000; low: $1,000).
Fields of interest: Education; Health; Religion.
Type of support: General support; Annual campaigns; Capital campaigns; Capital and infrastructure; Program development.

Limitations: Applications accepted. Giving primarily in PA. No grants to individuals, or for endowment funds or matching gifts; no loans.
Application information: Application form required.
Initial approach: Letter
Copies of proposal: 3
Deadline(s): None
Board meeting date(s): June and Dec.
Trustees: Elizabeth A. Donnelly; M. Megan Donnelly; Frederick N. Egler, Jr.; Ruth D. Egler.
EIN: 256037469

7964
The Double Eagle Foundation
c/o Glenmede Trust Co., N.A.
1650 Market St., Ste. 1200
Philadelphia, PA   19103-7391
Application address: c/o Raymond John Wean, III, Chair., 280 Millview Dr., Pittsburgh, PA 15238-1642, tel.: (412) 551-8063

Established in 2006 in Pennsylvania.
Donor: The Raymond John Wean Foundation.
Foundation type: Independent foundation.
Financial data (yr. ended 03/31/13): Assets, $8,465,930 (M); expenditures, $434,201; qualifying distributions, $373,099; giving activities include $362,250 for 55 grants (high: $50,000; low: $250).
Fields of interest: Arts and culture; Education; Higher education; Undergraduate education; University education.
Type of support: Capital campaigns.
Limitations: Applications accepted. Giving in the U.S., with emphasis on FL, PA and SC. No grants to individuals.
Application information:
Initial approach: Letter
Deadline(s): None
Officers: Raymond John Wean III, Chair.; Susan Wean, Secy.-Treas.
EIN: 256875219

7965
Peter C. Dozzi Family Foundation
(also known as Eugene Dozzi Charitable Foundation)
2000 Lincoln Rd.
Pittsburgh, PA   15235-1129

Established in 1969 in Pennsylvania.
Donors: Domenic P. Dozzi; Peter C. Dozzi; Dwight E. Kuhn; Petrina A. Lloyd; Thomas J. Murphy; EPIC Metals Corp.; Jendoco Construction Corp.; Theresa K. Dozzi; Plum Corp.; Theresa K. Dozzi.
Foundation type: Independent foundation.
Financial data (yr. ended 04/30/13): Assets, $5,376,231 (M); gifts received, $103,500; expenditures, $234,070; qualifying distributions, $226,195; giving activities include $216,655 for 83 grants (high: $50,000; low: $100).
Fields of interest: Arts and culture; Natural history museums; Historic preservation; Higher education; Health; Hospital care; Diseases and conditions; Judaism; Human services.
Type of support: General support.
Limitations: Applications not accepted. Giving primarily in Pittsburgh, PA. No grants to individuals.
Application information: Unsolicited requests for funds not accepted.

Officer and Trustees: Petrina A. Lloyd, Mgr. and Trustee; Domenic P. Dozzi; Peter C. Dozzi; Theresa K. Dozzi.
EIN: 237023479

7966
Drueding Foundation

c/o Mrs. James J. Stokes, III
669 Dodds Ln.
Gladwyne, PA   19035-1514

Established in 1986 in Pennsylvania.
Foundation type: Independent foundation.
Financial data (yr. ended 06/30/14): Assets, $8,344,783 (M); expenditures, $377,275; qualifying distributions, $344,790; giving activities include $342,400 for 40 grants (high: $121,160; low: $500).
Purpose and activities: Giving primarily to hospitals and health organizations; funding also for human services.
Fields of interest: Health; Hospital care; Diseases and conditions; Human services; Child welfare; Females; Homeless people.
Type of support: Research.
Limitations: Applications not accepted. Giving primarily in PA. No grants to individuals.
Application information: Contributes only to pre-selected organizations.
Officers: Mary Beth Lopiccolo, Pres.; Nanny G. Gifford, V.P.; James Drueding, Secy.; Patricia D. Stokes, Treas.
Trustees: Richard Drueding; Lizanne Michener; Diana D. Stewart; Caroline M. Stokes.
EIN: 232418214

7967
Dull Casper Trust

c/o BNY Mellon, N.A.
P.O. Box 185
Pittsburgh, PA   15230-0185

Foundation type: Independent foundation.
Financial data (yr. ended 09/30/14): Assets, $8,643,053 (M); expenditures, $386,451; qualifying distributions, $350,782; giving activities include $327,688 for 1 grant.
Fields of interest: Convalescent care.
Limitations: Applications not accepted. Giving primarily in Harrisburg, PA. No grants to individuals.
Application information: Contributes only to pre-selected organizations.
Trustee: BNY Mellon, N.A.
EIN: 236236573

7968
Eakins O For B E Endowment Fund

c/o BNY Mellon, N.A.
P.O. Box 185
Pittsburgh, PA   15230-0185

Foundation type: Independent foundation.
Financial data (yr. ended 09/30/14): Assets, $3,030,955 (M); expenditures, $153,228; qualifying distributions, $143,102; giving activities include $138,000 for 3 grants.
Fields of interest: Education; Health; Human services; Children; People with vision impairments.
Limitations: Applications not accepted. Giving primarily in Pittsburgh, PA.

Application information: Unsolicited requests for funds not accepted.
Trustee: BNY Mellon, N.A.
EIN: 256121513

7969
The Eberly Foundation

2 W. Main St., Ste. 101
Uniontown, PA   15401-3448   (724) 438-3789
Contact: Robert E. Eberly Jr., Pres. and Treas.

Established in 1963 in Pennsylvania.
Foundation type: Independent foundation.
Financial data (yr. ended 12/31/13): Assets, $7,663,489 (M); gifts received, $6,000; expenditures, $473,907; qualifying distributions, $420,260; giving activities include $312,756 for 43 grants (high: $40,000; low: $100).
Purpose and activities: Giving primarily for higher education, arts and culture; support also for youth, hospitals, and public policy.
Fields of interest: Arts and culture; Education; Higher education; Public policy; Community and economic development; Human services.
Type of support: Program development; Professorships; Scholarships; Policy, advocacy and systems reform.
Limitations: Applications accepted. Giving primarily in PA.
Publications: Annual report.
Application information: Application form required.
   Initial approach: Letter
   Copies of proposal: 1
   Deadline(s): Aug. 1
   Board meeting date(s): Oct.
Officers: Robert E. Eberly, Jr., Pres. and Treas.; Ruth B. Carter, V.P. and Secy.
Trustees: Carolyn E. Blany; Carolyn J. Drost; Paul O. Eberly; Robert E. Eberly III; Dana B. Pancoast; Tana M. Shirk.
Number of staff: 2 full-time professional; 1 part-time professional; 2 full-time support.
EIN: 237070246

7970
Theodore W. and Betty J. Eckels Foundation

c/o BNY Mellon Trust of Delaware
P.O. Box 185
Pittsburgh, PA   15230-0185

Donor: Betty Jean Eckels.
Foundation type: Independent foundation.
Financial data (yr. ended 12/31/14): Assets, $4,467,616; expenditures, $265,568; qualifying distributions, $234,885.
Fields of interest: Education; Religion; Human services.
Limitations: Applications not accepted. Giving primarily in CT, GA, TN and VA.
Application information: Unsolicited requests for funds not accepted.
Trustees: Betty Jean Eckels; Emerson F. Markham; BNY Mellon Trust of Delaware.
EIN: 452941744

7971
Eden Charitable Foundation

Strafford Bldg. 2
200 Eagle Rd., Ste. 204
Wayne, PA   19087-3166
Contact: John M. Kapp, Pres.; Earl Eden, Tr.

Established in 1993 in Pennsylvania.
Donor: Franklin C. Eden Revocable Trust.
Foundation type: Independent foundation.
Financial data (yr. ended 12/31/13): Assets, $8,946,251 (M); gifts received, $632,308; expenditures, $476,208; qualifying distributions, $455,631; giving activities include $370,500 for 43 grants (high: $12,500; low: $500).
Fields of interest: Arts and culture; Education; Diseases and conditions; Christianity; Human services.
Type of support: General support.
Limitations: Applications not accepted. Giving limited to PA. No grants to individuals.
Application information: Contributes only to pre-selected organizations.
   Board meeting date(s): As needed
Trustees: Donald E. Parlee; Kim S. P. Eble; Brooks Eden; Maria B. Eden.
Number of staff: 1 full-time professional.
EIN: 232706163

7972
Catherine Edwards Trust

c/o BNY Mellon, N.A.
P.O. Box 185
Pittsburgh, PA   15230-0185

Foundation type: Independent foundation.
Financial data (yr. ended 06/30/12): Assets, $4,711,664 (M); expenditures, $296,692; qualifying distributions, $274,474; giving activities include $259,663 for 5 grants (high: $51,933; low: $51,932).
Fields of interest: Health; Religion; People with vision impairments.
Type of support: General support.
Limitations: Applications not accepted. Giving primarily in CO, GA and PA.
Application information: Unsolicited requests for funds not accepted.
Trustee: BNY Mellon, N.A.
EIN: 900330808

7973
Catherine R. Edwards Trust

c/o BNY Mellon, N.A.
P.O. Box 185
Pittsburgh, PA   15230-0185

Foundation type: Independent foundation.
Financial data (yr. ended 06/30/13): Assets, $5,001,875 (M); expenditures, $246,177; qualifying distributions, $218,774; giving activities include $200,505 for 5 grants (high: $40,101; low: $40,101).
Fields of interest: Health; Diseases and conditions; Religion; Children; People with vision impairments.
Type of support: General support.
Limitations: Applications not accepted. Giving primarily in CO, GA, NY and PA.
Application information: Unsolicited requests for funds not accepted.

Trustee: BNY Mellon, N.A.
EIN: 236225449

7974
The EFM Foundation
P.O. Box 467
Newtown Square, PA 19073
Application address: c/o Margaret Gallagher
Thompson, Esq., 200 Four Falls Corporation Ctr.,
Ste. 400, West Conshohocken, PA 19428 tel: (610)
941-2370.

Established in 2006 in Pennsylvania.
Donors: Marie E. Dooner; Peter S. Dooner, Jr.;
Maneely Fund.
Foundation type: Independent foundation.
Financial data (yr. ended 12/31/13): Assets,
$8,232,544 (M); expenditures, $417,880;
qualifying distributions, $378,515; giving activities
include $374,500 for 50 grants (high: $53,000;
low: $1,000).
Fields of interest: Education; Housing development;
Religion.
Type of support: General support.
Limitations: Applications accepted. Giving primarily
in PA.
Application information:
  Initial approach: Proposal
  Deadline(s): None
Trustees: Amy Dooner Brennan; Diane Dooner
Murphy; Katherine Dooner Loftus; Marie E. Dooner;
Peter S. Dooner, Jr.
EIN: 206967970

7975
Elk County Community Foundation
(doing business as Community Foundation of North
Central Pennsylvania)
32 S. St.Marys St., Ste. 4
P.O. Box 934
Saint Marys, PA 15857 (814) 834-2125
Contact: Paula Fritz Eddy, Exec. Dir.
FAX: (814) 834-2126; E-mail: eccf@windstream.net;
Main URL: http://www.elkcountyfoundation.com
Facebook: https://www.facebook.com/
elkcountycommunityfoundation

Established in 2000 in Pennsylvania.
Foundation type: Community foundation.
Financial data (yr. ended 12/31/13): Assets,
$8,165,724 (M); gifts received, $1,680,833;
expenditures, $451,814; giving activities include
$234,938 for 15+ grants (high: $30,485), and
$108,215 for 124 grants to individuals.
Purpose and activities: The foundation provides a
vehicle that will enable citizens of Elk County to
achieve their philanthropic expectations and in so
doing strengthen the quality of life in the region.
Fields of interest: Arts and culture; Education;
Higher education; Environment; Health; Diseases
and conditions; Economic development; Human
services; Child welfare; Seniors.
Type of support: Capital and infrastructure;
Program-related investments; Matching grants;
Equipment; Program development; Scholarships;
Student aid.
Limitations: Applications accepted. Giving primarily
in Elk County, PA. No grants for ongoing operational
support or event sponsorship.
Publications: Application guidelines; Annual report;
Grants list; Informational brochure; Informational

brochure (including application guidelines);
Newsletter.
Application information: Visit foundation web site
for application form and guidelines. Application form
required.
  Initial approach: Mail application form and
    attachments
  Copies of proposal: 1
  Deadline(s): Jan. 15 and July 15
  Board meeting date(s): Mar., May, Aug., and Nov.
Officers and Directors: Donald Valone, Pres. and
Director; James A. Meyer, V.P. and Director; Barb
Duff, Secy. and Director; Ham Johnson, Treas. and
Director; Paula Fritz Eddy, Exec. Dir.; Gennaro Aiello;
William Conrad; Charles Constable; John Dippold III;
Nancy Hoffman Chritine Imbrogno; Frtiz Lecker;
Carol Pontzer; Mike Renaud; Judy Manno Stager;
Charlie Steger.
Number of staff: 1 part-time professional; 1
part-time support.
EIN: 251859637

7976
S. Mcintyre Elkins For Abington
c/o PNC Bank
620 Liberty Ave., 10th Fl.
Pittsburgh, PA 15222-2705

Foundation type: Independent foundation.
Financial data (yr. ended 12/31/13): Assets,
$3,848,664 (M); expenditures, $159,819;
qualifying distributions, $148,133; giving activities
include $148,133 for 1 grant.
Fields of interest: Health.
Limitations: Applications not accepted. Giving
primarily in PA.
Application information: Unsolicited requests for
funds not accepted.
Trustee: PNC Bank, N.A.
EIN: 236205270

7977
William and Muriel Elliott Foundation
c/o Bryn Mawr Trust Co.
1 E. Chocolate Ave., No. 200
Hershey, PA 17033-1314

Donors: Muriel D. Elliott Declaration of Trust; William
Elliot Declaration of Trust.
Foundation type: Independent foundation.
Financial data (yr. ended 12/31/13): Assets,
$8,804,602 (M); gifts received, $8,452;
expenditures, $501,269; qualifying distributions,
$487,833; giving activities include $405,000 for 7
grants (high: $125,000; low: $10,000).
Fields of interest: Arts and culture; Education.
Limitations: Applications not accepted. Giving
primarily in GA, NY and PA.
Application information: Unsolicted requests for
funds not accepted.
Trustees: Neil E. Cass; Katherine D. Elliott; William
L. McKernan; Bryn Mawr Trust Co.
EIN: 273855059

7978
Elizabeth B. Ellis Foundation Trust
540 Swede St.
Norristown, PA 19401-4807

Donor: Thomas Deliberato†.

Foundation type: Independent foundation.
Financial data (yr. ended 05/31/14): Assets,
$3,298,635; expenditures, $242,389; qualifying
distributions, $198,538.
Fields of interest: Arts and culture; Museums;
Higher education; Hospital care; Human services;
Child welfare.
Type of support: General support.
Limitations: Applications not accepted. Giving
primarily in PA.
Application information: Unsolicited requests for
funds not accepted.
Trustees: William Allen; Amy Sosnov; Lynne A.
Tsvetkov; Sergei Tsvetkov.
EIN: 236851809

7979
Charles C. Ely Trust
c/o BNY Mellon, N.A.
P.O. Box 185
Pittsburgh, PA 15230-0185

Established in 1987 in Massachusetts.
Foundation type: Independent foundation.
Financial data (yr. ended 08/31/14): Assets,
$3,891,092; expenditures, $209,760; qualifying
distributions, $177,647.
Purpose and activities: Giving for scholarship funds
at degree-granting institutions of higher education in
the Boston, MA, area. Preference for programs
providing emergency scholarship support to
students who have encountered financial difficulties
while in school, and scholarship programs for
low-income and minority students.
Fields of interest: Education; Ethnic and racial
groups.
Type of support: Scholarships; Student aid.
Limitations: Applications not accepted. Giving
primarily in the Boston, MA, area.
Application information: Unsolicited requests for
funds not accepted.
Trustee: BNY Mellon, N.A.
EIN: 046091865

7980
Emporium Foundation, Inc.
2 E. 4th St.
Emporium, PA 15834-1443 (814) 486-3333

Established in 1929 in Pennsylvania.
Foundation type: Independent foundation.
Financial data (yr. ended 12/31/14): Assets,
$4,171,103; expenditures, $252,078; qualifying
distributions, $221,702.
Purpose and activities: Established for the benefit
of local residents for maintaining or assisting public
schools, public libraries, recreation areas,
community buildings, and similar facilities.
Fields of interest: Elementary and secondary
education; Higher education; Environment; Public
libraries; Public administration; Community and
economic development; Sports and recreation.
Type of support: Building and renovations;
Equipment.
Limitations: Applications accepted. Giving limited to
Cameron County, PA. No grants to individuals.
Application information: Application form required.
  Initial approach: Proposal
  Deadline(s): None

Officers: John T. Rogers, Pres.; Edward B. Lundberg, V.P.; Edwin W. Tompkins III, Secy.; David E. Guloien, Treas.
EIN: 250995760

7981
Engel f/b/o AA CM State University of New York

c/o BNY Mellon, N.A.
P.O. Box 185
Pittsburgh, PA 15230-0185

Foundation type: Independent foundation.
Financial data (yr. ended 07/31/14): Assets, $4,354,129 (M); expenditures, $213,880; qualifying distributions, $202,260; giving activities include $195,000 for 1 grant.
Fields of interest: Education; Hospital care.
Limitations: Applications not accepted. Giving primarily in CT and NY.
Application information: Unsolicited requests for funds not accepted.
Trustee: BNY Mellon, N.A.
EIN: 136143215

7982
Alvin S. Engle Foundation

P.O. Box 500
Mount Joy, PA 17552

Established in 1993 in Pennsylvania.
Donors: C.A. Engle; Pauline H. Engle; Audrey E. Rutt; Dennis L. Engle; Engle Printing & Publishing Co., Inc.
Foundation type: Independent foundation.
Financial data (yr. ended 12/31/13): Assets, $1,114,410 (M); gifts received, $350,000; expenditures, $148,051; qualifying distributions, $148,051; giving activities include $148,015 for 4 grants (high: $50,000; low: $15,015).
Purpose and activities: Giving primarily for Christian education, with emphasis on Mennonite education.
Fields of interest: Education; Christianity; Protestantism.
Limitations: Applications not accepted. Giving primarily in PA. No grants to individuals.
Application information: Unsolicited requests for funds not accepted.
Officers: C.A. Engle, Pres.; Dennis L. Engle, V.P.; Pauline H. Engle, V.P.; Audrey E. Rutt, Secy.-Treas.
EIN: 232747886

7983
The Samuel Epstein Foundation Trust

c/o PNC Bank, N.A.
P. O. Box 609
Pittsburgh, PA 15230-9738

Established in 1988 in Pennsylvania.
Donor: Samuel Epstein†.
Foundation type: Independent foundation.
Financial data (yr. ended 12/31/13): Assets, $5,276,241 (M); expenditures, $263,549; qualifying distributions, $235,732; giving activities include $208,360 for 11 grants (high: $85,300; low: $12,306).
Purpose and activities: Giving primarily for human services, and Jewish organizations; scholarships are limited to Sheffield High School, Warren County, Pennsylvania.

Fields of interest: Education; Nonprofits; Judaism; Human services.
International interests: Israel.
Type of support: General support; Student aid; Regranting.
Limitations: Applications not accepted. Giving primarily in New York, NY, Saint Peter, MN and Warren, PA,.
Application information: Unsolicited requests for grants not accepted.
Trustee: PNC Bank, N.A.
EIN: 256311365

7984
Gene & Marlene Epstein Humanitarian Fund

1238 Wrightstown Rd.
Newtown, PA 18940-9602 (215) 968-2200
Contact: Gene Epstein, Dir.
E-mail: gboyle@gpboyle.com

Established in 2007 in Pennsylvania.
Donors: Gene Epstein; Marlene Epstein.
Foundation type: Operating foundation.
Financial data (yr. ended 12/31/13): Assets, $0 (M); gifts received, $272,934; expenditures, $137,175; qualifying distributions, $136,316; giving activities include $125,765 for 21 grants (high: $75,000; low: $15), and $10,551 for 3 grants to individuals (high: $5,600; low: $1,651).
Purpose and activities: Giving for troops stationed in war zones and to aid returning veterans in need.
Fields of interest: Judaism; International development; Military personnel; Veterans.
International interests: Israel.
Type of support: General support; Grants to individuals.
Limitations: Applications accepted. Giving primarily in PA.
Application information: Application form required.
Initial approach: Letter or Telephone call
Deadline(s): None
Directors: Gene Epstein; Marlene Epstein.
EIN: 061813910

7985
Alice Everard Charitable Foundation

c/o Daniel J. Paci
P.O. Box 215
Perkasie, PA 18944-0215

Established in 2004 in Pennsylvania.
Donor: Herbert Ward†.
Foundation type: Independent foundation.
Financial data (yr. ended 12/31/13): Assets, $5,857,104 (M); expenditures, $215,498; qualifying distributions, $196,150; giving activities include $195,300 for 21 grants (high: $50,000; low: $500).
Fields of interest: Education; Animal welfare; Human services; Child welfare; Domestic violence shelters; Victims of crime and abuse.
Limitations: Applications not accepted. Giving primarily in FL and NJ. No grants to individuals.
Application information: Contributes only to pre-selected organizations.
Trustee: Joseph R. Detrano.
EIN: 201608878

7986
Joseph R. Every Scholarship Fund

c/o Citizens & Northern Bank, Trust Dept.
90 Main St.
Wellsboro, PA 16901-1517
Application address: c/o Lori B. Blascak, Citizens Northern Bank, 428 Main St., Towanda, PA 18848, tel.: (570) 268-3041

Established in 2007 in Pennsylvania.
Donor: Joseph R. Every†.
Foundation type: Independent foundation.
Financial data (yr. ended 12/31/13): Assets, $3,725,380 (M); expenditures, $185,589; qualifying distributions, $162,000; giving activities include $6,000 for 1 grant, and $156,000 for 16 grants to individuals (high: $10,000; low: $6,000).
Purpose and activities: Scholarship awards to residents of Chemung County, New York, and Bradford and Tioga counties, Pennsylvania, pursuing careers in medicine, teaching, or engineering, who do not smoke tobacco or use illegal drugs or alcoholic beverages, and have a G.P.A. of at least 2.0.
Fields of interest: Graduate and professional education; Medical education; Teacher education; Engineering.
Type of support: Student aid.
Limitations: Applications accepted. Giving limited to residents of Chemung County, NY, and Bradford and Tioga counties, PA.
Application information: Application form required.
Initial approach: Letter or telephone
Deadline(s): Apr. 15
Trustee: Citizens & Northern Bank.
Committee Members: Larry D. Alderson; Lori B. Blascak; Michael G. Charles; Joseph R. Maresco; Deborah E. Scott.
EIN: 206949515

7987
Frederick and Ellen Fair Memorial Fund

c/o PNC Bank, N.A.
P.O. Box 609
Pittsburgh, PA 15230-9738
Application address: c/o Stephen Kosak, 248 Seneca St., Oil City, PA 16301, tel.: (814) 678-3545; E-mail: stephen.kosak@pnc.com

Foundation type: Independent foundation.
Financial data (yr. ended 12/31/13): Assets, $7,073,862 (M); expenditures, $254,979; qualifying distributions, $189,425; giving activities include $157,300 for 11 grants (high: $50,000; low: $1,000).
Fields of interest: Education; Health; Human services.
Limitations: Applications accepted. Giving primarily in PA.
Application information: Visit http://www.pncsites.com/pncfoundation/charitable_trusts.html for complete application guidelines. Application form required.
Deadline(s): Feb. 1, May 1, Aug. 1 and Oct. 1
Trustee: PNC Bank, N.A.
EIN: 256082935

7988
Rudderow Family Foundation Inc.

5595 Ridge Rd.
New Hope, PA 18938-5420

Established in 2006 in Pennsylvania.
Donor: Timothy J. Rudderow.
Foundation type: Independent foundation.
Financial data (yr. ended 12/31/13): Assets, $911,033 (M); gifts received, $45,000; expenditures, $194,255; qualifying distributions, $194,255; giving activities include $189,500 for 7 grants (high: $67,000; low: $8,000).
Fields of interest: Christianity; Human services; Food aid.
Limitations: Applications not accepted. Giving primarily in NY. No grants to individuals.
Application information: Contributes only to pre-selected organizations.
Directors: Judith M. Rudderow; Timothy J. Rudderow.
EIN: 204981849

7989
Lucy C. Farnsworth Trust
c/o BNY Mellon, N.A.
P.O. Box 185
Pittsburgh, PA   15230-0185

Foundation type: Independent foundation.
Financial data (yr. ended 08/31/14): Assets, $7,020,280 (M); expenditures, $377,010; qualifying distributions, $335,526; giving activities include $319,286 for 1 grant.
Fields of interest: Museums.
Limitations: Applications not accepted. Giving primarily in ME; some giving also in PA.
Application information: Contributes only to pre-selected organizations.
Trustee: BNY Mellon, N.A.
EIN: 041302043

7990
The Female Association of Philadelphia
c/o Haverford Trust Company
3 Radnor Corp. Ctr.
Radnor, PA   19087-4580

Established in 1800 in Pennsylvania.
Foundation type: Independent foundation.
Financial data (yr. ended 09/30/14): Assets, $2,686,019 (M); gifts received, $1,150; expenditures, $179,390; qualifying distributions, $152,950; giving activities include $152,950 for 355+ grants.
Purpose and activities: Modest, individual grants awarded only to women 60 years of age or older, who reside in the Philadelphia, PA, area with a per annum income under $12,000, and who do not receive Supplemental Security Income (SSI).
Fields of interest: Seniors; Females; Low-income and poor people.
Type of support: Grants to individuals.
Limitations: Applications not accepted. Giving primarily in PA.
Application information: Unsolicited requests for funds not accepted.
Officers and Trustees: Rodney D. Day III, Pres. and Trustee; Jack M. Maxwell III, V.P. and Trustee; Anne Pringle III, Secy. and Trustee; Ellen G. Anderson III, Treas. and Trustee; Mrs. Pierce Archer; Mrs. William L. Hires; Mrs. Robert B. Hobbs, Jr.; Pamela W. Leighton; Mrs. Brian J. Linz; Mrs. Marg Macdonald; Mrs. David Maxey; Mrs. Philip A. McMunigal.
EIN: 236214961

7991
Lela M. Fetters Charitable Trust
c/o PNC Bank, N.A.
P.O. Box 609
Pittsburgh, PA   15230-9738

Foundation type: Independent foundation.
Financial data (yr. ended 12/31/14): Assets, $3,437,589 (M); expenditures, $187,815; qualifying distributions, $167,866; giving activities include $152,934 for 9 grants (high: $38,233; low: $7,647).
Fields of interest: Domesticated animals; Christianity; Human services.
Limitations: Applications not accepted. Giving primarily in Ft. Wayne, IN.
Application information: Unsolicited requests for funds not accepted.
Trustee: PNC Bank, N.A.
EIN: 356245279

7992
Fierce Advocacy Fund, Inc.
(formerly Stephen and Ellen Solms Family Foundation)
1520 Spruce St., Apt. 1207
Philadelphia, PA   19102-4509

Donors: Stephen E. Solms; Ellen Solms; Food and Freedom Foundation.
Foundation type: Independent foundation.
Financial data (yr. ended 12/31/13): Assets, $1,500,830 (M); expenditures, $189,356; qualifying distributions, $170,415; giving activities include $170,400 for 8 grants (high: $50,250; low: $1,000).
Fields of interest: Arts and culture; Theater; Health; Agriculture; Females.
Limitations: Applications not accepted. Giving primarily in PA.
Application information: Unsolicited requests for funds not accepted.
Officer and Directors: Ellen Solms, Pres. and Treas. and Director; Elizabeth B. Solms.
EIN: 261749268

7993
The Fine Family Charitable Foundation
c/o FFC Capital Corporation
EQT Plz., 625 Liberty Ave., Ste. 3110
Pittsburgh, PA   15222-3115   (412) 444-3511
Contact: Susan H. Brownlee

Established in 2007 in Pennsylvania.
Donors: Milton Fine; Milton Fine 2000 Charitable Trust; The Fine Foundation.
Foundation type: Independent foundation.
Financial data (yr. ended 12/31/13): Assets, $216,441 (M); gifts received, $200,000; expenditures, $208,937; qualifying distributions, $208,937; giving activities include $208,937 for 27 grants (high: $70,000; low: $250).
Fields of interest: Philanthropy; Judaism.
International interests: England.
Limitations: Applications accepted. Giving primarily in MA.
Application information: Application form required.
Initial approach: Letter
Deadline(s): None

Officers: David Fine, Chair.; Rachel Fine, Secy.-Treas.
EIN: 208852301

7994
The Fine Fund
c/o FFC Capital Corporation
625 Liberty Ave., Ste. 3110
Pittsburgh, PA   15222-3115   (412) 444-3511
Contact: Susan H. Brownlee, Secy.

Established in 2007 in Pennsylvania.
Donors: Milton Fine; Milton Fine Trust.
Foundation type: Independent foundation.
Financial data (yr. ended 12/31/12): Assets, $541,872 (M); gifts received, $200,000; expenditures, $182,373; qualifying distributions, $167,500; giving activities include $167,500 for grants.
Purpose and activities: Giving primarily to the environment and visual arts.
Fields of interest: Higher education; Environment; Health.
Limitations: Applications accepted. Giving primarily in Boston, MA. No grants to individuals.
Application information:
Initial approach: Letter
Deadline(s): None
Officers and Directors: Carolyn Fine Friedman, Chair. and C.E.O. and Director; Susan Brownlee, Secy. and Director; Thomas J. Lavelle, Treas. and Director.
EIN: 260697144

7995
J. B. Finley Charitable Trust
c/o PNC Charitable Trusts
249 Fifth Ave.
1 PNC Plz., 20th Fl.
Pittsburgh, PA   15222
E-mail: charitabletrusts@pnc.com; Main URL: https://www.pncsites.com/pncfoundation/charitable_trusts.html

Established in 1919 in Pennsylvania.
Donor: J.B. Finley†.
Foundation type: Independent foundation.
Financial data (yr. ended 09/30/14): Assets, $3,641,665 (M); expenditures, $220,250; qualifying distributions, $194,806; giving activities include $178,174 for 16 grants (high: $25,000; low: $5,000).
Fields of interest: Arts and culture; Education; Christianity; Human services.
Type of support: General support; Matching grants; Capital and infrastructure; Equipment; Program development; Seed money.
Limitations: Applications accepted. Giving primarily in PA. No support for political organizations, or for labor, fraternal, or advocacy organizations. No grants to individuals, or for events or general operating costs.
Application information: Application form required.
Initial approach: Letter of inquiry
Copies of proposal: 1
Trustee: PNC Bank, N.A.
EIN: 256024443

7996
First Cornerstone Foundation Inc
c/o BNY Mellon Trust of Delaware
P.O. Box 185
Pittsburgh, PA 15230-0185

Foundation type: Independent foundation.
Financial data (yr. ended 06/30/14): Assets, $4,918,260; expenditures, $248,896; qualifying distributions, $229,334.
Fields of interest: Education; Environment; Health; Hospital care; Human services.
Type of support: General support.
Limitations: Applications not accepted. Giving primarily in MT and PA. No grants to individuals.
Application information: Contributes only to pre-selected organizations.
Trustee: Frances Abbott.
EIN: 421653252

7997
First Federal Charitable Foundation
8 W. Broad St.
Hazleton, PA 18201 (570) 501-2784
Contact: Megan Kennedy, Exec. Dir.
E-mail for Megan Kennedy:
megan.kennedy@verizon.net; Main URL: http://www.1stfederalcharitable.com

Established in 1998 in Pennsylvania.
Donor: Northeast Pennsylvania Financial Corp.
Foundation type: Independent foundation.
Financial data (yr. ended 09/30/13): Assets, $7,722,392 (M); expenditures, $357,317; qualifying distributions, $265,630; giving activities include $192,160 for 14 grants (high: $50,000; low: $160).
Purpose and activities: The foundation supports organizations involved with arts and culture, education, health, home ownership, human services, community economic development, and civic affairs.
Fields of interest: Arts and culture; Education; Health; Human services.
Type of support: General support; Capital and infrastructure; Equipment; Endowments; Program development; Sponsorships.
Limitations: Applications accepted. Giving limited to areas of company operations in northeast PA, with emphasis on Carbon, Columbia, Luzerne, Monroe, and Schuylkill counties. No support for churches or sectarian organizations, fraternal organizations, political campaigns/parties or candidates, specialized health campaigns, or statewide, national, or international projects. No grants to individuals, or for conferences or seminar attendance.
Publications: Application guidelines; Grants list; Informational brochure.
Application information: Application form required.
  Initial approach: Download application form and mail to foundation
  Copies of proposal: 1
  Board meeting date(s): 3 times per year
  Final notification: Following review
Officers and Directors: Thomas Kennedy, Chair. and Director; Anthony Cusatis, Pres. and Director; Megan Kennedy, Exec. Dir.; R.P. Haentjens; Jospeh Osiecki; John Raynock; Nancy Schlitzer; William Spear.
EIN: 061512796

7998
First Savings Community Foundation
219 S. 9th St.
P.O. Box 176
Perkasie, PA 18944-0176 (215) 257-5035
Contact: Frederick E. Schea, Pres. and C.E.O.
Main URL: https://www.firstsavingsonline.com/top_about_community.php

Donor: First Savings Bank of Perkasie.
Foundation type: Company-sponsored foundation.
Financial data (yr. ended 12/31/13): Assets, $2,749,272 (M); expenditures, $190,300; qualifying distributions, $190,275; giving activities include $190,275 for 73 grants (high: $25,000; low: $100).
Purpose and activities: The foundation supports museums, hospitals, and fire departments and organizations involved with mental health, housing development, youth development, and human services.
Fields of interest: Disasters and emergency management; Housing development; Human services.
Type of support: General support; Employee matching gifts; Annual campaigns; Capital campaigns; Program development.
Limitations: Applications accepted. Giving limited to Bethlehem, Bucks, Lehigh, and Montgomery counties, PA. No grants to individuals.
Application information: Application form required.
  Initial approach: Letter
  Deadline(s): None
Officers: Frederick E. Schea, C.E.O. and Pres.; Todd Hurley, Secy. and C.O.O.; Caroline H. Doyle, C.F.O.
Directors: E. Richard Aichele III; Robert L. Byers, Jr.; Walter H. Cressman; Cheri Freeh; W. Thomas Lomax; Jeffrey A. Naugle.
EIN: 232984663

7999
Five Together Foundation
1900 Market St., 6th Fl.
Philadelphia, PA 19103-2097

Established in 2006 in Pennsylvania.
Donor: Robert I Toll.
Foundation type: Independent foundation.
Financial data (yr. ended 12/31/13): Assets, $11,830,693 (M); expenditures, $438,008; qualifying distributions, $429,877; giving activities include $418,000 for 12 grants (high: $100,000; low: $7,000).
Fields of interest: Human services; Family services; Child welfare.
Limitations: Applications not accepted. No grants to individuals.
Application information: Contributes only to pre-selected organizations.
Officers: Laurie T. Franz, Pres.; Rachel Toll Grassi, V.P.; Jacob Toll, V.P.; Joshua Goldfein, Secy.; Deborah Toll Gruelle, Treas.
EIN: 256889820

8000
Fleming Foundation
7661 Beryl Rd.
Zionsville, PA 18092-2302

Established in 1990 in Pennsylvania.
Donor: Richard Fleming.

Foundation type: Independent foundation.
Financial data (yr. ended 12/31/13): Assets, $9,389,036 (M); gifts received, $300,149; expenditures, $473,768; qualifying distributions, $370,839; giving activities include $370,839 for 47 + grants (high: $256,074).
Purpose and activities: Giving primarily for higher education, health organizations and human services.
Fields of interest: Higher education; Hospital care; Diseases and conditions; Christianity; Human services.
Type of support: Capital campaigns.
Limitations: Applications not accepted. Giving primarily to Allentown, PA. No grants to individuals.
Application information: Contributes only to pre-selected organizations.
Trustees: Kathleen Arnold; Richard Fleming; Robert L. Gorman.
EIN: 232585510

8001
Negley Flinn Charitable Foundation
c/o PNC Bank
620 Liberty Ave., 10th Fl.
Pittsburgh, PA 15222-2719 (412) 768-7519
E-mail: bruce.bickel@pnc.com

Established in 2000 in Pennsylvania.
Donor: Negley Flinn.
Foundation type: Independent foundation.
Financial data (yr. ended 06/30/13): Assets, $13,927,727 (M); gifts received, $8,234,768; expenditures, $293,319; qualifying distributions, $238,023; giving activities include $234,000 for 19 grants (high: $30,000; low: $3,000).
Purpose and activities: Giving primarily for social services, youth education, and the environment.
Fields of interest: Education; Environment; Human services.
Type of support: Continuing support; Matching grants; Equipment; Emergency funds.
Limitations: Applications accepted. Giving primarily in PA. No grants to individuals.
Publications: Application guidelines.
Application information: Application form required.
  Initial approach: Letter or Telephone
  Copies of proposal: 1
  Deadline(s): None
  Board meeting date(s): Telephone for board meeting dates
Officers: Negley Flinn, Pres.; David Petty, V.P.; Jill Petty, V.P.; Lorien M. Flinn, Secy.; Robert W. Allen, Jr., Treas.
Number of staff: 2 full-time professional.
EIN: 256755515

8002
Fortinsky Charitable Foundation Inc.
315 Simpson St.
Swoyersville, PA 18704-3045

Established in 1985 in Pennsylvania.
Donor: Robert Fortinsky.
Foundation type: Independent foundation.
Financial data (yr. ended 12/31/13): Assets, $65,217 (M); expenditures, $209,701; qualifying distributions, $209,460; giving activities include $209,460 for 19 grants (high: $175,000; low: $100).

Fields of interest: Education; Judaism; Human services.

Type of support: General support; Continuing support; Annual campaigns; Scholarships.

Limitations: Applications not accepted. Giving limited to PA. No grants to individuals.

Publications: Annual report.

Application information: Unsolicited requests for funds not accepted.

Director: Jill F. Schwartz.

EIN: 232338218

8003
Foster Charitable Trust

681 Andersen Dr., Ste. 300
Pittsburgh, PA   15220-2747   (412) 928-8900
Contact: Peter F. Mars, Tr.

Established in 1962 in Pennsylvania.

Donors: Foster Industries, Inc.; Foster Investment Co.

Foundation type: Independent foundation.

Financial data (yr. ended 12/31/13): Assets, $3,552,752 (M); expenditures, $245,230; qualifying distributions, $225,035; giving activities include $225,035 for 13 grants (high: $41,800; low: $2).

Fields of interest: Arts and culture; Museums; Education; Higher education; Nonprofits; Judaism; Human services.

Type of support: Regranting.

Limitations: Applications accepted. Giving primarily in Chicago, IL, and Pittsburgh, PA. No grants to individuals, or for endowment funds or operating budgets.

Application information: Application form required.

   Initial approach: Typewritten letter
   Copies of proposal: 1
   Deadline(s): None

Trustees: Bernard S. Mars; Craig J. Foster; James R. Foster; Kim Foster Petracca; Lee B. Foster II; Penny Foster; Peter F. Mars.

EIN: 256064791

8004
Fountainhead Foundation

200 Alpha Dr.
Pittsburgh, PA   15238-2927   (412) 963-3165
Contact: Michelle R. Bitzer, Pres.

Established in 1989 in Pennsylvania.

Donor: ABARTA Inc.

Foundation type: Company-sponsored foundation.

Financial data (yr. ended 12/31/13): Assets, $194,222 (M); expenditures, $212,074; qualifying distributions, $210,721; giving activities include $210,700 for 13 grants (high: $75,000; low: $500).

Purpose and activities: The foundation supports organizations involved with education, health, recreation, children, and human services.

Fields of interest: Education; Elementary and secondary education; Higher education; Health; Hospital care; Sports and recreation; Human services; Child welfare.

Type of support: General support.

Limitations: Applications accepted. Giving on a national basis, with emphasis on PA. No grants to individuals.

Application information: Application form required.

Initial approach: Contact foundaion for application form

   Deadline(s): None

Officers: Michelle R. Bitzer, Pres.; Astrid S. Bitzer, V.P.; Susan Marie Forsyth, Secy.; John F. Bitzer III, Treas.

EIN: 251605441

8005
Freas Foundation, Inc.

1340 Broadcasting Rd., Ste. 100
Wyomissing, PA   19610-5703
Contact: David M. Trout, Mgr.

Foundation type: Independent foundation.

Financial data (yr. ended 12/31/13): Assets, $3,969,908 (M); expenditures, $187,127; qualifying distributions, $170,676; giving activities include $170,676 for 29 grants (high: $14,500; low: $500).

Purpose and activities: Giving primarily for the arts, education, and human services.

Fields of interest: Arts and culture; Higher education; Human services; Child welfare.

Type of support: General support; Matching grants; Annual campaigns; Capital campaigns; Program development; Scholarships.

Limitations: Applications not accepted. Giving primarily in PA. No grants to individuals.

Application information: Contributes only to pre-selected organizations.

Officers: Donald Freas, Pres.; Nancy Pratt, V.P.; Susan Magargee, Secy.; Lawrence Freas, Treas.

EIN: 221714810

8006
George A. & Mary E. Frederick Memorial Foundation

c/o PNC Bank
620 Liberty Ave., 10th Fl.
Pittsburgh, PA   15222-2705

Foundation type: Independent foundation.

Financial data (yr. ended 12/31/13): Assets, $6,674,502 (M); expenditures, $285,404; qualifying distributions, $272,390; giving activities include $271,798 for 2 grants (high: $135,899; low: $135,899).

Fields of interest: Education; Religion.

Limitations: Applications not accepted. Giving primarily in MD.

Application information: Unsolicited requests for funds not accepted.

Trustee: PNC Bank, N.A.

EIN: 900398149

8007
The French Foundation

c/o BNY Mellon, N.A.
P.O. Box 185
Pittsburgh, PA   15230-0185

Established in 1947 in Massachusetts.

Foundation type: Independent foundation.

Financial data (yr. ended 12/31/13): Assets, $6,002,268 (M); expenditures, $381,544; qualifying distributions, $346,940; giving activities include $341,085 for 70 grants (high: $21,000; low: $1,000).

Purpose and activities: Giving primarily for conservation and the environment; support also for the arts and social services.

Fields of interest: Arts and culture; Environment; Natural resources; Human services.

Limitations: Applications not accepted. Giving in ME, NH and VT. No grants to individuals.

Application information: Unsolicited requests for funds not accepted.

   Board meeting date(s): Mar., June, Sept., and Dec.

Trustee: Jameson S. French.

EIN: 046053426

8008
Friends Foundation for the Aging

606 W. Upsal St.
Philadelphia, PA   19119-3626

Donors: NYYM - Dietrich Fund; Marjorie E. Vail Revocable Trust; Roger P. Vail Revocable Trust.

Foundation type: Independent foundation.

Financial data (yr. ended 04/30/13): Assets, $12,704,567 (M); gifts received, $404,912; expenditures, $735,834; qualifying distributions, $721,466; giving activities include $393,336 for 17 grants (high: $89,329; low: $2,209).

Fields of interest: Health; Religion; Human services.

Limitations: Applications not accepted.

Application information: Unsolicited requests for funds not accepted.

Officers: James Whitely, Pres.; Eric Andrews, V.P.; Beth Yingling, Secy.; Howard Freund, Treas.; Deborah Frazer, Exec. Dir.

Trustee: Charley Flint; Susan Hoskins; Daphne Joslin; Beth Hudson Keller; Charles McCutchen; Paula McClure.

EIN: 221524182

8009
Friendship Fund Inc.

c/o BNY Mellon, N.A.
P.O. Box 185
Pittsburgh, PA   15230-0185   (617) 426-7080
Contact: Katy Fyrberg, Fdn. Asst.

Established in 1918 in New York.

Donor: Charles R. Crane†.

Foundation type: Independent foundation.

Financial data (yr. ended 06/30/14): Assets, $4,532,318 (M); expenditures, $269,241; qualifying distributions, $240,223; giving activities include $208,417 for 65 grants (high: $10,000; low: $435).

Purpose and activities: Giving for the advancement of the humanities and the sciences and for the welfare of humanity. Emphasis on local giving for environmental protection, social services, and international affairs. Funds largely committed in advance.

Fields of interest: Education; Environment; Science; Human services; International relations.

Type of support: Capital campaigns; Capital and infrastructure; Equipment; Land acquisitions; Program development; Publications; Seed money.

Limitations: Applications accepted. Giving primarily in CA, CO, CT, MA, NY and VA. No grants to individuals.

Application information:

   Initial approach: Letter

· *Deadline(s):* 4/1
Board meeting date(s): Aug.
Officers and Trustees: Diana H. Crane, Pres. and Trustee; Ellen D.B. F. Tully, V.P. and Trustee; Andrea Erda, Treas. and Trustee; Bronwen Bradley Ballou; Charles Bradley, Jr.; Charles M. Crane, MD; Thomas S. Crane; Frances Crane Manson; Kat Bradley Bennet, Secy. and Trustee; Lynn Bradley Leopold.
EIN: 136089220

8010
William O. and Gertrude Lewis Frohring Foundation
c/o Glenmede Trust Co.
1650 Market St., Ste. 1200
Philadelphia, PA   19103-7391

Established in 1958 in Ohio.
Donors: William O. Frohring†; Gertrude L. Frohring†.
Foundation type: Independent foundation.
Financial data (yr. ended 12/31/14): Assets, $5,678,463; expenditures, $329,958; qualifying distributions, $237,365.
Fields of interest: Arts and culture; Education; Higher education; Health; Diseases and conditions; Human services; Child welfare.
Type of support: General support; Continuing support; Annual campaigns; Capital and infrastructure; Equipment; Land acquisitions; Emergency funds; Seed money.
Limitations: Applications not accepted. Giving primarily in Geauga, Lake, and Cuyahoga counties, OH. No grants to individuals, or for deficit financing, endowment funds, matching gifts, scholarships, or fellowships; no loans.
Application information: Unsolicited requests for funds not accepted.
Board meeting date(s): May and Oct.
Officers: Glenn H. Frohring, Pres.; Steven Szilagyi, V.P.; Evelyn Frohring, Secy.; William W. Falsgraf, Treas.
EIN: 346516526

8011
Gamber Foundation
2220 Dutch Gold Dr.
Lancaster, PA   17601-1997   (717) 393-1716
Contact: Michael T. Kane, Pres.

Established in 1984 in Pennsylvania.
Donors: Dutch Gold Honey, Inc.; Gamber Glass Container, Inc.; W. Ralph Gamber†; Luella M. Gamber.
Foundation type: Company-sponsored foundation.
Financial data (yr. ended 09/30/13): Assets, $2,885,479 (M); gifts received, $124,000; expenditures, $145,515; qualifying distributions, $144,750; giving activities include $144,000 for 27 grants (high: $25,000; low: $1,500).
Purpose and activities: The foundation supports organizations involved with higher education, health, birth defects, housing development, and human services.
Fields of interest: Education; Health; Human services.
Type of support: General support; Capital campaigns; Equipment; Endowments; Program development; Scholarships.
Limitations: Applications accepted. Giving primarily in Lancaster, PA.
Application information:

Initial approach: Proposal
Deadline(s): None
Officers: Michael T. Kane, Pres.; Julie A. Good, Secy.; Nancy J. Gamber, Treas.
Directors: Kitty L. Gamber; Luella M. Gamber; Marianne M. Gamber; W.R. Gamber II; Steven E. Kane; Christopher Markley; Timothy M. Zimmerman.
EIN: 232331958

8012
The Gerald & Suzanne Ganse Family Foundation
2929 Lititz Pike
P.O. Box 5555
Lancaster, PA   17606-5555

Established in 2001 in Pennsylvania.
Donors: Gerald E. Ganse; Suzanne H. Ganse.
Foundation type: Independent foundation.
Financial data (yr. ended 06/30/13): Assets, $427,633 (M); gifts received, $10,000; expenditures, $165,632; qualifying distributions, $163,365; giving activities include $161,877 for 24 + grants (high: $75,100).
Fields of interest: Education; Catholicism; Human services.
Limitations: Applications not accepted. Giving primarily in NE and PA. No grants to individuals.
Application information: Unsolicited requests for funds not accepted.
Officers: Gerald E. Ganse, Pres.; Jeremy J. Ganse, V.P.; Suzanne H. Ganse, Secy.; Gregory P. Ganse, Treas.
EIN: 311789280

8013
Elsie Lee Garthwaite Memorial Foundation
P.O. Box 274
Newtown Square, PA   19073-0274   (610) 356-3585

Established in 1943 in Pennsylvania.
Donor: Albert A. Garthwaite, Jr.†.
Foundation type: Independent foundation.
Financial data (yr. ended 12/31/14): Assets, $9,263,250; expenditures, $499,872; qualifying distributions, $436,219.
Purpose and activities: The foundation has adopted new, more narrowly defined guidelines centered on the children and youth of Lower Montgomery County, PA, and the nearby surrounding communities. Giving primarily to organizations that: 1) provide for the physical and emotional well-being of children and young people; 2) seek to enable young people, particularly the needy, to reach their fullest potential through education, empowerment, and exposure to the arts; and 3) are smaller organizations, with budgets under $1 million per year.
Fields of interest: Arts and culture; Education; Diseases and conditions; Family services; Child welfare; Homeless services; Children and youth; Low-income and poor people; Slum youth.
Type of support: General support.
Limitations: Applications accepted. Giving primarily in Philadelphia, Chester, Montgomery and Delaware counties, PA. No grants to individuals, public, private, or parochial schools, colleges and universities.
Publications: Application guidelines; Grants list.
Application information: Application form required.

Initial approach: Letter of intent 30 days prior to deadlines
Copies of proposal: 1
Deadline(s): Mar. 31 and Aug. 31
Board meeting date(s): Spring and fall
Final notification: Within 10 days following Board meetings
Officers and Trustees: Diane Garthwaite, Pres. and Trustee; John Acuff, V.P. and Trustee; Thomas Kaneda, Secy. and Trustee; A. Alexander Ridley, Treas. and Trustee.
EIN: 236290877

8014
William F. and Lynn D. Gauss Foundation
c/o PNC Bank, N.A.
620 Liberty Ave.,10th Fl.
Pittsburgh, PA   15222-2705   (412) 762-9965
Contact: Jaco B. Reinhart

Established in 2001 in Iowa.
Donor: William F. Gauss.
Foundation type: Independent foundation.
Financial data (yr. ended 12/31/13): Assets, $4,796,174 (M); expenditures, $251,094; qualifying distributions, $198,967; giving activities include $178,400 for 10 grants (high: $35,000; low: $8,000).
Fields of interest: Education; Domesticated animals; Hospital care; Pediatrics; Cystic fibrosis; Protestantism; Human services; Food banks; Adoption; Scouting programs; Children; Ethnic and racial groups.
Type of support: General support; Individual development; Research.
Limitations: Applications accepted. Giving primarily in Pittsburgh, PA. No grants to individuals.
Application information:
Initial approach: Proposal
Deadline(s): None
Trustees: R. Michael Daniel; Mary S. Kroll; PNC Bank, N.A.
EIN: 256784891

8015
Joel and Elaine Gershman Foundation
(formerly Joel Gershman Foundation)
c/o Jager Management, Inc.
261 Old York Rd., Ste. 814
Jenkintown, PA   19046-2837

Donors: Joel Gershman; Elaine Gershman.
Foundation type: Independent foundation.
Financial data (yr. ended 11/30/12): Assets, $3,856,286 (M); expenditures, $262,499; qualifying distributions, $258,630; giving activities include $258,630 for 78 grants (high: $100,000; low: $10).
Purpose and activities: Giving primarily for the arts, education, health, federated giving programs, and human services.
Fields of interest: Arts and culture; Education; Higher education; Nonprofits; Diseases and conditions; Judaism; Human services.
Type of support: Research; Regranting.
Limitations: Applications not accepted. Giving primarily in Philadelphia, PA. No grants to individuals.
Application information: Unsolicited requests for funds not accepted.

Officer: Elaine Levitt Gershman, Secy.-Treas.
EIN: 222529629

8016
Richard P. Gibson and Rosemary Kirr Charitable Trust
P.O. Box 110
Latrobe, PA   15650-0110

Donors: Rosemary Kirr†; Richard P. Gibson.
Foundation type: Independent foundation.
Financial data (yr. ended 12/31/12): Assets, $0 (M); gifts received, $9,500; expenditures, $312,095; qualifying distributions, $311,736; giving activities include $311,736 for 17 grants (high: $301,336; low: $300).
Fields of interest: Education; Philanthropy; Diseases and conditions.
Limitations: Applications not accepted. Giving primarily in PA. No grants to individuals.
Application information: Unsolicited requests for funds not accepted.
Trustee: Richard P. Gibson.
EIN: 256727717

8017
James and Marilyn A. Gilmore Foundation
20 Stanwix St., Ste. 650
Pittsburgh, PA   15222-4801

Established in 2000 in Pennsylvania.
Donor: James Gilmore†.
Foundation type: Independent foundation.
Financial data (yr. ended 12/31/13): Assets, $6,031,090 (M); expenditures, $292,334; qualifying distributions, $240,000; giving activities include $240,000 for 20 grants (high: $61,000; low: $1,000).
Purpose and activities: Giving primarily for the arts, human services, education, a Presbyterian church, and to a theological seminary.
Fields of interest: Arts and culture; Education; Elementary and secondary education; Graduate and professional education; Protestantism; Theology; Human services.
Limitations: Applications not accepted. Giving primarily in Pittsburgh, PA. No grants to individuals.
Application information: Unsolicited requests for funds not accepted.
Trustees: Janet W. Danforth; Marilyn A. Gilmore; David M. Walradt.
EIN: 256699697

8018
Sonia Raiziss Giop Charitable Foundation
c/o Bank of New York Mellon, N.A.
P.O. Box 185
Pittsburgh, PA   15230-0185

Established in 1994 in Pennsylvania.
Donors: Sonia Giop†; Ines Giop Trust; Benz Charitable Remainder Unitrust.
Foundation type: Independent foundation.
Financial data (yr. ended 12/31/14): Assets, $3,551,316 (M); expenditures, $338,723; qualifying distributions, $324,267; giving activities include $322,700 for 27 grants (high: $140,700; low: $2,000).

Purpose and activities: Giving primarily for education, the arts, particularly for poetry and other literary organizations, and animal welfare.
Fields of interest: Arts and culture; Music; Literature and writing; Higher education; Animal welfare.
Limitations: Applications not accepted. Giving primarily in Washington, D.C. and NY. No grants to individuals.
Application information: Contributes only to pre-selected organizations.
Trustees: Alfredo De Palchi; Antoinette Denisof; Bank of New York Mellon, N.A.
EIN: 256453053

8019
Elizabeth M. Gitt Foundation
53 Sage Dr.
Pottstown, PA   19465

Donor: Elizabeth M. Gitt†.
Foundation type: Independent foundation.
Financial data (yr. ended 05/31/13): Assets, $1,587,610 (M); expenditures, $129,545; qualifying distributions, $122,300; giving activities include $122,300 for 26 grants (high: $56,500; low: $300).
Purpose and activities: Giving primarily to civil rights, health associations, family planning, animal welfare, and human services.
Fields of interest: Community and economic development; Human services.
Limitations: Applications not accepted. Giving primarily in Hanover, PA. No grants to individuals.
Application information: Contributes only to pre-selected organizations.
Officers: Carson G. Taylor, Esq., Pres.; Cynthia Gitt, Secy.; Andrew L. Schaeffer, Treas.
Directors: Jessica G. Nembhard; Douglas F. Rebert.
EIN: 232790834

8020
Glendorn Foundation
78 Main St.
Bradford, PA   16701-2026
Contact: William F. Higie, Mgr.

Established in 1953 in Texas.
Donors: Forest Oil Corp.; Ruth H. Dorn†.
Foundation type: Independent foundation.
Financial data (yr. ended 12/31/13): Assets, $4,329,868 (M); gifts received, $100; expenditures, $259,915; qualifying distributions, $196,833; giving activities include $196,833 for 13 grants (high: $41,000; low: $5,000).
Purpose and activities: Giving primarily for education and for health care.
Fields of interest: Education; Health; Diseases and conditions.
Type of support: Scholarships; Research; Research and evaluation.
Limitations: Applications not accepted. Giving on a national basis.
Publications: Financial statement.
Application information: Funds currently committed. Only trustee-originated requests considered.
   Board meeting date(s): Apr. and Oct.
Officer: William F. Higie, Secy. and Mgr.
Trustees: Clayton D. Coburn; John C. Dorn; Dale Bird Grubb; Jeffrey W. Miller; Brooks Dorn Stewart; Carolynn D. Warner; Leslie D. Young.

Number of staff: 1 part-time support.
EIN: 251024349

8021
Raymond & Ellen Goldberg Foundation
P.O. Box 1655
Horsham, PA   19044-6655

Established in 1986 in Pennsylvania.
Donors: Ellen Goldberg; Raymond Goldberg.
Foundation type: Independent foundation.
Financial data (yr. ended 11/30/13): Assets, $138,904 (M); gifts received, $199,309; expenditures, $162,295; qualifying distributions, $148,295; giving activities include $148,295 for 64 grants.
Fields of interest: Education; Health; Judaism.
Limitations: Applications not accepted. Giving primarily in PA, with some giving in FL. No grants to individuals.
Application information: Unsolicited requests for funds not accepted.
Trustees: Ellen Goldberg; Raymond Goldberg.
EIN: 222787780

8022
Golden Slipper Senior Care Foundation I
c/o Paul Geller
215 N Presidential Blvd., 1s Fl.
Bala-Cynwyd, PA   19004-1201   (610) 660-0510
Contact: Neal Grabell, Pres.

Foundation type: Independent foundation.
Financial data (yr. ended 09/30/13): Assets, $3,092,380 (M); expenditures, $356,874; qualifying distributions, $330,510; giving activities include $322,901 for 2 grants (high: $217,407; low: $105,494).
Fields of interest: Community service.
Limitations: Applications accepted. Giving primarily in PA.
Application information:
   Initial approach: Proposal
   Deadline(s): None
Officer: Neal Grabell, Pres.
Directors: Bernie Brown; Allan M. Dabrow; Michael Finkelstein; Susan R. Freedman; Stephen Frishberg; Mark Greene; David Horowitz; Scott Isdaner; Fred Kaplan; Betsy Klausman; Howard Lapensohn; Debbie Rasansky; Michael Steinberg.
EIN: 203275598

8023
Harvey Goodstein Charitable Trust
540 Pennsylvania Ave., Ste. 323
Fort Washington, PA   19034-3311

Established in 1999 in Pennsylvania.
Foundation type: Independent foundation.
Financial data (yr. ended 12/31/13): Assets, $7,600,269 (M); expenditures, $786,492; qualifying distributions, $355,000; giving activities include $355,000 for 7 grants (high: $125,000; low: $5,000).
Fields of interest: Education; Human services.
Limitations: Applications not accepted. Giving primarily in New York, NY, and Devon and Philadelphia, PA. No grants to individuals.
Application information: Contributes only to pre-selected organizations.

Trustees: Sandra Goodstein; Meyer Koplow.
EIN: 237992456

8024
Reuben & Mollie Gordon Foundation

1116 Mason Ave.
Drexel Hill, PA 19026-2510
Contact: Harry Lieberman, Pres.

Established in 1960 in Pennsylvania.
Donors: Reuben Gordon; Fred Lieberman†.
Foundation type: Independent foundation.
Financial data (yr. ended 12/31/13): Assets, $2,624,121 (M); expenditures, $441,394; qualifying distributions, $251,601; giving activities include $154,500 for 19 grants (high: $25,000; low: $1,000).
Purpose and activities: Giving primarily for health and medical education, services, and research; giving also for the arts and to human service organizations.
Fields of interest: Arts and culture; Diseases and conditions; Judaism; Human services.
Limitations: Applications not accepted. Giving primarily in CA, FL and PA. No grants to individuals.
Application information: Contributes only to pre-selected organizations.
Officers and Directors: Harry Lieberman, Pres. and Director; Annette Lieberman, V.P. and Director; Marla Lieberman, Secy. and Director; Anthony Mignogna, Treas. and Director.
EIN: 236251826

8025
Goshen Hill Foundation, Inc.

c/o BNY Mellon Trust of Delaware
P.O. Box 185
Pittsburgh, PA 15230-0185

Foundation type: Independent foundation.
Financial data (yr. ended 06/30/14): Assets, $3,598,062 (M); expenditures, $179,280; qualifying distributions, $167,186; giving activities include $163,600 for 13 grants (high: $25,000; low: $2,500).
Fields of interest: Animal welfare; Nonprofits; Equestrianism; Human services; Food aid.
Type of support: General support; Regranting.
Limitations: Applications not accepted. Giving primarily in Washington, DC, NC and PA. No grants to individuals.
Application information: Unsolicited requests for funds not accepted.
Trustee: BNY Mellon Trust of Delaware, N.A.
Director: Caroline A. Moran.
EIN: 412160007

8026
Greater Erie Economic Development Corporation

18 W. 9th St.
Erie, PA 16501-1343 (814) 459-4581
Contact: Gerald L. Blanks

Foundation type: Independent foundation.
Financial data (yr. ended 12/31/13): Assets, $17,817,618 (M); gifts received, $20,000; expenditures, $1,660,124; qualifying distributions, $594,489; giving activities include $256,262 for 15

grants (high: $229,667; low: $80), and $46,860 for 14 grants to individuals (high: $8,593; low: $838).
Fields of interest: Education; Higher education; Community and economic development; Human services.
Type of support: Grants to individuals.
Limitations: Applications accepted. Giving primarily in PA.
Application information: Applications are only selected from residents from the Erie County area and only for colleges and universities that confer four year degrees. Application form required.
  Initial approach: Contact foundation for application form
  Deadline(s): Apr. 15th for fall; Nov. 25th for Spring
Officers: Tessie Blanchard, Jr., Chair.; Vernon D. Dobbs, Vice-Chair.; Ronald A. Steele, C.E.O.; Carla Johnson, Secy.; Eva Tucker, Jr., Treas.
Board Members: Gerald L. Blanks; Barbara L. Drew; Melvin Witherspoon.
EIN: 251269138

8027
The Mary E. Groff Surgical and Medical Research and Education Charitable Trust

5 Radnor Corporate Ctr.
100 Malsonford Rd., Ste. 450
Radnor, PA 19087-4526

Established in 1999 in Pennsylvania.
Donor: Mary E. Groff†.
Foundation type: Independent foundation.
Financial data (yr. ended 12/31/14): Assets, $4,833,830; expenditures, $255,369; qualifying distributions, $199,308.
Purpose and activities: Giving primarily for higher education.
Fields of interest: Higher education; Hospital care.
Limitations: Applications not accepted. Giving primarily in PA. No grants to individuals.
Application information: Unsolicited requests for funds not accepted.
Trustees: Adam Burkey, MD; Fatema E.F. Burkey, Esq.; Coryell Urban.
EIN: 232725113

8028
The M. S. Grumbacher Foundation

c/o Cozen O'Connor
1900 Market St.
Philadelphia, PA 19103-3508 (215) 665-4117
Contact: David Glyn, Dir.

Established in 1992 in Pennsylvania.
Donor: M.S. Grumbacher.
Foundation type: Independent foundation.
Financial data (yr. ended 08/31/14): Assets, $6,833,029 (M); expenditures, $339,382; qualifying distributions, $300,832; giving activities include $284,500 for 12 grants (high: $105,000; low: $2,000).
Fields of interest: Arts and culture; Performing arts; Education; Higher education; Foundations; Health; Diseases and conditions; Alzheimer's disease; Community and economic development; Judaism; Human services; Child welfare.
Limitations: Applications accepted. Giving limited to PA, with emphasis on the York area. No grants to individuals.
Application information: Application form required.

Initial approach: Letter
Deadline(s): Submit application between Nov. 1 and Apr. 30
Officer: Joshua G. Schultz, Pres.
Directors: David R. Glyn; Susan Gregory; Mary Jo Grumbacher; Rowan Shultz.
EIN: 232697348

8029
The Grundy Foundation

680 Radcliffe St.
Bristol, PA 19007-5136 (215) 788-5460
Contact: Eugene J. Williams, Exec. Dir.
FAX: (215) 788-0915;
E-mail: info@grundyfoundation.com; Main URL: http://www.grundyfoundation.com
Philanthropical Endeavors: http://www.grundyfoundation.com/content/philanthropy

Established in 1961 in Pennsylvania.
Donor: Joseph R. Grundy†.
Foundation type: Independent foundation.
Financial data (yr. ended 12/31/13): Assets, $60,918,312 (M); gifts received, $858; expenditures, $2,347,660; qualifying distributions, $2,237,174; giving activities include $143,500 for 4 grants (high: $90,000; low: $10,000), and $1,293,601 for foundation-administered programs.
Purpose and activities: Grants for civic affairs and community planning, social service and youth agencies, a community fund, the arts, higher education, and health. Giving restricted to organizations supported by Mr. Grundy during his lifetime.
Fields of interest: Arts and culture; Higher education; Hospital care; Public administration; Community and economic development; Child welfare.
Type of support: General support; Capital and infrastructure; Equipment; Land acquisitions; Program development.
Limitations: Applications accepted. Giving limited to Bucks County, PA. No support for religious organizations. No grants to individuals, or for endowment funds, research, scholarships, or fellowships; no loans.
Publications: Application guidelines; Informational brochure (including application guidelines).
Application information: Application and guidelines available on foundation web site. Delaware Valley Grantmakers Common Grant Application Form accepted.
  Initial approach: Letter
  Copies of proposal: 1
  Deadline(s): None
  Board meeting date(s): Monthly except in Aug.
Officer: Eugene J. Williams, Exec. Dir.
Trustees: Frederick J.M. LaValley; Bonnie J. O'Boyle; Thomas F. Praiss; Leonard N. Snyder; Wells Fargo Bank.
Number of staff: 2 full-time professional.
EIN: 231609243

8030
GT Foundation

P.O. Box 305
Kulpsville, PA 19443-0305

Established in 1998 in Pennsylvania.
Donor: Green Tweed & Co.
Foundation type: Company-sponsored foundation.

Financial data (yr. ended 12/31/13): Assets, $6,151,195 (M); gifts received, $480,000; expenditures, $329,476; qualifying distributions, $325,000; giving activities include $325,000 for 5 grants (high: $180,000; low: $6,000).
Purpose and activities: The foundation supports organizations involved with animals and wildlife, patient services, horses, children and youth, homelessness, and Judaism.
Fields of interest: Education; Religion; Human services.
Type of support: General support.
Limitations: Applications not accepted. Giving primarily in CA, MT, NY, and PA. No grants to individuals.
Application information: Contributes only to pre-selected organizations.
Trustees: Hannah Delfiner; Michael Delfiner; Ruth Delfiner; Joan Stanley; Kenneth Stanley; Nancy Stanley.
EIN: 237927474

8031

Guild of the Dome Inc.
18695 Greenleaf Dr.
Saegertown, PA 16433-4429

Donors: James Greenleaf; Lawrence Raia; Thierry Porte.
Foundation type: Independent foundation.
Financial data (yr. ended 12/31/13): Assets, $5,041 (M); gifts received, $462,036; expenditures, $456,995; qualifying distributions, $456,995; giving activities include $299,406 for 1 grant.
Fields of interest: Arts and culture.
Limitations: Applications not accepted.
Application information: Unsolicited requests for funds not accepted.
Officers: James Greenleaf, Pres. and Treas.; Ennco Marinelli, Secy.
Directors: Annamaria Giusti; Mark Snyder.
EIN: 461139253

8032

The Gulati Family Foundation
c/o Rosemary M. Gulati
413 Long Ln.
Oley, PA 19547-9016

Donors: Jack D. Gulati; Rosemary M. Gulati.
Foundation type: Independent foundation.
Financial data (yr. ended 12/31/14): Assets, $2,968,217; gifts received, $30; expenditures, $294,597; qualifying distributions, $292,267.
Purpose and activities: Giving to educational institutions at every level, from early childhood through graduate school.
Fields of interest: Education; Diseases and conditions; Human services.
Type of support: Continuing support; Annual campaigns; Capital campaigns; Capital and infrastructure.
Limitations: Applications not accepted. No grants to individuals.
Application information: Unsolicited requests for funds not accepted.
Trustees: Allison Gulati; Charles J. Gulati; Jack D. Gulati; Jack D. Gulati II; Jennifer Gulati; Loretta Gulati; Michael E. Gulati; Rosemary M. Gulati.
EIN: 756669847

8033

The Gureghian Charitable Foundation
841 Merion Square Rd.
Gladwyne, PA 19035-1507 (610) 447-0400
Contact: Vahan H. Gureghian, Pres.

Donors: Vahan H. Gureghian; Danielle Gureghian.
Foundation type: Independent foundation.
Financial data (yr. ended 12/31/13): Assets, $16,168 (M); gifts received, $219,000; expenditures, $275,025; qualifying distributions, $271,055; giving activities include $271,055 for 14 grants (high: $64,951; low: $3,200).
Fields of interest: Secondary education.
Type of support: Scholarships.
Limitations: Applications accepted. Giving primarily in DE and PA.
Application information: Application form required.
Initial approach: Letter
Deadline(s): None
Officers and Directors: Vahan H. Gureghian, Pres. and Director; Danielle Gureghian, Secy.-Treas.
EIN: 272512489

8034

The Gypsy Hill Conservation Charitable Trust
P.O. Box 559
Gwynedd Valley, PA 19437-0559

Donor: Saly A. Glassman.
Foundation type: Operating foundation.
Financial data (yr. ended 12/31/12): Assets, $6,913,788 (M); gifts received, $375,000; expenditures, $165,948; qualifying distributions, $157,358; giving activities include $157,358 for 5 grants (high: $54,115; low: $2,500).
Purpose and activities: Giving to maintain an open space conservancy for the general public.
Fields of interest: Arts and culture; Education; Environment.
Limitations: Applications not accepted. Giving primarily in PA.
Application information: Unsolicited requests for funds not accepted.
Trustee: Martin J. Satinsky.
Director: Saly A. Glassman.
EIN: 237987715

8035

Hager Family Charitable Foundation
210 W. Ritten House Sq., Unit 2805
Philadelphia, PA 19103
Contact: D. Daniele Hager

Established in 2007 in Pennsylvania.
Donor: George V. Hager.
Foundation type: Independent foundation.
Financial data (yr. ended 12/31/13): Assets, $589,029 (M); gifts received, $150,000; expenditures, $286,398; qualifying distributions, $279,702; giving activities include $279,000 for 7 grants (high: $150,000; low: $5,000).
Fields of interest: Education; Philanthropy; Religion.
Type of support: General support.
Limitations: Applications not accepted. No grants to individuals.
Application information: Unsolicited requests for funds not accepted.

Trustees: Mark A. Daniele; D. Daniele Hager; Mark Eileen Tambellini.
EIN: 261378182

8036

The Norman & Elizabeth Hahn Family Foundation
1686 Weaverland Rd.
East Earl, PA 17519-9476

Established in 2002 in Pennsylvania.
Donors: Norman Hahn; Elizabeth Hahn; Conestoga Wood Specialities Corp.
Foundation type: Independent foundation.
Financial data (yr. ended 12/31/13): Assets, $735,801 (M); gifts received, $342,465; expenditures, $357,132; qualifying distributions, $348,120; giving activities include $347,500 for 19 grants (high: $50,000; low: $2,500).
Fields of interest: Christianity; Senior services.
Limitations: Applications not accepted. Giving primarily in PA. No grants to individuals.
Application information: Unsolicited requests for funds not accepted.
Trustee: Susquehanna Bank.
Number of staff: None.
EIN: 256818477

8037

The Hall Foundation
c/o Robert E. Hall
P.O. Box 1200
Camp Hill, PA 17001-1200 (717) 761-1057
Contact: Robert E. Hall, Exec. Dir.

Established in 1952 in Pennsylvania.
Donors: John N. Hall†; Hall's Motor Transit Co.
Foundation type: Independent foundation.
Financial data (yr. ended 12/31/14): Assets, $7,076,874 (M); expenditures, $497,793; qualifying distributions, $361,330; giving activities include $282,840 for 113 grants (high: $22,000; low: $100).
Purpose and activities: Emphasis on scholarship funds available to local area graduates chosen by their high school administrators; support also for higher education, youth agencies, health services, and sports and recreation.
Fields of interest: Arts and culture; Higher education; Health; Sports and recreation; Human services; Youth services.
Type of support: General support; Scholarships.
Limitations: Applications accepted. Giving primarily in PA.
Application information:
Initial approach: Letter
Copies of proposal: 1
Deadline(s): 3 months prior to date of requested contribution or grant
Board meeting date(s): Quarterly
Officers and Trustees: Gerald Hall, Jr., V.P. and Trustee; Robert E. Hall, Exec. Dir. and Trustee; R. Jarek Hall; Leroy Zimmerman.
EIN: 236243044

8038
Hankin Foundation
(formerly Bernard & Henrietta Hankin Foundation)
P.O. Box 562
Exton, PA   19341-0562
Contact: Robert S. Hankin, Pres.
Application address: 707 Eagleview Blvd., Exton, PA
19341, tel.: (610) 458-1900

Established in 1984 in Pennsylvania.
Donors: Bernard Hankin†; Robert Hankin; Richard
Hankin; Henrietta Hankin.
Foundation type: Independent foundation.
Financial data (yr. ended 11/30/13): Assets, $0
(M); gifts received, $228,000; expenditures,
$219,028; qualifying distributions, $217,911;
giving activities include $217,911 for 82 grants
(high: $30,000; low: $50).
Purpose and activities: Giving for health care, youth
and social services, and education.
Fields of interest: Education; Nonprofits; Health;
Human services; Child welfare.
Type of support: General support; Employee
matching gifts; In-kind gifts; Continuing support;
Annual campaigns; Capital campaigns; Capital and
infrastructure; Emergency funds; Regranting.
Limitations: Applications accepted. Giving primarily
in PA. No grants to individuals.
Application information:
   Initial approach: Proposal
   Deadline(s): None
Officers: Robert S. Hankin, Pres.; Henrietta Hankin,
Secy.-Treas.
EIN: 251479501

8039
Thomas S. Harrison 12Th Item
c/o BNY Mellon, N.A.
P.O. Box 185
Pittsburgh, PA   15230-0185

Foundation type: Independent foundation.
Financial data (yr. ended 12/31/14): Assets,
$3,320,934 (M); expenditures, $183,526;
qualifying distributions, $164,132; giving activities
include $160,000 for 1 grant.
Fields of interest: Human services.
Limitations: Applications not accepted.
Application information: Unsolicited requests for
funds not accepted.
Trustee: BNY Mellon, N.A.
EIN: 236225608

8040
Harsco Corporation Fund
c/o Harsco Corp.
350 Poplar Church Rd.
Camp Hill, PA   17011   (717) 763-7064
Contact: Robert G. Yocum, Chair.
Application address for charitable gifts: c/o Robert G.
Yocum, Chair., Harsco Corporation Fund, P.O. Box
8888, Camp Hill, PA 17001-8888

Established in 1956 in Pennsylvania.
Donor: Harsco Corp.
Foundation type: Company-sponsored foundation.
Financial data (yr. ended 12/31/13): Assets,
$8,037 (M); gifts received, $369,100;
expenditures, $369,118; qualifying distributions,
$368,880; giving activities include $285,150 for 12

grants (high: $159,100; low: $100), and $83,730
for 26 employee matching gifts.
Purpose and activities: The foundation supports
organizations involved with arts and culture,
education, health, housing development, human
services, and the steel industry.
Fields of interest: Arts and culture; Education;
Higher education; Nonprofits; Health;
Communication media; Housing development;
Business and industry; Human services.
Type of support: General support; Employee
matching gifts; Continuing support; Scholarships;
Individual development; Regranting.
Limitations: Applications accepted. Giving on a
national basis in areas of company operations, with
some emphasis on NY and PA. No grants to
individuals (except for employee-related
scholarships), or for special projects, building or
endowments, or research; no loans.
Application information: Application form required.
   Initial approach: Letter
   Deadline(s): None
   Board meeting date(s): Apr. and as required
Officer and Trustee: Robert G. Yocum, Chair. and
Trustee.
EIN: 236278376

8041
The Hartfield Foundation, Inc.
c/o Glenmede Trust Co.
1650 Market St., Ste. 1200
Philadelphia, PA   19103-7391

Established in 2001 in New Jersey.
Donor: C. Austin Buck.
Foundation type: Independent foundation.
Financial data (yr. ended 12/31/13): Assets,
$3,623,824 (M); expenditures, $171,385;
qualifying distributions, $153,580; giving activities
include $143,500 for 12 grants (high: $25,000;
low: $5,000).
Fields of interest: Art museums; Natural resources;
Gardening; Adolescents.
Type of support: General support.
Limitations: Applications not accepted. Giving
primarily in NJ, NY and VA. No grants to individuals.
Application information: Contributes only to
pre-selected organizations.
Officers: Marguerite D. Buck, Chair.; C. Austin Buck,
Pres. and Treas.; Wendy B. Brown, V.P. and Secy.;
Leonard J. Buck, V.P.; Belinda B. Kielland, V.P.
EIN: 223844906

8042
The Hassel Foundation
c/o BNY Mellon Center
1735 Market St., Ste. 600
Philadelphia, PA   19103-7513
Contact: Michael H. Krekstein, Tr.

Established in 1961 in Pennsylvania.
Donors: Morris Hassel†; Calvin Hassel†.
Foundation type: Independent foundation.
Financial data (yr. ended 12/31/13): Assets,
$6,945,162 (M); expenditures, $359,039;
qualifying distributions, $285,627; giving activities
include $270,700 for 44 grants (high: $40,000;
low: $700).
Purpose and activities: Support primarily for higher
and other education, human services, and the arts;
scholarships are awarded annually to graduating

seniors of Reading Senior High School, Exeter
Township Senior High School, and Twin Valley High
School, in PA.
Fields of interest: Arts and culture; Education;
Higher education; Human services; Seniors.
Type of support: General support; Continuing
support; Capital and infrastructure; Student aid.
Limitations: Applications accepted. Giving primarily
in Philadelphia and Reading, PA. No grants to
individuals (except for scholarships at specified high
schools).
Application information:
   Initial approach: Letter
   Deadline(s): None
   Board meeting date(s): June and Nov.
Trustees: Rodger Citron; Andrea Cohen; Barbara
Cohen; Elizabeth Cohen; Ellen Cohen; Mark
Deitcher; Andrew Goldberg; Jay L. Goldberg; Maxine
Goldberg; Michael Goldberg; David Khoury; Lisa
Khoury; Marilyn Khoury; Michael H. Krekstein; David
Whellan; Merle A. Wolfson.
Number of staff: None.
EIN: 236251862

8043
Hauber Foundation
c/o Gregory Harbaugh, Houston Harbaugh
401 Liberty Ave., 22nd Fl.
Pittsburgh, PA   15222-1005   4122815060

Established in 1997 in Pennsylvania.
Donors: William M. Hauber†; Jean D. Hauber.
Foundation type: Independent foundation.
Financial data (yr. ended 12/31/14): Assets,
$3,761,949; expenditures, $279,895; qualifying
distributions, $246,515.
Fields of interest: Education; Nonprofits; Human
services.
Type of support: Regranting.
Limitations: Applications not accepted. No grants to
individuals.
Application information: Unsolicited requests for
funds not accepted.
Officer: Gregory A. Harbaugh, Secy.-Treas.
Trustees: Nancy Bedwell; Gregory Hauber; Pamela
Hauber; Paul Hauber; Beth Stewart.
EIN: 237887198

8044
Alexandra G. Hawkins Foundation
c/o Morgan, Lewis & Bockius, LLP
1701 Market St.
Philadelphia, PA   19103-2903

Donors: A. Grange Trust; Alexandra Hawkins Trust.
Foundation type: Independent foundation.
Financial data (yr. ended 12/31/13): Assets,
$3,989,951 (M); gifts received, $36,691;
expenditures, $301,778; qualifying distributions,
$266,087; giving activities include $257,400 for 2
grants (high: $220,000; low: $37,400).
Fields of interest: Arts and culture.
Limitations: Applications not accepted. Giving
primarily in PA.
Application information: Unsolicited requests for
funds not accepted.
Trustees: Francis J. Mirabello; Marianna O.
Mirabello.
EIN: 943454881

8045
The Hawksglen Foundation
c/o BNY Mellon, N.A.
P.O. Box 185
Pittsburgh, PA 15230-0185
Application address: c/o BNY Mellon, N.A.,
Attn.: Richard Coleman, 1 Mellon Ctr., 151-3711,
Pittsburgh, PA 15258, tel.: (412) 234-8338

Established in 2002 in Pennsylvania.
Donor: Rebecca Barclay Humphrey.
Foundation type: Independent foundation.
Financial data (yr. ended 12/31/14): Assets,
$4,138,479; expenditures, $258,804; qualifying
distributions, $221,360.
Fields of interest: Natural resources; Biodiversity;
Wildlife biodiversity; Cancers; Archives and special
collections; Community beautification.
Limitations: Applications accepted. Giving primarily
in PA. No grants to individuals.
Application information:
Initial approach: Letter
Deadline(s): None
Trustees: Rebecca Barclay Humphrey; BNY Mellon,
N.A.
Number of staff: None.
EIN: 256820594

8046
The Ralph Hayes Common Wealth Foundation
c/o PNC Bank, N.A., Tax Dept.
1600 Market St.
Philadelphia, PA 19103-7240

Foundation type: Independent foundation.
Financial data (yr. ended 12/31/13): Assets,
$181,915 (M); expenditures, $345,905; qualifying
distributions, $345,905; giving activities include
$75,000 for 1 grant, and $225,000 for 3 grants to
individuals (high: $75,000; low: $75,000).
Fields of interest: Arts and culture.
Limitations: Applications not accepted.
Application information: Unsolicited requests for
funds not accepted.
Officers: Nicholas Marsini, Jr., Pres.; Linda R.
Manfredonia, V.P.; Richard E . Menkiewicz,
Secy.-Treas.
Directors: Mary Liz Biddle; Jaqueline Lessman;
Thomas P. Melcher; Connie Bond Staurt.
Trustee: PNC Bank, N.A.
EIN: 263603811

8047
The HBE Foundation
c/o Beucler, Kelly & Irwin, Ltd.
125 Strafford Ave., No. 116
Wayne, PA 19087
Application address: c/o Bruce M. Brown, 709 Great
Springs Rd., Bryn Mawr, PA 19010-1703

Established in 1988 in Pennsylvania.
Donor: Bruce Maitland Brown.
Foundation type: Independent foundation.
Financial data (yr. ended 06/30/13): Assets,
$970,729 (M); gifts received, $1,452;
expenditures, $199,484; qualifying distributions,
$193,517; giving activities include $182,400 for 30
grants (high: $30,000; low: $1,000).
Fields of interest: Education; Mental health care;
Community and economic development.

Type of support: General support; In-kind gifts;
Capital campaigns; Capital and infrastructure;
Program development; Publications; Seed money;
Scholarships; Research.
Limitations: Applications accepted. Giving primarily
in NJ and PA. No grants to individuals, for debt
reduction, emergencies, tickets, tables or ad books.
Application information: Unsolicited proposals not
acknowledged unless trustee is interested; contact
foundation to determine if a proposal is advisable.
Delaware Valley Grantmakers Common Grant
Application Form accepted.
Initial approach: Proposal
Deadline(s): Rolling basis
Trustee: Bruce M. Brown.
Number of staff: None.
EIN: 236910944

8048
Health and Welfare Foundation of Southern Chester County
P.O. Box 374
West Grove, PA 19390-0374 (610) 925-5925
Contact: William D. Pugh, Vice-Chair.
E-mail: wdp123@gmail.com; Main URL: http://
www.hwfscc.org

Foundation type: Independent foundation.
Financial data (yr. ended 09/30/13): Assets,
$5,352,473 (M); gifts received, $3,640;
expenditures, $236,881; qualifying distributions,
$168,500; giving activities include $168,500 for 32
grants (high: $15,000; low: $1,000).
Fields of interest: Education; Health; Community
and economic development.
Limitations: Giving primarily in PA.
Application information: Application guidelines for
grants and scholarships are available on foundation
web site.
Officers: Richard E. White, Chair.; William D. Pugh,
Vice-Chair.; Richard I. Wade, Treas.
Directors: Tamara K. Brosius; William L. Cook; Joan
M. Holliday; David L. Myers; Cheryl J. McConnell.
EIN: 233090992

8049
Health Care and Education Trust
600 W. Germantown Pike, Ste. 400
Plymouth Meeting, PA 19462-1046

Foundation type: Independent foundation.
Financial data (yr. ended 12/31/13): Assets,
$1,327 (M); expenditures, $300,147; qualifying
distributions, $300,000; giving activities include
$300,000 for 1 grant.
Fields of interest: Health.
Limitations: Applications not accepted.
Application information: Unsolicited requests for
funds not accepted.
Trustee: David A. Peckman, Esq.
EIN: 456182332

8050
Hecht Family Charitable Foundation
3920 Ravenswood Rd.
Allentown, PA 18103-9661

Established in 2006 in Pennsylvania.
Donor: William F. Hecht.
Foundation type: Independent foundation.

Financial data (yr. ended 09/30/13): Assets,
$2,930,324 (M); expenditures, $205,385;
qualifying distributions, $201,000; giving activities
include $201,000 for 13 grants (high: $50,000;
low: $2,500).
Fields of interest: Art museums; Higher education;
Nonprofits; Domestic violence shelters.
Type of support: General support; Regranting.
Limitations: Applications not accepted. Giving
primarily in PA and CT. No grants to individuals.
Application information: Contributes only to
pre-selected organizations.
Officers and Directors: William F. Hecht, Chair.;
Margaret D. Hecht, Pres.; Michael G. Hecht, Secy.;
Gregory B. Hecht, Treas.; Kimberly Hecht.
EIN: 203958008

8051
Lewis & Marguerite Herndon Memorial Fund
P.O. Box 609
Pittsburgh, PA 15230-9738

Foundation type: Independent foundation.
Financial data (yr. ended 07/31/13): Assets,
$3,940,618 (M); expenditures, $183,735;
qualifying distributions, $174,812; giving activities
include $167,413 for 5 grants (high: $74,407; low:
$18,601).
Fields of interest: Health; Children's hospital care;
Religion; Human services; Children.
Type of support: General support.
Limitations: Applications not accepted. Giving
primarily in KY.
Application information: Unsolicited requests for
funds not accepted.
Trustee: PNC Bank, N.A.
EIN: 616063431

8052
Jacob E. Heyl Trust
c/o PNC Bank
620 Liberty Ave., 10th Fl.
Pittsburgh, PA 15222

Foundation type: Independent foundation.
Financial data (yr. ended 12/31/14): Assets,
$5,382,814; expenditures, $282,055; qualifying
distributions, $227,615 and $0 for set-asides.
Fields of interest: Education; Health; Human
services.
Limitations: Applications not accepted. Giving
primarily in PA.
Application information: Unsolicited requests for
funds not accepted.
Trustee: PNC Bank, N.A.
EIN: 236203493

8053
HFO Foundation
c/o B. Rosenfield
1600 Market St., Ste. 3600
Philadelphia, PA 19103-7212

Established in 1989 in Pennsylvania.
Donors: John J. Harmon; Elaine Harmon; Debra
Abdo; Wendy Gironda.
Foundation type: Independent foundation.
Financial data (yr. ended 11/30/13): Assets,
$1,166,478 (M); expenditures, $362,303;

qualifying distributions, $357,849; giving activities include $355,000 for 11 grants (high: $50,000; low: $10,000).

Fields of interest: Elementary and secondary education; Nonprofits; Specialty hospital care; Human services; Family services; Child welfare.

Type of support: Regranting.

Limitations: Applications not accepted. Giving primarily in CT, MA, MD, NJ, NY, PA, TX, UT, and VA. No grants to individuals.

Application information: Contributes only to pre-selected organizations.

Board meeting date(s): Nov.

Trustees: Debra Abdo; Wendy Gironda; Elaine Harmon; John J. Harmon.

EIN: 236870251

8054
The S. Dale High Family Foundation
(formerly The High Foundation)
P.O. Box 10008
Lancaster, PA   17605-0008
Contact: Robin D. Stauffer, Exec. Dir.
E-mail: rstauffer@high.net

Established in 1980 in Pennsylvania.

Donors: Calvin G. High; High Industries, Inc.; S. Dale High; Mark Wagner.

Foundation type: Independent foundation.

Financial data (yr. ended 08/31/13): Assets, $9,994,712 (M); gifts received, $3,121,016; expenditures, $383,791; qualifying distributions, $312,846; giving activities include $278,296 for 46 grants (high: $50,000; low: $100), and $32,000 for 7 grants to individuals (high: $5,000; low: $4,000).

Purpose and activities: Giving for scholarships for higher education only to High Companies co-workers' children; support also for educational, social service, cultural and religious organizations.

Fields of interest: Arts and culture; Higher education; Christianity; Human services.

Type of support: Capital campaigns; Capital and infrastructure; Scholarships.

Limitations: Applications accepted. Giving primarily in south central PA, including Lancaster County. No grants to individuals (except for employee-related scholarships).

Publications: Application guidelines; Program policy statement.

Application information: Application form required.

Initial approach: Proposal
Copies of proposal: 1
Deadline(s): Nov. 1
Board meeting date(s): Annually
Final notification: 1st quarter of following year

Officers and Trustees: Gregory A. High, Chair. and Trustee; Robin D. Stauffer, Secy. and Exec. Dir.; S. Dale High, Treas. and Trustee.

Number of staff: None.

EIN: 232149972

8055
Ruth A. Hill Trust
c/o BNY Mellon, N.A.
P.O. Box 185
Pittsburgh, PA   15230-0185
Application address: C/O Matthew Loeffler, 100 State St., Erie, PA 16570 Tel.: (814) 874-5209

Foundation type: Independent foundation.

Financial data (yr. ended 12/31/13): Assets, $7,671,084 (M); expenditures, $390,308; qualifying distributions, $367,237; giving activities include $358,105 for 23 grants (high: $169,283; low: $72).

Fields of interest: Vocational education; Higher education; Graduate and professional education; Protestantism; Theology; Ethnic and racial groups.

Type of support: General support; Student aid.

Limitations: Applications accepted. Giving limited to Venango County, PA, for scholarships; giving primarily in Atlanta, GA, and Pittsburgh, PA, for churches, seminaries and educational institutions.

Application information: Application form required.

Initial approach: Request application form
Deadline(s): Mar. 15

Trustee: BNY Mellon, N.A.

EIN: 256031644

8056
Paul E. & Mildred L. Hill
c/o PNC Bank, N.A.
P.O. Box 609
Pittsburgh, PA   15230-9738

Foundation type: Independent foundation.

Financial data (yr. ended 12/31/14): Assets, $4,130,377; expenditures, $212,273; qualifying distributions, $187,617.

Fields of interest: Undergraduate education; Religion.

Type of support: General support.

Limitations: Applications not accepted. Giving primarily in PA.

Application information: Unsolicited requests for funds not accepted.

Trustee: PNC Bank, N.A.

EIN: 256156794

8057
Allen Hilles Fund
c/o Pembroke Philanthropy Advisors
16 E. Lancaster Ave., Plz. 16, Ste. 102
Ardmore, PA   19003
Contact: Marge Brennan, Grants Manager
FAX: (610) 896-3869;
E-mail: mbrennan@pembrokephilanthropy.net; Main URL: http://www.hillesfund.org

Established in 1983 in Pennsylvania.

Donor: Edith Hilles Dewees†.

Foundation type: Independent foundation.

Financial data (yr. ended 12/31/14): Assets, $7,241,277 (M); expenditures, $372,518; qualifying distributions, $309,050; giving activities include $273,000 for 58 grants (high: $6,000; low: $3,000).

Purpose and activities: The fund seeks to enhance the quality of life of disadvantaged and vulnerable children, youth and women in the city of Philadelphia, PA. The fund supports direct services as well as advocacy strategies that focus on education, youth development and community development. The fund also supports certain projects of the Religious Society of Friends, usually in the Philadelphia area.

Fields of interest: Arts and culture; Education; Elementary and secondary education; Community and economic development; Economic development; Human services; Family services;

Child welfare; Women's services; Children and youth; Females; Low-income and poor people.

Type of support: General support; Public engagement and education.

Limitations: Applications accepted. Giving primarily in the greater Philadelphia, PA area. No grants to individuals or for capital projects, endowments, conferences and seminars, or agency promotion, such as marketing, development, publication of annual reports, or sponsorship of fundraising events.

Publications: Application guidelines.

Application information: Applications by mail only. Applicants limited to 1 request per calendar year. Delaware Valley Grantmakers Common Grant Application Form accepted (with foundation's cover sheet). Preference is given to organizations with operating budgets of less than $2 million. Application form required.

Initial approach: Proposal with cover sheet; see Fund web site for complete guidelines and forms
Copies of proposal: 2
Deadline(s): Sept. 15 and Feb. 15
Board meeting date(s): May and Dec.
Final notification: 2 months

Directors: Daphne Rowe, Exec. Dir.; Brian Armstead; Edward D. Dewees; Robert L. Dewees; Stephanie Judson.

Number of staff: 2 part-time professional.

EIN: 516154986

8058
Orris C. Hirtzel and Beatrice Dewey Hirtzel
Memorial Foundation
(formerly Elec Material Hirtzel Memorial Foundation)
c/o BNY Mellon, N A
P.O. Box 185
Pittsburgh, PA   15230-0185
Contact: Laurie Moritz
Application address: c/o, Laurie Moritz, 500 Grant St., Ste. 3825, Pittsburgh, PA 15258, tel.: (412) 234-0023.

Established in 1956 in Pennsylvania.

Donors: Orris C. Hirtzel; Beatrice Dewey Hirtzel.

Foundation type: Independent foundation.

Financial data (yr. ended 12/31/13): Assets, $23,499,548 (M); expenditures, $367,576; qualifying distributions, $222,378; giving activities include $159,000 for 37 grants (high: $24,500; low: $1,500).

Fields of interest: Higher education; Community and economic development; Human services.

Type of support: General support; Capital campaigns; Capital and infrastructure; Equipment; Fellowships; Research; Student aid.

Limitations: Applications accepted. Giving primarily for the Town of Ripley in Chautauqua County, NY and the City of North East in Erie County, PA.

Application information: Application form required.

Initial approach: Contact Foundation for Application Form
Deadline(s): Contact Foundation for Application Deadline

Trustee: BNY Mellon, N.A.

EIN: 256018933

8059
The Margaret M. Hitchcock Foundation
c/o BNY Mellon, N.A.
P.O. Box 185
Pittsburgh, PA   15230-0185   4122345436

Established in 1961 in Pennsylvania.
Donor: Margaret Mellon Hitchcock.
Foundation type: Independent foundation.
Financial data (yr. ended 12/31/14): Assets, $4,727,231; expenditures, $325,381; qualifying distributions, $312,928.
Fields of interest: Arts and culture; Elementary and secondary education; Higher education; Hospital care; Rehabilitation; Human services.
Limitations: Applications not accepted. Giving on a national basis. No grants to individuals.
Application information: Unsolicited requests for funds not accepted.
   Board meeting date(s): Dec.
Trustee: BNY Mellon, N.A.
Number of staff: None.
EIN: 256018992

8060
Charles H. Hoch Foundation
c/o National Penn Investment Trust Co.
645 Hamilton St., Ste. 900
Allentown, PA   18101   6105306818
Application address: c/o National Penn Investors Trust Co., Attn: Sharon Malia, 1620 Pond Rd., Ste. 200, Allentown, PA 18104, tel.:(610) 366-9934, Fax: (610) 759-3144

Foundation type: Independent foundation.
Financial data (yr. ended 12/31/14): Assets, $5,575,367; expenditures, $413,770; qualifying distributions, $373,462.
Fields of interest: Arts and culture; Music; Education; Higher education; Diseases and conditions; Human services; Food aid; Food delivery; Child welfare; Youth services; Homeless people.
Limitations: Applications accepted. Giving primarily in Allentown, PA. No grants to individuals.
Application information: Application form required.
   Initial approach: Letter
   Deadline(s): Apr. 1 or Oct. 1
Officers: Kenneth Beisel, Pres. and Treas.; Richard DeMott, Secy.
Trustees: Thomas M. Buxton; Richard S. Miller; Deborah A. Sciher.
EIN: 236265016

8061
Emma Clyde Hodge Memorial Fund
c/o PNC Bank
620 Liberty Ave., 10th Fl.
Pittsburgh, PA   15222-2705

Established in 1990 in Pennsylvania.
Donor: Edwin Hodge, Jr.†.
Foundation type: Independent foundation.
Financial data (yr. ended 06/30/13): Assets, $9,465,657 (M); expenditures, $492,422; qualifying distributions, $421,500; giving activities include $421,500 for grants.
Purpose and activities: Giving primarily for the arts, education, health care, and human services.
Fields of interest: Arts and culture; Orchestral music; Education; Health; Human services.
Type of support: Capital and infrastructure.

Limitations: Applications not accepted. Giving primarily in the U.S., with some emphasis on Pittsburgh, PA. No grants to individuals.
Application information: Contributes only to pre-selected organizations.
Trustees: L. Van V. Dauler, Jr.; Anne Gordon Earle; Emma Sarosdy; PNC Bank, N.A.
EIN: 256227653

8062
Robert C. Hoffman Charitable Endowment Trust
c/o PNC Bank, N.A., Tax Dept.
1600 Market St.
Philadelphia, PA   19103-7240
E-mail: bernico@att.net; Mailing address: c/o Barbara B. Ernico, P.O. Box 3547, Gettysburg, PA 17325; tel.: (717) 338-0344

Established in 1999 in Pennsylvania.
Donor: Robert C. Hoffman†.
Foundation type: Independent foundation.
Financial data (yr. ended 07/31/13): Assets, $7,137,891 (M); expenditures, $334,178; qualifying distributions, $294,345; giving activities include $239,263 for 27 grants (high: $30,000; low: $1,000).
Purpose and activities: Giving for the betterment of the citizens and organizations of Adams County, PA and to benefit, promote, and support religious, educational, and vocational organizations. Giving also for the prevention of abuse to children and animals, to help the needy and underprivileged, for medical organizations and youth organizations, including youth sports, for the promotion of social welfare and lessening the burdens of government, and for Lutheran and Mennonite churches.
Fields of interest: Vocational post-secondary education; Undergraduate education; Hospital care; Housing development; Methodism; Housing for the homeless; Children and youth; Infants and toddlers; Children; Adults; Young adults; Seniors; Single parents; Ethnic and racial groups; People of Latin American descent; Migrant workers; Homeless people; Low-income and poor people; Incarcerated people; Victims of crime and abuse; People with disabilities; People with physical disabilities; People with vision impairments; People with hearing impairments; People with psychosocial disabilities; People with HIV/AIDS; Terminally ill people; Substance abusers.
Type of support: General support; Pro bono consulting services; Continuing support; Matching grants; Financial sustainability; Capacity-building and technical assistance; Annual campaigns; Capital campaigns; Capital and infrastructure; Equipment; Program development; Convening; Recordings; Publications; Curriculum development; Research; Technical assistance; Program evaluations.
Limitations: Applications accepted. Giving limited to Adams County, PA. No grants for debt retirement, or to heirs, personal representatives or other contributors to the Trust.
Publications: Annual report.
Application information: Considers up to 4 applications per organization each year; application may be re-typed, but should be no longer than 3 pages, 12-point type, single-spaced, on letter-size paper. Application form required.
   Initial approach: Letter
   Copies of proposal: 4
   Deadline(s): Jan. 15 and July 15

Board meeting date(s): Sept. and Feb.
   Final notification: Eight weeks
Trustee: PNC Bank, N.A.
Advisory Committees: David K. Heiges; Linda Lundberg; Tonya K. White.
Number of staff: None.
EIN: 256658643

8063
R. M. Hoffman Family Memorial Trust
c/o PNC Bank N.A.
620 Liberty Ave., 10th Fl.
Pittsburgh, PA   15222

Established in 2000 in Pennsylvania.
Foundation type: Independent foundation.
Financial data (yr. ended 12/31/14): Assets, $4,619,380; expenditures, $244,931; qualifying distributions, $189,813 and $0 for set-asides.
Fields of interest: Nonprofits; Hospital care; Diseases and conditions; Cancers; Public libraries; Human services.
Type of support: Regranting.
Limitations: Applications not accepted. Giving primarily in PA. No grants to individuals.
Application information: Contributes only to pre-selected organizations.
Trustee: PNC Bank, N.A.
EIN: 256500388

8064
Gibson E. Holden Foundation
1760 Market St.
Philadelphia, PA   19103-4134
Contact: Howard Soloman, Tr.
E-mail: howard@soloman-law.com

Foundation type: Independent foundation.
Financial data (yr. ended 12/31/13): Assets, $4,604,884 (M); expenditures, $427,921; qualifying distributions, $427,921; giving activities include $147,000 for 3 grants (high: $106,000; low: $16,000).
Fields of interest: Health; Diseases and conditions; Religion.
Type of support: Research.
Limitations: Applications accepted. Giving primarily in PA.
Application information:
   Initial approach: Proposal
   Deadline(s): None
Trustee: Howard M. Soloman.
EIN: 277052536

8065
Homeless Assistance Fund, Inc.
P.O. Box 40787
Philadelphia, PA   19107-0787

Foundation type: Operating foundation.
Financial data (yr. ended 06/30/14): Assets, $6,184,375 (M); expenditures, $277,392; qualifying distributions, $247,857; giving activities include $166,000 for 5 grants (high: $34,000; low: $30,000).
Fields of interest: National defense; Community and economic development; Human services; Homeless people.
Limitations: Applications not accepted. Giving primarily in Philadelphia, PA.

Application information: Unsolicited requests for funds not accepted.
Officers: Trino Boix, Esq., Chair.; Thelma Jacks, Secy.-Treas.
Trustees: Robin Ingram; Janet Kroll; Deborah McColloch; Dainette Mintz; Kate Reivera; Dina Schlossberg; Karen Vesely; Beatriz Vieira.
EIN: 920183166

8066
Lynne & Harold Honickman Foundation
210 W. Rittenhouse Sq., Ste. 3303
Philadelphia, PA 19103-5780 (215) 790-1710
Contact: Lynne Honickman, Pres.
Main URL: http://www.honickmanfoundation.org
Facebook: https://www.facebook.com/pages/The-Honickman-Foundation/232318940115941?sk=wall

Established in 1988 in Pennsylvania.
Donors: Lynne Honickman; Pepsi Cola & National Brand Beverage.
Foundation type: Independent foundation.
Financial data (yr. ended 12/31/13): Assets, $11,431,667 (M); gifts received, $531,932; expenditures, $532,219; qualifying distributions, $493,861; giving activities include $428,703 for 160 grants (high: $122,000; low: $50).
Purpose and activities: Giving primarily to support projects that promote the arts, education, health, social change, and heritage.
Fields of interest: Arts and culture; Art museums; Education; Nonprofits; Health; Family services.
Type of support: General support; Grants to individuals; Regranting.
Limitations: Applications not accepted. Giving primarily in Philadelphia, PA, and the surrounding 5 counties.
Publications: Grants list.
Application information: Unsolicited requests for funds are currently not accepted.
Officers: Lynne Honickman, Pres.; Kathy H. Ruyak, Exec. V.P., Dir. Progs.
Number of staff: 1 full-time professional.
EIN: 232513138

8067
David A. & Helen P. Horn Charitable Trust
c/o Archer & Greiner
1650 Market St., 32nd Fl.
Philadelphia, PA 19103-7393 (215) 246-3132
Contact: Kenneth E. Ahl, Tr.

Established in 2006 in Pennsylvania.
Foundation type: Independent foundation.
Financial data (yr. ended 12/31/13): Assets, $3,625,585 (M); expenditures, $192,210; qualifying distributions, $163,000; giving activities include $163,000 for 6 grants (high: $41,500; low: $19,000).
Fields of interest: Arts and culture; Museums; Religion; Human services; Youth services.
Limitations: Applications accepted. Giving primarily in OH and PA.
Application information:
  Initial approach: Proposal
  Deadline(s): None
Trustees: Kenneth E. Ahl; Helen H. Bickell; Carolyn H. Seidle.
EIN: 208091817

8068
The Horner Foundation
610 W. Germantown Pike, Ste. 400
Plymouth Meeting, PA 19462-1058
E-mail: HornerEd@gmail.com; *Main URL:* http://thehornerfoundation.org
Grants List: http://www.thehornerfoundation.org/donations.html

Established in 2007 in New Jersey.
Foundation type: Independent foundation.
Financial data (yr. ended 12/31/13): Assets, $6,964,106 (M); expenditures, $517,885; qualifying distributions, $414,770; giving activities include $414,770 for 30 grants (high: $54,566; low: $500).
Purpose and activities: Giving primarily for health care and education for youth, with a particular focus on at-risk or vulnerable youth.
Fields of interest: Education; Health; Youth development.
International interests: Canada; England.
Limitations: Applications accepted. Giving primarily in southern NJ; Philadelphia, PA; Salt Lake City, UT; Victoria, British Columbia; and central England. No grants to individuals.
Application information: See foundation website for complete application guidelines.
Officers and Trustees: Ann Marie Horner, Chair. and Trustee; Tracy Cullen, Exec. Dir.; Carolyn Horner; Kathryn Horner; Terry Horner; Meghann Horner-Smith; Damon Levy.
EIN: 260697610

8069
Milton G. Hulme Charitable Foundation
1146 Old Freeport Rd.
Pittsburgh, PA 15238-3109 (412) 781-5660

Established in 1960 in Pennsylvania.
Donors: Glover & MacGregor, Inc.; Jocelyn H. MacConnell; Natalie H. Curry; Holiday H. Shoup.
Foundation type: Independent foundation.
Financial data (yr. ended 12/31/13): Assets, $11,651,551 (M); expenditures, $573,895; qualifying distributions, $567,500; giving activities include $410,500 for 37 grants (high: $25,000; low: $5,000).
Purpose and activities: Giving primarily for the arts, children and family services, and social services.
Fields of interest: Performing arts; Education; Health; Christianity; Human services; Family services; Child welfare.
Type of support: General support; Capital campaigns.
Limitations: Applications accepted. Giving primarily in Pittsburgh, PA. No grants to individuals.
Application information: Application form required.
  Initial approach: Proposal
  Copies of proposal: 1
  Deadline(s): Aug. 31
Trustees: Natalie H. Curry; Aura R. Hulme; John P. Krivda; Holiday H. Shoup.
Number of staff: 2 part-time support.
EIN: 256062896

8070
Horace C. Hunt Memorial Foundation
(formerly Horace C. Hunt Foundation)
c/o BNY Mellon, N.A.
P.O. Box 185
Pittsburgh, PA 15230-0185

Foundation type: Independent foundation.
Financial data (yr. ended 10/31/13): Assets, $4,289,039 (M); expenditures, $220,524; qualifying distributions, $196,555; giving activities include $180,000 for 8 grants (high: $35,000; low: $10,000).
Fields of interest: Diseases and conditions; Cancers; Christianity; Human services; Family services.
Limitations: Applications not accepted. Giving primarily in the Boston, MA, area. No grants to individuals.
Application information: Contributes only to pre-selected organizations.
Trustees: Robert G. Bannish; Ronald Garmey; BNY Mellon, N.A.
EIN: 046171963

8071
Myrtle V. C. Huplits & Woodman E. Huplits Foundation Trust
c/o Todd E. Peskin
213 Regency Blvd.
Yardley, PA 19067

Foundation type: Independent foundation.
Financial data (yr. ended 12/31/14): Assets, $4,545,427; expenditures, $302,028; qualifying distributions, $250,000.
Fields of interest: Natural resources; Wildlife biodiversity; Zoos; Human services.
Type of support: General support; Advocacy.
Limitations: Applications not accepted. Giving primarily in PA. No grants to individuals.
Application information: Unsolicited requests for funds not accepted.
Trustees: Todd E. Peskin; Marni Zwick.
EIN: 237451411

8072
Diamond Ice Foundation
c/o Superior Family Office Inc.
100 Front St., Ste. 525
West Conshohocken, PA 19428-2800

Established in 2006 in Pennsylvania.
Donors: Mary G. Warden; William G. Warden III.
Foundation type: Independent foundation.
Financial data (yr. ended 12/31/13): Assets, $535,151 (M); gifts received, $300,000; expenditures, $224,540; qualifying distributions, $224,540; giving activities include $222,500 for 18 grants (high: $120,000; low: $1,000).
Fields of interest: Education; Hospital care; Christianity.
Limitations: Applications not accepted. Giving primarily in PA. No grants to individuals.
Application information: Contributes only to pre-selected organizations.
Trustees: Mary G. Warden; William G. Warden III.
EIN: 870790142

8073
IGN Foundation
435 Devon Park Dr.
Wayne, PA 19087-1900
Application address: c/o Frank S. Polizzi, 300
Berwyn Park, Ste. 100, Berwyn, PA 19312,
tel.: (610) 408-8600

Established in 1990 in Pennsylvania.
Donor: Frank Polizzi.
Foundation type: Independent foundation.
Financial data (yr. ended 06/30/13): Assets,
$6,325,897 (M); expenditures, $331,287;
qualifying distributions, $306,500; giving activities
include $306,500 for 8 grants (high: $105,000;
low: $2,500).
Fields of interest: Education; Nonprofits;
Catholicism; Human services.
Type of support: General support; Regranting.
Limitations: Applications accepted. Giving primarily
in IL and PA. No grants to individuals.
Application information:
Initial approach: Letter
Deadline(s): None
Trustee: Frank S. Polizzi.
EIN: 237653516

8074
The II Corinthians 9:7 Foundation
P.O. Box 687
Unionville, PA 19375-0687

Donor: American Gift Fund.
Financial data (yr. ended 12/31/13): Assets,
$5,593,049 (M); gifts received, $7,566;
expenditures, $264,583; qualifying distributions,
$243,511; giving activities include $223,212 for 7
grants (high: $98,212; low: $5,000).
Fields of interest: Education; Protestantism; Sports
and recreation.
Limitations: Applications not accepted.
Application information: Unsolicited requests for
funds not accepted.
Trustee: Judith Jefferis.
EIN: 900852219

8075
Invisible Prince Charitable Foundation
Inc.
c/o Glenmede Trust Co., N.A.
1650 Market St., Ste. 1200
Philadelphia, PA 19103-7391
Application address: c/o Steven Lewis Lloyd, 1523
Mount Zion Rd., Harding, PA 18643, tel.: (717)
233-1000

Donor: Steven Lewis Lloyd.
Foundation type: Independent foundation.
Financial data (yr. ended 12/31/13): Assets,
$5,110,826 (M); expenditures, $157,978;
qualifying distributions, $133,609; giving activities
include $123,540 for 10 grants (high: $30,000;
low: $500).
Limitations: Applications accepted. Giving primarily
in NY and PA.
Application information: Application form required.
Initial approach: Letter
Deadline(s): Feb. 28, Aug. 31

Officers: Steven Lewis Lloyd, Pres.; Jane Lewis
Lloyd, V.P.; Amy Lloyd Switzer, Secy.; Thomas
Coridon Lloyd, Treas.
Director: Gregory S. Chelap.
EIN: 454103342

8076
The Ithan Foundation, Inc.
c/o J. Terrill - HTT&S
100 4 Falls Corporate Ctr., Ste. 300
West Conshohocken, PA 19428-2950

Established in 1997 in Pennsylvania.
Donors: Ethyl S. Levenson; George R. Atterbury†.
Foundation type: Independent foundation.
Financial data (yr. ended 12/31/14): Assets,
$5,761,856 (M); gifts received, $298,986;
expenditures, $271,453; qualifying distributions,
$205,000; giving activities include $205,000 for 4
grants (high: $82,000; low: $41,000).
Fields of interest: Education; Human services.
Type of support: General support.
Limitations: Applications not accepted. Giving
primarily in PA. No grants to individuals.
Application information: Unsolicited requests for
funds not accepted.
Officers and Directors: Colin Gardner, V, Pres. and
Director; Kristin L. Gardner, V.P. and Director;
Susannah A. Gardner, Secy. and Director; Jennifer
Gardner Glose, Treas. and Director.
EIN: 232896573

8077
Adrian H. Jackson Charitable Trust
c/o BNY Mellon, N.A.
P.O. Box 185
Pittsburgh, PA 15230-0185

Foundation type: Independent foundation.
Financial data (yr. ended 12/31/14): Assets,
$5,564,296 (M); expenditures, $318,931;
qualifying distributions, $285,823; giving activities
include $279,192 for 6 grants (high: $46,532; low:
$46,532).
Fields of interest: Education; Health; Human
services.
Limitations: Applications not accepted. Giving
primarily in New York, NY.
Application information: Unsolicited requests for
funds not accepted.
Trustee: BNY Mellon, N.A.
EIN: 136078615

8078
John E. & Sue M. Jackson Charitable
Trust
c/o PNC Bank, N.A.
P.O. Box 609
Pittsburgh, PA 15230-9738
Application address: c/o PNC Charitable Trust,
Review Committee, PNC Bank, N.A., 249 5th Ave.,
20th Fl., Pittsburgh, PA 15222, tel.: (412) 768-8248

Foundation type: Independent foundation.
Financial data (yr. ended 12/31/13): Assets,
$11,128,929 (M); expenditures, $523,254;
qualifying distributions, $451,844; giving activities
include $432,362 for 81 grants (high: $37,000;
low: $484).

Fields of interest: Museums; Historic preservation;
Higher education; Graduate and professional
education; Foundations; Hospital care; Social
sciences; Public interest law; Employment;
Christianity; Theology; Human services; Family
services; Child welfare.
Type of support: Research and evaluation; Policy,
advocacy and systems reform.
Application information: Application form required.
Initial approach: See website
Deadline(s): None
Trustees: William R. Jackson, Jr.; Polly J. Townsend;
N.A. PNC Bank.
EIN: 256019484

8079
Jansing-Cook Foundation
(formerly Louella Cook Foundation)
3 Radnor Corp. Ctr., Ste. 450
Radnor, PA 19087-4546

Established in 1976 in Washington.
Donor: Ice Systems, Inc.
Foundation type: Independent foundation.
Financial data (yr. ended 12/31/13): Assets,
$5,197,166 (M); expenditures, $280,137;
qualifying distributions, $223,058; giving activities
include $223,058 for 43 grants (high: $25,000;
low: $250).
Fields of interest: Education; Cancers; Religion;
Human services; Homeless services; Homeless
people.
Type of support: General support.
Limitations: Applications not accepted. Giving
primarily in WA, with emphasis on Seattle. No grants
to individuals.
Application information: Unsolicited requests for
funds not accepted.
Trustees: Christopher C. Jansing; John Cook
Jansing; Caroline C. Jansing Vohr.
EIN: 911098016

8080
Jewish Family Assistance Fund
828 Hazelwood Ave.
Pittsburgh, PA 15217-2967
Application address: c/o Louise Silk, Tr., P.O. Box
8197, Pittsburgh, PA 15217, tel.: (412) 414-6050

Donors: Giant Eagle Foundation; Jewish Federation
of Greater Pittsburgh Foundation; Lipsitz Family
Foundation; Pittsburgh Foundation; Fine Family
Foundation; Herman Lipsitz; Mrs. Herman Lipsitz;
Jewish Healthcare Foundation; Charles Morris
Charitable Trust; PNC Foundation; A & M Porter
Charitable Foundation; Ladies Hospital Aid Society;
Sylvia and Martin Snow Foundation; Max Markovitz
Charitable Trust; Hyman Family Foundation; Helen
N. Nobel Lipsitz Family Foundation.
Foundation type: Independent foundation.
Financial data (yr. ended 12/31/13): Assets,
$1,587,703 (M); gifts received, $222,227;
expenditures, $219,740; qualifying distributions,
$219,740; giving activities include $187,548 for
grants.
Purpose and activities: Giving primarily for human
services, including grants to individuals for
expenses related to food, shelter, medicine, and
education.
Fields of interest: Judaism; Human services.

Type of support: General support; Grants to individuals.
Limitations: Applications accepted. Giving limited to residents of Pittsburgh, PA.
Application information: Application form required.
Initial approach: Letter
Deadline(s): None
Officer: David M. Maretsky, Pres.
Trustee: Louise Silk.
EIN: 251512726

8081

John Family Foundation

3855 County Line Rd.
Winfield, PA 17889

Established in 1991 in Pennsylvania.
Donors: Paul R. John; Mildred D. John.
Foundation type: Independent foundation.
Financial data (yr. ended 12/31/13): Assets, $7,800,871 (M); gifts received, $498,387; expenditures, $352,631; qualifying distributions, $330,850; giving activities include $330,850 for 47 grants (high: $50,000; low: $250).
Fields of interest: Higher education; Diseases and conditions; Human services; Child welfare.
Type of support: Capital and infrastructure.
Limitations: Applications accepted. Giving primarily in PA. No grants to individuals.
Application information: Application form required.
Initial approach: Letter
Deadline(s): None
Officers: Paul R. John, Pres.; Mildred D. John, V.P.
EIN: 232616038

8082

The Jordan Charitable Foundation

c/o Donnelly, Boyce & Associates, LLC
806 Darby Rd.
Havertown, PA 19083-4607

Established in 1999 in Delaware.
Donors: Barbara L. Jordan; John L. Jordan.
Foundation type: Operating foundation.
Financial data (yr. ended 02/28/13): Assets, $335,522 (M); gifts received, $183,245; expenditures, $168,435; qualifying distributions, $168,435; giving activities include $151,785 for 7 grants (high: $107,867; low: $150).
Fields of interest: Education; Philanthropy; Domestic violence; Housing development; Females.
Type of support: Individual development.
Limitations: Applications not accepted. Giving primarily in FL and PA. No grants to individuals.
Application information: Unsolicited requests for funds not accepted.
Officers and Directors: John L. Jordan, Pres. and Treas. and Director; Barbara L. Jordan, Secy. and Director; Bernard Eizen.
EIN: 510381471

8083

Joyce Family Foundation Trust

c/o Pitcairn Trust
165 Township Rd., Ste. 3000
Jenkintown, PA 19046-3593

Established in 1990 in Tennessee.
Donors: Kathryn Craig Henry; TCH M Wood/Joyce FDN Dec 90; TCH M Wood/JFF De-Clt May 92; TCH

M Wood/JFF De-Clt 9/16/93; TCH M Wood/JFF N-DCLT May 92.
Foundation type: Independent foundation.
Financial data (yr. ended 12/31/13): Assets, $2,158,242 (M); gifts received, $14,000; expenditures, $300,690; qualifying distributions, $192,419; giving activities include $192,419 for 12 grants (high: $100,000; low: $5).
Fields of interest: University education; Diseases and conditions; Religion; Human services.
Limitations: Applications not accepted. Giving primarily in TN. No grants to individuals.
Application information: Unsolicited requests for funds not accepted.
Trustees: SunTrust Bank; Pitcairn Trust Co.
EIN: 626225946

8084

Barbara R. and Charles Kahn, Jr. Foundation, Inc.

2600 One Commerce Sq.
Philadelphia, PA 19103-7098

Established in 1997 in Pennsylvania.
Donors: Charles Kahn, Jr.; Barbara R. Kahn.
Foundation type: Independent foundation.
Financial data (yr. ended 06/30/13): Assets, $1,427,478 (M); expenditures, $144,939; qualifying distributions, $144,939; giving activities include $144,102 for 21 grants (high: $75,000; low: $1,000).
Fields of interest: Museums; Education; University education; Nonprofits; Health; Judaism; Interfaith.
Type of support: Regranting.
Limitations: Applications not accepted. Giving primarily in Philadelphia, PA. No grants to individuals.
Application information: Contributes only to pre-selected organizations.
Officers and Directors: Charles Kahn, Jr., Pres. and Director; Barbara R. Kahn, Secy.-Treas. and Director; Bruce Goodman; Todd C. Vanett.
EIN: 232898465

8085

Nicholas J. & Celeste G. Karamatsoukas Family Foundation

1880 John F. Kennedy Blvd.
Philadelphia, PA 19103-7426

Donors: Nicholas J. Karamatsoukas; Celeste G. Karamatsoukas.
Foundation type: Independent foundation.
Financial data (yr. ended 06/30/14): Assets, $698,620 (M); gifts received, $350,400; expenditures, $317,909; qualifying distributions, $317,489; giving activities include $317,489 for 30 grants (high: $231,060; low: $30).
Fields of interest: Education; Catholicism; Human services.
Limitations: Applications not accepted. Giving primarily in PA. No grants to individuals.
Application information: Contributes only to pre-selected organizations.
Officer: Nicholas J. Karamatsoukas, Pres.
Director: Celeste G. Karamatsoukas.
EIN: 262852051

8086

The Katherine Alexandra Charitable Foundation

c/o Michael Kalogris
P.O. Box 431
Devault, PA 19432-0431
E-mail: info@katherinealexandra.org

Established in 2001 in Pennsylvania.
Donors: Elisabeth Kalogris; Michael E. Kalogris; Melanie Stewart Dance Theater.
Foundation type: Independent foundation.
Financial data (yr. ended 12/31/13): Assets, $162,769 (M); gifts received, $37; expenditures, $170,465; qualifying distributions, $166,406; giving activities include $157,500 for 9 grants (high: $101,500; low: $500).
Fields of interest: Arts and culture; Education; Health.
Limitations: Applications not accepted. Giving primarily in New York, NY and Philadelphia, PA. No grants to individuals.
Application information: Unsolicited requests for funds not accepted.
Trustees: Katherine Cipriano; Elisabeth Kalogris; Michael E. Kalogris; Alexandra McCloud.
EIN: 256799731

8087

The Katsaros Family Foundation

2450 Ballybunion Rd.
Center Valley, PA 18034-8901

Established in 2007 in Pennsylvania.
Donors: Arthur T. Katsaros; Denise S. Katsaros.
Foundation type: Independent foundation.
Financial data (yr. ended 12/31/13): Assets, $7,499,061 (M); gifts received, $984,764; expenditures, $226,635; qualifying distributions, $214,400; giving activities include $214,400 for 23 grants (high: $52,900; low: $500).
Fields of interest: Arts and culture; Education; Health.
Limitations: Applications not accepted. Giving primarily in MA and PA. No grants to individuals.
Application information: Unsolicited requests for funds not accepted.
Trustees: Arthur T. Katsaros; Denise S. Katsaros.
EIN: 261373188

8088

The Harold Katz Family Foundation

928 Jaymor Rd., Ste. A-100
Southampton, PA 18966-3869 (215) 364-0400
Contact: Harold Katz, Pres.

Established in 1986 in Pennsylvania.
Donors: Harold Katz; Creative Investments L.P.; Creative Investment Ltd. Partnership.
Foundation type: Independent foundation.
Financial data (yr. ended 12/31/14): Assets, $35,644 (M); gifts received, $250,000; expenditures, $238,925; qualifying distributions, $238,925; giving activities include $238,925 for 21 grants (high: $200,000; low: $125).
Purpose and activities: oGiving primarily for higher education, as well as for health organizations, including kidney research, and human services.
Fields of interest: Health; Diseases and conditions; Human services.

Limitations: Applications accepted. Giving primarily in Coral Gables, FL, MO and PA. No grants to individuals.
Application information: Application form required.
Initial approach: Letter
Deadline(s): None
Final notification: Within 3 months
Officer: Harold Katz, Pres.
Directors: David Katz; Diane Katz; Marlene Katz; Peggy Katz.
EIN: 232439844

8089
The Katz Family Foundation
c/o Diamatrix
225 Lincoln Hwy.
Fairless Hills, PA   19030-1103
Contact: F. Katz

Established in 1998 in Massachusetts.
Donors: Frank L. Katz; Elise Katz.
Foundation type: Independent foundation.
Financial data (yr. ended 06/30/14): Assets, $8,558,450 (M); gifts received, $500,000; expenditures, $414,990; qualifying distributions, $375,000; giving activities include $375,000 for 4 grants (high: $150,000; low: $25,000).
Purpose and activities: Giving primarily for medical and health care services.
Fields of interest: Education; Health; Hospital care; Human services.
Limitations: Applications not accepted. Giving primarily in IN, MA and PA. No grants to individuals.
Application information: Contributes only to pre-selected organizations.
Trustees: Benjamin A. Katz; Brooke D. Katz; Elise R. Katz; Frank L. Katz; Philip J. Katz.
EIN: 237996192

8090
The Calvin K. Kazanjian Economics Foundation, Inc.
P.O. Box 300
Dallas, PA   18612-0300   (570) 675-7074
Contact: Dr. Michael A. MacDowell, Mgr.
FAX: (570) 675-8436;
E-mail: director@kazanjian.org; Main URL: http://www.kazanjian.org

Established in 1947 in Connecticut.
Donor: Calvin K. Kazanjian†.
Foundation type: Independent foundation.
Financial data (yr. ended 12/31/13): Assets, $6,893,806 (M); expenditures, $218,339; qualifying distributions, $218,339; giving activities include $139,983 for 7 grants (high: $34,183; low: $10,000).
Purpose and activities: Giving limited to economics education programs for teachers to increase the understanding of economics and to disseminate such knowledge utilizing various media.
Fields of interest: Education; Business education; Adult education; Economics.
Type of support: Program development; Convening; Seed money; Curriculum development.
Limitations: Applications accepted. Giving primarily in Washington, DC and New York, NY, VA. No grants to individuals, or for capital or endowment funds, operating budgets, continuing support, annual campaigns, emergency funds, deficit financing,

matching gifts, scholarships, fellowships, or general purposes; no loans.
Publications: Application guidelines; Informational brochure.
Application information: See web site for additional information, as well as for application policies and guidelines.
Initial approach: Proposal of no more than 10 double-spaced pages, including either an abstract or executive summary of no more than one page
Copies of proposal: 1
Deadline(s): April 1 and Oct. 1
Board meeting date(s): May and Nov.
Officers: Richard L. Elston, Pres. and Treas.; Harold Buckingham, Jr., Secy.; Michael A. MacDowell, Exec. Dir.
Trustees: Caleb T. Elston; Lloyd W. Elston; Fred Finkenauer; Marnie W. Mueller; John F. VanGorder.
Number of staff: 1 part-time professional.
EIN: 060665174

8091
Kate M. Kelley Foundation
625 Stanwix St., Ste. 2104
Pittsburgh, PA   15222-1417

Established in 1976 in Pennsylvania.
Donor: Edward J. Kelley†.
Foundation type: Independent foundation.
Financial data (yr. ended 12/31/14): Assets, $4,497,919; expenditures, $279,266; qualifying distributions, $245,500.
Purpose and activities: Giving largely for Roman Catholic church support and church-related education; some support also for other higher and secondary education.
Fields of interest: Secondary education; Higher education; Graduate and professional education; Nonprofits; Catholicism; Theology; Human services.
Type of support: Regranting.
Limitations: Applications not accepted. Giving primarily in Pittsburgh, PA.
Application information: Unsolicited requests for funds not accepted.
Trustees: Frank D. Almade; Edward M. Bryce; Edward C. Ifft, Jr.
EIN: 256090985

8092
Kinney Memorial Foundation
c/o BNY Mellon, N.A.
P.O. Box 185
Pittsburgh, PA   15230-0185

Established in 1991 in New York.
Foundation type: Independent foundation.
Financial data (yr. ended 12/31/14): Assets, $4,591,153; expenditures, $262,406; qualifying distributions, $239,422.
Fields of interest: Health; Disasters and emergency management; Christianity.
Type of support: General support.
Limitations: Giving primarily in NJ, NY, and PA. No grants to individuals.
Application information: Unsolicited requests for funds not accepted.
Copies of proposal: 1
Trustees: Hope L. Holloway; Josephine J. Kinney; BNY Mellon, N.A.
EIN: 136968427

8093
Kittenbrink Family Foundation
300 California Ave.
Pittsburgh, PA   15202-2337

Established in 2006 in Pennsylvania.
Donors: Douglas A. Kittenbrink; Leslie Kittenbrink.
Foundation type: Independent foundation.
Financial data (yr. ended 12/31/14): Assets, $1,972,128 (M); expenditures, $235,263; qualifying distributions, $201,431; giving activities include $96,500 for 19 grants (high: $96,500; low: $100).
Fields of interest: Nonprofits; Diseases and conditions; Christianity.
Type of support: Regranting; Research.
Limitations: Applications accepted. Giving primarily in PA.
Application information:
Initial approach: Proposal
Deadline(s): None
Trustees: Douglas Kittenbrink; Leslie Kittenbrink.
EIN: 205918986

8094
KL Felicitas Foundation
(formerly Kleissner Family Foundation)
c/o Febert & Assocs., LLC
707 Grant St., Ste. 1140
Pittsburgh, PA   15219-1909
Contact: Lisa Kleissner, Pres.
E-mail: info@klfelicitasfoundation.org; Main URL: http://www.klfelicitasfoundation.org

Established in 2000 in California.
Donors: Karl Kleissner; Lisa Kleissner; KD Primus Trust.
Foundation type: Independent foundation.
Financial data (yr. ended 12/31/13): Assets, $10,410,296 (M); gifts received, $12,173; expenditures, $618,557; qualifying distributions, $542,420; giving activities include $221,162 for 20 grants (high: $35,000; low: $100), and $161,761 for loans/program-related investments.
Purpose and activities: Giving to enable social entrepreneurs worldwide to develop and grow economically sustainable, scalable enterprises with high measurable social impact and to empower rural communities and families through sustainable economic and social change.
Fields of interest: Environment; Community and economic development.
International interests: Brazil; India; Sri Lanka.
Type of support: General support; Mission-related investments; Pro bono consulting services; Financial sustainability; Capacity-building and technical assistance; Program-related investments; Matching grants; Annual campaigns; Capital campaigns; Capital and infrastructure; Endowments; Program development; Seed money; Curriculum development; Research; Technical assistance.
Limitations: Applications not accepted. Giving in the U.S., as well as in Brazil, India, and Sri Lanka. No support for religious organizations. No grants to individuals.
Application information: Contributes only to pre-selected organizations.
Board meeting date(s): Jan. 2, June 12-13, and Oct. 30-31
Officers: Lisa Kleissner, Pres.; Alex Kleissner, V.P.; Karl Kleissner, Secy.; Andrea Kleissner, Treas.
EIN: 770539366

8095
Emilie J. Klahr No. 2 Testamentary Trust
c/o PNC Bank
620 Liberty Ave., 10th Fl.
Pittsburgh, PA 15222-2705

Foundation type: Independent foundation.
Financial data (yr. ended 12/31/13): Assets, $7,015,976 (M); expenditures, $434,646; qualifying distributions, $279,047; giving activities include $270,858 for 2 grants (high: $135,429; low: $135,429).
Fields of interest: Education; Medical education; Human services.
Type of support: General support.
Limitations: Applications not accepted. Giving primarily in Philadelphia, PA.
Application information: Unsolicited requests for funds not accepted.
Trustee: PNC Bank, N.A.
EIN: 236205830

8096
The Raymond Klein Charitable Foundation
1735 Market St., Ste. 4010
Philadelphia, PA 19103-7501 (215) 751-9600

Established in 1988 in Pennsylvania.
Donor: Raymond Klein.
Foundation type: Independent foundation.
Financial data (yr. ended 10/31/14): Assets, $6,941,469; expenditures, $417,605; qualifying distributions, $392,750.
Fields of interest: Arts and culture; Nonprofits; Health; Diseases and conditions; Judaism; Human services.
Type of support: General support; Regranting.
Limitations: Applications accepted. Giving primarily in Philadelphia, PA. No grants to individuals.
Application information:
  Initial approach: Proposal
  Deadline(s): None
Trustee: Stephen B. Klein.
EIN: 232535513

8097
E. Ann Klein Charitable Trust
P.O. Box 3215
Lancaster, PA 17604-3215

Established in 2008 in Pennsylvania.
Donor: E. Ann Klein Irrevocable Trust.
Foundation type: Independent foundation.
Financial data (yr. ended 10/31/13): Assets, $7,030,586 (M); expenditures, $463,165; qualifying distributions, $351,279; giving activities include $351,279 for 9 grants (high: $122,948; low: $5,000).
Fields of interest: Arts and culture; Museums; Education; Higher education; Christianity; Human services.
Limitations: Applications not accepted. Giving primarily in Lancaster, PA. No grants to individuals.
Application information: Contributes only to pre-selected organizations.
Trustees: Bloor Redding; Walter J. Blenko, Jr.; William M. Davis; Fulton Bank, N.A.
EIN: 300455805

8098
Charles and Figa Kline Foundation
c/o Commerce Corporate Ctr.
5050 Tilghman St., Ste. 115
Allentown, PA 18104-9114 (610) 437-4077

Established in 1957 in Pennsylvania.
Donors: Charles Kline†; Figa Cohen Kline†.
Foundation type: Operating foundation.
Financial data (yr. ended 10/31/13): Assets, $8,752,975 (M); expenditures, $494,561; qualifying distributions, $431,200; giving activities include $431,200 for 12 grants (high: $178,200; low: $1,000).
Purpose and activities: Giving largely for Jewish welfare and community service agencies, temple support, and education.
Fields of interest: Education; Nonprofits; Judaism; Human services.
Type of support: Capital campaigns; Capital and infrastructure; Regranting.
Limitations: Applications accepted. Giving primarily in Allentown, PA. No grants to individuals.
Application information:
  Initial approach: Proposal
  Deadline(s): Sept. 30
Officers: Stewart Furmansky, Pres.; Barnet H. Fraenkel, V.P.; Roberto Fischmann, Secy.
EIN: 236262315

8099
The KMJ Family Foundation
826 Turnbridge Rd.
Wayne, PA 19087-2070

Established in 2007 in Pennsylvania.
Donor: Arnold C. Schneider III.
Foundation type: Independent foundation.
Financial data (yr. ended 12/31/13): Assets, $10,862,988 (M); gifts received, $327,180; expenditures, $358,325; qualifying distributions, $356,200; giving activities include $352,750 for 9 grants (high: $125,000; low: $250).
Fields of interest: Nonprofits; Christianity.
Type of support: Regranting.
Limitations: Applications not accepted. Giving primarily in PA. No grants to individuals.
Application information: Contributes only to pre-selected organizations.
Officers: Arnold C. Schneider III, Chair.; Mary M. Schneider, Pres.
EIN: 260554486

8100
The Knoll Charitable Foundation
1235 Water St.
P.O. Box 157
East Greenville, PA 18041-0157 (507) 931-1682

Established in 1999 in Pennsylvania.
Donors: Knoll, Inc.; Warburg Pincus Foundation.
Foundation type: Company-sponsored foundation.
Financial data (yr. ended 12/31/14): Assets, $5,000,137 (M); expenditures, $220,605; qualifying distributions, $193,200; giving activities include $185,000 for grants.
Purpose and activities: The foundation awards college scholarships to children of full-time employees of Knoll, Inc. The program is administered by Scholarship America.

Fields of interest: Higher education.
Type of support: Scholarships; Employee-related scholarships.
Limitations: Applications not accepted. Giving limited to areas of company operations in PA.
Application information: Contributes only through employee-related scholarships.
Officers and Directors: Karen Clary, Pres. and Director; Craig Spray, V.P. and Treas. and Director; Roxanne Klein, V.P.; Michael Pollner, Secy.; Lynn Utter.
EIN: 232939762

8101
Knox Family Foundation
2113 Delancey St.
Philadelphia, PA 19103-6511

Established in 1961 in Unspecified.
Donors: Eleanor E. Knox†; Knox Gelatine, Inc.
Foundation type: Independent foundation.
Financial data (yr. ended 12/31/14): Assets, $7,376,418; expenditures, $508,839; qualifying distributions, $413,449.
Fields of interest: Secondary education; Higher education; Hospital care; Protestantism; Human services.
Limitations: Applications not accepted. Giving primarily in NY and PA. No grants to individuals.
Application information: Contributes only to pre-selected organizations.
Officers: Eleanor G. Nalle, Pres. and Director; John K. Graham, V.P. and Secy. and Director; Nora Armstrong, V.P.; Rose Anne Armstrong, V.P. and Director; Roseann K. Beaudoin, V.P. and Director; Rosemary Birchard, V.P. and Director; Amy Brumley, V.P. and Director; Kimberly Knox, V.P. and Director.
EIN: 146017797

8102
Earl Knudsen Charitable Foundation
c/o PNC Bank, N.A.
P.O. Box 609
Pittsburgh, PA 15230-9738
Application address: c/o Judith D. Morrison, P.O. Box 1, Imperial, PA 15126-0001, tel.: (800) 622-8036

Donor: Earl Knudsen†.
Foundation type: Independent foundation.
Financial data (yr. ended 12/31/13): Assets, $1,957,553 (M); expenditures, $206,500; qualifying distributions, $190,566; giving activities include $182,000 for 23 grants (high: $20,000; low: $2,000).
Purpose and activities: Giving primarily for education, health organizations, and social services.
Fields of interest: Arts and culture; Education; Diseases and conditions; Christianity; Human services; Family services; Child welfare.
Type of support: General support; Annual campaigns; Capital campaigns.
Limitations: Applications accepted. Giving primarily in PA, with emphasis on Pittsburgh. No grants to individuals, or for scholarships, or fellowships; no loans.
Application information: Application form available at Grantmakers of Western Pennsylvania web site: http://www.gwpa.org. Application form required.
  Initial approach: See Website
  Copies of proposal: 3

Deadline(s): None
Board meeting date(s): Quarterly and as required
Final notification: Affirmative replies only
Trustee: PNC Bank, N.A.
EIN: 256062530

8103
Flora Dale Krouse Foundation
c/o PNC Bank, N.A.
P.O. Box 609
Pittsburgh, PA 15230-9738   (412) 762-8133
Application Address: c/o PNC Charitable Trust Grant
Review C, PNC Bank, 249 Fifth Ave., 20th Fl.,
Pittsburgh, PA, 15222, Application Phone: (216)
222-3226

Donor: F.B. Krouse Unitrust.
Foundation type: Independent foundation.
Financial data (yr. ended 09/30/14): Assets,
$3,796,877 (M); expenditures, $213,154;
qualifying distributions, $183,379; giving activities
include $142,000 for 11 grants (high: $25,000;
low: $2,000).
Fields of interest: Education; Sports and recreation;
Human services.
Type of support: General support.
Limitations: Applications accepted. Giving primarily
in Fort Wayne, IN; some giving also in OH. No grants
to individuals.
Application information: Consult web site.
Application form required.
  Initial approach: Letter
  Deadline(s): None
Trustee: PNC Bank, N.A.
EIN: 310902923

8104
Kurtz Family Foundation
7200 Sherman St.
Philadelphia, PA   19119-3353

Established in 2005 in Pennsylvania.
Donors: Esther A. Kurtz; Esther A. Kurtz Irrevocable
Trust.
Foundation type: Independent foundation.
Financial data (yr. ended 12/31/13): Assets,
$457,656 (M); gifts received, $1,580;
expenditures, $161,580; qualifying distributions,
$160,000; giving activities include $160,000 for 4
grants (high: $100,000; low: $5,000).
Fields of interest: Elementary and secondary
education; Higher education.
Limitations: Applications not accepted. Giving
primarily in Philadelphia, PA. No grants to
individuals.
Application information: Contributes only to
pre-selected organizations.
Officer: Ellen Kurtz, Pres.
EIN: 203687991

8105
Edna G. Kynett Memorial Foundation, Inc.
c/o Pembroke Philanthropy Advisors
16 E. Lancaster Ave., Plz. 16, Ste. 102
Ardmore, PA   19003-2228   (610) 896-3868
Contact: Martha E. Morse, Exec. Dir.; Marge
Brennan, Grants Mgr.
FAX: (610) 896-3869; Email for Martha E. Morse:
mmorse@pembrokephilanthropy.net; Main
URL: http://www.kynett.org/index.htm

Established in 1954 in Delaware.
Donor: Harold H. Kynett†.
Foundation type: Independent foundation.
Financial data (yr. ended 12/31/14): Assets,
$8,618,224 (M); expenditures, $606,701;
qualifying distributions, $540,549; giving activities
include $333,000 for grants.
Purpose and activities: Harold H. Kynett created the
Edna G. Kynett Memorial Foundation to improve
cardiovascular health in the Delaware Valley through
education, research and community health
programs. The foundation seeks to fulfill Mr.
Kynett's vision by funding innovative projects which
will advance the understanding of cardiac disease,
as well as those which contribute to improved
prevention and treatment. The foundation currently
accepts proposals in any of three broad areas:
professional education, research and programs to
improve cardiovascular health in certain
communities or populations. The Board encourages
and gives particular consideration to proposals
designed to improve the cardiac health of
populations that have a higher than average risk of
heart disease and that are generally underserved by
the current health system. Kynett funding may not
be utilized for routine medical care unless such
services are provided as an essential component of
a program to test innovative methods of health
service delivery.
Fields of interest: Higher education; Medical
education; Continuing education; Heart and
circulatory system diseases.
Type of support: Program development; Convening;
Seed money; Curriculum development.
Limitations: Applications accepted. Giving primarily
in the greater Philadelphia, PA, area.
Application information: Applicants should submit
2 proposal copies by mail and one full copy emailed
to mbrennan@pembrokephilanthropy.net.
Application form required.
  Initial approach: Proposal
  Deadline(s): Oct. 15th and Apr. 15th
  Board meeting date(s): Nov. and May
Officers: Jeane Ann Grisso, MD, Pres.; Victoria
Vetter, MD, V.P.; Dwayne Wharton, M.Ed., Secy.;
Amanda Agati, C.F.A., Treas.; Martha E. Morse,
Exec. Dir.
Directors: Nathalie Bartle, Ed.D.; Verdi DiSesa,
M.B.A.; Ruth DuBois; Frank James, MD; Ann
O'Sullivan, Ph.D; Walter H. Tsou, MD; Thomas
Vernon, MD; Roy Wade, MD; Gerald DeVaughn, MD.
Number of staff: 1 part-time professional.
EIN: 236296592

8106
Robert E. Lamb Foundation Inc.
21 Rebel Rd.
Radnor, PA   19087-2809

Established in 2003 in Pennsylvania.
Donors: Robert E. Lamb II; Walter E. Lamb Trust.
Foundation type: Independent foundation.
Financial data (yr. ended 12/31/13): Assets,
$5,630,717 (M); expenditures, $267,179;
qualifying distributions, $251,872; giving activities
include $243,500 for 19 grants (high: $25,000;
low: $1,000).
Fields of interest: Education; Higher education;
Animal welfare; Foundations; Community and
economic development; Reproductive rights.
Type of support: General support.
Limitations: Applications not accepted. Giving
primarily in PA. No grants to individuals.

Application information: Unsolicited requests for
funds not accepted.
Officer and Trustee: Robert E. Lamb II, Pres. and
Trustee.
EIN: 810606210

8107
Grace F. Lamb Trust A
c/o BNY Mellon, N.A.
P.O. Box 185
Pittsburgh, PA   15230-0185

Foundation type: Independent foundation.
Financial data (yr. ended 12/31/14): Assets,
$8,927,455; expenditures, $462,819; qualifying
distributions, $411,283.
Fields of interest: Diseases and conditions;
Arthritis; Heart and circulatory system diseases;
Cancers.
Limitations: Applications not accepted. Giving
primarily in NY; some giving also in OK. No grants to
individuals.
Application information: Contributes only to
pre-selected organizations.
Trustee: BNY Mellon, N.A.
EIN: 136210809

8108
Alice & Leslie E. Lancy Foundation
c/o PNC Bank, N.A.
P.O. Box 609
Pittsburgh, PA   15230-9738
Application address: c/o PNC Bank, N.A.,
Attn.: Shaun Byrne, 2 PNC Plz., 620 Liberty Ave., 7th
Fl., Pittsburgh, PA 15222, tel.: (412) 768-8248

Donor: Leslie E. Lancy†.
Foundation type: Independent foundation.
Financial data (yr. ended 12/31/13): Assets,
$3,654,039 (M); expenditures, $188,423;
qualifying distributions, $155,936; giving activities
include $155,936 for 2 grants (high: $129,815;
low: $26,121).
Purpose and activities: Giving primarily for
educational services.
Fields of interest: Education; Environment.
Limitations: Applications accepted. Giving primarily
in CA and VA.
Application information: Application form required.
  Initial approach: Proposal
  Deadline(s): None
Trustee: David F. Lancy.
EIN: 251371367

8109
Landenberger Family Foundation
c/o Cozen O' Connor
1900 Market St.
Philadelphia, PA   19103

Donor: J. William Landenberger†.
Foundation type: Independent foundation.
Financial data (yr. ended 12/31/14): Assets,
$6,475,058 (M); expenditures, $315,271;
qualifying distributions, $306,183; giving activities
include $300,000 for 36 grants (high: $40,000;
low: $500).
Fields of interest: Arts and culture; Religion;
Christianity; Sports and recreation; Human services.

Limitations: Applications accepted. Giving primarily in PA.
Application information:
   Initial approach: Contact foundation
   Deadline(s): none
Directors: Joseph A. Glyn; David R. Glyn.
EIN: 275009621

8110
Arthur E. and Hilda C. Landers Charitable Trust
c/o PNC Bank, N.A.
620 Liberty Ave., 10th Fl.
Pittsburgh, PA   15222-2729   4127689969
Application address: c/o PNC Charitable Trust Grant Review C, PNC Bank, 249 5th Ave., 20th Fl., Pittsburgh, PA 15222 tel.: (412) 762-2864

Established in 1998 in Maryland.
Donor: Arthur Landers Martial Trust.
Foundation type: Independent foundation.
Financial data (yr. ended 12/31/14): Assets, $8,544,332; expenditures, $445,876; qualifying distributions, $391,029 and $0 for set-asides.
Fields of interest: Higher education.
Type of support: General support.
Limitations: Applications accepted. Giving primarily in MD. No grants to individuals.
Application information: See c/o website. Application form required.
   Initial approach: See Website
   Deadline(s): See Website
Trustees: Donald R. Mering; PNC Bank, N.A.
EIN: 311612150

8111
Langner Charitable Trust
c/o PNC Bank, N.A.
620 Liberty Ave., 10th Fl.
Pittsburgh, PA   15222-2705

Donor: PNC Bank Trust.
Foundation type: Independent foundation.
Financial data (yr. ended 11/30/14): Assets, $7,434,844 (M); expenditures, $356,711; qualifying distributions, $276,874; giving activities include $273,498 for 3 grants (high: $123,074; low: $27,350).
Fields of interest: Domesticated animals; Protestantism.
Limitations: Applications not accepted. Giving primarily in PA.
Application information: Unsolicited requests for funds not accepted.
Trustees: Robert E. Ward, Esq.; PNC Bank, N.A.
EIN: 256866136

8112
Larking Hill Foundation
c/o Thomas L. Bennett
330 Thornbrook Ave.
Rosemont, PA   19010-1637   (610) 527-5634
Contact: Thomas L. Bennett, Tr.

Established in 1998 in Pennsylvania.
Donor: Thomas L. Bennett.
Foundation type: Independent foundation.
Financial data (yr. ended 05/31/13): Assets, $2,657,636 (M); gifts received, $29; expenditures, $201,838; qualifying distributions, $190,500;

giving activities include $190,500 for 14 grants (high: $60,000; low: $1,500).
Fields of interest: Arts and culture; Education; Human services.
Type of support: Capital campaigns.
Limitations: Applications accepted. Giving primarily in NC and PA. No grants to individuals.
Application information: Application form required.
   Initial approach: Letter
   Deadline(s): None
Trustees: Carolyn E. Bennett; Christopher F. Bennett; Geoffrey T. Bennett; Thomas L. Bennett.
EIN: 237978393

8113
Pamela Whitcomb Larsen Foundation
2364 Rte. 66
Delmont, PA   15626-1454

Established in 2003 in Pennsylvania.
Foundation type: Independent foundation.
Financial data (yr. ended 12/31/13): Assets, $3,774,751 (M); expenditures, $175,420; qualifying distributions, $161,000; giving activities include $161,000 for 6 grants (high: $30,000; low: $25,000).
Fields of interest: Cancers; Christianity; International development.
Limitations: Applications not accepted. Giving primarily in CT, MA, and PA. No grants to individuals.
Application information: Unsolicited requests for funds not accepted.
Trustee: Allan MacDougall III.
EIN: 043777113

8114
Laughlin Memorial, Inc.
5700 Corporate Dr., Ste. 800
Pittsburgh, PA   15237-5851   (412) 348-3106
Contact: Todd A. Sacco, Tr.

Established in 1927 in Pennsylvania.
Donors: Mary M. Laughlin†; PNC Bank.
Foundation type: Independent foundation.
Financial data (yr. ended 12/31/13): Assets, $3,309,347 (M); gifts received, $8,502; expenditures, $241,341; qualifying distributions, $198,838; giving activities include $198,838 for 16 grants (high: $127,838; low: $1,000).
Purpose and activities: Giving support for libraries, health, and human services.
Fields of interest: Rehabilitation; Libraries; Human services; Child welfare.
Type of support: General support.
Limitations: Applications accepted. Giving limited to the Ambridge, PA, area. No grants to individuals.
Application information: Application form required.
   Initial approach: Letter
   Copies of proposal: 1
   Deadline(s): Nov. 15
   Board meeting date(s): Dec.
Trustees: Fred C. Emerick; Alexander M. Laughlin; Alexander M. Laughlin, Jr.; David W. Laughlin; Todd A. Sacco; James F. Schell; William J. Simpson; Robert E. Taggart; James P. Wetzel, Jr.
Number of staff: 1 part-time professional.
EIN: 251072140

8115
Le Vine Family Foundation
506 Gulph Rd.
Bryn Mawr, PA   19010

Donor: Victory Foundation.
Foundation type: Independent foundation.
Financial data (yr. ended 12/31/14): Assets, $3,487,222; expenditures, $166,355; qualifying distributions, $163,276.
Fields of interest: Arts and culture; Education.
Limitations: Applications not accepted. Giving primarily in PA.
Application information: Contributes only to pre-selected organizations.
Trustees: D. Christopher LeVine; Victoria McNeil LeVine.
EIN: 262038890

8116
Susan D. Leakin Trust
c/o PNC Bank, N.A.
620 Liberty Ave., 10th Fl.
Pittsburgh, PA   15222

Foundation type: Independent foundation.
Financial data (yr. ended 12/31/14): Assets, $4,425,841; expenditures, $249,921; qualifying distributions, $215,409 and $0 for set-asides.
Fields of interest: Education; Health.
Type of support: General support.
Limitations: Applications not accepted. Giving primarily in MD.
Application information: Unsolicited requests for funds not accepted.
Trustee: PNC Bank, N.A.
EIN: 526022358

8117
The Leary Research Fund
c/o PNC Bank, N.A.
620 Liberty Ave., 10th Fl.
Pittsburgh, PA   15222-2705

Foundation type: Independent foundation.
Financial data (yr. ended 12/31/14): Assets, $9,615,693; expenditures, $444,258; qualifying distributions, $349,006 and $0 for set-asides.
Fields of interest: Diseases and conditions; Multiple sclerosis; Cancers.
Type of support: General support.
Limitations: Applications not accepted. Giving primarily in Washington, DC, FL and OK.
Application information: Unsolicited requests for funds not accepted.
Trustee: PNC Bank, N.A.
EIN: 266300509

8118
The Leeway Foundation
The Philadelphia Bldg.
1315 Walnut St., Ste. 832
Philadelphia, PA   19109-1025   (215) 545-4078
FAX: (215) 545-4021; E-mail: info@leeway.org; Main URL: http://www.leeway.org
Blog: http://www.leeway.org/blog
Facebook: http://www.facebook.com/leewayfoundation
Flickr: https://www.flickr.com/photos/leewayfoundation

Foundation's Instagram Profile: http://
instagram.com/leewayfound
Grants List: http://www.leeway.org/grantees
Tumblr: http://leewayfoundation.tumblr.com
Twitter: http://twitter.com/leewayfound
Vimeo: http://vimeo.com/leeway

Established in 1993 in Pennsylvania.
Donors: Linda L. Alter; Helen Berman Alter†; Bertha
Dagan Berman†.
Foundation type: Independent foundation.
Financial data (yr. ended 12/31/12): Assets,
$16,849,379 (M); gifts received, $2,000;
expenditures, $874,986; qualifying distributions,
$805,284; giving activities include $214,360 for 74
grants to individuals (high: $15,000; low: $100).
Purpose and activities: The foundation supports
individual women and transgender artists in order to
help them achieve individual and community
transformation in Camden County, New Jersey and
the Philadelphia, Pennsylvania, 5-county area.
Fields of interest: Arts and culture; Females.
Type of support: Grants to individuals.
Limitations: Applications accepted. Giving to
residents in the Delaware Valley area.
Publications: Application guidelines; Annual report;
Grants list.
Application information: Complete guidelines and
application form available on foundation web site.
Application form required.
  Initial approach: Letter, telephone or e-mail
    inquiry
  Copies of proposal: 1
  Deadline(s): See foundation web site for current
    deadlines
  Board meeting date(s): Six times per year
  Final notification: 60 days after deadline
Officers: Amandee Braxton, Pres.; Gretjen Clausing,
Treas.; Denise Brown, Exec. Dir.
Board Members: Carolyn Chernoff; Tina Morton;
Patience Rage; Virginia P. Sikes, Esq.
Number of staff: 3 full-time professional; 1 full-time
support; 1 part-time support.
EIN: 232727140

8119
The Lemole Family Charitable Trust
(formerly The Building Bridges Foundation)
2771 Philmont Ave.
Huntingdon Valley, PA   19006-5303

Established in 1996 in Pennsylvania.
Donors: Emily Jane A. Lemole; Gerald M. Lemole; G.
Michael Lemole.
Foundation type: Independent foundation.
Financial data (yr. ended 10/31/13): Assets,
$570,001 (M); gifts received, $255,000;
expenditures, $180,821; qualifying distributions,
$180,775; giving activities include $180,775 for 34
grants (high: $60,000; low: $250).
Fields of interest: Education; Higher education;
Health; Christianity; Human services.
Limitations: Applications not accepted. Giving in the
U.S., with emphasis on PA. No grants to individuals.
Application information: Contributes only to
pre-selected organizations.
Trustees: Laura Lemole Dupont; Christopher R.
Lemole; Emily Jane A. Lemole; G. Michael Lemole,
Jr.; Gerald M. Lemole; Samantha M. Lemole; Lisa
Lemole Oz; Emily A. Lemole Smith.
EIN: 232887165

8120
Peter And Judy Leone Foundation
P.O. Box 1393
Bryn Mawr, PA   19010-7393

Foundation type: Independent foundation.
Financial data (yr. ended 12/31/13): Assets,
$5,351,900 (M); expenditures, $243,831;
qualifying distributions, $220,000; giving activities
include $220,000 for 2 grants (high: $200,000;
low: $20,000).
Fields of interest: Arts and culture; Education.
Limitations: Applications not accepted. Giving
primarily in PA.
Application information: Unsolicited requests for
funds not accepted.
Trustees: Judy L. Leone; Peter G. Leone.
EIN: 461588133

8121
Polly A. Levee Charitable Trust B - La Vea
Trust
c/o PNC Bank, N.A.
620 Liberty Ave., 10th Fl.
Pittsburgh, PA   15222-2705

Established in 1993 in Pennsylvania.
Donor: Polly Annenberg Levee†.
Foundation type: Independent foundation.
Financial data (yr. ended 12/31/13): Assets,
$566,033 (M); expenditures, $262,158; qualifying
distributions, $244,669; giving activities include
$238,358 for 37 grants (high: $14,302; low:
$4,767).
Purpose and activities: Giving primarily for health
care and health associations.
Fields of interest: Education; Hospital care;
Diseases and conditions; Community and economic
development.
Type of support: General support; Annual
campaigns; Research; Research and evaluation.
Limitations: Applications not accepted. Giving
primarily in FL, IL and NY. No grants to individuals.
Application information: Contributes only to
pre-selected organizations.
Trustees: William J. Henrich, Jr., Esq.; PNC Bank,
N.A.
Number of staff: None.
EIN: 232735662

8122
The Adolph & Rose Levis Family
Foundation
c/o BNY Mellon, N.A.
P.O. Box 185
Pittsburgh, PA   15230-0185

Established in 1993 in Pennsylvania.
Donor: Adolph Levis†.
Foundation type: Independent foundation.
Financial data (yr. ended 11/30/13): Assets,
$7,866,638; expenditures, $391,944; qualifying
distributions, $365,924.
Purpose and activities: Giving primarily for Jewish
organizations.
Fields of interest: Foundations; Nonprofits;
Judaism; Human services.
Type of support: Regranting.
Limitations: Applications not accepted. Giving
primarily in Boca Raton, FL. No grants to individuals.

Application information: Contributes only to
pre-selected organizations.
Trustee: BNY Mellon, N.A.
EIN: 650211764

8123
Mabelle McLeod Lewis Memorial Fund
c/o Wells Fargo Bank, N.A.
101N Independence Mall E., MACY1372-062
Philadelphia, PA   19106-2112
Application address: P.O. Box 3730, Stanford, CA
94305

Established in 1968 in California.
Donor: Donald McLeod Lewis†.
Foundation type: Operating foundation.
Financial data (yr. ended 03/31/13): Assets,
$4,955,806 (M); expenditures, $283,530;
qualifying distributions, $247,412; giving activities
include $217,185 for 9 grants to individuals (high:
$35,306; low: $3,404).
Purpose and activities: Grants to scholars in the
humanities affiliated with northern CA universities
and colleges to bring about the completion of a
scholarly dissertation on which a substantial
amount of work has already been completed; also
awards grants to doctoral candidates who are in
their last year of study.
Fields of interest: Humanities.
Type of support: Fellowships; Research; Student
aid.
Limitations: Applications accepted. Giving limited to
northern CA.
Publications: Application guidelines; Program policy
statement.
Application information: Submit application by mail
only. Application form required.
  Initial approach: Letter
  Deadline(s): Jan. 15
  Board meeting date(s): Feb. or Mar.
Trustees: Robert M. Raymer; Wells Fargo Bank, N.A.
Number of staff: 1
EIN: 237079585

8124
Andrew and Janet Lyman Lewis Private
Foundation
c/o PNC Bank, N.A.
1600 Market St., Tax Dept.
Philadelphia, PA   19103-7240

Foundation type: Independent foundation.
Financial data (yr. ended 12/31/13): Assets,
$9,095,955 (M); expenditures, $449,979;
qualifying distributions, $390,347; giving activities
include $371,988 for 4 grants (high: $92,997; low:
$92,997).
Fields of interest: Elementary and secondary
education; Disasters and emergency management;
Search and rescue; Fire prevention and control;
Protestantism.
Type of support: Volunteer development.
Limitations: Applications not accepted. Giving
primarily in NJ and PA.
Application information: Contributes only to
pre-selected organizations.
Trustee: PNC Bank, N.A.
EIN: 256862301

8125
Hannah Lewis Scott 5
c/o PNC Bank
620 Liberty Ave., 10th Fl.
Pittsburgh, PA   15222-2705

Foundation type: Independent foundation.
Financial data (yr. ended 12/31/14): Assets,
$7,179,390; expenditures, $326,465; qualifying
distributions, $277,948 and $0 for set-asides.
Fields of interest: Human services; Children.
Limitations: Applications not accepted. Giving
primarily in PA.
Application information: Unsolicited requests for
funds not accepted.
Trustee: PNC Bank, N.A.
EIN: 236205614

8126
Park Lewis Trust
c/o BNY Mellon, N.A.
P.O. Box 185
Pittsburgh, PA   15230-0185

Foundation type: Independent foundation.
Financial data (yr. ended 09/30/14): Assets,
$8,255,007; expenditures, $404,615; qualifying
distributions, $380,326.
Fields of interest: Hospital care.
Limitations: Applications not accepted. Giving
primarily in Pittsburgh, PA.
Application information: Contributes only to
pre-selected organizations.
Trustee: BNY Mellon, N.A.
EIN: 256036857

8127
The Lida Foundation
504 W. Mermaid Ln.
Philadelphia, PA   19118-4206   (215) 247-5578

Established in 1993 in Pennsylvania.
Donor: Linda Glickstein.
Foundation type: Independent foundation.
Financial data (yr. ended 12/31/14): Assets,
$6,108,145; gifts received, $331,366;
expenditures, $238,775; qualifying distributions,
$220,280.
Fields of interest: Arts and culture; Theater; Opera;
Art museums; Education; University education;
Teacher education; Nonprofits; Radio; Reproductive
rights; Human services.
Type of support: General support; Regranting.
Limitations: Applications accepted. Giving primarily
in PA. No grants to individuals.
Application information:
   Initial approach: Proposal
   Deadline(s): None
Trustees: David L. Glickstein; Linda S. Glickstein.
EIN: 232706456

8128
Margaret Lienemann Perpetual Charitable Trust
77 E. King St.
Shippensburg, PA   17257-1307

Foundation type: Independent foundation.
Financial data (yr. ended 12/31/13): Assets,
$5,167,666 (M); expenditures, $224,053;

qualifying distributions, $181,426; giving activities
include $181,426 for 4 grants (high: $45,357; low:
$45,356).
Fields of interest: Education; Diseases and
conditions; Human services.
Limitations: Applications not accepted.
Application information: Unsolicited requests for
funds not accepted.
Trustee: Orrstown Bank.
EIN: 206609415

8129
The Lipstein Family Foundation
417 Conestoga Rd.
Malvern, PA   19355-1009

Established in 1999 in Pennsylvania.
Donors: Sanford Lipstein; Gail Lipstein.
Foundation type: Independent foundation.
Financial data (yr. ended 12/31/14): Assets,
$2,667,256 (M); gifts received, $2,308;
expenditures, $144,300; qualifying distributions,
$144,300; giving activities include $142,800 for 58
grants (high: $25,200; low: $100).
Fields of interest: Arts and culture; Diseases and
conditions; Sports and recreation.
Limitations: Applications not accepted. No grants to
individuals.
Application information: Unsolicited requests for
funds not accepted.
Officers: Sanford Lipstein, Pres.; Gail Lipstein, Secy.
EIN: 233008418

8130
James H. and Florence D. Lockhard Trust
c/o BNY Mellon, N.A.
P.O. Box 185
Pittsburgh, PA   15230-0185

Foundation type: Independent foundation.
Financial data (yr. ended 09/30/13): Assets,
$3,374,273 (M); expenditures, $171,647;
qualifying distributions, $168,914; giving activities
include $168,213 for 34 grants (high: $18,153;
low: $1,210).
Fields of interest: Higher education; Foundations;
Human services.
Limitations: Applications not accepted. Giving
primarily in NY and PA.
Application information: Unsolicited requests for
funds not accepted.
Trustee: BNY Mellon, N.A.
EIN: 256018608

8131
Lockhart Eastminster Presby Ch Pgh
c/o PNC Bank, N.A.
P.O. Box 609
Pittsburgh, PA   15230-9738

Foundation type: Independent foundation.
Financial data (yr. ended 12/31/14): Assets,
$5,996,570; expenditures, $297,562; qualifying
distributions, $260,078 and $0 for set-asides.
Fields of interest: Religion.
Type of support: General support.
Limitations: Applications not accepted. Giving
primarily in PA.
Application information: Unsolicited requests for
funds not accepted.

Trustee: PNC Bank, N.A.
EIN: 256021055

8132
Thomas Lord Charitable Trust
c/o PNC Bank, N.A.
P.O. Box 609
Pittsburgh, PA   15230-9738
Application address: c/o Michael Yoder, PNC Bank,
N.A., 620 Liberty Ave., Pittsburgh, PA 15222,
tel.: (412) 762-4106

Established in 1955 in Pennsylvania.
Donor: Thomas Lord.
Foundation type: Independent foundation.
Financial data (yr. ended 12/31/13): Assets,
$2,913,518 (M); expenditures, $152,900;
qualifying distributions, $149,513; giving activities
include $148,000 for 5 grants (high: $38,000; low:
$25,000).
Fields of interest: Undergraduate education;
Hospital care.
Limitations: Applications accepted. Giving primarily
in PA. No grants to individuals.
Application information: Application form required.
   Initial approach: Letter
   Deadline(s): None
Trustee: PNC Bank, N.A.
EIN: 256028793

8133
The Lubert Family Foundation, Inc.
2929 Arch St., 13th Fl.
Philadelphia, PA   19104-2868

Established in 2004 in Virgin Islands.
Donor: Ira M. Lubert.
Foundation type: Independent foundation.
Financial data (yr. ended 12/31/13): Assets,
$7,448,177 (M); expenditures, $519,300;
qualifying distributions, $378,683; giving activities
include $378,683 for 51 grants (high: $33,333;
low: $500).
Fields of interest: University education; Nonprofits;
Diseases and conditions; Christianity; Judaism.
Type of support: Research; Regranting.
Limitations: Applications not accepted. Giving
primarily in PA. No grants to individuals.
Application information: Unsolicited requests for
funds not accepted.
Officers: Ira M. Lubert, Pres.; Kristine Lubert, V.P.;
Tricia Billings, Secy.; Jonathan Lubert, Treas.
EIN: 660639002

8134
Christopher Ludwick Foundation
(formerly The Ludwick Institute)
16 N. Bryn Mawr Ave.
P.O. Box 1313
Bryn Mawr, PA   19010-3379
Contact: Trina Vaux, Secy.
E-mail: info@ludwickfoundation.org; Main
URL: http://www.ludwickfoundation.org

Established in 1799 in Pennsylvania.
Donor: Christopher Ludwick†.
Foundation type: Independent foundation.
Financial data (yr. ended 04/30/14): Assets,
$5,654,535 (M); expenditures, $220,835;
qualifying distributions, $216,729; giving activities

include $204,500 for 40 grants (high: $20,000; low: $500).

Purpose and activities: Giving primarily for the education of poor youth in Philadelphia, Pennsylvania. For a list of recent grants, see foundation web site.

Fields of interest: Arts and culture; Museums; Secondary education; Botanical gardens; Child welfare; Children; Adolescents; Young adults; Ethnic and racial groups; Low-income and poor people.

Type of support: Continuing support; Program development.

Limitations: Applications accepted. Giving limited to the City of Philadelphia, PA. No support for political organizations or programs targeted at children with disabilities for which other funding sources exist. No grants to individuals, or for building campaigns, endowments, equipment, or general operating support.

Publications: Application guidelines; Grants list.

Application information: 2 paper copies of proposal should be submitted (in addition to online submission). Application form required.

  Initial approach: Use application form on foundation web site
  Deadline(s): Applications accepted between Feb. 1 and Feb. 28
  Board meeting date(s): May and Oct.
  Final notification: Approx. June 15

Officers: Susan W. Catherwood, Pres.; William M. Davison IV, V.P. and Treas.; Rhonda Cohen, V.P.; Trina Vaux, Secy.

Number of staff: 1 part-time support.

EIN: 236256408

8135
M&P Family Foundation Inc.
20 Stanwix St., Ste. 650
Pittsburgh, PA   15222-4801

Established in 2007 in Pennsylvania.

Donor: Mildred Stern.

Foundation type: Independent foundation.

Financial data (yr. ended 12/31/12): Assets, $1,919,154 (M); expenditures, $156,355; qualifying distributions, $137,158; giving activities include $130,000 for 5 grants (high: $50,000; low: $10,000).

Fields of interest: Nonprofits.

Type of support: Regranting.

Limitations: Applications not accepted. Giving primarily in PA. No grants to individuals.

Application information: Unsolicited requests for funds not accepted.

Officers and Directors: Barbara S. Burstin, Chair. and Director; Andrea K. Schneider, Pres. and Director; Jeffrey F. Kupfer, V.P. and Director; Deborah K. Cosgrove, Secy.-Treas. and Director; Nancy K. Strichman.

EIN: 510648670

8136
John S. Mack Charitable Trust
c/o PNC Bank, N.A.
P.O. Box 609
Pittsburgh, PA   15230-9738

Foundation type: Independent foundation.

Financial data (yr. ended 12/31/13): Assets, $6,224,022 (M); expenditures, $302,074;

qualifying distributions, $266,239; giving activities include $237,849 for 1 grant.

Fields of interest: Health.

Limitations: Applications not accepted. Giving primarily in PA.

Application information: Unsolicited requests for funds not accepted.

Trustee: PNC Bank, N.A.

EIN: 256019551

8137
The Magee Foundation
212 Fair St.
Bloomsburg, PA   17815

Established in 1964 in Pennsylvania.

Donor: Magee Industrial Enterprises.

Foundation type: Independent foundation.

Financial data (yr. ended 10/31/13): Assets, $2,086,370 (M); expenditures, $169,995; qualifying distributions, $150,000; giving activities include $150,000 for 29 grants (high: $11,500; low: $1,000).

Fields of interest: Education; Health; Human services.

Limitations: Applications not accepted. Giving primarily in PA. No grants to individuals.

Application information: Unsolicited requests for funds not accepted.

Trustees: Stephen Hummel; Audrey R. Magee; Drue A. Magee; Elizabeth Magee.

EIN: 236398294

8138
The Mango Tree Foundation
c/o Aufman Associates
2200 Georgetown Dr.
Sewickley, PA   15143-8753

Donors: Alain J.P. Belda; Alcoa, Inc.

Foundation type: Independent foundation.

Financial data (yr. ended 12/31/13): Assets, $1,373,389 (M); gifts received, $750,000; expenditures, $336,606; qualifying distributions, $327,138; giving activities include $327,138 for 13 grants (high: $50,000; low: $5,400).

Fields of interest: Education; Higher education; Environment; Health.

International interests: Brazil.

Type of support: General support.

Limitations: Applications not accepted. Giving primarily in NY and VA; with some giving in Brazil.

Application information: Unsolicited requests for funds not accepted.

Officer: Edward Aufman, Mgr.

Director: Alain Belda.

EIN: 271825537

8139
Maple Hill Foundation
c/o Miller Assoc.
100 Front St., Ste. 950
West Conshohocken, PA   19428-2878   (610) 941-5011
Contact: Ella Warren Miller, Dir.

Established in 1986 in Pennsylvania.

Donors: Paul F. Miller, Jr.; Ella Warren Miller.

Foundation type: Independent foundation.

Financial data (yr. ended 07/31/14): Assets, $819,652 (M); expenditures, $220,991; qualifying distributions, $219,000; giving activities include $219,000 for 18 grants (high: $50,000; low: $1,000).

Purpose and activities: Giving primarily for education and human services.

Fields of interest: Arts and culture; Education; Higher education; Natural resources; Public policy; Human services.

Type of support: Policy, advocacy and systems reform.

Limitations: Applications not accepted. Giving primarily in CA, MA, NH, and Philadelphia, PA. No grants to individuals.

Application information: Contributes only to pre-selected organizations.

Officers and Directors: Ella Warren Merrill, Pres. and Director; Katharine S. Miller, V.P. and Secy. and Director; Paul F. Miller III, V.P. and Treas. and Director; Ella Warren Miller; Paul F. Miller, Jr.

EIN: 222751182

8140
The Maronda Foundation
11 Timberglen Dr.
Imperial, PA   15126-9267   (724) 695-1200
Contact: Ronald W. Wolf, Tr.

Donor: William J. Wolf.

Foundation type: Operating foundation.

Financial data (yr. ended 12/31/13): Assets, $30,948,862 (M); gifts received, $1,850; expenditures, $2,227,973; qualifying distributions, $753,214; giving activities include $177,252 for 3 grants (high: $129,130; low: $7,000), and $2,682,304 for 4 foundation-administered programs.

Purpose and activities: Giving primarily to Roman Catholic schools for grade school, high school and college scholarships, which will help financially needy students.

Fields of interest: Elementary and secondary education; Higher education; Catholicism; Low-income and poor people.

Type of support: Scholarships.

Limitations: Applications accepted. Giving primarily in PA.

Application information:
  Initial approach: Letter
  Deadline(s): None

Officer: Mary Wolf, Secy.

Director: Timothy O'Sullivan.

Trustee: Ronald W. Wolf.

EIN: 251386730

8141
Marstine Family Foundation
50 32nd St.
Pittsburgh, PA   15201-1402

Donor: Sheldon Marstine.

Foundation type: Independent foundation.

Financial data (yr. ended 12/31/13): Assets, $7,842,565 (M); gifts received, $2,091,000; expenditures, $381,554; qualifying distributions, $322,500; giving activities include $322,500 for 14 grants (high: $225,000; low: $3,000).

Fields of interest: Education; Judaism; Human services.

Limitations: Applications not accepted.

Application information: Unsolicited requests for funds not accepted.
Officer: Sheldon Marstine, Chair. and Fdn. Mgr.
Director: Janet Marstine.
EIN: 261529893

8142
Martin Foundation
(formerly Martin Family Foundation, Inc.)
c/o Kreischer Miller
100 Witmer Rd., Ste. 350
Horsham, PA 19044-2369
Application address: c/o Jessica M. Thompson, P.O. Box 749, Doylestown, PA 18901, tel.: (215) 348-8149

Donors: Sydney F. Martin; Sharon B. Martin.
Foundation type: Independent foundation.
Financial data (yr. ended 12/31/13): Assets, $10,638,659 (M); gifts received, $164,189; expenditures, $556,205; qualifying distributions, $491,683; giving activities include $420,000 for 16 grants (high: $135,690; low: $5,000).
Fields of interest: Arts and culture; Agriculture; Human services.
Application information: Application form required.
Initial approach: Proposal
Deadline(s): June 30
Officer: Sydney F. Martin, Pres.
Directors: Sharon B. Martin; Jessica E. Thompson.
EIN: 272178874

8143
The Martin Foundation
1936 S. Easton Rd., 2nd Fl.
Doylestown, PA 18901-2749 (267) 247-5036
Contact: Diane Armento

Foundation type: Independent foundation.
Financial data (yr. ended 03/31/14): Assets, $3,878,510 (M); expenditures, $182,201; qualifying distributions, $169,296; giving activities include $166,000 for 40 grants (high: $20,000; low: $1,000).
Fields of interest: Education; Human services.
Type of support: General support.
Limitations: Applications accepted. Giving primarily in MA, ME and PA. No grants to individuals.
Application information: Application form required.
Initial approach: Letter
Deadline(s): None
Trustees: George J. Hartnett; Laurel G. Martin; Zachary S. Martin; W. James Quigley.
EIN: 232182719

8144
Martin Guitar Charitable Foundation
510 Sycamore St.
Nazareth, PA 18064-1000

Established in 1996 in Pennsylvania.
Donors: C.F. Martin & Co., Inc.; C.F. Martin Guitar Co.
Foundation type: Company-sponsored foundation.
Financial data (yr. ended 12/31/13): Assets, $5,517,776 (M); gifts received, $502,940; expenditures, $258,501; qualifying distributions, $228,000; giving activities include $228,000 for 53 grants (high: $25,000; low: $1,000).

Purpose and activities: The foundation supports hospitals and organizations involved with arts and culture, higher education, and human services.
Fields of interest: Arts and culture; Education; Human services.
Type of support: General support.
Limitations: Applications not accepted. Giving primarily in PA. No grants to individuals.
Application information: Unsolicited requests for funds not accepted.
Officers: Christian F. Martin IV, Pres.; Diane S. Martin, V.P.; Theresa Rothrock, Secy.; John A. Messer, Treas.
EIN: 311483218

8145
J.P. Mascaro & Sons Charitable Trust
2650 Audubon Rd.
Audubon, PA 19403

Donor: Solid Waste Services, Inc.
Foundation type: Independent foundation.
Financial data (yr. ended 12/31/14): Assets, $5,413,699; gifts received, $350,000; expenditures, $284,862; qualifying distributions, $260,000.
Fields of interest: Religion.
Limitations: Applications not accepted. Giving primarily in PA.
Application information: Unsolicited requests for funds not accepted.
Trustees: William F. Fox, Jr.; Pasquale Mascaro.
EIN: 208254657

8146
Maslow Family Foundation Inc.
30 Hayfield Rd.
Shavertown, PA 18708-9748 (570) 674-6532
Contact: Marilyn J. O'Boyle

Established in 1994 in Pennsylvania.
Donor: Richard Maslow.
Foundation type: Independent foundation.
Financial data (yr. ended 12/31/12): Assets, $7,363,513 (M); expenditures, $413,882; qualifying distributions, $376,000; giving activities include $376,000 for grants.
Purpose and activities: Giving for the special needs children, and for the arts and cultural enrichment, and to improve the overall quality of life.
Fields of interest: Arts and culture; Child welfare; Children and youth; Adolescents; Low-income and poor people.
Type of support: General support; Matching grants; Continuing support; Capital campaigns; Capital and infrastructure; Equipment; Endowments; Emergency funds; Program development; Seed money; Scholarships.
Limitations: Applications accepted. Giving primarily in the greater Wyoming Valley area, in Luzerne County, PA. No grants to individuals, or for capital campaigns for colleges.
Publications: Financial statement.
Application information: Application form required.
Initial approach: Letter
Deadline(s): Aug. 1
Board meeting date(s): May, July and Sept.
Final notification: 3 months
Officers: Richard Maslow, Pres. and Director; Melanie Maslow Lumia, V.P. and Director; Hilary

Maslow Naud, Secy. and Director; Allison Maslow, Treas. and Director.
Directors: Douglas Maslow; Jennifer Holtzman Maslow; Eugene Roth.
Number of staff: 1 part-time support.
EIN: 232791676

8147
Martha Lockhart Mason Fund
c/o BNY Mellon, N.A.
P.O. Box 185
Pittsburgh, PA 15230-0185

Foundation type: Independent foundation.
Financial data (yr. ended 12/31/14): Assets, $7,238,398; expenditures, $422,583; qualifying distributions, $369,110.
Purpose and activities: The fund supports education, hospitals and other health organizations, human services and youth, and Presbyterian associations.
Fields of interest: Education; Elementary and secondary education; Higher education; Health; Hospital care; Protestantism; Human services; Child welfare; Youth development.
Limitations: Applications not accepted. Giving limited to PA.
Application information: Contributes only to pre-selected organizations.
Trustee: BNY Mellon, N.A.
EIN: 256018595

8148
M.L. Mason Memorial Fund
c/o PNC Bank, N.A.
P.O. Box 609
Pittsburgh, PA 15230-9738

Foundation type: Independent foundation.
Financial data (yr. ended 12/31/14): Assets, $10,311,776; expenditures, $483,658; qualifying distributions, $433,755 and $0 for set-asides.
Fields of interest: Health; Religion; Human services.
Type of support: General support.
Limitations: Applications not accepted. Giving primarily in PA.
Application information: Unsolicited requests for funds not accepted.
Trustee: PNC Bank, N.A.
EIN: 256020714

8149
M. L. Mason-Alleg Health Ed Research
c/o PNC Bank, N.A.
P.O. Box 609
Pittsburgh, PA 15230-9738

Foundation type: Independent foundation.
Financial data (yr. ended 12/31/14): Assets, $6,783,763; expenditures, $339,620; qualifying distributions, $303,658 and $0 for set-asides.
Fields of interest: Health.
Limitations: Applications not accepted. Giving primarily in PA.
Application information: Unsolicited requests for funds not accepted.
Trustee: PNC Bank, N.A.
EIN: 256020717

8150
Donald D. Mateer Foundation
c/o C. Stephenson
110 Crescent Dr.
Pittsburgh, PA 15228-1050

Foundation type: Independent foundation.
Financial data (yr. ended 12/31/14): Assets, $1,312,068; expenditures, $160,077; qualifying distributions, $153,162.
Fields of interest: Education; Christianity; Human services.
Limitations: Applications not accepted. Giving primarily in PA. No grants to individuals.
Application information: Unsolicited requests for funds not accepted.
Officer and Trustees: Charlotte M. Stephenson, Secy. and Trustee; Donald D. Mateer; Charlotte B. Obert.
EIN: 251895885

8151
Allen S. Mattingly Trust B
c/o PNC Bank
620 Liberty Ave., 10th Fl.
Pittsburgh, PA 15222-2722

Foundation type: Independent foundation.
Financial data (yr. ended 03/31/14): Assets, $6,982,716 (M); expenditures, $338,734; qualifying distributions, $289,503; giving activities include $287,311 for 5 grants (high: $91,940; low: $34,477).
Fields of interest: Animal welfare; Religion; Human services; Homeless people.
Type of support: General support.
Limitations: Applications not accepted. Giving primarily in KY.
Application information: Unsolicited requests for funds not accepted.
Trustee: PNC Bank, N.A.
EIN: 386814676

8152
Arthur Mayer Charitable Foundation
c/o PNC Bank, N.A.
620 Liberty Ave., 10th Fl.
Pittsburgh, PA 15222-2722

Foundation type: Independent foundation.
Financial data (yr. ended 12/31/14): Assets, $7,439,309; expenditures, $396,196; qualifying distributions, $303,530 and $0 for set-asides.
Fields of interest: Education; Health; Protestantism.
Limitations: Applications not accepted. Giving primarily in OH and PA.
Application information: Unsolicited requests for funds not accepted.
Trustee: PNC Bank, N.A.
EIN: 256155876

8153
James Frances McCandless Trust
c/o PNC Charitable Trusts
249 5th Ave.
1 PNC Plz., 20th Fl.
Pittsburgh, PA 15222 4127622950
E-mail: charitabletrusts@pnc.com; Application address: c/o PNC Bank, N.A., Attn.: Charitable Trust Grant Review Comm., One PNC Plz., 20th Fl., 249

5th Ave., Pittsburgh, PA 15222, tel.: (412) 762-5157 or (513) 651-8463; Main URL: https://www.pncsites.com/pncfoundation/charitable_trusts.html

Foundation type: Independent foundation.
Financial data (yr. ended 12/31/14): Assets, $5,546,640; expenditures, $272,200; qualifying distributions, $206,845 and $0 for set-asides.
Purpose and activities: Giving primarily to charitable or religious organizations for the benefit of sick, disabled or otherwise needy children.
Fields of interest: Child welfare.
Type of support: Capital campaigns; Matching grants; Capital and infrastructure; Equipment; Program development; Seed money.
Limitations: Applications accepted. Giving primarily in PA. No support for private foundations, or for fraternal, political, labor or advocacy groups. No grants to individuals, or for general operating costs or events.
Application information: Full proposals will not be accepted. Proposals will be invited upon review of inquiry. See web site PNC.com, under "Corporate & Institutional", then under "Special Segments", click on "Non-profits and Government Institutions", and then "Charitable Trust Grants".
Initial approach: Call or submit a letter of inquiry
Board meeting date(s): Quarterly
Trustee: PNC Bank, N.A.
EIN: 251347840

8154
Elinor Jones McConnell Trust Fund
P.O. Box 11054
Pittsburgh, PA 15237-0354

Established in 2000 in Pennsylvania.
Foundation type: Operating foundation.
Financial data (yr. ended 12/31/13): Assets, $3,033,906 (M); expenditures, $233,578; qualifying distributions, $180,000; giving activities include $180,000 for 18 grants (high: $40,000; low: $2,500).
Fields of interest: Animal welfare.
Limitations: Applications not accepted. Giving primarily in PA. No grants to individuals.
Application information: Contributes only to pre-selected organizations.
Trustee: William M. McKay.
EIN: 256747287

8155
Janet W. McCune for Charities
c/o PNC Bank, N.A.
P.O. Box 609
Pittsburgh, PA 15230-9738

Foundation type: Independent foundation.
Financial data (yr. ended 12/31/14): Assets, $8,300,874; expenditures, $464,394; qualifying distributions, $406,959 and $0 for set-asides.
Fields of interest: Health; Hospital care; Religion; Human services.
Type of support: General support.
Limitations: Applications not accepted. Giving primarily in PA.
Application information: Unsolicited requests for funds not accepted.
Trustee: PNC Bank, N.A.
EIN: 256020682

8156
Rita M. McGinley Foundation
600 Grant St., Ste. 4400
Pittsburgh, PA 15219-2713 (412) 566-1984

Established in 2003 in Pennsylvania.
Donor: Rita M. McGinley.
Foundation type: Independent foundation.
Financial data (yr. ended 12/31/14): Assets, $16,530,225; gifts received, $5,000; expenditures, $497,549; qualifying distributions, $345,150.
Fields of interest: Education; Diseases and conditions; Human services; Women's services.
Limitations: Applications accepted. Giving primarily in PA.
Application information:
Initial approach: Letter
Deadline(s): None
Officers and Directors: John R. McGinley, Jr., Pres. and Director; John C. McGinley, V.P. and Treas. and Director; Nancy Palamara, Secy.
EIN: 432024870

8157
McHale Memorial Trust
P. O. Box 609
Pittsburgh, PA 15230-9738

Donor: McHale Memorial Irrevocable Trust.
Foundation type: Independent foundation.
Financial data (yr. ended 12/31/13): Assets, $4,681,534 (M); expenditures, $250,737; qualifying distributions, $227,991; giving activities include $210,078 for 1 grant.
Fields of interest: Education.
Limitations: Applications not accepted. Giving primarily in IN.
Application information: Unsolicited requests for funds not accepted.
Trustee: PNC Bank, N.A.
EIN: 356334022

8158
The McKamish Family Foundation
50 55th St.
Pittsburgh, PA 15201-2311 (412) 781-6262
E-mail: themckamishfamilyfoundation@gmail.com

Donor: McKamish Inc.
Foundation type: Independent foundation.
Financial data (yr. ended 12/31/13): Assets, $4,741,633 (M); gifts received, $8,000; expenditures, $271,624; qualifying distributions, $254,779; giving activities include $244,437 for 13 grants (high: $85,000; low: $2,000).
Fields of interest: Education; Health; Children's hospital care; Human services; Children.
Limitations: Applications accepted. Giving primarily in Pittsburgh, PA.
Application information: Application form required.
Deadline(s): None
Officers and Directors: Joseph D. Osborn, Pres. and Director; Kevin McKamish, V.P.; Maria McKamish, Secy.; Melissa McKamish, Treas.; David McKamish; Dennis R. McKamish.
EIN: 275137609

8159
Virginia A. Mckee First Presbyterian Church
c/o PNC Bank, N.A.
620 Liberty Ave., 10th Fl.
Pittsburgh, PA 15222-2705

Foundation type: Independent foundation.
Financial data (yr. ended 12/31/13): Assets, $4,249,323 (M); expenditures, $203,421; qualifying distributions, $164,603; giving activities include $163,199 for 1 grant.
Fields of interest: Religion.
Limitations: Applications not accepted. Giving primarily in PA.
Application information: Unsolicited requests for funds not accepted.
Trustee: PNC Bank, N.A.
EIN: 256023290

8160
John McKee Trust
(also known as Trust Under Will of John McKee)
c/o John McKee Scholarship Comm.
P.O. Box 144
Merion Station, PA 19066 (484) 323-1348
Contact: Robert J. Stern, Exec. Secy.
FAX: (610) 640-1965;
E-mail: secretary@mckeescholars.org; Main URL: http://www.mckeescholars.org

Established in 2002 in Pennsylvania.
Donor: John McKee†.
Foundation type: Independent foundation.
Financial data (yr. ended 12/31/13): Assets, $6,093,230 (M); expenditures, $284,997; qualifying distributions, $228,844; giving activities include $228,844 for 30 grants to individuals (high: $34,619; low: $3,500).
Purpose and activities: Scholarship awards for college or vocational training to high school seniors who are fatherless boys (either because the father is actually deceased or has been declared missing by a competent authority) and who are native to one of the five counties of Bucks, Chester, Delaware, Montgomery, or Philadelphia, Pennsylvania. These seniors may attend school anywhere in the United States, or abroad if part of a U.S.-based college degree program. Preference for those desirous of obtaining a naval education. No giving to attend graduate school.
Fields of interest: Vocational education; Vocational post-secondary education; Higher education; Children and youth; Adolescents.
Type of support: Student aid.
Limitations: Applications accepted. Giving limited to natives of Bucks, Chester, Delaware, Montgomery, and Philadelphia counties, PA.
Publications: Application guidelines.
Application information: See Trust web site for complete application guidelines. Application form required.
Copies of proposal: 1
Deadline(s): Mar. 1
Board meeting date(s): 1st Tues. in Apr.
Officers and Committee Members: Joseph L. Zazyczny, Chair.; Robert J. Stern, Exec. Secy.; Capt. Frank E. Falcone, VSNR; Prof. James H. Kelch, Jr.; Hon. Theodore A. McKee; Thomas J. Smith.
Number of staff: 1 part-time professional.
EIN: 237675490

8161
William V. and Catherine A. McKinney Charitable Foundation
c/o PNC Bank, N.A.
P.O. Box 609
Pittsburgh, PA 15230-9738

Established in 1990 in Pennsylvania.
Donor: Catherine A. McKinney†.
Foundation type: Independent foundation.
Financial data (yr. ended 03/31/14): Assets, $11,971,993 (M); expenditures, $573,055; qualifying distributions, $495,647; giving activities include $436,456 for 31 grants (high: $30,000; low: $2,259).
Purpose and activities: Giving limited to organizations in western PA whose activities aid the elderly, disadvantaged youth and/or the disabled and support the arts.
Fields of interest: Arts and culture; Public affairs; Human services.
Type of support: General support; Matching grants; Capital campaigns; Endowments; Program development.
Limitations: Applications not accepted. Giving limited to western PA. No grants to individuals.
Application information: Contributes only to pre-selected organizations.
Board meeting date(s): 3 times per year
Trustee: PNC Bank.
EIN: 251641619

8162
The Mclelland Family Foundation
c/o Michael B. McLelland
795 E. Lancaster Ave., Ste. 280
Villanova, PA 19085-1525

Donor: Michael B. McLelland.
Foundation type: Independent foundation.
Financial data (yr. ended 12/31/13): Assets, $7,767,373 (M); gifts received, $473,497; expenditures, $197,346; qualifying distributions, $193,606; giving activities include $185,000 for 5 grants (high: $150,000; low: $5,000).
Fields of interest: Education; Health; Human services.
Limitations: Applications not accepted.
Application information: Unsolicited requests for funds not accepted.
Officers: Michael B. McLelland, Pres.; Nancy McLelland, Secy.-Treas.
Director: Laura McLelland.
EIN: 272995394

8163
William J. McMannis and A. Haskell McMannis Educational Trust Fund
c/o PNC Bank
620 Liberty Ave., 10th Fl.
Pittsburgh, PA 15222-2708
Scholarship address: c/o PNC Wealth Mgmt., Attn.: Ann O'Neil, P.O. Box 8480, Erie, PA 16553, tel.: (814) 871-9362

Donors: Haskell McMannis†; Naomi Haskell.
Foundation type: Independent foundation.
Financial data (yr. ended 08/31/13): Assets, $7,481,287 (M); expenditures, $441,317; qualifying distributions, $374,026; giving activities include $347,415 for 165 grants to individuals (high: $4,500; low: $500).
Purpose and activities: Giving for higher education scholarship funds only; grants paid directly to institutions for the benefit of students (U.S. citizens only) who are enrolled and in good standing. Awards granted for one degree only.
Fields of interest: Higher education.
Type of support: Student aid.
Limitations: Applications accepted. Giving primarily in PA.
Publications: Informational brochure (including application guidelines).
Application information: Applications must be submitted through qualified schools; applications directly from individual students not considered. Application form required.
Initial approach: Contact participating schools
Copies of proposal: 4
Deadline(s): None
Board meeting date(s): Apr. and Nov.
Trustee: PNC Bank, N.A.
EIN: 256191302

8164
Peter F. McManus Charitable Trust
31 Independence Pl.
Chesterbrook, PA 19087-5824 (610) 647-4974
Contact: Katharine G. Lidz, Tr.

Established in 2000 in Pennsylvania.
Foundation type: Independent foundation.
Financial data (yr. ended 12/31/13): Assets, $2,853,241 (M); expenditures, $228,803; qualifying distributions, $211,696; giving activities include $199,781 for 4 grants (high: $50,000; low: $49,781).
Purpose and activities: Giving to non-profit 501(c)(3) organizations for research into the causes of alcoholism and substance abuse. Basic, clinical, and social-environmental proposals will all be considered.
Fields of interest: Addiction services; Alcoholism.
Type of support: Research.
Limitations: Applications accepted. Giving primarily in CA, CT, MA and MD.
Application information: Grants may be requested in an amount up to $50,000. No grant money may be used for tuition, and no more than 10% of grant money may be used for indirect costs. Additional information may be requested by the Trust after initial review of application. Before any grant may be renewed, the grant recipient must submit a report to the Trust.
Initial approach: Send brief summary proposal (2-3 pages) describing the project and the amount of funding requested, along with investigator's biosketch, proposed budget for the project, and a copy of the organization's IRS determination letter.
Copies of proposal: 1
Deadline(s): Aug. 31
Board meeting date(s): Oct. or Nov.
Trustee: Katharine G. Lidz.
EIN: 256666319

8165
McSwigan Family Foundation
217 Tennyson Ave.
Pittsburgh, PA 15213-1415

Donor: Mary A. McDonough.
Foundation type: Independent foundation.
Financial data (yr. ended 06/30/14): Assets, $4,784,045; expenditures, $255,983; qualifying distributions, $222,500.
Fields of interest: Arts and culture; Agriculture; Human services.
Limitations: Applications not accepted. Giving primarily in Pittsburgh, PA.
Application information: Unsolicited requests for funds not accepted.
Officer: Mary A. McDonough, Chair.
Trustees: Stephen R. Kossuth; Carroll R. Quinn.
EIN: 326080749

8166
Glen and Diane Meakem Foundation, Inc.
1 PPG Pl., Ste. 2050
Pittsburgh, PA 15222-5417

Established in 2000 in Pennsylvania.
Donors: Glen T. Meakem; Diane B. Meakem; Snowline Partners, LP; Chamberlain Irrevocable Investment Trust.
Foundation type: Independent foundation.
Financial data (yr. ended 12/31/13): Assets, $830,981 (M); gifts received, $100,000; expenditures, $183,038; qualifying distributions, $170,725; giving activities include $163,786 for 31 grants (high: $43,850; low: $100).
Purpose and activities: Giving primarily for education, as well as for the arts, particularly to museums, including a science center; some funding also for Christian ministries, churches, and schools, and children, youth, and social services, including a women's shelter.
Fields of interest: Education; Religion; Human services.
Limitations: Applications not accepted. Giving primarily in PA. No grants to individuals.
Application information: Unsolicited requests for funds not accepted.
Officers: Glen T. Meakem, Pres.; Diane B. Meakem, V.P.; Raymond P. Parker, Esq., Secy.-Treas.
EIN: 251877307

8167
Matthew T. Mellon Foundation
c/o BNY Mellon, N.A.
P.O. Box 185
Pittsburgh, PA 15230-0185

Established in 2001 in Pennsylvania.
Foundation type: Independent foundation.
Financial data (yr. ended 12/31/14): Assets, $3,058,914 (M); expenditures, $201,701; qualifying distributions, $183,453; giving activities include $178,000 for 10 grants (high: $42,000; low: $10,000).
Fields of interest: Elementary and secondary education; Nonprofits; Hospital care; Immune system diseases; Human services.
Type of support: Regranting.
Limitations: Applications not accepted. Giving primarily in MA and NY. No grants to individuals.
Application information: Unsolicited requests for funds not accepted.
Trustees: Diana Mellon; James R. Mellon; Vivian R. Mellon.
EIN: 311734222

8168
Solomon & Sylvia Mendel Charitable Trust
c/o PNC Bank, N.A.
620 Liberty Ave., 10th Fl.
Pittsburgh, PA 15222-2705

Established in 1986 in Pennsylvania.
Foundation type: Independent foundation.
Financial data (yr. ended 07/31/13): Assets, $4,681,011 (M); expenditures, $246,935; qualifying distributions, $206,026; giving activities include $184,312 for 15 grants (high: $20,000; low: $7,500).
Fields of interest: History museums; Education; Higher education; Nonprofits; Specialty hospital care; Judaism; People with vision impairments.
Type of support: General support; Regranting.
Limitations: Applications not accepted. Giving primarily in Pittsburgh, PA. No grants to individuals.
Application information: Contributes only to pre-selected organization.
Trustee: PNC Bank, N.A.
EIN: 256271818

8169
The Merops Foundation
c/o Glenmede Trust Co., N.A.
1650 Market St., Ste. 1200
Philadelphia, PA 19103-7391

Donor: Crawford H. Greenewalt Jr. Trust.
Foundation type: Independent foundation.
Financial data (yr. ended 12/31/13): Assets, $10,810,441 (M); expenditures, $423,943; qualifying distributions, $381,933; giving activities include $335,000 for 7 grants (high: $160,000; low: $5,000).
Fields of interest: Arts and culture; Education.
Limitations: Applications not accepted.
Application information: Unsolicited requests for funds not accepted.
Trustees: Nicholas D. Cahill; David Lammot Greenewalt; Benjamin H. Testerman; The Glenmede Trust Co., N.A.; Wilmington Trust Co.
EIN: 456870036

8170
Merwin Foundation
2200 Asbury Rd.
Erie, PA 16506-1402

Donor: Robert F. Merwin.
Foundation type: Independent foundation.
Financial data (yr. ended 12/31/13): Assets, $6,781,763 (M); expenditures, $318,611; qualifying distributions, $273,800; giving activities include $273,800 for 22 grants (high: $100,000; low: $350).
Fields of interest: Music; Orchestral music; Art museums; Elementary and secondary education; Higher education; University education; Nonprofits; Human services; Food banks; Youth services; Senior assisted living.
Type of support: Regranting.
Limitations: Applications not accepted. Giving primarily in Erie and University Park, PA. No grants to individuals.
Application information: Contributes only to pre-selected organizations.

Officers and Directors: Richard A. Merwin, Pres. and Treas. and Director; James E. Spoden, Secy. and Director; James R. Walczak.
EIN: 256060860

8171
MHB Foundation
160 N. Pointe Blvd., Ste. 200
Lancaster, PA 17601-4134

Donors: James J. Bruder, Jr.; Margaret Anne Nolen.
Foundation type: Independent foundation.
Financial data (yr. ended 12/31/13): Assets, $545,054 (M); gifts received, $89,528; expenditures, $241,574; qualifying distributions, $233,000; giving activities include $233,000 for 8 grants (high: $100,000; low: $3,000).
Fields of interest: Education; Diseases and conditions.
Limitations: Applications not accepted. Giving primarily in PA.
Application information: Unsolicited requests for funds not accepted.
Officers and Directors: Margaret Anne Nolen, Pres. and Director; James J. Bruder, Jr., V.P. and Treas. and Director; Gene P. Otto, Secy.; Jennifer M. Bruder.
EIN: 264598771

8172
The Mill Spring Foundation
(formerly The Houghton-Carpenter Foundation)
P.O. Box 270
Ambler, PA 19002-0270   (215) 643-9916
Contact: William F. MacDonald Jr., Tr.
E-mail: WFMACDJR@gmail.com

Established in 1951 in Pennsylvania.
Donors: Aaron E. Carpenter†; Edythe A. Carpenter†; E.F. Houghton & Co.
Foundation type: Independent foundation.
Financial data (yr. ended 06/30/14): Assets, $4,721,334 (M); expenditures, $314,626; qualifying distributions, $249,800; giving activities include $249,800 for 39 grants (high: $25,000; low: $500).
Purpose and activities: Giving primarily for children's services, education, and the arts.
Fields of interest: Arts and culture; Education; Elementary and secondary education; Zoos; Communication media; Human services; Child welfare; Youth development; Children and youth; Children; Young adults; Female young adults; Male young adults; Low-income and poor people; People with disabilities; People with physical disabilities; People with vision impairments; People with psychosocial disabilities.
Type of support: Program development; Matching grants; General support; Continuing support; Annual campaigns; Capital campaigns; Equipment; Emergency funds.
Limitations: Applications accepted. Giving primarily in PA. No grants to individuals.
Publications: Application guidelines.
Application information: Application form required.
   Initial approach: Letter
   Copies of proposal: 1
   Deadline(s): None
Trustees: William F. MacDonald, Jr.
Number of staff: None.
EIN: 236230874

8173
Howard E. & Nell E. Miller Charitable Foundation
c/o PNC Advisors, Trust Comm.
620 Liberty Ave., 10th Fl.
Pittsburgh, PA 15222-2705
Application address: c/o Thomas M. Mulroy, Esq.,
2829 Shamrock Dr., Allison Park, PA 15101-3748,
tel.: (412) 471-3300

Established in 1988 in Pennsylvania.
Donor: Nellie E. Miller†.
Foundation type: Independent foundation.
Financial data (yr. ended 05/31/13): Assets,
$7,298,744 (M); expenditures, $427,164;
qualifying distributions, $379,743; giving activities
include $351,650 for 39 grants (high: $15,650;
low: $2,500).
Purpose and activities: Giving primarily for the
performing arts, as well as for children, youth and
social services.
Fields of interest: Arts and culture; Performing arts;
Human services; Child welfare.
Type of support: General support; Matching grants;
Capital and infrastructure; Equipment; Program
development; Seed money.
Limitations: Applications accepted. Giving primarily
in southwestern PA. No grants to individuals.
Application information: Common Grant Form
available from Grantmakers of Western
Pennsylvania at http://www.gwpa.org. Application
form required.
  Deadline(s): Apr. 1 and Oct. 1
Trustees: Thomas M. Mulroy, Esq.; John Pillar; PNC
Bank, N.A.
EIN: 256305933

8174
J. Clawson Mills Charitable Trust
c/o BNY Mellon, N.A.
P.O. Box 185
Pittsburgh, PA 15230-0185

Foundation type: Independent foundation.
Financial data (yr. ended 12/31/14): Assets,
$5,250,104; expenditures, $299,131; qualifying
distributions, $272,906.
Fields of interest: Architecture; Art museums.
Limitations: Applications not accepted. Giving
primarily in NY.
Application information: Unsolicited requests for
funds not accepted.
Trustee: BNY Mellon, N.A.
EIN: 136079334

8175
Robert Y. Moffat Family Charitable Trust
c/o PNC Bank, N.A.
620 Liberty Ave., 30th Fl.
Pittsburgh, PA 15222-2722 (412) 762-9942
Contact: Bruce Bickel

Established in 2002 in Pennsylvania.
Donor: Robert Y. Moffat†.
Foundation type: Independent foundation.
Financial data (yr. ended 12/31/14): Assets,
$8,330,777 (M); expenditures, $441,692;
qualifying distributions, $343,439; giving activities
include $293,000 for 14 grants (high: $75,000;
low: $5,000).

Fields of interest: Arts and culture; Education;
Higher education; Health; Hospital care; Community
and economic development; Human services.
Type of support: General support.
Limitations: Applications accepted. Giving primarily
in the Scranton, PA area (Lackawanna, Wyoming,
and Luzerne counties).
Application information:
  Initial approach: Letter
  Deadline(s): Apr. 1 and Oct. 1
Trustees: Yvette Wentland; PNC Bank, N.A.
EIN: 256823427

8176
The Anna-Maria Moggio Foundation
P.O. Box 11
Haverford, PA 19041-0011 (215) 298-3899
Contact: Joseph T. Rogers, Tr.

Foundation type: Independent foundation.
Financial data (yr. ended 05/31/13): Assets,
$5,430,988 (M); expenditures, $351,479;
qualifying distributions, $270,791; giving activities
include $203,156 for 16 grants (high: $25,600;
low: $2,285).
Fields of interest: Education; Higher education;
Christianity.
Limitations: Applications accepted. Giving primarily
in ME, PA and RI.
Application information: Application form required.
  Initial approach: Request application form
  Deadline(s): Mar. 1
Trustees: Joseph S. Falzone; Joseph T. Rogers.
EIN: 770667200

8177
P. M. Moore Foundation
P.O. Box 416
Beaver, PA 15009-0416 (724) 774-4997
Contact: Dana L. Duff, Pres.

Established in 1958 in Pennsylvania.
Donor: Paul M. Moore†.
Foundation type: Independent foundation.
Financial data (yr. ended 12/31/14): Assets,
$5,111,947 (M); expenditures, $278,507;
qualifying distributions, $271,000; giving activities
include $271,000 for 17 grants (high: $75,000;
low: $500).
Purpose and activities: Giving primarily to youth
scouting agencies, YMCAs, libraries, and for social
services, arts and culture, higher education,
federated giving programs, and Presbyterian
churches.
Fields of interest: Arts and culture; Higher
education; Nonprofits; Diseases and conditions;
Libraries; Protestantism; Human services; Scouting
programs.
Type of support: Regranting.
Limitations: Applications accepted. Giving primarily
in Beaver County, PA and OH. No grants to
individuals.
Application information:
  Initial approach: Letter
  Deadline(s): None
Officers: Dana L. Duff, Pres. and Treas.; Ruth Ann
Duff, Secy.
Trustee: Paul W. Duff.
EIN: 256066268

8178
The Eleanor & Howard Morgan Family Foundation
764 Mt. Moro Rd.
Villanova, PA 19085-2007

Established in 1996 in Pennsylvania.
Donors: Howard L. Morgan; Eleanor Morgan.
Foundation type: Independent foundation.
Financial data (yr. ended 12/31/12): Assets,
$160,859 (M); gifts received, $177,120;
expenditures, $400,599; qualifying distributions,
$400,324; giving activities include $400,324 for
grants.
Fields of interest: Arts and culture; Education;
University education; Judaism; International
relations.
Limitations: Applications not accepted. Giving
primarily in NY. No grants to individuals.
Application information: Contributes only to
pre-selected organizations.
Trustees: Kimberly Morgan Blank; Elizabeth Morgan
Hammack; Danielle Morgan Koplin; Eleanor K.
Morgan; Howard L. Morgan.
EIN: 232868322

8179
Mosi Foundation
c/o Gerald A. Isom
202 Valley Forge Lookout Pl.
Radnor, PA 19087-4673

Established in 2002 in Pennsylvania.
Donors: Gerald A. Isom; Lucille E. Isom.
Foundation type: Operating foundation.
Financial data (yr. ended 12/31/13): Assets,
$3,894,751 (M); gifts received, $324,388;
expenditures, $470,507; qualifying distributions,
$429,145; giving activities include $429,145 for 15
grants (high: $250,194; low: $1,500).
Fields of interest: Education; Undergraduate
education; Autism; Christianity; Camps.
Type of support: Research.
Limitations: Applications not accepted. No grants to
individuals.
Application information: Unsolicited requests for
funds not accepted.
Officers: Gerald A. Isom, Pres.; Lucille E. Isom, V.P.;
Jana L. de Leon, Secy.; Jennifer A. O'Malley, Treas.
Director: Karen M. Schmid.
EIN: 743071480

8180
W. Melvin & Mary L. Moyer Trust
c/o Mauch Chunk Trust Co.
P.O. Box 289
Jim Thorpe, PA 18229-0289

Donors: W. Melvin Moyer Trust; Mary L. Moyer†.
Foundation type: Independent foundation.
Financial data (yr. ended 12/31/13): Assets,
$4,609,178 (M); expenditures, $220,800;
qualifying distributions, $188,732; giving activities
include $179,500 for 6 grants (high: $165,500;
low: $2,000).
Fields of interest: Protestantism; Human services.
Limitations: Applications not accepted. No grants to
individuals.
Application information: Contributes only to
pre-selected organizations.

Trustee: Mauch Chunk Trust Co.
EIN: 056140215

8181
Mudge Foundation
c/o PNC Bank, N.A.
620 Liberty Ave., 10th Fl.
Pittsburgh, PA 15222-2705 (412) 762-4133

Established in 1955 in Pennsylvania.
Foundation type: Independent foundation.
Financial data (yr. ended 12/31/14): Assets,
$3,919,658; expenditures, $254,928; qualifying
distributions, $237,629 and $0 for set-asides.
Fields of interest: Museums; Higher education;
Natural resources; Nonprofits; Hospital care;
Diseases and conditions; Protestantism; Children.
Type of support: Research; Regranting.
Limitations: Applications accepted. Giving primarily
in ME, PA, and TX. No grants to individuals.
Application information:
  Initial approach: Letter
  Copies of proposal: 1
  Deadline(s): None
Trustee: PNC Bank, N.A.
EIN: 256023150

8182
Muirfield Foundation
(formerly Sherrerd Foundation)
c/o Dechert LLP
Cira Centre
2929 Arch St.
Philadelphia, PA 19104-2808

Established in 1986 in Pennsylvania.
Donors: John J.F. Sherrerd†; Kathleen C. Sherrerd†.
Foundation type: Independent foundation.
Financial data (yr. ended 07/31/13): Assets,
$21,642,568 (M); expenditures, $456,537;
qualifying distributions, $310,000; giving activities
include $310,000 for 5 grants (high: $140,000;
low: $20,000).
Fields of interest: University education.
Limitations: Giving primarily in Princeton, NJ. No
grants to individuals.
Application information:
  Initial approach: Letter
  Deadline(s): None
Officers: Susan M. Sherrerd, Pres.; Ellen D. Harvey,
V.P.; Anne C. Sherrerd, Secy.; John J.F. Sherrerd, Jr.,
Treas.
EIN: 222751186

8183
The Mukaiyama-Rice Foundation
c/o Lance Eastman
199 Bolivar Dr.
Bradford, PA 16701

Established in 1998 in Pennsylvania.
Donors: KOA Speer Electronics, Inc.; Katsuhiko
Kichiji.
Foundation type: Company-sponsored foundation.
Financial data (yr. ended 12/31/14): Assets,
$3,937,175; expenditures, $195,240; qualifying
distributions, $186,949.
Purpose and activities: The foundation supports
performing arts centers and organizations involved
with education, health, and housing development.

Fields of interest: Arts and culture; Performing arts;
Education; Higher education; Nonprofits; Health;
Hospital care; Public libraries; Housing
development; Human services.
Type of support: General support; Scholarships;
Regranting.
Limitations: Applications not accepted. Giving
limited to Bradford, PA. No grants to individuals.
Application information: Contributes only to
pre-selected organizations.
Officers and Board Members: Lance E. Eastman,
Pres. and Director; Jeff Rice, Secy. and Treas. and
Director; Scott Rice; Timothy D. Rice.
EIN: 232949160

8184
The Mullen Family Foundation
(formerly The Mullen Family Foundation)
P.O. Box 199
Newtown Square, PA 19073-0199 (215)
265-5617
Contact: Joan J. Mullen, Dir.

Established in 1979 in Pennsylvania.
Donors: John J. Mullen; Joan A. Mullen.
Foundation type: Independent foundation.
Financial data (yr. ended 09/30/14): Assets,
$2,334,868 (M); expenditures, $197,488;
qualifying distributions, $180,820; giving activities
include $180,820 for 14 grants (high: $57,500;
low: $500).
Fields of interest: Education; Diseases and
conditions; Human services; Orphanages; Children.
Type of support: General support; Program
development; Scholarships.
Limitations: Applications accepted. Giving primarily
in the Philadelphia, PA, area. No grants to
individuals.
Application information: Application form required.
  Initial approach: Completed application form
  Deadline(s): None
Directors: Joan A. Mullen; John J. Mullen.
Number of staff: 3 part-time support.
EIN: 232125388

8185
G. C. Murphy Company Foundation
211 Oberdick Dr.
McKeesport, PA 15135-2213 (412) 751-6649
Main URL: http://www.gcmurphy.org/
foundation.html

Established in 1952 in Pennsylvania.
Donor: G.C. Murphy Co.
Foundation type: Independent foundation.
Financial data (yr. ended 12/31/14): Assets,
$4,216,165; gifts received, $1,015; expenditures,
$300,053; qualifying distributions, $262,700.
Purpose and activities: Emphasis on youth and
social services, including women, child welfare,
family services, and hunger; support also for health
associations and services, and programs for cancer
care and the mentally ill, community funds and
development, the arts, and higher education.
Fields of interest: Arts and culture; Higher
education; Nonprofits; Health; Hospital care; Mental
health care; Diseases and conditions; Cancers;
Community and economic development; Human
services; Food aid; Family services; Child welfare;
Women's services; Children and youth;
Adolescents; Seniors; Females; Female children

and youth; Male children and youth; People with
psychosocial disabilities.
Type of support: General support; Continuing
support; Annual campaigns; Capital campaigns;
Capital and infrastructure; Scholarships;
Regranting.
Limitations: Applications accepted. Giving primarily
in southeastern Allegheny County, PA. No support
for political organizations or to churches. No grants
to individuals.
Application information:
  Initial approach: Proposal
  Copies of proposal: 1
  Deadline(s): None
  Board meeting date(s): Apr., July, and Nov.
  Final notification: Positive responses only
Officers and Directors: C.A. McElhinny, Pres. and
Director; T.F. Hudak, V.P. and Treas. and Director;
Charles W. Breckenridge, V.P. and Director; William
T. Cullen, V.P. and Director; Alice J. Hajduk, V.P. and
Director; Robert T. Messner, V.P. and Director;
Edwin W. Davis, Secy. and Director.
Number of staff: 1 part-time professional.
EIN: 256028651

8186
The Mutual Fire Foundation, Inc.
120 E. Uwchlan Ave., Ste. 101
Exton, PA 19341-1275

Established in 2004 in Pennsylvania.
Donors: The Mutual Fire Marine and Inland
Insurance Co.; Franklin Homeowners Assurance
Co.; FHA Holding Co.
Foundation type: Company-sponsored foundation.
Financial data (yr. ended 12/31/13): Assets,
$3,510,579 (M); gifts received, $834,589;
expenditures, $263,410; qualifying distributions,
$183,000; giving activities include $183,000 for 34
grants (high: $23,000; low: $1,000).
Purpose and activities: The foundation supports
nonprofit organizations involved with education,
human services, and religion.
Fields of interest: Education; Religion; Human
services.
Limitations: Applications not accepted. No grants to
individuals.
Application information: Unsolicited requests for
funds not accepted.
Officers and Directors: Michael J. Petrelia, Chair.;
Caroline Mazza, Pres. and Director; G. Alan Bailey,
Secy.; James McGuigan, Treas.; Walter Bratic.
EIN: 383704483

8187
The Mylan Charitable Foundation
1500 Corporate Dr., Ste. 400
Canonsburg, PA 15317-8580

Donors: Mylan Laboratories Inc.; Mylan
Pharmaceuticals.
Foundation type: Company-sponsored foundation.
Financial data (yr. ended 12/31/13): Assets,
$13,798,921 (M); gifts received, $4,000,000;
expenditures, $426,904; qualifying distributions,
$408,053; giving activities include $335,470 for 12
grants (high: $50,000; low: $5,000).
Purpose and activities: The foundation supports
organizations involved with education, health,
human services, and community development.

Fields of interest: Arts and culture; Education; Health.
Type of support: General support; Capital and infrastructure.
Limitations: Applications not accepted. Giving primarily in PA and WV as well as Rockford, IL, Sugar Land, TX, and St. Albans, VT. No grants to individuals.
Application information: Unsolicited requests for funds not accepted.
Officers: Rodney L. Piatt, Chair.; C. B. Todd, Secy.; Brian Byala, Treas.
Directors: Heather Bresch; Robert J. Coury.
Number of staff: 1 full-time professional.
EIN: 431954390

8188
The Nathan Foundation, Inc.

c/o PNC Bank, N.A.
1600 Market St. - Tax Dept.
Philadelphia, PA 19103-7240
Application address: c/o Robert S. Collison, Esq., 314 High St., Cambridge, MD 21613

Established in 1961 in Maryland.
Foundation type: Independent foundation.
Financial data (yr. ended 12/31/13): Assets, $5,501,866 (M); expenditures, $262,435; qualifying distributions, $241,802; giving activities include $233,100 for 49 grants (high: $40,000; low: $500).
Fields of interest: University education; Hospital care; Fire prevention and control; Sports and recreation; Human services.
Application information: Application form required.
　Initial approach: Letter
　Deadline(s): None
Officers: Edward H. Nabb, Jr., Pres.; T. Sewell Hubbert, V.P.; Robert Collison, Secy.; Linda K. Nabb, Treas.
Director: William Batson.
Trustee: PNC Bank, N.A.
EIN: 526033999

8189
Ray and Lynn Wood Neag Charitable Foundation

1216 Old Mill Rd.
Wyomissing, PA 19610-2853

Established in 1992 in Pennsylvania.
Donors: Raymond Neag; Lynn J. Neag; Letitia Morgan Charitable Remainder.
Foundation type: Independent foundation.
Financial data (yr. ended 06/30/13): Assets, $1,196,266 (M); gifts received, $10,000; expenditures, $189,140; qualifying distributions, $181,177; giving activities include $155,000 for 15 grants (high: $55,000; low: $2,500).
Purpose and activities: Giving primarily for education.
Fields of interest: Education; Health; Human services.
Type of support: General support; Scholarships.
Limitations: Applications not accepted. Giving primarily in CT.
Application information: Unsolicited requests for funds not accepted.
Trustees: Harriet H. Lawson; Carole Neag; Raymond Neag; Nancy Neag Satalino.
EIN: 232712023

8190
Neal Martin Christensen Foundation

127 Anderson St., Ste. 127
Pittsburgh, PA 15212-5803
Application address: Mr. Neal M. Christensen, 675 Saxonburg Rd., Butler, PA, 16002, tel.: (724) 352-3790

Donor: Neal M. Christensen.
Foundation type: Independent foundation.
Financial data (yr. ended 10/31/13): Assets, $906,476 (M); gifts received, $1,150,000; expenditures, $316,062; qualifying distributions, $315,950; giving activities include $315,950 for 6 grants (high: $158,000; low: $1,000).
Fields of interest: Arts and culture; Religion; Human services.
Limitations: Applications accepted. Giving primarily in PA.
Application information: Application form required.
　Initial approach: Contact Foundation
　Deadline(s): None
Officers: Neal M. Christensen, Pres.; Benjamin M. Burtner, V.P.; Stefanie L. Christensen, Secy.
EIN: 461569569

8191
Florence Nesh Charitable Trust

c/o PNC Bank
620 Liberty Ave., 10th Fl.
Pittsburgh, PA 15222-2705
Application address: c/o PNC Charitable Trust Grant Review Committee, 1 PNC Plz., 249 Fifth Ave., 20th Fl., Pittsburgh, PA 15222-2705, tel.: (412) 768-7716

Established in 2006 in District of Columbia.
Donor: Florence Nesh†.
Foundation type: Independent foundation.
Financial data (yr. ended 06/30/13): Assets, $5,550,377 (M); expenditures, $321,356; qualifying distributions, $269,973; giving activities include $245,000 for 3 grants (high: $90,000; low: $75,000).
Fields of interest: University education; Graduate and professional education; Children's hospital care; Nursing care; Children.
Limitations: Applications accepted. Giving primarily in Washington, DC, MD and VA.
Application information: Application form required.
　Initial approach: See website
　Deadline(s): See website
Trustee: PNC Bank, N.A.
EIN: 206758590

8192
Pryor E. & Arlene R. Neuber Charitable Trust

c/o PNC Bank, N.A.
1600 Market St., Tax Dept.
Philadelphia, PA 19103-7240

Foundation type: Independent foundation.
Financial data (yr. ended 12/31/13): Assets, $9,517,395 (M); expenditures, $375,760; qualifying distributions, $333,181; giving activities include $294,684 for 14 grants (high: $107,560; low: $4,569).
Fields of interest: Arts and culture; Community and economic development; Human services.

Limitations: Applications not accepted. Giving primarily in Lancaster, PA.
Application information: Unsolicited requests for funds not accepted.
Trustee: PNC Bank, N.A.
EIN: 016208130

8193
Nikolaus Family Foundation

327 Locust St.
Columbia, PA 17512-1120

Established in 2002 in Pennsylvania.
Donor: Donald H. Nikolaus.
Foundation type: Independent foundation.
Financial data (yr. ended 12/31/13): Assets, $3,603,744 (M); gifts received, $200,000; expenditures, $354,732; qualifying distributions, $354,636; giving activities include $354,636 for 10 grants (high: $131,000; low: $5,000).
Fields of interest: Education; Religion; Catholicism; Human services.
Limitations: Applications not accepted. Giving primarily in PA; some giving in MD. No grants to individuals.
Application information: Contributes only to pre-selected organizations.
Trustee: Donald H. Nikolaus.
EIN: 256823641

8194
John H. Noll Foundation

c/o PNC Bank, N.A.
P.O. Box 609
Pittsburgh, PA 15230-9738
Application address: c/o PNC Bank, N.A., Attn.: Jane Kleinsmith, 1900 E. 19th St., Cleveland, OH 44114, tel.: (216) 222-9815

Established in 1967 in Indiana.
Foundation type: Independent foundation.
Financial data (yr. ended 09/30/14): Assets, $4,153,683 (M); expenditures, $234,719; qualifying distributions, $207,269; giving activities include $187,100 for 24 grants to individuals (high: $49,900; low: $5,000).
Purpose and activities: Scholarship awards to graduating seniors of Fort Wayne, Indiana, community high schools, Bishop Dwenger, Bishop Luers, and Concordia high schools, and the Homestead High School.
Fields of interest: Education.
Type of support: Student aid.
Limitations: Applications accepted. Giving limited to residents of IN.
Application information: Application forms are available from guidance counselors at participating Fort Wayne, IN, high schools. Application form required.
　Initial approach: Proposal
　Deadline(s): Mar. 31
Trustee: PNC Bank, N.A.
EIN: 237082877

8195
The Norbell Foundation

(formerly The Stuckeman Foundation)
20 Stanwix St., Ste. 650
Pittsburgh, PA 15222-4801

Established in 1994 in Pennsylvania.
Donors: H. Campbell Stuckeman; Smithfield Trust Company.
Foundation type: Independent foundation.
Financial data (yr. ended 12/31/14): Assets, $4,852,924; expenditures, $298,421; qualifying distributions, $273,500.
Fields of interest: University education; In-patient medical care; Protestantism.
Type of support: General support; Annual campaigns; Capital campaigns; Capital and infrastructure; Equipment; Endowments.
Limitations: Applications not accepted. No grants to individuals.
Application information: Unsolicited requests for funds not accepted.
Trustees: Joyce S. Biffar; Travis S. Biffar; Ellen S. Easley; Charles C. Stuckeman; Smithfield Trust Co.
EIN: 251757468

8196
The Edward R. Norford Charitable Foundation
19 S. 19th St.
Camp Hill, PA   17011-5402

Donor: Edward R. Norford†.
Foundation type: Independent foundation.
Financial data (yr. ended 07/31/14): Assets, $3,557,516 (M); gifts received, $3,349,255; expenditures, $268,130; qualifying distributions, $207,192; giving activities include $207,192 for 11 grants (high: $100,000; low: $1,000).
Fields of interest: Education; Religion; Human services.
Limitations: Applications not accepted. Giving primarily in PA.
Application information: Unsolicited requests for funds not accepted.
Directors: Richard W. Stewart; Ralph W. Wire, Jr.
EIN: 462149884

8197
O'Brien-Veba Scholarship Trust
c/o PNC Bank, N.A.
P.O. Box 609
Pittsburgh, PA   15230-9738

Established in 1991 in Illinois.
Foundation type: Independent foundation.
Financial data (yr. ended 09/30/14): Assets, $3,742,772 (M); expenditures, $217,882; qualifying distributions, $198,863; giving activities include $40,000 for 4 grants (high: $10,000; low: $10,000), and $139,579 for grants to individuals.
Purpose and activities: Giving for higher education, primarily to individuals of Roman Catholic faith.
Fields of interest: Higher education; Catholicism.
Type of support: General support; Scholarships; Student aid.
Limitations: Applications not accepted. Giving primarily to residents of IA, IL, IN, MI, and WI.
Application information: Unsolicited requests for funds not accepted.
Trustee: PNC Bank, N.A.
Directors: John Bass; Thomas C. Brady; Ann Hupert; Harvey Share; Cindy Summers.
EIN: 376277500

8198
The Olitsky Family Foundation Inc
P.O. Box 514
Gwynedd Valley, PA   19437-0514

Donors: E. Goldberg; T. Olitsky.
Foundation type: Independent foundation.
Financial data (yr. ended 12/31/13): Assets, $6,048,353 (M); expenditures, $432,431; qualifying distributions, $302,000; giving activities include $302,000 for 31 grants (high: $75,000; low: $500).
Fields of interest: Education; University education; Nonprofits; Specialty hospital care; Diseases and conditions; Judaism; Human services; Family services; Child welfare.
Type of support: Regranting; Grants to individuals.
Limitations: Applications not accepted. Giving primarily in MA, NY and PA.
Application information: Unsolicited requests for funds not accepted.
Officers: Tamar Olitsky, Pres.; Stephen Olitsky, V.P.
EIN: 311750884

8199
Oppenheim Foundation
718 Taylor Ave.
Scranton, PA   18510-1819   (570) 347-5208
Contact: Jane Oppenheim, Pres.

Established in 1992 in Pennsylvania.
Foundation type: Independent foundation.
Financial data (yr. ended 12/31/13): Assets, $1,205,907 (M); expenditures, $236,743; qualifying distributions, $216,534; giving activities include $216,534 for 42 grants (high: $44,000; low: $100).
Fields of interest: Higher education; Nonprofits; Diseases and conditions; Judaism; Human services.
Type of support: General support; Regranting.
Limitations: Giving primarily in Lackawanna County, PA, with emphasis on Scranton. No grants to individuals.
Application information:
  Initial approach: Letter on letterhead
  Deadline(s): None
Officers: Jane Oppenheim, Pres. and Treas.; Susan Dimond, Secy.
EIN: 236296919

8200
O'Reilly H. and H. O'Reilly Char Trust
c/o BNY Mellon, N.A.
P.O. Box 185
Pittsburgh, PA   15230-0185

Donors: O'Reilly Rev. Trust Bypass Tr.; Helen O'Reilly Survivors Trust.
Foundation type: Independent foundation.
Financial data (yr. ended 12/31/14): Assets, $7,651,368 (M); gifts received, $396; expenditures, $355,360; qualifying distributions, $306,144; giving activities include $278,854 for 7 grants (high: $52,614; low: $5,261).
Fields of interest: Children's hospital care; Family services; Children.
Type of support: General support.
Limitations: Applications not accepted. Giving primarily in CA and TN.
Application information: Unsolicited request for funds not accepted.

Trustee: BNY Mellon, N.A.
EIN: 386892966

8201
Horace B. Packer Foundation Inc.
P.O. Box 732
Wellsboro, PA   16901-0732   (570) 724-1800

Established in 1951 in Pennsylvania.
Donors: Horace B. Packer†; Horace B. Packer Trust.
Foundation type: Independent foundation.
Financial data (yr. ended 12/31/13): Assets, $111,040 (M); gifts received, $183,000; expenditures, $263,326; qualifying distributions, $263,326; giving activities include $252,563 for 24 grants (high: $60,000; low: $1,000).
Purpose and activities: Giving for services to benefit the youth of Tioga County, PA, and to educational institutions for scholarships to students residing in the county.
Fields of interest: Education; Health; Hospital care; Public libraries; Community and economic development; Christianity; Special Olympics; Child welfare.
Type of support: Capital campaigns; Scholarships.
Limitations: Applications accepted. Giving limited to the Tioga County, PA, area.
Application information: Application form required.
  Initial approach: Completed application form
  Copies of proposal: 1
  Deadline(s): None
Officers: Eugene Seelye, Pres.; R. James Dunham, V.P.; Robert F. Cox, Jr., Secy.; Rhonda Litchfield, Treas.
Directors: Jeffrey A. Fetzer; Thomas Freeman; Gregory P. Hinton.
Number of staff: None.
EIN: 236390932

8202
The Panama Street Fund
c/o Langer, Grogan & Diver, P.C.
1717 Arch St., Ste. 4130
Philadelphia, PA   19103-2846

Established in 2004 in Pennsylvania.
Donors: Howard I. Langer; Barbara Jaffe.
Foundation type: Independent foundation.
Financial data (yr. ended 12/31/12): Assets, $2,301,489 (M); expenditures, $224,802; qualifying distributions, $193,235; giving activities include $193,235 for grants.
Fields of interest: Legal services; Judaism; Family services.
Limitations: Applications not accepted. No grants to individuals.
Application information: Contributes only to pre-selected organizations.
Officers: Barbara Jaffe, Pres.; Howard I. Langer, Secy.
EIN: 201877195

8203
John C. Pangborn Trust
c/o PNC Bank, N.A.
620 Liberty Ave., 10th Fl.
Pittsburgh, PA   15222

Foundation type: Independent foundation.

Financial data (yr. ended 12/31/13): Assets, $10,039,361 (M); expenditures, $482,871; qualifying distributions, $425,536; giving activities include $421,731 for 35 grants (high: $126,519; low: $2,126).
Fields of interest: Education; Religion; Human services.
Limitations: Applications not accepted. Giving primarily in MD.
Application information: Unsolicited requests for funds not accepted.
Trustee: PNC Bank, N.A.
EIN: 526024502

8204
Frank J. & Sylvia T. Pasquerilla Foundation
c/o Mark E. & Leah M. Pasquerilla
1 Pasquerilla Plz.
Johnstown, PA   15901-1999

Established in 2000 in Pennsylvania.
Donor: Sylvia T. Pasquerilla†.
Foundation type: Independent foundation.
Financial data (yr. ended 12/31/14): Assets, $250,254; expenditures, $168,925; qualifying distributions, $140,685.
Fields of interest: Folk arts.
Type of support: Research.
Limitations: Applications not accepted. Giving primarily in PA. No grants to individuals.
Application information: Unsolicited requests for funds not accepted.
Trustees: Leah M. Pasquerilla; Mark E. Pasquerilla.
EIN: 256690814

8205
W. I. Patterson Charitable Fund
1 Oxford Ctr., Ste. 2100
Pittsburgh, PA   15219-1400
Application address: c/o Timothy F. Burke, Jr., Nancy L. Rackoff, or Robert B. Wolf, 301 Grant St., 20th Fl., Pittsburgh, PA 15219, tel.: (412) 281-5580

Established in 1955 in Pennsylvania.
Donor: W.I. Patterson†.
Foundation type: Independent foundation.
Financial data (yr. ended 07/31/13): Assets, $5,436,173 (M); expenditures, $272,315; qualifying distributions, $252,501; giving activities include $222,689 for 57 grants (high: $44,538; low: $1,000).
Fields of interest: Arts and culture; Ballet; Theater; Opera; Vocal music; Children's museums; Historic preservation; Education; Higher education; Hospital care; Diseases and conditions; Public libraries; Camps; Reproductive rights; Human services; Food banks; Child welfare; Adult and child mentoring; People with vision impairments.
Type of support: General support; Continuing support; Annual campaigns; Capital campaigns; Capital and infrastructure; Equipment; Land acquisitions; Debt reduction; Emergency funds; Publications; Seed money; Research.
Limitations: Applications accepted. Giving limited to Allegheny County, PA. No grants to individuals or for endowment funds, scholarships, fellowships, or matching gifts; no loans.
Application information:
  Initial approach: Letter

Copies of proposal: 1
Deadline(s): Trustees review applications quarterly for consideration within the fund's fiscal year
Trustees: Timothy F. Burke, Jr.; Nancy L. Rackoff; Robert B. Wolf.
EIN: 256028639

8206
George & Rita Patterson Foundation
P.O. Box 6595
Harrisburg, PA   17112-0595

Established in 2000 in Pennsylvania.
Foundation type: Independent foundation.
Financial data (yr. ended 12/31/12): Assets, $5,215,829 (M); expenditures, $292,270; qualifying distributions, $278,000; giving activities include $278,000 for grants.
Fields of interest: Education; Elementary and secondary education; Higher education; Christianity; Human services.
Limitations: Applications not accepted. Giving primarily in PA. No grants to individuals.
Application information: Contributes only to pre-selected organizations.
Trustees: M. Geralyn Patterson Hempt; George Patterson, Jr.; Nathaniel J. Patterson III; M. Sharon Patterson Turner.
EIN: 256719662

8207
Richard L. & Marion K. Pearsall Family Foundation Inc.
Highland Acres, R.R. 4
Dallas, PA   18612-9804

Established in 1998 in Pennsylvania.
Foundation type: Independent foundation.
Financial data (yr. ended 12/31/13): Assets, $1,041,348 (M); expenditures, $129,504; qualifying distributions, $121,000; giving activities include $121,000 for 3 grants (high: $70,000; low: $20,000).
Fields of interest: Arts and culture; Education; Nonprofits; Religion.
Type of support: Regranting.
Limitations: Applications not accepted. Giving primarily in PA. No grants to individuals.
Application information: Unsolicited requests for funds not accepted.
Officers: Amy C. Pearsall, Pres.; Marion K. Pearsall, V.P.; Tamara L. Pearsall, V.P.; Yvonne P. Eckman, Secy.-Treas.
EIN: 232954560

8208
Penn National Gaming Foundation
825 Berkshire Blvd., Ste. 200
Wyomissing, PA   19610-1247   (610) 378-8325
Contact: Amanda Garber, Exec. Dir.
FAX: (610) 375-7632; *Main URL:* http://www.pngaming.com/Community

Established in 2005 in Pennsylvania.
Donor: Penn National Gaming, Inc.
Foundation type: Company-sponsored foundation.
Financial data (yr. ended 12/31/13): Assets, $29,175 (M); gifts received, $214,137; expenditures, $298,807; qualifying distributions,

$298,480; giving activities include $298,140 for 58 grants (high: $90,500; low: $50).
Purpose and activities: The foundation supports organizations involved with cultural affairs and diversity, education, health, human services, and community development.
Fields of interest: Arts and culture; Cultural awareness; Historic preservation; Education; Elementary and secondary education; Higher education; Health; Disasters and emergency management; Public affairs; Leadership development; Community and economic development; Housing development; Human rights; Human services; Child welfare; Senior services; Low-income and poor people.
Type of support: General support; Grants to individuals; Emergency funds; Program development; Equal access.
Limitations: Applications accepted. Giving primarily in areas of company operations in CO, FL, IL, IN, IA, LA, ME, MS, MO, NJ, NM, OH, PA, TX, and WV.
Publications: Application guidelines; Program policy statement.
Application information: Application form required.
  Initial approach: Download application form and mail to headquarters
  Copies of proposal: 2
  Deadline(s): Jan. 1, Apr. 1, July 1, and Oct. 1
  Board meeting date(s): Quarterly
  Final notification: 3 months
Officers and Directors: D. Eric Schippers, Chair. and Director; Robert S. Ippolito, Secy.-Treas. and Director; Amanda Garber, Exec. Dir.; Thomas Burke; Eugene Clark; John Finamore; Jordan B. Savitch, Esq.; Timothy Wilmott.
EIN: 203477997

8209
Jennie Perelman Foundation
1 Bala Ave., Ste. 310
Bala-Cynwyd, PA   19004-3210

Established in 1985 in Pennsylvania.
Donor: General Refractories Co.
Foundation type: Independent foundation.
Financial data (yr. ended 02/28/13): Assets, $2,566,543 (M); expenditures, $239,648; qualifying distributions, $231,880; giving activities include $231,880 for 11 grants (high: $107,250; low: $20).
Fields of interest: Arts and culture; Museums; Higher education; Nonprofits; Eye diseases; Cancers; Community and economic development; Judaism; Child welfare.
Type of support: Regranting.
Limitations: Applications not accepted. Giving primarily in PA. No grants to individuals.
Application information: Unsolicited requests for funds not accepted.
Trustee: Raymond G. Perelman.
EIN: 236251650

8210
Raymond & Ruth Perelman Judaica Foundation
1 Bala Ave., Ste. 310
Bala-Cynwyd, PA   19004-3210

Foundation type: Independent foundation.
Financial data (yr. ended 04/30/13): Assets, $30,217,308 (M); expenditures, $1,002,424;

qualifying distributions, $250,550; giving activities include $250,550 for 4 grants (high: $250,000; low: $100).
Fields of interest: Medical education; Foundations; Human services.
Limitations: Applications not accepted. Giving primarily in Philadelphia, PA. No grants to individuals.
Application information: Contributes only to pre-selected organizations.
Trustee: Raymond G. Perelman.
EIN: 232820841

8211
Perlow Family Foundation
The Grant Bldg.
310 Grant St., Ste. 2500
Pittsburgh, PA   15219-2303   (412) 623-8250

Established in 1997 in Pennsylvania.
Donors: Charles S. Perlow; Rita Perlow Langue Trust.
Foundation type: Independent foundation.
Financial data (yr. ended 12/31/14): Assets, $2,144,568; expenditures, $267,200; qualifying distributions, $203,296.
Fields of interest: Judaism.
Type of support: General support.
Limitations: Applications accepted. Giving primarily in the western PA area. No grants to individuals.
Application information: Application form required.
  Initial approach: Letter
  Deadline(s): None
Officers and Directors: Charles S. Perlow, V.P. and Director; Lori Perlow, V.P. and Director; Rodney W. Fink, Secy.-Treas.
EIN: 232894160

8212
John M. and Gertrude E. Petersen Foundation
124 Voyageur Dr.
Erie, PA   16505-5435
Application address: c/o John M. Petersen, 1550 El Camino Real, Apt. 234, Lady Lake, FL 32159, tel.: (814) 836-0365

Established in 2000 in Pennsylvania.
Donors: John M. Petersen; Gertrude Petersen.
Foundation type: Independent foundation.
Financial data (yr. ended 12/31/13): Assets, $16,507,809 (M); expenditures, $254,995; qualifying distributions, $244,000; giving activities include $244,000 for 18 grants (high: $150,000; low: $2,000).
Fields of interest: Education; Higher education; Environment; Human services.
Limitations: Applications accepted. Giving primarily in Erie and Pittsburgh, PA. No grants to individuals.
Application information: Application form required.
  Initial approach: Request application form
  Deadline(s): None
Officers: John M. Petersen, Pres.; Gertrude E. Petersen, V.P. and Treas.; James D. Cullen, Secy.
EIN: 251859031

8213
Pfundt Foundation
3111 Old Lincoln Hwy.
Trevose, PA   19053-4931   (215) 357-5500
Contact: Lauren P. Meyer, Dir.

Established in 1967 in Pennsylvania.
Donors: General Machine Products Co., Inc.; G. Nelson Pfundt.
Foundation type: Independent foundation.
Financial data (yr. ended 09/30/13): Assets, $3,006,207 (M); expenditures, $182,222; qualifying distributions, $155,996; giving activities include $155,996 for 27 grants (high: $50,000; low: $100).
Purpose and activities: Giving for art and cultural centers, education, health, and community development.
Fields of interest: Education; Health; Human services.
Type of support: General support; Employee matching gifts; Matching grants; Continuing support; Annual campaigns; Capital campaigns; Capital and infrastructure; Equipment.
Limitations: Applications accepted. Giving primarily in PA.
Publications: Application guidelines.
Application information: Application form required.
  Initial approach: Letter
  Copies of proposal: 1
  Deadline(s): None
Officer: G. Nelson Pfundt, Mgr.
Directors: Lauren P. Meyer; William N. Pfundt.
EIN: 236442007

8214
Marjorie M. & Irwin Nat Pincus Fund
277 Northwestern Ave.
Philadelphia, PA   19128-1808   (610) 941-3353

Established in 1984 in Pennsylvania.
Donor: Irwin Nat Pincus.
Foundation type: Independent foundation.
Financial data (yr. ended 12/31/13): Assets, $4,571,958 (M); gifts received, $1,848; expenditures, $186,951; qualifying distributions, $182,075; giving activities include $182,000 for 3 grants (high: $162,000; low: $10,000).
Fields of interest: University education; Nonprofits; Judaism.
Type of support: General support; Regranting.
Limitations: Applications accepted. Giving limited to Washington, DC, and Philadelphia, PA. No grants to individuals.
Application information:
  Initial approach: Proposal
  Deadline(s): None
Officers: Elizabeth M.P. Rubin, Pres.; Anne M. Pincus, V.P.; Nora M. Pincus Schwarz, Secy.-Treas.
EIN: 232751330

8215
The Pittsburgh Children's Foundation, Inc.
124 Bittersweet Cir.
Venetia, PA   15367-1000

Donors: William Zalewski; Louis E. Valli; Ron Burkle Foundation.
Foundation type: Independent foundation.
Financial data (yr. ended 12/31/13): Assets, $1,935,613 (M); gifts received, $387,515;

expenditures, $310,118; qualifying distributions, $300,514; giving activities include $300,514 for 24 grants (high: $125,000; low: $250).
Fields of interest: Health; Agriculture; Human services.
Limitations: Applications not accepted. No grants to individuals.
Application information: Unsolicited requests for funds not accepted.
Officers: William Zalewski, Chair. and Treas.; Louis E. Valli, Pres. and Secy.
EIN: 300022490

8216
Pittsburgh Foundation Charles H. Spang
c/o PNC Bank, N.A.
620 Liberty Ave., 10th Fl.
Pittsburgh, PA   15222

Foundation type: Independent foundation.
Financial data (yr. ended 12/31/13): Assets, $4,296,940 (M); expenditures, $178,509; qualifying distributions, $166,115; giving activities include $165,516 for 1 grant.
Fields of interest: Human services.
Type of support: General support.
Limitations: Applications not accepted. Giving primarily in PA.
Application information: Unsolicited requests for funds not accepted.
Trustee: PNC Bank, N.A.
EIN: 256077922

8217
The Plainfield Foundation
c/o PNC Bank, N.A.
1600 Market St.
Philadelphia, PA   19103-7240

Established in 1935 in New Jersey.
Foundation type: Independent foundation.
Financial data (yr. ended 12/31/13): Assets, $12,755,096 (M); expenditures, $436,326; qualifying distributions, $327,187; giving activities include $223,582 for 59 grants (high: $15,000; low: $20), and $47,950 for 49 grants to individuals (high: $1,750; low: $450).
Purpose and activities: The foundation primarily provides support for higher and other education, as well as for the arts, social services, and community development.
Fields of interest: Arts and culture; Orchestral music; Education; Higher education; Community and economic development; Religion; Protestantism; Human services.
Limitations: Applications not accepted. Giving limited to the Plainfield, NJ, area.
Application information: Contributes only to pre-selected organizations.
Trustee: PNC Bank, N.A.
EIN: 226023276

8218
Plaisance for Case Western
c/o PNC Bank, N.A.
620 Liberty Ave., 10th Fl.
Pittsburgh, PA   15222-2705

Foundation type: Independent foundation.

Financial data (yr. ended 12/31/13): Assets, $6,126,163 (M); expenditures, $304,433; qualifying distributions, $248,380; giving activities include $245,869 for 2 grants (high: $244,869; low: $1,000).
Fields of interest: Education.
Limitations: Applications not accepted. Giving primarily in OH.
Application information: Unsolicited requests for funds not accepted.
Trustee: PNC Bank, N.A.
EIN: 256071144

8219
Harry Plankenhorn Foundation Inc.
c/o New Covenant United Church of Christ
202 E. 3rd St.
Williamsport, PA 17701-6625

Donor: Harry Plankenhorn†.
Foundation type: Independent foundation.
Financial data (yr. ended 12/31/13): Assets, $7,482,663 (M); gifts received, $5,000; expenditures, $478,157; qualifying distributions, $435,867; giving activities include $433,910 for 20 grants (high: $125,000; low: $4,000).
Purpose and activities: Giving for human services, including programs for the visually handicapped, children and youth, and emergency aid.
Fields of interest: Camps; Human services; Basic and emergency aid; Child welfare; Youth development.
Type of support: Annual campaigns; Capital and infrastructure; General support; Program development.
Limitations: Applications not accepted. Giving primarily in Lycoming County, PA. No grants to individuals.
Application information: Unsolicited requests for funds not accepted.
Officers: Charles F. Greevy III, Pres.; Robert Reeder, V.P.; Nancy Stearns, Secy.; Carl O. Hieber, Treas.
Directors: Barbara Ertel; Mark A. Huffman; Philip D. Landers; Dean F. Rabert; J. Michael Wiley.
EIN: 246023579

8220
The Mary Jane & Joseph P. Platt, Jr. Family Foundation, Inc.
401 Wood St., Ste. 1100
Pittsburgh, PA 15222-1838   4125860226

Established in 1998 in Pennsylvania.
Donors: Mary Jane Platt; Joseph P. Platt, Jr.
Foundation type: Independent foundation.
Financial data (yr. ended 12/31/14): Assets, $2,467,853; expenditures, $286,955; qualifying distributions, $239,886.
Fields of interest: Arts and culture; Health; Human services.
Limitations: Applications not accepted. Giving primarily in PA. No grants to individuals.
Application information: Unsolicited requests for funds not accepted.
Officers: Mary Jane Platt, Pres.; Joseph P. Platt, Jr., Secy.; Denise M. Augelo, Exec. Dir.
EIN: 251815288

8221
Pogo Family Foundation
c/o Haney & Hecht
795 E. Lancaster Ave.
Villanova, PA 19085

Established in 2006 in Pennsylvania.
Donor: Peter Gould.
Foundation type: Independent foundation.
Financial data (yr. ended 12/31/13): Assets, $624,721 (M); expenditures, $245,509; qualifying distributions, $242,425; giving activities include $240,950 for 9 grants (high: $78,000; low: $3,000).
Fields of interest: Undergraduate education; Zoos; Gardening.
Limitations: Applications not accepted. Giving primarily in Philadelphia, PA. No grants to individuals.
Application information: Unsolicited requests for funds not accepted.
Officers: Peter G. Gould, Pres.; Alexandra P. Gould, V.P.; Robin M. Potter, Secy.-Treas.
EIN: 205989350

8222
The Douglas W. Pollock Foundation
c/o Michael L. Bangs, Esq.
429 S. 18th St.
Camp Hill, PA 17011-5902

Established in 2007 in Pennsylvania.
Foundation type: Independent foundation.
Financial data (yr. ended 06/30/13): Assets, $4,105,335 (M); expenditures, $220,149; qualifying distributions, $180,000; giving activities include $180,000 for 5 grants (high: $50,000; low: $25,000).
Fields of interest: Higher education; Diseases and conditions.
Limitations: Applications not accepted. Giving primarily in PA. No grants to individuals.
Application information: Contributes only to pre-selected organizations.
Directors: Michael L. Bangs; Douglas W. Pollock.
EIN: 205087721

8223
Wilbur E. Postles Scholarship Fund
c/o PNC Bank, N.A.
1600 Market St., Tax Dept.
Philadelphia, PA 19103-7240   2155855597
Application address: c/o Laura Schumache, PNC Bank, N.A., 222 Delaware Ave., 16th Fl., Wilmington, DE 19801-1637, tel.: (302) 429-1481

Established in 2002 in Delaware.
Foundation type: Independent foundation.
Financial data (yr. ended 12/31/14): Assets, $5,755,703; expenditures, $269,180; qualifying distributions, $202,351.
Purpose and activities: Scholarship awards to residents of Delaware who were residents for four years prior to applying, and who will attend a college, professional or technical school.
Fields of interest: Education; Higher education.
Type of support: Student aid; Individual development.
Limitations: Applications accepted. Giving limited to residents of DE.
Application information: Application form required.

Initial approach: Letter
Deadline(s): May 1
Trustees: John R. Twombly, Jr., Esq.; PNC Bank, N.A.
EIN: 516010602

8224
Dorothy M. Potter Irrevocable Trust
c/o PNC Bank, N.A.
620 Liberty Ave., 10th Fl.
Pittsburgh, PA 15222-2705

Foundation type: Independent foundation.
Financial data (yr. ended 12/31/14): Assets, $4,778,600; expenditures, $248,344; qualifying distributions, $191,943 and $0 for set-asides.
Fields of interest: Health.
Limitations: Applications not accepted. Giving primarily in Pittsburgh, PA.
Application information: Unsolicited requests for funds not accepted.
Trustee: PNC Bank, N.A.
EIN: 256715126

8225
Price Foundation
2364 Rte. 66
Delmont, PA 15626-1454

Established in 1993 in Pennsylvania.
Donor: Wendell Price.
Foundation type: Independent foundation.
Financial data (yr. ended 12/31/14): Assets, $4,905,063; expenditures, $228,532; qualifying distributions, $215,000.
Fields of interest: Natural resources; Family planning; HIV/AIDS; Population studies; Child welfare.
Type of support: General support; Program development; Research.
Limitations: Applications not accepted. Giving primarily in CT, MA, NY, and VA. No grants to individuals.
Application information: Unsolicited requests for funds not accepted.
Trustees: Allan MacDougall; Wendell B. Price.
EIN: 251701024

8226
John W. Price Jr. Fund
c/o PNC Bank, N.A.
P.O. Box 609
Pittsburgh, PA 15230-9738

Foundation type: Independent foundation.
Financial data (yr. ended 12/31/13): Assets, $3,610,781 (M); expenditures, $182,759; qualifying distributions, $152,419; giving activities include $143,764 for 1 grant.
Fields of interest: University education.
Limitations: Applications not accepted. Giving limited to Philadelphia, PA. No grants to individuals.
Application information: Contributes only to a pre-selected organization.
Trustee: PNC Bank, N.A.
EIN: 616058937

8227
Price Trust Fund
c/o PNC Bank, N.A.
P.O. Box 609
Pittsburgh, PA 15230-9738

Donor: Catherine Price Bass.
Foundation type: Independent foundation.
Financial data (yr. ended 12/31/13): Assets, $7,566,697 (M); expenditures, $354,343; qualifying distributions, $304,768; giving activities include $289,740 for 1 grant.
Fields of interest: University education.
Type of support: General support.
Limitations: Applications not accepted. Giving limited to Louisville, KY.
Application information: Unsolicited requests for funds not accepted.
Trustee: PNC Bank, N.A.
EIN: 616023009

8228
The Quaker Chemical Foundation
1 Quaker Park
901 Hector St.
Conshohocken, PA 19428-2307 (610) 832-4301
FAX: (610) 832-8682; Main URL: http://www.quakerchem.com/about_us/about_foundation.html

Established in 1959 in Pennsylvania.
Donor: Quaker Chemical Corp.
Foundation type: Company-sponsored foundation.
Financial data (yr. ended 06/30/14): Assets, $22,335 (M); gifts received, $155,000; expenditures, $157,245; qualifying distributions, $153,374; giving activities include $87,575 for grants, $26,000 for 1 grant to an individual, and $39,799 for 4 employee matching gifts.
Purpose and activities: The foundation supports organizations involved with arts and culture, health, human services, community development, and civic affairs. Special emphasis is directed toward programs designed to promote education and science, especially chemistry.
Fields of interest: Arts and culture; Education; Nonprofits; Health; Hospital care; Physical and earth sciences; Chemistry; Public affairs; Community and economic development; Human services.
Type of support: General support; Employee matching gifts; Scholarships; Matching grants; Regranting.
Limitations: Applications accepted. Giving limited to areas of company operations in Santa Fe Springs, CA, Downers Grove, IL, Bingham Farms and Detroit, MI, Batavia, NY, Dayton, OH, and Conshohocken, PA. Generally, no support for national organizations. No grants to individuals (except for employee-related scholarships), or for building or endowments; no loans.
Publications: Application guidelines.
Application information: Grants range from $1,000 to $5,000. National organizations and bricks and mortar projects are rarely supported. Application form required.
   Initial approach: Download application form and mail to foundation
   Copies of proposal: 1
   Deadline(s): Apr. 30
   Board meeting date(s): June
   Final notification: Aug.

Officer and Trustees: Jackie Porreca, Secy.; Palitha Abeywardena; Micheal F. Barry; Cindy Cetnar; Jennifer Hill; Irene M. Kisleiko; Christian Scholund; Jane L. Williams.
Number of staff: None.
EIN: 236245803

8229
The Henry A. Quinn Charitable Foundation
100 Chetwynd Dr.
Rosemont, PA 19010-1453

Established in 2006 in Pennsylvania.
Donor: Henry A. Quinn†.
Foundation type: Independent foundation.
Financial data (yr. ended 12/31/13): Assets, $13,059,533 (M); gifts received, $154,769; expenditures, $642,138; qualifying distributions, $418,795; giving activities include $402,000 for 12 grants (high: $75,000; low: $1,000).
Fields of interest: Arts and culture; Education; Elementary and secondary education; Human services.
Type of support: Capital campaigns.
Limitations: Applications not accepted. Giving primarily in PA. No grants to individuals.
Application information: Unsolicited requests for funds not accepted.
Officer: Susan Ilsemann, Pres.
EIN: 233092270

8230
Charity Randall Foundation
6031 Wallace Rd., Ext., Ste. 202
Wexford, PA 15090 (724) 799-8680
Contact: Robert P. Randall, Pres.

Donors: Earl R. Randall; Three Rivers Aluminum Co.
Foundation type: Independent foundation.
Financial data (yr. ended 06/30/13): Assets, $5,097,997 (M); expenditures, $258,986; qualifying distributions, $233,425; giving activities include $233,425 for 7 grants (high: $100,000; low: $4,725).
Purpose and activities: Grants primarily for higher education and to encourage literary and environmental conservation endeavors; also giving for fine arts, social service and community development.
Fields of interest: Arts and culture; Theater; Museums; Literature and writing; Education; Higher education; Environment; Zoos; Botanical gardens; Domesticated animals; Archives and special collections.
Type of support: General support; Scholarships.
Limitations: Applications accepted. Giving primarily in Pittsburgh, PA.
Application information: Individuals should submit a resume of academic qualifications, and, in the case of research grants, an outline of the proposed investigation and a proposed budget. Organizations must use the foundation's standard grant application. Application form required.
   Initial approach: Letter
   Deadline(s): Apr. 30th
   Final notification: Within 1 month
Officers and Directors: Robin S. Randall, Chair.; Robert P. Randall, Pres. and Director; Adam Randall, Treas.; Brett Randall; Chris Randall; Rita Randall.
EIN: 251329778

8231
The Frank E. Rath Spang & Company Charitable Trust
(formerly Spang and Company Charitable Trust)
c/o Spang Co.
P.O. Box 11422
Pittsburgh, PA 15238-0422 (412) 963-9363
Contact: Robert C. Harbage

Established in 1972 in Pennsylvania.
Donors: Spang and Co.; Magnetics, Inc.; F.E. Rath Trust.
Foundation type: Company-sponsored foundation.
Financial data (yr. ended 12/31/13): Assets, $6,175,540 (M); expenditures, $325,217; qualifying distributions, $320,600; giving activities include $320,600 for 42 grants (high: $75,000; low: $50).
Purpose and activities: The trust supports zoos and fire departments and organizations involved with performing arts, higher education, health, and cancer.
Fields of interest: Arts and culture; Health; Human services.
Type of support: General support.
Limitations: Applications accepted. Giving primarily in Butler and Pittsburgh, PA. No grants to individuals.
Application information: Application form required.
   Initial approach: Proposal
   Deadline(s): 90 days prior to end of calendar quarter
   Board meeting date(s): Apr., Aug., and Dec.
Trustees: David F. Rath; Frank E. Rath, Jr.
EIN: 256020192

8232
Reese Foundation
P.O. Box 3215, Tax Dept.
Lancaster, PA 17604-3215
Application address: c/o Fulton Financial Advisors, N.A., Attn.: Vince Lattanzio, P.O. Box 7988, Lancaster, PA 17604-7989, tel.: (717) 291-2523

Established in 1996 in Pennsylvania.
Foundation type: Independent foundation.
Financial data (yr. ended 05/31/13): Assets, $4,090,634 (M); expenditures, $225,780; qualifying distributions, $196,000; giving activities include $196,000 for 11 grants (high: $46,000; low: $2,500).
Purpose and activities: Giving primarily to theological seminaries, and to Christian agencies and churches.
Fields of interest: Undergraduate education; Graduate and professional education; Christianity; Theology; Human services.
Type of support: General support.
Limitations: Applications accepted. Giving primarily in CA, PA and TX.
Application information: Application form required.
   Initial approach: Letter
   Deadline(s): None
Trustees: I. Philip Reese; Kim Seldomridge; Fulton Bank, N.A.
EIN: 232349281

8233
The Reidler Foundation
c/o Zator Law Offices
4400 Walbert Ave.
Allentown, PA   18104-1619   (570) 454-7654

Established in 1944 in Pennsylvania.
Donors: John W. Reidler†; Verna C. Reidler†;
Howard D. Fegan; Ann B. Fegan; Hazelton Lutheran
Home Irrevocable Trust.
Foundation type: Independent foundation.
Financial data (yr. ended 10/31/13): Assets,
$8,995,453 (M); gifts received, $28,620;
expenditures, $465,737; qualifying distributions,
$416,106; giving activities include $400,000 for 44
grants (high: $47,500; low: $1,000).
Fields of interest: Education; Higher education;
Environment; Public libraries; Protestantism; Human
services; Youth services.
Type of support: General support; Capital
campaigns; Capital and infrastructure;
Endowments.
Limitations: Applications not accepted. Giving
primarily in the Ashland, Hazleton, and Lehigh
Valley, PA, areas. No grants to individuals.
Application information: Unsolicited requests for
funds not accepted.
Officers: Ann B. Fegan, Pres.; Howard D. Fegan,
V.P.; Diane K. Reidler, V.P.; Diana L. James,
Secy.-Treas.; John H. Fegan; Sarah K. Fegen;
Jessica Lupold; Barbara Subber.
EIN: 246022888

8234
Jacob L. Reiss Foundation
c/o BNY Mellon, N.A.
P.O. Box 185
Pittsburgh, PA   15230-0185   2129226636

Established in 1953 in New York.
Donor: Jacob L. Reiss†.
Foundation type: Independent foundation.
Financial data (yr. ended 12/31/14): Assets,
$5,656,525; expenditures, $278,996; qualifying
distributions, $259,052.
Purpose and activities: Giving primarily to health
and human service organizations and Roman
Catholic agencies.
Fields of interest: Secondary education; Hospital
care; Substance abuse prevention; Catholicism;
Human services; Senior assisted living.
Type of support: Continuing support; Capital
campaigns; Capital and infrastructure; Equipment;
Curriculum development.
Application information: Application form required.
   Initial approach: Letter
   Deadline(s): None
Trustee: BNY Mellon, N.A.
EIN: 136064123

8235
W. H. and Althea F. Remmel Foundation
c/o PNC Charitable Trusts
249 5th Ave.
1 PNC Plz., 20th Fl.
Pittsburgh, PA   15222
E-mail: charitabletrusts@pnc.com; Application
address: c/o PNC Charitable Trust Grant Review
Committee, 1 PNC Plz., 20th Fl., 249 5th Ave.,
Pittsburgh, PA 15222, tel.: (412) 762-3413

Established in 1951 in Pennsylvania.
Donors: William H. Remmel†; Althea F. Remmel†.
Foundation type: Independent foundation.
Financial data (yr. ended 12/31/13): Assets,
$4,938,456 (M); gifts received, $38,074;
expenditures, $260,911; qualifying distributions,
$207,515; giving activities include $190,450 for 17
grants (high: $30,000; low: $2,500).
Fields of interest: Education; Health; Religion;
Human services; Food banks; Women's services.
Type of support: Capital campaigns; Matching
grants; Capital and infrastructure; Equipment; Seed
money.
Limitations: Giving primarily in Pittsburgh, PA. No
support for private foundations, or for political,
fraternal, labor or advocacy groups. No grants to
individuals, or for events and operating costs.
Application information: Full proposals will not be
accepted. Proposals will be invited upon review of
inquiry.
   Initial approach: Letter of inquiry or telephone call
   Copies of proposal: 1
   Deadline(s): Feb.1, May 1, Aug. 1, and Oct. 1
Trustee: PNC Bank, N.A.
EIN: 237009732

8236
Helen R. Richards Trust
c/o BNY Mellon, N.A.
P.O. Box 185
Pittsburgh, PA   15230-0185

Donor: Castor Theodore H Trust.
Foundation type: Independent foundation.
Financial data (yr. ended 09/30/14): Assets,
$4,845,770 (M); expenditures, $260,854;
qualifying distributions, $221,050; giving activities
include $206,400 for 4 grants (high: $103,000;
low: $400).
Fields of interest: Higher education; Hospital care;
Public libraries.
Limitations: Applications not accepted. Giving
primarily in MA. No grants to individuals.
Application information: Unsolicited requests for
funds not accepted.
Trustee: BNY Mellon, N.A.
EIN: 046092036

8237
Ricon Americas Foundation
(formerly IKON Office Solutions Foundation, Inc)
70 Valley Stream Pkwy.
Malvern, PA   19355

Established in 1974 in Pennsylvania.
Donor: IKON Office Solutions, Inc.
Foundation type: Company-sponsored foundation.
Financial data (yr. ended 12/31/14): Assets,
$1,700,838 (M); expenditures, $174,010;
qualifying distributions, $171,260; giving activities
include $171,260 for 9 grants.
Purpose and activities: The foundation supports
organizations involved with secondary and higher
education.
Fields of interest: Education; Diseases and
conditions; Human services.
Type of support: General support; Employee
matching gifts; Cash grants.
Limitations: Applications not accepted. Giving
primarily in areas of company operations in

Washington, DC, IL, NJ, and PA. No grants to
individuals.
Application information: Grantmaking suspended
until further notice.
Officers: Gary Crowe, Pres.; Greg Weixel, V.P. and
Treas.; William LaSalle, Secy.
EIN: 237378726

8238
The Rider-Pool Foundation
645 W. Hamilton St., Ste. 202
Allentown, PA   18101   (610) 770-9346
Contact: Edward F. Meehan, Exec. Dir.
FAX: (610) 770-9361; E-mail: info@pooltrust.org;
Additional contact: Bridget I. Rassler, Mgr., Fin. and
Admin.; Main URL: http://rider.pooltrust.org

Established in 1957 in Pennsylvania.
Donor: Dorothy Rider-Pool†.
Foundation type: Independent foundation.
Financial data (yr. ended 12/31/13): Assets,
$11,670,236 (M); gifts received, $106,434;
expenditures, $359,024; qualifying distributions,
$322,783; giving activities include $208,625 for 67
grants (high: $21,000; low: $1,000).
Purpose and activities: The foundation's purpose is
to serve as a means to improve the quality of life in
the community, to build on the community's
strengths and add to its vitality, and to increase the
capacity of the community to serve the needs of all
its citizens.
Fields of interest: Arts and culture; Art museums;
Education; Health; Community and economic
development; Human services; Youth services.
Type of support: General support; Continuing
support; Program development.
Limitations: Applications accepted. Giving primarily
in the Lehigh Valley, PA, area. No support for
fraternal organizations or organizations outside the
U.S. or its territories; generally no support for
sectarian institutions, religious organizations for
religious purposes, hospitals, or United Way
member agencies. No grants to individuals, or for
fundraising or related advertising, testimonial
dinners, subsidization of books, mailings, or articles
in professional journals.
Publications: Application guidelines; Biennial
report; Financial statement; Grants list;
Informational brochure (including application
guidelines).
Application information: Requests for funds are
accepted through an electronic application process
described on foundation web site. See foundation
web site for application guidelines and procedures.
   Copies of proposal: 1
   Deadline(s): Aug. 15
   Board meeting date(s): May and Oct.
Officer and Trustees: Edward F. Meehan, Exec. Dir.
and Trustee; Denise M Gargan; Leon C. Holt, Jr.;
John P. Jones III; John E. McGlade; J. Scott Pidcock.
Number of staff: None.
EIN: 236207356

8239
William H. Ritter Trust
c/o PNC Bank, N.A.
620 Liberty Ave., 10th Fl.
Pittsburgh, PA   15222-2705

Foundation type: Independent foundation.

Financial data (yr. ended 12/31/13): Assets, $7,293,097 (M); expenditures, $339,103; qualifying distributions, $266,307; giving activities include $263,341 for 1 grant.
Fields of interest: Health.
Limitations: Applications not accepted.
Application information: Unsolicited requests for funds not accepted.
Trustee: PNC Bank, N.A.
EIN: 226018818

8240
Ralph & Suzanne Roberts Foundation
c/o Comcast Corp.
1701 John F. Kennedy Blvd., 52nd Fl.
Philadelphia, PA 19103-2899

Established in 1963 in Pennsylvania.
Donors: Ralph J. Roberts; Suzanne F. Roberts.
Foundation type: Independent foundation.
Financial data (yr. ended 11/30/13): Assets, $4,564,476 (M); expenditures, $335,784; qualifying distributions, $325,925; giving activities include $325,925 for 33 grants (high: $105,000; low: $100).
Purpose and activities: Giving primarily for the performing arts, particularly theater, as well as for higher education, and to Jewish organizations and temples.
Fields of interest: Arts and culture; Performing arts; Theater; Higher education; Judaism.
Limitations: Applications not accepted. Giving primarily in Philadelphia, PA. No grants to individuals.
Application information: Grants initiated by trustees.
Trustees: Ralph J. Roberts; Suzanne F. Roberts.
EIN: 237015984

8241
Donald & Sylvia Robinson Family Foundation
(formerly Alex & Leona Robinson Family Foundation)
6507 Wilkins Ave.
Pittsburgh, PA 15217-1305 (412) 661-1200
Contact: Donald Robinson, Dir.

Established in 2001 in Pennsylvania.
Donor: Donald Robinson.
Foundation type: Independent foundation.
Financial data (yr. ended 12/31/13): Assets, $6,961,258 (M); gifts received, $138,258; expenditures, $315,940; qualifying distributions, $300,690; giving activities include $300,690 for 184 grants (high: $25,000; low: $50).
Fields of interest: Museums; Nonprofits; Judaism.
Type of support: Regranting.
Limitations: Applications accepted. Giving primarily in PA.
Application information: Grantmakers of Western Pennsylvanias Common Grant Application Format accepted. Application form required.
 Initial approach: Letter
 Deadline(s): None
Directors: Carol Robinson; Donald Robinson; Stephen Robinson; Sylvia Robinson.
EIN: 311711937

8242
W. F. and L. C. Roemer Charitable Foundation
c/o Jack Crogan, PNC
2 PNC Plz., 620 Liberty Ave.
Pittsburgh, PA 15222 (412) 768-2629
Contact: William F. Roemer

Established in 1999 in Pennsylvania.
Donors: William F. Roemer; Linda C. Roemer.
Foundation type: Independent foundation.
Financial data (yr. ended 03/31/13): Assets, $3,070,005 (M); expenditures, $249,151; qualifying distributions, $225,000; giving activities include $225,000 for 5 grants (high: $100,000; low: $25,000).
Purpose and activities: Giving primarily to religious organizations or institutions of the Christian faith; at least two-thirds of distributions are made to such organizations during the year.
Fields of interest: Performing arts; Elementary and secondary education; Christianity; Human services.
Type of support: General support.
Limitations: Applications accepted. Giving primarily in PA. No grants to individuals.
Application information: Application form required.
 Initial approach: Letter
 Deadline(s): None
Trustee: Jack Crogan.
Distribution Committee Members: Linda C. Roemer; William F. Roemer.
EIN: 256636816

8243
The Kelly Rooney Foundation
5 Boulder Creek Ln.
Newtown Square, PA 19073-1703 (610) 745-2002
Contact: Sean Rooney, Tr.
E-mail: info@kellyrooney.org; *Main URL:* http://kellyrooney.org
Facebook: https://www.facebook.com/kellyrooneyfoundation
Twitter: https://twitter.com/KellyRooneyFdn

Established in 2006 in Pennsylvania.
Donors: Save 2nd Base; Comcast Spectator; Joann Rooney; Carter Sims; Gail Connor; Kevin Connor; Jenn Sims; John Rooney; ARAMARK; American Ireland Fund; IMX; INFOR; Thomas & Jane Dooner; Tom & Jill Nerney; Sean Rooney; Palm Beach Kennel Club; Nearney Family Foundation; Charles O'Brein; Mari O'Brein; Davis Foundation; Pittsburgh Steelers; PNC; Thomas Dooner; Adernaline Lacrosse; Steve Siegfried; Jane Dooner.
Foundation type: Independent foundation.
Financial data (yr. ended 12/31/13): Assets, $121,808 (M); gifts received, $30,024; expenditures, $298,132; qualifying distributions, $178,043; giving activities include $178,043 for 11 grants (high: $100,000; low: $546).
Fields of interest: Education; University education; Diseases and conditions; Breast cancer.
Limitations: Applications accepted. Giving primarily in PA. No grants to individuals.
Application information:
 Initial approach: Proposal
 Deadline(s): None
Trustee: Sean Rooney.
EIN: 207003413

8244
The David M. and Marjorie D. Rosenberg Foundation
893 Parkes Run Ln.
Villanova, PA 19085-1124 (610) 458-4175
Contact: Marjorie D. Rosenberg, Tr.; David M. Rosenberg, Tr.

Established in 1993 in Pennsylvania.
Donors: David M. Rosenberg; Marjorie D. Rosenberg; Rosenberg Family Charitable Lead Trust.
Foundation type: Independent foundation.
Financial data (yr. ended 12/31/13): Assets, $2,593,129 (M); expenditures, $333,541; qualifying distributions, $308,765; giving activities include $304,800 for 30 grants (high: $83,500; low: $100).
Purpose and activities: Giving primarily for education; health organizations and hospitals; Jewish organizations; and children and social services.
Fields of interest: Philosophy; Education; Higher education; Nonprofits; Hospital care; Specialty hospital care; Diseases and conditions; Judaism; Human services; Child welfare.
Type of support: Regranting.
Limitations: Applications accepted. Giving primarily in PA, with some giving in CA. No grants to individuals.
Application information: Application form required.
 Initial approach: Letter
 Deadline(s): None
Trustees: David M. Rosenberg; Marjorie D. Rosenberg.
EIN: 237715847

8245
The Rosenlund Family Foundation
P.O. Box 297
Haverford, PA 19041-0297
Contact: Dale Mitchell, Exec. Dir.
E-mail: dalemitch@verizon.net; *Main URL:* http://rosenlundfamilyfoundation.org

Established in 1962 in Pennsylvania.
Donor: Arthur O. Rosenlund‡.
Foundation type: Independent foundation.
Financial data (yr. ended 06/30/13): Assets, $2,789,694 (M); expenditures, $166,286; qualifying distributions, $160,498; giving activities include $147,000 for 47 grants (high: $5,000; low: $1,000).
Purpose and activities: Supports high quality small and medium sized organizations (with budgets of $1.5 million or less) whose priorities and ongoing commitment are to arts and environmental education programs for under-served children and youth in southeastern Pennsylvania.
Fields of interest: Arts education; Environmental education; Children and youth.
Type of support: Program development; General support.
Limitations: Applications accepted. Giving primarily in Philadelphia and southeastern Pennsylvania's most disadvantaged neighborhoods. No support for elementary, secondary or higher educational institutions, endowments, political groups or related think tanks, fraternal organizations, or religious organizations in support of their sacramental or theological functions. No grants to individuals, or for capital projects or endowments; the foundation does not support pilot/demonstration projects or

new initiatives that do not have sufficient committed funding to be sustained over time.

Publications: Application guidelines; Grants list.
Application information: Application form required. Application form required.

Initial approach: Submit proposal as outlined on foundation web site
Copies of proposal: 1
Deadline(s): Between Jan. 1 and 5:00 p.m. on the last business day of Feb.
Board meeting date(s): Varies
Final notification: All grants awarded in June. Declined applications will receive e-mail notification

Trustees: Hope Rosenlund, Managing Tr.; April Rosenlund Ford; Alarik A. Rosenlund; Alarik A. Rosenlund, Jr.; Stephanie Rosenlund Shim; Kristin Rosenlund Turrill.
Number of staff: 1 full-time professional.
EIN: 236243642

8246
Rubin Family Foundation
4201 Neshaminy Blvd.
P.O. Box 207
Bensalem, PA 19020

Donor: Michael Rubin.
Foundation type: Independent foundation.
Financial data (yr. ended 12/31/13): Assets, $4,929,740 (M); expenditures, $451,734; qualifying distributions, $425,000; giving activities include $425,000 for 48 grants (high: $62,500; low: $500).
Fields of interest: Arts and culture; Health; Human services.
Limitations: Applications not accepted. Giving primarily in NY and VA.
Application information: Unsolicited requests for funds not accepted.
Officers: Paulette Rubin, Pres.; Michael Rubin, Secy.; Michele Reardon, Treas.
EIN: 452485007

8247
Samuel & Lottie Rudin Scholarship Foundation
c/o Heather S. Hebert & E.H. Baum
422 Strathmore Rd.
Havertown, PA 19083-3736

Established in 2005 in Nevada.
Donor: Abraham Rudin†.
Foundation type: Independent foundation.
Financial data (yr. ended 12/31/13): Assets, $8,905,792 (M); expenditures, $343,489; qualifying distributions, $307,694; giving activities include $202,500 for 1 grant.
Fields of interest: Education; Judaism.
Type of support: General support; Scholarships.
Limitations: Applications not accepted.
Application information: Contributes only to pre-selected organizations.
Trustees: E. Harris Baum; Heather S. Herbert.
EIN: 486396189

8248
Kal and Lucille Rudman Foundation
c/o Eisneramper LLP
101 West Ave.
Jenkintown, PA 19046

Donors: Kal Rudman; Lucille Rudman.
Foundation type: Independent foundation.
Financial data (yr. ended 12/31/13): Assets, $7,660,913 (M); expenditures, $417,009; qualifying distributions, $384,655; giving activities include $376,950 for 23 grants (high: $165,000; low: $550).
Fields of interest: Higher education.
Limitations: Applications not accepted. Giving primarily in Philadelphia, PA.
Application information: Contributes only to pre-selected organizations.
Trustees: Lucille Rudman; Mitchell Rudman; Solomon Rudman.
EIN: 223237107

8249
Thomas A. and Georgina T. Russo Foundation
P.O. Box 6339
Lancaster, PA 17607-6339

Established in 2005 in Pennsylvania.
Donors: Thomas A. Russo; Georgina Russo.
Foundation type: Independent foundation.
Financial data (yr. ended 12/31/13): Assets, $6,389,056 (M); gifts received, $1,542,202; expenditures, $433,635; qualifying distributions, $361,112; giving activities include $361,112 for 19 grants (high: $60,409; low: $8).
Fields of interest: Law education; Nonprofits; Hospice care; Human services.
Type of support: Regranting.
Limitations: Applications not accepted. Giving primarily in PA.
Application information: Unsolicited requests for funds not accepted.
Directors: Georgina T. Russo; Thomas A. Russo.
EIN: 203980555

8250
The Rust Foundation
1305 Parkview Blvd.
Pittsburgh, PA 15217-2589

Established in 1950 in Pennsylvania.
Foundation type: Independent foundation.
Financial data (yr. ended 12/31/13): Assets, $6,217,026 (M); gifts received, $2,583; expenditures, $369,071; qualifying distributions, $299,685; giving activities include $291,500 for grants.
Purpose and activities: Giving limited to interests of individual trustees, including grants for health care, education, environmental conservation, church support, and community funds.
Fields of interest: Community and economic development; Human services.
Type of support: Continuing support; Annual campaigns; Capital campaigns; Capital and infrastructure; Land acquisitions; Endowments; Emergency funds; Seed money; Research.
Limitations: Applications not accepted. Giving on a national basis. No grants to individuals.

Application information: Unsolicited requests for funds not accepted.
Board meeting date(s): Late Dec. and early Aug.
Officers: Murray S. Rust III, Pres.; James O. Rust, V.P.; Molly R. Montgomery, Secy.; Thatcher O. Montgomery, Treas.
Trustees: Robert C. Gillies; Sean D. Montgomery; J Mead Rust, Jr.
EIN: 256049037

8251
The Ryan Family Foundation
2875 Country Club Rd.
Allentown, PA 18103-9258

Established in 1997 in Pennsylvania.
Donor: Frank Ryan†.
Foundation type: Independent foundation.
Financial data (yr. ended 12/31/13): Assets, $7,051,617 (M); expenditures, $407,021; qualifying distributions, $306,550; giving activities include $306,050 for 20 grants (high: $125,000; low: $500).
Fields of interest: Arts and culture; Elementary and secondary education; University education; Hospital care; Catholicism.
Limitations: Applications not accepted. Giving primarily in PA. No grants to individuals.
Application information: Contributes only to pre-selected organizations.
Trustees: Carolyn Healey; Christopher G. Ryan; Laurie Ryan; William D. Ryan.
EIN: 232901049

8252
The H. Glenn Sample, Jr., M.D. Memorial Fund
c/o PNC Bank, N.A.
620 Liberty Ave., 10th Fl.
Pittsburgh, PA 15222-2705
Application address: PNC Advisors Charitable Trust Grant, 1 PNC Plz., 249 5th Ave., 20th Fl., Pittsburgh, PA 15222, Tel.: (412) 762-9965

Established in 1999 in Pennsylvania.
Donor: H. Glenn Sample, Jr.†.
Foundation type: Independent foundation.
Financial data (yr. ended 12/31/13): Assets, $5,316,046 (M); expenditures, $285,600; qualifying distributions, $231,158; giving activities include $214,892 for 20 grants (high: $20,000; low: $4,500).
Fields of interest: Diseases and conditions; Human services; Child welfare.
Limitations: Applications accepted. Giving primarily in PA. No support for private foundations, or for political, labor, fraternal or advocacy groups. No grants to individuals, or for general operating costs, or for events.
Application information: See web site PNC.com, under "Corporate & Institutional", then under "Special Segments", click on "Non-profits and Government Institutions", and then "Charitable Trust Grants". Application form required.
Initial approach: See website www.pnc.com
Deadline(s): See website www.pnc.com
Trustee: PNC Bank, N.A.
EIN: 916453143

8253
The Saramar Charitable Fund
130 S. 18th St., Ste. 3301
Philadelphia, PA 19103 (856) 661-4515
Contact: Marjorie Honickman, Tr.
Application address: 8275 N. US Rte. 130,
Pennsauken, NJ 08110-1435

Established in 2003 in Pennsylvania.
Donors: Manhattan Beer Distributors, LLC; Marjorie Honickman.
Foundation type: Company-sponsored foundation.
Financial data (yr. ended 12/31/13): Assets, $3,927,693 (M); gifts received, $125,000; expenditures, $186,761; qualifying distributions, $185,267; giving activities include $183,772 for 109 grants (high: $17,402; low: $100).
Purpose and activities: The foundation supports organizations involved with arts and culture, education, cancer, human services, and Judaism.
Fields of interest: Arts and culture; Performing arts; Art museums; Education; Elementary education; Secondary education; Higher education; Nonprofits; Health; Hospital care; Cancers; Judaism; Human services; Senior services.
Type of support: General support; Program development; Scholarships; Regranting.
Limitations: Applications accepted. Giving primarily in Philadelphia, PA. No grants to individuals.
Application information:
   Initial approach: Proposal
   Deadline(s): None
Trustees: Jeffrey A. Honickman; Marjorie Honickman.
EIN: 256839698

8254
Satell Family Foundation
c/o Edward M. Satell
370 Technology Dr.
Malvern, PA 19355-1315

Established in 1995 in Pennsylvania.
Donors: Edward M. Satell; American Future Systems, Inc.; CMS Companies.
Foundation type: Independent foundation.
Financial data (yr. ended 12/31/13): Assets, $8,448,007 (M); gifts received, $2,500; expenditures, $368,951; qualifying distributions, $358,145; giving activities include $346,621 for 33 grants (high: $115,000; low: $100).
Fields of interest: Education; Higher education; Nonprofits; Judaism.
Type of support: Regranting.
Limitations: Applications not accepted. Giving primarily in PA; some funding also in New York, NY. No grants to individuals.
Application information: Contributes only to pre-selected organizations.
Trustee: Edward M. Satell.
EIN: 237769039

8255
The Sherrie R. Savett Family Foundation
c/o Mark Blaskey
3000 Two Logan Sq.
Philadelphia, PA 19103-2799

Established in 2007 in Pennsylvania.
Donor: Sherrie R. Savett.
Foundation type: Independent foundation.

Financial data (yr. ended 12/31/14): Assets, $1,195,164 (M); expenditures, $203,088; qualifying distributions, $190,053; giving activities include $187,180 for 26 grants (high: $135,250; low: $25).
Fields of interest: Education; Diseases and conditions; Judaism.
Limitations: Applications not accepted. Giving primarily in NY and PA. No grants to individuals.
Application information: Unsolicited requests for funds not accepted.
Trustees: Mark S. Blaskey; Sherrie R. Savett.
EIN: 256912746

8256
The Leonard A. and Mary Jane Schafer Charitable Foundation Trust
20 Stanwix St., Ste. 650
Pittsburgh, PA 15222-4801

Established in 2002 in Pennsylvania.
Donor: Mary Jane Schafer†.
Foundation type: Independent foundation.
Financial data (yr. ended 12/31/14): Assets, $3,655,258; expenditures, $257,102; qualifying distributions, $169,500.
Fields of interest: Higher education; Christianity; Human services.
Limitations: Applications not accepted. Giving primarily in PA. No grants to individuals.
Application information: Contributes only to pre-selected organizations.
Trustee: Jeffrey W. Sterling.
EIN: 226912465

8257
The Walter L. Schautz Foundation
150 E. Grove St.
Scranton, PA 18510-1200 (570) 344-1174
Contact: Walter L. Schautz, Pres. and Treas.

Established in 1948 in Pennsylvania.
Donors: Walter L. Schautz; Madalene L. Schautz; Grove Silk Co.
Foundation type: Independent foundation.
Financial data (yr. ended 01/31/14): Assets, $6,532,496 (M); expenditures, $331,136; qualifying distributions, $303,068; giving activities include $299,950 for 89 grants (high: $35,000; low: $100), and $3,118 for foundation-administered programs.
Purpose and activities: Grants for welfare programs, youth agencies, church support, higher education, health associations, animal welfare, and community funds. The foundation also operates a sports stadium.
Fields of interest: Arts and culture; Higher education; Graduate and professional education; Animal welfare; Nonprofits; Diseases and conditions; Public libraries; Christianity; Theology; Human services; Child welfare; Senior services.
Type of support: Regranting; Research; Research and evaluation.
Limitations: Applications accepted. Giving primarily in PA, with some emphasis on Jim Thorpe and Scranton. No grants to individuals.
Application information:
   Deadline(s): None
Officers: Walter Schautz, Pres. and Treas.; Nancy Miles, Secy.

Directors: John Cherb; James Reid.
EIN: 246018362

8258
Joseph B. Scheller and Rita P. Scheller Foundation
1 S. Church St., Ste. 400
Hazleton, PA 18201-6200

Established in 1995 in Pennsylvania.
Donors: Joseph B. Scheller; Rita P. Scheller; Schellers Mugget Fund.
Foundation type: Independent foundation.
Financial data (yr. ended 12/31/12): Assets, $2,708,041 (M); gifts received, $384,506; expenditures, $344,345; qualifying distributions, $311,000; giving activities include $311,000 for grants.
Fields of interest: Education; Higher education.
Limitations: Applications not accepted. Giving primarily in Cambridge, MA, and PA. No grants to individuals.
Application information: Contributes only to pre-selected organizations.
Officer: Joseph B. Scheller, Chair.
Trustees: Nancy Scheller Hays; Michael H. Scheller; Rita P. Scheller; Sarah E. Scheller.
EIN: 237824343

8259
Schlarbaum Family Foundation
c/o Gary G. Schlarbaum
231 Trianon Ln.
Villanova, PA 19085-1444

Established in 1999 in Pennsylvania.
Donor: Gary G. Schlarbaum.
Foundation type: Independent foundation.
Financial data (yr. ended 12/31/13): Assets, $2,892,140 (M); expenditures, $196,530; qualifying distributions, $196,400; giving activities include $196,400 for 20 grants (high: $65,000; low: $500).
Fields of interest: Arts and culture; Undergraduate education; Religion.
Type of support: Annual campaigns; Capital campaigns; Endowments.
Limitations: Applications not accepted. Giving primarily in PA; some giving also in AL. No grants to individuals.
Application information: Contributes only to pre-selected organizations.
Officers: Gary G. Schlarbaum, Pres.; Ruth Anne Schlarbaum, Secy.
Directors: Melinda Bradley; Mark R. Schlarbaum.
EIN: 232996673

8260
J. & L. Schoonmaker Trust
c/o BNY Mellon, N.A.
P.O. Box 185
Pittsburgh, PA 15230-0185

Foundation type: Independent foundation.
Financial data (yr. ended 09/30/14): Assets, $8,005,915 (M); expenditures, $429,735; qualifying distributions, $401,511; giving activities include $391,000 for 25 grants (high: $50,000; low: $7,500).

Purpose and activities: Giving limited to those organizations that are of special interest to the donors.

Fields of interest: Arts and culture; Orchestral music; Museums; Education; Higher education; Alumni relations; Foundations; Nonprofits; Hospital care; Christianity; Scouting programs.

Type of support: Regranting.

Limitations: Applications not accepted. Giving primarily in Pittsburgh, PA.

Application information: Unsolicited requests for funds not accepted.

Board meeting date(s): Feb., and Aug.

Trustee: BNY Mellon, N.A.

EIN: 256016020

8261
C. W. Schrenk and Marjorie J. Schrenk Family Foundation

130 Buck Rd., Ste. 201
Holland, PA 18966-1743   (215) 357-6195
Contact: Robert Pritz, Treas.

Foundation type: Operating foundation.

Financial data (yr. ended 12/31/13): Assets, $3,009,010 (M); gifts received, $1,050; expenditures, $169,507; qualifying distributions, $151,041; giving activities include $151,041 for 32 grants (high: $30,000; low: $457).

Purpose and activities: Giving primarily to organizations that provide education, food, and housing for underprivileged families with young children.

Fields of interest: Education; Religion; Human services.

Type of support: General support.

Limitations: Applications accepted. Giving limited to DE, NJ, and PA. No grants to individuals.

Application information:

Initial approach: Letter

Deadline(s): None

Officers: Marjorie J. Schrenk, Chair.; Bonnie Beth Stellwagon, Recording Secy.; Robert F. Pritz, Treas.

Trustees: Beverly Claire Gormley; Susan Marquiss; Barbara Jean Traub.

EIN: 236906460

8262
Robert E. Schultz Trust

c/o PNC Bank, N.A.
620 Liberty Ave., 10th Fl.
Pittsburgh, PA 15222-2705

Foundation type: Independent foundation.

Financial data (yr. ended 12/31/13): Assets, $3,708,648 (M); expenditures, $170,352; qualifying distributions, $146,702; giving activities include $145,669 for 6 grants (high: $36,745; low: $488).

Fields of interest: Education; Religion; Human services.

Limitations: Applications not accepted. Giving primarily in PA.

Application information: Unsolicited requests for funds not accepted.

Trustee: PNC Bank, N.A.

EIN: 246021696

8263
Schuylkill Area Community Foundation

(formerly Ashland Trusts)
216 S. Centre St.
Pottsville, PA 17901-3501   (570) 624-7223
Contact: Eileen Kuperavage, Exec. Dir.
FAX: (570) 624-7256;
E-mail: ekuperavage@verizon.net; Main URL: http://www.sacfoundation.com

Established in 1967 in Pennsylvania.

Foundation type: Community foundation.

Financial data (yr. ended 12/31/12): Assets, $13,292,779 (M); gifts received, $944,756; expenditures, $573,421; giving activities include $130,032 for 132+ grants (high: $26,918), and $221,628 for 104 grants to individuals.

Purpose and activities: The foundation's grant program provides a means for Schuylkill County nonprofit charitable organizations to apply for financial assistance to fund projects and programs that will enhance the quality of life of Schuylkill County, PA and its surrounding area. Scholarships are available for various schools throughout Schuylkill County, PA.

Fields of interest: Arts and culture; Education; Environment; Animal welfare; Voluntarism; Health; Libraries; Public administration; Community and economic development; Sports and recreation; Human services; Child welfare.

Type of support: General support; Capacity-building and technical assistance; Equipment; Endowments; Emergency funds; Program development; Publications; Curriculum development; Scholarships; Technical assistance; Student aid.

Limitations: Applications accepted. Giving primarily in the Schuylkill County, PA and surrounding area. No grants to individuals (except for scholarships), or for capital campaigns, operating expenses, salaries, or debt reduction.

Application information: Visit foundation web site for application and additional guidelines. Application form required.

Initial approach: Complete online application

Deadline(s): Mar. 15

Officer and Board Members: Eileen Kuperavage, Exec. Dir.; Marie Beauchamp; Richard L. Berger; James C. Bohorad, Esq.; Carl D. Edling; Dabbie Yuengling Ferhat; Gary R. Glessner; Charles Hiezenroth III; M. Irvil Kear, D.A.; G. Fred Schilling; Ann F. Snyder; Mark Snyder; Frank J. Staudenmeier; Keith J. Strouse; Louis David Truskowsky; J. Robert Zane; Joann Zogby, Ed. D.

Number of staff: 1 full-time professional; 1 full-time support.

EIN: 236422789

8264
Schwab-Silfen Foundation

(formerly Schwab Rainess Foundation)
P.O. Box 5796
Harrisburg, PA 17110-0967   (717) 233-8083
Contact: Israel Schwab, Pres.

Established in 1965 in Pennsylvania.

Donors: Morris Schwab; D & H Distributing Co.; Israel Schwab; Andrew E. Schwab; Dorothy B. Schwab; D & H Cares; JARB.

Foundation type: Independent foundation.

Financial data (yr. ended 12/31/13): Assets, $6,428,802 (M); gifts received, $324,963; expenditures, $419,522; qualifying distributions,

$397,077; giving activities include $389,391 for 70 grants (high: $132,818; low: $100).

Purpose and activities: Giving primarily to Jewish agencies and temples.

Fields of interest: Museums; University education; Sororities and fraternities; Nonprofits; Diseases and conditions; Judaism; Human services.

Type of support: Regranting.

Limitations: Applications accepted. Giving primarily in Baltimore, MD, New York, NY and Harrisburg, PA.

Application information: Application form required.

Initial approach: Letter

Deadline(s): None

Officers: Israel Schwab, Pres.; Andrew Schwab, Secy.-Treas.

Trustees: Daniel Schwab; Michael Schwab; Amy Silfen.

EIN: 236401901

8265
The Jane & Martin Schwartz Family Foundation

c/o Bruce A. Rosenfield
1600 Market St., Ste. 3600
Philadelphia, PA 19103-7212
Application address: c/o Martin Schwartz, 60 Orchard Farm Rd., Port Washington, NY 11050, tel.: (516) 883-4581

Established in 1988 in Pennsylvania.

Donors: Martin Schwartz; Jane Schwartz†.

Foundation type: Independent foundation.

Financial data (yr. ended 12/31/13): Assets, $77,535 (M); gifts received, $149,026; expenditures, $183,232; qualifying distributions, $176,914; giving activities include $172,325 for 125 grants (high: $20,000; low: $25).

Fields of interest: Museums; History museums; Foundations; Nonprofits; Hospital care; Judaism; Interfaith; Human services; Family services.

Type of support: Regranting.

Limitations: Applications accepted. Giving primarily in NY. No grants to individuals.

Application information:

Initial approach: Proposal

Deadline(s): None

Trustees: Julie Schwartz Gabay; Betsy A. Schwartz; Jane Schwartz; Martin Schwartz; Matthew S. Schwartz; Suzanne A. Schwartz.

EIN: 236913820

8266
The Joseph C. Scott Foundation

1515 The Fairway, 182 Woodside
Jenkintown, PA 19046

Donor: Patrica S. Scott.

Foundation type: Independent foundation.

Financial data (yr. ended 12/31/13): Assets, $3,022,730 (M); expenditures, $191,609; qualifying distributions, $154,600; giving activities include $154,600 for 20 grants (high: $75,000; low: $500).

Fields of interest: Arts and culture; Education; Higher education; Hospital care; Sports and recreation; Youth development.

Limitations: Applications not accepted. Giving primarily in PA.

Application information: Unsolicited requests for funds not accepted.

Trustee: Patricia S. Scott.
EIN: 263892199

8267
Secrist Family Charitable Foundation
c/o PNC Bank, N.A.
1600 Market St., Tax Dept.
Philadelphia, PA   19103-7240

Donor: Gail K. Secrist†.
Foundation type: Independent foundation.
Financial data (yr. ended 12/31/13): Assets, $4,457,362 (M); expenditures, $237,178; qualifying distributions, $198,749; giving activities include $187,967 for 9 grants (high: $52,518; low: $4,173).
Fields of interest: Education; Philanthropy; Diseases and conditions.
Limitations: Applications not accepted.
Application information: Unsolicited requests for funds not accepted.
Trustee: PNC Bank, N.A.
EIN: 800540881

8268
Frances Seebe Trust
c/o Wells Fargo Bank, N.A.
101N Independence Mall E., MACY1372-062
Philadelphia, PA   19106-2112

Established in 1983 in California.
Foundation type: Independent foundation.
Financial data (yr. ended 01/31/15): Assets, $4,154,381; expenditures, $294,384; qualifying distributions, $255,131.
Purpose and activities: Giving primarily for wildlife research and animal protection; support also for medical research.
Fields of interest: Education; Wildlife biodiversity; Domesticated animals; Animal welfare; Arthritis.
Type of support: Research.
Limitations: Applications not accepted. Giving primarily in Los Angeles, CA, Washington, DC, GA, and NM. No grants to individuals.
Application information: Contributes only to pre-selected organizations.
Trustee: Wells Fargo Bank, N.A.
EIN: 956795278

8269
Adam and Maria Sarah Seybert Institution for Poor Boys and Girls
(also known as Seybert Institution)
P.O. Box 1286
Doylestown, PA   18901-0100   (215) 696-9336
Contact: Diana Loukedis Doherty, Mgr.
E-mail: admin@seybertfoundation.org; Main URL: http://seybertfoundation.org/index.html
Grants List: http://seybertfoundation.org/grantees.html

Established in 1914 in Pennsylvania.
Donor: Henry Seybert†.
Foundation type: Independent foundation.
Financial data (yr. ended 12/31/13): Assets, $6,908,633 (M); expenditures, $416,835; qualifying distributions, $384,325; giving activities include $330,000 for 73 grants (high: $5,000; low: $1,000).

Purpose and activities: Support for projects and services for disadvantaged children in Philadelphia, Pennsylvania, primarily through community-based organizations.
Fields of interest: Education; Early childhood education; Elementary education; Child educational development; Human services; Family services; Child welfare; Child development; Ethnic and racial groups; Low-income and poor people.
Type of support: Program development; Matching grants; Seed money.
Limitations: Giving limited to Philadelphia, PA. No grants to individuals, or for building or endowment funds; low priority given to capital expenditures.
Publications: Annual report (including application guidelines).
Application information: Applicants limited to 1 request per calendar year; accepts Delaware Valley Grantmakers Common Grant Application and Common Report Form. For regular programs submit 1 original and 10 copies of proposal, 3 copies of the most recent audited annual financial report and 1 copy of the tax-exempt determination letter. See web site for additional application policies and guidelines and for application forms for all programs. Application form required.
  Initial approach: Proposal (no more than 6 pages)
  Copies of proposal: 10
  Deadline(s): Mar. 15 and Sept. 15
  Board meeting date(s): Last Wed. in Jan., Apr., and Oct.
  Final notification: Feb. 15, May 15 and Nov. 15
Officers and Directors: Dwayne Wharton, Pres. and Director; Aishah Miller, V.P.; Julie Cousler-Emig, Ph.D, Secy.; Dario Bellot, Treas.; Obinna Abara, Esq.; Sara S. Moran; Deepa Vasudevan; Linda White.
Number of staff: None.
EIN: 236260105

8270
Shady Maple Foundation
1324 Main St.
P.O. Box 157
East Earl, PA   17519   (717) 354-4981
Contact: Betty Weaver
E-mail: bweaver@shady-maple.com

Established in 2004 in Pennsylvania.
Donors: Miriam M. Weaver; Marvin R. Weaver; Shady Maple Smorgasbord Inc.; Shady Maple Farm Market Inc.
Foundation type: Independent foundation.
Financial data (yr. ended 12/31/14): Assets, $5,329,055 (M); gifts received, $200,000; expenditures, $137,394; qualifying distributions, $130,000; giving activities include $130,000 for 26 grants (high: $5,000; low: $5,000).
Fields of interest: Christianity.
Limitations: Applications accepted. Giving primarily in PA. No grants to individuals.
Application information: Application form required.
  Initial approach: Letter
  Deadline(s): None
Officers: Marvin R. Weaver, Pres.; Philip E. Weaver, 1st V.P.; Miriam M. Weaver, 2nd V.P.; Curtis R. Weaver, Secy.; Linford L. Weaver, Treas.
EIN: 200903361

8271
The Shaner Family Foundation
1965 Waddle Rd.
State College, PA   16803

Established in 2008 in Pennsylvania.
Donors: Lance T. Shaner Chaitable Lead Annuity Trust; Lance T. Shaner.
Foundation type: Independent foundation.
Financial data (yr. ended 12/31/14): Assets, $1,750,356; gifts received, $0; expenditures, $203,538; qualifying distributions, $191,000.
Fields of interest: Education; Health; Catholicism.
Limitations: Applications not accepted. Giving primarily in PA.
Application information: Unsolicited requests for funds not accepted.
Trustees: Sarah Shaner Mayville; Ellen R. Shaner; Justin Shaner; Lance T. Shaner; Mathias Shaner.
EIN: 166568964

8272
Emma Sharp Ochiltree Foundation
c/o BNY Mellon, N.A
P.O. Box 185
Pittsburgh, PA   15230-0185

Established in 1997 in Pennsylvania.
Donor: Emma O. Sharp.
Foundation type: Independent foundation.
Financial data (yr. ended 12/31/14): Assets, $6,670,967 (M); gifts received, $369,342; expenditures, $402,141; qualifying distributions, $351,224; giving activities include $325,000 for 20 grants (high: $80,000; low: $3,000).
Purpose and activities: Giving primarily for medical research and animal welfare.
Fields of interest: Animal welfare; Arthritis; Alzheimer's disease; Diabetes; Cancers.
Limitations: Applications not accepted. Giving primarily in GA. No grants individuals.
Application information: Unsolicited requests for funds not accepted.
Trustees: John C. Harmon, Esq.; BNY Mellon, N.A.
EIN: 237883781

8273
Ranjit Shastri Charity Trust
7540 Windsor Dr., Ste. 101
Allentown, PA   18195-1015

Established in 2002 in Pennsylvania.
Donors: Bhavna K. Shastri; Kalpendu R. Shastri.
Foundation type: Independent foundation.
Financial data (yr. ended 12/31/13): Assets, $21,933,488 (M); expenditures, $457,556; qualifying distributions, $406,806; giving activities include $406,806 for 2 grants (high: $400,000; low: $6,806).
Fields of interest: Human services.
International interests: India.
Type of support: General support.
Limitations: Applications not accepted. Giving primarily in NJ. No grants to individuals.
Application information: Unsolicited requests for funds not accepted.
Trustees: Shreyasi H. Dalal; Amit D. Shah; Bhavna K. Shastri; Kalpendu R. Shastri; Mrugank H. Shastri.
EIN: 256798195

8274
Willis and Elsie Shenk Foundation
(formerly The Weld Foundation)
P.O. Box 128
Lancaster, PA 17608-0128

Donors: Willis W. Shenk; Elsie S. Shenk†.
Foundation type: Independent foundation.
Financial data (yr. ended 12/31/13): Assets, $7,023,259 (M); expenditures, $300,263; qualifying distributions, $252,000; giving activities include $252,000 for 49 grants (high: $25,000; low: $1,500).
Fields of interest: Performing arts education; Art museums; Education; Higher education; Hospice care; Public libraries; Human services; Child welfare.
Limitations: Applications not accepted. Giving primarily in Lancaster County, PA. No grants to individuals.
Application information: Unsolicited requests for funds not accepted.
Officers: Willis W. Shenk, Pres.; J. David Shenk, V.P.; Wesley S. Lewis, Secy.; Michael J. Piascinski, Treas.
EIN: 232680871

8275
The Thomas H. and Mary Williams Shoemaker Fund
c/o Greene Street Friends School
5511 Greene St.
Philadelphia, PA 19144-2805 (215) 545-7099
Contact: Anne L. Edmunds, Admin. Asst.
E-mail: aedmunds@shoemakerfund.org; Main URL: http://www.shoemakerfund.org

Established in 1953 in Pennsylvania.
Donors: Mary Williams Shoemaker†; Thomas H. Shoemaker†; Thomas H. and Mary Williams Shoemaker Trust.
Foundation type: Independent foundation.
Financial data (yr. ended 09/30/14): Assets, $8,536,696 (M); expenditures, $407,885; qualifying distributions, $345,331; giving activities include $328,235 for 10 grants (high: $101,000; low: $1,000).
Purpose and activities: Giving to organizations that are investing specifically in the growth and development of the Society of Friends.
Type of support: General support; Continuing support; Capital campaigns; Capital and infrastructure; Endowments; Program development; Publications; Seed money; Curriculum development; Scholarships.
Limitations: Applications accepted. Giving primarily in PA. No grants to individuals, or for matching gifts; no loans.
Publications: Application guidelines; Informational brochure (including application guidelines).
Application information: After reviewing the concept at the inquiry stage, the fund will decide whether to request full proposals from an organization. Application form required.
Initial approach: Online letter of inquiry
Board meeting date(s): May and Nov.
Officers and Trustees: Edward W. Marshall III, Chair. and Trustee; Martha B. Bryans, Secy. and Trustee; Samuel D. Caldwell; Mary Ellen McNish; Parker Snowe; Advisory Trust Co. of Delaware.
Number of staff: 1 full-time support.
EIN: 236209783

8276
The Shore Fund
c/o BNY Mellon, N.A.
P.O. Box 185
Pittsburgh, PA 15230-0185

Established in 1982 in Pennsylvania.
Donors: Benjamin R. Fisher; Fisher Charitable Trusts I and II.
Foundation type: Independent foundation.
Financial data (yr. ended 12/31/14): Assets, $4,666,465; expenditures, $205,778; qualifying distributions, $176,852.
Fields of interest: Arts and culture; Education; Environment.
Type of support: General support; Annual campaigns; Capital campaigns; Program development.
Limitations: Applications not accepted. Giving primarily in NY. No grants to individuals.
Application information: Unsolicited requests for funds not accepted.
Trustee: BNY Mellon, N.A.
EIN: 256220659

8277
The Robbins Shuman Scholarship Fund Trust
P.O. Box 3215
Lancaster, PA 17604-3216
Application address: FNB Bank, c/o Fulton Financial Advisors, 344 Mill St., Danville, PA 17821, tel.: (717) 291-2523

Established in 2005 in Pennsylvania.
Foundation type: Independent foundation.
Financial data (yr. ended 04/30/15): Assets, $3,160,815 (M); expenditures, $187,597; qualifying distributions, $148,923; giving activities include $147,488 for grants, and $147,488 for 44 grants to individuals (high: $4,000; low: $1,000).
Purpose and activities: Giving only to full time students who are residents of Columbia County, Pennsylvania, and who have a 3.0 GPA.
Fields of interest: Education.
Type of support: Student aid.
Limitations: Applications accepted. Giving primarily to residents of PA.
Application information: Application form required.
Deadline(s): None
Trustee: Fulton Bank, N.A.
EIN: 256857939

8278
The Sidewater Family Foundation Inc.
(formerly The Morris & Evelyn Sidewater Foundation, Inc.)
308 E. Lancaster Ave., Ste. 235
Wynnewood, PA 19096

Established in 1989 in Pennsylvania.
Donor: Morris Sidewater.
Foundation type: Independent foundation.
Financial data (yr. ended 12/31/13): Assets, $5,113,932 (M); expenditures, $272,266; qualifying distributions, $243,164; giving activities include $240,050 for 45 grants (high: $40,000; low: $200).
Fields of interest: Arts and culture; Education; Nonprofits; Diseases and conditions; Alzheimer's disease; Judaism; Human services; International relations.
Type of support: Research; Regranting.
Limitations: Applications not accepted. Giving primarily in PA. No grants to individuals.
Application information: Unsolicited requests for funds not accepted.
Officers: Steven Sidewater, Pres. and Secy.; Samuel Sidewater, V.P. and Treas.
EIN: 232573603

8279
Singer Family C & E Foundation
(formerly C & E Foundation)
c/o Judith A. Harris
1611 Pond Rd.
Allentown, PA 18104-2258

Established in 1997 in Pennsylvania.
Foundation type: Independent foundation.
Financial data (yr. ended 12/31/13): Assets, $5,734,531 (M); expenditures, $219,902; qualifying distributions, $196,040; giving activities include $165,040 for 40 grants to individuals (high: $7,540; low: $2,500).
Purpose and activities: Giving primarily for scholarships for higher education.
Fields of interest: Higher education.
Type of support: General support; Student aid.
Limitations: Applications not accepted. Giving primarily to residents of NJ and PA.
Application information: Unsolicited requests for funds not accepted.
Officers and Trustees: Clint Denyse, Chair. and Trustee; Gavin J. Denyse, Treas. and Trustee; Bernetta Avery-Denyse, Scholarship Coordinator and Trustee; Marilyn Bronzi; Judith A. Harris; James R. Singer; Joanne Singer.
EIN: 232929096

8280
Arlene H. Smith Charitable Foundation
100 State St., Ste. 700
Erie, PA 16507-1459

Established in 1982 in Pennsylvania.
Donor: Arlene H. Smith†.
Foundation type: Independent foundation.
Financial data (yr. ended 12/31/14): Assets, $5,922,712; expenditures, $330,097; qualifying distributions, $295,207.
Fields of interest: Education; Higher education; Foundations; Hospital care; Cancers; Public libraries; Sports; Human services; Child welfare.
Type of support: General support; Employee matching gifts; Matching grants; Continuing support; Annual campaigns; Capital campaigns; Capital and infrastructure; Equipment; Debt reduction; Emergency funds; Program development; Curriculum development; Scholarships.
Limitations: Applications accepted. Giving limited to the Corry, PA, area. No grants to individuals.
Publications: Application guidelines; Grants list.
Application information: Application form required.
Initial approach: Completed application form
Deadline(s): None
Board meeting date(s): June and Dec.
Officers and Directors: James W. Anundson, Pres. and Director; Mamie S. Sprandel, V.P. and Director; Russell S. Warner, Secy. and Director; James D. Cullen, Treas. and Director.

Number of staff: None.
EIN: 251515142

8281
Frank J. Smith Foundation
c/o PNC Bank, N.A.
P.O. Box 609
Pittsburgh, PA   15230-9738

Established in 1994 in Indiana.
Donors: Frank J. Smith; Geraldine Schmidt Trust.
Foundation type: Independent foundation.
Financial data (yr. ended 01/31/13): Assets,
$3,723,229 (M); expenditures, $210,914;
qualifying distributions, $189,939; giving activities
include $170,861 for 25 grants (high: $29,283;
low: $976).
Fields of interest: Elementary and secondary
education; Protestantism; Catholicism; Human
services.
Limitations: Applications not accepted. Giving
primarily in Fort Wayne, IN. No grants to individuals.
Application information: Contributes only to
pre-selected organizations.
Trustee: PNC Bank, N.A.
EIN: 356598564

8282
Marguerite Carl Smith Foundation
c/o Woodlands Bank
2450 E. 3rd St.
Williamsport, PA   17701-4006

Established in 1989 in Pennsylvania.
Donor: Marguerite Carl Smith.
Foundation type: Independent foundation.
Financial data (yr. ended 05/31/13): Assets,
$2,652,610 (M); expenditures, $158,315;
qualifying distributions, $139,000; giving activities
include $24,000 for 5 grants (high: $13,000; low:
$1,000), and $115,000 for grants to individuals.
Fields of interest: Education; Human services.
Type of support: General support; Student aid.
Limitations: Applications not accepted. Giving
primarily in PA.
Application information: Unsolicited requests for
funds not accepted.
Trustees: Randy Laird; Sebastian Salvaton; Lee
Smith; Lynne Smith; Sharon Sutkins.
EIN: 232564406

8283
Stephen S. and Dolores R. Smith Foundation
1246 Forrest Hill Dr.
Lower Gwynedd, PA   19002-2058

Established in 1999 in Pennsylvania.
Donor: Stephen S. Smith.
Foundation type: Independent foundation.
Financial data (yr. ended 12/31/13): Assets,
$1,001,296 (M); gifts received, $340,052;
expenditures, $186,345; qualifying distributions,
$186,173; giving activities include $186,173 for 30
grants (high: $50,000; low: $50).
Purpose and activities: Giving primarily for higher
education, human services, Christian churches, and
to a children's hospital.

Fields of interest: Education; Higher education;
Specialty hospital care; Christianity; Human
services.
Limitations: Applications not accepted. Giving
primarily in PA. No grants to individuals.
Application information: Unsolicited requests for
funds not accepted.
Officers: Stephen S. Smith, Pres.; Dolores R. Smith,
Secy.-Treas.
EIN: 233019893

8284
Shirley A. Smith Revocable Trust
c/o BNY Mellon, N.A.
P.O. Box 185
Pittsburgh, PA   15230-0185

Foundation type: Independent foundation.
Financial data (yr. ended 12/31/14): Assets,
$3,254,614 (M); expenditures, $203,926;
qualifying distributions, $175,199; giving activities
include $164,370 for 8 grants (high: $20,547; low:
$20,546).
Fields of interest: Philanthropy; Diseases and
conditions; Human services.
Limitations: Applications not accepted.
Application information: Unsolicited requests for
funds not accepted.
Trustee: BNY Mellon, N.A.
EIN: 256291905

8285
The Jack J. Smith, Jr. Charitable Trust
c/o PNC Bank, N.A.
620 Liberty Ave., 10th Fl.
Pittsburgh, PA   15222-2729
Application address: P.O. Box 1198, Cincinnati, OH
45201; tel.: (513) 651-8463

Established in 1972 in Ohio.
Donor: Jack J. Smith, Jr.†
Foundation type: Independent foundation.
Financial data (yr. ended 09/30/13): Assets,
$9,328,175 (M); expenditures, $410,751;
qualifying distributions, $341,055; giving activities
include $334,000 for 29 grants (high: $20,000;
low: $3,000).
Purpose and activities: Giving primarily for health
and social services that benefit needy or
handicapped children in greater Cincinnati, OH.
Fields of interest: Child welfare.
Type of support: Capital campaigns; Capital and
infrastructure; Equipment; Program development;
Seed money.
Limitations: Applications accepted. Giving limited to
organizations serving the greater Cincinnati, OH,
area, including those in Hamilton, Butler, Clermont
and Warren counties in OH, and Boone, Campbell
and Kenton counties in KY. No grants to individuals,
or for operating budgets, continuing support, annual
campaigns, emergency funds, deficit financing,
endowment funds, scholarships, research, or
conferences; no loans.
Publications: Application guidelines.
Application information: Application form required.
Initial approach: Greater Cincinnati Common
   Grant Application Form required
Copies of proposal: 3
Deadline(s): Feb. 1, Aug. 1
Board meeting date(s): Mar. and Sept.
Final notification: 1 month after meetings

Trustees: Karen Wachs; PNC Bank, N.A.
Number of staff: None.
EIN: 310912146

8286
Dorothy Melcher Sneath Trust
c/o BNY Mellon, N.A.
P.O. Box 185
Pittsburgh, PA   15230-0185

Foundation type: Independent foundation.
Financial data (yr. ended 08/31/13): Assets,
$5,181,957 (M); expenditures, $287,228;
qualifying distributions, $257,274; giving activities
include $240,000 for 9 grants (high: $55,000; low:
$15,000).
Purpose and activities: Giving primarily to provide
scholarship funds to independent private
preparatory schools in New England with preference
to the following schools in MA: Winsor School,
Beaver County Day School, Milton Academy, Noble
and Greenough School, Middlesex School, and
Brooks School.
Fields of interest: Education; Secondary education.
Type of support: Scholarships.
Limitations: Applications not accepted. Giving
limited to MA. No grants to individuals directly.
Application information: Contributes primarily to
pre-selected private preparatory schools in New
England.
Trustees: Ronald Garmey, Esq.; BNY Mellon, N.A.
EIN: 046093840

8287
Snyder Charitable Foundation
c/o Charles H. Snyder, Jr.
P.O. Box 1022
Kittanning, PA   16201-5022

Established in 1987 in Pennsylvania.
Donors: Allegheny Mineral Corp.; Armstrong Cement
& Supply Corp.; Snyder Brothers, Inc.
Foundation type: Independent foundation.
Financial data (yr. ended 12/31/14): Assets,
$786,542 (M); gifts received, $75,000;
expenditures, $163,120; qualifying distributions,
$162,982; giving activities include $162,982 for 73
grants (high: $25,000; low: $75).
Fields of interest: Arts and culture; Education;
Nonprofits; Cancers; Protestantism; Human
services.
Type of support: Regranting.
Limitations: Applications not accepted. Giving
primarily in PA. No grants to individuals.
Application information: Unsolicited requests for
funds not accepted.
Trustees: Charles H. Snyder, Jr.; David E. Snyder.
EIN: 251551808

8288
Bruce R. Snyder & Madelyn G. Snyder Foundation
3090 Cape Horn Rd.
Red Lion, PA   17356-9068   (717) 244-1099
Contact: B. Robert Snyder, Pres.

Established in 1992 in Pennsylvania.
Donors: B. Robert Snyder; William Snyder; Carolyn
Kline; Joann Seindenstricker.
Foundation type: Independent foundation.

Financial data (yr. ended 09/30/13): Assets, $7,050,713 (M); gifts received, $179,222; expenditures, $374,177; qualifying distributions, $370,000; giving activities include $370,000 for 46 grants (high: $20,000; low: $2,000).
Fields of interest: Health; Diseases and conditions; Protestantism.
Type of support: Research.
Limitations: Applications accepted. Giving primarily in PA. No grants to individuals.
Application information: Application form required.
Initial approach: Proposal
Deadline(s): None
Officers: Joann Seidenstricker, Pres.; Carolyn Kline, V.P.; B. Robert Snyder, V.P.; William Snyder, V.P.; Holly Seace, Secy.; Daria Holtzapple, Treas.
EIN: 232706874

8289
Society for Analytical Chemists of Pittsburgh
300 Penn Ctr. Blvd., Ste. 332
Pittsburgh, PA 15235-5503 (412) 825-3220; 204
Contact: Valerie Daugherty, Admin. Asst.
FAX: (412) 825-3224; E-mail: sacpinfo@pittcon.org; E-mail for Valerie Daughtery: daugherty@pittcon.org; Main URL: http://www.sacp.org
Facebook: https://www.facebook.com/SocietyForAnalyticalChemistsOfPittsburgh
LinkedIn: http://www.linkedin.com/groups/Society-Analytical-Chemists-Pittsburgh-4823656?gid=4823656&trk=hb_side_g

Donors: James L. Waters Fund; PGH Conf. on Analytical Chemistry and Applied Spectroscopy.
Foundation type: Independent foundation.
Financial data (yr. ended 06/30/13): Assets, $175,753 (M); gifts received, $512,283; expenditures, $519,746; qualifying distributions, $507,998; giving activities include $402,254 for 152 grants (high: $59,489; low: $50).
Purpose and activities: Giving primarily for education and research projects in the field of analytical chemistry and applied spectroscopy.
Fields of interest: Education; Physical and earth sciences.
Type of support: General support; Conferences and exhibits; Internships; Scholarships; Research; Student aid.
Limitations: Giving primarily in the Pittsburgh, PA, area.
Publications: Informational brochure.
Application information: See foundation web site for application policies, guidelines, and form. Application form required.
Deadline(s): Varies
Officers: Susan Zawacky, Chair.; Amit Ghosh, Secy.; Michelle Ward, Treas.
EIN: 256072976

8290
Somerset Amish Helping Hands Inc.
7012 Mount Davis Rd.
Meyersdale, PA 15552-6505

Foundation type: Operating foundation.
Financial data (yr. ended 06/30/14): Assets, $2,857,907 (M); expenditures, $199,505; qualifying distributions, $156,200; giving activities include $156,200 for grants to individuals.

Purpose and activities: Giving to advance the religious beliefs, cultural traditions, and lifestyle of the Old Order Amish by providing loans and other financial assistance for land purchases and other farm-related purposes to young Amish persons interested in establishing themselves in the Old Order Amish community.
Type of support: Loans to individuals.
Limitations: Applications not accepted.
Application information: Unsolicited requests for funds not accepetd.
Officers: Henry Yoder, Pres.; Alvin S. Yoder, V.P.; Joseph E. Brenneman, Secy.; Menno J. Yoder, Treas.; Samuel A. Brenneman, Admin.
Director: Simon C. Yoder.
EIN: 204224257

8291
Graham and Thelma Somerville Charitable Trust
c/o PNC Bank, N.A.
P.O. Box 609
Pittsburgh, PA 15230-9738

Established in 1993 in Indiana.
Foundation type: Independent foundation.
Financial data (yr. ended 10/31/13): Assets, $3,459,530 (M); expenditures, $232,323; qualifying distributions, $213,163; giving activities include $198,165 for 11 grants (high: $35,670; low: $2,972).
Fields of interest: Diseases and conditions; Arthritis; Alzheimer's disease; Respiratory system diseases; Cancers; Catholicism; Human services; Child welfare.
Limitations: Applications not accepted. Giving limited to IN.
Application information: Contributes only to pre-selected organizations; unsolicited requests for funds not considered or acknowledged.
Trustee: PNC Bank, N.A.
EIN: 356547211

8292
Ann & Murray Spain Foundation
1308 Meeting House Rd.
P.O. Box 290
Gwynedd, PA 19436-0290

Established in 2000 in Pennsylvania.
Donor: Murray Spain.
Foundation type: Independent foundation.
Financial data (yr. ended 12/31/13): Assets, $3,249,923 (M); expenditures, $150,153; qualifying distributions, $150,000; giving activities include $150,000 for 8 grants (high: $52,000; low: $2,000).
Fields of interest: Education; Philanthropy; Judaism.
Limitations: Applications not accepted. Giving primarily in PA. No grants to individuals.
Application information: Unsolicited requests for funds not accepted.
Trustee: Murray Spain.
EIN: 256728781

8293
Mary C. & Perry F. Spencer Foundation
P.O. Box 609
Pittsburgh, PA 15230-9738 (260) 461-6218
Application Address: PNC Bank, N.A., P.O. Box 110, Fort Wayne, IN 46801, tel.: (260) 461-6218

Donor: Mary Spencer†.
Foundation type: Independent foundation.
Financial data (yr. ended 12/31/14): Assets, $5,127,590; expenditures, $246,802; qualifying distributions, $224,179 and $0 for set-asides.
Fields of interest: Arts and culture; Education; Natural resources; Christianity; Human services; Family services; Child welfare.
Application information: Application form required.
Initial approach: Letter
Deadline(s): None
Trustee: PNC Bank, N.A.
Directors: Jon Brandenberger; Mitch Harper; Don A. Wolf.
EIN: 311016213

8294
Alexander C. & Tillie S. Speyer Foundation
1202 Benedum Trees Bldg.
Pittsburgh, PA 15222-1719

Established in 1962 in Pennsylvania.
Foundation type: Independent foundation.
Financial data (yr. ended 12/31/13): Assets, $7,517,037 (M); expenditures, $505,974; qualifying distributions, $354,911; giving activities include $354,911 for 106 grants (high: $36,000; low: $200).
Fields of interest: Arts and culture; Visual arts; Museums; Elementary and secondary education; Higher education; Nonprofits; Human services.
Type of support: Regranting.
Limitations: Applications not accepted. Giving primarily in Pittsburgh, PA.
Application information: Unsolicited requests for funds not accepted.
Trustees: Christopher Fromboluti; A.C. Speyer III; James M. Speyer.
EIN: 256051650

8295
Florence M. and Paul M. Staehle Foundation
c/o PNC Bank, N.A.
P.O. Box 609
Pittsburgh, PA 15230-9738 4127625188
Application address: c/o Margaret Sturm, PNC Bank, 110 West Berry St., Fort Wayne, IN 46802, tel.: (260) 461-6218

Established in 1980 in Indiana.
Foundation type: Independent foundation.
Financial data (yr. ended 12/31/14): Assets, $5,242,610; expenditures, $272,970; qualifying distributions, $235,868 and $0 for set-asides.
Fields of interest: Education; Diseases and conditions; Catholicism; Human services.
Type of support: General support; Annual campaigns; Equipment; Scholarships.
Limitations: Applications accepted. Giving primarily in Fort Wayne, IN. No grants to individuals.
Application information: Application form required.
Initial approach: Letter
Deadline(s): None

Trustee: PNC Bank, N.A.
EIN: 356255328

8296
Thomas F. Staley Foundation
c/o Diane S. Bernard
520 Frutchey Hill Rd.
Easton, PA 18040-7109

Established in 1943 in Michigan.
Donors: Thomas F. Staley†; Shirley H. Hunter†.
Foundation type: Independent foundation.
Financial data (yr. ended 12/31/13): Assets, $5,362,328 (M); expenditures, $508,166; qualifying distributions, $409,406; giving activities include $277,000 for 51 grants (high: $34,000; low: $500).
Fields of interest: Education; Christianity; Protestantism; Family services; Child welfare.
Type of support: Curriculum development.
Limitations: Applications not accepted. Giving primarily in PA. No grants to individuals.
Publications: Informational brochure; Program policy statement.
Application information: Contributes only to pre-selected organizations.
  Board meeting date(s): June
Officers: Stuart Staley, Chair.; Robert G. Howard, Treas.
Trustees: Diane Staley Bernard; Susan H. Canada; Janet Howard; Catherine Staley; Sarah H. Wichert.
Number of staff: 1 full-time professional.
EIN: 136071888

8297
The Star Foundation
1775 Arden Ln.
Bethlehem, PA 18015-5829

Established in 2001 in Unspecified.
Donors: John Stella; Aurelia Stella.
Foundation type: Independent foundation.
Financial data (yr. ended 12/31/14): Assets, $2,995,793 (M); gifts received, $25,000; expenditures, $171,394; qualifying distributions, $171,394; giving activities include $170,000 for 11 grants (high: $80,000; low: $3,000).
Fields of interest: Arts and culture; Environment; Human services.
Limitations: Applications not accepted. No grants to individuals.
Application information: Unsolicited request for funds not accepted.
Trustees: Jenifer Indresano; Elisabeth Moughty; Aurelia A. Stella; John A. Stella; John C. Stella; Krista Stella; Matthew Stella; Lisa M. Weissberg.
Number of staff: None.
EIN: 256761169

8298
The Fred Stein Family Foundation
(formerly The Fred & Sharon Stein Foundation, Inc.)
306 Brentford Rd.
Haverford, PA 19041-1719
Application address: c/o CAB, Attn: Mark Stein, 950 3rd Ave., 20th Fl., New York, NY 10022, tel.: (212) 371-4446

Established in 1985 in New York.
Donors: Fred Stein; Susan Haugh Stein.

Foundation type: Independent foundation.
Financial data (yr. ended 11/30/14): Assets, $1,071,403 (M); expenditures, $198,779; qualifying distributions, $175,000; giving activities include $175,000 for 12 grants (high: $35,000; low: $10,000).
Fields of interest: Arts and culture; Performing arts; Nonprofits.
Type of support: Regranting.
Limitations: Applications accepted. Giving primarily in Washington, DC, NY and PA. No grants to individuals.
Application information:
  Initial approach: Proposal
  Deadline(s): None
Officers and Directors: Mark Stein, Pres. and Director; Carol Baker, V.P. and Secy.-Treas.; James Kaufman, V.P.
EIN: 133389107

8299
Louis and Bessie Stein Foundation/Fund No. 2
100 Greys Ln., Ste. 302
Haverford, PA 19041-1753 (267) 239-0923
Contact: Audrey Merves, Tr.

Established in 2001 in Pennsylvania.
Donor: Louis and Bessie Stein Fund No. 1.
Foundation type: Independent foundation.
Financial data (yr. ended 06/30/14): Assets, $5,724,455 (M); expenditures, $393,114; qualifying distributions, $372,684; giving activities include $370,709 for 14 grants (high: $150,000; low: $9).
Fields of interest: Arts and culture; Elementary education; Higher education; Graduate and professional education; Health; Judaism; Theology.
Type of support: Continuing support; Employee matching gifts; Annual campaigns; Capital campaigns; Capital and infrastructure; Professorships; Scholarships; Research.
Limitations: Applications accepted. Giving primarily in New York, NY, and Philadelphia, PA. No grants to individuals.
Application information: Application form required.
  Initial approach: Letter
  Copies of proposal: 1
  Deadline(s): None
Trustee: Audrey Merves.
EIN: 251899982

8300
Stein/Bellet Foundation, Inc.
1820 Rittenhouse Sq., Ste. 902
Philadelphia, PA 19103-5824 (215) 732-7781
Contact: Sally Bellet, Pres.

Established in 2004 in Pennsylvania.
Donor: Edward Bellet.
Foundation type: Independent foundation.
Financial data (yr. ended 12/31/14): Assets, $8,352,782 (M); expenditures, $637,324; qualifying distributions, $434,400; giving activities include $434,400 for 17 grants (high: $145,000; low: $250).
Fields of interest: Art museums; Law education; Specialty hospital care; Diseases and conditions.
Type of support: General support.
Limitations: Giving primarily in PA; funding also in NY. No grants to individuals.

Application information:
  Initial approach: Letter
  Deadline(s): Dec. 31
Officers and Trustees: Sally Bellet, Pres. and Trustee; Laura Bellet, V.P. and Trustee; Alison Kessler, Co-Secy.-Treas.; Matthew Kessler, Co-Secy.-Treas. and Trustee.
EIN: 562491254

8301
The Stewart Foundation
P.O. Box 902
York, PA 17405-0902

Established in 1986 in Pennsylvania.
Donors: York Building Products Inc.; Stewart & March, Inc.; Apple Chevrolet; Stewart & Tate Inc.; Stewart Associates Land Development; TRM LLC.
Foundation type: Independent foundation.
Financial data (yr. ended 12/31/13): Assets, $1,267,122 (M); gifts received, $210,000; expenditures, $243,385; qualifying distributions, $242,250; giving activities include $242,250 for 37 grants (high: $100,000; low: $100).
Purpose and activities: Giving primarily for education, hospitals and health care, and children, youth and social services.
Fields of interest: Education; Health; Hospital care; Human services; Child welfare.
Limitations: Applications not accepted. Giving primarily in York, PA; funding also in Elkton, MD. No grants to individuals.
Application information: Contributes only to pre-selected organizations.
Officers: Gary A. Stewart, Pres.; Robert H. Stewart, Jr., V.P.; Gary A. Stewart, Jr., Secy.; Mark Harrold, Treas.
EIN: 222762903

8302
Alexander Stewart, M.D. Foundation
c/o BNY Mellon, N.A.
P.O. Box 185
Pittsburgh, PA 15230-0185

Established in 1981 in Pennsylvania.
Foundation type: Independent foundation.
Financial data (yr. ended 06/30/13): Assets, $8,077,494 (M); expenditures, $406,375; qualifying distributions, $374,873; giving activities include $374,873 for grants.
Fields of interest: Arts and culture; Historic preservation; Sports and recreation; Human services.
Type of support: General support; Volunteer development.
Limitations: Applications not accepted. Giving limited to Shippensburg, PA, and vicinity, including Cumberland, Franklin, Fulton, and Perry counties.
Application information: Contributes only to pre-selected organizations.
Trustee: BNY Mellon, N.A.
EIN: 236732616

8303
Joseph and Lorraine Stotland Charitable Trust
c/o Bryn Mawar Trust Co.
1 E. Chocolate Ave., Ste. 200
Hershey, PA 17033-1314

Foundation type: Independent foundation.
Financial data (yr. ended 12/31/13): Assets, $5,128,424 (M); expenditures, $273,212; qualifying distributions, $232,431; giving activities include $221,618 for 1 grant.
Fields of interest: Hospital care.
Limitations: Applications not accepted.
Application information: Unsolicited requests for funds not accepted.
Trustees: Emanuel Lauria, Jr.; Bryn Mawr Trust Co.
EIN: 026184974

8304
The Louis L. Stott Foundation
P.O. Box 23
Pocopson, PA   19366-0023

Established in 1968 in Pennsylvania.
Donor: Martha Stott Diener†.
Foundation type: Independent foundation.
Financial data (yr. ended 09/30/13): Assets, $2,906,333 (M); expenditures, $181,939; qualifying distributions, $181,939; giving activities include $170,000 for 10 grants (high: $85,000; low: $1,000).
Purpose and activities: Giving primarily for education; funding also for health and human services.
Fields of interest: Philanthropy; Health.
Type of support: General support; Continuing support; Annual campaigns; Capital and infrastructure; Equipment; Research.
Limitations: Applications not accepted. Giving primarily in CA, DE, and MD. No grants to individuals, or for endowment funds, scholarships, fellowships, conferences, or matching gifts; no loans.
Application information: Unsolicited requests for funds not accepted.
Trustees: Benjamin W. Stott; Edward B. Stott; Kristine Stott.
Number of staff: None.
EIN: 237009027

8305
Margaret Dorrance Strawbridge Foundation of Pennsylvania II, Inc.
2011 Renaissance Blvd., Ste. 102
King of Prussia, PA   19406-2782
Contact: Diana S. Wister, Pres. and Dir.

Established in 1985 in Pennsylvania.
Donors: Margaret Dorrance Strawbridge Foundation; Diana S. Wister.
Foundation type: Independent foundation.
Financial data (yr. ended 12/31/13): Assets, $14,539,830 (M); expenditures, $423,650; qualifying distributions, $330,725; giving activities include $328,100 for 25 grants (high: $40,000; low: $1,000).
Purpose and activities: Giving primarily for education and health, and to Christian organizations and ministries.
Fields of interest: Higher education; Environment; Health; Diseases and conditions; Christianity; Human services.
Type of support: General support; Continuing support; Annual campaigns; Research; Research and evaluation.
Limitations: Applications accepted. Giving primarily in FL, ME, New York, NY and PA. No grants to

individuals, or for capital or endowment funds, scholarships, or fellowships; no loans.
Application information:
Initial approach: Proposal
Deadline(s): None
Officers and Directors: Diana S. Wister, Pres. and Director; William R. Wister, Jr., V.P. and Director; Joseph W. Roskos, Secy.-Treas. and Director.
EIN: 232371943

8306
The Walter M. and Alice Washco Strine Foundation
630 Fairview Rd., Ste. 205
Swarthmore, PA   19081-2336

Donor: Walter M. Strine, Jr.
Foundation type: Independent foundation.
Financial data (yr. ended 11/30/13): Assets, $323,897 (M); expenditures, $160,965; qualifying distributions, $160,815; giving activities include $159,250 for 15 grants (high: $90,000; low: $250).
Fields of interest: Arts and culture; Opera; Education; Youth development.
Limitations: Applications not accepted. Giving primarily in PA.
Application information: Unsolicited requests for funds not accepted.
Officers and Directors: Walter M. Strine, Jr., Pres. and Treas. and Director; Alice Washco Strine, Secy. and Director.
EIN: 743198099

8307
The William B. and Judith Baeshore Strine Foundation
203 E. Baltimore Ave.
Media, PA   19063

Donor: William B. Strine.
Foundation type: Independent foundation.
Financial data (yr. ended 11/30/13): Assets, $742,876 (M); expenditures, $248,547; qualifying distributions, $239,100; giving activities include $239,100 for 8 grants (high: $105,000; low: $1,800).
Fields of interest: Education; Environment; Religion.
Limitations: Applications not accepted. Giving primarily in PA.
Application information: Unsolicited requests for funds not accepted.
Officers and Directors: William B. Strine, Pres. and Treas. and Director; Judith Baeshore Strine, Secy. and Director.
EIN: 743198105

8308
Beatrice Moore Stump Endowment Fund
34 S. State St.
Newtown, PA   18940-1953

Foundation type: Independent foundation.
Financial data (yr. ended 12/31/13): Assets, $6,999,785 (M); gifts received, $358,486; expenditures, $320,000; giving activities include $320,000 for 1 grant.
Fields of interest: Education.
Limitations: Applications not accepted.
Application information: Unsolicited requests for funds not accepted.

Trustee: Julie Newhouse.
EIN: 276464048

8309
Stutzman Family Foundation
c/o BNY Mellon, N.A.
P.O. Box 185
Pittsburgh, PA   15230-0185

Donor: Stutzman Charitable Lead Trust.
Foundation type: Independent foundation.
Financial data (yr. ended 12/31/13): Assets, $13,138,526 (M); gifts received, $2,331,807; expenditures, $475,493; qualifying distributions, $351,707; giving activities include $313,750 for 7 grants (high: $183,750; low: $9,000).
Fields of interest: Education; Higher education; Religion.
Limitations: Applications not accepted. Giving primarily in CA, CT and NY.
Application information: Unsolicited requests for funds not accepted.
Trustees: Andrew Krause; Walter Stutzman.
EIN: 347218543

8310
Susquehanna Foundation
401 City Line Ave., Ste. 220
Bala-Cynwyd, PA   19004-1117

Donors: Jeffrey Yass; Eric Brooks; Andrew Frost; Arthur Datnchik; Joel Greenberg.
Foundation type: Operating foundation.
Financial data (yr. ended 12/31/13): Assets, $194,285 (M); gifts received, $385,000; expenditures, $377,123; qualifying distributions, $377,000; giving activities include $377,000 for 31 grants (high: $52,500; low: $500).
Purpose and activities: Giving primarily for education, hospitals, and children's services.
Fields of interest: Education; Hospital care; Child welfare.
Type of support: Program-related investments.
Limitations: Applications not accepted. Giving on a national basis. No support for religious organizations. No grants to individuals.
Application information: Contributes only to pre-selected organizations.
Officers: Arthur Dantchik, Pres.; Joel Greenberg, V.P. and Secy.; Jeffrey Yass, V.P.; Brian Sullivan, Treas.
EIN: 232732477

8311
Anne Brossman Sweigart Charitable Foundation
c/o PNC Bank, N.A.
620 Liberty Ave., 10th Fl.
Pittsburgh, PA   15222-2705
Application address: Anne Brosman Sweigart Charitable Foundation, P.O. Box 757, Ephrata, PA 17522, tel.: (717) 581-9321

Established in 2005 in Pennsylvania.
Donor: A. Sweigart Trust.
Foundation type: Independent foundation.
Financial data (yr. ended 12/31/13): Assets, $9,690,420 (M); expenditures, $474,124; qualifying distributions, $391,871; giving activities

include $300,700 for 38 grants (high: $100,000; low: $1,500).

Fields of interest: Performing arts; Graduate and professional education; Protestantism; Theology; Community recreation.

Limitations: Applications accepted. Giving primarily in NJ and PA. No grants to individuals.

Application information: Application form required.

Initial approach: Letter
Deadline(s): Sept. 1 for Nov. distribution

Trustees: W. Craig Brossman; Fred N. Buch; Richard Cummings; Robert M. Lauman.

EIN: 202751003

8312
The Harriette Steelman and Charles L. Tabas Foundation

(formerly Charles L. Tabas Foundation)
737 Montgomery Ave.
Narberth, PA 19072-2011
Contact: Gerald Levinson, Exec. Dir.

Established in 1984 in Pennsylvania.

Donor: Charles L. Tabas Memorial Lead Trust.

Foundation type: Independent foundation.

Financial data (yr. ended 03/31/13): Assets, $4,692,594 (M); expenditures, $322,819; qualifying distributions, $205,267; giving activities include $205,267 for grants.

Fields of interest: Arts and culture; Education; Medical education; Environment; Animal welfare; Nonprofits; Health; Geriatrics; Diseases and conditions; Judaism; Human rights; Reproductive rights; Human services; Food banks; Youth development; People with vision impairments.

Type of support: General support; Research; Regranting.

Limitations: Applications not accepted. Giving primarily in Philadelphia, PA. No grants to individuals.

Application information: Contributes only to pre-selected organizations.

Officers: Harriette S. Tabas, Pres.; Nancy T. Fleming, V.P.; Andrew R. Tabas, V.P.; Richard S. Tabas, Secy.; Gerald Levinson, Exec. Dir.

EIN: 222630429

8313
The Tally Foundation

c/o E.R. Boynton
30 Valley Stream Pkwy.
Malvern, PA 19355

Donor: Ithan Foundation.

Foundation type: Independent foundation.

Financial data (yr. ended 12/31/14): Assets, $6,532,689 (M); gifts received, $317,428; expenditures, $390,489; qualifying distributions, $330,000; giving activities include $330,000 for 24 grants (high: $30,000; low: $5,000).

Fields of interest: Education; Environment; Diseases and conditions.

Limitations: Applications not accepted. Giving primarily in AZ, CA and PA.

Application information: Unsolicited requests for funds not accepted.

Officers and Directors: Elizabeth G. Atterbury, Pres. and Director; Amanda A. Ryan, Secy.-Treas. and Director; Edwin R. Boynton.

EIN: 275271301

8314
Teleflex Foundation

550 E. Swedesford Rd.
Limerick, PA 19468-1603
E-mail: foundation@teleflex.com; Main URL: http://www.teleflex.com/en/aboutUs/teleflexFoundation/index.html

Established in 1980 in Pennsylvania.

Donor: Teleflex Inc.

Foundation type: Company-sponsored foundation.

Financial data (yr. ended 12/31/13): Assets, $3,747,160 (M); expenditures, $234,254; qualifying distributions, $215,273; giving activities include $209,013 for 64 grants (high: $2,000; low: $50), and $6,260 for 24 employee matching gifts.

Purpose and activities: The foundation supports programs designed to promote arts and culture, education, and human services.

Fields of interest: Arts and culture; Performing arts; Education; Elementary education; Higher education; Reading promotion; Domesticated animals; Health; Housing development; Human services; Child welfare; Youth services; Adult and child mentoring.

Type of support: Program development; Employee matching gifts; Curriculum development; Scholarships.

Limitations: Applications not accepted.

Application information: Unsolicited requests for funds not accepted.

Directors: Chris Brady; Cathy Bucci; Matt Howald.

Number of staff: 1 part-time professional.

EIN: 232104782

8315
The Terryglass Foundation

P. O. Box 212
Media, PA 19063-0212
Contact: H. Edward Hanway

Donors: H. Edward Hanway; Ellen M. Hanway.

Foundation type: Independent foundation.

Financial data (yr. ended 12/31/13): Assets, $9,931,872 (M); gifts received, $2,839,378; expenditures, $279,462; qualifying distributions, $274,500; giving activities include $274,500 for 15 grants (high: $115,000; low: $1,000).

Fields of interest: Education; Diseases and conditions; Religion.

Limitations: Applications not accepted. Giving primarily in PA.

Application information: Unsolicited requests for funds not accepted.

Officer and Directors: H. Edward Hanway, Mgr. and Director; Edward B. Hanway; Elizabeth A. Hanway; Ellen M. Hanway; Patrick N. Hanway.

EIN: 386988295

8316
G. Frank Thomas Foundation Inc.

c/o PNC Bank
620 Liberty Ave., 10th Fl.
Pittsburgh, PA 15222-2722 3016636592
Application address: c/o Charles F. Trunk III, 506 Fairview Ave., Frederick, MD 21701, tel.: (301) 663-6592

Established in 1954 in Maryland.

Foundation type: Independent foundation.

Financial data (yr. ended 12/31/14): Assets, $3,806,828; expenditures, $212,578; qualifying distributions, $181,833 and $0 for set-asides.

Purpose and activities: Giving primarily for higher education, hospitals, and human services.

Fields of interest: History museums; Historic preservation; Higher education; Hospital care; Public libraries; Human services; Food aid.

Limitations: Applications accepted. Giving primarily in Frederick County and Westminster, MD. No grants to individuals.

Application information:

Initial approach: Letter
Deadline(s): Nov. 1
Final notification: Dec.

Officers and Directors: Pamela I. Martin, Pres. and Director; Charles F. Trunk III, Secy. and Director; Adrian L. Winpigler.

EIN: 526039803

8317
Clara E. Thompson Trust for Charities

c/o PNC Bank, N.A.
P.O. Box 609
Pittsburgh, PA 15230-9738 4127628133

Foundation type: Independent foundation.

Financial data (yr. ended 12/31/14): Assets, $4,742,918; expenditures, $256,308; qualifying distributions, $220,329 and $0 for set-asides.

Fields of interest: Health; Religion; Human services.

Type of support: General support.

Limitations: Applications not accepted. Giving primarily in PA.

Application information: Unsolicited requests for funds not accepted.

Trustee: PNC Bank, N.A.

EIN: 656438868

8318
Tippins Foundation

209 4th Ave.
Pittsburgh, PA 15222-1707 (412) 391-0300

Established in 1987 in Pennsylvania.

Donors: TMC Investment Co.; Carolyn M. Tippins; George W. Tippins†; Tippins, Inc.; Carolyn H. Tippins.

Foundation type: Independent foundation.

Financial data (yr. ended 12/31/13): Assets, $1,433,022 (M); gifts received, $490,700; expenditures, $422,334; qualifying distributions, $417,948; giving activities include $416,750 for 58 grants (high: $75,000; low: $500).

Purpose and activities: The foundation supports organizations involved with arts and culture, education, animal welfare, health, medical research, and human services.

Fields of interest: Arts and culture; Performing arts; Education; Higher education; Domesticated animals; Animal welfare; Health; Hospital care; Diseases and conditions; Entrepreneurship; Human services.

Type of support: Annual campaigns; Capital campaigns; Capital and infrastructure; Research and evaluation; Research.

Limitations: Applications not accepted. Giving primarily in Pittsburgh, PA. No grants to individuals.

Application information: Contributes only to pre-selected organizations.

Board meeting date(s): Dec.

Officer and Trustees: George R. Knapp, Exec. Dir. and Trustee; Carolyn H. Tippins; John H. Tippins; William H. Tippins.
EIN: 256282382

8319
The Todi Foundation
P.O. Box 348
Gwynedd Valley, PA   19437-0348   (215) 362-1217
Contact: Nand Todi, Pres.

Donor: Nand Todi.
Foundation type: Independent foundation.
Financial data (yr. ended 12/31/13): Assets, $3,671,929 (M); gifts received, $400,000; expenditures, $174,713; qualifying distributions, $153,850; giving activities include $153,850 for 3 grants (high: $70,000; low: $40,000).
Fields of interest: Education; Health; Hinduism.
Type of support: General support.
Application information: Application form required.
Initial approach: Request application form
Deadline(s): None
Officer: Nand Todi, Pres.
EIN: 232744913

8320
Tompkins-Broll Family Foundation
710 Strawbridge Ln.
Wayne, PA   19087-2066
Contact: David Broll

Established in 2004 in Delaware.
Donor: Arthur G. Broll Jr. Charitable Lead Trust.
Foundation type: Independent foundation.
Financial data (yr. ended 06/30/14): Assets, $4,118,457 (M); gifts received, $448,160; expenditures, $251,841; qualifying distributions, $181,375; giving activities include $181,375 for 22 grants (high: $75,000; low: $500).
Fields of interest: Education; Environment; Health; Domestic violence; Human services.
Limitations: Applications not accepted. Giving primarily in PA, CA, TN, IL, and NJ. No grants to individuals.
Application information: Unsolicited requests for funds not accepted.
Officers: Arthur G. Broll, Jr., Pres.; Daniel W. Broll, V.P.; David A. Broll, V.P.; Geoffrey T. Broll, V.P.; Carolyn Broll Overton Kelly, V.P.; Julie Broll Lord, V.P.; Nancy T. Broll, Secy.-Treas.
EIN: 201516022

8321
Virginia S. Trax Trust
c/o BNY Mellon, N.A.
P.O. Box 185
Pittsburgh, PA   15230-0185

Foundation type: Independent foundation.
Financial data (yr. ended 12/31/13): Assets, $7,137,920 (M); expenditures, $392,067; qualifying distributions, $334,124; giving activities include $301,556 for 34 grants (high: $123,623; low: $636).
Fields of interest: Education; Christianity; Human services.
Limitations: Applications not accepted. Giving primarily in PA.

Application information: Contributes only to pre-selected organizations.
Trustee: BNY Mellon, N.A.
EIN: 237903348

8322
The Triple T Foundation
c/o Glenmede Trust Co., N.A.
1650 Market St., Ste. 1200
Philadelphia, PA   19103-7391

Established in 1996 in Ohio.
Donors: Alison C. Jones; Ellen W. Jones; Theodore T. Jones; Warren Tanner Jones; Edith J. Bastian; A.C. & T.T. Jones 1997 Trust; Edith J. Bastian 2001 Trust; Alison C. Jones 1999 Trust; Ellen W. Jones Nordell 2001 Trust; American Foundation Trust.
Foundation type: Independent foundation.
Financial data (yr. ended 12/31/14): Assets, $11,565,094 (M); expenditures, $387,906; qualifying distributions, $358,265; giving activities include $354,115 for 80 grants (high: $64,202; low: $50).
Purpose and activities: Giving primarily for education, social services, and health, particularly a therapeutic horse riding center.
Fields of interest: Arts and culture; Elementary and secondary education; Higher education; Health; Human services.
Limitations: Applications not accepted. Giving primarily in OH, with some emphasis on the greater Cleveland area. No grants to individuals.
Application information: Contributes only to pre-selected organizations.
Trustee: Edith J. Bastian; Alison C. Jones; Warren Tanner Jones; Ellen Nordell.
EIN: 341811968

8323
S. Edna Troemner No. 5 Phila Baptist Association
c/o PNC Bank, N.A.
620 Liberty Ave., 10th Fl.
Pittsburgh, PA   15222-2705

Foundation type: Independent foundation.
Financial data (yr. ended 12/31/13): Assets, $5,339,688 (M); expenditures, $243,188; qualifying distributions, $205,258; giving activities include $203,430 for 1 grant.
Fields of interest: Religion.
Limitations: Applications not accepted. Giving limited to Philadelphia, PA.
Application information: Unsolicited requests for funds not accepted.
Trustee: PNC Bank, N.A.
EIN: 237666715

8324
Leanne Freas Trout Foundation
1340 Broadcasting Rd., Ste. 100
Wyomissing, PA   19610-1190

Foundation type: Independent foundation.
Financial data (yr. ended 12/31/13): Assets, $4,185,146 (M); expenditures, $199,807; qualifying distributions, $180,055; giving activities include $180,055 for 40 grants (high: $46,355; low: $100).
Fields of interest: Higher education.

Limitations: Applications not accepted. Giving primarily in PA. No grants to individuals.
Application information: Contributes only to pre-selected organizations.
Directors: D. Leanne Ledgerwood; Linda Beth Mansfield; Rebecca L.F. Trout.
EIN: 205898335

8325
Tuttleman Family Foundation
23 Tettemer Rd.
Erwinna, PA   18920-9259
Contact: Jan S. Tuttleman, Tr.
FAX: (858) 457-7790; E-mail: jtuttleman@gmail.com

Established in 1993 in Pennsylvania.
Foundation type: Independent foundation.
Financial data (yr. ended 12/31/13): Assets, $5,019,863 (M); expenditures, $221,944; qualifying distributions, $191,500; giving activities include $191,500 for 12 grants (high: $62,500; low: $1,000).
Purpose and activities: The mission of the foundation is to support programs that enrich the quality of life for Jewish and secular children, their families, and the elderly in the Philadelphia, PA, area who are underprivileged, disadvantaged, or at risk. The foundation also supports medical research for Type II diabetes.
Fields of interest: Arts and culture; Education; Nonprofits; Diseases and conditions; Sustainable development; Urban development; Human services; Child welfare; Women's services.
Type of support: Technical assistance; Curriculum development; General support; Emergency funds; Program development; Convening; Seed money; Internships; Research; Regranting.
Limitations: Applications not accepted. Giving primarily in Philadelphia, PA. No support for capital campaigns. No grants to individuals.
Application information: Contributes only to pre-selected organizations.
Trustees: David Z. Tuttleman; Steven M. Tuttleman.
EIN: 237715836

8326
Union Benevolent Association
c/o Kasey Thompson
1528 Walnut St., Ste. 1002
Philadelphia, PA   19102-3627   (215) 763-7670
E-mail: info@uba1831.org; Main URL: http://www.uba1831.org
Facebook: https://www.facebook.com/UBA1831
Grants List: http://uba1831.org/index.php/about-our-grants/recent-recipients

Established in 1831 in Pennsylvania.
Foundation type: Independent foundation.
Financial data (yr. ended 12/31/13): Assets, $4,661,899 (M); gifts received, $2,036; expenditures, $240,817; qualifying distributions, $218,720; giving activities include $207,350 for 115 grants (high: $7,650; low: $500).
Fields of interest: Education; Child educational development; Basic and remedial instruction; Reading promotion; Family planning; Addiction services; HIV/AIDS; Community and economic development; Housing development; Diversity and intergroup relations; Human services; Child development; Housing for the homeless; Homeless

services; Ethnic and racial groups; Homeless people; Low-income and poor people.
Type of support: General support; Continuing support; Capital and infrastructure; Equipment; Emergency funds; Research.
Limitations: Applications accepted. Giving limited to Philadelphia, PA. No support for national organizations, religious organizations for religious purposes, or government agencies. No grants to individuals, or for capital renovations.
Publications: Annual report (including application guidelines).
Application information: Delaware Valley Grantmakers Common Application Form (including coversheet, summary, narrative and budget) required. The Association will only fund an organization for three years (not necessarily consecutive) out of five. Application form required.
Initial approach: Letter
Copies of proposal: 1
Deadline(s): Apr. 30 and Sept. 30
Officers and Directors: Phyllis Martino, Pres.; Michael Hinson, V.P. and Director; Tiffany Tavarez, Secy. and Director; William J. Burke, Jr., Treas. and Director; David R. Fair; Will Gonzalez; Danie Greenwell; Sigrid Lundby; Shawn McGill.
EIN: 231360861

8327
Up East, Inc.
P.O. Box 48
Chadds Ford, PA   19317-0048   (610) 793-1356

Established in 1995 in Pennsylvania.
Donors: Andrew N. Wyeth; Betsy James Wyeth.
Foundation type: Independent foundation.
Financial data (yr. ended 06/30/14): Assets, $10,434,414 (M); expenditures, $961,576; qualifying distributions, $904,708; giving activities include $282,828 for 6 grants (high: $200,000; low: $4,000), and $607,302 for foundation-administered programs.
Fields of interest: Art museums; Higher education; Environment; Wildlife biodiversity; Archives and special collections.
Type of support: Research and evaluation.
Limitations: Applications accepted. Giving primarily in ME.
Application information:
Initial approach: Letter of no more than 2 pages
Deadline(s): June 15 and Dec. 15
Officers and Trustees: J. Robinson West, Pres. and Trustee; Amy Morey, V.P. and Trustee; William J. Martin, Secy.-Treas.; Charles M. Cawley; Christopher B. Crosman; John Wilmerding; Betsy James Wyeth; James Browning Wyeth; Phyllis Wyeth.
EIN: 510367586

8328
Valentine Foundation
409 Merion Hill Ln.
West Conshohocken, PA   19428   (610) 525-7200
Contact: Alexandra V.A. Frazier, Exec. Dir.
E-mail: info@valentinefoundation.org; Main URL: http://www.valentinefoundation.org
Facebook: https://www.facebook.com/pages/The-Valentine-Foundation/127542280618958
Grants List: http://www.valentinefoundation.org/2013-grantees/grantee

Grants List: http://www.valentinefoundation.org/2014-grantees

Established in 1985 in Pennsylvania.
Donors: Phoebe V. Valentine†; The Hess Foundation; Pam Phelan; Walter R. Garrison; Susan Garrison.
Foundation type: Independent foundation.
Financial data (yr. ended 11/30/13): Assets, $3,613,726 (M); gifts received, $104,931; expenditures, $244,717; qualifying distributions, $199,149; giving activities include $176,319 for 23 grants (high: $12,000; low: $500).
Purpose and activities: The foundation makes grants to organizations or programs that empower women and girls to recognize and develop their full potential or that work to change established attitudes that discourage them from recognizing their potential. Grants will be given for endeavors to effect fundamental change - to change attitudes, policies, or social patterns. The trustees commit a minimum of half of their grants to programs for girls and the balance to programs for women. The programs for women must include advocacy for social change.
Fields of interest: Education; Women's services; Females; Female children and youth.
Type of support: General support; Continuing support; Program development; Seed money.
Limitations: Applications not accepted. Giving primarily in the Philadelphia, PA, area. No support for capital campaigns, religious organizations for religious purposes or political organizations for political purposes, and no support for international initiatives. No grants to individuals, or for scholarships, endowments, or capital campaigns.
Application information: Unsolicited requests for funds not accepted.
Officers: Alexandra V. A. Frazier, Exec. Dir.
Trustees: Brenda DeFeo; Jennifer Hope; Tara F. Jones; Laura Morris; Farrah Parkes; Hannah Jane Sassaman.
Number of staff: 1 part-time professional.
EIN: 236806061

8329
Herbert W. Vaughan Charitable Foundation
c/o The Philadelphia Trust Company
1760 Market St.
Philadelphia, PA   19103-4134

Donor: Herbert W. Vaughan†.
Foundation type: Independent foundation.
Financial data (yr. ended 06/30/13): Assets, $3,800,930 (M); gifts received, $3,731,792; expenditures, $261,373; qualifying distributions, $260,686; giving activities include $260,000 for 2 grants (high: $160,000; low: $100,000).
Fields of interest: Higher education.
Limitations: Applications not accepted. Giving primarily in Princeton, NJ. No grants to individuals.
Application information: Unsolicited requests for funds not accepted.
Trustees: Christopher C. DeMuth; Robert P. George; James R. Stoner, Jr.
EIN: 456911090

8330
Velma Moore T/W Charities
c/o PNC Bank
620 Liberty Ave., 10th Fl.
Pittsburgh, PA   15222-2722

Foundation type: Independent foundation.
Financial data (yr. ended 06/30/13): Assets, $5,625,331 (M); expenditures, $290,284; qualifying distributions, $234,460; giving activities include $234,460 for grants.
Fields of interest: Foundations; Community and economic development; Religion; Human services.
Type of support: General support.
Limitations: Applications not accepted. Giving primarily in NY and PA.
Application information: Unsolicited requests for funds not accepted.
Trustee: PNC Bank.
EIN: 900052174

8331
Clarence J. Venne Foundation
444 S. State St.
Newtown, PA   18940-1945   2159684224

Established in 2000 in Pennsylvania.
Donors: Clarence J. Venne†; Richard A. Venne.
Foundation type: Independent foundation.
Financial data (yr. ended 12/31/14): Assets, $7,589,216; expenditures, $329,983; qualifying distributions, $304,635.
Fields of interest: Education; Cancers; Christianity.
Limitations: Applications not accepted. Giving primarily in PA. No grants to individuals.
Application information: Unsolicited requests for funds not accepted.
Officers and Directors: Joanne Quinn, Pres. and Director; Patricia Venne, V.P. and Director; Margaret Brower, Secy. and Director; Nancy Venne, Treas. and Director; Marie Pendergast.
EIN: 233040515

8332
The Lois B. Victor Foundation
(formerly The Lois and Morton Victor Foundation)
c/o Cozen O'Connor
1900 Market St.
Philadelphia, PA   19103-3527

Established in 2000 in Pennsylvania.
Donor: Lois B. Victor.
Foundation type: Independent foundation.
Financial data (yr. ended 09/30/13): Assets, $506,756 (M); gifts received, $304,978; expenditures, $250,612; qualifying distributions, $244,955; giving activities include $239,700 for 7 grants (high: $221,200; low: $125).
Purpose and activities: Giving primarily for health care and Jewish organizations.
Fields of interest: Health; Diseases and conditions; Judaism; Human services.
Limitations: Applications not accepted. Giving primarily in FL and Philadelphia, PA. No grants to individuals.
Application information: Contributes only to pre-selected organizations.
Officer and Director: Lois Victor, Pres. and Treas. and Director.
EIN: 233058320

8333
Viii Brothers Family Charitable Foundation
c/o Parentebeard, LLC
1800 Byberry Rd., Ste. 1100
Huntingdon Valley, PA   19006-3523

Donor: Carl H.J. Asplundh, Jr.
Foundation type: Independent foundation.
Financial data (yr. ended 12/31/13): Assets,
$7,076,597 (M); gifts received, $194;
expenditures, $347,346; qualifying distributions,
$338,576; giving activities include $328,650 for 33
grants (high: $82,900; low: $150).
Fields of interest: Religion.
Limitations: Applications not accepted.
Application information: Unsolicited requests for
funds not accepted.
Trustees: Carl H.J. Asplundh, Jr.; Pamela S.
Asplundh.
EIN: 262541707

8334
Anna M. Vincent Trust
c/o BNY Mellon, N.A.
P.O. Box 185
Pittsburgh, PA   15230-0185

Established in 1967 in Pennsylvania.
Donor: Anna M. Vincent‡.
Foundation type: Independent foundation.
Financial data (yr. ended 06/30/13): Assets,
$6,404,276 (M); expenditures, $284,995;
qualifying distributions, $171,500; giving activities
include $171,500 for grants.
Fields of interest: Higher education.
Type of support: Scholarships; Student aid.
Limitations: Applications not accepted. Giving
limited to residents of the Delaware Valley, PA, area.
No grants for building or endowment funds,
operating budgets, or special projects.
Application information: Unsolicited requests for
funds not accepted.
   Board meeting date(s): Mar. and Apr.
Trustees: Robert Whitelaw; BNY Mellon, N.A.
EIN: 236422666

8335
Wabtec Foundation
1001 Air Brake Ave.
Wilmerding, PA   15148

Established in 2007 in Pennsylvania.
Donor: Westinghouse Air Brake Technologies Corp.
Foundation type: Company-sponsored foundation.
Financial data (yr. ended 12/31/14): Assets,
$4,590,779; expenditures, $351,699; qualifying
distributions, $319,310.
Purpose and activities: The foundation supports
nonprofit organizations involved with education,
human services, and community development.
Fields of interest: Education; Community and
economic development; Human services.
Application information: Application form required.
   Initial approach: Completed application form
   Deadline(s): 1 week prior to foundation meeting
Officers and Directors: Albert J. Neupaver, Pres. and
Director; Scott E. Walhstrom, V.P. and Director;
David M. Seitz, Secy.; Keith P. Hildum, Treas.; Lee
B. Foster II; William E. Kassling.
EIN: 141994641

8336
Judith & David Wachs Family Foundation
215 W. Church Rd., Ste. 108
King of Prussia, PA   19406-3209

Established in 1985 in Pennsylvania.
Donors: Second Chance Fund; David Wachs; Judith
Wachs.
Foundation type: Independent foundation.
Financial data (yr. ended 09/30/13): Assets,
$5,274,147 (M); expenditures, $259,725;
qualifying distributions, $244,590; giving activities
include $216,141 for grants.
Fields of interest: Education; Health; Diseases and
conditions; Diabetes; Judaism.
Type of support: Research.
Limitations: Applications not accepted. Giving
primarily in PA. No grants to individuals.
Application information: Unsolicited requests for
funds not accepted.
Trustee: Rachel A. Wachs.
EIN: 222682604

8337
Wachs-Weingarten Charitable Trust
c/o M. Wachs Weingarten & B. Weingarten Trust
1706 Rittenhouse Sq., Unit 701
Philadelphia, PA   19103-6235   (610) 687-1600
Contact: Bryan Weingarten, Tr.

Established in 1997 in Pennsylvania.
Donors: Bryan Weingarten; Marjorie Wachs
Weingarten.
Foundation type: Independent foundation.
Financial data (yr. ended 10/31/13): Assets,
$895,819 (M); gifts received, $308,434;
expenditures, $376,609; qualifying distributions,
$374,594; giving activities include $374,594 for 27
grants (high: $100,000; low: $50).
Fields of interest: Education; Judaism; Human
services.
Type of support: General support.
Limitations: Applications accepted. Giving primarily
in PA. No grants to individuals.
Application information:
   Initial approach: Proposal
   Deadline(s): None
Trustees: Bryan Weingarten; Marjorie Wachs
Weingarten.
EIN: 237922107

8338
Wagner Family Charitable Trust
c/o PNC Bank
620 Liberty Ave., 10th Fl.
Pittsburgh, PA   15222

Established in 2000 in Pennsylvania.
Donors: Robert K. Wagner; Elinor R. Wagner.
Foundation type: Independent foundation.
Financial data (yr. ended 12/31/12): Assets,
$2,223,496 (M); expenditures, $129,620;
qualifying distributions, $121,678; giving activities
include $119,124 for 39 grants (high: $36,000;
low: $500).
Fields of interest: Nonprofits; Christianity; Human
services.
Type of support: Regranting.
Limitations: Applications not accepted. Giving
primarily in Pittsburgh, PA. No grants to individuals.

Application information: Unsolicited requests for
funds not accepted.
Trustee: PNC Bank, N.A.
EIN: 256735042

8339
George P. Wakefield Residuary Trust
c/o BNY Mellon N.A.
P.O. Box 185
Pittsburgh, PA   15230-0185

Foundation type: Independent foundation.
Financial data (yr. ended 06/30/13): Assets,
$2,629,857 (M); expenditures, $237,331;
qualifying distributions, $216,850; giving activities
include $216,600 for 12 grants (high: $30,000;
low: $5,000).
Purpose and activities: Support primarily for Jewish
organizations; giving also to child welfare
organizations, hospitals and medical research.
Fields of interest: Human services; People with
vision impairments.
Limitations: Applications not accepted. Giving
primarily in New York, NY. No grants to individuals.
Application information: Contributes only to
pre-selected organizations.
Trustee: BNY Mellon, N.A.
EIN: 136079388

8340
The Waldo Trust
c/o BNY Mellon, N.A.
P.O. Box 185
Pittsburgh, PA   15230-0185

Established in 1996 in Connecticut.
Donors: Disney Shares; Anne F. Jeffery.
Foundation type: Independent foundation.
Financial data (yr. ended 10/31/14): Assets,
$5,823,055 (M); gifts received, $1,951,013;
expenditures, $242,369; qualifying distributions,
$223,171; giving activities include $206,000 for 23
grants (high: $65,000; low: $1,000).
Fields of interest: Education; Health; Community
and economic development.
Limitations: Applications not accepted. Giving
primarily in CT. No grants to individuals.
Application information: Unsolicited requests for
funds not accepted.
Trustee: BNY Mellon, N.A.
EIN: 137102854

8341
R. Walton Family Foundation
c/o BNY Mellon, N.A.
P.O. Box 185
Pittsburgh, PA   15230-0185   (412) 234-2332

Established in 1996 in Pennsylvania.
Donors: Rachel Mellon Walton; R. Walton.
Foundation type: Independent foundation.
Financial data (yr. ended 12/31/14): Assets,
$5,008,467; expenditures, $297,216; qualifying
distributions, $266,313.
Fields of interest: Nonprofits; Human services.
Type of support: General support; Regranting.
Limitations: Applications accepted. Giving primarily
in Pittsburgh, PA. No grants to individuals.
Application information: Application form required.

Initial approach: Request application form
Deadline(s): None
Trustees: Farley Walton Whetzel; James M. Walton; Mary Walton; William C. Walton.
EIN: 256568399

8342
The Ralph T. & Esther L. Warburton Foundation
c/o Glenmede Trust Co., N.A.
1650 Market St., Ste. 1200
Philadelphia, PA 19103-7391

Established in 1966 in Ohio.
Donor: Ralph T. Warburton†.
Foundation type: Independent foundation.
Financial data (yr. ended 12/31/14): Assets, $11,459,339 (M); expenditures, $602,868; qualifying distributions, $467,602; giving activities include $403,195 for 7 grants (high: $250,000; low: $3,195).
Purpose and activities: Giving primarily to a health organization, as well as for higher education, and to an Anglican church.
Fields of interest: Higher education; Health; Episcopalianism and Anglicanism.
Type of support: General support.
Limitations: Applications not accepted. Giving primarily in Stark County, OH. No grants to individuals.
Application information: Contributes only to pre-selected organizations.
Trustees: Betsy Warburton Downs; Mike D. Downs; Alex W. Montalto; Carrie Warburton Montalto; Phillip L. Warburton; Sally Warburton.
EIN: 346574882

8343
Ward Foundation
1 Charles St.
P.O. Box 878
Wellsboro, PA 16901-0878

Donor: Marjorie S. Ward.
Foundation type: Independent foundation.
Financial data (yr. ended 12/31/13): Assets, $4,385,540 (M); expenditures, $236,187; qualifying distributions, $204,161; giving activities include $185,698 for 25 grants (high: $50,000; low: $1,000).
Fields of interest: Diseases and conditions; Television; Religion; Christianity; Catholicism; Human services; Child welfare; Women's services.
Limitations: Applications not accepted. No grants to individuals.
Application information: Unsolicited requests for funds not accepted.
Trustees: Thomas M. Owlett; Joseph P. Ward; Patricia A. Ward-McGuire; Kathryn A. Ward-O'Malley; Marjorie A. Ward-Resnikoff.
EIN: 251877478

8344
The Paul D. Wasserott Foundation
P.O. Box 349
Wilkes-Barre, PA 18703-0349 (570) 287-2176
Contact: Paul D. Wasserott Jr., Pres. and Treas.

Established in 2002 in Pennsylvania.
Donor: Paul D. Wasserott, Jr.

Foundation type: Independent foundation.
Financial data (yr. ended 12/31/13): Assets, $3,804,075 (M); expenditures, $219,081; qualifying distributions, $179,621; giving activities include $175,675 for 15 grants (high: $100,550; low: $25).
Fields of interest: Education; Nonprofits; Health; Human services.
Type of support: Regranting.
Limitations: Applications accepted. Giving primarily in PA. No grants to individuals.
Application information: Application form required.
Initial approach: Letter
Deadline(s): None
Officers: Paul D. Wasserott, Jr., Pres. and Treas.; Elizabeth F. Wasserott, V.P.; Michael Molewski, Secy.
EIN: 043729982

8345
Wayne County Community Foundation
214 9th St., 2nd Fl.
Honesdale, PA 18431-1911 (570) 499-4299
Contact: Paul J. Edwards, Exec. Dir.
FAX: (570) 251-9904; E-mail: wccf@ptd.net; Main URL: http://www.waynefoundation.org
Facebook: https://www.facebook.com/pages/Wayne-County-Community-Foundation/281411003324

Established in 1991 in Pennsylvania.
Foundation type: Community foundation.
Financial data (yr. ended 06/30/13): Assets, $2,414,117 (M); gifts received, $374,376; expenditures, $261,268; giving activities include $183,320 for 7+ grants (high: $22,120).
Purpose and activities: The foundation seeks to serve as a publicly supported charity dedicated to preserving and enhancing the future quality of life in Wayne County by supporting that which is good about the present and that which seeks to do good in the future.
Fields of interest: Economic development; Community improvement.
Limitations: Applications accepted. Giving primarily in Wayne County, PA. No grants for advertising, individual conferences or trips, re-granting, endowments, deficit financing, or routine operating expenses.
Publications: Application guidelines.
Application information: Visit foundation web site for application information. Application form required.
Initial approach: Submit application
Deadline(s): Feb. 1, May 1, Aug. 1, and Nov. 1
Board meeting date(s): Mar., June, Sept., and Dec.
Officers and Directors: Vicki J. Botjey, Pres. and Director; Warren Schloesser, 1st V.P. and Director; William Gershey, 2nd V.P. and Director; Ann O'Hara, Secy. and Director; Thomas Sheridan, Treas. and Director; Pam J. Edwards, Exec. Dir.; Mary Ellen Bentler; Peter Bochnovich; John Carmody; Bill Douglass; Frances Gruber; Sharon Herzog; Kuni Holbert; James B. Kilgore; Robert Kramer; Thomas E. LaTournous; William B. McAllister; Paul Meagher; Patricia Mohn; Dan O'Neill; Jay Starnes; Jane Varcoe; Bob Zabady.
EIN: 232656896

8346
The Weil Family Foundation
(formerly Critical Care Foundation)
400 Woodward Rd.
Rose Valley, PA 19063-4227

Donor: Max Harry Weil, M.D., Ph.D.
Foundation type: Independent foundation.
Financial data (yr. ended 11/30/14): Assets, $6,124,141 (M); gifts received, $210,000; expenditures, $263,986; qualifying distributions, $230,600; giving activities include $230,600 for 4 grants (high: $200,000; low: $600).
Fields of interest: Health; Diseases and conditions.
Limitations: Applications not accepted. Giving primarily in CA. No grants to individuals.
Application information: Unsolicited requests for funds not accepted.
Officers: Michael Adesman, M.D., Ph.D., Pres.; Carol Weil, V.P.; Susan Weil, Secy.; Dianne Greenstein, Treas.
Trustee: Marianne Weil.
EIN: 952379787

8347
The Weiler Family Foundation, Inc.
160 North Pointe Blvd., Ste. 200
Lancaster, PA 17601

Established in 1998 in Pennsylvania.
Donors: Karl M. Weiler; Ann Weiler; James Weiler; Christopher Weiler; Richard K. Weiler; Weiler Corp., Inc.
Foundation type: Independent foundation.
Financial data (yr. ended 12/31/13): Assets, $4,488,421 (M); gifts received, $600,000; expenditures, $391,978; qualifying distributions, $378,402; giving activities include $374,217 for 20 grants (high: $100,000; low: $1,000).
Fields of interest: Higher education; Human services.
Limitations: Applications not accepted. Giving primarily in PA, some giving also in FL. No grants to individuals.
Application information: Contributes only to pre-selected organizations.
Officers: Karl M. Weiler, Pres.; Ann Weiler, V.P.; Richard K. Weiler, Secy.
Directors: Jennifer O'Hara; Christopher Weiler; James Weiler.
EIN: 232962255

8348
Weiler-Miller Fund, Inc.
(formerly Weiler-Miller Foundation)
c/o PNC Bank, N.A.
1600 Market St., 29th Fl.
Philadelphia, PA 19103-7260

Established in 1997 in Maryland.
Donors: Josepha S. Miller Revocable Trust; Schoeneman-Halle Foundation.
Foundation type: Independent foundation.
Financial data (yr. ended 11/30/13): Assets, $414,825 (M); expenditures, $178,995; qualifying distributions, $173,843; giving activities include $171,186 for 53 grants (high: $10,000; low: $500).
Fields of interest: Arts and culture; Museums; Education; Foundations; Nonprofits; Health; Hospital care; Diseases and conditions; Cancers; Human services.

Type of support: Annual campaigns; Capital campaigns; Capital and infrastructure; Regranting.
Limitations: Applications not accepted. Giving primarily in Baltimore, MD. No grants to individuals.
Application information: Contributes only to pre-selected organizations.
Officers: Anne W. Miller, Pres. and V.P.; Pamela Himmelrich, Secy.; Joshua M. Miller, Treas.
EIN: 522109374

8349
Weiner Family Foundation
(formerly Community Involvement Foundation)
139 Freeport Rd., Ste. 100
Pittsburgh, PA 15215-2943 (412) 782-0200
Contact: Christopher P. Smith, Exec. Dir.

Established in 1993 in Pennsylvania.
Donors: Bruce B. Weiner; Susan Weiner.
Foundation type: Independent foundation.
Financial data (yr. ended 12/31/13): Assets, $1,328,470 (M); expenditures, $336,664; qualifying distributions, $274,363; giving activities include $253,050 for grants.
Purpose and activities: Giving primarily for youth services.
Fields of interest: Community and economic development; Child welfare; Youth development.
Type of support: General support; In-kind gifts; Annual campaigns; Capital and infrastructure.
Limitations: Applications accepted. Giving primarily in Pittsburgh, PA. No grants to individuals.
Application information: Application form required.
Initial approach: Letter
Deadline(s): None
Officers and Trustees: Bruce B. Weiner, Chair. and Trustee; Susan Weiner, Pres. and Trustee; George L. Stewart, V.P.; Michele L. Decarlo, Secy.-Treas.; Christopher Smith, Exec. Dir. and Trustee.
Number of staff: 1 part-time professional.
EIN: 251724052

8350
Wells Fargo Community Development Corp.
(formerly Wachovia Regional Community Development Corporation)
123 S. Broad St., MAC Y1379-030
Philadelphia, PA 19109-1029 (215) 670-4300
Contact: Kimberly J. Allen, V.P.
Main URL: https://www.wellsfargo.com/about/regional-foundation/regional-community-development-corporation

Established in 1993 in Pennsylvania.
Donors: CoreStates Financial Corp; Wachovia Corp.; First Union Corp.
Foundation type: Company-sponsored foundation.
Financial data (yr. ended 12/31/13): Assets, $8,625,057 (M); expenditures, $202,093; qualifying distributions, $1,023,206; giving activities include $150,000 for 2 grants (high: $100,000; low: $50,000).
Purpose and activities: The foundation provides loans to organizations with programs designed to promote community and economic development for low-income individuals and communities.
Fields of interest: Community and economic development.
Type of support: Program-related investments.

Limitations: Applications not accepted. Giving primarily in DE, NJ, and the eastern half of PA.
Application information: Unsolicited applications are not accepted. Program-related investments are awarded by invitation only.
Officers: C. Kent McGuire, Ph.D, Chair.; Austin Burke, Vice-Chair; Denise McGregor Armbrister, Sr. V.P. and Exec. Dir.; Kimberly J. Allen, V.P.
Board Members: Fernando Chang-Muy; Lucia N. Gibbons; Stacy Holland; Maria Matos; Gabriella Morris; Robert Torres, Esq.; Ralph Smith, Esq.; John Thurber, Esq.
Number of staff: None.
EIN: 232735410

8351
Robert C. Wenger Charitable Trust
c/o Ephrata National Bank
47 E. Main St.
Ephrata, PA 17552-2713
Main URL: http://www.epnb.com

Donors: Robert C. Wenger†; Carolyn C. Wenger.
Foundation type: Independent foundation.
Financial data (yr. ended 12/31/13): Assets, $8,172,673 (M); expenditures, $462,743; qualifying distributions, $399,000; giving activities include $399,000 for 108 grants (high: $35,000; low: $500).
Fields of interest: Public affairs; Religion; Human services.
Limitations: Applications not accepted.
Application information: Unsolicited requests for funds not accepted.
Trustee: Ephrata National Bank.
EIN: 233835057

8352
The Wenger Foundation, Inc.
P.O. Box 409
Myerstown, PA 17067-0409 (717) 866-2130
Contact: Rose E. Walmer, Pres.

Established in 1995 in Pennsylvania.
Donor: Dutchvalley Food Distributors, Inc.
Foundation type: Independent foundation.
Financial data (yr. ended 12/31/13): Assets, $681,150 (M); gifts received, $726,250; expenditures, $225,076; qualifying distributions, $169,343; giving activities include $169,343 for 42 grants (high: $37,603; low: $35).
Purpose and activities: Giving primarily for education, health care, and family services.
Fields of interest: Education; Health; Religion; Human services; Family services.
Type of support: General support; Continuing support; Annual campaigns; Capital campaigns; Capital and infrastructure; Equipment; Emergency funds; Scholarships.
Limitations: Applications accepted. Giving primarily in south central PA. No support for political and socially progressive organizations.
Publications: Annual report; Informational brochure.
Application information:
Initial approach: Letter
Copies of proposal: 1
Board meeting date(s): Flexible
Final notification: 3 months from receipt
Officers and Directors: Rose E. Walmer, Pres.; Stacy Dieffenbach, Secy. and Director; Nancy L.

Layser, Treas.; Adam Wenger; Carl I. Wenger; Kitty Wenger; Margaret Wenger.
Number of staff: 1 part-time professional.
EIN: 251779023

8353
Whalley Charitable Trust
1206 Graham Ave.
Windber, PA 15963-1706 (814) 467-6656
Contact: David Klementik, Tr.

Established in 1961 in Pennsylvania.
Donors: John J. Whalley; John J. Whalley, Jr.; Mary Whalley.
Foundation type: Independent foundation.
Financial data (yr. ended 12/31/13): Assets, $4,004,972 (M); expenditures, $388,256; qualifying distributions, $341,359; giving activities include $331,285 for 56 grants (high: $55,000; low: $100).
Purpose and activities: Giving primarily for education and health care.
Fields of interest: Arts and culture; Education; Hospital care; Public libraries; Fire prevention and control; Community and economic development; Protestantism; Sports and recreation; Human services.
Limitations: Applications accepted. Giving primarily in PA, with emphasis on Windber and Johnstown.
Application information:
Initial approach: Proposal
Deadline(s): None
Trustees: David Klementik; Ruth Klementik.
EIN: 237128436

8354
Whimsie Fund
c/o E.R. Boynton
30 Valley Stream Pkwy.
Malvern, PA 19355-1462

Donor: Ithan Foundation.
Foundation type: Independent foundation.
Financial data (yr. ended 12/31/14): Assets, $6,071,945 (M); gifts received, $315,438; expenditures, $412,365; qualifying distributions, $284,500; giving activities include $284,500 for 18 grants (high: $150,000; low: $1,000).
Fields of interest: Arts and culture; Education; Higher education; Youth development.
Limitations: Applications not accepted. Giving primarily in Santa Barbara, CA, and RI.
Application information: Unsolicted requests for funds not accepted.
Officers and Directors: Harry L. Atterbury, Pres.; Wendy S. Atterbury, Secy.-Treas.; Edwin R. Boynton.
EIN: 275271127

8355
The White Pine Fund
c/o BNY Mellon
1 Mellon Ctr., Ste. 151
Pittsburgh, PA 15258
Contact: Richard Coleman

Established in 2009 in Pennsylvania.
Foundation type: Independent foundation.
Financial data (yr. ended 12/31/13): Assets, $6,802,696 (M); expenditures, $390,644; qualifying distributions, $349,688; giving activities

include $321,000 for 40 grants (high: $15,000; low: $3,000).
Fields of interest: Natural resources; Biodiversity; Wildlife biodiversity.
Limitations: Applications not accepted. Giving primarily in Washington, DC, and PA.
Application information: Unsolicited requests for funds not accepted.
Officer: Rebecca Barclay Humphrey, Pres.
EIN: 263168334

8356
Willary Foundation
P.O. Box 283
Scranton, PA 18501-0283 (570) 961-6952
Contact: Linda Donovan
FAX: (570) 961-7269; E-mail: info@willary.org; Main URL: http://www.willary.org
Grants List: http://www.willary.org/granthistory.html

Established in 1968 in Pennsylvania.
Donors: William W. Scranton; Mary L. Scranton.
Foundation type: Independent foundation.
Financial data (yr. ended 12/31/13): Assets, $5,316,926 (M); gifts received, $14,325; expenditures, $195,849; qualifying distributions, $173,027; giving activities include $155,162 for 11 grants (high: $25,000; low: $3,500).
Purpose and activities: The foundation wishes to promote the special qualities of the people of northeastern Pennsylvania, and is particularly interested in projects that support leadership and the development of leadership in business, the economy, education, human services, government, the arts, media and research.
Fields of interest: Education; Community and economic development; Human services.
Type of support: Program development; Matching grants.
Limitations: Applications accepted. Giving primarily in Lackawanna and Luzerne counties, PA. No grants to individuals, or for capital campaigns or annual drives; no loans.
Publications: Application guidelines; Grants list.
Application information: Application guidelines and form available on foundation web site. Application form required.
  Copies of proposal: 6
  Deadline(s): Mar. 10 for the spring board meeting; Aug. 27 for the winter board meeting
Trustees: Susan Scranton Dawson; Joseph C. Scranton; Julien Scranton; Mary L. Scranton; Peter K. Scranton; S. Caitlin Scranton; William W. Scranton III; Elizabeth S. Valosek.
EIN: 237014785

8357
John C. Williams Charitable Trust
c/o PNC Bank, N.A.
620 Liberty Ave., 10th Fl.
Pittsburgh, PA 15222-2719

Established in 1936 in Pennsylvania.
Donor: John C. Williams†.
Foundation type: Independent foundation.
Financial data (yr. ended 12/31/13): Assets, $7,770,960 (M); expenditures, $436,509; qualifying distributions, $379,832; giving activities include $352,500 for 19 grants (high: $60,000; low: $5,000).

Fields of interest: Human services; Food delivery; Family services; Child welfare.
Type of support: General support; Matching grants; Capital campaigns; Capital and infrastructure; Equipment; Program development.
Limitations: Applications accepted. Giving limited to Steubenville, OH, and Weirton, WV. No support for private foundations, or for political, labor, fraternal or advocacy groups. No grants to individuals, or for events or general operating costs.
Application information: See web site www.pnc.com. for application guidelines and deadlines. Click "Corporate & Institutional". Under "Special Segments" click "Non-profits and Government Institutions" and then "Charitable Trust Grants". Application form required.
  Initial approach: See website
  Copies of proposal: 1
  Deadline(s): See website
  Board meeting date(s): Mar., June, Sept., and Nov.
Trustee: PNC Bank, N.A.
EIN: 256024153

8358
The C. K. Williams Foundation
c/o BNY Mellon, N.A.
P.O. Box 185
Pittsburgh, PA 15230-0185

Established in 1963 in Pennsylvania.
Foundation type: Independent foundation.
Financial data (yr. ended 12/31/14): Assets, $10,586,254 (M); gifts received, $470,863; qualifying distributions, $431,980; giving activities include $410,500 for 12 grants (high: $263,000; low: $5,000).
Fields of interest: Museums; Elementary and secondary education; Higher education; Protestantism.
Type of support: General support.
Limitations: Applications not accepted. Giving in the U.S., with emphasis on PA. No grants to individuals.
Application information: Contributes only to pre-selected organizations.
  Board meeting date(s): Oct.
Trustee: Joan W. Rhame.
EIN: 236292772

8359
Jessie A. Williams Trust
(formerly The Frank O. and Clara R. Williams Scholarship Fund)
c/o PNC Bank, N.A.
P.O. Box 609
Pittsburgh, PA 15230-9738
Application address: c/o PNC Bank, N.A., Attn.: Michael Yoder, Trust Off., 2 PNC Plz., 7th Fl., 620 Liberty Ave., Pittsburgh, PA 15222, tel.: (412) 762-4106

Established in 1992 in Pennsylvania.
Foundation type: Independent foundation.
Financial data (yr. ended 12/31/14): Assets, $7,339,627 (M); expenditures, $336,889; qualifying distributions, $285,047; giving activities include $245,300 for 21 grants (high: $105,800; low: $100).
Purpose and activities: Scholarships to high school graduates who are residents of Venango County,

Pennsylvania, who intend to enroll in a four-year college or university.
Fields of interest: Higher education.
Type of support: Student aid.
Limitations: Applications accepted. Giving primarily to residents of Venango County, PA.
Publications: Application guidelines.
Application information: Application form required.
  Initial approach: Request application form
  Copies of proposal: 1
  Deadline(s): Apr. 30
Trustee: PNC Bank, N.A.
Number of staff: None.
EIN: 256031440

8360
Willow Tree Foundation
975 Georges Station Rd., Ste. 310
Greensburg, PA 15601

Donors: Michael J. Walker; Janice K. Walker.
Foundation type: Independent foundation.
Financial data (yr. ended 10/31/13): Assets, $429,273 (M); gifts received, $200,000; expenditures, $244,320; qualifying distributions, $244,099; giving activities include $239,135 for 4 grants (high: $100,000; low: $32,290).
Fields of interest: Mental health care; Human services.
Limitations: Applications not accepted. Giving primarily in PA.
Application information: Unsolicited requests for funds not accepted.
Officers: Michael J. Walker, Pres.; Janice K. Walker, Secy.
EIN: 263933599

8361
Phillip H. Wimmer and Betty L. Wimmer Family Foundation
c/o Samuel P. Kamin, Esq.
1806 Frick Building
Pittsburgh, PA 15219-6101

Established in 1997 in Pennsylvania.
Donor: Betty L. Wimmer†.
Foundation type: Independent foundation.
Financial data (yr. ended 12/31/14): Assets, $5,938,879; gifts received, $0; expenditures, $365,811; qualifying distributions, $290,025 and $0 for set-asides.
Fields of interest: Arts and culture; Education; Nonprofits; Health; Judaism.
Type of support: Regranting.
Limitations: Applications not accepted. Giving primarily in Pittsburgh, PA.
Application information: Unsolicited requests for funds not accepted.
Trustee: Samuel P. Kamin, Esq.
EIN: 251795161

8362
Winokur Foundation
c/o B. J. Winokur Cira Ctr.
2929 Arch St.
Philadelphia, PA 19104-2808

Established in 1986 in Pennsylvania.
Donor: Barton J. Winokur.
Foundation type: Independent foundation.

Financial data (yr. ended 07/31/14): Assets, $5,454,064 (M); gifts received, $1,600,000; expenditures, $283,196; qualifying distributions, $280,552; giving activities include $280,552 for 6 grants (high: $190,252; low: $1,800).
Fields of interest: Higher education; Law education; Philanthropy; Human services.
Type of support: General support.
Limitations: Applications not accepted. No grants to individuals.
Application information: Unsolicited requests for funds not accepted.
Trustee: Barton J. Winokur.
EIN: 236856163

8363
Benjamin & Fredora K. Wolf Memorial Foundation
12 Watson Mill Ln.
Newtown, PA 18940
Contact: Sue Gleeksman, Secy.Treas.

Established in 1955 in Pennsylvania.
Donor: Fredora K. Wolf†.
Foundation type: Independent foundation.
Financial data (yr. ended 05/31/14): Assets, $3,391,072 (M); expenditures, $178,289; qualifying distributions, $144,400; giving activities include $144,400 for grants to individuals.
Purpose and activities: Primarily awards scholarships for higher education to local area young men and women.
Type of support: Student aid.
Application information: Application form required.
Initial approach: Letter
Deadline(s): None
Officers and Trustees: Thomas Ginsberg, Pres. and Trustee; Sue Gleeksman, Secy.-Treas.; Marya Fogel Flanagan; Mary Hurtig; Suzanne Simons; John Tuton, Trustee; Flora Barth Wolf; Dennie Wolf; Martha Wolf.
Number of staff: 1 part-time support.
EIN: 236207344

8364
June & Steve Wolfson Family Foundation
(formerly Arthur & Estelle Sidewater Foundation)
c/o Lafayette Financial Services
215 W. Church Rd., Ste. 108
King of Prussia, PA 19406-3209

Established in 1990 in Pennsylvania.
Donors: Arthur Sidewater; Steve Wolfson; June Wolfson.
Foundation type: Independent foundation.
Financial data (yr. ended 12/31/13): Assets, $4,939,255 (M); gifts received, $1,148,102; expenditures, $196,680; qualifying distributions, $180,000; giving activities include $180,000 for 32 grants (high: $35,000; low: $1,000).
Fields of interest: Arts and culture; Education; Human services.
Limitations: Applications not accepted. Giving primarily in PA. No grants to individuals.
Application information: Unsolicited requests for funds not accepted.
Officers: June Wolfson, Pres.; Stephen Wolfson, V.P. and Secy.-Treas.
EIN: 232582882

8365
The Norman and Marian Wolgin Family Charitable Foundation
615 Chestnut St., Ste. 120
Philadelphia, PA 19106-4416 (215) 923-3001
Contact: R.M. Day

Donors: Norman Wolgin; Marian Wolgin.
Foundation type: Independent foundation.
Financial data (yr. ended 12/31/13): Assets, $2,000,962 (M); expenditures, $170,478; qualifying distributions, $160,000; giving activities include $160,000 for 5 grants (high: $50,000; low: $5,000).
Fields of interest: Diseases and conditions; Agriculture; Judaism.
Limitations: Applications accepted. Giving primarily in NY and PA.
Application information: Application form required.
Initial approach: Letter
Deadline(s): June 30
Trustees: Marian Wolgin; Norman Wolgin.
EIN: 386916704

8366
Wolstenholme Charitable Foundation
121 Pritchard Hollow Rd.
Westfield, PA 16950-1416 (607) 742-9284

Established in 1998 in Pennsylvania.
Donors: Eugene B. Wolstenholme; Jean M. Wolstenholme; Joseph Wright.
Foundation type: Independent foundation.
Financial data (yr. ended 06/30/15): Assets, $5,271,000 (M); gifts received, $90,000; expenditures, $345,508; qualifying distributions, $265,000; giving activities include $265,000 for 6 grants (high: $146,000; low: $15,000).
Purpose and activities: Giving primarily to Roman Catholic agencies, churches, and schools.
Fields of interest: Housing development; Religion; Human services.
Type of support: General support.
Limitations: Applications accepted. Giving primarily in MA and PA. No grants to individuals.
Application information:
Initial approach: Proposal
Deadline(s): None
Officers: Ralph Wolstenholme, Mgr.
EIN: 232937483

8367
Ira R. and Frances Wood Charitable Trust
301 Grant St., 14th Fl.
Pittsburgh, PA 15219-1407

Donor: Ira R. Wood Trust.
Foundation type: Independent foundation.
Financial data (yr. ended 12/31/13): Assets, $9,110,438 (M); gifts received, $957,720; expenditures, $343,007; qualifying distributions, $371,483; giving activities include $286,248 for 52 grants (high: $35,000; low: $500).
Purpose and activities: Giving primarily to Lutheran, Presbyterian, and United Methodist Churches.
Fields of interest: Methodism; Presbyterianism; Human services.
Limitations: Applications not accepted. Giving primarily in PA.
Application information: Unsolicited requests for funds not accepted.

Trustees: Michael J. Husarik; Sara A. Mercer.
EIN: 256897871

8368
The Marvin and Dee Woodall Charitable Foundation
775 Pebble Hill Rd.
Doylestown, PA 18901-3224
Contact: Marvin L. Woodall, Dir.

Donors: Cardiovascular Research Foundation; International Society of Endovacular Specialists; Dee Ann Woodall; Marvin L. Woodall; Secor Medical, LLC; X-Site Medical LLC; Surginex, Inc.
Foundation type: Independent foundation.
Financial data (yr. ended 12/31/13): Assets, $4,079,327 (M); expenditures, $175,390; qualifying distributions, $174,470; giving activities include $174,470 for 29 grants (high: $59,500; low: $35).
Fields of interest: Historic preservation; Hospital care; Diseases and conditions; Protestantism.
Type of support: General support; Research.
Application information: Application form required.
Initial approach: Letter
Deadline(s): None
Directors: Amy Carroll; Dee Ann Woodall; Mark E. Woodall; Marvin L. Woodall.
EIN: 233097172

8369
Wright-Cook Foundation
c/o The Glenmede Trust Company, N.A.
1650 Market St., Ste. 1200
Philadelphia, PA 19103-7391 (215) 419-6000

Established in 1990 in Pennsylvania.
Donor: Susanna W. Cook.
Foundation type: Independent foundation.
Financial data (yr. ended 12/31/14): Assets, $5,268,429; expenditures, $315,359; qualifying distributions, $272,830.
Fields of interest: Higher education; Natural resources; Environmental education; Cancers; Senior services.
Type of support: General support.
Limitations: Applications accepted. Giving primarily in MA and PA.
Application information:
Initial approach: Proposal
Deadline(s): None
Trustees: John D. Iskrant, Esq.; The Glenmede Trust Company, N.A.
EIN: 236962132

8370
Henrietta Tower Wurts Memorial Foundation
1234 Market St., Ste. 1800
Philadelphia, PA 19107-3704 (215) 563-6417
Contact: Libby Walsh

Established in 1934 in Pennsylvania.
Donor: Henrietta Tower Wurts†.
Foundation type: Independent foundation.
Financial data (yr. ended 12/31/13): Assets, $5,362,031 (M); expenditures, $367,283; qualifying distributions, $351,307; giving activities include $312,000 for 107 grants (high: $10,000; low: $1,000).

Purpose and activities: To contribute to nonsectarian corporate institutions which are engaged in helping or caring for people in need, or alleviating the conditions under which they live; grants primarily for the elderly, women, family and child welfare services.
Fields of interest: Arts and culture; Education; Early childhood education; Dental care; Community and economic development; Water sports; Human services; Victim aid; Family services; Child welfare; Homeless services; Senior services; Women's services; Children; Seniors; Females; Ethnic and racial groups; Homeless people; Low-income and poor people.
Type of support: General support; Continuing support; Annual campaigns; Equipment; Emergency funds; Seed money.
Limitations: Applications accepted. Giving limited to Philadelphia, PA. No grants to individuals, or for endowment funds, scholarships, fellowships, or matching gifts; no loans.
Publications: Application guidelines.
Application information: Application form required.
  Initial approach: Request application form
  Copies of proposal: 1
  Deadline(s): Feb. 1, May 1, Sept. 1
  Board meeting date(s): Apr., June, and Nov.
Officer: Ellen Nalle Hass, Pres.
Board Members: Allison Anderson; Patricia Blakley; Denise Brown; Tony Laduca, Ph.D; Sarah Laughlin; Joyce C. Mantell; Fred Neibauer.
Number of staff: None.
EIN: 236297977

8371
The Wyeth Foundation
101 S. Fairville Rd.
Chadds Ford, PA   19317-9440

Established in 2001 in Pennsylvania.
Donors: Phyllis M. Wyeth; James B. Wyeth.
Foundation type: Independent foundation.
Financial data (yr. ended 12/31/13): Assets, $12,592,706 (M); expenditures, $400,080; qualifying distributions, $552,875; giving activities include $288,000 for 20 grants (high: $115,000; low: $500).
Fields of interest: Arts and culture; Museums; Education; Higher education; Environment; Libraries; Human services.
Limitations: Applications not accepted. No grants to individuals.
Application information: Unsolicited applications not accepted.
Officer: Lisa A. Flagg, Secy.
Trustees: Mary Beth Dolan; Gregory F. Fields; Wendy Makins; James B. Wyeth; Phyllis M. Wyeth.
Number of staff: None.
EIN: 260002833

8372
Prince Lucinda Wyman Trust
c/o BNY Mellon, N.A.
P.O. Box 185
Pittsburgh, PA   15230-0185

Foundation type: Independent foundation.
Financial data (yr. ended 08/31/14): Assets, $3,593,303 (M); expenditures, $178,985; qualifying distributions, $147,525; giving activities include $135,540 for 1 grant.

Fields of interest: Higher education.
Limitations: Applications not accepted. Giving primarily in MA. No grants to individuals.
Application information: Unsolicited requests for funds not accepted.
Trustee: BNY Mellon, N.A.
EIN: 046237788

8373
Karen B. Yoh Foundation
c/o Edwin R. Boynton
30 Valley Stream Pkwy.
Malvern, PA   19355-1481

Donor: Karen B. Yoh Trust.
Foundation type: Independent foundation.
Financial data (yr. ended 12/31/13): Assets, $7,672,854 (M); gifts received, $3,200; expenditures, $404,495; qualifying distributions, $356,212; giving activities include $315,000 for 4 grants (high: $150,000; low: $15,000).
Fields of interest: Storms; Community improvement; Housing development.
Limitations: Applications not accepted. Giving primarily in New Orleans, LA. No grants to individuals.
Application information: Contributes only to pre-selected organizations.
Officers and Directors: Edwin R. Boynton, Pres. and Director; Russell J. Ressler, V.P. and Secy.-Treas.
EIN: 262950728

8374
The York Children's Foundation
2 Northshore Ctr.
Pittsburgh, PA   15212
Contact: Joseph C. Bartolacci

Established in 1991 in Pennsylvania.
Donor: The York Group, Inc.
Foundation type: Independent foundation.
Financial data (yr. ended 12/31/13): Assets, $191,000 (M); expenditures, $205,367; qualifying distributions, $205,367; giving activities include $200,000 for 217 grants (high: $6,000; low: $500).
Purpose and activities: Giving primarily to organizations whose main service is benefiting children in the U.S.
Fields of interest: Education; Nonprofits; Health; Diseases and conditions; Family services; Child welfare.
Type of support: Regranting.
Limitations: Applications accepted. Giving primarily in NY and PA.
Application information: Application form required.
  Initial approach: Proposal
  Deadline(s): None
  Board meeting date(s): Quarterly
Officers: Harry Pontone, Chair.; Ed Wolford, Pres.; Steve Duffy, V.P.; Doreen Klein, Treas.
EIN: 760353019

8375
Ralph W. Young Family Foundation
1050 Meridian Dr.
Presto, PA   15142-1029

Established in 2002 in Pennsylvania.
Donors: Sally J. Young†; Ralph W. Young Unitrust.
Foundation type: Independent foundation.

Financial data (yr. ended 12/31/13): Assets, $9,741,364 (M); expenditures, $456,821; qualifying distributions, $358,817; giving activities include $355,000 for 13 grants (high: $129,000; low: $1,000).
Purpose and activities: Giving primarily for scholarships for higher education.
Fields of interest: Higher education.
Type of support: Student aid; Scholarships.
Limitations: Applications not accepted. Giving primarily in PA.
Application information: Unsolicited requests for funds not accepted.
Officers and Trustees: Sandra Lee Blackwood, Mgr. and Trustee; Eileen E. Woodside, Mgr. and Trustee.
EIN: 306009141

8376
Zeldin Family Foundation
2039 Delancey St.
Philadelphia, PA   19103-6509

Established in 1986 in Pennsylvania.
Donors: Martin Zeldin; Claudia Zeldlin; Martex Fiber Southern Corp.; Stephanie Zeldin.
Foundation type: Independent foundation.
Financial data (yr. ended 11/30/13): Assets, $4,521,946 (M); gifts received, $311,000; expenditures, $275,208; qualifying distributions, $271,762; giving activities include $269,172 for 78 grants (high: $59,572; low: $200).
Purpose and activities: Giving primarily for education, youth and children's services, and for women's interests.
Fields of interest: Arts and culture; Education; Higher education; Diseases and conditions; Basic and emergency aid; Child welfare; Women's services; International development.
Type of support: General support; Matching grants; Annual campaigns; Capital campaigns; Emergency funds; Program development; Scholarships.
Limitations: Applications not accepted. Giving on a national basis. No support for religious or political organizations. No grants to individuals.
Application information: Unsolicited requests for funds will not be accepted.
  Board meeting date(s): Nov.
Trustees: Claudia Zeldin; Jessica Zeldin; Martin Zeldin; Stephanie Zeldin; Sybille Zeldin.
Number of staff: None.
EIN: 236861835

8377
The Zisman Family Foundation
311 Orchard Way
Wayne, PA   19087-4833

Established in 2000 in Pennsylvania.
Donors: Michael D. Zisman; Michael Zisman; Zisman Equities Group; Linda J. Gamble.
Foundation type: Independent foundation.
Financial data (yr. ended 12/31/13): Assets, $473,248 (M); gifts received, $395,134; expenditures, $178,472; qualifying distributions, $173,500; giving activities include $173,500 for 14 grants (high: $50,000; low: $1,000).
Purpose and activities: Giving primarily for education.
Fields of interest: Education; Higher education; Human services.

Limitations: Applications not accepted. Giving primarily in Philadelphia, PA. No grants to individuals.

Application information: Unsolicited requests for funds not accepted.

Officers and Directors: Linda J. Gamble, Pres. and Secy. and Director; Michael D. Zisman, V.P. and Treas. and Director.
EIN: 233033239

RHODE ISLAND

8378
Acriel Foundation
P.O. Box 1802
Providence, RI 02901-1802

Established in 1994 in New York.
Foundation type: Operating foundation.
Financial data (yr. ended 11/30/13): Assets, $1,385,197 (M); expenditures, $300,278; qualifying distributions, $288,873; giving activities include $285,000 for 6 grants (high: $100,000; low: $10,000).
Fields of interest: Higher education; Environmental justice; Natural resources.
Type of support: Equal access.
Limitations: Applications not accepted. No grants to individuals.
Application information: Contributes only to pre-selected organizations.
Trustees: Stuart Buice; Bank of America, N.A.
EIN: 133802863

8379
William Hadwen Ames Memorial Fund
(formerly Fanny H. Ames and Edna L. Holt Trust)
P.O. Box 1802
Providence, RI 02901-1802

Established in 2000 in Massachusetts.
Foundation type: Independent foundation.
Financial data (yr. ended 12/31/14): Assets, $6,285,126; expenditures, $374,370; qualifying distributions, $325,498.
Fields of interest: Public libraries.
Type of support: General support.
Limitations: Applications not accepted. Giving primarily in MA. No grants to individuals.
Application information: Unsolicited requests for funds not accepted.
Trustee: Bank of America, N.A.
EIN: 046905273

8380
Anne Apperson Trust
P.O. Box 1802
Providence, RI 02901-1802

Foundation type: Independent foundation.
Financial data (yr. ended 12/31/13): Assets, $3,984,797 (M); expenditures, $221,498; qualifying distributions, $183,074; giving activities include $166,101 for 3 grants (high: $55,367; low: $55,367).
Fields of interest: Education; Higher education.
Limitations: Applications not accepted. Giving primarily in Berkeley, CA, New Haven, CT and Princeton, NJ.
Application information: Unsolicited requests for funds not accepted.
Trustee: Bank of America, N.A.
EIN: 066169025

8381
Mary Alice Arakelian Foundation
P.O. Box 1802
Providence, RI 02901-1802
Application address: Mark Welch, P.O. Box 695, Newburyport, MA 01950-0895

Established in 1966 in Massachusetts.
Foundation type: Independent foundation.
Financial data (yr. ended 12/31/14): Assets, $7,358,777 (M); expenditures, $367,606; qualifying distributions, $321,549; giving activities include $290,833 for 15 grants (high: $100,000; low: $2,000).
Fields of interest: Arts and culture; Higher education; Health; Hospital care; Human services; Youth services.
Limitations: Applications accepted. Giving primarily in Newburyport, MA. No grants to individuals.
Application information:
  Initial approach: Proposal
  Deadline(s): Sept. 15
  Board meeting date(s): Oct.
Trustees: Mary E. Larnard; John F. Leary III; Donald D. Mitchell; Kimberly A. Rock; Mark F. Welch; Bank of America, N.A.
EIN: 046155695

8382
George Arents, Jr. Cerimon Fund
(formerly The Cerimon Fund)
P.O. Box 1802
Providence, RI 02901-1802

Foundation type: Independent foundation.
Financial data (yr. ended 01/31/15): Assets, $4,160,333 (M); expenditures, $262,586; qualifying distributions, $208,020; giving activities include $184,650 for 6 grants (high: $80,000; low: $850).
Fields of interest: Education; Higher education.
Type of support: General support.
Limitations: Applications not accepted. Giving primarily in NJ and New York, NY. No grants to individuals.
Application information: Unsolicited requests for funds not accepted.
Trustees: Patricia F. Davidson; Bank of America, N.A.
EIN: 136069576

8383
The Arr Trust D Charitable Trust
c/o Bank of America, N.A.
P. O. Box 1802
Providence, RI 02901-1802

Foundation type: Independent foundation.
Financial data (yr. ended 11/30/13): Assets, $4,720,822 (M); expenditures, $239,148; qualifying distributions, $215,727; giving activities include $200,041 for 1 grant.
Fields of interest: Catholicism.
Limitations: Applications not accepted. Giving primarily in Dubuque, IA. No grants to individuals.
Application information: Contributes only to pre-selected organizations.
Trustee: Bank of America, N.A.
EIN: 366944752

8384
Bailey Foundation
P.O. Box 1802
Providence, RI 02901-1802

Established in 2002 in Massachusetts.
Donor: Hamilton Bailey Charitable Trust.
Foundation type: Independent foundation.
Financial data (yr. ended 07/31/14): Assets, $3,444,996 (M); expenditures, $201,861; qualifying distributions, $166,967; giving activities include $150,000 for 16 grants (high: $40,000; low: $2,000).
Fields of interest: Natural resources; Domesticated animals; Emergency medical services; Public libraries; Christianity; Human services.
Limitations: Applications not accepted. No grants to individuals.
Application information: Unsolicited requests for funds not accepted.
Trustee: Bank of America.
EIN: 161625656

8385
Edward S. Barton Trust
c/o Bank of America, N.A.
P.O. Box 1802
Providence, RI 02903-1802

Established in 1993 in New York.
Donor: Edward S. Barton†.
Foundation type: Independent foundation.
Financial data (yr. ended 07/31/13): Assets, $4,242,534 (M); expenditures, $199,687; qualifying distributions, $183,214; giving activities include $179,663 for 5 grants (high: $50,000; low: $17,400).
Fields of interest: Public affairs; Community and economic development.
Type of support: General support.
Limitations: Applications not accepted. Giving primarily in Waterville, NY. No grants to individuals.
Application information: Contributes only to pre-selected organizations.
Trustees: Richard S. Woodman; Bank of America, N.A.
EIN: 166385508

8386
Christine L. Beck Trust
c/o Bank of America, N.A.
P.O. Box 1802
Providence, RI 02901-1802

Established in 1998 in Massachusetts.
Foundation type: Independent foundation.
Financial data (yr. ended 12/31/14): Assets, $3,352,327 (M); expenditures, $318,933; qualifying distributions, $293,286; giving activities include $279,795 for 15 grants (high: $70,655; low: $2,826).
Fields of interest: Education; Health; Youth development.
Limitations: Applications not accepted. Giving primarily in MA, with emphasis on Clinton. No grants to individuals.
Application information: Unsolicited requests for funds not accepted.
Trustee: Bank of America, N.A.
EIN: 046427501

8387
Helene and Bertram Bernhardt Foundation
55 Dorrance St., Ste. 400
Providence, RI 02903-2221   (401) 861-2900
Contact: Samuel D. Zurier Esq.

Established in 2007 in Rhode Island.
Donor: The Bertram L. Bernhardt Trust.
Foundation type: Independent foundation.
Financial data (yr. ended 04/30/14): Assets,
$11,775,720 (M); expenditures, $613,391;
qualifying distributions, $584,888; giving activities
include $434,580 for 24 grants (high: $186,300;
low: $200).
Fields of interest: Nonprofits; Judaism.
Type of support: Capital campaigns; Regranting.
Limitations: Applications accepted. Giving primarily
in Providence, RI.
Application information: Application form required.
   Initial approach: Letter
   Deadline(s): None
Officer: Samuel D. Zurier, Esq., Secy.
Trustees: Leslie Gutterman; Robert G. Huckins.
EIN: 342053837

8388
Grace Bersted Foundation
P.O. Box 1802
Providence, RI 02901-1802
E-mail: ilgrantmaking@ustrust.com; Main
URL: https://www.bankofamerica.com/
philanthropic/grantmaking.go

Established in 1986 in Illinois.
Donor: Grace A. Bersted†.
Foundation type: Independent foundation.
Financial data (yr. ended 12/31/14): Assets,
$9,306,309 (M); expenditures, $461,914;
qualifying distributions, $399,913; giving activities
include $338,000 for 25 grants (high: $50,000;
low: $5,000).
Purpose and activities: Giving primarily for health
care programming for underserved populations.
Special consideration is given to charitable
organizations that serve the needs of children or the
disabled.
Fields of interest: Secondary education; Higher
education; Natural resources; Foundations; Health;
Human services; Family services; Children.
Limitations: Applications accepted. Giving limited to
DuPage, Kane, Lake, and McHenry counties, IL. No
grants to individuals.
Application information: Application form required.
   Initial approach: Online through foundation web
   site
   Deadline(s): Aug. 1
Trustee: Bank of America, N.A.
EIN: 366841348

8389
Lizzie & Edward V. Bird Trust
P.O. Box 1802
Providence, RI 02901-1802   8888663275
Application address: c/o Susan Morrissey, Dept. of
Social Svcs., Massachusetts General Hospital, 15
Parkman St., Boston, MA 02114-3117

Foundation type: Independent foundation.
Financial data (yr. ended 02/28/15): Assets,
$5,654,274; expenditures, $291,013; qualifying
distributions, $251,919.

Purpose and activities: Provides medical aid,
through Massachusetts General Hospital, to needy
individuals.
Fields of interest: Health; Hospital care.
Limitations: Applications accepted. Giving limited to
MA.
Application information: Application forms available
only at Massachusetts General Hospital. Application
form required.
   Deadline(s): None
Trustee: Bank of America, N.A.
EIN: 046020389

8390
Robert Black Charitable Foundation
P.O. Box 1802
Providence, RI 02901-1802
Application address: c/o Christine O'Donnell, Bank
of America, 1 Bryant Park, New York, NY 10036

Established in 1998 in New York.
Donor: Robert Black†.
Foundation type: Independent foundation.
Financial data (yr. ended 12/31/13): Assets,
$8,781,770 (M); expenditures, $440,521;
qualifying distributions, $380,590; giving activities
include $325,105 for 7 grants (high: $53,000; low:
$10,105).
Purpose and activities: Grants limited to medical
research preferably for lung, pancreatic, and liver
cancers, and gastrointestinal problems.
Fields of interest: Digestive system diseases;
Pancreatic cancer; Lung cancer.
Type of support: Research.
Limitations: Applications accepted. Giving on a
national basis. No grants to individuals.
Application information:
   Initial approach: Proposal
   Deadline(s): None
Trustee: Bank of America, N.A.
Number of staff: 1 part-time professional.
EIN: 137174452

8391
Eugene B. Bowen Universalist Trust
(formerly E Bowen Bo Universalist Church Fund)
P.O. 1802
Providence, RI 02901-1802

Foundation type: Independent foundation.
Financial data (yr. ended 12/31/13): Assets,
$2,030,168 (M); expenditures, $186,794;
qualifying distributions, $168,136; giving activities
include $155,822 for 2 grants (high: $155,622;
low: $200).
Fields of interest: Housing development; Religion.
Type of support: General support.
Limitations: Applications not accepted. Giving
primarily in MA.
Application information: Unsolicited request for
funds not accepted.
Trustee: Bank of America, N.A.
EIN: 046437940

8392
The Joan H. Brack Charitable Foundation
c/o RBS Citizens N.A.
10 Tripps Ln.
Riverside, RI 02915-7995
Application address: c/o Kenneth B. Brack, 6 Soule
St., Plympton, MA 02367

Established in 2000 in Massachusetts.
Donors: Barker Steel Co. Golf Tournaments;
Leonard Trudell; Robert Brack; Bars Co., Inc.
Foundation type: Independent foundation.
Financial data (yr. ended 12/31/13): Assets,
$1,542,577 (M); expenditures, $202,477;
qualifying distributions, $163,766; giving activities
include $162,215 for 14 grants (high: $40,000;
low: $500).
Fields of interest: Education; Cancers; Human
services.
Type of support: Student aid.
Limitations: Applications accepted. Giving primarily
in MA.
Application information: Application form required.
   Initial approach: Request application
   Deadline(s): Apr. 4
Trustees: Denise Brack; Kenneth B. Brack; Robert
B. Brack; Virginia C. Brack, MD; William H. Brack.
EIN: 316632672

8393
The Chace Fund Inc
46 Aborn St., 4th Fl.
Providence, RI 02903-7104   (401) 854-0520
Contact: Elizabeth Z. Chace, Pres.

Established in 1947 in Rhode Island.
Donors: Malcolm G. Chace III; Arnold B. Chace;
Berkshire Hathaway Inc.; Kathleen Osborne†;
Beatrice O. Chace†; Patricia Kent; Arnold B. Chace,
Jr.; Bank Rhode Island; Elizabeth Z. Chace.
Foundation type: Independent foundation.
Financial data (yr. ended 12/31/13): Assets,
$1,246,306 (M); expenditures, $327,227;
qualifying distributions, $299,155; giving activities
include $299,155 for 28 grants (high: $50,000;
low: $200).
Fields of interest: Arts and culture; Education;
Environment; Health; Human services.
Type of support: General support.
Limitations: Applications accepted. Giving primarily
in MA, NY, and RI. No grants to individuals.
Application information: Application form required.
   Initial approach: Letter
   Deadline(s): None
Officers and Directors: Elizabeth Z. Chace, Pres.
and Director; Arnold B. Chace, Jr., V.P. and Secy.
and Director; Linda Deangelis, Treas. and Director;
Johnnie C. Chase.
EIN: 056008849

8394
Earle P. Charlton, Jr. Discretionary
Charitable Trust
(formerly Earle P. Charlton, Jr. Charitable Trust)
P.O. Box 1802
Providence, RI 02901-1802
Application address: Bank of America c/o Lauren
Cerullo 100 Federal St., Boston, MA 02110,
tel.: (617) 434-0225

Established in 1973 in Massachusetts.

Donor: Earle P. Charlton, Jr.†.
Foundation type: Independent foundation.
Financial data (yr. ended 12/31/14): Assets, $7,797,678 (M); expenditures, $434,767; qualifying distributions, $363,906; giving activities include $300,000 for 2 grants (high: $200,000; low: $100,000).
Fields of interest: Nonprofits; Health; Hospital care; Diabetes; Youth services.
Type of support: Regranting; General support.
Limitations: Applications accepted. Giving primarily in Boston and Fall River, MA. No grants to individuals.
Application information: Application form required.
Initial approach: Letter
Deadline(s): None
Trustees: E.P. Charlton; Stacy Charlton; Michael Garfield; Bank of America, N.A.
EIN: 046334412

8395
Vera J. Clark Irrevocable Trust-Balance
P.O. Box 1802
Providence, RI   02901-1802

Established in 2001 in Rhode Island.
Foundation type: Independent foundation.
Financial data (yr. ended 12/31/13): Assets, $6,424,788 (M); expenditures, $361,992; qualifying distributions, $308,144; giving activities include $283,290 for 8 grants (high: $141,645; low: $16,477).
Fields of interest: Education; Higher education; Human services; Scouting programs.
Limitations: Applications not accepted. Giving primarily in Brooklyn and West Nyack, NY, and RI. No grants to individuals.
Application information: Unsolicited requests for funds not accepted.
Trustee: Bank of America, N.A.
EIN: 056126789

8396
Mary M. Coes Charitable Trust
P.O. Box 1802
Providence, RI   02901-1802

Foundation type: Independent foundation.
Financial data (yr. ended 12/31/13): Assets, $4,518,021 (M); expenditures, $203,278; qualifying distributions, $170,976; giving activities include $146,790 for 5 grants (high: $29,358; low: $29,358).
Fields of interest: Animal welfare; Nursing care; Youth services; Female children and youth.
Type of support: General support.
Limitations: Applications not accepted. Giving primarily in MA.
Application information: Unsolicited requests for funds not accepted.
Trustee: Bank of America.
EIN: 046023228

8397
The Collis Foundation
10 Weybosset St., Ste. 302
Providence, RI   02903-2215
Contact: James D. Cregan

Application address: c/o Everwatch Financial, Attn: Astrid C. Womble, 8 Sound Shore Dr., Greenwich, CT 06830, tel.: (203) 629-7950

Established in 1997 in Rhode Island.
Donor: Charles A. Collis.
Foundation type: Independent foundation.
Financial data (yr. ended 02/28/14): Assets, $11,751,955 (M); gifts received, $2,984,838; expenditures, $198,321; qualifying distributions, $198,321; giving activities include $183,500 for 7 grants (high: $50,000; low: $10,000).
Purpose and activities: The primary focus is on children's education, scholarships and literacy programs, and basic human needs.
Fields of interest: Education; Human services.
Type of support: General support; Matching grants; Continuing support; Annual campaigns; Capital campaigns; Capital and infrastructure; Endowments; Emergency funds; Program development; Scholarships.
Limitations: Applications accepted. Giving primarily in RI; giving also in CT and MA. No support for environmental, rehabilitation, addiction or adoption programs.
Application information:
Initial approach: 2 page letter of inquiry
Deadline(s): None
Officer and Directors: Astrid C. Womble, Pres. and Director; Frohman Anderson; Charles A. Collis; Elfried A. Collis.
Number of staff: 1 full-time professional.
EIN: 061472006

8398
Richter E. E. Cook Memorial Fund
P.O. Box 1802
Providence, RI   02901-1802

Foundation type: Independent foundation.
Financial data (yr. ended 12/31/14): Assets, $4,200,955; expenditures, $245,439; qualifying distributions, $210,035 and $0 for set-asides.
Fields of interest: Education.
Limitations: Applications not accepted. Giving primarily in CA and IL.
Application information: Unsolicited requests for funds not accepted.
Trustee: Bank of America, N.A.
EIN: 366038368

8399
Margarette G. Crossman Trust
P.O. Box 1802
Providence, RI   02901-1802

Foundation type: Independent foundation.
Financial data (yr. ended 12/31/14): Assets, $5,415,227; expenditures, $240,033; qualifying distributions, $201,376.
Fields of interest: Animal welfare.
Limitations: Applications not accepted. Giving limited to Boston, MA.
Application information: Unsolicited requests for funds not accepted.
Trustee: Bank of America, N.A.
EIN: 046028852

8400
Robert Darling Educational Memorial Fund
P.O. Box 1802
Providence, RI   02901-1802

Foundation type: Independent foundation.
Financial data (yr. ended 12/31/14): Assets, $4,402,872; expenditures, $259,736; qualifying distributions, $221,969 and $0 for set-asides.
Fields of interest: Higher education.
Type of support: General support.
Limitations: Applications not accepted. Giving primarily in CT and NH. No grants to individuals.
Application information: Unsolicited requests for funds not accepted.
Trustee: Bank of America, N.A.
EIN: 066032895

8401
Del Prete Family Foundation
251 Smith St.
Providence, RI   02908-4954

Established in 1999 in Rhode Island.
Donor: Daniel B. Del Prete.
Foundation type: Independent foundation.
Financial data (yr. ended 12/31/13): Assets, $1,869,974 (M); gifts received, $200,000; expenditures, $162,172; qualifying distributions, $161,580; giving activities include $161,000 for 8 grants (high: $135,000; low: $1,000).
Fields of interest: Health; Housing development; Human services.
Type of support: General support.
Limitations: Applications not accepted. Giving primarily in RI. No grants to individuals.
Application information: Unsolicited requests for funds not accepted.
Trustee: Daniel B. Del Prete.
EIN: 050508471

8402
Elmer Hobson DeLoura Trust for Scholarships
(formerly The DeLoura Family Trust)
P.O. Box 1802
Providence, RI   02901-1802
Contact: Susanna Posteo-Castillo
Application address: c/o Scholarship America, Inc., P.O. Box 297, St. Peter, MN 56802

Established in 1981 in Texas.
Foundation type: Independent foundation.
Financial data (yr. ended 01/31/15): Assets, $4,597,638 (M); expenditures, $251,887; qualifying distributions, $209,383; giving activities include $165,000 for grants.
Purpose and activities: Giving primarily for scholarship funds for graduates of Martha's Vineyard, Massachusetts schools.
Fields of interest: Education.
Type of support: Scholarships.
Limitations: Applications accepted. Giving limited to Martha's Vineyard, MA and St. Peter, MN. No grants to individuals directly.
Application information: Applications available at the guidance office of Martha's Vineyard, MA, schools. Application form required.
Deadline(s): Mar. 15
Board meeting date(s): None

Trustee: Bank of America, N.A.
EIN: 046460749

8403
Lane and Elizabeth Dwinell Charitable Trust
P.O. Box 1802
Providence, RI 02901-1802 8888663275

Established in 1997 in New Hampshire.
Donor: Lane Dwinell†.
Foundation type: Independent foundation.
Financial data (yr. ended 12/31/14): Assets, $4,770,362; expenditures, $329,450; qualifying distributions, $262,101.
Purpose and activities: Giving primarily for education and social services.
Fields of interest: Higher education; Reading promotion; Health; Residential mental health care; Public libraries; Public policy; Community and economic development; Special population support; Children and youth; Homeless people; People with psychosocial disabilities.
Type of support: Policy, advocacy and systems reform.
Limitations: Applications accepted. Giving limited to organizaztions serving the city of Lebanon and upper valley of NH. No support for private foundations. No grants to individuals.
Application information: Only 501(c)(3) organizations considered. Application form required.
  Initial approach: Letter
Trustee: Bank of America, N.A.
Advisory Committee: Pamela B. Bean; Paul Boucher; Doug Britton; Roger D. Carroll; James Vanier.
EIN: 161543787

8404
Estate Of Elizabeth Straut
P.O. Box 1802
Providence, RI 02901-1802

Foundation type: Independent foundation.
Financial data (yr. ended 04/30/14): Assets, $4,556,847 (M); expenditures, $253,114; qualifying distributions, $220,825; giving activities include $199,302 for 3 grants (high: $66,434; low: $66,434).
Fields of interest: Environment; Religion; Youth development.
Type of support: General support.
Limitations: Applications not accepted. Giving primarily in IL.
Application information: Unsolicited requests for funds not accepted.
Trustee: Bank of America, N.A.
EIN: 366038536

8405
The Feibelman Foundation
c/o H. Jack Feibelman
11 Baldwin Orchard Dr.
Cranston, RI 02920-3901

Established in 1998 in Puerto Rico.
Donors: H. Jack Feibelman; AFCO, Inc.; Jack Feibelman; Barbara Feibelman; AFCO L.P.
Foundation type: Independent foundation.

Financial data (yr. ended 12/31/13): Assets, $4,393,917 (M); gifts received, $115,978; expenditures, $379,781; qualifying distributions, $359,836; giving activities include $359,836 for 31 + grants (high: $120,000).
Purpose and activities: Giving primarily for Jewish organizations; funding also for health associations, and human services.
Fields of interest: Education; Nonprofits; Diseases and conditions; Judaism; Human services.
Type of support: Regranting.
Limitations: Applications not accepted. Giving primarily in MA, New York, NY, and RI. No grants to individuals.
Application information: Contributes only to pre-selected organizations.
Trustee: H. Jack Feibelman.
EIN: 050499644

8406
Felicia Fund, Inc.
90 Elm St.
Providence, RI 02903-4647 (401) 274-1550
Contact: Pauline C. Metcalf, Pres.

Established in 1985 in Rhode Island.
Donor: Pauline C. Metcalf.
Foundation type: Independent foundation.
Financial data (yr. ended 11/30/14): Assets, $11,276,915 (M); expenditures, $467,009; qualifying distributions, $353,406; giving activities include $353,326 for 44 grants (high: $100,000; low: $250).
Purpose and activities: Giving primarily to fund projects that relate to architecture, decorative art, historic preservation, conservation, and related educational pursuits.
Fields of interest: Architecture; History museums; Historic preservation; Education; Graduate and professional education; Zoos.
Type of support: Individual development.
Limitations: Applications accepted. Giving primarily in MA, NY, and RI. No grants to individuals.
Application information:
  Initial approach: Proposal
  Deadline(s): None
Officers and Trustees: Pauline C. Metcalf, Pres. and Trustee; Frank Mauran, Secy. and Trustee; Paul W. Whyte, Treas. and Trustee; Joseph Spang.
EIN: 050420703

8407
Daniel W. Field Trust
P. O. Box 1802
Providence, RI 02901-1802

Foundation type: Independent foundation.
Financial data (yr. ended 12/31/13): Assets, $9,912,714 (M); expenditures, $442,627; qualifying distributions, $361,659; giving activities include $324,809 for 25 grants (high: $105,563; low: $1,776).
Fields of interest: Arts and culture; Community and economic development; Protestantism; Human services.
Type of support: General support.
Limitations: Applications not accepted.
Application information: Unsolicited requests for funds not accepted.
Trustee: Bank of America.
EIN: 046009552

8408
Herman Frasch Foundation for Chemical Research
P.O. Box 1802
Providence, RI 02901-1802

Established in 1924 in New York.
Donor: Elizabeth Blee Frasch†.
Foundation type: Independent foundation.
Financial data (yr. ended 12/31/13): Assets, $9,454,897 (M); expenditures, $506,026; qualifying distributions, $448,899; giving activities include $400,000 for 8 grants (high: $50,000; low: $50,000).
Purpose and activities: Grants for research in agricultural chemistry made for 5-year periods to nonprofit incorporated institutions in the U.S., selected with the advice of the American Chemical Society as well as Frasch committee members.
Fields of interest: Chemistry; Agriculture.
Type of support: Research.
Limitations: Applications accepted. Giving primarily in CA, CO, DC, FL, GA, MI, NJ, OR, and UT. No grants to individuals, or for endowment funds, building funds, operating budgets, scholarships, fellowships, or matching gifts; no loans.
Application information:
  Initial approach: Proposal
  Deadline(s): None
Trustee: Bank of America, N.A.
Number of staff: 1 part-time professional.
EIN: 136073145

8409
Fuller Family Charitable Trust
23 Broad St.
Westerly, RI 02891 (401) 348-1265

Foundation type: Independent foundation.
Financial data (yr. ended 06/30/13): Assets, $2,544,377 (M); expenditures, $261,957; qualifying distributions, $240,434; giving activities include $237,500 for 110 grants (high: $5,000; low: $500).
Fields of interest: Health; Agriculture; Human services.
Application information:
  Initial approach: Letter
  Deadline(s): None
Trustees: John W. Fuller; Penelope F. Petrone; The Washington Trust Company.
EIN: 356819590

8410
Galkin Private Foundation
155 Brookside Ave.
West Warwick, RI 02893-3865

Established in 1996 in Rhode Island.
Donors: Natco Home Fashions; Robert T. Galkin; Warren B. Galkin; Natco Products Corp.
Foundation type: Independent foundation.
Financial data (yr. ended 12/31/13): Assets, $2,184,261 (M); gifts received, $304,179; expenditures, $407,648; qualifying distributions, $399,795; giving activities include $399,795 for 8 grants (high: $112,775; low: $10,000).
Purpose and activities: Giving primarily for education, health care, and human services.

Fields of interest: Maritime museums; University education; Nonprofits; Hospital care; Human services; Youth services.
Type of support: Regranting.
Limitations: Applications not accepted. Giving primarily in RI. No grants to individuals.
Application information: Unsolicited requests for funds not accepted.
Officers: Robert T. Galkin, Pres.; Steven Rosenbaum, Secy.; Warren B. Galkin, Treas.
EIN: 050494243

8411
Harold S. Geneen Charitable Trust
P.O. Box 1802
Providence, RI   02901-1802

Established in 1999 in New York.
Donors: Harold S. Geneen†; UW HS Geneen f/b/o June Geneen.
Foundation type: Independent foundation.
Financial data (yr. ended 12/31/13): Assets, $36,045,388 (M); gifts received, $27,105,552; expenditures, $414,273; qualifying distributions, $352,329; giving activities include $277,335 for 3 grants (high: $150,000; low: $62,500).
Fields of interest: Higher education; Heart and circulatory system diseases.
Type of support: Research.
Limitations: Applications not accepted. Giving primarily in MA and NY. No grants to individuals.
Application information: Contributes only to pre-selected organizations.
Trustees: June Geneen; Allen Keesee; Thomas Silbiger; Bank of America, N.A.
EIN: 137163001

8412
Arthur L. Getz Charitable Trust
10 Tripps Ln.
Riverside, RI   02915-7995
Application address: c/o Bill Sirail, 875 Elm St., Manchester, NH 03101, tel.: (603) 634-7752

Established in 1995 in New Hampshire.
Foundation type: Independent foundation.
Financial data (yr. ended 04/30/13): Assets, $3,366,894 (M); expenditures, $259,155; qualifying distributions, $238,705; giving activities include $222,409 for 47 grants (high: $15,000; low: $1,000).
Fields of interest: Arts and culture; Religion; Human services.
Type of support: Capital and infrastructure; Pro bono consulting services; Equipment; Emergency funds; Program development; Convening; Curriculum development; Internships; Research.
Limitations: Applications accepted. Giving limited to NH. No grants to individuals.
Application information: Application form required.
Initial approach: Letter
Deadline(s): None
Trustee: RBS Citizens, N.A.
Number of staff: None.
EIN: 226701239

8413
Helen Wade Greene Charitable Trust
P.O. Box 1802
Providence, RI   02901-1802

Established in 1957 in Ohio.
Foundation type: Independent foundation.
Financial data (yr. ended 12/31/13): Assets, $12,086,725 (M); expenditures, $467,405; qualifying distributions, $441,249; giving activities include $430,000 for 10 grants (high: $310,000; low: $5,000).
Fields of interest: Arts and culture; Art museums; Education; Higher education; Foundations; Nonprofits; Hospital care; Human services.
Type of support: General support; Regranting.
Limitations: Applications not accepted. Giving primarily in Boston, MA; some funding also in Cleveland, OH. No grants to individuals.
Application information: Unsolicited requests for funds not accepted.
Trustees: Anne Hollis Perkins; E. Lee Perry; Slocumb Hollis Perry; Bank of America, N.A.
EIN: 346527172

8414
Maurice R. & Meta G. Gross Foundation
c/o Bank of America, N.A.
P. O. Box 1802
Providence, RI   02901-1802

Established in 1992 in Illinois.
Donor: Meta G. Gross Irrevocable Trust.
Foundation type: Independent foundation.
Financial data (yr. ended 11/30/14): Assets, $7,283,418 (M); expenditures, $443,133; qualifying distributions, $368,265; giving activities include $319,760 for 37 grants (high: $50,000; low: $1,000).
Purpose and activities: Giving primarily for museum support, higher education, and youth programs.
Fields of interest: Arts and culture; Museums; Higher education; Nonprofits; Diseases and conditions; Child welfare.
Type of support: Research; Research and evaluation; Regranting.
Limitations: Applications accepted. Giving primarily in AZ and IL. No grants to individuals, or for building or capital campaigns.
Publications: Application guidelines.
Application information:
Initial approach: Telephone
Copies of proposal: 2
Deadline(s): None
Board meeting date(s): Oct.
Trustee: Bank of America, N.A.; John D. Marshall.
EIN: 367013665

8415
Louise Davis Halsted Charitable Foundation
P.O. Box 1802
Providence, RI   02901-1802

Donor: Louise Davis Halsted.
Foundation type: Independent foundation.
Financial data (yr. ended 09/30/14): Assets, $3,250,868 (M); expenditures, $178,589; qualifying distributions, $152,367; giving activities include $136,969 for 10 grants (high: $29,997; low: $1,670).
Fields of interest: Education; Health; Religion.
Limitations: Applications not accepted. Giving primarily in VT.
Application information: Unsolicited request for funds not accepted.

Trustee: Bank of America, N.A.
EIN: 306257040

8416
Gutsave Hartman Trust
P.O. Box 1802
Providence, RI   02901-1802

Foundation type: Independent foundation.
Financial data (yr. ended 12/31/14): Assets, $4,479,415 (M); expenditures, $261,325; qualifying distributions, $202,358; giving activities include $181,370 for 2 grants (high: $145,096; low: $36,274).
Fields of interest: Domesticated animals; Health.
Type of support: General support.
Limitations: Applications not accepted. Giving primarily in MA.
Application information: Unsolicited requests for funds not accepted.
Trustee: Bank of America.
EIN: 046027388

8417
Harry C. Hartman Trust
c/o Bank of America, N.A.
P.O. Box 1802
Providence, RI   02901-1802

Foundation type: Independent foundation.
Financial data (yr. ended 12/31/13): Assets, $3,758,349 (M); expenditures, $241,381; qualifying distributions, $212,166; giving activities include $199,781 for 3 grants (high: $87,404; low: $37,459).
Fields of interest: Hospital care; Human services.
Limitations: Applications not accepted. No grants to individuals.
Application information: Unsolicited requests for funds not accepted.
Trustee: Bank of America, N.A.
EIN: 226302588

8418
Leslie L. & Mary B. Hecht Memorial Fund
P.O. Box 1802
Providence, RI   02901-1802

Foundation type: Independent foundation.
Financial data (yr. ended 03/31/15): Assets, $5,845,564; expenditures, $329,038; qualifying distributions, $289,237.
Fields of interest: Specialty hospital care; Cancers; Human services.
Limitations: Applications not accepted. Giving limited to Tampa, FL, Chicago, IL, and Oklahoma City, OK.
Application information: Contributes only to pre-selected organizations.
Trustee: Bank of America, N.A.
EIN: 366774670

8419
Nan and Matilda Heydt Fund
P.O. Box 1802
Providence, RI   02901-1802
Contact: Sheila Toto, Prog. Off.

Established in 1966 in Massachusetts.

Donor: Matilda L. Heydt†.
Foundation type: Independent foundation.
Financial data (yr. ended 12/31/14): Assets,
$6,690,403 (M); expenditures, $367,114;
qualifying distributions, $319,296; giving activities
include $285,728 for 44 grants (high: $17,100;
low: $2,900).
Purpose and activities: Grants for public charitable
purposes including health, welfare, the humanities,
and education; emphasis on child welfare and youth
agencies, community funds, and aid to the
handicapped in the vicinity of Springfield,
Massachusetts.
Fields of interest: Education; Environment;
Foundations; Nonprofits; Health; Diseases and
conditions; Mental and behavioral disorders; Child
welfare; Youth development; People with
disabilities.
Type of support: Capital campaigns; Matching
grants; Capital and infrastructure; Equipment; Land
acquisitions; Program development; Publications;
Seed money; Regranting.
Limitations: Applications accepted. Giving primarily
in MA. No grants to individuals, or for endowment
funds, scholarships, fellowships, or operating
budgets; no loans.
Application information: The application review
process involves a face-to-face meeting.
 Initial approach: Applications not accepted by fax
  or e-mail
 Deadline(s): 2/23
Trustee: Bank of America, N.A.
EIN: 046136421

8420
Carl & Anne Hirsch Family Charitable Foundation
P. O. Box 1802
Providence, RI   02901-1802   8888663275

Established in 1998 in South Carolina.
Donor: Carl H. Hirsch.
Foundation type: Independent foundation.
Financial data (yr. ended 12/31/14): Assets,
$121,572; gifts received, $100,000; expenditures,
$150,165; qualifying distributions, $149,013 and
$0 for set-asides.
Fields of interest: Arts and culture; Education;
Religion.
Limitations: Applications not accepted. Giving
primarily in OH. No grants to individuals.
Application information: Unsolicited requests for
funds not accepted.
Trustee: Bank of America, N.A.
EIN: 137141065

8421
Hoag Family Charitable Foundation
P.O. Box 1802
Providence, RI   02901-1802   8888663275
Application address: Lynn Dashevsky, c/o Bank of
America, 200 Glastonbury Blvd., Glastonbury, CT
06033

Established in 2005 in New York.
Donors: Barbara Hoag; Bruce Hoag.
Foundation type: Independent foundation.
Financial data (yr. ended 12/31/14): Assets,
$4,354,486; expenditures, $328,891; qualifying
distributions, $270,830.

Fields of interest: Education; Human services;
Basic and emergency aid; International
development.
Application information:
 Initial approach: Proposal
 Deadline(s): None
Trustee: Bank of America, N.A.
EIN: 204058314

8422
Hope Foundation
50 S. Main St.
Providence, RI   02903-2919   (401) 272-5050
Contact: Angela B. Fischer, Tr.

Established in 1960 in Rhode Island.
Donors: Angela B. Fischer; J. Carter Brown; Nicholas
Brown; Nicholas Brown; Sylvia Brown.
Foundation type: Independent foundation.
Financial data (yr. ended 12/31/13): Assets,
$3,830,389 (M); expenditures, $196,031;
qualifying distributions, $169,950; giving activities
include $169,950 for 59 grants (high: $20,000;
low: $225).
Purpose and activities: Giving primarily for the arts
and education.
Fields of interest: Arts and culture; Education;
Human services.
Type of support: General support; Continuing
support; Annual campaigns; Capital campaigns;
Capital and infrastructure.
Limitations: Applications accepted. Giving primarily
in MA, MD, RI, and VA.
Application information: Application form required.
 Initial approach: Letter
 Deadline(s): None
Trustees: John C. Brown IV; Nicholas Brown; Angela
B. Fischer.
EIN: 056006366

8423
Harry M., Miriam C. & William C. Horton Foundation
P.O. Box 1802
Providence, RI   02901-1802

Established in 2004 in Rhode Island.
Donor: Miriam C. Horton.
Foundation type: Independent foundation.
Financial data (yr. ended 12/31/14): Assets,
$7,207,633 (M); expenditures, $349,067;
qualifying distributions, $331,228; giving activities
include $305,000 for 37 grants (high: $77,500;
low: $2,000).
Fields of interest: Arts and culture; Higher
education; Health; Hospital care; Human services.
Limitations: Applications not accepted.
Application information: Unsolicited requests for
funds not accepted.
Trustee: Bank of America, N.A.
EIN: 010810723

8424
Edward Wagner and George Hosser Scholarship Fund Trust
c/o Citizens Bank
10 Tripps Ln.
Riverside, RI   02915-7995
Application Address: c/o RBS Citizens, N.A.,
Attn.: Bill Dirak, 900 Elm St., Manchester, NH,
03101, Application Phone: (603) 634-7752

Established in 1964 in New Hampshire.
Donor: Ottilie Wagner Hosser†.
Foundation type: Independent foundation.
Financial data (yr. ended 06/30/14): Assets,
$6,204,189 (M); expenditures, $354,542;
qualifying distributions, $327,277; giving activities
include $278,570 for 1 grant.
Purpose and activities: Scholarship grants for
college or professional education to worthy boys and
young men from Manchester, New Hampshire, who
wish to pursue an undergraduate program at an
accredited school.
Fields of interest: Foundations.
Type of support: Student aid.
Limitations: Applications accepted. Giving limited to
residents of Manchester, NH.
Application information: Application form required.
 Initial approach: Letter
 Copies of proposal: 1
 Deadline(s): May 31
 Board meeting date(s): Aug.
 Final notification: Approx. the 3rd week in Aug.
Trustee: RBS Citizens, N.A.
Number of staff: None.
EIN: 026005491

8425
Nathaniel Hubbard Charitable Trust
P.O. Box 1802
Providence, RI   02901-1802

Foundation type: Independent foundation.
Financial data (yr. ended 12/31/13): Assets,
$5,556,784 (M); expenditures, $298,899;
qualifying distributions, $248,495; giving activities
include $225,345 for 4 grants (high: $96,560; low:
$25,757).
Fields of interest: Christianity; Catholicism.
Limitations: Applications not accepted.
Application information: Unsolicited requests for
funds not accepted.
Trustee: Bank of America, N.A.
EIN: 066265198

8426
Jacbel Foundation
P.O. Box 1802
Providence, RI   02901-1802

Established in 1995 in Massachusetts.
Foundation type: Independent foundation.
Financial data (yr. ended 12/31/14): Assets,
$4,758,519; expenditures, $234,188; qualifying
distributions, $209,342.
Fields of interest: Education; Law education;
Natural resources; Nonprofits; Hospital care;
Alzheimer's disease; Public libraries; Judaism;
Human services.
Type of support: Regranting.
Limitations: Applications not accepted. No grants to
individuals.

Application information: Unsolicited requests for funds not accepted.
Trustees: Jamie L. Schreiber; Jeffrey W. Stulin; Rita J. Stulin.
EIN: 046796689

8427
Wilhelmina W. Jackson Trust
P.O. Box 1802
Providence, RI   02901-1802
Application address: Bank of America, N.A., 100 Federal St., Boston, MA 02110

Foundation type: Independent foundation.
Financial data (yr. ended 12/31/13): Assets, $8,750,485 (M); expenditures, $493,410; qualifying distributions, $429,178; giving activities include $500 for 1 grant, and $350,000 for 76 grants to individuals (high: $10,000; low: $500).
Purpose and activities: Scholarships to residents of Swampscott and Marblehead, MA, for the study of medicine, and for the study of any form of the creative arts at a college, university or art school.
Fields of interest: Higher education.
Type of support: Student aid.
Limitations: Applications accepted. Giving limited to residents of Swampscott and Marblehead, MA.
Application information: Application forms available through Marblehead and Swampscott high school guidance offices. Application form required.
   Initial approach: Completed application form
   Copies of proposal: 3
   Deadline(s): Feb. 15
   Final notification: July 30th
Trustee: Bank of America, N.A.
EIN: 046024405

8428
Janci Foundation
8 Whitney Dr.
Lincoln, RI   02865-4640

Established in 2000 in Rhode Island.
Donors: Jeffrey Weiss; Nancy Freeman.
Foundation type: Independent foundation.
Financial data (yr. ended 12/31/13): Assets, $3,093 (M); gifts received, $176,510; expenditures, $186,561; qualifying distributions, $186,561; giving activities include $185,000 for 12 grants (high: $65,000; low: $1,000).
Purpose and activities: Giving primarily for education and human services; funding also to a zoological society.
Fields of interest: Education; Higher education; Zoos; Nonprofits; Human services; Food banks.
Type of support: Regranting.
Limitations: Applications not accepted. No grants to individuals.
Application information: Contributes only to pre-selected organizations.
Trustees: Bruce J. Bettigole, Esq.; Nancy Freeman; Jeffrey Weiss.
EIN: 043506575

8429
Clara L. D. Jeffery Charitable Trust
P.O. Box 1802
Providence, RI   02901-1802

Donor: Clara L.D. Jeffery†.

Foundation type: Independent foundation.
Financial data (yr. ended 12/31/14): Assets, $8,355,101; expenditures, $455,160; qualifying distributions, $405,314.
Purpose and activities: Giving primarily for education, conservation, and animal welfare.
Fields of interest: Education; Natural resources; Domesticated animals.
Limitations: Applications not accepted. Giving on a national basis. No grants to individuals.
Application information: Unsolicited requests for funds not accepted.
   Board meeting date(s): Dec.
Trustees: Coleman P. Burke, Jr.; Daniel Burke II; Mary B. Partridge; Bank of America, N.A.
EIN: 226138410

8430
The Howard Johnson Foundation
P.O. Box 1802
Providence, RI   02901-1802   8888663275
Application address: Anne Hennessey, One Bryant Park, New York, NY 10036

Established in 1961 in Massachusetts.
Donors: Howard D. Johnson†; Dorothy J. Henry; William H. Weeks; Howard Brennan Johnson.
Foundation type: Independent foundation.
Financial data (yr. ended 12/31/14): Assets, $5,080,049; expenditures, $218,569; qualifying distributions, $196,354.
Fields of interest: Museums; Education; Secondary education; Higher education; Environment; Animal welfare; Nonprofits; Health; Hospital care; Diseases and conditions; Religion; Human services.
Type of support: General support; Regranting.
Limitations: Applications accepted. Giving primarily in CT, NC and NY. No grants to individuals.
Application information: Application form required.
   Initial approach: Letter
   Deadline(s): None
   Board meeting date(s): Varies
Trustees: Marissa J. Brock; Patricia B. Crawford; Dorothy J. Henry; Howard Bates Johnson; Howard Brennan Johnson; Joshua J. Weeks; William H. Weeks; Bank of America, N.A.
Number of staff: 1 part-time support.
EIN: 046060965

8431
Ralph & Helen Kelley Foundation
P.O. Box 1802
Providence, RI   02901-1802   (888) 866-3275

Established in 1989 in Maryland.
Donor: Ralph W. Kelley Trust.
Foundation type: Independent foundation.
Financial data (yr. ended 12/31/13): Assets, $12,533,628 (M); expenditures, $557,834; qualifying distributions, $432,412; giving activities include $350,500 for 1 grant.
Purpose and activities: Scholarships to high school students in the Gardner, Massachusetts, area.
Fields of interest: Higher education.
Type of support: Student aid.
Limitations: Applications accepted. Giving limited to students in the Gardner, MA, area.
Application information: Application form required.
   Initial approach: Application available at Bank of America
   Deadline(s): May 1

Trustees: G. Albert Anderson; John F. Bohman; Bank of America, N.A.
EIN: 043042476

8432
U. D. Kelly Family Foundation
P.O. Box 1802
Providence, RI   02901-1802

Established in 2003 in New York.
Donor: James P. Kelly.
Foundation type: Independent foundation.
Financial data (yr. ended 12/31/13): Assets, $2,205,704 (M); expenditures, $181,992; qualifying distributions, $174,000; giving activities include $169,000 for 16 grants (high: $55,000; low: $1,000).
Fields of interest: Education; Catholicism; Human services.
Limitations: Applications not accepted. Giving primarily in ME, NJ, and NY. No grants to individuals.
Application information: Unsolicited requests for funds not accepted.
Trustee: Bank of America, N.A.
EIN: 481270396

8433
Walter J. Kenney Scholarship Fund
P.O. Box 1802
Providence, RI   02901-1802

Established in 1990 in Connecticut.
Foundation type: Independent foundation.
Financial data (yr. ended 12/31/14): Assets, $3,600,602; expenditures, $189,525; qualifying distributions, $164,392.
Purpose and activities: Scholarship awards to residents of New Britain, Connecticut, who are accepted to an engineering college or seminary.
Fields of interest: Education.
Limitations: Applications accepted. Giving limited to residents of New Britain, CT.
Application information: Application form required.
   Initial approach: Completed Application Form
   Deadline(s): Apr. 15
Trustee: Bank of America, N.A.
EIN: 066111411

8434
Horace A. Kimball and S. Ella Kimball Foundation
23 Broad St.
Westerly, RI   02891-1879
Application address: c/o Thomas F. Black, III, Pres., 130 Woodville Rd., Hope Valley, RI 02832-2423, tel.: (401) 364-7799; Main URL: http://www.hkimballfoundation.org

Established in 1956 in Delaware.
Donor: H. Earle Kimball†.
Foundation type: Independent foundation.
Financial data (yr. ended 10/31/14): Assets, $9,896,107 (M); expenditures, $495,446; qualifying distributions, $469,800; giving activities include $421,525 for 30 grants (high: $50,000; low: $2,500).
Purpose and activities: Giving broadly in the areas of human services, the environment, and health care.

Fields of interest: Arts and culture; Education; Secondary education; Environment; Natural resources; Animal welfare; Health; Hospital care; Diseases and conditions; Human services; Food banks; Child welfare; Youth services; Homeless services; Senior services; Seniors; Homeless people; Low-income and poor people; People with disabilities.

Type of support: General support; Matching grants; Capital campaigns; Capital and infrastructure; Emergency funds; Seed money.

Limitations: Applications accepted. Giving primarily in RI. No support for religious organizations. No grants to individuals, or for feasibility studies, capital projects or multi-year commitments.

Publications: Financial statement; Grants list.

Application information: Application form and guidelines available on foundation web site; online application preferred. Application form required.

   Initial approach: Use application process on foundation web site

   Copies of proposal: 3

   Deadline(s): None, but preferably by July 15

   Board meeting date(s): Mar., June, Aug., and Oct.

Officers and Trustees: Thomas F. Black III, Pres. and Trustee; Norman D. Baker, Jr., Secy.-Treas. and Trustee; Edward C. Marth.

Number of staff: 1 part-time support.

EIN: 056006130

8435

The Kingsbury Fund

P.O. Box 1802
Providence, RI 02901-1802

Established in 1952 in New Hampshire.

Donor: Kingsbury Corp.

Foundation type: Company-sponsored foundation.

Financial data (yr. ended 12/31/14): Assets, $3,862,058; expenditures, $193,953; qualifying distributions, $165,731.

Purpose and activities: The foundation supports organizations involved with arts and culture, education, the environment, animal welfare, health, human services, and community economic development.

Fields of interest: Arts and culture; Music; Historic preservation; Education; Early childhood education; Elementary education; Higher education; Adult education; Environment; Natural resources; Animal welfare; Environmental education; Nonprofits; Health; Hospital care; Community and economic development; Business promotion; Human services; Family services; Child welfare; Senior services.

Type of support: Annual campaigns; Employee matching gifts; Matching grants; Sponsorships; Capital campaigns; Equipment; Program development; Seed money; Scholarships; Regranting.

Limitations: Applications accepted. Giving limited to Cheshire County, Keene, and the Monadnock region of NH. No support for religious or political organizations.

Application information: Application form required.

   Initial approach: Proposal

   Deadline(s): None

Trustees: James Koontz; Bank of America.

EIN: 026004465

8436

The Koffler Bornstein Family Foundation

(formerly The Koffler Family Foundation)

c/o The Koffler Group

10 Memorial Blvd., Ste. 901
Providence, RI 02903-1152

Established in 1978 in Rhode Island.

Donors: The Koffler Corp.; Lillian Koffler; Richard J. Bornstein.

Foundation type: Independent foundation.

Financial data (yr. ended 07/31/13): Assets, $5,354,764 (M); gifts received, $250,000; expenditures, $404,394; qualifying distributions, $307,860; giving activities include $307,860 for 41 grants (high: $50,000; low: $200).

Purpose and activities: Giving primarily to Jewish organizations, including welfare funds, congregations, and yeshivas; support also for higher education and hospitals.

Fields of interest: Elementary and secondary education; Higher education; Nonprofits; Hospital care; Judaism.

Type of support: Regranting.

Limitations: Applications not accepted. Giving primarily in RI, with emphasis on Providence; some giving in FL. No grants to individuals.

Application information: Contributes only to pre-selected organizations.

Trustees: Richard Bornstein; Sandra Bornstein; Jo-An Kaplan; Ben Pastor.

EIN: 050376269

8437

Kupher f/b/o Faxton St. Luke

P.O. Box 1802
Providence, RI 02901-1802

Donor: Mary Leary Trust.

Foundation type: Independent foundation.

Financial data (yr. ended 12/31/13): Assets, $108,039 (M); expenditures, $159,750; qualifying distributions, $155,460; giving activities include $150,000 for 1 grant.

Fields of interest: Health.

Limitations: Applications not accepted. Giving primarily in Utica, NY.

Application information: Unsolicited requests for funds not accepted.

Trustee: Bank of America, N.A.

EIN: 306306782

8438

The R.D. La Penta Medical Scholarship Trust

10 Tripps Ln.
Riverside, RI 02915-7995

Application address: RBS Citizens, N.A., 875 Elm St., NE4-06, Manchester, NH 03101,
e-mail: lapentascholarship@citizensbank.com

Foundation type: Independent foundation.

Financial data (yr. ended 12/31/14): Assets, $7,921,808 (M); expenditures, $497,885; qualifying distributions, $456,746; giving activities include $392,538 for 1 grant.

Purpose and activities: Giving primarily for scholarships in the study of medicine to candidates who have attended secondary schools in the last 3 years in CT, MA, or NH. Preference is given to candidates from NH.

Fields of interest: Education; Medical education.

Type of support: Scholarships.

Limitations: Applications accepted. Giving primarily in NH.

Application information: Application form required.

   Initial approach: Completed application form

   Deadline(s): May 31

Trustee: RBS Citizens Bank, N.A.

EIN: 266218956

8439

Leroe Family Charitable Foundation

P.O. Box 1802
Providence, RI 02901-1802

Application address: c/o Bank of America, N.A., Attn.: Maryann Clemente, 1 Bryant Park, New York, NY 10036

Foundation type: Independent foundation.

Financial data (yr. ended 12/31/14): Assets, $3,378,289 (M); expenditures, $172,821; qualifying distributions, $164,074; giving activities include $155,000 for 11 grants (high: $45,000; low: $5,000).

Fields of interest: Education; Higher education; Environment; Christianity; Human services.

Type of support: General support.

Limitations: Applications accepted. Giving primarily in NJ.

Application information: Application form required.

   Initial approach: To Be Determined By Selection Committee

   Deadline(s): None

Trustees: Bernard A. Leroe; Jane M. Leroe; Bank of America, N.A.

EIN: 161687981

8440

Liberty Mutual Scholarship Foundation

c/o Bank of America, N.A.
P.O. Box 1802
Providence, RI 02901-1802

Established in 2001 in Massachusetts.

Donor: Liberty Mutual Insurance Co.

Foundation type: Company-sponsored foundation.

Financial data (yr. ended 12/31/14): Assets, $3,695,085 (M); expenditures, $192,819; qualifying distributions, $162,100; giving activities include $149,035 for grants.

Purpose and activities: The foundation awards college scholarships to children of employees of Liberty Mutual Insurance Co. The program is administered by National Merit Scholarship Corporation.

Fields of interest: Higher education.

Type of support: Scholarships; Employee-related scholarships.

Limitations: Applications not accepted. Giving limited to areas of company operations, with emphasis on IL and RI.

Application information: Contributes only through employee-related scholarships.

Trustee: Bank of America, N.A.

EIN: 043548586

8441
Ida Ballou Littlefield Memorial Trust
50 Kennedy Plz., Ste. 1500
Providence, RI 02903-2319 (401) 274-2000
Contact: Joachim A. Weissfeld, Tr.

Established in 1989 in Rhode Island.
Foundation type: Independent foundation.
Financial data (yr. ended 12/31/13): Assets,
$7,372,376 (M); expenditures, $470,260;
qualifying distributions, $393,997; giving activities
include $350,599 for 51 grants (high: $40,000;
low: $1,000).
Fields of interest: Museums; Higher education;
Health; Hospital care; Diseases and conditions;
Family services; Children; Seniors; People with
physical disabilities.
Type of support: Continuing support; Capital
campaigns; Program development; Scholarships;
Research; Research and evaluation.
Limitations: Applications accepted. Giving primarily
in MA and RI. No grants to individuals.
Publications: Application guidelines.
Application information:
Initial approach: Letter
Copies of proposal: 3
Deadline(s): None
Board meeting date(s): 1st Fri. in May and Nov.
Trustees: William A. Viall; Joachim A. Weissfeld;
Citizens Bank.
Number of staff: None.
EIN: 222994936

8442
LLH/LHM Foundation
c/o Bank of America, N.A., Mary & Margaret Baird
100 Westminster St., Mail Stop RI1-5360202
Providence, RI 02903-2318

Established in 1999 in Massachusetts.
Donors: Mary Baird; Margaret Baird.
Foundation type: Independent foundation.
Financial data (yr. ended 12/31/13): Assets,
$4,355,867 (M); expenditures, $219,587;
qualifying distributions, $201,475; giving activities
include $200,000 for 30 grants (high: $10,000;
low: $1,500).
Fields of interest: Arts and culture; Education; Early
childhood education; Human services; Child
welfare.
Limitations: Applications not accepted. Giving
primarily in MA. No grants to individuals.
Application information: Contributes only to
pre-selected organizations.
Trustees: David A. Baird; Margaret Baird; Martha
Baird; Susan Lillia Baird Kennedy.
EIN: 043469581

8443
Dr. Ralph F. & Pearl A. Long Trust
P.O.Box 1802
Providence, RI 02901-1802 8888663275

Established in 1991 in Connecticut.
Donor: Ralph F. Long†.
Foundation type: Independent foundation.
Financial data (yr. ended 12/31/14): Assets,
$3,955,893; expenditures, $229,443; qualifying
distributions, $203,112.
Purpose and activities: Scholarship awards to
graduates of Terryville High School, Connecticut.

Fields of interest: Education.
Type of support: Scholarships.
Application information: Application form required.
Initial approach: Letter
Copies of proposal: 1
Deadline(s): None
Trustee: Bank of America, N.A.
EIN: 223010188

8444
Longfield Family Charitable Foundation
c/o U.S. Trust
P.O. Box 1802
Providence, RI 02901-1802

Established in 2007 in South Carolina.
Donor: William H. Longfield.
Foundation type: Independent foundation.
Financial data (yr. ended 12/31/14): Assets,
$3,023,293 (M); expenditures, $157,326;
qualifying distributions, $149,375; giving activities
include $141,000 for 17 grants (high: $25,000;
low: $1,000).
Fields of interest: Human services.
Limitations: Applications not accepted. Giving
primarily in MI, SC and VA. No grants to individuals.
Application information: Unsolicited requests for
funds not accepted.
Officers: William H. Longfield, Pres.; Sandy Tullo,
Secy.-Treas.; Kelly H. Longfield.
Trustees: Mitchell Longfield; Nancy S. Longfield;
Scott P. Longfield; Susan Longfield; William J.
Longfield; William R. Longfield.
EIN: 260430160

8445
Lorber Foundation
11 Ridgewood Rd.
Barrington, RI 02806-5032

Donors: M. Philip Lorber; Joan H. Lorber†.
Foundation type: Independent foundation.
Financial data (yr. ended 12/31/14): Assets,
$5,986,547; expenditures, $284,754; qualifying
distributions, $282,885 and $0 for set-asides.
Fields of interest: Education; Environment; Human
services.
Type of support: General support.
Limitations: Applications not accepted. Giving
primarily in Boca Raton, FL. No grants to individuals.
Application information: Unsolicited requests for
funds not accepted.
Officers: Bryan I. Lorber, Chair.; Leslie W. Lorber,
Vice-Chair. and Treas.; Jora Rehm-Lorber, Secy.
EIN: 237003984

8446
Edward K. Love Conservation Foundation
P.O. Box 1802
Providence, RI 02901-1802
Application address: c/o Andrew S. Love, Jr., 414
Olive St., Ste. 1400, St. Louis, MO 63101,
tel.: (314) 621-1200

Foundation type: Independent foundation.
Financial data (yr. ended 09/30/13): Assets,
$7,996,941 (M); expenditures, $364,487;
qualifying distributions, $334,270; giving activities
include $319,026 for 9 grants (high: $95,000; low:
$15,000).

Purpose and activities: Giving is limited to
recipients who aid in the protection and
conservation of wildlife in Missouri.
Fields of interest: Higher education; Natural
resources; Biodiversity; Wildlife biodiversity.
Limitations: Applications accepted. Giving limited to
MO.
Application information:
Initial approach: Proposal
Deadline(s): None
Trustee: Bank of America, N.A.
Board of Governors: Andrew Sproule Love, Jr.;
Daniel Spoule Love; Stephen C. Bradford; Scott
Schnuck.
EIN: 436022352

8447
Luke Charitable Foundation
333 Roosevelt Ave.
Pawtucket, RI 02860-2123

Established in 2005 in Unspecified.
Donor: Chinese Christian Church.
Foundation type: Independent foundation.
Financial data (yr. ended 12/31/13): Assets,
$5,158,222 (M); expenditures, $306,587;
qualifying distributions, $235,995; giving activities
include $229,000 for 17 grants (high: $47,000;
low: $200).
Purpose and activities: Giving primarily to Chinese
organizations.
Fields of interest: Cultural awareness; Higher
education; Human services; Basic and emergency
aid; International development.
Type of support: General support.
Limitations: Applications not accepted. Giving
primarily in RI. No grants to individuals.
Application information: Unsolicited requests for
funds not accepted.
Trustees: Robert Billington; Tze Ping Ng; Nai Che
Tsai; Shirley Wu; Chiu Yip.
EIN: 202597824

8448
The Mann Family Foundation
57 Stimson Ave.
Providence, RI 02906-5511 (401) 521-1580
Contact: Robert Mann, Pres., Treas., and Tr.

Established in 1996 in Rhode Island.
Donors: Robert Mann; Leon Mann; Carol Mann;
Judith Mann; Inga Mann.
Foundation type: Independent foundation.
Financial data (yr. ended 12/31/13): Assets,
$2,446,408 (M); gifts received, $184,744;
expenditures, $401,183; qualifying distributions,
$400,751; giving activities include $397,681 for 59
grants (high: $107,000; low: $250).
Purpose and activities: Giving for Jewish
organizations, health and medical services, and for
education.
Fields of interest: Education; Higher education;
Nonprofits; Hospital care; Judaism; Human
services.
Type of support: Regranting.
Limitations: Applications accepted. Giving primarily
in MI and RI. No grants to individuals.
Application information:
Initial approach: Proposal
Deadline(s): None

Officers and Trustees: Robert Mann, Pres. and Treas. and Trustee; Leon Mann, Secy. and Trustee; Carol Mann.
EIN: 050494136

8449
Masonic Grand Lodge Charities of Rhode Island, Inc.
222 Taunton Ave.
East Providence, RI 02914-4556 (401) 435-4650
Contact: Wyman P. Hallstrom Jr., Secy.

Established in 1912 in Rhode Island.
Donors: Edward M. Docherty Memorial Fund; W. Farnum Residual Charity Trust.
Foundation type: Independent foundation.
Financial data (yr. ended 10/31/13): Assets, $7,375,077 (M); gifts received, $177,841; expenditures, $565,788; qualifying distributions, $337,527; giving activities include $337,527 for grants.
Purpose and activities: Giving for the benefit of those with a Masonic affiliation or who have been a Rhode Island resident for at least five years.
Fields of interest: Education; Higher education; Human services.
Type of support: General support; Student aid.
Limitations: Applications accepted. Giving primarily in RI.
Application information: Application form required.
  Deadline(s): Apr. 18
Officers: Russell R. Davis, Jr., Pres.; Wyman P. Hallstrom III, V.P.; Wyman P. Hallstrom, Jr., Secy.; Michael J. Barboza, Treas.
Directors: Raymond E. Hassell; James Lapostora; David Lavery; Manuel M. Lewis; Kenneth B. Phillips.
EIN: 056014340

8450
Jean Mauze Charitable Trust
c/o Bank of America
P.O. Box 1802
Providence, RI 02901-1802 8888663275

Established in 1977 in New York.
Donor: Jean Mauze†.
Foundation type: Independent foundation.
Financial data (yr. ended 12/31/14): Assets, $8,879,888; expenditures, $504,713; qualifying distributions, $447,824 and $0 for set-asides.
Fields of interest: Education; Hospital care.
Limitations: Applications not accepted. Giving primarily in NC and NY. No grants to individuals.
Application information: Unsolicited requests for funds not accepted.
Trustee: Bank of America, N.A.
EIN: 136690071

8451
McCabe Catholic Charities
c/o Bank of America, N.A.
P.O. Box 1802
Providence, RI 02901-1802

Foundation type: Independent foundation.
Financial data (yr. ended 06/30/13): Assets, $5,254,237 (M); expenditures, $398,915; qualifying distributions, $366,869; giving activities

include $344,988 for 13 grants (high: $49,284; low: $24,642).
Fields of interest: Catholicism.
Limitations: Applications not accepted.
Application information: Unsolicited requests for funds not accepted.
Trustee: Bank of America, N.A.
EIN: 366774682

8452
Catherine McCarthy Memorial Trust Fund
P.O. Box 1802
Providence, RI 02901-1802

Established in 1984 in Massachusetts.
Donor: John J. McCarthy†.
Foundation type: Independent foundation.
Financial data (yr. ended 06/30/14): Assets, $4,242,609 (M); gifts received, $140,894; expenditures, $230,370; qualifying distributions, $200,025; giving activities include $140,894 for 31 grants (high: $15,000; low: $500).
Fields of interest: Elementary and secondary education; Hospital care; Human services.
Type of support: Capital campaigns; Capital and infrastructure; Equipment; Endowments; Program development; Seed money; Scholarships.
Limitations: Applications accepted. Giving limited to MA, with emphasis on the greater Lawrence area. No support for national health organizations or private foundations. No grants to individuals, or for annual campaigns or operating funds for standard educational programs.
Application information:
  Initial approach: Proposal
  Copies of proposal: 1
  Deadline(s): None
Trustees: Thomas F. Caffrey, Esq.; Bank of America, N.A.
EIN: 222549008

8453
The McWethy Foundation
P.O. Box 1802
Providence, RI 02901-1802
Application address: c/o Bank of America, N.A., 231 S. Lasalle St., Chicago, IL 60697. tel: (312) 828-2055

Established in 1993 in Illinois.
Donor: James B. McWethy.
Foundation type: Independent foundation.
Financial data (yr. ended 12/31/14): Assets, $7,362,057 (M); expenditures, $469,686; qualifying distributions, $404,078; giving activities include $379,500 for 34 grants (high: $100,000; low: $1,000).
Fields of interest: Education; Higher education; Foundations; Health; Hospital care; Diseases and conditions; Protestantism; Child welfare.
Application information:
  Initial approach: Proposal
  Deadline(s): None
Trustee: Bank of America, N.A.
Directors: James B. McWethy; Susan McWethy.
EIN: 363912789

8454
Morey and Helen McCarthy Miller Scholarship Fund
P.O. Box 1802
Providence, RI 02901-1802
Application address: c/o Rockland High School, Attn.: Karen Booth, 70 Loveland Hill Rd., Vernon, CT 06066-6836

Established in 1994 in Connecticut.
Foundation type: Independent foundation.
Financial data (yr. ended 02/28/15): Assets, $3,608,692 (M); expenditures, $212,415; qualifying distributions, $172,407; giving activities include $152,000 for 1 grant.
Purpose and activities: Scholarship awards paid through Scholarship America, St. Peter, Minnesota for college bound seniors from Rockville High School, Connecticut.
Fields of interest: Education.
Type of support: Scholarships.
Limitations: Applications accepted. Giving limited to Rockville, CT.
Application information: Application form required.
  Initial approach: Contact foundation for application form
  Deadline(s): None
Trustee: Bank of America, N.A.
EIN: 043222995

8455
The Molder Family Foundation
P.O. Box 1802
Providence, RI 02901-1802

Established in 1997 in Rhode Island.
Foundation type: Independent foundation.
Financial data (yr. ended 12/31/14): Assets, $4,231,754; expenditures, $237,034; qualifying distributions, $218,835.
Fields of interest: Education; Higher education; Undergraduate education; Nonprofits; Human services; Family services; Child welfare.
Type of support: Regranting.
Limitations: Applications not accepted. No grants to individuals.
Application information: Unsolicited requests for funds not accepted.
Trustee: Bank of America, N.A.
EIN: 056115363

8456
Marjorie Moore Charitable Foundation
P.O. Box 1802
Providence, RI 02901-1802
E-mail: kim.m.igoe-kasper@ustrust.comkate.kerchaert@ustrust.com; *Application address:* c/o Bank of America, N.A., Attn.: Carmen Britt, Trust Off., 77 Main St., Hartford, CT 06115

Established in 1958 in Connecticut.
Donor: Marjorie Moore†.
Foundation type: Independent foundation.
Financial data (yr. ended 07/31/14): Assets, $3,467,377; expenditures, $171,090; qualifying distributions, $141,492.
Fields of interest: Education; Human services; Youth development.
Type of support: Continuing support; Matching grants; Equipment; Program development; Seed money.

Limitations: Applications accepted. Giving limited to Berlin and Kensington, CT. No grants to individuals, or for scholarships or fellowships; no loans.
Application information: Application form required.
Initial approach: Letter
Deadline(s): None
Trustee: Bank of America, N.A.
EIN: 066050196

8457
Mary S. Mulligan Charitable Trust
c/o Bank of America, N.A.
P.O. Box 1802
Providence, RI   02901-1802
Application address: c/o Bank of America, N.A., Attn.: John Murphy, 1 East Ave., NY7-144-07-01, Rochester, NY 14638

Established in 1967 in New York.
Donor: Mary S. Mulligan†.
Foundation type: Independent foundation.
Financial data (yr. ended 05/31/13): Assets, $3,518,805 (M); expenditures, $262,287; qualifying distributions, $239,851; giving activities include $224,400 for 25 grants (high: $55,000; low: $1,000).
Fields of interest: Theater; Museums; Education; Graduate and professional education; Basic and remedial instruction; Nonprofits; Reproductive rights; Human services; Child welfare; Adult and child mentoring.
Type of support: Continuing support; Program development; Regranting; Scholarships; Research.
Limitations: Applications accepted. Giving primarily in Rochester, NY. No grants to individuals.
Application information: Application form required.
Initial approach: Request application form
Deadline(s): None
Trustee: Bank of America, N.A.
EIN: 166076169

8458
Mulvaney Family Foundation
P.O. Box 1802
Providence, RI   02901-1802

Established in 2001 in New York.
Donor: Eileen Mulvaney.
Foundation type: Independent foundation.
Financial data (yr. ended 12/31/13): Assets, $5,401,789 (M); expenditures, $280,428; qualifying distributions, $247,224; giving activities include $215,000 for 10 grants (high: $100,000; low: $6,000).
Fields of interest: Education; Secondary education; Catholicism; Human services.
Limitations: Applications not accepted. Giving primarily in MA, MD, and New York, NY. No grants to individuals.
Application information: Contributes only to pre-selected organizations.
Trustee: Bank of America, N.A.
Directors: Anne Davoren; Kathleen Faherty; Lynn Iafrate; Eileen Mulvaney.
EIN: 137304246

8459
N. Prince Trust No. 1
P.O. Box 1802
Providence, RI   02901-1802

Foundation type: Independent foundation.
Financial data (yr. ended 09/30/14): Assets, $3,630,540 (M); expenditures, $206,402; qualifying distributions, $178,269; giving activities include $158,168 for 4 grants (high: $59,313; low: $19,771).
Fields of interest: Graduate and professional education; Christianity; Theology; Cemeteries and burial services.
Type of support: General support.
Limitations: Applications not accepted. Giving primarily in CT and MA.
Trustee: Bank of America, N.A.
EIN: 066031328

8460
Alban B. and Edna B. Nixon Fund
P.O. Box 1802
Providence, RI   02901-1802

Foundation type: Independent foundation.
Financial data (yr. ended 05/31/14): Assets, $2,515,554 (M); expenditures, $169,989; qualifying distributions, $149,879; giving activities include $137,306 for 2 grants (high: $68,653; low: $68,653).
Fields of interest: Human services.
Limitations: Applications not accepted. Giving primarily in Chicago, IL.
Application information: Unsolicited requests for funds not accepted.
Trustee: Bank of America, N.A.
EIN: 366037818

8461
Grace Noyes Bo 7 Charities
P.O. Box 1802
Providence, RI   02901-1802

Foundation type: Independent foundation.
Financial data (yr. ended 12/31/13): Assets, $1,857,272 (M); expenditures, $251,915; qualifying distributions, $234,034; giving activities include $218,263 for 7 grants (high: $85,189; low: $22,179).
Fields of interest: Health; Human services; Youth development.
Limitations: Applications not accepted. Giving primarily in MA.
Application information: Unsolicited requests for funds not accepted.
Trustee: Bank of America.
EIN: 046019184

8462
The O'Halloran Family Foundation
158 Main St.
North Kingstown, RI   02852-5034

Established in 2000 in Rhode Island.
Donors: Alice O'Halloran; Gerard O'Halloran.
Foundation type: Independent foundation.
Financial data (yr. ended 12/31/14): Assets, $4,286,072 (M); expenditures, $198,569; qualifying distributions, $182,965; giving activities include $180,665 for 37 grants (high: $30,000; low: $500).
Fields of interest: Arts and culture; Education; Nonprofits; Christianity; Human services; Child welfare.

Type of support: General support; Regranting.
Limitations: Applications not accepted. Giving primarily in CT, NY and RI. No grants to individuals.
Application information: Contributes only to pre-selected organizations.
Trustees: Gerard O'Halloran; Mary Ann O'Halloran.
EIN: 050514803

8463
The David and Roberta Olsen Family Foundation
c/o Bank of America, N.A.
P.O. Box 1802
Providence, RI   02901-1802

Established in 1997 in Connecticut.
Donors: David A. Olsen; Roberta G. Olsen.
Foundation type: Independent foundation.
Financial data (yr. ended 12/31/13): Assets, $3,471,805 (M); expenditures, $200,209; qualifying distributions, $186,480; giving activities include $180,325 for 35 grants (high: $25,000; low: $25).
Fields of interest: Theater; Undergraduate education; Community and economic development; Christianity.
Limitations: Applications not accepted. No grants to individuals.
Application information: Contributes only to pre-selected organizations.
Trustees: Roberta G. Olsen; Bank of America, N.A.
EIN: 061485843

8464
Pacifica Foundation
336 Main St.
Wakefield, RI   02879-7404

Established in 2007 in Rhode Island.
Donors: Joan W. Sorensen; E. Paul Sorensen.
Foundation type: Independent foundation.
Financial data (yr. ended 03/31/13): Assets, $1,488,434 (M); gifts received, $3,351; expenditures, $185,987; qualifying distributions, $181,800; giving activities include $181,800 for 14 grants (high: $25,000; low: $500).
Fields of interest: Education; Higher education; Health.
Limitations: Applications not accepted. Giving primarily in RI.
Application information: Unsolicited requests for funds not accepted.
Trustees: E. Paul Sorensen; Joan W. Sorensen.
Directors: Alice A. Sorensen; Christian P. Sorensen.
EIN: 204733627

8465
Paine Charitable Trust
P.O. Box 1802
Providence, RI   02901-1802

Foundation type: Independent foundation.
Financial data (yr. ended 12/31/13): Assets, $5,569,003 (M); expenditures, $251,546; qualifying distributions, $206,721; giving activities include $185,118 for 5 grants (high: $90,559; low: $500).
Fields of interest: Art museums; History museums; Historic preservation.
Type of support: General support.

Limitations: Applications not accepted. Giving limited to Worcester, MA.
Application information: Unsolicited requests for funds not accepted.
Trustee: Bank of America, N.A.
EIN: 046036990

8466
Peter J. Palermo Scholarship
c/o Bank of America, N.A.
P.O. Box 1802
Providence, RI   02901-1802   8888663275

Donor: Peter J. Palermo.
Foundation type: Independent foundation.
Financial data (yr. ended 12/31/14): Assets, $2,672,492; expenditures, $318,718; qualifying distributions, $296,118.
Purpose and activities: Scholarship awards to high school graduates and residents of Albany County, New York.
Fields of interest: Higher education.
Type of support: Student aid.
Limitations: Applications accepted. Giving limited to residents of Albany County, NY.
Application information: Application form required.
  Initial approach: Proposal
  Deadline(s): May 1
Trustee: Bank of America, N.A.
EIN: 546898253

8467
The Papitto Foundation
c/o Kentron Inc.
201 Hillside Rd., No. 101
Cranston, RI   02920-5602

Established in 1986 in Rhode Island.
Donors: Ralph R. Papitto; Mario Gabelli.
Foundation type: Independent foundation.
Financial data (yr. ended 12/31/12): Assets, $11,364,457 (M); expenditures, $467,645; qualifying distributions, $368,790; giving activities include $368,790 for grants.
Purpose and activities: Giving primarily for education.
Fields of interest: Education; Human services.
Type of support: Annual campaigns; Loans to individuals; Endowments; Professorships; Scholarships; Individual development; Student aid.
Limitations: Applications not accepted. Giving primarily in RI, with emphasis on Cranston. No grants to individuals (except for student loans).
Publications: Annual report; Informational brochure; Newsletter.
Application information: Unsolicited requests for funds not accepted.
Officers: Ralph R. Papitto, Pres. and Treas.
Director: Barbara A. Papitto.
Trustees: David J. Papitto; Edward P. Peroni.
Number of staff: 2 full-time professional; 3 part-time support.
EIN: 050426569

8468
Sarah N. Pardee Estate Trust
P.O. Box 1802
Providence, RI   02901-1802

Foundation type: Independent foundation.

Financial data (yr. ended 12/31/14): Assets, $8,294,397; expenditures, $471,353; qualifying distributions, $414,585.
Fields of interest: Higher education; Graduate and professional education; Hospital care; Home health care; Catholicism; Theology; Human services; Females.
Limitations: Applications not accepted. Giving limited to CT. No grants to individuals.
Application information: Contributes only to pre-selected organizations; unsolicited requests for funds not considerd or acknowledged.
Trustee: Bank of America, N.A.
EIN: 066029233

8469
A. R. Peacock Trust
P. O. Box 1802
Providence, RI   02901-1802

Established in 2007 in New York.
Foundation type: Independent foundation.
Financial data (yr. ended 12/31/13): Assets, $8,039,045 (M); expenditures, $475,769; qualifying distributions, $399,481; giving activities include $346,700 for 10 grants (high: $52,005; low: $17,335).
Fields of interest: Health; Muscular dystrophy; Eye diseases; Heart and circulatory system diseases; Christianity; Human services; People with vision impairments.
Type of support: Research.
Limitations: Applications not accepted. Giving primarily in CT and NY; some giving also in AZ, IL, and MO.
Application information: Contributes only to pre-selected organizations.
Trustee: Bank of America, N.A.
EIN: 900288454

8470
Mary L. Perkins Trust
P. O. Box 1802
Providence, RI   02901-1802

Foundation type: Independent foundation.
Financial data (yr. ended 12/31/13): Assets, $4,724,968 (M); expenditures, $215,903; qualifying distributions, $178,983; giving activities include $157,435 for 5 grants (high: $31,487; low: $31,487).
Fields of interest: Education; Higher education; Religion; People with vision impairments; People with hearing impairments.
Limitations: Applications not accepted. Giving primarily in MA, MO and New York, NY.
Application information: Unsolicited requests for funds not accepted.
Trustee: Bank of America.
EIN: 046018695

8471
Perpetual Benevolent Fund
P.O. Box 1802
Providence, RI   02901-1802   8888663275
Application address: Augusta Haydock, 300 Washington St., Newton, Massachusetts 02158

Established in 1932 in Massachusetts.

Donors: Nathan P. Cutler†; William H. Cutler†; Howard A. Haney†; Giles E. Moser.
Foundation type: Independent foundation.
Financial data (yr. ended 12/31/14): Assets, $6,455,391; expenditures, $360,529; qualifying distributions, $288,325.
Purpose and activities: To assist local needy individuals. Individuals are referred by health, welfare, hospitals, or other organizations; support also for child welfare, social services, the homeless and disadvantaged, and restricted funds for the elderly.
Fields of interest: Human services; Child welfare; Homeless services; Senior services; Seniors; Homeless people; Low-income and poor people.
Type of support: Continuing support; Grants to individuals; Emergency funds.
Limitations: Applications accepted. Giving limited to Newton, Waltham, and adjacent communities in MA. No grants for scholarships.
Application information: Application form required.
  Initial approach: Proposal
  Copies of proposal: 1
  Deadline(s): None
Trustee: Bank of America, N.A.
Number of staff: 1 full-time professional.
EIN: 237011723

8472
Louise B. Phillips Trust
P.O. Box 1802
Providence, RI   02901-1802

Foundation type: Independent foundation.
Financial data (yr. ended 12/31/14): Assets, $6,035,808; expenditures, $308,019; qualifying distributions, $238,923.
Fields of interest: Education; Health; Diseases and conditions; Cancers.
Limitations: Applications not accepted. Giving primarily in AZ, MA and NJ.
Application information: Unsolicited requests for funds not accepted.
Trustee: Bank of America, N.A.
EIN: 046025374

8473
Pillsbury Hospital Residents Trust
P.O. Box 1802
Providence, RI   02901-1802   8888663275

Foundation type: Independent foundation.
Financial data (yr. ended 03/31/15): Assets, $3,012,603; expenditures, $164,757; qualifying distributions, $139,800.
Fields of interest: Education; Health; Hospital care.
Type of support: General support.
Limitations: Applications not accepted. Giving primarily in Chicago, IL.
Application information: Unsolicited requests for funds not accepted.
Trustee: Bank of America, N.A.
EIN: 366037703

8474
Pisa Foundation
121 Hidden Mere Ln.
North Kingstown, RI   02852-3700
Contact: Alan Perlman

Established in 1996 in Rhode Island.
Donors: Ann Perlman; Alan Perlman; Rosalind Perlman.
Foundation type: Independent foundation.
Financial data (yr. ended 11/30/13): Assets, $4,227,533 (M); gifts received, $170,904; expenditures, $195,793; qualifying distributions, $160,529; giving activities include $160,529 for 4 grants (high: $155,000; low: $100).
Fields of interest: Education; Domesticated animals; Diseases and conditions.
Type of support: General support.
Limitations: Applications not accepted. Giving primarily in RI. No grants to individuals.
Application information: Unsolicited requests for funds not accepted.
Trustees: Alan Perlman; Ann Perlman.
EIN: 050494285

8475
Evelyn W. Preston Trust
P.O. Box 1802
Providence, RI   02901-1802

Established in 1978 in Connecticut.
Donors: Mary Yale Bettis†; Evelyn Preston†.
Foundation type: Independent foundation.
Financial data (yr. ended 12/31/14): Assets, $4,405,732 (M); expenditures, $214,787; qualifying distributions, $176,799; giving activities include $145,355 for 28 grants (high: $20,000; low: $80).
Purpose and activities: Grants for free band and orchestral concerts in the City of Hartford from June through Sept.
Fields of interest: Music.
Type of support: General support; Grants to individuals; Continuing support; Program development.
Limitations: Applications not accepted. Giving limited to Hartford, CT.
Application information: Unsolicited requests for funds not accepted.
Trustee: Bank of America.
EIN: 060747389

8476
Olive Higgins Prouty Foundation, Inc.
c/o Bank of America, N.A.
P.O. Box 1802
Providence, RI   02901-1802   8888663275
Application address: c/o Bank of America, N.A., 100 Federal St., Boston, MA 02110, tel.: (617) 434-6565

Established in 1952 in Massachusetts.
Donors: Olive Higgins Prouty†; Richard Prouty - Literary Rights.
Foundation type: Independent foundation.
Financial data (yr. ended 12/31/14): Assets, $3,654,777; expenditures, $264,769; qualifying distributions, $243,773.
Purpose and activities: Giving primarily for education, conservation and human services.
Fields of interest: Arts and culture; Music; Secondary education; Higher education; Hospital care; Child welfare.
Type of support: Continuing support; Annual campaigns; Capital campaigns.

Limitations: Applications accepted. Giving primarily in the greater New Bedford and Worcester, MA, areas. No grants to individuals.
Application information: Application form required.
Initial approach: Letter
Deadline(s): Sept. 30th
Board meeting date(s): Mid-Nov.
Officer: William Mason Smith III, Pres.
Trustees: Thomas P. Jalkut; Olivia M. Leale; Hillary Prouty; Jonathan Prouty; Lewis I. Prouty; Caroline P. Smith.
EIN: 046046475

8477
Rainbow Fund
P.O. Box 1802
Providence, RI   02901-1802
Application address: US Trust and Co. of DE, c/o Patricia G. Kelly, 1100 N. King St., DE5-002-04-02, Wilmington, DE 19884, tel.: (302) 432-6706

Established in 1954 in Georgia.
Donors: J.P. Luce†; Barbara L. Abney; Albert L. Luce, Jr.
Foundation type: Independent foundation.
Financial data (yr. ended 12/31/14): Assets, $5,004,629 (M); expenditures, $191,177; qualifying distributions, $171,919; giving activities include $160,000 for 7 grants (high: $45,000; low: $5,000).
Purpose and activities: Giving primarily for theological education and other Christian endeavors; support also for substance abuse treatment and music education through mentoring high school students and conservatory musicians.
Fields of interest: Education; Religion; Youth development.
Type of support: Program development.
Limitations: Applications accepted. Giving primarily in FL, GA, IN, KY, MS, TN and TX.
Application information:
Initial approach: Proposal
Deadline(s): None
Officer: Burton S. Luce, Mgr.
Trustees: Stephen Luce; Beth Reed; Jenny Shattuck; US Trust Delaware.
EIN: 586043659

8478
The Robertson Foundation
c/o Jocelin G. Hamblett
66 Williams St.
Providence, RI   02906-1029

Established in 1994 in Rhode Island.
Donor: Stephen Hamblett†.
Foundation type: Independent foundation.
Financial data (yr. ended 12/31/13): Assets, $2,590,670 (M); expenditures, $208,763; qualifying distributions, $192,685; giving activities include $192,685 for 17 grants (high: $100,000; low: $35).
Fields of interest: Arts and culture; Community and economic development; Human services.
Limitations: Applications not accepted. Giving primarily in Providence, RI, with some giving in CT. No grants to individuals.
Application information: Contributes only to pre-selected organizations.

Officers and Directors: Jocelin G. Hamblett, Pres. and Treas. and Director; Christopher S. Hamblett, Secy. and Director; Paul P. St. Onge.
EIN: 050481538

8479
The Sachem Foundation
90 Elm St.
Providence, RI   02903-4647
Contact: Esther E.M. Mauran, Pres.

Established in 1997 in Rhode Island.
Donor: Esther E.M. Mauran.
Foundation type: Independent foundation.
Financial data (yr. ended 12/31/13): Assets, $3,829,443 (M); expenditures, $288,340; qualifying distributions, $254,300; giving activities include $254,300 for 18 grants (high: $70,000; low: $100).
Purpose and activities: Giving for nature conservation and for art and cultural programs.
Fields of interest: Education; Health; Human services.
Limitations: Applications accepted. Giving primarily in RI. No grants to individuals.
Application information:
Initial approach: Proposal
Deadline(s): None
Officers and Directors: Esther E.M. Mauran, Pres. and Director; Paul W. Whyte, Treas. and Director; Pauline C. Metcalf.
EIN: 061483391

8480
D.J. and R.G. Salerno Private Foundation
P.O. Box 1802
Providence, RI   02901-1802   8888663275
Application address: 225 Franklin St., Boston, MA 02110

Donor: Lucinda Salerno†.
Foundation type: Independent foundation.
Financial data (yr. ended 03/31/15): Assets, $4,426,473; expenditures, $227,669; qualifying distributions, $200,385.
Fields of interest: Higher education; Health care administration and financing.
Limitations: Applications accepted. Giving primarily in MA.
Application information:
Initial approach: Proposal
Deadline(s): None
Trustees: Ronald Garney; Bank of America.
EIN: 306228583

8481
Donald Salmanson Foundation
155 S. Main St.
Providence, RI   02903-2963

Donor: Donald Salmanson.
Foundation type: Independent foundation.
Financial data (yr. ended 09/30/14): Assets, $1,428,313 (M); gifts received, $250,280; expenditures, $204,162; qualifying distributions, $184,165; giving activities include $166,165 for 15 grants (high: $105,000; low: $1,000).
Fields of interest: Nonprofits; Hospital care; Judaism.
Type of support: Regranting.

Limitations: Applications not accepted. No grants to individuals.
Application information: Contributes only to pre-selected organizations.
Trustee: Donald Salmanson.
EIN: 222571911

8482
Jacob F. & Wilma S. Schoellkopf Foundation

c/o Bank of America, N.A.
P.O. Box 1802
Providence, RI 02901-1802

Foundation type: Independent foundation.
Financial data (yr. ended 09/30/13): Assets, $22,873,497 (M); expenditures, $492,692; qualifying distributions, $408,366; giving activities include $406,071 for 3 grants (high: $346,071; low: $10,000).
Fields of interest: Philanthropy; Foundations.
International interests: Germany.
Limitations: Applications not accepted. Giving in NY and Germany. No grants to individuals.
Application information: Contributes only to pre-selected organizations.
Trustee: Bank of America, N.A.
EIN: 046008242

8483
F. A. O. Schwarz Family Foundation

P.O. Box 1802
Providence, RI 02901-1802

Established in 1991 in New York.
Donors: Frederick A.O. Schwarz III; Dorothy S. Hines; H. Marshall Schwarz; Eric Schwarz; Alex Millard.
Foundation type: Independent foundation.
Financial data (yr. ended 04/30/14): Assets, $2,995,138; expenditures, $450,786; qualifying distributions, $405,998.
Fields of interest: Museums; Education; Higher education; Nonprofits; Health; Hospital care; Human services; Child welfare; Youth development.
Type of support: Regranting.
Limitations: Applications not accepted. Giving primarily in Gainesville, FL; Boston, MA; and New York, NY. No grants to individuals.
Application information: Contributes only to pre-selected organizations.
Trustees: Alex Millard; Peter Schastny; Eliza Ladd Schwarz; Frederick A.O. Schwarz III; Rae Paige Schwarz; Molly Wing-Berman; Bank of America, N.A.
EIN: 136986221

8484
Fred M. Seed Foundation

c/o Astra Ventures, Inc.
42 Ladd St.
East Greenwich, RI 02818

Donors: Fred M. Seed Annuity Trust; Fred M. Seed‡.
Foundation type: Independent foundation.
Financial data (yr. ended 12/31/13): Assets, $492,123 (M); expenditures, $241,387; qualifying distributions, $234,800; giving activities include $234,800 for 12 grants (high: $166,000; low: $250).

Purpose and activities: Support primarily for higher and secondary education; limited giving for cultural programs, social services, and civic affairs.
Fields of interest: Arts and culture; Secondary education; Higher education; Public administration; Human services.
Limitations: Applications not accepted. Giving primarily in RI. No grants to individuals.
Application information: Unsolicited requests for funds not accepted.
Officers: John C. Seed, Pres.; James M. Seed, V.P. and Secy.
EIN: 416029620

8485
George Dudley Seymour Trust

c/o Fiduciary Tax Services
P.O. Box 1802
Providence, RI 02901-1802
Application Address: c/o Bank of America, Attn.: Carmen Britt, 200 Glastonbury Blvd., Glastonbury, CT 06033

Established in 1986 in Connecticut.
Foundation type: Independent foundation.
Financial data (yr. ended 07/31/14): Assets, $6,331,116 (M); expenditures, $277,012; qualifying distributions, $239,619; giving activities include $214,000 for 1 grant.
Purpose and activities: Grants are made primarily for purchase of lands within the state of Connecticut to be delivered as recreational centers in the towns, and secondarily for the preservation of the history of Connecticut and its cities and towns.
Fields of interest: Public affairs.
Type of support: General support; Land acquisitions.
Limitations: Applications accepted. Giving limited to CT. No grants to individuals.
Publications: Application guidelines.
Application information: Application form required.
  Initial approach: Letter
  Deadline(s): None
  Board meeting date(s): June
Trustee: Bank of America, N.A.
Number of staff: None.
EIN: 066021772

8486
Mary E. Shea Trust

P.O. Box 1802
Providence, RI 02901-1802 8888663275
Application address: Bank of America, N.A., 777 Main St., Hartford, CT 06115

Foundation type: Independent foundation.
Financial data (yr. ended 12/31/14): Assets, $4,184,681 (M); expenditures, $304,780; qualifying distributions, $216,047.
Fields of interest: Education; Public libraries; Christianity; Human services; Family services; Child welfare; Homeless services.
Limitations: Applications accepted. Giving primarily in CT.
Application information: Application form required.
  Initial approach: Complete application form
  Copies of proposal: 8
  Deadline(s): Feb. 28
Trustee: Bank of America, N.A.
EIN: 066029604

8487
Simionescu Scholarship Foundation

P.O. Box 1802
Providence, RI 02901-1802

Established in 1987 in New Jersey.
Foundation type: Independent foundation.
Financial data (yr. ended 11/30/14): Assets, $3,261,510 (M); expenditures, $218,516; qualifying distributions, $191,195; giving activities include $165,040 for 18 grants (high: $27,040; low: $4,000).
Purpose and activities: Giving limited to Hackensack High School students in need of financial assistance with tuition, student housing, textbooks, and related expenses.
Fields of interest: Education.
Type of support: Student aid.
Limitations: Applications not accepted. Giving limited to residents of Hackensack, NJ.
Application information: Unsolicited requests for funds not accepted.
Trustees: Eugene H. Gilmartin; Claire J. Lavache-Mackey; James Montesano; Talin Young; Bank of America, N.A.
EIN: 222878206

8488
The Joseph S. and Rosalyn K. Sinclair Family Foundation

140 Westminster St., Ste. 200
Providence, RI 02903-2101

Established in 1978 in Rhode Island.
Donors: Joseph S. Sinclair‡; Rosalyn K. Sinclair.
Foundation type: Independent foundation.
Financial data (yr. ended 09/30/13): Assets, $3,645,839 (M); expenditures, $305,641; qualifying distributions, $279,100; giving activities include $279,100 for 15 grants (high: $101,500; low: $1,000).
Fields of interest: Health; Hospital care; Diseases and conditions; Community and economic development; Human services; Women's services; Females.
Type of support: General support; Continuing support; Annual campaigns; Capital campaigns; Capital and infrastructure.
Limitations: Applications not accepted. Giving primarily in RI. No grants to individuals.
Application information: Unsolicited requests for funds not accepted.
Officers: Rosalyn K. Sinclair, Pres.; William Piccerelli, Secy. and Treas.
Director: Sarah Sinclair.
EIN: 050380039

8489
Mynde & Gary Siperstein Charitable Foundation

130 Joseph Ct.
Warwick, RI 02886-9564

Established in 2000 in Rhode Island.
Donors: Mynde S. Siperstein; Gary S. Siperstein.
Foundation type: Independent foundation.
Financial data (yr. ended 12/31/13): Assets, $948,135 (M); expenditures, $195,239; qualifying distributions, $192,550; giving activities include $191,500 for 7 grants (high: $100,000; low: $500).
Fields of interest: Education; Nonprofits; Judaism.

Type of support: Regranting.
Limitations: Applications not accepted. Giving primarily in RI; some giving in GA and MA. No grants to individuals.
Application information: Contributes only to pre-selected organizations.
Trustees: Gary S. Siperstein; Mynde S. Siperstein.
EIN: 050514202

8490
Slemons Foundation
P.O. Box 1802
Providence, RI 02901-1802
Contact: Kate Luckert
Application address: 185 Oakes St., S.W., Grand Rapids, MI 49503, tel.: (616) 454-1754

Established in 1995 in Michigan.
Donor: Elmer & Mabel Slemons Trust.
Foundation type: Independent foundation.
Financial data (yr. ended 08/31/12): Assets, $0 (M); gifts received, $394,549; expenditures, $394,550; qualifying distributions, $394,550; giving activities include $384,500 for 24 grants (high: $36,000; low: $3,000).
Fields of interest: Museums; Education; Cancers; Public libraries; Protestantism; Human services.
Type of support: General support; Capital campaigns; Capital and infrastructure; Program development.
Limitations: Applications accepted. Giving primarily in MI. No grants to individuals.
Application information: Application form required.
   Initial approach: Proposal
   Deadline(s): None
Officers: John Bergstrom, Pres.; Larry Robson, V.P.; Michael R. Curtis, Secy.-Treas.
EIN: 386107913

8491
The Slingerland Foundation
P.O. Box 1802
Providence, RI 02901-1802
Application address: Craig C. Chenevert., 69 State St., Albany, NY 12207, tel.: (518) 626-2763

Established in 1991 in New York.
Donor: Donald M. Slingerland.
Foundation type: Independent foundation.
Financial data (yr. ended 06/30/13): Assets, $1,453,057 (M); expenditures, $240,552; qualifying distributions, $231,636; giving activities include $225,000 for 7 grants (high: $45,000; low: $15,000).
Fields of interest: Education; Religion; Human services.
Type of support: Scholarships.
Limitations: Applications accepted. Giving primarily in Albany, NY. No grants to individuals.
Application information: Recipient selected by advisory committee. Application form required.
   Initial approach: Letter
   Deadline(s): None
Trustees: Donald M. Slingerland; Frank M. Slingerland; Bank of America, N.A.
EIN: 146102644

8492
M. J. Smith Family Foundation
P.O. Box 1802
Providence, RI 02901-1802

Foundation type: Independent foundation.
Financial data (yr. ended 12/31/14): Assets, $5,358,273; expenditures, $250,597; qualifying distributions, $218,339.
Fields of interest: Catholicism; Shelter and residential care.
Limitations: Applications not accepted. Giving limited to Nashville, TN.
Application information: Unsolicited requests for funds not accepted.
Trustee: Bank of America, N.A.
EIN: 626075182

8493
Hervey L. Smith Trust
P.O. Box 1802
Providence, RI 02901-1802

Foundation type: Independent foundation.
Financial data (yr. ended 12/31/13): Assets, $5,179,927 (M); expenditures, $277,333; qualifying distributions, $229,630; giving activities include $205,287 for 6 grants (high: $51,322; low: $17,107).
Fields of interest: Undergraduate education; Health; Protestantism; Youth services.
Limitations: Applications not accepted. Giving limited to MA.
Application information: Unsolicited requests for funds not accepted.
Trustee: Bank of America, N.A.
EIN: 046033808

8494
The Alice I. Sullivan Charitable Foundation
(also known as AIS)
162 Middle St.
Pawtucket, RI 02860-1013
Main URL: http://www.collettefoundation.org/blog
Blog: http://www.collettefoundation.org/blog

Established in 2007 in Rhode Island.
Donors: Collette Travel Service, Inc.; Tides Foundation.
Foundation type: Company-sponsored foundation.
Financial data (yr. ended 12/31/13): Assets, $369,574 (M); gifts received, $366,000; expenditures, $321,618; qualifying distributions, $318,572; giving activities include $318,572 for 93 grants (high: $25,000; low: $50).
Purpose and activities: The foundation supports organizations involved with arts and culture, education, health, hunger, athletics, human services, and community development.
Fields of interest: Education; Health; Human services.
Type of support: Annual campaigns; Employee volunteer services; Capital campaigns; Program development; Scholarships; Sponsorships.
Limitations: Applications not accepted. Giving primarily in RI. No grants to individuals.
Application information: Contributes only to pre-selected organizations.
Trustees: John Galvin; Daniel J. Sullivan, Jr.
Director: Michael Horan.
EIN: 208256471

8495
Harry & Dolly Swarts Memorial Fund
c/o U.S. Trust Fiduciary Tax Svcs.
P.O. Box 1802
Providence, RI 02901-1802

Foundation type: Independent foundation.
Financial data (yr. ended 03/31/14): Assets, $8,969,445 (M); expenditures, $483,948; qualifying distributions, $410,020; giving activities include $376,041 for 10 grants (high: $188,021; low: $18,802).
Fields of interest: Higher education; Nonprofits; Mental health care; Diseases and conditions; Judaism; Human services.
Type of support: Regranting.
Limitations: Applications not accepted.
Application information: Unsolicited requests for funds not accepted.
Trustee: Bank of America, N.A.
EIN: 366693648

8496
Willard E. & Ella P. Thompson Educational Fund
P.O. Box 1802
Providence, RI 02901-1802 8888663275
Application address: c/o Thompson Scholarship Selection Committee, 600 S. Hale, Algona, IA 50511, tel.: (515) 295-7207

Donors: Henrietta R. Thompson Annuity Trust; Willard E. Thompson Trust.
Foundation type: Independent foundation.
Financial data (yr. ended 12/31/14): Assets, $5,093,199; expenditures, $250,858; qualifying distributions, $226,363.
Purpose and activities: Scholarship awards to graduates of Iowa high schools in the Algona School District.
Fields of interest: Higher education.
Type of support: Student aid.
Limitations: Applications accepted. Giving limited to residents of Algona, IA.
Application information: Applicants should submit resume or biographical information, 2 recommendations, high school transcript and a student aid report. Application form required.
   Initial approach: Proposal
   Deadline(s): First week in Apr.
Trustee: Bank of America, N.A.
EIN: 366028029

8497
W. A. Thompson Trust
P.O. Box 1802
Providence, RI 02901-1802

Foundation type: Independent foundation.
Financial data (yr. ended 12/31/14): Assets, $7,717,034; expenditures, $426,844; qualifying distributions, $380,479.
Fields of interest: Nonprofits; Diseases and conditions; Human services.
Type of support: Regranting.
Limitations: Applications not accepted. Giving limited to CT, NY and RI. No grants to individuals.
Application information: Contributes only to pre-selected organizations; unsolicited requests for funds not considered or acknowledged.

Trustee: Bank of America.
EIN: 056039819

8498
Unfi Foundation
c/o Lisa N'Chonon
313 Iron Horse Way
Providence, RI 02908-5637 (401) 528-8634
Contact: Melody Meyer, Exec. Dir.
Main URL: http://www.unfifoundation.org

Donor: United Natural Foods, Inc.
Foundation type: Independent foundation.
Financial data (yr. ended 07/31/13): Assets, $14,606 (M); gifts received, $367,042; expenditures, $358,436; qualifying distributions, $341,850; giving activities include $341,850 for 28 grants (high: $55,000; low: $250).
Purpose and activities: The foundation supports organizations that work to: 1) Increase organic food production; 2) Provide research and science to develop organic farming practices; 3) Protect the biodiversity of our seed supply and the stewardship of genetic resources of organic seed; 4) Teach organic farming practices that promote conservation of resources; and 5) Foster the next generation of organic farmers.
Fields of interest: Education; Health; Agriculture.
Limitations: Applications accepted. Giving primarily in CA, Washington, DC and VT.
Publications: Application guidelines.
Application Information: Complete application guidelines available on foundation web site. Application form required.
  Initial approach: Use online application system on foundation web site
  Deadline(s): See foundation web site for current deadlines
Officers and Directors: Steven Spinner, Chair. and Director; Anne Nichelson, Secy.; Lisa N'Chonon, Treas.; Melody Meyer, Exec. Dir.; Thomas Dziki; Michael Funk; Lisa Madsen.
EIN: 455023490

8499
Barrie Vanderpoel Family Charitable Trust
P.O. Box 1802
Providence, RI 02901-1802

Donor: E. B. Osborn Charitable Trust.
Foundation type: Independent foundation.
Financial data (yr. ended 12/31/14): Assets, $4,158,620; expenditures, $209,506; qualifying distributions, $194,290.
Fields of interest: Education; Health; Sports and recreation; Youth development.
Limitations: Applications not accepted.
Application Information: Unsolicted requests for funds not accepted.
Trustee: Bank of America.
EIN: 356888591

8500
The Washington Trust Charitable Foundation
c/o The Washington Trust Co.
23 Broad St.
Westerly, RI 02891-1879 (401) 348-1207
Contact: Dennis L. Algiere, Dir., Community Affairs

Main URL: http://www.washtrust.com/home/about/community

Established in 1994 in Rhode Island.
Donor: The Washington Trust Co.
Foundation type: Company-sponsored foundation.
Financial data (yr. ended 12/31/13): Assets, $3,123,336 (M); gifts received, $400,000; expenditures, $395,678; qualifying distributions, $388,833; giving activities include $388,833 for 97 grants (high: $50,000; low: $250).
Purpose and activities: The foundation supports programs designed to promote affordable housing and revitalization; business and economic development; youth and family services; health and human services; arts and culture; colleges, universities, and libraries; and conservation and the environment.
Fields of interest: Arts and culture; Museums; Education; Higher education; Environment; Natural resources; Nonprofits; Health; Hospital care; Public libraries; Community and economic development; Housing development; Business and industry; Human services; Family services; Youth services.
Type of support: General support; Continuing support; Capital campaigns; Capital and infrastructure; Program development; Regranting.
Limitations: Applications accepted. Giving primarily in areas of company operations in southeastern CT, MA, and RI. No grants to individuals.
Publications: Application guidelines.
Application information: Application form required.
  Initial approach: Letter
  Copies of proposal: 1
  Deadline(s): Oct. 1
Trustee: The Washington Trust Co.
EIN: 050477294

8501
Fred W. Wells Trust Fund
P.O. Box 1802
Providence, RI 02901-1802

Donor: Fred W. Wells†.
Foundation type: Independent foundation.
Financial data (yr. ended 06/30/13): Assets, $4,633,658 (M); expenditures, $211,444; qualifying distributions, $200,911; giving activities include $200,911 for grants.
Purpose and activities: Grants for medical and other health care programs, and agricultural accomplishment prizes; support also for scholarships.
Fields of interest: Education; Health; Hospital care; Agriculture.
Type of support: Scholarships.
Limitations: Applications not accepted. Giving limited to Franklin County, MA; scholarships limited to residents of Ashfield, Bernardston, Buckland, Charlemont, Conway, Deerfield, Gill, Greenfield, Hawley, Heath, Leyden, Monroe, Montague, Northfield, Rowe, and Shelburne, MA.
Application information: Unsolicited requests for funds not accepted.
Officers and Trustees: Pamela W. Walker, Chair. and Trustee; Suzanne Bishop, Vice-Chair. and Trustee; Gail Bissell; Elizabeth Braccia; Frank J. Cutting; Lois Feldman; Dianne Grinnell; Elizabeth Kirkwood; Carol G. Letson; Donald F. O'Hara.
EIN: 046412350

8502
Georgina B. West Trust
P.O. Box 1802
Providence, RI 02901-1802

Foundation type: Independent foundation.
Financial data (yr. ended 12/31/13): Assets, $7,230,586 (M); expenditures, $385,578; qualifying distributions, $330,741; giving activities include $299,529 for 1 grant.
Fields of interest: Hospital care.
Limitations: Applications not accepted. Giving primarily in Medford, MA. No grants to individuals.
Application information: Unsolicited requests for funds not accepted.
Trustee: Bank of America.
EIN: 046026094

8503
The White Family Foundation
(formerly The John and Happy White Foundation)
c/o Taco, Inc.
1120 Cranston St.
Cranston, RI 02920-7334 (401) 942-8000
Contact: Glenn Graham, Treas.
Main URL: http://www.thewhitefamilyfoundation.com

Established in 2000 in Rhode Island.
Donor: Taco, Inc.
Foundation type: Independent foundation.
Financial data (yr. ended 12/31/13): Assets, $1,568,813 (M); gifts received, $398,000; expenditures, $428,672; qualifying distributions, $425,902; giving activities include $405,143 for 16 grants (high: $166,667; low: $5,000).
Fields of interest: Arts and culture; Education; Hospital care.
Limitations: Applications accepted. Giving primarily in RI. No grants to individuals.
Application information:
  Initial approach: Proposal
  Deadline(s): None
Officers: Thomas J. Farrell, Pres.; Kyle Adamonis, Secy.; Glenn Graham, Treas.
Board Members: David Gilden; Irving Schneider; Ben White; John Hazen White, Jr.; John Hazen White III.
EIN: 050509502

8504
Annie E. Wilson Trust
P.O. Box 1802
Providence, RI 02901-1802

Foundation type: Independent foundation.
Financial data (yr. ended 12/31/13): Assets, $4,277,192 (M); expenditures, $177,801; qualifying distributions, $158,832; giving activities include $130,648 for 3 grants (high: $65,324; low: $32,662).
Fields of interest: Housing development; Human services; Family services; Child welfare; Seniors; Female young adults.
Type of support: General support.
Limitations: Applications not accepted. Giving primarily in MA.
Application information: Unsolicited requests for funds not accepted.
Trustee: Bank of America, N.A.
EIN: 046037210

8505
Woodward Fund
c/o Bank of America, N.A.
P.O. Box 1802
Providence, RI   02901-1802
Application address: 1 East Ave., Rochester, NY 14638

Established in 1965 in New York.
Donor: Florence S. Woodward.
Foundation type: Independent foundation.
Financial data (yr. ended 11/30/14): Assets, $4,008,059 (M); expenditures, $194,653; qualifying distributions, $192,091; giving activities include $192,091 for 37 grants (high: $20,000; low: $500).
Fields of interest: Arts and culture; Higher education; Wildlife biodiversity; Zoos; Nonprofits; Christianity; Human services.
Type of support: Regranting.
Limitations: Giving primarily in AZ, CA, and ME. No grants to individuals.
Application information: Application form required.
Initial approach: Proposal
Deadline(s): None
Trustee: Bank of America, N.A.
EIN: 166064221

8506
George R. Wright Trust For Charities
P.O. Box 1802
Providence, RI   02901-1802

Foundation type: Independent foundation.
Financial data (yr. ended 12/31/13): Assets, $3,923,082 (M); expenditures, $244,266; qualifying distributions, $206,061; giving activities include $185,631 for 4 grants (high: $62,650; low: $34,806).
Fields of interest: Education; Health; Hospital care; Christianity.
Limitations: Applications not accepted.
Application information: Unsolicited requests for funds not accepted.
Trustee: Bank of America.
EIN: 046020498

8507
Otto H. York Foundation Inc.
44 Hazard Ave.
Providence, RI   02906-1511   (407) 421-0738
Contact: Myrth York, Pres.

Donor: Otto H. York†.
Foundation type: Independent foundation.
Financial data (yr. ended 02/28/13): Assets, $6,127,200 (M); expenditures, $342,757; qualifying distributions, $305,042; giving activities include $221,610 for 19 grants (high: $25,000; low: $1,500).
Fields of interest: Arts and culture; Education; University education; Health; Hospital care; Family planning; Libraries; Reproductive rights; Human services; Food banks; People with physical disabilities.

Limitations: Applications accepted. Giving primarily in NJ and RI. No grants to individuals.
Application information: Application form required.
Initial approach: Letter
Deadline(s): None
Officer: Myrth York, Pres.
Trustees: Deborah M. Brayton; Amy Gabarra.
EIN: 225154083

8508
Otto & Margaret Zack Charitable Trust
P.O. Box 1802
Providence, RI   02901-1802

Donor: Margaret M. Zack Trust.
Foundation type: Independent foundation.
Financial data (yr. ended 12/31/13): Assets, $7,557,398 (M); expenditures, $267,642; qualifying distributions, $222,800; giving activities include $175,000 for 4 grants (high: $60,000; low: $20,000).
Fields of interest: Domesticated animals; Human services.
Limitations: Applications not accepted.
Application information: Unsolicited requests for funds not accepted.
Trustee: Bank of America, N.A.
EIN: 306283082

SOUTH CAROLINA

8509
P. S. and Ouida C. Bailey Foundation
P.O. Box 380
Clinton, SC 29325-0380

Donors: Emily F. Bailey; Clinton Investment Co.
Foundation type: Independent foundation.
Financial data (yr. ended 12/31/14): Assets, $7,453,924; expenditures, $417,976; qualifying distributions, $365,162.
Purpose and activities: Giving primarily for the revitalization of Clinton, South Carolina's downtown area; some giving also to Anglican missions, and to a home for the aged.
Fields of interest: Community and economic development; Religion; Human services.
Limitations: Applications not accepted. Giving primarily in SC, with some emphasis on Clinton. No grants to individuals.
Application information: Unsolicited requests for funds not accepted.
Officer and Trustees: Emily F. Bailey, Chair. and Trustee; Bishop Alex D. Dickson.
EIN: 570813063

8510
The Bailey Foundation
c/o TD Bank, N.A.
P.O. Box 494
Clinton, SC 29325-0494 (864) 938-2632
Contact: Robert S. Link Jr., Admin.

Established in 1951 in South Carolina.
Donors: M.S. Bailey & Son, Bankers; Clinton Investment Co.
Foundation type: Operating foundation.
Financial data (yr. ended 08/31/13): Assets, $4,435,587 (M); gifts received, $10,000; expenditures, $310,935; qualifying distributions, $278,510; giving activities include $209,100 for 32 grants (high: $50,000; low: $1,500), $40,000 for 10 grants to individuals (high: $5,000; low: $2,500), and $29,410 for 13 employee matching gifts.
Purpose and activities: The foundation supports health clinics and organizations involved with education, human services, community development, and Christianity and awards college scholarships to students graduating from public high schools in Laurens County, South Carolina.
Fields of interest: Education; Higher education; Nonprofits; Health care clinics; Community and economic development; Christianity; Human services; Child welfare; Senior assisted living.
Type of support: Annual campaigns; Employee matching gifts; Matching grants; Capital campaigns; Capital and infrastructure; Endowments; Scholarships; Student aid; Regranting.
Limitations: Applications accepted. Giving limited to Laurens County, SC. No grants to individuals (except for scholarships), or for general operating support.
Publications: Annual report; Informational brochure (including application guidelines).
Application information: An application form is required for scholarships.
Initial approach: Proposal; contact guidance counselor at Clinton High School or Laurens

High School for application form for scholarships
Copies of proposal: 1
Deadline(s): Oct. 1; Apr. 15 of applicant's senior year in high school for scholarships
Board meeting date(s): Periodically
Final notification: May 15
Advisory Committee: George H. Cornelson IV, Chair.; Martin S. Cornelson; C. Bailey Dixon; Norman W. Dixon; Walter S. Montgomery, Sr.; Fleming Patterson; James L. Switzer, Jr.; Toccoa W. Switzer; Virginia G. Vance.
EIN: 576018387

8511
The Bannon Foundation
P.O. Box 9097
Greenville, SC 29604-9097

Established in 1987 in South Carolina.
Foundation type: Independent foundation.
Financial data (yr. ended 12/31/14): Assets, $3,601,263 (M); expenditures, $203,750; qualifying distributions, $14,650; giving activities include $146,500 for 28 grants (high: $20,000; low: $500).
Purpose and activities: Giving primarily for education and community improvement.
Fields of interest: Higher education; Community improvement; Christianity; Human services.
Limitations: Applications not accepted. Giving primarily in SC and VA. No grants to individuals.
Application information: Unsolicited requests for funds not accepted.
Trustees: Judy B. Ballew; James G. Bannon, Jr.; James G. Bannon III; John Thomas.
EIN: 570833931

8512
Bignon Family Foundation
204 Montclair Rd.
Irmo, SC 29063-9154

Donor: Bernard H. Bignon.
Foundation type: Independent foundation.
Financial data (yr. ended 12/31/13): Assets, $1,499,043 (M); expenditures, $198,183; qualifying distributions, $172,000; giving activities include $172,000 for 3 grants (high: $137,000; low: $5,000).
Fields of interest: Education; Religion; Human services.
Limitations: Applications not accepted. Giving primarily in SC.
Application information: Contributes only to pre-selected organizations.
Trustees: Edward L. Bignon; W. Edward Howard; A. Dowl Knight.
EIN: 204753405

8513
Bonner Family Private Foundation, Inc.
129 Morning Shore Ct.
Lexington, SC 29072-7438 (803) 951-3033

Established in 1987 in South Carolina.
Donors: Hazel A. Bonner; T.L. Bonner; Northwoods, LP.
Foundation type: Independent foundation.

Financial data (yr. ended 12/31/14): Assets, $4,647,329; expenditures, $276,224; qualifying distributions, $239,000.
Purpose and activities: Giving primarily for hospitals, health associations, human services, and Christian agencies and churches.
Fields of interest: Nonprofits; Hospital care; Diseases and conditions; Christianity; Human services; Child welfare.
Type of support: General support; Regranting; Capital and infrastructure.
Limitations: Applications accepted. Giving primarily in Perry, GA and Columbia, SC. No grants to individuals.
Application information: Application form required.
Initial approach: Proposal
Deadline(s): Dec. 1
Officer: Sheila B. Kolb, Pres.
Trustee: Janice B. Norman.
EIN: 570844469

8514
Darnall W. Boyd Foundation, Inc.
7700 N. Trenholm Rd. Extension
Columbia, SC 29223-1724

Donor: Darnall W. Boyd.
Foundation type: Independent foundation.
Financial data (yr. ended 12/31/14): Assets, $9,503,125 (M); gifts received, $1,431,040; expenditures, $352,381; qualifying distributions, $293,500; giving activities include $293,500 for 19 grants (high: $120,000; low: $1,500).
Fields of interest: Arts and culture; Education; Environment.
Limitations: Applications not accepted. Giving primarily in SC.
Application information: Unsolicited requests for funds not accepted.
Officers: Darnall W. Boyd, Pres.; Susan F. Boyd, V.P.; George S. Bailey, Secy.; Joseph P. Wilczewski, Treas.
Directors: Ford B. Bailey; Johnson Small; Walter Taylor.
EIN: 272559583

8515
Betsy M. Campbell Foundation
104 Broadus Ave.
Greenville, SC 29601-3040

Established in 1997 in South Carolina.
Donor: Betsy McDavid Campbell Remainder Unitrust.
Foundation type: Independent foundation.
Financial data (yr. ended 12/31/13): Assets, $8,274,931 (M); expenditures, $604,949; qualifying distributions, $458,278; giving activities include $422,500 for 4 grants (high: $415,000; low: $2,000).
Fields of interest: Protestantism; Youth development.
Type of support: General support.
Limitations: Applications not accepted. Giving primarily in Greenville, SC. No grants to individuals.
Application information: Contributes only to pre-selected organizations.
Trustee: William W. Brown.
EIN: 586346237

8516
Edgar T. Cato Foundation, Inc.
5350 Woodside Executive Ct.
Aiken, SC 29803-3818

Established in 1998 in Florida.
Donors: Edgar T. Cato; Christine A. Cato Charitable Lead Annuity Trust.
Foundation type: Independent foundation.
Financial data (yr. ended 12/31/13): Assets, $4,664,091 (M); expenditures, $351,923; qualifying distributions, $270,000; giving activities include $270,000 for 4 grants (high: $100,000; low: $20,000).
Fields of interest: Education; Botanical gardens; Nonprofits; Archives and special collections; Fire prevention and control; Public policy; Equestrianism; Water sports.
Type of support: Regranting; Policy, advocacy and systems reform.
Limitations: Applications not accepted. Giving primarily in NC, SC, RI, and VA. No grants to individuals.
Application information: Unsolicited requests for funds not accepted.
Officers and Directors: Christine Anne Cato, Pres. and Director; Edgar T. Cato III, V.P. and Director; Tom Cannon.
EIN: 650450989

8517
The Chapman Family Charitable Trust
5033 Wittering Dr.
Columbia, SC 29206-2922
Contact: Scott Boyd
Application address: c/o U.S. Trust, Attn.: Laura Pease, 3414 Peachtree Rd. N.E., Ste. 1475, Atlanta, GA 30326-1113, tel.: (404) 264-2885

Established in 1994 in Georgia.
Donor: Hugh M. Chapman.
Foundation type: Independent foundation.
Financial data (yr. ended 12/31/13): Assets, $5,834,940 (M); expenditures, $312,210; qualifying distributions, $263,940; giving activities include $262,500 for 23 grants (high: $40,000; low: $1,000).
Purpose and activities: Giving for education, museums, children and youth services, and religion.
Fields of interest: Museums; Education; Foundations; Hospital care; Christianity; Child welfare.
Limitations: Applications accepted. Giving primarily in New York, NY and SC.
Application information:
Initial approach: Proposal
Deadline(s): None
Officers: Scott Boyd, Chair.; Anne Allston Chapman, Vice-Chair.; Rachel Chapman, Vice-Chair.; Mary Boyd, Secy.
EIN: 582105766

8518
The Childress Foundation
P.O. Box 1367
Easley, SC 29641-1367

Donor: Janice Childress.
Foundation type: Independent foundation.
Financial data (yr. ended 12/31/12): Assets, $9,058 (M); expenditures, $142,180; qualifying distributions, $140,750; giving activities include $140,750 for 10 grants (high: $50,000; low: $750).
Fields of interest: Education; Agriculture; Religion; Human services.
Limitations: Applications not accepted. Giving primarily in SC.
Application information: Unsolicited requests for funds not accepted.
Officer and Trustees: Janice E. Childress, Chair. and Trustee; Brandi N. Childress; Elizabeth C. Covil; Christopher I. Lupo; Gerald Reese.
EIN: 204365847

8519
Joan Sasser Coker and Charles Westfield Coker Charitable Foundation
1100 W. Carolina Ave.
Hartsville, SC 29550-4452

Established in 1998 in South Carolina.
Donors: Charles W. Coker, Sr.; Charles W. Coker, Jr.; Ellen C. Baldwin; Margaret C. Galloway; Carrie C. Haley; Robert Howard Coker; Thomas Lide Coker; Charles W. Coker.
Foundation type: Independent foundation.
Financial data (yr. ended 12/31/14): Assets, $4,897,365 (M); expenditures, $139,436; qualifying distributions, $135,648; giving activities include $135,648 for 29 grants (high: $12,500; low: $1,000).
Fields of interest: Education; Protestantism; Human services.
Limitations: Applications not accepted. Giving primarily in NC and SC. No grants to individuals.
Application information: Unsolicited requests for funds not accepted.
Trustees: Ellen C. Baldwin; Charles W. Coker; Charles W. Coker, Jr.; Robert Howard Coker; Margaret C. Galloway; Carrie C. Haley.
EIN: 571067455

8520
Fred Collins Foundation
3453 Pelham Rd., Ste. 103
Greenville, SC 29615-7400 8642681111

Established in 1986 in South Carolina.
Donor: Fred Collins†.
Foundation type: Independent foundation.
Financial data (yr. ended 12/31/14): Assets, $6,765,843; expenditures, $288,283; qualifying distributions, $198,200.
Fields of interest: Orchestral music; Education; Elementary and secondary education; Higher education; Law education; Foundations; Christianity; Protestantism; Human services; Food aid.
Type of support: Scholarships; Individual development.
Limitations: Applications not accepted. Giving primarily in the Greenville, SC, area. No grants to individuals.
Application information: Contributes only to pre-selected organizations.
Trustee: Felicia C. Robbins.
EIN: 576107255

8521
Davis Family Foundation, Inc.
P.O. Box 428
Greenwood, SC 29648-0428 (864) 229-5211
Contact: Emmett I. Davis Jr.

Established in 1999 in South Carolina.
Donors: Emmett I. Davis, Jr.; Davis & Floyd Inc.; Mona R. Davis.
Foundation type: Independent foundation.
Financial data (yr. ended 12/31/13): Assets, $5,343,772 (M); gifts received, $66,173; expenditures, $269,179; qualifying distributions, $199,343; giving activities include $197,200 for 42 grants (high: $50,000; low: $500).
Fields of interest: Higher education; Environment; Philanthropy; Housing development; Religion; Christianity.
Type of support: General support.
Limitations: Applications not accepted. Giving primarily in Greenwood, SC. No grants to individuals.
Application information: Unsolicited requests for funds not accepted.
Officers: Emmett I. Davis III, Vice-Chair.; Emmett I. Davis, Jr., Pres.; Stephen L. Davis, Secy.-Treas.
EIN: 582432024

8522
Eastern Carolina Community Foundation
154 W. Evans St.
Florence, SC 29501 (843) 667-1131
Contact: Sarah Shelley, Exec. Dir.
E-mail: info@easterncarolinacf.org; Mailing address: P.O. Box 1615, Florence, SC 29503; Main URL: http://www.easterncarolinacf.org
Facebook: https://www.facebook.com/easterncarolinacommunityfoundation
RSS feed: http://easterncarolinacf.org/feed

Established in 2006 in South Carolina.
Foundation type: Community foundation.
Financial data (yr. ended 12/31/13): Assets, $3,063,258 (M); gifts received, $246,949; expenditures, $349,927; giving activities include $198,767 for 15+ grants (high: $41,950).
Purpose and activities: The foundation seeks to improve the quality of life in this area of South Carolina through inspired philanthropy and innovative community programs.
Fields of interest: Health; Community and economic development; Human services.
Type of support: Annual campaigns; Endowments.
Limitations: Applications accepted. Giving primarily in Chesterfield, Darlington, Dillon, Florence, Marion, Marlboro, and Williamsburg counties, SC.
Publications: Newsletter.
Application information: When a grant cycle is announced, the foundation will define eligibility and deadlines. Visit web site for application information. Application form required.
Deadline(s): Varies
Officers and Board Members: Tom Ewart, Chair. and Director; Ken Charles, Vice-Chair. and Director; Katherine Griggs, Secy. and Director; Robert G. Vassy, Jr., Treas. and Director; Sarah Shelley, Exec. Dir.; Mary Wood Beasley; Charlie Blake; Marion Coxe; Wade R. Crow; Lola Coggeshall Early; Parks Garrison; Evans P. Holland; Judith H. Kammer; Corey Phillips; Linda P. Russell; Rev. Jeffrey W. Shealy.
Advisory Board: Frank Avent; Dr. Fred Carter; Emerson Gower; Bill Kinney, Jr.; Heyward L. King, Jr.; Buzz Rogers; Marguerite Willis.

Number of staff: 1 full-time professional.
EIN: 204654550

8523
Harry H. Gibson Family Foundation
P. O. Box 1724
Spartanburg, SC   29304-1724

Donor: Harry H. Gibson†.
Foundation type: Independent foundation.
Financial data (yr. ended 12/31/13): Assets, $2,293,843 (M); expenditures, $254,026; qualifying distributions, $232,200; giving activities include $232,200 for 54 grants (high: $30,000; low: $500).
Fields of interest: Undergraduate education; Christianity.
Limitations: Applications not accepted. No grants to individuals.
Application information: Contributes only to pre-selected organizations.
Trustees: Harry H. Gibson, Jr.; Joan B. Gibson; Colonial Trust Co.
EIN: 205338528

8524
The Gleason Family Foundation, Inc.
15 Man O War
Hilton Head Island, SC   29928-5248   (843) 842-3775
Contact: Martin Gleason, Pres.

Established in 1998 in New Jersey.
Donors: Martin Gleason; Lenore Gleason.
Foundation type: Independent foundation.
Financial data (yr. ended 12/31/12): Assets, $4,232,902 (M); expenditures, $266,707; qualifying distributions, $235,900; giving activities include $235,900 for grants.
Fields of interest: Arts and culture; Elementary and secondary education; Higher education; Hemophilia; Catholicism; Human services.
Limitations: Applications accepted. Giving primarily in NJ and SC.
Application information:
   Initial approach: Proposal
   Deadline(s): None
Officers and Trustees: Martin Gleason, Pres. and Treas. and Trustee; Lenore Gleason, V.P. and Secy. and Trustee; Bonnie Gleason; Mary Gleason; Nancy Gleason.
EIN: 223628310

8525
Greenleaf Foundation Inc.
951 S. Pine St., Ste. 100
Spartanburg, SC   29302-3370   (864) 515-9515
Contact: Robert E. Caldwell Sr., Chair.

Established in 1993 in South Carolina.
Donor: Greenleaf, Inc.
Foundation type: Independent foundation.
Financial data (yr. ended 12/31/13): Assets, $6,374,341 (M); expenditures, $350,807; qualifying distributions, $310,140; giving activities include $242,778 for 13 grants (high: $96,337; low: $650).
Fields of interest: Education; Christianity; Human services.

Limitations: Applications accepted. Giving primarily in Spartanburg, SC. No grants to individuals directly.
Application information: Application form required.
   Initial approach: Letter
   Deadline(s): None
Officers: Robert E. Caldwell, Sr., Chair.; Sylvia R. Caldwell, Vice-Chair.
Director: Hugh H. Brantley.
EIN: 570989702

8526
Greenwood County Community Foundation
929 Phoenix St.
Greenwood, SC   29646   (864) 223-1524
Contact: Mark Kasper, C.E.O. and Pres.
FAX: (815) 351-7408;
E-mail: staff@greenwoodcf.org; Grant inquiry e-mail: grants@greenwoodcf.org; Grant submission e-mail: mkasper@greenwoodcf.org; Main URL: http://www.greenwoodcf.org
E Newsletter: http://www.greenwoodcf.org/recent-newsletters

Established in 2009 in South Carolina.
Foundation type: Community foundation.
Financial data (yr. ended 12/31/13): Assets, $4,050,927 (M); gifts received, $594,923; expenditures, $475,906; giving activities include $285,178 for 15+ grants (high: $40,000).
Purpose and activities: The foundation works collaboratively with all individuals and organizations that are interested in improving the quality of life in Greenwood County.
Fields of interest: Arts and culture; Education; Environment; Land resources; Community and economic development; Sustainable development; Parks; Human rights; Children and youth.
Type of support: Program development.
Limitations: Applications accepted. Giving limited to Greenwood County, SC. No grants to individuals, or for general operations, capital expenditures or endowments; no loans.
Publications: Application guidelines; Financial statement; Newsletter.
Application information: Visit foundation web site for application and guidelines. Application form required.
   Initial approach: E-mail completed application to Exec. Dir.
   Deadline(s): Varies per focus area
Officers and Directors: Sam Tolbert, Chair. and Director; Linda Dolny, Vice-Chair. and Director; Sam Leaman, Secy. and Director; Peter Manning, Treas. and Director; Mark Kasper, Exec. Dir.; Joe Chandler; Dru James; Darrell Johnson; Sid Johnston; Megah Lal; Julius Leary, Jr.; Mamie Nicholson.
EIN: 270388708

8527
Ralph and Virginia Hendricks Foundation
7 Ralph Henrdicks Dr.
Simpsonville, SC   29681-0278

Established in 1986 in South Carolina.
Donor: Ralph S. Hendricks.
Foundation type: Independent foundation.
Financial data (yr. ended 12/31/13): Assets, $4,792,661 (M); gifts received, $164,918; expenditures, $265,066; qualifying distributions,

$225,329; giving activities include $225,000 for 20 grants (high: $50,000; low: $2,000).
Purpose and activities: Giving for education, human services, and Protestant agencies.
Fields of interest: Higher education; Protestantism; Human services; Food aid.
Limitations: Applications not accepted. Giving primarily in SC. No grants to individuals.
Application information: Contributes only to pre-selected organizations.
   Board meeting date(s): 1st Mon. in Dec.
Officer: Ralph S. Hendricks, Chair.
Trustees: Robert Hamby; Randy Harling; G. Wilson Jenkins; Richard C. Moore; Marc L. Saunders; John R. Thomas.
Number of staff: None.
EIN: 570822180

8528
Dick Horne Foundation
P.O. Box 306
Orangeburg, SC   29116-0306   (803) 534-2096
Contact: Karen Snell

Established in 1966 in South Carolina.
Donor: Amelia S. Horne†.
Foundation type: Independent foundation.
Financial data (yr. ended 12/31/13): Assets, $6,915,610 (M); expenditures, $390,238; qualifying distributions, $322,373; giving activities include $309,576 for 49 grants (high: $79,100; low: $200).
Purpose and activities: Giving primarily for community affairs and social services, and for educational scholarships based on need, character and ability.
Fields of interest: Arts and culture; Education; Public administration; Community and economic development; Sports and recreation; Human services.
Type of support: Student aid; General support; Scholarships.
Limitations: Applications accepted. Giving primarily in Orangeburg and Calhoun counties, SC. No loans or program-related investments.
Application information: Applicant should include information relating to their income and resources, their educational background and the purpose for which the grant is requested. Application form required.
   Initial approach: Letter
   Deadline(s): None
Trustees: W. Louis Griffith; Buster Smith; Bernice W. Tribble.
Number of staff: 1 full-time professional.
EIN: 237015996

8529
The Solomon Jackson Jr. Foundation
P.O. Box 90326
Columbia, SC   29290-1326
Application address: c/o South State Bank, Attn.: Ann Gluse, 520 Gervais St., Columbia, SC 29201, tel.: (803) 540-3941

Donor: Solomon Jackson, Jr.
Foundation type: Independent foundation.
Financial data (yr. ended 12/31/13): Assets, $6,192,883 (M); expenditures, $258,610; qualifying distributions, $238,504; giving activities include $197,125 for grants.

Fields of interest: Arts and culture; Education; Community and economic development.
Type of support: Student aid.
Limitations: Applications accepted. Giving primarily in Allendale, Dillon, Fairfield, Florence, Hampton, Jasper, Lee, Karshaw, Marion, Orangeburg, Richland, SC.
Application information: Application form required.
Initial approach: Request application
Deadline(s): April 1
Officers and Directors: Solomon Jackson, Jr., Pres. and Director; Winston Thomas, Secy. and Director; Robert Squirewell, Treas. and Director.
EIN: 271218152

8530
The Edward and Dorothy Kendall Foundation
P.O. Box 2767
Columbia, SC   29202-2767

Established in 2007 in South Carolina.
Donor: Donald M. Kendall.
Foundation type: Independent foundation.
Financial data (yr. ended 12/31/13): Assets, $5,140,098 (M); expenditures, $266,503; qualifying distributions, $222,037; giving activities include $222,037 for grants.
Fields of interest: Historic preservation; Higher education; Medical education; Nonprofits; Human services.
Type of support: Regranting.
Limitations: Applications not accepted. Giving primarily in RI and SC.
Application information: Contributes only to pre-selected organizations.
Officers: Edward Kendall, Pres.; Dorothy Kendall, V.P. and Secy.-Treas.
EIN: 260723656

8531
The Philip and Linda LeSourd Lader Foundation
151 Meeting St., Ste. 600
Charleston, SC   29401-2233

Established in 1986 in South Carolina.
Donors: Linda Lesourd Lader; Philip Lader.
Foundation type: Independent foundation.
Financial data (yr. ended 12/31/13): Assets, $3,712,984 (M); gifts received, $8,028; expenditures, $153,090; qualifying distributions, $148,895; giving activities include $148,895 for 6 grants (high: $135,395; low: $1,000).
Fields of interest: Arts and culture; Education; Religion.
International interests: United Kingdom of Great Britain and Northern Ireland.
Type of support: General support.
Limitations: Applications not accepted. Giving on a national and international basis. No grants to individuals.
Application information: Contributes only to pre-selected organizations.
Officer and Trustees: Linda LeSourd Lader, Mgr. and Trustee; Kenneth D. Fullerton; Marc A. Puntereri.
EIN: 576111836

8532
C. W. and Dorothy G. Love Foundation
P.O. Box 158
McColl, SC   29570-0158

Established in 2005 in South Carolina.
Donor: Charles W. Love.
Foundation type: Independent foundation.
Financial data (yr. ended 12/31/13): Assets, $0 (M); gifts received, $4,584,797; expenditures, $334,868; qualifying distributions, $242,690; giving activities include $242,690 for 28 grants (high: $64,910; low: $100).
Fields of interest: Arts and culture; Philanthropy; Protestantism.
Type of support: General support.
Limitations: Applications not accepted. Giving primarily in McColl, SC. No grants to individuals.
Application information: Unsolicited requests for funds not accepted.
Officer and Trustees: Charles Love, Jr., C.E.O. and Trustee; Dottie Farfone; Linda L. Levkoff; Alan Love; Catherine L. Vitale.
EIN: 202865906

8533
Clarence H. and Anna E. Lutz Foundation
P.O. Box 147
Chester, SC   29706-0147   (803) 385-5357
Contact: Joan L. Guyton, V.P. and Treas.; Dewey G. Guyton, Pres.
FAX: (803) 385-6666;
E-mail: Mjolley@lutzfoundation.org; Additional e-mails: Jguyton@lutzfoundation.org, Sbishop@lutzfoundation.org; Main URL: http://www.lutzfoundation.org
Grants List: http://www.lutzfoundation.org/index.php?location=Grants2011

Foundation type: Independent foundation.
Financial data (yr. ended 02/28/14): Assets, $6,243,912 (M); expenditures, $340,260; qualifying distributions, $332,723; giving activities include $285,000 for 18 grants (high: $50,000; low: $4,000).
Purpose and activities: The purpose of the foundation is to help fund various religious and community needs, as well as educational, health and welfare programs.
Fields of interest: Arts and culture; Theater; Education; Higher education; Hospice care; Public utilities; Community and economic development; Protestantism; Human services; Food aid; Family services; Children and youth; Adults; Low-income and poor people.
Type of support: Continuing support; Capital campaigns; Capital and infrastructure; Equipment; Program development.
Limitations: Applications accepted. Giving primarily in Chester County, SC, and the surrounding areas. No support for political organizations. No grants to individuals, or for scholarships, general operating expenses, or general fund campaigns.
Publications: Application guidelines; Annual report; Annual report (including application guidelines); Grants list; Program policy statement.
Application information: Application form required.
Initial approach: Letter (on letterhead) of no more than 2 pages
Copies of proposal: 2
Deadline(s): Sep. 30th
Board meeting date(s): Jan. and July, plus meetings as needed

Officers and Directors: Dewey G. Guyton, Pres. and Director; Joan L. Guyton, V.P. and Treas. and Director; Shelia Bishop, V.P.; Susan L. Stephenson, V.P., Public Rels. and Director; Mary S. Jolley, V.P., Tech. and Director.
Number of staff: None.
EIN: 570940342

8534
Stephen D. Mitchell Foundation Inc.
P.O. Box 3666
Greenville, SC   29608-3666

Foundation type: Independent foundation.
Financial data (yr. ended 12/31/14): Assets, $2,763,593 (M); expenditures, $186,916; qualifying distributions, $184,871; giving activities include $144,000 for 5 grants (high: $80,000; low: $2,000).
Fields of interest: Religion.
Limitations: Applications not accepted. Giving primarily in SC.
Application information: Unsolicited requests for funds not accepted.
Officers and Trustees: Hume Lucas Mitchell, Jr., Chair. and Trustee; Mary Lucas Mitchell, Secy. and Trustee.
EIN: 460743407

8535
Nalley Charitable Trust
P.O. Box 1929
Easley, SC   29641-1929

Established in 1980 in South Carolina.
Donors: George B. Nalley, Jr.; Anita L. Nalley.
Foundation type: Independent foundation.
Financial data (yr. ended 11/30/14): Assets, $2,960,101 (M); gifts received, $414,626; expenditures, $183,732; qualifying distributions, $175,550; giving activities include $175,550 for 26 grants (high: $67,000; low: $50).
Fields of interest: Education; Religion; Human services.
Type of support: General support.
Limitations: Applications not accepted. Giving primarily in SC. No grants to individuals.
Application information: Unsolicited requests for funds not accepted.
Officer: George B. Nalley, Jr., Chair.
EIN: 570727567

8536
The James B. Near Family Foundation
c/o Jim Near
225 Indigo Bay Cir.
Mount Pleasant, SC   29464-3973

Established in 2000 in South Carolina.
Donor: James B. Near, Jr.
Foundation type: Independent foundation.
Financial data (yr. ended 12/31/13): Assets, $3,282,435 (M); gifts received, $453,663; expenditures, $232,645; qualifying distributions, $202,357; giving activities include $192,000 for 19 grants (high: $28,000; low: $2,000).
Fields of interest: Education; Foundations; Health; Protestantism; Human services.
Type of support: Volunteer development.

Limitations: Applications not accepted. Giving primarily in OR and SC. No grants to individuals.
Application information: Contributes only to pre-selected organizations.
Board Members: Susan Near; Jean Rouse.
Director: James B. Near, Jr.
EIN: 571109864

8537
The Peery/Cauthen Foundation
(formerly Peery/Cauthen Charitable Trust)
c/o Colonial Trust Co.
P.O. Box 1724
Spartanburg, SC 29304-1724 (800) 225-2603

Established in 1989 in West Virginia.
Donor: Charles Cauthen.
Foundation type: Independent foundation.
Financial data (yr. ended 12/31/13): Assets, $1,880,339 (M); gifts received, $67,244; expenditures, $218,885; qualifying distributions, $169,650; giving activities include $169,650 for 54 grants (high: $45,000; low: $100).
Fields of interest: Higher education; Nonprofits; Christianity; Human services.
Type of support: General support; Regranting.
Application information: Application form required.
Initial approach: Letter
Deadline(s): None
Trustee: Colonial Trust Co.
Selection Committee: Matthews S. Bullard; Sidney C. Bullard; Charles E. Cauthen; Hazel Cauthen; Sara C. Landfear; Wesley E. Landfear; J. Phillip Rohrer; Rachel C. Rohrer; Portia C. White; Richard L. White.
EIN: 556065070

8538
John M. Rivers, Jr. Foundation
(formerly The John & Kathleen Rivers Foundation, Inc.)
40 Calhoun St., Ste. 500
Charleston, SC 29401-3530
Application address: P.O. Box 21050, Charleston, SC 29413

Foundation type: Independent foundation.
Financial data (yr. ended 12/31/14): Assets, $2,631,863; gifts received, $795; expenditures, $177,821; qualifying distributions, $141,295.
Purpose and activities: Giving primarily in the Cashiers, NC and Charleston, SC area for the arts and education to strengthen the quality of life in communities that have a special relationship with the Rivers family. The foundation periodically supports the work of artistic, educational and other charitable programs that it, or the Rivers family, has established. Giving also to provide seed money and matching or impact funds for new programs that promote the aforementioned concepts.
Fields of interest: Education; Religion; Sports and recreation.
Limitations: Applications accepted. Giving primarily in Cashiers NC, and the Charleston, SC, tri-county area (Berkeley, Dorchester and Charleston). No grants to individuals.
Application information: Application form required.
Initial approach: Letter
Deadline(s): None
Officers and Directors: John M. Rivers, Jr., Pres. and Director; J. Rutledge Young, Jr., V.P.; A. Baron Holmes IV, Secy. and Director; Edward H. Daniell,

Treas. and Director; David H. Maybank; Karen Phillips; Anne T. Pope; Thomas Waring.
EIN: 570907666

8539
Security's Lending Hand Foundation
P.O. Box 811
Spartanburg, SC 29304

Established in 1994 in South Carolina.
Donors: Security Finance Corp.; Security Finance Corporation of Spartanburg.
Foundation type: Company-sponsored foundation.
Financial data (yr. ended 12/31/13): Assets, $28,658 (M); gifts received, $420,000; expenditures, $391,500; qualifying distributions, $391,500; giving activities include $391,500 for 10 grants (high: $217,500; low: $1,500).
Purpose and activities: The foundation supports children's hospitals.
Fields of interest: Mental health care.
Type of support: General support.
Limitations: Applications not accepted. Giving primarily in FL, GA, LA, MO, NC, OK, SC, TN, and TX. No grants to individuals.
Application information: Contributes only to pre-selected organizations.
Officers: Susan A. Bridges, Chair.; A. Ray Biggs, Pres.; Jonathan W. Norwood, Treas.
EIN: 571012986

8540
Singing for Change
(also known as SFC Charitable Foundation)
P.O. Box 729
Sullivans Island, SC 29482-0729 (843) 388-7730
Contact: Judith Ranger Smith, Exec. Dir.
E-mail: info@singingforchange.com; Main URL: http://www.singingforchange.org
Grants List: http://www.singingforchange.org/previous_grants.html

Donors: Jimmy Buffett; Live Nation Worldwide, Inc.
Foundation type: Independent foundation.
Financial data (yr. ended 12/31/13): Assets, $545,662 (M); gifts received, $475,085; expenditures, $463,679; qualifying distributions, $248,383; giving activities include $248,383 for 14 grants (high: $100,000; low: $2,500).
Purpose and activities: Funding primarily for children and families, the environment, and disenfranchised groups.
Fields of interest: Education; Environmental education; Human services; Child welfare.
Type of support: General support; Continuing support.
Limitations: Applications accepted. Giving in the U.S., with emphasis on FL and LA. No support for religious organizations, public or private schools, or for medical research or disease treatment organizations. No grants to individuals, or for art, music, or recreational purposes.
Publications: Application guidelines; Annual report; Grants list.
Application information: Full proposals are by invitation only, upon review of letter of interest. Unsolicited full proposals are not considered. See foundation web site for additional information.
Initial approach: 1-page letter of interest via e-mail or USPS

Deadline(s): None
Board meeting date(s): Quarterly
Officers and Trustees: Howard Kaufman, Pres. and Trustee; Joel A. Katz, Secy. and Trustee; Irwin L. Rennert, Treas. and Trustee.
Number of staff: 1 full-time professional.
EIN: 650565248

8541
John T. Stevens Foundation
P.O. Box 158
Kershaw, SC 29067-0158 (803) 475-3655
Contact: Steve G. Williams Sr.

Established in 1948 in South Carolina.
Donor: John T. Stevens†.
Foundation type: Independent foundation.
Financial data (yr. ended 05/31/13): Assets, $6,643,194 (M); expenditures, $422,372; qualifying distributions, $345,588; giving activities include $345,588 for 52 grants (high: $26,000; low: $1,000).
Purpose and activities: Giving primarily for community funding.
Fields of interest: Arts and culture; Education; Community and economic development; Protestantism; Human services; Youth services.
Limitations: Applications accepted. Giving primarily in Kershaw and Lancaster County, SC. No grants to individuals.
Application information: Application form required.
Initial approach: Letter
Deadline(s): None
Officers: Steve G. Williams, Jr., Pres.; Lanny M. Williams, V.P.; Jason Munn, Secy.; Joey Munn, Treas.
EIN: 576005554

8542
The Stony Point Foundation
c/o Dixon Hughes Goodman
P.O. Box 973
Charleston, SC 29402

Established in 1993 in New York.
Donor: John O. Downing.
Foundation type: Independent foundation.
Financial data (yr. ended 01/31/14): Assets, $15,348,002 (M); expenditures, $343,067; qualifying distributions, $172,194; giving activities include $144,425 for 36 grants (high: $36,175; low: $100).
Purpose and activities: Giving primarily for education, the environment, and human services.
Fields of interest: Museums; Elementary and secondary education; Higher education; Natural resources; Human services.
Limitations: Applications not accepted. Giving in the U.S., with emphasis on CT, NJ, TN, and VT. No grants to individuals or for scholarships; no loans.
Application information: Contributes only to pre-selected organizations.
Officers: Frances V.S. Downing, Treas.; John O. Downing, Pres.
EIN: 133766973

8543

The Stringer Foundation
402 Boulevard
Anderson, SC 29605 (864) 222-0804
Contact: John S. Rainey, Chair.

Established in 1947 in South Carolina.
Foundation type: Independent foundation.
Financial data (yr. ended 12/31/13): Assets,
$2,475,621 (M); expenditures, $249,008;
qualifying distributions, $230,373; giving activities
include $223,692 for 35 grants (high: $127,500;
low: $300).
Fields of interest: Foundations.
Application information: Application form required.
  Initial approach: Letter
  Copies of proposal: 4
  Deadline(s): Sept. 10
Officer: John S. Rainey, Chair. and Pres.
Trustees: Nancy R. Crowley; Mary R. Belser; Robert
M. Rainey.
EIN: 576022719

8544

The Sunshine Foundation, Inc.
1664 Jackson St.
Barnwell, SC 29812-2156

Established in 1997 in South Carolina.
Donors: Terry E. Richardson, Jr.; Gail Ness
Richardson; Katherine J. Richardson; Julius N.
Richardson.
Foundation type: Independent foundation.
Financial data (yr. ended 12/31/13): Assets,
$8,066,339 (M); gifts received, $160,926;
expenditures, $412,554; qualifying distributions,
$342,961; giving activities include $329,397 for 62
+ grants (high: $59,000; low: $15), and $13,564
for 1 grant to an individual.
Purpose and activities: Giving for human services
and education.
Fields of interest: Education; University education;
Public libraries; Legal services; Christianity; Human
services.
Limitations: Applications not accepted. Giving
primarily in SC.
Application information: Unsolicited requests for
funds not accepted.
Board Members: David G. Bundy; Gail Ness
Richardson; Julius N. Richardson; Katherine J.
Richardson; Macon D.M. Richardson; Terry E.
Richardson, Jr.
EIN: 571060737

8545

Robert and Molly Tarr Charitable Foundation
58 River Marsh Ln.
Kiawah Island, SC 29455-5202 (843) 243-9948
Contact: Robert J. Tarr Jr., Tr.

Established in 1992 in Massachusetts.
Donors: Robert J. Tarr, Jr.; Molly U. Tarr.
Foundation type: Independent foundation.
Financial data (yr. ended 11/30/13): Assets,
$3,859,168 (M); gifts received, $2,117;
expenditures, $237,505; qualifying distributions,
$207,252; giving activities include $202,035 for 29
grants (high: $50,000; low: $1,000).
Fields of interest: Elementary and secondary
education; Higher education; Medical education;
Nonprofits; Specialty hospital care; Christianity.
Type of support: Regranting.
Limitations: Giving primarily in MA and SC. No
grants to individuals.
Application information:
  Initial approach: Letter
  Deadline(s): None
Trustees: Molly U. Tarr; Robert J. Tarr, Jr.
EIN: 043173231

8546

T-Bonz Foundation, Inc.
1177 Southgate Dr.
Charleston, SC 29407-4209

Established in 2009 in South Carolina.
Donors: Jerald Scheer; TBonz Restaurant Group.
Foundation type: Independent foundation.
Financial data (yr. ended 12/31/13): Assets,
$270,467 (M); gifts received, $275,830;
expenditures, $211,952; qualifying distributions,
$210,457; giving activities include $210,457 for 9
grants (high: $74,700; low: $5,637).
Fields of interest: Education; Agriculture; Human
services.
Type of support: General support.
Limitations: Applications not accepted. Giving
primarily in SC.
Application information: Unsolicited requests for
funds not accepted.
Officer: Jerald Scheer, Pres.
EIN: 542082714

8547

Verhagen Foundation
P.O. Box 31934
Charleston, SC 29417-1934

Established in 2005 in South Carolina.
Donor: Raoul M. Verhagen†.
Foundation type: Independent foundation.
Financial data (yr. ended 12/31/13): Assets,
$3,371,512 (M); expenditures, $227,748;
qualifying distributions, $154,500; giving activities
include $154,500 for 15 grants (high: $25,000;
low: $500).
Fields of interest: Animal welfare; Health;
Christianity; Food banks.
Limitations: Applications not accepted. Giving
primarily in SC. No grants to individuals.
Application information: Contributes only to
pre-selected organizations.
Officers: Mark Van Hook, Pres.; Dana Van Hook,
Secy.
EIN: 203604163

8548

The WebbCraft Family Foundation, Inc.
938 Simpson Rd.
Belton, SC 29627-8970 (864) 338-9734
Contact: Jerri Lynn Sharpe, Exec. Dir.
FAX: (864) 338-9737; E-mail: info@webbcraft.org;
Main URL: http://www.webbcraft.org

Established in 2000 in South Carolina.
Donor: Joy Craft Malcolm.
Foundation type: Independent foundation.
Financial data (yr. ended 12/31/14): Assets,
$3,184,866 (M); gifts received, $3,000;
expenditures, $216,738; qualifying distributions,
$189,491; giving activities include for 14 grants
(high: $35,240; low: $848).
Purpose and activities: The foundation supports
education and the development of individuals in the
Belton and Honea Path, South Carolina, areas.
Fields of interest: Arts and culture; Arts education;
Museums; Education; Secondary education; Higher
education.
Limitations: Applications accepted. Giving primarily
in SC. No grants to individuals.
Application information: Application guidelines and
form available on foundation web site. Application
form required.
  Initial approach: Applicants must contact the
    foundation prior to submitting an application
  Deadline(s): Apr. 1 and Oct. 1
Officers and Directors: Jerri Lynn Craft Sharpe,
Chair. and Director; Joy Craft, Vice-Chair. and
Director; Jana Craft Burdette, Secy. and Director;
Michael Pascuzzi, Treas. and Director; Julie Kay Bell;
Jimmy Craft; Lindy Craft Fullbright; Jane Craft Kay;
Faye Staton.
EIN: 571111833

8549

The Williams/Brice-Edwards Charitable Trust
110 Mason Croft Dr.
Sumter, SC 29150-4014 (803) 773-5407
Contact: Philip L. Edwards, Tr.

Established in 1988 in South Carolina.
Donor: Philip L. Edwards.
Foundation type: Independent foundation.
Financial data (yr. ended 12/31/13): Assets,
$5,972,607 (M); gifts received, $200,000;
expenditures, $206,473; qualifying distributions,
$205,000; giving activities include $205,000 for 9
grants (high: $50,000; low: $2,000).
Fields of interest: Arts and culture; Museums;
Historic preservation; Higher education; Nonprofits;
Community and economic development; Housing
development; Religion; Human services; Scouting
programs.
Type of support: Regranting.
Limitations: Applications accepted. Giving primarily
in Sumter, SC.
Application information:
  Initial approach: Proposal
  Deadline(s): None
Trustees: Frank O. Edwards; Philip L. Edwards;
Florence M. Ervin.
EIN: 576105891

8550

John Winthrop Charitable Trust
P.O. Box 22527
Charleston, SC 29413-2527

Donors: John Winthrop; John Winthrop, Jr.
Foundation type: Independent foundation.
Financial data (yr. ended 06/30/13): Assets,
$3,408,632 (M); gifts received, $100,139;
expenditures, $193,244; qualifying distributions,
$150,380; giving activities include $150,380 for 97
grants (high: $30,000; low: $100).
Fields of interest: Arts and culture; Education;
Human services.

Limitations: Applications not accepted. Giving on a national basis. No grants to individuals.
Application information: Unsolicited requests for funds not accepted.
Trustees: John Winthrop; John Winthrop, Jr.
EIN: 132982306

8551
The WPW Foundation
c/o Arthur State Bank
P.O. Box 481
Clinton, SC   29325-0481   (866) 266-5140

Established in 1997 in South Carolina.
Donor: Wilford P. Wood Trust.
Foundation type: Independent foundation.
Financial data (yr. ended 12/31/14): Assets, $3,716,534; expenditures, $237,829; qualifying distributions, $230,206.
Fields of interest: Elementary and secondary education; Christianity; Human services.
Type of support: General support.
Application information:
 Initial approach: Letter of request
 Deadline(s): Sept. 15 for letter of request
Trustees: Parnell Wood Buhlman; Estelle J. Wood; Arthur State Bank.
EIN: 586338488

8552
Carey Cox Wyatt Charitable Foundation
274 Doral Open
Kiawah Island, SC   29455

Established in 1995 in Georgia.
Foundation type: Independent foundation.
Financial data (yr. ended 12/31/13): Assets, $1,958,773 (M); expenditures, $161,130; qualifying distributions, $149,598; giving activities include $146,800 for 23 grants (high: $50,000; low: $100).
Fields of interest: Education; Health; Religion.
Type of support: General support.
Limitations: Applications not accepted. Giving primarily in GA. No grants to individuals.
Application information: Unsolicited requests for funds not accepted.
Directors: Gwyneth M. Dennard; Linda L. Wyatt; W. Whitlow Wyatt.
EIN: 582142054

8553
The Zvejnieks Foundation of South Carolina Inc
113 Beaver Ridge Dr.
Elgin, SC   29045-8211   (803) 699-5323
Contact: Peter Zvejnieks, Tr.

Foundation type: Independent foundation.
Financial data (yr. ended 12/31/12): Assets, $3,966,647 (M); expenditures, $375,177; qualifying distributions, $238,274; giving activities include $238,274 for grants.
Purpose and activities: Giving primarily for educational and financial support to students from any of the Baltic states, and to U.S. students studying or competent in the Latvian language.
Fields of interest: Arts and culture; Education; Human services.
International interests: Latvia.
Type of support: General support.
Limitations: Applications accepted. Giving primarily in SC; funding also in Latvia.
Application information: Application form required.
 Initial approach: Letter
 Deadline(s): None
Trustee: Peter Zvejnieks.
EIN: 262848806

SOUTH DAKOTA

8554
L. A. Amundson Scholarships, Inc.
c/o Barbara J. Hegelund
P.O. Box 1270
Sioux Falls, SD   57101-1270   (605) 335-1508

Established in 1992 in Minnesota.
Donors: First Security State Bank; First Security Bank, N.A.; Bank of Beulah; Lloyd and Barbara Amundson Charity Foundation, Inc.
Foundation type: Independent foundation.
Financial data (yr. ended 12/31/13): Assets, $7,128,977 (M); gifts received, $903,566; expenditures, $422,765; qualifying distributions, $313,874; giving activities include $305,500 for 54 grants (high: $34,000; low: $1,000).
Purpose and activities: Scholarship awards to residents of various locations in Iowa, Minnesota, Montana, and North Dakota, with special emphasis on students majoring in the areas of health care, business fields and technical trades.
Fields of interest: Higher education.
Limitations: Giving primarily in IA, MN, MT, and ND.
Application information: Application form required.
   Initial approach: Letter
   Deadline(s): Mar. 16
Officers and Directors: Barbara Hegelund, Pres. and Director; Jane Harberts, V.P. and Director; A.R. Mixner, Secy.-Treas. and Director; Matt Amundson; Philip Amundson.
Number of staff: None.
EIN: 411692528

8555
Orrion and Edith Barger Memorial Foundation
P.O. Box 609
Chamberlain, SD   57325-0609   (605) 734-5555
Contact: Lindsey Huether

Foundation type: Independent foundation.
Financial data (yr. ended 12/31/13): Assets, $8,308,176 (M); expenditures, $462,495; qualifying distributions, $360,830; giving activities include $360,830 for 28 grants (high: $60,000; low: $415).
Fields of interest: Education; Health; Public affairs.
Limitations: Applications accepted. Giving primarily in SD.
Application information: Application form required.
   Initial approach: Request application form
   Deadline(s): None
Officers: Denise Hyland, Pres.; Carson Pringle, V.P.; Cindy Adams, Secy.-Treas.
Directors: Gailen Meyerink; Douglas Nelson.
EIN: 261875189

8556
Black Hills Corporation Foundation
625 9th St.
P.O. Box 1400
Rapid City, SD   57709-1400
Contact: Kim Schneider

Established in 2001 in South Dakota.

Donors: Black Hills Corp.; Black Hills Service Co., LLC.
Foundation type: Company-sponsored foundation.
Financial data (yr. ended 12/31/13): Assets, $4,730,971 (M); gifts received, $300,000; expenditures, $250,688; qualifying distributions, $245,261; giving activities include $245,007 for 51 grants (high: $37,770; low: $100).
Purpose and activities: The foundation supports organizations involved with arts and culture, education, the environment, youth development, human services, community development, and civic affairs.
Fields of interest: Education; Domesticated animals; Religion.
Limitations: Applications accepted. Giving primarily in areas of company operations in CO, SD and WY. No support for political organizations, religious organizations not of direct benefit to the entire community, or discriminatory organizations. No grants to individuals, or for endowments, conferences, seminars, or festivals, tours, trips, or pageants, endowments, debt reduction, or athletic sponsorships.
Publications: Application guidelines.
Application information: Application form required.
   Initial approach: Request application form
   Deadline(s): None
   Board meeting date(s): Mar. 11, June 17, Sept. 16, and Dec. 16
Officers: Lori Rainwater, Pres.; Linden R. Evans, V.P.; Jafar Karim, Secy.; Perry Krush, Treas.
Directors: Susan Bailey; John Benton; David R. Emery; Nick Herman; Jason Ketchum; Tracy Peterson; Mark Stege; Jeff Sylvester.
EIN: 752986866

8557
The Mike Cindy and Kylie Huether Family Foundation
2815 S. Saint Charles Ln.
Sioux Falls, SD   57103-4671

Donors: Mike Huether; Cindy Huether.
Foundation type: Independent foundation.
Financial data (yr. ended 12/31/13): Assets, $0 (M); gifts received, $75,000; expenditures, $183,292; qualifying distributions, $178,333; giving activities include $178,333 for 44 grants (high: $51,150; low: $20).
Fields of interest: University education; Foundations.
Limitations: Applications not accepted. Giving primarily in SD.
Application information: Unsolicited requests for funds not accepted.
Officers: Mike Huether, Pres.; Cindy Huether, V.P.
Director: Kylie Huether.
EIN: 273665401

8558
Clarkson Family Foundation
c/o Pioneer Trust Bank
P.O. Box 729
Belle Fourche, SD   57717-0729

Established in 2001 in South Dakota.
Donor: Ferman L. Clarkson.
Foundation type: Independent foundation.

Financial data (yr. ended 12/31/14): Assets, $4,175,706; expenditures, $236,931; qualifying distributions, $194,092.
Fields of interest: Arts and culture; Education; Community and economic development; Human services.
Limitations: Applications not accepted. Giving primarily in SD. No grants to individuals.
Application information: Unsolicited requests for funds not accepted.
Officer and Directors: Ferman L. Clarkson, Pres. and Director; Mary Clarkson Buchholz; Thad Milton Buchholz.
Trustee: Pioneer Trust Bank.
EIN: 460460142

8559
Eleanor's Fund
117 E. Capitol Ave.
Pierre, SD   57501-3105

Established in 2009 in South Dakota.
Donor: Neal Wanless.
Foundation type: Independent foundation.
Financial data (yr. ended 12/31/13): Assets, $4,836,361 (M); expenditures, $396,383; qualifying distributions, $350,000; giving activities include $350,000 for 12 grants (high: $70,000; low: $10,000).
Fields of interest: Specialty hospital care; Hospice care; Human services.
Limitations: Applications accepted. Giving primarily in SD. No support for Private. No grants for International Organizations, Non 501(c)(3) Organizations, Individuals and Endowments.
Application information: Application form required.
   Initial approach: Letter
   Deadline(s): By 1st of Mar., June, Sept., and Dec.
Directors: Arlen Wanless; James Wanless; Nancy Wanless; Neal Wanless.
EIN: 271020259

8560
The James and Eloise Elmen Foundation
P.O. Box 5103
Sioux Falls, SD   57117

Established in 2007 in South Dakota.
Donors: James W. Elmen†; Eloise N. Elmen; Elmen Family Foundation.
Foundation type: Independent foundation.
Financial data (yr. ended 12/31/13): Assets, $10,584,080 (M); gifts received, $71,980; expenditures, $453,697; qualifying distributions, $420,849; giving activities include $341,560 for 23 grants (high: $200,000; low: $100).
Fields of interest: Foundations; Christianity.
Limitations: Applications not accepted. Giving primarily in SD.
Application information: Contributes only to pre-selected organizations.
Officers: Richard Elmen, Pres.; Eloise N. Elman, V.P.; Connie Renee Elmen, Secy.
Director: Rebecca Sue Elmen Lam.
EIN: 205767706

8561
The Robert and Rita Elmen Foundation
2901 W. 11th St.
Sioux Falls, SD   57104-2538

Established in 2007 in South Dakota.
Donors: Robert C. Elmen; Elmen Family Foundation.
Foundation type: Independent foundation.
Financial data (yr. ended 12/31/13): Assets, $11,416,912 (M); gifts received, $600,168; expenditures, $519,109; qualifying distributions, $482,823; giving activities include $402,275 for 27 grants (high: $250,000; low: $25).
Fields of interest: Higher education; Nonprofits; Christianity.
Type of support: Regranting.
Limitations: Applications not accepted. Giving primarily in SD.
Application information: Unsolicited requests for funds not accepted.
Officers: Robert C. Elmen, Pres.; Julie D. Elmen, V.P.; Sarah Kopp, V.P.; Vance Goldammer, Secy.; Thomas J. Whalen, Treas.
EIN: 205767798

8562
Emerald Foundation
401 E. 8th St., Ste. 319
Sioux Falls, SD   57103

Foundation type: Independent foundation.
Financial data (yr. ended 12/31/13): Assets, $6,263,945 (M); expenditures, $318,136; qualifying distributions, $295,673; giving activities include $273,000 for 12 grants (high: $65,000; low: $4,000).
Fields of interest: Education; Hospital care; Human services.
Limitations: Applications not accepted.
Application information: Unsolicited requests for funds not accepted.
Trustees: Thomas R. Youngren; Dorsey & Whitney Trust Co., LLC.
EIN: 376439234

8563
Engelsma Family Foundation
401 E. 8th St., Ste. 319
Sioux Falls, SD   57103

Foundation type: Independent foundation.
Financial data (yr. ended 12/31/13): Assets, $6,356,141 (M); expenditures, $319,574; qualifying distributions, $296,798; giving activities include $255,451 for 38 grants (high: $50,000; low: $50).
Fields of interest: Arts and culture; Performing arts; Education; Higher education; Hospital care; Diseases and conditions; Protestantism; Human services; Child welfare.
Type of support: Research.
Limitations: Applications not accepted. Giving primarily in MN. No grants to individuals.
Application information: Unsolicited requests for funds not accepted.
Officers: Sharon Korsch, Pres.; Susan Wilcox, V.P.; Barbara Diessner, Secy.; Daniel Engelsma, Treas.
Directors: Jonathon Diessner; Bruce Engelsma; Kirsten Engelsma; Jina Engelsma Opsahl; Nicole Slattery; Paige Wilcox.
EIN: 710924087

8564
The Ferguson Family Foundation Trust
c/o Delta Trust
330 S. Poplar Ave., Ste. 103
Pierre, SD   57501-2476

Donors: James Terese Ferguson; Terese M. Ferguson; J. Brian Ferguson.
Foundation type: Independent foundation.
Financial data (yr. ended 12/31/12): Assets, $3,031,110 (M); gifts received, $300,000; expenditures, $156,003; qualifying distributions, $125,000; giving activities include $125,000 for 5 grants (high: $25,000; low: $25,000).
Fields of interest: Education; Catholicism; Youth development.
Limitations: Applications not accepted.
Application information: Unsolicited requests for funds not accepted.
Trustee: Delta Trust.
EIN: 276633327

8565
John F. Grundhofer Charitable Foundation
P.O. Box 425
Plankinton, SD   57368-0425

Donors: John F. and Beverly G. Grundhofer Charitable Foundation; John F. Grundhofer.
Foundation type: Independent foundation.
Financial data (yr. ended 12/31/13): Assets, $5,547,949 (M); gifts received, $136,546; expenditures, $489,880; qualifying distributions, $413,980; giving activities include $391,177 for 42 grants (high: $77,500; low: $100).
Fields of interest: Arts and culture; Education; Youth development.
Limitations: Applications not accepted.
Application information: Unsolicited requests for funds not accepted.
Officers and Trustees: John F. Grundhofer, Pres. and Trustee; Patricia Meier Grundhofer, Exec. Dir.
EIN: 272440735

8566
The Hatterscheidt Foundation Inc.
c/o Dacotah Bank Trust
P.O. Box 1210
Aberdeen, SD   57402-1210
Application address: c/o Tyler DeBoer, 204 S. 1st St., P.O. Box 849, Aberdeen, SD 57402-0849, tel.: (605) 229-8223

Established in 1947 in Delaware.
Donors: Ruth K. Hatterscheidt†; F.W. Hatterscheidt Trusts.
Foundation type: Independent foundation.
Financial data (yr. ended 12/31/12): Assets, $4,436,799 (M); expenditures, $298,153; qualifying distributions, $240,513; giving activities include $232,000 for 33 grants (high: $65,500; low: $500).
Purpose and activities: Giving primarily to assist graduating seniors from South Dakota high schools with a 3.0 GPA or better for their freshman year of college in the state; some support also for local charitable organizations.
Fields of interest: Higher education.
Type of support: Scholarships; Student aid.
Limitations: Applications accepted. Giving primarily in SD. No grants for matching gifts; no loans.

Application information: Application form required.
Initial approach: Proposal
Copies of proposal: 1
Deadline(s): None
Board meeting date(s): Apr. and Nov.
Officers: Jack Thompson, Pres.; Harvey Jewett, Secy.-Treas.
Trustees: Dennis Kraft; Dorothy O'Keefe.
Number of staff: None.
EIN: 466012543

8567
The Houston Family Foundation
401 E. 8th St., Ste. 319
Sioux Falls, SD   57103-7031

Established in 2005 in South Dakota.
Foundation type: Independent foundation.
Financial data (yr. ended 12/31/13): Assets, $8,111,157 (M); expenditures, $524,447; qualifying distributions, $440,104; giving activities include $285,000 for 13 grants (high: $75,000; low: $10,000).
Fields of interest: Arts and culture; Education; Graduate and professional education; Health; Nursing care; Substance abuse treatment; Food banks.
Limitations: Applications not accepted. Giving primarily in CA and WA. No grants to individuals.
Application information: Contributes only to pre-selected organizations.
Officer: James R. Houston II, Pres. and Exec. Dir.
Trustees: Richard Fordiani; Theodore Giatas; David N. Rennie; Dorsey & Whitney Trust Co. LLC.
EIN: 203853573

8568
J&L Foundation
c/o Adler Trust Co.
401 E. 8th St., Ste. 250A
Sioux Falls, SD   57103-7034

Established in 2003 in South Dakota.
Donors: Sieben Foundation; Opus Corp.; Joseph Rauenhorst; Loretta Rauenhorst.
Foundation type: Independent foundation.
Financial data (yr. ended 12/31/13): Assets, $4,128,417 (M); expenditures, $168,346; qualifying distributions, $166,923; giving activities include $162,000 for 14 grants (high: $52,115; low: $1,050).
Fields of interest: Education; Youth development.
Type of support: Capital campaigns; General support.
Limitations: Applications not accepted. Giving primarily in FL. No grants to individuals.
Application information: Contributes only to pre-selected organizations.
Officers and Directors: Joseph J. Rauenhorst, Pres. and Director; Paul Lewis, V.P.; Loretta Rauenhorst, V.P. and Director; Suzanne Flannigan, Secy.-Treas. and Director.
EIN: 020694762

8569
Fred & Mary Maas Private Foundation
P. O. Box 205
Gettysburg, SD 57442-0205 6057652494
Application address: c/o, Lila Hericks, 408 E.
Commercial Ave., Gettysburg, SD 57442, tel.: (605)
765-2494

Established in 2000 in South Dakota.
Donor: Melvin Maas†.
Foundation type: Independent foundation.
Financial data (yr. ended 12/31/14): Assets,
$3,373,324; expenditures, $197,864; qualifying
distributions, $157,100.
Fields of interest: Education.
Limitations: Applications accepted. Giving primarily
in SD. No grants to individuals.
Application information: Application form required.
  Initial approach: Letter
  Deadline(s): None
Officers: Norman Kostboth, Pres.; Monty Harer,
V.P.; Lila Hericks, Secy.-Treas.
Board Members: Tim Hagedorn; Ken Iverson.
EIN: 460458582

8570
Mike Miller Foundation
9107 W. 32nd St.
Sioux Falls, SD 57106 (605) 770-4541
Contact: Thomas J. Miller, Pres.
Main URL: http://www.mikemiller33.com/
foundation.php

Established in 2002 in South Dakota.
Donors: Michael L. Miller; Miami Heat Foundation;
Randy Goldfarb; James Sensale; EquineTack and
Nutritionals; Incapital, LLC; Diane Fahey; Fed Ex
Services; Paul Tudor Jones; Sanford Health
Foundation; John D. Fleenor, MD; HFP Capital
Markets; Youth Athletic Foundation; Miriam
Sensale; Pat Riley Family Foundation; Africk
Holdings, Inc.; John B.A. Haggin, Jr.; Caesar's
Entertainment Operation Co.; Alain Trodec; Truth
Design; Jay D. Wilson; Abror's Edge Residential Lots
LLC; John Radtke; Poplar Foundation; Scott
Abdullah; Patricia Abdullah; First Premier Bank; First
Dakota National Bank.
Foundation type: Independent foundation.
Financial data (yr. ended 12/31/13): Assets,
$49,017 (M); gifts received, $370,795;
expenditures, $433,719; qualifying distributions,
$214,465; giving activities include $214,465 for 13
grants (high: $74,240; low: $1,000).
Fields of interest: Education; Health; Christianity;
Child welfare.
Type of support: Individual development.
Limitations: Applications accepted. Giving primarily
in SD and TN.
Application information:
  Initial approach: Proposal
  Deadline(s): None
Officers: Thomas J. Miller, Pres.; Jennifer Miller,
V.P.; Sheryl Miller, Secy.-Treas.
Directors: Chelsey S. Dockter; Jared Miller; Michael
Miller.
EIN: 300015773

8571
Harvey W. Peters Research Foundation
c/o First Premier Bank Trust Dept.
601 S. Minnesota Ave.
Sioux Falls, SD 57101-4824

Established in 1999 in Unspecified.
Donor: Edward Becher Via.
Foundation type: Independent foundation.
Financial data (yr. ended 06/30/14): Assets,
$49,282,036 (M); gifts received, $235,000;
expenditures, $2,416,068; qualifying distributions,
$271,000; giving activities include $271,000 for 1
grant.
Purpose and activities: Giving primarily for
osteopathic medicine.
Fields of interest: Education.
Limitations: Applications not accepted. Giving
primarily in VA.
Application information: Unsolicited request for
fund snot accepted.
Officer and Directors: John G. Rocovich, Pres. and
Director; David G. Hottman; J. Tracy O'Rourke;
Frederick P. Stratton, Jr.
EIN: 460459671

8572
Bob & Ginny Peterson Foundation
324 Dakota Dunes Blvd., Ste. 200
Dakota Dunes, SD 57049-5391

Established in 1996 in Iowa.
Donors: Robert L. Peterson; G. Virginia Peterson;
Mark R. Peterson.
Foundation type: Independent foundation.
Financial data (yr. ended 12/31/13): Assets,
$3,632,556 (M); expenditures, $282,732;
qualifying distributions, $210,070; giving activities
include $206,033 for 31 grants (high: $52,000;
low: $250).
Fields of interest: Education; Higher education;
Foundations; Diseases and conditions;
Protestantism; Human services; Child welfare;
Youth services.
Limitations: Applications not accepted. Giving
primarily in Sioux City, IA. No grants to individuals.
Application information: Contributes only to
pre-selected organizations.
Officers: G. Virginia Peterson, Pres.; Mark R.
Peterson, Secy.-Treas.
EIN: 911753779

8573
Sheldon F. Reese Foundation
P.O. Box 89704
Sioux Falls, SD 57109-1010
Application address: c/o John Quello, P.O. Box
1428, Sioux Falls, SD 57109-1010, tel.: (605)
336-1699

Established in 1980 in South Dakota.
Donor: Sheldon F. Reese†.
Foundation type: Independent foundation.
Financial data (yr. ended 12/31/13): Assets,
$4,570,933 (M); expenditures, $220,752;
qualifying distributions, $218,989; giving activities
include $211,767 for 28 grants (high: $25,000;
low: $500).
Fields of interest: Human services.
Type of support: General support.

Limitations: Applications accepted. Giving primarily
in Sioux Falls, SD.
Application information: Application form required.
  Initial approach: Contact foundation for
    application form
  Deadline(s): None
Officers: John Quello, Pres.; Ernest G. Carlson, V.P.;
Virginia Pavelka Luke, Secy.; Vance R.C.
Goldammer, Treas.
Director: Curtis L. Hage.
EIN: 460358682

8574
Edward L. Schwab Memorial Foundation
c/o Dacotah Bank
P.O. Box 1210
Aberdeen, SD 57402-1210 (605) 229-7122
Contact: Tom Appletoft

Established in 1996 in South Dakota.
Foundation type: Operating foundation.
Financial data (yr. ended 08/31/13): Assets,
$3,202,604 (M); expenditures, $240,723;
qualifying distributions, $184,169; giving activities
include $175,000 for 5 grants (high: $58,950; low:
$4,500).
Fields of interest: Higher education.
Type of support: Scholarships.
Limitations: Applications accepted. Giving limited to
residents of Henry, Willow Lake, Clark, Florence and
Hamlin counties, school districts, SD.
Application information: Application form required.
  Initial approach: Contact foundation
  Deadline(s): 180 days after publication notice
Officers: Kevin Wegehaupt, Pres.; Marci Caster,
V.P.; Tom Labrie, Secy.-Treas.
Directors: Henry Desnoyers; Gary Neuberger.
Trustee: Dacotah Bank, N.A.
EIN: 911770168

8575
Gwendolyn L. Stearns Foundation Inc.
246 Founders Park Dr., Ste. 101
Rapid City, SD 57701-8092
Application address: c/o James Clement, 3724 Park
Dr., Rapid City, SD 57702

Established in 2001 in South Dakota.
Donor: Gwendolyn L. Stearns†.
Foundation type: Independent foundation.
Financial data (yr. ended 12/31/13): Assets,
$6,249,376 (M); expenditures, $427,466;
qualifying distributions, $390,000; giving activities
include $390,000 for 33 grants (high: $40,000;
low: $3,000).
Fields of interest: Education; Human services; Food
aid; Family services; Child welfare.
Limitations: Applications accepted. Giving primarily
in Rapid City, SD.
Application information: Applicants must be from
the Rapid City, SD, area. Application form required.
  Initial approach: Letter requesting application
  Deadline(s): None
Officers: Judy Olson Duhamel, Pres.; Larry
Dahlstrom, V.P.; Phyllis S. Dixon, Secy.; Dave True,
Treas.
Directors: Robert Cook; William Howard; Janine
Kern; Kathy Miller; Terry Whiting.
EIN: 311737658

8576
Watertown Community Foundation

211 E. Kemp Ave.
P.O. Box 116
Watertown, SD   57201-0116   (605) 882-3731
Contact: Jan DeBerg, Exec. Dir.
FAX: (605) 753-5731;
E-mail: assistant@watertowncommunityfoundation.
org; Main URL: http://
www.watertowncommunityfoundation.org

Established in 1979 in South Dakota.
Foundation type: Community foundation.
Financial data (yr. ended 12/31/13): Assets,
$13,418,754 (M); gifts received, $2,625,455;
expenditures, $556,699; giving activities include
$168,514 for 11+ grants (high: $66,183), and
$136,242 for 30 grants to individuals.
Purpose and activities: The Watertown Community
Foundation invests in the vitality and future of
Watertown by supporting community priorities,
responding to human service needs and enhancing
recreation, education, arts and culture.
Fields of interest: Arts and culture; Education;
Environment; Natural resources; Health; Disasters
and emergency management; Public affairs;
Housing development; Sports and recreation;
Human services; Family services; Women's
services.
Type of support: Capital campaigns; Pro bono
consulting services; Capital and infrastructure;
Equipment; Emergency funds; Program
development; Convening; Seed money;
Scholarships; Student aid.
Limitations: Applications accepted. Giving limited to
the metropolitan Watertown, SD, area. No support
for private foundations. No grants to individuals
(except for designated scholarships), or for
operating expenses.
Publications: Annual report (including application
guidelines); Informational brochure; Newsletter.

Application information: The foundation's staff is
available to counsel with interested parties
regarding the appropriateness of a project for
consideration by the foundation's Board. Visit
foundation web site for application form and
guidelines. Application form required.
  Initial approach: Submit grant application
  Copies of proposal: 8
  Deadline(s): None, applications are accepted at
    any time and are considered at monthly Board
    meetings
  Board meeting date(s): Monthly
  Final notification: Monthly
Officers and Directors: Dr. Lesli Jutting, Chair. and
Director; Lee Schull, Vice-Chair. and Director; Jan
DeBerg, Exec. Dir.; Dale Christenson; Laurie
Benson; Angie Reppe.
Trustees: Great Western Bank; Wells Fargo Bank,
N.A.
Number of staff: 1 full-time professional.
EIN: 460350319

8577
Welk Family Foundation

c/o Dacotah Bank
P.O. Box 1210
Aberdeen, SD   57402-1210
Application address: Dacotah Bank, 308 S. Main St.,
Aberdeen, SD 57401, tel.: (605) 225-5611

Established in 1988 in South Dakota.
Foundation type: Independent foundation.
Financial data (yr. ended 12/31/14): Assets,
$4,100,447 (M); expenditures, $202,287;
qualifying distributions, $178,882; giving activities
include $165,594 for 34 grants (high: $45,000;
low: $489).
Purpose and activities: Giving primarily to human
services, education, and religious organizations.

Fields of interest: Education; Hospital care;
Libraries; Christianity; Human services.
Type of support: Scholarships; Individual
development.
Publications: Grants list.
Application information: Application form required.
  Initial approach: Contact foundation for
    application form
  Deadline(s): None
  Board meeting date(s): Apr.
Trustee: Dacotah Bank.
Advisory Committee: Kaye Cahill; Royce Grimsrud;
June Helgeson; Pat Dady.
EIN: 363579562

8578
Wolfe Family Charitable Foundation

201 S. Phillips Ave., Ste. 200
Sioux Falls, SD   57104-6449

Established in 2007 in Illinois.
Donor: Anna H. Wolfe.
Foundation type: Independent foundation.
Financial data (yr. ended 12/31/13): Assets,
$2,328 (M); gifts received, $152,500;
expenditures, $151,280; qualifying distributions,
$150,000; giving activities include $150,000 for 1
grant.
Purpose and activities: Giving primarily to an
organization that promotes spiritual, physical, and
mental health.
Fields of interest: Education; Environment; Human
services.
Limitations: Applications not accepted. Giving
primarily in Moline, IL. No grants to individuals.
Application information: Contributes only to
pre-selected organizations.
Trustee: South Dakota Trust Co.
EIN: 260600136

TENNESSEE

8579
Adams Family Foundation I
2217 Battleground Dr.
Murfreesboro, TN 37129-6006 (615) 890-2020
Contact: Robert G. Adams, Tr.

Established in 1993 in Tennessee.
Donors: Carl E. Adams; W. Andrew Adams; Gerald Coggin; Jennie Mae Adams.
Foundation type: Independent foundation.
Financial data (yr. ended 12/31/14): Assets, $10,633,442 (M); expenditures, $412,391; qualifying distributions, $412,391; giving activities include $410,750 for 40 grants (high: $141,000; low: $500).
Fields of interest: Arts and culture; Elementary and secondary education; University education; Christianity; Human services; Child welfare.
Type of support: General support.
Limitations: Applications accepted. Giving primarily in TN.
Application information: Application form required.
Initial approach: Letter
Deadline(s): None
Trustees: Alan B. Adams; Carl Adams; Fred Adams; Robert A. Adams; W. Andrew Adams; Joanne Coggin.
EIN: 621515107

8580
Agape Love Foundation, Inc.
650 25th St. N.W., Ste. 100
Cleveland, TN 37311-1353 (423) 476-9160
Contact: Kenneth D. Higgins, Pres.

Established in 1997 in Tennessee.
Donor: Kenneth D. Higgins.
Foundation type: Independent foundation.
Financial data (yr. ended 12/31/13): Assets, $12,766 (M); gifts received, $241,500; expenditures, $247,437; qualifying distributions, $241,578; giving activities include $241,578 for 25 grants (high: $99,996; low: $250).
Fields of interest: University education; Protestantism; Human services.
Type of support: General support.
Limitations: Applications accepted. Giving primarily in TN.
Application information:
Initial approach: Proposal
Deadline(s): None
Officer: Kenneth D. Higgins, Pres.
Directors: Edward Caylor; Joe Rodgers.
EIN: 621731414

8581
The Aim Charity
6075 Poplar Ave., Ste. 700
Memphis, TN 38119-0100

Donors: Advisory Research; RAB Capital PLC; Kurt Voldeng; Ironwood Capital Management; WCM Investments; Ore Hill Partners; Pontchatrain Capital; Fred Hodges.
Foundation type: Independent foundation.
Financial data (yr. ended 12/31/12): Assets, $31,385 (M); gifts received, $251,400;

expenditures, $229,600; qualifying distributions, $150,000; giving activities include $150,000 for grants.
Fields of interest: Christianity; Child welfare.
Limitations: Applications not accepted. Giving primarily in Memphis, TN. No grants to individuals.
Application information: Contributes only to pre-selected organizations.
Officers: Miles S. Fortas, Pres.; Robert Longfield, Secy.
Director: Brian Jones.
EIN: 270047198

8582
Atticus Trust
(formerly The Atticus Foundation)
c/o Martin S. Brown, Jr., Tr.
424 Church St., Ste. 2800
Nashville, TN 37219-2386

Established in 1986 in Tennessee.
Donor: Sara S. Brown.
Foundation type: Independent foundation.
Financial data (yr. ended 12/31/14): Assets, $19,322,478 (M); expenditures, $545,675; qualifying distributions, $394,054; giving activities include $368,500 for 41 grants (high: $100,000; low: $1,000).
Purpose and activities: Giving primarily for the arts, education, conservation, and to Episcopal organizations and churches; support also for a law center.
Fields of interest: Arts and culture; Visual arts; Performing arts; Art museums; Historic preservation; Education; Higher education; Environment; Environmental justice; Natural resources; Domesticated animals; Nonprofits; Hospice care; Radio; Television; Episcopalianism and Anglicanism; Lutheranism; Human services; Family services; Child welfare; Scouting programs.
Type of support: Public engagement and education; Equal access; Regranting.
Limitations: Applications not accepted. Giving primarily in TN. No grants to individuals.
Application information: Contributes only to pre-selected organizations.
Trustee and Committee Members: Elizabeth M. Brown; Martin S. Brown, Trustee; Martin S. Brown, Sr.; Margaret DeClercq; Susannah Scott-Barnes.
EIN: 581796390

8583
B & B Foundation
(formerly Betty and Bernard Werthan, Jr. Foundation)
P.O. Box 1310
Nashville, TN 37208-2729

Established in 1993 in Tennessee.
Donor: Leah Rose Werthan†.
Foundation type: Independent foundation.
Financial data (yr. ended 12/31/13): Assets, $1,812,826 (M); expenditures, $153,106; qualifying distributions, $130,630; giving activities include $129,030 for 88 grants (high: $21,600; low: $25).
Fields of interest: Arts and culture; Education; Nonprofits; Judaism; Human services.
Type of support: Regranting.
Limitations: Applications not accepted. No grants to individuals.

Application information: Contributes only to pre-selected organizations.
Officers: Bernard Werthan, Jr., Pres.; Betty Werthan, Secy.
EIN: 621543218

8584
Wayne G. Basler Charitable Foundation
P.O. Box 2049
Kingsport, TN 37662-2049 (423) 246-4546
Contact: Shari Hillman, Fdn. Mgr.

Established in 1988 in Tennessee.
Donor: Wayne G. Basler.
Foundation type: Independent foundation.
Financial data (yr. ended 12/31/14): Assets, $9,881,724 (M); expenditures, $458,339; qualifying distributions, $328,725; giving activities include $324,500 for 5 grants (high: $300,000; low: $500).
Fields of interest: Higher education; Nonprofits; Human services.
Type of support: Regranting.
Limitations: Applications accepted. Giving primarily in TN. No grants to individuals.
Application information: Application form required.
Initial approach: Letter
Deadline(s): Sept. 30
Officer: Shari L. Hillman, Fdn. Mgr.
Trustee: Wayne G. Basler.
EIN: 621347054

8585
Belz Foundation
100 Peabody Pl., Ste. 1400
Memphis, TN 38103-3648

Established in 1952 in Tennessee.
Donors: Philip Belz†; Martin S. Belz; Ronald A. Belz; Jack A. Belz; Andrew Groveman; Jan B. Groveman; Philip Bell Charitable Lead Annuity II; The 1992 Belz Charitable Trust.
Foundation type: Independent foundation.
Financial data (yr. ended 12/31/13): Assets, $27,610,196 (M); gifts received, $1,502,800; expenditures, $768,583; qualifying distributions, $345,873; giving activities include $345,873 for 155 grants (high: $50,000; low: $18).
Purpose and activities: Giving primarily for Jewish welfare funds, temple support, Israel, education, including higher education and yeshivas, cultural organizations, and health and welfare organizations.
Fields of interest: Arts and culture; Education; Elementary and secondary education; Higher education; Graduate and professional education; Nonprofits; Health; Diseases and conditions; Judaism; Theology; Human services.
International interests: Israel.
Type of support: Research; Research and evaluation; Regranting.
Limitations: Applications not accepted. Giving primarily in Memphis, TN. No grants to individuals.
Application information: Contributes only to pre-selected organizations.
Officers and Directors: Jack A. Belz, Pres. and Director; Martin S. Belz, V.P. and Director; Ronald A. Belz, V.P. and Director; Jimmie D. Williams, Secy.-Treas. and Director; Andrew Groveman; Jan B. Groveman; Raymond Shainberg.
EIN: 626046715

8586
The Benjamin & Heather Crane Foundation Inc.

390 Grovehurst Ln.
Brentwood, TN 37027-4461 (817) 296-9890

Foundation type: Independent foundation.
Financial data (yr. ended 12/31/13): Assets, $135,975 (M); gifts received, $506,554; expenditures, $544,909; qualifying distributions, $326,404; giving activities include $325,480 for 5 grants (high: $150,000; low: $3,980).
Fields of interest: Leadership development; Religion; Male children and youth.
Limitations: Applications accepted. Giving primarily in CT and TX.
Application information: Application form required.
Initial approach: Proposal
Deadline(s): None
Officers: Benjamin Crane, Pres.; Heather Crane, V.P.
Director: Katherine Crane.
EIN: 274268415

8587
Berman Charitable Foundation Inc.

P.O. Box 400
Winchester, TN 37398-0400

Donor: Farley L. Berman†.
Foundation type: Independent foundation.
Financial data (yr. ended 12/31/13): Assets, $4,838,459 (M); expenditures, $287,160; qualifying distributions, $255,636; giving activities include $192,000 for 20 grants (high: $25,000; low: $1,000).
Fields of interest: Museums; Elementary and secondary education; Substance abuse prevention; Substance abuse treatment; Diabetes; Christianity; Human services.
Limitations: Applications accepted. Giving primarily in AL, with emphasis on Anniston and Birmingham. No grants to individuals.
Application information:
Initial approach: Proposal
Deadline(s): None
Officers: Anne H. Norred, Pres.; William Henry Agee, Secy.; Dave Prosser, Treas.; Deanne H. Robinson, Exec. Dir.
EIN: 631229394

8588
BGL Foundation

(formerly Creating Christmas Memories)
3855 Ocoee St. N., 5th Fl.
Cleveland, TN 37312-4457

Established in 1997 in Tennessee.
Donors: Steve McKenzie; Brenda McKenzie; Brenda Lawson; Stanley C. Lawson; Lawson Trust.
Foundation type: Independent foundation.
Financial data (yr. ended 06/30/13): Assets, $540 (M); gifts received, $157,120; expenditures, $156,993; qualifying distributions, $156,993; giving activities include $150,726 for 4 grants (high: $115,214; low: $500).
Purpose and activities: Giving primarily to buy clothes and Christmas presents for economically disadvantaged children.
Fields of interest: Human services; Child welfare.

Limitations: Applications not accepted. Giving primarily in TN.
Application information: Unsolicited requests for funds not accepted.
Officers: Brenda Lawson, Pres., Treas. and C.E.O.; Stanley C. Lawson, V.P. and Secy.
Board Member: Sandra Rowland.
Number of staff: None.
EIN: 621714714

8589
The Blum Family Foundation

909 Bowring Pk.
Nashville, TN 37215-2456

Established in 2001 in Tennessee.
Donors: Lauren Blum; Joan B. Shayne.
Foundation type: Independent foundation.
Financial data (yr. ended 12/31/12): Assets, $2,207,157 (M); gifts received, $186,385; expenditures, $262,324; qualifying distributions, $224,805; giving activities include $224,805 for grants.
Fields of interest: Arts and culture; Museums; Education; Diseases and conditions; Judaism; Human services.
Limitations: Applications not accepted. Giving primarily in TN and NY. No grants to individuals.
Application information: Contributes only to pre-selected organizations.
Trustees: Jennifer L. Blum; Lauren Blum; Emily Blum Haslett; Joan B. Shayne.
EIN: 621871174

8590
Kenneth E. Boring Charitable Foundation, Inc.

P.O. Box 1258
Chattanooga, TN 37401-1258
Application address: c/o, Dorothy Boring, P.O. Box 1608, Dalton, GA 30722-1608, tel.: (706) 226-7625

Established in 2003 in Georgia.
Donor: Kenneth E. Boring.
Foundation type: Independent foundation.
Financial data (yr. ended 12/31/13): Assets, $3,588,869 (M); expenditures, $161,049; qualifying distributions, $158,620; giving activities include $158,620 for 23 grants (high: $35,000; low: $220).
Purpose and activities: Giving primarily for higher education.
Fields of interest: Higher education; Nonprofits; Health.
Type of support: Annual campaigns; Regranting; Scholarships.
Limitations: Applications accepted. Giving primarily in Atlanta and Dalton, GA, SC, and TN. No grants to individuals.
Application information: Application form required.
Initial approach: Proposal
Deadline(s): Dec. 31
Officer and Trustees: Dorothy S. Boring, Pres. and Trustee; Harold E. Abrams, Secy.; Laura Lynn Boring; Leah Boring Hill; Robert S. Riley.
EIN: 270063662

8591
The Bornblum Foundation

c/o Alvin A. Gordon
100 N. Main St., Ste. 3020
Memphis, TN 38103-0550 (901) 525-5744
Contact: Alvin A. Gordon, Exec. Dir.

Established in 1991 in Georgia.
Donors: Bert Bornblum; David Bornblum†.
Foundation type: Independent foundation.
Financial data (yr. ended 12/31/12): Assets, $10,842,001 (M); expenditures, $250,614; qualifying distributions, $218,970; giving activities include $218,970 for grants.
Purpose and activities: Giving primarily to Jewish agencies, temples, and schools.
Fields of interest: Education; Judaism.
Limitations: Applications accepted. Giving primarily in Memphis, TN. No grants to individuals.
Application information: Application form required.
Deadline(s): None
Officers: Bert Bornblum, V.P.; Bruce L. Feldbaum, Secy.-Treas.; Alvin A. Gordon, Exec. Dir.
Directors: Joel Felt; Elaine Gordon; Jerome Makowsky; Jack Rosenweig; Ira Weinstein; Barrie Weiser; Ted Winestone; Jocelyn Dan Wurzburg.
EIN: 621448070

8592
Bradford Family Foundation

(formerly The Lillian Foundation)
c/o J. C. Bradford
530 Belle Meade Blvd.
Nashville, TN 37205-3424

Established in 1990 in Tennessee.
Donors: Eleanor Bradford Unitrust; James C. Bradford†.
Foundation type: Independent foundation.
Financial data (yr. ended 12/31/13): Assets, $7,395,054 (M); gifts received, $740,253; expenditures, $175,035; qualifying distributions, $153,258; giving activities include $151,873 for 65 grants (high: $19,500; low: $50).
Fields of interest: Opera; Orchestral music; Education; Nonprofits; Religion; Human services.
Type of support: General support; Regranting.
Limitations: Applications not accepted. Giving primarily in TN. No grants to individuals.
Application information: Unsolicited requests for funds not accepted.
Trustees: Bryan R. Bradford; James C. Bradford III; Lillian R. Bradford.
EIN: 626344538

8593
Elizabeth Caldwell Charitable Trust

4385 Poplar Ave.
Memphis, TN 38117-3715

Donor: Elizabeth T. Caldwell Living Trust.
Foundation type: Independent foundation.
Financial data (yr. ended 12/31/13): Assets, $794,540 (M); gifts received, $1,034,000; expenditures, $243,659; qualifying distributions, $242,450; giving activities include $241,255 for 5 grants (high: $137,860; low: $10,340).
Fields of interest: Health; Religion; Human services.
Limitations: Applications not accepted. Giving primarily in TN.

Application information: Unsolicited requests for funds not accepted.
Trustee: First Tennessee Bank.
EIN: 466860147

8594
John and Jane Campbell Family Foundation
43 Laurelwood Cove
Jackson, TN 38305-8559 7316682799

Donors: Jane Campbell; John Campbell.
Foundation type: Independent foundation.
Financial data (yr. ended 12/31/14): Assets, $3,648,472; gifts received, $200,000; expenditures, $164,843; qualifying distributions, $154,000.
Fields of interest: Education; Sports and recreation.
Type of support: General support.
Limitations: Applications accepted. Giving primarily in TN.
Application information: Application form required.
Deadline(s): None
Officers and Directors: John Campbell, Pres. and Director; Jane Campbell, Secy. and Director.
EIN: 263889261

8595
Charles and Debby Campbell Family Foundation
26 Okeena Dr.
Jackson, TN 38305-8887 (731) 668-8934

Donors: Charles Campbell; Debby Campbell.
Foundation type: Independent foundation.
Financial data (yr. ended 12/31/14): Assets, $3,650,197; gifts received, $200,000; expenditures, $155,473; qualifying distributions, $144,500.
Fields of interest: Religion.
Type of support: Capital campaigns.
Limitations: Applications accepted. Giving primarily in TN.
Application information: Application form required.
Initial approach: Proposal
Deadline(s): None
Officers and Directors: Charles Campbell, Pres. and Director; Debby Campbell, Secy. and Director.
EIN: 263889103

8596
The Bob and Susan Card Charitable Foundation
1800 Mt. Vernon Dr., N.W.
Cleveland, TN 37311-3500 (423) 559-1196
Contact: Robert G. Card Jr., Pres.,Secy. and Dir.; Susan Card

Established in 2004 in Tennessee.
Donors: Susan Card; Robert G. Card, Jr.; Sunrise Acceptance, Inc.; Easy Auto, Inc.; Robert Card III; Augusta H. Card.
Foundation type: Independent foundation.
Financial data (yr. ended 12/31/13): Assets, $953,437 (M); gifts received, $28,860; expenditures, $232,966; qualifying distributions, $229,303; giving activities include $229,168 for 17 grants (high: $54,020; low: $128).
Fields of interest: Human services.
Type of support: General support.

Limitations: Applications accepted. Giving primarily in TN.
Application information: Application form required.
Initial approach: Letter (2 pages)
Deadline(s): None
Officer and Director: Robert G. Card, Jr., Pres. and Secy. and Director.
EIN: 200875812

8597
The Cartinhour-Woods Foundation, Inc.
2626 Clifftops Ave.
Monteagle, TN 37356-2088

Donor: W.C. Cartinhour, Sr.†.
Foundation type: Independent foundation.
Financial data (yr. ended 06/30/13): Assets, $4,946,303 (M); expenditures, $270,836; qualifying distributions, $251,321; giving activities include $200,000 for 16 grants (high: $40,000; low: $500).
Fields of interest: Education; Elementary and secondary education; Higher education; Foundations; Christianity.
Type of support: General support; Scholarships.
Limitations: Applications not accepted. Giving primarily in TN and VA. No grants to individuals.
Application information: Contributes only to pre-selected organizations.
Officers and Trustees: Margaret C. Woods, Chair. and Trustee; Ellen L. Woods, Pres. and Trustee; Caroline T. Woods, V.P. and Trustee; Sandra M. Thurmond, Secy.-Treas.; Kathleen E. Woods.
EIN: 621504440

8598
The Chrysalis Foundation
2444 Broad St.
Chattanooga, TN 37408-2909 (423) 756-0882
Contact: Mary N. Moore, Pres.

Established in 1992 in Tennessee.
Donor: Mary N. Moore.
Foundation type: Independent foundation.
Financial data (yr. ended 12/31/13): Assets, $1,896,984 (M); expenditures, $274,282; qualifying distributions, $251,935; giving activities include $244,250 for 21 grants (high: $51,000; low: $250).
Purpose and activities: Giving primarily for human services and food programs; funding also for land conservation.
Fields of interest: Natural resources; Nonprofits; Human services; Food aid.
Type of support: General support; Regranting.
Limitations: Applications accepted. Giving primarily in TN. No grants to individuals.
Application information: Application form required.
Initial approach: Letter of not more than 2 pages
Deadline(s): None
Officers: Mary N. Moore, Pres.; Patricia W. Unruh, Secy.; William N. Bailey, Treas.
EIN: 621497058

8599
Citizens Bank Tri-Cities Foundation Ltd.
(formerly Joe LaPorte, Jr. Foundation, Ltd.)
1 Citizens Plz.
300-304 E. Broad St., Ste. 301
Elizabethton, TN 37643-2715 (423) 547-2084
Contact: Sam J. LaPorte, Dir.

Established in 1990 in Tennessee.
Donors: Citizens Bank; GSC, Inc.; Sam LaPorte; Joseph LaPorte; Christopher LaPorte; Stephen LaPorte.
Foundation type: Independent foundation.
Financial data (yr. ended 12/31/13): Assets, $2,797,805 (M); gifts received, $605,000; expenditures, $336,640; qualifying distributions, $321,657; giving activities include $321,657 for 23 grants (high: $125,000; low: $250).
Purpose and activities: Giving primarily for higher education and to Christian ministries and churches.
Fields of interest: Education; Higher education; Nonprofits; Christianity; Human services; Youth development.
Type of support: Regranting.
Limitations: Applications accepted. Giving primarily in TN, with emphasis on Elizabethon and Johnson City. No grants to individuals.
Application information: Application form required.
Initial approach: Proposal
Deadline(s): None
Directors: Christopher LaPorte; Joseph LaPorte III; Sam LaPorte; Stephen LaPorte.
EIN: 581914223

8600
Robert H. & Monica M. Cole Foundation
515 Market St.
Knoxville, TN 37902-2145
Contact: Robert Page, Trust Off., Home Federal Bank

Foundation type: Independent foundation.
Financial data (yr. ended 09/30/13): Assets, $5,248,083 (M); expenditures, $355,982; qualifying distributions, $260,000; giving activities include $260,000 for 36 grants (high: $85,000; low: $1,000).
Purpose and activities: Giving primarily for arts and culture, education, children and social services, and health associations, particularly a neuroscience clinic.
Fields of interest: Arts and culture; Performing arts; Opera; Performing arts education; Historic preservation; Education; Higher education; Hospital care; Neurology; Diseases and conditions; Human services; Child welfare.
Type of support: General support; Research.
Limitations: Applications accepted. Giving primarily in TN; some funding in New York, NY. No support for political groups.
Application information:
Initial approach: Letter
Deadline(s): None
Board meeting date(s): Oct.
Final notification: Nov.
Trustee: Home Federal Bank Trust Dept.
Directors: William W. Davis, Jr.; Cole McKenry Johnson; James R. McKenry, Jr.; Margaret McKenry-Nash; Sarah C. Page.
EIN: 626137973

8601
Community Health Systems Foundation
4000 Meridian Blvd.
Franklin, TN 37067-6325

Established in 2005 in Tennessee.
Donor: Community Health Systems.
Foundation type: Company-sponsored foundation.
Financial data (yr. ended 12/31/13): Assets,
$7,177,425 (M); expenditures, $387,925;
qualifying distributions, $387,925; giving activities
include $387,925 for 82 grants (high: $35,000;
low: $100).
Purpose and activities: The foundation supports
organizations involved with education, health,
human services, and international development.
Fields of interest: Elementary and secondary
education; Higher education; Graduate and
professional education; Medical education;
Nonprofits; Health; Hospital care; Nursing care;
Human services; Basic and emergency aid; Child
welfare; Youth organizing; International
development.
Type of support: Program development; Employee
matching gifts; General support; Scholarships;
Regranting.
Limitations: Applications not accepted. Giving
primarily in KY, MA, NY, PA, and TN. No grants to
individuals.
Application information: Contributes only to
pre-selected organizations.
Officers: Wayne T. Smith, Chair., Pres., and C.E.O.;
Rachel A. Seifert, Exec. V.P. and Secy.; W. Larry
Cash, Exec. V.P.; Martin G. Schweinhart, Sr. V.P.;
James W. Doucette, V.P. and Treas.; Kevin J.
Hammons, V.P.
EIN: 203323391

8602
Cornerstone Foundation
P.O. Box 12489
Knoxville, TN 37912-0489 (865) 693-7000
Contact: Tim A. Graham, Tr.

Established in 1997 in Tennessee.
Donors: Graham GP; Tim A. Graham.
Foundation type: Independent foundation.
Financial data (yr. ended 12/31/13): Assets,
$426,839 (M); expenditures, $256,271; qualifying
distributions, $243,340; giving activities include
$243,340 for 47 grants (high: $75,250; low: $100).
Purpose and activities: Giving primarily for Christian
and Protestant organizations.
Fields of interest: Christianity; Protestantism; Youth
development.
Limitations: Applications accepted. Giving primarily
in TN, with emphasis on Knoxville. No grants to
individuals.
Application information: Application form required.
Initial approach: Letter
Deadline(s): None
Trustee: Tim A. Graham.
EIN: 311497257

8603
**Cracker Barrel Old Country Store
Foundation**
305 Hartmann Dr.
Lebanon, TN 37087 (615) 443-5533
Contact: Penny Carroll, Secy.

FAX: (615) 443-9874;
E-mail: foundation@crackerbarrel.com; Main
URL: http://www.crackerbarrel.com/about/
foundation#foundation

Donor: Cracker Barrel Old Country Store, Inc.
Foundation type: Company-sponsored foundation.
Financial data (yr. ended 07/31/14): Assets,
$5,022,914 (M); gifts received, $160,000;
expenditures, $285,444; qualifying distributions,
$278,491; giving activities include $183,250 for 28
grants (high: $100,000; low: $500), and $82,500
for 55 grants to individuals (high: $1,500; low:
$1,500).
Purpose and activities: The foundation supports
organizations involved with arts and culture,
education, the environment, and human services.
Special emphasis is directed toward programs
designed to improve access to education;
strengthen the bonds of military families; and
provide opportunities for minorities, children, and
low-income famailies.
Fields of interest: Arts and culture; Education;
Higher education; Reading promotion; Environment;
Human services; Family services; Child welfare;
Children; Economically disadvantaged people;
Low-income and poor people; Military personnel.
Type of support: Equipment; Matching grants;
Scholarships; Cash grants; Program development;
Employee-related scholarships; General support.
Limitations: Applications accepted. Giving primarily
in Lebanon and Nashville, TN. No support for
religious, political, fraternal, athletic, or veterans'
organizations. No grants to individuals (except
employee-related scholarships), or for disease or
health-related causes, capital campaigns,
conferences, seminars, or reunions.
Publications: Application guidelines; Informational
brochure (including application guidelines); Program
policy statement.
Application information: Letters of inquiry should be
no longer than 1 to 2 pages. A full proposal may be
requested at a later date.
Initial approach: E-mail letter of inquiry for new
applicants
Deadline(s): None, but Dec. 31 for the current
funding cycle
Board meeting date(s): Quarterly
Final notification: Apr.
Officers: Penny Carroll, Secy.; Doug Couvillion,
Treas.; Mike Mott, Pres.
Directors: Terry Deas.
Number of staff: 2 full-time professional.
EIN: 621577717

8604
Deupree Family Foundation
c/o Regions Morgan Keegan
1100 Ridgeway Loop, Ste. 100
Memphis, TN 38120-4060 (901) 818-7600

Established in 1998 in Tennessee.
Donors: William W. Dupree, Jr.; Angela Kaye
Deupree; William W. Dupree III; Reed Deupree.
Foundation type: Independent foundation.
Financial data (yr. ended 12/31/13): Assets,
$4,522,419 (M); gifts received, $1,247,737;
expenditures, $195,152; qualifying distributions,
$179,535; giving activities include $167,950 for 46
grants (high: $12,500; low: $500).
Fields of interest: Arts and culture; Higher
education; Human services.

Limitations: Applications accepted. Giving limited to
the Memphis, TN, area.
Application information: Application form required.
Initial approach: Letter
Deadline(s): None
Trustees: Angela Kaye Deupree; Rebecca Deupree;
Reed Deupree; Roberta Deupree; William Dupree,
Jr.; William W. Deupree III; Regions Morgan Keegan
Trust.
EIN: 626334424

8605
Doochin Family Charitable Foundation
(formerly Interstate Packaging Foundation
Charitable Trust)
P.O. Box 789
White Bluff, TN 37187 (615) 797-9000
Contact: Jerald Doochin, Tr.

Donors: Interstate Packaging Corp.; Women In
Printing.
Foundation type: Company-sponsored foundation.
Financial data (yr. ended 04/30/14): Assets,
$1,507,117 (M); gifts received, $15,000;
expenditures, $195,504; qualifying distributions,
$195,504; giving activities include $195,504 for 68
grants (high: $52,200; low: $50).
Purpose and activities: The foundation supports
community foundations and organizations involved
with arts and culture, education, children and youth,
and Judaism.
Fields of interest: Arts and culture; Theater;
Orchestral music; Education; Elementary and
secondary education; Higher education;
Foundations; Nonprofits; Diseases and conditions;
Judaism; Human services; Child welfare.
Type of support: General support; Research;
Regranting.
Limitations: Applications accepted. Giving primarily
in Nashville, TN. No grants to individuals.
Application information: Application form required.
Initial approach: Letter
Deadline(s): None
Trustees: Jerald Doochin; Michael Doochin.
EIN: 621031459

8606
The Drake Foundation
482 Halle Park Dr., Ste. 101
Collierville, TN 38017-7089
Contact: Pansy L. Drake, Pres. and Dir.

Established in 1997 in Tennessee.
Donors: Hendrick Manufacturing Co.; Drake
Industries, LLC.
Foundation type: Company-sponsored foundation.
Financial data (yr. ended 12/31/13): Assets,
$368,347 (M); gifts received, $168,635;
expenditures, $305,658; qualifying distributions,
$305,652; giving activities include $305,652 for 11
grants (high: $215,000; low: $500).
Purpose and activities: The foundation supports
organizations involved with cancer, domestic
violence, international relief, leadership
development, and Christianity.
Fields of interest: Cancers; Leadership
development; Christianity; Human services; Basic
and emergency aid; Domestic violence shelters;
International development.
Type of support: General support.

Limitations: Applications accepted. Giving primarily in KY, MO, TN, and TX. No grants to individuals.
Application information: Application form required.
Initial approach: Proposal
Deadline(s): None
Officers and Directors: Pansy L. Drake, Pres. and Director; Darin Drake, Secy. and Director.
EIN: 621684643

8607
Louis R. Draughon Foundation
150 4th Ave., N., 9th Fl.
Nashville, TN 37219

Established in 1982 in Tennessee.
Donor: Elizabeth F. Draughon†.
Foundation type: Independent foundation.
Financial data (yr. ended 12/31/13): Assets, $6,494,223 (M); expenditures, $483,306; qualifying distributions, $423,378; giving activities include $412,300 for 35 grants (high: $80,000; low: $900).
Purpose and activities: Giving primarily to educational institutions, human services, and Christian agencies, churches, and schools.
Fields of interest: Education; Higher education; Christianity; Human services; Child welfare.
Type of support: General support.
Limitations: Applications not accepted. Giving primarily in TN. No grants to individuals.
Application information: Contributes only to pre-selected organizations.
Officers and Directors: James Wilhite, Pres. and Director; Jeanette Dorris, V.P. and Director; Bob Andrews; Jerome Ellis; Dr. Joe Jackson.
Trustee: Regions Bank, N.A.
EIN: 621147685

8608
H. W. Durham Foundation
5050 Poplar Ave., Ste. 1007
Memphis, TN 38157-1007 (901) 683-3583
Main URL: http://www.durhamfoundation.org

Established in 1955 in Tennessee.
Donor: H.W. Durham†.
Foundation type: Independent foundation.
Financial data (yr. ended 12/31/13): Assets, $11,830,787 (M); expenditures, $676,651; qualifying distributions, $524,260; giving activities include $301,654 for 27+ grants (high: $100,000).
Purpose and activities: Giving primarily for the elderly and issues relating to the aging process.
Fields of interest: Senior services; Seniors.
Type of support: Program development; Program-related investments; Convening; Publications; Seed money; Fellowships; Scholarships; Research; Technical assistance.
Limitations: Applications accepted. Giving primarily in Memphis and western TN.
Publications: Application guidelines; Informational brochure (including application guidelines).
Application information:
Initial approach: Proposal
Copies of proposal: 5
Deadline(s): None
Board meeting date(s): Feb., May, and Sept.
Officers: Jenks E. McCrory, Pres.; John B. Coleman, Jr., V.P.; Chris Cooper, Secy.

Directors: Larry Boone; Kaye D. Brooksbank; Susan Cooper; Bettie Durham; Erich Durham; Lisa Durham; Hugh McHenry; Linda Nichols.
Number of staff: 2 full-time professional; 1 part-time support.
EIN: 620583854

8609
The Ebert-Leblanc Family Foundation Inc.
9020 Rocky Cannon Rd.
Cordova, TN 38018-6934

Foundation type: Independent foundation.
Financial data (yr. ended 12/31/13): Assets, $3,387,208 (M); expenditures, $191,864; qualifying distributions, $191,864; giving activities include $180,000 for 24 grants (high: $30,310; low: $500).
Fields of interest: Education; Health; Religion; Human services.
Limitations: Applications not accepted. Giving primarily in TN.
Application information: Unsolicited requests for funds not accepted.
Officers: Adrienne Ebert Leblanc, Pres.; Joseph Christopher Leblanc, Secy.
Directors: Chelsea A. Leblanc; Jessica N. Miller.
EIN: 455333162

8610
EBS Foundation
c/o Pinnacle Bank
P.O. Box 291947
Nashville, TN 37229-1947

Established in 1989 in Tennessee.
Donor: Ella Hayes.
Foundation type: Independent foundation.
Financial data (yr. ended 12/31/13): Assets, $9,533,169 (M); expenditures, $452,509; qualifying distributions, $356,594; giving activities include $280,500 for 160 grants (high: $50,000; low: $50).
Purpose and activities: Giving primarily for the arts, education, youth and social services, health organizations, Christian organizations, and Presbyterian churches.
Fields of interest: Arts and culture; Orchestral music; Education; University education; Botanical gardens; Hospice care; Diseases and conditions; Christianity; Protestantism; Human services; Child welfare.
Type of support: General support; Continuing support; Annual campaigns.
Limitations: Applications not accepted. Giving primarily in TN. No grants to individuals.
Application information: Contributes only to pre-selected organizations.
Trustee: Elizabeth Bullard Stadler; Pinnacle Bank.
EIN: 581797047

8611
The Annette & Irwin Eskind Family Foundation
541 Jackson Blvd.
Nashville, TN 37205-3453

Established in 1986 in Tennessee.
Donors: Annette Eskind; Irwin Eskind; Jeffrey Eskind; Steven Eskind.

Foundation type: Independent foundation.
Financial data (yr. ended 06/30/13): Assets, $1,457,445 (M); expenditures, $173,241; qualifying distributions, $168,515; giving activities include $168,515 for grants.
Purpose and activities: Giving primarily for higher education, health care, the arts, social services and Jewish organizations and temples.
Fields of interest: Arts and culture; Performing arts; Orchestral music; Art museums; Education; Elementary and secondary education; Higher education; Nonprofits; Diseases and conditions; Judaism; Human services.
Type of support: Regranting.
Limitations: Applications not accepted. No grants to individuals.
Application information: Unsolicited requests for funds not accepted.
Officers: Annette Eskind, Pres.; Jeffrey Eskind, Secy.
Director: Steven Eskind.
EIN: 621289997

8612
The Jeffrey and Donna Eskind Family Foundation
416 Ellendale Ave.
Nashville, TN 37205-3402

Established in 1986 in Tennessee.
Donors: Jeffrey B. Eskind; Donna G. Eskind; Irwin Eskind†.
Foundation type: Independent foundation.
Financial data (yr. ended 06/30/14): Assets, $5,326,397 (M); expenditures, $354,267; qualifying distributions, $343,735; giving activities include $343,735 for 64 grants (high: $50,000; low: $100).
Purpose and activities: Giving primarily for education, health care, federated giving programs, Jewish agencies, and temples.
Fields of interest: Arts and culture; Performing arts; Education; Health; Judaism; Human services.
Limitations: Applications not accepted. Giving primarily in Nashville, TN. No grants to individuals.
Application information: Unsolicited requests for funds not accepted.
Officers: Jeffrey B. Eskind, Pres.; Donna G. Eskind, Secy.
EIN: 621306904

8613
The Steven & Laurie Eskind Family Foundation
2322 Golf Club Ln.
Nashville, TN 37215-1155

Donors: Steven Eskind; Laurie Eskind; Irwin Eskind 2000 Charitable Lead Annuity Trust.
Foundation type: Independent foundation.
Financial data (yr. ended 06/30/13): Assets, $5,773,192 (M); expenditures, $345,023; qualifying distributions, $332,190; giving activities include $328,198 for 167 grants (high: $50,000; low: $100).
Purpose and activities: Giving primarily for education.
Fields of interest: Ballet; Elementary and secondary education; Higher education; Foundations; Judaism; Human services.
Type of support: General support.

Limitations: Applications not accepted. Giving primarily in Nashville, TN. No grants to individuals.
Application information: Contributes only to pre-selected organizations.
Officers: Steven Eskind, Pres.; Laurie Eskind, Secy.
EIN: 621306903

8614
Firstfruits Foundation
2 Brentwood Commons, Ste. 150
Brentwood, TN 37027-5239

Established in 2007 in Tennessee.
Donors: Felicia Haynes; Bobby Haynes; Tennessee Industrial Electronics.
Foundation type: Independent foundation.
Financial data (yr. ended 12/31/13): Assets, $770,979 (M); expenditures, $415,701; qualifying distributions, $415,060; giving activities include $415,060 for 5 grants (high: $200,000; low: $5,000).
Fields of interest: Elementary and secondary education; Christianity; Protestantism.
Limitations: Applications not accepted. Giving primarily in TN.
Application information: Unsolicited requests for funds not accepted.
Officers: Bobby R. Haynes, Pres.; Felicia B. Haynes, Secy.
EIN: 208962234

8615
The Samuel M. Fleming Foundation
1205 3rd Ave. N.
Nashville, TN 37208-2703

Established in 1993 in Tennessee.
Donors: Joanne Fleming Hayes; Fleming Trust; Fleming CLAT.
Foundation type: Independent foundation.
Financial data (yr. ended 12/31/13): Assets, $8,414,253 (M); gifts received, $401,676; expenditures, $486,851; qualifying distributions, $374,400; giving activities include $357,500 for 25 grants (high: $75,000; low: $2,500).
Fields of interest: Arts and culture; Performing arts; Historic preservation; Education; Higher education; Medical counseling; Cancers; Christianity; Human services.
Limitations: Applications not accepted. Giving primarily in the Nashville, TN, area. No grants to individuals.
Application information: Contributes only to pre-selected organizations.
Officers: Alden H. Smith, Jr., Secy.; Elizabeth B. Davie, Treas.
Trustees: Joanne Fleming Hayes; Samuel Fleming Wilt.
EIN: 582026295

8616
M. Stratton Foster Charitable Foundation
c/o Nashville Bank & Trust
4525 Harding Rd., Ste. 300
Nashville, TN 37205-2119

Established in 1986 in Tennessee.
Donor: M. Stratton Foster†.
Foundation type: Independent foundation.

Financial data (yr. ended 04/30/15): Assets, $4,922,732; expenditures, $270,399; qualifying distributions, $239,917.
Fields of interest: Education; University education; Land resources; Health care clinics; Religion; Christianity; Human services; Family services; Youth development; Low-income and poor people.
Limitations: Applications accepted. Giving primarily in Nashville, TN and the surrounding area. No grants to individuals.
Publications: Application guidelines; Informational brochure.
Application information: Application form required.
  Initial approach: Letter
  Copies of proposal: 2
  Deadline(s): Apr. 30
  Board meeting date(s): June
Trustees: Bob L. Andrews; Clay T. Jackson; Adelaide D. Stevens.
EIN: 626195713

8617
Malcolm Fraser Foundation
1805 Moriah Woods Blvd., Ste. 3
Memphis, TN 38117-7121
Contact: Joe R.G. Fulcher, V.P.

Established in 1992 in Tennessee.
Donor: Malcolm Fraser†.
Foundation type: Independent foundation.
Financial data (yr. ended 05/31/13): Assets, $3,690,953 (M); expenditures, $339,061; qualifying distributions, $337,061; giving activities include $330,700 for 22 grants (high: $50,000; low: $2,000).
Purpose and activities: Giving primarily for higher education to support programs in stuttering and speech pathology. Giving also for medical research and human services.
Fields of interest: Special needs education; Higher education; Speech and hearing rehabilitation; Diseases and conditions; Human services.
Type of support: Research; Research and evaluation.
Limitations: Applications accepted. Giving on a national basis. No grants to individuals.
Application information:
  Initial approach: Proposal
  Deadline(s): None
  Board meeting date(s): May and Dec.
Officers and Directors: Jane Hough Fraser, Pres. and Director; Joe R.G. Fulcher, V.P. and Secy.-Treas.; Celia Fraser Gruss, V.P. and Director; Jean F.R. Gruss, V.P. and Director.
Number of staff: 1 part-time professional.
EIN: 582026294

8618
Fugitive Foundation
(formerly Wills Foundation)
2156 Golf Club Ln.
Nashville, TN 37215-1224 (615) 269-5429

Established in 1992 in Tennessee.
Donors: W. Ridley Wills II; Irene J. Wills; Morgan J. Wills; Thomas W. Wills; W. Ridley Wills III.
Foundation type: Independent foundation.
Financial data (yr. ended 12/31/13): Assets, $5,017,545 (M); expenditures, $323,812; qualifying distributions, $269,000; giving activities

include $269,000 for 70 grants (high: $12,500; low: $500).
Fields of interest: Arts and culture; Historical activities; Education; Health; Christianity; Human services; Children and youth; Infants and toddlers; Children; Adolescents; Adults; Young adults; Females; Female infants and toddlers; Female adults; Female young adults; Males; Male children and youth; Male infants and toddlers; Male adults; Male young adults; Single parents; Ethnic and racial groups; People of African descent; People of Latin American descent; Migrant workers; Homeless people; Low-income and poor people; People with physical disabilities.
International interests: Ghana.
Type of support: General support; Annual campaigns; Capital campaigns; Capital and infrastructure; Endowments; Scholarships.
Limitations: Applications accepted. Giving primarily in Nashville, TN.
Application information: Application form required.
  Initial approach: Letter
  Deadline(s): None
  Board meeting date(s): late Dec.
Trustees: Irene J. Wills; Morgan J. Wills; Thomas W. Wills; W. Ridley Wills II; W. Ridley Wills III.
Number of staff: None.
EIN: 626245453

8619
Eldon and Emma Belle Gardner Charitable Foundation
c/o Cumberland Trust
40 Burton Hills Blvd., Ste. 300
Nashville, TN 37215-6292

Foundation type: Independent foundation.
Financial data (yr. ended 12/31/14): Assets, $1,152,158; expenditures, $229,430; qualifying distributions, $224,614.
Fields of interest: Higher education; Christianity.
Limitations: Applications not accepted. Giving primarily in TN. No grants to individuals.
Application information: Unsolicited requests for funds not accepted.
Trustee: Cumberland Trust.
EIN: 466336914

8620
Gaylord Entertainment Foundation
One Gaylord Dr.
Nashville, TN 37214-1207 (615) 316-6000
Contact: Jacque Layfield

Established in 2005 in Tennessee.
Donor: Gaylord Entertainment Co.
Foundation type: Company-sponsored foundation.
Financial data (yr. ended 12/31/13): Assets, $419,786 (M); gifts received, $600,000; expenditures, $254,006; qualifying distributions, $254,006; giving activities include $253,950 for 65 grants (high: $15,000; low: $250).
Purpose and activities: The foundation supports organizations involved with arts and culture, education, and youth.
Fields of interest: Arts and culture; Arts education; Performing arts; Historic preservation; Education; Elementary and secondary education; Higher education; Child welfare; Adolescents; Low-income and poor people.

Type of support: General support; Annual campaigns; Program development.
Limitations: Applications accepted. Giving primarily in areas of company operations in TN. No support for religious, political, veterans', fraternal, labor, lobbying, civic, social, or fraternal organizations. No grants to individuals, or for trusts or endowments.
Application information: Requests for multi-year commitments are not accepted. Contact hotels directly for in-kind donations.
  Initial approach: Proposal
  Copies of proposal: 1
  Deadline(s): None
  Board meeting date(s): Monthly
  Final notification: 30 days
Officers: Colin V. Reed, Chair.; Mark Fioravanti, Pres.; Scott J. Lynn, Secy.; Jennifer Hutcheson, Treas.
EIN: 202573370

8621
The Goad Family Foundation
c/o Truxton Trust
4525 Harding Rd., Ste. 300
Nashville, TN 37205-2119

Established in 2004 in Tennessee.
Donors: Fred C. Goad, Jr.; Deana Ross Goad.
Foundation type: Independent foundation.
Financial data (yr. ended 12/31/13): Assets, $3,115,724 (M); expenditures, $200,935; qualifying distributions, $167,500; giving activities include $167,500 for 22 grants (high: $100,000; low: $80).
Fields of interest: Education; Children's hospital care; Religion; Human services; Children.
Limitations: Applications not accepted. Giving primarily in TN and VA. No grants to individuals.
Application information: Contributes only to pre-selected organizations.
Trustees: Deana Ross Goad; Fred C. Goad, Jr.
EIN: 626402695

8622
The Goldsmith Family Foundation, Inc.
(formerly The Goldsmith Foundation)
1900 Union Ave.
Memphis, TN 38104-4029   9017284600

Established in 1944 in Tennessee.
Foundation type: Independent foundation.
Financial data (yr. ended 12/31/14): Assets, $8,307,934; expenditures, $494,896; qualifying distributions, $406,875.
Purpose and activities: Giving primarily to Jewish organizations and for education.
Fields of interest: Arts and culture; Education; Higher education; Nonprofits; Health; Diseases and conditions; Judaism; Interfaith; Human services; Child welfare; Youth services.
Type of support: Regranting.
Limitations: Applications accepted. Giving primarily in TN. No grants to individuals.
Application information:
  Initial approach: Proposal
  Deadline(s): None
Officers: Harry L. Goldsmith, Pres.; Beth Goldsmith Brown, V.P.; Jane Goldsmith Butler, V.P.; Peggy Goldsmith Fineman, V.P.; Elvis G. Goldsmith, V.P.; Fred Goldsmith III, V.P.; Jack L. Goldsmith III, V.P.; Melvin Goldsmith, V.P.; Thomas B. Goldsmith, V.P.;

Sylvia Goldsmith Marks, V.P.; Jennifer Entine Matz, V.P.; Larry J. Goldsmith, Secy.-Treas.
EIN: 626039604

8623
Goodlett Foundation
1779 Kirby Pkwy. 1, Ste. 223
Memphis, TN 38138-0631

Established in 1997 in Tennessee.
Donor: Robert B. Blow.
Foundation type: Independent foundation.
Financial data (yr. ended 09/30/13): Assets, $5,009,154 (M); expenditures, $297,935; qualifying distributions, $250,177; giving activities include $172,350 for 21 grants (high: $50,000; low: $500).
Purpose and activities: Giving primarily for education and to Christian agencies and churches.
Fields of interest: Education; Health; Agriculture.
Limitations: Applications not accepted. Giving primarily in Memphis, TN. No grants to individuals.
Application information: Unsolicited requests for funds not accepted.
Officers and Directors: David A. Dunehew, Pres. and Director; Kathleen S. Williams, Treas. and Director; Pamela D. Blow; Warner B. Rodda.
Number of staff: 1 part-time professional.
EIN: 621663934

8624
The Joel C. and Bernice W. Gordon Family Foundation
3102 West End Ave., Ste. 650
Nashville, TN 37203-1498

Established in 1986 in Tennessee.
Donors: Joel C. Gordon; Bernice W. Gordon; Sherrie Gordon Eisenman; Robert A. Gordon; Frank E. Gordon; Gail E. Gordon.
Foundation type: Independent foundation.
Financial data (yr. ended 06/30/13): Assets, $3,693,686 (M); expenditures, $401,525; qualifying distributions, $397,260; giving activities include $389,948 for 172 grants (high: $27,500; low: $15).
Purpose and activities: Giving primarily to Jewish agencies and temples, as well as for education, the arts, and health and social services.
Fields of interest: Arts and culture; Education; Health; Judaism; Human services.
Limitations: Applications not accepted. No grants to individuals.
Application information: Unsolicited requests for funds not accepted.
Officers: Joel C. Gordon, Pres.; Bernice W. Gordon, Secy.
Trustees: Alan J. Eisenman; Sherrie Gordon Eisenman; Frank E. Gordon; Gwen L. Gordon; Julie S. Gordon; Robert A. Gordon; Gail Gordon Jacobs; Jeffrey M. Jacobs.
Number of staff: None.
EIN: 621306906

8625
Grandview Foundation, Inc.
1200 Mountain Creek Rd.
Chattanooga, TN 37405

Established in 1991 in Georgia.

Donors: Carter N. Paden, Jr.; Janet C. Paden.
Foundation type: Independent foundation.
Financial data (yr. ended 11/30/13): Assets, $981,897 (M); gifts received, $148,789; expenditures, $197,456; qualifying distributions, $185,783; giving activities include $176,865 for 19 grants (high: $60,000; low: $100).
Purpose and activities: Giving primarily for Christian evangelism and education.
Fields of interest: Higher education; Christianity; Protestantism; Human services; Youth development.
Type of support: Capital campaigns.
Limitations: Applications not accepted. Giving primarily in TN. No grants to individuals.
Application information: Contributes only to pre-selected organizations.
  Board meeting date(s): May and Dec.
Directors: Carter N. Paden III; Dean P. North; Robert M. Paden; Janet C. Paden; Thomas C. Paden.
Number of staff: None.
EIN: 582004351

8626
Hawthorn Charitable Foundation
c/o Truxton Trust
4525 Harding Pike, Ste. 300
Nashville, TN 37205-2190

Established in 1995 in Tennessee.
Donors: W.L. Davis, Jr.; Adelaide Shull Davis; Harrison S. Davis; Florence S. Davis; W.L. Davis III; Virginia A. Davis.
Foundation type: Independent foundation.
Financial data (yr. ended 06/30/13): Assets, $119,379 (M); gifts received, $106,900; expenditures, $160,466; qualifying distributions, $159,450; giving activities include $159,450 for 66 grants (high: $30,000; low: $50).
Purpose and activities: Giving for secondary education, colleges, and youth programs.
Fields of interest: Education; Religion; Human services.
Limitations: Applications not accepted. Giving primarily in TN. No grants to individuals.
Application information: Unsolicited requests for funds not accepted.
Trustees: Adelaide Shull Davis; W. Lipscomb Davis, Jr.
EIN: 621624638

8627
Heagele-Blount Animal Shelters
800 S. Gay St.
Knoxville, TN 37995-1230
Application address: c/o First Tennessee Bank, Trust Div., Attn.: Rob Dancu, Knoxville, TN 37995-1230, tel.: (865) 971-2165

Foundation type: Independent foundation.
Financial data (yr. ended 12/31/13): Assets, $1,892,136 (M); expenditures, $222,910; qualifying distributions, $207,360; giving activities include $196,100 for 3 grants (high: $96,100; low: $50).
Fields of interest: Domesticated animals; Human services.
Limitations: Applications accepted. Giving primarily in TN.
Application information: Application form required.

Initial approach: Written
Deadline(s): None
Trustee: First Tennessee Bank, N.A.
EIN: 276808263

8628
HMA Foundation, Inc.
4000 Meridian Blvd.
Franklin, TN 37067 (239) 598-3131
Contact: Joe Meek
Application address: 5811 Pelican Bay Blvd., Ste. 500, Naples, FL 34108, tel.: (239) 598-3131

Donor: Health Management Associates, Inc.
Foundation type: Company-sponsored foundation.
Financial data (yr. ended 12/31/13): Assets, $869,012 (M); expenditures, $170,729; qualifying distributions, $160,000; giving activities include $160,000 for 7 grants (high: $100,000; low: $2,500).
Purpose and activities: The foundation supports organizations involved with orchestras, higher education, and cancer.
Fields of interest: Arts and culture; Education; Diseases and conditions.
Type of support: Sponsorships.
Limitations: Applications accepted. Giving primarily in Ava Maria and Naples, FL.
Application information:
Initial approach: Proposal
Deadline(s): None
Officers: William J. Schoen, Chair.; Gary D. Newsome, Pres.; Robert E. Farnham, V.P.
EIN: 651115909

8629
Hollingsworth Foundation, Inc.
2 Centre Plz.
Clinton, TN 37716-3960

Established in 2005 in Tennessee.
Donor: Joe Hollingsworth.
Foundation type: Independent foundation.
Financial data (yr. ended 09/30/13): Assets, $880,605 (M); gifts received, $100,022; expenditures, $182,683; qualifying distributions, $178,119; giving activities include $178,119 for 5 grants (high: $134,119; low: $500).
Fields of interest: Protestantism; Youth development.
Limitations: Applications not accepted. Giving primarily in TN.
Application information: Unsolicted requests for funds not accepted.
Officers and Directors: Joe Hollingsworth, Pres. and Director; Marsha Hollingsworth, Secy. and Director; Tim Lennon, Treas.; Brenda K. Bice.
EIN: 203632621

8630
The Houghland Foundation
1600 Division St., Ste. 700
Nashville, TN 37203-2771
Application address: c/o Davis Carr, P.O. Box 340025, Nashville, TN 37203

Established in 1986 in Tennessee.
Donor: Calvin Houghland.
Foundation type: Independent foundation.

Financial data (yr. ended 12/31/13): Assets, $4,386,628 (M); expenditures, $342,223; qualifying distributions, $334,458; giving activities include $315,000 for 53 grants (high: $50,000; low: $1,000).
Fields of interest: Education; Nonprofits; Diseases and conditions; Protestantism; Human services.
Type of support: Regranting.
Limitations: Applications accepted. Giving primarily in Nashville, TN. No grants to individuals.
Application information: Application form required.
Initial approach: Letter
Deadline(s): None
Trustees: Davis H. Carr; Joseph V. Russell; Jamie Sochovka.
EIN: 626199041

8631
Hazel Montague Hutcheson Foundation
c/o John L. Hutcheson, IV
1237 Browns Ferry Rd.
Chattanooga, TN 37419-1531
Application address: c/o Brooks, Moore & Assoc., Inc., Att.: Ricky Moore, 3905 St. Elmo Ave., Chattanooga, TN 37409, tel.: (423) 756-8628

Established in 1962 in Tennessee.
Donor: Hazel G.M. Montague†.
Foundation type: Independent foundation.
Financial data (yr. ended 06/30/13): Assets, $5,664,277 (M); expenditures, $335,693; qualifying distributions, $311,872; giving activities include $292,000 for 81 grants (high: $37,000; low: $300).
Fields of interest: Education; Protestantism; Human services; Child welfare.
Type of support: General support; Annual campaigns.
Limitations: Applications accepted. Giving primarily in TN. No grants for scholarships; no loans.
Application information: Application form required.
Initial approach: Letter
Deadline(s): None
Board meeting date(s): Varies
Trustees: John Banks; Hazel H. Bell; John L. Hutcheson IV; Theodore M. Hutcheson, Jr.
EIN: 626045925

8632
The Ingram Foundation
40 Burton Hills Blvd., Ste. 300
Nashville, TN 37215-2311

Foundation type: Independent foundation.
Financial data (yr. ended 10/31/14): Assets, $3,340,450; expenditures, $172,144; qualifying distributions, $165,043.
Purpose and activities: Support primarily for federated giving programs, arts and culture, and children and youth services.
Fields of interest: Education; Health; Human services.
Type of support: General support.
Limitations: Applications accepted. Giving primarily in CA and TN. No grants to individuals.
Application information: Application form required.
Initial approach: Letter
Deadline(s): None
Final notification: Within three months

Trustees: Patricia I. Hart; Alice I. Hooker; Joseph Presley.
EIN: 416011520

8633
The Daniel Ashley and Irene Houston Jewell Memorial Foundation
2221 Fox Run Dr.
Signal Mountain, TN 37377 (404) 624-7636
Contact: George McMillan Jr., Treas.
Application address: c/o D. Ashley Jewell, V, 115 Old Homestead Dr., Chickamauga, GA 30707, tel.: (404) 624-7636

Established in 1951 in Georgia.
Donor: The Crystal Springs Textiles Corp.
Foundation type: Independent foundation.
Financial data (yr. ended 06/30/13): Assets, $5,225,781 (M); expenditures, $272,378; qualifying distributions, $241,103; giving activities include $182,000 for 32 grants (high: $20,000; low: $500), and $48,000 for 12 grants to individuals (high: $4,000; low: $4,000).
Purpose and activities: Giving primarily for education, health care, and human services; giving also for scholarships to graduates of Gordon Lee Memorial High School, located in Chickamauga, GA.
Fields of interest: Education; Higher education; Public libraries; Human services; Child welfare.
Type of support: Annual campaigns; Capital campaigns; Capital and infrastructure; Individual development; Equipment; Scholarships; Student aid.
Limitations: Applications accepted. Giving primarily in GA.
Application information:
Initial approach: Proposal
Deadline(s): None
Officers and Trustees: D. Ashley Jewell, V, Chair. and Trustee; Elizabeth J. Berry, Vice-Chair. and Trustee; Carol J. Browder, Secy. and Trustee; George M. McMillan, Jr., Treas. and Trustee; Juanita C. Crowder; E. Dunbar Jewell, Jr.; Robert Houston Jewell III; Ellen J. Siegfried; Irene Jewell Staub; W. Miller Welborn; Michael S. Wright.
EIN: 586034213

8634
The Edith Carell Johnson Foundation
4407 Iroquois Ave.
Nashville, TN 37205-3831

Established in 1996 in Tennessee.
Donor: Edith Carell Johnson.
Foundation type: Independent foundation.
Financial data (yr. ended 12/31/13): Assets, $2,908,780 (M); expenditures, $298,724; qualifying distributions, $297,782; giving activities include $295,767 for 11 grants (high: $178,167; low: $1,000).
Fields of interest: Education; University education; Zoos; Hospital care; Child welfare.
Limitations: Applications not accepted. Giving primarily in Nashville, TN. No grants to individuals.
Application information: Unsolicited requests for funds not accepted.
Officer: Edith Carell Johnson, Chair.
Board Member: David B. Johnson.
EIN: 626314839

8635
Jennings & Rebecca Jones Foundation Inc.
2308 Londonderry Dr.
Murfreesboro, TN   37129

Donor: Jennings A. Jones.
Foundation type: Independent foundation.
Financial data (yr. ended 12/31/13): Assets,
$5,126,203 (M); expenditures, $398,029;
qualifying distributions, $320,200; giving activities
include $320,200 for 7 grants (high: $65,000; low:
$27,500).
Fields of interest: Education; Elementary education;
Community and economic development.
Type of support: Regulation and administration.
Limitations: Applications not accepted. Giving
primarily in Murfreesboro, TN. No grants to
individuals.
Application information: Contributes only to
pre-selected organizations.
Officers: W. Ransom Jones, Chair.; James Burton,
Vice-Chair.; Christina Jones, Secy.-Treas.
Directors: Jennings H. Jones; Andrea J. Loughry; Lee
Moss; J. Paul Vaughan.
EIN: 581698633

8636
The Jordan Family Foundation
5409 Maryland Way, Ste. 215
Brentwood, TN   37027-5068

Established in 2004 in Tennessee.
Donors: Joan C. Jordan; John F. Jordan III.
Foundation type: Independent foundation.
Financial data (yr. ended 12/31/13): Assets,
$3,545,833 (M); expenditures, $194,142;
qualifying distributions, $165,280; giving activities
include $165,280 for 35 grants (high: $16,400;
low: $500).
Fields of interest: Fire prevention and control;
Human services.
Limitations: Applications not accepted. Giving
primarily in MN and TN. No grants to individuals.
Application information: Contributes only to
pre-selected organizations.
Trustees: Joan C. Jordan; John F. Jordan III.
EIN: 626402992

8637
Kappa Delta Private Foundation
3205 Players Ln.
Memphis, TN   38125-8897
E-mail: kappadelta@kappadelta.org; Main
URL: http://www.kappadelta.org/
aboutthekdfoundation

Established in 2008 in Tennessee.
Foundation type: Independent foundation.
Financial data (yr. ended 07/31/14): Assets,
$9,272,853 (M); expenditures, $471,685;
qualifying distributions, $437,714; giving activities
include $436,000 for 7 grants (high: $325,000;
low: $2,500).
Fields of interest: Philanthropy; Scouting programs.
Limitations: Applications not accepted. Giving
primarily in NY and TN.
Application information: Contributes only to
pre-selected organizations.
Officers: Corre A. Stegall, Pres.; Elizabeth A. Wibker,
Secy.-Treas.

Directors: Nell K. Bieger; Beth Martin Langford;
Winsome McIntosh.
EIN: 261382185

8638
Kennedy Foundation, Inc.
P.O. Box 1607
Chattanooga, TN   37401-1607   (423) 756-5552
Contact: Shelia Crane, Secy.-Treas.

Established in 1986 in Tennessee.
Donor: James D. Kennedy NonGrantor Charitable
Lead Annuity Trust, Jr.
Foundation type: Independent foundation.
Financial data (yr. ended 12/31/13): Assets,
$4,335,556 (M); gifts received, $21,104;
expenditures, $228,599; qualifying distributions,
$200,965; giving activities include $198,850 for 46
grants (high: $49,000; low: $50).
Purpose and activities: Giving primarily for
education and social services.
Fields of interest: Arts and culture; Museums;
Education; Higher education; Nonprofits; Hospital
care; Diseases and conditions; Christianity; Human
services; Food banks.
Type of support: General support; Regranting.
Limitations: Applications accepted. Giving primarily
in Chattanooga, TN. No grants to individuals.
Application information:
   Initial approach: Proposal
   Deadline(s): None
Officers and Directors: James D. Kennedy, Jr., Pres.
and Director; Shelia M. Crane, Secy.-Treas. and
Director; Jane K. Green.
EIN: 621296643

8639
Kite Foundation
5100 Poplar Ave., Ste. 1400
Memphis, TN   38137-1499

Established in 2002 in Tennessee.
Donor: Nancye B. Starnes.
Foundation type: Independent foundation.
Financial data (yr. ended 12/31/13): Assets,
$6,202,232 (M); expenditures, $421,222;
qualifying distributions, $336,009; giving activities
include $299,000 for 9 grants (high: $60,000; low:
$15,000).
Fields of interest: Arts education; Performing arts;
Education; Higher education; Family services; Child
welfare.
Type of support: General support; Matching grants;
Program-related investments.
Limitations: Applications not accepted. Giving
primarily in DC, MS, NY, SC, and TN. No grants to
individuals.
Application information: Contributes only to
pre-selected organizations.
Officers and Directors: Nancye B. Starnes, Pres.
and Director; William A. Frazee, Secy.-Treas. and
Director; Cindy Johnson; Peggy Seessel.
EIN: 043613913

8640
Knight Charitable Foundation
8901 Forrest Ridge Cove
Cordova, TN   38018-7622

Foundation type: Independent foundation.

Financial data (yr. ended 12/31/13): Assets,
$313,439 (M); expenditures, $186,561; qualifying
distributions, $186,500; giving activities include
$186,500 for 6 grants (high: $100,000; low: $500).
Fields of interest: Education; Protestantism; Human
services.
Limitations: Applications not accepted.
Application information: Unsolicited requests for
funds not accepted.
Trustees: Barry Knight; Lana Knight.
EIN: 466315139

8641
LaRoche Family Foundation
2103 Shannon Dr.
Murfreesboro, TN   37129-1334
Contact: Richard F. LaRoche, Tr.

Established in 2004 in Tennessee.
Donors: Gloria LaRoche; Richard F. LaRoche;
LaRoche Enterprise; Laroche Family LP.
Foundation type: Independent foundation.
Financial data (yr. ended 12/31/13): Assets,
$171,001 (M); gifts received, $349,980;
expenditures, $376,562; qualifying distributions,
$375,833; giving activities include $374,634 for 40
grants (high: $50,500; low: $25).
Fields of interest: Arts and culture; Education;
Higher education; Hospital care; Youth
development.
Limitations: Applications accepted. Giving primarily
in Murfreesboro, Rutherford County, TN. No support
for religious or political organizations.
Application information: Application form required.
   Initial approach: Letter
   Deadline(s): None
Trustees: Ashley L. Heren; David LaRoche; Gloria
LaRoche; Richard F. LaRoche.
Number of staff: None.
EIN: 710944751

8642
LDB Foundation
5004 Hill Place Dr.
Nashville, TN   37205-2705

Established in 1997 in Texas.
Donors: Sam A. Brooks; Linda D. Brooks.
Foundation type: Independent foundation.
Financial data (yr. ended 12/31/13): Assets,
$3,777,989 (M); gifts received, $43,775;
expenditures, $233,573; qualifying distributions,
$155,000; giving activities include $155,000 for 14
grants (high: $50,000; low: $500).
Fields of interest: Education; Health; Mental health
care; Diabetes; Christianity; Human services.
Limitations: Applications not accepted. Giving
primarily in GA and TN. No grants to individuals.
Application information: Contributes only to
pre-selected organizations.
Officers and Directors: Linda D. Brooks, Pres. and
Director; Daniel A. Brooks, V.P. and Director;
Elizabeth Heaston, Secy.-Treas.; E. Ashley Brooks
Whitaker.
EIN: 742829433

8643
LifeWorks Foundation
(formerly George N. Bullard Foundation)
P.O. Box 50276
Nashville, TN 37205-0276
Contact: George Bullard, Dir.

Established in 1967 in Tennessee.
Donor: Ella Hayes Trust.
Foundation type: Independent foundation.
Financial data (yr. ended 12/31/13): Assets, $4,299,401 (M); expenditures, $405,400; qualifying distributions, $368,707; giving activities include $268,500 for 6 grants, and $10,766 for foundation-administered programs.
Purpose and activities: The foundation enables other charitable organizations to further their charitable activities. Interests include animals and wildlife, agriculture and food security in middle Tennessee.
Fields of interest: Domesticated animals; Agriculture.
Limitations: Applications not accepted. Giving limited to Nashville, TN, and the surrounding area. No support for religious organizations. No grants to individuals.
Publications: Financial statement.
Application information: Unsolicited applications not considered.
Board meeting date(s): Monthly
Director: George Bullard.
Number of staff: 2 part-time professional.
EIN: 621428468

8644
Louisiana-Pacific Foundation
414 Union Street, Ste. 2000
Nashville, TN 37219-1711 (615) 986-5886
E-mail: lpfoundation@lpcorp.com; *Main URL:* http://lpcorp.com/community/community-engagement
Grants List: http://www.lpcorp.com/sustainability/grants_awarded

Established in 1973 in Oregon.
Donor: Louisiana-Pacific Corp.
Foundation type: Company-sponsored foundation.
Financial data (yr. ended 12/31/14): Assets, $572,613; expenditures, $331,765; qualifying distributions, $329,895.
Purpose and activities: The foundation supports programs designed to promote shelter; public education; the environment; and social services.
Fields of interest: Education; Elementary and secondary education; Environment; Housing development; Human services; Food banks.
International interests: Canada.
Type of support: General support; Employee matching gifts; Public engagement and education; Sponsorships.
Limitations: Applications not accepted. Giving primarily in areas of company operations, with emphasis on Hanceville, AL, Red Bluff, CA, Athens, GA, MN, Wilmington, NC, Nashville, TN, Carthage, TX, WI, and Canada.
Publications: Grants list; Informational brochure.
Application information: Unsolicited applications are currently not accepted.
Board meeting date(s): Quarterly
Officers and Trustees: Mary Louise Cohn, Chair. and Pres. and Trustee; Ashley Koch, Secy.; Robert Hopkins, Treas.; Russell L. Carroll; Tamara Lester; Laura Proctor; William B. Southern.
EIN: 237268660

8645
William P. and Marie R. Lowenstein Foundation
22 N. Front St., Ste. 1055
Memphis, TN 38103-0550 (901) 525-5744
Contact: Alvin A. Gordon, Dir.

Established in 1959 in Tennessee.
Donor: Marie R. Lowenstein†.
Foundation type: Independent foundation.
Financial data (yr. ended 12/31/13): Assets, $1,722,478 (M); expenditures, $259,339; qualifying distributions, $207,552; giving activities include $177,184 for 16 grants (high: $45,000; low: $154).
Fields of interest: Nonprofits; Judaism.
International interests: Israel.
Type of support: General support; Regranting; Equipment; Seed money; Fellowships; Scholarships.
Limitations: Applications accepted. Giving primarily in NY and TN. No grants to individuals or for endowment funds or matching gifts; no loans.
Application information:
Initial approach: Proposal
Deadline(s): None
Officer: Elaine Gordon, Secy.
Director: Alvin A. Gordon.
Number of staff: 1 full-time professional; 1 full-time support.
EIN: 626037976

8646
The Barbara J. Mapp Foundation
6878 Walnut Hills Dr.
Brentwood, TN 37027-7813

Donor: Barbara J. Mapp Trust.
Foundation type: Independent foundation.
Financial data (yr. ended 03/31/14): Assets, $3,973,773 (M); expenditures, $276,077; qualifying distributions, $266,022; giving activities include $237,650 for 26 grants (high: $100,500; low: $500).
Fields of interest: Environment; Domesticated animals.
Type of support: General support.
Limitations: Applications not accepted. Giving primarily in TN.
Application information: Unsolicited requests for funds not accepted.
Officer and Directors: Norman Miede, Fdn. Mgr. and Director; John M. Dab; Laurence M. Weissman.
EIN: 264817582

8647
Massengill-DeFriece Foundation, Inc.
P.O. Box 966
Bristol, TN 37621-0966
Application address: c/o C. Thomas Davenport, 640 State St., Ste. 201, Bristol, TN 37620, tel.: (423) 989-6500

Established in 1949 in Tennessee.
Donors: Frank W. DeFriece†; Pauline M. DeFriece†; Frank W. DeFriece, Jr.; Josephine D. Wilson; The S.E. Massengill Co.
Foundation type: Independent foundation.
Financial data (yr. ended 12/31/13): Assets, $4,258,151 (M); expenditures, $219,446; qualifying distributions, $216,523; giving activities

include $169,750 for 12 grants (high: $99,250; low: $500).
Fields of interest: Museums; Historic preservation; Education; Diseases and conditions; Religion; Child welfare.
Type of support: General support; Continuing support; Annual campaigns; Capital campaigns; Equipment; Emergency funds; Program development; Seed money; Scholarships.
Limitations: Applications accepted. Giving primarily in the tri-city area, including Bristol, TN-VA, and Kingsport and Johnson City, TN. No grants to individuals; no loans.
Application information:
Initial approach: 1 or 2 page letter
Copies of proposal: 1
Deadline(s): None
Officers: C. Thomas Davenport, Jr., Pres.; C. Richard Hagerstrom, Jr., Secy.-Treas.
Directors: Paul E. DeFriece; Stephen L. Everhart; Ronan King; Chet Sikorski; Polly D. Wills.
EIN: 626044873

8648
McGehee Family Foundation
700 Colonial Rd., Ste. 110
Memphis, TN 38117-5191 (901) 763-1666
Contact: James E. McGehee III, Pres.

Established in 1999 in Tennessee.
Donor: James E. McGehee, Jr.
Foundation type: Independent foundation.
Financial data (yr. ended 12/31/12): Assets, $195,751 (M); gifts received, $755,471; expenditures, $281,257; qualifying distributions, $201,709; giving activities include $201,709 for grants.
Fields of interest: Education; University education; Foundations; Health; Protestantism.
Type of support: General support.
Limitations: Applications accepted. Giving primarily in TN.
Application information: Application form required.
Initial approach: Letter
Deadline(s): None
Officers and Directors: James E. McGehee III, Pres. and Director; Andrew P. McGehee, V.P. and Director; J. Clifton Paessler, Secy. and Director; Stuart C. McGehee, Treas. and Director; James E. McGehee, Jr.
EIN: 621801291

8649
Ned R. McWherter Charitable Foundation, Inc.
P.O. Box 1762
Jackson, TN 38302-1762

Established in 1996 in Tennessee.
Donor: Ned R. McWherter Charitable Lead Unity Trust.
Foundation type: Independent foundation.
Financial data (yr. ended 12/31/13): Assets, $2,308,721 (M); gifts received, $162,888; expenditures, $134,236; qualifying distributions, $132,891; giving activities include $114,000 for 7 grants (high: $100,000; low: $500).
Fields of interest: Health; Diseases and conditions; Human services.
Type of support: General support; Scholarships.

Limitations: Applications not accepted. Giving primarily in TN. No grants to individuals.
Application information: Unsolicited requests for funds not accepted.
Officers: Michael R. McWherter, Pres.; Madelyn B. Pritchett, Secy.
Director: Mary Jane McWherter.
EIN: 621657841

8650
The Mercy Foundation
9266 Wardley Park Ln.
Brentwood, TN 37027

Established in 1998 in Tennessee.
Donors: Scott L. Mercy; Harrell Mercy; Joy M. Mercy.
Foundation type: Independent foundation.
Financial data (yr. ended 12/31/13): Assets, $1,323,569 (M); expenditures, $173,200; qualifying distributions, $166,000; giving activities include $166,000 for 10 grants (high: $75,000; low: $500).
Fields of interest: Education; Diseases and conditions; Christianity; Human services; Family services; Child welfare.
Limitations: Applications not accepted. Giving primarily in TN. No grants to individuals.
Application information: Contributes only to pre-selected organizations.
Trustee: Joy M. Mercy.
EIN: 626351496

8651
The Mick Foundation
9230 Old Smyrna Rd.
Brentwood, TN 37027-6115 (615) 347-1315
Contact: John R. Mick, V.P. and Dir.
Main URL: http://themickfoundation.com

Established in 1992 in Tennessee.
Donors: Roger E. Mick; Barbara D. Mick.
Foundation type: Independent foundation.
Financial data (yr. ended 12/31/14): Assets, $3,568,826 (M); expenditures, $395,448; qualifying distributions, $284,524; giving activities include $284,524 for 23 grants (high: $145,000; low: $500).
Fields of interest: Arts and culture; Education; University education; Nonprofits; Health; Christianity; Human services; Child welfare.
Type of support: Regranting.
Limitations: Applications accepted. Giving primarily in KY and TN. No grants to individuals.
Application information:
Initial approach: Proposal
Deadline(s): None
Officers and Directors: Roger E. Mick, Pres. and Director; Jennifer Mick McKenzie, V.P. and Director; John R. Mick, V.P. and Director; Barbara D. Mick, Secy. and Director.
EIN: 621491417

8652
Gene & Florence Monday Foundation, Inc.
1810 Ailor Ave.
Knoxville, TN 37921-5802
Application address: c/o Ron Cunningham, P.O. Box 1, Knoxville, TN 37901, tel.: (865) 525-0238

Established in 1994 in Tennessee.

Donor: GFM, Inc.
Foundation type: Independent foundation.
Financial data (yr. ended 12/31/13): Assets, $4,875,864 (M); gifts received, $10,314; expenditures, $228,388; qualifying distributions, $214,000; giving activities include $214,000 for 22 grants (high: $25,000; low: $1,000).
Fields of interest: Education; Alzheimer's disease; Sexual abuse; Christianity; Human services; Child welfare; Youth services; Homeless shelters.
Type of support: Research.
Limitations: Applications accepted. Giving primarily in Knoxville, TN. No grants to individuals.
Application information: Application form required.
Initial approach: Letter
Deadline(s): July 1
Board meeting date(s): Sept.
Officers and Directors: Ron Cunningham, Pres.; William E. Monday III, V.P. and Director; Joan Vestal Ellis, Secy.; Kenneth W. Holbert, Treas.; John Lacy, MD; James S. Monday; Robert W. Monday; William E. Monday IV; James Stogner.
EIN: 621518306

8653
Nehemiah Foundation Inc.
4564 Peytonsville Rd.
Franklin, TN 37064-7611 (615) 794-7029
Contact: Thomas W. Singleton, Pres.

Established in 1987 in Tennessee.
Donors: Thomas Singleton; Robert Brolund.
Foundation type: Independent foundation.
Financial data (yr. ended 12/31/12): Assets, $464,148 (M); gifts received, $192,186; expenditures, $173,088; qualifying distributions, $151,591; giving activities include $151,591 for grants.
Fields of interest: Elementary and secondary education; Higher education; Christianity; Human services; Women's services.
Limitations: Applications accepted. Giving primarily in TN. No grants to individuals.
Application information: Application form required.
Initial approach: Letter
Deadline(s): None
Officer: Thomas W. Singleton, Pres.
Director: Silvia A. Singleton.
EIN: 621281778

8654
New Charitable Foundation
(formerly The N.E.W. Relief Fund, Inc.)
c/o The Company
648 Grassmere Park, Ste. 300
Nashville, TN 37211

Donors: N.E.W. Customer Service Cos., Inc.; AIG Warranty Guard; National Electronics Warranty Corp.
Foundation type: Company-sponsored foundation.
Financial data (yr. ended 03/31/14): Assets, $45,463 (M); expenditures, $234,150; qualifying distributions, $234,000; giving activities include $234,000 for 29 grants (high: $90,000; low: $500).
Purpose and activities: The foundation supports community foundations and organizations involved with performing arts, health, cancer, disaster relief, youth development, and human services.
Fields of interest: Performing arts; Foundations; Nonprofits; Health; Hospital care; Cancers; Disaster

relief; Special Olympics; Human services; Youth development; Youth services; Victims of disaster.
Type of support: General support; Regranting.
Limitations: Applications not accepted. Giving primarily in FL, MT, and VA. No grants to individuals.
Application information: Contributes only to pre-selected organizations.
Officers and Board Member: Frederick Schaufeld, Chair. and Pres.; Anthony Nader, V.P. and Director; Terri Feely, Secy.-Treas.
EIN: 542055525

8655
Paddison Charitable Foundation
(formerly Roger B. & Evelyn W. Paddison Charitable Foundation)
c/o Jim Baugh
1111 Northshore Dr., Ste. 800
Knoxville, TN 37919 (865) 766-3017

Established in 1996 in Tennessee.
Donor: Paddison Charitable Lead Trusts.
Foundation type: Independent foundation.
Financial data (yr. ended 12/31/14): Assets, $3,258,843 (M); gifts received, $112,500; expenditures, $186,486; qualifying distributions, $165,587; giving activities include $160,000 for 16 grants (high: $15,000; low: $3,000).
Fields of interest: Education; Health; Community and economic development.
Limitations: Applications accepted. Giving primarily in TN.
Application information: Application form required.
Initial approach: Contact foundation for application
Deadline(s): Jan. 31
Trustees: Mary Paddison James; Pinnacle Bank, N.A.
EIN: 626310121

8656
The Pattee Foundation, Inc.
c/o David Smith
605 Chestnut St., Ste. 1100
Chattanooga, TN 37450 (423) 756-6585
Contact: Gordon B. Pattee, Pres.

Established in 1989 in Tennessee.
Foundation type: Independent foundation.
Financial data (yr. ended 06/30/13): Assets, $3,989,011 (M); expenditures, $307,822; qualifying distributions, $248,662; giving activities include $242,175 for 20 grants (high: $50,000; low: $1,000).
Purpose and activities: Giving primarily for wildlife conservation; funding also for the arts, education, and hospitals.
Fields of interest: Arts and culture; Ballet; Children's museums; Education; University education; Wildlife biodiversity; Hospital care; Protestantism.
Limitations: Applications accepted. Giving primarily in Washington, DC, NY, TN, and VA. No grants to individuals.
Application information:
Initial approach: Letter or proposal
Deadline(s): None
Officers and Directors: Gordon B. Pattee, Pres. and Director; Anne L. Pattee, Secy. and Director; Dorothy E. Pattee.
EIN: 621376116

8657
The Pedigree Foundation
(formerly The Pedigree Adoption Drive Foundation)
315 Cool Spring Blvd.
Franklin, TN 37067-1632
E-mail: info@pedigreefoundation.org; Main
URL: http://www.pedigreefoundation.org
Facebook: https://www.facebook.com/
pedigreefoundation
Google Plus: https://plus.google.com/
116719576015704217580/about
Instagram: https://instagram.com/
pedigreefoundation
Pinterest: http://www.pinterest.com/Pedigreefou
Twitter: https://twitter.com/PedigreeFound
YouTube: https://www.youtube.com/channel/
UC8TDVpJsdXzxcGURtj5w6wQ

Established in 2007 in Tennessee.
Donors: Lisa Liewald; Omnicom Group; Mars
Petcare; Jacqueline Autry; Pedigree Brand; Meryl
Hartsband; Atlas Bass Fund; Linda Mars; Angelici
Estate.
Foundation type: Independent foundation.
Financial data (yr. ended 12/31/13): Assets,
$1,351,542 (M); gifts received, $946,676;
expenditures, $600,999; qualifying distributions,
$600,673; giving activities include $396,182 for
169 grants (high: $25,000; low: $1,000).
Fields of interest: Animal welfare.
Limitations: Applications not accepted. Giving
primarily in CA, FL and MA.
Application information: Unsolicited requests for
funds not accepted.
Officers and Directors: Debra Fair, Pres. and
Director; Bo Segers, Secy. and Director; Denise
Battaglini, Treas. and Director; Steve Capitani; Chris
Hamilton; Chris Mondzelewski; Linda Mars; Angel
May.
EIN: 261121498

8658
Jane L. Pettway Foundation
4823 Old Kingston Pike, Ste. 100
Knoxville, TN 37919-6499 (865) 971-1902
Contact: Charles Purkey

Established in 1999 in Tennessee.
Foundation type: Independent foundation.
Financial data (yr. ended 08/31/14): Assets,
$8,837,446 (M); expenditures, $478,531;
qualifying distributions, $453,315; giving activities
include $433,514 for 34 grants (high: $55,000;
low: $1,450).
Purpose and activities: Giving primarily for human
services, libraries, including the education and
training of library employees, financially-needy
women, and Episcopal parishes or ministries.
Fields of interest: Elementary and secondary
education; Public libraries; Christianity; Human
services; Low-income and poor people.
Limitations: Applications accepted. Giving primarily
in Anderson, Blount, Grainger, Jefferson, Knox,
Loudon, Roane, Sevier, and Union counties, TN.
Application information: Application may also be
hand delivered during normal business hours.
Application form required.
Initial approach: Request application form
Deadline(s): Mar. 31
Board meeting date(s): Annually, late Apr. or early
May
Trustee: The Trust Company of Knoxville.

Directors: Myretta Black; Stacy E. Roettger; Dean
John Ross.
EIN: 626371465

8659
The Pfeffer Foundation
836 Treemont Ct.
Oak Hill, TN 37220-1536

Established in 1997 in Tennessee.
Donors: Philip M. Pfeffer; Pamela K. Pfeffer.
Foundation type: Independent foundation.
Financial data (yr. ended 12/31/14): Assets,
$244,737 (M); gifts received, $45,723;
expenditures, $298,658; qualifying distributions,
$280,931; giving activities include $280,931 for 50
grants (high: $53,394; low: $25).
Fields of interest: Arts and culture; Education;
Health; Protestantism; Child welfare.
Limitations: Applications not accepted. No grants to
individuals.
Application information: Contributes only to
pre-selected organizations.
Trustee: Pamela K. Pfeffer.
Board Member: Philip M. Pfeffer.
EIN: 621694538

8660
The James W. Pickle Charitable
Foundation
905 Harpeth Valley Pl., Ste. 7057
Nashville, TN 37221-1141 (615) 662-2727
Contact: Lawrence J. Sacks, Pres.
E-mail: dking@atacpa.net

Established in 2004 in Tennessee.
Donor: James W. Pickle†.
Foundation type: Independent foundation.
Financial data (yr. ended 12/31/13): Assets,
$5,073,334 (M); expenditures, $671,832;
qualifying distributions, $353,949; giving activities
include $286,646 for 16 grants (high: $50,000;
low: $890).
Purpose and activities: Giving for life altering
medical care, services, and equipment.
Fields of interest: Higher education; Health;
Hospice care.
Type of support: Public engagement and education.
Limitations: Applications accepted. Giving primarily
in Nashville, TN.
Application information: Application form required.
Initial approach: Letter
Deadline(s): None
Officers: Lawrence J. Sacks, Pres.; Charlene
Sanders, Secy.
Trustee: Lynn Boone.
EIN: 200485515

8661
The Powell Foundation
3622 Bristol Hwy.
Johnson City, TN 37601-1324 (423) 282-0111
Contact: James J. Powell, Chair.

Established in 2000 in Tennessee.
Donor: James J. Powell.
Foundation type: Independent foundation.
Financial data (yr. ended 12/31/12): Assets,
$12,780,863 (M); gifts received, $4,000,000;
expenditures, $433,519; qualifying distributions,

$385,000; giving activities include $385,000 for
grants.
Fields of interest: Education; Higher education;
Health; Housing development; Christianity; Child
welfare; Scouting programs.
Type of support: Volunteer development.
Limitations: Applications accepted. Giving primarily
in TN.
Application information:
Initial approach: Letter
Deadline(s): None
Officers: James J. Powell, Chair.; Gary F. Clayton,
Secy.
Directors: James J. Powell, Jr.; Jeffrey J. Powell;
Michael W. Powell.
EIN: 621819796

8662
Elizabeth Craig Weaver Proctor Charitable
Foundation
215 Evelyn Ave.
Nashville, TN 37205-3307

Established in 2000 in Tennessee.
Donors: Elizabeth C. Proctor; E.C.W. Proctor Trust.
Foundation type: Independent foundation.
Financial data (yr. ended 12/31/14): Assets,
$6,217,244; gifts received, $130,575;
expenditures, $200,360; qualifying distributions,
$150,000.
Fields of interest: Education; Nonprofits; Health;
Multiple sclerosis; Christianity; Scouting programs.
Type of support: General support; Endowments;
Regranting.
Limitations: Applications not accepted. Giving
primarily in Nashville, TN. No grants to individuals.
Application information: Unsolicited requests for
funds not accepted.
Officer: Elizabeth Craig Weaver Proctor, Chair.
Trustees: Kathryn L. Berschback; Craig W. Friedrich;
Collins W. Hooper; Elizabeth W. Lane; Elizabeth
McAlister; Margaret A. Robinson; William C. Weaver
IV.
EIN: 621819464

8663
Provision Charitas, Inc.
2095 Lakeside Centre Way, Ste. 101
Knoxville, TN 37922-6647

Donors: Terry Douglas; Provision Trust; Vision
Investments.
Foundation type: Independent foundation.
Financial data (yr. ended 12/31/13): Assets,
$48,713 (M); gifts received, $680,000;
expenditures, $722,848; qualifying distributions,
$722,203; giving activities include $412,200 for 13
grants (high: $100,000; low: $1,000).
Fields of interest: Education; Diseases and
conditions; Religion; Christianity.
Limitations: Applications not accepted. Giving
primarily in CA and TN.
Application information: Unsolicited requests for
funds not accepted.
Officers: Terry Douglass, Pres.; Anne Swartz, Secy.
Board Member: Rosann Douglass.
EIN: 454784073

8664
Redbird Foundation
4624 Chambliss Ave.
Knoxville, TN   37919-5118

Established in 1995 in Tennessee.
Donors: B. Ray Thompson Charitable Trust; Juanne Thompson Charitable Trust.
Foundation type: Independent foundation.
Financial data (yr. ended 06/30/13): Assets, $7,901,128 (M); expenditures, $428,484; qualifying distributions, $352,326; giving activities include $352,326 for grants.
Fields of interest: Education; Christianity; Basic and emergency aid; International development.
Limitations: Applications not accepted. Giving on a national basis. No grants for endowments or funds to support operating deficits.
Publications: Annual report.
Application information: Contributes only to pre-selected organizations.
Officers and Directors: B. Ray Thompson, Jr., Pres. and Director; Juanne J. Thompson, Secy. and Director; Rebekah Thompson Palmer; Sarah Thompson Tarver; Adella Sands Thompson; B. Ray Thompson III; Catherine Vance Thompson.
EIN: 621591527

8665
The Restoration Foundation
2112 Hampton Ave.
Nashville, TN   37215-1402   6152559337

Established in 1999 in Tennessee.
Donors: John Elam; Lulu Elam.
Foundation type: Independent foundation.
Financial data (yr. ended 02/28/15): Assets, $3,342,089; gifts received, $1,200; expenditures, $303,329; qualifying distributions, $259,400.
Fields of interest: Health; Religion; Human services.
Limitations: Applications not accepted. Giving limited to Nashville, TN. No grants to individuals.
Application information: Unsolicited requests for funds not accepted.
Trustees: John Elam; Lulu Elam.
EIN: 626355168

8666
The James and Laura Rogers Foundation
105 Coventry Wynde Rd.
Kingsport, TN   37664-4877

Donors: James Rogers; Laura Rogers.
Foundation type: Independent foundation.
Financial data (yr. ended 11/30/13): Assets, $6,626,481 (M); expenditures, $323,472; qualifying distributions, $283,022; giving activities include $275,000 for 6 grants (high: $180,000; low: $5,000).
Fields of interest: Arts and culture; Human services; Youth development.
Limitations: Applications not accepted. Giving primarily in Kingsport, TN.
Application information: Unsolicited requests for funds not accepted.
Officers: James P. Rogers, Pres.; Laura C. Rogers, Secy.-Treas.
Directors: Tamara M. Cottingim; Anna K. Rogers; Jessica L. Rogers.
EIN: 274283892

8667
The Rose Foundation
1779 Kirby Pkwy., Ste. 1, PMB 320
Memphis, TN   38138-0631

Established in 1990 in Tennessee.
Donors: Gayle S. Rose; Michael D. Rose.
Foundation type: Independent foundation.
Financial data (yr. ended 12/31/13): Assets, $3,690,755 (M); gifts received, $333,708; expenditures, $303,192; qualifying distributions, $265,350; giving activities include $265,350 for 20 grants (high: $75,000; low: $250).
Purpose and activities: Giving primarily for higher education, youth services and the arts.
Fields of interest: Arts and culture; Museums; Education; Higher education; Natural resources; Foundations; Health; Diseases and conditions; Child welfare.
Limitations: Applications not accepted. Giving primarily in CO, GA, IL and Memphis, TN. No grants to individuals.
Application information: Contributes only to pre-selected organizations.
Officers: Michael D. Rose, Pres.; Norma Egbert, Secy.
Directors: Gabrielle E. Rose; Matthew D. Rose; Morgan D. Rose.
Number of staff: 1 full-time support.
EIN: 621450062

8668
Rucker-Donnell Foundation
110 S. Maple St.
Murfreesboro, TN   37130-3530   (615) 890-5700
Contact: Rick Mansfield, Tr.

Established in 2001 in Tennessee.
Donor: James Donnell.
Foundation type: Operating foundation.
Financial data (yr. ended 12/31/13): Assets, $6,008,477 (M); expenditures, $439,178; qualifying distributions, $317,062; giving activities include $276,800 for 2 grants (high: $275,718; low: $1,082).
Purpose and activities: Giving primarily to a United Methodist college; some giving also to a polytechnic university.
Fields of interest: Undergraduate education; Graduate and professional education; Engineering.
Limitations: Applications accepted. Giving primarily in Pulaski, TN; some giving also in Marietta, GA.
Application information:
Initial approach: Letter
Deadline(s): None
Trustees: J. Kent Burklow; Rick G. Mansfield; William E. Rowland.
EIN: 621856912

8669
Sasco Foundation Corporation
6000 Poplar Ave., Ste. 250
Memphis, TN   38119-3974

Donor: Larry H. Smead.
Foundation type: Independent foundation.
Financial data (yr. ended 06/30/13): Assets, $9,028,681 (M); expenditures, $565,666; qualifying distributions, $436,880; giving activities include $427,863 for 12 grants (high: $125,000; low: $1,009).

Fields of interest: Foundations; Diseases and conditions; Human services; Child welfare.
Limitations: Applications not accepted. Giving primarily in CA and WA.
Application information: Unsolicited requests for funds not accepted.
Officers: Larry H. Smead, Chair.; Preston Smead, Vice-Chair.
EIN: 452286657

8670
The Schadt Foundation, Inc.
P.O. Box 242049
Memphis, TN   38124-2049

Established in 1958 in Tennessee.
Donors: Charles F. Schadt, Sr.; Harry E. Schadt, Sr.†; Harry E. Schadt, Jr.
Foundation type: Independent foundation.
Financial data (yr. ended 12/31/12): Assets, $4,479,426 (M); expenditures, $384,153; qualifying distributions, $352,833; giving activities include $352,833 for grants.
Purpose and activities: Giving primarily for the arts, education, and children, youth, and social services.
Fields of interest: Arts and culture; Education; Elementary and secondary education; Human services; Child welfare.
Limitations: Applications not accepted. Giving limited to Memphis, TN. No grants to individuals.
Application information: Contributes only to pre-selected organizations.
Board meeting date(s): Annually
Officers: Stephen C. Schadt, Pres.; Lynn Schadt Thomas, Secy.
Director: Charles Schadt, Jr.
EIN: 626040050

8671
William E. Schmidt Foundation, Inc.
3712 Central Ave., Ste. 500
Nashville, TN   37205-2434
Application address for Schmidt Youth Vocal Competition: c/o Linda McAlister, Coor., 109 Presser Hall, 501 S. Patterson Ave., Miami University, Oxford, OH 45056, tel.: (513) 529-3046; Main URL: http://www.schmidtfoundation.org Grants List: http://www.schmidtfoundation.org/grants.shtml

Established in 1993 in Indiana.
Donor: William E. Schmidt.
Foundation type: Independent foundation.
Financial data (yr. ended 12/31/13): Assets, $3,763,117 (M); expenditures, $256,925; qualifying distributions, $230,177; giving activities include $213,533 for 15 grants (high: $156,000; low: $250).
Purpose and activities: Giving to support youth in the musical arts and through education.
Fields of interest: Opera; Education; Higher education; Christianity; Youth services; Young adults.
Type of support: Annual campaigns; Matching grants; Capital campaigns.
Limitations: Applications accepted. Giving primarily in Evansville, IN, KY and FL.
Application information: See foundation web site for complete application guidelines. Application form required.

Officers: William E. Schmidt, Chair.; Casiana Schmidt, Pres.; J. Michael Small, Secy.; Chester Schmidt, Treas.
Board Members: David F. Hamilton; Elizabeth Hamilton; John Hamilton; Chad Schmidt; Douglas M. Schmidt; Steven Schmidt; Lea Schmidt-Rogers.
EIN: 351884241

8672
P. K. Seidman Charitable Trust
3173 Kirby Whitten Pkwy., Ste. 105
Bartlett, TN 38134-2881 (901) 527-6666
Contact: Marcia R. Brasel, Tr.

Established in 1986 in Tennessee.
Donors: Thomas Erler Foundation; Seidman Foundation.
Foundation type: Independent foundation.
Financial data (yr. ended 12/31/13): Assets, $4,451,112 (M); expenditures, $254,579; qualifying distributions, $204,793; giving activities include $130,114 for 5 grants (high: $81,314; low: $800).
Purpose and activities: Giving primarily for higher education including awards, scholarships, and lecture programs; support also for arts and culture and health services.
Fields of interest: Performing arts; Higher education; Health; Christianity.
Type of support: General support; Scholarships.
Limitations: Applications accepted. Giving primarily in TN. No grants to individuals.
Application information: Application form required.
 Initial approach: Letter
 Deadline(s): None
Trustees: Marcia R. Brasel; Lori C. Locke.
EIN: 626034052

8673
Seme Foundation, Inc.
455 Security Pl.
Cookeville, TN 38506-4941

Established in 2002 in Tennessee.
Donors: Lisa L. Jones; Thomas H. Jones.
Foundation type: Independent foundation.
Financial data (yr. ended 06/30/14): Assets, $5,157,875 (M); gifts received, $1,000,000; expenditures, $273,808; qualifying distributions, $273,250; giving activities include $273,250 for 16 grants (high: $75,000; low: $350).
Fields of interest: Education; Christianity; Family services; Child welfare; Children.
Type of support: General support.
Limitations: Applications not accepted. Giving primarily in OH and TN. No grants to individuals.
Application information: Contributes only to pre-selected organizations.
Officers and Directors: Thomas H. Jones, Pres. and Director; Lisa L. Jones, Secy. and Director; Bruce R. Barsumian.
EIN: 383656678

8674
Richard Siegel Foundation
P.O. Box 7100
Murfreesboro, TN 37133-1700 (615) 278-7111
Contact: Gina King

Established in 2000 in Tennessee.

Donor: Richard Siegel†.
Foundation type: Independent foundation.
Financial data (yr. ended 01/01/15): Assets, $4,034,717 (M); gifts received, $90,612; expenditures, $218,457; qualifying distributions, $166,736; giving activities include $60,000 for 11 grants (high: $32,900; low: $1,000), and $95,800 for 27 grants to individuals (high: $2,500; low: $1,250).
Fields of interest: Elementary and secondary education; Child welfare.
Type of support: Student aid.
Limitations: Applications accepted. Giving primarily in Murfreesboro and Rutherford County, TN.
Application information: Application form required.
 Initial approach: Contact Foundation
 Deadline(s): None
Officers: John Sallee, Chair.; Bill Reid, Vice-Chair.
Trustees: Dianna Cantrell; Jamie Evans; Susan O'guin; Ray Thomas; David Chavis; Gordon Ferguson; Andrea Loughry.
EIN: 311646336

8675
Irvin and Beverly Small Foundation
409 W. Tyne Dr.
Nashville, TN 37205-4433

Established in 1995 in Tennessee.
Donors: Irvin Small; Beverly Small.
Foundation type: Independent foundation.
Financial data (yr. ended 12/31/13): Assets, $220,931 (M); expenditures, $127,558; qualifying distributions, $123,800; giving activities include $123,800 for 18 grants (high: $19,700; low: $2,000).
Fields of interest: Arts and culture; Orchestral music; Diseases and conditions; Cancers; Community and economic development; Judaism; Child welfare.
Limitations: Applications not accepted. No grants to individuals.
Application information: Unsolicited requests for funds not accepted.
Officers: Irvin Small, Pres.; Beverly Small, Secy.-Treas.
Directors: Linda S. Gluck; Douglas Small.
EIN: 621639814

8676
Jim and Leah Sohr Family Foundation
2002 Tyne Blvd.
Nashville, TN 37215-4705

Donor: James M. Sohr.
Foundation type: Independent foundation.
Financial data (yr. ended 12/31/14): Assets, $5,848,401; expenditures, $414,965; qualifying distributions, $377,500.
Fields of interest: University education; Foundations; Human services.
Limitations: Applications not accepted.
Application information: Unsolicited requests for funds not accepted.
Officer: James M. Sohr, Pres.
Director: Leah E. Sohr.
EIN: 356810134

8677
Don & Roy Splawn Charitable Foundation
(formerly The Don Splawn Charitable Foundation)
c/o East, Inc.
1163 Gateway Ln.
Nashville, TN 37220-1007
Contact: Jeffrey Gould, Board Member

Established in 1997 in California.
Donors: Don H. Splawn; Don Splawn Recovable Trust.
Foundation type: Independent foundation.
Financial data (yr. ended 12/31/13): Assets, $4,116,311 (M); expenditures, $363,284; qualifying distributions, $243,145; giving activities include $184,939 for 18 grants (high: $60,000; low: $280).
Fields of interest: Arts and culture; Ballet; Education; Health.
Type of support: General support; Student aid.
Limitations: Applications accepted. Giving primarily in TN.
Application information: Application form required.
 Initial approach: Letter
 Deadline(s): None
Directors: Jeff Gould; Jimmy Gould.
EIN: 770420822

8678
The Julia Carell Stadler Foundation
4432 Tyne Blvd.
Nashville, TN 37215-4505

Established in 1997 in Tennessee.
Donor: Julia Carell Stadler.
Foundation type: Independent foundation.
Financial data (yr. ended 12/31/13): Assets, $3,924,265 (M); expenditures, $279,208; qualifying distributions, $265,057; giving activities include $263,042 for 13 grants (high: $163,500; low: $500).
Fields of interest: Education; Environment; Hospital care; Religion; Human services; Child welfare.
Type of support: General support.
Limitations: Applications not accepted. Giving primarily in Nashville, TN. No grants to individuals.
Application information: Contributes only to pre-selected organizations.
Officer: Julia Carell Stadler, Chair.
Board Member: George B. Stadler.
EIN: 626314877

8679
Earl & Mary Storey Charitable Trust
800 S. Gay St.
Knoxville, TN 37995-1230

Foundation type: Independent foundation.
Financial data (yr. ended 12/31/13): Assets, $6,732,084 (M); expenditures, $350,780; qualifying distributions, $320,461; giving activities include $294,000 for 1 grant.
Fields of interest: Education.
Limitations: Applications not accepted. Giving primarily in TN.
Application information: Unsolicited requests for funds not accepted.
Trustee: First Tennessee Bank, N.A.
EIN: 266399772

8680
Stuttering Foundation of America, Inc.
(also known as The Stuttering Foundation)
(formerly Speech Foundation of America)
1805 Moriah Woods Blvd., Ste. 3
Memphis, TN 38117-7121 (800) 992-9392
Contact: Jane Fraser, Pres.
FAX: (901) 761-0484;
E-mail: info@stutteringhelp.org; Mailing address:
Stuttering Foundation of America, Inc., c/o Jane
Fraser, Pres., P.O. Box 11749, Memphis, TN
38111-0749. Additional toll-free tel.: (901)
761-0343; Main URL: http://
www.stutteringhelp.org
E Newsletter: http://www.stutteringhelp.org/
newsletters
Facebook: https://www.facebook.com/
stutteringhelp
Pinterest: http://www.pinterest.com/stutteringfdn
Podcasts: http://www.stutteringhelp.org/podcasts
RSS feed: http://feeds.feedburner.com/blogspot/
CLLc
Twitter: http://twitter.com/stutteringfdn
YouTube: http://www.youtube.com/user/
stutteringfdn

Established in 1947 in Tennessee.
Donor: Jane Fraser.
Foundation type: Operating foundation.
Financial data (yr. ended 12/31/13): Assets,
$31,029,694 (M); gifts received, $354,293;
expenditures, $1,847,457; qualifying distributions,
$1,673,479; giving activities include $250,000 for
1 grant, $5,000 for grants to individuals, and
$1,570,363 for 4 foundation-administered
programs.
Purpose and activities: Giving for
foundation-initiated programs in therapy and the
prevention of stuttering.
Type of support: Convening; Grants to individuals;
Publications.
Limitations: Applications not accepted.
Publications: Annual report; Informational brochure;
Newsletter.
Application information: Unsolicited requests for
funds not accepted.
   Board meeting date(s): May
Officers: Jane Fraser, Pres.; Joe Fulcher, V.P.;
Joseph Walker, Secy.; Donald Edwards, Treas.
Directors: Frances Cook; Dennis Drayna; Jean
Fraser Gruss; Robert M. Kurtz, Jr.; Donald Lineback;
Alan Rabinowitz.
Number of staff: 1 full-time professional; 3 full-time
support; 2 part-time support.
EIN: 626047678

8681
Sunlight Foundation
P.O. Box 150123
Nashville, TN 37215-0123

Established in 1999 in Tennessee.
Donors: Deborah D. Sherman; Timothy J. Siktberg.
Foundation type: Independent foundation.
Financial data (yr. ended 12/31/13): Assets,
$4,298,478 (M); gifts received, $30,000;
expenditures, $198,853; qualifying distributions,
$164,756; giving activities include $164,756 for 19
grants (high: $30,000; low: $456).
Fields of interest: Education; Environment;
Protestantism.
Limitations: Applications not accepted. Giving
primarily in CO. No grants to individuals.

Application information: Unsolicited requests for
funds not accepted.
Officers: Deborah D. Sherman, Pres.; Timothy J.
Siktberg, Secy.
Director: Billie Don Sherman.
EIN: 621809916

8682
Deborah Dunklin Tipton Charitable Foundation
1867 Kilbirnie Dr.
Germantown, TN 38139-3419

Donors: L.A. Black & J.H. Boone Foundation;
Deborah Dunklin Tipton; DDT Descendants
Charitable Lead Annuity Trust.
Foundation type: Independent foundation.
Financial data (yr. ended 12/31/13): Assets,
$8,299,502 (M); gifts received, $2,101,404;
expenditures, $424,182; qualifying distributions,
$369,325; giving activities include $367,575 for 38
grants (high: $280,500; low: $50).
Fields of interest: Arts and culture; Education;
Higher education; Domesticated animals.
Type of support: General support.
Limitations: Applications not accepted. Giving
primarily in TN. No grants to individuals.
Application information: Unsolicited requests for
funds not accepted.
Trustees: Harry C. Erwin III; Deborah Dunklin Tipton.
EIN: 300056706

8683
The Emmy Lou Tompkins Foundation
(formerly The West Virginia Foundation)
2020 Willowmet Ln.
Brentwood, TN 37027-8949 (615) 469-0810
Contact: Ryan Altizer, Tr.

Established in 1998 in West Virginia.
Donor: Emmy Lou Tompkins.
Foundation type: Independent foundation.
Financial data (yr. ended 12/31/14): Assets,
$2,508,012 (M); expenditures, $171,577;
qualifying distributions, $151,935; giving activities
include $147,500 for 15 grants (high: $20,000;
low: $5,000).
Purpose and activities: Giving primarily for human
services with an emphasis on families.
Fields of interest: Education; Diseases and
conditions; Human services.
Type of support: General support; Capital and
infrastructure; Equipment; Emergency funds;
Program development; Curriculum development.
Limitations: Applications accepted. Giving primarily
in NC and Charleston, WV. No support for political
organizations. No grants for scholarships to
individuals, or for income development, investments
or loans.
Application information:
   Initial approach: Proposal
   Deadline(s): None
Trustees: Betsy Altizer; Ryan Altizer; Joanna Dye;
Boydie Girimont; Heidi Dye Raines; Blair Sechrest.
EIN: 550759620

8684
Robert Lee Weiss Foundation
800 S. Gay St.
Knoxville, TN 37995-1230 (865) 971-2023
Contact: David B. Lantz, Exec. V.P. and Mgr.

Established in 1985 in Tennessee.
Donor: Robert Lee Weiss, Jr.†.
Foundation type: Independent foundation.
Financial data (yr. ended 08/31/14): Assets,
$3,004,944 (M); expenditures, $177,968;
qualifying distributions, $160,197; giving activities
include $145,000 for 32 grants (high: $20,000;
low: $1,000).
Fields of interest: Health; Religion; Human services.
Type of support: General support; Scholarships;
Student aid.
Limitations: Applications accepted. Giving primarily
in the eastern TN, area, with emphasis on Knoxville.
Application information: Application form required.
   Initial approach: Contact foundation for
      application form
   Deadline(s): June 30
Officers: David Lantz, Exec. V.P. and Mgr.; Robert
McDonald, Mgr.; Mrs. Mary Ellen Roddy Mitchell,
Mgr.
Trustee: First Tennessee Bank, N.A.
EIN: 621261218

8685
The Williamson, Martin & Brooke Family Foundation
(formerly The John Williamson Family Foundation)
2310 Golf Club Ln.
Nashville, TN 37215-1108

Established in 1988 in Alabama.
Donors: John A. Williamson; Jean C. Williamson;
Margaret W. Brooke; Linda W. Martin; C. Molton
Williams; John A. Williamson, Jr.
Foundation type: Independent foundation.
Financial data (yr. ended 05/31/14): Assets,
$1,588,086 (M); gifts received, $32,185;
expenditures, $177,586; qualifying distributions,
$149,750; giving activities include $149,750 for 22
grants (high: $30,000; low: $100).
Fields of interest: Religion; Sports and recreation;
Human services; Youth development.
Type of support: General support.
Limitations: Applications not accepted. Giving
primarily in AL. No grants to individuals.
Application information: Contributes only to
pre-selected organizations.
Officers: Raymond S. Martin III, Pres.; John A.
Williamson, Jr., V.P.; Margaret W. Brooke, Secy.;
Linda W. Martin, Treas.
EIN: 630983566

8686
Charles P. Wilson Foundation Inc.
829 Grant St.
Paris, TN 38242-5211 (731) 642-3180
Contact: Charles P. Wilson, Pres.

Donors: Charles P. Wilson; Progressive Financial
Services, Inc.; Ben Sherard; Chad P. Wilson.
Foundation type: Independent foundation.
Financial data (yr. ended 12/31/13): Assets,
$3,883,818 (M); gifts received, $296,451;
expenditures, $448,311; qualifying distributions,

$190,800; giving activities include $190,800 for 24 grants (high: $66,000; low: $500).

Fields of interest: Protestantism.

Limitations: Applications accepted. Giving primarily in TN.

Application information: Application form required.

Initial approach: Proposal

Deadline(s): None

Officers: Charles P. Wilson, Pres.; Ben Sherard, Secy.

Director: Chad P. Wilson.

EIN: 320249019

8687
Toby S. Wilt Family Foundation

P.O. Box 50879

Nashville, TN   37205-0879   (615) 383-4330

Established in 1987 in Tennessee.

Donors: Toby S. Wilt; Music City Bowl; Snedekar Charity Event.

Foundation type: Independent foundation.

Financial data (yr. ended 12/31/14): Assets, $2,453,761; expenditures, $158,945; qualifying distributions, $128,175.

Fields of interest: Undergraduate education; Health; Golf; Human services; Youth services.

Limitations: Applications accepted. Giving primarily in TN. No grants to individuals.

Application information: Application form required.

Initial approach: Letter

Deadline(s): None

Advisory Committee: Toby S. Wilt.

EIN: 626195897

8688
WTC Foundation

425 Jackson Blvd.

Nashville, TN   37205-3407

Established in 2006 in Tennessee.

Donor: Kimberly W. Coakley.

Foundation type: Independent foundation.

Financial data (yr. ended 12/31/13): Assets, -$3,789 (M); gifts received, $227,896; expenditures, $226,310; qualifying distributions, $186,325; giving activities include $186,325 for 18 grants (high: $150,000; low: $25).

Fields of interest: Education; Diseases and conditions; Human services.

Type of support: Capital campaigns.

Limitations: Applications not accepted. Giving primarily in TN. No grants to individuals.

Application information: Unsolicited requests for funds not accepted.

Trustee: Kimberly W. Coakley.

EIN: 020779716

TEXAS

8689
A Glimmer of Hope Foundation - Austin
(also known as A Glimmer of Hope Foundation Austin)
3600 N. Capital of Texas Hwy., Bldg. B., Ste. 330
Austin, TX 78746-3314   (512) 328-9944
FAX: (512) 328-8872;
E-mail: inquiries@aglimmerofhope.org; Application
e-mail: austin@aglimmerofhope.org; Main
URL: http://www.aglimmerofhopeaustin.org
Facebook: https://www.facebook.com/
aglimmerofhopeaustin
Twitter: https://twitter.com/glimmeraustin

Donors: A Glimmer of Hope Foundation; Ross
Garber; Austin Athletic Scholarship Foundation;
Cumberland Continental; Wells Fargo Bank, N.A.;
Silverton Foundation; Mydna Media, Inc.; The
Andrew S. Roddick Foundation.
Foundation type: Independent foundation.
Financial data (yr. ended 12/31/13): Assets,
$143,700 (M); gifts received, $392,104;
expenditures, $591,623; qualifying distributions,
$567,812; giving activities include $359,970 for 29
grants (high: $26,516; low: $1,000).
Purpose and activities: A Glimmer of Hope Austin
supports innovative programs that improve the lives
of youth and senior populations who suffer from
exclusion, social injustice and neglect.
Fields of interest: Human services; Child welfare;
Seniors.
Limitations: Applications accepted. Giving primarily
in East and South Austin, TX, with the following
boundaries: North (Rundberg Ln.), South (Slaughter
Ln.), East (Decker Ln./Hwy. 183 Corridor), and West
(IH 35 Corridor). The following postal codes are also
eligible to apply: 78751, 78752, 78757, and
78758. No support for cultural exchange programs.
No grants to individuals, or for travel or scholarship
assistance, general operating funds, construction
projects, hardware upgrades or labs, fundraising
events, mass mailings, advertising projects,
conferences or symposia, out-of-state performances
or competition expenses, or for academic or
scientific research.
Publications: Application guidelines; Grants list.
Application information: Complete application
guidelines available on foundation web site.
   Initial approach: Download grant application form
      from foundation web site, and send an
      electronic copy and two hard copies
   Deadline(s): See foundation web site for current
      deadlines
Officers: Donna Berber, Pres.; Philip Berber, V.P.;
Stephanie Fast, C.F.O.; David Porter, Exec. Dir.
Directors: Ryan Berber; Shane Berber.
EIN: 200733502

8690
Taylor S. & Patti Harding Abernathy
   Charitable Trust
c/o Bank of America, N.A.
P.O. Box 831041
Dallas, TX 75283-1041   (816) 292-400
Contact: Scott Berghaus, S.V.P., Sr. Philanthropic
Relationship Mgr.

E-mail: mo.grantmaking@ustrust.com; E-mail for
Scott Berghaus: scott.berghaus@ustrust.com; Main
URL: https://www.bankofamerica.com/
philanthropic/foundation.go

Established in 1988 in Missouri.
Donor: Spence Heddens.
Foundation type: Independent foundation.
Financial data (yr. ended 12/31/14): Assets,
$5,963,255 (M); expenditures, $306,686;
qualifying distributions, $281,182; giving activities
include $249,000 for 13 grants (high: $50,000;
low: $5,000).
Purpose and activities: The trust provides grants
that support and promote quality educational,
cultural, human services, and health care
programming.
Fields of interest: Arts and culture; Education;
Human services.
Type of support: General support; Program
development.
Limitations: Applications accepted. Giving primarily
in the greater bi-state metropolitan Kansas City
area. No grants for capital campaigns.
Application information: Application form required.
   Initial approach: Online application
   Deadline(s): May 31
   Final notification: July 31
Trustee: Bank of America, N.A.
EIN: 436343880

8691
The Donald A. Adam Family Foundation
1 Momentum Blvd., Ste. 1000
College Station, TX 77845-6335

Established in 2004 in Texas.
Donors: First American Bank, N.A.; The Adam
Corporation/Group.
Foundation type: Independent foundation.
Financial data (yr. ended 12/31/13): Assets,
$4,500,928 (M); gifts received, $125,000;
expenditures, $216,657; qualifying distributions,
$211,151; giving activities include $93,790 for 8
grants (high: $50,290; low: $1,000), and $116,268
for 14 grants to individuals (high: $28,973; low:
$1,734).
Fields of interest: Education; Health; Housing
development; Child welfare.
Limitations: Applications not accepted. Giving
primarily in TX. No grants to individuals.
Application information: Contributes only to
pre-selected organizations.
Officers: Donald A. Adam, Pres.; Donna J. Adam,
V.P.; Steven Bradley Adam, V.P.; Stephanie A.
Malechek, V.P.; James L. Wolfe, Secy.-Treas.
EIN: 260080253

8692
Adler Foundation
4899 Montrose Blvd., Ste. 1312
Houston, TX 77006-6169

Established in 1982 in Texas.
Donors: Gail F. Adler; Louis K. Adler.
Foundation type: Independent foundation.
Financial data (yr. ended 06/30/13): Assets,
$5,454,331 (M); expenditures, $238,098;
qualifying distributions, $233,936; giving activities
include $231,248 for 51 grants (high: $50,215;
low: $1).

Purpose and activities: Giving primarily to Jewish
agencies and temples, and for education and the
arts.
Fields of interest: Arts and culture; Art museums;
Education; Secondary education; Judaism.
Type of support: General support; Continuing
support; Annual campaigns; Capital campaigns;
Emergency funds.
Limitations: Applications not accepted. Giving
primarily in TX. No grants to individuals.
Publications: Annual report.
Application information: Unsolicited requests for
funds not accepted.
   Board meeting date(s): Varies
Officers: Louis K. Adler, Pres. and Treas.; Gail F.
Adler, V.P.
Trustee: Marc F. Adler.
Number of staff: 1 part-time professional.
EIN: 760001183

8693
The ADR Foundation, Inc.
P.O. Box 118953
Carrollton, TX 75011-8953

Established in 1999 in Texas.
Donors: Danny L. Dansby; Linda L. Dansby.
Foundation type: Independent foundation.
Financial data (yr. ended 12/31/14): Assets,
$3,162,935; expenditures, $256,666; qualifying
distributions, $235,000.
Fields of interest: Christianity; Family services;
Child welfare; Shelter and residential care;
International development.
Limitations: Applications not accepted. Giving
primarily in TX. No grants to individuals.
Application information: Unsolicited requests for
funds not accepted.
Officers: Danny L. Dansby, Pres.; David L. Dansby,
V.P.; Ryan L. Dansby, V.P.; Amy D. Dansby, Secy.
EIN: 752849058

8694
Agee Family Foundation
800 Gessner Rd., Ste. 1000
Houston, TX 77024-4257   (713) 468-6866
Contact: Richard Agee, Secy.-Treas.

Donors: Richard Agee; Judith Agee.
Foundation type: Independent foundation.
Financial data (yr. ended 12/31/13): Assets,
$11,039,427 (M); expenditures, $437,723;
qualifying distributions, $406,000; giving activities
include $406,000 for 9 grants (high: $150,000;
low: $10,000).
Fields of interest: Education.
Limitations: Applications accepted. Giving primarily
in TX.
Application information: Application form required.
   Initial approach: Letter
   Deadline(s): None
Officers: Judith Agee, Pres.; Erin Agee Riley, V.P.;
Richard Agee, Secy.-Treas.
EIN: 010939828

8695
The Andrew and Julie Alexander
   Foundation
2600 Citadel Plz. Dr., Ste. 300
Houston, TX 77008-1315

Established in 1998 in Texas.
Donors: Andrew Mark Alexander; Julie Alexander.
Foundation type: Independent foundation.
Financial data (yr. ended 12/31/13): Assets,
$3,411,195 (M); expenditures, $142,510;
qualifying distributions, $140,022; giving activities
include $139,050 for 27 grants (high: $32,000;
low: $100).
Fields of interest: Diseases and conditions;
Agriculture; Judaism.
Limitations: Applications not accepted. Giving
primarily in TX. No grants to individuals.
Application information: Unsolicited requests for
funds not accepted.
Officers and Directors: Andrew Mark Alexander,
Pres. and Treas. and Director; Julie Alexander, V.P.
and Secy. and Director; Martin Debrovner.
EIN: 760573347

8696
Robert D. and Catherine R. Alexander Foundation
4200 S. Hulen St., Ste. 617
Fort Worth, TX   76109-4913   (817) 731-1317
Contact: R. Denny Alexander, Tr.

Established in 1962 in Texas.
Donors: R.D. Alexander Trust; Catherine R.
Alexander†.
Foundation type: Independent foundation.
Financial data (yr. ended 12/31/13): Assets,
$6,194,439 (M); expenditures, $232,381;
qualifying distributions, $180,275; giving activities
include $178,300 for 26 grants (high: $50,000;
low: $300).
Purpose and activities: Giving primarily for
programs for visually impaired children; support also
for the arts.
Fields of interest: Arts and culture; Higher
education; Children's hospital care; Human
services; Child welfare; Children; People with vision
impairments.
Limitations: Applications accepted. Giving primarily
in Tarrant County, TX, with emphasis on Fort Worth.
No grants to individuals.
Application information:
  Initial approach: Letter
  Copies of proposal: 1
  Deadline(s): None
Trustee: R. Denny Alexander.
Number of staff: 1 part-time professional; 1
part-time support.
EIN: 756012124

8697
Amarillo Business Foundation
P.O. Box 389
Amarillo, TX   79105-0389

Established in 1999 in Texas.
Donor: Amarillo Credit Association Inc.
Foundation type: Independent foundation.
Financial data (yr. ended 12/31/13): Assets,
$5,229,667 (M); expenditures, $267,373;
qualifying distributions, $204,000; giving activities
include $204,000 for 15 grants (high: $25,000;
low: $5,000).
Purpose and activities: Giving primarily for the
purpose of improving and constructing buildings for
various organizations in Potter and Randall
counties, Texas.

Fields of interest: Museums; Historic preservation;
Education; Hospital care; Television; Human
services; Food banks.
Type of support: Capital campaigns; Building and
renovations.
Limitations: Applications accepted. Giving primarily
in Potter and Randall counties, TX. No grants to
individuals.
Application information: Application form required.
  Initial approach: Letter
  Copies of proposal: 8
  Deadline(s): None
Officers: William T. Ware, Pres.; Benjamin
Whttenburg, V.P.; Andrew Mitchell, Secy.; George
Raffkind, Treas.
Directors: Louise Ross; Edward R. Scott, Jr.
Number of staff: 1 part-time professional.
EIN: 752859752

8698
AMD Foundation, Inc.
7171 Southwest Pkwy., MS 100.3
Austin, TX   78735-8953
Contact: Kristi Fontenot
E-mail: amd.foundation@amd.com; Main
URL: http://www.amd.com/en-us/who-we-are/
corporate-responsibility/community/foundation
AMD Changing the Game on Facebook: http://
www.facebook.com/AMDChangingTheGame?ref=ts

Donor: Advanced Micro Devices, Inc.
Foundation type: Company-sponsored foundation.
Financial data (yr. ended 12/31/13): Assets,
$22,912 (M); gifts received, $15,000;
expenditures, $234,931; qualifying distributions,
$234,931; giving activities include $75,453 for 1
grant, and $159,478 for employee matching gifts.
Purpose and activities: The foundation supports
programs designed to provide future generations
with critical science, technology, engineering, and
mathematics (STEM) skills and life skills.
Fields of interest: Education; Higher education;
Science; Technology; Engineering; Mathematics;
Disasters and emergency management; Human
services; Youth services.
International interests: Asia; Canada; China; India;
Malaysia; Singapore; Taiwan.
Type of support: General support; Employee
volunteer services; Program development;
Employee matching gifts.
Limitations: Applications accepted. Giving primarily
in areas of company operations in San Jose and
Silicon Valley, CA, Ft. Collins, CO, Orlando, FL,
Boston, MA, Portland, OR, Austin, TX, and Bellevue,
WA, and in Beijing, Shanghai, and Suzhou, China,
Toronto, Canada, Bangalore and Hyderabad, India,
Cyberjaya and Penang, Malaysia, Singapore, and
Taipei, Taiwan.
Publications: Application guidelines.
Application information:
  Initial approach: E-mail foundation for AMD
    Changing the Game
  Deadline(s): None for AMD Changing the Game
Officers and Directors: Alex Brown, Chair.; J.
Michael Woollems, Vice-Chair.; Allyson W. Peerman,
Pres.; Devinder Kumar, Treas.; Ben Bar-Haim;
Robert Feldstein; Annie Flaig; Thomas Seifert; Leslie
Sobon; Kathleen Woodhouse.
EIN: 711036553

8699
American Airlines Foundation
(also known as AMR)
P.O. Box 619616, MD5656
DFW Airport, TX   75261-9616
Contact: Tiana Saenz
E-mail for Tiana Saenz: Tiana.Saenz@aa.com

Foundation type: Independent foundation.
Financial data (yr. ended 12/31/12): Assets,
$587,946 (M); gifts received, $219,123;
expenditures, $341,730; qualifying distributions,
$260,000; giving activities include $260,000 for 4
grants (high: $75,000; low: $35,000).
Fields of interest: Health; Human services;
Children.
Limitations: Applications accepted. Giving primarily
in CA.
Application information: Application form required.
  Initial approach: Letter
  Deadline(s): None
Officers and Directors: Thomas W. Horton, Pres.
and Director; Andrew M. Backover, V.P. and Director;
Kenneth W. Wimberly, Secy. and Director; Peter M.
Warlick, Treas.
EIN: 752086656

8700
American Campus Charities Foundation
12700 Hill Country Blvd., Ste. T-2
Austin, TX   78738

Established in 2006 in Texas.
Donors: Locke, Liddell & Sapp, LLP; Glast, Phillips
& Murray; Merrill Lynch; GPS Construction Services,
LLC; KeyBank Capital Markets; Apex Construction;
Davis Brothers Construction; Hardison Downey
Kitchell; University Loft Co.; Faver Gray; Hunter
Roberts Construction; Ryan Reid; RBC Capital
Markets; Community Bank of Texas; Hardman
Signs; Morley Group, Inc.; American Campus
Communities Services, Inc.; Bank of America Merrill
Lynch; American Campus Communities Services,
Inc.
Foundation type: Company-sponsored foundation.
Financial data (yr. ended 12/31/13): Assets,
$755,180 (M); gifts received, $323,334;
expenditures, $357,088; qualifying distributions,
$226,312; giving activities include $220,776 for 16
grants (high: $75,000; low: $35).
Purpose and activities: The foundation supports
nonprofit organizations involved with arts,
education, and youth development.
Fields of interest: Arts and culture; Education; Youth
development.
Limitations: Applications not accepted. Giving
primarily in Washington, DC, and Austin, TX. No
grants to individuals.
Application information: Unsolicited requests for
funds not accepted.
Officers: William Bayless, Pres.; Greg Dowell, V.P.;
Jonathan Graf, Secy.
EIN: 743061377

8701
American Community Trust
4514 Cole Ave., Ste. 405
Dallas, TX   75205-4100

Donors: Carol Barger; Ed Nance; The Nancy Morre
Marwill 1996 CRT #2.

Foundation type: Independent foundation.
Financial data (yr. ended 12/31/13): Assets, $3,327,851 (M); gifts received, $2,368,618; expenditures, $326,338; qualifying distributions, $317,407; giving activities include $310,116 for 8 grants (high: $215,192; low: $2,500).
Fields of interest: Arts and culture; Education; Domesticated animals.
Limitations: Applications not accepted.
Application information: Unsolicited requests for funds not accepted.
Trustees: William D. Elliott; William M. Marsh.
EIN: 752791649

8702
Amherst Foundation
5001 Plaza on the Lake Dr., No. 200
Austin, TX 78746-1053

Donor: Amherst Holdings LLC.
Foundation type: Independent foundation.
Financial data (yr. ended 12/31/13): Assets, $26,478 (M); gifts received, $353,007; expenditures, $432,526; qualifying distributions, $432,526; giving activities include $430,774 for 44 grants (high: $100,000; low: $75).
Fields of interest: Arts and culture; Education; Diseases and conditions.
Limitations: Applications not accepted.
Application information: Unsolicited requests for funds not accepted.
Directors: Sean Dobson; Michael Sullivan; Roxann Taylor.
EIN: 451559309

8703
AMR/American Airlines Foundation
P.O. Box 619616, MD5656
DFW Airport, TX 75261-9616

Established in 1985 in Texas.
Donors: AMR Corp.; Flagship Charities; Chicago Charities.
Foundation type: Company-sponsored foundation.
Financial data (yr. ended 12/31/13): Assets, $662,660 (M); gifts received, $320,552; expenditures, $123,022; qualifying distributions, $291,366; giving activities include $150,500 for 4 grants (high: $45,000; low: $20,000).
Purpose and activities: The foundation supports organizations involved with health, pediatrics, human services, and children.
Fields of interest: Health; Patient social services; Health care clinics; Pediatrics; Family services; Senior services; Children; Low-income and poor people.
Type of support: General support.
Limitations: Applications accepted. Giving primarily in areas of company operations, with emphasis on CA and Fort Worth, TX; giving also to regional and national organizations. No support for discriminatory organizations, religious, fraternal, social, or veterans' organizations, political or partisan organizations or candidates, or lobbying organizations. No grants to individuals, or for endowments, annual campaigns, basic academic or scientific research, athletic events or sponsorships, or social functions or advertising; generally, no multi-year grants.
Application information: Application form required.

Initial approach: Letter
Deadline(s): None
Officers and Directors: Kenneth W. Wimberly, Secy. and Director; Peter M. Warlick, Treas.; Bernie Willet, Fdn. Mgr. and Director.
EIN: 762086656

8704
Josephine Anderson Charitable Trust
P.O. Box 1
Amarillo, TX 79105-0001 (806) 378-8376
Contact: Jacque Branch, V.P. and Trust Officer

Donor: Josephine Anderson†.
Foundation type: Independent foundation.
Financial data (yr. ended 02/28/15): Assets, $8,040,828 (M); expenditures, $523,769; qualifying distributions, $470,060; giving activities include $429,000 for 69 grants (high: $15,000; low: $500).
Purpose and activities: Giving primarily for the arts, education, health care, Christian agencies and churches, and children, youth, and social services.
Fields of interest: Arts and culture; Performing arts; Education; Elementary and secondary education; Higher education; Health; Hospital care; Diseases and conditions; Christianity; Human services; Family services; Child welfare.
Type of support: General support; Capital and infrastructure.
Limitations: Applications accepted. Giving primarily in the TX Panhandle, with emphasis on Amarillo. No grants to individuals.
Application information:
Initial approach: Letter
Deadline(s): None
Trustee: Amarillo National Bank.
EIN: 751469596

8705
Robert A. and Kathey K. Anderson Foundation
10100 Reunion Pl., Ste. 635
San Antonio, TX 78216-4128 (210) 377-0669
Contact: Robert A. Anderson, Pres.

Established in 2001 in Texas.
Donor: Robert A. Anderson.
Foundation type: Independent foundation.
Financial data (yr. ended 08/31/13): Assets, $6,995,825 (M); expenditures, $327,873; qualifying distributions, $307,450; giving activities include $307,450 for 46 grants (high: $74,000; low: $500).
Fields of interest: Higher education; Protestantism; Human services.
Type of support: General support.
Limitations: Applications accepted. Giving primarily in TX, with emphasis on San Antonio. No grants to individuals.
Application information: Application form required.
Initial approach: Proposal
Deadline(s): None
Officers: Robert A. Anderson, Pres.; Kathey K. Anderson, V.P.; Thomas L. Keller, Secy.-Treas.
EIN: 743015784

8706
The Aragona Family Foundation
(formerly The Sandra and Joseph Aragona Family Foundation)
3311 Westlake Dr.
Austin, TX 78746-1901 (512) 328-2178
Contact: Joseph C. Aragona, Pres.

Established in 1997 in Texas.
Donors: Joseph C. Aragona; Sandra R. Aragona; Kenneth DeAngelis.
Foundation type: Independent foundation.
Financial data (yr. ended 12/31/12): Assets, $638,340 (M); gifts received, $500; expenditures, $235,186; qualifying distributions, $219,156; giving activities include $161,947 for 13 grants (high: $71,075; low: $430).
Fields of interest: Elementary and secondary education; Higher education; Foundations; Human services.
Type of support: General support.
Limitations: Giving primarily in Austin, TX.
Application information:
Deadline(s): None
Officers: Joseph C. Aragona, Pres.; Sandra R. Aragona, V.P.; Chris Earthman, Exec. Dir.
Director: Jeffrey C. Garvey.
EIN: 742833147

8707
The Arena Energy Foundation
4200 Research Forest Dr., Ste. 500
The Woodlands, TX 77381-4224

Donors: Don Metz; Larry Hoelscher; Arena Energy, LLC; William Companies, Inc.
Foundation type: Independent foundation.
Financial data (yr. ended 12/31/13): Assets, $6,662 (M); expenditures, $144,095; qualifying distributions, $141,867; giving activities include $141,867 for 31 grants (high: $20,000; low: $400).
Fields of interest: Health; Child abuse; Human services; Child welfare.
Limitations: Applications not accepted. Giving primarily in LA, MI and TX. No grants to individuals.
Application information: Unsolicited requests for funds not accepted.
Directors: Renee Kelly; Don Metz; Jane C. Minarovic; Jennifer Stone.
EIN: 261636123

8708
The Terry and Regina Armstrong Family Charitable Foundation
1826 N. Loop, 1604 W., Ste. 260
San Antonio, TX 78248-4531 2104027200

Donors: Terry Armstrong; Regina Armstrong.
Foundation type: Independent foundation.
Financial data (yr. ended 12/31/14): Assets, $5,281,781; gifts received, $0; expenditures, $319,895; qualifying distributions, $260,000 and $0 for set-asides.
Fields of interest: Education; Diseases and conditions; Human services.
Limitations: Applications not accepted. Giving primarily in NY and TX.
Application information: Unsolicited requests for funds not accepted.

Directors: Lisa Renee Armstrong; Cheryl Lynn Armstrong Remmert.
EIN: 274252565

8709
The H. G. Ash Foundation
13519 Kingsride Ln.
Houston, TX 77079-3432

Established in 2001 in Oklahoma.
Donors: Henry G. Ash; AG Equipment Co., Inc.; H. Grady Ash.
Foundation type: Independent foundation.
Financial data (yr. ended 12/31/13): Assets, $5,485,992 (M); expenditures, $464,891; qualifying distributions, $343,650; giving activities include $343,650 for 39 grants (high: $25,000; low: $1,000).
Fields of interest: Foundations; Health care administration and financing; Hospital care; Christianity; Sports and recreation; Youth development.
Type of support: General support.
Limitations: Applications not accepted. Giving primarily in TX; some funding also in Tulsa, OK. No grants to individuals.
Application information: Unsolicited requests for funds not accepted.
Officer: Stephen C. Ash, Mgr.
EIN: 731614119

8710
Nina Heard Astin Charitable Trust
c/o Wells Fargo Bank, N.A., Trust Dept.
P.O. Box 913
Bryan, TX 77805-0913
E-mail: grantadministration@wellsfargo.com;
Application address: c/o Wells Fargo Bank, N.A., Trust Dept., 3000 Briarcrest, Bryan, TX 77805, tel.: (979) 776-3267; Main URL: https://www.wellsfargo.com/privatefoundationgrants/astin
Scholarship application addresses: c/o Bryan High School Counselors, 3401 E. 29th St., Bryan, TX 77802, tel.: (979) 774-3276; c/o A&M Consolidated High School, 701 West Loop S., Bryan, TX 77840, tel.: (979) 696-0544

Established in 1975 in Texas.
Foundation type: Independent foundation.
Financial data (yr. ended 03/31/13): Assets, $7,837,833 (M); expenditures, $338,603; qualifying distributions, $249,136; giving activities include $227,750 for 22 grants (high: $50,000; low: $750).
Purpose and activities: Scholarships limited to graduating seniors attending Bryan High School or A&M Consolidated High School, TX; also giving for the arts, youth services, and Presbyterian agencies and churches.
Fields of interest: Arts and culture; Education; Nonprofits; Health; Diseases and conditions; Protestantism.
Type of support: General support; Program development; Student aid; Regranting.
Limitations: Applications accepted. Giving primarily in TX.
Application information: Application form required for scholarships.
Initial approach: Letter
Deadline(s): May 1 for scholarships; no set deadline for other grant proposals

Trustee: Wells Fargo Bank, N.A.
EIN: 741721901

8711
Astri Foundation
11777 Katy Freeway, Ste. 470
Houston, TX 77079-1785

Established in 2007 in Texas.
Donors: Hyatt Shipping Company, Inc.; Samson Lone Star, Ltd.; Martin Mosvold†; Jerald Whitten; Kandara Investment, Ltd.; Bob Wilson; Joyce Whitten; Open It; Gunnar Skarbovik; Kenneth Torsoe; Word of Life Armenia; Jerald Witten Investments.
Foundation type: Independent foundation.
Financial data (yr. ended 12/31/13): Assets, $39,872 (M); gifts received, $213,636; expenditures, $291,323; qualifying distributions, $289,228; giving activities include $289,228 for 11 grants (high: $95,000; low: $4,500).
Fields of interest: Housing development; Christianity; Human services; Children.
International interests: Armenia; Mozambique; Norway; South Africa; Sri Lanka; Sweden.
Limitations: Applications not accepted. Giving primarily in Armenia, Sofia, Bulgaria, Mozambique, Norway, South Africa, Sri Lanka, and Sweden; some funding also in the U.S., particularly in TX.
Application information: Unsolicited requests for funds not accepted.
Officers and Directors: Astri Mosvold, V.P.; Paul Mosvold, V.P. and Director; Torrey Mosvold, V.P. and Director; Bobby O'Neal, Secy.-Treas. and Director.
EIN: 450576135

8712
The Marilyn Augur Family Foundation
(formerly The Marilyn Augur Foundation)
6060 N. Central Expy., Ste. 616
Dallas, TX 75206-5236
Contact: Tracey Frattaroli, Exec. Dir.
FAX: (214) 526-0253; E-mail: maff@maugur.com;
Main URL: http://www.maugur.org

Established in 1990 in Texas.
Donor: Marilyn H. Augur.
Foundation type: Independent foundation.
Financial data (yr. ended 12/31/13): Assets, $7,010,092 (M); expenditures, $336,325; qualifying distributions, $263,329; giving activities include $147,938 for 67 grants (high: $25,000; low: $100).
Purpose and activities: Giving primarily for basic human needs (defined by the MAFF Board as food, shelter, clothing, health, and education aimed at transforming lives of those living in poverty or prison). The foundation funds non-profits which provide services for those who are economically, physically, emotionally and spiritually needy as it seeks to accomplish the mission stated in Matthew 25:35-40.
Fields of interest: Hospital care; Christianity; Human services; Child welfare.
Type of support: General support; Continuing support; Annual campaigns; Capital campaigns; Emergency funds; Program development; Scholarships.
Limitations: Applications not accepted. Giving primarily in Dallas, TX. No support for arts and culture. No grants to individuals.

Application information: Unsolicited requests for funds not accepted. Check foundation web site for updates.
Board meeting date(s): Spring and fall
Officers and Trustees: Marilyn H. Augur, Pres. and Trustee; Nancy Elizabeth Roberts, V.P.; Elizabeth T. Jones Turner, V.P. and Trustee; P. Mike McCullough, Secy. and Trustee; Margaret M. Augur Hancock, Treas. and Trustee; Tracey Frattaroli, Exec. Dir.
Number of staff: 1 part-time support.
EIN: 752358239

8713
The B.E.L.I.E.F. Foundation
(formerly Janet Jarie Jensen Foundation)
130 E. John Carpenter Fwy.
Irving, TX 75062-2708   (972) 999-4564
FAX: (972) 999-4568;
E-mail: info@thebelieffoundation.com; Main URL: http://www.thebelieffoundation.org
Grants List: http://www.thebelieffoundation.org/recipients.php

Established in 1997 in Texas.
Donor: Janet Jarie Jensen.
Foundation type: Independent foundation.
Financial data (yr. ended 12/31/13): Assets, $9,206,978 (M); expenditures, $291,938; qualifying distributions, $164,876; giving activities include $139,380 for 5 grants (high: $74,380; low: $5,000).
Purpose and activities: The philosophy of the B.E.L.I.E.F. Foundation's Scholarship Program is to give financial assistance to deserving college, vocational or technical school students as well as provide encouragement and support to the students and their families.
Fields of interest: Education; Higher education; Adolescents.
Type of support: Scholarships; Individual development.
Limitations: Applications not accepted. Giving limited to 22 zip codes within the Dallas, TX area. No grants to individuals.
Application information: Contributes only to pre-selected organizations. Scholarship applicants refer to foundation web site.
Trustee: Janet Jarie Jensen.
EIN: 752707934

8714
Sylvan T. Baer Foundation
c/o Bank of America, N.A.
P.O. Box 831041
Dallas, TX 75283-1041
Application Address: c/o Sylvan T. Baer Trust Comm., 7800 Northaven Rd. , Ste. A, Dallas, TX, 75230-3226

Foundation type: Independent foundation.
Financial data (yr. ended 01/31/14): Assets, $3,649,887 (M); expenditures, $192,656; qualifying distributions, $170,769; giving activities include $154,503 for 24 grants (high: $49,312; low: $472).
Purpose and activities: Giving primarily for Jewish organizations.
Fields of interest: Education; Judaism; Human services.
Limitations: Applications accepted. Giving primarily in the greater metropolitan Dallas, TX, area.

Application information: Application form required.
Initial approach: Proposal
Deadline(s): Apr. 30 and Sept. 30
Trustee: Bank of America, N.A.
EIN: 756044967

8715
The Baldridge Foundation
4925 Greenville, Ste. 1050
Dallas, TX 75206

Established in 2004 in Texas.
Donor: Jerald T. Baldridge.
Foundation type: Independent foundation.
Financial data (yr. ended 12/31/13): Assets,
$1,282,949 (M); expenditures, $397,699;
qualifying distributions, $395,881; giving activities
include $395,881 for 46 grants (high: $80,000;
low: $250).
Fields of interest: Museums; Humanities; Reading
promotion; Public policy; Human services;
International relations; International development.
Type of support: General support; Policy, advocacy
and systems reform.
Limitations: Applications not accepted. Giving
primarily in New York, NY, and Dallas, TX.
Application information: Contributes only to
pre-selected organizations.
Officers and Directors: Jerald T. Baldridge, Pres.
and Treas. and Director; Emily Z. Baldridge, V.P. and
Secy. and Director; Jeffrey Turner Baldridge;
Kimberly Baldridge Solomon.
EIN: 201806185

8716
The Ballard Foundation
4403 Perdido Bay
Katy, TX 77450-8656 (281) 451-2351

Donor: Triumph MC LP.
Foundation type: Independent foundation.
Financial data (yr. ended 12/31/13): Assets,
$9,739,235 (M); expenditures, $402,132;
qualifying distributions, $2,520,073; giving
activities include $169,780 for 9 grants (high:
$112,000; low: $100).
Fields of interest: Education; Health; Community
and economic development.
Limitations: Applications not accepted. Giving
primarily in TX. No grants to individuals.
Application information: Unsolicited requests for
funds not accepted.
Directors: Edwin Lee Ballard; Rachel Maria Ballard;
Duval Meade McDaniels.
EIN: 454077080

8717
The Barnabas Fund, Inc
4710 Northaven Rd.
Dallas, TX 75229-4227

Established in 2010 in Texas.
Donors: Cinthia Brinker Simmons; William Brinker
Simmons.
Foundation type: Independent foundation.
Financial data (yr. ended 12/31/13): Assets,
$119,752 (M); gifts received, $135,000;
expenditures, $218,311; qualifying distributions,
$218,285; giving activities include $215,325 for 46
grants (high: $105,700; low: $100).

Fields of interest: Education; Christianity; Human
services.
Limitations: Applications not accepted. Giving
primarily in Dallas, TX.
Application information: Unsolicted requests for
funds not accepted.
Directors: Cinthia Brinker Simmons; Betty Lovell;
George Edward Seay III; William Brinker Simmons.
EIN: 271491108

8718
Louis & Madlyn Barnett Family Foundation
P.O. Box 11739
Fort Worth, TX 76110-0739 (817) 921-0165
Contact: Laurie B. Werner, Tr.

Established in 1966 in Texas.
Donors: Louis Barnett; Madlyn Barnett.
Foundation type: Independent foundation.
Financial data (yr. ended 12/31/13): Assets,
$1,302,986 (M); expenditures, $194,749;
qualifying distributions, $182,447; giving activities
include $182,447 for 3 grants (high: $161,962;
low: $1).
Fields of interest: Higher education; Nonprofits.
Type of support: Regranting.
Limitations: Applications accepted. Giving primarily
in MA and NY. No grants to individuals.
Application information:
Initial approach: Proposal
Deadline(s): None
Trustees: Eliot B. Barnett; Louis H. Barnett; Laurie
B. Werner.
EIN: 751855078

8719
Barrow Foundation
P.O. Box 2510
Rockport, TX 78381-2510

Established in 1952 in Texas.
Donor: Nellie Dell Barrow‡.
Foundation type: Independent foundation.
Financial data (yr. ended 12/31/13): Assets,
$6,636,997 (M); expenditures, $349,403;
qualifying distributions, $286,436; giving activities
include $236,000 for 18 grants (high: $30,000;
low: $2,000).
Fields of interest: Arts and culture; Performing arts;
Museums; Higher education.
Limitations: Applications not accepted. Giving
primarily in MA and TX. No grants to individuals.
Application information: Unsolicited requests for
funds not accepted.
Trustees: Roxann Day; Randall E. Kemper; Marvin
H. Seline.
EIN: 746041372

8720
Beaird Family Foundation
18039 Windtop Ln.
Dallas, TX 75287-6659

Established in 2000 in Texas.
Donors: Pat C. Beaird; Colleen C. Beaird; Bosque
River Investments, Ltd.
Foundation type: Independent foundation.
Financial data (yr. ended 12/31/14): Assets,
$614,110 (M); expenditures, $206,428; qualifying

distributions, $206,345; giving activities include
$206,345 for 19 grants (high: $85,835; low: $145).
Fields of interest: Diseases and conditions;
Protestantism; Human services.
Type of support: General support.
Limitations: Applications not accepted. Giving
primarily in Plano, TX; giving also in Dallas. No grants
to individuals.
Application information: Unsolicited requests for
funds not accepted.
Officers and Trustees: Pat C. Beaird, Pres. and
Trustee; Colleen C. Beaird, Mgr. and Trustee;
Morgan E. Beaird.
EIN: 752912647

8721
Bearden Foundation
10510 W. Sam Houston Pkwy. S.
Houston, TX 77099-2848
Application address: c/o Bill Hall, 10460 W. Sam
Houston Pkwy. S., Houston, TX 77099, tel.: (281)
568-4185

Donor: Dennis Bearden.
Foundation type: Independent foundation.
Financial data (yr. ended 10/31/14): Assets,
$3,230,627 (M); expenditures, $207,817;
qualifying distributions, $173,772; giving activities
include $59,680 for 15 grants (high: $35,000; low:
$50), and $114,092 for 22 grants to individuals
(high: $12,250; low: $634).
Purpose and activities: Scholarships are given to
individuals.
Fields of interest: Education; Higher education;
Domesticated animals; Human services.
Type of support: Grants to individuals.
Limitations: Applications accepted. Giving primarily
in TX.
Application information: Application form required.
Initial approach: Letter
Deadline(s): Jun. 30
Officer and Directors: Bill Hall, V.P. and Secy.-Treas.
and Director; Barry Bearden; Dennis Bearden.
EIN: 263710470

8722
Beauchamp Foundation
P.O. Box 272906
Houston, TX 77277-2906

Established in 2000 in Texas.
Donors: Gary V. Beauchamp; Marian Wilfert
Beauchamp.
Foundation type: Independent foundation.
Financial data (yr. ended 12/31/13): Assets,
$6,620,816 (M); gifts received, $1,510,167;
expenditures, $225,016; qualifying distributions,
$175,000; giving activities include $175,000 for 5
grants (high: $50,000; low: $10,000).
Fields of interest: Higher education; Homeless
services.
Limitations: Applications not accepted. Giving
primarily in LA and TX. No grants to individuals.
Application information: Unsolicited requests for
funds not accepted.
Officers: Gary V. Beauchamp, Pres.; Marian Wilfert
Beauchamp, V.P.
EIN: 760663469

8723
Philip Theodore Bee Charitable Trust
5600 W. Lovers Ln., Ste. 116
P.O. Box 136
Dallas, TX   75209-4360

Foundation type: Independent foundation.
Financial data (yr. ended 12/31/13): Assets,
$4,440,548 (M); expenditures, $462,129;
qualifying distributions, $374,221; giving activities
include $349,906 for 51 grants (high: $138,500;
low: $100).
Fields of interest: Education; Health; Agriculture;
Human services.
Limitations: Applications not accepted. Giving
primarily in TX.
Application information: Unsolicited request for
funds not accepted.
Trustees: Jill C. Bee; Ross B. Bee.
EIN: 272006474

8724
The Victor and Anna Mae Beghini
Charitable Foundation
9686 Longmont
Houston, TX   77063-1029

Established in 2004 in Texas.
Donors: Anna Mae Beghini; Victor G. Beghini.
Foundation type: Independent foundation.
Financial data (yr. ended 11/30/13): Assets,
$671,291 (M); gifts received, $155,220;
expenditures, $147,514; qualifying distributions,
$147,500; giving activities include $147,500 for 9
grants (high: $49,000; low: $2,500).
Fields of interest: Philanthropy; Religion;
Christianity; Youth development.
Type of support: General support.
Limitations: Applications not accepted. Giving
primarily in TX.
Application information: Unsolicited requests for
funds not accepted.
Officers: Victor G. Beghini, Pres.; Anna Mae Beghini,
V.P.; John T. Mills, Secy.-Treas.
EIN: 201879154

8725
Behmann Brothers Foundation
P.O. Box 271486
Corpus Christi, TX   78427-1486   (361) 438-1589
Contact: Charles L. Kosarek Jr., Pres.
E-mail: info@behmannbrothersfoundation.org; Main
URL: http://behmannbrothersfoundation.org

Donors: Herman W. Behmann†; Arno W. Behmann†.
Foundation type: Independent foundation.
Financial data (yr. ended 06/30/13): Assets,
$6,798,027 (M); expenditures, $429,347;
qualifying distributions, $321,490; giving activities
include $310,232 for 61 grants (high: $30,000;
low: $250).
Purpose and activities: Giving primarily for
agricultural research and education, schools, youth
groups, health care and service organizations.
Fields of interest: Education; Higher education;
Diseases and conditions; Farmlands; Community
and economic development; Christianity; Human
services; Child welfare.
Type of support: Program development.
Limitations: Applications accepted. Giving limited to
TX, with an emphasis on the counties of Aransas,

Bee, Kleberg, Live Oak, Nueces, San Patricio,
Refugio, and Jim Wells. No support for political
organizations. No grants to individuals.
Application information: See web site for
application policies, guidelines and forms.
Application form required.
  Initial approach: Proposal
  Copies of proposal: 1
  Deadline(s): May 1
  Board meeting date(s): June
  Final notification: June, positive replies only
Officers and Directors: Charles L. Kosarek, Jr.,
Pres. and Director; T. Mark Anderson, V.P. and
Director; Sherry Kosarek, Secy. and Director; Willie
J. Kosarek, Treas. and Director; John Lloyd Bluntzer.
EIN: 742146739

8726
Fox and Monica Benton Foundation
8818 Stable Crest Blvd.
Houston, TX   77024-7034

Established in 2004 in Texas.
Donors: Monica K. Benton; F. Fox Benton III.
Foundation type: Independent foundation.
Financial data (yr. ended 12/31/13): Assets,
$5,520,614 (M); gifts received, $5,950;
expenditures, $217,682; qualifying distributions,
$136,000; giving activities include $136,000 for 1
grant.
Fields of interest: Natural history museums;
Science museums; Zoos.
Limitations: Applications not accepted. Giving
primarily in TX. No grants to individuals.
Application information: Unsolicited requests for
funds not accepted.
Officers and Directors: F. Fox Benton III, Pres. and
Director; Monica K. Benton, Secy. and Director;
Lucia Benton.
EIN: 202034030

8727
The Bergstrom Family Foundation
461 Edgewood Dr.
Montgomery, TX   77356-8428

Established in 1997 in Texas.
Donor: Stephen W. Bergstrom.
Foundation type: Independent foundation.
Financial data (yr. ended 12/31/13): Assets,
$3,358,484 (M); gifts received, $1,000,062;
expenditures, $242,034; qualifying distributions,
$236,285; giving activities include $236,285 for 13
grants (high: $177,085; low: $500).
Purpose and activities: Giving for primarily for higher
education.
Fields of interest: Education; Health; Protestantism.
Limitations: Applications not accepted. No grants to
individuals.
Application information: Unsolicited requests for
funds not accepted.
Officers: Stephen W. Bergstrom, Chair. and Pres.;
Debora Bergstrom, V.P. and Treas.; Wayne
Bergstrom, Secy.
EIN: 760563582

8728
F.M. Bernardin Charitable Trust
c/o Bank of America, N.A.
P.O. Box 831041
Dallas, TX   75283-1041

Foundation type: Independent foundation.
Financial data (yr. ended 12/31/14): Assets,
$4,374,102; expenditures, $237,064; qualifying
distributions, $184,865.
Fields of interest: Arts and culture; Education;
Health.
Limitations: Applications not accepted. Giving
primarily in MO.
Application information: Unsolicited requests for
funds not accepted.
Trustee: Bank of America, N.A.
EIN: 446008545

8729
Bertha Foundation
P.O. Box 1110
Graham, TX   76450-1110   (940) 549-1400

Established in 1967 in Texas.
Donors: E. Bruce Street; M. Boyd Street†.
Foundation type: Independent foundation.
Financial data (yr. ended 12/31/13): Assets,
$7,939,312 (M); expenditures, $404,617;
qualifying distributions, $377,288; giving activities
include $371,901 for 10 grants (high: $155,000;
low: $174).
Purpose and activities: Giving primarily for
charitable and civic causes.
Fields of interest: Education; Hospital care;
Libraries; Public administration; Sports and
recreation; Human services.
Type of support: General support; Capital and
infrastructure; Scholarships.
Limitations: Applications accepted. Giving limited to
Young County, TX. No grants to individuals.
Application information: Application form required.
  Initial approach: Letter
  Deadline(s): None
Officers: Alice Ann Street, Pres.; Joe R. Montgomery,
Secy.-Treas.
Directors: E. Bruce Street, Jr.; Malcolm B. Street,
Jr.; Melissa Street York.
Number of staff: 2 full-time professional.
EIN: 756050023

8730
Bhutada Family Foundation
4018 Westhollow Pkwy.
Houston, TX   77082-4604

Established in 2005 in Texas.
Donors: Rishi Bhutada; Ramesh Bhutada.
Foundation type: Independent foundation.
Financial data (yr. ended 12/31/13): Assets,
$1,934,999 (M); expenditures, $202,238;
qualifying distributions, $198,867; giving activities
include $155,102 for 10 grants (high: $46,001;
low: $500).
Fields of interest: Education; Religion; Hinduism;
Human services.
International interests: India.
Type of support: General support.
Limitations: Applications not accepted. Giving in the
U.S., with emphasis on TX. No grants to individuals.

Application information: Unsolicited requests for funds not accepted.
Officers: Ramesh Bhutada, Pres.; Kiren Bhutada, V.P.; Rishi Bhutada, Secy.
EIN: 202051596

8731
David E. Bloxom, Sr. Foundation
305 N.E. Loop 820, Ste. 109
Hurst, TX   76053-7211

Established in 1999 in Texas.
Donor: David E. Bloxom.
Foundation type: Independent foundation.
Financial data (yr. ended 12/31/14): Assets, $7,155,839; expenditures, $975,581; qualifying distributions, $314,910.
Fields of interest: Higher education; Nonprofits; Religion; Christianity; Protestantism; Human services.
Type of support: General support; Regranting.
Limitations: Applications not accepted. Giving primarily in TX.
Application information: Contributes only to pre-selected organizations.
Directors: Bonnie D. Dowdy; Darrell Lester; Lynn Ross, Jr.
EIN: 752793902

8732
Bodhi Foundation
9701B Solana Vista Loop
Austin, TX   78750-8539

Established in 1998 in Texas.
Donor: David Lunsford.
Foundation type: Independent foundation.
Financial data (yr. ended 06/30/12): Assets, $0 (M); gifts received, $100,000; expenditures, $168,994; qualifying distributions, $156,689; giving activities include $156,689 for 5 grants (high: $80,000; low: $189).
Fields of interest: Foundations; Buddhism; Family services.
Limitations: Applications not accepted. Giving primarily in CA, OR and TX.
Application information: Unsolicited requests for funds not accepted.
Officers and Directors: David Lunsford, Pres.; Sherri Matthews, V.P. and Director; Christina Mendoza, Secy.-Treas.
Number of staff: 2 full-time professional; 1 part-time professional.
EIN: 742890569

8733
Boeing Company Charitable Trust
c/o Bank of America, N.A.
P.O. Box 831041
Dallas, TX   75283-1041   (312) 544-2071
Contact: Bridget Sweeney-Renzulli
Application contact: 100 N. Riverside Plaza, Chicago, IL 60606, tel.: (312) 544-2071

Established in 1952 in Washington.
Donor: The Boeing Co.
Foundation type: Company-sponsored foundation.
Financial data (yr. ended 12/31/13): Assets, $65,294,977 (L); expenditures, $887,726; qualifying distributions, $516,106; giving activities

include $400,000 for 3 grants (high: $150,000; low: $125,000).
Purpose and activities: The foundation supports organizations involved with arts and culture, education, the environment, health, employment, human services, community development, science, civic affairs, and economically disadvantaged people.
Fields of interest: Arts and culture; Visual arts; Performing arts; Education; Elementary and secondary education; Early childhood education; Education services; Reading promotion; Environment; Climate change; Natural resources; Recycling; Health; Science; Mathematics; Public affairs; Public administration; Community and economic development; Sustainable development; Green building; Employment; Job training; Financial counseling; Business and industry; Human rights; Human services; Parent education; Low-income and poor people.
Type of support: Building and renovations; In-kind gifts; Matching grants; Equipment; Emergency funds; Program development; Seed money; Curriculum development; Research; Sponsorships; Equal access.
Limitations: Applications accepted. Giving on a national and international basis in areas of company operations, with emphasis on WA. No support for political candidates or organizations, religious organizations not of direct benefit to the entire community, athletic groups, hospitals, school-affiliated orchestras, bands, choirs, or drama groups. No grants to individuals, or for adoption services, memorials, endowments, travel, walk-a-thons, athletic events (except for Special Olympics), door prizes or raffles, medical research, school-affiliated trips, yearbooks, or class parties, general operating support, fundraising events or activities, advertising, t-shirts, giveaways or promotional items, documentary films or books, debt reduction, dissertations or student research projects, loans, scholarships, fellowships, gifts, honoraria, gratuities, or capital campaigns for rental properties.
Publications: Application guidelines; Annual report (including application guidelines); Program policy statement.
Application information: Application form required.
Initial approach: See website for application form
Deadline(s): See website for deadline
Trustee: Bank of America, N.A.
EIN: 916056738

8734
Dorothy M. Booth Charitable Trust
c/o Bank of America, N.A.
P.O. Box 831041
Dallas, TX   75283-1041

Established in 1988 in California.
Donor: Dorothy M. Booth Living Trust.
Foundation type: Independent foundation.
Financial data (yr. ended 12/31/14): Assets, $1,923,861 (M); expenditures, $181,688; qualifying distributions, $163,894; giving activities include $150,000 for 29 grants (high: $10,000; low: $5,000).
Fields of interest: Health; Diseases and conditions; Human services.
Type of support: Research.
Limitations: Applications not accepted. Giving primarily in CA. No grants to individuals.

Application information: Unsolicited requests for funds not accepted.
Trustees: R. Mac Jacobs; Bank of America, N.A.
EIN: 336051591

8735
Suzanne Deal Booth and David G. Booth Inc.
4107 Lakeplace Ln.
Austin, TX   78746-1623

Donors: Suzanne Deal Booth; David G. Booth.
Foundation type: Independent foundation.
Financial data (yr. ended 01/31/15): Assets, $11,169 (M); expenditures, $421,169; qualifying distributions, $419,834; giving activities include $418,500 for 11 grants (high: $270,000; low: $500).
Fields of interest: Arts and culture; Education; Higher education; Human services.
Limitations: Applications not accepted. Giving primarily in New York, NY, and Austin and Houston, TX.
Application information: Contributes only to pre-selected organizations.
Officers: Suzanne Deal Booth, Pres.; David G. Booth, V.P. and Secy.; Beverly G. Irick, V.P.
EIN: 454364494

8736
Bowers Foundation
P.O. Box 56048
Houston, TX   77256-6048

Established in 1988 in Texas.
Donors: Hugh R. Bowers; Ryn R. Bowers.
Foundation type: Independent foundation.
Financial data (yr. ended 12/31/14): Assets, $4,252,870; expenditures, $229,562; qualifying distributions, $178,983.
Purpose and activities: Giving primarily for education; support also for churches.
Fields of interest: Museums; Education; Higher education; Hospital care; Protestantism; Youth services.
Limitations: Applications not accepted. Giving primarily in TX. No grants to individuals.
Application information: Unsolicited requests for funds not accepted.
Officers: Carin M. Barth, Pres.; Todd F. Barth, V.P. and Co-Treas.; Hugh R. Bowers, V.P. and Co-Treas.
EIN: 760260739

8737
Bowling Family Charitable Foundation
4655 Cohen Ave.
El Paso, TX   79924-4415   (915) 821-3550

Donors: Randall J. Bowling; Robert L. Bowling III; Gregory B. Bowling; Robert L. Bowling IV.
Foundation type: Independent foundation.
Financial data (yr. ended 12/31/14): Assets, $7,556; gifts received, $339,225; expenditures, $337,785; qualifying distributions, $336,867.
Fields of interest: Human services; Youth development.
Limitations: Applications accepted. Giving primarily in El Paso, TX.
Application information: Application form required.

Initial approach: Letter
Deadline(s): None
Officers and Directors: Robert L. Bowling III, Pres. and Director; Gregory B. Bowling, Secy. and Director; Randall J. Bowling, Treas. and Director; Robert L. Bowling IV.
EIN: 272955506

8738
Brass Family Foundation

11 Greenway Plz., Ste. 2950
Houston, TX   77046-1107

Established in 2008 in Texas.
Donors: Michael Mithoff; Ned Davenport; Mithoff Family Foundation; Ernest Scalamandre; Matthew Johnson; Joseph Mattingly; Lou Anne Kellman; Philip Laak; Brad Scott; Lester Smith; Gulf Coast Asphalt Company; Chris Wilbratte.
Foundation type: Independent foundation.
Financial data (yr. ended 12/31/13): Assets, $197,377 (M); gifts received, $510,000; expenditures, $389,349; qualifying distributions, $387,036; giving activities include $386,779 for 7 grants (high: $343,279; low: $2,500).
Fields of interest: Arts and culture; Health; Diseases and conditions.
Limitations: Applications not accepted. Giving primarily in TX. No grants to individuals.
Application information: Unsolicited requests for funds not accepted.
Officers and Directors: Catherine M. Brass, Pres. and Treas. and Director; Arthur J. Brass, V.P. and Secy. and Director; Joyce Brass.
EIN: 263882953

8739
Meta Alice Keith Bratten Foundation

P.O. Box 707
Fort Worth, TX   76101-0707   (817) 924-4134

Foundation type: Independent foundation.
Financial data (yr. ended 12/31/14): Assets, $25,373,396; gifts received, $0; expenditures, $289,320; qualifying distributions, $1,213,351.
Fields of interest: Religion; Sports and recreation; Human services.
Limitations: Applications accepted. Giving primarily in TX.
Application information: Application form required.
Initial approach: Letter
Deadline(s): None
Officers: Adelaide Leavens, Pres.; Joann Means, Secy.; Elaine Petrus, Treas.
EIN: 261338655

8740
Thelma Braun & Bocklett Family Foundation

c/o Bank of America N.A
P.O. Box 831041
Dallas, TX   75283-1041   (214) 209-2396
Contact: Kelly Donohue
E-mail: kim.m.igoe-kasper@ustrust.comtx.philanthropic@ustrust.com; Application Address: c/o Bank of America Attn; Kelly Donhue, 901 Main St.Fl. 19, Dallas TX 75202; Main URL: http://www.bankofamerica.com/grantmaking

Established in 2001 in Texas.

Donor: Thelma Braun†.
Foundation type: Independent foundation.
Financial data (yr. ended 05/31/14): Assets, $3,645,861 (M); expenditures, $191,885; qualifying distributions, $167,611; giving activities include $130,900 for 14 grants (high: $25,000; low: $4,400).
Purpose and activities: To support and promote quality education, cultural, human services, and health care programming for underserved populations.
Fields of interest: Arts and culture; Education; Youth development.
Limitations: Applications accepted. Giving primarily in Grayson County, TX. No grants to individuals.
Application information: Application guidelines available on foundation web site.
Initial approach: Letter
Copies of proposal: 6
Deadline(s): Feb. 1 and Aug. 1
Final notification: May 31 or Nov. 30
Trustee: Bank of America, N.A.
EIN: 527186004

8741
Brentwood Foundation

3198 Parkwood Blvd., Ste. 11076
Frisco, TX   75034-9518

Donors: Thomas Teague; Syd Teague; George Allen; Holt Lunsford; Michael Ording; Elizabeth Ording; Donal Berg.
Foundation type: Independent foundation.
Financial data (yr. ended 12/31/14): Assets, $43,503; gifts received, $32,050; expenditures, $293,824; qualifying distributions, $157,550.
Fields of interest: Christianity; Human services.
Limitations: Applications not accepted. Giving primarily in TX. No grants to individuals.
Application information: Contributes only to pre-selected organizations.
Officer: Michael G. Jaccar, Pres.
Director: Thomas Teague.
EIN: 752032865

8742
The Bridge Foundation, Inc.

c/o Bruce Petty
201 Main St., Ste. 600
Fort Worth, TX   76102-3110   (817) 339-1156
Contact: Marguerite M. Gordon, Pres.

Donor: Anna Melissa Gordon.
Foundation type: Independent foundation.
Financial data (yr. ended 12/31/13): Assets, $10,038,692 (M); expenditures, $437,909; qualifying distributions, $420,000; giving activities include $420,000 for 3 grants (high: $315,000; low: $5,000).
Fields of interest: Animal welfare.
Limitations: Giving in the U.S., with emphasis on NM and VA. No grants to individuals.
Application information:
Initial approach: Letter
Deadline(s): None
Officers: Marguerite M. Gordon, Pres.; Anna Melissa Gordon, V.P. and Treas.; Bruce Petty, Secy.
EIN: 850476426

8743
Charles & Lois Marie Bright Foundation

P.O. Box 635001
Nacogdoches, TX   75963-5001   (936) 564-8378
Contact: Billy J. Earley, Pres.

Established in 1997 in Texas.
Donors: Charles R. Bright; Billy Earley.
Foundation type: Independent foundation.
Financial data (yr. ended 09/30/14): Assets, $26,975,055 (M); gifts received, $22,718,817; expenditures, $530,339; qualifying distributions, $217,491; giving activities include $213,681 for 10 grants (high: $101,500; low: $100).
Fields of interest: Education; Higher education; Public affairs; Religion.
Limitations: Applications accepted. Giving primarily in TX.
Application information:
Initial approach: Proposal
Deadline(s): None
Officers: Billy J. Earley, Pres.; Greg Williams, V.P.
Directors: Stanley Jones; John Mast.
EIN: 752717755

8744
Brisley Scholarship Loan Fund

(formerly Ella Frances Brisley & Noma Brisley Phillips Scholarship Loan Fund)
c/o Bank of America, N.A.
P.O. Box 831041
Dallas, TX   75283-1041
Application address: c/o Bank of America, N.A., Attn.: Maria Botelho, 111 Westminster St., Providence, RI 02903, tel.: (401) 278-6039

Established in 1984 in Missouri.
Foundation type: Independent foundation.
Financial data (yr. ended 02/28/13): Assets, $2,747,033 (M); expenditures, $358,274; qualifying distributions, $325,036; giving activities include $310,600 for 10 grants (high: $52,500; low: $400).
Purpose and activities: Scholarships limited to needy medical and nursing students attending Methodist colleges.
Fields of interest: Education; Health; Religion.
Type of support: Scholarships; Student aid.
Limitations: Applications accepted. Giving primarily to American-born residents of KS and MO.
Application information: Applications should be filed directly with financial aid office or school committee. The application consists of a standard form provided by the school. Application form required.
Initial approach: Proposal
Deadline(s): None
Trustee: Bank of America, N.A.
EIN: 431343600

8745
George K. & Eleanor J. Broady Family Opportunity Foundation

751 Canyon Dr., Ste. 100
Coppell, TX   75019-3857
Contact: George K. Broady, Dir.

Established in 1997 in Texas.
Donor: George K. Broady.
Foundation type: Independent foundation.

Financial data (yr. ended 12/31/13): Assets, $12,460 (M); gifts received, $52,235; expenditures, $219,387; qualifying distributions, $217,542; giving activities include $217,542 for 12 grants to individuals (high: $71,000; low: $1,500).
Purpose and activities: Scholarship awards to high school graduates from Dallas, Texas.
Fields of interest: Higher education.
Type of support: Student aid.
Limitations: Applications not accepted. Giving limited to residents of Dallas, TX.
Application information: Contributes only to pre-selected organizations.
Director: George K. Broady.
EIN: 752739287

8746
Raymond & Susan Brochstein Foundation
407 Thamer Cir.
Houston, TX 77024-6918

Donors: Raymond D. Brochstein; Susan Brochstein.
Foundation type: Independent foundation.
Financial data (yr. ended 12/31/14): Assets, $1,970,550 (M); expenditures, $181,638; qualifying distributions, $169,067; giving activities include $167,905 for 8 grants (high: $135,000; low: $825).
Fields of interest: Music; Art museums; Education; Higher education; Graduate and professional education; Cancers; Judaism; Human services.
Type of support: General support.
Limitations: Applications not accepted. Giving limited to Houston, TX. No grants to individuals.
Application information: Contributes only to pre-selected organizations.
Trustees: Raymond D. Brochstein; Susan Brochstein.
EIN: 760039176

8747
The Brodsky Foundation
c/o Donald W. Brodsky
1000 Louisiana St., Ste. 2000
Houston, TX 77002-5227

Established in 1966 in Texas.
Donors: Alexander E. Brodsky, MD†; Ruth W. Brodsky.
Foundation type: Independent foundation.
Financial data (yr. ended 12/31/13): Assets, $3,400,027 (M); expenditures, $188,149; qualifying distributions, $174,367; giving activities include $172,702 for 103 grants (high: $30,000; low: $50).
Purpose and activities: Giving primarily for Jewish organizations, and for the performing arts.
Fields of interest: Performing arts; Orchestral music; Education; Nonprofits; Health; Judaism; Human services.
Type of support: Regranting.
Limitations: Applications not accepted. Giving primarily in Houston, TX. No grants to individuals.
Application information: Contributes only to pre-selected organizations.
Officers: Ruth W. Brodsky, Pres.; Donald W. Brodsky, V.P. and Secy.-Treas.; James W. Brodsky, MD, V.P.; Ellen Brodsky Gaber, V.P.
Directors: Charles Alexander Brodsky; Gregor Lang Brodsky; Harris Elliot Brodsky; Lela Alexis Brodsky; Leonore Elizabeth Brodsky; Max Emmanuil

Schneidler Brodsky; Alicia Leonore Gaber; Nathan Solman Gaber.
EIN: 746089484

8748
Dr. Leon Bromberg Charitable Trust Fund
2200 Market St., Ste. 710
Galveston, TX 77550-1532 (409) 762-5890
Contact: Charles G. Dibrell III, Chair.

Established in 1985 in Texas.
Donor: Leon Bromberg†.
Foundation type: Independent foundation.
Financial data (yr. ended 04/30/14): Assets, $9,628,532 (M); expenditures, $596,389; qualifying distributions, $396,695; giving activities include $346,820 for 52 grants (high: $100,000; low: $250).
Fields of interest: Education; Health; Religion; Human services.
Type of support: Capital campaigns; Capital and infrastructure; Equipment; Endowments; Emergency funds; Convening; Professorships; Scholarships; Research.
Limitations: Applications accepted. Giving primarily in Austin, Corpus Christi, Galveston, and Houston, TX. No support for private foundations, conduit organizations, or government or tax-supported institutions. No grants to individuals, or for scholarships, operating funds, or debt retirement.
Application information: Application form required.
  Initial approach: Letter
  Copies of proposal: 2
  Deadline(s): None
  Board meeting date(s): 3rd Fri. monthly
Officer and Trustee: Charles G. Dibrell III, Chair. and Trustee.
Number of staff: 1
EIN: 760193007

8749
Guy I. Bromley Trust
c/o Bank of America, N.A.
P.O. Box 831041
Dallas, TX 75283-1041
E-mail: kim.m.igoe-kasper@ustrust.com; Application Address: c/o Bank of America, N.A., P.O. Box 219119, Kansas City, MO 64121-9119; tel.: (816) 292-4300

Established in 1964 in Missouri.
Donor: Guy I. Bromley.
Foundation type: Independent foundation.
Financial data (yr. ended 12/31/13): Assets, $5,664,409 (M); expenditures, $304,793; qualifying distributions, $272,978; giving activities include $234,400 for 16 grants (high: $50,000; low: $100).
Purpose and activities: The trust supports and promotes quality educational, cultural, human services, and health care programming.
Fields of interest: Arts and culture; Higher education; Christianity; Human services; Child welfare.
Type of support: Program development; Seed money.
Limitations: Applications accepted. Giving primarily in Atchison, KS and the greater Kansas City bi-state metropolitan area. No grants to individuals, or for capital campaigns.
Application information:

Initial approach: Letter (not exceeding 3 pages)
Copies of proposal: 2
Deadline(s): None
Trustee: Bank of America, N.A.
EIN: 436157236

8750
Margaret C. B. & S. Spencer N. Brown Foundation Inc.
c/o Extra Co. Trust Services
P.O. Box 6101
Temple, TX 76503-6101

Established in 1983 in Texas.
Donors: Margaret Boyce Brown; S. Spencer Brown, Sr.; National Diversified; Extraco Corp.
Foundation type: Independent foundation.
Financial data (yr. ended 12/31/13): Assets, $3,127,593 (M); gifts received, $4,680; expenditures, $197,003; qualifying distributions, $181,823; giving activities include $178,078 for 79 grants (high: $33,333; low: $100).
Purpose and activities: Giving primarily for education and religion.
Fields of interest: Elementary and secondary education; Religion; Christianity.
Limitations: Applications not accepted. Giving primarily in TX. No grants to individuals; or for fellowships.
Application information: Contributes only to pre-selected organizations.
Trustees: Margaret Boyce Brown; S. Spencer Brown, Jr.; Stanton Boyce Brown; Margaret Brown Lewis; M.Stanton Brown Sattler.
EIN: 746046197

8751
M. K. Brown Foundation, Inc.
P.O. Box 581
Pampa, TX 79066-0581 (806) 669-6890
Contact: Leland W. Waters, Chair.

Established in 1960 in Texas.
Donor: M.K. Brown†.
Foundation type: Independent foundation.
Financial data (yr. ended 12/31/13): Assets, $6,847,358 (M); expenditures, $504,456; qualifying distributions, $409,638; giving activities include $343,500 for 40 grants (high: $41,000; low: $1,250).
Fields of interest: Arts and culture; Education; Nonprofits; Christianity; Human services.
Type of support: Individual development; Regranting.
Limitations: Applications accepted. Giving limited to the TX Panhandle area, with emphasis on Gray and Pampa County, TX. No grants to individuals.
Application information: Application form required.
  Initial approach: Proposal
  Deadline(s): None
Officers: Leland W. Waters, Chair.; Doug Carmichael, Vice. Chair.; J. A. Johnson, Secy.-Treas.
Number of staff: 1 part-time support.
EIN: 756034058

8752
Brownsville Foundation for Health and Education

c/o Wells Fargo
P.O. Box 41629
Austin, TX 78704-9926
Application address: c/o United Way, 634 E. Levee, Brownsville, TX 78520

Foundation type: Independent foundation.
Financial data (yr. ended 05/31/14): Assets, $7,488,184 (M); expenditures, $449,178; qualifying distributions, $3,387,002; giving activities include $387,002 for 27 grants (high: $125,000; low: $1,250).
Purpose and activities: Giving primarily for health care and education.
Fields of interest: Arts and culture; Education; Nonprofits; Health; Public affairs; Human services.
Type of support: Regranting.
Limitations: Applications accepted. Giving primarily in Brownsville, TX.
Application information: Application form required.
  Initial approach: Proposal
  Deadline(s): Jan. 31
Officers: David Garza, Chair.; Renato E. Cardenas, Vice-Chair.; Antonio M. Diaz, MD, Secy.-Treas.
EIN: 741818930

8753
Budd Family Foundation

2615 State St.
Dallas, TX 75204-2632

Donors: Russell W. Budd; Dorothy R. Budd.
Foundation type: Independent foundation.
Financial data (yr. ended 12/31/13): Assets, $3,186,564 (M); expenditures, $265,781; qualifying distributions, $250,000; giving activities include $250,000 for 1 grant.
Fields of interest: Christianity.
Limitations: Applications not accepted. Giving primarily in Dallas, TX.
Application information: Contributes only to pre-selected organizations.
Officers: Russell W. Budd, Chair.; Dorothy R. Budd, Pres.; Charlie McBride, Secy.-Treas.
EIN: 263836252

8754
W. J. & Lela Budwine Foundation, Inc.

P.O. Box 6007
Huntsville, TX 77342-6007

Established in 1997 in Texas.
Donors: Lela Budwine; W.J. Budwine.
Foundation type: Independent foundation.
Financial data (yr. ended 06/30/13): Assets, $5,317,435 (M); expenditures, $300,097; qualifying distributions, $251,400; giving activities include $248,400 for 28 grants (high: $72,500; low: $400).
Fields of interest: Elementary and secondary education; Higher education; Hospital care.
Limitations: Applications not accepted. Giving primarily in TX. No grants to individuals.
Application information: Unsolicited requests for funds not accepted.
Officers: Wayne Budwine, Pres.; Sharon Boudreaux, V.P.
EIN: 760520860

8755
Mary Ellen Kent Bunyard Family Foundation

P.O. Box 271
San Angelo, TX 76902-0271   (325) 658-2728

Donor: Mary Ellen Bunyard†.
Foundation type: Independent foundation.
Financial data (yr. ended 04/30/13): Assets, $10,088,722 (M); gifts received, $175,000; expenditures, $419,181; qualifying distributions, $400,647; giving activities include $392,428 for 12 grants (high: $125,000; low: $5,000).
Fields of interest: Performing arts; Human services; Child welfare.
Limitations: Applications accepted. Giving primarily in San Angelo, TX.
Application information:
  Initial approach: Proposal
  Deadline(s): None
Officers and Directors: William Keith Davis, Pres. and Director; Gus Alexander, V.P. and Director; Wylie O. Webb, Secy.-Treas. and Director.
EIN: 264175604

8756
Burch Family Foundation

784 Drifting Wind Run
Dripping Springs, TX 78620-4463
Contact: Berkely Burch-Martinez, Tr.

Established in 1984 in California.
Donor: Robert D. Burch.
Foundation type: Independent foundation.
Financial data (yr. ended 05/31/13): Assets, $6,865,161 (M); expenditures, $404,368; qualifying distributions, $336,371; giving activities include $336,371 for 28 grants (high: $100,000; low: $1,000).
Purpose and activities: Giving primarily for higher and other education, and for social services.
Fields of interest: Education; Public affairs; Human services.
Type of support: General support; Continuing support; Annual campaigns; Endowments; Program development; Professorships.
Limitations: Applications accepted. Giving primarily in CA; some funding also in Washington, DC, and Arlington, VA. No grants to individuals.
Application information:
  Initial approach: Proposal
  Deadline(s): None
Trustees: Barry B. Burch; Berkeley Burch-Martinez.
EIN: 953924403

8757
Paul H. & Faye P. Burgett Trust

c/o Bank of America, N.A.
P.O. Box 831041
Dallas, TX 75283-1041   8003577094

Foundation type: Independent foundation.
Financial data (yr. ended 12/31/14): Assets, $3,078,059; expenditures, $172,191; qualifying distributions, $148,582 and $0 for set-asides.
Fields of interest: Education.
Limitations: Applications not accepted. Giving primarily in IA.
Application information: Unsolicited request for funds not accepted.

Trustee: Bank of America, N.A.
EIN: 956240155

8758
Catherine and Francis Burzik Foundation

7700 Broadway, Ste. 104
P. O. Box 308
San Antonio, TX 78209-3260

Donors: Catherine Burzik; Frank Burzik.
Foundation type: Independent foundation.
Financial data (yr. ended 12/31/13): Assets, $1,621,121 (M); gifts received, $90,552; expenditures, $420,875; qualifying distributions, $403,000; giving activities include $403,000 for 12 grants (high: $100,000; low: $3,000).
Fields of interest: Arts and culture; Education; Human services.
Limitations: Applications not accepted. Giving primarily in TX.
Application information: Unsolicited requests for funds not accepted.
Officers and Directors: Catherine Burzik, Pres. and Director; Frank Burzik, V.P. and Director; Cecelia Abel, Secy.-Treas. and Director.
EIN: 453975185

8759
Calpine Foundation

717 Texas Ave., Ste. 1000
Houston, TX 77002-2761   (713) 830-8883
Contact: Norma Dunn, Pres. and Dir.
E-mail: foundation@calpine.com

Established in 2002 in California.
Donors: Calpine Corp.; Paramount Pictures; Gas Turbine Efficiency; Calpine Corporation; TRS Services; Power Systems MFG, LLC.
Foundation type: Company-sponsored foundation.
Financial data (yr. ended 12/31/13): Assets, $1,124,917 (M); gifts received, $873,235; expenditures, $314,033; qualifying distributions, $314,033; giving activities include $248,751 for 12 grants (high: $105,251; low: $1,000).
Purpose and activities: The foundation supports organizations involved with arts and culture, education, lung disease, housing, human services, and community development.
Fields of interest: Arts and culture; Diseases and conditions; Human services.
Type of support: General support; Employee volunteer services; Employee matching gifts.
Limitations: Applications accepted. Giving primarily in TX; giving also to national organizations. No support for religious or political organizations.
Publications: Application guidelines.
Application information: Application form required.
  Initial approach: E-mail
  Copies of proposal: 1
  Deadline(s): None
Officers and Directors: Jack A. Fusco, Chair. and C.E.O.; Norma Dunn, Pres. and Director; Hether Benjamin-Brown, V.P.; John B. Hill, V.P. and Director; Michael Rogers, V.P. and Director; Thaddeus W. Miller, Secy. and Director; Zamir Rauf, Treas. and Director.
EIN: 260025038

8760
Cambridge Mindful Living Foundation
8383 Preston Center Plaza Dr., 5th Fl.
Dallas, TX 75225-5510

Donors: Jean-Claude Saada; Cambridge Real Estate Holdings Inc.
Foundation type: Independent foundation.
Financial data (yr. ended 12/31/13): Assets, $4,495 (M); gifts received, $290,416; expenditures, $291,446; qualifying distributions, $286,095; giving activities include $280,832 for 2 grants (high: $250,000; low: $30,832).
Fields of interest: Health.
Limitations: Applications not accepted.
Application information: Unsolicited requests for funds not accepted.
Officer and Directors: Jean-Claude Saada, Pres. and Director; Robert J. Brill; Leslie Deshazer.
EIN: 463466852

8761
Robert L. and Sara Lou Cargill Charitable Trust
4701 Alta Mesa Blvd.
Fort Worth, TX 76133-6112

Established in 1987 in Texas.
Donors: Robert L. Cargill; Sara Lou Cargill.
Foundation type: Independent foundation.
Financial data (yr. ended 12/31/13): Assets, $456,205 (M); gifts received, $20,215; expenditures, $188,700; qualifying distributions, $182,000; giving activities include $181,700 for 7 grants (high: $166,000; low: $500).
Fields of interest: Education; Philanthropy; Protestantism.
Limitations: Applications not accepted. Giving primarily in TX, with some emphasis on Fort Worth and Tarrant County. No grants to individuals.
Application information: Unsolicited requests for funds not accepted.
Trustees: Robert L. Cargill; Frost Bank.
EIN: 756365424

8762
Mildred Cariker Charitable Trust
c/o Bank of America, N.A.
P.O. Box 831041
Dallas, TX 75283-1041

Foundation type: Independent foundation.
Financial data (yr. ended 05/31/13): Assets, $2,430,782 (M); expenditures, $288,189; qualifying distributions, $272,279; giving activities include $261,072 for 3 grants (high: $130,536; low: $65,268).
Fields of interest: Education; University education; Housing development; Human services; Female children and youth; Male children and youth.
Limitations: Applications not accepted. Giving primarily in OK and TX.
Application information: Unsolicited requests for funds not accepted.
Trustee: Bank of America, N.A.
EIN: 756351870

8763
Caritas Veritatis Foundation
800 Gessner Rd., Ste. 1260
Houston, TX 77024-4273

Donor: Loughrea Trust.
Foundation type: Independent foundation.
Financial data (yr. ended 12/31/14): Assets, $519,150; gifts received, $0; expenditures, $468,074; qualifying distributions, $427,671.
Fields of interest: History; Archaeology; Catholicism.
International interests: Canada; Croatia; Czech Republic; France; Switzerland.
Limitations: Applications not accepted. Giving primarily in Canada, Croatia, the Czech Republic, France, and Switzerland.
Application information: Unsolicited requests for funds not accepted.
Officers and Directors: Jacques LeBlevennec, Pres. and Director; Francois Letaconnoux, V.P. and Director; Marvin A. Wurzer, Secy.-Treas. and Director.
EIN: 352340863

8764
John & Mildred Cauthorn Charitable Trust
P.O. Box 678
Sonora, TX 76950-0678 (325) 387-2711
Contact: Jessie Kerbow

Established in 1985 in Texas.
Donor: Mildred Cauthorn†.
Foundation type: Independent foundation.
Financial data (yr. ended 12/31/13): Assets, $13,529,957 (M); expenditures, $527,288; qualifying distributions, $190,938; giving activities include $178,796 for grants.
Purpose and activities: Giving primarily for health and human services.
Fields of interest: Human services.
Type of support: General support; Scholarships.
Limitations: Applications accepted. Giving limited to Sutton County, TX. No grants to individuals.
Application information:
   Initial approach: Proposal
   Copies of proposal: 1
   Deadline(s): None
   Board meeting date(s): 1st Tues. monthly
Trustees: Milton Cavaness; Michael V. Hale; Jo Ann Jones; Nelda Mayfield.
Number of staff: 1 part-time support.
EIN: 751977779

8765
Michael and Rebecca Cemo Foundation
4015 Inverness Dr.
Houston, TX 77019-1005
FAX: (713) 355-4702; E-mail: mcemo@comcast.net

Established in 1997 in Texas.
Donors: Michael J. Cemo; Rebecca A. Cemo.
Foundation type: Independent foundation.
Financial data (yr. ended 04/30/13): Assets, $7,775,341 (M); gifts received, $999,800; expenditures, $289,982; qualifying distributions, $278,136; giving activities include $275,500 for 16 grants (high: $115,000; low: $1,000).
Fields of interest: Arts and culture; Performing arts; Museums; Education; University education; Animal

welfare; Diseases and conditions; Religion; Human services.
Type of support: Annual campaigns; Capital and infrastructure; Scholarships; Research.
Limitations: Applications not accepted. Giving primarily in Houston, TX. No support for religious or political organizations. No grants to individuals.
Application information: Contributes only to pre-selected organizations.
   Board meeting date(s): Apr. 30
Officers and Directors: Michael J. Cemo, Pres. and Treas. and Director; Rebecca A. Cemo, V.P. and Secy. and Director; Jason M. Cemo; Stephanie C. Cemo.
Number of staff: None.
EIN: 760537009

8766
Central Texas Foundation Inc.
(also known as Central Texas Foundation, Inc.)
109 N. Fisk Ave.
Brownwood, TX 76801 (325) 646-4443
FAX: (325) 646-2738; E-mail: bellisbell@verizon.net

Established in 1982 in Texas.
Donor: James R. Beadel†.
Foundation type: Independent foundation.
Financial data (yr. ended 12/31/13): Assets, $5,001,444 (M); expenditures, $295,051; qualifying distributions, $291,900; giving activities include $282,000 for 34 grants (high: $45,000; low: $500).
Purpose and activities: Giving primarily for education, children's organizations, and health and human services.
Fields of interest: Historic preservation; Education; Early childhood education; Child educational development; Higher education; Health; Diseases and conditions; Domestic violence; Community and economic development; Human services; Family services; Child welfare; Child development; Low-income and poor people.
Type of support: General support; Matching grants; Continuing support; Annual campaigns; Capital and infrastructure; Emergency funds; Scholarships.
Limitations: Applications accepted. Giving limited to Brown County, TX, and immediate adjacent counties surrounding Brown County. The organization requesting funds must be located in either Brown, Callahan, Coleman, Comanche, Eastland, Mills or San Saba counties. No support for political organizations, or for athletic programs or scholarships for athletics. No grants to individuals.
Publications: Application guidelines; Financial statement.
Application information: Application form required.
   Initial approach: Contact foundation for application form
   Copies of proposal: 1
   Deadline(s): Dec. 31
   Board meeting date(s): Quarterly and as needed
Officers: Stuart Coleman, Pres.; Robert Porter, V.P.; Bob Beadel, Secy.-Treas.
Trustees: Don Jordan, Jr.; Tom Munson.
Number of staff: None.
EIN: 751848800

8767
The Mary Cecile Chambers Charitable Trust

(formerly The Mary Cecile Chambers Scholarship Fund)
c/o Moody National Bank
P.O. Box 1139
Galveston, TX 77553-1139 (409) 765-5561
FAX: (409) 763-8925; E-mail for Luann Bland: LBland@moodytrust.com

Established in 1991 in Texas.
Donor: Mary Cecile Chambers Scholarship Trust.
Foundation type: Independent foundation.
Financial data (yr. ended 03/31/14): Assets, $5,995,493 (M); expenditures, $267,287; qualifying distributions, $244,837; giving activities include $1,000 for grants, and $212,917 for grants to individuals.
Purpose and activities: Support primarily for education, including scholarships limited to worthy young men of the State of Texas.
Fields of interest: Vocational education; Higher education; Male young adults.
Type of support: Scholarships; Student aid.
Limitations: Applications accepted. Giving limited to residents of TX.
Publications: Application guidelines.
Application information: Application form required.
  Initial approach: Letter or telephone
  Deadline(s): None
  Board meeting date(s): Annually
Trustee: Moody National Bank, N.A.
Number of staff: None.
EIN: 766071425

8768
Younas & Bushra Chaudhary Foundation

15603 Kuykendahl Rd., No. 200
Houston, TX 77090-3655 (281) 893-9400
Contact: Younas Chaudhary, Dir.

Donor: Younas Chaudhary.
Foundation type: Independent foundation.
Financial data (yr. ended 12/31/12): Assets, $735,981 (M); gifts received, $250,000; expenditures, $198,922; qualifying distributions, $187,933; giving activities include $187,933 for 21 grants (high: $125,933; low: $500).
Fields of interest: Higher education.
Type of support: Student aid.
Limitations: Applications accepted. Giving primarily to residents of Houston, TX.
Application information:
  Initial approach: Proposal
  Deadline(s): None
Directors: Bushra Chaudhary; Maria Chaudhary; Younas Chaudhary.
EIN: 200479199

8769
The Chisholm Trail Communities Foundation

(formerly The Georgetown Area Community Foundation)
116 W. 8th St., Ste. 105
P.O. Box 1060
Georgetown, TX 78626-5847 (512) 863-4186
Contact: Mike Weir, Managing Dir.

FAX: (866) 348-8033;
E-mail: friends@chisholm-trail.org; Main
URL: http://www.chisholm-trail.org
Facebook: https://www.facebook.com/CTCFoundation
LinkedIn: http://www.linkedin.com/company/2460698
Twitter: http://twitter.com/chisholmtrail

Established in 1998 in Texas.
Foundation type: Community foundation.
Financial data (yr. ended 12/31/13): Assets, $2,913,120 (M); gifts received, $1,117,598; expenditures, $699,417; giving activities include $315,359 for 15+ grants (high: $22,500), and $54,800 for 13 grants to individuals.
Purpose and activities: The foundation grants funds for projects and programs that address community needs in the areas of community development and community services, education and training, arts and culture, health, and human services.
Fields of interest: Arts and culture; Education; Health; Community and economic development; Human services.
Limitations: Applications accepted. Giving primarily in the greater Georgetown, TX area. No support for religious organizations for religious purposes. No grants to individuals (except for scholarships).
Publications: Application guidelines.
Application information: Visit foundation web site for application form and guidelines. Application form required.
  Initial approach: Full proposal, e-mail, or telephone
  Copies of proposal: 5
  Deadline(s): Feb. 1, May 1, Aug. 1, and Nov. 1
  Board meeting date(s): Quarterly
  Final notification: Within 2 weeks after quarterly board meeting
Officer and Directors: Dr. Nelson Avery, Chair. and Director; Ray Barron; Dr. Barbara Brightwell; Eric Cooper; Karen Cole; Howard Faske; Jack Garey; Ron Greening; Hayden Johnson; Lynne Moore; Gary Newman.
EIN: 742786718

8770
Chrest Foundation, Inc.

(formerly J. Jensen Family Foundation, Inc.)
130 E. John Carpenter Freeway
Irving, TX 75062-2708 (972) 999-4514
Contact: Lou Anne King Jensen, Pres.
FAX: (972) 999-4502;
E-mail: administrator@chrestfoundation.org; Main
URL: http://www.chrestfoundation.org
Grants List: http://www.chrestfoundation.org/EN/grantsawarded.asp

Established in 1999 in Texas.
Donors: Jeffrey J. Jensen; Gladys Margaret Jensen.
Foundation type: Independent foundation.
Financial data (yr. ended 12/31/13): Assets, $8,687,375 (M); gifts received, $35,582; expenditures, $411,020; qualifying distributions, $327,077; giving activities include $327,077 for 9 grants (high: $98,090; low: $18,425).
Purpose and activities: The foundation believes that social action and civic participation contribute to the creation of a more equitable and tolerant society. The foundation concentrates its resources on civil society organizations in Turkey that focus on increasing gender equality and fostering

communication and dialogue through arts and culture.
Fields of interest: Children; Adolescents; Females; Female adults.
International interests: Cyprus; Turkey.
Type of support: Emergency funds; Matching grants; Program-related investments; Recordings; Capacity-building and technical assistance; Program development; Program evaluations; Research; Technical assistance.
Limitations: Applications accepted. Giving primarily in Turkey, with occasional support to Cyprus and the Caucasus. No grants to individuals.
Publications: Application guidelines; Grants list; Program policy statement; Program policy statement (including application guidelines).
Application information: Application guidelines available on foundation web site. Application form required.
  Initial approach: E-mail, telephone, or grant inquiry form on foundation web site
  Copies of proposal: 1
  Deadline(s): None
  Board meeting date(s): Two times per year
  Final notification: Ranges from days to eight weeks
Officers and Directors: Lou Anne King Jensen, Pres.; Jeffrey J. Jensen, V.P. and Director; Haley Barb, Secy. and Director; Julie J. Jensen, Treas. and Director.
Number of staff: 1 full-time professional; 1 part-time support.
EIN: 752840026

8771
Cielo Azul Foundation

3500 Ranch Rd., Ste. 620 N.
Austin, TX 78734-2111

Established in 2000 in Texas.
Donors: Betsy Blair; James Van Winkle.
Foundation type: Independent foundation.
Financial data (yr. ended 12/31/14): Assets, $2,306,849 (M); expenditures, $191,711; qualifying distributions, $182,130; giving activities include $180,505 for 20 grants (high: $50,000; low: $5).
Fields of interest: Education; Health; Religion.
Limitations: Applications not accepted. Giving primarily in TX. No grants to individuals.
Application information: Unsolicited requests for funds not accepted.
Officers and Directors: Betsy Blair, Pres. and Director; James Van Winkle, V.P. and Secy.-Treas. and Director; Kathryn Van Winkle.
EIN: 742982455

8772
Clear Channel Communications Foundation

250 W. Nottingham, Ste. 400
San Antonio, TX 78209-8328

Established in 1999 in Texas.
Donors: Clear Channel Communications, Inc.; J. Walter Thompson USA, Inc.
Foundation type: Company-sponsored foundation.
Financial data (yr. ended 12/31/13): Assets, $1,761,648 (M); expenditures, $363,322; qualifying distributions, $353,897; giving activities

include $353,425 for 26 grants (high: $100,000; low: $500).

Purpose and activities: The foundation supports parks and playgrounds and organizations involved with arts and culture, education, health, disaster relief, human services, and minority civil rights.

Fields of interest: Arts and culture; Education; Health.

Type of support: General support; Capital and infrastructure; Convening.

Limitations: Applications not accepted. Giving limited to San Antonio, TX. No grants to individuals.

Application information: Contributes only to pre-selected organizations.

Officers and Directors: L. Lowry Mays, Pres. and Director; Mark P. Mays, V.P. and Secy. and Director; Randall T. Mays, V.P. and Treas. and Director.

EIN: 742908486

8773

Bill and Gigi Clements Foundation

(formerly William Perry Clements Foundation)
404 Hamvasy Ln.
Tyler, TX   75701-5323

Established in 2002 in Texas.

Donor: Pauline Allen Gill Foundation.

Foundation type: Independent foundation.

Financial data (yr. ended 12/31/13): Assets, $14,210,856 (M); expenditures, $452,450; qualifying distributions, $317,291; giving activities include $317,291 for 10 grants (high: $130,000; low: $51).

Purpose and activities: Giving primarily to an Episcopal school, as well as for human services.

Fields of interest: Elementary and secondary education; Episcopalianism and Anglicanism; Lutheranism; Human services.

Type of support: General support; Matching grants; Annual campaigns; Capital campaigns; Scholarships.

Limitations: Applications not accepted. Giving limited to TX, primarily Tyler. No grants to individuals.

Application information: Contributes only to pre-selected organizations.

Officers: William Perry Clements III, Pres. and Secy. and Director; Georgia M. Clements, V.P. and Director.

Trustee: Loren Runnels.

EIN: 731645124

8774

Clifford Foundation, Inc.

P.O. Box 1001
Corsicana, TX   75151-1001   (903) 874-4725
Contact: Clifford L. Brown III, Pres.

Established in 1993 in Texas.

Donor: C.L. Brown III.

Foundation type: Independent foundation.

Financial data (yr. ended 06/30/13): Assets, $3,793,111 (M); gifts received, $276,308; expenditures, $218,632; qualifying distributions, $214,061; giving activities include $212,675 for 35 grants to individuals (high: $12,962; low: $1,007).

Purpose and activities: Scholarship awards to high school graduates of Navarro County, Texas.

Fields of interest: Higher education.

Type of support: Student aid.

Limitations: Applications accepted. Giving limited to residents of Navarro County, TX.

Application information: Applicants must be current high school graduates from Navarro County, TX, attending TX state-supported schools only. Application form required.

Initial approach: Proposal
Deadline(s): Apr. 1

Officers: Clifford L. Brown III, Pres.; Larry Morrison, V.P.; William S. Maupin, Secy.-Treas.

Committee Members: Mary E. Brown; Carla Dyess; Jane Fouty; Susan Cason Laird; Terry Seth; Nellie Carr Thorogood.

EIN: 752506394

8775

Samuel H. Clinedinst Trust

c/o Bank of America, N.A.
P.O. Box 831041
Dallas, TX   75283-1041

Foundation type: Independent foundation.

Financial data (yr. ended 07/31/13): Assets, $3,359,880 (M); expenditures, $274,451; qualifying distributions, $230,175; giving activities include $215,717 for 6 grants (high: $86,286; low: $21,572).

Fields of interest: Education; Health; Youth development.

Limitations: Applications not accepted. No grants to individuals.

Application information: Unsolicited requests for funds not accepted.

Trustee: Bank of America, N.A.

EIN: 956015486

8776

Bill Pace Cogdell Charitable Trust

2005 W. Missouri Ave.
Midland, TX   79701-6401

Foundation type: Independent foundation.

Financial data (yr. ended 12/31/13): Assets, $8,336,142 (M); expenditures, $341,886; qualifying distributions, $133,791; giving activities include $133,791 for 66 grants to individuals (high: $7,434; low: $186).

Fields of interest: Higher education.

Type of support: Student aid.

Limitations: Giving primarily in TX.

Trustees: Dennis Sever; Carol C. Subia.

EIN: 752737902

8777

Martha Ann Cogdell Hospital Trust

701 S. Taylor, Ste. 200
Amarillo, TX   79101-2425   (866) 356-8787

Established in 1951 in Texas.

Foundation type: Independent foundation.

Financial data (yr. ended 09/30/14): Assets, $4,162,856 (M); expenditures, $475,767; qualifying distributions, $400,789; giving activities include $394,000 for 15 grants (high: $50,000; low: $14,000).

Purpose and activities: Giving primarily in the health care field.

Fields of interest: Health; Hospital care; Emergency medical services; Fire prevention and control.

Limitations: Applications accepted. Giving primarily in TX. No grants to individuals.

Application information: Application form required.

Initial approach: Proposal
Deadline(s): Sept. 30

Trustee: Happy State Bank, N.A.

EIN: 756013973

8778

Dale & John Coleman Charitable Trust

P.O. Box 1
Amarillo, TX   79105-0001

Foundation type: Independent foundation.

Financial data (yr. ended 12/31/13): Assets, $7,924,604 (M); expenditures, $814,779; qualifying distributions, $349,241; giving activities include $349,241 for 9 grants (high: $122,235; low: $6,985).

Fields of interest: Education; University education; Religion; Human services.

Type of support: Endowments.

Limitations: Applications not accepted. Giving primarily in AR and KS.

Application information: Unsolicited requests for funds not accepted.

Trustee: Amarillo National Bank.

EIN: 752857586

8779

College First Foundation

130 E. John Carpenter Freeway
Irving, TX   75062-2708   (972) 999-4560
Contact: Toppy Cantrell, Admin.

Established in 1996 in Texas.

Donors: Ronald L. Jensen; Alliance for Affordable Healthcare Association, Inc.; UGSC; Alliance For Affordable Services, Inc.; Americans for Financial Security; B.E.L.I.E.F. Foundation; Health Markets.

Foundation type: Independent foundation.

Financial data (yr. ended 12/31/12): Assets, $560,235 (M); gifts received, $365,956; expenditures, $395,105; qualifying distributions, $389,457; giving activities include $325,000 for 191 grants to individuals (high: $5,000; low: $1,000).

Purpose and activities: The foundation seeks to improve the quality of life of well deserving students by promoting higher education though scholarship programs for children of active employees or agents of participating companies and associations.

Fields of interest: Education.

Type of support: Student aid; Individual development.

Limitations: Applications accepted. Giving primarily to residents of TX.

Application information: Application form required.

Deadline(s): Varies

Officers and Directors: Jeff Jensen, Pres. and Director; Lou Anne Jensen, V.P. and Director; Janet Jensen, Secy.-Treas. and Director.

EIN: 752638941

8780

James W. Collins Family Foundation

900 E. Lakeview Dr.
McAllen, TX   78501-5723   (956) 630-9400
Contact: Kathleen C. Collins, Pres. and Dir.

Established in 2006 in Texas.
Donors: Vanco Trust; James W. Collins.
Foundation type: Independent foundation.
Financial data (yr. ended 12/31/13): Assets, $2,038,527 (M); expenditures, $263,874; qualifying distributions, $233,205; giving activities include $233,050 for 24 grants (high: $117,000; low: $100).
Fields of interest: Education; Philanthropy; Diseases and conditions.
Limitations: Applications accepted. Giving primarily in McAllen, TX.
Application information: Application form required.
Initial approach: Letter
Deadline(s): None
Officers and Directors: Kathleen C. Collins, Pres. and Director; Caroline M. Collins, V.P. and Director; Courtney C. Collins, V.P. and Director; James W. Collins, Jr., V.P. and Director; Jennifer L. Collins, V.P.; Vannie C. Collins, V.P. and Director; Susan Simpson, Secy.; Robert J. Morehead, Treas. and Director; James W. Collins.
EIN: 161767144

8781
Collins Fisher Foundation
3644 Beverly Dr.
Dallas, TX   75205-2868   (214) 665-6905

Established in 2001 in Texas.
Donor: James M. Collins Foundation.
Foundation type: Independent foundation.
Financial data (yr. ended 12/31/13): Assets, $5,292,792 (M); expenditures, $289,136; qualifying distributions, $256,400; giving activities include $256,400 for 9 grants (high: $200,000; low: $700).
Fields of interest: Historic preservation; Education; Elementary and secondary education; Higher education; Foundations; Film and video; Human services.
Limitations: Applications accepted. Giving primarily in CA and CT. No grants to individuals and no loans or scholarships.
Application information:
Initial approach: Letter
Deadline(s): None
Officers: Nancy Collins Fisher, Pres.; Jan McMinn, Secy.; Andersen Collins Fisher, Treas.
Trustee: Alison Fisher Smith.
EIN: 311736933

8782
Community Hospital Foundation
13301 East Freeway, Ste. 307
Houston, TX   77015-5815

Established in 1986 in Texas.
Foundation type: Independent foundation.
Financial data (yr. ended 05/31/14): Assets, $2,723,332 (M); expenditures, $330,566; qualifying distributions, $302,844; giving activities include $262,000 for 32 grants (high: $50,000; low: $1,000).
Purpose and activities: Giving primarily for higher and other education, as well as for health care, youth and social services, and to recognized religious, nonprofit affiliations.
Fields of interest: Education; Higher education; Health; Protestantism; Catholicism; Human services; Youth services.

Type of support: General support; Capital campaigns; Capital and infrastructure; Equipment; Scholarships.
Limitations: Applications not accepted. Giving primarily in TX. No support for organizations without 501(c)(3) status. No grants to individuals.
Application information: Contributes only to pre-selected organizations.
Officers and Directors: Patsy Simon, Pres.; John Ward, V.P. and Director; Kay Howard, Secy.-Treas.; Gerald Cobb, C.F.O. and Director; Gary Rohr.
Number of staff: 1 part-time support.
EIN: 741470290

8783
The Coneway Family Foundation
(formerly Lynn & Peter Coneway Foundation)
2247 Troon Rd.
Houston, TX   77019-1417

Established in 1983 in Texas.
Donors: Lynn M. Coneway; Peter R. Coneway; Peter R. Coneway Charitable Lead Trust; Natalie Coneway Page.
Foundation type: Independent foundation.
Financial data (yr. ended 04/30/13): Assets, $12,357,587 (M); expenditures, $559,526; qualifying distributions, $514,375; giving activities include $347,000 for 37 grants (high: $54,000; low: $1,000).
Purpose and activities: Giving primarily for the arts, higher education, health care, and human services.
Fields of interest: Arts and culture; Art museums; Education; Higher education; Foundations; Health; Cancers; Human services.
International interests: Switzerland.
Type of support: Continuing support; Endowments; Fellowships.
Limitations: Applications not accepted. Giving primarily in TX, with emphasis on Austin and Houston. No grants, scholarships, or loans to individuals.
Application information: Unsolicited requests for funds not accepted.
Trustees: Lynn M. Coneway; Natalie Coneway; Peter R. Coneway; Cecile Coneway Puckett.
Number of staff: 1 full-time professional.
EIN: 133188841

8784
Gene Conley Foundation
P.O. Box 41629
Austin, TX   78704-9926   1-888-234-1999
FAX: 1-877-746-5889;
E-mail: grantsadministration@wellsfargo.com; *Main URL:* https://www.wellsfargo.com/privatefoundationgrants/conley

Established in 1989 in Texas.
Foundation type: Independent foundation.
Financial data (yr. ended 12/31/13): Assets, $12,454,577 (M); expenditures, $595,543; qualifying distributions, $407,333; giving activities include $349,179 for 31 grants (high: $50,855; low: $1,000).
Fields of interest: Arts and culture; Education; Environment; Animal welfare; Diseases and conditions; Science; Religion; Human services; Child welfare; Youth services; Scouting programs.

Limitations: Applications accepted. Giving primarily in the North Central area of TX. No grants to individuals.
Application information: See foundation website for complete application guidelines. Application form required.
Initial approach: Proposal
Copies of proposal: 8
Deadline(s): May 1
Final notification: July 31
Trustee: Wells Fargo Bank Texas, N.A.
Advisory Board Members: Mac Cannedy; Bill Daniel; Mike Elyea; Steve McSpadden; Terry Pence; Barry Plaxco; Rhonda Poirot; David I. Ramsey; Joseph N. Sherrill, Jr.; Chris Travelstead.
EIN: 752224430

8785
Ruth and Paul Connor Foundation
2112 Rio Grande St.
Austin, TX   78705   (512) 477-7543
Contact: Mark B. Schreiber, Pres. and Treas.

Established in 2000 in Texas.
Donor: Ruth P. Connor†.
Foundation type: Independent foundation.
Financial data (yr. ended 12/31/13): Assets, $5,750,266 (M); expenditures, $344,684; qualifying distributions, $290,371; giving activities include $285,000 for 10 grants (high: $73,000; low: $5,000).
Fields of interest: Christianity; Human services; Senior services.
Type of support: General support.
Limitations: Applications accepted. Giving primarily in Austin, TX. No grants to individuals.
Application information: Application form required.
Initial approach: Letter
Deadline(s): None
Officers: Mark B. Schreiber, Pres. and Treas.; Robert M. Sumners, Secy.
Trustee: Christopher Acton.
Number of staff: None.
EIN: 742946783

8786
Joe and Louise Cook Foundation
505 Cherokee Dr.
Temple, TX   76504

Established in 1989 in Texas.
Donors: Louise P. Cook†; Joe B. Cook†.
Foundation type: Independent foundation.
Financial data (yr. ended 12/31/13): Assets, $8,239,905 (M); expenditures, $394,135; qualifying distributions, $327,786; giving activities include $327,388 for 30 grants (high: $50,155; low: $1,000).
Fields of interest: Arts and culture; Education; Foundations; Protestantism.
Type of support: General support; Matching grants; Continuing support; Annual campaigns; Capital campaigns; Capital and infrastructure; Endowments; Program development; Professorships; Scholarships.
Limitations: Applications not accepted. Giving primarily in TX. No grants to individuals.
Application information: Contributes only to pre-selected organizations.

Directors: Barbara Wendland; C. Wendland; E. Wendland.
EIN: 742541278

8787

Mark and Judith Cook Foundation
103 Baronet Woods Ct.
The Woodlands, TX   77382-2649
Application address: c/o OAKS, Hartline & Daly,
Attn.: Daniel W. Daly, III, 2323 S. Shepherd, 14th
Fl., Houston, TX 77019, tel.: (713) 979-5566

Donors: Mark Cook; Judith Cook.
Foundation type: Independent foundation.
Financial data (yr. ended 12/31/13): Assets,
$9,064,856 (M); expenditures, $435,041;
qualifying distributions, $274,200; giving activities
include $269,450 for 10 grants (high: $75,000;
low: $1,000).
Fields of interest: Arts and culture; Education;
Environment.
Limitations: Applications accepted. Giving primarily
in TX.
Application information: Application form required.
Initial approach: Letter
Deadline(s): None
Officers and Directors: Mark Dewayne Cook, Pres.
and Treas. and Director; Judith Claire Womack Cook,
V.P. and Secy. and Director; Chloe Hope Cook; Kevin
Michael Cook; Molly Claire Cook.
EIN: 452423522

8788

Elizabeth Corlin Charitable Trust
c/o Bank of America, N.A.
P.O. Box 831041
Dallas, TX   75283-1041

Foundation type: Independent foundation.
Financial data (yr. ended 05/31/14): Assets,
$6,710,147 (M); expenditures, $337,460;
qualifying distributions, $306,037; giving activities
include $288,807 for 3 grants (high: $96,269; low:
$96,269).
Fields of interest: Hospital care; Cancers; Children.
Limitations: Applications not accepted. Giving
primarily in CA and FL.
Application information: Unsolicited requests for
funds not accepted.
Trustee: Bank of America, N.A.
EIN: 956855324

8789

Corrigan-Goddard Foundation
(formerly Charles B. Goddard Foundation of Texas)
8117 Preston Rd., Ste. 610
Dallas, TX   75225-6366   2147392025

Established in 2008 in Texas.
Foundation type: Independent foundation.
Financial data (yr. ended 12/31/13): Assets,
$9,025,200 (M); expenditures, $501,164;
qualifying distributions, $387,245; giving activities
include $375,300 for 21 grants (high: $50,000;
low: $550).
Fields of interest: Education; Health; Religion.
Limitations: Applications not accepted. Giving
primarily in OK and TX.
Application information: Contributes only to
pre-selected organizations.

Officers and Directors: Ann G. Corrigan, Chair. and
Pres. and Director; Bryan H. Corrigan, V.P. and
Director; Elaine Benningfield, Treas. and Director;
Blake G. Corrigan; William E. Corrigan.
EIN: 262556805

8790

Opal G. Cox Charitable Trust
c/o Bank of America, N.A.
P.O. Box 831041
Dallas, TX   75283-1041
Scholarship application addresses: Office of
Academic Scholarships and Financial Aid, Baylor
University, 1 Bear Pl., No. 97028, Waco, TX
76798-7028, tel.: (254) 710-2611; Office of
Financial Aid, Southwestern Baptist Theological
Seminary, P.O. Box 22510, Fort Worth, TX 76122,
tel.: (817) 923-1921

Established in 1982 in Texas.
Donor: Opal G. Cox†.
Foundation type: Independent foundation.
Financial data (yr. ended 08/31/14): Assets,
$8,478,990 (M); expenditures, $525,078;
qualifying distributions, $392,577; giving activities
include $372,420 for 2 grants (high: $186,210;
low: $186,210).
Purpose and activities: Provides educational funds
available to students attending or wishing to attend
Baylor University or Southwestern Baptist
Theological Seminary. Preference is given to
students studying to become missionaries or
medical missionaries.
Fields of interest: University education; Graduate
and professional education; Theology.
Type of support: Scholarships.
Limitations: Applications accepted. Giving primarily
in TX. No grants to individuals directly.
Application information: Applications are available
at financial aid office. Application form required.
Deadline(s): May 15 for Baylor University; for
Southwestern Baptist Theological Seminary
call for deadline
Trustee: Bank of America, N.A.
EIN: 746307500

8791

Crossroads Foundation
(formerly Twin Pines Foundation)
1 O'Connor Plz., Ste. 1100
Victoria, TX   77901-6549   (361) 578-6796
Contact: Robert L. Coffey, Pres.

Established in 1995 in Texas.
Foundation type: Independent foundation.
Financial data (yr. ended 12/31/13): Assets,
$2,884,447 (M); expenditures, $156,479;
qualifying distributions, $153,000; giving activities
include $153,000 for 23 grants (high: $15,000;
low: $1,000).
Purpose and activities: Funding primarily for historic
preservation, community development, arts and
culture, and human services.
Fields of interest: Arts and culture; Historic
preservation; Education; Community and economic
development; Human services.
Limitations: Applications accepted. Giving primarily
in Victoria County, TX, or adjacent counties.
Application information: Application form required.
Initial approach: Letter

Copies of proposal: 1
Deadline(s): None
Officers and Board Members: Robert L. Coffey,
Pres.; Bland Proctor, Secy.; Bruce Woolson, Treas.
and Director; David Drost; Betty Hedgelough; Danny
Hiller; Joseph M. Long, MD; John McNeil, MD.
Number of staff: None.
EIN: 741382486

8792

The Bill and Helen Crowder Foundation
6005 Fairmont Pkwy., Ste. I
Pasadena, TX   77505-4099   (281) 998-7499
Contact: Marilyn Sims

Established in 1999 in Texas.
Foundation type: Independent foundation.
Financial data (yr. ended 12/31/13): Assets,
$5,036,653 (M); expenditures, $247,837;
qualifying distributions, $240,089; giving activities
include $225,000 for grants.
Purpose and activities: Giving primarily for
hospitals, health associations, and human services;
funding also for children and youth services and an
Episcopal church.
Fields of interest: Nonprofits; Hospital care;
Diseases and conditions; Episcopalianism and
Anglicanism; Lutheranism; Human services; Child
welfare.
International interests: Africa; Asia.
Type of support: General support; Annual
campaigns; Capital campaigns; Emergency funds;
Program development; Scholarships; Regranting;
Research.
Limitations: Applications accepted. Giving primarily
in TX. No support for political organizations. No
grants to individuals.
Application information: Application form required.
Initial approach: Proposal
Copies of proposal: 1
Deadline(s): None
Board meeting date(s): Quarterly
Officers: Marilyn Sims, Pres.; R. N. Domec, V.P.;
Beverly Lively, Secy.
Directors: Steele Arthur; Stephen Arthur; Rodney A.
Rothermel.
Number of staff: 1 part-time professional; 1
part-time support.
EIN: 760555573

8793

D3 Foundation
5330 Montrose
Houston, TX   77005-1831
Contact: Andrew A. Schatte, Treas.

Established in 2003 in Texas.
Donors: Annette Clark Schatte; Andrew A. Schatte.
Foundation type: Independent foundation.
Financial data (yr. ended 12/31/12): Assets,
$873,088 (M); gifts received, $3,000;
expenditures, $203,118; qualifying distributions,
$196,793; giving activities include $196,793 for
grants.
Fields of interest: Disasters and emergency
management; Christianity; Low-income and poor
people; People with HIV/AIDS.
Type of support: General support; Grants to
individuals.
Limitations: Applications accepted. Giving primarily
in Houston, TX.

Application information:
Initial approach: Letter
Deadline(s): None
Officers: Ali Smith Williams, Pres.; Annette Clark Schatte, V.P. and Secy.; Andrew A. Schatte, Treas.
EIN: 200528919

8794
Lawrence B. Dale Family Foundation

2100 Ross Ave., Ste. 1870
Dallas, TX 75201-6773

Established in 2007 in Texas.
Donors: Lawrence B. Dale; Beverley B. Dale.
Foundation type: Independent foundation.
Financial data (yr. ended 12/31/13): Assets, $3,875,000 (M); expenditures, $444,218; qualifying distributions, $415,500; giving activities include $415,500 for 23 grants (high: $100,000; low: $1,000).
Purpose and activities: Giving primarily for education, children, youth and social services, and to hospitals, including a children's hospital.
Fields of interest: Elementary and secondary education; Hospital care; Specialty hospital care; Human services; Child welfare.
Type of support: General support; Financial sustainability; Capital campaigns; Program development.
Limitations: Applications not accepted. Giving primarily in TX, with emphasis on the greater metropolitan Dallas-Fort Worth area. No grants to individuals.
Application information: Unsolicited requests for funds not accepted.
Officers and Directors: Lawrence B. Dale, Pres. and Treas. and Director; Beverley B. Dale, V.P. and Secy. and Director; Edward B. Dale; Jayne K. Dale; John R. Dale; Peter L. Dale.
EIN: 260265867

8795
Dallas Mavericks Foundation
(formerly The New Mavericks Foundation)
2909 Taylor St.
Dallas, TX 75226-1909 (214) 747-6287
Main URL: http://www.mavsfoundation.com
Grants List: http://www.nba.com/mavericks/community/Dallas_Mavericks_Foundation_Past_Grants.html

Established in 2000 in Texas.
Donors: The Dallas Mavericks Foundation; Minyard Food Stores, Inc.; Once Upon A Time Foundation; The Michael Finley Foundation; Dallas Basketball Ltd.; Ed Ewing; Pro Players Foundation; Friends of the Trinity Stand trail; A.H. Belo-Corp the Dallas Morning News, Inc.; Fox Sports Southwest; Anschutz Entertainment Group, Inc.; Dallas Morning News; Coca Cola.
Foundation type: Company-sponsored foundation.
Financial data (yr. ended 06/30/14): Assets, $2,119,563 (M); gifts received, $96,384; expenditures, $163,562; qualifying distributions, $163,324; giving activities include $150,089 for 9 grants (high: $25,000; low: $10,000).
Purpose and activities: The foundation supports programs designed to assist young people through programs stressing education, good health, and skills necessary for their future success.

Fields of interest: Agriculture; Community and economic development; Human services.
Limitations: Applications accepted. Giving primarily in the metropolitan Dallas/Fort Worth, TX, area. No support for churches, public or private schools, or national organizations without locally, financially independent chapters. No grants to individuals, or for multi-year support, medical research, travel, salaries, general operating support for established organizations, political campaigns or fundraising events, continuing support of programs lasting more than one year, endowments, administrative costs, advertising or fundraising, or research.
Publications: Application guidelines; Grants list.
Application information: Application form required.
Initial approach: Completed Application Form
Deadline(s): June 30
Officers: Terdema L. Ussery, Pres.; Floyd Jahner, V.P. and Treas. and Director; Cheryl Karalla, Secy. and Director.
Directors: Donna Carlisle; Brian Cuban; Jeff Cuban; Kim Cuban; Mark Cuban; Tiffany Cuban; Gretchen Minyard Williams.
EIN: 311767408

8796
The Malcolm C. Damuth Foundation

P.O. Box 685168
Austin, TX 78768-5168

Established in 2006 in Texas.
Donor: S. Craig Damuth.
Foundation type: Independent foundation.
Financial data (yr. ended 12/31/14): Assets, $3,854,189 (M); gifts received, $249,000; expenditures, $314,085; qualifying distributions, $295,418; giving activities include $283,213 for 9 grants (high: $55,000; low: $500).
Fields of interest: Animal welfare.
Type of support: General support.
Limitations: Applications not accepted. Giving primarily in TX. No grants to individuals.
Application information: Contributes only to pre-selected organizations.
Officers and Trustees: Bob Warneke, Jr., Pres. and Trustee; Craig Damuth, V.P. and Trustee; Richard Gibbons; Mollie Fischer; Cullen Hanks; Sandra Skrei, Secy.; James R. Stewart, Jr.
EIN: 203673795

8797
Leo Daniel Foundation

1500 Stag Meadow
San Antonio, TX 78248-1346 (210) 617-4728

Established in 2006 in Texas.
Donors: Bryan Grundhoefer; Mary Jo Grundhoefer.
Foundation type: Independent foundation.
Financial data (yr. ended 12/31/13): Assets, $7,224,696 (M); expenditures, $339,908; qualifying distributions, $279,130; giving activities include $275,880 for 39 grants (high: $87,200; low: $100).
Fields of interest: Education; Higher education; Foundations; Christianity; Women's services.
Limitations: Applications accepted. Giving primarily in TX. No grants to individuals.
Application information: Application form required.
Initial approach: Prposal
Deadline(s): None

Officers: Bryan Grundhoefer, Pres.; Mary Jo Grundhoefer, V.P. and Secy.; Daniel Grundhoefer, Treas.
EIN: 205086929

8798
Sidney and Charline Dauphin Foundation
(formerly Texas Home Health, Inc.)
4140 Gladys Ave., Ste. 101
Beaumont, TX 77706-3648

Established in 2001 in Texas.
Foundation type: Independent foundation.
Financial data (yr. ended 12/31/13): Assets, $420,886 (M); expenditures, $263,857; qualifying distributions, $250,838; giving activities include $250,000 for 7 grants (high: $125,000; low: $5,000).
Purpose and activities: Giving primarily for cancer research, as well as for education.
Fields of interest: Education; Diseases and conditions; Protestantism; Human services.
Type of support: Research; Research and evaluation.
Limitations: Applications not accepted. Giving primarily in TX. No grants to individuals.
Application information: Contributes only to pre-selected organizations.
Officers: Charline Dauphin, Pres. and Secy.; Robin Dauphin, Treas.
Trustee: Jimmy Willis.
EIN: 237009052

8799
George H. Davis Trust for Employees

c/o Bank of America, N.A.
P.O. Box 831041
Dallas, TX 75283-1041

Donor: G.H. Davis for Employees.
Foundation type: Independent foundation.
Financial data (yr. ended 12/31/13): Assets, $3,829,677 (L); expenditures, $253,412; qualifying distributions, $147,033; giving activities include $139,566 for 11 grants (high: $34,888; low: $680).
Fields of interest: Education; Religion; Human services.
Limitations: Applications not accepted. Giving primarily in MO.
Application information: Unsolicited requests for funds not accepted.
Trustee: Bank of America, N.A.
EIN: 306314801

8800
James C. and Teresa K. Day Foundation

2277 Plaza Dr., Ste. 630
Sugar Land, TX 77478-6608

Donors: James C. Day; Teresa K. Day.
Foundation type: Independent foundation.
Financial data (yr. ended 11/30/13): Assets, $7,208,477 (M); expenditures, $499,766; qualifying distributions, $465,650; giving activities include $436,900 for 22 grants (high: $100,000; low: $1,500).
Fields of interest: Arts and culture; Education; Human services.
Limitations: Applications not accepted.

Application information: Unsolicited requests for funds not accepted.
Officers: James C. Day, Pres.; Andrew Kanaly, Secy.; James C. Day, Jr., Treas.
EIN: 061742265

8801
DDM Foundation
108 E. Mistletoe Ave.
San Antonio, TX 78212-3407

Donors: Darcy S. Mix; Darryl W. Mix.
Foundation type: Operating foundation.
Financial data (yr. ended 12/31/13): Assets, $1,862,939 (M); gifts received, $17,295; expenditures, $254,372; qualifying distributions, $237,295; giving activities include $237,295 for 8 grants (high: $200,000; low: $500).
Fields of interest: Domesticated animals; Human services.
Limitations: Applications not accepted. Giving primarily in TX.
Application information: Unsolicited requests for funds not accepted.
Directors: Darcy S. Mix; Darryl W. Mix.
EIN: 271180664

8802
The Wallace de Compiegne Foundation
P.O. Box 10808
Midland, TX 79702-7808 4326825371

Established in 1994 in Texas.
Foundation type: Independent foundation.
Financial data (yr. ended 12/31/14): Assets, $3,129,101; expenditures, $240,173; qualifying distributions, $207,500.
Purpose and activities: Giving primarily for human service organizations.
Fields of interest: Arts and culture; Education; Human services.
Type of support: General support; Capital campaigns; Capital and infrastructure; Endowments; Scholarships; Research.
Limitations: Applications not accepted. Giving primarily in NM and TX. No grants to individuals.
Application information: Unsolicited requests for funds not accepted.
Trustees: Henri Joseph de Compiegne; Mary Wallace de Compiegne; Anne de Compiegne Lutz; Elise de Compiegne Shatto.
EIN: 752533153

8803
Matias De Llano Charitable Trust
c/o International Bank of Commerce
1200 San Bernardo Ave.
Laredo, TX 78042-1359

Established in 2003 in Texas.
Donor: Matias De Llano†.
Foundation type: Independent foundation.
Financial data (yr. ended 12/31/13): Assets, $10,132,785 (M); expenditures, $493,086; qualifying distributions, $439,892; giving activities include $410,000 for 2 grants (high: $400,000; low: $10,000).
Purpose and activities: Giving primarily for education, and children, youth, and social services.

Fields of interest: Education; Higher education; Human services; Child welfare; Youth services.
Limitations: Applications not accepted. Giving primarily in Laredo, TX. No grants to individuals.
Application information: Contributes only to pre-selected organizations.
Trustee: International Bank of Commerce.
EIN: 743013012

8804
Katrine Menzing Deakins Charitable Trust
c/o U.S. Trust, Bank of America, N.A.
500 W. 7th St., 15th Fl., TX-1-497-15-08
Fort Worth, TX 76102-4700 (817) 390-6028
Contact: Mark J. Smith, Philanthropic Rels. Mgr.
E-mail: tx.philanthropic@ustrust.com; Main URL: https://www.bankofamerica.com/philanthropic/grantmaking.go

Established in 1987 in Texas.
Foundation type: Independent foundation.
Financial data (yr. ended 03/31/13): Assets, $6,637,392 (M); expenditures, $434,664; qualifying distributions, $393,834; giving activities include $364,950 for 20 grants (high: $62,000; low: $2,500).
Fields of interest: Arts and culture; Performing arts; Education; Health; Diseases and conditions; Human services.
Type of support: General support.
Limitations: Applications accepted. Giving limited to TX. No grants to individuals.
Publications: Annual report (including application guidelines).
Application information:
Initial approach: Consult online guidelines on Trust web site
Deadline(s): Mar. 31 and Sept. 30
Trustee: Bank of America, N.A.
EIN: 756370503

8805
The Deason Foundation
5956 Sherry Ln., Ste. 800
Dallas, TX 75225-8035

Established in 1997 in Texas.
Donor: Darwin Deason.
Foundation type: Independent foundation.
Financial data (yr. ended 12/31/14): Assets, $26,937,295 (M); gifts received, $10,012,114; expenditures, $494,855; qualifying distributions, $430,987; giving activities include $425,650 for 15 grants (high: $150,000; low: $1,000).
Fields of interest: Education; Diseases and conditions; Christianity.
Type of support: General support; Research; Research and evaluation.
Limitations: Applications not accepted. Giving primarily in TX. No grants to individuals.
Application information: Contributes only to pre-selected organizations.
Officers: Darwin Deason, Pres. and Treas.; Asher Ladner, V.P. and Secy.; Douglas Deason, V.P.
EIN: 752715549

8806
DeBusk Foundation
207 E. Virginia St., Ste. 205
McKinney, TX 75069-4374 (972) 542-0811
E-mail: director@debuskfoundation.org; Main URL: http://www.debuskfoundation.org
Grants List: http://www.debuskfoundation.org/fundedprograms.html

Foundation type: Independent foundation.
Financial data (yr. ended 12/31/14): Assets, $6,275,039; expenditures, $376,486; qualifying distributions, $304,000.
Purpose and activities: The DeBusk Foundation makes grants to educational organizations for the purpose of providing financial assistance to gifted students 12 years of age and under who are classified as elementary students. Grants will be limited to the state of Texas and priority will be given to established organizations.
Fields of interest: Elementary and secondary education; Elementary education.
Type of support: Scholarships.
Limitations: Applications accepted. Giving limited to TX.
Publications: Application guidelines.
Application information: Application guidelines available on foundation web site. Application form required.
Copies of proposal: 8
Deadline(s): Oct. 15
Board meeting date(s): Feb., May, Aug., and Nov.
Final notification: Within 8-10 weeks of the deadline
Officers and Directors: Patricia McNutt, Pres. and Director; Diane Cooper, V.P. and Director; Kari Kolber, Secy. and Director; Keith Belcher, Treas. and Director; Mike Tibbals; Marty Webb.
EIN: 751671193

8807
The Patricia Dedman Family Foundation
5956 Sherry Ln., Ste. 1800
Dallas, TX 75225-8029

Established in 2007 in Texas.
Donor: Nancy Dedman.
Foundation type: Independent foundation.
Financial data (yr. ended 12/31/12): Assets, $4,333,689 (M); expenditures, $214,669; qualifying distributions, $174,762; giving activities include $174,762 for 23 grants (high: $77,737; low: $64).
Purpose and activities: Giving primarily for the arts, education, and human services.
Fields of interest: Visual arts; Performing arts; Education; Botanical gardens; Foundations; Community and economic development; Protestantism; Human services.
Limitations: Applications not accepted. Giving primarily in Aspen, CO, and TX, with emphasis on Dallas.
Application information: Contributes only to pre-selected organizations.
Directors: Patricia Brown Dedman; Christina Dedman Dietz; Jonathan Dedman Dietz.
EIN: 260209206

8808
The Robert H. Dedman, Jr. Family Foundation
5956 Sherry Ln., Ste. 1800
Dallas, TX 75225-8029

Established in 2007 in Texas.
Donor: Nancy M. Dedman.
Foundation type: Independent foundation.
Financial data (yr. ended 12/31/13): Assets, $4,686,605 (M); expenditures, $275,331; qualifying distributions, $232,132; giving activities include $232,132 for 8 grants (high: $86,336; low: $2,000).
Fields of interest: Art museums; Education; Elementary and secondary education; Air quality; Nonprofits; Community and economic development; Protestantism; Human services.
Type of support: Regranting.
Limitations: Applications not accepted. Giving primarily in Dallas, TX. No grants to individuals.
Application information: Contributes only to pre-selected organizations.
Officer: Robert H. Dedman, Jr., Pres. and Treas.
Directors: Rachael Redekker Dedman; Forest Bradford Kelly.
EIN: 260209159

8809
Dehan Family Foundation
c/o Stephen E. Dehan
P.O. Box 92889
Austin, TX 78709-2889

Established in 1997 in Texas.
Donors: Stephen E. Dehan; Alison Dehan.
Foundation type: Independent foundation.
Financial data (yr. ended 12/31/13): Assets, $8,213,807 (M); gifts received, $983,712; expenditures, $389,334; qualifying distributions, $300,000; giving activities include $300,000 for 15 grants (high: $50,000; low: $10,000).
Fields of interest: Catholicism.
Limitations: Applications not accepted. Giving primarily in Austin, San Antonio, and Fort Worth, TX. No grants to individuals.
Application information: Unsolicited requests for funds not accepted.
Officers and Directors: Stephen E. Dehan, Pres. and Treas. and Director; Alison Dehan, V.P. and Secy. and Director; Kristin Baier; Laura Byrne; Susan Dehan.
EIN: 742807323

8810
Denman Family Foundation
4208 Versailles
Dallas, TX 75205

Established in 2003 in Texas.
Donor: John L. Denman, Jr.
Foundation type: Independent foundation.
Financial data (yr. ended 12/31/13): Assets, $1,531,163 (M); gifts received, $128,726; expenditures, $209,863; qualifying distributions, $198,077; giving activities include $195,877 for 45 grants (high: $85,000; low: $50), and $2,200 for 1 grant to an individual.
Fields of interest: Education; Religion; Christianity; Human services.
Type of support: Grants to individuals.

Limitations: Applications not accepted. Giving primarily in TX.
Application information: Unsolicited requests for funds not accepted.
Officers and Directors: John L. Denman, Jr., Pres. and Director; Patricia Denman, Secy.-Treas.; Alexander Chae.
EIN: 200222678

8811
David H. Dewhurst Foundation
109 N. Post Oak Ln., Ste. 540
Houston, TX 77024-7791

Established in 1993 in Texas.
Donors: David H. Dewhurst; The David Dewhurst Blind Trust; Harlan R. Crow.
Foundation type: Independent foundation.
Financial data (yr. ended 12/31/13): Assets, $39,156 (M); gifts received, $550; expenditures, $388,677; qualifying distributions, $344,880; giving activities include $344,880 for 4 grants (high: $136,807; low: $15,736).
Purpose and activities: Giving primarily to a D-day-related museum in France.
Fields of interest: Museums.
International interests: France.
Limitations: Applications not accepted. Giving primarily in France. No grants to individuals.
Application information: Unsolicited requests for funds not accepted.
Officers: David H. Dewhurst, Pres.; Howard Wolf, V.P.; Eugene H. Dewhurst, Secy.-Treas.
EIN: 760420739

8812
The Enrico & Sandra di Portanova Charitable Foundation
P.O. Box 27285
Houston, TX 77227-7285

Established in 1993 in Texas.
Foundation type: Independent foundation.
Financial data (yr. ended 12/31/14): Assets, $5,793,814 (M); expenditures, $516,072; qualifying distributions, $275,000; giving activities include $275,000 for 31 grants (high: $15,000; low: $500).
Purpose and activities: Giving primarily for children, youth, and social services, as well as for higher education and health care.
Fields of interest: Higher education; Medical education; Health; Human services; Family services; Child welfare.
Type of support: General support.
Limitations: Applications not accepted. Giving primarily in Houston, TX. No grants to individuals.
Application information: Contributes only to pre-selected organizations.
Officers: Lewis M. Linn, Pres.; Esther M. Perrine, Secy.-Treas.
Director: Jennifer Hovas.
EIN: 760408460

8813
Diamond M Foundation, Inc.
c/o Mark Mclaughlin
2201 Sherwood Way, Ste. 201
San Angelo, TX 76901-3081

Established in 1950 in Texas.
Donor: C.T. McLaughlin†.
Foundation type: Operating foundation.
Financial data (yr. ended 12/31/13): Assets, $6,948,329 (M); expenditures, $199,708; qualifying distributions, $160,715; giving activities include $160,715 for 4 grants (high: $61,740; low: $18,975).
Purpose and activities: Giving primarily for activities relating to ranching history, including a ranching heritage museum.
Fields of interest: Historical activities; Higher education.
Type of support: General support.
Limitations: Applications not accepted. Giving primarily in TX. No grants to individuals.
Application information: Contributes only to pre-selected organizations.
Officer: John Mark McLaughlin, Pres.
Directors: Evelyn McLaughlin Davies; Deborah Deford Dunkum; Barbara Riddle Fendley; Brian T. McLaughlin.
Number of staff: 1 full-time professional; 1 full-time support; 1 part-time support.
EIN: 756015426

8814
Bruce B. Dice Foundation
c/o Bruce B. Dice
4355 Sylvanfield Dr., Ste. 200
Houston, TX 77014-1612

Donor: Bruce B. Dice.
Foundation type: Independent foundation.
Financial data (yr. ended 05/31/13): Assets, $458,868 (M); gifts received, $220,936; expenditures, $234,282; qualifying distributions, $227,313; giving activities include $227,313 for grants.
Fields of interest: Education; Higher education.
Type of support: General support; Individual development.
Limitations: Applications not accepted. Giving primarily in TX. No grants to individuals.
Application information: Contributes only to pre-selected organizations.
Officers: Bruce B. Dice, Chair.; Kevin B. Dice, Pres.; Kirk Brian Dice, Secy.-Treas.
EIN: 760538023

8815
Albert & Mary Dick Charitable Trust
1 Oconnor Plz.
Victoria, TX 77901
Application address: c/o Gary Worsham, P. O. Box 511, Victoria, TX 77902, tel.: (361) 574-5111

Established in 1991 in Unspecified.
Donors: Albert Dick†; Betty Zoe†.
Foundation type: Independent foundation.
Financial data (yr. ended 12/31/13): Assets, $3,525,522 (M); expenditures, $229,395; qualifying distributions, $191,266; giving activities include $181,000 for 27 grants (high: $20,000; low: $2,000).
Fields of interest: Addiction services; Human services.
Type of support: Program development; Matching grants; Equipment; Continuing support; General support.

Limitations: Applications accepted. Giving primarily in Victoria County, TX. No grants to individuals.
Application information: Application form required.
Initial approach: Letter
Deadline(s): Semiannually May 5 and Nov. 5
Trustees: Gary Worsham; Wells Fargo Trust Department.
Number of staff: None.
EIN: 746388649

8816
The Discovery Fund
P.O. Box 2140
Fort Worth, TX 76113-2140
Application address: c/o Lucy Darden, 801 Cherry St., Ste. 3700, Fort Worth, TX 76102, tel.: (817) 665-5000

Established in 1984 in Texas.
Donors: Frank Darden†; Glenn Darden; Thomas Darden.
Foundation type: Operating foundation.
Financial data (yr. ended 12/31/13): Assets, $2,485,782 (M); expenditures, $226,569; qualifying distributions, $225,567; giving activities include $222,000 for 26 grants (high: $20,000; low: $2,000).
Fields of interest: Museums; Science museums; Education; Diseases and conditions.
Limitations: Applications accepted. Giving primarily in Fort Worth, TX. No grants to individuals.
Application information: Application form required.
Initial approach: Letter
Deadline(s): None
Officers: Lucy Darden, Chair. and Pres.; Paul Coulter, V.P. and Secy.-Treas.
Director: Peter Philpott.
EIN: 751989523

8817
DKG Foundation
4501 W. Lake Dr.
Austin, TX 78746 (832) 721-5600
Contact: Dean B. Truitt, Pres. and Dir.

Donors: Dean B. Truitt; Glenda A. Truitt; Citi Global Impact Funding Trust, Inc.; Dean B. Truitt Individual Retirement Account.
Foundation type: Operating foundation.
Financial data (yr. ended 12/31/13): Assets, $855,584 (M); gifts received, $68,800; expenditures, $166,917; qualifying distributions, $160,250; giving activities include $160,250 for 8 + grants (high: $120,000).
Fields of interest: Christianity; Human services.
Limitations: Applications accepted. Giving primarily in AZ and TX. No grants to individuals.
Application information: Application form required.
Initial approach: Letter
Deadline(s): None
Officers and Directors: Dean B. Truitt, Pres. and Director; Krista Truitt Borgen, V.P. and Director; Dean B. Truitt II, V.P. and Director; Glenda A. Truitt, Secy.-Treas. and Director.
EIN: 721521260

8818
Clifton C. and Henryetta C. Doak Charitable Trust
c/o Wells Fargo Bank Texas, N.A.
P.O. Drawer 913
Bryan, TX 77805-0913 (979) 776-3267
E-mail: grantadministration@wellsfargo.com; Main URL: https://www.wellsfargo.com/privatefoundationgrants/doak

Established in 1993 in Texas.
Donor: Henryetta C. Doak†.
Foundation type: Independent foundation.
Financial data (yr. ended 12/31/13): Assets, $3,580,022 (M); expenditures, $193,802; qualifying distributions, $160,975; giving activities include $144,000 for 12 grants (high: $25,000; low: $2,000).
Fields of interest: Arts and culture; Education; Higher education; Human services; Youth development.
Limitations: Applications accepted. Giving limited to the Brazos County, TX area. No grants to individuals.
Publications: Application guidelines.
Application information: Complete application guidelines and procedures available on trust web site. Application form required.
Initial approach: Online application system on trust web site
Deadline(s): July 31
Trustee: Wells Fargo Bank Texas, N.A.
EIN: 746402510

8819
Mary Louise Dobson Foundation
P.O. Box 588
Wharton, TX 77488-7727 (979) 282-7000

Established in 2001 in Texas.
Donors: Story Estate; Mary Louise Dobson; Dwight D. King; Jane Dobson Rice; TEAM Wharton.
Foundation type: Independent foundation.
Financial data (yr. ended 12/31/13): Assets, $5,994,546 (M); gifts received, $193,065; expenditures, $419,494; qualifying distributions, $326,114; giving activities include $326,114 for 10 grants (high: $282,655; low: $200).
Fields of interest: Education; Christianity; Human services; Child welfare.
Application information: Application form required.
Initial approach: Proposal
Deadline(s): None
Officers: Mary Louise Dobson, Pres.; Jane Dobson Rice, V.P.; Jeanene D. Merka, Secy.-Treas.; Abby K. Burditt, Exec. Dir.
Directors: Don Hillis; Billie H. Jones; Jimmy Schulze.
EIN: 760690889

8820
The Sean Joslyn Sean-Karl and Johanna Grace Dobson Foundation
2916 Waterbank Cove
Austin, TX 78746-4137

Foundation type: Independent foundation.
Financial data (yr. ended 12/31/13): Assets, $63,762 (M); gifts received, $300,000; expenditures, $261,228; qualifying distributions, $255,927; giving activities include $255,927 for 14 grants (high: $118,977; low: $50).
Fields of interest: Education; Health.

Limitations: Applications not accepted. Giving primarily in MA.
Application information: Unsolicited requests for funds not accepted.
Directors: Joslyn Dobson; Sean Dobson; Valari Dobson Staab.
EIN: 274335578

8821
James M. Donnell Family Foundation
c/o Andrew B. Linbeck
4265 San Felipe St., Ste. 900
Houston, TX 77027-2929

Donor: James Donna Donnell.
Foundation type: Independent foundation.
Financial data (yr. ended 12/31/13): Assets, $950,093 (M); gifts received, $3,680; expenditures, $337,148; qualifying distributions, $331,840; giving activities include $330,000 for 5 grants (high: $160,000; low: $10,000).
Fields of interest: Health; Protestantism.
Limitations: Applications not accepted. Giving primarily in TX.
Application information: Unsolicited requests for funds not accepted.
Officers: James M. Donnell, Pres.; Donna P. Donnell, Secy.; Andrew B. Linbeck, Treas.
EIN: 383733222

8822
Dooley Family Foundation
P.O. Box 6149
San Antonio, TX 78209-0149 (210) 824-0187
Contact: Arthur Rhew Dooley, Tr.; Sally Conway Dooley, Tr.

Established in 1997 in Texas.
Donors: Arthur Rhew Dooley; Sally C. Dooley; Sally C. Dooley Family Trust.
Foundation type: Independent foundation.
Financial data (yr. ended 12/31/13): Assets, $1,124,253 (M); gifts received, $319,162; expenditures, $179,778; qualifying distributions, $166,850; giving activities include $166,850 for 39 grants (high: $50,000; low: $100).
Fields of interest: Education; Protestantism; Human services.
Limitations: Applications accepted. Giving primarily in TX.
Application information: Application form required.
Initial approach: Letter or Telephone call
Deadline(s): None
Trustees: Arthur R. Dooley, Jr.; Chris C. Dooley; Sally C. Dooley; Courtney Dooley Duphorne.
EIN: 760536719

8823
The Ben and Mary Frances Doskocil Private Foundation
P.O. Box 180277
Arlington, TX 76096-0277

Established in 2004 in Texas.
Donors: Twelve D Limited; Benjamin L. Doskocil, Sr.; Edward Joseph Doskocil; Mary Frances Doskocil.
Foundation type: Independent foundation.
Financial data (yr. ended 12/31/13): Assets, $10,101,379 (M); gifts received, $940,008; expenditures, $437,810; qualifying distributions,

$392,917; giving activities include $386,450 for 15 grants (high: $100,000; low: $2,000).
Fields of interest: Education; Catholicism; Youth services.
Limitations: Applications not accepted. Giving primarily in TX. No grants to individuals.
Application information: Unsolicited requests for funds not accepted.
Officers: Benjamin L. Doskocil, Sr., Pres. and Treas.; Edward Joseph Doskocil, V.P.; Mary Frances Doskocil, Secy.
EIN: 752715940

8824
Lucille and John B. Dougherty Trust
c/o Wells Fargo Bank, N.A.
P.O. Box 913
Bryan, TX   77805-0913   (979) 776-3267
E-mail: grantadministration@wellsfargo.com; Main URL: https://www.wellsfargo.com/privatefoundationgrants/dougherty

Established in 2008 in Texas.
Foundation type: Independent foundation.
Financial data (yr. ended 12/31/13): Assets, $5,682,902 (M); expenditures, $341,215; qualifying distributions, $273,288; giving activities include $248,500 for 18 grants (high: $45,000; low: $1,000).
Fields of interest: Education; Health; Christianity.
Limitations: Applications accepted. Giving primarily in Bryan, The Woodlands, College Station, TX.
Application information: See foundation website for complete application guidelines. Application form required.
   Initial approach: Proposal
   Deadline(s): July 31
Trustees: William S. Thornton; Wells Fargo Bank, N.A.
EIN: 261444071

8825
James R. Dougherty, Jr. Foundation, Inc
P.O. Box 640
Beeville, TX   78104-0640   (361) 358-3560
Contact: Daren R. Wilder, Treas.

Established in 1950 in Texas.
Foundation type: Independent foundation.
Financial data (yr. ended 12/31/13): Assets, $7,322,766 (M); expenditures, $421,244; qualifying distributions, $357,461; giving activities include $338,500 for 122 grants (high: $15,000; low: $50).
Fields of interest: Human services; Domestic violence shelters; Females.
Type of support: General support; Matching grants; Continuing support; Financial sustainability; Capacity-building and technical assistance; Annual campaigns; Capital campaigns; Capital and infrastructure; Equipment; Endowments; Program development; Seed money; Curriculum development; Scholarships; Research; Technical assistance; Program evaluations.
Limitations: Applications accepted. Giving primarily in TX. No grants to individuals.
Application information:
   Initial approach: Letter
   Copies of proposal: 1
   Deadline(s): Mar. 1 and Sept. 1
   Board meeting date(s): Spring and fall

Officers and Directors: Ben F. Vaughan III, Pres. and Director; Frances Carr Tapp, Secy. and Director; Daren R. Wilder, Treas.; Rachael Carr; Racheel Pauley; Beatrice Rossi-Landi; Genevieve Vaughan.
Number of staff: 1 part-time professional; 2 part-time support.
EIN: 020583552

8826
Grant A. and Peg Brady Dove Foundation
c/o BOA/ US Trust
P.O. Box 831041
Dallas, TX   75283-1041
Application address: c/o Peg Dove, P.O Box 2349, Rancho de Taos, NM 87557, (972) 931-8217

Established in 2001 in Texas.
Donors: Grant Dove; Margaret Dove.
Foundation type: Independent foundation.
Financial data (yr. ended 12/31/13): Assets, $2,287,856 (M); gifts received, $200,000; expenditures, $193,525; qualifying distributions, $179,262; giving activities include $165,000 for 7 grants (high: $50,000; low: $10,000).
Fields of interest: Education; Diseases and conditions; Human services.
Type of support: Research.
Limitations: Applications accepted. Giving primarily in TX.
Application information: Application form required.
   Initial approach: Letter
   Deadline(s): None
Officer: Timothy L. Dove, Secy.
Directors: Brian J. Dove; Eugene M. Dove; Margaret Dove; Terence B. Dove.
EIN: 752877193

8827
Mario Dozzo Foundation
14500 Winwood Rd.
Dallas, TX   75254-7639

Established in 2007 in Texas.
Donor: Mario Dozzo.
Foundation type: Independent foundation.
Financial data (yr. ended 12/31/12): Assets, $3,735,367 (M); expenditures, $179,975; qualifying distributions, $150,168; giving activities include $150,168 for 10 grants (high: $30,000; low: $5,000).
Fields of interest: Diseases and conditions.
Type of support: Research.
Limitations: Applications not accepted. Giving primarily in TX and VA.
Application information: Contributes only to pre-selected organizations.
Directors: David Dozzo; Joseph Dozzo; Mario Dozzo; Katherine Fletcher; Allison Wright.
EIN: 392050389

8828
Dubose Family Foundation
P.O. Box 2990
Fort Worth, TX   76113-2990
Application address: c/o Anna Adams Dubose, 2624 West Freeway, Fort Worth, TX 76102, tel.: (817) 390-2202

Established in 2004 in Texas.
Donors: James S. Dubose; JS & JL Subose Trust.

Foundation type: Independent foundation.
Financial data (yr. ended 12/31/13): Assets, $13,354,302 (M); gifts received, $1,323,558; expenditures, $459,304; qualifying distributions, $401,721; giving activities include $401,721 for 94 grants (high: $60,000; low: $100).
Fields of interest: Arts and culture; Elementary and secondary education; Nonprofits; School-based health care; Diseases and conditions; Protestantism.
Type of support: Regranting.
Limitations: Applications accepted. Giving primarily in TX. No grants to individuals.
Application information: Application form required.
   Initial approach: Letter
   Deadline(s): None
Officer: Anna A. Dubose, Pres.
Directors: James E. Dubose; James S. Dubose; Christopher J. Keyland; Kathryn J. Roberts.
EIN: 201588677

8829
Wayne Duddlesten Foundation
2600 S. Gessner Rd., Ste. 111
Houston, TX   77063-3214

Donors: Wayne B. Duddlesten; TBJ Properties, Inc.
Foundation type: Independent foundation.
Financial data (yr. ended 12/31/13): Assets, $29,792,905 (M); gifts received, $24,133,232; expenditures, $423,348; qualifying distributions, $265,069; giving activities include $243,500 for 15 grants (high: $50,000; low: $500).
Fields of interest: Education; Human services; Youth development.
Limitations: Applications not accepted. Giving primarily in TX. No grants to individuals.
Application information: Unsolicited requests for funds not accepted.
Officers and Directors: Charles McMahen, Pres. and Director; Karen A. Duddlesten, V.P. and Director; Jerri Moore, Secy. and Director; David Kantorczyk, Treas. and Director; Terri Duddlesten; Kathy L. Young.
EIN: 760003093

8830
Joseph F. Dulaney Foundation
c/o Bank of America, N.A.
P.O. Box 831041
Dallas, TX   75283-1041

Foundation type: Independent foundation.
Financial data (yr. ended 08/31/13): Assets, $4,728,524 (M); expenditures, $209,602; qualifying distributions, $208,535; giving activities include $207,285 for 3 grants (high: $190,703; low: $8,291).
Fields of interest: Education; Religion; Human services.
Limitations: Applications not accepted. Giving primarily in CA, some giving also in TX. No grants to individuals.
Application information: Unsolicited requests for funds not accepted.
Trustee: Bank of America, N.A.
EIN: 756085990

8831
Dunagan Foundation, Inc.
P.O. Box 387
Monahans, TX   79756-0387

Established in 1976 in Texas.
Donors: John C. Dunagan; J. Conrad Dunagan†; Kathlyn C. Dunagan.
Foundation type: Independent foundation.
Financial data (yr. ended 12/31/13): Assets, $9,295,053 (M); expenditures, $438,816; qualifying distributions, $339,783; giving activities include $309,250 for 37 grants (high: $100,000; low: $500).
Purpose and activities: Giving primarily for education, youth and the arts.
Fields of interest: Arts and culture; Theater; Education; Cancers; Christianity; Human services; Youth development.
Type of support: Continuing support; Capital and infrastructure; Equipment; Program development; Professorships; Scholarships.
Limitations: Applications not accepted. No grants to individuals.
Application information: Unsolicited requests for funds not accepted.
  Board meeting date(s): Jan., Apr., July, and Oct.
Officers: John C. Dunagan, Pres.; Kathy Dunagan, Secy.
Trustees: Carol Husbands; Clay Dunagan; Deanna Dunagan.
EIN: 751561848

8832
The Carol Winn and James Reed Dunaway Family Foundation, Inc.
777 Taylor St., Ste. 1040
Fort Worth, TX   76102-4910

Established in 1999 in Texas.
Donors: James Reed Dunaway; Carol Winn Dunaway.
Foundation type: Independent foundation.
Financial data (yr. ended 12/31/13): Assets, $1,432,233 (M); expenditures, $319,738; qualifying distributions, $312,750; giving activities include $312,750 for 34 grants (high: $200,000; low: $200).
Fields of interest: Diseases and conditions; Human services; Youth development.
Type of support: General support; Annual campaigns; Capital and infrastructure.
Limitations: Applications not accepted. Giving primarily in Fort Worth, TX. No grants to individuals.
Application information: Contributes only to pre-selected organizations.
Officers: Carol Winn Dunaway, Co-Chair.; James Reed Dunaway, Co-Chair.
Directors: Bryan Winn Dunaway; Scott Michael Dunaway; Christina Dunaway-Smith.
EIN: 752770176

8833
The Lillian H. and C. W. Duncan Foundation
600 Travis St., Ste. 6100
Houston, TX   77002-3013
Application address: c/o Sherry Ashley, Salient Partners, 4265 San Felipe St., 8th Fl., Houston, TX 77027-2920; tel.: (713) 993-4695

Established in 1964 in Texas.
Donor: C.W. Duncan†.
Foundation type: Independent foundation.
Financial data (yr. ended 12/31/13): Assets, $5,179,847 (L); expenditures, $291,055; qualifying distributions, $231,257; giving activities include $231,242 for 28 grants (high: $48,000; low: $500).
Purpose and activities: Giving primarily to museums and education.
Fields of interest: Arts and culture; Performing arts; Museums; Education; Elementary and secondary education; Diseases and conditions; Human services; Child welfare.
Limitations: Applications accepted. Giving primarily in Houston, TX. No grants to individuals.
Publications: Application guidelines.
Application information: Application form required.
  Initial approach: Letter
  Copies of proposal: 1
  Deadline(s): None
  Board meeting date(s): 3 times per-year
Officers: John H. Duncan, Jr., Chair.; C.W. Duncan, Jr., Pres.; C.W. Duncan III, V.P.; Nena Marsh, V.P.; Laura Meinharot, Secy.-Treas.
Directors: Mary A. Dingus; Anne S. Duncan; Emily C. Duncan; Kate D. Oshins.
EIN: 746064215

8834
The Dunham Charitable Foundation
c/o Woodway Financial Advisors
10000 Memorial Dr., Ste. 650
Houston, TX   77024-3417

Established in 1997 in Texas.
Donors: Archie Dunham; Linda Dunham.
Foundation type: Independent foundation.
Financial data (yr. ended 09/30/13): Assets, $3,161,588 (M); expenditures, $210,237; qualifying distributions, $190,010; giving activities include $190,010 for 5 grants (high: $172,510; low: $2,500).
Fields of interest: Education; Religion.
Type of support: General support.
Limitations: Applications not accepted. Giving primarily in CA. No grants to individuals.
Application information: Unsolicited requests for funds not accepted.
Officers and Directors: Archie Dunham, Pres. and Director; Cary Dunham, V.P. and Director; Linda Dunham, V.P. and Director; Steve Dunham, V.P. and Director; Laura Shook, V.P. and Director.
EIN: 760554767

8835
Devary Durrill Foundation, Inc.
615 S. Upper Broadway
Corpus Christi, TX   78401-3432
Contact: Donna Kelly
Main URL: http://devarydurrillfoundation.org

Established in 1984 in Texas.
Donor: William R. Durrill.
Foundation type: Independent foundation.
Financial data (yr. ended 12/31/14): Assets, $8,908,208; gifts received, $47,500; expenditures, $868,163; qualifying distributions, $485,450.
Purpose and activities: Giving primarily, but not limited to projects such as educational, medical, social services, civic beautification and development, and environmental.
Fields of interest: University education; Human services.
Limitations: Giving primarily in the Corpus Christi, TX, area. No grants to individuals, or for debt, or administration costs.
Publications: Application guidelines.
Application information: Application form available on foundation web site. Application form required.
  Initial approach: Refer to guidelines on foundation web site
Officer: William R. Durrill, Pres.
Directors: Ginger Durrill; Melissa Durrill; Michele Durrill; William R. Durrill, Jr.
EIN: 742370613

8836
Educational Advancement Foundation
327 Congress Ave., Ste. 500
Austin, TX   78701-3656   (512) 469-1700
E-mail: info@edu-adv-foundation.org; Application address: c/o Grant Committee: 2303 Rio Grande St., Austin, TX 78705; Main URL: http://www.educationaladvancementfoundation.org
Grants List: http://www.eduadvance.org/history_files/grants_2013.pdf

Established in 1969 in Texas.
Donors: Harry Lucas, Jr.; Louis Beecherl; Kodosky Foundation; Lucas Petroleum Group; Gayle Ball; William Mahavier; E. Paul Mosbo; David Murphy; Allen Stenger; Larry Wadle; Kenneth Whipple; Coke S. Reed.
Foundation type: Independent foundation.
Financial data (yr. ended 12/31/13): Assets, $3,430,815 (M); gifts received, $608,849; expenditures, $927,901; qualifying distributions, $810,481; giving activities include $293,905 for 29 grants (high: $91,696; low: $1,500), and $308,401 for 4 foundation-administered programs.
Purpose and activities: Giving primarily to organizations that support 1) the development and implementation of inquiry-based learning at all educational levels in the U.S., particularly in the fields of mathematics and science, and 2) the preservation and dissemination of the inquiry-based learning methodology of Dr. R.L. Moore (1882-1974), renowned professor of mathematics at the University of Texas at Austin from 1920-1969.
Fields of interest: Education; Higher education; Mathematics.
Type of support: Endowments; Grants to individuals; Seed money; Research.
Limitations: Applications accepted. Giving primarily in TX. No grants for operating expenses, endowments, scholarships, or for capital projects.
Publications: Application guidelines; Informational brochure.
Application information: See foundation web site for downloadable grant application package, application guidelines and procedures. Application form required.
  Initial approach: Use online application form only. See foundation web site for specific instructions
  Deadline(s): See web site for current deadlines
Officers and Trustees: Harry Lucas, Chair. and Trustee; Albert Lewis, Ph.D, Secy. and Trustee; Fain Brock, Treas.; Hamilton Beazley, Ph.D; Ron Douglas, Ph.D; Tina Straley.

Advisory Committee: Greg Cotter; Bob Lawless; Carol Lucas.
Number of staff: 1 part-time support.
EIN: 237001761

8837
Kirk Edwards Foundation
4201 Bluff View Dr.
Granbury, TX 76048-5013

Established in 1966 in Texas.
Donor: A.B. Kirk Edwards†.
Foundation type: Independent foundation.
Financial data (yr. ended 10/31/14): Assets, $3,444,994 (M); expenditures, $231,271; qualifying distributions, $183,657; giving activities include $174,500 for 17 grants (high: $40,000; low: $1,500).
Fields of interest: Education; University education; Children's hospital care; Rehabilitation; Catholicism; Human services; Child welfare; Youth development; Youth services; Children and youth; People with disabilities.
Type of support: General support; Scholarships.
Limitations: Applications not accepted. Giving in TX, primarily in Dallas, Henrietta, Houston, and Wichita Falls. No grants to individuals.
Application information: Contributes only to pre-selected organizations.
Officers and Trustees: Carolyn Sullivan, Pres. and Trustee; George Slagle, V.P. and Trustee; Elizabeth Young, Secy. and Trustee; David J. Walch, Treas. and Trustee; Henry Medaris; Wilson Scaling; Edwin Taegel.
EIN: 756054922

8838
J. A. and Isabel M. Elkins Foundation
c/o Paraffine Management
1001 Fannin St., Ste. 1001
Houston, TX 77002-6708
Contact: Larry Medford

Established in 1956 in Texas.
Foundation type: Independent foundation.
Financial data (yr. ended 08/31/13): Assets, $5,210,478 (M); expenditures, $288,057; qualifying distributions, $240,000; giving activities include $240,000 for grants.
Purpose and activities: Grants primarily for religious, charitable, scientific, or educational agencies, institutions, and corporations. General focus on churches and religious associations; child welfare, hospitals, and health agencies; scientific organizations sponsoring research; and schools and universities.
Fields of interest: Education; Higher education; Hospital care; Diseases and conditions; Science; Technology; Religion; Child welfare.
Type of support: Capital campaigns; Capital and infrastructure; Equipment; Endowments; Research; Emergency funds; Research and evaluation; Program development.
Limitations: Applications accepted. Giving primarily in TX, with emphasis on the metropolitan Houston area. No grants to individuals, or for deficit financing; generally no grants for continuing operating support.
Application information:
Initial approach: Letter
Deadline(s): None

Trustees: Margaret Elise Elkins Joseph; William L. Medford; Leslie Keith Elkins Sasser.
Number of staff: None.
EIN: 746047894

8839
The Aaron and Catie Enrico Family Foundation
3601 Greenbrier Dr.
University Park, TX 75225-5106

Established in 2007 in Texas.
Donor: Roger A. Enrico.
Foundation type: Independent foundation.
Financial data (yr. ended 12/31/13): Assets, $5,979,191 (M); gifts received, $313,323; expenditures, $258,200; qualifying distributions, $258,200; giving activities include $258,200 for 24 grants (high: $59,875; low: $10).
Fields of interest: Higher education; Family services.
Limitations: Applications not accepted. No grants to individuals.
Application information: Unsolicited requests for funds not accepted.
Officers and Directors: Aaron J. Enrico, Chair.; Catherine B. Enrico, Pres. and Director; Rosemary Enrico, V.P.; Terence C. Sullivan, Secy.-Treas. and Director.
EIN: 261548483

8840
EOS Foundation
P.O. Box 121938
Fort Worth, TX 76121-1938

Donor: Gwendolyn Weiner.
Foundation type: Independent foundation.
Financial data (yr. ended 09/30/13): Assets, $6,408,550 (M); gifts received, $1,100,000; expenditures, $205,884; qualifying distributions, $201,241; giving activities include $193,850 for 42 grants (high: $40,000; low: $600).
Fields of interest: Arts and culture; Education; Human services.
Type of support: General support.
Limitations: Applications not accepted. Giving in the U.S., with emphasis on CA, MO, NY, TX, and the metropolitan Washington, DC, area, including MD and VA. No grants to individuals.
Application information: Contributes only to pre-selected organizations.
Officers: Gwendolyn Weiner, Pres.; Carol Klein, Secy.
Directors: Joanie Harris; Marion Holbrook.
EIN: 205202818

8841
Esping Family Foundation
2828 Routh St., Ste. 500
Dallas, TX 75201-1438 (214) 849-9808
Contact: Heather H. Esping, Pres.
FAX: (214) 849-9807;
E-mail: hesping@espingfamilyfoundation.org; Main URL: http://www.espingfamilyfoundation.org

Established in 1997 in Texas.
Donor: Perry E. Esping†.
Foundation type: Independent foundation.

Financial data (yr. ended 12/31/13): Assets, $9,574,626 (M); expenditures, $644,992; qualifying distributions, $459,885; giving activities include $406,000 for 11 grants (high: $200,000; low: $10,000).
Purpose and activities: Giving to help others help themselves by supporting active programs with strong leadership and entrepreneurial activity. Grants are made in four categories: education, human services, health, and arts and culture. Within these categories, the foundation gives priority to projects that target 3 primary program areas: improving the education outcomes of Texas children (K-12), children and families, and youth development.
Fields of interest: Arts and culture; Education; Elementary and secondary education; Health; Human services; Family services; Child welfare; Youth development.
Type of support: Continuing support; Equipment; Program development; Curriculum development; Scholarships; Research.
Limitations: Applications accepted. Giving limited to the Dallas-Fort Worth, TX, Metroplex, with most of its grant resources going to organizations helping those in the Dallas area. No support for school sports or bands, church or seminary construction, or single artistic events or performances. No grants for individual scholarships, underwriting for charity balls or fundraising events, endowment or permanent funds, professional conferences and symposia (unless directly related to the foundation's areas of high interest), travel, or capital campaigns; no loans.
Publications: Grants list.
Application information: See foundation website for complete application guidelines. Application form required.
Initial approach: Proposal
Copies of proposal: 1
Board meeting date(s): May and Nov.
Officers and Directors: William P. Esping, Chair.; Heather H. Esping, Pres. and Director; Jennifer E. Kirtland, V.P. and Secy. and Director; Julie E. Blanton, V.P. and Treas. and Director; Darren Blanton; John E. Kirtland; Kathryn Esping Woods; Rodney Woods.
Number of staff: 2 part-time support.
EIN: 752702676

8842
Ethel Frends Charitable Foundation
c/o Bank of America, N.A.
P.O. Box 831041
Dallas, TX 75283-1041
E-mail: hector.m.santillan@ustrust.com

Established in 1997 in California.
Donor: Ethel Frends†.
Foundation type: Independent foundation.
Financial data (yr. ended 02/28/13): Assets, $3,712,640 (M); expenditures, $246,534; qualifying distributions, $181,220; giving activities include $135,000 for 31 grants (high: $16,000; low: $1,500).
Purpose and activities: To support and promote canine care and/or canine education.
Fields of interest: Domesticated animals; Animal welfare.
Limitations: Applications not accepted. Giving primarily in Los Angeles, Ventura, Santa Barbara, San Luis Obispo, Orange, Riverside, San Bernardino, and San Diego counties, CA. No grants to individuals.

Application information: Unsolicited requests for funds not accepted.
Trustee: Bank of America, N.A.
EIN: 597246019

8843
Fabenco Founding Fathers Foundation
2001 Karbach St., Ste. J
Houston, TX 77092-8425
Main URL: http://www.the4f.org

Established in 2007 in Texas.
Donor: David H. LaCook.
Foundation type: Independent foundation.
Financial data (yr. ended 09/30/13): Assets, $570,677 (M); gifts received, $450,000; expenditures, $186,334; qualifying distributions, $186,000; giving activities include $186,000 for 27 grants (high: $150,000; low: $1,000).
Fields of interest: Education; Health; Religion.
Limitations: Applications not accepted. Giving primarily in PA, TX. No grants to individuals.
Application information: Unsolicited requests for funds not accepted.
Directors: Dou B. Henderson; Diane H. Holhain; David LaCook; Michele LaCook.
EIN: 205114069

8844
The R. W. Fair Foundation
P.O. Box 689
Tyler, TX 75710-0689 (903) 510-6535
Contact: Barbara King Fair, Pres.

Donors: R.W. Fair†; Mattie Allen Fair†; R.W. Fair Trust.
Foundation type: Independent foundation.
Financial data (yr. ended 12/31/13): Assets, $13,706,218 (M); expenditures, $416,279; qualifying distributions, $270,556; giving activities include $270,000 for 51 grants (high: $50,500; low: $500).
Purpose and activities: Giving primarily for education, health, youth and social services, and United Methodist agencies and churches.
Fields of interest: Higher education; Diseases and conditions; Community and economic development; Presbyterianism; Human services; Family services; Child welfare.
Type of support: Capital and infrastructure; Matching grants; Equipment; Endowments; Program development; Seed money; Research.
Limitations: Applications accepted. Giving primarily in TX, with emphasis on Tyler. No grants to individuals, or for operating budgets.
Publications: Application guidelines.
Application information: Application form required.
  Initial approach: Letter
  Copies of proposal: 1
  Deadline(s): None
  Board meeting date(s): Mar., June, Sept., and Dec.
Officers: Barbara King Fair, Pres.; John R. "Bob" Garrett, V.P.; Sherri Harris, Secy.-Treas.
Directors: Harold Beaird; Allen Fair; Mel Lovelady; Randy Roberts.
Number of staff: 2 part-time professional.
EIN: 756015270

8845
I. D. & Marguerite Fairchild Foundation
517 S. First St.
Lufkin, TX 75901-3867
Application address: c/o Phil Medford, Pres., P.O. Box 150143, Lufkin, TX 75915, tel.: (936) 632-6661

Established in 1977 in Texas.
Donor: Marguerite Fairchild†.
Foundation type: Independent foundation.
Financial data (yr. ended 06/30/13): Assets, $5,650,234 (M); expenditures, $264,897; qualifying distributions, $247,124; giving activities include $235,000 for 7 grants (high: $90,000; low: $10,000).
Fields of interest: Arts and culture; Museums; Education; Zoos.
Type of support: General support; Endowments; Program development; Scholarships.
Limitations: Applications accepted. Giving primarily in the Angelina County, TX, area. No grants to individuals.
Application information:
  Initial approach: Letter
  Deadline(s): None
  Board meeting date(s): June
Officers: Phil Medford, Pres.; Hilda Mitchell, V.P.; Mary Duncan, Secy.
Directors: Bob Flournoy; C. James Haley, Jr.; Jay Shands; Ellen Temple; George Thannisch.
EIN: 751572514

8846
The Barnabas Faith Foundation
3536 Centenary Ave.
Dallas, TX 75225-5013 (214) 202-8715
Contact: Tara E. Bozman, Secy.

Established in 2006 in Texas.
Foundation type: Independent foundation.
Financial data (yr. ended 12/31/13): Assets, $2,989,602 (M); expenditures, $265,586; qualifying distributions, $260,839; giving activities include $258,459 for 13 grants (high: $100,000; low: $1,090).
Purpose and activities: Giving primarily to education and religious agencies and churches.
Fields of interest: Higher education; Protestantism; Human services; Child welfare.
Type of support: General support.
Limitations: Applications accepted. Giving primarily in Dallas, TX. No grants to individuals.
Application information:
  Deadline(s): None
Officers: Blake P. Bozman, Pres. and Treas.; Tara E. Bozman, Secy.
Director: Lance Bozman.
EIN: 743195686

8847
The Farris Foundation
(formerly Robert Houston & Hollyanne Frances Farris Foundation)
P.O. Box 1870
Harlingen, TX 78551-1870

Established in 1997 in Texas.
Donors: Robert R. Farris; Robin Farris.
Foundation type: Independent foundation.

Financial data (yr. ended 12/31/14): Assets, $7,381,240; expenditures, $407,543; qualifying distributions, $395,885.
Fields of interest: Domesticated animals; Christianity; Protestantism; Catholicism; Human services.
Limitations: Applications not accepted. Giving primarily in TX. No grants to individuals.
Application information: Unsolicited requests for funds not accepted.
Officer and Directors: Robert R. Farris, Pres. and Director; Robin Farris, Secy.-Treas. and Director; R. Houston Farris; Hollyanne Farris Jenkins.
EIN: 742855935

8848
Fash Foundation
c/o Fort Worth Club
306 W. 7th St., Ste. 605
Fort Worth, TX 76102-4906 (817) 535-3852
Contact: Linda Fash Bush, Pres.
FAX: (817) 348-0860; *Main URL:* http://www.fashfoundation.com

Established in 1990 in Texas.
Donors: Annie G. Fash†; Ralph E. Fash.
Foundation type: Independent foundation.
Financial data (yr. ended 12/31/13): Assets, $6,292,460 (M); expenditures, $368,938; qualifying distributions, $263,860; giving activities include $171,318 for 67 grants (high: $10,000; low: $500).
Fields of interest: Higher education; Energy resources; Philanthropy; Health; Publishing; Child welfare.
Type of support: Capital and infrastructure; Equipment; Program development; Publications.
Limitations: Applications accepted. Giving primarily in Chicago, IL, Concord, NH, and Fort Worth, TX. No grants to individuals.
Application information:
  Deadline(s): July 31
Officers and Directors: Linda F. Bush, Pres. and Director; Kirk Manning, Secy. and Director; William A. Podsednik, Jr., Treas. and Director; James L. Kaiser.
EIN: 752327856

8849
Robert E. Fennell Foundation
c/o Virginia K. Simons, BBVA Compass
2200 Post Oak Blvd., 19th Fl.
Houston, TX 77056-4706

Donor: Robert E. Fennell†.
Foundation type: Independent foundation.
Financial data (yr. ended 12/31/13): Assets, $67,712 (M); expenditures, $157,738; qualifying distributions, $152,273; giving activities include $145,000 for 3 grants (high: $100,000; low: $10,000).
Fields of interest: Secondary education; Foundations; Specialty hospital care.
Limitations: Applications not accepted. Giving primarily in IL, TN, TX, and WA. No grants to individuals.
Application information: Unsolicited requests for funds not accepted.
Trustees: Beverly A. Manders; Virginia K. Simons; Leon Stanley White II.
EIN: 766228708

8850
Fenner Family Charitable Foundation
600 Goodwin Dr.
Richardson, TX 75081-5603 (972) 231-7289

Established in 2006 in Texas.
Donors: Peter R. Fenner; Suzan E. Fenner; Laura E. Fenner.
Foundation type: Independent foundation.
Financial data (yr. ended 12/31/14): Assets, $1,161,697; expenditures, $135,949; qualifying distributions, $124,502.
Fields of interest: Protestantism; Human services; Youth development.
Type of support: General support; Capital campaigns; Program development.
Limitations: Applications accepted. Giving primarily in TX, with emphasis on Dallas; minor giving also in New York, NY. No grants to individuals.
Application information: Application form required.
  Initial approach: Letter
  Deadline(s): None
Directors: Adam K. Fenner; Laura E. Fenner; Peter R. Fenner; Suzan E. Fenner.
EIN: 113790003

8851
The Fentress Foundation
P.O. Box 8359
Waco, TX 76714-8359 (254) 772-7800
Contact: Sara Humphreys Warren, Pres. and Secy.-Treas.

Established in 1959 in Texas.
Foundation type: Independent foundation.
Financial data (yr. ended 08/31/13): Assets, $3,776,146 (M); gifts received, $97,078; expenditures, $258,111; qualifying distributions, $170,232; giving activities include $170,232 for 22 grants (high: $30,000; low: $500).
Fields of interest: Arts and culture; University education; Christianity; Scouting programs.
Type of support: General support; Scholarships.
Limitations: Applications accepted. Giving limited to the Waco, TX area. No grants to individuals.
Application information: Application form required.
  Initial approach: Letter
  Deadline(s): June 1
Officer: Sara Humphreys Warren, Pres. and Secy.-Treas.
EIN: 746048267

8852
Tilman and Paige Fertitta Family Foundation
1510 W. Loop S.
Houston, TX 77027-9505

Established in 2000 in Texas.
Donors: Landry's Seafood Restaurants, Inc.; Landry's Restaurants, Inc.
Foundation type: Company-sponsored foundation.
Financial data (yr. ended 12/31/13): Assets, $1,877,233 (M); gifts received, $250,000; expenditures, $365,220; qualifying distributions, $361,800; giving activities include $361,800 for 8 grants (high: $200,000; low: $300).
Purpose and activities: The foundation supports police agencies and organizations involved with education, heart disease, and children.

Fields of interest: Education; Secondary education; Higher education; Heart and circulatory system diseases; Police agencies; Child welfare.
Type of support: General support; Capital campaigns; Scholarships.
Limitations: Applications not accepted. Giving limited to Houston, TX. No grants to individuals.
Application information: Unsolicited requests for funds not accepted.
Officers: Tilman J. Fertitta, Pres.; Paige Fertitta, V.P.; Steven Scheinthal, Secy.
EIN: 760626357

8853
The FHC Foundation
301 Commerce St., Ste. 1500
Fort Worth, TX 76102-4115 (817) 877-1088
Application address: c/o Bobby F. Sammons; 2512 Thomas Pl., Fort Worth, TX 76107

Established in 1996 in Tennessee.
Donors: Bobby F. Sammons; Lynda R. Sammons.
Foundation type: Independent foundation.
Financial data (yr. ended 12/31/13): Assets, $2,942,577 (M); expenditures, $217,416; qualifying distributions, $211,000; giving activities include $211,000 for 12 grants (high: $30,000; low: $6,000).
Purpose and activities: Giving primarily for children and youth services.
Fields of interest: Arts and culture; Education; Domestic violence; Human services; Child welfare; Homeless people.
Application information: Application form required.
  Initial approach: Letter
  Deadline(s): Determined Annually
Officers and Directors: Bobby F. Sammons, Pres. and Treas. and Director; Lynda R. Sammons, V.P. and Secy. and Director; Elizabeth P. Sammons Rauzi.
EIN: 621594775

8854
Franklin I. Fickett Charitable Foundation
100 Congress Ave., Ste. 1100
Austin, TX 78701-4042

Donor: Franklin I. Fickett‡.
Foundation type: Independent foundation.
Financial data (yr. ended 12/31/13): Assets, $2,396,801 (M); gifts received, $53,542; expenditures, $317,632; qualifying distributions, $190,015; giving activities include $180,015 for 5 grants (high: $100,015; low: $5,000).
Fields of interest: Education; Diseases and conditions; Community and economic development.
Type of support: Research.
Limitations: Applications not accepted. Giving primarily in TX.
Application information: Unsolicited requests for funds not accepted.
Officers: Edward C. Small, Pres.; Steve D. Moore, V.P.; Michael J. Baldwin, Secy.
EIN: 454078116

8855
Field-Day Foundation
20742 Stone Oak Pkwy., Ste. 107
San Antonio, TX 78258-7538

Established in 2001 in Texas.
Donor: Julia N.H. Widdowson.
Foundation type: Independent foundation.
Financial data (yr. ended 09/30/13): Assets, $69,866 (M); gifts received, $100,000; expenditures, $151,500; qualifying distributions, $149,200; giving activities include $147,300 for 21 grants (high: $34,000; low: $100).
Purpose and activities: Giving primarily to environmental organizations for the protection and conservation of our natural resources.
Fields of interest: Natural resources; Land resources.
Limitations: Applications not accepted. Giving primarily in NY. No grants to individuals.
Application information: Contributes only to pre-selected organizations.
Officers and Directors: Julia N.H. Widdowson, Pres. and Director; Nigel D. Widdowson, V.P. and Secy. and Director; David L. Sinak.
EIN: 522364623

8856
Fifth Age of Man Foundation
4211 Long Champ Dr.
Austin, TX 78746-1161
Main URL: http://www.5thage.org
Facebook: https://www.facebook.com/pages/Fifth-Age-of-Man-Foundation/180777262003582
Grants List: http://www.5thage.org/recipients

Foundation type: Independent foundation.
Financial data (yr. ended 12/31/13): Assets, $5,662,596 (M); expenditures, $483,012; qualifying distributions, $300,000; giving activities include $300,000 for 16 grants (high: $50,000; low: $2,500).
Fields of interest: Education.
Limitations: Applications accepted. Giving primarily in CA and TX.
Application information: Application form required.
  Deadline(s): None
Officers: A. Chandler, Pres.; C. Vitlin, V.P.; M. Vitlin, V.P.; V. Vitlin, Treas.
EIN: 352403651

8857
Jerry and Nanette Finger Foundation
520 Post Oak Blvd., Ste. 750
Houston, TX 77027-9409

Donors: Jerry E. Finger; Nanette B. Finger.
Foundation type: Independent foundation.
Financial data (yr. ended 12/31/13): Assets, $3,605,229 (M); gifts received, $120,000; expenditures, $364,170; qualifying distributions, $332,185; giving activities include $331,742 for 143 grants (high: $25,000; low: $25).
Purpose and activities: Giving for theatrical arts, Jewish organizations, food services, and health and medical services.
Fields of interest: Arts and culture; Museums; Education; Higher education; Nonprofits; Judaism; Senior services; Seniors.
Type of support: General support; Annual campaigns; Capital and infrastructure; Endowments; Scholarships; Regranting.
Limitations: Applications not accepted. Giving primarily in Aspen, CO, and Houston, TX. No grants to individuals.

Application information: Contributes only to pre-selected organizations.
Officers: Jerry E. Finger, Pres.; Nanette B. Finger, V.P.; Walter G. Finger, Secy.-Treas.; Jonathan S. Finger, Mgr.
EIN: 760209018

8858
Stanford C. and Mary Clare Finney Foundation

8201 Preston Rd., Ste. 440
Dallas, TX   75225-6209   2146923667

Established in 1999 in Texas.
Donors: Stanford C. Finney, Jr.; Mary Clare Finney.
Foundation type: Independent foundation.
Financial data (yr. ended 12/31/14): Assets, $2,128,221; expenditures, $194,325; qualifying distributions, $190,641.
Fields of interest: Education; Religion; Human services.
Limitations: Applications accepted. Giving primarily in Dallas, TX.
Application information:
  Initial approach: Proposal
  Deadline(s): None
Trustee: Mary Clare Finney.
EIN: 752809984

8859
Fired Up Foundation

1514 Ranch Rd. 620 S.
Austin, TX   78734

Established in 1999 in Texas.
Donors: Mazzetta Company, LLC; Trinity Valley Foods, Inc.; Illes Seasoning & Flavors; Maple Leaf Bakery; Produce Alliance, LLC; Nestle Prepared Foods Company; Ken's Food, Inc.; Distribution Market Advantage; Dr. Pepper/Seven Up, Inc.; Christofferson Commercial; Edward Don & Co.; A. Zerega's Sons, Inc.; Arthur Schuman, Inc.; Cargill Meat Solutions Corp.; Tyson Foods, Inc.; Fisherman's Pride Processors, Inc.; Nagle Veal; Saputo Cheese USA Inc.; American Roland Food Corp.; National Food and Beverage, Inc.; Maple Leaf Bakery; Ecolab, Inc.; Nestle; Illes; Heinz North America; Syracuse's Italian Sausage Co.; Heinz North America; Koch Foods Chicago; Coca-Cola North America; Cargill Inc.; Neptune Fisherman's Pride Processor; Arthur Schuman Inc.; Windsor; Sargento Foods Inc.; Grace Bakingmaple Leaf Baking; Diannes Fine Desserts; Farmland; Pactiv; Ventura Foods LLC.
Foundation type: Independent foundation.
Financial data (yr. ended 12/31/13): Assets, $394,549 (M); gifts received, $250,200; expenditures, $277,149; qualifying distributions, $225,317; giving activities include $225,317 for 13 grants (high: $50,000; low: $3,000).
Fields of interest: Human services; Child welfare.
Limitations: Applications not accepted. Giving primarily in Austin, TX. No grants to individuals.
Application information: Unsolicited requests for funds not accepted.
Director: Creed L. Ford III.
EIN: 742933083

8860
Rena Fleming Foundation for Boys, Inc.

c/o Community National Bank
P.O. Box 624
Corsicana, TX   75151-9004   (903) 654-4500
Contact: Les Leskoven, Secy.-Treas.

Established in 1970 in Texas.
Foundation type: Independent foundation.
Financial data (yr. ended 10/31/14): Assets, $3,783,573 (M); expenditures, $187,309; qualifying distributions, $171,546; giving activities include $167,393 for 11 grants (high: $31,000; low: $2,000).
Purpose and activities: Giving primarily for youth services and organizations.
Fields of interest: Christianity; Sports and recreation; Food banks; Child welfare; Youth development.
Type of support: General support.
Limitations: Applications accepted. Giving limited to Navarro County, TX. No grants to individuals.
Application information:
  Initial approach: Letter
  Deadline(s): None
Officers: Gail Cummins, Pres.; Les Leskoven, Secy.-Treas.
Directors: Jenny Braton; C.L. Brown III; Frank Murchison.
EIN: 751045968

8861
The Flohr Family Foundation

127 Grant Ave.
San Antonio, TX   78209-5618   (210) 822-1363
Contact: Bruce Flohr, Pres.

Donor: Bruce Flohr.
Foundation type: Independent foundation.
Financial data (yr. ended 02/28/13): Assets, $1,998,650 (M); expenditures, $249,252; qualifying distributions, $200,500; giving activities include $200,500 for 77 grants (high: $20,000; low: $500).
Fields of interest: Arts and culture; Education; Nonprofits; Diseases and conditions; Christianity; Human services; Youth development.
Type of support: Regranting.
Limitations: Applications accepted. Giving primarily in TX.
Application information: Application form required.
  Initial approach: Proposal
  Deadline(s): None
Officers: Bruce Flohr, Pres.; Janet Flohr, Secy.
EIN: 742944303

8862
H. Fort Flowers Foundation

2001 Kirby Dr., Ste. 1200
Houston, TX   77019-6044   (713) 529-3729
Contact: Leslie K. Kaminaris

Established in 1951 in Delaware.
Donors: Daniel Fort Flowers FD-4 Trust; Daniel Fort Flowers SD-3 Trust; Jane M. Davis SB-3 Trust; John R. Murray SB-3 Trust; Julia Mather Flowers FF-4 Trust; Julia Mather Flowers F-1 Trust; Mark McClelland Foster J-1 Trust; Julia Mather Flowers FF-4 Trust; Joseph Knowles Flowers D-1; Katherine M. Henderson SB-3; Julia Mather Flowers SF-3 Trust; Lynne Davis Flowers D-1; Mark McClelland Foster

FJ-4 Trust; Sara Fort Paschall SS-3 Trust; Sara Fort Paschall FS-4 Trust; Richard Warren Flowers FF-4 Trust; Mark McClelland Foster SJ-3 Trust; Patricia Anne Foster J-1 Trust; Patricia Anne Foster FJ-4 Trust; Patricia Anne Foster SJ-3 Trust; Richard Warren Flowers F-1 Trust; Richard Warren Flowers SF-3 Trust; Sara Fort Paschall S-1 Trust; Sara M. Beall SB-3 Trust.
Foundation type: Independent foundation.
Financial data (yr. ended 12/31/13): Assets, $1,585,094 (M); gifts received, $361,152; expenditures, $338,274; qualifying distributions, $313,389; giving activities include $306,000 for 82 grants (high: $45,000; low: $200).
Fields of interest: Arts and culture; Elementary and secondary education; Higher education; Graduate and professional education; Health; Diseases and conditions; Engineering; Christianity; Human services.
Type of support: General support; Capital and infrastructure; Equipment; Endowments; Program development.
Limitations: Applications accepted. Giving primarily in MA, OH and TX. No grants to individuals.
Application information:
  Initial approach: Proposal
  Deadline(s): None
Officers and Trustees: S.F. Dodd, Pres. and Trustee; R.W. Flowers, V.P. and Secy. and Trustee; D.F. Flowers, Jr., V.P. and Treas. and Trustee; S.M. Beall, V.P. and Trustee; L.F. Carlton; A.S. Collins; J.M. Davis; J.K. Flowers; J.M. Flowers; L.K. Kaminaris; Everett A. Marley, Jr.; J.R. Murray, Jr.; P.F. Sullivan.
EIN: 346513672

8863
Folsom Charitable Foundation, Inc.

16475 Dallas Pkwy., Ste. 800
Addison, TX   75001-6856

Established in 1984 in Texas.
Donors: Margaret D. Folsom; Robert Stephen Folsom.
Foundation type: Independent foundation.
Financial data (yr. ended 12/31/13): Assets, $45,513 (M); gifts received, $335,000; expenditures, $327,190; qualifying distributions, $327,040; giving activities include $324,240 for 10 grants (high: $200,000; low: $40).
Fields of interest: Education; Higher education; Health; Diseases and conditions; Protestantism; Human services.
Limitations: Applications not accepted. Giving primarily in TX, with emphasis on Dallas. No grants to individuals.
Application information: Contributes only to pre-selected organizations.
Officers and Trustees: Robert Stephen Folsom, Pres. and Trustee; Diane Folsom Frank, V.P. and Trustee; Debra Folsom Jarma, V.P. and Trustee; Haddon O. Winckler, Secy.-Treas.
EIN: 751862254

8864
The Jo and Joe Ford Family Foundation

2828 Hood St., Ste. 1303
Dallas, TX   75219-7810   (214) 252-0970
Contact: Joe T. Ford, Pres.

Established in 2007 in Texas.
Donors: Joe T. Ford; Jo Ellen Ford; Scott T. Ford.

Foundation type: Independent foundation.
Financial data (yr. ended 12/31/14): Assets, $4,764,954 (M); expenditures, $321,300; qualifying distributions, $300,000; giving activities include $300,000 for 2 grants (high: $200,000; low: $100,000).
Purpose and activities: Giving primarily to a Christian liberal arts college and to a presidential center.
Fields of interest: Higher education.
Type of support: General support.
Limitations: Applications accepted. Giving primarily in NY and TX.
Application information: Application form required.
 Initial approach: Letter
 Deadline(s): None
Officers: Joe T. Ford, Pres.; Peggy Mathews, Secy.-Treas.
Directors: Alison Ford Crawford; Jo Ellen Ford; Scott T. Ford.
EIN: 260513516

8865
Fort Worth Wildlife Conservation Fund
201 Main St., Ste. 2300
Fort Worth, TX 76102-3137

Established in 2000 in Texas.
Donors: Perry R. Bass†; Nancy Lee Bass.
Foundation type: Independent foundation.
Financial data (yr. ended 06/30/14): Assets, $6,804,562; expenditures, $374,506; qualifying distributions, $374,500.
Purpose and activities: Giving primarily to a zoological association; some funding also for higher education.
Fields of interest: Education; Domesticated animals.
Limitations: Applications not accepted. Giving primarily in TX. No grants to individuals.
Application information: Contributes only to pre-selected organizations.
Officers and Directors: Lee M. Bass, Chair., Pres. and Treas. and Director; Ramona S. Bass, Vice-Chair. and V.P. and Director; Thomas W. White, V.P. and Secy. and Director; Pete Geren, V.P.; Gary W. Reese, V.P.
EIN: 752901907

8866
Joe B. Foster Family Foundation
325 Sugarberry Cir.
Houston, TX 77024-7215 (713) 789-3757
Contact: Harriet R. Foster, Secy. and Dir.

Established in 1998 in Texas.
Donor: Joe B. Foster.
Foundation type: Independent foundation.
Financial data (yr. ended 04/30/13): Assets, $2,272,507 (M); expenditures, $217,213; qualifying distributions, $201,147; giving activities include $201,147 for 23 grants (high: $75,000; low: $1,000).
Fields of interest: Education; Religion; Human services.
Limitations: Applications accepted. Giving primarily in Austin and Houston, TX. No grants to individuals.
Application information: Application form required.
 Initial approach: Letter
 Deadline(s): None

Officers and Directors: Joe B. Foster, Pres.; Jennifer Kate Foster, V.P. and Director; Kenneth Knox Foster, V.P. and Director; William Warren Foster, V.P. and Director; Harriet R. Foster, Secy. and Director.
EIN: 760538109

8867
The Kent and JoAnn Foster Family Foundation
c/o Ken Travis
15950 N. Dallas Pkwy., Ste. 600
Dallas, TX 75248-6685

Established in 2007 in Texas.
Donors: JoAnn B. Foster; Kent B. Foster.
Foundation type: Independent foundation.
Financial data (yr. ended 12/31/13): Assets, $10,522,068 (M); gifts received, $400,000; expenditures, $441,120; qualifying distributions, $361,488; giving activities include $357,135 for 12 grants (high: $235,000; low: $20).
Fields of interest: Hospital care; Christianity; Catholicism.
Type of support: General support.
Limitations: Applications not accepted. Giving primarily in TX. No grants to individuals.
Application information: Contributes only to pre-selected organizations.
Officers: Kent Foster, Pres. and Treas.; JoAnn Foster, V.P. and Secy.
EIN: 261564242

8868
Harriet and Joe Foster Foundation
(formerly Joe B. Foster Family Foundation)
325 Sugarberry Cir.
Houston, TX 77024-7215 (713) 789-3757
Contact: Harriet R. Foster, Pres. and Treas.

Established in 1995 in Texas.
Donor: JB Foster Qual Gr Charitable Lead Trust.
Foundation type: Independent foundation.
Financial data (yr. ended 12/31/12): Assets, $2,481,430 (M); gifts received, $105,000; expenditures, $360,881; qualifying distributions, $351,000; giving activities include $351,000 for grants.
Fields of interest: Museums; Higher education; Hospice care; Diseases and conditions; Human services.
Type of support: Continuing support; Annual campaigns.
Application information: Application form required.
 Initial approach: Letter
 Deadline(s): None
Officers: Harriet R. Foster, Pres. and Treas.; William Warren Foster, V.P.; D. Bryan Ruez, Secy.
Directors: Jennifer Kate Foster; Kenneth Knox Foster.
EIN: 760464978

8869
Foundation for Southeast Texas, Inc.
700 N. St., Ste. C
P.O. Box 3092
Beaumont, TX 77704 (409) 833-5775
Contact: Mellie Bevilacqua, Exec. Dir.

FAX: (409) 833-7885;
E-mail: carolflatten@cfsetx.org; Main URL: http://www.cfsetx.org
Facebook: https://www.facebook.com/cfsetx

Established in 1996 in Texas.
Donors: John Laing; Mrs. John Liang; Jewel Curtis Spayth†; The Garth House; Walter Crawford, Jr.; Gisela Houseman; CASA of Southeast Texas; Maurine Gray†; H.O.W. Center, Inc.; Elizabeth Gilbert†.
Foundation type: Community foundation.
Financial data (yr. ended 12/31/12): Assets, $11,076,001 (M); gifts received, $107,536; expenditures, $568,186; giving activities include $290,664 for 4+ grants (high: $56,702).
Purpose and activities: The foundation manages, invests, and administers charitable funds given by numerous donors to numerous to numerous community charities.
Fields of interest: Arts and culture; Education; Nonprofits; Health; Public affairs; Economic development; Human services; Children and youth; Children; Adolescents; Adults; Seniors; Ethnic and racial groups; Low-income and poor people; Victims of crime and abuse; People with psychosocial disabilities.
Type of support: General support; Continuing support; Capital and infrastructure; Equipment; Program development; Scholarships; Regranting.
Limitations: Applications accepted. Giving limited to Hardin, Jefferson, and Orange counties, TX for competitive grants. No support for religious purposes. No grants to individuals (except for scholarships), or for financing fundraisers, endowments, or debt reduction.
Publications: Application guidelines; Annual report; Informational brochure; Newsletter.
Application information: Visit foundation web site for application guidelines. Application forms are also available at the foundation's office and local libraries in January. Application form required.
 Initial approach: Submit grant application form
 Copies of proposal: 10
 Deadline(s): Mar.
 Board meeting date(s): Quarterly- 4th Thurs. of Jan., Apr., July, and Oct.
 Final notification: May
Officers and Directors: Jason Fuller, Pres. and Director; Tammy Kotzur, V.P. and Director; Shaun Davis, Secy. and Director; Robert Edgar, Treas. and Director; Mellie Bevilacqua, Exec. Dir.; Chris Akbari; Johnnie Andrus; A.B. Bernard; Debbie Bishop; Tom Broussard; Rod Carroll; Shirlene Cook; Charles Cox; Colby Crenshaw; Todd Dunkleberger; Scott Hall; Kathleen Hardy; Andrea Johnson; David Locke; Brian Mills; Shawn Oubre; Mary Ann Reid; Ida Schossow; Ross Smith; Penny Sullivan; Ronnie Turner; Joe Vernon; Nancy Vincent; Boyd Wells; Jim Willis.
Number of staff: 1 full-time professional.
EIN: 760530567

8870
The Douglass Foundation
200 Patterson, No. 808
San Antonio, TX 78209-6268
Application address: c/o Donald J. Douglass, 330 Argyle Ave., San Antonio, TX 78209, tel.: (210) 824-1149

Established in 1984 in Texas.
Donors: Donald J. Douglass; Douglass Charitable Lead Trust.

Foundation type: Independent foundation.
Financial data (yr. ended 12/31/13): Assets, $5,518,825 (M); gifts received, $30,361; expenditures, $272,102; qualifying distributions, $217,182; giving activities include $205,720 for 15 grants (high: $55,620; low: $150).
Purpose and activities: Giving primarily for higher education, through grants to colleges and universities, Episcopal schools, and scholarships to seminary students.
Fields of interest: Museums; Art museums; Higher education; Undergraduate education; Nonprofits; Episcopalianism and Anglicanism; Lutheranism.
Type of support: General support; Fellowships; Student aid; Regranting.
Limitations: Applications accepted. Giving primarily in TX.
Application information:
  Initial approach: Proposal
  Deadline(s): None
Officers and Directors: Helen D. Douglass, Pres. and Director; Stanley L. Blend, V.P.; Deborah K. Samuel, Secy.; Marylee D. Browning; Scott E. Douglass; C. Michael Gentry.
EIN: 742239830

8871
C. J. and Syble Fowlston Charitable Trust
P.O. Box 51259
Amarillo, TX   79124-1259   (806) 355-7640
Contact: Joyce Perkins, Tr.

Established in 1981 in Texas.
Donors: Syble E. Fowlston†; C.J. Fowlston†.
Foundation type: Independent foundation.
Financial data (yr. ended 12/31/13): Assets, $7,495,547 (M); expenditures, $653,361; qualifying distributions, $399,801; giving activities include $371,750 for 18 grants (high: $100,000; low: $5,000).
Fields of interest: Arts and culture; Higher education; Botanical gardens; Diseases and conditions; Television; Community service; Protestantism; Human services; Food aid.
Type of support: General support; Equipment.
Limitations: Applications accepted. Giving limited to the 20 northernmost counties of the TX Panhandle. No grants to individuals.
Application information: Application form required.
  Initial approach: Letter
  Deadline(s): None
  Final notification: Within 2 months
Trustee: Joyce Perkins.
EIN: 756281596

8872
Frankel Family Foundation, Inc.
(formerly The Leonard R. Frankel Family Foundation)
c/o Russell M. Frankel
19 Briar Hollow Ln., Ste. 238
Houston, TX   77027-2820

Established in 1991 in Texas.
Donor: Marjorie L. Frankel†.
Foundation type: Independent foundation.
Financial data (yr. ended 12/31/13): Assets, $6,496,873 (M); expenditures, $298,516; qualifying distributions, $283,013; giving activities include $280,500 for 18 grants (high: $100,000; low: $500).

Fields of interest: Orchestral music; Higher education; Diabetes; Technology; Christianity; Judaism.
Type of support: General support.
Limitations: Applications not accepted. Giving primarily in MA and Houston, TX, with some giving in CA. No grants to individuals.
Application information: Contributes only to pre-selected organizations.
Officers: Russell M. Frankel, Chair.; Sherry G. Frankel, V.P.; Marvin D. Nathan, Secy.
Trustees: Julia Frankel; Barry H. Margolis.
EIN: 760354825

8873
The Eleanor and Frank Freed Foundation
1415 Louisiana St., 36th Fl.
Houston, TX   77002-2756

Established in 1992 in Texas.
Donor: Eleanor Freed Stern†.
Foundation type: Independent foundation.
Financial data (yr. ended 09/30/14): Assets, $2,390,130 (M); expenditures, $277,373; qualifying distributions, $238,500; giving activities include $50,000 for 10 grants (high: $238,500; low: $3,500).
Fields of interest: Visual arts; Art museums; Public libraries; Judaism; Adoption.
Limitations: Applications not accepted. Giving primarily in Houston, TX. No grants to individuals.
Application information: Unsolicited requests for funds not accepted.
Officers: Randall E. Evans, Chair. and Pres.; Gloria L. Herman, Secy.; Benjamin D. Rosenberg, Treas.
Trustees: Joanne Fishbein Brodsky; William A. Camfield; Stephen M. Kaufman; Fletcher Thorne-Thomsen, Jr.
EIN: 760385085

8874
Freescale Foundation
(formerly Freescale Relief Foundation)
6501 W. William Cannon Dr.
Austin, TX   78735-8523

Donors: Freescale Semiconductor Inc.; Permira; Solebury Capital LLC.; Fulbright & Jaworski, LLP; Skadden, Arps, Slate, Meagher & Flom, LLP.
Foundation type: Independent foundation.
Financial data (yr. ended 12/31/13): Assets, $4,846,950 (M); gifts received, $5,000,000; expenditures, $154,400; qualifying distributions, $154,150; giving activities include $153,400 for 6 grants (high: $48,400; low: $5,000).
Purpose and activities: Giving to provide assistance to victims of disasters.
Fields of interest: Education; Human services; Youth development.
Limitations: Applications not accepted. Giving primarily in TX.
Application information: Unsolicited requests for funds not accepted.
Officers and Directors: Alan Campbell, Pres. and Director; Dathan C. Voelter, Secy. and Director; Giovanni Pacelli, Treas. and Director; Pamela Brown; Robert Conrad; Jeffrey Elson; Ritu Favre; Mitch Haws; Diana Lowe; Rick Morales; Karen Rapp.
EIN: 450667916

8875
Friedel Family Foundation
5327 Valburn Cir.
Austin, TX   78731-1144

Established in 1998 in Arizona.
Donors: Leonard L. Friedel†; Phyllis J. Friedel.
Foundation type: Independent foundation.
Financial data (yr. ended 12/31/13): Assets, $5,295,654 (M); expenditures, $290,653; qualifying distributions, $249,357; giving activities include $249,357 for 147 grants (high: $83,234; low: $20).
Fields of interest: Arts and culture; Education; Higher education; Nonprofits; Judaism; Human services; Child welfare.
Type of support: Regranting.
Limitations: Applications not accepted. Giving primarily in AZ, NY and TX. No grants to individuals.
Application information: Contributes only to pre-selected organizations.
Officers: Randi F. Jablin, Pres.; Steve Gellman, V.P.; Lynne F. Gellman, Secy.-Treas.
EIN: 860938348

8876
Friedman Foundation
800 Bering Dr., Ste. 210
Houston, TX   77057-2130

Established in 1998 in Texas.
Donor: Esther Friedman Blonstein.
Foundation type: Independent foundation.
Financial data (yr. ended 12/31/13): Assets, $6,840,980 (M); gifts received, $70,000; expenditures, $325,097; qualifying distributions, $268,610; giving activities include $268,610 for 92 grants (high: $20,000; low: $250).
Fields of interest: Education; Higher education; Domesticated animals; Nonprofits; Health; Child welfare.
Type of support: General support; Regranting.
Limitations: Applications not accepted. Giving primarily in Houston, TX. No grants to individuals.
Application information: Contributes only to pre-selected organizations.
Officers: Morton A. Cohn, Pres.; J. Kent Friedman, V.P.
EIN: 311629811

8877
The Frill Foundation
5120 Woodway, Ste. 6000
Houston, TX   77056-1791   (713) 333-2200

Established in 1997 in Texas.
Donors: France S. B. Lummis; William R. Lummis.
Foundation type: Independent foundation.
Financial data (yr. ended 12/31/14): Assets, $5,652,736 (M); expenditures, $369,011; qualifying distributions, $332,662; giving activities include $300,000 for 18 grants (high: $80,000; low: $2,500).
Purpose and activities: Giving primarily for museums, education, particularly secondary schools, the environment, hospitals, and community services.
Fields of interest: Arts and culture; Education; Environment; Hospital care; Community and economic development.

Limitations: Applications accepted. Giving primarily in TX and VA.
Application information:
Initial approach: Letter
Deadline(s): Oct. 1
Board meeting date(s): Nov.
Officers: Frederick R. Lummis II, Pres. and Treas.; Ransom C. Lummis, V.P. and Secy.; Palmer Bradley Lummis, V.P.; William R. Lummis, Jr., V.P.
Number of staff: None.
EIN: 311505628

8878
Pat & Tom Frost Foundation
c/o Frost Bank, Frost Financial Management Services
P.O. Box 2950
San Antonio, TX 78299

Established in 1994 in Texas.
Donors: Patricia H. Frost; Thomas C. Frost.
Foundation type: Independent foundation.
Financial data (yr. ended 12/31/14): Assets, $7,328,171; gifts received, $0; expenditures, $366,987; qualifying distributions, $356,130 and $0 for set-asides.
Fields of interest: Museums; Education; University education; Natural resources; Health; National defense; Religion; Human services; Youth services.
Type of support: Capital campaigns; Research.
Limitations: Applications not accepted. Giving primarily in San Antonio, TX. No grants to individuals.
Application information: Unsolicited requests for funds not accepted.
Trustees: Patricia H. Frost; Thomas C. Frost.
EIN: 742699577

8879
The Fruehauf Foundation
c/o Sentinel Trust
2001 Kirby Dr., Ste. 1200
Houston, TX 77019-6081 (713) 529-3729
Contact: Lisa Fruehauf Prast, Pres. and Treas.

Established in 1968 in Michigan.
Donors: Angela Fruehauf; Barbara F. Bristol; Harvey C. Fruehauf, Jr.; Susanne M. Fruehauf.
Foundation type: Independent foundation.
Financial data (yr. ended 12/31/13): Assets, $5,326,077 (M); expenditures, $291,846; qualifying distributions, $251,103; giving activities include $220,000 for 57 grants (high: $16,000; low: $1,000).
Fields of interest: Arts and culture; Higher education; Graduate and professional education; Health; Hospital care; Christianity; Theology; Human services.
Type of support: General support; Endowments; Program development.
Limitations: Applications accepted. Giving primarily in states where directors reside (FL, MA, MI, and VA). No grants to individuals.
Application information: Application form required.
Initial approach: Letter
Deadline(s): None
Board meeting date(s): As required
Officers and Directors: Lisa Fruehauf Prast, Pres. and Treas.; Barbara F. Bristol, V.P. and Director; Bartley J. Rainey, V.P.; Virginia L. Kirila, Secy.; Harvey C. Fruehauf, Jr.; Martha S. Fruehauf.
EIN: 237015744

8880
FSR Foundation
c/o Encore Trust
Nine Greenway Plz., Ste. 1000
Houston, TX 77046-0900
Contact: Denise M. Saenz

Established in 1989 in Texas.
Donors: Fred S. Robertson III; Sara Kolin Robertson.
Foundation type: Independent foundation.
Financial data (yr. ended 12/31/13): Assets, $680,119 (M); expenditures, $224,028; qualifying distributions, $218,065; giving activities include $215,000 for 33 grants (high: $100,000; low: $500).
Fields of interest: Elementary and secondary education; Christianity.
Type of support: General support.
Limitations: Giving primarily in TX. No grants to individuals.
Application information: Application form required.
Initial approach: Letter
Copies of proposal: 1
Deadline(s): None
Board meeting date(s): Annually
Trustees: Fred S. Robertson III; Sara Kolin Robertson; Denise M. Saenz; Encore Trust.
EIN: 766053774

8881
Sally and Bernard Fuchs Charitable Foundation
c/o Bernard Fuchs
121 N. Post Oak Ln., Apt. 2206
Houston, TX 77024-7717

Established in 1985 in Texas.
Donors: Sally Fuchs; Bernard Fuchs.
Foundation type: Independent foundation.
Financial data (yr. ended 12/31/14): Assets, $472,381; gifts received, $179,150; expenditures, $153,899; qualifying distributions, $149,855.
Fields of interest: Arts and culture; Nonprofits; Hospital care; Diseases and conditions; Judaism; Human services.
Type of support: Regranting.
Limitations: Applications not accepted. Giving primarily in Houston, TX. No grants to individuals.
Application information: Unsolicited requests for funds not accepted.
Officers: Bernard Fuchs, Pres. and Treas.; Roslyn Beth Fuchs Haikin, V.P. and Secy.
EIN: 760155368

8882
William M. Fuller Foundation
1010 W. Wall St.
Midland, TX 79701-6638

Donors: First United Methodist Church; Marcia Fuller French.
Foundation type: Independent foundation.
Financial data (yr. ended 12/31/13): Assets, $6,198,837 (M); expenditures, $305,906; qualifying distributions, $238,924; giving activities include $236,453 for 22 grants (high: $93,703; low: $750).
Purpose and activities: Giving primarily for education, health associations, and human services.

Fields of interest: Education; Higher education; Foundations; Diseases and conditions; Community and economic development; Human services; Child welfare.
Type of support: General support; Scholarships.
Limitations: Applications not accepted. Giving primarily in Fort Worth and Midland, TX. No grants to individuals.
Application information: Contributes only to pre-selected organizations.
Officers: Marcia F. French, Chair., Pres. and Treas.; Powhatan Ernest K. French, V.P.; Richard West Bo French, V.P.; William Fuller K. French, Secy.
Director: Dee J. Kelly.
EIN: 752335552

8883
Garver Foundation
1901 Lexington St.
Houston, TX 77098-4219

Established in 1997 in Texas.
Donor: C. Michael Garver.
Foundation type: Independent foundation.
Financial data (yr. ended 12/31/13): Assets, $5,290,687 (M); expenditures, $174,834; qualifying distributions, $160,000; giving activities include $160,000 for 17 grants (high: $80,000; low: $500).
Fields of interest: Education; Environment; Diseases and conditions.
Limitations: Applications not accepted. Giving limited to Houston, TX. No grants to individuals.
Application information: Unsolicited requests for funds not accepted.
Trustee: C. Michael Garver.
EIN: 760556696

8884
Garvey Texas Foundation, Inc.
P.O. Box 9600
Fort Worth, TX 76147-2600 (817) 335-5881
Contact: Richard F. Garvey, Pres.

Established in 1962 in Texas.
Donors: James S. Garvey; Shirley F. Garvey; Garvey Foundation.
Foundation type: Independent foundation.
Financial data (yr. ended 12/31/13): Assets, $6,071,583 (M); expenditures, $500,364; qualifying distributions, $335,920; giving activities include $335,920 for 78 grants (high: $30,000; low: $100).
Purpose and activities: Giving primarily for secondary and higher education, the arts, youth organizations, social services, and Protestant agencies and churches.
Fields of interest: Arts and culture; Performing arts; Orchestral music; Museums; Historic preservation; Elementary and secondary education; Higher education; Health; Diseases and conditions; Protestantism; Human services; Child welfare.
Limitations: Applications accepted. Giving primarily to organizations operating in the immediate geographic area of the foundation. No grants, scholarships or loans to individuals.
Application information: Application form required.
Initial approach: Letter
Copies of proposal: 1
Deadline(s): None

Officers: Richard F. Garvey, Pres.; Carol G. Sweat, V.P.; Jacob G. Sweat, Secy.; Reece Pettigrew, Treas.
Trustee: Kathryn G. Cain.
EIN: 756031547

8885
Gatewood Family Foundation
16211 Park Ten Pl.
Houston, TX 77084-7016

Established in 1999 in Texas.
Donors: E. Michael Gatewood; Gatewood Family Partnership.
Foundation type: Independent foundation.
Financial data (yr. ended 12/31/13): Assets, $1,874,633 (M); gifts received, $276,500; expenditures, $344,953; qualifying distributions, $328,045; giving activities include $326,845 for 22 grants (high: $134,405; low: $1,000).
Purpose and activities: Giving primarily for children and youth services, particularly a home for children from families in crisis; funding also for education and human services.
Fields of interest: Education; Human services; Child welfare; Shelter and residential care.
Type of support: General support.
Limitations: Applications not accepted. Giving primarily in Houston, TX. No grants to individuals.
Application information: Contributes only to pre-selected organizations.
Officers: E. Michael Gatewood, Pres.; Nathan Stedham, Exec. Dir.
Directors: Cindy L. Gatewood; Paige E. Kelly; Kristen J. Stedham.
EIN: 760595111

8886
A. S. Genecov Foundation
P.O. Box 132450
Tyler, TX 75713-2450 (903) 509-8844
E-mail: freedy@genecov.com

Established in 1955 in Texas.
Donors: A.S. Genecov†; Hilda J. Genecov†; Terry Muntz Darryl; Linda Lynn; Debra Janelle; Martin Muntz.
Foundation type: Independent foundation.
Financial data (yr. ended 12/31/13): Assets, $5,768,602 (M); gifts received, $4,403; expenditures, $460,688; qualifying distributions, $431,350; giving activities include $430,500 for 42 grants (high: $100,000; low: $250).
Purpose and activities: Giving primarily for public service organizations, including support for the aged and education.
Fields of interest: Education; Foundations; Judaism; Human services; Seniors.
Type of support: Scholarships; Continuing support; Individual development; Annual campaigns.
Limitations: Applications accepted. Giving primarily in TX. No grants to individuals.
Application information: Application form required.
  Initial approach: Letter
  Copies of proposal: 1
  Deadline(s): None
Officers: Dennis D. Darryl, Mgr.; Terry Muntz Darryl, Mgr.; Maurine Genecov Muntz, Mgr.
Number of staff: None.
EIN: 756023698

8887
The Vincent Genovese Memorial Foundation
3243 Bryan Ave.
Fort Worth, TX 76110-4222

Donor: Clovis Genvese†.
Foundation type: Independent foundation.
Financial data (yr. ended 12/31/14): Assets, $5,417,232; expenditures, $330,984; qualifying distributions, $259,178.
Fields of interest: Education; Agriculture; Christianity; Protestantism.
Type of support: General support; Endowments.
Limitations: Applications not accepted. Giving primarily in CT and TX.
Application information: Unsolicited request for funds not accepted.
Officers: Karol Genovese Del Real, Pres.; Lucille Cline-Conway, Secy. and Exec. Dir.
Directors: Katie Peterson; Donna Saunders.
EIN: 262798439

8888
Richard W. George Jr. Charitable Foundation
c/o Citizens National Bank
400 W. Collin St.
Corsicana, TX 75110

Foundation type: Independent foundation.
Financial data (yr. ended 12/31/13): Assets, $10,140,760 (M); expenditures, $370,915; qualifying distributions, $312,152; giving activities include $272,976 for 2 grants (high: $136,488; low: $136,488).
Fields of interest: Education; Protestantism.
Limitations: Applications not accepted.
Application information: Unsolicited requests for funds not accepted.
Trustee: Citizens National Bank.
EIN: 166565730

8889
Sondra & Charles Gilman, Jr. Foundation, Inc.
2101 Glenoak
Corpus Christi, TX 78418-8904
Contact: Sondra G. Gonzalez-Falla, Chair.

Established in 1981 in New York.
Foundation type: Independent foundation.
Financial data (yr. ended 04/30/14): Assets, $5,214,295 (M); expenditures, $763,541; qualifying distributions, $388,904; giving activities include $388,904 for 13+ grants (high: $190,000).
Purpose and activities: Giving primarily for enhancement of the arts.
Fields of interest: Arts and culture; Visual arts; Theater; Art museums; Natural history museums; Education; Health; Diseases and conditions; Judaism.
Type of support: General support; Continuing support; Endowments; Program development.
Limitations: Applications not accepted. Giving on a national basis, with some emphasis on GA, New York, NY, and TX. No grants to individuals.
Publications: Program policy statement.
Application information: Contributes only to pre-selected organizations.
  Board meeting date(s): Quarterly

Officers: Sondra Gilman Gonzalez-Falla, Chair.; Celso M. Gonzalez-Falla, Pres.; Jack Friedland, V.P.; Walter Bauer, Treas.
Directors: Charles Gilman III; Myrna Schatz.
Number of staff: None.
EIN: 133097485

8890
Give to Life Foundation
6612 Cherry Hills Dr.
Fort Worth, TX 76132-4510 (817) 271-7379
Contact: Jennifer Smith, Pres. and Dir.
E-mail: jennifer@givetolife.com

Donors: Jennifer Smith; Mark A. Smith.
Foundation type: Independent foundation.
Financial data (yr. ended 12/31/13): Assets, $41,013 (M); gifts received, $470,472; expenditures, $473,133; qualifying distributions, $449,552; giving activities include $425,972 for 34 grants (high: $323,470; low: $30).
Fields of interest: Christianity; Human services.
Limitations: Applications accepted. Giving primarily in TX and WA.
Application information: Application form required.
  Initial approach: Letter
  Deadline(s): None
Officers and Directors: Jennifer Smith, Pres. and Director; Mark A. Smith, Secy.-Treas. and Director; Linda Osborn.
EIN: 462780353

8891
Go Inc.
P.O. Box 1196
Helotes, TX 78023-1196

Established in 2000 in Texas.
Donor: Research Educational Fdn. Inc.
Foundation type: Independent foundation.
Financial data (yr. ended 12/31/14): Assets, $9,727,630; expenditures, $615,620; qualifying distributions, $508,535.
Purpose and activities: Giving primarily to Protestant churches, organizations, and ministries.
Fields of interest: Protestantism; Human services; Child welfare.
Limitations: Applications not accepted. Giving primarily in TX. No grants to individuals.
Application information: Contributes only to pre-selected organizations.
Officers: Scott E. Thomas, Pres.; Stephanie Thomas, Secy.-Treas.
EIN: 752386869

8892
Meyer and Ida Gordon Foundation 2
109 N. Post Oak Ln., Ste. 300
Houston, TX 77024-7755

Established in 2007 in Texas.
Foundation type: Independent foundation.
Financial data (yr. ended 12/31/13): Assets, $2,810,592 (M); expenditures, $158,341; qualifying distributions, $149,848; giving activities include $147,580 for 21 grants (high: $65,000; low: $100).
Fields of interest: Arts and culture; Diseases and conditions; Judaism.

Limitations: Applications not accepted. Giving primarily in Houston, TX.
Application information: Unsolicited requests for funds not accepted.
Officers and Directors: Daniel Gordon, Pres. and Treas. and Director; Annette Gordon, V.P. and Director; W. Lowrey Barfield, Secy. and Director; James Gordon.
EIN: 260307538

8893
Meyer and Ida Gordon Foundation
1616 S. Voss Rd., Ste. 840
Houston, TX 77057-2626

Established in 1950 in Texas.
Donor: Gordon's Jewelry Co.
Foundation type: Independent foundation.
Financial data (yr. ended 12/31/13): Assets, $3,577,228 (M); expenditures, $224,065; qualifying distributions, $196,750; giving activities include $196,750 for 16 grants (high: $75,000; low: $1,000).
Purpose and activities: Giving primarily to Jewish organizations.
Fields of interest: Education; Nonprofits; Judaism; Human services.
Type of support: Regranting.
Limitations: Applications not accepted. Giving primarily in Houston, TX. No grants to individuals.
Application information: Unsolicited requests for funds not accepted.
Officers: James C. Gordon, Pres.; Daniel P. Gordon, V.P.; W. Lowry Barfield, Secy.
Trustees: Matthew Gordon; Nancy Gordon; Ryan Gordon; Scott Gordon.
EIN: 746046795

8894
The Gottlieb Foundation of Texas
279 Hostetter Rd.
New Waverly, TX 77358-4066

Donor: T. Wayne Register.
Foundation type: Independent foundation.
Financial data (yr. ended 10/31/13): Assets, $4,167,046 (M); gifts received, $108,381; expenditures, $287,250; qualifying distributions, $240,000; giving activities include $240,000 for 4 grants (high: $100,000; low: $15,000).
Fields of interest: Health; Christianity; Protestantism.
Limitations: Applications not accepted. Giving primarily in TX.
Application information: Unsolicited requests for funds not accepted.
Officers: T. Wayne Register, Pres.; Betty Anne Register, V.P.; T. Matthew Register, Secy.; Sara Rigister Smith, Treas.
EIN: 261440562

8895
Grace Foundation
1423-B Brazos Dr.
Huntsville, TX 77320

Donors: F T Services Trust; Wilson Heirs Trust; Wilson Kasowski Trust; Stephens Associates Trust.
Foundation type: Independent foundation.

Financial data (yr. ended 12/31/13): Assets, $1,898,600 (M); gifts received, $245,000; expenditures, $242,279; qualifying distributions, $242,134; giving activities include $236,100 for 12 grants (high: $54,000; low: $1,000).
Fields of interest: Education; Religion; Human services.
Limitations: Applications not accepted. Giving primarily in TX. No grants to individuals.
Application information: Contributes only to pre-selected organizations.
Trustees: Kay Ohendalski; R.S. Ohendalski.
EIN: 260225881

8896
Graham Benevolent Foundation
P.O. Box 1567
Graham, TX 76450-7567

Established in 1928 in Texas.
Donor: M.K. Graham†.
Foundation type: Independent foundation.
Financial data (yr. ended 12/31/13): Assets, $3,878,798 (M); expenditures, $185,218; qualifying distributions, $182,000; giving activities include $182,000 for 2 grants (high: $177,000; low: $5,000).
Fields of interest: Arts and culture; Foundations; Hospital care; Human services.
Type of support: General support; Matching grants; Capital campaigns; Capital and infrastructure.
Limitations: Applications not accepted. Giving limited to Graham, TX. No grants to individuals.
Application information: Unsolicited requests for funds not accepted.
Officers: N.D. Stovall, Jr., Pres.; John C. Graham, Secy.
EIN: 756022754

8897
Grant Me the Wisdom Foundation
203 Lakemere
Houston, TX 77079-7317

Donors: Debra McLeod Sears; Jay Sears.
Foundation type: Independent foundation.
Financial data (yr. ended 12/31/13): Assets, $2,295,534 (M); gifts received, $773,878; expenditures, $278,973; qualifying distributions, $505,895; giving activities include $278,973 for 38 grants (high: $110,000; low: $100).
Fields of interest: Education; Religion.
Limitations: Applications not accepted. Giving primarily in Washington, DC and TX.
Application information: Unsolicited requests for funds not accepted.
Officers and Directors: Jay K. Sears, Chair.; Debra McLeod Sears, Pres. and Treas. and Director; William J. McLeod.
EIN: 454059674

8898
Graue Family Foundation
c/o William D. Graue
P.O. Box 671327
Dallas, TX 75367-1327

Foundation type: Independent foundation.
Financial data (yr. ended 12/31/13): Assets, $5,816,220 (M); expenditures, $271,424;

qualifying distributions, $240,874; giving activities include $239,950 for 29 grants (high: $35,000; low: $50).
Fields of interest: Art museums; Education.
Limitations: Applications not accepted. Giving primarily in CA and TX.
Application information: Contributes only to pre-selected organizations.
Officers and Trustees: Marjory Louise Graue, Pres. and Trustee; William Douglas Graue, V.P. and Secy. and Trustee; Martin Bloes; Mona Graue.
EIN: 752840076

8899
The Gray Foundation
P.O. Box 45
Houston, TX 77001-0045

Established in 1960 in Texas.
Donors: Elaine H. Gray†; James A. Gray†.
Foundation type: Independent foundation.
Financial data (yr. ended 08/31/14): Assets, $2,309,917 (M); expenditures, $159,054; qualifying distributions, $253,275; giving activities include for 35 grants (high: $28,000; low: $1,000).
Purpose and activities: Giving primarily for health care, Christian agencies and churches, human services, and education.
Fields of interest: Education; Elementary and secondary education; Health; Religion; Christianity; Human services.
Limitations: Applications not accepted. Giving primarily in LA and TX. No grants to individuals.
Application information: Contributes only to pre-selected organizations.
Officer: Emily Gray Elmore, Pres.
EIN: 746040504

8900
Gray-Pampa Foundation, Inc.
P.O. Box 2436
Pampa, TX 79066-2436 (806) 669-6801
Contact: W. Wesley Green, Chair.

Established in 1954 in Texas.
Foundation type: Independent foundation.
Financial data (yr. ended 12/31/13): Assets, $3,337,452 (M); gifts received, $255; expenditures, $191,237; qualifying distributions, $167,240; giving activities include $167,240 for 23 grants (high: $20,740; low: $2,000).
Purpose and activities: Giving primarily to library endeavors and for aid to the underserved and underprivileged.
Fields of interest: Education; Philanthropy; Religion.
Type of support: General support; Equipment.
Limitations: Applications accepted. Giving limited to the Panhandle of TX, with emphasis on Gray and Pampa counties.
Application information:
Initial approach: Proposal
Deadline(s): July 1 and Dec. 1
Officer: W. Wesley Green, Chair.
Trustees: Kenneth W. Fields; Jay Johnson; Mark McVay; Doug Ware.
EIN: 756021715

8901
The Greentree Fund
5130 Green Tree
Houston, TX 77056-1406

Established in 1968 in Texas.
Donor: Nancy C. Allen.
Foundation type: Independent foundation.
Financial data (yr. ended 06/30/14): Assets,
$7,757,252 (M); expenditures, $374,008;
qualifying distributions, $274,713; giving activities
include $270,950 for 53 grants (high: $50,000;
low: $100).
Purpose and activities: Giving primarily for
education and the arts.
Fields of interest: Arts and culture; Museums;
Elementary and secondary education; Higher
education; Hospital care; Diseases and conditions;
Christianity; Human services.
Limitations: Applications not accepted. Giving
primarily in Austin and Houston, TX. No grants to
individuals.
Application information: Unsolicited requests for
funds not accepted.
Trustees: Edward R. Allen III; Nancy C. Allen; Wilson
G. Allen.
EIN: 237065240

8902
Rosa May Griffin Foundation
P.O. Box 1790
Kilgore, TX 75663-1775 (903) 983-2051

Established in 1960 in Texas.
Donor: Rosa May Griffin†.
Foundation type: Independent foundation.
Financial data (yr. ended 12/31/14): Assets,
$5,999,099; expenditures, $321,780; qualifying
distributions, $219,270.
Purpose and activities: Giving for Presbyterian
church support, higher education, and hospitals.
Fields of interest: Arts and culture; Theater; Higher
education; Hospital care; Christianity;
Protestantism; Human services.
Type of support: General support; Matching grants;
Continuing support; Annual campaigns; Capital and
infrastructure; Equipment; Emergency funds.
Limitations: Applications accepted. Giving limited to
TX. No grants to individuals, or for endowment
funds, scholarships, or fellowships; no loans.
Publications: Program policy statement.
Application information: Application form required.
  Initial approach: Letter
  Copies of proposal: 1
  Deadline(s): None
Officers: Ebb Mobley, Pres.; Dan Phillips, C.F.O.
Trustees: Helena T. Mobley; Francye W. Phillips.
EIN: 756011866

8903
Mary Hobbs Griffith Foundation
c/o Wells Fargo Bank Texas, N.A.
P.O. Box 41629
Austin, TX 78704-9926

Foundation type: Independent foundation.
Financial data (yr. ended 10/31/13): Assets,
$5,408,266 (M); expenditures, $288,619;
qualifying distributions, $178,361; giving activities
include $170,300 for 18 grants (high: $25,000;
low: $2,500).

Fields of interest: Art museums; Catholicism;
Human services.
Type of support: General support.
Limitations: Applications not accepted. Giving
primarily in TX. No grants to individuals.
Application information: Contributes only to
pre-selected organizations.
Trustee: Wells Fargo Bank, N.A.
EIN: 237000801

8904
Grits Foundation
5005 Woodway, Ste. 200
Houston, TX 77056-1789 (713) 850-7702
Contact: George A. Peterkin Jr., Pres.

Established in 1997 in Texas.
Donors: Winston Hey; Gap III Family Trust; Susan
Hey; Lynn Peterkin; Gail Peterkin; John Peterkin;
Susan Peterkin.
Foundation type: Independent foundation.
Financial data (yr. ended 12/31/13): Assets,
$5,128,764 (M); gifts received, $66,969;
expenditures, $234,170; qualifying distributions,
$341,690; giving activities include $230,000 for 15
grants (high: $95,000; low: $5,000).
Fields of interest: Education; Specialty hospital
care; Family planning; Human services.
Type of support: General support.
Limitations: Applications accepted. Giving primarily
in Houston, TX. No grants to individuals.
Application information:
  Initial approach: Proposal
  Deadline(s): None
Officers and Directors: George A. Peterkin, Jr., Pres.
and Director; Nancy G. Peterkin, V.P. and Secy. and
Director; John T. Peterkin, Treas. and Director;
George A. Peterkin III; Lynn Peterkin; Susan Peterkin
Hey.
EIN: 311505617

8905
Guetz Foundation
7650 County Line Rd., Ste. 3
Mobeetie, TX 79061

Established in 1999 in Colorado.
Donors: Michael H. Guetz; Mrs. Michael H. Guetz;
Linda Guetz.
Foundation type: Independent foundation.
Financial data (yr. ended 11/30/13): Assets,
$4,717,239 (M); expenditures, $194,500;
qualifying distributions, $193,000; giving activities
include $193,000 for 23 grants (high: $75,000;
low: $1,000).
Fields of interest: Nonprofits; Human services;
Child welfare.
Type of support: Regranting.
Limitations: Applications not accepted. Giving
primarily in CO. No grants to individuals.
Application information: Contributes only to
pre-selected organizations.
Officers: Michael H. Guetz, Pres.; John T. Kearns,
V.P.; Linda R. Guetz, Secy.
EIN: 841525284

8906
Guinn Foundation, Inc.
1111 7th St.
Wichita Falls, TX 76301-2301

Established in 1980 in Texas.
Donors: Alfred B. Guinn; Patricia A. Guinn.
Foundation type: Independent foundation.
Financial data (yr. ended 12/31/14): Assets,
$6,315,546; expenditures, $314,954; qualifying
distributions, $309,200.
Fields of interest: Higher education; Protestantism;
Human services.
Limitations: Applications not accepted. Giving
primarily in TX. No grants to individuals.
Application information: Unsolicited requests for
funds not accepted.
Officers: Alfred B. Guinn, Pres. and Treas.; A. Patrick
Guinn, V.P. and Secy.; Melissa G. Rothwell, V.P.
EIN: 751735688

8907
Ed Haggar Family Foundation
3198 Royal Ln., Ste. 100-B
Dallas, TX 75229-3798 (469) 335-0110
Contact: Patricia J. Haggar, Pres. and Treas.; Jimmie
N. Morin

Established in 1995 in Texas.
Foundation type: Independent foundation.
Financial data (yr. ended 12/31/13): Assets,
$4,439,362 (M); expenditures, $318,334;
qualifying distributions, $198,540; giving activities
include $198,540 for 42 grants (high: $15,000;
low: $300).
Fields of interest: Arts and culture; Education;
Diseases and conditions; Human services.
Limitations: Applications accepted. Giving primarily
in TX, with emphasis on Dallas. No grants to
individuals.
Application information: Application form required.
  Initial approach: Letter
  Deadline(s): None
Officers: Patricia J. Haggar, Pres. and Treas.;
Patricia A. Haggar, V.P. and Secy.
Directors: Daley Haggar; John Daley Haggar;
Michael Haggar; Anthony Stedillie.
EIN: 752565413

8908
The Isabell and J.M. Haggar, Jr. Family Foundation
(formerly The J. M. Haggar, Jr. Family Foundation)
5500 Preston Rd., Ste. 250
Dallas, TX 75205-2699

Donors: Joseph M. Haggar, Jr.; Isabell Hagar.
Foundation type: Independent foundation.
Financial data (yr. ended 12/31/12): Assets,
$6,170,202 (M); expenditures, $386,122;
qualifying distributions, $306,405; giving activities
include $306,405 for grants.
Purpose and activities: Giving primarily to Roman
Catholic organizations, as well as for education,
health, and human services.
Fields of interest: Education; Nonprofits; Diseases
and conditions; Catholicism; Human services.
Type of support: Research; Research and
evaluation; Regranting.
Limitations: Applications not accepted. Giving
primarily in Dallas, TX. No grants to individuals.
Application information: Contributes only to
pre-selected organizations.

Officers and Directors: Isabell Haggar, Pres. and Director; Lydia H. Novakov, V.P.; Marian H. Bryan, Secy.; J.M. Haggar III, Treas.; J.M. Haggar, Jr. **EIN:** 752565414

8909

Thomas A. Hall Jr. Family Foundation

19115 Aldine Westfield
Houston, TX 77073-3813

Donor: Thomas A. Hall, Jr.
Foundation type: Independent foundation.
Financial data (yr. ended 12/31/12): Assets, $13,372 (M); gifts received, $300,000; expenditures, $300,500; qualifying distributions, $300,500; giving activities include $300,500 for grants.
Fields of interest: Religion.
Limitations: Applications not accepted. Giving primarily in TX.
Application information: Unsolicited requests for funds not accepted.
Officers and Trustees: Thomas A. Hall, Jr., Pres. and Trustee; Sean P. Hall, Secy.-Treas. and Trustee; Janet C. Hall; Shannon E. Hall; Thomas A. Hall III.
EIN: 263976153

8910

The Howard Hallam Family Foundation

1805 Record Crossing
Dallas, TX 75235-6220

Established in 1993 in Texas.
Donor: Howard Hallam.
Foundation type: Independent foundation.
Financial data (yr. ended 12/31/13): Assets, $185,883 (M); gifts received, $15,983; expenditures, $237,614; qualifying distributions, $225,095; giving activities include $224,970 for 26 grants (high: $90,000; low: $100).
Fields of interest: Arts and culture; Performing arts; Orchestral music; Art museums; Education; Higher education; Protestantism.
Limitations: Applications not accepted. Giving primarily in Dallas, TX. No grants to individuals.
Application information: Contributes only to pre-selected organizations.
Officers: Howard Hallam, Pres.; Fanchon Hill Hallam, V.P.; Rhonda Harden-Polichino, Secy.
EIN: 752448134

8911

Elizabeth L. and Russell F. Hallberg Foundation

(also known as E. L. & R. F. Hallberg Foundation)
2705 S. Cooper St., Ste. 300
Arlington, TX 76015-2400 (817) 261-8419
Contact: Virginia L. Winker

Established in 1986 in Texas.
Foundation type: Independent foundation.
Financial data (yr. ended 09/30/13): Assets, $3,623,890 (M); expenditures, $195,988; qualifying distributions, $171,708; giving activities include $163,000 for 13 grants (high: $55,000; low: $2,000).
Fields of interest: Arts and culture; Orchestral music; Art museums; Higher education; University education; Health; Protestantism; Human services.
Type of support: Scholarships.

Limitations: Applications accepted. Giving primarily in TX. No grants to individuals.
Application information:
Initial approach: Letter
Trustees: Virginia L. Winker; JPMorgan Chase Bank, N.A.
EIN: 756356892

8912

James and Gayle Halperin Foundation

(formerly James Halperin Foundation)
3500 Maple Ave., 17th Fl.
Dallas, TX 75219-3941

Established in 1989 in Texas.
Donor: James L. Halperin.
Foundation type: Independent foundation.
Financial data (yr. ended 12/31/13): Assets, $10,156,143 (M); gifts received, $1,242,500; expenditures, $335,435; qualifying distributions, $284,620; giving activities include $284,620 for 20 grants (high: $120,000; low: $1,000).
Purpose and activities: Giving primarily for the arts, education, health, and international relief.
Fields of interest: Performing arts; Dance; Education; Health; Diseases and conditions; Genetic conditions and birth defects; Basic and emergency aid; Youth services; International development.
Type of support: Research.
Limitations: Applications not accepted. Giving primarily in TX. No grants to individuals.
Application information: Unsolicited requests for funds not accepted.
Officers: James L. Halperin, Pres.; Marjorie Halperin, V.P.; Sharon Halperin, V.P.
EIN: 752294319

8913

Tom and Carolyn Hamilton Family Foundation

c/o Woodway Financial Advisors
10000 Memorial Dr., Ste. 650
Houston, TX 77024-3417

Established in 1998 in Texas.
Foundation type: Independent foundation.
Financial data (yr. ended 05/31/13): Assets, $2,868,973 (M); expenditures, $201,838; qualifying distributions, $191,165; giving activities include $172,200 for 21 grants (high: $67,000; low: $200).
Fields of interest: Education; Mental health care; Housing development.
Limitations: Applications not accepted. Giving primarily in NY, OH, SC and TX. No grants to individuals.
Application information: Unsolicited requests for funds not accepted.
Officers: Carolyn E. Hamilton, Pres.; Thomas M. Hamilton, V.P. and Secy.-Treas.
Directors: Scott T. Hamiton; Brett A. Hamilton; Janet J. Hamilton.
EIN: 760573521

8914

Nancy and Alan Hamm Foundation, Inc.

411 Harwood Rd.
Bedford, TX 76021-4151

Established in 2002 in Texas.
Donors: Alan W. Hamm; Nancy Jane Hamm.
Foundation type: Independent foundation.
Financial data (yr. ended 12/31/13): Assets, $3,503,895 (M); expenditures, $207,352; qualifying distributions, $173,924; giving activities include $173,674 for 7 grants (high: $64,688; low: $2,500).
Fields of interest: Education; Diseases and conditions; Religion.
Limitations: Applications not accepted. Giving primarily in TX. No grants to individuals.
Application information: Unsolicited requests for funds not accepted.
Directors: Carolyn J. Deguire; David Alan Hamm; Jean Anne Hamm.
EIN: 810587502

8915

Dr. Mike & Patricia Hanley Charitable Foundation, Inc.

903 David Dr.
Palestine, TX 75803-8598

Donors: M.J. & P.C. Hanley Living Trust; Patricia C. Hanley†.
Foundation type: Independent foundation.
Financial data (yr. ended 12/31/13): Assets, $6,523,338 (M); gifts received, $3,470,613; expenditures, $198,312; qualifying distributions, $184,100; giving activities include $173,200 for 2 grants (high: $132,000; low: $41,200).
Fields of interest: Religion; Human services.
Limitations: Applications not accepted. Giving primarily in TX.
Application information: Unsolicited requests for funds not accepted.
Officers: Linda Davis, Pres. and Treas.; Larry Davis, V.P.; Julie Law, Secy.
EIN: 461430835

8916

The Bryant & Nancy Hanley Foundation

5455 Northbrook Dr.
Dallas, TX 75220-2256
Contact: Tim Hanley

Established in 1996 in Texas.
Donors: Bryant M. Hanley; Nancy Hanley.
Foundation type: Independent foundation.
Financial data (yr. ended 12/31/13): Assets, $78,170 (M); expenditures, $198,054; qualifying distributions, $194,525; giving activities include $193,750 for 34 grants (high: $45,000; low: $250).
Purpose and activities: Giving primarily for education and the arts.
Fields of interest: Arts and culture; Performing arts; Art museums; Education; Higher education; Human services.
Limitations: Applications accepted. Giving primarily in TX. No grants to individuals.
Application information: Application form required.
Initial approach: Letter
Deadline(s): None
Officer and Directors: Bryant M. Hanley, Pres. and Director; Barbara Hanley Caldas; Sarah E. Hanley.
EIN: 752683075

8917

The Haraldson Foundation
25025 I-45 N., Ste. 410
The Woodlands, TX 77380-3034 (281)
362-9909
Contact: Dale A. Dossey, Dir.
FAX: (281) 476-7045;
E-mail: ndossey@haraldsonfoundation.org; Main
URL: http://www.haraldsonfoundation.org

Established in 1993 in Texas.
Donor: Beulah M. Haraldson†.
Foundation type: Operating foundation.
Financial data (yr. ended 09/30/13): Assets,
$6,174,859 (M); expenditures, $469,278;
qualifying distributions, $244,400; giving activities
include $244,400 for 3 grants (high: $225,600;
low: $4,700).
Purpose and activities: To encourage individual
students to become Texas leaders for the 21st
century, by providing scholarships for study at the
University of Texas.
Fields of interest: Education.
Type of support: Scholarships; Student aid.
Limitations: Applications accepted. Giving limited to
TX.
Publications: Application guidelines; Annual report;
Grants list; Informational brochure (including
application guidelines); Newsletter.
Application information: Application form and
guidelines available on foundation web site.
Application form required.
  Initial approach: Telephone or letter
  Deadline(s): Dec. 1
  Board meeting date(s): After Jan. 1
Officers and Directors: Karen Sue Emami, Chair.
and Director; Betty Jean Cook, Vice-Chair. and
Director; Dale A. Dossey, Secy. and Director; John
Emami; Scott Emami; Tiffany Emami.
Number of staff: 1 part-time professional.
EIN: 760420758

8918

Norbert H. Hardner Foundation
115 Wild Basin, Ste. 106
Austin, TX 78746-3305

Established in 2000 in Texas.
Donor: Norbert H. Hardner†.
Foundation type: Independent foundation.
Financial data (yr. ended 12/31/13): Assets,
$5,408,513 (M); expenditures, $305,306;
qualifying distributions, $257,000; giving activities
include $257,000 for 12 grants (high: $30,000;
low: $3,000).
Fields of interest: Education; Health; Catholicism;
Camps; Child welfare; Child development.
Limitations: Applications not accepted. Giving
primarily in CT, PA and TX. No grants to individuals.
Application information: Contributes only to
pre-selected organizations.
Officers: Jared Hardner, Pres.; Sara Hardner Leon,
V.P.; Rebecca Haverly, Secy.; Margaret Hardner,
Treas.
EIN: 742952380

8919

Harrell Family Foundation
14214 Bonney Brier
Houston, TX 77069-1326

Donor: Forrest E. Harrell.
Foundation type: Independent foundation.
Financial data (yr. ended 12/31/13): Assets,
$5,040,128 (M); gifts received, $1,265,000;
expenditures, $328,672; qualifying distributions,
$295,000; giving activities include $295,000 for 5
grants (high: $120,000; low: $25,000).
Fields of interest: Education; Health; Human
services; Indigenous peoples.
Limitations: Applications not accepted. Giving
primarily in Houston, TX.
Application information: Contributes only to
pre-selected organizations.
Officers and Directors: Forrest E. Harrell, Pres. and
Director; Sandra H. Harrell, V.P. and Director;
Forrest E. Harrell, Jr., Secy. and Director; Curtis F.
Harrell, Treas. and Director.
EIN: 263687254

8920

The Hartman Foundation, Inc.
3345 Bee Cave Rd., Ste. 203
Austin, TX 78746-6692

Established in 1999 in Texas.
Donors: David A. Hartman; Claudette L. Hartman;
Douglas M. Hartman.
Foundation type: Operating foundation.
Financial data (yr. ended 05/31/13): Assets,
$1,975,974 (M); expenditures, $139,004;
qualifying distributions, $389,436; giving activities
include $328,528 for 3 grants (high: $145,000;
low: $93,496).
Purpose and activities: Giving for human services,
education, public policy, and the arts; funding also
for a weekly newsletter devoted exclusively to
coverage of Texas politics and government.
Fields of interest: Arts and culture; Education;
Higher education; Economics; Public affairs; Human
services.
Type of support: General support.
Limitations: Applications not accepted. Giving
primarily in TX. No grants to individuals.
Publications: Newsletter.
Application information: Unsolicited requests for
funds not accepted.
Officers and Directors: Douglas M. Hartman, Chair.
and Pres. and Director; Claudette L. Hartman, V.P.
and Director; Shirley Wolfe, Secy.-Treas. and
Director; John E. Hartman; Wayne P. Hartman.
EIN: 582471439

8921

W.A. Harwi Testamentary Trust
c/o Bank of America, N.A.
P.O. Box 831041
Dallas, TX 75283-1041

Foundation type: Independent foundation.
Financial data (yr. ended 10/31/13): Assets,
$5,704,265 (M); expenditures, $215,724;
qualifying distributions, $194,015; giving activities
include $180,000 for 1 grant.
Fields of interest: Nursing care.
Limitations: Applications not accepted. Giving
primarily in KS.
Application information: Unsolicited requests for
funds not accepted.
Trustee: Bank of America, N.A.
EIN: 486154436

8922

The George and Claudette Hatfield
Foundation, Inc.
2475 Discovery Blvd.
Rockwall, TX 75032
Application address: The George and Claudette
Hatfield Foundation Inc., 1 Shadydale Ln., Rockwall,
TX 75032, tel.: (972) 288-7625

Established in 1997 in Texas.
Donors: Claudette Hatfield; George R. Hatfield;
Hatfield and Co., Inc.
Foundation type: Independent foundation.
Financial data (yr. ended 12/31/13): Assets,
$2,960,470 (M); gifts received, $706,000;
expenditures, $280,933; qualifying distributions,
$279,600; giving activities include $279,600 for 20
grants (high: $100,000; low: $800).
Fields of interest: Higher education; Specialty
hospital care; Christianity; Human services; Food
aid; Child welfare.
Type of support: General support; Scholarships;
Student aid.
Limitations: Applications accepted. Giving primarily
in TX, with emphasis on Rockwall.
Application information: Application form required.
  Initial approach: Completed application form
  Deadline(s): None
Officers and Directors: George R. Hatfield, Pres.
and Director; John G. Hatfield, V.P. and Director;
Susan Wheelis, V.P. and Director; Claudette
Hatfield, Secy. and Director.
EIN: 752706578

8923

Hawkins Family Foundation
9 Greenway Plz., Ste. 2400
Houston, TX 77046-0909

Established in 2006 in Texas.
Donors: Renee D. Hawkins; John D. Hawkins.
Foundation type: Independent foundation.
Financial data (yr. ended 12/31/13): Assets,
$826,549 (M); expenditures, $241,801; qualifying
distributions, $240,000; giving activities include
$240,000 for 27 grants (high: $111,500; low:
$250).
Fields of interest: Arts and culture; Education;
Health.
Limitations: Applications not accepted. Giving
primarily in TX. No grants to individuals.
Application information: Unsolicited requests for
funds not accepted.
Officers and Directors: John D. Hawkins, Pres. and
Treas. and Director; Renee D. Hawkins, V.P. and
Secy. and Director; Anna Grace Hawkins; John D.
Hawkins, Jr.
EIN: 208060303

8924

Healthcare and Nursing Education
Foundation
(formerly Visiting Nurse Association of Houston
Foundation)
3120 Southwest Fwy., Ste. 215
Houston, TX 77098-4510
FAX: (713) 868-2619; E-mail: info@hnef.org;
Additional e-mail: grants@hnef.org; Main
URL: http://www.hnef.org

Established in 1996 in Texas.

Donor: Vaughan Nelson Investment Mgmt.
Foundation type: Independent foundation.
Financial data (yr. ended 06/30/15): Assets, $11,220,622 (M); expenditures, $371,295; qualifying distributions, $341,769; giving activities include $87,502 for 1 grant (high: $87,502), and $213,167 for 64 grants to individuals.
Purpose and activities: It is the foundation's mission to address unmet healthcare needs in the greater Houston, Texas, community through the provision of educational scholarships in nursing and community grants supporting the delivery of health care. Scholarships are awarded to students who have graduated from high school and will be attending an accepted undergraduate program in preparation for entry into an accredited college program leading to a bachelor's degree in nursing.
Fields of interest: Education; Higher education; Graduate and professional education; Nursing care; Home health care.
Type of support: Continuing support; Program development; Seed money; Individual development; Student aid.
Limitations: Applications not accepted. Giving primarily in the greater Houston, TX, area.
Application information: Unsolicited requests for funds not accepted.
　　Board meeting date(s): Quarterly
Officer and Directors: Henry A. de La Garza, Pres. and Director; Lewis E. Brazelton III; Sandra Cashaw, MPH, RN; Alan Fisherman, MD; Noel Graubart; Shirley Gee Henry, R.N., Ph.D.; Donald S. Huge, MD; Michael K. Jhin; Ann P. Kaufman; Willy Kuehn; David Lummis; Marylou Robins, Ph.D; Elsa Tansey, Ph.D; Peter K. Thompson, M.D., Dr. P.H.; Geri Wood, Ph.D.
EIN: 760454511

8925
Heavin Family Foundation
P.O. Box 531785
Harlingen, TX　78553

Established in 2005 in Texas.
Donor: Gary Heavin.
Foundation type: Independent foundation.
Financial data (yr. ended 12/31/13): Assets, $3,179,258 (M); expenditures, $163,661; qualifying distributions, $160,350; giving activities include $160,350 for 1 grant.
Fields of interest: Community and economic development; Protestantism.
Limitations: Applications not accepted. No grants to individuals.
Application information: Unsolicited requests for funds not accepted.
Officers: Glenna L. Heavin, Pres.; Nicole Heavin, V.P.; Linda Dehne, Secy.-Treas.
EIN: 203143695

8926
Hegi Family Foundation
4805 St. Johns Dr.
Dallas, TX　75205-3143
E-mail: fredhegi@wingatepartners.com; Application address: c/o Frederick B. Hegi, Jr., 50 N. St Paul, Ste. 1200, Dallas, TX 75201, tel.: (214) 720-1313

Established in 1987 in Texas.
Donor: Frederick B. Hegi, Jr.
Foundation type: Independent foundation.

Financial data (yr. ended 12/31/13): Assets, $5,590,717 (M); expenditures, $155,408; qualifying distributions, $153,157; giving activities include $151,300 for 60 grants (high: $20,417; low: $200).
Fields of interest: Performing arts; Art museums; Education; Higher education; Foundations; Cancers; Christianity; Human services; Homeless services.
Type of support: General support; Scholarships.
Limitations: Applications accepted. Giving primarily in Dallas, TX. No grants to individuals.
Application information: Application form required.
　　Initial approach: Letter
　　Deadline(s): None
Officers: Frederick B. Hegi, Jr., Pres.; Margie Ann Hegi, V.P.; Louise Backa, Secy.-Treas.
EIN: 752217565

8927
Robert A. and Virginia Heinlein Prize Trust
3106 Beauchamp St., 2nd Fl.
Houston, TX　77019-7206　(713) 861-3600
Contact: Arthur Dula, Dir.
FAX: (713) 861-3620;
E-mail: info@heinleinprize.com; Main URL: http://www.heinleinprize.com
RSS feed: http://www.heinleinprize.com/?feed=rss2

Foundation type: Independent foundation.
Financial data (yr. ended 12/31/13): Assets, $10,846,423 (M); expenditures, $919,455; qualifying distributions, $183,054; giving activities include $151,101 for 12 grants (high: $60,000; low: $862), and $13,163 for 2 grants to individuals (high: $10,000; low: $3,163).
Purpose and activities: The purpose of the Heinlein Prize is to encourage and reward progress in commercial space activities that advances the dream of humanity's future in space.
Fields of interest: Aerospace engineering.
Type of support: Program-related investments; Grants to individuals.
Application information: Application form required.
　　Initial approach: Letter
　　Deadline(s): None
Directors: Art Dula; Buckner Hightower; James M. Vaughn, Jr.
EIN: 766079186

8928
The Helm Foundation, Inc.
2901 Wilcrest Dr., Ste. 217
Houston, TX　77042-6071

Established in 1993 in Texas.
Donors: Glora Bee Helm; Tair, Ltd.
Foundation type: Independent foundation.
Financial data (yr. ended 12/31/13): Assets, $9,284,310 (M); expenditures, $605,560; qualifying distributions, $387,426; giving activities include $380,000 for 11 grants (high: $253,000; low: $1,000).
Purpose and activities: Giving primarily for education, including Protestant schools.
Fields of interest: Education; Protestantism; Human services.
Limitations: Applications not accepted. Giving primarily in TX. No grants to individuals.
Application information: Contributes only to pre-selected organizations.

Officers and Directors: Glora Bee Helm, Chair. and Director; Cyrus Vard Helm, Pres. and Director; Susan Helm, Secy. and Director.
EIN: 760419884

8929
Helmle-Shaw Foundation
2603 Bayshore Dr.
Bacliff, TX　77518-3002　(713) 787-7730
Contact: Roy C. Shaw Jr.

Established in 1994 in Texas.
Donors: Judith Helmle Shaw; Roy C. Shaw, Jr.
Foundation type: Independent foundation.
Financial data (yr. ended 12/31/13): Assets, $3,492,475 (M); expenditures, $181,160; qualifying distributions, $158,516; giving activities include $155,411 for 30 grants (high: $30,000; low: $500).
Fields of interest: Arts and culture; Education; Religion.
Type of support: General support.
Application information:
　　Initial approach: Letter
　　Deadline(s): None
Officers: Roy C. Shaw, Jr., Pres.; Judith Helmle Shaw, Secy.-Treas.
EIN: 760420414

8930
C. T. Herring Charitable Foundation
P.O. Box 50488
Amarillo, TX　79159-0488

Established in 2004 in Texas.
Foundation type: Independent foundation.
Financial data (yr. ended 12/31/12): Assets, $1,747,797 (M); expenditures, $171,784; qualifying distributions, $133,619; giving activities include $133,619 for 3 grants (high: $73,619; low: $10,000).
Fields of interest: Arts and culture; Education; Religion.
Limitations: Applications not accepted. Giving primarily in TX.
Application information: Unsolicited requests for funds not accepted.
Officer: C.C. Burgess, Chair.
EIN: 200548629

8931
Jacob and Terese Hershey Foundation
2121 San Felipe., Ste. 122
Houston, TX　77019-5600　(713) 529-7611
Contact: Terese T. Hershey, Pres.
E-mail: judyboyce@jthershey.org

Foundation type: Independent foundation.
Financial data (yr. ended 12/31/13): Assets, $3,696,867 (M); expenditures, $438,534; qualifying distributions, $425,261; giving activities include $420,100 for 83 grants (high: $30,250; low: $100).
Fields of interest: Environment; Domesticated animals; Human services.
Limitations: Applications accepted. Giving primarily in TX.
Application information:
　　Initial approach: Proposal
　　Deadline(s): None

Officers: Terese T. Hershey, Pres.; Amie Rodnick, Secy.; Andrew H. Sansom, Treas.
Directors: Jeffrey Hershey; Olive Hershey.
EIN: 746039126

8932
Hervey Foundation

P.O. Box 221138
El Paso, TX 79913-4138 (915) 532-2621
Contact: Georgiana Garcia, Secy.

Established in 1957 in Texas.
Foundation type: Independent foundation.
Financial data (yr. ended 01/31/13): Assets, $4,584,324 (M); expenditures, $220,861; qualifying distributions, $200,200; giving activities include $200,200 for 28 grants (high: $30,000; low: $3,000).
Fields of interest: Arts and culture; Nonprofits; Home health care; Diseases and conditions; Special Olympics; Human services; Child welfare; Scouting programs; Domestic violence shelters; People with vision impairments.
Type of support: Continuing support; Matching grants; Annual campaigns; Regranting; Equipment; Program development; Scholarships; Research.
Limitations: Applications accepted. Giving limited to El Paso and El Paso County, TX. No grants to individuals, or for endowment funds; no loans.
Publications: Annual report (including application guidelines).
Application information: Application form required.
  Initial approach: Letter
  Copies of proposal: 1
  Deadline(s): Quarterly
Officer: Georgiana Garcia, Secy.
Trustees: Sherleen Lockhart Hervey; Eric D. Payne.
EIN: 746068068

8933
Hext Family Foundation, Inc.

5704 Ponderosa
Odessa, TX 79762-9431 (432) 561-5043
Contact: Jane Hext, Pres.

Established in 1998 in Texas.
Donors: Jane Hext; Hext Management, LLC; Mark Palmer; Susan Palmer; Melinda Spencer; Tim Spencer.
Foundation type: Independent foundation.
Financial data (yr. ended 12/31/13): Assets, $2,791,631 (M); expenditures, $179,939; qualifying distributions, $156,573; giving activities include $155,000 for 42 grants (high: $30,000; low: $1,000).
Purpose and activities: Giving primarily for cancer research, vocational education, and religious charities in the Permian Basin area.
Fields of interest: Vocational education; Christianity; Human services.
Type of support: General support; Pro bono consulting services; Matching grants; Capital campaigns; Capital and infrastructure; Equipment; Land acquisitions; Emergency funds; Program development; Convening; Publications; Seed money; Scholarships; Research; Technical assistance.
Limitations: Giving primarily in the Permian Basin, TX area.

Publications: Application guidelines; Grants list; Informational brochure (including application guidelines); Program policy statement.
Application information: Application form required.
  Initial approach: Letter
  Copies of proposal: 1
  Deadline(s): Annually
  Final notification: Mar. 15
Officers: Jane Hext, Pres.; Melinda Spencer, V.P.
Trustee: Tim Spencer.
EIN: 752754667

8934
Hibbs Family Foundation

P.O. Box 8357
Tyler, TX 75711-8357

Established in 1999 in Texas.
Donors: Billy E. Hibbs, Jr.; Billy E. Hibbs, Jr.; Hibbs-Hallmark & Company; Claims Administrative Services; Hibbs Charitable Trust.
Foundation type: Independent foundation.
Financial data (yr. ended 12/31/13): Assets, $886,397 (M); gifts received, $175,780; expenditures, $325,410; qualifying distributions, $325,293; giving activities include $325,293 for 28 grants (high: $200,000; low: $100).
Fields of interest: Art museums; Higher education; Diseases and conditions; Human services; Child welfare.
Type of support: Capital campaigns; Research.
Limitations: Applications not accepted. Giving primarily in Tyler, TX. No grants to individuals.
Application information: Contributes only to pre-selected organizations.
Officers and Directors: Eugenia A. Hibbs, Pres.; Billy E. Hibbs, Jr., V.P. and Secy. and Director; Teresa W. Hibbs.
EIN: 752851757

8935
The Hicks Family Charitable Foundation

1703 W. 5th St., Ste. 800
Austin, TX 78703

Established in 1997 in Texas.
Donors: R. Steven Hicks; Donna Stockton Hicks.
Foundation type: Independent foundation.
Financial data (yr. ended 04/30/14): Assets, $7,896 (M); gifts received, $169,100; expenditures, $169,346; qualifying distributions, $168,473; giving activities include $167,600 for 6 grants (high: $100,000; low: $5,000).
Fields of interest: Education; Higher education; Substance abuse treatment; Christianity; School athletics; Human services; Child welfare.
Limitations: Applications not accepted. Giving primarily in Austin, TX. No grants to individuals.
Application information: Contributes only to pre-selected organizations.
Officers: R. Steven Hicks, Pres. and Treas.; Donna Stockton Hicks, V.P. and Secy.
Trustee: Lew Little.
EIN: 742877054

8936
The Thomas O. and Cinda Hicks Foundation

(formerly The Thomas O. Hicks Family Foundation)
100 Crescent Ct., Ste. 1200
Dallas, TX 75201-7860

Established in 1994 in Texas.
Donor: Thomas O. Hicks.
Foundation type: Independent foundation.
Financial data (yr. ended 11/30/13): Assets, $2,080,300 (M); expenditures, $330,981; qualifying distributions, $327,867; giving activities include $327,867 for 10 grants (high: $125,000; low: $500).
Purpose and activities: Giving primarily for higher education and the performing arts.
Fields of interest: Arts and culture; Performing arts; Elementary and secondary education; Higher education; Hospital care; Diseases and conditions; Human services; Child welfare.
Limitations: Applications not accepted. Giving primarily in TX, with emphasis on Dallas; some giving also in NJ and VA. No grants to individuals.
Application information: Contributes only to pre-selected organizations.
Officers: Thomas O. Hicks, Pres.; Cinda C. Hicks, V.P.
Director: Rebecca A. McConnell.
EIN: 752570214

8937
Hill Country Community Foundation

P.O. Box 848
Burnet, TX 78611 (512) 756-8211
Contact: Pat Williams
E-mail: pwilliams200@austin.rr.com; Additional e-mail: support@thehccf.com; Main URL: http://www.thehccf.org
Facebook: https://www.facebook.com/pages/Hill-Country-Community-Foundation/117940184977074
YouTube: https://www.youtube.com/user/BurnetHCCF

Established in 1982 in Texas.
Foundation type: Community foundation.
Financial data (yr. ended 12/31/12): Assets, $5,515,008 (M); gifts received, $388,506; expenditures, $341,339; giving activities include $59,455 for 9 grants (high: $26,000), and $254,532 for 193 grants to individuals.
Purpose and activities: The foundation, by investing endowment money to earn income, provides funding for certain local benefits. Specifically, the foundation seeks to advance the following goals: 1) grant multi-year scholarships to college freshman and sophomore students who are pursuing collegiate or other advanced educations; and 2) aid a variety of local youth and health organizations.
Fields of interest: Health; Economic development; Community improvement; Family services; Youth development; Young adults.
Type of support: Endowments; Student aid.
Limitations: Giving limited to residents of the Texas Hill Country area.
Publications: Annual report.
Application information: The foundation does not accept unsolicited grant applications.
  Initial approach: Submit letter
  Board meeting date(s): Bi-monthly

Officers and Directors: Mike Lucksinger, Pres. and Director; Ken Graham, V.P. and Director; Dennis Hoover, Secy. and Director; Glen Bible, Treas. and Director; Stan Hemphill; John Hoover; Cary Johnson; Sallye Long; Keith McBurnett; David Nantz; T.J. Reed; Kyle Stripling.
Number of staff: 1 part-time support.
EIN: 742452519

8938
The Margaret and Al Hill Family Foundation
(formerly Hill Foundation)
2001 Ross Ave., Ste. 4600
Dallas, TX   75201-8007   (214) 922-1100
Contact: Lyda Hill, Pres.

Donor: Margaret Hunt Hill†.
Foundation type: Independent foundation.
Financial data (yr. ended 02/28/13): Assets, $4,647,048 (M); expenditures, $248,953; qualifying distributions, $149,596; giving activities include $149,461 for 12 grants (high: $45,000; low: $300).
Fields of interest: Hospice care; Family planning; Diseases and conditions; Human services.
Type of support: General support; Annual campaigns; Capital campaigns; Capital and infrastructure; Scholarships.
Limitations: Applications accepted. Giving primarily in CO, with emphasis on Colorado Springs. No grants to individuals.
Application information: Application form required.
  Initial approach: Letter
  Deadline(s): None
Officers and Trustees: Lyda Hill, Chair. and Pres.; Al G. Hill, Jr., V.P. and Trustee; Alinda H. Wikert, V.P. and Trustee; Heather H. Washburne, Secy.-Treas. and Trustee; Elisa Hill Summers; Cody M. Wikert; Margretta H. Wikert; Michael B. Wisenbaker, Jr.; Wesley Hill Wisenbaker.
EIN: 756010533

8939
The Hillcrest Foundation
P.O. Box 132961
The Woodlands, TX   77393-2961

Established in 2003 in Texas.
Donor: L.C. Kung†.
Foundation type: Independent foundation.
Financial data (yr. ended 12/31/13): Assets, $8,227,399 (M); expenditures, $429,490; qualifying distributions, $341,000; giving activities include $341,000 for 65 grants (high: $34,100; low: $842).
Fields of interest: Higher education; Health; Hospital care; Cancers; Community and economic development; Protestantism; Human services; Temporary accommodations.
Limitations: Applications not accepted. Giving primarily in TX. No grants to individuals.
Application information: Contributes only to pre-selected organizations.
Directors: Elizabeth Gimmler; Diane Keir; Renee J. Kelly; David Mouton; David Myers; William Panill; Kelly Reed.
EIN: 311501699

8940
The Tim and Karen Hixon Foundation
315 E. Commerce St., Ste. 300
San Antonio, TX   78205-2947

Established in 1994 in Texas.
Donors: Karen J. Hixon; George C. Hixon; Hixon Charitable Lead Trust.
Foundation type: Independent foundation.
Financial data (yr. ended 12/31/13): Assets, $7,051,550 (M); expenditures, $312,191; qualifying distributions, $269,419; giving activities include $269,169 for 28 grants (high: $41,669; low: $2,500).
Purpose and activities: Giving primarily to support wildlife and zoological organizations and programs.
Fields of interest: Arts and culture; Education; Higher education; Natural resources; Wildlife biodiversity.
Type of support: General support; Continuing support; Annual campaigns; Capital campaigns; Land acquisitions; Research and evaluation; Research.
Limitations: Applications not accepted. Giving primarily in TX. No grants to individuals.
Application information: Contributes only to pre-selected organizations.
Officers and Directors: Bryan S. Hixon, V.P. and Director; George S. Hixon, V.P. and Director; Kathryn N. Sanco, Secy. and Director; George C. Hixon; Karen J. Hixon; Jack J. Spector.
Number of staff: None.
EIN: 742730275

8941
The Hoak Foundation
(formerly James M. and Nancy J. Hoak Foundation)
500 Crescent Ct., Ste. 220
Dallas, TX   75201-7808
Contact: Kate Hoak Power
E-mail: kate@hoakfoundation.org; Main URL: http://www.hoakfoundation.org

Established in 1990 in Texas.
Donors: James M. Hoak; Nancy J. Hoak.
Foundation type: Independent foundation.
Financial data (yr. ended 12/31/13): Assets, $1,597,800 (M); expenditures, $157,715; qualifying distributions, $152,485; giving activities include $151,150 for 26 grants (high: $50,000; low: $100).
Purpose and activities: Giving primarily for education and human services.
Fields of interest: Education; Health; Diseases and conditions.
Limitations: Applications not accepted. Giving primarily in Dallas, TX. No grants to individuals.
Application information: Unsolicted requests for funds not accepted.
Officers: James M. Hoak, Pres. and Treas.; Nancy J. Hoak, V.P. and Secy.; Kathleen Hoak Power, Exec. Dir.
Directors: Abigail Stevens Hoak; Jonathan Hale Hoak; Mary Margaret Hoak; Samuel E. Todd.
EIN: 752357697

8942
Irene Cafcalas Hofheinz Foundation
2000 Bering Dr., Ste. 909
Houston, TX   77057-3746

Established in 2007 in Texas.
Donor: Irene Cafcalas Hofheinz Foundation.
Foundation type: Independent foundation.
Financial data (yr. ended 12/31/14): Assets, $1,238,930; expenditures, $137,979; qualifying distributions, $134,606.
Fields of interest: Diseases and conditions; Protestantism; Human services.
Limitations: Applications not accepted. Giving primarily in Houston, TX. No grants to individuals.
Application information: Unsolicited requests for funds not accepted.
Officers and Directors: James Fred Hofheinz, Pres. and Director; Linda Hickerson Hofheinz, Secy. and Director; Dene Hofheinz Anton.
EIN: 260479856

8943
Bessie I. Hofstetter Trust
400 W. Collin St.
Corsicana, TX   75110-5124

Established in 1934 in Texas.
Donor: Bessie I. Hofstetter.
Foundation type: Independent foundation.
Financial data (yr. ended 06/30/13): Assets, $4,508,457 (M); expenditures, $222,518; qualifying distributions, $206,952; giving activities include $196,574 for 18 grants (high: $85,000; low: $1,000).
Fields of interest: Nonprofits; Protestantism; Human services; Family services; Child welfare; Youth services; Low-income and poor people.
Type of support: Regranting.
Limitations: Applications not accepted. Giving primarily in TX. No grants to individuals.
Application information: Unsolicited requests for funds not accepted.
Trustee: Citizens National Bank.
EIN: 756006485

8944
Joan Hohlt and J. Roger Wich Foundation
3210 Ferndale St.
Houston, TX   77098-2012

Established in 2004 in Texas.
Donors: Joan Hohlt Wich†; J. Roger Wich.
Foundation type: Independent foundation.
Financial data (yr. ended 12/31/13): Assets, $7,581,101 (M); expenditures, $930,694; qualifying distributions, $405,811; giving activities include $380,000 for 15 grants (high: $60,000; low: $2,500).
Fields of interest: Cultural awareness; Visual arts; Higher education; Community improvement.
Limitations: Applications not accepted. Giving primarily in TX. No grants to individuals.
Application information: Unsolicited requests for funds not accepted.
Officers: Paul Brockman, Pres.; Dawn Fudge, V.P.; Charles Lowery, Secy.
Trustees: Sandra Lowery; John Pecore.
EIN: 202045780

8945
Patsy B. Hollandsworth Family Foundation
P. O. Box 62
Judson, TX   75660-0062   (870) 540-6112
Contact: Gregory Courington, Pres.

Established in 1996 in Texas.
Donor: Patsy B. Hollandsworth†.
Foundation type: Independent foundation.
Financial data (yr. ended 12/31/13): Assets, $4,217,765 (M); expenditures, $246,670; qualifying distributions, $178,250; giving activities include $178,250 for 22 grants (high: $25,000; low: $2,500).
Fields of interest: Education; Higher education; Protestantism; Human services; Scouting programs.
Limitations: Applications accepted. Giving primarily in TX. No grants to individuals.
Application information: Application form required.
 Initial approach: Proposal
 Deadline(s): None
 Final notification: Within 2 months
Officers: Gregory Courington, Pres.; Lawrence Courington, V.P.; Alyce Sparks, Secy.-Treas.
EIN: 752655126

8946
The Graham and Carolyn Holloway Family Foundation

P.O. Box 989
Colleyville, TX 76034-0989
Contact: Valerie Holloway Skinner, V.P.
E-mail: valerie@hollowayfamilyfoundation.org; Main URL: http://www.hollowayfamilyfoundation.org
Grants List: http://www.hollowayfamilyfoundation.org/giving2014.htm
Grants List: http://www.hollowayfamilyfoundation.org/grants.htm

Established in 1994 in Texas.
Donors: E. Graham Holloway†; Carolyn G. Holloway.
Foundation type: Independent foundation.
Financial data (yr. ended 12/31/13): Assets, $4,826,111 (M); gifts received, $18,312; expenditures, $252,766; qualifying distributions, $212,500; giving activities include $212,500 for 55 grants (high: $20,000; low: $1,500).
Purpose and activities: Giving primarily to aid the elderly, individuals with developmental and/or physical disabilities, the chronically or terminally ill, and disadvantaged children.
Fields of interest: Arts and culture; Education; Hospital care; Alzheimer's disease; HIV/AIDS; Human services; Youth services; Children; Seniors; Homeless people; Low-income and poor people; People with disabilities; People with physical disabilities; People with psychosocial disabilities; People with intellectual disabilities; People with HIV/AIDS; Terminally ill people.
Type of support: General support; Program development; Research.
Limitations: Applications accepted. Giving primarily in NC, TN and TX. No support for churches or political interest groups. No grants to individuals and no loans; no international giving.
Publications: Application guidelines; Financial statement; Grants list.
Application information: See grantmaker web site for application policies and guidelines.
 Initial approach: Create account on foundation web site
 Copies of proposal: 1
 Deadline(s): See foundation web site for current deadlines
 Board meeting date(s): May and Nov.
Officer and Trustees: Valerie Holloway Skinner, V.P. and Trustee; Elizabeth Holloway Heinburger; Carolyn

G. Holloway; E. Graham Holloway; Ellen Ward; Susan Holloway Ward.
Number of staff: 1 part-time support.
EIN: 752569765

8947
John & Mildred Holmes Family Foundation

c/o Legacy Trust Co.
600 Jefferson, Ste. 350
Houston, TX 77002-7376 (713) 651-8800

Established in 1999 in Texas.
Donor: Mildred McDannald Holmes†.
Foundation type: Independent foundation.
Financial data (yr. ended 12/31/14): Assets, $4,909,167; expenditures, $282,549; qualifying distributions, $250,883.
Fields of interest: Elementary and secondary education; Higher education; Nonprofits; Hospice care; Christianity; School athletics; Family services.
Type of support: Regranting.
Application information: Application form required.
 Initial approach: Contact Foundation for application form
 Deadline(s): None
Officers and Directors: Mildred H. Bridges, Pres. and Director; Betty Holmes, V.P. and Director; Joe D. Untermeyer, Secy.-Treas.; Carter Crites; Katherine Crites; Jennifer G. Holmes; John B. Holmes III; Eleanor Johnson; Lucy H. Orens.
EIN: 311645204

8948
Hope 2 Others Foundation

2300 W. Pike Blvd., Ste. 105
Weslaco, TX 78596-5656 (956) 447-4115
Contact: Rocio P. Tanus, Secy. and Dir.
Main URL: http://hope2others.info/site

Donors: MV Flight Service LLC; Abraham Tanus.
Foundation type: Independent foundation.
Financial data (yr. ended 12/31/13): Assets, $5,022,068 (M); gifts received, $2,281,944; expenditures, $335,746; qualifying distributions, $329,746; giving activities include $300,000 for 1 grant.
Fields of interest: Religion.
Limitations: Applications accepted. Giving primarily in TX.
Application information: Application form required.
 Initial approach: Completed application form
 Deadline(s): None
Officers and Directors: Abraham Tanus, Pres. and Director; Rocio Tanus, V.P. and Director; Rocio P. Tanus, Secy. and Director; Sarah Tanus, Treas. and Director; Sam Lugo; Ricardo Villarreal.
EIN: 463579283

8949
Hope Charitable Foundation

610 N. Town East Blvd.
Mesquite, TX 75150-4736 (972) 329-9453
Contact: Jim Wade, Pres.

Donor: Ida Hope Thornton†.
Foundation type: Independent foundation.
Financial data (yr. ended 12/31/13): Assets, $848,901 (M); expenditures, $210,435; qualifying distributions, $210,435; giving activities include

$188,000 for 10 grants (high: $100,000; low: $3,000).
Purpose and activities: b.
Fields of interest: Education.
Limitations: Applications accepted. Giving primarily in TX.
Application information:
 Initial approach: Letter
 Deadline(s): None
Officers: Jim Wade, Pres.; Ronald Rhodes, V.P.; Amy Allen, Secy.
Directors: Robert Bowmer; Kathleen Brewer; Michael Mcilwain.
EIN: 275454671

8950
Hord Foundation

(formerly Passion Support, Inc.)
P.O. Box 882
Midland, TX 79701-0882

Established in 2006 in Texas.
Donors: W.D. Hord, Jr.; W.D. Hord III; Jennifer D. Hord.
Foundation type: Operating foundation.
Financial data (yr. ended 12/31/13): Assets, $2,636,002 (M); gifts received, $2,500,937; expenditures, $464,935; qualifying distributions, $412,028; giving activities include $412,028 for 8 grants (high: $369,378; low: $250).
Fields of interest: Foundations; Leadership development.
Limitations: Applications not accepted. Giving primarily in Washington, DC and Waco, TX.
Application information: Unsolicited requests for funds not accepted.
Officers: Jennifer D. Hord, Mgr.; W.D. Hord III, Mgr.
EIN: 208836849

8951
The Horizon Foundation

5601 Democracy Dr., Ste. 300
Plano, TX 75024-3674

Established in 2001 in Texas.
Donor: Rodger M. Sanders.
Foundation type: Independent foundation.
Financial data (yr. ended 12/31/12): Assets, $2,436,904 (M); gifts received, $1,500,000; expenditures, $250,464; qualifying distributions, $247,100; giving activities include $247,100 for grants.
Fields of interest: Natural resources; Human services; Child welfare; Youth services.
Limitations: Applications not accepted. Giving primarily in VA and TX. No grants to individuals.
Application information: Unsolicited requests for funds not accepted.
Officers: Rodger M. Sanders, Chair., Pres. and Treas.; Jean Ann Brock, V.P. and Secy.
EIN: 752947962

8952
Ralph & Genevieve B. Horween Foundation

Triad Bldg., 14887 Hwy., 105 W., Ste. 201
Montgomery, TX 77356-5670

Established in 1993 in Texas.
Foundation type: Independent foundation.

Financial data (yr. ended 12/31/14): Assets, $4,755,555; expenditures, $230,469; qualifying distributions, $220,963.
Fields of interest: Music; Orchestral music; Education; Protestantism; Child welfare.
Type of support: Regranting; Fundraising.
Limitations: Applications not accepted. No grants to individuals.
Application information: Unsolicited requests for funds not accepted.
Officers: Frederick Stow, Pres.; Frederick Stow, Jr., V.P.; Ralph Stow, V.P.; Stuart F. Chase, Secy.
EIN: 760401800

8953
Harvey R., Jr. and Patricia W. Houck Foundation, Inc.
8811 Westheimer Rd., Ste. 208
Houston, TX   77063-3617

Established in 1994 in Texas.
Donors: Harvey R. Houck, Jr.†; Patricia West Houck†; Houck Management Trust.
Foundation type: Independent foundation.
Financial data (yr. ended 12/31/13): Assets, $13,156,512 (M); gifts received, $500,000; expenditures, $555,868; qualifying distributions, $437,337; giving activities include $435,000 for 28 grants (high: $55,000; low: $500).
Fields of interest: Education; Christianity; Children's rights; Human services.
Type of support: General support; Capital campaigns.
Limitations: Applications not accepted. Giving primarily in MI and TX. No grants to individuals.
Application information: Contributes only to pre-selected organizations.
Officers: Patricia West Houck, Pres.; Gordon B. Rose, V.P. and Treas.; Mary Elizabeth Houck Moore, V.P.; Dunham F. Jewett, Secy.
EIN: 760435413

8954
Ruth S. Howard Family Trust
c/o Wells Fargo Bank, N.A.- Trust Tax Dept.
P.O. Box 41629, MAC T7061-021
Austin, TX   78704-1629

Foundation type: Independent foundation.
Financial data (yr. ended 12/31/13): Assets, $4,572,894 (M); expenditures, $260,151; qualifying distributions, $211,706; giving activities include $191,345 for 7 grants (high: $57,404; low: $9,567).
Fields of interest: Education; Health; Christianity; Protestantism.
Limitations: Applications not accepted. Giving primarily in TX.
Application information: Unsolicited requests for funds not accepted.
Trustee: Wells Fargo Bank, N.A.
EIN: 746375010

8955
Virginia Martin Howard Foundation
7230 Acacia Dr.
Leander, TX   78641-9385

Donor: Virginia Martin Howard†.
Foundation type: Independent foundation.

Financial data (yr. ended 12/31/13): Assets, $9,400,931 (M); expenditures, $420,351; qualifying distributions, $393,500; giving activities include $393,500 for 10 grants (high: $160,000; low: $3,500).
Fields of interest: Education; Graduate and professional education; Community and economic development; Theology; Food banks.
Type of support: General support.
Limitations: Applications not accepted. Giving primarily in Alexandria, LA; some funding also in Dallas, TX. No grants to individuals.
Application information: Unsolicited requests for funds not accepted.
Officers and Trustees: Joel E. Howard, Pres. and Trustee; Mark E. Howard II, V.P. and Trustee; Irma Howard, Secy. - Treas. and Trustee; Nathan Eric Howard; Rebecca Morris; William Owens.
EIN: 582022021

8956
The Howell Family Foundation
c/o Steven K. Howell
P.O. Box 22053
Houston, TX   77227-2053

Established in 2003 in Texas.
Donors: Evelyn E. Howell; The Howell Founation.
Foundation type: Independent foundation.
Financial data (yr. ended 12/31/13): Assets, $3,040,844 (M); expenditures, $183,630; qualifying distributions, $146,798; giving activities include $141,000 for 17 grants (high: $25,000; low: $1,000) and $186,000 for set-asides.
Fields of interest: Education; Elementary and secondary education; Diseases and conditions; Christianity; Human services.
Type of support: General support; Research; Scholarships.
Limitations: Applications not accepted. Giving primarily in TX and VA. No grants to individuals.
Application information: Unsolicited requests for funds not accepted.
Trustees: Charles W. Hall; Bradley N. Howell; David L. Howell; Douglas W. Howell; Evelyn E. Howell; Steven K. Howell; Thomas M. Wright.
EIN: 912192196

8957
RD Hunter Family Foundation
2829 Texas Ave.
Texas City, TX   77590-8259

Foundation type: Independent foundation.
Financial data (yr. ended 12/31/13): Assets, $0 (M); gifts received, $77,116; expenditures, $150,005; qualifying distributions, $150,000; giving activities include $150,000 for 2 grants (high: $100,000; low: $50,000).
Fields of interest: Education; Christianity.
Limitations: Applications not accepted. Giving primarily in TX.
Application information: Unsolicited requests for funds not accepted.
Director: Roy D. Hunter, Jr.
EIN: 455190876

8958
II Corinthians 9:7 Foundation
1409 Wathen Ave.
Austin, TX   78703-2527

Donors: Charles J. Anderson; Theresa M. Anderson.
Foundation type: Independent foundation.
Financial data (yr. ended 12/31/13): Assets, $4,218,162 (M); gifts received, $250,000; expenditures, $230,060; qualifying distributions, $183,080; giving activities include $183,080 for 26 grants (high: $105,250; low: $50).
Fields of interest: Education; Environment; Protestantism.
Limitations: Applications not accepted. Giving primarily in Austin, TX. No grants to individuals.
Application information: Contributes only to pre-selected organizations.
Officers: Charles J. Anderson, Pres.; Leslie H. Schievelbein, V.P.; Theresa M. Anderson, Secy.-Treas.
EIN: 274299005

8959
Ik Manzil
24902 Miranda Ridge
Boerne, TX   78006-8439

Foundation type: Independent foundation.
Financial data (yr. ended 12/31/13): Assets, $89,988 (M); gifts received, $400,000; expenditures, $330,917; qualifying distributions, $330,917; giving activities include $330,917 for 4 grants (high: $115,000; low: $39,525).
Fields of interest: Education; Religion; Human rights.
Limitations: Applications not accepted.
Application information: Unsolicited requests for funds not accepted.
Trustee: Gurvendera S. Suri.
Directors: Parvinderjit S. Khanuja; Gurvender P. Singh.
EIN: 461477271

8960
May H. Ilgenfritz Testamentary Trust
c/o Bank of America, N.A.
P.O. Box 831041
Dallas, TX   75283-1041
*Application address:*C/O John Swearingen, P.O. Box 311, Sedalia, MO 65302-0311, tel.: (816) 292-4342

Established in 1941 in Missouri.
Foundation type: Independent foundation.
Financial data (yr. ended 12/31/13): Assets, $4,320,432 (M); expenditures, $243,914; qualifying distributions, $201,466; giving activities include $175,000 for 76 grants to individuals (high: $4,400; low: $650).
Purpose and activities: Emphasis on scholarships to needy students residing in Sedalia, MO; support also for children and youth groups.
Fields of interest: Education; Human services.
Type of support: General support; Student aid.
Limitations: Applications accepted. Giving limited to residents and organizations of Sedalia, MO.
Application information: Application form required.
Initial approach: Letter (no more than 3 pages)
Deadline(s): July and Dec.

Trustees: John Swearingen; Stafford Swearingen; Bank of America, N.A.
EIN: 440663403

8961
The Inge Foundation
207 S. Brazos St.
Granbury, TX 76048-2253

Established in 2000 in Texas.
Donors: Charles Inge; Dominique Inge.
Foundation type: Independent foundation.
Financial data (yr. ended 12/31/14): Assets, $922,722 (M); expenditures, $203,581; qualifying distributions, $196,333; giving activities include $193,694 for 48 grants (high: $25,000; low: $500).
Fields of interest: Education; Environment; Nonprofits; Diseases and conditions.
Type of support: Regranting.
Limitations: Applications not accepted. Giving primarily in TX. No grants to individuals.
Application information: Unsolicited requests for funds not accepted.
Trustees: Charles Inge; Dominique Inge; Rust E. Reid.
EIN: 752913283

8962
The Isaac I Foundation
2312 Cedar Elm Terr.
Westlake, TX 76262-9030

Established in 2001 in Texas.
Donors: Ronald E. Rinard; Asher Resources Partnership.
Foundation type: Independent foundation.
Financial data (yr. ended 12/31/13): Assets, $8,015,972 (M); expenditures, $455,548; qualifying distributions, $385,452; giving activities include $384,727 for 10 grants (high: $135,000; low: $400).
Fields of interest: Undergraduate education; Youth services.
Limitations: Applications not accepted. Giving primarily in TX, with emphasis on Houston; some funding also in Marietta, OH.
Application information: Unsolicited requests for funds not accepted.
Directors: Cecilia M. Rinard; Ronald E. Rinard; John R. Stoika.
EIN: 752965575

8963
Crawford and Hattie Jackson Foundation
c/o J. Steven Awalt
9 Greenway Plz., Ste. 1700
Houston, TX 77046-0946

Established in 1997 in Texas.
Donor: Hattie Jackson†.
Foundation type: Independent foundation.
Financial data (yr. ended 12/31/13): Assets, $8,691,300 (M); expenditures, $402,400; qualifying distributions, $390,126; giving activities include $300,000 for 11 grants (high: $50,000; low: $5,000).
Fields of interest: Higher education; University education.
Type of support: General support.

Limitations: Applications not accepted. Giving primarily in TX. No grants to individuals.
Application information: Contributes only to pre-selected organizations.
Officers: J. Steven Awalt, Pres.; Rodney C. Koenig, V.P.; Brenda Harral, Secy.
EIN: 760526233

8964
The Charles E. Jacobs Foundation
P.O. Box 2770
Albany, TX 76430-1178

Established in 2000 in Texas.
Donors: C.E. Jacobs; Marcia Jacobs.
Foundation type: Independent foundation.
Financial data (yr. ended 12/31/13): Assets, $4,848,309 (M); expenditures, $160,051; qualifying distributions, $156,250; giving activities include $156,250 for 18 grants (high: $52,500; low: $250).
Fields of interest: Arts and culture; Christianity; Sports and recreation.
Limitations: Applications not accepted. Giving primarily in Albany, TX. No grants to individuals.
Application information: Unsolicited requests for funds not accepted.
Officers: Glenn A. Picquet, Pres.; Dan Neff, V.P. and Treas.; Marcia Carol Brewer Jacobs, Secy.
EIN: 752859040

8965
The Jamail Galveston Foundation
1200 Smith St., Ste. 1135
Houston, TX 77002-4592

Established in 1992 in Texas.
Donors: Joseph D. Jamail; Lillie H. Jamail†.
Foundation type: Independent foundation.
Financial data (yr. ended 12/31/14): Assets, $3,456,062 (M); expenditures, $260,500; qualifying distributions, $225,000; giving activities include $225,000 for 12 grants (high: $50,000; low: $10,000).
Fields of interest: Arts and culture; Education; Agriculture.
Type of support: General support.
Limitations: Applications accepted. Giving limited to the Galveston, TX, area. No grants to individuals.
Application information: Application form required.
  Initial approach: Letter on organization letterhead
  Copies of proposal: 1
  Deadline(s): None
Officers: Donald P. Stevens, V.P.; Robert L. Jamail, Secy.-Treas.
Trustees: J. Dahr Jamail III; Randall H. Jamail.
Number of staff: 1 part-time professional.
EIN: 760370098

8966
The Janszen Charitable Trust
4831 Merlot Ave., Ste. 320
Grapevine, TX 76051-7384

Established in 1992 in Texas.
Foundation type: Independent foundation.
Financial data (yr. ended 12/31/13): Assets, $25,966 (M); gifts received, $315,100; expenditures, $436,610; qualifying distributions,

$435,650; giving activities include $435,650 for 34 grants (high: $159,000; low: $250).
Purpose and activities: Giving primarily for evangelical Christian churches and agencies.
Fields of interest: Christianity; Human services.
Limitations: Applications not accepted. Giving primarily in TX. No grants to individuals.
Application information: Contributes only to pre-selected organizations.
Trustee: Ronald D. Ray.
EIN: 756423830

8967
Jastrow Foundation
6300 Bee Caves Rd., Bldg. 1, 6th Fl.
Austin, TX 78746-5833

Established in 2007 in Texas.
Donors: Susan T. Jastrow; Kenneth M. Jastrow II.
Foundation type: Independent foundation.
Financial data (yr. ended 12/31/13): Assets, $1,975,437 (M); expenditures, $331,430; qualifying distributions, $323,167; giving activities include $323,167 for 14 grants (high: $110,000; low: $1,000).
Fields of interest: Higher education; Protestantism.
Limitations: Applications not accepted. Giving primarily in TX. No grants to individuals.
Application information: Unsolicited requests for funds not accepted.
Officers: Kenneth M. Jastrow II, Pres.; Martha J. McCartt, Secy.-Treas.
Directors: Corbin T. Jastrow; Kenneth M. Jastrow III; Susan T. Jastrow.
EIN: 261635125

8968
Caroline Lott Jessen Foundation
770 S. Post Oak Ln., Ste. 460
Houston, TX 77056-2042
Application address: c/o Caroline Lott Jessen, Pres., 370 S. Main St., Yuma, AZ 85364

Established in 2004 in Texas.
Donors: Caroline Lott Jessen; Jon Jessen; Gowan Co.
Foundation type: Independent foundation.
Financial data (yr. ended 12/31/14): Assets, $635,496 (M); gifts received, $500,000; expenditures, $233,400; qualifying distributions, $229,258; giving activities include $229,258 for 12 grants (high: $175,138; low: $400).
Fields of interest: Education; Diseases and conditions; Agriculture.
Limitations: Applications accepted. Giving primarily in Yuma, AZ.
Application information: Application form required.
  Initial approach: Letter
  Deadline(s): None
Officers: Caroline Lott Jessen, Pres.; Jon Jessen, V.P.; Dirk Jessen, Secy.; Gowan Jessen Deckey, Treas.
EIN: 202056562

8969
Joe & Nan Johnson Family Foundation
P.O. Box 2249
Wichita Falls, TX   76307-2249
Application address: c/o Nan H. Johnson, 811 6th
St., Ste. 300, Wichita Falls, TX 76301, tel.: (940)
723-2166

Established in 2005 in Texas.
Donors: Nan H. Johnson; Joe L. Johnson, Jr.
Foundation type: Independent foundation.
Financial data (yr. ended 12/31/14): Assets,
$1,838,024 (M); gifts received, $16,258;
expenditures, $276,746; qualifying distributions,
$265,498; giving activities include $263,000 for 42
grants (high: $50,000; low: $1,000).
Fields of interest: Education; Alumni relations;
Diseases and conditions; Protestantism; Human
services; Food banks; Child welfare.
Type of support: General support.
Limitations: Applications accepted. Giving primarily
in TX, with some emphasis on Wichita Falls.
Application information: Application form required.
  Initial approach: Request application form
  Deadline(s): None
Officers and Directors: Joe L. Johnson III, Pres. and
Director; Nan H. Johnson, V.P. and Secy. and
Director; Nancy Isom; Jeannie Ralston.
EIN: 202784844

8970
The Wece B. and Martha A. Johnson Foundation
P.O. Box 4019
Longview, TX 75606-4019   (903) 758-1200
Contact: Jennifer Slade, Dir.
E-mail: johnsonfoundation1@gmail.com

Established in 1997 in Texas.
Donor: Martha A. Johnson†.
Foundation type: Independent foundation.
Financial data (yr. ended 12/31/13): Assets,
$4,431,704 (L); expenditures, $237,303;
qualifying distributions, $171,075; giving activities
include $169,000 for 9 grants (high: $71,100; low:
$1,000).
Fields of interest: University education; Christianity.
Limitations: Applications accepted. Giving primarily
in Longview, TX.
Application information: Application form required.
  Initial approach: Letter or E-mail
  Deadline(s): Mar. 15 for Spring and Sep. 15 for
    Fall
Officers: C. Mark Abernathy, Pres.; Ed Moore, V.P.;
Roy E. Price, Jr., Secy.; Sally Brown, Treas.
Directors: Howard P. Coghlan; Kellyn Drayer; Bob
Dyer; Lottie Guttry; Hazel Hickey; Cindy Jordan; Jack
Lenhart; Jennifer Slade; Joe Wallace.
EIN: 752659420

8971
R. C. Johnson, Jr. Foundation, Inc.
12002 Trafalgar Ave., Ste. 300
Lubbock, TX 79424
Contact: Nelda R. Johnson, Pres.
Application Address: c/o Nad Johnson, 9600
Quacker Ave. Ste. 10, Lubbock, TX 79424

Established in 2002 in Texas.
Donor: Nelda R. Johnson.
Foundation type: Independent foundation.

Financial data (yr. ended 12/31/13): Assets,
$4,176,927 (M); expenditures, $185,657;
qualifying distributions, $185,657; giving activities
include $178,627 for 11 grants (high: $49,000;
low: $307).
Fields of interest: Music; Education; Graduate and
professional education; Nonprofits; Nursing care;
Disasters and emergency management.
Type of support: Regranting.
Limitations: Applications accepted. Giving primarily
in TX. No grants to individuals.
Application information: Application form required.
  Initial approach: Letter
  Deadline(s): None
Officers: Jan Johnson, Pres.; Kathy Johnson Hurley,
V.P.; Jeremy Velasquez, Secy.; Justin Velasquez,
Treas.
EIN: 752954057

8972
The Ralph A. Johnston Foundation, Inc.
P.O. Box 10
Burton, TX   77835-0010

Established in 1959 in Texas.
Donor: Ralph A. Johnston†.
Foundation type: Independent foundation.
Financial data (yr. ended 05/31/13): Assets,
$3,830,166 (M); expenditures, $217,336;
qualifying distributions, $199,192; giving activities
include $182,500 for 18 grants (high: $25,000;
low: $2,500).
Purpose and activities: Giving primarily for
education and human services.
Fields of interest: Higher education; Hospital care;
Diseases and conditions; Human services; Child
welfare; Single parents; Homeless people; People
with disabilities; People with physical disabilities;
People with psychosocial disabilities.
Type of support: Capital campaigns; Fellowships;
Research; Research and evaluation.
Limitations: Applications not accepted. Giving
primarily in TX. No grants to individuals.
Application information: Unsolicited requests for
funds not accepted.
  Board meeting date(s): Varies
Officers: Jerry J. Andrew, Pres.; Lyle E. Carbaugh,
V.P. and Treas.; Cheryl Duff, Secy.
Directors: Brad Duff; Jill Lewis; Dee S. Osborne;
Carroll Phillips.
EIN: 746051797

8973
Charles S. Jones Memorial Trust
c/o Bank of America, N.A.
P.O. Box 831
Dallas, TX   75283-1041

Foundation type: Independent foundation.
Financial data (yr. ended 12/31/14): Assets,
$4,519,368 (M); expenditures, $285,743;
qualifying distributions, $236,628; giving activities
include $209,951 for 2 grants (high: $157,463;
low: $52,488).
Fields of interest: Specialty hospital care; Shelter
and residential care.
Limitations: Applications not accepted. No grants to
individuals.
Application information: Unsolicited requests for
funds not accepted.

Trustee: Bank of America, N.A.
EIN: 486166410

8974
Carolyn H. Joseph Charitable Trust
2211 Norfolk, Ste. 375
Houston, TX   77098

Donor: CHJ Trust.
Foundation type: Independent foundation.
Financial data (yr. ended 03/31/15): Assets,
$927,819 (M); expenditures, $315,607; qualifying
distributions, $302,279; giving activities include
$300,000 for 3 grants (high: $100,000; low:
$100,000).
Fields of interest: Health; Hospital care; Diseases
and conditions; Cancers.
Type of support: General support.
Limitations: Applications not accepted. Giving
primarily in FL, OK and VA.
Application information: Unsolicited requests for
funds not accepted.
Trustee: Patricia G. Ferguson.
EIN: 760679752

8975
Journey Charitable Foundation
9129 Briar Forest Dr.
Houston, TX   77024-7213

Established in 1998 in Texas.
Donor: Francine M. Fleming.
Foundation type: Independent foundation.
Financial data (yr. ended 12/31/13): Assets,
$4,219,454 (M); gifts received, $250,000;
expenditures, $209,795; qualifying distributions,
$160,500; giving activities include $160,500 for 19
grants (high: $12,500; low: $5,000).
Purpose and activities: `.
Fields of interest: Housing development; Religion;
Human services.
Limitations: Applications not accepted. Giving
primarily in TX. No grants to individuals.
Application information: Unsolicited requests for
funds not accepted.
Trustees: Francine M. Fleming; Weldon Mikulik;
Janice Oettmeier.
EIN: 760574341

8976
The Doris Pilgrim Julian Charitable Trust
c/o Bank of America, N.A.
P.O. Box 831041
Dallas, TX   75283-1041

Donor: Doris F. Julian†.
Foundation type: Independent foundation.
Financial data (yr. ended 07/31/13): Assets,
$6,043,649 (M); expenditures, $270,808;
qualifying distributions, $254,869; giving activities
include $243,914 for 3 grants (high: $150,000;
low: $10,000).
Fields of interest: Education; Housing development.
Limitations: Applications not accepted. Giving
primarily in TX.
Application information: Unsolicited requests for
funds not accepted.
Trustees: Aubrey Hal Pilgrim; Evanne Pilgrim;
Paulette Rolston; Bank of America, N.A.
EIN: 546882534

8977
The Kabacoff Family Foundation
4106 Ave. F
Austin, TX 78751-4624

Donors: Gloria S. Kabacoff; Lester E. Kabacoff.
Foundation type: Independent foundation.
Financial data (yr. ended 12/31/13): Assets, $6,453,412 (M); expenditures, $325,377; qualifying distributions, $241,550; giving activities include $241,550 for 100 grants (high: $30,000; low: $100).
Fields of interest: Arts and culture; Historic preservation; Education; Higher education; Family planning; Police agencies; Human services.
Limitations: Applications not accepted. Giving primarily in New Orleans, LA. No grants to individuals.
Application information: Unsolicited requests for funds not accepted.
Officers: Margot K. Thomas, Pres.; Maurice P. Kabacoff, Secy.-Treas.
EIN: 721307912

8978
Fannie and Stephen Kahn Charitable Foundation
10440 N. Central Expy., Ste. 1280
Dallas, TX 75231-5817

Donor: Stephen S. Kahn†.
Foundation type: Independent foundation.
Financial data (yr. ended 12/31/13): Assets, $10,030,867 (M); expenditures, $535,567; qualifying distributions, $403,113; giving activities include $222,600 for grants.
Fields of interest: Performing arts; Museums; Elementary and secondary education; Higher education; Hospital care; Diseases and conditions; Judaism; Human services; Females.
Type of support: Endowments; Annual campaigns; Scholarships; Research; Program development; General support.
Limitations: Applications not accepted. Giving primarily in Dallas, TX; giving also in Washington, DC. No grants to individuals.
Application information: Contributes only to pre-selected organizations.
Officers: Sallie A. Scanlan, Pres.; Susan S. Cameron, V.P. and Secy.
Directors: Courtenay S. Wood; Heather W. Wood.
EIN: 752873734

8979
Joan and Marvin Kaplan Foundation
(formerly The Joan and Marvin Kaplan Family Charitable Foundation)
c/o Marvin Kaplan
3411 Richmond, Ste. 750
Houston, TX 77046

Established in 1986 in Texas.
Donors: Marvin Kaplan; Joan Kaplan; Moselle Pollack†.
Foundation type: Independent foundation.
Financial data (yr. ended 12/31/14): Assets, $6,492,034; expenditures, $386,586; qualifying distributions, $306,149.
Fields of interest: Arts and culture; Education; Medical education; Foundations; Nonprofits; Judaism; Human services.

Type of support: General support; Annual campaigns; Capital campaigns; Capital and infrastructure; Endowments; Research; Regranting.
Limitations: Applications not accepted. Giving primarily in Houston, TX. No grants to individuals.
Application information: Contributes only to pre-selected organizations.
Officers: Marvin Kaplan, Pres. and Treas.; Joan Kaplan, V.P. and Secy.
Directors: Susan K. Bruch; Richard Kaplan.
EIN: 760205105

8980
The Kayser Foundation
600 Travis St., Ste. 2800
Houston, TX 77002-2926 (713) 226-1393
Contact: Jeff Love, Pres.

Established in 1961 in Texas.
Donors: Paul Kayser; Mrs. Paul Kayser.
Foundation type: Independent foundation.
Financial data (yr. ended 12/31/13): Assets, $4,276,229 (M); expenditures, $236,530; qualifying distributions, $216,051; giving activities include $202,400 for 53 grants (high: $30,000; low: $500).
Purpose and activities: Giving primarily for youth services, higher education, and medical research.
Fields of interest: Higher education; Hospital care; Diseases and conditions; Human services; Child welfare; Youth services.
Type of support: Annual campaigns; Capital and infrastructure; Equipment; Program development; Research.
Limitations: Applications accepted. Giving primarily in TX. No grants to individuals.
Application information: Application form required.
Initial approach: Letter
Deadline(s): None
Officers: Jeff Love, Pres.; Don Glendenning, V.P.; Kenneth Simon, Secy.-Treas.
EIN: 746050591

8981
KCL Foundation
(formerly KPW Foundation)
c/o Karyn Buchanan
600 Congress Ave., Ste. 200
Austin, TX 78701-2995

Established in 1993 in Texas.
Donors: Jerald Winetroub; Robert W. Hughes.
Foundation type: Independent foundation.
Financial data (yr. ended 12/31/13): Assets, $4,282,109 (M); expenditures, $211,892; qualifying distributions, $198,799; giving activities include $195,000 for 62 grants (high: $15,250; low: $500).
Purpose and activities: Giving primarily to 501(c)(3) organizations.
Fields of interest: Education; Higher education; In-patient medical care; Cancers; Human services.
Type of support: General support; Matching grants; Continuing support; Annual campaigns; Capital campaigns; Capital and infrastructure; Land acquisitions; Endowments; Debt reduction; Emergency funds; Program development; Scholarships; Program evaluations.
Limitations: Applications not accepted. Giving primarily in central TX, with emphasis on the area of

Travis, Williamson, and Hays counties. No grants to individuals.
Application information: Contributes only to pre-selected organizations.
Board meeting date(s): Dec.
Officers and Directors: Robert W. Hughes, Pres. and Director; Kyle L. Hughes, 1st V.P. and Director; Craig Hughes, 2nd V.P. and Director; Lee Walker, V.P. and Director; M. Gail Hughes, Secy. and Director; Karyn Buchanan, Treas.
Number of staff: 1 part-time professional; 1 part-time support.
EIN: 742707482

8982
The Kellam Foundation, Inc.
256 Rainbow Dr., Ste. 15682
Livingston, TX 77399-2056

Donor: ASU Foundation.
Foundation type: Independent foundation.
Financial data (yr. ended 12/31/13): Assets, $1,446,929 (M); expenditures, $170,817; qualifying distributions, $169,715; giving activities include $169,715 for 14 grants (high: $63,000; low: $675).
Fields of interest: Arts and culture; Diseases and conditions; Community and economic development.
Limitations: Applications not accepted. Giving primarily in AZ.
Application information: Unsolicited request for funds not accepted.
Officers: L. Birt Kellam, Pres.; Louisa J. Kellam, Secy.
EIN: 263920321

8983
The Boyd and Joan Kelley Charitable Foundation
2412 Bryan Glen
Wichita Falls, TX 76308-4734

Established in 1998 in Texas.
Donor: Joan Kelley.
Foundation type: Independent foundation.
Financial data (yr. ended 12/31/13): Assets, $12,199,730 (M); gifts received, $68,706; expenditures, $441,903; qualifying distributions, $361,500; giving activities include $361,500 for 20 grants (high: $109,000; low: $2,000).
Fields of interest: Christianity; Human services.
Type of support: General support.
Limitations: Applications not accepted. Giving primarily in TX; some funding nationally. No grants to individuals.
Application information: Contributes only to pre-selected organizations.
Officers and Trustees: Joan Kelley, Fdn.Mgr. and Trustee; Jack Hill, Mgr.
EIN: 742897733

8984
W. D. Kelley Foundation
(formerly W. D. Kelley Charitable Trust)
c/o Grants Committee
707 Rock St.
Georgetown, TX 78626-5718 (512) 863-2575
Contact: Dale Illig, Pres.

Established in 1996 in Texas.

Foundation type: Independent foundation.
Financial data (yr. ended 12/31/13): Assets, $8,251,142 (M); expenditures, $493,363; qualifying distributions, $425,074; giving activities include $329,364 for 20 grants (high: $32,900; low: $350).
Purpose and activities: Funding for projects directed at youth and family, with preference given to faith-based programs.
Fields of interest: Education; Health; Religion; Human services; Family services; Child welfare.
Type of support: General support.
Limitations: Applications accepted. Giving primarily within 20 miles of Georgetown, TX. No grants to individuals, or for endowments, capital campaigns, events or galas.
Application information:
  Deadline(s): July and Dec.
  Board meeting date(s): June and Nov.
Officers: Dale Illig, Pres.; Sandra Illig, Secy.
Directors: Thomas Baird; Herbert Nelson.
Number of staff: 1 part-time support.
EIN: 743007226

8985
Betty Stieren Kelso Foundation
640 Ivy Ln.
San Antonio, TX 78209-2827

Established in 1986 in Texas.
Donor: Betty Kelso.
Foundation type: Independent foundation.
Financial data (yr. ended 12/31/13): Assets, $5,429,139 (M); expenditures, $397,997; qualifying distributions, $322,488; giving activities include $322,488 for 20 grants (high: $122,958; low: $100).
Fields of interest: Music; Art museums; Nonprofits.
Type of support: Regranting.
Limitations: Applications not accepted. Giving limited to San Antonio, TX. No grants to individuals.
Application information: Unsolicited requests for funds not accepted.
Officers: Betty Kelso, Pres.; Robert Kelso, V.P.; Barry Roberts, Secy.-Treas.
EIN: 742442790

8986
Keown Charitable Foundation
P.O. Box 41629
Austin, TX 78704-0028

Established in 1993 in Texas.
Donor: Alvin V. Keown†.
Foundation type: Independent foundation.
Financial data (yr. ended 06/30/13): Assets, $7,404,132 (M); expenditures, $341,470; qualifying distributions, $303,676; giving activities include $225,052 for 29 grants (high: $46,250; low: $1,000).
Fields of interest: Education; Higher education; Health care administration and financing; Protestantism; Human services.
Limitations: Applications not accepted. Giving primarily in TX. No grants to individuals.
Application information: Contributes only to pre-selected organizations.
Trustees: Ira Betts; Laverne Klenk; Mitchell Koop; Kenneth Loke; Charles Wendt.
EIN: 742668057

8987
Carl E. Kessler Family Foundation
P.O. Box 121579
Fort Worth, TX 76121-1579

Established in 1994 in Texas.
Donors: Carl E. Kessler; Kenneth R. Kessler.
Foundation type: Independent foundation.
Financial data (yr. ended 12/31/13): Assets, $7,681,493 (M); gifts received, $100,000; expenditures, $737,417; qualifying distributions, $422,324; giving activities include $421,835 for 104 grants (high: $120,000; low: $5).
Fields of interest: Higher education; Community and economic development; Christianity; Children and youth.
Limitations: Applications not accepted. Giving primarily in Bloomington, IN; giving also in TX, with some emphasis on Mineral Wells. No grants to individuals.
Application information: Contributes only to pre-selected organizations.
Officers: Kenneth R. Kessler, Pres.; David R. Kessler, V.P.; Carla Kay Kessler, Secy.-Treas.
EIN: 752567397

8988
James L. & Kathryn Ketelsen Charitable Foundation
4265 San Felipe, No. 970
Houston, TX 77027-2960

Established in 1998 in Texas.
Donors: James L. Ketelsen; Kathryn Ketelsen.
Foundation type: Independent foundation.
Financial data (yr. ended 12/31/13): Assets, $10,279 (M); gifts received, $158,700; expenditures, $153,989; qualifying distributions, $153,975; giving activities include $153,975 for 25 grants (high: $63,500; low: $50).
Fields of interest: Arts and culture; Education; Human services.
Type of support: General support.
Limitations: Applications not accepted. Giving primarily in Houston, TX. No grants to individuals.
Application information: Contributes only to pre-selected organizations.
Trustees: James L. Ketelsen; Kathryn Ketelsen.
EIN: 311601478

8989
David & Margaret Kilgore Foundation
4700 Bluffview Blvd.
Dallas, TX 75209-1906

Established in 1988 in Texas.
Donors: David P. Kilgore; Margaret W. Kilgore; Therese Hendrix; J. Scott Hendrix.
Foundation type: Independent foundation.
Financial data (yr. ended 12/31/13): Assets, $459,093 (M); gifts received, $173,856; expenditures, $180,885; qualifying distributions, $180,874; giving activities include $180,727 for 16 grants (high: $55,389; low: $1,250).
Purpose and activities: Support primarily for Christian missionary programs.
Fields of interest: Linguistics; Christianity; Human services.
International interests: Russia.

Limitations: Applications not accepted. Giving primarily in FL; with some giving to Russia. No grants to individuals.
Application information: Unsolicited requests for funds not accepted.
Officers and Trustees: David P. Kilgore, Chair. and Trustee; Margaret W. Kilgore, Vice-Chair. and Trustee.
EIN: 752279050

8990
Winifred & B. A. Killson Educational Foundation
(formerly Killson Educational Foundation)
c/o Bank of America, N.A.
P.O. Box 831041
Dallas, TX 75283-1041

Established in 1996 in Texas.
Foundation type: Independent foundation.
Financial data (yr. ended 01/31/15): Assets, $3,437,589 (M); expenditures, $200,083; qualifying distributions, $166,250; giving activities include $165,000 for 4 grants (high: $80,000; low: $20,000).
Purpose and activities: Support for higher education, including scholarship awards to students who are residents of Texas at the time of high school graduation to enable them to complete their education at colleges and universities (which may or may not be located in Texas).
Fields of interest: Undergraduate education; University education; Medical education.
Type of support: Scholarships; Student aid.
Limitations: Applications not accepted. Giving limited to residents of TX. No grants to individuals (directly).
Application information: Unsolicited requests for funds not accepted.
Officers and Trustees: Robert L. Allbritton, Chair. and Pres.; Charles W. Hall, V.P. and Trustee; Dennis A. Young; Jeanne Lawyer, Secy.-Treas.
EIN: 752650791

8991
Kimble Foundation Trust
c/o Amarillo National Bank Trust
P.O. Box 1
Amarillo, TX 79105-0001

Foundation type: Independent foundation.
Financial data (yr. ended 12/31/13): Assets, $5,081,202 (M); expenditures, $295,209; qualifying distributions, $232,995; giving activities include $232,995 for 26 grants (high: $25,000; low: $500).
Fields of interest: Education; Human services.
Limitations: Applications not accepted.
Application information: Unsolicited requests for funds not accepted.
Trustee: Amarillo National Bank.
EIN: 134308100

8992
King Benjamin Fund
5500 Preston Rd., Ste. 250
Dallas, TX 75205-2699

Established in 2005 in Texas.
Donor: Mark Palmer.

Foundation type: Independent foundation.
Financial data (yr. ended 12/31/13): Assets, $4,027,288 (M); expenditures, $209,454; qualifying distributions, $185,000; giving activities include $185,000 for 7 grants (high: $65,000; low: $5,000).
Fields of interest: University education; Public libraries; Gift distribution.
Limitations: Applications not accepted. Giving primarily in Austin, TX, and UT. No grants to individuals.
Application information: Contributes only to pre-selected organizations.
Officers and Directors: Mark Palmer, Pres. and Director; Jacqueline Palmer, V.P. and Director; Jasmine Palmer, Secy. and Director; Chelsea Beauchamp, Treas. and Director; Whitney Lewis; Angela Palmer; Geoffrey Palmer; Nathan Palmer.
EIN: 202274344

8993
Luther & Teresa King Family Foundation
301 Commerce St., No. 1600
Fort Worth, TX 76102-4116

Donors: Luther King; Teresa King; J. Luther King, Jr.
Foundation type: Independent foundation.
Financial data (yr. ended 06/30/13): Assets, $3,283,342 (M); gifts received, $537,800; expenditures, $275,629; qualifying distributions, $272,000; giving activities include $272,000 for grants.
Fields of interest: Education; Higher education.
Limitations: Applications not accepted. Giving primarily in TX. No grants to individuals.
Application information: Unsolicited requests for funds not accepted.
Officers: Teresa King, Pres.; J. Luther King, Jr., V.P. and Secy.-Treas.; John Bryan King, V.P.; Mason Daniel King, V.P.
EIN: 203781741

8994
King Ranch Family Trust
P.O. Box 1418
Kingsville, TX 78364-1418
Contact: Paula Smith, Secy.
E-mail: krft@intcomm.net

Established in 1946 in Texas.
Donor: King Ranch Family.
Foundation type: Independent foundation.
Financial data (yr. ended 12/31/13): Assets, $6,805,740 (M); expenditures, $338,315; qualifying distributions, $291,238; giving activities include $268,386 for 15 grants (high: $35,000; low: $500).
Purpose and activities: Giving primarily for education, and youth, family and social services.
Fields of interest: Education; Hospital care; Family planning; Addiction services; Community and economic development; Human services; Family services; Youth development.
Type of support: Equipment; Matching grants; Program development; Professorships.
Limitations: Applications accepted. Giving limited to TX, with emphasis on the Kingsville and Corpus Christi, area. No grants to individuals, or for endowment funds; no loans.

Publications: Application guidelines; Annual report; Financial statement; Informational brochure (including application guidelines).
Application information:
  Initial approach: Letter on organization letterhead
  Copies of proposal: 1
  Deadline(s): None
  Board meeting date(s): June
  Final notification: 30 days after board meeting
Trustees: Leslie C. Clement; Richard M. Kleberg III.
Number of staff: 1 part-time professional.
EIN: 746044809

8995
Kingdom Foundation
c/o Ironwood Capital Partners
322 Boerne Stage Airfield
Boerne, TX 78006-5152

Established in 2005 in New Mexico.
Donors: Charles J. Gyurko; Paul C. Arthur; Claire Arthur Honsalek; James A. Arthur; William H. Arthur; Sadie D. Gyurko.
Foundation type: Independent foundation.
Financial data (yr. ended 12/31/13): Assets, $122,843 (M); gifts received, $23,537; expenditures, $200,123; qualifying distributions, $195,698; giving activities include $195,698 for 1 grant.
Purpose and activities: Giving primarily to further the charitable and religious mission of a Christian organization in Japan.
Fields of interest: Maternal and perinatal health; Christianity.
International interests: Japan.
Limitations: Applications not accepted. Giving primarily in Japan; some giving also in TX.
Application information: Contributes only to pre-selected organizations.
Officers and Directors: Charles J. Gyurko, Pres. and Exec. Dir.; Sadie D. Gyurko, V.P. and Director; William H. Arthur, Secy.-Treas. and C.F.O.; James A. Arthur.
EIN: 203816832

8996
Kirwan Family Foundation, Inc.
c/o Bank of America, N.A.
P.O. Box 831041
Dallas, TX 75283-1041
Application address: c/o Roger Kirwan, Pres., 19700 Fairchild, Ste. 350, Irvine, CA 92612-2522

Established in 1997 in California.
Donors: Roger Kirwan; Gail Kirwan.
Foundation type: Independent foundation.
Financial data (yr. ended 12/31/13): Assets, $2,331,669 (M); expenditures, $204,783; qualifying distributions, $193,879; giving activities include $186,300 for 17 grants (high: $33,000; low: $2,500).
Fields of interest: Education; Secondary education; Catholicism; Human services; Youth services.
Limitations: Applications accepted. Giving primarily in CA and NY. No grants to individuals.
Application information: Application form required.
  Initial approach: Letter
  Deadline(s): None
Officers: Roger T. Kirwan, Pres.; Sean R. Kirwan, V.P.; Virginia Kirwan, V.P.

Directors: Carol Aikenhead; Dave Logozzo; Nicole S. Kirwan; Terry Morrison.
Trustee: Bank of America, N.S.
EIN: 330755324

8997
Alvin A. & Roberta T. Klein Trust Fund
7715 Hertfordshire
Spring, TX 77379-4650
Contact: Allan Klein, Dir.

Donor: Roberta T. Klein.
Foundation type: Independent foundation.
Financial data (yr. ended 12/31/13): Assets, $5,469,624 (M); expenditures, $239,346; qualifying distributions, $239,346; giving activities include $235,000 for 48 grants (high: $20,000; low: $1,000).
Fields of interest: Arts and culture; Education; Higher education; Hospital care; Protestantism; Human services.
Type of support: Research.
Limitations: Applications accepted. Giving primarily in TX, with emphasis on Houston. No grants to individuals.
Application information: Application form required.
  Initial approach: Letter
  Deadline(s): Dec. 1
Directors: Allan R. Klein; David R. Klein; John W. Klein; Sonja Klein.
EIN: 746055506

8998
The Klesse Foundation
c/o Margaret Klesse
109 Turnberry way
San Antonio, TX 78230-5639

Established in 2005 in Texas.
Donors: Margaret A. Klesse; William R. Klesse.
Foundation type: Independent foundation.
Financial data (yr. ended 12/31/13): Assets, $157,163 (M); expenditures, $437,328; qualifying distributions, $434,328; giving activities include $434,328 for 70 grants (high: $50,000; low: $250).
Fields of interest: Education; Nonprofits; Multiple sclerosis; Catholicism; Human services.
Type of support: Regranting.
Limitations: Applications not accepted. Giving primarily in TX.
Application information: Contributes only to pre-selected organizations.
Officers and Directors: William R. Klesse, Pres. and Director; Laura Klesse, V.P. and Director; Julie Klesse Linderman, V.P. and Director; Allison Klesse Smith, V.P. and Director; Margaret A. Klesse, Secy. and Director.
EIN: 202666212

8999
Robert W. Knox, Sr. and Pearl Wallis Knox Charitable Foundation
c/o Bank of America, N.A.
P.O. Box 831041
Dallas, TX 75283-1041
Application address: c/o Bank of America, N.A., Attn.: Debra Phares, 901 Main St., 19th Fl., Dallas, TX 75202-3714, tel.: (214) 209-1830

Established in 1964 in Texas.

Donor: Robert W. Knox, Jr.‡.
Foundation type: Independent foundation.
Financial data (yr. ended 08/31/14): Assets, $5,780,893 (M); expenditures, $334,118; qualifying distributions, $305,719; giving activities include $273,100 for 66 grants (high: $20,000; low: $1,000).
Purpose and activities: Giving primarily for the arts, education, and for medical and human services.
Fields of interest: Arts and culture; Performing arts; Opera; Children's museums; Historic preservation; Education; Higher education; Plant biodiversity; Animal welfare; Environmental studies; Health; Diseases and conditions; Christianity; Human services; Family services; Child welfare; Youth services; Adult and child mentoring; People with disabilities.
Type of support: Individual development.
Limitations: Applications accepted. Giving primarily in Houston and Galveston, TX. No grants to individuals.
Application information: Application form required.
   Initial approach: Obtain application form from Bank of America, N.A.
   Copies of proposal: 1
   Deadline(s): Aug. 31, Nov. 30, Feb. 28, and June 30
   Board meeting date(s): Quarterly
Trustee: Bank of America, N.A.
EIN: 746064974

9000
Kolitz Foundation Inc.
425 W. Bitters
San Antonio, TX 78216-1604   (210) 493-7743
Contact: Robert Kolitz, Dir.

Established in 2005 in Texas.
Donors: Robert Kolitz; Sandora Kolitz.
Foundation type: Independent foundation.
Financial data (yr. ended 12/31/13): Assets, $10,490 (M); gifts received, $430,000; expenditures, $440,307; qualifying distributions, $440,307; giving activities include $429,862 for 20 grants (high: $15,000; low: $5,000).
Purpose and activities: Giving primarily to Jewish agencies and temples, including a Jewish day school; funding also for health organizations and children, youth, and social services.
Fields of interest: Art museums; Elementary and secondary education; Nonprofits; Diseases and conditions; Judaism; Child welfare.
Type of support: Regranting.
Limitations: Applications accepted. Giving primarily in San Antonio, TX.
Application information:
   Initial approach: Proposal
   Deadline(s): None
Directors: Robert Kolitz; Sandora Kolitz.
EIN: 412181211

9001
The Harold and Patricia Korell Foundation
3333 Allen Pkwy., Ste. 2708
Houston, TX 77019-1851   (713) 522-2293
Contact: Harold M. Korell, Pres.

Donors: Harold M. Korell; Traded Securities with a Market Val; Patricia Korell.
Foundation type: Independent foundation.

Financial data (yr. ended 12/31/13): Assets, $4,785,491 (M); expenditures, $219,000; qualifying distributions, $219,000; giving activities include $219,000 for 7 grants (high: $120,032; low: $500).
Fields of interest: Education; Health; Human services.
Limitations: Applications accepted. Giving primarily in CO, MT and TX.
Application information: Application form required.
   Initial approach: Letter
   Deadline(s): None
Officers and Directors: Harold M. Korell, Pres. and Director; Patricia Korell, Secy. and Director; Roger D. Goddard, Treas. and Director.
EIN: 271507283

9002
Kowitz Family Foundation
1901 N. Akard St.
Dallas, TX 75201-2305

Established in 1997 in Texas.
Donors: Sarah Kowitz; David Kowitz.
Foundation type: Independent foundation.
Financial data (yr. ended 12/31/14): Assets, $1,620,003 (M); gifts received, $22,492; expenditures, $348,120; qualifying distributions, $345,651; giving activities include $345,651 for 15 grants (high: $150,000; low: $250).
Fields of interest: Arts and culture; Education; Human services.
International interests: England.
Type of support: General support; Student aid.
Limitations: Applications not accepted. Giving primarily in NY, with emphasis on Garrison and New York; giving also in Washington, DC, and London, England.
Application information: Unsolicited requests for funds not accepted.
Officers and Trustees: David Kowitz, Pres. and Treas. and Trustee; Sarah Kowitz, V.P. and Secy. and Trustee; Julie Miller.
EIN: 752707561

9003
Kramer Family Foundation
(formerly Power Service Products Foundation)
513 Peaster Hwy.
Weatherford, TX 76086

Established in 1997 in Texas.
Donor: Power Service Products, Inc.
Foundation type: Company-sponsored foundation.
Financial data (yr. ended 12/31/13): Assets, $1,160,750 (M); gifts received, $1,000,000; expenditures, $178,665; qualifying distributions, $178,250; giving activities include $178,250 for 10 grants (high: $100,000; low: $2,500).
Purpose and activities: The foundation supports organizations involved with health, Alzheimer's disease, children, and gift distribution.
Fields of interest: Education; Mental health care; Human services.
Type of support: General support; Research.
Limitations: Applications not accepted. Giving primarily in north TX, with emphasis on Weatherford. No grants to individuals.
Application information: Contributes only to pre-selected organizations.

Officers: Eddie M. Kramer, Pres. and Treas.; Patricia A. Kramer, V.P.; Ruth B. Swain, Secy.
EIN: 752693125

9004
The Krist Foundation
2600 S. Shore Blvd., Ste. 120
League City, TX 77573-3367   (281) 283-8500
Contact: Ronald D. Krist, Pres.

Established in 1998 in Texas.
Donor: Ronald D. Krist.
Foundation type: Independent foundation.
Financial data (yr. ended 03/31/13): Assets, $1,081,992 (M); expenditures, $164,409; qualifying distributions, $149,740; giving activities include $149,740 for 20 grants (high: $25,240; low: $500).
Fields of interest: Arts and culture; Education; Human services.
Type of support: General support; Scholarships.
Limitations: Applications accepted. Giving primarily in TX.
Application information:
   Initial approach: Proposal
   Deadline(s): None
Officer: Ronald D. Krist, Pres. and Director.
Directors: Carole D. Krist; Karyn D. Krist; Kevin D. Krist; Scott C. Krist.
EIN: 311594569

9005
The Anna Belle Kritser, II Foundation
P.O. Box 9238
Amarillo, TX 79105-9238   (806) 372-5569

Established in 2009 in Texas.
Foundation type: Independent foundation.
Financial data (yr. ended 12/31/14): Assets, $5,686,286; expenditures, $416,688; qualifying distributions, $295,000.
Fields of interest: Education; Human services.
Limitations: Applications accepted. Giving primarily in Amarillo, TX.
Application information: Application form required.
   Initial approach: Request application form
   Deadline(s): None
Trustees: Bill Countiss; David S. Kritser III.
EIN: 266730610

9006
Michael & Alice Kuhn Foundation
609B Wood St.
Austin, TX 78703-5417

Established in 1997 in Texas.
Donors: Michael Kuhn; Alice Kuhn.
Foundation type: Independent foundation.
Financial data (yr. ended 12/31/13): Assets, $10,232,598 (M); gifts received, $1,177,500; expenditures, $278,900; qualifying distributions, $219,000; giving activities include $219,000 for 16 grants (high: $33,000; low: $1,000).
Fields of interest: Community and economic development; Judaism.
Limitations: Applications not accepted. Giving primarily in NY,TX and DC. No grants to individuals.
Application information: Contributes only to pre-selected organizations.

Officers: Michael Kuhn, Pres. and C.E.O.; Alice Kuhn, V.P.; Jeffrey Kuhn, Treas.
Directors: Eric Kuhn; Randall S. Kuhn.
EIN: 742791217

9007
The L & M Charitable Foundation, Inc.
550 W. Texas Ave., Ste. 945
Midland, TX 79701-4233

Established in 2000 in Texas.
Donors: Hazel Valeria Late; Jan Late McMillan.
Foundation type: Independent foundation.
Financial data (yr. ended 12/31/12): Assets, $6,448,297 (M); gifts received, $1,855,714; expenditures, $273,033; qualifying distributions, $222,000; giving activities include $222,000 for grants.
Fields of interest: Education; Religion; Sports and recreation.
Limitations: Applications not accepted. Giving primarily in TX. No grants to individuals.
Application information: Unsolicited requests for funds not accepted.
Officer and Directors: Richard T. McMillan, Pres. and Director; Kirstin Elizabeth McMillan Gillespie; Jan Late McMillan.
EIN: 752874187

9008
Julian G. Lange Family Foundation I
7 Elmcourt St.
San Antonio, TX 78209-2811 (210) 826-8804
Contact: Richard A. Lange, Tr.

Established in 1999 in Texas.
Donor: Julian G. Lange†.
Foundation type: Independent foundation.
Financial data (yr. ended 12/31/13): Assets, $4,605,501 (M); expenditures, $230,278; qualifying distributions, $185,600; giving activities include $185,600 for 37 grants (high: $25,000; low: $1,000).
Fields of interest: Higher education; Health; Human services; Food banks.
Limitations: Applications accepted. Giving primarily in OH.
Application information: Application form required.
  Initial approach: Letter
  Deadline(s): None
Trustee: Richard A. Lange.
EIN: 311663386

9009
Lantana Education Charitable Foundation
c/o Mark Kiker
8401 N. Central Expwy., Ste. 350
Dallas, TX 75225-4404 (214) 292-3400
Contact: Richard Strauss, Pres.

Established in 2000 in Texas.
Donors: Rayzor Ranch LP; Weekley Homes; WRH Texas Ltd. Partnership; Dress Custom Homes; New Haven Custom Homes; Balmoral Homes Ltd.; Huntington Homes/Sanders Custom Homes; Kimball Hill Homes Texas, Inc.; Grand Homes; Laurel Development II LP; Highland Homes Ltd.; Landstar Homes Dallas Ltd.; CLRPG Land Co. LP; Newport Homes; Starlight Builders; Altura Homes; Banderalantana LP; 4SRPG Land Co. LP; Standard

Pacific of Texas Inc.; Newport Homebuilders Ltd.; Madisonlantana LP; ISA Bellantana LP; Lions Gate Homes; Sanders Custom Builders Ltd.
Foundation type: Independent foundation.
Financial data (yr. ended 12/31/12): Assets, $649,546 (M); gifts received, $681,826; expenditures, $234,617; qualifying distributions, $193,000; giving activities include $193,000 for grants.
Fields of interest: Education; Elementary and secondary education; Higher education; Hospital care; Diseases and conditions; Human services; Child welfare.
Limitations: Applications accepted. Giving primarily in TX. No grants to individuals.
Application information:
  Initial approach: Proposal
  Deadline(s): None
Officers and Directors: Richard C. Strauss, Pres. and Director; Mark R. Wagner, V.P. and Treas. and Director; John P. Wagner, V.P. and Director; Timothy B. McKnight, Secy.
EIN: 752882214

9010
Laredo Area Community Foundation
P.O. Box 450223
Laredo, TX 78045 (956) 796-1700
Contact: Elizabeth Romano Sames, Pres.
E-mail: esames@laredofoundation.org; Main URL: http://www.laredofoundation.org

Established in 2004 in Texas.
Foundation type: Community foundation.
Financial data (yr. ended 12/31/13): Assets, $4,691,102 (M); gifts received, $1,117,820; expenditures, $307,180; giving activities include $221,407 for 5+ grants (high: $65,000).
Purpose and activities: The foundation acts as a driving force to develop a permanent endowment, to assess and to respond to emerging and changing community needs, to provide a vehicle and service donors with varied interest and levels of giving, and to serve as a resource catalyst for charitable activities in the community.
Fields of interest: Arts and culture; Education; Environment; Health; Human services.
Limitations: Applications accepted. Giving primarily in Laredo, TX. No grants to individuals, or for fundraising events or campaigns, endowments, debt reduction, or operating deficits.
Publications: Annual report; Financial statement; Grants list; Informational brochure.
Application information: Application form required.
  Board meeting date(s): Monthly
Officers and Directors: Elizabeth R. Sames, Pres. and Director; William B. Green, V.P. and Director; Roseann C. Glassford, Secy. and Director; Nancy de Anda, Treas. and Director; Maria Eugenia Calderon-Porter; Rosendo Carranco; Christine H. Cerda; Irving I. Greenblum; Jim Harrell; Ray M. Keck III; Melissa M. Peters; Toni L. Ruiz; Robert H. Summers.
EIN: 311742706

9011
The LBJ Family Foundation
(formerly The LBJ Nonprofit Corporation)
114 W. 7th St., Ste. 900
Austin, TX 78701-3062

Established in 1996 in Texas.
Donors: The LBJ Family Foundation; Claudia T. Johnson Lifetime Trust.
Foundation type: Independent foundation.
Financial data (yr. ended 12/31/13): Assets, $3,109,743 (M); expenditures, $164,108; qualifying distributions, $138,188; giving activities include $129,000 for 27 grants (high: $20,000; low: $1,000).
Fields of interest: Education; Health; Human services.
Limitations: Applications not accepted. Giving primarily in TX. No grants to individuals.
Application information: Unsolicited requests for funds not accepted.
Officers and Trustees: Luci Baines Johnson, Chair. and Trustee; Claudia Taylor Brod, V.P. and Trustee; Nicole Marie Nugent Covert, V.P. and Trustee; Rebekah McIntosh, V.P. and Trustee; Patrick Lyndon Nugent, V.P. and Trustee; Willyn Wahl, Secy.-Treas.
EIN: 742715123

9012
The Terry and Laurie Ledbetter Foundation
P.O. Box 24622
Fort Worth, TX 76124-1622

Donors: Terry L. Ledbetter; Reta L. Ledbetter.
Foundation type: Independent foundation.
Financial data (yr. ended 12/31/12): Assets, $5,625,157 (M); gifts received, $2,488,163; expenditures, $284,724; qualifying distributions, $250,000; giving activities include $250,000 for grants.
Fields of interest: Religion.
Limitations: Applications not accepted. Giving primarily in TX.
Application information: Unsolicited requests for funds not accepted.
Officers and Directors: Reta L. Ledbetter, Pres. and Director; Terry L. Ledbetter, Treas. and Director; Kay Gaudin; Bradford L. Ledbetter; Terry L. Ledbetter, Jr.
EIN: 800188174

9013
Lesley Family Foundation, Inc.
c/o Bank of America, N.A.
P.O. Box 831041
Dallas, TX 75283-1041
Application address: c/o Debra Phares, Bank of America, N.A., 901 Main St., 19 Fl., Dallas, TX 75202-3714

Established in 2001 in Texas.
Donors: Hattie Mae Lesley†; Sarah A. Lesley Charitable Trust.
Foundation type: Independent foundation.
Financial data (yr. ended 12/31/14): Assets, $13,135,079 (M); gifts received, $847,380; expenditures, $469,772; qualifying distributions, $436,457; giving activities include $422,846 for 3 grants (high: $200,000; low: $97,846).
Fields of interest: Higher education; Domesticated animals; Food banks; Youth development.
Limitations: Applications accepted. Giving primarily in TX; some funding also in Honolulu, HI. No grants to individuals.
Application information: Application form required.
  Initial approach: Contact foundation for application form
  Deadline(s): None

Trustee: Bank of America, N.A.
Directors: Sarah A. Keeyes; Joseph D. Lesley; Sammy Joe Ramsey.
EIN: 752936755

9014
The Meyer Levy Charitable Foundation
P.O. Box 146
Austin, TX 78767-0146

Established in 2002 in Texas.
Donor: Myer Levy†.
Foundation type: Independent foundation.
Financial data (yr. ended 01/31/13): Assets, $9,252,332 (M); expenditures, $529,199; qualifying distributions, $432,481; giving activities include $310,237 for 46 grants (high: $20,000; low: $200).
Purpose and activities: Giving primarily for the basic needs of children and their families.
Fields of interest: Arts and culture; Arts education; Art museums; Children's museums; Education; Early childhood education; Child educational development; Climate change; Foundations; Infant care; Art and music therapy; HIV/AIDS; Housing development; Judaism; Human services; Adolescent parenting; Child welfare; Child care; Child development; Family counseling; Parent education; Single parent support; Youth development; Youth services; Youth mentoring; Temporary accommodations; Women's services.
Type of support: Public engagement and education.
Limitations: Applications not accepted. Giving primarily in Austin, TX. No grants to individuals.
Application information: Unsolicited requests for funds not accepted.
Officers: Jean Karotkin, Pres. and Treas.; Michael R. Levy, V.P. and Secy.
Director: James A. Flieller.
EIN: 752963800

9015
Paul A. Lewis College Fund
c/o Bank of America, N.A.
P.O. Box. 831041
Dallas, TX 75283-1041

Foundation type: Independent foundation.
Financial data (yr. ended 12/31/14): Assets, $3,189,215; expenditures, $190,769; qualifying distributions, $160,582.
Fields of interest: Education.
Limitations: Applications not accepted.
Application information: Unsolicited requests for funds not accepted.
Trustee: Bank of America, N.A.
EIN: 956112853

9016
Jack H. & William M. Light Charitable Trust
P.O. Box 17001-Trust
San Antonio, TX 78217-0001
Main URL: http://broadwaybank.com/wealthmanagement/FoundationWilliamMLight.html

Established in 1998 in Texas.
Donors: Jack H. Light†; William M. Light†; William M. Light Community Property Trust.
Foundation type: Independent foundation.

Financial data (yr. ended 12/31/13): Assets, $10,875,582 (M); expenditures, $520,293; qualifying distributions, $471,703; giving activities include $440,000 for 43 grants (high: $30,000; low: $2,500).
Purpose and activities: Giving primarily for health and human services for the benefit of children.
Fields of interest: Human services.
Type of support: Continuing support; Annual campaigns; Capital campaigns; Capital and infrastructure; Equipment; Endowments; Emergency funds; Program development; Curriculum development; Research.
Limitations: Applications accepted. Giving primarily in Bexar, Denton, and Harris counties, TX. No grants to individuals.
Application information: See foundation website for complete application guidelines and form. Application form required.
  Deadline(s): Apr. 30 and Oct. 31
  Final notification: June and Dec.
Trustee: Broadway National Bank, N.A.
Number of staff: None.
EIN: 742874941

9017
Lighthouse Foundation
P.O. Box 9542
The Woodlands, TX 77387-9542

Established in 2003 in Texas.
Donor: Watcham Trust.
Foundation type: Independent foundation.
Financial data (yr. ended 12/31/13): Assets, $1,845,272 (M); expenditures, $344,739; qualifying distributions, $343,646; giving activities include $343,646 for 11 grants (high: $276,000; low: $25).
Fields of interest: Christianity; Human services.
Limitations: Applications not accepted. Giving primarily in NC. No grants to individuals.
Application information: Contributes only to pre-selected organizations.
Trustees: Mitzi M. Pudlo; Richard T. Pudlo.
EIN: 200271577

9018
Ligon-Lamsam Foundation
c/o Megan Flynn
6615 Vaught Ranch Rd., Ste. 200
Austin, TX 78730—2314

Donor: W. Austin Ligon.
Foundation type: Independent foundation.
Financial data (yr. ended 12/31/13): Assets, $1,530,650 (M); expenditures, $275,508; qualifying distributions, $273,000; giving activities include $273,000 for 14 grants (high: $75,000; low: $500).
Fields of interest: Education; Adolescents.
Limitations: Applications not accepted. Giving primarily in MD and VA.
Application information: Unsolicited requests for funds not accepted.
Officer: W. Austin Ligon, Pres.
EIN: 205791016

9019
The Kevin and Lesley Lilly Foundation
3424 Robinhood St.
Houston, TX 77005-2228
Application address: c/o Kevin J. Lilly, 717 Texas Ave., Ste. 3000, Houston, TX 77002, tel.: (713) 238-2050

Established in 1996 in Texas.
Donors: Kevin J. Lilly; Lesley Lilly.
Foundation type: Independent foundation.
Financial data (yr. ended 07/31/13): Assets, $492,614 (M); gifts received, $300,000; expenditures, $236,187; qualifying distributions, $223,110; giving activities include $223,110 for 21 grants (high: $100,000; low: $250).
Fields of interest: Orchestral music; Museums; Education; Nonprofits; Community service; Religion; Protestantism; Females.
Type of support: Regranting.
Limitations: Applications accepted. Giving primarily in TX.
Application information: Application form required.
  Initial approach: Letter
  Deadline(s): None
  Board meeting date(s): Within 2 months
Officers and Directors: Kevin J. Lilly, Pres. and Treas. and Director; Lesley K. Lilly, V.P. and Secy. and Director; Joseph W. Thomson.
EIN: 311518662

9020
The Link Foundation
401 Congress Ave., Ste. 2424
Austin, TX 78701-3711 (512) 480-0010
Contact: Joe W. Bratcher III, Pres. and Treas.

Established in 1985 in Texas.
Donors: Joe W. Bratcher III; Joe W. Bratcher, Jr.
Foundation type: Independent foundation.
Financial data (yr. ended 12/31/13): Assets, $4,448,632 (M); expenditures, $466,238; qualifying distributions, $429,259; giving activities include $425,195 for 19 grants (high: $66,666; low: $5,000).
Purpose and activities: Giving primarily for human services, health care, and relief organizations.
Fields of interest: Arts and culture; Health; Human services.
Limitations: Applications accepted. Giving primarily in Austin, TX. No grants to individuals.
Application information: Application form required.
  Initial approach: Proposal
  Deadline(s): Sept. 30
Officers: Joe W. Bratcher III, Pres. and Treas.; Brigid Anne Cockrum, V.P. and Secy.
Director: Wendy Albrecht.
EIN: 742387802

9021
Helen Irwin Littauer Educational Trust
c/o Bank of America, N.A.
P.O. Box 831041
Dallas, TX 75283-1041
E-mail: kim.m.igoe-kasper@ustrust.com; E-mail: tx.philanthropic@ustrust.com (please indicate the foundation name in the subject line); Main URL: http://www.bankofamerica.com/grantmaking

Established in 1969 in Texas.
Foundation type: Independent foundation.

Financial data (yr. ended 04/30/14): Assets, $8,939,785 (M); expenditures, $517,172; qualifying distributions, $465,268; giving activities include $393,000 for 19 grants (high: $35,000; low: $3,000).

Purpose and activities: The trust is particularly interested in, but not limited to charitable organizations that focus on: scholarships that enable needy, but worthy boys and girls and young adults to attend school, college, or university, with a particular emphasis on making scholarships available for attending schools of journalism; promotion of art, education, and good citizenship; alleviating human suffering; medical care and treatment for all needy persons, including hospitals and clinics; providing care, education, recreation and/or physical training for needy, orphaned or disabled children; care of needy persons who are sick, aged or disabled; and improvement of living and working conditions of all persons.

Fields of interest: Arts and culture; Performing arts; Opera; Education; Health; Housing development; Human services; Child welfare; Youth development.

Type of support: General support; Matching grants; Fundraising; Capital and infrastructure; Program development.

Limitations: Applications accepted. Giving primarily in Tarrant County, TX. No grants to individuals.

Application information: Application guidelines on Trust web site. Application form required.

Initial approach: Use application process on foundation web site

Deadline(s): Mar. 1

Trustee: Bank of America, N.A.

EIN: 237029857

9022
C. L. and Gladys Lloyd Trust
c/o Bank of America, N.A.
P.O. Box 831041
Dallas, TX 75283-1041

Foundation type: Independent foundation.

Financial data (yr. ended 12/31/14): Assets, $7,872,663; expenditures, $433,960; qualifying distributions, $372,217.

Fields of interest: University education; Protestantism.

Limitations: Applications not accepted. Giving primarily in Dallas, TX.

Application information: Unsolicited request for funds not accepted.

Trustee: Bank of America, N.A.

EIN: 756066777

9023
The Long Foundation
(formerly The Joe and Teresa L. Long Foundation for the Arts)
40 N. I-H 35, Ste. 7C2
Austin, TX 78701-4359 (512) 479-4080
Contact: Mitchell Long, Secy.-Treas.
FAX: (512) 479-4182;
E-mail: mitchell@longfoundation.org; Main URL: http://www.longfoundation.org/content/nav_lf.html
Grants List: http://www.longfoundation.org/content/history.html

Established in 1999 in Texas.

Donor: Joe R. Long.

Foundation type: Independent foundation.

Financial data (yr. ended 12/31/14): Assets, $8,812,119; expenditures, $583,997; qualifying distributions, $442,889.

Purpose and activities: Giving primarily for education and youth services, particularly Texas Hispanic youth.

Fields of interest: Education; Higher education; Student retention; Reading promotion; Health care clinics; Community and economic development; Child welfare; People of Latin American descent.

Type of support: General support; Matching grants; Program development; Scholarships.

Limitations: Applications accepted. Giving primarily in TX. No support for religious programs or environmental organizations. No grants to individuals.

Application information: See foundation website for complete application guidelines. Application form required.

Initial approach: Letter

Officers: Joe R. Long, Pres.; Teresa L. Long, V.P.; Mitchell Long, Secy.-Treas. and Exec. Dir.

Director: Ruby Long.

EIN: 742916682

9024
Harry F. Lose Testamentary Trust
c/o Bank of America, N.A.
P.O. Box 831041
Dallas, TX 75283-1041

Foundation type: Independent foundation.

Financial data (yr. ended 12/31/14): Assets, $7,169,710; expenditures, $357,947; qualifying distributions, $319,459.

Fields of interest: Education.

Limitations: Applications not accepted. Giving primarily in KS.

Application information: Unsolicited requests for funds not accepted.

Trustee: Bank of America, N.A.

EIN: 486313319

9025
Lowdon Family Foundation
1400 W. 7th St., Ste. 400
Fort Worth, TX 76102-2628

Established in 1997 in Texas.

Donors: Maria M. Lowdon; Robert R. Lowdon; Lowdon Revocable Trust.

Foundation type: Operating foundation.

Financial data (yr. ended 12/31/13): Assets, $7,044,501 (M); expenditures, $362,838; qualifying distributions, $326,318; giving activities include $315,846 for 35 grants (high: $115,000; low: $200).

Purpose and activities: Giving primarily for the arts, particularly the performing arts; some funding also for health and human services.

Fields of interest: Arts and culture; Performing arts; Opera; Museums; Health; Diseases and conditions; Diabetes; Christianity; Human services; Child welfare.

Type of support: General support; Research.

Limitations: Applications not accepted. Giving primarily in Palm Beach, FL and Fort Worth, TX. No grants to individuals.

Application information: Contributes only to pre-selected organizations.

Officers and Directors: Ethel Patty Lowdon, Pres. and Director; Lili Lowdon Luth, Secy.-Treas. and Director; Matthew Hyder; Matt Luth.

EIN: 752688118

9026
LSF Foundation
11303 Williamsburg Dr.
Houston, TX 77024-7420 (713) 464-6441

Established in 1996 in Texas.

Donors: Lisa S. Frantz; Lisa M. Frantz.

Foundation type: Independent foundation.

Financial data (yr. ended 06/30/14): Assets, $2,357,025 (M); expenditures, $256,380; qualifying distributions, $251,250; giving activities include $250,000 for 11 grants (high: $50,000; low: $10,000).

Fields of interest: Education; Health; Human services.

Limitations: Applications not accepted. Giving primarily in TX, with emphasis on Houston. No grants to individuals.

Application information: Unsolicited requests for funds not accepted.

Officers: Lisa S. Frantz, Pres.; Jonda Watson, Secy.; Carol A. Cantrell, Treas.

Director: Jennifer Albitz.

EIN: 760506645

9027
The LSG Charitable Foundation
c/o Sanford L. Gottesman
P.O. Box 709
Coppell, TX 75019-0709

Established in 1998 in Texas.

Donors: Sanford Lee Gottesman; Austin Gottesman Family, LP; Lisa T. Gottesman.

Foundation type: Independent foundation.

Financial data (yr. ended 12/31/12): Assets, $5,150,135 (M); gifts received, $618,295; expenditures, $208,490; qualifying distributions, $205,163; giving activities include $205,163 for grants.

Fields of interest: Education; Human services; Youth development.

Limitations: Applications not accepted. Giving primarily in Austin, TX. No grants to individuals.

Application information: Contributes only to pre-selected organizations.

Trustees: Lisa T. Gottesman; Sanford Lee Gottesman.

EIN: 742900154

9028
T. C. Lupton Family Foundation
3811 Turtle Creek Blvd., No. 480
Dallas, TX 75219-4474

Established in 1994 in Texas.

Donors: Carolyn C. Lupton; T.C. Lupton, Jr.

Foundation type: Independent foundation.

Financial data (yr. ended 06/30/13): Assets, $4,654,131 (M); expenditures, $239,547; qualifying distributions, $220,895; giving activities include $220,895 for 44 grants (high: $30,702; low: $500).

Purpose and activities: Giving primarily for youth services and education.

Fields of interest: Education; Archives and special collections; Religion; Human services; Child welfare; Youth mentoring.
Limitations: Applications not accepted. Giving primarily in Dallas, TX. No grants to individuals.
Application information: Contributes only to pre-selected organizations.
Officers: T.C. Lupton, Jr., Chair.; Carol L. Huckin, Pres.; Carolyn C. Lupton, Secy.; Tavenner C. Lupton III, Treas.
Director: Laurie L. Liedtke.
EIN: 752549244

9029
W. P. & Bulah Luse Foundation
c/o U.S. Trust, Philanthropic Solutions
901 Main St., 19th Fl., TX1-492-19-11
Dallas, TX   75202-3714   8003577094
Contact: David T. Ross, Sr. V.P.
E-mail: tx.philanthropic@ustrust.com; Main
URL: https://www.bankofamerica.com/
philanthropic/grantmaking.go

Established in 1947 in Texas.
Donors: Bulah Luse†; W.P. Luse†.
Foundation type: Independent foundation.
Financial data (yr. ended 12/31/14): Assets, $16,262,433; expenditures, $770,952; qualifying distributions, $488,287.
Purpose and activities: Giving to support and promote quality education, human services, and health care programming for underserved populations.
Fields of interest: Education; Medical education; Diseases and conditions; Human services.
Type of support: General support; Continuing support; Annual campaigns; Capital campaigns; Capital and infrastructure; Equipment; Scholarships.
Limitations: Applications accepted. Giving limited to Dallas County, TX. No support for political or religious organizations. No grants to individuals.
Publications: Application guidelines.
Application information: Complete application guidelines are available on foundation web site.
  Initial approach: Online through foundation web site
  Deadline(s): June 30 and Dec. 31
Trustees: James P. Bevans; Karen Shuford; Kelly Watson; Bank of America, N.A.
Number of staff: None.
EIN: 756007639

9030
Lykes-Knapp Family Fund
(formerly J. M. Lykes Family Foundation)
1177 W. Loop S., Ste. 1310
Houston, TX   77027-9062
Contact: Christopher L. Knapp

Established in 1997 in Texas.
Donors: Christopher L. Knapp; Breck L. Knapp; James M.L. Grace; R. Randall Grace, Jr.; Genevieve K. O'Sullivan; A. John Knapp, Jr.
Foundation type: Independent foundation.
Financial data (yr. ended 12/31/13): Assets, $879,778 (M); expenditures, $184,733; qualifying distributions, $158,050; giving activities include $158,050 for 21 grants (high: $44,250; low: $1,000).

Fields of interest: Education; Environment; Youth development.
Limitations: Applications not accepted. Giving primarily in OK and TX. No grants to individuals.
Application information: Unsolicited requests for funds not accepted.
Officer: Christopher L. Knapp, Pres.
Directors: Breckenridge L. Knapp; Genevieve K. O'Sullivan.
EIN: 760411686

9031
Ruth Jones MacDonald Charitable Trust
5773 Woodway Dr., No. 630
Houston, TX   77057-1501

Established in 1998 in Texas.
Foundation type: Independent foundation.
Financial data (yr. ended 06/30/13): Assets, $5,216,282 (M); expenditures, $617,316; qualifying distributions, $366,449; giving activities include $200,000 for 10 grants (high: $35,000; low: $5,000).
Fields of interest: Education; Foundations; Depression; Human services; Family services.
Limitations: Applications not accepted. Giving primarily in Brookshire and Houston, TX. No grants to individuals.
Application information: Contributes only to pre-selected organizations.
Trustee: Bruce C. Arendale.
EIN: 766143209

9032
MacDonald-Peterson Foundation
1 Riverway, Ste. 1900
Houston, TX   77056-1944   (713) 623-2210
Contact: Guy Tabor

Established in 1995 in Texas.
Foundation type: Independent foundation.
Financial data (yr. ended 12/31/14): Assets, $9,535,403 (M); expenditures, $495,597; qualifying distributions, $463,027; giving activities include $420,000 for 30 grants (high: $50,000; low: $2,500).
Purpose and activities: Giving primarily for health and human services.
Fields of interest: Orchestral music; Higher education; University education; Nonprofits; Hospital care; Mental health counseling; Diseases and conditions; Community and economic development; Christianity; Human services; Food banks; Child welfare; Community service for youth.
Type of support: Research; Research and evaluation; Regranting.
Limitations: Applications not accepted. Giving primarily in TX; some funding also in New York, NY. No grants, loans or scholarships to individuals.
Application information: Contributes only to pre-selected organizations.
Officers: Erik G. Peterson, Pres. and Director; William T. Miller, V.P. and Secy.; Diana MacDonald Moore, V.P.
EIN: 760430319

9033
Majella Foundation
(also known as Majella Society)
11615 Angus Rd., Ste. 102
Austin, TX   78759-4064
Main URL: http://www.majellasociety.org/site/
PageServer?pagename=homepage

Donors: Brian R. Follett; The Life Foundation; Sally Follett; Scott Follett; Joan Follett; Robert Follett; Darlena Mead; Ron Mead; The Staubach Family Foundation; The Catholic Foundation; Dyatech; Nichole Tucker; Shane Tucker; Ann Quest; Bill Quest; Maureen Hafertepe; Joe Hafertepe; Shyla High; Thank Heaven Foundation; Don High; Heartbeat International, Inc.; Carenet; Life Education Fund; Jeffery S. Bogan; Joe Malone; Edward Mello; Marcus Fisher; Sumter Pregnancy Center; The J. Christopher and Ann C. Donahue Charitable Foundation; Douglas Libertore; Curtis L. Donahou.
Foundation type: Operating foundation.
Financial data (yr. ended 06/30/13): Assets, $495,642 (M); gifts received, $1,287,917; expenditures, $1,092,507; qualifying distributions, $853,448; giving activities include $349,999 for 1 grant.
Purpose and activities: The foundation's primary goal and purpose is to educate persons about issues regarding the value of life and its need for protection from the time of conception.
Fields of interest: Right to life.
Limitations: Applications not accepted. Giving primarily in Austin, TX.
Application information: Contributes only to pre-selected organizations.
Officers: Brian R. Follett, Pres.; Steve Kienlen, V.P., Opers.
Directors: Keith Armato; Alejandro Bermudez; Patrick D'Andrea; Barbara L. Lyons.
EIN: 203992655

9034
Manna International Charitable Foundation
P.O. Box 607
Greenwood, TX   76246-0607

Donors: Blake Sandford; Carole Sandford; Western Transportation Company; Coastline Transportation Inc; Sanford Oil South Texas; Sanford Fuels Ltd.; Sanford Oil Company; Sanford Petroleum Inc.
Foundation type: Independent foundation.
Financial data (yr. ended 12/31/13): Assets, $912,710 (M); gifts received, $553,000; expenditures, $140,780; qualifying distributions, $138,466; giving activities include $138,466 for 20 grants (high: $25,000; low: $215).
Fields of interest: Christianity.
Limitations: Applications not accepted. Giving primarily in TX.
Application information: Unsolicited requests for funds not accepted.
Trustees: Blake Sandford; Carole Sandford.
EIN: 276601355

9035
Harl & Evelyn Mansur Foundation
P.O. Box 4726
Wichita Falls, TX   76308-0726   (940) 691-4342

Donors: Evelyn L. Mansur; Harl D. Mansur, Jr.
Foundation type: Independent foundation.
Financial data (yr. ended 12/31/14): Assets, $5,998,499; expenditures, $374,020; qualifying distributions, $339,800.
Fields of interest: Education; Christianity; Human services.
International interests: Nicaragua.
Limitations: Applications accepted. Giving primarily in TX. No grants to individuals.
Application information: Application form required.
Initial approach: Letter
Deadline(s): None
Officers: Jonathan Mansur, Pres.; Miguel Miguel, V.P.; Thomas D. Barber, Treas.
EIN: 756085383

9036
Ernest A. Mantzel Foundation
c/o Frost National Bank
P.O. Box 179
Galveston, TX 77553-0179
Application Address: P. O. Box 8210, Galveston, TX, 77553, Application Phone: (409) 770-5665

Donor: Ernest A. Mantzel†.
Foundation type: Independent foundation.
Financial data (yr. ended 12/31/14): Assets, $6,807,094 (M); expenditures, $367,078; qualifying distributions, $296,635; giving activities include $270,000 for 68 grants to individuals.
Purpose and activities: Provides educational loans to Texas residents who attend a Texas university.
Fields of interest: Education; Vocational education.
Type of support: Student aid; Loans to individuals.
Limitations: Applications accepted. Giving limited to residents of TX.
Application information: Application form required.
Initial approach: Completed application form
Deadline(s): None
Trustee: Frost National Bank.
Directors: Harris L. Kempner, Jr.; Katherine Konkel; Freddie Meier.
EIN: 746155151

9037
The Edward and Betty Marcus Foundation
P.O. Box 5623
Austin, TX 78763-5623 (512) 478-4675
Contact: Linda Murdock

Established in 1984 in Texas.
Donor: Betty B. Marcus†.
Foundation type: Independent foundation.
Financial data (yr. ended 12/31/13): Assets, $10,002,132 (M); expenditures, $486,872; qualifying distributions, $407,630; giving activities include $355,000 for 1 grant.
Purpose and activities: Giving limited to entities that involve artworks and/or art education in the state of Texas.
Fields of interest: Arts education.
Type of support: Program development; Matching grants; Seed money; Curriculum development.
Limitations: Applications accepted. Giving limited to TX. No grants to individuals, or for capital campaigns, operating support, or endowment funds.
Application information: Application form required.
Initial approach: Letter
Copies of proposal: 1
Deadline(s): Mar. 1

Officers: Melba Davis Whatley, Chair.; Richard C. Marcus, Secy.-Treas.
Trustees: Norine Haynes; Susan Russell Marcus; Carolyn Levy Clark.
Number of staff: 1 part-time professional.
EIN: 751989529

9038
The Joseph & Bernice Margolin Foundation
5620 S. Rice Ave.
Houston, TX 77081-2118

Established in 1994 in Texas.
Donor: Bernice Margolin.
Foundation type: Independent foundation.
Financial data (yr. ended 11/30/13): Assets, $831,710 (M); expenditures, $203,905; qualifying distributions, $203,905; giving activities include $202,280 for 8 grants (high: $60,000; low: $1,000).
Purpose and activities: Giving for Jewish organizations.
Fields of interest: Arts and culture; Museums; Education; Human services.
Limitations: Applications not accepted. Giving primarily in OR and TX. No grants to individuals.
Application information: Unsolicited requets for funds not accepted.
Trustee: Allan Margolin.
EIN: 760463240

9039
Jay & Shirley Marks Foundation
585 Trianon St.
Houston, TX 77024-4619
Application address: Jay Shirley Marks Foundation, 858 Trianon, Houston, TX 770244619, tel.:(713) 202-0427

Established in 1972 in Texas.
Donors: Jay Marks; Shirley Marks.
Foundation type: Independent foundation.
Financial data (yr. ended 11/30/13): Assets, $157,152 (M); gifts received, $70,157; expenditures, $165,629; qualifying distributions, $159,877; giving activities include $157,728 for 14 grants (high: $100,200; low: $525).
Fields of interest: Arts and culture; Judaism; Human services.
Limitations: Applications accepted. Giving primarily in Houston, TX. No grants to individuals.
Application information:
Initial approach: Letter
Deadline(s): Nov. 30
Directors: Francis Marks Lowe; Jay M. Marks; Lester A. Marks; Shirley Marks.
EIN: 237253928

9040
Willie I., Wanda & W. F. Martin Charitable Trust
P.O. Box 701
Abilene, TX 79604-0701

Donor: Wanda Walker Martin†.
Foundation type: Independent foundation.
Financial data (yr. ended 09/30/13): Assets, $6,936,319 (M); expenditures, $413,105; qualifying distributions, $323,815; giving activities

include $305,750 for 6 grants (high: $125,000; low: $3,000).
Purpose and activities: Giving primarily for education.
Fields of interest: Education; Higher education; Youth organizing.
Type of support: Scholarships.
Limitations: Applications not accepted. Giving primarily in NM and TX. No grants to individuals.
Application information: Contributes only to pre-selected organizations.
Trustees: Linda Cain; First Financial Trust & Asset Management.
EIN: 756334363

9041
The Charles C. Matthews Foundation
P.O. Box 427
Carthage, TX 75633-0427

Donors: Charles Matthews†; Charles Matthews, LP; Charles Matthews Charitable Remainder Unitrust; C & M Ranch, Inc.
Foundation type: Independent foundation.
Financial data (yr. ended 12/31/13): Assets, $15,357,856 (M); expenditures, $736,478; qualifying distributions, $361,750; giving activities include $361,750 for 24 grants (high: $137,500; low: $250).
Purpose and activities: Giving primarily to benefit local communities.
Fields of interest: Education; Community and economic development.
Limitations: Applications not accepted. Giving primarily in the Carthage, TX, area. No grants to individuals.
Application information: Unsolicited requests for funds not accepted.
Trustees: Richard Ballenger; David Bush; John W. Conway; Jimmy D. Payne; Vermoyn D. Reeder; Robert M. Underwood.
EIN: 752741045

9042
The Mattsson McHale Foundation
3300 Bee Cave Rd., Ste. 650, No. 1311
Austin, TX 78746-6663 (512) 681-8402
Contact: Christine Mattsson, Dir.

Established in 1995 in Texas.
Donors: John McHale; Christine Mattsson.
Foundation type: Independent foundation.
Financial data (yr. ended 12/31/13): Assets, $2,035,594 (M); expenditures, $220,562; qualifying distributions, $217,902; giving activities include $217,027 for 14 grants (high: $64,000; low: $1,000).
Fields of interest: Art museums; Elementary and secondary education; National security.
Limitations: Applications accepted. Giving primarily in TX; some giving also in Washington, DC. No grants to individuals.
Publications: Annual report.
Application information:
Initial approach: Contact foundation
Deadline(s): None
Directors: Christine Mattsson; John McHale.
EIN: 752623152

9043
James & Eva Mayer Foundation
P.O. Box 328
Plainview, TX 79073-0328 (806) 296-6304

Established in 1987 in Texas.
Donor: Eva H. Mayer†.
Foundation type: Independent foundation.
Financial data (yr. ended 12/31/14): Assets, $4,719,814; expenditures, $284,263; qualifying distributions, $232,159.
Fields of interest: Child educational development; Higher education; Diseases and conditions; Children and youth.
Type of support: Capital campaigns; Matching grants; Capital and infrastructure; Equipment.
Limitations: Applications accepted. Giving primarily in TX, with an emphasis on the West Texas and Panhandle areas. No support for political or religious organizations, or for tax supported organizations. No grants to individuals, or generally for operating budgets or fundraising projects.
Application information: Application form required.
Initial approach: Letter
Copies of proposal: 3
Deadline(s): None
Trustees: Paul Lyle; Rudd F. Owen; David Wilder.
Number of staff: 1 part-time professional.
EIN: 756360908

9044
Mayfield Foundation Inc
P.O. Box 570365
Houston, TX 77257-0365

Established in 1996 in Texas.
Donor: Jack H. Mayfield, Jr.
Foundation type: Independent foundation.
Financial data (yr. ended 12/31/13): Assets, $3,486,111 (M); expenditures, $280,966; qualifying distributions, $280,966; giving activities include $240,167 for 18 grants (high: $50,000; low: $2,000).
Fields of interest: Education; Natural resources; Water resources; Protestantism; Youth services.
Limitations: Applications not accepted. Giving primarily in TX. No grants to individuals.
Application information: Unsolicited requests for funds not accepted.
Officers: Jack H. Mayfield, Jr., Pres.; Don W. Pisklak, Treas.
EIN: 760495695

9045
Mays Foundation
914 S. Tyler St.
Amarillo, TX 79101-3430 (806) 376-5417
Contact: Stacy Mays Sharp, Pres.

Donor: W.A. Mays and Agnes Mays Trust.
Foundation type: Independent foundation.
Financial data (yr. ended 07/31/13): Assets, $7,754,427 (M); expenditures, $281,639; qualifying distributions, $222,185; giving activities include $219,710 for 35 grants (high: $98,000; low: $150).
Fields of interest: Higher education; Protestantism; Youth development.
Type of support: Annual campaigns; Capital campaigns; Capital and infrastructure.

Limitations: Applications accepted. Giving primarily in TX. No grants to individuals.
Application information: Application form required.
Initial approach: Letter
Copies of proposal: 1
Deadline(s): None
Board meeting date(s): Jan.
Officers: Stacy Mays Sharp, Pres.; Karra Mays Hill, V.P.; Randy Sharp, Secy.-Treas.
Number of staff: None.
EIN: 751213346

9046
Hugh A. McAllister Charitable Foundation
(formerly McAllister Foundation)
840 Gessner Rd., No. 150
Houston, TX 77024-4153

Established in 1997 in Texas.
Donor: Hugh A. McAllister, Jr.
Foundation type: Independent foundation.
Financial data (yr. ended 12/31/13): Assets, $3,204,644 (M); expenditures, $307,502; qualifying distributions, $282,329; giving activities include $246,620 for 12 grants (high: $130,545; low: $75).
Fields of interest: Wildlife biodiversity; Aquariums; Health.
Type of support: General support.
Limitations: Applications not accepted. Giving primarily in Monterey, CA, Washington, DC and Davidson, NC. No grants to individuals.
Application information: Contributes only to pre-selected organizations.
Officers: Hugh A. McAllister, Jr., Pres.; Dana Leigh McAllister, Treas.
EIN: 760556345

9047
McCarty Family Foundation
P. O. Box 2271
Vernon, TX 76385-2271

Established in 2005 in Texas.
Donor: D.M. Robb†.
Foundation type: Independent foundation.
Financial data (yr. ended 12/31/13): Assets, $3,252,677 (M); expenditures, $190,625; qualifying distributions, $160,000; giving activities include $160,000 for 6 grants (high: $60,000; low: $10,000).
Fields of interest: Animal welfare; Housing development; Religion.
Type of support: General support.
Limitations: Applications not accepted. Giving primarily in Wichita Falls, TX, with some giving in CA and UT. No grants to individuals.
Application information: Contributes only to pre-selected organizations.
Officer: Greta Robb McCarty, Pres.
Trustee: Waggoner National Bank.
EIN: 203103094

9048
John H. & Tommie E. McCoy Charitable Foundation
2900 St. Michael Dr., Ste. 302
Texarkana, TX 75503-5212

Established in 2007 in Texas.

Foundation type: Independent foundation.
Financial data (yr. ended 12/31/14): Assets, $5,546,314; expenditures, $243,500; qualifying distributions, $243,500.
Fields of interest: Protestantism.
Limitations: Applications not accepted. Giving primarily in TX.
Application information: Unsolicited requests for funds not accepted.
Trustees: Monty Casteel; Raymond Wesley Jordan.
EIN: 208943856

9049
Sollie & Lilla McCreless Foundation for Christian Evangelism, Christian Missions, and Christian Education
P.O. Box 10
Waring, TX 78074-0010 (830) 995-2252
Contact: Jimmie L. Joffe, Secy.

Established in 1958 in Texas.
Donors: Sollie E. McCreless†; Lilla M. McCreless†.
Foundation type: Independent foundation.
Financial data (yr. ended 12/31/14): Assets, $2,330,429 (M); expenditures, $183,368; qualifying distributions, $162,064; giving activities include $145,319 for 18 grants (high: $35,000; low: $500).
Purpose and activities: Giving primarily to United Methodist churches, theological schools, and mission societies.
Fields of interest: Graduate and professional education; Christianity; Presbyterianism; Theology.
Type of support: General support; Program development.
Limitations: Applications accepted. Giving on a national basis. No grants to individuals.
Publications: Financial statement; Program policy statement.
Application information: Application form required.
Initial approach: Letter
Deadline(s): None
Board meeting date(s): Annually
Officers and Directors: Frances Jean Sunderland, Pres. and Director; Robert B. Sunderland, V.P. and Director; Elaine B. Hutzler, Treas.; Douglas E. Jividen; David W. Sunderland.
Number of staff: None.
EIN: 741485541

9050
McDaniel Charitable Foundation
P.O. Box 2968
Texas City, TX 77592-2968 (409) 942-2940
FAX: (409) 944-0120;
E-mail: contactus@mcdanielcharitablefoundation.org; Main URL: http://mcdanielcharitablefoundation.org

Established in 1999 in Texas.
Donors: Lola McDaniel†; Jene M. Moseley; Melissa Lyons-Gardner; Mark A. Lyons; Michelle Spier.
Foundation type: Independent foundation.
Financial data (yr. ended 12/31/13): Assets, $6,901,013 (M); expenditures, $674,997; qualifying distributions, $560,242; giving activities include $164,005 for 6 grants (high: $93,000; low: $1,500), $59,000 for 21 grants to individuals (high: $5,000; low: $500), and $162,524 for foundation-administered programs.

Purpose and activities: Giving to support programs, projects, and education that enhance the quality of life within the local community and State of Texas.
Fields of interest: Education; Higher education.
Type of support: Individual development.
Limitations: Applications not accepted. Giving primarily in TX.
Application information: Unsolicited requests for grant funding not accepted. See foundation web site for renewal scholarship application information.
Officers and Directors: Mark A. Lyons, Pres. and Director; Michelle Lyons Spier, V.P. and Director; Melissa Lyons Gardner, Secy.-Treas. and Director; R. Stewart Campbell, Jr.; Randall Harris; Robert Harris.
EIN: 760538313

9051
The Jim and Paula McDonald Charitable Trust
2900 N. Quinlan Park Rd., Ste. 239/240
Austin, TX   78732-6083

Established in 2000 in Georgia.
Donors: James F. McDonald; Paula S. McDonald.
Foundation type: Independent foundation.
Financial data (yr. ended 12/31/13): Assets, $10,410,276 (M); gifts received, $371,332; expenditures, $379,686; qualifying distributions, $326,495; giving activities include $278,630 for 12 grants (high: $200,000; low: $630).
Fields of interest: Foundations; Diseases and conditions; Diabetes; Human services.
Type of support: Research.
Limitations: Applications not accepted. No grants to individuals.
Application information: Unsolicited requests for funds not accepted.
Trustee: James F. McDonald.
Directors: Paula S. McDonald; Ashley M. Taylor.
EIN: 586429849

9052
Robert E. and Evelyn McKee Foundation
5835 Cromo Dr., Ste. 1
El Paso, TX   79912-5501   (915) 581-4025
Contact: Louis B. McKee, Pres.
FAX: (915) 833-3714;
E-mail: mckeefoundation@att.net; Application address: P.O. Box 220599, El Paso, TX 79913-2599; Main URL: http://www.mckeefoundation.org
Grants List: http://www.mckeefoundation.org/Donation%20List%202014.pdf

Established in 1952 in Texas.
Donors: Robert E. McKee†; Evelyn McKee†; Robert E. McKee, Inc.; The Zia Co.
Foundation type: Independent foundation.
Financial data (yr. ended 12/31/13): Assets, $8,528,217 (M); gifts received, $500; expenditures, $536,752; qualifying distributions, $399,506; giving activities include $371,374 for 62 grants (high: $50,000; low: $1,000).
Purpose and activities: Emphasis on local hospitals, community funds, and rehabilitation and the handicapped; grants also for religious organizations, higher and other education, youth agencies, child welfare, and medical research.
Fields of interest: Education; Higher education; Nonprofits; Hospital care; Rehabilitation; Diseases

and conditions; Christianity; Child welfare; People with disabilities.
Type of support: General support; In-kind gifts; Continuing support; Annual campaigns; Capital campaigns; Capital and infrastructure; Research; Equipment; Research and evaluation; Emergency funds; Program development; Regranting; Convening; Seed money; Scholarships.
Limitations: Applications accepted. Giving primarily in TX, with emphasis on El Paso. No support for organizations limited by race or ethnic origin, other private foundations (except for a local community foundation), religious organizations (except local Episcopal churches), or attempts to influence legislation. No grants or loans to individuals, or for endowment funds or deficit financing.
Publications: Application guidelines; Annual report (including application guidelines); Program policy statement.
Application information: Application guidelines available on foundation web site.
  Initial approach: Proposal
  Copies of proposal: 1
  Deadline(s): Dec. 15
  Board meeting date(s): June
  Final notification: After Feb. 15
Officers and Trustees: Louis B. McKee, Pres. and Treas. and Trustee; Helen Lund Yancey, V.P. and Secy. and Trustee; Margaret McKee Lund, Sr. V.P.; Charlotte McKee Cohen, V.P. and Trustee; Sharon Hays Herrera, V.P. and Trustee; F. James McKee, V.P.; James T. McKee, V.P. and Trustee; Philip Russell McKee, V.P. and Trustee; Susan J. McKee, V.P.; Linda Hays Gunter; C. Steven McKee; R. Brian McKee; Robert E. McKee IV; H.A. Woods.
Number of staff: 1 part-time professional; 1 part-time support.
EIN: 746036675

9053
The McLaughlin Doty Foundation
P.O. Box 769
Hunt, TX   78024-0769   (830) 238-3575

Donors: Beth Doty; Mark Doty.
Foundation type: Independent foundation.
Financial data (yr. ended 12/31/14): Assets, $5,370,072; expenditures, $309,685; qualifying distributions, $224,736.
Fields of interest: Arts and culture; Education; Elementary and secondary education; Foundations; Disasters and emergency management; Human services.
Type of support: Systems reform.
Limitations: Applications accepted. Giving primarily in TX.
Application information: Application form required.
  Initial approach: Contact foundation for application form
  Deadline(s): None for grant application; Apr. 1 for scholarship application
Directors: Beth Doty; Mark Doty; Stephanie Herman.
EIN: 274319466

9054
Bruce McMillan, Jr. Foundation Inc.
P.O. Box 9
Overton, TX   75684-0009   (903) 834-3148
Contact: Todd Meadows, Pres.

Established in 1951 in Texas.
Donors: V. Bruce McMillan, MD†; Mary Moore McMillan†.
Foundation type: Independent foundation.
Financial data (yr. ended 06/30/13): Assets, $19,830,479 (M); expenditures, $827,820; qualifying distributions, $537,774; giving activities include $268,760 for 21 grants (high: $100,000; low: $250), and $84,689 for 15 grants to individuals (high: $15,000; low: $1,000).
Purpose and activities: Grants largely for higher education, including a scholarship program for graduates of West Rusk, Overton, Henderson, Leverett Chapel, Kilgore, Troup, Arp, Carlisle and Troup Hill high schools in the immediate Overton, TX, area; support also for Baptist churches, agricultural conservation, and human services.
Fields of interest: Education; Higher education; Agriculture; Baptist; Human services.
Type of support: General support; Program development; Scholarships; Student aid.
Limitations: Applications accepted. Giving primarily in the Overton, TX, area.
Publications: Application guidelines.
Application information: Application form required.
  Initial approach: Letter
  Deadline(s): June 15
  Board meeting date(s): June and Oct.
Officers and Directors: Rogers Pope, Sr., Chair.; Rogers Pope, Jr., Vice-Chair.; Todd Meadows, Pres. and Treas. and Director; Tyree Collier, V.P.; Brenda Roach, Secy.
Number of staff: 2 full-time professional; 4 full-time support.
EIN: 750945924

9055
V. H. McNutt Memorial Foundation, Inc.
153 Treeline Park, Ste. 300
San Antonio, TX   78209-1880   2108291800

Foundation type: Independent foundation.
Financial data (yr. ended 12/31/14): Assets, $9,585,292; expenditures, $461,592; qualifying distributions, $434,895.
Fields of interest: Museums; Art museums; Education; Secondary education; Higher education; Biomedicine; Science; Technology; Human services; Child welfare.
Type of support: Capital campaigns; Research.
Limitations: Applications accepted. Giving primarily in the metropolitan San Antonio, TX, area. No grants to individuals, or for scholarships.
Application information: Newsletters and unsolicited applications from outside the metropolitan San Antonio, TX, area, will not be considered. IRS determination letter must be currently dated (within 3 years). Application form required.
  Initial approach: Letter (not exceeding 3 pages)
  Deadline(s): May 31 and Nov. 30
  Board meeting date(s): June and Dec.
Officers: Jack Guenther, Chair. and Pres.; Abigail G. Kampmann, V.P. and Secy.; Valerie Guenther, V.P. and Treas.
EIN: 820569927

9056
Trini and O. C. Mendenhall Foundation
55 Waugh Dr., No. 550
Houston, TX   77007-5800

Established in 1998 in Texas.
Donors: Trinidad Mendenhall Sosa; Trinidad V. Mendenhall.
Foundation type: Independent foundation.
Financial data (yr. ended 12/31/13): Assets, $53,218 (M); gifts received, $217,725; expenditures, $169,575; qualifying distributions, $169,575; giving activities include $165,095 for 17 grants (high: $50,000; low: $1,000).
Fields of interest: Higher education; Diseases and conditions; Christianity; Human services.
Type of support: Annual campaigns; Capital campaigns; Endowments.
Limitations: Applications not accepted. Giving primarily in Harris County, TX. No grants to individuals.
Application information: Contributes only to pre-selected organizations.
  Board meeting date(s): End of each quarter
Officers: Trinidad V. Mendenhall, Chair.; Oniel Mendenhall, Jr., Secy.
EIN: 760530965

9057
Mercy International
2734 Harvest Creek Ln.
Boerne, TX   78006-7603

Established in 1992 in Texas.
Donors: Jeffrey E. Leininger; John H. Leininger; Diane J. Leininger; J. Ryan Leininger.
Foundation type: Independent foundation.
Financial data (yr. ended 12/31/13): Assets, $377,340 (M); gifts received, $148,341; expenditures, $728,938; qualifying distributions, $179,674; giving activities include $167,962 for 15 grants (high: $93,874; low: $25).
Purpose and activities: Giving primarily to Christian churches, schools, charities, and agencies.
Fields of interest: Education; Diseases and conditions; Christianity; Human services.
Limitations: Applications not accepted. Giving primarily in FL and TX. No grants to individuals.
Application information: Unsolicited requests for funds not accepted.
Directors: Diane J. Leininger; John H. Leininger; J. Ryan Leininger; Shantel Leininger.
EIN: 742633786

9058
Merfish-Jacobson Foundation
38 Crestwood Dr.
Houston, TX   77007   (713) 869-5731

Established in 1988 in Texas.
Donors: Merfish Pipe & Supply; Ida K. Merfish; Gerald Merfish; Abe Merfish; Rochelle Jacobson.
Foundation type: Company-sponsored foundation.
Financial data (yr. ended 12/31/13): Assets, $4,218,789 (M); gifts received, $1,009,970; expenditures, $175,015; qualifying distributions, $159,922; giving activities include $149,250 for 27 grants (high: $30,000; low: $250).
Purpose and activities: The foundation supports organizations involved with higher education, family planning, patient services, children and youth, and Judaism.
Fields of interest: Health; Religion; Human services.
Limitations: Applications not accepted. Giving primarily in Houston, TX. No grants to individuals.

Application information: Unsolicited requests for funds not accepted.
Trustees: Rochelle M. Jacobson; Gerald Merfish; Ida K. Merfish.
EIN: 760239810

9059
Merrick Family Foundation
c/o Nicholas A. Merrick
3625 Greenbrier
Dallas, TX   75225-5106

Established in 1999 in Texas.
Donors: Nicholas A. Merrick; Leslie T. Merrick.
Foundation type: Independent foundation.
Financial data (yr. ended 12/31/13): Assets, $891,989 (M); gifts received, $116,900; expenditures, $417,688; qualifying distributions, $393,523; giving activities include $393,523 for 40 grants (high: $100,000; low: $200).
Fields of interest: Elementary and secondary education; Higher education; Christianity; Human services.
Limitations: Applications not accepted. Giving primarily in Dallas County, TX; giving also in AZ, CO, PA and VA. No grants to individuals.
Application information: Unsolicited requests for funds not accepted.
Officers: Nicholas A. Merrick, Pres.; Leslie T. Merrick, Secy.
Director: Judith L. Merrick.
EIN: 752851383

9060
The Michael and Linda Mewhinney Foundation
c/o Michael C. Mewhinney
4242 Cochran Chapel Rd.
Dallas, TX   75209-1506

Established in 1999 in Texas.
Donors: Michael C. Mewhinney; Linda D. Mewhinney.
Foundation type: Independent foundation.
Financial data (yr. ended 05/31/14): Assets, $2,396,663 (M); expenditures, $190,267; qualifying distributions, $188,917; giving activities include $188,917 for 14 grants (high: $61,320; low: $100).
Purpose and activities: Giving primarily for higher education; funding also for social services and Protestant and Roman Catholic organizations.
Fields of interest: Higher education; Nonprofits; Protestantism; Catholicism; Human services.
Type of support: Regranting.
Limitations: Applications not accepted. Giving primarily in MA, WA and TX.
Application information: Unsolicited requests for funds not accepted.
Officers: Michael C. Mewhinney, Pres. and Treas.; Linda D. Mewhinney, Secy.
Director: James S. Mewhinney.
EIN: 752828954

9061
The Meyer Foundation Inc.
6802 Mapleridge, Ste. 210
Bellaire, TX   77401
Application address: c/o Joseph F. Meyer, IV, 5402 Chevy Chase Dr., Houston, TX 77024-4229, tel.: (713) 668-2369

Established in 1999 in Texas.
Donors: Joseph F. Meyer III; Rosemary Meyer†.
Foundation type: Independent foundation.
Financial data (yr. ended 12/31/13): Assets, $3,471,121 (M); expenditures, $270,885; qualifying distributions, $233,003; giving activities include $227,500 for 35 grants (high: $28,500; low: $1,000).
Fields of interest: Protestantism; Child welfare; Homeless services.
Limitations: Applications accepted. Giving primarily in Houston, TX. No grants to individuals.
Application information: Application form required.
  Initial approach: Letter
  Deadline(s): None
Officers: Lucy Mitchell, Pres.; Kenneth Meyer, V.P.; C. Fred Meyer, Secy.-Treas.
Director: Joseph F. Meyer IV.
EIN: 760613316

9062
Marlene Nathan Meyerson Family Foundation
2800 Post Oak Blvd., 61st Fl.
Houston, TX   77056-6102

Established in 1999 in Texas.
Donor: Marlene N. Meyerson.
Foundation type: Independent foundation.
Financial data (yr. ended 12/31/13): Assets, $3,984,512 (M); expenditures, $362,808; qualifying distributions, $315,520; giving activities include $296,400 for 10 grants (high: $140,800; low: $600).
Fields of interest: Photography; Art museums; Higher education; Foundations; Judaism; Human rights; Child welfare; Female children and youth.
Limitations: Applications not accepted. Giving primarily in NM, NY and TX. No grants to individuals.
Application information: Unsolicited requests for funds not accepted.
Officers: Marlene Nathan Meyerson, Pres.; Marti Meyerson Hooper, V.P.; Marvin D. Nathan, Secy.
Directors: Brenda F. Brand; Elizabeth Glassman; Barry H. Margolis.
EIN: 752797176

9063
MHR Family Foundation Inc
4400 Windsor Ridge Dr.
Irving, TX   75038-6300

Donors: Michael H. Renzulli; Victoria A. Renzulli.
Foundation type: Independent foundation.
Financial data (yr. ended 12/31/13): Assets, $337,374 (M); expenditures, $201,855; qualifying distributions, $201,430; giving activities include $201,430 for 4 grants (high: $200,000; low: $80).
Fields of interest: University education.
Limitations: Applications not accepted. Giving primarily in PA.
Application information: Unsolicited requests for funds not accepted.

Officers: Michael H. Renzulli, Pres.; Victoria A. Renzulli, Secy.
Directors: Dante W. Renzulli; Michael H. Renzulli, Jr.
EIN: 261790581

9064

K. R. & Laura Miller Foundation

(formerly K. R. Miller Foundation)
736 FM 2341 N.
Edna, TX 77957 (361) 782-5852
Contact: Darrell Sklar, Tr.

Established in 2000 in Texas.
Donors: K.R. Miller; Laura Miller†.
Foundation type: Independent foundation.
Financial data (yr. ended 12/31/13): Assets, $4,508,302 (M); expenditures, $260,927; qualifying distributions, $222,479; giving activities include $207,479 for 16 grants (high: $47,255; low: $500).
Fields of interest: Undergraduate education; Community and economic development; Christianity.
Limitations: Applications accepted. Giving primarily in TX. No grants to individuals.
Application information: Application form required.
    Initial approach: Letter
    Deadline(s): None
Trustees: Michael Maraggia; Darrell Sklar; Kim Smith.
EIN: 742941588

9065

Monty Miller Living Legacy Foundation

1117 65th Dr.
Lubbock, TX 79412-3722 (806) 747-2542
Contact: Gary Light, Pres.

Established in 2002 in Texas.
Donors: Monty Miller; David Moody; Wendell Moore.
Foundation type: Independent foundation.
Financial data (yr. ended 12/31/13): Assets, $2,524,599 (M); gifts received, $3,000; expenditures, $342,416; qualifying distributions, $259,508; giving activities include $258,836 for 34 grants (high: $43,625; low: $711).
Fields of interest: Christianity; Child welfare.
Limitations: Applications accepted. Giving primarily in Lubbock, TX.
Application information: Application form required.
    Initial approach: Letter
    Deadline(s): None
Officers: Gary Light, Pres.; Chris Bost, V.P.; Quency Light, Secy.
Directors: Anna Purdue; Kyle Purdue.
EIN: 752941956

9066

Richard G. Miller Memorial Foundation

P.O. Box 1977
El Paso, TX 79950-1977
Application address: c/o Theodore F. Lange, 6300 Ridglea Pl., Ste. 500, Fort Worth TX 76116

Donor: Philip F. Schoch Trust.
Foundation type: Operating foundation.
Financial data (yr. ended 05/31/13): Assets, $5,831,433 (M); gifts received, $10,910; expenditures, $251,907; qualifying distributions,

$178,550; giving activities include $178,500 for 6 grants (high: $60,000; low: $5,000).
Fields of interest: Education; Religion; Human services.
Application information: Application form required.
    Initial approach: Letter
    Deadline(s): None
Trustees: John Birkelbach; Mike McCune.
EIN: 540852892

9067

The Walter M. Mischer & Mary A. Mischer Foundation

9 Greenway Plz., Ste. 2900
Houston, TX 77046-0923

Established in 1998 in Texas.
Donors: Mary A. Mischer; Walter M. Mischer, Sr.
Foundation type: Independent foundation.
Financial data (yr. ended 12/31/14): Assets, $3,284,490 (M); expenditures, $178,955; qualifying distributions, $175,000; giving activities include $175,000 for 4 grants (high: $100,000; low: $25,000).
Purpose and activities: Giving primarily for neuroscience, spinal cord injury, recovery and rehabilitation.
Fields of interest: Education; Health; Neurology; Diseases and conditions; Prostate cancer.
Type of support: Research.
Limitations: Applications not accepted. Giving primarily in Houston, TX. No grants to individuals.
Application information: Contributes only to pre-selected organizations.
Officers: Mary A. Mischer, Pres.; John W. Storms, V.P.; Sheryl Taylor, Secy.
Directors: Paula Mischer; Walter M. Mischer, Jr.
EIN: 760574194

9068

Mithoff Family Charitable Foundation, Inc.

(formerly Richard Warren Mithoff Family Charitable Foundation)
500 Dallas St., Ste. 3450
Houston, TX 77002-4800

Established in 1984 in Texas.
Donors: Richard Warren Mithoff, Jr.; Virginia Mithoff.
Foundation type: Independent foundation.
Financial data (yr. ended 12/31/13): Assets, $1,973,156 (M); expenditures, $414,895; qualifying distributions, $362,579; giving activities include $362,579 for 70 grants (high: $30,000; low: $3).
Fields of interest: Arts and culture; Performing arts; Museums; Science museums; University education; Human services; Child welfare.
Type of support: Capital campaigns; General support.
Limitations: Applications not accepted. Giving primarily in Houston, TX. No grants to individuals.
Application information: Contributes only to pre-selected organizations.
Officers: Virginia Mithoff, Pres.; V. Richard Viebig, Jr., Secy.; Michael K. Mithoff, Treas.
Directors: Caroline R. Mithoff; Melissa Mithoff; Richard Warren Mithoff, Jr.; Scott Perez.
EIN: 760094136

9069

Roy F. and Joann Cole Mitte Foundation

1008 West Ave.
Austin, TX 78701-2019 (512) 233-5599
Contact: Cheryl Nolting, Exec. Dir.
FAX: (512) 233-5542;
E-mail: info@mittefoundation.org; Grant application e-mail: communitygrants@mittefoundation.org;
Main URL: http://www.mittefoundation.org

Established in 1994 in Texas.
Donors: Roy F. Mitte†; Joann Cole Mitte†.
Foundation type: Independent foundation.
Financial data (yr. ended 12/31/13): Assets, $20,808,997 (M); expenditures, $851,291; qualifying distributions, $474,453; giving activities include $348,660 for 29 grants (high: $50,000; low: $1,500).
Purpose and activities: Giving primarily for: 1) Education, particularly college access and readiness preparation in grades 6-12; 2) Aging, with emphasis on aging in place and increasing public awareness of aging issues; and 3) Therapeutic and rehabilitative services for the mentally and/or physically disabled, with focus upon individual self sufficiency, functionality, and improved quality of life.
Fields of interest: Education; University education; Philanthropy; Health; Seniors.
Type of support: General support; Continuing support; Capacity-building and technical assistance; Individual development; Annual campaigns; Capital campaigns; Capital and infrastructure; Equipment; Endowments; Program development; Professorships; Curriculum development; Fellowships; Scholarships; Research.
Limitations: Applications accepted. Giving primarily in the central TX area. Generally, no support for religious or political organizations, private foundations, community foundations, or the United Way. No grants to individuals, indirect costs, or loans or program-related investments.
Publications: Application guidelines; Newsletter.
Application information: See foundation web site for more application information, including acceptable proposal formats. Online submissions only. Application form required.
    Initial approach: Letter of inquiry via foundation web site only
    Deadline(s): See foundation web site
    Board meeting date(s): Twice a year
    Final notification: Up to 6 months following deadline
Officers and Directors: Dilum Chandrasoma, Pres. and Director; Dyna Mitte, Secy.; Mark Davis, Treas.; Coleith Molstad, Exec. Dir.; Bob Burton; Dianne Carriere; Joseph "Dusty" McCormick; R.J. Mitte; Denise Nance Pierce.
Number of staff: 2 full-time professional.
EIN: 742766058

9070

Montgomery County Community Foundation

9320 Lakeside Blvd., Ste. 200
Bldg. 2
The Woodlands, TX 77381 (281) 363-8158
Contact: Shannon L. Kidd, Exec. Dir.
FAX: (281) 363-8191;
E-mail: skidd@mccfoundation.org; Main URL: http://www.mccfoundation.org

Established in 1983 in Texas.
Donors: Eric J. Bauer; Mrs. Eric J. Bauer.
Foundation type: Community foundation.
Financial data (yr. ended 12/31/13): Assets, $4,709,117 (M); gifts received, $228,851; expenditures, $200,752; giving activities include $115,509 for 6+ grants (high: $15,000), and $6,700 for 10 grants to individuals.
Purpose and activities: The foundation seeks to match community resources with community needs.
Fields of interest: Arts and culture; Historical activities; Education; Environment; Health; Community and economic development; Sports and recreation; Human services; Youth development; Children and youth; Seniors; Low-income and poor people; People with vision impairments.
Type of support: Student aid; General support.
Limitations: Applications accepted. Giving primarily in Montgomery County, TX. No support for lobbying activities. No grants to individuals (except for scholarships).
Publications: Annual report.
Application information: Visit foundation web site for application form and guidelines. Application form required.
  Initial approach: Submit application form and required attachments
  Copies of proposal: 2
  Deadline(s): Sept. 15
  Final notification: Applicants will be notified in early November and grants will be given in December.
Officers and Directors: Donnie Buckalew, Pres. and Director; John D. Webb, V.P. and Director; Nick VanderPool, Secy. and Director; Gregg Hope, Treas. and Director; Shannon L. Kidd, Exec. Dir.; Henry Brooks; Don Carter; Emily Cook; Roz Dauzat; Nancy Martin; Richie Ray; Luciano Reyes; Steve Sanders; Alex Sutton; Amanda Trapp; Jill Vaughan.
Number of staff: 1 full-time professional.
EIN: 760082098

9071
Hazel Montgomery, M.D., Memorial Scholarship Trust
P.O. Box 6170
Tyler, TX 75711-6170

Established in 1997 in Texas.
Donor: Hazel I. Montgomery†.
Foundation type: Independent foundation.
Financial data (yr. ended 05/31/13): Assets, $1,300,036 (M); expenditures, $191,746; qualifying distributions, $171,764; giving activities include $170,272 for grants to individuals.
Purpose and activities: Scholarship awards to students of West Independent School District, Texas.
Type of support: Student aid.
Limitations: Applications not accepted. Giving limited to residents of TX.
Application information: Unsolicited requests for funds not accepted.
Trustee: Southside Bank, N.A.
EIN: 756498847

9072
Ardon and Iris Moore Foundation
201 Main St., Ste. 300
Fort Worth, TX 76102

Donor: Ardon Iris Moore.
Foundation type: Independent foundation.
Financial data (yr. ended 11/30/13): Assets, $6,411,018 (M); gifts received, $439,624; expenditures, $381,938; qualifying distributions, $381,080; giving activities include $381,080 for 26 grants (high: $150,000; low: $1,000).
Purpose and activities: Giving primarily to a university.
Fields of interest: Elementary and secondary education; Higher education; Zoos.
Type of support: General support.
Limitations: Applications not accepted. Giving primarily in Austin and Fort Worth, TX. No grants to individuals.
Application information: Unsolicited requests for funds not accepted.
Officers: Ardon E. Moore, Pres. and Treas.; Iris H. Moore, V.P. and Secy.
Director: Ardon Tucker Moore.
EIN: 208090599

9073
Morrison Trust
c/o Frost National Bank Trust Dept.
P.O. Box 2950
San Antonio, TX 78299-2950   (210) 220-4438

Foundation type: Independent foundation.
Financial data (yr. ended 09/30/14): Assets, $3,761,922 (M); expenditures, $248,422; qualifying distributions, $232,182; giving activities include $209,834 for 4 grants (high: $35,160; low: $58,050).
Purpose and activities: Giving primarily to support the remedy, research, and improvement of existing methods of treating and preventing human sickness, and the development of new methods of treatment within the fields of nutrition, blood chemistry, and radionics and electricity.
Fields of interest: Medical education; Nutrition; Biomedicine; Diseases and conditions.
Type of support: Research; Research and evaluation.
Limitations: Applications accepted. Giving primarily in TX.
Application information: Proposal should include the following information: name of sponsoring institution and individual performing research, summary of research, budget request, and the signature of the sponsoring institution representative.
  Initial approach: Proposal
  Deadline(s): July 1
Trustee: Frost National Bank.
EIN: 746013340

9074
Paul and Katherine Morrow Family Foundation
P.O. Box 61447
Midland, TX 79711-1447

Foundation type: Independent foundation.
Financial data (yr. ended 12/31/13): Assets, $4,275,736 (M); expenditures, $222,753; qualifying distributions, $222,584; giving activities include $222,400 for 43 grants (high: $30,000; low: $500).
Fields of interest: Health; Religion; Human rights.

Limitations: Applications not accepted. Giving primarily in TX.
Application information: Unsolicited requests for funds not accepted.
Directors: Katherine Morrow; Paul Morrow.
EIN: 453981868

9075
Mosbacher Foundation, Inc.
712 Main St., Ste. 2200
Houston, TX 77002-3206

Established in 1948 in New York.
Donors: Barbara Mosbacher; Robert A. Mosbacher, Jr.; Emil Mosbacher; Gertrude Mosbacher; Emil Mosbacher, Jr.†; A.W. Downing Mears, Jr.; Diane Mosbacher; Kathryn Mosbacher; Lisa M. Mears; Robert A. Mosbacher†.
Foundation type: Independent foundation.
Financial data (yr. ended 12/31/13): Assets, $4,900 (M); gifts received, $315,000; expenditures, $315,025; qualifying distributions, $315,000; giving activities include $315,000 for 9 grants (high: $200,000; low: $1,000).
Fields of interest: Higher education; Foundations; Hospital care.
Limitations: Applications not accepted. Giving primarily in TX, with emphasis on College Station, Galveston, and Houston. No grants to individuals.
Application information: Unsolicited requests for funds not accepted.
Officers: Robert A. Mosbacher, Jr., Chair. and Pres.; A.W. Downing Mears, Jr., V.P.; Jason Hanlon, Secy.; Gerald Bendele, Treas.
EIN: 136155392

9076
Harry S. Moss Foundation
3838 Oak Lawn Ave., Ste. 1516
Dallas, TX 75219-4516   (214) 754-2984
Contact: Frank S. Ryburn, Pres.

Established in 1952 in Texas.
Donors: Harry S. Moss; Florence M. Moss; Moss Petroleum Co.
Foundation type: Independent foundation.
Financial data (yr. ended 11/30/14): Assets, $7,579,125 (M); expenditures, $338,404; qualifying distributions, $318,148; giving activities include $311,250 for 45 grants (high: $35,000; low: $1,000).
Fields of interest: Performing arts; Museums; Humanities; Education; Domesticated animals; Community and economic development; Human services; Child welfare.
Type of support: General support.
Limitations: Applications accepted. Giving primarily in the Dallas, TX, area. No grants to individuals.
Application information:
  Initial approach: Proposal
  Deadline(s): None
Officers: Frank S. Ryburn, Pres.; Mary Jane Ryburn, V.P. and Secy.-Treas.
EIN: 756036333

9077
The Jane P. and Wiley L. Mossy, Jr. Foundation
12150 Katy Freeway
Houston, TX 77079-1105

Established in 2002 in Texas.
Donor: Wiley L. Mossy, Jr.
Foundation type: Independent foundation.
Financial data (yr. ended 12/31/13): Assets,
$2,806,628 (M); gifts received, $175,000;
expenditures, $173,175; qualifying distributions,
$160,000; giving activities include $160,000 for 9
grants (high: $75,000; low: $2,500).
Fields of interest: Education; Health; Catholicism.
Limitations: Applications not accepted. Giving
primarily in Houston, TX. No grants to individuals.
Application information: Unsolicited requests for
funds not accepted.
Officers: Wiley L. Mossy, Jr., Pres.; David L. Mossy,
Secy.
EIN: 300070599

9078
The MST Foundation
P.O. Box 5585
Kingwood, TX   77325-5585

Established in 2006 in Texas.
Donors: Mark D. Manifould; Mary S. Manifould.
Foundation type: Independent foundation.
Financial data (yr. ended 12/31/14): Assets,
$4,184,817; expenditures, $226,977; qualifying
distributions, $189,632.
Fields of interest: University education; Cancers.
Limitations: Applications not accepted. Giving
primarily in TX, with some giving in IL. No grants to
individuals.
Application information: Contributes only to
pre-selected organizations.
Directors: Mark D. Manifould; Mary S. Manifould;
Richard Withey.
EIN: 208065954

9079
Austin James Mummert Trust
c/o Bank of America, N.A.
P.O. Box 831041
Dallas, TX   75283-1041

Foundation type: Independent foundation.
Financial data (yr. ended 12/31/13): Assets,
$1,824,718 (M); expenditures, $147,440;
qualifying distributions, $143,294; giving activities
include $140,418 for 2 grants (high: $70,209; low:
$70,209).
Fields of interest: Health; Housing development.
Limitations: Applications not accepted. Giving
primarily in CA.
Application information: Unsolicited requests for
funds not accepted.
Trustee: Bank of America, N.A.
EIN: 956014224

9080
The Muse Educational Foundation
2100 McKinney Ave., Ste. 1600
Dallas, TX   75201-1829   (214) 740-7236
Contact: Linda Ehlers

Established in 1999 in Texas.
Donors: John R. Muse; Lyn R. Muse.
Foundation type: Independent foundation.
Financial data (yr. ended 12/31/13): Assets,
$12,767,040 (M); gifts received, $6,500,000;
expenditures, $245,523; qualifying distributions,

$212,165; giving activities include $211,136 for 18
grants (high: $100,000; low: $100).
Purpose and activities: Giving primarily for
education.
Fields of interest: Performing arts; Education;
Elementary and secondary education; Alumni
relations; Diseases and conditions; Child welfare.
Limitations: Applications accepted. Giving primarily
in TX, with emphasis on Dallas.
Application information: Letter directed to the muse
educational foundation: John Muse. Application
form required.
   Initial approach: Letter
   Deadline(s): None
Officers and Directors: John R. Muse, Pres. and
Treas. and Director; Lyn R. Muse, Exec. V.P.; H.
Rand Reynolds.
EIN: 752824936

9081
Mike A. Myers Foundation
6310 Lemmon Ave., Ste. 200
Dallas, TX   75209

Established in 1982 in Texas.
Donors: Mike A. Myers; Sammye Myers.
Foundation type: Independent foundation.
Financial data (yr. ended 12/31/13): Assets,
$4,032,425 (M); expenditures, $464,626;
qualifying distributions, $378,013; giving activities
include $378,013 for 63 grants (high: $36,000;
low: $500).
Purpose and activities: Giving primarily for higher
education and human services.
Fields of interest: Higher education; Health; Human
services; Youth development.
Type of support: General support; Capital and
infrastructure; Program development; Scholarships.
Limitations: Applications not accepted. Giving
primarily in Dallas, TX. No grants to individuals.
Application information: Contributes only to
pre-selected organizations.
Officers: Mike A. Myers, Chair.; Nancy Turley, Secy.;
Joe Pipes, Treas.
Trustees: Curtis W. Meadows, Jr.; Amanda S.
Myers; Robert Myers; Sammye Myers; Larry Temple;
Carol M. Wilcox.
EIN: 751832130

9082
N.H. Foundation
11602 Haley Hollow
Richmond, TX   77469-7915   7132423497

Established in 1995 in Texas.
Donors: L. David Sparks; Kay E. Sparks; Southern
Slope Trust.
Foundation type: Operating foundation.
Financial data (yr. ended 12/31/14): Assets,
$5,104,380; expenditures, $190,953; qualifying
distributions, $150,000.
Fields of interest: Christianity.
Limitations: Applications accepted. Giving primarily
in Tulsa, OK.
Application information:
   Initial approach: Letter
   Deadline(s): None
Trustees: Bryan K. Sparks; Kay E. Sparks.
EIN: 766108510

9083
Nabors Charitable Foundation
515 W. Greens Rd., Ste. 1200
Houston, TX   77067-4536

Established in 2005 in Texas.
Foundation type: Independent foundation.
Financial data (yr. ended 12/31/13): Assets,
$17,350,133 (M); gifts received, $4,500;
expenditures, $329,463; qualifying distributions,
$329,463; giving activities include $326,782 for
100 grants to individuals (high: $10,000; low:
$159).
Purpose and activities: Giving to support and assist
victims and their family members, of natural and civil
disasters.
Fields of interest: Disasters and emergency
management.
Type of support: Grants to individuals.
Limitations: Applications accepted. Giving primarily
in CA, LA and TX.
Application information:
   Initial approach: Proposal
   Deadline(s): None
Officers: Laura W. Doerre, Chair.; Julia W. Wright,
Secy.; Jose S. Cadena, Treas.
EIN: 030569199

9084
Navarro County Educational Foundation
401 N. 14th St.
Corsicana, TX   75110-4509
Application address: c/o Navarro College, 3200 W.
7th Ave., Corsicana, TX 75110, tel.: (903)
874-6501

Established in 1988 in Texas.
Foundation type: Independent foundation.
Financial data (yr. ended 12/31/13): Assets,
$4,527,176 (M); expenditures, $216,661;
qualifying distributions, $183,010; giving activities
include $174,823 for 1 grant.
Purpose and activities: Support only for Navarro
College, TX, through a scholarship fund.
Fields of interest: Higher education.
Type of support: Scholarships.
Limitations: Applications accepted. Giving primarily
in TX.
Application information: Application form required.
   Initial approach: Completed application form
   Deadline(s): See application form for current
      deadline
Officers: C. David Campbell, MD, Pres.; Barbara
Moe, Secy.-Treas.
Directors: Don Denbow; Mike Gage; Mickey Hillock;
Larry Morrison.
EIN: 752227788

9085
Navarro County Health Services
Foundation
4200 S. Hulen St., Ste. 417
Ft. Worth, TX   76109
Application address: c/o Dora Chavez, Columbia
Navarro Regional Hospital, Corsiana, TX 75110,
tel.: (903) 654-6800

Foundation type: Independent foundation.
Financial data (yr. ended 12/31/13): Assets,
$7,617,830 (M); expenditures, $372,750;
qualifying distributions, $349,992; giving activities

include $348,264 for 3 grants (high: $181,114; low: $15,750).

Purpose and activities: The foundation primarily pays Navarro Regional Hospital for services provided to indigent individuals.

Fields of interest: Health; Low-income and poor people.

Type of support: Grants to individuals.

Limitations: Applications accepted. Giving to residents of Navarro County, TX, particularly Corsicana.

Application information: Application form required.
  Initial approach: Proposal
  Deadline(s): None

Officers: JoAnn H. Means, Pres.; David Campbell, V.P.; A.L. Atkiesson, Secy.

Director: Betty Armstrong.

Trustees: James Chapman; Walker Lea; Bob Scott; Harrison Sloan.

EIN: 751767188

9086
Clara Freshour Nelson Foundation
18 Cutter Green Dr.
San Antonio, TX 78248-2412

Established in 1996 in Texas.

Donors: Harold S. Nelson; Helen E. Nelson; Harold S. Nelson Charitable Remainder Annuity Trust; Nelson 1998 Charitable Remainder Annuity Trust.

Foundation type: Independent foundation.

Financial data (yr. ended 12/31/13): Assets, $6,900,916 (M); expenditures, $406,965; qualifying distributions, $341,700; giving activities include $341,700 for 4 grants (high: $330,700; low: $1,000).

Fields of interest: Education; University education.

Type of support: Scholarships; Individual development.

Limitations: Applications not accepted. Giving primarily in Houston, TX. No grants to individuals.

Application information: Contributes only to pre-selected organizations.

Trustee: Helen E. Nelson.

EIN: 746436452

9087
New Beginning Resources, Inc.
P.O. Box 509
Porter, TX 77365-0509 (713) 494-0596
Contact: Russell Leatherman, C.O.O.
FAX: (281) 354-2110; E-mail: nbri@earthlink.net;
Main URL: http://www.nbri.net

Established in 2004 in Texas.

Donors: Perry L. Shaw; Patricia Shaw.

Foundation type: Operating foundation.

Financial data (yr. ended 12/31/13): Assets, $1,059,198 (M); gifts received, $557,320; expenditures, $714,419; qualifying distributions, $600,861; giving activities include $427,180 for grants, and $554,546 for 4 foundation-administered programs.

Purpose and activities: Grants primarily for Christian missionary work and human services.

Fields of interest: Christianity; Human services.

International interests: Ecuador; Guatemala; Haiti.

Type of support: General support; Grants to individuals.

Limitations: Applications accepted. Giving primarily in TX.

Application information:
  Initial approach: Letter
  Deadline(s): None

Officer: Russell Leatherman, C.O.O.

Board Members: Matthew P. Brouwer; Perry L. Shaw.

EIN: 200432677

9088
James Nislar Foundation
c/o Prosperity Bank
1401 Avenue Q
Lubbock, TX 79408-1401 (806) 741-2178
Contact: Holly Brake

Established in 2002 in Texas.

Donor: James Nislar†.

Foundation type: Independent foundation.

Financial data (yr. ended 12/31/13): Assets, $4,392,513 (M); expenditures, $245,640; qualifying distributions, $199,242; giving activities include $182,850 for 2 grants (high: $91,425; low: $91,425).

Fields of interest: Human services; Youth services.

Limitations: Applications accepted. Giving primarily in the Lubbock, TX, area. No grants to individuals.

Application information:
  Initial approach: Proposal
  Deadline(s): None

Trustee: Prosperity Bank.

EIN: 756555318

9089
North American Communities Foundation
791 Town and Country Blvd., Ste. 250
Houston, TX 77024-3925

Donor: Combeewood Partners.

Foundation type: Independent foundation.

Financial data (yr. ended 12/31/13): Assets, $3,815,287 (M); gifts received, $10,192; expenditures, $333,564; qualifying distributions, $314,027; giving activities include $314,027 for 13 grants (high: $200,000; low: $50).

Fields of interest: Health; Hospital care; Cancers; Human services.

Limitations: Applications not accepted. Giving primarily in FL.

Application information: Unsolicited requests for funds are not accepted.

Officers and Trustees: Madeline R. Lay, Pres. and Trustee; Philip O. Allen, V.P. and Trustee; Robert W. Scharar, Secy. and Trustee; Herbert F. Hunter, Treas. and Trustee.

EIN: 591987265

9090
The Nowiczewski Foundation
623 Buffington St.
Houston, TX 77060-4603 (281)445-6393
Contact: Joseph Nowiczewski, Pres.

Donor: Joseph Nowiczewski.

Foundation type: Independent foundation.

Financial data (yr. ended 03/31/14): Assets, $0 (M); expenditures, $163,650; qualifying distributions, $163,650; giving activities include $163,650 for 14 grants (high: $83,300; low: $250).

Fields of interest: Education; Christianity; Human services.

Type of support: General support.

Limitations: Applications accepted. Giving primarily in TX. No grants to individuals.

Application information: Application form required.
  Initial approach: Letter
  Deadline(s): Dec. 31

Officers and Directors: Joseph Nowiczewski, Pres. and Treas. and Director; Paula Nowiczewski, Secy.

EIN: 760569596

9091
The Bill Nowotny Foundation
5309 Huisache St.
Bellaire, TX 77401-4933

Established in 2010 in Texas.

Donors: Suzanne Nowotny; Barbara K. Nowotny.

Foundation type: Independent foundation.

Financial data (yr. ended 12/31/13): Assets, $720,835 (M); gifts received, $1,000; expenditures, $520,944; qualifying distributions, $426,000; giving activities include $426,000 for 15 grants (high: $96,000; low: $5,000).

Fields of interest: Christianity; Sports and recreation; Human services.

Limitations: Applications not accepted. Giving primarily in TX. No grants to individuals.

Application information: Unsolicited requests for funds not accepted.

Officers: Barbara K. Nowotny, Pres. and Treas.; John Nowotny, V.P.; Rusty Folk, Secy.

EIN: 271508254

9092
Roger Nuncio Foundation
c/o William H. Crook, Jr.
6433 Long Meadow Dr.
Corpus Christi, TX 78413-2828

Established in 2003 in Texas.

Donors: Caryl W. Crook; William H. Crook.

Foundation type: Independent foundation.

Financial data (yr. ended 12/31/13): Assets, $758,224 (M); gifts received, $450,000; expenditures, $131,163; qualifying distributions, $130,550; giving activities include $130,550 for 7 grants (high: $69,500; low: $1,750).

Fields of interest: Education; Agriculture; Religion; Christianity.

Limitations: Applications not accepted. Giving primarily in TX. No grants to individuals.

Application information: Unsolicited requests for funds not accepted.

Directors: Caryl Wilson Crook; Christine Rebecca Crook; William H. Crook.

EIN: 270076168

9093
The Kathryn O'Connor Foundation
P.O. Box 400
Victoria, TX 77902-0400 (361) 578-6271
Contact: Venable Proctor, Secy.

Established in 1951 in Texas.

Donors: Kathryn S. O'Connor†; Tom O'Connor, Jr.†; Dennis O'Connor†; Mary O'Connor Braman†; The O'Connor & Hewitt Foundation.

Foundation type: Independent foundation.

Financial data (yr. ended 12/31/13): Assets, $8,962,606 (M); gifts received, $20,000;

expenditures, $391,742; qualifying distributions, $313,719; giving activities include $313,719 for 39 grants (high: $72,169; low: $500).
Purpose and activities: Giving primarily for education, human services, and Christian churches.
Fields of interest: Education; Elementary and secondary education; Secondary education; Christianity; Human services.
Type of support: General support; Continuing support; Annual campaigns; Capital and infrastructure.
Limitations: Applications accepted. Giving limited to southern TX, with emphasis on Victoria and Refugio counties and the surrounding area. No support for political organizations. No grants to individuals, or for matching gifts; no loans.
Publications: Annual report.
Application information: Application form required.
Initial approach: Letter
Deadline(s): None
Board meeting date(s): As required
Officers and Trustees: D.H. Braman III, Pres. and Trustee; Kathryn O'Connor Counts, V.P. and Trustee; Louise O'Connor, V.P. and Trustee; Venable B. Proctor, Secy. and Trustee; Ralph R. Gilster III, Treas. and Trustee; Kathryn C. Dunnam; Virginia D. Lebermann; Junie G. Meskey.
EIN: 746039415

9094
The Sydnor & Olga Oden Foundation
c/o Kanaly Trust LTA
5555 San Felipe St., Ste. 200
Houston, TX 77056-2760

Established in 1988 in Texas.
Donor: Sydnor & Olga Oden Charitable Trust.
Foundation type: Independent foundation.
Financial data (yr. ended 12/31/14): Assets, $5,396,222 (M); expenditures, $342,674; qualifying distributions, $274,000; giving activities include $274,000 for 29 grants (high: $126,000; low: $1,000).
Fields of interest: Education; University education; Specialty hospital care; Speech and hearing rehabilitation; Christians.
Limitations: Applications not accepted. Giving primarily in IN and TX. No grants to individuals.
Application information: Contributes only to pre-selected organizations.
Trustees: Carol Brollier Deason; Zillan T. Oden.
EIN: 766029653

9095
The O'Hare Family Private Foundation
c/o W. Scott O'Hare
2905 Popano Cove
Austin, TX 78746-1974

Established in 1999 in Texas.
Donor: W. Scott O'Hare.
Foundation type: Independent foundation.
Financial data (yr. ended 12/31/13): Assets, $435,448 (M); gifts received, $199,159; expenditures, $431,668; qualifying distributions, $429,750; giving activities include $429,750 for 21 grants (high: $133,000; low: $500).
Purpose and activities: Giving primarily for education and to Protestant churches; funding also for social services.

Fields of interest: Elementary and secondary education; Higher education; Health; Protestantism; Human services; Children.
Limitations: Applications not accepted. Giving primarily in Austin, TX. No grants to individuals.
Application information: Unsolicited requests for funds not accepted.
Officers: W. Scott O'Hare, Pres.; Kathryn Angell Sackett O'Hare, V.P. and Secy.
Director: Jody Cole.
EIN: 752802946

9096
One in Heart Foundation
11 Liberty Bell Cir.
Houston, TX 77024-6303   (281) 833-9200
Contact: Robert K. Hillin Jr., Pres.

Donors: Robert K. Hillin, Jr.; Hillin II.
Foundation type: Independent foundation.
Financial data (yr. ended 06/30/14): Assets, $2,700,579 (M); gifts received, $500; expenditures, $155,641; qualifying distributions, $151,250; giving activities include $151,250 for 6 grants (high: $90,000; low: $250).
Fields of interest: Education; Protestantism; Human services.
Limitations: Applications accepted. Giving primarily in TX.
Application information: Application form required.
Initial approach: Proposal
Deadline(s): None
Officers: Robert K. Hillin, Jr., Pres. and Treas.; Lake Chambers Speed, V.P.; Danny Scheaffer, Secy.
EIN: 270249416

9097
The Pat O'Neal Educational Foundation
675 N. Henderson St.
Fort Worth, TX 76107-1479   (817) 625-8246
Contact: Patricia J. O'Neal, Pres.

Established in 2004 in Texas.
Donor: Patricia J. O'Neal.
Foundation type: Independent foundation.
Financial data (yr. ended 12/31/13): Assets, $208,454 (M); gifts received, $150,000; expenditures, $168,835; qualifying distributions, $168,835; giving activities include $50,000 for 1 grant, and $117,441 for 13 grants to individuals (high: $15,944; low: $200).
Purpose and activities: Scholarship awards to graduating seniors from high schools in the Fort Worth, Texas, area.
Fields of interest: Higher education.
Type of support: Scholarships; Student aid.
Limitations: Applications accepted. Giving primarily to residents of the Fort Worth, TX, area.
Application information: Application form required.
Initial approach: Completed application form
Deadline(s): None
Officers: Patricia J. O'Neal, Pres.; Cathy Blackwell, Secy.
Directors: David Dean Diment; Jesse Miles.
EIN: 202055414

9098
OneSight Research Foundation
(formerly Pearle Vision Foundation, Inc.)
2465 Joe Field Rd.
Dallas, TX 75229-3402   (972) 277-6191
Contact: Trina Parasiliti, Secy.
FAX: (972) 277-6422;
E-mail: tparasil@onesight.org; Main URL: http://www.onesight.org
Block Grant Recipients: http://www.onesight.org/na/about_us/research_education/block_grant_recipients
Dr. Panley Pearle Scholarship Fund Recipients: http://www.onesight.org/na/about_us/research_education/scholarship_recipients
Facebook: http://www.facebook.com/pages/OneSight/42105750215?ref=ts
Twitter: http://twitter.com/onesightorg
YouTube: http://www.youtube.com/user/OneSightOrg

Established in 1986 in California.
Donors: Pearle Vision, Inc.; Cole National Foundation; Luxottica Retail; Lenscrafters, Inc.; OneSight.
Foundation type: Operating foundation.
Financial data (yr. ended 12/31/13): Assets, $1,663,048 (M); gifts received, $277,297; expenditures, $379,060; qualifying distributions, $372,520; giving activities include $250,000 for 5 + grants (high: $125,000; low: $20,000), and $40,000 for 1 grant to an individual (high: $40,000).
Purpose and activities: The foundation supports research projects designed to find better treatments and cures for vision threatening diseases and disorders with a focus on diabetic and pediatric eye diseases; and awards scholarships to optometry students through the Dr. Stanley Pearle Scholarship Fund.
Fields of interest: Medical education; Eye diseases; Diabetes.
Type of support: Research; Student aid.
Limitations: Applications accepted. Giving on a national basis. No grants for endowments or general operating support.
Publications: Application guidelines; Grants list.
Application information: Starting in the Fall, only 2nd, 3rd, and 4th year students are eligible for Optometry Scholarships (application available online at www.onesight.org). Application form required.
Initial approach: Download application form and mail to foundation
Copies of proposal: 1
Deadline(s): Postmarked by Dec. 31 and June 30 for Block grants; Apr. 15 for Dr. Stanley Pearle Scholarship Fund
Board meeting date(s): Feb. and Aug.
Final notification: Mid-Mar. and mid-Sept.; June 15 for Dr. Stanley Pearle Scholarship Fund
Officers and Directors: Jason Singh, OD, Chair. and Exec. Dir.; Mark Jacquot, OD, V.P. and Director; Trina Parasiliti, Secy. and Admin.; Teresa Benson, Treas.; Tifani DeMaria; Srini Kumar; Joe Neville.
Number of staff: 1 part-time professional.
EIN: 752173714

9099
John T. Opie Charitable Trust No 1
c/o Bank of America, N.A.
P.O. Box 831041
Dallas, TX   75283-1041

Foundation type: Independent foundation.
Financial data (yr. ended 12/31/13): Assets, $5,595,955 (M); expenditures, $269,431; qualifying distributions, $249,317; giving activities include $241,632 for 4 grants (high: $120,816; low: $12,082).
Fields of interest: Health; Children's hospital care; Housing development; Religion; Children.
Limitations: Applications not accepted. Giving primarily in FL and MA.
Application information: Unsolicited requests for funds not accepted.
Trustee: Bank of America, N.A.
EIN: 431764088

9100
The Edward and Helen Oppenheimer Foundation
3435 Westheimer Rd., Ste. 1506
Houston, TX   77027-5363

Established in 1993 in Texas.
Donor: Edward Oppenheimer, Jr.
Foundation type: Independent foundation.
Financial data (yr. ended 12/31/13): Assets, $5,093,105 (M); expenditures, $313,953; qualifying distributions, $277,600; giving activities include $277,600 for 35 grants (high: $130,000; low: $500).
Purpose and activities: Giving primarily for education, human services, and religious organizations.
Fields of interest: Education; University education; Nonprofits; Health; Judaism; Human services; Child welfare.
Type of support: Regranting.
Limitations: Applications not accepted. Giving limited to Houston, TX. No grants to individuals.
Application information: Unsolicited requests for funds not accepted.
Officers: Carl Herman, Pres.; Gloria Herman, V.P.; Paul F. Herman, V.P.; Lee E. Herman, Treas.
EIN: 760403101

9101
The Jesse H. and Susan R. Oppenheimer Foundation
312 E. Hermosa Dr.
San Antonio, TX   78212-1732

Established in 1964 in Texas.
Donors: Jesse H. Oppenheimer; Susan R. Oppenheimer; J. David Oppenheimer.
Foundation type: Independent foundation.
Financial data (yr. ended 12/31/13): Assets, $6,029,095 (M); expenditures, $284,369; qualifying distributions, $268,600; giving activities include $268,600 for 107 grants (high: $31,500; low: $100).
Purpose and activities: Giving for conservation, education, and medical purposes.
Fields of interest: Arts and culture; Education; Environment; Nonprofits; Family planning; Diseases and conditions; International peace and security;

People with disabilities; People with hearing impairments; People with psychosocial disabilities.
Type of support: Endowments; Scholarships; Research; Research and evaluation; Regranting.
Limitations: Applications not accepted. Giving primarily in Bexar County, TX.
Application information: Unsolicited requests for funds not accepted; all donations are trustee-generated.
  Board meeting date(s): Varies
Trustees: J. David Oppenheimer; Susan R. Oppenheimer.
Number of staff: None.
EIN: 746032845

9102
Orant Charities
2536 N.E. Loop 820
Fort Worth, TX   76106-1809   (817) 378-5237
Main URL: http://www.orantcharities.org
Facebook: https://www.facebook.com/orantcharities
Twitter: https://twitter.com/OrantCharities

Donors: Michael Tenny; Sporting Supplies International, Inc.; Spencer Tien; Claudia Larry Rovens.
Foundation type: Independent foundation.
Financial data (yr. ended 12/31/13): Assets, $925,188 (M); gifts received, $290,158; expenditures, $279,968; qualifying distributions, $278,770; giving activities include $272,147 for 9 grants (high: $105,025; low: $830).
Fields of interest: Religion.
International interests: Malawi.
Limitations: Applications not accepted. Giving primarily in TX and internationally in Malawi.
Application information: Unsolicited requests for funds not accepted.
Officers: Seth Morgan, Pres.; John Turner, C.O.O., V.P. and Treas.; Michael Tenny, V.P. and Secy.
EIN: 208042971

9103
The Oriska Foundation
P.O. Box 672265
Houston, TX   77267-2265
Application address: C/o Allen Boutte, P.O. Box 301078, Houston, TX 77230; tel.: (713) 673-8440

Established in 2006 in Texas.
Foundation type: Independent foundation.
Financial data (yr. ended 12/31/13): Assets, $3,470,266 (M); expenditures, $240,473; qualifying distributions, $239,626; giving activities include $208,000 for 17 grants (high: $45,000; low: $1,000).
Fields of interest: Christianity; Human services.
Limitations: Applications accepted. Giving primarily in TX. No grants to individuals.
Application information:
  Initial approach: None
  Deadline(s): None
Officer: Luckett Johnson, Pres.
Directors: James Douglas; Wanda Wilson.
EIN: 205963834

9104
Waldon H. and Adele Orr Charitable Trust
c/o Wells Fargo Bank, N.A.
P.O. Box 41629
Austin, TX   78704-9926   (979) 776-3237
E-mail: grantadministration@wellsfargo.com; Main URL: https://www.wellsfargo.com/privatefoundationgrants/orr

Established in 2003 in Texas.
Donors: Waldon H. Orr†; Adele S. Orr†.
Foundation type: Independent foundation.
Financial data (yr. ended 12/31/13): Assets, $5,477,495 (M); expenditures, $267,817; qualifying distributions, $218,656; giving activities include $203,500 for 19 grants (high: $30,000; low: $1,500).
Fields of interest: Ethnic museums; Nonprofits; Protestantism; Human services; Youth development.
Type of support: Regranting.
Limitations: Applications accepted. Giving primarily in TX. No grants to individuals.
Application information: See foundation website for complete application guidelines. Application form required.
  Initial approach: Letter
  Deadline(s): July 31
Trustee: Wells Fargo Trust Dept.
EIN: 746523535

9105
The Osberg Family Trust
c/o Bank of America, N.A.
P.O. Box 831041
Dallas, TX   75283-1041
Contact: Nancy Atkinson
Application address: c/o Bank of America, N.A., P.O. Box 24565, Seattle, WA 98124-0565, tel.: (206) 358-0912

Donors: Hilma Osberg†; Axel Osberg†; Osberg Construction Co.
Foundation type: Independent foundation.
Financial data (yr. ended 12/31/14): Assets, $5,983,880 (M); expenditures, $333,985; qualifying distributions, $287,522; giving activities include $263,273 for 22 grants (high: $25,000; low: $2,000).
Fields of interest: History museums; Higher education; Natural resources; Voluntarism; Nonprofits; Science; Human services.
Type of support: Regranting.
Limitations: Applications accepted. Giving primarily in WA. No grants to individuals.
Application information: Application form required.
  Initial approach: Letter
  Deadline(s): None
Trustees: Allan F. Osberg; John W. Osberg; Bank of America, N.A.
EIN: 943067305

9106
Overlake Foundation Inc.
P.O. Box 2549
Victoria, TX   77902-2549   (361) 573-4383
Contact: Thomas L. Keller, Secy.-Treas.

Established in 1981 in Texas.
Donor: Mary Alice Fitzpatrick.
Foundation type: Independent foundation.

Financial data (yr. ended 11/30/13): Assets, $8,845,259 (M); expenditures, $347,137; qualifying distributions, $323,000; giving activities include $323,000 for 20 grants (high: $175,000; low: $1,250).
Fields of interest: Arts and culture; Education; Mental health counseling; Diseases and conditions; Fire prevention and control; Christianity; Human services; Child welfare; Senior services.
Type of support: Research.
Limitations: Applications accepted. Giving primarily in TX. No grants to individuals.
Application information: Application form required.
   Initial approach: Proposal
   Deadline(s): Contact foundation for deadline
Officers: Steven C. Anderson, Pres.; Michael S. Anderson, V.P.; Donald J. Malouf, V.P.; Thomas L. Keller, Secy.-Treas.
EIN: 751793068

9107
George and Angelina Owusu Foudnation
510 Bering Dr., Ste. 300
Houston, TX 77057-1400

Donor: George Owusu.
Foundation type: Independent foundation.
Financial data (yr. ended 12/31/13): Assets, $0 (M); gifts received, $200,100; expenditures, $189,585; qualifying distributions, $189,585; giving activities include $180,000 for 3 grants (high: $100,000; low: $5,000).
Fields of interest: Education; Health; Religion.
International interests: Ghana.
Limitations: Applications not accepted. Giving primarily in Ghana.
Application information: Unsolicited requests for funds not accepted.
Officers: George Owusu, Pres.; Angelina Owusu, V.P.
EIN: 462345449

9108
The P Twenty-One Foundation
c/o Joseph W. Ryan
P.O. Box 27883
Houston, TX 77227-7883 (832) 228-8974

Established in 2000 in Texas.
Donors: Joseph W. Ryan; Yolanda V. Ryan.
Foundation type: Independent foundation.
Financial data (yr. ended 11/30/13): Assets, $3,247,437 (M); expenditures, $155,629; qualifying distributions, $148,000; giving activities include $148,000 for 15 grants (high: $25,000; low: $2,000).
Purpose and activities: Giving primarily for public health and ecological activities.
Fields of interest: Orchestral music; Elementary and secondary education; Environment; Domesticated animals; Health; Community mental health care; Public health; Catholicism.
Type of support: General support; Capital campaigns.
Limitations: Applications accepted. Giving primarily in CA, GA, NY and TX.
Application information: Application form required.
   Initial approach: Letter
   Deadline(s): None

Officers and Directors: Joseph W. Ryan, Pres. and Treas. and Director; Yolanda V. Ryan, V.P. and Secy. and Director; Noralisa Villarreal, MD.
EIN: 760628482

9109
Jay and Ruth Pack Family Foundation
2000 McKinney Ave., Ste. 1200
Dallas, TX 75201

Donors: Ruth A. Pack; Brian M. Lidji.
Foundation type: Independent foundation.
Financial data (yr. ended 12/31/12): Assets, $2,836,700 (M); expenditures, $325,795; qualifying distributions, $304,805; giving activities include $304,805 for grants.
Fields of interest: Arts and culture; Education; Religion.
Type of support: Annual campaigns; Capital campaigns; Scholarships.
Limitations: Applications not accepted. Giving primarily in TX.
Application information: Contributes only to pre-selected organizations.
Directors: Brian M. Lidji; Jay A. Pack; Ruth A. Pack.
EIN: 510441897

9110
Charles Y.C. Pak Foundation
7107 Churchill Way
Dallas, TX 75230-1906

Established in 1988 in Texas.
Donors: Charles Y.C. Pak; Vitel, Inc.; Bone Quality Research Institute.
Foundation type: Independent foundation.
Financial data (yr. ended 12/31/14): Assets, $5,613,390 (M); gifts received, $200,000; expenditures, $299,463; qualifying distributions, $291,500; giving activities include $291,500 for 2 grants (high: $290,000; low: $1,500).
Fields of interest: Medical education; Hospital care; Diseases and conditions.
Type of support: Research; Research and evaluation.
Limitations: Applications not accepted. Giving primarily in Dallas, TX.
Application information: Unsolicited requests for funds not accepted.
Officers and Trustees: Charles Y.C. Pak, Pres. and Trustee; Jane Pak, Secy.; Tom Dooley; Christopher J. Huber; Gregory Pak; Laura Kim Pak; Neill Walsdorf.
EIN: 752267679

9111
The PAL Foundation
12000 Huebner Rd., Ste. 103
San Antonio, TX 78230-1209

Established in 1993 in Texas.
Donors: Berneta Leininger; Peter A. Leininger.
Foundation type: Independent foundation.
Financial data (yr. ended 12/31/13): Assets, $4,330,112 (M); expenditures, $275,135; qualifying distributions, $230,710; giving activities include $230,710 for 44 grants (high: $64,750; low: $50).
Fields of interest: Reproductive health care; Christianity; Human services.

Limitations: Applications not accepted. Giving primarily in TX. No grants to individuals.
Application information: Contributes only to pre-selected organizations.
Directors: Daniel E. Leininger; James R. Leininger; John H. Leininger; Peter A. Leininger.
EIN: 742692751

9112
Palmer Foundation
520 Post Oak Blvd., Ste. 780
Houston, TX 77027-9481
Contact: C. Robert Palmer, Pres.

Established in 1997 in Texas.
Donors: C. Robert Palmer; Charles R. Palmer.
Foundation type: Independent foundation.
Financial data (yr. ended 12/31/13): Assets, $7,979,748 (M); gifts received, $25,250; expenditures, $311,703; qualifying distributions, $251,067; giving activities include $248,630 for 24 grants (high: $125,000; low: $30).
Fields of interest: Education; Human services; Youth development.
Limitations: Applications accepted. Giving primarily in TX. No grants to individuals.
Application information: Application form required.
   Initial approach: Letter
   Deadline(s): None
Officers: C. Robert Palmer, Pres.; Rebecca T. Palmer, V.P.; Shelley P. Hayes, Secy.-Treas.
EIN: 760565827

9113
C. N. and Maria Papadopoulos Charitable Foundation
3939 Hartsdale Dr.
Houston, TX 77063-6403

Established in 1999 in Texas.
Donors: Maria Papadopoulos; C.N. Papadopoulos.
Foundation type: Independent foundation.
Financial data (yr. ended 03/31/13): Assets, $4,043,627 (M); expenditures, $235,094; qualifying distributions, $200,725; giving activities include $198,228 for 22 grants (high: $92,200; low: $250).
Fields of interest: Arts and culture; Education; Protestantism; Human services; Child welfare.
Type of support: Annual campaigns; Capital campaigns; Endowments.
Limitations: Applications not accepted. Giving primarily in TX. No grants to individuals.
Application information: Unsolicited requests for funds not accepted.
Officers and Directors: Maria Papadopoulos, Pres. and Director; Helena P. Johnson, V.P. and Director; Christina P. Papandreau, Treas.; Neofytos Papadopoulos; William C. Papadopoulos.
EIN: 760604133

9114
Paris Legacy Foundation Inc
(formerly Paris Regional Health Care Endowment Fund, Inc.)
P.O. Box 1815
Paris, TX 75461-0919 (903) 754-5297
Contact: Frank Ray, Treas.

Donor: L.P. McCuistion Sanitarium Foundation.

Foundation type: Independent foundation.
Financial data (yr. ended 12/31/13): Assets, $8,070,230 (M); expenditures, $505,381; qualifying distributions, $421,779; giving activities include $416,337 for 8 grants (high: $150,000; low: $1,250).
Purpose and activities: Giving for the general health of the community of Lamar County, Texas.
Fields of interest: Health; Agriculture; Human services.
Limitations: Applications accepted. Giving primarily in Lamar County, TX.
Application information: Application form required.
  Initial approach: Letter
  Deadline(s): None
Officers: E. Sims Norment, Chair.; Carl Cecil, Secy.; Frank Ray, Treas.
Trustees: Richard Amis; Philip Cecil; Sam Hocker; Brad Hutchison; Robert S. Norment; G. Bert Strom, MD; George Struve; Bobby Walters; Barbara Wilson.
EIN: 752198726

9115
Parks Family Foundation
c/o John Mike Parks
3601 Princeton Ave.
Dallas, TX   75205-1387

Established in 2007 in Texas.
Foundation type: Independent foundation.
Financial data (yr. ended 12/31/13): Assets, $5,508,243 (M); expenditures, $318,259; qualifying distributions, $290,000; giving activities include $290,000 for 26 grants (high: $35,000; low: $5,000).
Fields of interest: Education; Domesticated animals; Health; Family services; People with disabilities.
Limitations: Applications not accepted. Giving primarily in TX. No grants to individuals.
Application information: Unsolicited requests for funds not accepted.
Officers and Directors: Maureen C. Parks, Pres.; J. Michael Parks, V.P. and Treas. and Director; Christopher Michael Parks, Secy.; Daniel John Parks.
EIN: 261480405

9116
The Partnership Foundation
6031 Woodland Dr.
Dallas, TX   75225-2834

Established in 1999 in Texas.
Foundation type: Independent foundation.
Financial data (yr. ended 12/31/13): Assets, $10,800,502 (M); expenditures, $475,154; qualifying distributions, $431,242; giving activities include $425,000 for 32 grants (high: $35,000; low: $1,000).
Fields of interest: Arts and culture; Education; Environment; Human services.
Limitations: Applications not accepted. Giving primarily in Berkeley and Alameda County, CA, Providence, RI, and Dallas, TX. No grants to individuals.
Application information: Contributes only to pre-selected organizations.

Officers: Anne Paxton Wagley, Pres.; B. Allyn Copp, V.P.; James F.P. Wagley, V.P.; Mary Wagley Copp, Secy.; Sue Wagley, Treas.
EIN: 752796975

9117
Partridge Foundation
100 E. Kleberg Ave. Ste. 200
Kingsville, TX   78363-4571
E-mail: waring@partridge.vi; Application address: c/o Mr. B. Waring Partridge, IV, 6906 Vessup Ln., Saint Thomas, VI 00802; tel.: (361) 595-0411

Established in 1994 in Texas.
Donor: B. Waring Partridge III.
Foundation type: Independent foundation.
Financial data (yr. ended 12/31/13): Assets, $14,806,459 (M); expenditures, $313,333; qualifying distributions, $275,240; giving activities include $275,240 for 15 grants (high: $50,000; low: $100).
Fields of interest: Education; Health; Religion.
International interests: Virgin Islands of the United States.
Limitations: Applications accepted. Giving primarily in CT, NY and the U.S. Virgin Islands. No grants to individuals.
Application information:
  Initial approach: Letter
  Deadline(s): None
Officers and Directors: B. Waring Partridge IV, Pres. and Director; Linda M. Hahn, Secy.-Treas. and Director; Tatiana A. Jitkoff.
Number of staff: None.
EIN: 742712637

9118
Patterson Foundation Inc.
P.O. Box 5608
Texarkana, TX   75505-5608

Established in 1994 in Texas.
Donors: Jessica B. Patterson†; Nancy P. Troike.
Foundation type: Independent foundation.
Financial data (yr. ended 12/31/13): Assets, $8,750,560 (M); gifts received, $216,284; expenditures, $459,329; qualifying distributions, $415,058; giving activities include $404,019 for 29 grants (high: $150,000; low: $280).
Fields of interest: Arts and culture; Museums; Education; Community and economic development; Human services.
Limitations: Applications not accepted. Giving primarily in Texarkana, TX. No grants to individuals.
Application information: Contributes only to pre-selected organizations.
Directors: Ron Mills; Donna Stewart; Nancy P. Troike.
EIN: 752561756

9119
Paul Patton Charitable Trust
c/o Bank of America, N.A.
P.O. Box 831041
Dallas, TX   75283-1041   8003577094
Application address: c/o Anthony Twyman, Bank of America, N.A., P.O. Box 219119, Kansas City, MO 64121-9119, tel.: (816) 292-4342

Established in 1989 in Missouri.

Foundation type: Independent foundation.
Financial data (yr. ended 12/31/14): Assets, $4,403,659; expenditures, $236,500; qualifying distributions, $200,728.
Purpose and activities: Giving limited to organizations that serve needy individuals suffering from diseases or deformities of body or mind and/or that conduct medical research for the treatment or cure of such diseases.
Fields of interest: Hospital care; Pediatrics; Diseases and conditions; Child welfare.
Type of support: Research.
Limitations: Applications accepted. Giving primarily in the greater Kansas City, MO, area. No grants to individuals.
Application information: Application form required.
  Initial approach: Letter not more than 3 pages
  Deadline(s): None
Trustees: William L. Evans, Jr.; C. Ted McCarter; Bank of America, N.A.
EIN: 446009254

9120
The Paulos Foundation
6708 Ashbrook Dr.
Fort Worth, TX   76132-1140

Established in 1990 in Texas.
Donors: James J. Paulos; Paulos Charitable Lead Annuity Trust Ventures Ltd.; Paulos FJS Ventures Ltd.
Foundation type: Independent foundation.
Financial data (yr. ended 12/31/14): Assets, $7,438,934; expenditures, $365,900; qualifying distributions, $348,673.
Purpose and activities: Giving for arts, education, youth services and religion.
Fields of interest: Arts and culture; Performing arts; Education; Natural resources; Nonprofits; Diseases and conditions; Protestantism; Orthodox Christianity; Human services; Child welfare.
Type of support: Regranting.
Limitations: Applications not accepted. Giving in Fort Worth, TX. No grants to individuals.
Application information: Contributes only to pre-selected organizations.
Officer: Flora A. Brewer, Chair. and Pres.
Directors: John J. Paulos; Sam G. Paulos.
EIN: 752353196

9121
Jack & Katherine Pearce Educational Foundation
c/o Frost National Bank
P.O. Box 8210
Galveston, TX   77553-8210
Contact: Janet Gathright

Established in 1950 in Texas.
Foundation type: Operating foundation.
Financial data (yr. ended 12/31/13): Assets, $2,450,130 (M); expenditures, $197,909; qualifying distributions, $190,349; giving activities include $177,500 for 36 loans to individuals (high: $5,000; low: $5,000).
Purpose and activities: Gives interest-free loans only to students in Galveston, TX, pursuing college or professional education.
Fields of interest: Higher education.
Type of support: Student aid; Loans to individuals.

Limitations: Applications accepted. Giving limited to residents of Galveston, TX.
Publications: Informational brochure (including application guidelines).
Application information: Application form required.
  Deadline(s): Jan. 1 through Mar. 31
  Board meeting date(s): Apr.
Trustee: Frost National Bank.
Directors: Edward J. Patterson; Rev. Ronald Pogue; Albert Shannon.
EIN: 746035546

9122
Pearlman Family Foundation
200 Crescent Ct., Ste. 1550
Dallas, TX 75201-1580

Established in 2001 in Texas.
Donors: Elaine Pearlman; Trevor Pearlman; Rymorg Investments.
Foundation type: Independent foundation.
Financial data (yr. ended 12/31/13): Assets, $1,650,855 (M); expenditures, $161,809; qualifying distributions, $157,660; giving activities include $157,660 for 21 grants (high: $100,000; low: $100).
Fields of interest: Arts and culture; Education; University education; Religion.
Type of support: General support.
Limitations: Applications not accepted. Giving primarily in Addison and Dallas County, TX. No grants to individuals.
Application information: Unsolicited requests for funds not accepted.
Officers: Trevor Pearlman, Pres.; Cynthia Shipper, V.P.; Elaine Pearlman, Secy.-Treas.
EIN: 752858215

9123
Peine Charitable Foundation for Manhattan Fund
c/o Bank of America, N.A.
P.O. Box 831041
Dallas, TX 75283-1041
Application address: c/o Bank of America, N.A., Attn.: Trust Off., Ref.: Manhattan Community Fdn., P.O. Box 1127, Manhattan, KS 66505, tel.: (785) 587-8995; Main URL: http://peinefoundation.org

Established in 2005 in Texas.
Donor: Caroline F. Peine†.
Foundation type: Independent foundation.
Financial data (yr. ended 08/31/14): Assets, $8,876,101 (M); expenditures, $502,436; qualifying distributions, $463,044; giving activities include $413,341 for 18 grants (high: $77,519; low: $500).
Purpose and activities: Giving to organizations that improve the quality of life in the city of Manhattan, Kansas, including, but not limited to, parks and recreation, arts and theater, historical preservation, and human services.
Fields of interest: Arts and culture; Education; Foundations; Health; Community and economic development; Sports and recreation; Youth services.
Type of support: General support.
Limitations: Applications accepted. Giving limited to Manhattan, KS. No support for industrial development, organized athletics, or church or religious purposes. No grants to individuals.

Application information: Application form required.
  Initial approach: See foundation web site
  Deadline(s): See foundation web site
  Final notification: Accepted applicants only by May 26
Trustee: Bank of America, N.A.
Distribution Committee: Diana Chapel; Kathy Dzewaltowski; Geri Simon; Bruce C. Snead; Stan Ward.
EIN: 597250365

9124
Penland Foundation
6550 Tram Rd.
Beaumont, TX 77713-8703 (409) 722-4594
Contact: Joe Penland Sr., Pres.

Established in 2007 in Texas.
Donors: Joe Penland, Sr.; Tram Road Partners, LP.
Foundation type: Independent foundation.
Financial data (yr. ended 09/30/14): Assets, $4,815,041 (M); gifts received, $1,665,752; expenditures, $264,011; qualifying distributions, $259,548; giving activities include $259,548 for 38 grants (high: $100,000; low: $100).
Fields of interest: Education; Health; Cancers; Christianity; Human services; Child welfare.
Limitations: Applications accepted. Giving primarily in TX.
Application information:
  Initial approach: Proposal
  Deadline(s): None
Officers: Joe Penland, Sr., Pres.; Linda Penland, V.P.
Director: Joe Penland, Jr.; Joe C. Vernon.
EIN: 205692339

9125
James I. Perkins Family Foundation
P.O. Box 9339
Tyler, TX 75711

Established in 2005 in Texas.
Donors: James I. Perkins; Margaret Perkins.
Foundation type: Independent foundation.
Financial data (yr. ended 12/31/13): Assets, $6,611,756 (M); gifts received, $1,787,509; expenditures, $420,630; qualifying distributions, $402,190; giving activities include $383,753 for 48 grants (high: $103,750; low: $100).
Fields of interest: Arts and culture; Education; Elementary and secondary education; Higher education; Law education; Nonprofits; Community and economic development; Protestantism; Human services; Child welfare; Youth organizing.
Type of support: Regranting.
Limitations: Applications not accepted. Giving primarily in TX.
Application information: Unsolicited requests for funds not accepted.
Officers: James I. Perkins, Pres.; Margaret H. Perkins, V.P.; Nancy McKean, Secy.-Treas.
Directors: James I. Perkins, Jr.; Laura C. Perkins.
EIN: 020762991

9126
The Scott Petty Foundation
1027 Austin Hwy., Ste. 200
San Antonio, TX 78209-4717
Contact: Eleanor H. Petty, Dir.

Application address: c/o Scott Petty Jr., 711 Navarro, Ste. 235, San Antonio, TX 78208

Established in 1980 in Texas.
Donors: Edwina H. Petty†; O.S. Petty†; Scott Petty, Jr.
Foundation type: Independent foundation.
Financial data (yr. ended 11/30/13): Assets, $4,051,546 (M); gifts received, $921,123; expenditures, $374,012; qualifying distributions, $356,091; giving activities include $350,173 for 85 grants (high: $100,000; low: $15).
Fields of interest: Museums; Education; Animal welfare; Nonprofits; Geriatrics; Abuse prevention; Disasters and emergency management; Sports and recreation; Child welfare.
Type of support: General support; Matching grants; Continuing support; Annual campaigns; Capital campaigns; Research; Equipment; Program development; Curriculum development; Regranting.
Limitations: Applications accepted. Giving primarily in San Antonio, TX. No grants to individuals.
Application information:
  Initial approach: Contact foundation
  Deadline(s): None
Directors: Eleanor H. Petty; Scott Petty, Jr.
Number of staff: None.
EIN: 742146978

9127
Pevehouse Family Foundation Inc.
3300 North A St., Bldg. 1-201
Midland, TX 79705-5416

Donor: Beverly Pevehouse.
Foundation type: Independent foundation.
Financial data (yr. ended 12/31/13): Assets, $10,798,246 (M); gifts received, $1,000,000; expenditures, $516,819; qualifying distributions, $422,642; giving activities include $420,000 for 12 grants (high: $72,674; low: $6,662).
Fields of interest: Education; Diseases and conditions; Human services.
Limitations: Applications not accepted. Giving primarily in TX.
Application information: Unsolicited requests for funds not accepted.
Officer: Beverly Pevehouse, Pres.
Directors: Melissa Hoelscher; Clay Pevehouse; Jan Watson.
EIN: 263401629

9128
The Phoenix Charitable Foundation
100 N.E. Loop 410, Ste. 1300
San Antonio, TX 78216-4736

Established in 2006 in Texas.
Donors: Rex Amini; Margaret Amini; Deborah Amini.
Foundation type: Independent foundation.
Financial data (yr. ended 12/31/12): Assets, $25,343 (M); gifts received, $325,000; expenditures, $348,802; qualifying distributions, $348,166; giving activities include $348,166 for grants.
Fields of interest: Philanthropy; Christianity; Human services.
Limitations: Applications not accepted. Giving primarily in San Antonio, TX.
Application information: Unsolicited requests for funds not accepted.

Trustees: Deborah Amini; Rex Amini.
EIN: 206954843

9129
Earl W. and Hazel C. Pierson Foundation
1245 County Rd. 400
Dime Box, TX 77853-5095

Established in 1993 in Texas.
Donor: Hazel C. Pierson†.
Foundation type: Independent foundation.
Financial data (yr. ended 12/31/13): Assets, $2,524,418 (M); expenditures, $339,921; qualifying distributions, $322,500; giving activities include $322,500 for 16 grants (high: $250,000; low: $2,500).
Fields of interest: Human services; Developmental disability services.
Type of support: General support; Scholarships.
Limitations: Applications not accepted. Giving primarily in Houston, TX. No grants to individuals.
Application information: Contributes only to pre-selected organizations.
Officers and Directors: Marion B. Armstrong, Pres. and Director; Jerry M. Armstrong, V.P. and Treas. and Director; Jack B. Manning, Secy. and Director; Julie Armstrong; Terri Armstrong; Gloria Borreca; Sue Manning.
EIN: 760394931

9130
Pipe Line Contractors Association Scholarship Foundation
c/o Pat Tielborg
1700 Pacific Ave.
Dallas, TX 75201-4675
Application address: c/o Scholarship Management Svcs., 1505 Riverview Rd., P.O. Box 297, St. Peter, MN 56082

Donors: C. Paul Evans; Henkels Mccoy Inc; Sheehan Pipe Line Construction Co; Phillips Jordan Inc.; Letourneau Products; Rockford Corp.; Chase, Inc.; OTIS Eastern Service Inc; US Pipeline Inc.; Precision Pipeline LLC; Western Supplies Inc; Ozzie's Pipeline Padder Inc; Price Gregory International Inc; Sunbelt Equipment Marketing Inc; Utility Line Services Inc; Kelly W. Osborn; Welded Construction Company; Appalachian Pipeline; Latex Construction Co; Laney Inc; Wasatch Pipeline Supply Inc.
Foundation type: Independent foundation.
Financial data (yr. ended 12/31/12): Assets, $4,184,389 (M); gifts received, $637,000; expenditures, $369,278; qualifying distributions, $349,750; giving activities include $349,750 for grants to individuals.
Purpose and activities: Scholarship awards to children or grandchildren, age 25 or younger, of full-time employees of regular or associated members of the Pipe Line Contractors Assn. or one of its subsidiaries.
Fields of interest: Higher education.
Type of support: Student aid.
Limitations: Applications accepted. Giving primarily in CA, TX and WI.
Application information: Application form required.
  Initial approach: Proposal
  Deadline(s): Jan. 7
Officers: Don W. Thorn, Chair.; Pat Tielborg, Secy.

Directors: John Allen; C. Paul Evans; Karma Newberry; Ronnie Wise.
EIN: 752744096

9131
Pisani Family Foundation
3129 Bass Pro Dr.
Grapevine, TX 76051-1987

Donor: Dean C. Pisani.
Foundation type: Independent foundation.
Financial data (yr. ended 12/31/13): Assets, $1,172,808 (M); expenditures, $266,165; qualifying distributions, $249,160; giving activities include $249,160 for 14 grants (high: $125,000; low: $200).
Fields of interest: Diseases and conditions.
Limitations: Applications not accepted. Giving in the U.S., with emphasis on NY and TX.
Application information: Unsolicited requests for funds not accepted.
Directors: Dean C. Pisani; Jacqueline Pisani; Philip J. Pisani.
EIN: 274399564

9132
The Planetary Trust
7149 Hillgreen Dr.
Dallas, TX 75214-1933

Established in 1994 in Texas.
Donors: John M. Haley; Margaret J. Haley; Garland Eye Associates, P.A.
Foundation type: Independent foundation.
Financial data (yr. ended 12/31/13): Assets, $1,125,783; gifts received, $50,000; expenditures, $311,473; qualifying distributions, $311,270.
Purpose and activities: Giving primarily for environmental conservation and issues of economic, environmental and social sustainability.
Fields of interest: Higher education; Natural resources; Community and economic development; Sustainable development; Business promotion.
Type of support: Ethics and accountability.
Limitations: Applications not accepted. Giving primarily in CO and Dallas, TX; giving also to national organizations. No grants to individuals.
Application information: Unsolicited requests for funds not accepted.
Trustee: Margaret J. Haley.
EIN: 752567517

9133
Pogue Family Missions Society
1512 Bray Central Dr.
McKinney, TX 75069

Donors: Paul Pogue; Radiant Church; Mark Nevil; John D. Fulkerson; Sandra Clemons; Sharon Berry; Melvin Clearman, Jr.; David Taylor; Bob Tomes; Matt Burk; Lee Dunlap; David Clemons; Gayla Cotton; Nita Williams; George Williams; Elizabeth Genzel; Judy Pogue; Robert Genzel; Bob Cotton; Jenny Brown; Jessica Clemons; Jamie Dunlap; Jessica Burk; Barbara Tomes; Stacy Taylor; Buddy Berry; Sam Clemons; Donna L. Carter; Minuteman Disaster Response Foundation; Heath Morel.
Foundation type: Independent foundation.

Financial data (yr. ended 12/31/13): Assets, $26,006 (M); gifts received, $193,197; expenditures, $177,892; qualifying distributions, $177,892; giving activities include $168,183 for 16 grants (high: $69,629; low: $100).
Fields of interest: Religion; Human services.
Limitations: Applications not accepted. Giving primarily in TX.
Application information: Unsolicited requests for funds not accepted.
Directors: Benjamin P. Pogue; Judy L. Pogue; Paul H. Pogue.
EIN: 274285936

9134
Poncin Scholarship Fund
c/o Bank of America, N.A.
P.O. Box 831041
Dallas, TX 75283-1041
Application address: c/o Bank of America, N.A., P.O. Box 24565, Seattle, WA 98124, tel.: (206) 358-3079

Established in 1966 in Washington.
Donor: Cora May Poncin†.
Foundation type: Independent foundation.
Financial data (yr. ended 12/31/14): Assets, $7,327,178; expenditures, $442,426; qualifying distributions, $384,529.
Purpose and activities: Scholarships awarded to people engaged in advanced medical research in connection with, or as a part of, any recognized institution of learning within the state of Washington.
Fields of interest: Diseases and conditions.
Type of support: Research; Student aid; Research and evaluation.
Limitations: Applications accepted. Giving limited to WA.
Publications: Application guidelines.
Application information: Application form required.
  Initial approach: Required application form
  Copies of proposal: 1
  Deadline(s): May 1
Trustee: Bank of America, N.A.
EIN: 916069573

9135
Andrew & Lillian A. Posey Foundation
5905 Northern Dancer Dr.
Austin, TX 78746-2105

Donor: Andrew J. Posey, Jr.
Foundation type: Independent foundation.
Financial data (yr. ended 12/31/12): Assets, $2,979,334 (M); expenditures, $147,443; qualifying distributions, $141,000; giving activities include $141,000 for 8 grants (high: $25,000; low: $10,000).
Fields of interest: Education; Health; Diseases and conditions.
Limitations: Applications not accepted. Giving primarily in TX; funding also in AZ, OH and NY.
Application information: Unsolicited requests for funds not accepted.
Officers: Robert F. Glickert, Pres. and C.E.O.; Anita Posey Glickert, Secy.; Keith E. Glickert, Treas.
Board Members: Audrey M. Glickert; Michael W. Glickert.
EIN: 261794495

9136

The Postl Family Foundation

5338 Doliver Dr.
Houston, TX 77056-2316

Established in 2003 in Texas.
Donors: James J. Postl; Beverly A. Postl.
Foundation type: Independent foundation.
Financial data (yr. ended 12/31/13): Assets, $1,061,968 (M); expenditures, $169,785; qualifying distributions, $167,050; giving activities include $167,050 for 26 grants (high: $30,000; low: $500).
Fields of interest: Elementary and secondary education; Nonprofits; Diseases and conditions; Human services.
Type of support: General support; Regranting.
Limitations: Applications not accepted. Giving primarily in TX. No grants to individuals.
Application information: Unsolicited requests for funds not accepted.
Officers and Directors: James J. Postl, Pres. and Director; Beverly A. Postl, Secy. and Director; Jennifer Boston; Erin Postl.
EIN: 141856946

9137

The Aileen and Jack Pratt Foundation

13355 Noel Rd., Ste. 1865
Dallas, TX 75240-6835

Established in 2002 in Texas.
Donors: Aileen Pratt; Jack E. Pratt, Sr.
Foundation type: Independent foundation.
Financial data (yr. ended 09/30/13): Assets, $2,805,476 (M); gifts received, $25,000; expenditures, $390,301; qualifying distributions, $382,375; giving activities include $320,791 for 47 grants (high: $33,334; low: $500).
Fields of interest: Education; Higher education; Diseases and conditions; Christianity; Catholicism; Human services.
Type of support: Capital and infrastructure; General support.
Limitations: Applications not accepted. Giving primarily in Dallas, TX. No grants to individuals.
Application information: Contributes only to pre-selected organizations.
Officers and Directors: Jack E. Pratt, Sr., Pres. and Director; Aileen Pratt, Secy.-Treas. and Director.
EIN: 820576238

9138

The Prayer Closet

6505 W. Park Blvd., Ste. 306-361
Plano, TX 75093

Foundation type: Independent foundation.
Financial data (yr. ended 12/31/13): Assets, $4,532,169 (M); expenditures, $361,811; qualifying distributions, $293,795; giving activities include $243,500 for 38 grants (high: $50,000; low: $500).
Fields of interest: Health; Diseases and conditions; Religion; Christianity; Human services.
Limitations: Applications not accepted. Giving primarily in TX.
Application information: Unsolicited requests for funds not accepted.
Officers: Sharon N. Thomas, Pres.; Sam H. Thomas, Secy.

Directors: Sara Whitney Standerfer; Samuel Judson Thomas.
EIN: 201849802

9139

Hahl Proctor Charitable Trust

c/o U.S. Trust, Bank of America, N.A.
500 W. 7th St., 15th Fl., TX1-497-15-08
Fort Worth, TX 76102-4700 (817) 390-6028
Contact: Mark J. Smith, Philanthropic Relationship Mgr.
E-mail: tx.philanthropic@ustrust.com; Application address: P.O. Box 270, Midland, TX 79702-0270; Main URL: https://www.bankofamerica.com/philanthropic/grantmaking.go

Established in 1987 in Texas.
Foundation type: Independent foundation.
Financial data (yr. ended 04/30/13): Assets, $5,510,178 (M); expenditures, $298,092; qualifying distributions, $266,231; giving activities include $240,000 for 15 grants (high: $40,000; low: $4,500).
Purpose and activities: Giving primarily for youth development and education, including education and services for children who are mentally or physically disabled; funding also for other children, youth, and social services and for the performing arts.
Fields of interest: Performing arts; Education; Special needs education; Human services; Child welfare; Youth organizing; Shelter and residential care; Developmental disability services; People with physical disabilities.
Limitations: Applications accepted. Giving primarily in Midland, TX. No grants to individuals.
Application information: Application form required.
  Initial approach: Online proposal via Trust web site
  Deadline(s): May 15
Committee Members: Bob Elliott; Sean Low; Jeff Morton; David Smith; Mark Smith; Lisa Van der Zanden.
EIN: 756382699

9140

Margot Rosenberg Pulitzer Foundation

12020 Excelsior Way
Dallas, TX 75230-2243 (972) 934-1850
Contact: Ann P. Rosenberg, Dir.

Donor: Margot Rosenberg Pulitzer Charitable lead Unity Trust.
Foundation type: Independent foundation.
Financial data (yr. ended 12/31/13): Assets, $7,286,588 (M); gifts received, $628,056; expenditures, $326,853; qualifying distributions, $292,000; giving activities include $292,000 for 10 grants (high: $100,000; low: $500).
Fields of interest: Education; Nonprofits; Cancers.
Type of support: Regranting.
Limitations: Applications not accepted. Giving primarily in New York, NY, TX and WA. No grants to individuals.
Application information: Contributes only to pre-selected organizations.
Directors: Elizabeth Rosenberg Grief; Jules Grief; Ann P. Rosenberg; Sheri Rosenberg; Steven Rosenberg; Helen Rosenberg Waldman.
EIN: 260017254

9141

Quanex Foundation

1800 W. Loop S., Ste. 1500
Houston, TX 77027-3267 (713) 961-4600

Established in 1951 in Illinois.
Donors: LaSalle Steel Co.; Quanex Corp.
Foundation type: Company-sponsored foundation.
Financial data (yr. ended 12/31/14): Assets, $8,040,317; expenditures, $390,298; qualifying distributions, $365,381.
Purpose and activities: The foundation supports organizations involved with education, health, Parkinson's disease research, rodeos, human services, and the forging industry.
Fields of interest: Diseases and conditions; Agriculture; Human services.
Type of support: General support; Employee matching gifts; Scholarships.
Limitations: Applications accepted. No support for organizations supporting dependent children . No grants to individuals.
Application information: Application form required.
  Initial approach: Proposal
  Copies of proposal: 1
  Deadline(s): Oct. 31
Officers: Kevin P. Delaney, Pres.; Brent L. Korb, V.P.
EIN: 366065490

9142

Quest Family Foundation

5609 Ursula Ln.
Dallas, TX 75229-6429
Contact: William J. Quest, V.P. and Secy.

Donors: Ann L. Quest; William J. Quest.
Foundation type: Independent foundation.
Financial data (yr. ended 12/31/13): Assets, $3,244,473 (M); gifts received, $100,000; expenditures, $431,593; qualifying distributions, $431,593; giving activities include $376,700 for 39 grants (high: $161,000; low: $1,000).
Fields of interest: Education; Health; Religion.
Limitations: Applications not accepted. Giving primarily in TX.
Application information: Contributes only to pre-selected organizations.
Officers: Ann L. Quest, Pres. and Treas.; William J. Quest, V.P. and Secy.
Directors: Julie Q. Brooks; Melissa Q. Hays; Michael E. Quest.
EIN: 273773219

9143

The Jerry S. Rawls Scholarship Foundation

6204 17th St.
Lubbock, TX 79416-6133

Established in 2001 in California.
Donor: Jerry S. Rawls.
Foundation type: Independent foundation.
Financial data (yr. ended 06/30/14): Assets, $4,326,369 (M); gifts received, $30; expenditures, $217,860; qualifying distributions, $169,343; giving activities include $166,325 for 87 grants to individuals (high: $4,675; low: $500).
Fields of interest: Education.
Type of support: Student aid.
Limitations: Applications not accepted. Giving primarily in TX.

Application information: Unsolicited requests for funds not accepted.
Trustees: Bobby M. Gleason; Owen McWhorter, Jr.; Glenn D. Moor; Jerry S. Rawls.
Number of staff: None.
EIN: 916530654

9144
The Ray H. Marr Foundation
325 N. St. Paul, Ste. 2500
Dallas, TX 75201-3854

Donor: Ray H. Marr.
Foundation type: Independent foundation.
Financial data (yr. ended 12/31/13): Assets, $3,502,897 (M); expenditures, $339,176; qualifying distributions, $171,951; giving activities include $167,400 for 9 grants (high: $57,500; low: $650).
Fields of interest: Education; Graduate and professional education; Engineering; Religion; Youth development; Scouting programs.
Type of support: General support.
Limitations: Applications not accepted. Giving primarily in TX.
Application information: Unsolicited requests for funds not accepted.
Officers and Directors: Ray H. Marr, Pres. and Director; Douglas W. Bonner, V.P. and Director; Phyllis Weir, Secy.; Judith Elder, Treas.; G. Todd Bright.
EIN: 263172622

9145
Raygar Foundation
23790 Champion Dr.
Lindale, TX 75771-5554

Established in 1993 in Florida.
Donors: Annie M. Sloan; Garrett Sloan; Raygar Realty Group; Annie Sloan Trust; Garrett Sloan Trust.
Foundation type: Independent foundation.
Financial data (yr. ended 08/31/13): Assets, $23,359,069 (M); gifts received, $16,234,216; expenditures, $225,112; qualifying distributions, $219,000; giving activities include $219,000 for 8 grants (high: $100,000; low: $3,000).
Purpose and activities: Giving primarily to Christian ministries and organizations.
Fields of interest: Graduate and professional education; Christianity; Theology; Human services.
Limitations: Applications not accepted. Giving in the U.S., with some emphasis on CA and CO. No grants to individuals.
Application information: Contributes only to pre-selected organizations.
Trustee: Thomas G. Sloan.
EIN: 656128544

9146
RDM Positive Impact Foundation
81 N. Bay Blvd.
The Woodlands, TX 77380-1069

Established in 2005 in California.
Donors: Ronald J. Mittelstaedt; Darin Mittelstaedt.
Foundation type: Independent foundation.
Financial data (yr. ended 12/31/12): Assets, $1,612,927 (M); gifts received, $131,434; expenditures, $296,382; qualifying distributions,

$286,675; giving activities include $286,675 for 11 grants (high: $100,000; low: $3,000).
Fields of interest: Diseases and conditions; Protestantism; Human services; Child welfare.
Type of support: Research.
Limitations: Applications not accepted. Giving primarily in CA. No grants to individuals.
Application information: Contributes only to pre-selected organizations.
Officers: Ronald J. Mittelstaedt, C.E.O.; Darin Mittelstaedt, Secy.
EIN: 203502111

9147
Redman Foundation Inc
P.O. Box 38567
Dallas, TX 75238-0567 (214) 221-5999
Contact: Marti Royer, Exec. Dir.
Main URL: http://redmanfoundation.org

Foundation type: Independent foundation.
Financial data (yr. ended 12/31/13): Assets, $8,408,978 (M); expenditures, $436,729; qualifying distributions, $390,700; giving activities include $328,095 for 27 grants (high: $35,000; low: $500).
Fields of interest: Religion; Christianity.
Type of support: General support; Matching grants; Continuing support; Public engagement and education; Capital campaigns; Capital and infrastructure.
Limitations: Applications accepted. Giving primarily in Dallas and North TX. Generally, no support for galas, special events, testimonial or fund-raising luncheons or dinners or honoraria for guest speakers or panelists. No grants to individuals; no loans.
Application information: Application form required.
   Initial approach: Letter
   Deadline(s): None
Officers: Janey Bills, Pres.; Kay Chafin, V.P.; Joy Henderson, Secy.; Amy Williams-Getzoff, Treas.; Marti Royer, Exec. Dir.
Trustees: Megan Flowers; Carol Martin.
Number of staff: 1 part-time professional.
EIN: 752617664

9148
The Reilly Family Foundation
1017 S. FM Rd. 5
Aledo, TX 76008-4558 (817) 265-2364
Contact: Beverly A. Reilly, V.P.; Michael A. Reilly, Chair.

Established in 1996 in Texas.
Donors: John C. Franklin; Stars for Children; Peter Baldwin; Reilly Parkway; Beverly A. Reilly; Michael A. Reilly.
Foundation type: Independent foundation.
Financial data (yr. ended 12/31/14): Assets, $1,834,021 (M); expenditures, $329,322; qualifying distributions, $318,323; giving activities include $318,323 for 47 grants (high: $40,000; low: $250).
Purpose and activities: Giving primarily for education, including scholarships to high school graduates pursuing higher education.
Fields of interest: Education; Higher education; Health; Christianity; Human services; International development.

Type of support: General support; Scholarships; Student aid.
Limitations: Applications accepted. Giving in the U.S., primarily in the Dallas-Fort Worth, TX, area.
Application information: An application and list of information required to be submitted will be mailed or faxed to the applicant upon such request. Application form required.
   Initial approach: Letter of telephone
   Deadline(s): None
Officers and Directors: Michael A. Reilly, Chair. and Director; Richard D. Trubitt, V.P. and Secy.-Treas. and Director; Beverly A. Reilly, V.P. and Director; Robert Barnes; Anson Reilly; Asher Reilly; Atlee Reilly; Austin Reilly; Axton Reilly.
EIN: 752366809

9149
Tom C. & Mary B. Reitch Charitable Trust
c/o Bank of America, N.A.
P.O. Box 831041
Dallas, TX 75283-1041 8003577094

Established in 2000 in Texas.
Donor: Mary B. Reitch†.
Foundation type: Independent foundation.
Financial data (yr. ended 12/31/14): Assets, $7,662,515; expenditures, $462,179; qualifying distributions, $355,149.
Purpose and activities: Giving primarily for scholarships available to students at Texas Woman's University.
Fields of interest: Higher education; Christianity; Females.
Type of support: General support; Scholarships.
Limitations: Applications accepted. Giving primarily in TX.
Application information: For Texas Woman's University application form and eligibility requirements, see the web site http://www.twu.edu/finaid/scholarship-application-form.asp. Application form required.
   Initial approach: Request application form
   Deadline(s): Mar. 1
Trustee: Bank of America, N.A.
EIN: 527033945

9150
Reuhl Family Foundation
P.O. Box 132099
Houston, TX 77219-2099

Established in 1997 in Texas.
Donor: Gerald G. Reuhl.
Foundation type: Independent foundation.
Financial data (yr. ended 12/31/13): Assets, $3,789,947 (M); expenditures, $160,006; qualifying distributions, $153,524; giving activities include $150,000 for 5 grants (high: $70,000; low: $7,500).
Purpose and activities: Funding primarily for hospitals, human services, and higher education.
Fields of interest: Higher education; Hospital care; Human services; Child welfare; Youth services.
Type of support: General support.
Limitations: Applications not accepted. Giving primarily in TX. No grants to individuals.
Application information: Contributes only to pre-selected organizations.

Officers: Gerald G. Reuhl, Pres. and Treas.; Ellen Ann Reuhl, V.P. and Secy.
Trustees: Brooks McGee; Catherine Reuhl; Sarah Wilbanks.
EIN: 760559539

9151
Sid Richardson Memorial Fund
309 Main St.
Fort Worth, TX 76102-4006 (817) 336-0494
Contact: Mary Kuykendall
FAX: (817) 332-2176;
E-mail: mkuykendall@sidrichardson.org; Main URL: https://www.sidrichardsonmemorialfund.org
Grant Database: http://www.sidrichardson.org/grants/prior

Established in 1965 in Texas.
Donor: Sid W. Richardson†.
Foundation type: Independent foundation.
Financial data (yr. ended 12/31/13): Assets, $8,616,954 (M); expenditures, $455,548; qualifying distributions, $374,099; giving activities include $314,750 for 67 grants to individuals (high: $8,000; low: $1,250).
Purpose and activities: Giving limited to scholarships for direct descendants of donor's employees.
Fields of interest: Higher education.
Type of support: Scholarships.
Limitations: Applications accepted. Giving primarily in TX. No grants for capital or endowment funds, operating budgets, general purposes, special projects, research, or matching gifts; no loans.
Application information: Application form required.
  Initial approach: Letter, telephone, or fax
  Copies of proposal: 1
  Deadline(s): Submit application between Jan. and Mar.; deadline Mar. 31
  Board meeting date(s): Sept./Oct.; selection committee meets annually in May
  Final notification: 2 months
Officers and Directors: John Hogg, Pres. and Director; Peggy Laskoski, Secy.; Cynthia K. Alexander, Treas.; Robert E. Kolba; Valleau Wilkie, Jr.
Number of staff: None.
EIN: 751220266

9152
Wade Richmond Foundation
1009 Austin Hwy.
San Antonio, TX 78209-4729 2108269507

Donors: Jack C. Richmond; Laura G Richmond; Leffingwell Ltd.
Foundation type: Independent foundation.
Financial data (yr. ended 12/31/14): Assets, $3,023,255; expenditures, $220,392; qualifying distributions, $200,000.
Fields of interest: Mental health care; Religion.
Limitations: Applications not accepted. Giving primarily in TX.
Application information: Contributes only to pre-selected organizations.
Directors: Clay P. Richmond; Gail Richmond; Jack C. Richmond; John M. Richmond; Laaura G. Richmond; Stephanie Richmond; Steven J. Richmond; Victoria Richmond.
EIN: 462179454

9153
Adam Richter Charitable Trust
c/o Bank of America, N.A.
P.O. Box 831041
Dallas, TX 75283-1041 8003577094
Application address: c/o Bank of America, N.A., Att.: Constance Morrow, 901 Main St., 9th Fl., Dallas, TX 75202-3714, tel.: (866) 461-7281

Established in 1994 in California.
Foundation type: Independent foundation.
Financial data (yr. ended 09/30/14): Assets, $5,369,412; expenditures, $278,092; qualifying distributions, $209,722.
Fields of interest: Arts and culture; Higher education; Environment; Animal welfare; Hospital care; Diseases and conditions; Christianity; Human services.
Limitations: Applications accepted. Giving primarily in CA. No grants to individuals.
Application information: Application form required.
  Initial approach: Letter
  Deadline(s): None
Trustee: Bank of America, N.A.
EIN: 956978793

9154
A. W. Riter, Jr. Family Foundation
1012 Pruitt Pl.
Tyler, TX 75703-1132

Established in 1997 in Texas.
Donors: A.W. Riter, Jr.; Betty Jo B. Riter.
Foundation type: Independent foundation.
Financial data (yr. ended 12/31/13): Assets, $7,311,875 (M); expenditures, $614,911; qualifying distributions, $489,966; giving activities include $416,551 for 21 grants (high: $108,000; low: $1,000).
Fields of interest: Elementary and secondary education; Higher education; School-based health care; Diseases and conditions; Human services; Food banks; Child welfare.
Type of support: General support; Research.
Limitations: Applications not accepted. Giving primarily in Tyler, TX. No grants to individuals.
Application information: Contributes only to pre-selected organizations.
Officers: A.W. Riter III, Pres. and Treas.; Betty Jo B. Riter, V.P.; Cynthia S. Riter, Secy.
Directors: Melvin B. Lovelady; Paxton W. Riter; Melinda Shoemake; Tom Shoemake.
EIN: 752707712

9155
Dr. Kent and Ilene Roberts Balliet Foundation
P.O. Box 1
Amarillo, TX 79105-0001

Foundation type: Independent foundation.
Financial data (yr. ended 08/31/14): Assets, $8,734,275; expenditures, $471,280; qualifying distributions, $383,850.
Fields of interest: Arts and culture; Education; Agriculture.
Limitations: Applications not accepted. Giving primarily in Amarillo, TX.
Application information: Unsolicited requests for funds not accepted.

Trustee: Amarillo National Bank, N.A.
EIN: 272885140

9156
Ed and Margaret Roberts Foundation
P.O. Box 9294
Amarillo, TX 79105-9294

Established in 2006 in Texas.
Donors: Margaret Roberts†; E.L. Roberts.
Foundation type: Independent foundation.
Financial data (yr. ended 12/31/12): Assets, $2,329,249 (M); expenditures, $237,587; qualifying distributions, $139,518; giving activities include $133,750 for grants.
Fields of interest: Arts education.
Type of support: Scholarships.
Limitations: Applications not accepted. Giving primarily in TX. No grants to individuals.
Application information: Unsolicited requests for funds not accepted.
Trustee: Bill Countiss.
EIN: 756600063

9157
Summerfield G. Roberts Foundation
c/o Bank of America, N.A.
P.O. Box 831041
Dallas, TX 75283-1041
Application address: c/o David D. Jackson, 5556 Caruth Haven Ln., Dallas, TX 75225, tel.: (214) 363-9000

Established in 1990 in Texas.
Donor: Summerfield G. Roberts†.
Foundation type: Independent foundation.
Financial data (yr. ended 03/31/13): Assets, $8,343,403 (M); expenditures, $466,995; qualifying distributions, $315,001; giving activities include $315,001 for grants.
Purpose and activities: Giving primarily through scholarship funds earmarked for the advanced study of business, commerce, banking, oil and gas, and other related subjects and for medical students and doctors performing medical research on diseases or disorders of the human body. Support also to educational institutions for the advancement of the study, research, and teaching of Texas history.
Fields of interest: Education; Higher education; Diseases and conditions.
Type of support: Publications; Research; Scholarships.
Limitations: Applications accepted. Giving limited to TX.
Publications: Application guidelines; Financial statement.
Application information: Scholarship application forms provided by educational institutions must be completed by prospective award recipients. The foundation does not make the final selection of individuals receiving support.
  Initial approach: Letter
  Copies of proposal: 1
  Deadline(s): Dec. 31
  Board meeting date(s): Quarterly
Trustees: David D. Jackson; Bank of America, N.A.
Number of staff: None.
EIN: 752341916

9158
George A. Robinson IV Foundation
5005 Riverway, Ste. 200
Houston, TX 77056 (713) 627-9440
Contact: Robert S. Pulitzer, V.P., Treas. and Tr.

Foundation type: Independent foundation.
Financial data (yr. ended 12/31/13): Assets,
$5,632,042 (M); expenditures, $323,938;
qualifying distributions, $250,625; giving activities
include $250,625 for 8 grants (high: $110,000;
low: $500).
Purpose and activities: Giving for medical research,
child welfare, and education.
Fields of interest: Museums; Higher education;
Medical education; Hospital care; Christianity;
Human services.
Limitations: Applications accepted. Giving primarily
in Houston, TX.
Application information:
Initial approach: Proposal
Copies of proposal: 1
Deadline(s): None
Officers and Trustees: George A. Robinson IV, Pres.
and Trustee; Robert S. Pulitzer, V.P. and Treas. and
Trustee; Jay Houren, Secy. and Trustee; Larry
Hollier, MD.
EIN: 760399825

9159
John William and Lena Wells Rogers Trust
c/o Bank of America, N.A.
P.O. Box 831041
Dallas, TX 75283-1041

Foundation type: Independent foundation.
Financial data (yr. ended 12/31/13): Assets,
$4,959,843 (M); expenditures, $246,497;
qualifying distributions, $224,091; giving activities
include $210,429 for 1 grant.
Fields of interest: Community and economic
development.
Limitations: Applications not accepted. Giving
primarily in Dallas, TX.
Application information: Unsolicited requests for
funds not accepted.
Trustee: Bank of America, N.A.
EIN: 756063759

9160
Sam Roosth Foundation
P.O. Box 8300
Tyler, TX 75711-8300

Established in 1953 in Texas.
Donor: Jake Roosth Trust.
Foundation type: Independent foundation.
Financial data (yr. ended 12/31/13): Assets,
$6,376,372 (M); expenditures, $271,080;
qualifying distributions, $243,240; giving activities
include $242,880 for 15 grants (high: $40,000;
low: $5,000).
Fields of interest: Higher education; Health;
Community and economic development; Judaism;
Human services; Food banks; Family services; Child
welfare; Child care.
Type of support: General support; Annual
campaigns; Scholarships.
Limitations: Applications not accepted. Giving
primarily in TX, with emphasis on Tyler. No grants to
individuals.

Publications: Annual report.
Application information: Contributes only to
pre-selected organizations.
Officers: Wiley Roosth, Pres.; Steven C. Roosth,
V.P.; Sam Roosth, Secy.-Treas.
Directors: Kenneth Roosth; Toni Roosth; Celia
Schoenbrun; Marleen Swerdlow.
EIN: 756023828

9161
The Dr. A. Everett & Ruth E. Rosen Foundation
c/o Walter Rosen
49 Briar Hollow Ln., Ste. 1802
Houston, TX 77027-9352

Donors: A. Everett Rosen†; Ruth E. Rosen; Abraham
E. Rosen†.
Foundation type: Independent foundation.
Financial data (yr. ended 12/31/13): Assets,
$4,931,896 (M); expenditures, $357,265;
qualifying distributions, $223,404; giving activities
include $223,404 for 43 grants (high: $36,550;
low: $800).
Fields of interest: Education; University education;
Hospital care; Judaism; Human services.
Limitations: Applications not accepted. No grants to
individuals.
Application information: Unsolicited requests for
funds not accepted.
Trustee: Walter M. Rosen.
EIN: 042915665

9162
Michael L. Rosenberg Foundation
4831 Brookview Dr.
Dallas, TX 75229

Established in 1997 in Texas.
Donors: Sonia Rosenberg; Michael L. Rosenberg†.
Foundation type: Independent foundation.
Financial data (yr. ended 12/31/13): Assets,
$4,267,702 (M); expenditures, $294,296;
qualifying distributions, $234,596; giving activities
include $234,596 for 4 grants (high: $157,096;
low: $2,500).
Purpose and activities: Giving primarily for the arts.
Fields of interest: Orchestral music; Art museums;
University education; Foundations; Child welfare;
Women's services.
Type of support: General support.
Limitations: Applications not accepted. Giving
primarily in TX. No grants to individuals.
Application information: Contributes only to
pre-selected organizations.
Officers and Directors: Lawrence Barzune, MD,
Pres. and Treas. and Director; Deborah Gage, V.P.
and Secy. and Director; Bob Harrison.
EIN: 752736174

9163
The Rosenthal Foundation
604 E. 4th St., Ste. 201
Fort Worth, TX 76102-4074

Established in 1979 in Texas.
Donor: E.M. Rosenthal.
Foundation type: Independent foundation.

Financial data (yr. ended 12/31/14): Assets,
$4,997,239 (M); expenditures, $253,925; qualifying
distributions, $205,250.
Fields of interest: Arts and culture; Health;
Diseases and conditions.
Type of support: General support.
Limitations: Applications not accepted. Giving
primarily in St. Louis, MO, New York, NY, and Fort
Worth, TX. No grants to individuals.
Application information: Unsolicited requests for
funds not accepted.
Trustees: Marcia Cohen; Rosalyn G. Rosenthal;
William Rosenthal.
EIN: 751675127

9164
The Dale and Deborah Ross Foundation
P.O. Box 17149
Sugar Land, TX 77496-7149

Established in 1997 in Texas.
Donors: Deborah H. Ross; R. Dale Ross.
Foundation type: Independent foundation.
Financial data (yr. ended 12/31/14): Assets,
$166,875 (M); expenditures, $205,898; qualifying
distributions, $203,000; giving activities include
$203,000 for 9 grants (high: $140,000; low: $500).
Purpose and activities: Giving primarily to Christian
churches.
Fields of interest: Art museums; Education;
Elementary and secondary education; Early
childhood education; Higher education;
Protestantism.
Limitations: Applications not accepted. Giving
primarily in Houston, TX. No grants to individuals.
Application information: Contributes only to
pre-selected organizations.
Officers: R. Dale Ross, Pres.; David J. Ross, V.P.;
Michael A. Ross, Secy.-Treas.
EIN: 760551779

9165
The Marshal Verne Ross Foundation
c/o Mary Frances Ross
2200 Quail Hollow Dr.
Bryan, TX 77802-2919 (806) 745-6789

Established in 1998 in Texas.
Foundation type: Independent foundation.
Financial data (yr. ended 12/31/13): Assets,
$6,367,018 (M); expenditures, $475,966;
qualifying distributions, $305,472; giving activities
include $300,000 for 13 grants (high: $80,000;
low: $5,000).
Fields of interest: Education; Higher education;
Protestantism.
Type of support: General support; Individual
development.
Limitations: Applications accepted. Giving primarily
in TX. No grants to individuals.
Application information: Application form required.
Initial approach: Letter
Deadline(s): June 30
Officers: Mary Frances Ross, Pres.; Margaret Purvis,
V.P.; Wendell D. Moore, Treas.
Directors: Amanda Lee Ross; Marsha Frances Ross
Shaer.
EIN: 742864663

9166
The Arch and Stella Rowan Foundation Inc.
c/o Findling Milam & Pyle
3011 Nacogdoches Rd., Bldg. 2
San Antonio, TX 78217-4541 (210) 824-3224

Established in 1963 in Texas.
Donors: Stella S. Rowan†; Arch H. Rowan†.
Foundation type: Independent foundation.
Financial data (yr. ended 08/31/13): Assets, $4,616,630 (M); expenditures, $235,249; qualifying distributions, $223,000; giving activities include $223,000 for 98 grants (high: $20,000; low: $100).
Fields of interest: Arts and culture; Education; Health; Diseases and conditions; Human services.
Type of support: General support; Continuing support; Annual campaigns; Capital campaigns; Equipment; Research; Scholarships.
Limitations: Applications accepted. Giving limited to TX. No grants to individuals.
Application information: Application form required.
   Initial approach: Letter
   Deadline(s): None
   Board meeting date(s): Varies
Officers: Eloise Rowan, Pres.; James E. Altgelt, Jr., V.P.; Dave Zurbriggen, Secy.; Erica Laughlin, Treas.
Number of staff: 1 part-time professional.
EIN: 756030348

9167
The Jerry and Maury Rubenstein Foundation
2330 Holmes Rd.
Houston, TX 77051-1014 (713) 799-5732

Established in 2000 in Texas.
Donor: Texas Pipe & Supply Co, Ltd.
Foundation type: Independent foundation.
Financial data (yr. ended 05/31/13): Assets, $1,117,710 (M); expenditures, $318,800; qualifying distributions, $318,800; giving activities include $318,000 for 6 grants (high: $150,000; low: $1,000).
Fields of interest: Diseases and conditions; Judaism; Family services; Child welfare.
Type of support: Research.
Limitations: Applications not accepted. Giving primarily in Houston, TX. No grants to individuals.
Application information: Contributes only to pre-selected organizations.
Trustees: Jerry Rubenstein; Maury Rubenstein.
EIN: 316645608

9168
Margaret Sue Rust Foundation
2602 Hwy. 35 N.
Rockport, TX 78382-5707
Application address: c/o Susie Bracht Black, P.O. Box 2659, Rockport, TX 78381-2659, tel.: (361) 729-2321

Established in 1998 in Texas.
Donor: Margaret S. Rust†.
Foundation type: Independent foundation.
Financial data (yr. ended 12/31/13): Assets, $7,272,249 (M); expenditures, $459,918; qualifying distributions, $378,319; giving activities include $378,319 for 19 grants (high: $59,648; low: $5,000).

Fields of interest: Arts and culture; Maritime museums; Education; Health; Christianity; Human services; Scouting programs.
Type of support: General support.
Limitations: Applications accepted. Giving primarily in Rockport, TX. No grants to individuals.
Application information:
   Initial approach: Proposal
   Deadline(s): None
Officers: Susie Bracht Black, Pres.; Michael Johnson, Secy.-Treas.
Directors: Mindy Durham; John P. Jackson; Al Johnson.
EIN: 742832533

9169
The Ryrie Foundation
3310 Fairmount St., Apt. 5D
Dallas, TX 75201-1232 (972) 383-5700
Contact: Charles C. Ryrie, Tr.

Donors: Charles C. Ryrie; Association of Baptist World Evangelism, Inc.
Foundation type: Independent foundation.
Financial data (yr. ended 12/31/12): Assets, $2,472,773 (M); gifts received, $50,547; expenditures, $247,570; qualifying distributions, $240,200; giving activities include $240,200 for grants.
Fields of interest: Graduate and professional education; Protestantism; Theology.
Type of support: General support; Grants to individuals; Student aid.
Limitations: Applications accepted. Giving nationally to religious organizations; scholarships to residents of TX.
Application information: Application form required.
   Initial approach: Proposal
   Deadline(s): None
Trustee: Charles C. Ryrie.
EIN: 752001540

9170
San Marcos Civic Foundation
c/o BDO USA LLP
2579 Western Trails Blvd., Ste. 110
Austin, TX 78745-1496 (512) 328-6696
Contact: Susan Hinton, Tr.

Established in 1968 in Texas.
Donors: H.Y. Price, Jr.†; Lois Pollard Price†.
Foundation type: Independent foundation.
Financial data (yr. ended 12/31/13): Assets, $6,862,695 (M); expenditures, $428,357; qualifying distributions, $343,307; giving activities include $120,709 for 40 grants (high: $39,677; low: $110).
Purpose and activities: Giving primarily for literacy programs and to train teachers working with dyslexia.
Fields of interest: Education; Elementary and secondary education; Higher education; Learning disorders.
Type of support: Convening; Matching grants; Scholarships; Program evaluations.
Limitations: Applications accepted. Giving primarily in Hays County, TX and central TX. No grants for capital campaigns.
Application information: Application form required.
   Initial approach: Request application form

Copies of proposal: 1
Deadline(s): None
Trustees: Mary Davis; Susan Hinton; Timothy M. Price.
Number of staff: 2 part-time professional.
EIN: 746109230

9171
The Sanders Foundation
201 E. Main St., Ste. 350
El Paso, TX 79901-1416

Donor: William D. Sanders.
Foundation type: Independent foundation.
Financial data (yr. ended 12/31/13): Assets, $4,311,614 (M); expenditures, $342,133; qualifying distributions, $327,125; giving activities include $327,125 for 20 grants (high: $50,000; low: $1,500).
Fields of interest: Education; Higher education.
Limitations: Applications not accepted. Giving primarily in NM, NY and TX. No grants to individuals.
Application information: Unsolicited requests for funds not accepted.
Directors: Barry A. Kobren; Louann F. Sanders; Marianna E. Sanders; William D. Sanders.
EIN: 742698726

9172
Annunziata Sanguinetti Foundation
c/o Wells Fargo Bank, N.A.
P.O. Box 41629
Austin, TX 78704-0028
Application address: c/o Wells Fargo Bank, N.A., Attn.: Grant Administration Team, 1 W. 4th St., 2nd Fl., Winston-Salem, NC 27101, tel.: (888) 234-1999; Main URL: https://www.wellsfargo.com/privatefoundationgrants/sanguinetti

Established in 1958 in California.
Donor: Annunziata Sanguinetti†.
Foundation type: Independent foundation.
Financial data (yr. ended 09/30/14): Assets, $4,964,572 (M); expenditures, $369,523; qualifying distributions, $299,110; giving activities include $279,000 for 16 grants (high: $35,000; low: $5,000).
Purpose and activities: Giving to organizations that benefit children.
Fields of interest: Health; Hospital care; Family services; Child welfare; Adult and child mentoring; People with disabilities.
Limitations: Applications accepted. Giving limited to San Francisco County, CA. No grants to individuals or for building or endowment funds.
Publications: Application guidelines.
Application information:
   Initial approach: Letter
   Copies of proposal: 1
   Deadline(s): June 30
   Board meeting date(s): Nov. or Dec.
Trustee: Wells Fargo Bank, N.A.
EIN: 946073762

9173
Santander Consumer USA Inc. Foundation
(formerly Drive With A Heart Foundation)
8585 N. Stemmons Fwy., Ste. 1100 N.
Dallas, TX 75247-3836

Established in 2004 in Texas.
Donors: Scot A. Foith; Drive Financial Services LP; Santander Consumer Inc.; Blake Bozman; Concorde Group Corp.; Doug Natalie John.
Foundation type: Company-sponsored foundation.
Financial data (yr. ended 12/31/13): Assets, $0 (M); gifts received, $9,500; expenditures, $198,006; qualifying distributions, $191,600; giving activities include $191,600 for 18 grants (high: $72,600; low: $500).
Purpose and activities: The foundation supports organizations involved with education, health, and poverty and awards college scholarships to K-12 and GED students.
Fields of interest: Education; Health; Low-income and poor people.
Type of support: General support; Student aid.
Limitations: Applications not accepted. Giving primarily in Dallas, TX.
Application information: Contributes only to pre-selected organizations and individuals.
Officers: Thomas Dundon, Pres. and C.E.O.; Jason Kulas, Treas.
EIN: 201519185

9174
The Saramco Foundation
P.O. Box 542329
Houston, TX   77254

Donors: James A. Gilligan; Julie J. Gilligan.
Foundation type: Independent foundation.
Financial data (yr. ended 12/31/13): Assets, $3,990,139 (M); gifts received, $550,000; expenditures, $178,000; qualifying distributions, $178,000; giving activities include $175,000 for 7 grants (high: $58,000; low: $7,500).
Fields of interest: Education.
Limitations: Applications not accepted. Giving primarily in TX. No grants to individuals.
Application information: Contributes only to pre-selected organizations.
Officers: James Gilligan, Pres.; Julie Gilligan, Secy.
Trustee: Judith Smith.
EIN: 208358255

9175
Saulsbury Family Foundation, Inc.
P.O. Box 12770
Odessa, TX   79768-2770

Established in 2007 in Texas.
Donor: Saulisbury Electric Co., Ltd.
Foundation type: Independent foundation.
Financial data (yr. ended 12/31/12): Assets, $116,611 (M); gifts received, $18,605; expenditures, $305,620; qualifying distributions, $303,900; giving activities include $303,900 for grants.
Fields of interest: Arts and culture; Performing arts; Education.
Limitations: Applications not accepted. Giving primarily in TX.
Application information: Unsolicited requests for funds not accepted.
Officers and Directors: Amelia Dianne Saulsbury Zugg, Pres. and Director; Mark A. Saulsbury, V.P. and Director; Charles R. Saulsbury, Jr., Secy. and Director; Matthew D. Saulsbury, Treas. and Director.
EIN: 261396903

9176
Saunders Foundation
7500 San Felipe St., Ste. 1070
Houston, TX   77063-1716

Established in 1998 in Texas.
Donors: Frederic M. Saunders; Mission-Heights Management Co. Ltd.
Foundation type: Independent foundation.
Financial data (yr. ended 12/31/13): Assets, $6,024,358 (M); expenditures, $293,955; qualifying distributions, $277,296; giving activities include $208,000 for 33 grants (high: $50,500; low: $100), and $62,535 for 6 grants to individuals (high: $26,180; low: $4,500).
Fields of interest: Higher education; Christianity; Human services.
Type of support: General support; Student aid.
Limitations: Applications not accepted. Giving primarily in TX.
Application information: Unsolicited requests for funds not accepted.
Directors: Meredith S. Mason; Frederic M. Saunders; Gayle D. Saunders; Stuart D. Saunders.
EIN: 760574880

9177
A. I. and Manet Schepps Foundation
(formerly Schepps Charitable Foundation, Inc.)
P. O. Box 539
Bellaire, TX   77402-0539

Established in 1962 in Texas.
Donors: A.I. Schepps; Manet Schepps†.
Foundation type: Independent foundation.
Financial data (yr. ended 12/31/13): Assets, $6,669,729 (M); gifts received, $1,408,860; expenditures, $517,011; qualifying distributions, $467,286; giving activities include $356,181 for 35 grants (high: $260,000; low: $30).
Fields of interest: Education; Nonprofits; Judaism; Human services.
Type of support: General support; Regranting.
Limitations: Applications not accepted. No grants to individuals.
Application information: Contributes only to pre-selected organizations.
Officer: Nancy Brand, Pres.
Directors: Jennifer Brand; Gilda Sprung.
EIN: 746050262

9178
Sonnie Schepps Robinson Foundation
1330 Post Oak Rd.
Houston, TX   77056

Foundation type: Independent foundation.
Financial data (yr. ended 12/31/13): Assets, $6,198,800 (M); expenditures, $238,794; qualifying distributions, $213,938; giving activities include $212,640 for 28 grants (high: $60,000; low: $200).
Fields of interest: Education; Diseases and conditions; Religion; Judaism.
Type of support: Research.
Limitations: Applications not accepted. Giving primarily in TX.
Application information: Unsolicited requests for funds not accepted.

Officers: Cary Robinson, Pres.; Scott Schepps, Secy.; Melissa Schepps, Treas.
EIN: 452074253

9179
The Schissler Foundation
(formerly Schissler Charitable Foundation)
c/o Nancy Lynn Red
P.O. Box 272805
Houston, TX   77277-2805   (713) 626-3890
Contact: Richard P. Schissler, Pres.

Established in 1983 in Texas.
Donors: Nancy R. Schissler; Richard P. Schissler; Chifton Ltd Co.
Foundation type: Independent foundation.
Financial data (yr. ended 03/31/13): Assets, $242,922 (M); gifts received, $200,000; expenditures, $189,663; qualifying distributions, $182,850; giving activities include $181,250 for 14 grants (high: $100,000; low: $500).
Purpose and activities: Giving primarily for education and human services, including a YMCA.
Fields of interest: Opera; Orchestral music; Education; Higher education; Graduate and professional education; Nonprofits; Human services.
Type of support: Regranting.
Limitations: Applications accepted. Giving primarily in Houston, TX. No grants to individuals.
Application information:
  Initial approach: Proposal
  Deadline(s): None
Officers and Trustees: Richard P. Schissler, Pres. and Trustee; Richard P. Schissler III, V.P.; Nancy Lynn Red, Secy.-Treas.; Laura Lee Jenkins; Nancy R. Schissler.
EIN: 760056884

9180
The Phyllis L. Schoener Foundation
3011 Nacogdoches Rd., Bldg. 2
San Antonio, TX   78217-4541

Established in 2004 in Texas.
Donor: Phyllis L. Schoener†.
Foundation type: Independent foundation.
Financial data (yr. ended 06/30/14): Assets, $5,676,706 (M); expenditures, $282,412; qualifying distributions, $275,000; giving activities include $275,000 for 20 grants (high: $35,000; low: $2,500).
Fields of interest: Education; Higher education; Christianity; Protestantism; Judaism.
Type of support: Scholarships.
Limitations: Applications accepted. Giving primarily in San Antonio, TX.
Application information: Application form required.
  Initial approach: Letter
  Deadline(s): Apr. 30
Officers: Jerry A. Pyle, Pres. and Treas.; Caroline P. Lochte, V.P.; Barbara A. Blass, Secy.
EIN: 900197155

9181
Schulte Charitable Foundation
9977 W. Sam Houston Pkwy. N., Ste. 150
Houston, TX   77064-7509

Established in 1994 in Texas.

Donors: Johnie Schulte, Jr.; Ca Rundell; Barbara Schulte; Schulte Enterprises Ltd.
Foundation type: Independent foundation.
Financial data (yr. ended 12/31/13): Assets, $42,744 (M); gifts received, $160,000; expenditures, $164,209; qualifying distributions, $163,246; giving activities include $162,300 for 9 grants (high: $115,500; low: $150).
Purpose and activities: Giving primarily for education, health organizations, children, youth and social services, and to a Baptist church.
Fields of interest: Education; Diseases and conditions; Baptist; Human services; Child welfare.
Type of support: General support.
Limitations: Applications not accepted. Giving primarily in Houston, TX. No grants to individuals.
Application information: Unsolicited requests for funds not accepted.
Officers: Barbara Schulte, V.P. and Secy.-Treas.; Gary Kolkhorst, V.P.; Karen Rosales, Mgr.
EIN: 760455567

9182
The Richard & Enika Schulze Foundation
8150 N. Central Expwy., No. 725
Dallas, TX 75206-1889

Established in 2007 in Texas.
Donors: Richard H. Schulze; Enika Schulze.
Foundation type: Independent foundation.
Financial data (yr. ended 12/31/13): Assets, $7,401,040 (M); gifts received, $465,806; expenditures, $457,493; qualifying distributions, $350,012; giving activities include $350,012 for 5 grants (high: $250,000; low: $1).
Fields of interest: Performing arts; Opera.
Limitations: Applications not accepted. Giving primarily in Dallas, TX. No grants to individuals.
Application information: Contributes only to pre-selected organizations.
Directors: Carl W. Schulze; Enika Schulze; Richard H. Schulze.
EIN: 261614982

9183
Robert J. and Edith K. Schumacher Foundation
777 Main St., No. 3200
Fort Worth, TX 76102-5304

Donors: Robert J. Schumacher; Edith K. Schumacher.
Foundation type: Independent foundation.
Financial data (yr. ended 12/31/13): Assets, $1,630,787 (M); expenditures, $218,311; qualifying distributions, $194,334; giving activities include $194,334 for 3 grants (high: $90,000; low: $51,000).
Fields of interest: Education; Catholicism.
Limitations: Applications not accepted. Giving primarily in NM and TX.
Application information: Unsolicited requests for funds not accepted.
Officers and Directors: Frank Kyle, Pres. and Treas. and Director; Katherine Ann Schumacher Kyle, V.P. and Director; Mary Elizabeth Schumacher Millett, V.P. and Director; William G. Schumacher, V.P. and Director; Leah Gurley, Secy.; Edith K. Schumacher.
EIN: 271346180

9184
Schwab-Rosenhouse Memorial Foundation
c/o Wells Fargo Bank, N.A.
P.O. Box 41629, MAC T7061-021
Austin, TX 78704-9926
E-mail: mnovember@applyists.com; C/o Schwab-rosenhouse Memorial Scholarship, M.D. November, Int'l Scholarship & Tuition Services Inc., 1321 Murfreesboro Rd., Ste 800, Nashville, TN 37217 Tel.: (615) 627-3834

Established in 1997 in California.
Donor: Rosenhouse Family Trust.
Foundation type: Independent foundation.
Financial data (yr. ended 12/31/13): Assets, $6,735,823 (M); expenditures, $453,644; qualifying distributions, $390,575; giving activities include $305,831 for 230 grants to individuals (high: $3,000; low: $500).
Purpose and activities: Awards scholarships to high school students who live in the 4 counties in and around the Sacramento, CA metropolitan area. Students planning to enroll at a college or university, community or an accredited vocational/technical institution located within a 100-mile radius of Sacramento are invited to apply. Variable grants of $1,000 to $3,500 will be awarded. The purpose of the program is to encourage deserving students to pursue their educational career goals by providing funds to continue their studies beyond high school.
Fields of interest: Education.
Type of support: Student aid.
Limitations: Applications accepted. Giving limited to high school seniors residing in the 4 counties in and around Sacramento, CA, including El Dorado, Placer, Sacramento, and Yolo counties and who will enroll at a post secondary institution within a 100-mile radius of Sacramento.
Application information: Application form required.
Initial approach: Completed application form
Deadline(s): Feb.
Trustees: Frank Gumpert; Marvin Kamras, MD; Neil Levy; John Lewis; Alan Rabishaw; Julie Small; Jana Uslan; Linda Van Rees.
EIN: 686136241

9185
SCP Foundation
100 Highland Park Village, Ste. 211
Dallas, TX 75205-2722

Donors: Christine Pitzer; Starr Pitzer.
Foundation type: Independent foundation.
Financial data (yr. ended 12/31/13): Assets, $96,373 (M); gifts received, $501,000; expenditures, $392,465; qualifying distributions, $392,500; giving activities include $392,500 for 8 grants (high: $150,000; low: $20,000).
Fields of interest: Health; Protestantism; Human services.
Limitations: Applications accepted. Giving primarily in Dallas, TX.
Application information: Application form required.
Initial approach: Letter
Deadline(s): None
Officers: Starr L. Pitzer, Chair.; R.L. Bramble, Secy.; Christine H. Pitzer, Treas.
Directors: Chaney Pitzer; Gavin Pitzer.
EIN: 453833676

9186
Sear Family Foundation
4301 County Rd., Ste. 707
Cleburne, TX 76031-7986 (817) 790-5444
Contact: Timothy R.G. Sear, Pres.

Established in 1996 in Texas.
Donors: Judith Sear; Timothy R.G. Sear.
Foundation type: Independent foundation.
Financial data (yr. ended 12/31/13): Assets, $2,544,274 (M); gifts received, $335,000; expenditures, $273,771; qualifying distributions, $271,360; giving activities include $260,166 for 85 grants (high: $69,300; low: $35).
Fields of interest: Arts and culture; Higher education; Hospital care; Diseases and conditions; Eye diseases; Human services.
Type of support: General support; Capital campaigns; Scholarships; Research.
Limitations: Applications accepted. Giving primarily in MA and TX.
Application information:
Initial approach: Proposal
Deadline(s): None
Officers: Timothy R.G. Sear, Pres.; Judith Sear, Secy.-Treas.
Directors: Katherine M. Johnson; Adam J.T. Sear; Charles D. Sear.
EIN: 752673430

9187
Stephen M. Seay Foundation, Inc.
4611 Travis St., Ste. 1409A
Dallas, TX 75205-5581 (214) 855-7955
Contact: Stephen M. Seay, Dir.

Established in 2007 in Texas.
Foundation type: Independent foundation.
Financial data (yr. ended 12/31/12): Assets, $31,483,629 (M); expenditures, $772,344; qualifying distributions, $472,541; giving activities include $279,190 for 20 grants (high: $60,000; low: $1,500), and $122,597 for 8 grants to individuals (high: $36,349; low: $3,875).
Fields of interest: Arts and culture; Education; Human services.
Application information: Application form required.
Initial approach: Contact foundation
Deadline(s): Apr. 1st
Directors: Lee-Ann Graham; Peter K. Lutken III; Stephen M. Seay; David J. Wood.
EIN: 364613275

9188
Serafy Foundation
205 W. Levee St.
Brownsville, TX 78520-5558 (956) 564-5313
Contact: Nicholas T. Serafy Jr., Tr.

Established in 1997 in Texas.
Donors: Nicholas T. Serafy; Jean H. Serafy; Nicholas T. Serafy, Sr.‡; The Barbara Bush Texas Fund for Family Literacy.
Foundation type: Independent foundation.
Financial data (yr. ended 12/31/13): Assets, $9,613,434 (M); expenditures, $758,701; qualifying distributions, $394,896; giving activities include $394,896 for 32 grants (high: $50,000; low: $100).
Fields of interest: Arts and culture; Education; Human services.

Limitations: Applications accepted. Giving primarily in IN and Brownsville, TX.
Application information: Application form required.
Initial approach: Letter
Deadline(s): None
Trustee: Nicholas T. Serafy, Jr.
EIN: 742861035

9189
Seven Cities Foundation
314 S. 11th St.
McAllen, TX   78501-2822
Contact: Charles E. Thompson Jr., Pres.

Established in 2006 in Texas.
Donor: Charles E. Thompson, Jr.
Foundation type: Independent foundation.
Financial data (yr. ended 12/31/13): Assets, $3,295,324 (M); expenditures, $226,891; qualifying distributions, $224,527; giving activities include $224,500 for 41 grants (high: $71,500; low: $1,000).
Fields of interest: Education; National defense; Christianity; Human services.
Limitations: Applications not accepted. Giving primarily in San Antonio, TX.
Application information: Unsolicited requests for funds not accepted.
Officers: Charles E. Thompson, Jr., Pres.; Jonathan Bevil, V.P.; Marla Luce, Secy.
EIN: 320181077

9190
The Sharma Foundation
P.O. Box 802090
Dallas, TX   75380

Established in 2000 in Texas.
Donor: Bianca Sharma.
Foundation type: Independent foundation.
Financial data (yr. ended 12/31/13): Assets, $4,580,416 (M); expenditures, $506,548; qualifying distributions, $236,000; giving activities include $236,000 for 10 grants (high: $100,000; low: $2,500).
Fields of interest: Arts and culture; Philanthropy; Specialty hospital care; Health care clinics; Cancers; Human services; Child welfare.
Limitations: Applications not accepted. Giving primarily in CO, KS, KY, NY and SC. No grants to individuals.
Application information: Contributes only to pre-selected organizations.
Officer: Bianca Sharma, Pres.
Directors: Michael R. Held; Roy Monk.
EIN: 752857275

9191
Shepherds for the Savior
19380 Hwy. 105 W., Ste. 516
Montgomery, TX   77356   (936) 582-7997
Contact: Tracey Magee
Main URL: http://shepherdsforthesavior.com

Established in 2004 in Texas.
Donor: Christ Church of Conroe.
Foundation type: Independent foundation.
Financial data (yr. ended 12/31/14): Assets, $5,563,424 (M); gifts received, $3,570; expenditures, $434,183; qualifying distributions,

$284,167; giving activities include $178,167 for 24 + grants, and $106,000 for 102 grants to individuals (high: $6,000; low: $1,500).
Fields of interest: Wildfires; Christianity; Human services; Child welfare; International development.
Limitations: Applications accepted. Giving primarily in TX.
Publications: Informational brochure; Informational brochure (including application guidelines); Newsletter.
Application information: Application form required.
Initial approach: Mail or Hand Delivered
Deadline(s): Ministry Grant Application: June 15 & Dec. 15, Ministry Education Grant Application: April 1 and Nov. 1, Widow Grant Application and Retired Pastor Grant Applications: June 1 and Dec. 1
Officers and Directors: Becky Thompson, Pres. and Director; Bill Hamlin, V.P.; Ed Bishop, Secy.; Scott Barr, Treas.
Board Members: Bill Garrett; David Johnson; Rhonda Saldivar.
EIN: 200554658

9192
The Sherman Foundation
7502 Shadyvilla Ln.
Houston, TX   77055-5006

Foundation type: Independent foundation.
Financial data (yr. ended 12/31/13): Assets, $8,771,318 (M); expenditures, $282,579; qualifying distributions, $280,129; giving activities include $280,129 for 19 grants (high: $75,000; low: $1,000).
Fields of interest: Domesticated animals; Diseases and conditions; Religion; People with vision impairments.
Type of support: General support; Research.
Limitations: Applications not accepted. Giving primarily in Houston, TX. No grants to individuals.
Application information: Unsolicited requests for funds not accepted.
Trustee: Jim Sherman.
EIN: 912136222

9193
The Shiloff Family Foundation
c/o Robert M. Shiloff
5709 Burning Tree Dr.
El Paso, TX   79912-4105

Established in 1994 in Texas.
Donors: Robert M. Shiloff; Sara P. Shiloff.
Foundation type: Independent foundation.
Financial data (yr. ended 12/31/14): Assets, $4,026,095; expenditures, $216,831; qualifying distributions, $205,000.
Purpose and activities: Giving primarily for the arts, wildlife preservation, and human services.
Fields of interest: Arts and culture; Education; Zoos; Human services.
Limitations: Applications not accepted. Giving primarily in the El Paso, TX area. No grants to individuals.
Application information: Unsolicited requests for funds not accepted.
Officers and Directors: Robert M. Shiloff, Pres. and Director; Robyn Shiloff Kelly, V.P.; Bryan Shiloff,

V.P.; Stuart P. Shiloff, V.P.; Sara P. Shiloff, Secy.-Treas. and Director.
EIN: 742691141

9194
SHT Foundation
16433 Jersey Hollow Dr.
Jersey Village, TX   77040-1133

Foundation type: Independent foundation.
Financial data (yr. ended 12/31/14): Assets, $949,409; gifts received, $700,000; expenditures, $200,069; qualifying distributions, $200,000.
Fields of interest: Education.
Limitations: Applications not accepted.
Application information: Unsolicited requests for funds not accepted.
Officers: Rajani K. Shah, Pres. and Treas.; Darshana Shah, V.P. and Secy.
EIN: 273648426

9195
Yvonne H. Simard Foundation
6153 Lemans Dr.
Corpus Christi, TX   78414-6100

Established in 2005 in Texas.
Foundation type: Independent foundation.
Financial data (yr. ended 12/31/14): Assets, $6,448,935; expenditures, $365,762; qualifying distributions, $329,581.
Fields of interest: Diabetes; Storms; Christianity; Human services.
Type of support: Research.
Limitations: Applications accepted. Giving primarily in south TX.
Application information:
Initial approach: Proposal
Copies of proposal: 1
Deadline(s): Nov. 1
Board meeting date(s): Dec. 1
Final notification: On or before Dec. 31
Officer: Willie J. Kosarek, Pres.
Directors: Connie V. Kosarek; Jay A. Kosarek; Willie J. Kosarek.
EIN: 203411622

9196
Simpson-Omohundro Foundation
(also known as Omohundro Educational Trust)
P.O. Box 7343
Beaumont, TX   77726-7343

Established in 1988 in Texas.
Donors: Helen Omohundro†; Ed Omohundro†.
Foundation type: Independent foundation.
Financial data (yr. ended 12/31/13): Assets, $3,526,236 (M); expenditures, $191,870; qualifying distributions, $151,934; giving activities include $148,000 for 15 grants (high: $74,000; low: $2,000).
Purpose and activities: Giving limited to qualified charities that provide for the health and educational needs of school children in Flora, MS, or Beaumont, TX.
Fields of interest: Arts and culture; Education; Health; Religion; Youth services.
Type of support: General support.

Limitations: Applications not accepted. Giving limited to Flora, MS, and Beaumont, TX. No grants to individuals.
Application information: Unsolicited requests for funds not accepted.
Trustees: Eva Connell; Paul Parker; Peter Boyd Wells III.
EIN: 760260102

9197
M. E. Singleton Scholarship Trust
P.O. Box 717
Waxahachie, TX 75168-0717

Donors: Jeannette Singleton Cloyd; George H. Singleton; Citizens National Bank; Martha Singleton†; Robin Cloyd.
Foundation type: Independent foundation.
Financial data (yr. ended 12/31/13): Assets, $3,708,131 (M); gifts received, $94,674; expenditures, $205,880; qualifying distributions, $198,000; giving activities include $198,000 for 119 grants to individuals (high: $3,000; low: $1,000).
Fields of interest: Education.
Type of support: Student aid.
Limitations: Applications not accepted. Giving primarily in TX.
Application information: Unsolicited requests for funds not accepted.
Trustees: Robin Cloyd; Terry Gibson; Joe Langley; Pat Merrill; Jennifer Rash; George H. Singleton; Mark Singleton.
EIN: 756037399

9198
SK Foundation
2001 Kirby Dr., Ste. 510
Houston, TX 77019-6046

Established in 1996 in Texas.
Foundation type: Independent foundation.
Financial data (yr. ended 12/31/14): Assets, $6,219,664 (M); expenditures, $325,288; qualifying distributions, $305,300; giving activities include $304,000 for 77 grants (high: $22,000; low: $100).
Fields of interest: Education; Domesticated animals; Religion.
Limitations: Applications not accepted. Giving primarily in TX. No grants to individuals.
Application information: Unsolicited requests for funds not accepted.
Officers: W.A. Stockard, Jr., Pres.; Sue Stockard Schaefer, V.P.; Jan Stockard Cato, Secy.-Treas.
EIN: 760500154

9199
The Sklar Family Foundation
6344 Wakeforest
Houston, TX 77005-3454

Established in 2004 in Texas.
Donors: Barbara S. Sklar; Louis S. Sklar.
Foundation type: Independent foundation.
Financial data (yr. ended 12/31/13): Assets, $1,851,744 (M); gifts received, $2,290; expenditures, $178,019; qualifying distributions, $168,650; giving activities include $168,650 for 2 + grants (high: $62,750; low: $4,750).

Fields of interest: Education; Community and economic development; Human services.
Limitations: Applications not accepted.
Application information: Unsolicited requests for funds not accepted.
Officers and Directors: Barbara S. Sklar, Pres. and Director; Louis S. Sklar, Secy. and Director; Suzanne Sklar McCarthy; Michael Alan Sklar.
EIN: 200098248

9200
The Ted and Shannon Skokos Foundation
P.O. Box 670219
Dallas, TX 75367-0219
Main URL: http://www.skokosfoundation.com

Donors: Cartier; Shannon B. Skokos; Theodore C. Skokos.
Foundation type: Independent foundation.
Financial data (yr. ended 12/31/13): Assets, $15,784,059 (M); expenditures, $515,862; qualifying distributions, $163,360; giving activities include $157,500 for 7 grants (high: $50,000; low: $2,500).
Purpose and activities: Giving for the advancement of education, the arts, science, and religion.
Fields of interest: Performing arts; Protestantism; Food aid.
Limitations: Applications accepted. Giving primarily in Dallas, TX.
Application information:
  Initial approach: Letter
  Deadline(s): None
Officers and Directors: Theodore C. Skokos, Pres. and Director; Mary Ellen VanGilder, Secy. and Director; Shannon B. Skokos, Treas. and Director.
EIN: 262190216

9201
Herman & Patsy Smith Charitable Foundation
3700 Cheek Sparger Rd., Ste.180
Bedford, TX 76021-3058

Established in 1996 in Texas.
Donor: Patsy R. Smith.
Foundation type: Independent foundation.
Financial data (yr. ended 12/31/14): Assets, $4,150,079; expenditures, $239,939; qualifying distributions, $236,990.
Fields of interest: Higher education; Housing development; Protestantism.
Type of support: Capital and infrastructure; Scholarships; General support.
Limitations: Applications accepted. Giving primarily in Washington, DC, and TX, with some emphasis on Bedford and Dallas. No grants to individuals.
Application information: Application form required.
  Initial approach: Request application form
  Deadline(s): June 1 or Nov. 1
Officers and Directors: Patsy R. Smith, Pres. and Treas. and Director; Madelyn B. Ivey, V.P. and Director; Linda L. Hamilton.
EIN: 752610418

9202
Ray and June Smith Charitable Foundation
355 N. Post Oak Ln. 834
Houston, TX 77024-5958

Donor: Raymond K. Smith†.
Foundation type: Independent foundation.
Financial data (yr. ended 12/31/13): Assets, $8,408,241 (M); expenditures, $317,673; qualifying distributions, $245,700; giving activities include $235,000 for 14 grants (high: $125,000; low: $5,000).
Fields of interest: Arts and culture; Religion; Protestantism; Human services.
Type of support: General support.
Limitations: Applications not accepted. Giving primarily in TX.
Application information: Unsolicited requests for funds not accepted.
Trustees: Mike Gaus; Carol Haney.
EIN: 264442351

9203
The Will Smith Charitable Foundation
4242 Broadway St., Apt. 1503
San Antonio, TX 78209-6469 (210) 559-4044
Main URL: http://www.willsmithfoundation.org/

Established in 2007 in Texas.
Donor: B. Naylor Morton.
Foundation type: Independent foundation.
Financial data (yr. ended 12/31/13): Assets, $1,195,944 (M); gifts received, $774,696; expenditures, $220,730; qualifying distributions, $174,924; giving activities include $174,924 for 18 grants (high: $75,000; low: $1,365).
Purpose and activities: The foundation's mission is to provide the means of giving positive life experiences to children through art, music and acts of compassion, and to assist in bringing emergency medical services to areas in need.
Fields of interest: Philanthropy; Community and economic development; Human services.
International interests: Botswana; Mexico; Zambia.
Limitations: Applications accepted. Giving primarily in HI and TX.
Application information:
  Initial approach: Letter
  Deadline(s): None
Officers: Susan N.M. Moulton, Pres.; Charles Naylor Moulton, V.P.; Theresa Brandon, Secy.-Treas.
EIN: 371545757

9204
Pat & Emmitt Smith Charities
(also known as Emmitt Smith Charities)
(formerly Emmitt Smith Charities, Inc.)
c/o Tolleson Wealth Management
5500 Preston Rd.
Dallas, TX 75205-2699 (214) 252-3250
Contact: Emmitt J. Smith III, V.P.
E-mail: info@patandemmittsmithcharities.org; Main URL: https://smithcharities.wordpress.com
Facebook: https://www.facebook.com/SmithCharities
RSS feed: https://smithcharities.wordpress.com/feed
Twitter: http://twitter.com/SmithCharities

Established in 2004 in Texas.
Donors: Emmitt J. Smith III; Walt Brown; Clint Herzog; Breah Herzog; David Weinreb; Karen Weinreb.
Foundation type: Independent foundation.
Financial data (yr. ended 09/30/13): Assets, $0 (M); gifts received, $991,328; expenditures,

$1,058,350; qualifying distributions, $969,455; giving activities include $378,336 for 50 grants (high: $113,580; low: $200).

Purpose and activities: Giving primarily for unique educational experiences and enrichment opportunities for underserved children.

Fields of interest: Education; Human services; Youth development; Children; Low-income and poor people.

Limitations: Applications accepted. Giving primarily in North TX.

Application information:

Initial approach: Letter or Telephone call

Deadline(s): None

Officers: Patricia A. Smith, Pres.; Emmitt J. Smith III, V.P.; Marvin E. Blum, Secy.-Treas.

EIN: 201895778

9205
Vivian L. Smith Foundation for Neurological Research

(formerly Vivian L. Smith Foundation for Restorative Neurology)

1900 W. Loop S., Ste. 1050

Houston, TX 77027-3295

Contact: Amy M. Meckel

Established in 1981 in Texas.

Donor: Vivian L. Smith†.

Foundation type: Independent foundation.

Financial data (yr. ended 06/30/13): Assets, $10,783,147 (M); expenditures, $270,859; qualifying distributions, $198,360; giving activities include $198,360 for grants.

Purpose and activities: Giving primarily for restorative neurology, clinical activities and scientific research in the areas of medicine which diagnose, treat and seek improvements in the quality of people who are afflicted with injury and disease related to the brain, spinal cord and nervous system.

Fields of interest: Biomedicine; Neurology; Diseases and conditions.

Type of support: Research; Research and evaluation.

Limitations: Giving primarily in Houston, TX.

Application information:

Initial approach: Proposal

Copies of proposal: 1

Deadline(s): None

Board meeting date(s): Varies

Officers and Trustees: Steven H. Gerdes, Pres. and Trustee; Dee S. Osborne, V.P.; Suzanne R. Benson, Secy.-Treas. and Trustee; Cynthia Adkins; Dr. Guy Clifton; Sandra Smith Dompier; Dr. Brent Masel.

EIN: 742139770

9206
James C. & Norma I. Smith Foundation

P.O. Box 190369

Dallas, TX 75219-0369

Donors: James C. and Norma I. Smith Foundation; Gartner, Inc.; Norma I. Smith; James C. Smith.

Foundation type: Operating foundation.

Financial data (yr. ended 11/30/13): Assets, $13,722,573 (M); gifts received, $1,020,000; expenditures, $357,265; qualifying distributions, $357,245; giving activities include $355,000 for 2 grants (high: $350,000; low: $5,000).

Fields of interest: Arts and culture; Health; Health care clinics.

Type of support: General support.

Limitations: Applications not accepted. Giving in the U.S., primarily in AZ. No grants to individuals.

Application information: Contributes only to pre-selected organizations.

Officers and Directors: James C. Smith, Pres. and Director; Norma I. Smith, Treas. and Director; Joseph E. Witters.

EIN: 710938986

9207
Julia and Albert Smith Foundation

c/o Inwood Mgmt., LP

7660 Woodway Dr., Ste. 595

Houston, TX 77063-1528

Established in 1986 in Texas.

Donors: Albert J. Smith III; Gwendolyn Smith; Albert J. Smith, Jr.; Julia C. Smith.

Foundation type: Independent foundation.

Financial data (yr. ended 11/30/13): Assets, $6,222,210 (M); expenditures, $341,052; qualifying distributions, $291,466; giving activities include $270,094 for 16 grants (high: $100,000; low: $500).

Fields of interest: Arts and culture; Elementary and secondary education; Higher education; Diseases and conditions; Religion; Christianity; Human services; Women's services; Females.

Type of support: General support; Program development; Fellowships; Scholarships; Research; Research and evaluation.

Limitations: Applications not accepted. Giving primarily in Houston, TX. No grants to individuals.

Application information: Unsolicited requests for funds not accepted.

Officers: Julia C. Smith, Pres.; Albert J. Smith, Jr., Secy.-Treas.

Directors: Julia Anne Smith Rawson; Albert J. Smith III; William C. Smith.

Number of staff: 1 part-time professional.

EIN: 760207247

9208
Soonae Foundation, Inc.

(formerly Sparrows' Home Foundation, Inc.)

4303 Innovation Loop

Marble Falls, TX 78654-9792 (830) 798-5446

Established in 2007 in Texas.

Donors: National Christian Foundation; Gibraltar Material Distribution, LP; Gibraltar Cable Barrier Systems, LP; Foundation Fence, Inc.

Foundation type: Operating foundation.

Financial data (yr. ended 12/31/13): Assets, $6,615,196 (M); gifts received, $406,100; expenditures, $883,449; qualifying distributions, $854,437; giving activities include $223,600 for 7 grants (high: $175,000; low: $1,600).

Purpose and activities: The foundation supports programs designed to alleviate spiritual, physical, and economic suffering for orphans and widows in distress.

Fields of interest: Education; Christianity; Human services; Adoption; Children; Low-income and poor people.

International interests: Asia; North Korea.

Type of support: General support; Program development; Sponsorships.

Limitations: Applications accepted. Giving primarily in CA, CO, NE, TX, Asia, and North Korea. No grants to individuals.

Application information: Unsolicited applications for general funding are not accepted. Application form required.

Initial approach: Download application form and mail to foundation for Adoption Fund

Deadline(s): None for Adoption Fund

Officers: William H. Neusch, Pres.; Agnes Neusch, V.P. and Secy.; Regina Ahn, Genl. Counsel; Sarah Neusch, Prog. Coord.

EIN: 261571372

9209
South Plains Foundation

511 Ave. K

Lubbock, TX 79408-1800 (806) 747-9009

Contact: Sue Hudson, Exec. Dir.

FAX: (806) 762-8622; E-mail: sueh24@gmail.com;

Main URL: http://www.southplainsfoundation.com

Established in 1989 in Texas.

Foundation type: Independent foundation.

Financial data (yr. ended 06/30/13): Assets, $5,099,421 (M); expenditures, $286,422; qualifying distributions, $203,535; giving activities include $203,535 for grants.

Purpose and activities: Giving primarily for innovative programs providing effective health care services and in-service training in schools, institutions, and agencies in west Texas; giving also for a research grant program which encourages medical and behavioral science research focused on health care.

Fields of interest: University education; Medical education; Adult education; Health; Rehabilitation; Mental health care; Diseases and conditions; Kidney diseases; Food banks; Food delivery.

Type of support: Program development; Grants to individuals; Research; Matching grants; Seed money; Scholarships; Research and evaluation.

Limitations: Applications accepted. Giving limited to the Lubbock, TX, area.

Application information: See foundation website for complete application guidelines. Application form required.

Initial approach: Proposal

Deadline(s): Varies

Officers: Max Ince, Pres.; Sandy Ogletree, V.P.; Jim Moore, Secy.; Sue Hudson, Exec. Dir.

Board Member: Bill Miller.

Number of staff: 1 part-time professional.

EIN: 752294100

9210
South Texas Charitable Foundation

P.O. Box 2549

Victoria, TX 77902-2549 (361) 573-4383

Contact: Thomas L. Keller, Secy.-Treas.

Established in 1981 in Texas.

Donor: Maude O'Connor Williams.

Foundation type: Independent foundation.

Financial data (yr. ended 12/31/13): Assets, $9,277,968 (L); expenditures, $317,598; qualifying distributions, $294,770; giving activities include $294,770 for 18 grants (high: $106,020; low: $1,250).

Purpose and activities: Giving primarily for the arts, education, and social services.

Fields of interest: Arts and culture; Education; Catholicism; Human services; Food aid; Child welfare; Senior services.
Limitations: Applications accepted. Giving primarily in NY and TX. No grants to individuals.
Application information: Application form required.
  Initial approach: Proposal
  Deadline(s): None
Officers: Ann W. Harithas, Pres.; Molly O. Kemp, V.P.; Thomas L. Keller, Secy.-Treas.
EIN: 742148107

9211
Ruth Parr Sparks Foundation
1220 N. Texas Blvd., Ste. 5
Alice, TX 78332-4828
Contact: David Leon McNinch, Chair.
Application address: P.O. Box 728, Alice, TX 78333-0728

Established in 1998 in Texas.
Donor: Ruth Sparks†.
Foundation type: Operating foundation.
Financial data (yr. ended 12/31/13): Assets, $5,015,913 (M); expenditures, $326,454; qualifying distributions, $232,178; giving activities include $215,000 for 16 grants (high: $56,500; low: $1,500).
Purpose and activities: Giving primarily for education, youth services, and for community and civic organizations.
Fields of interest: Education; Undergraduate education; Foundations; Youth development.
Type of support: General support; Scholarships; Individual development.
Limitations: Applications not accepted. Giving limited to TX.
Application information: Contributes only to pre-selected organizations.
Officers: David Leon McNinch, Chair.; Hilda Resendez, Secy.
Directors: Olga Galindo; Susan Swinney.
EIN: 742844494

9212
The Sparrow Foundation
5601 Democracy Dr., Ste. 300
Plano, TX 75024-3674

Established in 2004 in Texas.
Donor: Jean Ann Brock.
Foundation type: Independent foundation.
Financial data (yr. ended 12/31/13): Assets, $0 (M); gifts received, $500,000; expenditures, $250,175; qualifying distributions, $250,000; giving activities include $250,000 for 1 grant.
Fields of interest: Education.
Limitations: Applications not accepted. Giving primarily in Dallas, TX. No grants to individuals.
Application information: Unsolicited request for funds not accepted.
Officer and Directors: Jean Ann Brock, Pres. and Director; Rodger M. Sanders.
EIN: 200253717

9213
The Stanzel Family Foundation, Inc.
P.O. Box 6
Schulenburg, TX 78956-0006
Application address: c/o Robert R. Stanzel, Pres., 311 Baumgarten St., Schulenberg, TX 78956-2101, tel.: (979) 743-6559

Established in 1989 in Texas.
Donors: Joseph Stanzel†; Victor Stanzel†.
Foundation type: Independent foundation.
Financial data (yr. ended 07/31/13): Assets, $17,727,999 (M); gifts received, $219,893; expenditures, $1,032,331; qualifying distributions, $799,619; giving activities include $168,770 for 11 grants (high: $91,000; low: $100), and $101,000 for 56 grants to individuals (high: $2,000; low: $1,000).
Purpose and activities: Scholarships only to graduating high school seniors who reside within a 30-mile radius of Schulenburg or Weimar independent school districts in TX, and who plan to enroll at any institution of higher education after graduation; other community programs are restricted to those that provide educational and medical benefits to residents of the Schulenberg and Weimar communities.
Fields of interest: Education; Human services.
Type of support: Research; Student aid; Individual development.
Limitations: Giving limited to Schulenburg and Weimar, TX.
Application information: Application form required.
  Deadline(s): Mar. 31
  Board meeting date(s): Jan., Mar., May, July, Sept. and Nov.
Officers: Robert R. Stanzel, Pres.; Theodore E. Stanzel, V.P.; Helen Niesner, Secy.; Ginger Bosl, Treas.
Directors: Melinda Barneycastle; Tonia Livingston.
EIN: 742579827

9214
The Dixie Starnes Wenger Foundation
(formerly The Dixie and Cedric Wenger 1994 Foundation)
8610 N. New Braunfels Ave., Ste. 101
San Antonio, TX 78217-6359 (210) 829-1300
Contact: David J. Doherty, Tr.
E-mail address for David J. Doherty: david@adkf.com

Established in 1994 in Texas.
Donor: Olga Starnes Kuhn Wenger.
Foundation type: Independent foundation.
Financial data (yr. ended 12/31/12): Assets, $6,229,305 (M); expenditures, $432,250; qualifying distributions, $320,000; giving activities include $320,000 for grants.
Fields of interest: Protestantism; Human services; Child welfare.
Limitations: Applications accepted. Giving primarily in TX. No grants to individuals.
Application information: Application form required.
  Initial approach: Request application form
  Deadline(s): May 31
  Board meeting date(s): June and Nov.
Officers: Laura Garrett, Mgr.; Gloria S. Lamascus, Mgr.; Sue C. Ortman, Mgr.
Trustee: David J. Doherty.
EIN: 742719361

9215
The Staubach Family Foundation
4916 Gulfstream Dr.
Dallas, TX 75244-7632 (972) 386-6237
Contact: Amy S. Mentgen, Secy.-Treas.

Established in 1986 in Texas.
Donors: Roger T. Staubach; Phillips Brokerage; Balloons Over Texas; Marsh & McLennan; Holloway-Staubach Co.; Harold Simmons.
Foundation type: Independent foundation.
Financial data (yr. ended 12/31/12): Assets, $2,837,576 (M); gifts received, $1,000,000; expenditures, $339,470; qualifying distributions, $263,790; giving activities include $263,790 for grants.
Fields of interest: Arts and culture; Education; Undergraduate education; Nonprofits; Diseases and conditions; Camps; Basketball; Human services; Child welfare.
Type of support: Regranting.
Limitations: Applications accepted. Giving primarily in OH and Dallas, TX. No grants to individuals.
Application information:
  Initial approach: Letter
  Deadline(s): None
Officers and Trustees: Roger T. Staubach, Pres. and Trustee; Marianne H. Staubach, V.P. and Trustee; Amy S. Mentgen, Secy.-Treas.; Stephanie Staubach Phillips.
EIN: 752123195

9216
Don and Trudy Steen Charitable Foundation
c/o William Miranda, CPA
5715 Thames Ct.
Dallas, TX 75252-5032

Donors: Donald E. Steen; Trudy K. Steen.
Foundation type: Independent foundation.
Financial data (yr. ended 12/31/13): Assets, $787,410 (M); gifts received, $302,600; expenditures, $381,125; qualifying distributions, $380,000; giving activities include $380,000 for 10 grants (high: $125,000; low: $1,500).
Fields of interest: Diseases and conditions; Public affairs; Community and economic development.
Type of support: Research.
Limitations: Applications not accepted.
Application information: Unsolicited requests for funds not accepted.
Officers and Directors: Donald E. Steen, Pres. and Director; Trudy K. Steen, Secy.-Treas. and Director.
EIN: 208198307

9217
Stephens Family Foundation
P.O. Box 2249
Wichita Falls, TX 76307-2249
Application address: c/o Fred Stephens, Pres., 811 6th St., Wichita Falls, TX 76301, tel.: (940) 723-2166

Established in 2005 in Texas.
Donors: Fred Stephens 2005 Trust; Fred Stephens; Fred Stephens 2005 Charitable Lead Annuity Trust.
Foundation type: Independent foundation.
Financial data (yr. ended 12/31/13): Assets, $290,550 (M); expenditures, $202,143; qualifying distributions, $192,499; giving activities include

$190,000 for 9 grants (high: $100,000; low: $10,000).

Fields of interest: Health; Religion.

Type of support: General support.

Limitations: Applications accepted. Giving primarily in Wichita Falls, TX.

Application information: Application form required.
Initial approach: Request Application form
Deadline(s): None

Officers and Directors: Fred Stephens, Pres. and Director; Thomas P. Stephens, V.P. and Secy. and Director; Susan S. Geyer; Katherine S. Smethie.

EIN: 202784814

9218
Leonard and Shirley Sterling Charitable Foundation
c/o Tax Dept., T-8
P.O. Box 2950
San Antonio, TX 78299-2950

Established in 2008 in Texas.

Donor: Shirley Sterling†.

Foundation type: Independent foundation.

Financial data (yr. ended 06/30/13): Assets, $5,718,549 (M); expenditures, $285,399; qualifying distributions, $251,625; giving activities include $219,950 for 13 grants (high: $23,153; low: $11,576).

Fields of interest: Education; University education; Health; Diseases and conditions.

Limitations: Applications not accepted. Giving primarily in FL and TX.

Application information: Unsolicited requests for funds not accepted.

Trustees: Marilynn Gerson; Hershel Oliff; Frost Bank.

EIN: 263746420

9219
Sterling Family Foundation
P.O. Box 1837
Bellaire, TX 77402-1837 (713) 659-6551
Contact: Daniel Dominguez, Tr.; Jay Epstein, Tr.

Established in 2003 in Texas.

Donor: Lillie Sterling†.

Foundation type: Independent foundation.

Financial data (yr. ended 12/31/13): Assets, $7,316,362 (M); expenditures, $579,358; qualifying distributions, $421,500; giving activities include $421,500 for 20 grants (high: $195,000; low: $500).

Fields of interest: Education; Nonprofits; Diseases and conditions; Christianity; Human services.

Type of support: Regranting.

Limitations: Applications accepted. Giving primarily in TX.

Application information: Application form required.
Initial approach: Letter
Deadline(s): None

Trustees: Daniel Dominguez; Jay A. Epstein.

EIN: 046995246

9220
Keith & Mattie Stevenson Foundation
c/o Sequent Asset Management
952 Echo Ln., Ste. 115
Houston, TX 77024-2828 (713) 467-0008

Established in 1992 in Texas.

Donors: Keith T. Stevenson; Mattie Stevenson.

Foundation type: Independent foundation.

Financial data (yr. ended 12/31/14): Assets, $4,129,878; expenditures, $250,633; qualifying distributions, $225,747.

Fields of interest: Higher education; Environment; Wildlife biodiversity; Animal welfare; Veterinary medicine; Nonprofits; Health; Neurology; Child welfare.

Type of support: General support; Regranting.

Limitations: Applications accepted. Giving primarily in TX. No grants to individuals.

Application information:
Initial approach: Proposal
Deadline(s): None

Trustees: Keith T. Stevenson; Mattie Stevenson.

EIN: 760366599

9221
The Marlene and J.O. Stewart, Jr. Foundation
124 W. Castellano, Ste. 100
El Paso, TX 79912-6139 (915) 833-6488
Contact: Ron F. Acton, Pres. and Dir.

Established in 2000 in Texas.

Donors: Marlene Stewart; James O. Stewart, Jr.

Foundation type: Independent foundation.

Financial data (yr. ended 12/31/13): Assets, $1,053,516 (M); expenditures, $361,494; qualifying distributions, $283,717; giving activities include $283,717 for 43 grants (high: $39,647; low: $100).

Purpose and activities: Giving primarily for Christian agencies and churches.

Fields of interest: Arts and culture; Higher education; Diseases and conditions; Christianity; Human services; International relations.

Limitations: Applications accepted. Giving primarily in TX. No grants to individuals.

Application information: Application form required.
Initial approach: Letter
Copies of proposal: 1
Deadline(s): None
Board meeting date(s): Annually, in Jan, and thereafter as needed

Officers and Directors: Ron F. Acton, Pres. and Director; Myron Brown, V.P. and Director; James O. Stewart, Jr., V.P. and Director; James O. Stewart III, V.P. and Director; Marlene Stewart, V.P. and Director.

EIN: 742958268

9222
The Stoller Foundation
9600 Long Point Rd., Ste. 201
Houston, TX 77055-4200
Contact: Jonathan Schinzler
E-mail: jschinzler@stollerfoundation.org

Established in 2006 in Texas.

Donor: Jerry H. Stoller.

Foundation type: Independent foundation.

Financial data (yr. ended 12/31/13): Assets, $5,149,426 (M); gifts received, $3,427,609; expenditures, $903,627; qualifying distributions, $411,563; giving activities include $302,671 for 16 grants (high: $125,000; low: $700).

Fields of interest: Christianity.

Limitations: Applications accepted. Giving primarily in TX. No grants to individuals.

Application information:
Initial approach: Letter of inquiry

Officers and Directors: Jerry H. Stoller, Chair. and Director; Sandra Lund-Diaz, Exec. Dir.

Trustees: Karen White; Hank Winfield.

EIN: 204729632

9223
Storehouse Foundation
(formerly FSH Properties Foundation)
3794-C W. Hwy. 67
Glen Rose, TX 76043-5854

Established in 2001 in Texas.

Donors: Hill Ranch, Ltd.; Bobby Hill; Ounita Hill†.

Foundation type: Independent foundation.

Financial data (yr. ended 12/31/13): Assets, $1,076,482 (M); expenditures, $166,503; qualifying distributions, $165,500; giving activities include $165,500 for 17 grants (high: $32,500; low: $1,000).

Fields of interest: Diseases and conditions; Christianity; Sports and recreation.

Type of support: General support; Research.

Limitations: Applications not accepted. Giving primarily in TX, with some emphasis on North TX. No grants to individuals.

Application information: Unsolicited requests for funds not accepted.

Directors: B.F. Hill; Dottie Hill; Amy Hill Kozelsky.

EIN: 752907765

9224
The Linda & Jerry Strickland Family Foundation
3019 Sunset Blvd.
Houston, TX 77005-2149

Established in 2007 in Texas.

Donors: Jerry Strickland; Linda Strickland.

Foundation type: Independent foundation.

Financial data (yr. ended 09/30/13): Assets, $3,983,540 (M); gifts received, $655,835; expenditures, $390,184; qualifying distributions, $386,181; giving activities include $385,538 for 33 grants (high: $50,000; low: $1,000).

Fields of interest: Addiction services; Children; Adolescents; People with disabilities; Military personnel.

Type of support: Advocacy.

Limitations: Applications not accepted. Giving primarily in GA and TX. No grants to individuals.

Application information: Contributes only to pre-selected organizations.

Officers: Jerry Strickland, Pres.; Linda Strickland, V.P.

Directors: Lisa Baker; Terri Gainor; Steve Rothbauer; Carter Strickland; Patia Strickland; Whitney Strickland.

EIN: 208102548

9225
Sure Foundation Inc
P.O. Box 3487
Pasadena, TX 77501-3487
Contact: John H. Moon Sr., Pres. and Dir.

Established in 1987 in Texas.

Donors: John H. Moon, Sr.; Moon Credit Corp.
Foundation type: Independent foundation.
Financial data (yr. ended 12/31/13): Assets, $1,734,041 (M); expenditures, $215,838; qualifying distributions, $214,527; giving activities include $214,527 for 10 grants (high: $100,000; low: $250).
Fields of interest: Religion; Human services; Youth development.
Limitations: Applications accepted. Giving primarily in Baytown, TX. No grants to individuals.
Application information: Application form required.
  Initial approach: Proposal
  Deadline(s): None
  Final notification: Within 3 months
Officer and Directors: John H. Moon, Sr., Pres. and Director; A. Rose Moon; John H. Moon, Jr.
EIN: 760219600

9226
Mark B. Sutton Family Foundation
4433 River Garden Trail
Austin, TX 78746-2016

Established in 2004 in Texas.
Donors: Dayna Sutton; Mark Sutton.
Foundation type: Independent foundation.
Financial data (yr. ended 12/31/13): Assets, $188,753 (M); gifts received, $457,493; expenditures, $334,610; qualifying distributions, $330,000; giving activities include $330,000 for 3 grants (high: $304,000; low: $1,000).
Fields of interest: Education; Religion; Human services.
Limitations: Applications not accepted. Giving primarily in AR, IN, and TX. No grants to individuals.
Application information: Contributes only to pre-selected organizations.
Trustees: Kent Anderson; Dayna Sutton; Mark B. Sutton.
EIN: 300245632

9227
Ralph & Eileen Swett Foundation
2802 Flintrock Trace, Ste. B101
Austin, TX 78738-1743

Established in 1999 in Nevada.
Donors: Ralph Swett; Eileen Swett.
Foundation type: Independent foundation.
Financial data (yr. ended 05/31/14): Assets, $1,799,561 (M); expenditures, $410,450; qualifying distributions, $258,588; giving activities include $230,066 for 17 grants (high: $50,000; low: $10).
Purpose and activities: The foundation's mission is to make a positive difference in the lives of individuals. It has identified: 1) the assistance of orphaned children including the promotion of their adoption, and 2) intervention in the lives of troubled youths as two areas of interest to which it expects to direct a portion of its funding each year. Funding, however, is by no means limited to these areas.
Fields of interest: Religion; Human services; Adoption; Children.
Limitations: Applications not accepted. Giving primarily in CA, FL, IL, MO, OH, and TX. No grants to individuals.
Application information: Contributes only to pre-selected organizations.
Officer: Robin Swett Wooten, Pres.

Directors: Eileen Swett; Jeffrey Swett; Michael Swett; Ralph Swett; Timothy Swett.
EIN: 742940596

9228
Tabani Family Foundation
16600 Dallas Pkwy., Ste. 300
Dallas, TX 75248-2608

Established in 2007 in Texas.
Donor: Tabani Group, Inc.
Foundation type: Independent foundation.
Financial data (yr. ended 12/31/13): Assets, $3,085,840 (M); gifts received, $1,000,000; expenditures, $290,028.
Purpose and activities: Giviing primarily to Islamic organizations.
Fields of interest: Health; Religion; Human services.
Limitations: Applications not accepted. Giving primarily in TX. No grants to individuals.
Application information: Unsolicited requests for funds not accepted.
Officers: Zaffar S. Tabani, Chair. and Pres.; Tahira B. Tabani, V.P. and Secy.; Aliya Khatri, V.P. and Treas.
EIN: 208058783

9229
Taub Foundation
Texan Bldg.
333 W. Loop N., 4th Fl.
Houston, TX 77024-7776

Established in 1953 in Texas.
Donors: Henry J.N. Taub; H. Ben Taub; Neurological Research Foundation.
Foundation type: Independent foundation.
Financial data (yr. ended 06/30/14): Assets, $6,365,815 (M); gifts received, $80,000; expenditures, $454,182; qualifying distributions, $417,600; giving activities include $417,600 for 17 grants (high: $180,000; low: $250).
Purpose and activities: Giving primarily for health, education, the arts, and religious causes.
Fields of interest: Arts and culture; Education; Medical education; Hospital care; Diseases and conditions; Christianity; Judaism; Human services; Child welfare.
Limitations: Applications not accepted. Giving primarily in TX. No grants to individuals.
Application information: Contributes only to pre-selected organizations.
Officers: Henry J.N. Taub II, Pres.; Marcy E. Taub, V.P.
Trustee: Gail Hendrix.
EIN: 746060216

9230
Tennessee Titans Foundation
P.O. Box 844
Houston, TX 77001-0844
Contact: K.S. Adams Jr., Pres.
Main URL: http://www.titansonline.com/community/in-the-community.html

Established in 1999 in Tennessee.
Donors: Tennessee Football, Inc.; K.S. Adams, Jr.; Garth Brooks Teammates for Kids Foundation; Handback Group; Purities Dairies; Carol Ducey;

Metro Nashville Airport; M. Collins Cambridge Focus; Taitantown Tailgaters.
Foundation type: Company-sponsored foundation.
Financial data (yr. ended 12/31/13): Assets, $2,357,012 (M); gifts received, $350,186; expenditures, $294,303; qualifying distributions, $276,038; giving activities include $276,038 for 34 grants (high: $80,000; low: $1,000).
Purpose and activities: The foundation supports hospitals, camps, and community foundations and organizations involved with arts and culture, higher education, football, youth development, and human services.
Fields of interest: Education; Community and economic development; Human services.
Type of support: General support; Employee volunteer services; Annual campaigns; Capital campaigns; Capital and infrastructure; Equipment; Program development; Scholarships.
Limitations: Applications accepted. Giving limited to TN. No grants to individuals.
Application information:
  Initial approach: Proposal
  Deadline(s): None
Officer: K.S. Adams IV, Corp. Secy.
Director: John A. Barrett.
EIN: 760611503

9231
The Texas Area Fund Foundation, Inc.
207 W. Spring St.
P.O. Box 283
Palestine, TX 75802-0283 (903) 729-6048
Contact: Connie Fain, Admin.
Main URL: http://www.txareafundfoundation.org
Facebook: https://www.facebook.com/taffactionfund
Picasa Album: https://picasaweb.google.com/115520342924674979263

Established in 1999 in Texas.
Foundation type: Community foundation.
Financial data (yr. ended 12/31/12): Assets, $1,374,956 (M); gifts received, $184,739; expenditures, $208,736; giving activities include $93,544 for 2+ grants (high: $35,100), and $57,250 for 15 grants to individuals.
Purpose and activities: The foundation seeks to help Palestine and Anderson County, TX, become a better place through directed funds and projects in these areas: Community Pride, Education, Recreation, Health Care, and Culture and the Arts.
Fields of interest: Arts and culture; Education; Higher education; Environment; Health; Community and economic development; Community beautification; Sports and recreation; Human services.
Type of support: Scholarships; Grants to individuals; Student aid.
Limitations: Applications not accepted. Giving limited to Palestine and Anderson County, TX.
Application information:
  Board meeting date(s): Monthly
Officers and Directors: Jackson Hanks, Pres. and Director; David Barnard, V.P., Governance and Director; Cad Williams, V.P. and Director; Russ Gideon, Secy. and Director; Cecil Staples, Treas. and Director; Danice Brumley; Linda Dickens; Alan George; Allyson Mitchell; Freta Parkes; Dorenda Smith; Ahnise Summers; Jeff Watson.
EIN: 752834546

9232
Texas Bankers Foundation
203 W. 10th St.
Austin, TX 78701-2321 (512) 472-8388
Contact: Gabrielle Adams
Main URL: http://www.texasbankers.com/web/
Foundation/Overview/Texas_Bankers/
Foundation_Overview.aspx?
hkey=10dee388-37f5-4e25-b864-022fb7ab9bf8

Established in 1995 in Texas.

Donors: Texas Bankers Assoc.; Comerica Bank; Federal Home Loan Bank of Dallas; Southside Bank; The Independent Bankers Bank; American National Bank of Texas.
Foundation type: Company-sponsored foundation.
Financial data (yr. ended 05/31/13): Assets, $362,692 (M); gifts received, $166,195; expenditures, $169,323; qualifying distributions, $146,115; giving activities include $143,533 for 1 grant, and $2,000 for 2 grants to individuals (high: $1,500; low: $500).
Purpose and activities: Scholarship awards to residents and employees of the Texas Bankers Association, Wisconsin.
Fields of interest: Human services.
Type of support: Student aid.
Limitations: Applications accepted. Giving primarily in areas of company operations in TX.
Application information: See foundation web site for complete application guidelines. Application form required.
Officers: William M. Lucas, Chair. and Director; J. Enc T. Sandberg, Jr., Secy. -Treas.
Directors: Jerrica Anderson; Joe Brown; Danny B. Butler; Heather Keith; Pamela H. Lovett; Mindy Nelson; Sue L. Owens; Aaron L. Ring; Amanda Stephens; Anita G. Werner; Lea Ann Wilson.
EIN: 742602147

9233
Texas House Foundation
(formerly Texas House Foundation)
143 Glynn Way Dr.
Houston, TX 77056-1111 7139566337
Main URL: http://www.texas-house.org/

Established in 2001 in Texas.
Foundation type: Independent foundation.
Financial data (yr. ended 12/31/13): Assets, $2,542,277 (M); expenditures, $248,649; qualifying distributions, $128,500; giving activities include $128,500 for 2 grants (high: $127,000; low: $1,500).
Fields of interest: Foundations; Mental health care.
Limitations: Applications not accepted. Giving limited to TX. No grants to individuals.
Application information: Unsolicited requests for funds not accepted.
Directors: Ralph Berkeley; Wyatt Heard; Joe Knauth; George McDonald; Robert Paddock; Jim Weatherall.
EIN: 760502916

9234
Jim and Angela Thompson Foundation
(also known as The James and Angela Thompson Foundation)
6125 Luther Ln., No. 386
Dallas, TX 75225-6202
Contact: Angela M. Thompson, Pres.
Main URL: http://www.jatf.us

Established in 2006 in Texas.
Donors: James R. Thompson; Clifford M. Weiner.
Foundation type: Independent foundation.
Financial data (yr. ended 12/31/13): Assets, $914,287 (M); expenditures, $139,104; qualifying distributions, $136,134; giving activities include $131,755 for 9 grants (high: $45,000; low: $2,500).
Purpose and activities: Giving primarily for children and family services, education, general aviation, free speech and animal services.
Fields of interest: Education; Animal welfare; Diseases and conditions; Aerospace engineering; Family services; Child welfare.
Type of support: Research.
Limitations: Applications accepted. Giving primarily in TX, with some emphasis on Dallas. No grants to individuals.
Publications: Application guidelines.
Application information: See foundation web site for current application information and guidelines.
Initial approach: Submit written request
Officers: James R. Thompson, Chair.; Angela M. Thompson, Pres.; Andrew P. Lester, Secy.
EIN: 205856025

9235
Dorothy F. Thorne Foundation
c/o Bank of America, N.A.
P.O. Box 831040
Dallas, TX 75283-1040 (206) 709-1565
Application address: c/o John Akin, Jr., Treas., 110 Lakeside Ave., Apt. A Seattle, WA, 98122-6594; tel.:(206) 709-1565

Established in 1997 in Washington.
Donors: Dorothy F. Thorne; Thorne Lead Charitable Trust.
Foundation type: Independent foundation.
Financial data (yr. ended 04/30/13): Assets, $601,744 (M); gifts received, $213,667; expenditures, $233,140; qualifying distributions, $196,360; giving activities include $196,360 for grants.
Fields of interest: Arts education; Botanical gardens; Health; Hospital care; Family services.
Limitations: Applications accepted. Giving primarily in NM, NY, SC, and WA. No support for political causes and candidates. No grants to individuals.
Application information: Application form required.
Initial approach: Proposal
Deadline(s): None
Officers and Directors: Nina Righter, Pres. and Director; Gwen Akin, V.P. and Director; Lisa Sloan, Secy. and Director; John Akin, Jr., Treas. and Director; Anne Akin; John A. Akin; Alison Righter; Alex Simmons; Matt Sloan; Mary Stevens.
EIN: 911817980

9236
John H. Tietze Foundation Trust
7511 Glenshannon Cir.
Dallas, TX 75225-2063

Donor: John H. Tietze†.
Foundation type: Independent foundation.
Financial data (yr. ended 12/31/13): Assets, $7,674,766 (M); expenditures, $362,420; qualifying distributions, $354,000; giving activities include $354,000 for 5 grants (high: $211,000; low: $10,000).

Fields of interest: Arts and culture; Education; Higher education; Cancers; Human services.
Limitations: Applications not accepted. Giving primarily in AZ, KS, NE and WA. No grants to individuals.
Application information: Contributes only to pre-selected organizations.
Directors: Andrew Billingsley; Eileen Tietze; John L. Tietze; Judith T. Trowbridge; Stephen D. Trowbridge.
EIN: 486282494

9237
The Tobin Theatre Arts Fund
(formerly The Tobin Foundation for Theatre Arts)
P.O. Box 91019
San Antonio, TX 78209-9094 (210) 227-6065
Contact: Mel L. Weingart, Chair.

Donors: Edgar G. Tobin†; Margaret Batts Tobin†; Robert L.B. Tobin†; The Tobin Endowment.
Foundation type: Operating foundation.
Financial data (yr. ended 12/31/13): Assets, $54,040,829 (M); gifts received, $508,500; expenditures, $831,801; qualifying distributions, $698,856; giving activities include $362,410 for 10 grants (high: $235,810; low: $1,500).
Purpose and activities: Support for theater design as a distinct and worthy art form through programs aimed at stimulating interest through exhibitions, financial assistance to exceptional talents and encouraging studies; also supports ballet, opera, theatre and the arts. The foundation also holds exhibits and educational seminars at local museums.
Fields of interest: Arts and culture; Art museums; Education.
Type of support: Continuing support; Convening; Curriculum development.
Limitations: Applications accepted. Giving on a national basis, with emphasis on NM, New York City, and San Antonio, TX. No grants for debt retirement, tuition, real estate or equipment purchases; no loans.
Publications: Informational brochure.
Application information:
Initial approach: Letter requesting application guidelines
Copies of proposal: 1
Deadline(s): None
Board meeting date(s): 4 times per year
Officers and Directors: Mel L. Weingart, Chair. and C.E.O. and Director; Linda Hardberger, Secy. and Director; Robert F. Perdziola.
Number of staff: 2 full-time professional.
EIN: 742921417

9238
The Tolleson Family Foundation
5500 Preston Rd., Ste. 250
Dallas, TX 75205-1241

Established in 1994 in Texas.
Donors: John C. Tolleson; Kevin Howe; Debra J. Tolleson.
Foundation type: Independent foundation.
Financial data (yr. ended 12/31/13): Assets, $6,607,627 (M); gifts received, $749,406; expenditures, $470,736; qualifying distributions, $432,900; giving activities include $432,900 for 28 grants (high: $163,800; low: $100).

Fields of interest: Arts and culture; Higher education; Nonprofits; Diseases and conditions; Brain and nervous system disorders; Protestantism; Human services; Child welfare; Homeless services.
Type of support: Research; Regranting.
Limitations: Applications not accepted. Giving primarily in Austin and Dallas, TX. No grants to individuals.
Application information: Contributes only to pre-selected organizations.
Officers: Debra J. Tolleson, Pres.; John C. Tolleson, V.P.; Amy Tolleson Baldwin, Secy.; John Carter Tolleson, Jr., Treas.
EIN: 752567318

9239
Shirley and David Toomim Foundation
5333 Gulfton St.
Houston, TX 77081-2801 (713) 662-7784
Contact: Bruce M. Levy, V.P. and Secy.-Treas.

Established in 1999 in Texas.
Donor: Shirley Toomin.
Foundation type: Independent foundation.
Financial data (yr. ended 12/31/14): Assets, $3,864,512 (M); expenditures, $392,050; qualifying distributions, $332,723; giving activities include $305,800 for 36 grants (high: $50,000; low: $1,000).
Fields of interest: Education; Higher education; Judaism; Food delivery.
Limitations: Applications accepted. Giving primarily in Houston, TX.
Application information:
  Initial approach: Proposal
  Deadline(s): None
Officers: Bruce M. Levy, V.P. and Secy.-Treas.; Ellen T. Robinson, Pres.; Shirley W. Toomim, V.P.
Trustees: Steve Robinson.
EIN: 760585077

9240
Torchmark Benevolent Foundation
3700 S. Stonebridge Dr.
P.O. Box 8080
McKinney, TX 75070-8080
Contact: Arvelia Bowie, Dir.
E-mail: TBF@torchmarkcorp.com

Donors: C.B. Hudson; Torchmark Corporation; Andrew King; Mark McAndrew; Surace-Smith Agency.
Foundation type: Company-sponsored foundation.
Financial data (yr. ended 12/31/13): Assets, $42,797 (M); gifts received, $126,417; expenditures, $283,943; qualifying distributions, $241,856; giving activities include $241,856 for 55 grants (high: $50,000; low: $250).
Purpose and activities: The foundation supports nonprofit organizations involved with education, housing and shelter, and human services.
Fields of interest: Education; Housing development; Human services.
Application information: Application form required.
  Initial approach: Letter
  Deadline(s): None
Directors: Arvelia Bowie; Larry Hutchison; Mark McAndrew.
EIN: 274829618

9241
E. L. & Ruth Torrance Memorial Trust
c/o Community Bank
P.O. Box 2303
Waco, TX 76703-2303
Application address: Community Bank and Trust, 1900 Washington Ave., Waco, TX 76703, tel.: (254) 753-1521

Established in 1991 in Texas.
Donor: Helon Hiatt†.
Foundation type: Independent foundation.
Financial data (yr. ended 12/31/14): Assets, $5,253,067 (M); expenditures, $279,149; qualifying distributions, $228,236; giving activities include $228,236 for 7 grants (high: $57,059; low: $11,412).
Fields of interest: Health; Children's hospital care; Religion; Human services; Children.
Type of support: General support.
Limitations: Applications accepted. Giving primarily in FL, NE and TX. No grants to individuals.
Application information:
  Initial approach: Proposal
  Deadline(s): None
Trustee: Community Bank & Trust.
EIN: 746447246

9242
Trojan Real Properties Inc.
17001 Addison Rd.
Addison, TX 75001-5027

Established in 2007 in Texas.
Donor: Trinity Christian Academy.
Foundation type: Operating foundation.
Financial data (yr. ended 07/31/13): Assets, $43,918,809 (M); gifts received, $479,715; expenditures, $668,765; qualifying distributions, $219,870; giving activities include $210,000 for 1 grant.
Fields of interest: Education; Christianity.
Limitations: Applications not accepted. Giving primarily in Addison, TX. No grants to individuals.
Application information: Unsolicited requests for funds not accepted.
Officers: Jeff Price, Chair.; Robbie Fusch, Vice-Chair.; Scott Dennis, Secy.; Ron Crosby, Treas.
Director: David Ward.
EIN: 261484901

9243
Massey Tucker Foundation
P.O. Box 1373
Houston, TX 77251-1373

Established in 1989 in Texas.
Foundation type: Independent foundation.
Financial data (yr. ended 01/31/14): Assets, $3,452,187 (M); expenditures, $209,802; qualifying distributions, $160,000; giving activities include $160,000 for 1 grant.
Fields of interest: Education; Protestantism; Shelter and residential care.
Limitations: Applications not accepted. Giving primarily in TX.
Application information: Unsolicited requests for funds not accepted.
Trustees: Bradley Bracewell; Bradford Tucker; Louis Tucker.
EIN: 760276670

9244
Tyler Foundation
c/o Tyler Technologies Inc.
5101 Tennyson Pkwy.
Plano, TX 75024 (972) 713-3700
Contact: Terri L. Alford, Secy.

Established in 1971 in Texas.
Donors: Tyler Technologies, Inc.; Tyler Corp.
Foundation type: Company-sponsored foundation.
Financial data (yr. ended 12/31/13): Assets, $4,035,190 (M); expenditures, $211,715; qualifying distributions, $190,328; giving activities include $190,328 for 57 grants (high: $17,900; low: $50).
Purpose and activities: The foundation supports hospitals and services clubs and organizations involved with education, patient services, cystic fibrosis, breast cancer, diabetes, housing development, golf, and human services.
Fields of interest: Education; Diseases and conditions; Youth development.
Type of support: General support.
Limitations: Applications accepted. Giving primarily in areas of company operations, with emphasis on ME and Dallas, TX. No grants to individuals, or for scholarships or fellowships; no loans; no matching gifts.
Application information:
  Initial approach: Proposal
  Copies of proposal: 1
  Deadline(s): None
Officers and Trustees: John M. Yeaman, Pres. and Trustee; Brian K. Miller, C.F.O. and Treas.; Terri L. Alford, Secy.
EIN: 237140526

9245
USD Foundation
9590 New Decade Dr.
Pasadena, TX 77507-1076

Donors: US Development Group, LLC; Total Depth Foundation; Michael R. Curry.
Foundation type: Independent foundation.
Financial data (yr. ended 10/31/13): Assets, $2,208,478 (M); gifts received, $190,000; expenditures, $361,066; qualifying distributions, $296,765; giving activities include $296,765 for 35 grants (high: $75,000; low: $100).
Fields of interest: Diseases and conditions; Sports and recreation; Golf; Youth development; Youth services.
Type of support: Research.
Limitations: Applications not accepted. Giving primarily in GA and TX.
Application information: Unsolicited requests for funds not accepted.
Officer: Michael R. Curry, Secy.
Directors: Dan Borgen; Clyde Crutchmer; Dale Norris.
EIN: 271561110

9246
Valero Scholarship Trust
c/o Corp. Tax
P.O. Box 696000
San Antonio, TX 78269-6000
Contact: Debbie McNaul

Established in 1996 in Texas.

Donor: Valero Energy Corp.
Foundation type: Company-sponsored foundation.
Financial data (yr. ended 12/31/14): Assets, $168,092 (M); gifts received, $309,500; expenditures, $266,124; qualifying distributions, $265,224; giving activities include $255,000 for grants to individuals.
Purpose and activities: The trust awards college scholarships to the children of employees of Valero Energy and its affiliates.
Fields of interest: Higher education.
Type of support: Scholarships; Employee-related scholarships.
Limitations: Applications not accepted. Giving limited to areas of company operations in AL, CA, FL, LA, MI, MN, OH, OK, TN, TX and the United Kingdom.
Application information: Contributes only through employee related scholarships.
Trustees: Donna M. Titzman; Frost Bank, N.A.
EIN: 746437579

9247
Van Dyke Charitable Foundation
13650 Karah Ln.
Lindale, TX   75771   (256) 651-0262
Contact: Lois T. Van Dyke, Pres.

Established in 2000 in Alabama.
Donors: Earl B. Van Dyke; Lois T. Van Dyke.
Foundation type: Independent foundation.
Financial data (yr. ended 12/31/13): Assets, $1,577,594 (M); expenditures, $381,035; qualifying distributions, $356,562; giving activities include $356,562 for 7 grants (high: $235,060; low: $1,000).
Fields of interest: Education; Christianity; Human services.
Limitations: Applications accepted. Giving primarily in AL and TX.
Application information: Application form required.
Initial approach: Proposal
Deadline(s): None
Final notification: Within 2 months
Officers: Lois T. Van Dyke, Pres.; Suzanne Van Dyke, Secy.
EIN: 311719202

9248
Rosemary Haggar Vaughan Family Foundation
16135 Preston Rd., Ste. 212
Dallas, TX   75248
Contact: Martha A. Rumble, Mgr.

Foundation type: Independent foundation.
Financial data (yr. ended 12/31/13): Assets, $5,807,916 (M); expenditures, $440,798; qualifying distributions, $383,163; giving activities include $290,500 for 64 grants (high: $50,000; low: $250).
Purpose and activities: Giving primarily for education, health associations including hospitals, the arts, and human services.
Fields of interest: Arts and culture; Performing arts; Art museums; Education; Elementary and secondary education; Health; Hospital care; Specialty hospital care; Diseases and conditions; Eye diseases; Diabetes; Catholicism; Human services; Child welfare.
Type of support: Research.

Limitations: Applications accepted. Giving primarily in Dallas, TX. No grants to individuals.
Application information:
Initial approach: Proposal
Deadline(s): Dec. 31
Officers: Rosemary H. Vaughan, Pres.; Mary Lynn Vaughan, V.P.; Vicki Miller, Secy.-Treas.; Martha A. Rumble, Mgr.
EIN: 752577797

9249
The Rachael & Ben Vaughan Foundation
P.O. Box 460968
San Antonio, TX   78246-0968   (210) 222-0335
Contact: James C. Vaughan

Established in 1952 in Texas.
Donors: Ben F. Vaughan, Jr.†; Rachael Vaughan†; Ben F. Vaughan III.
Foundation type: Independent foundation.
Financial data (yr. ended 11/30/13): Assets, $7,045,771 (M); gifts received, $2,100; expenditures, $302,517; qualifying distributions, $297,271; giving activities include $285,493 for 61 grants (high: $15,000; low: $1,000).
Purpose and activities: Support for educational, cultural, environmental, community, and religious development of central and south Texas; support for the needy and disadvantaged in this area.
Fields of interest: Arts and culture; Education; Child educational development; Environment; Natural resources; Biodiversity; Wildlife biodiversity; Nonprofits; Health; Family planning; Legal services; Community and economic development; Catholicism; Human services; Child development; Females.
Type of support: General support; Pro bono consulting services; Matching grants; Annual campaigns; Research and evaluation; Capital campaigns; Capital and infrastructure; Equipment; Land acquisitions; Endowments; Program development; Convening; Professorships; Publications; Curriculum development; Fellowships; Internships; Scholarships; Regranting; Research.
Limitations: Applications accepted. Giving primarily in southern and central TX. No grants to individuals; no loans.
Publications: Application guidelines; Grants list.
Application information: Application form required.
Initial approach: Proposal
Copies of proposal: 1
Deadline(s): June 1
Officers and Trustees: Ben F. Vaughan III, Pres. and Trustee; Ben F. Vaughan IV, V.P. and Trustee; Genevieve Vaughan, V.P. and Trustee; Daphne duPont Vaughan, Secy.-Treas. and Trustee.
Number of staff: 1 part-time professional; 1 part-time support.
EIN: 746040479

9250
Andrew F. & Barbara Veres Charitable Trust
101 Westcott, No. 506
Houston, TX   77007-7030
E-mail: andrewveres@gmail.com

Established in 2000 in Texas.
Donors: Andrew F. Veres; Barbara Veres; Hepatitis Support Association.
Foundation type: Independent foundation.

Financial data (yr. ended 12/31/13): Assets, $12,583 (M); gifts received, $218,000; expenditures, $208,332; qualifying distributions, $207,800; giving activities include $207,800 for 3 grants (high: $200,000; low: $1,000).
Fields of interest: Higher education.
Limitations: Applications not accepted. Giving primarily in OH. No grants to individuals.
Application information: Unsolicited requests for funds not accepted.
Trustee: Andrew F. Veres.
EIN: 766166971

9251
Vetter Foundation
4126 Meadowdale Ln.
Dallas, TX   75229-5317   (214) 351-0914

Donor: Edward O. Vetter.
Foundation type: Independent foundation.
Financial data (yr. ended 12/31/13): Assets, $2,116,080 (M); expenditures, $145,191; qualifying distributions, $143,665; giving activities include $143,240 for 28 grants (high: $25,000; low: $500).
Fields of interest: Elementary and secondary education; Undergraduate education; Christianity; Human services; Unknown or not classified.
Type of support: General support.
Limitations: Applications accepted. Giving primarily in the Dallas, TX, area.
Application information: Application form required.
Initial approach: Letter
Deadline(s): None
Trustee: Sally Vetter.
EIN: 756038164

9252
VMP Nutrition Foundation
(formerly CCS Foundation)
1750 Valley View Ln.
Farmers Branch, TX   75234

Donors: Bekins Distribution Center Co.; Greg Deman; Bekins Investments.
Foundation type: Company-sponsored foundation.
Financial data (yr. ended 12/31/12): Assets, $0 (M); expenditures, $414,765; qualifying distributions, $414,750; giving activities include $414,750 for 1 grant.
Purpose and activities: The foundation supports organizations involved with education, health, youth development, and Catholicism.
Fields of interest: Human services.
Type of support: General support.
Limitations: Applications not accepted. Giving primarily in Sioux City, IA. No grants to individuals.
Application information: Contributes only to pre-selected organizations.
Directors: Greg Deman; Dale C. Tigges.
EIN: 421517830

9253
E. F. Von Seggern Charitable Foundation
P.O. Box 6497
McKinney, TX   75071-5113

Established in 1994 in Texas.
Donor: E.F. Von Seggern†.
Foundation type: Independent foundation.

Financial data (yr. ended 12/31/13): Assets, $10,824,323 (M); expenditures, $594,114; qualifying distributions, $491,913; giving activities include $314,000 for 2 grants (high: $274,000; low: $40,000), and $75,000 for 1 employee matching gift.

Purpose and activities: Giving limited to the opera, symphony, and ballet, primarily the Dallas Symphony Orchestra and the Dallas Opera.

Fields of interest: Opera; Orchestral music.

Type of support: Matching grants.

Limitations: Applications not accepted. Giving limited to Dallas, TX. No grants to individuals.

Application information: Contributes only to pre-selected organizations.

> *Board meeting date(s):* Quarterly

Trustee: Dwight E. Saur, Jr., Tr.

Directors: Charles Campbell; Ronald B. Daniel; Rogene Russell; Joe Lyn Sharp.

Number of staff: 1 full-time professional; 1 part-time professional.

EIN: 752304039

9254
E. Paul and Helen Buck Waggoner Foundation, Inc.

P.O. Box 2130
Vernon, TX 76385-2130 (940) 552-2521
Contact: Gene W. Willingham, Secy.-Treas.

Established in 1966 in Texas.

Donors: E. Paul Waggoner†; Helen Buck Waggoner†.

Foundation type: Independent foundation.

Financial data (yr. ended 04/30/14): Assets, $5,315,984 (M); expenditures, $296,338; qualifying distributions, $287,093; giving activities include $287,093 for 36 grants (high: $50,000; low: $329).

Fields of interest: Museums; Education; Elementary and secondary education; Higher education; Christianity; Human services; Child welfare; Youth services.

Type of support: General support; Capital and infrastructure; Scholarships; Research; Individual development.

Limitations: Applications accepted. Giving primarily in TX; some giving also in FL.

Application information: Application form required.

> *Initial approach:* Letter
> *Deadline(s):* None

Officers: Helen Willingham, Pres.; Electra Moulder, V.P.; Gene W. Willingham, Secy.-Treas.

Director: Bill Moulder.

EIN: 751243673

9255
Waggoners Foundation

19500 State Hwy. 249, Ste. 295
Houston, TX 77070-3062

Established in 1993 in Texas.

Donors: J. Virgil Waggoner; June Waggoner.

Foundation type: Independent foundation.

Financial data (yr. ended 12/31/14): Assets, $4,073,786; expenditures, $386,987; qualifying distributions, $210,000.

Fields of interest: Higher education; Diseases and conditions; Alcoholism; Human services; Homeless services; Females; Victims of crime and abuse.

Type of support: General support; Scholarships.

Limitations: Applications not accepted. Giving primarily in Houston, TX. No grants to individuals.

Application information: Contributes only to pre-selected organizations.

Officers: Marjorie J. Waggoner, Pres.; Liz A. Waggoner, V.P.; Katherine A. Fleck, Secy.

Director: Blake W. Quisenberry.

EIN: 760404981

9256
Wal-Dot Foundation

7557 Rambler Rd., Ste. 268
Dallas, TX 75231-2390 2148915933
E-mail: dotneu412@aol.com

Established in 1993 in Oklahoma.

Donors: Walter Neustadt, Jr.; Dolores K. Neustadt.

Foundation type: Independent foundation.

Financial data (yr. ended 12/31/14): Assets, $4,906,568; gifts received, $131,148; expenditures, $428,086; qualifying distributions, $365,400.

Purpose and activities: Giving primarily for education and human services.

Fields of interest: Arts education; Museums; Education; Elementary and secondary education; Higher education; Hospice care; Human services; Family services; Child welfare.

Type of support: Continuing support; Annual campaigns; Capital campaigns; Emergency funds; Professorships; Scholarships; Research.

Limitations: Applications not accepted. Giving primarily in TX. No grants to individuals.

Application information: Contributes only to pre-selected organizations.

> *Board meeting date(s):* Jan. and July

Officer and Director: Dolores K. Neustadt, Pres. and Director.

Number of staff: None.

EIN: 731414803

9257
The Carmage And Martha Ann Walls Foundation

5701 Woodway Dr., Ste. 131
Houston, TX 77057-1589

Donor: Jean Walls Garcich†.

Foundation type: Independent foundation.

Financial data (yr. ended 06/30/13): Assets, $5,673,257 (M); expenditures, $361,254; qualifying distributions, $288,500; giving activities include $288,500 for grants.

Purpose and activities: Giving primarily for education and human services.

Fields of interest: Arts and culture; Arts education; Education; Higher education; Graduate and professional education; Nonprofits; Health; Diseases and conditions; News and public information; Human services; Youth development.

Type of support: Endowments; Program development; Scholarships; Capital and infrastructure; Research; Research and evaluation; Regranting.

Limitations: Applications not accepted. Giving primarily in AL and TX. No grants to individuals.

Application information: Contributes only to pre-selected organizations.

Officers and Trustees: Lissa Walls Vahldiek, Pres. and Trustee; Martha Ann Walls, V.P. and Trustee; John R. Allender, Secy.-Treas. and Trustee.

EIN: 760031815

9258
Marjorie T. Walthall Perpetual Charitable Trust

151 Rockhill Dr.
San Antonio, TX 78209-2219
Application address: c/o Wilson J. Walthall, III, 1220 Arroyo Blanco St., McKinney, TX 75069, tel.: (972) 562-3118

Established in 1976 in Texas.

Donors: Marjorie T. Walthall; NETTING PACE CPAS.

Foundation type: Independent foundation.

Financial data (yr. ended 12/31/12): Assets, $3,893,964 (M); expenditures, $212,776; qualifying distributions, $175,189; giving activities include $160,000 for 2 grants (high: $155,000; low: $5,000).

Purpose and activities: Giving primarily for nursing education, human services, health, and animal welfare.

Fields of interest: Arts and culture; Education; Diseases and conditions.

Type of support: General support; Scholarships.

Limitations: Applications accepted. Giving primarily in San Antonio, TX. No grants to individuals.

Application information: Application form required.

> *Initial approach:* Letter
> *Deadline(s):* None

Trustees: Marjorie Walthall Fry; Wilson J. Walthall III.

EIN: 510170313

9259
The Waltrip-McGee Foundation

P.O. Box 130548
Houston, TX 77219-0548
Application address: c/o Robert L. Waltrip, 1929 Allen Pkwy., 12th Fl., Houston TX 77019-2506, tel.: (713) 525-5264

Established in 1998 in Texas.

Donor: Robert L. Waltrip.

Foundation type: Independent foundation.

Financial data (yr. ended 04/30/13): Assets, $4,238,268 (M); expenditures, $164,261; qualifying distributions, $159,141; giving activities include $157,041 for 7 grants (high: $50,000; low: $7,500).

Purpose and activities: Giving primarily to an aviation museum.

Fields of interest: Museums.

Type of support: Continuing support.

Limitations: Applications accepted. Giving primarily in TX. No grants to individuals.

Application information:

> *Initial approach:* Contact foundation
> *Deadline(s):* None

Officers: Robert L. Waltrip, Pres.; William Blair Waltrip, V.P.; Robert L. Waltrip, Jr., Secy.-Treas.

Directors: Claire H. Waltrip; Holly Waltrip.

EIN: 311608714

9260
The Ward Family Foundation

5949 Sherry Ln., Ste. 1735
Dallas, TX 75225-8048

Established in 1993 in Texas.
Donors: William C. Ward; Cynthia R. Ward.
Foundation type: Independent foundation.
Financial data (yr. ended 12/31/13): Assets, $5,682,514 (M); expenditures, $383,547; qualifying distributions, $289,246; giving activities include $286,596 for 22 grants (high: $100,000; low: $45).
Purpose and activities: Giving primarily for education and children, youth, and social services.
Fields of interest: Arts and culture; Elementary and secondary education; Higher education; Specialty hospital care; Community and economic development; Human services; Child welfare.
Type of support: General support; Capital campaigns.
Limitations: Applications not accepted. Giving primarily in TX, with emphasis on Dallas. No grants to individuals.
Application information: Contributes only to pre-selected organizations.
Officers: William C. Ward, Pres.; Cynthia R. Ward, V.P. and Secy.; Katherine J. Ward, Treas.
EIN: 752514341

9261
Naomi and Martin Warren Family Foundation
c/o JPMorgan Chase Bank
P.O. Box 2558
Houston, TX 77252-2558

Established in 1998 in Texas.
Donors: Geraldine Roper; Jim Roper; Andrew Spector; Helen Spector; Benjamin Warren; Joy Warren.
Foundation type: Independent foundation.
Financial data (yr. ended 12/31/13): Assets, $2,226,565 (M); expenditures, $212,511; qualifying distributions, $212,473; giving activities include $195,000 for 6 grants (high: $80,000; low: $10,000).
Purpose and activities: The foundation supports projects in justice and human rights, environmental quality, reduction of hunger and homelessness, education of children, and re-education and re-training of unemployed adults.
Fields of interest: Arts and culture; Education.
Type of support: General support.
Limitations: Applications not accepted. Giving primarily in NJ, New York, NY, and the greater Houston, TX, area. No support for organizations whose purpose is strictly religious or political in nature. No grants to individuals.
Application information: Unsolicited requests for funds not accepted.
Officers and Directors: Naomi Warren, Pres. and Director; Geraldine Roper, V.P. and Director; Jessica Schaeppi, V.P. and Director; Helen Spector, V.P. and Director; Benjamin Warren, V.P. and Director; Joy Warren, V.P. and Director.
EIN: 760588400

9262
Watford Family Foundation Inc.
2 Villeroy Way
The Woodlands, TX 77382-2711

Donor: Watford Interests, Ltd.
Foundation type: Independent foundation.

Financial data (yr. ended 12/31/14): Assets, $5,870,527; expenditures, $427,718; qualifying distributions, $417,196.
Fields of interest: University education; Religion; Youth services.
Limitations: Applications not accepted. Giving primarily in FL and TX.
Application information: Unsolicited requests for funds not accepted.
Officer: Michael D. Watford, Pres. and Secy.-Treas.
Directors: Amanda N. Watford; Jason M. Watford.
EIN: 274187713

9263
The Watson Foundation
(formerly The Mark and Kathleen Watson Charitable Foundation)
P.O. Box 6886
San Antonio, TX 78209-0886
Contact: Mark E. Watson Jr., Pres. and Treas.

Established in 1997 in Texas.
Donor: Mark E. Watson, Jr.
Foundation type: Independent foundation.
Financial data (yr. ended 09/30/13): Assets, $91,227 (M); gifts received, $75,000; expenditures, $241,460; qualifying distributions, $239,682; giving activities include $237,909 for 40 grants (high: $52,500; low: $80).
Fields of interest: Arts and culture; Higher education; Environment; Zoos; Nonprofits; Diseases and conditions; Community and economic development; Religion; Human services.
Type of support: General support; Regranting.
Limitations: Applications accepted. Giving primarily in San Antonio, TX.
Application information: Application form required.
   Initial approach: Letter
   Deadline(s): None
Officer: Mark E. Watson, Jr., Pres. and Treas.
EIN: 742825092

9264
The Way Ahead Trust
P.O. Box 99
Westhoff, TX 77994-0099
Contact: Teddy Aven

Donors: Teddy Aven; Frances Aven.
Foundation type: Independent foundation.
Financial data (yr. ended 12/31/13): Assets, $1,785,467 (M); expenditures, $217,878; qualifying distributions, $155,000; giving activities include $155,000 for 8 grants (high: $50,000; low: $5,000).
Fields of interest: Higher education; Christianity; Human services.
Limitations: Applications accepted. Giving primarily in GA; funding also in MS, TX and VA.
Application information:
   Initial approach: Letter
   Deadline(s): None
Trustees: Frances J. Aven; Teddy W. Aven.
EIN: 456533936

9265
Bill & Katie Weaver Charitable Trust
1845 Woodall Rogers Freeway, Ste. 1275
Dallas, TX 75201-2299 (214) 999-9497
Contact: William R. Weaver, Tr.

Donors: William R. Weaver; Kaethe M. Weaver.
Foundation type: Independent foundation.
Financial data (yr. ended 11/30/13): Assets, $5,427,821 (M); gifts received, $182,353; expenditures, $392,618; qualifying distributions, $188,099; giving activities include $187,655 for 94 grants (high: $25,000; low: $65).
Fields of interest: Orchestral music; Higher education; Community and economic development; Religion; Human services.
Type of support: General support; Continuing support; Annual campaigns; Regranting; Fundraising.
Limitations: Giving primarily in Dallas, TX. No grants to individuals.
Publications: Application guidelines.
Application information:
   Initial approach: Letter
   Copies of proposal: 1
   Deadline(s): None
Trustees: William R. Weaver.
Number of staff: None.
EIN: 752001841

9266
The Iris and Lloyd Webre Foundation
4800 San Felipe St., Ste. 100
Houston, TX 77056-3908

Established in 1987 in Texas.
Donors: Texas Brine Co., LLC; Iris Paine Webre†.
Foundation type: Company-sponsored foundation.
Financial data (yr. ended 09/30/14): Assets, $7,598,214 (M); expenditures, $355,089; qualifying distributions, $291,000; giving activities include $291,000 for 23 grants (high: $35,000; low: $2,500).
Purpose and activities: The foundation supports museums and women's clubs and organizations involved with education, health, youth development, human services, and Catholicism.
Fields of interest: Art museums; Education; Health; Organ and tissue banks; Catholicism; Human services; Youth development; Youth services.
Type of support: General support; Cash grants; Capital campaigns; Equipment; Program development; Scholarships; Building and renovations; Research.
Limitations: Applications not accepted. Giving limited to Houston, TX. No grants to individuals.
Application information: Contributes only to pre-selected organizations.
Officers: Robert W. Sneed, Pres.; Roberta Rude, V.P.; Mary Iris Webre, V.P.; Marjorie Pribyl, Secy.-Treas.
EIN: 760240169

9267
Weir Foundation
c/o Dan Weir
P.O. Box 600125
Dallas, TX 75360-0125
Application address: c/o D 'Ann Moore, P.O. Box 720158, Dallas, TX 75372-0158

Donor: Weir Furniture Village, Inc.
Foundation type: Independent foundation.
Financial data (yr. ended 02/28/13): Assets, $335,121 (M); gifts received, $198,148; expenditures, $372,232; qualifying distributions,

$371,000; giving activities include $371,000 for 32 grants (high: $47,000; low: $3,000).

Purpose and activities: Giving to aid the furtherance of the Gospel of Jesus Christ, teach the word of God, and discipline individuals in accordance with Christian doctrines.

Fields of interest: Religion.

Limitations: Applications accepted. Giving primarily in TX, with emphasis on Dallas. No grants to individuals.

Application information:

Initial approach: Proposal

Deadline(s): None

Officers and Directors: Dan R. Weir, Pres.; Jack Brady, V.P.; D'Ann Moore, Secy.; Laura Weir, Treas.

Directors: Mike Clubb; Amy Fullerton; Brad Weir.

EIN: 751943678

9268

Weir Foundation Trust

464 Little Bear Rd.

Buda, TX   78610-2961

Established in 1953 in District of Columbia.

Donor: Davis Weir†.

Foundation type: Independent foundation.

Financial data (yr. ended 12/31/12): Assets, $1,514,044 (M); expenditures, $241,100; qualifying distributions, $234,000; giving activities include $234,000 for grants.

Fields of interest: Arts and culture; Art museums; Higher education; Protestantism; Human services; Child welfare; Youth services.

Type of support: General support; Scholarships; Research.

Limitations: Applications not accepted. Giving primarily in MD and TX. No grants to individuals.

Application information: Contributes only to pre-selected organizations.

Trustee: Scott Sandahl.

EIN: 526029328

9269

Leroy and Merle Weir Trust

c/o Frost National Bank

P.O. Box 2127

Austin, TX   78768-2127

Established in 2002 in Texas.

Foundation type: Independent foundation.

Financial data (yr. ended 12/31/13): Assets, $14,817,148 (M); expenditures, $497,784; qualifying distributions, $456,594; giving activities include $420,500 for 6 grants (high: $160,200; low: $10,000).

Purpose and activities: Giving primarily for higher education; some funding also for a health organization and children services.

Fields of interest: Higher education; Diseases and conditions; Child welfare.

Limitations: Applications not accepted. Giving primarily in TX.

Application information: Contributes only to pre-selected organizations.

Trustee: Frost National Bank.

EIN: 742656448

9270

Welch Family Foundation

1716 Briarcrest Dr., Ste. 700

Bryan, TX   77802-2760   (979) 846-0303

Contact: Finis Welch, Pres.

Donor: Finis Welch.

Foundation type: Independent foundation.

Financial data (yr. ended 12/31/13): Assets, $101,504 (M); gifts received, $293,952; expenditures, $193,858; qualifying distributions, $191,500; giving activities include $191,500 for 2 grants (high: $141,500; low: $50,000).

Fields of interest: Arts and culture; Education.

Limitations: Applications not accepted.

Application information: Unsolicited requests for funds not accepted.

Officers: Finis Welch, Pres.; James Pearce, V.P.; Lara Anderson, Secy.-Treas.

EIN: 274470063

9271

The Damon Wells Foundation

2001 Kirby Dr., Ste. 806

Houston, TX   77019

Established in 1993 in Texas.

Donors: Damon Wells, Jr.; Damon Wells.

Foundation type: Independent foundation.

Financial data (yr. ended 12/31/14): Assets, $3,889,859 (M); expenditures, $398,753; qualifying distributions, $395,825; giving activities include $395,000 for 7 grants (high: $250,000; low: $5,000).

Fields of interest: Museums; Higher education; Graduate and professional education; Christianity.

Type of support: General support; Endowments; Program development; Professorships.

Limitations: Applications not accepted. Giving primarily in MO, NY, and TX. No grants to individuals.

Application information: Contributes only to pre-selected organizations.

Officers and Directors: Damon Wells, Pres. and Director; David M. Underwood, V.P. and Director; Carol Billups, Secy.-Treas. and Director.

EIN: 760419933

9272

Dan Kirkland Wells Foundation

P.O. Box 513

Clifton, TX   76654-0709

Donor: Stephen A. Wells.

Foundation type: Independent foundation.

Financial data (yr. ended 11/30/14): Assets, $3,661,288 (M); expenditures, $147,772; qualifying distributions, $147,772; giving activities include $144,120 for 24 grants (high: $35,420; low: $200).

Fields of interest: Education; Health; Religion.

Limitations: Applications not accepted. No grants to individuals.

Application information: Contributes only to pre-selected organizations.

Officers and Directors: Stephen A. Wells, Pres. and Director; Judy K. Wells, Secy. and Director; Dansby Erwin; Cayce W. McCormick; Ran K. Wells.

EIN: 751822990

9273

Westcott Foundation

100 Crescent Ct., Ste. 1620

Dallas, TX   75201-1884   (214) 777-5000

Established in 1989 in Texas.

Donors: Carl Westcott; Jimmy Westcott.

Foundation type: Independent foundation.

Financial data (yr. ended 12/31/14): Assets, $1,082,221; expenditures, $277,566; qualifying distributions, $274,909.

Purpose and activities: Giving primarily for higher education, and federated giving programs; funding also for hospitals, and human services.

Fields of interest: Arts and culture; Elementary and secondary education; Higher education; Nonprofits; Diseases and conditions; Golf; Human services; Child welfare; Youth services.

Type of support: General support; Regranting.

Limitations: Applications accepted. Giving primarily in Nashville, TN, and Dallas, TX.

Application information: Application form required.

Initial approach: E-Mail

Copies of proposal: 1

Deadline(s): None

Officers: Chart Westcott, Chair.; Jack T. Smith, Pres.; Jimmy Westcott, V.P.; Beth Prothro, Secy.-Treas.

Director: Diane Adler.

Number of staff: 1 part-time support.

EIN: 752304233

9274

Barbara F. Wheeler Foundation

P. O. Box 985

Aledo, TX   76008-0985

Foundation type: Independent foundation.

Financial data (yr. ended 12/31/13): Assets, $9,267,689 (M); expenditures, $531,905; qualifying distributions, $478,052; giving activities include $440,000 for 14 grants (high: $55,000; low: $15,000).

Fields of interest: Agriculture; Housing development; Religion; Human services; Food delivery; Homeless people.

Limitations: Applications not accepted.

Application information: Unsolicited requests for funds not accepted.

Officers: Diane Stavens, Pres.; James Stavens, V.P.; Phillip Stavens, Secy.-Treas.

EIN: 752838312

9275

White Family Foundation

205 Lighthouse Dr.

Horseshoe Bay, TX   78657

Donor: Charles C. White†.

Foundation type: Independent foundation.

Financial data (yr. ended 12/31/14): Assets, $5,027,838; expenditures, $318,974; qualifying distributions, $282,500.

Fields of interest: Arts and culture; Education; Health.

Limitations: Applications not accepted.

Application information: Unsolicited requests for funds not accepted.

Trustee: Charles C. White, Jr.

EIN: 208657835

9276
The Whitley Charitable Foundation
8911 N. Capital of Texas Hwy., Bldg. 3, Ste. 3120
Austin, TX 78759-7247 (512) 476-7101
Contact: Ronald Jones, Pres.

Established in 1990 in Texas.
Donors: Ronald Jones; Whitley Company, LP; Matthew Jones; Stephine Jones Dent.
Foundation type: Company-sponsored foundation.
Financial data (yr. ended 12/31/13): Assets, $2,096,973 (M); expenditures, $156,642; qualifying distributions, $138,095; giving activities include $138,095 for 8 grants (high: $115,345; low: $250).
Purpose and activities: The foundation supports organizations involved with higher education, hunger, athletics, human services, and Christianity.
Fields of interest: Higher education; Christianity; Track and field; Human services; Food delivery; Women's services.
Type of support: General support.
Limitations: Applications accepted. Giving primarily in TX. No grants to individuals.
Application information:
Initial approach: Proposal
Deadline(s): None
Officers: Ronald Jones, Pres.; Matthew Jones, V.P. and Secy.-Treas.
Director: Stephanie Jones Dent.
EIN: 742588216

9277
John and Susan Wilder Foundation
200 Crescent Ct., No. 200
Dallas, TX 75201-1875

Established in 2007 in Texas.
Donors: C. John Wilder; Susan A. Wilder.
Foundation type: Independent foundation.
Financial data (yr. ended 06/30/13): Assets, $837,463 (M); expenditures, $168,802; qualifying distributions, $167,496; giving activities include $165,380 for 12 grants (high: $122,500; low: $500).
Purpose and activities: The foundation's mission seeks to improve the lives of families through funding initiatives and programs that foster youth development, Christian ministries, and public school education. The foundation believes that child's future begins with a healthy environment, which includes access to educational, sports, and Christian development opportunites.
Fields of interest: Education; Nonprofits; Christianity; Human services; Child welfare.
Type of support: Regranting.
Limitations: Applications not accepted. Giving primarily in TX, with emphasis on Dallas; giving also in Branson, MO. No support for marketing opportunities. No grants to individuals.
Application information: Contributes only to pre-selected organizations.
Officers and Directors: C. John Wilder, Exec. Chair. and Director; Susan A. Wilder, Pres. and Director; Nathan E. Langston, Exec. V.P. and C.F.O.; Harold M. King, Exec. V.P.; Lillian S. Meyer, Secy. and Cont.; Janice E. Wallace, Treas. and Director; Jeffrey S. Agree.
EIN: 260281707

9278
Cecilia Young Willard Helping Fund
c/o Broadway National Bank
P.O. Box 17001
San Antonio, TX 78217-0001
Main URL: http://broadwaybank.com/wealthmanagement/FoundationCeciliaYoungWillard.html

Established in 1987 in Texas.
Donor: Cecilia Young Willard Trust.
Foundation type: Independent foundation.
Financial data (yr. ended 05/31/13): Assets, $5,041,295 (M); expenditures, $260,651; qualifying distributions, $216,360; giving activities include $216,360 for grants.
Purpose and activities: Giving primarily for health organizations, and children, youth and social services.
Fields of interest: Orchestral music; Education; Diseases and conditions; Human services; Child welfare.
Type of support: General support; Continuing support; Annual campaigns; Capital campaigns; Capital and infrastructure; Emergency funds; Curriculum development; Research.
Limitations: Applications accepted. Giving primarily in MD, NC, PA, and TX. No grants to individuals.
Application information: See foundation website for complete application guidelines. Application form required.
Deadline(s): May 31
Trustee: Broadway National Bank.
Number of staff: None.
EIN: 746350893

9279
Elizabeth P. and Harold R. Williams Foundation
P.O. Box 741709
Houston, TX 77274-1709

Established in 2007 in Texas.
Donor: Harold R. Williams†.
Foundation type: Independent foundation.
Financial data (yr. ended 12/31/13): Assets, $5,434,709 (M); gifts received, $200,000; expenditures, $274,982; qualifying distributions, $216,589; giving activities include $205,608 for 9 grants (high: $105,000; low: $2,804).
Fields of interest: Elementary and secondary education; Higher education.
Limitations: Applications not accepted. Giving primarily in TX. No grants to individuals.
Application information: Unsolicited requests for funds not accepted.
Officers: James E. Miles, Pres. and Treas.; Diana Miles, V.P.; Rodney C. Koenig, Secy.
EIN: 260796372

9280
J.L. Williams Foundation, Inc.
P.O. Box 797464
Dallas, TX 75379-7464 (972) 588-3636
Contact: Julia Underwood, Secy.-Treas.

Established in 2000 in Texas.
Donors: J.L. Williams†; The Barbara Barton Trust.
Foundation type: Independent foundation.
Financial data (yr. ended 12/31/13): Assets, $15,867,954 (M); expenditures, $626,940; qualifying distributions, $333,843; giving activities include $309,500 for 20 grants (high: $125,000; low: $1,000).
Fields of interest: Health; Christianity; Human services; Food banks; Child welfare; Homeless people.
Limitations: Applications accepted. Giving primarily in Dallas, TX.
Application information:
Initial approach: Proposal
Deadline(s): None
Officers: R.J. Pipes, Chair.; Jonell H. Williams, Pres.; Julia Underwood, Secy.-Treas.
Directors: Andrea Connolly; Richard Williams.
EIN: 752671320

9281
Lester and Beatrice Williams Foundation
168 Butler St.
Onalaska, TX 77360-7317 (936) 646-3335
Contact: Beverly Elliott, Dir.
FAX: (936) 646-5769;
E-mail: info@thewilliamsfoundation.org; *Main URL:* http://www.thewilliamsfoundation.org

Established in 1997 in Texas.
Donor: Beatrice Williams†.
Foundation type: Operating foundation.
Financial data (yr. ended 12/31/13): Assets, $5,844,108 (M); expenditures, $552,617; qualifying distributions, $470,034; giving activities include $250,000 for 8 grants (high: $80,000; low: $5,000).
Purpose and activities: A private operating foundation, giving primarily for education and community organizations.
Fields of interest: Education; Community and economic development; Protestantism; Food aid; Child welfare.
Limitations: Applications accepted. Giving primarily in Cameron, TX. No grants, loans or scholarships to individuals or for annual funds, galas, and fundraising activities, debt reduction, emergency or disaster relief efforts, administrative and operating expenses or for conferences, seminars or workshops.
Application information: Generally contributes to pre-selected organizations. Application information available on foundation web site.
Initial approach: Letter, fax or e-mail
Copies of proposal: 3
Deadline(s): None
Directors: Beverly Elliott; William Elliott; Amy Poe; Charles S. Poe.
EIN: 742847229

9282
The Winston Charitable Foundation
c/o Salient Trust Co.
4625 San Felipe, Ste. 900
Houston, TX 77027 (713) 993-4675
Contact: Sherry Ashley

Established in 1998 in Texas.
Donor: Bert F. Winston, Jr.
Foundation type: Independent foundation.
Financial data (yr. ended 12/31/12): Assets, $3,892,798 (M); expenditures, $225,349; qualifying distributions, $200,000; giving activities include $200,000 for 7 grants (high: $70,000; low: $10,000).

Fields of interest: Arts and culture; Education; Housing development.
Limitations: Applications accepted. Giving primarily in TX.
Application information:
Initial approach: Letter
Deadline(s): None
Officers and Directors: Lynn David Winston, V.P. and Director; Chaille Winston Hawkins, Secy. and Director.
EIN: 742877210

9283
The William and Marie Wise Family Foundation
10223 Broadway, Ste. P257
Pearland, TX 77584-7880

Established in 1998 in Texas.
Donor: William A. Wise.
Foundation type: Independent foundation.
Financial data (yr. ended 12/31/13): Assets, $2,091,167 (M); expenditures, $241,332; qualifying distributions, $236,100; giving activities include $236,100 for 22 grants (high: $50,000; low: $500).
Purpose and activities: Giving primarily for higher education and social services.
Fields of interest: Art museums; Education; Higher education; Nonprofits; Diseases and conditions; Christianity; Human services.
Type of support: General support; Regranting.
Limitations: Applications not accepted. Giving primarily in Davenport, IA and Houston, TX. No grants to individuals.
Application information: Unsolicited requests for funds not accepted.
Officers: Marie Figge Wise, Pres. and Treas.; William A. Wise, V.P. and Secy.; Genevieve Wise Evans, Exec. Dir.
EIN: 311519664

9284
Kalman & Ida Wolens Foundation
P.O. Box 863717
Plano, TX 75086-3717 (972) 960-1881
Contact: Joe Milkes, Pres. and Treas.

Established in 1972 in Texas.
Donor: Louis Wolens†.
Foundation type: Independent foundation.
Financial data (yr. ended 07/31/14): Assets, $6,467,102 (M); expenditures, $304,405; qualifying distributions, $251,750; giving activities include $250,500 for 10 grants (high: $50,000; low: $1,000).
Fields of interest: Community and economic development; Religion; Judaism; Human services; Seniors.
Type of support: Endowments; Program development; Scholarships; Research.
Limitations: Applications accepted. Giving primarily in TX, with emphasis on Dallas. No grants to individuals.
Application information: Application form required.
Initial approach: Letter
Deadline(s): None
Officers and Directors: Joe Milkes, Pres. and Treas.; Bette Miller, Secy. and Director.
EIN: 237222516

9285
The Erving and Joyce Wolf Foundation
700 Louisiana St., Ste. 1100
Houston, TX 77002-2731
Contact: Erving Wolf

Donors: Erving Wolf; Joyce Wolf.
Foundation type: Independent foundation.
Financial data (yr. ended 02/28/14): Assets, $5,017,353 (M); expenditures, $261,392; qualifying distributions, $248,875; giving activities include $248,875 for 43 grants (high: $40,000; low: $100).
Fields of interest: Arts and culture; Higher education; Nonprofits; Hospital care; Diseases and conditions; Religion; Judaism.
Type of support: Regranting.
Limitations: Applications not accepted. Giving primarily in NY and TX. No grants to individuals.
Application information: Contributes only to pre-selected organizations.
Officers and Trustees: Erving Wolf, Pres. and Trustee; Joyce Wolf, V.P. and Trustee; Gary Winston, Secy. and Trustee; M. Daniel Wolf, Treas. and Trustee; Mathew D. Wolf.
EIN: 364504334

9286
Wolff-Toomim Foundation
P.O. Box 219169
Houston, TX 77218-7026

Established in 1990 in Texas.
Donors: Shirley W. Toomin; David R. Toomin†; Melvyn L. Wolff; Cylvia Wolff.
Foundation type: Independent foundation.
Financial data (yr. ended 12/31/13): Assets, $0 (M); gifts received, $215,000; expenditures, $241,758; qualifying distributions, $241,758; giving activities include $238,796 for 53 grants (high: $150,000; low: $75).
Fields of interest: Arts and culture; Nonprofits; Cancers; Catholicism; Judaism; Human services.
Type of support: Annual campaigns; Capital campaigns; Regranting.
Limitations: Applications not accepted. Giving primarily in the Harris County, TX, area. No grants to individuals.
Application information: Contributes only to pre-selected organizations.
Trustees: Shirley W. Toomim; Cylvia Wolff; Melvyn L. Wolff.
EIN: 760324661

9287
Gus & Ethel Wolters Foundation Trust
c/o Tax Dept. T-8
P.O. Box 2950
San Antonio, TX 78299-2950 (210) 220-4620
Contact: Ryland Howard, V.P.

Foundation type: Independent foundation.
Financial data (yr. ended 08/31/13): Assets, $7,403,667 (M); expenditures, $278,509; qualifying distributions, $254,325; giving activities include $243,050 for 15 grants (high: $90,250; low: $750).
Purpose and activities: Scholarship awards to graduates of Shriner High School and St. Paul's High School, Lavaca County, Texas, to attend a Texas

college or university. Awards are paid directly to the college or university.
Fields of interest: Higher education.
Type of support: Scholarships.
Limitations: Applications accepted. Giving limited to residents of Lavaca County, TX. No grants to individuals directly.
Application information: Must be a graduate of Shriner or St Pauls Catholic High School. Application form required.
Initial approach: Proposal
Deadline(s): Before beginning of school year
Trustee: Frost Bank.
EIN: 742335544

9288
B. M. Woltman Foundation
2525 N. Loop W., Ste. 102
Houston, TX 77008-1024
Application address: c/o Lutheran Church, Missouri Synod, 7900 East Hwy. 290, Austin, TX 78724-2499, tel.: (512) 926-4272

Established in 1948 in Texas.
Donors: B.M. Woltman†; Woltman Furniture Co.
Foundation type: Independent foundation.
Financial data (yr. ended 12/31/13): Assets, $6,723,988 (M); expenditures, $354,998; qualifying distributions, $292,844; giving activities include $223,200 for 12 grants (high: $116,300; low: $5,342), and $62,000 for 24 grants to individuals (high: $3,930; low: $1,115).
Purpose and activities: Giving only for Lutheran church support, local church-related secondary schools, hospitals, and higher education; scholarships for students preparing for the Lutheran ministry or for teaching in Lutheran schools.
Fields of interest: Secondary education; Higher education; Graduate and professional education; Methodism; Theology.
Type of support: General support; Student aid.
Limitations: Applications accepted. Giving primarily in TX; some giving in IN and MO.
Application information: Application form required.
Initial approach: Completed Application form
Deadline(s): Before school term begins for scholarships
Officers and Trustees: Mary McCanne Currin, Pres. and Trustee; Rev. Donald G. Black, Secy.-Treas. and Trustee; Rev. Kenneth Hennings; James E. Kellerman; R. Lynn Moers; Louis L. Pabor; Ben G. Schoppe; Kurt Rosenhagen.
EIN: 741402184

9289
The Eva and Marvin Womack Foundation
4305 Waterford Pl.
Austin, TX 78731-4635

Established in 1997 in Texas.
Donors: Eva Robuck Womack; R. Marvin Womack.
Foundation type: Independent foundation.
Financial data (yr. ended 12/31/13): Assets, $1,968,199 (M); expenditures, $191,637; qualifying distributions, $189,817; giving activities include $186,652 for 14 grants (high: $44,610; low: $500).
Purpose and activities: Giving primarily for opera and music, education, and children's services.

Fields of interest: Music; Higher education; Christianity; Sports and recreation; Child welfare; Youth development.
Limitations: Applications not accepted. Giving primarily in TX, with emphasis on Austin. No grants to individuals.
Application information: Contributes only to pre-selected organizations.
Officers and Directors: R. Marvin Womack, Pres. and Director; Eva Robuck Womack, Secy. and Director; Deanna Lynn Womack; Michael Scott Womack.
EIN: 742831302

9290
Wood Family Memorial Trust
P.O. Box 1338
Victoria, TX   77902-1338
Contact: Garry Petras
Application address: 101 S. Main, Victoria, TX 7790,
tel.: (361) 573-6321

Foundation type: Independent foundation.
Financial data (yr. ended 11/30/13): Assets, $3,742,110 (M); expenditures, $196,070; qualifying distributions, $174,721; giving activities include $174,721 for 22 grants (high: $30,000; low: $500).
Purpose and activities: Giving primarily for human services and education.
Fields of interest: Education; Fire prevention and control; Housing development; Human services.
Type of support: General support; Capital and infrastructure; Equipment; Endowments; Emergency funds; Scholarships.
Limitations: Giving primarily in Victoria, TX.
Publications: Annual report.
Application information: Application form required.
  Initial approach: Letter
  Copies of proposal: 1
  Deadline(s): None
Trustees: Joe Bland; Richard T. "Terry" Cullen; Elvin "Al" Koehn; Garry Petras; Prosperity Bank.
EIN: 746307476

9291
Woods Foundation
755 E. Mulberry St., Ste. 600
San Antonio, TX   78212-6013
Contact: Gary V. Woods, Pres.

Established in 2000 in Texas.
Donor: Gary V. Woods.
Foundation type: Independent foundation.
Financial data (yr. ended 12/31/13): Assets, $1,340,747 (M); expenditures, $335,230; qualifying distributions, $333,500; giving activities include $333,500 for 9 grants (high: $200,000; low: $1,000).
Fields of interest: Education; Health; Nursing care; Cancers; Human services.
Type of support: Research.
Limitations: Applications accepted. Giving primarily in TX. No grants to individuals.
Application information: Application form required.
  Initial approach: Proposal
  Deadline(s): None
Officers: Gary V. Woods, Pres.; Steven L. Cummings, Secy.
EIN: 742955600

9292
Orien and Dr. Jack Woolf Charitable Foundation
612 Forest Bend Dr.
Plano, TX   75025-6105

Donor: Orien Levy Woolf†.
Foundation type: Independent foundation.
Financial data (yr. ended 11/30/13): Assets, $4,154,390 (M); expenditures, $261,188; qualifying distributions, $203,050; giving activities include $203,050 for 6 grants (high: $60,700; low: $350).
Fields of interest: Arts and culture; Education; Human services.
Limitations: Applications not accepted. Giving primarily in Dallas, TX.
Application information: Unsolicited requests for funds not accepted.
Officers: Roberta Shapiro, Pres.; Michelle Devereux, V.P.; John Broude, Secy.
Trustees: Katy Crowe; Barbara Devereux.
EIN: 272113885

9293
The Works of Grace Foundation
201 Lavaca St., Unit 3701
Austin, TX   78701
Main URL: http://www.worksofgracefoundation.org

Established in 2000 in Texas.
Donors: Theresa Castellano; The Angel Trust.
Foundation type: Independent foundation.
Financial data (yr. ended 12/31/13): Assets, $3,584,855 (M); gifts received, $100,000; expenditures, $204,677; qualifying distributions, $175,617; giving activities include $155,300 for 13 grants (high: $40,725; low: $500).
Purpose and activities: The foundation's mission is to provide support and inspiration to individuals, programs and organizations that make a difference in the lives of children and families. The foundation also supports a scholarship program for children of Blaine County, ID, teachers.
Fields of interest: Education; Cancers; Human services; Family services; Child welfare.
Type of support: General support; Program-related investments; Continuing support; Financial sustainability; Annual campaigns; Capital campaigns; Capital and infrastructure; Program development; Convening; Curriculum development; Scholarships; Program evaluations.
Limitations: Applications not accepted. No grants to individuals.
Application information: Unsolicited request for funds not accepted.
Officers: Benjamin David Wood, Pres.; Theresa Castellano, V.P.; Vicki Browne, Secy.-Treas.
Number of staff: 1 part-time support.
EIN: 752906814

9294
Patti and Jim Wright Family Foundation
6 Steeplechase Tr.
Longview, TX   75605-7561
Application address: c/o Jim R. Wright, 4 Steeplechase Tr., Longview, TX 75605, tel.: (903) 663-6866

Established in 2007 in Texas.
Foundation type: Independent foundation.

Financial data (yr. ended 12/31/13): Assets, $5,246,724 (M); expenditures, $310,568; qualifying distributions, $310,568; giving activities include $294,850 for 26 grants (high: $65,000; low: $500).
Fields of interest: Education; Religion; Human services.
Limitations: Applications accepted. Giving primarily in CO and TX.
Application information:
  Initial approach: Letter
  Deadline(s): None
Officers: James Richard Wright, Pres.; Melissa Wright Hurt, V.P.; Jessica Wright Marshall, V.P.; Patti L. Wright, Secy.-Treas.
EIN: 261331625

9295
William Wright Family Foundation
P.O. Box 4517
Wichita Falls, TX   76308-0517
Contact: W. Dan Wright

Established in 1998 in Texas.
Donors: William E. Wright; William Dan Wright.
Foundation type: Independent foundation.
Financial data (yr. ended 12/31/13): Assets, $5,656,835 (M); expenditures, $368,440; qualifying distributions, $345,590; giving activities include $345,590 for 6 grants (high: $125,000; low: $5,000).
Fields of interest: Higher education; Foundations; Youth services.
Limitations: Applications not accepted. Giving primarily in La Jolla, CA, and Vernon, TX. No grants to individuals.
Application information: Contributes only to pre-selected organizations.
Officers and Directors: William Dan Wright, Pres. and Director; Betty J. Wright, V.P. and Director; William E. Wright, Secy.-Treas. and Director; Betty Duane Bolton; James L. Bolton; Patricia L. Wright.
EIN: 752743584

9296
The David & Willa Grace Wynne Foundation
1021 Main St., Ste. 1275, 1 City Ctr.
Houston, TX   77002-2851

Established in 2006 in Texas.
Donor: Kenneth R. Wynne.
Foundation type: Independent foundation.
Financial data (yr. ended 12/31/13): Assets, $3,076,067 (M); gifts received, $31,940; expenditures, $191,391; qualifying distributions, $191,391; giving activities include $183,050 for 9 grants (high: $90,300; low: $500).
Fields of interest: Graduate and professional education; Christianity; Protestantism; Theology; Family services.
Limitations: Applications not accepted. Giving primarily in NC and TX. No grants to individuals.
Application information: Unsolicited requests for funds not accepted.
Trustee: Kenneth R. Wynne.
EIN: 300363741

9297
Young Family Charitable Foundation

5601 Banister Ct.
Plano, TX 75093-4227 (972) 964-6674
Contact: Chick Diane Young
E-mail: cym@chickyoung.com

Established in 1997 in Texas.
Donors: Charles M. Young; Dianne P. Young; Jennifer Timmons; Brad M. Young; Kyle A. Young; Michelle N. Young; R.J. Timmons.
Foundation type: Independent foundation.
Financial data (yr. ended 12/31/13): Assets, $617,228 (M); gifts received, $29,406; expenditures, $415,900; qualifying distributions, $415,450; giving activities include $415,000 for 8 grants (high: $205,000; low: $5,000).
Purpose and activities: Giving primarily to Christian churches.
Fields of interest: Education; Religion.
Limitations: Applications accepted. Giving primarily in Metairie, LA and Dallas, TX.
Application information: Application form required.
  Initial approach: Letter
  Deadline(s): None
Trustee: Merrill Lynch Trust Co.
Advisory Committee: Charles Young; Diane Young.
EIN: 226705354

9298
Youth Emergency Services

P.O. Box 13549
Austin, TX 78711-3549

Donor: Michael Kleinman.

Foundation type: Independent foundation.
Financial data (yr. ended 12/31/12): Assets, $492,471 (M); gifts received, $83,030; expenditures, $414,595; qualifying distributions, $398,350; giving activities include $398,350 for 139 grants (high: $106,000; low: $300).
Fields of interest: Museums; Services for offenders; Human services.
Limitations: Applications not accepted. Giving primarily in TX. No grants to individuals.
Application information: Contributes only to pre-selected organizations.
Officers: Michael Kleinman, Pres.; Mariann Garner-Wizard, V.P.; Roland De Noire, Secy.-Treas.
EIN: 741723924

9299
The Abe Zale Foundation

6360 LBJ Freeway, Ste. 205
Dallas, TX 75240

Established in 1995 in Texas.
Foundation type: Independent foundation.
Financial data (yr. ended 12/31/13): Assets, $3,553,856; expenditures, $347,961; qualifying distributions, $172,688.
Fields of interest: Arts and culture; Health; Human services.
Type of support: Capital campaigns; Equipment; Professorships; Research.
Limitations: Applications not accepted. Giving primarily in TX. No grants to individuals.
Application information: Unsolicited requests for funds not accepted.

Officers: Donald Zale, Chair.; George Tobolowsky, Pres.; Leonard R. Krasnow, Secy. and Exec. Dir.
Number of staff: None.
EIN: 752580972

9300
William & Sylvia Zale Foundation

16990 N. Dallas Pkwy., Ste. 210
Dallas, TX 75248-1952
Contact: Jack Chen

Established in 1951 in Texas.
Donors: Eugene Zale; Sylvia Zale; Lew D. Zale.
Foundation type: Independent foundation.
Financial data (yr. ended 08/31/14): Assets, $5,154,677 (M); expenditures, $334,459; qualifying distributions, $312,600; giving activities include $312,600 for 27 grants (high: $50,000; low: $1,000).
Purpose and activities: Giving primarily to Jewish agencies and temples, as well as for education and human services.
Fields of interest: Elementary and secondary education; Nonprofits; Judaism; Human services.
Type of support: Regranting.
Limitations: Applications not accepted. Giving primarily in Dallas, TX. No grants to individuals, or for scholarships, fellowships, or prizes; no loans.
Application information: Contributes only to pre-selected organizations.
Officers: Mark Zale, Pres.; Leslie Greco, V.P.
Directors: Cindy Zale Sollie; Daniel B. Zale; Gregory R. Zale; Stacy Zale.
EIN: 756037591

UTAH

9301
Brent & Cheri Andrus Charitable Trust
15 Sandstone Cove
Park City, UT 84060-6869

Donors: Brent Andrus; Cheri Andrus.
Foundation type: Independent foundation.
Financial data (yr. ended 12/31/13): Assets, $281,009 (M); gifts received, $200,000; expenditures, $223,879; qualifying distributions, $223,768; giving activities include $223,768 for 13 grants (high: $201,200; low: $50).
Fields of interest: Education; Nonprofits; Mormonism.
Type of support: Regranting.
Limitations: Applications not accepted. Giving primarily in UT. No grants to individuals.
Application information: Unsolicited requests for funds not accepted.
Trustees: Brent Andrus; Cheri Andrus.
EIN: 208074132

9302
The B. Attitudes Foundation
6949 S. High Tech Dr.
Midvale, UT 84047
Contact: Ginny U. Smith

Established in 2003 in Utah.
Donor: Brent L. Bishop.
Foundation type: Independent foundation.
Financial data (yr. ended 12/31/13): Assets, $6,658,939 (M); gifts received, $79,596; expenditures, $340,257; qualifying distributions, $283,399; giving activities include $126,727 for 23 grants (high: $36,800; low: $109), and $83,673 for grants to individuals.
Fields of interest: Arts and culture; Humanities; Education; Health; Community and economic development; Religion; Human services.
Type of support: Student aid.
Limitations: Applications not accepted. Giving primarily in UT.
Application information: Contributes only to pre-selected organizations.
Officers and Directors: Jill J. Bishop, Chair. and Director; Brent L. Bishop, Pres. and Treas. and Director; Bryan Bishop, V.P. and Director; Jamie Bishop, Secy.; Brandon J. Bishop; David B. Bishop; Betsy B. Blake.
Number of staff: 1 full-time professional.
EIN: 550828666

9303
The Backcountry Charitable Trust
1678 W. Redstone Ctr. Dr., Ste. 210
Park City, UT 84098-7614

Established in 2007 in Utah.
Donors: James H. Holland; Joseph J. Holland.
Foundation type: Independent foundation.
Financial data (yr. ended 12/31/13): Assets, $4,861,861 (M); gifts received, $10,027; expenditures, $226,750; qualifying distributions, $207,347; giving activities include $205,200 for 8 grants (high: $142,500; low: $2,000).

Fields of interest: Environment; Sports and recreation.
Limitations: Applications not accepted. Giving primarily in UT. No grants to individuals.
Application information: Unsolicited requests for funds not accepted.
Trustees: James H. Holland; Joseph J. Holland.
EIN: 261214808

9304
The M. Bastian Family Foundation
51 W. Center St., Ste. 305
Orem, UT 84057-4605

Established in 1993 in Utah.
Donor: Melanie L. Bastian.
Foundation type: Independent foundation.
Financial data (yr. ended 12/31/14): Assets, $4,461,829; expenditures, $213,187; qualifying distributions, $205,634.
Purpose and activities: Giving primarily for education, health care and medical research, and children's health services.
Fields of interest: Orchestral music; Education; Secondary education; Higher education; Nonprofits; Health; Diseases and conditions; Diabetes; HIV/AIDS; Cystic fibrosis; Radio; Television; Food aid; Child welfare; Homeless shelters; Women's services.
Type of support: Research; Research and evaluation; Regranting.
Limitations: Applications not accepted. Giving primarily in UT. No grants to individuals.
Application information: Unsolicited requests for funds not accepted.
Trustees: Melanie L. Bastian; McKay S. Matthews.
EIN: 876225255

9305
The Gail L. & Arthur E. Benjamin Foundation
10062 S. Stone Mountain Cove
Sandy, UT 84092-6542

Donor: Stephen Brewster.
Foundation type: Independent foundation.
Financial data (yr. ended 12/31/13): Assets, $486,478 (M); expenditures, $285,584; qualifying distributions, $223,886; giving activities include $218,485 for 33 grants (high: $25,050; low: $25).
Fields of interest: Orchestral music; Animal welfare; Diseases and conditions; Human services.
Limitations: Applications not accepted.
Application information: Unsolicited requests for funds not accepted.
Officer: Joseph Benjamin, Treas.
Trustees: Brent Anderson; Arthur E. Benjamin; Lee M. Brower; Patricia Ann Rhein.
EIN: 200200319

9306
The Bourne-Spafford Foundation
11201 S. Susan Dr.
Sandy, UT 84092-5102 (801) 277-5111
Contact: David R. Spafford, Tr.

Established in 1994 in Utah.
Donors: David R. Spafford; Susan B. Spafford.
Foundation type: Independent foundation.

Financial data (yr. ended 12/31/13): Assets, $2,056,589 (M); expenditures, $304,018; qualifying distributions, $271,500; giving activities include $271,500 for 5 grants (high: $250,000; low: $1,500).
Fields of interest: Orchestral music; Nonprofits.
Type of support: General support; Regranting.
Limitations: Applications accepted. Giving primarily in Salt Lake City, UT.
Application information: Application form required.
Initial approach: Letter
Deadline(s): None
Trustees: David R. Spafford; Susan B. Spafford.
EIN: 870533046

9307
Ruth H. Brown Foundation
2931 E. Bench Rd.
Moab, UT 84532-3607

Established in 1959 in Colorado.
Donor: Ruth H. Brown.
Foundation type: Independent foundation.
Financial data (yr. ended 12/31/13): Assets, $4,998,884 (M); expenditures, $230,362; qualifying distributions, $222,500; giving activities include $222,500 for grants.
Purpose and activities: Giving primarily for environmental education, protection and enhancement.
Limitations: Applications not accepted. Giving on a national basis, with a western emphasis. No support for religious organizations.
Application information: Unsolicited requests for funds not accepted.
Officers: Laurene Cochran, Pres.; Albert Brown, Secy.; Darcey Brown, Treas.
Trustee: Charla Brown.
Number of staff: 1 part-time support.
EIN: 846023395

9308
Kenneth P. & Sally Rich Burbidge Foundation
1725 Yalecrest Ave.
Salt Lake City, UT 84108-1839

Established in 1998 in Utah.
Donor: Sally Rich Burbidge.
Foundation type: Independent foundation.
Financial data (yr. ended 12/31/13): Assets, $5,011,730 (M); expenditures, $240,393; qualifying distributions, $201,384; giving activities include $201,384 for 14 grants (high: $115,255; low: $250).
Fields of interest: Education; University education; Human services.
Limitations: Applications not accepted. Giving primarily in UT. No grants to individuals.
Application information: Contributes only to pre-selected organizations.
Trustee: Karin Cook.
EIN: 870622260

9309
The Frances W. Burton Foundation
c/o First Western Advisors
6440 S. Millrock Dr., Ste. 150
Holladay, UT 84121-5893 (801) 269-1818
Contact: Gary W. Teran, Board Member

E-mail: email@fwbfoundation.org; Main URL: http://fwbfoundation.org

Foundation type: Independent foundation.
Financial data (yr. ended 12/31/13): Assets, $6,565,909 (M); gifts received, $17,019; expenditures, $292,703; qualifying distributions, $251,903; giving activities include $232,500 for 26 grants (high: $35,000; low: $2,500).
Purpose and activities: Giving primarily to organizations serving children and the underprivileged.
Fields of interest: Education; Cancers; Human services; Child welfare.
Limitations: Applications accepted. Giving primarily in UT. No grants to individuals.
Application information: Application form required.
Initial approach: Letter or E-mail
Deadline(s): Dec. 31
Trustee: Kim Plautz.
Board Members: Andrea W. Bauer; John S. Bradley; Scott Burton; Bret Gunderson; Gary W. Teran.
EIN: 204214804

9310
Paul Q. Callister Foundation Inc.
(formerly Louise E. Callister Foundation)
2005 S. 300 W.
Salt Lake City, UT 84115-1808

Established in 1958 in Utah.
Donors: Paul Q. Callister; Mary B. Callister.
Foundation type: Independent foundation.
Financial data (yr. ended 06/30/14): Assets, $7,665,210 (M); expenditures, $370,574; qualifying distributions, $306,000; giving activities include $306,000 for 4 grants (high: $160,000; low: $1,000).
Fields of interest: Arts and culture; Hospital care; Mormonism; American Indians.
Type of support: General support.
Limitations: Applications not accepted. Giving primarily in Salt Lake City, UT. No grants to individuals.
Application information: Unsolicited requests for funds not accepted.
Directors: Andrew Callister; Jan Callister; Paul Q. Callister; Sara McConkie; Jeanne C. Thorne.
EIN: 876118299

9311
Jeffrey S. and Helen H. Cardon Foundation
1663 Devonshire Dr.
Salt Lake City, UT 84108-2560   (801) 581-9333
Contact: Helen H. Cardon, Pres. and Dir.

Established in 2004 in Utah.
Donors: Helen H. Cardon; Jeffrey S. Cardon.
Foundation type: Independent foundation.
Financial data (yr. ended 12/31/13): Assets, $12,134,202 (M); gifts received, $1,500,000; expenditures, $384,229; qualifying distributions, $374,600; giving activities include $374,600 for 25 grants (high: $54,000; low: $200).
Fields of interest: Museums; University education; Cancers; Child welfare.
Limitations: Applications accepted. Giving primarily in IN and UT. No grants to individuals.
Application information:
Initial approach: Proposal
Deadline(s): None

Officers and Directors: Helen H. Cardon, Pres. and Director; Jeffrey S. Cardon, Secy.-Treas. and Director; Jane H. Mason.
EIN: 202029087

9312
CASA Family Foundation
115 W. 2150 N.
Centerville, UT 84014-2708

Established in 2005 in Utah.
Donors: Hermila Cutler; Christopher A. Cutler.
Foundation type: Independent foundation.
Financial data (yr. ended 12/31/13): Assets, $7,294,278 (M); expenditures, $391,513; qualifying distributions, $339,033; giving activities include $336,083 for 17 grants (high: $50,350; low: $5,000).
Fields of interest: Education; Human services; Adoption; Homeless shelters; Low-income and poor people.
Limitations: Applications not accepted. No grants to individuals.
Application information: Unsolicited requests for funds not accepted.
Officers: Christopher A. Cutler, Co-Chair.; Hermila Cutler, Co-Chair.
EIN: 203909377

9313
Catalyst Foundation
10 Exchange Pl., Ste. 520
Salt Lake City, UT 84111-2334   (801) 532-7900
Contact: Diana Lady Dougan, Chair. and Pres.

Established in 2000 in Utah.
Donors: J. Lynn Dougan; Galena Group; Diana Lady Dougan.
Foundation type: Independent foundation.
Financial data (yr. ended 12/31/13): Assets, $9,284,488 (M); gifts received, $214,488; expenditures, $319,111; qualifying distributions, $313,445; giving activities include $312,400 for 33 grants (high: $145,000; low: $250).
Fields of interest: Arts and culture; Education; Mental health care; Radio; Public policy.
Type of support: General support; Policy, advocacy and systems reform.
Limitations: Applications accepted. Giving primarily in CA, Washington, DC and UT. No grants to individuals.
Application information:
Initial approach: Proposal
Deadline(s): None
Officers and Trustees: Diana Lady Dougan, Chair. and Pres. and Trustee; Gavin M. Dougan, Secy. and Trustee; Elena Lady Minton, Treas. and Trustee; J. Lynn Dougan.
EIN: 870666762

9314
The Crawford Family Foundation
4760 Highland Dr.
P.O. Box 125
Holladay, UT 84117-5149

Established in 2004 in Utah.
Donor: Barbara Crawford Huppe.
Foundation type: Independent foundation.

Financial data (yr. ended 03/31/14): Assets, $3,399,931 (M); expenditures, $168,190; qualifying distributions, $166,540; giving activities include $151,000 for 6 grants (high: $70,000; low: $1,000).
Fields of interest: Health care clinics; Family planning; Child welfare; Homeless services.
Limitations: Applications not accepted. Giving primarily in UT. No grants to individuals.
Application information: Unsolicited requests for funds not accepted.
Officer and Directors: Barbara C. Huppe, Pres. and Director; George E. Mulligan; Lisa M. Sponaugle; William Lee Sponaugle.
EIN: 201724534

9315
David E. Cumming Family Foundation
P.O. Box 570
Oakley, UT 84055-0570
Contact: David E. Cumming, Pres. and Treas.

Donor: David E. Cumming.
Foundation type: Independent foundation.
Financial data (yr. ended 12/31/13): Assets, $9,079,175 (M); expenditures, $187,363; qualifying distributions, $164,671; giving activities include $162,395 for 15 grants (high: $50,000; low: $400).
Fields of interest: Child educational development; Maternal and perinatal health; Adult and child mentoring.
Limitations: Applications accepted. Giving primarily in Park City and Salt Lake City, UT.
Application information: Application form required.
Initial approach: Letter
Deadline(s): None
Officers: David E. Cumming, Pres. and Treas.; Allison R. Cumming, V.P.; Cathy McNab, Secy.-Treas.; Stephen D. Swindle, Secy.
EIN: 260403789

9316
John D. Cumming Family Foundation
1115 W. Old Ranch Rd.
Park City, UT 84098-6700
Contact: John D. Cumming, Pres. and Treas.

Donor: John D. Cumming.
Foundation type: Independent foundation.
Financial data (yr. ended 12/31/13): Assets, $7,792,527 (M); expenditures, $422,798; qualifying distributions, $403,832; giving activities include $356,000 for 6 grants (high: $250,000; low: $1,000).
Fields of interest: Education; Graduate and professional education; Medical education; Nursing care.
Limitations: Applications accepted. Giving primarily in Park City and Salt Lake City, UT.
Application information: Application form required.
Initial approach: Letter
Deadline(s): None
Officers: John D. Cumming, Pres. and Co-Treas.; Kristi Terzian Cumming, V.P.; Cathy Handley, Co-Secy.-Co-Treas.; Stephen D. Swindle, Co-Secy.
EIN: 260403677

9317
Donald D. & Elaine F. Davis Trust
966 Wintook Dr.
Ivins, UT   84738-6438

Established in 1986 in Virginia.
Donors: Donald D. Davis; Elaine F. Davis.
Foundation type: Independent foundation.
Financial data (yr. ended 12/31/13): Assets,
$527,533 (M); gifts received, $351,341;
expenditures, $196,082; qualifying distributions,
$192,620; giving activities include $192,620 for 21
grants (high: $86,966; low: $25).
Fields of interest: Higher education; Floods;
Mormonism.
Type of support: General support.
Limitations: Applications not accepted. Giving
primarily in UT; some giving in VA. No grants to
individuals.
Application information: Contributes only to
pre-selected organizations.
Trustees: Donald D. Davis; Elaine F. Davis.
EIN: 541398502

9318
Stephen G. and Susan E. Denkers Family Foundation
5210 Skyline Dr.
Ogden, UT   84403-4692

Established in 2000 in Utah.
Donors: Stephen G. Denkers; Susan E. Denkers.
Foundation type: Independent foundation.
Financial data (yr. ended 09/30/13): Assets,
$8,909,965 (M); expenditures, $492,487;
qualifying distributions, $383,571; giving activities
include $372,000 for 36 grants (high: $37,000;
low: $1,000).
Purpose and activities: Giving primarily for human
services, education, and nature conservancies.
Fields of interest: Natural history museums;
Education; Natural resources; Human services.
Limitations: Applications not accepted. Giving
primarily in UT and WA. No grants to individuals.
Application information: Contributes only to
pre-selected organizations.
Trustees: Stephen G. Denkers; Susan E. Denkers.
Directors: Ashley Nicole Bishop; Matthew Bishop;
Julie Denkers-Bishop; Kelli Sue Denkers; Madison
Denkers; Stephen E. Denkers.
EIN: 870659552

9319
Dialysis Research Foundation
5575 S. 500 E.
Ogden, UT   84405-6907

Foundation type: Independent foundation.
Financial data (yr. ended 12/31/13): Assets, $0
(M); expenditures, $455,107; qualifying
distributions, $323,912; giving activities include
$204,200 for 4 grants (high: $156,000; low: $700).
Purpose and activities: Giving limited to renal
disease research and treatment, and for non-profit
kidney disease foundations.
Fields of interest: Diseases and conditions.
Type of support: Research; Research and
evaluation.
Limitations: Applications not accepted. Giving
primarily in UT. No grants to individuals.

Application information: Contributes only to
pre-selected organizations.
Officers and Board Members: Fred Galvez, Pres.
and Director; Mardee Hagen, Secy. and Exec. Dir.;
Todd Schenck, Treas. and Director; Allen Berrett;
Neal Berube; Pam Corbridge; Jerald Israelsen;
Kelvin Jackson; Harry Senekjian, MD.
EIN: 942819009

9320
Dreamweaver Foundation
6300 Sagewood Dr., Ste. H502
Park City, UT   84098   (801) 281-7644
Contact: William C. Klintworth, Tr.

Established in 2000 in Utah.
Donor: John B. Benear.
Foundation type: Independent foundation.
Financial data (yr. ended 12/31/12): Assets,
$5,409,243 (M); expenditures, $168,387;
qualifying distributions, $162,082; giving activities
include $159,758 for 15 grants (high: $23,500;
low: $1,000).
Purpose and activities: Giving primarily to a medical
foundation which assists in the transfer of medical
supplies to medical mission agencies.
Fields of interest: Education; Health; Human
services.
Type of support: General support.
Limitations: Applications accepted. Giving primarily
in UT.
Application information: Application form required.
 Initial approach: Contact foundation
 Deadline(s): Aug. 31
Trustee: William C. Klintworth.
Directors: John B. Benear II; Bradford C. Bond.
EIN: 870648469

9321
Dry Creek Road
(formerly Pro Health Lab Park City)
6871 S. 700 W., Ste. 200
Midvale, UT   84047

Foundation type: Independent foundation.
Financial data (yr. ended 12/31/13): Assets,
$2,598,976 (M); gifts received, $1,016,573;
expenditures, $464,278; qualifying distributions,
$447,645; giving activities include $391,625 for 14
grants (high: $110,262; low: $168).
Fields of interest: Education; Employment; Human
services.
Limitations: Applications not accepted. Giving
primarily in Park City, UT.
Application information: Unsolicited requests for
funds not accepted.
Directors: Brent Griffiths; Lee McCullough; Thomas
Rosenberg; Saurabh Shah; Darin Zwick.
EIN: 204351350

9322
Eccles First Security Foundation
79 S. Main St., 2nd Fl.
Salt Lake City, UT   84111

Established in 1952 in Utah.
Donor: First Security Corp.
Foundation type: Company-sponsored foundation.
Financial data (yr. ended 12/31/13): Assets,
$4,000,338 (M); expenditures, $181,884;

qualifying distributions, $161,032; giving activities
include $120,000 for 7 grants (high: $50,000; low:
$10,000).
Purpose and activities: The foundation supports
organizations involved with higher education.
Fields of interest: Education.
Type of support: General support; Scholarships.
Limitations: Applications not accepted. Giving
limited to ID, UT, and WY. No grants to individuals.
Application information: Contributes only to
pre-selected organizations.
Officers and Trustees: Spencer F. Eccles, Chair. and
Trustee; Spencer P. Eccles, Pres. and Trustee;
Verna Lee Johnston, Secy.; Katherine Ann Eccles.
EIN: 876118149

9323
Henry W. & Leslie M. Eskuche Charitable Foundation
c/o U.S. Bank, N.A.
170 S. Main St., Ste. 600
Salt Lake City, UT   84101-3600   (801) 534-6045
Contact: Songa Corbin; Michael Poulter

Donor: Leslie M. Eskuche†.
Foundation type: Independent foundation.
Financial data (yr. ended 02/28/14): Assets,
$6,743,402 (M); expenditures, $392,512;
qualifying distributions, $308,955; giving activities
include $288,065 for 69 grants (high: $30,000;
low: $1,000).
Purpose and activities: Giving primarily for
education and health care.
Fields of interest: Education; Elementary and
secondary education; Higher education; Health;
Hospital care; Community and economic
development; Christianity; Human services; Child
welfare.
Type of support: General support; Capital
campaigns; Capital and infrastructure; Equipment;
Scholarships.
Limitations: Applications accepted. Giving primarily
in UT. No grants to individuals.
Publications: Application guidelines.
Application information: Application form required.
 Initial approach: Proposal
 Copies of proposal: 4
 Deadline(s): None
 Board meeting date(s): Jan., May, and Sept.
Trustee: U.S. Bank, N.A.
Advisory Committee: Paula Julander; Brian
Levin-Stankevich; Keith Odendahl.
EIN: 876179296

9324
Foothold
P.O. Box 712320
Salt Lake City, UT   84171—2320

Established in 2007 in Utah.
Donors: Independence Square, LLC; Richard N.
Beckstrand.
Foundation type: Operating foundation.
Financial data (yr. ended 12/31/13): Assets,
$3,087,910 (M); gifts received, $273,425;
expenditures, $367,914; qualifying distributions,
$368,026; giving activities include $350,384 for 4
grants (high: $254,000; low: $15,425).
Fields of interest: Education.
Limitations: Applications not accepted.

Application information: Unsolicited requests for funds not accepted.
Officers: Richard N. Beckstrand, Chair. and Pres.; Jonathan Beckstrand, Secy.
Board Members: Amy Marie Driggs; Carol B. Beckstrand.
EIN: 208968356

9325
The Funding Passion and Love Foundation Inc
9993 S. 3100 E.
Sandy, UT 84092-4205

Donor: Schutz Engel Trust.
Foundation type: Independent foundation.
Financial data (yr. ended 12/31/12): Assets, $365,828 (M); gifts received, $250,000; expenditures, $286,174; qualifying distributions, $263,780; giving activities include $263,780 for grants.
Fields of interest: Wildlife sanctuaries; Human services; Victim aid; Homeless services.
Limitations: Applications not accepted. Giving primarily in CA and UT. No grants to individuals.
Application information: Contributes only to pre-selected organizations.
Officers: David Mock, Pres.; Jeffrey G. Korn, Secy.-Treas.
EIN: 200451720

9326
Sterling & Shelli Gardner Foundation
610 W. Westfield Rd.
Alpine, UT 84004-1501
Application address: c/o Megan White, 732 W. 600 N., Alpine, UT 84004, tel.: (801) 717-6789

Established in 2002 in Utah.
Donors: Shelli Gardner; Sterling Gardner.
Foundation type: Independent foundation.
Financial data (yr. ended 12/31/13): Assets, $479,802 (M); gifts received, $200,000; expenditures, $194,889; qualifying distributions, $194,889; giving activities include $187,120 for 37 grants (high: $40,000; low: $620).
Fields of interest: Education; Community and economic development; Human services.
Limitations: Applications accepted. Giving primarily in UT.
Application information: Application form required.
Initial approach: Letter
Deadline(s): None
Trustees: Jon Brown; Shale Brown; Sara Douglas; Sean Douglas; Shelli Gardner; Sterling Gardner; Jason Hoopiiaina; Sage Hoopiiaina; Megan White; Nate White.
EIN: 870686202

9327
Val A. Green and Edith D. Green Foundation
4660 McKinney Ct.
Park City, UT 84098-8515 (801) 560-9326
Main URL: http://fdnweb.org/green

Established in 1997 in Utah.
Donors: Edith D. Green; Val A. Green.
Foundation type: Independent foundation.

Financial data (yr. ended 03/31/14): Assets, $8,134,872 (M); expenditures, $414,187; qualifying distributions, $387,118; giving activities include $206,000 for 9 grants (high: $100,000; low: $1,000).
Purpose and activities: The foundation's mission is to fund health care, medical research, local and higher education, and community projects in UT.
Fields of interest: Arts and culture; Elementary and secondary education; Higher education; Health; School-based health care; Diseases and conditions; Eye diseases; Community and economic development; Human services.
Type of support: Capital campaigns; Equipment; Scholarships; Research.
Limitations: Applications accepted. Giving limited to UT, with emphasis placed along the Wasatch Front. No support for foreign organizations. No grants to individuals.
Application information: See foundation web site for full application guidelines and requirements, including downloadable application form. Application form required.
Initial approach: Summary letter and application form
Deadline(s): Dec. 31
Final notification: Within 30 to 60 days
Officer and Trustees: Val J. Green, Pres. and Trustee; Brody Hamblin; Holly Hamblin; Kenlon Reeve; Aaron Green.
EIN: 841407030

9328
John and Wauna Harman Foundation
7838 River Oaks Cir.
Salt Lake City, UT 84093

Established in 1999 in Washington.
Donor: Wauna Harman.
Foundation type: Independent foundation.
Financial data (yr. ended 12/31/13): Assets, $8,467,184 (L); expenditures, $512,686; qualifying distributions, $501,917; giving activities include $402,920 for 11 grants (high: $262,920; low: $2,500).
Fields of interest: Foundations; Television; Human services.
Limitations: Applications not accepted. Giving primarily in Washington, DC, MA and WA. No grants to individuals.
Application information: Contributes only to pre-selected organizations.
Officers: Barry W. Harman, Pres.; Dawn Cook, V.P.; Julie A. Berrey, Secy.
Directors: Elaine Harman; Mark B. Harman; Todd B. Harman.
EIN: 911999241

9329
C. Charles Jackson Foundation
6193 W. Ridge Rd.
Highland, UT 84003-3623
Contact: Dr. Bruce H. Jackson, Tr.
E-mail for Dr. Bruce H. Jackson: BruceHJackson@comcast.net

Established in 2002 in Minnesota.
Donor: C. Charles Jackson†.
Foundation type: Independent foundation.
Financial data (yr. ended 12/31/13): Assets, $7,357,494 (M); expenditures, $464,091;

qualifying distributions, $315,572; giving activities include $268,500 for 35 grants (high: $12,000; low: $2,500).
Purpose and activities: Giving for leadership, character and life skills development programs, projects, and research for grades kindergarten through college.
Fields of interest: Education; Higher education; Community and economic development; Human services; Youth development.
Limitations: Applications accepted. Giving primarily in MN, with some giving on a national basis. No grants to individuals.
Publications: Informational brochure.
Application information: All applications and support materials must be in either PDF or Microsoft word format. Paper documentation is not accepted. Application form required.
Initial approach: Only e-mail inquiries pertaining to leadership programs, projects and research accepted
Copies of proposal: 1
Deadline(s): Nov. 1
Board meeting date(s): Four times a year
Final notification: 60 days after Nov. 1
Trustees: Dr. Bruce H. Jackson; Wells Fargo Bank Minnesota, N.A.
Number of staff: None.
EIN: 411996905

9330
JKS Foundation
6440 S. Wasatch Blvd., Ste. 105
Holladay, UT 84121-3559

Donors: Joseph Sorenson; Kathleen Sorenson.
Foundation type: Operating foundation.
Financial data (yr. ended 12/31/13): Assets, $5,925,358 (M); gifts received, $789,264; expenditures, $328,073; qualifying distributions, $256,865; giving activities include $250,000 for 6 grants (high: $200,000; low: $5,000).
Fields of interest: Education; Human services; Youth development.
Limitations: Applications not accepted. Giving primarily in UT.
Application information: Unsolicited requests for funds not accepted.
Officer: Joseph Sorenson, Treas.
Directors: Heather S. Baugh; Holly Grierson; Jason Sorenson; Jessica Sorenson; Katelyn Sorenson; Kathleen Sorenson.
EIN: 263948638

9331
JNF Foundation
c/o S. Warburton
1968 Lincoln Ln., Ste. 2A
Salt Lake City, UT 84124-2753

Established in 2007 in Utah.
Donors: James Fosgate; Norma Fosgate.
Foundation type: Independent foundation.
Financial data (yr. ended 12/31/13): Assets, $1,410,868 (M); gifts received, $500,000; expenditures, $278,034; qualifying distributions, $210,527; giving activities include $210,527 for 17 grants (high: $40,000; low: $500).
Fields of interest: Human services.

Limitations: Applications not accepted. Giving primarily in Salt Lake City, UT. No grants to individuals.
Application information: Unsolicited requests for funds not accepted.
Directors: Cameron Bennee; Kaira Bennee; Betty McElroy; Christine Paramore; Susan Warburton.
EIN: 260523149

9332
Robert W. & Barbara J. Keener Foundation
P.O. Box 9360
Salt Lake City, UT   84109-0360

Established in 1995 in Utah.
Donors: Robert W. Keener; Barbara J. Keener.
Foundation type: Independent foundation.
Financial data (yr. ended 05/31/14): Assets, $4,825,226 (M); gifts received, $100,000; expenditures, $204,738; qualifying distributions, $161,957; giving activities include $82,700 for 12 grants (high: $25,000; low: $500), and $78,250 for 42 grants to individuals (high: $5,000; low: $500).
Purpose and activities: Giving for education, health, housing, and Christian organizations.
Fields of interest: Education; Religion; Human services.
Type of support: Student aid; Grants to individuals.
Limitations: Applications not accepted. Giving primarily in CA, MO and UT.
Application information: Unsolicited requests for funds not accepted.
Trustees: Daniel D. Garner IV; Robert W. Keener.
Director: Mary D. Draper.
EIN: 876232895

9333
Kennecott Utah Copper Visitors Center Charitable Foundation
4700 Daybreak Pkwy.
South Jordan, UT   84095-5120   (801) 204-2000
Contact: Brian Davis, Tr.
Main URL: http://www.kennecott.com/kennecott-foundation

Established in 1994 in Utah.
Donors: Kennecott Utah Copper Corp.; Mrs. Herb Babcock; David Moffatt; Kennecott Employee Care & Share Campaign.
Foundation type: Company-sponsored foundation.
Financial data (yr. ended 12/31/13): Assets, $1,099,738 (M); gifts received, $247,613; expenditures, $252,957; qualifying distributions, $252,781; giving activities include $252,676 for 114 grants (high: $28,806; low: $20).
Purpose and activities: The foundation supports organizations involved with health, human services, senior citizens, disabled people, and homeless people.
Fields of interest: Health; Human services; Child welfare; Seniors; Homeless people; People with disabilities.
Type of support: General support; Continuing support; Annual campaigns; Program development.
Limitations: Applications accepted. Giving primarily in areas of company operations in Salt Lake, UT.
Publications: Application guidelines.
Application information: Application form required.

Initial approach: Download application form and mail proposal and application form to foundation
Copies of proposal: 1
Deadline(s): Oct. 15
Board meeting date(s): 2 to 3 times per year
Officers and Trustees: Ted Himebaugh, Pres. and Trustee; Julie Cummings, Secy. and Trustee; Jack Welch, Treas. and Trustee; Rev. Patrick Carley; Gary Curtis; Norm Fitzgerald; Scott Whipple.
EIN: 870560044

9334
Kirk Humanitarian
201 S. Main St., Ste. 1100
Salt Lake City, UT   84111-4904

Established in 2006 in Utah.
Donors: Spencer Kirk; Kirk 101 Trust; Krispen Family Holdings.
Foundation type: Operating foundation.
Financial data (yr. ended 06/30/13): Assets, $937,180 (M); gifts received, $3,435,426; expenditures, $462,142; qualifying distributions, $462,139; giving activities include $434,455 for 3 grants (high: $214,455; low: $60,000).
Fields of interest: Human services.
Limitations: Applications not accepted. Giving primarily in OR.
Application information: Unsolicited requests for funds not accepted.
Officers and Directors: Spencer Kirk, Pres. and Director; Kristen Kirk, Secy.-Treas.; Ronald Moffitt.
EIN: 203920671

9335
Kyle Korver Foundation
1780 Sunrise Park Cir.
Sandy, UT   84093-2451
Main URL: http://www.kylekorverfoundation.com

Donors: Kyle Korver; Seer Outfitters LLC; Kind LLC.
Foundation type: Independent foundation.
Financial data (yr. ended 12/31/13): Assets, $959,222 (M); gifts received, $697,839; expenditures, $629,906; qualifying distributions, $534,711; giving activities include $177,000 for 3 grants (high: $150,000; low: $2,000), and $332,711 for 2 foundation-administered programs.
Fields of interest: Education; Religion; Human services.
Limitations: Applications not accepted. Giving primarily in Omaha, NE.
Application information: Unsolicited requests for funds not accepted.
Officers: Kyle Korver, Pres.; Laine Korver, V.P.; Jeff Schwartz, Secy.; Lester Knispel, Treas.
EIN: 205879443

9336
Sally Langdon Barefoot Foundation
2490 Wall Ave.
Ogden, UT   84401-3057   8016210440
Application address: c/o W. Rory Youngberg, 2050 Combe Rd., Ogden, UT 84403; tel.: (801) 479-3021

Donors: Sally Barefoot; S. J. Barefoot Irrevoc Trust.
Foundation type: Independent foundation.

Financial data (yr. ended 12/31/14): Assets, $5,660,628; expenditures, $383,994; qualifying distributions, $272,520.
Fields of interest: Education; Health; Protestantism.
Limitations: Applications accepted. Giving primarily in UT.
Application information: Application form required.
Initial approach: Contact foundation for application form
Deadline(s): Sept. 30
Trustees: Lisha Y. Rudd; Barbara Youngberg; Kristian R. Youngberg; Lance L. Youngberg; Rory Youngberg.
EIN: 200342204

9337
E. & B. Larsen Family Foundation
252 N. 950 E.
Orem, UT   84097-4977

Foundation type: Independent foundation.
Financial data (yr. ended 12/31/13): Assets, $3,782,674 (L); gifts received, $2,779,312; expenditures, $199,161; qualifying distributions, $199,161; giving activities include $199,161 for 6 grants (high: $110,086; low: $1,175).
Fields of interest: Education; Mormonism.
Type of support: General support.
Limitations: Applications not accepted. Giving primarily in UT. No grants to individuals.
Application information: Unsolicited requests for funds not accepted.
Officers: Eric Larsen, Pres.; Brenda Larsen, Secy.
EIN: 760792103

9338
The Michael & Jacalyn Leavitt Foundation
216 S. 200 W.
Cedar City, UT   84720-3207

Donors: Michael O. Leavitt; Jacalyn S. Leavitt; University of Utah; Third Chapter, Inc.; Utah Valley University.
Foundation type: Independent foundation.
Financial data (yr. ended 12/31/13): Assets, $1,827,741 (M); gifts received, $170,500; expenditures, $173,941; qualifying distributions, $173,600; giving activities include $173,600 for 5 grants (high: $147,000; low: $100).
Fields of interest: Education; Mormonism; Human services.
Limitations: Applications not accepted. Giving limited to UT. No grants to individuals.
Application information: Contributes only to pre-selected organizations.
Officer: Jim Douglas, Treas.
Trustees: Jacalyn S. Leavitt; Michael O. Leavitt.
EIN: 202361058

9339
Bruce Lindorf Memorial Foundation
51 W. Center St., Ste. 604
Orem, UT   84057-4605   (801) 426-4366
Contact: Ronald S. Lindorf, Pres.

Donors: Ronald S. Lindorf; David Forsyth; Howard Wahl.
Foundation type: Independent foundation.
Financial data (yr. ended 11/30/13): Assets, $3,707,503 (M); gifts received, $14,150;

expenditures, $366,010; qualifying distributions, $280,098; giving activities include $263,590 for 16 grants (high: $88,800; low: $200).
Purpose and activities: Giving for primarily to the Mormon Church, some giving to education for scholarships.
Fields of interest: Education; Health; Religion.
Limitations: Applications accepted. Giving limited to residents of UT.
Application information: Application form required.
   Initial approach: Mail
   Deadline(s): Apr. 1
Officers: Ronald S. Lindorf, Pres.; Terri Lindorf, Secy.
EIN: 237061702

9340
Low Book Sales Foundation
590 N. State St.
Lindon, UT   84042-1321   (801) 922-9191
Contact: David Nielson, Dir.

Donor: Low Book Sales Management Group.
Foundation type: Independent foundation.
Financial data (yr. ended 12/31/13): Assets, $36,189 (M); gifts received, $285,425; expenditures, $251,595; qualifying distributions, $251,595; giving activities include $251,085 for 16 grants (high: $90,985; low: $500).
Purpose and activities: Grants to provide adoption service, education to students K-12, worldwide humanitarian service and for cancer research.
Fields of interest: Education; Health; Human services.
Limitations: Applications accepted. Giving primarily in UT.
Application information: Application form required.
   Initial approach: Proposal
   Deadline(s): None
Directors: Chas Felt; David Nielson; Jody Nielson.
EIN: 208967423

9341
The Leslie DeeAnn Mower Foundation
3189 Canyon Rd.
Springville, UT   84663-9538   (801) 426-8600
Contact: Leslie DeeAnn Mower, Tr.

Established in 2007 in Utah.
Donor: Leslie DeeAnn Mower.
Foundation type: Independent foundation.
Financial data (yr. ended 12/31/13): Assets, $5,180,581 (M); gifts received, $4,090; expenditures, $302,738; qualifying distributions, $250,000; giving activities include $250,000 for 3 grants (high: $150,000; low: $30,000).
Fields of interest: Foundations; Television.
Limitations: Applications accepted. Giving primarily in UT. No grants for Contact for information.
Application information: Application form required.
   Initial approach: Contact foundation for
      application form
   Deadline(s): Contact foundation for deadlines
Trustees: Leslie DeeAnn Mower; Jamie Ross; Robert Steed.
EIN: 260507671

9342
Odyssey Foundation
P.O. Box 712320
Salt Lake City, UT   84171-2320

Established in 1999 in Nevada.
Donors: Frank Roberts; Jean Roberts.
Foundation type: Independent foundation.
Financial data (yr. ended 12/31/13): Assets, $4,546,650 (M); expenditures, $203,188; qualifying distributions, $247,931; giving activities include $156,500 for 2 grants (high: $150,000; low: $6,500).
Fields of interest: Arts and culture; Education; Environment; Health; Human services.
Type of support: Continuing support; In-kind gifts; Capital and infrastructure; General support; Equipment; Program development; Seed money.
Limitations: Applications not accepted. Giving primarily in CO and NV.
Application information: Unsolicited requests for funds not accepted.
Officers and Board Members: Frank Roberts, Chair.; Eric Roberts, Pres. and Director; Donald Roberts, Secy. and Director; Katherine Farrell; Tim Farrell; Doug Roberts; Jean Roberts; Joan Roberts.
EIN: 880436019

9343
Charles Maxfield & Gloria F. Parrish Foundation
c/o Erika Parrish Bunnell
2195 Dallin St.
Salt Lake City, UT   84109-1116

Established in 1992 in Utah.
Donors: Charles Maxfield Parrish†; Gloria F. Parrish.
Foundation type: Independent foundation.
Financial data (yr. ended 12/31/14): Assets, $10,551,599; expenditures, $521,826; qualifying distributions, $428,923.
Fields of interest: Historical activities.
Type of support: General support.
Limitations: Applications not accepted. Giving primarily in Washington, DC; some giving in TN, UT and WY. No grants to individuals.
Application information: Unsolicited requests for funds not accepted.
Officers: Erika Marie Parrish, Pres.; Kristine Ann Parrish, V.P.; Charles Kurt Parrish, Secy.; Charles Bryan Parrish, Treas.
EIN: 870490763

9344
Dinesh and Kalpana Patel Foundation
P.O. Box 58887
Salt Lake City, UT   84158-0887

Established in 1994 in Utah.
Donors: Dinesh C. Patel; Kalpana Patel.
Foundation type: Independent foundation.
Financial data (yr. ended 12/31/13): Assets, $239,304 (M); gifts received, $434,265; expenditures, $448,984; qualifying distributions, $441,606; giving activities include $441,606 for 59 grants (high: $134,000; low: $20).
Fields of interest: Arts and culture; Education; University education; Hinduism.
Type of support: Annual campaigns; Matching grants; Capital campaigns; Capital and infrastructure; Convening; Scholarships.

Limitations: Applications not accepted. Giving primarily in MI and UT. No grants to individuals.
Application information: Contributes only to pre-selected organizations.
Trustees: Dinesh C. Patel; Kalpana D. Patel; Kiran C. Patel.
EIN: 870532423

9345
Promontory Foundation
8758 N. Promontory Ranch Rd.
Park City, UT   84098-6226   (435) 333-4204
Contact: Beth Armstrong, Secy.
Main URL: http://www.promontoryclub.com

Donors: Paul Jennings; Donald Robert; Ronald Ormand; Francis Najafi; Robert Marling; Ken Abdalla; Mark Gurvitz; Pivotal Foundation; Jennings Family Foundation; Terry Hartshorn; Claire Van Konynenburg; John Michael Corder; Robert Marling; Jim Laub; Leonard Marek; Dale Miller; Thomas Raffa; E.L. Shannon; Ruth B. Shannon; Robert Barrett; William Taylor; Braden Hopkins; The Ron and Nancy Ormand Family Foundation; Richard Wallace; Gary Mandel; Barry Holden; John Piecush.
Foundation type: Independent foundation.
Financial data (yr. ended 12/31/13): Assets, $59,130 (M); gifts received, $246,735; expenditures, $295,196; qualifying distributions, $295,196; giving activities include $218,000 for 16 grants (high: $40,000; low: $7,500).
Fields of interest: Arts and culture; Education; Diseases and conditions.
Limitations: Applications accepted. Giving primarily in Park City, UT.
Application information: Application form required.
   Initial approach: Proposal
   Deadline(s): Jul. 5
Officers: Rich Sonntag, Pres.; Francis Najafi, V.P.; Beth Armstrong, Secy.; Stephen Lees, Treas.
EIN: 205016814

9346
Questar Corporation Arts Foundation
QC 690
P.O. Box 45433
Salt Lake City, UT   84145-0433
FAX: (801) 324-5483;
E-mail: debra.hoyt@questar.com; Main URL: http://www.questar.com/4EnvironmentCommunity/Community.php

Established in 1991 in Utah.
Donor: Questar Corp.
Foundation type: Company-sponsored foundation.
Financial data (yr. ended 12/31/14): Assets, $2,870,843; gifts received, $0; expenditures, $282,135; qualifying distributions, $280,000 and $0 for set-asides.
Purpose and activities: The foundation supports organizations involved with arts and culture.
Fields of interest: Arts and culture.
Type of support: Continuing support; Program-related investments; Capital and infrastructure.
Limitations: Applications not accepted. Giving limited to UT. No grants to individuals.
Publications: Annual report.
Application information: Contributes only to pre-selected organizations.

Officers and Trustees: Ronald W. Jibson, Chair. and Pres. and Trustee; Allan Bradley, V.P. and Trustee; Debra Hoyt, Secy.; Kevin Hadlock, Treas. and Trustee; Thomas Jepperson.
Number of staff: None.
EIN: 870489086

9347
Questar Corporation Educational Foundation
QC 690
P.O. Box 45433
Salt Lake City, UT 84145-0433
FAX: (801) 324-5483;
E-mail: debra.hoyt@questar.com; Main URL: http://www.questar.com/4EnvironmentCommunity/Community.php

Established in 1988 in Utah.
Donor: Questar Corp.
Foundation type: Company-sponsored foundation.
Financial data (yr. ended 12/31/14): Assets, $4,269,526; gifts received, $0; expenditures, $288,181; qualifying distributions, $286,000 and $0 for set-asides.
Purpose and activities: The foundation supports institutions of higher education.
Fields of interest: Education.
Type of support: Capital campaigns; Capital and infrastructure; Student aid.
Limitations: Applications not accepted. Giving limited to areas of company operations in AZ, CO, OK, TX, UT, and WY. No grants to individuals (except for scholarships).
Application information: Contributes only to pre-selected organizations.
Officers and Trustees: Ronald W. Jibson, Chair. and Pres. and Trustee; Allan Bradley, V.P. and Trustee; Kevin Hadlock, Treas. and Trustee; Debra Hoyt, Secy.; Thomas Jepperson.
Number of staff: None.
EIN: 870461487

9348
The Scott and Robyn Scharman Family Foundation Inc.
19 Crosshill Ln.
Sandy, UT 84092-6512

Donors: Cross Hill Venturs, LLC; Schemco FLP; Scott & Robyn Scharman Charitable Remainder Unitrust; Bentwood Family LP; Quorus Ventures LLC.
Foundation type: Independent foundation.
Financial data (yr. ended 12/31/13): Assets, $1,139 (M); gifts received, $186,500; expenditures, $185,615; qualifying distributions, $185,500; giving activities include $185,500 for 5 grants (high: $164,000; low: $500).
Fields of interest: Education; Mormonism.
Limitations: Applications not accepted. Giving primarily in UT.
Application information: Unsolicited requests for funds not accepted.
Trustees: Christopher Scharman; Robyn Scharman; Scott Scharman.
EIN: 270158181

9349
Theodore & Elizabeth Schmidt Family Foundation
2115 Connor Park Cove
Salt Lake City, UT 84109-2468

Established in 1998 in California.
Donors: Elizabeth Schmidt; Theodore Schmidt, Jr.
Foundation type: Independent foundation.
Financial data (yr. ended 07/31/14): Assets, $4,569,996 (M); expenditures, $419,345; qualifying distributions, $382,388; giving activities include $382,388 for 47 grants (high: $96,948; low: $200).
Purpose and activities: Giving primarily for education and hospitals; funding also for human services.
Fields of interest: Arts and culture; Performing arts; Education; Higher education; Nonprofits; Hospital care; Christianity; Mormonism; Human services.
Type of support: Regranting.
Limitations: Applications not accepted. Giving primarily in CA and UT. No grants to individuals.
Application information: Contributes only to pre-selected organizations.
Officers: Theodore Schmidt, Pres.; Sandefur Schmidt, Treas.
EIN: 680422838

9350
Duane and Marci Shaw Foundation, Inc.
1220 E. 7800 S.
Sandy, UT 84094-7285 (801) 530-7359

Donors: John Duane Shaw; Marchelle Marie Shaw.
Foundation type: Independent foundation.
Financial data (yr. ended 12/31/13): Assets, $5,816,290 (M); gifts received, $450; expenditures, $268,100; qualifying distributions, $266,100; giving activities include $266,100 for 1 grant.
Fields of interest: Education.
Limitations: Applications accepted. Giving primarily in UT.
Application information: Application form required.
    Initial approach: Contact Foundation or Telephone
    Deadline(s): None
Directors: Rebecca Lyn Alder; Karen Marie Bitton; Natalie Anne Kessler; John Duane Shaw; John William Shaw; Marchelle Marie Shaw.
EIN: 455628049

9351
Joanne L. Shrontz Family Foundation
P.O. Box 45385
Salt Lake City, UT 84145-0385

Donors: Ellen S. Erlingsson; Ellen E. Rossi.
Foundation type: Independent foundation.
Financial data (yr. ended 12/31/13): Assets, $4,238,738 (M); expenditures, $280,800; qualifying distributions, $243,179; giving activities include $240,000 for 27 grants (high: $42,000; low: $1,000).
Fields of interest: Arts and culture; Education; Environment; Diseases and conditions.
Limitations: Applications not accepted. Giving primarily in UT.
Application information: Unsolicited requests for funds not accepted.

Trustees: Erik C. Erlingsson; Clark P. Giles; Herbert C. Livsey; Ellen E. Rossi; Maywood Trust Company, LLC.
EIN: 208515544

9352
The Skolnick Foundation
1553 Connecticut Dr.
Salt Lake City, UT 84103-4204 (801) 364-0936

Established in 1996 in Utah.
Donors: Angela A. Skolnick; Mark H. Skolnick.
Foundation type: Independent foundation.
Financial data (yr. ended 12/31/14): Assets, $3,852,679; expenditures, $439,445; qualifying distributions, $427,879.
Fields of interest: Museums; Education; Health; Disasters and emergency management; Human services.
International interests: Mexico.
Limitations: Applications accepted. Giving primarily in Salt Lake City, UT and Zuni, NM. No grants to individuals.
Application information:
    Initial approach: Proposal
    Deadline(s): None
Trustees: Angela A. Skolnick; Giancarlo Skolnick; Joshua Skolnick; Mark H. Skolnick.
EIN: 870567067

9353
William E. Slaughter, Jr. Foundation, Inc.
375 S. Main St., No. 144
Moab, UT 84532-2557

Established in 1959 in Michigan.
Donor: William E. Slaughter, Jr.‡
Foundation type: Independent foundation.
Financial data (yr. ended 12/31/13): Assets, $0 (M); expenditures, $168,840; qualifying distributions, $160,000; giving activities include $160,000 for 32 grants (high: $20,000; low: $1,000).
Purpose and activities: Giving primarily for wildlife and animal preservation, world improvement, and the environment.
Fields of interest: Environment; Natural resources; Animal welfare; International peace and security.
Type of support: General support; Continuing support; Annual campaigns; Seed money.
Limitations: Applications not accepted. Giving primarily in AZ, HI, and UT. No grants to individuals or for scholarships.
Application information: Contributes only to pre-selected organizations.
Officers and Directors: Kent C. Slaughter, Pres. and Secy. and Director; Gloria Slaughter, V.P. and Director; William E. Stillwater, V.P. and Director; William A. Corbett, Treas.
Number of staff: None.
EIN: 386065616

9354
SmartGo Foundation
3021 Chaucer Pl.
Salt Lake City, UT 84108-2503

Established in 2006 in Utah.
Foundation type: Independent foundation.

Financial data (yr. ended 12/31/12): Assets, $4,245,775 (M); expenditures, $312,874; qualifying distributions, $156,000; giving activities include $156,000 for grants.
Fields of interest: Education; Gardening; Human services; Basic and emergency aid; International development.
Limitations: Applications not accepted. Giving primarily in UT, with some giving in CA, GA, and NY. No grants to individuals.
Application information: Contributes only to pre-selected organizations.
Directors: Anders Kierulf; Bjorn Kierulf; Sara A. Rich.
EIN: 205290408

9355
Beverley Taylor Sorenson Foundation
299 S. Main St., Ste. 2200
Salt Lake City, UT   84111-2288

Donor: Beverley Taylor Sorenson Revocable Trust.
Foundation type: Independent foundation.
Financial data (yr. ended 12/31/13): Assets, $299,087 (M); gifts received, $452,750; expenditures, $153,663; qualifying distributions, $153,663; giving activities include $152,750 for 1 grant.
Fields of interest: Arts and culture.
Limitations: Applications not accepted. Giving primarily in Salt Lake City, UT.
Application information: Unsolicited requests for funds not accepted.
Directors: Joan Fenton; James Lee Sorenson; Joseph Sorenson.
EIN: 463784084

9356
James LeVoy Sorenson Foundation
2511 S. West Temple St.
Salt Lake City, UT   84115-3060   (801) 461-9700
Contact: James Lee Sorenson, Tr.

Established in 1986 in Utah.
Donor: James LeVoy Sorenson†.
Foundation type: Independent foundation.
Financial data (yr. ended 12/31/12): Assets, $0 (M); expenditures, $235,242; qualifying distributions, $235,242; giving activities include $234,381 for 1 grant.
Fields of interest: Arts and culture.
Type of support: General support; Matching grants.
Limitations: Applications accepted. Giving primarily in Salt Lake City, UT. No grants to individuals.
Application information:
    Initial approach: Contact foundation
    Deadline(s): None
Trustees: Beverly Sorenson; James Lee Sorenson.
Directors: Ann Crocker; Gary Crocker; Joan Fenton; Christine Harris; Shauna Johnson; Carol Smith; Kathleen Sorenson; Gail Williamsen.
EIN: 870440827

9357
Spendlove Research Foundation
365 N. 600 W.
Logan, UT   84321

Established in 1989 in Utah.
Donors: Rex S. Spendlove; Reta A. Spendlove; Alan Spendlove.

Foundation type: Operating foundation.
Financial data (yr. ended 12/31/13): Assets, $3,760,000 (M); expenditures, $412,355; qualifying distributions, $396,510; giving activities include $396,510 for 1 grant.
Fields of interest: Diseases and conditions.
Type of support: Research; Research and evaluation.
Limitations: Applications not accepted. Giving primarily in Logan, UT.
Application information: Unsolicited requests for funds not accepted.
Officers: Rex S. Spendlove, Pres.; Debbi Spendlove, Secy.
Directors: Lori Arnold; Lisa Cornwell; Cheri Murdock; Reta A. Spendlove.
EIN: 870461699

9358
Steiner Foundation, Inc.
505 E. South Temple St.
Salt Lake City, UT   84102-1004   (801) 328-8831
Contact: Kevin K. Steiner, Pres. and Dir.

Established in 1959 in Utah.
Donors: Steiner Corp.; Alsco Inc.; Richard R. Steiner†.
Foundation type: Company-sponsored foundation.
Financial data (yr. ended 06/30/13): Assets, $6,466,491 (M); gifts received, $500,000; expenditures, $416,115; qualifying distributions, $403,375; giving activities include $403,375 for 32 grants (high: $120,000; low: $1,000).
Purpose and activities: The foundation supports organizations involved with dance, theater, education, family planning, substance abuse services, human services, and economically disadvantaged people.
Fields of interest: Dance; Theater; Education; Elementary and secondary education; Higher education; Education services; Family planning; Addiction services; Human services; Scouting programs; Homeless services; Low-income and poor people.
Type of support: General support; Scholarships.
Limitations: Applications accepted. Giving primarily in UT.
Application information:
    Initial approach: Proposal
    Deadline(s): None
Officers and Directors: Kevin K. Steiner, Pres. and Director; Timothy L. Weiler, Treas.; Piper Rogers; Richard A. Rogers; Melissa Steiner-Griffiths; Robert C. Steiner; David Winder.
EIN: 876119190

9359
Telemachus: Foundation to Empower the Poor and End War
549 Cortez St.
Salt Lake City, UT   84103-2122   (801) 364-2971

Established in 2003 in Utah.
Donors: Deb Sawyer; Kimber Martinson-Sawyer.
Foundation type: Independent foundation.
Financial data (yr. ended 12/31/13): Assets, $3,405,930 (M); expenditures, $209,052; qualifying distributions, $185,940; giving activities include $185,940 for 17 grants (high: $52,000; low: $1,500).

Fields of interest: Education; Natural resources; Science; International relations.
Limitations: Applications accepted. Giving primarily in Washington, DC, New York, NY and UT.
Application information:
    Initial approach: Proposal
    Deadline(s): None
Officers: Deb Sawyer, Pres. and Secy.; Wayne Martinson, Treas.
EIN: 743078500

9360
Harold & Elaine Turley Foundation
2857 Willow Creek Dr.
Sandy, UT   84093-2048

Donors: Harold E. & Elaine Turley Trust; Harold E. & Elaine Turley Charitable Remainder Unitrust.
Foundation type: Independent foundation.
Financial data (yr. ended 12/31/13): Assets, $141,892 (M); gifts received, $255,000; expenditures, $214,804; qualifying distributions, $214,800; giving activities include $214,800 for 35 grants (high: $95,687; low: $15).
Fields of interest: Education; Christianity; Mormonism; Sports and recreation.
Limitations: Applications not accepted. Giving primarily in UT.
Application information: Unsolicited requests for funds not accepted.
Trustees: Kathryn T. Sonne; Susan Steiner; Derek J. Turley; Elaine E. Turley; Harold E. Turley, Jr.; Harold E. Turley III; Kalei T. Wyatt.
EIN: 262008261

9361
Utah Medical Association Foundation
310 E. 4500 S.
Salt Lake City, UT   84107-4250   (801) 747-3500
Contact: Michelle S. McOmber, Secy.-Treas.
E-mail: michelle@utahmed.org; *Main URL:* http://www.utahmed.org/WCM/Health_Promotion/UMA_Foundation/wcm/_HealthPromotion/Foundation3.aspx

Foundation type: Independent foundation.
Financial data (yr. ended 12/31/13): Assets, $0 (M); gifts received, $2,611; expenditures, $503,828; qualifying distributions, $226,433; giving activities include $209,500 for 25 grants (high: $20,000; low: $3,000).
Fields of interest: Education; Domesticated animals; Health.
Limitations: Applications accepted. Giving primarily in UT.
Application information: See foundation website for complete application guidelines. Application form required.
    Initial approach: Proposal
    Deadline(s): Apr. 15, Oct. 15
Officers: Scott A. Leckman, MD, Chair.; Michelle S. McOmber, Secy.-Treas.
Directors: Stewart E. Barlow, MD; George W. Cannon, MD; F. James Cowan; John Gates; Richard Home; Val B. Johnson, MD; Richard J. Sperry, MD.
EIN: 876122299

9362
Wadman Foundation
2920 S. 925 W.
Ogden, UT   84401-3800
Contact: David L. Wadman, Pres.

Established in 1998 in Utah.
Donors: David Wadman; V. Jay Wadman†.
Foundation type: Independent foundation.
Financial data (yr. ended 12/31/14): Assets,
$4,365,680 (M); gifts received, $200,000;
expenditures, $214,093; qualifying distributions,
$207,428; giving activities include $207,428 for 40
grants (high: $140,000; low: $100).
Purpose and activities: Giving primarily for
education and human services, particularly to an
organization for Native Americans.
Fields of interest: Elementary and secondary
education; Higher education; Youth development;
American Indians.

Limitations: Applications accepted. Giving primarily
in UT. No grants to individuals.
Application information:
  Initial approach: Proposal
  Deadline(s): None
Officers: David L. Wadman, Pres.; Ronda Wadman,
V.P.
EIN: 841392243

9363
The Zions Bancorporation Foundation
1 S. Main St., 15th Fl.
Salt Lake City, UT   84133-1109

Established in 1997 in Utah.
Donor: Zions Bancorporation.
Foundation type: Company-sponsored foundation.

Financial data (yr. ended 12/31/13): Assets,
$3,020,124 (M); gifts received, $2,500;
expenditures, $204,015; qualifying distributions,
$201,500; giving activities include $201,500 for 25
grants (high: $50,000; low: $500).
Purpose and activities: The foundation supports
organizations involved with performing arts, the
environment, health, cancer, legal aid, and
community development.
Fields of interest: Human services.
Type of support: General support; Program
development.
Limitations: Applications not accepted. Giving
limited to CA, Las Vegas, NV, Portland, OR, Houston,
TX, and Salt Lake City, UT. No grants to individuals.
Application information: Unsolicited requests for
funds not accepted.
Officers and Trustees: Harris H. Simmons, Pres.
and Trustee; W. David Hemingway, Treas.
EIN: 841411938

VERMONT

9364
The Morris and Bessie Altman Foundation
P.O. Box 458
Shelburne, VT 05482-0458 (802) 985-9943
Contact: Peter Stern, Dir.

Established in 1989 in Vermont.
Donors: P. Stern Charitable Remainder Trust; Peter Stern; Bernice and Milton Stern Foundation.
Foundation type: Independent foundation.
Financial data (yr. ended 06/30/14): Assets, $4,741,680 (M); gifts received, $102,500; expenditures, $331,660; qualifying distributions, $294,744; giving activities include $290,350 for 76 grants (high: $120,000; low: $100).
Purpose and activities: Giving primarily for higher and other education.
Fields of interest: Arts and culture; Elementary and secondary education; Special needs education; Higher education; Medical education; Health; School-based health care; Human services; Food aid.
Type of support: General support.
Limitations: Applications accepted. Giving primarily in VT, with some emphasis on Burlington. No grants to individuals.
Application information:
  Initial approach: Letter
  Deadline(s): None
Directors: Abbi Stern; Marjorie Stern; Peter Stern; Sarena Stern.
EIN: 030323120

9365
Blittersdorf Family Foundation Inc.
(formerly Jan & David Blittersdorf Foundation, Inc.)
1042 Dorset St.
Charlotte, VT 05445-9270 (802) 872-9600
Contact: David C. Blittersdorf
E-mail: info@blittersdorffamilyfoundation.org;
Application address: c/o Allearth Renewables, 94 Harvest Ln., Williston, VT 05495-8997

Established in 2005 in Vermont.
Donors: David C. Blittersdorf; Jan L. Blittersdorf.
Foundation type: Independent foundation.
Financial data (yr. ended 12/31/13): Assets, $1,108,717 (M); expenditures, $205,838; qualifying distributions, $204,500; giving activities include $204,500 for 12 grants (high: $75,000; low: $1,500).
Purpose and activities: Giving primarily for promoting the development of renewable energy sources, building a sustainable world infrastructure, and celebrating arts and culture in order to help society make better long term choices while lessening the impact on world energy and natural resources.
Fields of interest: Environment.
Type of support: General support; Program development; Seed money; Scholarships.
Limitations: Applications accepted. Giving primarily in Vermont, with some support to national nonprofits connected to renewable energy and the environment. No grants to individuals.
Application information: Unsolicited full proposals not accepted. However, grantseekers may contact the foundation by e-mail to discuss funding priorities and opportunities to submit a proposal.
  Initial approach: Proposal
  Deadline(s): None
Officers: David C. Blittersdorf, Pres.; Alyssa L. Blittersdorf, V.P.; Evan D. Blittersdorf, Secy.
EIN: 061764244

9366
Harris & Frances Block Foundation Inc.
c/o Betsy Chodorkoff
491 Ennis Hill Rd.
Marshfield, VT 05658-8250 (802) 426-2026
E-mail: info@blockfound.org; Main URL: http://www.blockfound.org
Grants List: http://blockfound.org/what-we-fund

Established in 2001 in Vermont.
Donor: Carol Maurer†.
Foundation type: Independent foundation.
Financial data (yr. ended 12/31/13): Assets, $8,827,904 (M); gifts received, $865,000; expenditures, $522,366; qualifying distributions, $450,802; giving activities include $415,108 for 47 grants (high: $15,000; low: $500).
Purpose and activities: Giving primarily in the areas of economic justice, environmental protection, arms control, community development, and historic preservation.
Fields of interest: Historic preservation; Natural resources; Sustainable development; Human rights; Arms control.
Limitations: Applications accepted. Giving in the U.S., primarily in VT; giving also in CT, MA, NC, and VA.
Application information: Complete application guidelines available on foundation web site. Application form required.
  Initial approach: Letter of inquiry
  Deadline(s): None
Officers: Nancy M. Sluys, V.P.; Diane Maurer Schatz, Secy.; Betsy M. Chodorkoff, Treas.
EIN: 311784246

9367
Carris Corporate Foundation, Inc.
(formerly The Carris Reels Fund)
49 Main St.
Proctor, VT 05765-1178

Donors: Carris Reels, Inc.; Bridge Manufacturing, Inc.; Vermont Tubbs, Inc.; Carris Financial Corp.; Carris Reels of Connecticut, Inc.; Carris Reels of California, Inc.
Foundation type: Company-sponsored foundation.
Financial data (yr. ended 12/31/13): Assets, $83,533 (M); gifts received, $181,173; expenditures, $223,770; qualifying distributions, $223,694; giving activities include $223,694 for 114 grants (high: $43,484; low: $150).
Purpose and activities: The foundation makes charitable contributions to nonprofit organizations recommended by Carris employees and approved by local giving committees.
Fields of interest: Community and economic development; Housing development; Human services.
Type of support: General support.
Limitations: Applications not accepted. Giving primarily in areas of company operations in VT. No grants to individuals.

Application information: Contributes only to pre-selected organizations.
Officers: David Ferraro, Pres. and Secy.; David Fitz-Gerald, V.P. and Treas.
Director: Alberto Aguilar.
EIN: 030326934

9368
Castanea Foundation, Inc.
P.O. Box 64
Montpelier, VT 05601-0064
Contact: Tim Storrow
FAX: (802) 225-1182;
E-mail: timstorrow@comcast.net; Main URL: http://www.castaneafoundation.org

Established in 2005 in Vermont.
Donors: Fidelity Charitable Gift Fund; The Green Acres Fund; The Conservation Fund.
Foundation type: Operating foundation.
Financial data (yr. ended 03/31/13): Assets, $8,448,129 (M); gifts received, $2,017,500; expenditures, $864,173; qualifying distributions, $702,176; giving activities include $224,687 for 11 grants, $924,825 for 2 foundation-administered programs and $219,144 for loans/program-related investments.
Purpose and activities: The foundation's mission is to conserve and protect agriculturally productive and environmentally significant lands and water resources in Vermont and in select areas of New York State.
Fields of interest: Water resources; Land resources; Farmlands.
Type of support: General support; Pro bono consulting services; Program-related investments; Capacity-building and technical assistance; Loans to individuals; Capital campaigns; Capital and infrastructure; Mission-related investments; Equipment; Land acquisitions; Endowments; Program development; Technical assistance.
Limitations: Applications not accepted. Giving primarily in VT, with priority given to projects in the watershed of Lake Champlain, southwestern Vermont, and the Hoosic River and Batten Kill watersheds, and Washington and Rensselaer counties, NY. No grants to individuals.
Publications: Occasional report.
Application information: Contributes only to pre-selected organizations.
  Board meeting date(s): Quarterly
Officers: Megan Camp, Chair.; Robert E. Woolmington, Secy.; Alec Webb, Treas.; Thomas Storrow, Exec. Dir.
Number of staff: 2 full-time professional.
EIN: 202727759

9369
Ben Cohen Charitable Trust
c/o GHP Advisors, PC
P.O. Box 5550
Burlington, VT 05402-5550 (802) 863-5099
Contact: Ben Cohen, Tr.

Established in 2000 in Vermont.
Donor: Bennet R. Cohen.
Foundation type: Independent foundation.
Financial data (yr. ended 10/31/13): Assets, $4,882,285 (M); gifts received, $1,346,717; expenditures, $390,711; qualifying distributions,

$371,760; giving activities include $349,802 for 23 grants (high: $176,752; low: $100).

Purpose and activities: The trust gives to qualified charitable or educational organizations that have a demonstrated history or intention for involvement in socially responsible issues.

Fields of interest: Public affairs; Leadership development.

Limitations: Applications accepted. Giving primarily in Washington, DC, NY, PA and VT.

Application information: Application form required.
  Initial approach: Letter
  Deadline(s): None

Trustees: Bennet R. Cohen; Charles Lacy.

EIN: 030368595

9370
The Copley Fund
P.O. Box 696
Morrisville, VT   05661-0696   (802) 888-2000
Contact: Richard C. Sargent Esq., Tr.

Established in 1969 in Vermont.

Foundation type: Independent foundation.

Financial data (yr. ended 12/31/13): Assets, $4,466,176 (M); expenditures, $217,887; qualifying distributions, $200,000; giving activities include $200,000 for 16 grants (high: $120,600; low: $1,000).

Purpose and activities: Giving to organizations providing services to the elderly, as well as direct grants to individuals for housing assistance.

Fields of interest: Food aid; Senior assisted living; Retirement housing; Senior services; Seniors.

Type of support: Program development; Grants to individuals.

Limitations: Applications accepted. Giving primarily in Lamoille County, VT.

Application information: Application form required.
  Initial approach: Letter
  Deadline(s): Dec. 31

Trustees: Richard C. Sargent, Esq.; Gloria Wing.

EIN: 036006013

9371
Helen E. Daly Narthex Project Charitable Remainder Unitrust
P.O. Box 1280
Brattleboro, VT   05302-1280

Donor: Helen Daly Irrevocable Trust.

Foundation type: Independent foundation.

Financial data (yr. ended 12/31/14): Assets, $1,893,590; gifts received, $40,000; expenditures, $270,166; qualifying distributions, $246,184.

Fields of interest: Religion.

International interests: Canada.

Limitations: Applications not accepted. Giving primarily in Binghamton and Syracuse, NY; some funding also in Victoria, British Columbia, Canada.

Application information: Unsolicited requests for funds not accepted.

Trustee: Trust Company of Vermont.

EIN: 207037351

9372
Charles P. Ferro Foundation
88 Sunset Cliff
Burlington, VT   05408-1325   (802) 660-2765
Contact: Bonnie Ferro, Tr.
E-mail: bferro@me.com; Application address: c/o Ferro Foundation, Sonnenschein, Nath & Rosenthal LLP, 1221 Avenue of the Americas, New York, NY 10020

Established in 1993 in New York.

Donor: Charles P. Ferro†.

Foundation type: Independent foundation.

Financial data (yr. ended 12/31/13): Assets, $5,108,330 (M); expenditures, $167,769; qualifying distributions, $219,193; giving activities include $159,000 for 15 grants (high: $10,000; low: $1,000).

Purpose and activities: Giving primarily for health related causes and children's services.

Fields of interest: Education; Human services; Youth development.

Limitations: Applications accepted. Giving primarily in CT, FL, NY, RI, and VT. No support for religious organizations.

Application information:
  Initial approach: Letter
  Deadline(s): None

Trustees: Vera Dosky; Bonnie Ferro; Marc Ferro; Marianne Ferro; Edward Friedhoff; Jennifer Ferro Lessieu; Maren Tripolitsiotis.

Number of staff: 2 part-time professional.

EIN: 223253710

9373
Philip S. Harper Foundation
P.O. Box 96
Weston, VT   05161-0086

Established in 1953 in Illinois.

Donors: Philip S. Harper; Harper-Wyman Co.

Foundation type: Independent foundation.

Financial data (yr. ended 09/30/13): Assets, $6,817,838 (M); expenditures, $365,384; qualifying distributions, $331,828; giving activities include $304,500 for 170 grants (high: $15,000; low: $250).

Fields of interest: Arts and culture; Elementary and secondary education; Higher education; Natural resources; Health; Diseases and conditions; Communication media; Legal services; Public affairs; Christianity; Protestantism; Human services; Family services; Child welfare; Females; Female children and youth; Low-income and poor people.

Type of support: Research; Research and evaluation.

Limitations: Applications not accepted. Giving primarily in CA, CO, Washington, DC, FL, Atlanta, GA, IA, Chicago, IL, MA, MI, New York, NY, VA, and VT. No grants to individuals.

Application information: Unsolicited requests for funds not accepted.

Officers: Lamar Williams, Pres.; Kirk Harper William, V.P.; Andrew Harper, Secy.-Treas.

Director: Steven Palumbo.

EIN: 366049875

9374
S & C Harvest Foundation Inc.
2504 N. Bingham St.
Cornwall, VT   05753-4469

Established in 2003 in Vermont.

Donors: Charles W. Grigg; Grigg Family Lead Trust 2011; Grigg Family Charitable Lead Trust; Grigg Family Charitable Lead Trust 201.

Foundation type: Independent foundation.

Financial data (yr. ended 12/31/13): Assets, $4,004,857 (M); gifts received, $266,000; expenditures, $191,647; qualifying distributions, $190,254; giving activities include $190,200 for 47 grants (high: $15,000; low: $200).

Fields of interest: Arts and culture; Elementary and secondary education; Natural resources; Community and economic development; Christianity; Human services; Basic and emergency aid; International development.

Limitations: Applications not accepted. Giving primarily in VT. No grants to individuals.

Application information: Contributes only to pre-selected organizations.

Officers: Charles W. Grigg, Pres.; Susan K. Grigg, V.P. and Secy.-Treas.

Trustees: Donald W. Grigg; Laurie D. Grigg; Sally G. Olmstead.

EIN: 200443423

9375
Robert & Helen Holland Charitable Annuity Trust
P.O. Box 1280
Brattleboro, VT   05302-1280

Foundation type: Independent foundation.

Financial data (yr. ended 12/31/13): Assets, $3,897,655 (M); expenditures, $206,922; qualifying distributions, $182,892; giving activities include $182,342 for 1 grant.

Fields of interest: Health.

Limitations: Applications not accepted. Giving primarily in NH.

Application information: Unsolicited requests for funds not accepted.

Trustee: Trust Company of Vermont.

EIN: 206554587

9376
Huntington Tracy Foundation, Inc.
c/o CFC
49 Main St.
Proctor, VT   05765-1178   8027739111

Donors: Carris Corporate Foundation; Barbara T. Carris; William H. Carris.

Foundation type: Independent foundation.

Financial data (yr. ended 12/31/14): Assets, $3,840,301; gifts received, $49,000; expenditures, $192,524; qualifying distributions, $179,556.

Fields of interest: Arts and culture; Education; Agriculture.

Limitations: Applications not accepted. Giving primarily in Rutland, VT.

Application information: Unsolicited requests for funds not accepted.

Officers: William H. Carris, Pres. and Treas.; Barbara T. Carris, V.P. and Secy.

Board Member: Jennifer Carris Swetland.
EIN: 261548756

9377

Wolf Kahn And Emily Mason Foundation Inc.

P.O. Box 2314
West Brattleboro, VT   05301-0001

Established in 1998 in New York.
Donors: Wolf Kahn; Emily Mason Kahn.
Foundation type: Independent foundation.
Financial data (yr. ended 08/31/13): Assets, $2,806,103 (M); expenditures, $261,177; qualifying distributions, $184,725; giving activities include $184,725 for 26 grants (high: $25,000; low: $1,000).
Fields of interest: Arts and culture; Arts education; Art museums.
Type of support: General support.
Limitations: Applications not accepted. Giving primarily in NY and VT. No grants to individuals.
Application information: Unsolicited requests for funds not accepted.
Officers: Wolf Kahn, Pres.; Emily Mason, V.P.
EIN: 134036532

9378

C. Kaufman Family Foundation

c/o Stacey Gerrish, Jenifer Mathieu & CFSG
P.O. Box 120
Newport, VT   05855-0120

Established in 2004 in Vermont.
Donors: Barbara Kaufman; Kaufman Revocable Trust "B"; Barbara Kaufmann Trust.
Foundation type: Independent foundation.
Financial data (yr. ended 12/31/13): Assets, $7,367,861 (M); expenditures, $349,731; qualifying distributions, $327,748; giving activities include $320,000 for 25 grants (high: $30,000; low: $2,000).
Fields of interest: Education; Wildlife biodiversity; Diseases and conditions; Economic development; Human rights; International development.
Type of support: General support.
Limitations: Applications not accepted. No grants to individuals.
Application information: Unsolicited requests for funds not accepted.
Trustee: Community Financial Services Group.
EIN: 036111428

9379

Andree Leboeuf Foundation Inc.

20 Ian Pl.
Williston, VT   05495-4408

Foundation type: Independent foundation.
Financial data (yr. ended 11/30/14): Assets, $3,185,195 (M); expenditures, $176,877; qualifying distributions, $149,750; giving activities include $146,000 for 3 grants (high: $91,000; low: $5,000).
Fields of interest: Health; Agriculture; Human services.
Limitations: Applications not accepted.
Application information: Unsolicited requests for funds not accepted.

Trustee: Andree Leboeuf.
EIN: 451055677

9380

Maverick Lloyd Foundation

(formerly Maverick Foundation)
c/o Arthur Berndt
426 Maverick Farm Rd.
P.O. Box 100
Sharon, VT   05065
Main URL: http://www.mavericklloyd.org

Established in 1995 in Illinois.
Donors: Georgia Lloyd†; Lloyd Charitable Trust No. 2; Manfred Beshears Annuity Trust.
Foundation type: Independent foundation.
Financial data (yr. ended 12/31/13): Assets, $6,790,788 (M); gifts received, $336,073; expenditures, $285,681; qualifying distributions, $237,409; giving activities include $223,500 for 12 grants (high: $150,000; low: $1,000).
Purpose and activities: The foundation is committed to creating a more equitable world and supports innovative projects that focus on building a non-violent, just, and sustainable future.
Type of support: General support; System and operational improvements; Public engagement and education.
Limitations: Applications not accepted. Giving on a national basis. No support for religious organizations, colleges, or universities. No grants to individuals, or for general operating support, travel, scholarships, new construction or endowments, or to the medical fields.
Publications: Grants list.
Application information: Unsolicited requests for funds not accepted.
Trustees: Anne Berndt; Arthur Berndt.
Number of staff: 1 part-time professional.
EIN: 367093389

9381

George W. Mergens Foundation

P.O. Box 633
Milton, VT   05468-0633   (802) 862-6770
Contact: Paul Mergens, Pres.
FAX: (802) 863-5968;
E-mail: info@mergensfoundation.org

Established in 1994 in Vermont.
Donors: Paul Mergens; Mary Mergens-Loughran.
Foundation type: Independent foundation.
Financial data (yr. ended 08/31/13): Assets, $9,858,324 (M); expenditures, $540,044; qualifying distributions, $358,790; giving activities include $148,500 for 14 grants (high: $20,000; low: $500).
Purpose and activities: Giving primarily for educational, cultural, medical and general welfare needs of children in Vermont.
Fields of interest: Arts and culture; Education; Elementary and secondary education; Christianity; Human services; Youth services; Scouting programs; Children and youth; Children.
Type of support: General support; Matching grants; Continuing support; Financial sustainability; Annual campaigns; Capital and infrastructure; Equipment; Program development; Scholarships.
Limitations: Applications accepted. Giving primarily in VT. No grants to individuals.
Publications: Application guidelines.

Application information: Application form required.
Initial approach: Letter requesting grant guidelines and information, including a brief introduction of the applicant
Copies of proposal: 1
Deadline(s): None
Officers: Paul Mergens, Pres.; Mary Mergens-Loughran, V.P.; Lenora Mergens, Secy.
Number of staff: 2 full-time support.
EIN: 030345055

9382

NSB Foundation Inc.

c/o Northfield Savings Bank, N.A.
33 S. Main St.
Northfield, VT   05663-6703
Main URL: https://www.nsbvt.com

Established in 2000 in Vermont.
Donor: Northfield Savings Bank.
Foundation type: Company-sponsored foundation.
Financial data (yr. ended 12/31/13): Assets, $1,766,150 (M); gifts received, $150,000; expenditures, $154,542; qualifying distributions, $153,337; giving activities include $150,000 for 1 grant.
Purpose and activities: The foundation supports Hunger Free Vermont to expand access to healthy meals in Central Vermont and Chittenden County.
Fields of interest: Agriculture; Human services.
Type of support: General support; Continuing support.
Limitations: Applications not accepted. Giving limited to central VT. No grants to individuals.
Application information: Contributes only to a pre-selected organization.
Board meeting date(s): Feb., June, and Oct.
Officers and Directors: J. Timothy Burke, Chair. and Director; Eileen Bradley, V.P. and Secy.; Edward T. Sulva, Treas.; Laura Carlsmith; Samuel FitzPatrick; L. Stephen Hackett; Stephanie Hainley; Sandra Rousse; Nancy Zom.
EIN: 311713065

9383

The Redducs Chartered Foundation Corp.

c/o Sue Conley
119 Pleasant View Ln.
Hinesburg, VT   05461-9779

Donors: Mary Gale Scudder; Edward Scudder, Jr.; Edward Scudder III; Katherine Scudder Tiballi.
Foundation type: Independent foundation.
Financial data (yr. ended 12/31/14): Assets, $3,588,648; expenditures, $211,197; qualifying distributions, $189,321.
Purpose and activities: Giving primarily for education and social services.
Fields of interest: Arts and culture; Education; Natural resources; Animal welfare; Human services.
Type of support: General support; Continuing support; Annual campaigns; Capital campaigns; Land acquisitions; Emergency funds; Program development; Curriculum development.
Limitations: Applications not accepted. Giving primarily in CA and VT. No support for private foundations. No grants to individuals.
Application information: Contributes only to pre-selected organizations.
Board meeting date(s): Mid-July

Officers: Katherine Tiballi, Pres.; Mary Gale Scudder, V.P.; Jason Tiballi, Secy.; Sue Conley, Exec. Dir.
Number of staff: 1 part-time professional.
EIN: 650840245

9384
Seventh Generation Foundation, Inc

60 Lake St.
Burlington, VT 05401
Main URL: http://www.seventhgeneration.com

Donor: Seventh Generation.
Foundation type: Company-sponsored foundation.
Financial data (yr. ended 12/31/12): Assets, $3,872 (M); gifts received, $175,600; expenditures, $177,728; qualifying distributions, $148,635; giving activities include $142,900 for 9 grants (high: $30,000; low: $900).
Fields of interest: Zoos; Health; Diseases and conditions; Breast cancer; Human services.
Limitations: Applications not accepted. Giving primarily in VT.
Application information: Unsolicited requests for funds not accepted.
Officer: Ashley Orgain, Pres. and Exec. Dir.; Chris Lyon, Secy.; Cindy Fuller, Treas.

Directors: Chrystie Heimert; Peter Graham; John Replogle.
EIN: 455204475

9385
Lydia B. Stokes Foundation

P.O. Box 5777
Burlington, VT 05402-5777
Main URL: http://www.lydiabstokesfoundation.org
Grants List: http://www.lydiabstokesfoundation.org/currentgrants.php
Grants List: http://www.lydiabstokesfoundation.org/currentgrants.php?year=2012
Grants List: http://www.lydiabstokesfoundation.org/currentgrants.php?year=2013

Established in 1959 in New Jersey.
Donor: Lydia B. Stokes†.
Foundation type: Independent foundation.
Financial data (yr. ended 06/30/13): Assets, $6,472,435 (M); gifts received, $2,985,370; expenditures, $315,866; qualifying distributions, $474,801; giving activities include $209,500 for 26 grants (high: $25,000; low: $1,500), and $228,990 for 3 loans/program-related investments.

Purpose and activities: Giving primarily for women's issues, the environment, children, education, peace, and social and economic justice.
Fields of interest: Education; Environment; Natural resources; Community and economic development; Human services; Family services; Child welfare; Women's services; Children and youth; Adolescents; Females; Low-income and poor people.
Type of support: General support; Program-related investments; Matching grants; Land acquisitions; Program development; Recordings; Seed money; Curriculum development.
Limitations: Applications not accepted. Giving primarily in FL, MA, NH, and NM; giving also to certain organizations that are national or international in scope. No grants to individuals.
Publications: Grants list.
Application information: Unsolicited requests for funds not accepted.
 Board meeting date(s): May and Nov.
Trustees: Nancy V. Deren; Thalia Venerable; Thomas R. Willits.
Number of staff: None.
EIN: 216016107

VIRGINIA

9386
American Friends of Eton College, Inc.
7521 Royal Oak Dr.
McLean, VA 22102-2114
Contact: Henry D. Edelman, Dir.
E-mail: AFEtonC@aol.com

Established in 2005 in District of Columbia.
Donors: Harry D. Edelman; Armins K. Rusis; John M. Hennessey; Margarita Hennessey; Leander McCormick-Goodhart; Colin Hely-Hutchinson; Bernard Liataud; N. Minter Dial; Columbia Foundation; Dominic Moross Foundation; H.R. Howard Foundation; Michael J. McDonough; James I. McLaren; James McBurney; Dominic H.R. Moross; Mrs. Bernard Liataud; Andrew John Rolfe; James McM Wilson; Peter-John Kuttel; Mrs. James McBurney; The Townes Foundation; Sanjay H. Patel; Bryann Nuzzo; James Nuzzo; Dominic H. R. Moross; Charles Shabica; Garett Albert; Henry D. Edelman; Arthur G. Armstrong; William Blair & Co.
Foundation type: Independent foundation.
Financial data (yr. ended 12/31/13): Assets, $170,679 (M); gifts received, $139,747; expenditures, $163,434; qualifying distributions, $163,014; giving activities include $163,014 for 1 grant.
Purpose and activities: Scholarship awards for a U.S. student to attend Eton College, Windsor, England.
Fields of interest: Undergraduate education.
International interests: England.
Type of support: Student aid.
Limitations: Applications accepted. Giving primarily in Windsor, England; scholarships to U.S. citizens to study at Eaton College in Windsor.
Application information: Application form required.
Deadline(s): Jan. 31 (for scholars seeking admission into Eaton College in the fall of the same year)
Officer and Directors: James I. McLaren, Chair. and Pres. and Director; Henry D. Edelman; Andrew L.H. Gailley; John Hennessy; Anthony Little; George C. McNamee; Dominic H.R. Moross; Lord William Waldegrave.
EIN: 522273240

9387
American Woodmark Foundation, Inc.
3102 Shawnee Dr.
Winchester, VA 22601-4208 (540) 665-9129
Contact: Brenda K. Dupont, Chair. and Dir.
E-mail: awfoundation@woodmark.com; Main URL: http://www.americanwoodmark.com/about.asp?iAreaID=1&iSectionID=7

Established in 1995 in Virginia.
Donor: American Woodmark Corp.
Foundation type: Company-sponsored foundation.
Financial data (yr. ended 04/30/14): Assets, $320,193 (M); gifts received, $98,000; expenditures, $216,603; qualifying distributions, $215,937; giving activities include $215,365 for 140 grants (high: $10,000; low: $500).
Purpose and activities: The foundation supports organizations involved with education, domestic violence, housing, and public safety. Support is limited to areas of company operations.
Fields of interest: Education; Domestic violence; Disasters and emergency management; Housing development; Human services.
Type of support: General support; Continuing support; Annual campaigns; Capital campaigns; Capital and infrastructure; Equipment; Curriculum development.
Limitations: Applications accepted. Giving limited to areas of company operations in Kingman, AZ, Jackson and Toccoa, GA, Grant County, IN, Monticello and Hazard, KY, Cumberland, MD, Tahlequah, OK, Humboldt, TN, Winchester-Frederick County, Clarke County and Orange, VA, and Moorefield, WV. No support for private foundations, political organizations, or religious organizations not of direct benefit to the entire community. No grants to individuals.
Application information: Application form required.
Initial approach: Letter of inquiry signed by official with organization applying
Copies of proposal: 1
Deadline(s): None
Board meeting date(s): Jan., Apr., July, and Oct.
Officers and Directors: Brenda K. Dupont, Chair. and Director; Wendy W. Armel, Secy. and Director; Douglas Boucher, Treas. and Director.
EIN: 541759773

9388
George Andreas Foundation, Inc.
c/o Ursula E. Andreas
43670 Trade Center Pl., Ste. 145
Dulles, VA 20166

Established in 1993 in Virginia.
Donors: George C. Andreas‡; Ursula E. Andreas.
Foundation type: Independent foundation.
Financial data (yr. ended 12/31/13): Assets, $542,671 (M); expenditures, $267,987; qualifying distributions, $263,432; giving activities include $263,432 for 8 grants (high: $100,000; low: $1,000).
Fields of interest: Performing arts; Art museums; Education; Hospital care; Antidiscrimination.
Type of support: General support.
Limitations: Applications not accepted. Giving primarily in Washington, DC, and New York, NY; funding also in Baltimore, MD. No grants to individuals.
Application information: Unsolicited requests for funds not accepted.
Officers: Ursula E. Andreas, Pres.; Christopher Andreas, V.P.
EIN: 541691040

9389
The William M. Backer Foundation, Inc.
7181 Smitten Farm Ln.
The Plains, VA 20198-1930

Established in 1990 in Delaware.
Donors: William M. Backer; Ann Backer.
Foundation type: Independent foundation.
Financial data (yr. ended 07/31/14): Assets, $8,330,234 (M); gifts received, $100,222; expenditures, $381,561; qualifying distributions, $315,129; giving activities include for 43 grants (high: $202,000; low: $25).
Fields of interest: Arts and culture; Education; Environment; Nonprofits; Protestantism; Human services.
Type of support: General support; Continuing support; Capital campaigns; Capital and infrastructure; Land acquisitions; Regranting; Endowments; Scholarships; Research.
Limitations: Applications not accepted. Giving primarily in VA. No grants to individuals.
Application information: Contributes only to pre-selected organizations.
Officer: William M. Backer, Pres. and Treas.
Directors: Ann M. Backer; Georgia H. Herbert; David Moltke-Hansen.
EIN: 133579157

9390
The William and Karin Banks Foundation, Inc.
2205 Big Lonely Ln.
Monterey, VA 24465-2218

Established in 2002 in Virginia.
Donors: Karin Banks; William Banks.
Foundation type: Independent foundation.
Financial data (yr. ended 12/31/14): Assets, $6,798,035 (M); expenditures, $350,046; qualifying distributions, $327,646; giving activities include $314,916 for 55 grants (high: $20,500; low: $500).
Fields of interest: Education; Higher education; Foundations; Health; Diseases and conditions.
Type of support: General support.
Limitations: Applications not accepted. Giving primarily in VA. No grants to individuals.
Application information: Contributes only to pre-selected organizations.
Officers: Karin Banks, Pres.; Harald Mangold, V.P.
EIN: 010758677

9391
Bassett Furniture Industries Foundation, Inc.
P.O. Box 626
Bassett, VA 24055-0626

Established in 1992 in Virginia.
Donor: Bassett Furniture Industries, Inc.
Foundation type: Company-sponsored foundation.
Financial data (yr. ended 11/30/13): Assets, $1,656,464 (M); gifts received, $10,000; expenditures, $267,098; qualifying distributions, $267,098; giving activities include $260,791 for 12 grants (high: $128,791; low: $1,000).
Purpose and activities: The foundation supports organizations involved with arts and culture, higher education, athletics, children's services, and Christianity.
Fields of interest: Arts and culture; Natural history museums; Higher education; Community and economic development; Track and field; Human services; Child welfare; Scouting programs.
Type of support: General support; Program development.
Limitations: Applications not accepted. Giving primarily in VA. No grants to individuals.
Application information: Unsolicited requests for funds not accepted.
Officer and Director: Robert H. Spilman, Jr., Pres. and Director.

Trustees: J. Michael Daniel; Eddie White.
EIN: 541652381

9392
The Beck Foundation Inc.
P.O. Box 7486
Fairfax Station, VA   22039-7486
E-mail: beckfoundation@cox.net

Established in 2005 in Virginia.
Donors: Charlotte V. Beck; Buddy G. Beck.
Foundation type: Independent foundation.
Financial data (yr. ended 01/31/14): Assets,
$4,400,908 (M); expenditures, $334,056;
qualifying distributions, $245,450; giving activities
include $245,450 for 24 grants (high: $154,500;
low: $200).
Fields of interest: Education; Higher education.
Limitations: Applications not accepted. Giving
primarily in VA. No grants to individuals.
Application information: Contributes only to
pre-selected organizations.
Officers: Buddy G. Beck, Chair.; Charlotte V. Beck,
Pres.
Directors: Michael S. Beck; Deborah B. Corbatto.
EIN: 202214025

9393
Tad Beck Fund
P.O. Box 1566
Lexington, VA   24450-1566

Established in 1968 in Delaware.
Donors: Ann M. Beck; T.E. Beck, Jr.; Beck
Foundation; Avent C. Beck; T.E. Beck III†.
Foundation type: Independent foundation.
Financial data (yr. ended 12/31/14): Assets,
$4,646,525 (M); expenditures, $211,430;
qualifying distributions, $211,430; giving activities
include $175,000 for 3 grants (high: $100,000;
low: $5,000), and $12,000 for 2 grants to
individuals (high: $10,000; low: $2,000).
Fields of interest: Arts and culture; Higher
education.
Type of support: General support; Matching grants;
Continuing support; Capital and infrastructure;
Program development; Convening; Curriculum
development; Scholarships.
Limitations: Applications not accepted. Giving
primarily in NE, SD,VA and VT.
Application information: Unsolicited requests for
funds not accepted.
Officers: T.E. Beck, Jr., Pres.; Ann M. Beck, V.P.;
Avent C. Beck, Secy.; John C. Beck, Treas.
EIN: 476057394

9394
The Gloria Wille Bell and Carlos R. Bell
Charitable Trust
c/o McGuire Woods, LLP
One James Center
901 E. Cary St.
Richmond, VA   23219-4030
Contact: John O'Grady, Tr.
E-mail for John O'Grady:
jogrady@mcguirewoods.com; Main URL: http://
www.bellscholarship.org

Established in 2002 in Virginia.
Donor: Carlos R. Bell†.

Foundation type: Independent foundation.
Financial data (yr. ended 06/30/13): Assets,
$4,932,289 (M); expenditures, $355,251;
qualifying distributions, $311,689; giving activities
include $240,000 for grants to individuals.
Purpose and activities: Scholarship awards to first
year students attending the University of Michigan,
Ann Arbor, entering the College of Engineering or the
College of Literature, Science, and the Arts, who are
enrolled in an undergraduate degree program in the
sciences and who meet specific geographic criteria.
Fields of interest: Higher education.
Type of support: Scholarships; Student aid.
Limitations: Applications accepted. Giving limited to
benefit University of Michigan students at Ann Arbor
who also meet one of the following geographic
criteria: resident of the Commonwealth of VA;
graduate of the Chicago, IL public, parochial, private
school system, New Trier High School in Winnetka,
IL, or Illinois Mathematics and Science Academy in
Aurora; or resident of Allegan, Barry, Berrien,
Branch, Calhoun, Cass, Eaton, Hillsdale, Ingham,
Jackson, Kalamazoo, Lenawee, Livingston, Monroe,
Oakland, St. Joseph, Van Buren, Washtenaw, or
Wayne counties, MI.
Application information: Applications must be
submitted online through Trust web site. See Trust
web site for complete application guidelines.
Application form required.
    Deadline(s): Feb. 1
Trustee: John B. O'Grady.
EIN: 546500526

9395
The Berni Family Charitable Foundation
7808 Preakness Ln.
Fairfax Station, VA   22039-3413

Donors: John V. Adams; Mary B. Adams.
Foundation type: Independent foundation.
Financial data (yr. ended 06/30/14): Assets,
$71,427 (M); gifts received, $170,300;
expenditures, $254,882; qualifying distributions,
$254,882; giving activities include $253,250 for 6
grants (high: $220,000; low: $250).
Fields of interest: Arts and culture; Education;
Health; Religion; Christianity.
Limitations: Applications not accepted. No grants to
individuals.
Application information: Contributes only to
pre-selected organizations.
Trustee: John V. Adams.
EIN: 541843093

9396
The Better Living Foundation
P.O. Box 7627
Charlottesville, VA   22906-7627   (434)
973-4333
Contact: Richard L. Nunley, Pres. and Dir.

Established in 1985 in Virginia.
Donors: Richard L. Nunley; Julia G. Nunley; John G.
Nunley.
Foundation type: Independent foundation.
Financial data (yr. ended 12/31/13): Assets,
$959,311 (M); gifts received, $25,525;
expenditures, $207,227; qualifying distributions,
$197,578; giving activities include $194,953 for 57
grants (high: $20,000; low: $125).

Fields of interest: Education; Nonprofits; Health;
Diseases and conditions; Protestantism; Human
services; Food banks; Child welfare.
Type of support: Regranting.
Limitations: Applications accepted. Giving primarily
in Charlottesville, VA. No grants to individuals.
Application information: Application form required.
    Initial approach: Letter
    Deadline(s): None
Officers and Directors: Richard L. Nunley, Pres. and
Director; Julia G. Nunley, Secy.-Treas. and Director;
John G. Nunley; Caroline N. Satira.
EIN: 541324304

9397
Eric and Marianne Billings Foundation
1001 19th St., 18th Fl.
Arlington, VA   22209-1722

Established in 1993 in Virginia.
Donors: Eric Billings; Marianne Billings; Marilyn C.
Pownall.
Foundation type: Independent foundation.
Financial data (yr. ended 06/30/13): Assets,
$3,843 (M); gifts received, $315,000;
expenditures, $314,166; qualifying distributions,
$310,000; giving activities include $310,000 for 7
grants (high: $60,000; low: $10,000).
Fields of interest: Higher education; Business
education; Catholicism.
Type of support: Capital campaigns.
Limitations: Applications not accepted. Giving
primarily in Washington, DC and MD; funding also in
Atlanta, GA. No grants to individuals.
Application information: Unsolicited requests for
funds not accepted.
Directors: Eric Billings; Marianne Billings; Ned S.
Scherer.
EIN: 521853715

9398
The Birk Family Foundation
P.O. Box 1840
Vienna, VA   22183-1840

Established in 1996 in Florida.
Donor: Roger E. Birk.
Foundation type: Independent foundation.
Financial data (yr. ended 12/31/13): Assets,
$5,016,573 (M); expenditures, $228,227;
qualifying distributions, $228,227; giving activities
include $190,000 for 33 grants (high: $15,000;
low: $1,000).
Purpose and activities: Giving primarily for
education, medical care, and multiple sclerosis
research.
Fields of interest: Secondary education;
Undergraduate education; Health; Multiple
sclerosis; Catholicism.
Type of support: General support; Research.
Limitations: Applications not accepted. Giving
primarily in FL. No grants to individuals or for private
foundations.
Application information: Unsolicited requests for
funds not accepted.
Officer and Directors: Mary E. Colas, Pres. and
Director; Barbara J. Billstrand; Dr. Kathleen A. Birk;
Mary L. Birk; Roger E. Birk; Timothy Colas.
EIN: 650661100

9399
The Black Dog Foundation
P.O. Box 338
Rectortown, VA 20140-0338 (540) 364-3469
Contact: Timothy P. Dunn, Tr.

Established in 2002 in Virginia.
Donors: Ellen R. Stofan; Timothy P. Dunn.
Foundation type: Independent foundation.
Financial data (yr. ended 06/30/13): Assets,
$1,848,287 (M); gifts received, $60,688;
expenditures, $154,587; qualifying distributions,
$151,183; giving activities include $151,183 for 17
grants (high: $40,000; low: $1,000).
Fields of interest: Environment; Health; Human
services.
Application information: Application form required.
Initial approach: Letter
Deadline(s): None
Trustees: Ryan Dunn; Timothy P. Dunn; Ellen R.
Stofan.
EIN: 043721096

9400
Blue Dot Foundation
(formerly Satori Foundation)
8404 Parham Ct.
McLean, VA 22102-1533

Established in 1994 in Virginia.
Donors: Steven M. Rales; Mitchell P. Rales.
Foundation type: Independent foundation.
Financial data (yr. ended 12/31/13): Assets,
$35,566,860 (M); gifts received, $26,356,699;
expenditures, $741,325; qualifying distributions,
$197,317; giving activities include $195,912 for 9
grants (high: $83,333; low: $4).
Fields of interest: Education; Elementary and
secondary education; University education;
Diseases and conditions; Breast cancer.
Limitations: Applications not accepted. Giving
primarily in CA and NY; some funding also in
Washington, DC. No grants to individuals.
Application information: Contributes only to
pre-selected organizations.
Officers and Directors: Steven M. Rales, Chair. and
Director; Michael G. Ryan, Pres.; Joseph O. Bunting
III, V.P.; Teresa L.C. Baldwin, Secy.-Treas.
EIN: 541739160

9401
Blue Earth Foundation Inc.
P.O. Box 934
McLean, VA 22101

Established in 2000 in Delaware.
Donors: Daniel F. Akerson; Karin A. Akerson.
Foundation type: Independent foundation.
Financial data (yr. ended 12/31/13): Assets,
$2,428,007 (M); expenditures, $268,031;
qualifying distributions, $260,274; giving activities
include $215,000 for 5 grants (high: $150,000;
low: $5,000).
Fields of interest: Education; Catholicism; Child
welfare.
Type of support: General support; Individual
development.
Limitations: Applications not accepted. No grants to
individuals.
Application information: Contributes only to
pre-selected organizations.

Officers and Directors: Daniel F. Akerson, Chair. and
Director; Karin A. Akerson, Pres. and Director;
Gretchen E. Akerson, V.P. and Exec. Dir.; Keith D.
Akerson, Secy. and Director; Elizabeth C. Akerson,
Treas. and Director.
EIN: 541991343

9402
Blueberry Hill Agm Foundation
1493 Chain Bridge Rd., Ste. 200
McLean, VA 22101-5726 (703) 847-8799
Contact: Robert J. Freda, V.P.

Donor: Angela G. Mernone.
Foundation type: Independent foundation.
Financial data (yr. ended 12/31/13): Assets,
$130,600 (M); gifts received, $161,000;
expenditures, $229,054; qualifying distributions,
$227,704; giving activities include $226,250 for 22
grants (high: $50,000; low: $1,000).
Fields of interest: Education; Domesticated
animals; Human services.
Application information:
Initial approach: Request application form
Deadline(s): None
Officers and Directors: Angela G. Mernone, Pres.
and Director; Robert J. Freda, V.P. and Director;
Patricia A. Freda, Secy.-Treas. and Director.
EIN: 274824652

9403
The Brandt Foundation
201 Fox Meadow Ln.
Winchester, VA 22602-2339 (540) 665-9100
Contact: William F. Brandt Jr., Pres.

Donors: William F. Brandt, Jr.; Elaine Brandt.
Foundation type: Independent foundation.
Financial data (yr. ended 12/31/13): Assets,
$404,074 (M); expenditures, $230,576; qualifying
distributions, $230,426; giving activities include
$222,054 for 33 grants (high: $55,000; low: $200).
Fields of interest: Education; Protestantism; Human
services.
Limitations: Applications accepted. Giving primarily
in VA; some giving in CO. No grants to individuals.
Application information: Application form required.
Initial approach: Letter
Deadline(s): None
Officers and Directors: William F. Brandt, Jr., Pres.
and Treas. and Director; Elaine K. Brandt, Secy. and
Director.
EIN: 541392294

9404
The Ramon W. Breeden, Jr. Foundation
560 Lynnhaven Pkwy.
Virginia Beach, VA 23452-7312 (757) 486-1000
Contact: Ramon W. Breeden Jr., Pres.

Donor: Ramon W. Breeden, Jr.
Foundation type: Independent foundation.
Financial data (yr. ended 12/31/13): Assets,
$307,704 (M); gifts received, $200,000;
expenditures, $176,615; qualifying distributions,
$174,720; giving activities include $174,720 for 15
grants (high: $40,000; low: $100).
Fields of interest: Natural resources; Animal
welfare.

Limitations: Applications accepted. Giving primarily
in Virginia Beach, VA.
Application information: Application form required.
Initial approach: Letter
Deadline(s): None
Officer: Ramon W. Breeden, Jr., Pres.
EIN: 541167246

9405
The BRI Foundation, Inc.
c/o MJW
6402 Arlington Blvd., Ste. 1130
Falls Church, VA 22042-2300

Established in 1997 in Virginia.
Donors: Catharine C. Dorrier; Frank L. Hurley.
Foundation type: Independent foundation.
Financial data (yr. ended 04/30/13): Assets,
$513,768 (M); expenditures, $207,658; qualifying
distributions, $202,392; giving activities include
$200,000 for 1 grant.
Fields of interest: Higher education; Human
services.
Limitations: Applications not accepted. Giving
primarily in MA, and Baltimore, MD. No grants to
individuals.
Application information: Contributes only to
pre-selected organizations.
Officers: Frank L. Hurley, Chair.; Catharine C.
Dorrier, Pres.; John Hurley, Secy.-Treas.
EIN: 541848984

9406
The Brink's Foundation
(formerly The Pittston Foundation)
1801 Bayberry Ct.
P.O. Box 18100
Richmond, VA 23226-8100

Established in 1997 in Virginia.
Donors: The Pittston Co.; The Brink's Co.
Foundation type: Company-sponsored foundation.
Financial data (yr. ended 12/31/13): Assets,
$117,369 (M); gifts received, $5,951;
expenditures, $145,506; qualifying distributions,
$142,319; giving activities include $142,319 for 17
grants (high: $32,260; low: $500).
Purpose and activities: The foundation supports
children's hospitals and organizations involved with
education.
Fields of interest: Arts and culture; Education;
Health.
Type of support: General support; Scholarships.
Limitations: Applications not accepted. Giving
primarily in VA. No grants to individuals.
Application information: Unsolicited requests for
funds not accepted.
Officers and Directors: McAlister C. Marschall II,
Pres. and Director; Joseph W. Dzledzic, V.P. and
Director; Jonathan Andrew Leon, Secy.-Treas.; Holly
R. Tyson.
EIN: 541815655

9407
**Charles S. and Millicent P. Brown
Foundation**
2841 Bennett's Pond Rd.
Williamsburg, VA 23185

Established in 2000 in Illinois.

Donors: Charles S. & Millicent P. Brown Charitable Lead Annuity Trust; Brown Clat-15.
Foundation type: Independent foundation.
Financial data (yr. ended 12/31/13): Assets, $6,487,019 (M); gifts received, $290,577; expenditures, $360,851; qualifying distributions, $309,857; giving activities include $298,020 for 26 grants (high: $46,500; low: $1,000).
Fields of interest: Higher education; Diseases and conditions; Christianity; Protestantism; Infants and toddlers; Children; Adults; Seniors; Females; Incarcerated people; Terminally ill people.
Type of support: Research; Matching grants; Scholarships; Program development; Emergency funds; Curriculum development; Capital campaigns; General support.
Limitations: Applications not accepted. Giving on a national basis, with some emphasis on IL. No support for political organizations. No grants to individuals.
Application information: Contributes only to pre-selected organizations.
 Board meeting date(s): June
Trustees: Charles S. Brown, Jr.; Keith Brown DuBois; Robert A. Brown.
Number of staff: None.
EIN: 367295068

9408
Bruhn-Morris Family Foundation Inc.
311 Cameron St.
Alexandria, VA 22314-3219

Donors: Nigel W. Morris; Lori M. Morris.
Foundation type: Independent foundation.
Financial data (yr. ended 12/31/13): Assets, $11,955,813 (M); expenditures, $611,480; qualifying distributions, $602,781; giving activities include $368,645 for 35 grants (high: $125,000; low: $190).
Fields of interest: Education; Foundations; Venture philanthropy; Health; Child welfare.
Limitations: Applications not accepted. Giving primarily in Washington, DC, and VA. No grants to individuals.
Application information: Unsolicited requests for funds not accepted.
Officers: Lori M. Morris, Pres. and Secy.; Nigel W. Morris, V.P. and Treas.
Director: Ellen Folts.
EIN: 562315079

9409
The Bryant Foundation
P.O. Box 1239
Stephens City, VA 22655-1239 (540) 868-2183
Contact: Arthur H. Bryant II, Pres. and Treas.

Donor: J.C. Herbert Bryant†.
Foundation type: Independent foundation.
Financial data (yr. ended 12/31/13): Assets, $4,114,629 (M); expenditures, $222,612; qualifying distributions, $160,425; giving activities include $156,500 for 23 grants (high: $60,000; low: $500).
Purpose and activities: Giving for higher and other education, health care, and the arts.
Fields of interest: Arts and culture; Education; Higher education; Foundations; Health; Human services; Child welfare.
Type of support: Employee matching gifts.

Limitations: Applications accepted. Giving primarily in VA. No grants to individuals.
Application information:
 Initial approach: Proposal
 Deadline(s): None
Officers: Arthur H. Bryant II, Pres. and Treas.; Arthur H. Bryant, Jr., Secy.
Trustees: Gary F. Bryant; Taylor C. Bryant; James T. Holland.
EIN: 546032840

9410
George and Sarah Buchanan Foundation
(formerly Smith & Woodford Foundation)
400 Bridge St.
Danville, VA 24541-1404 (434) 797-3543

Established in 2006 in Virginia.
Donor: George B. Buchanan, Jr.
Foundation type: Independent foundation.
Financial data (yr. ended 02/28/13): Assets, $2,055,273 (M); expenditures, $304,649; qualifying distributions, $303,610; giving activities include $303,610 for 20 grants (high: $215,110; low: $100).
Fields of interest: Health; Diseases and conditions; Religion.
Type of support: General support.
Limitations: Applications accepted. Giving primarily in VA.
Application information:
 Initial approach: Proposal
 Deadline(s): None
Officers and Directors: George Buchanan, Jr., Pres. and Director; Donna Gibson, Secy.-Treas. and Director; Sally Alexander; George Buchanan III; Robert Buchanan.
EIN: 204479813

9411
The Burford Leimenstoll Foundation Inc.
P.O. Box 1998
Richmond, VA 23218-1998

Established in 1991 in Virginia.
Donor: Betty Sams Christian.
Foundation type: Independent foundation.
Financial data (yr. ended 12/31/13): Assets, $6,776,910 (M); expenditures, $339,193; qualifying distributions, $237,500; giving activities include $237,500 for 39 grants (high: $35,500; low: $500).
Fields of interest: Arts and culture; Education; University education; Environment; Diseases and conditions; Housing development; Human services; Child welfare.
Limitations: Applications not accepted. Giving primarily in VA. No grants to individuals.
Application information: Contributes only to pre-selected organizations.
Officer: Bruce L. Mertens, Secy.
Director: W. Bates Chappell.
EIN: 541608741

9412
Bw718 Foundation Inc.
P.O. Box 29628
Richmond, VA 23242-0628

Donor: E. Carlton Wilton Foundation.

Foundation type: Independent foundation.
Financial data (yr. ended 12/31/13): Assets, $2,066,156 (M); gifts received, $83,977; expenditures, $358,376; qualifying distributions, $357,418; giving activities include $355,946 for 25 grants (high: $90,000; low: $300).
Fields of interest: Education; Health; Human services.
Limitations: Applications not accepted.
Application information: Unsolicited requests for funds not accepted.
Officer: E. Carlton Wilton, Jr., Pres.
Directors: David H. Charlton; JoAnne D. Monday; Cameron Vaughn.
EIN: 271874537

9413
J. L. Camp Foundation, Inc.
100 73rd St.
Virginia Beach, VA 23451-1902 (757) 705-9498
Contact: James L. Camp IV, Pres.

Established in 1946 in Virginia.
Donors: J.L. Camp, Jr.†; Mrs. J.L. Camp, Jr.†; James L. Camp III†.
Foundation type: Independent foundation.
Financial data (yr. ended 12/31/13): Assets, $3,620,356 (M); expenditures, $144,988; qualifying distributions, $132,800; giving activities include $130,500 for 19 grants (high: $15,000; low: $2,500).
Purpose and activities: Emphasis on higher and secondary education, medical research and hospitals, the arts, and religion; some support for child welfare and youth development organizations.
Fields of interest: Education; Health; Agriculture.
Type of support: Continuing support; Capital and infrastructure; Emergency funds.
Limitations: Applications accepted. Giving primarily in VA. No grants to individuals.
Application information: Application form required.
 Initial approach: Letter
 Deadline(s): None
Officers: James L. Camp IV, Pres.; Toy D. Savage, Jr., V.P.; Karen A. Cavanaugh, Secy.-Treas.
Director: Peter M. Huber.
Number of staff: 1 full-time professional.
EIN: 540742940

9414
Cartledge Charitable Foundation, Inc.
4235 Electric Rd. S.W., Ste. 100
Roanoke, VA 24018-8445 (540) 776-7000
Contact: George B. Cartledge Jr., Chair.

Established in 1960 in Virginia.
Donors: Olive M. Cartledge Chantable Lead Trust; Grand Piano and Furniture Co.
Foundation type: Independent foundation.
Financial data (yr. ended 08/31/13): Assets, $3,707 (M); gifts received, $156,292; expenditures, $250,274; qualifying distributions, $248,255; giving activities include $248,255 for 69 grants (high: $68,250; low: $50).
Purpose and activities: Giving primarily for the arts and culture, higher and other education, social services, health associations, and youth organizations.
Fields of interest: Arts and culture; Performing arts; Theater; Museums; Education; Higher education; Diseases and conditions; Community and economic

development; Protestantism; Human services; Child welfare.
Type of support: General support.
Limitations: Applications accepted. Giving primarily in VA, with emphasis on Roanoke.
Application information:
  Initial approach: Letter
  Deadline(s): None
Officers: George B. Cartledge, Jr., Chair.; George B. Cartledge III, Pres.; Robert G. Bennett, Exec. V.P.; Randall Lundy, Secy.
Director: Pat Bennett.
EIN: 546044831

9415
Catesby Foundation
6384 Stuart St.
P.O. Box 500
The Plains, VA   20198-0500

Established in 1971 in Virginia.
Donor: Richard R. Ohrstrom†.
Foundation type: Independent foundation.
Financial data (yr. ended 12/31/13): Assets, $5,931,177 (M); expenditures, $280,734; qualifying distributions, $253,765; giving activities include $230,000 for 2 grants (high: $185,000; low: $45,000).
Purpose and activities: Giving primarily to a donor-advised fund.
Fields of interest: Foundations.
Limitations: Applications not accepted. Giving primarily in Southeastern, PA. No grants to individuals.
Application information: Unsolicited requests for funds not accepted.
Officers: George L. Ohrstrom II, Pres.; Mark J. Ohrstrom, V.P.; Kenneth M. Ohrstrom, Secy.; Barnaby A. Ohrstrom, Treas.
EIN: 237149750

9416
Cedars Foundation, Inc.
40123 Bond St.
P.O. Box 55
Waterford, VA   20197

Donor: W. Bowman Cutter.
Foundation type: Independent foundation.
Financial data (yr. ended 12/31/13): Assets, $2,278,937 (M); gifts received, $1,291,926; expenditures, $343,704; qualifying distributions, $308,275; giving activities include $308,275 for 28 grants (high: $129,600; low: $75).
Purpose and activities: Giving primarily for environmental conservation and international relief efforts.
Fields of interest: Higher education; Natural resources; Public policy; Human services; Basic and emergency aid; International development.
Type of support: Policy, advocacy and systems reform.
Limitations: Applications not accepted. Giving primarily in GA. No grants to individuals.
Application information: Unsolicited requests for funds not accepted.
Director: W. Bowman Cutter III.
EIN: 223651734

9417
Kamlesh and Luci Chainani Foundation
c/o BDO USA, LLP
8405 Greensboro Dr., Ste. 700
McLean, VA   22102-5108

Established in 2001 in Virginia.
Donors: Kamlesh Chainani; FC Business Systems; Luci Chainani.
Foundation type: Independent foundation.
Financial data (yr. ended 12/31/13): Assets, $3,921,605 (M); expenditures, $203,231; qualifying distributions, $176,736; giving activities include $170,201 for 2 grants (high: $165,201; low: $5,000).
Fields of interest: Health; Specialty hospital care; Human services; Basic and emergency aid; Food aid; Child welfare; International development.
Limitations: Applications not accepted. Giving primarily in OH.
Application information: Unsolicited requests for funds not accepted.
Officers: Kamlesh Chainani, Pres.; Angela Gilbert, V.P. and Secy.
EIN: 542061344

9418
The Charles Fund, Inc.
c/o Richmond and Fishburne
250 E. High St.
Charlottesville, VA   22902-5177   (434) 977-8590
Contact: Joseph W. Richmond Jr., Pres.

Donors: Edward C. Eisenhart; Edward Eisenhart Marital Trust; Sarah Eisenhart Trust.
Foundation type: Independent foundation.
Financial data (yr. ended 12/31/13): Assets, $10,660,387 (M); gifts received, $18,307; expenditures, $562,461; qualifying distributions, $482,707; giving activities include $435,000 for 60 grants (high: $75,000; low: $250).
Fields of interest: Science museums; Nonprofits; Hospital care; Geriatrics.
Type of support: General support; Regranting.
Limitations: Applications accepted. Giving primarily in Charlottesville, VA; with some giving in NY. No grants to individuals.
Application information: Application form required.
  Initial approach: Contact foundation for application form
  Deadline(s): None
Officers: Joseph W. Richmond, Jr., Pres.; Betsy Carver, V.P.; Deborah Maggs, V.P.; J. Walker Richmond III, Secy.-Treas.
Directors: Timothy Alexander; Gregory Carver; Anne M. Farnham.
EIN: 168064401

9419
The Chastain Home for Gentlewomen
370 Mountain Rd.
P. O. Box 756
Halifax, VA   24558-0756

Established in 2007 in Virginia.
Foundation type: Independent foundation.
Financial data (yr. ended 03/31/13): Assets, $10,930,800 (M); expenditures, $550,925; qualifying distributions, $171,750; giving activities include $171,750 for grants.

Fields of interest: Education; Hospice care; Christianity; Human services.
Limitations: Applications not accepted. Giving primarily in VA. No grants to individuals.
Application information: Unsolicited requests for funds not accepted.
Officers and Trustees: Tucker Henley, Chair. and Pres. and Trustee; Chandler A. Nelson, V.P. and Trustee; W. Bates Chappell, Secy.-Treas.; Hugh G. Edmonds, Jr.; Carl Espy IV; Brockenbrough Lamp, Jr.; Connie Zamora.
EIN: 202949635

9420
The Gladys and Franklin Clark Foundation
809 Richmond Rd.
Williamsburg, VA   23185-3543

Established in 1992 in Virginia.
Donor: Gladys & Franklin Clark Revocable Trust.
Foundation type: Independent foundation.
Financial data (yr. ended 12/31/13): Assets, $6,598,543 (M); expenditures, $501,254; qualifying distributions, $376,773; giving activities include $360,000 for 3 grants (high: $200,000; low: $60,000).
Fields of interest: Historical activities; Law education.
Limitations: Applications not accepted. Giving primarily in Williamsburg, VA. No grants to individuals.
Application information: Unsolicited requests for funds not accepted.
Officers and Directors: Gilbert A. Bartlett, Pres. and Director; L. Alvin Garrison, Secy. and Director; Joseph W. Montgomery, Treas. and Director.
EIN: 541640751

9421
The Clark-Nexsen Foundation Inc.
6160 Kempsville Cir., Ste. 200A
Norfolk, VA   23502-3945

Donor: Clark Nexsen.
Foundation type: Independent foundation.
Financial data (yr. ended 12/31/13): Assets, $33,668 (M); gifts received, $31,000; expenditures, $164,476; qualifying distributions, $164,413; giving activities include $163,063 for 23 grants (high: $33,114; low: $250).
Fields of interest: Arts and culture; Education; Human services.
Limitations: Applications not accepted. Giving primarily in VA. No grants to individuals.
Application information: Contributes only to pre-selected organizations.
Officers: Christopher M. Stone, Chair.; Kenneth G. Stepka, Vice-Chair. and Treas.; Susan B. Drew, Secy.
Directors: Joseph H. Bushey; Gregory J. Hall; Garry G. Kiskinis.
EIN: 262652520

9422
The Helen C. Cobbs Foundation
P.O. Box 90
Roanoke, VA   24002-0090   (540) 512-1801
Contact: Olin R. Melchionna Jr., Tr.

Donor: Helen C. Cobbs.

Foundation type: Independent foundation.
Financial data (yr. ended 12/31/13): Assets, $5,537,360 (M); expenditures, $309,591; qualifying distributions, $264,403; giving activities include $230,000 for 13 grants (high: $34,500; low: $5,750).
Fields of interest: Education; Community and economic development; Protestantism.
Limitations: Applications accepted. Giving primarily in Roanoke, VA. No grants to individuals.
Application information: Application form required.
  Initial approach: Letter
  Deadline(s): None
Trustee: Olin R. Melchionna, Jr.
EIN: 276251236

9423
S. Mason and Lula P. Cole Charitable Trust
P.O. Box 1419
Kilmarnock, VA 22482

Donors: S. Mason Cole Trust; Lula P. Cole Trust.
Foundation type: Independent foundation.
Financial data (yr. ended 12/31/14): Assets, $4,217,162; expenditures, $285,058; qualifying distributions, $216,000.
Fields of interest: Arts and culture; Education; Community and economic development; Human services.
Limitations: Applications not accepted. Giving primarily in Virginia.
Application information: Unsolicited requests for funds not accepted.
Trustee: Chesapeake Trust Co.
EIN: 266779458

9424
The Vicky Collins Charitable Foundation, Inc.
c/o David Sher
3800 N. Fairfax Dr., Ste. 7
Arlington, VA 22203-1703 (703) 525-1200
Main URL: http://www.vickycollinsfoundation.com

Established in 2004 in Virginia.
Donor: Vicky G. Collins†.
Foundation type: Independent foundation.
Financial data (yr. ended 12/31/14): Assets, $3,908,026; expenditures, $259,263; qualifying distributions, $212,548.
Purpose and activities: Giving to organizations that assist disabled children.
Fields of interest: Health care clinics; Family services; Domestic violence shelters; Children; Females; People with disabilities.
Limitations: Applications accepted. Giving primarily in VA. No grants to individuals.
Application information: Application form required.
  Initial approach: Letter
  Deadline(s): None
Officers and Directors: David E. Sher, Pres. and Director; Mark D. Cummings, V.P. and Director; A. Paul Lanzillotta, Secy. and Director.
EIN: 320105718

9425
Alisann and Terry Collins Foundation
6713 Bellamy Ave.
Springfield, VA 22152-3026

Foundation type: Independent foundation.
Financial data (yr. ended 12/31/14): Assets, $8,697,430; gifts received, $1,483; expenditures, $357,353; qualifying distributions, $355,350.
Fields of interest: Education; Health; Human services.
Limitations: Applications not accepted.
Application information: Unsolicited requests for funds not accepted.
Officers: Terry L. Collins, Pres. and Treas.; Alisann A. Collins, V.P. and Secy.
EIN: 272764310

9426
The Community Foundation of the New River Valley
990 Cambria St., N.E.
Christiansburg, VA 24073-1602 (540) 381-8999
Contact: Jessica Wirgau, Exec. Dir.
FAX: (540) 381-1406; E-mail: cfnrv@cfnrv.org; Additional e-mail: jessicawirgau@cfnrv.org; Mailing address: P.O. Box 6009, Christiansburg 24068-6009; Main URL: http://www.cfnrv.org

Established in 1994 in Virginia.
Foundation type: Community foundation.
Financial data (yr. ended 12/31/13): Assets, $8,637,133 (M); gifts received, $722,563; expenditures, $595,181; giving activities include $217,304 for 6+ grants (high: $32,842), and $82,650 for grants to individuals.
Purpose and activities: The mission of the Community Foundation of the New River Valley is to enrich the community by providing professional management services to donors for their charitable causes, awarding visionary grants and scholarships, and nurturing collaborations in the local community.
Fields of interest: Arts and culture; Cultural awareness; Museums; Historic preservation; Education; Natural resources; Domesticated animals; Health; Libraries; Public administration; Community and economic development; Community improvement; Religion; Human services; Civics for youth.
Type of support: General support; Matching grants; Continuing support; Equipment; Publications; Seed money; Scholarships.
Limitations: Applications accepted. Giving primarily in the City of Radford and Floyd, Giles, Montgomery, and Pulaski counties, VA. No grants for "bricks and mortar" projects (generally).
Publications: Application guidelines; Annual report; Financial statement; Grants list; Informational brochure; Newsletter.
Application information: Applicants are invited to submit a full application at the invitation of the foundation after reviewing Intent to Apply Forms. Faxed or e-mailed full applications are not accepted. Visit foundation website for more information. Application form required.
  Initial approach: Submit Intent to Apply Form
  Copies of proposal: 1
  Deadline(s): Apr. 4 for Intent to Apply Form, July 18 for Full Application
  Board meeting date(s): 4th Tues. of each month
Officers and Directors: Courtney Grohs, Pres. and Director; Ed Lawhorn, V.P. and Director; Terri Fisher, Secy. and Director; Katy Kirk, Treas. and Director; Jessica Wirgau, Exec. Dir.; C.J. Carter; Belva Collins; Peggy Eaton; Nancy Eiss; Ginny Gardner; Gary Hancock; Pat Huber; Hugh Jenkins; Dwayne Kittle;

Mike Larrowe; Carlotta Lewis; Hing-Har Lo; Barbara Michelsen; Sam Minner; John Muffo; Andrew Warren.
Number of staff: 1 full-time professional; 1 full-time support; 1 part-time support.
EIN: 541740455

9427
William A. Cooke Foundation
P.O. Box 462
Louisa, VA 23093-0462 (540) 967-0881
Contact: Wallace L. Tingler CPA, Pres.
FAX: (540) 967-0711; E-mail: rltingler1@gmail.com; Main URL: http://wacookefoundation.com
Grants List: http://wacookefoundation.com/pages/grants

Donors: William A. Cooke, Incorporated; William A. Cooke Trust.
Foundation type: Independent foundation.
Financial data (yr. ended 12/31/13): Assets, $9,483,058; gifts received, $115,823; expenditures, $720,835; qualifying distributions, $304,535; giving activities include $245,550 for 71 grants to individuals (high: $25,000; low: $300).
Fields of interest: Arts and culture; Education; Health.
Limitations: Applications accepted. Giving limited to Louisa and Orange counties, VA.
Application information: Application form required.
  Initial approach: Proposal
  Deadline(s): None
Officers: Wallace L. Tingler, CPA, Pres.; Randall L. Tingler, V.P.; Rebecca B. Cavanaugh, Secy.
Directors: Dean P. Agee; C. Champian Bowles; Gloria G. Layne; Linda J. Parker; Deborah Pettit.
EIN: 542012726

9428
The Joshua P. & Elizabeth D. Darden Foundation
1303 Ballantrae Ct.
McLean, VA 22101-3001 (757) 640-1414
Contact: E. Holley Darden, Secy. and Dir.

Established in 1993 in Virginia.
Donor: Joshua P. Darden.
Foundation type: Independent foundation.
Financial data (yr. ended 12/31/13): Assets, $1,253,644 (M); gifts received, $25,000; expenditures, $379,405; qualifying distributions, $367,050; giving activities include $367,050 for 27 grants (high: $150,000; low: $100).
Fields of interest: Health; Catholicism; Human services.
Type of support: General support; Program development.
Limitations: Applications accepted. Giving limited to VA, with some emphasis in Norfolk and Virginia Beach. No grants to individuals.
Application information: Application form required.
  Initial approach: Letter
  Deadline(s): None
Officers and Directors: Joshua P. Darden, Jr., Pres. and Director; E. Holley Darden, Secy. and Director; Elizabeth D. Darden, Treas. and Director; Audrey D. Parrott.
Number of staff: 1 part-time support.
EIN: 541661365

9429
The Charles Delmar Foundation
5205 Leesburg Pike, Ste. 209
Falls Church, VA 22041-3858

Established in 1957 in District of Columbia.
Donors: Charles Delmar†; Mareen D. Hughes; Roland H. Delmar†; Elizabeth A. Delmar†.
Foundation type: Independent foundation.
Financial data (yr. ended 12/31/13): Assets, $7,633,757 (M); expenditures, $356,211; qualifying distributions, $332,874; giving activities include $301,000 for 110 grants (high: $10,000; low: $500).
Purpose and activities: Special interests include inter-American studies, higher, secondary, elementary, and other education, underprivileged youth, the disadvantaged, the aged, the homeless and housing issues, general welfare organizations, and fine and performing arts.
Fields of interest: Performing arts; Higher education; Natural resources; Hospital care; Family planning; Diseases and conditions; Protestantism; Catholicism; Human services; Child welfare; Children and youth; Infants and toddlers; Children; Adolescents; Adults; Seniors; Females; Female children and youth; Female adults; Males; Male children and youth; Male adults; Ethnic and racial groups; People of African descent; People of Latin American descent; Indigenous peoples; American Indians; Migrant workers; Homeless people; Low-income and poor people; Out-of-home youth; People with disabilities; People with physical disabilities; People with vision impairments; People with hearing impairments; People with psychosocial disabilities; People with HIV/AIDS; Substance abusers; Veterans.
International interests: Europe; Latin America; South America.
Type of support: General support; Continuing support; Annual campaigns; Capital campaigns; Capital and infrastructure; Endowments; Convening; Seed money; Internships; Scholarships.
Limitations: Applications accepted. Giving primarily in the Washington, DC area in the U.S., and in Europe and South America. No support for religious or political organizations. No grants to individuals, or for building or endowment funds, or matching gifts; no loans.
Publications: Financial statement.
Application information:
   Initial approach: Letter
   Copies of proposal: 1
   Deadline(s): None
   Board meeting date(s): As required
Officers and Trustees: Mareen D. Hughes, Pres. and Trustee; R. Bruce Hughes, Secy.-Treas. and Trustee.
EIN: 526035345

9430
Helen Pumphrey Denit Charitable Trust
(formerly The Helen Pumphrey Denit Trust for Charitable and Educational Purposes)
c/o U.S. Trust, Bank of America, N.A.
1111 E. Main St., VA2-300-12-92
Richmond, VA 23219 (804) 788-2673
Contact: Sarah Kay, V.P.
E-mail: sarah.kay@ustrust.com; Main URL: https://www.bankofamerica.com/philanthropic/grantmaking.go

Donor: Helen P. Denit†.
Foundation type: Independent foundation.

Financial data (yr. ended 06/30/15): Assets, $7,109,957 (M); expenditures, $449,121; qualifying distributions, $355,348; giving activities include $305,000 for 29 grants (high: $50,000; low: $5,000).
Purpose and activities: Giving to support charitable organizations that promote quality education, culture, human service, health service, and arts opportunities.
Fields of interest: Arts and culture; Art museums; Higher education; Graduate and professional education; Hospital care; Theology; Human services.
Type of support: General support.
Limitations: Applications accepted. Giving primarily in Washington, DC and Baltimore, MD. No grants to individuals.
Application information:
   Initial approach: Online via Trust web site
   Deadline(s): Feb. 1
Trustee: Bank of America, N.A.
EIN: 526401248

9431
Douglas & Marianne Dickerson Foundation
1204 Kamichi Ct.
Virginia Beach, VA 23451-4918 (757) 428-1080
Contact: Douglas Dickerson, Pres. and Treas.

Established in 2004 in Virginia.
Donors: Douglas Dickerson; Marianne Dickerson.
Foundation type: Independent foundation.
Financial data (yr. ended 12/31/13): Assets, $4,482,910 (M); expenditures, $237,522; qualifying distributions, $210,000; giving activities include $210,000 for 18 grants (high: $103,000; low: $500).
Fields of interest: Undergraduate education; Nonprofits; Specialty hospital care; Human services; Developmental disability services.
Type of support: Capital campaigns; Regranting.
Limitations: Applications accepted. Giving primarily in VA and CA.
Application information: Application form required.
   Initial approach: Letter
   Deadline(s): None
Officers: Douglas Dickerson, Pres. and Treas.; Marianne Dickerson, V.P. and Secy.
EIN: 201577084

9432
The Donohue Family Foundation, Inc.
4109 N. Randolph Ct.
Arlington, VA 22207-4863

Donors: Thomas J. Donohue; Elizabeth A. Donohue.
Foundation type: Independent foundation.
Financial data (yr. ended 06/30/13): Assets, $552,321 (M); gifts received, $300,000; expenditures, $169,550; qualifying distributions, $167,100; giving activities include $167,100 for 24 grants (high: $25,000; low: $100).
Fields of interest: Higher education; Health; Community and economic development; Christianity; Human services.
Type of support: General support.
Limitations: Applications not accepted. Giving primarily in NY. No grants to individuals.
Application information: Unsolicited requests for funds not accepted.

Officers: John L. Donohue, Pres.; Elizabeth A. Donohue, Treas.
Directors: Keith M. Donohue; Thomas J. Donohue; Thomas J. Donohue, Jr.
EIN: 522127961

9433
The Dorothy-Ann Foundation
1177 Jamestown Rd.
Williamsburg, VA 23185-3315 7572206500

Established in 1999 in Virginia.
Donors: Darwin O'Ryan Curtis; Darwin O'Ryan Curtis Charitable Lead Annuity Trust.
Foundation type: Independent foundation.
Financial data (yr. ended 12/31/14): Assets, $465,494; gifts received, $307,851; expenditures, $227,936; qualifying distributions, $221,563.
Purpose and activities: Giving primarily for international health and environmental conservation.
Fields of interest: Natural resources; Health.
International interests: Africa; Australia; Latin America.
Type of support: General support; Matching grants; Program development; Seed money.
Limitations: Applications not accepted. Giving primarily to ME, New York, NY, NC and VA. No grants to individuals.
Publications: Occasional report.
Application information: Contributes only to pre-selected organizations.
   Board meeting date(s): Fall
Officers: Randall K. Curtis, Pres.; Vernon M. Geddy III, Secy.-Treas.
Directors: Mieke Bowman; John D. Curtis; Laura Curtis; Simon B. Curtis.
Number of staff: None.
EIN: 541965966

9434
The Doudera Family Foundation
2940 N. Lynnhaven Rd., Ste. 200
Virginia Beach, VA 23452-6949

Established in 1996 in Virginia.
Donor: Ralph J. Doudera.
Foundation type: Independent foundation.
Financial data (yr. ended 12/31/13): Assets, $7,784,629 (M); expenditures, $276,994; qualifying distributions, $253,500; giving activities include $253,500 for 3 grants (high: $250,000; low: $1,000).
Purpose and activities: Giving primarily to promote fundamentalist Christianity and for human services.
Fields of interest: Christianity; Human services.
Limitations: Applications not accepted. Giving primarily in GA, NC and VA. No grants to individuals.
Application information: Unsolicited requests for funds not accepted.
Officers and Directors: Ralph J. Doudera, Pres. and Secy.-Treas. and Director; Richard C. Mapp III, V.P.
EIN: 541817654

9435
Dreaming Hand Foundation
1050 Broomley Rd.
Charlottesville, VA 22901-7824

Established in 2000 in Virginia.

Donors: Kay F. Bechtel; Stefan D. Bechtel; Kay L. Ferguson.
Foundation type: Independent foundation.
Financial data (yr. ended 12/31/13): Assets, $114,027 (M); gifts received, $109,162; expenditures, $171,460; qualifying distributions, $166,570; giving activities include $166,570 for 48 grants (high: $50,000; low: $100).
Purpose and activities: Giving primarily for the arts.
Fields of interest: Arts and culture; Education; Environment; Human services.
Limitations: Applications not accepted. Giving primarily in Charlottesville, VA. No grants to individuals.
Application information: Unsolicited requests for funds not accepted.
Officers: Kay L. Ferguson, Pres. and Treas.; David W. Kudravetz, Secy.
Directors: Lilly A. Becthel.
EIN: 542014866

9436
Dreyfus Foundation
5555 Greenwich Rd., No. 600
Virginia Beach, VA 23462-6542

Established in 1997 in Virginia.
Donors: Mark Dreyfus; Alfred Dreyfus.
Foundation type: Independent foundation.
Financial data (yr. ended 12/31/13): Assets, $6,193,980 (M); gifts received, $487,795; expenditures, $470,751; qualifying distributions, $438,607; giving activities include $437,375 for 7 grants (high: $300,895; low: $10,239).
Purpose and activities: Giving for education and community organizations.
Fields of interest: Education; Community and economic development.
Limitations: Applications not accepted. Giving primarily in VA. No grants to individuals.
Application information: Contributes only to pre-selected organizations.
Officers and Directors: Alfred Dreyfus, Pres. and Director; Mildred Dreyfus, Secy. and Director; Mark Dreyfus, Treas. and Director; Claudia Dreyfus Levi.
EIN: 541851411

9437
Dun Foundation
P.O. Box 346
Middleburg, VA 20118-0346 (540) 687-6057

Established in 2006 in Virginia.
Foundation type: Independent foundation.
Financial data (yr. ended 12/31/14): Assets, $4,297,649; expenditures, $244,142; qualifying distributions, $243,657.
Fields of interest: Museums; Education; Environment; Equestrianism; Human services; Child welfare.
Application information:
   Initial approach: Proposal
   Deadline(s): None
Officers: P. Douglas Fout, Pres. and Treas.; Virginia Fout, V.P.; Nina Fout, Secy.
EIN: 204463281

9438
The Constance Dundas Foundation
c/o Fred J. Bernhardt, Jr.
901 E. Cary St., Ste. 1900
Richmond, VA 23219-4049

Established in 1997 in Virginia.
Donor: Constance Dundas†.
Foundation type: Independent foundation.
Financial data (yr. ended 09/30/14): Assets, $6,743,576; expenditures, $354,021; qualifying distributions, $305,528.
Fields of interest: Foundations; Community and economic development; Christianity; Human services.
Limitations: Applications not accepted. Giving primarily in VA. No grants to individuals.
Application information: Contributes only to pre-selected organizations.
Trustee: Fred J. Bernhardt, Jr.
EIN: 541894989

9439
The Richard J. Dwyer, Jr. & Mary B. Dwyer Charitable Foundation Trust
2322 Staley Rd.
Reston, VA 20191-4619

Established in 1996 in Virginia.
Donors: Mary B. Dwyer; Richard J. Dwyer, Jr.
Foundation type: Independent foundation.
Financial data (yr. ended 06/30/13): Assets, $1,122,463 (M); expenditures, $245,587; qualifying distributions, $222,500; giving activities include $222,500 for 21 grants (high: $20,000; low: $5,000).
Fields of interest: Housing development; Religion; Human services.
Limitations: Applications not accepted. Giving primarily in VA. No grants to individuals.
Application information: Unsolicited requests for funds not accepted.
Trustees: Kathryn A. Dwyer; Kevin Dwyer; Paul B. Dwyer; Richard Dwyer; Nancy McKenzie; Mary D. Rinaldi.
EIN: 541815672

9440
The Irwin P. Edlavitch Foundation, Inc.
185 Chain Bridge Rd.
McLean, VA 22101-1907

Established in 1998 in Virginia.
Donor: Irwin P. Edlavitch.
Foundation type: Independent foundation.
Financial data (yr. ended 12/31/13): Assets, $2,124,266 (M); gifts received, $202,975; expenditures, $304,126; qualifying distributions, $293,313; giving activities include $282,500 for 5 grants (high: $200,000; low: $12,500).
Fields of interest: Arts and culture; Nonprofits; Hospital care.
Type of support: General support; Regranting.
Limitations: Applications not accepted. Giving primarily in MD. No grants to individuals.
Application information: Unsolicited requests for funds not accepted.
Officers and Directors: Irwin P. Edlavitch, Pres. and Director; Ginny S. Abrams, Secy. and Director.
EIN: 541907348

9441
Leifur Eiriksson Foundation
c/o University of Virginia Foundation
P.O. Box 400222
Charlottesville, VA 22904-4222 (434) 982-4849
Contact: Margo Eppard, Treas.
E-mail: mde5c@virginia.edu; Application address: c/o Karen Torgersen, Coordinator, 1209 Redbud Rd., Blacksburg, VA 24060, tel.: (434) 981-2061, e-mail: eiriksson.foundation@gmail.com; Additional contact: c/o Susan G. Harris, Secy., tel.: (434) 924-7120, e-mail: sgh4c@virginia.edu; Main URL: http://www.leifureirikssonfoundation.org

Foundation type: Independent foundation.
Financial data (yr. ended 06/30/13): Assets, $5,364,449 (M); expenditures, $314,050; qualifying distributions, $261,712; giving activities include $187,500 for 8 grants to individuals (high: $25,000; low: $12,500).
Purpose and activities: The foundation funds a graduate fellowship exchange program between Iceland and the United States.
Fields of interest: Education.
International interests: Iceland.
Type of support: Fellowships.
Application information: See foundation web site for complete application guidelines. Application form required.
   Initial approach: Email or complete online application form
   Deadline(s): Applications by Dec. 2; supporting documents by Dec. 13
Officers: John T. Casteen III, Chair.; Susan G. Harris, Secy.; Margo D. Eppard, Treas.
Trustees: Thrainn Eggertsson; Joan Fry; Halla Tomasdottir; Richard S. Williams, Jr.
EIN: 542056415

9442
The Elmwood Fund
P.O. Box 85678
Richmond, VA 23285-5678 8047802115
Application address: Walter M. Dotts, 2720 Broad St., Richmond, VA 23223; tel.: (804) 780-2115

Established in 1970 in Virginia.
Foundation type: Independent foundation.
Financial data (yr. ended 12/31/14): Assets, $1,435,238; expenditures, $204,460; qualifying distributions, $188,400.
Purpose and activities: Giving for historical preservation, youth services, and park and recreation services.
Fields of interest: Arts and culture; Education; Human services.
Limitations: Applications accepted. Giving primarily in NY and Richmond, VA. No grants to individuals.
Application information: Application form required.
   Initial approach: Letter
   Copies of proposal: 4
   Deadline(s): None
Officers: Walter M. Dotts, Pres.; Mary Zuegner, Secy.-Treas.
EIN: 237075321

9443

The English Foundation

(formerly The English Foundation-Trust)
c/o English's Inc.
1522 Main St.
Altavista, VA 24517-1132 (434) 369-4771
Contact: E.R. English Jr., Tr.

Established in 1956 in Virginia.
Donor: E.R. English, Sr.‡
Foundation type: Independent foundation.
Financial data (yr. ended 12/31/12): Assets,
$2,141,434 (M); gifts received, $10,000;
expenditures, $207,687; qualifying distributions,
$168,350; giving activities include $168,350 for 30
grants (high: $73,250; low: $100).
Fields of interest: Education; Sports and recreation;
Youth development.
Limitations: Applications accepted. Giving primarily
in Campbell County, VA, area.
Application information: Application form required.
  Initial approach: Letter for organizations; letter
    requesting application form for scholarships
  Deadline(s): None
Trustees: E.R. English, Jr.; Rita T. English; James P.
Kent, Jr.
EIN: 546036409

9444

The Jacquemin Family Foundation Inc.

8609 Westwood Center Dr., Ste. 45
Vienna, VA 22182 (703) 917-0707
Contact: John M. Jacquemin, Mgr.

Established in 1997 in Virginia.
Donors: John M. Jacquemin; Brookewood
Investment Company LLC.
Foundation type: Independent foundation.
Financial data (yr. ended 12/31/13): Assets,
$3,975,414 (M); expenditures, $216,630;
qualifying distributions, $213,875; giving activities
include $213,875 for 28 grants (high: $30,000;
low: $725).
Purpose and activities: Giving to organizations that
give specific attention to promote education and the
arts for under-served children.
Fields of interest: Arts education; Education; Youth
development; Low-income and poor people.
Type of support: Program development;
Scholarships.
Limitations: Applications accepted. Giving primarily
in NY and VA.
Application information:
  Initial approach: Proposal
  Deadline(s): None
Officers: Tracie Jensen Jacquemin, Secy.; John M.
Jacquemin, Mgr.
Director: Claude Jacquemin.
EIN: 541887187

9445

The Farkas Family Foundation

1720 Brown's Gap Tpke.
Charlottesville, VA 22901—6312

Established in 2000 in Virginia.
Donor: Thomas Farkas Marital Trust.
Foundation type: Independent foundation.
Financial data (yr. ended 06/30/13): Assets,
$9,998,911 (M); expenditures, $395,850;

qualifying distributions, $305,000; giving activities
include $305,000 for grants.
Fields of interest: Arts and culture; Higher
education; Hospital care; Human services.
Limitations: Applications not accepted. Giving
primarily in NY and VA. No grants to individuals.
Application information: Contributes only to
pre-selected organizations.
Trustee: Gail Munger.
EIN: 061593377

9446

Andrew U. Ferrari Foundation

c/o BDO USA, LLP
8405 Greensboro Dr., Ste. 700
McLean, VA 22102-5108

Donors: Andrew U. Ferrari; Barbara Q. Ferrari.
Foundation type: Independent foundation.
Financial data (yr. ended 12/31/13): Assets,
$339,045 (M); expenditures, $153,806; qualifying
distributions, $151,600; giving activities include
$151,600 for 27 grants (high: $60,000; low: $100).
Purpose and activities: Giving primarily for higher
and other education, health associations, and
children, youth, and social services.
Fields of interest: Education; Employment.
Limitations: Applications not accepted. Giving
primarily in VA, with emphasis on the Shenandoah
Valley; some funding nationally.
Application information: Unsolicited requests for
funds not accepted.
Trustees: Andrew U. Ferrari; Barbara Q. Ferrari.
EIN: 206084198

9447

R. and M. Fink Family Trust

5873 Iron Stone Ct.
Centreville, VA 20120-4915 (212) 935-1555
Contact: Richard Fink

Established in 1999 in Virginia.
Donors: Mary Fink; Richard H. Fink.
Foundation type: Independent foundation.
Financial data (yr. ended 12/31/13): Assets,
$8,506,457 (M); gifts received, $1,000,000;
expenditures, $211,355; qualifying distributions,
$211,330; giving activities include $211,330 for 22
grants (high: $100,000; low: $30).
Fields of interest: Education; Higher education;
Housing development; Christianity; Right to life;
Human services.
Limitations: Applications accepted. Giving primarily
in KS and VA. No grants to individuals.
Application information:
  Initial approach: Letter
  Deadline(s): None
Trustee: Richard Fink.
EIN: 546466359

9448

Alan & Esther Fleder Foundation

500 E. Main St., Ste. 1424
Norfolk, VA 23510-2206 (757) 623-1062
Contact: Lawrence Fleder, Pres.

Established in 1977 in Virginia.
Donors: Alan Fleder; Esther Fleder; CGEL
Associates, LLP.
Foundation type: Independent foundation.

Financial data (yr. ended 09/30/14): Assets,
$3,032,700 (M); expenditures, $155,264;
qualifying distributions, $154,734; giving activities
include $154,734 for 93 grants (high: $20,500;
low: $100).
Fields of interest: Community and economic
development; Religion; Human services.
Limitations: Applications accepted. Giving primarily
in Norfolk, VA.
Application information: Application form required.
  Initial approach: Letter
  Deadline(s): None
Officers and Directors: Lawrence Fleder, Pres. and
Director; Janice L. Cabacungan, Secy.; Eileen Kahn,
Treas. and Director.
EIN: 510217379

9449

The Jane and Arthur Flippo Foundation

P.O. Box 38
Doswell, VA 23047-0038
Application address: Sylvia S. Acors, Secy.-Treas.,
16415 Washington Hwy., Doswell, VA 23047

Established in 1988 in Virginia.
Donors: Arthur P. Flippo; Arthur P. Flippo Trust.
Foundation type: Independent foundation.
Financial data (yr. ended 12/31/14): Assets,
$4,681,586 (M); expenditures, $318,778;
qualifying distributions, $256,000; giving activities
include $256,000 for 27 grants (high: $105,000;
low: $250).
Fields of interest: Education; Protestantism; Human
services.
Type of support: General support.
Limitations: Applications accepted. Giving primarily
in VA. No grants to individuals.
Application information: Application form required.
  Initial approach: Letter
  Deadline(s): None
Officers: J. Franklin Jones, Pres.; Norman L. Long,
V.P.; Sylvia S. Acors, Secy.-Treas.
EIN: 541479553

9450

Foundation of the Pierre Fauchard Academy

11654 Plaza American Dr., Ste. 901
Reston, VA 20190 (703) 217-1480
Contact: Jennifer Teale, Exec. Dir.
E-mail: information@foundationpfa.org; Email for
completed applications: jteale@foundationpfa.org;
Main URL: http://www.foundationpfa.org
Grants List: https://www.foundationpfa.org/grants

Established in 1986 in California.
Foundation type: Independent foundation.
Financial data (yr. ended 12/31/13): Assets,
$7,151,745 (M); gifts received, $26,807;
expenditures, $401,876; qualifying distributions,
$292,336; giving activities include $119,750 for 15
grants (high: $10,000; low: $5,000), and $78,900
for 65 grants to individuals (high: $10,000; low:
$1,000).
Purpose and activities: Support primarily for dental
schools and for the study and research of dentistry.
Support also for programs that support dental care
for the underserved world wide.
Fields of interest: Graduate and professional
education; Dental care; Human services.
Type of support: General support; Student aid.

Limitations: Applications accepted. Giving on a national basis.
Application information: See Academy web site for application information for grants and scholarships.
Board meeting date(s): Oct.
Officers: Dr. Gary W. Lowder, Pres.; Dr. Howard Mark, V.P.; Dr. Michael J. Perpich, Treas.; Dr. Steven Hedlund, Grants. Chair.; Jennifer Teale, Exec. Dir.
Trustees: Dr. Malcolm David Campbell; Dr. Charles G. Eller; Joseph Harris; Steven Hedlund; William B. Kort; James Long.
EIN: 770120371

9451
The Lewis and Butler Foundation
(formerly Sydney & Frances Lewis Foundation)
2601 Monument Ave.
Richmond, VA   23220-2620

Established in 1966 in Virginia.
Donors: Sydney Lewis†; Frances A. Lewis.
Foundation type: Independent foundation.
Financial data (yr. ended 06/30/13): Assets, $4,492,791 (M); expenditures, $333,046; qualifying distributions, $300,355; giving activities include $300,355 for 33 grants (high: $100,000; low: $90).
Fields of interest: Museums; Education; Higher education; Nonprofits; Human services.
Type of support: Regranting.
Limitations: Applications not accepted. Giving primarily in New York, NY, and VA, with emphasis on Richmond. No grants to individuals.
Application information: Contributes only to pre-selected organizations.
Officers and Directors: Frances A. Lewis, Pres. and Director; Susan L. Butler, V.P. and Director; Andrew M. Lewis, Secy. and Director.
EIN: 546061170

9452
The Franklin Federal Foundation
4501 Cox Rd.
Glen Allen, VA   23060-3381

Established in 2000 in Virginia.
Donors: Franklin Federal Savings & Loan; Franklin Financial Corporation.
Foundation type: Company-sponsored foundation.
Financial data (yr. ended 09/30/13): Assets, $9,991,750 (M); expenditures, $366,345; qualifying distributions, $346,308; giving activities include $248,450 for 66 grants (high: $25,000; low: $100), and $97,858 for 69 employee matching gifts.
Purpose and activities: The foundation supports hospitals and organizations involved with arts and culture, education, hunger, school athletics, human services, and the banking industry.
Fields of interest: Arts and culture; Orchestral music; Art museums; Education; Higher education; Hospital care; Financial counseling; Business and industry; School athletics; Human services; Food banks; Food delivery.
Type of support: General support; Employee matching gifts.
Limitations: Applications not accepted. Giving primarily in VA. No grants to individuals.
Application information: Contributes only to pre-selected organizations.

Officers: William E. W. Frayser, Jr., V.P.; Jennifer R. Merritt, V.P.; Donald F. Marker, Secy.-Treas.
Directors: George C. Freeman III; Hugh T. Harrison II; Erin S. Jewett; L. Gerald Roach; Richard T. Wheeler, Jr.
Number of staff: None.
EIN: 541996321

9453
Fraser Family Foundation, Inc.
9239 Old Green Mountain Rd.
Esmont, VA   22937-2306

Established in 2000 in New York.
Donors: Corey F. Huber; Katherine L. Huber.
Foundation type: Independent foundation.
Financial data (yr. ended 12/31/13): Assets, $1,067,672 (M); expenditures, $235,448; qualifying distributions, $221,891; giving activities include $221,891 for 7 grants (high: $177,576; low: $500).
Purpose and activities: Giving primarily to Roman Catholic organizations, and to individuals who desire to follow their vocational call to religious life, but are prevented from doing do by the debt they acquired to pay for an education.
Fields of interest: Education; Catholicism; Human services.
Limitations: Applications not accepted. Giving primarily in the Washington, DC, area, including MD and VA.
Application information: Unsolicited requests for funds not accepted.
Officers: Corey F. Huber, Pres. and C.E.O.; Katherine L. Huber, V.P. and Secy.-Treas.
Director: Laurence G. Bousquet, Esq.
EIN: 161584090

9454
Fredericksburg Rescue Squad Foundation
P.O. Box 4101
Fredericksburg, VA   22402-4101

Foundation type: Independent foundation.
Financial data (yr. ended 12/31/13): Assets, $3,632,501 (M); gifts received, $1,000; expenditures, $180,285; qualifying distributions, $156,743; giving activities include $151,432 for 1 grant.
Fields of interest: Disasters and emergency management.
Limitations: Applications not accepted. Giving primarily in Fredericksburg, VA.
Application information: Unsolicited requests for funds not accepted.
Officers: Steve Ennis, Pres.; Kevin Jones, Secy.; John Thompson, Treas.
Directors: Francis Curtis; Daryl Labre; Troy E. Payne; Gerald Snellings; Harry Snellings; Richard Wright.
EIN: 541892320

9455
Fund for Innovation and Public Service
1200 N. Nash St.
Arlington, VA   22209-3616

Foundation type: Independent foundation.
Financial data (yr. ended 12/31/13): Assets, $4,819,089 (M); gifts received, $44,778; expenditures, $230,797; qualifying distributions,

$202,910; giving activities include $202,910 for 23 grants (high: $134,000; low: $35).
Purpose and activities: Giving to organizations supporting employment opportunities in the U.S., helping young people start their own community service organizations, and encouraging social entrepreneurship globally.
Fields of interest: Education; Environment; Employment.
Type of support: Capacity-building and technical assistance; Grants to individuals; Endowments; Program development; Seed money; Fellowships.
Limitations: Applications not accepted. Giving globally and within the U.S., primarily to social entrepreneurs and also to national organizations in Washington, DC, New York, NY, and VA. No support for political or religious organizations. No grants to conventional institutions or services.
Publications: Occasional report.
Application information: Unsolicited requests for funds not accepted.
Board meeting date(s): As necessary
Officer: William Drayton, Pres. and Treas.
Directors: Ann Simon Hadley; Steven Hadley; David C. Oxman.
Number of staff: 1 part-time professional.
EIN: 133384072

9456
The Geary-O'Hara Family Foundation
(formerly The Geary-O'Hara Trust)
1412 N. Meade St.
Arlington, VA   22209
Contact: Michael Geary, Tr.

Donors: The Geary Family Charitable Lead Annuity Trust; Michael Geary.
Foundation type: Independent foundation.
Financial data (yr. ended 06/30/13): Assets, $4,576,582 (M); gifts received, $350,000; expenditures, $224,844; qualifying distributions, $224,844; giving activities include $191,405 for 17 grants (high: $30,000; low: $30).
Fields of interest: Pediatrics; Homeless shelters; Low-income and poor people.
Type of support: General support.
Limitations: Applications not accepted. No grants to individuals.
Application information: Unsolicited requests for funds not accepted.
Trustees: Caitlin Geary; Michael Geary.
EIN: 546462110

9457
Helen G. Gifford Foundation
(formerly The Lee A. & Helen G. Gifford Foundation)
1004 Witch Point Trail
Virginia Beach, VA   23455-5645   (757) 412-1467
FAX: (757) 412-1468; E-mail: WHearst@cox.net

Established in 1997 in Virginia.
Donor: Helen G. Gifford†.
Foundation type: Independent foundation.
Financial data (yr. ended 02/28/13): Assets, $4,131,459 (M); expenditures, $505,980; qualifying distributions, $400,140; giving activities include $393,500 for 52 grants (high: $115,000; low: $1,000).
Purpose and activities: Funding primarily for Jewish agencies, temples, and federated giving programs.

Funding also for arts and culture, and human services.
Fields of interest: Arts and culture; Performing arts; Museums; Nonprofits; Judaism; Human services.
Type of support: Regranting.
Limitations: Applications not accepted. Giving primarily in Hampton Roads, VA. No support for political organizations. No grants to individuals.
Application information: Unsolicited requests for funds not accepted.
 Board meeting date(s): Quarterly
Officers and Directors: William A. Hearst, Pres. and Director; Zelma G. Rivint, Exec. V.P. and Director; Patricia M. Rowland, 1st V.P. and Director; Jennifer Rosenberg, 2nd V.P. and Director; Michael E. Barney, Secy. and Director; Joseph B. Hearst, Treas. and Director.
EIN: 541850266

9458
David and Lorna Gladstone Foundation
1521 Westbranch Dr., Ste. 100
McLean, VA   22102-3211

Donors: David Gladstone; Lorna Gladstone.
Foundation type: Independent foundation.
Financial data (yr. ended 06/30/13): Assets, $14,178 (M); gifts received, $175,000; expenditures, $169,061; qualifying distributions, $164,316.
Limitations: Applications not accepted.
Application information: Unsolicited requests for funds not accepted.
Officers: David Gladstone, Pres.; Michael LiCalsi, Secy.
EIN: 900705352

9459
Richard S. Glasser Family Foundation
580 E. Main St., Ste. 600
Norfolk, VA   23510-2322

Established in 2001 in Virginia.
Donors: Richard S. Glasser; Martha Mednick-Glasser.
Foundation type: Independent foundation.
Financial data (yr. ended 12/31/13): Assets, $2,273,871 (M); gifts received, $199,936; expenditures, $174,065; qualifying distributions, $170,478; giving activities include $170,478 for 39 grants (high: $71,000; low: $15).
Fields of interest: Arts and culture; Nonprofits; Health; Religion.
Type of support: Annual campaigns; Regranting.
Limitations: Applications not accepted. Giving primarily in VA. No grants to individuals.
Application information: Unsolicited requests for funds not accepted.
Officers: Richard S. Glasser, Pres.; Michael A. Glasser, Secy.; Martha Mednick-Glasser, Treas.
Director: Hara B. Glasser-Frei.
EIN: 542061975

9460
The Glencairn Foundation
P.O. Box 635
Clifton Forge, VA   24422-0635
Application address: c/o Michele A. Elmore, Alleghany High School, 210 Mountaineer Dr., Covington, VA 24426, tel.: 540-863-1703

Donor: Mary Jane Luke Trust.
Foundation type: Independent foundation.
Financial data (yr. ended 12/31/13): Assets, $6,817,690 (L); expenditures, $343,900; qualifying distributions, $303,506; giving activities include $240,000 for 30 grants to individuals (high: $8,000; low: $8,000).
Fields of interest: Education.
Limitations: Applications accepted. Giving primarily in VA.
Application information: Application form required.
 Initial approach: Contact foundation for application form
 Deadline(s): Contact foundation for deadline
Trustees: James D. Snyder; R. Meade Snyder.
EIN: 266761893

9461
Good News Foundation
753-C Thimble Shoals Blvd.
Newport News, VA   23606-3564

Donors: Caleb D. West, Jr.; Virginia C. West Revocable Trust.
Foundation type: Independent foundation.
Financial data (yr. ended 12/31/13): Assets, $3,557,542 (M); expenditures, $184,501; qualifying distributions, $183,340; giving activities include $181,512 for 11 grants (high: $40,000; low: $2,000).
Fields of interest: Education; Health care administration and financing; Christianity.
Limitations: Applications not accepted. No grants to individuals.
Application information: Unsolicited requests for funds not accepted.
Officer: C. Dwight West III, Pres. and Secy.-Treas.
Director: Robert W. Crowe.
EIN: 541812414

9462
Harry and Harriet Grandis Family Foundation
c/o Grandis Properties
P.O. Box 3029
Glen Allen, VA   23058-3029

Established in 1998 in Virginia.
Donors: Sophia Gumenick; Harry Grandis; Harriet Grandis.
Foundation type: Independent foundation.
Financial data (yr. ended 01/31/13): Assets, $6,756,135 (M); expenditures, $351,216; qualifying distributions, $340,810; giving activities include $340,810 for 57 grants (high: $30,460; low: $1,000).
Purpose and activities: Giving primarily for education, health organizations, human services, and to Jewish organizations and temples; funding also for the arts.
Fields of interest: Arts and culture; Museums; Education; Higher education; Foundations; Nonprofits; Hospital care; Diseases and conditions; Judaism; Human services.
Type of support: Regranting.
Limitations: Applications not accepted. Giving primarily in Richmond, VA. No grants to individuals.
Application information: Unsolicited requests for funds not accepted.

Officers: Harry Grandis, Pres. and Treas.; Betty G. Lepage, V.P.; Nancy Grandis White, Secy.
EIN: 541922209

9463
The Violet H. Greco Foundation, Inc.
P.O. Box 5423
Suffolk, VA   23435-5423

Established in 1997 in Virginia.
Foundation type: Independent foundation.
Financial data (yr. ended 06/30/13): Assets, $4,450,227 (M); expenditures, $239,586; qualifying distributions, $229,794; giving activities include $202,000 for 17 grants (high: $25,000; low: $3,000).
Purpose and activities: Giving primarily for first-responder organizations and for health and human services.
Fields of interest: Health; Search and rescue; Fire prevention and control; Housing development; Christianity; Baseball and softball; Human services; Cemeteries and burial services; Females.
Type of support: General support.
Limitations: Applications not accepted. Giving primarily in VA. No grants to individuals.
Application information: Contributes only to pre-selected organizations.
Officers and Directors: S. Chris Jones, Pres. and Director; Susan Mansfield, Secy. and Director; Richard R. Harris; John P. Leigh; Lynne W. Stockman.
EIN: 541859728

9464
Greensville Memorial Foundation
(formerly Greensville Memorial Hospital)
P.O. Box 1015
Emporia, VA   23847-1015   (434) 336-9822
Contact: Jill Slate, Exec. Dir.

Foundation type: Independent foundation.
Financial data (yr. ended 08/31/13): Assets, $13,704,862 (M); expenditures, $854,455; qualifying distributions, $384,991; giving activities include $326,098 for 14 grants (high: $127,708; low: $160).
Purpose and activities: Giving primarily to community organizations for equipment procurement; some funding for education, particularly a nursing program, social services, and to a YMCA.
Fields of interest: Graduate and professional education; Nursing care; Disasters and emergency management; Fire prevention and control; Human services.
Type of support: Volunteer development.
Limitations: Applications accepted. Giving restricted to areas serviced by the Greensville Memorial Hospital, Greensville, VA.
Application information: Application form required.
 Initial approach: Proposal
 Deadline(s): Aug. 1 for fall grant cycle and Feb. 1 for spring grant cycle
Officers: Michael S. Anderson, MD, Chair.; Robert Grizzard, Jr., Vice-Chair.; Angela B. Wilson, MD, Secy.; Frank E. Kientz, Treas.; Jill Slate, Exec. Dir.
Board Members: Theopolis Gilliam; Brian K. Roberts; James C. Saunders.
EIN: 540645217

9465
Hansen Family Foundation
2241 Hatton St.
Virginia Beach, VA 23451-1703

Donors: Richard C. Hansen; Cherrie L. Hansen.
Foundation type: Independent foundation.
Financial data (yr. ended 12/31/12): Assets,
$2,427,365 (M); expenditures, $208,566;
qualifying distributions, $125,700; giving activities
include $125,700 for grants.
Fields of interest: Education; Specialty hospital
care; Catholicism; Basic and emergency aid; Child
welfare; International development.
Limitations: Applications not accepted. Giving
primarily in VA. No grants to individuals.
Application information: Unsolicited requests for
funds not accepted.
Officers and Directors: Richard D. Hansen, Pres.
and Director; Cherrie L. Hansen, Secy. and Director;
Larry Biddle; Keith Carl; John T. Cole; Caitlin
Hansen; Caleb Hansen; Rebecca Hansen.
EIN: 208102394

9466
The Ron and Debra Harris Charitable
Foundation Inc.
P. O. Box 446
Palmyra, VA 22963-0446

Established in 1994 in Delaware.
Donors: Ronald Harris; Debra Harris.
Foundation type: Independent foundation.
Financial data (yr. ended 10/31/14): Assets,
$3,360,596 (M); expenditures, $320,923;
qualifying distributions, $270,000; giving activities
include $270,000 for 3 grants (high: $150,000;
low: $105,000).
Fields of interest: Education; Higher education;
Hospital care.
Limitations: Applications not accepted. Giving
primarily in CT, NH, RI, TX and VA. No grants to
individuals.
Application information: Contributes only to
pre-selected organizations.
Officers: Ronald Harris, Pres.; Debra Harris, V.P.
Director: Howard Presant.
EIN: 133793221

9467
Harris Foundation
c/o H. Hiter Harris, III
6315 3 Chopt Rd.
Richmond, VA 23226-3134

Established in 1997 in Virginia.
Donors: Elizabeth Harris; H. Hiter Harris III; Jil W.
Harris; H. Hiter Harris, Jr.
Foundation type: Independent foundation.
Financial data (yr. ended 12/31/13): Assets,
$3,432,610 (M); expenditures, $286,390;
qualifying distributions, $264,960; giving activities
include $264,960 for 29 grants (high: $33,000;
low: $500).
Fields of interest: Higher education; Protestantism.
Limitations: Applications not accepted. Giving
primarily in Richmond, VA. No grants to individuals.
Application information: Contributes only to
pre-selected organizations.
Officers: H. Hiter Harris III, Pres.; Jil W. Harris,
Secy.-Treas.

Director: Katherine Alexander Harris.
EIN: 541844579

9468
Floyd W. Harris Foundation for Personal
Evangelism
6817 Alpine Dr.
Annandale, VA 22003-3444

Established in 1986 in Virginia.
Donor: Floyd W. Harris.
Foundation type: Independent foundation.
Financial data (yr. ended 12/31/13): Assets,
$3,806,394 (M); expenditures, $248,585;
qualifying distributions, $225,681; giving activities
include $205,000 for 2 grants (high: $175,000;
low: $30,000).
Fields of interest: Protestantism.
Type of support: General support.
Limitations: Applications not accepted. Giving
primarily in VA. No grants to individuals.
Application information: Contributes only to
pre-selected organizations.
Officers and Directors: Bonnie Harris Ferrer, Pres.
and Treas. and Director; Jeffrey G. Wiletts, V.P. and
Director; Nuria C Ferrer, Secy.; F. Aaron Harris;
Nimrod McNair.
EIN: 541384875

9469
The Hausfeld Family Charitable
Foundation
9207 Coronado Terr.
Fairfax, VA 22031-3833
Contact: Michael Hausfeld

Established in 2001 in Virginia.
Donors: Michael D. Hausfeld; Marilyn Hausfeld.
Foundation type: Independent foundation.
Financial data (yr. ended 12/31/13): Assets,
$490,628 (M); gifts received, $111,650;
expenditures, $161,638; qualifying distributions,
$157,300; giving activities include $157,300 for 16
grants (high: $53,300; low: $150).
Purpose and activities: Giving primarily to Jewish
schools, temples, and federated giving programs;
some support also for an arts council.
Fields of interest: Arts and culture; Education;
Nonprofits; Religion; Judaism.
Type of support: Regranting.
Limitations: Applications not accepted. Giving
primarily in Washington, DC, MD and Fairfax, VA. No
grants to individuals.
Application information: Unsolicited requests for
funds not accepted.
Directors: Marilyn Hausfeld; Michael D. Hausfeld.
EIN: 311677290

9470
The Hilltop Foundation
P.O. Box 223
Charlottesville, VA 22902-0223

Donors: Greyson P. Williams; Ariana C.A. Williams.
Foundation type: Independent foundation.
Financial data (yr. ended 12/31/13): Assets,
$3,421,058 (M); gifts received, $100,000;
expenditures, $236,265; qualifying distributions,
$235,375; giving activities include $235,000 for 12
grants (high: $40,000; low: $5,000).

Fields of interest: Education; Housing development;
Human services; Youth development.
Limitations: Applications not accepted. Giving
primarily in VA.
Application information: Unsolicited requests for
funds not accepted.
Trustees: Ariana C.A. Williams; Greyson P. Williams.
EIN: 276204423

9471
Honey Foundation
2001 Maywill St., Ste. 100
Richmond, VA 23230-3236
Contact: Susan Heath

Donor: The Ukrop Foundation.
Foundation type: Independent foundation.
Financial data (yr. ended 12/31/13): Assets,
$9,960,871 (M); gifts received, $4,980,625;
expenditures, $229,253; qualifying distributions,
$283,263; giving activities include $206,750 for 12
grants (high: $60,000; low: $500).
Fields of interest: Community and economic
development; Protestantism; Youth development.
Limitations: Applications not accepted. Giving
primarily in VA.
Application information: Contributes only to
pre-selected organizations.
Officers: Robert S. Ukrop, Pres.; David J. Naquin,
Secy.-Treas.
Director: Robert S. Ukrop, Jr.
EIN: 272314439

9472
Cecil R. & Edna S. Hopkins Family
Foundation
P.O. Box 1779
Glen Allen, VA 23060-0660

Established in 2004 in Virginia.
Donor: Edna S. Hopkins Charitable Trust.
Foundation type: Independent foundation.
Financial data (yr. ended 12/31/13): Assets,
$2,279,007 (M); gifts received, $230,673;
expenditures, $176,351; qualifying distributions,
$157,960; giving activities include $157,960 for 26
grants (high: $22,000; low: $500).
Fields of interest: Health; Diseases and conditions;
Human services.
Limitations: Applications not accepted. Giving
primarily in VA. No grants to individuals.
Application information: Unsolicited requests for
funds not accepted.
Officers: Brenda Hopkins Eggleston, Pres.; Thomas
B. Eggleston, V.P.; Mary Butler Eggleston, Secy.;
David Reid Eggleston, Treas.
Directors: Karen O. Atwood; B.W. Edmonds; John B.
O'Grady.
EIN: 201350070

9473
Houff Foundation
P.O. Box 220
Weyers Cave, VA 24486-0220 (540) 234-9233
Contact: Dwight E. Houff, Secy.

Established in 1979 in Virginia.
Donors: Cletus E. Houff†; Houff Transfer, Inc.;
Charlotte R. Houff†.
Foundation type: Independent foundation.

Financial data (yr. ended 12/31/13): Assets, $6,118,728 (M); expenditures, $356,583; qualifying distributions, $337,300; giving activities include $337,300 for 47 grants (high: $55,500; low: $500).
Purpose and activities: Giving primarily for education, particularly higher education, and Protestant organizations, ministries, and churches, with emphasis on the Brethren, Nazarene, Presbyterian, and United Methodist churches; some funding also for human services, including fire department control/rescue services, and health care.
Fields of interest: Hospital care; Presbyterianism; Human services; Child welfare.
Type of support: Volunteer development.
Limitations: Giving primarily in the Shenandoah Valley, VA, area. No grants to individuals.
Application information:
  Deadline(s): None
Officers: Roxie White, Pres.; Douglas Houff, V.P.; Dwight E. Houff, Secy.
EIN: 540236893

9474
Hughes Memorial Home

P.O. Box 5371
Danville, VA   24540-5371   (434) 724-6525
Contact: Edward O. Blount
Application address: 508 Oxford Pl., Danville, VA 24541

Donor: Eugene Thompson Trust.
Foundation type: Independent foundation.
Financial data (yr. ended 06/30/14): Assets, $10,163,634 (M); expenditures, $268,913; qualifying distributions, $402,426; giving activities include $307,982 for 32 grants (high: $88,233; low: $200).
Purpose and activities: Giving primarily to benefit needy and at-risk children.
Fields of interest: Human services; Family services; Child welfare.
Limitations: Applications accepted. Giving primarily in NC and VA.
Application information:
  Initial approach: Letter & website
  Deadline(s): None
Officers: Gene Hayes, V.P.; Becky Medema, Secy.; Kelvin Perry, Treas.
Trustees: John Collins; Gwen Edwards; Ray Beale, Jr.; Connie Fletcher; Rodney Reynolds; Nick Argyrakis; Gary Cotta; Jay I. Hayes, Jr.; Harry J. Johnson; Kent Shelton; Dave Zook; Gayle Breakley; Kim Clifton; Linda Copeland; Mark Moore; Bob Newnam; John Parris.
EIN: 540519574

9475
II Corinthians Foundation

7149 Rock Hill Mill Rd.
The Plains, VA   20198-1909
Contact: Barbara Giuliano

Established in 2002 in Virginia.
Donor: Louis J. Giuliano.
Foundation type: Independent foundation.
Financial data (yr. ended 12/31/13): Assets, $5,964,076 (M); gifts received, $3,053; expenditures, $260,053; qualifying distributions,

$257,542; giving activities include $256,000 for 17 grants (high: $50,000; low: $4,000).
Fields of interest: Education; Christianity; Human services.
Limitations: Applications not accepted. Giving primarily in VA. No grants to individuals.
Application information: Unsolicited requests for funds not accepted.
Officers: Barbara J. Giuliano, Chair.; Louis J. Giuliano, Pres.; Kristie Giuliano Stover, Secy.; Victoria Jennifer Stapleton, Treas.
Directors: Mark Zachary Glascock; Rex Stover.
EIN: 223887024

9476
Immixgroup Foundation

8444 Westpark Dr., Ste. 200
McLean, VA   22102-5112
Main URL: http://www.immixgroup.com/company/philanthropy/
Twitter: http://www.immixgroup.com/company/philanthropy/#.VjuBZ6FNJpw.twitter

Established in 2007 in Virginia.
Donor: Immixgroup, Inc.
Foundation type: Independent foundation.
Financial data (yr. ended 05/31/14): Assets, $75,201 (M); gifts received, $74,743; expenditures, $238,846; qualifying distributions, $238,447; giving activities include $149,048 for 6 + grants (high: $125,000).
Fields of interest: Oncology; Diseases and conditions; Cancers; Human services.
Type of support: Research; Employee matching gifts; Research and evaluation.
Limitations: Applications not accepted. Giving primarily in Baltimore, MD. No grants for individuals.
Application information: Unsolicited requests for funds not accepted.
Officers: Jeffery L. Copeland, Pres.; Arthur A. Richer, V.P.; Stephen G. Charles, Secy.; Peter G. Baker, Treas.
EIN: 208938162

9477
Ivakota Association, Inc.

913 Cameron St.
Alexandria, VA   22314-2424   (703) 548-3299

Established in 1919 in Virginia.
Donor: Kate Waller Barrett†.
Foundation type: Independent foundation.
Financial data (yr. ended 12/31/13): Assets, $4,140,952 (M); expenditures, $265,770; qualifying distributions, $252,832; giving activities include $239,000 for 39 grants (high: $16,000; low: $3,000).
Purpose and activities: Primary interest is support of needy women and children in Alexandria, Virginia, but grants for other purposes in other locations are made from time to time.
Fields of interest: Education; Early childhood education; Child educational development; Higher education; Crime prevention; Housing development; Human services; Child welfare; Child development; Senior services; Women's services; Children; Young adults; Seniors; Females; Ethnic and racial groups; Low-income and poor people.
Type of support: General support; Continuing support; Scholarships.

Limitations: Applications accepted. Giving primarily in Alexandria, VA. No grants to individuals.
Application information: Application form required.
  Initial approach: Letter
  Copies of proposal: 1
  Deadline(s): Apr. 15
Officers and Trustees: Douglas G. Lindsay, Pres. and Trustee; Louis B. Rodenberg, Jr., Secy.-Treas. and Trustee; Stephen W. Rideout; Louis B. Rodenberg III; Robert N. Sayler; Oran Warder.
Number of staff: None.
EIN: 540505919

9478
Jain Family Foundation, Inc.

10421 Lawyers Rd.
Vienna, VA   22181-2822   (703) 319-2265

Foundation type: Independent foundation.
Financial data (yr. ended 12/31/13): Assets, $3,412,354 (M); gifts received, $4,182; expenditures, $164,513; qualifying distributions, $162,218; giving activities include $160,600 for 15 grants (high: $30,000; low: $50).
Fields of interest: Education; Human services.
International interests: India.
Limitations: Applications accepted. Giving primarily in CA and VA; some giving internationally in India.
Application information: Application form required.
  Initial approach: Request application form
Officers and Directors: Narendra Kumar Jain, Pres. and Director; Atul Jain, V.P. and Secy. and Director; Priti Agarwal Jain, Treas. and Director.
EIN: 271530085

9479
Homer A. and Ida S. Jones Trust

P.O. Box 1689
Bristol, VA   24203-1689

Established in 1983 in Tennessee.
Donor: Homer A. Jones, Jr.
Foundation type: Independent foundation.
Financial data (yr. ended 12/31/14): Assets, $1,105,787; gifts received, $0; expenditures, $204,062; qualifying distributions, $189,301 and $0 for set-asides.
Fields of interest: Education; Human services; Youth development.
Limitations: Applications not accepted. Giving primarily in TN and VA. No grants to individuals.
Application information: Unsolicited requests for funds not accepted.
Trustees: Nell King Bieger; Sara J. Konhaus; Diana J. Mawhinney.
EIN: 581535978

9480
Kahn Lyons Foundation, Inc.

909 Lynton Pl.
McLean, VA   22102-2113   (703) 847-4279
Contact: Patrice A. Lyons, Pres.

Established in 2007 in Virginia.
Donors: Robert E. Kahn; Patrice A. Lyons.
Foundation type: Independent foundation.
Financial data (yr. ended 12/31/13): Assets, $5,089,878 (M); gifts received, $200,000; expenditures, $438,088; qualifying distributions,

$400,000; giving activities include $400,000 for 1 grant.
Fields of interest: Computer science; Internet.
Limitations: Applications accepted. Giving primarily in Reston, VA. No grants to individuals.
Application information: Application form required.
> *Initial approach:* Letter
> *Deadline(s):* None

Officers: Patrice A. Lyons, Pres.; Robert E. Kahn, Secy.-Treas.
Director: Brian D. Taylor.
EIN: 261603096

9481
Karlgaard Family Foundation
5 Clarks Branch Rd.
Great Falls, VA   22066-4157

Established in 2001 in Virginia.
Donors: David C. Karlgaard; Marilyn E. Karlgaard.
Foundation type: Independent foundation.
Financial data (yr. ended 12/31/13): Assets, $8,413,903 (M); gifts received, $421,520; expenditures, $345,334; qualifying distributions, $345,334; giving activities include $342,000 for 5 grants (high: $100,000; low: $2,000).
Fields of interest: Education; Higher education.
Type of support: Individual development.
Limitations: Applications not accepted. Giving primarily in WI. No grants to individuals.
Application information: Unsolicited requests for funds not accepted.
Officers: David C. Karlgaard, Pres. and Treas.; Marilyn E. Karlgaard, V.P. and Secy.
EIN: 311810538

9482
Kaufman Americana Foundation
480 World Trade Ctr.
Norfolk, VA   23510   (757) 625-1627
Contact: Linda H. Kaufman, Pres.

Established in 1977 in Virginia.
Donors: George M. Kaufman†; Linda H. Kaufman; HCH Family Foundation.
Foundation type: Operating foundation.
Financial data (yr. ended 11/30/13): Assets, $27,554,472 (M); gifts received, $469,000; expenditures, $347,958; qualifying distributions, $327,333; giving activities include $290,724 for 3 grants (high: $250,000; low: $7,000).
Purpose and activities: Awards are generally made for the encouragement, promotion and enhancement of the study of American decorative arts or design, or related items; funding also for health.
Fields of interest: Arts and culture; Visual arts; Art museums; Hospital care.
Type of support: Program development.
Limitations: Giving primarily in Cleveland, OH and Washington, DC; some giving also in Wilmington, DE.
Application information:
> *Initial approach:* Letter
> *Deadline(s):* None

Officers and Directors: Linda H. Kaufman, Pres. and Director; Lisa Hurst, Secy.; Luke Beckerdite; Claire K. Benjack; Wendy A. Cooper; Thomas G. Johnson, Jr.; Edward G. Kaufman; Mark Leithauser.
EIN: 510217081

9483
The Keenan Family Foundation
1750 Tysons Blvd., 12th Fl.
McLean, VA   22102-4232

Donors: Timothy P. Keenan; Kathleen F. Keenan.
Foundation type: Independent foundation.
Financial data (yr. ended 12/31/14): Assets, $5,670,964; gifts received, $0; expenditures, $305,517; qualifying distributions, $264,695 and $0 for set-asides.
Fields of interest: Education; Youth development.
Limitations: Applications not accepted.
Application information: Unsolicited requests for funds not accepted.
Officers: Kathleen F. Keenan, Pres.; Timothy P. Keenan, V.P.
EIN: 452955455

9484
The William M. King Foundation
182 Spottswood Ln.
McGaheysville, VA   22840-2807
Contact: Theresa King, Pres.
E-mail: proposals@wmkingfoundation.org;
Additional address: Mira Zergani, Secy., 427 E. Allens Ln., Philadelphia, PA 19119; Main URL: http://www.wmkingfoundation.org

Established in 1996 in Pennsylvania.
Donor: William M. King†.
Foundation type: Independent foundation.
Financial data (yr. ended 12/31/13): Assets, $6,273,669 (M); gifts received, $112,413; expenditures, $248,824; qualifying distributions, $177,000; giving activities include $177,000 for 12 grants (high: $60,000; low: $2,000).
Fields of interest: Arts and culture; Education; Secondary education; Cancers; Human services.
Limitations: Giving primarily in the Greater Philadelphia, PA, region. No grants for fundraising activities, benefits, dinners, theater, or sporting events.
Application information: Applicants may also include one publication or brochure of their choice (no CDs or videos).
> *Initial approach:* Brief, 2-3 page letter via U.S. mail or e-mail

Officers and Trustees: Theresa King, Pres. and Trustee; Mira Zergani, Secy. and Trustee; Lamont D. King, Treas. and Trustee.
EIN: 237788220

9485
Lacy Foundation
P.O. Box 3084
Martinsville, VA   24115-3084

Established in 1980 in Virginia.
Foundation type: Independent foundation.
Financial data (yr. ended 08/31/13): Assets, $2,950,282 (M); expenditures, $301,517; qualifying distributions, $270,400; giving activities include $270,400 for 15 grants (high: $30,000; low: $2,400).
Fields of interest: Arts services; Education; Health; Hospice care; Human services; Child welfare.
Type of support: Research.
Limitations: Applications not accepted. Giving limited to NC and VA. No grants to individuals.

Application information: Unsolicited requests for funds not accepted.
Officers: Frank M. Lacy, Jr., Pres.; Adele James, Secy.-Treas.
Directors: Richard W. Critz; Frank M. James IV; Brent M. Lacy; Slate Lacy.
EIN: 521205924

9486
The Minnie and Bernard Lane Foundation
P.O. Box 359
Altavista, VA   24517-1952   (434) 369-6663

Established in 1957 in Virginia.
Donors: Bernard B. Lane†; Minnie B. Lane.
Foundation type: Independent foundation.
Financial data (yr. ended 03/31/13): Assets, $4,450,281 (M); expenditures, $280,604; qualifying distributions, $250,105; giving activities include $250,105 for 27 grants (high: $135,000; low: $150).
Purpose and activities: Giving primarily for a food distribution program; support also for Methodist churches and other Christian organizations, social and human services, and international giving, including relief and missionary programs. Support is for U.S.-based organizations only, and primarily for projects in Campbell County, VA.
Fields of interest: Christianity; Presbyterianism; Human services; Basic and emergency aid; Food aid; International development.
Type of support: Seed money; Matching grants.
Limitations: Applications accepted. Giving primarily in Campbell County, VA, for new projects. No support for foreign organizations. No grants to individuals; no loans.
Application information: Application form required.
> *Initial approach:* Letter
> *Deadline(s):* None

Trustees: Douglas B. Lane; Rick Lane.
Number of staff: 1 part-time professional.
EIN: 546052404

9487
Lind Lawrence Foundation
4132 Innslake Dr.
Glen Allen, VA   23060-3344
Contact: Lee P. Martin Jr., Tr.

Established in 1973 in Virginia.
Donors: Lind Lawrence†; Lloyd B. Gee Family Trust.
Foundation type: Independent foundation.
Financial data (yr. ended 09/30/13): Assets, $7,752,345 (M); gifts received, $350,000; expenditures, $446,088; qualifying distributions, $386,500; giving activities include $377,500 for 21 grants (high: $115,000; low: $1,500).
Purpose and activities: Giving primarily for neurosurgical research; funding also for social services.
Fields of interest: Neurology; Human services; Youth mentoring.
Type of support: General support; Capital campaigns; Research; Capital and infrastructure.
Limitations: Applications accepted. Giving primarily in Richmond, VA.
Application information:
> *Initial approach:* Letter
> *Deadline(s):* None

Trustees: Fred J. Bernhardt, Jr.; Lee P. Martin, Jr.
EIN: 237310359

9488
Lee-Jackson Educational Foundation
(also known as Lee-Jackson Educational
Foundation)
(formerly The Lee-Jackson Foundation)
P.O. Box 8121
Charlottesville, VA 22906-8121 4349771861
Contact: Stephanie P. Leech, Secy.
E-mail: leejacksonfoundation@yahoo.com; Main
URL: http://www.lee-jackson.org

Established in 1953 in Virginia.
Donors: Jay W. Johns; Civil War Preservation Trust.
Foundation type: Independent foundation.
Financial data (yr. ended 03/31/13): Assets, $0
(M); expenditures, $260,054; qualifying
distributions, $231,661; giving activities include
$155,000 for 20 grants (high: $25,000; low:
$1,000), and $30,000 for 16 grants to individuals
(high: $10,000; low: $1,000).
Purpose and activities: The foundation works to
increase educational opportunities for Virginia's
youth with scholarships awarded through an essay
competition; an applicant must be a junior or senior
in a Virginia public or private high school who is a
resident of Virginia. Funding also for museums and
historical activities, secondary schools, and higher
education.
Fields of interest: Museums; Historic preservation;
Secondary education; Higher education;
Foundations.
Type of support: General support; Student aid.
Limitations: Applications accepted. Giving limited to
residents of VA.
Application information: See foundation web site
for complete application guidelines. Application
form required.
Initial approach: Proposal
Deadline(s): Mid-Feb.
Officers: John P. Ackerly III, Pres.; William W.
Bergen, V.P.; Stephanie Leech, Secy.; Robert R.
Humphris, Treas. and Director.
Directors: Adm. Thomas E. Bass III; Richard H.
Britton; Claude P. Foster; Gary W. Gallagher;
Donovan E. Hower, Sr.; Robert K. Krick; Richard
Bland Lee, V; Alexander C. Von Thelen; David M.
West.
EIN: 540581000

9489
The Leonard Family Foundation
P.O. Box 8200
Bristol, VA 24203-8200 (423) 764-5535

Established in 2006 in Virginia.
Donors: Electro-Mechanical Corp.; Jacqueline F.
Leonard; Francis L. Leonard.
Foundation type: Independent foundation.
Financial data (yr. ended 12/31/14): Assets,
$55,297; gifts received, $20,000; expenditures,
$375,037; qualifying distributions, $365,000.
Fields of interest: Undergraduate education;
Hospital care.
Limitations: Applications accepted. Giving primarily
in TN and VA.
Application information: Application form required.
Initial approach: A written summary of not more
than two pages
Deadline(s): None
Trustees: Renee L. Kennedy; Roger L. Leonard;
Russell F. Leonard; Robin L. North.
EIN: 208100510

9490
The Levmar Foundation, Inc.
P.O. Box 10705
McLean, VA 22102-8705

Established in 1998 in Virginia.
Donors: Lev Volftsun; Margarita Volftsun.
Foundation type: Independent foundation.
Financial data (yr. ended 12/31/14): Assets,
$2,305,597 (M); expenditures, $172,954;
qualifying distributions, $145,600; giving activities
include $145,600 for 17 grants (high: $50,000;
low: $500).
Fields of interest: Education; Religion; Human
services.
Limitations: Applications not accepted. Giving
primarily in Washington, DC and MD. No grants to
individuals, or for capital campaigns.
Application information: Unsolicited requests for
funds not accepted.
Officer: Margarita Volftsun, Pres.
Directors: Amy Rosenblatt Lui; Lev Volftsun.
EIN: 510387146

9491
The Lincoln-Lane Foundation
c/o Edith Grandy
207 Granby St., Ste. 302
Norfolk, VA 23510-1825 (757) 622-2557
FAX: (757) 623-2698;
E-mail: contact@lincolnlanefoundation.org; Main
URL: http://www.lincolnlanefoundation.org

Established in 1928 in Virginia.
Donor: John H. Rogers†.
Foundation type: Independent foundation.
Financial data (yr. ended 07/31/13): Assets,
$7,152,364 (M); gifts received, $26,000;
expenditures, $588,447; qualifying distributions,
$521,592; giving activities include $377,000 for
147 grants to individuals (high: $4,000; low: $250).
Purpose and activities: Giving limited to awards for
college scholarships to individuals.
Fields of interest: Higher education.
Type of support: Student aid.
Limitations: Applications accepted. Giving limited to
permanent residents of the Tidewater, VA, area. No
grants for endowment or building programs,
operating budgets, special projects, or annual
fundraising campaigns; no loans.
Publications: Application guidelines; Program policy
statement.
Application information: Application form required.
Initial approach: Letter requesting application
form
Copies of proposal: 1
Deadline(s): Sept. 1 through Oct. 15. Letters
requesting applications must be postmarked
no later than Oct. 15
Board meeting date(s): Apr., May, Oct., and Dec.
Final notification: Early April
Officers: Ruth P. Acra, Pres.; Walter M. Moore IV,
V.P.; Edith G. Grandy, Secy.-Treas.
Directors: John M. Ankerson; Patricia J. Shotton.
Number of staff: 1 part-time professional; 1
part-time support.
EIN: 540601700

9492
May Liang & James Lintott Foundation
c/o Sterling Foundation Mgmt., LLC
2325 Dulles Corner Blvd., Ste. 670
Herndon, VA 20171-4683

Established in 1998 in Virginia.
Donors: May Liang; James Lintott.
Foundation type: Independent foundation.
Financial data (yr. ended 11/30/13): Assets,
$1,854,719 (M); expenditures, $242,300;
qualifying distributions, $242,000; giving activities
include $242,000 for 9 grants (high: $95,000; low:
$2,000).
Purpose and activities: Giving primarily for
children's services, including a children's hospital,
as well as for education.
Fields of interest: Education; Elementary and
secondary education; Specialty hospital care; Child
welfare.
Limitations: Applications not accepted. Giving in the
U.S., primarily in Washington, DC, Falls Church, VA,
and Chehalis and Seattle, WA. No grants to
individuals.
Application information: Unsolicited requests for
funds not accepted.
Officers: James Lintott, Pres.; May Liang, Secy.
EIN: 541920378

9493
The Jesse and Rose Loeb Foundation, Inc.
P.O. Box 803
Warrenton, VA 20188-0803 (540) 428-1960
Contact: Thomas H. Kirk, Exec. Dir.
E-mail: kirk@loebfoundation.org; Main URL: http://
www.loebfoundation.org

Established in 1991 in Virginia.
Donor: Rose Loeb.
Foundation type: Independent foundation.
Financial data (yr. ended 09/30/14): Assets,
$9,890,278 (M); expenditures, $461,491;
qualifying distributions, $400,451; giving activities
include $285,700 for 18 grants (high: $35,000;
low: $1,000), and $60,000 for 12 grants to
individuals (high: $5,000; low: $5,000).
Purpose and activities: Giving primarily for human
services and community development. Funding also
for scholarships to student graduates of Liberty High
School in Fauquier County, Virginia, who are
pursuing higher education in the state of Virginia.
Fields of interest: Arts and culture; Education;
Public health; Community and economic
development; Human services.
Limitations: Applications accepted. Giving limited to
the Fauquier County, VA, region. No grants to.
Publications: Application guidelines.
Application information: Application guidelines
available on foundation web site. Application form
required.
Copies of proposal: 5
Deadline(s): Between Feb. 1 and Apr. 30; mid-Apr.
for scholarships
Offices and Directors: Sue Ann Meek, Pres.;
Thomas H. Kirk, Secy.-Treas. and Director; G. Wayne
Eastham; Richard Monahan; Donald R. Yowell.
EIN: 541604839

9494
Longview Foundation for Education in World Affairs and International Understanding, Inc.
1069 W. Broad St., Ste. 801
Falls Church, VA 22046-4610
Contact: Jennifer Manise, Exec. Dir.
E-mail: globaled@longviewfdn.org; Main URL: http://www.longviewfdn.org
Grant Database: http://www.longviewfdn.org/grants-grantees/grants-awarded
LinkedIn: http://www.linkedin.com/company/the-longview-foundation
Twitter: https://twitter.com/LongviewGlobal

Established in 1966 in Maryland.
Donor: William L. Breese†.
Foundation type: Independent foundation.
Financial data (yr. ended 09/30/13): Assets, $6,487,045 (M); expenditures, $466,144; qualifying distributions, $398,237; giving activities include $241,359 for 11 grants (high: $32,377; low: $4,550).
Purpose and activities: Giving to foster greater awareness of world affairs and international understanding within American schools at the K-12 grade level.
Fields of interest: Education; Teacher education.
Type of support: Program development; Matching grants; Policy, advocacy and systems reform; Convening; Publications; Seed money; Curriculum development; Research; Technical assistance.
Limitations: Applications accepted. Giving on a national basis. No support for individual schools or foundations. No grants to individuals or for indirect costs not directly related to a project.
Publications: Application guidelines; Grants list; Occasional report.
Application information: Proposals are accepted by invitation only. Guidelines available on web site. Electronic submissions required. Application form required.
   Initial approach: E-mail inquiry form
   Copies of proposal: 1
   Deadline(s): See foundation web site for deadlines
   Board meeting date(s): Apr. and Oct.
   Final notification: May 15 and Nov. 15
Officers and Trustees: Lois Adams-Rodgers, Pres. and Trustee; Anthony Jackson, V.P.; Susan Sclafani, Secy.; Yvonne Chan, Treas.; John Friedland; Breese McIlvaine; Caryn Stedman; Ron Thorpe; John Wilson.
Number of staff: 1 part-time professional.
EIN: 526070327

9495
Ludington, Inc.
P.O. Box 12641
Roanoke, VA 24027-2641

Established in 1984 in Kentucky.
Foundation type: Independent foundation.
Financial data (yr. ended 12/31/14): Assets, $6,807,844 (M); expenditures, $291,284; qualifying distributions, $290,642; giving activities include $290,000 for 3 grants (high: $205,000; low: $35,000).
Fields of interest: Natural resources; Health; Family planning.
Limitations: Applications not accepted. No grants to individuals; no loans.

Application information: Contributes only to pre-selected organizations.
Directors: Philip Abbey; Emily Parrino; Greta Tisdale.
EIN: 311128833

9496
Macedonian Call Inc.
P.O. Box 573
Dryden, VA 24243-0573

Donors: Seth Ross Kegan; Black Mountian Resources; Richard Gilliam; Blue Ridge Services; Leslie Gilliam; Sharra C. Kegan.
Foundation type: Independent foundation.
Financial data (yr. ended 06/30/13): Assets, $659,191 (M); gifts received, $200,150; expenditures, $198,916; qualifying distributions, $192,409; giving activities include $192,409 for 17 grants (high: $80,150; low: $150).
Fields of interest: Education; Religion; Human services; International relations.
Type of support: General support.
Limitations: Applications not accepted. Giving primarily in VA.
Application information: Unsolicited requests for funds not accepted.
Officers: Seth Ross Kegan, Pres.; Sharra C. Kegan, Secy.-Treas.
EIN: 272104610

9497
MAIHS Foundation
11835 Fishing Piont Dr., Ste. 101
Newport News, VA 23606-2584
Contact: Carolyn Abbitt

Donors: Richard F. Abbitt†; Carolyn S. Abbitt.
Foundation type: Independent foundation.
Financial data (yr. ended 07/31/14): Assets, $6,538,240 (M); expenditures, $296,092; qualifying distributions, $260,407; giving activities include $260,407 for 26 grants (high: $132,700; low: $500).
Fields of interest: Museums; Education; University education; Education services; Aquariums; Autism; Protestantism.
Limitations: Applications not accepted. Giving primarily in VA. No grants to individuals.
Application information: Contributes only to pre-selected organizations.
Officer: Carolyn S. Abbitt, Pres.
Directors: Matthew M. Abbitt; Stephen M. Abbitt.
EIN: 521441636

9498
The Steven & Katherine Markel Foundation
119 Tempsford Ln.
Richmond, VA 23226-2318

Established in 2006 in Virginia.
Donor: Steven A. Markel.
Foundation type: Independent foundation.
Financial data (yr. ended 12/31/13): Assets, $9,782,150 (M); gifts received, $565,130; expenditures, $336,800; qualifying distributions, $335,000; giving activities include $335,000 for 10 grants (high: $100,000; low: $10,000).
Fields of interest: Arts and culture; Visual arts; History museums; Botanical gardens; Food banks.

Limitations: Applications not accepted. Giving primarily in VA.
Application information: Unsolicited requests for funds not accepted.
Officers and Directors: Steven A. Markel, Pres. and Director; Katherine N. Markel, Secy.-Treas. and Director.
EIN: 205331849

9499
The McWaters Family Foundation
1207 Laskin Rd.
Virginia Beach, VA 23451-5211
Application address: c/o Cynthia L. McWaters Revocable Trust, Virginia Beach, VA 23454, tel.: (757) 473-2706

Established in 2004 in Virginia.
Donors: Jeffery L. McWaters; McWaters Family L.P.; Cynthia L. McWaters.
Foundation type: Independent foundation.
Financial data (yr. ended 12/31/13): Assets, $3,192,160 (M); gifts received, $450; expenditures, $316,936; qualifying distributions, $299,234; giving activities include $299,234 for 30 grants (high: $100,000; low: $25).
Fields of interest: Christianity; Human services.
Limitations: Applications accepted. Giving primarily in VA.
Application information: Application form required.
   Initial approach: Letter
   Deadline(s): None
Officers: Jeffery L. McWaters, Pres.; Hunter McWaters, V.P.; Megan Rathbone, V.P.; Cynthia L. McWaters, Secy.-Treas.
EIN: 201053280

9500
James A. Meador Foundation
305 Boulevard
Salem, VA 24153-5009
Application addresses: c/o Guidance Office, Staunton River High School, Rte. 4, Box 732, Moneta, VA 24121, tel.: (540) 947-2867; c/o Salem High School, 400 Spartan Dr., Salem, VA 24153, tel.: (540) 387-2437; c/o Glenvar High School, 4549 Malus Dr., Salem, VA 24153, tel.: (540) 387-6536

Foundation type: Independent foundation.
Financial data (yr. ended 12/31/13): Assets, $9,846,908 (M); expenditures, $504,816; qualifying distributions, $390,000; giving activities include $390,000 for 21 grants (high: $70,000; low: $1,000).
Purpose and activities: Scholarships to seniors at Staunton River High School, Salem High School or Glenvar High School in VA, who plan to attend college. Grants also for health associations, human services, federated giving programs, and Protestant organizations and churches.
Fields of interest: Education; Nonprofits; Diseases and conditions; Protestantism; Human services.
Type of support: Individual development; Regranting.
Limitations: Giving primarily in Washington, DC, and VA.
Application information: Application forms available at each high school. Application form required.
   Deadline(s): May 15

Officers: C.M. Thomas, Pres. and Treas.; Susan Tinsley, V.P. and Secy.
EIN: 540795438

9501
Mody Foundation
c/o BDO
8405 Greensboro Dr., Ste. 700
McLean, VA 22102-5108

Established in 2002 in Virginia.
Donors: Roger Mody; Roger Mody Trust.
Foundation type: Independent foundation.
Financial data (yr. ended 12/31/13): Assets, $1,955,765 (M); gifts received, $203,000; expenditures, $175,666; qualifying distributions, $175,550; giving activities include $171,250 for 9 grants (high: $52,500; low: $2,500).
Purpose and activities: Giving primarily for children's services.
Fields of interest: Arts and culture; Education; Human services.
Limitations: Applications not accepted. Giving primarily in Washington, DC, NY and VA. No grants to individuals.
Application information: Unsolicited requests for funds not accepted.
Officer: Roger Mody, Pres. and Treas.
Directors: Sharon Berman; Katherine Kyle Mody.
EIN: 542065054

9502
Williams Mullen Foundation
(formerly WMCD Charitable Foundation)
P.O. Box 1320
Richmond, VA 23218-1320

Established in 1994 in Virginia.
Donors: Julious P. Smith, Jr.; M. Keith Kapp.
Foundation type: Company-sponsored foundation.
Financial data (yr. ended 01/31/14): Assets, $182,506 (M); gifts received, $332,300; expenditures, $293,513; qualifying distributions, $293,513; giving activities include $293,263 for 160 grants (high: $20,000; low: $100).
Purpose and activities: The foundation supports nonprofit organizations involved with arts and health organizations.
Fields of interest: Arts and culture; Theater; Museums; Higher education; Aquariums; Diseases and conditions; Technology; Business and industry; Human services.
Limitations: Applications not accepted. Giving primarily in VA. No grants to individuals.
Application information: Contributes only to pre-selected organizations.
Officer and Directors: John L. Walker, Pres. and Director; Thomas R. Frantz, V.P. and Director; Craig L. Rascoe, Treas. and Director.
EIN: 541700227

9503
Northern Piedmont Community Foundation
102 S. Main St., Ste. 207
P.O. Box 5
Culpeper, VA 22701 (540) 349-0631
Contact: M. Cole Johnson, Exec. Dir.

FAX: (540) 349-0633; E-mail: info@npcf.org; Main URL: http://www.npcf.org
-: https://plus.google.com/118191100098081751625/videos
Facebook: https://www.facebook.com/northernpiedmontcommunityfoundation
YouTube: https://www.youtube.com/channel/UCTk_MQELZ85HIWwam_elpQA

Established in 2000 in Virginia.
Foundation type: Community foundation.
Financial data (yr. ended 06/30/13): Assets, $6,104,597 (M); gifts received, $299,970; expenditures, $492,450; giving activities include $284,794 for 16+ grants (high: $40,000), and $27,850 for 23 grants to individuals.
Purpose and activities: The foundation seeks to build philanthropic capital to enhance and preserve the quality of life in Culpepper, Fauquier, Rappahannock and Madison counties, and to strengthen the region's nonprofit organizations.
Fields of interest: Arts and culture; Education; Higher education; Environment; Health; Community and economic development; Human services; Family services.
Type of support: Capacity-building and technical assistance; Building and renovations; Equipment; Program development; Publications; Research; Program evaluations.
Limitations: Applications accepted. Giving primarily in Culpeper, Fauquier, Madison, and Rappahannock counties, VA. No support for religious purposes, or national or international organizations. No grants to individuals (except for scholarships), or for ongoing operating support or annual fund drives, endowment, debt or operating deficit reduction, scholarly research, or fellowships or travel.
Publications: Application guidelines; Annual report; Informational brochure; Newsletter.
Application information: Visit foundation web site for application cover sheet and guidelines. Faxed or e-mailed applications are not accepted. Application form required.
  Initial approach: Letter or telephone
  Copies of proposal: 5
  Deadline(s): Oct. 15 for Community Fund
  Board meeting date(s): Monthly
  Final notification: 3 months
Officers and Directors: John W. McCarthy, Chair. and Director; Carlton M. Yowell, Secy. and Director; Eugene F. Triplett, Treas. and Director; M. Cole Johnson, Exec. Dir.; Robert C. Dart, MD; Marshall deF. Doeller; Jeffrey C. Early; M. Andrew Gayheart; Hilary Scheer Gerhardt; Trice Gravatte, MD; Michael T. Leake; Sharon Genebach Luke, Esq.; William L. Walton; Elizabeth M. Yates.
Number of staff: 2 part-time professional.
EIN: 311742955

9504
The Ochsman Foundation, Inc.
1650 Tysons Blvd., Ste. 820
McLean, VA 22102-4844

Established in 1998 in Maryland.
Donors: Ralph Ochsman; Meurice C. Ochsman; Yetta K. Cohen†.
Foundation type: Independent foundation.
Financial data (yr. ended 12/31/13): Assets, $11,479,963 (M); expenditures, $419,866; qualifying distributions, $279,900; giving activities include $279,900 for 36 grants (high: $100,000; low: $500).

Purpose and activities: Giving primarily for health associations, particularly for Tourette syndrome, as well as for education, social services, and Jewish organizations.
Fields of interest: Education; Animal welfare; Nonprofits; Hospital care; Diseases and conditions; Brain and nervous system disorders; Mental and behavioral disorders; Judaism; Human services; Children.
Type of support: Regranting.
Limitations: Applications not accepted. Giving primarily in the eastern U.S., with emphasis on Washington, DC, MD, New York, NY, NC, and VA. No grants to individuals.
Application information: Contributes only to pre-selected organizations.
Officers: Ralph Ochsman, Pres.; Jeffrey Wayne Ochsman, V.P.; Michael Paul Ochsman, V.P.; Bruce David Ochsman, Secy.
EIN: 541893317

9505
The O'Shaughnessy-Hurst Memorial Foundation
602 S. King St., Ste. 200
Leesburg, VA 20175-3919

Donors: Mary Hurst O'Shaughnessy†; M. O'Shaughnessy†.
Foundation type: Independent foundation.
Financial data (yr. ended 12/31/12): Assets, $7,947,146 (M); expenditures, $525,581; qualifying distributions, $369,520; giving activities include $369,520 for grants.
Fields of interest: Education; Human services.
Limitations: Applications not accepted. Giving primarily in VA. No grants to individuals.
Application information: Unsolicited requests for funds not accepted.
Officers: William Soza, Chair.; Deborah Dech Piland, Pres.; Richard Piland, V.P.; Stephanie Marsh, Secy.; Kurt Pfluger, Treas.
EIN: 541394736

9506
The Overton Family Foundation
5859 Harbour View Blvd., Ste. 300
Suffolk, VA 23435

Established in 2003 in Virginia.
Donors: Overyork, LLC; Etheridge Construction Corporation; BSJ, LLC; William S. Overton; Victor R. Wilfore; Fairways Crossing LLC; Overton Family Partnership.
Foundation type: Independent foundation.
Financial data (yr. ended 12/31/12): Assets, $4,544,759 (M); gifts received, $200,000; expenditures, $259,876; qualifying distributions, $207,000; giving activities include $207,000 for grants.
Fields of interest: Leadership development; Christianity; Child welfare.
Limitations: Applications not accepted. Giving primarily in VA. No grants to individuals.
Application information: Unsolicited requests for funds not accepted.
Officers: William S. Overton, Pres.; Alton S. Overton, V.P.; Jefferey S. Benson, Secy.; William J. Overton, Treas.
EIN: 200081041

9507
Page Family Foundation
6715 Arlington Blvd.
Falls Church, VA   22042-2728   (703) 533-9700
Contact: William J. Page, Pres.

Established in 1992 in District of Columbia.
Donor: William H. Page.
Foundation type: Independent foundation.
Financial data (yr. ended 12/31/12): Assets, $6,892,386 (M); expenditures, $349,312; qualifying distributions, $287,000; giving activities include $287,000 for grants.
Fields of interest: Elementary and secondary education; Catholicism; Human services.
Limitations: Applications accepted. Giving primarily in Washington, DC, and MD.
Application information: Application form required.
 Initial approach: Letter
 Deadline(s): None
Officer: William J. Page, Pres.
Director: W. Raymond Page.
EIN: 541595128

9508
Peachtree House Foundation
c/o McGuire Woods, LLP
P.O. Box 397
Richmond, VA   23218-0397

Established in 1992 in Virginia.
Donors: Elizabeth Gray Duff; CF & EG Duff 2002 Charitable Lead Annuity Trust; EG Duff Charitable Lead Trust.
Foundation type: Independent foundation.
Financial data (yr. ended 06/30/14): Assets, $5,864,995 (M); gifts received, $187,279; expenditures, $347,270; qualifying distributions, $301,793; giving activities include $300,000 for 24 grants (high: $100,000; low: $1,000).
Fields of interest: Visual arts; Museums; Higher education; Animal welfare; Nonprofits; Hospital care; Autism; Heart and circulatory system diseases; Cancers; Catholicism; Human services.
Type of support: Regranting.
Limitations: Applications not accepted. Giving primarily in VA.
Application information: Unsolicited requests for funds not accepted.
Officers: Elmon F. Duff, Pres.; Elizabeth Gray Duff, V.P.; James Carlton Duff, V.P.; Rita M. Smith, Secy.-Treas.
Director: Rachel M. Duff.
EIN: 541633892

9509
Pensmore Foundation
19108 Harmony Church Rd.
Leesburg, VA   20175-9001
Main URL: http://www.pensmore.org

Established in 2005 in Virginia.
Donor: Steven T. Huff.
Foundation type: Independent foundation.
Financial data (yr. ended 12/31/13): Assets, $6,715,978 (M); expenditures, $392,255; qualifying distributions, $349,161; giving activities include $345,000 for 9 grants (high: $100,000; low: $5,000).

Fields of interest: Graduate and professional education; Science; Protestantism; Theology; Human services.
Type of support: Policy, advocacy and systems reform.
Limitations: Applications not accepted. Giving primarily in PA, VA and WA. No grants to individuals.
Application information: Contributes only to pre-selected organizations.
Trustees: Steven T. Huff; Susan A. Huff; Thomas M. Huff.
EIN: 546681072

9510
Perlin Family Foundation
10301 Firefly Cir.
Fairfax Station, VA   22039-2504

Donors: Amy R. Perlin; Gary L. Perlin.
Foundation type: Independent foundation.
Financial data (yr. ended 12/31/13): Assets, $4,983,193 (M); expenditures, $267,472; qualifying distributions, $256,952; giving activities include $255,450 for 14 grants (high: $61,000; low: $3,600).
Fields of interest: Education; Judaism; Human services.
Limitations: Applications not accepted. Giving primarily in Washington, DC, OH, NY and VA.
Application information: Unsolicited requests for funds not accepted.
Officers: Amy R. Perlin, Pres.; Gregory R. Davis, Secy.; Gary L. Perlin, Treas.
EIN: 452467431

9511
Petersburg Hospital, Inc.
228 S. Sycamore St.
Petersburg, VA   23803-4260

Foundation type: Independent foundation.
Financial data (yr. ended 12/31/12): Assets, $7,022,214 (M); expenditures, $381,974; qualifying distributions, $350,000; giving activities include $350,000 for grants.
Fields of interest: Foundations.
Limitations: Applications not accepted. Giving primarily in Petersburg, VA.
Application information: Unsolicited requests for funds not accepted.
Officers: Grady W. Powell, Chair.; Cleveland A. Wright, Vice-Chair.; Donald L. Haraway, Treas.
EIN: 540800802

9512
Harry and Zoe Poole Foundation
3877 Fairfax Ridge Rd.
Fairfax, VA   22030   (703) 591-7200

Established in 2004 in Virginia.
Donor: Zoe Stamm Poole Trust.
Foundation type: Independent foundation.
Financial data (yr. ended 12/31/13): Assets, $3,846,101 (M); expenditures, $271,759; qualifying distributions, $196,050; giving activities include $196,050 for 22 grants (high: $25,000; low: $500).
Purpose and activities: Giving primarily to promote education and benefit children.

Fields of interest: Education; Religion; Human services; Child welfare.
Type of support: General support; Scholarships; Individual development.
Limitations: Applications accepted. Giving primarily in DC, Cambridge, MA and VA. No grants to individuals.
Application information: Application form required.
 Initial approach: Letter
 Deadline(s): None
Officer: Paul M. Gurman, Pres.
Directors: John Riley; Charles Wight.
EIN: 201360297

9513
Powell Charitable Foundation
6629 Fairway View Tr.
Roanoke, VA   24018-7473

Foundation type: Independent foundation.
Financial data (yr. ended 12/31/12): Assets, $5,744,201 (M); gifts received, $582,160; expenditures, $544,963; qualifying distributions, $369,552; giving activities include $311,300 for 27 grants (high: $40,000; low: $500).
Fields of interest: Higher education; Community and economic development; Religion; Youth development.
Limitations: Applications not accepted. Giving primarily in MD and VA. No grants to individuals.
Application information: Unsolicited requests for funds not accepted.
Trustee: Paul Powell, Jr.
EIN: 651175747

9514
Praktikos Institute
P.O. Box 457
Edinburg, VA   22824-0457   (540) 984-3829
Toll-free tel.: (888) 542-9467; *Main URL:* http://www.praktikosinstitute.org

Donor: Hunter Lewis.
Foundation type: Independent foundation.
Financial data (yr. ended 12/31/14): Assets, $5,438,168 (M); gifts received, $1,900,000; expenditures, $790,656; qualifying distributions, $790,656; giving activities include $333,240 for 2 grants (high: $332,240; low: $1,000), and $62,916 for 3 foundation-administered programs.
Purpose and activities: Praktikos Institute was established specifically to promote consumer healthcare information and education-particularly information about natural, integrative, and preventive medicine.
Fields of interest: Diseases and conditions.
International interests: United Kingdom of Great Britain and Northern Ireland.
Type of support: Research; Research and evaluation.
Limitations: Applications not accepted. Giving primarily in the U.S., as well as in the U.K.
Application information: Unsolicited requests for funds not accepted.
Officers and Directors: Deborah Ray, Pres. and Director; Stephanie Bosserman, Treas. and Director; Ivana Mestrovic; Elizabeth Sidamon-Eristoff; Alec Webb.
EIN: 743201821

9515

The Praxis Foundation

(formerly The James B. and Bruce R. Murray, Jr. Foundation)
455 2nd St. S.E., Ste. 402
Charlottesville, VA 22902-5793 (434) 971-8080
Contact: James B. Murray Jr., Pres.

Established in 1996 in Virginia.
Donors: James B. Murray, Jr.; Bruce R. Murray.
Foundation type: Independent foundation.
Financial data (yr. ended 12/31/13): Assets, $1,488,847 (M); expenditures, $209,910; qualifying distributions, $177,601; giving activities include $172,730 for 36 grants (high: $100,000; low: $100).
Fields of interest: Education; Health; Youth development.
Limitations: Applications accepted. Giving primarily in VA. No grants to individuals.
Application information: Application form required.
  Initial approach: Letter
  Deadline(s): None
Officers and Directors: James B. Murray, Jr., Pres. and Director; Bruce R. Murray, Secy. and Director.
EIN: 541830546

9516

Theodore H. & Nancy Price Foundation, Inc.

c/o Theodore W. Price
P.O. Box 85678
Richmond, VA 23285-5678

Donors: Theodore W. Price; Gail Trust.
Foundation type: Independent foundation.
Financial data (yr. ended 03/31/13): Assets, $701,754 (M); gifts received, $95,506; expenditures, $182,234; qualifying distributions, $171,700; giving activities include $171,700 for 21 grants (high: $64,000; low: $500).
Fields of interest: Ballet; Theater; Natural history museums; Historic preservation; Elementary and secondary education; Higher education; Foundations; Nonprofits.
International interests: France.
Type of support: Regranting.
Limitations: Applications not accepted. Giving primarily in VA; giving also in Paris, France. No grants to individuals.
Application information: Unsolicited requests for funds not accepted.
Officers: Theodore W. Price, Pres. and Treas.; Gail P. Messiqua, V.P.; Carol B. Price, Secy.
EIN: 136199406

9517

The Pruden Foundation

6464 Hampton Blvd.
Norfolk, VA 23508 (757) 425-3011
Contact: Peter D. Pruden III, Pres.

Established in 1972 in Virginia.
Donors: Peter D. Pruden, Jr.; Peter D. Pruden, Sr.†.
Foundation type: Independent foundation.
Financial data (yr. ended 02/28/13): Assets, $3,001,885 (M); expenditures, $178,169; qualifying distributions, $152,500; giving activities include $152,500 for 20 grants (high: $20,000; low: $2,500).

Fields of interest: Arts and culture; Education; Health; Housing development; Human services.
Type of support: General support; Continuing support; Annual campaigns; Capital campaigns; Capital and infrastructure; Equipment; Emergency funds; Program development; Scholarships.
Limitations: Applications accepted. Giving primarily in VA.
Application information:
  Copies of proposal: 1
  Board meeting date(s): Mar., Sept., and Dec.
Officers: Peter D. Pruden III, Pres.; Thomas F. Hofler, V.P.; Jonathan E. Pruden, Secy.-Treas.
Directors: J. Brooke Pruden III; Bobby L. Ralph; Whitney G. Saunders; Vernon Towler.
EIN: 540923448

9518

R & R Foundation

1650 Tysons Blvd., Ste. 900
McLean, VA 22101-1569

Established in 2002 in Virginia.
Donors: AGR Family Limited Partnership; EGR Family Limited Partnership.
Foundation type: Independent foundation.
Financial data (yr. ended 12/31/12): Assets, $1,621,755 (M); expenditures, $166,700; qualifying distributions, $166,700; giving activities include $162,000 for 7 grants (high: $70,000; low: $2,000).
Fields of interest: Arts and culture; Performing arts; University education; Law education; Medical education; Film and video.
Type of support: General support.
Limitations: Applications not accepted. Giving primarily in Washington, DC, New York, NY, TN and VA. No grants to individuals.
Application information: Contributes only to pre-selected organizations.
Trustees: Edgar G. Rios; Lillian Rios.
EIN: 527318076

9519

W. Russell and Norma Ramsey Foundation Inc.

11911 Freedom Dr., No. 710
Reston, VA 20190-5629

Established in 1993 in Virginia.
Donors: W. Russell Ramsey; Norma Ramsey.
Foundation type: Independent foundation.
Financial data (yr. ended 06/30/13): Assets, $21,516 (M); gifts received, $175,000; expenditures, $171,049; qualifying distributions, $170,600; giving activities include $170,600 for 14 grants (high: $35,000; low: $100).
Fields of interest: Education; Religion; Human services.
Limitations: Applications not accepted. Giving primarily in the Washington, DC, area, including MD and VA. No grants to individuals.
Application information: Contributes only to pre-selected organizations.
Directors: Norma Ramsey; W. Russell Ramsey; Ned S. Scherer.
EIN: 521853713

9520

Aaron Rashti Family Foundation Inc.

6012 S. River Rd.
Norfolk, VA 23505-4728 (757) 489-0100

Established in 1993 in Texas.
Donor: Aaron Rashti†.
Foundation type: Independent foundation.
Financial data (yr. ended 12/31/14): Assets, $4,177,998; expenditures, $248,511; qualifying distributions, $228,000.
Fields of interest: Arts and culture; Health; Maternal and perinatal health; Human services.
Limitations: Applications accepted. Giving primarily in NH, TX and VA.
Application information: Application form required.
  Initial approach: Letter
  Deadline(s): None
Trustee: Robert A. Rashti.
EIN: 752437335

9521

The Ratner Family Foundation

1577 Spring Hill Rd., Ste. 500
Vienna, VA 22182-2223

Established in 1990 in Virginia.
Donors: Creative Hairdressers, Inc.; Dennis F. Ratner; Warren A. Ratner.
Foundation type: Company-sponsored foundation.
Financial data (yr. ended 12/31/13): Assets, $44,996 (M); gifts received, $400,000; expenditures, $428,770; qualifying distributions, $482,770; giving activities include $428,770 for 47 grants (high: $120,500; low: $100).
Purpose and activities: The foundation supports museums and camps and organizations involved with education, science, and Judaism.
Fields of interest: Museums; Education; Nonprofits; Science; Judaism; Camps; Group homes.
Type of support: General support; Program development; Regranting.
Limitations: Applications not accepted. Giving primarily in CO, Washington, DC, and MD, with emphasis on Bethesda, and Rockville. No grants to individuals.
Application information: Contributes only to pre-selected organizations.
Officers: Dennis F. Ratner, Pres.; Warren A. Ratner, Secy.
EIN: 521099125

9522

The RECO Foundation

P.O. Box 25189
Richmond, VA 23260-5189 (804) 644-2800
Contact: Robert C. Courain Jr., Pres. and Treas.
Application address: 720 Hospital St., Richmond, VA 23219

Donors: RECO Constructors, Inc.; RECO Industries, Inc.; Virginia American Industries, Inc.; Robert C. Courain, Jr.; Ruth D. Courain.
Foundation type: Company-sponsored foundation.
Financial data (yr. ended 09/30/14): Assets, $8,567,347 (M); gifts received, $100,076; expenditures, $442,488; qualifying distributions, $380,600; giving activities include $380,600 for 90 grants (high: $178,500; low: $100).
Purpose and activities: The foundation supports food banks and health clinics and organizations

involved with historic preservation, education, cancer, temporary housing, youth, and family services.

Fields of interest: Education; Diseases and conditions; Human services.

Type of support: General support; Annual campaigns; Capital campaigns; Program development; Scholarships; Research.

Limitations: Applications accepted. Giving primarily in Richmond, VA. No grants to individuals.

Application information:
Initial approach: Proposal
Deadline(s): None

Officers and Directors: Robert C. Courain, Jr., Pres. and Treas. and Director; Ruth D. Courain, V.P. and Director; William M. Richardson, Secy. and Director; Jennifer R. Courain; Robert C. Courain III; Allen C. Goolsby III; Frank G. Louthan, Jr.; Lauren C. Luke.

EIN: 546039609

9523
C. E. Richardson Benevolent Foundation

P.O. Box 1120
Pulaski, VA 24301-1120
Application address: c/o Ruth S. Looney, 202 N. Washington Ave., Pulaski, VA 24301-1120, tel.: (540) 980-6628

Established in 1979 in Virginia.
Foundation type: Independent foundation.
Financial data (yr. ended 05/31/14): Assets, $4,743,779 (M); expenditures, $214,443; qualifying distributions, $207,493; giving activities include $194,470 for 50 grants (high: $10,000; low: $970).

Purpose and activities: Support for programs for needy children, women, aged people, and indigent or handicapped persons; support also for private colleges and universities.

Fields of interest: Education; Higher education; Nonprofits; Health; Community and economic development; Human services.

Type of support: Regranting.

Limitations: Applications accepted. Giving limited to VA. No grants to individuals.

Publications: Application guidelines; Program policy statement.

Application information: Contact foundation for application. Application form required.
Initial approach: Obtain and complete application
Copies of proposal: 1
Deadline(s): Sept. 15
Board meeting date(s): Oct.

Trustees: James D. Miller; James C. Turk.
Number of staff: 1 part-time support.
EIN: 510227549

9524
The Rimora Foundation

1065 Wood Ln.
Charlottesville, VA 22901-5038

Donor: Richard L. Booth, Jr.
Foundation type: Independent foundation.
Financial data (yr. ended 12/31/13): Assets, $9,459,307 (M); gifts received, $500,000; expenditures, $444,676; qualifying distributions, $442,500; giving activities include $442,500 for 26 grants (high: $210,500; low: $1,000).

Fields of interest: Performing arts; Education; Higher education; Human services; Family services.

Limitations: Applications not accepted. Giving primarily in Charlottesville, VA.

Application information: Unsolicited requests for funds not accepted.

Director: Richard L. Booth, Jr.
EIN: 611579580

9525
The Roller-Bottimore Foundation

c/o Bank of America, N.A.
1111 E. Main St., 12th Fl.
Richmond, VA 23219-3531 (804) 788-2963
Contact: Elizabeth D. Seaman, Advisor

Established in 1981 in Virginia.
Donor: Elizabeth R. Bottimore†.
Foundation type: Independent foundation.
Financial data (yr. ended 12/31/13): Assets, $8,268,687 (M); expenditures, $483,825; qualifying distributions, $385,119; giving activities include $340,000 for 12 grants (high: $50,000; low: $15,000).

Purpose and activities: Giving for capital projects and specific programs of an educational, historical or charitable nature, primarily to organizations in central VA; primary interests are historic preservation and Virginia history.

Fields of interest: Historic preservation.

Type of support: Capital and infrastructure; Matching grants; Program development.

Limitations: Applications accepted. Giving primarily in central VA. No grants to individuals, or for endowments, annual campaigns, debt reduction, national fund drives, scholarship funds or general operating expenses.

Publications: Informational brochure (including application guidelines).

Application information:
Initial approach: Request guidelines via letter or telephone to advisor
Copies of proposal: 1
Deadline(s): May 1 and Nov. 1
Board meeting date(s): June and Dec.
Final notification: In writing, following board meetings

Officers and Directors: Henry Spalding, Jr., Pres. and Director; Lucy P. Summerell, V.P. and Director; John Thomas King, Treas. and Director.

Number of staff: None.
EIN: 541201084

9526
Rouse-Bottom Foundation

P.O. Box 1326
Hampton, VA 23661-0326

Established in 1989 in Virginia.
Donor: Dorothy Bottom†.
Foundation type: Independent foundation.
Financial data (yr. ended 12/31/13): Assets, $3,265,378 (M); expenditures, $179,918; qualifying distributions, $173,879; giving activities include $131,500 for 46 grants (high: $7,500; low: $500).

Fields of interest: Arts and culture; Education; Human services.

Limitations: Applications not accepted. Giving primarily in VA, with emphasis on the Lower Peninsula, Hampton Roads, and Tidewater areas. No support for health, political or religious

organizations, social services, or youth or civic programs. No grants to individuals.

Application information: Unsolicited requests for funds not accepted.

Officers: Raymond B. Bottom, Jr., Pres. and Director; M. Whitney Gilkey, Secy.-Treas.
Directors: Lewis T. Booker; Jesse R. Forst.
EIN: 541521527

9527
Sauer Lewis Foundation

c/o Janet Lewis Sauer
204 S. Erlwood Ct.
Richmond, VA 23229-7665

Established in 2003 in Virginia.
Donors: Janet P. Lewis†; The Flager Foundation.
Foundation type: Independent foundation.
Financial data (yr. ended 12/31/13): Assets, $8,555,980 (M); gifts received, $26,182; expenditures, $243,339; qualifying distributions, $219,063; giving activities include $216,619 for 14 grants (high: $50,000; low: $2,000).

Fields of interest: Undergraduate education; Christianity.

Limitations: Applications not accepted. Giving primarily in VA. No grants to individuals.

Application information: Contributes only to pre-selected organizations.

Officers and Directors: Janet Lewis Sauer, Pres. and Director; Bradford B. Sauer, Secy. and Director.
EIN: 200059321

9528
The J. V. Schiro-Zavela Foundation

1223 Earnestine St.
McLean, VA 22101-2646 (703) 749-7679
Contact: Jean L. Schiro-Zavela, Tr.

Established in 1993 in Maryland.
Donor: Schiro Fund, Inc.
Foundation type: Independent foundation.
Financial data (yr. ended 12/31/13): Assets, $4,023,118 (M); expenditures, $170,088; qualifying distributions, $158,969; giving activities include $157,900 for 144 grants (high: $5,000; low: $100).

Purpose and activities: Giving to relief service organizations, conservation and animal welfare, health services, art and cultural programs, and to education.

Fields of interest: Arts and culture; Education; Natural resources; Domesticated animals; Nonprofits; Diseases and conditions; Human services.

Type of support: Regranting.

Limitations: Applications accepted. Giving primarily in the greater metropolitan Washington, DC area, including MD and VA. No grants to individuals.

Application information:
Initial approach: Proposal
Deadline(s): None

Trustees: Jean L. Schiro-Zavela; Vance S. Zavela.
EIN: 521802117

9529
The Abe & Kathryn Selsky Foundation Inc.

c/o RPK
1950 Old Gallows Rd., Ste. 440
Vienna, VA 22182-3920

Established in 1996 in Maryland.
Donor: Abe Selsky†.
Foundation type: Independent foundation.
Financial data (yr. ended 12/31/13): Assets, $4,735,466 (M); expenditures, $265,112; qualifying distributions, $220,500; giving activities include $220,500 for 28 grants (high: $22,500; low: $1,000).
Fields of interest: Domesticated animals; Diseases and conditions; Judaism; Human services.
Type of support: Research.
Limitations: Applications not accepted. Giving primarily in Washington, DC, and New York, NY. No grants to individuals.
Application information: Unsolicited requests for funds not accepted.
Officers and Directors: Jeffrey S. Abramson, Pres. and Director; Lisa Reich Dillion, V.P.; Beth Rubinstein, V.P.; Ronald D. Abramson, Secy.-Treas.; Gary M. Abramson.
EIN: 522006783

9530
George, Clarence & Dorothy Shaffer Charitable Foundation
8621 Clydesdale Rd.
Springfield, VA   22151-1428

Established in 1998 in Virginia.
Donor: Dorothy S. Shaffer†.
Foundation type: Independent foundation.
Financial data (yr. ended 08/31/13): Assets, $3,015,851 (M); expenditures, $210,529; qualifying distributions, $185,000; giving activities include $185,000 for 18 grants (high: $90,000; low: $2,500).
Fields of interest: Elementary and secondary education; University education; Family planning; Storms; Christianity; Catholicism; Human services; Child welfare.
Limitations: Applications not accepted. Giving primarily in Washington, DC, MD, MO, and VA. No grants to individuals.
Application information: Contributes only to pre-selected organizations.
Officers and Directors: Vera D. Schleeter, Pres. and Treas. and Director; James S. Regan, V.P and Secy. and Director.
EIN: 541856732

9531
The Charles and Marie Shepherdson Family Foundation
321 S. Columbus St.
Alexandria, VA   22314-3603

Established in 2003 in Virginia.
Donors: Charles J. Shepherdson; Sharon Schambra; William Schambra.
Foundation type: Independent foundation.
Financial data (yr. ended 06/30/13): Assets, $466,541 (M); expenditures, $160,377; qualifying distributions, $160,377; giving activities include $155,000 for 3 grants (high: $55,000; low: $50,000).
Fields of interest: Health.
Limitations: Applications not accepted. Giving primarily in VA. No grants to individuals.
Application information: Unsolicited requests for funds not accepted.

Trustees: Emily Schambra; Sharon Schambra; William Schambra.
EIN: 550839714

9532
Short Pump Ruritan/Civic Foundation, Inc.
P.O. Box 2773
Glen Allen, VA   23058-2773

Foundation type: Independent foundation.
Financial data (yr. ended 12/31/13): Assets, $925,233 (M); expenditures, $197,187; qualifying distributions, $180,000; giving activities include $180,000 for 3 grants (high: $65,000; low: $50,000).
Fields of interest: Arts and culture; Education; Health.
Limitations: Applications not accepted.
Application information: Unsolicited requests for funds not accepted.
Officers: Donald L. Fitzgerald, Pres.; Harold E. Englert, V.P.; Kevin J. McGovern, Secy.; Norwood Nuckols, Treas.
Directors: Frances Boswell; Clay R. Leonard.
EIN: 611629933

9533
Sirad Foundation Inc.
21570 Schoolhouse Ct.
Ashburn, VA   20148-5018
Contact: John Hopkinson

Donor: Jeffrey Zinsmeyer.
Foundation type: Independent foundation.
Financial data (yr. ended 09/30/13): Assets, $3,444,494 (M); expenditures, $208,336; qualifying distributions, $181,182; giving activities include $178,866 for 21 grants (high: $32,266; low: $600).
Purpose and activities: Giving primarily to improve job opportunities, wages and benefits for poor and low-income working people, including workfare participants.
Fields of interest: Education; Community and economic development; Religion.
Type of support: General support.
Limitations: Applications not accepted. Giving primarily in Washington, DC; some giving also in NY and MA. No grants to individuals.
Application information: Unsolicited requests for funds not accepted.
Officer and Director: Jeffrey Zinsmeyer, Pres. and Treas. and Director.
EIN: 043484554

9534
Hunter Smith Family Foundation
1 Boar's Head Pt., Ste. 150
Charlottesville, VA   22903-4656

Established in 2007 in Virginia.
Donor: Hunter J. Smith.
Foundation type: Independent foundation.
Financial data (yr. ended 12/31/14): Assets, $51,125 (M); gifts received, $418,000; expenditures, $423,692; qualifying distributions, $423,676; giving activities include $418,683 for 13 grants (high: $107,183; low: $1,000).

Fields of interest: Arts and culture; Higher education; Camps; Human services.
Limitations: Applications not accepted. Giving primarily in Charlottesville, VA.
Application information: Contributes only to pre-selected organizations.
Officers: Hunter J. Smith, Pres.; Randolph H. Huffman, Treas. and C.F.O.; Stuart P. Smith, Secy.
EIN: 261607153

9535
Stafford Foundation
(formerly The Stafford Family Foundation)
P.O. Box 2665
Reston, VA   20195-0665   (703) 689-9849
Facebook: https://www.facebook.com/pages/The-Stafford-Foundation/83603224718
Flickr: https://www.flickr.com/photos/thestaffordfoundation
RSS feed: https://www.thestaffordfoundation.org/feed
Twitter: https://twitter.com/staffordfnd

Donors: Earl W. Stafford, Sr.; Amanda Stafford.
Foundation type: Independent foundation.
Financial data (yr. ended 12/31/13): Assets, $382,460 (M); gifts received, $117,514; expenditures, $367,741; qualifying distributions, $428,791; giving activities include $259,800 for 9 grants (high: $135,000; low: $2,000).
Fields of interest: Christianity; Youth organizing.
Type of support: General support.
Limitations: Applications accepted. Giving primarily in DC, MD and VA.
Application information: Application form required.
Initial approach: Letter
Deadline(s): None
Officers: Earl W. Stafford, Sr., Chair.; Adam Grotke, C.F.O.; Robin F. Forrest, Secy.
EIN: 753072793

9536
Philip Stephenson Foundation
c/o Freedom Capital Partners
132 King St., 2ndFl.
Alexandria, VA   22314-3208

Established in 2005 in Unspecified.
Donor: Philip Stephenson.
Foundation type: Independent foundation.
Financial data (yr. ended 12/31/13): Assets, $31,428 (M); gifts received, $300,000; expenditures, $282,368; qualifying distributions, $282,018; giving activities include $246,000 for 4 grants (high: $100,000; low: $1,000).
Fields of interest: Arts and culture; Education; Science; Human services.
Limitations: Applications not accepted. Giving primarily in CT. No grants to individuals.
Application information: Unsolicited requests for funds not accepted.
Trustees: John P. Dedon; Colin Hart; Charles Stephenson; Philip Stephenson.
EIN: 546669190

9537
Whitney and Anne M. Stone Foundation
c/o Silvercrest
614 E. High St.
Charlottesville, VA   22902-5122

Established in 1986 in Virginia.
Donor: Anne M. Stone†.
Foundation type: Independent foundation.
Financial data (yr. ended 12/31/13): Assets, $4,441,310 (M); expenditures, $256,259; qualifying distributions, $209,147; giving activities include $200,000 for 52 grants (high: $24,000; low: $1,000).
Fields of interest: Higher education; Nonprofits; Diseases and conditions; Christianity; Sports and recreation; Human services.
Type of support: General support; Regranting; Scholarships.
Limitations: Applications not accepted. Giving primarily in VA. No grants to individuals.
Application information: Contributes only to pre-selected organizations.
Trustees: Mary Minor Henderson; David J. Wood, Jr.; Elizabeth Wood.
EIN: 133394681

9538
Barry S. and Evelyn M. Strauch Foundation, Inc.
1468 Evans Farm Dr.
McLean, VA 22101-5652

Established in 1986 in Virginia.
Donors: Barry S. Strauch, MD; Evelyn M. Strauch; Gerald N. Springer.
Foundation type: Independent foundation.
Financial data (yr. ended 09/30/13): Assets, $1,128,686 (M); gifts received, $100,000; expenditures, $220,394; qualifying distributions, $215,510; giving activities include $214,249 for 39 grants (high: $100,000; low: $100).
Purpose and activities: Giving primarily for arts and culture, including a center for Jewish history; funding also for education, health, and children and social services.
Fields of interest: Arts and culture; Art museums; Ethnic museums; Education; Higher education; Health; Human services; Child welfare.
Limitations: Applications not accepted. Giving primarily in Washington, DC, MD, and VA. No grants to individuals.
Application information: Contributes only to pre-selected organizations.
Officers: Evelyn M. Strauch, Pres.; Barry S. Strauch, MD, Secy.-Treas.
EIN: 541407386

9539
The Stultz Foundation
P.O. Box 3344
Charlottesville, VA 22903-0344 (434) 971-7802

Foundation type: Independent foundation.
Financial data (yr. ended 12/31/13): Assets, $15,640 (M); gifts received, $210,000; expenditures, $208,981; qualifying distributions, $207,468; giving activities include $207,468 for 27 grants (high: $75,000; low: $250).
Fields of interest: Education; Health; Housing development; Religion.
Limitations: Applications accepted. Giving primarily in VA.
Application information: Application form required.
Initial approach: Letter
Deadline(s): Dec. 31

Officers: Cynthia B. Stultz, Pres.; James D. Stultz, Jr., V.P.
EIN: 271024255

9540
Tara Foundation Inc.
P.O. Box 1850
Middleburg, VA 20118-0193 5406878884
Application address: P.O. Box 1000, Middleburg, VA 20118

Donor: Magalen O. Bryant.
Foundation type: Independent foundation.
Financial data (yr. ended 12/31/13): Assets, $6,862,139 (M); expenditures, $274,946; qualifying distributions, $268,500; giving activities include $268,500 for 59 grants (high: $46,000; low: $500).
Fields of interest: Arts and culture; Education; Natural resources; Libraries; Public administration; Religion; Human services.
Limitations: Applications accepted. Giving on a national basis. No grants to individuals.
Application information:
Initial approach: Proposal
Deadline(s): None
Officers: W. Carey Crane, Pres.; John C.O. Bryant, V.P.; Magalen C. Webert, Treas.
Directors: Magalen O. Bryant; Michael R. Crane; Kristiane W. Graham.
Number of staff: None.
EIN: 541596203

9541
Tesco Foundation
2001 Maywill St., Ste. 100
Richmond, VA 23230-3236
Application address: c/o Barbara B. Ukrop, 4306 Sulgrave Rd., Richmond, VA 23230, tel.: (804) 340-4094

Established in 2010 in Virginia.
Donors: The Ukrop Foundation; The Ukrop Educational Foundation.
Foundation type: Independent foundation.
Financial data (yr. ended 12/31/13): Assets, $4,853,740 (M); gifts received, $1,625; expenditures, $276,026; qualifying distributions, $245,530; giving activities include $245,324 for 122 grants (high: $20,000; low: $100).
Fields of interest: Education; Protestantism; Human services.
Limitations: Applications accepted. Giving primarily in Richmond, VA. No grants to individuals.
Application information: Application form required.
Initial approach: Letter
Deadline(s): None
Officers: Barbara B. Ukrop, Pres.; Robert S. Ukrop, Secy.
Directors: James E. Ukrop; Joseph E. Ukrop.
EIN: 272314595

9542
Adele M. Thomas Charitable Foundation, Inc.
304 Buxton Rd.
Falls Church, VA 22046-3618 (703) 533-9566
Contact: John V. Thomas, Pres. and Dir.

Established in 2000 in Virginia.

Donor: Adele M. Thomas Trust.
Foundation type: Independent foundation.
Financial data (yr. ended 12/31/13): Assets, $6,078,963 (M); expenditures, $249,756; qualifying distributions, $249,756; giving activities include $242,850 for 76 grants (high: $30,000; low: $100).
Fields of interest: Education; Higher education; Human services.
Type of support: General support; Individual development.
Limitations: Applications accepted. Giving primarily in CA and VA. No grants to individuals.
Application information: Application form required.
Initial approach: Proposal
Deadline(s): None
Officers and Directors: John V. Thomas, Pres. and Director; Eunice W. Thomas, V.P. and Director.
EIN: 311704650

9543
The J. Edwin Treakle Foundation, Inc.
P.O. Box 1157
Gloucester, VA 23061-1157 (804) 693-0881
Contact: Harry E. Dunn, Pres.

Established in 1963 in Virginia.
Donor: J. Edwin Treakle†.
Foundation type: Independent foundation.
Financial data (yr. ended 04/30/13): Assets, $6,346,265 (M); expenditures, $487,160; qualifying distributions, $374,000; giving activities include $374,000 for grants.
Purpose and activities: Giving primarily to local and educational organizations.
Fields of interest: Arts and culture; Education; Animal welfare; Health; Diseases and conditions; Public libraries; Fire prevention and control; Community and economic development; Protestantism; Human services; Child welfare.
Type of support: General support; Continuing support; Annual campaigns; Capital campaigns; Capital and infrastructure; Equipment; Scholarships.
Limitations: Giving primarily in VA. No grants to individuals.
Application information: Application form required.
Initial approach: Letter or telephone requesting application form
Copies of proposal: 1
Deadline(s): Submit proposal between Jan. 1 and Apr. 30
Board meeting date(s): Thurs. after 2nd Mon. in Feb., Apr., June, Aug., Oct., and Dec.
Final notification: After June meeting
Officers and Directors: John Warren Cooke, Pres. and Genl. Mgr. and Director; Robert A. May, V.P.; Nancy Powell, Secy.-Treas.; Cynthia B. Horsley, Secy. and Director.
Number of staff: 2 part-time professional; 2 part-time support.
EIN: 546051620

9544
Two Mauds, Inc.
P.O. Box 792
Exmore, VA 23350-0792 (757) 442-9297
Contact: James B. Mason, Secy.
FAX: (757) 442-9297;
E-mail: jbmason40@verizon.net

Donor: Dallas Pratt, MD†.
Foundation type: Independent foundation.
Financial data (yr. ended 12/31/13): Assets, $3,520,797 (M); gifts received, $25,948; expenditures, $349,620; qualifying distributions, $303,244; giving activities include $145,000 for 16 grants (high: $15,000; low: $5,000), and $42,000 for 14 employee matching gifts.
Purpose and activities: Grants to support animal welfare and prevention of cruelty to animals, with a priority on spay/neutering programs.
Fields of interest: Animal welfare; Low-income and poor people.
Type of support: General support; Continuing support; Capital and infrastructure; Equipment; Program development; Seed money.
Publications: Application guidelines; Grants list; Program policy statement.
Application information:
Initial approach: E-mail or letter
Copies of proposal: 1
Deadline(s): Sept. 1
Board meeting date(s): Oct.
Final notification: Dec.
Officers and Directors: Linda L. Hackett-Munson, Pres. and Director; David Finkbeiner, 1st V.P. and Director; Melinda Hackett-Hutchins, 2nd V.P. and Director; James B. Mason, Secy. and Director; Mark E. Haranzo.
Number of staff: 2 part-time professional; 2 part-time support.
EIN: 132665313

9545
The Valentine Charitable Foundation Inc.
c/o BDO, USA LLP
8405 Greensboro Dr., 7th Fl.
McLean, VA 22102-5104

Established in 1998 in Florida.
Donors: Audrey I. Clark Charitable Lead Trust; Reed Clark Dynasty Chartiable Lead Unitrust; Reed Clark Charitable Lead Annuity Trust; Dynasty Charitable Lead Unitrust.
Foundation type: Independent foundation.
Financial data (yr. ended 12/31/13): Assets, $1,431,301 (M); gifts received, $437,587; expenditures, $321,796; qualifying distributions, $314,129; giving activities include $307,181 for 113 grants (high: $20,000; low: $500).
Purpose and activities: Giving primarily to Christian churches and organizations; funding also for education.
Fields of interest: Education; Foundations; Christianity.
Type of support: General support.
Limitations: Applications not accepted. Giving primarily in NY. No grants to individuals.
Application information: Unsolicited requests for funds not accepted.
Officers and Directors: Audrey I. Clark, Pres. and Director; Peter R. Clark, V.P. and Treas. and Director; Sandra C. Moore, Secy. and Director.
EIN: 223603584

9546
George Verlander & Cornelis M. Verlander Foundation
P.O. Box 629
Irvington, VA 22480-0629 (804) 435-1635
Contact: Jack Neal

Donors: George W. Veralander Marital Tr.; James & Allien Taylor Trust.
Foundation type: Independent foundation.
Financial data (yr. ended 12/31/13): Assets, $8,146,541 (M); expenditures, $597,917; qualifying distributions, $429,323; giving activities include $408,500 for 8 grants (high: $216,000; low: $5,000).
Fields of interest: Higher education.
Limitations: Applications accepted. Giving primarily in VA.
Application information:
Initial approach: Proposal
Deadline(s): None
Officers: Graham H. Neal, Jr., Pres.; H. Scott Neal, V.P.; Murrell McLeod, Secy.
Director: Dexter C. Rumsey.
EIN: 200482028

9547
Vinoskey Family Foundation
13150 E. Lynchburg-Salem Tpke.
Forest, VA 24551-3135

Donors: Adam V. Vinoskey; Carole J. Vinoskey.
Foundation type: Independent foundation.
Financial data (yr. ended 12/31/13): Assets, $2,206,921 (M); expenditures, $349,014; qualifying distributions, $330,000; giving activities include $330,000 for 9 grants (high: $200,000; low: $5,000).
Fields of interest: Higher education; Human services.
Limitations: Applications not accepted. Giving primarily in VA. No grants to individuals.
Application information: Unsolicited requests for funds not accepted.
Officers and Directors: Adam V. Vinoskey, Pres. and Director; Barbara Holcomb, Secy.-Treas.
EIN: 261498897

9548
VuBay Foundation
6160 Kempsville Cir., Ste. 101A
Norfolk, VA 23502 (757) 466-0464
Contact: Cyrus A. Dolph IV Esq.

Established in 1997 in Virginia.
Donor: Gertrude S. Dixon.
Foundation type: Independent foundation.
Financial data (yr. ended 06/30/13): Assets, $3,338,112 (M); expenditures, $173,498; qualifying distributions, $168,330; giving activities include $168,330 for grants.
Purpose and activities: Giving primarily for education.
Fields of interest: Arts and culture; Museums; Elementary and secondary education; Higher education; Foundations; Human services.
Type of support: General support.
Limitations: Applications accepted. Giving primarily in VA. No grants to individuals.
Application information: Application form required.
Initial approach: Proposal
Deadline(s): Sept. 30
Officers: Ann D. Wallace, Pres.; Robert F. Shuford, V.P. and Secy.; James R. Chisman, Treas.
EIN: 541840750

9549
Walter Family Foundation
c/o Sterling Foundation Management, LLC
2325 Dulles Corner Blvd., Ste. 670
Herndon, VA 20171-4683 (703) 437-9720

Donor: W. Edward Walter.
Foundation type: Independent foundation.
Financial data (yr. ended 12/31/13): Assets, $1,363,824 (M); gifts received, $120,000; expenditures, $200,025; qualifying distributions, $200,000; giving activities include $200,000 for 1 grant.
Fields of interest: Diseases and conditions.
Application information:
Initial approach: Proposal
Deadline(s): None
Officers and Directors: W. Edward Walter, Pres. and Director; Carole Walter, Secy.-Treas. and Director.
EIN: 461181153

9550
Weil Foundation
c/o Gaffey Deane & Talley, PLC
3400 Franklin Manor Ct.
Fairfax, VA 22033—1130

Established in 1998 in Ohio.
Donors: Kenneth M. Weil; Audrey York Weil.
Foundation type: Independent foundation.
Financial data (yr. ended 06/30/14): Assets, $7,007,476 (M); gifts received, $1,142; expenditures, $389,828; qualifying distributions, $334,661; giving activities include $298,573 for 46 grants (high: $126,500; low: $100).
Fields of interest: Museums; Education; Higher education; Nonprofits; Diseases and conditions; Human services.
Type of support: General support; Research; Regranting.
Limitations: Applications not accepted. Giving primarily in NC. No grants to individuals.
Application information: Unsolicited requests for funds not accepted.
Officers: Audrey York Weil, Pres.; Kenneth M. Weil, Secy.-Treas.
Advisory Committee: Elizabeth W. Betts; Alan R. York.
EIN: 311627660

9551
The Nettie L. and Charles L. Wiley Foundation
P.O. Box 126
Irvington, VA 22480-0126
E-mail: grants@wileyfdn.org; Main URL: http://www.wileyfdn.org

Established in 1981 in Virginia.
Donor: Nettie L. Lokey Wiley†.
Foundation type: Independent foundation.
Financial data (yr. ended 12/31/13): Assets, $9,708,472 (M); expenditures, $441,805; qualifying distributions, $419,281; giving activities include $391,145 for 26 grants (high: $100,000; low: $500).
Purpose and activities: The foundation's mission includes support to organizations whose programs and projects educate and benefit young children (pre-school through 3rd grade) of Lancaster County, Virginia. The foundation also grants scholarships or

loans to students seeking an undergraduate degree in a field that focuses on the educational well-being of young children, like teaching or health care.

Fields of interest: Education; Health care clinics; Human services; Child development; Children.

Type of support: Scholarships; Student aid.

Limitations: Applications accepted. Giving primarily in VA.

Application information: See foundation web site for application guidelines for student scholarships and loans. Application form required.

> *Initial approach:* Letter of Inquiry for organizations
> *Deadline(s):* Mar. 30 and Sept. 30 for organizations; June 1 for scholarships
> *Final notification:* 60 days

Officers: Thomas A. Gosse, Pres.; Gloria C. Conley, V.P.; Catherine B. Moore, Secy.; B.H.B. Hubbard, Treas.

Board Member: Leslie Franklin.

EIN: 521231771

9552
The William Gerald Willett Charitable Foundation

2809 Whirlaway Cir.
Oak Hill, VA 20171-2031

Established in 2007 in Virginia.

Donors: William G. Willett; Lynne Willett.

Foundation type: Independent foundation.

Financial data (yr. ended 12/31/14): Assets, $6,493,814; gifts received, $379,314; expenditures, $383,939; qualifying distributions, $380,974.

Purpose and activities: Giving primarily for higher education; some funding also for Christian and Catholic church support.

Fields of interest: Higher education; Christianity; Catholicism.

Limitations: Applications not accepted. Giving primarily in KY, TN and VA. No grants to individuals.

Application information: Unsolicited requests for funds not accepted.

Officer: William G. Willett, Pres.

EIN: 260890463

9553
The Dave H. & Reba W. Williams Foundation

c/o Silvercrest
614 E. High St.
Charlottesville, VA 22902-5122

Established in 1986 in New York.

Donors: Dave H. Williams; Reba W. Williams.

Foundation type: Independent foundation.

Financial data (yr. ended 06/30/13): Assets, $33,855 (M); gifts received, $50,004; expenditures, $178,950; qualifying distributions, $166,850; giving activities include $161,800 for 24 grants (high: $25,000; low: $100).

Purpose and activities: Funding primarily for museums and arts programs.

Fields of interest: Arts and culture; Education; Religion.

Limitations: Applications not accepted. Giving primarily in New York, NY and Fairfield County, CT. No grants to individuals.

Publications: Annual report.

Application information: Unsolicited requests for funds not accepted.

Trustees: Dave H. Williams; Reba W. Williams.

Number of staff: None.

EIN: 133381821

9554
Williams-Berry Charitable Foundation

P.O. Box 1327
Bristol, VA 24203-1327

Contact: Jane L. Sheffey, Pres.

FAX: (423) 968-2233; E-mail for Jane L. Sheffey: jlsheffey@aol.com

Established in 1998 in Virginia.

Donors: Patsy B. Williams†; Harry S. Williams†.

Foundation type: Independent foundation.

Financial data (yr. ended 12/31/13): Assets, $2,151,635 (M); gifts received, $65,000; expenditures, $317,426; qualifying distributions, $311,223; giving activities include $293,750 for 18 grants (high: $102,000; low: $1,000).

Fields of interest: Education; Higher education; Diseases and conditions; Christianity; Human services.

Limitations: Applications accepted. Giving primarily in VA. No grants to individuals.

Application information:

> *Initial approach:* Letter
> *Copies of proposal:* 2
> *Deadline(s):* Nov.
> *Board meeting date(s):* Dec.
> *Final notification:* Varies

Officers and Trustees: Jane L. Sheffey, Pres. and Trustee; James H. Long, V.P. and Treas. and Trustee; Jesse A. Jones, Secy.

Number of staff: None.

EIN: 541884873

9555
The Bob Wiser Charitable Foundation Trust

11032 Brent Town Rd.
Catlett, VA 20119-2404

Established in 1994 in Virginia.

Donor: Bob Wiser.

Foundation type: Independent foundation.

Financial data (yr. ended 06/30/14): Assets, $4,775,245 (M); expenditures, $316,422; qualifying distributions, $277,124; giving activities include $273,900 for 2 grants (high: $253,900; low: $20,000).

Purpose and activities: Giving primarily to a youth organization; some funding also for a boarding and training facilities for dogs .

Fields of interest: Animal rescue and rehabilitation; Youth services; Children and youth.

Limitations: Applications not accepted. Giving primarily in VA; with emphasis on Bristow. No grants to individuals.

Application information: Contributes only to pre-selected organizations.

Trustees: Nancy B. Padgett; Tammy Jo Suter.

EIN: 546372531

9556
Womack Foundation

419 Maple Ln.
Danville, VA 24541-3531

Application address: c/o James Daniel, P.O. Box 720, Danville, VA 24543-0720; tel.: (434) 792-3911

Established in 1963 in Virginia.

Donors: Charles Womack, Sr.†; Womack Company; Charles A. Womack, Jr.

Foundation type: Independent foundation.

Financial data (yr. ended 03/31/14): Assets, $5,510,774 (M); expenditures, $386,844; qualifying distributions, $357,077; giving activities include $357,077 for 40 grants (high: $54,400; low: $500).

Purpose and activities: Giving primarily for children and youth services, including camps and swimming programs.

Fields of interest: Art museums; Education; Camps; Human services; Child welfare.

Type of support: General support; Loans to individuals; Student aid.

Limitations: Applications accepted. Giving primarily in Pittsylvania and Caswell counties.

Application information: Application form required.

> *Initial approach:* Proposal
> *Deadline(s):* None

Officers and Trustees: James A.L. Daniel, Chair. and Trustee; Charles Womack, Jr., Vice-Chair. and Trustee; Bobbye Rae Womack, Secy. and Trustee; Mark Gignac, Treas. and Trustee; Pamela Boor; Rev. Lawrence Campbell, Sr.; R.Timothy Davis; Deborah Fitzgerald; John B. Gilstrap; Shannon Hair; Jonathan Hollie; Alonzo Jones; Lauren Mathena; Amanda Oakes; Kelvin Perry; Richard Turner; Charles A. Womack III; Patrick Womack.

EIN: 546053255

9557
The Zeiders Family Charitable Foundation Trust

1532 Duke of Windsor Rd.
Virginia Beach, VA 23454-2504

Established in 1997 in Virginia.

Donors: Michael D. Zeiders; Charlotte A. Zeiders.

Foundation type: Independent foundation.

Financial data (yr. ended 06/30/14): Assets, $6,763,721 (M); gifts received, $2,600,000; expenditures, $288,357; qualifying distributions, $288,345; giving activities include $287,650 for 7 grants (high: $205,000; low: $3,000).

Fields of interest: Performing arts; Health; Religion; Human services.

Type of support: General support.

Limitations: Applications not accepted. Giving primarily in VA. No grants to individuals.

Application information: Unsolicited requests for funds not accepted.

Trustees: Charlotte A. Zeiders; Michael D. Zeiders.

EIN: 546417943

WASHINGTON

9558
Kenneth and Marleen Alhadeff Charitable Foundation
1752 N.W. Market St. 808
Seattle, WA 98107-5264
E-mail: rcoleman@elttaes.com

Established in 1997 in Washington.
Donors: Kenneth Alhadeff; Marleen Magnoni Alhadeff.
Foundation type: Independent foundation.
Financial data (yr. ended 07/31/14): Assets, $401,653 (M); gifts received, $522,968; expenditures, $156,553; qualifying distributions, $154,239; giving activities include $153,773 for 54 grants (high: $58,407; low: $92).
Fields of interest: Arts and culture; Catholicism; Judaism; Human services.
Limitations: Applications not accepted. Giving primarily in WA. No grants to individuals.
Application information: Unsolicited requests for funds not accepted.
Officers and Directors: Kenneth Alhadeff, Pres. and Treas. and Director; Marleen Alhadeff, Secy.
EIN: 911760871

9559
Amelia Charitable Foundation
P.O. Box 12535
Olympia, WA 98508-2535

Donor: Alfred Vendegna Irrevocable Trust.
Foundation type: Independent foundation.
Financial data (yr. ended 12/31/13): Assets, $131,733 (M); gifts received, $331,667; expenditures, $200,000; qualifying distributions, $200,000; giving activities include $200,000 for 1 grant.
Fields of interest: Mental health care; Housing development.
Limitations: Applications not accepted.
Application information: Unsolicited requests for funds not accepted.
Director: Barbara A. Weaver.
EIN: 271058390

9560
Ames Family Foundation
c/o Gary Ames
10566 N.E. Country Club Rd.
Bainbridge Island, WA 98110

Established in 2000 in Washington.
Donors: A. Gary Ames; Barbara J. Ames.
Foundation type: Independent foundation.
Financial data (yr. ended 12/31/13): Assets, $462,971 (M); expenditures, $451,714; qualifying distributions, $448,000; giving activities include $423,000 for 9 grants (high: $250,000; low: $1,000).
Fields of interest: Arts and culture; Education; Higher education; Human services.
Limitations: Applications not accepted. Giving primarily in NM, OR, and WA. No grants to individuals.

Application information: Contributes only to pre-selected organizations.
Trustees: A. Gary Ames; Barbara J. Ames; Eric C. Ames; Megan E. Barjesteh.
EIN: 916511506

9561
The Peter Amstein Foundation
1823 Terry Ave., Ste. 3701
Seattle, WA 98101-2421

Established in 2001 in Washington.
Donor: Peter Amstein Charitable Remainder Unitrust.
Foundation type: Independent foundation.
Financial data (yr. ended 06/30/14): Assets, $2,695,940 (M); expenditures, $293,530; qualifying distributions, $256,000; giving activities include $256,000 for 1 grant.
Fields of interest: Human services.
Limitations: Applications not accepted. Giving primarily in NJ and WA. No grants to individuals.
Application information: Unsolicited requests for funds not accepted.
Officers: Peter Amstein, Pres. and Treas.; Cathy Boyce, V.P.; Michael Amstein, Secy.
EIN: 912164797

9562
Arise Charitable Trust
P.O. Box 1014
Freeland, WA 98249-1014 (360) 331-5792
E-mail: info@arisecharitabletrust.org; Main
URL: http://www.arisecharitabletrust.org

Established in 1986 in Washington.
Donor: Judith P. Yeakel.
Foundation type: Independent foundation.
Financial data (yr. ended 09/30/13): Assets, $4,670,278 (M); expenditures, $245,098; qualifying distributions, $208,095; giving activities include $95,620 for 7 grants (high: $30,000; low: $3,000), and $94,842 for 56 grants to individuals (high: $3,500; low: $194).
Purpose and activities: Giving limited to aid programs benefiting local women in the form of scholarships to individuals and grants to social service agencies.
Fields of interest: Human services; Women's services; Females.
Type of support: General support; Student aid.
Limitations: Applications accepted. Giving limited to residents of the South Whidbey, WA, area.
Publications: Informational brochure.
Application information: See trust web site for complete application guidelines. Application form required.
   Copies of proposal: 1
   Board meeting date(s): Varies
Officer and Trustees: Charles W. Edwards, Mgr. and Trustee; Carolyn Cliff; Anne Pettit; Barbara Yeakel; Judith P. Yeakel.
EIN: 911350780

9563
George & Dorothy Babare Family Foundation
6442 N. View Ridge Dr.
Tacoma, WA 98407-1118 (253) 756-5576
Contact: Martin Babare, Treas.

Established in 1995 in Washington.
Donor: The Babare Foundation.
Foundation type: Independent foundation.
Financial data (yr. ended 12/31/13): Assets, $4,469,785 (M); expenditures, $424,846; qualifying distributions, $338,900; giving activities include $338,900 for 23 grants (high: $40,000; low: $500).
Fields of interest: Health; Religion; Human services.
Limitations: Applications accepted. Giving primarily in Tacoma, WA.
Application information:
   Initial approach: Proposal
   Deadline(s): None
Officers: Martin D. Babare, Pres.; Evelyn G. Babare, V.P.; Angela Lusk, Secy.; Martin Babare, Treas.
EIN: 912065206

9564
The Babare Foundation
11222 74th Ave. N.W.
Gig Harbor, WA 98332-6803 (253) 549-6464

Established in 1989 in Washington.
Donors: Mary Babare†; Robert S. Babare; George M. Babare; Robert M. Barbare.
Foundation type: Independent foundation.
Financial data (yr. ended 12/31/14): Assets, $3,954,591 (M); expenditures, $218,449; qualifying distributions, $178,785.
Fields of interest: Arts and culture; Health; Religion.
Type of support: General support.
Limitations: Applications accepted. Giving primarily in Tacoma, WA. No grants to individuals.
Application information: Application form required.
   Initial approach: Letter
   Deadline(s): None
Officers: Robert M. Babare, Pres.; Cynthia Louise Babare, V.P.
EIN: 943099309

9565
The John and Debra Bacon Family Foundation
P.O. Box 848
Medina, WA 98039-0848
E-mail: info@baconfamilyfoundation.org
Blog: http://baconfamilyfoundation.blogspot.com
Facebook: http://www.facebook.com/baconfamilyfoundation
Twitter: http://twitter.com/baconfoundation

Established in 2002 in Washington.
Donors: Debra Becon; John E. Bacon; Par 4 Financial, LLC.
Foundation type: Independent foundation.
Financial data (yr. ended 12/31/13): Assets, $2,523,801 (M); gifts received, $100,200; expenditures, $249,896; qualifying distributions, $234,051; giving activities include $234,051 for 13 grants (high: $150,000; low: $428).
Purpose and activities: Giving primarily to organizations that support children and their families in greater King County, Washington.
Fields of interest: Nonprofits; Human services; Child welfare.
Type of support: Regranting.
Limitations: Applications not accepted. Giving primarily in King County, WA. No grants to individuals.

Application information: Contributes only to pre-selected organizations. Please do not send unsolicited materials.
Officers: John E. Bacon, Pres.; Debra Bacon, V.P.; Michael V. Griffith, Secy.-Treas.
Directors: Alissa B. Bacon; Anthony R. Bacon; John D. Bacon; Joseph A. Bacon.
EIN: 743070936

9566
The Baker Foundation
1201 Pacific Ave., Ste. 1475
Tacoma, WA   98402-4325   (253) 383-7055
Contact: Sydney Parker

Established in 1987 in Washington.
Donors: Elbert H. Baker II; Martine Baker; Suzanne Bethke; Robert W. Bethke; Jay Prince; Debra Prince; Melissa Nelson.
Foundation type: Independent foundation.
Financial data (yr. ended 12/31/13): Assets, $7,377,016 (M); expenditures, $467,141; qualifying distributions, $324,677; giving activities include $204,300 for 30 grants (high: $25,000; low: $1,500).
Purpose and activities: Giving to organizations which are primarily dedicated to the youth of Pierce County, Washington, and specifically address the areas of education, the fine arts, and health care.
Fields of interest: Performing arts; Secondary education; Human services; Child welfare; Youth development.
Type of support: Capital campaigns; Endowments; Program development; Student aid.
Limitations: Applications accepted. Giving primarily in Pierce County, WA. No grants to individuals, except for scholarships.
Application information: Application form required.
Initial approach: Request application form
Copies of proposal: 2
Deadline(s): None
Officer: Robert W. Bethke, Exec. Dir.
Directors: Melissa Nelson; Debra Prince; Jay Prince.
EIN: 943027892

9567
Bayley Family Foundation
c/o Foundation Mgmt. Group LLC
1000 2nd Ave., 34th Fl.
Seattle, WA   98104-1022

Established in 2006 in Washington.
Donors: Jacquelin R.G. Bayley; N.P. Bjorn Bayley.
Foundation type: Independent foundation.
Financial data (yr. ended 12/31/13): Assets, $4,083,511 (M); expenditures, $271,374; qualifying distributions, $221,978; giving activities include $201,000 for 13 grants (high: $33,000; low: $1,000).
Fields of interest: Higher education; Nonprofits; Children's hospital care; Diseases and conditions; Judaism; Human services; Children.
Type of support: Research; Regranting.
Limitations: Applications not accepted. Giving primarily in WA. No grants to individuals.
Application information: Unsolicited requests for funds not accepted.
Officers and Directors: Bjorn Bayley, Pres. and Director; Daniella Bayley, V.P. and Director; David

Bayley, V.P. and Director; Daniel Asher, Secy.; Jacquelin Bayley, Treas. and Director.
EIN: 208113775

9568
Dave Beck, Sr. Foundation
3307 W. Queen Pl.
Spokane, WA   99205-5965

Established in 1997 in Washington.
Foundation type: Independent foundation.
Financial data (yr. ended 12/31/12): Assets, $0 (M); gifts received, $246,476; expenditures, $261,546; qualifying distributions, $259,970; giving activities include $258,393 for 1 grant.
Fields of interest: Human services.
Limitations: Applications not accepted. Giving primarily in WA. No grants to individuals.
Application information: Contributes only to pre-selected organizations.
Officers and Directors: Paul R. Cressman, Sr., Pres. and Director; Robert E. Heaton, Secy. and Director; Paul R. Cressman, Jr.
EIN: 911401746

9569
Bishop Family Foundation
8040 161st Ave. N.E.
P.O. Box 303
Redmond, WA   98052

Established in 2003 in Washington.
Donors: Byron D. Bishop; Sheila M. Bishop.
Foundation type: Independent foundation.
Financial data (yr. ended 12/31/13): Assets, $3,813,178 (M); expenditures, $158,715; qualifying distributions, $155,000; giving activities include $155,000 for 9 grants (high: $50,000; low: $5,000).
Fields of interest: Natural resources; Aquariums; Human services.
Limitations: Applications not accepted. Giving primarily in WA. No grants to individuals.
Application information: Unsolicited requests for funds not accepted.
Trustees: Byron D. Bishop; Sheila M. Bishop.
Number of staff: None.
EIN: 916560117

9570
The Abe & Sidney Block Foundation
c/o Foundation Management Group
1000 2nd Ave., 34th Fl.
Seattle, WA   98104

Donors: Abe Block; Sidney Block†; Martha Block.
Foundation type: Independent foundation.
Financial data (yr. ended 12/31/13): Assets, $776,656 (M); expenditures, $302,400; qualifying distributions, $297,150; giving activities include $290,900 for 32 grants (high: $55,500; low: $400).
Fields of interest: Education; Health; Religion.
Limitations: Applications not accepted. No grants to individuals.
Application information: Contributes only to pre-selected organizations.
Officers and Directors: Joseph Buchman, Pres. and Treas. and Director; Barbara Buchman, V.P. and Director; Daniel M. Asher, Secy.; Joyce Rivkin.
EIN: 133394916

9571
The Boeschoten Foundation
10901 176th Cir. N.E., Ste. 3524
Redmond, WA   98052-7218

Donors: Adrian P. Boeschoten†; Anna M. Boeschoten.
Foundation type: Independent foundation.
Financial data (yr. ended 12/31/13): Assets, $1,274,906 (M); expenditures, $192,864; qualifying distributions, $182,100; giving activities include $182,100 for 21 grants (high: $51,500; low: $500).
Fields of interest: Education; Kidney diseases; Protestantism; Catholicism; Human services.
Type of support: Research.
Limitations: Applications not accepted. Giving primarily in WA. No grants to individuals.
Application information: Unsolicited requests for funds not accepted.
Trustees: Anna M. Boeschoten; Paul A. Boeschoten; Monique G. Williams.
EIN: 470667399

9572
Robert E. and Adele Boydston Foundation
c/o Mark R. Boydston
7507 Boston Harbor Rd.
Olympia, WA   98506-9720
Main URL: http://boydstonfoundation.org
Grants List: http://boydstonfoundation.org/grants.php

Established in 2003 in Delaware.
Donors: Adele M. Boydston†; Robert E. Boydston†.
Foundation type: Independent foundation.
Financial data (yr. ended 12/31/14): Assets, $2,777,588 (M); gifts received, $100; expenditures, $217,750; qualifying distributions, $217,750; giving activities include for 20 grants (high: $12,000; low: $3,000).
Fields of interest: Arts and culture; Education; Environment; Human services.
Limitations: Applications not accepted. No grants to individuals.
Application information: Unsolicited requests for funds not accepted.
Officers and Directors: Mark R. Boydston, Pres. and Treas. and Director; Shiraz Kotadia, V.P. and Director; Grace Brewer; Anar Kotadia.
EIN: 562396839

9573
Brookshire-Green Foundation
250 39th Ave. E.
Seattle, WA   98112-5019

Established in 1997 in Washington.
Donors: Bert Green; Alexandra Brookshire.
Foundation type: Independent foundation.
Financial data (yr. ended 12/31/13): Assets, $882,676 (M); gifts received, $300,000; expenditures, $161,346; qualifying distributions, $148,978; giving activities include $148,978 for 37 grants (high: $21,500; low: $25).
Fields of interest: Music; Education; Cystic fibrosis; Cancers; Judaism; Human services; Youth services.
Limitations: Applications not accepted. No grants to individuals.
Application information: Unsolicited requests for funds not accepted.

Officers: Alexandra Brookshire, Pres.; Bert Green, V.P.
EIN: 911868189

9574
Brotman Family Foundation
c/o Carol Fyall
999 Lake Dr., Ste. 300
Issaquah, WA 98027-8990

Established in 2001 in Washington.
Donors: Jeffrey H. Brotman; Susan T. Brotman; Brotman Charitable Unitrust.
Foundation type: Independent foundation.
Financial data (yr. ended 12/31/13): Assets, $11,172,008 (M); gifts received, $3,107,250; expenditures, $376,700; qualifying distributions, $375,335; giving activities include $375,000 for 3 grants (high: $250,000; low: $25,000).
Fields of interest: Arts and culture; Community and economic development.
Limitations: Applications not accepted. Giving primarily in Seattle, WA. No grants to individuals.
Application information: Unsolicited requests for funds not accepted.
Officers: Susan T. Brotman, Pres. and Treas.; Jeffrey H. Brotman, V.P. and Secy.
EIN: 522364320

9575
Joe & Roberta Bulleri Foundation
c/o R. Kiesz
P.O. Box 1606
Wenatchee, WA 98807-1606

Established in 2004 in Washington.
Donors: Irrevocable Trust of Jr Bulleri; Roberta Bulleri†; Joseph A. Bulleri Marital Trust.
Foundation type: Independent foundation.
Financial data (yr. ended 12/31/13): Assets, $1,096,039 (M); expenditures, $335,082; qualifying distributions, $334,787; giving activities include $320,730 for 10 grants (high: $109,350; low: $5,000), and $62,615 for 1 foundation-administered program.
Fields of interest: Education; Health; Human services.
Limitations: Applications not accepted. Giving primarily in OR. No grants to individuals.
Application information: Unsolicited requests for funds not accepted.
Officers: Albert W. Libke, MD, Pres.; Jeff Rounds, Secy-Treas.
EIN: 201227283

9576
The Bungie Foundation
550 106th Ave. N.E., Ste. 207
Bellevue, WA 98004-5088
Main URL: https://www.bungie.net/en/aboutus?page=foundation
Twitter: https://twitter.com/bungielove

Established in 2010 in Washington.
Donors: Bungie, LLC; Brent Abrahamsen; Ondraus Jenkins; Pete Parsons; Zach Russell; Harold Ryan.
Foundation type: Company-sponsored foundation.
Financial data (yr. ended 12/31/13): Assets, $910,389 (M); gifts received, $20,120; expenditures, $357,177; qualifying distributions,

$354,086; giving activities include $244,234 for 135 grants (high: $51,409; low: $50), and $104,219 for 2 loans/program-related investments (high: $93,699; low: $10,520).
Purpose and activities: The foundation supports programs designed to reduce distressing and suffering of children.
Fields of interest: Performing arts; Health; Patient-centered care; Children's hospital care; Disaster relief; Human services; Food aid; Child care; Youth development; Children.
Type of support: General support; Cash grants; Matching grants; Program development.
Limitations: Applications not accepted. Giving primarily in WA.
Application information: Unsolicited requests for funds not accepted.
Officers: Harold Ryan, Pres.; Brent Abrahamsen, Secy.
Directors: Ondraus Jenkins; Pete Parsons; Zach Russell.
EIN: 272313989

9577
Daniel and Margaret Carper Foundation
P.O. Box 1026
Eastsound, WA 98245-1026 (360) 376-5357

Donors: The Carper Foundation; Daniel E. Carper; Margaret A. Carper.
Foundation type: Independent foundation.
Financial data (yr. ended 12/31/14): Assets, $2,094,301; expenditures, $296,367; qualifying distributions, $283,172.
Fields of interest: History museums; Education; Higher education; Land resources.
Limitations: Applications accepted. Giving primarily in WA.
Application information: Application form required.
  Initial approach: Letter
  Deadline(s): None
Trustees: Daniel E. Carper; Margaret A. Carper.
EIN: 260196143

9578
John A. and Helen M. Cartales Foundation
8710 S.E. Porter Cir.
Vancouver, WA 98664-2866

Established in 1998 in Washington.
Donors: John A. Cartales; Helen M. Cartales.
Foundation type: Independent foundation.
Financial data (yr. ended 06/30/13): Assets, $8,729,228 (M); gifts received, $34,000; expenditures, $426,117; qualifying distributions, $374,000; giving activities include $374,000 for 3 grants (high: $174,000; low: $100,000).
Fields of interest: Education; Community college education; Diseases and conditions; Child welfare.
Limitations: Applications not accepted. Giving primarily in Portland, OR, and Vancouver, WA. No grants to individuals.
Application information: Unsolicited requests for funds not accepted.
Trustee: Helen M. Cartales.
EIN: 911940389

9579
Children's Chance for Life
20720 Snag Island Dr.
Lake Tapps, WA 98391-8712
E-mail: teeter@attglobal.net; Main URL: http://www.ccfl-online.org
Blog: http://ccfl-online.org/category/blog
Facebook: https://www.facebook.com/ChildrensChanceForLife
RSS feed: http://ccfl-online.org/comments/feed
Twitter: https://twitter.com/CCFLfoundation

Donors: Roger Teeter; Vicky Moore; Jennifer Teeter; Timothy Moore.
Foundation type: Independent foundation.
Financial data (yr. ended 12/31/13): Assets, $391,499 (M); gifts received, $414,762; expenditures, $220,682; qualifying distributions, $221,344; giving activities include $214,300 for 6 grants (high: $115,000; low: $2,000).
Purpose and activities: Giving primarily for children that are raised by Christian foster mothers and currently have the choice to attend Faith-way, a Christian school, or one of the other schools in town.
Fields of interest: Christianity; Human services.
International interests: Africa.
Limitations: Applications not accepted. Giving primarily in South Africa. No grants to individuals.
Application information: Contributes only to pre-selected organizations.
Officers: Roger C. Teeter, Pres.; Ann Rylie Teeter, V.P.; Jennifer M. Teeter, Secy.-Treas.
EIN: 450490401

9580
The Coleman Family Foundation
P.O. Box 4012
Sequim, WA 98382-4012

Established in 2001 in Washington.
Donor: James M. Coleman.
Foundation type: Independent foundation.
Financial data (yr. ended 12/31/13): Assets, $1,799,317 (M); expenditures, $196,040; qualifying distributions, $194,804; giving activities include $194,268 for 2 grants (high: $163,593; low: $30,675).
Fields of interest: Christianity.
Limitations: Applications not accepted. Giving primarily in Seattle, WA. No grants to individuals.
Application information: Unsolicited requests for funds not accepted.
Director: Judy A. Mann.
EIN: 260014877

9581
Viola Vestal Coulter Foundation, Inc.
3004 Viewcrest Dr. N.E.
Bremerton, WA 98310-9740
Contact: Mary Lynne Braun, Secy.

Donor: Mabel Munro Coulter†.
Foundation type: Independent foundation.
Financial data (yr. ended 12/31/13): Assets, $6,929,046 (M); expenditures, $455,394; qualifying distributions, $359,037; giving activities include $305,250 for 45 grants (high: $38,000; low: $1,000).
Purpose and activities: Grant awards paid directly to designate institutions of higher education in the

western U.S., including funding scholarships for undergraduate and graduate programs.
Fields of interest: Higher education; Graduate and professional education; Nursing care; Diseases and conditions; Engineering.
Type of support: Scholarships; General support; Research; Research and evaluation.
Limitations: Applications not accepted. Giving primarily in CO. No grants to individuals directly.
Application information: Applications available at financial aid offices at pre-selected universities; unsolicited requests for funds not considered; grants do not go directly to individuals.
Officers and Trustees: Bruce T. Buell, Pres. and Trustee; Judy G. Ward, V.P. and Trustee; Mary Lynne Braun, Secy. and Trustee; James S. Gutshall, Treas.; Pamela L. Saxton; Priscilla Ann Barsotti; Alan D. Buell; Eric P. Turner; Ellen M. Vestal.
EIN: 846029641

9582
William H. Cowles Foundation
999 W. Riverside Ave., No. 605
Spokane, WA 99201-1006

Established in 1952 in Washington.
Foundation type: Independent foundation.
Financial data (yr. ended 12/31/13): Assets, $5,854,598 (M); expenditures, $298,552; qualifying distributions, $253,000; giving activities include $253,000 for 2 grants (high: $192,000; low: $61,000).
Fields of interest: Education; Foundations; Human services.
Limitations: Applications not accepted. Giving primarily in Spokane, WA. No grants to individuals.
Application information: Unsolicited requests for funds not accepted.
Officers and Trustees: W.S. Cowles, Pres. and Trustee; E.A. Cowles, V.P. and Trustee; S.R. Rector, Secy.
EIN: 916020496

9583
Crete Family Foundation
925 4th Ave., Ste. 2288
Seattle, WA 98104-1145

Established in 2007 in Unspecified.
Donor: Michael Crete.
Foundation type: Independent foundation.
Financial data (yr. ended 12/31/13): Assets, $10,438,761 (M); gifts received, $7,250; expenditures, $315,887; qualifying distributions, $259,295; giving activities include $259,295 for 22 grants (high: $41,000; low: $1,000).
Fields of interest: Higher education; Foundations; Hospital care; Youth services.
Limitations: Applications not accepted. Giving primarily in CA.
Application information: Contributes only to pre-selected organizations.
Officers: Michael Crete, Pres.; Matthew McCutchen, Secy.
EIN: 261593512

9584
CSM Foundation
2001 6th Ave., Ste. 3434
Seattle, WA 98121-2807

Established in 1986 in Washington.
Donor: Cynthia Stroum.
Foundation type: Independent foundation.
Financial data (yr. ended 12/31/12): Assets, $4,213,161 (M); expenditures, $233,337; qualifying distributions, $196,920; giving activities include $196,920 for grants.
Fields of interest: Dance; Higher education; Nonprofits; Hospital care; Cancers.
Type of support: Regranting.
Limitations: Applications not accepted. Giving primarily in CA and WA. No grants to individuals.
Application information: Unsolicited requests for funds not accepted.
Officers: Cynthia Stroum, Pres. and Treas.; Irwin L. Treiger, Secy.
EIN: 911362111

9585
DeFalco Family Foundation
3125 N. 33rd St.
Tacoma, WA 98407-6422
Contact: Santina De Falco, Pres.

Established in 1992 in California.
Donors: Goodwill Industries of Tacoma; Shoes That Fit; Tears Foundation.
Foundation type: Independent foundation.
Financial data (yr. ended 09/30/13): Assets, $6,974,312 (M); expenditures, $504,111; qualifying distributions, $419,350; giving activities include $397,600 for 58 grants (high: $60,000; low: $1,000).
Fields of interest: Arts and culture; Education; Aquariums; Zoos; Health; In-patient medical care; Pediatrics; Food delivery; Child welfare; Homeless services; Children and youth; Adolescents; Homeless people; People with vision impairments.
Type of support: General support; Continuing support; Annual campaigns; Scholarships; Research; Individual development.
Limitations: Applications not accepted. Giving primarily in Phoenix, AZ, San Diego, CA, and WA (Tacoma, Seattle, Kitsap County, and Gig Harbor). No support for religious or political organizations. No grants to individuals.
Application information: Contributes only to pre-selected organizations.
Board meeting date(s): June and Sept.
Officers and Trustees: Santina DeFalco, Pres. and Trustee; Victoria J. Shrewsbury, V.P.; Darrell F. Johnson, Secy.; David A. Johnson, Treas.
EIN: 330526533

9586
The DG Foundation
425 Lagoon Point Rd.
GreenBank, WA 98253-9768

Foundation type: Independent foundation.
Financial data (yr. ended 12/31/13): Assets, $1,370,947 (M); gifts received, $148,307; expenditures, $256,522; qualifying distributions, $242,065; giving activities include $238,500 for 37 grants (high: $45,000; low: $1,000).
Fields of interest: Education; Environment; Housing development.
Limitations: Applications not accepted. Giving primarily in Seattle, WA.
Application information: Unsolicited requests for funds not accepted.

Officers: Donald Guthrie, Pres.; Candace Y. Tkachuck, V.P.; Donald G. Guthrie, Secy.-Treas.
EIN: 262061646

9587
Fred H. & Mary S. Dore Charitable Foundation
117 E. Louisa St., Ste. 293
Seattle, WA 98102-3203

Established in 2006 in Washington.
Donor: Mary S. Dore†.
Foundation type: Independent foundation.
Financial data (yr. ended 12/31/14): Assets, $2,625,741; expenditures, $217,508; qualifying distributions, $196,241.
Fields of interest: Education; Diseases and conditions; Human services.
Type of support: Research.
Limitations: Applications not accepted. Giving primarily in WA. No grants to individuals.
Application information: Unsolicited requests for funds not accepted.
Officers: Jane Kuper, Pres.; Eric Dore, V.P; Frederick H. Dore, Jr., MD, V.P.; Pam Dore, V.P.; Bill Kuper, V.P.; Tim W. Dore, Secy.-Treas.
EIN: 204749617

9588
The Dudley Foundation
609 N. Shore Dr.
Bellingham, WA 98226-4414

Established in 1990 in Washington.
Donors: Tilford E. Dudley†; Gerric W. Dudley.
Foundation type: Independent foundation.
Financial data (yr. ended 12/31/13): Assets, $4,446,746 (M); expenditures, $191,888; qualifying distributions, $186,079; giving activities include $186,079 for 33 grants (high: $19,000; low: $100).
Purpose and activities: To alleviate present and future unnecessary suffering of all sentient beings by addressing its social and environmental roots, e.g.: (human) overpopulation, intolerance, excessive consumption (greed), and ecological destruction.
Fields of interest: Environment; Natural resources; Population studies; Consumer protection; Public affairs.
Type of support: General support; Continuing support.
Limitations: Applications not accepted. Giving primarily in WA. No grants to individuals.
Application information: Unsolicited requests for funds not accepted.
Board meeting date(s): Varies
Officers: Rick W. Dudley, Pres.; Justin Dudley, V.P.; Eric Dudley, Secy.
Directors: Todd Jones; Bob Keller; Frank Morrow.
EIN: 911474291

9589
R. B. and Ruth H. Dunn Charitable Foundation
P.O. Box 82222
Kenmore, WA 98028-0222

Donors: R.B. Dunn; Ruth H. Dunn; Revocable Living Trust.

Foundation type: Independent foundation.
Financial data (yr. ended 09/30/14): Assets, $6,841,601 (M); expenditures, $528,558; qualifying distributions, $473,633; giving activities include $350,867 for 15 grants (high: $142,857; low: $10).
Fields of interest: Arts and culture; Agriculture; Religion.
Limitations: Applications not accepted. Giving primarily in Seattle, WA.
Application information: Unsolicited requests for funds not accepted.
Officers: Neil E. Larson, Pres.; Irwin L. Treiger, V.P.
EIN: 270601430

9590
Echo Bay Foundation
c/o Anders Berglund
7055 Beach Dr. S.W.
Seattle, WA 98136

Established in 2005 in Washington.
Donors: Anders Berglund; Janet Berglund.
Foundation type: Independent foundation.
Financial data (yr. ended 09/30/14): Assets, $7,410,126; expenditures, $366,283; qualifying distributions, $341,819.
Fields of interest: Performing arts; Education; Child welfare.
Type of support: Individual development.
Limitations: Applications not accepted. Giving primarily in CA and WA. No grants to individuals.
Application information: Contributes only to pre-selected organizations.
Trustees: Anders Berglund; Janet Berglund.
EIN: 201985227

9591
Erickson Family Charitable Foundation
2027 Narrows View Cir. N.W., E-141
Gig Harbor, WA 98335-6814

Established in 2007 in Washington.
Donors: David L. Erickson; Sandra C. Erickson.
Foundation type: Independent foundation.
Financial data (yr. ended 12/31/14): Assets, $1,401,636 (M); expenditures, $161,663; qualifying distributions, $155,000; giving activities include $155,000 for 12 grants (high: $40,000; low: $5,000).
Fields of interest: Arts and culture; Education; Human services.
Type of support: Research; Policy, advocacy and systems reform; Capital campaigns.
Limitations: Applications not accepted. Giving primarily in CA, Washington, DC, and PA. No grants to individuals.
Application information: Unsolicited request for funds not accepted.
Officers: David L. Erickson, C.E.O.; Sandra C. Erickson, Secy. and C.F.O.
EIN: 331184117

9592
The Greater Everett Community Foundation
(formerly Everett Parks Foundation)
2823 Rockefeller Ave.
P.O. Box 5549
Everett, WA 98201-3524 (425) 212-4056
Contact: Maddy Metzger-Utt, Pres. and C.E.O.; Karri Matau
FAX: (425) 212-4059;
E-mail: maddy@greatereverettcf.org; Mailing address: P.O. Box 5549, Everett, WA 98206-5549; Additional e-mail: info@greatereverettcf.org; Grant inquiry tel. 425-212-4056; Main URL: http://www.greatereverettcf.org

Established in 2001 in Washington.
Foundation type: Community foundation.
Financial data (yr. ended 12/31/12): Assets, $10,525,375 (M); gifts received, $714,245; expenditures, $866,736; giving activities include $414,719 for 23+ grants (high: $25,840), and $28,200 for 16 grants to individuals.
Purpose and activities: The foundation works in partnership with donors to strengthen communities in greater Everett and Snohomish County, WA, by building permanent charitable funds, connecting donors to the causes they care about, making effective grants, and providing leadership to address community issues.
Fields of interest: Arts and culture; Education; Environment; Health; Human services; Youth mentoring; Developmental disability services; Children; Adolescents; People with psychosocial disabilities; People with intellectual disabilities.
Type of support: General support; Employee matching gifts; Annual campaigns; Equipment; Endowments; Program development; Scholarships; Student aid.
Limitations: Applications accepted. Giving primarily in Snohomish County, WA.
Publications: Application guidelines; Annual report.
Application information: Visit foundation web site for application forms and guidelines per grant type. Application form required.
Initial approach: Submit application form
Copies of proposal: 1
Deadline(s): Apr. 30 for Spring Grants and Oct. 31 for Fall Grants
Board meeting date(s): 4th Wed. of every other month
Final notification: 60 days
Officers and Directors: Patty DeGroodt, Chair. and Director; Martha Danker, Vice-Chair. and Director; Maddy Metzger-Utt, Pres. and C.E.O. and Director; Karri Matau, V.P., Grantmaking and Partnerships and Director; Elena Pullen-Venema, V.P., Devel. and Director; John Middleton, Secy. and Director; Scott Murphy, Treas. and Director; Sarah Duncan; Bonnie Eckley; Melinda Grout; Kelly Johnson; Phil McConnell; Laron Olson; Ross Rettenmier.
Number of staff: 1 full-time professional; 2 part-time professional.
EIN: 943188703

9593
Excel at Sports Foundation
P.O. Box 956
Mercer Island, WA 98040-0956

Donor: Scott Gibson.
Foundation type: Independent foundation.

Financial data (yr. ended 12/31/13): Assets, $2,133,033 (M); expenditures, $163,377; qualifying distributions, $157,926; giving activities include $155,000 for 2 grants (high: $130,000; low: $25,000).
Fields of interest: Sports and recreation.
Type of support: General support.
Limitations: Applications not accepted. Giving primarily in Seattle, WA.
Application information: Unsolicited requests for funds not accepted.
Officer: Scott Gibson, Pres.
EIN: 271463855

9594
Fales Foundation Trust
c/o Union Bank, N.A.
1201 3rd Ave., Ste. 900
Seattle, WA 98101-3054 (206) 781-3472
E-mail: OgleFounds@aol.com; Main URL: http://fdnweb.org/fales
Grants List: http://fdnweb.org/fales/grants/year/2013
Grants List: http://fdnweb.org/fales/grants/year/2014

Established in 1985 in Washington.
Donor: Gilbert R. Fales†.
Foundation type: Independent foundation.
Financial data (yr. ended 01/31/15): Assets, $4,555,735; expenditures, $300,570; qualifying distributions, $256,636.
Purpose and activities: Giving primarily to programs serving the homeless and hungry, and to arts and culture (primarily community-based arts programs related to issues of homelessness and hunger, providing arts opportunities for underserved constituencies).
Fields of interest: Arts and culture; Education; Human services; Food aid; Homeless shelters.
Type of support: General support; Annual campaigns; Program development.
Limitations: Applications accepted. Giving limited to Seattle, WA. No grants to individuals, or for film/video, computers, office equipment, or software.
Publications: Application guidelines.
Application information: Application form required.
Initial approach: Proposal
Copies of proposal: 1
Deadline(s): Mar. 15 and Oct. 15
Board meeting date(s): May and Dec.
Final notification: Following board meetings
Trustee: Union Bank, N.A.
Number of staff: 1 part-time professional.
EIN: 916087669

9595
FAR Family Foundation
P.O. Box 863
Auburn, WA 98071

Established in 2006 in Washington.
Donors: Ron Schaafsma; Faith Schaafsma.
Foundation type: Independent foundation.
Financial data (yr. ended 12/31/14): Assets, $4,030,427; expenditures, $248,049; qualifying distributions, $244,700.
Fields of interest: Education; Christianity; Human services.
Limitations: Applications not accepted. Giving primarily in WA. No grants to individuals.

Application information: Contributes only to pre-selected organizations.
Officers: Faith Schaafsma, Pres.; Ron Schaafsma, V.P.; David B. Schaafsma, Secy.; Lori J. Schaafsma, Treas.
EIN: 205615052

9596
The Hugh and Jane Ferguson Foundation
6723 Sycamore Ave. NW
Seattle, WA 98117-4849 (206) 781-3472
Contact: Therese Ogle, Fdn. Advisor
E-mail: OgleFounds@aol.com; Main URL: http://fdnweb.org/ferguson
Alaska Grants: http://fdnweb.org/ferguson/grants/category/alaska-groups
Cultural Grants: http://fdnweb.org/ferguson/grants/category/cultural-projects
Oregon Environmental Grants: http://fdnweb.org/ferguson/grants/category/oregon-environmental-groups
Washington Environmental Grants: http://fdnweb.org/ferguson/grants/category/washington-environmental-groups

Established in 1986 in Washington.
Donors: Hugh S. Ferguson; Jane Avery Ferguson†.
Foundation type: Independent foundation.
Financial data (yr. ended 09/30/13): Assets, $5,358,017 (M); gifts received, $3,594,822; expenditures, $358,100; qualifying distributions, $340,285; giving activities include $330,860 for 43 grants (high: $50,000; low: $300).
Purpose and activities: The foundation is dedicated to the preservation and restoration of nature, including wildlife and their required habitats. It also supports the institutions that present nature and the cultural heritage of the greater Puget Sound area to the public—museums, libraries, aquariums, zoos and public media.
Fields of interest: Museums; Education; Higher education; Natural resources; Aquariums; Zoos; Domesticated animals; Nonprofits; Public libraries; Human services.
Type of support: General support; Continuing support; Capital campaigns; Land acquisitions; Program development; Seed money; Technical assistance; Regranting.
Limitations: Applications not accepted. Giving primarily in AK, OR, and WA, with emphasis on WA. No support for social service agencies, schools or government agencies or collaborations between nonprofits and government agencies in which the government provides majority funding or leadership. No grants to individuals or for research projects, book publications, web or video/film productions, capital campaigns, curriculum development, or scholarships.
Publications: Grants list.
Application information: The foundation is not accepting unsolicited proposals.
Board meeting date(s): Mar. and Sept.
Officers and Directors: Hugh S. Ferguson, Pres. and Director; Ellen Lee Ferguson, Secy. and Director.
Number of staff: None.
EIN: 911357603

9597
Fletcher Bay Foundation
P.O. Box 11788
Bainbridge Island, WA 98110-5788

Established in 2003 in Washington.
Donors: J. Glenn Haber; Nancy J. Haber.
Foundation type: Independent foundation.
Financial data (yr. ended 12/31/14): Assets, $7,262,462 (M); expenditures, $320,484; qualifying distributions, $310,306; giving activities include $300,855 for 60 grants (high: $50,000; low: $500).
Fields of interest: Arts and culture; Foundations; Health; Human services.
Limitations: Applications not accepted. Giving primarily in WA. No grants to individuals.
Application information: Contributes only to pre-selected organizations.
Officers: J. Glenn Haber, Pres.; Emily J. Haber, V.P.; Kellie Haber, V.P.; Nancy J. Haber, V.P.; Jeffrey Schlueter, V.P.; E. Jeb Haber, Secy.-Treas.
EIN: 200194109

9598
June & Julian Foss Foundation
(also known as Foss Foundation)
6824 19th St. W., #116
University Place, WA 98466-5528
Contact: Julie Stuhr, Administrator; Kyle J. Foss, V.P.
E-mail: administrator@foss-foundation.org; Mailing address: c/o Julie Stuhr, Administrator, 419 W. Hillsdale Blvd., San Mateo, CA 94403; E-mail for Julie Stuhr: administrator@foss-foundation.org; Main URL: http://foss-foundation.org

Established in 1997 in Washington.
Foundation type: Independent foundation.
Financial data (yr. ended 03/31/15): Assets, $7,791,536 (M); expenditures, $378,476; qualifying distributions, $303,751; giving activities include $228,000 for 80 grants (high: $12,000; low: $100).
Purpose and activities: The foundation's mission is to promote change in the life situations of young people to help them grow into healthy, responsible adults, and to promote philanthropy within the family.
Fields of interest: Education; Early childhood education; Student retention; Reading promotion; Mental health care; Brain and nervous system disorders; Mental and behavioral disorders; Abuse prevention; Child abuse; Sexual abuse; Human services; Family services; Child welfare; Foster care; Family counseling; Parent education; Single parent support; Youth development; Youth services; Youth mentoring; Domestic violence shelters; Children and youth; Adolescents; Young adults; Single parents; Foster and adoptive children; Ethnic and racial groups; Homeless people; Low-income and poor people; Victims of crime and abuse.
Type of support: General support; Matching grants; Capacity-building and technical assistance; Equipment; Program development; Publications; Seed money; Curriculum development; Internships; Research; Technical assistance; Program evaluations.
Limitations: Applications accepted. Giving primarily in the San Francisco Bay Area, CA; Miami, FL; Minneapolis, MN; Portland, OR; and Seattle and Tacoma, WA. No support for organizations that discriminate on any basis including age, gender, race, ethnicity, sexual orientation, physical or mental ability, national origin, political affiliation, or religious belief. No grants to individuals.
Publications: Application guidelines; Grants list; Informational brochure (including application

guidelines); Multi-year report; Program policy statement.
Application information: Applications must be made through the online system on foundation web site. Complete application policies and guidelines available on foundation web site. A site visit is required before a grant can be made.
Initial approach: Check eligibility quiz available on foundation web site; online Letter of Inquiry required
Deadline(s): Mar. 15 for Letters of Inquiry
Board meeting date(s): Three times per year
Final notification: Applicants should receive final decision by late Sept.
Officers and Directors: Jillian Foss, Pres. and Director; Kyle J. Foss, V.P.; Jerry M. Foss, Treas. and Director; JulieAnn Foss Stuhr, Admin. and Director; Jamie Foss Devore; James M. Foss; Telma Pena.
Number of staff: None.
EIN: 911798171

9599
Fries-Tait Foundation
c/o Biddle Group, LLC
P.O. Box 70897
Seattle, WA 98107-0897

Established in 1998 in Washington.
Donors: William Rashkov†; Richard Tait; Karen Fries.
Foundation type: Independent foundation.
Financial data (yr. ended 12/31/12): Assets, $2,847,944 (M); expenditures, $204,439; qualifying distributions, $173,550; giving activities include $173,550 for grants.
Fields of interest: Education; Higher education; Natural resources; Animal welfare; Human services.
Limitations: Applications not accepted. Giving primarily in WA. No grants to individuals.
Application information: Unsolicited requests for funds not accepted.
Trustees: Karen Fries; Richard Tait.
EIN: 916458447

9600
FTJ Charitable Foundation
P.O. Box 1781
Longview, WA 98632-8101

Established in 2005 in Washington.
Donors: Steve Wilcox; Ellen Wilcox.
Foundation type: Independent foundation.
Financial data (yr. ended 12/31/13): Assets, $11,567 (M); gifts received, $175,000; expenditures, $178,527; qualifying distributions, $177,791; giving activities include $177,791 for 9 grants (high: $51,600; low: $3,000).
Fields of interest: Education; Community and economic development; Human services.
Limitations: Applications not accepted. Giving primarily in WA. No grants to individuals.
Application information: Contributes only to pre-selected organizations.
Officers: Steve Wilcox, Pres. and Treas.; Ellen Wilcox, V.P. and Secy.
EIN: 203269055

9601

David and Amy Fulton Foundation
c/o K&L Gates
925 4th Ave., Ste. 2900
Seattle, WA 98104-1158

Established in 1997 in Washington.
Donors: Amy Fulton; David Fulton.
Foundation type: Independent foundation.
Financial data (yr. ended 08/31/13): Assets, $4,477,847 (M); expenditures, $297,559; qualifying distributions, $247,140; giving activities include $245,600 for 7 grants (high: $67,000; low: $1,000).
Purpose and activities: Giving primarily to Jewish agencies, and for Jewish education and temples; some funding also for arts and education.
Fields of interest: Arts and culture; Education; Human services.
Limitations: Applications not accepted. Giving primarily in WA. No grants to individuals.
Application information: Unsolicited requests for funds not accepted.
Officers: David Fulton, Pres.; Amy Fulton, Secy.-Treas.
EIN: 911811411

9602

The Furnessville Foundation
2125 1st Ave., Ste. 2904
Seattle, WA 98121-2121

Established in 2005 in California.
Donor: Andrew Conru.
Foundation type: Independent foundation.
Financial data (yr. ended 12/31/13): Assets, $4,885,188 (M); expenditures, $281,116; qualifying distributions, $225,000; giving activities include $225,000 for 12 grants (high: $80,000; low: $2,500).
Fields of interest: Museums; University education; Reading promotion; Foundations; Hospital care; Diseases and conditions; Human services.
Limitations: Applications not accepted. Giving primarily in CA and WA. No grants to individuals.
Application information: Unsolicited requests for funds not accepted.
Officer: Andrew Conru, Pres.
EIN: 203421585

9603

Richard and Barrie Galanti Foundation
c/o Foundation Mangement Group, LLC
1000 2nd Ave., Ste. 3400
Seattle, WA 98104-1022

Donors: Barrie Galanti; Richard Galanti.
Foundation type: Independent foundation.
Financial data (yr. ended 12/31/13): Assets, $46,306 (M); gifts received, $288,341; expenditures, $270,065; qualifying distributions, $264,835; giving activities include $260,000 for 6 grants (high: $250,000; low: $500).
Fields of interest: Nonprofits.
Type of support: Regranting.
Limitations: Applications not accepted. Giving primarily in Seattle, WA.
Application information: Contributes only to pre-selected organizations.

Officers and Directors: Richard Galanti, Pres. and Treas. and Director; Barrie Galanti, V.P. and Director; Daniel M. Asher, Secy.
EIN: 911728733

9604

The Gibson Family Foundation
89 Cascade Key
Bellevue, WA 98006-1023

Foundation type: Independent foundation.
Financial data (yr. ended 12/31/13): Assets, $4,105,632 (M); expenditures, $231,211; qualifying distributions, $192,135; giving activities include $189,000 for 34 grants (high: $30,000; low: $1,000).
Fields of interest: Education; Cancers; Human services; Child welfare; Adoption.
Type of support: General support.
Limitations: Applications not accepted. Giving primarily in WA.
Application information: Unsolicited requests for funds not accepted.
Officers: Burke F. Gibson, Pres.; Dolores M. Gibson, V.P.; Bruce F. Gibson, Secy.; Scott S. Gibson, Treas.
EIN: 611584784

9605

Elmer and Iva Gilmore Education Fund
15215 52nd Ave. S., Ste. 9
Tukwila, WA 98188-2354

Established in 2001 in Washington.
Donor: Amy L. Hendrickson.
Foundation type: Independent foundation.
Financial data (yr. ended 06/30/13): Assets, $2,190,091 (M); expenditures, $208,382; qualifying distributions, $154,180; giving activities include $154,180 for grants.
Fields of interest: Education.
Type of support: Student aid; General support.
Limitations: Applications not accepted.
Application information: Unsolicited requests for funds not accepted.
Trustee: Jeff M. Wilson.
EIN: 912096568

9606

Gius Foundation
P.O. Box 277
Quincy, WA 98848-0277 (509) 787-3501

Donors: Leslie Ann Gius; Margaret Gius†.
Foundation type: Independent foundation.
Financial data (yr. ended 12/31/13): Assets, $6,738,440 (M); expenditures, $449,699; qualifying distributions, $435,811; giving activities include $435,811 for 14 grants (high: $163,000; low: $985).
Purpose and activities: Giving primarily for services for senior citizens, as well as for social services, a hospital and Roman Catholic churches. Scholarships are also made to students who are graduates of Quincy High School in WA, have a GPA of 2.3 or higher, and plan on attending a 2-year community college or technical or trade school to pursue a vocational career. The scholarship must be used at a program located in the state of WA.

Fields of interest: Education; Hospital care; Christianity; Catholicism; Human services; Senior services.
Type of support: General support; Student aid.
Limitations: Applications not accepted. Giving primarily in WA, with emphasis on Quincy and Wenatchee.
Application information: Unsolicited requests for funds not accepted.
Trustee: Marie Helen Gius.
Advisory Committee: Leslie Ann Gius; David R. Lemon; Douglas Spaulding.
EIN: 911511475

9607

Goodfellow Fund
433 13th Ave. E., Ste. 101
Seattle, WA 98102-5175

Established in 1999 in Washington.
Donor: John Goodfellow.
Foundation type: Independent foundation.
Financial data (yr. ended 12/31/13): Assets, $161,069 (M); gifts received, $274,543; expenditures, $153,479; qualifying distributions, $150,563; giving activities include $150,563 for 14 grants (high: $63,575; low: $1,000).
Fields of interest: Education; Sports and recreation; Human services.
Limitations: Applications not accepted. Giving primarily in PA and WA. No grants to individuals.
Application information: Unsolicited requests for funds not accepted.
Officers: John Goodfellow, Pres.; Barbara Peterson, V.P. and Secy.
EIN: 912000453

9608

The Goodman Foundation
2801 Alaskan Way, Ste. 310
Seattle, WA 98121-1136 (206) 438-6902
Contact: Teresa Beattie
E-mail for Teresa Beattie:
teresa@goodmanfound.org; Main URL: http://www.goodmanfound.org

Established in 2005 in Washington.
Donors: John Goodman; Shawn Goodman.
Foundation type: Independent foundation.
Financial data (yr. ended 12/31/13): Assets, $639 (M); gifts received, $375,900; expenditures, $377,333; qualifying distributions, $376,242; giving activities include $374,500 for 20 grants (high: $100,000; low: $600).
Purpose and activities: The foundation's mission is to fund organizations that support children and their families.
Fields of interest: Education; Christianity; Human services; Family services; Child welfare; Youth services.
Limitations: Applications not accepted. No grants to individuals.
Application information: Unsolicited requests for funds not accepted.
Officers and Directors: John A. Goodman, Pres. and Treas. and Director; Shawn Goodman, Secy. and Director.
EIN: 203215663

9609
The John Graham Foundation
c/o Thomas C. Gores
1201 3rd Ave., Ste. 4800
Seattle, WA 98101-1345

Established in 1992 in Washington.
Donor: John Graham†.
Foundation type: Independent foundation.
Financial data (yr. ended 12/31/13): Assets, $1,719,296 (M); gifts received, $3,295; expenditures, $321,365; qualifying distributions, $300,752; giving activities include $300,000 for 6 grants (high: $100,000; low: $25,000).
Fields of interest: Performing arts; Opera.
Limitations: Applications not accepted. Giving primarily in WA. No grants to individuals.
Application information: Unsolicited requests for funds not accepted.
Trustees: J. Kevin Callaghan; Thomas C. Gores; Stanley D. Savage.
EIN: 916339306

9610
Grindstone Foundation
9916 Peacock Hill Ave. N.W., Bldg. A
Gig Harbor, WA 98332-1076
Application address: c/o Ronna L. Schreiner, 5224 Olympic Dr. N.W., Gig Harbor, WA 98335, tel.: (253) 225-4566

Foundation type: Independent foundation.
Financial data (yr. ended 12/31/13): Assets, $5,893,241 (M); expenditures, $640,495; qualifying distributions, $350,000; giving activities include $350,000 for 8 grants (high: $100,000; low: $25,000).
Fields of interest: Arts and culture; Education; Religion.
Application information: Application form required.
Initial approach: Contact foundation for application form
Deadline(s): Apr. 30 for June Grants; Sept. 30 for Nov. Grants
Officers: Steven C. Schreiner, Pres.; Ronna L. Schreiner, V.P. and Treas.
Board Members: Kristina Hatley; James B. Lynch; Stephanie Sagle.
EIN: 900351007

9611
Grousemont Foundation
(formerly Howard S. Wright Family Foundation)
511 Boren Ave. N., Ste. 300
Seattle, WA 98109-5505

Established in 1984 in Washington.
Donors: Howard S. Wright†; T.Y. Scheumann.
Foundation type: Independent foundation.
Financial data (yr. ended 12/31/13): Assets, $17,317,755 (M); gifts received, $10,057,250; expenditures, $432,232; qualifying distributions, $390,291; giving activities include $340,450 for 55 grants (high: $50,000; low: $100).
Purpose and activities: Giving primarily for the arts, education and health.
Fields of interest: Arts and culture; Education; Higher education; Environment; Health; Diseases and conditions; Christianity.

Type of support: Annual campaigns; Capital campaigns; Capital and infrastructure; Endowments.
Limitations: Applications not accepted. Giving primarily in the Pacific Northwest, with emphasis on Seattle, WA. No support for religious organizations. No grants to individuals.
Publications: Annual report.
Application information: Unsolicited requests for funds not accepted.
Board meeting date(s): Quarterly
Officers and Directors: Sally S. Wright, Pres. and Director; Korynne Wright, Secy. and Director; Erin Wright, Treas. and Director; Lee Rolfe; Kate Janway Wright.
Number of staff: 1 part-time support.
EIN: 911276047

9612
Hagan Foundation
(formerly Cornelius and Lydiellen Hagan Foundation)
15326 N. Edencrest Ct.
Spokane, WA 99208-9738 (509) 443-1933

Established in 1997 in Washington.
Donor: Cornelius E. Hagan, MD.
Foundation type: Independent foundation.
Financial data (yr. ended 12/31/13): Assets, $8,818,074 (M); expenditures, $498,730; qualifying distributions, $441,918; giving activities include $441,918 for 14 grants (high: $93,549; low: $4,000).
Fields of interest: Education; Agriculture.
Type of support: General support.
Limitations: Applications accepted. Giving primarily in the Spokane, WA, area. No grants to individuals.
Application information: At present, no application for a grant in an amount greater than $5,000 will be considered. Application form required.
Initial approach: Letter
Deadline(s): Sept. 1
Board meeting date(s): Feb.
Officer: Roger Bragdon, Chair.
Board Members: Robert Blume; Kathie Burch, MD; Ross Wood.
EIN: 911762315

9613
Benjamin & Margaret Hall Foundation
310 120th Ave. N.E., Ste. 201
Bellevue, WA 98005-3013

Established in 1995 in Washington.
Donors: Benjamin Hall; Margaret Hall.
Foundation type: Independent foundation.
Financial data (yr. ended 12/31/13): Assets, $4,399,548 (M); gifts received, $345,542; expenditures, $202,205; qualifying distributions, $186,000; giving activities include $186,000 for 6 grants (high: $71,000; low: $10,000).
Fields of interest: Education.
Type of support: Endowments; General support.
Limitations: Applications not accepted. Giving primarily in KS and WA.
Application information: Unsolicited requests for funds not accepted.
Officers: Benjamin Hall, Pres.; Charles Hall, V.P.; Anne Hall, Secy.; Margaret Hall, Treas.
EIN: 911705444

9614
Adrian Hanauer Foundation
925 4th Ave., Ste. 2288
Seattle, WA 98104-1145

Donor: Gerald L. Hanauer†.
Foundation type: Independent foundation.
Financial data (yr. ended 12/31/13): Assets, $3,420,147 (M); expenditures, $408,747; qualifying distributions, $387,297; giving activities include $387,297 for 12 grants (high: $100,000; low: $1,000).
Fields of interest: Arts and culture; Environment; Human services.
Limitations: Applications not accepted. Giving primarily in Seattle, WA.
Application information: Unsolicited requests for funds not accepted.
Director: Adrian Hanauer.
EIN: 261820315

9615
Carl M. Hansen Foundation, Inc.
422 W. Riverside, Ste. 1420
Spokane, WA 99201-0305 5097472158

Donor: Carl M. Hansen†.
Foundation type: Independent foundation.
Financial data (yr. ended 12/31/14): Assets, $3,165,998; expenditures, $277,988; qualifying distributions, $236,881.
Purpose and activities: Awards scholarships and grants in the fields of art, science, literature, and education, particularly as they apply to engineering.
Fields of interest: Arts and culture; Higher education; Graduate and professional education; Engineering; Human services; Food banks; Youth services.
Limitations: Applications not accepted.
Application information: Unsolicited requests for funds not accepted.
Trustees: James R. Harless; Betty Lukins.
EIN: 916063191

9616
Hanson Family Foundation
P.O. Box 4246
Bellevue, WA 98009-4246

Foundation type: Independent foundation.
Financial data (yr. ended 12/31/13): Assets, $5,130,853 (M); gifts received, $2,189,539; expenditures, $268,492; qualifying distributions, $239,505; giving activities include $230,000 for 1 grant.
Fields of interest: Museums.
Limitations: Applications not accepted.
Application information: Unsolicited requests for funds not accepted.
Officers: James R. Ladd, Pres. and Treas.; Sharon S. Ladd, Secy.
Trustees: Christopher B. Smith; Randolph C.H. Smith.
EIN: 204562272

9617
Jackson Heath Foundation
c/o Trust Tax Dept.
P.O. Box 21927, MAC P6540-400
Seattle, WA 98111-3927

Established in 2002 in Montana.
Foundation type: Independent foundation.
Financial data (yr. ended 12/31/13): Assets, $2,755,875 (M); expenditures, $202,624; qualifying distributions, $153,663; giving activities include $138,100 for 6 grants (high: $27,600; low: $100).
Fields of interest: Diseases and conditions; Cancers; Christianity; Human services.
Limitations: Applications not accepted. Giving primarily in MT. No grants to individuals.
Application information: Contributes only to pre-selected organizations.
Trustee: Wells Fargo Bank, N.A.
EIN: 816061603

9618
Marco J. Heidner Charitable Trust
2825 Colby Ave., Ste. A
Everett, WA 98201

Established in 1995 in Washington.
Donor: Marco J. Heidner Trust B.
Foundation type: Independent foundation.
Financial data (yr. ended 12/31/14): Assets, $6,078,269 (M); expenditures, $334,841; qualifying distributions, $270,337; giving activities include $255,000 for 11 grants (high: $70,000; low: $5,000).
Fields of interest: Foundations; Diseases and conditions; Human services.
Limitations: Applications not accepted. Giving primarily in WA. No grants to individuals.
Application information: Unsolicited requests for funds not accepted.
Trustee: Union Bank, N.A.
EIN: 943219943

9619
The Helstrom Foundation
4500 3rd Ave. S.E., Ste. 2
Lacey, WA 98503-1002 (360) 491-6320

Established in 1991 in Washington.
Donors: Robert L. Helstrom; Norris Helstrom.
Foundation type: Operating foundation.
Financial data (yr. ended 06/30/13): Assets, $14,790,116 (M); gifts received, $482,558; expenditures, $1,356,158; qualifying distributions, $365,022; giving activities include $350,194 for 3 grants (high: $316,000; low: $6,000).
Purpose and activities: Giving primarily for Christian education and organizations.
Fields of interest: Higher education; Christianity.
Type of support: General support; Scholarships.
Limitations: Applications accepted. Giving primarily in ID, KS and WA. No grants to individuals directly.
Application information: Include evidence of charitable status or demonstration of financial need, academic achievement, and recommendation by principal, teacher, or youth program or civic leader. Scholarship awards will be granted to candidates selected from public, parochial, and other private elementary, secondary, and post-secondary schools in the U.S. who have demonstrated academic success, social responsibility, and financial need.
  Initial approach: Letter
  Deadline(s): None

Officers: Robert L. Helstrom, Pres.; Brian L. Helstrom, V.P.; Yvonne E. Helstrom, Secy.; Phillip G. Harris, Treas.
EIN: 943124662

9620
Herbold Foundation
1106 108th Ave. N.E., Ste. 203
Bellevue, WA 98004-8609 4254539796
Application address: Donna M. Herbold, 10353 Timber Leaf Ct., Indianapolis, IN 46236, tel.: (317) 823-7555

Established in 2002 in Washington.
Donors: Patricia L. Herbold; Robert J. Herbold.
Foundation type: Independent foundation.
Financial data (yr. ended 12/31/14): Assets, $9,102,167; gifts received, $280,000; expenditures, $374,570; qualifying distributions, $370,493.
Purpose and activities: Giving for college scholarships for science, math, and engineering students; giving also for human services and public affairs.
Fields of interest: Education; Public affairs; Human services.
Type of support: Individual development.
Limitations: Applications accepted. Giving primarily in CA, Washington, DC and WA.
Application information: Application form required.
  Initial approach: 3 pages request application form
  Deadline(s): Apr. 1st
Officers: Robert J. Herbold, Pres. and Treas.; Patricia L. Herbold, V.P. and Secy.; Donna M. Herbold, Exec. Dir.
Number of staff: 1 part-time professional.
EIN: 320046141

9621
Herray Foundation
816 35th Ave.
Seattle, WA 98122-5234

Donors: Gretl Dupre Galgon; Roots and Wings.
Foundation type: Independent foundation.
Financial data (yr. ended 12/31/13): Assets, $9,635,055 (M); gifts received, $7,689,364; expenditures, $306,311; qualifying distributions, $226,600; giving activities include $226,600 for 4 grants (high: $185,250; low: $1,350).
Fields of interest: Education; Domesticated animals; Human services.
Limitations: Applications not accepted. Giving primarily in WA.
Application information: Unsolicited requests for funds not accepted.
Officer and Director: Gretl Dupre Galgon, V.P. and Director.
EIN: 461394812

9622
Ray Hickey Foundation
16420 S.E. McGillivray, Ste. 103
P.O. Box 193
Vancouver, WA 98683-3461
Contact: Linda Rae Hickey, Exec. Dir. and Tr.

Established in 1998 in Washington.
Donors: Raymond Hickey†; Hickey Family Co.
Foundation type: Independent foundation.

Financial data (yr. ended 12/31/13): Assets, $15,444,564 (M); expenditures, $588,467; qualifying distributions, $407,450; giving activities include $407,450 for 20 grants (high: $75,000; low: $5,000).
Fields of interest: Education; Natural resources; Health; Sports and recreation; Human services; Family services; Child welfare.
Limitations: Applications accepted. Giving primarily in the Portland, OR and Vancouver, WA, area. No grants to individuals.
Application information: Application form required.
  Initial approach: Letter
  Deadline(s): None
Officer and Trustees: Linda Rae Hickey, Exec. Dir. and Trustee; Cindy Nesbitt.
EIN: 911887342

9623
Hilal Foundation
6582 169th Pl. S.E.
Bellevue, WA 98006-6010

Established in 2003 in Washington.
Donors: Wael Bahaa-El-Din; Amira Youssef El-Bastawissi.
Foundation type: Independent foundation.
Financial data (yr. ended 12/31/13): Assets, $2,273,447 (M); gifts received, $150,000; expenditures, $295,647; qualifying distributions, $289,832; giving activities include $288,210 for 11 grants (high: $214,650; low: $1,000).
Fields of interest: Community and economic development; Religion.
Limitations: Applications not accepted. Giving primarily in WA; some giving in CA. No grants to individuals.
Application information: Unsolicited requests for funds not accepted.
Board Members: Wael Bahaa-El-Din; Amira Youssef El-Bastawissi.
EIN: 200439076

9624
HIS Foundation
(formerly TCT Foundation)
2737 78th Ave. S.E., Ste. 201
Mercer Island, WA 98040-2843

Established in 2000 in Washington.
Donors: Doris Cassan; James Cassan; Cassan Enterprises, Inc.; Dollar Fly; Park Fly; Todd Investment Company.
Foundation type: Independent foundation.
Financial data (yr. ended 09/30/14): Assets, $597,710 (M); gifts received, $258,000; expenditures, $189,892; qualifying distributions, $189,257; giving activities include $189,257 for 24 grants (high: $45,608; low: $750).
Fields of interest: Education; Christianity; Child welfare.
Limitations: Applications not accepted. Giving primarily in WA. No grants to individuals.
Application information: Unsolicited requests for funds not accepted.
Trustees: Doris O. Cassan; James T. Cassan.
EIN: 916512367

9625
Thomas & Martina Horn Foundation
P.O. Box 3130
Bellingham, WA 98227-3130 (360) 734-3300
Contact: Donna MacDonald, Exec. Dir.

Donor: Thomas Horn†.
Foundation type: Independent foundation.
Financial data (yr. ended 12/31/13): Assets, $3,511,980 (M); expenditures, $219,018; qualifying distributions, $196,160; giving activities include $173,300 for 36 grants (high: $26,000; low: $250).
Fields of interest: Education; Higher education; Hospice care; HIV/AIDS; Human services; Food banks; Family services; Youth services.
Type of support: General support; Endowments; Individual development; Scholarships.
Limitations: Applications not accepted. Giving primarily in Bellingham and Whatcom County, WA. No support for religious or political organizations. No grants to individuals.
Application information: Contributes only to pre-selected organizations.
Officer: Donna MacDonald, Exec. Dir.
Board Members: J. Bruce Smith; Orphalee Smith.
Number of staff: 2 part-time support.
EIN: 911701495

9626
Howarth Trust, Inc.
(formerly Cawsey Trust Fund)
P.O. Box 5397
Everett, WA 98206-5397
E-mail: pcarpenter@andersonhunterlaw.com

Established in 1960 in Washington.
Donor: Mrs. Hugh R. Cawsey†.
Foundation type: Independent foundation.
Financial data (yr. ended 12/31/14): Assets, $4,052,634 (M); gifts received, $580,000; expenditures, $181,915; qualifying distributions, $189,099; giving activities include $187,949 for 19 grants (high: $20,000; low: $605).
Purpose and activities: Giving generally to organizations working in conjunction with other United Way organizations benefiting youth located for the most part in Snohomish County, Washington.
Fields of interest: Education; Child welfare; Youth services.
Type of support: General support; Capital campaigns; Capital and infrastructure; Equipment; Emergency funds.
Limitations: Applications not accepted. Giving primarily in Everett, WA. No support for religious or political organizations. No grants to individuals.
Application information: Unsolicited requests for funds not accepted.
Officers and Trustees: G. Paul Carpenter, Pres.; H. Roy Yates, V.P.; Elizabeth M. Campbell, Secy. and Trustee; Mary Ellen Denman; Thomas Lane.
EIN: 916053815

9627
The Hyde Foundation
4715 133rd St. N.W.
Gig Harbor, WA 98332-8887

Established in 1997 in Washington.
Donor: William B. Hyde.
Foundation type: Independent foundation.

Financial data (yr. ended 12/31/13): Assets, $4,018,806 (M); expenditures, $207,256; qualifying distributions, $200,000; giving activities include $200,000 for 18 grants (high: $34,000; low: $1,000).
Purpose and activities: Giving primarily for education and conservation.
Fields of interest: Art museums; Education; Higher education; Natural resources; Biodiversity; Wildlife biodiversity; Domesticated animals; Animal welfare; Foundations; Hospital care; Learning disorders.
Type of support: Research.
Limitations: Applications not accepted. Giving primarily in VA and WA. No grants to individuals.
Application information: Unsolicited requests for funds not accepted.
Officers: William B. Hyde, Pres.; Elizabeth D. Hyde, V.P.; Pamela Hyde Smith, Treas.
Directors: Catherine E. Smith; Marian Smith.
EIN: 911797073

9628
Jacobi Family Foundation
4699 Woodson Way, Ste. 310A
Bainbridge, WA 98110-2385

Donor: John W. Jacobi.
Foundation type: Independent foundation.
Financial data (yr. ended 12/31/13): Assets, $1,296,649 (M); expenditures, $279,601; qualifying distributions, $248,986; giving activities include $248,986 for 17 grants (high: $108,471; low: $250).
Fields of interest: Domesticated animals; Religion; Human services.
Type of support: General support.
Limitations: Applications not accepted. Giving primarily in HI and WA.
Application information: Contributes only to pre-selected organizations.
Officers: John Jacobi, Pres.; Rosalind Jacobi, V.P.; Victoria Dotson, Secy.-Treas.
EIN: 273985046

9629
The Bernard M. and Audrey Jaffe Foundation
P.O. Box 1151
Bellingham, WA 98227-1151

Established in 1988 in Washington.
Donors: Bernard M. Jaffe†; Audrey Jaffe; BMJ Holdings, Inc.
Foundation type: Independent foundation.
Financial data (yr. ended 03/31/15): Assets, $944,646 (M); expenditures, $140,429; qualifying distributions, $139,000; giving activities include $139,000 for 13 grants (high: $31,000; low: $700).
Fields of interest: Education; Nonprofits; Science; Judaism.
Type of support: Regranting.
Limitations: Applications not accepted. Giving primarily in CA, New York, NY, and WA. No grants to individuals.
Application information: Unsolicited requests for funds not accepted.
Officers and Trustees: Audrey Jaffe; Jeffery Jaffe, Pres.; Joel Jaffe; Roberta Jaffe; Mark B. Packer, Secy.
EIN: 911409921

9630
Jefferson County Community Foundation
201-B Patison St.
Port Hadlock, WA 98339 (360) 385-1729
Contact: Kris Nelson, Pres.
E-mail: info@jccfgives.org; *Main URL:* http://www.jccfgives.org
Facebook: https://www.facebook.com/JeffersonCountyCommunityFoundation

Established in 2005 in Washington.
Foundation type: Community foundation.
Financial data (yr. ended 12/31/13): Assets, $1,305,078 (M); gifts received, $178,252; expenditures, $260,616; giving activities include $197,700 for 5+ grants (high: $118,000).
Purpose and activities: The foundation is dedicated to strengthening the community both now and for future generations through engaged philanthropy. The goals of the foundation are to: 1) expand philanthropic giving in the community; 2) facilitate legacy giving from one generation to another; 3) strengthen local nonprofits through education and grant making; 4) educate community members, organizations and businesses about the services offered through the Community Foundation; 5) engage and collaborate, as appropriate, with organizations addressing systemic community issues; and 6) increase growth and sustainability of the foundation through fund development, donor engagement, and participation in community problem-solving.
Fields of interest: Arts and culture; Education; Environment; Health; Human services; Seniors.
Type of support: Program development; System and operational improvements.
Limitations: Giving primarily in Jefferson County, WA. No grants to individuals, or for endowments or fundraising events.
Publications: Annual report; Financial statement.
Application information: Visit foundation web site for more information.
Initial approach: Contact foundation
Deadline(s): Apr. 15
Officers and Directors: Kris Nelson, Pres. and Director; Ned Luce, V.P. and Director; Liesl Slabaugh, Secy. and Director; Doug Van Allen, Treas. and Director; Carla Caldwell, Exec. Dir.; Kate Burke; Jill Landes; Laurie Liske; Earll Murman; Roger Hagen.
EIN: 841682682

9631
The Jernigan Foundation
343 Westhampton Ln. S.W.
Olympia, WA 98512-9475 (360) 791-3917
Contact: Tanya S. Jernigan, V.P. and Secy.

Established in 2006 in Washington.
Donors: Austin Community Foundation; Thomas Burns; Lacie Crow; Patrick Crow; Lane Grigsby; Mallory E. Hensley; Maria A. Hensley; Jeff Holmes; Lori Holmes; Tanya S. Jernigan; Theodore E. Jernigan; Bradford Kline; Theresa Kline; Lee Ann Miller; Linda Muzyl; William Muzyl; Brad Parker; Kathleen Parker; Schwab Charitable Fund; Marc A. Sparks; Loralee S. West; Bibler Allen; James Allen; Laurie Allen; Four Special Daughters LP; Allen Hodges III; Janet Hodges III; Todd Mueller; Amy Mueller; National Christian Foundation; Cree Land and Cattle Co Ltd.; Robbie Mayfield; Treeta Mayfield; Mzuri Wildlife Foundation; Richard Rose; Sandra E.

Rutherford; Steve Skinner; Leanne Skinner; David Wheeler; Marta Wheeler.
Foundation type: Independent foundation.
Financial data (yr. ended 06/30/14): Assets, $279,344 (M); gifts received, $438,068; expenditures, $289,351; qualifying distributions, $279,660; giving activities include $279,660 for 7 grants (high: $250,000; low: $2,000).
Fields of interest: Orchestral music; Education; Nonprofits; Maternal and perinatal health; Christianity; Human rights; Youth development; Youth services.
International interests: South Africa.
Type of support: General support; Scholarships; Regranting.
Limitations: Applications accepted. Giving primarily in WA and South Africa. No grants to individuals.
Application information:
   Initial approach: Proposal
   Deadline(s): None
Officers: Theodore E. Jernigan, Pres. and Treas.; Tanya S. Jernigan, V.P. and Secy.
EIN: 208111798

9632
The Ji Ji Foundation
2730 Westlake Ave. N.
Seattle, WA 98109-1916   (206) 328-2393
Contact: Anne McEnany
E-mail: anne@jiji.org; *Main URL:* http://www.jiji.org

Established in 1994 in Washington.
Donors: Alan B. Harper; Louise G. Harper Charitable Lead Annuity Trust.
Foundation type: Independent foundation.
Financial data (yr. ended 09/30/13): Assets, $3,174,031 (M); gifts received, $323,750; expenditures, $404,610; qualifying distributions, $381,285; giving activities include $357,877 for 22 grants (high: $130,100; low: $2,800); and $22,830 for 5 grants to individuals (high: $9,500; low: $2,330).
Purpose and activities: Giving primarily to support conservation, research, and public education on environmental issues.
Fields of interest: Education; Environment; Natural resources.
International interests: Mexico.
Type of support: General support; Grants to individuals; Research and evaluation; Land acquisitions; Convening; Publications; Seed money; Curriculum development; Research.
Limitations: Applications accepted. Giving primarily in CA, and Baja California, Mexico. No grants for endowments.
Publications: Application guidelines; Grants list.
Application information: Applications are also accepted for small conservation grants ($1,000-3,000) for field research related to coastal sage scrub, chaparral, and desert ecosystems in Baja California, Mexico. Any application for a small conservation grant must demonstrate how the project is directly related to the goals of the foundation for Baja California, Mexico. The foundation will not be funding any work in island ecosystems or on the Gulf of California coastline at this time. See foundation web site for specific application guidelines. Application form required.
   Initial approach: Letter of request (for grants between $3,000-10,000) or a letter of inquiry (for grants between $10,000-50,000). A cover sheet (which can be downloaded from foundation web site) should also be included

Copies of proposal: 1
Deadline(s): See foundation web site for current deadlines
Board meeting date(s): Quarterly
Officers: Alan B. Harper, Pres.; Carol J. Baird, Secy.; Anne McEnany, Treas.
Trustee: Bruce Sherman.
Number of staff: None.
EIN: 911664723

9633
Johnson & Haefling Family Foundation
9615 N.E. Watch Hill Dr.
Bainbridge Island, WA 98110-2394

Established in 2002 in Washington.
Donors: Carl Haefling; Pamela Johnson.
Foundation type: Independent foundation.
Financial data (yr. ended 12/31/13): Assets, $1,080,173 (M); expenditures, $381,776; qualifying distributions, $379,385; giving activities include $377,500 for 15 grants (high: $50,000; low: $7,000).
Fields of interest: Natural resources; Food aid; Housing services; International relations.
Limitations: Applications not accepted. Giving primarily in Seattle, WA. No grants to individuals.
Application information: Unsolicited requests for funds not accepted.
Officers: Carl Haefling, Pres. and Treas.; Pamela Johnson, V.P. and Secy.
EIN: 270036658

9634
Johnston-Fix Foundation
2903 E. 25th Ave., Ste. 226
Spokane, WA 99223-1728
Application address: c/o Harriet J. Fix, Pres., 2812 E. Foxwood Dr., Spokane, WA 99223-3418

Donor: Eric Johnston†.
Foundation type: Independent foundation.
Financial data (yr. ended 12/31/13): Assets, $7,177,142 (M); expenditures, $327,720; qualifying distributions, $301,400; giving activities include $299,000 for grants.
Purpose and activities: Giving primarily for private higher and independent secondary education and cultural programs; support also for youth groups.
Fields of interest: Arts and culture; Secondary education; Higher education; Radio; Youth services.
Application information:
   Initial approach: Telephone Call
   Copies of proposal: 1
   Deadline(s): None
Officer: Harriet J. Fix, Pres.
Directors: Thomas M. Culbertson; Allan C. Fix; Harold J. Fix; William C. Fix; Rob Lindsay.
Number of staff: 1 part-time professional.
EIN: 943076779

9635
Johnston-Hanson Foundation
5118 S. Perry St.
Spokane, WA 99223-6356
Contact: Elizabeth J. Hanson, Chair.

Established in 1948 in Washington.
Donor: Eric Johnston†.
Foundation type: Independent foundation.

Financial data (yr. ended 12/31/13): Assets, $7,188,666 (M); expenditures, $444,770; qualifying distributions, $433,682; giving activities include $401,398 for 40 grants (high: $100,242; low: $500).
Purpose and activities: Giving primarily for higher and other education; support also for the arts, including music and museums and social services.
Fields of interest: Arts and culture; Music; Museums; Education; Higher education; Human services.
Type of support: Continuing support; Annual campaigns; Endowments; Scholarships.
Limitations: Applications accepted. Giving primarily in the Spokane, WA, area. No support for publicly supported institutions or medical institutions. No grants to individuals.
Publications: Annual report; Annual report (including application guidelines).
Application information: Application form required.
   Initial approach: Letter
   Copies of proposal: 7
   Deadline(s): May 1 for June; July 1 for Aug. or Sept.; and Nov. 1 for Dec.
   Board meeting date(s): 2 conference calls yearly when needed
   Final notification: Two weeks following board meeting
Officers and Directors: Elizabeth J. Hanson, Chair. and Secy.-Treas. and Director; Fred L. Hanson, Vice-Chair.; Victoria Carney; Eric Hanson; Ann Hanson Scarborough; Gil Zwetsch.
Number of staff: 1 part-time professional; 1 part-time support.
EIN: 943077091

9636
Joint Heirs Ministry
2959 - 81st Pl., S.E.
Mercer Island, WA 98040-3057

Donors: George Duff; Marilyn Duff.
Foundation type: Independent foundation.
Financial data (yr. ended 03/31/13): Assets, $1,472,402 (M); expenditures, $258,288; qualifying distributions, $245,077; giving activities include $240,641 for 20 grants (high: $150,000; low: $100), and $4,436 for 1 foundation-administered program.
Fields of interest: Religion; Christianity; Sports and recreation; Human services.
Limitations: Applications not accepted. Giving primarily in GA and WA. No grants to individuals.
Application information: Unsolicited requests for funds not accepted.
Officers: George Duff, Pres.; Marilyn Duff, V.P.; Bruce Duff, Secy.-Treas.
EIN: 911726394

9637
Margery Jones Charitable Trust
9115 Fortuna Dr., Apt. 6412
Mercer Island, WA 98040-3158

Donor: Margery M. Jones†.
Foundation type: Independent foundation.
Financial data (yr. ended 09/30/14): Assets, $8,029,559; expenditures, $429,684; qualifying distributions, $408,040.
Fields of interest: Arts and culture; Education; Human services.

Limitations: Applications not accepted. Giving primarily in CA and WA.
Application information: Unsolicited requests for funds not accepted.
EIN: 276589503

9638
The Herbert B. Jones Foundation
c/o Key Private Bank
601 108th Ave. N.E., Ste. 260
Bellevue, WA 98004-8606 (206) 285-1729
Main URL: http://www.hbjfoundation.com
Grant Database: http://www.hbjfoundation.com/grant_history.html

Established in 1989 in Washington.
Donor: Herbert B. Jones.
Foundation type: Independent foundation.
Financial data (yr. ended 08/31/14): Assets, $12,745,436 (M); expenditures, $476,983; qualifying distributions, $398,972; giving activities include $396,246 for 18 grants (high: $80,000; low: $9,000).
Purpose and activities: The foundation promotes small-business and entrepreneurism through programs managed by post-secondary educational institutions.
Fields of interest: Education; Higher education; Business education.
Type of support: Program development; Convening; Seed money; Curriculum development.
Limitations: Applications accepted. Giving limited to WA. No grants to individuals, or for equipment, capital projects, gifts, endowments or food costs.
Publications: Application guidelines.
Application information: Refer to foundation web site for complete guideline information. Application form required.
   Initial approach: Proposal (2 pages maximum, with a minimum font size of 11)
   Copies of proposal: 6
   Deadline(s): First Mon. in Apr.
   Board meeting date(s): May
   Final notification: Within 8 weeks
Trustees: Michael R. Bauer; Tom Crha; Bill Erwert; Tammy Miller; Terry Smith; Teri Tingvall; Janet Woods.
Number of staff: None.
EIN: 943124801

9639
Zelma May Josi Charitable Trust
c/o Jack L. Robson
6220 S.E. Riverside Dr.
Vancouver, WA 98661-7643

Foundation type: Independent foundation.
Financial data (yr. ended 12/31/13): Assets, $3,727,374 (M); expenditures, $207,052; qualifying distributions, $167,220; giving activities include $167,220 for 1 grant.
Fields of interest: Human services.
Limitations: Applications not accepted.
Application information: Unsolicited requests for funds not accepted.
Trustee: Jack L. Robson.
EIN: 376445616

9640
Juniper Foundation
c/o Daniel Asher
1000 2nd Ave., 34th Fl.
Seattle, WA 98104

Established in 1998 in Washington.
Donors: Sheila Wyckoff-Dickey; Charles D. Dickey III.
Foundation type: Independent foundation.
Financial data (yr. ended 12/31/13): Assets, $11,071,033 (M); gifts received, $400,000; expenditures, $413,908; qualifying distributions, $378,673; giving activities include $370,500 for 46 grants (high: $50,000; low: $1,000).
Fields of interest: Arts and culture; Art museums; Education; Environment; Health; Diseases and conditions; Human services; Youth development; Scouting programs.
Type of support: Research.
Limitations: Applications not accepted. Giving primarily in WA. No grants to individuals.
Application information: Unsolicited requests for funds not accepted.
Officers and Directors: Sheila Wyckoff-Dickey, Pres. and Treas. and Director; Charles D. Dickey III, V.P. and Director; Daniel M. Asher, Secy.
EIN: 911908199

9641
Kaleidoscope Foundation
c/o Richard Leeds
227 Bellevue Way N.E., Ste. 543
Bellevue, WA 98004-5721

Established in 1997 in Washington.
Donors: Gerard Leeds; Liselotte Leeds; Richard Leeds.
Foundation type: Independent foundation.
Financial data (yr. ended 11/30/13): Assets, $3,873,990 (M); gifts received, $70,000; expenditures, $402,657; qualifying distributions, $386,657; giving activities include $310,735 for 59 grants (high: $136,500; low: $100).
Purpose and activities: Giving primarily for the arts, education, the environment, animals and wildlife, and human services.
Fields of interest: Performing arts; Museums; Education; Higher education; Environment; Land resources; Domesticated animals; Human services.
Limitations: Applications not accepted. Giving primarily in WA, with emphasis on Seattle. No grants to individuals.
Application information: Unsolicited requests for funds not accepted.
Officers and Directors: Anne F. Kroeker, Co-Pres. and V.P. and Director; Richard Leeds, Co-Pres. and V.P. and Director; Robert H. Blais, Secy.; Michael Sweeney, Treas. and Director.
EIN: 911874926

9642
Kawabe Memorial Fund
(also known as Harry S. Kawabe Trust)
c/o Bank of America, Philanthropic Mgmt.
P.O. Box 3977, WA1-501-33-23
Seattle, WA 98124-2477
E-mail: natalie.grantwork@gmail.com; Toll-free tel.: (800) 848-7177; Additional contact: Natalie Lecher; e-mail: natalie.grantwork@gmail.com, tel.: (206) 406-6124; Main URL: http://fdnweb.org/kawabe

Established in 1972 in Washington.
Donors: Tomo Kawabe†; Harry Kawabe†.
Foundation type: Independent foundation.
Financial data (yr. ended 12/31/14): Assets, $4,420,245 (M); expenditures, $248,036; qualifying distributions, $198,638; giving activities include $164,200 for 45 grants (high: $22,000; low: $500).
Purpose and activities: Giving to support and promote quality human services programming for the economically disadvantaged, children and the elderly. Some giving also as capital grants to churches, as well as scholarships to support teachers and the clergy. The Fund typically supports organizations serving the people of the Puget Sound area.
Fields of interest: Graduate and professional education; Theology; Human services; Child welfare; Senior services; Seniors; Low-income and poor people.
Type of support: General support; Continuing support; Capital and infrastructure; Equipment; Program development; Seed money; Student aid.
Limitations: Applications accepted. Giving primarily to organizations serving the people of the Puget Sound area.
Publications: Application guidelines.
Application information: Complete application guidelines available on Fund web site.
   Initial approach: Online grant application
   Deadline(s): Second Fridays of Jan. (spring cycle), April (summer cycle) and Aug. (fall cycle)
Trustee: Bank of America, N.A.
Allocation Committee: Yasue Brevig; Thomas M. Ikeda; Tsuyoshi Nakano; Katsumi Tanino; Warren Yasutake; Bruce Tadashi Abe; Gary Kiyonaga; Dale Kaku; Rev. Donald Castro.
EIN: 916116549

9643
Keller Foundation
1701 S.E. Columbia River Dr., Ste. 100
Vancouver, WA 98661-8029

Established in 1997 in Oregon.
Donor: Richard B. Keller.
Foundation type: Independent foundation.
Financial data (yr. ended 12/31/13): Assets, $4,568,016 (M); gifts received, $136,040; expenditures, $213,502; qualifying distributions, $209,776; giving activities include $175,500 for 29 grants (high: $18,000; low: $2,500).
Fields of interest: Arts and culture; Orchestral music; Early childhood education; Higher education; Business education; Law education; Environment; Health; Human services.
Limitations: Applications not accepted. Giving primarily in Portland, OR. No grants to individuals.
Application information: Contributes only to pre-selected organizations.
Officers and Directors: Richard B. Keller, Chair. and Pres. and Director; Gary W. Stachlowski, V.P., Vice-Chair. and Director; Ruth E. Keller, V.P. and Director; Kevin C. Kuch, Exec. Dir. and Treas.; Carol J. Frohoff, Secy.; Brian G. Booth; Charles Keller; Elizabeth K. McCaslin; Peter F. Bechen; Richard Keller III.
EIN: 911811697

9644
Florence B. Kilworth Charitable Trust Foundation
2825 Colby Ave., Ste. A
Everett, WA 98201-3554

Foundation type: Independent foundation.
Financial data (yr. ended 12/31/14): Assets, $6,624,261 (M); expenditures, $367,940; qualifying distributions, $318,166; giving activities include $299,050 for 68 grants (high: $11,000; low: $1,000).
Purpose and activities: Giving primarily for the arts and human services.
Fields of interest: Arts and culture; Education; Elementary and secondary education; Diseases and conditions; Human services; Child welfare.
Type of support: General support; Annual campaigns; Capital campaigns; Capital and infrastructure; Equipment; Program development; Scholarships.
Limitations: Applications not accepted. Giving primarily in WA. No grants to individuals.
Application information: Unsolicited requests for funds not accepted.
Trustee: Union Bank, N.A.
Number of staff: 1 part-time support.
EIN: 916221495

9645
Paul L. King Charitable Foundation
P.O. Box 61669
Vancouver, WA 98666-1669

Established in 1997 in Washington.
Donors: Paul L. King; Mary-Claire King.
Foundation type: Independent foundation.
Financial data (yr. ended 12/31/13): Assets, $3,648,952 (M); expenditures, $150,025; qualifying distributions, $150,025; giving activities include $150,000 for 2 grants (high: $100,000; low: $50,000).
Fields of interest: Land resources.
Limitations: Applications not accepted. Giving primarily in Boston, MA and Portland, OR. No grants to individuals.
Application information: Contributes only to pre-selected organizations.
Trustee: Paul L. King.
EIN: 911811633

9646
Kismet 805 Foundation
P.O. Box 3831
Bellevue, WA 98009

Established in 2002 in Washington.
Donors: Brad A. Silverberg; Janice M. Silverberg.
Foundation type: Independent foundation.
Financial data (yr. ended 12/31/13): Assets, $6,862,171 (M); expenditures, $469,370; qualifying distributions, $407,070; giving activities include $401,600 for 34 grants (high: $60,000; low: $1,000).
Fields of interest: Education; Health; Religion.
Limitations: Applications not accepted. Giving primarily in WA; some funding also in Providence, RI. No grants to individuals.
Application information: Contributes only to pre-selected organizations.

Trustees: Brad A. Silverberg; Janice M. Silverberg.
EIN: 916557030

9647
Klaue Family Foundation
14 E. Main Ave.
Spokane, WA 99202-1620   (509) 534-0266

Established in 1990 in Washington.
Donors: August V. Klaue; Mary E. Klaue.
Foundation type: Independent foundation.
Financial data (yr. ended 12/31/13): Assets, $4,085,949 (M); expenditures, $242,303; qualifying distributions, $232,096; giving activities include $193,125 for 23 grants (high: $18,125; low: $5,000).
Fields of interest: Arts and culture; Education; University education; Hospice care; Human services.
Limitations: Applications accepted. Giving primarily in the Spokane, WA, area. No grants to individuals.
Application information: Application form required.
 Initial approach: Phone or E-mail
 Deadline(s): None
Officer: David A. Klaue, Pres.
EIN: 911503434

9648
Korum for Kids Foundation
P.O. Box 538
Puyallup, WA 98371   (253) 845-6600
Contact: Jerry Korum, Tr.

Established in 1994 in Washington.
Donors: Korum Automotive Group Inc.; Jerry Korum Investments; Jerome Korum; Korum Family Limited Partnership.
Foundation type: Company-sponsored foundation.
Financial data (yr. ended 12/31/13): Assets, $7,829,642 (M); gifts received, $801,000; expenditures, $328,413; qualifying distributions, $256,626; giving activities include $229,434 for 70 grants (high: $35,500; low: $25).
Purpose and activities: The foundation supports programs designed to promote and improve the health, welfare, and future of young people.
Fields of interest: Arts and culture; Education; Health; Sports and recreation; Human services; Children and youth.
Type of support: General support; Matching grants; Capital campaigns; Capital and infrastructure; Equipment; Program development; Scholarships; Sponsorships.
Application information: Application form required.
 Initial approach: Contact foundation for application form
 Copies of proposal: 3
 Deadline(s): None
Officer and Trustees: Sophia Hall, Mgr. and Trustee; Germaine R. Korum; Jerry Korum.
EIN: 916528752

9649
The Lanterman Foundation
221 1st Ave. W., Ste. 108
Seattle, WA 98119-4223

Donors: A. Kirk Lanterman; Janet O. Lanterman.
Foundation type: Independent foundation.

Financial data (yr. ended 12/31/14): Expenditures, $381,208; qualifying distributions, $344,458.
Fields of interest: Historic preservation; Higher education; Nonprofits; Human services.
Type of support: Regranting.
Limitations: Applications not accepted. Giving primarily in CA, ND, and WA. No grants to individuals.
Application information: Contributes only to pre-selected organizations.
Officers: A. Kirk Lanterman, Pres. and Treas.; Janet O. Lanterman, Sr. V.P. and Secy.; Barbara Nixon, V.P.; Dorothy Heberling, V.P.; Linda Young, V.P.; Patricia Gable, V.P.
EIN: 911789916

9650
Reed and Jeanne Larson Foundation
11311 116th Pl., N.E.
Kirkland, WA 98033-3865

Established in 1987 in Virginia.
Donors: Reed E. Larson; Reed Larson Charitable Remainder.
Foundation type: Independent foundation.
Financial data (yr. ended 06/30/13): Assets, $810,811 (M); expenditures, $170,487; qualifying distributions, $168,195; giving activities include $168,195 for 38 grants (high: $28,750; low: $300).
Fields of interest: Education; Religion; Human services.
Limitations: Applications not accepted. Giving primarily in VA. No grants to individuals.
Application information: Unsolicited requests for funds not accepted.
Officer and Trustees: Reed E. Larson, Chair. and Trustee; Marcia Larson Craig; Barbara Larson Finnegan; Patricia Larson Sween.
EIN: 541443620

9651
Paul Lauzier Scholarship Foundation
117 Basin St. N.W.
P.O. Box 1230
Ephrata, WA 98823-1623   (509) 754-3209
E-mail: ck.lauzier@nwi.net; *Main URL:* http://www.lauzier.org/scholarship-foundation

Donor: Paul Lauzier†.
Foundation type: Independent foundation.
Financial data (yr. ended 12/31/13): Assets, $9,060 (M); gifts received, $445,000; expenditures, $443,195; qualifying distributions, $438,983; giving activities include $438,983 for 209 grants to individuals (high: $5,000; low: $1,000).
Purpose and activities: Scholarships to graduates of Grant County, WA, high schools who attend a college or vocational school (full time) within the State of Washington. Students pursuing graduate degrees are also eligible for scholarship awards. Applicants must reside in Grant County for a minimum of 2 years prior to high school graduation.
Fields of interest: Higher education.
Type of support: Student aid.
Limitations: Applications accepted. Giving limited to residents of Grant County, WA. No grants for salaries, debt retirement, or tuitions assistance.
Publications: Application guidelines.
Application information: Application forms available on foundation web site. There are two different application forms: one for graduating seniors, and

another for students who are out of high school. Applicants should make sure they complete the appropriate form. All applications must be typed. Handwritten applications, as well as faxed or e-mailed applications will not be considered. Applicants should not use folders, binders, covers, or double-sided copies, or staple any material. Application form required.

Deadline(s): See application form for current deadlines

Trustee: Michael Rex Tabler.
EIN: 911701545

9652
The Jane Isakson Lea Foundation

c/o Kristine Leander
5608 34th Ave. N.W.
Seattle, WA   98107-3335
Main URL: http://www.thejanefoundation.org

Established in 2011 in Washington.
Donors: James Lea; Jane Isakson Lea; Judy Cooper.
Foundation type: Independent foundation.
Financial data (yr. ended 11/30/13): Assets, $3,200,031 (M); expenditures, $179,788; qualifying distributions, $171,000; giving activities include $171,000 for 7 grants (high: $158,000; low: $1,000).
Fields of interest: Arts and culture; Public affairs; Human services.
Limitations: Applications not accepted. Giving primarily in WA.
Application information: Unsolicited requests for funds not accepted.
Officers: Kristine Leander, Pres.; Donald Wahlquist, Secy.-Treas.
Director: Judy Cooper.
EIN: 454050643

9653
Levitan Family Foundation

411 1st Ave. S., No. 600
Seattle, WA   98104-3846   (206) 288-1722
Contact: Andra Hall

Established in 2004 in Washington.
Donors: Stacey Rae Winston Levitan; Daniel G. Levitan; Daniel Stacey Levitan.
Foundation type: Independent foundation.
Financial data (yr. ended 12/31/13): Assets, $68,348 (M); gifts received, $303,125; expenditures, $238,422; qualifying distributions, $235,785; giving activities include $228,410 for 19 grants (high: $100,000; low: $250).
Fields of interest: Education; Philanthropy; Nonprofits; Human services.
Type of support: Regranting.
Limitations: Applications accepted. Giving primarily in Seattle, WA. No grants to individuals.
Application information: Application form required.
Initial approach: Letter
Deadline(s): None
Officers: Stacey Rae Winston Levitan, Pres.; Daniel G. Levitan, V.P. and Treas.
EIN: 202071411

9654
Richard and Francine Loeb Family Foundation

c/o Foundation Management Grp. LL
1000 2nd. Ave., 34th Fl.
Seattle, WA   98104-1022

Donor: Alex Shulman Family Foundation.
Foundation type: Independent foundation.
Financial data (yr. ended 12/31/13): Assets, $6,077,034 (M); expenditures, $207,218; qualifying distributions, $181,606; giving activities include $177,500 for 5 grants (high: $100,000; low: $10,000).
Fields of interest: Education; Health; Children's hospital care; Agriculture; Children.
Limitations: Applications not accepted. Giving primarily in Seattle, WA. No grants to individuals.
Application information: Contributes only to pre-selected organizations.
Officers: Richard Loeb, Pres. and Treas.; Francine Loeb, V.P.; Dan Asher, Secy.
EIN: 200334683

9655
The Longbrake Family Foundation

P.O. Box 21027
Seattle, WA   98111-3027
E-mail: info@longbrakefamilyfoundation.org; *Main URL:* http://www.longbrakefamilyfoundation.org

Established in 1999 in Washington.
Donors: Martha Longbrake; William A. Longbrake.
Foundation type: Independent foundation.
Financial data (yr. ended 12/31/13): Assets, $8,521,477 (M); expenditures, $480,496; qualifying distributions, $372,978; giving activities include $277,872 for 11 grants (high: $37,024; low: $3,400).
Fields of interest: Performing arts education; Secondary education; Higher education; Graduate and professional education; Housing development; Christianity; Theology; Homeless services.
Limitations: Applications not accepted. Giving primarily in IL and WA. No grants to individuals.
Application information: Contributes only to pre-selected organizations.
Officers: William A. Longbrake, Pres. and Treas.; Martha Longbrake, V.P. and Secy.; Dorothy Longbrake, Exec. Dir.
Trustees: David Longbrake; Derek C. Longbrake; Erin Longbrake; Mark W. Longbrake.
EIN: 912014805

9656
Lott Foundation

22833 S.E. Black Nugget Rd., Ste. 130
Issaquah, WA   98029-3621

Donors: Martin Lott; Sharon Lott.
Foundation type: Independent foundation.
Financial data (yr. ended 12/31/13): Assets, $7,453,879 (M); expenditures, $257,234; qualifying distributions, $212,350; giving activities include $212,350 for 24 grants (high: $106,000; low: $100).
Purpose and activities: Grants for general support in children's hospital, heart association, school and family service.
Fields of interest: Arts and culture; Education; Nonprofits; Human services.

Type of support: Regranting.
Limitations: Applications not accepted. Giving primarily in WA.
Application information: Unsolicited requests for funds not accepted.
Officers and Directors: Martin Lott, Pres.; Sharon Lott, V.P. and Secy. and Director.
EIN: 274359837

9657
Madrona Foundation

1000 2nd Ave., 34th Fl.
Seattle, WA   98104-1022

Established in 2004 in Washington.
Donor: Lois Fish.
Foundation type: Independent foundation.
Financial data (yr. ended 12/31/12): Assets, $7,027,961 (M); expenditures, $397,348; qualifying distributions, $350,000; giving activities include $350,000 for grants.
Fields of interest: Education; Human rights; Human services.
Limitations: Applications not accepted. Giving primarily in WA, with some giving in Washington, DC and NY. No grants to individuals.
Application information: Contributes only to pre-selected organizations.
Officers and Directors: Brian Fish, Pres. and Treas. and Director; Susanne L. Fish-Sadin, V.P. and Secy. and Director.
EIN: 200780447

9658
Magdalen Foundation

10655 N.E. 4th St., Ste. 611
Bellevue, WA   98004-5038

Established in 1980 in Washington.
Donor: Nicholas J. Bez.
Foundation type: Independent foundation.
Financial data (yr. ended 08/31/14): Assets, $2,340,967 (M); expenditures, $301,180; qualifying distributions, $267,000; giving activities include $267,000 for 15 grants (high: $125,000; low: $1,000).
Purpose and activities: Giving primarily for a Roman Catholic monastery, as well as for arts and culture, particularly the ballet.
Fields of interest: Arts and culture; Performing arts; Ballet; Orchestral music; Education; Health; Catholicism.
Type of support: General support.
Limitations: Applications not accepted. Giving primarily in Seattle, WA. No grants to individuals.
Application information: Contributes only to pre-selected organizations.
Trustee: Nicholas J. Bez.
EIN: 911114068

9659
Martin Family Foundation

13964 Biz Point Ln.
Anacortes, WA   98221-8417

Established in 2000 in Washington.
Donors: Darlene E. Martin; Roy W. Martin.
Foundation type: Independent foundation.
Financial data (yr. ended 12/31/13): Assets, $3,940,219 (M); expenditures, $231,495;

qualifying distributions, $231,495; giving activities include $208,000 for 36 grants (high: $60,000; low: $200).
Fields of interest: Diseases and conditions; Religion; Christianity; Human services.
Limitations: Applications not accepted. Giving primarily in Seattle, WA. No grants to individuals.
Application information: Contributes only to pre-selected organizations.
Trustees: Darlene E. Martin; Roy W. Martin.
EIN: 912089435

9660
The Martin Family Foundation
c/o Secure Tax Group Inc.
P.O. Box 1
Auburn, WA 98071-1542

Established in 1991 in Washington.
Donor: Benn Martin.
Foundation type: Independent foundation.
Financial data (yr. ended 12/31/13): Assets, $3,656,441 (M); expenditures, $226,411; qualifying distributions, $226,411; giving activities include $207,900 for 6 grants (high: $188,900; low: $500).
Purpose and activities: The foundation is dedicated to assisting students who are Washington state residents, enrolled in Washington state community colleges, and wish to pursue a college degree at the University of Washington.
Fields of interest: Higher education.
Type of support: Scholarships.
Limitations: Applications not accepted. Giving limited to WA. No grants to individuals.
Application information: Unsolicited requests for funds are not accepted. Funding is very specific in nature.
Officer: James M. Palmer, Pres.
Directors: Howard Greenwald; Neal Hardin; Gwen Jackson; Richard Lassman; Ray Lundeen; Cynthia Masterson; Robert Valentine.
EIN: 911455940

9661
Edmund F. Maxwell Foundation
P.O. Box 55548
Seattle, WA 98155-0548
Contact: David G. Johansen
E-mail: admin@maxwell.org; *Main URL:* http://www.maxwell.org
Grants List: http://www.maxwell.org/awardrecipients.aspx

Established in 1992 in Washington.
Foundation type: Independent foundation.
Financial data (yr. ended 12/31/13): Assets, $9,510,450 (M); expenditures, $474,572; qualifying distributions, $415,394; giving activities include $347,854 for 76 grants to individuals (high: $5,000; low: $1,324).
Purpose and activities: Scholarships for residents of western Washington attending accredited independent colleges or universities. Grants are dependent on financial need, as determined by the college or university attended.
Fields of interest: Higher education.
Type of support: Student aid.
Limitations: Applications accepted. Giving limited to students residing in western WA attending

accredited private colleges and universities. No grants to individuals directly.
Application information: Complete application guidelines available on foundation web site. Application form required.
   Deadline(s): Varies
   Board meeting date(s): Varies
Trustees: David G. Johansen; David D. Lewis; William S. Macgeorge.
Number of staff: 2 part-time professional.
EIN: 916181008

9662
David McKinlay Trust
(formerly Orphans Home of Seattle, Inc.)
c/o Habib, Zillen & Russell, P.S.
1220 116th Ave. N.E., Ste. 201
Bellevue, WA 98004-3826

Established in 1948 in Washington.
Foundation type: Independent foundation.
Financial data (yr. ended 12/31/13): Assets, $3,045,192 (M); expenditures, $148,760; qualifying distributions, $127,112; giving activities include $122,500 for 9 grants (high: $20,000; low: $7,500).
Purpose and activities: Giving limited to organizations involved in long-term care of orphans, or children in need or in foster care, who reside in King County, Washington.
Fields of interest: Arts and culture; Religion; Human services.
Type of support: General support.
Limitations: Applications not accepted. Giving limited to King County, WA. No grants to individuals.
Application information: Contributes only to pre-selected organizations.
   Board meeting date(s): Quarterly
Officers: Douglas Monaghan, Pres.; Carolee Nunn, V.P.; Corliss Nystrom, Secy.; Henry J. Iske, Treas.
Directors: David Harrison; C. William Rehm; Frederic L. Roebke; Margaret Symons; Curtis A. West.
Number of staff: None.
EIN: 910586921

9663
Mize Family Foundation
c/o Anne B. Mize
USPS 112, 1463 E. Republican St., Ste. 132
Seattle, WA 98112-4517

Established in 2010 in Washington.
Donor: Anne B. Mize.
Foundation type: Independent foundation.
Financial data (yr. ended 12/31/13): Assets, $627,303 (M); gifts received, $90,000; expenditures, $258,220; qualifying distributions, $239,476; giving activities include $231,500 for 15 grants (high: $25,000; low: $10,000).
Fields of interest: Environment; Human services.
Limitations: Applications not accepted.
Application information: Unsolicited requests for funds not accepted.
Officer: Anne B. Mize, Pres.
Board Members: Nanette Fok; Bill Mitchell; Savitha Reddy Pathi; Katrin Wilde.
EIN: 271374636

9664
The Moraine Foundation
c/o Susan W. Pohl
14419 Greenwood Ave. N.
P.O. Box 334
Seattle, WA 98133-6865
Main URL: http://www.morainefoundation.org

Donor: Susan W. Pohl.
Foundation type: Independent foundation.
Financial data (yr. ended 12/31/13): Assets, $6,606,940 (M); gifts received, $393,881; expenditures, $434,822; qualifying distributions, $430,348; giving activities include $425,000 for 4 grants (high: $250,000; low: $25,000).
Purpose and activities: Giving primarily for higher education, as well as for social services, and children services, including a children's hospital.
Fields of interest: Arts and culture; Education; Human services.
Limitations: Applications not accepted. Giving primarily in Seattle, WA; funding also in Carlisle, PA. No grants to individuals.
Application information: Contributes only to pre-selected organizations.
Officers: Susan W. Pohl, Pres.; John C. Pohl, V.P. and Secy.-Treas.
EIN: 204195024

9665
Morningside Foundation
8061 Lakemont Dr. N.E.
Seattle, WA 98115-5235   (206) 729-0349
Contact: Thomas W. Phillips, Pres. and Treas.

Established in 1999 in Washington.
Donor: Thomas W. Phillips.
Foundation type: Independent foundation.
Financial data (yr. ended 12/31/13): Assets, $4,170,164 (M); expenditures, $173,113; qualifying distributions, $168,250; giving activities include $168,250 for 75 grants (high: $15,000; low: $250).
Fields of interest: Education; University education; Nonprofits; Protestantism; Child welfare.
Type of support: Regranting.
Limitations: Applications accepted. Giving primarily in WA. No grants to individuals.
Application information:
   Initial approach: U.S. mail
   Copies of proposal: 1
   Deadline(s): None
Officers: Thomas W. Phillips, Pres. and Treas.; Peggy Van Slice Phillips, V.P. and Secy.
EIN: 912010842

9666
The Laura Ellen & Robert Muglia Family Foundation
1215 4th Ave., Ste. 1225
Seattle, WA 98161-1008

Established in 2000 in Washington.
Donors: Laura Ellen Muglia; Robert Muglia.
Foundation type: Independent foundation.
Financial data (yr. ended 01/31/13): Assets, $7,672,132 (M); expenditures, $270,752; qualifying distributions, $225,475; giving activities include $221,500 for 9 grants (high: $100,000; low: $1,000).

Purpose and activities: Giving primarily to Episcopal churches and organizations, and for education.
Fields of interest: Education; Health; Episcopalianism and Anglicanism; Lutheranism.
Limitations: Applications not accepted. Giving primarily in New York, NY, and Seattle, WA. No grants to individuals.
Application information: Contributes only to pre-selected organizations.
Trustees: Laura Ellen Muglia; Robert Muglia.
EIN: 916525838

9667
Murray Foundation
1201 Pacific Ave., Ste. 1750
Tacoma, WA 98402-4389 (253) 383-4911
Contact: Kathleen Brossoit

Established in 1952 in Washington.
Donors: L.T. Murray†; Mrs. L.T. Murray†.
Foundation type: Independent foundation.
Financial data (yr. ended 12/31/13): Assets, $5,727,281 (M); expenditures, $342,699; qualifying distributions, $271,544; giving activities include $252,500 for 17 grants (high: $50,000; low: $5,000).
Purpose and activities: Giving for higher and secondary education, hospitals, museums, cultural programs, and community funds. Priority given to capital programs in the Puget Sound area.
Fields of interest: Arts and culture; Education; Hospital care; Community and economic development.
Type of support: Continuing support; Annual campaigns; Capital campaigns; Capital and infrastructure; Endowments; Program development; Professorships; Publications; Scholarships; Research; Technical assistance.
Limitations: Applications accepted. Giving limited to Tacoma and Pierce County, WA. No grants to individuals, or for scholarships or fellowships; no loans.
Application information:
  Initial approach: Letter
Officers and Directors: Anne Murray Barbey, Pres. and Director; L.T. Murray III, V.P. and Director; Steve Larson, Secy. and Exec. Dir.; L.T. Murray, Jr., Treas. and Director; Anita Barbey; Amy Butson; Gary Coover.
Number of staff: 1 part-time professional.
EIN: 510163345

9668
Nordstrom/Seifert Family Foundation
650 Bellevue Way N.E., Ste. 3304
Bellevue, WA 98004

Established in 2000 in Washington.
Donors: Linda Nordstrom; Christian M. Seifert.
Foundation type: Independent foundation.
Financial data (yr. ended 12/31/14): Assets, $3,661,466 (M); expenditures, $192,528; qualifying distributions, $161,187; giving activities include $160,000 for 6 grants (high: $50,000; low: $5,500).
Fields of interest: Arts and culture; Education; Health.
Limitations: Applications not accepted. Giving primarily in Seattle, WA; some giving in Washington, DC. No grants to individuals.

Application information: Unsolicited requests for funds not accepted.
Trustee: Linda Nordstrom.
EIN: 916516127

9669
Northwest Fund for the Environment
1904 3rd Ave., Ste. 615
Seattle, WA 98101-3326 (206) 386-7220
Contact: Pamela Fujita-Yuhas, Fdn. Dir.; Zoe Rothchild, Fdn. Dir.
FAX: (206) 386-7223; E-mail: staff@nwfund.org; E-mail for Pamela Fujita-Yuhas: pamf@nwfund.org; e-mail for Zoe Rothchild: zoer@nwfund.org; Main URL: http://www.nwfund.org
Grants List: http://www.nwfund.org/2013-charitable-grants
Grants List: http://www.nwfund.org/2011-charitable-grants
Grants List: http://www.nwfund.org/2014-charitable-grants
Grants List: http://www.nwfund.org/charitable-grants-2009
Grants List: http://www.nwfund.org/charitable-grants-2010
Grants List: http://www.nwfund.org/2012-standard-grants

Established in 1971 in Washington.
Donor: Helen May Marcy Johnson†.
Foundation type: Independent foundation.
Financial data (yr. ended 12/31/14): Assets, $6,572,694; expenditures, $419,881; qualifying distributions, $335,745.
Purpose and activities: Giving for environmental purposes, including grants for protection of wildlife habitats, water quality, and shoreline and wetland environments, enforcement of environmental regulations, and capacity building for conservation organizations.
Fields of interest: Environment; Natural resources; Oceans and coastal waters; Wetlands; Biodiversity; Wildlife biodiversity.
Type of support: General support; Matching grants; Advocacy; Program development; Seed money.
Limitations: Applications accepted. Giving limited to WA. No support for partisan political activities or purely educational programs, art projects, Web page development, youth groups, museum displays, government agencies, or field research. No grants to individuals, or for academic research, endowment funds, land acquisition, or capital projects or debt reduction; no loans.
Publications: Annual report.
Application information: Call the Fund office to discuss project. If staff determines that the project meets guidelines and criteria, they will e-mail a cover letter and guidelines for the Letter of Inquiry. Unsolicited Letter of Inquiry or applications will not be accepted. Complete application guidelines are available on Fund web site. Application form required.
  Initial approach: Telephone to discuss project
  Deadline(s): See Fund web site for deadlines
  Final notification: Within 3 weeks
Officers and Trustees: Jennifer Dold, Pres. and Trustee; David Harrison, V.P.; Susan Markey, Secy.; Jim Harless, Treas.; Hellmut Golde; Rick Moore; Claudia Newman; Janna Rolland; Annette Sommers.
Number of staff: 2 part-time professional.
EIN: 237134880

9670
Not Yet Foundation
P.O. Box 17
Issaquah, WA 98027-0001
Main URL: http://www.notyetfoundation.org
Grants List: http://www.notyetfoundation.org/funded-projects

Donor: Laura J. Brancato.
Foundation type: Independent foundation.
Financial data (yr. ended 12/31/13): Assets, $143,381 (M); gifts received, $400,000; expenditures, $352,475; qualifying distributions, $231,590; giving activities include $231,590 for 10 grants (high: $150,000; low: $2,500).
Fields of interest: Environment; Disasters and emergency management; Human services.
Limitations: Applications not accepted. Giving primarily in WA.
Application information: Unsolicited requests for funds not accepted.
Officers: Laura J. Brancato, Pres.; Shane M. Moss, V.P.; Barbara A. Peters, Secy.
EIN: 455472839

9671
The Nysether Family Foundation
(formerly The Eldon & Shirley Nysether Family Foundation)
P.O. Box 1201
Everett, WA 98206-1201

Established in 2000 in Washington.
Donors: Eldon M. Nysether; Shirley Nysether; Sea-Real Corporation; Sea-Dog Corporation; Mark Nysether; Vickie Nysether; Sea-Land Corporation.
Foundation type: Independent foundation.
Financial data (yr. ended 01/20/16): Assets, $7,225,457 (M); gifts received, $604,000; expenditures, $365,673; qualifying distributions, $326,754; giving activities include $326,754 for 46 grants (high: $30,000; low: $1,000).
Purpose and activities: Giving to improve the quality of life by providing services for programs to challenge individuals of all ages, in conservation, preservation, and restoration of the natural environment, including wildlife, within specific counties in Washington.
Fields of interest: Land resources; Forest preservation; Domesticated animals; Animal welfare; Child welfare.
Type of support: General support; Annual campaigns; Capital campaigns; Capital and infrastructure; Land acquisitions; Endowments.
Limitations: Applications not accepted. Giving primarily in the Puget Sound region of WA, with emphasis on Snohomish, Skagit and Okanogan counties. No grants to individuals.
Application information: Contributes only to pre-selected organizations.
Officers: Eldon M. Nysether, Pres.; Shirley Nysether, 1st V.P.; Mark A. Nysether, 2nd V.P.; Bradley Nysether, 3rd V.P.
Directors: Vickie Nysether; Kathy Nysether.
EIN: 912084108

9672
O'Donnell Family Charitable Foundation
c/o Jim O'Donnell
1326 5th Ave., Ste. 703
Seattle, WA 98101-2604

Established in 1996 in Washington.
Donors: Jim O'Donnell; Harry J. O'Donnell; Mariette E. O'Donnell; The O'Donnell Children's Trust.
Foundation type: Independent foundation.
Financial data (yr. ended 12/31/13): Assets, $812,096 (M); gifts received, $18,803; expenditures, $177,175; qualifying distributions, $168,903; giving activities include $166,853 for 25 grants.
Purpose and activities: Giving primarily for education, health care, particularly medical rehabilitation, and for medical research, children and youth, including an after-school program, and social services, with emphasis on a community health program and disaster relief services.
Fields of interest: Arts and culture; Education; Elementary and secondary education; Higher education; Multiple sclerosis; Human services; Child welfare; Youth services.
Type of support: Research.
Limitations: Applications not accepted. Giving primarily in Seattle, WA. No grants to individuals.
Application information: Unsolicited requests for funds not accepted.
Officers: Harry J. O'Donnell, Jr., Pres.; Mariette E. O'Donnell, Secy.-Treas.
EIN: 911712175

9673
Ignatius Ohno Foundation
9416 Martin Luther King Jr. Way S.
Seattle, WA 98118-5418

Established in 2006 in Washington.
Donors: Yoshio A. Ohno; I.F. Ohno; Ohno Construction Co.
Foundation type: Independent foundation.
Financial data (yr. ended 12/31/13): Assets, $432,294 (M); gifts received, $219,000; expenditures, $149,406; qualifying distributions, $143,150; giving activities include $143,150 for 18 grants (high: $100,000; low: $150).
Fields of interest: Religion; Human services; International relations.
Limitations: Applications not accepted. Giving primarily in OR and WA. No grants to individuals.
Application information: Unsolicited requests for funds not accepted.
Directors: Barbara Ohno; Yoshio A. Ohno.
EIN: 205861148

9674
Ormsby Hill Trust
c/o Maitland Hardyman
310 Saddle Dr.
Port Townsend, WA 98368-9438

Established in 1962 in California.
Foundation type: Independent foundation.
Financial data (yr. ended 06/30/13): Assets, $2,089,247 (M); expenditures, $251,414; qualifying distributions, $234,700; giving activities include $234,700 for 1 grant.
Fields of interest: Education; Camps; Child welfare.
International interests: Mexico.
Limitations: Applications not accepted. Giving on a national and international basis. No grants to individuals.
Application information: Contributes only to pre-selected organizations.
Officer: Maitland Hardyman, Pres.

Trustee: Norman Frank.
EIN: 951866004

9675
Sujal and Meera Patel Foundation
c/o Stetson Koenes PLLC
155 108th Avenue N.E., Ste. 320
Bellevue, WA 98004-5901

Donors: Meera Patel; Sujal Patel.
Foundation type: Independent foundation.
Financial data (yr. ended 12/31/13): Assets, $5,783,065 (M); gifts received, $6,332; expenditures, $270,370; qualifying distributions, $233,353; giving activities include $230,000 for 8 grants (high: $122,500; low: $7,500).
Fields of interest: Arts and culture; Higher education; Foundations; Diseases and conditions.
Type of support: Research.
Limitations: Applications not accepted. Giving primarily in CA and WA.
Application information: Unsolicited requests for funds not accepted.
Officers: Sujal Patel, Pres. and Treas.; Meera Patel, V.P. and Secy.
EIN: 274038029

9676
Paulus Family Foundation
P.O. Box 178
Bow, WA 98232-0178

Established in 2003 in Washington.
Donors: Werner K. Paulus; C. Michelle Paulus; Andrew E. Beldin; Ana Sophia Augustenborg; Lia G. Beldin.
Foundation type: Independent foundation.
Financial data (yr. ended 12/31/13): Assets, $688,784 (M); gifts received, $861,720; expenditures, $275,645; qualifying distributions, $275,000; giving activities include $275,000 for 7 grants (high: $75,000; low: $10,000).
Fields of interest: Education; Environment; Domesticated animals.
Limitations: Applications not accepted. Giving primarily in CA and WA. No grants to individuals.
Application information: Unsolicited requests for funds not accepted.
Officers: Werner K. Paulus, Pres.; C. Michelle Paulus, Secy.
EIN: 200351925

9677
Paul Pigott Scholarship Foundation
P.O. Box 1518
Bellevue, WA 98009-1518 (425) 468-7890
Contact: Jack K. Levier, Secy.

Established in 1961 in Washington.
Foundation type: Independent foundation.
Financial data (yr. ended 12/31/13): Assets, $1,582,005 (M); gifts received, $1,000,000; expenditures, $245,748; qualifying distributions, $245,469; giving activities include $245,469 for 26 grants to individuals (high: $10,000; low: $2,274).
Purpose and activities: Scholarship awards to children of employees of PACCAR, Inc. and its subsidiaries for the first college year.
Fields of interest: Higher education.
Type of support: Scholarships.

Limitations: Applications accepted. Giving primarily in TX and WA.
Application information: Application form required. *Initial approach:* Request application form *Deadline(s):* Dec. 1
Officers and Directors: Mark C. Pigott, Pres. and Director; R.E. Armstrong, V.P. and Treas.; David C. Anderson, V.P. and Director; Robert J. Christensen, V.P. and Director; Dan D. Sobic, V.P. and Director; Jack K. Levier, Secy.
EIN: 916030639

9678
Riley & Nancy Pleas Family Foundation
2410 Boyer Ave. E., Ste. 1
Seattle, WA 98112-2157

Established in 1995 in Washington.
Donors: Riley W. Pleas; Nancy A. Pleas.
Foundation type: Independent foundation.
Financial data (yr. ended 12/31/13): Assets, $178,138 (M); gifts received, $122,000; expenditures, $177,899; qualifying distributions, $174,791; giving activities include $174,791 for 70 grants (high: $42,050; low: $50).
Fields of interest: Education; Religion; Human services.
Limitations: Applications not accepted. Giving primarily in WA. No grants to individuals.
Application information: Unsocilisited requests for funds not accepted.
Officers and Directors: Maureen P. Brotherton, Pres. and Director; Nancy A. Pleas, V.P. and Director; Theresa A. James, Secy. and Director; Colleen P. Raymond, Treas. and Director.
EIN: 911663829

9679
Lily Pointe Family Foundation
P.O. Box 40329
Bellevue, WA 98015-4329

Established in 2009 in Washington.
Donor: Carol-Ann O'Mack.
Foundation type: Independent foundation.
Financial data (yr. ended 12/31/13): Assets, $3,639,688 (M); expenditures, $213,917; qualifying distributions, $187,730; giving activities include $187,500 for 14 grants (high: $85,000; low: $2,500).
Fields of interest: Health; Diseases and conditions; Human services.
Type of support: Research.
Limitations: Applications not accepted.
Application information: Unsolicited requests for funds not accepted.
Officers: Carol-Ann O'Mack, Pres.; John Deininger, Secy.-Treas.
EIN: 271540216

9680
Prairie Foundation
c/o Colin Moseley
P.O. Box 21866
Seattle, WA 98111-3866

Established in 1998 in Washington.
Donors: Martha P. Moseley; Colin Moseley.
Foundation type: Independent foundation.

Financial data (yr. ended 12/31/13): Assets, $4,991,225 (M); expenditures, $411,723; qualifying distributions, $407,371; giving activities include $401,580 for 42 grants (high: $250,000; low: $50).

Fields of interest: Arts and culture; Education; Higher education; Environment; Nonprofits; Diseases and conditions; Science; Judaism; Human services.

Type of support: Regranting.

Limitations: Applications not accepted. Giving primarily in Seattle, WA. No grants to individuals.

Application information: Contributes only to pre-selected organizations.

Officers and Directors: Martha P. Moseley, Pres. and Treas. and Director; Colin Moseley, V.P. and Secy. and Director.

EIN: 911939662

9681
Quest for Truth Foundation
7890 Fletcher Bay Rd., N.E.
Bainbridge Island, WA 98110-2651

Established in 1982 in Washington.

Foundation type: Independent foundation.

Financial data (yr. ended 09/30/13): Assets, $7,158,273 (M); expenditures, $303,685; qualifying distributions, $300,000; giving activities include $300,000 for 12 grants (high: $75,000; low: $10,000).

Purpose and activities: Grants for research and publication of papers dealing with history, geography, politics, economics, sociology, health care and related subjects without restriction as to geographic areas or political jurisdiction, for the education of the reading public.

Fields of interest: Museums; History; Hospital care; Blood banks; Sociology; Economics; Political science.

Type of support: Publications; Research.

Limitations: Applications not accepted. Giving primarily in CA, ID, MT, NY, OR, and WA.

Application information: Unsolicited requests for funds not accepted.

Officers: DeLancey B. Lewis, Pres.; Bradley F. Henke, V.P.; Paul K. Scripps, V.P.

Directors: Roxanne D. Greene; Marion W. Roozen.

EIN: 911190760

9682
Razore Foundation
3927 Lake Washington Blvd., N.E.
Kirkland, WA 98033-7867

Established in 1997 in Washington.

Donors: Joan M. Razore; Josie Razore; Sanitary Service Co., Inc.

Foundation type: Independent foundation.

Financial data (yr. ended 04/30/13): Assets, $4,529,090 (M); gifts received, $19,200; expenditures, $345,119; qualifying distributions, $332,800; giving activities include $332,800 for 10 grants (high: $261,000; low: $100).

Purpose and activities: Giving primarily for human services.

Fields of interest: Education; Nonprofits; Community and economic development; Religion.

Type of support: Regranting.

Limitations: Applications not accepted. Giving primarily in WA. No grants to individuals.

Application information: Contributes only to pre-selected organizations.

Officer: Joan M. Razore, Pres. and Treas.

EIN: 911877166

9683
Satya and Rao Remala Foundation
c/o Smith Sunday Berman Britton
11808 Northup Way, Ste. 240
Bellevue, WA 98005-1936

Established in 1998 in Washington.

Donors: Rao V. Remala; Satya K. Remala.

Foundation type: Independent foundation.

Financial data (yr. ended 12/31/13): Assets, $11,692,021 (M); gifts received, $339,100; expenditures, $546,011; qualifying distributions, $448,716; giving activities include $439,834 for 65 grants (high: $201,000; low: $65).

Fields of interest: Elementary and secondary education; Higher education; Philanthropy; Nonprofits; Hinduism; Human services.

Type of support: General support; Regranting.

Limitations: Applications not accepted. Giving primarily in WA. No grants to individuals.

Application information: Contributes only to pre-selected organizations.

Trustees: Rao V. Remala; Satya K. Remala.

EIN: 916477106

9684
Rita & Herbert Rosen Family Foundation
P.O. Box 5003
Bellevue, WA 98009-5003 (425) 454-3030
Contact: Stanley Rosen, Pres.; Michele Rosen, V.P.; Miriam Rosen, Secy.-Treas.

Established in 1986 in Washington.

Donors: Stanley Rosen; Judith de Jonge; Rosen Dejonge Properties LLC.

Foundation type: Independent foundation.

Financial data (yr. ended 12/31/13): Assets, $7,743,400 (M); gifts received, $32,227; expenditures, $1,831,596; qualifying distributions, $411,240; giving activities include $401,167 for 20 grants (high: $70,000; low: $1,000).

Fields of interest: Nonprofits.

Type of support: Capital campaigns; Regranting.

Limitations: Applications accepted. Giving limited to Seattle, WA.

Application information:
Initial approach: Proposal
Deadline(s): None

Officers: Stanley G. Rosen, Pres.; Judith de Jonge, V.P.; Michele Rosen, V.P.; Miriam Rosen, Secy.-Treas.

Director: Jacob Rosen.

EIN: 911304542

9685
Rotalia Foundation
9133 View Ave. N.W.
Seattle, WA 98117-2654
Application address: c/o Mark Kask, 8 Lindley Rd., Mercer Island, WA 98040, tel.: (206) 275-0140

Donors: Paul a. Raidna; Estate of Anne J. Smith.

Foundation type: Independent foundation.

Financial data (yr. ended 12/31/14): Assets, $2,643,384 (M); expenditures, $180,391;

qualifying distributions, $180,391; giving activities include $23,320 for 7 grants (high: $10,000; low: $1,500), and $132,083 for 50 grants to individuals.

Purpose and activities: Scholarship awards to U.S. citizens for study abroad in Estonia, majoring in the studies relating to the Estonian homeland; some giving move to Estonians for study in the United States.

Fields of interest: Arts and culture; Education.

International interests: Estonia.

Type of support: Student aid.

Limitations: Applications accepted. Giving in Washington, DC and Estonia.

Application information: Application form required.
Initial approach: Letter
Deadline(s): None

Officers: Mart Kask, Chair.; Uve Kapsi, Vice-Chair.; Paul Raidna, Treas.

Board Members: Veljo Areng; Rein Grabbi; Bruno Laan; Tom Napa; Tiina Oviir; Vaho Rebassoo; Kalev Sepp; Thomas Tuling.

EIN: 911409344

9686
Runstad Foundation
c/o Judith M. Runstad
1201 3rd Ave., Ste. 2700
Seattle, WA 98101-3274

Established in 1999 in Washington.

Donors: H. Jon Runstad; Judith M. Runstad.

Foundation type: Independent foundation.

Financial data (yr. ended 12/31/14): Assets, $32,484; gifts received, $430,000; expenditures, $434,676; qualifying distributions, $432,576.

Fields of interest: Education; Higher education; Natural resources; Nonprofits; Health.

Type of support: General support; Regranting.

Limitations: Applications not accepted. Giving primarily in Seattle, WA. No grants to individuals.

Application information: Contributes only to pre-selected organizations.

Directors: H. Jon Runstad; Judith M. Runstad.

EIN: 911873948

9687
John and Nancy Sabol Foundation
3100 W. Commodore Way, Ste. 208
Seattle, WA 98199-1117

Established in 2000 in Washington.

Donors: John M. Sabol; Nancy A. Sabol.

Foundation type: Independent foundation.

Financial data (yr. ended 12/31/13): Assets, $4,817,763 (M); gifts received, $800,000; expenditures, $246,880; qualifying distributions, $216,776; giving activities include $205,000 for 12 grants (high: $45,000; low: $5,000).

Fields of interest: Education; Neurology.

International interests: Canada.

Type of support: Research; Regranting; Fundraising.

Limitations: Applications not accepted. Giving primarily in Seattle, WA. No grants to individuals.

Application information: Unsolicited requests for funds not accepted.

Officers: John M. Sabol, Pres. and Treas.; Nancy A. Sabol, V.P. and Secy.

EIN: 912061780

9688
Herman & Faye Sarkowsky Charitable Foundation

(formerly Sarkowsky Family Charitable Foundation)
1201 3rd Ave., Ste. 5450
Seattle, WA 98101-3018

Established in 1991 in Washington.
Donors: Herman Sarkowsky; Faye Sarkowsky.
Foundation type: Independent foundation.
Financial data (yr. ended 12/31/13): Assets, $1,228,105; gifts received, $8,750; expenditures, $424,943; qualifying distributions, $417,557.
Purpose and activities: Giving primarily for the arts and Jewish organizations.
Fields of interest: Arts and culture; Performing arts; Art museums; Nonprofits; Judaism.
Type of support: Regranting.
Limitations: Applications not accepted. Giving primarily in WA. No grants to individuals.
Application information: Contributes only to pre-selected organizations.
Officers: Faye Sarkowsky, Pres.; Herman Sarkowsky, V.P. and Treas.; Cathy Sarkowsky, V.P.; Steve Sarkowsky, V.P.; Louis Treiger, Secy.
EIN: 911479527

9689
S. B. Schaar & P. K. Whelpton Foundation

10655 N. E. 4th St., Ste. 510
Bellevue, WA 98004-5039 (425) 213-1550

Established in 1998 in Washington.
Donors: Jabe Blumenthal; Julie Edsforth.
Foundation type: Independent foundation.
Financial data (yr. ended 12/31/14): Assets, $6,995,848; expenditures, $341,761; qualifying distributions, $295,981.
Fields of interest: Higher education; Foundations; Females.
Type of support: Research.
Limitations: Applications accepted. Giving primarily in Seattle, WA. No grants to individuals.
Application information: Application form required.
  Initial approach: Letter
  Deadline(s): None
Trustees: Jabe Blumenthal; Julie E. Edsforth.
EIN: 916468169

9690
Schuler Family Foundation

(formerly Force Schuler Family Foundation)
P.O. Box 2438
Seattle, WA 98111-2438

Established in 2002 in Washington.
Donor: Jean A. Schuler.
Foundation type: Independent foundation.
Financial data (yr. ended 12/31/13): Assets, $5,747,929 (M); expenditures, $315,065; qualifying distributions, $285,863; giving activities include $284,500 for 12 grants (high: $100,000; low: $2,000).
Fields of interest: Higher education; Hospital care; Housing development; Human services; Family services; Child development; Domestic violence shelters; Women's services; International development.
Limitations: Applications not accepted. Giving primarily in AR, CA and WA. No grants to individuals.

Application information: Contributes only to pre-selected organizations.
Trustee: Jean A. Schuler.
EIN: 916557029

9691
Schwab Charitable Foundation

c/o M. Waldman
1508 N.E. 88th St.
Vancouver, WA 98665-9622

Foundation type: Independent foundation.
Financial data (yr. ended 12/31/13): Assets, $3,580,676 (M); expenditures, $249,457; qualifying distributions, $173,550; giving activities include $173,550 for 12 grants (high: $30,000; low: $5,000).
Fields of interest: Education; Human services.
Limitations: Applications not accepted.
Application information: Unsolicited requests for funds not accepted.
Officer: Marshall H. Waldman, CPA, Pres.
Directors: John Callegari; Frank Falbee; Dwight L. Schwab, Jr.
Trustee: Sterling Savings Bank.
EIN: 261997839

9692
Esther Totten Seager Trust

P.O Box 21927, MAC P6540-11K
Seattle, WA 98111-3927

Established in 2000 in Montana.
Foundation type: Independent foundation.
Financial data (yr. ended 12/31/14): Assets, $3,443,013; expenditures, $208,174; qualifying distributions, $175,405.
Purpose and activities: Support only for Rock Mountain College, MT.
Fields of interest: Education; Geology.
Limitations: Applications not accepted. Giving primarily in MT. No grants to individuals.
Application information: Contributes only to a pre-selected organization.
Trustee: Wells Fargo Private Client Serv.
EIN: 841595869

9693
Alfred & Tillie Shemanski Testamentary Trust

c/o Bank of America, N.A.
800 5th Ave. WA1-501-33-23
Seattle, WA 98104-3176
E-mail: wa.grantmaking@ustrust.com; Main
URL: https://www.bankofamerica.com/philanthropic/grantmaking.go

Established in 1974 in Washington.
Donors: Alfred Shemanski†; Tillie Shemanski†.
Foundation type: Independent foundation.
Financial data (yr. ended 12/31/14): Assets, $8,160,624; expenditures, $392,167; qualifying distributions, $326,524 and $0 for set-asides.
Purpose and activities: Giving primarily to: 1) Improve the capacity of and cooperation among Jewish congregations in the City of Seattle, Washington; 2) Support interfaith tolerance and understanding; 3) Provide scholarship assistance, primarily to the University of Washington and Seattle University; 4) Support and promote quality

educational, human services, and health care programming for economically disadvantaged individuals and families.
Fields of interest: Higher education; Nonprofits; Hospital care; Diseases and conditions; Religion; Judaism; Human services; Child welfare; Youth services.
Type of support: Regranting.
Limitations: Giving primarily in the greater Seattle, WA, area. No grants to individuals.
Application information: Application guidelines available on Trust web site.
  Initial approach: Online through Trust web site
  Deadline(s): Oct. 15
Trustee: Bank of America, N.A.
EIN: 916196855

9694
Harold and Helen Shepherd Foundation

P.O. Box 1757
Walla Walla, WA 99362-0348 5095273500
Application address: c/o Gary Houser, Tr., 56 Lewis Rd., Pomeroy, WA 99347, tel.: (509) 525-0220

Established in 1996 in Washington.
Donors: Harold Shepherd†; Helen Shepherd†.
Foundation type: Independent foundation.
Financial data (yr. ended 12/31/14): Assets, $6,039,037; expenditures, $381,396; qualifying distributions, $343,994.
Purpose and activities: Giving primarily for education and to civic organizations.
Fields of interest: Education; Community and economic development; Human services.
Type of support: General support.
Limitations: Applications accepted. Giving primarily in Asotin, Columbia, Garfield, and Walla Walla counties, WA. No grants to individuals.
Application information:
  Initial approach: Letter
  Deadline(s): None
Trustees: H.H. Hayner; Gary Houser.
EIN: 911708510

9695
Singh Family Foundation

2609 Evergreen Point Rd.
Medina, WA 98039-1528
E-mail: Gopal@Singhfoundation.com; Main
URL: http://singhfamilyfoundation.com
E Newsletter: http://singhfamilyfoundation.com/about-us/newsletter

Established in 2006 in Michigan.
Donors: Gopal Singh; Kamala Singh; Rajeev Singh; Jill Singh; Mahendra Amin; Saroj Amin; Rajat Bhargava; Thomas Despasquale; Dean Morehouse.
Foundation type: Independent foundation.
Financial data (yr. ended 12/31/13): Assets, $9,724,761 (M); gifts received, $6,097; expenditures, $277,498; qualifying distributions, $256,974; giving activities include $256,410 for 9 grants (high: $93,260; low: $500).
Purpose and activities: The foundation's mission provides: 1) Quality middle and high school education to young rural girls, 2) Urgently needed medical care to the elderly, and 3) Community outreach programs designed to meet basic needs.
Fields of interest: Health; Female children and youth; Low-income and poor people.
International interests: India.

Limitations: Applications not accepted. Giving primarily in WA and Jaunpur, India. No grants to individuals.
Application information: Unsolicited requests for funds not accepted.
Officers: Gopal Singh, Pres.; Kamala Singh, Secy.
Board Member: Sudhir Singh.
EIN: 300360186

9696
The Skagit Community Foundation
1204 Cleveland Ave.
P.O. Box 1763
Mount Vernon, WA 98273 (360) 419-3181
Contact: Mary J. McGoffin, Exec. Dir.
FAX: (360) 299-0979; E-mail: director@skagitcf.org;
Main URL: http://www.skagitcf.org
Facebook: https://www.facebook.com/Skagitcf

Established in 1993 in Washington.
Foundation type: Community foundation.
Financial data (yr. ended 12/31/13): Assets, $4,830,813 (M); gifts received, $133,395; expenditures, $490,353; giving activities include $277,874 for 14+ grants (high: $50,000).
Purpose and activities: The foundation exists to enhance the social, cultural, educational and health programs for the residents of the greater Skagit, WA community.
Fields of interest: Arts and culture; Education; Environment; Health; Housing development; Sports and recreation; Child welfare; Youth services; Senior services.
Type of support: Capital campaigns; Equipment; Program development; Seed money.
Limitations: Applications accepted. Giving limited to Skagit County, WA. No grants for general operating support or endowment funds.
Publications: Application guidelines.
Application information: Visit foundation web site for application and guidelines. Application form required.
Initial approach: Complete online proposal
Copies of proposal: 1
Deadline(s): Feb. 1
Board meeting date(s): Monthly
Officers and Directors: Nancy Loftis, Chair. and Director; Stacey Knutzen Betz, Secy. and Director; Matt Lehman, Treas. and Director; Mary J. McGoffin, Exec. Dir.; Anthony Asp; Cheryl Bishop; Peter Carletti; Paula Dey; Mike Fohn; Jeremy McCullough; Tom Moser; Pamela Nelson; Joan Penney; Nancy Williams.
EIN: 911572414

9697
Slingshot Development Fund
220 2nd Ave. S., Ste. 92
Seattle, WA 98104 (206) 498-4643
Main URL: http://slingshotdf.org

Foundation type: Independent foundation.
Financial data (yr. ended 12/31/13): Assets, $6,662,401 (M); expenditures, $563,446; qualifying distributions, $480,211; giving activities include $415,640 for 11 grants (high: $226,039; low: $4,000).
Fields of interest: Education; Community and economic development; Human services.
Application information: Application form required.

Initial approach: Letter
Deadline(s): None
Officers: Therese Caouette, Pres.; Nai Aue Mon, V.P.; Anne Richardson, Secy.; Danny L. Dukes III, Treas.
Board Members: Paul Hoffman; Susanna Soe; Ko Kyaw Thu.
EIN: 450579461

9698
The Lester M. Smith Foundation
P.O. Box 3010
Bellevue, WA 98009-3010

Established in 1981 in Washington.
Donor: Lester M. Smith.
Foundation type: Independent foundation.
Financial data (yr. ended 10/31/14): Assets, $5,138,848 (M); expenditures, $362,818; qualifying distributions, $323,950; giving activities include $320,547 for 48 grants (high: $50,000; low: $250).
Fields of interest: Arts and culture; Education; Nonprofits; Diseases and conditions.
Type of support: General support; Research; Regranting.
Limitations: Applications not accepted. Giving primarily in WA. No grants to individuals.
Application information: Contributions only to pre-selected organizations.
Directors: Alexander M. Smith; Bernice R. Smith.
EIN: 911156087

9699
Doris E. Snyder Foundation
4727 44th Ave., S.W., Ste. 201
Seattle, WA 98116-4467 (253) 383-7058
Contact: Michael Turnbull, Tr.

Foundation type: Independent foundation.
Financial data (yr. ended 12/31/13): Assets, $1,505,614 (M); expenditures, $201,620; qualifying distributions, $180,000; giving activities include $180,000 for 6 grants (high: $46,000; low: $3,000).
Fields of interest: Education; Community and economic development; Catholicism.
Limitations: Applications accepted. Giving primarily in Seattle, WA.
Application information: Application form required.
Initial approach: Proposal
Deadline(s): None
Trustees: Robert Rebar; Michael Turnbull.
EIN: 261327904

9700
The Gordon D. Sondland and Katherine J. Durant Foundation
(formerly Gordon D. Sondland Foundation)
1531 7th Ave., 20th Fl.
Seattle, WA 98101-1703
Main URL: http://www.sondlanddurant.org

Established in 1991 in Washington.
Donors: Gordon D. Sondland; Katherine Durant.
Foundation type: Independent foundation.
Financial data (yr. ended 12/31/13): Assets, $2,977 (M); gifts received, $380,250; expenditures, $455,874; qualifying distributions,

$436,036; giving activities include $432,502 for 22 grants (high: $150,000; low: $500).
Fields of interest: Art museums; Education; Foundations; Medical support services; Religion; Judaism; Human services; Females.
Limitations: Applications not accepted. Giving primarily in OR, with emphasis on Portland. No grants to individuals.
Application information: Contributes only to pre-selected organizations.
Officer: Gordon D. Sondland, Pres.
EIN: 911534721

9701
Spark Charitable Foundation
c/o Nahwatzel, LLC
P.O. Box 21866
Seattle, WA 98111-3866

Established in 2008 in Washington.
Donors: Furman C. Moseley; Susan R. Moseley.
Foundation type: Independent foundation.
Financial data (yr. ended 05/31/14): Assets, $1,396,706 (M); expenditures, $291,225; qualifying distributions, $290,325; giving activities include $287,480 for 43 grants (high: $125,000; low: $250).
Purpose and activities: Giving primarily for the arts, and to Episcopal churches; funding also for higher education and human services.
Fields of interest: Arts and culture; Museums; Higher education; Science; Episcopalianism and Anglicanism; Lutheranism; Human services.
Type of support: Capital campaigns.
Limitations: Applications not accepted. Giving primarily in WA, with emphasis on Seattle.
Application information: Unsolicited requests for funds not accepted.
Officers: Susan R. Moseley, Pres. and Treas.; Furman C. Moseley, V.P. and Secy.
EIN: 262667609

9702
Spring Forth Foundation
2611 Evergreen Point Rd.
Medina, WA 98039-1528

Established in 2005 in Washington.
Donors: Russell Zylstra; Julie Zylstra; Renaware International.
Foundation type: Independent foundation.
Financial data (yr. ended 12/31/13): Assets, $1,955,490 (M); gifts received, $999,123; expenditures, $417,500; qualifying distributions, $416,050; giving activities include $411,500 for 8 grants (high: $121,500; low: $500).
Fields of interest: Nonprofits; Christianity; Human services; Child welfare.
Type of support: Regranting.
Limitations: Applications not accepted. Giving primarily in WA, with some giving in CA. No grants to individuals.
Application information: Contributes only to pre-selected organizations.
Officers: Julie J. Zylstra, Pres. and Treas.; Russell J. Zylstra, V.P. and Secy.
EIN: 202615628

9703
The Stars Foundation of Thurston County
P. O. Box 12600
Olympia, WA 98508-2600 (360) 528-3701
Contact: Jennifer Valdenegro, Exec. Dir.

Established in 2001 in Washington.
Donors: Steve Boone; Michele Boone.
Foundation type: Independent foundation.
Financial data (yr. ended 12/31/13): Assets, $520,986 (M); gifts received, $125,280; expenditures, $153,594; qualifying distributions, $153,107; giving activities include $153,105 for 8 grants (high: $103,655; low: $3,500).
Fields of interest: Nonprofits; Youth services.
Type of support: Regranting.
Limitations: Applications accepted. Giving primarily in Thurston County, WA.
Application information: Application form required.
  Initial approach: Proposal
  Deadline(s): None
Directors and Trustees: Michele Boone; Amee Kiefer; Craig Kiefer; Julio Valdenegro.
Officers and Directors: Stephen K. Boone, Chair. and Director; Joe S. Deck, Treas. and Director; Jennifer Valdenegro, Exec. Dir.
EIN: 912084967

9704
Stevens Family Foundation
P.O. Box 702
Medina, WA 98039-0702
Contact: Delphine Stevens, Tr.

Established in 2004 in Washington.
Donors: Delphine S. Stevens; Charles G.V. Stevens.
Foundation type: Independent foundation.
Financial data (yr. ended 12/31/13): Assets, $4,400,250 (M); expenditures, $263,388; qualifying distributions, $246,853; giving activities include $245,134 for 28 grants (high: $75,834; low: $35).
Purpose and activities: To provide community support for the arts, education, health and human services, religious life, animals and the environment.
Fields of interest: Arts and culture; Education; Higher education; Environment; Diseases and conditions; Religion; Human services.
Type of support: Continuing support; Annual campaigns; Capital campaigns; Capital and infrastructure; Emergency funds; Program development; Fellowships; Scholarships; Research.
Limitations: Applications not accepted. Giving primarily in WA. No grants to individuals.
Application information: Contributes only to pre-selected organizations.
Trustees: Charles G.V. Stevens; Delphine S. Stevens.
EIN: 201998989

9705
The Suen Family Foundation
13500 Linden Ave. N.
Seattle, WA 98133-7538

Established in 2008 in Washington.
Donors: US Biotek Laboratories Inc.; Raymond M. Suen; Margaret W. Suen.
Foundation type: Independent foundation.

Financial data (yr. ended 12/31/13): Assets, $23,741 (M); gifts received, $304,000; expenditures, $398,915; qualifying distributions, $398,915; giving activities include $398,300 for 12 grants (high: $148,000; low: $200).
Fields of interest: Christianity.
Limitations: Applications not accepted. Giving primarily in CA and TX.
Application information: Unsolicited requests for funds not accepted.
Officers: Raymond M. Suen, Pres.; Margaret W. Suen, V.P.
EIN: 261218419

9706
Svanees Foundation
P.O. Box 77012
Seattle, WA 98177-0012   2069496898

Donor: Svanhild S. Castner.
Foundation type: Independent foundation.
Financial data (yr. ended 12/31/14): Assets, $5,506,230; expenditures, $283,146; qualifying distributions, $247,541.
Fields of interest: Domesticated animals.
Limitations: Applications not accepted. Giving primarily in WA.
Application information: Unsolicited requests for funds not accepted.
Directors: Russell Castner; Cari Wyszynski.
EIN: 461169463

9707
The Tamaki Foundation
4616 25th Ave. N.E., No. 37
Seattle, WA 98105-4183   (206) 233-7550

Established in 1988 in Washington.
Donor: Meriko Tamaki.
Foundation type: Independent foundation.
Financial data (yr. ended 12/31/13): Assets, $4,980,372 (M); gifts received, $15,000; expenditures, $178,118; qualifying distributions, $158,855; giving activities include $151,006 for 9 grants (high: $45,000; low: $4,506).
Purpose and activities: Giving primarily for education and social services.
Fields of interest: Higher education; University education; Domesticated animals; Catholicism; Human services.
Limitations: Applications accepted. Giving primarily in CA and WA.
Application information: Application form required.
  Initial approach: Letter
  Deadline(s): None
Officers: Meriko Tamaki, Pres.; Fr. John Martin, Secy.; Steven Boyd, Treas.
Director: John F. Hopkins.
EIN: 943099647

9708
Teel Charitable Foundation
c/o Seattle Pacific Foundation
3307 3rd Ave. W.
Seattle, WA 98119 (206) 281-2308
Contact: Gordan Nygard

Foundation type: Independent foundation.
Financial data (yr. ended 12/31/14): Assets, $5,732,833 (M); expenditures, $318,148;

qualifying distributions, $267,645; giving activities include $267,645 for 19 grants (high: $160,145; low: $500).
Fields of interest: Education; Higher education; Christianity; Sports training; Human services; Child welfare.
Limitations: Applications accepted. Giving primarily in WA, with emphasis on Seattle.
Application information: Application form required.
  Initial approach: Letter
  Deadline(s): None
Officers: E. Gerald Teel, Pres.; Chuck Teel, V.P.; Daryl Vander Pol, Secy.
EIN: 911083941

9709
The Templin Foundation
P. O. Box 397
Seaview, WA 98644
Application address: c/o James B. Finlay, P.O. Box 755, Long Beach, WA 98631, tel.: (360) 642-3108

Established in 1992 in Washington.
Donors: Allys M. Templin†; Russell B. Templin.
Foundation type: Independent foundation.
Financial data (yr. ended 12/31/13): Assets, $4,139,233 (M); gifts received, $1,120; expenditures, $266,079; qualifying distributions, $210,766; giving activities include $198,315 for 12 grants (high: $40,000; low: $1,000).
Fields of interest: Arts and culture; Education; Nonprofits; Search and rescue; Fire prevention and control; Community improvement; Human services; Senior services.
Type of support: Regranting.
Limitations: Applications accepted. Giving primarily in WA. No grants to individuals.
Application information: Application form required.
  Initial approach: Letter
  Deadline(s): Prior to next board meeting
Officer: James B. Finlay, Pres.
Directors: K. David Aase; Dian Barker-Sayce; Patricia C. Nelson; Gustave A. Wiegardt, Jr.
EIN: 943166824

9710
Dorothy M. Thayer Memorial Trust
P.O. Box 21927, MAC P6540-400
Seattle, WA 98111-3927

Donor: Dorothy M. Thayer Admin Trust.
Foundation type: Independent foundation.
Financial data (yr. ended 12/31/14): Assets, $3,689,814; expenditures, $205,344; qualifying distributions, $172,505.
Fields of interest: Education; Human services.
Limitations: Applications not accepted. Giving primarily in MT.
Application information: Unsolicited requests for funds not accepted.
Trustee: Wells Fargo Wealth Mgmt.
EIN: 816075781

9711
The Jean E. Thomson Foundation
1740 S. Karl Johan Ave.
Tacoma, WA 98465-1224
Contact: Kenneth J. Zajac, Pres.
E-mail: zmail@harbornet.com; Main URL: http://www.JeanEThomsonFoundation.org

Established in 1999 in Washington.
Donor: Jean E. Thomson†.
Foundation type: Independent foundation.
Financial data (yr. ended 12/31/13): Assets, $2,824,475 (M); expenditures, $281,772; qualifying distributions, $163,500; giving activities include $163,500 for grants.
Purpose and activities: Giving to programs and research institutions that benefit advancements in human disease treatments and cures.
Fields of interest: Literature and writing; Education; Health; Diseases and conditions; Science; Community and economic development; Religion; Christianity; Human services.
Type of support: General support; Research; Continuing support; Equipment; Emergency funds; Program development; Curriculum development; Fellowships.
Limitations: Applications accepted. Giving primarily in Minneapolis, MN, and Tacoma and Seattle, WA. No support for political organizations. No grants to individuals.
Publications: Annual report; Financial statement.
Application information: Applicants must complete the grant application form found at foundation web site. Application form required.
   Initial approach: Letter
   Copies of proposal: 1
   Deadline(s): Oct. 1
   Board meeting date(s): Oct.
Officers: Kenneth J. Zajac, Pres. and Treas.; Debbie L. Zajac, V.P. and Secy.
Board Members: Cindy Baldwin; Crystal Godfrey.
Number of staff: None.
EIN: 911962581

9712
Three Rivers Community Foundation

1333 Columbia Park Trail, Ste. 310
Richland, WA   99352   (509) 735-5559
Contact: Carrie Green, Secy. and Exec. Dir.
E-mail: carrie@3rcf.org; *Main URL:* http://www. 3rcf.org
Facebook: https://www.facebook.com/ 3RiversCommunityFoundation

Established in 1999 in Washington.
Foundation type: Community foundation.
Financial data (yr. ended 12/31/13): Assets, $2,541,689 (M); gifts received, $951,997; expenditures, $516,718; giving activities include $246,249 for 51+ grants (high: $31,398; low: $500), and $45,721 for 12 grants to individuals.
Purpose and activities: The Three Rivers Community Foundation is a community endowment whose mission is to strengthen and improve the quality of life in the Three Rivers Community by supporting and enhancing philanthropy and charitable activities.
Fields of interest: Unknown or not classified.
Limitations: Giving primarily in Benton or Franklin counties, WA.
Publications: Grants list.
Application information: Visit foundation web site for application guidelines. The foundation accepts draft proposals for review prior to formal application.
   Initial approach: Telephone or e-mail
   Copies of proposal: 1
   Deadline(s): Sept. 15
Officers and Directors: Matt Hammer, Chair. and Director; Tim Anderson, Vice-Chair. and Director; Carrie Green, Secy. and Exec. Dir.; Dale Burgeson, Treas. and Director; Jim Dillman; Jeanne

McPherson; Ian Mitz; Bill Moffitt; Sheri Noland; Erik Pielstik; Rella Reimann; Sharon Rhodes; Muriel Templeton; Christopher Turner; Tony Umek; Mel Wicks.
EIN: 912049302

9713
Thurston Charitable Foundation

c/o S. Finley, C.P.A
P.O. Box 430
Milton, WA   98354-0430

Established in 1962 in Washington.
Donor: Ellen E. Thurston†.
Foundation type: Independent foundation.
Financial data (yr. ended 06/30/13): Assets, $4,260,520 (M); expenditures, $252,806; qualifying distributions, $206,525; giving activities include $204,000 for 69 grants (high: $25,000; low: $100).
Purpose and activities: Giving primarily for health care, the arts, education, and to Christian churches and organizations.
Fields of interest: Arts and culture; Ballet; Higher education; Health; Hospital care; Christianity; Human services; Child welfare.
Limitations: Applications not accepted. Giving primarily in WA. No grants to individuals.
Application information: Contributes only to pre-selected organizations.
Officers: Severt W. Thurston, Jr., Pres.; Robert H. Thurston, V.P.; Susan E. Thurston, Secy.; Sherrie Tossell, Treas.
EIN: 916055032

9714
The Titus-Will Families Foundation

616 Broadway
Tacoma, WA   98402-3899   (253) 272-8311
Contact: James W. Will, Pres. and Tr.

Established in 1994 in Washington.
Donors: James W. Will; Leon E. Titus, Jr.; James M. Will; Carolyn Titus; Graham A. Tash, Jr.; Stephen E. Anderson.
Foundation type: Independent foundation.
Financial data (yr. ended 12/31/13): Assets, $2,489,658 (M); expenditures, $200,981; qualifying distributions, $195,800; giving activities include $195,800 for 71 grants (high: $25,000; low: $300) and $1 for set-asides.
Fields of interest: Arts and culture; Museums; Education; Higher education; Health; Hospital care; Human services; Child welfare; Youth development.
Limitations: Applications accepted. Giving primarily in Pierce County, WA. No grants for individuals.
Application information:
   Initial approach: Contact foundation for application form
   Deadline(s): None
Officers and Trustees: James W. Will, Pres. and Trustee; James M. Will, Secy. and Trustee; Leon E. Titus, Jr., Treas. and Trustee; Joanne S. Titus Thompson; Carolyn A. Titus; Muriel J. Will.
EIN: 911659510

9715
Tom & Helen Tonkin Foundation

c/o Wells Fargo Bank Wyoming, N.A.
P.O. Box 21927
Seattle, WA   98111-3927
Application address: c/o Wells Fargo Bank Wyoming, N.A., P.O. Box 2799, Casper, WY 82602, tel.: (307) 235-7744

Established in 1956 in Wyoming.
Donors: Helen B. Tonkin†; T.C. Tonkin†.
Foundation type: Independent foundation.
Financial data (yr. ended 07/31/13): Assets, $3,304,446 (M); expenditures, $282,823; qualifying distributions, $221,285; giving activities include $219,000 for 19 grants (high: $60,677; low: $1,000).
Purpose and activities: Giving to aid the youth of Wyoming, particularly those between the ages of 5-21 handicapped by illness, injury, or poverty.
Fields of interest: Child educational development; Human services; Child welfare; Child development; Low-income and poor people; People with disabilities.
Type of support: General support; Matching grants; Debt reduction; Emergency funds; Program development; Convening; Publications; Seed money; Curriculum development; Scholarships.
Limitations: Applications accepted. Giving limited to WY, with emphasis on the Casper area. No grants to individuals, or for continuing support, annual campaigns, building or endowment funds, land acquisition, special projects, or research; no loans.
Publications: Application guidelines.
Application information: Application form required.
   Initial approach: Letter
   Copies of proposal: 7
   Deadline(s): None
   Board meeting date(s): As required
   Final notification: 60 days
Trustee Bank: Wells Fargo Bank Wyoming Investment.
EIN: 836002200

9716
True North Family Foundation

4215 91st Ave. N.E.
Yarrow Point, WA   98004-1211

Established in 2007 in Washington.
Donors: Robert R. Wilkerson; Peggy B. Wilkerson.
Foundation type: Independent foundation.
Financial data (yr. ended 12/31/14): Assets, $3,969,635 (M); gifts received, $406,485; expenditures, $286,039; qualifying distributions, $275,760; giving activities include $272,750 for 26 grants (high: $143,750; low: $250).
Fields of interest: Education; Hospital care; Human services; Children; Females.
Limitations: Applications not accepted. Giving primarily in WA. No grants to individuals.
Application information: Unsolicited requests for funds not accepted.
Trustees: Peggy B. Wilkerson; Robert R. Wilkerson.
EIN: 916577620

9717
The Tudor Foundation

411 University St., Ste. 1200
Seattle, WA   98101-2519

Established in 1996 in Washington.
Donors: E. Annette Rieger; Roger A. Rieger.
Foundation type: Operating foundation.
Financial data (yr. ended 12/31/13): Assets, $1,095,501 (M); gifts received, $12,500; expenditures, $265,201; qualifying distributions, $265,201; giving activities include $52,847 for 6 grants (high: $20,543; low: $180), and $208,512 for grants to individuals.
Fields of interest: Education.
Type of support: Scholarships; Grants to individuals; Student aid.
Limitations: Applications not accepted. Giving primarily in Seattle, WA.
Application information: Unsolicited requests for funds not accepted.
Officers: Roger A. Rieger, Pres.; Erin R. Baranick, V.P.; E. Annette Rieger, Secy.
EIN: 911708176

9718
Zeneth F. & Lanetta S. Ward Foundation Inc.
12313 N.W. 43rd Ct.
Vancouver, WA 98685-2185

Established in 2000 in Oregon.
Foundation type: Independent foundation.
Financial data (yr. ended 12/31/13): Assets, $10,428,778 (M); expenditures, $229,596; qualifying distributions, $200,000; giving activities include $200,000 for 2 grants (high: $100,000; low: $100,000).
Purpose and activities: Giving primarily to a Christian high school; support also for a Christian church.
Fields of interest: Secondary education; Christianity.
Limitations: Applications not accepted. Giving primarily in WA. No grants to individuals.
Application information: Contributes only to pre-selected organizations.
Directors: Cheryl Johnson; Dan Kristensen; Douglas G. Ward; Lanetta S. Ward; Steve Butler.
EIN: 931269745

9719
The Weidner Foundation
9757 N.E. Juanita Dr., Ste. 300
Kirkland, WA 98034-4201

Established in 2004 in Washington.
Donor: W. Dean Weidner.
Foundation type: Independent foundation.
Financial data (yr. ended 12/31/13): Assets, $31,865 (M); gifts received, $365,000; expenditures, $373,854; qualifying distributions, $366,705; giving activities include $366,705 for 10 grants (high: $121,936; low: $1,000).
Fields of interest: Domesticated animals.
Limitations: Applications not accepted. No grants to individuals.
Application information: Contributes only to pre-selected organizations.
Officer: Ana Maria Weidner, Pres. and C.E.O.
Trustee: W. Dean Weidner.
EIN: 916564978

9720
Weier Family Foundation
820 Blanchard St., Unit 1702
Seattle, WA 98121-2658

Donors: G. William Weier; Patricia R. Weier.
Foundation type: Independent foundation.
Financial data (yr. ended 06/30/13): Assets, $137,491 (M); gifts received, $154,190; expenditures, $172,390; qualifying distributions, $170,000; giving activities include $170,000 for 2 grants (high: $150,000; low: $20,000).
Fields of interest: Education; Religion.
Limitations: Applications not accepted.
Application information: Unsolicited requests for funds not accepted.
Trustees: G. William Weier; John W. Weier; Patricia R. Weier.
EIN: 326081823

9721
George T. Welch Testamentary Trust
c/o Baker Boyer National Bank
P.O. Box 1796
Walla Walla, WA 99362-0353
Contact: Peter J. Allen, Trust Off., Baker Boyer National Bank

Established in 1938 in Washington.
Foundation type: Independent foundation.
Financial data (yr. ended 09/30/13): Assets, $3,803,441 (M); expenditures, $204,300; qualifying distributions, $169,938; giving activities include $57,073 for 21 grants (high: $4,000; low: $997), and $106,835 for 61 grants to individuals (high: $12,900; low: $114).
Purpose and activities: Grants to the needy, including medical assistance, and scholarships; some support also for youth agencies, cultural programs, and education, especially a community college.
Fields of interest: Arts and culture; Education; Higher education; Health; Human services; Child welfare; Low-income and poor people.
Type of support: Program development; Grants to individuals; Student aid.
Limitations: Applications accepted. Giving limited to Walla Walla County, WA.
Publications: Application guidelines; Program policy statement.
Application information: Application form required.
  Initial approach: Proposal
  Copies of proposal: 1
  Deadline(s): Feb. 15, May 15, Aug. 15, and Nov. 15 for medical requests, Apr. 1 for academic requests and July 31 for community requests
  Board meeting date(s): Feb., May, Aug., and Nov.
  Final notification: 30 days
Trustee: Baker Boyer National Bank.
EIN: 916024318

9722
The Wellworth Foundation
11055 - 204th Ave. N.E.
Redmond, WA 98053-5106

Established in 1997 in Washington.
Donors: David J. Thacher; Nancy C. Thacher.
Foundation type: Independent foundation.
Financial data (yr. ended 12/31/13): Assets, $2,586,282 (M); expenditures, $208,363;

qualifying distributions, $204,561; giving activities include $203,700 for 16 grants (high: $50,000; low: $1,200).
Fields of interest: Arts and culture; Education; Higher education; Natural resources; Human services.
Limitations: Applications not accepted. Giving primarily in WA. No grants to individuals.
Application information: Unsolicited requests for funds not accepted.
Trustees: David T. Thacher; Nancy C. Thacher.
EIN: 916438273

9723
The Wiebe Foundation
2252 Odell St.
Blaine, WA 98230-9754 (604) 385-1117
Contact: John Hugh Wiebe, V.P.

Donor: John Hugh Wiebe.
Foundation type: Independent foundation.
Financial data (yr. ended 12/31/13): Assets, $4,535,319 (M); expenditures, $370,855; qualifying distributions, $289,373; giving activities include $187,000 for 8 grants (high: $66,000; low: $10,000).
Fields of interest: Health; Religion; Christianity; Human services.
International interests: Canada.
Limitations: Applications accepted. Giving primarily in CA; with some giving in Canada.
Application information:
  Initial approach: Proposal
  Deadline(s): None
Officers: Barbara J. Wiebe, Pres.; John Hugh Wiebe, V.P.; Ruthanne Wartman, Secy.-Treas.
Director: Henry J. Wiebe.
EIN: 453998241

9724
Catherine Holmes Wilkens Charitable Foundation
(formerly Wilkins Charitable Foundation)
c/o Bank of America, N.A., Philanthropic Solutions
P.O. Box 24565, WA1-501-33-23
Seattle, WA 98124-0565 (206) 604-5374
E-mail: healey7556@msn.com; Main URL: http://fdnweb.org/wilkins

Donor: Catherine Wilkins†.
Foundation type: Independent foundation.
Financial data (yr. ended 08/31/14): Assets, $4,450,314 (M); expenditures, $247,373; qualifying distributions, $191,141; giving activities include $158,000 for 42 grants (high: $7,500; low: $2,000).
Purpose and activities: Giving primarily to medical and academic centers conducting research and training in areas such as cancer, heart disease, and mental illness, community nonprofit agencies providing direct social services to people with physical disabilities or mental illness, and community-based programs providing immediate support to the needy, with particular emphasis on services for abused women and children.
Fields of interest: Education; Hospital care; Diseases and conditions; Human services; People with physical disabilities; People with psychosocial disabilities.
Type of support: Research; Research and evaluation.

Limitations: Applications accepted. Giving limited to the greater Seattle, WA area (Tacoma to Everett). No grants to individuals, or for scholarships, or debt retirement.
Publications: Application guidelines; Grants list.
Application information: Application guidelines available on foundation web site. Application form required.

Initial approach: Proposal
Copies of proposal: 4
Deadline(s): None
Board meeting date(s): Quarterly

Officers: Brian Comstock, Chair.; Bob Bunting, Vice-Chair.; Loy D. Smith, Secy. and Mgr.
Trustee: Bank of America, N.A.
EIN: 916277933

9725
George A. and Marion M. Wilson Foundation
7900 S. E. 28th St., Ste. 416
Mercer Island, WA 98040-4823
Application address: c/o Laura W. Kilkelly, Amicus Law Group, 1325 4th Ave., Ste. 940, Seattle, WA 98101-2509, tel.: (206) 624-9410

Established in 1999 in Washington.
Donors: George A. Wilson; Marion M. Wilson.
Foundation type: Independent foundation.
Financial data (yr. ended 12/31/13): Assets, $2,836,048 (M); expenditures, $190,048; qualifying distributions, $174,400; giving activities include $174,400 for 7 grants (high: $65,000; low: $5,000).
Fields of interest: Elementary and secondary education; Higher education; Children's hospital care; Family services; Children and youth; Homeless people.
Type of support: General support; Capital campaigns.
Limitations: Applications accepted. Giving primarily in Seattle, WA; some giving also in CA. No grants to individuals.
Application information: Application form required.

Initial approach: Letter
Deadline(s): Nov. 1

Officers and Directors: George A. Wilson, Pres. and Director; Marion M. Wilson, V.P. and Director; Laura W. Kilkelly, Secy. and Exec. Dir.; Lesley Wilson; Michael Wilson; Nancy Wilson.
EIN: 911952034

9726
Winter Cove Foundation
c/o Wellspring Group PS CPAS
10885 N.E. 4th St., Ste. 320
Bellevue, WA 98004-5525

Donor: Lewis Levin.
Foundation type: Independent foundation.
Financial data (yr. ended 12/31/13): Assets, $2,530,918 (M); gifts received, $639,080; expenditures, $194,378; qualifying distributions, $181,458; giving activities include $180,251 for 5 grants (high: $105,161; low: $5,065).
Fields of interest: Education; Religion; Human services.
Limitations: Applications not accepted. Giving primarily in Seattle, WA.
Application information: Unsolicited requests for funds not accepted.

Officer: Emily W. Neilson, Secy.
Director: Lewis Levin.
EIN: 263917620

9727
Wissner-Slivka Foundation
c/o Lisa Wissner-Slivka
P.O. Box 3904
Clyde Hill, WA 98009-3904
Main URL: http://www.slivka.org

Established in 1997 in Washington.
Donors: Benjamin W. Slivka; Stella Wissner; Lisa Wissner-Slivka.
Foundation type: Independent foundation.
Financial data (yr. ended 12/31/14): Assets, $3,954,235; gifts received, $0; expenditures, $316,334; qualifying distributions, $307,223 and $0 for set-asides.
Purpose and activities: Giving primarily to assist children in special needs, cancer research and education.
Fields of interest: Children's museums; Education; Diseases and conditions; Human services; Children.
Type of support: Research.
Limitations: Applications not accepted. Giving primarily in WA. No grants to individuals.
Application information: Unsolicited requests for funds not accepted.
Trustees: Benjamin W. Slivka; Max Slivka; Nathaniel Slivka; Lisa Wissner-Slivka.
EIN: 916458451

9728
Woodworth Family Foundation
3110 Ruston Way, Ste. D
Tacoma, WA 98402-5308 (253) 759-0165
Contact: Jeffrey A. Woodworth, Pres.
FAX: 2537593841;
E-mail: info@woodworthfamilyfoundation.org; Main URL: http://www.woodworthfamilyfoundation.org

Established in 2005 in Washington.
Donors: Jeffrey A. Woodworth; John A. Woodworth; Woodworth & Company, Inc.; Woodworth Capital Inc.; Gary E. Milgard Family Foundation.
Foundation type: Independent foundation.
Financial data (yr. ended 12/31/13): Assets, $4,066,192 (M); gifts received, $36,805; expenditures, $384,937; qualifying distributions, $196,750; giving activities include $196,750 for 23 grants (high: $45,000; low: $1,000).
Fields of interest: Human services.
Limitations: Applications not accepted. Giving primarily in Tacoma, WA. No grants to individuals.
Application information: Contributes only to pre-selected organizations.
Officers: Jeffrey A. Woodworth, Pres.; John A. Woodworth, V.P.; Nancy Woodworth, Secy.; William Starks, Treas.
EIN: 900283284

9729
Richard & Lois Worthington Foundation
15203 Gibralter Rd.
Anacortes, WA 98221-8615 (360) 293-9647
Contact: Barbara Matheson, Pres.

Established in 1998 in Washington.
Donor: Lois M. Worthington.

Foundation type: Independent foundation.
Financial data (yr. ended 09/30/13): Assets, $6,113,197 (M); expenditures, $319,162; qualifying distributions, $266,500; giving activities include $251,500 for 24 grants (high: $70,000; low: $1,000), and $15,000 for 5 grants to individuals (high: $5,000; low: $2,500).
Purpose and activities: The foundation makes grants primarily to support educational institutions, Bothell high school students, education-related activities, and religious organizations.
Fields of interest: Performing arts; Education; Elementary and secondary education; Higher education; Sororities and fraternities; Nursing care; Family planning; Christianity; Human services; Family services.
Type of support: General support; Scholarships; Student aid; Individual development.
Limitations: Applications accepted. Giving primarily in WA.
Application information: Application form required.

Initial approach: Request application form
Deadline(s): Various

Officers: Barbara Matheson, Pres.; Molly Hendricks, 1st V.P.; Richard Matheson, 2nd V.P.; Katherine Metcalf, Secy.; B. Michael Matheson, Treas.
EIN: 911909665

9730
Charles and Barbara Wright Foundation
407 Dexter Ave. N.
Seattle, WA 98109-4704

Established in 2009 in Washington.
Donors: Barbara Wright; Charles Wright.
Foundation type: Independent foundation.
Financial data (yr. ended 12/31/13): Assets, $2,707,951 (M); gifts received, $39,201; expenditures, $362,476; qualifying distributions, $348,239; giving activities include $344,503 for 15 grants (high: $125,000; low: $1,000).
Fields of interest: Arts and culture; Human services.
Limitations: Applications not accepted. Giving primarily in WA.
Application information: Unsolicited requests for funds not accepted.
Trustees: Barbara Schuchart Wright; Charles Bagley Wright III.
EIN: 270400040

9731
Wyman Youth Trust
104 30th Ave. S.
Seattle, WA 98144-2502

Established in 1951 in Washington.
Foundation type: Independent foundation.
Financial data (yr. ended 12/31/13): Assets, $5,614,669 (M); expenditures, $481,367; qualifying distributions, $383,320; giving activities include $368,078 for 137 grants (high: $15,000; low: $250).
Purpose and activities: Support primarily for youth-oriented projects, civic and cultural development, and special community endeavors; support also for schools and health services.
Fields of interest: Arts and culture; Education; Health; Children and youth.
Limitations: Giving primarily in York, Custer and Lancaster counties, NE, and King, Pierce, and Snohomish counties, WA, with emphasis on King

County. No grants to individuals, or for scholarships, capital funds or aggregate donors.

Application information: Telephone calls are not accepted.

Initial approach: Letter

Copies of proposal: 1

Deadline(s): June 15 (Grant review for Arts and Culture), Sept. 15 (Grant review for Civic and Education), and Dec. 1 (Grant review for Social/Health Services)

Board meeting date(s): Mar., June, Sept., and Dec.

Final notification: Positive responses only

Trustees: Deehan M. Wyman; Hal Wyman; Merrily Wyman.

Number of staff: 1 part-time professional.

EIN: 916031590

9732
Peg and Rick Young Foundation

P.O. Box 31878
Seattle, WA 98103-1878
Contact: Joanne Young

Established in 2003 in Washington.

Donor: Peg and Rick Young Family Trust.

Foundation type: Independent foundation.

Financial data (yr. ended 12/31/13): Assets, $4,947,607 (M); expenditures, $345,042; qualifying distributions, $305,449; giving activities include $256,000 for 70 grants (high: $15,000; low: $1,000).

Fields of interest: Arts and culture; Education; Environment; Zoos; Child welfare; Youth development.

Type of support: Annual campaigns.

Limitations: Applications not accepted. Giving primarily in WA. No grants to individuals.

Application information: Contributes only to pre-selected organizations.

Officers: Joanne Young, Pres.; Kermit Anderson, V.P.; Robert Ness, Secy.; Debra Nordby, Treas.

EIN: 731661452

9733
Zufall Family Foundation

c/o Kathryn A. Zufall, M.D.
2420 NW 201st Pl.
Shoreline, WA 98177-2427

Established in 1998 in New Jersey.

Donors: Robert Zufall; Kay Zufall.

Foundation type: Independent foundation.

Financial data (yr. ended 09/30/14): Assets, $621,904 (M); expenditures, $151,687; qualifying distributions, $142,000; giving activities include $142,000 for 19 grants (high: $24,000; low: $375).

Fields of interest: Education; Health; Religion.

Limitations: Applications not accepted. No grants to individuals.

Application information: Unsolicited requests for funds not accepted.

Trustees: Margaret Zufall Roberts; Nancy Zufall Stetten; David Zufall; Kathryn A. Zufall.

EIN: 223611396

WEST VIRGINIA

9734
Appalachian Stewardship Foundation

P.O. Box 2567
Elkins, WV   26241-2567
Contact: Shanda Minney
E-mail: shanda@appalachianstewards.org; Main
URL: http://www.appalachianstewards.org
Facebook: https://www.facebook.com/pages/
Appalachian-Stewardship-Foundation-ASF/
263784936992126
RSS feed: http://appalachianstewards.org/
index.php/feed

Foundation type: Independent foundation.
Financial data (yr. ended 12/31/13): Assets,
$370,243 (M); gifts received, $500,000;
expenditures, $340,506; qualifying distributions,
$340,506; giving activities include $270,901 for 13
grants (high: $50,000; low: $3,000).
Fields of interest: Education; Public affairs; Human
services.
Limitations: Applications accepted. Giving primarily
in VA and WV.
Publications: Application guidelines.
Application information: See foundation web site
for complete application guidelines. Application
form required.
Officers and Directors: Charles L. Harris, Chair. and
Director; William DePaulo, C.E.O. and Secy. and
Director; Kathy Harman-Stokes, Pres. and Treas.
and Director; Shanda Minney, Exec. Dir.
EIN: 273190444

9735
Sara E. Blake Charitable Foundation

1 Bank Plz.
Wheeling, WV   26003-3543

Foundation type: Independent foundation.
Financial data (yr. ended 12/31/13): Assets,
$9,447,846 (M); expenditures, $458,348;
qualifying distributions, $436,833; giving activities
include $420,009 for 2 grants (high: $357,008;
low: $63,001).
Fields of interest: Education; Higher education;
Religion.
Limitations: Applications not accepted. Giving
primarily in WV.
Application information: Unsolicited requests for
funds not accepted.
Trustee: WesBanco Bank.
EIN: 556091949

9736
Franklin W. & Helen S. Bowen Charitable Trust

300 Summers St., 6th Fl.
Charleston, WV   25301
Contact: John Barry
E-mail: bowentrust@wvbc.org

Donors: Franklin W. Bowen†; Joan F. Bowen†.
Foundation type: Independent foundation.
Financial data (yr. ended 12/31/13): Assets,
$6,210,372 (M); expenditures, $399,541;
qualifying distributions, $342,517; giving activities

include $309,863 for 89 grants (high: $23,000;
low: $500).
Purpose and activities: Scholarship awards paid
directly to college or university for individuals who
are pursuing a theological education and are
members of Baptist religious organizations.
Fields of interest: Higher education; Graduate and
professional education; Christianity; Theology.
Type of support: Scholarships; Grants to
individuals; Student aid.
Limitations: Applications not accepted. Giving
primarily in WV.
Application information: Unsolicited requests for
funds not accepted.
Trustee: John Barry.
Number of staff: 1 part-time professional; 1
part-time support.
EIN: 256091907

9737
Ethel N. Bowen Foundation

c/o First Century Bank, N.A.
500 Federal St.
Bluefield, WV   24701-3010   (304) 325-8181

Established in 1968 in West Virginia.
Donor: Ethel N. Bowen†.
Foundation type: Independent foundation.
Financial data (yr. ended 12/31/13): Assets,
$10,027,059 (M); expenditures, $529,682; giving
activities include $142,210 for 39 grants (high:
$25,000; low: $150), and $281,940 for 510 grants
to individuals (high: $1,000; low: $250).
Purpose and activities: Giving primarily for
scholarships to further the education of students in
southern WV and southwestern VA; support also for
higher, secondary, and other education, and a
municipality.
Fields of interest: Education; Secondary education;
Higher education; Public administration.
Type of support: General support; Scholarships;
Student aid.
Limitations: Giving limited to residents of
southwestern VA and southern WV.
Application information: Students required to
submit transcript.
 Initial approach: Letter
 Copies of proposal: 1
 Deadline(s): Prior to beginning of academic year
  for scholarships.
 Board meeting date(s): Monthly
Officers and Directors: Frank W. Wilkinson, Pres.
and Director; R.W. Wilkinson, Secy. and Director;
B.K. Satterfield, Treas. and Director; Henry Bowen.
Investment Agent: First Century Bank, N.A.
Number of staff: None.
EIN: 237010740

9738
George W. Bowers Family Charitable Trust

c/o Wesbanco Bank
1 Bank Plz.
Wheeling, WV   26003-3543   (304) 234-9400
Contact: R. Bruce Bandi
E-mail: barnett@wesbanco.com

Established in 2001 in West Virginia.
Donor: Frances B. Bowers†.
Foundation type: Independent foundation.
Financial data (yr. ended 12/31/13): Assets,
$5,891,583 (M); expenditures, $295,729;

qualifying distributions, $277,272; giving activities
include $261,100 for 23 grants (high: $35,000;
low: $3,000).
Purpose and activities: Grants awarded to public,
charitable, civic, and governmental organizations for
the civic improvement of the community; giving also
for college scholarships.
Fields of interest: Historical activities; Education;
Secondary education; Hospital care; Community
improvement; Human services; Food banks; Senior
services.
Type of support: General support; Student aid.
Limitations: Applications accepted. Giving primarily
in the city of Mannington and Marion County, WV.
Application information: Application form required.
 Initial approach: Submit completed application
  form
 Deadline(s): May 1 - June 15
Trustee: WesBanco Bank.
EIN: 556140783

9739
John Mathew Gay Brown Family Foundation

P.O. Box 633
Charleston, WV   25322-0633   (304) 348-4582

Established in 1989 in West Virginia.
Donor: Mary Virginia Brown†.
Foundation type: Operating foundation.
Financial data (yr. ended 12/31/13): Assets,
$2,650,031 (M); expenditures, $162,551;
qualifying distributions, $138,635; giving activities
include $135,000 for 28 grants (high: $20,000;
low: $500).
Purpose and activities: Giving primarily for human
services and federated giving programs.
Fields of interest: Arts and culture; Nonprofits;
Health; Human services; Family services.
Type of support: General support; Capital
campaigns; Regranting.
Limitations: Applications accepted. Giving limited to
Morgantown, WV. No grants to individuals.
Application information: Application form required.
 Initial approach: Letter
 Copies of proposal: 6
 Deadline(s): Oct. 1
Trustee: Huntington National Bank, N.A.
Directors: Jack L. Britton; John Fahey; Vaughn L.
Kiger; Douglas J. Leech; Chad Prather; Tom Rogers;
Reed Tanner.
EIN: 550685612

9740
The Warren and Betty Burnside Foundation, Inc.

300 W. Pike St.
Clarksburg, WV   26301-2710   (304) 623-3668
Contact: James C. West Jr.
E-mail: burnsidefoundation@frontier.com; Main
URL: http://www.burnsidefoundation.org

Established in 1991 in West Virginia.
Donors: Warren Burnside; Betty Burnside.
Foundation type: Independent foundation.
Financial data (yr. ended 01/31/13): Assets,
$6,668,370 (M); gifts received, $65,290;
expenditures, $318,728; qualifying distributions,
$309,794; giving activities include $213,000 for
grants to individuals.

Purpose and activities: Scholarships for higher education only to deserving and achieving students from Harrison County, WV.
Fields of interest: Higher education.
Type of support: Student aid.
Limitations: Applications accepted. Giving limited to residents of Harrison County, WV.
Publications: Application guidelines.
Application information: See foundation web site for application information. Application form required.
　Initial approach: Download application on foundation web site
Officers and Directors: James C. West, Jr., Pres. and Director; John L. Westfall, V.P. and Director; Dean C. Ramsey, Secy. and Director; Kathryn K. Allen, Treas. and Director; Jean Hardesty; Robert Kittle; Harry Murray, Jr.; Robert Tolley; Tim Whalen; Becky Wilson.
EIN: 550709158

9741
Carter Family Foundation
P.O. Box 393
Charleston, WV　25322-0393　(304) 256-7301
Contact: Maria L. Miller

Established in 1981 in West Virginia.
Donors: Bernard E. Carter†; Georgia Carter†; Leslie R. Carter†.
Foundation type: Operating foundation.
Financial data (yr. ended 06/30/13): Assets, $14,447,897 (M); expenditures, $528,629; qualifying distributions, $478,141; giving activities include $398,066 for 50 grants (high: $50,000; low: $1,000).
Purpose and activities: Giving primarily for education, health organizations, children and youth services, and Christian and Protestant churches. The foundation also provides scholarships and student loans to individuals willing to continue their education and teaching profession within West Virginia.
Fields of interest: Higher education; Hospice care; Diseases and conditions; Christianity; Protestantism; Human services; Child welfare.
Type of support: Program development; Loans to individuals; Scholarships; Student aid.
Limitations: Giving limited to WV, with emphasis on Raleigh County residents for scholarships.
Application information:
　Initial approach: Letter and resume
　Deadline(s): None
Trustee: United Bank.
EIN: 550606479

9742
James B. Chambers Memorial
P.O. Box 3047
Wheeling, WV　26003-0207　(304) 243-9373
Contact: Emily Schramm-Fisher
Main URL: http://jbchambersfoundation.org

Established in 1924 in West Virginia.
Foundation type: Independent foundation.
Financial data (yr. ended 12/31/13): Assets, $11,204,509 (M); expenditures, $594,164; qualifying distributions, $471,611; giving activities include $424,704 for 15 grants (high: $150,000; low: $2,500).

Purpose and activities: Giving limited to funding for indigent children in Ohio County, WV.
Fields of interest: Education; Foundations; Community and economic development; Sports and recreation; Human services; Child welfare; Children; Low-income and poor people.
Type of support: Capital campaigns; Matching grants; Capital and infrastructure; Equipment; Program development; Seed money; Technical assistance.
Limitations: Applications accepted. Giving limited to Ohio County, WV. No support for political organizations, or for non-501(c)3 organizations. No grants to individuals, or for salaries.
Application information: Application form required.
　Initial approach: Proposal
　Deadline(s): None
　Board meeting date(s): Bimonthly
Officers: Thomas L. Thomas, Pres.; James E. Altmeyer, V.P.; Edward G. Sloane, Jr., Secy.-Treas.
Directors: Thomas L. Gompers; Brian E. Joseph; Arthur M. Recht; C. Jack Savage.
Number of staff: 1 part-time professional.
EIN: 550360517

9743
The Driehorst Family Foundation
(formerly Frederick C. Driehorst and Nancy W. Driehorst Charitable Foundation)
c/o Security National Trust Co.
1300 Chapline St.
Wheeling, WV　26003-6645　(304) 233-5215

Established in 2003 in West Virginia.
Donors: Nancy W. Driehorst†; The Frederick C. and Nancy W. Driehorst Charitable Remainder Unitrust No II.
Foundation type: Independent foundation.
Financial data (yr. ended 12/31/14): Assets, $3,856,063; expenditures, $208,804; qualifying distributions, $187,000 and $0 for set-asides.
Fields of interest: Arts and culture; Education; Animal welfare; Foundations; Hospital care; Human services.
Type of support: General support; Capital campaigns.
Limitations: Applications accepted. Giving primarily in Wheeling, WV. No grants to individuals.
Application information: Application form required.
　Initial approach: Letter
　Deadline(s): None
Trustees: Joyce P. Jefferson; Wilbur S. Jones, Jr.; Larry Schultz; Judith J. Vance; Security National Trust Co.
EIN: 306061768

9744
Esbenshade Foundation
166 60th St.
Vienna, WV　26105

Established in 2001 in West Virginia.
Donors: Harry H. Esbenshade III; Whitley/Service Roofing & Sheet Metal Co.; The Laurel Management Group, Inc.; Tri-State Roofing & Sheet Metal Co.; Service Roofing & Sheet Metal Co.; The Mountain Co.
Foundation type: Independent foundation.
Financial data (yr. ended 12/31/13): Assets, $2,806,746 (M); gifts received, $294,447; expenditures, $238,180; qualifying distributions,

$222,726; giving activities include $222,700 for 9 grants (high: $100,000; low: $2,000).
Fields of interest: Education; Sports and recreation.
Limitations: Applications not accepted. Giving primarily in NC. No grants to individuals.
Application information: Unsolicited requests for funds not accepted.
Officers: Harry H. Esbenshade III, Pres.; Thomas R. Davies, V.P.; Michael D. Cain, Secy.-Treas.
Director: Bryan J. Ream.
EIN: 550779947

9745
Frada L. Fine Scholarship Fund
148 S. Queen St.
Martinsburg, WV　25401-3316

Established in 2004 in West Virginia.
Donor: Frada L. Fine†.
Foundation type: Independent foundation.
Financial data (yr. ended 03/31/13): Assets, $4,830,204 (M); expenditures, $311,494; qualifying distributions, $277,351; giving activities include $241,815 for 5 grants (high: $107,929; low: $39).
Purpose and activities: Scholarship awards available to graduates of Martinsburg High School, who will attend Shepherd University, WV.
Fields of interest: Performing arts education; Education; University education; Foundations.
Type of support: Scholarships; Student aid.
Limitations: Applications not accepted. Giving primarily in WV.
Application information: Unsolicited requests for funds not accepted.
Trustee: Branch Banking & Trust Co.
EIN: 556164208

9746
The Hamer Foundation
P.O. Box 418
Kenova, WV　25530-0418

Established in 1973 in West Virginia.
Donors: J.C. Hamer; J.P. Hamer; Gladys F. Hamer; Lori Dale Hamer; Leola D. Frazier Estate.
Foundation type: Independent foundation.
Financial data (yr. ended 11/30/13): Assets, $2,474,117 (M); gifts received, $76,008; expenditures, $212,888; qualifying distributions, $207,100; giving activities include $207,100 for 14 grants (high: $145,000; low: $1,000).
Fields of interest: Education; Religion; Christianity; Human services.
Type of support: General support.
Limitations: Applications accepted. Giving primarily in WV.
Application information: Application form required.
　Initial approach: Letter
　Deadline(s): Dec. 15
Trustees: Gladys F. Hamer; Lori Dale Hamer.
EIN: 237349926

9747
Hess Family Foundation
1 Bank Plz.
Wheeling, WV　26003　(304) 234-9400
Contact: Steven Kellas

Established in 1997 in West Virginia.

Donors: Andrew C. Hess; Mary Ann Hess.
Foundation type: Independent foundation.
Financial data (yr. ended 12/31/13): Assets, $5,370,376 (M); expenditures, $291,267; qualifying distributions, $276,267; giving activities include $265,000 for 19 grants (high: $51,205; low: $1,000).
Fields of interest: Elementary and secondary education; Higher education; Catholicism; Human services; Youth services.
Limitations: Applications accepted. Giving primarily in Wheeling, WV.
Application information: Application form required.
 Initial approach: Letter
 Deadline(s): None
Trustees: Christina H. Hess; Andrew P. Hogan; Jessica B. Hogan; Margaret B. Hogan; William N. Hogan; Wesbanco Bank.
EIN: 550751425

9748
Paul J. Hewgill Charitable Foundation Inc.
c/o Charles Clark
P.O. Box 479
Alderson, WV 24910-0479

Donor: Patricia J. Hewgill.
Foundation type: Independent foundation.
Financial data (yr. ended 12/31/14): Assets, $626,077; expenditures, $192,078; qualifying distributions, $177,250.
Fields of interest: Wildlife biodiversity; Animal welfare; Hospice care; Heart and circulatory system diseases.
Type of support: General support.
Limitations: Applications not accepted. No grants to individuals.
Application information: Contributes only to pre-selected organizations.
Officers and Directors: Charles C. Clark, Pres. and Director; Joseph E. Murphy, V.P. and Director; Mary E. Murphy, Secy. and Director.
EIN: 541796090

9749
August J. & Thelma S. Hoffmann Foundation
83 Edgington Ln.
Wheeling, WV 26003-1541 (304) 242-2300
Contact: Robert J. Krall, Tr.

Established in 2000 in West Virginia.
Donor: Thelma S. Hoffman†.
Foundation type: Independent foundation.
Financial data (yr. ended 12/31/13): Assets, $7,416,585 (M); expenditures, $342,469; qualifying distributions, $314,836; giving activities include $287,125 for 16 grants (high: $100,000; low: $1,000).
Purpose and activities: Giving primarily to Roman Catholic organizations and schools.
Fields of interest: Education; Catholicism; Food aid.
Type of support: General support.
Limitations: Applications accepted. Giving primarily in Wheeling, WV.
Application information: Application form required.
 Initial approach: Contact foundation for application
 Deadline(s): None

Trustees: Robert P. Fitzsimmons; Robert J. Krall; Holly S. Planinsic; William J. Yaeger, Jr.
EIN: 550769742

9750
P.G. and Ruby Hollandsworth Memorial Trust
349 Buckhannon Ave.
Clarksburg, WV 26301-3134 (304) 624-0022
Contact: Terring M. Weaver, Tr.

Foundation type: Independent foundation.
Financial data (yr. ended 12/31/13): Assets, $4,886,133 (M); expenditures, $343,636; qualifying distributions, $343,636; giving activities include $183,700 for 14 grants (high: $27,400; low: $3,000), and $105,000 for 24 grants to individuals (high: $6,000; low: $500).
Purpose and activities: Scholarships awarded to graduating seniors in North Central West Virginia with preference given to graduating seniors in Harrison and Nicholas counties with an overall preference given to students with physical impairments as defined by the Americans with Disabilities Act.
Fields of interest: Education.
Type of support: General support; Student aid.
Application information: Application form required.
 Initial approach: Completed aplication form
 Deadline(s): Mar.-May
Trustee: Terring M. Weaver.
EIN: 266577320

9751
Hollowell Foundation, Inc.
(formerly Hollowell-Ford Foundation, Inc.)
103 E. Washington St.
Lewisburg, WV 24901-1427 (304) 645-3313
Application address: c/o Allen Carson, Pres., 117 N. Court St., Lewisburg, WV 24901

Established in 1975 in West Virginia.
Donors: Margaret F. Hollowell†; Otto Hollowell Unitrust; John R. Dawkins†; The Greater Kanawha Valley Foundation.
Foundation type: Independent foundation.
Financial data (yr. ended 06/30/14): Assets, $8,423,427 (M); gifts received, $35,000; expenditures, $626,179; qualifying distributions, $458,703; giving activities include $439,750 for 53 grants (high: $45,000; low: $250).
Purpose and activities: Giving primarily for community improvement and renovation projects.
Fields of interest: Arts and culture; Higher education; Community and economic development; Human services.
Type of support: Capital campaigns; Matching grants; General support; Building and renovations.
Limitations: Applications accepted. Giving limited to Greenbrier County, WV. No grants to individuals.
Application information: Application form required.
 Initial approach: Letter
 Copies of proposal: 1
 Deadline(s): Apr. 1
 Board meeting date(s): Jan., Apr., June, and Sept.
 Final notification: June 30
Officers: Allen Carson, Pres.; Thomas G. McMillan, V.P.; Marshall Musser, Secy.; H. Richard Marshall, Treas.; Jesse O. Guills, Jr.; Thomas G. McMillian.
Number of staff: 1 part-time professional.
EIN: 510183517

9752
Hope, Love and Charity Foundation
c/o John Cook
P.O. Box 492
Thomas, WV 26292-0492

Established in 1994 in West Virginia.
Foundation type: Independent foundation.
Financial data (yr. ended 12/31/14): Assets, $3,223,780 (M); gifts received, $5,119; expenditures, $167,953; qualifying distributions, $147,148; giving activities include $139,500 for 43 grants (high: $12,000; low: $250).
Purpose and activities: Giving primarily for education and community services.
Fields of interest: Education; Religion; Human services.
Limitations: Applications not accepted. No grants to individuals.
Application information: Unsolicited requests for funds not accepted.
Officer: Ladonna Teets, Secy.
Trustees: John J. Cook; Patrick A. Nichols; Larry Roth; Mark Teets.
EIN: 550616253

9753
George D. Hott Memorial Foundation
P.O. Box 633
Charleston, WV 25322-0633 (304) 285-2359
Contact: Carla Parsons
E-mail: carlaparsons@huntington.com

Established in 1980 in West Virginia.
Donor: George D. Hott†.
Foundation type: Operating foundation.
Financial data (yr. ended 12/31/13): Assets, $2,738,898 (M); expenditures, $170,395; qualifying distributions, $145,994; giving activities include $142,000 for 32 grants (high: $20,000; low: $500).
Fields of interest: Arts and culture; Education; Nonprofits; Health; Hospital care; Diseases and conditions; Libraries; Community improvement; Protestantism; Human services; Food aid; Youth services; Scouting programs.
Type of support: Equipment; Endowments; Scholarships; Regranting.
Limitations: Applications accepted. Giving primarily in Morgantown, WV. No grants to individuals.
Application information: Application form required.
 Initial approach: Completed application form
 Copies of proposal: 6
 Deadline(s): Oct. 1
Trustee: Huntington National Bank, N.A.
Directors: Jack L. Britton; John Fahey; Vaughn L. Kiger; Douglas J. Leech; Chad Prather; Thomas P. Rogers; Reed J. Tanner.
EIN: 556085230

9754
The Huntington Foundation, Inc.
P.O. Box 2548
Huntington, WV 25726-2548 3045220611
Application address: The Huntington Foundation, Inc., 916 5th Ave., Ste. 207, Huntington, WV 25701, tel.: (304) 522-0611

Established in 1986 in West Virginia.
Foundation type: Independent foundation.

Financial data (yr. ended 12/31/14): Assets, $6,960,157; expenditures, $377,289; qualifying distributions, $302,906.
Purpose and activities: Giving primarily for higher education, hospitals and human services, including services for people who are blind.
Fields of interest: Higher education; Hospital care; Human services; People with vision impairments.
Type of support: General support; Equipment; Land acquisitions.
Limitations: Applications accepted. Giving primarily in WV. No grants to individuals.
Application information: Application form required.
  Initial approach: Request application form
  Copies of proposal: 6
  Deadline(s): None
Officers: Frank Hanshaw, Jr., Pres.; Leon K. Oxley, V.P.; Kermit E. McGinnis, Secy.-Treas.
Director: Joseph B. Touma.
Number of staff: 1 part-time support.
EIN: 550370129

9755
The Larch Foundation
26 Park Rd.
Wheeling, WV   26003-6642

Established in 2004 in Maine.
Donors: Irvin Shapell; David Shapell Lead Unitrus; David Shapell 2009 Charitable Lead; Fela Shapell Lead Unitrus; Fela Shapell 2009 Charitable Lead A.
Foundation type: Independent foundation.
Financial data (yr. ended 12/31/13): Assets, $2,121,607 (M); gifts received, $621,092; expenditures, $150,147; qualifying distributions, $146,800; giving activities include $146,800 for 24 grants (high: $41,500; low: $500).
Fields of interest: Education; Human services; Child welfare; People with disabilities.
Limitations: Applications not accepted. Giving primarily in MA, ME and WV.
Application information: Contributes only to pre-selected organizations.
Officers: Irvin Shapell, Pres. and Secy.-Treas.; Charles E. Miller, Clerk.
EIN: 202012929

9756
Henry Logan Childrens Home Inc.
c/o Wesbanco Trust Dept.
415 Market St.
Parkersburg, WV   26101-5338
Application address: c/o Barbara Smith,1736 Woodland Dr., Vienna, WV 26105, tel.:(304) 295-8397

Established in 1952 in West Virginia.
Foundation type: Independent foundation.
Financial data (yr. ended 12/31/13): Assets, $3,983,514 (M); expenditures, $195,512; qualifying distributions, $176,228; giving activities include $176,228 for 17 grants (high: $28,100; low: $500).
Purpose and activities: Giving to organizations that provide education and training to needy and disadvantaged children in Wood County, WV.
Fields of interest: Higher education; Sports and recreation; Family services; Child welfare; Youth services.

Type of support: Continuing support; Program-related investments; Annual campaigns; Equipment; Emergency funds; Seed money.
Limitations: Applications accepted. Giving primarily in Wood County, WV. No grants to individuals.
Application information: Application form required.
  Initial approach: Proposal
  Copies of proposal: 5
  Deadline(s): None
  Board meeting date(s): 3rd Wed. of each month
Officers: Bob Waters, Pres.; Betty Rathbone, Secy.; Katie Morris, Treas.
Directors: Bill Butler; John Coffman; Marian Dauphin; John Fanta; Randy Law; Tom Murray; Steve Reger; Michelle Sandy; Lynn Schwartz; Barbara Smith.
EIN: 550365258

9757
Logan Healthcare Foundation, Inc.
P.O. Box 1725
Logan, WV   25601-1725   (304) 752-7244
Main URL: http://www.loganhealthcare.com

Established in 2003 in West Virginia.
Donor: Logan Medical Foundation.
Foundation type: Independent foundation.
Financial data (yr. ended 12/31/14): Assets, $11,564,165; gifts received, $100,000; expenditures, $641,683; qualifying distributions, $584,655.
Purpose and activities: Giving primarily to enhance health initiatives, which include seeking to improve the health status of, and access to, health care for the residents of the grantmaker's service area.
Fields of interest: Health.
Limitations: Applications accepted. Giving restricted to the geographic service area formerly served by the Logan General Hospital and the residents of Logan, Boone, Lincoln, Mingo, and Wyoming counties in southern WV.
Publications: Application guidelines.
Application information: Application form required.
  Initial approach: See website
  Deadline(s): Oct. 2
Officers: Roger McGrew, Chair.; John Earles, Pres.; Judith McCormick, Secy.
Directors: Anita Amburgey; Ed Napier; Bob Whitler.
EIN: 201337361

9758
Robert W. McCormick Scholarship Fund
c/o Bank of Charles Town
P.O. Drawer 40
Charles Town, WV   25414-0040   (304) 728-2435

Established in 1994 in West Virginia.
Donor: Robert W. McCormick.
Foundation type: Independent foundation.
Financial data (yr. ended 04/30/13): Assets, $4,363,924 (M); expenditures, $225,066; qualifying distributions, $169,005; giving activities include $38,240 for 1 grant, and $130,765 for 14 grants to individuals (high: $21,617; low: $1,100).
Purpose and activities: Giving primarily for education; scholarships are available only to students graduating from a high school in the Jefferson County, West Virginia, area, who will attend a public college or university in West Virginia.
Fields of interest: Education.
Type of support: General support; Student aid.

Limitations: Applications accepted. Giving limited to residents of Jefferson County, WV.
Application information: Students must graduate with a "B" average from a high school located in Jefferson County, West Virginia. Application form required.
  Deadline(s): Feb. 20
Trustees: F. Samuel Byrer; Bank of Charles Town.
EIN: 550734149

9759
Robert W. McCormick Trust f/b/o
Jefferson High School
c/o Bank of Charles Town
P.O. Box 40
Charles Town, WV   25414-0040

Foundation type: Independent foundation.
Financial data (yr. ended 04/30/14): Assets, $3,115,661 (M); expenditures, $182,106; qualifying distributions, $141,585; giving activities include $141,585 for 1 grant.
Fields of interest: Education.
Limitations: Applications not accepted. Giving primarily in WV.
Application information: Unsolicited requests for funds not accepted.
Trustee: Bank of Charles Town.
EIN: 556124577

9760
McDavid Foundation
1410 Woodmere Dr.
Charleston, WV   25314-1940   (304) 346-9001
Main URL: http://www.mcdavidfoundation.org

Donor: William R. McDavid.
Foundation type: Independent foundation.
Financial data (yr. ended 12/31/14): Assets, $1,723,063; expenditures, $171,300; qualifying distributions, $166,119.
Fields of interest: Education; University education; Human services.
Limitations: Applications accepted. Giving primarily in Charleston, WV. No grants to individuals.
Application information: Application form required.
  Initial approach: Contact foundation for application form
  Deadline(s): Dec. 1
Officers and Directors: Bradford A. McDavid, Pres. and Treas. and Director; Diana L. Long, Secy. and Director; Anne R. Haakenson; Dean Haakenson; Sandra McDavid.
EIN: 550730152

9761
The Berkeley Minor and Susan F. Minor
Foundation
300 Summers St., Ste. 620
Charleston, WV   25301
Contact: John L. Ray
Application address: c/o John L. Ray, 109 Capitol St., Ste. 700, Charleston, WV 25301-2609, tel.: (304) 342-1141

Established in 1957 in West Virginia.
Donor: Berkeley Minor, Jr.†
Foundation type: Independent foundation.
Financial data (yr. ended 12/31/14): Assets, $2,729,548 (M); expenditures, $195,859;

qualifying distributions, $178,184; giving activities include $175,000 for 3 grants (high: $100,000; low: $15,000).

Purpose and activities: Giving primarily for scholarship awards for higher education.

Fields of interest: University education; Graduate and professional education; Theology.

Type of support: General support; Student aid.

Limitations: Applications accepted. Giving primarily in VA and WV.

Application information: Students attending the University of Charleston, the University of Virginia, and the Protestant Episcopal Theological Seminary of Virginia should contact their respective schools for scholarship application information. Students attending West Virginia University and other schools should apply directly to the foundation for scholarship aid.

Initial approach: Letter
Deadline(s): Aug. 1
Board meeting date(s): Aug. and as required
Trustees: Mark W. Kelley; John L. Ray; Christopher J. Winston; Branch Banking & Trust Co.
EIN: 556014946

9762
Robinson S. Parlin Trust
1 Bank Plz.
Wheeling, WV   26003-3543   (304) 234-9400
Contact: Anthony J. Habbit
E-mail: habbit@wesbanco.com

Foundation type: Independent foundation.

Financial data (yr. ended 12/31/13): Assets, $4,615,583 (M); expenditures, $220,295; qualifying distributions, $207,681; giving activities include $196,460 for 12 grants (high: $40,000; low: $1,860).

Purpose and activities: Giving for the promotion of the health and welfare of crippled or mentally retarded children, underprivileged children, and the blind of Ohio County, West Virginia.

Fields of interest: Camps; Scouting programs; Developmental disability services; People with disabilities; People with physical disabilities; People with vision impairments; People with psychosocial disabilities; People with intellectual disabilities.

Type of support: General support.

Application information: Application form required.
Initial approach: Letter
Deadline(s): None
Trustee: Wesbanco Bank.
EIN: 556162728

9763
Herschel C. Price Educational Foundation
P.O. Box 412
Huntington, WV   25708-0412
Contact: Jonna Hughes, Tr.

Established in 1975 in West Virginia.
Donor: Herschel C. Price†.
Foundation type: Independent foundation.

Financial data (yr. ended 04/30/13): Assets, $4,472,767 (M); expenditures, $250,976; qualifying distributions, $200,000; giving activities include $200,000 for grants.

Purpose and activities: Scholarships awarded directly to deserving students for attendance at accredited local educational West Virginia institutions. Interviews generally required with

selection based on financial need as well as scholastic standing.

Fields of interest: University education.

Type of support: Student aid.

Limitations: Applications not accepted. Giving limited to WV residents and those attending WV colleges.

Application information: Unsolicited requests for funds not accepted.
Board meeting date(s): May and Nov.
Trustees: Jonna L. Hughes; Chandos H. Peak; City National Bank.
Number of staff: 1 part-time professional.
EIN: 556076719

9764
Raymond Brooks Vanscoy Testamentary Trust
P.O. Box 1152
Fairmont, WV   26555-1152

Foundation type: Independent foundation.

Financial data (yr. ended 12/31/13): Assets, $3,853,061 (M); expenditures, $208,863; qualifying distributions, $172,925; giving activities include $172,925 for 5 grants (high: $34,585; low: $34,585).

Fields of interest: Education; Diseases and conditions; Arthritis; Religion.

Limitations: Applications not accepted. Giving primarily in AZ, FL, OH and WV.

Application information: Unsolicited requests for funds not accepted.
Trustees: Argyle Shingleton; Wesbanco Bank, Inc.
EIN: 376453534

9765
The June Oblinger Shott Foundation, Inc.
P.O. Box 1559
Bluefield, WV   24701-1559   (304) 324-3214
Contact: Frank W. Wilkinson, Chair.

Established in 2007 in West Virginia.
Donor: June Oblinger Shott†.
Foundation type: Independent foundation.

Financial data (yr. ended 12/31/14): Assets, $5,921,211 (M); expenditures, $320,412; qualifying distributions, $284,622; giving activities include $284,622 for 17 grants (high: $121,000; low: $1,000).

Fields of interest: Education; Community and economic development; Sports and recreation.

Limitations: Applications accepted. Giving primarily in VA and West Virginia. No grants to individuals.

Application information: Application form required.
Initial approach: Completed Application form
Deadline(s): None
Officers: Frank W. Wilkinson, Chair.; Byron K. Satterfield, Vice-Chair.; Gary D. Cornwell, Treas.
EIN: 870786480

9766
Skewes Family Foundation
P.O. Box 1014
Bluefield, WV   24701-1014

Established in 2004 in West Virginia.
Donors: Concept Mining, Inc.; William G. Skewes†; Ridgeland Company, Inc.
Foundation type: Company-sponsored foundation.

Financial data (yr. ended 12/31/13): Assets, $5,196,962 (M); expenditures, $311,486; qualifying distributions, $305,735; giving activities include $283,800 for 42 grants (high: $52,000; low: $300).

Purpose and activities: The foundation supports museums and community foundations and organizations involved with education and recreation.

Fields of interest: Education; Sports and recreation; Human services.

Type of support: General support; Capital and infrastructure; Program development; Scholarships.

Limitations: Applications not accepted. Giving primarily in VA, WV, and WY.

Application information: Unsolicited requests for funds not accepted.
Officer: William G. Skewes, Chair.
Directors: Jack Caffrey; Ronald Campbell; James C. Mulkey.
EIN: 201978793

9767
Starvaggi Charities, Inc.
401 Pennsylvania Ave.
Weirton, WV   26062-2322
Contact: James A. O'Brien, V.P. and Treas.

Donor: Mike Starvaggi†.
Foundation type: Operating foundation.

Financial data (yr. ended 01/31/13): Assets, $23,109,154 (M); gifts received, $2,100; expenditures, $177,242; qualifying distributions, $159,619; giving activities include $159,619 for 76 grants (high: $50,000; low: $50).

Fields of interest: Secondary education; Higher education; Nonprofits; Economic development; Protestantism; Catholicism; Human services; Indigenous peoples.

Type of support: General support; Fellowships; Regranting.

Limitations: Applications accepted. Giving primarily in WV. No grants to individuals.

Application information:
Initial approach: Proposal
Deadline(s): None
Officers: G. Michael Wehr, Pres.; James A. O'Brien, V.P. and Treas.; Richard Trzaskoma, Secy.
EIN: 550602138

9768
Agnita M. Stine Schreiber Foundation Inc.
(formerly Agnita M. Schreiber Foundation, Inc.)
c/o Lee E. Stine, Jr.
P.O. Box 1680
Shepherdstown, WV   25443   (301) 730-7677

Established in 1999 in Maryland.
Donor: Agnita M. Schreiber.
Foundation type: Independent foundation.

Financial data (yr. ended 12/31/13): Assets, $5,108,661 (M); gifts received, $1,000; expenditures, $235,912; qualifying distributions, $193,500; giving activities include $189,800 for 22 grants (high: $58,750; low: $750).

Fields of interest: Art museums; Women's services.

Limitations: Applications accepted. Giving primarily in Washington County, MD. No grants to individuals.

Application information: Application form required.
Initial approach: Letter
Deadline(s): None

Officers: Lee E. Stine, Jr., Pres.; Sally Pfaeffle, V.P.; John H. Urner, Secy.; Larry W. Stine, Treas.
Directors: Sandra S. Tillou.
EIN: 522206796

9769
O. J. Stout Scholarship Fund
c/o United National Bank
P.O. Box 1508
Parkersburg, WV 26102-1508
Contact: Catherine L. Houser, V.P.

Established in 1973 in West Virginia.
Foundation type: Independent foundation.
Financial data (yr. ended 12/31/14): Assets, $10,621,388 (M); expenditures, $459,045; qualifying distributions, $457,066; giving activities include $312,000 for 27 grants to individuals (high: $4,000; low: $400).
Purpose and activities: Scholarship awards and loans to male high school graduates residing in Wood County, West Virginia, and adjacent WV counties. Preference given to applicants studying for the ministry at West Virginia Wesleyan College in Buckhannon.
Fields of interest: Graduate and professional education; Theology.
Type of support: Student aid; Loans to individuals.
Limitations: Applications accepted. Giving limited to residents of WV from Wood and adjacent counties.
Application information: Application form required.
Initial approach: Completed application form
Deadline(s): Mar. 31 and Apr. 1
Officer: Catherine L. Houser, V.P.
EIN: 556029015

9770
The Vecellio Family Foundation, Inc.
(formerly The Enrico Vecellio Family Foundation, Inc.)
P.O. Box 2438
Beckley, WV 25802-2438

Established in 1972 in West Virginia.
Donors: Erma V. Grogan; Evelyn P. Vecellio; Leo A. Vecellio, Sr.†; Anna M. Vecellio†.
Foundation type: Independent foundation.
Financial data (yr. ended 12/31/14): Assets, $7,461,720 (M); expenditures, $426,508; qualifying distributions, $372,175; giving activities include $365,750 for grants.
Purpose and activities: Grants for higher education, social service agencies, health services, and churches. Support also for scholarships to local area residents and children of employees of Vecellio Group, Inc. and subsidiaries.
Fields of interest: Arts and culture; Performing arts; Art museums; Education; Higher education; Health; Hospice care; Heart and circulatory system diseases; Leukemia; Catholicism; Human services; Youth services; Scouting programs.
Type of support: General support; Scholarships; Student aid; Research; Individual development.
Limitations: Applications accepted. Giving primarily in FL and WV. No grants to individuals directly and no loans.
Application information:
Initial approach: Proposal
Deadline(s): Nov. 15
Officers and Trustees: Leo A. Vecellio, Jr., Pres. and Trustee; Christopher S. Vecellio, V.P. and Trustee; Michael A. Vecellio, V.P. and Trustee; Michael J. Sullivan, Secy.- Co-Treas.; L. L. Gwinn, Co-Treas.; Robert L. Castrodale; Patricia Vecellio Cunningham; Kathryn C. Vecellio.
EIN: 550538242

9771
H.B. Wehrle Foundation
c/o Henry B. Wehrle, Jr.
835 Hillcrest Dr. E.
Charleston, WV 25311—1627

Foundation type: Independent foundation.

Financial data (yr. ended 12/31/12): Assets, $8,255,950 (M); expenditures, $516,187; qualifying distributions, $438,945; giving activities include $429,500 for 31 grants (high: $75,000; low: $1,000).
Fields of interest: Education; Higher education; Diseases and conditions; Libraries; Community and economic development; Child welfare.
Limitations: Applications not accepted. Giving primarily in WV.
Application information: Unsolicited requests for funds not accepted.
Trustees: F. Thomas Graff, Jr.; Thomas Newton; Elizabeth Marie Wehrle; H. Bernard Wehrle III; Henry B. Wehrle, Jr.; Stephen D. Wehrle; Lynne Wehrle-Zande.
EIN: 266449761

9772
W. A. Jr. and Phyllis P. Wolfe Foundation, Inc.
500 Federal St.
Bluefield, WV 24701-3010 (304) 325-8181
Contact: John Beckett, Dir.

Foundation type: Independent foundation.
Financial data (yr. ended 12/31/14): Assets, $3,751,254 (M); expenditures, $171,564; qualifying distributions, $145,500; giving activities include $145,500 for 73 grants (high: $3,000; low: $250).
Fields of interest: Education.
Type of support: General support; Student aid.
Limitations: Applications accepted. Giving primarily in VA and WA.
Application information: Application form required.
Initial approach: Letter
Deadline(s): None
Officers and Directors: John Beckett, Pres. and Director; Julie Johnson, V.P. and Director; Elizabeth Prue, Secy.-Treas.; Amy Havens; Mark Hipes; Tony Reed; Kathy Shott; R. W. Wilkinson.
Trustee: First Century bank.
EIN: 550684389

WISCONSIN

9773
Donald W. & Margaret M. Anderson Foundation

c/o Martha A. Van De Ven
3901 Signature Dr.
Middleton, WI 53562-2388

Established in 1998 in Florida.
Donors: Donald W. Anderson; Margaret M. Anderson.
Foundation type: Independent foundation.
Financial data (yr. ended 12/31/14): Assets, $4,402,283; expenditures, $317,516; qualifying distributions, $275,000.
Purpose and activities: Giving primarily for education and social services.
Fields of interest: Education; Higher education; Nonprofits; Health; Hospice care; Christianity; Human services.
Type of support: Regranting.
Limitations: Applications not accepted. Giving primarily in WI. No grants to individuals.
Application information: Contributes only to pre-selected organizations.
Trustee: Martha van De Ven.
EIN: 656254236

9774
AnnMarie Foundation, Inc.

1245 N. Airport Rd.
Phillips, WI 54555 (715) 381-3213
Contact: Lori Feiten
E-mail: lorl.feiten@annmariefoundation.org; Main
URL: http://annmariefoundation.org

Established in 1973 in Wisconsin.
Donors: Phillips Plastics Corp.; Mike Litvinoff Memorial; Robert Cervenka; Debbie Cervenka; Louis Vokurka.
Foundation type: Company-sponsored foundation.
Financial data (yr. ended 04/30/14): Assets, $7,555,900 (M); gifts received, $166,000; expenditures, $373,281; qualifying distributions, $347,018; giving activities include $265,674 for 164 grants (high: $6,550; low: $160), and $65,500 for 40 grants to individuals (high: $4,000; low: $1,500).
Purpose and activities: The foundation supports organizations involved with arts and culture, education, recreation, youth development, and human services and awards college scholarships to high school seniors located in areas where Philip Plastics Corporation has a facility.
Fields of interest: Arts and culture; Education; Public libraries; Sports and recreation; Human services; Youth development; Youth services.
Type of support: General support; Student aid.
Limitations: Applications accepted. Giving limited to areas of company operations in WI (not Milwaukee). No support for cities, counties, or municipalities, foundations, or individual colleges. No grants to individuals (except for AnnMarie scholarships), or for political or religious purposes, discretionary funds, salaries, or state or national fundraising.
Publications: Application guidelines; Program policy statement.
Application information: Application form required.

Initial approach: Completed application form
Deadline(s): May 17
Board meeting date(s): Quarterly
Final notification: Following board meetings
Officers: Jeff Heinzen, Pres.; Ann Mike, V.P.; Kris Becker, Secy. and Treas.
Members: Lynn Downing; Ed Lucas; Pat Quinn; Steve Russ; Richard Thomas.
EIN: 237301323

9775
Antonia Foundation Inc.

c/o F. Michael Arnow
3966 N. Lake Dr.
Milwaukee, WI 53211-2448 (414) 964-4000
Contact: Laura J. Arnow, CPA

Established in 1991 in Wisconsin.
Donors: Annette Marra; John M. Marra.
Foundation type: Independent foundation.
Financial data (yr. ended 03/31/15): Assets, $3,062,913 (M); gifts received, $344,539; expenditures, $238,621; qualifying distributions, $212,182; giving activities include $205,600 for 12 grants (high: $47,000; low: $2,000).
Purpose and activities: The purpose of the foundation is to benefit wildlife education and conservation efforts and to protect wildlife and wildlife habitat in and around southeastern WI.
Fields of interest: Environment; Wildlife biodiversity; Zoos.
Type of support: Public engagement and education.
Limitations: Applications accepted. Giving primarily in WI. No grants for endowments, debt reduction, or annual drives.
Application information: Application form required.
Initial approach: Proposal
Deadline(s): None
Officers: Annette Marra, Pres.; John M. Marra, V.P.; F. Michael Arnow, Treas.; Denasha A. Scott, Secy.
Director: Kathleen Ryan.
Number of staff: None.
EIN: 391717099

9776
Ariens Foundation, Ltd.

655 W. Ryan St.
Brillion, WI 54110-1072 (920) 756-4273
Contact: Leone M. Pahl, V.P.

Established in 1967 in Wisconsin.
Donors: Ariens Corp.; Francis Ariens Memorial; Ariens Co.; Ariens Company.
Foundation type: Company-sponsored foundation.
Financial data (yr. ended 06/30/14): Assets, $375,716 (M); gifts received, $196,575; expenditures, $227,744; qualifying distributions, $227,463; giving activities include $217,560 for 36 grants (high: $111,575; low: $60), and $9,650 for grants to individuals.
Purpose and activities: The foundation supports community foundations and organizations involved with secondary and higher education, the environment, homeless shelters, athletics, civil liberties, and human services and awards scholarships to individuals.
Fields of interest: Secondary education; Higher education; Environment; Environmental education; Track and field; Right to life; Human services; Economics for youth; Homeless shelters.

Type of support: Capital and infrastructure; General support; Scholarships; Student aid.
Limitations: Applications accepted. Giving primarily in northeastern WI, with emphasis on Brillion.
Application information: Application form required.
Initial approach: Proposal
Deadline(s): None
Officers: Mary M. Ariens, Pres.; Leone M. Pahl, V.P.; Stephen Letourneaux, Secy.; H. James Jensen, Treas.
EIN: 396102058

9777
Arzbaecher Family Foundation

c/o Robert C. Arzbaecher
17425 Morningview Ct.
Brookfield, WI 53045-4359

Established in 2007 in Wisconsin.
Donor: Robert C. Arzbaecher.
Foundation type: Independent foundation.
Financial data (yr. ended 12/31/13): Assets, $7,804,217 (M); gifts received, $1,463,200; expenditures, $429,316; qualifying distributions, $407,801; giving activities include $393,765 for 27 grants (high: $93,000; low: $40).
Purpose and activities: Giving primarily for the arts, particularly a children's theater, as well as for education and federated giving programs.
Fields of interest: Theater; Education; Nonprofits; Children and youth.
Type of support: Regranting.
Limitations: Applications not accepted. Giving primarily in Milwaukee, WI.
Application information: Unsolicited requests for funds not accepted.
Officer and Director: Robert C. Arzbaecher, Pres. and Director.
EIN: 261148157

9778
Associated Banc-Corp Foundation Charitable Trust

(formerly First Financial Foundation, Inc.)
P.O. Box 12800
Green Bay, WI 54307-2800

Established in 1977 in Wisconsin.
Donors: First Financial Bank; Associated Banc-Corp.
Foundation type: Company-sponsored foundation.
Financial data (yr. ended 12/31/13): Assets, $16,634 (M); gifts received, $260,001; expenditures, $270,147; qualifying distributions, $269,585; giving activities include $263,667 for 30 grants (high: $50,000; low: $1,000).
Purpose and activities: The trust supports hospitals and organizations involved with television, cancer, youth development, and community development.
Fields of interest: Education; Health; Human services.
Type of support: Program development.
Limitations: Applications accepted. Giving limited to areas of company operations in IL and WI; giving also to national organizations. No support for political, labor, or veterans' organizations or religious organizations. No grants to individuals.
Application information: Application form required.
Initial approach: Request application form
Deadline(s): Sept. 1
Officers: Philip Flynn, Pres.; Christopher Del Moral Niles, V.P.

Directors: Oliver Buechse; Gwen Dansby; Breck Hanson; Donna Smith; David Stein; John Utz.
Trustee: Associated Trust Co., N.A.
Number of staff: 1 part-time professional.
EIN: 391277461

9779
Aylward Family Foundation
(formerly Neenah Foundry Foundation, Inc.)
P.O. Box 409
Neenah, WI 54957-0409

Donor: Neenah Foundry Co.
Foundation type: Company-sponsored foundation.
Financial data (yr. ended 12/31/14): Assets, $3,525,467; expenditures, $136,611; qualifying distributions, $133,715.
Purpose and activities: The foundation supports organizations involved with television, secondary and higher education, substance abuse treatment, human services, and Christianity.
Fields of interest: Arts and culture; Education; Health; Human services.
Limitations: Applications accepted. Giving primarily in Appleton, Menasha, Neenah, and New London, WI. No grants to individuals.
Application information: Application form required.
  Initial approach: Letter
  Deadline(s): Oct. 31
  Board meeting date(s): May and as required
Officers: E.W. Aylward, Pres.; A.A. Aylward, V.P.; R.J. Aylward, Secy.-Treas.
EIN: 396042143

9780
Baker Family Foundation, Inc.
N5279 County Rd. G
Saint Cloud, WI 53079-1602

Established in 2003 in Wisconsin.
Donors: Baker Cheese Factory, Inc.; Rosie Baker; Bob Baker.
Foundation type: Independent foundation.
Financial data (yr. ended 09/30/13): Assets, $1,069,945 (M); gifts received, $726,040; expenditures, $399,757; qualifying distributions, $398,030; giving activities include $397,500 for 11 grants (high: $327,000; low: $500).
Fields of interest: Education; Christianity; Human services.
Limitations: Applications not accepted. Giving primarily in WI. No grants to individuals.
Application information: Unsolicited requests for funds not accepted.
Trustees: Brian Baker; Kevin Baker; Richard Baker.
EIN: 200529206

9781
BayCare Clinic Foundation, Ltd.
164 N. Broadway
Green Bay, WI 54303-2728 (920) 405-5382
Contact: Ann Seidl, Dir.
FAX: (920) 405-8004; E-mail: aseidl@baycare.net; Main URL: http://www.baycare.net/about-us/baycare-clinic-foundation

Established in 2000 in Wisconsin.
Donors: BayCare Health Systems, LLC; Mrs. Kevin Wienkers; Dr. Kevin Wienkers; Dr. Ahmet Dervish; Bruce Neal, MD; Joseph Hodgson, MD; Dr.

Christopher Sorrells; Dr. John Lee; Dr. Alex Roitstein; Dr. Richard Harrison; Paul Summerside, MD; Dr. Per Anderas; Dr. Scott Gage; Dr. Stephen Brada.
Foundation type: Independent foundation.
Financial data (yr. ended 12/31/13): Assets, $213,268 (M); gifts received, $248,584; expenditures, $251,721; qualifying distributions, $251,659; giving activities include $251,550 for 174 grants (high: $25,000; low: $22).
Purpose and activities: Giving to promote the health and well-being of residents within Green Bay, Northeast Wisconsin and Michigan's Upper Peninsula.
Fields of interest: Arts and culture; Education; Diseases and conditions; Religion; Christianity; Human services; Child welfare.
Type of support: General support; Grants to individuals.
Limitations: Applications accepted. Giving primarily in Green Bay, WI.
Publications: Application guidelines.
Application information: See foundation web site for complete application guidelines. Application form required.
  Initial approach: Download application from foundation web site
  Deadline(s): Jan. 14, Apr. 14, July 14, and Oct. 13
Officers and Directors: Joseph Hodgson, MD, Pres. and Director; Bruce Neal, MD, V.P. and Director; Dianna Bordewick, MD, Secy.-Treas. and Director; Lesley O'Connell; Ann Seidl; Christopher Sorrells, MD; William Witmer.
EIN: 392000503

9782
Berbeewalsh Foundation, Inc.
c/o Fred G. Broihahn, C.P.A.
P.O. Box 620676
Middleton, WI 53562-0676

Established in 2006 in Wisconsin.
Donors: James G. Berbee; Karen A. Berbee; Karen A. Walsh.
Foundation type: Independent foundation.
Financial data (yr. ended 12/31/14): Assets, $3,345,402; expenditures, $265,110; qualifying distributions, $242,500.
Fields of interest: Opera; Education; Human services.
Type of support: Regranting; Fundraising.
Limitations: Applications not accepted. Giving primarily in Madison, WI. No grants to individuals.
Application information: Contributes only to pre-selected organizations.
Officers and Directors: James G. Berbee, Pres. and Treas. and Director; Karen A. Walsh, V.P. and Director; Paul S. Peercy; Paul S. Shain.
EIN: 205892278

9783
Alvin and Marion Birnschein Foundation
111 E. Wisconsin Ave., Ste. 1800
Milwaukee, WI 53202-4809 (414) 276-3400
Contact: Peter C. Haensel, Dir.

Established in 1968 in Wisconsin.
Donors: Alvin Birnschein†; Marion Birnschein†.
Foundation type: Independent foundation.
Financial data (yr. ended 12/31/13): Assets, $4,439,416 (M); expenditures, $297,002;

qualifying distributions, $214,407; giving activities include $214,407 for 25 grants (high: $25,500; low: $3,000).
Fields of interest: Arts and culture; Higher education; Graduate and professional education; Hospital care; Diseases and conditions; Engineering; Human services; Child welfare; Developmental disability services; Low-income and poor people; People with disabilities; People with vision impairments; People with hearing impairments.
Type of support: General support; Endowments; Scholarships; Research.
Limitations: Giving primarily in the greater Milwaukee, WI, area. No support for religious purposes, or for elementary and secondary schools. No grants to individuals, or for salaries.
Publications: Informational brochure (including application guidelines).
Application information: Application form required.
  Initial approach: Contact foundation via letter of intent to request application form
  Copies of proposal: 1
  Deadline(s): July 31
Directors: Peter C. Haensel; Janet M. Hoehnen; Ronald Jodat.
Number of staff: 1 full-time professional; 1 part-time support.
EIN: 396126798

9784
Blooming Prairie Foundation, Inc.
c/o Willy St. Grocery Co-op
1457 E. Main St.
Madison, WI 53703 (608) 216-8152
Contact: Sverre D. Roang, Dir.
E-mail: bloomingprairiefoundation@gmail.com; Main URL: http://www.bloomingprairiefoundation.org

Established in 2003 in Wisconsin.
Foundation type: Independent foundation.
Financial data (yr. ended 06/30/13): Assets, $1,864,704 (M); expenditures, $301,048; qualifying distributions, $278,785; giving activities include $270,000 for 2 grants (high: $250,000; low: $20,000).
Purpose and activities: The foundation makes grants to non-profit, charitable organizations that conduct any of the following activities: 1) developmental, research, and educational efforts in the organic industry and the cooperative community; 2) the development of organic and natural products; or 3) cooperative development in the natural products industry.
Fields of interest: Cooperative education; Environmental education; Nutrition; Agricultural cooperatives; Organic farming.
Type of support: Debt reduction; Matching grants; Program development; Scholarships.
Limitations: No support for organizations lacking 501(c)(3) status . No grants to individuals.
Application information: See foundation web site for current application guidelines.
Officers and Directors: Anya Firszt, Chair. and Director; Leslie Campbell, Secy. and Director; Allan Gallant; Pam Kringlund; Sheila Phillips-Hawkins; Sverre David Roang.
Number of staff: 2 part-time support.
EIN: 450511132

9785
Duane & Dorothy Bluemke Foundation, Ltd.

(formerly Duane H. & Dorothy M. Bluemke Charitable Foundation, Ltd.)
P.O. Box 425
Sturgeon Bay, WI   54235-0425

Established in 2004 in Wisconsin.
Donors: Duane H. Bluemke; Dorothy M. Bluemke.
Foundation type: Independent foundation.
Financial data (yr. ended 12/31/13): Assets, $8,098,691 (M); expenditures, $379,087; qualifying distributions, $272,793; giving activities include $220,926 for 46 grants (high: $41,576; low: $200).
Fields of interest: Higher education; Foundations; Diseases and conditions; Christianity; Human services; Child welfare.
Limitations: Applications not accepted. Giving primarily in WI. No grants to individuals.
Application information: Unsolicited requests for funds not accepted.
Officers: Duane H. Bluemke, Pres. and Treas.; Dorothy M. Bluemke, V.P. and Secy.
Director: Christine A. Miller.
EIN: 202058965

9786
John C. Bock Foundation

411 E. Wisconsin Ave., Ste. 1000
Milwaukee, WI   53202-4409   (414) 276-1122
Contact: Sally C. Merrell Esq.
FAX: (414) 978-8877; E-mail for Sally C. Merrell: smerrell@vonbriesen.com; Main URL: http://www.bockfoundation.com
Grants List: http://www.bockfoundation.com/bock/testimonials_and_portfolio.htm

Established in 2002 in Wisconsin.
Donor: John C. Bock Revocable Trust.
Foundation type: Independent foundation.
Financial data (yr. ended 12/31/13): Assets, $7,443,470 (M); expenditures, $351,726; qualifying distributions, $293,333; giving activities include $218,500 for 18 grants (high: $25,000; low: $5,000).
Purpose and activities: Giving for the preservation, maintenance and enhancement of land areas in their natural or undeveloped state that support woodlands and old-growth forests, principally those proximate to Lake Mendota, WI, and generally in the state of WI.
Fields of interest: Undergraduate education; Environmental justice; Natural resources; Environmental education.
Type of support: Equal access.
Limitations: Applications accepted. Giving primarily in WI.
Application information: Application form required.
  Initial approach: See website for application form and details
  Deadline(s): May 31
Trustees: Carl J. Bock; Sharon L. Bock; Albert Goldstein; Luke Seggelink; Jeremy C. Shea.
EIN: 266014448

9787
Victor F. Braun Foundation Inc.

W. 1781 Washington Rd.
Oconomowoc, WI   53066-9561

Established in 1956 in Wisconsin.
Donor: Victor F. Braun†.
Foundation type: Independent foundation.
Financial data (yr. ended 11/30/13): Assets, $4,112,470 (M); expenditures, $216,063; qualifying distributions, $187,913; giving activities include $187,000 for 7 grants (high: $90,000; low: $2,700).
Fields of interest: Education; Diseases and conditions; Cancers; Protestantism; Child welfare; Youth services.
Type of support: General support.
Limitations: Applications not accepted. No grants to individuals.
Application information: Unsolicited requests for funds not accepted.
Officers and Directors: Cole M. Braun, Pres.; Jeffrey V. Braun, V.P. and Director; Jennifer C. Braun, Secy. and Director; Diane Braun, Treas. and Director.
EIN: 396043684

9788
Edward A. and Lois L. Brennan Family Foundation

c/o Donald A. Brennan
6052 N. Lake Drive Ct.
Whitefish Bay, WI   53217-4648

Established in 1995 in Illinois.
Donor: Edward A. Brennan†.
Foundation type: Independent foundation.
Financial data (yr. ended 12/31/14): Assets, $3,548,972; gifts received, $0; expenditures, $427,266; qualifying distributions, $380,500 and $0 for set-asides.
Purpose and activities: Giving primarily for higher education and a university medical center.
Fields of interest: Arts and culture; Education; Higher education; Catholicism.
Limitations: Applications not accepted. Giving primarily in IL, with emphasis on Chicago and River Forest. No grants to individuals.
Application information: Contributes only to pre-selected organizations.
Officers: Donald A. Brennan, Pres.; Lois L. Brennan, V.P.; Edward J. Brennan, Secy.; John L. Brennan, Treas.
Directors: Sharon M. Lisnow; Cynthia J. Walls.
EIN: 363993265

9789
Brillion Public High School Scholarship Trust Fund

315 S. Main St.
Brillion, WI   54110-3038

Donor: R.D. & Linda Peters Foundation.
Foundation type: Independent foundation.
Financial data (yr. ended 11/30/14): Assets, $3,587 (M); gifts received, $207,409; expenditures, $208,076; qualifying distributions, $208,076; giving activities include $208,076 for 108 grants to individuals (high: $6,270; low: $500).
Fields of interest: Higher education.
Type of support: Student aid.
Limitations: Applications not accepted.
Application information: Contributes only to pre-selected organizations.
Trustees: Dominick Madison; Jeff VandeHey; Ken Wagner.
EIN: 396365622

9790
The Robert and Susan Brown Family Foundation Inc.

P.O. Box 201
Neenah, WI   54957-0201   (920) 727-1137
Contact: Melinda S. Brown
E-mail: info@red-canoe.org; Main URL: http://red-canoe.org

Established in 2009 in Wisconsin.
Donors: Robert W. Brown; Susan T. Brown.
Foundation type: Independent foundation.
Financial data (yr. ended 12/31/13): Assets, $2,965,433 (M); gifts received, $489,777; expenditures, $173,677; qualifying distributions, $160,396; giving activities include $159,000 for 19 grants (high: $25,000; low: $500).
Fields of interest: Education; Housing development; Human services.
Application information: The foundation is currently not accepting any grant applications.
Officers: Daniel T. Brown, Pres.; Robert W. Brown, V.P. and Secy.; Susan T. Brown, Treas.
EIN: 260743538

9791
Caritas Foundation

P.O. Box 1150
Madison, WI   53701-1150

Established in 2002 in Wisconsin.
Donors: Frederick Schwartz; Deborah Schwartz.
Foundation type: Independent foundation.
Financial data (yr. ended 12/31/13): Assets, $7,452,402 (M); expenditures, $411,014; qualifying distributions, $354,344; giving activities include $330,000 for 4 grants (high: $200,000; low: $35,000).
Fields of interest: Higher education; Nonprofits; Hospice care; Community and economic development; Human services; Food banks.
Type of support: General support; Regranting.
Limitations: Applications not accepted. Giving primarily in WI. No grants to individuals.
Application information: Contributes only to pre-selected organizations.
Trustees: Deborah A. Schwartz; Frederick P. Schwartz.
Executive Committee Members: Richard J. Langer; Sarah A. Kuemmel.
EIN: 416487728

9792
Michael Carlisle Charitable Trust 2

P.O. Box 509
Eau Claire, WI   54702-0509   (715) 833-3940
Contact: Robert A. Kerbell, Tr.

Established in 2003 in Wisconsin.
Donor: Robert A. Kerbell.
Foundation type: Independent foundation.
Financial data (yr. ended 12/31/13): Assets, $1,043,424 (L); expenditures, $176,185; qualifying distributions, $170,600; giving activities include $168,000 for 8 grants (high: $65,000; low: $500).
Fields of interest: Education; Higher education; Christianity.
Type of support: General support; Grants to individuals; Student aid.

Limitations: Applications accepted. Giving primarily in WI.
Application information: Application form required.
   Initial approach: Letter
   Deadline(s): For scholarships: Apr. 30; for organizations: no deadline
Trustee: Robert A. Kerbell.
EIN: 206001882

9793
Betty B. Chastain Educational Foundation
P.O. Box 0634
Milwaukee, WI 53201-0634
Contact: U.S. Bank N.A.
Application address: c/o U.S. Bank, Att.: Kerry Hall, 101 N. First Ave., Ste. 1600, Phoenix, AZ 85003, tel.: (602) 257-5443

Established in 2002 in Arizona.
Donor: Betty Chastain Trust.
Foundation type: Independent foundation.
Financial data (yr. ended 11/30/14): Assets, $3,681,310 (M); expenditures, $408,078; qualifying distributions, $358,355; giving activities include $351,643 for 1 grant.
Fields of interest: University education.
Limitations: Applications accepted. Giving primarily in Tucson, AZ.
Application information: Application form required.
   Initial approach: Letter or telephone
Trustee: U.S. Bank, N.A.
EIN: 916561080

9794
Chipstone Foundation
c/o Foley & Lardner LLP
777 E. Wisconsin Ave., Ste. 3600
Milwaukee, WI 53202-5306
Main URL: http://www.chipstone.org
Facebook: https://www.facebook.com/pages/Chipstone-Foundation/142603039504
Foundation's ArtBabble Profile: http://www.artbabble.org/partner/chipstone
Foundation's Instagram Profile: http://instagram.com/chipstone_org
Twitter: https://twitter.com/chipstone_org

Donors: Stanley Stone†; Ivor Noel Hume; Mrs. Ivor Noel Hume; I. Stanley Stone Charitable Trust; Carol Hume.
Foundation type: Operating foundation.
Financial data (yr. ended 12/31/13): Assets, $76,752,605 (M); gifts received, $1,017,725; expenditures, $4,061,457; qualifying distributions, $5,263,172; giving activities include $248,278 for 20+ grants (high: $141,341), and $2,732,665 for foundation-administered programs.
Purpose and activities: Giving to institutions dedicated to the study and preservation of American material culture and related activities, and education.
Fields of interest: Museums; Historic preservation; Higher education; Nonprofits; Human services; Child welfare.
Type of support: General support; Regranting.
Limitations: Applications not accepted. Giving primarily in Madison and Milwaukee, WI. No grants to individuals.
Application information: Contributes only to pre-selected organizations.

Officers and Directors: W. David Knox II, Chair., Pres. and Treas. and Director; Ted D. Kellner, Vice-Chair. and Director; Jacquelyn A. Sarich, V.P., Admin.; L. Elizabeth Beetz, Secy.; Jonathan Prown, Exec. Dir.; Edward S. Cook, Jr.; Charles F. Hummel; Peter M. Kenny; John S. McGregor; Alison Stone; Stanley Stone III; Gustavus F. Taylor.
Number of staff: 2 full-time professional.
EIN: 396096593

9795
Lau & Bea Christensen Charitable Foundation
(formerly Laurits R. Christensen Charitable Foundation)
723 Wilder Dr.
Madison, WI 53704-6011

Donor: Laurits R. Christensen.
Foundation type: Independent foundation.
Financial data (yr. ended 12/31/13): Assets, $9,690,057 (M); gifts received, $1,076,901; expenditures, $326,047; qualifying distributions, $324,000; giving activities include $324,000 for 31 grants (high: $115,000; low: $100).
Fields of interest: Performing arts; Higher education; Nonprofits; Maternal and perinatal health.
Type of support: Regranting.
Limitations: Applications not accepted. Giving primarily in WI. No grants to individuals.
Application information: Contributes only to pre-selected organizations.
Directors: Christopher Bugg; Laurits R. Christensen; Scott Christensen.
EIN: 208837127

9796
Cloud Family Foundation Inc.
(formerly U.S. Paper Mills Foundation Inc.)
P.O. Box 5876
De Pere, WI 54115-5876

Donor: U.S. Paper Mills Corp.
Foundation type: Company-sponsored foundation.
Financial data (yr. ended 09/30/13): Assets, $5,952,294 (M); expenditures, $327,857; qualifying distributions, $284,400; giving activities include $284,400 for 12 grants (high: $75,000; low: $1,000).
Purpose and activities: The foundation supports organizations involved with education and hunger.
Fields of interest: Education; Domesticated animals; Community and economic development.
Type of support: General support; Scholarships.
Limitations: Applications not accepted. Giving primarily in areas of plant locations in DePere and Green Bay, WI. No grants to individuals.
Application information: Contributes only to pre-selected organizations.
Officers: Walter J. Cloud, Pres.; Thomas L. Olson, V.P.; Kathleen T. Riley, Treas.
Directors: Sam R. Cloud; Theodore Cloud; Nancy Gustavson; Thomas Lemorande; Eric Wimberger.
EIN: 391432753

9797
Community Foundation of Chippewa County
(formerly Chippewa Area Community Foundation)
404 1/2 N. Bridge St.
P.O. Box 153
Chippewa Falls, WI 54729 (715) 723-8125
Contact: Melinda Haun, Secy. and Exec. Dir.
FAX: (715) 720-0834;
E-mail: info@yourlegacyforever.org; Main
URL: http://www.yourlegacyforever.org
E Newsletter: http://www.yourlegacyforever.org/library/includes/newsletter_signup.phtml
Facebook: http://www.facebook.com/pages/Community-Foundation-of-Chippewa-County/261672217694
Twitter: https://twitter.com/comfdncc

Established in 2001 in Wisconsin.
Foundation type: Community foundation.
Financial data (yr. ended 06/30/13): Assets, $10,208,905 (M); gifts received, $419,869; expenditures, $287,826; giving activities include $117,718 for 9+ grants (high: $24,503).
Purpose and activities: The foundation enables donors to achieve their philanthropic goals, to meet changing community needs, and thereby to benefit the communities, people, and other nonprofit organizations of Chippewa County.
Fields of interest: Education; Community and economic development; Human services.
Limitations: Applications accepted. Giving primarily in Chippewa County, WI. No support for sectarian causes. No grants to individuals, or for annual campaigns, routine operating expenses, or debt retirement.
Publications: Application guidelines; Annual report.
Application information: Visit foundation web site for application information. Application form required.
   Copies of proposal: 2
   Deadline(s): Nov. 7
Officers and Directors: Rick Schafer, Chair. and Director; Susan Kern, 1st Vice-Chair. and Director; Dave Jankoski, 2nd Vice-Chair. and Director; Melinda Haun, Secy. and Exec. Dir.; Paul Salm, Treas. and Director; Linda Bergen; Jeanne Boisvert; Ken Custer; Patti Darley; Dave Fish; Megan MacLaughlin-Barck; Tim Scobie; Dean White.
EIN: 392024542

9798
Courtier Foundation Inc.
c/o Foley & Lardner, LLP
P.O. Box 1497
Madison, WI 53701-1497 (608) 258-4224
Contact: David W. Reinecke

Established in 1999 in Wisconsin.
Donors: Veryl F. Courtier Survivor's Trust; Wilma W. Courtier Residual Trust.
Foundation type: Independent foundation.
Financial data (yr. ended 12/31/14): Assets, $4,174,131 (M); expenditures, $249,085; qualifying distributions, $206,251; giving activities include $158,000 for 38 grants (high: $12,000; low: $1,000).
Purpose and activities: Giving primarily to organizations which provide services for children, and housing and other services for elderly individuals in financial need.
Fields of interest: Child welfare; Senior services.

Type of support: Program development.
Limitations: Applications accepted. Giving generally limited to Dane County, WI. No grants to individuals.
Application information: Application form required.
  Initial approach: Request application form
  Copies of proposal: 4
  Deadline(s): None
  Board meeting date(s): Semiannually, usually June and Dec.
Officers and Directors: Thomas G. Ragatz, Pres. and Director; Ronald M. Wanek, V.P. and Director.
Trustee: Foley & Lardner, LLP.
EIN: 391935038

9799
Geoffrey T. Crowley Family Foundation Inc.
6610 N. Purdy Pkwy.
Appleton, WI 54913-7843

Established in 2008 in Wisconsin.
Donor: Geoffrey T. Crowley.
Foundation type: Independent foundation.
Financial data (yr. ended 06/30/14): Assets, $2,470,295 (M); gifts received, $406,898; expenditures, $317,930; qualifying distributions, $305,551; giving activities include $304,561 for 12 grants (high: $250,000; low: $1,000).
Fields of interest: University education; Engineering.
Limitations: Applications not accepted. Giving primarily in IN and WI. No grants to individuals.
Application information: Contributes only to pre-selected organizations.
Officers: Geoffrey T. Crowley, Pres. and Treas.; Elizabeth V. Crowley, V.P. and Secy.
EIN: 261385752

9800
The Cudahy Foundation
(formerly Michael J. Cudahy Foundation)
c/o Kevin I. Lindsey
925 E. Wells St., Ste. 420
Milwaukee, WI 53202-3954

Established in 1999 in Wisconsin.
Donors: Michael J. Cudahy; The Endeavors Group LLC.
Foundation type: Independent foundation.
Financial data (yr. ended 12/31/13): Assets, $9,313,182 (M); gifts received, $37,485; expenditures, $385,681; qualifying distributions, $340,237; giving activities include $303,932 for 17 grants (high: $100,000; low: $1,000).
Fields of interest: Ballet; Theater; Education; Health; Human services; Child welfare.
Limitations: Applications not accepted. Giving primarily in Milwaukee, WI. No grants to individuals.
Application information: Contributes only to pre-selected organizations.
Trustees: Julia A. Cudahy; Lisa A. Cudahy; Joanna D. Hamadi; Kevin L. Lindsey; John W. Linnen; Melvin S. Newman.
EIN: 396720806

9801
Cummings-Christensen Family Foundation
(formerly Laurits R. and Dianne Cummings-Christensen Foundation, Inc.)
701 Deming Way, Ste. 100
Madison, WI 53717-2916

Established in 2001 in Wisconsin.
Donors: Laurits R. Christensen; Dianne C. Christensen.
Foundation type: Independent foundation.
Financial data (yr. ended 12/31/13): Assets, $9,863,949 (M); expenditures, $358,374; qualifying distributions, $348,100; giving activities include $348,100 for 28 grants (high: $50,000; low: $500).
Fields of interest: Arts and culture; Nonprofits; Family planning; Human services.
Type of support: Regranting.
Limitations: Applications not accepted. Giving primarily in NY and WI. No grants to individuals.
Application information: Contributes only to pre-selected organizations.
Directors: Christopher Bugg; Dianne C. Christensen; Scott Christensen.
EIN: 392041875

9802
Dwight and Linda Davis Foundation
P.O. Box 8010
Wausau, WI 54402-8010

Donors: Dwight E. Davis; Greenheck Fan Corporation; Linda Davis.
Foundation type: Independent foundation.
Financial data (yr. ended 12/31/13): Assets, $11,736,942 (M); gifts received, $2,055,592; expenditures, $367,230; qualifying distributions, $316,531; giving activities include $310,800 for 21 grants (high: $60,000; low: $500).
Fields of interest: Domesticated animals; Philanthropy; Foundations; Community and economic development.
Limitations: Applications not accepted. Giving primarily in WI.
Application information: Unsolicited requests for funds not accepted.
Officers and Directors: Dwight E. Davis, Pres. and Director; Linda Davis, V.P. and Director; Lon Robets, Secy. and Director; Jeffrey Stubbe, Treas. and Director.
EIN: 263604136

9803
Gretchen & Andrew Dawes Charitable Trust
c/o Provident Trust Co.
N16 W23217 Stone Ridge Dr., Ste. 310
Waukesha, WI 53188-1155

Established in 2003 in Wisconsin.
Foundation type: Independent foundation.
Financial data (yr. ended 12/31/12): Assets, $0 (M); expenditures, $389,591; qualifying distributions, $388,651; giving activities include $356,112 for 11 grants (high: $50,000; low: $10,000).
Purpose and activities: Giving primarily for the arts, education, and human services.
Fields of interest: Arts and culture; Performing arts; Orchestral music; Education; Higher education; Medical education; Human services; Youth services.
Limitations: Applications not accepted. No grants to individuals.
Application information: Contributes only to pre-selected organizations.

Trustees: Stephen M. Fisher; Max E. Grefig; Janis C. Lenz.
EIN: 367407807

9804
Debbink Family Foundation, Inc.
c/o MSI General Corp.
P.O. Box 7
Oconomowoc, WI 53066-0007

Established in 1997 in Wisconsin.
Donors: Dirk J. Debbink; Teresa L. Debbink; John P. Debbink; Joan C. Debbink.
Foundation type: Independent foundation.
Financial data (yr. ended 12/31/14): Assets, $3,238,277 (M); gifts received, $82,000; expenditures, $172,635; qualifying distributions, $170,760; giving activities include $170,500 for 26 grants (high: $25,000; low: $1,000).
Fields of interest: Education; Health; Human services.
Type of support: General support.
Limitations: Applications not accepted. Giving primarily in WI. No grants to individuals.
Application information: Unsolicited requests for funds not accepted.
Officers: Teresa L. Debbink, Pres.; Joan C. Debbink, V.P.; Dirk J. Debbink, Secy.-Treas.
Director: John P. Debbink.
EIN: 391904743

9805
Frances R. Dewing Foundation
P.O. Box 45259
Madison, WI 53744-5259 (401) 749-8550
Contact: Ann Z. Avery, Mgr.
FAX: (608) 298-7601; Main URL: http://www.frd-foundation.org

Established in 1976 in Massachusetts.
Donor: Frances R. Dewing‡.
Foundation type: Independent foundation.
Financial data (yr. ended 12/31/13): Assets, $2,499,573 (M); expenditures, $172,742; qualifying distributions, $148,736; giving activities include $145,089 for 19 grants (high: $20,000; low: $2,000).
Purpose and activities: The foundation gives grants only to programs that deal directly with early childhood education. Within that context, support is given for the fine and performing arts and other cultural programs, social services, conservation and environmental protection, pre-school, elementary, and other education. Programs must serve children under 12. Emphasis is on new untried or unusual educational organizations or institutions which endeavor to introduce new educational methods.
Fields of interest: Early childhood education.
Type of support: Equipment; Program development; Seed money; Curriculum development.
Limitations: Giving on a national basis. No support for non-501(c)(3) organizations, or organizations funded by the United Way or any other major source of funding. No grants to individuals, or for operating expenses and salaries, general funds, capital campaigns, endowment funds, or scholarships, camperships or transportation.
Publications: Application guidelines; Program policy statement.

Application information: Application guidelines and proposal summary sheet available on foundation web site. Application form required.

> *Initial approach:* Letter or telephone, or see foundation web site
> *Copies of proposal:* 6
> *Deadline(s):* Apr. 1 and Oct. 1
> *Board meeting date(s):* End of Apr. and Oct.

Officers and Trustees: Roger C. Avery, Treas. and Trustee; Ann Z. Avery, Mgr.; Margaret A. Avery; Susan R. Avery; Ruth D. Ewing; Marilyn London-Ewing.

Number of staff: 1 part-time support.

EIN: 046114839

9806

Dohmen Company Foundation, Inc.

215 N. Water St., No. 300
Milwaukee, WI 53202-6055 (414) 299-4914
Contact: Carol Pfeil, V.P., Corp. Comms.
E-mail: cpfeil@dohmen.com; Main URL: http://dohmencompanyfoundation.org

Donor: The F. Dohmen Co.

Foundation type: Company-sponsored foundation.

Financial data (yr. ended 12/31/13): Assets, $3,878,651 (L); expenditures, $362,703; qualifying distributions, $336,000; giving activities include $336,000 for 4 grants (high: $250,000; low: $1,000).

Purpose and activities: The foundation's mission is to connect people in need with lifesaving healthcare products and services.

Fields of interest: Higher education; Health; Human services.

Limitations: Applications not accepted. Giving primarily in WI.

Application information: Unsolicited requests for funds not accepted.

Officers and Directors: Cynthia LaConte, Pres. and Director; Robert Dohmen, V.P. and Director; Ted Dohmen, Secy.-Treas. and Director.

EIN: 352317921

9807

Dohmen Family Foundation, Inc.

3903 W. Mequon Rd., Ste. 112N
Mequon, WI 53092-2727

Established in 2007 in Wisconsin.

Donors: Mary H. Dohmen; Robert C. Dohmen.

Foundation type: Independent foundation.

Financial data (yr. ended 12/31/12): Assets, $8,769 (M); gifts received, $350,064; expenditures, $373,525; qualifying distributions, $370,000; giving activities include $370,000 for grants.

Fields of interest: Ballet; Wildlife biodiversity; Zoos.

Limitations: Applications not accepted. Giving primarily in WI. No grants to individuals.

Application information: Contributes only to pre-selected organizations.

Officers and Directors: Robert C. Dohmen, Pres. and Secy. and Director; Mary H. Dohmen, V.P. and Treas. and Director.

EIN: 208179222

9808

Arnold and Lois Domer Foundation

10466 26th Ave.
Eau Claire, WI 54703-0298 (715) 720-9107
Contact: Mickey Crothers, Exec. Dir.

Donors: Arnold Domer; Lois Domer.

Foundation type: Independent foundation.

Financial data (yr. ended 12/31/13): Assets, $2,122,160 (M); expenditures, $184,448; qualifying distributions, $156,000; giving activities include $156,000 for 41 grants (high: $20,000; low: $1,000).

Fields of interest: Education; Philanthropy; Health.

Limitations: Applications accepted. Giving limited to the Eau Claire, WI, area.

Application information: Application form required.

> *Initial approach:* Letter
> *Deadline(s):* None

Officer: Mickey Crothers, Exec. Dir.

Trustees: Larry R. Domer; Linda A. Roe.

EIN: 391966526

9809

Elizabeth Elser Doolittle Charitable Trust No. 1

777 E. Wisconsin Ave., Ste. 3080
Milwaukee, WI 53202-5302
Contact: Richard S. Gallagher, Tr.; Adam J. Wiensch, Tr.

Established in 1988 in Wisconsin.

Foundation type: Independent foundation.

Financial data (yr. ended 12/31/13): Assets, $2,539,410 (M); expenditures, $207,920; qualifying distributions, $170,286; giving activities include $152,522 for 13 grants (high: $21,227; low: $5,000).

Purpose and activities: Particular consideration given to organizations which provide hospital care and/or provide care or services in the fields of physical or mental health; organizations dealing with or benefiting children under age 18, and particularly physically handicapped and/or mentally handicapped and/or otherwise disadvantaged children; and organizations of an educational and cultural character that provide broad segments of society with an opportunity for self-improvement, self-development, and for an enriched understanding, enjoyment, and appreciation of the quality of life. Priority given to organizations operating in the metropolitan Milwaukee, Wisconsin, area.

Fields of interest: Arts and culture; Education; Philanthropy.

Type of support: Capital campaigns; Equipment; Endowments.

Limitations: Applications accepted. Giving primarily in the Milwaukee, WI, metropolitan area. No grants to individuals, or for operating expenses.

Application information:

> *Initial approach:* Contact foundation
> *Deadline(s):* Aug. 31

Trustees: Richard S. Gallagher; Adam J. Wiensch.

EIN: 391602180

9810

Door County Community Foundation, Inc.

342 Louisiana St., Historic Downtown
Sturgeon Bay, WI 54235 (920) 746-1786
Contact: Bret Bicoy, Pres. and C.E.O.

FAX: (920) 473-2066;
E-mail: bret@doorcountycommunityfoundation.org;
Mailing Address: P.O. Box 802, Sturgeon Bay, WI 54235; Main URL: http://www.doorcountycommunityfoundation.org
Facebook: https://www.facebook.com/doorcountycommunityfoundation

Established in 1999 in Wisconsin.

Foundation type: Community foundation.

Financial data (yr. ended 06/30/13): Assets, $10,805,399 (M); gifts received, $3,311,060; expenditures, $610,275; giving activities include $402,559 for 13+ grants (high: $75,000), and $8,900 for 9 grants to individuals.

Purpose and activities: The foundation seeks to enhance the quality of life in Door County by perpetually serving the charitable needs of the community, and encouraging the continued and expanded philanthropic activities of citizens.

Fields of interest: Arts and culture; Environment; Wildlife biodiversity; Human services.

Type of support: General support; Program development.

Limitations: Applications accepted. Giving primarily in Door County, WI. No support for religious purposes. No grants to individuals (except for scholarships), or for debt retirement, normal operating expenses, annual campaigns, or endowments.

Publications: Informational brochure; Newsletter.

Application information: Visit foundation web site for application form and guidelines per grant type. Application form required.

> *Initial approach:* Telephone, e-mail, or letter
> *Deadline(s):* Varies
> *Final notification:* 6 to 8 weeks

Officers and Directors: David Eliot, Chair. and Director; Polly Alberts, Vice-Chair. and Director; Bret Bicoy, Pres. and C.E.O. and Director; Dick Egan, Secy. and Director; Richard Hauser, Treas. and Director; Bill Boettcher; Jacinda Duffin; Michael Felhofer; John Herlache; Mark Jinkins; Linda Laarman; Frank Maxwell; Michael McCoy; Kaaren Northrop; Sally O'Brien; Nancy Sargent; Marcia Smith; Jane Stevenson.

Number of staff: 1 part-time professional.

EIN: 391980685

9811

Dudley Foundation Inc.

500 1st St., Ste. 2
Wausau, WI 54403-4881 (715) 849-5729

Established in 2000 in Wisconsin.

Donor: Richard D. Dudley.

Foundation type: Independent foundation.

Financial data (yr. ended 06/30/13): Assets, $5,538,109 (M); expenditures, $272,881; qualifying distributions, $250,427; giving activities include $215,750 for 26 grants (high: $50,000; low: $500).

Purpose and activities: Support for organizations benefiting WI, with emphasis on Marathon County, WI.

Fields of interest: Arts and culture; Education; Environment; Home health care; Disasters and emergency management; Economic development; Housing development; Sports and recreation; Human services; Child welfare.

Type of support: General support; Matching grants; Capital campaigns; Capital and infrastructure; Equipment; Land acquisitions; Emergency funds;

Program development; Public engagement and education; Seed money; Technical assistance; Program evaluations.

Limitations: Applications accepted. Giving primarily in WI, with emphasis on Marathon County, WI. No grants to individuals or private businesses.

Application information: Application form required.

Initial approach: Proposal
Copies of proposal: 8
Deadline(s): 1 month before board meeting
Board meeting date(s): Mar., June, Sept., and Dec.
Final notification: 2 months from receipt

Officers: Richard D. Dudley, Chair.; Ann Dudley Shannon, Pres.; John D. Dudley, V.P.; Paul C. Schlindwein II, Secy.; Gary W. Freels, Treas.

Directors: Mary C. Dudley; Robert J. Dudley II; Chad D. Kane.

Number of staff: None.

EIN: 392003427

9812
James E. Dutton Foundation, Inc.

6655 Rainbow Dr.
Merrill, WI 54452-9134 (414) 640-0523
E-mail: silvercreek.fenske@gmail.com; Main
URL: http://www.jameseduttonfoundation.org
Facebook: https://www.facebook.com/pages/
James-E-Dutton-Foundation-Inc/
103622556352989
Grants List: http://
www.jameseduttonfoundation.org/grants/
previous-awards/2014-grant-recipients

Established in 2006 in Wisconsin.

Foundation type: Independent foundation.

Financial data (yr. ended 12/31/14): Assets, $3,844,565; expenditures, $319,723; qualifying distributions, $183,730.

Fields of interest: Education; Environment; Domesticated animals.

Limitations: Applications accepted. Giving primarily in WI. No grants to individuals.

Application information: Application guidelines available on foundation web site.

Initial approach: Letter
Deadline(s): None

Officers: Dean W. Fenske, Pres. and Treas.; John Dutton, V.P.; J. Lewis Perlson, Secy.

EIN: 710985492

9813
Easter Foundation Inc.

958 Hickory Ave.
De Pere, WI 54115-3016

Established in 2003 in Wisconsin.

Donors: Bruce A. Bell; Carol H. Bell; Karen B. Schmidt; Karl A. Schmidt; Paul Elizabeth Keppeler; Warren Brenda Pfohl Family.

Foundation type: Independent foundation.

Financial data (yr. ended 06/30/13): Assets, $13,357,574 (M); gifts received, $6,020,585; expenditures, $286,420; qualifying distributions, $208,530; giving activities include $205,634 for 33 grants (high: $75,000; low: $100).

Fields of interest: Diseases and conditions; Housing development; Human services.

Limitations: Applications not accepted. Giving primarily in NY and WI. No grants to individuals.

Application information: Unsolicited requests for funds not accepted.

Officers: Bruce A. Bell, Pres. and Treas.; Carol H. Bell, V.P. and Secy.

Directors: Betsy B. Keppeler; Paul Keppeler; Brenda B. Pfohl; Warren C. Pfohl; Karen B. Schmidt; Karl A. Schmidt.

EIN: 200499778

9814
Eau Claire Community Foundation

(formerly Eau Claire Area Foundation)
306 S. Barstow, Ste. 104
P.O. Box 511
Eau Claire, WI 54702-0511 (715) 552-3801
Contact: Sue Bornick, Exec. Dir.
FAX: (715) 552-3802;
E-mail: info@eccommunityfoundation.org; Additional
e-mail: suebornick@eccommunityfoundation.org;
Main URL: http://www.eccommunityfoundation.org
Facebook: https://www.facebook.com/
eccommunityfoundation
LinkedIn: https://www.linkedin.com/company/
eau-claire-community-foundation

Established in 1997 in Wisconsin.

Donors: Interfaith Hospitality; Roger & Sue Tietz.

Foundation type: Community foundation.

Financial data (yr. ended 12/31/13): Assets, $9,350,617 (M); gifts received, $535,225; expenditures, $469,691; giving activities include $257,414 for 18+ grants (high: $38,003).

Purpose and activities: The foundation strengthens the community by offering donors opportunities to establish charitable legacies, by making grants, and by serving as a catalyst to address community needs.

Fields of interest: Arts and culture; Education; Environment; Sports and recreation; Human services.

Type of support: Capital campaigns; Matching grants; Capital and infrastructure; Equipment; Program development; Seed money; Research; Technical assistance; Program evaluations.

Limitations: Applications accepted. Giving limited to the greater Eau Claire, WI, area. No support for sectarian causes. No grants to individuals, or for annual campaigns, capital campaigns, debt retirement, endowments, lobbying, or routine operating expenses.

Publications: Annual report; Financial statement; Grants list; Informational brochure (including application guidelines); Newsletter.

Application information: Visit foundation web site for application form and guidelines. Full proposals sent by fax or e-mail are not accepted. The foundation strongly encourages applicants to attend one of the orientation sessions prior to submitting an application. Application form required.

Initial approach: Contact foundation
Copies of proposal: 16
Deadline(s): 1 month prior to grant deadline for Letter of Intent; Feb. 8 for full grant application
Board meeting date(s): Monthly
Final notification: 90 days

Officers and Trustees: Jane Lokken, Chair. and Trustee; Mark Faanes, Vice-Chair. and Trustee; Laura Talley, Secy. and Trustee; Lois Krause, Treas. and Trustee; Sue Bornick, Exec. Dir.; Suzanne Ashley; Jill Barland; Thomas Dow; Joe Fesenmaier; Dave Frederikson; Charlie Grossklaus; Jeff Halloin; Chris Hasenberg; Betsy Kell; Laurie Klinkhammer;

Nicole Lasker; Leland Meyer, MD; Wayne Peters; Pat Quinn.

Number of staff: 1 full-time professional; 3 part-time support.

EIN: 391891064

9815
Einhorn Family Foundation Inc.

(formerly Einhorn Family Charitable Trust)
8205 N. River Rd.
Milwaukee, WI 53217-2546 (414) 351-3169
Contact: Nancy Einhorn, Pres.
E-mail: rwalmer@wengers.com; Main URL: http://
www.einhornfamilyfoundation.org

Donors: Stephen Einhorn; Nancy Einhorn.

Foundation type: Independent foundation.

Financial data (yr. ended 12/31/13): Assets, $3,347,117 (M); expenditures, $384,495; qualifying distributions, $377,375; giving activities include $372,500 for 31 grants (high: $100,000; low: $1,000).

Purpose and activities: Giving primarily for the arts and education.

Fields of interest: Arts and culture; Ballet; Art museums; Education; Higher education.

Type of support: General support.

Limitations: Applications accepted. Giving limited to the greater Milwaukee, WI area. No grants to individuals, or for annual campaigns or endowments.

Application information: Application forms are by invitation only, upon review of initial proposal. Application form required.

Initial approach: Short proposal via U.S. mail or e-mail
Deadline(s): None

Officers: Nancy Einhorn, Pres.; Stephen Einhorn, V.P.

EIN: 396643717

9816
Daniel W. Erdman Foundation

c/o U.S. Bank, N.A.
P.O. Box 7900
Madison, WI 53707-7900

Established in 2000 in Wisconsin.

Donor: Daniel W. Erdman.

Foundation type: Independent foundation.

Financial data (yr. ended 12/31/13): Assets, $3,003,097 (M); gifts received, $163,098; expenditures, $202,598; qualifying distributions, $178,250; giving activities include $177,500 for 6 grants (high: $125,000; low: $5,000).

Fields of interest: Arts and culture; Historic preservation; Natural resources; Foundations; Nonprofits; Diseases and conditions; Eye diseases; Housing development; Human services.

Type of support: Capital campaigns; Regranting; Research; Research and evaluation.

Limitations: Applications not accepted. Giving primarily in AZ, VA and WI. No grants to individuals.

Application information: Contributes only to pre-selected organizations.

Directors: Darrell W. Behnke; Daniel W. Erdman; Deborah Erdman-Luder; Natalie Bock Erdman.

EIN: 392012234

9817

F.K. Bemis Family Foundation
300 Mill St.
Sheboygan Falls, WI 53085-0901 (920)
467-4621
Contact: Karen E. Hoefler, Secy.

Donor: Bemis Manufacturing Co.
Foundation type: Company-sponsored foundation.
Financial data (yr. ended 12/31/13): Assets,
$2,156,300 (M); gifts received, $1,809,379;
expenditures, $358,729; qualifying distributions,
$358,727; giving activities include $358,727 for 50
grants (high: $75,000; low: $250).
Purpose and activities: The foundation supports
gardens and hospices and organizations involved
with arts and culture, education, children and youth,
and community development.
Fields of interest: Education; Community and
economic development; Human services.
Limitations: Applications accepted. Giving primarily
in Sheboygan County, WI.
Application information: Application form required.
  Initial approach: Proposal
  Deadline(s): Dec. 1
Officers: Erin E. Bemis, Pres.; Wendy Bemis, V.P.;
Karen E. Hoefler, Secy.; Frank J. Poja, Treas.
EIN: 396067930

9818

Charles E. Fahrney Education Foundation
(also known as Fahrney Education Foundation)
c/o U.S. Bank, N.A.
P.O. Box 2043
Milwaukee, WI 53201-9668
Application address: c/o US Bank, N.A., Trust Dept.,
123 E. 3rd St., Ottumwa, IA 52501, tel.: (641)
683-2053

Established in 1979 in Iowa.
Donors: Helen Fahrney†; Blanche Peck Charitable
Remainder Unitrust.
Foundation type: Independent foundation.
Financial data (yr. ended 02/28/13): Assets,
$4,935,298 (M); expenditures, $270,416;
qualifying distributions, $231,648; giving activities
include $215,000 for 87 grants to individuals (high:
$2,500; low: $1,250).
Purpose and activities: Provides scholarships for
full-time students who are Wapello County, Iowa,
residents and are attending a college or university
in Iowa.
Fields of interest: Education.
Type of support: Student aid.
Limitations: Applications accepted. Giving limited to
residents of Wapello County, IA, attending IA
colleges or universities.
Publications: Application guidelines.
Application information: Include an official high
school or college/university transcript, along with a
signed personal letter. Application form required.
  Initial approach: E-Mail.
  Copies of proposal: 1
  Deadline(s): Feb. 15
Trustee: U.S. Bank, N.A.
EIN: 426295370

9819

**Ferguson Family Baptist Missionary &
Educational Foundation, Ltd.**
2450 Old Plank Rd.
De Pere, WI 54115-8658

Established in 2004 in Wisconsin.
Donor: Larry P. Ferguson.
Foundation type: Independent foundation.
Financial data (yr. ended 12/31/12): Assets,
$29,589,370 (M); gifts received, $3,495,850;
expenditures, $693,154; qualifying distributions,
$188,550; giving activities include $188,550 for
grants.
Fields of interest: Education; Religion.
Limitations: Applications not accepted. Giving
primarily in WI; some funding also in FL.
Application information: Unsolicited requests for
funds not accepted.
Officers: Larry P. Ferguson, Pres.; Kayleen H.
Ferguson, V.P.; Bryant Ferguson, Secy.; Kyle
Ferguson, Treas.
EIN: 201554053

9820

Foley Family Foundation
c/o Stephen M. Fisher & Assocs. LLP
11414 W. Park Pl., Ste. 107
Milwaukee, WI 53224-3500

Established in 1993 in Wisconsin.
Donor: Mildred Foley†.
Foundation type: Independent foundation.
Financial data (yr. ended 12/31/14): Assets,
$3,470,346; gifts received, $0; expenditures,
$487,959; qualifying distributions, $432,466 and
$0 for set-asides.
Fields of interest: Higher education; Nonprofits.
Type of support: General support; Regranting.
Limitations: Applications not accepted. Giving
primarily in Milwaukee, WI; some giving also in
Evanston, IL. No grants to individuals.
Application information: Contributes only to
pre-selected organizations.
Trustees: Wendy Reed Bosworth; Stephen M.
Fisher.
EIN: 396551865

9821

**Duane and Kathleen Foulkes Foundation,
Inc.**
P.O. Box 337
Beaver Dam, WI 53916-0337

Established in 2006 in Wisconsin.
Donors: Duane E. Foulkes; Kathleen M. Foulkes.
Foundation type: Independent foundation.
Financial data (yr. ended 12/31/14): Assets,
$4,796,107 (M); expenditures, $259,348;
qualifying distributions, $207,268; giving activities
include $207,268 for 46 grants (high: $130,821;
low: $50).
Fields of interest: Diseases and conditions;
Religion; Human services.
Type of support: Research.
Limitations: Applications not accepted. Giving
primarily in WI. No grants to individuals.
Application information: Unsolicited requests for
funds not accepted.

Directors: Kristine M. Eckles; Duane E. Foulkes;
Kathleen M. Foulkes.
EIN: 205592397

9822

**John J. Frautschi Family Foundation,
Inc.**
303 Lakewood Blvd.
Madison, WI 53704-5917

Established in 1986 in Wisconsin.
Donor: John J. Frautschi.
Foundation type: Independent foundation.
Financial data (yr. ended 12/31/13): Assets,
$4,640,521 (M); expenditures, $463,417;
qualifying distributions, $436,297; giving activities
include $423,000 for 77 grants (high: $175,000;
low: $1,000).
Purpose and activities: Giving primarily for
education, the arts, health associations, human
services, and to a Presbyterian church.
Fields of interest: Arts and culture; Performing arts;
Museums; Education; Elementary and secondary
education; Higher education; Natural resources;
Nonprofits; Diseases and conditions;
Protestantism; Human services.
Type of support: General support; Regranting.
Limitations: Applications not accepted. Giving
primarily in Madison, WI. No grants to individuals.
Application information: Contributes only to
pre-selected organizations. Unsolicited requests for
funds not considered.
  Board meeting date(s): Annually
Officers and Directors: John J. Frautschi, Pres. and
Director; Elizabeth J. Frautschi, V.P. and Director;
Christopher J. Frautschi, Co-Secy.-Co-Treas. and
Director; Peter W. Frautschi, Co-Secy.-Co-Treas. and
Director.
EIN: 391561017

9823

**Walter and Mabel Fromm Scholarship
Trust**
c/o U.S. Bank N.A.
P.O. Box 7900
Madison, WI 53707-7900

Established in 1975 in Wisconsin.
Donors: Mabel Fromm†; Walter Fromm†.
Foundation type: Independent foundation.
Financial data (yr. ended 02/28/15): Assets,
$3,793,834 (M); expenditures, $212,352;
qualifying distributions, $160,877; giving activities
include $155,000 for 36 grants to individuals (high:
$4,750; low: $1,500).
Purpose and activities: Support limited to college,
vocational, and nursing school scholarships for
graduates of the Maple Grove School and/or Merrill
Senior Public High School.
Fields of interest: Vocational education; Graduate
and professional education; Nursing care.
Type of support: Student aid.
Limitations: Applications not accepted. Giving
primarily in WI.
Application information: Unsolicited requests for
funds not accepted.
Trustee: U.S. Bank, N.A.
Number of staff: None.
EIN: 396250027

9824
Fromstein Foundation Ltd.
5205 N. Ironwood Rd., Ste. 100
Milwaukee, WI 53217-4907

Established in 1977 in Wisconsin.
Donor: Mitchell S. Fromstein.
Foundation type: Independent foundation.
Financial data (yr. ended 06/30/13): Assets,
$2,113,110 (M); expenditures, $324,204;
qualifying distributions, $314,468; giving activities
include $307,600 for 11 grants (high: $200,000;
low: $100).
Purpose and activities: Giving primarily for
federated giving programs, as well as human
services.
Fields of interest: Arts and culture; Philanthropy;
Religion.
Type of support: General support.
Limitations: Applications not accepted. Giving
primarily in FL and Milwaukee, WI. No grants to
individuals.
Application information: Contributes only to
pre-selected organizations.
Officers: Mitchell S. Fromstein, Pres. and Treas.;
Lita Fromstein, V.P. and Secy.
Directors: John L. Fromstein; Jane F. Henley.
EIN: 391287508

9825
Gardner Foundation
322 E. Michigan St., Ste. 250
Milwaukee, WI 53202-5010 (414) 273-0308
Contact: Theodore Friedlander III, Pres.

Established in 1947 in New York.
Donor: Herman Gardner‡.
Foundation type: Independent foundation.
Financial data (yr. ended 12/31/13): Assets,
$2,210,516 (M); expenditures, $161,379;
qualifying distributions, $151,975; giving activities
include $151,975 for 45 grants (high: $6,000; low:
$975).
Purpose and activities: Giving for arts and culture,
education, and youth services.
Fields of interest: Performing arts; Museums;
Elementary and secondary education; Hospice care;
Reproductive health care; Mental health care;
Community and economic development;
Employment; Human services; Child welfare;
Homeless services.
Type of support: General support; Continuing
support; Annual campaigns; Capital campaigns;
Capital and infrastructure; Emergency funds.
Limitations: Applications accepted. Giving primarily
in the greater Milwaukee, WI, area.
Publications: Application guidelines; Program policy
statement.
Application information: Application form required.
  Initial approach: Contact foundation for
    application form
  Copies of proposal: 1
  Deadline(s): One month before each board
    meeting
  Board meeting date(s): Apr., Sept., and Dec.
Officers: Theodore Friedlander III, Pres.; Gardner L.
R. Friedlander, V.P.; Sarah O. Zimmerman, Treas.
Directors: Clifford M. Asmuth; Margaret Brinig; Jean
W. Friedlander; Louise Friedlander; C. Frederick
Geilfuss; Barbara Brown Lee; Lynde Uihlein.
Number of staff: None.
EIN: 396076956

9826
Gebhardt Foundation, Inc.
c/o BMO Harris Bank N.A.
P.O. Box 2980
Milwaukee, WI 53201-2977 (239) 597-2771
Application address: 5601 Turtle Bay Dr., No. 1204,
Naples, FL 34108-2702

Established in 2000 in Florida.
Donors: Arthur A. Gebhardt; Gebhardt Charitable
Lead Annuity Trust.
Foundation type: Independent foundation.
Financial data (yr. ended 12/31/14): Assets,
$862,741; gifts received, $204,586; expenditures,
$379,739; qualifying distributions, $377,700.
Fields of interest: Education; Higher education;
Religion; Human services.
Limitations: Applications accepted. Giving primarily
in SD and WI.
Application information:
  Initial approach: Letter
  Deadline(s): None
Officers: Arthur A. Gebhardt, Pres.; Patricia A.
Gebhardt, V.P.; Ellen C. Nygaard, Secy.; Sarah
Hammill, Treas.
EIN: 651059870

9827
Karen J. Glanert Charitable Trust
2933 W. Range Line Ct., Unit 102N
Mequon, WI 53092-5328

Established in 1998 in Wisconsin.
Donor: Karen J. Glanert.
Foundation type: Independent foundation.
Financial data (yr. ended 12/31/13): Assets,
$3,900,605 (M); expenditures, $215,909;
qualifying distributions, $188,488; giving activities
include $185,000 for 9 grants (high: $75,000; low:
$1,500).
Fields of interest: Historic preservation; Nonprofits;
Hospital care; Pediatrics; Cancers; Child welfare;
Youth services.
Type of support: General support; Regranting.
Limitations: Applications not accepted. Giving
primarily in CO, FL, and WI. No grants to individuals.
Application information: Contributes only to
pre-selected organizations.
Trustees: Jennifer G. Callahan; Karen J. Glanert.
EIN: 396695585

9828
Glendenning Family Foundation, Inc.
c/o Jack Glendenning, Abbot Downing
200 West Ave. S.
La Crosse, WI 54061

Established in 1999 in Wisconsin.
Donors: Jack L. Glendenning; Rosanne
Glendenning; Mark T. Glendenning; John H.
Glendenning; Inland Label & Marketing Services,
LLC.
Foundation type: Independent foundation.
Financial data (yr. ended 12/31/13): Assets,
$5,393,105 (M); gifts received, $383,506;
expenditures, $278,097; qualifying distributions,
$252,069; giving activities include $243,000 for 11
grants (high: $140,000; low: $2,000).
Fields of interest: Health; Human services; Youth
services.

Limitations: Applications not accepted. No grants to
individuals.
Application information: Unsolicited requests for
funds not accepted.
Officers: John H. Glendenning, Pres.; Rosanne
Glendenning, V.P.; Jill Keck, Secy.; Mark
Glendenning, Treas.
Director: John Glendenning.
EIN: 391981729

9829
Global Christian Interaction, Inc.
9667 S. 20th St.
Oak Creek, WI 53154-4931

Established in 1990 in Wisconsin.
Donor: Michael H. Polaski.
Foundation type: Operating foundation.
Financial data (yr. ended 12/31/13): Assets,
$6,390,353 (M); gifts received, $356,916;
expenditures, $419,628; qualifying distributions,
$407,695; giving activities include $202,700 for 1
grant.
Fields of interest: Christianity; Human services.
International interests: Bulgaria; Global Programs;
Kenya.
Limitations: Applications not accepted. Giving
primarily in Bulgaria and Kenya. No grants to
individuals.
Application information: Unsolicited requests for
funds not accepted.
Officers and Directors: Michael H. Polaski, Pres.
and Treas. and Director; Michael J. Polaski, Secy.
and Director; Catherine J. Polaski.
EIN: 391695712

9830
Donald A. Gordon Foundation
c/o Trust Point, Inc.
230 Front St. N.
La Crosse, WI 54601-3219

Foundation type: Independent foundation.
Financial data (yr. ended 12/31/14): Assets,
$5,314,928; gifts received, $0; expenditures,
$308,914; qualifying distributions, $234,688 and
$0 for set-asides.
Fields of interest: Higher education; Foundations;
Nonprofits; Health; Public libraries; Human services;
Youth services.
Type of support: Regranting; Fundraising.
Limitations: Applications not accepted. Giving
primarily in La Crosse, WI. No grants to individuals.
Application information: Unsolicited requests for
funds not accepted.
Trustee: Trust Point, Inc.
EIN: 316672086

9831
Gertrude S. Gordon Foundation
c/o Trust Point Inc.
230 Front St. N.
La Crosse, WI 54601-3219

Foundation type: Independent foundation.
Financial data (yr. ended 12/31/13): Assets,
$10,656,810 (M); expenditures, $526,745;
qualifying distributions, $435,171; giving activities
include $431,171 for 10 grants (high: $112,657;
low: $21,486).

Fields of interest: Foundations; Protestantism; Human services; Youth services.
Limitations: Applications not accepted. Giving primarily in La Crosse, WI. No grants to individuals.
Application information: Contributes only to pre-selected organizations.
Trustee: Trust Point.
EIN: 316672080

9832
Grande Foundation
301 E. Main St.
Lomira, WI 53048-9548 (920) 269-7200

Donor: Grande Cheese Co.
Foundation type: Independent foundation.
Financial data (yr. ended 03/31/13): Assets, $1,240 (M); gifts received, $230,000; expenditures, $231,405; qualifying distributions, $231,405; giving activities include $228,055 for 50 grants (high: $125,000; low: $250).
Fields of interest: Education; Health; Human services.
Limitations: Applications accepted. Giving primarily in WI.
Application information:
 Initial approach: Letter
 Deadline(s): None
Officers and Directors: John Candela, Chair. and Director; Wayne E. Matzke, Pres. and Director; Todd H. Koss, Secy.-Treas. and Director.
EIN: 208316469

9833
Arno Gunther Charitable Foundation
P.O. Box 649
Neenah, WI 54957-0649 9209675020

Foundation type: Independent foundation.
Financial data (yr. ended 12/31/14): Assets, $3,793,347; expenditures, $248,249; qualifying distributions, $212,622 and $0 for set-asides.
Fields of interest: Education; Philanthropy; Religion.
Limitations: Applications not accepted. Giving primarily in WI.
Application information: Unsolicited requests for funds not accepted.
Trustee: Legacy Private Trust Company.
EIN: 262522556

9834
Hamilton Family Foundation Inc.
411 E. Wisconsin Ave. von Briesen
Milwaukee, WI 53202

Established in 2000 in Wisconsin.
Donor: William H. Hamilton†.
Foundation type: Independent foundation.
Financial data (yr. ended 12/31/13): Assets, $4,022,337 (M); expenditures, $193,301; qualifying distributions, $173,765; giving activities include $154,500 for 24 grants (high: $20,000; low: $500).
Fields of interest: Undergraduate education; Religion; Children and youth; Infants and toddlers; Adolescents; Adults.
Limitations: Applications not accepted. Giving primarily in WI. No support for political organizations. No grants to individuals.
Publications: Annual report.

Application information: Contributes only to pre-selected organizations.
Officers and Directors: Douglas H. Hamilton, Pres. and Director; Jane Musich Hamilton, V.P.; Sally H. Lensink, Treas. and Director.
Number of staff: None.
EIN: 391980599

9835
The Robert E. Hansen Family Foundation
c/o Inge Alverson Bacon, CPA
253 N. 1st Ave., Ste. 1
Sturgeon Bay, WI 54235-2500

Established in 1988 in Texas.
Donor: Margaret W.H. Hansen.
Foundation type: Independent foundation.
Financial data (yr. ended 08/31/13): Assets, $1,399,977 (M); gifts received, $14,790; expenditures, $217,819; qualifying distributions, $212,200; giving activities include $212,200 for 70 grants (high: $100,000; low: $100).
Fields of interest: Arts and culture; Higher education; Environment; Domesticated animals; Protestantism; Human services.
Limitations: Applications not accepted. Giving primarily in TX. No grants to individuals.
Application information: Unsolicited requests for funds not accepted.
Officers: Margaret W.H. Hansen, Pres. and Treas.; Alexander E. Hansen, V.P.; Laurie H. Saxton, Secy.
EIN: 760259279

9836
Hartwig Family Foundation, Inc.
P.O. Box 733
Appleton, WI 54912-0733

Established in 1999 in Wisconsin.
Donor: Christopher Hartwig.
Foundation type: Independent foundation.
Financial data (yr. ended 06/30/14): Assets, $3,928,540 (M); gifts received, $212,754; expenditures, $182,177; qualifying distributions, $168,000; giving activities include $168,000 for 51 grants (high: $25,000; low: $1,000).
Fields of interest: Education; Elementary and secondary education; Foundations; Catholicism; Human services; Child welfare.
Limitations: Applications not accepted. Giving primarily in WI. No grants to individuals.
Application information: Unsolicited requests for funds not accepted.
Officers and Directors: Christopher Hartwig, Pres. and Treas. and Director; Evelyn Hartwig, Secy. and Director; Joseph Bielinski; Dana Hartwig; Hans Hartwig; Dennis Wojahn; Gary Wynveen.
EIN: 391977500

9837
Deena Hatch Foundation
N15301 13th Ave. N.
Necedah, WI 54646-7021

Established in 1998 in Wisconsin.
Donors: William G. Hatch; Sandra L. Hatch.
Foundation type: Independent foundation.
Financial data (yr. ended 06/30/14): Assets, $4,573,538 (M); gifts received, $454,170; expenditures, $208,445; qualifying distributions,

$175,756; giving activities include $172,000 for 8 grants (high: $50,000; low: $7,500).
Fields of interest: Education; Human services.
Type of support: Scholarships.
Limitations: Applications not accepted. Giving primarily to residents of Necedah, WI. No grants to individuals.
Application information: Unsolicited requests for funds not accepted.
Trustees: William T. Curran; Sandra L. Hatch; William G. Hatch.
EIN: 391943131

9838
Helios Foundation
c/o Schaper, Benz & Wise Investment Counsel
18 Jewelers Park, Ste. 200
P.O. Box 628
Neenah, WI 54957-0628

Established in 1986 in Wisconsin.
Donor: Marjorie Klewit.
Foundation type: Independent foundation.
Financial data (yr. ended 05/31/14): Assets, $4,905,021 (M); expenditures, $273,960; qualifying distributions, $232,981; giving activities include $229,500 for 31 grants (high: $40,000; low: $1,000).
Fields of interest: Arts and culture; Theater; Education; Graduate and professional education; Environment; Natural resources; Foundations; Addiction services; Theology.
Limitations: Applications accepted. Giving on a national basis. No grants to individuals.
Officer and Directors: Barbara B. Aalfs; John H. Buchanan, Pres.; Linda Jacob; Marjorie Kiewit; Nancy McLoughlin; Pat McLoughlin; Daniel Jacob; Juliana Kelly; Christina M. Aalfs; Ben McLoughlin; Schaper, Benz & Wise Investment Counsel.
EIN: 391532106

9839
Heller Foundation, Inc.
c/o Godfrey & Kahnsc
780 N. Water St., 15th Fl.
Milwaukee, WI 53202-3512

Established in 1957 in Wisconsin.
Foundation type: Independent foundation.
Financial data (yr. ended 11/30/13): Assets, $4,203,629 (M); expenditures, $198,779; qualifying distributions, $189,652; giving activities include $189,652 for 47 grants (high: $18,706; low: $250).
Purpose and activities: Support primarily for higher education and health services.
Fields of interest: Arts and culture; Higher education; Community health care.
Type of support: General support; Scholarships; Research.
Limitations: Applications not accepted. Giving primarily in AZ and Milwaukee, WI. No grants to individuals.
Application information: Contributes only to pre-selected organizations.
Officers and Trustees: Joan Heller, Pres. and Treas.; Gretchen Farmer, V.P. and Secy.; J. Andrew Heller; Nancy Joan Heller; William J. Heller; Heidi Kieslerco.
EIN: 396045338

9840
Nelson G. and Vera C. Hicks Charitable Foundation

5339 Irish Ln.
Madison, WI 53711-5517
Contact: John Karsten, Pres.
Application address: 4 Fond du Lac St., Waupun, WI
53963-1939, tel.: (920) 324-8658

Foundation type: Independent foundation.
Financial data (yr. ended 12/31/13): Assets,
$4,544,572 (M); expenditures, $212,753;
qualifying distributions, $204,083; giving activities
include $202,500 for 46 grants (high: $25,000;
low: $500).
Fields of interest: Education; Health; Public
libraries; Christianity; Human services; Family
services; Youth development.
Limitations: Applications accepted. Giving primarily
in Beaver Dam, WI.
Application information:
Initial approach: Proposal
Deadline(s): None
Officers: John Karsten, Pres.; Robert H. Keller, V.P.;
W.E. Kinney, Secy.-Treas.
EIN: 391582654

9841
Highlands Foundation, Inc.

4717 Hammersley Rd.
Madison, WI 53711-2708

Established in 2005 in Wisconsin.
Donors: Susan A. Bakke; James J. Bakke.
Foundation type: Independent foundation.
Financial data (yr. ended 12/31/13): Assets,
$5,259,809 (M); expenditures, $294,680;
qualifying distributions, $251,700; giving activities
include $251,700 for 7 grants (high: $110,700;
low: $2,500).
Fields of interest: Arts and culture; Performing arts;
Children's museums; Education; Foundations;
Nonprofits; Christianity; Winter sports; Human
services.
Type of support: General support; Public
engagement and education; Regranting.
Limitations: Applications not accepted. Giving
primarily in WI and DC. No grants to individuals.
Application information: Unsolicited requests for
funds not accepted.
Officers: Susan A. Bakke, Pres; James J. Bakke,
V.P.; Blaine R. Renfert, Secy.-Treas.
EIN: 203941123

9842
Harri Hoffmann Family Foundation Inc.

125 N. Water St.
Milwaukee, WI 53202-6011 (414) 276-6190
Contact: Lorraine Hoffmann, Pres.

Established in 1985 in Wisconsin.
Donors: Harri Hoffmann; Herta Hoffmann†; Lorraine
Hoffmann.
Foundation type: Independent foundation.
Financial data (yr. ended 12/31/13): Assets,
$3,095,343 (M); gifts received, $15,800;
expenditures, $220,781; qualifying distributions,
$217,835; giving activities include $217,835 for 2
+ grants.
Purpose and activities: Giving primarily for Jewish
agencies and temples.

Fields of interest: Education; Diseases and
conditions; Judaism.
Limitations: Applications accepted. Giving primarily
in WI.
Application information:
Initial approach: Letter
Deadline(s): None
Officers: Lorraine Hoffmann, Pres.; Evelyn
Hoffmann, V.P.; Alan Matsoff, Secy.
EIN: 391537228

9843
The Terri & Verne Holoubek Family Foundation, Inc.

6545 Donegal Rd.
Hartford, WI 53027-8829

Established in 2005 in Wisconsin.
Donors: Carol A. Holoubek; Verne A. Holoubek; Terri
Holoubek.
Foundation type: Independent foundation.
Financial data (yr. ended 12/31/13): Assets,
$5,108,864 (M); expenditures, $283,199;
qualifying distributions, $250,350; giving activities
include $250,350 for 20 grants (high: $50,000;
low: $100).
Fields of interest: Art museums; University
education; Catholicism; Child welfare; Youth
development; Low-income and poor people.
Limitations: Applications not accepted. Giving
primarily in GA, MD, NE and WI. No grants to
individuals.
Application information: Contributes only to
pre-selected organizations.
Officers: Verne A. Holoubek, Pres.; Carol A.
Holoubek, V.P.; Richard Vanderheiden, Secy.; Sara
Holoubek, Treas.
EIN: 204002202

9844
Ralph J. Huiras Foundation, Inc.

(formerly Ralph J. Huiras Family Foundation, Inc.)
2560 Hwy. 32
P.O. Box 366
Port Washington, WI 53074-0366 (262)
377-6160
Contact: William J. Farrell, Pres. and Dir.

Established in 1996 in Wisconsin.
Donor: Ralph J. Huiras.
Foundation type: Operating foundation.
Financial data (yr. ended 12/31/13): Assets,
$5,169,199 (M); expenditures, $375,149;
qualifying distributions, $322,980; giving activities
include $303,000 for 25 grants (high: $105,000;
low: $1,000).
Fields of interest: Arts and culture; Education; Law
education; Foundations; Diseases and conditions;
Catholicism; Human services.
Limitations: Applications accepted. Giving primarily
in WI.
Application information: Application form required.
Initial approach: Proposal
Deadline(s): None
Officer and Directors: William Farrell, Pres. and
Director; John Farrell; Margaret Schreiner.
EIN: 391844576

9845
Frieda & William Hunt Memorial Trust

c/o Foley & Lardner LLP
777 E. Wisconsin Ave., Ste. 3500
Milwaukee, WI 53202-5306

Established in 1988 in Wisconsin.
Donor: Frieda E. Hunt†.
Foundation type: Independent foundation.
Financial data (yr. ended 12/31/14): Assets,
$8,426,982; expenditures, $438,741; qualifying
distributions, $403,695.
Fields of interest: Arts and culture; Performing arts;
Opera; Museums; Education; University education;
Natural resources; Biodiversity; Wildlife biodiversity;
Health; Protestantism; Human services.
Type of support: General support; Annual
campaigns; Capital campaigns; Capital and
infrastructure; Equipment; Emergency funds;
Program development; Seed money.
Limitations: Applications accepted. Giving primarily
in Milwaukee, WI.
Application information:
Initial approach: Proposal
Deadline(s): None
Trustees: Wayne R. Lueders; Jeffrey M. Seaman;
John T. Seaman, Jr.; John T. Seaman III.
EIN: 391642918

9846
The Hyde Family Charitable Fund

c/o James J. Malczewski, Virchaw Krause
P.O. Box 2459
Appleton, WI 54912

Established in 1996 in New York.
Donors: Charles F. Hyde, Jr.; Thomas R. Hyde.
Foundation type: Independent foundation.
Financial data (yr. ended 12/31/13): Assets,
$5,411,364 (M); expenditures, $366,879;
qualifying distributions, $334,875; giving activities
include $334,000 for 13 grants (high: $250,000;
low: $2,000).
Fields of interest: Orchestral music; Art museums;
Literature and writing; Education; Housing
development; Human services; Youth services.
Limitations: Applications not accepted. Giving
primarily in Buffalo, NY. No grants to individuals.
Application information: Contributes only to
pre-selected organizations.
Trustees: Douglas W. Hyde; Joyce W. Hyde; Thomas
R. Hyde; Margaret H. Wachtel.
EIN: 161502229

9847
Dorothy Inbusch Foundation, Inc.

(formerly Charles E. & Dorothy Watkins Inbusch
Foundation, Inc.)
111 E. Kilbourn Ave., Ste. 1400
Milwaukee, WI 53202-6677 (414) 225-1404

Donor: Dorothy Watkins Inbusch†.
Foundation type: Independent foundation.
Financial data (yr. ended 12/31/14): Assets,
$3,027,548; expenditures, $240,410; qualifying
distributions, $210,819 and $0 for set-asides.
Purpose and activities: Funding primarily for arts
and culture, health and human services, education,
environmental and historic preservation.
Fields of interest: Arts and culture; Historic
preservation; Education; Natural resources; Health;

Human services; Children; Adults; Seniors; Female adults; Male adults; Ethnic and racial groups; People of African descent; People of Latin American descent; Homeless people; Low-income and poor people; People with disabilities; People with physical disabilities; People with vision impairments; People with hearing impairments.

Type of support: General support; Continuing support; Capital campaigns; Capital and infrastructure; Program development; Seed money.

Limitations: Applications accepted. Giving primarily in the greater Milwaukee, WI, area. No grants to individuals.

Publications: Application guidelines.

Application information:
Initial approach: Proposal
Copies of proposal: 1
Deadline(s): Oct. 31

Officers and Directors: Kathy L. Nusslock, V.P. and Director; Thomas J. Drought, Secy.-Treas. and Director.

Number of staff: None.

EIN: 396084238

9848
J.P.C. Foundation
c/o Stephen Wisnefsky
P.O. Box 1957
Janesville, WI 53547-1957

Established in 1991 in Wisconsin.

Donors: J.P. Cullen & Sons, Inc.; John P. Cullen.

Foundation type: Company-sponsored foundation.

Financial data (yr. ended 05/31/14): Assets, $3,205,002 (M); gifts received, $340,000; expenditures, $312,083; qualifying distributions, $296,450; giving activities include $296,450 for 32 grants (high: $100,000; low: $200).

Purpose and activities: The foundation supports organizations involved with arts and culture, education, health, human services, and Catholicism.

Fields of interest: Arts and culture; Health; Religion; Human services.

Type of support: General support; Capital and infrastructure; Scholarships.

Limitations: Applications not accepted. Giving primarily in WI; some giving also in Honolulu, HI. No grants to individuals.

Application information: Contributes only to pre-selected organizations.

Trustees: John P. Cullen; Mark A. Cullen.

EIN: 391703739

9849
Charles D. Jacobus Family Foundation
11815 W. Bradley Rd.
Milwaukee, WI 53224-2532 (414) 577-0252
Contact: Missy MacLeod, Pres.
FAX: (414) 359-1357;
E-mail: foundation@jacobusenergy.com; Mailing address: P.O. Box 13009, Milwaukee, WI 53213-0009; Toll free tel.: (800) 242-4702 ext. 1252; Main URL: http://www.cdjff.org
Grants List: http://www.cdjff.org/pastrecipients.html

Established in 1986 in Wisconsin.

Donors: Jacobus Co.; Charles D. Jacobus†; Eugene T. Jacobus.

Foundation type: Independent foundation.

Financial data (yr. ended 12/31/13): Assets, $5,045,968 (M); expenditures, $454,476; qualifying distributions, $432,307; giving activities include $340,948 for 22 grants (high: $50,000; low: $3,500), and $24,000 for 6 grants to individuals (high: $15,000; low: $1,000).

Purpose and activities: Giving primarily for youth development in the areas of preventive programs, positive youth activities, and strengthening families and research; also funding for scholarships to children of full time employees of Jacobus Energy, Inc., or Quick Fuel Fleet Services, LLC.

Fields of interest: Arts and culture; Early childhood education; Nonprofits; Family services; Child welfare; Children and youth; Children; Adolescents.

Type of support: Continuing support; Annual campaigns; Capital campaigns; Capital and infrastructure; Program development; Publications; Research; Technical assistance; Regranting; Program evaluations; Student aid.

Limitations: Applications accepted. Giving limited to Milwaukee, WI, specifically Milwaukee County. No support for religious or political organizations. No grants for scholarships (except employee-related), tuition, seminars, fundraisers, travel, legislative or lobbying activities, or for benefits (sponsoring tables, buying auction items, etc.), competitions, parades, or camps.

Publications: Application guidelines.

Application information: Application forms available on foundation web site. Application form required.
Initial approach: Use pre-application format on foundation web site
Copies of proposal: 1
Deadline(s): See foundation web site for current deadlines
Board meeting date(s): Sept. and Nov.

Officers: Missy MacLeod, Pres.; Eugenia Jacobus, V.P. and Secy.; Eugene T. Jacobus, Treas.

Director: Charles D. Jacobus, Jr.

Number of staff: 1 full-time professional.

EIN: 391559892

9850
Janesville Foundation, Inc.
121 N. Parker Dr.
P.O. Box 8123
Janesville, WI 53547-8123 (608) 752-1032
Contact: Ronald K. Ochs, C.E.O.; Diane K. Brown, Admin.
FAX: (608) 752-1952;
E-mail: contact@janesvillefoundation.org; Main URL: http://www.janesvillefoundation.org

Established in 1944 in Wisconsin.

Donor: The Parker Pen Co.

Foundation type: Independent foundation.

Financial data (yr. ended 12/31/13): Assets, $8,810,485 (M); expenditures, $467,057; qualifying distributions, $404,607; giving activities include $334,958 for 17 grants (high: $55,000; low: $290).

Purpose and activities: Primary areas of interest include community/economic development and education. All giving must impact the Janesville, Wisconsin, area.

Fields of interest: Education; Community and economic development.

Type of support: Equipment; Matching grants; Capital campaigns; Land acquisitions; Program development; Seed money.

Limitations: Applications accepted. Giving limited to grants that impact the local Janesville, WI, area. No

support for programs that do not impact the local Janesville, WI, area, or for religious or partisan organizations, or non-501(c)(3) organizations. No grants to individuals or for operating budgets, endowment or investment funds, or medical research.

Application information: Application guidelines and application available upon request. Application form required.
Initial approach: Online inquiry through foundation web site or letter of inquiry
Copies of proposal: 1
Deadline(s): None
Board meeting date(s): Varies
Final notification: After board meetings

Officers and Directors: Rowland J. McClellan, Chair. and Director; Dennis L. Hansch, Vice-Chair. and Treas.; Ronald K. Ochs, C.E.O. and Pres. and Director; Martha E. Parker, V.P. and Director; Dolores M. Dilley, Secy.

Number of staff: 1 part-time professional; 2 part-time support.

EIN: 396034645

9851
C. Paul Johnson Family Charitable Foundation
10000 Innovation Dr., No. 250
Milwaukee, WI 53226-4837

Established in 1988 in Illinois.

Donor: C. Paul Johnson.

Foundation type: Independent foundation.

Financial data (yr. ended 12/31/12): Assets, $107,753 (M); gifts received, $383,077; expenditures, $442,138; qualifying distributions, $427,747; giving activities include $427,747 for grants.

Fields of interest: Education; Higher education; Natural resources; Science; Human services.

International interests: Africa; Israel.

Type of support: Endowments; Capital campaigns; General support; Scholarships; Research.

Limitations: Applications not accepted. Giving in the U.S., with emphasis on CA. No grants to individuals.

Application information: Contributes only to pre-selected organizations.

Trustees: Deborah De La Reguera; Adrienne Johnson; C. Paul Johnson; Debra Johnson; Julianne Johnson; Vince Mancuso; Rebecca Milne.

EIN: 366891454

9852
Charles E. and Andriene M. Johnson Foundation
P.O. Box 12800
Green Bay, WI 54307-2800

Established in 1992 in Minnesota.

Donors: Charles E. Johnson; Andriene M. Johnson Annuity Hartford.

Foundation type: Independent foundation.

Financial data (yr. ended 12/31/13): Assets, $5,861,278 (M); expenditures, $253,784; qualifying distributions, $224,476; giving activities include $224,301 for 3 grants (high: $214,801; low: $3,500).

Fields of interest: Immune system diseases; Community and economic development; Housing development; Human services.

Limitations: Applications not accepted. Giving primarily in MN. No grants to individuals.
Application information: Unsolicited requests for funds not accepted.
Officers: Kirsten L. O'Brien, Pres.; Tyler H. O'Brien, V.P.; Collin L. O'Brien, Secy.; Justin F. O'Brien, Treas.
EIN: 411736857

9853
Claire and Marjorie Johnson, Inc.
397 24 3/4 Ave.
Cumberland, WI 54829-8839   (715) 822-5124
Application address: c/o Principal, Cumberland High School, 1000 8th Ave., Cumberland, WI 54829, tel.: (715) 822-5124

Established in 1998 in Wisconsin.
Donors: Claire Johnson; Marjorie Johnson.
Foundation type: Independent foundation.
Financial data (yr. ended 12/31/13): Assets, $6,409,500 (M); gifts received, $6,409,500; expenditures, $417,871; qualifying distributions, $372,652; giving activities include $278,550 for 10 grants (high: $100,750; low: $800), and $81,250 for 50 grants to individuals (high: $2,500; low: $1,250).
Purpose and activities: Giving primarily for education, including scholarship awards to Cumberland High School, Wisconsin, juniors with a B average and a family income under $75,000.
Fields of interest: Children's museums; Education; Youth services.
Type of support: General support; Scholarships; Student aid.
Limitations: Applications accepted. Giving primarily in MN and WI.
Application information: Application form required.
   Initial approach: Proposal
   Deadline(s): Apr. 30
Officers: Claire Johnson, Pres.; Marjorie Johnson, V.P.
Directors: Teresa Devenecia; Mary Kay Hanson; Kelly Kautz; Karen Pardyjak.
EIN: 391874405

9854
Stella H. Jones Foundation
100 E. Wisconsin Ave., Ste. 3300
Milwaukee, WI 53202-4108

Established in 1997 in Wisconsin.
Donor: Jones Living Trust.
Foundation type: Independent foundation.
Financial data (yr. ended 12/31/14): Assets, $3,280,993 (M); expenditures, $252,824; qualifying distributions, $177,955; giving activities include $144,000 for 17 grants (high: $25,000; low: $2,500).
Purpose and activities: Giving primarily for social services, health care and the arts.
Fields of interest: Education; Health; Human services.
Limitations: Applications not accepted. Giving primarily in WI. No grants to individuals.
Application information: Unsolicited requests for funds not accepted.
Trustees: Carol A. Bourne; Richard P. Bourne; Arthur F. Jeske; J. Lewis Perlson.
EIN: 396630656

9855
William Stark Jones Foundation
c/o Kathleen W. Lambert
250 W Coventry Ct., Ste. 207
Milwaukee, WI 53217

Established in 2005 in Wisconsin.
Donor: William Stark Jones Admin. Tr.
Foundation type: Independent foundation.
Financial data (yr. ended 12/31/13): Assets, $3,162,378 (M); expenditures, $211,631; qualifying distributions, $200,000; giving activities include $200,000 for 68 grants (high: $30,000; low: $1,000).
Fields of interest: Arts and culture; Education; Christianity; Protestantism; Adult day care.
Limitations: Applications not accepted. Giving primarily in Milwaukee, WI; some giving in FL. No grants to individuals.
Application information: Unsolicited requests for funds not accepted.
Trustees: Kathleen F. DeMarinis; Peter Klode; Katherine W. Lambert; Thomas J. Landers.
EIN: 396786974

9856
Karl Junginger Foundation, Inc.
P.O. Box 185
Waterloo, WI 53594-0185
Application address: P.O. Box 127, Waterloo, WI 53594, tel.: (920) 478-2101

Established in 1988 in Wisconsin.
Donor: Karl Junginger‡.
Foundation type: Independent foundation.
Financial data (yr. ended 12/31/13): Assets, $1,769,535 (M); expenditures, $187,423; qualifying distributions, $167,398; giving activities include $166,900 for 2 grants (high: $108,400; low: $58,500).
Purpose and activities: Giving primarily for community support and for scholarships to Waterloo High School seniors in Waterloo, Wisconsin.
Fields of interest: Higher education; Public libraries; Public administration; Community and economic development.
Type of support: General support; Scholarships.
Limitations: Applications accepted. Giving primarily in Waterloo, WI.
Application information: Application form required.
   Initial approach: Proposal
   Deadline(s): None
Officers: Tim Jonas, Pres. and Treas.; Lee Fiedorowicz, V.P.; Kevin Fiedorowicz, V.P.
EIN: 391602319

9857
Kachel Family Foundation Inc.
144 N. Tratt St.
Whitewater, WI 53190-1205   (262) 473-3355
Contact: Michael S.D. Kachel, Pres., Treas., and Dir.

Established in 2006 in Wisconsin.
Donor: Kachel 2005 Charitable Lead Annuity Trust.
Foundation type: Independent foundation.
Financial data (yr. ended 12/31/13): Assets, $304,414 (M); gifts received, $468,750; expenditures, $212,196; qualifying distributions, $211,613; giving activities include $211,031 for 7 grants (high: $167,601; low: $500).

Fields of interest: Education; Higher education; Hospital care; Protestantism.
Type of support: Annual campaigns.
Limitations: Applications accepted. Giving primarily in WI.
Application information:
   Initial approach: Proposal
   Deadline(s): None
Officers and Directors: Michael S.D. Kachel, Pres. and Treas. and Director; Laurence D. Kachel, V.P. and Secy. and Director; Mitchell Simon.
EIN: 204009911

9858
Kalscheur Family Foundation
(formerly James & Joyce Kalscheur Foundation)
1221 John Q Hammons Dr.
Madison, WI 53717
Application Address: 3234 Valley Spring Rd., Mt. Horeb, WI 53572 1236, Tel.: (608) 355-3040

Established in 1997 in Wisconsin.
Donors: Steven Kalscheur; James H. Kalscheur; Joyce J. Kalscheur; Scott Kalscheur; Amy Lanham.
Foundation type: Independent foundation.
Financial data (yr. ended 12/31/13): Assets, $10,594,222 (M); expenditures, $487,181; qualifying distributions, $407,825; giving activities include $376,046 for 60 grants (high: $50,000; low: $100).
Purpose and activities: Giving primarily to Roman Catholic churches and schools, for human services, and for children's and youth services.
Fields of interest: Education; Hospice care; Catholicism; Human services; Child welfare.
Type of support: General support.
Limitations: Applications accepted. Giving primarily in WI. No grants to individuals.
Application information:
   Initial approach: Proposal
   Deadline(s): None
Trustee: Baraboo National Bank.
EIN: 396681490

9859
The Karol Fund
c/o Edward P. Mooney, Jr.
7038 N. Beach Rd.
Fox Point, WI 53217-3657   (414) 228-5124
Contact: Edward P. Mooney Jr., Tr.

Established in 2003 in Wisconsin.
Donor: Edward P. Mooney, Jr.
Foundation type: Independent foundation.
Financial data (yr. ended 12/31/13): Assets, $663,913 (M); gifts received, $400,000; expenditures, $328,900; qualifying distributions, $228,200; giving activities include $227,500 for 13 grants (high: $80,000; low: $2,500).
Fields of interest: Catholicism.
Type of support: General support.
Limitations: Applications accepted. Giving primarily in Milwaukee, WI; some giving also in Washington, DC. No support for organizations that support or advocate abortion, euthanasia, or capital punishment. No grants to individuals.
Application information: Application form required.
   Initial approach: Typed letter
   Deadline(s): None
Trustees: Bridie Ann Mooney; Edward P. Mooney, Jr.
EIN: 200350673

9860
Kaztex Foundation, Inc.
N28 W23000 Roundy Dr., No. 203
Pewaukee, WI 53072-7300

Established in 1993 in Wisconsin.
Donors: John C. Kasdorf; Elmbrook Church; Kaztex Enterprises, Inc.
Foundation type: Independent foundation.
Financial data (yr. ended 12/31/13): Assets, $10,027,469 (M); gifts received, $263,001; expenditures, $427,395; qualifying distributions, $421,449; giving activities include $405,529 for 61 grants (high: $30,000; low: $14).
Purpose and activities: Giving primarily to organizations in southeast Wisconsin that assist those in need and share the gospel.
Fields of interest: Christianity; Human services.
Type of support: General support.
Limitations: Applications not accepted. Giving primarily in Milwaukee and southeast WI. No grants to individuals.
Application information: Contributes only to pre-selected organizations.
Officers and Directors: John C. Kasdorf, Pres. and Director; Michael D. Murphy, V.P.; Jessica L. Stenz, Secy. and Director; Michael C. Kasdorf, Treas.; Cheryl N. Kasdorf.
Number of staff: None.
EIN: 391774373

9861
Kelly Family Foundation, Inc.
401 Charmany Dr., Ste. 320
Madison, WI 53719-1270

Established in 2002 in Wisconsin.
Donors: Mary Kelly; Terry Kelly; Terence Kelly.
Foundation type: Independent foundation.
Financial data (yr. ended 12/31/13): Assets, $97,118 (M); expenditures, $190,070; qualifying distributions, $185,915; giving activities include $184,502 for 27 grants (high: $25,000; low: $100).
Fields of interest: Arts and culture; Education; Environment.
Type of support: General support.
Limitations: Applications not accepted. Giving primarily in WI. No grants to individuals.
Application information: Unsolicited requests for funds not accepted.
Officers: Mary Kelly, Pres.; Christopher Kelly, V.P.; Matthew Kelly, V.P.; Terry Kelly, Secy.-Treas.
EIN: 392030686

9862
Kenosha Community Foundation
600 52nd St., Ste. 110
Kenosha, WI 53140-3423 (262) 654-2412
Contact: Robert B. Schneider, Exec. Dir.
FAX: (262) 654-2615;
E-mail: email@kenoshafoundation.org; Additional e-mail: rschneider@kenoshafoundation.org; Main URL: http://www.kenoshafoundation.org
Facebook: https://www.facebook.com/kenoshafoundation

Established in 1926 in Wisconsin.
Foundation type: Community foundation.
Financial data (yr. ended 12/31/13): Assets, $7,003,436 (M); gifts received, $205,210; expenditures, $555,723; giving activities include

$286,363 for 3+ grants (high: $11,435), and $32,167 for 41 grants to individuals.
Purpose and activities: The foundation seeks to provide philanthropic leadership to address the changing needs of the people of Greater Kenosha in order to enhance their quality of life. The foundation is structured to receive charitable gifts of any size to advance civic, cultural, educational, health, and welfare causes.
Fields of interest: Arts and culture; Historic preservation; Education; Environment; Health; Public affairs; Human services.
Type of support: General support; Matching grants; Seed money; Scholarships.
Limitations: Applications accepted. Giving primarily in Kenosha County, WI. No support for sectarian religious programs. No grants to individuals (except for scholarships), or for endowment funds, annual campaigns, debt retirement, or emergency funding; or will repeat grants to the same project on an open-ended basis.
Publications: Application guidelines; Annual report; Grants list; Informational brochure.
Application information: Visit foundation web site for application form and guidelines. Application form required.
Initial approach: Telephone or letter of intent
Copies of proposal: 18
Deadline(s): Feb. 27
Board meeting date(s): Quarterly
Officers and Directors: Kenneth L. Fellman, Pres. and Director; Robert B. Schneider, Exec. Dir.; Cathryn S. Bothe; Marsha Caporaso; Gary Dickes; David Geertsen; Neil F. Guttormsen; Jack S. Harris; Jane Harrington Heide; J. Michael McTernan; Joan Wilk; Victor N. Weiler; Jamie Young.
Board of Advisors: Elynor Chemerow; Robert A. Cornog; Mary P. Enroth; Connie Ferwerda; Samuel Seavitte; James D. Seymour; Gene F. Soens.
Number of staff: 1 full-time professional; 1 part-time support.
EIN: 396045289

9863
John & Ruth Kloss Charitable Trust
c/o US Bank N.A.
P.O. Box 2043
Milwaukee, WI 53201-9668
Application address: c/o U.S. Bank, N.A. Foundation Team, 777 E. Wisconsin Ave., MK-WI-TWPT, Milwaukee, WI 53202, tel.: (414) 765-5672

Established in 2006 in Wisconsin.
Foundation type: Independent foundation.
Financial data (yr. ended 05/31/14): Assets, $9,462,575 (M); expenditures, $546,409; qualifying distributions, $440,036; giving activities include $428,500 for 24 grants (high: $85,000; low: $2,000).
Fields of interest: Education; Animal welfare; Human services.
Limitations: Applications accepted. Giving primarily in southeastern WI, with emphasis on Kenosha County.
Application information: Application form required.
Initial approach: Letter requesting application form
Deadline(s): None
Trustee: U.S. Bank, N.A.
Board Members: Bryan Albrecht; John Antaramian; Jane Harrington-Heide; Mary Plunkett.
EIN: 396790033

9864
Herbert H. Kohl Charities, Inc.
825 N. Jefferson St., Ste. 350
Milwaukee, WI 53202-3731

Established in 1977 in Wisconsin.
Donors: Herbert H. Kohl; Mary Kohl.
Foundation type: Independent foundation.
Financial data (yr. ended 06/30/14): Assets, $7,226,868 (M); expenditures, $395,070; qualifying distributions, $381,210; giving activities include $378,150 for 504 grants (high: $60,000; low: $100).
Purpose and activities: Giving primarily for higher and other education, health associations, children, youth and social services, arts and culture, federated giving programs, and community development; some funding also for Christian organizations and churches, and Jewish organizations.
Fields of interest: Arts and culture; Education; Elementary and secondary education; Higher education; Nonprofits; Diseases and conditions; Community and economic development; Protestantism; Catholicism; Judaism; Human services; Child welfare; Youth services.
Type of support: Research; Research and evaluation; Regranting.
Limitations: Applications not accepted. Giving primarily in WI, with strong emphasis on Milwaukee. No grants to individuals.
Application information: Contributes only to pre-selected organizations.
Officers and Directors: Herbert H. Kohl, Pres. and Director; Allen D. Kohl, V.P. and Director; Sidney A. Kohl, Secy. and Director; Dolores K. Kohl, Treas. and Director.
EIN: 391300476

9865
Herb Kohl Educational Foundation
825 N. Jefferson St., Ste. 350
Milwaukee, WI 53202-3731
Main URL: http://www.kohleducation.org
Grant Database: http://www.kohleducation.org/recipients
Scholarship address: c/o Elaine Strom, Education Consultant, Wisconsin Dept. of Public Instruction, P.O. Box 7841, Madison, WI 53707-7841, tel.: (608) 266-3089, e-mail: elaine.strom@dpi.wi.gov

Established in 1989 in Wisconsin.
Donors: Herbert H. Kohl; Herbert H. Kohl Charities, Inc.
Foundation type: Independent foundation.
Financial data (yr. ended 12/31/13): Assets, $736,910 (M); expenditures, $415,871; qualifying distributions, $402,930; giving activities include $398,500 for 360 grants to individuals (high: $4,000; low: $1,000).
Purpose and activities: Scholarship awards to graduating seniors of public and private Wisconsin high schools; also awards fellowships for teachers of public and private WI schools. Giving also for elementary and secondary education.
Fields of interest: Elementary education; Secondary education; Higher education; Teacher education.
Type of support: General support; Grants to individuals; Student aid.
Limitations: Applications accepted. Giving primarily in WI.

Application information: Teaching awards by nomination only. Application form required.

Deadline(s): Generally the second week of Nov. for scholarships. Check with school principal or counselor for current deadline information. See foundation web site for current deadline date for teaching awards

Officers and Directors: Herbert H. Kohl, Pres. and Director; Allen D. Kohl, V.P. and Director; Sidney A. Kohl, Secy. and Director; Dolores Kohl.

EIN: 391661743

9866
Koss Foundation Inc.

(formerly John C. Koss Family Foundation, Inc.)
4129 N. Port Washington Rd.
Milwaukee, WI 53212-1029 (414) 964-5000

Established in 1968 in Wisconsin.
Donor: Koss Corp.
Foundation type: Company-sponsored foundation.
Financial data (yr. ended 12/31/14): Assets, $725,987; expenditures, $164,731; qualifying distributions, $163,600.
Purpose and activities: The foundation supports organizations involved with arts and culture, education, health, Crohn's disease, youth development, and Christianity.
Fields of interest: Education; Religion; Youth development.
Type of support: Continuing support; Matching grants; Annual campaigns; Capital campaigns.
Limitations: Applications accepted. Giving primarily in the Milwaukee, WI, area. No grants to individuals.
Application information:

Initial approach: Letter
Deadline(s): None

Officers and Directors: John C. Koss, Pres. and Director; Michael J. Koss, Secy.-Treas.; Nancy L. Koss.
Number of staff: 1 part-time support.
EIN: 391098935

9867
Lakeshore Community Foundation, Inc.

915 Memorial Drive
Manitowoc, WI 54220 (920) 682-5222
Contact: Rachel E. Wiegert, Exec. Dir.
E-mail: rwiegert@lakeshorecommunityfoundation.or g; Additional tel. (Sheboygan office): (920) 458-1920; Main URL: http://www.lakeshorecommunityfoundation.org

Established in 2009 in Wisconsin.
Foundation type: Community foundation.
Financial data (yr. ended 12/31/13): Assets, $10,415,224 (M); gifts received, $3,515,866; expenditures, $395,849; giving activities include $196,410 for 6+ grants (high: $70,000).
Limitations: Applications accepted. Giving primarily in the Lakeshore Area of East Central Wisconsin. No support for religious organizations for religious purposes. No grants to individuals, or for general operating expenses, debt reduction, or agency endowments.
Application information: Application form required.
Officers and Directors: Rachel Wiegert, Exec. Dir.; Thomas Aschenbrenner; Richard Balge; Thomas Bare; Joseph DiRaimondo, MD; Edward McKelvey; Jane Pfeffer; Timothy Schroeder.
EIN: 270978059

9868
The Lakeview Foundation, Inc.

P.O. Box 253
Thiensville, WI 53092-2053
Contact: William H. Foshag, Dir.

Established in 1996 in Wisconsin.
Foundation type: Independent foundation.
Financial data (yr. ended 07/31/14): Assets, $10,710,375 (M); expenditures, $499,636; qualifying distributions, $375,250; giving activities include $375,250 for 8 grants (high: $100,000; low: $250).
Purpose and activities: Giving primarily for programs benefiting youth in the inner city of Milwaukee, WI.
Fields of interest: Education; Youth services; Children and youth; Children; Adolescents; Female children and youth; Male children and youth; Slum youth.
Type of support: Capital campaigns; Capital and infrastructure; Equipment; Program development; Curriculum development.
Limitations: Giving primarily in the inner city of Milwaukee, WI. No grants to individuals.
Application information: Unsolicited requests for funds are generally not accepted. Application form required.

Deadline(s): Mar. 31
Board meeting date(s): Quarterly
Final notification: 90-120 days

Officers and Directors: Charles J. Osborne, Pres.; John H. Woodin, V.P. and Director; Ruth H. McGuire, Secy. and Director; Robert R. Magliocco, Treas. and Director; Fred J. Bartkowski; Robert H. Brogan; Kelly Denk; William H. Foshag; Ron Perri; E. Thomas Sheahan; Vernon H. Swanson.
EIN: 391857646

9869
Lato Family Foundation, Inc.

S27 W29293 Jennie Ct.
Waukesha, WI 53188-9518
Contact: Joan M. Lato, Pres.

Established in 2006 in Wisconsin.
Donors: Gary J. Lato; Joan M. Lato; Robert D. Kern.
Foundation type: Independent foundation.
Financial data (yr. ended 12/31/13): Assets, $1,567,784 (M); expenditures, $209,405; qualifying distributions, $209,405; giving activities include $167,100 for 19 grants (high: $38,500; low: $500).
Fields of interest: Education; Christianity.
Application information:

Initial approach: Proposal
Deadline(s): None

Officers: Joan M. Lato, Pres.; Gary J. Lato, V.P. and Treas.
EIN: 205677633

9870
Robert William, M.D. and June M. Lloyd Charitable Trust

P.O. Box 0634
Milwaukee, WI 53201-0634

Foundation type: Independent foundation.
Financial data (yr. ended 11/30/14): Assets, $3,470,026 (M); expenditures, $220,686;

qualifying distributions, $174,920; giving activities include $168,654 for 1 grant.
Fields of interest: Education.
Type of support: General support.
Limitations: Applications not accepted. Giving primarily in OR. No grants to individuals.
Application information: Unsolicited requests for funds not accepted.
Trustee: U.S. Bank, N.A.
EIN: 916573273

9871
Alain Locke Scholarship Trust

P.O. Box 39
Wisconsin Rapids, WI 54495-0039 (715) 424-3004
Contact: George Mead, Tr.

Donor: George Mead.
Foundation type: Independent foundation.
Financial data (yr. ended 12/31/14): Assets, $2,788,779 (M); gifts received, $1,042; expenditures, $151,056; qualifying distributions, $150,355; giving activities include $150,000 for 1 grant.
Fields of interest: Education; Higher education.
Limitations: Applications accepted. Giving primarily in Chicago, IL.
Application information: Application form required.

Initial approach: Proposal
Deadline(s): None

Trustees: James Alexander; Deborah Mead; George Mead.
EIN: 326098483

9872
Loehrke Family Charitable Foundation

N29 W27510 Peninsula Dr.
Pewaukee, WI 53072-4328

Established in 2003 in Wisconsin.
Donors: Kent Loehrke; Wynne Loehrke.
Foundation type: Independent foundation.
Financial data (yr. ended 12/31/14): Assets, $1,039,775; gifts received, $600,000; expenditures, $201,543; qualifying distributions, $188,820.
Fields of interest: Higher education; Diseases and conditions; Christianity; Human services.
Type of support: General support; Research.
Limitations: Applications not accepted. Giving primarily in WI. No grants to individuals.
Application information: Unsolicited requests for funds not accepted.
Trustees: Kent Loehrke; Wynne Loehrke.
EIN: 396779459

9873
Lutsey Family Foundation, Inc.

P.O. Box 22074
Green Bay, WI 54305-2074
Contact: Sharon L. Lutsey, Dir.; Thomas J. Lutsey, Pres.
Application address: 1675 Remington Ridge Rd., Depere, WI 54115, tel.: (920) 339-9823

Established in 1989 in Wisconsin.
Donor: Thomas J. Lutsey.
Foundation type: Independent foundation.

Financial data (yr. ended 12/31/13): Assets, $5,139,137 (M); gifts received, $7,620; expenditures, $219,601; qualifying distributions, $223,271; giving activities include $219,601 for 29 grants (high: $80,000; low: $75).
Fields of interest: Arts and culture; Education; Higher education; Foundations; Nonprofits; Hospital care; Diseases and conditions; Human services; Youth services.
Type of support: Capital campaigns; Matching grants; Seed money; Scholarships; Regranting.
Limitations: Applications accepted. Giving primarily in WI, with emphasis on Green Bay. No grants to individuals.
Application information:
Initial approach: Proposal
Deadline(s): None
Officer: Thomas J. Lutsey, Pres.
Directors: Andrew J. Lutsey; Jeffrey K. Lutsey; Matthew T. Lutsey; Nicholas P. Lutsey; Sharon L. Lutsey.
EIN: 391657029

9874
LUX Foundation Inc.
c/o Stephen M. Fisher & Assoc., LLP
11414 W. Park Pl., Ste. 107
Milwaukee, WI 53224-3500

Established in 1988 in Wisconsin.
Donors: Barbara E. Manger; William H. Lynch; Edmund B. Manger; Matthew Manger-Lynch.
Foundation type: Independent foundation.
Financial data (yr. ended 12/31/13): Assets, $8,691,813 (M); expenditures, $430,168; qualifying distributions, $387,038; giving activities include $377,500 for 32 grants (high: $30,000; low: $5,000).
Fields of interest: Education; Higher education; Graduate and professional education; Natural resources; Biodiversity; Wildlife biodiversity; Botanical gardens; Nursing care; Human services; Youth services.
Type of support: General support; Matching grants; Endowments; Scholarships.
Limitations: Applications not accepted. Giving primarily in WI, with emphasis on Green Bay and Milwaukee. No grants to individuals.
Application information: Contributes only to pre-selected organizations.
Officers and Directors: Barbara E. Manger, Pres. and Director; Robert E. Manger, V.P. and Director; Stephen M. Fisher, Secy.; William H. Lynch, Treas. and Director; Luke M. Lynch.
EIN: 391618778

9875
Lyche Family Foundation, Inc.
1820 Ironwood Pl.
Onalaska, WI 54650-8211

Donors: John Lyche; Linda Lyche.
Foundation type: Independent foundation.
Financial data (yr. ended 12/31/13): Assets, $8,620,327 (M); expenditures, $445,557; qualifying distributions, $392,575; giving activities include $392,575 for 35 grants (high: $263,500; low: $50).
Fields of interest: Arts and culture; Human services; Youth development.

Limitations: Applications not accepted. Giving primarily in WI.
Application information: Unsolicited requests for funds not accepted.
Trustees: Eric J. Lyche; John Lyche; Linda Lyche.
EIN: 262410775

9876
The Manitowoc Company Foundation
(formerly Welbilt Corporation Foundation)
2400 S. 44th St.
Manitowoc, WI 54220-5846

Established in 1972 in Michigan.
Donors: Kysor Industrial Corp.; Manitowoc Company.
Foundation type: Company-sponsored foundation.
Financial data (yr. ended 05/31/14): Assets, $2,245,702 (M); gifts received, $322,060; expenditures, $334,380; qualifying distributions, $327,408; giving activities include $321,200 for 51 grants (high: $60,000; low: $60).
Purpose and activities: The foundation supports organizations involved with education, health, cancer, and human services.
Fields of interest: Education; Higher education; Nonprofits; Health; Patient social services; Cancers; Public libraries; Human services; Child welfare; Youth services; Adult and child mentoring.
Type of support: General support; Continuing support; Capital campaigns; Capital and infrastructure; Publications; Research; Regranting.
Limitations: Applications not accepted. Giving primarily in areas of company operations in CO, GA, LA, MD, PA, and TX; giving also to national organizations. No support for political organizations, religious organizations not of direct benefit to the entire community, or national or international organizations. No grants to individuals or for political campaigns.
Application information: Contributes only to pre-selected organizations.
Officers: Robert M. Hund, Pres.; Maurice D. Jones, V.P. and Secy.; Carl J. Laurino, V.P.; Therese C. Houlahan, Treas.
EIN: 237199469

9877
Marcus Family Charitable Trust
301 N. Broadway, No. 300
Milwaukee, WI 53202-2660
Application address: c/o Stephen Marcus, 100 E. Wisconsin Ave., Ste. 1900, Milwaukee, WI 53202, tel.: (414) 905-1530

Established in 1997 in Wisconsin.
Donors: Ben Marcus; Celia Marcus; Joan Marcus; Stephen Marcus.
Foundation type: Independent foundation.
Financial data (yr. ended 12/31/12): Assets, $4,916,531 (M); gifts received, $91,588; expenditures, $259,660; qualifying distributions, $208,932; giving activities include $208,932 for grants.
Purpose and activities: Giving for human services and Jewish organizations.
Fields of interest: Foundations; Nonprofits; Kidney diseases; Judaism; Human services.
Type of support: General support; Research; Regranting.

Limitations: Applications accepted. Giving primarily in Milwaukee, WI. No grants to individuals.
Application information:
Initial approach: Brochures preferred
Deadline(s): None
Trustee: Stephen Marcus.
EIN: 391891090

9878
Marshfield Area Community Foundation
P.O. Box 456
Marshfield, WI 54449-0456   (715) 384-9029
Contact: Amber Kigins-Leifheit, Exec. Dir.
FAX: (715) 384-9229;
E-mail: macf@marshfieldareacommunityfoundation.org; Main URL: http://marshfieldareacommunityfoundation.org

Established in 1993 in Wisconsin.
Donors: Harry Chronquist†; Gladys Chronquist†; G. Stanley Custer†; Violet Custer†; Leonard L. Hartl†; Margaret Quirt Heck†; Melvin A. Hintz†; LaVerne R. Kohs†; Patrice LeGrand†; J.P. Leonard†; George Mac Kinnon†; Joseph Lang†; Bette Adler; Anne Adler; Pat Hamus; Floyd Hamus; Roberta DeVetter; Dennis DeVetter; Margaret B. King†.
Foundation type: Community foundation.
Financial data (yr. ended 06/30/13): Assets, $5,639,442 (M); gifts received, $380,383; expenditures, $287,600; giving activities include $131,405 for 6+ grants (high: $27,355), and $51,802 for grants to individuals.
Purpose and activities: The purpose of the foundation is to receive and accept property exclusively for educational, recreational, artistic/cultural, conservation, community development, charitable or benevolent purposes for the benefit and improvement of residents of the Marshfield, WI, area.
Fields of interest: Arts and culture; Education; Environment; Domesticated animals; Community and economic development; Community improvement; Religion; Sports and recreation; Children and youth; Infants and toddlers; Children; Adolescents; Adults; Young adults; Seniors; Females; Female children and youth; Female infants and toddlers; Female adults; Female young adults; Males; Male children and youth; Male infants and toddlers; Male adults; Male young adults; Single parents; Ethnic and racial groups; People of Latin American descent; Immigrants and migrants; Migrant workers; Low-income and poor people; Victims of crime and abuse; People with physical disabilities; People with psychosocial disabilities; Military personnel.
Type of support: General support; Grants to individuals; In-kind gifts; Continuing support; Capacity-building and technical assistance; Matching grants; Annual campaigns; Equipment; Endowments; Program development; Convening; Publications; Scholarships; Technical assistance; Student aid.
Limitations: Applications accepted. Giving limited to Marshfield, WI and surrounding areas. No grants for capital campaigns or debt reduction.
Publications: Application guidelines; Annual report; Financial statement; Grants list; Informational brochure; Informational brochure (including application guidelines); Newsletter.
Application information: Visit foundation web site for application form and guidelines. Application form required.

Initial approach: Submit application form and attachments
Copies of proposal: 8
Deadline(s): June 1
Board meeting date(s): Third Tues. in Jan., Feb., Apr., May, Sept., Oct., and Nov.
Final notification: Following Sept. board meeting
Officers and Trustees: Marty Reinhart, Chair. and Trustee; Pat Saucerman, Vice-Chair. and Trustee; Amber Kiggens-Leifheit, Exec. Dir.; Kathleen Anderson; Ed Englehart; Paula Jero; Scott Larson; Graham Olson; Pete Schmeling; Patricia Stuhr; Ron Wilczek; Don Zais.
Number of staff: 1 part-time professional; 1 part-time support.
EIN: 396578767

9879
Martin Family Foundation
2601 W. Cedar Ln.
Milwaukee, WI 53217-1138

Donors: Janet Dowler Martin; Vincent L. Martin.
Foundation type: Independent foundation.
Financial data (yr. ended 07/31/13): Assets, $6,635,838 (M); gifts received, $300,000; expenditures, $384,907; qualifying distributions, $333,165; giving activities include $331,900 for 34 grants (high: $65,000; low: $1,000).
Purpose and activities: Giving primarily for higher education and the arts; funding also for a Presbyterian church.
Fields of interest: Arts and culture; Theater; Education; Higher education; Nonprofits; Protestantism; Human services.
Type of support: General support; Capital campaigns; Regranting.
Limitations: Applications not accepted. Giving primarily in IA and WI. No grants to individuals.
Application information: Contributes only to pre-selected organizations.
Trustees: Janet Dowler Martin; Vincent L. Martin.
EIN: 396584789

9880
B. A. Mason Trust
1251 1st Ave.
Chippewa Falls, WI 54729-1408 (715) 723-1871
Contact: Timothy Scobie, Tr.

Established in 1953 in Wisconsin.
Donors: Mason Shoe Manufacturing Co.; Tim Scobie; Mason Companies.
Foundation type: Independent foundation.
Financial data (yr. ended 12/31/13): Assets, $3,981,701 (M); gifts received, $390,703; expenditures, $271,909; qualifying distributions, $240,500; giving activities include $240,500 for 13 grants (high: $75,000; low: $2,500).
Purpose and activities: Giving primarily to Chippewa Valley, Wisconsin community organizations, cultural associations, and youth hockey .
Fields of interest: Elementary and secondary education; Natural resources; Foundations; Hospital care; Community and economic development; Human services.
Type of support: General support.
Limitations: Applications accepted. Giving primarily in Chippewa Falls, WI. No grants to individuals.
Application information: Application form required.

Initial approach: Letter
Deadline(s): None
Trustees: Lori Geissler; Stephanie Niebergail; Timothy Scobie; William M. Scobie.
EIN: 396075816

9881
Isadore Mednikow Educational Trust
c/o Cecile Faller
126 S. Washington St.
Green Bay, WI 54301-4211

Established in 2002 in Wisconsin.
Donor: Isadore Medikow†.
Foundation type: Independent foundation.
Financial data (yr. ended 07/31/13): Assets, $6,640,250 (M); expenditures, $387,846; qualifying distributions, $365,450; giving activities include $350,000 for 25 grants (high: $50,000; low: $1,000).
Purpose and activities: Giving primarily for education, including Baptist, Lutheran and Roman Catholic schools.
Fields of interest: Education; Technology; Human services.
Limitations: Applications not accepted. Giving primarily in WI. No grants to individuals.
Application information: Contributes only to pre-selected organizations.
Trustee: Leland E. Rogers.
EIN: 276004423

9882
Meehan Family Foundation
(formerly Daniel E. Meehan Foundation, Inc.)
c/o Feld, Schumacher & Co., LLP
P.O. Box 270407
West Allis, WI 53227-2950
Contact: Daniel E. Meehan, Chair.

Established in 1983 in Wisconsin.
Donors: Daniel E. Meehan; Eileen Meehan.
Foundation type: Independent foundation.
Financial data (yr. ended 12/31/13): Assets, $2,320,991 (M); expenditures, $310,657; qualifying distributions, $308,813; giving activities include $308,650 for 17 grants (high: $189,606; low: $160).
Purpose and activities: Support for higher and secondary education, and social services. Also awards scholarships to children of employees of Meehan Seaway Service.
Fields of interest: Secondary education; Higher education; Specialty hospital care; Catholicism; Judaism; Human services; Basic and emergency aid; International development.
Type of support: Scholarships.
Publications: Application guidelines.
Application information: Individual scholarships are awarded only to children or grandchildren of employees of Meehan Seaway Service. Foundation is currently accepting applications from organizations. Application form required.
Initial approach: Letter or inter-company mail
Deadline(s): May 15
Board meeting date(s): June and Nov.
Officers: Daniel E. Meehan, Chair.; Laurie Lukaszewicz, Pres.; Eileen Meehan, V.P.; Theresa R Meehan-Felknor, Treas.
Director: Henry Loos.

Number of staff: None.
EIN: 391445333

9883
Archie & Viola Meinerz Family Foundation Inc.
622 N. Water St., Ste. 500
Milwaukee, WI 53202-4910

Established in 1992 in Wisconsin.
Donor: Viola Meinerz.
Foundation type: Independent foundation.
Financial data (yr. ended 12/31/13): Assets, $5,753,761 (M); expenditures, $304,758; qualifying distributions, $245,000; giving activities include $245,000 for 11 grants (high: $65,000; low: $2,000).
Purpose and activities: Giving primarily for education, the arts, and to Roman Catholic education, organizations and churches.
Fields of interest: Museums; Education; Secondary education; Higher education; Medical education; Diseases and conditions; Catholicism; Child welfare; Youth services.
Type of support: Research; Research and evaluation.
Limitations: Applications not accepted. Giving primarily in WI. No grants to individuals.
Application information: Unsolicited requests for funds not accepted.
Officers and Directors: Leigh Peterson, Pres. and Director; Nancy Meinerz, Secy. and Director; William Fitzhugh Fox, Treas. and Director.
EIN: 391713840

9884
Merkel Foundation, Inc.
3712 Bismarck Cir.
Sheboygan, WI 53083-2653

Established in 1986 in Wisconsin.
Donors: Daniel A. Merkel; Betty Merkel; American Orthodontics Corp.
Foundation type: Independent foundation.
Financial data (yr. ended 07/31/13): Assets, $9,489,986 (M); gifts received, $100,000; expenditures, $384,253; qualifying distributions, $365,755; giving activities include $362,000 for 32 grants (high: $125,000; low: $1,000).
Purpose and activities: Support primarily for Roman Catholic services and organizations, social services and youth, and health associations.
Fields of interest: Arts and culture; Higher education; Nonprofits; Diseases and conditions; Cancers; Catholicism; Human services; Child welfare.
Type of support: Regranting.
Limitations: Applications not accepted. Giving primarily in WI. No grants to individuals.
Application information: Contributes only to pre-selected organizations.
Officers: Betty Merkel, Pres. and Treas.; Daniel A. Merkel, V.P. and Secy.
EIN: 391582624

9885
Robert and Betty Meyer Family Foundation

(formerly Robert T. Meyer Foundation)
469 Security Blvd.
Green Bay, WI 54313-9707
Application address: c/o Associated Bank, P.O. Box 19006, Green Bay, WI 54307-9006, tel.: (920) 433-3257

Established in 1985 in Wisconsin.
Donor: Janet E. Meyer†.
Foundation type: Independent foundation.
Financial data (yr. ended 12/31/13): Assets, $2,463,231 (M); expenditures, $149,819; qualifying distributions, $130,000; giving activities include $130,000 for 1 grant.
Fields of interest: Arts and culture; Education; Health.
Limitations: Applications accepted. Giving primarily in Green Bay, WI.
Application information: Application form required.
Initial approach: Proposal
Copies of proposal: 1
Deadline(s): None
Director: Christine E. Mayer.
EIN: 396413619

9886
Dorothy I. Meyer Trust

P.O. Box 2043
Milwaukee, WI 53201-9668

Donor: Gordon Meyer Trust.
Foundation type: Independent foundation.
Financial data (yr. ended 12/31/13): Assets, $920,837 (M); expenditures, $427,567; qualifying distributions, $396,545; giving activities include $392,357 for 41 grants (high: $101,157; low: $3,000).
Fields of interest: Protestantism.
Limitations: Applications not accepted. Giving primarily in IL.
Application information: Unsolicited requests for funds not accepted.
Trustee: US Bank, N.A.
EIN: 366829833

9887
Mid-States Aluminum Foundation, Inc.

132 Trowbridge Dr.
Fond du Lac, WI 54937-9177

Established in 2001 in Wisconsin.
Donor: Mid-States Aluminum, Inc.
Foundation type: Company-sponsored foundation.
Financial data (yr. ended 12/31/13): Assets, $552,414 (M); gifts received, $463,695; expenditures, $423,841; qualifying distributions, $416,951; giving activities include $415,953 for 51 grants (high: $202,600; low: $75).
Purpose and activities: The foundation supports public libraries and organizations involved with arts and culture, K-12 education, human services, and Christianity.
Fields of interest: Arts and culture; Education; Human services.
Type of support: General support; Capital and infrastructure.
Limitations: Applications not accepted. Giving primarily in Fond du Lac, WI.

Application information: Unsolicited requests for funds not accepted.
Directors: Dawn Colwin; Betty Koenigs.
EIN: 392014920

9888
Mielcarek Family Foundation Inc.

3139 Vinburn Rd.
Sun Prairie, WI 53590-9362
E-mail: tim.mielcarek@hallmanlindsay.com

Established in 2000 in Wisconsin.
Donors: Timothy A. Mielcarek; Beth A. Mielcarek; Hallman Lidnsay Paints, Inc.
Foundation type: Independent foundation.
Financial data (yr. ended 12/31/13): Assets, $1,678,354 (M); gifts received, $200,000; expenditures, $136,119; qualifying distributions, $131,010; giving activities include $131,000 for 9 grants (high: $50,000; low: $2,500).
Fields of interest: Agriculture; Religion; Human services.
Limitations: Applications not accepted. Giving primarily in WI. No grants to individuals.
Application information: Unsolicited requests for funds not accepted.
Officers: Timothy A. Mielcarek, Pres.; Beth A. Mielcarek, V.P. and Treas.; Rebecca Nelson, Secy.
EIN: 392008964

9889
The Modine Manufacturing Company Foundation, Inc.

1500 DeKoven Ave.
Racine, WI 53403 (262) 636-1200
Contact: Valerie Madala

Established in 1995 in Wisconsin.
Donor: Modine Manufacturing Co.
Foundation type: Company-sponsored foundation.
Financial data (yr. ended 03/31/14): Assets, $443,322 (M); gifts received, $305,000; expenditures, $277,159; qualifying distributions, $277,159; giving activities include $276,972 for 48 grants (high: $50,193; low: $100).
Purpose and activities: The foundation supports organizations involved with arts and culture, education, health, human services, community development, and civic affairs.
Fields of interest: Arts and culture; Performing arts; Historic preservation; Education; Elementary and secondary education; Higher education; Nonprofits; Health; Science; Technology; Mathematics; Public affairs; Community and economic development; Manufacturing; Human services; Low-income and poor people.
Type of support: Continuing support; Employee volunteer services; Capital campaigns; Matching grants; Capital and infrastructure; Program development; Scholarships; Sponsorships; Regranting.
Limitations: Applications accepted. Giving limited to areas of company operations, with emphasis on Racine, WI. No support for religious or political organizations, organizations lacking a business plan, political parties or candidates, or discriminatory organizations. No grants for travel or debt reduction.
Publications: Application guidelines.
Application information: Application form required.

Initial approach: See website www.modline.com for application form
Copies of proposal: 1
Deadline(s): Quaterly on Mar 31, Jun. 30, Sept. 30, and Dec. 31
Board meeting date(s): Quarterly
Final notification: 1 to 2 months
Officers: Thomas A. Burke, Pres.; Brian J. Agen, V.P.; Margaret C. Kelsey, Secy. and Director; Michael B. Lucareli, Treas.
EIN: 391818362

9890
Mortenson Family Foundation

P.O. Box 486
Belleville, WI 53508

Established in 1997 in Wisconsin.
Donor: Loren D. Mortenson.
Foundation type: Independent foundation.
Financial data (yr. ended 12/31/12): Assets, $0 (M); expenditures, $448,984; qualifying distributions, $442,330; giving activities include $442,330 for grants.
Fields of interest: Nonprofits; Christianity; Child welfare.
Type of support: Regranting.
Limitations: Applications not accepted. No grants to individuals.
Application information: Unsolicited requests for funds not accepted.
Trustees: Ryan Henderson; Joelle Mortenson Hunter; Barbara J. Mortenson; Jay P. Mortenson; Loren D. Mortenson.
EIN: 396659441

9891
Mound Properties Inc.

1525 Howe St.
Racine, WI 53403-2237 (262) 260-0185

Foundation type: Independent foundation.
Financial data (yr. ended 08/31/14): Assets, $1,735,058 (M); expenditures, $360,485; qualifying distributions, $360,485; giving activities include $360,485 for 8 grants (high: $184,692; low: $1,632).
Fields of interest: Philanthropy; Human services; Youth development.
Limitations: Applications accepted. Giving primarily in Racine, WI.
Application information: Application form required.
Initial approach: Proposal
Deadline(s): None
Officers and Directors: Matthew L. Wagner, Pres. and Director; Julie Branick, V.P. and Director; William Harold Van Lopik, V.P.; Thomas S. Simpson, Secy. and Director; Kristi Peterson, Treas. and Director.
EIN: 043610852

9892
Harry and Virginia Murray Foundation

c/o U.S. Bank, N.A.
P.O. Box 2043
Milwaukee, WI 53201-9668
Application address: U.S. Bank, N.A., 201 Jefferson St., Burlington, IA 52601-5260, tel.: (319) 753-8761

Foundation type: Independent foundation.
Financial data (yr. ended 12/31/13): Assets, $9,142,111 (M); expenditures, $479,175; qualifying distributions, $403,841; giving activities include $392,000 for 20 grants (high: $55,000; low: $1,000).
Fields of interest: Historic preservation; Education; Diseases and conditions; Protestantism; Human services.
Type of support: Capital campaigns.
Limitations: Applications accepted. Giving limited to Des Moines County, IA. No grants to individuals.
Application information: Application form required.
  Initial approach: Letter
  Deadline(s): None
Trustee: U.S. Bank, N.A.
EIN: 426291207

9893
Frances L. Nelson Foundation, Ltd.
c/o Sheri Kole
2201 Lakeland Ave.
Madison, WI 53704-5636

Donor: Dale Leibowitz.
Foundation type: Independent foundation.
Financial data (yr. ended 12/31/13): Assets, $3,476,936 (M); gifts received, $3,476,936; expenditures, $182,268; qualifying distributions, $180,000; giving activities include $180,000 for 1 grant.
Fields of interest: Human services.
Limitations: Applications not accepted. Giving primarily in Madison, WI.
Application information: Unsolicited requests for funds not accepted.
Officers and Directors: Dale Leibowitz, Pres. and Director; Frances L. Nelson, V.P. and Director; Sheri L. Kole, Secy.-Treas. and Director.
EIN: 392033920

9894
Victor & Mary D. Nelson Scholarship Fund
c/o BMO Harris Bank, N.A.
P.O. Box 2980
Milwaukee, WI 53201-2980
Scholarship address: c/o William Retinstrand, Superior Senior High School, 2600 Catlin Ave., Superior, WI 54880, tel.: (715) 384-0271

Established in 1973 in Wisconsin.
Donor: Mary D. Nelson†.
Foundation type: Independent foundation.
Financial data (yr. ended 06/30/13): Assets, $4,802,303 (M); expenditures, $273,483; qualifying distributions, $229,316; giving activities include $209,833 for grants.
Purpose and activities: Awards scholarships for higher and vocational education to graduates of Superior High School in WI.
Fields of interest: Education; Vocational education; Higher education.
Type of support: Student aid.
Limitations: Applications accepted. Giving limited to Superior, WI.
Application information: Application form required.
  Initial approach: Contact WM Retinstrand Superior Senior High School Counseling Office for application form
  Deadline(s): Apr. 15

Trustee: BMO Harris Bank, N.A.
EIN: 396184729

9895
Ocular Physiology Research and Education Foundation, Inc.
3006 Harvard Dr.
Madison, WI 53705-2107

Established in 1989 in Wisconsin.
Donors: Pfizer (Pharmacia) Corp.; Inspire Pharmaceuticals; MEMX; Alcon Foundation; Frey Research; NU Lens, Ltd.; QLT, Inc.; Santen, Inc.; Edward W. Smith Jr. Foundation.
Foundation type: Independent foundation.
Financial data (yr. ended 06/30/14): Assets, $215,038 (M); expenditures, $302,901; qualifying distributions, $301,060; giving activities include $300,000 for 1 grant.
Purpose and activities: Giving primarily for eye research, particularly ocular physiology.
Fields of interest: Eye diseases.
Type of support: General support; Research.
Limitations: Applications not accepted. Giving primarily in Madison, WI. No grants to individuals.
Application information: Unsolicited requests for funds not accepted.
Officers and Directors: Paul L. Kaufman, MD, Pres. and Director; Howard S. Goldman, V.P.; Margaret G. Kaufman, Secy.-Treas.; Katherine B. Foehl, V.P.
EIN: 391661745

9896
Edward J. Okray Foundation Inc.
(formerly Edward J. Okray & Lucille S. Okray Foundation, Inc.)
P.O. Box 489
Plover, WI 54467-0489

Established in 1984 in Wisconsin.
Donors: Edward J. Okray; Lucille S. Okray.
Foundation type: Independent foundation.
Financial data (yr. ended 09/30/14): Assets, $6,333,579 (M); expenditures, $300,973; qualifying distributions, $277,500; giving activities include $275,500 for 29 grants (high: $62,000; low: $500).
Fields of interest: Health; Human services; Youth development.
Limitations: Applications not accepted. Giving primarily in WI. No grants to individuals.
Application information: Unsolicited requests for funds not accepted.
Officers: Carol Okray, Pres.; Michael J. Finnessy, V.P.; Richard W. Okray, Secy.
EIN: 391501333

9897
Jennie H. Olson Charitable Foundation Inc.
2 E. Mifflin St., Ste. 200
Madison, WI 53703-4269
Application address: c/o John C. Mitby, Pres., P.O. Box 1767, Madison, WI 53701-1767, tel.: (608) 257-5661

Established in 1995 in Wisconsin.
Donor: Jennie H. Olson.
Foundation type: Independent foundation.
Financial data (yr. ended 12/31/13): Assets, $7,690,335 (M); expenditures, $473,595;

qualifying distributions, $388,357; giving activities include $388,357 for 32 grants (high: $40,667; low: $2,500).
Purpose and activities: Giving primarily for services to the elderly and handicapped.
Fields of interest: Elementary and secondary education; School-based health care; Community and economic development; Community recreation; Human services.
Limitations: Applications accepted. Giving limited to Iowa County, WI. No grants to individuals.
Application information: Application form required.
  Initial approach: Letter
  Deadline(s): Oct. 1
Officers: John C. Mitby, Pres. and Treas.; Edward M. Terry, V.P. and Secy.
Director: Steven A. Brezinski.
EIN: 391818653

9898
Ronald L. Olson Charitable Foundation Inc.
716 Pine St.
Green Bay, WI 54301-4929

Established in 2005 in Wisconsin.
Donor: Ronald L. Olson.
Foundation type: Independent foundation.
Financial data (yr. ended 12/31/14): Assets, $6,857; gifts received, $220,925; expenditures, $238,250; qualifying distributions, $238,250 and $0 for set-asides.
Fields of interest: Foundations; Diseases and conditions; Human services; Low-income and poor people.
Type of support: General support.
Limitations: Applications not accepted. Giving primarily in WI. No grants to individuals.
Application information: Unsolicited requests for funds not accepted.
Officers: Ronald L. Olson, Pres.; Rudy Hanamann, V.P.; Kenneth G. Calewarts, Secy.-Treas.
EIN: 203102236

9899
Park Bank Foundation, Inc.
330 E. Kilbourn Ave., Ste. 150
Milwaukee, WI 53202-6619 (414) 270-3209
Contact: Susan Baudo, Secy.

Established in 1980 in Wisconsin.
Donor: Park Bank.
Foundation type: Company-sponsored foundation.
Financial data (yr. ended 12/31/13): Assets, $399,045 (M); gifts received, $200,000; expenditures, $223,086; qualifying distributions, $219,595; giving activities include $206,795 for 101 grants (high: $40,000; low: $250).
Purpose and activities: The foundation supports hospitals and organizations involved with arts and culture, education, hunger, human services, and community development.
Fields of interest: Arts and culture; Religion; Human services.
Limitations: Applications accepted. Giving limited to the greater Milwaukee, WI, area. No grants to individuals.
Application information:
  Initial approach: Proposal
  Deadline(s): None
Officers and Directors: P. Michael Mahoney, Pres. and Director; Michael J. Kelly, V.P. and Director;

Lorraine A. Kelly, V.P. and Director; Susan Baudo, Secy.; James W. Wright, Treas. and Director.
EIN: 391365837

9900
Pelz Family Foundation
318 W. Seacroft Ct.
Mequon, WI 53092-3561

Established in 1995 in Wisconsin.
Donors: Harry Pelz; Marilyn Pelz.
Foundation type: Independent foundation.
Financial data (yr. ended 12/31/13): Assets, $967,363 (M); gifts received, $204,945; expenditures, $253,683; qualifying distributions, $242,795; giving activities include $242,795 for 25 grants (high: $100,000; low: $75).
Fields of interest: Education; Nonprofits; Health; Religion; Judaism.
Type of support: Regranting.
Limitations: Applications not accepted. Giving primarily in WI. No grants to individuals.
Application information: Contributes only to pre-selected organizations.
Officers and Directors: Harry Pelz, Pres. and Treas. and Director; Marilyn Pelz, Secy. and Director; Mara Lappin; Daniel Pelz; David Pelz; Jason Pelz.
EIN: 391837448

9901
John & Carolyn Peterson Charitable Foundation, Inc.
P.O. Box 1507
Brookfield, WI 53005

Donor: John L. Peterson.
Foundation type: Independent foundation.
Financial data (yr. ended 12/31/13): Assets, $6,885,870 (M); expenditures, $288,115; qualifying distributions, $239,191; giving activities include $231,000 for 9 grants (high: $65,000; low: $5,000).
Fields of interest: Arts and culture; Arts education; Orchestral music; Education; Foundations; Television.
Limitations: Applications not accepted. Giving primarily in WI. No grants to individuals.
Application information: Unsolicited requests for funds not accepted.
Officers and Directors: Elinor Guzniczak, Pres. and Director; Mark L. Peterson, V.P. and Director; Ryia R. Peterson, Secy. and Director; Michael J. Guzniczak, Treas. and Director; Emily C. Guzniczak; Lauren A. Guzniczak.
EIN: 431974269

9902
Charles H. Phipps Foundation Agency
c/o M I Trust Co., N.A.
11270 W. Park Pl. S.
Milwaukee, WI 53224-3623
Contact: Charles H. Phipps, Tr.
Application address: c/o Charles H. Phipps, 6600 Lyndon B. Johnson Freeway, Ste. 155, Dallas, TX 75240-6511, tel.: (972) 960-1186

Established in 1997 in Texas.
Donors: Charles H. Phipps; Mary K. Phipps.
Foundation type: Independent foundation.

Financial data (yr. ended 04/30/13): Assets, $4,005,886 (M); expenditures, $198,573; qualifying distributions, $185,300; giving activities include $185,300 for grants.
Fields of interest: Education; University education; Down syndrome; Human services.
Type of support: General support; Individual development.
Limitations: Giving primarily in Dallas, TX and WI. No grants to individuals.
Application information:
   Initial approach: Letter
   Deadline(s): None
Trustee: Charles H. Phipps.
EIN: 752750645

9903
William H. Phipps Foundation
P.O. Box 653
Hudson, WI 54016-0653 (715) 386-3352

Established in 1946 in Wisconsin.
Donors: Helen Clark Phipps†; Stephen C. Phipps†; John Harding†.
Foundation type: Independent foundation.
Financial data (yr. ended 04/30/14): Assets, $6,912,837 (M); expenditures, $392,676; qualifying distributions, $381,220; giving activities include $368,000 for 13 grants (high: $205,000; low: $2,000).
Purpose and activities: Support primarily for an arts center, as well as for education, and youth, family and social services. The foundation may also make grants to the Hudson, WI, school district for scholarships to graduating seniors.
Fields of interest: Arts and culture; Education; Secondary education; Human services; Family services; Child welfare; Scouting programs.
Type of support: Capital and infrastructure; Curriculum development; Scholarships.
Limitations: Applications accepted. Giving primarily in St. Croix County and Hudson, WI, area. No grants to individuals.
Application information: Application form required.
   Initial approach: Letter outlining request
   Copies of proposal: 1
   Deadline(s): None
   Board meeting date(s): May 1 and as needed
   Final notification: 3 months
Officers and Directors: Frederick E. Nagel, Pres. and Director; John Clymer, Secy. and Director; Kitty Rhoades; Monica Weekes; Charles Huntley; Ken Heiser.
EIN: 396043312

9904
Thomas A. Plein Foundation, Ltd.
3415 Commerce Ct.
Appleton, WI 54911-8439
Application address: c/o H. Matthew Frazier, 1920 Spyglass Dr., Henderson, NV 89074, tel.: (702) 492-1177

Donor: Thomas A. Plein.
Foundation type: Independent foundation.
Financial data (yr. ended 12/31/13): Assets, $7,923,262 (M); expenditures, $404,503; qualifying distributions, $355,650; giving activities include $355,650 for 25 grants (high: $32,250; low: $650).

Fields of interest: Education; Health; Christianity; Catholicism; Human services.
Limitations: Applications accepted. Giving primarily in NV and WI; some funding in FL, IL, IN, NY, PA, and UT.
Application information: Application form required.
   Initial approach: Proposal
   Deadline(s): None
   Final notification: 2 months
Officers: H. Matthew Frazier, Pres.; Jason W. Ketter, Exec. V.P.
Directors: Jim Paulsen; Steven Plein.
EIN: 391558684

9905
Prescott Family Foundation, Inc.
c/o Beth Fellenz
2412 W. Washington St., Ste. 200
West Bend, WI 53095-2120

Established in 2002 in Wisconsin.
Donors: Prescott's Supermarket, Inc.; George Prescott.
Foundation type: Independent foundation.
Financial data (yr. ended 12/31/13): Assets, $5,031,918 (M); gifts received, $47,500; expenditures, $310,404; qualifying distributions, $268,626; giving activities include $262,900 for 37 grants (high: $31,500; low: $125).
Purpose and activities: The foundation supports organizations involved with underprivileged families and youth, as well as health organizations.
Fields of interest: Diseases and conditions; Cancers; Human services; Youth services.
Type of support: Continuing support; Matching grants; Annual campaigns; Capital campaigns; Capital and infrastructure; Program development; Seed money; Curriculum development.
Limitations: Applications not accepted. Giving primarily in Washington County, WI. No support for religious or political organizations.
Publications: Annual report; Grants list.
Application information: Contributes only to pre-selected organizations.
Officers and Directors: Judith A. Prescott, Pres. and Director; Matthew Prescott, Secy. and Director; George E. Prescott, Treas.; Beth Fellenz, Exec. Dir.; Cheryl Prescott; Dawn Prescott; Kelly Prescott; Patrick Prescott.
EIN: 061667125

9906
Pritchett Foundation
c/o BMO Harris Bank, N.A.
P.O. Box 2980
Milwaukee, WI 53201-2977
Application address: c/o Traci Williams, 1251 N.W. Briarcliff Pkwy., Ste. 140, Kansas City, MO 64116, tel.: (816) 584-4009

Established in 1994 in Kansas.
Donor: First State Bank & Trust Co.
Foundation type: Independent foundation.
Financial data (yr. ended 05/31/13): Assets, $9,081,452 (M); expenditures, $491,701; qualifying distributions, $400,119; giving activities include $399,358 for 39 grants (high: $50,000; low: $600).
Purpose and activities: The foundation's mission is to improve the quality of life in Pittsburg and Crawford County, KS, by strengthening children,

youth, and families, and by supporting projects that serve these populations.

Fields of interest: Education; Elementary and secondary education; Higher education; Foundations; Human services; Family services; Child welfare; Youth services.

Limitations: Applications accepted. Giving limited to Crawford County and Pittsburg, KS. No grants to individuals.

Application information: All documents must be submitted on 8 1/2 x 11 inch sheets of paper printed on one side. Do not bind papers or set them in bulky notebooks; the complete proposal and its 1-page synopsis must be submitted at the same time.

> *Initial approach:* Complete proposal, and a 1-page synopsis thereof
> *Copies of proposal:* 1
> *Deadline(s):* Jan. 2
> *Final notification:* End of Feb.

Trustee: BMO Harris Bank, N.A.
EIN: 481210113

9907
Puelicher Foundation, Inc.
111 E. Kilbourn Ave.
Milwaukee, WI 53202-6633
Application address: c/o James B. Wigdale, 770 N. Water St., Milwaukee, WI 53202, tel.: (414) 765-7707

Donor: John A. Puelicher†.
Foundation type: Independent foundation.
Financial data (yr. ended 12/31/13): Assets, $2,978,197 (M); expenditures, $234,856; qualifying distributions, $222,800; giving activities include $222,000 for 28 grants (high: $40,000; low: $1,000).
Fields of interest: Museums; Higher education; Environment; Nonprofits; Human services.
Type of support: General support; Scholarships; Regranting.
Limitations: Applications accepted. Giving primarily in Milwaukee, WI.
Application information: Application form required.
> *Initial approach:* Letter, including expected community benefits
> *Copies of proposal:* 1
> *Deadline(s):* None

Officers and Directors: James B. Wigdale, Pres.; Diane L. Sebion, Secy.-Treas.; Judith C. Murphy, C.F.O. and Director; Melissa D. Smid; Mary P. Uihlein.
EIN: 396055461

9908
Purple Moon Foundation, Inc.
2201 Lakeland Ave.
Madison, WI 53704-5636

Established in 1999 in Wisconsin.
Donor: Dale Leibowitz.
Foundation type: Independent foundation.
Financial data (yr. ended 12/31/13): Assets, $3,081,799 (M); gifts received, $1,000,000; expenditures, $224,248; qualifying distributions, $220,000; giving activities include $220,000 for 18 grants (high: $50,000; low: $1,000).
Fields of interest: Arts and culture; Judaism; Human services.

Limitations: Applications not accepted. Giving primarily in Madison, WI. No grants to individuals.
Application information: Unsolicited requests for funds not accepted.
Officers and Directors: Dale Leibowitz, Pres. and Director; Sheri Kole, Secy.-Treas. and Director; Amy Kaster.
EIN: 391975376

9909
RCP Christian Foundation
12489 N. Larson Rd.
Hayward, WI 54843-5162

Established in 2000 in Iowa.
Donors: Ronald W. Parr; Cheryl A. Parr; Catherine Parr.
Foundation type: Independent foundation.
Financial data (yr. ended 05/31/14): Assets, $246,610 (M); expenditures, $146,210; qualifying distributions, $1,438,805; giving activities include $141,550 for 9 grants (high: $44,000; low: $2,000).
Fields of interest: Higher education; Christianity; Child welfare.
Limitations: Applications not accepted. Giving primarily in IL and WI. No grants to individuals.
Application information: Contributes only to pre-selected organizations.
Officers: Ronald W. Parr, Pres.; Cheryl A. Parr, V.P.
EIN: 421508114

9910
Redmond Family Foundation
W228 N745 Westmound Dr.
Waukesha, WI 53186

Established in 2004 in Wisconsin.
Donors: Kathleen J. Redmond; Mark Redmond.
Foundation type: Independent foundation.
Financial data (yr. ended 12/31/13): Assets, $2,088,544 (M); gifts received, $900,077; expenditures, $312,249; qualifying distributions, $292,148; giving activities include $289,833 for 5 grants (high: $183,333; low: $1,000).
Fields of interest: Environment; Domesticated animals; Christianity.
Type of support: General support.
Limitations: Applications not accepted. Giving primarily in FL. No grants to individuals.
Application information: Unsolicited requests for funds not accepted.
Officer: James Voelz, Secy.
Trustee: Kathleen J. Redmond.
EIN: 201940725

9911
Regal-Beloit Charitable Foundation
200 State St.
Beloit, WI 53511-6254

Established in 1995 in Wisconsin.
Donor: Regal-Beloit Corp.
Foundation type: Company-sponsored foundation.
Financial data (yr. ended 12/31/13): Assets, $2,269,101 (M); expenditures, $302,275; qualifying distributions, $296,939; giving activities include $296,939 for 63 grants (high: $40,000; low: $60).

Purpose and activities: The foundation supports organizations involved with health and recreation.
Fields of interest: Education; Sports and recreation; Human services.
Type of support: Capital campaigns; Capital and infrastructure.
Limitations: Applications not accepted. Giving primarily in areas of company operations, with emphasis on Beloit, WI. No grants to individuals.
Application information: Unsolicited requests for funds not accepted.
Officer and Trustees: Mark Gliebe, Chair. and Trustee; Charles Hinrichs.
EIN: 391814812

9912
Religious Care Foundation, Inc.
P.O. Box 12800
Green Bay, WI 54307-2800

Established in 1990 in Wisconsin.
Donors: Rev. Henry H. Lee; Henry H. Lee Agency Trust.
Foundation type: Independent foundation.
Financial data (yr. ended 12/31/13): Assets, $14,237,595 (M); gifts received, $70,000; expenditures, $436,371; qualifying distributions, $349,910; giving activities include $337,500 for 11 grants (high: $150,000; low: $5,000).
Fields of interest: Catholicism.
Type of support: General support.
Limitations: Applications not accepted. Giving primarily in WI. No grants to individuals.
Application information: Contributes only to pre-selected organizations.
Officers: Don L. Komis, Pres.; James Bartelt, Treas.
Director: Ed M. Lee.
EIN: 391684392

9913
AB Rewald and Jeanette Rewald Scholarship Trust
c/o BMO Harris Bank, N.A.
P.O. Box 2980
Milwaukee, WI 53201

Foundation type: Independent foundation.
Financial data (yr. ended 12/31/13): Assets, $8,729,074 (M); expenditures, $420,691; qualifying distributions, $342,512; giving activities include $342,512 for 4 grants (high: $111,068; low: $71,185).
Fields of interest: Secondary education; Protestantism; Catholicism.
Limitations: Applications not accepted. Giving primarily in WI.
Application information: Unsolicited requests for funds not accepted.
Trustee: BMO Harris Bank, N.A.
Board of Directors: Eric Henderson; Loretta Jackson; Margaret Pietsch; Phil Rehberger; John Smith; Steven Vonderheide.
EIN: 396591984

9914
The Albert and Mary Rhodes Museum and Charitable Foundation Inc.
c/o Steven D. Shambeau
P.O. Box 111
Waupaca, WI 54981-0111

Established in 1999 in Wisconsin.
Donor: Charles B. Sanford & Lorinda Sanford Family Trust.
Foundation type: Independent foundation.
Financial data (yr. ended 12/31/13): Assets, $6,947,397 (M); expenditures, $401,171; qualifying distributions, $369,433; giving activities include $340,550 for 8 grants (high: $200,000; low: $3,000).
Fields of interest: Arts and culture; Higher education.
Type of support: Scholarships.
Limitations: Applications not accepted. Giving primarily in WI.
Application information: Unsolicited requests for funds not accepted.
Directors: Phillip Abendschein; Ted Galloway; Gary E. Janssen; Earl Lindsay; Tom Remley; Steven D. Shambeau.
EIN: 391982685

9915
RITE-HITE Corporation Foundation Inc.
8900 N. Arbon Dr.
Milwaukee, WI 53223-2451 (414) 355-2600
Contact: Mark S. Kirkish, Treas. and Dir.

Donors: RITE-HITE Corp.; RITE-HITE Holding Corp.
Foundation type: Company-sponsored foundation.
Financial data (yr. ended 12/31/13): Assets, $19,659 (M); gifts received, $130,000; expenditures, $155,510; qualifying distributions, $155,500; giving activities include $155,500 for 17 grants (high: $100,000; low: $500).
Purpose and activities: The foundation supports museums and organizations involved with performing arts, higher education, legal aid, youth development, and children and youth.
Fields of interest: Performing arts; Museums; Higher education; Nonprofits; Health; Legal aid; Human services; Youth services.
Type of support: General support; Regranting.
Limitations: Applications accepted. Giving primarily in Milwaukee, WI.
Application information:
Initial approach: Letter
Deadline(s): None
Officers and Directors: Michael H. White, Pres. and Director; Paul J. Maly, V.P. and Director; Antonio P. Catalano, Secy.; Mark S. Kirkish, Treas. and Director.
EIN: 391522057

9916
Hamilton Roddis Foundation, Inc.
1213 N. Sherman Ave., Ste. 175
Madison, WI 53704-4236

Established in 1953 in Wisconsin.
Donors: Hamilton Roddis†; Augusta D. Roddis; Catherine P. Roddis; Roddis Plywood Corp.
Foundation type: Independent foundation.
Financial data (yr. ended 12/31/13): Assets, $6,394,454 (M); expenditures, $356,356; qualifying distributions, $328,810; giving activities include $321,500 for 24 grants (high: $50,000; low: $2,000).
Purpose and activities: Giving primarily to Episcopal churches, higher education, the arts, and health and human services.

Fields of interest: Historic preservation; Education; Higher education; Nonprofits; Health; Cancers; Public policy; Episcopalianism and Anglicanism; Lutheranism; Human services.
Type of support: Regranting; Policy, advocacy and systems reform.
Limitations: Applications not accepted. Giving primarily in Washington, DC, NC, and WI. No grants to individuals.
Application information: Contributes only to pre-selected organizations.
Officers: Thomas Roddis, Pres.; Phil Prange, V.P.; Douglas Lempereur, Secy.; Catherine Roddis Peck, Treas.
Director: James Greer.
EIN: 396077001

9917
Roehl Foundation, Inc.
P.O. Box 168
Oconomowoc, WI 53066-0168

Donor: Peter G. Roehl.
Foundation type: Independent foundation.
Financial data (yr. ended 06/30/13): Assets, $4,637,786 (M); expenditures, $259,824; qualifying distributions, $239,783; giving activities include $237,210 for 40 grants (high: $40,000; low: $110).
Fields of interest: Arts and culture; Education; Human services; Youth development.
Type of support: Continuing support; Capital campaigns; Capital and infrastructure; Equipment.
Limitations: Applications not accepted. Giving primarily in WI. No grants to individuals.
Application information: Unsolicited request for funds not accepted.
Officers and Directors: Peter G. Roehl, Pres. and Director; Wendy A. Luengen, Secy. and Director; Nancy A. Roehl, Treas. and Director.
EIN: 366048089

9918
The ROS Foundation
c/o Robert O. Schlytter
4811 S. 76th St., Ste. 211
Greenfield, WI 53220-4352 (414) 281-6000

Established in 1998 in Wisconsin.
Donors: Robert O. Schlytter; Marion C. Schlytter.
Foundation type: Independent foundation.
Financial data (yr. ended 12/31/13): Assets, $10,956,376 (M); gifts received, $1,094,910; expenditures, $484,758; qualifying distributions, $429,161; giving activities include $425,500 for 50 grants (high: $75,000; low: $500).
Fields of interest: Higher education; Hospital care; Public libraries; Human services.
Type of support: General support.
Limitations: Applications accepted. Giving primarily in the Milwaukee, WI, area. No support for abortion proponents, extremist environmental groups or for left-wing extremist groups.
Application information:
Initial approach: Letter
Deadline(s): None
Trustees: Susan L. Riordan; Robert B. Schlytter; Robert O. Schlytter.
EIN: 391948463

9919
Rosemann Family Foundation Inc
11473 Beach Rd.
Sister Bay, WI 54234-9658

Established in 1988 in Wisconsin.
Donors: Russell R. Rosemann; Virginia V. Rosemann; Virginia Roseman Charitable Trust.
Foundation type: Independent foundation.
Financial data (yr. ended 07/31/13): Assets, $4,404,729 (M); gifts received, $162,313; expenditures, $239,623; qualifying distributions, $239,420; giving activities include $239,240 for 31 grants (high: $50,000; low: $250).
Fields of interest: Arts and culture; Performing arts; Environment; Health; Protestantism; Human services.
Type of support: General support; Research and evaluation.
Limitations: Applications not accepted. Giving primarily in WI; some giving in NV. No grants to individuals.
Application information: Contributes only to pre-selected organizations.
Officers: Gayle Rosemann, Pres.; Jeff Rosemann, Treas.
Director: Rachel Rosemann.
EIN: 391621252

9920
Rusinow Family Charitable Foundation
384 Lake Shore Rd.
Grafton, WI 53024-9550

Donors: Jeffrey Rusinow; Kimberly Rusinow; Jennifer Ellis.
Foundation type: Independent foundation.
Financial data (yr. ended 12/31/13): Assets, $285,412 (M); gifts received, $150,000; expenditures, $149,478; qualifying distributions, $149,478; giving activities include $143,640 for 33 grants (high: $40,000; low: $100).
Fields of interest: Environment; Domesticated animals; Human services.
Limitations: Applications not accepted. No grants to individuals.
Application information: Unsolicited requests for funds not accepted.
Officers: Jeffrey Rusinow, Pres.; Jennifer Ellis, Secy.
EIN: 392012636

9921
The Sartori Foundation Inc.
P.O. Box 258
Plymouth, WI 53073-0258 (920) 918-9477
Contact: Frederick M. Bowes II, Secy.-Treas.

Donors: Sartori Food Corp.; Sartori Co.
Foundation type: Company-sponsored foundation.
Financial data (yr. ended 12/31/13): Assets, $1,412,979 (M); gifts received, $180,000; expenditures, $228,524; qualifying distributions, $209,410; giving activities include $209,410 for 13 grants (high: $53,000; low: $1,000).
Purpose and activities: The foundation supports hospices and organizations involved with education, health, and civil liberties.
Fields of interest: Education; Secondary education; Health; Hospital care; Hospice care; Right to life.
Type of support: General support; Annual campaigns.

Limitations: Applications accepted. Giving primarily in the Sheboygan County, WI, area. No grants to individuals.
Application information:
Initial approach: Proposal
Deadline(s): None
Officers: James C. Sartori, Pres.; Janet L. Sartori, V.P.; Frederick M. Bowes II, Secy.-Treas.
EIN: 391933307

9922
Oscar C. & Augusta Schlegel Foundation
c/o BMO Harris Bank, N.A.
P.O. Box 2980
Milwaukee, WI 53201-2980

Established in 1987 in Wisconsin.
Foundation type: Independent foundation.
Financial data (yr. ended 03/31/13): Assets, $7,748,544 (M); expenditures, $386,154; qualifying distributions, $348,300; giving activities include $348,300 for 28 grants (high: $85,000; low: $1,000).
Fields of interest: Arts and culture; Secondary education; Hospital care; Human services; Youth services; Scouting programs.
Limitations: Applications not accepted. Giving limited to WI. No grants to individuals.
Application information: Contributes only to pre-selected organizations.
Officers: Marilyn L. Holmquist, Chair.; Roger T. Stephenson, Vice-Chair.; Kim Palleon, Secy.
Trustee: BMO Harris Bank, N.A.
EIN: 391586544

9923
Swanson Schmucker Charitable Trust
P.O. Box 2043
Milwaukee, WI 53201-9668

Established in 2008 in Wisconsin.
Donor: Virginia Schmucker Trust.
Foundation type: Independent foundation.
Financial data (yr. ended 05/31/14): Assets, $4,981,072 (M); expenditures, $206,588; qualifying distributions, $196,028; giving activities include $193,312 for 4 grants (high: $48,328; low: $48,328).
Fields of interest: Education; Diseases and conditions; Christianity.
Type of support: General support; Research.
Limitations: Applications not accepted. Giving primarily in IA and IN. No grants to individuals.
Application information: Contributes only to pre-selected organizations.
Trustee: U.S. Bank, N.A.
EIN: 396795378

9924
Schoenleber Foundation, Inc.
111 E. Wisconsin Ave., Ste. 1800
Milwaukee, WI 53202-4809 (414) 276-3400
Contact: Peter C. Haensel, Pres.

Established in 1965 in Wisconsin.
Donors: Marie Schoenleber†; Louise Schoenleber†; Gretchen Schoenleber†.
Foundation type: Independent foundation.
Financial data (yr. ended 12/31/13): Assets, $8,707,098 (M); expenditures, $565,933;

qualifying distributions, $437,500; giving activities include $437,500 for 29 grants (high: $100,000; low: $1,000).
Fields of interest: Arts and culture; Performing arts; Museums; Education; Higher education; Natural resources; Libraries; Human services; Developmental disability services.
Type of support: General support; Endowments; Scholarships.
Limitations: Giving primarily in WI, with emphasis on Milwaukee. No support for religious purposes, or for primary or secondary education. No grants to individuals or for salaries.
Publications: Informational brochure (including application guidelines).
Application information: Application form required.
Initial approach: Letter or telephone requesting application form
Copies of proposal: 1
Deadline(s): July 31
Directors: Frank W. Bastian; Peter C. Haensel; Michael Orgeman.
Number of staff: 1 full-time professional; 1 part-time support.
EIN: 391049364

9925
Seeds of Faith, Inc.
P.O. Box 197
Hartland, WI 53029-0197 (262) 367-1990

Established in 1999 in Wisconsin.
Donor: Ralph Findley Charitable Rem Trust.
Foundation type: Independent foundation.
Financial data (yr. ended 12/31/14): Assets, $6,110,231; expenditures, $363,877; qualifying distributions, $302,265.
Fields of interest: Higher education; Graduate and professional education; Natural resources; Public libraries; Christianity; Theology; Child welfare.
Type of support: General support; Scholarships.
Limitations: Applications accepted. Giving primarily in WI.
Application information:
Initial approach: Letter
Deadline(s): None
Officers: William A. Rose, Pres. and Treas.; Susan F. Rose, V.P. and Secy.
Director: Gretchen Petraske.
EIN: 391938697

9926
Seramur Family Foundation Inc.
2026 County Rd., Ste. HH
Plover, WI 54467-2653

Established in 1994 in Wisconsin.
Donor: John C. Seramur.
Foundation type: Independent foundation.
Financial data (yr. ended 09/30/13): Assets, $5,518,853 (M); gifts received, $500,005; expenditures, $229,646; qualifying distributions, $193,850; giving activities include $193,850 for 17 grants (high: $100,000; low: $250).
Purpose and activities: Giving primarily for educational and community oriented programs; funding also for medical research, and to a Roman Catholic church.
Fields of interest: Children's museums; Education; Higher education; Diseases and conditions; Catholicism.

Type of support: Equipment; Research; Research and evaluation.
Limitations: Applications not accepted. Giving primarily in WI. No grants to individuals.
Application information: Contributes only to pre-selected organizations.
Officers: John C. Seramur, Pres.; Gary T. Pucci, V.P.; Joan Seramur, Secy.-Treas.
Directors: Brian Seramur; Brenda S. Thompson.
EIN: 391806609

9927
Mike Shannon Automotive Foundation Inc.
321 N. Rolling Meadows Dr.
Fond du Lac, WI 54935

Established in 2001 in Wisconsin.
Donors: Holiday Auto & Truck Inc.; Mike Shannon Automotive, Inc.
Foundation type: Company-sponsored foundation.
Financial data (yr. ended 12/31/13): Assets, $311,987 (M); gifts received, $187,530; expenditures, $345,672; qualifying distributions, $342,321; giving activities include $341,500 for 15 grants (high: $244,000; low: $100).
Purpose and activities: The foundation supports fire associations and organizations involved with secondary education, health, ice skating, and youth services.
Fields of interest: Education; Health; Religion.
Type of support: General support.
Limitations: Applications not accepted. Giving primarily in Fond du Lac, WI. No grants to individuals.
Application information: Unsolicited requests for funds not accepted.
Officers: Michael R. Shannon, Pres.; Patrick McCullough, Secy.-Treas.
EIN: 392018969

9928
George T. & Margaret E. Shoemaker Charitable Trust
c/o U.S. Bank, N.A.
P.O. Box 2043
Milwaukee, WI 53201-9668

Established in 1990 in Iowa.
Donor: Shoemaker Family Trust.
Foundation type: Independent foundation.
Financial data (yr. ended 12/31/13): Assets, $5,167,139 (M); expenditures, $269,979; qualifying distributions, $224,917; giving activities include $219,500 for 6 grants (high: $43,900; low: $35,120).
Fields of interest: Nonprofits; Christianity; Human services.
Type of support: Regranting.
Limitations: Applications not accepted. Giving limited to Ottumwa, IA. No grants to individuals.
Application information: Contributes only to pre-selected organizations.
Trustee: U.S. Bank, N.A.
EIN: 426448073

9929
The Simms Family Foundation
c/o Vogel Consulting SC
3415 Gateway Rd.
Brookfield, WI 53045-5166

Established in 1985 in Illinois.
Donors: Merkle-Korff Industries, Inc.; Elmco Industries, Inc.
Foundation type: Independent foundation.
Financial data (yr. ended 12/31/14): Assets, $7,194,635; expenditures, $458,808; qualifying distributions, $392,670.
Fields of interest: Arts and culture; Education; Hospital care; Christianity; Human services; Child welfare; Developmental disability services.
Limitations: Applications not accepted. Giving primarily in FL, IL and WI. No grants to individuals.
Application information: Contributes only to pre-selected organizations.
Officers and Directors: John D. Simms, Jr., Pres. and Director; Frederick V. Simms, V.P. and Secy. and Director; Michael P. Simms, Treas.; Mary Jean Beck-Calcagno; Jean M. Simms; John D. Simms.
EIN: 363413327

9930
Single Step Foundation
5210 County Rd., Ste. C
Spring Green, WI 53588-8915

Established in 2008 in Illinois.
Donors: Denise Marino; Herbert E. Paaren.
Foundation type: Independent foundation.
Financial data (yr. ended 12/31/13): Assets, $50,553 (M); gifts received, $200,215; expenditures, $184,653; qualifying distributions, $183,000; giving activities include $183,000 for 16 grants (high: $100,000; low: $1,000).
Fields of interest: Education; Higher education; Natural resources.
Limitations: Applications not accepted. Giving primarily in IL and WI.
Application information: Unsolicited requests for funds not accepted.
Officers and Directors: Herbert E. Paaren, Pres. and Director; Jonathan Michael, Secy. and Director; Denise Marino, Treas. and Director.
EIN: 262691592

9931
Everett Smith Group Foundation, Ltd.
(formerly Maysteel Foundation, Ltd.)
800 N. Marshall St.
Milwaukee, WI 53202-3911

Established in 1983 in Wisconsin.
Donors: OEM Worldwide; Maysteel, LLC; Eagle Ottawa, LLC; Everett Smith Group, Ltd.; Trostel, Ltd.
Foundation type: Independent foundation.
Financial data (yr. ended 12/01/14): Assets, $2,507,259 (M); gifts received, $225,000; expenditures, $268,589; qualifying distributions, $257,700; giving activities include $218,950 for 26 grants (high: $22,000; low: $12,100), and $38,750 for 9 grants to individuals (high: $5,000; low: $1,250).
Fields of interest: Art museums; University education; Natural resources; Nonprofits; Hospital care; Religion; Youth services.
Type of support: General support; Scholarships; Student aid; Regranting.
Limitations: Applications accepted. Giving primarily in WI.
Application information:
Initial approach: Proposal
Deadline(s): None

Officers and Directors: Thomas J. Hauske, Jr., Pres. and Director; Steven J. Hartung, V.P. and Secy.; Bruce J. Betters, V.P. Finance and Director; J. Douglas Gray, V.P. and Director; Becky J. Beth, Treas.
EIN: 391480641

9932
Russell L. & Vera M. Smith Private Foundation
230 Front St. N.
La Crosse, WI 54601-3219 (608) 782-1148

Donor: Russell L. Smith.
Foundation type: Independent foundation.
Financial data (yr. ended 12/31/14): Assets, $5,638,270; expenditures, $303,766; qualifying distributions, $241,568 and $0 for set-asides.
Fields of interest: Education; Nonprofits; Health; Protestantism; Human services; Youth services.
Type of support: Regranting.
Limitations: Applications accepted. Giving primarily in La Crosse County, WI. No grants to individuals.
Application information: Application form required.
Initial approach: Letter
Deadline(s): None
Directors: Mark Chamberlain; Darwin Isaacson; George E. Smith; Trust Point, Inc.
EIN: 391744162

9933
SMS Foundation, Inc
P.O. Box 5324
Madison, WI 53705-0324

Established in 2004 in Wisconsin.
Donor: Matthew D. Silverstein.
Foundation type: Independent foundation.
Financial data (yr. ended 12/31/14): Assets, $6,721,750 (M); gifts received, $671,920; expenditures, $355,583; qualifying distributions, $331,035; giving activities include $331,035 for 34 grants (high: $50,000; low: $3,000).
Fields of interest: Arts and culture; Education; Christianity; Human services.
Limitations: Applications not accepted. Giving primarily in WI. No support to individuals.
Application information: Unsolicited requests for funds not accepted.
Officers and Directors: Sarah E. Spencer, Pres. and Director; Matthew D. Silverstein, V.P. and Director; David B. Billing, Secy. and Director; Thomas G. Tierney, Treas. and Director; Mark Spencer.
EIN: 201878599

9934
Sonnentag Foundation Ltd.
P.O. Box 100
Marathon, WI 54448-0100
Application address: c/o Carolyn Sonnentag, P.O. Box 435, Astatula, FL 34705, tel.: (715) 848-1365

Foundation type: Independent foundation.
Financial data (yr. ended 09/30/14): Assets, $25,597,471 (M); gifts received, $79,968; expenditures, $255,951; qualifying distributions, $232,917; giving activities include $206,417 for grants, and $26,500 for 18 grants to individuals (high: $1,500; low: $1,500).

Fields of interest: Education; Adult and child mentoring.
Type of support: General support; Student aid.
Application information: Application form required.
Initial approach: Letter
Deadline(s): None
Officers: John Sonnentag, Pres.; Carolyn Sonnentag, V.P.
Directors: Bill Sonnentag; Tim Sonnentag.
EIN: 391597420

9935
Spider Shores Foundation, Inc.
4 Gusty Ct.
Verona, WI 53593-7903 (608) 219-0119

Established in 2006 in Wisconsin.
Donor: Helen Bakke.
Foundation type: Independent foundation.
Financial data (yr. ended 12/31/14): Assets, $3,314,594; expenditures, $344,388; qualifying distributions, $306,642.
Fields of interest: Religion.
Limitations: Applications accepted. Giving primarily in WI.
Application information:
Initial approach: Proposal
Deadline(s): None
Officers: Helen Bakke, Pres.; Gregory Monday, V.P. and Secy.; Marvin Ganser, V.P. and Treas.
EIN: 205706620

9936
St. Piran's Foundation
6536 Hillcrest Dr.
Wauwatosa, WI 53213-2462

Established in 1997 in Wisconsin.
Donors: Elizabeth W. Boyce; Thomas C. Boyce; Iunia L. Boyce.
Foundation type: Independent foundation.
Financial data (yr. ended 06/30/13): Assets, $178,092 (M); expenditures, $171,223; qualifying distributions, $167,535; giving activities include $167,535 for grants.
Purpose and activities: Giving for Christian religion and education.
Fields of interest: Education; University education; Christianity; Human services.
Type of support: General support.
Limitations: Applications not accepted. Giving primarily in CA and IL. No grants to individuals.
Application information: Contributes only to pre-selected organizations.
Trustees: Iunia L. Boyce; Thomas C. Boyce.
EIN: 396675978

9937
The Stateline Community Foundation
(formerly The Greater Beloit Community Foundation)
690 3rd St., Ste. 110
Beloit, WI 53511-6210 (608) 362-4228
Contact: Tara Jean Tinder, Exec. Dir.
FAX: (608) 362-0056; E-mail: statelinecf@aol.com; Additional E-mail: tara@statelinecf.com; Main URL: http://www.statelinecf.org
Facebook: http://www.facebook.com/StatelineCommunityFoundation

Established in 1986 in Wisconsin.

Foundation type: Community foundation.
Financial data (yr. ended 12/31/12): Assets, $9,741,658 (M); gifts received, $202,690; expenditures, $653,284; giving activities include $184,717 for 14+ grants (high: $15,291), and $132,514 for grants to individuals.
Purpose and activities: The foundation seeks to provide for the betterment of the greater Beloit, WI, Stateline area and the enhancement of the quality of life for all of its citizens.
Fields of interest: Arts and culture; Performing arts; Education; Early childhood education; Higher education; Environment; Diseases and conditions; Leadership development; Community and economic development; Sustainable development; Urban development; Sports and recreation; Human services; Child welfare; Youth organizing; Homeless services; Adolescents; Seniors; Ethnic and racial groups; Homeless people; People with disabilities.
Type of support: Equipment; Matching grants; Emergency funds; Program development; Seed money; Curriculum development; Scholarships; Program evaluations.
Limitations: Applications accepted. Giving limited to the greater Stateline area encompassing Rock County, WI, and northern Winnebago County, IL. No support for scholarly research. No grants to individuals (except for designated scholarship funds), or for ongoing operating expenses, building funds or capital campaigns, endowments and debt reduction, annual fundraising drives or travel grants.
Publications: Application guidelines; Annual report; Grants list; Informational brochure; Newsletter.
Application information: Visit foundation web site for application guidelines. Selected organizations will be notified of their status within 10 days following submission of their letter of inquiry for the Community Needs Grant Program. Application form required.
  Initial approach: Submit online Letter of Inquiry
  Deadline(s): Jan. 1 for Community Needs Grant Program full proposal; None for Discretionary grants; Jan. 21, Apr. 21, July. 21, Oct. 21 For J.E.T. Grants and Destination Grants. Oct. 31 for Teachers Mini-Grant.
  Final notification: 6 to 8 weeks for Community Needs Grant Program
Officers and Directors: Bill Lock, Chair. and Director; Martha Mitchell, 1st Vice-Chair. and Director; J. Marc Perry, Secy. and Director; Don Huebschen, Treas. and Director; Tara Jean Tinder, Exec. Dir.; Joanne Acomb; Francisca Amadore; Heidi Eldred; William Flanagan; Jeff Johnson; Sarah Kruse; Bruce Lans; Kay Nightingale; Lynee Tourdot; Mike Wickiser; Cecil Youngblood.
Number of staff: 2 full-time professional.
EIN: 391585271

9938
The J. Vernon Steinle & Elmyra K. Steinle Foundation, Inc.
7200 Washington Ave., Ste. 102
Racine, WI 53406-6516

Established in 1998 in Wisconsin.
Donor: Elmyra K. Steinle†.
Foundation type: Operating foundation.
Financial data (yr. ended 12/31/13): Assets, $3,194,907 (M); expenditures, $318,634; qualifying distributions, $290,000; giving activities include $290,000 for 4 grants (high: $150,000; low: $5,000).

Purpose and activities: Giving primarily for health care.
Fields of interest: Nonprofits; Health; Alcoholism; Cancers; Females.
Type of support: General support; Regranting.
Limitations: Applications not accepted. Giving limited to Racine, WI. No grants to individuals directly.
Application information: Contributes only to pre-selected organizations.
Officers: Robert F. Siegert, MD, Pres.; John G. Schulz, V.P.; Kenneth E. Rusch, Secy.-Treas.
EIN: 391934819

9939
R. A. Stevens Family Foundation
445 S. Moorland Rd., Ste. 400
Brookfield, WI 53005-4254 4143139310

Established in 1999 in Wisconsin.
Donors: Andrew J. Fleckenstein; Rita A. Stevens; Carolyn J. Scott.
Foundation type: Independent foundation.
Financial data (yr. ended 12/31/14): Assets, $4,800,665; expenditures, $285,993; qualifying distributions, $263,050.
Purpose and activities: Giving primarily for higher education, health care and human services, including services for adults and children who are blind, visually impaired, and/or deaf.
Fields of interest: Arts and culture; Education; Health.
Limitations: Applications accepted. Giving primarily in Milwaukee, WI.
Application information: Application form required.
  Initial approach: Letter
  Deadline(s): None
Officer: Carolyn J. Scott, Exec. Dir.
Trustee: Rita A. Stevens.
EIN: 396711913

9940
Lester W. Stevenson Charitable Trust
230 Front St. N.
La Crosse, WI 54601

Donors: Stevenson Trust; Stevenson Irrevocable Trust.
Foundation type: Independent foundation.
Financial data (yr. ended 12/31/14): Assets, $3,300,759; expenditures, $217,744; qualifying distributions, $171,551 and $0 for set-asides.
Fields of interest: Health; Diseases and conditions.
Limitations: Applications not accepted. Giving primarily in MN.
Application information: Unsolicited requests for funds not accepted.
Trustees: W. Thomas Wheeler; Anchor Trust; Trust Point Inc.
EIN: 356890177

9941
Paul E. Stry Foundation, Inc.
230 Front St., N.
La Crosse, WI 54601-3219

Established in 1988 in Wisconsin.
Donor: Paul E. Stry†.
Foundation type: Independent foundation.

Financial data (yr. ended 12/31/13): Assets, $4,481,735 (M); expenditures, $268,353; qualifying distributions, $238,922; giving activities include $181,500 for 20 grants (high: $60,000; low: $500).
Fields of interest: Arts and culture; Historic preservation; Higher education; Natural resources; Child welfare.
Type of support: Land acquisitions; Program development; Convening; Publications; Curriculum development.
Limitations: Applications not accepted. Giving primarily in WI. No grants to individuals.
Application information: Unsolicited requests for funds not accepted.
Officers: Robert Swartz, Pres.; Robert Skemp, V.P.; Robert Skemp, Jr., Secy.-Treas.
EIN: 391598681

9942
E. C. Styberg Foundation, Inc.
P.O. Box 788
Racine, WI 53401-0788
Contact: E.C. Styberg Jr., Pres.

Established in 1981 in Wisconsin.
Donors: E.C. Styberg, Jr.; Bernice M. Styberg.
Foundation type: Independent foundation.
Financial data (yr. ended 06/30/13): Assets, $9,134,938 (M); gifts received, $100,000; expenditures, $283,717; qualifying distributions, $201,903; giving activities include $198,800 for 57 grants (high: $25,000; low: $500).
Purpose and activities: Giving primarily for education, including a theological seminary, as well as for health organizations, and social services.
Fields of interest: Arts and culture; Education; Graduate and professional education; Diseases and conditions; Community and economic development; Theology; Human services.
Type of support: General support; Capital campaigns.
Limitations: Applications accepted. Giving primarily in southeastern WI; with some giving in IL. No grants to individuals.
Application information: Application form required.
  Initial approach: Proposal
  Deadline(s): None
Officers: E.C. Styberg, Jr., Pres.; Bernice M. Styberg, V.P. and Secy.; Paul L. Guenther, Treas.
EIN: 391410323

9943
Sub-Zero Wolf Foundation, Inc.
c/o Sub-Zero Wolf, Inc.
4717 Hammersley Rd.
Madison, WI 53711-2708 (608) 271-2233
Contact: Marge Bien

Established in 1998 in Wisconsin.
Donors: Sub-Zero Freezer Co., Inc.; Sub-Zero Wolf, Inc.; Sub-Zero Group, Inc.
Foundation type: Company-sponsored foundation.
Financial data (yr. ended 04/30/14): Assets, $244,269 (M); gifts received, $200,000; expenditures, $120,250; qualifying distributions, $120,250; giving activities include $120,250 for 68 grants (high: $50,000; low: $150).
Purpose and activities: The foundation supports zoos and organizations involved with arts and culture, education, conservation, health,

Alzheimer's disease, diabetes, athletics, human services, and business promotion.
Fields of interest: Education; Health; Diseases and conditions; Community and economic development; Human services.
Type of support: General support; Program development; Research.
Limitations: Applications accepted. Giving primarily in Madison, WI.
Application information: Application form required.
Initial approach: Letter
Deadline(s): None
Officers and Directors: Helen A. Bakke, Pres. and Director; James J. Bakke, V.P. and Director; Marjorie Bien, Secy.; Deborah A. Schwartz, Treas. and Director.
EIN: 391918462

9944
The Robert J. Sullivan Family Foundation
W302 S1638 Brandybrook Rd.
Waukesha, WI 53188-9319 (262) 968-4665
Contact: Katherine Sullivan, Dir.

Established in 1990 in Wisconsin.
Donor: Robert J. Sullivan.
Foundation type: Independent foundation.
Financial data (yr. ended 12/31/13): Assets, $4,093,223 (M); expenditures, $197,637; qualifying distributions, $173,222; giving activities include $170,000 for 6 grants (high: $50,000; low: $5,000).
Fields of interest: Hospital care; Diseases and conditions; Developmental disability services.
Type of support: Research.
Limitations: Applications accepted. Giving primarily in CA and WI.
Application information: Application form required.
Initial approach: Letter
Copies of proposal: 1
Deadline(s): None
Directors: Elizabeth Ann Cimler; Mary Kathleen Schwanke; Katherine Sullivan; Robert J. Sullivan, Jr.; Timothy J. Sullivan.
Number of staff: 1 part-time professional.
EIN: 391686475

9945
T & O Foundation Inc.
6101 N. Shore Dr.
Eau Claire, WI 54703-2040

Established in 1987 in Wisconsin.
Donor: David B. Westrate.
Foundation type: Independent foundation.
Financial data (yr. ended 12/31/13): Assets, $3,354,073 (M); expenditures, $312,180; qualifying distributions, $300,380; giving activities include $300,380 for 10 grants (high: $150,000; low: $500).
Purpose and activities: Giving primarily for family values and Christian evangelical causes.
Fields of interest: Christianity; Family services.
Type of support: General support; Equipment; Seed money; Scholarships.
Limitations: Applications not accepted. Giving primarily in OR. No grants to individuals.
Application information: Unsolicited requests for funds not accepted.

Officers: David B. Westrate, Pres.; Mike Westrate, V.P.; Brian Westrate, Secy.-Treas.
EIN: 391615711

9946
Elizabeth J. Tellier Foundation Inc.
1000 N. Water St., Ste. 1500
Milwaukee, WI 53202-6649

Established in 1995 in Wisconsin.
Donor: Elizabeth J. Tellier.
Foundation type: Independent foundation.
Financial data (yr. ended 03/31/13): Assets, $3,711,288 (M); expenditures, $213,249; qualifying distributions, $178,000; giving activities include $178,000 for grants.
Purpose and activities: Giving for the preservation of wildlife or to benefit the public.
Fields of interest: Arts and culture; Education; Wildlife biodiversity; Forest preservation; Crime prevention; Public affairs; Christianity.
Limitations: Applications not accepted. Giving primarily in WI. No grants to individuals.
Application information: Unsolicited request for funds not accepted.
Officers and Directors: Robert W. Chernow, Pres. and Director; John C. Dowd, Treas. and Director; John M. Marra.
Number of staff: None.
EIN: 391777930

9947
Patrick J. and Janet L. Thompson Family Foundation Inc.
9 N. Kurt Ave.
Appleton, WI 54913-9715

Established in 2007 in Wisconsin.
Donors: Patrick J. Thompson; Janet L. Thompson.
Foundation type: Independent foundation.
Financial data (yr. ended 06/30/13): Assets, $4,021,483 (M); expenditures, $226,896; qualifying distributions, $207,500; giving activities include $207,500 for grants.
Fields of interest: Education; Foundations; Religion.
Limitations: Applications not accepted. Giving primarily in MN and WI. No grants to individuals.
Application information: Contributes only to pre-selected organizations.
Officers: Patrick J. Thompson, Pres. and Treas.; Janet L. Thompson, V.P. and Secy.
EIN: 261404215

9948
Trek Scholarship Foundation Inc.
801 W. Madison St.
Waterloo, WI 53594-1379 (920) 478-2191
Contact: Heather Sexton

Established in 2005 in Wisconsin.
Donors: Richard Burke; Trek Bicycle Corporation.
Foundation type: Independent foundation.
Financial data (yr. ended 07/31/14): Assets, $4,139,583 (M); expenditures, $199,554; qualifying distributions, $159,500; giving activities include $159,500 for grants to individuals.
Purpose and activities: Scholarship awards to residents of Wisconsin for tuition, housing, books, fees and/or transportation expenses at any

accredited postsecondary educational program/institution.
Fields of interest: Higher education.
Type of support: Scholarships; Student aid.
Limitations: Applications accepted. Giving primarily in WI and MN.
Application information: Applicants must include resume, transcripts, essay, 2 recommendation letters and photograph. Application form required.
Initial approach: Request application form
Officers and Directors: Elaine Burke, Pres. and Director; Michele Deubel, Secy.-Treas. and Director; Mark Joslyn.
EIN: 204143271

9949
David V. Uihlein Foundation
(formerly David Uihlein Racing Museum Foundation)
322 E. Michigan St., Ste. 302
Milwaukee, WI 53202—4104

Donor: David V. Uihlein.
Foundation type: Operating foundation.
Financial data (yr. ended 12/31/13): Assets, $9,778,289 (M); expenditures, $470,234; qualifying distributions, $426,320; giving activities include $425,000 for 30 grants (high: $50,000; low: $5,000).
Fields of interest: Education; Environment; Diseases and conditions; Human services.
Type of support: General support.
Limitations: Applications not accepted. Giving in the U.S., with emphasis in WI. No grants to individuals.
Application information: Contributes only to pre-selected organizations.
Trustees: Kathryn M. Kuehn; Philip G. Kuehn, Jr.; Margery H. Uihlein.
EIN: 391284018

9950
Robert A. Uihlein Foundation
c/o Glenora Co.
322 E. Michigan St., Ste. 302
Milwaukee, WI 53202-4104

Established in 1942 in Wisconsin.
Donors: Robert A. Uihlein III; James J. Uihlein.
Foundation type: Independent foundation.
Financial data (yr. ended 12/31/13): Assets, $4,276,090 (M); expenditures, $187,690; qualifying distributions, $181,230; giving activities include $180,000 for 6 grants (high: $120,000; low: $12,000).
Fields of interest: Arts and culture; Sport and hobby museums; Education; Nonprofits; Health; Diseases and conditions; Cancers; Christianity; Human services; Youth services.
Type of support: Regranting.
Limitations: Applications not accepted. Giving primarily in Milwaukee, WI. No grants to individuals.
Application information: Unsolicited requests for funds not accepted.
Officers and Directors: Robert A. Uihlein III, Pres. and Director; Jill Mnewman, V.P. and Secy.-Treas. and Director; James I. Uihlein.
EIN: 396033236

9951
John & Janet Van Den Wymelenberg Foundation Inc.
1570 Mesa Dr.
Green Bay, WI 54313-9366

Donor: John Van Den Wymelenberg.
Foundation type: Independent foundation.
Financial data (yr. ended 08/31/13): Assets, $4,390,004 (M); expenditures, $220,629; qualifying distributions, $215,647; giving activities include $215,647 for 31 grants (high: $17,500; low: $750).
Fields of interest: Christianity; Human services; Youth services.
Limitations: Applications not accepted. Giving primarily in WI. No grants to individuals.
Application information: Contributes only to pre-selected organizations.
Officers and Directors: Kathy Rolling, Pres. and Director; Fr. Richard Mauthe, V.P.; Linda Boss; Mary Ann Hunt; Susan Martell.
EIN: 391392405

9952
Joseph & Sarah Van Drisse Charitable Trust
111 N. Washington St.
Green Bay, WI 54305

Established in 2000 in Wisconsin.
Foundation type: Independent foundation.
Financial data (yr. ended 12/31/14): Assets, $4,972,075 (M); expenditures, $250,124; qualifying distributions, $177,808; giving activities include $166,500 for 14 grants (high: $50,000; low: $1,000).
Purpose and activities: Giving primarily for Roman Catholic organizations, as well as for education, the arts, and human services.
Fields of interest: Orchestral music; Children's museums; Education; Higher education; Nonprofits; Hospital care; Rehabilitation; Catholicism; Human services; Child welfare; Youth services.
Type of support: Individual development; Regranting.
Limitations: Applications not accepted. Giving primarily in Green Bay, WI. No grants to individuals.
Application information: Unsolicited requests for funds not accepted.
Trustee: JPMorgan Chase Bank, N.A.
EIN: 396719617

9953
Gregory C. Van Wie Charitable Foundation
2 E. Mifflin St., Ste. 200
Madison, WI 53703-4269

Established in 1996 in Wisconsin.
Foundation type: Independent foundation.
Financial data (yr. ended 12/31/13): Assets, $4,190,955 (M); expenditures, $428,564; qualifying distributions, $220,700; giving activities include $220,700 for 6 grants (high: $136,000; low: $5,000).
Fields of interest: Historic preservation; Education; Nonprofits; Sports and recreation; Human services; Developmental disability services; People with disabilities.
Type of support: General support; Scholarships; Regranting.

Limitations: Applications not accepted. Giving primarily in WI. No grants to individuals.
Application information: Contributes only to pre-selected organizations.
Officers: John C. Mitby, Pres.; John van Wie, V.P.; Bruce C. Rodger, Secy.
EIN: 391822927

9954
Marvin P. Verhulst Foundation, Inc.
3821 Signature Dr.
Middleton, WI 53562-2387

Established in 2002 in Wisconsin.
Donors: Marvin P. Verhulst; Kenneth M. Burbach; Mary S. Burbach.
Foundation type: Independent foundation.
Financial data (yr. ended 12/31/13): Assets, $4,701,535 (M); expenditures, $201,830; qualifying distributions, $197,187; giving activities include $195,500 for 19 grants (high: $75,000; low: $1,000).
Fields of interest: Museums; Education; University education; Christianity; Human services; Senior assisted living.
Limitations: Applications not accepted. Giving primarily in FL and WI. No grants to individuals.
Application information: Contributes only to pre-selected organizations.
Officers: Mary S. Burbach, Pres. and Treas.; Kenneth M. Burbach, Secy.
Directors: Sarah Bruch; Brian Burbach; Patricia Dorfman; Robert Dorfman.
EIN: 330998350

9955
Melvin F. and Ellen L. Wagner Foundation
(formerly Melvin F. Wagner Foundation)
c/o U.S. Bank, N.A.
P.O. Box 2043
Milwaukee, WI 53201-9668

Donor: Ellen L. Wagner†.
Foundation type: Independent foundation.
Financial data (yr. ended 12/31/13): Assets, $9,037,593 (M); expenditures, $471,221; qualifying distributions, $421,726; giving activities include $413,820 for 11 grants (high: $56,430; low: $18,810).
Purpose and activities: Giving primarily for education, health care, particularly hospitals and health organizations, Christian churches, and human services.
Fields of interest: Higher education; Nonprofits; Hospital care; Muscular dystrophy; Alzheimer's disease; Christianity; Human services.
Type of support: General support; Regranting.
Limitations: Applications not accepted. Giving primarily in Sheboygan, WI. No grants to individuals.
Application information: Contributes only to pre-selected organizations.
 Board meeting date(s): Quarterly
Trustees: James Kitzinger; James E. Raffel; Dolores V. Slesrick; Eugene D. Weber; U.S. Bank, N.A.
EIN: 396129125

9956
Watertown Area Community Foundation
c/o Thomas Levi
P.O. Box 351
Watertown, WI 53094-0351 (920) 261-8720
Contact: Tom Schultz, Pres.

Established in 1992 in Wisconsin.
Foundation type: Community foundation.
Financial data (yr. ended 06/30/13): Assets, $4,710,217 (M); gifts received, $5,343; expenditures, $257,827; giving activities include $55,333 for grants, and $167,448 for grants to individuals.
Purpose and activities: Provide for the betterment and improvement of Watertown, WI.
Fields of interest: Secondary education; Community and economic development; Human services; Senior services.
Limitations: Giving limited to the Watertown, WI, area.
Officers and Directors: Tom Schultz, Pres. and Director; James Clifford, V.P. and Director; Bruce Kasten, Treas. and Director; Thomas Levi; Dave Pederson; Sue Rhodes.
EIN: 391708484

9957
Webcrafters-Frautschi Foundation, Inc.
2211 Fordem Ave.
Madison, WI 53704-4611
Application address: c/o Jac B. Garner, P.O. Box 7608, Madison, WI 53707, tel.: (608) 244-3561

Established in 1961 in Wisconsin.
Donors: John J. Frautschi; Christopher Frautschi; Jac B. Garner; Judy Peirick; John C. Weston; John J. Frautschi Family Foundation.
Foundation type: Independent foundation.
Financial data (yr. ended 06/30/13): Assets, $3,434 (M); gifts received, $180,000; expenditures, $186,510; qualifying distributions, $186,500; giving activities include $186,500 for grants.
Purpose and activities: Grants are limited to human services, arts, and education.
Fields of interest: Arts and culture; Education; Higher education; Nonprofits; Hospice care; Public libraries; Human services; Child welfare.
Type of support: General support; Annual campaigns; Capital campaigns; Capital and infrastructure; Regranting.
Limitations: Applications accepted. Giving primarily in WI, with emphasis on the Madison area. No grants to individuals.
Application information:
 Initial approach: Letter
 Deadline(s): None
Officers: Jac B. Garner, Pres.; Christopher J. Frautschi, 1st V.P.; Judy A. Perick, 2nd V.P.; Robert A. Lay, Secy.-Treas.
Board Member: John J. Frautschi.
EIN: 396045309

9958
Weyco Group Charitable Trust
P.O. Box 1188
Milwaukee, WI 53201-1188 (414) 908-1880
Contact: John F. Wittkowske, Tr.

Established in 1996 in Wisconsin.

Donor: Weyco Group, Inc.
Foundation type: Company-sponsored foundation.
Financial data (yr. ended 12/31/13): Assets, $211,521 (M); gifts received, $250,000; expenditures, $211,169; qualifying distributions, $211,158; giving activities include $211,158 for 59 grants (high: $25,370; low: $180).
Purpose and activities: The trust supports civic centers and organizations involved with arts and culture, education, human services, the footwear industry, and leadership development.
Fields of interest: Education; Community and economic development; Human services.
Type of support: General support; Program development; Scholarships.
Limitations: Applications accepted. Giving primarily in Milwaukee, WI. No grants to individuals.
Application information: Application form required.
Initial approach: Letter
Deadline(s): None
Trustees: John W. Florsheim; Thomas W. Florsheim, Sr.; Thomas W. Florsheim, Jr.; John F. Wittkowske.
EIN: 396645370

9959
Weyers Family Foundation Inc.
P.O. Box 12057
Green Bay, WI 54307-2057 (920) 434-5812
Contact: Ronald Weyers, Mgr.

Established in 1997 in Wisconsin.
Donors: Ronald Weyers; Secura Insurance; Tosca, Ltd.; Robert J. Weyers; Weyers Charitable Lead Annuity Trust of 2010.
Foundation type: Independent foundation.
Financial data (yr. ended 12/31/13): Assets, $3,481,635 (M); gifts received, $55,086; expenditures, $310,030; qualifying distributions, $295,850; giving activities include $295,850 for 50 grants (high: $55,000; low: $200).
Fields of interest: Performing arts; Education; Foundations; Hospital care; Diseases and conditions; Cerebral palsy; Community and economic development; Human services; Food banks; Youth services.
Type of support: Research; Research and evaluation.
Limitations: Applications accepted. Giving primarily in Green Bay, WI. No grants to individuals.
Application information: Application form required.
Initial approach: Letter
Deadline(s): None
Officer: Ronald Weyers, Mgr.
EIN: 391901443

9960
Wilson Family Foundation, Inc.
(formerly FMI Soccer Club, Inc.)
19160 Still Pt. Trail
Brookfield, WI 53045-4809

Donor: Donald S. Wilson.
Foundation type: Independent foundation.
Financial data (yr. ended 12/31/14): Assets, $3,857,406; expenditures, $223,445; qualifying distributions, $222,476.

Fields of interest: Arts and culture; University education.
Type of support: Capital campaigns; General support.
Limitations: Applications not accepted. Giving primarily in WI. No grants to individuals.
Application information: Contributes only to pre-selected organizations.
Officers: Donald S. Wilson, Pres.; Kathleen Wilson, V.P.
Director: Katharine Otto Lockwood.
EIN: 391656189

9961
Windway Foundation, Inc.
P.O. Box 897
Sheboygan, WI 53081 (920) 457-8600
Contact: Terry Kohler, Pres.
Application Address: 630 Riverfront Dr., Ste. 200, Sheboygan, WI, 53081

Donors: The Vollrath Co., LLC; Windway Capital Corp.
Foundation type: Company-sponsored foundation.
Financial data (yr. ended 09/30/14): Assets, $46,610 (M); gifts received, $180,000; expenditures, $182,868; qualifying distributions, $182,868; giving activities include $182,000 for 39 grants (high: $30,000; low: $500).
Purpose and activities: The foundation supports museums and organizations involved with education, conservation, human services, civil rights, and public policy.
Fields of interest: Museums; History museums; Education; Higher education; Law education; Water resources; Bird preservation; Public policy; Human services; Youth services.
Type of support: Equipment; Cash grants; Program development; Scholarships; Research.
Limitations: Applications accepted. Giving primarily in areas of company operations in IL and Sheboygan, WI. No grants to individuals.
Application information: Application form required.
Initial approach: Letter
Deadline(s): None
Officers and Directors: Terry J. Kohler, Pres. and Dir.; Mary S. Kohler, V.P. and Dir.; Mary Theune, Secy. and Dir.; Roland M. Neumann, Treas. and Dir.
Number of staff: None.
EIN: 396046987

9962
John H. Witte, Jr. Foundation Trust
c/o U.S. Bank, N.A.
P.O. Box 7900
Madison, WI 53707-7900
Application address: c/o U.S. Bank, N.A., Attn.: Terri Dowell, 201 Jefferson St., Burlington, IA 52601, (319) 753-8761

Established in 1979 in Iowa.
Donor: John H. Witte, Jr.†
Foundation type: Independent foundation.
Financial data (yr. ended 08/31/13): Assets, $7,454,214 (M); expenditures, $377,685;

qualifying distributions, $339,776; giving activities include $301,230 for 27 grants (high: $55,000; low: $500).
Purpose and activities: Giving primarily for education and social services.
Fields of interest: Arts and culture; Elementary and secondary education; Higher education; Natural resources; Nonprofits; Public libraries; Community and economic development; Human services; Child welfare.
Type of support: Annual campaigns; Capital and infrastructure; Equipment; Program development; Regranting.
Limitations: Applications accepted. Giving primarily in the Burlington, IA, area. No grants to individuals.
Application information: Application form required.
Initial approach: Letter
Deadline(s): None
Trustee: U.S. Bank, N.A.
EIN: 426297940

9963
Woodtrust-Bell Foundation Inc.
(formerly Bell Family Charitable Foundation, Inc.)
181 2nd St. S.
Wisconsin Rapids, WI 54494-4100

Established in 1992 in Wisconsin.
Donors: Steven C. Bell; Margaret L. Bell; Wood County National Bank; WCN Bancorp; Paula J. Bell; Wood County Trust Co.; Woodtrust Financial Corp.; Margaret L. Bell Administrative Trust.
Foundation type: Company-sponsored foundation.
Financial data (yr. ended 12/31/13): Assets, $3,997,968 (M); gifts received, $25,000; expenditures, $263,371; qualifying distributions, $233,705; giving activities include $223,498 for 30 grants (high: $50,000; low: $169).
Purpose and activities: The foundation supports recreation centers and community foundations and organizations involved with secondary and higher education, health, employment, and children services.
Fields of interest: Secondary education; Higher education; Foundations; Health; Employment; Community recreation; Human services; Child welfare.
Type of support: General support; Capital campaigns; Capital and infrastructure; Equipment; Endowments; Program development; Scholarships; Sponsorships.
Limitations: Applications not accepted.
Application information: Unsolicited requests for funds not accepted.
Officers: Steven C. Bell, Co-Chair.; Chad D. Kane, Co-Chair.; Rebecca L. Kettleson, Pres.; Paula J. Bell, V.P.; Sandra L. Oleson, Secy.; Deborah N. Kane, Treas.
Directors: Margaret S. Bell; Elizabeth A. Bell Killian.
EIN: 396572208

WYOMING

9964
Jim and Audrey Bailey Foundation
2578 Painted Horse Trail
Casper, WY 82604-3783

Established in 1991 in Wyoming.
Donors: Jim M. Bailey; Audrey W. Bailey.
Foundation type: Independent foundation.
Financial data (yr. ended 12/31/14): Assets, $2,945,067 (M); expenditures, $211,781; qualifying distributions, $160,650; giving activities include $160,650 for 12 grants (high: $39,000; low: $500).
Fields of interest: Education; Diseases and conditions.
Type of support: Scholarships; Research.
Limitations: Applications not accepted. Giving primarily in WY. No grants to individuals.
Application information: Unsolicited requests for funds not accepted.
Officers: James M. Bailey, Pres. and V.P.; Judith Bailey Scully, Secy.; Walter M. Bailey, Treas.
Trustee: Audrey W. Bailey.
EIN: 363776545

9965
Brendsel Family Foundation
735 Swan Rd.
P.O. Box 6547
Jackson, WY 83002-6547

Established in 2004 in Wyoming.
Donors: Billie D. Brendsel; Leland C. Brendsel.
Foundation type: Independent foundation.
Financial data (yr. ended 12/31/13): Assets, $760,576 (M); expenditures, $229,009; qualifying distributions, $215,000; giving activities include $215,000 for 7 grants (high: $175,000; low: $5,000).
Fields of interest: Higher education; Environment.
Limitations: Applications not accepted. Giving primarily in MD.
Application information: Contributes only to pre-selected organizations.
Trustees: Billie D. Brendsel; Leland C. Brendsel.
EIN: 202068409

9966
C & N Foundation
P.O. Box 767
Wilson, WY 83014-0767 3077337727

Established in 1987 in Michigan.
Donors: Norman H. Hofley; Carole S. Hofley.
Foundation type: Independent foundation.
Financial data (yr. ended 05/31/15): Assets, $3,688,631; gifts received, $43,686; expenditures, $204,507; qualifying distributions, $183,272.
Fields of interest: Arts and culture; Music; Orchestral music; Historic preservation; Undergraduate education; Environment; Foundations; Health; Libraries; Radio; Protestantism; Human services.
Type of support: General support.

Limitations: Applications not accepted. Giving primarily in MI and WY. No grants to individuals.
Application information: Unsolicited requests for funds not accepted.
Officers: Norman H. Hofley, Pres. and Treas.; Carole S. Hofley, V.P. and Secy.
EIN: 382746657

9967
Connemara Fund
c/o Polly J. Friess
P.O. Box 11655
Jackson, WY 83002-1655

Established in 1968 in North Carolina.
Donor: Mary R. Jackson†.
Foundation type: Independent foundation.
Financial data (yr. ended 06/30/13): Assets, $5,653,540 (M); expenditures, $422,094; qualifying distributions, $363,699; giving activities include $319,530 for 42 grants (high: $90,000; low: $30).
Purpose and activities: Grants primarily for church support and religious welfare associations; support also for social services, cultural programs, and education.
Fields of interest: Arts and culture; Historic preservation; Education; Higher education; Environment; Nonprofits; Hospital care; Legal services; Religion; Christianity; Interfaith; Human services; Child welfare.
Type of support: General support; Continuing support; Regranting; Equal access.
Limitations: Applications not accepted. Giving primarily in CT and NY. No grants to individuals.
Application information: Unsolicited requests for funds not accepted.
Trustees: Polly J. Friess; Herrick Jackson; Alison J. Van Dyk.
Number of staff: None.
EIN: 566096063

9968
The Allen B. Cutting Foundation
c/o Rebecca Broderick
P.O. Box 10516
Jackson, WY 83002-0516

Established in 1996 in Michigan.
Donors: Joan L. Cutting; Margaret Cutting Manuel; Rebecca Cutting Broderick; Amy E. Cutting.
Foundation type: Independent foundation.
Financial data (yr. ended 12/31/13): Assets, $7,529,634 (M); gifts received, $5,900; expenditures, $409,006; qualifying distributions, $370,000; giving activities include $370,000 for 9 grants (high: $90,000; low: $10,000).
Fields of interest: Arts education; Elementary and secondary education; School-based health care; Kidney diseases; Human rights; Minority rights; Domestic violence shelters; American Indians.
Limitations: Applications not accepted. Giving primarily in FL, Interlochen, MI, Kansas City, MO, Pine Ridge, SD, and Plano, TX, Jackson, WY. No grants to individuals.
Application information: Contributes only to pre-selected organizations.
Officers: Joan L. Cutting, Pres.; Margaret Cutting Manuel, V.P. and Secy.; Rebecca Cutting Broderick, Treas.
EIN: 383319000

9969
Matthew and Virgie O. Dragicevich Wyoming Foundation Trust No. 1
P.O. Box 385
Teton Village, WY 83025-0385 (307) 733-4520

Established in 1998 in New York.
Donor: Calvin Mathieu.
Foundation type: Independent foundation.
Financial data (yr. ended 09/30/12): Assets, $6,898,380 (M); expenditures, $502,148; qualifying distributions, $433,782; giving activities include $321,000 for 11 grants (high: $101,000; low: $5,000).
Fields of interest: Arts and culture; Education; Foundations; Human services; Child welfare; Seniors; People of Latin American descent; Homeless people; Low-income and poor people.
Type of support: General support.
Limitations: Applications not accepted. Giving primarily in Jackson, WY.
Application information: Contributes only to pre-selected organizations.
Trustees: Jolene C. Harms; Calvin N. Mathieu.
EIN: 836046045

9970
The Carine and Jacques Dubois Family Foundation
(formerly The Jacques & Lucille Dubois Charitable Foundation)
P.O. Box 10100
Jackson, WY 83002-0100

Established in 1998 in Connecticut.
Donor: Jacques E. Dubois.
Foundation type: Independent foundation.
Financial data (yr. ended 06/30/14): Assets, $6,280,724 (M); gifts received, $8,925; expenditures, $327,676; qualifying distributions, $258,835; giving activities include $255,000 for 4 grants (high: $100,000; low: $30,000).
Fields of interest: Education; Higher education; Foundations; Human services; Scouting programs.
Limitations: Applications not accepted. Giving primarily in CT, NM, RI, and WY. No grants to individuals.
Application information: Contributes only to pre-selected organizations.
Officers: Carine R. Klein, Chair.; Jacques E. Dubois, Pres.
EIN: 061529842

9971
Ruth R. Ellbogen Foundation
P.O. Box 70
Casper, WY 82602-0070

Established in 1999 in Wyoming.
Donor: Ruth R. Ellbogen.
Foundation type: Independent foundation.
Financial data (yr. ended 07/31/14): Assets, $2,392,267 (M); gifts received, $103,235; expenditures, $351,829; qualifying distributions, $337,366; giving activities include $331,886 for 30 grants (high: $120,000; low: $100).
Fields of interest: Education; University education; Foundations; Hospital care; Hospice care; Child welfare.
Limitations: Applications not accepted. Giving primarily in WY. No grants to individuals.

Application information: Contributes only to pre-selected organizations.
Officers: Thomas M. Ellbogen, Pres.; John P. Ellbogen II, V.P.; Mary L. E. Garland, Secy.-Treas.
Directors: Ruth R. Ellbogen; Theresa A. Ellbogen.
EIN: 830327143

9972
Guthrie Family Foundation
P.O. Box 1242
Laramie, WY 82070-4337 (307) 742-7117
Contact: John Guthrie

Established in 2001 in Wyoming.
Donors: Jack Guthrie; Pat Guthrie.
Foundation type: Independent foundation.
Financial data (yr. ended 09/30/13): Assets, $6,081,581 (M); expenditures, $350,393; qualifying distributions, $312,913; giving activities include $312,913 for 17 grants (high: $60,000; low: $2,800).
Fields of interest: Arts and culture; Foundations; Nonprofits; Community and economic development; Christianity; Human services; Low-income and poor people.
Type of support: Regranting.
Limitations: Applications accepted. Giving primarily in Laramie, WY.
Application information: Application form required.
  Initial approach: Letter
  Copies of proposal: 7
  Deadline(s): July 1
Officer: John A. Guthrie III, Pres.; Brenda Hunter, Secy.-Treas.
Board Members: Margaret Dickman; Dan Furphy; Pat Guthrie.
EIN: 830314146

9973
Norman Hirschfield Foundation
P.O. Box 7443
Jackson, WY 83002-7443

Donors: Alan J. Hirschfield; Berte E. Hirschfield.
Foundation type: Independent foundation.
Financial data (yr. ended 11/30/13): Assets, $7,051,632 (M); expenditures, $238,494; qualifying distributions, $226,271; giving activities include $224,300 for 18 grants (high: $89,000; low: $50).
Purpose and activities: Giving primarily for education, human services, and to health organizations, including an animal cancer center.
Fields of interest: Education; Health; Human services.
Limitations: Applications not accepted. Giving primarily in Jackson, WY. No grants to individuals.
Application information: Contributes only to pre-selected organizations.
Officers: Alan J. Hirschfield, Pres.; Berte E. Hirschfield, V.P. and Secy.-Treas.
EIN: 736092984

9974
The Imig Family Foundation
1110 W. Powell Rd.
Cheyenne, WY 82009

Donors: Gary R. Imig; Pamela L. Imig.
Foundation type: Independent foundation.

Financial data (yr. ended 12/31/14): Assets, $236,243; gifts received, $104,663; expenditures, $127,804; qualifying distributions, $125,817.
Fields of interest: Arts and culture; Christianity; Human services.
Limitations: Applications not accepted. Giving primarily in Cheyenne, WY.
Application information: Unsolicited requests for funds not accepted.
Directors: Gary R. Imig; Pamela L. Imig.
EIN: 274243009

9975
Jaquith Family Foundation
4515 Willowbrook Ln.
Wilson, WY 83014-9208

Established in 1986 in Illinois.
Donors: Richard D. Jaquith; Patricia P. Jaquith.
Foundation type: Independent foundation.
Financial data (yr. ended 12/31/13): Assets, $2,055,769 (M); gifts received, $1,313; expenditures, $159,500; qualifying distributions, $158,750; giving activities include $158,750 for 29 grants (high: $25,000; low: $200).
Fields of interest: Performing arts; Higher education; Family planning; International development.
Type of support: General support.
Limitations: Applications not accepted. Giving primarily in IL and MA, with some giving in NY. No grants to individuals.
Application information: Contributes only to pre-selected organizations.
Officers and Directors: Richard D. Jaquith, Pres. and Director; Patricia P. Jaquith, V.P. and Secy.-Treas. and Director; David W. Jaquith; Susan L. Musich.
EIN: 363487797

9976
Joannides Family Foundation
10013 Wayne Rd.
Cheyenne, WY 82009-9644

Established in 2008 in Wyoming.
Donors: Timothy J. Joannides; Halladay Motors; Joannides Family Properties.
Foundation type: Independent foundation.
Financial data (yr. ended 12/31/14): Assets, $8,080 (M); gifts received, $235,000; expenditures, $231,743; qualifying distributions, $227,315; giving activities include $220,269 for 101 grants (high: $72,145; low: $100).
Fields of interest: Education; Religion; Orthodox Christianity; Human services.
Limitations: Applications not accepted. Giving primarily in WY.
Application information: Unsolicited requests for funds not accepted.
Directors: Andrew L. Joannides; Angela S. Joannides; Christopher J. Joannides; Kathy A. Joannides; Nickolas S. Joannides; Timothy J. Joannides.
EIN: 263903831

9977
Karl M. Johnson Foundation
P.O. Box 7
Jackson, WY 83001-0007 (307) 733-2772

Established in 1989 in Wyoming.
Donor: Karl M. Johnson.
Foundation type: Independent foundation.
Financial data (yr. ended 12/31/13): Assets, $3,659,193 (M); expenditures, $1,253,925; qualifying distributions, $378,053; giving activities include $366,258 for 64 grants (high: $20,000; low: $50).
Fields of interest: Elementary and secondary education; Hospital care; Fire prevention and control; Christianity; Human services.
Limitations: Applications accepted. Giving primarily in the Teton Valley, WY, area.
Application information:
  Initial approach: Proposal
  Deadline(s): None
Directors: Bret King; Richard Palmer.
EIN: 742554281

9978
The JWJ Family Foundation Inc.
P.O. Box 7241
Jackson, WY 83002-7241

Foundation type: Independent foundation.
Financial data (yr. ended 12/31/14): Assets, $2,888,605 (M); expenditures, $139,796; qualifying distributions, $130,760; giving activities include $130,760 for grants (high: $10,000; low: $260).
Fields of interest: Education.
Type of support: General support.
Limitations: Applications not accepted. Giving primarily in VT and WY.
Application information: Unsolicited requests for funds not accepted.
Officers: Maria Johnson, Pres.; Nina Johnson Lynch, Secy.; Worthington Johnson, Jr., Treas.
EIN: 208411928

9979
Marna M. Kuehne Foundation
P.O. Box 6064
Sheridan, WY 82801-1464
Application address: c/o Edward A. Hoffman, 1949 Sugarland Dr., Ste. 220, Sheridan, WY 82801; tel.: (307) 672-8956

Established in 1997 in Wyoming.
Donor: Marna M. Kuehne†.
Foundation type: Independent foundation.
Financial data (yr. ended 10/31/13): Assets, $24,531,351 (M); expenditures, $869,129; qualifying distributions, $869,129; giving activities include $334,323 for 16 grants (high: $104,097; low: $1,380).
Purpose and activities: Grants are restricted to organizations serving veterans.
Fields of interest: National defense; Veterans.
Limitations: Applications accepted. Giving primarily in northwestern WY. No grants to individuals.
Application information: Application form required.
  Initial approach: Letter
  Deadline(s): Ten days before the next scheduled board of directors meet
Officers: Edward A. Hoffman, Pres.; Jack Tarter, V.P.; Dan B. Riggs, Secy.
Director: Richard Hammer.
EIN: 742276741

9980
Marine Ventures Foundation, Inc.
P.O. Box 30000, PMB 61
Jackson, WY 83002-0600
E-mail: info@marineventures.org
Blog: http://www.marineventures.org/blog

Established in 2001 in District of Columbia.
Donor: John Thomas McMurray.
Foundation type: Independent foundation.
Financial data (yr. ended 12/31/13): Assets, $3,355,782 (M); expenditures, $241,585; qualifying distributions, $200,086; giving activities include $200,086 for 10 grants (high: $75,000; low: $282).
Purpose and activities: Giving to fund new conservation efforts to ensure healthy fish populations in the world's rivers and oceans. The grantmaker's vision is to shift the cultural focus of short-term wealth extraction of our limited natural resources in the world's river and marine ecosystems, to long-term stewardship for the benefit of the rivers and oceans and all of us who depend on them.
Fields of interest: Education; Aquatic wildlife protection; Domesticated animals; Human services.
Limitations: Applications not accepted. No grants to individuals.
Application information: Contributes only to pre-selected organizations.
Officer: Tom McMurray, C.E.O. and Pres.
Directors: Carson Reid McMurray; John Thomas McMurray; McCain Jay McMurray; Brandon C. White.
EIN: 522297698

9981
Anne & Scott Nickerson Family Foundation
P.O. Box 278
Big Horn, WY 82833-0278 (307) 674-9875

Established in 1997 in Wyoming.
Donors: Scott Nickerson; Anne Nickerson.
Foundation type: Independent foundation.
Financial data (yr. ended 05/31/13): Assets, $3,729,137 (M); gifts received, $100,000; expenditures, $256,993; qualifying distributions, $211,162; giving activities include $210,500 for grants.
Fields of interest: Historic preservation; Education; Community and economic development; Human services.
Type of support: General support.
Limitations: Applications accepted. Giving primarily in WY. No grants to individuals.
Application information: Application form required.
  Initial approach: Request application
  Deadline(s): None
Officers: Scott Nickerson, Pres.; Anne Nickerson, Secy.-Treas.
Directors: David Nickerson; Gregory Nickerson; Phillip Nickerson.
EIN: 841409098

9982
B. F. & Rose H. Perkins Foundation
45 E. Loucks St., Ste. 110
Sheridan, WY 82801-6329 (307) 674-8871
FAX: (307) 674-8803;
E-mail: bfperkin@fiberpipe.net; Mailing address:

P.O. Box 1064, Sheridan, WY 82801; Main URL: http://www.perkinsfoundation.org

Established in 1933 in Wyoming.
Donor: Benjamin F. Perkins†.
Foundation type: Independent foundation.
Financial data (yr. ended 12/31/13): Assets, $10,020,413 (M); expenditures, $490,866; qualifying distributions, $554,119; giving activities include $177,250 for 15 grants (high: $57,600; low: $1,750), $134,924 for 71 grants to individuals, $124,400 for 38 loans to individuals, and $30,825 for 1 foundation-administered program.·
Purpose and activities: Medical and educational assistance to individuals under the age of 21; recipients of educational loans must be graduates of a Sheridan County, Wyoming, high school.
Fields of interest: Higher education; Youth services; Low-income and poor people.
Type of support: General support; Loans to individuals; Student aid; Grants to individuals.
Limitations: Applications accepted. Giving limited to residents of Sheridan County, WY.
Publications: Application guidelines; Informational brochure.
Application information: Minimum 1 year residency in Sheridan County, WY. Application form required.
  Initial approach: Letter
  Copies of proposal: 1
  Deadline(s): June 1 for fall registration; 1st of each month for other educational grants and for medical grants
  Board meeting date(s): Third Tues. or second to last Tues. of each month
Officers and Trustees: Victor Garber, Chair. and Trustee; Paddy Bard, Vice-Chair. and Trustee; Stephen D. Carroll, Treas. and Trustee; George P. Fletcher; Michael Pilch.
Number of staff: 1 full-time professional; 5 full-time support; 2 part-time support.
EIN: 830138740

9983
The Richardson Family Foundation
5025 Campstool Rd.
Cheyenne, WY 82007-1816
Contact: Keith W. Richardson, Pres.

Established in 1994 in Wyoming.
Donors: Sierra Trading Post; Keith Richardson; Richardson Family Partnership.
Foundation type: Independent foundation.
Financial data (yr. ended 03/31/13): Assets, $5,458,227 (M); gifts received, $5,490,000; expenditures, $377,017; qualifying distributions, $351,981; giving activities include $351,981 for grants.
Purpose and activities: Funding primarily for social services and Christian organizations that have an established relationship with foundation officials.
Fields of interest: Christianity; Human services; Family services.
Limitations: Applications accepted. Giving in the U.S., with emphasis on AZ and CO. No grants to individuals.
Application information: Application form required.
  Initial approach: Letter
  Deadline(s): None
Officers: Keith W. Richardson, Pres.; Roberta Richardson, V.P.; Norman J. Wyman, Secy.-Treas.
EIN: 830310875

9984
The Riehm Family Foundation, Inc.
P.O. Box 603
Sheridan, WY 82801-0603 (307) 672-6494

Established in 2007 in Wyoming.
Donors: John Riehm Trust; Riehm Realty, Inc.; John W. Riehm Irrevocable Trust; Doris Riehm.
Foundation type: Independent foundation.
Financial data (yr. ended 09/30/14): Assets, $2,156,352; expenditures, $147,949; qualifying distributions, $120,544.
Fields of interest: Education; Health; Human services.
Application information: Application form required.
  Initial approach: Letter
  Deadline(s): None
Directors: Elizabeth Ganin; Doris N. Riehm; John W. Riehm III.
EIN: 260631873

9985
Newell B. Sargent Foundation
P.O. Box 50581
Casper, WY 82605-0581 (307) 577-0724
Contact: Charles W. Smith, Dir.

Donor: Newell B. Sargent.
Foundation type: Independent foundation.
Financial data (yr. ended 10/31/13): Assets, $24,547,927 (M); expenditures, $754,852; qualifying distributions, $299,123; giving activities include $188,323 for 17 grants (high: $30,000; low: $1,000).
Purpose and activities: Giving primarily to a local museum for building and general support.
Fields of interest: Museums; Education; Hospital care; Human services; Child welfare.
Type of support: General support; Building and renovations; Land acquisitions; Endowments.
Limitations: Applications accepted. Giving primarily in WY, with emphasis on Washakie County.
Application information: Application form required.
  Initial approach: Letter
  Copies of proposal: 1
  Deadline(s): None
  Board meeting date(s): Apr. and Oct. (Other months via teleconference)
  Final notification: Oct. meeting
Directors: Ron Hansen; Kent Richins; Charles W. Smith.
EIN: 830271536

9986
The Arthur B. Schultz Foundation
P.O. Box 1570
Lander, WY 82520-1570 (307) 714-5665
Contact: Erik B. Schultz, Chair.; Rachael K. Richards, Exec. Dir.
E-mail: rachel@absfoundation.org; E-mail for Erik B. Schultz: ebs@absfoundation.org.; Main URL: http://www.absfoundation.org
Facebook: http://www.facebook.com/pages/The-Arthur-B-Schultz-Foundation/103668762718
Grants List: http://absfoundation.org/current-grants
LinkedIn: https://www.linkedin.com/company/the-arthur-b-schultz-foundation

Established in 1985 in California.
Donor: Arthur B. Schultz.

Foundation type: Independent foundation.
Financial data (yr. ended 11/30/13): Assets, $5,677,962 (M); gifts received, $216,665; expenditures, $642,865; qualifying distributions, $604,547; giving activities include $438,348 for 26 grants (high: $250,000; low: $1,000), and $27,044 for 2 loans/program-related investments.
Purpose and activities: Advancing opportunities for women, entrepreneurs, and people with disabilities.
Fields of interest: Elementary and secondary education; Higher education; Physical therapy; Economic development; Young adults; Females; Female children and youth; Low-income and poor people; People with disabilities; People with physical disabilities.
International interests: Cambodia; Central America; Guatemala; Honduras; Israel; Jordan; Kenya; Nicaragua; Rwanda; Tanzania; Vietnam; West Bank/ Gaza (Palestinian Territories).
Type of support: General support; Program-related investments; Matching grants; Continuing support; Fundraising; Leadership and professional development; Equipment; Program development; Seed money; Scholarships.
Limitations: Applications accepted. Giving currently limited to Guatemala, Honduras, and Nicaragua in Central America, Kenya, Rwanda, and Tanzania in East Africa, Palestine and Jordan in the Middle East, and Vietnam and Cambodia in Southeast Asia. No support for strictly religious organizations. No grants to individuals.
Publications: Application guidelines; Financial statement; Grants list; Program policy statement; Program policy statement (including application guidelines).
Application information: Electronic submission only. Application guidelines are available on foundation web site; unsolicited letters of inquiry are accepted but unsolicited proposals are not accepted. Other publications available online include grant guidelines, program descriptions and selected grant descriptions. The foundation requires letters of inquiry received by e-mail, with attachments in MS Office (Word, Excel, etc.), and/ or Adobe PDF format. Eligible organizations will be invited to submit a full proposal.
   Initial approach: See foundation web site for letter of inquiry guidelines. Letter of inquiry required; electronic submissions only.
   Copies of proposal: 1
   Deadline(s): Varies
   Board meeting date(s): Annually, typically in the spring or early summer
   Final notification: For letters of inquiry, no response if guidelines are not met.
Officers and Board Members: Erik B. Schultz, Chair. and Director; Arthur B. Schultz, Chair. Emeritus and Director; Rachael K. Richards, Exec. Dir.; Einar Christensen; John Schultz; Dave Straley; Mike Testa.
Number of staff: 1 full-time professional; 1 part-time professional.
EIN: 953980014

9987
The Joseph J. Scott Foundation
123 W. 1st St., Ste. 620
Casper, WY 82601

Donor: Joseph J. Scott.
Foundation type: Independent foundation.
Financial data (yr. ended 12/31/13): Assets, $6,201,253 (M); expenditures, $326,944;

qualifying distributions, $279,191; giving activities include $279,191 for 14 grants (high: $134,858; low: $833).
Fields of interest: Education; Housing development; Christianity; Sports and recreation; Child development.
Limitations: Applications not accepted. Giving primarily in WY.
Application information: Unsolicited requests for funds not accepted.
Officers and Directors: Joseph J. Scott, Pres. and Director; Cordell Fonnesbeck, V.P. and Director; Mark Petrie, V.P. and Director.
EIN: 263374979

9988
Walter Scott Foundation
6705 Foxglove Dr.
Cheyenne, WY 82009-5707
Contact: Thorpe A. Nickerson, Pres.

Foundation type: Independent foundation.
Financial data (yr. ended 09/30/14): Assets, $6,664,211 (M); expenditures, $343,629; qualifying distributions, $272,158; giving activities include $247,500 for 15 grants (high: $100,000; low: $1,000).
Purpose and activities: Aid to institutions concerned with handicapped children and adults; some giving also for medical research.
Fields of interest: Diseases and conditions; Child welfare; People with disabilities.
Type of support: Research; General support; Research and evaluation; Continuing support; Annual campaigns; Capital and infrastructure; Equipment; Endowments; Seed money.
Limitations: Applications accepted. Giving primarily in WY. No support for political or religious organizations. No grants to individuals, or for matching gifts; no loans.
Application information:
   Initial approach: Letter
   Copies of proposal: 1
   Deadline(s): None
   Board meeting date(s): Semiannually in the spring and early Sept.
Officers and Directors: Thorpe A. Nickerson, Pres. and Secy. and Director; Brett R. Nickerson, V.P. and Treas. and Director; Jocelyn A. Nickerson, V.P. and Exec. Dir.; Elizabeth Nickerson, V.P. and Director.
Number of staff: None.
EIN: 135681161

9989
Myra Fox Skelton Trust Foundation
c/o Wells Fargo Bank, N.A., Trust Dept.
P.O. Box 2799
Casper, WY 82602-2799   (307) 235-7744

Established in 1987 in Wyoming.
Foundation type: Independent foundation.
Financial data (yr. ended 12/31/14): Assets, $3,212,671; expenditures, $358,592; qualifying distributions, $262,882.
Purpose and activities: Giving primarily for higher education; support also for a community fund and social services.
Fields of interest: Higher education; Nonprofits; Religion; Human services.

Type of support: Program development; Equipment; Capital and infrastructure; Regranting; Annual campaigns; General support; Scholarships.
Limitations: Applications accepted. Giving limited to WY. No grants to individuals.
Application information: Contributes mostly to pre-selected organizations as only limited funds are available.
   Initial approach: Letter
   Copies of proposal: 1
   Deadline(s): Jan. 1 through Mar. 31, and June 1 through Sept. 30
   Board meeting date(s): May and Nov.
Advisory Committee: Charles Chapin; Rick Mason; John S. Miracle; Joseph Sramek; Tom Valdez.
EIN: 836029858

9990
Skilling Foundation
212 Arapahoe Dr.
Saratoga, WY 82331

Established in 1996 in California.
Donors: Barbara C. Skilling; David Van Skilling.
Foundation type: Independent foundation.
Financial data (yr. ended 11/30/13): Assets, $1,038,563 (M); gifts received, $116,391; qualifying distributions, $191,547; giving activities include $182,000 for 7 grants (high: $85,000; low: $500).
Purpose and activities: Giving primarily to education and health organizations.
Fields of interest: Undergraduate education; Domesticated animals; Eye diseases; Cancers.
Type of support: Research.
Limitations: Applications not accepted. Giving primarily in CA, CO, VA and WA. No grants to individuals.
Application information: Contributes only to pre-selected organizations.
Officers: David Van Skilling, Pres.; Barbara C. Skilling, Secy.
Directors: Steve Ranney; Jean Skilling; Kim Skilling; Mark Skilling.
EIN: 330735035

9991
StoneRiver Foundation
(formerly The Vega Foundation)
P.O. Box 9580
Jackson, WY 83002-1663

Established in 2000 in Wyoming.
Donors: Gary K. Silberberg; Veronica Silberberg; Stoneriver Capital.
Foundation type: Independent foundation.
Financial data (yr. ended 11/30/13): Assets, $5,403,277 (M); gifts received, $3,839; expenditures, $274,345; qualifying distributions, $274,320; giving activities include $266,900 for 5 grants (high: $80,000; low: $10,000).
Fields of interest: Education; Foundations; Nonprofits; Diseases and conditions; Public libraries; Human services.
Type of support: Regranting; Research.
Limitations: Applications not accepted. Giving primarily in MT, NY, and WY. No grants to individuals.
Application information: Contributes only to pre-selected organizations.

Officers: Gary K. Silberberg, Pres.; Veronica K. Silberberg, V.P. and Treas.; Jane Emmer, Secy.
EIN: 223787992

9992
Mary H. Storer Foundation
P.O. Box 1088
Cheyenne, WY 82003-1088

Established in 2001 in Wyoming.
Donor: Mary H. Storer.
Foundation type: Independent foundation.
Financial data (yr. ended 12/31/12): Assets, $3,087,733 (M); expenditures, $167,751; qualifying distributions, $144,724; giving activities include $140,010 for 10 grants (high: $40,000; low: $10,000).
Fields of interest: Higher education; Environment; Health; Agriculture.
Limitations: Applications not accepted. Giving primarily in CA, WI and WY. No grants to individuals.
Application information: Contributes only to pre-selected organizations.
Officers and Directors: Mary H. Storer, Pres. and Director; James W. Hearne, Secy.-Treas. and Director; Charles B. Begg, Jr.; Lantson E. Eldred; Katherine H. Manning; David C. Wind.
EIN: 830335956

9993
Elbridge & Evelyn Stuart Foundation
c/o Pendleton Fiduciary Management, Inc.
P.O. Box 1905
Jackson, WY 83001-1905
Application address: c/o BNY Mellon, 1 Wall St., New York, NY 10286, tel.: (310) 551-7618

Established in 1961 in California.
Foundation type: Independent foundation.
Financial data (yr. ended 12/31/13): Assets, $7,286,333 (M); expenditures, $518,116; qualifying distributions, $425,000; giving activities include $425,000 for 44 grants (high: $100,000; low: $500).
Purpose and activities: Giving primarily for higher and other education.
Fields of interest: Secondary education; Higher education; Science; Christianity; Youth services.
Limitations: Applications accepted. Giving primarily in CA; funding also in WY. No grants to individuals.
Application information: Application form required.
    Initial approach: Letter
    Deadline(s): None
Trustees: Evelyn Nelson Attaway; Clarke A. Nelson.
EIN: 956014019

9994
Harry & Thelma Surrena Memorial
P.O. Box 603
Sheridan, WY 82801-0603
Application address: P.O. Box 27, Buffalo, WY 82834-0027, tel.: (307) 684-5574

Established in 1973 in Wyoming.
Foundation type: Independent foundation.
Financial data (yr. ended 10/31/13): Assets, $5,378,062 (M); expenditures, $297,259; qualifying distributions, $262,691; giving activities include $248,500 for 23 grants (high: $45,000; low: $500).

Fields of interest: Education; Protestantism; Human services; Child welfare.
Limitations: Applications accepted. Giving primarily in WY. No grants to individuals.
Application information:
    Initial approach: Letter
    Deadline(s): None
Trustees: John Pradere; Ralph C. Robinson; Robert Wyatt.
EIN: 237435554

9995
Tate Foundation
c/o Chris Muirhead
P.O. Box 2750
Casper, WY 82602-2280
Application address: c/o Diane Harrop, P.O. Box 2280, Casper, WY 82602, tel.: (307) 359-0738

Established in 1994 in Wyoming.
Donor: Inez M. Tate.
Foundation type: Independent foundation.
Financial data (yr. ended 11/30/14): Assets, $6,212,286 (M); expenditures, $264,601; qualifying distributions, $313,178; giving activities include $195,820 for 13 grants (high: $125,000; low: $2,000).
Fields of interest: Foundations; Health; Public libraries; Community and economic development; Human services.
Type of support: General support.
Limitations: Applications accepted. Giving primarily in WY.
Application information: Application form required.
    Initial approach: Contact foundation
    Deadline(s): None
Officers: T. Chris Muirhead, Pres.; Jennifer McDowell, Secy.; John Masterson, Treas.
EIN: 830310832

9996
The Mary K. Weiss Foundation
P.O. Box 2589
Jackson, WY 83001-2589

Established in 1999 in Wyoming.
Donor: Mary K. Weiss.
Foundation type: Independent foundation.
Financial data (yr. ended 12/31/13): Assets, $30,151 (M); gifts received, $286,512; expenditures, $334,586; qualifying distributions, $328,911; giving activities include $323,600 for 11 grants (high: $243,000; low: $500).
Fields of interest: Arts and culture; Education; Community and economic development.
Type of support: General support.
Limitations: Applications not accepted. No grants to individuals.
Application information: Unsolicited requests for funds not accepted.
    Board meeting date(s): 2nd Tues. in Apr.
Officers and Directors: Mary K. Weiss, Pres. and Director; Arturo H. Peralta-Ramos III, V.P. and Director; Lorian Peralta-Ramos, Secy.-Treas. and Director.
Number of staff: 1 part-time support.
EIN: 830325778

9997
William E. Weiss Foundation, Inc.
P.O. Box 14270
Jackson, WY 83002-4270
Contact: Liz D. Hutchinson

Established in 1955 in New York.
Donors: William E. Weiss, Jr.†; Helene K. Brown†.
Foundation type: Independent foundation.
Financial data (yr. ended 03/31/13): Assets, $7,226,931 (M); expenditures, $429,942; qualifying distributions, $339,775; giving activities include $339,500 for 26 grants (high: $44,500; low: $1,500).
Purpose and activities: Giving primarily to museums and for arts and cultural programs.
Fields of interest: Arts and culture; Education; Environment.
Type of support: General support; Continuing support; Capital campaigns; Capital and infrastructure; Program development.
Limitations: Applications not accepted. Giving primarily in CA, MO, NY, TN and WY. No grants to individuals.
Application information: Contributes only to pre-selected organizations.
Officers: Monte Brown, Pres.; William U. Weiss, V.P.; Katrina W. Ryan, Secy.; Dwyer Brown, Treas.
Number of staff: 1 part-time support.
EIN: 556016633

9998
William F. & Lorene W. Welch Foundation
P.O. Box J
Sheridan, WY 82801-0620   (307) 674-1770

Established in 1993 in Wyoming.
Donor: Lorene W. Welch.
Foundation type: Independent foundation.
Financial data (yr. ended 08/31/13): Assets, $3,658,616 (M); expenditures, $243,288; qualifying distributions, $189,000; giving activities include $180,500 for 16 grants (high: $77,500; low: $500).
Purpose and activities: Giving primarily for education and health facilities.
Fields of interest: Arts and culture; Higher education; Hospital care; Catholicism; Human services.
Limitations: Applications accepted. Giving primarily in MT and WY.
Application information: Application form required.
    Initial approach: Letter
    Deadline(s): None
Trustees: Frank Rotellini; Richard M. Davis, Jr.; William B. Ebzery.
EIN: 836033434

9999
Windy Ridge Foundation
c/o Dennis Cook
P.O. Box 1345
Laramie, WY 82073-3252
Application address: American Meteorological Society,

Established in 2003 in Wyoming.
Donor: Harry Vaughan.
Foundation type: Independent foundation.
Financial data (yr. ended 12/31/14): Assets, $4,741,140 (M); expenditures, $293,043;

qualifying distributions, $230,000; giving activities include $230,000 for 3 grants (high: $175,000; low: $25,000).

Fields of interest: Science.

Limitations: Applications accepted. Giving primarily in CA, MA, TX and WY.

Application information:
Initial approach: Proposal
Deadline(s): None

Directors: Dennis Cook; Nickolas Floyd; Ann Nelson.

EIN: 431982457

10000
Witzel Family Foundation
P.O. Box 603
Sheridan, WY 82801-0603
E-mail: contact@witzelfamilyfoundation.org;
Application address: 1 S. Tschirgi St., Sheridan, WY

82801; tel.: (307) 751-7723; Main URL: http://witzelfamilyfoundation.org

Donor: Sarah E. Witzel Trust.

Foundation type: Independent foundation.

Financial data (yr. ended 12/31/13): Assets, $3,104,754 (M); expenditures, $152,437; qualifying distributions, $137,354; giving activities include $17,020 for 7 grants, and $113,580 for 18 grants to individuals.

Purpose and activities: The Witzel Family Foundation awards grants and scholarships to special needs students, or students pursuing music education. In some instances the Foundation may support students pursuing a general education. On a case by case basis, the Foundation may fund presentations by visiting artists, or assist with purchase of musical instruments for local schools.

Fields of interest: Music; Education; Higher education.

Limitations: Applications accepted. Giving primarily in Sheridan, WY.

Publications: Application guidelines.

Application information: See foundation web site for complete application guidelines and procedures. Application form required.

Officers: John A. Meyer, Pres.; Mary Beth Evers, V.P.; Karen E. Nicolarsen, Secy.; David J. Nicolarsen, Treas.

Directors: Michael J. Evers; Frederick E. Kehrwald.

EIN: 263239496

APPENDIX A

The following foundations appeared in the previous edition of *The Foundation Directory Part 2* but are not included in this edition for the reasons stated.

Bain, Jr. Charitable Trust, William W.
Boston, MA
The trust terminated in 2014.

Beach Foundation Trust B for First Baptist Church
Mobile, AL
Specified beneficiary.

Beach Foundation Trust D for Baptist Village
Mobile, AL
Specified beneficiary.

Burchell Charitable Trust, Llewellyn
Chicago, IL
Specified beneficiaries.

Congregation Shaaray Tefila Endowment Trust
New York City, NY
Specified beneficiary.

Ellison Charitable Remainder Trust
Montgomery, AL
Specified beneficiary.

Friedman Foundation, Robert G.
Fort Lauderdale, FL
The foundation terminated on Dec. 31, 2014.

Glyndebourne Association America Inc., The
New York City, NY
Specified beneficiary.

Golden Slipper Club Uptown Home for the Aged
Bala-Cynwyd, PA
Specified beneficiary.

Gross Charitable Foundation, William, The
Newark, NJ
The foundation terminated and transferred its assets to The William Gross Charitable Foundation, Inc.

Harlan Scholarship Trust, Wilbur V.
Philomath, OR
Specified beneficiary.

Herscher Family Foundation, Myna & Uri, The
Los Angeles, CA
Specified beneficiary.

Hillback Foundation, Elliott and Marjorie, The
Needham, MA
The foundation terminated in 2012.

Hull Charitable Trust A, Cora A.
Dallas, TX
Specified beneficiaries.

Imerman Memorial Foundation, Stanley
Bloomfield Hills, MI
The foundation terminated in 2014.

J. N. M. Gift Trust
(Formerly J.N.M. 1966 Gift Trust)
Winston-Salem, NC

J.N.M. 1966 Gift Trust
See J. N. M. Gift Trust

Lance Charitable Foundation, Howard and Christine
Indian Harbour Beach, FL
The foundation terminated in 2012 and transferred its assets to the Community Foundation for Brevard.

Lessman Foundation, Andrew
Henderson, NV
Specified beneficiary.

Lloyd Trust, C.L. & Gladys
Dallas, TX
Specified beneficiary.

Maynard Blackard Charitable Trust
Fort Smith, AR
Specified beneficiaries.

Merrick Medical Equip. Trust, Bette M.
Winston-Salem, NC
Specified beneficiary.

Mooney Charitable Trust
Seattle, WA
Specified beneficiary.

Petunia Foundation
Seattle, WA
The foundation terminated on Dec. 31, 2013 and transferred its assets to American Endowment Fund.

Quaker Hill Foundation, The
North Andover, MA
The foundation terminated in 2012.

Ruddy Charitable Trust, Raymond & Marilyn
Dover, MA
Specified beneficiary.

Todd Foundation, Roland R. and Hazel C.
Winston-Salem, NC
Specified beneficiary.

INDEX TO DONORS, OFFICERS, TRUSTEES

10 East Side LLC, 6858
107 Kensington Partners, LLC, 5338
107 Northern Boulevard Realty LLC, 6914
11400, 7925
115 CCD Partners, LP, 5338
1219 Avenue J LLC, 6914
16W Marketing LLC, 1408
1790 Building Corp., 5823
1804 76th Street LLC, 6914
1820 Security Corp., 3992
1903-1909 Broadway LLC, 6914
1957 Charity Foundation, 7841
1960 IRR Trust No. 3 SMWS, 4815
1969 IRR Trust No. 2 SMWS, 4815
1992 Belz Charitable Trust, The, 8585
1998 Black Family Charitable Lead
   Annuity Trust, 7876
1999 Bistricer Family Trust, 6425
1st Source Bank, 3444

20/20 Inspections, 6203
2007 David R. Goetz Delaware Gift Trust, 2044
2012 Hein Foundation Trust, 6184

333 LP LLC, 4594
36 Plaza Corp., 7008

4SRPG Land Co. LP, 9009

618 Main Clothing Corp., 6216
63rd Street Equities, 6996
687 BR, 2763

9th Avenue Equities, 6996

A & A Fuel Oil Co., 5500
A & E Family Partnership, 6101
A & E Trust, 5923, 6575, 6920
A & M Porter Charitable Foundation, 8080
A & RW Properties LLC, 5633
A & S Bleichroeder Holdings, 5826
A Friends' Fund, 5240
A Glimmer of Hope Foundation, 8689
A Good Neighbor Foundation, 7299
A&E Trust, 6965
A. and R. Enterprises LP, 153
A. Duda & Sons, Inc., 1983
Aalfs, Barbara B., 9838
Aalfs, Christina M. , 9838
Aanestad, Douglas I., 2673
Aardema, Diane, 3407
Aardema, Norman, 3407
Aardema, Peter, 3407
Aaron's, 2621
Aaron, Daniel, 7835
Aaron, Geraldine, 7835
Aase, K. David, 9709
ABA Realty, 5484
Ababa Co., 153

Abadie, Jacque, 1316
Abadrabo, Gary, 5385
Aballe, Mel, 581
Abara, Obinna, 8269
ABARTA Inc., 7836, 8004
ABB Foundation, 7368
Abbattista, Gerard, 5582
Abbey, Philip, 9495
Abbitt, Carolyn S., 9497
Abbitt, Matthew M., 9497
Abbitt, Richard F., 9497
Abbitt, Stephen M., 9497
Abbott, Frances, 7996
Abbott, Janet, 464
Abbott, Kyle C., 4369
Abbott, Susan L., 1393
Abbott/Wendermere, 2406
Abboy, Chandar, 651
Abboy, Rajamannar, 651
Abboy, Ramadas, 651
Abboy, Sridevi, 651
Abdalla, Ken, 9345
Abdella, Leo, 2261
Abdo, Debra, 8053
Abdullah, Patricia, 8570
Abdullah, Scott, 8570
Abe, Bruce Tadashi , 9642
Abe, Kazuharu, 679
Abecassis, Max, 2231
Abel, Cecelia, 8758
Abel, Jack, 3911
Abel, James P., 5067
Abeles, Damaris, 3880
Abell, Christopher S., 3842
Abell, Gregory T., 3842
Abell, W. Shepherdson, 3842
Abelson, Benjamin, 2692
Abelson, Jesse F., 2693
Abendschein, Phillip, 9914
Abercrombie, Josephine E., 3645
Aberley, Janet, 238
Aberlich, Marilyn, 780
Abernathy, C. Mark, 8970
Abernethy, Bruce R., 1879
Abernethy, Bruce, Jr., 2148
Abernethy, Claude, 7037
Abernethy, Claude S., III, 7037
Abess, Ashley, 5636, 5637
Abess, Brett U., 5636, 5637
Abess, Jayne Harris, 5636, 5637
Abess, Leonard L., 5636
Abess, Leonard L., Jr., 5637
Abess, Leonard L., Sr., 5637
Abess, Mathew U., 5636
Abess, Matthew U., 5637
Abeywardena, Palitha, 8228
Abishai Financial II, LP, 3343
Abland Family Partnership, 5923
Abney, Barbara L., 8477
Aboia, Patricia, 2154
Aboia, Richard, 2154
Aboia-Vall, Regina, 2154
Aboud, J.R., 260
Abplanalp, Josephine, 5944
Abplanalp, Robert H., 5944
Abraham Foundation, Anthony, 3238

Abrahams, Kenneth, 108
Abrahamsen, Brent, 9576
Abrahamson, Ernest, 5639
Abrahamson, Kathleen, 5639
Abrahamson, Kurt, 5639
Abrahamson, Mark, 5639
Abram, Sam, 3421
Abramowitz, Kenneth, 1384
Abramowitz, Nira, 1384
Abrams Charitable Remainder Unitrust, Nina, The , 224
Abrams Rev. Trust, Jessie H., 7300
Abrams Rev. Trust, Marlyon E., 7300
Abrams Revocable Trust, Nina, 224
Abrams, Brian, 7300
Abrams, David C., 5241
Abrams, Donald, 181
Abrams, Georgia, 588
Abrams, Ginny S., 9440
Abrams, Harold E., 2537, 8590
Abrams, Isaac N., 588
Abrams, Jessica L., 4001
Abrams, Jessie H., 7300
Abrams, Jonathan, 1599
Abrams, Kenneth L., 4001
Abrams, Leota, 4369
Abrams, Marlyon E., 7300
Abrams, Nat, 588
Abrams, Nina, 224
Abrams, Susan N., 4001
Abrams, Talbert, 4369
Abrams, Vicki, 5241
Abrams, Vicki S., 5241
Abrams, William H., 5241
Abramson, Daniel, 5905
Abramson, David A., 5905
Abramson, Ellen M., 5905
Abramson, Gary M., 9529
Abramson, Gregg, 5640
Abramson, Harriet A., 5905
Abramson, Jeffrey S., 9529
Abramson, Jill, 5640
Abramson, Lauren, 5640
Abramson, Lorraine, 5640
Abramson, Marc A., 5905
Abramson, Nathan S., 4344
Abramson, Richard, 5640
Abramson, Ronald D., 9529
Abreu Trust, Francis, 2431
Abreu, Claire, 2431
Abreu, Katherine M., 2431
Abreu, Michael, 2431
Abreu, Mike, 2431
Abroms, Harold L., 2
Abroms, James M., 2
Abroms, Judith E., 2
Abror's Edge Residential Lots LLC, 8570
ABS Partners Real Estate, LLC, 6655
Absolute Yacht Refinishing, 2261
Acacia Life Insurance Co., 3807
Accademia Charitable Foundation, 1455
Access All Directory Placement, 461
Accessory Exchange, LLC, 6881
Accurate Castings, 6207
Aceveda, Russell A., 6922
Ach, Andrew, 226

Ach, Linda Rosenberg, 226
Achatz, John, 3789
Achepohl, E., 3138, 3140
Acheson, Adele F., 4370
Acheson, Michael H., 4370
Achor, Robert L., 2252
Ackapo-Satchiavi, Cecile, 6820
Ackerly, John P., III, 9488
Ackerman, Edward, 6681
Ackerman, James F., 3339
Ackerman, John F., 3339
Ackerman, Joseph D., 5003
Ackerman, Lily, 257
Ackerman, Sybil, 7781
Ackerman, Thomas C., Jr., 227
Ackley Trust, R.V., 7740
Ackley, Tom, 5104
Ackman, Lawrence, 6655
Acme Sponge and Chamois Co., 1915
Acomb, Joanne, 9937
Acorn Composite Corporation, 3201
Acors, Sylvia S., 9449
ACP Loan Repayment, 2844
Acra, Ruth P., 9491
Acree, Lucy, 2570
Act Trust, 5309
Active Network, 684
Acton, Christopher, 8785
Acton, Pam W., 3362
Acton, Ron F., 9221
Acton, Susan E., 4216
Acuff, John, 8013
Acushnet Company, 7209
Acuthan, Lakshman, 5485
Acworth, Brian, 5642
Adair Family Foundation Inc., 153
Adair, Earnest L., 153
Adair, Marsha A., 3553
Adair, Paul H., 3553
Adam Corporation/Group, The, 8691
Adam, Donald A., 8691
Adam, Donna J., 8691
Adam, Kathy, 4119
Adam, Steven Bradley, 8691
Adame, Margaret Hayes, 1548
Adame, Omar R., 1548
Adamonis, Kyle, 8503
Adams Charitable Trust, Gladis H., 7258
Adams Plaza, 228
Adams, Alan B., 8579
Adams, Brett, 3379
Adams, Carl, 8579
Adams, Carl E., 8579
Adams, Carla W., 2259
Adams, Caryl W., 6032
Adams, Cindy, 8555
Adams, Clyde T., 2599
Adams, Daniel F., 2267
Adams, David V., 228
Adams, Edward Thomas, 1404
Adams, Elizabeth Helms, 615
Adams, Ellen H., 1386
Adams, Fred, 8579
Adams, Heather B., 1404
Adams, J. Dann, 2592
Adams, James W., 1386

Adams, Jennie Mae, 8579
Adams, Joanna, 2576
Adams, Joanne, 2706
Adams, John H., 5662
Adams, John King, 228
Adams, John V., 9395
Adams, K.S., IV, 9230
Adams, K.S., Jr., 9230
Adams, Karen, 1386
Adams, Katrina, 3144
Adams, Ken, 3535
Adams, Kendall Wishnick, 2690
Adams, Louise B., 1404
Adams, Marjorie Carr, 2696
Adams, Mary, 7097
Adams, Mary B., 9395
Adams, Megan, 4234
Adams, Morgan, Jr., 228
Adams, Peter D., 229
Adams, Ralph W., Jr., 3
Adams, Rebecca B., 229
Adams, Richard, 7764
Adams, Robert A., 8579
Adams, Roger, 4739
Adams, Rolland L., 7836
Adams, Samuel, 3
Adams, Susan C., 4059
Adams, Thomas L., 2259
Adams, Thomas T., 1392
Adams, W. Andrew, 8579
Adams, Walter F., III, 1864
Adams, Warren, 4234
Adams, Wendy E., 1404
Adams, William James "will.i.am", Jr., 645
Adams, William L., 3808
Adams-Rodgers, Lois, 9494
Adamson, Katharine J., 1566
Adaya, Muhammad, 1011
Adaya, Salim, 1011
Adaya, Yasmin, 1011
Addeo, Gina, 5954
Adelberg, Stuart D., 1413
Adelman, Barry A., 5643
Adelman, Lauren B., 5643
Adelman, Lucy, 231
Adelman, Robin, 5643
Adelman, Susan, 231
Adelman, Todd M., 5643
Adelsberg, Steve, 6023
Adelsberg, Steven, 6023, 6658, 6822
Ader, Pamela, 5644
Ader, Richard, 5644
Aderhold, John E., 2597
Ades, Alan M., 5645
Ades, Jane, 5645
Ades, Joan, 5645
Adesman, M.D., Ph.D., Michael, 8346
Adikes, Maryedith, 5646
Adikes, Park T., 5646
Adikes-Hill, Patricia, 5646
Adkerson, Richard C., 94
Adkerson, Richard Clark, 94
Adkerson, William Tyler, 94
Adkins, Cynthia, 9205
Adkins, Ruth F., 3710
Adler, Alan, 5282
Adler, Anne, 9878
Adler, Bette, 9878
Adler, Chaim Meir, 5666
Adler, Constance, 2854
Adler, David F., 7474
Adler, Diane, 9273
Adler, Donald James, 5242

Adler, Elaine, 5242
Adler, Eric S., 3809
Adler, Esther G., 3809
Adler, Esthy, 3809
Adler, Gail F., 8692
Adler, Harry, 5452
Adler, Hedy Kangesser, 7474
Adler, James B., 3809
Adler, Jeffrey A., 1842
Adler, Jordan, 5282
Adler, Judith, 5282
Adler, Louis K., 8692
Adler, Marc F., 8692
Adler, Marie, 546
Adler, Mitchell, 6498
Adler, Myron, 5242
Adler, Richard S., 5242
Adler, Rita N., 1842
Adler, Rothstein Rosenfeldt, 5482
Adler, William S., 5242
Adleta, Charles Derek, 1699
ADM Charitable Lead Annuity Trust, 6679
Admire, Jack G., 2102
Adreani, Raymond J., 2697
Advance Carter Co., 4711
Advanced Micro Devices, 8698
Advisory Research, 8581
Advisory Trust Co. of Delaware, 1655, 8275
Advisory Trust Company of Delaware, 1732
Advocate and Greenwich Times Holiday Fund, The, 1566
AEC Trust, 2391
Aehle Living Trust, 7038
AFCO, 8405
AFCO L.P., 8405
Afeyan, Noubar, 3996
Afeyan, Noubar B., 3996
Africk Holdings, 8570
AG 1991 Trust, 2927
AG Equipment Co., 8709
Against All Odds U.S.A., 5545
Agarwal Charitable Lead Annuity Trust, 7039
Agarwal, Ankit K., 7039
Agarwal, Asha R., 7039
Agarwal, Rohit K., 7039
Agarwal, Sajjan Kumar, 7039
Agate, Anita, 5649
Agati, C.F.A., Amanda, 8105
Agee Trust, Sternee, 51
Agee, Dean P., 9427
Agee, Judith, 8694
Agee, Richard, 8694
Agee, Robert D., 1640
Agee, William Henry, 8587
Agen, Brian J., 9889
Agency Serv. Consolidated, 7647
Agg Rok Materials Co., 7443
Agha, Hassnain, 1196
Agha, Jaffar H., 1196
Agha, Sara, 1196
Aghjayan, George M., 5562
Agli, Andria, 82
Aglietti, Wendy, 6536
Agnes, Michael A., 6669
Agness, Lance, 3340
Agnew, Mary Elizabeth, 3740
Agnew, Patricia S., 7221
Agnone, Charlotte, Dr. , 7357
AGR Family Limited Partnership, 9518
AGR Trust, The, 3206

Agree, Jeffrey S., 9277
Agudath Israel of Long Island, 5247
Aguerre, Fernando, 945
Aguilar, Alberto, 9367
Aguilo, Elizabeth, 4352
Ahart, Edward W., 5510
Ahdout, William, 6718, 7011
Ahearn, Charles J., 1861, 2275
Ahearn, Gayle S., 95
Ahearn, Michael J., 95
Ahern, Marilynn, 1095
Ahl, Kenneth E., 8067
Ahlstrand, Armer F., 2700
Ahlswede, Kent, 516
Ahmed, Afshan, 7611
Ahmed, Ashfaq, 7611
Ahmed, Ayesha, 6793
Ahmed, Mohammed Raheemuddin, 236
Ahmed, Nasser, 6793
Ahmed, Shahana, 7611
Ahmed, Tajuddin, 7611
Ahn, Regina, 9208
Ahrens, Lydia, 2803
Ahuja, Namrata, 90
Ahuja, Natasha, 90
Aibel, Daniel, 1388
Aibel, David, 1388
Aibel, Howard J., 1388
Aibel, Jonathan, 1388
Aichele, E. Richard, III, 7998
Aidnoff, Ellen F. Vanderbilt, 5983
Aiello, Gennaro, 7975
Aiello, Mark, 4410
AIG 2001 Trust, 6142
AIG Warranty Guard, 8654
Aijian, Mark M., 1018
Aiken, J. Kirby, 1735
Aikenhead, Carol, 8996
Ailes, Gary, 5121
Ain, Aron, 4289
Ain, Carolyn C., 3997
Ain, Mark S., 3997
Ainyff, 6256
Aisenbrey, John C., 4995
Aitken, Jonathan, 4508
Aitken, Randi Ross, 375
Ajalat, Charles R., 890
Ajalat, Marilee N., 890
Ajemian Trust, Robert, 4371
Akbari, Chris, 8869
Akcan, Carolyn Snorf, 305
Akers, C. Scott, Jr., 2432
Akers, J. Frederick, 2432
Akers, Mary Kathleen, 2432
Akerson, Daniel F., 9401
Akerson, Elizabeth C., 9401
Akerson, Gretchen E., 9401
Akerson, Karin A., 9401
Akerson, Keith D., 9401
Akerson, Loretta D., 5604
Akerson, Warren, 5604
Akhoury, Priya Joy, 5243
Akhoury, Ravindranath, 5243
Akhoury, Virginia, 5243
Akian, Haig P., 234
Akian, Lena G., 234
Akian, Sonia, 234
Akian, Zaven P., 234
Akien, Zaven P., 234
Akin, Anne, 9235
Akin, Gwen, 9235
Akin, John A., 9235
Akin, John, Jr., 9235
AKP Gourmet Inc., 5670

Akre, Elizabeth I., 5016
Akridge, John E., III, 3810
Akridge, Sarah B., 3810
Al-Alusi, Hesham, 236
Alabama Sports Foundation, 9
Alafi Capital Company, LLC, 235
Alafi, Christopher, 235
Alafi, Margaret, 235
Alafi, Moshe, 235
Alafi, Shireen, 235
Alaska Airlines, 80
AlaTrust, 66
Albergotti, Lia F., 7106
Albers, Julie, 3126
Albers, Mark N., 2193
Albert, Garett, 9386
Albert, John R., 1389
Alberts, Polly, 9810
Albertson, Crista, 7159
Albertson, William J., 7159
Albin, Arthur E., 4387
Albitz, Jennifer, 9026
Albrecht Grocery Co., Fred W., 7301
Albrecht Inc., 7301
Albrecht, Bryan, 9863
Albrecht, F. Steven, 7301
Albrecht, Steve, 5235
Albrecht, Steven A., 5206
Albrecht, Wendy, 9020
Albright, Alice, 3067
Albright, Amy, 4565
Albright, Anne, 3067
Albright, Anne K., 1826
Albright, Carolyn, 4625
Albright, Jeanette, 4625
Albright, Joseph M.P., 1826
Albright, Julie, 4625
Albright, Katharine, 3067
Albright, Madeleine K., 3067
Albright, Robert, 4625
Albritton, Tom, 4
Alcadan, LLC, 7365
Alcalde, Gabriela, 3669
Alcantara, Oscar L., 2919
Alcas Corp., 5890
Alcoa, 8138
Alcock, Gudrun, 2749
Alcon Foundation, 9895
Alcon Foundation Inc., The, 6539
Alcon Laboratories, 5244
Alden, Priscilla, 3999
Alden, Robin B., 102
Alder, Rebecca Lyn, 9350
Aldercrest Development Corp., 5281
Alderson, Larry D., 7986
Aldredge, Alison, 5871
Aldredge, Deborah L., 496
Aldrich, Kent, 7774
Aldridge, John, 1794
Aldrovandi, Judith, 1856
Aldsworth, Pamela, 1038
Alegi, Peter, 1456
Aleppo, Georgia, 1860
Aleppo, Joseph A., 1860
Alesci, Pattijo, 5642
Alessi, Evelyn, 5660
Alex, Josephine, 5681
Alexander Trust, R.D., 8696
Alexander, Andrew Mark, 8695
Alexander, Bobby, 7715
Alexander, Brenda, 7715
Alexander, Catherine R., 8696
Alexander, Cynthia K., 9151
Alexander, Diomy, 652

Alexander, Ethel Dolores, 1120
Alexander, Gaylord D., 4570
Alexander, Gregory G., 7318
Alexander, Gus, 8755
Alexander, Hana Basal, 5653
Alexander, J. Kobi, 5653
Alexander, James, 9871
Alexander, John, 6208
Alexander, Julie, 8695
Alexander, Juliet, 6437
Alexander, Lu Ann, 7724
Alexander, Marjorie, 5655
Alexander, Mary, 5094
Alexander, Patrick, 7654
Alexander, Paula, 1635
Alexander, R. Denny, 8696
Alexander, Rebecca Bogle, 191
Alexander, Richard M., 1787
Alexander, Sally, 9410
Alexander, Sandrea Sue Goerlich, 7428
Alexander, Shana, 5654
Alexander, Sydenham B., 7258
Alexander, Ted J., 4847
Alexander, Timothy, 9418
Alexander, W. Robert, 130
Alexander-Cameron Services, 1316
Alfirevic, Susan, 2055
Alfond, Peter G., 3764
Alfond, William, 3764
Alford, Paul R., 3859
Alford, Susan Hager, 3687
Alford, Terri L., 9244
Alhadeff, Kenneth, 9558
Alhadeff, Marleen, 9558
Alhadeff, Marleen Magnoni, 9558
Alistar Corp., 283
Alkhatib, Hala, 4420
All American Products, 5034
Allan-Hodge, Elizabeth, 2686
Allard, Pablo, 4234
Allatt, Nancy C., 5659
Allatt, Peter J.D., Jr., 5659
Allbritton, Robert L., 8990
Allegheny Mineral Corp., 8287
Allegood, Tommy, 2463
Alleman, Charles, Jr., 421
Allen, Amy, 8949
Allen, Barbara, 1220, 2148
Allen, Bibler, 9631
Allen, Brad, Dr. , 500
Allen, Buddy, 2437
Allen, Cristi, 3614
Allen, David F., 7357
Allen, David, Dr. , 2437
Allen, Debbie, 3566
Allen, Douglas F., Jr., 5384
Allen, E. Thomas, 5301
Allen, Edward R., III, 8901
Allen, Elizabeth Peale, 6582
Allen, Eric R., 3775
Allen, George, 8741
Allen, Gordon, 6625
Allen, H. Rollin, 4405
Allen, James, 9631
Allen, James C., 1220
Allen, John, 9130
Allen, John R., Jr., 1952
Allen, Kathryn K., 9740
Allen, Kimberly J., 8350
Allen, L.D., 3255
Allen, Laurie, 9631
Allen, Linda A., 3704
Allen, Marci, 306
Allen, Marcia M., 3967

Allen, Mark, 306
Allen, Marsha, 7803
Allen, Matthew, 1220
Allen, Mimi, 306
Allen, Nancy C., 8901
Allen, Philip O., 9089
Allen, Ralph C., 2222
Allen, Robert W., Jr., 8001
Allen, Shelley Anne, 1609
Allen, Timothy, 4521
Allen, Timothy J., 377
Allen, William, 4008, 7978
Allen, Wilson G., 9130
Allender, John R., 9257
Alley, Albert A., 7837
Alley, Kerry H., 4239
Alley, Richard, 7837
Alley, Teresa, 1295
Alley, Tom, 1295
Alliance Bank, 3394
Alliance for Affordable Healthcare
    Association, 8779
Alliance For Affordable Services, 8779
Alliant Credit Union, 2702
Allied Farms, 698
Allied Trades Council, 5245
Allison, Elisabeth, 4000
Allison, Graham, Jr., 4000
Allison, John, 4221
Allphin, Robert, 870
AllPro, 253
Allred, Dan, 1038
Allsbrook, David N., III, 966
Allscripts Healthcare Solutions Inc.,
    7176
Allwin, James M., 1390
Allwin, Maria, 1390
Allyn, John W., Jr., 2703
Almade, Frank D., 8091
Alman, Larry, 213
Almeida, Alexis, 2704
Almeida, Jill F., 2704
Almeida, Richard J., 2704
Almo, Eli, 5665
Alon, Margo S., 949
Alord, Nicolas A., 5507
Alpaugh Family 15 Year Charitable Lead
    Trust, The, 7302
Alpaugh Family 20 Year Charitable Lead
    Trust, The, 7302
Alpaugh, Peter A., 7302
Alper, Penni A., 2549
Alpha Bancorp, 2866
Alpha I Marketing Corp., 6344
Alpine Bank & Trust Co., 3116, 3325
Alpizar, Sandra, 2944
Alroc Real Estate Associates LTD, 2380
ALS Therapy Development Foundation,
    7209
Alsco Inc., 9358
Alshar, Ayam, 236
Alsman, Brent R., 3160
Alston, John G., 2453
Alt, Christina G., 2099, 5571
Altamore, Ellen, 4426
Altenbaumer, Luanne E., 2109
Alter, Daniel M., 2398
Alter, David, 7577
Alter, Helen Berman, 8118
Alter, Linda L., 8118
Alter, Lisa, 5654
Altgelt, James E., Jr., 9166
Altitude Sports & Entertainment, 1295
Altizer, Betsy, 8683

Altizer, Ryan, 8683
Altman, D. David, 7582
Altman, David, 7030
Altman, Earle S., 6655
Altman, Louis, 7030
Altman, Peter M., 5788
Altman, Thomas L., 2077
Altmeyer, James E., 9742
Altschul, Mark, 6149
Altura Homes, 9009
Alvarado, Carlos, 3969
Alvarez, Sofia, 2970
Alverno Health Care Corp., 3372
Alves, John, 1552
Alvis, Patricia, 3413
Alvord, Joel B., 4002
Alvord, Sarah H., 4002
Alvord, Seth W., 4002
Alyeska Pipeline Co., 89
Alzohaili, Opada, 4420
Amadore, Francisca, 9937
Amalse, John, 5573
Amar Industries, 1931
Amar Infinity Foundation, 449
Amarillo Credit Association Inc., 8697
Amarillo National Bank, 8704, 8778,
    8991, 9155
Ambach, Lucy E., 3222
Ambasta, Rajesh, 6015
Ambasta, Sumita, 6015
Ambler, David, 4251
Ambler, Sarah H. C., 4251
Amboian, Andrew L., 3292
Amboian, Ann L., 3292
Amboian, John P., Jr., 3292
Amboy National Bank, 5246
Ambrose LLC, 153
Ambrose, Robert F., 6084
Ambrosiani Foundation, 2663
Ambrosiani, Irene, 2663
Ambrosiani, Jack, 2663
Ambrosiani, Mary J., 2663
Amburgey, Anita, 9757
Amen, Charles A., 4908
Amendola, Laura, 1938
Amerian, Michael, 648
America First Cos. L.L.C., 5066
American Academy of Orthopaedic
    Surgeons, 3144
American Campus Communities
    Services, 8700
American Civil Liberties Union, 1787
American Eagle Outfitters, 7839
American Electric Power Co., 7303
American Express, 5664
American Flange & Manufacturing Co.,
    2247
American Foundation Trust, 8322
American Friends of Hebrew University,
    5668
American Future Systems, 8254
American General Finance, 3455
American Gift Fund, 8074
American Golf Corp., 2642
American Homecare Federation, 1421
American Ireland Fund, 8243
American Microproducts, 7333
American National Bank of Texas, 9232
American Orthodontics Corp., 9884
American Pulverizer, 4925
American Roland Food Corp., 8859
American Seafoods Co., 91
American Seniors, 3440
American Standard Inc., 3600

American Warrior, 3612
American Woodmark Corp., 9387
Americans for Financial Security, 8779
Ameringen, Henry Van, 6053
Amerisure Mutual Holdings, 4375
Amerisure Mutual Insurance Co., 4375
Ameritas Life Insurance Corp., 5067
Amerman, Anne J., 239
Amerman, Garrett J., 239
Amerman, Jerome T., 239
Amerman, John W., 239
Ames, A. Gary, 9560
Ames, Barbara J., 9560
Ames, Donald S., 5880
Ames, Eric C., 9560
Ames, Harriett, 7840
Ames, Kathleen L., 6170
Ames, Steven, 7840
Amestoy, Jay, 810
Amethyst, 375
Amgen USA Inc., 825
AmGraph, 1408
Amherst Holdings LLC, 8702
Amick, Abby, 3592
Amid Metro Partnership, LLC, 3749
Amin, Chirag, 240
Amin, Kelly, 240
Amin, Mahendra, 9695
Amin, Mohammed Mark, 241
Amin, Reza, 241
Amin, Saroj, 9695
Amini, Deborah, 9128
Amini, Margaret, 9128
Amini, Rex, 9128
Amis, Richard, 9114
Ammerman, Bruce, 3813
Ammerman, Don, 2260
Ammerman, Joshua M., 3813
Ammerman, Joy, 3813
Ammerman, Lenell, 3813
Ammerman, Matthew D., 3813
Amon, Thomas G., 7035
Amor, Jack, 2367
Amos, Courtney G., 2615
Amos, Daniel P., 2615
Amos, Elena Diaz-Verson, 2433
Amos, John Shelby, II, 2433
Amos, Lauren A., 2615
Amos, Mable, 4
Amos, Paul, II, 2615
Amplatz, Caroline, 4654
AMR Corp., 8703
AmSouth Bank, 58
Amsted Industries Inc., 2708
Amstein Charitable Remainder Unitrust,
    Peter, 9561
Amstein, Michael, 9561
Amstein, Peter, 9561
Amster, Harvey, 1156
Amsterdam, Jack, 5672
Amstore Corporation, 4479
Amtekco Industries, 7632
Amundson Charity Foundation, Lloyd and
    Barbara, 8554
Amundson, Karen Onan, 4754
Amundson, Matt, 8554
Amundson, Philip, 8554
Anast-May, Linda, 3372
Anastas, Lila L., 643
Anbinder, Madeline, 1611
Anbinder, Stephen, 1611
Anbinder, Tyler, 1611
Anchor Mosn, LLC, 2390
Anchor Trust, 9940

Anderas, Per, Dr. , 9781
Andersen Foundation, Elmer L. & Eleanor J., 4801
Andersen, Amy, 4626
Andersen, Anthony L., 4626
Andersen, Anthony L. "Tony", 4801
Andersen, Crystal, 420
Andersen, Eleanor J., 4626
Andersen, Elmer L., 4626
Andersen, Frank N., 4377
Andersen, G. Chris, 6925
Andersen, Holly S., 6211
Andersen, Julian, 4626
Andersen, Kathleen S., 6490
Anderson Columbia Co., 1846
Anderson Foundation, Charlie and Moll, 5
Anderson Foundation, Terry and Susan, 5
Anderson Irrevocable Trust CLAT, Particia A., 7271
Anderson, Alan C., 4678
Anderson, Alan J., 3548
Anderson, Allison, 8370
Anderson, Amy, 4801
Anderson, Angela L., 3057
Anderson, Annie W., 7304
Anderson, Blair, 2103
Anderson, Brent, 9305
Anderson, Brian, 5352
Anderson, Brian A., 1393
Anderson, Carl T., 7168
Anderson, Charles C., 5, 6
Anderson, Charles J., 8958
Anderson, Charles L., Sr., 2085
Anderson, Clyde B., 6
Anderson, Cynthia T., 1846
Anderson, David C., 9677
Anderson, Deborah L., 4207
Anderson, Diana, 1304
Anderson, Diana Zeff, 1383
Anderson, Dick, 2686
Anderson, Don, 2687
Anderson, Donald, 1505
Anderson, Donald W., 9773
Anderson, Douglas E., 7055
Anderson, Douglas G., 5674
Anderson, E. Martin, 244
Anderson, Ed L., 370
Anderson, Elizabeth Milbank, 6490
Anderson, Ellen G., III, 7990
Anderson, Frederick P., 1394
Anderson, Frohman, 8397
Anderson, G. Albert, 8431
Anderson, Gail, 2178
Anderson, Gary, 5352
Anderson, Gordon, 3493
Anderson, Gregory S., 1393
Anderson, Grenville, 7305
Anderson, Harlan E., 1393
Anderson, Harold M., 5
Anderson, Hilda, 5
Anderson, Illie, 244
Anderson, James C., 7587
Anderson, James D., 2989
Anderson, James M., 7616
Anderson, Jane G., 5674
Anderson, Jason, 7747
Anderson, Jason M., 7827
Anderson, Jerrica, 9232
Anderson, Joe H., III, 1846
Anderson, Joe H., Jr., 1846
Anderson, John, 2090
Anderson, John R., 1845

Anderson, Josephine, 8704
Anderson, Judy, 802
Anderson, Julie, 84
Anderson, Kathey K., 8705
Anderson, Kathleen, 9878
Anderson, Kayrita, 5
Anderson, Kenneth G., 2361
Anderson, Kent, 9226
Anderson, Kermit, 9732
Anderson, Lara, 9270
Anderson, Lawrence C., 6049
Anderson, Linda, 1845
Anderson, Lois J., 1393
Anderson, Loren, 89
Anderson, Lorraine W., 1351
Anderson, M. Douglas, 1846
Anderson, Margaret M., 9773
Anderson, Marion, 7031
Anderson, Marion Douglas, 1846
Anderson, Michael S., 9106, 9464
Anderson, Nancy, 4666
Anderson, Nicholas R., 7305
Anderson, Nicole, 726
Anderson, P.K., 3814
Anderson, Patricia A., 7271
Anderson, Porter W., 5676
Anderson, Porter W., Jr., 5676
Anderson, Raymond E., 1351
Anderson, Richard L., 2982
Anderson, Robert, 1291
Anderson, Robert A., 8705
Anderson, Robert C., 1847
Anderson, Robert P., Jr., 1394
Anderson, Robert S., 1568
Anderson, Roger, 802
Anderson, RuthAnne, 5161
Anderson, S. Stormy, 1248
Anderson, Sadie Gaither, 1847
Anderson, Samuel A., 5651
Anderson, Stephen E., 9714
Anderson, Steven C., 9106
Anderson, Summer, 6
Anderson, Susan E., 1393
Anderson, T. Mark, 8725
Anderson, Terry C., 6
Anderson, Theresa M., 8958
Anderson, Thomas, 3092, 5249
Anderson, Thomas M., 7545
Anderson, Tim, 9712
Anderson, V, William P., 7305
Anderson, W.T., 1848
Anderson, Zeff, 1304
Anderson-Owens, Edna V., 575
Andeson, Victor, 688
Andolshek, Richard, 4702
Andre, Edward A., 1849
Andre, Jeanne M., 1849
Andre, Jessica L., 1849
Andreas, Christopher, 9388
Andreas, George C., 9388
Andreas, Ursula E., 9388
Andreassi, James, 1427
Andreassi, Margaret, 1427
Andreassi, Margaret C., 1427
Andreef, Carla, 1850
Andreef, Starr, 1850
Andreeff, Dane, 1850
Andreoli, Rennick, 7358
Andreski, Claudia, 5582
Andress, Don, 5132
Andress, Louwanna, 5132
Andress, Madeleine, 5132
Andrew Julie Klingenstein Family, 6328
Andrew, Jerry J., 8972

Andrews, Bob, 8607
Andrews, Bob L., 8616
Andrews, Christie F., 1292
Andrews, David J., 5235
Andrews, Eric, 8008
Andrews, Harry C., 1221
Andrews, Hugh T., 4860
Andrews, James C., 4860
Andrews, Joan K., 5677
Andrews, Karen E., 1221
Andrews, Kathleen C., 4886
Andrews, Kathleen W., 4860
Andrews, Matthew, Mrs. , 7307
Andrews, Patricia Totemoff, 83
Andrews, Peter C., 5677
Andrews, Renee Elise, 1292
Andrews, Richard J., 1292
Andrews, Robert L., 1923
Andrews, Robert S., 2434
Andringa, Dale J., 3470
Andringa, Mary A., 3470
Androscoggin Bank, 3787
Andrus, Brent, 9301
Andrus, Cheri, 9301
Andrus, Johnnie, 8869
Anema, Sophia Gebhard, 1831
Angel Trust, The, 9293
Angel, Dolores W., 5678
Angel, Stephen F., 5678
Angelici Estate, 8657
Angelo, Bonnie, 5879
Angelo, John M., 5863
Angelos, Georgia K., 3817
Angelos, John Peter, 3817
Angelos, Louis Francis, 3817
Angelos, Peter G., 3817
Angelson, Genevieve, 5679
Angelson, Jessica, 5679
Angelson, Lynn F., 1397
Angelson, Marilyn, 5679
Angelson, Mark, 5679
Angelson, Meredith, 5679
Angner, Dennis P., 4468
Angove, Vicki, 3495
Anhaltzer, Gregory C., 245
Anhaltzer, Jeffrey O., 245
Anheuser Busch, 5369
Aniello, Maura E., 4353
Anjargolian, Sara, 5562
Ankeny Charitable Lead Trust, Marie H., 4628
Ankeny, Dewalt, 4628
Ankeny, Dewalt H., Jr., 4628
Ankeny, Michael H., 4628
Ankerson, John M., 9491
Ann Christy, Thomas and Lee, 3593
Annala, Don, 4666
Anning, Dulany, 2773
Annis, Linda, 3771
Anschel, Daniel, 2709
Anschel, Trude, 2709
Anschutz Entertainment Group, 8795
Anschutz Foundation, The, 1243, 1296
Ansin, Harold S., 4003
Ansin, Joseph L., 4003
Anson, Catherine K., 4670
Anson, Sally A., 4628
Antaramian, John, 9863
Antebi, Albert, 6199
Antebi, Moris, 6199
Antes, Shirley, 3635
Anthon, John, 3991
Anthony, Carmelo K., 247
Anthony, Frederick W., 6569

Anthony, Frenny Thomas, 2501
Anthony, Grant, 1096
Anthony, June, 217
Anton Trust, Barbara, 1851
Anton, Dene Hofheinz, 8942
Anton, Patricia, 5133
Anton, William, 5133
Antonacci, Frank, 1395
Antonacci, Gaetano, 1395
Antonacci, Gerald, 1395
Antonetti, Chris, 7354
Antonetti, Emilie, 6091
Antun, Frank J., 5681
Anundson, James W., 8280
Apex Construction, 8700
Apicella, Achille A., 1482, 1505
Appalachian Pipeline, 9130
Appel, Richard, 6559
Appell, George N., 3778
Appell, Laura W. R., 3778
Appell, Laura W.R., 3778
Appell, Lloyd E., 4606
Appellof, Elaine, 5532
Applbaum, Edward A., 567
Apple Chevrolet, 8301
Apple, Virginia Reeves, 967
Applebaum, Irwyn, 5683
Applebaum, Stuart S., 5683
Appleby, Scott B., 2711
Appler, Samantha, 3867
Applied Dynamics, 4088
April, Anne M., 5204
AptarGroup, 2712
Arader, Walter, 7868
Arago, Judith, 1209
Aragona, Joseph C., 8706
Aragona, Sandra R., 8706
Aramark, 3867
ARAMARK, 8243
ARAMARK Corp., 3817
Arapahoe and Holly Self Storage, 1295
Arbabi, Deborah E., 1799
Arbesman, Linda Roberts, 1551
Arboit, Guy A., 2713
Arboit, N. Kay, 2713
Arbuckle, Allison Fridy, 1740
Arbuckle, Jeffrey D., 3637
Arbus, Loreen J., 6094
Arcade Trust, 1547
Archangeli, Elizabeth, 2265
Archangeli, Matthew, 2265
Archbold, Nadea R., 6229
Archbold, Paul S., 2614
Archbold, William J., 6229
Archer, Jessica, 3362
Archer, Pierce, Mrs., 7990
Archer, Robert A., 250
Archibald, Anne G., 4005
Archibald, Daniel Isaac, 1852
Archibald, Delbert M., 1852
Archibald, John L.G., 4005
Archibald, Kathy, 1852
Archibald, Kenneth Cole, 1852
Archibald, Simon, 5400
Arciero, Pam, 6194
Arctic Fjord, 91
Ardigo, Linda, 1633
Arditti, Elliot, 1800
Ardizzone, Leonisa, 6682
Arella, Christine, 6871
Arena Energy, LLC, 8707
Arena, David, 6655
Arendale, Bruce C., 9031
Arends, Darla, 3540

Arendt, William, 2776
Areng, Veljo, 9685
Arenz, Betty, 844
Arenz, Betty Money, 844
Arenz, John Marshall, 844
Arenz, Robert F., Jr., 844
Aresty, Joseph, 5686, 5687
Aresty, Peter, 5686
Aresty, Rosanne, 5686
Aresty, Sheila, 5687
Aresty, Steven, 5687
Arey, Lorene, 406
Arey, Paris, 406
Argent Trust Company of Tennessee, 15
Argenziano, Joseph, 2099
Argenziano, Susan E., 2099
Argo, Allison, 251
Arguetty, Isaac, 2212
Arguetty, Miriam, 2212
Argus, Saul G., 6374
Argyrakis, Nick, 9474
Argyris, George T., 952, 1033
ARH Revocable Trust, 4464
ARH Trust, 4464
Aria Foundation, 1826
Arias, Silvestre, 545
Ariens Co., 7520, 9776
Ariens Company, 9776
Ariens Corp., 9776
Ariens Memorial, Francis, 9776
Ariens, Mary M., 9776
Arison, Marilyn B., 1853
Arison, Sarah, 1853
Arizona Bank and Trust, 98
Arjani, Temo A., 476
Arjunan, S., 651
Arkansas Democrat-Gazette, 201
Arkema Inc., 7842
Arkin, Harry L., 1244
Arkwright, Richard T., 5979
Arlen, Alice, 1826
Arlington Center Service and Garage, 4204
Arlington, LLC, 804
Armagno, Valerie S., 2373
Armantrout, Natalie, 3623
Armato, Keith, 9033
Armbrister, Denise McGregor, 8350
Armel, Wendy W., 9387
Armellino, Michael R., 6953
Armiger, William, 3884
Armijo, Jil Wing, 1105
Armington, Everett, 7309
Armitage, Desiree C., 1415
Armknecht, Leila B., 1631
Armour Revocable Trust, Robert L., 5251
Armour, Karen Webb, 5196
Armstead, Brian, 8057
Armstrong Cement & Supply Corp., 8287
Armstrong, Arthur G., 9386
Armstrong, Beth, 9345
Armstrong, Betty, 9085
Armstrong, Connie M., 3580
Armstrong, Donald, 5880
Armstrong, Fred E., Jr., 97
Armstrong, Fred E., Sr., 97
Armstrong, Gerald S., 1416
Armstrong, Jerry M., 9129
Armstrong, Julie, 9129
Armstrong, Kathie, 945
Armstrong, Kelly R., 2624
Armstrong, Lisa Renee, 8708
Armstrong, Marcia, 5060
Armstrong, Marion B., 9129

Armstrong, Nora, 8101
Armstrong, R.E., 9677
Armstrong, Regina, 8708
Armstrong, Robert E., 5181
Armstrong, Robert H., 2624
Armstrong, Rose Anne, 8101
Armstrong, Samuel T., Jr., 97
Armstrong, Sidney O'Malley, 5054
Armstrong, Steven R., 7144
Armstrong, Terri, 9129
Armstrong, Terry, 8708
Armstrong, Whitney B., 1490
Armstrong, Whitney Brewster, 1490
Arnall, Daniel M., 423
Arnall, Judith A., 423
Arndt, Jennifer, 5463
Arnhold Ceramics, 5826
Arnhold Foundation, 5826
Arnhold, Henry H., 5826
Arnhold, John P., 5826
Arnoff, Cathy, 2509
Arnold & Porter, 1787
Arnold, Claire Lewis, 2461
Arnold, Ethan, 4044
Arnold, Gregory L., 3579
Arnold, Kathleen, 8000
Arnold, Lisa, 3360
Arnold, Lori, 9357
Arnold, Mary Ann, 2666
Arnold, Matthew C., Sr., 3631
Arnold, Michael, 108, 968
Arnovitz, Eliot M., 2509
Arnow, F. Michael, 9775
Arnstein, Beverly J., 254
Arnstein, Daniel C., 254
Arnstein, Frank G., 254
Arone, Vincent J., 4134
Aronov, Jake F., 7
Aronov, Teri, 7
Aronson, Adam, 5689
Aronson, Alan, 3048
Aronson, James, 5689
Aronson, Jonathan, 5689
Aronson, Joshua, 5689
Aronson, Judith, 5689
Aronson, Martha G., 4944
Arrien, Angeles, 574
Arrison Family Foundation, 5690
Arrison, Clement R., 5690
Arrison, Karen, 5690
Arronson, Gertrude, 7844
Arsenault, Cynda, 1224
Arsenault, Cynda Collins, 1224
Arsenault, John, 1224
Arsenault, John F.C., 1224
Arsenault, Marcel J.C., 1224
Art of the Game, 3817
Art, James B., 4057
Artemenko, Sherry Y., 2422
Arthur Patricia Price Family Trust, 938
Arthur Schuman Inc., 8859
Arthur State Bank, 8551
Arthur, James A., 8995
Arthur, Paul C., 8995
Arthur, Steele, 8792
Arthur, Stephen, 8792
Arthur, William H., 8995
Artic Storm, 91
Arts, Veerle, 4698
Arum 1988 Trust, Robert, 5202
Arumugam, Sivasenthil, 1599
Arundel, Morgan, 4653
Arvest Trust Co., 202
ArvinMeritor, 4511

Aryeh, Jason M., 6361
Aryeh, Vera, 6361
Arzbaecher, Robert C., 9777
Arzt, Gainor Wessinger, 7826
Asack, George, Jr., 4245
Asato, Saturu, 4671
Asbjornson, Norman H., 7655
Asbury, Mary, 7582
Ascena Retail Group, 5252
Asch, Leslee, 6194
Aschenbrenner, Thomas, 9867
Ascher, David S., 256
Ascher, David S., II, 256
Ascher, Deloris, 256
Ascher, Pamela, 256
Ascher, Shane, 256
Ascoli, Lucy B., 3059
Ascoli, Peter M., 3059
Asen, Robert Scott, 5694
Asgrimson, T., 4703
Ash Family Trust, 5134
Ash, Celia, 4514
Ash, Elizabeth, 5134
Ash, Elizabeth A., 3341
Ash, H. Grady, 8709
Ash, Henry G., 8709
Ash, Stephen C., 8709
Ash, Timothy E., 3341
Ashbritt Inc., 1840
Ashbrook, Mary K., 7656
Ashbrook, Thomas J., 4942
Ashby, Norma, 5054
Ashe, Brian T., 3242
Asher Resources Partnership, 8962
Asher, Dan, 9654
Asher, Daniel, 9567
Asher, Daniel M., 9570, 9603, 9640
Asher, Kenneth R., 6982
Ashford, Theodore H., 1677
Ashkenazi, David E., 5276
Ashkenazi, Ezra E., 5276
Ashkenazi, Isaac, 5276
Ashkenazi, Ronald, 5276
Ashla, Susan, 2688
Ashley, Daniel C., 6910
Ashley, Daniel J., 6910
Ashley, Suzanne, 9814
Ashok Patel Charitable Lead Annuity Trust, 5491
Ashton Trust, Elisha V., 4046
Ashton, Eric A., Jr., 421
Ashton, Jon M., 4742
Ashton, Kreea, 4742
Ashton, Kristie, 6644
Ashton, Nancy, 4742
Ashton, Rita Goldstein, 569
Ashton, Ryan, 945
Ashur, George, 4195
Ashworth, Sarah P., 3699
Askew, Rebecca, 4847
Askin, Chris, 5181
Asmat, Shereen, 4012
Asmuth, Clifford M., 9825
Asnani, Brijbala, 7871
Asnani, Gul, 7871
Asp, Anthony, 9696
Aspen Industries, 1295
Asplundh, Carl H.J., Jr., 8333
Asplundh, Pamela S., 8333
Assents LLC, 5482
Assink, Karen A.P., 7639
Associated Banc-Corp, 9778
Associated Media Group LLC, 3437
Associated Trust Co., 9778

Associates of the Bon-Ton Dept. Stores, 7884
Association of Baptist World Evangelism, 9169
Assurance Dimensions, 2348
Assurity Life Insurance Co., 5068
Ast, Alan, 6131
Astin, Katherine T., 1371
Astles, Geoffrey, 6559
Astman, Fred L., 552
Astman, Jean, 552
ASU Foundation, 3998, 8982
Atcheson, Elizabeth, 226
Atco Properties & Management, 6655
ATG Trust Company, 2813
Athanasuleas, C.L., 725
Athanasuleas, Constantine, 725
Athens, Susan Wood, 3644
Atherton, Delores Ann, 7657
Atherton, J. Thomas, 7657
Atherton, Michael Dirk, 7657
Atherton, William S., 7657
ATK, 3991
Atkiesson, A.L., 9085
Atkins North America, 1856
Atkins North America Holdings Corp., The, 1856
Atkins, Donald K., 4244
Atkins, Frederick J., 6032
Atkins, H. Kent, 6868
Atkins, Jeannine, 4365
Atkins, John B., 5092
Atkins, Margaret Quern, 2888
Atkinson, Ben, 13
Atkinson, Carol A., 1857
Atkinson, Eugene D., 1857
Atkinson, James F., III, 923
Atlanta Public Schools, 2621
Atlantic Foundation, 5485
Atlas Bass Fund, 8657
Atlas Carpet Mills, 632
Atlas Lighting Products Inc., 7135
Atnip, Janice Erion Pierce, 1265
Atofina Chemicals, 7842
Attal, Charles A., 2367
Attaway, Evelyn Nelson, 9993
Attaway, John, 2222
Atter, Michael, 1298
Atterbury, Alan L., 3554
Atterbury, Andrew L., 3554
Atterbury, Carol A., 7888
Atterbury, Darsie L., 7934
Atterbury, David A., 3554
Atterbury, Elizabeth G., 8313
Atterbury, George R., 8076
Atterbury, George R., Jr., 7934
Atterbury, Harry L., 8354
Atterbury, Jennifer L., 3554
Atterbury, Mary P., 3554
Atterbury, Michael B., 7888
Atterbury, Wendy S., 8354
Atwater, John, 4749
Atwater, Verne S., 6372
Atwood, Bruce, 4244
Atwood, Karen O., 9472
Atwood, Sarah, 3686
Auburn Construction, 4211
Aud, Michael, 210
Aud, Millard, 210
Aud, Theda, 210
Auda Advisor Associates, 6884
Audiocodes Inc., 3398
Audouze, Jean, 6585
Auerbach, Arlene, 260

Auerbach, Carol B., 1859
Auerbach, Isaac L., 1859
Auerbach, William, 6656
Aufman, Edward, 8138
Aufzien, Alan, 5253
Aufzien, Jonathan, 5253
Aufzien, Lisa, 5253
Aufzien, Norma, 5253
Augelo, Denise M., 8220
Augur, Marilyn H., 8712
August, Andrew, 5698
August, Burton S., 5698
August, Burton S., Jr., 5698
August, Burton Stuart, 5698
August, Charles J., 5698
August, Jan, 5698
August, Jean B., 5698
August, Joan, 5698
August, John, 5698
August, Leslie J., 7152
August, Robert, 5698
Augustenborg, Ana Sophia, 9676
Augustine, Lucile Cochrane, 1420
Augustine, Merlin, 188
Auletta, Frank, 138
Auriana, Lawrence, 1447
Auriana, Mark, 1447
Ausband, Allison, 2586
Ausch, Abraham, 5699
Ausch, Bella, 6649
Ausiello, Talia K., 3018
Austein Trust, 5705
Austein Trust, Susi, 5705
Austin Athletic Scholarship Foundation, 8689
Austin Community Foundation, 9631
Austin, Constance A., 5649
Austin, David, 2372
Austin, Jerry, 7691
Austin, Linda J., 1416
Austin, Mark D., 1958
Austin-Keevil, Wendy M., 2480
Autenreith, Penny S., 3751
Auto Vehicle Parts Co., 7451
Automatic Service Corp., 3905
Autozone, 215
Autry, Jacqueline, 8657
Autumn Health Svcs. of Kennebunk, 3786
Auyang, Angela, 8
Auyang, Eric, 8
Auyang, Sunny, 8
Avanessians, Armen A., 5701
Avansino, Malarkey, Knobel and Mulli, 4416
Avedisian, Berge, 6826
Aven, Frances, 9264
Aven, Frances J., 9264
Aven, Teddy, 9264
Aven, Teddy W., 9264
Avent, Frank, 8522
Averett, Joe N., Jr., 3750
Averitt, George R., 3372
Avery Foundation, R. Stanton, The , 261
Avery, Alicia, 1396
Avery, Ann Z., 9805
Avery, Chris, 6916
Avery, John E., 1396
Avery, Margaret A., 9805
Avery, Nelson, Dr. , 8769
Avery, Roger C., 9805
Avery, Sally M., 5702
Avery, Susan R., 9805
Avery-Denyse, Bernetta, 8279

Avlon, John, 6655
Avreichim, Keren, 5544
Awalt, J. Steven, 8963
Awerkamp, Alden, 5117
Awuondo, Isaac, 2622
Ax Family Foundation, James B., 695
Axe, Emerson W., 1397
Axelrod, Emily, 4030
Axelrod, Margaret G., 6048
Ayer, David, 4260
Ayer, Gordon C., 3803
Ayer, Susan, 3803
Ayer, William S., 80
Ayers, Ann, 6248
Ayers, Florence, 7848
Ayers, Genevieve S., 2319
Ayers, James A., II, 7848
Ayers, Paul W., 2272
Ayers, Penelope, 6759
Ayers, Renee, 7848
Ayers, Tobin, 71
Aylward, A.A., 9779
Aylward, E.W., 9779
Aylward, R.J., 9779
Ayotte, Mark, 4648
Ayres and Co., L.S., 3342
Ayres LP, 4841
Ayres, Nancy, 3342
Ayres, Nancy P., 2272
Ayyad, Daniel, 449
Ayyad, William G., 449
Azar, Eddie, 5704
Azar, Shawna, 5704
Azek Trim Boards, 3817
Azrack, Diana, 6513
Azrak, Albert, 6513
Azrak, Diane, 5705
Azrak, Raymond, 6513

B.E.L.I.E.F. Foundation, 8779
B.J. Development LLC, 7638
B.P.O.E., 1640
Baack, Jessica, 2986
Baas, Daniel G., 4382
Babab, Chaim, 6859
Babab, Joseph, 6859
Babare Foundation, The, 9563
Babare, Cynthia Louise, 9564
Babare, Evelyn G., 9563
Babare, George M., 9564
Babare, Martin, 9563
Babare, Martin D., 9563
Babare, Mary, 9564
Babare, Robert M., 9564
Babare, Robert S., 9564
Babbitt, George, 98
Babcock, Calvin H., 1972
Babcock, Charles I., III, 1972
Babcock, Charles I., Jr., 1972
Babcock, Evelyn E., 1972
Babcock, Fred C., 1612
Babcock, Guilford C., 580
Babcock, Gwendolyn Garland, 580
Babcock, Herb, Mrs. , 9333
Babcock, Mary A., 1612
Babcock, Mary H., 1972
Baber, Tom, 1107
Babinger, Emil, 3555
Babson, Averill, 4009
Babson, David F., 1479
Babson, Deborah E., 4009
Babson, James A., 4009
Babson, Richard L., 4009

Babson, Susan, 4009
Baby Boom Consumer, 5743
Bacardi, 2510
Bach, Duane R., 1845
Bachman, C. William, 6922
Bachman, Lois V., 4814
Bachmann, Bruce R., 3179
Bachrach, Ed, 2764
Bachrach, Laurie, 2764
Backa, Louise, 8926
Backer, Ann, 9389
Backer, Ann M., 9389
Backer, Edward, 1503
Backer, John W., 3645
Backer, Sary, 1503
Backer, William M., 9389
Backman, David, 6294
Backman, Sherrie, 6294
Backover, Andrew M., 8699
Bacon, Alissa B., 9565
Bacon, Anthony R., 9565
Bacon, Charles F., 4011
Bacon, Debra, 9565
Bacon, John D., 9565
Bacon, John E., 9565
Bacon, Joseph A., 9565
Bacon, Katherine Weld, 6992
Bacon, Kim Krasne, 6344
Bacon, Paul, 1442
Badali, Sally J., 1639
Badcock, Philip A., 2517
Badgley, Allison, 1202
Badgley, Coleman, 1202
Badgley, Judy Yoder, 1202
Baehr, Dolpha, 3556
Baehr, L.W., 3556
Baekgaard, Barbara B., 7850
Baer, Helen K., 4862
Baer, Henry, 2241
Baer, Kathy, 5069
Baer, Theodore, 5069
Baer, Zac, 5069
Baesler, Colin, 2425
Baesler, Jordan Z., 2425
Bag Bazaar, 6881
Bag One Arts, 6839
Baga, Louis S., 2475
Bagatelle, David, 6632
Bagatin, Jeffrey, 6087
Bagby, Alyson M., 48
Bagby, Glen S., 3674
Baggs, Darrell W., 874
Bagley, Martha R., 4075
Bagley, Ralph R., 4075
Bagshawe, E. N., 5341
Bagwell, John C., 1109
Bahaa-El-Din, Wael, 9623
Bahl, Felicia V., 4632
Bahl, Tracy L., 4632
Bahlman, William T., Jr., 7582
Bahmann, Emma Leah, 7313
Bahmann, Laura Belle, 7313
Bahora, Heather A., 3575
Baiardi, Angelo, 4381
Baiardi, Chris A., 4381
Baiardi, Cindy J., 4381
Baiardi, Kristen L., 4381
Baiardi, Suzanne M., 4381
Baic, Vojin, 4391
Baier, Kristin, 8809
Baig, Mirza, 236
Baig, Patricia, 236
Bailes, Jacqueline H., 2107
Bailey & Son, Bankers, M.S., 8510

Bailey, Audrey W., 9964
Bailey, Catherine T., 1878
Bailey, Dean R., 2217
Bailey, Don V., 1613
Bailey, Emily F., 8509
Bailey, Ford B., 8514
Bailey, G. Alan, 8186
Bailey, George S., 8514
Bailey, H.A. Ted, 187
Bailey, H.A. Ted, Jr., 187
Bailey, Irving W., II, 1878
Bailey, James L., 1862
Bailey, James M., 9964
Bailey, Jerome, 4633
Bailey, Jim, 5895
Bailey, Jim M., 9964
Bailey, John, 186
Bailey, John D., Jr., 2341
Bailey, John Hill, Jr., 2496
Bailey, John P., 5046
Bailey, Joseph, 4633
Bailey, Josh, 3623
Bailey, Judith A., 1862
Bailey, Kristin, 7787
Bailey, Lucia H., 1863
Bailey, Margaret, 4633
Bailey, Melanie, 3557
Bailey, Patricia, 186
Bailey, Penny, 4632
Bailey, Robert F., 7125
Bailey, Robert S., 7944
Bailey, Sara F., 1862
Bailey, Stephanie, 673
Bailey, Stephen M., 1863
Bailey, Susan, 8556
Bailey, Timothy A., 7784
Bailey, Verna, 7807
Bailey, Walter M., 9964
Bailey, William N., 8598
Bailey-Barnum, Vivien M., 6274
Bailon, Charlie, 921
Bain, St. John, 316
Bainum, Barbara, 3912
Bair, Jack, 3511
Bair, Judith, 1802
Baird & Warner, 2717
Baird Brothers Co., 7314
Baird, Brian D., 6365
Baird, Carol J., 9632
Baird, David A., 8442
Baird, John, 2717
Baird, Margaret, 8442
Baird, Martha, 8442
Baird, Mary, 8442
Baird, Philip F., Jr., 7795
Baird, Stephen W., 2717, 2718
Baird, Susan M., 2718
Baird, Thomas, 8984
Baird, Thomas A., 4454
Baird, William F., 4845
Baird, William Robert, 4822
Bais Yaakov Faigeh Schonberger Ofadas Ye, 5834
Baither, Thomas A., 4458
Bajandas, John, 3694
Bajandas, Laura D., 3694
Bajandas, Marlene Marie Smith, 3694
Bakalis, Desi, 2827
Baker Boyer National Bank, 9721
Baker Cheese Factory, 9780
Baker Corporation, Michael, 7851
Baker Enterprises, Bob, 264
Baker Trust, 3815
Baker, Bob, 9780

Baker, Brian, 9780
Baker, Carol, 8298
Baker, Carol Jean, 266
Baker, Carrie Lynn, 266
Baker, Christopher R., 264
Baker, Clark A., 2439
Baker, Douglas, 3427
Baker, Douglas W., 266
Baker, Edward D., III, 265
Baker, Elbert H., II, 9566
Baker, Eric H., 267
Baker, Frances W., 3815
Baker, Frederick M., 4590
Baker, Jayne, 6559
Baker, Joan, 2030
Baker, John, 2005, 5954
Baker, John C., 1244
Baker, Kate, 7543
Baker, Kevin, 9780
Baker, Lenox D., Jr., 3815
Baker, Linda, 2264
Baker, Lisa, 9224
Baker, Looe, 4660
Baker, Looe, III, 4660
Baker, Mack, 3655
Baker, Malcolm F., 267
Baker, Margaret W., 3815
Baker, Martine, 9566
Baker, Mary Ann, 4660
Baker, Natalie, 1260
Baker, Norma, 267
Baker, Norman D., Jr., 8434
Baker, Pamela, 1424
Baker, Peter G., 9476
Baker, Richard, 9780
Baker, Robert G., Jr., 1359
Baker, Robert H., 264
Baker, Rosemary Boccio, 265
Baker, Rosie, 9780
Baker, Sara F., 3815
Baker, Saul, 3251
Baker, Shawna, 7723
Baker, Solomon R., 267
Baker, Walter, 3799
Bakewell Corp., 4863
Bakewell, Edward L., III, 4863
Bakewell, Edward L., Jr., 4863
Bakke, Helen, 9935
Bakke, Helen A., 9943
Bakke, James J., 9841, 9943
Bakke, Susan A., 9841
Bakken, Eric A., 4770
Bakst, M., 6093
Bakwin, Edward Morris, 6693
Balakian Family Foundation, 1416
Balanced Tech. Corp., 5976
Balazs, Bryan, 912
Balbach, Carl T., 5707
Balbach, Charles E., 5707
Balbach, Margaret C., 5707
Balbach, Melissa T., 5707
Balch, Alan F., 3704
Balco Holdings, 1177
Baldacci, Elizabeth, 268
Baldacci, James, 268
Baldacci, Paul, 268
Baldacci, Paul R., Jr., 268
Baldi, Laura, 1295
Balding, Bruce, 6850
Baldinger, Howard, 5954
Baldini, Laura F., 1520
Baldor Electric Co., 188
Baldridge, Bill, 929
Baldridge, Emily Z., 8715

Baldridge, George C., 4959
Baldridge, Jeffrey Turner, 8715
Baldridge, Jerald T., 8715
Baldridge, Sharon, 3553
Baldwin, Amy Tolleson, 9238
Baldwin, Benjamin, 7742
Baldwin, Chi, 7742
Baldwin, Cindy, 9711
Baldwin, Dennis E., 1249
Baldwin, Edward, 2625
Baldwin, Eleanor R., 1864
Baldwin, Ellen C., 8519
Baldwin, Fred, 2625
Baldwin, Gregory S., 7742
Baldwin, Harriet D., 2629
Baldwin, Jeremy C., 2625
Baldwin, Joan Lamb, 7742
Baldwin, M. Dana, II, 4382
Baldwin, Michael J., 8854
Baldwin, Peter, 9148
Baldwin, Teresa L.C., 1809, 9400
Baldwin, Winifred B., 1399
Balenson, Brian, 3886
Balestra, Emily Saks, 4990
Balge, Richard, 9867
Balin, Karen, 1039
Balk, James H., 4383
Balk, James H., II, 4383
Balk, Martin, 4383
Balk, Shirley, 4383
Balk, Steven, 4383
Ball, Ann Marie, 4598
Ball, Gayle, 8836
Ball, George C., Jr., 5802
Ball, John R., 6490
Ball, Lamar Q., III, 2606
Ball, Nancy E., 110
Ball, Tracey, 3550
Ballantine, Christopher, 1226
Ballantine, David, 1226
Ballantine, Elizabeth, 1226, 3482
Ballantine, Morley C., 1226
Ballantine, Richard G., 1226
Ballard, Alexandra H., 3994
Ballard, Edwin Lee, 8716
Ballard, Lisa S., 7260
Ballard, Pamela, 7666
Ballard, Rachel Maria, 8716
Ballas, Jody, 7591
Ballenger, Richard, 9041
Baller Living Trust, 1370
Baller, Brenda L., 1370
Baller, M.L., 1370
Ballew, Judy B., 8511
Balloons Over Texas, 9215
Ballou, Bronwen Bradley, 8009
Ballou, Frederick D., 4038, 4356
Balmoral Homes Ltd., 9009
Balon, Donna, 5425
Balten, Leslee, 1242
Balthazard, Eileen M., 4358
Baltimore Capital Corp., 3966
Baltimore Equitable Society, The, 3816
Baltimore Orioles L.P., 3817
Baltoland Inc., 3905
Balus, Kathleen M., 6633
Balus, Mark S., 6633
Balzar, Rick, 726
Balzereit Trust, Leo C., 7853
Balzereit, Leo G., 7853
Bambeck, Alan, 7623
Bame, Christian, 4634
Bame, Christian N., 4634
Bame, Kevin F., 4634

Bame, Marna, 4634
Bame, Stacey L., 4634
Bame, Wendie M., 4634
Banaim, Darel, 5638
Banchik, Howard, 269
Banchik, Jacqueline, 269
Banchik, Randall, 269
Bancroft Unitrust, James M., 270
Bancroft, Elizabeth, 2274
Bancroft, Gail, 5549
Bancroft, James R., 270
Bancroft, John R., 270
Bancroft, Paul M., 270
Bancroft, William N., 4276
Bander, Patricia A., 4867
Bander, Steven, 4867
Bander, Steven Joseph, 4867
Banderalantana LP, 9009
Bandier, Dorothy, 5709
Bandier, Martin, 5709
Bandler, Jean P., 5109
Bandy, Michael C., 7652
Bane, Earl, 3557
Bane, Eugene M., 7043
Bangs, Michael L., 8222
Bangsund, Lynne, 7807
Banhardt Manufacturigng Co., 7202
Bank of America, 545, 1458, 1460,
    1473, 1475, 1553, 1582, 1595,
    1847, 1848, 1907, 1920, 1956,
    2000, 2009, 2014, 2038, 2224,
    2262, 2263, 2302, 2322, 2333,
    2342, 2439, 2451, 2483, 2486,
    2487, 2768, 2783, 3087, 3153,
    3177, 3329, 3999, 4011, 4025,
    4045, 4049, 4124, 4136, 4183,
    4225, 4241, 4265, 4874, 4881,
    5042, 5277, 5356, 5475, 5754,
    6678, 6844, 7185, 7193, 7250,
    7283, 7284, 7456, 7667, 7899,
    8378, 8379, 8380, 8381, 8382,
    8383, 8384, 8385, 8386, 8388,
    8389, 8390, 8391, 8394, 8395,
    8396, 8398, 8399, 8400, 8402,
    8403, 8404, 8407, 8408, 8411,
    8413, 8414, 8415, 8416, 8417,
    8418, 8419, 8420, 8421, 8423,
    8425, 8427, 8429, 8430, 8431,
    8432, 8433, 8435, 8437, 8439,
    8440, 8443, 8446, 8450, 8451,
    8452, 8453, 8454, 8455, 8456,
    8457, 8458, 8459, 8460, 8461,
    8463, 8465, 8466, 8468, 8469,
    8470, 8471, 8472, 8473, 8475,
    8480, 8482, 8483, 8485, 8486,
    8487, 8491, 8492, 8493, 8495,
    8496, 8497, 8499, 8502, 8504,
    8505, 8506, 8508, 8690, 8714,
    8728, 8733, 8734, 8740, 8744,
    8749, 8757, 8762, 8775, 8788,
    8790, 8799, 8804, 8830, 8842,
    8921, 8960, 8973, 8976, 8999,
    9013, 9015, 9021, 9022, 9024,
    9029, 9079, 9099, 9105, 9119,
    9123, 9134, 9149, 9153, 9157,
    9159, 9430, 9642, 9693, 9724
Bank of America Merrill Lynch, 4028,
    4357, 8700
Bank of America Private Client Group,
    214
Bank of America, N.S., 8996
Bank of Beulah, 8554
Bank of Charles Town, 9758, 9759
Bank of China, 6558

Bank of Hawaii, 2626, 2630, 2634,
    2643, 2649, 2653
Bank of Herrin, The, 2761
Bank of New York, 7905
Bank of New York Mellon, 6655, 8018
Bank of Oklahoma, 7672, 7733, 7738
Bank of Texas, 7698
Bank of the Ozarks, 7118
Bank of the West, 587
Bank of Tokyo, Mitsubishi Trust Co., The,
    5795
Bank of Tokyo, Mitsubishi UFJ Trust Co.,
    The, 5795
Bank of Utica, 5710
Bank Rhode Island, 8393
Bank, Helen S., 3818
Bank, Herbert M., 3818
Bank, Merrill L., 3818
Bank, Penny, 3818
Banks, Jerry, 3527
Banks, John, 8631
Banks, Karin, 9390
Banks, Lincoln H., 433
Banks, Roberta F., 3775
Banks, William, 9390
Bankston, Denise M., 3712
Bannan, C. Forrest, 897
Bannett, Michael L., 3474
Bannigan, Patrick, 1330
Banning, Edmund, 402
Bannish, Robert G., 4230, 4314, 8070
Bannon, Alexandra Laboutin, 312
Bannon, James G., III, 8511
Bannon, James G., Jr., 8511
Bannon, Mel B., 312
Banta, Berton M., 2719
Banta, Bradford C., 2719
Banta, June M., 2719
Banta, Merle H., 2719
Bantle, Louis F., 1401
Bantle, Robert C., 1401
Bantle, Virginia C., 1401
Baptie, T.J., 361
Baptist, Megan, 2280
Baptiste, Kim E., 5781
Baptiste, Pamela, 5781
Bar Harbor Trust Svcs., 3788
Bar-Haim, Ben, 8698
Barabino, John P., 1199
Baraboo National Bank, 9858
Baragli, Judith O., 4754
Barakas, Eve, 1593
Baran, Helen, 6540
Baran, Nicole, 281
Baranick, Erin R., 9717
Baratz, Shirley, 4635
Baratz, Stan, 4635
Baratz, Zollie, 4635
Barb, Haley, 8770
Barbagelata, Louise, 754
Barbara Bush Texas Fund for Family
    Literacy, The, 9188
Barbara Oil Co., 2758
Barbare, Robert M., 9564
Barbaro, Joseph, 5954
Barbaro, Michael, 1586
Barbarow, Carol, 813
Barbash, Bernard, 1865
Barbash, Cathy, 5714
Barbash, Lillian, 5714
Barbash, Maurice, 5714
Barbash, Pamela, 1865
Barbash, Shepard, 5714
Barbash, Susan, 5714

Barbee, Ronald M., 7075
Barber Co., Fred Lee, 5762
Barber, Daniel, 5762
Barber, David, 5762
Barber, Fred Lee, 5762
Barber, Gerald, 4377
Barber, Jane C., 7569
Barber, Patrick, 617
Barber, Thomas D., 9035
Barbera, Concetta, 3963
Barbera, Josephine, 275
Barbera, Mary Poppert, 3963
Barbera, Robert, 275
Barbera, Thomas, 3963
Barberich, Timothy J., 6528
Barbey, Anita, 9667
Barbey, Anne Murray, 9667
Barbo, A. Dennis, 4247
Barbonchielli Trust, Joseph L., 276
Barbour, Christine, 7757
Barboza, Michael J., 8449
Barchas, Jack David, 906
Barclays Capital, 6524
Barco Uniforms, 277
Bard, Holly Hewitt, 5673
Bard, James R., 7339
Bard, Paddy, 9982
Barden Corp., The, 1402
Bardley, Dianne, 3366
Bare, Thomas, 9867
Barefoot, Geoffrey, 5791
Barefoot, Sally, 9336
Barela, Sandra, 5198
Baren, Charles, 363
Barenholtz, Michael, 5695
Bares, Eliot, 5157
Baretz, Anne, 5344
Barfield, Thomas J., 4012
Barfield, W. Lowrey, 8892
Barfield, W. Lowry, 8893
Barge, William F., 2592
Barger, Carol, 8701
Barham, Carole A., 5715
Barham, Norman, 5715
Baright, Hollis I., 5070
Barillaro, Laura, 6265
Bariteau, James, 427
Barjesteh, Megan E., 9560
Barkan, Mel, 5909
Barkan, Mel P., 5802
Barke, Laurie, 427
Barkema, Evelyn, 3471
Barkema, Foster, 3471
Barker Inc., Bob, 7044
Barker Steel Co. Golf Tournaments, 8392
Barker, Albert P., 2665
Barker, Allan M., 5204
Barker, Anne E., 157
Barker, Brett D., 5136
Barker, Bruce S., 5346
Barker, Charles H., 157
Barker, Daryl S., 5346
Barker, Deborah L., 5136
Barker, Dorothy A., 5204
Barker, Douglas M., 5204
Barker, Francis H., 5346
Barker, Irene L., 5204
Barker, Jacky, 1964
Barker, Joanne S., 3890
Barker, John, 1368
Barker, Leslie M., 3132
Barker, Mary L., 157
Barker, Patricia M., 7044

Barker, Peter K., 5716
Barker, Robert J., 7044
Barker, Robert J., Jr., 7044
Barker, Robin B., 5716
Barker, Thomas B., 5128
Barker, Walter, 5204
Barker-Sayce, Dian, 9709
Barkhurst, William J., 759
Barklage, Ferrol, 5071
Barklage, Oliver, 5071
Barkley Enterprises, 9
Barkley, Charles, 9
Barkley, Jan Schmidt, 7813
Barksdale, Heather, 4879
Barksdale, Kathleen M., 2576
Barkus, Paul R., 5283
Barland, Jill, 9814
Barley, Craig H., 3126
Barlow, Julie, 1816
Barlow, Stewart E., 9361
Barmada, Riad, 2771
Barna, Janet, 5104
Barnard, David, 9231
Barnard, E.H., 1866
Barnebl, David A., 6638
Barneby, Kenneth A., 2368
Barnes, Bill, 3359
Barnes, Bruce, 7452
Barnes, Carlyle F., 1404
Barnes, Carolyn, 7276
Barnes, Fuller F., 1404
Barnes, Harry Fuller, The , 1403
Barnes, James E., 7659
Barnes, Joan W., 1404
Barnes, Marsha K., 7658
Barnes, Mary M., 7659
Barnes, Michael G., 5718
Barnes, Myrtle I., 1404
Barnes, Robert, 9148
Barnes, Steve, 585
Barnes, Thomas O., 1403
Barnes, William C., 7658
Barnet, Geoff, 1694
Barnet, Howard, Jr., 1694
Barnet, Jane, 1694
Barnet, Peter, 1694
Barnet, Saretta, 1694
Barnett, Betty B., 2903
Barnett, Billie, 7660
Barnett, Eliot B., 8718
Barnett, Florence L.J., 7660
Barnett, Gary, 5794
Barnett, Glen C., 278
Barnett, Howard G., 7660
Barnett, Howard G., Jr., 7660
Barnett, John, 1599
Barnett, John W., 1427
Barnett, Louis, 8718
Barnett, Louis H., 8718
Barnett, Madlyn, 8718
Barnett, Preston B., 62
Barney, Michael E., 9457
Barneycastle, Melinda, 9213
Barnhardt, Thomas, 7202
Barnhart, Florence V.M., 7626
Barnhisel, Lana, 3340
Barnsley, Emma, 7091
Baroco, J. H., III, 1867
Baroco, James H., Sr., 1867
Baroco, Julie M., 1867
Baroco, Ronald Anthony, 1867
Baroco, Vicki Ann, 1867
Baron Technology, 3991
Baron, Arthur, 4497

Baron, Dave, 3991
Baron, Frank J., 1169
Baron, Harold M., 2801
Baron, Jami, 4973
Baron, Kathryn Lazarus, 7493
Baron, Marjorie A., 2277
Baron, Paula L., 2801
Baron, Tracy, 1611
Barone, Richard, 7330
Barone, Steve, 783
Barosko, Allison G., 4698
Barosko, James, 4698
Baroway, Richard, 7811
Barr Residuary Trust, George, 2720
Barr, Charles C., 3646
Barr, David S., 6316
Barr, J. McFerran, II, 3646
Barr, John McFerran, 3708
Barr, Mary Louise, 3646
Barr, Nancy, 3446
Barr, Scott, 9191
Barr, Steven, 7572
Barre, Bart A., 5573
Barreca, Anne, 5927
Barreca, Hugo, II, 5927
Barreca, Laura, 5927
Barrentine, Gana Griffin, 30
Barrera, Agustin, 2150
Barrett, Caroline, 6832
Barrett, Charles F., 4846
Barrett, Don, 4846
Barrett, Donna, 5426
Barrett, Gene R., 4849
Barrett, John A., 9230
Barrett, Kate Waller, 9477
Barrett, Laura K., 3239
Barrett, Melinda, 4107
Barrett, Nancy, 4846
Barrett, Peter, 4007
Barrett, Richard, 4846
Barrett, Robert, 9345
Barrett, S. Katherine, 4846
Barrett, Thomas J., Jr., 1302
Barrett, William L.D., 6739
Barrett, Yvonne, 4796
Barrick Gold Finance, 5198
Barrientos, Robert, 4983
Barriere Construction Company, 4785
Barringer, Phil, 2367
Barringer, Terri C., 7255
Barrington, Arthur, 1868
Barrington, Bruce D., 1868
Barrington, Gayle M., 1868
Barrington, Kenneth, 1868
Barrionuevo, Helen J., 2193
Barron, David R., 7316
Barron, Eric, 4384
Barron, Guy, 4384
Barron, Guy L., 4384
Barron, Marc, 5193
Barron, Nora Lee, 4384
Barron, Ray, 8769
Barrow, Craig, III, 2619
Barrow, Diana D., 2619
Barrow, Elfrida Derenne, 2619
Barrow, Nellie Dell, 8719
Barrow, Thornton D., 2619
Barrow, Tommy, 2463
Barrows Foundation, Sidney and June, The , 2778
Barrows, Donna E., 2715, 2778
Barrows, Erin Lin Frautschy, 3304
Barrows, G.M., 4864
Barrows, Geoffrey M., 3304

Barrows, June H., 2778
Barrows, Linda Masters, 3304
Barrows, Robert Lewis, 2715, 2778, 3304
Barrows, Stephen H., 3304
Barrows, William H., 2715, 2778
Barry, Alelia, 3356
Barry, Ann E., 3622
Barry, Jean M., 3093
Barry, John, 3093, 3313, 9736
Barry, Linda, 3313
Barry, Micheal F., 8228
Barry, Shana, 4778
Barry, Timothy, 3093
Barry, William S., 7591
Bars Co., 8392
Barsamian, Anthony J., 4008
Barse, David M., 1763
Barsotti, Priscilla Ann, 9581
Barstow, David O., 4385
Barstow, Florence K., 4385
Barstow, Frederick E., 4013
Barstow, James F., 4013
Barstow, John C., 4013, 4385
Barstow, Robert G., 4385
Barstow, Thomas R., 4013
Barsumian, Bruce R., 8673
Bart Partners, LP, 1708
Bart, Lydia, 2370
Bartalini, Karen, 7794
Bartel, Harry, 3251
Bartell, James R., 3147
Bartell, Laurence A., 7490
Bartels, Carol, 764
Bartelt, James, 9912
Barten, Loren, 3567
Barth Memorial Fund, Louise K., 2705
Barth Memorial Trust, Louise K., 2705
Barth, Aneila, 279
Barth, Carin M., 8736
Barth, Deborah, 2146
Barth, Eugene F., 279
Barth, Todd F., 8736
Barth, Wayne, 3867
Barthelmes, Albert J., 7661
Barthelmes, Hedwig, 7661
Bartholomay, Virginia, 3272
Bartholomay, William C., 2721
Bartkowski, Fred J., 9868
Bartle, Allissa Zolla, 1216
Bartle, Nathalie, 8105
Bartle, Peter, 1216
Bartles, Beth, 4736
Bartleson, Caroline, 1076
Bartleson, Leslie S., 1076
Bartlett and Co., 4865
Bartlett, Barbara, 3969
Bartlett, Dede, 1615
Bartlett, Gilbert A., 9420
Bartlett, J. Dennis, 128
Bartlett, Jim W., 1615
Bartlett, John P., 5256
Bartlett, Margaret W., 5256
Bartlett, Marshall P., 5256
Bartlett, Martha B., 7904
Bartlett, Paul D., Jr., 4865
Bartlett, Stephen W., 5256
Bartley, John, 6023
Bartner, Beverly D.N., 1869
Bartner, Nicole, 1869
Bartner, Robert G., 1869
Bartolommeo, Robert, 1557
Barton Malow Company, 4386
Barton Trust, Barbara, The , 9280

Barton, Babcock & Blair, 5245
Barton, Edward S., 8385
Barton, Florence Lucille, 99
Barton, James F., 6652
Barton, Lola, 5954
Barton-Malow Enterprises, 4386
Barton-Navitsky, Elizabeth, 6082
Bartow, Edwin B., 6912
Bartsch, Chris, 4633
Bartsch, Noel R., 4270
Bartsch, Ruth, 2722
Bartz, Robert , 2149
Bartz, Veronica, 154
Barulich, Aaron, 280
Barulich, Jeanne, 280
Barulich, Lauren, 280
Barulich, Nathan, 280
Barulich, William, 280
Barulich, Zachary, 280
Barz, Richard J., 4468
Barzune, Lawrence, 9162
Basant LTDA, 4234
Bascom, C. Perry, 5005
Bascom, Charles E., 4338
Bascom, Christina M., 4338
Basden, Mildred V., 1119
Basha, Edward N., Jr., 93
Basha, Nadine K. Mathis, 93
Basha, Regine, 5691
Basham, Robert D., 1870
Bashas Benefit Golf Classic, 93
Bashas', 93
Basile, Silverio, 2109
Basile, Vincent D., 4211
Baskerville, H.M., Jr., 4776
Baskett, Charles E., 7013
Baskin, Jack, 281
Baskin, Peggy Downes, 281
Baskins, Randolph S., 7712
Baskins, Steven E., 7712
Basler, Donald N., 3300
Basler, Wayne G., 8584
Bass, Adm. Thomas E., III, 9488
Bass, Catherine Price, 8227
Bass, Harris D., 1086
Bass, John, 8197
Bass, Lee M., 8865
Bass, Michael A., 1929
Bass, Nancy Lee, 8865
Bass, Perry R., 8865
Bass, Ramona S., 8865
Bass, Robert O., 2723
Bassett Furniture Industries, 9391
Bassett, Betty, 7299
Bassett, Tom, 7829
Bassmajian, Zouhrab, 853
Bassman, Harley, 5721
Bassman, Lori, 5721
Bastian 2001 Trust, Edith J., 8322
Bastian, Aaron C., 3577
Bastian, Christine C., 3577
Bastian, Edith J., 8322
Bastian, Frank W., 9924
Bastian, H. Clay, 3577
Bastian, H. Marvin, 3577
Bastian, M. Clark, 3577
Bastian, Melanie, 158
Bastian, Melanie L., 9304
Bastien, Nellie J., 1872
Basy, Christopher, 7373
Batchelder Interim Trust, Anne, 5072
Batchelder, Anne, 5072
Batchelder, Anne Stuart, 5072
Batchelder, Edward, 5072

Batchelor, Sean, 912
Bates Associates LLC, 4594
Bates, Dave, 7558
Bates, George A., 2725
Bates, Henry G., 2724
Bates, John C., 7317
Bates, John C., Jr., 7317
Bates, Sarah J., 7317
Bates, William F., 7428
Batliner, Kevin, 2223
Bato, Doris Z., 4620
Bator, Thomas E., 4128
Batsel, Teresa Stamm, 3456
Batson, William, 8188
Battaglini, Denise, 8657
Battery Park Mgmt., 7008
Battey-Simon, Patrice, 4081
Battison, Chad, 3594
Battista, Francis, 399
Battle, A. George, 282
Battle, Alice Ann, 10
Battle, Daniel K., 282
Battle, Emily T., 282
Battle, William P., 10
Battle, William R., III, 10
Batzer, Annette, 7761
Baudhuin, Annette, 2726
Baudhuin, Mike, 2726
Baudhuin, Paul, 2726
Baudhuin, Tom, 2726
Baudo, Susan, 9899
Bauer, Andrea W., 9309
Bauer, Betsy, 5257
Bauer, Eddie, 2683
Bauer, Eric J., 9070
Bauer, Eric J., Mrs. , 9070
Bauer, Janet, 4449
Bauer, Jeff, 1616
Bauer, Jon, 1616
Bauer, Jon R., 1616
Bauer, Keith, 7774
Bauer, Kevin, 6748
Bauer, Laura, 1616
Bauer, Meredith, 5253
Bauer, Michael R., 9638
Bauer, Nancy A, 1616
Bauer, Nancy A., 1616
Bauer, Walter, 8889
Bauernfiend, Deanna, 3363
Baugh, Heather S., 9330
Baughn, Mike, 3634
Baulch Trusts, Viola S., 1873
Baulch, R.E., Jr., 1873
Baulch, R.E., Jr., Mrs. , 1873
Baulch, Robert, Jr., 1873
Baum, A. Earlene, 4387
Baum, Andrea Terzi, 5258
Baum, Dan, 7218
Baum, David, 6368
Baum, David L., 4387
Baum, David M., 5258
Baum, E. Harris, 8247
Baum, Elizabeth, 5722
Baum, Floyd, 4497
Baum, James, 1316
Baum, Jim, 3125
Baum, Jody L., 3241
Baum, Kenneth D., 3241
Baum, Larry, 6373
Baum, Larry R., 4387
Baum, Linda, 2727
Baum, Melvin R., 2727
Baum, Ruth, 5722
Baum, Terry L., 3241

Baum, Theodore B., 5722
Bauman, Debra L., 7622
Bauman, Steve, 213
Baumann Charitable Lead Trust, Hannah
  H., 5723
Baumann, Alison, 283
Baumann, Hannah H., 5723
Baumann, James S., 5723
Baumann, Peter, 283
Baumberger, Leroy, 3590
Baumgart, Melissa G., 6058
Baumstein, Barbara Lieb, 6398
Baumstein, Jeffrey, 6398
Baxter Healthcare Corp., 1180
Baxter, Frank E., 284
Baxter, Gerald M., 2005
Baxter, Harold J., 1874
Baxter, John, 4853
Baxter, Lonnie C., 2435
Baxter, Matthew, 284
Baxter, Richard, 181
Baxter-Heuer, Laura, 7307
Bay Alarm Co., 1177
Bay Cedar Charitable Trust, 1656
Bay Mgmt., 6859
Bay Trust, Moore, The , 3201
Bayard, Jane U., 6450
BayCare Health Systems, LLC, 9781
Bayer, David S., 4353
Bayless, William, 8700
Bayley, Bjorn, 9567
Bayley, Daniella, 9567
Bayley, David, 9567
Bayley, Jacquelin, 9567
Bayley, Jacquelin R.G., 9567
Bayley, N.P. Bjorn, 9567
Bayley, Reginald E., 412
Bays, Barbara M., 3093
Bayuk, Florence, 1875
BB&T Corp., 7045
BBL Carlton, LLC, 5724
BBL Construction Services, LLC, 5724
BBL Equinox At Tradition, 5724
BCDG LP, 153
BCL, LLC, 7292
BDP International, 7882
Be'Ramatahava, L'Yeladim, 5947
Beach, Debra, 3513
Beach, Jonathan T., 7855
Beach, Theodore T., 7855
Beach, Thomas C., Jr., 5725
Beach, Thomas E., 7855
Beach, Walter T., 7855
Beacon, Owen, 2749
Beadel, Bob, 8766
Beadel, James R., 8766
Beaird, Carolyn W., 1295
Beaird, Charles T., 1295
Beaird, Colleen C., 8720
Beaird, Harold, 8844
Beaird, Morgan E., 8720
Beaird, Pat C., 8720
Beal, Barbara, 4046
Beale, Deborah B., 6560
Beale, Ray, Jr., 9474
Beall SB-3 Trust, Sara M., 8862
Beall's, 1876
Beall's Department Stores, 1876
Beall, Beverly, 1876, 2286
Beall, Kenneth S., Jr., 4812
Beall, Lisa A., 2597
Beall, Robert M., II, 1876
Beall, S.M., 8862
Beals, Eleanore M., 100

Beals, Jason, 7339
Beals, Vaughn L., 100
Beals, Vaughn L., Jr., 100
Beamsley, Teresa, 4411
Bean, Claire, 4267
Bean, George, 5511
Bean, Jane Riskin, 5511
Bean, Pamela B., 8403
Beane, Rosa T., 5259
Beane, Silas Robert, III, 5259
Beane, Silas Robert, Jr., 5259
Beane-Bonomet, Maria E., 5259
Bear Stearns & Co., 5249
Bear, Julie, 5104
Beard, Brad, 4671
Beard, Eugene P., 5727
Beard, Gregory Scott, 5727
Beard, Nancy J., 5727
Beard, Nancy Jones, 5727
Bearden, Barry, 8721
Bearden, Dennis, 8721
Beardslee, Robert, 1904
Beardsley, James M., 6570
Beardsley, Karen, 3860
Beardsley, Lynne A., 1590
Beasley Trust, Emily T., 2728
Beasley Trust, Robert P., 2728
Beasley, Jane, 1877
Beasley, Mary Wood, 8522
Beatitude Foundation Inc., The, 2344
Beattie, William H., 289
Beatty-Buller, Sarah, 5800
Beauchamp, Chelsea, 8992
Beauchamp, Gary V., 8722
Beauchamp, Marian Wilfert, 8722
Beauchamp, Marie, 8263
Beaudoin, Roseann K., 8101
Beaudoin, Terry, 369
Beaver Excavating Co., The, 7606
Beaver, Bernie, 4671
Beazley, Hamilton, 8836
Beber, Candace Clark, 7807
Bechen, Peter F., 9643
Bechinski, Linda, 3372
Bechler River Partners, LLC, 4234
Bechmann, Mary, 699
Bechtel, Kay F., 9435
Bechtel, Stefan D., 9435
Bechtel, Stephen D., Jr., 952
Bechtel, Stephen, Jr., 1033
Becily-Hodes, Maria, 2974
Beck Foundation, 9393
Beck, Ann M., 9393
Beck, Avent G., 9393
Beck, Buddy G., 9392
Beck, Carol Morley, 4518
Beck, Carol Schulte, 5031
Beck, Charlotte V., 9392
Beck, David, 7724
Beck, John A., 1819
Beck, John C., 5728, 9393
Beck, John M., 2729
Beck, Larry, 1242
Beck, Louis S., 7319
Beck, Mardi, 1135
Beck, Michael S., 9392
Beck, Patty S., 7319
Beck, Robert J., 5031
Beck, Robnett, 1135
Beck, Rosemary, 1135
Beck, Ryan, 7319
Beck, Steven, 7319
Beck, T. Edmund, 5728
Beck, T. Edmund, Jr., 5728

Beck, T.E., III, 9393
Beck, T.E., Jr., 9393
Beck, Ted, 1330
Beck-Calcagno, Mary Jean, 9929
Becker Charitable Lead Annuity Trust, Richard E. & Lillian M., 1879
Becker Family Foundation, Newton & Rochelle, 291
Becker Unitrust, Gary E., 292
Becker, Bruce, 5156
Becker, Charles E., 6631
Becker, David, 291
Becker, Gary, 292
Becker, Heidi, 4437
Becker, Hugh C., 4636
Becker, Jane Cleaver, 5915
Becker, Jeffrey, 3472
Becker, Jo Ann, 1879
Becker, Kris, 9774
Becker, Laura Lee Baskerville, 4776
Becker, Lillian M., 1879
Becker, Marc, 6165
Becker, Margaret, 4026
Becker, Mary, 292
Becker, Newton D., 291
Becker, Paul, 3611
Becker, Richard E., 1879
Becker, Robert A., 4250
Becker, Rochelle, 291
Becker, Sharon, 3472
Becker, Stephen, Dr. , 1633
Becker, Terry R., 4776
Beckerdite, Luke, 9482
Beckett, John, 9772
Beckley, Jacqueline P., 6551
Beckman Corp., Camille, 2665
Beckman, Jacob, 5729
Beckman, Joel S., 5729
Beckman, Jolene, 3617
Beckman, Paul A., 2665
Beckman, Shari L., 5729
Beckman, Steven B., 5729
Beckman, Susan, 7430
Beckstrand, Carol B., 9324
Beckstrand, Jonathan, 9324
Beckstrand, Richard N., 9324
Beckwith, Edward J., 1994
Beckwith, F. William, 3473
Beckwith, G. Nicholas, III, 5730
Beckwith, Leola I., 3473
Beckwith, Page, 1935
Beckwith, Virginia P., 5730
Becon, Debra, 9565
Becthel, Lilly A., 9435
Becton, Henry P., Jr., 1880
Bedecccare, Albert, 480
Bedford, Jerry, 205
Bediones, Dolores, 2638
Bedke, Michael A., 1330
Bedwell, Nancy, 8043
Bee, Jill C., 8723
Bee, Ross B., 8723
Beebe, Cheryl K., 2987, 2988
Beebe, Mary L., 5691
Beebe, Merrell, 2223
Beebe, Susan P., 3685
Beech Street Holdings LLC, 6478
Beecher, Florence Simon, 7320
Beecher, Ward, 7321
Beecher, William, 5053
Beecherl, Louis, 8836
Beeck, Alberto, 1881
Beeck, Alberto Miguel, 1881
Beeck, Olga Maria, 1881

Beede, Russell S., 4310
Beef Promotions of Iowa, 3511
Beeghly, Bruce R., 2730
Beeghly, Nancy W., 2730
Beekman, Blaine, 7641
Beelman, Maud, 1826
Beer, Robert A., 1406, 1410, 1470
Beerhalter, Mary, 3564
Beerman, Mona Zacharia, 1601
Beernink, Howard, 3528
Beeson, Gerald, 2791
Beeson, Gerald A., 2791
Beetz, L. Elizabeth, 9794
Begg, Charles B., Jr., 9992
Beghini, Anna Mae, 8724
Beghini, Victor G., 8724
Beha, James A., 5988
Beha, Macy Ann, 5988
Behan, Mark L., 6082
Behler, Albert P., 6655
Behmann, Arno W., 8725
Behmann, Herman W., 8725
Behnke, Darrell W., 9816
Behrakis, Drake, 4015
Behrakis, George D., 4015
Behrakis, Margo, 4015
Behrens, Bobbette, 3527
Behrens, Christopher C., 5731
Behrens, Mary Taylor, 5731
Behroozi, Helga, 2954
Beim, John, 3607
Beim, Phyllis, 293
Beim, Sanford, 293
Beimfohr, Edward G., 6446
Beinecke Foundation, The, 1816
Beinecke, Frances G., 5662
Beinecke, Walter, III, 6560
Beinhorn, Esther, 7007
Beinhorn, Marvin, 7007
Beir, Joan S., 5732
Beir, Robert L., 5732
Beirele, Tami Lee, 6660
Beischer, David D., 7103
Beischer, Susan Fox, 7103
Beisel, Kenneth, 8060
Beiser, Janis W., 1617
Beiser, John T., 1617
Beitzel, John, 7623
Bejcek, Kim, 4533
Bejtra LLC, 5399
Bekins Co., The, 294
Bekins Distribution Center Co., 9252
Bekins Investments, 9252
Bekins, Jacqueline, 294
Bekins, Michael D., 294
Bekins, Milo W., 294
Bekins, Richard, 294
Belcher, Keith, 8806
Belchez, Chito, 4983
Belda, Alain, 8138
Belda, Alain J.P., 8138
Belden, Christopher, 5573
Beldin, Andrew E., 9676
Beldin, Lia G., 9676
Belefonte, Carmen P., 7953
Beley, James F., 1357
Belic, Ellen Stone, 3269
Belin, David W., 3512
Belin, James M., 3480, 3512
Belin, Joy Elizabeth, 3480, 3512
Belin, Laurie, 3480, 3512
Belin, Thomas Richard, 3480, 3512
Belitz, K.C., 5105
Belk Charitable Lead Trusts, Irwin, 7046

Belk Charitable Lead Unitrust CW, Irwin, 7046
Belk Charitable Lead Unitrust DB, Irwin, 7046
Belk Charitable Lead Unitrust IB, Irwin, 7046
Belk Charitable Lead Unitrust JW, Irwin, 7046
Belk Charitable Lead Unitrust MM, Irwin, 7046
Belk Charitable Lead Unitrust PB, Irwin, 7046
Belk Charitable Lead Unitrust SB, Irwin, 7046
Belk, Bill, 7046
Belk, Carl G., 7046
Belk, Irwin, 7046
Belkin, Amy, 7794
Bell Administrative Trust, Margaret L., 9963
Bell Charitable Lead Annu, Charles H., 4756
Bell Charitable Lead Annuity II, Philip, 8585
Bell Charitable Lead Annuity Trust, Charles H., 4631
Bell Country Expo., 1046
Bell Family Trust, 295
Bell Investments Limited Partnership, 7047
Bell Marc Admin. Corp., 6656
Bell, Bruce A., 9813
Bell, Carlos R., 9394
Bell, Carol H., 9813
Bell, Charles H., 4631, 4638, 4731, 4756
Bell, Constance L., 1883
Bell, David A., 3708
Bell, Evan D., 7048
Bell, Ford W., 4638
Bell, Hazel H., 8631
Bell, Heidi Cracchiolo, 4414
Bell, James E., 1883
Bell, James Ford, 4638
Bell, James M., 1059
Bell, Jane McNair, 7047
Bell, Jennifer, 5734
Bell, John, 4
Bell, John H., Jr., 6437, 6809
Bell, John McNair, 7047
Bell, Jonathan D., 7048
Bell, Julie Kay, 8548
Bell, Laura Schaefer, 7047
Bell, Malcolm, III, 2619
Bell, Margaret L., 9963
Bell, Margaret S., 9963
Bell, Martha A., 295
Bell, Mary Grady Koonce, 7047
Bell, Patricia S., 1882
Bell, Paula J., 9963
Bell, Ron H., 1882
Bell, Samuel H., Jr., 4638
Bell, Shannon C., 5494
Bell, Stacey K., 284
Bell, Stephen Helms, 615
Bell, Steve, 2919
Bell, Steven C., 9963
Bell, Steven D., 7048
Bell, Stuart M., 1883
Bell, Thomas, 5734
Bell, Victor E., III, 7047
Bell, Victor E., Jr., 7047
Bell, Walter W., 3063, 3190, 3355
Bell-Flynn, Kathleen, 295

Bellairs, Robert J., Jr., 2743
Bellamy, Corky, 3634
Bellange, Debbie, 1624
Beller, Ron, 297
Bellet, Edward, 8300
Bellet, Laura, 8300
Bellet, Sally, 8300
Bellick, Robert R., 2732
Bellick, Sheryl D., 2732
Bellinger, Roger, 2660
Bellini, J., 298
Bellini, Michael J., 298
Bellini, Patrick W., 298
Bellman, David H., 5232
Bello, Debbie, 425
Belloir-Fairgrieve, Kristell, 6123
Belloit, Jerry, Rev. , 7891
Bellot, Dario, 8269
Belo-Corp the Dallas Morning News, A.H., 8795
Belser, Mary R., 8543
Belskus, Jeffrey G., 3396
Belson, Jerome, 6655
Beltax Corp., 7132
Beltramo, Larry, 1155
Beltramo, Lisa, 1155
Belz, Jack A., 8585
Belz, Martin S., 8585
Belz, Philip, 8585
Belz, Ronald A., 8585
Belzberg, Lisa, 6906
Belzberg, Wendy, 1602
Bemiller, F. Loyal, 1546
Bemis Manufacturing Co., 9817
Bemis, Erin E., 9817
Bemis, Wendy, 9817
Benaroya, Linda, 5260
Benaroya, Raphael, 5260
Benaroya, Shirley, 5260
Benbow, Brian, 1260
Benbow, Louann, 1260
Benbow, Robert, 3346
Bench, Kathleen, 176
Bendele, Gerald, 9075
Bender Charitable Lead Trust, Matthew, IV, 5735
Bender, Beth, 4931
Bender, Dorothy G., 1789
Bender, Florence H., 1405
Bender, Grace M., 1789
Bender, Helen Hadjiyannakis, 6280
Bender, Howard, 6720
Bender, Jay S., 1789
Bender, Jeffrey P., 5735
Bender, Kurt, 4598
Bender, M. Christian, 5735
Bender, Matthew, IV, 5735
Bender, Morris, 1405
Bender, Morton A., 1789
Bender, Phoebe P., 5735
Bender, Susan, 6720
Bendich, Albert, 2733
Bendich, Pamela, 2733
Bendit, Charles R., 5736
Bendit, Karyn K., 5736
Bendon, Dorothy F., 5137
Bendon, James A., 5137
Bendon, John James, 5137
Bendon, Susan Kaylor, 5137
Benear, John B., 9320
Benear, John B., II, 9320
Beneche, Elizabeth R., 6004
Benedek, Barbara, 300
Benedek, Peter, 300

Benedict, Bruce O., 7339
Benedict, Davis M., 1884
Benedict, Jennifer, 1628
Benedict, Laura G., 6099
Benedict, Nancy H., 1884
Benedict, Peter B., 1884
Benedict, Peter B., II, 1884
Benedict, Samuel, 7450
Benenson Capital Funding, 6655
Benenson Capital Partners, 6655
Benenson, Lawrence, 6655
Benerofe, Froma, 5719
Beneto, Darlene J., 301
Beneto, Stephen T., 301
Benglis, Lynda, 6114
Benhaim, Andre, 6820
Benjack, Claire K., 9482
Benjamin, Adelaide Wisdom, 3761
Benjamin, Arthur E., 9305
Benjamin, Ben, 5624
Benjamin, Joseph, 9305
Benjamin, Laurie A., 4957
Benjamin, Ned, 3761
Benjamin, Stuart, 3761
Benjamin-Brown, Hether, 8759
Benka, Carla, 1539
Benkert, Jerome A., Jr., 3450
Benna, Bruno, 5138
Benna, Edna B., 5138
Bennee, Cameron, 9331
Bennee, Kaira, 9331
Benner, Gene, 3796
Bennet, Kat Bradley , 8009
Bennett, Andy, 4806
Bennett, C. Eugene, 1618
Bennett, Carl J., 6062
Bennett, Carolyn E., 8112
Bennett, Christopher F., 8112
Bennett, Eleanore, 7860
Bennett, Elizabeth, 615
Bennett, Geoffrey T., 8112
Bennett, Gerald, 6033
Bennett, Glen Philip, 5607
Bennett, Jay L., 4806
Bennett, Jean, 2881
Bennett, Joanna, 4186
Bennett, John R., 2570
Bennett, John T., Jr., 1898
Bennett, Karl E., 1618
Bennett, Laura S., 5906
Bennett, Margie, 3474
Bennett, Michael L., 3474
Bennett, Ned W., 5607
Bennett, Pat, 9414
Bennett, R. Taylor, 5165
Bennett, Robert G., 9414
Bennett, Rodney K., 5660
Bennett, Shalini, 7233
Bennett, Shalini R., 7233
Bennett, Thomas L., 8112
Bennett, Twila, 7796
Benningfield, Elaine, 8789
Bennington, Kristi, 3125
Benoit, D. Ben, 1418
Benovitz, Lee, 3690
Benser, Bob, 4499
Bensink, Edith T., 5675
Benson, Andrew, 4559
Benson, Barbara F., 4559
Benson, Bill W., 3956
Benson, Brent, 4844
Benson, Brooks D., 1620
Benson, Cliff, 5799
Benson, Craig R., 4016

Benson, Craig T., 3356
Benson, Cynthia C., 1229
Benson, Dave, 1230, 4419
Benson, Denise A., 4016
Benson, Erik B., 1229
Benson, Jack, 1620
Benson, Jefferey S., 9506
Benson, Kiersa J., 1229
Benson, Kris, 3817
Benson, Laurie, 8576
Benson, Mary-Alice, 902
Benson, P. Bruce, 1230
Benson, Richard, 3421
Benson, Robert S., 1229
Benson, Roger, 2802
Benson, Sarah J., 404
Benson, Suzanne R., 9205
Benson, Teresa, 9098
Benson-Brown, Polly, 1230
Bentler, Mary Ellen, 8345
Bentley, Barton, 5475
Bentley, Kevin, 4960
Benton, F. Fox, III, 8726
Benton, John, 8556
Benton, Lucia, 8726
Benton, Lurner O., III, 2445
Benton, Lurner O., IV, 2445
Benton, Margaret, 2148
Benton, Monica K., 8726
Benton, Nancy T., 2445
Bentwood Family LP, 9348
Bentz, Arnold, 4735
Bentzen, Anne H., 6228
Benun, Morris C., 5261
Benun, Raymond M., 5261
Benun, Susan, 5261
Benz Charitable Remainder Unitrust,
    8018
Benz, Derek, 4702
Benz, Doris L., 4017
Benz, Margaret L., 7861
Benz, William, 4582
Bequette, Jim, 3991
Bequette, Mary Batchelder, 5072
Beracy, Rick, 4534
Berbee, James G., 9782
Berbee, Karen A., 9782
Berber, Donna, 8689
Berber, Philip, 8689
Berber, Ryan, 8689
Berber, Shane, 8689
Berckmann, Warren, 1624
Berding, John, 7322
Berding, Susan, 7322
Bere, Barbara L., 2734
Bere, Barbara V., 2734
Bere, David L., 2734
Bere, James F., 2734
Bere, James F., Jr., 2734
Bere, Robert P., 2734
Berelsman, David W., 1885
Beren Foundation, Robert M., The , 654
Beren, David, 1231, 1233
Beren, Sheldon K., 1231
Beren, Zev, 1231, 1232
Berens, William J., 4813
Berenson, David A., 5774
Beretta U.S.A. Corp., 3991
Bereuter, Honorable Douglas, 5105
Berg, Benjamin, 6098
Berg, Daniel, 6098
Berg, Donal, 8741
Berg, John A., 4809
Berg, Kristen A., 4809

Berg, Leon, 1066
Berg, Miriam, 6929
Berg, Nancy, 4809
Berg, Patricia, 5675
Berg, Sherman, 5074
Bergard, Carl A., 1174
Berge, B.B., 1863
Berge, David, 7294
Bergen, Linda, 9797
Bergen, William W., 9488
Berger Foundation, H.N. and Frances C.,
    1162
Berger, Barry S., 6211
Berger, E. Edith, 4018
Berger, Eva E., 4018
Berger, Eve Edith, 4018
Berger, Harold, 7862
Berger, Harold D., 2509
Berger, Harvey J., 4018
Berger, Jessoca, 7356
Berger, Leo V., 3821
Berger, Nancee Shannon R., 5128
Berger, Renee, 7862
Berger, Richard L., 8263
Berget, Jeff, 1316
Bergford, Dawn, 2944
Bergford, Jeffrey, 2944
Berghoef, Henry, 3146
Berghoff, Robert A., 3232
Berghorst, Alexander, 1619
Berghorst, Barb, 4736
Berghorst, David T., 1619
Berghorst, Deborah H., 1619
Berghorst, Linda E., 4527
Berghorst, Linda Ellen, 4527
Berghorst, Lisa Hinckley, 1619
Berghorst, Ryan, 4527
Berghorst, Sarah, 1619
Berglund, Anders, 9590
Berglund, Eric W., 303
Berglund, Janet, 9590
Berglund, Kenneth J., 4640
Berglund, Lisa, 286
Berglund, Sandra, 303
Berglund, Steven, 303
Berglund, Wesley E., 4640
Bergman, Alice, 4503
Bergman, Cordelia, 7863
Bergman, Garrett E., 7847
Bergman, James R., 304
Bergman, Judy G., 304
Bergman, Justin, Jr., 7863
Bergman, Robin, 1402
Bergman, Thomas, 5580
Bergman-Rallis, Mary Lynn, 951
Bergner, Michele L., 1651
Bergner, William S., 1651
Bergquist, Scott, 1038
Bergsma, Nancy, 4613
Bergsma, Nancy E., 4613
Bergson, Simon, 5738
Bergson, Stefany, 5738
Bergstein, Adam, 2735
Bergstein, Bertini, 2735
Bergstein, Melvyn, 2735
Bergstein, Seth, 2735
Bergstrom Climate Systems, Inc., 2736
Bergstrom Inc., 2736
Bergstrom Manufacturing Co., 2736
Bergstrom, Ashley F., 7864
Bergstrom, Craig A., 4019
Bergstrom, Debora, 8727
Bergstrom, Gary L., 4019
Bergstrom, Henry A., 7864

Bergstrom, Henry A., Jr., 7864
Bergstrom, Joan L., 4019
Bergstrom, John, 8490
Bergstrom, Margaret A., 7864
Bergstrom, Stephen W., 8727
Bergstrom, Wayne, 8727
Berguland, Kari D., 303
Berhendt, June, 440
Berk, Celia, 224
Berk, Tony B., 6578
Berkas, Ernest, 1288
Berkeley Philathropies Ltd., 1455
Berkeley, Ralph, 9233
Berkenstadt, James A., 2815
Berkenstadt, Rebecca, 2815
Berkley, Amy C., 1297
Berkley, E. Bertram, 5019
Berkley, Richard L., 5019
Berkley, William, 5019
Berkline Corp., The, 5304
Berkman, Deborah L., 7324
Berkman, Ellen F., 7324
Berkowitz, Alan, 7865
Berkowitz, Arthur M., 7865
Berkowitz, Barbara R., 7865
Berkowitz, Bernard S., 5451
Berkowitz, Daniel M., 7865
Berkowitz, Edwin J., 7865
Berkowitz, Ettil, 3970
Berkowitz, Hershel, 3970
Berkowitz, Jack, 5872
Berkowitz, Jeffrey, 1886
Berkowitz, Louis, 5739
Berkowitz, Nathan L., 285
Berkowitz, Pearl S., 285
Berkowitz, Richard, 1886
Berkowitz, Yolanda, 1886
Berkshire Hathaway Inc., 305, 3764,
    3897, 6806, 8393
Berkson, Daniel, 3036
Berkson, Kay, 3036
Berlin, Alice, 4388
Berlin, Carter F., 101
Berlin, Howard R., 101
Berlin, Howard R., Jr., 101
Berlin, Howard R., Sr., 101
Berlin, Jack, 306
Berlin, Jeffrey H., 306
Berlin, Joy M., 101
Berlin, Marvin, 4388
Berlin, Mary E., 306
Berlin, Rabbi Chaim, 7000
Berlin, Sheila, 306
Berlin, Thomas, 4426
Berlin, William E., 4388
Berlinger, Patricia, 5357
Berman, Bertha Dagan, 8118
Berman, David I., 7950
Berman, Edwin M., 3052
Berman, Elaine Gantz, 6056
Berman, Farley L., 8587
Berman, Marc H., 7950
Berman, Marc L., 3250
Berman, Michael, 4503
Berman, Michael P., 4503
Berman, Philip, 5476
Berman, Sharen, 3250
Berman, Sharon, 9501
Berman, Sheri, 5711
Berman, Sherrill, 4503
Bermas, Stephen, 1422
Bermingham, Linda, 4410
Bermudez, Alejandro, 9033
Bernacki, Robert, 1920

Bernard Oster, 5484
Bernard, A.B., 8869
Bernard, Cathy S., 3822
Bernard, Diane Staley, 8296
Bernard, Ginger , 471
Bernard, James H., 4901
Bernard, James H., Jr., 4901, 4948
Bernard, James H., Sr., 4948
Bernard, Pat Palmer, 6573
Bernard, Ralph L., 7325
Bernard, Ralph L., Jr., 7325
Bernard, William J., 3779
Bernardin, Thomas, 2769
Bernath & Rosenberg PC, 6930
Bernath, James H., 6930
Bernath, Susi, 6930
Berndt, Anne, 9380
Berndt, Arthur, 9380
Berndt, Richard O., 3816
Berne, Carol, 4735
Berner, Anthony, 6385
Bernfield, Craig, 2737
Bernfield, Craig M., 2737
Bernfield, Donna, 2737
Bernhard Foundation, The, 5741
Bernhard, Adele, 5635
Bernhard, Anna Wells, 5635
Bernhard, Jessica W., 5635
Bernhard, Michael, 5635
Bernhard, Steven, 5635
Bernhard, William L., 5741
Bernhardt Trust, Bertram L., The , 8387
Bernhardt, Anthony F., 1139
Bernhardt, Fred J., Jr., 9438, 9487
Bernheim, Charles A., 5740
Bernheim, Elinor K., 5740
Bernheim, Howard, 3978
Bernheim, Leonard H., Jr., 5740
Bernheim, Nelida, 2994
Bernheim, Rachel O., 5740
Bernheim, Stephanie H., 5740
Berning, Jane L., 1620
Berning, Paul, 802
Bernoudy Interim Trust, G., 2738
Bernstein & Co., Sanford C., 7141
Bernstein, Alan, Jr., 3897
Bernstein, Barbara K., 7049
Bernstein, Carolyn, 307
Bernstein, David, 307
Bernstein, Donald H., 7049
Bernstein, Douglas, 3897
Bernstein, Harold, 1518
Bernstein, Jane, 5489
Bernstein, Jeffrey, 307
Bernstein, Jonathan K., 1534
Bernstein, Laurel, 307
Bernstein, Leslie S., 308
Bernstein, Mark D., 2644
Bernstein, Marshal, 1611
Bernstein, Nina, 5630
Bernstein, Patricia, 307
Bernstein, Philip L., 308
Bernstein, Raphael, 5489
Bernstein-Mason, Shirley, 6308
Berol, Peter J., 7953
Berquist, Alice O'Brien, 4753
Berrett, Allen, 9319
Berrey, Julie A., 9328
Berry Companies, 3558
Berry, Anish, 5926
Berry, Archie W., Sr., 7867
Berry, Barbara, 7867
Berry, Bear, 3641
Berry, Bill, 309

Berry, Buddy, 9133
Berry, Charles D., 7490
Berry, David M., 2296
Berry, Deborah, 34
Berry, Derek W., 309
Berry, Elizabeth, 1588
Berry, Elizabeth J., 8633
Berry, Faith, 5226
Berry, Fred F., Jr., 3558
Berry, Gary, 34
Berry, Gary B., 34
Berry, Harold, 4596
Berry, Jacqueline L. Quern, 2888
Berry, Joanne, 309
Berry, Leah, 2803
Berry, Mark S., 306
Berry, Nella F., 309
Berry, Patrice E., 306
Berry, Robert R., 7867
Berry, Rodney, 3687
Berry, Sharon, 9133
Berry, Tristy, 7490
Berry, Viveca Ann S., 541
Berry, Waldron, 3448
Berry, Walter T., 3558
Berry, William F., 309
Berryhill, John A., 584, 731
Berryman, Hunt, 2222
Bersch, Neil, 1108
Berschback, Kathryn L., 8662
Bershad, Bradley J., 5262
Bershad, David J., 5263
Bershad, Elizabeth J., 5262
Bershad, Jeffrey, 5263
Bershad, Susan V., 5262
Bershad, William, 5263
Berson, Tom, 870
Bersted, Grace A., 8388
Bert, Kendall, 108
Bertacchi, Gary, 2811
Bertelsman, Arlene, 886
Bertelsmeyer, James, 7692
Bertha, Sandra Marriott, 3909
Berthelot, Anne, 6820
Bertholf, Teresa D., 1793
Bertsch Charitable Trust, 7050
Bertsch, Diane, 7050
Bertschy, Nannette, 4758
Berube, Neal, 9319
Berven, Blake, 7784
Berwind Corporation, 7868
Berwind, C. Graham, 7868
Berwind, Sandra, 7868
Beshara, David, 5230
Besharov, Douglas J., 3887
Besharov, Susan Hyman, 3887
Besl, James C., 7326
Besl, Joseph E., 7326
Besl, Lester J., 7326
Besl, Michael L., 7326
Beson Charitable Annuity Lead Trust, Robert J., 4389
Beson Charitable Trust, Beth Ann, 4413
Beson, Beth, 4413
Beson, Beth Ann, 4413
Beson, Elizabeth C., 4389
Bess, Barry R., 4455, 4494
Bess, Brian K., 1661
Besselman, Mary K. Crigler, 3726
Bessemer Charitable Reminder Unitrust, Mary Tilley, 6221
Bessemer Trust Co., 6897
Bessemer Trust Co., N.A., 6268
Bessemer Trust Company, 5202

Besser, Albert G., 5583
Bessie, Cornelia, 1407
Besson, Rebecca L., 3823
Best Buddies International, 4043
Best Buy, 684
Best Charitable Trust, Thilo M., 2739
Best Foods Educational Foundation, 2988
Best Trust, Jacob H., 2739
Best, Bryan, 2739
Best, Edith, 2740
Best, Eileen, 6585
Best, Michael, 3172
Best, Peter, 2739
Best, Thilo H., 2739
Best, Walter, 2740
Beswick, Julie, 3567
Beta II Marketing Corp., 6344
Betancourt, Shelly, 4534
Bete Fog Nozzle, 4088
Beten Imports Inc., 4390
Betesh, Elliot, 5743
Betesh, Michael, 5743
Betesh, Norma, 5743
Betesh, Sol E., 5743
Betesh, Steven, 5743
Betgold, 5743
Betgold International, 5743
Beth Oloth, 5794
Beth, Becky J., 9931
Beth, Richard E., 228
Bethel Performing Arts Ctr., The, 1046
Bethke, Robert W., 9566
Bethke, Suzanne, 9566
Betten, Ann, 3854
Betten, Gregory, 4390
Betten, Marion, 4390
Betten, Marlene, 4390
Betten, Rodney, 4390
Bettendorf, Phil, 2437
Bettenga, Joanne, 4739
Betters, Bruce J., 9931
Bettigole, Bruce J., 8428
Bettingen, Burton G., 310
Bettis, Mary Yale, 8475
Betts Industries, 7869
Betts, C.R., 7869
Betts, Elizabeth W., 9550
Betts, Ira, 8986
Betts, James T., 1522
Betts, Jarre Barnes, 1403
Betts, Jessica E., 5744
Betts, Lois P., 5744
Betts, M.J., 7869
Betts, Margaret W., 5744
Betts, R.E., 7869
Betts, Richard T., 7869
Betts, Roland W., 5744
Betts, T.E., 7869
Betz, Albert L., 2441
Betz, Judy, 4551
Betz, Kenneth, 4551
Betz, Stacey Knutzen, 9696
Betzler, Colleen, 5466
Beusse, Blake, 4543
Beusse, Heather, 4543
Beusse, Margaret, 4543
Beuttenmuller, David, 2407
Bevans, James P., 9029
Bevier, Carol E., 7384
Bevier, John E., 7384
Bevil, Jonathan, 9189
Bevilacqua, Mellie, 8869
Beyer, Andrew Owen, 3160

Beyer, Howard, 7294
Beyerlein, David, 4616
Beyerlein, David A., 4522
Beyman, Debbie, 7000
Beyman, Ezra, 7000
Beynon, Kathryne, 312
Beys, Froso, 6280
Beyster, John Robert, 520
Beyster, John Robert, Dr. , 520
Beyster, Mary Ann, 520
Bez, Nicholas J., 9658
Bezdek, Lynda, 1216
Bezdek, Patrick, 1216
Bezirgan, Brittney, 2180
Bezirgan, Yasir, 2180
BFT Carriers, 5140
BGK Equities II, LLC, 5616
BGK Property Mgmt. LLC, 5616
BGKP Properties, 5616
Bhappu, Candy L., 1234
Bhappu, Elizabeth M., 1234
Bhappu, Katherine L., 1234
Bhappu, Ross R., 1234
Bharat, Krishna, 1621
Bhargava, Rajat, 9695
Bhatia, Anu, 1768
Bhatia, Jyothi, 1768
Bhattacharya, Rasmani, 1368
Bhutada, Kiren, 8730
Bhutada, Ramesh, 8730
Bhutada, Rishi, 8730
Bialek, Hilton, 305
Bialek, Roberta Buffett, 305
Bialis Trading, 313
Bialis, Ellen G., 313
Bialis, Gary C., 313
Bialis, Jonathan G., 313
Bialkin, Kenneth J., 6949
Bianco, Joseph, 7370
Bianco, Lindsay, 7370
Bianco, Ronni Silverman, 2337
Biane, Rene, 882
Bibber, Richard V., 3786
Bible Believers of Lima, 7372
Bible, Glen, 8937
Bibliowicz, Jessica, 6949
Bibliowicz, Tommy, 6949
Bice, Ashley, 3344
Bice, Brenda K., 8629
Bice, William B., 5788
Bich, Bruno, 5669
Bickel, Bruce, 7848
Bickell, Helen H., 8067
Bickerton, James J., 2297
Bickford, Andrew G., 5205
Bickford, Benjamin, 5205
Bickford, Charles G., 5205
Bickford, John H., 5205
Bickford, John H., Jr., 5205
Bickford, Lydia B., 5205
Bickford, Tatyana, 5205
Bicknell, Kate H., 7327
Bicknell, Warren, III, 7327
Bicknell, Warren, Jr., 7327
Bicknell, Wendy H., 7327
Bicoy, Bret, 9810
Biddinger, Clay M., 1887
Biddle, Larry, 9465
Biddle, Mary Liz, 8046
Biddy, Ralph L., 5012
Bider, Leslie E., 314
Bider, Lynn, 314
Bidwell, Brian R., 2741
Bidwill, Charles W., Jr., 2741

Bidwill, Patricia M., 2741
Bidwill, Patricia S., 2741
Bieber, Julian M., 902
Bieber, William F., 4641
Biedenharn, Catherine Susan, 3713
Biedenharn, R.Z., 3713
Biedenharn, Sydney, 3713
Biederman Trust, Anne, 4391
Biederman, Anna R., 4391
Biederman, Lester M., 4391
Biederman, Paul M., 4391
Biederman, Ross, 4391
Bieger, Nell K., 8637
Bieger, Nell King, 9479
Biehl, Michele, 4497
Bieker, Dennis L., 3620
Biel, William H., 3585
Bielinski, Joseph, 9836
Bien, Marjorie, 9943
Bienenfeld, Helen, 7872
Bienenfeld, Henry, 7872
Bienenfeld, Jack, 7872
Bienenfeld, Michael, 7872
Bienfield, William H., 6084
Bierlein Companies, 4392
Bierlein Cos., 4392
Bierlein Demolition Contractors, 4392
Bierlein Environmental Services, 4392
Bierlein Services, 4392
Bierlein, Michael D., 4392
Bierlein, Ryan, 4392
Bierman, Kathy, 5992
Bierman, Kathy Fein, 5992
Bieser, Irvin G., Jr., 7610
Bieser, Jerry, 726
Bietler, Charles E., 4432
Biffar, Joyce S., 8195
Biffar, Travis S., 8195
Big Rock Sport, LLC, 3991
Big Y Foods, 4064
Bigelow Inc., R.C., 1408
Bigelow, Cynthia R., 1408
Bigelow, David C., 1408
Bigelow, Eunice J., 1408
Bigelow, Lori, 1408
Biggs, A. Ray, 8539
Biggs, Franklin B., 1641
Biggs, Margaret Cooper, 22
Biggs, Sewell C., 1641
Bigler, Deborah Kampen, 5413
Bigley, Thomas C., Jr., 3425
Biglow, Timothy B., 4358
Bignon, Bernard H., 8512
Bignon, Edward L., 8512
Bihn, Kenneth, 7368
Bihn, Robert, 7368
Bihn, Timothy, 7368
Bijou, Albert, 5264
Bijou, Joseph, 5264, 5327
Bijou, Renee, 5264
Bikubenfonden, 5746
Bilak, Dorian, 317
Bilak, Dorian Frances, 317
Bilak, Frances, 317
Bilak, Milton, 317
Bildirichi, David, 6199
Bill Hick & Co., 3991
Billig, Aaron, 5265
Billig, Gail, 5265
Billig, Gail A., 5265
Billig, Sali, 5265
Billing, David B., 9933
Billingham, Robert I.C., 998
Billings, Eric, 9397

Billings, Marianne, 9397
Billings, Tricia, 8133
Billingsley, Andrew, 9236
Billington, Robert, 8447
Billowitz, Edgar, 5247
Bills, Janey, 9147
Billstrand, Barbara J., 9398
Billups, Carol, 9271
Bilodeau, Ken, 4410
Bilstein, Dick, 5127
Bindeman, Stuart L., 3844
Binderman, Daniel, 5655
Binderman, Gail, 5655
Bingham Foundation, William, The ,
    7414, 7415
Bingham, Sallie, 3669
Bingham, W. Richard, 5747
Bingham, Winifred W., 5747
Binion, Jack, 5139
Binkhorst, Audrey, 6415
Binkhorst, Gordon, 6415
Binkhorst, Mark, 6415
Binkhorst, Sonja K., 6415
Binkley, Ken, 5610
Binkow, Maurice S., 4453
Binns, David, 520
Binns, Hugh, 3623
Binswanger, Louisa, 546
Binz, Donald, 4945
Binz, Margaret R., 1888
Birchard, Rosemary, 8101
Bircumshaw, Colin, Rev. , 1544
Bird License Plates Program, 3817
Bird, James G., 4260
Bird, Mary Lynne, 1816
Bird, Terry, 1117
Bird, Walter M., III, 4260
Birdsey, Barbara U., 4236
Birdsey, Charles J., 4236
Birdsong, Robert T., 1274
Birdsong, Teresa R., 1274
Birk, Kathleen A., Dr. , 9398
Birk, Mary L., 9398
Birk, Roger E., 9398
Birkelbach, John, 9066
Birker, Craig C., 902
Birkins, David A., 1590
Birmingham Hide & Tallow, 11
Birnbaum, Caroline, 5975
Birnbaum, Egon, 5751
Birnbaum, Ezra, 5975
Birnbaum, Irwin, 5752
Birnbaum, Milton, 5752
Birnbaum, Moshe, 5975
Birnbaum, Sylvia, 5752
Birnbaum, Telsi, 5751
Birnhak, J. Robert, 7873
Birnhak, Marilyn J., 7873
Birnschein, Alvin, 9783
Birnschein, Marion, 9783
Biros, Andrew, 7924
Bisco, 2742
Bishop, Andre, 6323
Bishop, Arthur Giles, 2743
Bishop, Ashley Nicole, 9318
Bishop, Brandon J., 9302
Bishop, Brent L., 9302
Bishop, Bryan, 9302
Bishop, Byron D., 9569
Bishop, Cheryl, 9696
Bishop, David, 498
Bishop, David B., 9302
Bishop, Debbie, 8869
Bishop, Ed, 9191

Bishop, Jamie, 9302
Bishop, Jill J., 9302
Bishop, John L., 1735
Bishop, Katherine J., 7874
Bishop, Margaret L., 6421
Bishop, Matthew, 9318
Bishop, Sheila M., 9569
Bishop, Shelia, 8533
Bishop, Suzanne, 8501
Bishop, Thomas C., 7874
Bishop, Timothy R., 7752, 7753
Bishop, Tricia, 4720
Bishop, Trudie, 7874
Bishow, Charles J., 3873
Bisio, Gabriel, 1437
Bissell, Gail, 8501
Bissett, William J., 215
Bisticer, Eliza, 6425
Bistline, Sharon, 1248
Bistricer, David, 6222
Bistricer, Eliza, 6425
Bistricer, Elsa, 6425
Bistricer, Moric, 6425
Bitar, Sam, 4353
Bitner, Donna, 5129
Bito, Laszlo, 5753
Bitter, Laurie A.Z., 2821
Bitter, Mark, 3582
Bitting, Elizabeth S., 4275
Bitton, Karen Marie, 9350
Bitzer, Astrid S., 8004
Bitzer, John F., III, 8004
Bitzer, Michelle R., 8004
Bivins, Jeffrey, 2252
Bixby, Brian D., 4247
Bjelland, Nancy, 3125
Bjork, Annette, 4820
BJP Ventures, LLC, 4234
Blachford, Norman, 318
Black & J.H. Boone Foundation, L.A.,
    194, 8682
Black Hills Corp., 8556
Black Hills Service Co., LLC, 8556
Black Mountian Resources, 9496
Black, Archie C., 4642
Black, Christine, 4518
Black, Dameron, III, 2476
Black, Dameron, IV, 2476
Black, Dennis, 2919
Black, Donald G., Rev. , 9288
Black, Frederick H., 7258
Black, Gary, 176
Black, George, 1407
Black, Harry S., 5754
Black, Helene B., 4021
Black, James Floyd, 2476
Black, Jane Cocke, 2476
Black, Jeff, 221
Black, John B., 7499
Black, John L., Jr., 4825
Black, Myretta, 8658
Black, Noel, 1374
Black, Peter M., 7499
Black, Robert, 8390
Black, Robert S., 2904
Black, Rusty, 4946
Black, Samuel P., III, 7876
Black, Sandra M., 4825
Black, Susan, 2081
Black, Susie Bracht, 9168
Black, Suzanne, 6916
Black, Thomas F., III, 8434
Blackburn, Marcia Ross, 2015
Blackburn, William Ross, 2015

Blackburn, William W., II, 2015
Blackford, Kristen, 554
Blackie, Florence M., 319
Blackie, Heather, 319
Blackie, Heidi, 319
Blackman, Bryce, 196
Blackman, Chad, 5139
Blackman, Dennis, 5116
Blackman, John, 5755
Blackman, John N., Jr., 5755
Blackman, Marie, 320
Blackman, Mark, 5755
Blackman, Mark W., 5755
Blackman, Radha, 595
Blackmon, Elaine O., 2440
Blackstone, Kathy C., 7401
Blackstone, Lisa, 3704
Blackwell, Cathy, 9097
Blackwell, Jessie L., 7717
Blackwell, Linda, 5409
Blackwell, Virgil, 5671
Blackwood, Sandra Lee, 8375
Blades, Margaret, 6357
Blades-Rodriguez, Virginia, 461
Blaesing, Janice, 3005
Blair & Co., William, 9386
Blair, Betsy, 8771
Blair, David J., 7938
Blair, Donna R., 1237
Blair, James R., 1237
Blair, Jim, 4962
Blair, Laura, 2041
Blair, Ronald J., 1237
Blair, Steven R., 1237
Blais, Robert H., 9641
Blake, Betsy B., 9302
Blake, Charlie, 8522
Blake, Karen, 1889
Blake, Karen S., 1889
Blake, Kathleen B., 723
Blake, Norman P., Jr., 1889
Blake, Steve, 408
Blake, Thomas G., 723
Blakeney, W. Carlyle, 2327
Blakeslee, Ann G., 1897
Blakeslee, Derek J., 1897
Blakley, Patricia, 8370
Blanchard Training & Development, 321
Blanchard, Andre, 541
Blanchard, Greg, 1242
Blanchard, Kenneth H., 321
Blanchard, Marcelle, 541
Blanchard, Marjorie M., 321
Blanchard, Maxine, 6820
Blanchard, Sofia, 1528
Blanchard, Tessie, Jr., 8026
Blanche Peck Charitable Remainder
    Unitrust, 9818
Blanchet, Patricia, 5775
Blanco, Eddie, 2329
Blanco, Odilo, 2457
Blanco, Pat, 1952
Bland, A. Stanley, III, 4868
Bland, Joe, 9290
Bland-Walsh, Hailee A., 3638
Blane, Jack B., 2970
Blaney, Thomas F., 6455
Blank Family Foundation, 1890
Blank, George W., 7859
Blank, Harriet I., 7859
Blank, John P., 4643
Blank, Karen L., 4643
Blank, Kimberly Morgan, 8178
Blank, Linda, 5011

Blank, Mark, 1890
Blank, Matthew S., 5756
Blank, Meredith L., 4643
Blank, Nancy L., 5756
Blank, Robert S., 5756
Blank, Samuel A., 5756
Blank, Tony, 1890
Blankenship Trust, 7729
Blankenship, Elizabeth Warren, 7729
Blanks, Gerald L., 8026
Blanksteen, David, 1891
Blanksteen, Goldie, 1891
Blanton, Darren, 8841
Blanton, Hilda Sutton, 1892
Blanton, Julie E., 8841
Blany, Carolyn E., 7969
Blascak, Lori B., 7986
Blasi, John R., 5283, 5332
Blaskey, Mark S., 8255
Blass, Barbara A., 9180
Blass, Gus, III, 213
Blass, Joseph, 4596
Blat, Cheryl, 4393
Blatchford, Laura A., 2086
Blatt, Elaine E., 4393
Blatt, John A., 4393
Blatt, Lee, 1893
Blatt, Leland D., 4393
Blatt, Sydell, 1893
Blatteis, Angela, 322
Blatteis, Daniel, 322
Blatz, Diana Gaede, 1055
Blauner, Peter, 5700
Blauwkamp, Carl, 4488
Blavatt, Jason, 3837
Blavatt, Jeffrey, 3837
Blavatt, Ronald, 3837
Blaylock, Elizabeth Eisold, 6849
Blazek, George, 5106
Blazek, George T., 5121
Blazek-White, Doris D., 1817
Blazey, Karen, 6559
Blechman Revocable Trust, Jean, 1894
Blechman, David, 1894
Blechman, Jean, 1894
Blee, Kristi A., 4780
Bleichroeder, A., 5826
Bleichroeder, S., 5826
Blend, Stanley L., 8870
Blenker, David, 3991
Blenko, Walter J., Jr., 8097
Blessing, Melissa W., 5635
Blevins, Kerrie, 4800
Blewett, Laura H., 3974
Blickhan, Jill Arnold, 2803
Blin, James L., 3476
Blin, Judy R., 3476
Blin, Randy, 3476
Blin, Randy A., 3476
Blin, Timothy L., 3476
Blinken Joint Account, 5757
Blinken, Alan J., 5757
Blinken, Allison, 5757
Blinken, Donald M., 5757
Blinken, Milt, 5757
Blinken, Robert J., 5757
Blisko, Elain, 7030
Blisko, Mark, 7030
Blisko, Mayer, 7030
Bliss, Barbara, 1578
Bliss, Cheryl, 5425
Blittersdorf, Alyssa L., 9365
Blittersdorf, David C., 9365
Blittersdorf, Evan D., 9365

Blittersdorf, Jan L., 9365
Bloch, Bernard L., 7878
Bloch, Raymond, 7878
Block Electric Co., 2745
Block, Abe, 9570
Block, Andrew K., 2746
Block, Barbara, 5759
Block, David R., 1624
Block, Diane M., 1624
Block, Freya, 5758
Block, James A., 5759
Block, John G., 2745
Block, Judith S., 2746
Block, Margaret S., 2746
Block, Martha, 9570
Block, Michael, 2745
Block, Nadia, 5758
Block, Patrick, 1624
Block, Peter M., 5759
Block, Philip D., III, 2746
Block, Richard H., 5758
Block, Richard L., 1624
Block, Shaun C., 2746
Block, Sidney, 9570
Block, Valerie M., 5759
Blodgett, Thomas H., Mrs. , 5760
Bloedorn, A.O., 1238
Bloedorn, C.F.W., 1238
Bloedorn, H.B., 1238
Bloedorn, J.H., 1238
Bloedorn, W.A., 1238
Bloedorn, Walter A., 1790
Bloem, Russell, 4408
Bloes, Martin, 8898
Blomenberg, Ralph, 3448
Blonstein, Esther Friedman, 8876
Bloom Charitable Lead Annuity Trust,
  Jamacha, 5403
Bloom Family 2009 Charitable Lead
  Trust, 5267
Bloom, Barry L., 6900
Bloom, Bradley M., 4171
Bloom, David, 5267
Bloom, Eric N., 4171
Bloom, Kara, 3033
Bloom, Kemery, 3033
Bloom, Mary, 7613
Bloom, Matthew R., 4171
Bloom, Myron, 6341
Bloom, Myron S., 2084
Bloom, Ruth, 5403
Bloom, Sam S., 1239
Bloom, Terrie F., 4171
Bloom, Whitney, 5267
Bloom, William, 5403
Bloomberg, Emma, 5761
Bloomberg, Georgina, 5761
Bloomberg, Michael R., 5761
Bloomberg, Susan E.B., 5761
Bloomfield, Margaret, 1186
Bloomington Acura, 4733
Blosser, Fred, 7442
Blossom, Dudley S., 7367
Blossom, Elizabeth B., 7414, 7415
Blossom, Kathryn F., 7367
Blount, Mildred W., 13
Blount, Tom, 7058
Blow, Pamela D., 8623
Blow, Robert B., 8623
Blowers, Alison, 1077
Blowers, Dorothy, 1077
Blowers, Steve, 7785
Bloxom, David E., 8731
Bloyd, Catherine Fox, 478

Blue Bell, 7053
Blue Cross of Northeastern
  Pennsylvania, 7879
Blue Deuce Ent., LLC, 1046
Blue Grass Comm. Foundation, 7333
Blue Ridge Services, 9496
Blue, Florida, 2005
Bluemke, Dorothy M., 9785
Bluemke, Duane H., 9785
Bluerock Capital, 5705
Blum Foundation, 6339
Blum, Alex D., 3825
Blum, Alvin H., 3825
Blum, Ari, 3825
Blum, Christine L., 7381
Blum, James, 3825
Blum, James D., 3825
Blum, Jennifer L., 8589
Blum, Lauren, 8589
Blum, Marc P., 3825
Blum, Mark, 1581
Blum, Marvin E., 9204
Blum, Mary J., 7381
Blum, Michael, 6709
Blum, Tracy A., 7381
Blum, W. Charles, 7381
Blume, Allen C., 5197
Blume, Casey, 3592
Blume, Elizabeth, 7582
Blume, Hazel, 5197
Blume, Hazel P., 5197
Blume, Robert, 9612
Blumenfeld, Jack, 1696
Blumenthal, Barbara, 6522
Blumenthal, David, 6522
Blumenthal, Jabe, 9689
Bluntzer, John Lloyd, 8725
BMJ Holdings, 9629
BMO Harris Bank, 2740, 2808, 2816,
  2831, 2859, 2900, 2920, 2954,
  3128, 3170, 3187, 3198, 3305,
  3326, 9894, 9906, 9913, 9922
BNG Management, 4701
BNS Family Trust, 1504
BNY Mellon, 2412, 2552, 6000, 6018,
  6202, 7849, 7854, 7858, 7861,
  7881, 7902, 7918, 7921, 7926,
  7939, 7957, 7967, 7968, 7972,
  7973, 7979, 7981, 7989, 8039,
  8045, 8055, 8058, 8059, 8070,
  8077, 8092, 8107, 8122, 8126,
  8130, 8147, 8174, 8200, 8234,
  8236, 8260, 8272, 8276, 8284,
  8286, 8302, 8321, 8334, 8339,
  8340, 8372
BNY Mellon Trust of Delaware, 7841,
  7970, 8025
Boa, Ray P., 1590
Boains, Douglas, 1552
Boak, Thomas B., 5257
Boand Marital Trust, 323
Boand, Catherine Jane, 323
Boand, Harry, Jr., 323
Boand, Nicole, 323
Boardman Charitable Lead Annuity,
  Jean, 7881
Boardman, Cynthia R., 7563
Boardman, Jean R., 7881
Bobak, Martin Cornelis, 5085
Bobb, John G., 1917
Boben, Linda, 4667
Bobins, Norman, 2747, 3151
Bobins, Norman R., 2786
Bobins, Virginia, 2747

Bobo, Ron, 2512
Bobrow, Edythe, 6739
Bobrow, Julia, 5765
Bobrow, Norman, 5765
Bocchino, Lisa Duda, 1983
Bochnovich, Peter, 8345
Bochnowski, James J., 325
Bochnowski, Janet A., 325
Bochnowski, Stasia M., 325
Bochnowski, Thomas J., 325
Bock Revocable Trust, John C., 9786
Bock, Carl J., 9786
Bock, Sharon L., 9786
Boddie Noell Enterprises Inc., 7055
Boddie, B. Mayo, 7054
Boddie, B. Mayo, Jr., 7054
Boddie, Mayo, Sr., 7055
Boddie, Michael W., 7054
Boddie, William L., 7054, 7055
Bodenhamer, Lee, 190
Bodenstein, Aric, 7030
Bodhi, Ven Bhikkhu, 5596
Bodie, C. William, 4836
Bodine, George, 5154
Bodine, James P., 7924
Bodnar, Andrew G., 4035
Bodner, Tim, 669, 985
Boeckman, Brad, 7666
Boedecker, K. Judson, 2221
Boeh, John, 5011
Boehm, Donna M., 2813
Boehm, Esther, 3826
Boehm, Hershel, 3826
Boehm, Howard M., 3826
Boehm, Ken, 7357
Boeing Co., The, 8733
Boerner, Richard, 1320
Boeschoten, Adrian P., 9571
Boeschoten, Anna M., 9571
Boeschoten, Paul A., 9571
Boettcher, Bill, 9810
Bogan, Ernest, 5668
Bogan, Jeffery S., 9033
Bogardus, Wayne E., 1764
Bogart, Martha, 6245
Bogart, Max, Dr. , 6245
Bogen, Stanley, 5668
Boger, Barbara C., 4023
Boger, Ethan, 7548
Boger, Jennifer B., 7258
Boger, Peter M., 6669
Boger, William P., III, 4023
Bogert, Carrol, 5879
Bogert, Jeremiah M., 6989
Bogert, Jeremiah M., Jr., 6989
Bogert, Margot C., 6989
Bogert, Millicent D., 6989
Boggess, Anna, 7826
Boggust, Paula Friedland, 5082
Bogle, David, 191
Bogle, Eve S., 7843
Bogle, John C., 7843
Bogle, Marilyn, 191
Bogle, Robert, 191
Bogner Trust, Charles, 7756
Bogoni, Irene, 5766
Bogoni, Paul, 5766
Bograd, Abe, 4870
Bohan, Jack, 427
Bohatch, John S., 6233
Bohemian Distributing Co., 2846
Bohm, Leona, 4871
Bohm, Leona Lee, 4871
Bohm, Milford, 4871

Bohman, John F., 8431
Bohman, Michael J., 7566
Bohnsack, Rob, 3511
Bohorad, James C., 8263
Boiling, Tim, 4082
Bois, Ken Du, 96
Boisi, Mark P., 6655
Boisseau, Gail, 3628
Boisvert, Jeanne, 9797
Boit, C-F David, 4155
Boix, Trino, 8065
Bokan-Blair, Marianne, 7938
BOKF, 7696
Bokoff, Steven L., 1438
Bokow, Barry, 6563
Boland, Joseph L., 2097
Bolano, Andres, Jr., 2150
Boldemann-Tatkin, Tracey, 630
Bolen, Ellen Stolzer, 3630
Bolen, Pamela A., 173
Boles, Joseph L., Jr., 2341
Boles, Penny, 3568
Bolick, Jerome W., 7056
Bolick, Judith L., 7056
Bolick, Linda B., 7056
Bolig, Ron, 7905
Bolinger, Martha, 4802
Bolling, Landrum R., 1807
Bollman, Milton W., 1249
Bolton, Betty Duane, 9295
Bolton, James L., 9295
Bolus, Paul P., 14
Bomberger, Andy, 2602
Bomberger, Frances N., 1896
Bon Appetit Danish, 804
Bonanno, Judith B., 7894
Bond, Bradford C., 9320
Bond, Ethelyn C., 3137
Bond, Jon, 3462
Bond, Walter, 1897
Bonder Irrevocable Trust, Seth, 4394
Bonder, Merrill, 4394
Bondy, Richard C., 2247
Bone Quality Research Institute, 9110
Bonhard, Mark, 7645
Bonn, Bernard, III, 4078
Bonn, Kelley R., 1552
Bonn, William A., 1952
Bonnell, Mary L., 6300
Bonner, Bonnie F., 2456
Bonner, Charles W., 326
Bonner, Clark J., 327
Bonner, Douglas W., 9144
Bonner, Elizabeth B., 326
Bonner, Gus, 326
Bonner, Hazel A., 8513
Bonner, Nancy S., 327
Bonner, T.L., 8513
Bonner, Teresa, 4698
Bonner-Cline, Christina, 326
Bonnie, Rodney M, 7596
Bonomi, Darby Furth, 540
Bontrager, Mahlon, 3412
Bonura, Michael, 5872
Bonvissuto, Donna, 7560
Boodro, Michael, 6075
Boogaard, Marcia, 3969
Boogaard, Thomas, 3969
Booher, Harry, 2108
Book, Holly, 563
Book, Hollyann, 563
Booker, Lewis T., 9526
Bookoff, Steven, 5742

Boone Jr. Charitable Remainder Unitrust, Hilary J., 3649
Boone, Alex, 3648
Boone, Charles E., 328
Boone, Daniel W., III, 2446
Boone, Daniel W., IV, 2446
Boone, Douglas, 3528
Boone, George N., 329
Boone, George N., Jr., 329
Boone, Hilary J., Jr., 3649
Boone, Joyce, 3081
Boone, Larry, 8608
Boone, Lynn, 8660
Boone, Mary Lou, 329
Boone, Merrie, 2446
Boone, Michele, 9703
Boone, Samuel A.B., 3649
Boone, Stephen K., 9703
Boone, Steve, 9703
Boone, Thomas H., 7817
Boone, Virginia M., 2446
Boor, Pamela, 9556
Boosalis, Dean J., 1326
Boote, Dana Larson, 5440
Booth Living Trust, Dorothy M., 8734
Booth, Brian G., 9643
Booth, David G., 8735
Booth, Debbie, 1928
Booth, Elizabeth, 6540
Booth, Lee, 4811
Booth, Lynn A., 487
Booth, Richard L., Jr., 9524
Booth, Suzanne Deal, 8735
Booth, Ulrika Rixon, 7223
Borch, Andrea W., 330
Borch, Christopher R., 330
Borchardt, Georges, 5700
Borcheck, Teresa W., 2123
Borcherding, Curt, 3991
Borczynski, Chester E., 6710
Borden, Neal D., 3871
Borden, Winifred, 3871
Borders, Gerry, 3744
Borders, William, 3443
Bordewick, Dianna, 9781
Borek, John M., Jr., 2484
Borer, Jeffrey, 6084
Borg, Bjorn, 6463
Borgcamp Ltd., 5085
Borgen, Dan, 9245
Borgen, Krista Truitt, 8817
Borges, Keith, 914
Borghi, Battista, 1180
Boring, Dorothy S., 8590
Boring, Kenneth E., 8590
Boring, Laura Lynn, 8590
Borkson, Elliot P., 2047
Borlinghaus, Scott R., 4907
Borman, Adam, 3767
Borman, Cornelius H., 3767
Borman, Donald, 3767
Borman, Elizabeth, 4644
Borman, Kate, 3767
Borman, Marvin, 4644
Borman, Matthew, 3767
Borman, Robert, 3767
Borman, Robert, Jr., 3767
Born, Jerry, 7357
Born, Ross J., 7885
Born, Wendy, 7885
Bornblum, Bert, 8591
Bornblum, David, 8591
Bornick, Sue, 9814
Bornstein, Joseph P., 2142

Bornstein, Lynn Harris, 2142
Bornstein, Richard, 8436
Bornstein, Richard J., 8436
Bornstein, Sandra, 8436
Borntraeger, Courtney B., 1612
Borod, Gerard I., 5839
Borodinsky, Louis, 6194
Borok, Jack, 331
Borok, Leonard, 331
Borok, Lois, 331
Borok, Robert, 331
Borok, Ronald, 331
Boronow, Anna M., 1585
Boronow, Gordon, 1585
Borowsky, Irvin J., 7886
Borowsky, Ned, 7886
Borreca, Gloria, 9129
Borsecnik, Katherine, 5329
Borthwick, Maribeth A., 961
Borthwick, William H., 961
Borton, Karl, 7637
Borton, Thomas, 7637
Borun, Anna, 7057
Borun, Harry, 7057
Borzi, Carol, 332
Borzi, Jay, 332
Borzi, William J., 332
Borzi, William Jay, 332
Bos, Mary Beth, 3347
Bos, Tony, 3347
Boscacci, Allan J., 333
Boscacci, Patricia A., 333
Boscia, Brandon J., 7887
Boscia, Donna L., 7887
Boscia, Jon A., 7887
Boscia, Nicole M., 7887
Bosen, John K., 4250
Boskofsky, Peter, 89
Bosl, Ginger, 9213
Bosque River Investments, 8720
Boss, Aldrich, 1955
Boss, Greg, 7847
Boss, Harlan, 4645
Boss, Linda, 4645, 9951
Boss, Mark H., 7519
Bossen, Connie Nickell, 7243
Bossen, Elliott G., 7243
Bosserman Revocable Trust, C.E., 2007
Bosserman Revocable Trust, Gladys, 2007
Bosserman, Nancy H., 2007
Bosserman, Richard E., 2007
Bosserman, Stephanie, 9514
Bost, Chris, 9065
Bost, Ruthanna Jolley, 2513, 2526
Bostic, Molly, 7276
Bostock, Anne Louise Zachry, 4395
Bostock, Kate, 4395
Bostock, Matthew, 4395
Bostock, Merilee, 4395
Bostock, Roy J., 4395
Boston Beer Co., The, 4399
Boston Foundation, 1467
Boston, Jennifer, 9136
Boston, Lorraine, 3766
Bostwick, Albert C., 5767
Bostwick, Albert C., Jr., 5767
Boswell Charitable Lead Trust, Lois K., The, 4872
Boswell Foundation, Amie, 4872
Boswell Foundation, Joe, 4872
Boswell Foundation, Johnathon, 4872
Boswell Foundation, Julie, 4872
Boswell House Ministries, 2261

Boswell, Barbara W., 2667
Boswell, Charlotte, 3446
Boswell, Frances, 9532
Boswell, J.G., II, 2667
Boswell, John Holly, 2261
Boswell, John J., 4872
Boswell, W.W., 425
Boswell, W.W., Mrs. , 425
Boswell-Healey, Sarah, 4754
Bosworth, Susan M., 3529
Bosworth, Wendy Reed, 9820
Bothe, Cathryn S., 9862
Bothmer, Leona, 5768
Bothwell, Julie, 4946
Botjey, Vicki J., 8345
Botkin, John, 3507
Botkin, Pat, 4410
Botsford, John, 7297
Botterman, Viola Ann Gammon, 3385
Bottimore, Elizabeth R., 9525
Botto, Gary E., 515, 1165
Bottom, Dorothy, 9526
Bottom, Raymond B., Jr., 9526
Bottomline Technologies,Inc., 2053
Bottoms, Dale, 5140
Bottoms, Gary T., 2463
Bottorff, 3535
Bottrall, David C., 4587
Botts, Patrick, 3421
Botwinoff, Neil E., 6946
Botzman, Lawrence J., 3657
Bouchard, Angelee F., 608
Boucher, Douglas, 9387
Boucher, Paul, 8403
Boudreau, Helen, 5244
Boudreaux, Sharon, 8754
Boukai, Akhram, 334
Boukai, Amer, 334
Boukai, Amer A., 334
Boukai, Issam, 334
Boukai, Ziad, 334
Boulanger, Carol, 5489
Bould, Eve H., 1838
Boulos Co., The, 3768
Boulos, Cheryl R., 3768
Boulos, Gretchen C., 3768
Boulos, Joseph F., 3768
Boulos, Stephanie J., 3768
Boult Cummings, LLP, Bradley Arant, 14
Bouma, John J., 171
Bound To Stay Bound Books, 2751
Bourdeau, Paul L., 1463
Bourgeois, Alain, 6630
Bourgeois, Alexander, 6630
Bourgeois, Claire, 6630
Bourke, Anita, 3587
Bourne, Carol A., 9854
Bourne, Richard P., 9854
Bourque, Katleen, 4299
Bousquet, Laurence G., 9453
Boustead, Douglas, 5632, 5769
Boustead, Michael, 5769
Bovin, Denis A., 5770
Bowden, Steve, 7209
Bowditch, Katherine, 4022
Bowditch, Louise J., 4022
Bowditch, Robert S., Jr., 4022
Bowe, M. Joseph, 1075
Bowen, Amanda J., 4133
Bowen, Elizabeth J., 7743
Bowen, Ethel N., 9737
Bowen, Franklin W., 9736
Bowen, Henry, 9737
Bowen, Jay, 4260

Bowen, Joan F., 9736
Bowen, Julie, 2803
Bowen, Kara J., 4133
Bowen, Peter G., 5300
Bowen, R. A., Jr., 2447
Bowen, R.A., Jr., 2447
Bowen, Richard, 4133
Bowen, Richard J., 4133
Bowen, Robert A., III, 2447
Bowen, Walter C., 7743
Bower Foundation, The, 4828
Bower, John D., 3593
Bower, Joseph B., Jr., 7929
Bower, Spencer, 3593
Bowers, Frances B., 9738
Bowers, Hugh R., 8736
Bowers, Ryn R., 8736
Bowes, Frederick M., II, 9921
Bowie, Arvelia, 9240
Bowler Charitable Lead Trust, 803
Bowler, Ann Martin, 803
Bowler, Francis, 803
Bowler, John, 803
Bowler, Nicole, 803
Bowles, Beatrice, 773
Bowles, C. Champian, 9427
Bowling, Ann J., 1409
Bowling, David J., 1958
Bowling, Gregory B., 8737
Bowling, Randall J., 8737
Bowling, Robert L., III, 8737
Bowling, Robert L., IV, 8737
Bowman, Joane Lappe, 7854
Bowman, Kathy, 4845
Bowman, Linda, 4555
Bowman, Lynn, 3039
Bowman, Marianne H., 2502
Bowman, Matthias B., 1625
Bowman, Mieke, 9433
Bowman, Paul, 4490
Bowman, Penny M., 1625
Bowman, S., 7449
Bowmer, Robert, 8949
Bowness, Suzanne Bruno, 17
Bowyer, Sara Willingham, 5589
Boxer, Leonard, 5772, 6656
Boxer, Steven, 5772
Boyajian, Vaughn, 4137
Boyce, Carole C., 4257
Boyce, Cathy, 9561
Boyce, Elizabeth W., 9936
Boyce, Iunia L., 9936
Boyce, Michael R., 4024
Boyce, Peter F., 4257
Boyce, Sandra, 1149
Boyce, Thomas C., 9936
Boyd Foundation, 5141
Boyd, Darnall W., 8514
Boyd, Dennis G., 1434
Boyd, Jeffrey, 1094
Boyd, Kevin M., 1434
Boyd, Mary, 8517
Boyd, Mary S., 2517
Boyd, Michael J., 1434
Boyd, Scott, 8517
Boyd, Steven, 9707
Boyd, Susan F., 8514
Boyd, Wiliam, 5156
Boydston, Adele M., 9572
Boydston, John, 7640
Boydston, Mark R., 9572
Boydston, Robert E., 9572
Boyer and Meyrovitz Foundation, 2253
Boyer, Dennis, 726

Boyer, Douglas M., 335
Boyer, Ethan T., 335
Boyer, Herbert W., 335
Boyer, Jeffrey, 4949
Boyer, John K., 5072, 5115
Boyer, Marigrace, 335
Boyer, Phoebe C., 5773
Boyett, Michael, 425
Boylan Trust, Helen S., 4873
Boylan, Elbert Elwyn, Jr., 4873
Boylan, Rebecca A., 2753
Boyle Desendants Charitable Lead Trust, 2754
Boyle, Barbara, 366
Boyle, Brian, 2754
Boyle, Gertrude, 7810
Boyle, Jay, 5582
Boyle, John, 366
Boyle, Kevin, 2754
Boyle, Lisa Fremont, 2891
Boyle, Michael, 2754
Boyle, Patrick J., 2754
Boyle, Theresa, 2754
Boymel, Rachel, 7329
Boymel, Sam, 7329
Boymel, Samuel, 7329
Boymel, Steve, 7329
Boynton, Dora C., 4025
Boynton, Edwin R., 7888, 8313, 8354, 8373
Bozarth, Glenn, 239
Bozman, Blake, 9173
Bozman, Blake P., 8846
Bozman, Lance, 8846
Bozman, Tara E., 8846
Bozorth, Louise M., 6739
BP Foundation, 81
Braaksma, Christopher, 2520
Brabson Trust, Evelyn, 4026
Brabson Trust, George, 4026
Brabson, Andrew, 4026
Brabson, Bennet, 4026
Brabson, G. Dana, Jr., 4026
Brabson, Jessica, 4026
Brabson, John, 4026
Brabson, Steve, 4026
Braccia, Elizabeth, 8501
Bracco, Michael, 272
Bracco, Sarah W., 3637
Brace Charitable Trust, W.J., 4874
Brace, Jack E., 7339
Bracewell, Bradley, 9243
Brachfeld, Jacob, 5474
Brachfeld, Mendel, 5474
Brachfeld, Tina, 5334, 5474
Brack, Denise, 8392
Brack, Kenneth B., 8392
Brack, Robert, 8392
Brack, Robert B., 8392
Brack, Virginia C., 8392
Brack, William H., 8392
Bracken, Julie H., 3792
Brackett, Susan E., 7726
Brackin, Ellen Kate B., 1
Brad Henry for Governor, 7715
Brad Peterson, Brad, 1098
Brada, Stephen, Dr. , 9781
Bradbury, Elizabeth W., 3331
Braddock, Lois C., 336
Braddock, Robert C., 336
Braddock, Robert C., Jr., 336
Brademas, John, 5774
Bradford Unitrust, Eleanor, 8592
Bradford, Bryan R., 8592

Bradford, Hilary, 5842
Bradford, James C., 8592
Bradford, James C., III, 8592
Bradford, Kevin L., 42
Bradford, Lillian R., 8592
Bradford, Margaret, 7764
Bradford, Peter R., 337
Bradford, Ruth, 337
Bradford, Sharon, 566
Bradford, Stephen C., 8446
Bradley Family Foundation, William E., 4647
Bradley Trust, Eleanor R., 1411
Bradley, Allan, 9346, 9347
Bradley, Beverly K., 3420
Bradley, Bill H., 3420
Bradley, Charles, Jr., 8009
Bradley, David J., 4647
Bradley, Diane, 3927
Bradley, Edward R., Jr., 5775
Bradley, Eileen, 9382
Bradley, Eleanor R., 1411
Bradley, Elizabeth A., 4647
Bradley, Elizabeth P., 1546
Bradley, Erroll, 4824
Bradley, John F., 4151
Bradley, John S., 9309
Bradley, Karen, 439
Bradley, Kathy, 2438
Bradley, Kerry, 1626
Bradley, Laura, 1626
Bradley, Melinda, 8259
Bradley, Tim, 6971
Bradley, Timothy, 6971
Bradshaw, Darlene, 3402
Bradshaw, Gerald E., 7720
Bradshaw, Nicholas, 5573
Bradshaw, Philip L., 3932
Bradshaw, Tracy, 2602
Brady, Barrett, 4970
Brady, Betty, 456
Brady, Beverlye, 2456
Brady, Brad, 1323
Brady, C. Quinn, Jr., 456
Brady, Chris, 8314
Brady, Holly, 3445
Brady, Jack, 9267
Brady, James, 1298
Brady, Kaci, 3614
Brady, Katherine D., 3843
Brady, Mary, 6559
Brady, Nicholas F., 3843
Brady, Thomas C., 8197
Brady, Thomas, Jr., 4043
Braet, Christine, 7820
Braet, Joseph, 7820
Braff, Phyllis, 6219
Bragdon, Roger, 9612
Braham Securities, 6720
Braitmayer, Eric A., 3827
Braitmayer, John W., 3827
Braitmayer, Karen L., 3827
Braitmayer, Marian S., 3827
Brake, Timothy L., 5038
Brakora, Marianne, 4370
Bram, Linda Helmig, 4354
Bram, Tony, 4354
Braman, D.H., III, 9093
Braman, Mary O'Connor, 9093
Braman, Norman, 2315
Bramble, R.L., 9185
Bramhall, Emily B., 4239
Bramlage, Dorothy O., 3559
Bramlage, F. Robert, 3559

Bramlage, Fred C., 3559
Bramwell, Jim, 1772
Branam, Robin, 3735
Brancato, Laura J., 9670
Branch Banking & Trust Co., 7082, 7186, 7219, 7249, 7263, 7287, 7291, 9745, 9761
Branch Banking &Trust Co., 7045, 7169
Branch, Janet D., 1969
Branchfield, Barbara, 5003
Brand, Brenda F., 9062
Brand, Chase, 4518
Brand, Jennifer, 9177
Brand, Martha, 5776
Brand, Michael Morley, 4518
Brand, Nancy, 9177
Brandeis, E. John, 5069
Brandenberger, Jon, 8293
Brandes, Charles H., 6439
Brandes, Linda, 6439
Brandes, Tanya, 6439
Brandman, Etta, 5918, 6954
Brandman, Samuel, 3041
Brandon, Anthony D., 3359
Brandon, Edward B., 7568
Brandon, Theresa, 9203
Brandrup, Douglas W., 1399
Brandsgaard, Don, 189
Brandsma, Joshua, 1627
Brandsma, Lee, 1627
Brandsma, Pamela, 1627, 1673
Brandsma, Ryan, 1627
Brandsma, Tessa, 1627
Brandt, Barbara, 5777
Brandt, Elaine, 9403
Brandt, Elaine K., 9403
Brandt, Gary, 5777
Brandt, Joanne L., 6375
Brandt, William F., Jr., 9403
Branfman, Alan R., 5271
Branfman, Alan R., Mrs. , 5271
Branfman, Joyce, 5271
Branick, Julie, 9891
Branigar Charitable Lead Annuity Trust, Sarah L., 5606
Branigar, Harvey W., Jr., 5606
Branigar, Sarah L., 5606
Brankman, John David, 1101
Brankman, Maida Lynn, 1101
Brannan, Ruth, 96
Brannin, Alder, 7662
Brannin, Caroline, 7662
Brannin, Clark Stewart, 7662
Brannin, Dan Graham, 7662
Brannin, Joe, 7662
Brannin, Nancy Louise, 7662
Brannin, Neva L., 7662
Brannon, Mary, 1773
Branson, Chris, 3360
Branson, Steven A., 4142
Branstad, Christine W., 2755
Branstad, Paul A., 2755
Branstetter, Michael K., 2681
Brant, Terri, 6652
Branta Foundation, 5822
Brantley, Hugh H., 8525
Brantley, Max, 193
Brasel, Marcia R., 8672
Brasel, Susan S., 5018
Brass, Arthur J., 8738
Brass, Catherine M., 8738
Brass, Joyce, 8738
Brassard, Thanda, 4352
Bratcher, Joe W., III, 9020

Bratcher, Joe W., Jr., 9020
Bratic, Walter, 8186
Braton, Jenny, 8860
Bratt Trust, Henry, 5778
Bratton, William, 5872
Braun, Alan, 3349
Braun, Alan W., 3349
Braun, Andrew G., 4164
Braun, Byron, 3356
Braun, Cole M., 9787
Braun, Diane, 9787
Braun, Henry A., 5979, 6669
Braun, Jeffrey V., 9787
Braun, Jennifer C., 9787
Braun, Linda, 4352
Braun, Loyce, 471, 472
Braun, Mary Lynne, 9581
Braun, Mathew A., 3349
Braun, Phil, 2291
Braun, Sharon, 3349
Braun, Sharon A., 3349
Braun, Thelma, 8740
Braun, Victor F., 9787
Brauner, David, 5909
Brauner, David A., 5802
Braunlich, Paul, 4411
Braunstein, Colette, 2059
Braunstein, Richard L., 6077
Brause Realty Inc., 6655
Brause, Luis, 6655
Braverman, Carol, 1718
Braverman, Eva, 3208
Braverman, Henry, 4095
Bravo Foundation, The, 470
Brawer, Catherine Coleman, 6696
Brawer, Christopher P., 6696
Brawer, Nicholas A., 6696
Brawer, Robert A., 6696
Brawer, Wendy H., 6696
Braxton, Amandee, 8118
Bray, David, 4410
Bray, Elizabeth, 7899
Brayman, Beverly J., 4979
Brayman, Roger, 4979
Brayton, Deborah M., 8507
Brazelton, Lewis E., III, 8924
Breakey, Mark D., 7929
Breakley, Gayle, 9474
Brearton, Jess, 3580
Breaux-Wells, Shea, 5635
Brecher, Helen, 6697, 6858
Brecher, Joel, 6697
Brecher, Judah, 6697
Brecher, Michael, 6697
Brecher, Sharge, 7008
Brecher, Shimon, 7000
Brecher, Shraga, 6858
Brecher, Usher, 6697
Breck, Christopher, 5780
Breck, Henry, 5780
Breck, Wendy, 5780
Breckenridge, Bryan, 4964
Breckenridge, Charles W., 8185
Breech Charitable Lead Annuity Trust, Mara, 339
Breech Trust, Mara, 339
Breech, Andrew L., 339
Breech, Debra N., 339
Breech, Mara W., 339
Breed, Alan, 6868
Breed, Allen, 369
Breeden, Ramon W., Jr., 9404
Breeden, Russell, III, 539
Breedlove, Alan Merkle, 7890

Breedlove, Ann M., 7890
Breedlove, Howell A., 7890
Breedlove, John Adams, 7890
Breedlove, Mark Howell, 7890
Breedlove, William Parker, 7890
Breese, William L., 9494
Breidenthal Charitable Lead Trust, 4875
Breidenthal, George Gray, 4875
Breidenthal, McKenzie, 4875
Breidenthal, Willard J, 4875
Breier, Robert, 1921
Breiner, Nancy, 3397
Breit, Catherine S., 3238
Breitenbach, Thomas, 7610
Breitenfeld, Frederick, Jr., 7905
Bremer, Carin, 1647
Bremer, Larry, 4735
Brenalvirez, Meredith, 826
Brendle, Heather, 2881
Brendle, Jimmy, 2881
Brendsel, Billie D., 9965
Brendsel, Leland C., 9965
Brenman, Lawrence H., 3005
Brennan, Amy Dooner, 7974
Brennan, Donald A., 9788
Brennan, Edward A., 9788
Brennan, Edward J., 9788
Brennan, George G., 5246
Brennan, Jacqueline E., 5865
Brennan, James C., 7953
Brennan, John L., 9788
Brennan, John T., Jr., 1799
Brennan, Lois L., 9788
Brennan, Michael, 5369
Brennan, Nora, 5400
Brennan, Sybil Ann, 6026
Brenneman, Joseph E., 8290
Brenneman, Samuel A., 8290
Brenner, Abe, 2756
Brenner, Francis, 2756
Brenner, Frank, 2756
Brenner, Michael, 2756
Brenner, Miriam, 2756
Brenner, Susan, 2756, 6739
Brennock, Erin, 1100
Brenny, Bonita, 4656
Brent, Aaron, 256
Brent, Averil R., 1240
Brent, Douglas B., 1240
Bresch, Heather, 8187
Bresko, Andrew G., 7366
Bresler, Amanda, 3828
Bresler, Carol, 3828
Bresler, Charles S., 3828
Bresler, Edward, 3828
Breslow, Elaine R., 340
Breslow, Lauren Hammer, 6329
Breslow, Warren L., 340
Bresnan Family Foundation Trust, 1628
Bresnan, Ann, 1628
Bresnan, Ann L., 1628
Bresnan, William J., 1628
Brethen, David M., 7331
Brethen, Robert H., 7331
Brett, Bradford A., 4900
Brett, James, 4268
Bretzman, Merlin, 4734
Breuer, Chana, 6567
Breuer, Shmyer, 6567
Breunling, Debra L., 3424
Brevard, David E., 4826
Brevard, Elizabeth B., 4826
Brevard, Henry C., Jr., 4826
Brevig, Yasue, 9642

Brevorka, Peter J., 6710
Brewer, Barrett, 5610
Brewer, Charles H., 2757
Brewer, Charles M., 2448
Brewer, Flora A., 9120
Brewer, Grace, 9572
Brewer, Kathleen, 8949
Brewer, Laura W., 1639
Brewer, Lynn P., 2757
Brewer, Virginia F., 2448
Brewester Co., The, 153
Brewster, Antoinette B., 1490
Brewster, Benjamin, 1490
Brewster, Stephen, 9305
Brewster, Steve, 5105
Brey, Ingrid K., 4471
Brezinski, Alexandra K. Heath, 2701
Brezinski, Edwin, 2701
Brezinski, Steven A., 9897
Brezski, Richard J., 1743
Brick, Gary, 3370
Bridge Manufacturing, 9367
Bridgens, Pepper Woodard, 7831
Bridger, Barbara, 4880
Bridges, Alice M., 342
Bridges, C. Ray, 7255
Bridges, Dorothy J., 1330
Bridges, James, 343
Bridges, James R., 342
Bridges, Jeff, 498
Bridges, Mildred H., 8947
Bridges, Robert, 3441
Bridges, Robert L., 342
Bridges, Susan A., 8539
Bridges, Thomas S. , 2739
Bridgewater Crossing Developers, LLC, 5367
Bridgforth, Allen, 4832
Brier, Rachel Zacharia, 1601
Briger, Devon, 5784
Briger, Peter L., 5784
Briggs, Deborah Plutzik, 6103
Briggs, Lynn Bryan, 53
Briggs, Margaret, 7892
Briggs, Robert Stephen, Jr., 53
Briggs, Robert Stephen, Sr., 53
Briggs, Ronald P., 3714
Briggs, Stephen, 4947
Briggs, V. Gwendolyn, 3714
Brigham, Martha M., 260
Bright, Calvin E., 345
Bright, Charles R., 8743
Bright, G. Todd, 9144
Brighton, W. Curtis, 3396
Brightwell, Barbara, Dr. , 8769
Brightwood, Sarah Livia, 1102
Brigission, Gundmundur A., 1573
Briley, Bertha H., 1169
Brill, Arthur, 6988
Brill, Randall, 997
Brill, Robert J., 8760
Brillo, Lyn, 5785
Brimberg, Elizabeth, 6659
Brimberg, Stanlee, 6659
Brimmer, William A., 1532
Brinbaum, Issachar, 5794
Brinberg, Simeon, 6684
Brinck, Cynthia A., 7333
Brinck, Joseph, 7333
Brinck, Joseph A., 7333
Brinck, Joseph A., II, 7333
Brinckerhoff, Ashley M., 1900
Brinckerhoff, Coleman M., 1900
Brinckerhoff, Peter R., 1900

Brinckerhoff, Susan C., 1900
Briner, Kenneth R., 3449
Brinig, Margaret, 9825
Brink's Co., The, 9406
Brinkley, Hugh M., 15
Brinkman Trust, Richard G., 7893
Brinkman, Christina Rae, 5786
Brinkman, Robert J., 5786
Brinkmann, Cynthia, 900
Brinkmoeller, George E., 3393
Brinks, Brent, 4401
Brinn, Mildred C., 6353
Brinshore Development, LLC, 2881
Brint, Betsy, 2970
Brint, David, 2881
Brint, Elizabeth, 2881
Brinton, Joyce, 4120
Briscoe, D. Daniel, 7255
Briscoe, Robert B., 4824
Briskin, Bernard, 346
Briskin, Judy, 346
Bristol Bay Econ. Devel. Corp., 91
Bristol Bay Native Corp., 82
Bristol County Savings Bank, 1477
Bristol, Barbara F., 8879
Bristow, Aurelia B., 1404
Bristow, Elliott B., 1404
Bristow, Gail I., 1404
Bristow, Julie, 7647
Bristow, W. Scott, 7647
Brittain, Barbara, 3902
Brittan, Alexandra, 1127
Brittan, Gordon "Corky", 5047
Brittan, Graydon, 1127
Brittan, Linda, 1127
Brittan, Maynard, 1127
Brittan, Maynard M., 1127
Brittenham, K.C. Samson, 2678
Britton, Doug, 8403
Britton, Jack L., 9739, 9753
Britton, John E., 7894
Britton, John W., 7894
Britton, Kimberly, 1156
Britton, Richard H., 9488
Britton, Suzanne E., 7894
Broach, Mark A., 1579
Broad, Gary, 347
Broad, Marilyn S., 5272
Broadbent, Camille W., 5046
Broadbent, John H., Jr., 7895
Broadbent, Mary K., 5046
Broadbent, Richard L., 7895
Broadbent, Robert R., 5046
Broadbent, William S., 5046
Broadhead, Elaine, 3210
Broadhurst, William, 7663
Broadnax, Marcus, 2005
Broadus, Lucy E., 3829
Broadus, Thomas H., III, 3829
Broadway National Bank, 9016, 9278
Broady, Barbara, 3446
Broady, George K., 8745
Broccoli Foundation, 1176
Brochstein, Raymond D., 8746
Brochstein, Susan, 8746
Brock, Fain, 8836
Brock, Jean Ann, 8951, 9212
Brock, Marissa J., 8430
Brock, Susan L., 4104
Brock-Wilson, Jack, 4027
Brock-Wilson, Jane, 4027
Brocker, Bruce E., 7334
Brocker, Deborah J., 7334
Brocker, Matthew C., 7334

Brockett, Daniel, 480
Brockman, Paul, 8944
Brockmeier, Judy, 5105
Brockton Wholesale Beverage Co., 1833
Brockway, Eleanor, 4198
Brod, Claudia Taylor, 9011
Broder, Cynthia, 348
Broder, Hans, 2586
Broder, Paul G., 1629
Broder, Robert, 348
Broderick, Rebecca Cutting, 9968
Brodeur, Lawrence, 4095
Brodie, Renee, 6350
Brodnik, Kim, 709
Brodrick, James W., Jr., 4299
Brodsky, Alexander E., 8747
Brodsky, Charles Alexander, 8747
Brodsky, Daniel, 6656
Brodsky, Donald W., 8747
Brodsky, Gregor Lang, 8747
Brodsky, Harris Elliot, 8747
Brodsky, James W., 8747
Brodsky, Joan, 1901
Brodsky, Joan B., 1901
Brodsky, Joanne Fishbein, 8873
Brodsky, Jonathan P., 1901
Brodsky, Lela Alexis, 8747
Brodsky, Leonore Elizabeth, 8747
Brodsky, Max Emmanuil Schneidler, 8747
Brodsky, Michael B., 1901
Brodsky, Ruth W., 8747
Brodsky, Stephen A., 1901
Brodsky, William, 1901
Brodsky, William J., 1901
Brody 1998 Charitable Lead Unitrust #2, Sara Strouss, The , 1902
Brody 1998 Charitable Lead Unitrust, Sara Strouss, The , 1902
Brody, Caroline W., 1791
Brody, Carolyn, 1791
Brody, Carolyn Schwenker, 5787
Brody, Charles W., 1791
Brody, Elena, 5315
Brody, Kenneth D., 1791
Brody, Paula J., 1902
Brody, Sara S., 1902
Broer, Victoria Urban, 3545
Brogan, Jeffrey P., 825
Brogan, Mike, 4079
Brogan, Robert H., 9868
Broker, Gerald, 7896
Broker, Joshua, 7896
Broll Jr. Charitable Lead Trust, Arthur G., 8320
Broll, Arthur G., Jr., 8320
Broll, Daniel W., 8320
Broll, David A., 8320
Broll, Geoffrey T., 8320
Broll, Nancy T., 8320
Brolund, Robert, 8653
Bromberg, Dan, 480
Bromberg, Leon, 8748
Bromley, Guy I., 8749
Bronfman Foundation, Ann, 6906
Bronfman, Ann, 6906
Bronfman, Ann L., 5742
Bronfman, Matthew, 6906
Bronfman, Stacey K., 6906
Bronner Family Trust, Wallace and Irene, 4398
Bronner, Carla, 4398
Bronner, Irene R., 4398
Bronner, Maria, 4398

Bronner, Randy, 4398
Bronner, Wayne, 4398
Bronson, Robert, 7822
Bronson, Ryan, 3991
Bronstein, Sol, 3351
Bronstein, Solomon, 7896
Bronzi, Marilyn, 8279
Brook, Anthony, 3769
Brook, Cara Dingus, 7408
Brook, Nickolas, 3769
Brook, Paul, 3769
Brook, Robert L., 3769
Brook, Shirley, 3769
Brookbank, Nancy, 3435
Brooke, Margaret W., 8685
Brooke, William W., 79
Brooker, T. Kimball, 2758
Brookewood Investment Company LLC, 9444
Brookfield Financial Properties, 6655
Brooklyn Endoscopy and Surgery Center, 5697
Brookman, Michelle, 969
Brooks Resources Inc., 4639
Brooks Teammates for Kids Foundation, Garth, 9230
Brooks Teammates for Kids, Gasrth, 4399
Brooks Trust, John and Barbara, 350
Brooks, Barbara, 350
Brooks, Brian, 2123
Brooks, Cameron, 5463
Brooks, Catherine, 1151
Brooks, Colin, 4639
Brooks, Conley, Jr., 4639
Brooks, Daniel A., 8642
Brooks, Drew, 3192
Brooks, Eleine H., 7341
Brooks, Eric, 8310
Brooks, Harold, 4028
Brooks, Hattie H., 349
Brooks, Henry, 9070
Brooks, J. Michael, 7545
Brooks, John, 350
Brooks, Jonathan, 224
Brooks, Julie Q., 9142
Brooks, Karen Phifer, 54
Brooks, Kyle C., 7341
Brooks, Linda D., 8642
Brooks, Linda Leith, 5274
Brooks, Martha Finn, 2450
Brooks, Mike, 7408
Brooks, Oliver, Jr., 2450
Brooks, Owen E., 5979
Brooks, Robert J., 7897
Brooks, Sam A., 8642
Brooks, Sunshine, 349
Brooks, Susan C., 7897
Brooks, T. Anthony, 5274
Brooks, Tom, 2123
Brooks, William Mathews, 350
Brooks-Mullins, Nichelle, 1453
Brooks-Scanlon, 4639
Brooksbank, Kaye D., 8608
Brooksbank, Robin W., 4753
Brookshire, Alexandra, 9573
Broomfield Trust, Elizabeth, 5275
Broomhead, Paul, 1581
Brophy, John, 4362
Brosens, Deenie M., 5789
Brosens, Frank, 1791
Brosens, Frank P., 5789
Brosius, Tamara K., 8048
Brosnahan, Anne Laura, 6334

Brosnahan, Anne Laura K., 6334
Brosseau, Helen L., 6816
Brossman Charitable Foundation, William and Jemima, 7900
Brossman, W. Craig, 8311
Brothers, Elizabeth, 1485
Brothers, Kelly, 697
Brotherton, Maureen P., 9678
Brotman Charitable Unitrust, 9574
Brotman, Jeffrey H., 9574
Brotman, Susan T., 9574
Broman, Toni, 351
Broude, John, 9292
Brouder, Suzanne D'Addario, 5895
Broudy, Norma J., 230
Broughton Charitable Remainder Unitrust, William, 5790
Broughton, George W., 7546
Broussard, Donald J., 3715
Broussard, Merieda, 3715
Broussard, Michael, 3715
Broussard, Scott, 3760
Broussard, Stephen, 3715
Broussard, Tom, 8869
Brousseau, Theodore, Jr., 1861
Brouwer, Matthew P., 9087
Browder Charitable Lead Annuity Trust, 5277
Browder Trust, 5277
Browder, Carol J., 8633
Browder, R.J., 74
Browder, Rhea, 5277
Browder, William, 5277
Brower, Lee M., 9305
Brower, Margaret, 8331
Brown and Associates, Clayton, 2759
Brown Brothers Harriman Trust Co., 1713, 6528
Brown Charitable Lead Annuity Trust, Charles S. & Millicent P., 9407
Brown Charitable Lead, Janice, 7076
Brown Charitbale Rem Unitrust, William, 5791
Brown Clat-15, 9407
Brown Harris Stevens Residential, 6656
Brown Revocable Living Trust, Mary Helen, 4877
Brown Supply Co., 7372
Brown Trust, Helen M., 7337
Brown Trust, Mary Lore F., 7059
Brown Trust, Patricia A., 353
Brown, Adam R., 5278
Brown, Albert, 9307
Brown, Alex, 8698
Brown, Allen C., 3932
Brown, Andrea C., 2004
Brown, Ann N., 7664
Brown, Arnold H., 3639
Brown, Arthur H., 6676
Brown, Barbara, 7222
Brown, Barbara J., 4369
Brown, Barrie, Mrs. , 6643
Brown, Barry, 4054
Brown, Bennett A., III, 1631
Brown, Bernie, 8022
Brown, Beth Goldsmith, 8622
Brown, Beverly, 756
Brown, Brian, 5074
Brown, Bruce F., Jr., 1630
Brown, Bruce M., 7953, 8047
Brown, Bruce Maitland, 8047
Brown, C. Foster, III, 3106
Brown, C. Foster, IV, 3106
Brown, C.L., III, 8774, 8860

Brown, Candace, 389
Brown, Carlton D., 6443
Brown, Carol Anne Smullin, 1060
Brown, Catherine, 1906
Brown, Cee, 5691
Brown, Charla, 9307
Brown, Charles S., Jr., 9407
Brown, Charlotte G., 2759
Brown, Christina, 1904
Brown, Christopher, 5605
Brown, Christopher R., 2004
Brown, Clayton F., 2759
Brown, Clifford L., III, 8774
Brown, Colene, 352
Brown, Craig, 1904
Brown, Craig C., 4369
Brown, Cynthia, 153
Brown, Cynthia Marvell, 6283
Brown, D. Randolph, Jr., 7664
Brown, D. Warren, 7336
Brown, Daniel T., 9790
Brown, Darcey, 9307
Brown, David, 5278
Brown, David A., 620
Brown, David M., 5278
Brown, David R., 7664
Brown, Deirdre A., 2367
Brown, Denise, 8118, 8370
Brown, Donald, 3398
Brown, Donnaldson Kathryn, 1630
Brown, Douglas W., 7336
Brown, Dwyer, 9997
Brown, E. Wendy, 6189
Brown, Edith Rae, 5692
Brown, Elizabeth A., 1243
Brown, Elizabeth K., 2691
Brown, Elizabeth M., 8582
Brown, Elliot H., 6323
Brown, Ellis C., 7744
Brown, Eric, 4423
Brown, Florence Mavis, 4201
Brown, Garrett, 756
Brown, George, 7339
Brown, Harmon A., 2630
Brown, Harold, 352
Brown, Harry J., Jr., 1906
Brown, Helen, 7337
Brown, Helen M., 2191
Brown, Helene K., 9997
Brown, Himan, 6643
Brown, Howard J., 2691
Brown, Ian D., 2004
Brown, J. Carter, 8422
Brown, J. Stokes, 16
Brown, James, 6373
Brown, James E., 1632
Brown, Janice J., 7336
Brown, Jeffrey, 1904
Brown, Jennifer, 1904, 3106
Brown, Jenny, 9133
Brown, Jessica, 4220
Brown, Jim, 5628
Brown, Joe, 9232
Brown, Joel F., 2919
Brown, John C., IV, 8422
Brown, Jon, 9326
Brown, Judy, 5114
Brown, Julia, 6137
Brown, Julie A., 5025, 7339
Brown, Karen, 620
Brown, Katharine, 6632
Brown, Kathleen T., 4919
Brown, Kathryne L., 7058
Brown, Keith A., 2004

Brown, Kenneth F., 7833
Brown, Kevin Smullin, 1060
Brown, Kim R., 4490
Brown, Laura Lee Lyons, 3699
Brown, Leelee, 6372
Brown, Lorraine Eddy, 1630
Brown, Louis M., II, 3106
Brown, Lynn A., 353
Brown, Lynn M. Schilling, 4799
Brown, Lynn Marie, 3845
Brown, Lynora S., 1123
Brown, M.K., 8751
Brown, Margaret Boyce, 8750
Brown, Margarite, 436
Brown, Marilyn, 7372
Brown, Martin S., 8582
Brown, Martin S., Sr., 8582
Brown, Mary E., 8774
Brown, Mary Helen, 4877
Brown, Mary Virginia, 9739
Brown, Maxine, 1632
Brown, Melina, 6643
Brown, Meredith A., 1060
Brown, Michael R., 5036
Brown, Monica Welty, 7635
Brown, Monte, 9997
Brown, Morgan, 1906
Brown, Myron, 9221
Brown, Neil, 2362
Brown, Neil A., 7400
Brown, Nicholas, 8422
Brown, Nicholas C., 3106
Brown, Nicole, 1246
Brown, Nikki Mintz, 5278
Brown, Pamela, 8874
Brown, Pamela H., 7833
Brown, Patricia A., 310
Brown, Peter C., 4919
Brown, Peter C., Jr., 4919
Brown, Peter G., 4067
Brown, Peter P., 4363
Brown, Richard, 756
Brown, Richard F, 1905
Brown, Robert A., 9407
Brown, Robert W., 9790
Brown, Ruth H., 9307
Brown, S. Spencer, Jr., 8750
Brown, S. Spencer, Sr., 8750
Brown, S.M., 3561
Brown, Sally, 1630, 3444, 8970
Brown, Sara S., 8582
Brown, Shale, 9326
Brown, Shawn P., 7833
Brown, Stanton Boyce, 8750
Brown, Stephanie L., 4029
Brown, Stephen D., 1630
Brown, Steven C., 2759
Brown, Susan, 1568, 7664
Brown, Susan T., 9790
Brown, Sylvia, 8422
Brown, Tara, 620
Brown, Terry, 5692
Brown, Thomas E., 7372
Brown, Thomas M., 1630
Brown, Thomas P., 5660
Brown, Tiara, 817
Brown, Vicki, 1904
Brown, Virginia Sory, 16
Brown, Walt, 9204
Brown, Wendy B., 8041
Brown, Whitney, 3106
Brown, William V., 3080
Brown, William W., 8515
Brown, Zoe, 3471

Brown-Forman, 2510
Brown-Russ, Sarah M., 2691
Brown-Tuchler, Amy I., 2691
Browne, Caroline Muir, 2493
Browne, James J., 7901
Browne, Noel W., 7901
Browne, Vicki, 9293
Brownell, Debbie, 7764
Brownell, Jana, 4592
Browning, George, III, 2308
Browning, Marylee D., 8870
Browning, Steve, 5054
Brownlee, Susan, 7640, 7994
Brownlow, Ian, 5616
Broyhill, John M., 3932
Broze, Diana C., 3563
Brozowski, Catherine, 887
Brubaker, Alex, 1317
Bruce Living Trust, Julia, 2761
Bruce, Carl, 2761
Bruce, Carole, 7209
Bruce, David J., 4057
Bruce, Elizabeth Davison, 2470
Bruce, Julia H., 2761
Bruce, Robert, 2760
Bruce, Robert B., 2760
Bruch, Sarah, 9954
Bruch, Susan K., 8979
Brucia, Charles J., 6311
Brucia, Frank, 857
Bruder, James J., Jr., 8171
Bruder, Jennifer M., 8171
Brudny, Abraham, 5599
Brudos, Alan R., 355
Brueckner, Laurie C., 5279
Brueckner, Richard F., 5279
Brueggeman, Steve, 3175
Bruml, Jennifer, 7781
Brumley, Amy, 8101
Brumley, Danice, 9231
Brun, James, 7649
Brunce, Lynn S., 4116
Brundage, Edna T., 5280
Bruner, Joshua E., 4030
Bruner, Martha, 4030
Bruner, R. Simeon, 4030
Bruner, Rudy, 4030
Brunet, Whitney D., 4655
Brunetti, Joann H., 5281
Brunetti, John J., 5281
Brunetti, John J., Jr., 5281
Brunetti, Stephen P., 5281
Brunie, Charles H., 5792
Brunie, Jean I., 5792
Brunkow, Glenn, 3592
Brunn, Ralph A., 3929
Brunn, Simone, 3929
Brunnemer, James A., 3431
Brunner, Esther, 793
Bruno, Alan, 17
Bruno, Angelo J., 17
Bruno, Ann, 17
Bruno, David, 17
Bruno, Kenneth, 17
Bruno, Ronald, 17
Brunos Memorial Classic, 9
Bruns, Bonnie, 2977
Bruns, Daniel, 4938
Bruns, Kathleen, 4938
Brunswick Corp., 2762
Brunswick, Lewis, 354
Brunton, Steve, 3344
Brush, Charles F., 7338
Brush, Edwin F., 3993

Bryan Foundation of Greater GSO, Joseph M., The , 7209
Bryan, Amanda A., 355
Bryan, Anne E., 355
Bryan, Anne L., 355
Bryan, Cheryl, 7666
Bryan, David C., 4082
Bryan, Florence E., 355
Bryan, J.F., IV, 2280
Bryan, James E., 7060
Bryan, Jeff, 2280
Bryan, John M., 355
Bryan, Kathryn B., 355
Bryan, Marian H., 8908
Bryan, Mary Z., 7060
Bryan, Ralph, 997
Bryan, Suzanne E., 355
Bryan, William H., 7060, 7196
Bryans, Martha B., 8275
Bryant, Andy, 7807
Bryant, Arthur H., II, 9409
Bryant, Arthur H., Jr., 9409
Bryant, Barbara Murphy, 4878
Bryant, C.E., Jr., 42
Bryant, Christine, 966
Bryant, Dawn, 1421
Bryant, Gary F., 9409
Bryant, J.C. Herbert, 9409
Bryant, John C.O., 9540
Bryant, Magalen O., 9540
Bryant, Nancy Kay, 7807
Bryant, Natalie, 104
Bryant, Rachelle, 5077
Bryant, Taylor C., 9409
Bryce, Edward M., 8091
Bryce, James D., 2020
Bryer, Ben F., 7902
Bryers, Joanne E., 7923
Bryn Mawr Trust Co., 8303
Bryon, Kathy, 7761
Brzozowski, John, 4449
BSJ, LLC, 9506
BSP Group, The, 2150
BTIG, LLC, 1730
Btig, LLC, 6463
BTIG, LLC, 6720
Bub, Keith, 6245
Bucci, Cathy, 8314
Buch, Fred N., 8311
Buchalter, Lawrence R., 5796
Buchanan, George B., Jr., 9410
Buchanan, George, III, 9410
Buchanan, George, Jr., 9410
Buchanan, Janice B., 4541
Buchanan, Jayme, 3344
Buchanan, John H., 9838
Buchanan, Julia G., 2917
Buchanan, Karyn, 8981
Buchanan, Robert, 9410
Buchanan, Tim, 5198
Buchanan, Valda M., 7707
Buchele, Ken, 3635
Buchholz, Mary Clarkson, 8558
Buchholz, Thad Milton, 8558
Buchman, Barbara, 9570
Buchman, Joseph, 9570
Bucholtz, Gary A., 2356
Buchwald, Donald, 5797
Buchwald, Margaret, 5797
Buck, C. Austin, 8041
Buck, C. Austin, II, 7904
Buck, Haleryn A., 5635
Buck, Helen R., 7904
Buck, Jan G., 192

Buck, John Garner, 192
Buck, Julianne, 3125
Buck, Laura T., 7834
Buck, Leonard J., 8041
Buck, Marguerite D., 8041
Buck, Richard E., 192
Buck, Travis W., 5635
Buck, W. Lawrence, 5842
Buckalew, Donnie, 9070
Buckberg, Gerald D., 725
Buckingham, Eunice Hale, 7591
Buckingham, Greg, 884
Buckingham, Harold, Jr., 8090
Buckley, Jeremiah S., 1818
Buckley, John, 1856
Buckley, Mary K., 5798
Buckley, William , 4467
Buckley, William J., 5798
Bucknam, Elizabeth M., 5204
Bucknam, Susan, 5220
Buckner, Kamala, 6598
Buckner, Thomas W., 6598
Buckstead, Kevin, 4960
Budd, Dorothy R., 8753
Budd, Kim, 6979
Budd, Laura, 4667
Budd, MacDonald, 5957
Budd, McDonald, 5836
Budd, Russell W., 8753
Budds, Matt, 4411
Budge, Kathleen L., 4764
Budwig, Jennifer, 817
Budwine, Lela, 8754
Budwine, W.J., 8754
Budwine, Wayne, 8754
Buechel, Debra, 2647
Buechner, Robert, 7651
Buechse, Oliver, 9778
Buell, Alan D., 9581
Buell, Bruce T., 9581
Buell, Mark, 357
Buell, Sugirthamalar, 391
Buell, Susie R. Tompkins, 357
Buer, Bob, 4879
Buesching, Marlene, 3429
Buesing, Eric, 5426
Buesing, Gregory P., 5426
Buesing, Guy K., 5426
Buesing, Jean, 5426
Buffalo Bills Inc., 4399
Buffett Foundation, Howard G., 3235
Buffett, Doris, 4169
Buffett, Howard G., 3235
Buffett, Howard W., 3235, 4169
Buffett, Jimmy, 8540
Bufka, Andrea, 2763
Bufka, Carl K., 2763
Bufka, Karen L., 2763
Buford, Anne S., 3562
Buford, C. Robert, 3562
Buford, Martha C., 3562
Buford, R.C., 3562
Bugden, Stephanie, 5929
Bugg, Christopher, 9795, 9801
Buhler, Jill M., 2314
Buhlman, Parnell Wood, 8551
Buhr Machine Tool Co., 4400
Buhr, James D., 4400
Buhr, Richard J., 4400
Buhr, Thomas A., 4400
Buice, Stuart, 8378
Build-A-Bear Workshop, 4879
Build-A-Bear Workshop Canada Ltd, 4879

Builders, 3905
Buis, Paula, 7155
Buist Electric, 4401
Buist, Larry G., 4401
Buker, Margaret R., 2566
Buley, Gloria, 6929
Bulger, Elise Donaldson, 1760
Bulger, Gregory E., 4031
Bulkley, Everett S., Jr., 2765
Bull Ventures Limited Partnership, 4283
Bull, Belitje B., 2440
Bull, Maud L., 358
Bull, Randy, 2880
Bullard, George, 8643
Bullard, Ginger, 219
Bullard, Matthews S., 8537
Bullard, Sidney C., 8537
Bullen, Mary, 7452
Buller, Cheryl, 5800
Buller, James, 5800
Buller, Mark, 5800
Bulleri Marital Trust, Joseph A., 9575
Bulleri, Roberta, 9575
Bullington, Kendra Ladane, 7155
Bullington, Mitchell Grant, 7155
Bullington, Odell Frasier, 7155
Bullitt-Jonas, Margaret, 4730
Bullock, Alexandra, 6579
Bullock, Ellis F., 4702
Bullock, Whitney, 6579
Bumgarner, John T., 4649
Bumgarner, Terry L., 4649
Bump, Benjamin, 4299
Bumpass, Mike, 7209
Bunch and Assocs., 1922
Bunch, Cynthia L., 1922
Bunch, James D., 1922
Bundy Baking Solutions, 1362
Bundy, Anne S., 360
Bundy, Bruce, 360
Bundy, David G., 8544
Bundy, Tracy M., 1527
Bungie, LLC, 9576
Bunker, Brenda, 4499
Bunker, Irene, 3448
Bunn, Jeanette, 7646
Bunn, Mike, 2434
Bunnen, Lucinda W., 6417
Bunnen, Robert L., 6417
Bunnen, Robert L., Jr., 6417
Bunten, Paul, 4549
Bunting Family Foundation, The, 3928
Bunting, Anne R., 3928
Bunting, Bob, 9724
Bunting, Christopher L., 3928
Bunting, Dana L., 7895
Bunting, George L., Jr., 3816, 3928
Bunting, Joseph O., III, 1809, 9400
Bunting, Marc, 3928
Bunting, Mary Catherine, 3928
Bunting, Rebekah S., 3928
Buntrock, Dean L., 2766
Buntrock, Rosemarie, 2766
Buntz, M.A., 7729
Bunyard, Mary Ellen, 8755
Burbach, Brian, 9954
Burbach, Kenneth M., 9954
Burbach, Mary S., 9954
Burbidge, Sally Rich, 9308
Burch, Barry B., 8756
Burch, Kathie, 9612
Burch, Robert D., 8756
Burch-Martinez, Berkeley, 8756
Burchan, Anna H., 5801

Burchard, Marilyn, 268
Burd, Barb, 7652
Burdette, Jana Craft, 8548
Burdick, Christopher, 4164
Burdick, Lalor, 4164
Burdick, Marci, 3444
Burdick, Sheryl J., 2917
Burditt, Abby K., 8819
Burelle, Ralph, 7794
Burg, Anton, 362
Burgard, Christopher, 3476
Burgard, Sandra L. Blin, 3476
Burger, Ernest P., 421
Burger, Greg, 4736
Burgeson, Dale, 9712
Burgess, C.C., 8930
Burgess, Kathy, 4401
Burghardt, John L., 366
Burgin, Thomas, 3078
Burgoon, Patricia B., 1908
Burgoon, Richard R., 1908
Burgos-Rodriquez, Abner, 1590
Burianek, Karen A., 3477
Burk Trust, Henrietta Lange, 2768
Burk, Jessica, 9133
Burk, Matt, 9133
Burke Family Foundation, 147
Burke, Albert, 2438
Burke, Austin, 8350
Burke, Christine, 884
Burke, Coleman P., Jr., 8429
Burke, Colleen D., 2834
Burke, Daniel, II, 8429
Burke, Elaine, 9948
Burke, Elizabeth K., 1639
Burke, Franklin A., 1639
Burke, J. Timothy, 9382
Burke, James, 2357
Burke, John, 884
Burke, Kate, 9630
Burke, Kathleen A., 3477
Burke, Kathryn, 7730
Burke, Lisa V., 3302
Burke, Lucie, 1528
Burke, R. Taylor, Jr., 147
Burke, Richard, 9948
Burke, Robert, 1639
Burke, Robert E., 6177
Burke, Sharon, 2664
Burke, Thomas, 8208
Burke, Thomas A., 9889
Burke, Thomas C., 2451
Burke, Thomas J., 7063
Burke, Thomas J., Jr., 7063
Burke, Thomas R., 3477
Burke, Timothy F., Jr., 8205
Burke, Vincent, 1528
Burke, William J., Jr., 3477, 8326
Burke, William J., Sr., 3477
Burke, Woody, 67
Burke, Wylie G., 1169
Burket, Carmen W., 7906
Burkett, Ginger Griffin, 30
Burkett, Radford, 2962
Burkey, Adam, 8027
Burkey, Fatema E.F., 8027
Burkhardt, David, 3441
Burkhart, Bryan, 7665
Burkhart, Matt, 7665
Burkhart, Mike, 7665
Burkhart, Susan, 7665
Burkholder, Corby, 7907
Burkholder, Lane, 7907
Burkholder, Matthew V., 7907

Burkholder, Melvin S., 7907
Burkholtz, Joan, 5337
Burkle Foundation, Ron, 8215
Burklow, J. Kent, 8668
Burklund, Wayne, 3588
Burkom, Selma, 5940
Burks Charitable Lead Annuity Trust, Tina L., 1909
Burks, Ellis, 7354
Burks, Jami Lynn, 2639
Burks, Keith W., 1909
Burks, Margaret K., 457
Burks, Tina L., 1909
Burleigh, Anne O'Herron, 1536
Burles, John S., 7809
Burlington Capital Group LLC, The, 5066
Burlington Industries, 7062
Burlington Industries LLC, 7062
Burma Bibas, 6319, 6320, 6321
Burman, Lisa, 2701
Burn, Luan Wagner, 5610
Burnap, Candida D., 2823
Burnett Co., Leo, 2769
Burnett USA, Leo, 2769
Burnett, Alexander H., 1911
Burnett, Bill, Dr. , 3402
Burnett, Bruce K., 1910
Burnett, Candace, 6604
Burnett, Elaine B., 5586
Burnett, H.L., 2260
Burnett, J. Albert, 1910
Burnett, Jill, 3415
Burnett, Lynn, 4979
Burnett, Mary Ellen, 1911
Burnett, Matthew, 3415
Burnett, Nancy L., 1910
Burnett, R. Kenneth, 4979
Burnett, Rebecca, 4426
Burnett, Robert, 7558
Burnette, Leah B., 2280
Burnette, Thomas, 3707
Burnetti, Dean, 1912
Burnetti, Denise L., 1912
Burnetti, Douglas K., 1912
Burnetti, Patricia A., 1912
Burnham, Charles, 7773
Burnham, Cheryl, 7773
Burnham, Deborah, 5725
Burnham, Margaret E., 3770
Burnham, Mark, 7773
Burnham, Wendy, 1184
Burns Family Charitable Trust, 1663
Burns, Anne Klinger, 7063
Burns, Bettye Lou Geurin, 458
Burns, Brent, 5483
Burns, Caroline, 2901
Burns, Charles, 5133
Burns, Emily Wilson, 1412
Burns, Michael B., 7935
Burns, Scott, 498
Burns, Sheila, 3052
Burns, Thomas, 9631
Burnside, Betty, 9740
Burnside, Warren, 9740
Burr Charitable Trust, Charles, 6542
Burr, Anna Monteleone, 3741
Burr, Jeffrey L., 5156
Burrage, Michael, 7715
Burrage, Steve, 7705
Burrell, 2621
Burrill, W. Gregory, 4134
Burris Ice, Stacey L., 3352
Burris, Barbara J., 3352
Burris, Jerry L., 3352

Burrough, Rick, 4490
Burroughs, Michael L., 2069
Burrows Paper Corp., 5803
Burrows, Deborah, 363
Burrows, Gladys A., 5803
Burrows, James, 363
Burrows, Laura, 1560
Burrows, R.W., 5803
Burrows, R.W., Jr., 5803
Burson, John H., 7438
Burstin, Barbara S., 8135
Burstman, Ruth, 6290
Burt's Bees, 1635, 3777
Burt, Charles R., 2770
Burt, Donna, 7806
Burt, F.R., 1244
Burt, Lynn C., 2770
Burt, N.B., 1244
Burt, Paul J., 2027
Burt, Randolph N., 2770
Burt, Robert N., 2770
Burt, Tracy C., 2770
Burtner, Benjamin M., 8190
Burton Charitable Foundation, Robert G., 1416
Burton, Angus M., 6818
Burton, Bob, 9069
Burton, David G., 1634
Burton, James, 8635
Burton, Kate Sato, 1007
Burton, Matthew D., 2520
Burton, Paula, 1416
Burton, Robert G., 1416
Burton, Robert G., Sr., 1416
Burton, Scott, 9309
Burton, Stephen J., 4681
Burton, Terry C., 215
Burwell, Barbara E., 4650
Burwell, Rodney P., 4650
Burzik, Catherine, 8758
Burzik, Frank, 8758
Busby, Ann, 7058
Busch, Mike, 3462
Busemeyer, Daniel, 7342
Busemeyer, Michael, 7342
Busemeyer, Richard A., 7342
Bush, David, 9041
Bush, Greg, 7944
Bush, Janet, 4297
Bush, John L., 3519
Bush, Lawrence A., 230
Bush, Linda F., 8848
Bush, Mary Lou, 230
Bush, Melinda H., 2675
Bush, Tom, 3519
Bush, William, 5759
Bushee, Florence Evans, 4032
Bushey, Catherine G., 1913
Bushey, Joseph H., 9421
Bushong-Weeks, Sarah, 1636
Bushwell, Joy, 7956
Busse, Audrey, 3478
Busse, Jeffrey, 3478
Busse, Lavern T., 3478
Busse, Lori Ann, 3478
Busse, Thomas W., 7343
Busse, Wilfried, 3912
Bussing, Constance K., 3353
Bussing, Marie A., 3353
Bussing, Wilfred C., III, 3353
Bussman, Courtney, 6357
Bussmann, Claudia, 6357
Bussmann, Margaret, 6357
Bussmann, Martin, 6357

Bussmann, Martin, Dr. , 6357
Bussmann, Richard, 6357
Buster, Robert, 3557
Buster, Victoria D., 3700
Bustle, Larry , 2149
Busumeyer, Steven, 7342
Butcher, McBee, 7924
Butcher, Ruby, 3586
Butka, Byrdie, 4466
Butler Charitable Lead Annuity Trust
   6/30/99, The, 365
Butler Charitable Lead Annuity Trust
   9/30/97, The, 365
Butler Foundation, J.E. and Z.B., 1792
Butler Foundation, The, 5206
Butler Manufacturing Co., 4880
Butler, Bill, 9756
Butler, Brett Lee, 364
Butler, Danny B., 9232
Butler, David, 2109
Butler, David J., 3874
Butler, Dorene Nunley, 364
Butler, Edna Loewy, 6409
Butler, Eliot, 365
Butler, Eugene Britt, 1
Butler, George Lee, 364
Butler, Hillary, 365
Butler, Jane Goldsmith, 8622
Butler, Jill Roland, 6148
Butler, Judy W., 1
Butler, Katharine, 1410
Butler, Lawrence, 365
Butler, Marilyn, 365
Butler, Marshall D., 365
Butler, Michael, 365
Butler, Nancy Chasanoff, 5833
Butler, Nancy Oare, 4514
Butler, Nathaniel, 4352
Butler, Patti Dawn, 364
Butler, Steve, 9718
Butler, Susan L., 9451
Butler, Susan Storz, 5122
Butler, Willard G., 4829
Butson, Amy, 9667
Butt Foundation, H.E., 2621
Butterfield, Bruce, 7388
Butterfield, Mark, 5238
Buttress, Christine, 7304
Butz, Alvin H., 7908
Butz, Dolores A., 7908
Butz, Eric R., 7908
Butz, Greg L., 7908
Butz, Lee A., 7908
Butz, Shari L., 7908
Butzel, Laura E., 6135
Butzow, Barry W., 4651
Butzow, Bryan A., 4651
Butzow, Joni, 4651
Buxton, Thomas M., 8060
Buyan, Elizabeth S., 4848
Buzzeo, Michael A., 2172
Byala, Brian, 8187
Byers, Daphne, 7338
Byers, Robert L., Jr., 7998
Bynum, Jessie Sue, 18
Byrd, Dennis, 3786
Byrd, Julie A., 4410
Byrer, F. Samuel, 9758
Byrne Revocable Trust, Doris M., 5283
Byrne, James, 7850
Byrne, James R., 6884
Byrne, Kevin, 2597
Byrne, Laura, 8809
Byrne, Rebecca C., 6884

Byrne, Thomas, 7850
Byrne, Thomas J., 7476
Byrnes, James J., 6546
Byron, Larry, 4362
Byron-Weston Co., 4058
Byrski, Mary, 1938
Byzewski, Sandra, 4806

C & B Foundation, 2265
C & M Ranch, 9041
C&A Industries, 5098
C&D Zodiac, 461
C-CK's Inc., 153
C. A. Marketing Inc., 5953
CA Unlimited LLC, 153
Cabacungan, Janice L., 9448
Cabela, Jerome J., 5118
Cable, Cindy, 7829
Cable, Gay W., 2728
Cable, Howard W., Jr., 2728
Cabot, Frederick C., 4034
Cabot, Paul C., 4034
Cabot, Richard, 4035
Cabot, Virginia, 4034
Caccese, Maria, 6408
Cacchio, Steven, 1559
Cacciamani, Lauren P., 6616
Cacciamani, Paul A., 6616
Caccomo, Aurelio, 2771
Cachey, Theodore, 3078
Cactus Family Trust, 5167
Cad Capital, LLC, 7365
Caddell Construction Co., 19
Caddell, Cathy L., 19
Caddell, Christopher P., 19
Caddell, Jeffrey P., 19
Caddell, John A., 19
Caddell, John K., 19
Caddell, Joyce K., 19
Caddell, Michael A., 19
Cade, Martha, 1670
Cade, Mary, 1670
Cadena, Jose S., 9083
Cadena, Mona, 5235
Cader, Andrew, 5807
Cader, Michael, 5807
Cadinha, Harlan J., 2657
Cadle, Barbara J., 1112
Cadle, Carolyn, 1112
Cadle, LLC, 7365
Caesar's Entertainment Operation Co.,
   8570
Cafaro, Debra A., 2772
Caffrey, Jack, 9766
Caffrey, John, 6455
Caffrey, Thomas F., 8452
Cafritz Trust, William N., 3830
Cafritz, Buffy M., 3830
Cafritz, Carter, 1793
Cafritz, Melissa, 1793
Cafritz, Pamela Anne, 3830
Cafritz, William N., 3830
Cahill, Catherine G., 5741
Cahill, Kaye, 8577
Cahill, Nicholas D., 8169
Cahill, Robert L., Jr., 5906
Cahn, Adele, 3716
Cahn, James L., 3716
Cahn, June, 3716
Cahn, Richard M., 3716
Cail, Lois, 4036
Cail, Milton, 4036
Caille, Frances P., 5822

Caimi, Gina, 5968
Cain, Douglas M., 1273
Cain, Kathryn G., 8884
Cain, Linda, 9040
Cain, Michael, 3436
Cain, Michael D., 9744
Cain, Tyler R., 2773
Cain-Pozzo, Diane, 7796
Caine, Edward P., 7953
Caine, Karen, 4582
Cajthaml, Mary J., 2423
Calamari, Peter, 480
Calame, Paul, 2327
Calarco, Christopher, 1414
Calarco, David, 1414
Calarco, Linda, 1414
Calarco, Vincent, 1414
Calcara, Melanie, 3582
Calcaterra, Jenna, 1606
Caldas, Barbara Hanley, 8916
Calder, Ann Martin, 5810
Calder, Cornelia Martin, 5810
Calder, Donald, 5810
Calder, Donald Grant, 5810
Calder, Donald Grant, Jr., 5810
Calder, Frederick C., 6360
Calder, Isabella Swift, 5810
Calderon-Porter, Maria Eugenia, 9010
Caldwell Group Charitable Trust, 3796
Caldwell Living Trust, Elizabeth T., 8593
Caldwell Scholarship Fund, 3796
Caldwell, Betsey C., 1415
Caldwell, Carla, 9630
Caldwell, Cheryl L., 1239
Caldwell, Chris, 3421
Caldwell, Elvin, Jr., 1228
Caldwell, John, 3796
Caldwell, Lawrence C., 1415
Caldwell, Philip, 1415
Caldwell, R. Carter, 7924
Caldwell, Robert E., Sr., 8525
Caldwell, Robert P., Jr., 7097
Caldwell, Samuel D., 8275
Caldwell, Sylvia R., 8525
Caldwell, William H., 2296
Calewarts, Kenneth G., 9898
Calhoon, Ann, 4851
Calhoun, Brad Allen, 7366
Calhoun, Eric R., 7221
Calhoun, John C., 3724
Calhoun, Kenneth, 7344
Calhoun, Sallie, 644
Cali, Brant, 5284
Cali, John, 5284
Cali, John J., 5284
Cali, Rose, 5284
Cali, Rose C., 5284
Caliguri, Katie, 5016
Calkins, Christopher C., 227
Call, Linda C., 1297
Callaghan, Elizabeth H., 2083
Callaghan, J. Kevin, 9609
Callaghan, Lorraine M., 5897
Callahan, Carol, 110
Callahan, Eugene J., 6638
Callahan, F.J., 5284
Callahan, Jennifer G., 9827
Callahan, Maurice E., 4057
Callahan, Nancy, 7345
Callahan, Sandra W., 2367
Callahan, Timothy J., 7345
Callan, David J., 3946
Callans, Gwen, 3217
Callant Estate Trust, Marcel, 4439

Callas, Michael G., 1913
Calle, 90
Callea, Janet V., 6676
Callegari, John, 9691
Callen, Rudy, 4606
Calligan, Marian E., 7909
Calligan, Scott R., 7909
Calligaris, Alfred B., 6922
Callison, Fred W., 371
Callister, Andrew, 9310
Callister, Jan, 9310
Callister, Mary B., 9310
Callister, Paul Q., 9310
Calpin, William J., 7892
Calpine Corp., 8759
Calpine Corporation, 8759
Calumet Enterprises Inc., 7925
Calvanese, Emily, 5961
Calvary Baptist Church, 840
Calvo, Jose, 1952
Camacho, Victor, 1599
Camadeco, Benjamin, 5245
Camaliche, Raul A., 2150
Cambell, Catherine, 2909
Cambell, Levin H., Jr., 4251
Cambridge Real Estate Holdings Inc.,
   8760
Cambridge Trust Co., 4288, 4368
Camelo, Laura, 6669
Cameron Services, 1316
Cameron, Alpin J., 7911
Cameron, Alpin W., 7911
Cameron, Bruce S., 337
Cameron, Charlotte, 7065
Cameron, Daniel D., 7065
Cameron, Daniel D., Jr., 7065
Cameron, Elizabeth H., 7065
Cameron, John D., 3721
Cameron, John J., 4250
Cameron, Lynell D., 1885
Cameron, Lynn, 4592
Cameron, Robert C., 2161
Cameron, Ronald M., 3002
Cameron, Susan S., 8978
Cameron, William H., 7065
Camfield, William A., 8873
Camillus House, 1975
Cammarano, Philip, 1559
Cammarota, Edward D., 1637
Camp Chaviva, 5544
Camp, Gwen Borowsky, 7886
Camp, J.L., Jr., 9413
Camp, J.L., Jr., Mrs. , 9413
Camp, James L., III, 9413
Camp, James L., IV, 9413
Camp, Megan, 9368
Camp, Melvin R., 7698
Camp, Ruth Turner, 2177
Campanale, Frank, 4440
Campbell Remainder Unitrust, Betsy
   McDavid, 8515
Campbell, Alan, 8874
Campbell, Ardis, 4222
Campbell, Bruce S., III, 3831
Campbell, C. David, 9084
Campbell, Charles, 8595, 9253
Campbell, Charles Talbot, 7912
Campbell, Charles W., 5129
Campbell, Chris, 7637
Campbell, Craig Dobbs, 211
Campbell, David, 9085
Campbell, Debby, 8595
Campbell, Debra, 2862
Campbell, Douglas, Jr., 1426

Campbell, Elizabeth M., 9626
Campbell, Elizabeth Stephens, 211
Campbell, Eugenie, 7417
Campbell, J. Tyler, 3831
Campbell, Jane, 8594
Campbell, John, 7637, 8594
Campbell, John D., 5510
Campbell, John L., 7305
Campbell, Kate, 4542
Campbell, Lawrence, Sr., Rev. , 9556
Campbell, Leslie, 9784
Campbell, Levin H., 4251
Campbell, Lisa W., 1159
Campbell, Malcolm David, Dr. , 9450
Campbell, Mary Jo, 3831
Campbell, Nancy Harris, 5605
Campbell, Patrick, 7637
Campbell, R. Stewart, Jr., 9050
Campbell, Ronald, 9766
Campbell, Virginia T., 3831
Campbell, William Durant, 6989
Campen, Angelique , 471
Campey, Alan, 427
Camuto, Robert, 5812
Canada, Susan H., 8296
Canady, Gina, 3397
Candela, John, 9832
Candler, Sarah Graham, 2591
Candler, Shannon I., 2518
Candrian, Scott, 2109
Canfield, William W., 4882
Canida, Ben, Dr. , 3359
Canipe, Anne, 2452
Canipe, Virginia, 2452
Canipe, W. Kent, 2452
Cannedy, Mac, 8784
Canning, Charlotte H., 2975
Cannon Manufacturing Co., 577
Cannon Marital Trust, William C., 7067
Cannon, E. Rasha, 62
Cannon, Eleanor Rixon, 7223
Cannon, Francis, 374
Cannon, George W., 9361
Cannon, Lucinda Samford, 62
Cannon, Robert, 374
Cannon, Sara, 374
Cannon, Ted, 5113
Cannon, Tom, 8516
Cannon, William C., Jr., 7067
Canteen, 1362
Canton Investment Holdings LLC, 1367
Cantonis, Anastasia H., 1915
Cantonis, George H., 1915
Cantonis, George M., 1915
Cantonis, James M., 1915
Cantonis, Michael G., 1915
Cantor Fitzgerald Inc., 375
Cantor Fitzgerald Relief Fund Admin, 6463
Cantor Fitzgerald, LP, 375
Cantor, B. Gerald, 375
Cantor, Eddy, 1916
Cantor, Iris, 375
Cantor, Richard, 5285
Cantrell, Carol A., 9026
Cantrell, Dianna, 8674
Cantwell, Dick, 1272
Cantwell, Lucy, 1272
Cantwell, William R., 4405
Canty, Kristin M., 4104
Caouette, Therese, 9697
Capco Sales, 4966
Capellano, Mark, 1047
Capellupo, John, 4883

Capellupo, Kevin, 4883
Capellupo, Mark, 4883
Capellupo, Mary Ann, 4883
Capellupo, Matthew, 4883
Capellupo, Michael, 4883
Capital City Bank, 1918
Capital City First National Bank, 1918
Capital City Trust Co., 1973
Capital Guardian Trust Co., 289
Capital Investments & Ventures Corp., 898
Capital One, 1837, 3722, 3728
Capital One Bank, 3740, 3755, 6655
Capital Ventures of NV, 4408
Capital, Perry, 6884
Capitani, Steve, 8657
Caplan, Catherine, 3832
Caplan, Constance R., 3832
Caplan, Denise B., 2919
Caplan, Jonathan, 3832
Caplan, Mark M., 3832
Caplanson, Nicholas, 1438
Caplin, Edwin, 1638
Caplow, Mildred R., 6698
Caporale, Nicholas A., 4277
Caporale, Wende, 5692
Caporaso, Marsha, 9862
Capossela, Carmine, 4212
Capp, Stephen H., 5183
Cappelen, Ashley J. Knopf, 2155
Cappelletti, Matthew, Jr., 7923
Cappelloni, Robert J., 773
Cappuzzo, Salvatore, 6956
Capra, Ellen M., 6258
Capra, James R., 6258
Capranica, Ruth M., 3895
Capranica, Steven F., 3895
Capraro, James, 3078
Caprio, Anthony, 4116
Capshaw, Steven, 4088
Caraway, Ann Cracchiolo, 4415
Caraway, Roberta Gorenstein, 107
Carbaugh, Lyle E., 8972
Carberry, George, 3385
Carbiener, Pamela, 2001
Carbonari, Bruce A., 1919
Carbonari, Danielle M., 1919
Carbonari, Kathryn E., 1919
Carbonari, Kathy, 1919
Carbonari, Nicole K., 1919
Carbonell, John N., 3833
Carbonell, Michelle, 3833
Carbonell, Nelson, 3833
Card, Augusta H., 8596
Card, Robert G., Jr., 8596
Card, Robert, III, 8596
Card, Susan, 8596
Carden, Lance, 7388
Cardenas, Renato E., 8752
Cardinale, Ruth, 5018
Cardinali, Albert J., 6202
Cardiovascular Research Foundation, 8368
Cardon, Helen H., 9311
Cardon, Jeffrey S., 9311
Cardozo, Michael, 5886
Cardozo, V, Michael H., 5887
Carenet, 9033
Carey Trust, Jeanne M., 2775
Carey, C.M., 7765
Carey, Drew A., 311
Carey, John M., 7317
Carey, Linda, 3684
Carey, Patricia G., 7691

Carey, Patrick M., 1482
Cargill Inc., 8859
Cargill Meat Solutions Corp., 8859
Cargill, Kenneth V., 5238
Cargill, Robert L., 8761
Cargill, Sara Lou, 8761
Carillo, Gretchen Weisenburger, 1097
Carillon Importers, 6123
Carino, Olivia, 5753
Carion, Anthony P., 707
Caristo, Heather, 7358
Carl, Keith, 9465
Carle, Barbara, 4037
Carle, Eric, 4037
Carlee, Jane H., 4038
Carletti, Peter, 9696
Carley, Patrick, Rev. , 9333
Carli, Franco, 1180
Carlile, Rhett, 7822
Carlile, Richard F., 2296
Carlin, Audre, 1921
Carlin, Donald, 1921
Carlin, Wayne, 7339
Carlinski, Michael, 480
Carlisle, Donna, 8795
Carlman, Leonard R., 4163
Carlone, Robert, 4448
Carlozzi, Beth, 5287
Carlozzi, Margaret H., 5287
Carlozzi, Mark, 5287
Carlozzi, Nicholas, 5287
Carlozzi, Nicholas H., 5287
Carlozzi, Robert, 5287
Carlquist, Michelle J., 5786
Carlsmith, Laura, 9382
Carlson Living Trust, Arleen M., 4692
Carlson, Brenda, 5104
Carlson, C. Dean, 3479
Carlson, David, 1581
Carlson, Diane, 4689
Carlson, Ernest G., 8573
Carlson, Jay, 4396
Carlson, Mark, 7933
Carlson, Max E., 1360
Carlson, Merlyn, 5118
Carlson, Ronald P., 4139
Carlson, Sandra S., 3479
Carlson, Terri, 4334
Carlston, Alice, 377
Carlston, Don, 377
Carlston, Douglas G., 377
Carlston, Gary, 377
Carlton, Doyle E., III, 2239, 2413
Carlton, Doyle E., Jr., 2413
Carlton, L.F., 8862
Carlton, Uriel W., 1736
Carlyle, Shannon McLin, 2123
Carlyon, David, 6634
Carmack, Marion D., Jr., 3902
Carmichael, Doug, 8751
Carmichael, James, 89
Carmody, John, 8345
Carnahan, Katharine J., 7917
Carnegie, Helen, 1888
Carnegie, Henry, 1888
Carnell, J. Kevin, 3937
Carnes, Caleb J., 2555
Carnes, Clifford, 3359
Carney, Annelle I., 2093
Carney, Victoria, 9635
Carnivale, Nicholas, 5513
Carol Electric Company Inc., 382
Carolan, James M., 1456, 6679
Caroll, Jennifer, 1167

Caroll, John, 1167
Caron, Cynthia, 1816
Carosso, Virginia Peterson, 3614
Carothers Construction, 4827
Carothers, Lucille K., 7501
Carothers, Max E., 3366
Carothers, Sean B., 4827
Carpenter, Aaron E., 8172
Carpenter, Andy, 4824
Carpenter, Benjamin, 1549
Carpenter, Edythe A., 8172
Carpenter, Elaine, 2689
Carpenter, G. Paul, 9626
Carpenter, Michael, 6884, 7311
Carpenter, Michael, Mrs. , 6884
Carpenter, Wayne L., 3585
Carpenter, William, Jr., 4947
Carpentier, Lisa Busse, 3478
Carper Foundation, The, 9577
Carper, Daniel E., 9577
Carper, Margaret A., 9577
CARR Lane Manufacturing, 5034
Carr Trust, Robert L., 4484
Carr, Catherine E., 577
Carr, Davis H., 8630
Carr, Jerome D., 3896
Carr, Joe, 3514
Carr, Meredith G., 7425
Carr, Rachael, 8825
Carr, Rebecca, 211
Carr, Ronald, Mrs. , 6868
Carr, Tamara, 4472
Carranco, Rosendo, 9010
Carrick, David H., 3508
Carrico, Jennifer, 2681
Carriere, Dianne, 9069
Carrington, Janet A., 1923
Carris Corporate Foundation, 9376
Carris Financial Corp., 9367
Carris Reels, 9367
Carris Reels of California, 9367
Carris Reels of Connecticut, 9367
Carris, Barbara T., 9376
Carris, William H., 9376
Carroll Trust, Florence V., 3354
Carroll, Amy, 8368
Carroll, Catharine A., 2976
Carroll, Charlene P., 5816
Carroll, D.H., 2976
Carroll, David, 1368
Carroll, Frederick L., 359
Carroll, Frederick L., Mrs. , 359
Carroll, George, 3171
Carroll, Greg, 3911
Carroll, Jody, 3611
Carroll, Judith, 1167
Carroll, Ken, 1295
Carroll, Kevin, 5
Carroll, Marilyn, 1295
Carroll, Patsy R., 7068
Carroll, Penny, 8603
Carroll, Philip J., Jr., 5816
Carroll, Rod, 8869
Carroll, Roger D., 8403
Carroll, Roy E., II, 7068
Carroll, Russell L., 8644
Carroll, Stephen, 7953
Carroll, Stephen D., 9982
Carroll, Timothy G., 2893, 2939
Carroll, Vanessa Y., 7068
Carroll, Wendy I., 3888
Carroll-Pankhurst, Cindie, 7338
Carros Revocable Trust, Jean, 1924
Carros, Jean, 1924

Carruth, Laura T., 1134
Carruthers, Daniel J., 2132
Carse, Elizabeth, 1553
Carson, Allen, 9751
Carson, Mark H., 1350
Carson, Wayne, 2050
Carstens, Richard, 5090
Carswell, Bruce, 1507
Carswell, Gale Fisher, 2654
Carswell, Robert, 6135
Cartales, Helen M., 9578
Cartales, John A., 9578
Carter, Annie, 7356
Carter, Bernard E., 9741
Carter, C.J., 9426
Carter, Curt, 4490
Carter, David W., 7519
Carter, Don, 9070
Carter, Don E., 5325
Carter, Donna L., 9133
Carter, E. Eugene, 1794
Carter, Elliott C., Jr., 5671
Carter, Evelyn, 2776
Carter, Fred, Dr. , 8522
Carter, Georgia, 9741
Carter, James J., Jr., 71
Carter, Larry, 3702
Carter, Lee A., 7609
Carter, Leslie R., 9741
Carter, Lynne A., 4221
Carter, Richard J., Jr., 6000
Carter, Ruth B., 7969
Carter, Teron, 1937
Cartier, 9200
Cartiglia, Katherine Gilweit, 5190
Cartinhour, W.C., Sr., 8597
Cartledge Chantable Lead Trust, Olive
    M., 9414
Cartledge, George B., III, 9414
Cartledge, George B., Jr., 9414
Carty, Blair, 229
Caruana, Sal, 5582
Carusi, Bruce, 5154
Carusi, Sue, 5154
Caruso, Donna, 1917
Caruso, Frank, 5817
Caruso, Joseph, 1463
Caruso, Kim M., 2367
Caruso, Ruth, 5817
Caruthers, Witt, 3750
Carver, Betsy, 9418
Carver, Gregory, 9418
Carver, Judith G., 4067
Carver, Martin G., 5143
Carver, Ruth A., 5143
Carville, J., 3748
Cary Oil Co. Inc., 7070
Cary, A. Bray, Jr., 7069
Cary, Catherine Havens, 3727
CASA of Southeast Texas, 8869
Casaclang, Eisen Jo, 5964
Casady, Julia N., 4230
Casady, Mark S., 4230
Casagrande, Genevieve, 4938
Casali, John, 4228
Casalou, Allan, 509
Cascarilla, Charles, 6239
Case, Deborah J., 7469
Case, Donald, 1566
Case, Elmer, 5091
Case, Libby, 3691
Case, Nicole, 7558
Case, Pamela Jean, 1925
Case, Phil, 933

Case, Robert B., 1925
Case, Robert R., 933
Case, Samuel L., 1925
Case, Scott, 1038
Casebolt, Robert, 5011
Caselton, Stephen, Dr. , 4497
Casey, Carol, 1161
Casey, Coleman H., 1591
Casey, E. Paul, 4039
Casey, Edward G., 4195
Casey, J. Robert, 4325
Casey, Jennifer P., 4039
Casey, Kathy, 1291
Casey, Michael D., 2454
Casey, Sarah O'Herron, 1536
Casey, Sophia B., 5819
Casey, William J., 5819
Casey-Smith, Bernadette, 5819
Cash, James D., 7711
Cash, W. Larry, 8601
Cashaw, MPH, RN, Sandra, 8924
Cashill, Robert, 5513
Cashion Family Foundation, John L.,
    The , 884
Cashman, Kathryn Batchelder, 6739
Cashmere Capital, 5452
Casino, Artichoke Joe's, 996
Casner Family Fund, 3668
Caspall, Kenneth K., 4960
Cass, Neil E., 7977
Cassan Enterprises, 9624
Cassan, Doris, 9624
Cassan, Doris O., 9624
Cassan, James, 9624
Cassan, James T., 9624
Cassem, Tierney, Adams, Gotch, 5102
Cassidy, Ann S., 7663
Cassidy, Mary Lou, 4903
Cassidy, William L., 4903
Cassie, Beth, 5582
Cassin, Joseph M., 6368
Cassity, Dorothy J., 3589
Cassner, Alvin, 7348
Cassner, Brian, 7348
Cassner, Carl, 7348
Cassner, Jon, 7348
Cassullo, Joanne Leonhardt, 6381
Casteel, Monty, 9048
Casteen, John T., III, 9441
Castelano-Garcia, Carmela, 380
Castellani, Joan J., 1927
Castellani, Lawrence P., 1927
Castellani, Lawrence P., Jr., 1927
Castellano, Alcario, 380
Castellano, Armando, 380
Castellano, Carmen, 380
Castellano, Christine, 2987
Castellano, Theresa, 9293
Castellano-Garcia, Carmela, 380
Castelle, George, 5593
Castelnau Foundation, 1783
Caster, Marci, 8574
Castle Oil Corp., 5820
Castle, Courtney A., 1469
Castle, Gary S., 5843
Castle, George P., 2626
Castle, Ida Tenney, 2626
Castle, James H., 1469
Castle, Jennie Y., 1469
Castle, Jonatha Y., 1469
Castle, William H., 1469
Castleberry, Anne Pund, 7567
Castleberry, Edward F., 7567
Castleberry, Kelly, 7567

Castleberry, Susan, 7567
Castleman, Peter M., 5144
Castleman, Sloane C., 5144
Castner, Russell, 9706
Castner, Svanhild S., 9706
Castor Theodore H Trust, 8236
Castro, Donald , Rev., 9642
Castro, Jill C., 5494
Castrodale, Robert L., 9770
Caswell Caplan First Charitable Inc.
    Trust, 3832
Caswell Caplan Second Charitable Inc.
    Trust, 3832
Catalano, Antonio P., 9915
Catalde, Brian, 1130
Catalde, Michelle, 1130
Catalina Marketing Corp., 1928
Catanzaro, Terre R., 170
Catazaro-Perry, Katy, 7442
Cater, Annabel, 5280
Cater, Charles B., 5280
Cater, June B., 5280
Cater, Kerry, 5280
Cater, William B., Jr., 5280, 5566
Cathedral of St. John the Divine, 5220
Catherwood, Susan W., 8134
Catholic Foundation, The, 9033
Catholic Seminary Foundation of
    Indianapolis, 5358
Catino, Beverly, 4040
Catino, Theodore, 4040
Catlett, L. Reed, 2349
Cato Charitable Lead Annuity Trust,
    Christine A., 8516
Cato, Christine Anne, 8516
Cato, Edgar T., 8516
Cato, Edgar T., III, 8516
Cato, Jan Stockard, 9198
Cato, John P.D., 7071
Cato, Thomas E., 7071
Cato, Wayland H., 7071
Cato, Wayland H., Jr., 7071
Catsimatidis, John, 5823
Catsimatidis, Margo, 5823
Cattan, Ezra Jack, 5976
Cattan, Jack, 5976
Cattan, Judah, 5976
Cattan, Mary, 6542
Caudill, Loretta D., 2122
Caudill, Michael S., 2122
Caudill, Richard J., 2122
Caudill, Richard W., 2122
Caudill, William H., 5821
Caudle, Robert, 5620
Caulkins, Christina Radichel, 4765
Caulkins, David I., 1245
Caulkins, Eleanor N., 1245
Caulkins, George P., III, 1245
Caulkins, George P., Jr., 1245
Caulkins, John N., 1245
Caulkins, Mary I., 1245
Caulkins, Maxwell O.B., 1245
Causley, James F., Jr., 4405
Cauthen, Charles, 8537
Cauthen, Charles E., 8537
Cauthen, Hazel, 8537
Cauthen, William, 2291
Cauthorn, Mildred, 8764
Cavaliere, Anthony J., 7953
Cavallaro, Peter I., 6631
Cavanagh Trust, John C., The , 6265
Cavanagh, April, 5094
Cavanaugh, Karen A., 9413
Cavanaugh, March A., 5702

Cavanaugh, Paul, 4243
Cavanaugh, Philip G., 5702
Cavanaugh, Rebecca B., 9427
Cavanaugh, Sean A., 5702
Cavaness, Milton, 8764
Cavaricci, Caesar A., 381
Cavaricci, Diane L., 381
Cavaricci, James A., 381
Cavaricci, Marcello, 381
Cavender Charitable Lead Annuity Trust,
    S.S., 3248
Cavender, Susan S., 3248
Caveney Family Enterprises, LP, 2789
Cavins, Jennifer S., 2170
Cawley, Charles M., 1781, 8327
Cawsey, Hugh R., Mrs. , 9626
Cay, Christopher W., 2506
Caya, Renetta Ascher, 256
Cayard, Paul, 998
Caylor, Edward, 8580
Cayne, Richard, 3995
Cayrac Corp., 1246
CCC Wood Group, 1095
CCF I, 2141
Cebelak, Bernard J., 4406
Cebelak, Camille L., 4406
Cecil, Carl, 9114
Cecil, Philip, 9114
Cedar Hill Foundation, 6265
Cedar, William, 4576
Cedlair Corp., 3905
Ceglarski, Eileen, 1588
Celebrity Bowling Classic, 5414
Celebrity Golf Championship, 9
Celebrity International, 1931
Celer, Michael, 3065
Celestin, Roger, 6820
Celstar Group, 7331
Celusniak, Kristin, 1295
Celusniak, Mark, 1295
Cemex, 366
Cemo, Jason M., 8765
Cemo, Michael J., 8765
Cemo, Rebecca A., 8765
Cemo, Stephanie C., 8765
Cendant Corp., 5255
Ceniza, Natalie, 4414
Censullo, Marilyn A., 4211
Centaur, 7317
Centennial Consulting Corp., 190
Centerplate, 3867
Central Argentina Corp., 1336
Central Bank Illinois, 2909
Central Cheese Co., 5468
Central Concrete Supply Co., 366
Central Florida Investments, 2400
Central National Bank, 3564
Central Pacific Bank, 2627
Central Stearns Comsis, 4624
Central Trust and Investment Co., 5010
Centrella, Frank, 5461
Century 21 William B. May, 6656
Century Coin and Collectibles, 376
Century National Bank, 7518
Century, Jane Friedman, 6682
Cepko, Constance, 2881
Cerda, Christine H., 9010
Ceriale, John V., 5828
Ceriale, Melissa, 5828
Cermak, Mark, 3149
Cernak, Kenneth S., 4076
Cernera, Anthony J., 2022
Cerri 2002 Trust, Rossi, 384
Cerullo, Geraldine F., 5829

Cerullo, John J., III, 5829
Cervantes, Jennifer, 5610
Cervenak, Chris, 4234
Cervenka, Debbie, 9774
Cervenka, Robert, 9774
Cervone, Stefano, 6828
Cesare, Denise S., 7879
Cestac, Francoise, 5669
Cesta, Claire D., 422
Cetnar, Cindy, 8228
Ceunis, Irma, 385
CF & EG Duff 2002 Charitable Lead
    Annuity Trust, 9508
CGEL Associates, LLP, 9448
CGF Industries, 3563
CGS Industries, 6726
Chabner, Brandon S., 4041
Chabner, Bruce Allan, 4041
Chabner, Davi-Ellen, 4041
Chabrourne, Ruth, 1932
Chace, Arnold B., 8393
Chace, Arnold B., Jr., 8393
Chace, Beatrice O., 8393
Chace, Elizabeth Z., 8393
Chace, Malcolm G., III, 8393
Chadbourne, Doug, 921
Chadbourne, Edward M., III, 1932
Chadbourne, Edward M., Jr., 1932
Chadbourne, Edward M., Jr., Mrs. , 1932
Chadbourne, Ruth J., 1932
Chaddock, Jeffery, 7408
Chader, Gerald J., 2881
Chae, Alexander, 8810
Chaffee, Marcia G., 3806
Chaffee, Robert B., 3806
Chaffin, Greg, 42
Chaffins, Douglas H., 2463
Chaffiot, Mark K., 1933
Chaffiot, Robeana, 1933
Chaffiot, Robert R., 1933
Chaffiot, Robert R., Jr., 1933
Chaffiot, Victor, 1933
Chaffiot, Victor A., 1933
Chafin, James T., III, 2586
Chafin, Kay, 9147
Chai X Four Charitable Trust, 6151
Chai, Ping Yin, 4277
Chaikin, Wendy Blank, 5756
Chaim Electronic Corp., 6771
Chaim Foundation, 5705
Chainani, Kamlesh, 9417
Chainani, Luci, 9417
Chaintreuil, Renier F., 6939
Chait, Gerald, 7856
Chalfant, Henry, Mrs. , 5935
Chalfant, R. Peterson, 7335
Chamberlain Irrevocable Investment
    Trust, 8166
Chamberlain, Bryce B., 2909
Chamberlain, Mark, 9932
Chamberlain, Thomas, 2989
Chamberlin, Craig, 3567
Chamberlin, Glenn, 2708
Chambers Scholarship Trust, Mary
    Cecile, 8767
Chambers, Anne Cox, 5669
Chambers, Bradley T., 4499
Chambers, Jason R., 3718
Chambers, Ned, 1102
Chambers, Ray L., 3449
Chambers, Rhonda, 3485
Chambers, Russell C., 3718
Chameli, Kathleen C., 3544
Chami, George, 5146

Chami, George Albert, II, 5146
Chami, Marcia, 5146
Chami, Mardah, 5146
Chamley, Amy C. Kilgus, 3220
Champlain Valley Expo., 1046
Chan, Amy H. Caplow, 6698
Chan, Annie M.H., 387
Chan, Caleb, 388
Chan, Chia Hwa, 52
Chan, Christian, 388
Chan, David Y.W., 387
Chan, Dennis C.C., 52
Chan, Edward Y.C., 387
Chan, James, 2638
Chan, John, 6624
Chan, Pei Ling, 52
Chan, Pei Ling, Mrs. , 52
Chan, Shiu Leung, 387
Chan, Stephanie, 2638
Chan, Tom, 388
Chan, Yvonne, 9494
Chana Sasha Foundation Inc., 5878
Chance, Elizabeth B., 5582
Chance, V.E., 3633
Chancellor, Brian, 900
Chandler, A., 8856
Chandler, A. Russell, III, 2455
Chandler, Ashley E., 2455
Chandler, Carol, 4164
Chandler, Don, 1038
Chandler, Heather, 763
Chandler, Joe, 8526
Chandler, John W., 5393
Chandler, Maria Planes, 2455
Chandler, Morgan A., 2455
Chandler, Stephen, 1024
Chandler, Sue W., 1024
Chandler, Whitney R., 2455
Chandran, Rama E., 925
Chandrasoma, Dilum, 9069
Chanen, Franklin A., 3118
Chaney Enterprises, L.P., 1640
Chaney, Frances, 7747
Chaney, Francis H., II, 1640
Chaney, James B., 7349
Chaney, Robert, 7747
Chang, Charles K., 528
Chang, Chung Yuan, 255
Chang, Karin, 4983
Chang, Luanne, 533
Chang, Margaret S., 5289
Chang, Michelle, 1190
Chang, Phillip, 1190
Chang, Robert N., 5290
Chang, Shiu Run Shirley, 255
Chang, Yen Shiu-Run, 255
Chang-Muy, Fernando, 8350
Chang-Tzu, Ven Bhikkhu, 5596
Chanin, Leona F., 1934
Chapdelaine, Donald, 4657
Chapekis, Frederick, 2827
Chapel, Diana, 9123
Chapin, Charles, 9989
Chapin, Simeon B., 2782
Chapin, Stewart B., 7860
Chapin, Thomas M., 7860
Chaplin, Carolyn A., 4268
Chaplin, Christina Stafford, 2346
Chaplin, Harvey R., 4334
Chaplin, Laurie, 5739
Chapman, Alvah H., 1935
Chapman, Anna, 5832
Chapman, Anne Allston, 8517
Chapman, Betty Bateman, 1935

Chapman, Carl L., 3450
Chapman, Cynthia M., 4884
Chapman, Don, 4946
Chapman, George, 67
Chapman, Hugh M., 8517
Chapman, James, 9085
Chapman, Matthew, 3033
Chapman, Max C., Jr., 5292
Chapman, Nancy, 1117
Chapman, Patti, 7513
Chapman, Peter R., 6982
Chapman, Rachel, 8517
Chapman, Robert H., 4884
Chapman, Susan, 6982
Chapman, Wyline Page, 1935
Chappell, Katherine C., 3772
Chappell, Norman P., 3401
Chappell, Thomas M., 3772
Chappell, W. Bates, 9411, 9419
Chappuis, Jacques, 2109
Charach, Jeffrey, 4503
Charach, Manuel, 4503
Charach, Natalie, 4503
Charah Inc., 3686
Charbonnet, Carolyn H., 2361
Chardan Capital, 1730
Chardoul, Marion H., 2779
Charitable Lead Annuity Trust, 4631
Charitable Lead Annuity Trust No. 1,
    4677, 4731, 4756
Charity Appell Mcnabb, 3778
Charity Buzz, 1730
Charlene, Freda, 1072
Charles Schwab Bank, 1663
Charles, Ellen Macneille, 7213
Charles, Ken, 8522
Charles, Les, 390
Charles, Michael G., 7986
Charles, Stephen G., 9476
Charles, Zora, 390
Charlestein Foundation, Julius and Ray,
    7941
Charlestein, Gary, 7920
Charlestein, Morton L., 7920
Charlton Co., Harry, 5500
Charlton, David H., 9412
Charlton, E.P., 8394
Charlton, Earle P., Jr., 8394
Charlton, Stacy, 8394
Charter Charitable Foundation, 5235
Chartered Foundation, 2005
Chartis Group LLC, 4044
Chasanoff, Allan, 5833
Chasanoff, Judith, 5833
Chasanoff, Michael J., 5833
Chasanoff, Nancy, 5833
Chasanoff, Robert, 5833
Chasanoff, Stephen, 5833
Chasco Co., 5833
Chase, 9130
Chase, Alfred E., 4045
Chase, Alice P., 7921
Chase, Allison A. F., 6224
Chase, Charlene, 3796
Chase, David D., 5606
Chase, Joe, 4396
Chase, Johnnie C., 8393
Chase, Katherin Lee, 5606
Chase, Rahn, 7078
Chase, Sarah Tyler, 4599
Chase, Stuart F., 8952
Chase, Thomas, 4246
Chastain Trust, Betty, 9793
Chastain, Ricky, 2437

Chastain, Robert Lee, 7073
Chatham Investment Partners, 2714
Chatman, Cheryl, 4734
Chatterjee Charitable Foundation, 6884
Chatterjee, Jay, 7582
Chatters, Lawrence J., 5085
Chaudhary, Bushra, 8768
Chaudhary, Maria, 8768
Chaudhary, Younas, 8768
Chavis, David, 8674
Cheatham, Barbara Marlene M., 3753
Cheatham, Celeste W., 5836
Cheatham, Frank W., 3255
Cheatham, Owen Robertson, 5836
Cheatham, Scott Eric, 3753
Cheatham, Skye Edwards, 3753
Cheatham, Stanley Earl, 3753
Cheatham, Stanley Eugene, 3753
Cheatham, Steven Eugene, 3753
Chee, William, 2638
Cheek, Donna, 58
Cheek, H. Yvonne, 4796
Cheesman, Gary D., 3346
Cheetham, Allin, 5058
Cheever, Andrew, 6448
Cheever, Benjamin, 6448
Cheever, Janet, 6448
Cheever, John, 6448
Chehebar, Ezra A., 6069
Chehebar, Gabriel A., 6069
Chehebar, Josef A., 6069
Chehebar, Michael A., 6069
Cheiftain, 3516
Chelace Brand Inc., 153
Chelap, Gregory S., 8075
Chelm, Kerry, 7475
Chelsea Groton Bank, 1418
Chemed Corp., 7350
Chemerow, Elynor, 9862
Chemtob, Elka, 5837
Chemtob, Marc, 5837
Chen, Alice Der-Shan, 1939
Chen, Andrew H., 533
Chen, Edward, 5575
Chen, Gerald G., 1939
Chen, Janet, 5575
Chen, Jerome G., 1939
Chen, Shirley, 636
Chen, Stephen, 636
Chen, Sue, 533
Chen, Wan-Ju, 5596
Chen, Yuan-Tsong, 1939
Chenanar Valley Bus Lines, 5273
Chenega Corp., 83
Cheney, Arta, 4763
Cheney, Duane, 3634
Cheney, James E., 6626
Cheng, Angela Kamling, 1194
Cheng, Bob, 659
Cheng, Clifford, 659
Cheng, George, 659
Cheng, Jean, 659
Cherb, John, 8257
Cherington, Gretchen, 5223
Chermak, Renae, 4716
Chernick, Deborah, 4802
Chernoff, Carolyn, 8118
Chernow, Robert W., 9946
Cherry Jr. Trust, Walter L., 2784
Cherry Trust, Virginia B., 2784
Cherry, Adam Z., 1235
Cherry, Alison L., 1940
Cherry, Arthur L., 1940
Cherry, Beverly M., 1940

Cherry, Carolyn N., 1940
Cherry, Christopher R., 1940
Cherry, John Scott, 1940
Cherry, Mary Catherine, 1235
Cherry, Peter B., 2784
Cherry, Robert, 2842
Cherry, Virginia B., 2784
Cherundolo, John C., Hon. , 5154
Chervenak, James, 5839
Chesapeake Energy Corporation, 1785
Chesapeake Trust Co., 9423
Chesed Global Foundation, 5830
Cheshire, Marjorie J. Rodgers, 3808
Chesley, Richard A., 7351
Chesley, Stanley M., 7351
Chessed Congregations of America, 5544
Chessin, Vicki, 4459
Chetham, Enid, 4948
Cheung, Martin, 719
Chez, Eric J., 2785
Chez, Ronald L., 2785
Chiaro, Antoinette, 6408
Chiaro, Jonathan, 6408
Chiarotti, John M., 3348
Chiat, Jay, 393
Chiat, Marc, 393
Chiat-Rosales, Elyse, 393
Chiate, Kenneth, 480
Chic-Fil-A, 2621
Chicago Charities, 8703
Chicago Title and Trust Co., 2786
Chicago Tribune Co., 2787
Chicone, Jerry J., Jr., 1941
Chicopee Bancorp, 4047
Chiel, Judith Jacoby, 654
Chifton Ltd Co., 9179
Child, Julia, 394
Childers, Cynthia Anderson, 1846
Childers, Frank, 884
Childress, Brandi N., 8518
Childress, Francis B., 1942
Childress, J. Donald, 2459
Childress, Janice, 8518
Childress, Janice E., 8518
Childress, Miranda Y., 1942
Childs, Jim, 551
Childs, Kathleen L., 7736
Childs, Kathryn H., 5651
Childs, William F., IV, 1640
Chiles, Earle A., 7749
Chiles, Earle M., 7749
Chiles, Lois, 5843
Chiles, Virginia H., 7749
Chilo, Orille Rex, 157
Chilton, Arthur L., 7667
Chilton, Leonore, 7667
Chilton, Philip N., 4862
Chime on Inc., 684
Chin, Sharon I., 3495
Chinese Christian Church, 8447
Ching, Edric M., 2628
Ching, Elizabeth Lau, 2628
Ching, Glenn, 2627
Ching, Han Hsin, 2628
Ching, Han Ping, 2628
Ching, Hung Wo, 2628
Ching, Patrick D., 2645
Ching, Shelli Mei Li, 2628
Chinn, Louise, 6946
Chiodo, Kristen, 1499
Chipman, Wayne, 3427
Chishti, Muzaffar, 5630
Chisick, Brad, 395

Chisick, Brian, 395
Chisick, Jamie P., 395
Chisick, Mark D., 395
Chisick, Sarah, 395
Chisman, James R., 9548
Chisolm, Juliet, 2619
Chitjian, Zaruhy Sara, 396
Chizen, Bruce R., 397
Chizen, Gail B., 397
Chizen, Jessica H., 397
Chizen, Steven M., 397
CHJ Trust, 8974
Cho, IL Hwan, 5431
Cho, Soon Ja, 5431
Chod, Paul N., 3915
Chod, Ronald, 4885
Chodorkoff, Betsy M., 9366
Choi, Enoch, 900
Choksi, Armeane M., 1795
Choksi, Maaren A., 1795
Choksi, Mary C., 1795
Cholobel, Michael, 5667
Choma, Chris, 4079
Chomeau, Douglas B., 4886
Chomeau, Stuart G., 4886
Chong, Yeh Wah, 344
Choong, Gloria, 5298
Chopin, L. Frank, 2010, 2012
Chorbajian, Herbert G., 6546
Chormann Charitable, Richard and Carolyn, 5293
Chormann, James, 5293
Chormann, Richard F., 5293
Chosa, Carnell, 5609
Chotin Group Corp., The, 1246
Chotin, Robin, 1246
Chotin, Steven, 1246
Chotin, Steven B., 1246
Chouake, Benjamin, 5399
Chowdhury, Anand Preet Singh, 1943
Chowdhury, Malini, 398
Chowdhury, Ravneet, 1943
Chowdhury, Subir, 398
Chowning, Glenn S., 7789
Chris Carey Foundation, 7715
Chrisman, Clyde, 7734
Chrisman, Roger Packard, 1016
Chrisman, Sarah Schlinger, 1016
Christ Church of Conroe, 9191
Christ, Helen, 2788
Christensen, Amy, 400
Christensen, Andrew, 400
Christensen, Anker, 697
Christensen, Annika, 5180
Christensen, David A., 4713
Christensen, Dianne C., 9801
Christensen, Einar, 9986
Christensen, Gavin, 400
Christensen, Henry, III, 6274, 6357
Christensen, Herman, Jr., 400
Christensen, Isobel, 400
Christensen, Jack, 3535
Christensen, Jeannette L., 634
Christensen, Karen K., 694
Christensen, Laurits R., 9795, 9801
Christensen, Maren, 400
Christensen, Nadia, 4715
Christensen, Neal M., 8190
Christensen, Robert J., 9677
Christensen, Scott, 9795, 9801
Christensen, Stefanie L., 8190
Christensen, Vaughn, 5074
Christenson, Dale, 8576
Christenson, Sheila, 4032

Christian Community Foundation, 7333
Christian, Betty Sams, 9411
Christian, Don R., 2508
Christian, George, 257
Christian, Mary W., 2070
Christian, Ronald E., 3450
Christie Family Foundation, 5369
Christie, James D., 7208
Christie, Sharon A., 3956
Christine, Mark, 7442
Christman, Chip, 7452
Christofferson Commercial, 8859
Christofferson, Clare, 408
Christopher Trust, Louis J., 7089
Christopher, Mark M., 4014, 4248
Christopherson, Elizabeth G., 5510
Christopherson, Mark, 4672
Christy, Lee Ann, 3593
Christy, Thomas, 3593
Chronquist, Gladys, 9878
Chronquist, Harry, 9878
Chrysalis Holdings, LLC, 3925
Chrysiliou, Belinda Sue, 629
Chrysiliou, Chrysilios, 629
Chu, Chinh E., 6601
Chu, Daniel, 1195
Chu, Emily, 5294
Chu, Ha Phuong, 6601
Chu, Lam, 5294
Chu, Miriam, 232
Chu, Tony, 5294
Chu, Yuet-Ming, 232
Chuang, Juichang, 5596
Chubb, Thomas C., III, 2561
Chun, Marie, 6394
Chun-Deduonni, Gail, 6394
Chung, Henry, 7031
Chung, Ray Jui Chuang, 5596
Chup, Sharon, 3956
Chupp, Carrie N., 1997
Chupp, Charles O., 1997
Chupp, Charles O., Jr., 1997
Chupp, L. Gayle, 1997
Chupp, Todd M., 1997
Church, John Clayton, 2460
Church, Sally Hughes, 403
Church, Therese Maxwell, 2460
Churchman, Caroline A., 7903
Churchman, J. Alexander, 7903
Churchman, Lee Stirling, 7903
Churchman, Leidy McIlvaine, 7903
Churchman, W. Morgan, 7903
Churgin, Amy , 6148
Churgin, Gary, 6148
Ciampa, Christine, 5845
Ciampa, Dominick, 5845
Ciampa, Rose, 5845
Ciardelli, Anthony, 5217
Ciardelli, Lillian, 5217
Ciardelli, Thomas L., 5217
Cicek, Robert J., 7137
Cicero, Nina, 1822
Cicero, R.J., 1822
Cici, Michelle, 4672
Ciesielka, John, 5140
Cieslak, Peter, 3113
Cieslak, Peter F., 3113
CIMA Pollia Trust, 931
Ciment Foundation, Norman and Joan, The , 5665
Cimler, Elizabeth Ann, 9944
Cimpl, Donald A., 5076
Cimpl, Joan M., 5076

Cincinnati Foundation, Greater, The , 4326
Cinerar, Christine, 6585
Cipares, Tom, 3372
Cipriano, Katherine, 8086
Circle, Brendan, 785
Circle, Douglas, 785
Circle, Jan, 785
Circle, Kyle, 785
Circle, Leah, 785
Cisneros, Joe, 7303
Citco Fund Services USA Inc., 6042
Citco Technology Management Inc., 6042
Citi Global Impact Funding Trust, 8817
Citi Habits, 6656
CitiBank, 1623
CitiBank, 5900
CitiBank, 6014
Citibank, 6105
CitiBank, 6293
Citibank, 6693, 6758
CitiBank, 6792, 6829
Citigroup Trust, 6611
Citizens & Northern Bank, 7986
Citizens Bank, 4580, 8441, 8599
Citizens Bank & Trust, 4963
Citizens National Bank, 8888, 8943, 9197
Citrin, Jeffrey, 1419
Citrin, Rona Hollander, 1419
Citron, Joel-Tomas, 5847
Citron, Rodger, 8042
Citron, Ulrika, 5847
Citrone, Christopher J., 2241
Citrone, Debra A., 2241
Citta Family Charitable Lead Trust, 5295
Citta, Joseph A., Jr., 5295
Citta, Rosanne L., 5295
City National Bank, 7700, 9763
City of Hartford, 1595
City of Mission, 4956
Ciuffetelli, Vincent, 3455
Civic Riking Inc., 373
Civil War Preservation Trust, 9488
Claflin, Will, 7305
Clagg, Mickey, 7688
Claims Administrative Services, 8934
Clair, Sara B., 270
Clampco Products Inc., 7627
Clancy, Constance T., 1363
Clancy, Maureen, 6655
Clapis, Jerry, 1453
Clapp, Eugene H., II, 4156
Clapp, Eugene H., III, 4156
Clapp, M. Millicent, 4156
Clapp, Marjorie G., 4156
Clapp, Maud M., 4156
Clapp, Meredith P., 4156
Clapp, Sandra, 2673
Clarett Group, The, 6656
Clarey, Patricia, 608
Clarice, Michael, 3662
Clarie, D'Arcy R., 2008
Clark Associates, 7925
Clark Charitable Lead Annuity Trust, Reed, 9545
Clark Charitable Lead Trust, Audrey I., 9545
Clark Dynasty Chartiable Lead Unitrust, Reed, 9545
Clark Foundation, 6265
Clark Revocable Trust, Gladys & Franklin, 9420

Clark Trust, Edith Allen, 6265
Clark, Aaron C., 413
Clark, Andrew L., 7926
Clark, Ann M., 7927
Clark, Aubrey, 6230
Clark, Audrey I., 9545
Clark, beth, 3390
Clark, Beverly S., 3708
Clark, Carolyn C., 6490
Clark, Carolyn Levy, 9037
Clark, Charles C., 9748
Clark, David A., 4783
Clark, David L., 413
Clark, Dennis P., 6183
Clark, Doris D., 7927
Clark, Eleanor Cochrane, 1420
Clark, Elizabeth A., 7925
Clark, Eugene, 8208
Clark, Frank E., 5848
Clark, Fred E., 7925
Clark, Frederic H., 379
Clark, Gretchen R., 3691
Clark, Hollice, 2802
Clark, Holly, 172
Clark, James W., 106
Clark, Jane Rogers, 4108
Clark, Jennifer W., 46
Clark, Jody A., 413
Clark, John, 4049
Clark, John L., 4783
Clark, Judy, 3595
Clark, Laurel K., 413
Clark, Marcella S., 106
Clark, Margaret Nolan, 379
Clark, Martha, 7145
Clark, Mary Jane, 1226
Clark, Matthew H., 6452
Clark, Merrell F., 7927
Clark, Midge, 7882
Clark, Mitch, 3370
Clark, Nancy Considine, 2804
Clark, Nancy E., 4783
Clark, Ned, 6998
Clark, Nicholas J., 7379
Clark, Patricia P., 2272
Clark, Peter, 6540
Clark, Peter R., 9545
Clark, Randall D., 4957
Clark, Rhea P., 6603
Clark, Roger E., 1265
Clark, Sandra Martin, 7164
Clark, Sarah, 900
Clark, Teresa L., 3611
Clark, Thomas E., 106
Clark, Tom, 4847
Clark, Valentine, 461
Clark-Morey, Timothy, 7801
Clarke, Dave, 3662
Clarke, E. Boyd, 6590
Clarke, J. Dwaine, 2530
Clarke, Kay Knight, 5647
Clarke, Pat H., 1952
Clarkson, Bayard D., 5849
Clarkson, Ferman L., 8558
Clarkson, Virginia C., 5849
Clary, Eugene M., 2462
Clary, Jean, 2462
Clary, Karen, 8100
Clary, Kenneth B., 2462
Classen, Roger F., 7330
Clat Distribution, Robert Kirby, 6313
Clat, Florence Ragan, 5507
Clat, Robert A. Yanover, 2268
Clat, Wender, 1777

Clauder, Mary Frances W., 7638
Clausing, Gretjen, 8118
Clausing, W. Kirk, 7708
Clavell, Patricia, 356
Clavette, Alan C., 1532
Clavin, Andrew, 750
Clavin, Daniel, 750
Clavin, Nancy, 750
Claxton, John, 3371
Clay, Garland, 7684
Clay, Jennifer Mary Ellen, 6262
Clay, John Peter, 6262
Clay, Laura, 7707
Clayburn, D. Kent, 5190
Clayton, Bruce, 2463
Clayton, Emily, 3825
Clayton, Gary F., 8661
Clayton, T. Kevin, 2507
Clean Harbors Inc, 367
Clear Channel Communications, 8772
Clearman, Melvin, Jr., 9133
Cleary, Bernadette C., 4979
Cleary, Edward, 5954
Cleary, James P., 4107
Cleary, John M., 7427
Cleary, Patti, 7624
Cleary, Susan, 4107
Cleary, Timothy, 7427
Cleaves, Daniel, 5398
Cleland, Lynette, 754
Clelland, Ellie, 1095
Clemence, Richard R., 4139
Clement, Cordelia E., 5970
Clement, Don, 7298
Clement, Leslie C., 8994
Clementi, John, 4050
Clements, Alice B., 1945
Clements, Georgia M., 8773
Clements, Helen T., 1945
Clements, John B., 1945
Clements, Maurice, 2686
Clements, Robert M., 1945
Clements, Thomas, III, 1945
Clements, Tyler M., 1945
Clements, William Perry, III, 8773
Clemons, David, 9133
Clemons, Jessica, 9133
Clemons, Sam, 9133
Clemons, Sandra, 9133
Cless, Bryan C., 2793
Cless, Gerhard, 2793
Cless, Martin, 2793
Cless, Ruth I., 2793
Cless, Stephen G., 2793
Cleveland Indians Baseball Co., 7354
Cleveland Syrup Corp., 7349
Cleveland, C.H., Sr., 4793
Cleveland, Charles A., Jr., 4793
Cleveland, Thirza, 4793
Cleven, Carol C., 1898
Click, Betty J., 3614
Cliett, Charles B., Jr., 193
Cliff, Carolyn, 9562
Clifford Charitable Lead Annuity Trust,
    Stewart B., 5594
Clifford, A. Keena, 4051
Clifford, Bill, 2200
Clifford, Caroline M., 4051
Clifford, Catherine K., 4051
Clifford, Cornelia W., 5594
Clifford, Daniel F., 7434
Clifford, J. Christopher, 4051
Clifford, James, 9956
Clifford, John, 5573

Clifford, John C., 4051
Clifford, Stewart B., 5594
Clifford, Terry, 7790
Clifton, Guy, Dr. , 9205
Clifton, Karen A., 127
Clifton, Kim , 9474
Clifton, Paul T., 127
Clifton, Rick, 4
Clifton, Susan Lea, 127
Clime, J.R., 7449
Cline, J. Michael, 5851
Cline, Robert, 3531
Cline-Conway, Lucille, 8887
Clingen, Brian T., 2794
Clingen, Deidre M., 2794
Clingen, Kenneth W., 2794
Clinton Investment Co., 8509, 8510
Clinton Management, 6675
Clinton National Bank, 3522
Clinton, Lottie, 472
Clise, Al, 5156
Clore, Dale Ann, 3589
Close, Helen, 5148
Close, Kristi A., 7546
Cloud, Claire Goodman Pellegrini, 6107
Cloud, John M., 7593
Cloud, Randy, 7665
Cloud, Sam R., 9796
Cloud, Theodore, 9796
Cloud, Walter J., 9796
Clough, Charles I., III, 4104
Clough, Charles I., Jr., 4104
Clough, Gloria I., 4104
Clough, Gloria L., 4104
Clougherty, Anthony P., 409
Clougherty, Bernard J., 409
Clougherty, Joseph D., 409
Cloverdale Equipment Co., 4386
Cloyd, Jeannette Singleton, 9197
Cloyd, Robin, 9197
CLRPG Land Co. LP, 9009
Clubb, Mike, 9267
Clune, David F., Dr. , 1392
Clusen, Charles M., 5662
Clut, Bendon, 5137
Clymer, John, 9903
CMC Charitable Lead Annuity Trust,
    1822
CMC Trust, 1822
CME Group, 2800
Cmiel, David F., 4703
CMM Charitable Lead Trust I, 7710
CMM Charitable Lead Trust II, 7710
CMS Companies, 8254
CNB Bank, 7929
CNB Financial Corp., 7929
CNB Trust Dept., 4409
Coakley, Kimberly W., 8688
Coakley, Sean, 4362
Coast Grain Co., 1164
Coastline Transportation Inc, 9034
Coates, Thomas K., 3885
Coats, Cathy, 3344
Coaxium Enterprise, 153
Coaxum, Donna B., 3158
Coban, John, 2109
Cobb, Arletta, 3448
Cobb, Calvin Hayes, Jr., 1807
Cobb, Gerald, 8782
Cobbs, Helen C., 9422
Cobie, Nancy L., 7521
Coburn Survivor's Trust, 411
Coburn, Abbie, 483
Coburn, Clayton D., 8020

Coburn, Jean Crummer, 436
Coburn, Ron, 3991
Coca Cola, 8795
Coca Cola East Africa, 2621
Coca Cola Foundation, 2622
Coca-Cola North America, 8859
Cochener, Bruce G., 3565
Cochener, Nancy M., 3565
Cochener-Metcalfe, Donna M., 3565
Cochran, Laurene, 9307
Cochran, Paula, 7386
Cochran, Rick, 3431
Cochran, Robert P., 5853
Cochran, Suzanne H., 5853
Cochran, William, 58
Cochrane, Andrew R., 1420
Cochrane, Dorothy Lott, 1420
Cochrane, Dorothy Louise, 1420
Cochrane, Robert, 4514
Cocke, Frances F., 2476
Cockrum, Brigid Anne, 9020
Cocks, David, 5872
Cocola, David J., 1453
Cocumelli, Karen Smythe, 1061
Codding Enterprises, 412
Codding, Constance L., 412
Codding, Hugh B., 412
Coddington, Ricci, 574
Codman, Dorothy S.F.M., 4052
Coe, Charles R., Jr., 7707
Coe, Ross M. "Rick", 7707
Coe, Ward I., 7707
Coehlo, Kenneth B., 3921
Coen, Kent, 5114
Coen, Michael, 7809
Coffey Trust, Harold F., 7078
Coffey, Isabell, 6507
Coffey, Larry R., 3650
Coffey, Robert L., 8791
Coffin, Anne, 6739
Coffin, Elizabeth Robinson, 2306
Coffman, Adelia A., 7750
Coffman, Bryant J., 7706
Coffman, Jean, 4222
Coffman, John, 9756
Coffman, Rick, 2686
Coffman, Ronnie D., 7750
Cofrin, Cladys G., 2391
Cofrin, Gladys, 2391
Cogan Charitable Trust, 3837
Cogan, Gill, 448
Cogan, Laura, 448
Coggin, Elizabeth Jenks, 4953
Coggin, Gerald, 8579
Coggin, Joanne, 8579
Coghlan, Howard P., 8970
Cogut, Craig, 5856
Cogut, Deborah, 5856
Cohee, Lynn, 3024
Cohen Trust, Abraham J., 3838
Cohen, Aaron, 752, 6117
Cohen, Abby J., 5895
Cohen, Alan H., 3357, 3408
Cohen, Alvin, 4946
Cohen, Andrea, 8042
Cohen, Andrew, 5858
Cohen, Andrew M., 6958
Cohen, Aviezer, 5974
Cohen, Barbara, 8042
Cohen, Bennet R., 9369
Cohen, Bette D., 3905
Cohen, Bonnie, 1833
Cohen, Bradford S., 311
Cohen, Candice N., 1947

Cohen, Carolyn, 1948
Cohen, Charles, 3113
Cohen, Charlotte McKee, 9052
Cohen, Chief Rabbi Shear-Yashuv, 6009
Cohen, David, 7000
Cohen, David M., 5857
Cohen, Eileen F., 1643
Cohen, Elaine, 5974
Cohen, Eleanor, 1947
Cohen, Elizabeth, 8042
Cohen, Ellen, 4053, 8042
Cohen, Ellen M., 5857
Cohen, Ellen R., 4053
Cohen, Florence, 5858
Cohen, George M., 1948
Cohen, Howard, 5582
Cohen, Howard M., 3151
Cohen, Isabelle Hahn, 6407
Cohen, Jarrod, 5859
Cohen, Jeremy, 27
Cohen, Jerome J., 7031
Cohen, Jon S., 171
Cohen, Jonathan L., 6384
Cohen, Joseph M., 5859
Cohen, Julian, 4053, 4307
Cohen, Karen B., 5860
Cohen, Laura, 472
Cohen, Lauren, 5858
Cohen, Lauren Chesley, 7351
Cohen, Lauren G., 5857
Cohen, Lawrence B., 4189
Cohen, Lea, 7008
Cohen, Leah, 27, 6858
Cohen, Lee, 6764
Cohen, Leslie, 3783
Cohen, Linda M., 3357
Cohen, Marcia, 9163
Cohen, Maryjo, 1643
Cohen, Melvin S., 1643
Cohen, Michael, 5766
Cohen, Michele, 5858
Cohen, Natalie, 414
Cohen, Nathan, 3357
Cohen, Peter A., 5858
Cohen, Peter J., 414
Cohen, Rhonda, 8134
Cohen, Robert, 5149
Cohen, Robert L., 3587
Cohen, Robert S., 1422
Cohen, Ruth, 5299
Cohen, Susan, 7764
Cohen, Uriel, 6918
Cohen, William C., Jr., 3587
Cohen, William Finaly, 2401
Cohen, William L., 5858
Cohen, Yael, 6918
Cohen, Yetta K., 9504
Cohenca, Emy, 5861
Cohenca, Jacques, 5861
Cohenca, Philip, 5861
Cohn, Andrew, 2795
Cohn, Bernice, 5945
Cohn, Daniel, 5862
Cohn, David, 5945
Cohn, Doris, 5864
Cohn, Elizabeth, 750
Cohn, Elizabeth S., 5863
Cohn, Gerald L., 7931
Cohn, Harold, 5864
Cohn, Jamie, 2795
Cohn, Jonathan, 2795
Cohn, Lawrence, 2795
Cohn, Marc S., 5862

Cohn, Marcia, 2796
Cohn, Marshall S., 5864
Cohn, Martin, 5864
Cohn, Martin D., 7931
Cohn, Mary Louise, 8644
Cohn, Morton A., 8876
Cohn, Paul, 5864
Cohn, Peter, 5945
Cohn, Peter A., 5863
Cohn, Robert, 2795
Cohn, Rosaline, 2796
Cohn, Seymour, 5864
Cohn, Stacey, 6720
Cohn, Susie, 5083
Cohn, Terri L., 2795
Cohoes Savings Bank, 5865
Coit, Barbara E., 7751
Coit, Susan, 7751
Coit, William E., 7751
Coker, Charles W., 8519
Coker, Charles W., Jr., 8519
Coker, Charles W., Sr., 8519
Coker, Robert Howard, 8519
Coker, Thomas Lide, 8519
Colage, Vera L., 6224
Colangelo, Anna, 4050
Colangelo, Carol, 7396
Colaruotolo, Frank D., 5865
Colas, Mary E., 9398
Colas, Timothy, 9398
Colas, William, 1952
Colbert, Ann B., 4829
Colbert, Thomas W., 4829
Colbert, Thomas W., Jr., 4829
Colbert, Thomas W., Sr., 4829
Colburn Trust, Donald, 1421
Colburn, Deo B., 5866
Colburn, Donald, 1421
Colburn, Jane, 4297
Colby Unitrust, P., 5867
Colby, Benjamin N., 2711
Colby, F. Jordan, 2711
Colby, Patricia, 5867
Colby, Walter F., 3993
Cold, Kathleen, 2368
Coldwell, Colbert, 2797
Coldwell, Lizanell, 2797
Cole Family Investements, 2798
Cole National Foundation, 9098
Cole Trust, Lula P., 9423
Cole Trust, S. Mason, 9423
Cole, Adam, 3362
Cole, Amy, 6007
Cole, Anne R., 1726
Cole, Ben, 4054
Cole, Bob, 3592
Cole, Bonnie J., 3839
Cole, Catherine P., 1297
Cole, David G., 7431
Cole, Ellen G., 7431
Cole, Ellen L., 3839
Cole, Greg, 3948
Cole, Jeffrey, 4419
Cole, Jody, 9095
Cole, John T., 9465
Cole, Karen, 8769
Cole, Kenneth D., 5868
Cole, Lesle E., 4487
Cole, Lisa A., 1297
Cole, Madison F., 2798
Cole, Madison F., Jr., 2798
Cole, Maria Cuomo, 5868
Cole, Marlowe, 1531
Cole, Roland H., 3839

Cole, Rose, 4054
Cole, Sharon J., 2798
Cole, Theora Ruth, 415
Cole, William L., 839
Colella, Thomas C., 5154
Coleman Meadows Pate Drug Co., 2485
Coleman, Brett, 5150
Coleman, Clarence B., 416
Coleman, Elinor, 416
Coleman, Isobel, 5871
Coleman, James, 5870, 6588
Coleman, James M., 9580
Coleman, Janet M., 5870
Coleman, Joan F., 416
Coleman, John, 5870
Coleman, John A., III, 6821
Coleman, John B., Jr., 8608
Coleman, Karen, 5150
Coleman, Laura B., 7324
Coleman, M. Graham, 6311
Coleman, Magaret M., 5869
Coleman, Marjorie T., 1644
Coleman, Martin S., 5870
Coleman, Milton, 6950
Coleman, Roger V., 5869
Coleman, Ruth, 107
Coleman, Stuart, 8766
Coleman, Susan H., 1290
Coleman, William R., 1644
Colerain, Jeff Wyler, 7647
Coles, Douglas, 5871
Coles, Joan C., 5871
Coles, Michael, 6815
Coles, Michael H., 5871
Coles, Richard, 5871
Colgan, Patricia, 5681
Colgate, John C., Jr., 1645
Colin, Barbara, 1320
Colker, Becky, 2959
Colkitt Trust, Carol I., 7590
Coll, Carmen, 6820
Collado, Valerie, 1772
Collective Brands, 3614
College Gardens, 3905
Collette Travel Service, 8494
Colletti, Anthony, 6656
Colletti, Christina, 6233
Collier, Glenn W., 7585
Collier, Phyllis, 3362
Collier, Tyree, 9054
Colliers ABR, 6655
Collins Cambridge Focus, M., 9230
Collins Foundation, James M., 8781
Collins Pine Company, 7753
Collins, A.S., 8862
Collins, Alisann A., 9425
Collins, Andrew, 7668
Collins, Ann Childs, 5651
Collins, Anne B., 2799
Collins, Arthur D., Jr., 2799
Collins, Belva, 9426
Collins, Brian, 1949, 5635
Collins, Budge, 5288
Collins, Carol, 5288
Collins, Caroline M., 8780
Collins, Courtney, 1949
Collins, Courtney C., 8780
Collins, David S., 4193
Collins, Elizabeth, 2799
Collins, Frances R., 7668
Collins, Fred, 8520
Collins, George F., Jr., 7668
Collins, George Fulton, IV, 7669
Collins, H. Michael, 227

Collins, Holiday M., 4193
Collins, James W., 8780
Collins, James W., Jr., 8780
Collins, Janna C., 2805
Collins, Jennifer, 1949
Collins, Jennifer L., 8780
Collins, John, 9474
Collins, Kathleen C., 8780
Collins, Kathleen Fox, 1374
Collins, Larkin, 1046
Collins, Lee Diane, 7753
Collins, Lesley, 1949
Collins, Maribeth W., 7753
Collins, Michael E., 3643
Collins, Richard B., 4337
Collins, Roger, 7692
Collins, Roger B., 7668, 7669
Collins, Russell, 3401
Collins, Shawn, 3628
Collins, Susan B., 5635
Collins, Suzanne M., 7669
Collins, Terence W., 1802
Collins, Terrence Ray, 137
Collins, Terry L., 9425
Collins, Terry S., 7753
Collins, Theresa M., 7661
Collins, Thomas, 7690
Collins, Truman W., Jr., 7753
Collins, Vannie C., 8780
Collins, Vicky G., 9424
Collins, Wendy B., 102
Collins, William, 1949
Collis, Charles A., 8397
Collis, Elfried A., 8397
Collis, Robert H., 7111
Collison, Kevin, 4459
Collison, Robert, 8188
Colliton, Felice, 3776
Colonial Trust Co., 8523, 8537
Colonis, Harry, 1418
Colony, Ann B., 4261
Colony, George F., 4261
Colorado Business Bank, 1362
Colorado Rockies Baseball Club
   Foundation, 1730
Colorado State University, 1295
Colotto, James V., 5300
Colotto, Loretta, 5300
Colpitts, Richard P., 3796
Colten, Marsha L., 1422
Columbia Financial Inc., 5301
Columbia Foundation, 9386
Columbia Foundation, The, 7218
Columbus Foundation and Affiliated
   Organizations, The, 7545
Columbus Southern Power Co., 7303
Colver, David O., 1289
Colvin, Gill, 219
Colvis, Linda, 546
Colwell, Stephen B., 5166
Colwell, William S., 1560
Colwin, Dawn, 9887
Colyer, John Michael, 1772
Comb, David, 4220
Combeewood Partners, 9089
Combs, Christopher W., 419
Combs, Donald G., 4220
Combs, Earle M., III, 2800
Combs, Earle M., IV, 2800
Combs, Loula Long, 4948
Combs, Virginia M., 2800
Comcast Spectator, 8243
Comer, Adrian, 1293
Comer, John D., Mrs. , 2451

Comerchero, Jill, 5471
Comerchero, Leonard, 5471
Comerchero, Matthew, 5471
Comerchero, Melissa, 5471
Comerchero, Myrna, 5471
Comerford, Kevin, 3371
Comerica Bank, 2109, 4404, 4444, 4480, 4550, 4561, 4595, 9232
Comerica Bank and Trust, 4439
Comfort & Sons Inc., George, 6656
Comisky, Ian, 7896
Comisky, Matthew J., 7896
Comly, Joseph P., III, 5419
Commerce Bank, 4935, 4965, 4988
Commerce Construction, 784
Commerce Trust Co., 4894, 4902, 4918
Commerce Trust Co., The, 5039
Commerce Trust Company, 4913
Commercial Bank of Africa, 2622
Commercial Brick Corp., 7697
Commercial Federal Bank, FSB, 272
Commercial Realty, 5484
Commercial Stainless, 7925
Commers, Christen, 3361
Common Sense Fund, 6553
Community Action Network, 7258
Community Bank & Trust, 9241
Community Bank of Texas, 8700
Community Financial Services Group, 9378
Community Foundation of San Benito, 644
Community Foundation of Sarasota, 6542
Community Foundation of St. Joseph County, 3458
Community Foundation, The, 2005
Community Health Systems, 8601
Company & Sons, George, 6655
Comparato, Thomas F., 3993
Compass Bank, 37
Compass Group Management, LLC, 2475
Competitor Group Inc., 684
Compression, 3905
Compton, Elizabeth K., 6147
Compton, John G., 4830
Compton, Justine, 5827
Compton, Walter K., 206
Compton, Wilson, III, 5205
Computer Stock Forms, 7348
Comstock, Brian, 9724
Comunale, Amanda, 7358
Comunale, Jane, 7358
Comunale, John, 7358
Comunale, Stephen A., 7358
Comunale, Steve, 7358
Comunale, Steve Jane, 7358
Comus, Louis, Jr., 177
Conant, Douglas R., 5302
Conaway, Mary Ann, 7929
Conboy, Karen Boyle, 2754
Concannon, Craig A., 3591
Concept Mining, 9766
Concepts in Time, LLC, 6199
Conco Companies, 366
Concord Trust, 5923, 6965
Concorde Group Corp., 9173
Conder, Lisa, 3446
Condie, Parker B., 4951
Conditioned Air Systems, 2543
Condon, Edward, 3612
Condon, Paul S., 966
Cone, Edward H., 7936

Cone, Philip J., 7936
Cone, Robert L., 7936
Cone, Stephen E., 7936
Cone, Todd, 7717
Conelly Foundation, The, 7935
Conestoga Wood Specialities Corp., 8036
Coneway Charitable Lead Trust, Peter R., 8783
Coneway, Lynn M., 8783
Coneway, Natalie, 8783
Coneway, Peter R., 8783
Cong TA of KJ, 6444
Conger, Nancy P., 5303
Conger, Silvia, 4820
Conger, T.J., 7408
Conger, William F., 5303
Congregation Avreichim, 5705
Congregation Bais Mordechai, 5834
Congregation Bais Yisroel, 7000
Congregation Shaare Tefila, 5544
Congressional Quarterly, 2362
Congressional Youth Leadership Council, 1592, 3874
Conklin, Charles R., 7312
Conley, Bruce, 2321
Conley, Gloria C., 9551
Conley, John, 5874
Conley, Kathy, 211
Conley, Monika, 5874
Conley, Sue, 9383
Conlogue, Virginia, 7359
Conn, Andrew D., 7360
Conn, Joan D., 7360
Conn, Leon, 5954
Conn, Nicolette, 7360
Conn, Olivia D., 7360
Conn, Raymond A., 7360
Conn, Robert, 3432
Connable, Genevieve W., 4412
Connable, H.P., 4412
Connally, Ruth, 3469
Connell Charitable Lead Annuity Trust, William F., 4055
Connell, Courtenay E., 4055
Connell, Eva, 9196
Connell, George, 7903
Connell, Margot C., 4055
Connell, Michael, 1992
Connell, Terence A., 4055
Connell, Timothy P., 4055
Connell, Todd M., 3565
Connell, William C., 4055
Connell, William F., 4055
Connelly, David, 3056
Connelly, Linda, 2095
Connelly, Linda M., 2095
Connelly, Michael, 2095
Connelly, Michael J., 2095
Connelly, Patricia, 5573
Connelly, Sherry S., 3461
Conner, Elizabeth Ann, 5219
Conner, James, 3343
Conner, Marjorie L., 7373
Conner, Thomas, 3406
Conners, John, 239
Connoley, Clemenx, 5166
Connolly, Andrea, 9280
Connolly, Cynthia Sprague, 1070
Connolly, Darleen, 3359
Connolly, James, Jr., 4221
Connolly, John L., 2467
Connolly, Joseph G.J., 7958
Connolly, Leigh Z., 2467

Connolly, Thomas J., 4191
Connor, Christopher, 1250
Connor, Claire E., 1250
Connor, Gail, 8243
Connor, John J., II, 1250
Connor, Kevin, 8243
Connor, Larry, 7361
Connor, Lawrence S., 7361
Connor, Patricia A., 1250
Connor, Robert F., Jr., 1250
Connor, Robert F., Sr., 1250
Connor, Ruth P., 8785
Connors, Adele, 6360
Connors, Martin F., Jr., 4270
Connors, William, 7882
ConocoPhillips Co., 301
Conover, Catherine M., 1822
Conover, Kurt, 1950
Conover, Mary, 1822
Conrad, Arlene, 3364
Conrad, Beth, 3364
Conrad, Frank P., 4051, 4125
Conrad, Jean, 3364
Conrad, Karen N., 7287
Conrad, Mark, 3364
Conrad, Michelle, 2389
Conrad, Phyllis, 3364
Conrad, Robert, 8874
Conrad, William, 7975
Conrades, George, 3998
Conru, Andrew, 9602
Consentino, Jocelyne, 4222
Conservation Fund, The, 9368
Considine, Alison, 1599
Considine, Frank W., 2804
Considine, Kevin S., 2804
Considine, Nancy, 2804
Consolidated Supermarket Supply LLC, 6344
Constable, Charles, 7975
Constable, Mark, 7923
Constance, Jamie, 566
Constance, Marcia W., 566
Constantino, Mary, 3027
Construction, Turnbull-wahlert, 7647
Contaxis, Mary, 921
Continental Can Co., 1422
Continental Divide Electric Cooperative, 5612
Continental Food Mgmt., 334
Continium Healthcare Mgmt., LLC, 2424
Contino, Betty, 3840
Contino, Francis A., 3840
Contois, Leo, 1599
Contorer, David C., 4473
Contra Costa Waste, 546
Contribution of Securities, 2125
Conway Trust, William E., The , 7569
Conway, Greg, 4382
Conway, John W., 7935, 9041
Conway, Mary French, 7569
Conway, Pat, 4939
Conway, Peter F., 7569
Conway, Ron, 645
Conway, William E., 7569
Conway, William G., Dr. , 5662
Conway, William T., 7569
Conwill Co., 3905
Conwill, Daniel O., 689
Cook, Betty Jean, 8917
Cook, Bradley R., 4326
Cook, Carl A., 1797
Cook, Chloe Hope, 8787
Cook, Christopher, 3421

Cook, Claude P., Sr., 2468
Cook, Daniel L., 7047
Cook, David E., 7571
Cook, Dawn, 9328
Cook, Denise, 552
Cook, Dennis, 9999
Cook, Diane, 4658
Cook, Douglas E., 6790
Cook, Edward S., Jr., 9794
Cook, Emily, 9070
Cook, Fairley Bell, 7047
Cook, Frances, 8680
Cook, Gayle T., 1797
Cook, Gerald S., 4589
Cook, Gretchen Stone, 4056
Cook, James, 4658
Cook, James R., 4658
Cook, Jeffrey, 988
Cook, Joe B., 8786
Cook, John J., 9752
Cook, Judith, 8787
Cook, Judith Claire Womack, 8787
Cook, Julie Arcart, 4012
Cook, Karin, 9308
Cook, Katherine Hyman, 3887
Cook, Kevin Michael, 8787
Cook, Langdon P., 1432
Cook, Larry D., 4568
Cook, Laura, 1155
Cook, Louise P., 8786
Cook, Mark, 8787
Cook, Mark Dewayne, 8787
Cook, Molly Claire, 8787
Cook, Philip C., 2595
Cook, Robert, 8575
Cook, Royrickers, Dr. , 12
Cook, Shirlene, 8869
Cook, Susan, 3732
Cook, Susanna W., 8369
Cook, Thad, 3732
Cook, Trisha, 3235
Cook, V.L., 7124
Cook, Willard T., 3887
Cook, William L., 8048
Cooke Trust, William A., 9427
Cooke, Elizabeth G., 7080
Cooke, Incorporated, William A., 9427
Cooke, John D., 6978
Cooke, John Warren, 9543
Cooke, Trudi C., 7079
Cooke, V.V., 7079
Cooke, V.V., Jr., 7079
Cooke, V.V., Mrs. , 7079
Cooks, Jude, 377
Cooksey, Ben, 3707
Coolidge Trust, 4057
Coolidge Trust, Elizabeth S., 4057
Coolidge, Francis L., 4196
Coolidge, Peter, 5934
Coombe, Michael A., 7305
Coombe, Tucker J., 7305
Coonan, Joslin, 7649
Cooney, Barbara C., 2806
Cooney, Brendan H., 2777
Cooney, Christopher L., 2777
Cooney, John D., 2806
Cooney, Mary E., 2777
Coons, Christine S., 3481
Coons, Kenton D., 3481
Coons, Kevin, 3481
Coons, Kyle, 3481
Coons, Margaret L., 3481
Coons, Marion M., 3481

Cooper Charitable Lead Annuity Trust, John and Mary, 109
Cooper Charitable Lead Unitrust, A.S., 7096
Cooper Tire & Rubber Co., 7362
Cooper, Aaron, 4401
Cooper, Adam C., 2791
Cooper, Angus R., II, 23
Cooper, Angus R., III, 23
Cooper, Ann, 5879, 6114
Cooper, Barry C., 3020
Cooper, Beckwith Archer, 2469
Cooper, Bonaventura, 5317
Cooper, Chris, 8608
Cooper, Christine, 109
Cooper, David J., Jr., 22
Cooper, David J., Sr., 22
Cooper, Diane, 8806
Cooper, Elizabeth Elaine Fletcher, 4093
Cooper, Eric, 8769
Cooper, Frank G., 7107
Cooper, Frederick E., 2469
Cooper, Frederick E., Jr., 2469
Cooper, Gary, 109
Cooper, Helen D., 2469
Cooper, Herbert L., 3020
Cooper, Hilma F., 7952
Cooper, J. Fenimore, Jr., 2238
Cooper, Joanne K., 22
Cooper, John, 109
Cooper, Johnson Joseph, 2469
Cooper, Judy, 9652
Cooper, Katherine, 2238
Cooper, Leslie, 1539
Cooper, Leslie A.W., 1539
Cooper, Lisa, 1207
Cooper, Lisa Anne, 4456
Cooper, Mary, 109, 5855, 7769
Cooper, My, 7124
Cooper, Peter, 318
Cooper, Peter D., 5855
Cooper, Randall, 5855
Cooper, Scott H., 23
Cooper, Sloan, 5855
Cooper, Sonja J.M., Dr. , 1633
Cooper, Stuart, 3823
Cooper, Susan, 8608
Cooper, Wendy A., 9482
Cooperrider, Jon H., II, 7652
Coopersmith, Ari, 5247
Coopersmith, Gladys, 1646
Coors, Holly, 1647
Coors, Phyllis M., 1647
Coors, William Scott, 1647
Coover, Gary, 9667
Copaken, Jon, 4888
Copaken, Keith, 4888
Copaken, Lois, 4888
Copaken, Paul, 4888
Cope, Carol, 5077
Cope, Dennis W., 7031
Cope, Judy, 6826
Cope, Phyllis Mae, 5139
Copeland, Barbara, 367
Copeland, Carol, 1059
Copeland, Jeffery L., 9476
Copeland, Linda , 9474
Copeland, Loretta M., 2807
Copeland, Robert G., 227
Copp, B. Allyn, 1538, 9116
Copp, Betsey A., 1538
Copp, Eugenie C.T., 1538
Copp, Joseph A., 1538
Copp, Lucy A., 1538

Copp, Mary Wagley, 9116
Coppa Family LLC, Konover, 1501
Corallo, Christopher, 5872
Corbalis, Charles M., 424
Corbalis, Linda J., 424
Corbatto, Deborah B., 9392
Corbet, Daniel R., 324
Corbett Trust, E.L., 4176
Corbett, Alice, 2809
Corbett, Cornelia Gerry, 2037
Corbett, J. Ralph, 7363
Corbett, Jim, 2844
Corbett, Patricia A., 7363
Corbett, Sandra M., 2368
Corbett, William A., 9353
Corbin, Gene A., 4035
Corbin, Katharine, 5101
Corbin, Lee Harrison, 6224
Corbridge, Pam, 9319
Corcoran Group Real Estate, 6656
Corcoran, Gerald, 2810
Corcoran, Gerald F., 2810
Corcoran, Gerry, 3189
Corcoran, Mary, 4983
Corcoran, Maureen, 2810
Corcoran, Maureen A., 2810
Corcoran, William W., 4049
Corday, Eliot, 426
Corday, Marian, 426
Corday, Stephen, 426
Cordeiro, Carlos A., 2683
Corder, John Michael, 9345
Corder, Tyler, 5156
Cordevalle Golf Club, 427
Cordover, Barbara A., 5304
Cordover, Jeffrey A., 5304
Cordover, Ronald H., 5304
Corefirst Bank & Trust, 3626
Coressel, Justin F., 7364
CoreStates Financial Corp, 8350
Corfront, Linda, 7933
Corinaldi, Reginald, 1387
Cork, Susan Phifer, 54
Corkern, Wilton C., Jr., 3880
Corkery, Nancy W., 3827
Corkins, David, 1648
Corleto, Richard, 855, 1210
Corley, Dewey W., 3751
Corley, Gayle, 200
Corley, Nolly E., 4191
Corn, Wanda M., 1781
Cornblath, David, 2880
Cornbrooks, Ernest I., III, 3932
Cornelison, Jeff, 2530
Cornell, Alison A., 5305
Cornell, Barbara, 7591
Cornell, David, 5877
Cornell, Henry, 5876
Cornell, Michael, 5877
Cornell, Olivia, 5877
Cornell, Vanessa, 5876
Cornelsen, Floy L., 4889
Cornelsen, Kristina, 4889
Cornelsen, Paul F., 4889
Cornelson, George H., IV, 8510
Cornelson, Martin S., 8510
Corner Riverdale Trust, 6039
Corner, Rebecca, 4590
Cornerstone Farm & Gin Co., 218
Cornett, Wally, 3655
Cornick, Kenneth, 6165
Cornish, John M., 4117, 4143, 4214
Cornish, William G., 4117
Cornog, Robert A., 9862

Cornwell, Gary D., 9765
Cornwell, Lisa, 9357
Cornwell-Bruce, Denise, 1005
Corpus, Janet, 4008
Correstore LLC, 725
Corrie, Steve, 3534
Corrigan Family RevocTrust, Robert K., 110
Corrigan, Ann G., 8789
Corrigan, Blake G., 8789
Corrigan, Bryan H., 8789
Corrigan, Sean, 1649
Corrigan, Sigrun, 1649
Corrigan, Wilfred J., 1649
Corrigan, Wilfred James, 1649
Corrigan, William E., 8789
Corringan, Elsa, 1649
Corringan, Eric, 1649
Cortell, J., 7333
Cortell, J., Mrs. , 7333
Cortes, Francisca, 4234
Cortese, Lafcadio, 7781
Cortese, Paul, 5541
Cortese, Shannon, 5541
Cortessi, Claire, 2881
Cortessi, Richard, 2881
Cortez, Arline S., 5541
Cortez, Barrick, 5198
Cortez, Deborah A. Farley, 4813
Corty, Andrew P., 2362
Corwin, Bruce C., 428
Corwin, Daniel, 428
Corwin, David, 428
Corwin, Randall D., 1884
Corwin, Toni, 428
Corzine Foundation, John S., 2977
Cosby, Camille, 5775
Cosby, William, Jr., 5775
Cosentino, Julia Satti, 4331
Cosgrove, Deborah K., 8135
Cosh, Ian R., 195
Cosmo Co., 3905
Cossa, Joanne Hubbard, 6950
Cossyphas, Sherry, 3040
Cost, Charles L., 7937
Costa, Dan J., 429
Costa, Daniel S., 429
Costa, Denise L., 429
Costa, Kelsie L., 429
Costa, Lorelei, 7204
Costa, Mark, 3014
Costco Wholesale Corp., 349
Costello, Francis W., 679
Costello, James P., 6032
Costello, Timothy M., 1298
Costigan, C.F.A., Joe, 7953
Costigan, Virginia, 1482
Costlow, Kathleen A., 3902
Cote, Leann, 4237
Cote, Robert C., 4800
Cote, S. Ruggles, 4800
Cote, Samuel A., 4800
Cote, Stephen P., 3992
Cotner, David B., 5063
Cotsen, Lloyd, 430
Cotsen, Lloyd E., 430
Cotsen, Margit, 430
Cotsirilos, George G., Jr., 3774
Cotsirilos, George J., 3774
Cotsirilos, John G., 3774
Cotsirilos, Stephanie, 3774
Cotta, Gary , 9474
Cotter, Greg, 8836
Cotter, Jeffrey Louis, 4691

Cotter, Paula M., 4075
Cotter, Robert L., Jr., 2989
Cottille-Foley, Nora, 6820
Cottingim, Tamara M., 8666
Cotton, Bob, 9133
Cotton, Gayla, 9133
Cotton, Jon, 4460
Cotton, Michael, 4460
Cotton, Sean, 4460
Cotton, Shery, 4460
Cottrell, Pat, 840
Couch, Barbara J., 5209
Couch, Martha K., 1953
Couch, Richard W., 5209
Couch, Richard W., Jr., 5209
Couch, Theodore J., Jr., 1953
Couch, Theodore J., Sr., 1953
Coughlin, M.D., Ph.D, Shaun R., 906
Coules, Peter, 3231
Coulson, Larry, 3567
Coulter, Charles R., 3523
Coulter, June G., 2813
Coulter, Mabel Munro, 9581
Coulter, Paul, 8816
Coulter, Tom, 4459
Coulter-Jones, Laura Gene, 1954
Counce, Mitchell, 3624
Counselman, Albert R., 3937
Counselman, Catherine R., 3937
Counselman, Charles C., 3937
Counselman, Margaret K., 3937
Countiss, Bill, 9005, 9156
Country Club Trust Co., 4929
Country Trust Bank, 3021
Countryman, Gary, 4378
Counts, James, 4939
Counts, Kathryn O'Connor, 9093
Counts, Tommy, 35
Courain, Jennifer R., 9522
Courain, Robert C., III, 9522
Courain, Robert C., Jr., 9522
Courain, Ruth D., 9522
Courington, Gregory, 8945
Courington, Lawrence, 8945
Courtier Residual Trust, Wilma W., 9798
Courtier Survivor's Trust, Veryl F., 9798
Courtnage, Kathleen A., 5098
Courtnage, Larry J., 5098
Courtney, Thomas F., Sr., 3098
Courtsey Motors Inc., 4390
Coury, Robert J., 8187
Cousins, Frank G., Jr., 4250
Cousins, Thomas G., 2557
Cousler-Emig, Julie, 8269
Coutant, Barry, 1566
Couvillion, Doug, 8603
Covance Inc., 5305
Covarrubias, Abel, 5610
Covelli Enterprises, 7365
Covelli Family Limited Partnership, 7365
Covelli Family Limited Partnership, II, 7365
Covelli, Albert M., 7365
Covelli, Josephine, 7365
Covelli, Sam, 7365
Covelli, Sam A., 7365
Coveney, Kenneth G., 227
Covert, Nicole Marie Nugent, 9011
Covey, Joy D., 286
Covey, Patrick M., 7373
Covey, Yvonne, 7724
Covil, Elizabeth C., 8518
Coville, Betsy, 4596
Coville, Claudia, 4596

Coville, Margot E., 4596
Coville, Warren J., 4596
Covington, Marion Stedman, 7081
Covitz, Lisa Adler, 2707
Cowan, Debra, 1039
Cowan, F. James, 9361
Cowan, Greg, 1772
Cowan, Ivy, 7255
Cowan, James, 7255
Cowan, James R., 7255
Cowan, Myra, 7255
Cowan, R. Douglas, 7373
Cowart, Janice, 823
Cowell, Katherine, 4466
Cowell, MacKenzie, 4466
Cowell, Whitney, 4466
Cowen, Jon-Paul, 975
Cowen, Randolph L., 5882
Cowett, Anne F., 6411
Cowett, Fred, 6411
Cowett, Wilbur A., 6411
Cowles Charitable Trust, 6256
Cowles Media Co., 811
Cowles, E.A., 9582
Cowles, Florence C., 3482
Cowles, Gardner, Sr., 3482
Cowles, W.S., 9582
Cowlin Charitable Lead Trust, 2814
Cowlin Charitable Trust, W.J., 2814
Cowlin, Bill, 2814
Cowlin, Bridget, 2814
Cowlin, David A., 2814
Cowlin, Geraldine, 2814
Cowsert, Bill, 2437
Cowsert, Susan, 4672
Cox Enterprises, 2621
Cox, Betsy, 2368
Cox, Charles, 8869
Cox, Donald M., 5883
Cox, James, 859
Cox, James M., 4662
Cox, Jim, 7357
Cox, Lorine G., 7805
Cox, Maria R., 5883
Cox, Mike, 4736
Cox, Natasha, 3344
Cox, Opal G., 8790
Cox, Patricia O'Neill, 3028
Cox, Robert F., Jr., 8201
Cox, Russell N., 5219
Cox, Steven E., 7314, 7545
Cox, T.A., 5062
Cox, William J., 603
Coxe, Marion, 8522
Coy, Debra M., 3248, 3249
Coykendall, Robert, 1453
Coyle, Kathye, 912
Coyne, Anthony J., 7608
Coyne, Fran, 4801
Coyne, Kevin, 5154
Cozen, Stephen A., 7941
Cozort, Barbara Myers, 7097
Crabb, Anthony, 431
Crabb, Greg J., 4375
Crabill, John C., 5988
Crable, Steve E., 1958
Crabtree, John G., 942
Crabtree, Thomas S., II, 3462
Cracchiolo, Bernadette M., 4415
Cracchiolo, Carol A., 4415
Cracchiolo, David, 4414
Cracchiolo, Jane E., 4414
Cracchiolo, Raymond M., 4414
Cracchiolo, Thomas A., 4415

Cracker Barrel Old Country Store, 8603
Craft, Barbara, 3589
Craft, Carol L., 1856
Craft, Jimmy, 8548
Craft, Joy, 8548
Crahan, Caryl, 456
Crahan, Michelle, 456
Crahan, Sean, 456
Craig, Charles S., 1423
Craig, Emily C., 7111
Craig, Jeffrey A., 4511
Craig, Jerome H., 1040
Craig, Marcia Larson, 9650
Craig, Mary Ellen, 5664
Craig, Myrita J., 4713
Craig, Nancy, 3362
Craig, Richard, 6083
Craig-Scheckman, Michael, 1252
Craig-Scheckman, Sara, 1252
Cramblit, Geraldine, 432
Cramblit, Lue D., 432
Cramer, Joe, 4450
Cramer, Lauren, 6676
Crandall, J. Ford, 7366
Crane & Co., 4058
Crane 2007 Chairtable Lead Trust, Colleen A., 5884
Crane 2007 Chairtable Lead Trust, James D., 5884
Crane Co., 5306
Crane Trust, Colleen A., 5884
Crane Trust, James D., 5884
Crane, Alan L., 4007
Crane, Benjamin, 8586
Crane, Charles M., 8009
Crane, Charles R., 1816, 8009
Crane, David Radford, 1955
Crane, Diana H., 8009
Crane, Don, 7784
Crane, Ellen F., 1955
Crane, Heather, 8586
Crane, J.D., 5884
Crane, Jane, 2688
Crane, Katherine, 8586
Crane, Lucia L., 4764
Crane, Michael R., 9540
Crane, Raymond E., 1955
Crane, Shelia M., 8638
Crane, Thomas S., 8009
Crane, Tony, 2803
Crane, W. Carey, 9540
Crane-Spier, Kathryn, 2345
Craney, Brody, 5054
Craney, Darlene, 5054
Cranley Trust, The, 1881
Cranshaw, Crawford, 1735
Crary, Lawrence E., III, 2085
Crary, Sandy, 7295
Crat, B. Miller, 7185
Crate, Bradley, 4318
Cravens, Sylvia J., 3680
Cravens, Valerie K., 3680
Craver, Benjamin A., 4353
Craves, Frederick B., 434
Craves, Ryan Soulier, 434
Craves, Sara Soulier, 434
Crawford Trust for Children Northern Trust, The, 4023
Crawford Trust for Grand Children Northern Trust, The, 4023
Crawford, Alison Ford, 8864
Crawford, Denise V., 1330
Crawford, Dona, 435
Crawford, E.R., 7945

Crawford, Emily, 6739
Crawford, Gordon, 435
Crawford, James, 1593
Crawford, Jeffrey G., 435
Crawford, Lori Kulvin, 907
Crawford, Mike, 1295
Crawford, Nancy R., 4059
Crawford, Nancy S., 4059
Crawford, Orsi Z., 435
Crawford, Patricia B., 8430
Crawford, Peter T., 4059
Crawford, Thomas, IV, 4059
Crawford, Thomas, Jr., 4059
Crawford, Tim, 4410
Crawford, Walter, Jr., 8869
Crawley, Ethel W., 7082
Cray Estate, Sara J., 3569
Cray Family Trust, Cloud L., 3569
Cray, Cloud L., 3569
Cray, Cloud L., Jr., 3569, 4890
Cray, Sara Jane, 3569
Creal, Paul, 4396
Creamer, Joanna B., 7868
Creasey, Louise, 5159
Creative Hairdressers, 9521
Creative Investment Ltd. Partnership, 8088
Creative Investments L.P., 8088
Creative Sign Service, 4844
Creaturo, Marie, 1526
Cree Land and Cattle Co Ltd., 9631
Creedon, John F., 4137
Creedon, Richard, 6922
Creek, Jon, 3346
Creighton, G. Russell, 1485
Cremeans, Ron, 7408
Cremer, Frances, 2815
Cremer, Holly L., 2815
Cremins, John, 5681
Crenshaw, Colby, 8869
Crenshaw, Timothy M., 3248
Crescent Plastics, 3365
Cresline Plastics Pipe Co., 3365
Cresline-Northwest LLC, 3365
Cresline-West, 3365
Cress, Robert G., 214
Cressman, Barry, Rev. , 7944
Cressman, Paul R., Jr., 9568
Cressman, Paul R., Sr., 9568
Cressman, Walter H., 7998
Creston Electronics, 5344
Crete, Michael, 9583
Crevier, Donnie, 726
Crew, Kimberly, 1424
Crew, Pat, 238
Crew, Peggy Lynn, 1424
Crew, Ted J., 1424
Crews, Gary, 4598
Crews, Robert, 7782
Crha, Tom, 9638
Crickard, James L., 3847
Crider, Jack, 1965
Crilley, Terry K., 7468
Crimmings, Joann DeLorenzo, 4068
Crimson Shipping Company, 22
Criniti, Linda M., 4020
Crippen, Audrey, 2330
Crippen, Carolyn, 6946
Crippen, Scott, 2330
Crippen, Stan, 2330
Crippen, Standish, 2330
Criqui, Thomas H., 7438
Criscione, Joseph, 2141
Crisosostomo, Victor M., 1125

Crisp, Charles R., 2550
Crispo, Lori Windolf, 2614
Crissman, Philip, 104
Criste, Hildebert F., 3850
Criste, Mary Ellen, 3850
Crites, Carter, 8947
Crites, Katherine, 8947
Crittenden County-Crime Stoppers, 215
Critz, Richard W., 9485
Crivelli, Bill, 420
CRO America Charitable Trust, 388
Croce, Rudy G., 384
Crocker, Ann, 9356
Crocker, Gary, 9356
Crockett, Dick, 4671
Crockett, Kathleen H., 7081
Crocs Cares, 1295
Crocus, Gary E., 3065
Croff, James, 5053
Croft, Jane Aurell, 3841
Croft, Jocelyn, 4088
Croft, Kent Gordon, 3841
Croft, L. Gordon, 3841
Crogan, Jack, 8242
Croman Equities Limited, LLC, 5307
Croman, David, 5307
Croman, Edward L., 5307
Croman, Steven, 5307
Cronic, Steve, 92
Cronin, Carol, 3003
Cronin, David, 3003
Cronin, JD, BSW, Katie, 4983
Cronin, Pam, 1467
Cronin, William J., 2816
Cronk, Gerald M., 2817
Cronk, Lidia E., 2817
Cronquist, Kent, 7297
Crook, Caryl W., 9092
Crook, Caryl Wilson, 9092
Crook, Christine Rebecca, 9092
Crook, Frances C., 105
Crook, Sara B., 5106
Crook, William H., 9092
Croostelex, 2501
Cropp, Linda, 3880
Crosby, Beatrice Wells, 4680
Crosby, Brew, 158
Crosby, Harriett, 4680
Crosby, Ron, 9242
Crosland, Troy, 158
Crosman, Chris, 1781
Crosman, Christopher B., 8327
Cross Hill Venturs, LLC, 9348
Cross, Charles E., 1204
Cross, Frances Pilling, 2567
Cross, Jane C., 7079
Cross, Joe D., Jr., 7079
Crossen, Cynthia, 1854
Crosslands Inc., 4658
Crosson, Tami Lynn Trover, 7824
Crosstel, 2501
Crosswalk Ministry, 7792
Crothers, Mickey, 9808
Crouch, James B., Jr., 7209
Crouchly, Gabrielle, 1680
Crouse, Ann Reynolds, 2574
Crouse, Jacob, 3647
Crow, Harlan R., 8811
Crow, Lacie, 9631
Crow, Patrick, 9631
Crow, Wade R., 8522
Crowder, Juanita C., 8633
Crowder, William C., 1953
Crowe, Brynn, 708

Crowe, Charles, 708
Crowe, Gary, 8237
Crowe, Irene, 1828
Crowe, John, 3322
Crowe, Kathryn R., 3664
Crowe, Katy, 9292
Crowe, Kerridan, 4061
Crowe, Mary, 1828
Crowe, Michael K, 4061
Crowe, Michael K., 4061
Crowe, Robert W., 9461
Crowell & Moring LLP, 1799
Crowell, Richard L., Jr., 3729
Crowell, Susan M., 2917
Crowley Charitable Lead Trust, 4416
Crowley, C., 1239
Crowley, Colin P., 5788
Crowley, Elizabeth V., 9799
Crowley, Geoffrey T., 9799
Crowley, Ian, 4012
Crowley, James, 5245
Crowley, Joseph, Dr. , 7346
Crowley, Nancy R., 8543
Crowley, Samantha K., 7327
Crown Books Corp., 1800
Crowther, Bruce, 3092
Croxton, J. Huff, Jr., 2441
Cruden, John, 897
Cruikshank, Douglas A., 4620
Cruikshank, Lisa P., 4620
Crull, Linn A., 3421
Crum, Christine B., 2724
Crum, Dennis, 5398
Crummer, Donn J., 436
Crummer, Keith R., 436
Crummer, Roy E., III, 436
Crump, Katherine, 4845
Crumpton, Darren K., 3730
Crumrine, Marla, 3634
Crut No. 2, Dorothy M. Morrison, 3608
Crut, Dorothy B. Gackstatter, 4400
Crut, Dorothy M. Morrison, 3608
Crutchfield, Edward E., 1957
Crutchfield, Edward E., Jr., 1957
Crutchmer, Clyde, 9245
Cruz-Reis, Claudia, 1453
Cryan, Elizabeth S., 2306
Cryer, Gretchen, 5700
Crystal Springs Textiles Corp., The, 8633
CSL Behring, 7847
CSU Industries, 5733
CSW Foundation, 7303
CSX Corp., 1958
CSX Corporation, 2283
CSX Transportation, 1958
CTS Equities LP, 2357
Cuban, Brian, 8795
Cuban, Jeff, 8795
Cuban, Kim, 8795
Cuban, Mark, 8795
Cuban, Tiffany, 8795
Cuda, Richard S., 1612
Cuda, Sean, 2007
Cudahy, Julia A., 9800
Cudahy, Lisa A., 9800
Cudahy, Michael J., 9800
Cudd, Nancy H., 6481
Cudd, Robert A.N., 6481
Cudlie Accessories, LLC, 6882
Cudworth, Jane, 1130
Cuervo, Manuel A., 2150
Culbertson, Thomas M., 9634
Culbertson, William, 7396
Cullen & Sons, J.P., 9848

Cullen, Charles R., 4250
Cullen, James D., 7876, 8212, 8280
Cullen, John P., 9848
Cullen, Mark A., 9848
Cullen, Melissa, 4633
Cullen, Richard T. "Terry", 9290
Cullen, Tracy, 8068
Cullen, William T., 8185
Culler, Michael, 7339
Culley, Natalie C., Mrs. , 2830
Cullina LLP, Murtha, 1493
Cullinan, Alfreda S., 1131
Cullinan, Michael N., 2818
Cullinan, Stephen A., 2818
Cullinane, John, 6455
Cullis, Christopher, 7339
Cullman Trust, Joseph F., 5886, 5887
Culp, Missy, 3432
Cultural Survival, 4012
Culver, Erne Constans, 2805
Cumberland Continental, 8689
Cumberland Trust, 8619
Cumings, Susan, 7899
Cumings, Susan Hurd, 7899
Cumming, Allison R., 9315
Cumming, Barbara Bell, 5888
Cumming, David E., 9315
Cumming, John D., 9316
Cumming, Kristi Terzian, 9316
Cummings, Andrew, 4417
Cummings, Charles, 5874
Cummings, Charles K., III, 4155
Cummings, Gay C., 4417
Cummings, Harrington M., 4417
Cummings, Julie, 9333
Cummings, Kaye B., 326
Cummings, Kevin, 5513
Cummings, Mark D., 9424
Cummings, Mimi, 4417
Cummings, Pat, 5700
Cummings, Richard, 8311
Cummings, Samuel, 4417
Cummings, Steven L., 9291
Cummins, Gail, 8860
Cummins, Lisa, 6720
Cummins, Susan, 991
Cummins-Allison Corp., 3002
Cunha, Paul, 447
Cunnane, Edith C., 1959
Cunnane, James J., Jr., 1959
Cunnane, James J., Sr., 1959
Cunningham Charitable Lead
    AnnuityTrust, Rubye A., 3682
Cunningham, Amy, 2827
Cunningham, C. Frederick, 3428
Cunningham, Carlie, 2819
Cunningham, Edward V.K., Jr., 6544
Cunningham, Gertrude Oliver, 3428
Cunningham, J. Dawson, 7373
Cunningham, J. Oliver, 3428
Cunningham, Jane W., 7545
Cunningham, Judith L., 3682
Cunningham, Kurt, 7205
Cunningham, Pam, 7205
Cunningham, Patricia Vecellio, 9770
Cunningham, Ron, 8652
Cuomo, Paul, 6088
Cupp, Bob, 3367
Curby, John E., Jr., 5005
Curby, Nancy S., 5005
Curci-Turner Company LLC, 784
Curley, Maureen M., 3090
Curley, Stephen C., 2013
Curley, Walter J.P., 5669

Curmark, 1730
Curme, Cynthia K., 4180
Curme, Oliver D., 4180
Curran Foundation, 6542
Curran, Albert F., Jr., 4362
Curran, Daniel, 723
Curran, Jane F., 1427
Curran, Jennifer, 723
Curran, Lisa M., 1552
Curran, Richard E., Jr., 3795
Curran, Vincent, 5414
Curran, William E., 1427
Curran, William T., 9837
Currens, Tim, 3360
Currie Family Foundation, 1080
Currie, Andrew, 4130
Currie, William G., 4418
Currin, Mary McCanne, 9288
Curry, Bill, 4892
Curry, Clifford, 7755
Curry, Dorothy F., 4892
Curry, Doug, 4892
Curry, Jona Nusink, 5625
Curry, Kathy, 5094
Curry, Lee, 4892
Curry, Michael R., 9245
Curry, Natalie H., 8069
Curry, Richard L., 3052
Curry, William H., 4892
Curtin, Daniel F., 6134
Curtis Charitable Lead Annuity Trust,
    Darwin O'Ryan, 9433
Curtis Partnership, 5889
Curtis, Alan, 5889
Curtis, Bryan, 5889
Curtis, Christine W., 5889
Curtis, Darwin O'Ryan, 9433
Curtis, Donna, 7910
Curtis, Francis, 9454
Curtis, Gary, 9333
Curtis, Hugh V. Stan, 591
Curtis, Jackie, 4527
Curtis, Jacqueline, 4527
Curtis, James F., III, 3249
Curtis, John, 1929
Curtis, John D., 9433
Curtis, Kyle, 4527
Curtis, Laura, 9433
Curtis, Linda, 5889
Curtis, Michael R., 8490
Curtis, Pat, 4598
Curtis, Rachel, 3963
Curtis, Randall K., 9433
Curtis, Robert, 6290
Curtis, Roberta, 5889
Curtis, Simon B., 9433
Curtis, Tom, 785
Curtis, William, 3963
Curtiss Wright Corp., 6385
Curtiss, Jacqueline DeWitt, 4527
Curvey, J. Scott, 4062
Curvey, James C., 4062
Curvey, Jeffrey C., 4062
Cusatis, Anthony, 7997
Cushing, Margaret C., 7013
Cushman & Wakefield, 6655
Cushman, Marjorie L., 437
Cushman, Stephen P., 437
Cussins, R. Donald, 3847
Cusson, Craig, 4057
Custard, Lovell J., 7645
Custer, G. Stanley, 9878
Custer, Ken, 9797
Custer, Violet, 9878

Custom Nutrition Services, LLC, 181
Cusumano, Michael, 421
Cutco Corporation, 5890
Cutco Cutlery, 5890
Cutco Cutlery Corp., 5890
Cuthell, Catherine S., 1693
Cutler, Burt, 438
Cutler, Christopher A., 9312
Cutler, Diana, 438
Cutler, Hermila, 9312
Cutler, Jay, 438
Cutler, Linda, 3179
Cutler, Nathan P., 8471
Cutler, Sarah S., 7568
Cutler, William H., 8471
Cutrow, Allan, 839
Cutshall, Pat, 4667
Cutter, W. Bowman, 9416
Cutter, W. Bowman, III, 9416
Cutting, Amy E., 9968
Cutting, Carol Moore, 4337
Cutting, Carol T., 1134
Cutting, Frank J., 8501
Cutting, Joan L., 9968
Cutting, Richard W., 5842
Cuvelier, Andrea, 6355
Cuvelier, Guillaume, 6355
CVC Capital Partners, 6741
Cwysyshyn, Bradley, 4583
Cybelonics, 2406
Cyclops Family Partnership, LP, 3810
Cyr, Roderick J., 3570
Czap, Eugene A., 5891
Czermak, Elliot, 5875
Czerwinski, Frank, 5301
Czerwinski, Kathy, 4478
Czesak, Cynthia, 5493

D & H Cares, 8264
D & H Distributing Co., 8264
D & M Lumber Products Co., 6566
D'Addario Co. Inc., 5895
D'Addario, Joan, 5894
D'Addario, John, III, 5894, 5895
D'Addario, John, Jr., 5894, 5895
D'Addario, Laura, 5894
D'Addario, Michael, 5894
D'Addario, Suzanne, 5894
d'Adolf, Lila Gimprich, 6080
D'Agostino, John, 6540
D'Allessio, John, 1599
D'Aloia, G. Peter, 5311
D'Aloia, Marguerite, 5311
D'Amato, June, 6932
D'Amato, Lawrence L., 6932
D'Amour, Charles L., 4064
D'Amour, Donald H., 4064
D'Andrea, Patrick, 9033
D'Angelo, Debra Chiat, 393
D'Angelo, Kara, 6579
D'Anneo, Allan C., 7748
D'Anneo, Andrea J., 7748
D'Anneo, Roberta C., 7748
D'Anniballe, David E., 7335
D'Anto, Sarah, 2415
D'Arenberg, Pierre, 7857
D'Arrigo, Joseph W., 4268
D'Auria, Janet, 6408
D'Auria, Paul, 6408
D'Eredita, Bill, 6720
D'Onofrio, Donato, 5324
D'Onofrio, Linda, 5324
D'Onofrio, Mary, 5324

D.M. Merchandising, 3077
D.Q. Acquisition LLC, 6656
Dab, John M., 8646
Dabah Charitable Foundation Inc., Ezra & Renee, 5260
Dabah, Barbara, 5892
Dabah, Haim, 5892
Dabah, Morris, Jr., 5892
Dabah, Raquel, 5893
Dabah, Solomon, 5893
Dabah, Victor H., 5893
Dabek, Bozena, 4076
Daberko, David A., 7369
Daberko, Deborah L., 7369
Dabha Children Charitable Foundation, 7001
Dabkowski, Gary, 4389
Dabney, Edith LaCroix, 4150
Dabrow, Allan M., 8022
Dachs, Alan M., 527
Dacotah Bank, 8574, 8577
Dadakis, John D., 5731
Dady, Pat, 8577
Daeumer Trust No. 1, Harvey, 2821
Daeumer, Harvey E., 2821
Daft, Delphine H., 5310
Daft, Douglas N., 5310
Daggett, Brian, 6624
Dahab, Albert V., 5454
Dahl, David D., 7164
Dahl, Doris, 7697
Dahl, Keith, 439
Dahl, Kenneth, 439
Dahl, Matthew C., 7164
Dahl, Patricia, 439
Dahl, Robert, 439
Dahley Co., 3905
Dahlgren, Denis, 5660
Dahling, Nena, 4592
Dahlstrom, Larry, 8575
Daiger, Stephan, 2881
Daikeler, Carl, 7941
Dailey, John, 7794
Daily News, LP, 6909
Daimler Trucks North America, LLC, 7094
DaimlerChrysler Corp., 7209
Dain, Regina A., 7325
Daisy Outdoor Products, 3991
Daitch, Alexa, 4714
Daitch, Peter, 4714
Dake, Bradford G., 6238
Dal Pozzo, James A., 1118
Dalal, Shreyasi H., 8273
Dalcan, LLC, 7365
Dale, Beverley B., 8794
Dale, Bruce, 3567
Dale, Edward B., 8794
Dale, Jayne K., 8794
Dale, Joanne, 812
Dale, John R., 8794
Dale, Lauren Lipcon, 7468
Dale, Lawrence B., 8794
Dale, Peter L., 8794
Dale, Tom, 2803
Dale, William H., Jr., 3303
Dalen, James, 181
Dalessandro, Frances C., 4063
Dalessandro, John J., 4063
Dallas Basketball Ltd., 8795
Dallas Mavericks Foundation, The, 8795
Dallas Morning News, 8795
Dallmeyer, Dorinda, 2619
Dally, Rebecca P., 2604

Dalrymple, Elizabeth T., 5674
Dalsimer, Diane Kimmel, 6308
Dalsimer, Janet Craig, 7942
Dalton, Arthur R., 1960
Dalton, Janet B., 1960
Dalton, Mark F., 5896
Dalton, Paul J., 5324
Dalton, Susan K., 5896
Daly Irrevocable Trust, Helen, 9371
Daly, Bernard, 7756
Daly, Edward J., 440
Daly, James J., 5788
Daly, Joy Fox, 5349
Dama, Mike, 4497
Damba, Dwayne, 4961
Damba, Victoria, 4961
Damico, Joseph D., 7370
Damico, Joseph F., Jr., 7370
Damico, Lauren C., 7370
Damico, Pamela C., 7370
Damis, James, 7832
Damme, Lora, 5105
Damner, Bert, 773
Damuth Trust, Adeline J., 1428
Damuth, Craig, 8796
Damuth, S. Craig, 8796
Dan's Supreme Supermarkets, 6387
Dana Corporation, 4419
Dana Holding Corporation, 4419
Dana, Joseph, 78
Dana, Joseph F., 2434
Dana, Verrill, 3782
Danastasio, Cody, 4893
Danastasio, Erin D., 4893
Dane, Herbert P., 4276
Danella, Carmen, 7948
Danella, Sharon, 7948
Danforth, Janet W., 8017
Daniel, Bill, 8784
Daniel, J. Michael, 9391
Daniel, James A.L., 9556
Daniel, R. Michael, 8014
Daniel, Ronald B., 9253
Daniele, Mark A., 8035
Daniell, Edward H., 8538
Daniels 1986 Irrevocable Trust, Selma S., 3483
Daniels, Bruce, 7357
Daniels, Charles R., III, 6683
Daniels, Edgar Foster, 5613
Daniels, June E., 3483
Daniels, Laura Sue, 4942
Daniels, Ron, 7789
Daniels, Ronald L., 3483
Danielson, Barbara S., 2824
Danielson, Beverly, 2824
Danielson, Dick, 3511
Danielson, Zachary, 1272
Danis Building Construction Co., 7371
Danis, John, 7371
Danker, Martha, 9592
Danker, Richard, 1870
Dankis, Brian K., 5312
Dankis, Gary P., 5312
Dankis, Mark J., 5312
Dankis, Mildred L., 5312
Dankis, Victor J., 5312
Danksewicz, Jill Cosgrove, 4095
Danley, Frances A., 51
Danley, Franklin, 51
Dann, Harvey, IV, 6119
Dann, Tyler, 6119
Danner, J.C., 5594
Dansby, Amy D., 8693

Dansby, Danny L., 8693
Dansby, David L., 8693
Dansby, Gwen, 9778
Dansby, Linda L., 8693
Dansby, Ryan L., 8693
Dantchik, Arthur, 8310
Danzi LLC, John A., 5898
Danzi, John A., 5898
Danziger, Sidney, 5899
Danziger, Thomas C., 1778
Danzing, Lisa, 7781
DAR, 4966
Darcy, Larissa, 3766
Darcy, Thomas E., 520
Darden, E. Holley, 9428
Darden, Elizabeth D., 9428
Darden, Frank, 8816
Darden, Glenn, 8816
Darden, Joshua P., 9428
Darden, Joshua P., Jr., 9428
Darden, Lucy, 8816
Darden, Thomas, 8816
Dareus, Marcel, 4399
Darjess LLC, 6675
Darley, Patti, 9797
Darling, Anne Helow, 2089
Darling, Bradford L., 1249
Darnall Cemetery Fund, Eugenia B., 7949
Darney, Suzette M., 5199
Darr, Sr. Carolyn, 4035
Darr, William N., 4893
Danastasio, Cody, 4893
Darragh, Fred K., Jr., 193
Darrah, Jessie S., 5900
Darrigrand, Maritxu, 945
Darroch, Jacqueline, 7338
Darryl, Dennis D., 8886
Darryl, Terry Muntz, 8886
Dart Container Corporation, 4421
Dart Container Corporation of Georgia, 4421
Dart Container Corporation of Kentucky, 4421
Dart Container Sales Co., LLC, 4421
Dart, Ariane M., 4421
Dart, Robert C., 4421, 9503
Dartnell, Ashley, 6926
Das Ventures Ltd., 6839
Dasburg, John H., 1961
Dasburg, Mary L., 1961
Dasburg, Mary Lou, 1961
Dasher, Kevin, 5104
DaSilva, Diane Lynn, 1974
DaSilva, Krista Mary, 1974
Datnchik, Arthur, 8310
Dattner, Hezzy, 6052
Dauch, Gladys, 7372
Dauer, Anne, 900
Dauer, David R., 362
Dauer, Jason, 362
Daugherty, David, 3397
Daugherty, Mary Wilson, 1366
Daughters, Willie, 7558
Daughterty, Sally, 2055
Daughtrey, Margery, 6083
Daughtridge, Bill, 7227
Dauler, L. Van V., Jr., 8061
Daum, Deborah, 6508
Daum, John, 6508
Daum, Paul L., 6083
Dauphin, Charline, 8798
Dauphin, Marian, 9756
Dauphin, Robin, 8798
Dauphinais, Roger, 4095

Dauzat, Roz, 9070
Davenport, C. Thomas, Jr., 8647
Davenport, Gene, 4497
Davenport, George P., 3775
Davenport, Ned, 8738
Davey Tree Expert Co., The, 7373
David, Betty, 6739
David, Robert, 2872
David-Weill, Michel, 5669
Davidson Foundation, Marvin H., 5901
Davidson Trust Co., 5045, 5055
Davidson, Andrew, Dr., 2443
Davidson, Carleton F., 7374
Davidson, Deb Kmon, 3928
Davidson, James A., 1087
Davidson, Jeannie V., 2658
Davidson, John C., 3979
Davidson, Jonathan, 972
Davidson, Joyce, 471
Davidson, Julia Loewy, 1087
Davidson, Lorraine, 3125
Davidson, Park R., 7062
Davidson, Patricia F., 8382
Davidson, Richard, 283
Davidson, Scott E., 5901
Davidson, Spencer, 147
Davidson, Susan, 5901
Davidson, Suzanne Schwartz, 1397
Davie, Elizabeth B., 8615
Davies, Dennis, 840
Davies, Evelyn McLaughlin, 8813
Davies, George Aitken, 6775
Davies, John, 5872
Davies, John L., 1801
Davies, Marjorie, 7582
Davies, Natalie L., 762
Davies, Paul L., III, 762
Davies, Paul L., Jr., 762, 1142
Davies, Pilar H., 762
Davies, Ralph K., 444
Davies, Robert H., 762
Davies, Thomas R., 9744
Davies, Tyler S., 762
Davies, Virginia L., 5562
Davino, Anthony P., 5313
Davino, Frances, 5313
Davino, Salvatore A., 5313
Davis & Floyd Inc., 8521
Davis Brothers Construction, 8700
Davis for Employees, G.H., 8799
Davis Foundation, 8243
Davis SB-3 Trust, Jane M., 8862
Davis, A. Dano, 1962
Davis, Adelaide Shull, 8626
Davis, Anthony, 5556
Davis, Barbara, 7513
Davis, Bradley K., 2341
Davis, Catherine, 6909
Davis, Cora, 3844
Davis, Dana, 202
Davis, Daryl Rose, 1964
Davis, David, 7083
Davis, Diane, 1354
Davis, Diane Trombetta, 1128
Davis, Don, 3611
Davis, Donald D., 9317
Davis, Donna, 1204
Davis, Donna G., 2164
Davis, Dwight E., 9802
Davis, Edgar B., 4245
Davis, Edwin W., 8185
Davis, Elaine, 3771
Davis, Elaine F., 9317
Davis, Elwood, 1494

Davis, Elwood B., 1533
Davis, Emmett I., III, 8521
Davis, Emmett I., Jr., 8521
Davis, Ernie, 3666
Davis, Everett M., 4340
Davis, Florence S., 8626
Davis, G. Franklin T., 7084
Davis, Gary, 2959
Davis, Graeme W., 577
Davis, Gregory R., 9510
Davis, H. Stewart, 2465
Davis, Harrison S., 8626
Davis, Henry, 3948
Davis, Howard C., 4773
Davis, J.B., 7209
Davis, J.M., 8862
Davis, Jaimee Lisa, 299
Davis, James D., 25
Davis, James E., 1962
Davis, Jan, 5104
Davis, Jane C., 2095, 5314
Davis, Jefferson, 4107
Davis, Joan Goodman, 1213
Davis, John, 445, 4850
Davis, John C., 4995
Davis, John H., 3844
Davis, John S., 2465
Davis, Jordan, 445
Davis, Joseph P., III, 7064
Davis, Joy, 196
Davis, Karen, 5955
Davis, Kevin, 5902
Davis, Kevin J., 4568
Davis, Kevin R., 5902
Davis, King, 4107
Davis, L. Kelly, 2590
Davis, Larry, 8915
Davis, Linda, 8915, 9802
Davis, Lori, 4222
Davis, Louis J., 1345
Davis, Mark, 9069
Davis, Mary, 9170
Davis, Mary H., 7455
Davis, Maryellen, 7645
Davis, Mitchell R., 5314
Davis, Mona R., 8521
Davis, Nancy B., 3697
Davis, Nancy I., 7933
Davis, Paul Oliver, 299
Davis, Peggy, 5708
Davis, R.Timothy, 9556
Davis, Richard M., Jr., 9998
Davis, Richard P., 1963
Davis, Robert, 1402
Davis, Robert C., 3932
Davis, Robert E., 1790
Davis, Robert S., 1964
Davis, Robert T., 810
Davis, Ronald, 5054
Davis, Russell R., Jr., 8449
Davis, Sarah Crutchfield, 1957
Davis, Shaun, 8869
Davis, Sherry Sue, 7656
Davis, Stephen L., 8521
Davis, Steven D., 1130
Davis, Susan, 2373
Davis, Susan P., 1963
Davis, Terry, 5620, 7513
Davis, Thomas H., 7084
Davis, Thomas H., Jr., 7084
Davis, Thomas P., 726
Davis, Tom, Dr. , 7311
Davis, Virginia A., 8626
Davis, W. Lipscomb, Jr., 8626

Davis, W.L., III, 8626
Davis, W.L., Jr., 8626
Davis, Wendy, 612, 7923
Davis, William Keith, 8755
Davis, William M., 8097
Davis, William W., Jr., 8600
Davison Iron Works, 917
Davison, William M., IV, 8134
Davoli, Robert E., 4065
Davoren, Anne, 8458
Dawkins, John R., 9751
Dawson, Sue Ann, 6739
Dawson, Susan, 1060
Dawson, Susan Scranton, 8356
Day Interim Trust, Margaret, 1654
Day Trust, Rodney and Evelyn, 5980
Day, Barbara S., 4563
Day, Carl, 4832
Day, Evelyn S., 5980
Day, Gary Wayne, 3845
Day, H. Corbin, 25
Day, Harry M., 1965
Day, James C., 8800
Day, James C., Jr., 8800
Day, Jerry, 1965
Day, Jr. Trust, Rufus S., 7338
Day, Kelly G., 589
Day, Larry L., 120
Day, Mary Grace, 3845
Day, Michael G., 3814
Day, Rodney D., III, 5980, 7990
Day, Roxann, 8719
Day, Setsuko, 1965
Day, Teresa K., 8800
Dayal, Duke, 272
Daybrook Fisheries Inc., 3720
Dayton, Arlene J., 4655
Dayton, Chadwick L., 4655
Dayton, Charles, 4626
Dayton, Duncan N., 4797
Dayton, John W., 4655
Dayton, Paul K., 1858
Dayton, Paul K., Ph.D, 898
DBK Vision Inc., 153
DCD Marketing LTD, 6914
DCF Enterprises, 1046
DDR Invesment Co., 4966
DDT Descendants Charitable Lead
   Annuity Trust, 8682
de Allesandrini, Enrico, 7013
de Anda, Nancy, 9010
de Beaumont Trust, Mary Deland, 4266
de Beaumont, Mary Deland, 4266
de Compiegne, Henri Joseph, 8802
de Compiegne, Mary Wallace, 8802
De Cook, Daniel, 3484
De Cook, Kay, 3484
De Cook, Mark, 3484
De Cordova, Michael, 6544
De Cordova, Noel, Jr., 6544
De Dergh, Sue Anne, 6623
De Gaetano, Peter F., 6353
de Hoernle, Countess Henrietta, 1966
De Jacobo, Dilia Carmela, 1430
De Jong, Barb, 3487
De Jong, Dave, 3487
de Jonge, Judith, 9684
de Juan, Eugene, 2881
De La Cour, Edmund P., 5904
De La Cour, Lea, 5904
De La Cour, Willis S., 5904
De La Cour, Willis S., Jr., 5904
de La Garza, Henry A., 8924
de la Montana, Flores, 1102

De La Reguera, Deborah, 9851
De La Vega, Dania, 2182
De Lara, Angela D., 1430
De Lara, Jonne Low, 1430
de Leeuw, Debra Sylvan, 7722
de Leon, Jana L., 8179
de Lesseps, Geoffrey, 1391
De Lesseps, Tauni, 1391
De Llano, Matias, 8803
De McCarty, Jack, 7714
de Menil Foundation, Adelaide, 6679
de Menil, Adelaide, 6679
de Menil, George, 6679
de Menil, Victoria, 6679
De Miranda, Jay R., 446
De Miranda, Shirley Y., 446
De Noire, Roland, 9298
De Palchi, Alfredo, 8018
de Peyster, Electra Ducommun, 465
De Polo, Julie Huntington, 642
de rothschild, Victoria, 6749
de Roulet, Daniel C., 6579
de Roulet, Daniel C., Jr., 6579
de Roulet, Lorinda P., 6579
de Serio, Charlotte H., 1680
De Sieyes, Charles J., 5682
De Sieyes, David C., 5682
De Sieyes, Virginia, 5682
De Vink, L. Rupert A., 1967
De Vink, Lodewijk J.R., 1967
De Vink, Marijke B.E., 1967
De Vink, Rutger J.L., 1967
de Werd, Dolores G., 121
de Werd, Susan L., 121
De Z. Meyer, Maria Teresa, 3913
Dea, Cathy Carpenter, 1254
Dea, Peter A., 1254
Deacon, Steven D., 447
Dead River Co., 3792
Deakin, Scott M., 1442
Deaktor, Michael W., 421
Deal, Crystal S., 2328
Deal, Doris P., 7085
Deal, Harmon B., III, 2826
Deal, Jean F., 2826
Deal, Jennie Goodman, 7078
Deal, R.L., 7085
Dean Assoc. Corp., Joel, 3846
Dean, Aaron J., 5174
Dean, Arthur H., 6879
Dean, Doug, 3684
Dean, Emily R., 5174
Dean, Gillian, 3846
Dean, Gregory A., 5174
Dean, Jared G., 5174
Dean, Jason, 370
Dean, Jimmy, 1938
Dean, Joel, 3846
Dean, Joel, Jr., 3846
Dean, John, 2627
Dean, Jurrien, 3846
Dean, Kerry A.F., 5174
Dean, Laura, 2309
Dean, Lucas, 5174
Dean, Mary R., 3812
Dean, Patrick J., 3812
Dean, Tracy T., 2593
Deane, Brian C., 5788
Deane, Gordon L., 4066
Deane, Julie, 7358
Deane, Motoko T., 4066
Deane, Shelley W., 3779
DeAngelis, Kenneth, 8706
Deangelis, Linda, 8393

Deanovic, Anne, 4738
Dearing, Henry H., 977
Dearth, Marc J., 5595
Deary, Kenneth J., 4141
Deas, Terry, 8603
Dease, Clyde, 4847
Deason, Carol Brollier, 9094
Deason, Darwin, 8805
Deason, Douglas, 8805
Deaver, Francesca, 1125
Debauge, Jeff, 3635
Debaut, Elizabeth, 4756
Debbink, Dirk J., 9804
Debbink, Joan C., 9804
Debbink, John P., 9804
Debbink, Teresa L., 9804
DeBerg, Jan, 8576
Deberry, James A., 4873
DeBlasio, Alfred, Jr., 5513
Debode, Gary, 5330
DeBolt, Valerie, 3576
Debrovner, Martin, 8695
DeBuys, Paige, 7444
Decarlo, Michele L., 8349
Decatur Trust, Mary, 4314
DeCello, Anthony D., 7370
Deck, Joe S., 9703
Decker, Ann, 2148
Decker, Jim, 3651
Decker, Joyce, 3651
Decker, Kristen, 908
Decker, Margaret, 3651
Decker, Midge, 3397
Deckey, Gowan Jessen, 8968
DeClercq, Margaret, 8582
Decoteau, Jay M., 4288
DeCrane, Vincent F., 7330
Dedecker, Faith, 2909
Dedecker, Hayden, 2909
Dedham Institution for Savings, 4067
Dedick, Regina, 6408
Dedman, Nancy, 8807
Dedman, Nancy M., 8808
Dedman, Patricia Brown, 8807
Dedman, Rachael Redekker, 8808
Dedman, Robert H., Jr., 8808
Dedon, John P., 9536
Dedrick, George B., 2909
Deeb, Mark, 1950
Deer Park Road Corp., 1252
Deering Foundation, 2823, 2824, 2912
Deering, L. Patrick, 3937
Deering, Nicole, 7807
Dees, Kathleen P., 5181
Deeter, Leslie A. Pegler, 5110
Deeter, Trent, 5110
Deevy, Brian M., 1375
DeFalco, Santina, 9585
DeFeo, Brenda, 8328
Defeo, Elizabeth, 1968
Defeo, Julia, 1968
Defeo, Lauren, 1968
Defeo, Neil, 1968
Defeo, Sandra, 1968
Defilippo, Marsha, 6178
DeFriece, Frank W., 8647
DeFriece, Frank W., Jr., 8647
DeFriece, Paul E., 8647
DeFriece, Pauline M., 8647
Deggendorfer, Frank, 7810
Deggendorfer, Kathleen, 7810
Deggendorfer, Kathy, 7810
DeGiacomo, James R., 4068

Degnan 2011 Charitable Lead Annuity Trust, John J., 5315
Degnan, Cynthia, 5315
Degnan, Mary, 5315
Degnan, Philip, 5315
Degrandpre, Peter, 4076
DeGree, Kitty, 3721
DeGroodt, Patty, 9592
DeGroot, Katie, 3432
Degroot, Louise, 4423
Deguire, Carolyn J., 8914
Dehaemers, Barbara, 3572
Dehaemers, David, 3572
Dehan, Alison, 8809
Dehan, Stephen E., 8809
Dehan, Susan, 8809
Dehennis, Linda Dodwell, 1101
Dehne, Linda, 8925
DeHoff, Daniel J., 7376
DeHoff, Linda M., 7376
DeHoff, Robert J., 7376
Dehring, Jack E., 4499
Deikel, Beverly, 4683
Deikel, Theodore, 4663
Deininger, John, 9679
Deitch, Donna, 273
Deitch, Joseph, 4094
Deitcher, Mark, 8042
Deiter, David, 425
Dejonge Properties LLC., Rosen, 9684
Dejoy, Louis, 7209
DeKock, Douglas, 4425
DeKock, Sandra, 4425
Del Balso, Dudley, 5908
Del Balso, Michael, 5908
Del Buono, Barry, 740
Del Prete, Daniel B., 8401
Del Real, Karol Genovese, 8887
Del Vecchio, Claudio, 6091
Del Vecchio, Debra, 6091
DeLaere, Katie, 2695
Delagnes, Natalie J., 1104
Delagnes, R. Michael, 1104
DeLaMater, Chester C., 5865
Deland Turst I, 6965
Deland Turst II, 6965
Deland, Emme, 7021
Delaney, Diane, 3329
Delaney, Kevin P., 9141
Delaney, Rick, 3397
Delano, Mignon Sherwood, 4426
Delany, B. Cort, 1445
Delate, Edward M., 7910
Delavan Foundation, Nelson B., 1807
Delaware North, 3817
Delaware North Companies, 215
Delaware North Corporation, 3867
DeleDonne, John, 5790
DeLeo, Jean T., 1718
DeLesseps Charitable Reminder Unitrust, 1391
Delevati, Anthony, 385
Delevati, William Henry, 1135
Delfiner, Hannah, 8030
Delfiner, Michael, 8030
Delfiner, Ruth, 8030
Delhaise, Michel G., 3660
Deliberato, Thomas, 7978
Deliniere Trust, Selene, 4894
Deliniere Trust, Victor H., 4894
Delisle, Raymond C., 1249
Dell, Neva J., 2278
Dell, Steven G., 2122
DellaMaria, Matthew, 2712

Delles, Rose, 223
Dellinger, D.C., 651
Dellinger, Paul H., 7932
Delma, Linda A., 7961
Delmar, Charles, 9429
Delmar, Elizabeth A., 9429
Delmar, Roland H., 9429
Delmas, Gladys V.K., 1308
Deloach, Barbara, 4880
DeLoach, M.F., Jr., 2438
DeLoache, Waldo, 2471
DeLong, Christopher, 1791
Delong, James Wycliffe, 4427
Delong, John Wycliffe, 4427
DeLorenzo, Felicia, 4068
DelSignore, Carl, 3847
DelSignore, Carmen P., 3847
Delta Air Lines, 2621
Delta Trust, 8564
DeLuca, Elizabeth, 1431
Deluca, Ellen J., 3417
DeLuca, Frederick A., 1431
DeLuca, Jonathan, 1431
Deluxe Corp., 7311
Delzell Trust, Charles L., 450
Delzell, Robert M., 450
DeMaio, Stephen, 6405
Deman, Greg, 9252
DeMarea, Christine, 3602
Demarest, David P., 7754
Demarest, Frank C., 7754
Demarest, Harold H., Jr., 7754
DeMaria, Brian F., 1932
DeMaria, Caroline C., 1932
DeMaria, Sissy, 1952
DeMaria, Stacy L., 4133
DeMaria, Tifani, 9098
DeMarinis, Kathleen F., 9855
DeMars, Brian L., 1052
Demars, Galene J., 1052
DeMars, Gaylene J., 1052
Demattia, Amy, 4457
Demattia, Mary Ann, 4457
Dembitzer, Fran, 5692
DeMello, Ronald, 401
Demetros, Mary, 7377
DeMoon, Judith A., 5168
DeMoon, Patrick S., 5168
Demorest, Harry L., 7757
Demorest, Jon D., 926
Demorest, Kaaren M., 7757
Demorest, Scott E., 7757
Demos, Emanuel G., 6280
Demos, Nicholas, 2827
DeMott, Richard, 8060
Demoulas, Arthur S., 4324
Dempze, Nancy E., 4268
Demskey, Kathleen, 4998
Demski, Vaneetha R., 7233
DeMuth, Anne S., 3978
DeMuth, Christopher C., 8329
Demyanick, Dale B., 5677, 5999
DenBeste, Janet, 4805
Denbo, Monte, 3427
Denbow, Don, 9084
Denby, Stephanie Hopper, 2977
Denczi, Barbara A., 7953
Denham, Linda, 7548
Denis, Alan J., 3838
Denisof, Antoinette, 8018
Denison, Mary A., 3785
Denit, Helen P., 9430
Denk, Kelly, 9868
Denkers, Kelli Sue, 9318

Denkers, Madison, 9318
Denkers, Stephen E., 9318
Denkers, Stephen G., 9318
Denkers, Susan E., 9318
Denkers-Bishop, Julie, 9318
Denman, Anne M., 5842
Denman, John L., Jr., 8810
Denman, Mary Ellen, 9626
Denman, Patricia, 8810
Dennard, Gwyneth M., 8552
Dennen, Craig, 1599
Dennett, Marie G., 1432
Denney, Timothy, 4490
Denning, Carolyn, 5509
Dennis, Christina, 5254
Dennis, Elizabeth O., 1969
Dennis, Harriet C., 2939
Dennis, Janet J., 1969
Dennis, Jeffrey, 2939
Dennis, Minfong Ho, 6394
Dennis, Pat, 2030
Dennis, Scott, 9242
Dennis, Tina, 2030
Denny, Catherine M., 2828
Denny, James M., 2828
Denny, Prudence, 7825
Densch Charitable Trust, Wayne, 1970
Dent, F.B., 7040
Dent, F.B., Jr., 7040
Dent, Magruder H., 7040
Dent, Rebecca, 6599
Dent, Rebecca H., 7532
Dent, Stephanie Jones, 9276
Dent, Stephine Jones, 9276
Dental Components, 7820
DENTSPLY International Inc., 7954
DeNunzio, Jean Ames, 1433
DeNunzio, Ralph, 1433
Denyse, Clint, 8279
Denyse, Gavin J., 8279
Denzler, Henrietta, 1434
Denzler, Herman, 1434
Deon, Grace, 7905
Department of Justice, State of California, 898
Depaul, Carol, 4581
DePaulo, William, 9734
Deputy Charitable Lead Annuity Trust, William J., 3345
Deputy, Lawrence P., 3345
Deputy, Robert J., 3345
Derak, Tara, 1095
Derby, Steven R., 7953
Deren, Nancy V., 9385
DeRenzo, Linda, 4199
Dermalogica, 451
Dermer, Keri, 1295
Dermer, Neal, 1295
Dermody Properties, 5152
Dermody, Michael C., 5152
DeRoo, Curtis J., 4428
Derosa Dohoney LLP, 4249
deRosa, Paul, 5316
Derr, Laraine, 88
Derry, Chris, 2686
Derusha, Jerry, 4497
Dervish, Ahmet, Dr. , 9781
Derx Trust, Marguerite M., 1435
Desai, Katharine, 5910
Desai, Kulin S., 5574
Desai, Rohit M., 5910
Desai, Vanessa, 5910
Desanctis Trust, Alfred, 5911
Desenberg, Louis A., 4514

Deserio, Charlotte, 1680
Desert Champions, LLC., 386
Deshazer, Leslie, 8760
Deshetsky, Ralph, 4490
Desilva, Peter J., 5026
Desmarais, Jean, 2630
Desmond, William C., 2407
Desnoyers, Henry, 8574
Despasquale, Thomas, 9695
Desrosiers, Robert, 4244
DesRuisseaux, Angela H., 3794
DesRuisseaux, David, 3794
DesRuisseaux, Libby, 3794
DesRuisseaux, Reid, 3794
Dessauer Charitable Lead Unitrust, John H., 6452
Dessauer, John H., 6452
Dessauer, Margaret Lee, 6452
Desser, Orley M., 2707
deStwolinski, Elizabeth H., 3486
deStwolinski, Lance W., 3486
deStwolinski, Matthew, 3486
Deters, Garvin, 3699
Deters, Polk, 3699
Detisch, Ira J., 4285
Detjen, Mark, 4998
Detrano, Joseph R., 7985
Detter, Gerald, 1971
Detter, Iris F., 1971
Detter, Jason M., 1971
Dettlinger, Courtney, 833
Detweiler, John, 7905
Deubel, Michele, 9948
Deupree, Angela Kaye, 8604
Deupree, Rebecca, 8604
Deupree, Reed, 8604
Deupree, Roberta, 8604
Deupree, William W., III, 8604
Deutsch Co., The, 1765
Deutsch, Carl, 1765
Deutsch, David, 5912
Deutsch, Eleanor, 1765
Deutsch, Eugene H., 3404
Deutsch, Frances E., 1436
Deutsch, Isaac, 5912
Deutsch, Joseph, 3404
Deutsch, Lester, 1765
Deutsch, Robert, 5912
Deutsch, Shirley, 3404
Deutsch, William J., 1436
Deutsch-Adler, Alexis, 1765
Deutsch-Zakarin, Gina, 1765
Deutsche Bank Trust Co., 5750, 5813, 5973, 6471
Deutsche-Zakarin, Gina, 1765
Devane, Jim, 3758
Devanney, Timothy, 1544
DeVaughn, Gerald, 8105
DeVaughn, Richard, 7666
Developers, 3905
DeVene, Susan, 7362
Devenecia, Teresa, 9853
Devenoge, Marc, 6428
Devenoge, Mary Louise, 6428
Devereaux, Ann T., 4069
Devereaux, Ann Thompson, 4069
Devereaux, William Anderson, 4069
Devereux, Barbara, 9292
Devereux, Michelle, 9292
DeVetter, Dennis, 9878
DeVetter, Roberta, 9878
deVillers, Rebecca, 7545
Devine, Bonaventura, 5317
Devine, James, 2776

Devine, James P., Jr., 3171
DeVinney, Daniel, 5696
DeVisser, Sherwood, 4521
DeVito, Mathias J., 3848
DeVito, Rosetta K., 3848
DeVlieg Machine Co., 4428
DeVlieg, Charles B., 4428
DeVlieg, Charles R., 4428
DeVlieg, Julia C., 4428
DeVlieg, Kathryn S., 4428
Devlin, J. Hugh, 5477
Devlin, John P., 6682
Devlin, Nancy, 5477
Devlin, R. Sean, 5445
Devlin, Sean, 5303
Devlin, Shawn L., 697
Devnew, Edith S., 4275
Devoe, Stephen E., 3348
DeVore, Floyd, 3573
Devore, Jamie Foss, 9598
DeVore, Richard A., 3573
DeVore, William D., 3573
Devries, Christine, 399
DeVries, Matt, 4401
Dewald, Chris Noel, 2723
Dewald, Donald L., 7424
DeWees, Donald C., 1766
Dewees, Edith Hilles, 8057
Dewees, Edward D., 8057
Dewees, Robert L., 8057
Dewey, Fred, 7953
Dewey, Melvil, 6360
Dewhurst Blind Trust, David, The , 8811
Dewhurst, David H., 8811
Dewhurst, Eugene H., 8811
Dewing, Frances R., 9805
Dewitt, Donald L., 4429
Dewitt, Gary D., 4429
Dewitt, Jack L., 4429
DeWitt, Jack L., 4527
DeWitt, James Russell, 4527
Dewitt, Jerene L., 4429
DeWitt, Jim, 4527
Dewitt, Keith A., 4429
DeWitt, Lyne, 4527
Dewitt, Marvin, 4429
DeWitt, Mary, 4527
Dewitt, Mary E., 4527
DeWitt, Melissa, 4527
Dewitt, Merle J., 4429
DeWitt, Steve, 4527
DeWitt, Steven Lee, 4527
Dewolf, Margaret Lee, 1256
Dewolf, Nicholas, 1256
Dewolf, Nicole, 1256
Dexter, Mike, 2676
Dexter-Russell, 4139
Dey, Nancy, 1403
Dey, Paula, 9696
Dezii, Steve, 5202
Dezorillo, Sonja, 1573
DFM Investment Co., 4966
Dhaens, Lucia, 1230
Diaco, Frank P., 5318
Diaco, Joseph, 5318
Diaco, Theodore F., 5318
Diadamo, Harry P., 1482
Diageo North America, 1437
Dial, N. Minter, 9386
Diamantine, Frank A., 452
Diamantine, George, 452
Diamantine, James A., 452
Diamantine, Richard, 452

Diamond Charitable Remainder Trust, Ruby, 1973
Diamond Foundation, 7000
Diamond, Henry L., 5662
Diamond, Jennifer, 2829
Diamond, John, 2829
Diamond, Laraine, 6932
Diamond, Marilyn, 2829
Diamond, Susan, 6302, 7575
Diamond, Tamara K. Blin, 3476
Diamond, Terry, 2829
Diana, Brenda S., 4196
Diani, James A., 302
Diani, Michael J., 302
Diani, Robert P., 302
Diannes Fine Desserts, 8859
Dias, Dominic, 2657
Diaz, Antonio M., 8752
Diaz, Carol, 7741
Diaz, Joseph, 5648
Diaz-Verson, Salvador, 2433
Dibble, Dave, 1295
Dibble, Dottie, 1295
Dibert, Winifred Crawford, 5915
Dibert, Winifred S., 5915
DiBiasio, Robert A., 7354
Dible, Jeffery, 3410
Dibona, G. Fred, III, 7955
Dibona, Sylvia M., 7955
Dibrell, Charles G., III, 8748
Dibsie, Krista J., 5480
Dice, Bruce B., 8814
Dice, Kevin B., 8814
Dice, Kirk Brian, 8814
Dicerbo, Cheri, 7956
Dicerbo, Eileen Patricia, 7956
Dicerbo, Louis P., II, 7956
Dick, Albert, 8815
Dick, Bruce L., 2542
Dick, C. Trafford, 7591
Dick, Edison, 1807
Dick, Edison W., 2830
Dick, John H., 2830
Dick, John H., Jr., 2830
Dick, Mark, 7666
Dick, Sylvia L., 2542
Dick, Timothy, 4372
Dick, Timothy A., 4372
Dickason, Richard R., 3553
Dickens, Brian, 4947
Dickens, Helen, 1246
Dickens, Jill E., 2724
Dickens, Linda, 9231
Dickerson, Douglas, 9431
Dickerson, Marianne, 9431
Dickes, Gary, 9862
Dickey, Charles D., III, 9640
Dickey, Dave, 3514
Dickie, Elizabeth R., 1831
Dickins, Margaret E., 3651
Dickinson, Ann, 5319
Dickinson, Claire F., 5551
Dickinson, Cynthia, 4980
Dickinson, Elizabeth H., 5319
Dickinson, Fairleigh S., 5319
Dickinson, Haskell, 218
Dickinson, Jolynn, 1975
Dickinson, Robert H., 1975
Dickinson, Susan, 5625
Dickman, Margaret, 9972
Dickson Charitable Marital Trust, Fairleigh S., 5319
Dickson, Bishop Alex D., 8509
Dickson, Donald, 5234

Dickson, Greg, 1244
Dickson, Peggy, 3427
Didier, Calvin W., 4645
Didier, Kari, 7724
Didlake, Ralph, 4828
Diebold, Margaret E., 3652
Diebold, Stephen E., 3652
Diederich, Gene, 4962
Dieffenbach, Stacy, 8352
Diehl, J. Ted, 2670
Diekemper Trust, H., 4938
Diener, Lawrence B., 5445
Diener, Martha Stott, 8304
Dierberg, Ellen, 4895
Dierberg, James F., 4895
Dierberg, James F., II, 4895
Dierberg, Mary W., 4895
Dierberg, Michael J., 4895
Dieringer Trust, Victoria Evelyn, 7758
Dieringer, Eugene, 7758
Dierker, Dave, 2195, 2284
Dierksen, Fred, 3628
Diermeier, Jeffrey J., 1976
Diermeier, Julia M., 1976
Diermeier, Julie M., 1976
Diessner, Barbara, 8563
Diessner, Jonathon, 8563
Dieterle, Michael M., 4375
Dietrich American Foundation, 7958
Dietrich, Daniel W., II, 7958
Dietrich, Ralph, 3564
Dietz & Watson, 7959
Dietz, Christina Dedman, 8807
Dietz, Jonathan Dedman, 8807
Dietze, David L., 5320
Dietze, Joan M., 5320
Dietze, John A., 5320
Dietze, John A., Jr., 5320
Difabio, E. Michael, 5881
Difabio, Michael D., 5881
Digby Management, Co. LLC, 6655
Digges, Charles W., IV, 5016
Digges, Hester M., 3944
Digia, Robert, 4199
DiGiacomo, Anne, 6373
Dik, Edward, 4430
Dik, Evelyn, 4430
DiLeo, Victor, 5525
Dill, Anne E., 4931
Dill, David, 2034
Dill, G. Michael, 7671
Dill, Hilda C., 7065
Dill, Shelley M., 7671
Dillard, Anna Karin J., 5916
Dillard, Christopher, 5916
Dillard, David B., 5916
Dillard, James, 5916
Dilley, Dolores M., 9850
Dilling Mechanical, 2348
Dillingham, Peter, 7666
Dillion, Lisa Reich, 9529
Dillman, Jim, 9712
Dillon, Bill, 3402
Dillon, Catherine A., 4431
Dillon, Eileen White, 6875
Dillon, Norma, 7374
Dillon, Ray E., III, 3571
Dilworth Trust, Helen R., 1977
Dimarco, Janet, 1344
DiMaria, Anna R., 4211
Dime Bank, 1438
Dime Savings Bank of Norwich, 1438
Diment, David Dean, 9097
Dimick, John, 1803

Dimick, Marion T., 1803
Dimidjian, Sona, 283
Dimino, Joseph M., 7923
Dimond, Susan, 8199
Dinan Irrevocable Trust, John D., 4431
Dinan, J. Denise, 4431
Dinan, Jean E., 4431
Dinapoli, Douglas, 2458
DiNapoli, J. Philip, 454
DiNapoli, Jennifer, 454
DiNapoli, Jennifer G., 454
DiNapoli, John B., 454
Dineen, Christine, 5483
Dineen, John K., 4072
Dines, Allen, 1258
Dines, Connie, 1258
Dines, Sidney A., 1258
Dinesol Plastics, Inc., 7398
Dingle, Bill, 882
Dingman, James R., 2813
Dingus, Mary A., 8833
Dingwall Family, LP, 1804
Dingwall Trust, Marion Orr, 1804
Dingwell, Mark Edward, 1983
Dinkins, David, 5630
Dion, Donald R., 1656
Dion, Robert, 2776
Dipentino, Frank, 1316
DiPonio, Margaret E., 4432
Dippold, John, III, 7975
Diquollo, Robert, 5311
DiQuollo, Robert J., 5466
Diquollo, Robert J., 5496
DiRaimondo, Joseph, 9867
Directv, 1295
Dirks, Kari, 3507
Dirksen, Carri, 3359
Dirkx, Ryan, 7842
DiSabato, Christina S., 1571
Discovery Communications, 1295
DiSepio, Marguerite, 5246
DiSesa, Verdi, 8105
Dish Network, 1295
Dishong, Claudia, 2102
Dishong, William, 2102
Diskin Trust, The, 5697
Disney Shares, 8340
Dison, Linda, 3392
Distaola, Elio, 2877
Distribution Market Advantage, 8859
Ditmars, Joan B., 5286
Ditmore, Dana, 1100
Ditolla, Daniel, 6943
Dively, George S., 2226
Dively, Michael A., 1808, 2226
Dix, Richard J., 4031
Dix, Stuart, 6847
Dixie Mill Supply Co., 3716
Dixon Bros., 5500
Dixon, Adam H., 5919
Dixon, C. Bailey, 8510
Dixon, Charlotte B., 1631
Dixon, Christi C., 26
Dixon, David E., 26
Dixon, Edwin W., 26
Dixon, Gertrude S., 9548
Dixon, Hillary A., 5919
Dixon, James J., 6669
Dixon, Linda F., 5919
Dixon, Marny, 3229
Dixon, Norman W., 8510
Dixon, Phyllis S., 8575
Dixon, Ruth M., 4385
Dixon, Seth, 3229

Dixon, Thomas F., 5919
Dixon, William R., 4385
Dixson, Karen, 3481
Dixson, Mark A., 87
DJ Davbel Trust, 6354
DJ Grantor Trust, 6354
DJ Jadabe Trust, 6354
DLD Family, 1974
Doak, Henryetta C., 8818
Doan, Thu-Le, 5145
Doar, John, 6679
Dobbins, Hugh Trowbridge, 7748
Dobbins, Lewis M., 7748
Dobbins, Peter T., 7748
Dobbins, Roberta Lloyd, 7748
Dobbs, Frances, 221
Dobbs, Teneen L., 3368
Dobbs, Vernon D., 8026
Dobbs, W.M. Craig, 3368
Dobbs, Wm. Craig, 3368
Dobosz, Glen T., 2821
Dobrusin, Charles, 2970
Dobson, Joslyn, 8820
Dobson, Larry, 4978
Dobson, Mary Catherine, 4978
Dobson, Mary Louise, 8819
Dobson, Nellie, 7672
Dobson, Sean, 8702, 8820
Docherty Memorial Fund, Edward M.,
    8449
Docker, Christine, 244
Docker, W.F., 244
Dockham, Heather, 5206
Dockser, Bradford H., 3849
Dockser, Saundra L., 3849
Dockser, William B., 3849
Dockter, Chelsey S., 8570
Docktor, William, 5060
Doctor, Donald L., 5321
Doctor, Jordan, 5321
Doctor, Landon, 5321
Doctor, Mary, 5321
Doctors Hospital, 7545
Dodd, Allen Mckee, 3647
Dodd, Allen P., III, 3647
Dodd, Patricia, 2643
Dodd, S.F., 8862
Dodman, Mary Catherine, 6457
Dodwell, Linda, 1101
Doehrman, Druscilla, 1979
Doehrman, Druscilla S., 1979
Doelger, Susan, 457
Doeller, Marshall deF., 9503
Doerflinger, Steve, 3367
Doerr, Fred, 5622
Doerre, Laura W., 9083
Doherty, David J., 9214
Doherty, Janice L., 3590, 3627
Doherty, Patrick, 2712
Doherty, Phil, 2787
Dohmen Co., F., The, 9806
Dohmen, Mary H., 9807
Dohmen, Robert, 9806
Dohmen, Robert C., 9807
Dohmen, Ted, 9806
Dohrman, Pamela W., 2654
Dolan, Ann M., 874
Dolan, Charles, 6565
Dolan, Mary Beth, 8371
Dolan, Paul J., 7354
Dolan, Teresa A., 7954
Dold, Jennifer, 9669
Dole, Marvin G., 1128
Dolehide, John, 3521

Doleshek, Richard J., 1342
Dolgen, Jonathan, 5922
Dolgen, Susan, 5922
Dolgicer, Sasha, 1952
Dolgin, Jay, 3025
Doll, Carol Ann, 1657
Doll, David, 7645
Doll, Dixon R., 1657
Doll, Doris M., 4433
Doll, Henry C., 7338
Doll, Leslie L., 5322
Doll, Nancy, 5635
Doll, Robert C., Jr., 5322
Dolle, Molly W., 1198
Dolmatch, Rosalie, 6080
Dolny, Linda, 8526
Domec, R. N., 8792
Domenick-Muscat, Peggy, 4449, 4487
Domer, Arnold, 9808
Domer, Larry R., 9808
Domer, Lois, 9808
Domestic Air Conditioning Services,
    6681
Dominguez, Daniel, 9219
Domini, Amy L., 4022
Domino's Pizza, 4379
Domke, John, 4657
Domonkos, Carmen, 1566
Dompier, Sandra Smith, 9205
Don & Co., Edward, 8859
Donahou, Curtis L., 9033
Donahue Charitable Foundation, J.
    Christopher and Ann C., The, 9033
Donahue, Dolores, 892
Donahue, Greg, 1257
Donahue, Laura J., 1482
Donahue, Leonice M., 1257
Donahue, Mark, 1257
Donahue, Timothy J., 7935
Donahue, William L., 1257
Donahue, William P., 1257
Donahue-Goodwin, Lisa, 1257
Donald Heath Revocable Living Trust,
    7772
Donald Zucker Company, 6655
Donald, Sanford S., 3834
Donaldson, Charlotte D'Arcy, 4178
Donaldson, Evelyn, 1760
Donaldson, Michael R., 7475
Donatelli, Mark R., 3231
Donchian, Alma G., 1439
Donchian, Richard D., 1440
Donegan, Mark, 7759
Donegan, Pamela, 7759
Donithen, Joe D., 7336
Donlon, Marcia, 761
Donna, John C., 4057, 4254
Donnell, Donna P., 8821
Donnell, James, 8668
Donnell, James Donna, 8821
Donnell, James M., 8821
Donnelley Charitable Lead Trust, Laura,
    5691
Donnelley, Laura, 5691
Donnelley, Robert G., 3092
Donnelly, Elizabeth, 6081
Donnelly, Elizabeth A., 7963
Donnelly, John J., 7588
Donnelly, John W., 5575
Donnelly, M. Megan, 7963
Donnelly, Mary J., 7963
Donnelly, Patrick, 7673
Donnelly, Valarie, 176
Donnenfeld, Bernard, 575

Donner, Frida, 277
Donner, George R., 3424
Donohoe, John C., 4348
Donohue, Elise R., 4815
Donohue, Elizabeth A., 9432
Donohue, John L., 9432
Donohue, Keith M., 9432
Donohue, Louise, 6230
Donohue, Robert W., 6669
Donohue, Thomas J., 9432
Donohue, Thomas J., Jr., 9432
Donosky, Patricia Miller, 3114
Donovan Charitable Lead Trust, 4070
Donovan, Beverly A., 4070
Donovan, Catherine, 2833
Donovan, Celeste Rice, 2283
Donovan, Christine, 5206
Donovan, David E., 2832
Donovan, James P., 4070
Donovan, James R., 4070
Donovan, Karen M., 4070
Donovan, Keith, 2833
Donovan, Kenneth M., 2833
Donovan, Michael R., 4070
Donovan, Nancy S., 2832
Donovan, Raymond C., 2833
Donovan, Raymond J., 2833
Donovan, Thidie Delaine, 4070
Doochin, Jerald, 8605
Doochin, Michael, 8605
Doody, Tim, 3744
Dooley Family Trust, Sally C., 8822
Dooley, Arthur R., Jr., 8822
Dooley, Arthur Rhew, 8822
Dooley, Chris C., 8822
Dooley, Sally C., 8822
Dooley, Tom, 9110
Doolittle, Amity A., 3778
Doolittle, Barbara A., 7778
Doolittle, Michael J., 3778
Doon, James, 4142
Dooner, Jane, 8243
Dooner, Marie E., 7974
Dooner, Peter S., Jr., 7974
Dooner, Thomas, 8243
Dooner, Thomas & Jane, 8243
Dopp, Cynthia Hill, 5393
Dopson, Arnold, 13
Doran, Gail, 3431
Doran, Margaret E., 5866
Doran, Teri, 3402
Doran, Toan, 2638
Dore, Eric, 9587
Dore, Frederick H., Jr., 9587
Dore, Mary S., 9587
Dore, Pam, 9587
Dore, Tim W., 9587
Dorf, Alexandra N.P., 1539
Dorf, Alexis, 1539
Dorf, Matthew, 1539
Dorfman, David, 5580
Dorfman, Patricia, 9954
Dorfman, Robert, 9954
Dori, Bruno N., 5498
Dorian, Jennifer R., 1660
Dorman, John C., 1081
Dorman, Leslie A., 1081
Dorman, Robin, 4499
Dorn, Deborah K., 7380
Dorn, John C., 8020
Dorn, Philip R., 7380
Dorn, Robert F., 7380
Dorn, Ruth H., 8020

Dorn, Thomas C., 1619
Dornette, Martha, 7523
Dornette, W. Stuart, 7523
Dornfeld, Sharon, 1512
Dorr, Jamie C., 1294
Dorr, Jeffry B., 1294
Dorr, John, 5211
Dorr, Paul E., 1294
Dorr, Terri L., 1294
Dorrier, Catharine C., 9405
Dorris, Jeanette, 8607
Dorset, W.S., 1259
Dorsey & Whitney Trust Co. LLC, 8567
Dorsey & Whitney Trust Co., LLC, 8562
Dorsey, Carol, 3369
Dorsey, Erin, 3369
Dorsey, Jessica, 3978
Dorsey, Scott, 3369
Dorskind, Albert, 459
Dorskind, Dorothy D., 459
Dorskind, James A., 459
Dorskind, Sue M., 459
Dorsky, David A., 5924
Dorsky, Karen A., 5924
Dorsky, Noah P., 5924
Dorsky, Samuel, 5924
Dorst, Martha, 3487
Dortch, Blanche, 7560
Dortch, Sebastian, 2362
Doscas, Anne, 5925
Doscas, Christopher, 5925
Doscas, John, 5925
Doshi Trust FBO Neely Doshi-Cather,
    5926
Doshi Trust FBO Nishat Doshi, The, 5926
Doshi, Leena N., 5926
Doshi, Nishat, 5926
Doshi, Nitin V., 5926
Doshi-Cather, Neely, 5926
Doskocil, Benjamin L., Sr., 8823
Doskocil, Edward Joseph, 8823
Doskocil, Mary Frances, 8823
Dosky, Vera, 9372
Dossey, Dale A., 8917
Dossin, Mandi, 726
Dostal, Michael, 7356
Dotson, Darlene B., 7317
Dotson, Michael, 857
Dotson, Terry, 4979
Dotson, Victoria, 9628
Dotts, Walter M., 9442
Doty, Beth, 9053
Doty, Carol, 2492
Doty, Mark, 9053
Double V Growth, LLC, 7127
Doucette, James W., 8601
Doud, Margaret M., 4499
Doudera, Ralph J., 9434
Dougan, Diana Lady, 9313
Dougan, Frank, 6889
Dougan, Gavin M., 9313
Dougan, J. Lynn, 9313
Dougherty, Dale, 1658
Dougherty, Daniel P., 5586
Dougherty, Gayle, 2857
Dougherty, John P., 4331
Dougherty, Kathy, 2953
Dougherty, Nancy C., 1658
Dougherty, Patrick J., 2082
Dougherty, Ronald, 6912
Dougherty-Manners, Marie-France, 5928
Doughty, Hubert, 3401
Doughty, Merle, 4946
Douglas Development, 6675

Douglas Securitiies Corp., 2320
Douglas, Bill, 2437
Douglas, Charles, 2252
Douglas, David W., 5628
Douglas, Deborah S., 5628
Douglas, James, 9103
Douglas, Jean Wallace, 1806
Douglas, Jim, 9338
Douglas, Karen, 900
Douglas, Leslie, 1806
Douglas, Ron, 8836
Douglas, Sara, 9326
Douglas, Sarah, 6323
Douglas, Sean, 9326
Douglas, Sioux, 88
Douglas, Terry, 8663
Douglas, Virginia Sue, 7656
Douglass Charitable Lead Trust, 8870
Douglass, Bill, 8345
Douglass, Dick, 7357
Douglass, Donald J., 8870
Douglass, Helen D., 8870
Douglass, Rosann, 8663
Douglass, Scott E., 8870
Douglass, Terry, 8663
Dove Givings Foundation, 3995
Dove, Brian J., 8826
Dove, Eugene M., 8826
Dove, Grant, 8826
Dove, Kathy, 3402
Dove, Margaret, 8826
Dove, Terence B., 8826
Dove, Timothy L., 8826
Doverspike, Terry, 7682
Dow Jones Foundation, 5325
Dow, Peter A., 4462
Dow, Thomas, 9814
Dowd, John C., 9946
Dowdle, James C., 2834
Dowdle, James C., Jr., 2834
Dowdle, Sally S., 2834
Dowdy, Bonnie D., 8731
Dowell, Greg, 8700
Dowell, William, 3585
Dower, Thomas W., 2835
Dowicz, Stephen, 5901
Down, Ann M., 2673
Downeast Wholesalers, 3802
Downer, Leilani, 563
Downes, David, 3932
Downey, Harriette R., 7638
Downey, James E., 460, 461
Downey, Keith M., 460
Downey, Nancy A., 5930
Downey, Robert N., 5930
Downie, David L., 4615
Downie, William W., 4615
Downing, Danna, 4606
Downing, Frances V.S., 8542
Downing, Jack G., 7381
Downing, John C., 462
Downing, John O., 8542
Downing, Lynn, 9774
Downing, Tracy, 462
Downing, Tracy Toft, 4931
Downs, Abby W., 76
Downs, Bertis, 2437
Downs, Betsy Warburton, 8342
Downs, Jeanne Floyd, 513
Downs, Mike D., 8342
Dows, David A., 362
Doyle, Caroline H., 7998
Doyle, Daniel M., Jr., 1980
Doyle, Daniel M., Sr., 1980

Doyle, Dennis M., 7326
Doyle, Fr. Kenneth, 6966
Doyle, Jean, 4222
Doyle, Rosaleen J., 1980
Doyle, Sister Anna, 3098
Doyon Ltd. and Affiliates, 84
Dozier, Matthew B., 2556
Dozier, Robert L., 2556
Dozzi, Domenic P., 7965
Dozzi, Peter C., 7965
Dozzi, Theresa K., 7965
Dozzo, David, 8827
Dozzo, Joseph, 8827
Dozzo, Mario, 8827
DP Advisors LLC, 5152
DP Homes LLC, 5152
Dr. Cotton, 4460
Dr. Pepper/Seven Up, Inc., 8859
Dr. Phillips, 2260
Drackett, Charles M., Jr., 3706
Drackett, Marjorie W., 3706
Draft, David R., 1981
Draft, Robert, 1981
Drake Capital LLC, 967
Drake Industries, LLC, 8606
Drake, Darin, 8606
Drake, John, 3363
Drake, Mark, 2512
Drake, Pansy L., 8606
Drakulic, Joe, 516
Dranoff, David L., 2919
Draper Corp., 4134
Draper, Amy, 154
Draper, Katie, 154
Draper, Mary D., 9332
Draper, Michael J., 5066
Draughon, Elizabeth F., 8607
Drawdy, Larry, 4824
Drayer, Kellyn, 8970
Drayna, Dennis, 8680
Drayton, William, 9455
Dreher, Joan, 3582
Drehle, Raymond Von, 7274
Drehle, Steve Von, 7274
Dreman, David N., 5326
Dreman, Holly, 5326
Dreman, Solly, 5326
Drennan, James, 7410
Drennan, Joseph A., 7410
Dresner Sadaka, Jane, 4434
Dresner, Mary Ann, 4434
Dresner, Milton H., 4434
Dresner, Robert J., 4434
Dress Barn Inc., The, 5252
Dress Custom Homes, 9009
Drew, Barbara L., 8026
Drew, Pamela J., 3786
Drew, Susan B., 9421
Drew, Teha Colleen Eliassen, 242
Drewek, Mary Anne, 3549
Drexinger, Karen, 2522
Drexler Enterprises, 113
Drexler, Dan, 2896
Drexler, Harry, 2896
Drexler, Jason, 2896
Drexler, Jerome, 463
Drexler, John, 113
Drexler, Kathleen, 113
Drexler, Lloyd, 2896
Drexler, Pam, 113
Drexler, Richard, 2896
Drexler, Sylvia, 463
Drexler, Sylvia B., 463
Drexler, Tim, 113

Dreyer, Lucy Lewis, 444
Dreyfus, Alfred, 9436
Dreyfus, Jack, 5622
Dreyfus, Mark, 9436
Dreyfus, Mildred, 9436
Driano, Dominick V., Jr., 4782
Driehorst Charitable Remainder Unitrust No II, Frederick C. and Nancy W., The , 9743
Driehorst, Nancy W., 9743
Driemeyer Trust, Derick L., 4991
Driemeyer, Derick L., 4991
Driemeyer, Sally M., 4991
Driesman, Shelley, 4145
Driggs, Amy Marie, 9324
Drinkwater, Clover M., 5674, 6997
Dripchak, David A., 4243
Drisaldi, Cynthia F., 2591
Driscoll, Brent, 5890
Driscoll, Elizabeth, 7567
Drive Financial Services LP, 9173
Drivemax Ltd., 5085
Driver-Bishop, Robert, 3902
DRK Investment Co., 4966
Drone, Jack, Dr. , 3401
Droppa, Daniel Watson, 6260
Droppa, Jack J., 6260
Droppa, Jane W.I., 6260
Droppa, Larry D., 6260
Drost, Amanda R., 2390
Drost, Carl, 3487
Drost, Carolyn J., 7969
Drost, David, 8791
Drost, Martha, 3487
Drought, Thomas J., 9847
Drozd, Taras, 2967
Druckenmiller, Fiona, 6258
Druckenmiller, Stanley F., 6258
Druckman, Nicole E., 2301
Drueding, James, 7966
Drueding, Richard, 7966
Drugas, George, 2837
Drugas, Peter, 2837
Drugas, Theodore G., 2837
drugstore.com, 181
Druker, Bertram A., 4071
Druker, Ronald M., 4071
Drum, Frank G., 464
Drumm, Susan, 6248
Drushal, J. Douglas, 7470
Druskin, Ben, 5932
Druskin, Harriett A., 5932
Druskin, Melissa, 5932
Druskin, Robert A., 5932
Druz, David S., 5131
Dryco LLC., 2348
Dryren, Janet T., 1363
DS Associates, 6882
du Bois, E. Blois, 114
du Pont de Nemours and Co., E.I., 2406
Duarte Trust, Jose G., 7382
Dubin, Anne E., 2838
Dubin, Howard S., 2838
Dubin, Michael, 6720
Dubin, Thomas G., 2838
Dubin, Victoria, 6720
Dubinsky, John P., 4896
Dubois, Jacques E., 9970
DuBois, Jim, 3458
DuBois, John J., 2909
DuBois, Keith Brown, 9407
DuBois, Ruth, 8105
Dubon, Donald, 870
Dubose, Anna A., 8828

Dubose, James E., 8828
Dubose, James S., 8828
DuBow, Lawrence J., 1948
Dubrow, Lowell H., 1732
Dubs, Arthur R., 7760
Dubsky, Michael, Rev. , 3904
Ducey, Carol, 9230
Duchene CRUT, 4435
Duchene, Barbara, 4435
Duchene, Donald L., Sr., 4435
Duchene, Doris, 4435
Duckett, Lisa F., 485
Duckwall, Frank E., 1982
Duckwall, Ralph, 3371
Ducommun, Robert E., 465
Ducot, Elizabeth, 4130
Duda & Sons, A., 1983, 2132
Duda, Andrew, 2132
Duda, Andrew, Jr., 2132
Duda, Elizabeth Mikler, 2132
Duda, Luther, 2132
Duda, Melanie, 2132
Duda, Michael, 2132
Duda, Rebecca, 2132
Duda, Sandra, 2132
Duddlesten, Karen A., 8829
Duddlesten, Terri, 8829
Duddlesten, Wayne B., 8829
Dudley, Eric, 9588
Dudley, Gatewood, 2550
Dudley, Gerric W., 9588
Dudley, Henry A., Jr., 7213
Dudley, John D., 9811
Dudley, Justin, 9588
Dudley, Laura, 733
Dudley, Mary C., 9811
Dudley, Michael, 4830
Dudley, Richard D., 9811
Dudley, Rick W., 9588
Dudley, Robert J., II, 9811
Dudley, Spotswood P., 7213
Dudley, Tilford E., 9588
Dudte, James J., 7652
Duer, Wendy, 697
Duerr, Jennifer, 1486
Duesenberg, John R., 4897
Duesenberg, Lorraine F., 4897
Duesenberg, Robert H., 4897
Duesterberg, Kathleen, 4008
Duff, Barb, 7975
Duff, Brad, 8972
Duff, Bruce, 9636
Duff, Charles B., 131
Duff, Charles E., 131
Duff, Cheryl, 8972
Duff, Dana L., 8177
Duff, Dorie J., 131
Duff, Elizabeth Gray, 9508
Duff, Elmon F., 9508
Duff, George, 9636
Duff, Helen L., 4873
Duff, James Carlton, 9508
Duff, John B., 131
Duff, Marilyn, 9636
Duff, Paul W., 8177
Duff, Rachel M., 9508
Duff, Ruth Ann, 8177
Duffe, Kathy, 5385
Duffey, Thomas, 6477
Duffin, Jacinda, 9810
Duffy Homes, 7386
Duffy, Dorothy B., 3928
Duffy, Joseph J., Jr., 3928
Duffy, Michael G., 1686

Duffy, Paul, 6372
Duffy, Steve, 8374
Dufraine, William, 4088
Dufrane, Lynn, 4497
Dufrenoy, Louise, 6820
Dugan, Cecelia L., 1766
Dugan, Tom, 2400
Dugan, Vincent J., 1763
Dugas, Agnes, 3776
Dugas, Marc, 3776
Dugas, Normand, 3776
Dugas, Peter, 3776
Duguid, Anne H. Easterly, 1660
Duhamel, Judy Olson, 8575
Dujay, Eva, 3722
Duke Energy, 7340
Duke, Donald Led, 5724
Duke, John, 7761
Dukes County Savings Bank, 4239
Dukes, Danny L., III, 9697
Dukes, Faye O., 2508
Dula, Art, 8927
Dulaney, Richard P., 7674
Dulay, Jennifer, 942
Dullabh, Nitesh, 900
Dullard, Connie, 3081
Dumas, Ernie, 193
Dumas, Paul, 1772
Dumke, Andrew B., 2668
Dumke, Arlette Crane, 1955
Dumke, Carol B., 2668
Dumke, Edmund E., 2668
Dumke, Edmund W., 2668
Dumont Corp., 4088
Dumouchel, Patrick, 2769
Dunagan, Clay, 8831
Dunagan, Deanna, 8831
Dunagan, J. Conrad, 8831
Dunagan, John C., 8831
Dunagan, Kathlyn C., 8831
Dunagan, Kathy, 8831
Dunaway, Bryan Winn, 8832
Dunaway, Carol Winn, 8832
Dunaway, James Reed, 8832
Dunaway, Jane B., 653
Dunaway, Scott Michael, 8832
Dunaway-Smith, Christina, 8832
Dunbar, C. Wendell, 4400
Dunbar, Laura J., 3653
Dunbar, Thomas E., 3653
Dunbar, Wallace H., 3653
Dunbar, Wallace H., Jr., 3653
Duncan, Anne S., 8833
Duncan, Anneliese H., 3851
Duncan, Bruce W., 2839
Duncan, C.W., 8833
Duncan, C.W., III, 8833
Duncan, C.W., Jr., 8833
Duncan, Catriona, 3003
Duncan, Deborah E., 2839
Duncan, Deborah L., 527
Duncan, Emily C., 8833
Duncan, Harry F., 3851
Duncan, John G., 7086
Duncan, John H., Jr., 8833
Duncan, Juanita, 421
Duncan, Kathi, 883
Duncan, Louise Head, 2840
Duncan, Mary, 8845
Duncan, Sarah, 9592
Duncan, Susan M., 1349
Duncker, C. Steven, 6265
Dundas, Constance, 9438
Dunderdale, Beverly, 7778

Dunderdale, Nicole, 7778
Dundon, Thomas, 9173
Dunehew, David A., 8623
Dunford, Albert, 421
Dungan, Anna, 3379
Dungan, Neal, 5608
Dunham, Archie, 8834
Dunham, Cary, 8834
Dunham, Janet, 6585
Dunham, Joanie, 5413
Dunham, Linda, 8834
Dunham, R. James, 8201
Dunham, Steve, 8834
Dunhill, Linda, 7815
Dunkelmann, Dianne, 7340
Dunkerton, Donald, 7223
Dunkleberger, Todd, 8869
Dunklin Association, George H., 194
Dunklin Trust, M.E. Black, 194
Dunklin, George H., Jr., 194
Dunkum, Deborah Deford, 8813
Dunlap, Gertrude, 4496
Dunlap, Jamie, 9133
Dunlap, Lee, 9133
Dunlap-Shohl, Peter, 4297
Dunleary, Sally Anne, 6623
Dunlop Slazenger International, 6463
Dunn Construction, J.E., 4898
Dunn Family Trust, Robert P., 4898
Dunn Family Trust, Stephen D., 4898
Dunn Family Trust, Terry, 4898
Dunn Family Trust, William H., 4898
Dunn, Bryan C., 3411
Dunn, Dons L., 496
Dunn, Dorothy O., 5212
Dunn, Edward, 5936
Dunn, Edward B., 5936
Dunn, Erin, 817
Dunn, Giovannella, 5936
Dunn, James C., 7392
Dunn, Janet, 3400
Dunn, Jeanine E., 7521
Dunn, John, 345
Dunn, Kevin A., 4898
Dunn, Laurie Mitchell, 5626
Dunn, Luckey M., 2001
Dunn, Mary B., 1659
Dunn, Norma, 8759
Dunn, Patricia M., 1219
Dunn, R.B., 9589
Dunn, Robert P., 4898
Dunn, Ruth H., 9589
Dunn, Ryan, 9399
Dunn, Stephen D., 4898
Dunn, Steven D., 4898
Dunn, Terrence P., 4898
Dunn, Terry, 4898
Dunn, Timothy P., 9399
Dunn, William H., Jr., 4898
Dunn, William H., Sr., 4898
Dunnam, Kathryn C., 9093
Dunnan, Bruce B., 1399
Dunnan, D. Stuart, Rev. , 1399
Dunnan, Diana B., 1399
Dunnan, Douglas M., 1399
Dunnan, John M., 1399
Dunne, James, 6542
Dunne, James I., 6016, 6542
Dunne, James J., III, 6443
Dunne, Paige, 1868
Dunworth, Gerald J., 6569
Duphorne, Courtney Dooley, 8822
DuPont, Augustus I., 5306
Dupont, Brenda K., 9387

DuPont, Hewitt, 2263
Dupont, Laura Lemole, 8119
Dupree, William W., III, 8604
Dupree, William W., Jr., 8604
Dupree, William, Jr., 8604
Dupuis, Martin D., 2226
Duquette, Ron, 4552
Durand, Nancy, 2456
Durando, Jane Carlton, 2413
Durant, Joan S., 4072
Durant, Karen A., 4798
Durant, Katherine, 9700
Durant, Kingsley, 4072
Durden Enterprises II Inc., 1984
Durden, Janice H., 2611
Durden, K. Earl, 1984
Durden, Karen L., 1984
Durden, Michael E., 1984
Durden, Randall E., 2611
Durden, Randy, 2611
Durfinger, Marie, 652
Durham, Bettie, 8608
Durham, Brenton, 6248
Durham, Christine M., 7799
Durham, Erich, 8608
Durham, H.W., 8608
Durham, Lisa, 8608
Durham, Lori, 6248
Durham, Mindy, 9168
Durham, Wanda, 5608
Durkin, Elizabeth B., 1590
Durkin, Elizabeth M., 5358
Durlam, Patricia, 178
Durokovic, Samantha, 4537
Durr Heavy Construction, LLC, 3749
Durrant, Matthew, 7799
Durrill, Ginger, 8835
Durrill, Melissa, 8835
Durrill, Michele, 8835
Durrill, William R., 8835
Durrill, William R., Jr., 8835
Durst Fetner Residential, 6655
Durst Organization L.P., 6656
Durst Organization, The, 6655
Durst, Alexander, 6554
Durst, Anita, 6554
Durst, Douglas, 6554
Durst, Helena, 6554
Durst, Seymour, 6554
Dusenbury Marital Trust, Warren, 466
Dusenbury, Warren, 466
Dusenbury, Zoann L., 466
Dushel, Robert P., 3963
Dutch Gold Honey, 8011
Dutch Valley Food Distributors Inc., 7907
Dutchvalley Food Distributors, 8352
Dutriac, Rick, 158
Dutton, Craig, 3991
Dutton, John, 9812
Dutton, William, 2881
Duval, Carol, 5244
Duxbury, Jean M., 5790
Dvorak, Bernie, 1295
Dweck, Aboud, 1805
Dweck, Elana, 3855
Dweck, Florence, 5327
Dweck, Kathy, 3855
Dweck, Morris, 1805, 3855
Dweck, Murray, 5264, 5327
Dweck, Noah, 3855
Dweck, Ralph, 1805
Dweck, Rena, 1805
Dweck, Ronald, 3857
Dweck, Samuel R., 1805

Dweck, Susan, 1805, 3855
Dwelle, David, 467
Dwelle, Stephen, 467
Dwelle, Thomas, 467
Dwelle, Walter, 467
Dwinell, Lane, 8403
Dworkin, Lisa Fraites, 1454
Dworman Foundation, 1765
Dworman, Alvin, 5938
Dwyer, Amy, 4608
Dwyer, Christine M., 4074
Dwyer, Jason, 1703
Dwyer, Jeanne D., 2834
Dwyer, Kathleen, 1703
Dwyer, Kathryn A., 9439
Dwyer, Kevin, 9439
Dwyer, Mary B., 9439
Dwyer, Paul B., 9439
Dwyer, Richard, 9439
Dwyer, Richard F., 468
Dwyer, Richard J., Jr., 9439
Dwyer, William E., 4074
Dwyer, William E., III, 4074
Dwyer, William J., 6666
Dyatech, 9033
Dybsky, Thomas J., 4798
Dyco Petroleum Corp., 4669
Dye, Betty, 3373
Dye, James W., 3373
Dye, Joanna, 8683
Dyer Charitable Lead Trust, Betty Faye, 4669
Dyer Charitable Trust, 469
Dyer Family Charitable Lead Trust, Jaye F., The , 4669
Dyer, Betsy, 4845
Dyer, Bob, 8970
Dyer, Charon M., 2194
Dyer, Cristi Y., 469
Dyer, Darleen R., 469
Dyer, David F., 1985
Dyer, Harriet, 1985
Dyer, Jaye F., 4669
Dyer, Jill M., 4669
Dyer, Karen A., 2122
Dyer, Maura, 3938
Dyer, Michael J., 4669
Dyer, Rick, 4419
Dyess, Carla, 8774
Dygert, Justin, 2710
Dykema, Adam, 4502
Dykema, Alex, 4502
Dykema, Gabrielle, 4502
Dykema, John E., 4502
Dykema, Sara E., 4575
Dykema, Timothy J., 4575
Dykes, Martha Marshall, 2545
Dykshorn, Owen, 3528
Dylan, Robert, 6766
Dynasty Charitable Lead Unitrust, 9545
Dyson, Roger, 3397
Dzewaltowski, Kathy, 9123
Dziadzio, Doug, 4088
Dzielski, Lori, 5660
Dziki, Thomas, 8498
Dzledzic, Joseph W., 9406

E & C Trust, 6859
E 14 Realty, 6199
E.L.I.S., LLC, 6553
Eacho, Donna W., 3852
Eacho, William C., III, 3852
Eager, John J., 6455

Eagin, Mary Hoffer, 2975
Eagin, Sara, 2975
Eagle Capital, 6720
Eagle Ottawa, LLC, 9931
Eagletech International, 528
Eakins, Jon, 3379
Eanes, Meredith, 7058
Earl, Todd, 7666
Earle, Anne Gordon, 8061
Earle, Carol A., 5328
Earle, Dexter D., 5328
Earle, Linda, 5691
Earles, John, 9757
Earley, Billy, 8743
Earley, Billy J., 8743
Earls, Michael, 3445
Early, Caroline P., 3177
Early, Gilbert Gordon, 3177
Early, Jeffrey C., 9503
Early, Lola Coggeshall, 8522
Early, Mike, 4879
Earnhardt, Hazel, 7692
Earnhardt, Stan, 7692
Earthman, Chris, 8706
Easley, Ellen S., 8195
Easley, Richard, 2880
Eason-Watkins, Barbara, 3372
East Boston Savings Bank, 4075, 4211
Eastburn, Dave, 3514
Eastburn, David, 3514
Eastdil Secured, 6655
Easterlin, Nan S., 2589
Easterling, Stacey, 7338
Easterly, David E., 1660
Easterly, Gregory C., 1660
Easterly, Judy B., 1660
Eastern Bank Wealth Management, 4192
Eastern Consolidated Properties, 6655
Eastern Minerals Inc., 4184
Eastern Regional Medical Center, 6463
Eastern Union Funding, 5247
Eastgate, Jeff Wyler, 7647
Eastham, G. Wayne, 9493
Easthampton Savings Bank, 4076
Eastman, Benjamin, 5940
Eastman, Jennifer, 5940
Eastman, John, 5940
Eastman, Judy, 840
Eastman, Lance E., 8183
Eastman, Mark S., 3796
Easton, Diane T., 1363
Eastwood, Susan, 5698
Easy Auto, 8596
Eaton Charitable Trust, W.E., 6542
Eaton, Ann, 7094
Eaton, Carol E., 115
Eaton, Catherine L., 7383
Eaton, David H., 115
Eaton, James, 4961
Eaton, Jane E., 6542
Eaton, Kim, 3466
Eaton, Peggy, 9426
Eaton, William C., 4276
Eaves, Reuben E., 4290
Ebaugh, Emily, 7339
Ebbett, Denise, 369
Eberhart, David F., 5942
Eberhart, Frances A., 5942
Eberhart, Marcie, 7839
Eberhart, Tracy A., 5942
Eberhart, Wendy F., 5942
Eberly, Jane D., 1979
Eberly, Paul O., 7969

Eberly, Robert E., III, 7969
Eberly, Robert E., Jr., 7969
Eberspacher, Ursula, 1261
Eberspacher, Walter, 1261
Ebert, Lyda, 739
Eble, Kim S. P., 7971
Ebner, Carolyn, 6836
Ebzery, William B., 9998
Eccles, Katherine Ann, 9322
Eccles, M. E., 3410
Eccles, Margot L., 3410
Eccles, Mary, 3853
Eccles, Robert, 3853
Eccles, Spencer F., 9322
Eccles, Spencer P., 9322
Echevarria, Christina M., 1987
Echevarria, Emily C., 1987
Echevarria, Laurie B., 1987
Echevarria, Michael J., 1987
Echlin, Beryl G., 2472
Echlin, John E., 2472
Echlin, John E., Jr., 2472
ECI Opportunities LLC, 6447
Eck, E. Edwin, 5060
Eck, Jack, 6248
Eckel, Fred, 6666
Eckelberry, Robert L., 1305
Eckels, Betty Jean, 7970
Eckerd Family Foundation, 2360
Eckerd, Jack, 2360
Eckert, Elizabeth A., 2843
Eckert, Katherine Elizabeth, 2843
Eckert, Matt, 3370
Eckert, Theodore H., 2843
Eckert, Theodore Mark, 2843
Eckhardt, Laura, 7339
Eckhardt, Manah Kulp, 1635
Eckhoff, James D., 4859
Eckles, David, 2636
Eckles, Kristine M., 9821
Eckles, Morgan, 2636
Eckley, Bonnie, 9592
Eckman, Yvonne P., 8207
Eckroth, Jeff, 5135
Eckroth, Paul, 3078
Eckstein, Devorah, 5878
Eckstein, Gittel, 5878
Eckstein, Rafael, 5878
Eckstein, Richard J., 4143
Eclipse Inc., 2844
Ecolab, 8859
Ecolo Ltd, 6648
ECT Holdings, LLC, 6447
Edco Supply Corp., 5355
Eddy, Charles R., 4276
Eddy, Edwin H., Jr., 7087
Eddy, Mary-Louise, 4077
Eddy, Paula Fritz, 7975
Eddy, Ruth N., 4077
Eddy, Tristan, 4276
Edelman, Alex, 5943
Edelman, Daniel J., 2845
Edelman, Debra, 3374
Edelman, Harry D., 9386
Edelman, Henry D., 9386
Edelman, Inc. and Subsidiaries, Daniel J., 2845
Edelman, Jack, 3374
Edelman, Jeffrey, 5943
Edelman, John D., 2845
Edelman, Renee, 2845
Edelman, Richard W., 2845
Edelman, Ruth A., 2845
Edelman, Susan, 5943

Edelson, Carol, 6076
Edelstein, Arthur, 2846
Edelstein, James, 2846
Edelstein, Marian, 2846
Edelstone, Gary H., 493
Eden Revocable Trust, Franklin C., 7971
Eden, Brooks, 7971
Eden, Carl Lynn, 2473
Eden, Carol Lynn, 2473
Eden, Maria B., 7971
Edens, Wesley R., 5844
Eder Annuity Trust, Andrew, 1441
Eder Brothers, 1441
Eder, Andrew J., 1441
Eder, Eileen F., 1441
Edes, Claire Rosen, 3205
Edes, Nik B., 3205
Edgar, C. Ernest, 1856
Edgar, Robert, 8869
Edgcomb, Brian W., 7952
Edgecomb, Chris, 1090
Edgerly, Lois Stiles, 2847
Edgerly, William S., 2847
Edgerton, Adele P., 1470
Edible Arrangements Franchise Group, 1444
Edible Brands, LLC, 1444
Edina Realty, 4672
Edlavitch, Irwin P., 9440
Edling, Carl D., 8263
Edlund, Philip A., 142
Edmonds, B.W., 9472
Edmonds, Hugh G., Jr., 9419
Edmonds, Matthew J., 6256
Edmondson, Susan J., 1374
Edmonston, Miriam A., 4900
Edmunds, David, 5842
Edmunds, Donald, 5254
Edmundson, Diane, 2936
Edmundson, Lauren Cohen, 3357
Edsforth, Julie, 9689
Edsforth, Julie E., 9689
Edson, Brad, 145
Edson, Bret, 145
Edson, Jarvis, 6912
Edson, Patricia, 145
Education For Youth Society, 6200
Education for Youth Society, 6217
Education Measures, 1295
Educational Contractors of America, 698
Edwards Industries, 7386
Edwards Insulation, 7386
Edwards, A.B. Kirk, 8837
Edwards, Barbara A., 6682
Edwards, Charles C., Jr., 3482
Edwards, Charles W., 9562
Edwards, Donald, 8680
Edwards, Elizabeth McCarty, 4833
Edwards, Frank O., 8549
Edwards, Gary, 7358
Edwards, Gary R., 1799
Edwards, Grace M., 4078
Edwards, Gwen, 9474
Edwards, J., 1178
Edwards, Jeffrey W., 7386
Edwards, Jephtha Tausig, 6026
Edwards, Kip, 870
Edwards, Margaret Watt, 7825
Edwards, Pam J., 8345
Edwards, Peter H., 7386
Edwards, Philip L., 8549
Edwards, R.A., 3571
Edwards, Ray Thomas, 473
Edwards, Robert L., 7238

Edwards, Rodney, 7087
Edwards, Stephen McCarty, 4833
Edwards, T. Ashley, 4198
Edwards, Warren, 1712
Edwards, William, 221, 5512
Edwards, William Raynor, 4833
Edwardson Charitable Lead Annuity Trust 2, Catherine O., 3239
Edwardson Charitable Lead Annuity Trust, Catherine O., 3239
Edwardson Family Foundation, 3239
Edwardson, Anne L., 3239
Edwardson, Catharine O., 3239
Edwardson, Shelly M., 3239
Efird, H. Timothy, II, 7111
Efird, Tom D., 7097
Eftax, William P., 2955
EG Duff Charitable Lead Trust, 9508
EG&G, 4238
Egan, Amb. Christopher F., 4079
Egan, Brian, 3401
Egan, Dick, 9810
Egan, Dorothy Harrison, 4080
Egan, George, 2280
Egan, Jean, 4079
Egan, Jennifer, 5700
Egan, Katherine D., 3944
Egan, Linda, 88
Egan, Owen, 1462
Egan, Richard, 4079
Egan, Thomas J., 3944
Egan, Thomas J., Jr., 3944
Egbert, Norma, 8667
Egenolf, Robert, 776
Eggertsson, Thrainn, 9441
Eggleston, Brenda Hopkins, 9472
Eggleston, David Reid, 9472
Eggleston, Mary Butler, 9472
Eggleston, Thomas B., 9472
Egler, Frederick N., Jr., 7963
Egler, Ruth D., 7963
Eglisau Estate Family, LP, 6713
Eglisau Estates Ltd., 6713
Egnot, Barbara, 6666
Ego, Kathleen, 1566
EGR Family Limited Partnership, 9518
EGS Electrical Group, LLC, 7252
Ehara, George S., 1098
Ehlen, Carol K., 7786
Ehlen, Kate E., 7786
Ehlen, MacGregor, 7786
Ehlen, Nicholas R., 7786
Ehly, Marvin P., 5068
Ehrenkranz, Joel S., 492
Ehrenkranz, Sanford B., 6470
Ehret, Lynn Kuse, 7786
Ehrlich, Jonas, 5947
Ehrline, Leo, 6524
Ehrman, Alyssa, 5949
Ehrman, Eric, 5949
Ehrman, Fred, 5949
Ehrman, Suzan, 5949
Eich, Carol, 2695
Eichenberg, Ladorna, 474
Eichenberg, Robert, 474
Eicher, Warren, 3641
Eichner, Barbara R., 2849
Eichner, Ira A., 2849
Eickelberger, Scott D., 7533
Eickhoff, E. Frances, 3413
Eidhammer, Lillian, 6541
Eiduson, Mark, 274
Eigen, David L., 2146
Eigen, Joan K., 2146

Eighanayan, Frederick, 6656
Eighanayan, H. Henry, 6656
Eighanayan, Kamran, 6656
Eikelberner, Emily, 1761
Eilenberg, Moses, 6333, 6904
Eilian, Charlene, 2709
Eilian, Jonathan, 2709
Einess, Lucile, 4734
Einhorn, Nancy, 9815
Einhorn, Stephen, 9815
Einstein Noah Restaurant, 1362
Einstein, Jean M., 2755
Eisen, Julius, 5273, 5516
Eisen, Susan, 5273, 5516
Eisenberg, Alan, 6720
Eisenberg, Estelle, 2850
Eisenberg, Harry K., 3804
Eisenberg, Joan, 285
Eisenberg, Martin, 5331
Eisenberg, Rebecca, 5331
Eisenberg, Ronald, 5331
Eisenberg, Warren, 5331
Eisenberger, Jeffrey, 5950
Eisenberger, Lauren, 5950
Eisenhart Marital Trust, Edward, 9418
Eisenhart Trust, Sarah, 9418
Eisenhart, Edward C., 9418
Eisenhut, Steve, 3397
Eisenman, Alan J., 8624
Eisenman, Sherrie Gordon, 8624
Eisenstein, Marci A., 3224
Eisma, Doug, 4736
Eisman, George, 2229
Eisner, David, 5951
Eisner, Jeffrey, 5665
Eisner, Jonathan D., 3881
Eisner, Karen, 5951
Eisner, Michael D., 1665
Eisold, Barbara K., 6849
Eisold, Kenneth, 6849
Eiss, Nancy, 9426
Eiszner, James R., Jr., 2851
Eiszner, Joyce C., 2851
Eiszner, Timothy J., 2851
Eizen, Bernard, 8082
Eizikovitz, Jack, 6367
Ekern, Kirk, 4900
EKS Inv Ltd Partnership, 5000
Ekstein, Abraham, 5952
Ekstein, Raizel, 5952
El Reno Senior Citizens Center, 7656
El-Bastawissi, Amira Youssef, 9623
Ela, Dan, 1279
Elahaian, Zohre, 1095
Elahian, Kamran, 565
Elahian, Zohre, 565
Elam, John, 8665
Elam, Laura, 3126
Elam, Lulu, 8665
Elaree, Thompson, 2510
Elbaum, Abigail Black, 5941
Eldad, Gidon, 7329
Elder Groups, 3375
Elder Trust, Bruce E., 3375
Elder, Alan H., 3375
Elder, Amy, 3375
Elder, Coley K., 475
Elder, Jack E., 3375
Elder, Judith, 9144
Elder, Julie, 3375
Elder, Louise, 3375
Elder, Mary D., 1466, 1467
Elder, Paul A., 3375
Elder, Ralph K., 475

Elder, Robert C., 475
Eldred, Heidi, 9937
Eldred, Justin, 1317
Eldred, Kary, 1317
Eldred, Kenneth A., 1317
Eldred, Lantson E., 9992
Eldred, Monica, 1317
Eldred, Rachel, 1317
Eldred, Robert E., 1317
Eldred, Roberta E., 1317
Eldred, Wayne Cameron, 1952
Eldridge, Bob, 882
Eldridge, Doc, 2437
Eldridge, Loyal A., III, 4402, 4412, 4483
Eleanor King, Eleanor, 1305
Electric Furnace Foundation, 7473
Electro-Mechanical Corp., 9489
Elefante, Michael B., 4033
Elegant Headwear Co., 6253
Elements Therapeutic Massage, 1295
Eley, Hillary, 4396
Elf Atochem North America, 7842
Elg, Annette, 2685
Elghanayan, Sharon M., 6386
Elgin, Arthur, 1802
Eli Scholarship Fund, 7205
Elias, Robert C., 5147
Eliasberg, H. Voss, 3854
Eliasberg, Richard A., 3854
Eliason, Robert, 1729
Eliassen, John Todd, 242
Elibol, David, 5799
Eliezer, Kollel Damesek, 5720
Elihu, Rose, 6685
Eliot, David, 9810
Elite Self Park Services, LLC, 5648
Elkins, Fred, 314
Elkins, Scott, 4763
Ellard, Heidi, 4220
Ellbogen, John P., II, 9971
Ellbogen, Ruth R., 9971
Ellbogen, Theresa A., 9971
Ellbogen, Thomas M., 9971
Ellenbogen, Ilene, 3835
Ellenoff, Debra S., 6753
Ellenoff, Douglas, 6753
Ellenoff, Gregory, 6753
Ellenoff, Lois, 6753
Ellens, Brett, 4422
Ellens, Curtis J., 4422
Ellens, Dennis, 4422
Ellens, Eileen, 4422
Eller, Amy, 6090
Eller, Charles G., Dr. , 9450
Ellerbrake, Richard, 5012
Ellerbrook, Karen, 3376
Ellerbrook, Karen M., 3376
Ellerbrook, Niel C., 3376
Ellerman, Roberta J., 2961
Ellett Brothers, 3991
Ellett Brothers, LLC, 3991
Elli, Matt, 7408
Elliman, Douglas, 6656
Elliot Declaration of Trust, William, 7977
Elliot, Edward, 5381
Elliot, RADM. Thomas J., Jr., 7223
Elliott Declaration of Trust, Muriel D., 7977
Elliott, Beverly, 9281
Elliott, Bob, 9139
Elliott, Chad K., 4436
Elliott, Chelsea, 479
Elliott, Daniel Keith, 2218
Elliott, Deborah, 479

Elliott, E. Allen, 7440
Elliott, Harry C., 479
Elliott, Harry C., III, 479
Elliott, Harry C., IV, 479
Elliott, James Ray, Jr., 2218
Elliott, Katherine D., 7977
Elliott, Marjorie Phillips, 5609
Elliott, Mary Ann, 2218
Elliott, Mary Catherine Brannin, 7662
Elliott, Nancy N., 4436
Elliott, R. Hugh, 4436
Elliott, Roxanne, 479
Elliott, Sharon, 7204
Elliott, Thomas J., Sr., 7223
Elliott, William, 9281
Elliott, William D., 8701
Ellis, Barbara I., 5333
Ellis, Belle L., 1109
Ellis, C.B. Richard, 6655
Ellis, Caroline A., 4038
Ellis, Christian Foreman, 5408
Ellis, David W., III, 7583
Ellis, Donald, 1989
Ellis, Franklyn, 5603
Ellis, Franklyn R., 5603
Ellis, Gail G., 2853
Ellis, Hayne, III, 4948
Ellis, J. Wiley, 2506, 2619
Ellis, Janice B., 1989
Ellis, Jennifer, 9920
Ellis, Jerome, 8607
Ellis, Joan Vestal, 8652
Ellis, Joseph H., 5333
Ellis, Lavina O., 5603
Ellis, Long, Jr., 4948
Ellis, Madelon L., 1989
Ellis, Martha F., 3723
Ellis, Peter S., 4134
Ellis, R.A. Long, 4948
Ellis, Sally Long, 4948
Ellis, Scott D., 4327
Ellis, Seth E., 2271
Ellis, Steven G., 4134
Ellis, William D., 2541
Ellis, William D., Jr., 2541
Ellis, Winnifred, 1622
Ellis, Winnifred C., 1622
Ellison Company, The, 7090
Ellison, Elizabeth M., 7090
Ellison, Jane R., 7090
Ellison, Jody, 4963
Ellison, John G.B., Jr., 7090
Ellman, Esther, 5956
Ellman, Jan, 5956
Ellman, Lee E., 5956
Ellsworth, Linda, 5188
Elman, Eloise N., 8560
Elmbrook Church, 9860
Elmco Industries, 9929
Elmcroft Co., 3905
Elmen Family Foundation, 8560, 8561
Elmen, Connie Renee, 8560
Elmen, Eloise N., 8560
Elmen, James W., 8560
Elmen, Julie D., 8561
Elmen, Richard, 8560
Elmen, Robert C., 8561
Elmore, Emily Gray, 8899
Elmore, Joni, 1928
Elrod, Ben M., 195
Elrod, Betty Lou, 195
Elrod, Scott M., 3092
Elrod, William Searcy, 195
Elsberg, Andrew, 3856

Elsberg, Daniel, 3856
Elsberg, David, 480
Elsberg, Margery, 3856
Elsberg, Stuart M., 3856
Elsberry, Anne W., 3574
Elsberry, Howard, 3574
Elsberry, Terence L., Rev. , 6989
Elsey, Paul, 4484
Elson, Jeffrey, 8874
Elster, Robert S., 1990
Elston, Caleb T., 8090
Elston, Lloyd W., 8090
Elston, Richard L., 8090
Elvia Diamonds, LLC, 3877
Elvin, Norman S., 3785
Elwell, Joanne, 4656
Elwood, Gordon, 7761
Ely, Lenoard, III, 900
Ely, Roland P., Jr., 7483
Elyachar, Daniel, 5959
Elyachar, Jonathan, 5959
Elyea, Mike, 8784
Elzer, Robert, 3459
Emami, John, 8917
Emami, Karen Sue, 8917
Emami, Scott, 8917
Emami, Tiffany, 8917
Embassy Apparel, 5976
Emberton, Bonnie L., 2821
Emblidge, Warren E., Jr., 5842
Embree, Donna A., 3509
Emerald Management Corp., 153
Emerick, Fred C., 8114
Emerick, Katherine Woods, 6992
Emerson, Thomas Bonie, 6542
Emerson, Thomas C., 6016, 6542
Emerson, Warren, 5660
Emery, David R., 8556
Emery, James A., 5130
Emery, Katherine R., 3222
Emery, Linda Rodgers, 6680
Empedocles, Marianne, 794
Emperio, Stephanie, 5318
Empire Brushes, 6056
Empire Southwest LLC, 116
Empire State Certified Development Corporation, 6546
Employee Ownership Foundation, 520
Emswiler, David, 7284
Emet Corp., 2481
Emfinger, Lloyd F., Jr., 13
EMG Madonna Educational Foundation, 6884
Emig Trust A, John, 4576
Emig Trust B, John, 4576
Emig, Gerald M., 4576
Emig, John G., 1373
Eminent Services Corp., 3965
Emison, Elizabeth A., 5394
Emison, James W., 5394
Emison, Jane B. Larson, 5394
Emison, Thomas W., 5394
Emison, William A., 5394
Emmer, Jane, 9991
Emmerich, Karol D., 4673
Emmerich, Richard J., 4673
Emmett, Dan A., 481
Emmett, Daniel W., 481
Emmett, Morgan W., 481
Emmett, Rae M., 481
Emmett, Tyler A., 481
Emmons, Keith, Dr. , 361
Emmott, Helen, 4881
Emory, Benjamin, 3222
Emory, Katherine R., 3222
Emory, Linda Rodgers, 6680

Emunah Trust, The, 1844
Enchanted Candle Inc., 6906
Encore Trust, 8880
Endacott, Kent, 5081
Ende, Howard, 3919
Endeavors Group LLC, The, 9800
Enderman, Jason, 221
Endo Laboratories, 1694
Energy North, 1469
Engan, Daniella, 1542
Engdahl, Herbert A., 5122
Engebretson, Douglas, 4047
Engel Trust, Schutz, 9325
Engel, Andre, 5966
Engel, Andre S., 5334
Engel, Ary, 5334
Engel, Barry, 5334
Engel, Blima, 5334
Engel, Elizabeth Hunter, 5335
Engel, Gershon, 5334
Engel, Ivy, 1556
Engel, Jacob, 5334
Engel, Jan, 4845
Engel, Jane V., 5335
Engel, John P., 5863, 5897
Engel, Margaret, 1826
Engel, Ralph M., 1405
Engel, Robert A., 5335
Engel, Robert G., 5335
Engel, Sherman, 5334
Engel, Toby, 5966
Engel, William V., 5445
Engelbert, David E., 4498
Engelbert, Lynn H., 4498
Engelbert, Matthew T., 4498
Engelhorn, Claudia, 6357
Engellant, Francis, 5058
Engelman, Kendall Clark, 4365
Engels, Gayle, 3165
Engelsma, Bruce, 8563
Engelsma, Daniel, 8563
Engelsma, Kirsten, 8563
Engeman, Kathy H., 2586
Engle Printing & Publishing Co., 7982
Engle, C.A., 7982
Engle, Catherine C., 2855
Engle, Deborah, 2855
Engle, Dennis L., 7982
Engle, Pauline H., 7982
Engle, S. Cody, 2855
Englebardt, Bonnie, 6857
Englebardt, Bonnie S., 5965
Englehardt, Joseph, 1807
Englehart, Ed, 9878
Engleman, Thomas E., 5325
Englert, Harold E., 9532
Englert, Joe, 7114
English, Abigail, 7338
English, E.R., Jr., 9443
English, E.R., Sr., 9443
English, Florence Cruft, 2474
English, Rita T., 9443
Eni, Christopher W., 7959
Eni, Louis J., Jr., 7959
Eni, Ruth, 7959
Enivar Enterprises, 2856
Ennen, Philip L., 7339
Ennis, Steve, 9454
Enomoto, Tom, 2642
Enrico, Aaron J., 8839
Enrico, Catherine B., 8839
Enrico, Roger A., 8839
Enrico, Rosemary, 8839
Enright, Erin S., 5339

Enright, Joseph J., 4903
Enroth, Mary P., 9862
Ensign-Bickford Industries, 1442
Entaire Global Companies, 2577
Entegris, 4806
Entelco Corp., 7389
Enterline, Larry L., 2475
Enterprise Bank & Trust Co., 4149, 5029
Entertainment Industry Foundation, 645, 684
Entinger, Richard, 7802
Enzle, Susan, 5520
Enzor, Scott, 219
Epard, Richard, 3585
Epel, Elissa S., 283
Ephraim Family TSG II Trust, 6575
Ephraim Family TSG Trust II, 6965
Ephrata National Bank, 8351
Ephrata National Bank, The, 7900
EPIC Metals Corp., 7965
Episalla, Joy, 6075
Eplee, Gordon Kelly, 7092
Eplee, Herbert W., Jr., 7092
Eplee, Herbert W., Sr., 7092
Eplee, Melvin Glen, 7092
Eplee, Shirley J., 7092
Epley, Mike, 3735
Eppard, Margo D., 9441
Eppig, Marianne E., 7581
Eppig, Ruth Swetland, 7581
Epple, Karl H., 1559
Eppley, Marion, 5967
Epps, Charles, 870
Epstein & Assocs., Ben, 5705
Epstein, Andrew, 2890
Epstein, Barbara, 4084
Epstein, Ben, 5705
Epstein, Benjamin, 5891
Epstein, Colin, 483
Epstein, Danielle, 5672
Epstein, Dasha, 5672
Epstein, David, 1992
Epstein, Gene, 7984
Epstein, Geraldine, 1992
Epstein, Harris, 483
Epstein, Jay A., 9219
Epstein, Jodi, 4084
Epstein, Lewis, 4084
Epstein, Marlene, 7984
Epstein, Paul, 6585, 6950
Epstein, Reuven, 5705
Epstein, Richard, 7630
Epstein, Robert, 483
Epstein, Samuel, 7983
Epstein, Seymour, 7494
EquineTack and Nutritionals, 8570
Erath, Richard C., 7762
Erb, Donald R., 4359
Erb, Elisha W., 4359
Erb, Steve, 7794
Erbe, Loriann, 5295
Erbsen, Diana L., 6621
Erda, Andrea, 8009
Erdel, Dan K., 4921
Erdle, Harvey B., 1993
Erdle, Jack A., 1993
Erdle, Norma, 1993
Erdman, Daniel W., 9816
Erdman, Natalie Bock, 9816
Erdman-Luder, Deborah, 9816
Ergen, Cantey M., 1762
Ergen, Charles W., 1762
Ergen, Christopher, 1762

Ergen, Courtney, 1762
Ergen, Katherine, 1762
Ergen, Kerry, 1762
Erhardt, Ron, 4671
Erickson, Ann, 2678
Erickson, Bradford, 1581
Erickson, Brian A., 4674
Erickson, Carole I., 5049
Erickson, Constance, 2069
Erickson, David L., 9591
Erickson, Debra, 1858
Erickson, Galen, 4719
Erickson, Gerald A., 4675
Erickson, Jeanne, 3539
Erickson, Leif B., 5049
Erickson, Meredith, 2822
Erickson, Neal D., 4674
Erickson, Ronald A., 4674
Erickson, Sandra C., 9591
Erie Community Foundation, 7876
Erikson, Christopher, 5954
Erikson, Rolf F., 1696
Erion, Douglas J., 1265
Erion, Helen, 1265
Erion, Justin, 1265
Erion, Ken, 1265
Erion, Travis, 1265
Erisman, Otis W., 3674
ERJ Living Trust, 673
Erker, William H., 5030
Erkiletian, Lynda, 411
Erlandson, Sarah E., 2190
Erler Foundation, Thomas, 8672
Erler, Linda, 3402
Erley, Bruce, 1242
Erlich, Max, 4904
Erlich, Melba, 4904
Erlin, Beatrice, 5539
Erlingsson, Ellen S., 9351
Erlingsson, Erik C., 9351
Ernest, Max W., 3448
Ernst, Julia, 6872
Ernst, Nancy M., 5455
Ernst, Robin, 7944
Ernst, Valerie M., 1435
Erpf Charitable Trust, 5968
Erpf, Armand G., 5968
Erpf-Forsman, Cornelia A., 5968
Erskin, Joseph L., 3612
Ertel, Barbara, 8219
Ervin, Florence M., 8549
Ervin, Timmy L., 7222
Erwert, Bill, 9638
Erwin, Angela, 3420
Erwin, Anna P., 7145
Erwin, Dansby, 9272
Erwin, Harry C., 210
Erwin, Harry C., III, 8682
Erwin, John S., 6246, 6247
Erwin, Robert, 210
ESB Financial, 3555, 3635
ESB Securities Corp., 4076
Esbenshade, Harry H., III, 9744
Esber, Betsy, 5028
Escalante, Heidi, 5050
Esch, Rosemary, 4573
Eschhofen, Diana Moore, 7339
Eshbaugh, David C., 6189
Eshbaugh, W. Hardy, 6189
Eshbaugh, William H., 6189
Eshenbaugh, Jill, 415
Eshima, Sharon K., 1224
Eskenazi, Lois, 3377
Eskenazi, Sandra, 3377

Eskenazi, Sidney, 3377
Eskenazi, Sidney Lois, 3377
Eskind, Annette, 8611
Eskind, Donna G., 8612
Eskind, Irwin, 8611, 8612
Eskind, Jeffrey, 8611
Eskind, Jeffrey B., 8612
Eskind, Laurie, 8613
Eskind, Steven, 8611, 8613
Eskuche, Leslie M., 9323
ESL Federal Credit Union, 5969
Esma Basha Memorial, 93
Espenscheid, Dorothy, 2859
Espenscheid, Harry, 2859
Esping, Heather H., 8841
Esping, Perry E., 8841
Esping, William P., 8841
Espinosa, Marc, 1316
Espinoza, Richard, 4608
Espinoza, Toni Beck, 421
Esplain Associates Three, LLC, 6747
Esplanade Venture Partnership LP, The, 6302
Esposito, James, 1549
Esposito, Kathleen, 1998
Esptein, Eli, 5544
Espy, Carl, IV, 9419
Essig, Stuart, 5400
Essig, Stuart M., 5339
Essman, Alyn V., 4905
Essman, Marlyn R., 4905
Essman, Sharyn M., 4905
Estate of Anne J. Smith, 9685
Estate of John Shaughnessy, 4292
Estes, Debbie, 3628
Estes, Kelly, 3628
Estes, Mike, 5198
Estrada, Paul, 3641
Estreich & Co., 6655
Estridge, Larry, 7105
Estrin, Jesse, 763
Estrin, Mary Lloyd, 763
Estrin, Robert L., 763
Etchart, Sarah, 5054
Etheredge, Jeannette, 3145
Etheridge Construction Corporation, 9506
Etheridge, Chris P., 4849
Ethington, Brendan Damon, 2629
Etscorn, Alice S., 3654
Etters, Bonnie C., 2800
Ettinger, Brandie L., 2169
Ettinger, Mark, 7002
Ettinger, Mark I., 5891
Ettl, Alex J., 5970
Etzkorn Trust, Albert, 7379
Eule, Beth, 5971
Eule, Daniel, 5971
Eurich, Juliet A., 3816, 3966
Evans Charitable Lead Trust, Heather, 1783
Evans Telecommunication, 1994
Evans, Anne T., 1747
Evans, Ashley Reid, 5973
Evans, C. Paul, 9130
Evans, Carol, 1100
Evans, Dave, 1305
Evans, David, 240
Evans, Devorah Faiga, 5972
Evans, Eric D., 5972
Evans, Eva L., 4590
Evans, Gareth, 3781
Evans, Genevieve Wise, 9283
Evans, Glenn, 3988

Evans, Heather, 1783
Evans, Ivor J., 4511
Evans, J. Morris, 1747
Evans, Jack, 3781
Evans, Jamie, 8674
Evans, Jean, 3781
Evans, Joe, 7630
Evans, John A., III, 4831
Evans, John D., 1994
Evans, Jonathan Perry, 5973
Evans, Karen, 1053
Evans, Ken, 5058
Evans, Linden R., 8556
Evans, Mary Louise, 1289
Evans, Norman K., 486
Evans, Pamela S., 4276
Evans, Peter A., 1747
Evans, Peter M., 2109
Evans, Ph. D, Christopher J., 906
Evans, Ph. D, Ronald, 906
Evans, Randall E., 8873
Evans, Robert S., 5306, 5973
Evans, Sara G., 486
Evans, Saramel R., 4831
Evans, Saramel Repsher Crooks, 4831
Evans, Saramel Repsher Crooks, II, 4831
Evans, Shaun, 3711
Evans, Sian, 3781
Evans, Susan C., 5973
Evans, Teresa, 323
Evans, Tina, 7417
Evans, Tom, 7666
Evans, Trevor, 3781
Evans, Walter C., 1747
Evans, Walter O., 2506
Evans, William L., Jr., 9119
Evanson, Carol L., 1995
Evanson, Paul J., 1995
Evapco., Amex, 2348
Evavold, Dale, 4678
Even-Zohar, Adina, 4101
Evenson, David, 7295
Everbank, 2005
Everest, Bimla, 488
Everest, Christine G., 7676
Everest, James H., 7676
Everest, Jean I., 7676
Everest, Tricia L., 7676
Everets, John, 3766
Everett, Margaret P., 6582
Everett, Michael, 3446
Everhart, Stephen L., 8647
Everitt, Laurie B., 2232
Evernham Motorsports, LLC, 7094
Evernham, Mary, 7094
Evernham, Raymond D., Jr., 7094
Evernham, Raymond J., 7094
Evernham, William, 7094
Evers, Mary Beth, 10000
Evers, Michael J., 10000
Every, Joseph R., 7986
Ewart, Tom, 8522
EWB Charitable Trust, 7729
Ewen, Daniel C., 5056
Ewing, Ed, 8795
Ewing, Ruth D., 9805
Exburg Group S A, 5085
Exchange Bankshares Corp., 3553
Exchange National Bank, 3553
Exron Capital, 3257
Exstream, 3675
Extraco Corp., 8750
Exxon Mobil Corp., 5272

Exxon Mobile, 89
Eykamp Grandchildren's Trust, G&D, 4197
Eykamp Sons Trust, D&G, 4197
Eykamp, Dorothy, 4197
Eykamp, G.R., 4197
Eykamp, Philip, 4197
Eykamp, Richard, 4197
Eykamp, Rita, 4197
Eykamp, William, 4197
Ezra Trust Foundation, 7000
Ezra, David H., 1305
Ezrasons, 5976
Ezrilov, Bob, 4701

F T Services Trust, 8895
F&G Realty Recycling, LLC, 1395
F.A. Kohler, 7386
Faanes, Mark, 9814
Fabems, A.L., 7612
Faber, Alison W. Lufkin, 6421
Faber, Clara, 7392
Faber, Marilyn, 4621
Fabiano Brothers, 4438
Fabiano, Evangeline L., 4438
Fabiano, James C., 4438
Fabiano, James C., II, 4438
Fabiano, Joseph R., II, 4438
Fabick Tractor Co., John, 4907
Fabick, Harry, 4907
Fabrication Technologies, 3011
Fabyan, Nelle, 2862
Facciola, Tom, 6720
Fackler, Cynthia, 6559
Fadley, James P., 3381
Faechner, Al, 5045
Faerber, George O., 7545
Faesen, Virginia, 2877
Faessler, Thomas A., 2408
Fagan, John, 3526
Fagan, Susel A., 3526
Fagen, Ginny, 3015
Fagenson & Co., 5657
Fagenson, J., 6905
Fagenson, Robert, 5657, 6905
Fagert, William, 7407
Faggin, Elvia, 489
Faggin, Federico, 489
Fagin, Allen I., 5978
Fagin, Charles G., 5978
Fagin, Judith H., 5978
Fagin, Miriam, 5978
Fagin, Robert B., 5978
Fagnani, Laurie, 89
Fagundes, Heather L., 811
Faherty, Kathleen, 8458
Fahey, Diane, 8570
Fahey, John, 9739, 9753
Fahey, Peter M., 6078
Fahey, Richard, 4914
Fahey, Thomas M., 4914
Fahey, Todd C., 5237
Fahrer, Belle, 3365
Fahrney, Helen, 9818
Failinger, Ann L., 872
Fair Oaks Dairy Farm, LLC, 3347
Fair Trust, R.W., 8844
Fair, Allen, 8844
Fair, Barbara King, 8844
Fair, Clyde, 2085
Fair, David, 7613
Fair, David R., 8326
Fair, Debra, 8657

Fair, Mattie Allen, 8844
Fair, R.W., 8844
Fairbourne, Michael, 4719
Fairchild, Marguerite, 8845
Fairclo, Richard, 7768
Fairclough, John H., 5493
Fairfield, Freeman E., 7095
Fairley-Barlow, Trina, 1799
Fairman, David, 2970
Fairness Foundation, 3440
Fairways Crossing LLC, 9506
Falbaum, Rand H., 3750
Falbee, Frank, 9691
Falchuk, Z. Myron, Dr., 4054
Falcon's Flight, 175
Falcone, VSNR, Capt. Frank E., 8160
Falero, Ralph, 7202
Fales, Gilbert R., 9594
Falese, Robert D., 1841
Falese, Robert D., Jr., 1841
Falk, Annie, 1996
Falk, Benjamin D.E., 2390
Falk, Caroline Tell, 1580
Falk, Judi L., 5981
Falk, Maurice B., 5981
Falk, Michael, 1996
Falkenstein, Karin, 4514
Falkin, Joyce, 1595
Fallis, Helen, 238
Fallon, Judge Jim, 1259
Fallon, Tara L., 5251
Falsgraf, William W., 8010
Falzone, Joseph S., 8176
Fameco, LLC, 6438
Familian Foundation, Arnold & Edith, 1050
Familian Intervivos Trust, Isadore, 1050
Familian, Zalec, 491
Families Inc. of Arkansas, 196
Family Capital Trust Co., 4346
Family Development Ctr., 5592
Family Foods, 7174
Family Foundation, Aarwal, 1768
Family Foundation, Jennings, 9345
Family Foundation, Ron and Nancy Ormand, The , 9345
Fan, George, 5985
Fan, Katherine, 5985
Fancher, Christopher D., 3449
Fandino, Laura, 4229
Fanfest Merchandise/Autographs, 3817
Fang, Ying, 5162
Fanguy, D., 3748
Fankhouser, Alexis L., 2498
Fanning, Tom, 2357
Fanno, James T., Dr. , 7346
Fant, Beth, 5610
Fanta, John, 9756
Fantasy Diamond Co., 3315
Farabow, Sara Beiro, 3242
Faranna, Charles C., 7678
Farb, Gretchen Hoffer, 2975
Farber, Gail, 5987
Farber, Gerald, 5379
Farber, Gloria, 5986
Farber, Hilliard, 5986
Farber, Jack, 5987
Farber, James A., 495
Farber, Jennifer, 5986
Farber, Melissa, 5986
Farbman, Eileen, 6628
Farell, John M., 2351
Farfalla, Kristin, 5295
Farfone, Dottie, 8532

Farid, Kamran, 1444
Farid, Tariq, 1444
Faris, David C., 609
Faris, Heidi R., 4766
Faris, Noelle, 3998
Farish, William S., 3668
Farkas Marital Trust, Thomas, 9445
Farkas, Barbara, 5988
Farkovits, Esther, 6552
Farkovits, Josh, 6552
Farkovitz, Esther, 6552
Farley, Shauna, 1155
Farm, Jodee, 2638
Farm, Lis, 7829
Farmer, Debby, 3015
Farmer, Duncan C., 4107
Farmer, F.J., 7449
Farmer, Gretchen, 9839
Farmer, Jeremy G.O., 2710
Farmers & Mechanics Bank, 3039
Farmers and Merchants Bank & Trust Co., 2445
Farmers Bank Capital Trust, 3698
Farmers Bank, The, 2445
Farmers Group, 496
Farmers State Bank, The, 1300
Farmers Trust Co., 7625
Farmers Trust Company, 7385, 7630
Farmers Union Marketing & Processing Assoc., 4679
Farmland, 8859
Farnham, Anne M., 9418
Farnham, MerriBeth, 1917
Farnham, Robert E., 8628
Farnsworth, Randall, 6559
Farr, Caroline M., 1662
Farr, Catherine E., 1662
Farr, Joseph G., 1662
Farr, Leonard, 1359
Farr, Michael J., 1662
Farr, Patrick M., 1662
Farr, Rebecca C., 1662
Farr, Tena D., 653
Farr, Walter S., 2239, 2413
Farrar, Joan, 3988
Farrar, Robert R., 3988
Farrell, David J., 1998
Farrell, David V., 5788
Farrell, J. David, 7923
Farrell, James M., 1998
Farrell, Jeremiah E., 4494
Farrell, John, 6194, 9844
Farrell, Joseph, 5542
Farrell, Katherine, 9342
Farrell, Maxine P., 1998
Farrell, Sharon, 7375
Farrell, Thomas J., 8503
Farrell, Tim, 9342
Farrell, W. James, 1998
Farrell, William, 9844
Farrell, William J., 7879
Farrelly, Wendy M., 3745
Farris, David J., 5342
Farris, Jill, 5342
Farris, R. Houston, 8847
Farris, Robert R., 8847
Farris, Robin, 8847
Farrow, Jennifer Stafford, 2346
Farver, Charles S., 3491
Farver, Constance, 4441
Farver, Herbert, 4441
Farver, Mary Joan, 3491
Farver, Michael, 4441
Farver, Orville W., 4441

Farver, Patrick, 4441
Farver-Galiette, Cynthia, 4441
Fasenmyer Foundation, Richard J., 5724
Fash, Annie G., 8848
Fash, Ralph E., 8848
Faske, Howard, 8769
Fasseas, Alexis, 2866
Fasseas, Drew, 2866
Fasseas, Paula, 2866
Fasseas, Peter A., 2866
Fassino, Edward G., 4086
Fassino, Lillian M., 4086
Fast, Eric C., 5306
Fast, Stephanie, 8689
Faubert, Jessica Ann, 7657
Faulkner, Marianne Gaillard, 2867
Faulkner, Thomas, Jr., 4107
Faulkner, Thomas, Sr., 4107
Faust, Jon, 3371
Faust, Winifred D., 1399
Faversham, Lori Gray, 2927
Favre, Kathryn G., 4908
Favre, Ritu, 8874
Fawcett, Farrah, 500
Fawer, Estanne Abraham, 6151
Fawer, Martin, 6151
Fay, John T., 1669
FC Business Systems, 9417
FDH Enterprises Inc., 199
Feathers, Elizabeth, 4026
Fechser, Fancy, 5139
Fechser, T.J., 5139
Fechter, Debra, 6283
Fed Ex Services, 8570
Fedele, John E., 4068
Fedeli, Umberto, Jr., 7393
Feder, Arthur A., 6062
Feder, Donald L., 501
Feder, Helene T., 501
Feder, Margaret, 501
Feder, Paul E., 501
Feder, Steven H., 501
Feder, Susan, 5671, 6950
Federal Catridge Co., 3991
Federal Home Loan Bank of Dallas, 9232
Federici, Anthony, 6892
Federico, Kathleen, 4199
Fedje, Judith A., 7296
Fedje, Noel I., 7296
Fedor, Donald B., 5257
Fedor, John W., 5257
Fedorovich, Richard C., 7635
Fedyniak, Oresta, 3234
Fee Mission Council, 7513
Fee, Allen K., 3571
Fee, Frank H., III, 2148
Fee, Frank J., III, 5990
Fee, Kevin T., 5990
Feeley, Cathi, 7295
Feely, Terri, 8654
Feeney, Matthew, 171
Feeney, Patricia G., 7425
Feeney, Patrick F., 1174
Feenstra Investment, LLC, 118
Feenstra, Patrick W., 118, 2687
Feenstra, Tami, 118
Feeser, Barbara, 3956
Fefel, Jeremy, 3817
Fegan, Ann B., 8233
Fegan, Howard D., 8233
Fegan, John H., 8233
Fegen, Sarah K., 8233
Fehlman, Bruce, 2909
Fehr, Gloria J., 7299

Fehsenfeld, Fred M., Jr., 3387
Fehsenfeld, Suzanne, 3387
Feibelman, Barbara, 8405
Feibelman, H. Jack, 8405
Feibelman, Jack, 8405
Feidelson, Linn, 5465
Feidelson, Robert, 5465
Feierman, Dennis, 2424
Feig, Robert, 5688
Feigenbaum, Arieh, 5561
Feil Organization, The, 6655
Feil, Brian, 5991
Feil, Erika, 5991
Feil, Jeffrey J., 5991
Feil, Joshua, 5991
Feil, Lee, 5991
Fein, Adam, 5992
Fein, Bernard, 5992
Fein, Cecile, 5357
Fein, David, 5992
Fein, Edward, 5155, 5668
Fein, Elaine, 5992
Fein, Lawrence, 5992
Fein, Stephanie, 5357
Feinberg, Besty, 3857
Feinberg, Carol J., 5993
Feinberg, David, 5993
Feinberg, Harry, 3857
Feinberg, Mark, 2320
Feinberg, Maurice, 5993
Feinberg, Robert, 3857
Feinblatt, John A., 3971
Feiner, Lawrence, 6656
Feinman, Alfred, 5994
Feinman, Andrew, 5994
Feinman, Martin, 5994
Feinman, Robert, 5994
Feinstein, Debra, 5343
Feinstein, Jeffrey, 5343
Feinstein, Leonard, 5343
Feinstein, Michael, 5654
Feinstein, Richard, 5343
Feintech, Evelyn, 1139
Feintech, Evelyn M., 502
Feintech, Irving, 502
Feintech, Lynn, 1139
Feintech, Lynn Diane, 502
Feintech, Norman, 502
Feintech, Vivian A., 502
Feit, Roger, 6226
Fekete, Frank L., 5566
Fel-Pro Inc., 2908
Feld, Jeffrey, 3113
Feld, Marc, 4570
Feldbaum, Bruce L., 8591
Feldberger, Yechezkel, 1231
Feldhausen, Jil K., 138
Feldheim, Deborah, 6725
Feldheim, Herbert D., 6725
Feldman Revocable Trust, Samuel, 3858
Feldman, Dene E., 3858
Feldman, Donald, 7299
Feldman, Dr., Robert M., 5384
Feldman, Earl N., 567, 837, 871
Feldman, Franklin, 5692
Feldman, Gretchen V., 3858
Feldman, H. John, 1911
Feldman, Jeffrey, 5996
Feldman, Leigh E., 3858
Feldman, Leslie C., 5996
Feldman, Lois, 8501
Feldman, M.D., Ph.D., Eva, 2880
Feldman, Samuel M., 3858
Feldman, Seymour, 5996

Feldman, Steven, 5995
Feldstein, Daniel, 5344
Feldstein, David, 5344
Feldstein, George, 5344
Feldstein, Judith, 5997
Feldstein, Mark S., 7394
Feldstein, Richard, 5997
Feldstein, Robert, 8698
Felger, Edith M., 7395
Felhaber, Larson, Fenlon & Vogt, LLC, 4681
Felhofer, Michael, 9810
Felich, Georgia D., 386
Felis, Austin S., 2140
Felix, Nathan, 157
Fellenz, Beth, 9905
Feller, Robert D., 885
Fellman, Jennifer A., 4133
Fellman, Kenneth L., 9862
Fells, Andrea H., 1288
Feloney, James P., Dr., 361
Felson, Dan A., 1735
Felt Products Manufacturing Co., 2908
Felt, Chas, 9340
Felt, Joel, 8591
Felter, Timothy L., 4221
Felter, Tom, 912
Feltes, Karla, 1416, 2869
Feltes, Timothy, 1416, 2869
Feltl, Mary Jo, 4794
Fema Electronics Corp., 659
Feminella, Ann, 6154
Feminist Women's Health Center, 5206
Fenaroli, Paul, 3614
Fenderson, Timothy, 650
Fendley, Barbara Riddle, 8813
Fenech, Lisa R., 3380
Fenech, Michael J., 3380
Fenech, Ronald J., 3380
Fenech, Taylor R., 3380
Fenigstein, Jack, 768
Fenn, Nancy, 4534
Fennell, Robert E., 8849
Fenner, Adam K., 8850
Fenner, Laura E., 8850
Fenner, Mark, 4960
Fenner, Peter R., 8850
Fenner, Suzan E., 8850
Fenno, J. Brooks, 4127
Fenske, Dean W., 9812
Fenton, Devon, 5998
Fenton, Joan, 9355, 9356
Fenton, Joyce R., 2670
Fenton, Lance, 5998
Fenton, Noel, 5998
Fenton, Peter, 5998
Fenton, Sarah, 5998
Fenton, Steven, 2670
Fenton, Wendy, 5998
Fenzel, John, 3925
Ferber, James W., 2260
Ferber, JoAnn B., 4682
Ferber, Roman S., 4443
Ferber, Ronda, 4443
Ferber, Roy R., 4682
Ferebee, David, Jr., 1914
Ferenc, Sidney R., 5080
Fergenbaum, Josh, 6494
Ferger, Jane D., 2127
Fergus, Terrance P., 7459
Ferguson Construction Co., 5999
Ferguson, Brian C., 1446
Ferguson, Bryant, 9819
Ferguson, Carol J., 1446

Ferguson, Cathy, 1446
Ferguson, Daniel C., 1999
Ferguson, Dave, 3125
Ferguson, Donald R., 5999
Ferguson, Dorothy T., 5999
Ferguson, Ellen Lee, 9596
Ferguson, Gordon , 8674
Ferguson, Hugh S., 9596
Ferguson, J. Brian, 8564
Ferguson, James Terese, 8564
Ferguson, Jane Avery, 9596
Ferguson, Joe, 5105
Ferguson, John, 3445, 6284
Ferguson, John J., 1573
Ferguson, Kathy, 7033
Ferguson, Kathy L., 7033
Ferguson, Kay L., 9435
Ferguson, Kayleen H., 9819
Ferguson, Kyle, 9819
Ferguson, Larry P., 9819
Ferguson, Lori, 3607
Ferguson, Marissa V.G., 1715
Ferguson, Nancy L., 503
Ferguson, Patricia G., 8974
Ferguson, Richard, 1715
Ferguson, Richard A., 1715
Ferguson, Ronald E., 1446
Ferguson, Terese M., 8564
Ferhat, Dabbie Yuengling, 8263
Ferm, Mike, 5074
Fernandez, Alberto Eduardo Duarte, 7382
Fernandez, Cindy, 3783
Fernandez, Enriqueta, 2150
Fernandez, Roberto Duarte, 7382
Fernstrum, Lisa, 4497
Ferrara, Al, 4413
Ferrara, Alan, 4389
Ferrara, Joseph F., 5557
Ferrari, Andrew U., 9446
Ferrari, Barbara Q., 9446
Ferraro, David, 9367
Ferreira, Nelson, 5369
Ferrer, Bonnie Harris, 9468
Ferrer, Nuria C, 9468
Ferrero, John, Jr., 7442
Ferriday, Carolyn, 6000
Ferrie, Timothy, 6442
Ferrier, Ellen Roberts, 1551
Ferrio, George, 1564
Ferris, Bruce, 3576
Ferris, Carl W., 3859
Ferris, Constance F., 3859
Ferris, George M., Jr., 3860
Ferris, Nancy S., 3860
Ferro, Bonnie, 9372
Ferro, Charles P., 9372
Ferro, Marc, 9372
Ferro, Marianne, 9372
Ferry, Carolyn P., 7396
Ferry, Maude M., 504
Ferry, Richard M., 504
Ferry, Tom, 1100
Fertig, Alice, 5582
Fertitta, Paige, 8852
Fertitta, Tilman J., 8852
Ferwerda, Connie, 9862
Fesenmaier, Joe, 9814
Fessend, Susan-Louise, 5593
Festekjian, Raffi, 3996
Festinger, Trudy, 6300
Fetchig Charitable Remainder Unitrust, Allie Morriss, 7145
Feth, Karen W., 7397

Feth, William R., 7397
Fetridge, Kimberly, 375
Fetter, Lynda Boone, 329
Fetzer, Jeffrey A., 8201
Feuerring, Gertrude, 6001
Feuerring, Ralph, 6001
Feuerstein, Gary, 7755
Fezekas, Robert, 2437
Fezzey, Sarah, 4487
FHA Holding Co., 8186
Fibus Family Properties, LLC, 7398
Fibus, C. Kenneth, 7398
Fibus, M., 7398
Ficalora, Alice B., 6002
Ficalora, John J., 6002
Ficalora, Joseph R., 6002
Fickett, Franklin I., 8854
Fickling, Neva L., 2478
Fickling, Roy H., 2478
Fickling, William A., III, 2478
Fickling, William A., Jr., 2478
Fidelity Bank, 3577
Fidelity Charitable Gift Fund, 9368
Fidelity National Bank, 215
Fidelity State Bank and Trust Co., 3624
Fidgeon, Timothy F., 4233
Fidler, Genine Macks, 3906
Fidler, Josh, 3906
Fiduciary Trust Co., 4034, 4077, 4176, 4206, 4223
Fiduciary Trust Co. Int'l, 4227
Fiduciary Trust International - Delaware, 1769
Fiedler, David, 5969
Fiedorowicz, Kevin, 9856
Fiedorowicz, Lee, 9856
Field Trust, Daniel W., 4137
Field, Larry D., 4849
Fields Imports, 2870
Fields Jeep, 2870
Fields Motorcars of Florida, 2870
Fields Pag, 2870
Fields, Bill, 3655
Fields, Cary, 6003
Fields, Clinton, 4983
Fields, Gregory F., 8371
Fields, J. Alexander, 6003
Fields, John R., 2870
Fields, Kathleen, 6003
Fields, Kenneth W., 8900
Fields, Randolph, 4442
Fields, Rosemary, 7731
Fields, Samantha, 6003
Fields-Taylor, Joetta, 2787
Fieler, Sean, 379
Fierstadt, Marjorie, 472
Fife, Lori, 6005
Fife, Mark, 6005
Fifield, Helen D., 4198
Fifield, Randy A., 2871
Fifield, Steven D., 2871
Fifth Third Bank, 4430, 4452, 7306, 7390, 7440, 7447, 7450, 7462, 7479, 7481, 7492, 7506, 7508, 7509, 7544, 7549, 7552, 7586, 7607
Fifth Third Bank of Western Ohio, 7538
Figge, Thomas K., 3492
Figge, Vivian Otto, 3492
Figueroa, Laura, 5362
Filandro, Gerry, 6632
Filareki, Donald, 4732
Filbin, Thomas J., 4067
Filipelli, Joseph N., 384

Fillman, Gordon B., 5129
Fillman, Jay, 3125
Fillmore County Cinema Association, 5124
Fillmore County Foundation, 5124
Fillmore West Investment Trust, 2057
Filmer Estate Trust, Elizabeth, 4444
Finaldi, Arnold E., Jr., 1590
Finamore, John, 8208
Finch, Doak, 2000
Finch, Lawrence, 998
Findlay Cadillac, 5156
Findlay Management Group, 5156
Findlay Shack Properties LLC, 5156
Findlay, Clifford J., 5156
Findley Charitable Rem Trust, Ralph, 9925
Findley, Leslie E., 948
Findley, Ryan, 1346
Fine 2000 Charitable Trust, Milton, 7993
Fine Family Foundation, 8080
Fine Foundation, The, 7993
Fine Rev. Trust, Jerome M., 3861
Fine Sheer Industries, Inc., 6025
Fine Trust, Milton, 7994
Fine, David, 7993
Fine, Frada L., 9745
Fine, Jerome M., 3861
Fine, Milton, 7993, 7994
Fine, Rachel, 7993
Fineman, Peggy Goldsmith, 8622
Finerty, Linda, 4909
Finerty, Linda M., 4909
Finerty, Steve, 4909, 4962
Finerty, Steven L., 4909
Finestein, Russell, 5582
Finestra, Carmen J., 505
Finestra, Tonia Stivale, 505
Finger, Jerry E., 8857
Finger, Jonathan S., 8857
Finger, Nanette B., 8857
Finger, Walter G., 8857
Fingerhut, Manny, 4683
Fingerhut, Ronald, 4683
Fingerhut, Rose, 4683
Fingleson, Eric, 399
Finigan Estate, Pearlie F., 5081
Finigan, Pearle F., 5081
Finigan, William C., 5081
Fink Charitable Reminder Unitrust, Ruth G., 3565
Fink Charity Trust, Ruth G., 3563
Fink, Beverly, 4684
Fink, Ken, 4635
Fink, Kevin, 7358
Fink, Laurence D., 6006
Fink, Lori, 6006
Fink, Lori W., 6006
Fink, Mary, 9447
Fink, Richard, 4684, 9447
Fink, Richard H., 9447
Fink, Rodney W., 8211
Fink, Ruth G., 3563
Finkbeiner, David, 9544
Finke, John W., 4713
Finkel, Diana J., 1266
Finkel, Eileen, 1266
Finkel, Gerald, 5954
Finkel, Jill B., 1266
Finkel, Michael J., 1266
Finkel, Paul, 1266
Finkel, Paul A., 1266
Finkelstein, Alix, 1448
Finkelstein, David, 1448, 6007

Finkelstein, Howard, 6007
Finkelstein, Lauren, 6007
Finkelstein, Mark, 6573
Finkelstein, Michael, 1448, 8022
Finkelstein, Stan, 6007
Finkelstein, Susan, 6007
Finkenauer, Fred, 8090
Finkle, Nancy, 6559
Finlay, D.F.K., 6884
Finlay, James B., 9709
Finlay, Karin K., 5213
Finlay, Robert, 5213
Finlayson, Frank, 2666
Finlayson, Sharon, 5337
Finley Bros. Enterprises, 4653
Finley Foundation, Michael, The , 8795
Finley, J.B., 7995
Finley, Robert L., 4910
Finn, Arden, 6848
Finn, Bettina, 6848
Finn, Brian, 6848
Finn, Christopher, 1449
Finn, Daniel R., 1449
Finn, Daniel R., Jr., 1449
Finn, David, 1449, 6008
Finn, Laura, 6008
Finn, Marissa, 6848
Finn, Phyllis, 1449
Finn, Steven, 6848
Finnegan, Barbara Larson, 9650
Finnegan, Daniel, 3034
Finnegan, Jean M., 3034
Finnegan, John D., 7399
Finnegan, Rosemary, 2305
Finnegan, Rowan, 4073
Finneran, Gerard, 6910
Finneran, Laurey, 739
Finneran, Mary Ray, 6910
Finnessy, Michael J., 9896
Finney Trust, Lawrence, 3539
Finney, Mary Clare, 8858
Finney, Stanford C., Jr., 8858
Finocchiaro, Linda W., 1198
Finsen, Jean M., 5459
Fioravanti, Mark, 8620
Fippinger, Grace J., 1450
Fippinger, Robert A., 5656
Firman, Pamela H., 7400
Firman, Royal, III, 7400
Firman, Stephanie, 7400
First American Bank, 2713, 3536, 8691
First American Corp., The, 506
First American National Bank, 58
First American Real Estate Tax Svcs., 5255
First Baptist Church, 7792
First Bank of Coastal Georgia, 2445
First Banks, 4895
First Century Bank, 9737
First Century bank, 9772
First Citizens Bank, 7074, 7126
First Citizens Financial Corp., 3493
First Citizens National Bank, 3493
First County Bank, 1566
First Dakota National Bank, 8570
First Data Corp., 1269
First Financial Bank, 3366, 3425, 7402, 7483, 9778
First Financial Partners of Texas, 2061
First Financial Trust & Asset Management, 9040
First Hawaiian Bank, 2629, 2658
First Insurance Co. of Hawaii, 2631
First Kentucky Trust, 3660

First Mid-Illinois Bank & Trust, 2767
First National Bank, 1265, 3094, 3553, 3629
First National Bank and Trust of Newtown, 7905
First National Bank of Fort Smith, 198
First National Bank of La Grange, 3227
First National Bank of Mount Dora, 2223
First National Bank of Muscatine, 3475
First National Bank of Omaha, 5102
First Option Bank, 3556
First Premier Bank, 8570
First Savings Bank of Perkasie, 7905, 7998
First Security Bank, 8554
First Security Corp., 9322
First Security Federal Savings Bank, 2967
First Security State Bank, 8554
First Service Williams, 6655
First State Bank & Trust Co., 9906
First Sterling Corp., 6097
First Tennessee Bank, 8593, 8627, 8679, 8684
First Union Corp., 8350
First United Methodist Church, 8882
First Virginia Bank, 7045
First, Deborah, 4091
First, Robert, 4091
FirstBank Holding Company, 1316
FirstMerit Bank, 4512, 4515, 7466, 7503, 7561, 7598
FirstMerit Trust Co., 7377
Firszt, Anya, 9784
Firth, Judy, 3462
Fischel, Harry, 6009
Fischer, Angela B., 8422
Fischer, Barbara, 1075
Fischer, David, 4379
Fischer, Dean R., 3527
Fischer, Gerald, 3862
Fischer, Gerald, Dr. , 3862
Fischer, Larry, 2803, 3566
Fischer, Lisa, 4379
Fischer, Marlene Kay, 3862
Fischer, Mollie, 8796
Fischer, Richard, 4667
Fischer, Robert E., 5899
Fischer, Sonja H., 2874
Fischer, Steven P., 520
Fischer, Sylvia, 2874
Fischer, Tom, 3503
Fischil, Meir, 6552
Fischman, E. David, 4685
Fischman, Moses, 6567
Fischmann, Roberto, 8098
Fish, Brian, 9657
Fish, Dave, 9797
Fish, John, 4523
Fish, Lois, 9657
Fish, Robert H., 290
Fish, Valerie M. Johnson, 290
Fish-Sadin, Susanne L., 9657
Fishback, Harmes C., 1270
Fishel Co., 7401
Fisher 1998 Revocable Trust, Richard B., 3797
Fisher Brothers, 6655
Fisher Charitable lead Annuity Trust, Mary Elizabeth, 4397
Fisher Charitable Trusts I and II, 8276
Fisher Foundation, Max M. and Marjorie S., 4567
Fisher Trust, Julia A., 5011

Fisher, Alex, 3797
Fisher, Andersen Collins, 8781
Fisher, Angela, 1974
Fisher, Ann, 5347
Fisher, Benjamin R., 8276
Fisher, Catherine N., 2616
Fisher, Charles T., III, 4397
Fisher, David S., 2463
Fisher, Deb, 4497
Fisher, Dexter, 2437
Fisher, Elliott S., 5510
Fisher, Everett, 1432
Fisher, F. Conrad, 2874
Fisher, Frederick E., 1980
Fisher, George, 5347
Fisher, Gregg, 1298
Fisher, Harry, 4666
Fisher, Jim, 7798
Fisher, Joan M., 5766
Fisher, John R., 2435
Fisher, Judy, 246
Fisher, Linda, 6493
Fisher, Louise, 2616
Fisher, Marcus, 9033
Fisher, Marilyn Hope, 3946
Fisher, Mark, 498
Fisher, Mary B., 4046
Fisher, Misty, 3582
Fisher, Nancy Collins, 8781
Fisher, Peggy L., 3346
Fisher, Robert W., 2616
Fisher, Ryan, 375
Fisher, Sarah W., 4397
Fisher, Sonja H., 2874
Fisher, Stephen M., 9803, 9820, 9874
Fisher, Suzanne, 375
Fisher, Terri, 9426
Fisher, Walter B., 4397
Fisher, Wendy Perks, 2844
Fisherman's Pride Processors, 8859
Fisherman, Alan, 8924
Fishkin, Caleb, 5157
Fishkin, Cortney, 5157
Fishkin, Joshua, 5157
Fishley, Gail, 350
Fishman, David M., 6080
Fishman, Leora, 6080
Fishman, Leslie J., 5781
Fishman, Margaret I., 5334
Fisk, Robert C., 6170
Fiske, George F., Jr., 4203
Fister, Bruce, 7603
Fister, Kent D., 7603
Fitch, Eric, 3993
Fitch, Kathryn, 2876
Fitchburg Savings Bank, 4270
Fitt, Lawton W., 6010
Fitton, Chana, 5510
Fitton, Richard J., 7402
Fitts, David W., 4236, 4345
Fitts, Harriet W., 4805
Fitts, William S., 4805
Fitz-Gerald, David, 9367
Fitzgerald Cleaning, 4211
Fitzgerald, Alexandra K., 3901
Fitzgerald, Amber, 7666
Fitzgerald, Cantor, 5154
Fitzgerald, Deborah, 9556
Fitzgerald, Donald L., 9532
Fitzgerald, Dorothy K., 3901
Fitzgerald, Frances, 1826
Fitzgerald, Katharine, 5872
Fitzgerald, Msgr. J. Terrence, Rev. , 1544
Fitzgerald, Norm, 9333

Fitzgerald, Sarah S., 4004
Fitzgerald, Teresa, 1063
Fitzgerald, Thomas G., 3092
Fitzgibbon, Jennifer, 1549
Fitzgibbons, Christine, 6011
Fitzgibbons, John B., 6011
Fitzmaurice, Nessan, 2791
Fitzpatrick, Christopher, 508
Fitzpatrick, Elizabeth, 1595, 2699
Fitzpatrick, Frank, 607
Fitzpatrick, Kimberly, 508
Fitzpatrick, Kristen L., 3113
Fitzpatrick, Margart Mary, 6669
Fitzpatrick, Mary Alice, 9106
Fitzpatrick, Michael J., 508
Fitzpatrick, Michael J., Jr., 508
Fitzpatrick, Patricia W., 508
Fitzpatrick, Paul C., 6669
FitzPatrick, Samuel, 9382
Fitzsimmons, Ellen M., 1958
Fitzsimmons, Robert P., 9749
Fitzsimmons, Sue, 3904
Fix, Allan C., 9634
Fix, Harold J., 9634
Fix, Harriet J., 9634
Fix, William C., 9634
FJC Philanthropic Funds, 5665
Flager Foundation, The, 9527
Flagg, Lisa A., 8371
Flagship Charities, 8703
Flagstaff Financial Corp., 2156
Flaherty, Edward F., 4686
Flaherty, Jonathan P., 6012
Flaherty, Liss, 4417
Flaherty, Pamela, 6012
Flaherty, Pamela P., 6012
Flaherty, Peter A., 6012
Flaig, Annie, 8698
Flair Corp., 7252
Flamio, Donna, 1520
Flanagan Charitable Trust, Thomas & Esther, 6542
Flanagan, Darla, 510
Flanagan, Edward P., 1544
Flanagan, Esther C., 6542
Flanagan, Jennifer Z., 4012
Flanagan, Margaret, 4078
Flanagan, Marya Fogel, 8363
Flanagan, Patrick, 510, 6542
Flanagan, Quintin, 3634
Flanagan, Sheila B., 1544
Flanagan, William, 9937
Flanagan-Watson, Carrie E., 5660
Flanders, Fred J., 5054
Flanigan, James, 1928
Flannery, Dan, 5398
Flannigan, Cindy, 3991
Flannigan, Cyndi, 3991
Flannigan, Suzanne, 8568
Flanzer, Peter, 2970
Flapan, LLC, 7365
Flather, Newell, 4009
Flattery, Chris, 3592
Flattery, Sarah, 3514
Fleck, James, 178
Fleck, Katherine A., 9255
Fleck, Wanda, 3150
Fleckenstein, Andrew J., 9939
Fleder, Alan, 9448
Fleder, Esther, 9448
Fleder, Lawrence, 9448
Fleece, William H., 2878
Fleenor, John D., 8570
Fleet Street Ltd., 6794

Fleisch, Andrew P., 6181
Fleisch, Eleanor C., 6181
Fleisch, Harry M., 6181
Fleisch, Thomas, 6181
Fleischaker, David S., 7679
Fleischaker, Emily R., 7679
Fleischaker, Joseph L., 7679
Fleischaker, Paula Anne, 7679
Fleischer, Carl, 6013
Fleischer, Donald, 6013
Fleischer, Michael, 5791
Fleischer, Shirley, 6013
Fleischer, Steven, 6013
Fleischer, William R., 6013
Fleischman Foundation, Aaron I., The , 2003
Fleischman, Aaron I., 2003
Fleischman, Marc, 180
Fleischmann, Blair S., 7404
Fleischmann, Charles, III, 7404
Fleischmann, Charles, IV, 7404
Fleischmann, Julius, 7404
Fleischmann, Louisa, 7404
Fleischmann, Noah, 7404
Fleissig, Matthew, 5595
Flekman, Manny, 363
Fleming CLAT, 8615
Fleming Trust, 8615
Fleming, Donna Beaver, 7271
Fleming, Francine M., 8975
Fleming, James, 7892
Fleming, Jean, 5127
Fleming, Jeffrey, 2872
Fleming, Joseph M., 2240
Fleming, Martita, 6880
Fleming, Nancy M., 4092
Fleming, Nancy T., 8312
Fleming, Peggy J., 3547
Fleming, Richard, 8000
Fleming, Samuel C., 4092
Fleming, Sharon A., 5014
Fleming, Stephen, 697
Fleming, Terry P., 7408
Flessner, Marty, 1295
Fletcher, Connie, 9474
Fletcher, David A., 5332
Fletcher, George P., 9982
Fletcher, Jacquelyn, 4687
Fletcher, James P., 726
Fletcher, John, 4687
Fletcher, Joyce V., 4093
Fletcher, Katherine, 8827
Fletcher, Leonard H., 7405
Fletcher, Louise A., 7405
Fletcher, Nancy J., 4687
Fletcher, Pamela, 4093
Fletcher, Ronald R., 4687
Fletcher, Warner S., 4364
Fletcher, William C., 4093
Fletcher, William C., III, 4093
Fleugel, Donald J., 4820
Flexon, Courtney, 2457
Flicker, Louise M., 511
Flicker, Perry G., 511
Flickinger, Bonnie G., 5842
Flieller, James A., 9014
Flier, Edith, 1212
Flier, Jason, 4469
Flier, Jonathan, 1212
Flier, Patricia, 4469
Fliesbach, Gail, 512
Flinders, Boyd, Dr. , 361
Flinn, David B., 260
Flinn, Douglas A., 7301

Flinn, Lorien M., 8001
Flinn, Mary Ann, 1176
Flinn, Negley, 8001
Flinn, Patrick J., 2875
Flinn, Robyn, 2875
Flint, Alexis S., 288
Flint, Bryan H., 2436
Flint, Charley, 8008
Flint, David H., 2436
Flint, Katie L., 288
Flint, Lou Ann, 7497
Flint, Lucile E. Dupont, 288, 1608
Flint, Michael D., 2436
Flint, Richard N., 5220
Flint, Robert B., Jr., 288
Flint, Robert B., Mrs. , 1684
Flint, Susan J., 288
Flippo Trust, Arthur P., 9449
Flippo, Arthur P., 9449
Flisher, Leigh A., 4975
Floersheimer, Daniel, 2300
Flohr, Bruce, 8861
Flohr, Janet, 5118, 8861
Flood, Carol Ann, 5177
Flood, Carrie Hatch, 4203
Flora, Shirley, 2456
Floren, Douglas C., 1451
Florence, Jeff Wyler, 7647
Flores, Hope, 3363
Flores, Israel, 1453
Flores, Jenny, 272
Florida Institute of Technology, 2597
Floridamae Vanderpool 2005 Trust, 2811
Florin, John, 5348
Florin, Richard, 5348
Florin, Thelma, 5348
Florsheim, John W., 9958
Florsheim, Nancy R., 2856
Florsheim, Thomas W., Jr., 9958
Florsheim, Thomas W., Sr., 9958
Flournoy, Bob, 8845
Flours, Oren, 4735
Flowerree Residuary Marital Trust, 7763
Flowerree, Ann D., 7763
Flowerree, David R., 7763
Flowerree, Elaine D., 7763
Flowerree, John H., 7763
Flowerree, Robert E., 7763
Flowers D-1, Joseph Knowles, 8862
Flowers D-1, Lynne Davis, 8862
Flowers F-1 Trust, Julia Mather, 8862
Flowers F-1 Trust, Richard Warren, 8862
Flowers FD-4 Trust, Daniel Fort, 8862
Flowers FF-4 Trust, Julia Mather, 8862
Flowers FF-4 Trust, Richard Warren, 8862
Flowers SD-3 Trust, Daniel Fort, 8862
Flowers SF-3 Trust, Julia Mather, 8862
Flowers SF-3 Trust, Richard Warren, 8862
Flowers, D.F., Jr., 8862
Flowers, Doug, 4939
Flowers, Frank S., 7099
Flowers, J.K., 8862
Flowers, J.M., 8862
Flowers, Katie, 6998
Flowers, Megan, 9147
Flowers, R.W., 8862
Floyd, Charles B., 6380
Floyd, Dan B., 539
Floyd, Diana, 3567
Floyd, Frederick P., 6380
Floyd, Frederick P., Jr., 6380

Floyd, Kathleen E., 6380
Floyd, Marcia P., 6380, 6603
Floyd, Mary Bell, 513
Floyd, Nickolas, 9999
Floyd, Robert O., 7078
Floyd, William S., 513
Flug, Angela, 1271
Flug, Angie, 1271
Flug, James, 1320
Flug, Jeremy, 1271, 1320
Flug, Martin, 1320
Flug, Robert, 1320
Fluoroware, 4806
Fly, Dollar, 9624
Fly, Park, 9624
Flynn, Barbara L., 1520
Flynn, Brenna K., 1404
Flynn, Bryan, 884
Flynn, Corey W., 1404
Flynn, Garrett S., 1520
Flynn, Grayce B. Kerr, 7693
Flynn, Kenneth, 4228
Flynn, Nancy, 884
Flynn, Philip, 9778
Flynn, Russell B., 1104
Flynn, Ruth S., 3147
Flynn, Sara, 1104
Flynn, Steve, 295
Flynt, Allen, 4848
Flynt, Katherine McCarty, 4848
FM Bank and Trust Co., 4984
FNW Realty Corp., 6963
Focas, Jerry D., 3939
Foehl, Katherine B., 9895
Foellmer, Frank, 1098
Fogarty, W. Phillip, Rev. , 3902
Fogle, Jarrod, 447
Fogt, Mark, 3356
Fohn, Mike, 9696
Foith, Scot A., 9173
Fok, Nanette, 9663
Folcroft Co., 3905
Foldcraft, 4820
Folden, Dennis, 3516
Foley & Lardner, LLP, 9798
Foley Inc., 5584
Foley Inc., E.J., 5584
Foley, Donald, 4362
Foley, Edward J., III, 5584
Foley, J. Justin, 2876
Foley, James F., 2876
Foley, Jean I., 2876
Foley, Joan, 5584
Foley, John C., 5584
Foley, Kevin P., 5979
Foley, Lawrence G., 1452
Foley, Megan M., 1452
Foley, Melissa, 4222
Foley, Michael E., 7504
Foley, Mildred, 9820
Foley, Thomas, 5154
Foley, Tom, 5154
Folger, Beverly M., 515
Folger, Elizabeth J., 515
Folk, Rusty, 9091
Folkerts, Kevin, 4672
Follet, Roger, 6016
Follett Corp., 2877
Follett, Brian R., 9033
Follett, Britten, 2877
Follett, Dwight W., 2877
Follett, Joan, 9033
Follett, Julie, 2877
Follett, Kent, 2877

Follett, Matthew, 2877
Follett, Mildred, 2877
Follett, Nancy, 2877
Follett, Robert, 2877, 9033
Follett, Sally, 9033
Follett, Scott, 9033
Folsom, Margaret D., 8863
Folsom, Robert Stephen, 8863
Folts, Ellen, 9408
Foltz, Cyrene M., 5289
Foltz, David B., 5289
Fomer, Margaret, 1244
Fong, Ann, 1038
Fonnesbeck, Cordell, 9987
Fons, Joan, 3566
Fontaine, Denis L., 2006
Fontaine, Glenda C., 2006
Fontaine, Gregory J., 2006
Fontichiaro, James, 2753
Food and Freedom Foundation, 7992
Food Services of America, 5065
Foord, Elfrena, 248
Forbes, Herman, 2878
Forbes, Mary C., 2008
Force Control Industries, 7326
Force, Michelle, 4582
Forcum, Julie A., 3346
Ford, Alice D., 3863
Ford, Anne, 4447
Ford, Annette, 7365
Ford, April Rosenlund, 8245
Ford, Barbara S., 3839
Ford, Betty Jane, 7513
Ford, Celeste V., 1080
Ford, Charlotte M., 4447
Ford, Creed L., III, 8859
Ford, David C., 4758
Ford, Durand G., 4758
Ford, Dustin, 3511
Ford, Eugene F., 3863
Ford, Frank, 2001
Ford, Frederick B., 4597
Ford, Frederick S., 4597
Ford, Fredrica Pollack, 6614
Ford, Henry, III, 4447
Ford, Horace C., 4597
Ford, James W., 4597
Ford, Jo Ellen, 8864
Ford, Joe T., 8864
Ford, John M., Jr., 4823
Ford, Jr., William C., 4446
Ford, Kathleen DuRoss, 2010
Ford, Katie, 6030
Ford, Kevin E., 1080
Ford, Margaret, 4758
Ford, Martha F., 4445
Ford, Martha Firestone, 4445
Ford, Olivia C., 4758
Ford, Scott T., 8864
Ford, Silas M., III, 4758
Ford, William C., Jr., 4446
Ford, William Clay, 4445
Ford-Thomas, Allegra C., 4447
Ford-Werling, Kimberly, 4758
Fordiani, Richard, 8567
Forehand, David A., Jr., 2479
Forehand, Elizabeth G., 2479
Foreman, Barbara J., 5408
Foreman, Louis, 2842
Foreman, Robert B., 7252
Foren Irrevocable Trust, Frazier C., 4448
Foren, Belinda, 4448
Foren, Donald, 4448
Forer, David B., 6396

Forest City Ratner Companies, 6524
Forest City Ratner Companies
    Foundation, 6524
Forest Harlem Properties, 3075
Forest Oil Corp., 8020
Foresther, Charlotte, 7944
Forgatch, Gregory T., 517
Forgatch, Lorraine E., 517
Forger, Alexander D., 6381
Forgy, Pat, 200
Forkner, Larry, 4964
Forlenza, Thomas, 5874
Forman, Hamilton Collins, 2011
Forman, M. Austin, 2011
Forman, Walter Collins, 2011
Fornabaro, Michael, 6405
Fornander, Kenneth, 5118
Fornear, Ben, 4667
Forrest, Barbara J., 5614
Forrest, Betty J., 5614
Forrest, Richard J., 5614
Forrest, Richard J., Jr., 5608
Forrest, Robert H., 5614
Forrest, Robert J., 5614
Forrest, Robin F., 9535
Forrester, Margretta V.E., 5028
Fors, Erik, 4702
Forsman, Michael S., 5233
Forst, Jesse S., 9526
Forster, Charles, 1397
Forster, David, 6484
Forster, Ella B., 3494
Forster, James W., 3494
Forster, Paul, 6484
Forsyth, David, 9339
Forsyth, Susan Marie, 8004
Forsyth, T. Cole, 2429
Forsythe, Carola, 3432
Forsythe, Suzanne, 7605
Fort Management, 6858
Fort, Combs Lawson, 2080
Fortas, Miles S., 8581
Forte, Cheryl, 4191
Forthman, Teena, 221
Fortin Foundation of Florida, 2012
Fortin Foundation, Mary Alice, 2012
Fortin, Mary Alice, 2012
Fortino, Chuck, 4459, 4534
Fortinsky, Robert, 8002
Fortner, George C., 7542
Fortney, Robert L., 7406
Fortney, Ruth A., 7406
Fortson, Edred, 7100
Fortune Foundation, Martha Murray,
    1273
Fortune, Penny, 3381
Fortune, Russell, III, 3381
Fortune, Sheila M., 1273
Fosbel, 7368
Fosgate, James, 9331
Fosgate, Norma, 9331
Foshag, William H., 9868
Foss, Donald J., 7407
Foss, Donald J., Mrs., 7407
Foss, James M., 9598
Foss, Jerry M., 9598
Foss, Jillian, 9598
Foss, Joseph E., 3817
Foss, Kyle J., 9598
Foss, Walter R., 7407
Fosse, Darwin A., 4719
Foster FJ-4 Trust, Mark McClelland,
    8862
Foster FJ-4 Trust, Patricia Anne, 8862

Foster Industries, 8003
Foster Investment Co., 8003
Foster J-1 Trust, Mark McClelland, 8862
Foster J-1 Trust, Patricia Anne, 8862
Foster SJ-3 Trust, Mark McClelland,
    8862
Foster SJ-3 Trust, Patricia Anne, 8862
Foster Trust, James R., 4458
Foster, Adam Rockwood, 1827
Foster, Catherine Crystal, 900
Foster, Claude P., 9488
Foster, Craig J., 8003
Foster, David Jack, 2161
Foster, Debra L., 7244
Foster, Dorry, 7891
Foster, Eric, 1098
Foster, Esther J., 5615
Foster, F. Jay, 2963
Foster, F. Whittington, 4306
Foster, Frank, 2879
Foster, Fred L., Jr., 7106
Foster, Gina Dominique, 519
Foster, Harriet R., 8866, 8868
Foster, James R., 4458, 8003
Foster, Jane, 5660
Foster, Jennifer Kate, 8866, 8868
Foster, JoAnn, 8867
Foster, JoAnn B., 8867
Foster, Joe B., 8866
Foster, Joe C., 4369
Foster, John H., 2013
Foster, Joseph C., 5615
Foster, Kathleen A., 1781
Foster, Kenneth Knox, 8866, 8868
Foster, Kent, 8867
Foster, Kent B., 8867
Foster, Lee B., II, 8003, 8335
Foster, Leonard, 7624
Foster, Lorreva S., 4458
Foster, M. Stratton, 8616
Foster, Marguerite Peet, 1827
Foster, Penny, 8003
Foster, Robert D., 519
Foster, Therese, 2811
Foster, Thomas F., 7058
Foster, Timothy D., 2879
Foster, William Warren, 8866, 8868
Foszcz, Cooper, 2895
Foszcz, Joshua, 2895
Foszcz, Russell, 2895
Foszcz, Sara, 2895
Foto Electronic Supply Co. Inc., 6100
Fougnies, Douglas V., 120
Foulke, Thomas , 3210
Foulkes, Duane E., 9821
Foulkes, Kathleen M., 9821
Foundation Fence, 9208
Foundation Fighting Blindness, 7209
Foundation for Medical Research, 4235
Foundation for the Needs of Others,
    6598
Foundation Jewish Philanthropies of
    Buffalo, 5247
Foundation, H.R. Howard, 9386
Foundation, John Bandimere, 1362
Foundation, Samuel P. Pardoe, 3928
Founders Bank and Trust, 4382
Fountain, Brad, 4837
Fountain, Christopher G., 4837
Fountain, D.G., 4837
Fountain, James B., 4837
Fountain, James Bradley, 4837
Fountain, Karen, 5582
Fountain, Lynette, 4837

Fountain, Margaret B., 4837
Fountain, Monica, 4837
Four Special Daughters LP, 9631
Four Wheels, 2885
Fout, Nina, 9437
Fout, P. Douglas, 9437
Fout, Virginia, 9437
Fouts, Kimberly A., 4550
Fouty, Jane, 8774
Fowler, Judi, 237
Fowler, Mary Anna, 2198
Fowler, Theodore M., 7075
Fowler, Willa Jo, 7666
Fowlston, C.J., 8871
Fowlston, Syble E., 8871
Fox and Company, M.E., 478
Fox Charitable Lead Unitrust, 7103
Fox Residential Group Inc., 6656
Fox Sports Southwest, 8795
Fox, Alan C., 523
Fox, Amelia L., 3578
Fox, Amy, 4218
Fox, Ann, 7311
Fox, Belle, 3864
Fox, Bill C., 2016
Fox, Carolyn, 523
Fox, Cheryl Ann, 4952
Fox, Daveen, 523
Fox, David K., 2016
Fox, Debra, 4218
Fox, Dennis P., 478
Fox, Emma R., 7409
Fox, Frances Hill, 7103
Fox, Gerald C., 2016
Fox, Gregory, 4666
Fox, Gregory P., 3578
Fox, Ira, 4465
Fox, Jennifer L., 422
Fox, Joseph P., 3578
Fox, Katherine M., 2016
Fox, Keith, 524
Fox, Kenneth J., 3578
Fox, Kevin J., 3578
Fox, Lewis, 1453
Fox, Lori, 478
Fox, Margene B., 2016
Fox, Mark B., 5349
Fox, Mary Ellen, 478
Fox, Michael, 478
Fox, Michael E., Jr., 478
Fox, Michael E., Sr., 478
Fox, Michele, 478
Fox, Monica, 478
Fox, Pamela, 524
Fox, Sam, 4952
Fox, Terence, 478
Fox, Thomas F., 6442
Fox, Wallace, 6022
Fox, William F., Jr., 8145
Fox, William Fitzhugh, 9883
Foxley, Griff, 763
Foxley, Zoe Lloyd, 763
Foy, Deborah, 1241
Fr. Labat, 4772
Frackman, Russell, 839
Fraenkel, Barnet H., 8098
Fraiman, Chaim, 6023
Fraiman, Rose, 6023
Fraites, Christopher G., 1454
Fraites, Joseph L., 1454
Fraites, Joseph Lawrence, Sr., 1454
Fraley, George, 2408
Framel, James, 7722

Frampton Family Charitable Foundation, 6248
Francis, Clarence E., 708
Francis, G. Scott, 7282
Francis, G. Scott, Mrs. , 7282
Francis, Harry D., 1962
Francis, Juanita F., 117
Francis, Philip, 117
Francis, Philip L., 117
Francis, Ronald H., 2463
Franciscovich, Linda R., 5881
Franco, Isaac S., 6025
Franco, Joseph A., 6024
Franco, Joseph N., 6024
Franco, Marc, 6024
Franey, William G., 3865
Frangakis, F. John, 2017
Frangakis, Joyce, 2017
Frangella, Stacey L., 5345
Frangella, Stacy L., 5345
Frank Consolidated Enterprises, 2885
Frank Lumber Co., 7765
Frank Timber Products, 7765
Frank, A.J., 7765
Frank, Aaron, 2481
Frank, Adam, 2481
Frank, Charles E., 2885
Frank, Constance, 1111
Frank, D.D., 7765
Frank, David, 768
Frank, Diane Folsom, 8863
Frank, Dorothy J., 5393
Frank, Elaine S., 2885
Frank, Ernest H., 6026
Frank, Ernst L., 6026
Frank, Frederick, 6893
Frank, Fried, 6655
Frank, Isaac, 2481
Frank, J.T., 7765
Frank, James S., 2885
Frank, L.D., 7765
Frank, Larry, 2481
Frank, Lois, 2481
Frank, M. Joshua, 2481
Frank, Mary, 7705
Frank, Milton, 5350
Frank, Newmark Knight, 6655
Frank, Norman, 9674
Frank, Patricia, 6655
Frank, Paul M., 6018
Frank, Stefan, 5350
Frank, Z., 2885
Frank, Zollie S., 2885
Franke, Carter, 3978
Frankel Trading Corp, 5666
Frankel, Belinda, 526
Frankel, David F., 6027
Frankel, David W., Jr., 6027
Frankel, Elizabeth, 2886
Frankel, Erin R., 4540
Frankel, Gregory, 6027
Frankel, Herman, 2018
Frankel, Julia, 8872
Frankel, Linda, 6027
Frankel, Marjorie L., 8872
Frankel, Marshall, 2886
Frankel, Maxine, 526
Frankel, Raymond, 526
Frankel, Russell M., 8872
Frankel, Sherry G., 8872
Frankiel, Steven M., 719
Frankle, Mark A., 2019
Frankle, Mary A., 2019
Frankle, Mary D., 2019

Frankle, Nicholas A., 2019
Franklin Bancorp, Benjamin, 4267
Franklin Charitable Foundation, Julie and Martin, 6720
Franklin Electric Co., 3382
Franklin Federal Savings & Loan, 9452
Franklin Financial Corporation, 9452
Franklin Holdings, 1422
Franklin Homeowners Assurance Co., 8186
Franklin Savings Bank, 3779
Franklin, Alice, 5961
Franklin, Andrew, 5961
Franklin, Andrew D., 5961
Franklin, Audrey, 5961
Franklin, Audrey F., 5961
Franklin, Churchill G., 4096
Franklin, Churchill H., 4096
Franklin, Cynthia F., 6028
Franklin, George S., III, 6028
Franklin, Hugh, 1425
Franklin, Janet H., 4096
Franklin, Jennifer, 3402
Franklin, John C., 9148
Franklin, Katherine D., 4096
Franklin, Leslie, 9551
Franklin, Lindsey W., 4096
Franklin, Madeleine, 1425
Franklin, Richard R., 2020
Franklin, Samuel, 5961
Franklin, Tammy G., 2020
Franklin, W. Stevens, 2020
Franklin, Wilson P., 2020
Franks, Betty, 7339
Franks, J. Kevin, 3144
Franson, Wallace D., 669, 985
Fransway, Paul, 4379
Frantz, Lisa M., 9026
Frantz, Lisa S., 9026
Frantz, Thomas R., 9502
Frantze, David W., 4995
Franz, Jennifer A., 6846
Franz, Laurie T., 7999
Franz, Paul G., 3652
Frasch, Elizabeth Blee, 8408
Fraser Foundation, Richard M. & Helen T., 4097
Fraser, Duncan A., 5788
Fraser, George P., 4689
Fraser, Helen T., 4097
Fraser, Jane, 8680
Fraser, Jane Hough, 8617
Fraser, Malcolm, 8617
Fraser, Richard M., 4097
Fraser, Robert E., 4689
Frattalli, Dan, 591
Frattaroli, Tracey, 8712
Frautschi Family Foundation, John J., 9957
Frautschi, Christopher, 9957
Frautschi, Christopher J., 9822, 9957
Frautschi, Elizabeth J., 9822
Frautschi, John J., 9822, 9957
Frautschi, Peter W., 9822
Frawley, Arthur J., 4192
Fraydun Foundation, 5851, 6681
Frayser, William E. W., Jr., 9452
Frazee, William A., 8639
Frazer, Deborah, 8008
Frazier Estate, Leola D., 9746
Frazier, Alexandra V. A., 8328
Frazier, Bob, 3611
Frazier, H. Matthew, 9904
Frazier, Joyce, 3628

Frazier, Robert, 247
Frazier, W. Robinson, 2094
Freas, Donald, 8005
Freas, Lawrence, 8005
Freda, Patricia A., 9402
Freda, Robert J., 9402
Frede, Mary Ann, 1590
Frederick Foundation, The, 3711
Frederick, Bob, 5104
Frederick, Cathey, 7686
Fredericks, James, 4576
Frederikson, Dave, 9814
Fredland, Valita M., 2954
Fredman Bros. Furniture Co., 2890
Fredman, Aaron, 2890
Fredman, Yoseph, 2890
Fredricks, Robert, 1170
Freebairn Char Lead Annuity Trust, 3278
Freebairn, Elizabeth A., 3278
Freebairn, Kenneth T., 3278
Freebairn, William A., 3278
Freed, Dean, 1339, 7796
Freedburg, Louis, 1826
Freedland, Tzepah, 423
Freedman, Anne L., 5351
Freedman, Barry J., 5351
Freedman, Deborah S., 5351
Freedman, Douglas M., 1665
Freedman, Gerald H., 5351
Freedman, Len, 3452
Freedman, Marc, 5352
Freedman, Margot E., 1665
Freedman, Roy, 2880
Freedman, Susan R., 8022
Freedman, Twilight, 5352
Freedman, Wendy, 5352
Freedom Wireless Inc., 120
Freeh, Cheri, 7998
Freeland, Brooke, 5209
Freelander, Daniel H., 5353
Freelander, Michael S., 5353
Freels, Gary W., 9811
Freeman, Douglas K., 984
Freeman, George C., III, 9452
Freeman, Lida, 7942
Freeman, Lynn, 984
Freeman, Nancy, 8428
Freeman, Richard H., 5788
Freeman, Thomas, 8201
Freeman, William, 5969
Freeport McMoran Copper & Gold, 94
Freer, Charles L., 7414
Freer, Deborah G., 7414
Freescale Semiconductor Inc., 8874
Freeseman, Lisa A., 1219
Fregger, Stephan, 1973
Freiburger, Jared, 3521
Freidheim, Amandine, 6031
Freidheim, Cyrus, 6031
Freidheim, Marguerite, 6031
Freidheim, Scott, 6031
Freidheim, Stephen C., 6031
Freidkin, Norman, 3938
Freidland, Sheila G., 6037
Freidus, Bernice, 1376
Freightliner Corp., 301
Freightliner, LLC, 7094
Frein, Carl, 204
Freitas, David, 1599
Freitas, Mark E., 2022
Freitas, Mary Fairbanks, 2022
Frelinghuysen, Adaline H., 5354
Frelinghuysen, Alice C., 5354
Frelinghuysen, Frederick, 5354

Frelinghuysen, George L.K., 5354
Frelinghuysen, Henry, 5354
Frelinghuysen, Peter, 5354
Frelinghuysen, Virginia R., 5354
Fremont National Bank & Trust Co., 5126
Fremont Sequoia Holding, L.P., 527
Fremont Street Foundation, 4150
Fremont, Barbara, 2891
Fremont, Robert S., 2891
French Investing, Fred F., 6655
French, Charles H., 2671
French, Clara M., 6032
French, D.E., 6032
French, Duncan A., 2671
French, Elaine A., 2671
French, Eric R., 2671
French, Gabe, 7680
French, Gregory, 82
French, Hal, 7680
French, Jameson S., 8007
French, John K., 2671
French, Marcia F., 8882
French, Marcia Fuller, 8882
French, Megan, 7680
French, Mike, 3702
French, Powhatan Ernest K., 8882
French, Richard West Bo, 8882
French, William Fuller, 538
French, William Fuller K., 8882
Frends, Ethel, 8842
Fresh Direct, LLC, 6033
Fresno Clinton Operating Assoc., LP, 5616
Fretz, Michael, 7734
Freund, Bella, 6034
Freund, Dorothy, 2892
Freund, Henry, 2892
Freund, Howard, 8008
Freund, Hugh J., 6421
Freund, Joyce, 2892
Freund, Marilyn, 2892
Freund, Meir, 6034
Frey Foundation, Stephen, 4686
Frey Research, 9895
Frey, Allison, 416
Frey, Carolyn, 3402
Frey, Charles, 3127
Frey, David J., 4690
Frey, Jeanette, 5381
Frey, Karen B., 4690
Frey, Karen K., 97
Frey, Michael B., 4690
Frey, Michael J., 4690
Frey, Robert H., 6879
Frey, Sara J., 4690
Freyer, Carl J., 5355
Freyer, Sylvia, 5355
Freygang, Antje, 7410
Freygang, Dale G., 7410
Freygang, David B., 7410
Freygang, Katherine A., 7410
Freygang, Marie A., 7410
Freygang, W. Nicholas F., 7410
Freygang, Walter Henry, 7410
Freymark, Peter, 5101
Freymark, Sally, 5101
Friar, Craig, 7741
Frias, Antonio, 4079
Frick, Drew, 2034
Fricke, Alice, 6015
Fricks, Deanie D., 2023
Fricks, William P., 2023
Friday, Lucille R., 301

Fridman, Anne, 6035
Fridman, Anne H., 6035
Fridman, David, 6035
Fridman, David M., 6035
Fridman, Natalio, 6035
Fridman, Natalio S., 6035
Fridy, Tommy Joe, 1740
Fried, J. Michael, 6036
Fried, Janet C., 6036
Fried, Tammy D., 5664
Fried-Calcaterra, Donna L., 1606
Friedberg, Clayton A., 1564
Friedberg, Elinor, 6283
Friedberg, Leslie, 6283
Friedel, Leonard L., 8875
Friedel, Phyllis J., 8875
Friedheim, Edith H., 2024
Friedheim, Eric, 2024
Friedhoff, Edward, 9372
Friedland Realty, 6037
Friedland, Annette, 2025
Friedland, David L., 5082
Friedland, Edward, 5082
Friedland, Erin Pond, 3798
Friedland, Jack, 2025, 8889
Friedland, John, 9494
Friedland, Jonathan, 6777
Friedland, Nancy B., 5082
Friedland, Robert, 6037
Friedland, Rodger, 2025
Friedland, Sheila G., 6037
Friedlander, Gardner L. R., 9825
Friedlander, Jean W., 9825
Friedlander, Lee, 6038
Friedlander, Louise, 9825
Friedlander, Maria, 6038
Friedlander, Theodore, III, 9825
Friedlander, W. John, 6360
Friedman Admin Trust, Sid, 5356
Friedman Family Trust, J., 6039
Friedman Revocable Trust, Miriam S., 3866
Friedman, Adam B., 5649
Friedman, Albert H., 1952
Friedman, Anita Dann, 5649
Friedman, Arnold D., 6679
Friedman, Benjamin, 3027, 6784
Friedman, Bernard, 6039
Friedman, Brenda, 27
Friedman, Carole, 6212
Friedman, Carolyn Fine, 7994
Friedman, Chaim, 5247, 6039
Friedman, Chaya V., 6765
Friedman, Cheryl S., 6868
Friedman, D. Sylvan, 3866
Friedman, Edward, 6983
Friedman, Elizabeth L., 47
Friedman, Elliott, 3067
Friedman, Esther, 6039
Friedman, Eva, 6784
Friedman, Frank, 27
Friedman, Fred H., 27
Friedman, Freda, 880
Friedman, Harold E., 7409
Friedman, Isadore, 5083
Friedman, J. Kent, 8876
Friedman, Jacob, 6983
Friedman, Jordan, 27
Friedman, Julian W., 6003
Friedman, Leah, 6040
Friedman, Lisa, 530
Friedman, Louis F., 3851, 3861, 3866, 3873, 3882, 3888
Friedman, Marcine, 531

Friedman, Marianne, 2729
Friedman, Mark E., 7272
Friedman, Maury, 530
Friedman, Michael, 6040
Friedman, Miriam, 3866
Friedman, Morris, 6784
Friedman, Morton L., 531
Friedman, Nancy S., 7409
Friedman, Phyllis C., 3851, 3861, 3866, 3873, 3882
Friedman, Pinchas, 5665
Friedman, Robert, 6039
Friedman, Rosalie, 5083
Friedman, Samuel D., 6765
Friedman, Samuel H., 3866, 3882
Friedman, Sarah, 6039
Friedman, Saul N., 6784
Friedman, Simeon, 6784
Friedman, Sue-Ann, 1448
Friedmann, Debbie, 1834
Friedmann, Joseph W., 1834
Friedmann, Peter, 1834
Friedrich, Craig W., 8662
Friedrich, Fariha, 5703
Friedrich, Heiner, 5703
Friedrich, Matthew I., 543
Friedrich, Philippa de Menil, 5703
Friedt, Theodore, 2177
Friel, Robert F., 4238
Frieman, Rivka, 6041
Friend, Barrie, 4098
Friend, Charles, 4098
Friend, Howard M., 4098
Friend, Loren, 4098
Friend, Michelle, 532
Friend, Nicole, 532
Friend, Robert, 532
Friendly, Printer, 726
Friends of the Trinity Stand trail, 8795
Friends of Torrey Pines, LLC, 748
Friendship Fund, 1816
Friendship House, 1566
Frierson, Imogen M., 3723
Fries, Karen, 9599
Friesen, Gaylene, 3624
Friesen, Gilbert B., 492
Friess, Polly J., 9967
Friezo, Charles, 1457
Friezo, David, 1457
Friezo, Joan, 1457
Friezo, Jorgelina, 1457
Frigo, Arthur, Sr., 2109
Frink, Jeannine, 1402
Frisbee, Christine, 5317
Frisbie, Richard, 4099
Frisbie, Sharon W., 7638
Frisby, Daniel, 2893
Frisby, Kent, 2893
Frisby, Michael, 2893
Frisby, R. J., 2893
Frisby, Timothy, 2893
Frisch, Diane, 2987
Frisch, Diane J., 2988
Frische, Ivan, 3448
Frische, Ruth, 3448
Frishberg, Stephen, 8022
Frisk, Judith Harris, 601
Frith, Maria Teresa Amos, 2433
Fritsch, Sherri, 3442
Fritts, James A., 2285
Fritts, Phyllis, 2285
Fritz, Arthur J., Jr., 534
Fritz, Barbara, 534
Frizzell, Cadijah, 7663

Frizzell, Thomas A., 1590
Froderman, Carl, 3383
Froderman, Chris, 3383
Froderman, Harvey, 3383
Froderman, Harvey, Mrs. , 3383
Frohman, Blanche P., 7411
Frohman, Daniel C., 7411
Frohman, Sidney, 7411
Frohoff, Carol J., 9643
Frohring, Evelyn, 8010
Frohring, Gertrude L., 8010
Frohring, Glenn H., 8010
Frohring, William O., 8010
Fromberg, Lynn W., 2295
Fromboluti, Christopher, 8294
Frome, Mary, 535
Frome, Stan, 535
Frome, Walter, 535
Fromm, Mabel, 9823
Fromm, Walter, 9823
Fromme, Michelle Simon, 1042
Fromstein, John L., 9824
Fromstein, Lita, 9824
Fromstein, Mitchell S., 9824
Frontline Placement Technologies, 7936
Frost Bank, 8761, 9218, 9246, 9287
Frost National Bank, 9036, 9073, 9121, 9269
Frost, Andrew, 8310
Frost, Elise W., 2398
Frost, Elizabeth, 2048
Frost, George, 4686
Frost, Ira M., 2398
Frost, J., 939
Frost, Judy, 887
Frost, Karin A., 2632
Frost, Louis B., 2948
Frost, Meshech, 7412
Frost, Nancy E., 5034
Frost, Patricia H., 8878
Frost, Steven J., 7081
Frost, Thomas C., 8878
Frost, Will, 274
Frost, William D., 274
Frowery, Megan, 3767
Frozen Ropes of Morris County NJ, LLC, 1730
Fruchtzweig, Ben, 7000
Fruehauf, Angela, 8879
Fruehauf, Harvey C., Jr., 8879
Fruehauf, Martha S., 8879
Fruehauf, Susanne M., 8879
Frum, Jennifer, Dr. , 2437
Frum, Rita, 7518
Fry, Alice J., 536
Fry, Charles, 884
Fry, Charles L., 536
Fry, Cheryl E., 2027
Fry, Darryl D., 2027
Fry, Elizabeth H.W., 2285
Fry, Joan, 9441
Fry, John C., 536
Fry, Marjorie Walthall, 9258
Fry, Marlene D., 2027
Fry, Mary, 4552
Fry, William Henry, 1458
Fryar, Barbara, 221
Frye, John L., 7111
Frye, John C., 7111
Frys.com Open, 427
Fuchella, Carol, 3799
Fuchs, Bernard, 6043, 8881
Fuchs, Hannah, 6043
Fuchs, Lawrence M., 5603
Fuchs, Russell, 1459

Fuchs, Sally, 8881
Fuchsberg & Fuchsberg, 6044
Fuchsberg Family Foundation, 6044
Fuchsberg, Abraham, 6044
Fuchsberg, Rita, 6044
Fuchsberg, Seymour, 6044
Fucito, Thomas, 6229
Fudge, Austyn R., 537
Fudge, Dawn, 8944
Fudge, Gary A., 537
Fuel Delivery Services, 301
Fuentes, Eric, 5872
Fuesler, Larry, 3370
Fugitt, Gary, 7681
Fuguet, Darcy, 4046
Fuhr, Kathleen D., 2750
Fuhs, Kurt, 3370
Fuite, Grace A., 121
Fuite, Teaumen A., 121
Fuji Films, Japan, 6839
Fukami, Toshu, 6249
Fukunaga Memorial Fund, George J., 2633
Fukunaga, Eric S., 2633, 2645
Fukunaga, George J., 2633
Fukunaga, Grace M., 2633
Fukunaga, Mark H., 2633, 2645
Fulbright & Jaworski, LLP, 8874
Fulcher, Joe, 8680
Fulcher, Joe R.G., 8617
Fuld, David, 5666
Fuld, Robert A., 3866
Fuld, Sara R., 3873
Fuline, Daniel J., 7312
Fulkerson, John D., 9133
Fullbright, Lindy Craft, 8548
Fullenwider, Stuart, 1346
Fuller Family Irrevocable Trust, 2028
Fuller, Andrew P., 538
Fuller, Aulbrey G., 2591
Fuller, Charles A., Jr., 5009
Fuller, Cindy, 9384
Fuller, Fran, 1228
Fuller, Gary, 13
Fuller, Gillian, 538
Fuller, Jason, 8869
Fuller, John W., 8409
Fuller, Samuel P., 2591
Fuller, Sandra, 2028
Fuller, Stephen M., 2028
Fuller, Suzan T., 4835
Fuller, Thomas, IV, 2591
Fuller, Victor, 2028
Fuller, William M., 538
Fullerton, Amy, 9267
Fullerton, Kenneth D., 8531
Fullerton, Reginald, 5783
Fullerton, Scott, 945
Fullmer, Jeff, 4879
Fullmer, Mark A., 3730
Fulmer, David, 5671
Fulmer, Scott L., 5852
Fulop, Jack, 2274
Fulton Bank, 7930, 8097, 8232, 8277
Fulton, Amy, 9601
Fulton, David, 9601
Fulton, James A., 1547
Fulton, Paul, 7209
Fults, Frank B., 3440
Fulweiler, Pamela S., 7013
Funari, Robert, 539
Funderburk, Charles, 13
Fung, Alison G., 6713
Fung, Lai Wah, 6713

Fung, Stephen G., 6713
Funk, Charles, 1922
Funk, Charles A., 1922
Funk, Duncan, 2897
Funk, Michael, 8498
Funkhouser, Wilson P., 2856
Fuqua, John R., 382
Furgatch, Harvey, 1156
Furlong, Andrew T., Jr., 3786
Furman Foundation, Morris & Gertrude, 6681
Furman, Gail, 6045
Furman, Gail Ann, 6045
Furman, Jason, 6045
Furman, Jay, 6045, 6046
Furman, Richard I., 2246
Furmansky, Stewart, 8098
Furness, Deborra-Lee, 1683
Furney, Katharine S., 6004
Furnish, Ginger, 3362
Furniture Design Studios, 2400
Furphy, Dan, 9972
Furst, Michael, 2237
Furth, Donna W., 540
Furth, Frederick P., 540
Furth, Hope L., 6047
Furth, John L., 6047
Furth, Peggy J., 540
Fusch, Robbie, 9242
Fusco, Anthony P., 4157
Fusco, Jack A., 3868, 8759
Fusco, Joseph J., 6624
Fusco, Kristin A., 3868
Fusenot, Germaine, 541
Fuson, Brad, 3383
Fuson, Mark, 3383
Fusscas, Amanda C., 1308
Fusscas, Christopher P., 1308
Fux, Michael, 5359
Fux, Michael C., 5359
FWL Sons Inc., 153

G & M Capital Inc., 6961
G & W Laboratories, 5376
G&K Services, 4691
G-Bar Limited Partnership, 2927
Gabaldon, Eileen, 5616
Gabarra, Amy, 8507
Gabay, Andrea, 3180
Gabay, Julie Schwartz, 8265
Gabay, Michael, 3180
Gabbard, Robin, 3655
Gabbert, Vince, 3668
Gabel, Cindy, 91
Gabelli, Mario, 8467
Gaber, Alicia Leonore, 8747
Gaber, David, 5627
Gaber, Ellen Brodsky, 8747
Gaber, Nathan Solman, 8747
Gaber, Stephen, 5627
Gable, Patricia, 9649
Gabor, Vince, 5157
Gabrellian, Ani, 5360
Gabrellian, Mark, 5360
Gabrellian, Mark Ani, 5360
Gabriele, Stephanie K., 7594
Gadbois, Richard A., III, 945
Gaddy, Joe E., 7249
Gaebler, Raymond E., 4912
Gaeckler, Sylvie C., 6071
Gaede, Judy, 884
Gaede, Stan, 884
Gaede, Tracey L., 1055

Gaedke, Dorotha, 3495
Gaffney, David Miller, 6049
Gaffney, James T., 6049
Gaffney, Jeffrey T., 6049
Gaffney, Miller S., 6049
Gaffney, Philip W., 6049
Gafkay, Julie, 4450
Gagarin, Andrew, 3656
Gagarin, Jamie, 3656
Gage, Barbara C., 4692
Gage, Christine C., 4692
Gage, Deborah, 9162
Gage, Edwin C., 4692
Gage, James V., 825
Gage, Kasara, 6026
Gage, Kathy, 3456
Gage, Michele L., 6050
Gage, Mike, 9084
Gage, Robert T., 6050
Gage, Scott, Dr. , 9781
Gage, Thomas C., 6050
Gagen, Marianne, 812
Gagen, William, Jr., 812
Gagnon, Christie V., 2029
Gagnon, Christine L., 2029
Gagnon, Christy V., 2029
Gagnon, David, 7944
Gagnon, Eric E., 2029
Gagnon, Roberta, 4396
Gail Trust, 9516
Gailley, Andrew L.H., 9386
Gaines, Barbara, 3166
Gaines, John Austin, 5438
Gaines, Kevin T., 2607
Gaines, Sharon, 4963
Gaines, Thomas W., Jr., 2840
Gaines, Wade A., 2607
Gainor, Terri, 9224
Gaither, Bill, 3384
Gaither, Gloria, 3384
Gaither, Gloria L., 3384
Gaither, William J., 3384
Gala, Kanti, 5574
Galanti, Barrie, 9603
Galanti, Richard, 9603
Galantowicz, Barbara, 7513
Galantowicz, Mark, 7513
Galbraith, Amy, 7375
Galbraith, Peter, Rev. , 7311
Galbraith, Walter F., 3850
Gale, Alicia W., 7415
Gale, Barbara W., 7415
Gale, Benjamin, 7414
Gale, Deborah B., 7414
Gale, Elizabeth A., 7415
Gale, Lynn, 4100
Gale, Lynne M., 5041
Gale, Mary B., 7414
Gale, Nick, 5041
Gale, Peter, 4100
Gale, Thomas H., 7415
Gale, Thomas V., 7414
Galeana, Jerry L., 2030
Galen, Jessica A. Bloom, 4171
Galena Group, 9313
Galente, De Anna, 1610
Galente, Jonathan Nicolas, 1610
Galgon, Gretl Dupre, 9621
Galindo, Olga, 9211
Galines Foundation, Tony, 2761
Galinski, Paul, 3098
Galkin, Robert T., 8410
Galkin, Warren B., 8410

Gallagher Foundation, W.J. & Rosemary, 5052
Gallagher, A. James, 2898
Gallagher, Beth, 2710
Gallagher, Gary W., 9488
Gallagher, Hollie, 7560
Gallagher, Karen K., 7339
Gallagher, Kevin P., 2898
Gallagher, Marie P., 2898
Gallagher, Mary K., 6051
Gallagher, Ralph W., 7339
Gallagher, Richard S., 9809
Gallagher, Susan M., 5473
Gallagher, Thomas E., 5880, 6051
Gallagher, Thomas G., 7892
Gallagher, Whit, 3799
Gallagher, William T., 7935
Gallaher, George, 176
Gallant, Allan, 9784
Gallant, Theresa, 2085
Gallanter, Linda, 542
Gallanter, Sanford, 542
Galleher, Cathy Lee, 5607
Galleher, Christopher A., 5607
Galleher, Ian R., 5607
Galler, Beatrice, 6052
Galler, Lynne, 6052
Gallerstein, Gary, 1123
Gallman, Charles W., 7111
Gallman, Jean, 2604
Gallo Survivor's Trust, Aileen, 543
Gallo, Gina M., 543
Gallo, John R., 543
Gallo, Marie D., 543
Gallo, Mary E., 543
Gallo, Matthew J., 543
Gallo, Robert J., 543
Gallo, Thomas J., 543
Gallo-Ballatore, Amy M., 543
Galloway, Margaret C., 8519
Galloway, Richard W., 1856
Galloway, Sandra, 71
Galloway, T. Eric, 6053
Galloway, Ted, 9914
Galloway, Winslow Hayes, 7121
Galt, Martin E., III, 4951
Galter Corp., The, 2899
Galter, Dollie, 2899
Galter, Jack, 2899
Galter, William, 2899
Galvani, Paul V., 4216
Galvez, Fred, 9319
Galvin, Diane, 4107
Galvin, Jennifer , 4327
Galvin, John, 8494
Galvin, John R., 4327
Gamber Glass Container, 8011
Gamber, Kitty L., 8011
Gamber, Luella M., 8011
Gamber, Marianne M., 8011
Gamber, Nancy J., 8011
Gamber, W. Ralph, 8011
Gamber, W.R., II, 8011
Gamble Insurance Services, 7941
Gamble, Kenneth, 7941
Gamble, Kristin, 6539
Gamble, Linda, 8377
Gamble, Paul F., 4506, 4507
Gambrell, Sally, 7105
Gambrell, Sarah Belk, 7105
Gambrill, Anne J., 7106
Gammell, Tracy, 7789
Gammon, James A., III, 3385
Gammon, Jeanne, 80

Gamper, Albert, 5361
Gamper, Albert R., Jr., 5361
Gamper, Christopher, 5361
Gamper, Janice, 5361
Gamper, Maria, 3943
Gandhi, Meera T., 1668
Gandia, Naomi, 1730
Ganin, Elizabeth, 9984
Gann, Ronald, 2540
Gannett, John D., 4134
Gannett, Richard B., 4134
Gannett, William B., 4134
Ganot, Asaf, 5149
Ganot, Ruth, 5149
Gans, Frederick M., 544
Gans, Kim, 914
Gans, Rabbi Manferd, 6068
Gans, Shelby M., 544
Ganse, Gerald E., 8012
Ganse, Gregory P., 8012
Ganse, Jeremy J., 8012
Ganse, Suzanne H., 8012
Ganser, Marvin, 9935
Ganshirt, Clark E., 3092
Gansler, Jill, 3905
Gant, Alison A., 6054
Gant, Allen E., Jr., 7209
Gant, Christopher T., 6054
Gant, Donald R., 6054
Gantcher, Alice, 6055
Gantcher, Joel, 6055
Gantcher, Meredith, 6287
Gantcher, Michael, 6055
Gantcher, Nathan, 6055
Gantz Investment Co., The, 6056
Gantz Trust, Louis, 2900
Gantz, Joseph, 6056
Gantz, Linda, 2901
Gantz, Matthew, 2901
Gantz, Sarita, 6056
Gantz, Wilbur, 2901
Gantz, Wilbur H., 2901
Ganz, Simona A., 6151
Gap III Family Trust, 8904
Garabedian, John, 545
Garard, James L., Jr., 2902
Garaud, Jean-Jacques, 979
Garaventa Enterprises, 546
Garaventa, Mary, 546
Garaventa, Silvio, 546
Garber, Adele, 6057
Garber, Amanda, 8208
Garber, Anne M., 4451
Garber, Arnold P., 4492
Garber, Janine, 7625
Garber, Laura C., 4451
Garber, Laurie A., 6057
Garber, Richard J., 4451
Garber, Richard J., Jr., 4451
Garber, Ross, 8689
Garber, Ross B., 6057
Garber, Victor, 9982
Garbin, Ann Marie, 7890
Garboden, Sheri-Dee, 2657
Garcelon, Cherie, 5057
Garcia, Anna, 1100
Garcia, Carlos F., 1952
Garcia, Ernest C., II, 122
Garcia, Georgiana, 8932
Garcia, Joanne, 122
Garcia, Juan C., 7416
Garcia, Lillian D., 2379
Garcia, Maria N., 7416
Garcia, Pedro, 7749

Garcia, Roberta, 3150
Garcich, Jean Walls, 9257
Gard, Michael, 2702
Garden State Chassis, 5561
Garder, Denise B., 2903
Gardiner Savings Institution, F.S.B., 3766
Gardiner, Becky, 1063
Gardiner, Keith, 585
Gardiner, Nancy B., 4309
Gardner Equity Investments L.P., 2903
Gardner, Denise B., 2903
Gardner, Edward T., III, 7417
Gardner, Gary E., 2903
Gardner, George H., 7339
Gardner, George J., 4693
Gardner, George W., 4693
Gardner, Ginny, 9426
Gardner, Herman, 9825
Gardner, J. Alston, 2031
Gardner, J.B., 3441
Gardner, Jacqui, 4693
Gardner, Jennifer Ann, 1318
Gardner, Kristin L., 8076
Gardner, Lee H., 7417
Gardner, Mahershall, 3379
Gardner, Melissa Lyons, 9050
Gardner, Merritt A., 2006
Gardner, Olivia R., 2031
Gardner, Robert, III, 7417
Gardner, Shelli, 9326
Gardner, Stephen D., 6754
Gardner, Sterling, 9326
Gardner, Susan M., 4693
Gardner, Susanah A., 7417
Gardner, Susannah A., 8076
Gardner, Timothy N., 1355
Gardner, V, Colin, 8076
Garechana, Robert, 2858
Gareeb, Nabeel K., 548
Garey, Jack, 8769
Garfield, Michael, 8394
Garfinkel, James, 6294
Garfinkle, Lorraine, 5364
Garfinkle, Sandor A., 5364
Gargan, Denise M, 8238
Garguilo, Lorraine, 5280
Garibaldi, Wayne, 238
Garipoli, Rosemarie, 5852
Garland Eye Associates, P.A., 9132
Garland, Mary L. E., 9971
Garlich, Jill S., 5008
Garlotte, Helen, 3469
Garman, Richard E., 6058
Garmey, Ronald, 4205, 8070, 8286
Garmisa, William J., 3155
Garner, Daniel D., IV, 9332
Garner, Jac B., 9957
Garner, John Michael, 2032
Garner-Wizard, Mariann, 9298
Garnett, Sandra, 1349
Garney, Ronald, 8480
Garrels, Gary, 5558
Garret, Jack, 3641
Garrett, Benjamin E., 2604
Garrett, Bill, 9191
Garrett, Donald Lee, 2604
Garrett, John L., 6452
Garrett, John R. "Bob", 8844
Garrett, Laura, 9214
Garrett, Robert F., III, 5286
Garrigan, Casey, 5105
Garriott, Helen, 7666
Garriott, Owen, 7666

Garris, Garry A., 7145
Garrison, John D., 7728
Garrison, L. Alvin, 9420
Garrison, Parks, 8522
Garrison, Susan, 8328
Garrison, Walter R., 8328
Garside, Elizabeth R., 5651
Gart, John, 1275
Gart, Ken, 1275
Gart, Paul Gerald, 1275
Gart, Sally, 1275
Gart, Sally S., 1275
Gart, Thomas A., 1275
Garth House, The, 8869
Garth, Thomas F., 4836
Garthwaite, Albert A., Jr., 8013
Garthwaite, Diane, 8013
Gartner, 9206
Gartner, Barbara, 3496
Gartner, Carl, 3496
Gartner, Melissa, 3496
Gartner, Melissa M., 3496
Gartner, Michael C., 3496
Gartner, Michael G., 3496
Gartner, Philip A., 4755
Garver, C. Michael, 8883
Garvey Foundation, 8884
Garvey International, 1110
Garvey, Edward C., 4913
Garvey, James S., 8884
Garvey, Jeffrey C., 8706
Garvey, Nancy A., 5481
Garvey, Richard F., 8884
Garvey, Shirley F., 8884
Garvin, Eric, 6600
Garvin, Sam, 147
Garvy, Carol K., 2033
Garvy, Robert A., 2033
Gary, Kathryn W., 1276
Gary, Samuel, Jr., 1276
Garza, David, 8752
Gas Turbine Efficiency, 8759
Gase, Gerald R., 4501
Gasits, Laura Lee, 3699
Gaskin, Roy, 358
Gaspar, Angie, 3024
Gassel, James, 4310
Gassin, Benny, 2906
Gassin, Bernard, 2906
Gast, Michael, 2858
Gaster, Gordon, 2085
Gastis, George, 3699
Gaston, Don, 7666
Gaston, Joe, 16
Gatch, John T., 7313
Gatch, Lewis A., 7313, 7583
Gatch, Tonie L., 1239
Gate Petroleum Company, 2034
Gates, Janet G., 1057
Gates, John, 9361
Gates, Mimi Gardner, 7417
Gates, Nathan C., 1057
Gatewood Family Partnership, 8885
Gatewood, Cindy L., 8885
Gatewood, E. Michael, 8885
Gatewood, James C., 2550
Gathard, Lisa, 3289
Gatting, Carlene J., 4239
Gatto, Joseph D., 6061
Gatto, Susan, 6061
Gaudin, Kay, 9012
Gaughran, Robert J., 5425, 5435
Gault, Ronald, 5775
Gaunce Management Inc., 3658

Gaunce, Chapatcha, 3658
Gaunce, Patrick, 3665
Gaunce, Wayne, 3658
Gauntt Trust, Joanne W., 5365
Gauntt, Joanne W., 5365
Gauntt, Miles, 2395
Gaus, Mike, 9202
Gause, Dick, 3361
Gauss, William F., 8014
Gaut, Kevin E., 839
Gauthier, Anne S. Barrios, 3724
Gauthier, Celeste A., 3724
Gauthier, Cherie A., 3724
Gauthier, Michelle A., 3724
Gavegnano, Richard, 4211
Gavegnano, Richard J., 4075
Gavin, James J., 4237
Gavin, Michael J., 6230
Gawryk, Terry, 2967
Gay, Faith, 480
Gay, Tonee, 5104
Gayfield, Laura Lee, 4946
Gayheart, M. Andrew, 9503
Gaylord Entertainment Co., 8620
Gaylord, Catherine M., 4914
Gaylord, Clifford W., 4915
Gaylord, Guilford W., 6381
Gazaille, Denis H., 4080
Gazette Co., The, 3497
Gazley, Martha, 7807
GB Living Trust, 356
Geabler, Milton R., 4912
Geary Family Charitable Lead Annuity Trust, The, 9456
Geary, Bruce P., 6083
Geary, Caitlin, 9456
Geary, Jr. Irrevocable Trust, H.H., 7419
Geary, Michael, 9456
Gebhard, Elizabeth, 2827
Gebhard, Gwenn H.S., 1831
Gebhard, Paul R.S., 1831
Gebhardt Charitable Lead Annuity Trust, 9826
Gebhardt, Arthur A., 9826
Gebhardt, Patricia A., 9826
Gebhardt, Theresa, 7071
Gebrian, Eileen P., 6528
Geddes, Robert D., 7826
Geddy, Vernon M., III, 9433
Geduld, Emanuel E., 6062
Gee Family Trust, Lloyd B., 9487
Gee, Bruce, 900
Gee, Lynn, 3363
Geenen, Lenora, 5170
Geertsen, David, 9862
Gefen, Sidney, 2024
Gegwich, Grant, 7953
Geib, Barkley M., 2547
Geib, Denise N., 2547
Geier, Philip H., Jr., 6064
Geiger, Dennis Donald, 384
Geilfuss, C. Frederick, 9825
Geis, David M., 3448
Geis, Garry, 825
Geis, Mari, 4764
Geisenberger, Jacques M., Jr., 7932
Geiser, Jodi, 7340
Geiser, Kelsey Schweers, 1020
Geiser, Thomas C., 1020
Geisler, Gertrude, 3498
Geisler, Harold, 3498
Geisler, John, 3498
Geisler, Mavis, 3498
Geissler, Lori, 9880

Geistfeld, Elroy, 4735
Gel Spice Co., 5334
Gelbart, June Baumgardner, 2035
Gelber, Brian R., 3053
Gelber, Franklin A., 3053
Gelber, Sandra, 3053
Gelbman Charitable Trust, 7420
Gelbman Trust, Frank, 7420
Gelbman Trust, Pearl, 7420
Gelernter, Spencer, 2463
Gelfand, Bertram, 5245
Gelinas, Andre A., 4347
Geller, Judith, 6066
Geller, Michele, 375
Geller, Moshe, 6066
Gellert, Annette, 550
Gellert, Fred, 550
Gellert, Fred, Sr., 550
Gellert, Jay M., 608
Gelles, Phyllis, 6800
Gelles, Steven, 6800
Gelley, David, 5449, 6067
Gelley, Heidi, 6067
Gelley, Heidi S., 6067
Gelley, Meir, 5449
Gellin, Terry, 1552
Gellman, Lynne F., 8875
Gellman, Steve, 8875
Gelman, Corey, 5987
Gelman, Emmaia, 6830
Gelman, Felice, 6830
Gelman, Yoram, 6830
Geltzer, David R., 1666
Geltzer, Ethan M., 1666
Geltzer, Isaac S., 1666
Geltzer, Leslee, 1666
Geltzer, Leslee V., 1666
Gelvin, Lyle M., 7682
Gemini Motor Transport, LP, 7701
Gemmell, Nadema, 5230
Gemrich, Alfred J., 4602
Gemunder, Joel F., 2036
Genco Masonry, 3889
Genecov, A.S., 8886
Genecov, Hilda J., 8886
Geneen, Harold S., 8411
Geneen, June, 8411
General Accident Insurance Co. of America, 4231
General Chemical, 5228
General Iron Holdings Inc., 2907
General Iron Industries, 3208
General Machine Products Co., 8213
General Procument Inc., 334
General Refractories Co., 8209
Generativity Charitable Lead Trust, 2778
Geneseo Lions Club, 2909
Genesis Info Security, 5667
Geneva Partners, 6654
Gengras Motor Cars, 1461
Gengras, E. Clayton, Jr., 1461
Gengras, Edith P., 1461
Genie Energy Ltd., 5366
Geno, Dennis R., 4533
Gentry, C. Michael, 8870
Gentry, Patricia Boyd, 102
Genvese, Clovis, 8887
Genzel, Elizabeth, 9133
Genzel, Robert, 9133
Geoffrion, Jill K.H., 4677
Geoffrion, Timothy C., 4677
Geoghan, William, 5561
George Family Charitable Lead Unitrust, Jack M., 7421

George Trust, Noel, 7421
George, Alan, 9231
George, Anton H., 3396
George, Carol, 551, 7421
George, Edward M., 7335
George, Ellen, 4638
George, Elsie, 749
George, Emil J., 4057
George, Helen A., 2815
George, Jack, 7421
George, James, 4585
George, Joan, 7421
George, Joanne M., 551
George, John G., 2140
George, John G., Mrs., 2140
George, Katherine M., 3396
George, M. Josephine, 3396
George, Marcel, 551
George, Mari H., 3396
George, Nancy L., 3396
George, Nick, 7358
George, Rick, 684
George, Robert P., 8329
George, Ruthie, 7358
George, Sarah, 7421
George, Timothy M., 1667
Georgia Medical Plan, 2484
Georgia-Pacific, 2621
Georgino, Sue, 361
Georlach, Deborah, 4057
Gephart, Robert, 1724
Geraghty, John, 2195, 2284
Gerath, Clair, 1462
Gerber State Bank, The, 2911
Gerber, John Edward, 3824
Gerber, Robert R., 7623
Gerbic, Celina, 1463
Gerbic, Peter E., 1463
Gerbic, Verna A., 1463
Gerbitz, Brooks, 7608
Gerdes, Steven H., 9205
Gerel Corp., 5959
Geren, Pete, 8865
Gerfin, Michael, 7932
Gerhard, Greg, 2573
Gerhard, Kristen, 6072
Gerhard, Peter C., 6072, 6130
Gerhardt, Hilary Scheer, 9503
Gerhart, Marian, 5205
Gerhart, Thomas L., 5053
Germain, Steve, 6420
German, James L., III, Mrs., 6868
Gernant, Michael L., 2909
Gernatt, Daniel, Jr., 6073
Gernatt, Daniel, Sr., 6073
Gero, Jacqueline, 6590
Gerome-Acuff, Amy, 1990
Gerretse, Dale, 2802
Gerrish, Allan M., 1277
Gerrish, Allison D., 1277
Gerrish, Curtis L., 4217
Gerrish, Gail S., 1277
Gerrity, James F., III, 4102
Gerrity, Peter F., 4102
Gerrity, Ruth M., 4102
Gerry Charitable Lead Trust, 2037
Gerry Foundation, 5872
Gerry, Libbie F., 2037
Gerry, William F., 2037
Gershey, William, 8345
Gershman Investment Corp., 4916
Gershman, Bettie, 4916
Gershman, Elaine, 8015
Gershman, Elaine Levitt, 8015

Gershman, Jeffrey S., 4916
Gershman, Joel, 8015
Gershman, Mortimer, 5332
Gershon, Elliot S., 2707
Gerson, Marilynn, 9218
Gerstman LLC, 6074
Gerstman, Bradley, 6074
Gerstman, Carolyn, 6074
Gerstman, Cheryl, 6074
Gerstman, Daniel, 6074
Gerstman, Harvey, 6074
Gerstman, Linda, 6074
Gerstman, Pamela, 6074
Gertler, Charles Garrison, 4108
Gertler, Clark Chessin, 4108
Gertler, Jonathan P., 4108
Gertler, William R., 4108
Gerton, Janice, 5693
Gervais, John F., 4087
Gervais, Stephen L., 4087
Geschick Res. Trust, Mary W., 7109
Gessner, Robert, 7442
Gestetner, Hindy, 5367
Gestetner, Marcel, 5367, 5373
Getchell, Debra A., 3785
Getsch, David D., 4695
Getsch, Dianne H., 4695
Getsch, Edward W., 4695
Getsch, John H., 4695
Getsch, Marilyn R., 4695
Getsch, Marjorie D., 4695
Gettenberg Irrevocable Trust, Gary, 5697
Gettenberg Irrevocable Trust, Lynn, 5697
Gettenberg, Gary, 5697
Gettenberg, Lynn, 5697
Gettens, James, 4198
Getter, Philip, 6950
Gettinger, Clark, 6076
Gettinger, Robert, 6076
Getty, Ariadne, 5159
Getty, John Paul, III, 5159
Getz, Emma, 1278
Getz, Oscar, 1278
Getz, Richard, 1278
Getz, William M., 1278
Geurts, Kari, 4654
Gever, Laura Kies, 6307
Gewelber, Hali, 1164
Gewelber, Rhona Weinberg, 1164
Gewirtz, Michael, 6704
Gewirz, Carl, 3869
Gewirz, Nancy, 3869
Gewirz, Victoria, 3869
Geyelin, Erin, 3940
Geyen, Merritt L., 4634
Geyer, Bev, 4806
Geyer, Stan, 4806
Geyer, Susan S., 9217
GFM, 8652
Ghazy, Tarik, 5085
GHD Jr. Descendants Charitable Lead Annuity Trust, 194
Gherardi, Gai, 5691
Ghim, Mimi, 1804
GHO Venturer-Olsen Foundation, 5954
Gholston, J. Knox, 2486
Ghosh, Amit, 8289
GHP Horwath P.C., 1362
Giacoletto Living Trust, 3499
Giampaoli, Maria, 420
Gianatasio, Vincent P., 1610
Giancristofaro, Anthony, 5368
Giancristofaro, Suzan, 5368

Giangrasso, Chris, 7842
Gianna Sabella, 5400
Giannetto, Fred, 5493
Giannini, Duane, 1532
Gianninni, Julius, 411
Giant Eagle, 7856
Giant Eagle Foundation, 8080
Giant Experiences, 7715
Giat, Jane, 4181
Giatas, Theodore, 8567
Gibb, Jane, 3485
Gibber, Allan J., 3877
Gibber, Debbie, 3877
Gibber, Deborah S., 3877
Gibbons, Christine, 7330
Gibbons, David, 5332
Gibbons, Joseph M., 4277
Gibbons, Lucia N., 8350
Gibbons, Miles J., Jr., 6964
Gibbons, Richard, 8796
Gibbons, Richard V., 788
Gibbs, Daniel M., 1083
Gibbs, Sara C., 7352
Gibbs, Thomas E., 3329
Gibler-Zwick, Kathryn, 1218
Giblin, Kevin, 4079
Gibney, Jayne, 7741
Gibor Revocable Trust, Herbert and Sarah M., 1464
Gibraltar Cable Barrier Systems, LP, 9208
Gibraltar Material Distribution, LP, 9208
Gibson, Ami Jo, 2690
Gibson, Becky, 3379
Gibson, Brian, 6573
Gibson, Bruce F., 9604
Gibson, Burke F., 9604
Gibson, Cynthia D., 5634
Gibson, Dana, 5370
Gibson, Daniel, 5634
Gibson, Daniel F., 5634
Gibson, Dolores M., 9604
Gibson, Donna, 9410
Gibson, Elizabeth A., 5634
Gibson, Gregory, 3386
Gibson, Harry H., 8523
Gibson, Harry H., Jr., 8523
Gibson, Jacqueline, 3386
Gibson, Janell M., 5634
Gibson, Jean H., 7256
Gibson, Jennifer, 5634
Gibson, Jennifer L., 5634
Gibson, Joan B., 8523
Gibson, Joel T., 5634
Gibson, John F., 5634
Gibson, Kay, 4963
Gibson, Lisa, 3386
Gibson, Mary Jane, 4035
Gibson, Max L., 3386
Gibson, Peter, 5370
Gibson, Richard P., 8016
Gibson, Scott, 9593
Gibson, Scott S., 9604
Gibson, Terry, 9197
Giddings, Paula, 5700
Gideon, Russ, 9231
Gidwani, Gita P., 7338
Gidwitz 1999 Irrevocable Trust, Richard, 3870
Gidwitz Charitable Lead Annuity Trust, Adele, 3870
Gidwitz Charitable Lead Annuity Trust, Susan, 3870
Gidwitz, Adele, 3870

Gidwitz, Alan, 2914
Gidwitz, Betsy R., 2910, 2914
Gidwitz, Christina K., 2913
Gidwitz, Gail, 2914
Gidwitz, James G., 2914
Gidwitz, Jane B., 2914
Gidwitz, John, 3870
Gidwitz, John D., 3870
Gidwitz, Nancy, 2914
Gidwitz, Peter E., 2914
Gidwitz, Ralph, 2914
Gidwitz, Ralph W., 2914
Gidwitz, Ronald J., 2913, 2914
Gidwitz, Steven, 2910
Gidwitz, Susan, 3870
Gidwitz, Teri, 2910, 2914
Gidwitz, Thomas R., 2914
Gieske, Marguerite, 7595
Gifford, Anne, 977
Gifford, Helen G., 9457
Gifford, John F., 4361
Gifford, Nanny G., 7966
Gifford, Peter B., 900
Gignac, Mark, 9556
Gikoas, William J., 4047
Gil, Ady, 233
Gilbane, Cate S., 4306
Gilberg, Jacqueline, 1973
Gilberstadt, Terryl L. Schilling, 4799
Gilbert, Angela, 9417
Gilbert, Edward M., 5616
Gilbert, Elizabeth, 8869
Gilbert, Eric, 4917
Gilbert, Eric N., 4917
Gilbert, Gillett A., 6220
Gilbert, Gillett A., Jr., 6220
Gilbert, Helen A., 4917
Gilbert, James M., 7223
Gilbert, John N., Jr., 6220
Gilbert, Larry, 710
Gilbert, Sara, 4917
Gilbert, Sara E., 4917
Gilbert, Stacy L., 6163
Gilbert, William A., 4917
Gilbride, Frank J., II, 1391
Gilchrist, Anne, 5658
Gildea, Carol, 4103
Gildea, James F., 4103
Gildea, Scott, 6644
Gilden, David, 8503
Gilden, Jerry, 7379
Gilder, Richard, 5843
Gildred, Alison F., 966
Giles, Clark P., 9351
Giles, Cynthia C., 5935
Giles, Harlan R., 5935
Giles, Terry M., 554
Gililland, Nancy, 3427
Gilkey, Kirk, 425
Gilkey, M. Whitney, 9526
Gill Foundation, Pauline Allen, 8773
Gill, Douglas, 3948
Gill, Elisabeth C., 5651
Gill, Elizabeth O., 555
Gill, Frank C., 7766
Gill, Katherine, 6364
Gill, Katherine L., 7766
Gill, Margaret G., 555
Gill, Mary Kay, 7766
Gill, Megan K., 7766
Gill, Richard P., 555
Gill, Stephen P., 555
Gillam, Robert A., 85
Gillam, Robert Arthur, 85

Gillam, Robert B., 85
Gillard, Cynthia S., 3465
Gilleland, Carrie Jo, 556
Gilleland, Ellen, 556
Gilleland, Richard, 556
Gillen, Arlene, 4552
Gillen, Rex, 4552
Gillen, Valerie, 808
Giller, Mary Kevin Stolzer, 3630
Gillern, Michelle H., 2675
Gillespie, C.H., III, 7698
Gillespie, Kirstin Elizabeth McMillan, 9007
Gillete, Gordon L., 2367
Gillett, James, 1357
Gillett, Mary H., 2971
Gillett, Robert W., 2971
Gilliam, Deane A., 6078
Gilliam, John D., 6078
Gilliam, Leslie, 9496
Gilliam, Richard, 9496
Gilliam, Theopolis, 9464
Gillies, Robert C., 8250
Gillig, Donna J., 7297
Gilligan, Ann, 4696
Gilligan, James, 9174
Gilligan, James A., 9174
Gilligan, Julie, 9174
Gilligan, Julie J., 9174
Gilligan, Katherine Helow, 2089
Gilligan, Margaret, 4696
Gilligan, Michael, 4696
Gilligan, Peter J., 4696
Gillilan, John S., Jr., 7281
Gillis, Janie DeVore, 3566
Gilman, Allene N., 7423
Gilman, Charles, III, 8889
Gilman, Harriet, 4144
Gilmartin, Eugene H., 5300, 8487
Gilmartin, Wayne, 2919
Gilmore Co., A.F., 557
Gilmore, Dennis, 506
Gilmore, James, 8017
Gilmore, Julia W., 4805
Gilmore, Madeline K., 7708
Gilmore, Marguerite L., 7110
Gilmore, Marie Dent, 557
Gilmore, Marilyn A., 8017
Gilmore, R. Patrick, 7663
Gilmour, David W., 4210
Gilmour, John, 4377
Gilreath, Debbie, 3461
Gilroy, Beth, 5795
Gilsdorf, James R., 1249
Gilster, Ralph R., III, 9093
Gilstrap, John B., 9556
Gilweit, Alexa, 5190
Gilweit, Martha Stout, 5190
Gilweit, Samantha, 5190
Gimbel, Bailey, 6079
Gimbel, Leslie, 6079
Gimbel, Mary, 7424
Gimbel, Russell, 7424
Gimbel, Thomas S.T., 6079
Gimmler, Elizabeth, 8939
Gimprich, Marvin, 6080
Ginandes, Alice M., 6488
Ginder Charitable Lead Trust, 558
Ginder, Brad, 558
Ginder, Deborah A., 558
Ginder, Grant S., 558
Ginder, Reid G., 558
Ginder, Stephen P., 558
Gindi, Elizabeth, 5939

Gindi, Isaac, 5939
Gindi, Raymond, 5939
Giner, A. Silvana, 4132, 4195, 4351
Gingerich, Pastor Dennis, 1917
Ginn, Alexander, 7425
Ginn, Ann L., 7425
Ginn, Mary C., 7425
Ginn, Walter P., 7425
Ginn, William J., 7373
Ginsberg, Mark, 5889
Ginsberg, Thomas, 8363
Ginsburg, Dennis, 2277
Ginsburg, James A., 317
Ginsburg, Susan, 6974
Giop Trust, Ines, 8018
Giop, Sonia, 8018
Giordani, Leslie C., 2056
Giordani, Roseanne, 2056
Giordano, Catherine, 6081
Giornelli, Gregory J., 2557
Giornelli, Lillian C., 2557
Giovanetti, Louis, 4254
Gipson, Scott, 2689
Girard, Laura S., 4754
Girard, Sara, 3564
Girardat, Janet, 1482
Girimont, Boydie, 8683
Gironda, Wendy, 8053
Gish, Lillian D., 2915
Gish, Stephen J., 3614
Gissy, Jim, 2400
Gitlin, Joni, 1062
Gitlin, Stanley B., 1062
Gitt, Cynthia, 8019
Gitt, Elizabeth M., 8019
Giuliano, Barbara J., 9475
Giuliano, Louis J., 9475
Giullian, Susan, 5593
Gius, Leslie Ann, 9606
Gius, Margaret, 9606
Gius, Marie Helen, 9606
Giusti, Annamaria, 8031
Giusti, Robert, 1483
Giustina, L.M., 7767
Giustina, Natale B., 7767
Given, Robert H., 1217
Given, Suzi, 1217
GKD Trust, The, 5174
Glaceau, 90
Gladden, Gordon D., 3932
Gladden, William C., 2456
Gladding, Harry L., 3871
Glade, Fred, 5114
Glade, Gordon, 5114
Gladish, Nina, 773
Gladson, Linda, 882
Gladstein, Gary, 6720
Gladstein, Gary S., 1465
Gladstein, Jeff, 1465
Gladstone, David, 9458
Gladstone, Lorna, 9458
Glaeser, Elizabeth, 4693
Glancy, Alfred R., III, 2489
Glancy, Alfred R., IV, 2489
Glancy, Andrew Roby, 2489
Glancy, Douglas R., 2489
Glancy, Joan C., 2489
Glancy, Ruth R., 2489
Glanert, Karen J., 9827
Glascock, Mark Zachary, 9475
Glaser, D.J., 3635
Glasrud, Sharon E., 123
Glasrud, Theodore G., 123
Glass, Barbara Ann, 7736

Glass, Leslie Gordon, 2039
Glass, Marybeth, 7714
Glassberg, David M., 2229
Glassen, Harold, 4454
Glasser, Gerald, 5371
Glasser, Marlene, 5371
Glasser, Meg Bloom, 5371
Glasser, Michael A., 9459
Glasser, Richard S., 9459
Glasser, Steve, 7666
Glasser-Baker, Laura, 5371
Glasser-Frei, Hara B., 9459
Glassford, Roseann C., 9010
Glassman, Elizabeth, 9062
Glassman, Saly A., 8034
Glasson, Mary H., 3448
Glast, Phillips & Murray, 8700
Glatfelter, Philip H., II, 7932
Glaubinger, Jane, 2040
Glaubinger, Lawrence D., 2040
Glaubinger, Lucienne M., 2040
Glaubitz, Suzanne Cadle, 1112
Glaze, Helen M., 28
Glazer, Bradford A., 7426
Glazer, David H., 7426
Glazer, Diane, 562
Glazer, Emerson, 1092
Glazer, Erika J., 561
Glazer, Guilford, 562
Glazer, Jill N., 7426
Glazer, Margot, 2167
Glazer, Melissa A., 7426
Glazer, Michael F., 3844
Glazer, Michelle B., 7426
Glazer, Susan F., 7426
Gleason, Bobby M., 9143
Gleason, Bonnie, 8524
Gleason, Kathleen, 6058
Gleason, Kevin, 5724
Gleason, Lenore, 8524
Gleason, Martin, 8524
Gleason, Marty, 3514
Gleason, Mary, 8524
Gleason, Nancy, 8524
Gleeksman, Sue, 8363
Gleeson Constructors, 3500
Gleeson, Helen K., 3500
Gleeson, John W., 3500
Gleeson, Karen, 3500
Gleeson, Robert E., 3500
Gleichenhaus, Poly S., 3751
Gleicher, Warren, 6870
Gleick, James, 1854
Glem Co., 976
Glen, Michael, 6889
Glendenning, Don, 8980
Glendenning, Jack L., 9828
Glendenning, John, 9828
Glendenning, John H., 9828
Glendenning, Mark, 9828
Glendenning, Mark T., 9828
Glendenning, Rosanne, 9828
Glenmede Trust Co, The, 7904
Glenmede Trust Co., The, 7516, 7853, 7893, 8169
Glenmede Trust Company, The, 8369
Glenn, Camilla, 7137
Glenn, Carrie Eugenia, 7111
Glenn, Charles, 1770
Glenn, Lena Viola, 7111
Glenn, Michael S., 11
Glennon, Catherine B., 6880
Glennon, Cathie, 7807

Glens Falls National Bank & Trust Co., 6699
Glenview Trust Co., 3677
Glenwood Management Group, 6656
Glesener, Loretta, 268
Glessner, Gary R., 8263
Glezer, Maggie, 107
Glick Diamond Corporation, Louis, 6117
Glick, Adam P., 2235
Glick, Lawrence, 3207
Glick, Louis, 6117
Glick, Simon, 6117
Glickert, Anita Posey, 9135
Glickert, Audrey M., 9135
Glickert, Keith E., 9135
Glickert, Michael W., 9135
Glickert, Robert F., 9135
Glickstein, David L., 8127
Glickstein, Linda, 8127
Glickstein, Linda S., 8127
Glidden, Marie E., 7427
Gliebe, Mark, 9911
Glikbarg, Charlene, 564
Glikbarg, Steven, 564
Glikbarg, William K., 564
Glikman, Helen, 4035
Global Catalyst Partners, 565
Global Charitable Foundation, 5705
Global Green Solutions, 5452
Global Imports, 6390
Global Link Solutions, 334
Globerman, Michael, 470
Globke, Cheryl, 4396
Gloeckner, Frederick C., 6083
Glomb, Franny, 6432
Gloneck, Janice, 2270
Glose, Jennifer Gardner, 8076
Glossberg, Joseph, 3210
Glossberg, Joseph B., 2916
Glossberg, Madeleine K.B., 2916
Glotzbecker, Paul G., 6902
Glover & MacGregor, 8069
Glover, Becky, 4830
Glover, Ella, 5362
Glover, Glenn, 14
Glover, Jane E., 7952
Gloyd, Lawrence E., 2917
Gluck, Fred, 6235
Gluck, Irving, 6297
Gluck, Linda S., 8675
Gluck, Lisa, 6235
Gluck, Susan, 6235
Gluckstern, Judith, 6420
Gluckstern, Judith O'Connor, 6420
Gluckstern, Steven M., 6420
Glucoft, Frida, 839
Glumac, Kathleen, 7637
Glyn, David R., 7942, 8028, 8109
Glyn, Joseph A., 8109
Glynn, John J., 5494
Glynn, Suzanne M., 4860
Glynn, William C., 2677
GMO Renewable Resources LLC, 4264
Goad, Deana Ross, 8621
Goad, Fred C., Jr., 8621
Gober, Karen E., 3881
Gobis, Lou, 1295
Gochnauer, Beth A., 2918
Gochnauer, Grant D., 2918
Gochnauer, Meg, 2918
Gochnauer, Richard W., 2918
Gocht, Russell C., 1585
Godbold Foundation, 2362
Godbold, Elizabeth, 2041

Godbold, Francis, 2041
Godbold, John, 2041
Godby, Janet, 3657
Godby, Melvin, 3657
Godchaux, Charles R., 3734
Godchaux, Frank A., III, 3734
Godchaux, Frank K., 3734
Godchaux, Frank M., 3734
Godchaux, Leslie K., 3734
Goddard, Amanda, 6085
Goddard, Charles B., 7684
Goddard, Chuck, 4497
Goddard, Colin, 6085
Goddard, Jennifer, 7684
Goddard, Katherine, 7684
Goddard, Kathleen H., 2491
Goddard, Robert C., III, 2491
Goddard, Roger D., 9001
Goddard, Teri, 1257
Goddard, Terry, 172
Goddard, William R., Jr., 7684
Godfrey, Crystal, 9711
Godfrey, David L., 1408, 1529
Godfrey, John A., 5183
Godindger Silver Art Ltd., 6086
Godinger, Arnold, 6086
Godinger, Rita, 6086
Godley, Jeffrey, 1418
Godsey, Donald W., 2043
Godsey, Joyce W., 2043
Godson, Roy, 5630
Godwin, Armied A., III, 7281
Godwin, Cindy P., 7281
Godwin, Gary, 5004
Godwin, Gus T., 7125
Godwin, Sally Smythe, 1061
Godwin, Stephen, 1061
Goebel, Kathleen, 3580
Goebel, Patrick M., 3580
Goebel, Robert L., 3580
Goelkel, Andrea Marie Lieselotte, 7192
Goering, Randy, 3582
Goerlich, John, 7428
Goerlich, Selma E., 7428
Goeser, Greg, 158
Goetz, David R., 2044
Goetz, David R., Jr., 2044
Goetz, Gregory E., 2044
Goetz, Mary Sue, 2044
Goff, Chris, 7442
Goff, David F., 7601
Goff, Marcia L., 7601
Goff, Martin E., 7601
Goff-Davis, Annabel, 1906
Gogel, Donald J., 6087
Gogel, Leah G., 6087
Gogel, Rebecca, 6087
Goggin, Topher, 4534
Goheen, Gail H., 104
Golan, Stephen L., 2698
Gold Canyon Candle, 158
Gold, Bradd J., 6088
Gold, Julie Breidenthal, 3560
Gold, Randy, 832
Gold, Richard, 5631, 6427
Gold, Sidney, 925
Gold, Sophia, 1273
Goldammer, Vance, 8561
Goldammer, Vance R.C., 8573
Goldbach, Jeanne, 1595
Goldbaum, Chana, 6771
Goldbaum, Saul Elliot, 6771
Goldbeck, Irene Giustina, 7767
Goldberg Interim Trust, 567

Goldberg, Amy, 7844
Goldberg, Andrew, 8042
Goldberg, Arthur A., 6020
Goldberg, Barry, 124
Goldberg, Bradley, 5680
Goldberg, Brian L., 3872
Goldberg, Carol, 6020
Goldberg, Diana, 3872
Goldberg, Diana L., 3872
Goldberg, Dorothy, 567, 3780
Goldberg, E., 8198
Goldberg, Edward, 568
Goldberg, Ellen, 8021
Goldberg, Evelyn B., 4944
Goldberg, Frank M., 568
Goldberg, Gene, 124
Goldberg, Geraldine D., 3581
Goldberg, Ira, 5692
Goldberg, J. Arthur, 2045
Goldberg, Jay, 4763
Goldberg, Jay L., 8042
Goldberg, Joel S., 4238
Goldberg, John M., 3581
Goldberg, Lauren B., 3872
Goldberg, Lee, 568
Goldberg, Mark, 124
Goldberg, Maxine, 8042
Goldberg, Michael, 8042
Goldberg, Rae, 3872
Goldberg, Raymond, 8021
Goldberg, Rita, 124
Goldberg, Robert, 3780, 6090
Goldberg, Robert A., 3581
Goldberg, Robert S., 567
Goldberg, Stephen, 3872
Goldberg, Stephen A., 3872
Goldberg, Stuart W., 3872
Goldberger, Leah, 6333
Goldberger, Marjorie, 5372
Golde, Hellmut, 9669
Golden K. Kiwanis Club, 4484
Golden Partners LLC, 153
Golden, Avi, 5366
Golden, Bradley, 4455
Golden, Connie, 2672
Golden, Diana, 5368
Golden, Donald L., 4455
Golden, Grace E., 5790
Golden, John J., 3993
Golden, Kenneth, 503
Golden, Kenneth M., 926
Golden, Linda H., 2046
Golden, Marion, 4455
Golden, Michael, 4455
Golden, Morley, 2672
Golden, Nathan, 2046
Golden, Neal, 2046
Golden, Randal E., 4455
Golden, Raymond L., 2046
Golden, Richard S., 4455
Golden, Stephanie, 2046
Goldenberg, A., 6093
Goldenberg, Harold, 6093
Goldenberg, Jeffrey, 6092
Goldenberg, Leon, 6093
Goldenberg, Lloyd, 5630
Goldenberg, M., 6093
Goldenberg, Max, 2920
Goldenberg, Susan, 6092
Goldenson, Maxine W., 6094
Golder Family Partnership, 2921
Golder, David B., 2921
Golder, Joan J., 2921
Golder, Kenneth, 2921

Golder, Stanley C., 2921
Goldfarb Revocable Living Trust, Harry E., 1466
Goldfarb, Andrew, 915
Goldfarb, Denise, 915
Goldfarb, Francine L., 1467
Goldfarb, Harry E., 1466, 1467
Goldfarb, Jessica, 915
Goldfarb, Maureen, 1467
Goldfarb, Randy, 8570
Goldfarb, Rebecca, 915
Goldfarb, Robert B., 1466, 1467
Goldfarb, Robert D., 6095
Goldfarb, William H., 1466, 1467
Goldfeder, Avrom, 3175
Goldfein, Joshua, 7999
Goldfein, Myles S., 6096
Goldfein, Roanne, 6096
Goldfein, Stanley F., 6096
Goldfeiz, Emanuel, 2329
Goldgraber, Avigail, 4952
Goldin, Philippe, 5918
Golding, Faith, 6097
Golding, Melody, 4838
Golding, Stacy Rogers, 2058
Golding, Stephen D., 4838
Golding, Susan, 2986
Goldman and Brothers, William P., 4105
Goldman Capital Management, 6098
Goldman Sachs Family Office, 6851
Goldman Sachs Trust Co., 1687
Goldman, Aaron, 1810
Goldman, Amy R., 4697
Goldman, Belle, 180
Goldman, Brian A., 3838
Goldman, Bruce E., 5377
Goldman, Byron, 4105
Goldman, Carol, 2922
Goldman, Cecile, 1810
Goldman, Daniela, 6098
Goldman, Howard S., 9895
Goldman, Jacob, 6098
Goldman, Kenneth, 346
Goldman, Margaret B., 5803
Goldman, Marlene Mieske, 6098
Goldman, Michael, 5551
Goldman, Michael D., 1810
Goldman, Neal I., 6098
Goldman, Peter D., 2922
Goldman, Philip S., 4697
Goldman, Richard, 1100
Goldman, Robert P., 4021, 4293
Goldman, Ron, 820
Goldman, Sally, 2047
Goldman, Sheldon M., 5688
Goldman, Shmuel, 7015
Goldman, Steven, 180
Goldman, Tzirel, 7015
Goldman, William P., 4105
Goldmann, Stephen C., 6099
Goldmann, Stephen F., 6099
Goldmark Group, The, 5460
Goldner, David A., 3823
Goldrick, James M., 6403
Goldrick, Thomas F., Jr., 6546
Goldsmith, Ann, 448
Goldsmith, Deborah L., 7031
Goldsmith, Elvis G., 8622
Goldsmith, Fred, III, 8622
Goldsmith, Harry L., 8622
Goldsmith, Jack L., III, 8622
Goldsmith, Larry J., 8622
Goldsmith, Margaret Ann, 3958
Goldsmith, Melvin, 8622

Goldsmith, Stephen, 1837
Goldsmith, Thomas B., 8622
Goldspink, Christy P., 5220
Goldstein Family Charitable Foundation, The, 6100
Goldstein, Albert, 9786
Goldstein, Aryeh, 6444
Goldstein, Benjamin, 6100
Goldstein, David, 6100, 6101
Goldstein, Douglas R., 1990
Goldstein, Elizabeth Geer, 1990
Goldstein, Emerich, 6100
Goldstein, Esther, 6101
Goldstein, Heather Hart, 2792
Goldstein, Jerome E., 1990
Goldstein, Jonathan M., 4252
Goldstein, Joshua, 5373
Goldstein, Michael B., 2176
Goldstein, Michael L., 5909
Goldstein, Pearl, 5373
Goldstein, Robert, 5455
Goldstein, Robert L., 6720
Goldstein, Ruth, 569
Goldstein, Sanford, 5811
Goldstein, Sarah, 6444
Goldstein, Seth M., 6009
Goldstein, Sheldon, 569
Goldstein, Shulamith K., 6322
Goldstein, Sydney E., 1990
Goldstone, Arthur H., 6102
Goldstone, Herbert A., 6102
Golem, Tara, 825
Golf Tournament, 4133
Golichowski, Shirley, 3458
Golick, Ed, 4410
Golick, Morrie, 6104
Golick, Susan, 6104
Golieb, Abner J., 6048
Golieb, John A., 6048
Gollin, James D., 5605
Gollin, Suzanne D., 5605
Golub, Herman B., 6105
Gombos, David, 1400
Gomer, Brian D., 1917
Gomes, Lee-Ann, 1438
Gomez, Barbara, 425
Gompers, Thomas L., 9742
Gonter, Alex, 5960
Gonter, Joel, 5960
Gonter, Mark, 5960
Gonter, Neil, 5960
Gonter, Shlomo, 5960
Gonthier, Robert A., Jr., 4250
Gonya, Jeffrey K., 3919
Gonz, Marena, 6230
Gonzales, Debbie Strait, 1239
Gonzales, Rosemary, 652
Gonzalez, Alexander, 1330
Gonzalez, Camila, 1816
Gonzalez, Manuel A., 2150
Gonzalez, Pedro L., 2150
Gonzalez, Ricardo, 2150
Gonzalez, Rosa, 5842
Gonzalez, Will, 8326
Gonzalez-Falla, Celso M., 8889
Gonzalez-Falla, Sondra Gilman, 8889
Gooch, Chris, 3655
Gooch, Hubert L., Jr., 7276
Gooch, James, 2090
Goocher, Robert L., 3450
Good Works Foundation, 5691
Good, Adam P., 4698
Good, David F., 4698
Good, Julie A., 8011

Good, Rosemary H., 4698
Good, Seth H., 2919
Goodall, Jackson W., Jr., 570
Goodall, Jeff, 570
Goodall, John C., III, 2961
Goodall, John C., Jr., 2961
Goodall, Laura K., 3836
Goodall, Lauralea T., 3836
Goodall, Richard L., 3836
Goodall, Richard T., 3836
Goodall, Rosalie L., 3836
Goodfellow, John, 9607
Goodhardt, William A., 3905
Goodin, Janet, 7685
Goodin, Janet R., 7685
Goodin, Kenneth R., 7685
Goodin, Reggie, 7670
Gooding, Nancy A., 1268
Gooding, Richard L., 1268
Gooding, Terence J., 571
Goodman Foundation, Edward & Marion, 1213
Goodman, Asher, 6728
Goodman, Bruce, 8084
Goodman, Bruce K., 2970
Goodman, Carol Lanier, 2492
Goodman, Carolyn, 3918
Goodman, Deborah, 2887
Goodman, Dobert, 5247
Goodman, Donn, 5911
Goodman, George D., 4499
Goodman, Gilbert, 6106
Goodman, Hirshel, 2899
Goodman, James S., 6108
Goodman, John, 9608
Goodman, John A., 9608
Goodman, Joyce, 2887
Goodman, Judith, 6106
Goodman, Karen, 2899
Goodman, Leslie Ann, 6107
Goodman, Linda, 2887
Goodman, Mark, 6106
Goodman, Miriam, 4081
Goodman, Morris F., 2887
Goodman, Rachel, 6728
Goodman, Randolph B., 6107
Goodman, Robert P., 6108
Goodman, Roy M., 6107
Goodman, Scott, 2492
Goodman, Shawn, 9608
Goodman, Stanley, 2887
Goodman, Sylvia, 3750
Goodman, William Michael, 2887
Goodman, William R., III, 16
Goodman, Yitzchok, 6728
Goodman-Bowden, Jenny, 2887
Goodmaster, Carolyn E., 2086
Goodnews, 3641
Goodrich, Billie G., 29
Goodrich, Dennett W., 1432
Goodrich, Frances, 29
Goodrich, Henry C., 29
Goodrich, John A., 1432
Goodrich, Ramsey W., 1432
Goodrich, William, 29
Goodrum Enterprises Inc., 153
Goodson, Lief, 1922
Goodson, Lief G., 1922
Goodstein, Robert, 6612
Goodstein, Sandra, 8023
Goodwill Industries of Tacoma, 9585
Goodwin, Andrew, 6612
Goodwin, Carl, 2761
Goodwin, Charles S., 5232

Goodwin, Clay, 2761
Goodwin, Donald G., 572
Goodwin, Ed, 2761
Goodwin, Gillian, 6612
Goodwin, Greg, 7798
Goodwin, Harry B., 1279
Goodwin, Jeanne, 6612
Goodwin, Joanna, 5374
Goodwin, John, 5374
Goodwin, Linda, 7905
Goodwin, Patricia, 6358
Goodwin, Richard C., 5374
Goodwin, Robert, 5374
Goodwin, Scott J., 1416
Goodwin, Todd, 2048
Goody, Kenneth L., 7028
Goodyear, Clarice Cato, 7071
Google Inc., 1775
Google UK Ltd., 2622
Goolsby, Allen C., III, 9522
Gopher Smelting & Refining Corp., 3437
Gorab, Eugene A., 1468
Gorab, Suzanne H., 1468
Goranson, Richard A., 7704
Gorder, Charles F., 541
Gordon Charitable Lead Trust, Edward, 7112
Gordon Corporation, Nathan H., 6109
Gordon Meyer Trust, 9886
Gordon's Jewelry Co., 8893
Gordon, Albert H., 5934, 6112
Gordon, Allan S., 6110
Gordon, Alvin A., 8591, 8645
Gordon, Anna Melissa, 8742
Gordon, Annette, 8892
Gordon, Bernice W., 8624
Gordon, Cathy Anne, 2052
Gordon, Charlotte A., 3122
Gordon, Courtney P., 6616
Gordon, Daniel, 7112, 8892
Gordon, Daniel P., 8893
Gordon, Donald, 6283
Gordon, Elaine, 8591, 8645
Gordon, Elizabeth, 574, 6109
Gordon, Elizabeth Hekman, 4456
Gordon, Elizabeth M., 3079
Gordon, Ellen, 573
Gordon, Eugene, 3122
Gordon, Frank E., 8624
Gordon, Gail, 2050
Gordon, Gail E., 8624
Gordon, Gwen L., 8624
Gordon, Herbert, 5437
Gordon, James, 8892
Gordon, James C., 8893
Gordon, Jason, 2050
Gordon, Jay, 6836
Gordon, Jeffrey M., 7094
Gordon, Joel C., 8624
Gordon, John, 3079
Gordon, Julie S., 8624
Gordon, Kathleen, 6111
Gordon, Kevin Edward, 2052
Gordon, Laura, 6110
Gordon, Linda, 7112
Gordon, Lucy H., 4142
Gordon, Lynda S., 2052
Gordon, Marguerite M., 8742
Gordon, Mark J., 2051
Gordon, Marshall, 3122
Gordon, Mary, 3628
Gordon, Matthew, 8893
Gordon, Mayme, 3122
Gordon, Michael S., 2052

Gordon, Milton, 6177
Gordon, Nancy, 8893
Gordon, Paul M., 457
Gordon, Raymond P., 3122
Gordon, Reuben, 8024
Gordon, Robert A., 8624
Gordon, Ryan, 8893
Gordon, Sandy, 619
Gordon, Scott, 8893
Gordon, Timothy C., 6110
Gordon, William J.J., 6109
Gordon, Yale, 3873
Gordon, Yisrael, 619
Gordy, Berry, 575
Gordy, Berry, IV, 575
Goreham, Lucy, 4317
Gorelick, Robert, 5582
Gores, Thomas C., 9609
Gorga, Joseph L., 7062
Gorish, Frances M., 6945
Gorlin, Andrew, 4457
Gorlin, Jacques J., 3874
Gorlin, Robert H., 4457
Gorlin, Susan J., 3874
Gorlitz, Gail, 1811
Gorlitz, Grace K., 1811
Gorlitz, Paula, 1811
Gorman, Deb, 1316
Gorman, Robert L., 8000
Gorman, Thomas, 1316
Gormley, Beverly Claire, 8261
Gormley, Douglas, 7624
Gormley, John, 1279
Gorny, Thomas, 1671
Gorter Family Foundation, 2934
Gorton, Lawrence E., 4391
Gorzelanczyk, David, 7339
Gosiger, 7429
Gosnell, Elizabeth G., 6418
Goss, Ann Coit, 7751
Goss, Janet Reed, 7616
Gossard, Katherine, 3329
Gosse, Thomas A., 9551
Gossett, John, 884
Gossett, Lyn, 884
Gostomski Family Foundation, 2925
Gostomski, Michael M., 2925
Goswami, Aditi, 6015
Gotham Organization, 6655
Gother, Ronald, 1170
Gothorpe, William G., 4067
Gotlieb Family Trust, 5697
Goto, Greta L., 82
Goto, Noriaki, 5795
Gotsch, Pat, 2680
Gotschall, Clark, 5127
Gotterer, David, 6497
Gottesman Family, LP, Austin, 9027
Gottesman, Jerome, 5330
Gottesman, Lisa T., 9027
Gottesman, Margery, 5330
Gottesman, Sanford Lee, 9027
Gottfredson, Michael, 7744
Gottieb, Jaquelin, 2484
Gottlieb, Adolph, 6114
Gottlieb, Esther, 6114
Gottlieb, Keith, 5612
Gottlieb, Martin, 6115
Gottlieb, Michael, 6115
Gottlieb, Steven, 6905
Gottsegen, Peter M., 6490
Gottstein, Barnard J., 86
Gottstein, David R., 86
Gottstein, James B., 86

Gottstein, Rachel L., 86
Gottstein, Robert W., 86
Gottstein, Sandra L., 86
Gouger, William R., 1762
Gough, Richard, 3361
Gould, Stuart S., 6116
Gould, Alexandra P., 8221
Gould, Carolyn, 2494
Gould, Carolyn J., 2494
Gould, David, 2494
Gould, David B., 2494
Gould, Jay E., 4250
Gould, Jeff, 8677
Gould, Jimmy, 8677
Gould, Laurence K., Jr., 801, 1076
Gould, N. Jay, 6116
Gould, Nicole F., 5467
Gould, Peter, 8221
Gould, Peter G., 8221
Gould, Robert, 7430
Gould, Suzanne Grossinger, 2933
Gouldin, David M., 6049
Goulet, Tracey, 4268
Gouran, Lisa, 1242
Gourdeau, Richard, 4277
Gourger, Bill, 1316
Govil, Sanjay, 3875
Govil, Vidya, 3875
Gow, Ian F., 436
Gowan Co., 8968
Gower, Emerson, 8522
GPM 48th St. LLC, 6261
GPS Construction Services, LLC, 8700
Grabbi, Rein, 9685
Grabe, Douglas, 2053
Grabe, Joan H., 2053
Grabe, Laura, 2053
Grabe, William O., 2053
Grabe-Taffe, Lisa, 2053
Grabell, Neal, 8022
Grabow, Raymond J., 7330
Graboys, Ken, 4044
Grace Bakingmaple Leaf Baking, 8859
Grace Baptist Church, 840, 7205
Grace Charitable Lea Ann Trust, Ann K.,
    125
Grace, Anne E., 6118
Grace, Barb, 125
Grace, Betty Ann, 4245
Grace, Darrell, 5011
Grace, Howard T., 125
Grace, James M.L., 9030
Grace, Matt, 125
Grace, R. Randall, Jr., 9030
Grace, Thomas G., 6118
Grace, Thomas G., Jr., 6118
Grader, Evelyn L., 2054
Grader, K.W., 2054
Gradient, 3905
Grado, John, Jr., 4347
Grady, Caroline B., 1898
Grady, Edward R., Jr., 3727
Grady, Lance, 2803
Graeber, James P., Jr., 4839
Graeber, John C., 4839
Graeber, Josephine H., 6224
Graeber, Lewis A., 4839
Graeber, William M., 4839
Graef, Staci, 7319
Graese, Clifford E., 2055
Graese, Diane M., 2055
Graese, Larry, 2055
Graese, LaVonne B., 2055
Graf, Daniel J., 4375

Graf, Jonathan, 8700
Graff, Curtis, 4959
Graff, F. Thomas, Jr., 9771
Graff, Lee, 576
Graff, Nicole Bartner, 1869
Grafil Inc., 825
Grafstein, Bernice, 577
Grafstein, Mindy A., 1465
Graham GP, 8602
Graham Trust, Helen I., 6119
Graham, Barbara F., 2926
Graham, Cynthia S., 7257
Graham, Daniel A., 4915
Graham, Donald E., 1823
Graham, Eva C., 2495
Graham, G. Howard, 2444
Graham, Glenn, 8503
Graham, John, 4007, 5620, 7204, 9609
Graham, John C., 8896
Graham, John K., 8101
Graham, Ken, 8937
Graham, Kristi, 4499
Graham, Kristiane W., 9540
Graham, Lee-Ann, 9187
Graham, M.K., 8896
Graham, Mark E., 2495
Graham, Mary, 1823
Graham, Monica, 6120
Graham, Peter, 9384
Graham, Ray A., III, 2926
Graham, Robert W., 7784
Graham, Stephen B., 2495
Graham, Tim A., 8602
Gralnick, Helene B., 2056
Gralnick, Marvin J., 2056
Gralnick, William, 6121
Gramps, Nancy Bowling, 1409
Granberg-Michaelson, Wes, 2857
Grand Homes, 9009
Grand Piano and Furniture Co., 9414
Grande Cheese Co., 9832
Grandey, Linda G., 6638
Grandis, Harriet, 9462
Grandis, Harry, 9462
Grandy, Edith G., 9491
Grandy, John W., 4236
Grange Trust, A., 8044
Granger, Stephen, 4095
Granholm, Gundrun, 7807
Grano, Andrea J., 6128
Grano, Angela L., 6128
Grano, Jim, 7829
Grano, Joseph C., 6128
Grano, Joseph J., Jr., 6128
Grano, Kathleen J., 6128
Grant & Co. LLC., Eugene M., 6655
Grant Family Foundation, Eugene and
    Emily, 6655
Grant Family, Eugene & Emily, 6656
Grant& Co., Eugene M., 6655
Grant, Adrienne, 663
Grant, Alison A., 6054
Grant, Annette M., 6130
Grant, Anthony, 1096
Grant, Caroline, 1096
Grant, Debra, 7372
Grant, Donald R., 6078
Grant, Doug, 884
Grant, E. Reuben, 4918
Grant, Geoffrey T., 6130
Grant, Gladys Flora, 4918
Grant, Ian, 893
Grant, John R., 4407
Grant, Kelvin, 4459

Grant, Laurie, 4633
Grant, Mabel B., 1470
Grant, Madeline, 893
Grant, Mary D., 6129
Grant, Merwin D., 5203
Grant, Richard A., 368
Grant, Robert N., 237
Grant, Sandy, 884
Grant, Suzanne B., 1696
Grantham, Hillary, 7670
Grantmakers in Health, 5611
Grantor Trust, D.J., 5920
Granville Capital, 7209
Grass Instrument Co., 577
Grass Trust, Ellen R., The , 577
Grass, Albert M., 577
Grass, Ellen R., 577
Grass, Henry J., 577
Grasseschi, Barbara, 431
Grassi, Rachel Toll, 7999
Grassmyer, K. Scott, 2561
Grasso, Catherine Smythe, 1061
Grasso, Lorraine P., 5663
Grasso, Richard A., 5663
Grasso, Scott, 3497
Grateful Foundation, The, 6720
Gratzer, Robert T. , 3022
Graubart, Noel, 8924
Grauberger, Gary L., 5158
Grauberger, Linda K., 5158
Graue, Marjory Louise, 8898
Graue, Mona, 8898
Graue, William Douglas, 8898
Graunke, Terence M., 3092
Graus, Asher, 6089
Graus, Samuel, 6089
Gravatte, Trice, 9503
Graven, Irene C., 6912
Graves, Beverly Garner, 2032
Graves, Claire, 4080
Graves, Daniel, 4088
Graves, Frances B., 2496
Graves, Helen M., 1280
Graves, Jim, 5011
Graves, Martha Reese, 1280
Graves, Melonie, 3390
Graves, Ron, 2685
Graves, William H., 1280
Graves, William M., 2496
Graves, William M., Jr., 2496
Graves, William P., 1280
Gravin, Jennifer, 1792
Gravina, Amy, 1910
Gray Fund, Joseph J., 2927
Gray Revocable Trust, Mae K., 2927
Gray Trust Dated May 1, Anita Winton,
    4756
Gray Trust, Anita, 4731
Gray, Avrum, 2927
Gray, Charles D., III, 7198
Gray, David, 6137, 7027
Gray, Elaine H., 8899
Gray, Faver, 8700
Gray, Glenn, 1094
Gray, J. Douglas, 9931
Gray, James, 2927
Gray, James A., 8899
Gray, Jeffrey M., 36
Gray, Laura K.G., 3836
Gray, Lloyd H., Jr., 71
Gray, Matthew, 2927
Gray, Maurine, 8869
Gray, Melvin, 2928
Gray, Pearl, 421

Gray, Steven F., 2928
Gray, Susanne, 2928
Gray, Thomas H., 2336
Graycor, 2928
Grazia, Peri De, 5402
Graziano, Judith O., 7879, 7892
Great Chesapeake Bay Swim, 3924
Great Circle Trust, 5843
Great Pacific Land Corporation, 388
Great Plains Manufacturing Inc., 3593
Great River Productions, Inc. Profit
    Sharing Plan, 3181
Great Western Bank, 5070, 8576
Greater Kanawha Valley Foundation, The,
    9751
Greater Talent Network, 6900
Greathead, R. Scott, 5662
Greaton, Evelyn S., 2060
Greaton, Susan, 2060
Greaton, Wilson B., Jr., 2060
Greaves, Maryon, 421
Greco, Leslie, 9300
Greco, Marie Katherine, 6081
Greco, Phil, 1610
Green Acres Fund, The, 9368
Green Bay Converting, 1937
Green Bay Packers, 7520
Green Charitable Trust, Helen Wade,
    4240
Green Spring Foundation, 7176
Green Tweed & Co., 8030
Green, Aaron, 9327
Green, Alan, Jr., 7777
Green, Andrew, 2061
Green, Anne W., 2061
Green, Bert, 9573
Green, Brenda, 7747
Green, Carrie, 9712
Green, Christine H., 4332
Green, Edith D., 9327
Green, Friday A., 1364
Green, Georgie F., 3704
Green, Glenn, 3027
Green, Jane K., 8638
Green, Jason, 188
Green, Jason E., 2299
Green, Jean, 4901
Green, Jean McGreevy, 1838
Green, Jennifer D., 1624
Green, Jerome, 3081
Green, Justin, 6857
Green, Larry, 3389
Green, Leo, Dr., 2705
Green, Leonard C., 1416
Green, Louis B., 2061
Green, Margie R., 2299
Green, May O' Donnell, 3150
Green, Nancy, 3081
Green, Norman H., 421
Green, Oliver H., 2061
Green, Patricia, 3389
Green, Phyllis, 5882
Green, Randall E., 4891
Green, Scott, 6123
Green, Stuart, 1838
Green, Susan, 6857
Green, Sydney Goodrich, 29
Green, Thomas, 4920
Green, Thomas R., 1590
Green, Thomas R., Jr., 4920
Green, Val A., 9327
Green, Val J., 9327
Green, W. Wesley, 8900
Green, William B., 9010

Greenbaum, Don, 870
Greenbaum, Robin, 5396
Greenberg Charitable Lead Trust-2000, Jerry A., The , 4106
Greenberg Charitable Trust No. 1, 6132
Greenberg, Adi K., 4106
Greenberg, Allen, 6875
Greenberg, Bernard A., 579
Greenberg, Brett, 2062
Greenberg, Brett A., 2062
Greenberg, Corinne P., 6132
Greenberg, Edward, 1773
Greenberg, Evan G., 6132
Greenberg, Fay, 5943
Greenberg, Jane F., 2062
Greenberg, Jeffrey W., 6132
Greenberg, Jerry A., 4106
Greenberg, Joel, 8310
Greenberg, Kenneth, 1812, 2216
Greenberg, Lawrence S., 6132
Greenberg, Lenore S., 579
Greenberg, Martin F., 2062
Greenberg, Marvin A., 4106
Greenberg, Maurice R., 6132
Greenberg, Maurice R. "Hank", 6132
Greenberg, Michael, 2216, 6530
Greenberg, Norman, 6520
Greenberg, Paul, 1812
Greenberg, Robert, 6389
Greenberg, Roger, 2216
Greenberg, Sylvia, 1812
Greenblatt, Allan, 2063
Greenblatt, Anne C., 5376
Greenblatt, Burton G., 5376
Greenblatt, Joel, 2063, 6757
Greenblatt, Judith S., 6133
Greenblatt, Muriel, 2063
Greenblatt, Richard, 2063
Greenblatt, Ronald, 5376
Greenblatt, Steven Jacob, 6133
Greenblatt, William M., 6133
Greenblum, Irving I., 9010
Greene, Arthur B., 6178
Greene, Barbara, 754
Greene, Carolyn A., 2064
Greene, Douglas H.S., 2064
Greene, Marion E., 739
Greene, Mark, 8022
Greene, Myer, 3876
Greene, Nancy K., 6499
Greene, Roger W., 4198
Greene, Roxanne D., 9681
Greene, Sarah Haskell, 7439
Greene, Susan, 6178
Greene, Thomas, 5795
Greene, Thomas H., 3947
Greene, Valerie, 2389
Greene, Wade, 6974
Greene-Sawtell, Alice, 2065
Greenewalt Jr. Trust, Crawford H., 8169
Greenewalt, David Lammot, 8169
Greenfeder, Sam, 2047
Greenfeld, Jacob, 6065
Greenfeld, Joseph, 6065
Greenfield Cooperative Bank, 4088
Greenfield Savings Bank, 4088
Greenfield, James L., 5879
Greenfield, Malkie, 6924
Greenfield, Marguerite G., 2066
Greenfield, Marjorie Hanson, 2950
Greenfield, Richard D., 2066
Greenfield, Stewart H., 1471
Greenheck Fan Corporation, 9802
Greenhill, Gayle G., 1472

Greenhill, Hy, 2884
Greenhill, Mark A., 2884
Greenhill, Michael L., 2884
Greenhill, Robert F., 1472
Greening, Ron, 8769
Greenleaf, 8525
Greenleaf, James, 8031
Greenleaf, Jane S., 6850
Greenleaf, Michael, 5485
Greenleaf, Victoria Stebbins, 6850
Greenlee, Paul, Jr., 5674
Greenlight Capital, 6720
Greenough, Donald M., 3992
Greensboro Junior Chamber of Commerce, 7209
Greensher, Joseph, 1066
Greenspan, Esq., C.P.A., Raphael P., 6071
Greenspan, Louis, 6134
Greenstein, Dianne, 8346
Greenwald, Benjamin, 3854
Greenwald, Howard, 9660
Greenway, Lumina V., 5236
Greenwell, Danie, 8326
Greenwich Capital Markets, 1549
Greenwood, John T., 2909
Greenwood, Lewis, 581
Greenwood, Rita, 581
Greer, Homer, 3735
Greer, James, 9916
Greevy, Charles F., III, 8219
Grefig, Max E., 9803
Grega, Marianne, 7327
Gregg, Brian W., 1399
Gregg, Kevin, 3817
Gregor, Cairo, 936
Gregory International Inc, Price, 9130
Gregory, Alicia, 2288
Gregory, Kitsy, 1352
Gregory, Mary, 407
Gregory, Mary Carol, 149
Gregory, Paul, 3601
Gregory, Robert B., 3765
Gregory, Susan, 8028
Gregory, Wayne A., Jr., 2288
Gregory, William A., Jr., 2067
Greiner Trust, Lorine, 2498
Greiner, Albert L., 2498
Greiner, Josephine L., 2498
Greiner, Kaivan, 2498
Greiner, Lindsay, 3511
Greiner, Lorine, 2498
Grenke, John E., 4448
Grenon, David, 4095
Gresh, Kim, 2463
Gresham, Mary, 5842
Gresham, W.W., Jr., 4823
Greslick, Richard L., Jr., 7929
Gretz, Hannah Judy, 3003
Gretz, Stephen R., 3003
Greuling, Michelle, 2165
Grevey, Anne C., 7427
Grewcock, Bruce E., 5086
Grewcock, Debra K., 5086
Grewcock, William L., 5086
Grey, Alexander, 5691
Grey, Bonnie R., 582
Grey, Brad A., 582
Grey, Carolyn K., 583
Grey, Cassandra H., 582
Grey, Margaret, 583
Grey, Richard S., 583
Grey, Samuel I., 582
Gribetz, Judah, 6651

Gridley, William G., Jr., 6739
Grief, Elizabeth Rosenberg, 9140
Grief, Jules, 9140
Grier, Andrew, 5106
Grierson, Holly, 9330
Gries, Robert D., 7431
Gries, Sally P., 7431
Gries, Sarah, 7431
Griesedieck, Henry C., III, 4925
Griesedieck, Marilyn W., 4925
Griesedieck, Paul H., 4925
Griesinger, Janet M., 3093
Griffel, William "Bill", 3535
Griffen, Jill, 3422
Griffey, Romey, 3662
Griffin, Anna Margaret, 4921
Griffin, Clarence A., 7113
Griffin, Clarence A., III, 7113
Griffin, Cynthia, 7807
Griffin, Dorothy G., 6138
Griffin, Elizabeth, 5693
Griffin, Elizabeth S., 7113
Griffin, Haynes G., 7113
Griffin, Jean, 665
Griffin, Jeffrey, 7113
Griffin, Joe Lee, 30
Griffin, Judith, 7944
Griffin, Karol, 3458
Griffin, Kenneth C., 2791
Griffin, R.A., Jr., 2499
Griffin, Ron, 2877
Griffin, Rosa May, 8902
Griffin, William L., 6138
Griffis, Mary Helen McCarty, 4848
Griffith Laboratories, 2930
Griffith Laboratories U.S.A., 2930
Griffith Labs Worldwide, 2930
Griffith Micro Science, 2930
Griffith, Arden, 1897
Griffith, Bronwyn A.E., 4805
Griffith, Dean L., 2929, 2930
Griffith, Gerry, 3350
Griffith, Lois Jo, 2929
Griffith, Mark, 1897
Griffith, Mary Farver, 3491
Griffith, Michael V., 9565
Griffith, Philip Thomas, 1236
Griffith, Theodore B., 3342
Griffith, Theodore B., Mrs. , 3342
Griffith, W. Louis, 8528
Griffith, William, 3350
Griffiths, Brent, 9321
Griffiths, Harold F., 4700
Griffiths, Keith A., 4700
Griffiths, Kenneth H., 4700
Griffiths, Kimberly J., 1629
Grigg Family Charitable Lead Trust, 9374
Grigg Family Charitable Lead Trust 201, 9374
Grigg Family Lead Trust 2011, 9374
Grigg, Charles W., 9374
Grigg, Donald W., 9374
Grigg, Laurie D., 9374
Grigg, Susan K., 9374
Griggs, Katherine, 8522
Grigsby, Jack W., 3725
Grigsby, Lane, 9631
Grigsby, Morgan, 3725
Grilliland Living Trust, Carol Beth, 2005
Grimes, Connie, 7933
Grimes, Kim, 7933
Grimes, Martha B., 4400
Grimes, Michael, 4648

Grimm Family Foundation, Rodney, The , 585
Grimm, Robert, 921
Grimm, Sarah K., 3579
Grimm-Marshall, Barbara, 585
Grimsley, Michael A., 2429
Grimsrud, Royce, 8577
Grin, David, 5764
Grin, Eugene, 5764
Grinberg, Alexander, 6139
Grinberg, Efraim, 6139
Grinewicz, Alex, 5301
Grinnell Mutual Reinsurance Co., 3501
Grinnell, Dianne, 8501
Grippardi, Paul, 1049
Grissett, Anthony, 153
Grissett, Arminda, 153
Grissett, David, 7666
Grisso, Jeane Ann, 8105
Griswold Industries, 586
Griswold, Adelaide, 6908
Griswold, David E., 586
Grizzard, Robert, Jr., 9464
Grobman Foundation, Frank & Roslyn, 6387
Grobman, Frank, 6140
Grobman, Richard, 6140
Grodd, Barbara, 6561
Grodd, James, 6561
Grodin, Jay, 413
Grodin, Jay H., 1167
Grodnick, Edythe Roland, 6148
Grodnick, James M., 49
Grodnick, Joy Mitchell, 49
Groff, Mary E., 8027
Groff, Michael, 2689
Grogan, Erma V., 9770
Grohs, Courtney, 9426
Gromala, John A., 914
Gromet, Ben, 1672
Groner Trust, Grace, 2932
Groner, Grace, 2932
Groom, David, 2547
Groom, Michael P., 808
Groot, Larry, 1673
Groot, Phyllis Christine, 1673
Grose, George R., 3905
Grose, Peter, 3905
Grosman, Shea, 6791
Gross Family, LP, H., 6654
Gross Foundation, Donald & Linda, 6387
Gross Irrevocable Trust, Meta G., 8414
Gross Trust, Rosalind, 1473
Gross Unitrust, Rosalind, 1473
Gross, Allen I., 6142
Gross, Arye, 421
Gross, Betty, 4582
Gross, Brian, 6142
Gross, Charles E., 4582
Gross, Courtlandt D., 465
Gross, Cynthia Squires, 173
Gross, David B., 7432
Gross, Donald L., 1978
Gross, Edie, 6142
Gross, Heddy, 6143
Gross, Henry, 6654
Gross, Inez, 4108
Gross, Jonathan, 6142, 6143
Gross, Karen, 6931
Gross, Mark, 6654
Gross, Michael L., 7432
Gross, Peter, 6931
Gross, Richard, 5561
Gross, Sandra L., 7433

Gross, Sara, 6931
Gross, Stella B., 587
Gross, Thomas R., 7432
Gross, Thomas R., Jr., 7432
Gross, Wayne, 3055
Grossberger, George, 6261
Grossberger, Vickie, 6261
Grosser, Shawn, 3807
Grossinger Motorcorp, 2933
Grossinger, Gary, 2933
Grossinger, Irwin, 2933
Grossinger, Sharon, 2933
Grossinger-Schiller, Caroline, 2933
Grossklaus, Charlie, 9814
Grossman, Alan R., 6684
Grossman, Alison, 2068
Grossman, Beverly, 4701
Grossman, Bruce D., 6146
Grossman, Dena, 1225
Grossman, Dena Beren, 1231
Grossman, Devorah, 7011
Grossman, Dianne M., 6146
Grossman, Ephraim, 6291
Grossman, Geoffrey, 6778
Grossman, Gina, 2690
Grossman, Harold I., 126
Grossman, Hendel, 6291
Grossman, Isaac, 1225, 6144
Grossman, Jerome K., 1696
Grossman, Judd B., 6145
Grossman, Kenneth, 6718, 7011
Grossman, Louis, 2068
Grossman, Lynne, 2068
Grossman, Marilynn P., 6146
Grossman, Marion, 2068
Grossman, Marton B., 6144
Grossman, Matthew, 6778
Grossman, N. Bud, 4701
Grossman, Nancy, 6145, 6739
Grossman, Nathan M., 3338
Grossman, Peter, 6778
Grossman, Raphael, 6728
Grossman, Richard, 3784
Grossman, Richard L., 5863
Grossman, Robert, 2068
Grossman, Ronald, 6146
Grossman, Ryan Jean, 126
Grossman, Ryna Jean, 126
Grossman, Sanford J., 1281
Grossman, Sharon, 6778
Grossman, Sheila, 6144
Grossman, Stanley, 6145
Grosvenor Foundation, 1282, 1283
Grosvenor, Alexander Lusk, 1282
Grosvenor, Craig Lusk, 1282
Grosvenor, J. Mark, 1283
Grosvenor, Nicholas Craig, 1282
Grotke, Adam, 9535
Grotnes, Alice D., 26
Groudis, Ausra, 6150
Groudis, Victor G., 6150
Grout, Kelsey Green, 7777
Grout, Melinda, 9592
Grove Silk Co., 8257
Grove, Jane, 3361
Groveman, Andrew, 8585
Groveman, Jan B., 8585
Grover, Fred, 7839
Grover, Jason, 3341
Groves and Sons Co., S.J., 4703
Groves, Anne, 4191
Groves, F. N., Jr., 4703
Groves, Frank N., 4703
Groves, Franklin N., 4703

Growth Trust Fund, 7008
Grubb, Dale Bird, 8020
Grubb, John R., 3502
Grubb, John W., 3502
Grubbs, Melinda H., 7538
Gruber, David, 7408
Gruber, David P., 4364
Gruber, Frances, 8345
Gruber, James, 3948
Grubich, Kenneth E., 2979
Grubman, Eric P., 6147
Gruelle, Deborah Toll, 7999
Gruening, Clark, 88
Grumbach, Antonia M., 6260
Grumbacher, M.S., 8028
Grumbacher, Mary Jo, 8028
Grumbacher, Stanley, 6148
Grumhaus, David D., Jr., 2934
Grumhaus, Jennifer K., 2934
Grunberg, Ariel, 6149
Grunberg, Daniel, 5706
Grunberg, David, 5706
Grunberg, Fanny, 6149
Grunberg, Judith B., 5706
Grunberg, Michael, 6149
Grundfest, Julianne D., 213
Grundhoefer, Bryan, 8797
Grundhoefer, Daniel, 8797
Grundhoefer, Mary Jo, 8797
Grundhofer Charitable Foundation, John
    F. and Beverly G., 8565
Grundhofer, John F., 8565
Grundhofer, Patricia Meier, 8565
Grundman, Vincent, 4764
Grundy, Joseph R., 8029
Grunenberg, Lynette, 321
Grunwald, Meir, 6574
Gruodis, Victor G., 6150
Gruppo, David, 5795
Grusecki, Brenda S., 2935
Grusecki, James P., 2935
Grushkin, Steven D., 1464
Gruson, Jane B., 7853
Gruss, Celia Fraser, 8617
Gruss, Jean F.R., 8617
Gruss, Jean Fraser, 8680
Gryl, Kim, 3126
Grymes, Sandra, 4239
GSC, 8599
Guard, SuzanneClair, 6739
Guarino, Alice B., 7947
Guarino, Carl A., 7947
Guarino, Christopher, 7947
Guarino, Eric, 7947
Guarino, Karen, 7947
Guarino, Tiel Batters, 7947
Guarisco, Martha, 3756
Guarnieri, Philip, 5872
Guarnieri, Philip, Jr., 2241
Gudbranson, Robert N., 7530
Gudden, Cheryl, 5091
Gudebski, Jay A., 490
Gudebski, M. Jordan, 490
Gue, Floyd, 3736
Gue, Rita, 3736
Guenther, Jack, 9055
Guenther, Paul L., 9942
Guenther, Robert L., 1477
Guenther, Valerie, 9055
Guerin, Fabienne, 589
Guerin, J.P., 589
Guerra, James, 839
Guest, J. Rodney, 4509
Guest, Richard L., 7924

Guethle, Kenneth, 5012
Guetz, Linda, 8905
Guetz, Linda R., 8905
Guetz, Michael H., 8905
Guetz, Michael H., Mrs. , 8905
GuideOne Life Insurance Co., 3503
Guilander Trust, Robert M., 4922
Guilander, Robert, 4922
Guild, Charlotte, 96
Guilden, Louise B., 1633
Guilden, Paul B., 1633
Guilford County, 7209
Guilford, Zeke, 1952
Guillaume, Gabriel, 1241
Guillaume, Mary K., 2500
Guillaume, Roger N., Jr., 2500
Guills, Jesse O., Jr., 9751
Guindi, Helen, 7006
Guindi, Henry J., 7006
Guinn, A. Patrick, 8906
Guinn, Alfred B., 8906
Guinn, Jennifer, 4879
Guinn, Patricia A., 8906
Guinness UDV North America, 1437
Gulati, Allison, 8032
Gulati, Charles J., 8032
Gulati, Jack D., 8032
Gulati, Jack D., II, 8032
Gulati, Jennifer, 8032
Gulati, Loretta, 8032
Gulati, Michael E., 8032
Gulati, Rosemary M., 8032
Gulden, Shirley, 2110
Gulf Coast Asphalt Company, 8738
Gulf Power Co., 2069
Gulfco, 1320
Gulftech International, 1320
Gulick, Alice J., 7383
Gulick, Diane S., 3509
Gulick, Henry W., 7383
Gulling, Douglas R., 3547
Gullot, Richard, 6624
Guloien, David E., 7980
Gumbs, Richard, 912
Gumenick, Sophia, 9462
Gumpert, Frank, 9184
Gund, Catherine, 5691
Gund, George, III, 1652
Gundersen, Carl, 2857
Gundersen, Gary, 2857
Gunderson, Bret, 9309
Gunderson, Kim, 3370
Gunderson, Scott, 5134
Gunn, Louise Staton, 2523
Gunnarson, Anna Karin M., 3996
Gunnigle, Ryan T., 2530
Gunning, Thomas J., 4211
Gunter, Linda Hays, 9052
Guntermann, Tony, 899
Gupa, Doris, 4151
Gupa, Raymond, 4151
Gupitosi, Pam, 5737
Gupta, Kiran B., 443
Gupta, Ramesh C., 443
Gupta, Santosh, 443
Gupta, Vinod K., 443
Gupta, Vinod Kumar, 443
Gureghian, Danielle, 8033
Gureghian, Vahan H., 8033
Gurley, Leah, 9183
Gurman, Paul M., 9512
Gurney, Elizabeth S., 5842
Gurvitz, Mark, 9345
Gurwicz, Bonnie, 5378

Gurwicz, Helena, 5378
Gurwicz, Herzel, 5378
Guschausky, Pam, 5058
Gushiken, Reid A., 2627
Gussman Trust, Herbert, 7677
Gust, Christopher L., 2732, 2936
Gust, M. Susan, 2936
Gustafson, Clifford, 5063
Gustafson, Edwin, Jr., 6606
Gustavson, Nancy, 9796
Gutcher, Molly A. Langer, 4166
Gutchess, Homer C., 5880
Gutchess, Martha W., 5880
Gutfruend, Pauline, 7019
Gutfruend, S., 7019
Guthman, Sandra P., 3179
Guthridge, Dave, 3344
Guthrie, Donald, 9586
Guthrie, Donald G., 9586
Guthrie, Glenn, 9
Guthrie, Jack, 9972
Guthrie, John A., III, 9972
Guthrie, Pat, 9972
Guthrie, Sabrina, 3288
Gutierrez, Ethan, 5621
Gutierrez, Kelly S., 1734
Gutierrez, Kenneth, 1599
Gutis, Aiden, 4560
Gutman, Abe, 3877
Gutman, Abraham, 3877
Gutman, Edna C., 6152
Gutman, Ernst, 3877
Gutman, Mannie, 3877
Gutman, Marion, 3877
Gutman, Menachem, 3877
Gutman, Monroe C., 6152
Gutmann, Rachel, 2156
Gutmann, Paul P., 7395
Gutshall, James S., 9581
Guttag 2005 Annuity Trust A, 4109
Guttag 2005 Annuity Trust B, 4109
Guttag 2005 Annuity Trust C, 4109
Guttag 2005 Annuity Trust D, 4109
Guttag Trust, Marjorie V., The , 4109
Guttag, John, 4109
Guttenberg, Rachael K., 6340
Gutterman, Leslie, 8387
Guttman, Marton, 6514
Guttman, Moishe, 6514
Guttman, Sara, 6514
Guttormsen, Neil F., 9862
Guttridge, Nicholas, 2580
Guttry, Lottie, 8970
Gutwein, Yehuda, 6791
Guy Carpenter & Co., LLC, 4375
Guyas, Vickie, 3412
Guyer, Leigh, 913
Guylas, Joan D., 133
Guyton, Dewey G., 8533
Guyton, Joan L., 8533
Guyton, Michelle, 1273
Guzelimian, Ara, 5671
Guzman, Brian, 6243
Guzniczak, Elinor, 9901
Guzniczak, Emily C., 9901
Guzniczak, Lauren A., 9901
Guzniczak, Michael J., 9901
Guzy, D. James, 249
Guzy, Marcia O., 249
Gwaltney, Frank, 2034
Gwin, Dean, 2034
Gwinn, L. L., 9770
Gwyn, Owen, Jr., 7143
Gyeszly, Amanda, 5475

Gyllenhaal, Anders, 811
Gyurko, Charles J., 8995
Gyurko, Sadie D., 8995

H&A Partners, 449
H. Bell Charitable Lead Annuity, Charles, 4731
H.E. Northgate, 5338
H.E. Sevilla, 5338
H.M. Payson & Co., 3791
H.O.W. Center, Inc., 8869
Haakenson, Anne R., 9760
Haakenson, Dean, 9760
Haan, Bernard, 4006
Haan, Jennifer, 4006
Haarlow, A. William, III, 2940
Haarlow, Blair Richlay, 2940
Haarlow, Evangeline R., 2940
Haarlow, Evangeline Rupp, 2940
Haarlow, William Noble, 2940
Haas, Brian, 4625
Haas, Destin, 3344
Haas, Donald W., 3710
Haas, Dwight, 7944
Haas, Elinor, 3567
Haas, Gary, 4598
Haas, Jacob, 6203
Haas, Raizy, 6203
Haas, Stan, 1772
Habata, Toyokatsu, 6249
Habenicht, Brenda, 3402
Haber, Alan, 6881
Haber, E. Jeb, 9597
Haber, Emily J., 9597
Haber, Gary, 1046
Haber, J. Glenn, 9597
Haber, Kellie, 9597
Haber, Manny, 6794
Haber, Nancy J., 9597
Haber, Raymond, 6794
Haber, Stephen, 6794
Haber, William M., 1126
Haberg, Richard A., 5660
Habets, James, 147
Habicht, Robert N., 4514
Hackbarth, James, 7114
Hackbarth, James P., 7114
Hackerman, Willard, 3952
Hackett The Clarett Group, Veronica, 6656
Hackett, L. Stephen, 9382
Hackett, Leo A., 7953
Hackett, Linda, 5808
Hackett, Linda L., 5808
Hackett, Melinda, 5808
Hackett, Montague H., Jr., 5808
Hackett-Hutchins, Melinda, 9544
Hackett-Munson, Linda L., 9544
Hackney, Guy, 5286
Hackney, Melissa M., 4239
Hadar Charitable Lead Trust, The, 6154
Hadar, Mica B., 6154
Hadar, Richard, 6154
Hadaway, Phyllis G., 2122
Hadden, Alexander M., 7013
Hadden, Alexander M., Mrs. , 7013
Hadden, J.C. David, 5682
Haddix, George F., 5084
Haddix, Sally A., 5084
Haddock, Ann M., 174
Haddock, Rich, 5198
Haddock, Robert, 174
Haddock, Robert M., 174

Hadhazy, Allan E., 2193
Hadley, Albert, 7809
Hadley, Ann Simon, 9455
Hadley, Steven, 9455
Hadlock, Kevin, 9346, 9347
Hadriye, Isaac, 6553
Hadriye, Shelly, 6553
Haefling, Carl, 9633
Haenel, Elizabeth D., 1979
Haensel, Peter C., 9783, 9924
Haentjens, R.P., 7997
Haessig, Priscilla, 3531
Hafertepe, Joe, 9033
Hafertepe, Maureen, 9033
Haffenreffer, John D., 5014
Hafner, Robert, 6699
Hafner, Travis, 7354
Haft, Burt, 5615
Haft, Daniel Foster, 5615
Haft, Ronald, 1813
Haft, Ronald S., 1800, 1813
Hagadone Helicopters, LLC, 2674
Hagadone, Bradley D., 2674
Hagadone, Duane B., 2674
Hagadone, Lola C., 2674
Hagan, Cornelius E., 9612
Hagan, John J., 1674
Hagan, John, Jr., 1674
Hagan, Mike, 1674
Hagan, Sally Ann, 3043
Hagar, Isabell, 8908
Hagar, Kari, 591
Hagar, Randall, 1051
Hagar, Sam R., 591
Hagar-Otterman, Velma, 591
Hage, Curtis L., 8573
Hagedorn, Michael D., 5026
Hagedorn, Tim, 8569
Hagen, Alexander L., 4704
Hagen, Luania R., 4704
Hagen, Mardee, 9319
Hagen, Mary E., 4211
Hagen, Roger, 9630
Hagen, Russell B., 4704
Hagen, Steven H., 2410
Hagens, Annette J., 2071
Hager Jr., Larry, 3687
Hager, Bruce William, 3687
Hager, D. Daniele, 8035
Hager, Frankie, 3687
Hager, George V., 8035
Hager, John S., 3687
Hager, John Stewart, Jr., 3687
Hager, Marjorie, 3687
Hagerstrom, C. Richard, Jr., 8647
Hagerty, Jeanne M., 4110
Hagerty, Thomas M., 4110
Haggar, Daley, 8907
Haggar, Isabell, 8908
Haggar, J.M., III, 8908
Haggar, J.M., Jr., 8908
Haggar, John Daley, 8907
Haggar, Joseph M., Jr., 8908
Haggar, Michael, 8907
Haggar, Patricia A., 8907
Haggar, Patricia J., 8907
Haggard, Karla, 3634
Hagge, Stephen J., 2712
Haggerty, Daniel J., 4705
Haggerty, John, 4705
Haggerty, Ruth, 4705
Haggin, John B.A., Jr., 8570
Haggin, L.L., III, 3668
Haggstrom, Leslie J., 5660

Haglage, Dorothy Claire, 3584
Hagler, Jon L., 4111
Hagopian, B. Kipling, 592
Hagopian, Gina Lauren, 592
Hagopian, Mary Ann, 592
Hagopian, Todd Kipling, 592
Hagstrom, Kristen L., 1627
Hagstrom, Paul A., 6922
Hagy, Paul A., 2710
Hahn Estate, Stephen, 6419
Hahn Waianae Land, LLC, 2072
Hahn, Carla Brasseur, 6157
Hahn, Charles, 6156
Hahn, Charles D., 6156
Hahn, Charles J., 5842, 6156
Hahn, David J., 2072
Hahn, Elizabeth, 8036
Hahn, Eric S., 6156
Hahn, Hai Joung, 2072
Hahn, Hai Joung Yoon, 2072
Hahn, Helen F., 3902
Hahn, Lillian Sara, 6419
Hahn, Linda M., 9117
Hahn, Lowell, 3607
Hahn, Norman, 8036
Hahn, Paul, 2072
Hahn, Sang Hoon, 2072
Hahn, Stephen, 6407
Hahn, Stephen R., 6157
Hahn, Thomas A., 441
Hahn, Tracy Weeks, 1774
Hahn-Baker, Anne H., 6156
Haiken, Edward, 5451
Haikin, Roslyn Beth Fuchs, 8881
Haile Jr. Foundation, Carol Ann and Ralph V., 7340
Haimbaugh, Sally S., 5001
Haimes, Todd, 6585
Haims, Bruce D., 1397
Haines, Christopher, 3736
Haines, Dennis, 420
Haines, John J., 3382
Haines, Pamela H., 3794
Haines, Robert H., 6530
Haines, William, 3736
Hainley, Stephaine, 9382
Hair, Charles M., 761
Hair, Nancy S., 952, 1033
Hair, Shannon, 9556
Haire, Gerald L., 4661
Haire, Lucretia, 4661
Haire, Steven, 4661
Haisley, Jimmie Anne, 2148
Hajduk, Alice J., 8185
Hajek, Josef, 2379
Hajim, Barbara, 6158
Hajim, Edmund A., 6158
Hake, Gregory A., 4933
Hake, John J., 4933
Hake, Matthew D., 4933
Halbin, Karey, 2108
Halbrook, Benita K., 2073
Halbrook, John A., 2073
Halbrook, Nathan, 2073
Halbrook, Pamela Dietze, 5320
Haldan Family Charitable Foundation, 1675
Haldan Family Foundation, 1676
Haldan, Dwight S., 1676
Haldan, Ethelmae S., 1675
Haldan, James Stuart, 1675
Hale, Charles M., 4112
Hale, Martin M., 4112, 4113
Hale, Michael V., 8764

Haleen, Tobi, 3206
Halegoua, Jamie A., 5968
Hales Charitable Fund, 2779
Hales, Alice, 6159
Hales, Andrea, 4478
Hales, Burton W., 2779
Hales, Catherine L., 2941
Hales, Daniel B., 2779
Hales, Daniel R.J., 2779
Hales, Erick W., 2941
Hales, John W., 2941
Hales, Marion J., 2779
Hales, Mary C., 2941
Hales, Terence, 6159
Hales, Thomas E., 6159
Hales, William M., 2941
Haley Foundation, The, 7209
Haley Trust, Jane, 7429
Haley, Barbara, 1334
Haley, C. James, Jr., 8845
Haley, Carrie C., 8519
Haley, Jane Gosiger, 7429
Haley, John M., 9132
Haley, John R., 7429
Haley, Kathleen Powers, 4114
Haley, Margaret J., 9132
Haley, Mike, 7209
Haley, Peter G., 7429
Haley, Steven, 4114
Haliday, Alfred C., Jr., 2196
Hall's Motor Transit Co., 8037
Hall, Anne, 9613
Hall, Benjamin, 9613
Hall, Beverly, 2576
Hall, Bill, 8721
Hall, Charles, 9613
Hall, Charles W., 8956, 8990
Hall, Charlotte, 4588
Hall, Dave, 7132
Hall, David, 2520, 4588
Hall, Dena M., 4337
Hall, Douglas K., 7373
Hall, Eugene C., 4873
Hall, Gerald, Jr., 8037
Hall, Gregory J., 9421
Hall, Henry, 1553
Hall, James F., 5337
Hall, James N., 4877
Hall, Janet C., 8909
Hall, Jerry, 6540
Hall, Joan Byrne, 7850
Hall, Joe, 2467
Hall, John K., Dr. , 5760
Hall, John N., 8037
Hall, Joseph William, 2840
Hall, Kevin, 7620
Hall, Lisa Shara, 7762
Hall, Margaret, 9613
Hall, Martha D., 3653
Hall, Mia, 200
Hall, Nechie, 1359
Hall, Patricia, 39
Hall, Patrick C., 4215
Hall, R. Jarek, 8037
Hall, Robert, 39
Hall, Robert E., 8037
Hall, Scott, 8869
Hall, Sean P., 8909
Hall, Shannon E., 8909
Hall, Sophia, 9648
Hall, Steve R., 3547
Hall, Thomas A., III, 8909
Hall, Thomas A., Jr., 8909
Hall, Thomas H., III, 2597

Hall, Thomas L., Dr. , 5760
Hall, William M., 2074
Halladay Motors, 9976
Hallam, Fanchon Hill, 8910
Hallam, Howard, 8910
Halldane, 3905
Halle, Martha D., 3878
Halle, Warren E., 3878
Hallenbeck, Eleanor, 6908
Hallenbeck, William, Jr., 6908
Hallene, Alan M., Jr., 2943
Hallene, James N., 2943
Hallene, Phyllis W., 2943
Hallett, Jessie F., 4706
Hallgrimson, Steven L., 878
Halliburton, Ebony, 3144
Hallingby, Julia H., 6160
Hallingby, Paul L., 6160
Hallman Lidnsay Paints, 9888
Hallman, Edward S., 2552
Hallman, Michael J., 60
Hallock, Brooke, 1918
Hallock, Raymond G., 5301
Halloin, Jeff, 9814
Halloran, Christine M., 4252
Halls, Tim, 4962
Hallstrom, Wyman P., III, 8449
Hallstrom, Wyman P., Jr., 8449
Halm, Jeffrey, 7531
Halmos, Jeffry, 2075
Halmos, Madeline G., 2075
Halmos, Stephanie, 2075
Halmos, Steven J., 2075
Halperin, Alan, 6429
Halperin, Barry S., 2076
Halperin, James L., 8912
Halperin, Marjorie, 8912
Halperin, Sharon, 8912
Halpern 2003 Charitable Lead Annuity
    Trust, Stacie, 7526
Halpern 2007 Charitable Lead Annuity
    Trust, Stacie, 7526
Halpern Charitable Lead Annuity Trust,
    Stacie, 7526
Halpern Trust, 5309
Halpern, Gladys, 5380
Halpern, Jacob, 5309
Halpern, Marcelle, 5763
Halpern, Sam, 5380
Halpern, Stacie L., 7526
Halpert, Beverly, 1812
Halpert, Stuart, 1812
Halstead Charitable Trust, 2944
Halstead Lumber Co., J.D., 2944
Halstead Property LLC, Jack, 6656
Halstead Trust, 2944
Halstead, Joanne S., 2944
Halstead, Wade, 2550
Halsted, Louise Davis, 8415
Halter Foundation, Maurice, 4334
Halverson, Gelaine, 4807
Halvim, Nachlat, 7030
Ham, Rudman J., 4203
Hamadi, Joanna D., 9800
Hamar, G. David Phelps, 6109
Hamblett, Christopher S., 8478
Hamblett, Jocelin G., 8478
Hamblett, Stephen, 8478
Hamblin, Brody, 9327
Hamblin, Holly, 9327
Hamby, Robert, 8527
Hamer, Gladys F., 9746
Hamer, J.C., 9746
Hamer, J.P., 9746

Hamer, Lori Dale, 9746
Hamid Moghadam, 1095
Hamill, Frances, 5822
Hamilton Bailey Charitable Trust, 8384
Hamilton, Anne, 4608
Hamilton, Brett A., 8913
Hamilton, Carolyn E., 8913
Hamilton, Chris, 8657
Hamilton, Crawford M., 1285
Hamilton, David B., 7468
Hamilton, David F., 8671
Hamilton, David Ley, 1605
Hamilton, Douglas H., 9834
Hamilton, Elizabeth, 8671
Hamilton, Frederic C., 1285
Hamilton, Frederic C., Jr., 1285
Hamilton, Jacqueline, 7435
Hamilton, Jane M., 1285
Hamilton, Jane Musich, 9834
Hamilton, Janet J., 8913
Hamilton, Jeffrey R., 429
Hamilton, John, 5626, 8671
Hamilton, Linda L., 9201
Hamilton, Lynn, 7442
Hamilton, Mary C., 1054
Hamilton, Patricia, 968
Hamilton, Peggy, 4410
Hamilton, Rick, 2463
Hamilton, Scott, 1291
Hamilton, Thomas, 1711
Hamilton, Thomas M., 8913
Hamilton, William H., 9834
Hamiowitz, Joseph, 2329
Hamiton, Scott T., 8913
Hamlin, Bill, 9191
Hamlin, Fran, 1295
Hamm, Alan W., 8914
Hamm, Candace S., 4751
Hamm, Charles J., 1476
Hamm, David Alan, 8914
Hamm, Edward H., 4751
Hamm, Harold, 7666
Hamm, Harold G., 2947
Hamm, Irene F., 1476
Hamm, Jean Anne, 8914
Hamm, Liza H., 1476
Hamm, Nancy Jane, 8914
Hamm, Sue, 7666
Hamm, Sue A., 2947
Hamm, Sue Ann, 2947
Hamm, William H., 4751
Hammack, Elizabeth Morgan, 8178
Hamman, Beverly O., 5151
Hamman, Stephen R., 5151
Hammecker, Roy, 6625
Hammelrath, Thomas P., 7371
Hammer, Matt, 9712
Hammer, Paul Allen, 6083
Hammer, Richard, 9979
Hammerman, Alan H., 2733, 3336
Hammill, Sarah, 9826
Hammond, Joseph, 240
Hammond, Linda S., 1327
Hammond, Michael, 108
Hammons, Kevin J., 8601
Hammoud, Jamal, 4373
Hammoud, Khaled, 4373
Hammoud, Mai, 4373
Hamon, Patricia, 1404
Hamorsky, Cynthia, 7848
Hampar, Armen, 594
Hampar, Steven, 594
Hampden Bancorp, 4116
Hampson Estate, Lois J., 7436

Hampton, Kathryn B., 355
Hamsa, William R., 5112
Hamus, Floyd, 9878
Hamus, Pat, 9878
Han-Andersen, Sung, 6925
Hana Foundation, 3033
Hanafin, Ellen, 5381
Hanafin, Erika, 5381
Hanafin, Marcella G., 5381
Hanaghan, Dennis, 7631
Hanamann, Rudy, 9898
Hanauer, Adrian, 9614
Hanauer, Gerald L., 9614
Hancher, Bill, 3397
Hancock, D.D.S., Richard B., 966
Hancock, Elaine G., 4840
Hancock, Gary, 9426
Hancock, John, 7424
Hancock, L.D., 4840
Hancock, Margaret M. Augur, 8712
Hancock, Michael H., 7055
Hand, Frances R., 2077
Hand, Francis R., 2077
Hand, Homer J., 2077
Handback Group, 9230
Handel, Franklin, Mrs. , 2296
Handelman, Donald E., 6840
Handelman, Joseph W., 6727, 6840
Handelman, Russell J., 6727
Handelman, William R., 6727, 6840
Handler, David A., 5296
Handler, Martha, 6161
Handler, Milton, 6162
Handler, Richard, 6161
Handlery, Ardyce A., 596
Handlery, Margaret, 596
Handlery, Michael K., 596
Handlery, Paul R., 596
Handley, Cathy, 9316
Handley, Virginia, 1005
Haneline, Dan, 3411
Hanes, Daniel M., Ph.D, 898
Hanes, Meir Baal, 5666
Haney Foundation Trust, 7116
Haney, Carol, 9202
Haney, Cheryl, 5368
Haney, Dale, 2034
Haney, Howard A., 8471
Haney, Sloan M., 2417
Hangs, George L., Jr., 7686
Hanif, Jasmine M. Campirides, 6680
Hanisko, Louis, 4616
Hank, Allen B., 2865
Hank, John C., 2865
Hank, Sheri, 4720
Hank, Viola D., 2865, 3303
Hankel, Richard, 5129
Hankin, Bernard, 8038
Hankin, Henrietta, 8038
Hankin, Richard, 8038
Hankin, Robert, 8038
Hankin, Robert S., 8038
Hankins, Edward R., 7437
Hankins, James M., 2359
Hankins, Lynne A., 3642
Hankins, Ruth Leale, 7437
Hankins, Stephen M., 3224
Hankison, John E., 7438
Hanks, Cullen, 8796
Hanks, Jackson, 9231
Hanks, Merrill I., 32
Hanley Living Trust, M.J. & P.C., 8915
Hanley, Andria, 1952
Hanley, Bryant M., 8916

Hanley, Ed, 1101
Hanley, Kathryn J., 1814
Hanley, Michael J., 1814
Hanley, Nancy, 8916
Hanley, Norma, 3651
Hanley, Patricia C., 8915
Hanley, Sarah E., 8916
Hanlon, Jason, 9075
Hanlon, Judith, 4181
Hanlon, Thomas, LLC, 1284
Hanlon-Stolte, Mardy, 7357
Hann, Cynthia, 5293
Hanna, Therese, 4828
Hannah, Bill, 208
Hannah, Catha, 3659
Hannah, Marie C., 3659
Hannah, Wood, 3659
Hannah, Wood, III, 3659
Hannigan, Dan, 4497
Hannon, Brian T., 7953
Hannum, Diane, 6540
Hanrahan, Dan, 4770
Hanrahan, Pegeen, 2391
Hansch, Dennis L., 9850
Hanse, William C., 5581
Hansen, 2348
Hansen Irrevocable Trust, Elizabeth A.,
    2948
Hansen Revocable Trust, Elizabeth A.,
    2948
Hansen Trust, Elizabeth A., 2948
Hansen, Alexander E., 9835
Hansen, Allison C., 6572
Hansen, Barbara, 7408
Hansen, Bernice F., 5087
Hansen, Caitlin, 9465
Hansen, Caleb, 9465
Hansen, Carl M., 2079, 9615
Hansen, Charles R, Jr., 5219
Hansen, Cherrie L., 9465
Hansen, Harvey C., 2079
Hansen, Helen M., 2079
Hansen, Irving A., 2948
Hansen, Jamey, 5087
Hansen, Jill T., 3547
Hansen, John P., 127
Hansen, Julie, 1184
Hansen, Margaret W.H., 9835
Hansen, Marie E., 127
Hansen, Mark W., 127
Hansen, Mary Dale, 7295
Hansen, Olivia B., 1756
Hansen, Paul, 1786
Hansen, Phillip, 425
Hansen, Rebecca, 9465
Hansen, Richard C., 9465
Hansen, Richard D., 9465
Hansen, Robert, 1300
Hansen, Ron, 9985
Hansen, Thomas P., 587
Hanshaw, Frank, Jr., 9754
Hansmann, Ralph E., 7031
Hanson Trust, Constance B., 1830
Hanson, Abigail, 5383
Hanson, Alexander D., 5383
Hanson, Andrew, 2972
Hanson, Anna Emery, 2950
Hanson, Beverly D., 2461
Hanson, Breck, 9778
Hanson, Carrie, 7827
Hanson, Christy, 2972
Hanson, Derek, 723
Hanson, Eliza F., 5383
Hanson, Elizabeth, 1151

Hanson, Elizabeth J., 9635
Hanson, Ellen, 6587
Hanson, Eric, 9635
Hanson, Erik A., 6409
Hanson, Erinn, 723
Hanson, Fred L., 9635
Hanson, Jamie, 4623
Hanson, John Nils, 1286
Hanson, Laura F., 5383
Hanson, Linda H., 2972
Hanson, Margaret P., 1830
Hanson, Mark, 4623
Hanson, Mary Kay, 9853
Hanson, Matthew, 4623
Hanson, Robert B., 4067
Hanson, Sam, 4648
Hanson, Shirly, 4623
Hanson, Stephanie M., 1286
Hanson, Stephen P., 6163
Hanson, Susan, 564
Hanson, Theodre, 3275
Hanus, Barbara A., 2951
Hanus, George D., 2951
Hanus, Julie, 3432
Hanus, Magda, 2951
Hanway, Edward B., 8315
Hanway, Elizabeth A., 8315
Hanway, Ellen M., 8315
Hanway, H. Edward, 8315
Hanway, Patrick N., 8315
Happy State Bank, 8777
Hara, Rodger A., 1239
Harabedian, Robert, 411
Harada, Jan, 2657
Harahan, William J., IV, 4509
Haraldson, Beulah M., 8917
Haranas, Mark R., 4216
Haranzo, Mark E., 9544
Harary, Janet, 6166
Harary, Jerry, 6166
Harary, Leon J., 6166
Harary, Michael, 6166
Harary, Sarah, 5893
Haraway, Donald L., 9511
Harbaugh, Gregory A., 8043
Harbert, James, 2701
Harberts, Jane, 8554
Harbeson, Ellen, 1718
Harbor Fund, 4927
Harbor View Holdings Inc., 771
Harbour, Janet L., 7437
Harbour, Robert, 172
Harbrecht, Sandra W., 7373
Harcourt, Kelly Stewart, 1082
Harczak, Harry J., Jr., 2952
Harczak, Jason, 2952
Harczak, Marcy A., 2952
Hard, Rachel, 4396
Hardacre, David, 430
Hardart, Frank J., III, 6455
Hardaway, Harry, 2599
Hardberger, Linda, 9237
Harden, Gregory M., 6922
Harden-Polichino, Rhonda, 8910
Hardenbrook, Helen, 4260
Hardesty, Jean, 9740
Hardiek, Bernard, 2953
Hardiek, Greg, 2953
Hardiek, Mark, 2953
Hardiman, Donna Landau, 6955
Hardin, Dan, 5620
Hardin, Neal, 9660
Harding, Henry J., 2848
Harding, John, 9903

Harding, Judith I., 2518
Harding, Lillian R., 1174
Harding, Louis, 5525
Harding, Martha, 2848
Harding, Robert L., 2848
Harding, Robert L., Jr., 2848
Hardison, James, 2081
Hardison, Janet, 2081
Hardison, Jill, 2081
Hardison, John, 2081
Hardison, Leslie C., 2081
Hardison, Paul, 2081
Hardman Signs, 8700
Hardman, Grayson Kelsey, 6298
Hardner, Jared, 8918
Hardner, Margaret, 8918
Hardner, Norbert H., 8918
Hardon, Allen, 5211
Hardon, Roger, 5211
Hardy, Don Ed, 599
Hardy, Douglas, 599
Hardy, J.J., 3817
Hardy, Kathleen, 8869
Hardy, Richard B., 4139
Hardyman, Maitland, 9674
Hare, Bonnie, 3359
Hare, Daniel P., 2675
Hare, Laura, 2954
Hare, Richard, 2675
Hare, Susan, 2675
Hare, Susan F., 2675
Harelson, Julie, 346
Harer, Monty, 8569
Harford, Karen, 5091
Hargrave, Jeffrey, 7715
Hargrave, Louis W., 3978
Hargraves, John A., 6529
Hargreaves, John, 461
Hargrove, Brian, 6604
Hargrove, David Brian, 6604
Harithas, Ann W., 9210
Hariton, Leon, 2049
Hariton, Leon, Mrs. , 2049
Harjai, Sneha, 1768
Hark, Marguerite Delany, 2955
Harker, Jack, 5135
Harker, Joseph Edward, 3329
Harkness, Calvin, 12
Harla, JoAnne, 5400
Harlan Charitable Lead Trust, Hal P.,
    3391
Harlan, Doug, 3391
Harlan, Hal P., 3391
Harlan, Hugh, 3391
Harlan, Paul, 7752
Harlem Irving Companies, 3075
Harless, James R., 9615
Harless, Jim, 9669
Harley, Narley L., 7440, 7481
Harling, Cal C., 795
Harling, Randy, 8527
Harlo Investments, 4820
Harman, Barry W., 9328
Harman, Carla, 5386
Harman, David L., 7120
Harman, Elaine, 9328
Harman, Hayden K., 598
Harman, J. Patrick, 7120
Harman, Mark B., 9328
Harman, Nan M., 598
Harman, Patrick H., 7120
Harman, Phoebe N., 7120
Harman, Reed L., 598
Harman, Robert, 3796

Harman, Susan S., 7120
Harman, Todd B., 9328
Harman, Wauna, 9328
Harman-Stokes, Kathy, 9734
Harmeyer, Dave, 3515
Harmon Trust Foundation, 6168
Harmon Trust, William E., 6168
Harmon, Aaron, 7666
Harmon, Anna S., 3246
Harmon, Baron D., 3143
Harmon, Claude C., 7686
Harmon, Elaine, 8053
Harmon, Gail McGreevy, 1838
Harmon, Herbert N., 3944
Harmon, James, 6169
Harmon, James A., 6169
Harmon, Jane, 6169
Harmon, John C., 8272
Harmon, John J., 8053
Harmon, Julia J., 7686
Harmon, Kathleen, 238
Harmon, Martin A., 253
Harmon, Wayne, 607
Harmony, Jane E., 7314
Harms, George, 5385
Harms, Jolene C., 9969
Harms, Kevin, 5385
Harms, Robert, 5385
Harms, Ruth, 5385
Harmsen, Dorothy C., 128
Harmssen, Hilary Joy, 677
Harmssen, Joshua A., 677
Harned, Dave, 4552
Harnick, Sheldon, 6323
Harper Charitable Lead Annuity Trust,
    Louise G., 9632
Harper, Alan B., 9632
Harper, Andrew, 9373
Harper, Carolyn J., 5088
Harper, Charles M., Jr., 5088
Harper, Charles M., Sr., 5088
Harper, George, 2082
Harper, Harvey H., IV, 2259
Harper, Julie, 2706
Harper, Kimberly M., 2259
Harper, Mark, 7678
Harper, Mitch, 8293
Harper, Morris, 7933
Harper, Philip S., 9373
Harper, Robert W., 2082
Harper-Wyman Co., 9373
Harpest, Todd, 7375
Harral, Brenda, 8963
Harrbaugh, Bryce, 7587
Harrell, Bobbi, 591
Harrell, Curtis F., 8919
Harrell, Deloris, 7204
Harrell, Doug, 3485
Harrell, Forrest E., 8919
Harrell, Forrest E., Jr., 8919
Harrell, Jim, 9010
Harrell, Jimmy, 7698
Harrell, Robert L., 3814
Harrell, Sandra H., 8919
Harriman, Brown Brothers, 6506
Harriman, W. Averell, 6170
Harrington, Andrew, 4490
Harrington, Barbara, 4411
Harrington, Brent, 369
Harrington, Debbie Weil, 6204
Harrington, Deborah W., 6204
Harrington, Denise, 4598
Harrington, George, 4117
Harrington, John Timothy W., 6204

Harrington, Lydia L., 7581
Harrington, Samuel P., 6204
Harrington, Susan W., 1182
Harrington-Heide, Jane, 9863
Harris Bank, 2700, 2809
Harris Charitable Lead Annuity Trust,
    Winifred J. and John M., 4710
Harris Charitable Lead Trust, Brigitte P.,
    4461
Harris Charitable Lead Trust, Edward F.,
    2956
Harris Foundation, Irving, The , 2778
Harris Revocable Trust, Jonathan M.,
    6172
Harris, Alexander W., 2957
Harris, Andrew L., 600
Harris, Beth McCarty, 4841
Harris, Brigitte P., 4461
Harris, Charles L., 9734
Harris, Charles U., 600
Harris, Charles W., 5129, 7719
Harris, Christine, 9356
Harris, Christopher, 4620
Harris, Constance, 1063
Harris, David, 3279
Harris, Debra, 9466
Harris, Dee Ann, 7793
Harris, Diane B., 2957
Harris, Diane Lynn, 2401
Harris, Edward F., 2956
Harris, Elizabeth, 9467
Harris, Ellen T., 4035
Harris, F. Aaron, 9468
Harris, Floyd W., 9468
Harris, Gaylene V., 1228
Harris, H. Hiter, III, 9467
Harris, H. Hiter, Jr., 9467
Harris, J., 259
Harris, Jack S., 9862
Harris, James I. , 601
Harris, Jane, 2956
Harris, Janna, 471, 472
Harris, Jeffrey P., 7573
Harris, Jennifer, 6171
Harris, Jennifer Lynn, 6172
Harris, Jennifer M., 2957
Harris, Jessica, 1478, 6775
Harris, Jil W., 9467
Harris, Joanie, 8840
Harris, Johanna H., 4118
Harris, John, 3495
Harris, John C., 600
Harris, John H., II, 2957
Harris, Jonathan M., 6172
Harris, Joseph, 9450
Harris, Judith A., 8279
Harris, Judy H., 3659
Harris, Katherine A., 4710
Harris, Katherine Alexander, 9467
Harris, Ken, Jr., 34
Harris, Kenneth L., 34
Harris, Kenneth L., Jr., 34
Harris, Kenneth L., Sr., 34
Harris, Kiffi, 7801
Harris, Linda, 7863
Harris, Linda C., 3018
Harris, Margaret B., 34
Harris, Marjorie A., 4710
Harris, Mark, 2956
Harris, Martha, 4620
Harris, Mary, 446
Harris, Mary Ann, 2956
Harris, Matthew, 6171
Harris, Matthew C., 6171

Harris, Molly K., 2957
Harris, Morton E., 4461
Harris, Nicki, 6172
Harris, Patricia, 5761
Harris, Patricia W., 46
Harris, Phillip G., 9619
Harris, Randall, 9050
Harris, Randy A., 2658
Harris, Richard H., 7377
Harris, Richard R., 9463
Harris, Robert, 9050
Harris, Robert N., 259
Harris, Robert R., 2201
Harris, Robert W., 601
Harris, Roland J., 1438
Harris, Ronald, 9466
Harris, Roy W., 4841
Harris, Sally C., 1413
Harris, Scott, 4672
Harris, Sherri, 8844
Harris, Shirley M., 601
Harris, Susan G., 9441
Harris, Vera, 2956
Harris, Vonda, 34
Harris, W. Gordon, 4710
Harris, William H., 4118
Harris, William N., 259
Harris, William W., 259
Harris, Wilmot L., Jr., 1413
Harrison Industries, 35
Harrison, Albert E., 2502
Harrison, Angie, 2664
Harrison, Avery, 7204
Harrison, Bob, 9162
Harrison, Carol M., 35
Harrison, Cassidy, 5161
Harrison, David, 9662, 9669
Harrison, Douglas P., 2502
Harrison, Hugh T., II, 9452
Harrison, Jessica, 1355
Harrison, Jim, 5608
Harrison, John M., 2502
Harrison, Louis S., 3245
Harrison, Michele, 178
Harrison, Richard, Dr. , 9781
Harrison, William T., Jr., 2356
Harrold, Mark, 8301
Harrold, Mary Beth, 5104
Harryman, Robert J., 726
Harsco Corp., 8040
Harsh, Ed, 6950
Harshman, Deroy, 5121
Hart Trust, Olga B., 4708
Hart, Augustin, 2792
Hart, Colin, 9536
Hart, Gurnee F., 6173
Hart, Henry P., 5521
Hart, John H., 2958
Hart, Karl V., 3704
Hart, Kathleen M., 570
Hart, Kenneth A., 2977
Hart, Margaret S., 2792
Hart, Marjorie, 6173
Hart, Nellie, 3771
Hart, Patricia I., 8632
Hart, Timothy, 3134
Harter, Douglas, 7379
Harter, John Burton, 3660
Hartigan, Mary, 2835
Hartigan, Mary K., 2835
Hartl, Leonard L., 9878
Hartley, Mac, 2666
Hartley, Nedenia H., 6840
Hartman, Cherryl L., 7084

Hartman, Claudette L., 8920
Hartman, David, 3683
Hartman, David A., 8920
Hartman, Douglas M., 8920
Hartman, Jean, 1802
Hartman, Jerry J., 6922
Hartman, John E., 8920
Hartman, M.B., 557
Hartman, Malcolm J., 6070
Hartman, Paul, 4636
Hartman, Wayne P., 8920
Hartnett, George J., 8143
Hartquist, Jeff, 4736
Hartsband, Meryl, 8657
Hartshorn, Kelly, 1703
Hartshorn, Margaret, 1703
Hartshorn, Michael, 1703
Hartshorn, Terry, 9345
Hartshorn, Timothy, 1703
Hartung, Steven J., 9931
Hartvigsen, Keith, 5074
Hartwell, Anne C. Vanderbilt, 5983
Hartwell, Charles B., 4637
Hartwell, David B., 4637, 4756
Hartwell, Lucy B., 4637
Hartwell, Stephen, 1807
Hartwick Unitrust, Alice Kales, 4462
Hartwig, Christopher, 9836
Hartwig, Dana, 9836
Hartwig, Evelyn, 9836
Hartwig, Hans, 9836
Harty, Chris Breisch, 3125
Hartz, Greg, 6373
Hartzell Industries, 7538
Harvard University, 5707
Harvest Foundation, 4806
Harvey Enterprises Inc., 7119
Harvey Gerstman Associates, 6074
Harvey, Ann, 1319
Harvey, Ashton, 6868
Harvey, Brian L., 602
Harvey, Cannon, 6248
Harvey, Cannon Y., 1287
Harvey, Constance, 1319
Harvey, Darin, 602
Harvey, Ellen D., 8182
Harvey, J. Dale, 660
Harvey, Jim, 3807
Harvey, Larry D., 1326
Harvey, Laurel, 3919
Harvey, Lydia, 6248
Harvey, Lyndia K., 1287
Harvey, Mark, 1319
Harvey, Nelson, 1319
Harvey, Stephanie F., 660
Harvey, Tanya, 2803
Harvey, Thomas E., 6490
Harvey, Tim R., 3055
Harvey, Tyler Y., 1287
Harvill Trust, Jane, 243
Harwood, Amy W., 1423
Harwood, Charles E., 4119
Harzan, Annette, 884
Harzan, John, 884
Haseley, John, 7311
Hasenberg, Chris, 9814
Hasenfeld Stein, 5338
Hasenfeld, Alexander, 6174
Hasenfeld, Ephraim, 5338
Hasenfeld, Shoshana, 5338
Hasenfeld, Zissel, 6174
Hasenfeld, Zissy, 6174
Hasenfeld-Stein Inc., 6174, 6856
Hashemi, Nasrin, 595

Hashemi, Noosheen, 595
Haskell, Coburn, 7439
Haskell, Coburn T., 7439
Haskell, Eric T., 7439
Haskell, Joan, 2083
Haskell, Joan S., 2083
Haskell, Keith, 5091
Haskell, Mark, 7439
Haskell, Melville H., 7439
Haskell, Melville H., Jr., 7439
Haskell, Molly, 5700
Haskell, Naomi, 8163
Haskell, Preston, 2005
Haskell, Preston H., 2083
Haskell, Preston H., III, 2083
Haskell, Preston H., IV, 2083
Haskell, Schuyler A., 7439
Hasken, Sarah, 3520
Haskins, John C., 225
Haskins, Morris E., 3661
Haskins, Scott, 225
Hasler, Terry, 3363
Haslett, Emily Blum, 8589
Haslett, John J., II, 1764
Hass, Cindy, 3171
Hass, Ellen Nalle, 8370
Hassay-Savage Broach Co.Inc., 4088
Hassel, Bryan C., 1258
Hassel, Calvin, 8042
Hassel, Morris, 8042
Hassell, Raymond E., 8449
Hassenfeld, Merrill I., 1902
Hassett, Douglas, 4411
Hasson, Laurie, 7435
Hastings Trust, Jane Hope, 1479
Hastings, Diane F., 3785
Hatao, Katsumi, 5795
Hatch, Mary Alice Marriott, 3909
Hatch, Sandra L., 9837
Hatch, William G., 9837
Hatcher, Robert F., 2485
Hatfield and Co., 8922
Hatfield, Claudette, 8922
Hatfield, Eileen, 6175
Hatfield, George R., 8922
Hatfield, Jay, 6175
Hatfield, John G., 8922
Hathaway, David, 6176
Hathaway, Harry L., 973
Hathcoat, Annette, 7718
Hatleskog, E. Kweilen, 6309
Hatley, Kristina, 9610
Hatten, Dean E., 4731
Hatten, M. Kristen Kelleher, 4147
Hatten, Penelope B., 4731
Hatten, Penelope Bell, 4637
Hatterscheidt Trusts, F.W., 8566
Hatterscheidt, Ruth K., 8566
Hatton, Donald W., 3591
Hatton, Eugene, 5696
Hatton, Nikki C., 1060
Hattori-Roche, Ritsuko, 3201
Hattox, Ralph S., 6304
Hauben, Bruce M., 4120
Hauben, Craig, 4120
Hauben, Jason, 4120
Hauben, Michael, 4120
Hauber, Gregory, 8043
Hauber, Jean D., 8043
Hauber, Pamela, 8043
Hauber, Paul, 8043
Hauber, William M., 8043
Hauck, Frederick, 7440
Hauck, John W., 7440

Hauff, Robert V., 6177
Haug, William A., 4689
Haugen, Clifford, 1639
Haugen, Jon M., 4471
Haugland Group, LLC, 2084
Haugland, Linda, 2084
Haugland, William J., 2084
Haugse QTP Trust, Ralph A., 7771
Haun, Melinda, 9797
Haus, Elsie I., 5801
Haus, Ronald R., 5801
Haus, Scott, 7718
Hausback, Paul, 271
Hauser Family Revocable Living Trust,
    1678
Hauser, Julianne, 1678
Hauser, Richard, 9810
Hauser, W. Kurt, 1678
Hausfeld, Marilyn, 9469
Hausfeld, Michael D., 9469
Hauske, Thomas J., Jr., 9931
Hausman Felicidad LLC, 603
Hausman, Jerry A., 4121
Hausman, Margaretta S., 4121
Hausman, Marilyn E., 603
Hausman, Richard P., 603
Hausman, Richard P., Jr., 603
Hauthaway, Bartlett M., 4274
Hautman, April, 3427
Have Irrevocable Trust, Gregory A., 4933
Havel, Terry, 6097
Haveman, Nancy L., 4429
Havens, Amy, 9772
Havens, John P., 3727
Havens, Prentiss C., 3727
Haverkate, Jeffrey M., 1288
Haverkate, Mark, 1288
Haverkate, Mary Ann, 1288
Haverly, Rebecca, 8918
Haverstock, Mary, 900
Havican, John, 257
Haviland, Colleen A., 5131
Havner, LeeAnn R., 604
Havner, Ronald L., 604
Havner, Ronald L., Jr., 604
Havrilla, Edward J., 7704
Hawaiian Host, 2650
Hawes, Mary Catherine, 2432
Hawk Industries, 7925
Hawk Revocable Trust, Henry, 7434
Hawk Trust, Beverly A., 7434
Hawk, Beverly A., 7434
Hawkins Charitable Lead Trust, 7769
Hawkins Construction Co., 5089
Hawkins Family Charitable Annuity Trust,
    The, 2503
Hawkins Trust, Alexandra, 8044
Hawkins, Anna Grace, 8923
Hawkins, Benjamin, 7769
Hawkins, Beth, 7769
Hawkins, Catherine O., 1843
Hawkins, Chaille Winston, 9282
Hawkins, Chris, 5089
Hawkins, Daniel, 7769
Hawkins, Elsie, 7522
Hawkins, Fred, Jr., 5089
Hawkins, Fred, Sr., 5089
Hawkins, Jack , Esq., 2149
Hawkins, Jean K., 2598
Hawkins, John D., 8923
Hawkins, John D., Jr., 8923
Hawkins, Kate, 3363
Hawkins, Kim, 5089
Hawkins, Lauren, 3892

Hawkins, Renee D., 8923
Hawkins, Robert C., 7769
Hawkins, Scott D., 2503
Hawkins, Shirley Jean, 7769
Hawkins, Stan, 2686
Hawkins, Stephanie, 7769
Hawkins, Susan M., 2503
Hawkins, Winsome, 2461, 2576
Hawks, Richard, 6559
Hawley, Alexandra W., 605
Hawley, David S., 1590
Hawley, Gary W., 1559
Hawley, Wallace H., 605
Hawley, Wallace R., 605
Haworth Foundation, Richard and
  Ethelyn, 4575
Haworth, Anna, 4575
Haworth, Anna C., 4575
Haworth, Daniel, 179
Haworth, Donna, 179
Haworth, Ethelyn L., 4575
Haworth, Jennifer L., 4575
Haworth, Matthew R., 4575
Haworth, Richard G., 4575
Haworth, William Barr, 179
Haws, Mitch, 8874
Hawthome, Sarah Case, 1757
Hawthorne, Danielle K., 5786
Hawthorne, Eleanor, 5786
Hawthorne, Joan, 7295
Hawthorne, Kevin S., 5786
Hawthorne, Richard W., 2057
Hawver, Michelle, 3108
Hawxhurst, Jean, 3674
Hay Trust, John I., 2961
Hay, Bonita, 3057
Hayden, Agnes R., 4464
Hayden, Donald C., 4464
Hayden, Donald, Jr., 4464
Hayden, Douglas, 2998
Hayden, James G., 4076
Hayden, Jerry L., 2998
Hayden, Marilyn J., 2998
Hayden, Ted, 3589
Haydon, Richard L., 5154
Hayes Living Trust, Mariam Cannon,
  7121
Hayes Trust, Ella, 8643
Hayes, Barbara W., 7121
Hayes, Brett, 3448
Hayes, Charles W., 759
Hayes, Christina Anton, 5133
Hayes, Ella, 8610
Hayes, Gene, 9474
Hayes, Grace, 3390
Hayes, Harrison F., 1244
Hayes, Helen Young, 1247
Hayes, Jay I., Jr., 9474
Hayes, Joanne Fleming, 8615
Hayes, Linda Snyder, 5540
Hayes, Matthew S., 1247
Hayes, Robert C., 7121
Hayes, Robert C., Jr., 7121
Hayes, Shelley P., 9112
Hayes, Stewart L., 5165
Hayes, Tammy, 3462
Hayes, Tyan, 89
Hayes, Victor R., 4501
Hayford, David Patrick, 2086
Hayford, June, 2086
Hayford, Marylou, 2086
Hayford, Michael Edward, 2086
Hayford, V, Warren John, 2086
Hayford, Warren J., 2086

Hayford, Warren John, 2086
Haygood, Billy, 4840
Hayhoe, Christopher S., 4681
Haylor, Jane T., 7615
Hayman, Betty C., 606
Hayman, Fred J., 606
Hayman, Robert, 606
Hayner, H.H., 9694
Haynes, Bobby, 8614
Haynes, Bobby R., 8614
Haynes, Felicia, 8614
Haynes, Felicia B., 8614
Haynes, Norine, 9037
Haynes, Susan, 3360
Hays, Charles W., Jr., 3785
Hays, Melissa Q., 9142
Hays, Nancy Scheller, 8258
Hayse, Monica, 3628
Haystead, John, 2108
Hayton, Allan, 84
Hayunga, Del, 3699
Hayward, George Stewart Marshall,
  1605
Hayward, Marilyn Rushworth, 1605
Hayward, Nathan, III, 1605
Hayward, Nathan, IV, 1605
Hayward, Pierre duPont, 1641
Hayworth-Hopp, Ashley, 3401
Hazard Limited Partnership, 4123
Hazard, C. Michael, 4123
Hazard, George S., Jr., 4850
Hazard, Stephen, 5210
Hazard, Susan G., 4123
Hazelbaker, Billie E., 7441
Hazelbaker, R. Brian, 7441
Hazelbaker, Ralph E., 7441
Hazelton Lutheran Home Irrevocable
  Trust, 8233
Hazen, Judith E., 5970
Hazzard, Miriam, 4739
Hazzard, Yakub, 575
HCH Family Foundation, 9482
He, Qingdong, 5162
He, Zhengxu, 5162
Head, Carol A., 7961
Head, Douglas M., 4709
Head, Glenn O., 7961
Head, Jeffery A., 28
Head, Kathryn S., 7961
Head, Lynn, 5612
Head, Martha M., 4709
Head, Robert, 3024
Head, Virginia R., 4709
Header Products, 4509
Headrick Companies, 4844
Headrick Sign Company, 4844
Headrick, Gina, 4844
Headrick, Richard, 4844
Healey, Carolyn, 8251
Healey, Monica C., 4055
Healey, Robert K., 7542
Healey, Robert K., Jr., 7542
Healey, Robert K., Mrs. , 7542
Health Management Associates, 8628
Health Markets, 8779
Health Net, 608
Health Net of California, 608
Health Plan of Michigan Inc, 4460
Health, Trinity, 2109
Healy, Daniel M., 6179
Healy, Helen B., 1226
Healy, James T., 1131
Healy, Morley, 1226
Heaney, Cornelius, 5788

Heaney, Cornelius A., 5788
Heard, Wyatt, 9233
Hearing, Richard Scott, 2261
Hearne, James W., 9992
Hearne, Sheila, 1709
Hearst, Joseph B., 9457
Hearst, Victoria, 1339
Hearst, William A., 9457
Heartbeat International, 9033
Heaston, Elizabeth, 8642
Heath Irrevocable Trust, Laura, 7496
Heath, Charles K., 2701
Heath, Harriet A., 2701
Heath, John E.S., 2701
Heath, Karen, 5838
Heaton, Carmen, 3508
Heaton, Robert E., 9568
Heatter, Justin W., 1880
Heaven Hill Distilleries, 3693
Heavin, Gary, 8925
Heavin, Glenna L., 8925
Heavin, Nicole, 8925
Hebenstreit, James B., 4865
Hebenstreit, Julia, 5098
Hebenstreit, Marilyn B., 4865
Heberling, Dorothy, 9649
Hebert, Pattie J., 7213
Hebert, Terry P., 3711
Hebert, Tim, 4636
Hechenbleikner, Betty R., 7217
Hecht, David M., 4495
Hecht, Gregory B., 8050
Hecht, Joyce F., 4495
Hecht, Kimberly, 8050
Hecht, Margaret D., 8050
Hecht, Michael G., 8050
Hecht, William F., 8050
Heck, Gary B., 609
Heck, Julie, 3426
Heck, Margaret Quirt, 9878
Heck, Patricia DelTorro, 1422
Heckman, Margaret Jenks, 4953
Heddens, Spence, 4881, 8690
Hedgelough, Betty, 8791
Hedges, M.D., 7869
Hedinger, Nancy, 5337
Hedlund, Jean Knowles, 4150
Hedlund, Steven, 9450
Hedlund, Steven, Dr. , 9450
Heeke, Bernard Allen, 1736
Heekin Charitable Lead Annuity Trust,
  Charles L., II, 7628
Heekin Trust, Charles L., 7355
Heekin, Albert E., IV, 7355
Heekin, Charles L., II, 7628
Heekin, Christine H., 7355
Heekin, Christopher J., 7355
Heekin, Helen K., 7628
Heekin, James K., 7355
Heekin, Micaela, 7628
Heekin, Peter, 7628
Heekin, R. McShane, 7628
Heemstra, Linda R., 4478
Heerema, Bruce, 3504
Heerema, M. Timothy, 3504
Heerema, Sandy, 3504
Heerema, Steven, 3504
Heerwagen, John R., 4203
Heeschen, Paul C., 1171
Heeter, David, 3421
Heffer, Alison, 6180
Heffer, Barbara, 6180
Heffer, Douglas, 6180
Heffer, John, 6180

Hefferlin, Marian W., 610
Heffernan, Ann Marie, 611
Heffernan, F. Michael, III, 611
Heffernan, Frank, 611
Heffernan, Frank, Jr., 611
Heffernan, Gregory, 488
Heffernan, John Warren, 611
Heffernan, Joseph, 3485
Heffernan, Lenore, 611
Heffner, Kirsten, 2664
Heffner, William G., 7443
Heffron, Patricia, 6499
Heflin, J.N. Boo, 197
Heflin, Jay M., 197
Heflin, John L., Jr., 197
Heflin, Lynn, 197
Heflin, Marc W., 197
Heflin, Sharon, 197
Heflin, Sharon K., 197
Hefner, Henry Mason, 3358
Hefner, James Curtis, 3358
Hefner, Juanell, 608
Hefner, Patty M., 3358
Hefner, Thomas L., 3358
Hefty, Noel, 1708
Hefty, Noel Messing, 1708
Hefty, Terrance, 1708
Hegamyer, Katharine, 2087
Hegarty, Anita, 6182
Hegarty, Anita Lise-Ingrid, 6182
Hegarty, Michael, 6182
Hegarty, Paul, 835
Hegeler, Alix S., 2963
Hegeler, Julius W., II, 2963
Hegelund, Barbara, 8554
Hegi, Frederick B., Jr., 8926
Hegi, Margie Ann, 8926
Heginbotham, Will E., 1289
Heide, Elizabeth C., 4125
Heide, Elizabeth H., 4125
Heide, Jane Harrington, 9862
Heide, Ulf B., 4125
Heidlauf, David, 2857
Heidlauf, Valerie, 2857
Heidner Trust B, Marco J., 9618
Heidtman Steel Products, 7317
Heiges, David K., 8062
Heikkinen, Marvin, 4666
Heil Charitable Lead Unitrust, Janet,
  7380
Heil Trailer Intl. Inc., 301
Heil, Janet D., 7380
Heilbrunn Trust, Harriet, 6527
Heilbrunn Trust, Robert, 6527
Heilbrunn, Harriet, 6527
Heilicher, Amos, 4711
Heilicher, Daniel, 4711
Heilicher, Elissa, 4711
Heilicher, Matthew, 4711
Heilig, Clifford J., 6183
Heilmaier, Anna M., 4712
Heiman Charitable Remainder Trust,
  Florence, 4926
Heiman, Diane S., 2652
Heiman, Jan, 2581
Heiman, Stephen E., 2652
Heimann, Robert A., 7444
Heimann, Robert, Jr., 7444
Heimann, Sandra, 7444
Heimark, Craig F., 2781
Heimbinder, Isaac, 7445
Heimbinder, Sheila, 7445
Heimert, Chrystie, 9384
Hein, Diane S., 6184

Hein, William S., 6184
Heinburger, Elizabeth Holloway, 8946
Heinegg, James G., 6682
Heineken, 2510
Heinemann Irrevocable Trust, Ruth P., 7265
Heinemann, Susan E., 7265
Heinen, Stacy, 3501
Heinrich Charitable Lead Trust, Alfred D., The , 7446
Heinrich Charitable Lead Trust, Gladys L., The , 7446
Heinrich, Greg, 5156
Heinrich, James R., 7446
Heinrich, Janice E., 7446
Heinrich, Milt, 5074
Heinrich, Richard, 5692
Heinrich, Sharon L., 7446
Heintz, David, 657
Heintzman, David P., 3697
Heiny, James R., 3490
Heinz North America, 8859
Heinz, Cheri, 612
Heinz, Kenneth G., 612
Heinz, Patricia B., 612
Heinz, Scott K., 612
Heinze, Daniels, 3607
Heinzen, Jeff, 9774
Heise, Elsa Suleelsa Marie, 3663
Heisen, Joann Heffernan, 5389
Heiser, Christopher, 2678
Heiser, Ken, 9903
Heiser, Megan, 2678
Heisey, Charles E., 5056
Heisinger, Katie, 2774
Heisler, Clara, 6067, 6185
Heisler, Solomon, 6067, 6185
Heisman Trophy Trust, 2109
Heisser, Andrea, 680
Heitman, Dorothy, 1023
Heitmann, Kathryn, 5111
Hejl, David, 158
Hekemian Foundation, 5390
Hekemian, David B., 5390
Hekemian, Mary Jane, 5390
Hekemian, Robert S., 5390
Hekemian, Robert S., Sr., 5390
Hekimian, Catherine L., 3936
Hekimian, Christopher D., 3936
Hekimian, Joan E., 3936
Hekimian, Norris C., 3936
Held, James, 2088
Held, John, 7644
Held, Mary, 257
Held, Michael R., 9190
Helena Assoc., LLC, The, 6656
Helena Franklin, The, 6028
Helgerson, Margo, 7298
Helgerson, Zoe-Ann, 3513
Helgeson, June, 8577
Hellebuyck, Kathy, 3532
Heller Foundation, The, 6435
Heller, Carol Joy, 6774
Heller, Cynthia, 1915
Heller, David B., 6187
Heller, Elwyn, 613
Heller, Esther, 5391
Heller, Gary, 5391
Heller, Hermine Riegerl, 6187
Heller, J. Andrew, 9839
Heller, Joan, 9839
Heller, Joyce L., 5340
Heller, Melvin S., 5560
Heller, Moishe, 6186

Heller, Nancy Joan, 9839
Heller, Robert, 5391
Heller, Robert M., 6187
Heller, Ronald, 5340
Heller, Sarah, 6186
Heller, William J., 9839
Hellinghausen, Lorraine, 3991
Hellman, Barbara, 614
Hellman, Bud, 614
Hellmann, Dianna G., 2495
Hellweg, Kurt D., 4893
Hellweg, Priscilla Kane, 2137
Hellweg, Sheryl D., 4893
Hellweg, Tyler D., 4893
Helm, Cyrus Vard, 8928
Helm, Gladys M., 3879
Helm, Glora Bee, 8928
Helm, Lesley Malin, 3879
Helm, Meredith Fridy, 1740
Helm, Robert J., 4977
Helm, Scott, 3879
Helm, Susan, 8928
Helman, Elizabeth Daisy, 4234
Helman, Irving J., 4126
Helmbrecht, William, 3366, 3425
Helmkamp Trust, Donald Elizabeth, 7379
Helms Bakeries, 615
Helms, D. Scott, 1984
Helms, Michael, 440
Helms, Michael L., 515
Helmsbriscoe Performance Group Inc., 129
Helmstetter, Deidre, 616
Helmstetter, Erik M., 616
Helmstetter, Jeaninne, 616
Helmstetter, Richard C., 616
Helow, Joseph P., 2089
Helow, Margaret O., 2089
Helpenstell, Bonnie, 7818
Helpenstell, Emily, 7818
Helpenstell, Eric, 7818
Helpenstell, Lily, 7818
Helseth, Nancy L., 7753
Helstrom, Brian L., 9619
Helstrom, Jon, 4666
Helstrom, Norris, 9619
Helstrom, Robert L., 9619
Helstrom, Yvonne E., 9619
Helton, Barbara S., 7123
Helton, Laura Elaine, 7123
Helton, Thomas Dale, 7123
Helton, W. Charles, 7123
Hely-Hutchinson, Colin, 9386
Hemington, Stephen, 479
Hemingway, W. David, 9363
Hemm, Patricia, 6179
Hemp, Timothy, 4735
Hemphill, Stan, 8937
Hemphill, Suzanne, 3592
Hempstead, David M., 4445, 4446
Hempt, M. Geralyn Patterson, 8206
Hemrick, Christine F., 514
Henao, Marie, 1107
Hench Charitable Lead Trust, Mary A., The , 143
Hench, Deb, 7375
Hench, Mark, 7364
Hendel Foundation, The, 4644
Henderson SB-3, Katherine M., 8862
Henderson, Barclay, 4127
Henderson, Barclay C.S., 4128
Henderson, Brian E., 906
Henderson, Dou B., 8843

Henderson, E.W., 6189
Henderson, Eric, 9913
Henderson, Eric U., 4128
Henderson, Ernest, 4127
Henderson, Ernest, III, 4127
Henderson, Eugene L., 3348
Henderson, George B., 4127, 4128
Henderson, George W., III, 7062
Henderson, James L., Jr., 7100
Henderson, Janet, 1595
Henderson, Joel, 4838
Henderson, Joy, 9147
Henderson, Larry, 5608
Henderson, Mary Minor, 9537
Henderson, Roberta, 4127
Henderson, Ryan, 9890
Henderson, Thomas, 4211
Henderson, Vincent, 3458
Hendik, Susan, 6656
Hendler, Clifford, 1799
Hendler, Lee M., 3914
Hendrick Manufacturing Co., 8606
Hendricks, Janet, 3462
Hendricks, John C., 3922
Hendricks, Molly, 9729
Hendricks, Ralph S., 8527
Hendrickson, Amy L., 9605
Hendrickson, Douglas, 3662
Hendrickson, John, 6768
Hendrickson, Sara, 6768
Hendrickx, Sandra, 484
Hendrix Charitable Lead Annuity Trust, 2090
Hendrix, Allison, 2117
Hendrix, Frances, 2090
Hendrix, Gail, 9229
Hendrix, J. Scott, 8989
Hendrix, James, 2090
Hendrix, Tanya, 909
Hendrix, Therese, 8989
Hengehold, Mary Anne, 7456
Hengehold, Michael, 7456
Hengehold, Michael Mary Anne, 7456
Hengeveld, Ted, 3528
Henke, Bradley F., 9681
Henke, Frank X., III, 7736
Henke, Mark, 5017
Henkel, John R., 453
Henkels Mccoy Inc, 9130
Henkind, Lewis, 6190
Henkind, Sol, 6190
Henkind-Katz, Elie, 6190
Henley, Brian, 42
Henley, Jane F., 9824
Henley, Tucker, 9419
Henneman, Jack, 5400
Henneman, John Bell, III, 5339
Hennen, Joe, 4624
Hennessey, Jevera, 1566
Hennessey, John M., 9386
Hennessey, Margarita, 9386
Hennessy Testamentary Trust, W.T., 198
Hennessy Trust, May P., 198
Hennessy, Carol, 3149
Hennessy, Carole J., 2983
Hennessy, David B., 6191
Hennessy, John, 9386
Hennessy, John F., 6191
Hennessy, Jonathan M., 2983
Hennessy, Kathleen, 6191
Hennessy, Matthew H., 2983
Hennessy, Michael P., 7190
Hennessy, Michael W., 2983
Hennigh, Kaleb, 7666

Henning, Thomas E., 5068
Henninger, Ragan, 740
Hennings, Kenneth, Rev. , 9288
Henri, David, 480
Henrich, Peter, 3776
Henrich, William J., Jr., 8121
Henriksen Trust, The, 2005
Henry Funding Trust, Anne R., 3782
Henry Repeating Arms, 3991
Henry Repeating Arms Co., 3991
Henry Trust, Anne Randolph, 3782
Henry Trust, Sam, 104
Henry, Allen S., 3505
Henry, Charles S., 3505
Henry, Dorothy J., 8430
Henry, Douglas M., 3505
Henry, James B., 3505
Henry, Kathryn Craig, 8083
Henry, Kent, 7102
Henry, Michelle, 2338
Henry, Pierre C., 3585
Henry, R.N., Ph.D., Shirley Gee, 8924
Henry, Steve, 1950
Henry, Thornton, 2124
Hensely, Sharon Elliott, 2218
Hensey Properties, 6191
Henshel, Dayle, 6192
Henshel, Emily B., 6192
Henshel, Harry B., 6192
Henshel, Joy A., 6192
Henshel, Patti, 6192
Henshel, Patti J., 6192
Hensley, Mallory E., 9631
Hensley, Maria A., 9631
Henson Foundation, Jane, 6194
Henson, Brian, 6193
Henson, Cheryl, 6193, 6194
Henson, Heather, 6193, 6194
Henson, James Maury "Jim", 6194
Henson, Jane, 6193, 6194
Henson, Joan S., 3104
Henson, John P., 6193
Henson, Lisa, 6193
Henson, Robert Edward, 45
Henzy, Mary C., 1520
Hepatitis Support Association, 9250
Herald, Darrell A., 3703
Herandez, Lynnae, 652
Herb, Amanda, 7518
Herbert, Ann D., 7106
Herbert, Bernard E., Dr. , 2966
Herbert, Georgia H., 9389
Herbert, Heather S., 8247
Herbert, John K., III, 4128
Herbert, Marvin, 6526
Herbert, Patrick J., III, 3249
Herbert, Pauline I., 2966
Herbold, Donna M., 9620
Herbold, Patricia L., 9620
Herbold, Robert J., 9620
Herbsman, Jonas, 6839
Herbst, Janice, 6195
Herd, Victoria Prescott, 2805
Heren, Ashley L., 8641
Hergenhan, Joyce, 1481
Hericks, Lila, 8569
Hering, Jennifer A., 4873
Heritage Bank, 5078, 5079
Herlache, John, 9810
Herlihy, Richard G., 541
Herman Charitable Unitrust, Stanley H., 4606
Herman, Carl, 9100
Herman, Gloria, 9100

Herman, Gloria L., 8873
Herman, Jonathan, 5379
Herman, Lee E., 9100
Herman, Lisa, 1242
Herman, Margaret, 2968
Herman, Nick, 8556
Herman, Paul F., 9100
Herman, Richard L., 5090
Herman, Richard M., 5090
Herman, Russell, 5379
Herman, Sidney N., 2968
Herman, Stephanie, 9053
Herman, Thomas M., 7339
Hermann Trust, Catherine L., 618
Hermann, Diana P., 6739
Hermann, Robert R., Jr., 4927
Hernandez, Annie, 523
Hernandez, Arecio, 870
Hernandez, Carlos, 5940
Hernandez, Chon, 367
Hernandez, Daniel, 5954
Hernandez, Eugenio, 2150
Herndon, C. M., 7125
Herndon, Jana, 5547
Heron, George, 4533
Heron, James H., 4805
Heroy Partners LLC, 4360
Herr, Bryan, 3506
Herr, Delinda, 3506
Herrema, Caleb, 3347
Herrema, Derek, 3347
Herrema, Gavin, 3347
Herrema, Lara, 3347
Herren, K. Wood, 14
Herrera, Sharon Hays, 9052
Herreria, Robert, 1599
Herrin, Melva J., 2091
Herrin, Melvin B., 2091
Herring, Ann, 923
Herring, Benjamin Ari, 2878
Herring, J. Michael, 4930
Herring, Joseph L., 5305
Herring, Laura, 4930
Herring, Lauren, 4930
Herring, Lisa Butler, 364
Herring, Michael, 364, 923
Herringer, Frank C., 6196
Herringer, Maryellen C., 6196
Herrington, Ed, 6665
Herrington, Marion, 4573
Herrmann III Trust, Carl, 618
Herrmann Trust, Carron M., 618
Herrmann Trust, Christopher, 618
Herrmann, Carl L., III, 618
Herrmann, Carron M., 618
Herrmann, Christopher M., 618
Herron, Robert, 7391
Herschend, Austin, 4928
Herschend, Jack R., 4928
Herschend, James R., 4928
Herschend, Ronald, 4928
Herschend, Tiffany, 4928
Hersh, Dena, 6552
Hersh, Harry, 1853
Hershaft, Arthur N., 6197
Hershaft, Carol H., 6197
Hershaft, Janet, 6197
Hershberg, Sherrill, 5326
Hershey, Jeffrey, 8931
Hershey, Olive, 8931
Hershey, Terese T., 8931
Hershfield, Allan F., 503
Hershman, Hannah, 6198
Hershman, Ronnie A., 6198

Herskowitz & Hampton, LLC, 5414
Herskowitz, Barry, 5627
Herson, Mendy, 5601
Herts, Ken, 5325
Hertz, Chavi F., 619
Hertz, Douglas J., 2509
Hertz, Isaac, 619
Hertz, Meir, 6704
Hertz, Zev, 619
Hervey, Sherleen Lockhart, 8932
Herzka, Ralph, 6478
Herzog, Breah, 9204
Herzog, Clint, 9204
Herzog, Michael, 6791
Herzog, Sharon, 8345
Herzog, Yochanan, 6791
Heseltine, Sharon S., 6570
Hess Foundation, The, 8328
Hess, Alvin, 3970
Hess, Andrew C., 9747
Hess, Bev, 3605
Hess, Christina H., 9747
Hess, Mary Ann, 9747
Hess, Myrtle E., 2969
Hess, Nancy, 3623
Hess, Rick, 1258
Hess, Robert, 1992
Hess, Stephen, 7339
Hesselbein, Frances, 344
Hesselbrock, Steve, 3702
Hesser, Curtis B., 7670
Hesser, Ronald N., 7670
Hessinger, Jennifer C., 7927
Hester, Lauren K., 1815
Hester, R. Faison, 7196
Hetelle, Ron, 2931
Hetherington, Craig, 5873
Hettinger Foundation, 6265
Hettinger, Denis O., 458
Hettinger, John, 6265
Hetzel, Katherine, 5567
Hetzner, Marc A., 1273, 3381
Heubeck, Kerry, 257, 5622
Heublein, 1437
Heuer, Carl-Heinz, 7192
Heuer, Michael A., 7307
Heuer, Russell P., Jr., 1680
Heuermann, B. Keith, 5092
Heuermann, Bernard K., 5092
Heuermann, Norma F., 5092
Heuermann, Scott P., 5092
Heuvel, Melinda Vanden, 4447
Heuvel, Wendy Vanden, 5918
Hevner, Richard, 7948
Hewell, Joyce S., 1855
Hewell, Robert E., 1855
Hewey, Kristina B., 3827
Hewgill, Patricia J., 9748
Hewitt, Carl H., 6200
Hewitt, Carl N., 6200
Hewitt, Howard, 2291
Hewitt, Marsha A., 6200
Hewitt, Patricia, 5635
Hewitt, Rosie, 3427
Hewitt, Webster, 2437
Hext Management, LLC, 8933
Hext, Jane, 8933
Hey, Susan, 8904
Hey, Winston, 8904
Heydon, Michael, 4979
Heydt, Jessica D., 3093
Heydt, Matilda L., 8419
Heyer, Margaret R., 2505
Heyer, Steven J., 2505

Heylin, Martha, 3147
Heyman Family LLC, Annette, 6201
Heyman, Annette, 6201
Heyman, Barbara G., 7677
Heyman, Larry S., 6201
Heyman, Lazarus S., 6201
Heyman, Ronnie F., 6201
Heyman, Samuel J., 6201
Heyman, Stephen J., 7677
Heyman, Susan, 5299
Heyneman, Jennifer, 968
Heyward, Jenifer, 6202
HFP Capital Markets, 8570
HGK 2009 Trust, 712
HHD, LLC, 5210
Hiatt, Helon, 9241
Hiatt, Mark A., 5066
Hibberd, William F., 2948
Hibbs Charitable Trust, 8934
Hibbs, Billy E., Jr., 8934
Hibbs, Eugenia A., 8934
Hibbs, Teresa W., 8934
Hibbs-Hallmark & Company, 8934
Hickel, Ollie, 1378
Hickert-Hill, Diana, 2932
Hickey Family Co., 9622
Hickey Revocable Trust, Bonnie, 5093
Hickey, Bonnie, 5093
Hickey, Hazel, 8970
Hickey, Linda Rae, 9622
Hickey, Raymond, 9622
Hickey, William F., 6443
Hickingbotham Family Ltd Ptnr., 199
Hickingbotham, Frank D., 199
Hickman, Eric, 1770
Hickman, Franklin J., 7645
Hickman, Hilary I., 2093
Hickory Tech Corp., 4713
Hickox, Danielle, 2012
Hicks & Company, Jim, 493
Hicks Charitable Foundation, The, 6248
Hicks, Ann C., 2094
Hicks, Christian B., 4129
Hicks, Cinda C., 8936
Hicks, Coleman S., 4129
Hicks, Darlington P., 4129
Hicks, David M., 2094
Hicks, Donna Stockton, 8935
Hicks, Greg, 3402
Hicks, Jennifer E., 493
Hicks, Jim, 493
Hicks, Jutta B., 4129
Hicks, Michelle, 3362
Hicks, Neta, 493
Hicks, R. Steven, 8935
Hicks, Robert E., 2496
Hicks, Thomas O., 8936
Hicks, Valerie Bradley, 7645
Hicks, Wayland R., 493
Hidary & Co., M., 6205
Hidary, Abraham J., 6205
Hidary, Abraham J., Jr., 6205
Hidary, Abraham J., Sr., 6205
Hidary, Abraham M., 6205
Hidary, Eddie, 6205
Hidary, Fred M., 6205
Hidary, Jack A., 6205
Hidary, Morris, 6205
Hidary, Steven J., 6205
Hiden, Georgia G., 6071
Hieber, Carl O., 8219
Hiebert, Don, 3641
Hieronimus, Jill M., 3914
Hieronymus, Bryan, 7448

Hieronymus, Harriet, 7448
Hieronymus, Lee, 7448
Hieronymus, Paul, 7448
Hieronymus, Theodore, 7448
Hiezenroth, Charles, III, 8263
Higashi, Mildred, 2650
Higgins Community Property Trust, The, 2635
Higgins, Arabella, 1869
Higgins, Arabella Bartner, 1869
Higgins, Barbara, 4198
Higgins, Betty, 649
Higgins, Diane, 5122
Higgins, Kenneth D., 8580
Higgins, Patricia, 649
Higgins, Ralph, Jr., 7383
Higgins, Ron, 2635
Higgins, Sam, 649
Higgins, Sanne, 2635
Higginson, Corina, 3880
Higgs, George, 2096
High Industries, 8054
High Point Hospital, 6121
High, Calvin G., 8054
High, Charles F., 7449
High, Don, 9033
High, Gregory A., 8054
High, S. Dale, 8054
High, Shyla, 9033
Highet, Lea Paine, 5852
Highland Clinic, 6539
Highland Homes Ltd., 9009
Highsmith, Aubrey, 2438
Highsmith, Jane Jackson, 2438
Hightower, Buckner, 8927
Hightower, George H., Jr., 2465
Hightower, Jane, 591
Hightower, John B., 2465
Hightower, Julian T., 2465
Hightower, Neil H., Jr., 2465
Hightower, Neil H., Sr., 2465
Hightower, William H., IV, 2465
Highwoods Realty L.P., 4970
Higie, David G., 7851
Higie, William F., 8020
Hila, Greg, Mr., 2030
Hila, Greg, Mrs. , 2030
Hilbert, Barb, 4733
Hilbert, John H., Jr., 6220
Hilbert, Paul C., 6335, 6336
Hilboldt, James S., 4402, 4412, 4544
Hilburn, Ray, 5620
Hild, Guy M., 7340
Hilda Larson Trust, 7788
Hildebrand, Carl, 3811
Hilder, Elizabeth, 1799
Hilderbrand, Jane C., 7081
Hildner, Tim, 4450
Hildum, Keith P., 8335
Hilen, Andrew G., 557
Hilen, Frances Gilmore, 557
Hiler & Son, Charles D., 6207
Hiler, Margaret F., 6207
Hiler, Robert J., 6207
Hilgendorf, John, 4735
Hilger, Alison, 5625
Hilger, Deon T., 5625
Hilger, Kristin, 5625
Hill Charitable Trusts, 5393
Hill Ranch, 9223
Hill, Al G., Jr., 8938
Hill, Allen M., 7610
Hill, Alyssa Anne, 1681
Hill, B.F., 9223

Hill, Bobby, 9223
Hill, Brian, 7699
Hill, Catherine Woods, 3332
Hill, Cindy L., 4887
Hill, David J., 3023
Hill, David K., Sr., 7694
Hill, Dottie, 9223
Hill, Eugene, 1681
Hill, Eugene D., III, 1681
Hill, Gregory Alexander, 1681
Hill, Jack, 8983
Hill, James Scott, 5393
Hill, Jason S., 4887
Hill, Jeffrey S., 7851
Hill, Jennifer, 8228
Hill, Joan L., 1681
Hill, John B., 8759
Hill, Karen, 3398, 3700
Hill, Karra Mays, 9045
Hill, Kathrine, 4702
Hill, Kay, 7694
Hill, Kay K., 7694
Hill, Leah Boring, 8590
Hill, Louis F., 4702
Hill, Louis Shea, 4702
Hill, Louis W., Jr., 4702
Hill, Lyda, 8938
Hill, Margaret, 2098
Hill, Margaret Hunt, 8938
Hill, Mark, 3398
Hill, Mark S., 4887
Hill, Mary Jane, 2688
Hill, Mary Jane S., 7413
Hill, Michael, 5393
Hill, Nicole, 6001
Hill, Ounita, 9223
Hill, P. Jeffrey, 3674
Hill, Patty, 471, 472
Hill, Ranlyn Tilley, 826
Hill, Rebecca Travers, 2097
Hill, Richard, 5393
Hill, Robert, 2098
Hill, Shirley, 5392
Hill, Steven, 3595
Hill, Thomas A., 7694
Hill, Thomas A., III, 7694
Hill, Tom, 7694
Hill, Vernon W., II, 5392
Hill, Walter, 12
Hillard, Frank P., 7079
Hillenbrand Industries, 3393
Hillenbrand, John A., II, 3393
Hillenbrand, W. August, 3393
Hillenbrand, William A., II, 3393
Hillenburg Family Trust, 1136
Hillenburg, Karen, 1136
Hillenburg, Stephen, 1136
Hiller, Danny, 8791
Hillery, Matthew R., 4014
Hillesland Charitable Trust, 4954
Hilliard Corp., The, 6208
Hilliard Farber & Co., 5986
Hilliard Lyons Trust Co., 3654
Hilliard, Dozier, 2149
Hilliker, Richard O., 2313
Hillin, II, 9096
Hillin, Robert K., Jr., 9096
Hillis, Chyrl, 369
Hillis, Don, 8819
Hillman, Shari L., 8584
Hillock, Mickey, 9084
Hills, Carol T., 3507
Hills, Dave, 2687
Hills, Jared S., 3507

Hills, Paul, 3507
Hillsboro, 804
Hillside Plastics, 4088
Hillstrom, Michael C., 3092
Hillyer, Blair A., 7623
Hillyer, Kevin Pauley, 909
Hilson, Dwight, 6209
Hilson, John S., 6209
Hilson, William E., 6209
Hiltbrand, Bob, 7356
Hilton Foundation, Conrad, 3206
Hilton, Bob, 1935
Hilton, Chris, 1935
Hilton, Chris Chapman, 1935
Hilty, Henry L., Jr., 557
Himebaugh, Ted, 9333
Himelberg, David, 6210
Himelberg, Norman, 6210
Himelright, Carise M., 6229
Himelright, James H., III, 6229
Himeno, Yoshinori, 1
Himmelfarb, Paul, 1815
Himmelreich, David B., 1450
Himmelrich, Pamela, 8348
Himmelsbach, Donald, 4187
Hinck, Tina Marie, 5354
Hinckley, Harry, 2087
Hinckley, Jacquelyn Hegamyer, 2087
Hind, Pearl N., 1002
Hinderer, Walter, 6950
Hines, Christy, 4588
Hines, Dorothy S., 8483
Hines, Leslie D., Jr., 7078
Hing, Gerald, 371
Hinman, Beverly J., 2099
Hinman, Brian L., 622
Hinman, Larry J., 2099
Hinrichs, Charles, 9911
Hinrichsen, Ron, 3592
Hinshaw, Virginia, 2297
Hinson, Gertrude, 3904
Hinson, J.A., 2260
Hinson, Michael, 8326
Hinton, Gregory P., 8201
Hinton, Susan, 9170
Hinton-Irwin, Dorise Carlyon, 7777
Hintsa, Matthew, 1709
Hintsa, Michael, 1709
Hintsa, Moira, 1709
Hintz, Greg, 809
Hintz, Greg J.T, 6467
Hintz, Melvin A., 9878
Hintz, Rosemary-Mayer, 809
Hipes, Mark, 9772
Hires, William L., Mrs., 7990
Hirmes, Alan, 6036
Hirota, Masao, 6876
Hirsch Foundation, Fred and Lucille, 7089
Hirsch, Carl H., 8420
Hirsch, Clement L., 487
Hirsch, David, 6212
Hirsch, Douglas A., 6211
Hirsch, Gladys Ottenheimer, 213
Hirsch, Greg, 487
Hirsch, Henry, 6212
Hirsch, Jillian, 6145
Hirsch, Joseph B., 213
Hirsch, Myrtle G., 6212
Hirsch, Phineas, 1792
Hirsch, Richard, 6212
Hirsch, Sanford, 6114
Hirsch, Scott, 2880
Hirsched, Andrew Karen, 147

Hirschfield, Alan J., 9973
Hirschfield, Berte E., 9973
Hirschman, Becky, 4534
Hirschman, Doris, 2973
Hirschman, Esther, 3970
Hirschman, Jerome, 2973
Hirschman, Orin Z., 3970
Hirschmann, Doris, 2973
Hirschmann, George F., 2972
Hirschmann, Louis W., 2973
Hirschmann, Richard A., 2973
Hirschy, John A., 7762
Hirsh, Ben, 6632
Hirsh, Carol N., 6059
Hirsh, David, 6883
Hirsh, Jill, 3281
Hirsh, Michael G., 6059
Hirsh, Nicole, 5669
Hirsh, Steven A., 2970
Hirtzel, Beatrice Dewey, 8058
Hirtzel, Orris C., 8058
His Global Inc., 6248
Hiscock, Dana W., 6260, 6980
Hiscox, Harry, 7863
Hishmeh, Basem L., 2100
Hishmeh, Muna, 2100
Hishmeh, Robert, 2100
Hissong, Robert E., 2728
Hitchcock, Holly, 1439
Hitchcock, James, 4945
Hitchcock, Margaret Mellon, 8059
Hitchcock-Gear, Salene, 3807
Hite, Dustin, 5161
Hite, Haydn, 5161
Hite, Henry, 5161
Hite, Jessica, 5161
Hite, Lawrence, 6213
Hite, Lawrence D., 6213
Hite, Marilyn, 5161
Hitter, Anna, 624
Hitter, Sabrina, 624
Hitter, Steve, 624
Hittman, Fred, 3881
Hittman, Judith E., 3881
Hittman, Sandra, 3881
Hittman, Stephen J., 3881
Hixon Charitable Lead Trust, 8940
Hixon, Alexander P., 3994
Hixon, Bryan S., 8940
Hixon, Dylan H., 3994
Hixon, George C., 8940
Hixon, George S., 8940
Hixon, Karen J., 8940
Hixon, Shanti S., 3994
Hixon, Sheila K., 3994
HLM & JM Charitable Lead Trust, 3138
HLM and JM 2006 Charitable Lead Trust, 3140
Ho, Chiyun, 593
Ho, Douglas K.T., 2659
Ho, Rossana H., 376
Ho, Stuart, 2650
Hoag, Barbara, 8421
Hoag, Bruce, 8421
Hoag, C. Larry, 625
Hoag, Helen, 625
Hoag, LeVert W., 1293
Hoagland, Carolyn T., 4504
Hoagland, James H., 4504
Hoagland, Jim, 4967
Hoagland, John T., 4504
Hoagland, Nancy L., 4504
Hoaglin, Donna J., 3508
Hoaglin, William M., 3508

Hoak, Abigail Stevens, 8941
Hoak, James M., 8941
Hoak, Jonathan Hale, 8941
Hoak, Mary Margaret, 8941
Hoak, Nancy J., 8941
Hoar, Antoinette Geyelin, 5424
Hobart, Edward A., 3571
Hobbins, Robert, 4636
Hobbs, Debbie Riley, 7080
Hobbs, Emmett, 3882
Hobbs, Kevin F., 5275
Hobbs, Robert B., Jr., Mrs., 7990
Hoberman, Robert A., 5336
Hobish, Richard, 6021
Hoch, J. Herbert, 3394
Hochberg, David, 6928
Hochberg, Fred, 6928
Hochfelder, Peter, 6720
Hochfelder, Peter A., 6720
Hochfelder, Stacy, 6720
Hochman Family 2003 Trust, The, 6214
Hochman, Carol, 6214
Hochman, Carol J., 6214
Hochman, Cynthia, 2187
Hochman, David P., 2187
Hochman, Kenneth G., 7387, 7499
Hochman, Neal S., 2187
Hochman, Richard, 6214
Hochman, Richard H., 6214
Hochman, Sara B., 2187
Hochstein, Shaul, 2707
Hochwalt, J.R., 7631
Hocker, Sam, 9114
Hockett, Phylis, 2673
Hocking, Lydia, 230
Hoctor, Susan F., 3786
Hodes, Anthony S., 2974
Hodes, Michael C., 3924
Hodes, Scott, 2974
Hodge, Edwin, Jr., 8061
Hodge, Gail, 875
Hodge, John, 559
Hodge, Katherine K., 1502
Hodge, Sarah Mills, 2506
Hodges, Allen, III, 9631
Hodges, Bess J., 627
Hodges, Brett, 566
Hodges, Brian, 566
Hodges, Fred, 8581
Hodges, Janet, III, 9631
Hodges, John K., 7944
Hodges, Tim, 1316
Hodgson Charitable Remainder Trust, 2507
Hodgson, David C., 5631
Hodgson, John E., 4194
Hodgson, Joseph, 9781
Hodgson, Laurie B., 5631
Hodgson, Lydia A., 2507
Hodgson, Morton S., III, 2507
Hodgson, Patricia S., 2507
Hodos, William, 1804
Hodson, Harold, 3511
Hoechst, J.W., 2402
Hoecker, Thomas R., 171
Hoefener, Karen, 5739
Hoefer, Alan, 628
Hoefer, Alan, Jr., 628
Hoefer, Craig, 628
Hoefer, Gladys, 628
Hoefer, Kurt, 628
Hoeffner, Gail, 5739
Hoefler, Karen E., 9817
Hoeg, Thomas E., 4375

Hoehnen, Janet M., 9783
Hoejland, Peter, 5746
Hoellen, John J., 2864
Hoellen, R., 2864
Hoellen, Robert B., 3277
Hoelscher, Larry, 8707
Hoelscher, Melissa, 9127
Hoelzer, Alfred M., 6437
Hoeme, Kelly, 3623
Hoenle, W. Paul, 2101
Hoerle, Robert F., 6490, 6891
Hoerner, Marie, 2102
Hoesterey, Brian, 4234
Hoesterey, Dawn, 4234
Hoffberger, Douglas, 3854
Hoffen, Howard I., 6215
Hoffen, Sandra, 6215
Hoffer Plastics Corp., 2975
Hoffer, Helen C., 2975
Hoffer, Robert A., 2975
Hoffer, Robert A., Jr., 2975
Hoffer, Samuel R., 5583
Hoffer, William A., 2975
Hoffer, William Alex, 2975
Hoffheimer, Jon, 7548
Hoffman, Burton, 1576
Hoffman, Chad, 7357
Hoffman, David, 6216
Hoffman, Edna R., 1576
Hoffman, Edward A., 9979
Hoffman, Effe K.D., 4131
Hoffman, Elizabeth, 4980
Hoffman, Eric H. I., 7777
Hoffman, Gregory, 3395
Hoffman, Howard, 6216
Hoffman, Hyacinthe K., 1576
Hoffman, Jacob, 5834
Hoffman, Janet, 7127
Hoffman, Janet A., 7127
Hoffman, Jason, 6216
Hoffman, Jean I., 7777
Hoffman, John, 3575
Hoffman, John E., Jr., 4131
Hoffman, John R., 3575
Hoffman, Kim, 2842
Hoffman, Laurence K., 1576
Hoffman, Linda, 3575
Hoffman, Mabel, 1553
Hoffman, Matthew Payne, 2103
Hoffman, Nathan, 6216
Hoffman, Paul, 9697
Hoffman, Robert B., 7127
Hoffman, Robert C., 8062
Hoffman, Robert Jane, 7127
Hoffman, Robert S., III, 4010
Hoffman, Stephen J., 1576
Hoffman, Susan, 1799, 3395
Hoffman, Susanne, 3395
Hoffman, Thelma S., 9749
Hoffman, Wesley, 4497
Hoffmann, Evelyn, 9842
Hoffmann, Harri, 9842
Hoffmann, Herta, 9842
Hoffmann, Lorraine, 9842
Hoffmann-La Roche Inc., 979
Hoffmeyer, Jason, 4410
Hofheinz Foundation, Irene Cafcalas, 8942
Hofheinz, James Fred, 8942
Hofheinz, Linda Hickerson, 8942
Hofler, Thomas F., 9517
Hofley, Carole S., 9966
Hofley, Norman H., 9966
Hofstetter, Bessie I., 8943

Hogan, Andrew P., 9747
Hogan, Cheryl, 6082
Hogan, Christine, 2338
Hogan, David Patrick, 3455
Hogan, Elise W., 3758
Hogan, Gisela B., 4132
Hogan, Jessica B., 9747
Hogan, Lakelyn K., 5095
Hogan, Lori L., 5094, 5095
Hogan, Margaret B., 9747
Hogan, Mary Emily, 5617
Hogan, Paul R., 5094, 5095
Hogan, Richard, 5807, 6217
Hogan, Richard F., 2912
Hogan, Samalid, 4299
Hogan, Tracey Elise, 5617
Hogan, William Hobson, 5617
Hogan, William N., 9747
Hogan-Bechtel, Elizabeth, 1033
Hoge, Patrick, 1826
Hogen, Mary, 66
Hogg, John, 9151
Hognander, Gertrude, 4715
Hognander, Orville C., Jr., 4715
Hogue, Kristin M., 1975
Hogue, Thelma L., 12
Hogwild Associates, 2084
Hohl, Doren E., 496
Hohmann, Frank L., 6218
Hohmann, Jere, 7905
Hohmann, Kristin, 6218
Hohnstein, Philip, 629
Hoie Revocable Trust, Claus, 6219
Hojnacki, Christine, 7884
Hojnacki, William, 3458
Hokin, Richard, 2677
Holbert, Kenneth W., 8652
Holbert, Kuni, 8345
Holbrook, Marion, 8840
Holcomb, Barbara, 9547
Holcomb, James, 5468
Holcomb, John, 2139
Holcomb, Victor, 2139
Holcomb, Zelda J., 6922
Holcombe, Beth E., 1378
Holcombe, Marie, 5944
Holden, Barry, 9345
Holden, James S., 4467
Holden, Lynelle A., 4467
Holden, Richard S., 5325
Holder, Lacey, 3754
Holder, Sharon, 3754
Holding, Frank, Jr., 7060
Holding, Thomas Charles, 3794
Holding, Wendy S., 4022, 4038
Holdren, Larry E., 7546
Holefelder, Jack, Jr., 7953
Holhain, Diane H., 8843
Holiat, Lydia, 7953
Holiday Auto & Truck Inc., 9927
Holiday Companies, 4674
Holiday Stationstores, 4674, 4675
Holke, Rich, 2702
Hollabaugh, Beth, 7339
Holladay, Clay, 4830
Holland, Betty G., 2482
Holland, David K., 787
Holland, Eugene F., Jr., 7227
Holland, Evans P., 8522
Holland, James H., 9303
Holland, James T., 9409
Holland, James W., 3366
Holland, John G., Jr., 2960
Holland, Joseph J., 9303

Holland, L.A., 2508
Holland, Laura, 2021
Holland, Noel R., 5301
Holland, Richard, Dr. , 12
Holland, Stacy, 8350
Hollander Family Foundation, 5665
Hollander, Alan S., 7879
Hollander, Peter, 5357
Hollander, Sidney, 3036
Hollandsworth, Patsy B., 8945
Hollenkemp, Michael, 5003
Holler, Denis, 4199
Hollern, Michael P., 4639
Holley, Cheri T., 3286
Holliday, Joan M., 8048
Holliday, Susan, 4994
Hollie, Jonathan, 9556
Hollier, Larry, 9158
Holliman, Jean F., 7687
Holliman, Joe M., 7687
Holliman, John H., 7687
Hollingsworth, Betty, 617
Hollingsworth, Gail, 911
Hollingsworth, Joe, 8629
Hollingsworth, Mark, Jr., 7588
Hollingsworth, Marsha, 8629
Hollington, Richard R., Jr., 7437
Hollins, Karen E. Lemons, 1263
Hollister Inc., 3226
Hollister, Terry, 7613
Hollman, Daniel, 4970
Hollo, Jerome, 2105
Hollo, Sheila, 2105
Hollo, Tibor, 2105
Hollon, Leon L., 3703
Holloway Revocable Trust, John D., 2107
Holloway, B. Scott, 2106
Holloway, Carolyn G., 8946
Holloway, Caswell F., Jr., 2106
Holloway, Diane T., 4835
Holloway, E. Graham, 8946
Holloway, Gary F., 1443
Holloway, Hope L., 8092
Holloway, John W., 2107
Holloway, Julie D., 1443
Holloway, Kelly, 2437
Holloway, Marie B., 2106
Holloway, R. Kurtz, 7923
Holloway-Staubach Co., 9215
Hollowell Unitrust, Otto, 9751
Hollowell, Margaret F., 9751
Hollowell, Sharon, 3367
Holly, Deb, 7520
Holly, Mike, 7520
Hollyday, James, Jr., 6168
Hollyday, Michael B., 6168
Hollywood, Meggie, 1098
Holm, Brenda, 3567
Holman, Henry, 4748
Holman, Janelle, 4748
Holman, Kim D.L., 4748
Holman, Thomas H., Jr., 4748
Holman, Vanessa, 3751
Holmes Trust, Clarence C., 3371
Holmes, A. Baron, IV, 8538
Holmes, Alexandra T., 7594
Holmes, Allison, 4538
Holmes, Andrea L., 4403
Holmes, Betty, 8947
Holmes, Bradley W., 2438
Holmes, Christine M., 4403
Holmes, Elizabeth Peck Repass, 1727
Holmes, G. E., 7686
Holmes, George, 4488

Holmes, Gregory, 577
Holmes, Jeff, 9631
Holmes, Jennifer G., 8947
Holmes, John B., III, 8947
Holmes, Kristine A., 3477
Holmes, Lee, 7731
Holmes, Lori, 9631
Holmes, Mildred McDannald, 8947
Holmes, Raleigh, 4538
Holmes, Wendy B., 4538
Holmes, Whitney, 4538
Holmes, Will, 1105
Holmes, William B., 4538
Holmquist, Marilyn L., 9922
Holoch, Kristie, 5129
Holoubek, Carol A., 9843
Holoubek, Sara, 9843
Holoubek, Terri, 9843
Holoubek, Verne A., 9843
Holowaty, Michael, 7643
Holowka, Nick O., 4490
Holpsinger, Matthew M., 2191
Holsombach, Jennifer Lynn, 5352
Holsten, Diana L., 3346
Holt, Gregory F., 3720
Holt, Lauren, 3720
Holt, Leon C., Jr., 8238
Holt, Marilyn, 2872
Holt, Terrance, 2894
Holt, Terrance K., 2894
Holt, Virginia R., 2894
Holtel, Joseph A., 7545
Holthus, C.G., 5129
Holton, Carlota H., 4927
Holton, Jim, 6540
Holtsford, Jeanine, 2776, 3171
Holtz, Beth B., 2109
Holtz, Kevin R., 2109
Holtz, Louis Beth, 2109
Holtz, Louis L., 2109
Holtz, Louis L. "Lou", 2109
Holtz, Louis L. Skip, Jr., 2109
Holtzapple, Daria, 8288
Holtzer, Molly M., 7376
Holtzman, Samuel J., 6223
Holyoke, Thomas, 5130
Holzapfel, Alice A., 5332
Holzapfel, Bob, 7361
Holzer, Erich, 5396
Holzer, Eva, 5396
Holzer, Robert, 5396
Holzer, Vivian, 5396
Holzman, Becky, 7775
Holzman, Irwin B., 7775
Holzman, Jay L., 7775
Holzman, Lawrence J., 7775
Holzman, Lee M., 7775
Holzman, Renee R., 7775
Hom, Tom, 261
Homan, Frank X., 7451
Homan, Walter E., 7451
Home Federal Bank Trust Dept., 8600
Home Instead, 5094
Home State Bank, 1309
Home Towne Suites - Bowling Green LLC, 5034
Home Towne Suites - Clarksville LLC, 5034
Home, Richard, 9361
Homes, Elliott, 479
Homra, Jack, 7691
Hon, Maria, 704
Honek, Mellow, 5610
Honest Teas, 1295

Hong, Catherine, 631
Hong, Peter, 631
Honickman, Jeffrey A., 8253
Honickman, Lynne, 8066
Honickman, Marjorie, 8253
Honsalek, Claire Arthur, 8995
Hood, Bruce, 6884
Hood, Heidi, 552
Hood, J. Wilson, Jr., 4842
Hood, James W., 4842
Hood, Paula J., 4842
Hood, Scott, 552
Hood, Warren A., Jr., 4843
Hoogeboom, Marge, 4408
Hoogenboom, Barbara, 4553
Hook, June C., 7079
Hook, Robert L., Jr., 7079
Hook, Taber Campbell, 3831
Hooker, Alice I., 8632
Hooker, Craig, 3401
Hooks, George, 2550
Hooks, Larry, 2482
Hoon, Philip W., 3948
Hooper, Collins W., 8662
Hooper, Marti Meyerson, 9062
Hoopiiaina, Jason, 9326
Hoopiiaina, Sage, 9326
Hoops, Jeffrey A., 1682
Hoops, Patricia, 1682
Hooters, 2510
Hooters of America, 2510
Hootwinc 100, 2510
Hoover, Candace, 2586
Hoover, Charles H., 7453
Hoover, Dennis, 8937
Hoover, John, 8937
Hoover, Kimberly, 5345
Hoover, Lawrence R., 7453
Hoover, Lynn, 4946
Hoover, Timothy, 7453
Hoover, W. Henry, 7453
Hope, Gregg, 9070
Hope, Jennifer, 8328
Hopf, Carl, 7368
Hopf, Desiree, 7368
Hopkins Charitable Trust, Edna S., 9472
Hopkins, Adele, 3771
Hopkins, Alton H., 2567
Hopkins, Braden, 9345
Hopkins, Carolyn F., 2567
Hopkins, Donald J., 1296
Hopkins, E.L., 3586
Hopkins, Jan, 7276
Hopkins, John F., 9707
Hopkins, Kelly, 1725
Hopkins, Kenneth L., 3586
Hopkins, Margaret M., 183
Hopkins, Robert, 8644
Hopkins, T. Downing, 2567
Hopkins, Virginia C., 2567
Hopkins, Z. Irene, 3586
Hopmayer, Alec, 3074
Hopmayer, Jeffrey, 3074
Hopmayer, Marlene, 3074
Hoppe, Susan L. Pegler, 5110
Hopper Paper Co., 2977
Hopper, Austin W., 2977
Hopper, Bertrand C., 2977
Hopper, Dana Baum, 5722
Hopper, David W., 2977
Hopper, Marilyn M., 2977
Hopper, Randal B., 2977
Hopper, William B., 2977
Horak, Mark, 498

Horal, Sharon I., 2093
Horan, Debra, 4141
Horan, Michael, 8494
Hord, Janel, 7356
Hord, Jennifer D., 8950
Hord, W.D., III, 8950
Hord, W.D., Jr., 8950
Hori, George T., 647
Hori, Helen, 647
Hori, Jim, 1038
Horio, Yoshihiko, 5821
Hormel, James C., 1049
Horn, Albert, Jr., 7339
Horn, Daniel L., 7367, 7414
Horn, H.B., 5618
Horn, John, 200
Horn, Lucille L., 5618
Horn, Michael Andrew, 3664
Horn, Michael B., 1258
Horn, Michael E., 3664
Horn, Paula K., 3664
Horn, Robyn, 200
Horn, Thomas, 9625
Horn, Thomas E., 5618
Hornady Manufacturing Co., 3991
Hornady-David, Margaret, 3991
Hornblower & Weeks-Lothrop Withington, 4135
Hornblower, Josiah, 5233
Horne, Amelia S., 8528
Horne, Gail, 114
Horne, Mabel A., 4136
Horne, Robert, 114
Horner, Ann Marie, 8068
Horner, Carolyn, 8068
Horner, Gary, 7762
Horner, Kathryn, 8068
Horner, Terry, 8068
Horner-Smith, Meghann, 8068
Horney, Jeff, 7058
Hornik, Peter F., 2111
Hornik, Steven R., 2111
Hornik, Todd A., 2111
Hornor, Eileen, 1434
Hornsby, Doug, 3379
Horonzy, Joseph G., 4591
Horowitz Charitable Lead Trust, Gedale B., 6225
Horowitz March 31, 1994 Charitable Lead Annuity Trust, Gedale B. & Barbara S., 6225
Horowitz, Barbara S., 6225
Horowitz, David, 8022
Horowitz, Gedale B., 6225
Horowitz, Jeffrey, 1138
Horowitz, Leo, 5875
Horowitz, Lynn, 1138
Horowitz, Paul, 3145
Horowitz, Rachel, 6804
Horowitz, Ruth, 6225
Horowitz, Schmuel, 6804
Horowitz, Seth, 6225
Horras, Nancy, 3514
Horsburgh, Christopher, 7496
Horsey, Linda, 5135
Horsley, Cynthia B., 9543
Horst, Richard, 3492
Horton, Adelaind, 2248
Horton, David F., 7042
Horton, Gayle, 7787
Horton, Ken, 650
Horton, Miriam C., 8423
Horton, Stevie, 3363
Horton, Thomas W., 8699

Horvitz, Carol, 7454
Horvitz, Jane R., 7563
Horvitz, Jeffrey E., 7454
Horvitz, Michael J., 7484
Horvitz, Norma, 2288
Horvitz, Richard A., 7454
Horvitz, Samuel, 7454
Horvitz, William D., 2288
Horwich, Ada, 632
Horwich, Ada R., 632
Horwich, James, 632
Horwitch, Matthew, 4187
Horwitz, Bradley J., 633
Horwitz, Louis B., 633
Hoskins, Alyce B., 3649
Hoskins, Dowell, 3649
Hoskins, Susan, 8008
Hospital Service Assn. of N.E. PA, 7879
Hoss, Gregory M., 3947
Hosser, Ottilie Wagner, 8424
Host, W. James, 3684
Hotchkis, Carolyn R., 635
Hotchkis, Joan, 635
Hotchkis, John F., 635
Hotchkis, John F., Jr., 635
Hotchkis, Mark B., 635
Hotchkis, Maurine M., 634
Hotchkis, Preston B., 634
Hott, George D., 9753
Hotta, Keiichi, 5795
Hottman, David G., 8571
Hotz, Robert Lee, 1826
Houchens, Nell, 3658, 3665
Houchens, Ruel, 3665
Houchin, Regina, 367
Houck Management Trust, 8953
Houck, Harvey R., Jr., 8953
Houck, Patricia West, 8953
Houck, Richard I., 2978
Houff Transfer, 9473
Houff, Charlotte R., 9473
Houff, Cletus E., 9473
Houff, Douglas, 9473
Houff, Dwight E., 9473
Houghland, Calvin, 8630
Houghtaling, Dave, 4598
Houghton & Co., E.F., 8172
Houghton, Alanson B., II, 6908
Houghton, Alanson B., III, 6908
Houghton, Amory, III, 6908
Houghton, Amory, Jr., 6908
Houghton, Christina F., 6908
Houghton, James D., 6908
Houghton, James R., 6908
Houghton, Joanne, 6908
Houghton, John W., Jr., 912
Houghton, Nina B., 6908
Houghton, Ralph H., Jr., 4432
Houghton, Robert W., 6908
Houlahan, Therese C., 9876
Houlehan, John, 5017
Houlihan, Francis J., 2979
Houlihan, Patricia A., 2979
Houlihan, Sr. Patricia, 6966
Houlthouse, Ruth Ann, 4716
Hounahan, William P., 4080
Houren, Jay, 9158
House of Flavors, Inc., 3799
House, Carol, 3595
House, George, 7209
House, Patricia A., 780
House, William A., 1770
Household Bank, 1837
Houseknecht, Alice G., 6226

Houseknecht, Jaclyn Y., 6226
Houseman Charitable Trust, Jackie, 3728
Houseman, Dave, 4401
Houseman, Edna, 3728
Houseman, Gisela, 8869
Houser, Anouchka, 6227
Houser, Catherine L., 9769
Houser, Daniel, 6227
Houser, Gary, 9694
Houser, Michael, 4945
Houser, Samuel, 6227
Housh, Scot, 4671
Houssels FLP, 5163
Houssels, J.K., 5163
Houssels, Nancy C., 5163
Houston Charitable Lead Annuity Trust, Anne, 6228
Houston, Andrew G., 6228
Houston, Cynthia A., 6228
Houston, James R., II, 8567
Hovas, Jennifer, 8812
Hovde, Eric D., 1094
Hovis, Jennifer B., 2464
Hovland, James B., 4671
Howald, Matt, 8314
Howard, Andrea M., 4237
Howard, Barbara, 12
Howard, Barbara H., 2981
Howard, Betty Anne, 3978
Howard, Betty R., 242
Howard, Cheryl, 1484
Howard, Chrystal, 7666
Howard, Cynthia D., 242
Howard, Dale A., 3509
Howard, Eliza, 6027
Howard, Esme, 6027
Howard, Gary D., 1295
Howard, Gary S., 1295
Howard, Horace, 4137
Howard, Irma, 8955
Howard, Janet, 8296
Howard, Joe, 7375
Howard, Joel E., 8955
Howard, Johanna Geier, 6063, 6064
Howard, John D., 242
Howard, Judith S., 7689
Howard, Katherine Kelly, 3905
Howard, Kay, 8782
Howard, Leslie D., 1295
Howard, Marilyn J., 3509
Howard, Mark E., II, 8955
Howard, Melinda, 7756
Howard, Mike, 2602
Howard, Nathan Eric, 8955
Howard, Robert, 4612
Howard, Robert E., II, 7688
Howard, Robert G., 8296
Howard, Robert S., 5122
Howard, Ron, 1484
Howard, Scott A., 3509
Howard, Stephen R., 7388
Howard, Steven M., 3509
Howard, Vicki P., 7688
Howard, Virginia Martin, 8955
Howard, W. Edward, 8512
Howard, William, 8575
Howard, William F., 7689
Howard, Winnifred C., 7131
Howe Charitable Lead Trust, Roger L., 7455
Howe, Dave, 7132
Howe, H.R., 7132
Howe, H.T., 7132

Howe, Helen H., 3510
Howe, Isabel, 5700
Howe, James, 3510
Howe, Joyce L., 7455
Howe, Karen C., 7455
Howe, Kevin, 9238
Howe, Niloofar Razi, 957
Howe, R. Edwin, 7455
Howe, Richard V., 4317
Howe, Roger L., 7455
Howe, Stanley M., 3510
Howell Founation, The, 8956
Howell, Barbara N., 2511
Howell, Bradley N., 8956
Howell, Clark, 2512
Howell, Clark, III, 2512
Howell, David L., 8956
Howell, Don N., 2511
Howell, Douglas W., 8956
Howell, Elizabeth Kenan, 7143
Howell, Evelyn E., 8956
Howell, Faye, 2512
Howell, George L., 6208
Howell, John, 3400
Howell, Kendra, 447
Howell, Kim, 3363
Howell, Martha C., 5852
Howell, Michael, 3397
Howell, Nancy B., 5257
Howell, Steven K., 8956
Howell, W. Barrett, 2512
Howell, W. Barrett, II, 2512
Hower, Donovan E., Sr., 9488
Howerton, Jason K., 710
Howie, Michael B., 1180
Howitt, Bob, 5592
Howitt, Joan S., 5592
Howitt, Robert M., 5592
Howland, Edward M., 4276
Howley, Jon, 67
Hoy, Annette, 2797
Hoy, James A., 6542
Hoy, James Sue, 6542
Hoy, Ronald R., 577
Hoyem, David S., 3300
Hoyt, Debra, 9346, 9347
Hoyt, Fred A., Jr., 2514
Hoyt, Kathleen C., 5223
Hoyt, Lawrence C., Jr., 4250
Hoyt, Sara J., 2514
Hoyt, Walter J., 2514
Hoyt, William D., 2514
Hoyt, Willma C., 6230
HS Processing, LP, 7317
HSBC Bank USA, 6807, 6978
HSDC, 2899
Hsia, Sven E., 7013
Hsiao, Bernard, 2112
Hsiao, Jane H., 2112
Hsiao, Kristy, 2112
Hsiao, Michael, 2112
Hsieh, David, 4600
Hsieh, Douglas, 4600
Hsieh, Pai-Her, 636
Hsieh, Wen-Jai, 636
Hsieh, William, 4600
Hsu Family Trust, 637
Hsu, Chau, 637
Hsu, Christopher, 1455
Hsu, Kwei Kuang, 593
Hsu, Lynn, 4294
Hsu, Thomas, 1455
Huang Family Foundation, Inc., 2113
Huang, Adam, 2113

Huang, Lawrence P., 2113
Huang, Nancy J., 2113
Huang, Shu, 952
Huang, Shu C., 527
Hubay, Alfred F., 6364
Hubbard, A.C., 3883
Hubbard, A.C., Jr., 3883
Hubbard, Amy L., 4763
Hubbard, B.H.B., 9551
Hubbard, Erin G., 4704
Hubbard, Frank M., 5240
Hubbard, Howard, 6966
Hubbard, Linda, 5240
Hubbard, Michael E., 5240
Hubbard, Penney, 3883
Hubbard, Ward M., 3467
Hubbert, Becky, 5629
Hubbert, T. Sewell, 8188
Huber, Alexander L., 6231
Huber, Benjamin P., 6231
Huber, Caroline, 5553
Huber, Caroline P., 5553
Huber, Christopher J., 9110
Huber, Corey F., 9453
Huber, Eleanor H., 5553
Huber, J. David, 3443
Huber, Joseph W., 5553
Huber, Katherine L., 9453
Huber, M. Sebastian, 6231
Huber, Margaret L., 4903
Huber, Martha, 5553
Huber, Pat, 9426
Huber, Paul L., 7944
Huber, Peter M., 9413
Huber, Richard L., 6231
Huber, Roberta P., 6231
Huber, Samuel G., 5553
Hubert Family LLC, George, 7456
Hubert, Amanda, 7456
Hubert, Anthony, 7456
Hubert, Benjamin G., 7456
Hubert, Christopher, 7456
Hubert, Cynthia, 7456
Hubert, George J., 7456
Hubert, George J., Jr., 7456
Hubert, Joshua A., 7456
Hubert, Karen, 7456
Hubert, Robert, 7456
Hubert, Scott, 7456
Hubert, Tiffany, 7456
Hubert, Zachary, 7456
Hubler, Mildred, 7564
Hubspot Co., 5833
Huckin, Carol L., 9028
Huckins, Robert G., 8387
Hudak, Robert, 7283
Hudak, T.F., 8185
Huddart Family, LLC, 7776
Huddart, Aaron L., 7776
Huddart, Adam L., 7776
Huddart, James L., 7776
Huddart, Margaret M., 7776
Huddart, Peggy M., 7776
Huddart, Sarah, 7776
Hudkins, Steve, 4411
Hudner, Philip, 464
Hudnut, Paul, 1272
Hudock, Barbara, 5041
Hudson Foundation, The, 7133
Hudson River Bank & Trust Co., 5865
Hudson, Bill, 5626
Hudson, C.B., 9240
Hudson, Kenneth D., 7133
Hudson, Laura J., 3785

Hudson, Mary J., 7133
Hudson, Mary R., 7836
Hudson, Paul, 6559
Hudson, Rockney W., 2968
Hudson, Saundra, 2706
Hudson, Sue, 9209
Hudson, T. Warner, III, 7133
Hudson, Thomas W., Jr., 7133
Hudson-Jaccard Charitable Trust Fund,
     Aduh, 3611
Hudsonville Ice Cream, 4422
Hueblein, Colleen, 1075
Huebner, David, 1199
Huebschen, Don, 9937
Huelsmann, Jennifer A., 4688
Huelsmann, Richard L., 4688
Huesman, Terri Donlin, 7545
Huether, Ann Lee, 3884
Huether, Cindy, 8557
Huether, H. Douglas, 3884
Huether, Kylie, 8557
Huether, Mary Ellen, 3884
Huether, Mary Ellen M., 3884
Huether, Mike, 8557
Huether, Richard D., 3884
Huether, Ryan, 3884
Hufbauer, Ellen, 3137
Hufbauer, Gary C., 3137
Huff, Darla, 3084
Huff, Florida Ellis, 2541
Huff, Georgie, 427
Huff, Steven T., 9509
Huff, Susan A., 9509
Huff, Thomas M., 9509
Huff, W.C., 761
Huffington, Michael, 5685
Huffman, Daniel, 3707
Huffman, George, 4900
Huffman, Mark A., 8219
Huffman, Randolph H., 9534
Hufty, Frances Archbold, 2114
Hufty, John A., 2114
Hufty, Mary P., 2114
Huge, Donald S., 8924
Huggler, Tom, 4454
Hughan, Wade, 873
Hughes, Angela M., 3382
Hughes, Arthur H., 1807
Hughes, Betsey R., 4881
Hughes, Bradley E., 7362
Hughes, Brian, 3503
Hughes, Charlotte F., 419
Hughes, Craig, 8981
Hughes, Dale, 2463
Hughes, Eileen, 2786
Hughes, Jeanne T., 2983
Hughes, John E., 2983
Hughes, Jonna L., 9763
Hughes, Judy, 3513
Hughes, K., 2783
Hughes, Kim, 3390
Hughes, Kyle L., 8981
Hughes, M. Gail, 8981
Hughes, Mabel Y., 130
Hughes, Mareen D., 9429
Hughes, Michael, 2763
Hughes, Nancy C., 64
Hughes, Nita, 7944
Hughes, Patricia, 979
Hughes, Paul J., 639
Hughes, R. Bruce, 9429
Hughes, Robert M., 3637
Hughes, Robert W., 8981
Hughes, Teresa L., 639

Hughes, Vester T., 2310
Hughson, Susan, 5125
Hugo, Richard G., 3172
Huguenard, Breanne C., 1960
Huh, Young, 6600
Huiras, Ralph J., 9844
Huisinga, Audrey, 4716
Huisinga, Randall, 4716
Huisinga, Richard, 4716
Huisinga, Ronald, 4716
Huisinga, Theodore G., 4716
Huizenga Foundation, Elizabeth I., 4407
Huizenga, Elizabeth I., 4376
Huizenga, J.C., 4407
Huizenga, John C., 4407
Hulbert, Carolyn H., 6232
Hulbert, Christopher W., 6232
Hulbert, Maureen P., 6623
Hulbert, Nila B., 6232
Hulbert, William H., 6232
Hulburd, Carrie L., 142
Hull, Barbara Kelly, 3012
Hull, Brandon, 5322
Hull, David J., 1948
Hull, Kathleen Nicholson, 866
Hullender, Ashley W., 4848
Hulman & Co., 3396
Hulme, Aura R., 8069
Hulme, Charles Scott, 967
Hulme, Elizabeth R., 967
Huloschman, Lorraine, 2321
Hulsemann, Eric, 4411
Hultquist, Andrew, 2115
Hultquist, Cynthia M., 2115
Hultquist, Matthew, 2115
Hultquist, Timothy, 2115
Hultquist, Timothy A., 2115
Humayun, Mark, 2881
Humberston, Russ, Jr., 7798
Hume, Augusta, 1485
Hume, Carol, 9794
Hume, Christina, 1485
Hume, Gene, 301
Hume, Ivor Noel, 9794
Hume, Ivor Noel, Mrs., 9794
Hume, Tara Hefty, 1708
Hume, Warren C., 1485
Humes, Brian K., 5034
Hummel, Charles F., 9794
Hummel, Justin, 3674
Hummel, Stephen, 8137
Hummer, James, 7459
Hummer, James J., 7459
Humphrey, Rebecca Barclay, 8045,
     8355
Humphreys, B.J., 4522, 4616
Humphreys, John, 4522, 4616
Humphries, Cary, 4806
Humphries, Deborah, 458
Humphris, Robert R., 9488
Hunckler, Katherine Patricia, 3028
Hund, Robert M., 9876
Hund, Steve, 3592
Hundelt, Claire Vatterott, 5030
Hundert, Carol, 6536
Hundley, Linda, 7145
Hundred Foundation, The, 5094
Hung, Lyris, 5895
Hungerman, Sr. Marie Gabriel, 4411
Hungerpiller, James R., 2515
Hungerpiller, Susan, 2515
Hunsaker, Brain, 884
Hunsaker, Jean, 3658
Hunsaker, Nancy, 884

Hunsaker, Richard C., 640
Hunsaker, Virginia A., 640
Hunt Electric Supply, 7135
Hunt Foundation, William O. & Jeannette P., 1333
Hunt, C. Giles, 7134
Hunt, Carol W., 3893
Hunt, Christopher, 1333
Hunt, Christopher W., 1296
Hunt, Dan, 516
Hunt, Frieda E., 9845
Hunt, G. Ellis, 2059
Hunt, Ian C., 1333
Hunt, Mary Ann, 9951
Hunt, R. Samuel, III, 7135
Hunt, R. Samuel, IV, 7135
Hunt, Samuel P., 5214
Hunt, Sarah A., 1296
Hunt, Victoria S., 7135
Hunt, Virginia, 2984
Hunt, William O., Jr., 1333
Hunter Roberts Construction, 8700
Hunter, Blake C., 641
Hunter, Brenda, 9972
Hunter, Britton, 7721
Hunter, Carl, 3719
Hunter, Coleman A., 2116
Hunter, Dianne, 3719
Hunter, Edwin K., 3718, 3733
Hunter, Emily S., 2116
Hunter, Gerald L., 3557
Hunter, Herbert F., 9089
Hunter, Janet, 4459
Hunter, Joelle Mortenson, 9890
Hunter, Margaret, 7290
Hunter, Robert, 7212
Hunter, Roy D., Jr., 8957
Hunter, Shirley H., 8296
Hunter, Sue Stone, 7721
Hunter, Susan, 345
Hunter, Susan L., 7545
Hunter, Thomas, 4426
Hunter, Todd, 4082
Hunter, Tony, 2787
Hunter, Vernon, 3771
Huntington Atrium Development, 5642
Huntington Bancshares Inc., 7354
Huntington Charitable Trust, John B., 642
Huntington Homes/Sanders Custom Homes, 9009
Huntington National Bank, 7309, 7320, 7321, 7399, 7420, 7458, 7533, 7547, 7562, 7590, 7646, 7653, 9739, 9753
Huntington National Bank, The, 7314, 7366, 7457, 7618
Huntington, Al, 3359
Huntington, Elizabeth, 642
Huntington, Tom, 913
Huntley, Charles, 9903
Huntley, Jennifer, 6816
Huntley, Joanne, 7249
Hunziker, Gregory, 2727
Hupert, Ann, 8197
Huppe, Barbara C., 9314
Huppe, Barbara Crawford, 9314
Hurd, Jacklyn C., 4568
Hurlbert, Gordon C., 2516
Hurlbert, James G., 2516
Hurlbert, Patricia J., 2516
Hurlburt, Jean L., 6233
Hurlburt, Sunshine, 6233
Hurlburt, Wilbur F., III, 6233

Hurley, Barbara B., 1879
Hurley, Ed E., 2985
Hurley, Frank L., 9405
Hurley, John, 9405
Hurley, Jr., Joseph D., 892
Hurley, Kathy Johnson, 8971
Hurley, Patrick, 3134
Hurley, Phil, 2686
Hurley, Todd, 7998
Hurley, ToniRae, 1917
Hurliman, Edith E., 643
Huron & Orleans Building Corp., 1735
Huron Co., 3905
Hurst, Genna, 369
Hurst, Kathy, 3628
Hurst, Lisa, 9482
Hurston, Ronald O., 4138
Hurt, David, 1647
Hurt, Johnny, 153
Hurt, Melissa Wright, 9294
Hurtig, Mary, 8363
Hurwich, Joseph, 1216
Hurwitz Charitable Lead Trust, Benno & Elayne A., 3886
Hurwitz, Elayne A., 3886
Hurwitz, Jan C., 3886
Hurwitz, Markc L., 7030
Hurwitz, William A., 3886
Hurwitz, Zahava, 6142
Husarik, Michael J., 8367
Husbands, Carol, 8831
Husid, Jackie, 4317
Husmann, Joyce, 3361
Hussey, Alison, 1917
Hussey, Derrick M., 5647
Hussman, Robena, 201
Hussman, Walter, Jr., 201
Husted, Amy C., 7619
Hustler Conveyor Company, 4925
Hutcheson, Jennifer, 8620
Hutcheson, John L., IV, 8631
Hutcheson, Theodore M., Jr., 8631
Hutchings, Lisa, 5429
Hutchins, Daniel, 3584
Hutchins, Daniel F., 3584
Hutchins, Dorothy, 3623
Hutchinson, Christopher, 1637
Hutchinson, James S., 2595
Hutchinson, Merideth M., 6453
Hutchinson, Robert, 2391
Hutchinson, Sandra L., 1637
Hutchison, Brad, 9114
Hutchison, Catherine, 2117
Hutchison, Deanne, 2117
Hutchison, Jeffrey, 7545
Hutchison, Larry, 9240
Hutchison, Thomas, 2117
Hutton, Billy J., Jr., 7452
Hutton, John S., 7433
Hutton, Thomas C., 7350
Hutzler, Elaine B., 9049
Huynen, Diana, 2266
Huzella, Lisa W., 4612
Huzella, Lisa Wheeler, 4612
Hvalbukta Ans, 4234
Hwang, Chin Hee, 1093
Hwang, Sunny S., 705, 1093
Hwang, Willy, 1093
HXI, LLC, 4162
Hyatt Shipping Company, 8711
Hyatt, David P., 7760
Hyche, Mary Frank, 42
Hyde Manufacturing Co., 4139
Hyde Park, 247

Hyde, Charles F., Jr., 9846
Hyde, Douglas W., 9846
Hyde, Elizabeth D., 9627
Hyde, Joyce W., 9846
Hyde, Olin, 3601
Hyde, Steve, 7118
Hyde, Thomas R., 9846
Hyde, William B., 9627
Hyder, Matthew, 9025
Hyland, Denise, 8555
Hyland, John J., 6509
Hyland, Thomas, 5525
Hyman Family Foundation, 8080
Hyman Fund, Mark, 3887
Hyman, Mark, Jr., 3887
Hymowitz, Gregg S., 6234
Hynes, Eileen G., 1450
Hynes, Liz, 1450
Hynes, Mary Ann, 2988
Hynes, Thomas L., 1450
Hynes, Thomas W., 1450

I Run 4, 3711
Iacarella, Dawn, 4648
Iafrate, Lynn, 8458
IATSE, 6943
Ibarra, Martha Romero, 7382
Iberia Bank, 15
Ibrahim, Nina, 646
Ibrahim, S.A., 646
Ibrahimaj, Amal, 2100
Icap, 90
ICAP Holdings(USA) Inc., 5398
ICAP Services North America LLC, 5398
Ice Age Management, 153
Ice Systems, 8079
Ide, Greg, 4636
Ideal Industries Inc., 2986
Idema, William W., 4469
IF Bancorp Inc., 2989
Ifft, Edward C., Jr., 8091
IFO Enterprises, 6286
IGI Resources, 2677
Ignacio, Adriana, 4239
Igor Chesnomzav Trust, 5452
Iguchi, Debra, 7787
Ihrig, Frederick G., 1249
Iida, Henry T., 2642
Ilingworth, Calvin, 3401
IIMI, 6374
Ikeda, Thomas M., 9642
Ikeddi Enterprises Inc., 6240
Ikeddi Imports, LLC, 6240
IKON Office Solutions, 8237
Ilacqua, Glen, 4187
Iles, Erica, 3388
Illegal Pete's, 1295
Illes, 8859
Illes Seasoning & Flavors, 8859
Illges, Emmy Lou, 2518
Illges, John P., 2517
Illges, John P., III, 2517
Illges, Richard B., 2517
Illies, Barbara, 4693
Illig, Dale, 8984
Illig, Sandra, 8984
Ilsemann, Susan, 8229
IMA Financial Group Inc., The, 3587
Imbriani, Joseph G., 4029
Imbrogno, Nancy Hoffman Chritine, 7975
IMI, 2510
Imig, Gary R., 9974
Imig, Pamela L., 9974

Imler, Steve, 2463
Immixgroup, 9476
Imperato, Anthony, 3991
Impey, Kristine, 2113
IMX, 8243
Inbusch, Dorothy Watkins, 9847
Inc., Ingredion, 2987
Incantalupo, Michael T., 6152
Incapital, LLC, 8570
Ince, Max, 9209
Indeck, Jennifer, 1869
Indeck, Jennifer Bartner, 1869
Independence Bank, 3666
Independence Square, LLC, 9324
Independent Bankers Bank, The, 9232
Independent Can Co., 3884
Independent Stave Co., 4872
India Blake Foundation, 5485
Indian Hill Management, 153
Indiana Plumbing Supply Co., 850
Indianapolis Foundation Legacy, The, 3398
Indianapolis Motor Speedway, 3410
Indochino, 90
Indresano, Jenifer, 8297
Indus Capital Partners, LLC, 6243
Industrial Centers Corp., 242
Industrial Lumber & Plywood, 4661
Industry Initiatives, 1100
Indvik, Donald, 7294
INFOR, 8243
ING America, 2621
Ingalls Testamentary Trust II, Robert I., 64
Ingalls, Joan D., 2118
Ingalls, Paul, 4427
Inge, Charles, 8961
Inge, Dominique, 8961
Ingersoll Racing Co., 7094
Ingersoll, J. David, 7560
Ingham, Frederick H., 2093
Ingham, Helen Ann Hubbell, 2093
Ingham, Linda B., 342
Ingham, Richard S., 2093
Ingham, Richard S., Jr., 2093
Ingham, Timothy C., 2093
Inghram, Frank B., 3490
Ingle, John, 5620
Ingle, Tom, 7462
Ingold, Kurt, 5063
Ingraham, Barbara L.F., 1802
Ingram, G. Conley, Hon. , 2463
Ingram, John G., 5788
Ingram, Robert L., Jr., 2444
Ingram, Robin, 8065
Ingram, Scarlett, 3702
Ingrassia, Francis J., 6244
Inkster, Julie, 427
Inland Label & Marketing Services, LLC, 9828
Inman, Betty Ann, 2519
Inman, Frances L., 784
Inman, Hugh M., 2519
Inman, Hugh M., Jr., 2519
Inman, John S., 2519
Inman, William E., 2519
Innamorati, Joseph E., 4243
Inoue, Tomoatsu, 1334
Inouye, Glenn K., 2645
Insall Foundation, Mary V., 6246
Insall, Mary V., 6246, 6247
Insel, Michael S., 5888
Insetta, Diane, 2119
Insetta, Victor, 2119

Inskip, Gregory, 1669
Insley, Loudell, 3932
Inspire Pharmaceuticals, 9895
Inst. Advancement of Ed in Jaffa, 562
Instant Combo Savings, 2030
Instar Service, 1316
Institutional Leasing Trust, 1844
Institutional Venture Partners, 3456
Insultation Distributors, 4634
Insurance Management Associates, 3587
Integra LifeSciences Corp., 5400
Integrity Bank and Trust, 1365
Interactive Intelligence Inc., 3398
Interco, 7267
Interdigital, 1743
Interfaith Council, 1566
Interfaith Hope Maintenance, 7366
Interfaith Hospitality, 9814
Interlock Industries, 3673
Intermountain Gas Co., 2677
Intermountain Industries, 2677
International Bank of Commerce, 8803
International Bible College, 7205
International Dermal Institute, 451
International DX Association, 870
International Ladies Garment Workers Union, 5630
International Maintenance Corp., 3297
International Marketing Systems, 1408
International Piping Systems, 3297
International Shinto Foundation Tokyo, 6249
International Society of Endovacular Specialists, 8368
Interstate Packaging Corp., 8605
Interstate Realty, 5484
Intrater, Lynn G., 3581
INTRUST Bank, 3561
Inukai-Coffee, Shannon, 7798
Inverso, Peter A., 5513
Investment Rarities Inc., 4658
Investment, Freida and Leon Steinberg, 5189
Investors Management Corp., 7075
Invicta Watch Company, 6040
Iny, Joseph, 5405
Inzlicht, Daniel, 5712
Inzlicht, David, 5712
Inzlicht, Esther, 5712
Ioka Fund, 3100
Iott, Constance J., 7463
Iott, Devon E., 7463
Iott, Ian W., 7463
Iott, Richard B., 7463
Iott, W.D., 7463
Iowa Select Farms, 3511
Iowa State Chapter, P.E.O. Sisterhood, 3513
IP Mississippi Charities, LLC, 591
Ipema, Robin J., 1673
Ippel, Mary, 4648
Ippolito, Robert S., 8208
Ippoltti-Smith, Mary, 2391
IPSCO Foundation, 67
Ipswich Co-operative Bank, 3992
Ireland, C. Eugene, 39
Ireland, Katherine, 1167
Irick, Beverly G., 8735
Irish, Art, 2109
Irish, Jeff Q., 2109
Ironwood Capital Management, 8581
Irrevoc Trust, S. J. Barefoot, 9336
Irrevocable K-2 Trust, 3515

Irrevocable Trust of Jr Bulleri, 9575
Irvine, David C., 1274
Irvine, John D., 7762
Irvine, Ronald A., 7822
Irving, Joe D., 2521
Irving, Michael, 2521
Irwin Eskind 2000 Charitable Lead Annuity Trust, 8613
Irwin Schloss, 6664
Is Revocable Trust, 6743
ISA Bellantana LP, 9009
Isaac, Amy E. Saltonstall, 4276
Isaac, Mark, 763
Isaacson, Darwin, 9932
Isabella Bank and Trust, 4468
Isakson, Edward, 7456
Isakson, Kimberly, 7456
ISCO Holding Co., 4872
Iscol, Jill, 6237
Iscol, Kenneth, 6237
Isdaner, Scott, 8022
Isenberg, Alan L., 2720
Isenberg, Bill, 5873
Isenberg, Diane, 2121
Isenberg, Diane S., 2121
Isenberg, Eugene M., 2121
Isenberg, Holly, 5349
Isenberg, Howard, 2720
Isenberg, Marc S., 2720
Iser, Alan, 2183
Isern, Peter, 2150
Ish Shalom Trust, 6784
Isham, Duane, 7624
Ishida, Takuzo, 3024
Ishimaru, Todd, 7944
Ishmael, Jeffrey, 945
ISI International, 2510
Iske, Henry J., 9662
Iskowitz, Gary, 575
Iskrant, John D., 8369
Isom, Gerald A., 8179
Isom, Lucille E., 8179
Isom, Nancy, 8969
Ison, Donald, 3703
Isono, Denis K., 2627
Israel, Kilhillet, 1090
Israel, Steve, 6297
Israelsen, Jerald, 9319
Israelson, Bernice F., 3888
Israelson, Cynthia, 3888
Israelson, Max R., 3888
Israelson, Stuart G., 3888
Issa, Sakeba, 2990
Issa, Suad, 2990
Issa, Sultan, 2990
Issa, Sultan S., 3320
Issenberg, Sheila C., 3249
Issroff, David, 6251
Issroff, Lisa, 6251
Istock, Judith A., 2991
Istock, Verne G., 2991
Itell, John, 3814
Ithan Foundation, 8313, 8354
Itsmyseat.com, 5562
Ittner, Susan B., 5001
Ivancovich, Jane Harrison, 1355
Ivanko, Marika, 3604
Iversen, Alfred A., 4717
Iversen, Brenda C., 4717
Iversen, Emily A., 4717
Iverson Trust, Michelle A., 2480
Iverson, Amy E., 4493
Iverson, George D., 7213
Iverson, Ken, 8569

Iverson, Robert Michael F., 2480
Ivey, Madelyn B., 9201
Ivon and Jane Culver Irrevocable Trust, 5308
Ivory Residual Estate, 6542
Iwasawa, Hideki, 6876
Iyengar, Sarang, 4605
Izzo, Anthony J., III, 3889
Izzo, Anthony J., Jr., 3889

J&A Corporation, 1295
J.G. Petrucci Co., Inc., 5498
J.S. Leasing Company Inc. & Subsidiaries, 5008
Jablin, Randi F., 8875
Jaccar, Michael G., 8741
Jaccard Memorial Trust, A.H., 3611
Jaccard Memorial Trust, L.A., 3611
Jachter, Dave, 7798
Jackman, Hugh, 1683
Jackman, Wendy M., 3923
Jacks, Hugh B., 79
Jacks, Thelma, 8065
Jackson County Bank, 3448
Jackson Hole Preserve, 5662
Jackson, Alice, 260
Jackson, Angie, 7695
Jackson, Anthony, 9494
Jackson, Bill, 4946
Jackson, Blaine, 202
Jackson, Blake A., 3343, 3406
Jackson, Blake Renata, 3343
Jackson, Bruce H., Dr. , 9329
Jackson, C. Charles, 9329
Jackson, Carol M., 1640
Jackson, Clay T., 8616
Jackson, Cobi, 7807
Jackson, Darren R., 4718
Jackson, David, 237
Jackson, David D., 2757, 9157
Jackson, Deborah J., 4075
Jackson, Dorothy, 5725
Jackson, Douglas J., 58
Jackson, Elizabeth O., 2440
Jackson, Frank, 2522
Jackson, Franklin, 2522
Jackson, Glenn, 5398
Jackson, Gwen, 9660
Jackson, Hattie, 8963
Jackson, Henry, 3757
Jackson, Herrick, 9967
Jackson, Joe, Dr. , 8607
Jackson, John P., 9168
Jackson, Kate, 3704
Jackson, Kathleen, 4140
Jackson, Kelvin, 9319
Jackson, Kyle, 3406
Jackson, Linwood A., 7039
Jackson, Loretta, 9913
Jackson, Louise, 7389
Jackson, Marge N., 2608
Jackson, Mark, 237
Jackson, Mark A., 3378
Jackson, Marsha, 361
Jackson, Mary R., 9967
Jackson, Patricia, 2081
Jackson, Robert, 7692
Jackson, Ronald J., 4140
Jackson, Ryan D., 4718
Jackson, Sally, 1917, 6625
Jackson, Sherrlyn, 575
Jackson, Solomon, Jr., 8529
Jackson, Susan, 237

Jackson, Susan L., 4140
Jackson, Tarvaris, 4399
Jackson, Theresa A., 4718
Jackson, Wess, 3343
Jackson, William R., Jr., 8078
Jacksonville Housing Authority, 2094
Jacksonville Savings Bank, 2751
Jacob, Daniel, 9838
Jacob, John, 7375
Jacob, Linda, 9838
Jacob, Lynn H., 2941
Jacob, P. Bernard, 2069
Jacobi, John, 9628
Jacobi, John W., 9628
Jacobi, Judy, 3372
Jacobi, Rosalind, 9628
Jacobowitz, Berl, 5907
Jacobowitz, David, 5920, 6354
Jacobowitz, Gerald N., 5872
Jacobowitz, Isaac, 5815
Jacobs, Ann, 4242
Jacobs, Barbara, 2761
Jacobs, Brian, 1051
Jacobs, C.E., 8964
Jacobs, Carla, 1051
Jacobs, Donald R., 1239
Jacobs, Frank D., 7521
Jacobs, Gail Gordon, 8624
Jacobs, Harry, 5667
Jacobs, Isaac, 5815
Jacobs, Jeffrey M., 8624
Jacobs, Julie, 2180
Jacobs, Kevin, 1242
Jacobs, Leslie R., 3717
Jacobs, Linda K., 6254
Jacobs, Loraine, 1298
Jacobs, Marcia, 8964
Jacobs, Marcia Carol Brewer, 8964
Jacobs, Milton, 320
Jacobs, Nancy, 4796
Jacobs, R. Mac, 8734
Jacobs, Rachel, 5815
Jacobs, Richard D., 561
Jacobs, Scott, 3717
Jacobs, Yisroel Tzvi, 5667
Jacobs-Lowry, Sasha, 1239
Jacobsen, Eytan, 86
Jacobson Family Trust, Robert, 2124
Jacobson Trust, Claudia K., 7683
Jacobson, Eden, 5402
Jacobson, Glaudia K., 7683
Jacobson, Jed J., Dr. , 7346
Jacobson, Joan L., 6255
Jacobson, Julius N., II, 6255
Jacobson, Lyle G., 4713
Jacobson, Mark, 5402
Jacobson, Nelson C., 4474
Jacobson, Rochelle, 9058
Jacobson, Rochelle M., 9058
Jacobson, Roni, 2125
Jacobson, Sam, 2125
Jacobson, Theodore T., 7683
Jacobus Co., 9849
Jacobus, Charles D., 9849
Jacobus, Charles D., Jr., 9849
Jacobus, Eugene T., 9849
Jacobus, Eugenia, 9849
Jacobwitz, David, 6354
Jacoby, Lela, 654
Jacoby, Lela Beren, 654
Jacoby, Norman, 654
Jacoby, Susan, 5372
Jacoby, Tamar K., 3018
Jacquemin, Claude, 9444

Jacquemin, John M., 9444
Jacquemin, Tracie Jensen, 9444
Jacquot, Mark, 9098
Jadabe Trust, David Jacobowitz, 5920
Jadeja, Asha, 1685
Jaeger, Gerald, 5688
Jafek, Bruce W., 1244
Jaffe, Amy D., 1488
Jaffe, Audrey, 9629
Jaffe, Barbara, 8202
Jaffe, Bernard M., 9629
Jaffe, David, 1488
Jaffe, Douglas, 1488
Jaffe, Elliot S., 5252
Jaffe, Jeffery, 9629
Jaffe, Joel, 9629
Jaffe, Roberta, 9629
Jaffe, Roslyn E., 5252
Jaffe, Ruth M., 4478
Jaffee, Patricia, 1205, 1206
Jafferjee, Husein, 6890
Jagannathan, S., 651
Jagelski, Janice, 442
Jahn, Carolyn L., 2992
Jahn, Charles L., 2992
Jahn, Reinhardt E., 2992
Jahn, Reinhardt H., 2992
Jahn, Shirley R., 2992
Jahner, Floyd, 8795
Jain, Atul, 9478
Jain, Madhu, 657
Jain, Narendra Kumar, 9478
Jain, Navindra, 657
Jain, Navindra K., 657
Jain, Neeraj, 656
Jain, Parveen, 656
Jain, Priti Agarwal, 9478
Jakabovits, Elizabeth, 6424
Jakalow, Gary A., 5775
Jakmas, Wendy, 7311
Jakubiak, Krystyna, 6227
Jalaa Equities, LP, 6361
Jalkut, Thomas P., 4126, 4331, 8476
Jamail, J. Dahr, III, 8965
Jamail, Joseph D., 8965
Jamail, Lillie H., 8965
Jamail, Randall H., 8965
Jamail, Robert L., 8965
Jamakepe Investments LLC, 6256
Jambes Trust, Frederick A., 5927
James, Adele, 9485
James, Barbara L., 4602
James, Bob, 1752
James, Diana L., 8233
James, Dru, 8526
James, Frank, 8105
James, Frank M., IV, 9485
James, Jean Butz, 132
James, John, 5121
James, Laura, 132
James, Mary Paddison, 8655
James, Paula, 4851
James, Robert B., 132
James, Ronald E., 132
James, Stephen O., 1283
James, Theresa A., 9678
Jameson, Cindy, 2420
Jameson, Oleonda, 5215
Jamieson, Aileen, 658
Jamieson, Doug, 658
Jamieson, G.W., 658
Jamieson, Jennifer, 658
Janecka, Ivo P., 5874
Janelle, Debra, 8886

Janeway 1999 Charitable Remainder
Unitrust No. 1, 6635
Janeway 1999 Charitable Remainder
Unitrust No. 2, 6635
Janeway, Dean, 6387
Janeway, Weslie R., 6635
Janeway, William H., 6635
Janfaza, Melissa Weiner, 4355
Janke, Lalita, 2126
Janke, Walter, 2126
Janklow, Linda LeRoy, 6257
Janklow, Lucas, 6257
Janklow, Morton L., 6257
Jankoski, Dave, 9797
Jankowski, Carol, 3126
Janney, Eric, 1418
Jannusch, Rey, 2897
Jansen Charitable Lead Annuity Trust,
5164
Jansen Charitable Remainder Trust,
Avis, 5164
Jansen, Ben, 6042
Jansen, Larry, 3501
Jansing, Christopher C., 8079
Jansing, John Cook, 8079
Janssen, Gary E., 9914
Januzzi, Michael, 5642
Janz, Al, 921
Jaquish, Gail A., 5165
Jaquith, David W., 9975
Jaquith, Patricia P., 9975
Jaquith, Richard D., 9975
Jaramillo, George R., 5626
JARB, 8264
Jarma, Debra Folsom, 8863
Jarmusz, Molly, 5044
Jaros Declaration of Trust, Arthur G., Sr.,
2993
Jaros, Arthur G., Jr., 2993
Jaros, Randall S., 2993
Jaros, Wesley A., 2993
Jarrett, Diane K., 7312
Jarrett, James C., 5036
Jas Trust, 4932
Jaschke, Ginger, 5621
Jaskelevicus, Steven, 4107
Jason Industrial, 5861
Jason of Illinois, 5861
Jastrow, Corbin T., 8967
Jastrow, Kenneth M., II, 8967
Jastrow, Kenneth M., III, 8967
Jastrow, Susan T., 8967
Jattuso, Aj, 7796
Jauntig, Thomas F., Jr., 6632
Javitch, Jonathan, 1506
Javor, Kathy, 716
Jaworski, Gary D., Dr. , 6084
Jaye, Arthur N., 2896
Jayswal, B.K., 298
JB Foster Qual Gr Charitable Lead Trust,
8868
JCMC Custom Solutions, 7292
JD Rush Company, 1145
Jeangerard, Jack J., 661
Jeangerard, Ralph W., 661
Jeansonne, Susan, 3754
Jefferis, Judith, 8074
Jefferson Regional Health Alliance, 7761
Jefferson, Joyce P., 9743
Jeffery, Anne F., 8340
Jeffery, Clara L.D., 8429
Jeffery, W. Paul, 7486
Jeffords, Walter M., Jr., 5921
Jeffrey, Marie D., 1047

Jeffries Morris, 6655
Jel Family LP, 6675
Jelin, William S., 662
Jelks, Allen N., Jr., 2128
Jelks, Deborah Stephens, 2128
Jelks, Howard L., 2128
Jelks, Lisa Grace, 2128
Jelks, Mary, Dr. , 2128
Jellison, A.D., 3589
Jellison, Maude S., 3589
Jelm Trust, Charles R., 7137
Jelm, Charles L., 7137
Jelm, Cheryl A., 7137
Jencks, Anne B., 4310
Jendall, Donald M., Sr., 1498
Jendoco Construction Corp., 7965
Jenkins, Andrea L., 4470
Jenkins, Anita H., 4470
Jenkins, Anita Horne, 4470
Jenkins, Anne H., 7465
Jenkins, David A., 2129
Jenkins, G. Wilson, 8527
Jenkins, Hollyanne Farris, 8847
Jenkins, Hugh, 9426
Jenkins, James R., 4470
Jenkins, Karen, 7623
Jenkins, Kathryn M., 4910
Jenkins, Laura, 3651
Jenkins, Laura Lee, 9179
Jenkins, Lisa, 405
Jenkins, Ondraus, 9576
Jenkins, Stephen H., 7465
Jenkins, Timothy J., 7465
Jenkins, Tom H., 7465
Jenko, Mary E., 2222
Jenks, Margaret M., 4953
Jenney, Michelle, 4035
Jennings Trust, Edith, 7466
Jennings Trust, Wyman, 7466
Jennings, Adrienne, 663
Jennings, Barry W., 3384
Jennings, Bruce, 3494
Jennings, Christopher, 6259
Jennings, Elizabeth, 6259
Jennings, Ezra, 5303
Jennings, Frank G., 6245
Jennings, Jean Porter, 5099
Jennings, Joshua S., 663
Jennings, Judith, 3669
Jennings, Kayce Freed, 6259
Jennings, Libby, 4766
Jennings, Lisa, 3361
Jennings, Mary Ellen, 7198
Jennings, Michael, 7839
Jennings, Paul, 663, 9345
Jennings, Peter, 6259
Jennings, Robert, 5099
Jennings, Susan, 2347
Jennings, Suzanne G., 3384
Jennings, Thomas E., 2054
Jennings, William R., 3674
Jennison Assocs. Capital Corp., 5908
Jensen, Alice A., 3547
Jensen, Curtis, 1763
Jensen, Gladys Margaret, 8770
Jensen, H. James, 9776
Jensen, Janet, 8779
Jensen, Janet Jarie, 8713
Jensen, Jeff, 8779
Jensen, Jeffrey J., 8770
Jensen, John M., 7932
Jensen, Julie J., 8770
Jensen, Kenneth, 91
Jensen, Lou Anne, 8779

Jensen, Lou Anne King, 8770
Jensen, Nicole, 3925
Jensen, Pamela Simon, 1040
Jensen, Ronald C., 4662
Jensen, Ronald L., 8779
Jensen, Tom, 4706
Jentes, Janet O., 2995
Jentes, Justine O., 2995
Jentes, William R., 2995
Jentzen, Hank, 3446
Jeon, Brent, 704
Jephson, Lucretia Davis, 2996
Jepperson, Thomas, 9346, 9347
Jeppson, Nancy, 4198
Jepsen, Janet L., 4545
Jernigan, Matt, 4552
Jernigan, Melissa Bunnen, 6417
Jernigan, Tanya S., 9631
Jernigan, Theodore E., 9631
Jero, Paula, 9878
Jerviss, Shelly, 6245
Jeske, Arthur F., 9854
Jesse, Neil J., 3659
Jesse, Ulli Sir, 494
Jessen, Caroline Lott, 8968
Jessen, Dirk, 8968
Jessen, Helen, 3188
Jessen, Howard, 3188
Jessen, Jon, 8968
Jessup, Dan, 1352
Jessup, Jeanne, 780
Jesudason, Navaratnam M., 391
Jesus Fund, The, 3002
Jeter, George W., 2524
Jeter, Joseph W., 3622
Jewell, E. Dunbar, Jr., 8633
Jewell, Mary, 5093
Jewell, Robert Houston, III, 8633
Jewell, V, D. Ashley, 8633
Jewett, Dunham F., 8953
Jewett, Erin S., 9452
Jewett, Harvey, 8566
Jewish Federation of Greater Pittsburgh
Foundation, 8080
Jewish Healthcare Foundation, 8080
Jhin, Michael K., 8924
Ji, Wang, 1773
Jibson, Ronald W., 9346, 9347
JII Capital, 2637
Jinkerson, Lana L., 4961
Jinkins, Mark, 9810
Jinks, Lynn W., 69
Jirous, Barbara, 7690
Jirous, Jay, 7690
Jirous, Jeanette, 7690
Jirous, M.D., 7690
Jirous, Marvin, 7690
Jitkoff, Tatiana A., 9117
Jividen, Douglas E., 9049
JJSP LLC, 5443
JK Living Foundation, 684
JLRJ, 6374
JME Charitable Lead Trust, 6582
JME II Charitable Lead Trust, 6582
Joachim, Scott, 900
Joan Fabrics Corp., 4003
Joannides Family Properties, 9976
Joannides, Andrew L., 9976
Joannides, Angela S., 9976
Joannides, Christopher J., 9976
Joannides, Kathy A., 9976
Joannides, Nickolas S., 9976
Joannides, Timothy J., 9976
Joans, Barbara D., 2750

Jobe, Karen, 1075
Jobe, Kathy, 7624
Jochell, Dorothy B., 3647
Jochens, William, 4971, 5027
Jockers, Helen, 1687
Jockey International, 3265
Jodar, Carol W., 7638
Jodat, Ronald, 9783
Joerger, Dolores, 665
Joerger, Michael, 665
Joffe, Arnold, 5083
Joffe, Harvey G., 905
Joffe, Heidi, 7467
Joffe, Sandra, 7467
Joffe, Stephen, 7467
Johansen, David G., 9661
Johanson, Stephen H., 697
John, Dale, 5130
John, Doug Natalie, 9173
John, Mildred D., 8081
John, Paul R., 8081
Johns, Daniel T., 7359
Johns, Jasper, 1513
Johns, Jay W., 9488
Johns, Karen B., 7331
Johns, Nancy B., 7044
Johnsen, Sheila, 2986
Johnson 1998 Charitable Lead Tr. # 1,
    5406
Johnson 1998 Charitable Lead Tr. # 2,
    5406
Johnson 1998 Charitable Trust No. 1,
    5485
Johnson 1998 Charitable Trust No. 2,
    5485
Johnson and C.W. Wolzinger Charitable
    Lead Annuity Trust, J.A., 5200
Johnson Annuity Hartford, Andriene M.,
    9852
Johnson Charitable Lead UniTrust,
    Raymond C., 7469
Johnson Foundation, Joyce & Stuart,
    5485
Johnson Foundation, Robert Wood, 5611
Johnson Foundation, Walter S., 3711
Johnson Foundation, William M. and
    Phyllis B., The , 2477
Johnson Lifetime Trust, Claudia T., 9011
Johnson Supporting Foundation, 2477
Johnson, A.D., 3001
Johnson, Adrienne, 9851
Johnson, Al, 9168
Johnson, Allan, 7598
Johnson, Andrea, 8869
Johnson, Arlyn T., 7468
Johnson, Arnold L., 4377
Johnson, B. Kristine, 4726
Johnson, Barbara B., 341
Johnson, Barbara Hiller, 670
Johnson, Barbara J., 3519
Johnson, Bari S., 4474
Johnson, Barry, 1324
Johnson, Bernard J., 667
Johnson, Betty W., 6266, 6270
Johnson, Bill, 7209
Johnson, Blanche A., 6269
Johnson, Brenda LaGrange, 6267
Johnson, Bruce, 1242
Johnson, C. Paul, 9851
Johnson, Calvin M., 2217
Johnson, Candace J., 1292
Johnson, Carl W., 669
Johnson, Carla, 8026
Johnson, Cary, 8937

Johnson, Charles E., 9852
Johnson, Cheryl, 9718
Johnson, Cheryl J., 825
Johnson, Chris, Mrs. , 7145
Johnson, Christopher, 6269
Johnson, Christopher W., 6266
Johnson, Cindy, 8639
Johnson, Cindy M., 4217
Johnson, Claire, 9853
Johnson, Clarion E., 6490
Johnson, Cole McKenry, 8600
Johnson, Craig, 7711
Johnson, Curtis, 3456
Johnson, Darrell, 8526
Johnson, Darrell F., 9585
Johnson, David, 9191
Johnson, David A., 9585
Johnson, David B., 8634
Johnson, David Suzanne, 492
Johnson, Debra, 9851
Johnson, Derrick, 7295
Johnson, Diane T., 3001
Johnson, Don Robert, 6483
Johnson, Donald P., 668
Johnson, Donna Jill, 4822
Johnson, Donna M., 6682
Johnson, Douglas L., 973
Johnson, Douglas R., 6049
Johnson, Douglas W., 795
Johnson, Ed, 2680
Johnson, Edith Carell, 8634
Johnson, Edwina, 2525
Johnson, Eleanor, 8947
Johnson, Elizabeth B., 134
Johnson, Eric, 341, 2909
Johnson, Eric L., 341
Johnson, Erick P., 4474
Johnson, Erik, 2669
Johnson, Ethan W., 2388
Johnson, Eunice C., 4115
Johnson, Frances, 4471
Johnson, Frederica Wheeler, 6969
Johnson, Gary, 4722
Johnson, Gary W., 7712
Johnson, Geoffrey B., 134
Johnson, Glenn, 870
Johnson, Gwendolyn Kess, 7468
Johnson, Ham, 7975
Johnson, Harry J., 9474
Johnson, Hayden, 8769
Johnson, Helen May Marcy, 9669
Johnson, Helena P., 9113
Johnson, Howard Bates, 8430
Johnson, Howard Brennan, 8430
Johnson, Howard D., 8430
Johnson, J. A., 8751
Johnson, J. Howard, 6267
Johnson, J. Seward, Jr., 5406
Johnson, James, 3360, 4994, 5873
Johnson, James Hardy, Jr., 7215
Johnson, Jan, 8971
Johnson, Janissa, 89
Johnson, Jay, 8900
Johnson, Jean Ann, 5200
Johnson, Jeff, 9937
Johnson, Jessica, 7452, 7933
Johnson, Jill Fedje, 7296
Johnson, Joan, 2857
Johnson, Joanne, 4245
Johnson, Joe L., III, 8969
Johnson, Joe L., Jr., 8969
Johnson, Joel W., 134
Johnson, Johanna, 7468
Johnson, John B., 7734

Johnson, John S., III, 5485
Johnson, Johnny, 2463
Johnson, Joseph C., 6221
Johnson, Joyce H., 5406
Johnson, Jr. Trust, J. Seward, 5406
Johnson, Judy, 126
Johnson, Julianne, 9851
Johnson, Julie, 2669, 9772
Johnson, Karen W., 3637
Johnson, Karl, 461
Johnson, Karl M., 9977
Johnson, Katharine B., 2440
Johnson, Katherine M., 9186
Johnson, Kathryn, 3402
Johnson, Kathryn Shannon, 1030
Johnson, Katrina, 82
Johnson, Kelly, 9592
Johnson, Kimberly Leach, 2274
Johnson, LaVon, 83
Johnson, Lawrence D., 104
Johnson, Lemoyne , 2149
Johnson, Leonard W., 4260
Johnson, Leslie A., 6221
Johnson, Linda, 3456
Johnson, Luci Baines, 9011
Johnson, Luckett, 9103
Johnson, Lynn G., 2054
Johnson, M. Cole, 9503
Johnson, M.R., 978
Johnson, Maggie, 3456
Johnson, Margaret, 4169
Johnson, Margaret A., 2130
Johnson, Margaret Ann, 2130
Johnson, Maria, 9978
Johnson, Marie, 1566
Johnson, Marjorie, 9853
Johnson, Mark C., 667
Johnson, Mark Chapin, 670
Johnson, Martha A., 8970
Johnson, Martha C., 3001
Johnson, Mary A., 135
Johnson, Mary Ann K., 91
Johnson, Mary T., 667
Johnson, Mary W., 668
Johnson, Matthew, 2477, 8738
Johnson, Matthew S., 2477
Johnson, Melinda E., 4474
Johnson, Michael, 4962, 9168
Johnson, Michella L., 4714, 4768
Johnson, Mike, 3567
Johnson, Nan H., 8969
Johnson, Nancy, 1803
Johnson, Nelda R., 8971
Johnson, Pamela, 9633
Johnson, Pat, 1802
Johnson, Patricia, 275
Johnson, Paul, 4471
Johnson, Paula D., 4148
Johnson, Peter J., 134
Johnson, Peter James, Jr., 6269
Johnson, Peter James, Sr., 6269
Johnson, Philip, 997
Johnson, Philip B., 667
Johnson, Phyllis B., 2477
Johnson, R. Randall, 2054
Johnson, Ray A., 1918
Johnson, Robbin S., 4726
Johnson, Robert D., 7945
Johnson, Robert K., 5407
Johnson, Robert L., 135, 2456
Johnson, Robert W., 668
Johnson, Robert W., IV, 6270
Johnson, Russell M., 2477
Johnson, Ryan W., 2477

Johnson, Sally P., 4148
Johnson, Sally Patrick, 4148
Johnson, Sally S., 996
Johnson, Samuel J., IV, 7468
Johnson, Sandra, 1520
Johnson, Sarah, 3582
Johnson, Shauna, 9356
Johnson, Shirley W., 2604
Johnson, Spencer, 5700
Johnson, Stephanie, 7761
Johnson, Stephen P., 4148
Johnson, Steye, 4399
Johnson, Steven P., 122
Johnson, Sunni, 2440
Johnson, Tanya M., 6439
Johnson, Thomas G., Jr., 9482
Johnson, Thomas P., 2130
Johnson, Thomas S., 2130
Johnson, Tim, 2437, 3567
Johnson, Tom, 2525
Johnson, Tyler, 4798
Johnson, Val B., 9361
Johnson, Veronica, 6269
Johnson, Veronica F., 6269
Johnson, Virginia, 2812
Johnson, W. Macy, 6809
Johnson, William M., 2477
Johnson, Worthington, Jr., 9978
Johnson, Wyatt, III, 2525
Johnson, Zachary, 7468
Johnston Separate Party Trust, Harry E.,
    671
Johnston Trust, John A., 1802
Johnston, Ann Marie, 2539
Johnston, Bart A., 6331
Johnston, Catherine I., 6360
Johnston, Eric, 9634, 9635
Johnston, Frederick T., 2148
Johnston, Gretchen M., 7171
Johnston, James, 1680
Johnston, Julie Fedje, 7296
Johnston, M. James, 3445
Johnston, Mark L., 3785
Johnston, Penelope, 5897
Johnston, Peter E., 7545
Johnston, Ralph A., 8972
Johnston, Sally Curby, 5005
Johnston, Sid, 8526
Johnston, Verna Lee, 9322
Johnstone, Kyle, 1033
Johnstone, R. Clinton, Jr., 1033
Johnstone, R.C., Jr., 1033
Johnstone, Shana B., 1033
Jojola, Ted, 5609
Jolie Intimates, 6794
Jolley, F. Lex, Jr., 2513
Jolley, Mary S., 8533
Jolley, William Hoyt, 2513
Jolly, Jacqueline A., 3580
Jolson, Joseph A., 672
Jolson, Kathleen, 672
Jolson, Leon, 6522
Jonas, Adele M., 7778
Jonas, Gerald B., 65
Jonas, Jennifer, 65
Jonas, Jennifer M., 65
Jonas, Robert, 4730
Jonas, Robert A., 4730
Jonas, Tim, 9856
Jonas, William M., 7778
Jones 1997 Trust, A.C. & T.T., 8322
Jones 1999 Trust, Alison C., 8322
Jones Admin. Tr., William Stark, 9855

Jones Charitable Lead Trust, Janet Stone, 1490
Jones Charitable Trust, Anita C., 1614
Jones Charitable Trust, Anita R., 1614
Jones Development Co. Inc., Steven, 675
Jones Living Trust, 673, 9854
Jones Management, 153
Jones Nordell 2001 Trust, Ellen W., 8322
Jones Trust Co., Edward, 4956
Jones Trust Company, Edward, 4954
Jones Trust, William F., 5409
Jones, Abigail L., 1342
Jones, Alan, 2223
Jones, Alfred W., III, 2449
Jones, Alison C., 8322
Jones, Allie B., 7692
Jones, Alonzo, 9556
Jones, Amy F., 1489
Jones, Anita C., 1614
Jones, Anita R. Collier, 1614
Jones, Anthony, 2842
Jones, Arlene, 401
Jones, Belinda, 7408
Jones, Bernadette, 1593
Jones, Billie H., 8819
Jones, Blake W., 708
Jones, Brereton C., 3667
Jones, Brian, 8581
Jones, Carolyn, 4800, 7138
Jones, Cedric, 7276
Jones, Charlotte, 1425
Jones, Cheryl, 2451, 3361
Jones, Christina, 8635
Jones, Christine Newman, 136
Jones, Claiborne S., 3253
Jones, Clay, 2131
Jones, Dale P., 1614
Jones, Dana E., 4992
Jones, Daniel E., 674
Jones, David L., 4997
Jones, Debbie, 2131
Jones, Donna D., 674
Jones, E. Richard, 673
Jones, Edward A., 1425
Jones, Elizabeth L., 3667
Jones, Ellen W., 8322
Jones, Emily, 708
Jones, Ernest, 4362
Jones, Felecia L., 12
Jones, Gary Dean, 136
Jones, Greg, 7762
Jones, Henrietta, 6272
Jones, Herbert B., 9638
Jones, Herbert S., 4915
Jones, Homer A., Jr., 9479
Jones, Hugh R., 4199
Jones, J. Franklin, 9449
Jones, Jackson I., 3672
Jones, Jana, 2362
Jones, Janet Louise, 1911
Jones, Jeanette, 3580
Jones, Jennings A., 8635
Jones, Jennings H., 8635
Jones, Jerry K., 1238
Jones, Jesse A., 9554
Jones, Jo Ann, 8764
Jones, John E., 3002
Jones, John P., III, 8238
Jones, John T., 5065
Jones, Josephine F., 1425
Jones, Josh, 4396
Jones, Judge Steve, 2437

Jones, Judith G., 675
Jones, Judith R., 3425
Jones, K. Malcom, 5206
Jones, Kenneth M., 5235
Jones, Kevin, 4881, 9454
Jones, Leigh Smith, 3683
Jones, Linda Wallace, 3637
Jones, Lisa, 884
Jones, Lisa L., 8673
Jones, Louis E., 674
Jones, Lucy Rosenberry, 4815
Jones, Margery M., 9637
Jones, Marilee, 4327
Jones, Marilyn, 673
Jones, Matthew, 9276
Jones, Maurice D., 9876
Jones, Max, 4472
Jones, Michael J., 3992
Jones, Owen Brett, 7194
Jones, Patrick, 884
Jones, Patti, 3390
Jones, Paul A., 3002
Jones, Paul Tudor, 8570
Jones, Polly Swetland, 7581
Jones, Robert, 5188
Jones, Ron L., 5091
Jones, Ronald, 9276
Jones, S. Chris, 9463
Jones, Sam, 3771
Jones, Sara Kelly, 6360
Jones, Sarah Hopper, 2449
Jones, Shelly, 4472
Jones, Skipper K., 1846
Jones, Stanley, 8743
Jones, Steaven K., 675
Jones, Steve, 3655
Jones, Tara F., 8328
Jones, Theodore T., 8322
Jones, Thomas, 3255
Jones, Thomas H., 8673
Jones, Todd, 9588
Jones, Tyrena, 708
Jones, Victoria Philpott, 1326
Jones, W. Paul, 3614
Jones, W. Ransom, 8635
Jones, W.J., 7691
Jones, Warren Tanner, 8322
Jones, Wayne, 7138
Jones, Wayne D., 4472
Jones, Wendy H., 2147
Jones, Wilbur S., Jr., 9743
Jones, William E., 2418
Jones, William H., Jr., 3707
Jones, William J., 3002
Jones, William K., 708
Jonquill LLC, 2390
Jonson, Karl, 460
Joralemon, Jane G., 5674
Jordan Charitable Lead Anuity Trust, Wendy E., 490
Jordan Furniture Family Foundation, 4322
Jordan Furniture Foundation, 4323
Jordan Inc., Phillips, 9130
Jordan, Barbara L., 8082
Jordan, Cindy, 8970
Jordan, David B., 7083
Jordan, Don, Jr., 8766
Jordan, George, 3660
Jordan, Gloria Perez, 4763
Jordan, Jeff, 499
Jordan, Joan C., 8636
Jordan, John F., III, 8636
Jordan, John L., 8082

Jordan, Karen, 3928
Jordan, Karen Shishino, 499
Jordan, Kathryn H., 7471
Jordan, Kimberley, 1272
Jordan, Raymond Wesley, 9048
Jordan, Ron, 3401
Jordan, Tabitha, 1775
Jordan, Travis, 3928
Jordan, Vernon E., Jr., 5664
Jordan, Wendy E., 490
Jorgensen, Annette, 676
Jorgensen, David G., 676
Jorgensen, Jennifer A., 676
Jorgensen, Randy, 4449
Jorgensen, Thomas D., 676
Joscelyn, Verla Nesbitt, 3590
Joseph, Alice, 6283
Joseph, Andrew, 6283
Joseph, Barry T., 455
Joseph, Benjamin, 6283
Joseph, Brian E., 9742
Joseph, Capezza C., 608
Joseph, Carol, 6534
Joseph, Danielle, 6273
Joseph, Edward P., 1816
Joseph, Evelyn C., 6273
Joseph, James P., 1787
Joseph, Janet Lynn, 5166
Joseph, Marc, 6534
Joseph, Margaret Elise Elkins, 8838
Joseph, Pamela, 6568
Joseph, Peter T., 6273
Joseph, Robert, 2899
Joseph, S. Michael, 5166
Joseph, Sajan, 7223
Joseph, Todd M., 5884
Joseph, Wendy Evans, 6273
Joseph, William D., 7591
Josephson, J., 6106
Joslin, Daphne, 8008
Joslin, Gladys, 1300
Joslyn, Mark, 9948
Jospey, Maxwell, 4473
Jossi, Mike, 1761
Jostens, 4720
Joukowsky, Artemis A.W., 6274
Joukowsky, Martha S., 6274
Joy, Hayden N., 1301
Joy, Jennifer A., 677
Joy, Jessica M., 677
Joy, Judith C., 677
Joy, Ken E., 677
Joy, Madison C., 1301
Joy, Matthew T., 677
Joy, Sara R., 1301
Joy, William N., 1301
Joyce Foundation, John M. & Mary A., 6457
Joyce, Cynthia, 2527
Joyce, Jeffery, 2527
Joyce, Jeffrey, 2527
Joyce, Nancy D., 6275
Joyce, Timothy J., 6275
JP Morgan Chase, 684
JPMorgan Chase, 5369
JPMorgan Chase Bank, 2696, 2716, 2722, 2730, 2736, 2743, 2748, 2750, 2752, 2765, 2780, 2788, 2790, 2797, 2805, 2807, 2819, 2825, 2833, 2840, 2841, 2848, 2850, 2852, 2860, 2861, 2867, 2868, 2878, 2879, 2883, 2905, 2915, 2944, 2945, 2948, 2964, 2965, 2966, 2969, 2980, 2982,

2984, 2985, 2996, 3007, 3010, 3020, 3038, 3060, 3061, 3062, 3064, 3069, 3085, 3105, 3124, 3130, 3135, 3159, 3161, 3163, 3164, 3168, 3185, 3197, 3202, 3222, 3225, 3232, 3236, 3247, 3251, 3252, 3270, 3271, 3273, 3285, 3293, 3297, 3308, 3310, 3311, 3314, 3324, 3735, 5848, 5963, 6129, 6656, 6788, 6789, 6819, 8911, 9952
JREZ LLC, 6784
JRO Charitable Lead Annuity Trust, 7340
Jrr Mgmt., 7020
JSJ Corp., 4474
JSW & JCW, LP, 2415
JTB Americas, 679
JTL Consulting, 7333
JTM Provisions, Inc., 7333
Ju, David M.C., 5410
Ju, Doris, 5410
Ju, William, 5410
Jubas, Marvin, 680
Jubitz, Fred, 7779
Jubitz, Gail, 7779
Jubitz, Matthew, 7779
Juda, Felix M., 681
Juda, Helen, 681
Juda, Tom, 681
Juday, Dave, 2986
Juday, David W., 2986
Juday, Nancy, 2986
Juday, Patricia, 2986
Juday, Sally, 2986
Judd Wire, 4088
Judd, Robert, 2177
Judge, James, 3948
Judith, Judith, 7701
Judkins, Don, 682
Judkins, Donavan, 682, 683
Judkins, Greg, 682
Judkins, Maxine, 682
Judkins, Peter, 3779
Judkins, Randie, 683
Judson, Erna, 5411
Judson, Stephanie, 8057
Judson, Sundel, 5411
Judy, Mary Ann, 3003
Judy, Paul R., 3003
Jufa Capital LLC, 682
Juhasz, Katherine K., 6334
Jukiro, Joel, 5280
Jukoski, Mary Ellen, 1418
Jukosky, James A., 5280
Jukosky, Susan, 5280, 5566
Julander, Paula, 9323
Julian, Doris F., 8976
Julien, Michael R., 4587
Juline, Roger, 610
Juman, Robert, 480
Junginger, Karl, 9856
Jungreis, Aaron, 6276
Jungreis, Ruth, 6276
Junker, Christopher A., 7944
Junkin, Lora Dean, 3956
Jurdem, Ann, 5372
Jurrens, Candace, 7780
Jurrens, Jaime Grady, 7780
Jurrens, Joshua Martin, 7780
Jurrens, Robert Damion, 7780
Jurrens, Sara Beth, 7780
Jurries, James L., 4476
Jurries, Virginia L., 4476
Juster, Anne Conway, 7569

Justice, Deloris, 3655
Justin, Robert, 4410
Justis, Jane Leighty, 1311
Justis, Robert F., 1311
Jutagir, Hattie K., 6123
Jutting, Lesli, Dr. , 8576
JV Farms, 170
JWG Equipment Assocs., 5330

K Enterprises, 702
Kaare-Andersen, Soeren, 5746
Kabacoff, Gloria S., 8977
Kabacoff, Lester E., 8977
Kabacoff, Maurice P., 8977
Kabcenell, Charlene C., 685
Kabcenell, Dirk A., 685
Kachel 2005 Charitable Lead Annuity
    Trust, 9857
Kachel, Laurence D., 9857
Kachel, Michael S.D., 9857
Kadet, Philip C., 5999
Kadish, Steven A., 3141
Kafer, Megan E., 1747
Kagan, Alisa, 2924
Kagan, Leslie, 3784
Kagan, Paula, 3784
Kagen, Russell, 6079
Kahan, Donald, 5013
Kahan, Gita, 6934
Kahan, Jacob, 6934
Kahan, Lea, 6278
Kahan, Yudel, 6278
Kahl, Daid, 2934
Kahn, Ann, 6424
Kahn, Barbara R., 8084
Kahn, Charles, Jr., 8084
Kahn, David B., 2529
Kahn, Eileen, 9448
Kahn, Emily Mason, 9377
Kahn, Esther B., 4143
Kahn, Gerald J., 3237
Kahn, Gilbert S., 2133
Kahn, Irving, 6279
Kahn, Jennifer M., 2529
Kahn, John J. Noffo, 2133
Kahn, Jordan A., 4085
Kahn, Kris D., 4085
Kahn, Lawrence M., 4085
Kahn, Mitchell, 5800
Kahn, Peter A., 6068
Kahn, Richard, 5205
Kahn, Robert E., 9480
Kahn, Stephen S., 8978
Kahn, Susan R., 4085
Kahn, Thomas, 6279
Kahn, Wolf, 9377
Kainz, John, 3004
Kainz, Joseph A., 3004
Kainz, Michael J., 3004
Kainz, Patrick J., 3004
Kainz, Susan J., 3004
Kaiser, Bill, 3370
Kaiser, Elyse, 551
Kaiser, Fred, 230
Kaiser, Hayward, 839
Kaiser, Heather G., 125
Kaiser, James, 4471
Kaiser, James L., 8848
Kaiser, Kate, 125
Kaiser, Maruna, 7194
Kaiser, Richard, 2049
Kaiser, Steve, 1858
Kaiserman, J.J., 2134

Kaiserman, Rebecca, 2134
Kaish, Morton, 5692
Kaji, Pamela I., 3218
Kakiuchi, Clyde, 2648
Kaku, Dale, 9642
Kakups, Judy A., 2232
Kalamar, Kevin, 1316
Kalamaris, Nancy, 990
Kalikow, H.J., LLC, 6655
Kalina, R. Terence, 3065
Kalinauskas, Brooke, 2543
Kaliski, M.J., 455
Kalkin, Eugene, 5412
Kalkin, Joan, 5412
Kallaus, Kurt J., 5018
Kallenberger, Paul, 7704, 7736
Kallgren, Charles, 509
Kallick, Blackman, 2844
Kallick, Deborah B., 263
Kallick, Ivan L., 263
Kallin Terminating Trust, Alexandra,
    6280
Kallin, Alexandra, 6280
Kallins, Barbara, 687
Kallins, George, 687
Kallins, James G., 687
Kallins, Virginia, 687
Kalogris, Elisabeth, 8086
Kalogris, Michael E., 8086
Kalscheur, James H., 9858
Kalscheur, Joyce J., 9858
Kalscheur, Scott, 9858
Kalscheur, Steven, 9858
Kaltenbach, Rich, 5398
Kalter, Albert, 6162
Kalter, Dahlia, 6162
Kam, Wendell W.S., 2658
Kaman Corporation, 1493
Kaman, C. William, II, 1493
Kaman, Cathleen H., 1493
Kaman, Charles H., 1493
Kamas, John A., Rev. , 6405
Kamen, Dean, 5210
Kamerschen, Robert, 2592
Kamin, Peter H., 4144
Kamin, Samuel P., 8361
Kaminaris, L.K., 8862
Kaminer Partners, 6282
Kaminer, Ariel, 6282
Kaminer, Henry, 6282
Kaminer, Martin, 6282
Kaminer, Nina, 5807
Kaminer, Phyllis, 6282
Kaminetsky, Bernard, 2219
Kaminski Trust, Robert S., 3005
Kaminski, David M., 3005
Kaminski, Mary Ann, 3005
Kaminski, Robert M., 3005
Kaminski, Robert S., 3005
Kaminsky, Gary J., 6206
Kaminsky, Gerald P., 6206
Kaminsky, Jaclyn, 6206
Kamm, C.P., 7473
Kamm, J.O., 7473
Kamm, J.O., II, 7473
Kamm, J.S., 7473
Kamm, Roger D., 4108
Kammer, Judith H., 8522
Kammerer, Jane, 2472
Kammermeyer, Bruce, 3494
Kampen, Douglas S., 5413
Kampen, Emerson, 5413
Kampmann, Abigail G., 9055
Kamprath, Diane, 4411

Kamras, Marvin, 9184
Kanak, Bob, 7670
Kanak, Linda, 7670
Kanaly, Andrew, 8800
Kanarick, Herbert G., 6233
Kandara Investment, 8711
Kandel, William, 3455
Kandell Fund, The, 6656
Kandell, Alice, 6283
Kandell, Florence, 6283
Kandell, Leonard, 6283
Kandell, Leslie, 6283
Kanders Trust, Jeanne, 2135
Kanders, Alan, 2135
Kanders, Alan J., 2135
Kanders, Beatrice, 2135
Kanders, Emily, 2135
Kanders, Jeanne, 2135
Kanders, Warren B., 2135, 2136
Kane, Brandon, 1242
Kane, Brian J., 3544
Kane, Chad D., 9811, 9963
Kane, Deborah N., 9963
Kane, Diana, 5549
Kane, John, 7392
Kane, Mary, 6373
Kane, Michael F., 615
Kane, Michael T., 8011
Kane, Stanley, 2137
Kane, Steven E., 8011
Kane, Vivian, 477
Kane, William, 6876
Kane-Hartnett, Betsy, 2137
Kaneda, Thomas, 8013
Kanel, Ursula, 688
Kanemoto, Noele, 2638
Kaneta, Lester, 2637
Kaneta, Marian, 2637
Kang, Don, 1689
Kang, Susan, 1689
Kangas, Paul, 4557
Kangesser, Harry A., 7474
Kangesser, M. Sylvia, 7474
Kangesser, Robert E., 7474
Kangeter, Linda McCall, 369
Kania, Edwin Carol, 3996
Kaniewski, James, 1581
Kanis, Herman, 4376
Kanis, Michael J., 4376
Kanis, Suzanne, 4376
Kann, Nancy, 2242
Kanner, Raymond, 6374
Kanoff, Chris M., 689
Kanoff, Mary Ellen, 689
Kansas Medical Mutual Insurance Co.,
    3591
Kanter, Suzanne Rubens, 2301
Kantor, Connie, 1938
Kantor, Harris, 5557
Kantorczyk, David, 8829
Kantzler, Leopold J., 4478
Kao, Carly, 578
Kao, John E., 690
Kao, Susan S., 690
Kapaloski, Eugene, 418
Kaplan Trucking Co., 7421
Kaplan, Ann F., 5656
Kaplan, Arnold H., 2138
Kaplan, Carolyn M., 3738
Kaplan, David, 5783
Kaplan, David H., 1474
Kaplan, Deanne, 2138
Kaplan, Donald M., 4145
Kaplan, Faith, 4036

Kaplan, Fred, 8022
Kaplan, George R., 622
Kaplan, Harvey, 4721
Kaplan, Helen, 4721
Kaplan, Helen B., 1474
Kaplan, Jay M., 3738
Kaplan, Jo-An, 8436
Kaplan, Joan, 8979
Kaplan, Joel, 3242
Kaplan, Jonathan, 4145
Kaplan, Katherine, 5783
Kaplan, Laura, 4721
Kaplan, Leah, 4721
Kaplan, Lynne, 3194, 3245
Kaplan, Marjorie, 4721
Kaplan, Marjorie Sue, 3598
Kaplan, Marvin, 8979
Kaplan, Myron, 1744
Kaplan, Naomi, 6284
Kaplan, Paul D., 5783
Kaplan, Rachel, 4721
Kaplan, Richard, 8979
Kaplan, Robert S., 6951
Kaplan, Ross, 4721
Kaplan, Sidney, 2699
Kaplan, Tori, 1958
Kaplus, Laura Herzog, 7899
Kapnick, Michael, 4582
Kapp, Elizabeth R., 5206
Kapp, M. Keith, 9502
Kappe, Rudy, 4514
Kappos, George, Jr., 7330
Kapsi, Uve, 9685
Kapsner, Maurice, 3593
Karabian, Walter J., 648
Karaffa, Robert, 7513
Karaffa, Tracee, 7513
Karakul, Kenn, 2088
Karalla, Cheryl, 8795
Karamanoukian, Alber K., 5562
Karamatsoukas, Celeste G., 8085
Karamatsoukas, Nicholas J., 8085
Karami, Zahra, 1100
Karamitis, Linda, 2914
Karas & Karas Glass Co., 4146
Karas, Barbara, 4146
Karas, Joseph, 4146
Karas, Leo, 4146
Karasik, Marshall, 3006
Karasik, Paul, 4239
Karawan, Oleh, 3234
Karbel, Robert A., 4570
Kardos, David D., 1483
Karges, James M., 4797
Karim, Jafar, 8556
Karimi, Habibullah, 4012
Karinski, Edna, 421
Karl, Donald E., 630
Karl, Richard, 7368
Karlgaard, David C., 9481
Karlgaard, Marilyn E., 9481
Karlin, Trish Devine, 763
Karotkin, Jean, 9014
Karp, Haim, 2229
Karp, Jane, 5668
Karp, Jonathan A., 314
Karp, Marsha B., 1748
Karp, Richard, 5668
Karp, Richard A., 691
Karp, Robert N., 1748
Karpf, Zac, 5113
Karplus, Lisa, 1191
Karpus Investment Management, 5698
Karrash, W. Dean, 1639

Karsten, John, 9840
Kasbarian, John, 5562
Kasbarian, John Antranig, 5562
Kasdorf, Cheryl N., 9860
Kasdorf, John C., 9860
Kasdorf, Michael C., 9860
Kaser, Amy B., 5607
Kask, Mart, 9685
Kaslow, Nadine, Dr. , 2443
Kasowitz, Samantha, 6285
Kasowitz, Sheldon, 6285
Kaspar, Robert J., 3410
Kasper, Mark, 8526
Kassap, Harry, 3821
Kassap, Sigmund, 3821
Kassel, Ruth, 5872
Kassling, William E., 8335
Kassner, Fred, 7141
Kassner, Gerda, 7141
Kassner, Michelle, 7141
Kassover, Helene S., 1036
Kasten, Bruce, 9956
Kaster, Amy, 9908
Kaster, Lisa A., 3685
Kasting, Fredrick, 3448
Kaszovitz, Saul, 2219
Katabasis Intl., 7816
Katen, Karen L., 1494
Katen-Bahensky, Donna, 1494
Kathwari, Farah, 6286
Kathwari, Farida, 6286
Kathwari, M. Farooq, 6286
Kathwari, Omar, 6286
Katicich, Rosemary M., 384
Katka, Steve, 4624
Katlowitz, Moshe, 6771
Katris, Darcy M., 6018
Katsaros, Arthur T., 8087
Katsaros, Denise S., 8087
Katten, Melvin, 3037
Katten, Melvin L., 3037
Katula, Sharon E., 3944
Katz Family Trust, 6849
Katz, Andrew, 839
Katz, Audrey, 3891
Katz, Avrum S., 7475
Katz, Barbara, 5357
Katz, Benjamin A., 8089
Katz, Brooke D., 8089
Katz, Bruce, 692
Katz, Bruce R., 692
Katz, Charles J., Jr., 693
Katz, Dave, 178
Katz, David, 8088
Katz, Diane, 8088
Katz, Drew A., 5414
Katz, Elise, 8089
Katz, Elise R., 8089
Katz, Frank L., 8089
Katz, Gary, 6287
Katz, Harold, 8088
Katz, Jeffrey, 4352
Katz, Joel A., 8540
Katz, Larry, 6676
Katz, Marilyn, 6663
Katz, Marlene, 8088
Katz, Martha, 2484
Katz, Michael, 2028, 5732
Katz, Peggy, 8088
Katz, Philip J., 8089
Katz, Richard, 5959
Katz, Robert, 6704
Katz, Roberta B., 693
Katz, Roberta R., 693

Katz, Roger, 692
Katz, Rosalie, 6287
Katz, Sarah B., 693
Katz, Sheldon T., 3891
Katz, Stephen, 6448
Katz, Sydney M., 693
Katz, Teller, Brant & Hild, 7647
Katz, Valerie, 5304
Katzen, Seth J., 1696
Katzenstein, Nick, 899
Katzin, Alfred J., 1977
Katzin, Daniel, 6288
Katzin, David, 6288
Katzin, David, Dr. , 6288
Katzin, Diane, 6288
Katzin, Jerome S., 6288
Katzman, Jane Dray, 6289
Katzman, Richard, 6289
Katzman, Warren, 5875
Katzovitz, Kim, 6720
Katzovitz, Loren, 6720
Kau, Zachary, 2636
Kauffman Scholarship Foundation Trust,
    Gene, 4934
Kauffman, David, 7953
Kauffman, Katherine A., 3220
Kauffman, Welz, 6950
Kaufman Family Partnership, L.P., A. &
    E., 5415
Kaufman Family Trust, A & E, 6101
Kaufman Revocable Trust "B", 9378
Kaufman, Alon, 4374
Kaufman, Ann P., 8924
Kaufman, Armin, 6101
Kaufman, Barbara, 9378
Kaufman, David, 7942
Kaufman, Edward G., 9482
Kaufman, George, 6656
Kaufman, George M., 9482
Kaufman, George S., 6655
Kaufman, Harold, 5415
Kaufman, Howard, 8540
Kaufman, James, 8298
Kaufman, Jay, 2295
Kaufman, Lester, 408
Kaufman, Linda H., 9482
Kaufman, Margaret G., 9895
Kaufman, Paul L., 9895
Kaufman, Richard F., 4479
Kaufman, Shari, 4374
Kaufman, Stephen M., 8873
Kaufman, Steven B., 2349
Kaufman, Sylvia C., 4479
Kaufman, William, Dr. , 7891
Kaufman, Yenny, 5415
Kaufman-Bell, Yvette, 5611
Kaufmann Trust, Barbara, 9378
Kaufmann, Andrew, 1495
Kaufmann, Elizabeth, 7781
Kaufmann, Jeffrey, 3077
Kaufmann, Peter, 1495
Kaufmann, Ronald, 1495
Kaufmann, Ruth, 1495
Kaufmann, Thomas C., 2749
Kaul, Ralph, 2139
Kaung, Thomas TS, 7560
Kaus, Kathy, 6540
Kautz, Charles P., 6290
Kautz, Kelly, 9853
Kavanagh, Danielle H., 3730
Kavanagh, Dylan M., 3730
Kavanagh, Zachary P., 3730
Kavanaugh, Robert, 384
Kavoukjian, Michael, 6250

Kawabe, Harry, 9642
Kawabe, Tomo, 9642
Kawahara, Akito, 6556
Kawahara, Hiroko, 6556
Kawahara, On, 6556
Kawahara, Sahe, 6556
Kay, David R., 5909
Kay, Elizabeth D., 1258
Kay, Ina, 3892
Kay, Jack, 3892
Kay, Jane Craft, 8548
Kay, June E., 1496
Kay, Louis J., 1496
Kay, Richard, 6643
Kay, Sarah Ziegler, 2343
Kay, Shelley Joan, 3892
Kayden, Gabrielle Reem, 5404
Kayden, Herbert, 5404
Kayden-Killian, Joelle, 5404
Kaye Trust, Herman H., 1690
Kaye, Barry, 2141
Kaye, Carole, 2141
Kaye, Chip, 6720
Kaye, Howard, 2141
Kaye, Sheryl, 6720
Kayman, Brian, 3113
Kayser, Paul, 8980
Kayser, Paul, Mrs. , 8980
Kayton, Andrew H., 2193
Kazahaya, Kenneth, Dr. , 7924
Kazahaya, Masayuki, Dr. , 7924
Kazanjian, Calvin K., 8090
Kazanjian, Olivia A., 7439
Kazarian Family Charitable Foundation,
    Paul B., 6974
Kazarnowicz, Michael, 6463
Kazemi, Farhad, 6589
Kaztex Enterprises, 9860
KCH Group, 1730
KD Primus Trust, 8094
Keaffaber, Duane, 3379
Keaffaber, Jama, 3412
Kean, Reed, 5417
Kean, Thomas H., 5417
Kean, Thomas H., Jr., 5417
Kean-Strong, Alexandra, 5417
Keane Corporation, 2461
Keane, Marc, 7114
Kear, D.A., M. Irvil, 8263
Keare, Stacey, 559
Kearney County Gas Irrigators, 3641
Kearney, Christopher J., 7252
Kearney, Dawn, 3401
Kearney, Erica, 2344
Kearney, John E., 2152
Kearney, Mary Bernadette, 2344
Kearney, Michael, 349
Kearney, Michelle, 2344
Kearney, Scott, 2344
Kearns, John, 1428
Kearns, John F., III, 1411
Kearns, John T., 8905
Kearns, Thomas P., 1356
Kearny Foundation, The, 137
Keast, Walter, 3527
Keating, Arthur E., 102
Keating, Catherine N., 2190
Keating, Edward, 102
Keating, James J., III, 3786
Keating, Kevin, 695
Keating, Kevin B., 695
Keating, Masha, 695
Keating, Michael, 1100
Keaton, Mark, 6908

Keck, Jill, 9828
Keck, Joe, 1226
Keck, Ray M., III, 9010
Keck, Roger, 4459
Keckeis, Stephen L., 7524
Keeble, Toy D., 7619
Keebler, Joe, 7891
Keebler, William C., 2001
Keefe, Anita L., 1391, 1497
Keefe, Carol A., 1497
Keefe, Harry V., III, 1497
Keefe, Harry V., Jr., 1497
Keegan, Dennis J., 5416
Keegan, Karen S., 5416
Keegan, Michael, 931
Keel, Brian, 7218
Keeler Motor Car Co., 6292
Keeler, Alexander, 6292
Keeler, Diane L., 7401
Keemar, Cheryl Lee, 336
Keen, Diane Drugas, 2837
Keen, George Comforted, 4082
Keen, Gordon L., Jr., 7903
Keenan Advantage Group, 301
Keenan Trust, Kathy Ann, 1421
Keenan, Hilary, 1421
Keenan, James F., 4542
Keenan, Kathleen F., 9483
Keenan, Sue, 3412
Keenan, Timothy P., 9483
Keeneland Association Inc., 3668
Keener, Barbara J., 9332
Keener, Robert W., 9332
Keeney, Hattie Hannah, 3007
Keens, Catherine, 5542
Keeping, Troy, 215
Keesee, Allen, 8411
Keever, Carolyn, 7255
Keeyes, Sarah A., 9013
Keffeler, Adrienne, 2733
Kegan, Seth Ross, 9496
Kegan, Sharra C., 9496
Kehle, Gerald, 713
Kehle, Jacqueline, 713
Kehoe, Geoffrey, 4763
Kehoe, Leslie, 2463
Kehrwald, Frederick E., 10000
Keillor, Garrison, 5700
Keily-Kolb, Sandra L., 7622
Keir, Anne Swayne, 1097
Keir, Diane, 8939
Keith Trust, Aram & Margie, 696
Keith, Aram H., 696
Keith, Charles L., 6493
Keith, Garnett L., 5298
Keith, Heather, 9232
Keith, Margie R., 696
Keith, Martha H., 5298
Keith, Ryan Derrick, 696
Keith, Sally, 3371
Kejr, 3593
Kejr Family Foundation of Brookville, KS,
    3593
Kejr Trust, 3593
Kejr, Harry J., 3593
Kejr, Joseph, 3593
Kejr, Larry, 3593
Kejr, Mary, 3593
Kejr, Melvin, 3593
Kelch, James H., Jr., Prof. , 8160
Kelin, Carla S., 1499
Kell, Betsy, 9814
Kellam, L. Birt, 8982
Kellam, Louisa J., 8982

Kellar, Lorrence, 7340
Kelleher, Carol A., 6295
Kelleher, Caroline F., 4147
Kelleher, Cynthia A., 4348
Kelleher, Denis P., 6295
Kelleher, Denis P., Jr., 6295
Kelleher, Nancy S., 4147
Kelleher, Patrick, 4147
Kelleher, Richard M., 4147
Kelleher, Sean M., 6295
Kellen Foundation, A.M. & S.M., 5826
Kellen, Michael M., 5826
Kellen, Stephen M., 5826
Keller Charitable Remainder Annuity, 4481
Keller Group Investment, The, 5605
Keller, Andrew J., 4481
Keller, Bernedine, 4481
Keller, Beth Hudson, 8008
Keller, Betsy, 773
Keller, Betty S., 6297
Keller, Bob, 9588
Keller, C. Joyce, 6296
Keller, Chad, 1928
Keller, Charles, 9643
Keller, Christina L., 4481
Keller, Christoph, III, 5418
Keller, Constance T., 3009
Keller, Craig P., 6296
Keller, David M., 3009
Keller, Dennis, 3919
Keller, Dennis J., 3009
Keller, Frederick P., 4481
Keller, Jeffrey B., 3009
Keller, John T., 3009
Keller, Julie, 5418
Keller, Richard B., 9643
Keller, Richard, III, 9643
Keller, Robert H., 9840
Keller, Ruth E., 9643
Keller, Sally Anne, 5421
Keller, Thomas Christopher, 5418
Keller, Thomas L., 8705, 9106, 9210
Keller, Tracy, 4615
Kellerman, James E., 9288
Kellet, Shawn, 4636
Kellett, Martine, 4220
Kelley Trust, Ralph W., 8431
Kelley, Barbara R., 7725
Kelley, Edward J., 8091
Kelley, Gary, 5113
Kelley, Gwen, 7466
Kelley, Joan, 8983
Kelley, John, 4755
Kelley, Marilyn Golden, 2672
Kelley, Mark W., 9761
Kelley, Thomas C., 2001
Kelley, Thomas J., 1131
Kelling, Carla, 3501
Kellman, Lou Anne, 8738
Kellner, Ted D., 9794
Kellogg Foundation, 5611
Kellogg Trust, Mildred H., 4722
Kellogg, Frederic, 1830
Kellogg, June, 4482
Kellogg, Ryan, 4482
Kellogg, Thomas A., 4482
Kelly Broadcasting Co., 697
Kelly Buick Sales Corp., 3893
Kelly Television Co., 697
Kelly Trust, Eugene, 6245
Kelly, Arthur L., 3012
Kelly, Beverly, 2440
Kelly, C. Markland, 3893

Kelly, C.F.P., Michael J., Jr., 740
Kelly, Carolyn Broll Overton, 8320
Kelly, Christopher, 9861
Kelly, Colleen Monson, 852
Kelly, David M., 2144
Kelly, David M., Jr., 2144
Kelly, Dee J., 8882
Kelly, Eugene, 6245
Kelly, Eugene, Jr., 2604
Kelly, Forest Bradford, 8808
Kelly, G.G., LLC, 697
Kelly, Geri, 5301
Kelly, Gregory G., 697
Kelly, J.S., LLC, 697
Kelly, James P., 8432
Kelly, James S., 5463
Kelly, Jeannine, 2705
Kelly, Jon S., 697
Kelly, Juliana, 9838
Kelly, Karen, 1566
Kelly, Kathy, 2119
Kelly, Lauren D., 6780
Kelly, Lorraine A., 9899
Kelly, Mary, 9861
Kelly, Matthew, 9861
Kelly, Michael J., 9899
Kelly, Michele, 3011
Kelly, Michelle, 2144
Kelly, Michelle B., 2144
Kelly, Mike, 7204
Kelly, Nancy, 6265
Kelly, Paige E., 8885
Kelly, Paul, 3011
Kelly, Raymond, 6179
Kelly, Renee, 8707
Kelly, Renee J., 8939
Kelly, Robert, 2144
Kelly, Robyn Shiloff, 9193
Kelly, Susan B., 2144
Kelly, Terence, 9861
Kelly, Terry, 9861
Kelly, Thea, 3458
Kelly, Thomas, 2033
Kelly, Thomas A., 7935
Kelly, Tilsley H., 4306
Kelly, William M., 7031
Kelsey, Anne H.P., 6298
Kelsey, John L., 6298
Kelsey, Jonathan C., 6298
Kelsey, Margaret C., 9889
Kelso, Betty, 8985
Kelso, John G., 7215
Kelso, Robert, 8985
Keltner, Donald H., 1357
Keltner, Kathleen, 1357
Kelton, David, 698
Kelton, Louis L., 698
Kelton, Richard, 698
Kelz, Lynn, 3831
Kelzer, James, 4734
Kemly, Thomas J., 5301
Kemp, Beatrice W., 966
Kemp, Charleen M., 42
Kemp, Christopher, 3013
Kemp, G. Parker, 3013
Kemp, Molly O., 9210
Kemp, Parker, 3013
Kemper Enterprises, Jackson, 3014
Kemper, Jackson, 3014
Kemper, Jackson, Jr., 3014
Kemper, Mariner J., 5026
Kemper, Randall E., 8719
Kemper, Sharon J., 3014
Kempf, Donald G., Jr., 2995

Kempner, Harris L., Jr., 9036
Kempskie-Aquino, Karen M., 4353
Kempton, James M., 7851
Ken's Food, 8859
Kenan, Annice Hawkins, 7143
Kenan, Elizabeth Price, 7143
Kenan, Frank H., 7143
Kenan, James G., III, 5962
Kenan, Roberta Sterling, 7143
Kenan, Thomas S., III, 7143, 7144
Kendall Charitable Lead Unitrust, Alexander and Christopher, 700
Kendall Charitable Remainder, Evelyn L., 1898
Kendall, Alexander, 700
Kendall, Christopher, 700
Kendall, Donald M., 315, 701, 8530
Kendall, Donald M., Jr., 1498
Kendall, Donald M., Sr., 1498
Kendall, Donna L., 701
Kendall, Dorothy, 8530
Kendall, Edward, 8530
Kendall, Elaine, 700
Kendall, Fr. Daniell, 1204
Kendall, Herbert J., 700
Kendall, Kent C., 315
Kendall, Mac, 7218
Kendall, Philip A., 1374
Kendall, Richard, 700
Kendall, Richard C., 4058
Kendrick, E.G. Ken, Jr., 147
Kendrick, James M., 5671
Keng, Irene W., 373
Keng, James, 373
Kennamer, Richard, 1176
Kennamer, Seaborn, 1176
Kennebec Savings Bank, 3785
Kennebunk Savings Bank, 3786
Kennecott Employee Care & Share Campaign, 9333
Kennecott Utah Copper Corp., 9333
Kennedy Home, Catherine, The , 7145
Kennedy International Inc., 7006
Kennedy NonGrantor Charitable Lead Annuity Trust, James D., Jr., 8638
Kennedy, Brian J., 5169
Kennedy, Bruce, 6559
Kennedy, Eleanora, 5654
Kennedy, Jack, 1552
Kennedy, Jack, Dr. , 2463
Kennedy, James A., 1532
Kennedy, James D., Jr., 8638
Kennedy, James Lehr, 7476
Kennedy, Jan B., 1385
Kennedy, Kerry, 6430
Kennedy, Kit C., 1385
Kennedy, Megan, 7997
Kennedy, Nancy, 3710
Kennedy, Nancy J., 5169
Kennedy, Parker S., 506
Kennedy, R. Michael, 6945
Kennedy, Renee L., 9489
Kennedy, Robert D., 1398
Kennedy, Robert J., 1385
Kennedy, Roger B., 2400
Kennedy, Sally D., 1398
Kennedy, Susan Lillia Baird, 8442
Kennedy, Thomas, 7997
Kennedy, Traci, 5059
Kennelly, Karen A., 3387
Kenner, Jeffrey L., 6264
Kennerly, Kenneth R., 5836
Kennerly, Owen C., 5836
Kennett, H. Connor, 7288

Kenney, Alan P., 4138
Kenney, Chad, 1302
Kenney, Clayton Kendall, 1302
Kenney, Duncan Stross, 1302
Kenney, Jay P.K., 1302
Kenninger Trust, Ruth L., 5165
Kenninger, Steven C., 5165
Kenninger, Susan K., 5165
Kennis, Robert H., 794
Kennon, A. William, 7103
Kenny, Joseph W., 5218
Kenny, Mary Jane, 5317
Kenny, Peter M., 9794
Kenridge, LLC, 5697
Kent Foundation, Atwater, 1691
Kent Manufacturing Co., 4406
Kent, Evan, 839
Kent, Fred I., III, 5662
Kent, James P., Jr., 9443
Kent, Jennifer, 3389
Kent, Jim, 5091
Kent, Mitchell, 3157
Kent, Patricia, 8393
Kent, Ruth, 4921
Kent, Scott, 2252
Kenton, Donna, 6090
Kenton, Glenn C., 1641
Kentucky Bank, 3671
Kentucky Christian Foundation, 7333
Kentz, Frederick C., III, 979
Kenvin, Evelyn, 5265
Kenvin, Fred, 5265
Kenworthy, Marion E., 6300
Keny-Guyer, Alissa, 913
Kenya Embassy, 2622
Kenyon, Ann M., 6301
Kenyon, John C., 7952
Kenyon, Mark J., 6301
Keo Mill Cutters, 4088
Keown, Alvin V., 8986
Keppeler, Betsy B., 9813
Keppeler, Paul, 9813
Keppeler, Paul Elizabeth, 9813
Keppy Memorial Trust, Walter & Carol, 2909
Kerbell, Robert A., 9792
Kerdell, David, 6720
Kerdell, Wendy, 6720
Kerke, David G., 4937
Kerley, Catherine L. Herrmann, 618
Kerman, Barbara, 6338
Kerman, Neil, 6338
Kermanshachi, Shirin, 6120
Kern, Barbara M., 4906
Kern, Elsie, 4906
Kern, Fred J., 4906
Kern, Janine, 8575
Kern, Jerome, 1303
Kern, Mary, 1303
Kern, Robert D., 9869
Kern, Susan, 9797
Kerney, J. Regan, 5419
Kerney, John E., Jr., 5419
Kerney, T. Lincoln, II, 5419
Kernon, Janet W., 541
Kerr, Cody T., 7693
Kerr, E. Coe., 5570
Kerr, Ellen Stern, 7501
Kerr, Holly, 3015
Kerr, Lou C., 7693
Kerr, Lynda, 1692
Kerr, Mary, 7884
Kerr, Nancy, 3628
Kerr, Richard, 1692

Kerr, Steve, 1153
Kerr, Steven. S., 7693
Kerr, Vicki, 251
Kershaw, Thomas A., 4151
Kershner, Morrie, 4664
Kerst, Robert, 7424
Kerstein, Ruth, 6755
Kersten, Stephen, 3535
Kertz, Marion, 4960
Kertz, Susan E., 2189
Kerzner International Bahamas, 1858
Kerzner, Solomon, 5202
Keshishian, Onnik, 5562
Keske, David G., 4937
Keske, Karen A., 4937
Keslar, Peter, 7613
Kessel, George, 5420
Kessel, Jeffrey, 5420
Kessel, Steven, 5420
Kesselman, Edward N., 1239
Kessinger, Hunter R., 3692
Kessler Family Fund f/b/o Brian, The, 2145
Kessler Family Fund f/b/o David, The, 2145
Kessler, Alison, 8300
Kessler, Barbara W., 2863
Kessler, Carl E., 8987
Kessler, Carla Kay, 8987
Kessler, David, 500
Kessler, David R., 8987
Kessler, Dennis L., 2863
Kessler, Emily R., 6274
Kessler, Eric J., 2863
Kessler, Howard J., 2145
Kessler, Ira, 6044
Kessler, John A., 2880
Kessler, John E., 4385
Kessler, Kenneth R., 8987
Kessler, Matthew, 8300
Kessler, Michael, 6675
Kessler, Natalie Anne, 9350
Kessler, Patricia M., 2145
Kessler, Randall E., 495
Kessler, Ronnie, 6044
Kest, Anna, 392
Kest, Benjamin, 392
Kest, Clara, 392
Kest, Sol, 392
Kestenbaum, Alan, 5695
Kestenbaum, Deborah, 5695
Kestenbaum, Gitty, 5720
Kestner, R. Steven, 7568
Keswin, Erica, 6303
Keswin, Jeffrey, 6303
Ketchen, Jim, 3432
Ketcherside, James, 3605
Ketchum, Jason, 8556
Ketelsen, James L., 8988
Ketelsen, Kathryn, 8988
Keter Torah Synagogue Sephardic Community, 5976
Kettenbach, Mary Ruth, 2706
Ketter, Jason W., 9904
Ketterer, Sarah H., 635
Kettleson, Rebecca L., 9963
Keutgen, Christian, 6585
Kever, Kristos P., 7659
Kevorkian, Hagop, 6304
Kew, Julia Mirak, 4204
Key Food Stores Cooperative, 6387
KeyBank, 1945, 7318, 7328, 7343, 7394, 7416, 7419, 7427, 7453, 7460

Keybank, 7461
KeyBank, 7517, 7522, 7527, 7536, 7540, 7555, 7588, 7604, 7617, 7636
KeyBank Capital Markets, 8700
KeyBank N.A., 7332, 7337, 7338, 7344, 7378, 7477, 7480, 7494, 7512, 7539, 7589
Keybank N.A., 7614
Keyes, James H., 3016
Keyes, James P., 3016
Keyes, Kevin, 2109
Keyes, Kevin W., 3016
Keyes, Paul T., Rev. , 4273, 4311
Keyes, Timothy D., 3016
Keyland, Christopher J., 8828
Keys, Patricia M., 5246
Keyser, M. Anthony, 1169
Keyser, Mary Anne, 1169
Keystone Foods Corp., 7910
Keystone Foods LLC, 7910
KG Investments, 3516
Kgabo, Molapo, 7513
Kgil, Minchung, 3455
Khanuja, Parvinderjit S., 8959
Khanuk, L., 3140
Khanuk, T., 3140
Khatri, Aliya, 9228
Khaury, Susan M., 4693
Kheel, Kathleen, 6325
Khouri, Patricia, 6088
Khoury, Brian N., 702
Khoury, David, 8042
Khoury, Eileen M., 4273, 4311
Khoury, Jason B., 702
Khoury, Lisa, 8042
Khoury, Marilyn, 8042
Khoury, Richel G., 702
Khoury, Tawfiq, 702
Khoury, Tawfiq N., 702
Khym, Daewon, 5545
Khym, Esther, 5545
Khym, Kwangwon, 5545
Kibbey, Josephine, 4260
Kiburis, Doris, 3426
Kichiji, Katsuhiko, 8183
Kidd, Shannon L., 9070
Kidder, Michael R., 4152
Kids II Employees, 2530
Kids II Inc., 2530
Kids II Vendors, 2530
Kidwell, Gene, 7636
Kiefer, Amee, 9703
Kiefer, Craig, 9703
Kiefer, Kathryn, 4931
Kiel, Sue, 5843
Kielland, Belinda B., 8041
Kiely, Maryann S., 1590
Kiely, Timothy, 4057
Kienholz, Corey, 1546
Kienlen, Steve, 9033
Kienstra, Christina L., 4938
Kienstra, Faith, 4938
Kienstra, Theodore A., Jr., 4938
Kienstra, Theodore A., Sr., 4938
Kientz, Frank E., 9464
Kiernan, Eaddo H., 6306
Kiernan, Peter D., 6306
Kiersznowski Revocable Trust, David, 3594
Kiersznowski, David, 3594
Kierulf, Anders, 9354
Kierulf, Bjorn, 9354
Kies, David M., 6307

Kies, Kathryn L., 6307
Kieslerco, Heidi, 9839
Kieve, Lenoir, 703
Kieve, Robert S., 703
Kiewit, Marjorie, 9838
Kiffel, Aviva, 6931
Kifton Development, 7801
Kiger, Vaughn L., 9739, 9753
Kiggens-Leifheit, Amber, 9878
Kihlman, Dale, 3702
Kihm, Kimberly Dawn, 696
Kihn, Cecily, 1822
Kikuchi, Atsuko, 931
Kilbourne, Edgar, 5097
Kilbride, James, 2336
Kileen, Mary M., 4747
Kilen, C. Bruce, 7795
Kilgore, David P., 8989
Kilgore, James, 5513
Kilgore, James B., 8345
Kilgore, Margaret W., 8989
Kilgore, Patty, 2617
Kilgus, Adam, 3220
Kilgus, Joann A., 3220
Kilkelly, Laura W., 9725
Killam, Oliver P., 4153
Killeen, Michael F., 7330
Killen, Dina F., 503
Killen, James E., 503
Killian, Charles F., 3670
Killian, Elizabeth A. Bell, 9963
Killian, Helen C., 4154
Killian, Mildred A., 3670
Killian, Raymond L., 4154
Killingstad, H. Chris, 4798
Killingsworth, Dorothy, 7204
Killion, Benjamin C., 7717
Killmer, Walter J., Jr., 6826
Kilmurray, Dan, 6720
Kilpatrick, J. Thomas, 2461
Kilrea, Mary Beth, 3017
Kilrea, Scott, 3017
Kim Family Revocable Trust, 704
Kim, Andy, 4943
Kim, Anthony, 631
Kim, Chin-Wu, 1804
Kim, Dong Koo, 704
Kim, Geon Y., 705
Kim, Injoa, 5291
Kim, Jeanne M., 705
Kim, Jinsoo, 5375
Kim, Min, 883
Kim, Ock Hee, 883
Kim, Seong, 5375
Kim, Stephen, 5375
Kim, Sun Kee, 5291
Kim, Young-Key-Renaud, 1804
Kimball Hill Homes Texas, 9009
Kimball, Alberta S., 245
Kimball, Elizabeth, 1059
Kimball, H. Earle, 8434
Kimberly, James H., 7622
Kimberly, Newton S., Jr., 7622
Kimmel Trust, Edward A., 2146
Kimmel, David, 2146, 6308
Kimmel, Edward A., 2146
Kimmel, Howard J., 7782
Kimmel, Sandra F., 7782
Kimmel, Steve, 3397
Kimmell 2001 Rev. Trust, Garman O., 7694
Kimmell, Garman O., 7694
Kimmelman, Elbrun, 6309
Kimmelman, P. Damian, 6309

Kimmelman, Peter, 6309, 6761
Kimray Inc., 7694
Kimura, Brain, 7742
Kimura, Sera Baldwin, 7742
Kin, Lucy, 140
Kincaid, Nick, 7292
Kincaid, Pam B., 3645
Kincheloe, John B., Jr., 7227
Kind LLC, 9335
King Ranch Family, 8994
King, Adam, 4789
King, Amy, 2499
King, Andrew, 9240
King, Barbara, 4789
King, Benjamin A., 2128
King, Betty, 2148
King, Bret, 9977
King, Bryan, 2128
King, Carl K., 3993
King, Carol H., 2943
King, Charles H., III, 7834
King, Christopher B., Dr. , 2128
King, David P., 710
King, DeLutha H., Jr., 2504
King, Diana, 6311
King, Dorothy Warren, 7729
King, Douglas, 7118
King, Dr., Charles, 2435
King, Dwight D., 8819
King, Elizabeth, 7602
King, Elizabeth B., 7834
King, Ellen J., 5619
King, Erin, 4789
King, Harold M., 9277
King, Helen J., Dr. , 2128
King, Heyward L., Jr., 8522
King, J. Luther, Jr., 8993
King, Jacqueline E., 6926
King, James N., 5619
King, Jennifer, 4499
King, John Bryan, 8993
King, John Thomas, 9525
King, Jonathan Leroy, 6926
King, Kathy, 389
King, Kelly, 1295
King, Lamont D., 9484
King, Luther, 8993
King, Marcia, 1712
King, Margaret, 7602
King, Margaret B., 9878
King, Mark A., 1712
King, Mary-Claire, 9645
King, Mason Daniel, 8993
King, Michael S., 3780
King, Michele, 3441
King, Michelle E., 5619
King, Olin B., 43
King, Paul A., 5363
King, Paul L., 9645
King, Ronan, 8647
King, Shelbie A., 43
King, Shelbie Jean, 43
King, Stephen, 6178
King, Stephen E., 6178
King, Steven, 4789
King, Teresa, 8993
King, Theresa, 9484
King, Wendy, 5344
King, Wendy B., 2435
King, William M., 9484
King, William Toben, 4939
Kinghorn, Deloris W., 469
Kingsberg, Alan D., 5421
Kingsberg, Harold J., 5421

Kingsberg, Ruth J., 5421
Kingsbury Castings, 6207
Kingsbury Corp., 8435
Kingsbury, Gretchen, 238
Kingsbury, Sarah O., 831
Kingsley, F.G., 1693
Kingsley, Juanita Allen, 4046, 4067
Kingston, Jean, 4318
Kingston, John, 4318
Kingston, Kate, 3797
Kinko's Corporation, 887
Kinnaird, Margaret, 3919
Kinney, Bill, Jr., 8522
Kinney, Eva J., 4483
Kinney, H. Lee, 7551
Kinney, Jodona Morley, 4518
Kinney, Josephine J., 8092
Kinney, Madeleine B., 4724
Kinney, Ronald F., 4483
Kinney, W.E., 9840
Kinnie, Cynthia A., 7783
Kinnie, D. Craig, 7783
Kinnie, Kristin, 7783
Kinnie, Ryan, 7783
Kinning, Joseph, 4648
Kinsell, Stephen J., 3401
Kinser, Brenda, 3610
Kinsey, Joan, 707
Kinsey, Norman E., 707
Kinsolving, Dean, 5620
Kipper, Barbara, 3018
Kipper, Barbara Levy, 3018
Kipper, David, 3018
Kiralla, Gail, 784
Kirbo, Helen V., 2441
Kirbo, Kathy, 2437
Kirby Charitable Lead Annuity Trust, Robert, 6313
Kirby Family Trust, The, 708
Kirby, Ann, 6451
Kirby, Deborah, 5422
Kirby, Deborah Y., 5905
Kirby, G. Michael, 5422
Kirby, Kay Ellen, 1259
Kirby, Marvel B., 708
Kirby, Michael, 5422
Kirby, Paula C., 6451
Kirby, Robert E., 6313
Kirchhoff, Gregory, 1368
Kirchhoff, Lovelle, 3617
Kirchner Trust I, Garnett I., 4649
Kirchner Trust II, Garnett I., 4649
Kirihara, Wayne H., 2627
Kirila, Virginia L., 8879
Kirk 101 Trust, 9334
Kirk, Donald H., Jr., 3894
Kirk, Katy, 9426
Kirk, Kristen, 9334
Kirk, Mary C., 1645
Kirk, Michael C., 4881
Kirk, Patricia M., 3894
Kirk, Spencer, 9334
Kirk, Thomas H., 9493
Kirker, James M., 1438
Kirkham, Kate B., 7327
Kirkham, Ryan, 7546
Kirkham, W. Gates, 7327
Kirkish, Mark S., 9915
Kirkland, Keith, 4141
Kirkorian, John, 709
Kirkorian, Marguerite, 709
Kirkorian, Marleen, 709
Kirkpatrick, Charles, 3298
Kirkpatrick, Mary Alice, 7944

Kirkpatrick, Norma L., 3298
Kirkwood, Elizabeth, 8501
Kirkwood, Wayne R., 1917
Kirr, Rosemary, 8016
Kirsch, Gregory, 4945
Kirsch, Martin J., 3872
Kirschenbaum, Avrohom, 6294
Kirschenbaum, D. Maimon, 6314
Kirschenbaum, M.R., 2360
Kirschenbaum, Maurice, 6294
Kirschenbaum, Mordechai, 6294
Kirschenbaum, Ruth, 6314
Kirsh, Michael A., 2237
Kirtland, Jennifer E., 8841
Kirtland, John E., 8841
Kirwan, Christopher, 4709
Kirwan, Gail, 8996
Kirwan, Nicole S., 8996
Kirwan, Roger, 8996
Kirwan, Roger T., 8996
Kirwan, Sean R., 8996
Kirwan, Virginia, 8996
Kirwin, Martha E.H., 4709
Kirzner, Martin, 6315
Kiser, Robert R., 2463
Kishawi, Qassem, 1599
Kisker Court, Patricia, 7479
Kiskinis, Garry G., 9421
Kisleiko, Irene M., 8228
Kisling, Norman, 3508
Kisling, Sheryl, 2305
Kiss Investment Co., LLC, 4564
Kissner, Rita, 7375
Kistler, Brian G., 6316
Kistler, Eileen K., 6316
Kistler, William L., III, 6316
Kitchell, Hardison Downey, 8700
Kitchens, John L., 1958
Kitko, Paulette, 7439
Kitson, Kevin, 1610
Kittenbrink, Douglas, 8093
Kittenbrink, Douglas A., 8093
Kittenbrink, Leslie, 8093
Kittendorf, Anne, 4551
Kittillsen, Kjell, 6541
Kittle, Dwayne, 9426
Kittle, Jay S., 151
Kittle, Laura, 3918
Kittle, Robert, 9740
Kittredge, Charles J., 4058
Kittredge, John, 4058
Kittrell, John David, 4834
Kittrell, Kerry D., 4834
Kittrell, Lequita S., 4834
Kittsmiller, Katherine, 2365
Kitzinger, James, 9955
Kiwanis Club of Ann Arbor, 4484
Kiwanis Club of Bradenton, 2149
Kiwanis Club of Little Havana, 2150
Kiwanis Club of Traverse City, 4484
Kiyonaga, Gary, 9642
Kjellstrom, Janet Ann, 3019
Kjolhaug, Aaron, 4720
KKP Holdings LLC, 3045, 3136
KL Ventures LLC, 153
Klabin, Alexander, 6775
Klabin, Kristen, 6775
Kladder, Thomas B., 4621
Klafehn, Joan, 6898
Klagsbrun, Edward, 6970
Klagsbrun, Francine, 6318
Klagsbrun, Samuel C., 6318
Klaich, Daniel J., 5176
Klakamp, Willard, 3448

Klaphake, John, 4624
Klapp, Guy, 7392
Klapper, David I., 3357, 3408
Klapper, Mary Elizabeth, 3408
Klare, Daniel, 7456
Klare, Karen, 7456
Klarr, Louise S., 4539
Klarr, S. Gunnar, 4539
Klatskin, Charles, 5423
Klatskin, Deborah, 5423
Klatskin, Lynne, 5423
Klatskin, Samuel, 5423
Klau Foundation, David W. and Sadie, 5977
Klaue, August V., 9647
Klaue, David A., 9647
Klaue, Mary E., 9647
Klaus, Anne, 6321
Klaus, Arthur, 6319
Klaus, Barbara, 6321
Klaus, Barry, 6321
Klaus, Esther, 6320
Klaus, Jeffrey, 6320
Klaus, Lester, 6320
Klaus, Michael, 6320
Klaus, Mortimer, 6321
Klaus, Ryan, 6319
Klaus, Steven, 6320
Klaus, Vivian, 6319
Klausman, Betsy, 8022
Klavan, Harry S., 6322
Klavan, Rena S., 6322
Kleban, Edward L., 6323
Kleber, Charles F., 4499
Kleberg, Richard M., III, 8994
Klebuc-Simes, Michele, 3260
Kleiman, Steven M., 5184
Klein Foundation, Fritz, 370
Klein Irrevocable Trust, E. Ann, 8097
Klein, Abraham, 5748, 6469
Klein, Adele, 6324
Klein, Allan R., 8997
Klein, Avi, 2424
Klein, Barbara G., 6325
Klein, Benjamin, 6791
Klein, Carine R., 9970
Klein, Carla S., 1499
Klein, Carol, 8840
Klein, Chaim S., 6426
Klein, Christine Erion, 1265
Klein, Daniel V., 6294
Klein, David L., 1694
Klein, David R., 8997
Klein, Dinah, 6469
Klein, Doreen, 8374
Klein, Earl D., 2870
Klein, Eric, 1499
Klein, Feigie, 6426
Klein, Frank H., 6136
Klein, Fritz, 370
Klein, George, 6324
Klein, Herbert C., 4160
Klein, Jason A., 6325
Klein, John W., 8997
Klein, Linda Dorn, 763
Klein, Marcia, 4581
Klein, Margaret K., 5424
Klein, Mary Eddy, 5424
Klein, Mendel, 6426
Klein, Michele Gerber, 6396
Klein, Mike, 7375
Klein, Miriam, 1694
Klein, Mordechai, 6469
Klein, Patricia J., 2546

Klein, Randall L., 2919
Klein, Raymond, 8096
Klein, Regina, 370
Klein, Richard A., 4764
Klein, Richard C., 7553
Klein, Rivka, 6469
Klein, Roberta T., 8997
Klein, Roger D., 7553
Klein, Roger M., 4160
Klein, Rosalie, 389
Klein, Roxanne, 8100
Klein, Ruth L., 6325
Klein, Sara Dina, 5748
Klein, Seymour M., 6325
Klein, Sonja, 8997
Klein, Stephen B., 8096
Klein, Walter C., 5424
Klein, Zoe S., 6325
Kleinman Foundation, The, 4181
Kleinman, Doron L., 1326
Kleinman, Michael, 9298
Kleinman, Michael J., 1326
Kleinschmidt, Alexander, 6326
Kleinschmidt, Amy, 4672
Kleinschmidt, Lara, 6326
Kleinschmidt, Nell F., 6326
Kleinschmidt, Paul, 6326
Kleinschmidt, Robert W., 6326
Kleissner, Alex, 8094
Kleissner, Andrea, 8094
Kleissner, Karl, 8094
Kleissner, Lisa, 8094
Klementik, David, 8353
Klementik, Ruth, 8353
Klemm, Marianne, 4961
Klenk, Laverne, 8986
Kleppel, Lee G., 2054
Klesa, J. Michael, 6083
Kleshinski, Richard M., 7488
Klesius, Elaine, 2944
Klesius, Patrick, 2944
Klesius, Stephen, 2944
Klesse, Laura, 8998
Klesse, Margaret A., 8998
Klesse, William R., 8998
Kletscher, Joanne, 4631
Klette, Ruth, 3663
Klewit, Marjorie, 9838
Klier, Kareen, 7625
Klimas, Stan, 5058
Klimek, John, 2092
Kline, Anthony, 284
Kline, Bradford, 9631
Kline, Carolyn, 8288
Kline, Cary, 5110
Kline, Charles, 8098
Kline, Figa Cohen, 8098
Kline, John C., 1590
Kline, Lawrence E., 730
Kline, Michael H., Sr., 6233
Kline, Michael, Jr., 6233
Kline, Nancy W., 7826
Kline, Sherry M., 730
Kline, Theresa, 9631
Klingenmeyer, John D., 4493
Klingenmeyer, Joseph R., 4493
Klingenmeyer, Maggie, 4493
Klingenmeyer, Ralph E., 4493
Klingenstein Fund, Esther A. and Joseph, 6328
Klingenstein, Alan, 6327
Klingenstein, Alan L., 6327
Klingenstein, Andrew, 6328
Klingenstein, Frances S., 6327

Klingenstein, John, 6329
Klingenstein, Kathy, 6328
Klingenstein, Lee Paul, 6327
Klingenstein, Paul H., 6327
Klingenstein, Susan, 6328
Klingenstein, Thomas, 6328
Klinger Co., 3500
Klingner, Linda L., 2682
Klinkhammer, Laurie, 9814
Klintworth, William C., 9320
Klode, Peter, 9855
Kloeker, Nellie, 3448
Kloha, David, 2132
Kloha, Elizabeth, 2132
Kloha, Mark, 2132
Kloidt, William H., Jr., 7932
Klopp, David, 92
Klos, Diana Mitsu, 5325
Klose, Donna D., 6624
Klosk, Louis, 3020
Klosowski, Henry, 6769
Klubes, Benjamin B., 1818
Klueber, William J., 4107
Klumok, Lucy P., 916
Klump, Elizabeth, 2533
Klump, Michael, 2533
KML Royal Dutch Airlines, 2622
Knafel, Andrew G., 6330
Knafel, Douglas R., 6330
Knafel, Sidney R., 6330
Knakal, Robert, 6656
Knake, Cheryl, 3223
Knapp Foundation, The, 3895
Knapp, A. John, Jr., 9030
Knapp, Breck L., 9030
Knapp, Breckenridge L., 9030
Knapp, Charles, 2619
Knapp, Christopher L., 9030
Knapp, George O., 6331
Knapp, George O., III, 6331
Knapp, George R., 8318
Knapp, Gwen, 2153
Knapp, Jules, 2153
Knapp, Laurie H., 4250
Knapp, Scott, 3520
Knapp, W. Jared, III, 6331
Knappenberger, Burdette, 3021
Knaster, Martha, 6332
Knauer, Joann, 3922
Knauf, Robert J., 421
Knauth, Joe, 9233
Knechtel, A. Mark, 3936
Knedler, Marie, 3527
Kneisel, Anne H., 4157
Kneisel, Anne Hooper, 4157
Kneisel, William J., 4157
Knell, Ellen R., 712
Knell, Harvey, 712
Knell, Harvey G., 712
Knell, Paul, 497
Knepley, Katie, 1038
Knief, Byron L., 6490
Knight & Co Ltd., D.J., 6656
Knight 2000 Revocable Trust, Rebecca
     W., The , 7482
Knight Testamentary Clut, Edward R.,
     3731
Knight, A. Dowl, 8512
Knight, Amelia, 7482
Knight, Andrew M., 3022
Knight, Ann, 3731
Knight, Barry, 8640
Knight, Bryan, 3731
Knight, Charles, 7482

Knight, Colleen, 4396
Knight, Edward R., 3731
Knight, Elaine, 2546
Knight, Gerald C., 4574
Knight, H. Elvin, Jr., 3602
Knight, J.A., 5425
Knight, James, 7482
Knight, Jessica, 7482
Knight, Jr. Trust, Robert G., 3022
Knight, Lana, 8640
Knight, Lester B., 7482
Knight, Lisa, 5425
Knight, Mark, 3731
Knight, Mary K., 3022
Knight, Maureen, 4574
Knight, Patricia, 5198
Knight, Peggy, 1295
Knight, Peter, 147
Knight, Rebecca W., 7482
Knight, Robert D., 1917
Knight, Robert G., III, 3022
Knight, Robert G., Jr., 3022
Knight, Stephanie, 7807
Knight, William J., 5626
Knip, John J., Jr., 4811, 4812
Knippenberg, Ruth J., 2154
Knisely, Jay, 138
Knispel, Lester, 9335
Kniss, Lynee M., 726
Knistrom, Fanny, 5426
Knistrom, Svante, 5426
Knitcraft, 7132
Knobelauch, Karl, 238
Knobloch, George, 6387
Knoll, 8100
Knoll, Ruth, 4378
Knoll, Ruth S., 4378
Knoll, Thomas, 4378
Knopf Assocs., 2156
Knopf, Charles E., Jr., 2155
Knopf, Eli, 2156
Knopf, Eugene, 3498
Knopf, Max, 2156
Knopf, Rika, 2156
Knopf, Solomon, 2156
Knoph Foundation, Max, 7026
Knoph Foundation, Rika, 7026
Knopoff, Alejandro, 1566
Knotts, Bradley, 3024
Knowles Electronics, 3023
Knowles, Charles P., 4150
Knowles, James T., 4150
Knowles, Jean L., 4150
Knowles, John H, 4150
Knowles, John H., Jr., 4150
Knowles, Michael W., 2463
Knowles, Nancy, 3023
Knowles, Nancy W., 3023
Knowles, Robert M., 4150
Knowles-Hedlund, Jean, 4150
Knowlton, Calvin H., 5427
Knowlton, Nancy V., 4725
Knowlton, Reginald K., 5427
Knowlton, Richard L., 4725
Knox Gelatine, 8101
Knox, Eleanor E., 8101
Knox, Jeanne M., 1500
Knox, Jillian, 778
Knox, Kimberly, 8101
Knox, Martha, 5268
Knox, Molly, 778
Knox, Robert A., 1500
Knox, Robert W., Jr., 8999
Knox, Shell H., 2534

Knox, W. David, II, 9794
Knox, Wyckliffe A., 2534
Knox, Wyckliffe A., Jr., 2534
Knudsen, Earl, 8102
Knupp, Colleen Mitchell, 3189
Knupp, Jeffrey, 3189
Knuppe, Barbara, 714
Knuppe, H. James, 714
Knutson, Robert B., 6990
Knutson, Thomas K., 2679
Ko, Amy F.M., 715
Ko, J.J., 5795
Ko, Shannon J.S., 715
KOA Speer Electronics, 8183
Koblin, Ronald R., 343
Kobor, Carmen, 716
Kobor, Erika, 716
Kobor, George, 716
Kobren, Barry A., 9171
Koch Foods Chicago, 8859
Koch, Ashley, 8644
Koch, Donald G., 7411
Koch, Gary, 6134
Koch, Gloria, 512
Koch, Jacob, 3025
Koch, Leah, 3025
Koch, Loretta M., 3353
Koch, Priscilla, 6540
Koch, Rebecca, 3025
Koch, Steven, 3025
Kochis, S. Timothy, 1779
Kocurek, Arnold J., 5428
Kocurek, Irene B., 5428
Kocurek, Karen, 5428
Kocurek, Suzanne, 5428
Kodama, Mitchell M., 470
Kodosky Foundation, 8836
Koechlein, John H., 3456
Koechlein, Monica, 3456
Koegel, Albert J., 4535
Koegel, Barbara L., 4535
Koegel, Jane, 4535
Koegel, John, 4535
Koegel, John C., 4535
Koegel, Kathryn, 4535
Koegel, Lisa A., 4535
Koehm, Christopher J., 1396
Koehn, Elton, 3641
Koehn, Elvin "Al", 9290
Koehn, Kelly, 3641
Koehn, Max, 3641
Koelbel, Gene N., 1306
Koelbel, Walter A., 1306
Koelbel, Walter A., Jr., 1306
Koellner, Ben, 3539
Koenig, Bradford, 717
Koenig, John, 5113
Koenig, Lauren, 717
Koenig, Rodney C., 8963, 9279
Koenigs, Betty, 9887
Koentopf, Marin, 4720
Koepke, James E., 5078, 5079
Koeplin, John, 1204
Koeppel, Eliza, 225
Koeppel, Eliza Haskins, 225
Koerner, Jodi M., 1971
Koerselman, John, 3528
Koessler, Eric, 6335
Koessler, John W., Jr., 6335
Koessler, Kenneth L., Jr., 6334
Koessler, Mary M., 6336
Koessler, Mary R., 6335, 6933
Koessler, Paul J., 6335
Koessler, Paul J., Jr., 6335

Koester, William, 7375
Koffler Corp., The, 8436
Koffler, Lillian, 8436
Kofkoff, Susan Godwin, 5004
Kogan, Barton H., 5776
Kogan, Marjorie D., 5776
Kogan, Michael S., 5776
Koha, Irene M., 4158
Koha, Valdur, 4158
Kohan, Richard L., 1853
Kohl Charities, Herbert H., 9865
Kohl, Allen D., 9864, 9865
Kohl, Dolores, 9865
Kohl, Dolores K., 9864
Kohl, Herbert H., 9864, 9865
Kohl, Konrad D., 4506, 4507
Kohl, Mary, 9864
Kohl, Sidney A., 9864, 9865
Kohlberg, Andrew S., 710
Kohler, Mary S., 9961
Kohler, Terry J., 9961
Kohlhas, Susan Berry, 7867
Kohn Family Trust, 6339
Kohn, Asher, 5544
Kohn, Cookie Anspach, 2970
Kohn, David, 3120
Kohn, Ellen, 7844
Kohn, Herb, 6339
Kohn, Joseph C., 7844
Kohn, Josephine L., 3896
Kohn, Richard, 2919
Kohn, Robert A., 3694
Kohn, Sara, 6339
Kohn, Victoria C., 3120
Kohnen, David A., 7609
Kohorst, Kevin A., 1609
Kohorst, Matthew A., 1609
Kohorst, W. Robert, 1609
Kohrs, Craig, 7525
Kohrs, Shelly A. Mifsud, 7525
Kohs, LaVerne R., 9878
Koht-Phipps, Alice, 1038
Kokot, Eugene V., 2187, 6311
Kolar, Joseph M., 1818
Kolb, Sheila B., 8513
Kolba, Robert E., 9151
Kolber, George, 5429
Kolber, Kari, 8806
Kolber, Richard, 5429
Kolber, Vita, 5429
Kole, Sheri, 9908
Kole, Sheri L., 9893
Kolitsos, Socrates, 7366
Kolitz, Robert, 9000
Kolitz, Sandora, 9000
Kolkhorst, Gary, 9181
Kollel Kol Yakov, 5834
Kolton, Myra, 4283
Komich, Mary Patricia, 5573
Kominowski, Ed, 3360
Komis, Don L., 9912
Komos, Joseph P., 4931
Kompkoff, Joyce L., 83
Kompkoff, Lloyd, 83
Konar, Howard E., 6340
Konar, Sheila, 6340
Konar, William B., 6340
Konczyk, Erick, 6017
Konda Charitable Lead Annuity Trust,
     1107
Kondo, Hideo, 2650
Kong, Danette, 2648
Konhaus, Sara J., 9479
Konheim, Estelle M., 6499

Koniag, 89
Konig, Kasper, 6556
Konigsberg, Paul J., 5644
Koningstein, Ross, 943
Konkel, Katherine, 9036
Konover, Doris, 1501
Konover, Simon, 1501
Konst, Gary, 7375
Kontos, Arthur, 5430
Kontos, James, 5430
Kontos, Michael, 5430
Konwinski, Patrice, 4406
Konynenburg, Claire Van, 9345
Koo, Carlos Chang, 6394
Koo, Jackie, 2049
Koontz, Frederick P., 7736
Koontz, Frederick Singley, 3916, 3976, 3977
Koontz, James, 8435
Koop, Mitchell, 8986
Koosh, Susan, 7442
Kopac, Matt, 1635
Kopald, Andrea Nelson, 947
Kopczick, Elise M., 5306
Kopelman, Eli, 6643
Kopf, Richard S., 527
Kopko, Peter, 7312
Koplin, Danielle Morgan, 8178
Koplow, Florence, 4159
Koplow, Meyer, 8023
Koplow, Richard A., 4159
Kopnisky, Jack, 6632
Kopp, Ronald S., 7635
Kopp, Sarah, 8561
Kopperl, Joan H., 4266
Koprulu, Nina J., 6274
Kopsa, Lawrence R., 5129
Koranda Family Foundation, 3026
Koranda, John, 3026
Koranda, Katherine, 3026
Koranda, Kenneth R., 3026
Koranda, Susan W., 3026
Korb, Brent L., 9141
Korba, Robert W., 2310
Korbey, John, 5230
Korczak, Midge A., 6806
Korell, Harold M., 9001
Korell, Patricia, 9001
Korf, Gene R., 5583
Korn, Jeffrey G., 9325
Kornblum, Gay Klearman, 4940
Kornblum, Harvey, 4940
Kornblum, Kathy, 4940
Kornbluth, Phyllis, 6479
Korngold, Jonathan, 6427
Korngold, Kristen, 6427
Korniczky, Anna, 6170
Korniczky, Anna T., 5919
Kornitzer, Carol W., 3583
Kornitzer, John C., 3583
Kornitzer, Nicole M., 3583
Kornland Building Co., 718
Kornreich, Janet, 6341
Kornreich, John, 6341
Kornwasser, Joseph, 718
Kornwasser, Mark, 718
Kornwasser, Sonia, 718
Korsch, Sharon, 8563
Korsinsky, Eduard, 6241
Kort Marital Trust, Fred, 719
Kort, Barbara, 719
Kort, William B., 9450
Kortjohn, Martin D., 6083
Kortz, Jess, 1307

Korum Automotive Group Inc., 9648
Korum Family Limited Partnership, 9648
Korum Investments, Jerry, 9648
Korum, Germaine R., 9648
Korum, Jerome, 9648
Korum, Jerry, 9648
Korver, Kyle, 9335
Korver, Laine, 9335
Kos, MSN, RN, Jeanne R., 1914
Kosa, Peter, 5085
Kosarek, Charles L., Jr., 8725
Kosarek, Connie V., 9195
Kosarek, Jay A., 9195
Kosarek, Sherry, 8725
Kosarek, Willie J., 8725, 9195
Kosbab, Robert, 4735
Kosbruk, Gerda, 91
Kosch, Donald F., 4485
Kosch, Donald Mary, 4485
Kosch, Mary T., 4485
Koshal, Vipin, Dr., 7311
Koskey, Richard, 6665
Koski, Beverly L., 2157
Koski, Christine L., 2157
Koski, Robert C., 2157
Koski, Robert E., 2157
Koski, Thomas L., 2157
Koskoff, Richard, 5004
Kosky, Betty, 3078
Kosmatka, Dan, 7761
Koss Corp., 9866
Koss, Blair, 6540
Koss, Cornelia, 720
Koss, John C., 9866
Koss, Michael A., 720
Koss, Michael J., 9866
Koss, Nancy L., 9866
Koss, Todd H., 9832
Koss, Zane, 720
Kossel, Sylvia, 6755
Kossuth, Stephen R., 8165
Kost, Jamie, 2795
Kost, M., 825
Kostboth, Norman, 8569
Kosteck, Greg, 3991
Koster, Ardith A., 4486
Koster, Cheryl, 4486
Koster, Daniel J., 4486
Koster, Gail, 6956
Koster, Greg, 4486
Koster, Jeremy, 5414
Koster, Kurt, 4486
Koster, Linda, 4486
Koster, Rick, 4486
Koster, Susan, 4486
Kostohryz, Thomas, 7311
Kostyack, Ray, 5582
Kot, Mary Crane, 5884
Kotadia, Anar, 9572
Kotadia, Shiraz, 9572
Koth, Trandy G., 2498
Kotik, Charlotta, 6114
Kott Memorial Charitable Trust, 3027
Kottke, Keith, 4772
Kotzur, Tammy, 8869
Koubek, Dennis, 3863
Koulaieff, Ivan V., 1132
Koulajian, Carla, 6537
Koulajian, Laura, 6537
Koulajian, Nigol, 6537
Kourlesis, Suzanne, 5363
Kouroubacalis, Janet, 4304
Koury, Anne Kirkpatrick, 7150
Koury, Carol E., 5206, 5235

Koury, Ernest A., Jr., 7150
Koury, Maurice J., 7150
Koury, Michelle A., Dr., 5872
Koury-Jones, Carina, 5235
Koutz, Mick, 4534
Kovacs, Bernadine H., 7945
Kovacs, Ruth, 1720
Kovar, Lisa, 3217
Kovener, Gilbert, 3448
Kovensky, Nicole Greene, 6342
Kovensky, Stuart R., 6342
Kovner, Amy, 6972
Kovner, Jeffrey, 6972
Kovner, Kristin, 6972
Kovner, Nicholas, 6972
Kowalke, Kim H., 6950
Kowitz, David, 9002
Kowitz, Sarah, 9002
Kozak, Page Otenasek, 3931
Kozakis, Chris M., 4199
Kozberg, Anthony, 426
Kozberg, Joanne, 426
Kozelsky, Amy Hill, 9223
Kozicki, Judy, 6343
Kozicki, Zvi, 6343
Kozlik, Michael, 5093
Kozusko, Donald D., 1797
Kpaa-Kaiser Permanente, 5562
KPMG, 2510
Krabbe, Joseph, 7304
Kraby, Sharon J., 2217
Kracht, Hutch, 3501
Krafft, Dennis, 4450
Kraft Foods Inc., 3600
Kraft, Cynthia, 3635
Kraft, Dennis, 8566
Kraft, Kevin, 7932
Krahe, David, 7330
Krahling, David, 3528
Krahmer, Johannes R., 1641
Krahulik, David, 942
Kraines, Jeffrey L., 4105
Kraines, Merrill M., 4105
Krall, Robert J., 9749
Kram Construction, 718
Kramer, Catherine F., 5014
Kramer, Charlotte R., 7484
Kramer, Christopher M., 5897
Kramer, Daniel R., 5897
Kramer, Eddie M., 9003
Kramer, Elizabeth, 7484
Kramer, Joel, 159
Kramer, John N., Dr., 7346
Kramer, Kevin, 3390
Kramer, Louise, 7485
Kramer, Mark R., 7484
Kramer, Patricia A., 9003
Kramer, Robert, 8345
Kramer, Thomas, 7882
Kramer, Toby, 7484
Krammer, Susan, 7747
Krantz, Harriet, 6349
Kranz, Mary Jo, 4396
Kranzlin, Mary Ellen, 3928
Krarup, Irene, 5746
Krasberg, Corinne, 3029
Krasdale Foods Inc., 6344
Krasne, Charles A., 6344
Krasne, Kenneth, 6344
Krasne, Thatcher, 6344
Krasnow, Leonard R., 9299
Kratschmer, Mark, 2705
Kraunelis, Matthew A., 4311
Kraus, Avishai, 6009

Kraus, Paul V., 2244
Krause Gentle Corporation, 3516
Krause, Andrew, 8309
Krause, Andrew J., 2030
Krause, Kathryn, 2158
Krause, Lois, 9814
Krause, Lori, 3623
Krause, Martin, 4735
Krause, Robin, 6329
Krause, Roy, 2158
Krause, Simone, 6952
Krause, William A., 3516
Kraushaar, Charles W., 6946
Krausman, Lisa, 5824
Krausman, Steven, 5824
Krauss Miller Lutz Charitable Foundation, 2152
Krauss, Alan F., 7153
Krauss, Frederick G., 7153
Krauss, Irene, 6345
Krauss, Melvyn, 6345
Krauss, Otto F., 7153
Krauss, Virginia, 7153
Kravecas, Marie Adler, 5242
Kravitz, Barbara, 6153
Kravitz, Harriett B., 6153
Kravitz, Jennifer E., 1747
Krawitt, Andrew L., 5306
Krayer, Anthony, 1978
Krech, Douglas, 647
Krech, Jane, 647
Kreeger, Douglas, 6554
Kreeger, Evan, 6554
Kreeger, Keith, 6554
Kreeger, Wendy Durst, 6554
Krehbiel, Frederick L., 3030
Krehbiel, Jay F., 3030
Krehbiel, John H., III, 3030
Krehbiel, Kenton K., 3585
Krehbiel, William V., 3030
Krehbiel-Ellsworth, Margaret V., 3030
Kreider, James, 2987
Kreider, Matthew S., 5018
Kreisman, David S., 2159
Kreisman, Susan A., 2159
Kreitler, Hobart C., 1502
Kreitler, James S., 1502
Kreitler, John M., 1502
Kreitler, Karen R., 1502
Kreitler, Sally S., 1502
Kreitler, Thomas S., 1502
Kreitman, Jacob, 5667
Kreitman, Rabbi B., 5899
Kreitman, Rabbi J., 5899
Kreitman, Rivkah, 5667
Kreitzberg, Bruce, 721
Kreitzberg, Caroline, 721
Kreitzberg, Fred, 721
Kreitzer, JoAn, 7452
Krekstein, Michael H., 8042
Krems, David Z., 1212
Krendl, Kathy, 7545
Kresa, Joyce, 5432
Kresa, Kent, 5432
Kresa-Reahl, Kiren, 5432
Kretchmar, Brenda, 4845
Kretzschmar, Pastor Robert, 3904
Kreun, Curt, 7295
Kreuter, Annica, 710
Kreuzberger, Donald, 5426
Kreuzberger, Douglas, 5426
Kreuzberger, Kurt, 5426
Kreuzberger, Scott, 5426
Kreuzberger, Virginia, 5426

Krick, Robert K., 9488
Krieble, Frederick, 1308
Krieble, Frederick B., 1308
Krieble, Helen E., 1308
Kriesberg, Irving, 5977
Krikava, Michael, 4648
Krimendahl, Elizabeth K., 6346
Krimendahl, H. Frederick, II, 6346
Kring, Gary S., 1350
Kring, Matthew, 1350
Kringlund, Pam, 9784
Krinsky, John, 6578
Krinsky, Robert D., 6578
Kriser, David B., 6347
Krishnan, Raj, 722
Krishnan-Shah, Lata, 722
Krispen Family Holdings, 9334
Krist, Carole D., 9004
Krist, Karyn D., 9004
Krist, Kevin D., 9004
Krist, Ronald D., 9004
Krist, Scott C., 9004
Kristel, J., 3138
Kristensen, Dan, 9718
Kristiansen, Barbara, 6541
Kristoff, Sandy, 1914
Kritser, David S., III, 9005
Kritz, Paul, 3566
Krivda, John P., 8069
Krizek, Curtis A., 4932
Krizek, Jennifer S., 4932
Krizman, Dwight, 498
Kroack, Laurel, 3417
Krock, David C., 7434
Krodel, Greg, 3441
Krodel, Tom, 3370
Kroeker, Anne F., 9641
Kroene, Ann Walton, 5037
Kroenke Charitable Lead Trust, Ann
    Walton, 5037
Kroenke Sports Charities, 1295
Kroger, William, 3206
Kroh Marital Trust, Lois L., 1309
Kroll, Alan, 6050
Kroll, Dana, 6348
Kroll, Janet, 8065
Kroll, Jeremy, 6348
Kroll, Jules B., 6348
Kroll, Lynn Korda, 6348
Kroll, Mary S., 8014
Kroll, Nicholas, 6348
Kroll, Teresa, 4879
Kroll, Vanessa, 6348
Kromer, John P., 1818
Kroon, David Fleming, 5433
Kroon, Mary Jane Sheehan, 5433
Kroon, Richard E., 5433
Krotts, Kim Pralle, 933
Krouse Unitrust, F.B., 8103
Krueck, Anstiss, 3031
Krueck, Ronald, 3031
Krueger, Alma M., 7695
Krueger, Amy E., 7695
Krueger, Carol K., 7695
Krueger, Dorrie, 4879
Krueger, Jennifer, 2117
Krueger, Tom, 3586
Krueger, W.C., 7695
Krug, Henry, Jr., 5091
Kruger, Ron, 3432
Kruidenier, Lisa, 3482
Kruis, David S., 4402, 4412, 4483,
    4544
Krumholz, Roy, 6349

Krumholz, Terry, 6349
Krumm, Ann L., 3517
Krumm, Daniel J., 3517
Krumm, David J., 3517
Krumm, Timothy J., 3517
Krummerich, Kimberly, 7884
Krumsiek, Barbara, 3807
Krupa, John, 5434
Krupa, Margaret A., 5434
Krupp, George, 4161
Krupp, Lizbeth, 4161
Krupps, Philip, 2803
Kruse, Andrea, 2132
Kruse, Karl, 2802
Kruse, Katharine M., 3419
Kruse, Richard D., 3419
Kruse, Sarah, 9937
Krush, Perry, 8556
Krutulis, Marian Cline, 1952
Krywat, Favish, 2890
Ktsanes, Teresa Taylor, 4855
Kubal, Elizabeth, 2802
Kubasak, Thomas F., 1131
Kubiak, Julie R., 2670
Kubiak, Mark S., 2670
Kubiak, Susan L., 2670
Kubicka, Jacqueline Whittier, 1181
Kubli, Tim, 1063
Kucaj, Dale, 2004
Kuch, Kevin C., 9643
Kuchevsky, Olga, 7030
Kuchin, Kenneth, 5917
Kuchman, Kenneth, 1191
Kudas, Kris, 415
Kudravetz, David W., 9435
Kueffner, Eric, 88
Kuehn, Kathryn M., 9949
Kuehn, Philip G., Jr., 9949
Kuehn, Willy, 8924
Kuehne, Marna M., 9979
Kuehner, Patricia, 1695
Kuehner, Paul J., 1695
Kuemmel, Sarah A., 9791
Kuflik, Mitchell A., 6720
Kugelman, D. Jack, 2161
Kugelman, Jane S., 2161
Kugelman, Marsha Cameron, 2161
Kuhl, Michele, 3126
Kuhl, Phil, 3126
Kuhle Investments LP, 139
Kuhle, Richard, 139
Kuhle, Shelley, 139
Kuhle, Shelley Louise Inch, 139
Kuhlmann, John E., 3555
Kuhn, Alice, 9006
Kuhn, Bernard, 4576
Kuhn, Dwight E., 7965
Kuhn, Eric, 9006
Kuhn, Glen, 7375
Kuhn, Hilda Albers, 4859
Kuhn, James, 799
Kuhn, Jeffrey, 9006
Kuhn, Michael, 9006
Kuhn, Michael J., 4941
Kuhn, Randall S., 9006
Kuhn, Raymond, 2404
Kuhn, Robert, 2404, 2712
Kuhn, Robert M., 7932
Kuhn, Steven L., 4941
Kuhn, Thomas, 2740
Kuhn, Thomas E., 4941
Kuhn, Tom, 5359
Kuhnley, Marc, 4672
Kuiken, Tim, 3514

Kukla, Don, 4962
Kukla, Donald T., 4962
Kukla, Elizabeth, 5381
Kukla, Lawrence, 3521
Kukulus, JoAnn, 6021
Kula, Donald T., 4962
Kula, Rabbi Irwin, 6757
Kulas, Jason, 9173
Kulas, Julian E., 2967
Kulick, Alice L., 6350
Kum & Go LC, 3516
Kumar, Devinder, 8698
Kumar, Shivaram, 5574
Kumar, Srini, 9098
Kumm, Dan, 4880
Kummerow, Arnold, 4487
Kump, Marsha A., 4614
Kumpula, Kathy, 601
Kundtz, Mary Ann, 3296
Kung, L.C., 8939
Kunick, Marlene Holly, 4530
Kunis, Eric, 6475
Kunitzer, John, 4522
Kunsman, Jason, 7339
Kuntz, Jean M., 7686
Kuntz, Peter H., 7485
Kunzman, Edwin A., 5525
Kunzman, Steven, 5525
Kuper, Bill, 9587
Kuper, Jane, 9587
Kuperavage, Eileen, 8263
Kupfer, Jeffrey F., 8135
Kupferberg, Dorothy, 6351
Kupferberg, Jack, 6351
Kupferberg, Lawrence, 5340
Kupferberg, Lenn, 6351
Kupferberg, Marcia, 6351
Kupferberg, Max L., 6932
Kupferberg, Seth, 6351
Kurian Limited Partnership, 4162
Kurian, Molly, 4162
Kurian, Thampy, 4162
Kuriansky, Joan, 1503, 2162
Kurland, Sheila, 6352
Kurland, Stanford L., 6352
Kurren, Faye W., 2631
Kurschner, Terry, 4668
Kurth, Jeri, 4890
Kurth, Tineka, 4784
Kurtz Irrevocable Trust, Esther A., 8104
Kurtz, Carol, 5436
Kurtz, Ellen, 8104
Kurtz, Esther A., 8104
Kurtz, Evelyn, 4980
Kurtz, Faythe K., 6720
Kurtz, Gregory P., 7330
Kurtz, Robert M., Jr., 8680
Kurtz, Ronald, 5436
Kurzrok Foundation, The, 7340
Kusalava International, 3965
Kuse, James R., 7786
Kuse, Shirley R., 7786
Kushen, Ivan, 2924
Kushen, Marilyn, 2924
Kushnick, Barbara, 5602
Kusman, Shelley Trager, 3701
Kutcel, Sandra, 2122
Kuth, Byron, 739
Kuth, Lyda, 739
Kutnick, Dale, 5437
Kutnick, Laura Gordon, 5437
Kuttel, Peter-John, 9386
Kutz, Hattie, 1696
Kutz, Milton, 1696

Kutz, Robert A., 7486
Kuyper, Peter C., 1253
Kuza, William M., 4203
Kvandal, Michelle, 623
Kvandal, Scott, 623
Kwal, Jaclyn M., 2410
Kwal, Rachel A., 2410
Kwal, Richard M., 2410
Kwam, Nancy E., 4775
Kwast, Terry, 425
KWD Video, 301
Kwiecinski, Henry, 7870
Kwoh, Cassandra, 724
Kyle, Frank, 9183
Kyle, Katherine Ann Schumacher, 9183
Kyling, Mikael, 2200
Kynett, Harold H., 8105
Kysor Industrial Corp., 9876
Kyte, Lawrence H., Jr., 7638
Kyte, Ryan, 7638

L&L Holding Co., 6655
L.C. Page Char Tr f/b/o Page Fam Char,
    4530
L.P. McCuistion Sanitarium Foundation,
    9114
La Arcada Investments Corp., 1720
La Motta, Michael, 5395
La Rocque, Vilma Banky, 273
La, Robert, 344
Laabs, Charles W., 2729
Laak, Philip, 8738
Laan, Bruno, 9685
Laarman, Linda, 9810
LaBarbera, Michael D., 2372
Labe, L. Jay, 1239
Labkon, Adam, 2907, 3208
Labkon, Howard, 2907, 3208
Labkon, Lindsey Levin, 2907
Labkon, Marilyn, 2907, 3208
Labkon, Mark, 2907
Labre, Daryl, 9454
Labrecque, Dawn, 3867
Labrie, Tom, 8574
Lacasse, Joanne, 484
Lachman, Joan, 6356
Lachman, Julie, 6356
Lachman, Lawrence, 6356
Lachman, Leon, 6356
Lachnit, Karl-Heinz, 1141
Lachowicz, Cheryl, 5154
Lachowicz, Theodore, 5154
Lacinak, Charles, Jr., 3741
Lackey, Connie, 361
Lackey, Lee Anna Jones, 1614
Lackey, R. Brandon, 1614
Lackland, David, 5525
Lackland, Michael, 5525
Laclede Gas Co., 4967
LaConte, Cynthia, 9806
LaCook, David, 8843
LaCook, David H., 8843
LaCook, Michele, 8843
Lacritz, Robbie, 4094
LaCroix, Sara Morley, 4518
Lacrosse, Adernaline, 8243
Lacy Charitable Lead Annuity Trust,
    Linwood A., The, 2163
Lacy Charitable Trust, Andre B., 3410
Lacy Memorial, Edna B., 3410
Lacy, Adam M., 2163
Lacy, Andre B., 3410
Lacy, Brent M., 9485

Lacy, Charles, 9369
Lacy, Christopher L., 2163
Lacy, Constance C., 2163
Lacy, Frank M., Jr., 9485
Lacy, Jill S., 3410
Lacy, John, 8652
Lacy, Linwood A., Jr., 2163
Lacy, Nicole, 3108
Lacy, Slate, 9485
Ladd, Anne K., 4163
Ladd, Berthe K., 4163
Ladd, Edward H., 4163
Ladd, Edward L., 4163
Ladd, J.B., 1310
Ladd, James R., 9616
Ladd, Jerry D., 1310
Ladd, Lara L., 1086
Ladd, Laura Hewitt, 4163
Ladd, Sharon S., 9616
Lader, Linda LeSourd, 8531
Lader, Philip, 8531
Ladgrove, Julia, 945
Ladies Hospital Aid Society, 8080
Ladner, Asher, 8805
Ladner, John, 5159
Laduca, Tony, 8370
Laerdal Medical Corp., 6358
Laerdal, Tore, 6358
Lafayette 148, 6748
Lafayette College, 5987
Lafayette's Oceanfront Resort, 3787
Lafayette, Carla J., 3787
Lafayette, J. Daniel, 3787
Lafayette, J. Daniel, III, 3787
Lafer, Fred S., 5668
Laff, Kenneth M., 1307
Laffan, Louise B., 3647
Laffend, Jane, 1405
LaFleur, James, 3044
LaFleur, Johanna Leestma, 3044
LaFontaine, Marybeth, 5873
LaFontaine, Patrick "Pat", 5873
LaFrance, Dorothy, 4217
Lafrance, Dorothy, 4222
Lagasse, Ronald L., 5790
Lager, Aaron, 411
Lager, Martin H., 1298
Lagorio, Lisa, 912
LaGrassa, Carl, 5438
LaGrassa, Carl G., 5438
LaGrassa, Carla, 5438
LaGrassa, Gloria, 5438
Lahiff, Mary Elizabeth, 4764
Lahn, Patricia Davis, 5314
Laidig Charitable Trust, Jon & Sonja, 3399
Laidig Systems Inc., 3399
Laidig, Jon, 3399
Laidig, Sonja, 3399
Laidig, Wynn, 3399
Laidlaw Environmental Services, 4657
Laidlaw, Kathleen Muir, 4481
Laine, Erick, 5890
Laine, Richard, 3771
Laing, John, 8869
Laing, Kevin, Dr. , 7346
Lainoff, Carole, 6359
Lainoff, Irwin, 6359
Lainoff, Michael, 6359
Lainoff, Steven, 6359
Laiou, Evangelia, 3040
Laird Trust, Lisa K., 1135
Laird, Linda, 2573
Laird, Lisa K., 1135

Laird, Peter A., 4365
Laird, Randy, 8282
Laird, Susan Cason, 8774
Laird, Tony, 3441
LaKamp, Larry, 1352
LaKamp, Martha, 1352
Lake, Christopher, 4237
Lake, Cynthia G., 727
Lake, John Paul, 727
Lake, Melissa, 881
Lake, Sheila, 727
Lake, Sonia, 4552
Lake, Thomas H., 5012
Laketon Asphalt Refining Co., 3351
Lakin, Robert, 1586
Lakireddy, P., 958
Lakonishok, Josef, 3032
Lal, Megah, 8526
Lally, Ann R., 5230
Lalor, Willard A., 4164
Lam, Donald, 373
Lam, Kenneth, 655
Lam, Rebecca Sue Elmen, 8560
Lam, Sam, 373
Lam, Samantha, 655
Lam, Susan, 373
Lamale, John, 3515
Lamando, Stephen M., 1504
Lamar Construction, 4488
Lamar, Cynthia Chavez, 5609
Lamar, Stoney, 200
Lamascus, Gloria S., 9214
Lamb Trust, Walter E., 8106
Lamb Weston, 2510
Lamb, Barbara, 7787
Lamb, Brenda, 7787
Lamb, Carl, 7787
Lamb, Catherine L., 4805
Lamb, Chris, 2986
Lamb, Paige, 4514
Lamb, Robert E., II, 8106
Lambert Charitable Lead Annuity Trust, Jean Thomas, 7487
Lambert Trust, Jean Thomas, 7487
Lambert Trust, Lenore, 4942
Lambert, Clement T., 4216
Lambert, Darlene, 728
Lambert, Dave, 5626
Lambert, J. William, 7228
Lambert, Katherine W., 9855
Lambert, Lenore, 4942
Lambert, Mary Lynn, 2586
Lambert, Patsy J., 2164
Lambert, Philip A., 2164
Lambert, Ronald S., 2164
Lambert, Roy H., 2164
Lambert, Roy H., Jr., 2164
Lambert, Samuel W., III, 6464
Lambert, Thomas, 7487
Lambert, Thomas P., 839
Lambrecht, Melissa, 2165
Lambrecht, Patricia, 2165
Lamer, Laura, 4390
Lamka Trust, , 3034
Lamm, Deborah, 4165
Lamm, Peter D, 4165
Lammers, James D., 4421
Lamn, LLC, 4634
Lamond, Christine, 729
Lamond, Pierre, 729
Lamont, Sharon L., 5513
Lamoretti, Jill, 6595
Lamoretti, Michael, 6595
Lamoureux, John F., 2166

Lamoureux, Rita, 2166
Lamp, Brockenbrough, Jr., 9419
Lampl Trust, Scott, 6884
Lampl, Sir Peter, 6884
Lamprey, Robert P., 4216
Lancaster, Amy S., 3035
Lancaster, Bettina Jane, 6866
Lancaster, Christa, 6866
Lancaster, Craig J., 3035
Lancaster, Guy N., 6866
Lancaster, James R., 3035
Lancaster, Mark T., 3035
Lancaster, Timothy, 6866
Lance, 7250
Lancellot, Mike, 5890
Lanci, Marc, 802
Lanci, Susan, 802
Lanciault, Muriel E., 1989
Lancy, David F., 8108
Lancy, Leslie E., 8108
Land Charitable Lead Trust, Patricia Lloyd, 3594
Land Services, 1373
Land, Jennifer, 1246
Landa, Ben, 6552
Landau Trust, 6641
Landau Trust, A., 6575
Landau, Barbara, 6955
Landau, Chaim, 5923, 6920
Landau, Chanie, 6362
Landau, David, 5661, 5923
Landau, Efraim, 6575, 6920
Landau, Elizabeth, 6720
Landau, Ephraim, 5923, 6575, 6965
Landau, Goldy, 6575, 6965
Landau, Howard M., 3036
Landau, Jon, 1117
Landau, Kenneth J., 3036
Landau, Pinches, 6362
Landau, Rivka, 5661
Landau, Solomon, 6362
Landau, W. Loeber, 6955
Lande, Brooke Dana, 1318
Landenberger, J. William, 8109
Landers Martial Trust, Arthur, 8110
Landers, Arline J., 7488
Landers, Elizabeth, 320
Landers, Lynn, 219
Landers, Philip D., 8219
Landers, Richard I., 7488
Landers, Thomas J., 9855
Landes, Jill, 9630
Landes, Rodney, 219
Landfear, Sara C., 8537
Landfear, Wesley E., 8537
Landon, Jr. Estate, JC, 7158
Landow, Stephen, 1583
Landreville, Alan, 4774
Landreville, Julie, 4774
Landry's Restaurants, 8852
Landry's Seafood Restaurants, 8852
Landry, Kim, 7953
Landscape Structures, 4789
Landstar Homes Dallas Ltd., 9009
Landwirth, Gary M., 2167
Landwirth, Gregory D., 2167
Landwirth, Henri, 2167
Landwirth, Linda, 2167
Landwirth, Theresa, 2167
Landy, Eugene W., 5439
Landy, Gloria, 5439
Landy, Laura K., 5510
Landy, Michael, 5439
Landy, Samuel, 5439

Lane Texas Partners, 4487
Lane, Bernard B., 9486
Lane, Brigitte, 6820
Lane, Carol R., 2299
Lane, Charles G., 2536
Lane, Christine O'Connor, 3148
Lane, Douglas B., 9486
Lane, Elizabeth Blackburn, 2015
Lane, Elizabeth W., 8662
Lane, Hugh C., Jr., 2536
Lane, Jeffrey B., 6363
Lane, Kevin A., 2299
Lane, Minnie B., 9486
Lane, Nancy Z., 6363
Lane, Ray, 2296
Lane, Rick, 9486
Lane, Sandro, 88
Lane, Susan J., 4487
Lane, Thomas, 9626
Lane, W. Eugene, 4487
Laney Inc, 9130
Laney, Sandra E., 7350
Lanfer, Stephen, 3799
Lang, Charles B., 7489
Lang, Christine B., 7944
Lang, Electra V., 5465
Lang, Ellen H., 3885
Lang, Fritz, 3733
Lang, James R., 7489
Lang, Janet, 181
Lang, Jeffrey S., 7944
Lang, Joseph, 9878
Lang, Mary Sue, 7489
Lang, Rachel Boyce, 7489
Langdale, Noah N., Jr., 2537
Langdon, Marian B., 4868
Lange, Corlene, 3557
Lange, Julian G., 9008
Lange, Laurence E., 1191
Lange, Richard A., 9008
Langenstein, William H., III, 3730
Langer, Carol B., 4166
Langer, Howard I., 8202
Langer, Kurt W., 4166
Langer, Richard J., 9791
Langer, Todd H., 4166
Langert, Andrew, 3275
Langford, Beth Martin, 8637
Langford, Donovan A., III, 2766
Langford, George, 577
Langie, Louis A., Jr., 6452
Langley, Jim, Dr. , 5104
Langley, Joe, 9197
Langston, Nathan E., 9277
Langue Trust, Rita Perlow, 8211
Lanham, Amy, 9858
Laniak, Andrew J., 5786
Lanier Foundation, Helen S., 2492
Lanier, Bruce, Mrs. , 2517
Lanier, J. Hicks, 2561
Lanier, J. Reese, 2538
Lanier, J.W., 7713
Lanier, Lauren, 6030
Lanier, Reese J., 2538
Lanier, Robert, 7276
Lanier, Susan I., 2518
Lanigan, Bernard, Jr., 2469
Lanigan, Brian D., 4203
Lankes, J. B., 5692
Lankford, Mickey D., 2604
Lankton, Gordon B., 4228
Lankton, Janet K., 4228
Lanni, Allison Day, 5980
Lanphere, Bob, Jr., 7798

Lans, Bruce, 9937
Lansbury, Susan S., 305
Lansing, Jennifer Minor, 3117
Lansing, John, 5866
Lansing, John S., 6360
Lansing, Kathryn H., 2792
Lanterman, A. Kirk, 9649
Lanterman, Janet O., 9649
Lanting, Arlyn, 4489
Lanting, Marcia, 4489
Lantz, David, 8684
Lanza, Michael H., 5528
Lanzillotta, A. Paul, 9424
Lapadula, Kimberly A., 5480
Lapalombara, Joseph, 1456
Lapan, David, 140
Lapan, Joseph, 140
Lapan, Patricia, 140
Lapensohn, Howard, 8022
Lapidos Productions LTD, Mark, 6839
Lapidow, Seth J., 5807
LaPlace, William B., 7652
LaPlante, Carole, 6912
LaPorte, Christopher, 8599
LaPorte, Joseph, 8599
LaPorte, Joseph, III, 8599
LaPorte, Sam, 8599
LaPorte, Stephen, 8599
Lapostora, James, 8449
Lappin, Mara, 9900
LaPres, Theodore E., III, 4228
Laramie, Carole S., 4563
Lare, Rebekah, 1640
Largay, Dorothy F., 758
Largent, Joy, 3056
Larid, Lisa K., 1135
Larimer, Pamela, 7055
Lariviere, Jennifer D., 2268
Lariviere, Stephanae D., 6078
Larka Family Properties, 6655
Larkburger, 1295
Larkin, David P., 6720
Larkin, Joan, 3242
Larkin, Linda, 820
Larkin, Richard, 577
Larmann, Edward, 6775
Larmett, James C., Mrs. , 7013
Larnard, Mary E., 8381
LaRoche Enterprise, 8641
Laroche Family LP, 8641
LaRoche, David, 8641
LaRoche, Gloria, 8641
LaRoche, Richard F., 8641
LaRosa, Ann, 4824
Larose, Will, 3988
Larrowe, Mike, 9426
Larsen, Allan, 5979
Larsen, Brenda, 9337
Larsen, Brent, 3501
Larsen, Charles, 1216
Larsen, Craig, 3038
Larsen, Eric, 9337
Larsen, John A., 4728
Larsen, John E., 4728
Larsen, Karen R., 4728
Larsen, Marilyn, 3038
Larsen, Mark, 5154
Larsen, Martine B., 341
Larsen, Terrence, 3038
Larson Financial Foundation, The, 4943
Larson, Bernie, 421
Larson, Bruce, 4654
Larson, David M., 7788
Larson, Dexter, 4667

Larson, Dorothy, 421, 1400
Larson, Dorothy B., 1400
Larson, Geoff, 88
Larson, Harold B., 5170
Larson, Joan J., 6365
Larson, Kathleen C., 7788
Larson, Leland E.G., 7788
Larson, Mary, 4741
Larson, Maryle A., 5440
Larson, Monroe, 4801
Larson, Neil E., 9589
Larson, Orville H., 3039
Larson, Paul D., 4943
Larson, Peter N., 2762, 5440
Larson, Pippa, 2456
Larson, Reed E., 9650
Larson, Scott, 9878
Larson, Steve, 3549, 9667
Larson, Wilfred J., 6365
Larson-Fenton, Denise, 1400
Larson-Rabin, Leah, 3897
LaSalle Steel Co., 9141
LaSalle, Jones Lang, 6655
LaSalle, William, 8237
Lascelles, Scott, 3455
Laschober, James, 5014
Laser, Joan, 4181
Lasher, Allan, 468
Lasher, Darlene, 468
Lasher, Susan, 468
Lasker, Nicole, 9814
Laskoski, Peggy, 9151
Lasry, Evelyn Day, 5980
Lassalle, Gratia H., 6908
Lassalle, Nancy N., 6366
Lasser, Ethan, 5749
Lasser, Lawrence J., 5749
Lasser, Michelle, 5749
Lassiter, E.G., III, 2539
Lassiter, James, 1053
Lassiter, Marianne B., 2539
Lassiter, Richard G., 2539
Lassman, Richard, 9660
Lastavica, Catherine, 4345
Lastavica, Catherine C., 4345
Lastinger, Allen L., Jr., 2168
Lastinger, Beth, 2168
Lastinger, Delores T., 2168
Lastinger, Lane, 2168
Lastowka, Jr., Esq., Joseph E., 7953
Late, Hazel Valeria, 9007
Latex Construction Co, 9130
Lathrop, Alma, 3342
Latimer, James J., 3993
Latimer, Robert W., 625
Latkin Trust, Herbert and Gertrude, 731
Lato, Gary J., 9869
Lato, Joan M., 9869
LaTournous, Thomas E., 8345
Latshaw, Robert E., 7953
Latta, Lucile, 3518
Lau, Jannie K., 1743
Laub, Carol Cracchiolo, 4415
Laub, Elsie K., 7490
Laub, Herbert J., 7490
Laub, Irving, 6367
Laub, Jim, 9345
Lauderdale, Lauren S., 2317
Lauer, John A., 7876
Lauer, Kay, 3635
Laufer, Bradley W., 2169
Laufer, Doris, 5657
Laufer, Gayle M., 2169
Laufer, Mayer, 5657

Laufer, Wayne L., 2169
Laughlin, Alexander M., 5906, 8114
Laughlin, Alexander M., Jr., 8114
Laughlin, David W., 8114
Laughlin, Erica, 9166
Laughlin, Henry P., 3898
Laughlin, J.R., 3898
Laughlin, M. P., 3898
Laughlin, M.P., 3898
Laughlin, Mary M., 8114
Laughlin, Sarah, 8370
Laughren, Sara Stone, 7721
Lauman, Robert M., 8311
Laurance, Dale R., 732
Laurance, Lynda E., 732
Laurel Development II LP, 9009
Laurel Management Group, The, 9744
Laurel Wilt Bank, Peter Smith, 6542
Laurelwood Hospital, 7560
Lauren, Muriel, 6368
Lauria, Emanuel, Jr., 8303
Laurino, Carl J., 9876
Lause, Thomas N., 7362
Lauter, Larry, 7624
Lauter, Nancy A., 3091
Lauzier, Paul, 9651
Lavache-Mackey, Claire J., 8487
LaValley, Frederick J.M., 8029
Lavelle Fund for the Blind Inc., 6539
Lavelle, Thomas J., 7994
Lavery, Charlotte D., 5441
Lavery, David, 8449
Lavery, John W., 5441
Lavidge, Kathleen A., 940
Lavietes, Estelle, 1505
Lavietes, Raymond P., 1505
Lavin, Eric, 3157
Lavin, Jack, 3157
Lavin, Karen S., 3275
Lavin, Karen Sue, 3275
Lavin, Lisa, 2994
Lavin, Robin, 3157
Lavin, Ronald, 2994
Lavin, Sheldon, 3158
Lavin, Thomas, 2811
Lavine, Richard A., 733
Lavine, Ruth J., 733
Lavoie, Gerard R., 4067
Law Offices of Peter F. Davis, 4292
Law, D. Brian, 4478
Law, Douglas, 7899
Law, Julie, 8915
Law, Randy, 9756
Lawder, James A., 3255
Lawford Co., 3905
Lawhorn, Ed, 9426
Lawler, Maggie, 4198
Lawler, Michael J., 6071
Lawless, Bob, 8836
Lawlor, Evelyn M., 7625
Lawner, C.S.W., Lilli, 5680
Lawrence Foundation, The, 5202
Lawrence, Edward P., 2847, 4196
Lawrence, J. Vinton, 5651
Lawrence, James G., 6369
Lawrence, Jeff, 734
Lawrence, John S., 6369
Lawrence, Kathleen, Jr., 4552
Lawrence, Keith, 927
Lawrence, Ken, 3611
Lawrence, Lind, 9487
Lawrence, Peter, 5651
Lawrence, Priscilla, 4167
Lawrence, Warren, 4606

Lawry, Cynthia C., 4168
Lawry, Marion Schultz, 7491
Lawry, Seth W., 4168
Laws, Jean H., 3932
Lawson Rock and Oil Co., John R., 301
Lawson Trust, 8588
Lawson, Barbara, 1640
Lawson, Brenda, 8588
Lawson, Harriet H., 8189
Lawson, Jill T., 1872
Lawson, John K., 2170
Lawson, Katherine, 7492
Lawson, Robert J., 2170
Lawson, Stanley C., 8588
Lawson, Suzanne D., 2170
Lawson-Johnston, Peter, 6084
Lawter, Kathryn L., 4490
Lawther, Fonza Bell, 615
Lawton, Barbara P., 4915
Lawton, John T., 1639
Lawver, Jeanne, 8990
Lax, Lynn, 5398
Lay, Madeline R., 9089
Lay, Robert A., 9957
Layden Agency, Donald W., 2171
Layden, Barbara, 2171
Layden, Donald W., 2171
Laydon, Kimberly Lewan, 1314
Layne, Gloria G., 9427
Layral, Philip A., 81
Layser, Nancy L., 8352
Layton Trust, Bernard, 6370
Layton, Estelle M., 278
Lazar, Herman, 3041
Lazar, Robert W., 6546
Lazard, 5667
Lazarus, Charles, 5442
Lazarus, Gladys, 7493
Lazarus, James, 7493
Lazarus, John R., 7493
Lazarus, Rudolph G., 2172
Lazoff Irrevocable Trust, Alice E., 2173
Lazzara, Alan A., 3042
Lazzara, Angelo J., 3042
Lazzara, Antoinette, 3042
Lazzara, Antoniette, 3042
Lazzara, Gasper, 2174
Lazzara, Irene, 2174
Lazzara, Jack R., 3042
Lazzara, Philip, 3042
LBJ Family Foundation, The, 9011
LCMS Foundation, The, 4998
LCNB National Bank, 7403, 7504
Le Rud, Marilyn, 738
Le, Junming, 2175
Lea County Electric Cooperative, 5620
Lea, James, 9652
Lea, Jane Isakson, 9652
Lea, Walker, 9085
Leach, Anne C., 403
Leach, Elizabeth, 7494
Leach, Jennifer, 4204
Leach, Jennifer A., 1353
Leadbetter, Bonnie T., 2593
Leadingham, Toni M., 462
Leahy, Charles F., 5215
Leahy, Lynne B., 1404
Leahy, Margaret, 1116
Leahy, Richard T., 4353
Leake, Michael T., 9503
Leake, Nancy Johnson, 7736
Leake, Paul, 3707
Leale, Olivia M., 8476
Leaman, Sam, 8526

Leander, Kristine, 9652
Leap, Rose, 3462
Leap, Roy, 3362
Lear, Eric, 5513
Lear, William M., Jr., 3668
Leary Trust, Mary, 8437
Leary, Carol A., 4337
Leary, Daniel L., 1486
Leary, John F., III, 8381
Leary, Julius, Jr., 8526
Leary, Linda, 1486
Leary, Linda K., 1486
Leasure, Candace, 852
Leasure, Shantel, 3125
Leatherman, Russell, 9087
Leatherwood, Many, 5610
Leavens, Adelaide, 8739
Leavens, Bill, 5444
Leavens, Nancy, 5444
Leavens, William B., III, 5444
Leavitt, Jacalyn S., 9338
Leavitt, Michael O., 9338
Leavitt, Nathan R., 5445
Leavitt, Sarah, 1226
Leavitt, William, 1226
Lebaron, Marc E., 5068
Lebel, Katie, 3797
Lebermann, Virginia D., 9093
Lebesch, Nickolas, 1272
Lebherz, Phil, 735
Lebherz, Phillip, 735
Lebherz, Sharon, 735
LeBien, Harry A., 5850
LeBien, Laurent C., 5850
LeBien, Mary Ellen, 5850
LeBien, Thomas E., 5850
Leblanc, Adrienne Ebert, 8609
Leblanc, Chelsea A., 8609
Leblanc, Joseph Christopher, 8609
Leblanc, Richard P., 3768
LeBlevennec, Jacques, 8763
Leboeuf, Andree, 9379
Lebovitz, James, 1506
Lebovitz, Peter M., 1506
Lebowitz, Deborah, 736
Lebowitz, Steve, 736
Lebowitz, Steven D., 736
LeBuff, Robyn, 3786
Lebus, Frazer D., Jr., 3043
Lebus, W. Frank, Jr., 3671
Lecates, Deborah, 6183
Lecates, William, 6183
Lecatonnoux, Francois, 6123
Lecker, Frtiz, 7975
Leckman, Scott A., 9361
Leconte, Frantz-Antoine, 6820
LeCroy, Charles L., III, 421
LeCureux, Kenneth W., 4392
Ledbetter, Bradford L., 9012
Ledbetter, Reta L., 9012
Ledbetter, Terry L., 9012
Ledbetter, Terry L., Jr., 9012
Ledermann, Mary A., 6669
Ledesma, Ruben, Jr., 2077
Ledgerwood, D. Leanne, 8324
Ledonne, Edmond V., 6370
Ledoux, Beverly, 4250
Ledoux, Reinald, Jr., 4245
Lee Agency Trust, Henry H., 9912
Lee Charitable Lead Trust, 5171
Lee, Andrew J., 6083
Lee, Barbara Brown, 9825
Lee, Benjamin K., 737
Lee, Bill, 7295

Lee, Bonnie A., 737
Lee, Carl E., 4491
Lee, Carolyn, 5737
Lee, Charles R., 1507
Lee, Dave, 204
Lee, David L., 737
Lee, Debora, 1202
Lee, Deni, 921
Lee, Doris S., 5171
Lee, Ed M., 9912
Lee, Edward Y.H., 533
Lee, Ellen W., 737
Lee, Erin, 2266
Lee, Ernest T.H., 5171
Lee, Francis Childress, 1942
Lee, Frank, 824
Lee, George C., 1942
Lee, Gregory T.H., 5171
Lee, H.B., Jr., 9
Lee, Henry H., Rev. , 9912
Lee, Hwalin, Dr. , 777
Lee, iara, 1652
Lee, Ilda G., 1507
Lee, J. April, 2027
Lee, James T., 6372
Lee, John, Dr. , 9781
Lee, Jung, 6768
Lee, Lan Fong, 719
Lee, Larry, 3535
Lee, Leslie, 4466
Lee, Lewis S., 1942
Lee, Lewis S., Jr., 1942
Lee, M.D., Ph.D., Deborah, 2880
Lee, Mary Elizabeth, 2540
Lee, Megan, 1202
Lee, Michael S., 3292
Lee, Min Sok, 2791
Lee, Nikkel, 3641
Lee, Ning, 664
Lee, Portia, 471
Lee, Rachel R., 737
Lee, Ray M., 2540
Lee, Robert C., 6713
Lee, Robert E., 2710
Lee, Robert W., 7637
Lee, Rosemary K., 43
Lee, Stephen, 344
Lee, Theodore B., 5171
Lee, Tsuku, 5596
Lee, Tu-Lien, 664
Lee, V, Richard Bland, 9488
Lee, Wayne, 35
Lee-Gilligan, Joseph, 4696
Leeburg, Louis, 574
Leech, Douglas J., 9739, 9753
Leech, Stephanie, 9488
Leedom-Ackerman, Joanne, 5700
Leeds, Gerard, 9641
Leeds, Jennifer, 6077
Leeds, Lilo J., 6077
Leeds, Liselotte, 9641
Leeds, Liselotte Gerard, 6077
Leeds, Richard, 9641
Leedy, Michael, 7839
Leek, Beverly A., 6570
Leekley, John D., Jr., 6919
Lees, Stephen, 9345
Leestma, Jan E., 3044
Leestma, Louise M., 3044
Leetch, Thomas J., 4237
Leeth, Lori B., 4191
Lefcourt, Ilene Sackler, 6371
Lefcourt, Jeffrey, 6371
Lefcourt-Taylor, Karen, 6371

Leff, Eleanor, 6492
Leff, Joel B., 6827
Leff, Joseph, 6333
Leff, Julie Abrams, 5241
Leffingwell Ltd., 9152
Leffler, D.D.S., William, 7442
Lefkovits, Samuel, 7024
Lefkowitz, Leib, 7024
Lefkowitz, Samuel, 7024
Lefkowitz, Sarah, 7024
Lefkowitz, William, 6086
Legacy Partners Commercial, LP, 740
Legacy Private Trust Company, 9833
Legends, Irish, 2109
Legg, James S., 2929, 2930
Legg, Louis E., 4590
Leggat, Scott, 7204
Leggott, Garold, 5129
Legnini, Robert C., Mr. , 7915
Legnini, Robert C., Mrs. , 7915
LeGrand, Patrice, 9878
Legum, Harriett, 3899
Legum, Jeffrey, 3899
Legum, Laurie, 3899
Legum, Michael, 3899
Lehigh Southwest Cement Co., 366
Lehman 93E Descendants Trust, 3136
Lehman 93F Descendants Trust, 3136
Lehman, Allan G., 6375
Lehman, Amy G., 3008
Lehman, Elton D., 7312
Lehman, F., 3136
Lehman, Gene, 3401
Lehman, Jonathan, 3045
Lehman, Kathleen S., 4563
Lehman, Kenneth A., 3008
Lehman, Lucy G., 3008
Lehman, Matt, 9696
Lehman, Mildred K., 7495
Lehman, Paul, 3045
Lehman, Paul A., 3136
Lehman, Peter G., 3008
Lehman, William C., 7495
Lehmann, Daniel, 6235
Lehmann, Suzanne, 6235
Lehr, Deborah M., 6422
Lehrman, Lewis E., 6271
Lehrman, Louise S., 6271
Lehv, Spencer, 7027
Leiber, David, 6075
Leibold, John A., 7386
Leibold, William J., 7347
Leibowitz, Dale, 3046, 9893, 9908
Leibowitz, Jane, 6376
Leibowitz, Lew, 3046
Leibowitz, Marvin, 2176
Leibowitz, Pearl R., 3046
Leibowitz, Reuben S., 6376
Leibowitz, Sheldon L., 3046
Leidy, Frances H., 2114
Leifer, Annette, 326
Leigh, John P., 9463
Leighton, F. Thomson, 3998
Leighton, F. Thomson, Mrs. , 3998
Leighton, Pamela W., 7990
Leighty, H.D., 1311
Leighty, William C., 1311
Leighty, William Clyde, 1311
Leiman, Leonard, 6169
Leimanstoll, Jo Ramsey, 7081
Leinberger, Karl, 2822
Leiner, David, 5705
Leininger, B. Joseph, 1312
Leininger, Berneta, 9111

Leininger, Daniel E., 9111
Leininger, Diane J., 9057
Leininger, J. Ryan, 9057
Leininger, James R., 9111
Leininger, Jeffrey E., 9057
Leininger, John H., 9057, 9111
Leininger, Kathryn L., 1312
Leininger, Peter A., 9111
Leininger, Shantel, 9057
Leisch, Doris, 7947
Leiser, Josephine S., 2177
Leith, Eric M, 4423
Leith, Jessica M., 4423
Leith, Shirley, 4423
Leithauser, Mark, 9482
Leland, Ashleigh Cooper, 22
Leland, John D., Jr., 741
Leland, Sandra S., 741
LeLash, Curtis W., 2178
Lelash, Marie Keese, 2178
LeLash, Richard W., 2178
LeLash, William J., 2178
LeLaurin, Elaine H., 4227
Lem, Matthew, 7221
Lemann, Stephen B., 3745
Lemann, Thomas B., 3745
Lemay Family, Gene, 5172
LeMay, Carla A., 5172
LeMay, H. Eugene, Jr., 5172
Lemberg, Blimy, 5266
Lemberg, Daniel, 5266
Lemelson, Eric, 7781
Lemelson, Robert, 742
LeMieux, Linda J., 4614
Lemings, Laura, 3412
Lemle, Gertrude, 6377
Lemle, Gertrude B., 6378
Lemle, Laura C., 6377, 6378
Lemle, Leo K., 6378
Lemle, Robert S., 6378
Lemmo, Ronald, Dr. , 7346
Lemole, Christopher R., 8119
Lemole, Emily Jane A., 8119
Lemole, G. Michael, 8119
Lemole, G. Michael, Jr., 8119
Lemole, Gerald M., 8119
Lemole, Samantha M., 8119
Lemon, David R., 9606
Lemon, James H., Jr., 1819
Lemon, Martha McG., 1819
Lemons Charitable Lead Ann Trust, Brad, 743
Lemons Charitable Lead Unitrust, Brad, 743
Lemons Charitable Lead Unitrust, Karen E., 1263
Lemons Charitable Trust, Mark C., 744
Lemons, Brad, 743
Lemons, Mark C., 744
Lemons, William B., 743
Lemorande, Thomas, 9796
Lempereur, Douglas, 9916
Lenhart, Jack, 8970
Lenihan, David J., 5389
Lenk, Jack, 4998
Lenkin, Edward J., 2179
Lenkin, Melvin, 2179
Lenkin, Thelma, 2179
Lenner, Marc J., 5336
Lennon, John Ono, 6839
Lennon, Tim, 8629
Lennon, Yoko Ono, 6839
Lennox, Gregory P., 745
Lennox, Lillian, 745

Lenoir, Ernestine, 46
Lenscrafters, 9098
Lensink, Sally H., 9834
Lent, Daniel, 7436
Lent, Jay C., 1590
Lentsch, Deborah, 123
Lentsch, Deborah G., 123
Lenya, Lotte, 6950
Lenz, Janis C., 9803
Lenz, Tomme, 361
Leo, Marilyn, 610
Leof, David, 5414
Leominster, 3841
Leon, Iris Mireya, 7953
Leon, Jonathan Andrew, 9406
Leon, Sara Hardner, 8918
Leonard & Related Trusts, Gena, 7789
Leonard C. and Lois S. Charitable
    Foundation, 1416
Leonard, Angeline Brown, 3106
Leonard, Besty, 7145
Leonard, Charlie, 2463
Leonard, Clay R., 9532
Leonard, Francis L., 9489
Leonard, J.P., 9878
Leonard, Jacqueline F., 9489
Leonard, Randall, 3584
Leonard, Roger L., 9489
Leonard, Russell F., 9489
Leonard, Scot A., 2776, 3171
Leonards, H.H., 2324
Leone, Judy L., 8120
Leone, Peter G., 8120
Leong, Gregory, 2659
Leong, Maxine W., 2656
Leong, Randolph, 2659
Leong, Robert H.Y., 2656
Leonhardt, Clifton A., 701
Leonhardt, Frederick H., 6381
Leonian, Edith, 3047
Leonian, Phillip, 3047
Leopold, Geoff, 1242
Leopold, Lynn Bradley, 8009
Lepage, Betty G., 9462
LePell, Nancy, 3634
Lepitas Foundation, 1352
Lepp, Aaron, 7624
Leprino, Laura, 1313
Leprino, Mary, 1313
Leprino, Mike, 1313
Leprino, Nancy, 1313
Leprino, Terry L., 1316
Lerer, Daniel, 6367
Lerer, Kenneth B., 6382
Lerner Irrevocable Trust, Bernice L.,
    7160
Lerner, Amanda R., 7160
Lerner, Bernice L., 7160
Lerner, Dena P., 7160
Lerner, Donald, 2180
Lerner, Eleanor, 6383
Lerner, Eugene M., 3092
Lerner, Frederick M., 3011
Lerner, Helaine, 6527
Lerner, Judy Lenkin, 2179
Lerner, Kiyoko, 3048
Lerner, Marianne Minkoff, 3915
Lerner, Mark, 7160
Lerner, Michael, 2180, 3048
Lerner, Morton S., 7160
Lerner, Richard I., 7160
Lerner, Saul, 6383
Lerner, Stephen, 6383
Leroe, Bernard A., 8439

Leroe, Jane M., 8439
LeRoux, Tamara Brown, 7372
Leroy, Nancy R., 7229
Leroy, Stephen C., 7229
Leroy, W. Scott, 7229
Leroy, William B., 7229
Lerse, Ursula, 5783
Lesage, Carl R., 4250
Leshkowitz, Joseph, 6246, 6247, 6773
Leshner, Brian, 3890
Leskoven, Les, 8860
Lesley Charitable Trust, Sarah A., 9013
Lesley, Hattie Mae, 9013
Lesley, Joseph D., 9013
Leslie Metal Arts Co., Inc., The, 4587
Leslie, David, 4764
Leslie, Kathleen, 4764
Lesniak, Leonard, 7114
Lessieu, Jennifer Ferro, 9372
Lessman, Carl A., 57
Lessman, Jaqueline, 8046
Lester, Andrew P., 9234
Lester, Cynthia, 2437
Lester, Darrell, 8731
Lester, Emile, 6720
Lester, Karen, 747
Lester, Kenneth A., 747
Lester, Kinha, 6720
Lester, Kirk, 748
Lester, Lana Christine, 747
Lester, Mark, 4820
Lester, Mary, 748
Lester, Norman, 747
Lester, Tamara, 8644
Lester, W. Howard, 748
Lester, William W., 5067
Letaconnoux, Francois, 8763
Letcher, John, 4238
Letourneau Products, 9130
Letourneaux, Stephen, 9776
Letson, Carol G., 8501
Lett, Beth, 3363
Leu, Crystal, 3412
Leuman, Janet R., 4650
Leupold & Stevens, 7790
Leupold & Stevens, Inc., 3991
Leuschen, David M., 6384
Lev, Holly, 5742
Lev, Holly B., 5742
Lev, Yoav, 5742
Levandoski, Esther, 1124
Levangie, Aaron J., 4172
Levangie, Allison M., 4172
Levangie, Daniel J., 4172
Levangie, Joan, 4172
Levchuck, Sean, Dr., 5873
Levee, Polly Annenberg, 8121
Leven, Myron P., 4492
Levenson, Ethyl S., 8076
Levenson, Michelle Riley, 1803
Levenson, Ruth Leebron, 7693
Leventhal Foundation, Ira and Beth,
    3995
Leventhal, Harald, 865
Leventhal, Harald J., 998
Leventhal, Heidi, 1071
Leventhal, Kathy, 5550
Leventhal, Paul, 1071
Leventhal, Richard, 5550
Leverage Discovery LLC, 1352
Levere, Amy T., 6895
Leverence, Christine, 5414
Levey, Pearle Rae Kortz, 1307
Levey, Sharyn Nichols, 590

Levi & Korsinsky LLP, 6241
Levi, Claudia Dreyfus, 9436
Levi, Donald D., 4568
Levi, Joseph E., 6241
Levi, Judith, 6236
Levi, Mark, 6236
Levi, Thomas, 9956
Levie, George R., 2047
Levier, Jack K., 9677
Levikow, Jane, 972
Levin, Abbe, 3900
Levin, Adam, 839
Levin, Alan, 3900
Levin, Alan B., 1697
Levin, Andrew G., 1697
Levin, Charles, 3900
Levin, Daniel B., 1697
Levin, Ellen K., 1697
Levin, Emily, 749
Levin, H. Debra, 1278, 2692, 2693
Levin, Jacquelyn A., 1442
Levin, Jason S., 1697
Levin, Jerome L., 6667
Levin, Laurie, 2970
Levin, Lewis, 9726
Levin, Marc, 4419
Levin, Margaret, 3900
Levin, Peter, 7021
Levin, Richard, 749
Levin, Simon, 6213
Levin, Stanley L., 5296
Levin, Stephen D., 2873
Levin, Sydney, 749
Levin-Stankevich, Brian, 9323
Levine Builders, 6675
Levine Trust, Max A., 750
Levine Trust, Sid B., 750
Levine, A.L., 5446
Levine, Adam Paul, 750
Levine, Arthur L., 5446
Levine, Brenda A., 527
Levine, Cara E., 750
Levine, Caroline C., 5218
LeVine, D. Christopher, 8115
Levine, David, 7630
Levine, Diane L., 4916
Levine, Elliot H., 6258
Levine, Ilana, 5556
Levine, Jack, 2120
Levine, Jacob C., 750
Levine, Jay, 1549
Levine, Jeffrey, 6675
Levine, Jeffrey M., 1590
Levine, Jerome L., 5481
Levine, Joel A., 824
Levine, Lawrence I., 2181
Levine, Leslie, 5253
Levine, Loren L., 252
Levine, Meldon, 750
Levine, Michael, 6090
Levine, Michael F., 2181
Levine, Mildred, 2181
Levine, Nolan, Dr., 3282
Levine, Peter L., 5446
Levine, Randi, 6675
Levine, Richard J., 5325
Levine, Robert, 750
Levine, Shelley, 6779
Levine, Steven D., 252
Levine, Susan, 177, 2307
LeVine, Victoria McNeil, 8115
Levinson, Bernice S., 3949
Levinson, Donald, 3049
Levinson, Elaine, 3049

Levinson, Gerald, 8312
Levinson, Lilian, 491
Levinson, Robert, 1816
Levinson, Shmuel, 6117, 6222
Levio, Joy, 26
Levis, Adolph, 8122
Levison, S. Jarvin, 2484
Levitan, Daniel G., 9653
Levitan, Daniel Stacey, 9653
Levitan, Ken, 1046
Levitan, Stacey Rae Winston, 9653
Levitas, Catherine Otenasek, 3931
Levithan, Allen B., 5548
Levitin, Eli, 6388
Levitin, Raizy, 6388
Levitt, Jane, 4234
Levitt, Jim, 4234
Levitt, Madelyn M., 3538
Levitt, Steven, 5436
Levkoff, Linda L., 8532
Levy Foundation, Jerome, 6973
Levy, Amnon, 5670
Levy, Andrew H., 6530
Levy, Bruce M., 9239
Levy, Carolyne, 6389
Levy, Craig, 4259
Levy, Damon, 8068
Levy, David S., 421
Levy, Diane V.S., 3050
Levy, Donna, 752
Levy, Edward, 5247
Levy, Edwin A., 6389
Levy, Edwin Carolyn, 6389
Levy, Frances, 6391
Levy, Gloria, 751, 1141
Levy, Gloria K., 6281
Levy, Gregg H., 6374
Levy, Hyman, 752
Levy, Jack, 6391
Levy, Jacob, 5247
Levy, Jeffrey M., 6546
Levy, John, 4173
Levy, John F., 4174
Levy, Julian, 3113
Levy, Karen S., 4175
Levy, Kenneth, 751, 1141
Levy, M. William, 6441
Levy, Malka, 6918
Levy, Malky, 6423
Levy, Marion H., 6441
Levy, Meilech, 6423, 6918
Levy, Michael R., 9014
Levy, Milton, 4174
Levy, Myer, 9014
Levy, Nadine, 6525
Levy, Neil, 9184
Levy, Norman S., 6390
Levy, Peter B., 6281
Levy, Robert, 3146
Levy, Robert M., 3050
Levy, Roberta Morse, 4259
Levy, Shirley, 4174
Levy, Sid, 7250
Levy, Stanley H., 6281
Levy, Steven, 4174
Levy, Steven A., 2919
Levy, Steven M., 6281
Levy, William Guy, 6441
Lewan, Jennifer E., 1314
Lewan, Lloyd S., 1314
Lewan, Marjorie, 1314
Lewan, Marjorie A., 1314
Lewan, Matthew R., 1314
Lewan, Paul R., 1314

Lewin, Andrew, 6392
Lewin, Barbara, 925
Lewin, Marina, 6392
Lewin, Sheldon M., 7323
Lewinski, Sally, 2881
Lewinson, Lisa, 746
Lewis Family Foundation, Clark, 7807
Lewis Rollover Ira, Leonard D., 4303
Lewis Trust, Jonathan D., 2182
Lewis, Albert, 8836
Lewis, Andrew M., 9451
Lewis, Barbara, 5447
Lewis, Beverly J., 753
Lewis, Blanche, 4303
Lewis, Bradford H., 1315
Lewis, Burt, 6428
Lewis, Carlotta, 9426
Lewis, Carol A., 1315
Lewis, Charlie, 2531
Lewis, David D., 9661
Lewis, DeLancey B., 9681
Lewis, Diana B., 5447
Lewis, Diana M., 3745
Lewis, Donald McLeod, 8123
Lewis, Edith E., 5946
Lewis, Elizabeth, 5916
Lewis, Frances A., 9451
Lewis, George, 3593, 4122
Lewis, Hayes, 5609
Lewis, Hunter, 9514
Lewis, Ivy B., 5401
Lewis, J. Thomas, 3745
Lewis, Janet P., 9527
Lewis, Jeff, 5050
Lewis, Jeffrey, 753
Lewis, Jeffrey A., 3179
Lewis, Jill, 8972
Lewis, John, 9184
Lewis, John T., 225
Lewis, Jonathan D., 2182
Lewis, Leonard, 4303
Lewis, Lily, 6506
Lewis, Manuel M., 8449
Lewis, Margaret Brown, 8750
Lewis, Margery, 753
Lewis, Maryon Davies, 444
Lewis, Mildred Luck, 754
Lewis, Paul, 4767, 8568
Lewis, Renee, 810
Lewis, Richard H., 1315
Lewis, Robert, 753
Lewis, Salim B., 5447
Lewis, Shirley Long, 141
Lewis, Stephen, 1581
Lewis, Sydney, 9451
Lewis, Tony, 1258
Lewis, Warren Lloyd, 5251
Lewis, Wesley S., 8274
Lewis, Whitney, 8992
Lewis, William E., 5946
Lewy, Brooke, 6393
Lewy, Cheryl Winter, 6393
Lewy, Glen S., 6393
Lewy, Marshall, 6393
Lewy, Zachary, 6393
Lewy, Zachary Jason, 6393
Lezcano, Alice J., 2128
Lezcano, Edgar, 2128
LG & SG NY 1987 Trust, 6117
LG & SP NY 1987 Trust, 6117
Li, Anna, 6394
Li, Cheng, 1816
Li, Ling, 6394
Li, Min-Duo, 4600

Li, Philip, 1633
Li, Richard, 1457
Li, Taie, 6394
Li, Zheng, 1195
Liakos, Elisabeth B., 5109
Liakos, John G., 5109
Liakos, Stephanie B., 4015
Lian, Fred V., 1332
Liang, Charles, 578
Liang, John, Mrs. , 8869
Liang, May, 9492
Liang, Sara, 578
Liao, Jason S., 948
Liataud, Bernard, 9386
Liataud, Bernard, Mrs. , 9386
Liautaud, Bernard, 755
Liautaud, Susan, 755
Libby, Jocelyn, 6395
Libby, Kenneth, 6395
Libby, Louis S., 6395
Liberman, Eric, 5377
Liberman, Isaac, 6396
Liberman, Julie, 4987
Liberman, Martin, 5377
Liberotti, Gina, 766
Libertore, Douglas, 9033
Liberty Gives Foundation, 1295
Liberty Glass Co., 7668
Liberty Global, 1295
Liberty Mutual Insurance Co., 8440
Libke, Albert W., 9575
Liboff, Jerry, 82
Libov, Ann Neumann, 3957
LiCalsi, Michael, 9458
Licalsi, Paul, 839
Licata, Linda M., 3907
Lichner Trust, Anne, 3051
Lichner, John A., Jr., 3051
Lichtenstein, Leslie, 1765
Lichtenstein, Marita, 6397
Lichtenstein, Seymour, 6397
Lichter, Moishe, 5835
Lichtman, Jeff, 577
Lichtman, Kay, 3052
Lichtman, Marvin, 3052
Licursi, Kathryn, 6746
Liddell, Richard D., 7697
Lidji, Brian M., 9109
Lidrbauch, Elena, 7560
Lidz, Katharine G., 8164
Lieb, David L., 6398
Lieb, Sam, 6398
Lieb, Toby, 6398
Liebe, Randy F., 1643
Lieber, Frank, 2970
Lieber, Israel, 7000
Lieber, Sheila F., 6028
Lieberman, Amy F., 1665
Lieberman, Annette, 8024
Lieberman, Barbara, 3229
Lieberman, Charles, 1212
Lieberman, Dawn, 3229
Lieberman, Denise, 1104
Lieberman, Fred, 8024
Lieberman, Gloria, 6399
Lieberman, Harry, 8024
Lieberman, Jane, 5448
Lieberman, Jason, 3975
Lieberman, Joseph, 1518
Lieberman, Judith, 5448
Lieberman, Kenneth, 3229
Lieberman, Laurie A., 2885
Lieberman, Lester, 5448
Lieberman, Marla, 8024

Lieberman, Melvin, 3229
Lieberman, Michael, 3975
Lieberman, Moshe, 6399
Lieberman, Phyllis, 3229
Lieberman, Ruth, 1212
Lieberman, Susan, 5448
Liebhaber, Henia, 2183
Liebhaber, Marc, 2183
Liebhaber, Sharon F., 2183
Liebhard, Kranie, 6808
Liebhard, Sandy, 6808
Lieblich, Abraham, 5947
Lieblich, Asher, 5947
Lieblich, Chaya, 5947
Liebman, Vance, 2707, 2856
Liebowitz, David A., 6400
Liebscher, Anita, 7145
Liechenstein, Francesca, 5511
Liechenstein, Michael, 5511
Lieder, Erick, 7802
Liedtke, Laurie L., 9028
Liendecker, Katie, 6625
Lienemann, Charlotte, 5100
Lienemann, Del, Jr., 5100
Lienemann, Del, Sr., 5100
Lienemann, Douglas, 5100
Lies, Eric, 1316
Liewald, Lisa, 8657
Life Education Fund, 9033
Life Foundation, The, 9033
Life Rescue, 1316
Lifetime Systems Co., 4243
Lifton, Harvey, 5954
Light Community Property Trust, William M., 9016
Light Year Holdings, 344
Light, Gary, 9065
Light, Jack H., 9016
Light, Quency, 9065
Light, William M., 9016
Lighten, Adrienne J., 1698
Lighten, Alexis N., 1698
Lighten, Janifer Lynn, 1698
Lighten, William E., 1698
Lightner, Earl Sams, 1699
Lightner, Larry, 1699
Lightner, Robin H., 1699
Lightner, Sue B., 1699
Lightner-Scammahorn, Kamala A., 1699
Lightpen, Christopher W., 1698
Ligibel, Nancy Lee, 7438
Ligon, Robert M., 4487
Ligon, W. Austin, 9018
Liguori, Catherine E., 553
Liguori, Daniel T., 553
Liguori, Lisa A., 553
Liguori, Susan, 553
Liguori, Susan K., 553
Liguori, Thomas, 553
Liguori, Thomas A., 553
Liles, Herb, 1059
Lilienfield, Laura G., 6054
Lilja, Michael, 4802
Liljedahl, Kerdyle, 1952
Lillard, John, 3188
Lillard, John S., 3188
Lillard, Paula Polk, 3188
Lillehei, Craig, 4729
Lillehei, Katherine R., 4729
Lillehei, Kevin, 4729
Lillestolen, Ted, 1729
Lilley, Denise, 7743
Lillios, Judge Paul, 2827
Lillis, Chuck, 4396

Lilly, Brian, 1043
Lilly, Brian M., 1043
Lilly, Charlotte Johnson, 7468
Lilly, Denise L., 1043
Lilly, George D., 1043
Lilly, John, 2932
Lilly, Kevin, 1043, 7252
Lilly, Kevin J., 9019
Lilly, Kevin T., 1043
Lilly, Lesley, 9019
Lilly, Lesley K., 9019
Lilly, Parker, 1043
Lim Family Trust, Jonathan Conyee, 1642
Lim, Conyee, 1642
Lim, Jonathan, 1642
Lima, Karen, 1389
Lin, Alice P., Dr. , 6300
Lin, Dennis, 533
Lin, Eva, 5596
Lin, Fawn, 3566
Lin, Helene, 533
Lin, Joanne, 757
Lin, Raymond, 757
Lin, Rebecca E., 2399
Lin, Vincent, 757
Linbeck, Andrew B., 8821
Lincoln, Barbara, 4377
Lincoln, Brinton C., 7496
Lincoln, Constance P., 7496
Lincoln, Edward M., 3596
Lincoln, G. Russell, 7496
Lincoln, James D., 7496
Lincoln, Tim, 2252
Lincoln, William T., 7485
Lind, Kenneth, 610
Lindberg, Ken, 7944
Lindeborg, Ruth, Dr. , 2443
Lindemann, Paul, 3381
Linden, Dennis A., 7553
Lindenbaum, Carol S., 2587
Lindenbaum, David S., 2587
Lindenbaum, Samuel, 6656
Linderman, Julie Klesse, 8998
Lindgren Trust, Ruby F., 7791
Lindgren, Brooke E., 7791
Lindgren, Clarence R., 7791
Lindgren, Eric W., 7791
Lindgren, Paul E., 7791
Lindholm, John T., 4614
Lindley, W.B., 403
Lindner 2008 Charitable Lead Trust, Carl & Edyth, 7497
Lindner, Carl H., III, 7497
Lindner, Carl H., Jr., 7497
Lindner, Edyth B., 7497
Lindner, Keith E., 7497
Lindner, S. Craig, 7497
Lindon, Charlotte, 3054
Lindon, Elick, 3054
Lindorf, Ronald S., 9339
Lindorf, Terri, 9339
Lindquist, David S., 1735
Lindquist, Scott R., 496
Lindsay, Alan, 5512
Lindsay, Douglas G., 9477
Lindsay, Earl, 9914
Lindsay, Edwin B., 4176
Lindsay, Elizabeth S., 4176
Lindsay, Margaret S., 4176
Lindsay, Rob, 9634
Lindsey, John H., 2361
Lindsey, Kevin L., 9800
Lindsley, Janet, 2376

Lindsley, William, 2376
Lindstrom, Michael R., 2665
Line N Bath Creation, 6199
Lineback, Donald, 8680
Lineberger, Laura G., 7111
Linehan, Jerome, 4299
Linen, Ned, 5255
Ling, Kathie, 4388
Linger, Laura M., 4456
Lingkogin, 637
Lingos, John W., 4177
Lingos, Sonia Tasha, 4177
Lingos, Thalia I., 4177
Lingos-Utley, Tamara, 4177
Link, John, 5671
Link, Mary Pat, 1361
Linke, Gordon F., 1508
Linke, Jocelyn B., 1508
Linn, Erik, 3134
Linn, Kirk A., 7367, 7414
Linn, Lewis M., 8812
Linnell, Renee, 5219
Linnell, Robert C., 5219
Linnemann, Calvin C., 7498
Linnemann, Catherine A., 7498
Linnemann, Mark D., 7498
Linnemann, Patricia G., 7498
Linnen, John W., 9800
Linsley, Sarah M., 3205
Lintecum, Elaine, 811
Lintott, James, 9492
Linwood Mining & Minerals Corp., 3519
Linz, Brian J., Mrs., 7990
Linz, Brigitte Loewy, 6409
Linz, Peter Erwin, 6409
Lions Gate Homes, 9009
Lipcon, Jesse, 7468
Lipcon, Patricia L. Johnson, 7468
Lipcon, Scott, 7468
Lipcon, Todd, 7468
Lipkin, Barbara, 7031
Lipkin, Joan, 5576
Lipkin, John O., 7031
Lipkin, Mack, Jr., 7031
Lipkin, Richard, 5576
Lipkin, Richard M., 5384
Lipkin, Steven, 5576
Lipkin, Steven M., 5576
Lipman, Jane Sarah, 6108
Lipner, Wesley, 2057
Lipoff, Norman, 2035
Lipp Revocable Trust, David W., 759
Lipp, David W., 759
Lipp, Lee, Dr., 7295
Lipper, A. Michael, 5450
Lipper, Kenneth, 6219
Lipper, Ruth C., 5450
Lippert, Christine Castleberry, 7567
Lippes, Adam S., 6401
Lippes, David F., 6401
Lippes, Gerald L., 6401
Lippes, Gerald S., 6401
Lippes, Tracy G., 6401
Lippincott, Alfred, 1509
Lippincott, Diane, 1509
Lippincott, Donald B., 1509
Lippman, James, 1090
Lippman, Michael, 6796
Lipschitz, Chaim, 6402
Lipschitz, Fishel, 6402
Lipschitz, Yocheved, 6402
Lipschultz, Jennifer S., 6403
Lipschultz, Marc, 6403
Lipschultz, Marc S., 6403

Lipschutz, Neal, 5325
Lipscomb, Tabita, 202
Lipshutz, Menachem, 5824
Lipsitz Family Foundation, 8080
Lipsitz Family Foundation, Helen N. Nobel, 8080
Lipsitz, Herman, 8080
Lipsitz, Herman, Mrs. , 8080
Lipstein, Bruce J., 5302
Lipstein, Gail, 8129
Lipstein, Sanford, 8129
Liptack, Barbara Loomis, 5782
Liptack, Thomas, 5782
Lipton, Alan, 2185
Lipton, Janice, 2185
Lipton, Katherine B., 6404
Lipton, Martin, 6404
Lipton, Samantha D., 6404
Lipton, Susan L., 6404
Lis, Daniel T., 4467
Liske, Laurie, 9630
Lisker, Mitchell, 5247
Liskevych, Nancy L., 3035
Lisle, Lora Jane Harv, 760
Lisle, Philip, 7168
Lisle, Sally, 760
Lisnow, Sharon M., 9788
Lissack, Michael R., 2186
Lissner Foundation, Herman, The , 5700
Lissner, Elaine, 904, 5173
Lissner, Gerda, 6405
Lissner, Michael D., 7029
Lissner, R.J., 5173
List, Robert, 3220
List, Stephen C., 4450
Listeman, Kurt, 3055
Litchfield, Rhonda, 8201
Literacy Council of Jackson County, 7761
Litke, Gary, 6704
Litsch, Jim, 7724
Litterman, Adam J., 6406
Litterman, Mary, 6406
Litterman, Nadia K., 6406
Litterman, Robert, 6406
Litterman, Robert B., 6406
Little, Angela Flynt, 4848
Little, Anthony, 9386
Little, Espie Watts, 7162
Little, Lew, 8935
Littlefield, Corliss Bloedorn, 1238
Littlefield, Michael E., 1251
Littlejohn, Leonard, 5118
Littlejohns, Linda, 5400
Littles, Alma, 1918
Littman, Thomas N., 7622
Littmann, Jeffrey C., 4399
Litton Revocable Trust, Mildred, 4946
Litton, Mildred K., 4946
Litvinoff Memorial, Mike, 9774
Litwin, Leonard, 6656
Litwin, Nancy, 6114
Litz, Paul, 738
Liu, Allan, 5290
Liu, Andy, 1799
Liu, Chiu-Chu, 578
Liu, Sara, 578
Liu, Shalin, 4316
Liu, Steven, 5290
Live Nation, 1046
Live Nation Worldwide, 8540
Lively, Beverly, 8792
Living Memorial Trust, 4465
Livingston, Andrew M., 2970

Livingston, Janet K., 2161
Livingston, Lanien, 84
Livingston, Mitchel D., 7541
Livingston, Mollie Parnis, 2187
Livingston, Robert L., 2187
Livingston, Ruth Daily, 761
Livingston, Terrance K., 2772
Livingston, Tonia, 9213
Livney, Patrick, 3056
Livney, Roland, 3056
Livsey, Herbert C., 9351
Lizzadro, John S., 3057
Lizzadro, Joseph F., 3057
Lizzadro, Louis L., 3057
LJA Insurance Co., 674
LKB Investments, 4872
LKBOC LLC, 6656
Llanos, Aron Adelman, 231
Llanos, Claudio, 231
Llanos, Lisa Adelman, 231
Llewellyn, Kathleen, 3656
Llewellyn, Richard E., II, 566
Lloyd Charitable Trust No. 2, 9380
Lloyd Charitable Trust, Harry J., 1347
Lloyd Revocable Trust, Demi, 3594
Lloyd, Demi, 3594
Lloyd, Georgia, 9380
Lloyd, Heidi Mage, 763
Lloyd, Jane Lewis, 8075
Lloyd, Pat, 3594
Lloyd, Petrina A., 7965
Lloyd, Philip A., 7377
Lloyd, Roger, 7805
Lloyd, Roy, 1512
Lloyd, Steven Lewis, 8075
Lloyd, Terry, 975
Lloyd, Thomas Coridon, 8075
LMB Family Trust, 4660
LMB Funding, 5482
LMCL, 6374
Lo, Hing-Har, 9426
Load King Manufacturing Co., 1997
Loats, John, 3902
Lobel, Michael A., 6332
Lobell, Jay, 6478
Lobert, Sandra, 7340
Lobl, Frances, 5425
Lobley, Christine D., 7955
Locarni, Ida S., 4873
Locher, Michelle, 7027
Lochte, Caroline P., 9180
Lock, Bill, 9937
Lockard, Dorianne Cotter, 610
Locke, David, 8869
Locke, Deb, 3367
Locke, Gwendolyn, 764
Locke, Jeffery C., 1888
Locke, Liddell & Sapp, LLP, 8700
Locke, Lori C., 8672
Locke, William F., 6138
Locker, David S., 6009
Lockerby, Pat, 3560
Lockhart Revocable Trust, 7699
Lockhart, G. Robert, 5207
Lockhart, Marion S., 7699
Lockhart, Romona, 5207
Lockridge Trust, The, 765
Lockridge, B. Russell, 2762
Lockridge, Erika H., 765
Lockridge, John P., 765
Lockwood, Carol, 5105
Lockwood, Jackie, 7502
Lockwood, Jacquelyn E., 7502
Lockwood, Jane H., 7437

Lockwood, Katharine Otto, 9960
Lockwood, William D., 7502
Lococo, Elizabeth Dodd, 3647
Lococo, Louis, 6898
Loconsolo, Elizabeth, 6408
Loconsolo, Jacqueline, 6408
Loconsolo, John A., 6408
Lodato, Valery H., 2974
Lodder, Fran, 3978
Lodes, Robert R., 4849
Lodestone, 3905
Lodewick, Christine, 1512
Lodewick, Philip H., 1512
Lodging Kit Co., 2400
Loeb, Francine, 9654
Loeb, Fred, 2049
Loeb, Frederick, 7503
Loeb, Helen R., 47
Loeb, James L., 47
Loeb, James L., Jr., 47
Loeb, James L., Mrs. , 47
Loeb, Joan B., 47
Loeb, Justus H., 7504
Loeb, Matthew, 6943
Loeb, Richard, 9654
Loeb, Rose, 9493
Loeb, Steven, 6344
Loeb, Steven M., 5770, 6225
Loeding, Dahna, 4490
Loehmann, Frank M., Jr., 1520
Loehmann, Gregory M., 1520
Loehrke, Kent, 9872
Loehrke, Wynne, 9872
Loera, Beartriz, 275
Loesch, Collin, 2498
Loeschen, Larry, 4741
Loescher, Dan, 3019
Loesel, George F., 4433
Loesel, Susan D., 4433
Loewen, Rosalie L., 6385
Loewy, Alfred, 6409
Loft, Richard, 761
Loft, Sara Ognibene, 2458
Loftin, Jay G., Jr., 7261
Loftis, Nancy, 9696
Loftis, Robert W., 2188
Loftus, Georgia Z., 4620
Loftus, James, 4620
Loftus, John, 1700
Loftus, Katherine Dooner, 7974
Loftus-Mays, Maureen, 4620
Logan Medical Foundation, 9757
Logan, Eugene T., 3597
Logan, James, 3597
Logan, Jonathan, 6754
Logan, Margaret E., 3597
Logan, Penny, 2200
Logan, Robert E., 3597
Logan, Sheridan A., 4947
Logan, Thomas A., 4947
Logan, William W., 7494
Logemann, Darrell, 5074
Logies, Martin A., 376
Logli, Paul, 3019
Logozzo, Dave, 8996
Logser Charitable Lead Trust, John and Mary, 109
Logvinsky, Victoria, 5414
Loh, Daniella, 2175
Lohbeck, David J., 7350
Lohide, Mark, 3462
Lohide, Ruth, 3362
Lohman, Brett, 2909
Lohr, Walter G., Jr., 3903

Lohuis, Neal, 2164
Lok, Harvey, 6748
Lok, Yuk Chun, 6748
Loke, Kenneth, 8986
Loken, Kimberle, 4729
Loken, Troy, 4729
Lokken, Jane, 9814
Loll, Terry, 96
Lomas, Leslie S., 6806
Lomax, W. Thomas, 7998
Lombard, Edward M., 5542
Lombard, Patricia , 471
Lon, Les, 5105
London, Frances P., 7164
London-Ewing, Marilyn, 9805
Londono, Yolanda, 2379
Lonergan, James A., 801
Lonergan, Lauren, 4648
Loney, Chip, 3361
Long Family Foundation, Robert E., Jr.
    and Kathryn Scott, 7209
Long Trust, Sidne J., 1135
Long, Ann H., 7437
Long, Dale, 3506
Long, Daniel R., III, 2189
Long, Diana L., 9760
Long, Gordon, 7437
Long, Jacob F., 141
Long, James, 9450
Long, James H., 9554
Long, Joe R., 9023
Long, John F., 141
Long, Joseph M., 8791
Long, Kathryn G., 7470
Long, Laura, 5050
Long, Mary Balent, 2537
Long, Matthew A., 7470
Long, Mitchell, 9023
Long, Norman L., 9449
Long, Phillip C., 7541
Long, Ralph F., 8443
Long, Robert, 3932, 7209
Long, Robert E., Jr., 7209
Long, Ruby, 9023
Long, Sallye, 8937
Long, Sidne J., 1135
Long, Teresa L., 9023
Long, Tracy, 188
Longaberger Foundation, The, 7578
Longbrake Trust, Mary, 3024
Longbrake, David, 9655
Longbrake, Derek C., 9655
Longbrake, Dorothy, 9655
Longbrake, Erin, 9655
Longbrake, Mark W., 9655
Longbrake, Martha, 9655
Longbrake, William A., 9655
Longenecker, Kent, 3571
Longest, Mary B., 3672
Longfield, Kelly H. , 8444
Longfield, Mitchell, 8444
Longfield, Nancy S., 8444
Longfield, Robert, 8581
Longfield, Scott P., 8444
Longfield, Susan, 8444
Longfield, William H., 8444
Longfield, William J., 8444
Longfield, William R., 8444
Longhini-Halbin, Amanda, 2108
Longino, Fred, 3735
Longley, Grace M., 5101
Longley, Michael C., 5101
Longtine, Janina, 4179
Longyear, Mary Beecher, 7388

Loo, Janice Luke, 2650
Looker, Amy, 766
Looker, Erin, 766
Looker, Mary, 766
Looker, Mary M., 766
Looker, Monica, 766
Looker, Robert, 766
Looker, Robert L., 766
Looker, Tonia, 766
Loomis, Carol, 5782
Loomis, Carol J., 5782
Loomis, John, 5782
Loomis, Mark, 5782
Loomis, Peter, 6666
Loomis, Stephanie, 5782
Loomis, Tucker, 4772
Looney, Martha W., 2542
Looney, Wilton D., 2542
Looper, Deborah Beaver, 7271
Loos, Henry, 9882
Loosemore, Charles W., 4495
Lopatin, Brenda, 6412
Lopatin, Jonathan M., 6412
Lope, Matt, 1772
Lopes, Kristine N., 1180
Lopez, E. Zeke, 338
Lopez, Edwin, 5954
Lopez, Humberto S., 181
Lopez, Julie, 7102
Lopez, Mary K., 276
Lopez, Michael E., 7102
Lopez, Michael J., 338
Lopez, Virginia, 767
Lopez-Wessell, Cathy, 1241
Lopez-Wessell, Irene, 1241
Lopiccolo, Mary Beth, 7966
Lopiccolo, Matt, 7608
LoPrete, James H., 4496
LoPrete, James S., 4496
LoPrete, Robert D., 4496
Lord, Julie Broll, 8320
Lord, Thomas, 8132
Lorence, Chris, 6625
Lorenz, Andrew R., 7524
Lorenz, Glenn J., 7768
Lorenz, Glenn T., 7768
Lorenz, Susan M., 7768
Lorenzen, Marc, 5050
Loretto High School, 917
Loring, E. Amory, 4276
Loring, Patricia H., 4038
Loring, Peter B., 4356
Loring, Robert W., 4276
Lorren, Stanly, 7070
Lorusso, Kathryn A., 4104
Losardo, Kathleen, 4757
Loschen, Donna, 5129
Lossee, Joann Bullock, 5507
Lossi, Jean Howe, 6665
Lothlorien Enterprises, LP, 5101
Lott, Leon, 882

Lott, Martin, 9656
Lott, Sharon, 9656
Lott, T.E., Jr., 4850
Loucks, Donna, 6625
Lough, Donald, Jr., 5322
Lougheed, Linford L., 2003
Loughlin, Brian R., 5710
Loughman, Thomas F., 1402
Loughran, Marcia B., 3969
Loughrea Trust, 8763
Loughry, Andrea , 8674
Loughry, Andrea J., 8635
Louie, Betty B., 770
Louie, David, 770
Louis Berkman Investment Company,
    7324
Louis Charitable Trust, Henrietta J., 142
Louis Foundation, John J., 3063
Louis Revocable Trust, Herbert J., 142
Louis Revocable Trust, Julie D., 142
Louis, Herbert J., 142
Louis, J. Jeffry, 3063
Louis, John Jeffry, 3063
Louis, John Jeffry, III, 3063
Louis, Julie D., 142
Louis, Nelson, 6558
Louis, Timothy C., 142, 3063
Louisiana-Pacific Corp., 8644
Louisville Christian Foundation, 7333
Lounsbury, Tina, 6912
Lourd, Blaine, 684
Louthan, Frank G., Jr., 9522
Lovaas, Kati, 5558
Love Trusts, John Allan, 4951
Love, Alan, 8532
Love, Andrew Sproule, Jr., 8446
Love, Ben F., 3064
Love, Benton, 3064
Love, Charles W., 8532
Love, Charles, Jr., 8532
Love, Daniel Spoule, 8446
Love, Davis, III, 2449
Love, Frank C., IV, 7701
Love, Gregory M., 7701
Love, Hugh, Jr., 4832
Love, Jeff, 8980
Love, Jeff B., 3064
Love, John, 2651
Love, Judith M., 7701
Love, Katherine, 3064
Love, Laura A., 7701
Love, Margaret M., 3064
Love, Rosemarie J., 2651
Love, Steve, 5616
Love, Thomas, 7701
Love, Thomas E., 7701
Lovejoy, Joan D., 1442
Lovejoy, Joseph E., Jr., 1442
Lovelace, Mark, 4983
Lovelace, Richard M., 2348
Lovelady, Mel, 8844
Lovelady, Melvin B., 9154
Loveless, Barbara, 341
Loveless, Keith, 80
Lovell, Betty, 8717
Lovett, James W., 5305
Lovett, Pamela H., 9232
Lovik, Kathryn, 4798
Lovoi, P. Vincent, 7702
Lovoi, Sally S., 7702
Low Book Sales Management Group,
    9340
Low, Gabriel Lopez, 767
Low, Jesse Lopez, 767

Low, Lisa, 6878
Low, Nathan A., 6878
Low, Pamela, 7730
Low, Roger, 767
Low, Sean, 9139
Lowden, David W., 5233
Lowder, Gary W., Dr. , 9450
Lowdon Revocable Trust, 9025
Lowdon, Ethel Patty, 9025
Lowdon, Maria M., 9025
Lowdon, Robert R., 9025
Lowe, Betty M., 7505
Lowe, C. Marshall, 7505
Lowe, Catharine M., 3076
Lowe, Constance M., 7505
Lowe, Diana, 8874
Lowe, Francis Marks, 9039
Lowe, Henry T., 5037
Lowe, James T., 7505
Lowe, Margaret L., 4653
Lowe, Megan, 2412
Lowe, Peter A., 7505
Lowe, Richard, 2412
Lowe, Sandra Lois, 2412
Lowe, Thomas P., 4653
Lowe, Thomas P., III, 4653
Lowe, Walter M., 6032
Lowell, Charlotte, 410
Lowell, Dwight E., 399
Lowell, Jack, 1952
Lowell, Kimberly, 399
Lowell, Mandy, 900
Lowenbery, Greg, 3514
Lowenbraun, Chaim, 6414
Lowenbraun, Miriam, 6414
Lowenstein, Glenn L., 3598
Lowenstein, John, 3598
Lowenstein, Lon J., 3598
Lowenstein, Marie R., 8645
Lowenstein, Reed, 3598
Lowenstein, William B., 3598
Lowenthal, Paul, 1952
Lowery, Austin, 2057
Lowery, Brinck, 3994
Lowery, Charles, 8944
Lowery, Darlene, 7636
Lowery, Sandra, 8944
Lowery-Bregar, Nancy, 7645
Lowes Charitable Foundation, 140
Lowet, Henry A., 6020
Lowndes, Caroline M., 1701
Lowney, Ann, 4565
Lowrey, Thad, 1950
Lowry, Ivilyn, 2191
Lowry, L.L., 3446
Lowry, Sumter, 2191
Lowy, Rudolph, 768
Loy, R. Steve, 825
Loyd, Robert W., 4935
Lozick, Edward A., 7608
Lozier, Kaye R., 3547
LRFA LLC, 1168
LSL Productions, 6839
LSM Mgmt., 7008
LSM Mgmt. Co., 6858
LSR Fund, 5662
Lu, David, 637
Luaces, Maria Alonso, 4983
Lubben, David J., 4775
Luber, Howard J., 167
Luber, Howrd Lisa, 147
Lubert, Ira M., 8133
Lubert, Jonathan, 8133
Lubert, Kristine, 8133

Lubetkin, Arcie, 1578
Lubin, Amy S., 2720
Lubin, Donald, 3018
Lubin, Donald G., 2720
Lubin, Kenneth, 6536
Lubin, Tillie K., 6416
Lubitz, David M., 1785
Lubrication Technologies, 4634
Lucareli, Michael B., 9889
Lucas Petroleum Group, 8836
Lucas, Carol, 8836
Lucas, Ed, 9774
Lucas, Harry, 8836
Lucas, Harry, Jr., 8836
Lucas, Lawrence R., 3092
Lucas, Matt, 1063
Lucas, Tom, 1204
Lucas, William M., 9232
Lucast, Jodi, 4672
Luce, Albert L., Jr., 8477
Luce, Burton S., 8477
Luce, Dwain G., Jr., 4836
Luce, Elizabeth, 1227
Luce, Elizabeth Bardsley, 1227
Luce, J.P., 8477
Luce, Marla, 9189
Luce, Ned, 9630
Luce, Peter Paul, 1227
Luce, Stephen, 8477
Luce, Tom, 3344
Lucero, Wanda, 5626
Luciano, Mary, 1595
Luciu, Susan Marie, 2086
Luck, Suzanne, 4552
Lucksinger, Mike, 8937
Ludington, Cassandra V.A., II, 1691
Ludwick, Andrew, 1003
Ludwick, Christopher, 1003, 8134
Ludwick, Jocelyn, 1003
Ludwick, Theodore, 1003
Ludwick, Worth Z., 1003
Ludwig, Marianne, 3704
Ludwig, Noelle K., 702
Ludwig, Roger W., 5581
Ludwig, Samantha, 7422
Ludwigson, Jon, 1239
Luedders, Jerry D., 931
Luedeman, Craig, 3448
Lueders, Wayne R., 9845
Luegers, Jeryl, 3370
Luehring Irrevocable Trust, Ruth E., 3065
Luehring Trust, Marian D., 3065
Luempert-Coy, Molly, 4411
Luengen, Wendy A., 9917
Lufkin, Abigail F., 6421
Lufkin, Dan W., 6421
Lufkin, Elise G.B., 6421
Lugo, Sam, 8948
Lui, Amy Rosenblatt, 9490
Lui, Gorretti, 771
Lui, Lawrence, 771
Luikart, James S., 1950
Luing, Gary A., 2351
Lujan, Vernon, 5626
Lukaszewicz, Laurie, 9882
Luke Trust, Mary Jane, 9460
Luke, Craig, 3223
Luke, Lauren C., 9522
Luke, Sharon Genebach, 9503
Luke, Virginia Pavelka, 8573
Lukens, Ashley, 7507
Lukens, Chelsey, 7507
Lukens, Heidi, 7507
Lukens, Joseph T., 7507

Lukesn, H. Kimberly, 7507
Lukins, Betty, 9615
Lukis, Donna, 4732
Lukis, Donna B., 4732
Lukis, Lawrence, 4732
Lukis, Lawrence J., 4732
Lukowicz, Stan, 238
Lum, Lori, 1052
Lum, Lori R., 1052
Lum, Steve, 1052
Lum, Steven D., 1052
Lumia, Melanie Maslow, 8146
Lummis, David, 8924
Lummis, France S. B., 8877
Lummis, Frederick R., II, 8877
Lummis, Palmer Bradley, 8877
Lummis, Ransom C., 8877
Lummis, William R., 8877
Lummis, William R., Jr., 8877
Lumsden, Joann, 2638
Luna Investments, 1931
Luna, Kathryn T., 1477
Luna, Louis, 5611
Lunardon, Judy, 5608
Lunchpad Communication, 2622
Lund, Arthur K., 587
Lund, Bradford, 143
Lund, Bradford D., 143
Lund, Margaret McKee, 9052
Lund, Michelle, 143
Lund, Sherry L., 143
Lund, William S., 143
Lund-Diaz, Sandra, 9222
Lundberg, Edward B., 7980
Lundberg, Linda, 8062
Lundby, Sigrid, 8326
Lundeen, Gloria, 3019
Lundeen, Phoebe Weil, 5961
Lundeen, Ray, 9660
Lundell, Karin J., 6396
Lunden, Jeanne, 2857
Lundgard Trust, Ruth, 7509
Lundgren, Carolyn, 772
Lundgren, William J., III, 4277
Lundstrom, Bryan, 5033
Lundy, Randall, 9414
Lunsford, David, 8732
Lunsford, Holt, 8741
Lunsford, Travis, 1948
Lunsway, Ranell, 3634
Lunt, Bonnie, 2248
Lunt, Martha W., 4358
Lupica, Anne E., 6551
Lupo, Christopher I., 8518
Lupold, Chris, 7845
Lupold, Jessica, 7845, 8233
Lupton, Carolyn C., 9028
Lupton, T.C., Jr., 9028
Lupton, Tavenner C., III, 9028
Lurie, Heather, 1378
Lurie, Lori Christina, 3982
Lusardi, Debra E., 5175
Lusardi, Warner C., 5175
Lusby, Ronald L., 7451
Luse, Bulah, 9029
Luse, W.P., 9029
Lusk, Angela, 9563
Luster, Elizabeth, 880
Luster, Elizabeth S., 880
Lustig, Debra, 1318
Lustig, James A., 1318
Luth, Lili Lowdon, 9025
Luth, Matt, 9025
Luther Family Ford, 4733

Luther Nissan Kia, 4733
Luther, Charles David, 4733
Luther, Rudy Dan, 4733
Lutken, Peter K., III, 9187
Lutsey, Andrew J., 9873
Lutsey, Jeffrey K., 9873
Lutsey, Matthew T., 9873
Lutsey, Nicholas P., 9873
Lutsey, Sharon L., 9873
Lutsey, Thomas J., 9873
Lutz, Anne de Compiegne, 8802
Lutz, Kathleen, 7932
Lutz, Kevin, 7636
Lutzka, Claude, 4666
Lux, Miranda W., 773
Lux, Paul S., 1532
Luxottica Retail, 9098
Luy, Peg, 2959
Luzius, Kate B., 7327
Lyche, Eric J., 9875
Lyche, John, 9875
Lyche, Linda, 9875
Lykins, Elizabeth Welch, 4610
Lyle Pacific Corp., 7682
Lyle, James R., 2192
Lyle, Paul, 9043
Lyles, W.M., IV, 310
Lyman Banks Trust, 3371
Lyman, Elizabeth, 5795
Lyman, Steven A., 774
Lyman, Vicki Jo, 774
Lynam, Fred C., 3788
Lynch Trust Co., Merrill, 5254
Lynch, Daniel C., 775
Lynch, Edward, 4211
Lynch, James B., 9610
Lynch, James E., 7752
Lynch, James P., 4047
Lynch, John H., 5221
Lynch, Julie E., 775
Lynch, Karen D., 775
Lynch, Luke M., 9874
Lynch, Michael, 7794
Lynch, Michael J., 4662
Lynch, Nina Johnson, 9978
Lynch, Robert, 5233
Lynch, Susan E. Upton, 5221
Lynch, Thomas C., 3925
Lynch, Wendy J., 4618
Lynch, William H., 9874
Lynch, William W., Jr., 97
Lynch-Sasson, Julie E., 775
Lynehan, Linda, 4222
Lyneis, Mary M., 4496
Lynham, John M., Jr., 1803
Lynn, Chloe, 5059
Lynn, Elizabeth, 5059
Lynn, Elizabeth A., 5059
Lynn, June, 4890
Lynn, Linda, 8886
Lynn, Riley, 5059
Lynn, Scott J., 8620
Lyon, Chris, 9384
Lyon, David, 3066
Lyon, Donna, 3066
Lyon, Linda B., 4881
Lyon, Lynda, 1005
Lyon, Mark S., 1477
Lyon, Richard A.M., 4054
Lyons Magnus, Inc., 1059
Lyons, Barbara L., 9033
Lyons, Cynthia Willis, 776
Lyons, Evelyn, 776
Lyons, Joseph, 7483

Lyons, Kristina E., 2625
Lyons, Mark A., 9050
Lyons, Patrice A., 9480
Lyons, Shaun B., 2625
Lyons, Steve, 3362
Lyons, Steven, 776
Lyons, Tim, 4598
Lyons-Gardner, Melissa, 9050

M & T Trust Co., 6964
M and T Trust Co., 6805
M&A Partnership, 4985
M&T Bank, 6460, 6581, 6616, 6817
M&T Investment Group, 6912
M&T Trust Co., 3819, 6155, 6458, 6620
Ma, Yanling, 1195
Maas, Benard L., 4498
Maas, Diane, 3458
Maas, Melvin, 8569
Mabry, Nancy, 7789
Mac Kinnon, George, 9878
MacAdam, June, 1054
MacAllister, Lorissa K., 4481
MacAllister, Scott, 4153
MacAllister, Wesley, 4481
MacArthur, C.J., 6429
MacArthur, Gina G., 6429
Macauley, Alma Jane, 1514
Macauley, Melinda Rice, 1514
Macauley, Robert C., 1514
Macauley, Robert C., Jr., 1514
MacClure, Pablo, 1180
MacConnell, Diane, 4198
MacConnell, Gary, 4198
MacConnell, Jocelyn H., 8069
MacCready, Judith, 778, 5268
MacCready, Marshall, 778
MacCready, Parker, 778, 5268
MacCready, Tyler, 778
MacDonald, Ann M., 4296
MacDonald, Brad, 5453
MacDonald, Catherine, 3068
MacDonald, Donna, 9625
MacDonald, Donna Marie, 779
MacDonald, Joseph, 3068
Macdonald, Marg, Mrs., 7990
MacDonald, Margaret, 5453
MacDonald, Mark, 779
MacDonald, Marquis George, 3068
MacDonald, Robert, 1669
MacDonald, Robert B., 4296
MacDonald, Robert I., 5885
MacDonald, Shirley, 5453
MacDonald, Shirley D., 5555
MacDonald, William F., Jr., 8172
MacDonald-Pizzico, Kellie T., 5555
MacDonald-Sheetz, Margaret, 5555
MacDougall, Allan, 8225
MacDougall, Allan, III, 8113
MacDougall, Peter, 887
MacDowell, Michael A., 8090
Macek, Paul J., 4141
MacFie, Valerie A., 6818
Macgeorge, William S., 9661
Machine Builders & Design, 7118
Machones, Melinda, 4667
Macht, Amy, 3905
Macht, Philip, 3905
Macht, Sophia, 3905
Machtinger, Sidney J., 617
Machuga, John Victor, 5454
Maciariello, Joseph, 344

MacInnis, Beverly J., 1515
MacInnis, Frank T., 1515
MacInnis, Lauren, 1515
MacIntyre, Heidi, 1295
MacIntyre, John, 4497
Maciunas, Robert, Dr. , 872
Maciunas-Mockus, Dana, Dr. , 872
Mack Renaud, 2244
Mack, Beth L., 3839
Mack, David, 1170
Mack, Howard I., 5790
Mack, James, 1170
Mack, Jennifer, 1170
Mack, Kelly, 6430
Mack, Marcie, Dr. , 7666
Mack, Richard, 6430
Mack, Stephen, 6430
MacKay, B., 3748
Mackay-Smith, Alexander, Jr., 3880
Mackay-Smith, Virginia L., 3880
Mackens, Mike, 4410
MacKenzie, Jennifer P., 1829
Mackessey, Richard, 5332
Mackey, Dayton, 4977
Mackey, Eddina F., 4977
Mackey, Gail, 7845
Mackey, Keith, 7845
Mackey, Wendy, 7903
Mackie, Bert, 2947
Mackin, Craig L., 3673
Mackin, Jay Lawrence, 3673
Mackin, Jeffrey L., 3673
Mackin, Kimberly Ann, 3673
Mackin, Michael J., 3673
Mackin, Virginia, 3673
MacKing, V, 153
MacKnin, Elizabeth A., 2785
Mackowski, Maureen, 1141
Mackrell, Patrick J., 6546
Macks Charitable Lead Trust, Martha, 3906
Macks, Ellen A., 3906
Macks, Lawrence M., 3906
Macks, Louise D., 3906
Macks, Morton J., 3906
Macks-Kahn, Martha, 3906
MacLaughlin-Barck, Megan, 9797
MacLean, Mary Anna Hanson, 2950
MacLeod, Barbara B., 7347
Macleod, Karen B., 4236
MacLeod, Missy, 9849
MacLeod, Thomas D., 7347
Maclin, Alan, 4648
Macon, Randy, 7707
Macwell, 3905
Mada Charitable Lead Trust, 3309
MadAnt Energy, LLC, 1381
Madar, Gregory S., 1477
Madden, Diane, 4699
Madden, Francis T., 4699
Madden, John W., Jr., 1267
Madden, Mallory L., 4699
Madden, Melanie M., 4699
Madden, Michaela, 4699
Madden, Steven R., 3113
Madden, Timothy, 4699
Madden, W. H., 3602
Maddin, Michael W., 4473
Madding, Sherry, 260
Maddock, Paul L., Jr., 1423
Maddox, Ben, 5626
Maddox, Matt, 5202
Maddux, W.E., 7717
Madigan, Eileen, 2835

Madison Brands, 6216
Madison Dearborn Partners, 4199
Madison Holding Trust, 5953
Madison Title Agency, 5443, 6654
Madison, Dominick, 9789
Madison, J. Craig, 2310
Madison, Larry W., 36
Madison, Nellie, 7789
Madison, Steven, 480
Madisonlantana LP, 9009
Madley, Barbara A., 1684
Madonna, Robert P., 4182
Madorsky, Marsha, 2404
Madover, Arielle Tepper, 6431
Madover, Ian, 6431
Madrigal, Lydia H., 950
Madsen, Gary C., 3614
Madsen, Jacqueline, 89
Madsen, Lisa, 8498
Madzior, Aaron, 4533
Madzula, John S., 1532
Maetzold, Denny, 4671
Maffitt, James S., 3836
Mafrici, Elizabeth August, 5698
Magale, John F., 3735
Magargee, Susan, 8005
Magaro, Alex, 1516
Magaro, Diviya, 1516
Magazine, Sarah, 4199
Magee Carpet Co., 3674
Magee Industrial Enterprises, 8137
Magee, Audrey A., 8137
Magee, Drue A., 8137
Magee, Elizabeth, 8137
Magee, Ella G., 3674
Magee, Frances W., 5635
Magee, James, 3674
Magette, Cari, 2680
Maggard, Danny, 3655
Maggs, Deborah, 9418
Magid, Caryn L., 6441
Magill, R. Hugh, 2827
Magliocco, Robert R., 9868
Magnetics, 8231
Magnum Construction Corp., 2206
Magnus, Diane S., 2543
Magnus, James D., 2543
Magnus, Matthew, 2543
Magnuson, Amy, 432
Magnussen, David R., 4327
Magoon, Grace Previte, 4075
Magoon, Nancy, 2235
Magothy River Land Trust, 3824
Magoun, Anne H., 4504
Magoun, Peter R., 4504
Magowan Family Trust, 782
Magowan, Deborah, 782
Magowan, Peter, 782
Magrann, R.P., 2030
Magrann, R.P., Mrs. , 2030
Maguire Revocable Trust, James J., 6432
Maguire, Robert, 4362
Maguire, Sue, 6432
Maguire, Timothy, 6432
Mahadeva, Wijeyaraj A., 1517
Mahaffey, R. Ernest, 3166
Mahalak, Joan, 4411
Mahan, Ingrid T., 5455
Mahan, Marvin, 5455
Mahan, Tom, 3441
Mahavier, William, 8836
Maher, Basil, 5387
Maher, Christian, 7944

Maher, Helen S., 6434
Maher, James, 6433
Maher, Joan K., 783
Maher, John F., 6434
Maher, Miriam Duffy, 5387
Maher, Thomas C., 783
Maher, Tomas C., 783
Mahler, Ken, 7537
Mahler, Perin, 7537
Mahon, Arthur, 6949
Mahon, Deborah P., 4737
Mahon, Peter M., Jr., 4737
Mahoney, Anne, 4299
Mahoney, Carol L., 1532
Mahoney, David L., 1622
Mahoney, Joseph, 4738
Mahoney, Judith Rauenhorst, 4738
Mahoney, Lawrence, 2802
Mahoney, Leo D., 4184
Mahoney, Meghan L., 4184
Mahoney, P. Michael, 9899
Mahoney, Patrick L., 4184
Mahoney, Randolph B., 2074
Mahoney, Shelagh E., 4184
Mahoney, Thomas, 4738
Mahony, Joan, 5522
Mahuna, Dee Anne, 2643
Mahuna, Peter E., 2643
Mahuzier, Brigitte, 6820
Maibach Trust, Lorene M., 4500
Maibach, Benjamin C., Jr., 4500
Maibach, Douglas, 4386, 4500
Maidenbaum, Esther, 6435
Maidenbaum, Iris, 6435
Maidenbaum, Nathan, 6435
Maidenbaum, Shalom, 6435
Maier, Laura L., 7272
Maier, Peter K., 642
Maier, Steven F., 7272
Mailhot, Raymond E., 3786
Main, Anna, 4501
Main, John T., 69
Mainetti, Valter, 6828
Mainetti, Veronica, 6828
Mair, Bhavani, 3526
Maisel, Barbara, 4100
Maison Grande Assocs., 6784
Maize and Blue Charitable Trust, 6172
Majestic Realty Co., 784
Majid, Ameena, 3242
Majidi, Bryna, 5021
Major League Baseball, 1730
Major League Soccer, 90
Major, Gene, 3082
Majors, Maxine E. Devine, 5913
Majors, Robert I., 5913
Majors, William F., 5913
Majutana, Tirtanus, 2388
Makepeace, Christopher, 4186
Makepeace, Maurice, 4186
Maker's Mark, 3668
Makihara, Jun, 6436
Makins, Wendy, 8371
Makoff, John, 158
Makoujy, Joseph M., 5454
Makowsky, Jerome, 8591
Malabar J&J Halstead Survivors Trust, 2944
Malachowsky, Chris, 786
Malachowsky, Jeff, 913
Malachowsky, Melody, 786
Malachowsky, Sarah, 913
Malafarina, Gregory J., 7560
Malanga, Anthony, 6624

Malcolm, Joy Craft, 8548
Maldonado, Jeff, 6796
Maldonado, Maria, 6796
Maldonado, Melissa Lopez, 6796
Malechek, Stephanie A., 8691
Malenfant, David, 5244
Maleport, Jeff, 4401
Maley, Janet S., 1427
Maley, N. L., 787
Maley, Norman, 787
Malin, JoAnne C., 3879
Malkin Fund, The, 6656
Malkin Holdings, 6655
Malkmus, Stephen, 988
Mallah, Leo, 5544
Mallard Financial Group, 546
Mallard Oil Company, 7119
Mallard, John W., 7103
Mallel, Raymond, 752
Mallett, Amber, 2664
Mallett, Jennifer, 7533
Mallinger, Jeanette Witz, 3324
Mallon, Margaret, 3071
Mallon, Thomas J., 3071
Mallott, Amanda, 88
Malloy, George W., 4236
Malloy, John F., 7857
Malloy, Ken, 3514
Malloy, Vivian, 1611
Mallview, 3905
Malm, Laurie Howard, 5177
Malmgren, Arthur, 1092
Malo, J. Kenneth, Jr., 1329
Malo, John F., 1329
Malo, Kathleen M., 1329
Malone, Joe, 9033
Malone, Kathleen, 4705
Malone, Mollie, 1083
Malone, Ocllo S., 48
Malone, Richard G., 341
Malone, Robert E., 183
Malone, Sue, 4459
Malone, Thomas E., 183
Malone, Wallace D., Jr., 48
Malone, Wallace Davis, 48
Maloney, Patrick, 7781
Maloney, Scott R., 3255
Maloney, Timothy P., 6974
Maloof, Dee, 180
Malott, Gregg, 3432
Malott, Maxie A., 3346
Malouf, Donald J., 9106
Maloy, Jane, 7145
Maloy, Julia Strain, 68
Malpass, Barbara, 4536
Malpass, Barbara J., 4536
Malpass, Frederick F., 4536
Malser, Janet E., 4141
Malstrom, Robert A., 3012
Malt, R. Bradford, 4165
Maltby, Richard, Jr., 6323
Malutinok, David M., 4158
Malvini, Lisa, 248
Maly, Neil A., 7618
Maly, Paul J., 9915
Maly-Dykema, Michele, 4502
Mamary, Nicholas, 5785
Mamiye Brothers, 5456
Mamiye, Abraham, 5456
Mamiye, Charles D., 5456
Mamiye, Charles H., 5456
Mamiye, Hyman M., 5456
Mamula, Milosh, 7944
Man-Dell Food Stores, 6387

Manasia, Joseph, 5318
Manchester Resorts, 788
Manchester, Douglas F., 788
Manchester, M. Christina, 3076
Manchester, Wayne F., 3786
Manchikanti, Laxmaiah, 3678
Manchikanti, Murali Manohar, 3678
Manchikanti, Ram Mohan, 3678
Manchon, Meghan T., 3302
Mancini, Michelle M., 7868
Mancuso, Vince, 9851
Mandanis, Sarah G., 6054
Mandel, Gary, 9345
Mandel, Lawrence, 6387
Mandel, Rodger, 3210
Mandelbaum, Stacey, 6082
Mandell, Karen, 114
Mandelstamm, Ann, 4940
Manders, Beverly A., 8849
Mandeville, Josephine C., 7935
Maneely Fund, 7974
Maner, Hilary Day, 5980
Manes, Dennis L., 7316
Maness Living Trust, Carolyn J., 7166
Maness, Carolyn J., 7166
Maness, John R., 7166
Manett, Bruce, 7339
Manfred Beshears Annuity Trust, 9380
Manfredonia, Linda R., 8046
Mangano, Frank J., 7511
Mangano, Margaret E., 7511
Mangano, Ross J., 3355
Manger, Barbara E., 9874
Manger, Edmund B., 9874
Manger, Robert, 5811
Manger, Robert E., 9874
Manger-Lynch, Matthew, 9874
Mangin, Michael, 3078
Mangione, Ellen J., 1249
Mangione, Louis, 3907
Mangione, Mary C., 3907
Mangione, Nicholas B., 3907
Mangione, Samuel, 3907
Mangold, Harald, 9390
Mangold, Janet L., 789
Mangold, Karl G., 789
Mangold, Robert, 6114
Mangot, Neil, 2002
Manhattan Beer Distributors, LLC, 5738, 8253
Manhattan Charitable Foundation, 5925
Manhattan Mortgage, 6656
Manifould, Mark D., 9078
Manifould, Mary S., 9078
Manion, Mel, 6785
Manitowoc Company, 9876
Mank, Edward H., 4187
Mankiller, Rebecca, 5177
Manley Burke, LPA, 7566
Manley, Christopher, 6305
Manley, Dave, 1242
Manley, Edward, 6305
Manley, Frances, 6305
Manley, John, 6305
Manley, Justyn Haskell, 7439
Manley, Marguerite, 6305
Manley, Susanne, 6305
Mann Foundation, Ted, 790
Mann, Andrew L., 3975
Mann, Anthony E., 3738
Mann, Barbara L., 3599
Mann, Beth, 2695
Mann, Carol, 8448
Mann, Charlie, 4490

Mann, Curtis J., 4519
Mann, David, 7582
Mann, H. George, 3072
Mann, Hollis, 13
Mann, Inga, 8448
Mann, Jason, 3077
Mann, Judith, 8448
Mann, Judy A., 9580
Mann, Katharine, 2717
Mann, Leon, 8448
Mann, Lydia B., 6250
Mann, Madeline B., 1519
Mann, Milton, 1519
Mann, Norma, 1519
Mann, Pamela G., 1519
Mann, Robert, 8448
Mann, Ronald D., 3599
Mann, Sally M., 3738
Mann, Sheldon, 3072
Manne, Sharon, 3073
Manne, Stanley, 3073
Manning Trust, J.H., 6437
Manning, Andrew, 389
Manning, Beatrice Austin, 6437
Manning, Craig, 1316
Manning, Jack B., 9129
Manning, Jeffrey P., 2155
Manning, Katherine H., 9992
Manning, Kirk, 8848
Manning, Peter, 8526
Manning, Rick, 7354
Manning, Sue, 9129
Mannino, John, 5954
Mannion, Annette, 7588
Manocherian, Alan, 6438
Manocherian, Amir, 6438
Manocherian, Bernice, 5638
Manocherian, Fraydun, 6029
Manocherian, Fred, 6029
Manocherian, Greg, 6681
Manocherian, Jed, 6438, 6681
Manocherian, Jennifer, 6029
Manocherian, John, 6681
Manocherian, Kimberly, 6029
Manocherian, Mireille, 6438
Manocherian, Robert, 6438
Manocherian, Rosita, 6438
Mans, Ray, Dr. , 7829
Mansfield, Alexis, 3074
Mansfield, Benetta, 3074
Mansfield, David P., 4250
Mansfield, Justin, 3074
Mansfield, Linda Beth, 8324
Mansfield, Rick G., 8668
Mansfield, Seymour, 3074
Mansfield, Susan, 9463
Manske, Tippi, 650
Manson, Frances Crane, 8009
Manson, Kathleen, 4245
Mansour, John G., 726
Mansour, Lisa, 726
Mansur, Evelyn L., 9035
Mansur, Harl D., Jr., 9035
Mansur, Jonathan, 9035
Mantell, Joyce C., 8370
Mantzaris, Jennifer G., 7415
Mantzel, Ernest A., 9036
Manual, Eleanor M., 1174
Manuel, Margaret Cutting, 9968
Manuel, Michael B., 2919
Manufacturers and Traders Bank, 6790
Manufacturers and Traders Trust Co., 5867
Manus, Peter J., 4282

Manus, Vicki, 2535
Manz, Anne L., 6070
Manzanita Baptist Church, 840
Manzo, Cynthia, 1895
Manzo, Robert, 1895
Manzuk, Howard, 3156
Mapes Charitable Trust, 5103
Maple Leaf Bakery, 8859
Maples Burlingame, LLC, 477
Mapp Trust, Barbara J., 8646
Mapp, Richard C., III, 9434
Mara, Francis X., 5369
Mara, John K., 5369
Marable, Ned, 7145
Maraggia, Michael, 9064
Maraghy, Patrick B., 4003, 4302
Marandon, Jeanne, 6820
Marantes, Inna, 1599
Marbach, Beth, 3422
Marbach, Constance, 3422
Marbach, Terry, 3422
March, Barbara Baldieri, 791
March, J. Brad, 1379
March, John B., 4740
March, John D., 4740
March, Karen, 5400
March, Mary Chung, 4740
March, Roy Hilton, 791
March, Sallie S., 4740
March, Timothy S., 4740
March-Aurele, R. Drew, 3992
Marchell, John, 5954, 7295
Marchese, Chris, 792
Marchese, Margaret, 3075
Marchese, Marianne, 3075
Marchese, Mary, 792
Marchese, Michael, 3075
Marchi, Paul, 301
Marcil, Carol L., 793
Marcil, Gerald J., 793
Marcled Foundation, The, 316
Marco, Carolyn C., 2194
Marco, David A., 2194
Marco, Paul, 2244
Marco, Sol, 5667
Marcum, Joseph L., 3076
Marcum, Sarah, 3076
Marcum, Sarah S., 3076
Marcum, Stephen S., 3076
Marcus & Millichap Co., The, 794
Marcus, Ben, 9877
Marcus, Bernard, 2544, 2553
Marcus, Betty B., 9037
Marcus, Billi, 2544
Marcus, Celia, 9877
Marcus, Cynthia S., 4188
Marcus, Daniel H., 4188
Marcus, Frederick R., 2458
Marcus, George M., 794
Marcus, James S., 6346
Marcus, Joan, 9877
Marcus, Melanie L., 4188
Marcus, Nancy Dubois, 2458
Marcus, Norman, 746
Marcus, Paul R., 3993, 4007
Marcus, Richard C., 9037
Marcus, Richard S., 4188
Marcus, Stephen, 9877
Marcus, Susan Russell, 9037
Marcus, William M., 4188
Marder, Ruth R., 3834
Mardirosian, Anahid, 5562
Marek, Leonard, 9345
Marenghi, Julio, 6909

Maresco, Joseph R., 7986
Maretsky, David M., 8080
Margoes, John A., 795
Margolin, Allan, 9038
Margolin, Barbara, 5914
Margolin, Bernice, 9038
Margolin, David, 5914
Margolin, Jesse, 5914
Margolin, Michael, 5914
Margolin, Robert J., 5013
Margolin, Stephen M., 2998
Margolis, Alexandria A., 796
Margolis, Allegra H., 796
Margolis, Barry H., 8872, 9062
Margolis, Ben B., 144
Margolis, Deborah H., 796
Margolis, Iris M., 144
Margolis, Jeffrey H., 796
Margolis, Kenneth R., 2591
Margolis, Robert, 797
Margules, Rubein, 6994
Mariani, Linda L., 1438
Marie Crowley Charitable Lead Trust, 4416
Marietta college Trust, 7167
Marin, Carol, 5188
Marin, Joseph, 2030
Marinaro, Vincent P., 4254
Marineau, Philip A., 798
Marineau, Susan G., 798
Marinelli, Ennco, 8031
Mariners Care, 1730
Marino, Anthony, 5795
Marino, Cheryl, 5457
Marino, Denise, 9930
Marino, Douglas W., 5458
Marino, Gregory S., 5458
Marino, Joseph, 5457
Marino, Lauren M., 5458
Marino, Megan M., 5458
Marino, Michelle S., 4190
Marino, Paula, 5458
Marino, Roger M., 4190
Marino, Sharon, 840
Marino, William J., 5458
Marinos Charity, 2510
Marion County State Bank, 3541
Marion, Alexis, 523
Marital Trust, 6527
Marital Trust, The, 639
Maritime Heritage Alliance, 4466
Marittai, Tom, 4465
Mark Gold L.P., 5460
Mark, Bahr, 4500
Mark, Howard, Dr. , 9450
Mark, Melvyn I., 857
Markakis, Nicholas, 3817
Markantonis, George, 1858
Markel, Joel, 5379
Markel, Katherine N., 9498
Markel, Steven A., 9498
Markel, Virginia W., 541
Markely, James A., Jr., 7363
Marker, David, 4950
Marker, Dennis C., 4950
Marker, Donald F., 9452
Marker, Sara Lordi, 4950
Marker, Susan Lordi, 4950
Markes, Lori H., 7659
Markey, Andrew J., 5459
Markey, Elizabeth M., 5459
Markey, John C., 7168
Markey, John Clifton, II, 7168
Markey, Kevin A., 5459

Markey, Michael G., 5459
Markey, Susan, 9669
Markey, Timothy P., 5459
Markham, Emerson F., 7970
Markin, John, 1442
Markley, Christopher, 8011
Markley, Jean, 1899
Markley, Jeffrey D., 1899
Markley, Robert D., 1899
Markley, Robert J., 1899
Markovitz Charitable Trust, Max, 8080
Markowitz, Eugene, 5460
Markowitz, Renee, 5460
Marks, David, 1466, 3077
Marks, Dennis A, 2749
Marks, J. Alan, 5624
Marks, Jay, 9039
Marks, Jay M., 9039
Marks, Jim M., Jr., 1958
Marks, Lester A., 9039
Marks, Mara, 1350
Marks, Michael J., 2640
Marks, Murlin, 1100
Marks, Sarah, 1378
Marks, Shirley, 9039
Marks, Sylvia Goldsmith, 8622
Marks, Terrance, 2510
Marksbury Gifting Trust, 3675
Marksbury, Beverly E., 3675
Marksbury, Davis L., 3675
Marksbury, Davis L., III, 3675
Marksbury, Davis L., Jr., 3675
Marksbury, Logan Renee, 3675
Marlatt, William C., 2932
Marley, Everett A., Jr., 8862
Marlin, Charles, Dr. , 7891
Marlin, Jennifer W., 4239
Marling, Robert, 9345
Marlow, Rhett, 1770
Marmelstein, Marvin, 5247
Marmi, 2387
Marnell Foundation, 5202
Marois, Ralph D., 4095
Maron, Christina W., 3820
Marosek, Edwin P., 5674
Marples, Dean, 5123
Marquart, Aaron W., 5032
Marquart, William F., 5032
Marquiss, Susan, 8261
Marr, Dennis, 6666
Marr, Ray H., 9144
Marra, Annette, 9775
Marra, Gayle Susan, 6543
Marra, John M., 9775, 9946
Marra, Vincenzo R., 6543
Marram, Beverly G., 4189
Marriott Charitable Trust, Richard E., The , 3909
Marriott, Julie Ann, 3909
Marriott, Karen Christine, 3909
Marriott, Martha Graves, 2496
Marron, Dorothy, 5461
Marron, Martha, 5461
Marron, Peter, 5461
Marrow, Eugene, 4137
Marrow, James H., 6687
Mars Petcare, 8657
Mars, Bernard S., 8003
Mars, Linda, 8657
Mars, Peter F., 8003
Marschall, McAlister C., II, 9406
Marsh & McLennan, 9215
Marsh Assocs., 7171
Marsh Mortgage Co., 7171

Marsh Realty Co., 7171
Marsh, Eleanor, 4317
Marsh, G. Alex, III, 7171
Marsh, Gordon, 6114
Marsh, Hattie Heller, 613
Marsh, John D., 4740
Marsh, Kathleen A., 3051
Marsh, Kenneth, 5652
Marsh, Lee M., 3051
Marsh, Linda, 6559
Marsh, Nena, 8833
Marsh, Paul, 3458
Marsh, Richard S.T., 1807
Marsh, Stephanie, 9505
Marsh, William M., 8701
Marshal, Steven A., 7373
Marshall, Charlie, 7118
Marshall, Dennis, 5121
Marshall, Donna Ensign, 6446
Marshall, Edward W., III, 8275
Marshall, Elizabeth, 2356
Marshall, Gary, 6445
Marshall, Georgia Leupold, 7790
Marshall, H. Richard, 9751
Marshall, Harriet McDaniel, 2195
Marshall, Ina, 6445
Marshall, James Harper, 6446
Marshall, Jerry E., 7703
Marshall, Jessica Wright, 9294
Marshall, John D., 8414
Marshall, John W., 7703
Marshall, Katherine, 6249
Marshall, Kenneth, 2592
Marshall, Kent, 6445
Marshall, Laura B., 7834
Marshall, Lee Harper, 6446
Marshall, Margaret H., 5623
Marshall, Scot M., 7703
Marshall, Thomas O., 2545
Marshall, Thomas O., Mrs. , 2545
Marshall, W. Gilman, 6445
Marshall, Wally, 516
Marshburn, D.C., 799
Marshburn, Daniel, 799
Marshburn, Mark, 799
Marsico, Cydney, 5202
Marsilje Irrevocable Trust, I.H., 3044
Marsini, Nicholas, Jr., 8046
Marsteller Trust, Gloria C., 3079
Marstine, Janet, 8141
Marstine, Sheldon, 8141
Martell, Christopher Michael, 6329
Martell, Sally Klingenstein, 6328
Martell, Sarah, 6328
Martell, Sarah Klingenstein, 6329
Martell, Susan, 9951
Martelle, Tom, 92
Martens, Dawn, 1077
Martex Fiber Southern Corp., 8376
Marth, Edward C., 8434
Martin & Co., C.F., 8144
Martin Family Foundation, 5065
Martin Guitar Co., C.F., 8144
Martin Pringle Law Firm, 3561
Martin Trust, Karl & June, 7704
Martin, Aaron, 3970
Martin, Alan, 2989
Martin, Alfred S., 2196
Martin, Anne Marie, 1047
Martin, Benn, 9660
Martin, Carol, 9147
Martin, Catherine J., 96
Martin, Charles E., Jr., 4997
Martin, Christian F., IV, 8144

Martin, Daniel, 6305
Martin, Darlene E., 9659
Martin, Della, 801
Martin, Diane S., 8144
Martin, Dolores F., 2641
Martin, Dustin, 2464
Martin, E. Snow, Jr., 1892
Martin, Eille, 4666
Martin, Elizabeth C., 2196
Martin, Eva, 153
Martin, Fr. John, 9707
Martin, Freida H., 2082
Martin, G., 5222
Martin, G. Roxy, 2196
Martin, Gail, 3669
Martin, Gary, 2989
Martin, Gerard M., 5222
Martin, Gilbert J., 802
Martin, Harold L., Sr., 7209
Martin, J.W., 7100
Martin, Jackie, 7281
Martin, James G., 5222
Martin, Jane, 472
Martin, Janet Dowler, 9879
Martin, Jeffrey S., 1047
Martin, Jerria, 12
Martin, JoAnn M., 5067
Martin, John C., Jr., 7281
Martin, John G., 1520
Martin, Julie, 803
Martin, K., 5222
Martin, Kevin, 3466
Martin, Kristen H., III, 6922
Martin, Laurel G., 8143
Martin, Lee P., Jr., 9487
Martin, Linda, 3126
Martin, Linda M., 8685
Martin, Lockheed, 2621
Martin, Lynda J., 1047
Martin, Meghan, 803
Martin, Michael, 7866
Martin, Nancy, 9070
Martin, Noreen, 803
Martin, Pamela I., 8316
Martin, Patrick J., 2197
Martin, Raymond S., III, 8685
Martin, Richard, 4088
Martin, Richard L., 1047
Martin, Roberta, 7866
Martin, Roy W., 9659
Martin, Shari, 2463
Martin, Sharon B., 8142
Martin, Stephen G., 800
Martin, Susan B., 326
Martin, Susette M., 4997
Martin, Sydney F., 8142
Martin, Terry, 7591
Martin, Thomas, 4362
Martin, Tom, 803
Martin, Vincent L., 9879
Martin, Walter O., Jr., 2641
Martin, Wanda Walker, 9040
Martin, Watters O., Jr., 2641
Martin, Wayne, 5872
Martin, Wendy B., 4870
Martin, William, 7497
Martin, William G., 7339
Martin, William J., 1781, 7194, 8327
Martin, William, Mrs. , 7497
Martin, Zachary S., 8143
Martinez, Gary M., 3719
Martinez, Leslie H., 3719
Martinez, Michael L., 1799
Martini, John, 188

Martini, Samuel, 6447
Martino, Elizabeth, 268
Martino, Eva Amuri, 1004
Martino, Phyllis, 8326
Martinsen, Patricia M., 1521
Martinsen, Robert H., 1521
Martinson, Wayne, 9359
Martinson-Sawyer, Kimber, 9359
Martischang, Alphonse, 1321
Martocci, John J., 1532
Marton, Margy, 138
Martone, Craig, 5369
Maruk, Jon, 4651
Marusarz, Phil, 3260
Marwill 1996 CRT #2, Nancy Morre, The , 8701
Marx, Michael, 3506
Maryland Investments, 159
Maryland, LLC, 159
Maryott, Brian, 415
Mascaro, James, 5152
Mascaro, Pasquale, 8145
Mascerrella, Raymond M., II, 2118
Maschler, Erik, 5462
Maschler, Matthew, 5462
Maschler, Sheldon, 5462
Mascoma Savings Bank, 5223
Masel, Brent, Dr. , 9205
Mashhoon, Hamid R., 804
Mashhoon, Mahasti, 804
Mashni, 7333
Masin, Michael T., 6949
Maslick, Joseph R., Jr., 2929, 2930
Maslin 2000 Charitable Lead Trust, Lucille, 6448
Maslow, Allison, 8146
Maslow, Douglas, 8146
Maslow, Jennifer Holtzman, 8146
Maslow, Richard, 8146
Mason Companies, 9880
Mason Shoe Manufacturing Co., 9880
Mason, Beth, 1892, 3466
Mason, Bonnie Simpson, 3144
Mason, Brad L., 7422
Mason, Bruce E., 3029
Mason, Danna B., 805
Mason, David E., 3029
Mason, David M., 2919
Mason, Diane, 5580
Mason, Emily, 9377
Mason, Erik, 5628
Mason, James B., 9544
Mason, Jane H., 9311
Mason, Margaret K., 3029
Mason, Marilyn, 5590
Mason, Meredith S., 9176
Mason, Otis, 2341
Mason, Richard J., 805
Mason, Rick, 9989
Mason, Robert, 3024
Mason, Sarah C., 3029
Mason, Stephen, 6308
Masood, Aslam, 1986
Masood, Faheem A., 5969
Masood, Mona, 1986
Masood, Sohail, 1986
Masotti, Laura A., 1478
Masotti, Robert P., 1478
Massa, William, 7379
Massachusetts IOTA TAU, 3993
Massamillo, Eugene, 6892
Massengill Co., S.E., The , 8647
Masser, Frances, 3676
Massey Investment, 7705

Massey, Brenda R., 7776
Massey, Catherine Andrea, 2823
Massey, Christopher, 2823
Massey, Gregory L., 7705
Massey, John L., 7705
Massey, John Michael, 7705
Massey, Richard J., 3082
Massey, Richard S., 2823
Massey, Robert M., 4116
Massey, Ron, 5234
Massie, Clara K., 806
Massie, Debbie, 806
Massie, Perry, 146
Massie, Rick, 806
Massie, Rick W., 806
Massie, Sandy, 146
Massing, Michael, 1826
Massman, Michael, 3548
Masson, Maurice, 807
Masson, Melena, 807
Masson, Melinda, 807
Masson, Pierre, 807
Massoni, Carol, 4266
Massoud, Elizabeth Allman, 1704
Massoud, Ihab Joseph, 1704
Massoud, Joseph, 2475
Massry, Sam, 6199
Mast, John, 8743
Mastercard, 3639
Masterplan, Inc., 3905
Masterson, Cynthia, 9660
Masterson, John, 9995
Maston, Bill, 1316
Mastrinanni, Beverley, 2201
Mastrocola, David J., 6449
Mastrogiorgio, Maryellen, 6094
Mastropieri, Robert W., 3905
Matalon, Eli, 1931
Matalon, Michael, 1931
Matalon, Morris, 1931
Matalon, Morris D., 1931
Matalon, Samuel, 1931
Matalon, Sharon, 1931
Matanky, Robert W., 3143
Matau, Karri, 9592
Matchett, Terri E., 3469
Mateer, Donald D., 8150
Mateo, Gregory W., 1142
Mateo, Kenneth P., 1142
Mateo, Laura D., 1142
Mateo, Wesley D., 1142
Mater Trust, The, 6157
Mathena, Lauren, 9556
Mathenaeum Foundation, 1717
Mather, Elizabeth, 7380
Mather, Henry T., 4458
Mather, S. Livingston, 7516
Mathers, Elizabeth A., 2818
Mathers, Libby, 2818
Matheson, B. Michael, 9729
Matheson, Barbara, 9729
Matheson, Marjorie A., 5673
Matheson, Richard, 9729
Mathews Foundation, 4953
Mathews Trust, Devin, 243
Mathews Trust, Elaine, 243
Mathews, Cecelia, 39
Mathews, Elaine, 243
Mathews, Harry B., 4953
Mathews, Peggy, 8864
Mathey, Dean W., 6018
Mathiasen, Jerry, 3527
Mathies, Allen W., Jr., 801

Mathieu, Calvin, 9969
Mathieu, Calvin N., 9969
Mathis, Allen W., III, 21
Mathis, Allen W., Jr., 21
Mathis, Carol P., 1549
Mathis, Janice, 2437
Mathisen, Carole, 5148
Matoesian, Audrey L., 594
Matoff Admin Trust, Rebecca, The , 354
Matos, Maria, 8350
Matousek, Mary Therese, 7560
Matsoff, Alan, 9842
Matson, Alan, 6720
Matsukane, Melvin T., 805
Matsuo, Masayuki, 271
Matt, Nicholas O., 6922
Mattei, J. Scott, 7173
Mattern, Megan, 4999
Mattern, Steve, 4745
Mattesky, Katherine V., 3726
Mattessich, Michelle, 5582
Matthew, Amy, 509
Matthews Charitable Remainder
    Unitrust, Charles, 9041
Matthews, Alan, 39
Matthews, Ann C., 1165
Matthews, B. Frank, II, 7097
Matthews, Charles, 9041
Matthews, Elizabeth E., 1725
Matthews, Gail, 274
Matthews, George G., 1725
Matthews, George G., Jr., 1725
Matthews, John, 349
Matthews, Lori, 7839
Matthews, LP, Charles, 9041
Matthews, McKay S., 9304
Matthews, Robert E., 2520
Matthews, Robert S., 5406
Matthews, Ron, 7174
Matthews, Sharon, 7174
Matthews, Sherri, 8732
Matthews, William, 1725
Matthews, Yvonne Alexander, 3922
Matthewson, Chuck, 301
Mattingly, Joseph, 8738
Mattson, Maryanne, 3801
Mattsson, Christine, 9042
Matukewicz, Michael J., 5109
Matz, Israel, 6107
Matz, Jennifer Entine, 8622
Matzke, Wayne E., 9832
Mau, Gordon J., 2657
Mauch Chunk Trust Co., 8180
Mauck, Melody, 238
Maue, Richard A., 5306
Mauer, Daniel C., 4740
Mauer, Lisa M., 4740
Mauer, Marshall Gloria, 5665
Mauer, Patrick A., 925
Mauk, Anne S., 6331
Mauna Kea Villages, LLC, 2072
Maune, Christina, 825
Maune, John J., 5032
Maunz, Bettina, 5244
Maupin, Emily, 929
Maupin, Ernie, 5176
Maupin, William S., 8774
Mauran, Esther E.M., 8479
Mauran, Frank, 8406
Maurer, Ann, 6453
Maurer, Ann E., 6453
Maurer, Carol, 9366
Maurer, Christopher C., 6453
Maurer, David W., 6453

Maurer, Gilbert C., 6453
Maurer, Greg, 3415
Maurer, Janie, 3415
Maurer, Jonathan G., 6453
Maurer, Linda, 3415
Maurer, Michael S., 3415
Maurer, Peter J., 6453
Maurer, Todd J., 3415
Maurice, Mark A., 4508
Maurices, 5252
Maurray Hill Properties, 6655
Maust, Galen D., 3423
Mauthe, Fr. Richard, 9951
Mauze, Jean, 8450
Mavrogenis, Marion, 4192
Mawe, Lynn, 3501
Mawhinney, Diana J., 9479
Mawr Trust Co., Bryn, 7977
Max, Ricky L., 3113
Maxey, David, Mrs., 7990
Maxfield, Katherine, 808
Maxfield, Melinda C., 808
Maxfield, Robert, 105
Maxfield, Robert R., 808
Maxwell, Anita K., 2390
Maxwell, David O., 1817
Maxwell, Frank, 9810
Maxwell, Jack M., III, 7990
Maxwell, Jeffrey D., 264
Maxwell, Joan P., 1817
Maxwell, John, 7623
Maxwell, Laird, 2686
Maxwell, Lawrence W., 2390
Maxwell, Michele LeBien, 5850
Maxwell, Patrick, 5159
Maxwell, Virginia, 5211
May Co., William B., 6656
May Foundation, Wilbur, 1176
May, Alice Chapin, 2782
May, Angel, 8657
May, Anna L., 7794
May, Barbara V., 2384
May, Carolyn B., 3803
May, David, 58
May, Drew, 4497
May, Robert A., 9543
May, Tom, 4960
Maybank, David H., 8538
Mayberg, Louis, 2199
Mayberg, Manette, 2199
Mayer, Bob, 4396
Mayer, Christine E., 9885
Mayer, David, 809
Mayer, Eugene, 7357
Mayer, Eva H., 9043
Mayer, Kathryn R., 3203
Mayer, Mary Ellen, 5459
Mayer, Michael, 809
Mayer, Olivia, 809
Mayer, Sally, 809
Mayer, Stephen, 809
Mayer, Weiss, 5443
Mayes, Pamela E., 5413
Mayfield, Jack H., Jr., 9044
Mayfield, Nelda, 8764
Mayfield, Robbie, 9631
Mayfield, Treeta, 9631
Mayher, John W., Jr., 2517
Mayhew Steel Products, 4088
Mayhew, Karin D., 608
Maynard, Christy, 369
Maynard, David L., 7058
Maynard, Easter A., 7075
Maynard, James H., 7075

Mayne, Larry R., 1180
Mays Trust, W.A. Mays and Agnes, 9045
Mays, J.W., 6956
Mays, L. Lowry, 8772
Mays, Mark P., 8772
Mays, Randall T., 8772
Maysteel, LLC, 9931
Mayteles, Sara, 5661
Mayville, Sarah Shaner, 8271
Maywood Trust Company, LLC, 9351
Mazda Motor of America, 810
Mazda North American Opers., 810
Mazda Research & Development of
    North America, 810
Maze, Aubrey, 178
Mazenko, Francis, 2705
Mazer, Magdalena, 4089
Mazer, Robert, 4089
Mazur, Jay, 5630
Mazza, Caroline, 8186
Mazza, Donald J., 7411
Mazzarelli, Ester, 7192
Mazzetta Company, LLC, 3083, 8859
Mazzetta, Cynthia L., 3083
Mazzetta, Jordan J., 3083
Mazzetta, Thomas J., 3083
Mazzetta, Zachary D., 3083
MB 2006 Lead Trust, 6425
MB Kids Clothes LLC, 5456
MBNA Foundation, 1781
MBNA Mastercard, 7209
Mboya, Susan, 2622
Mc-Hale, Sir. M. Martin de Porres, 7879
McAdam, Jeanine, 4081
McAdams, Scott, 5626
McAdaragh, Pat, 4745
McAfee, Emily Jean H., 2548
McAfoos, Kerri Bieber, 4641
McAlister, Elizabeth, 8662
McAllister, Dana Leigh, 9046
McAllister, Holly, 6888
McAllister, Hugh A., Jr., 9046
McAllister, Martha Nicholson, 866
McAllister, William B., 8345
McAlpin Charitable Lead Trust, Joan R.,
    5809
McAlpin, David H., Jr., 5809
McAlpin, Loring, 5809, 6075
McAlpin, Loring R., 5809
McAlpine, Michael D., 3528
McAndrew, Mark, 9240
McAuliffe, E. Timothy, 7013
McAvoy Trust, Agnes K., 2749
McAvoy, Laura K., 761
McBee, Christopher, 1316
McBrayer, Keith, 7100
McBride, Angela M., 4375
McBride, Anne V., 1898
McBride, Charlie, 8753
McBride, Gary, 825
McBride, Renee, 825
McBurnett, Keith, 8937
McBurney, James, 9386
McBurney, James, Mrs. , 9386
McBurnie, Richard G., 1175
McCabe Charitable Lead Unitrust,
    William and Katherine, 700
McCabe, Ann, 4676
McCabe, Ann L., 4676
McCabe, David J., 1452
McCabe, Eleonora W., 2201
McCabe, Katherine, 700
McCabe, Lindsay, 4676
McCabe, Lindsay E., 4676

McCabe, Nancy, 3084
McCabe, Nancy Kendall, 700
McCabe, Philip R., 4327
McCabe, Robert F., 2201
McCabe, Roger, 3084
McCabe, William, 700
McCaffrey, Marian, 1450
McCain Foods, 2510
McCall, Matthew, 1057
McCallum, James, 2666
McCallum, Jean A., 260
McCann, Robert, 4063
McCannel, Dana D., 4805
McCannel, Louise W., 4805
McCardle, Burnice E., Jr., 4844
McCarl, Steven, 5624
McCarrey, J.L., III, 85
McCarter, C. Ted, 9119
McCarter, Tammy, 221
McCarthy Bush Corp., 3519
McCarthy Improvement Co., 3519
McCarthy, Denis, 4449
McCarthy, Jessica A., 7520
McCarthy, John J., 8452
McCarthy, John M., 6456
McCarthy, John W., 9503
McCarthy, Kathleen M., 4176
McCarthy, Kevin, 784
McCarthy, Laurette E., 6456
McCarthy, Mary A., 6456
McCarthy, Michael J., 7520
McCarthy, Mike, 461
McCarthy, Neil M., 6456
McCarthy, Paul, 3078
McCarthy, Priscilla, 5692
McCarthy, Robert, 3527
McCarthy, Stephen J., 6456
McCarthy, Suzanne Sklar, 9199
McCarthy, Tara A., 6456
McCartney, Brian, 1324
McCartney, James, 7466
McCartt, Martha J., 8967
McCarty Enterprises, LLC, 4848
McCarty, Cameron, 6633
McCarty, Greta Robb, 9047
McCarty, H.F., Jr., 4848
McCarty, Harrison Russel, 4841
McCarty, John R., 4848
McCarty, Judy, 3634
McCarty, Marshall, 6633
McCarty, Mary Ann, 4848
McCarty, Michael A., 4848
McCarty, Ned, 1624
McCarty, Sara, 4949
McCarty, Shellye S., 4848
McCarty, W.B., III, 4841
McCarver, James O., 2026
McCarver, Patsy E., 2026
McCaslin, Elizabeth K., 9643
McCaslin, Lynn, 7891
McCaul, Elizabeth, 6244
McCauley, Michael, 7707
McCauley, Richard, 2296
McCausland, Tim, 5872
McCellon-Allen, Venita, 7303
McClain, Carol F., 2565
McClain, Michael, 7330
McClain, Randolph S., 2565
McClain, Randy, 2565
McClain, Susie, 3442
McClanathan, Joseph W., 2202
McClanathan, Laura D., 2202
McClanathan, Robin, 2202
McClanathan, Susan A., 2202

McClary, Andrew F., 1238
McClatchey, Devereaux F., 2546
McClatchey, Dorothy M., 2546
McClatchy Co., The, 811
McClayton, Maureen, 3286
McClear, Chris R., 3139
McClear, Johanna N., 3139
McClear, Kevin R., 3139
McClear, Richard J., 3139
McCleery, William, Jr., 2803
McClellan, Ann, 5393
McClellan, Rowland J., 9850
McClelland, Catherine, 3884
McClelland, Catherine H., 3884
McClelland, George, 3884
McClelland, George R., 3884
McClelland, James F., 4505
McClelland, Pamela K., 4505
McClelland, Pamela T., 4505
McClerg, James E., 5068
McCleskey, Edwin, 577
McClimon, Timothy J., 5664
McClintic, William, 1831
McClinton, Dale, 3799
McCloud, Alexandra, 8086
McClung, Barbara, 795
McClure, Anne C., 3355
McClure, Archibald, 3355
McClure, Paula, 8008
McClure, William L., 835
McCluskey, Dennis, 7358
McCluskey, John M., 4258
McColl, Robert, 1816
McColl, Suzanne, 1816
McColloch, Deborah, 8065
McCollough, Pat, 4514
McCollum, Courtney H., 3792
McCollum, Yancey L., 2538
McConaughey, Camila, 684
McConaughey, Matthew, 684
McConkey, Kally, 3592
McConkie, Sara, 9310
McConnaughey and Young, LLC, 1284
McConnell Foundation, John, The , 7209
McConnell, Beverly Anne, 7903
McConnell, Cheryl J., 8048
McConnell, John, 7176, 7209
McConnell, M. Susan, 825
McConnell, Marion, 3777
McConnell, Nancy, 1836
McConnell, Nicholas C., 1836
McConnell, Phil, 9592
McConnell, Polly, 5463
McConnell, Rebecca A., 8936
McConnnell, John, 7209
McCooey, Mary C., 6457
McCooey, Michael P., 6457
McCord, Margot R., 5425
McCorkle, Roger, 7829
McCormack Charitable Lead Trust, 3086
McCormack, Bonnie, 1155
McCormack, Kathleen M., 6224
McCormack, Tommie Ann Fridy, 1740
McCormick Family Foundation, 6460
McCormick, Anne, 6460
McCormick, Cayce W., 9272
McCormick, Genine, 6459
McCormick, Genine R., 6459
McCormick, Joseph "Dusty", 9069
McCormick, Judith, 9757
McCormick, Michael, 6459
McCormick, Michael P., 6459
McCormick, Robert W., 9758
McCormick-Goodhart, Leander, 9386

McCourtney, Flora, 3087
McCourtney, Plato, 3087
McCown, Jean K., 900
McCown, Sylvia, 4521
McCoy, Ana Carmina, 7214
McCoy, Carolyn, 7541
McCoy, Dena Woodard, 7831
McCoy, Michael, 9810
McCracken, Kate, 2862
McCrane, John A., 5464
McCrane, Margit, 5464
McCrea, Mary Corling, 3088
McCree, Heidi B., 2067
McCreless, Lilla M., 9049
McCreless, Sollie E., 9049
McCrink, James E., 5153
McCrory, Jenks E., 8608
McCuiston, Stonewall, Dr. , 2802
McCulley, Paul A., 5989
McCulloch, Jonathon, 3218
McCullough, Elizabeth Lowman, 6997
McCullough, Jeremy, 9696
McCullough, Lee, 9321
McCullough, P. Mike, 8712
McCullough, Patrick, 9927
McCullough, Victoria, 1429
McCullough, Victoria Davis, 1429
McCune Foundation, 5611
McCune, Anne E., 6933
McCune, Mary W., 3089
McCune, Mike, 9066
McCurdy, Bob, 6844
McCurdy, Laura, 5465
McCutchen, Charles, 8008
McCutchen, Matthew, 9583
McCutcheon, Hilary H., 1333
McCutchin, John A., 4193
McDade, Herbert H., III, 6461
McDaneld, David, 3580
McDaniel Administrative Trust, Neil, 812
McDaniel Family Trust, 813
McDaniel, David, 3350
McDaniel, Douglas Pulliam, 3958
McDaniel, Lola, 9050
McDaniel, Neil, 812
McDaniel, Thomas R., 813
McDaniels, Duval Meade, 8716
McDavid, Bradford A., 9760
McDavid, Sandra, 9760
McDavid, William R., 9760
McDede, David P., 979
McDermott, C. David, 1359
McDermott, John, III, 6945
McDermott, Lucinda, 323
McDermott, Mildred Wetten Kelly, 3012
McDevitt, Nancy, 5517
McDevitt, William G., III, 1898
McDole Charitable Remainder Trust,
   June, 4507
McDole Trust, June, 4506
McDole, June, 4507
McDonagh, Eileen L., 4065
McDonald Industries, A.Y., 3520
McDonald Investments, 7354
McDonald, A. Jefferson, Jr., 65
McDonald, Albert, 3068
McDonald, Alonzo L., 4508
McDonald, Alonzo L., Jr., 4508
McDonald, April Shannon, 2328
McDonald, Charles R., 4548
McDonald, David G., 3158
McDonald, Dean, 2676
McDonald, Debbie, 2685
McDonald, Douglas B., 5190

McDonald, Ellice, Jr., 1669
McDonald, Evelyn M., 3313
McDonald, G. Patrick, 3991
McDonald, George, 9233
McDonald, Gregory C., 5065
McDonald, Helen, 3068
McDonald, Hilary, 6360
McDonald, Hollie, 7953
McDonald, J. M., III, 3520
McDonald, James F., 9051
McDonald, Jane, 4642
McDonald, Janet Strain, 68
McDonald, Jennifer C., 65
McDonald, Jim, 7311
McDonald, John, 3134, 5091
McDonald, John L., 65
McDonald, Kari Anne, 7787
McDonald, Kevin, 1321, 3068
McDonald, Kristen, 3068
McDonald, Lauren, 3068
McDonald, Lee, 3068
McDonald, Lynn, 1321
McDonald, Mackey, 7209
McDonald, Malcolm S., 2203
McDonald, Malcolm W., 4702
McDonald, Paula S., 9051
McDonald, Peter, 4508
McDonald, R. D., II, 3520
McDonald, Robert, 8684
McDonald, Rosa H., 1669
McDonald, Sam E., Jr., 5065
McDonald, Sheila, 4449
McDonald, Sonia R., 2203
McDonald, Steven, 4671
McDonald, Suzanne M., 4508
McDonnell, Archie, Jr., 4822
McDonnell, Maura, 4212
McDonnell, William Randall, 4992
McDonough, Jacqueline A., 3090
McDonough, James J., 3090
Mcdonough, James P., 3090
McDonough, Kathleen A., 6624
McDonough, Kimberly, 4938
McDonough, Mary A., 8165
McDonough, Michael J., 9386
McDonough, Paul H., 4231
McDonough, Sean J., 6812
McDougal, Alfred L., 3091
McDowell, Angela, 2706
McDowell, Electra V., 5465
McDowell, Fletcher H., 5465
McDowell, Jennifer, 9995
McDowell, John, Dr. , 3662
McDowell, Patricia M., 408
McDowell, Scott, 408
McDowell, Walter, 7209
McElhinny, C.A., 8185
McEllistrem, Michael, 4648
McElroy, Betty, 9331
McElroy, Gregory E., 7924
McElroy, John, 6178
McElroy, Tem, 3750
McElvaine, Ranae S., 1743
McElveen-Hunter, Bonnie, 7209
McElwain, William, 7551
McEnany, Anne, 9632
McEnroe, Erika Varga, 1100
McEnroe, John, 6463
McEnroe, John P., 6463
McEnroe, Mark T., 6463
McFadden, Robert, 6998
McFadden, Stova F., 28
McFarland, Catherine, 2319
McFarland, John, 188

McFarland, Mike, 402
McFarland, Sheila, 3771
McFarland, Teresa, 7118
McFarland, Tom, 461
McFarlin, George, 1023
McFarlin, Sarah, 1023
McFarlin, Tim, 1023
McFarlin, Tina, 1023
McFate, Robert W., 7858
McFetridge, Hallie Q., 2273
McGahren, Marjorie, 2204
McGahren, Richard, 2204
McGannon, Kathleen, 1434
McGarrah, Bill, 367
McGarrity, Michelle, 3776
McGarry, Nellie, 420
McGaughey, Linda Page, 899
McGee, Brooks, 9150
McGee, Darlene L., 4669
McGee, Dawn, 5057
McGee, Joan W., 3546
McGee, Marcella, 7807
McGee, Vincent, 3656, 5708
McGehee, Andrew P., 8648
McGehee, James E., III, 8648
McGehee, James E., Jr., 8648
McGehee, Stuart C., 8648
McGeorge Contracting Co., 218
McGeorge, Harvey W., 218
McGeorge, Scott, 218
McGeorge, Wallace P., III, 218
McGhee, Michelle, 7276
McGill, Shawn, 8326
McGillen, Edward J., 2775
McGimsey, Jane, 5846
McGinley, John C., 8156
McGinley, John R., Jr., 8156
McGinley, Rita M., 8156
McGinnes, Cynthia R., 2416
McGinness, Macy H. Allatt, 6908
McGinnis, Bonnie, 3403
McGinnis, Craig, 3403
McGinnis, Kermit E., 9754
McGinty, Ann Skiles, 4572
McGinty, Richard, 7785
McGlade, John E., 8238
McGladrey LLP, 2348
McGlenn, Michael, 4979
McGlensey, Marlene, 923
McGlothlin, Nancy D., 7084
McGoffin, Mary J., 9696
McGovern, Kevin J., 9532
McGowan, Gertude, 7879
McGowan, Jeannine L., 7801
McGrane, Sara G., 4681
McGrath, Barbara L., 1322
McGrath, Bonnie, 4671
McGrath, Bruce K., 1322
McGrath, Dorn, 2297
McGrath, J., 383, 894
McGrath, John J., 7442
McGrath, L., 7541
McGrath, Pat, 3134
McGrath, Patrick, 7624
McGrath, R., 383, 894
McGrath, Robert P., 383, 894
McGrath, Thomas F., III, 761
McGrath, Tracey F., 1322
McGraw Co., The, 814
McGraw Foundation, 3092
McGraw, Christy Hamilton, 1285
McGraw, Jack, 814
McGraw, Joan D., 814
McGraw, John M., 814

McGraw, John V., Jr., 814
McGraw, Joshua D., 4516
McGraw, Michael A., 4516
McGraw, Michael J., 814
McGraw, Michael R., 4516
McGreevy, Annie James, 1838
McGreevy, Milton, 1838
McGreevy, Pam, 1838
McGregor, Constance Bates, 2725
McGregor, Cynthia, 121
McGregor, John S., 9794
McGrew, Laura Adler, 3809
McGrew, Margery, 3107
McGrew, Roger, 9757
McGuigan, E. Gayle, Jr., 6572
McGuigan, James, 8186
McGuigan, Phillip P., 6572
McGuinness, J. Luke, 2865
McGuire, C. Kent, 8350
McGuire, Caroline R., 7177
McGuire, Mary Jo, 3149
McGuire, Molly L., 7177
McGuire, Patricia, 3807
McGuire, Ruth H., 9868
McGuire, Susanne H., 7177
McGuire, William B., Jr., 7177
McGuire, William H., 7177
McGurk, Thomas A., Jr., 3466
McHale Memorial Irrevocable Trust, 8157
McHale, John, 9042
McHale, Marcie, 3831
McHenry, Hugh, 8608
McHenry, William B., 5662
McHolme, Rebecca Shaw, 7945
McHugh, Paul, 7560
McIlquham, Lynne Caruso, 2771, 2886
McIlvaine, Breese, 9494
Mcilwain, Michael, 8949
McIninch, Douglas, 5224
McIninch, Douglas A., 5214
McIninch, Nancy M., 5224
McIninch, Ralph A., 5224
McIntire, Lorraine, 630
McIntosh, Carolyn, 1705
McIntosh, Ken, 3427
McIntosh, Rebekah, 9011
McIntosh, Robert E., 4900
McIntosh, Scott, 1705
McIntosh, Winsome, 8637
McIntyre, Christina W., 4360
McIver, Frances, 7276
McKamish Inc., 8158
McKamish, David, 8158
McKamish, Dennis R., 8158
McKamish, Kevin, 8158
McKamish, Maria, 8158
McKamish, Melissa, 8158
McKay, Carol, 6245
McKay, Chuck, 3359
McKay, Elaine, 815
McKay, Eleanor P., 7795
McKay, John P., 815
McKay, Lawrence I., III, 4471
McKay, Miles E., 7795
McKay, Neil, 2717
McKay, Olive B., 2717
McKay, Robert, 815
McKay, Robert L., Sr., 815
McKay, Shawn, 3501
McKay, William M., 8154
McKean, Nancy, 9125
McKee Foods Corp., 175

McKee Foundation, James W. & Jayne A., 2988
McKee, C. Steven, 9052
Mckee, Dorothy, 7698
McKee, Evelyn, 9052
McKee, F. James, 9052
McKee, Gregory A., 3093
McKee, Howard A., 3093
McKee, James T., 9052
McKee, Jay, 5799
McKee, John, 4824, 8160
McKee, Louis B., 9052
McKee, Lydia, 6248
McKee, Mary Ellen, 148
McKee, Meredith B., 3093
McKee, Philip Russell, 9052
McKee, R. Brian, 9052
McKee, Robert E., 9052
McKee, Robert E., IV, 9052
McKee, Robert H., 148
McKee, Susan J., 9052
McKee, Theodore A., Hon. , 8160
McKee, William A., 3093
McKellar, Archie C., 6896
McKellar, Marie T., 6896
McKelvey, Edward, 9867
McKelvin, Leodis, 4399
McKenna, Andrew J., 3322
McKenna, Erin A. O'Sullivan, 6565
McKenna, James, 6565, 6919
McKenna, Marion, 2457
McKenna, Marty, 2858
McKenna, Molly C., 3322
McKenna, William J., 3322
McKenney, Bruce J., 7868
McKenney, David M., 2597
McKennon, Keith, 180
McKenny Charitable Lead Trust, Charles A., 7510
McKenny Charitable Lead Trust, Mary L., 7510
McKenny, Anne E., 7510
McKenny, Arthur E., 7510
McKenny, Charles A., 7510
McKenny, Mary L., 7510
McKenry, James R., Jr., 8600
McKenry-Nash, Margaret, 8600
McKenzie, Barbara, 4459
McKenzie, Bonnie, 1248
McKenzie, Brenda, 8588
McKenzie, David Ryan, 1248
McKenzie, Floretta Dukes, 3880
McKenzie, Jennifer Mick, 8651
McKenzie, Leslie Ann Bogle, 191
McKenzie, Nancy, 9439
McKenzie, Steve, 8588
McKeown, Daniel W., 4646
McKeown, Desmond, 4646
McKeown, Heidi, 4646
McKeown, Isabella, 4646
McKernan, William L., 7977
McKiernan, William S., 1706
McKillip, Robert, 1549
McKim, Karen P., 7363
McKinlay, Scott D., 3455
McKinley Capital Management LLC, 85
McKinley, Edward J., 940
McKinley, Jeff, 3058
McKinley, Tyson, 4396
McKinney, Betsy Hall, 494
McKinney, Catherine A., 8161
McKinney, David, 7732
McKinney, John, 494, 4951
McKinney, Kent, 3416

McKinney, Kevin K., 3416
McKinney, Lisa C., 3416
McKinney, Marni, 3416
McKinney, Robert C., 3416
McKinney, Robert H., 3416
McKinney, Robert N., 3416
McKinnon, Noah C., Jr., 2001
McKissock, David L., 2247
McKittrick, Richard A., 3773, 3790
McKnight, H. James, 7851
McKnight, H. Turney, 3910
McKnight, Loretta Haley, 2548
McKnight, Sumner T., 3910
McKnight, Timothy B., 9009
McKrill, Mike, 88
McLamb, Catherine Canaday, 7066
McLamore, Leslie, 2901
McLane Securities, 5369
McLane Unitrust, K.K., 1522
McLane, David H., 6616
McLane, Henry, 1522
McLane, Henry R., III, 1522
McLane, John P., 6032
McLaren, James, 6010
McLaren, James I., 6010, 9386
McLaughlin Body Company, 3095
McLaughlin, Alan, 3439
McLaughlin, Brian T., 8813
McLaughlin, C.T., 8813
McLaughlin, Genevieve M., 1523
McLaughlin, James P., 1523
McLaughlin, Jean M., 1523
McLaughlin, John Mark, 8813
McLaughlin, John W., 2205
McLaughlin, Justin, 2897
McLaughlin, Matthew T., 6821
McLaughlin, Paul B., 1523
McLaughlin, Peter J., 3095
McLaughlin, Raymond L., 3095
McLaurin, Eric, 1856
McLawhorn, Hunter Johnston, 7171
McLawhorn, James H., 7171
McLean, Isabelle G., 7178
McLean, Jennifer S., 4280
McLean, John L., 7178
McLean, John P., 7178
McLean, Melvin F., 817
McLean, Michael H., 1082
McLeitch, Larry, 484
McLelland, Laura, 8162
McLelland, Michael B., 8162
McLelland, Nancy, 8162
McLendon, Barbara, 6739
McLennan, Douglas A., 3096
McLennan, Rebecca A., 3096
McLennan, Robert G., 3096
McLennan, Robert M., 3096
McLeod, Alice, 4222
McLeod, Carrie L. Bumgarner, 4649
McLeod, Christopher, 6015
McLeod, Christopher K., 1524
McLeod, Elaine M., 1524
McLeod, Kelly S., 818
McLeod, Murrell, 9546
McLeod, Scott, 1524
McLeod, Steve, 818
McLeod, Steven B., 818
McLeod, William J., 8897
McLoraine, Helen M., 1291
McLoughlin, Ben, 9838
McLoughlin, Mary Jo, 6579
McLoughlin, Nancy, 9838
McLoughlin, Pat, 9838
McMacken, Dave, 4459

McMackin, Ellen, 1814
McMahen, Charles, 8829
McMahon, Jacklyn K., 2161
McMahon, Joanne, 819
McMahon, John, 819
McMahon, John A., 819
McMahon, Mary, 4565
McMahon, Pat, 3514
McMannis, Haskell, 8163
McManus, Michael F., 4509
McManus, Patrick J., 6652
McManus, Sheila C., 4039
McMaster, Alan J., 7521
McMaster, Harold A., 7521
McMaster, Helen E., 7521
McMaster, Ronald A., 7521
McMeel, John P., 4860
McMeel, Maureen A., 4860
McMeel, Susan S., 4860
McMerty, Brian J., 7180
McMerty, Sarah Lyell Bellamy, 7180
McMillan, Barbara, 5211
McMillan, George, 12
McMillan, George M., Jr., 8633
McMillan, Gioconda, 4592
McMillan, Jan Late, 9007
McMillan, Kathleen M., 2373
McMillan, Mary Moore, 9054
McMillan, Peter, 5211
McMillan, Richard T., 9007
McMillan, Thomas G., 9751
McMillan, V. Bruce, 9054
McMillian, Priscilla, 5700
McMillian, Thomas G., 9751
McMillin, John, 6360
McMinn, Jan, 8781
McMullen, Justin, 7356
McMullin, John, 5621
McMunigal, Philip A., Mrs., 7990
McMurray, Carson Reid, 9980
McMurray, John Thomas, 9980
McMurray, McCain Jay, 9980
McMurray, Tom, 9980
Mcn Righter, Brewster, 2388
McNab, Alan C., 3778
McNab, Cathy, 9315
McNabb, Charity R. Appell, 3778
Mcnabb, Charlene, 2580
McNabola, Gwyneth B., 5289
McNair, Alfred, 4824
McNair, Nimrod, 9468
McNairy, John O., 7119
McNairy, Leigh H., 7119
McNally III Trust, A., 3097
McNally, Andrew, IV, 3097
McNally, Brian, 2417, 4510
McNally, Danny D., 7283, 7284
McNally, Dwight, 4510
McNally, Jeanine S., 3097
McNally, Jeff, 4510
McNally, Jeffrey W., 4377
McNally, Sean, 585
McNally, William F., 4510
McNamara, Christine, 2207
McNamara, Elizabeth, 2207
McNamara, Emily, 4743
McNamara, James, 6442
McNamara, James M., 2207
McNamara, Kathy, 403
McNamara, Kevin J., 7350
McNamara, Lana, 2207
McNamara, Lisa T., 4055
McNamara, Nicholas, 4198
McNamara, Pat, 403

McNamara, Peggy, 966
McNamara, Richard F., 4743
McNamara, Robert J., 4743
McNamara, Tom, 403
McNamee, George C., 9386
McNamee, Michael W., 58
McNamme, Norman L., 6669
McNary, Julie Anne, 4239
McNay, Colin, 1838
McNeely, Jason, 5106
McNeice, John, 4195
McNeice, John A., Jr., 4195
McNeil Pharmaceuticals, 2406
McNeil, John, 8791
McNeil, Sandi, 5395
McNeil, William B., 7395
McNeil-Rogers, Sandra, 5395
McNeill, George Reed, 3098
McNeill, William, 3662
McNeilus, Denzil, 4694
McNeilus, Garwin, 4694
McNeilus, Marilee, 4694
McNevin, A.C. Barnes, III, 6168
McNew, Stephen, 4411
McNicholas, Dennis, 1988
McNicholas, Dennis T., 1988
McNicholas, Lisa, 1988
McNicholas, Lisa M., 1988
McNinch, David Leon, 9211
McNinch, Jackie, 4057
McNish, Mary Ellen, 8275
McNulty, Anne Welsh, 6465
McNulty, James, 3099
McNulty, James J., 3099
McNulty, Kyle J., 3099
McNulty, Lucas H., 3099
McNutt, Patricia, 8806
McOmber, Michelle S., 9361
McPeek, Daniel J., 7301
McPherson, J. Mark, 1323
McPherson, Jeanne, 9712
McPherson, Kim L., 1323
McPhillips, Paul R., 6082
McQuade, Roberta, 2986
McQuillan, William P., 4020
McQuirk, Rt. Rev. John, 6455
McQuistion, Ethel K., 2208
MCR Foundation, 686
McRedmond, Eugene, 1435
McReynolds, Laura, 2803
McReynolds, Scott, 3655
McSherry, Constance, 7868
McShine, Kynaston, 6075
McSpadden, Steve, 8784
McSparran, Melody A., 7675
McSween Enterprises Inc., 153
McSweeney, Nancy K., 2161
McSweeny, Nancy K., 2161
McTernan, J. Michael, 9862
McTiernan, Megan, 1113
McVaney Family Foundation, 1352
McVay, Cathy, 12
McVay, Mark, 8900
McWaters Family L.P., 9499
McWaters, Cynthia L., 9499
McWaters, Hunter, 9499
McWaters, Jeffery L., 9499
McWethy, James B., 8453
McWethy, Susan, 8453
McWherter Charitable Lead Unity Trust, Ned R., 8649
McWherter, Mary Jane, 8649
McWherter, Michael R., 8649
McWhorter, Owen, Jr., 9143

Mead Charitable Remainder Trust, Nelson & Ruth, 3100
Mead, Betsy Boney, 7221
Mead, Darlena, 9033
Mead, Deborah, 9871
Mead, Elizabeth, 6466
Mead, George, 9871
Mead, Ron, 9033
Mead, Ruth C., 3100
Meade, Brianna, 3077
Meade, D.C., 6467
Meade, J.F., IV, 6467
Meade, Joseph F., III, 6467
Meade, Joseph F., Jr., 6467
Meadowbrook Investment Advisors, 4548
Meadows Consulting, 1316
Meadows, Curtis W., Jr., 9081
Meadows, Jean, 2970
Meadows, Todd, 9054
Meagher, Paul, 8345
Meaglia, Robert, 253
Meakem, Diane B., 8166
Meakem, Glen T., 8166
Means, Joann, 8739
Means, JoAnn H., 9085
Means, Mary C., 1175
Meara, Edward F., 5419
Meara, John W., 5038
Mears, A.W. Downing, Jr., 9075
Mears, Arnold W., 4911
Mears, Lisa M., 9075
Meckfessel, Mary Ann, 7736
Mecklenburg, William C., Jr., 7218
Medaris, Frank, Jr., 3655
Medaris, Henry, 8837
Medart, Cynthia B., 4868
Medart, James M., 5001
Medd, William L., 3796
Medema, Becky, 9474
Medford Multicare, 6469
Medford Schools Foundation, 7761
Medford, Phil, 8845
Medford, William L., 8838
Medical Arts Press, 1377
Medical Associates Clinic, P.C., 3521
Medical Mutual of Ohio, 7354
Medifast, 5555
Medikow, Isadore, 9881
Medley, Stacy, 196
Medlin, Steve L., 7162
Mednick-Glasser, Martha, 9459
Medore, Brenda G., 2310
Medore, Cuyler P., 2310
Medtronic, 2109
Medved, Jon J., 1359
Medvin, Harvey N., 2710
Meehan, Daniel E., 9882
Meehan, Edward F., 8238
Meehan, Eileen, 9882
Meehan, Kathryn, 2044
Meehan, Matthew, 1952
Meehan, Shealagh, 892
Meehan, Viola, 5825
Meehan-Felknor, Theresa R, 9882
Meek, Sue Ann, 9493
Meekins, Lois, 219
Meeks, Marion, 5322
Meeks, Terri, 1758
Meenan, Jennifer Gamper, 5361
Meengs, Cindy, 4401
Meerman, Sharon C., 4545
Meerwarth, Lurenna M., 2209
Meerwarth, Ralph N., 2209

Meerwarth, Tracy, 2209
Megibben, John, 7524
Mehl Family Trust, George and Deborah, 7523
Mehl, Bonnie, 7523
Mehl, David, 7523
Mehran, Alexander, 1126
Mehrberg, Dillon, 1325
Mehrberg, Randall E., 1325
Mehrberg, Randy, 1325
Mehta, Devangi, 889
Mehta, Manan, 889
Mehta, Rita, 889
Mehta, Samir, 889
Meier, Ana, 6470
Meier, Arlene, 3101
Meier, Chris, 7798
Meier, Craig, 488
Meier, Freddie, 9036
Meier, Marshall, 3101
Meier, Richard, 6470
Meier, Richard W., 4863
Meier, Sharon, 3609
Mein, Allison, 333
Meinberg, Gayle, 7656
Meinerding, James, 3361
Meiners, Gerald, 4911
Meinerz, Nancy, 9883
Meinerz, Viola, 9883
Meinhardt, Edward, 1834
Meinhardt, Evi, 1834
Meinharot, Laura, 8833
Meinstein, Edward, 2173
Meisel, J., 1178
Meisler, Herbert A., 60
Meissner, Edwin M., Jr., 2738
Meister, Barbara, 821
Meister, Larry, 821
Meister, Paul M., 5228
Mekhemar, Sami A., 5085
Melaleuca, 2679
Melampy, Patrick, 4167
Meland, Susan C., 7748
Melcher, Harold, 4957
Melcher, Harold S., 4957
Melcher, Lynne F., 4957
Melcher, Marilyn, 4957
Melcher, Marilyn B., 4957
Melcher, Richard A., 4957
Melcher, Thomas P., 8046
Melcher-Benjamin, Laurie Ann, 4957
Melchionna, Olin R., Jr., 9422
Melendez, Hector, 260
Melhado, Peter A.B., 6250
Melhorn, John, 3625
Melhorn, Julie E., 3625
Melick, Brian, 2270
Melick, John, 3289
Melick, Kimberly, 2270
Melin, David, 2210
Melin, Gina, 2210
Melin, Olga, 2210
Melius, Patrick, 7785
Mellen, Diane, 1525
Mellen, Michael, 1586
Mellen, Nancy, 1586
Mellen, Neil, 1525, 1586
Mellin, Jonathan B., 3248, 3249
Mellin, Kim, 5639
Mellion, Joseph T., Dr., 7346
Mello, Edward, 9033
Mellon, Darlene, 3432
Mellon, Diana, 8167
Mellon, James R., 8167

Mellon, Vivian R., 8167
Melo Enterprises, 247
Melo, Harry A., 7797
Melohn, Jonathan, 5794
Meloy, David, 1316
Melrose, Frances A., 1326
Melton, Terry, 7375
Melton, Terry L., 7364
Meltzer, Alan L., 3911
Meltzer, Amy, 3911
Meltzer, Janet, 7003
Meltzer, Mary L., 5946
Meltzer, Seth, 4564
Meltzner, Aron, 378
Meltzner, Carole J., 378
Meltzner, Sidney J., 378
Melville, Raymond, 5954
Melvin, Heather, 673
Melvin, James C., 4402, 4412, 4483, 4544
Melvin, Jim, 7209
MEMX, 9895
Menapace, John J., 7879
Mencotti, Melissa, 7944
Mendell, Ira L., 6472
Mendell, James, 6472
Mendell, Thomas G., 6472
Mendelsohn, Leslie, 768
Mendelson, Arlene H., 2211
Mendelson, Eric, 2211
Mendelson, Laurans A., 2211
Mendelson, Victor, 2211
Mendenhall, Oniel, Jr., 9056
Mendenhall, Trinidad V., 9056
Mendez, Bernardita, 1143
Mendlik, Paul M., 5128
Mendonca, Bob, 912
Mendoza, Christina, 8732
Mendoza, David, 5691
Menefee, Tandy, 219
Menezes, Ivan M., 1437
Menezes, M. Alia, 6473
Menezes, Mita N., 6473
Menezes, Pia A., 6473
Menezes, Tara A., 6473
Menezes, Victor J., 6473
Menges, Benjamin, 6474
Menges, Carl B., 6474
Menges, Cordelia S., 6474
Menges, J. Kenneth, Jr., 7749
Menges, James, 6474
Menges, Samuel, 6474
Menius, Donald, 7222
Menken, Alan, 6475
Menken, Janis, 6475
Menkiewicz, Richard E ., 8046
Menold, Wayne, 3126
Menoudakos, Chryssanthy, 5726
Menoudakos, John K., 5726
Menscher, Ellen, 5862
Menser, Charles D., Jr., 2431
Mentgen, Amy S., 9215
Menton, Bonnie M., 4246
Mentor Graphics Corp., 7796
MENTOR Network, The, 4199
Mentzinger, Elizabeth, 475
Menzer, Dov, 5665
Merage, Gregory, 822
Merage, Jeff, 822
Merage, Katherine, 822
Merage, Louise, 822
Merage, Paul, 822
Meraux, Arlene V., 3736
Mercadante, Anthony J., 4270

Mercadolibre,Inc., 2053
Mercantile Trust & Savings Bank, 3287
Mercardante, Pat, 2437
Mercer, Sara A., 8367
Merchant, Adnan, 1196
Merchant, David, 1581
Merchant, Steve, 870
Merchantz, Cathy Jo, 3102
Merchantz, William, 3102
Merck, Adele S., 4812
Merck, George G., 4812
Mercurio, Derrick, 323
Mercy Shared Services, 7715
Mercy, Harrell, 8650
Mercy, Joy M., 8650
Mercy, Scott L., 8650
Meredith, Audrey, 6477
Meredith, Gregory, 6477
Meredith, William, 3360
Merewether, Ellen Brown, 352
Merfish Pipe & Supply, 9058
Merfish, Abe, 9058
Merfish, Gerald, 9058
Merfish, Ida K., 9058
Mergener, Patricia O'Connor, 3148
Mergens, Lenora, 9381
Mergens, Paul, 9381
Mergens-Loughran, Mary, 9381
Merhoff, Theodore L., 7079
Meridian Capital Group LLC, 6478
Merillat, Nancy, 7339
Meriman, Peter, 1543
Mering, Donald R., 3834, 8110
Merit Consulting LLC, 5452
Merit Property Management, 807
Meritor, 4511
Meritor Automotive, 4511
Meriwether, Charles A., 2509
Merka, Jeanene D., 8819
Merkel, Beth, 3991
Merkel, Betty, 9884
Merkel, Daniel A., 9884
Merkel, Glen T., 4568
Merkle, Lyda T., 3737
Merkle, Paul E., 3737
Merkle, Robert J., 203
Merkle, Sarah E., 203
Merkle-Korff Industries, 9929
Merkley, Martha K., 4512
Merlin, Jean, 574
Merlo, Ellen, 6479
Merlo, Harry A., 7797
Merlo, Harry A., Jr., 7797
Mermelstein, Doreen, 3103
Mermelstein, Henry, 3103
Mermelstein, Joseph, 3103
Mermelstein, Louise, 3103
Mermelstein, Marvin, 3103
Mermelstein, Michael S., 1921
Mermin, Stephanie P., 6916
Mernone, Angela G., 9402
Mero, Steven C., 6449
Merrick, Frank W., 7707
Merrick, Frank W., Mrs. , 7707
Merrick, Judith L., 9059
Merrick, Leslie T., 9059
Merrick, Nicholas A., 9059
Merrick, Robert, 7707
Merrick, Ward S., III, 7707
Merrick, Will, 7707
Merrill Foundation, 6137
Merrill Lynch, 8700
Merrill Lynch Trust Co., 2618, 5240, 5275, 5293, 5320, 5341, 5365,

5409, 5428, 5434, 5486, 5519, 5521, 5522, 9297
Merrill Lynch Trust Company, 5308
Merrill, Abigail, 6480
Merrill, Amy, 4200
Merrill, Brooks, 158
Merrill, Bruce, 4200
Merrill, Catherin V., 3602
Merrill, Charles E., Jr., 4200
Merrill, Ella Warren, 8139
Merrill, Gilbert, 6480
Merrill, Joe, 2942
Merrill, Joseph W., 2942
Merrill, Judy Stewart, 1082
Merrill, Julia, 6480
Merrill, Oliver, 2942
Merrill, Pat, 9197
Merrill, Paul, 4200
Merrill, Paul D., 3789
Merrill, Peter, 1578
Merrill, Ross, 403
Merrill, Tracy Louis, 2942
Merriman, Elaine A., 1820
Merriman, Joe Jack, 1820
Merriman, Michael, 7330
Merriman, Michael A., 1820
Merrion Oil & Gas, 1707
Merrion, Anne M., 1707
Merrion, Brittany K.M., 1707
Merrion, Hannah J., 1707
Merrion, Molly J., 1707
Merrion, Ryan G., 1707
Merrion, Samantha C., 1707
Merrion, Sara L., 1707
Merrion, T. Greg, 1707
Merrion, Tori G., 1707
Merritt, Carrie, 1038
Merritt, Edward J., 4211
Merritt, Jennifer R., 9452
Merritt, Raymond, 5859
Merritt, William J., 1743
Mersfelder, James L., 5572
Mertens, Bruce L., 9411
Mertz, DeWitt W., 6481
Merves, Audrey, 8299
Mervis Industries, 3417
Mervis, Adam, 3417
Mervis, Ivan J., 7323
Mervis, Louis L., 3417
Mervis, Michael J., 3417
Mervis, Sybil S., 3417
Merwin, Richard A., 8170
Merwin, Robert F., 8170
Mesereau, Robert J., 4474
Meserve, Albert W., 7182
Meserve, Helen C., 7182
Meskey, Junie G., 9093
Mesler, Jennifer, 4569
Messaglia, Elizabeth H., 2109
Messemer, Glenn M., 1493
Messenger, Caroline, 3754
Messer Construction Co., 7524
Messer, John A., 8144
Messick Charitable Trust, Harry F., 4958
Messick Charitable Trust, Helena Blanch, 4958
Messina, Al, 1950
Messina, Salvadore, 3781
Messing Walsh, Jeanne Elise, 1708
Messing, Ali, 1708
Messing, Jake, 1708
Messing, Roswell, III, 1708
Messing, Roswell, Jr., 1708
Messing, Roswell, Jr., Mrs. , 1708

Messing, Wilma E., 1708
Messinger, Daryl, 6482
Messinger, Kera, 4784
Messinger, Lisa, 6482
Messinger, Martin, 6482
Messinger, Sarah, 6482
Messinger, William T., 4784
Messiqua, Gail P., 9516
Messler, Joseph D., Jr., 3790
Messler, Timothy P., 3790
Messner, Robert T., 8185
Mestrovic, Ivana, 9514
Metcalf, Jody, 3634
Metcalf, Katherine, 9729
Metcalf, Pauline C., 8406, 8479
Metcalf, Virginia, 2604
Metcalfe, Walter L., Jr., 4967
Metheny, Richard, 7713
Methfessel, John, 5569
Metro Nashville Airport, 9230
Metro Portland New Car Dealers Association, 7798
Metropolitan Bancorp, 2866
Metropolitan Bank Group, 2866
Metropolitan Iakovos, 2827
Metson, Taren Jacoby, 654
Metz, Dara, 6777
Metz, Don, 8707
Metzger, Belinda Bewkes, 1409
Metzger, Estelle, 6483
Metzger, John, 5091
Metzger, Leonard, 6483
Metzger, William C., 1273, 3381
Metzger, William L., 2762
Metzger-Utt, Maddy, 9592
Metzner, David B., 3104
Metzner, Gary F., 3104
Metzner, Mark J., 3104
Meuse, Kevin, 4291
Mewhinney, James S., 9060
Mewhinney, Linda D., 9060
Mewhinney, Michael C., 9060
Mewhort, Gail, 3000
Mewshaw, Linda K., 6313
Mewshaw, Marc P., 6313
Mewshaw, Michael F., 6313
Mewshaw, Sean K., 6313
Meyer Irrevocable Credit Trust, Paul, 5177
Meyer Irrevocable Non Credit Trust, Paul, 5177
Meyer, Alvin Reynold, 220
Meyer, Amy, 5177
Meyer, Anthony E., 6485, 6486
Meyer, Audrey H., 3261
Meyer, C. Fred, 9061
Meyer, Carlos Roberto Bensen, 3913
Meyer, Carol, 5414
Meyer, Charles R., 4959
Meyer, Constance F., 3859
Meyer, Daniel H., 3261
Meyer, Donald E., 3708
Meyer, Edward H., 6485, 6486
Meyer, Eva Chiles, 7749
Meyer, Gerald L., 2813
Meyer, Gordon D., 5362
Meyer, Helen, 5177
Meyer, Henry L., III, 7327
Meyer, James, 2086
Meyer, James A., 7975
Meyer, Jane A., 4959
Meyer, Janet E., 9885
Meyer, Jennifer Love, 7701
Meyer, Jerome, 6487

Meyer, John A., 10000
Meyer, Joseph F., III, 9061
Meyer, Joseph F., IV, 9061
Meyer, Katharine Maria, 3913
Meyer, Kenneth, 9061
Meyer, Kenneth E., 4959
Meyer, Kristine, 3567
Meyer, Larry W., 4959
Meyer, Lauren P., 8213
Meyer, Lawrence F., 421
Meyer, Leland, 9814
Meyer, Lillian S., 9277
Meyer, Linda L., 7735
Meyer, Margaret A., 6486
Meyer, Melba Bayers, 7183
Meyer, Melody, 8498
Meyer, Milton, 7184
Meyer, Mirth, 607
Meyer, Muffie, 6141
Meyer, Nancy, 3070, 3279
Meyer, Natalie, 1244
Meyer, Orin H., 4135
Meyer, Paul, 5414
Meyer, Paul E., 5177
Meyer, Pauline, 5177
Meyer, Robert D., 7735
Meyer, Rosemary, 9061
Meyer, Roslyn, 6487
Meyer, Sandra R., 6485
Meyer, Steve, 2670
Meyer, Steven A., 4335
Meyer, Thomas W., 3070
Meyer, Tom, 4583
Meyer, Valerie Kohn, 3120
Meyer, Virginia A.W., 1539
Meyer-Ploeger, Amy, Dr. , 3441
Meyerhoff, Joseph, II, 3914
Meyerhoff, Lenore P., 3914
Meyerink, Gailen, 8555
Meyers, Charles O., Jr., 7730
Meyers, Daniel M., 6939
Meyers, David R., 3107
Meyers, Dori, 3377
Meyers, Doris, 586
Meyers, Frederick C., 3107
Meyerson, Marlene N., 9062
Meyerson, Marlene Nathan, 9062
Meyhew, Brian, 662
Meza, Denise, 899
Meziab, Ziad, 128
Mezuman Associates LLC, 3437
Mezzapelle, Michael G., 1566
MFA Oil Co., 4960
MFA Petroleum Company, 4960
MFC Family Trust, 2798
Mhatre, Nitin J., 1477
Miami Corp., 2824, 2912
Miami Heat Foundation, 8570
Miami Perfume Junction Inc., 1943
Mibo Construction Co., 5414
Micallef, Joseph S., 4815
Micciantuono, Frank D., 4354
Michaan, Nevine, 5861
Michael, Elsa B., 7799
Michael, James R., 1836
Michael, Jonathan, 9930
Michael, Loretta, 7204
Michael, Mike, 7541
Michaels, Barbara R., 6488
Michaels, Gilbert N., 246
Michaels, Robert S., 4570
Michaels, Roger A., 6488
Michaelson, Robert, 2300, 6723
Michaelson, Ronald, 2857

Michalow, Daniel A., 6824
Michaud Administrative Trust, Dorothy P., 824
Michelin North America, 301
Michell, Roy G., 4513
Michell, Roy G., Jr., 4513
Michell, William, 4513
Michelotti, Carla, 2769
Michelsen, Barbara, 9426
Michelson, Joseph, 4289
Michener, Lizanne, 7966
Mick, Barbara D., 8651
Mick, Gregory, 3601
Mick, John R., 8651
Mick, Roger E., 8651
Mickelson, Amy, 825
Mickelson, Amy McBride, 825
Mickelson, Mary Santos, 825
Mickelson, Phil, 825
Mickelson, Phil, Sr., 825
Mickelson, Philip A., 825
Mickelson, Phillip A., 825
Mickens, Helen Pratt, 4590
Micklash, Ken, 4598
Mid-States Aluminum, 9887
Midcontinent Communications, 4745
Midcontinent Media, 4745
Middelthon, Ann E., 2430
Middendorf, Patricia A., 1349
Middlekauff Trust, Mildred, 3603
Middlesex Savings Bank, 4203
Middleton, Debra, 5140
Middleton, John, 9592
Middleton, Mike, 1640
Midland Manufacturing Money Purchase Plan and Trust, 2532
MidwayUSA, 3991
Miede, Norman, 8646
Miel, Karen, 3897
Mielcarek, Beth A., 9888
Mielcarek, Timothy A., 9888
Mielnicki, Daniel D., 2133
Miers, Fred, 6542
Miers, Frederic B., 6542
Mierswa, Charlie, 6524
Miesel, Deborah A., 4562
Miettinen, Richard M., 4573
Mifsud, Elizabeth, 7525
Mifsud, Judith D., 7525
Mifsud, Oscar J., 7525
Mifsud, Ryan S., 7525
Migdal, Lester C., 6895
Miglis, Thomas, 2791
Mignogna, Anthony, 8024
Miguel, Miguel, 9035
Mihelish, Gary, 5060
Mika, Susan, 2923
Mike, Ann, 9774
Mikels, Joseph, 3027
Mikelson, Thomas J.S., 4326
Mikkelsen, Chris D., 104
Mikler, Eleanor, 2132
Mikulik, Weldon, 8975
Milacek, George, 7666
Milanak, Susan Reichert, 3192
Milano Charitable Lead Trust, Sidonia, 5466
Milano, Jessie, 1710
Milano, Mark R., 1710
Milano, Robert J., 5466
Milazzo, Rick, 7839
Milbank, Samuel L., 6490
Mile Hi Bakery, 1362
Mile Hi Foods Co., 1362

Mile Hi Investments, 1362
Mile Hi Shared Service, 1362
Miles, Diana, 9279
Miles, James E., 9279
Miles, Jesse, 9097
Miles, Nancy, 8257
Miles, Phoebe C., 1670
Miley, Teresa, 4821
Milgard Family Foundation, Gary E., 9728
Milhoan, Susan, 6248
Milholland, Haley, 3702
Milhous, Gary, 493
Milinovich, Thomas G., 7933
Military Program, 3817
Milkes, Joe, 9284
Mill, Mary, 827
Millard, Adah K., 3109
Millard, Alex, 8483
Millard, Charles E. F. , 6455
Millbrook Partners LLC, 5576
Millennium Healthcare Mgmt., LLC, 2424
Miller 2013 Trust, Doreen D., 5931
Miller Brewing Co., 2510
Miller Charitable Annuity Trust, Kristie, 5469
Miller Charitable Lead Annuity Trust 1, Maya P., 5180
Miller Charitable lead Annuity Trust 2, Maya P., 5180
Miller Charitable Lead Annuity Trust, Sydell L., 7526
Miller Foundation, John D. and Doreen, 5931
Miller Irrevocable Trust, Dora, 2002
Miller Irrevocable Trust, Sadye, 2002
Miller Revocable Trust, Josepha S., 8348
Miller Trust, Louis H., 7708
Miller, Adaire R., 7811
Miller, Adonis E., 4299
Miller, Aishah, 8269
Miller, Angie, 726
Miller, Ann Marie, 4057
Miller, Anne W., 8348
Miller, Arjay, 831
Miller, Arjay R., 831
Miller, Barbara, 828
Miller, Bette, 9284
Miller, Betty Lou, 7078
Miller, Bill, 9209
Miller, Bonnie, 5104
Miller, Brain W., 6922
Miller, Brian K., 9244
Miller, Bruce, 5778
Miller, C. Richard, Jr., 3902
Miller, Carol, 5467
Miller, Carol P., 5467
Miller, Carole R., 832
Miller, Carolyn J., 5660
Miller, Carson A., 5180
Miller, Charles E., 9755
Miller, Christine A., 9785
Miller, Cindy, 900
Miller, Colin A., 1821
Miller, Connie H., 5240
Miller, Cooper & Co., Ltd., 3113
Miller, Dale, 9345
Miller, David A., 7312
Miller, David E., 832
Miller, Denis, 3607
Miller, Diane Duda, 1983
Miller, Donald J., 4467
Miller, Doreen D., 5931

Miller, Doris, 84
Miller, Dorothy M., 5289
Miller, Douglas E., 3414
Miller, Douglas V., 4746
Miller, E. Lynne, 1821
Miller, Edward F., 4239
Miller, Edward S., 6879, 6880
Miller, Elizabeth G., 6418
Miller, Ella Warren, 8139
Miller, Ellen K., 2181
Miller, Frances, 831
Miller, Fred, 828
Miller, G. Willard, 833
Miller, Gayle T., 832
Miller, Glen, 4454
Miller, Goldie Wolfe, 2880
Miller, H. Fred, 3372
Miller, Harvey R., 6491
Miller, Harvey Shipley, 5702
Miller, Henry S., III, 3114
Miller, Henry S., Jr., 3114
Miller, J.R., II, 7449
Miller, Jack, 2880
Miller, James, 2417
Miller, James D., 9523
Miller, James E., 7800
Miller, James J., 141
Miller, James Ludlow, 3604
Miller, Jared, 8570
Miller, Jason, 5467
Miller, Jay, 3027
Miller, Jean, 7802
Miller, Jeffrey, 830
Miller, Jeffrey W., 8020
Miller, Jennifer, 8570
Miller, Jennifer L., 1181
Miller, Jenny, 90
Miller, Jerome B., 7709
Miller, Jerry, 4463
Miller, Jerry L., 4463
Miller, Jessica N., 8609
Miller, Joe, 2689
Miller, John, 829, 870
Miller, Jonathan D., 3111
Miller, Joshua M., 8348
Miller, JoZach James, 3604
Miller, Juanita, 3114
Miller, Julie, 9002
Miller, K.R., 9064
Miller, Karen, 830
Miller, Katharine S., 8139
Miller, Katherine Eisold, 6849
Miller, Kathy, 2409, 8575
Miller, Kenneth F., 831
Miller, Kenneth H., 6494
Miller, Kenneth V., 4463
Miller, Ki, 1467
Miller, Kim S., 2152
Miller, Kristie, 5469
Miller, Laura, 9064
Miller, Laurence, 5691
Miller, Lee Ann, 9631
Miller, Lee J., 3986
Miller, Lila G., 7800
Miller, Lucy K., 1467
Miller, Luther, 6978
Miller, Margaret G., 2260
Miller, Marjorie, 6492
Miller, Mark, 7339
Miller, Mark C., 3111
Miller, Matthew B., 1821
Miller, Maureen E., 3111
Miller, Mavis S., 2267
Miller, Maya P., 5180

Miller, Michael, 3183, 8570
Miller, Michael E., 832
Miller, Michael L., 8570
Miller, Misdee Wrigley, 2417
Miller, Monty, 9065
Miller, Morgan, 6492
Miller, Nancy, 523
Miller, Nancy S., 833
Miller, Nellie E., 8173
Miller, Norman C., 5468
Miller, Norman F., 2213
Miller, Pat, 3370
Miller, Paul, 5133, 5467
Miller, Paul F., III, 8139
Miller, Paul F., Jr., 8139
Miller, Paul S., 5467
Miller, Paulina, 5468
Miller, Peggy, 3634
Miller, Peter, 5133
Miller, R., 3138
Miller, Richard, 283
Miller, Richard A., 6418
Miller, Richard J., Jr., 5957
Miller, Richard S., 8060
Miller, Rick, 7379
Miller, Robert, 2388
Miller, Robert J., 1430, 1507, 1533
Miller, Roger, 7356
Miller, Ruth, 6491
Miller, Ruth A., 5964
Miller, Sally H., 7777
Miller, Sean M., 3111
Miller, Sheryl, 8570
Miller, Stanley T., 5899
Miller, Stephen B., 7258
Miller, Stephen R., 833
Miller, Stephen R., Jr., 833
Miller, Steve, 3582, 3991, 7769
Miller, Steve J., 5468
Miller, Susan, 4463
Miller, Susan L., 4463
Miller, Sydell L., 7526
Miller, T. Wainwright, 2313
Miller, T. Wainwright, Jr., 2267
Miller, Tammy, 829, 9638
Miller, Ted, 7442
Miller, Ted M., 7800
Miller, Thaddeus W., 8759
Miller, Theodore W., 5468
Miller, Thomas, 5569
Miller, Thomas J., 8570
Miller, Tim, 4459
Miller, Tuck, 1467
Miller, Vance C., Sr., 3114
Miller, Vic, 5054
Miller, Vicki, 9248
Miller, Virginia R., 2152
Miller, Weston, 4746
Miller, William A., 7806
Miller, William G., 3112
Miller, William T., 9032
Millercoors, 7520
Milles, Evan, 3948
Millesen, Judith, 7311
Millett, Mary Elizabeth Schumacher, 9183
Milliken, Gerrish H., Jr., 1711
Milliken, John W., 1711
Milliken, Peter, 1711
Milliken, Phoebe, 1711
Milliken, Phoebe G., 1711
Milliken, Stephen G., 1711
Milliken, Weston, 2226
Milliken, Weston F., 1808

Million Dollars Media, 2510
Milliron, Grant, 7529
Millman, Gary, 5935
Millner Charitable Lead Annuity Trust, 3115
Millner, Gordon H., 3115
Millner, Karen M., 3115
Mills, Brian, 8869
Mills, David, 3126, 3567
Mills, David W., 834, 5548
Mills, Don, 4964
Mills, Frances Goll, 4515
Mills, Frank F., 7249
Mills, Helen, 2437
Mills, James R., 2426
Mills, John Clark, 6495
Mills, John T., 8724
Mills, Karen F., 2067
Mills, Larry, 7789
Mills, Linda, 7717
Mills, Marianne M., 6495
Mills, Nancy, 2970
Mills, Peter K., 1958
Mills, Ron, 9118
Mills, Ruth B., 3361
Mills, Sandra T., 3742
Mills, Sharon, 5152
Mills, Steven A., 6495
Mills, Tony G., 2521
Mills, William P., III, 3742
Millsaps, Audrey, 2214
Millsaps, Fred, 2214
Millstone, Jennifer H., 6201
Milne, Christopher B., 4365
Milne, Rebecca, 9851
Milstein Family Foundation, 6487, 6496
Milstein, Constance, 5941
Milstein, Constance J., 6886
Milstein, Edward L., 6496
Milstein, Herbert E., 3876
Milstein, Irma, 6487, 6496
Milstein, Mark B., 3876
Milstein, Nancy G., 3876
Milstein, Paul, 6487, 6496
Milstein, Philip L., 6886
Milstein, Richard S., 4312
Milstein, Seymour, 5941, 6886
Milstein, Vivian, 5941, 6778, 6886
Miltenberger, Carolyn Snyder, 5540
Miltimore, Irene Belk, 7046
Milton Home, 3418
Milton, Arthur, 6497
Milton, Phyllis, 6497
Mims Living Trust, Herman D., 7118
Mims, Darryl, 7118
Mims, David, 7118
Mims, Johnny, 4849
Minaci Charitable Lead Trust, Rose, 2215
Minarovic, Jane C., 8707
Minasian, Ralph, 6304
Minelli, Michael A., 7560
Miner, Daniel, 4130
Miner, Debbie, 4487
Miner, Jerry, 3116
Miner, Nina, 6802
Miner, Paula, 4082
Mineral Area Regional Medical Center, 4961
Mines, Tom, 4410
Mingenback, E.C., 3605
Mingst, Caryll S., 1070
Miniaci, Albert J., 2215
Miniaci, Dominick F., 2215

Miniaci, Rose, 2215
Minihan, Joe, 3592
Minio, Anthony, 5470
Minio, John, 5470
Minio, Loraine, 5470
Minis Charitable Trust, Edith, 2515
Minis, Margaret D., 2506
Minkin, Carol, 2076
Minkoff, Irene, 6044
Minkoff, Jonathan, 6044
Minkoff, Leon P., 3915
Minn, Lucille Brown, 2691
Minn, Steven, 2691
Minner, Sam, 9426
Minnesota Twins, 1730
Minnette, Dick, 3466
Minney, Shanda, 9734
Minnick, David M., 5014
Minnick, Margaret, 7787
Minor, Berkeley, Jr., 9761
Minor, Judith, 3117
Minor, Lucy, 3117
Minotto, S., 6212
Minow, Josephine B., 3118
Minow, Martha L., 3118
Minow, Mary R., 3118
Minow, Newton N., 3118
Minow, S. Nell, 3118
Minskoff Equities, 6655
Minsky, Leonard, 3793
Minsky, Renee, 3793
Minto Communities, 2216
Minton, Elena Lady, 9313
Mintz, Anna, 836
Mintz, Dainette, 8065
Mintz, Jean S., 3738
Mintz, Melinda F., 3738
Mintz, Morris F., 3738
Mintz, Neil, 836
Mintz, Saul a., 3738
Mintz, Ward L.E., 5852
Minuteman Disaster Response Foundation, 9133
Minutolo, James, 7299
Minyard Food Stores, 8795
Mirabello, Francis J., 8044
Mirabello, Marianna O., 8044
Miracle, John S., 9989
Mirak Building Trust, 4204
Mirak, Artemis, 4204
Mirak, John, 4204
Mirak, Robert, 4204
Miramonti, Dina, 4449
Mirapaul, Evan D., 3119
Mirapaul, Matthew R., 3119
Mirapaul, Walter N., 3119
Mirkovitch, Michel, 1132
Mischer, Mary A., 9067
Mischer, Paula, 9067
Mischer, Walter M., Jr., 9067
Mischer, Walter M., Sr., 9067
Mischinski, Maureen L., 4705
Mishler, Kristi, 7295
Miskavage, Kristin Z., 7028
Missad, Matthew J., 4418
Mission Linen Cos., 899
Mission-Heights Management Co. Ltd., 9176
Missouri Valley Steel Co., 5108
Mistele, Henry E., 4546
Mistler, Alvin J., 3606
Mistler, Richard E., 3606
Mistler, Thomas E., 3606
Mitby, John C., 9897, 9953

Mitchell Industries, 50
Mitchell Trust, Bernard A., 3120
Mitchell, Allyson, 9231
Mitchell, Amanda K., 2464
Mitchell, Andrew, 8697
Mitchell, Anna, 838
Mitchell, Arlene F., 49
Mitchell, Betsy, 3978, 5842
Mitchell, Bill, 9663
Mitchell, Bonnie, 4946
Mitchell, Braxton D., 3978
Mitchell, David C., 5698
Mitchell, Donald D., 1559, 8381
Mitchell, Dorothy L., 50
Mitchell, Edward C., III, 2464
Mitchell, Edward C., Jr., 2464
Mitchell, Edward D., 838
Mitchell, Elizabeth S., 5903
Mitchell, Everett W., 4205
Mitchell, Guy K., III, 50
Mitchell, Guy K., Jr., 50
Mitchell, Hank, 2292
Mitchell, Hilda, 8845
Mitchell, Hugh, 3655
Mitchell, Hume Lucas, Jr., 8534
Mitchell, James, 2687
Mitchell, Jason H., 838
Mitchell, Jill, 3521
Mitchell, Jonathan E., 838
Mitchell, Joseph, 7357
Mitchell, Joseph D., 6365
Mitchell, Katherine J., 50
Mitchell, Katherine W., 3318
Mitchell, Lee, 3120
Mitchell, Lee H., 3120
Mitchell, Lois, 721, 887
Mitchell, Lori, 4406
Mitchell, Lori Read, 734
Mitchell, Lucy, 9061
Mitchell, Marjorie I., 3120
Mitchell, Martha, 9937
Mitchell, Mary Ellen Roddy, Mrs. , 8684
Mitchell, Mary Lucas, 8534
Mitchell, Mayer, 49
Mitchell, Melanie, 4830
Mitchell, Michelle Rice, 2283
Mitchell, Pam, 3514
Mitchell, Richard A., 7545
Mitchell, Robert H., 7566
Mitchell, Sally R., 2292
Mitchell, Thomas, 2283
Mitchell, Virginia C., 2464
Mitchell, W. Bruce, 2680
Mitchell, William E., 3785
Mitchell, William H., 3885
Mitchell, Yvonnett, 837
Mithoff Family Foundation, 8738
Mithoff, Caroline R., 9068
Mithoff, Melissa, 9068
Mithoff, Michael, 8738
Mithoff, Michael K., 9068
Mithoff, Richard Warren, Jr., 9068
Mithoff, Virginia, 9068
Mitrani, Selma T., 5471
Mitte, Dyna, 9069
Mitte, Joann Cole, 9069
Mitte, R.J., 9069
Mitte, Roy F., 9069
Mittelstaedt, Darin, 9146
Mittelstaedt, Ronald J., 9146
Mittleman, Esther, 6188
Mittleman, Hershey, 6188
Mittleman, Joel, 6188
Mittlemann, Josef, 6500

Mittlemann, Marsy, 6500
Mitz, Ian, 9712
Mitzel, Maria, 4414
Mitzi International, 5743
Mix, Darcy S., 8801
Mix, Darryl W., 8801
Mix, Jeannette C., 2550
Mix, Kendall A., 4628
Mixner, A.R., 8554
Mixon, A. Malachi, III, 7530
Mixon, Barbara W., 7530
Miyazaki, Midori, 6249
Mize Estate, King Joshua, 7186
Mize Trust, Jose and Wynona, 7186
Mize, Ann, 3609
Mize, Anne B., 9663
Mize, David C., 3609
Mize, King Joshua, 7186
Mize, Ryan, 4983
Mizer, Ronald E., 2977
Mizner, Stephen P., 7944
MLF Charitable Lead Trust, The, 6040
MLTC, 5397
MMG, 4043
Mnewman, Jill, 9950
Mobile AL Bowl, 9
Mobley, Ebb, 8902
Mobley, Helena T., 8902
Mock, David, 9325
Mock, Randall D., 7691
Mockus, Vytautas, Dr. , 872
Modern Properties, 6097
Modglin, Donald L., 840
Modglin, Grace, 840
Modglin, Grace M., 840
Modglin, Steven, 840
Modine Manufacturing Co., 9889
Modungo, Thomas A., Rev., 6455
Mody Trust, Roger, 9501
Mody, Katherine Kyle, 9501
Mody, Roger, 9501
Moe, Barbara, 9084
Moe, Karin L., 2151
Moe, Robert S., 2151
Moeller, Joseph W., 150
Moeller, Mary, 150
Moeller, Mary F., 150
Moen, 2400
Moen, Stephanie, 3461
Moers, R. Lynn, 9288
Moffat Realty, 7020
Moffat, Robert Y., 8175
Moffatt, David, 9333
Moffatt, Joyce A., 3145
Moffett Holdings, LLC, 3739
Moffett, James R., 3739
Moffett, James R., Jr., 3739
Moffett, Louise H., 3739
Moffett-Lourd, Crystal L., 3739
Moffitt, Allen W., 382
Moffitt, Bill, 9712
Moffitt, F. Brower, 1406
Moffitt, Ronald, 9334
Mohammed, Halima, 1011
Moheban, Jeffrey, 3395
Mohler, Lowell, 4946
Mohn, Patricia, 8345
Mohr, Frank T., 3121
Mohr, Jean Whyte, 3121
Mojonnier, Alan L., 7223
Mokelke, Adam, 81
Molasky Revocable Trust, Irwin A., 5202
Moldow, Susan Jane, 350
Moldvay, Michael, 7624

Mole, Karen L., 7436
Molen, Sue, 1005
Moles, Charles F., 2887
Molesworth, Nancy Gassin, 2906
Molewski, Michael, 8344
Moley, Elizabeth, 841
Moley, Richard, 841
Molina, Polo, 645
Molinaro, Michelle R., 3586
Mollath, Louise, 842
Molleur, Danielle, 3776
Molleur, Dennis, 3776
Molloy, Ann K., 4083
Molnar, Marie, 4517
Molnar, William, 4517
Molstad, Coleith, 9069
Moltke-Hansen, David, 9389
Molyneux, Cynthia M., 3739
Molz, Kristi, 3628
Mon, Nai Aue, 9697
Monaco, Diane, 6720
Monadnock Paper Mills, 5236
Monaghan, Douglas, 9662
Monaghan, Helene, 6502
Monaghan, Helene M., 6502
Monaghan, Richard A., 6502
Monaghan, Thomas S., 4379
Monahan, Richard, 9493
Monahan, Susan T., 3999, 4052
Monastiere, Dominic, 4478
Moncada, George, 3078
Monck, Ronald R., 1938
Mondavi, Isabel, 843
Mondavi, Michael, 843
Monday, Gregory, 9935
Monday, James S., 8652
Monday, JoAnne D., 9412
Monday, Robert W., 8652
Monday, William E., III, 8652
Monday, William E., IV, 8652
Monderer, Benjamin, 6503
Mondzelewski, Chris, 8657
Moneo, Helen, 6280
Money, John Marshall, 844
Mong, David, 5825
Mong, Josephine, 5825
Mong, Stephen T., 5825
Monk, Roy, 9190
Monroe Bank & Trust, 4424
Monroe Securities, 2301
Monroe, Robert E., 7233
Monroe, Sarah, 138
Monroy, Marco, 591
Monserrate-McDade, Martha, 6461
Montag, Ken, 7944
Montag, Sara Lee, 7824
Montague, Hazel G.M., 8631
Montaldo, Maurice J., 3944
Montalto, Alex W., 8342
Montalto, Carrie Warburton, 8342
Montan, Christopher D., 669
Montana Mental Health Settlement
    Trust, 5060
Montanez, Thea, 1552
Monte, Constance, 6404, 6545
Montecito Bank & Trust, 292
Montecto Manufacturing Co., 899
Monteleone, David G., 3741
Monteleone, William A., III, 3741
Montemayor y Asociados, 2150
Montero, Andre, 1949
Montesano, James, 8487
Montford, Debbie, 929
Montford, John, 929

Montgageit Inc., 6656
Montgomery Foundation, The, 2551
Montgomery Trust, Gratia R., 5659
Montgomery, Carolyn, 5052
Montgomery, Carolyn R., 7817
Montgomery, Hazel I., 9071
Montgomery, Jeff, 1950
Montgomery, Joe R., 8729
Montgomery, Joseph W., 9420
Montgomery, Lovie K., 26
Montgomery, Marie, 608
Montgomery, Molly R., 8250
Montgomery, Nancy T., 2551
Montgomery, Sean D., 8250
Montgomery, Thatcher O., 8250
Montgomery, Walter S., Sr., 8510
Montuori, Michael E., 4270
Moody National Bank, 8767
Moody, Anna, 825
Moody, Becky, 5152
Moody, David, 9065
Moody, Melanie, 7582
Moody, Phyllis, 7408
Mook, Saundra, 7944
Moon Credit Corp., 9225
Moon, A. Rose, 9225
Moon, Jack, 7187
Moon, John H., Jr., 9225
Moon, John H., Sr., 9225
Mooney and Moses of Ohio, 7386
Mooney, Bill, 2681
Mooney, Bridie Ann, 9859
Mooney, David, 2702
Mooney, Edward P., Jr., 9859
Mooney, Richard G., III, 2583
Moor, Glenn D., 9143
Moorad, Amal E., 7715
Moore Family Trust, 1251
Moore Trust, Charles G., 3795
Moore, Alice W., 4576
Moore, Annette M., 3123
Moore, Ardon E., 9072
Moore, Ardon Iris, 9072
Moore, Ardon Tucker, 9072
Moore, Becky B., 1910
Moore, Billy S., 7641
Moore, C. Frank, 2598
Moore, Catherine B., 9551
Moore, Cathryn Mayo, 7710
Moore, Charles "Rick", 1098
Moore, Charles G., III, 3795
Moore, Christopher S., 3795
Moore, Clement C., II, 3917
Moore, Connie, 5016
Moore, Craig, 3988
Moore, D'Ann, 9267
Moore, Danielle, 2012
Moore, David, 5036
Moore, Dennis F., 7308
Moore, Diana MacDonald, 9032
Moore, Donald T., 7367
Moore, Dorothy, 6405
Moore, Douglas D., 3123
Moore, Ed, 8970
Moore, Eileen P., 7868
Moore, Elfrida B., 2619
Moore, Elizabeth W., 3917
Moore, Emily E., 3795
Moore, Everett H., 3123
Moore, Franklin H., 4576
Moore, George C., Mrs. , 6868
Moore, Gerald H., 7352
Moore, Gerald W., 2032
Moore, Iris H., 9072

Moore, J. A., 206
Moore, J. Kevin, 2463
Moore, J. W., Jr., 7725
Moore, James, 4961
Moore, James D., 7710
Moore, James W., 2032
Moore, Janet, 665
Moore, Jerri, 8829
Moore, Jerry, 7352
Moore, Jim, 9209
Moore, John, 3521
Moore, Joseph H., III, 1251
Moore, Joshua, 2643
Moore, Julie, 2959
Moore, Katherine F., 6504
Moore, Laura J., 3123
Moore, Leslie, 1255
Moore, Lori A., 437
Moore, Lucy S., 4004
Moore, Lynne, 8769
Moore, Marjorie, 8456
Moore, Mark, 3521
Moore, Mark , 9474
Moore, Martha G., 2217
Moore, Mary Elizabeth Houck, 8953
Moore, Mary N., 8598
Moore, Matthew W., 6221
Moore, Meredith, 4449
Moore, Michele, 3058
Moore, Michele, Mrs. , 3058
Moore, Mike, 7408
Moore, Nancy M., 4250
Moore, Nathaniel T., 3795
Moore, Nicholas, 6868
Moore, Noel G., 3058
Moore, Noel G., Mr. , 3058
Moore, O.L., 2643
Moore, Pamela, 3595
Moore, Patricia, 7352
Moore, Patricia P., 7352
Moore, Patrick, 6075
Moore, Paul M., 8177
Moore, Peter, 897
Moore, Peter M., 3123
Moore, Ralph, 1952
Moore, Rebecca, 6075
Moore, Richard C., 8527
Moore, Rick, 9669
Moore, Sandra, 7717
Moore, Sandra C., 9545
Moore, Shirley, 3988
Moore, Sonja, 4702
Moore, Stephen, 4822
Moore, Stephen A., 4131
Moore, Steve D., 8854
Moore, Thomas B., 4090
Moore, Timothy, 9579
Moore, Timothy R., 4601
Moore, Vicky, 9579
Moore, Vicky L., 7308
Moore, Walter M., IV, 9491
Moore, Wendell, 9065
Moore, Wendell D., 9165
Moore, William E., 2643
Moorman, Carol E., 3092
Mooty, Melvin R., 4747
Mooty, Paul, 4671
Mooty, Paul R., 4747
Mooty, Sally R., 4747
Mor, William, 4012
Mora, Melvin, 3817
Morales, Rick, 8874
Moran Charitable Remainder Net Income
    Unitrust, 5178

Moran, Caroline A., 8025
Moran, Edward P., Jr., 5204
Moran, Elizabeth, 7928
Moran, Garrett M., 6468
Moran, Jamey, 6184
Moran, Joan M., 7838
Moran, Joseph P., 5178
Moran, Joshua P., 5178
Moran, Karen A., 5801
Moran, Laura, 408
Moran, Laurel A., 5178
Moran, Lucille Ann, 5178
Moran, Michael, 2109, 7841
Moran, Ranney R., 7880
Moran, Richard Jerome, 5178
Moran, Sara S., 8269
Moran, Susan B., 5204
Moran, William C., 6184
Morasch, Linda F., 847
Morash, Douglas A., 4191
Moraski, Gwendolyn, 1599
Moravitz, Edward, 7856
Morawczyk, Laura Aryeh, 6361
Morawczyk, Richard, 6361
Morbeck, Frank A., 2681
More, Alexandra, 1088
More, Braden, 1088
More, Penelope Straus, 1088
More, Robert P., 1402
Moreau, Thomas, 4552
Moreco, IV, 153
Morehead, Robert J., 8780
Morehouse, C. Schuyler, 5539
Morehouse, Dean, 9695
Morehouse, Ellen S., 5539
Morel, Heath, 9133
Morell, Allen N., 1716
Morell, Patricia M., 1716
Morelock, John P., Jr., 7472
Moreton, Alma, 3124
Moretta, Daniel N., 7312
Morey, Amy, 8327
Morey, Robert, 7801
Morey, Robert Timi, 7801
Morey-Forest Grove I LLC, Wellner, 7801
Morf, Darrel A., 3507
Morgado, Mary Lou, 6505
Morgado, Robert J., 6505
Morgan Charitable Remainder, Letitia, 8189
Morgan Foundation, Pete, 1352
Morgan Guaranty Trust Co. of New York, 6656
Morgan Stanley Trust, 5911
Morgan, Albert, 3607
Morgan, Cassie, 196
Morgan, Eleanor, 8178
Morgan, Eleanor K., 8178
Morgan, Evalyn, 4963
Morgan, Gia, 3713
Morgan, Harry, 2551
Morgan, Howard L., 8178
Morgan, J.K., 7729
Morgan, James, 846
Morgan, James A., 4211
Morgan, James C., 846
Morgan, Jonathan, 196
Morgan, Judy B., 1962
Morgan, Judy L., 847
Morgan, Karin W., 3940
Morgan, Keith B., 5299
Morgan, Kile, Jr., 847
Morgan, Kim, 4396
Morgan, Leona, 3607

Morgan, Phillip, 3441
Morgan, Rebecca, 846
Morgan, Rebecca Q., 846
Morgan, Seth, 9102
Morgan, Stephen, 5299
Morgan, Warren, 4963
Morgan-Prager, Karole, 811
Morganstern, Stephen, 3720
Morgenstern, Daniel, 3918
Morgenstern, Frank N., 848
Morgenstern, Harry, 2890
Morgenstern, Morris, 848
Morgenstern, Richard, 848
Morgenthaler, Gary, 1168
Morger, Randal, 5054
Morhman, Fr. Gregory, 5022
Mori, Faith Harding, 2848
Moriarty, Edmond N., III, 5473
Moriarty, Elizabeth N., 5473
Moriarty, John D., 5473
Moriarty, Mary Ellen, 5473
Moriarty, Virginia H., 5473
Morielli, Scott, 576
Morin, Barbara, 2369
Morin, Stanley J., 5578
Morinelli, Mary, 5071
Morisey, Frances D., 7191
Morisey, John C., III, 7191
Morisey, John C., Jr., 7191
Morishita, Ken, 1103
Moritz, Terry, 2919
Morley Charitable Lead Trust No. 1, John C. and Sally S., 7532
Morley Charitable Lead Trust No. 2, John C. and Sally S., 7532
Morley Group, 8700
Morley, Burrows, Jr., 4518
Morley, Christopher, 4518
Morley, David H., 4518
Morley, George B., Jr., 4518
Morley, James T., Jr., 1532
Morley, John C., 7532
Morley, Katharyn, 4518
Morley, Michael, 4518
Morley, Peter, 4518
Morley, Peter, Jr., 4518
Morley, Ralph Chase, Sr., 4518
Morley, Ralph Chase, Sr., Mrs. , 4518
Morley, Sally S., 7532
Morlock, Danyle, 5011
Morneau, Bob, 5628
Morningstar, Betty, 4207
Morningstar, Jane, 4207
Morningstar, Otto, 4207
Moross Foundation, Dominic, 9386
Moross, Dominic H. R., 9386
Moross, Dominic H.R., 9386
Morrical, Ann McGraw, 814
Morrill, Alexandra Goldman, 6098
Morrill, Judith, 3356
Morrin, Patrick J., 442
Morris 1993 Descendants Trust, Bruce, 2908
Morris Charitable Trust, Charles, 8080
Morris Family Trust, John and Sharon, 2220
Morris Foundation, 936
Morris Weinman Co., The, 3981
Morris, Anthony J., 496
Morris, Belinda, 2553
Morris, Bruce, 2908
Morris, Cherie, 2220
Morris, Dorothy, 205
Morris, Earl W., 7802

Morris, Ellen, 2908
Morris, Gabriella, 8350
Morris, Gary Edward, 7695
Morris, Glendolyn M., 3679
Morris, Gordon, 205
Morris, Jeffery, 6508
Morris, John, 2220, 3679, 5660
Morris, John R., 3679
Morris, John Richard, 3679
Morris, John Ryan, 3679
Morris, Katie, 9756
Morris, L. Daniel, 39
Morris, Laura, 8328
Morris, Lauren, 6508
Morris, Lori M., 9408
Morris, Michael, 2553
Morris, Nigel W., 9408
Morris, Norman M., 6508
Morris, P. Kevin, 684
Morris, Peggy, 1295
Morris, Rebecca, 8955
Morris, Richard, 2908
Morris, Robert, 2908, 6508
Morris, Ronnie, 2219
Morris, Sally J., 4376
Morris, Sandi, 6508
Morris, Stephen A., 3786
Morris, W. Newton, 2552
Morris, Walter S., 205
Morrisey, John, 5322
Morrison Knudsen Corp., 2666
Morrison, Cary Jay, 2221
Morrison, Christine A., 4752
Morrison, Emily Cade, 1670
Morrison, G. Lowe, 1982
Morrison, Harry W., 2682
Morrison, John L., 4752
Morrison, Kent, 1799
Morrison, Larry, 8774, 9084
Morrison, Larry A., 7488
Morrison, Mark, 942
Morrison, Mills Lane, 2536
Morrison, Nina, 1792
Morrison, Robert H., 7193
Morrison, Robert L., 1670
Morrison, Terry, 8996
Morrison, Velma V., 2682
Morrisey, Scot, 2437
Morrone, Colleen P., 7953
Morrow, Claire, 1527
Morrow, Dillard, 7255
Morrow, Donna M., 1527
Morrow, Frank, 9588
Morrow, Joseph J., 1527
Morrow, Katherine, 9074
Morrow, Kim A., 1527
Morrow, Paul, 9074
Morrow, Sherry, 5077
Morse, Alan R., Jr., 4259
Morse, Alfred L., 4208
Morse, Annette S., 4208
Morse, Brent J., 1328
Morse, Charles W., Jr., 4217
Morse, Claire W., 4209
Morse, Eric Robert, 4259
Morse, Janice C., 4221
Morse, Jennifer, 4259
Morse, Julie, 1328
Morse, Julie A., 1328
Morse, Martha E., 8105
Morse, Mildred H., 6509
Morse, Phillip H., 4210
Morse, Richard P., 4209
Morse, Robert R., 6510

Morse, Ruth, 4209
Morse, Sandra, 121
Morse, Stacey C., 6510
Morse, Susan K., 4210
Morss, Everett, Jr., 4276
Mortenson, Barbara J., 9890
Mortenson, Jay P., 9890
Mortenson, Jill, 3513
Mortenson, Loren D., 9890
Mortenson, Stephen D., 1989
Mortimer, Averell H., 6170
Mortimer, Kathleen L., 6170
Mortin, Malinda J., 2526
Morton, B. Naylor, 9203
Morton, Claire R., 7565
Morton, Helene, 2199
Morton, James R., 3752
Morton, Jeff, 9139
Morton, Jennifer L., 994
Morton, John, 138
Morton, John B., 3127
Morton, Jordan, 650
Morton, Melinda, 5050
Morton, Thomas M., 3752
Morton, Tina, 8118
Mosbacher, Barbara, 9075
Mosbacher, Diane, 9075
Mosbacher, Emil, 9075
Mosbacher, Emil, Jr., 9075
Mosbacher, Gertrude, 9075
Mosbacher, Kathryn, 9075
Mosbacher, Peter, 1477
Mosbacher, Robert A., 9075
Mosbacher, Robert A., Jr., 9075
Mosbo, E. Paul, 8836
Moscow, John, 6396
Mosdos Gur, 5443
Moseley, Chessye, 5393
Moseley, Colin, 9680
Moseley, Furman C., 9701
Moseley, Jene M., 9050
Moseley, Lisa Dean, 7194
Moseley, Martha P., 9680
Moseley, Susan R., 9701
Moseley, Thomas A. , 2149
Moser, Caroline, 472
Moser, Constance B., 1883
Moser, Elizabeth K., 3918
Moser, G. Dewey, 5573
Moser, Giles E., 8471
Moser, Jeremy R.H., 3918
Moser, M. Peter, 3918
Moser, Martin P., Jr., 3918
Moser, Mike, 402
Moser, Moriah, 3918
Moser, Paul E., 7364
Moser, Tom, 9696
Moses, Alfred H., 7426
Moses, Donald, 6009
Moses, Janet, 6258
Moses, Jennifer, 297
Moses, John P., 7879
Moshe Isaac Foundation, 5524
Moshe, Yair Ben, 7000
Mosier, Jerrilee K., 3445
Mosier, Martha, 389
Moskoff, Judy, 4915
Moskovits, Judy, 718
Moskovits, William, 5665
Moskowitz, Henry, 6511
Moskowitz, Jeffrey, 849
Moskowitz, Madeleine, 849
Moskowitz, Mark, 6511
Moskowitz, Michael L., 6113

Moskowitz, Rose, 6511
Moss Foundation, 492
Moss Petroleum Co., 9076
Moss, Anne Palmer, 5872
Moss, Brenda E., 1993
Moss, Charles B., III, 5806
Moss, Charles B., Jr., 5806
Moss, Elizabeth H., 5806
Moss, Finis M., 4964
Moss, Florence M., 9076
Moss, Francis E., 4484
Moss, Gerald, 2878
Moss, Harry S., 9076
Moss, Jennifer Louise, 5342
Moss, Jody, 5059
Moss, Lee, 8635
Moss, Lee C., 1993
Moss, Marilyn R., 3228
Moss, Neil M., 7423
Moss, Robin H., 5806
Moss, Shane M., 9670
Mosseri, Joe, 5705
Mossy, David L., 9077
Mossy, Wiley L., Jr., 9077
Most, Jordan, 5247
Mostofizadeh, Javad, 900
Mosvold, Astri, 8711
Mosvold, Martin, 8711
Mosvold, Paul, 8711
Mosvold, Torrey, 8711
Mothershead, Katharine B., 3419
Motherwell, Marjorie, 3429
Motley, George B., 4276
Motley, Herbert J., Jr., 4805
Motley, Teri M., 4805
Motoshita, Toshihide, 5795
Motschall, Thomas J., 4447
Mott, Mike, 8603
Mottley, Elliott, 6585
Mouawad, Fred, 4234
Moughty, Elisabeth, 8297
Moul, Douglas G., 1913
Moul, Maxine, 5105
Moulder, Bill, 9254
Moulder, Electra, 9254
Moulder, Frances L., 2074
Moulin, Trenton, 7891
Moulton, Charles Naylor, 9203
Moulton, Susan N.M., 9203
Mount Olive Pickle Co., 7196
Mount Saint Clare Education Foundation, 3522
Mount Sinai Medical Center, 7560
Mountain Co., The, 9744
Mountain, Paul, 84
Mourer, Ryan, 6540
Mouron, Michael A., 69
Mouton, David, 8939
Moutray, Vicki, 5608
Mouw, Jim, 3528
Mowbray, Megan H., 6908
Mowbray, Tessa E., 6908
Mower, Leslie DeeAnn, 9341
Moye, Katherine, 3983
Moyer Trust, W. Melvin, 8180
Moyer, Mary L., 8180
Moyer, Robert W., 6623
Moylan, Laura, 2689
Moynihan, Merrily, 1461
Mozel, Claire A., 6512
Mozes, Jack, 2345
MPR Family Foundation, 1809
Mr. Holmberg, 6221
Mraz, Michael, 870

MRHM, 6374
Mroz, John D., 3696
Mroz, Judith A., 3696
Mroz-Bremner, Karen, 3696
Mrozek, Donald, 2789
Mrozik, Reiko, 3024
Mrozkowski, Phyllis J., 5790
Mrs. Bessemer, 6221
MSC Industrial, 7094
Msy Charitable Foundation, Dare, 6605
Mt. Washington Co-operative Bank, 4211
MTS Assocs. LLC, 6731
Muccia, Carrol A., Jr., 2225, 6455
Muccia, David C., 6455
Muccia, Margaret D., 2225
Muchin, Allan, 2999
Muchnic, Daphne Nan, 3609
Muchnic, H.E., 3609
Muchnic, Helen Q., 3609
Muchnick, Howard W., 6163
Muckel, John, 850
Muckel, Linda, 850
Mudd Charitable Remainder Uni-Trust, 851
Mudd, Dennis, 851
Mudd, Lance, 4379
Mudd, Pamela, 851
Mueller and Co., 5452
Mueller, Amy, 9631
Mueller, Amy Luster, 880
Mueller, Joyce Ann, 2234
Mueller, Marnie W., 8090
Mueller, Moshe, 5452
Mueller, Shoshana, 5452
Mueller, Todd, 9631
Muffo, John, 9426
Muffy, Terry, 147
Mugar, Carolyn G., 4008
Muglia, Laura Ellen, 9666
Muglia, Robert, 9666
Mugride, Jason, 7847
Muhart, Monica Ross, 375
Muhlbach, John L., Jr., 7312
Muir, Catherine L., 4481
Muir, David F., 4481
Muir, Douglas Gordon, III, 2493
Muir, Elizabeth M., 4481
Muir, Lea Ann, 4481
Muir, Molly, 4490
Muir, William M, 4481
Muirhead, T. Chris, 9995
Mujica-Larson, Evelyn, 82
Mulder, David, 3593
Mulder, Jeffrey, 4569
Mulder, Jeri, 4569
Muldoon, Joseph W., 6565
Mule Deer Foundation, 3991
Mule, Edward A., 6515
Mulhern, Sherrill Ann, 3600
Mulholland, James, 3350
Mulholland, Peter, 4345
Mulhollem, Paul B., Jr., 3680
Mulka, Susan Lane, 4487
Mulkey, James C., 9766
Mullan, C. Louise, 3920
Mullan, Thomas F., III, 3920
Mullan, Thomas F., Sr., 3920
Mullen Estate Trust, Boyd, 5475
Mullen Foundation, J.K., The , 1329
Mullen, Alicia C., 3129
Mullen, Catherine S., 1329
Mullen, Evelyn Z., 5475
Mullen, Joan A., 8184

Mullen, John J., 8184
Mullen, John K., 1329
Mullen, Joseph, 3129
Mullen, Mary L., 3129
Mullen, Timothy R., 3129
Mullen-Hohl, Anne, 6820
Muller, Abraham, 5793
Muller, Bob, 7204
Muller, Hans, 2234
Muller, Hyman, 2937
Muller, Jacob, 5793
Muller, Joyce, 2234
Muller, Joyce Ann, 2078
Muller, Marisa, 2078, 2234
Muller, Mark, 3566
Muller, Sally, 3251
Mulligan, George E., 9314
Mulligan, Janet L., 6102, 6786
Mulligan, Mary S., 8457
Mulligan, Nancy, 6111
Mulliken, Rosemary, 5234
Mulliner, Raymond L., 1049
Mullins, Jeffrey, 1549
Mullins, Marcus, 3703
Mullins, Susan Whittaker, 985
Mullins, Thomas, 2261
Mullins, Todd, 2261
Mulroy, Thomas M., 8173
Mulstay, John, 1341
Multack, Ellen, 3179
Multicon Builders, Inc., 7386
Multiple Sclerosis Society, 7209
Mulvaney, Brian, 1713
Mulvaney, Eileen, 8458
Mulvaney, Kay, 1713
Mulvany, Kate, 1566
Mulvehill, Urban S., 5813
Mulvihill, Heather, 6248
Mulzer, Edgar C., 3420
Mulzer, Rebecca, 3420
Mulzer, Roberta, 3420
Muma, Leslie M., 2227
Muma, Pamela S., 2227
Mumford, Carol, 1595
Munana, Carl, 1881
Mundia, Abdul, 6921
Mundia, Mubasir, 6921
Mundia, Munib, 6921
Mundia, Roshanara, 6921
Mundy, George E., 71
Munga, Susan, 7513
Mungenast Group Dealer Services, 4966
Mungenast, Barbara J., 4966
Mungenast, David F., 4966
Mungenast, David F., Jr., 4966
Mungenast, Kurt A., 4966
Mungenast, Raymond J., 4966
Munger, Barry A., 711
Munger, Charles, 961
Munger, Charles T., 711, 1070
Munger, Charles T., Jr., 410
Munger, Gail, 9445
Muni, Craig, 5799
Munilla, Fernando, 2206
Munilla, Jorge, 2206
Munilla, Juan, 2206
Munilla, Pedro, 2206
Munilla, Raul, 2206
Munitz, Barry, 430
Munk, Aaron, 5544
Munk, Ezrial, 5544
Munk, Judah, 5544
Munk, Nathan, 5544
Munk, Yaffa, 5544

Munkvold, Richard, 937
Munn, Jason, 8541
Munn, Joey, 8541
Munn, Monte, 2686
Munnelly, Kevin V., 666
Munro, David M., 7763
Munroe, Bobbie D., 2228
Munroe, Jan H., 2228
Munroe, Richard C., 2228
Munroe, Richard G., 2228
Munson, Alice, 852
Munson, Christine A., 3564
Munson, Kenneth R., 852
Munson, Tom, 8766
Munson, Ward, 852
Muntz, Martin, 8886
Muntz, Maurine Genecov, 8886
Munushian Revocable Trust of 1997, Jack, 853
Murad Family, 854
Murad Inc., 854
Murad, Hilarie, 854
Murad, Jeff, 854
Murad, Richard, 854
Muraglia, John, 1295
Muraski, Michael J., 4406
Murawczyk, Laura Aryeh, 6361
Murawczyk, Richard, 6361
Muraya, Eva, 2622
Murchison, Anne, 7145
Murchison, Frank, 8860
Murchison, George, 627
Murchison, Joyce, 627
Murchison, Michael, 627
Murdoch, Ann Troxell, 2688
Murdock, Bart A., 4519
Murdock, Cheri, 9357
Murdock, David C., 7952
Murdock, Donald L., 4519
Murdock, Marcia Jean, 4519
Murfin, Joe, 3991
Murla, Paula, 3744
Murman, Earll, 9630
Murnane Specialities, 3131
Murnane, Frank, Sr., 3131
Muro, Derek, 240
Murphy Charitable Trust, Isobel, 873
Murphy Co., G.C., 8185
Murphy Oil Corp., 206
Murphy, Adele A., 3132
Murphy, Anne, 2191
Murphy, Ashley, 3038
Murphy, Brian, 4079
Murphy, Bryan F., 496
Murphy, Candy, 3628
Murphy, Cecile Higginson, 4214
Murphy, Chris J., 5088
Murphy, Christopher M., 3132
Murphy, David, 8836
Murphy, David C., 7182
Murphy, David R., 2191
Murphy, Diane Dooner, 7974
Murphy, Edward, 4199
Murphy, Elizabeth, 5088
Murphy, Frank, 6626
Murphy, Glenn S., 3132
Murphy, Jan, 7761
Murphy, John D., 873
Murphy, John M., 1590
Murphy, Joseph E., 9748
Murphy, Judith C., 9907
Murphy, Laura, 6936
Murphy, Leo G., 825
Murphy, Maeve, 1184

Murphy, Martha W., 207
Murphy, Mary E., 4215, 9748
Murphy, Maura E., 4052, 4329
Murphy, Michael, 645
Murphy, Michael D., 9860
Murphy, Michael E., 3132
Murphy, Mike, 219, 3126
Murphy, Pam, 7802
Murphy, Richard, 1807
Murphy, Robert F., Jr., 4348
Murphy, Robert Madison, 207
Murphy, Scott, 9592
Murphy, Suzanne Nodini, 207
Murphy, Suzanne P., 3958
Murphy, Thomas J., 7965
Murphy, Tom, 3628
Murphy, Walter J., Jr., 3944
Murray Fortune Foundation, Martha, 3381
Murray SB-3 Trust, John R., 8862
Murray, Andy, 14
Murray, Ann, 7636
Murray, Anne, 7375
Murray, Bruce R., 9515
Murray, David, 1806
Murray, Edward, 2200
Murray, Harry, Jr., 9740
Murray, J.R., Jr., 8862
Murray, James B., Jr., 9515
Murray, Jason, 7488
Murray, Joan, 1806
Murray, Joan Douglas, 1806
Murray, John F., Jr., 6683
Murray, Karen, 7543
Murray, Kelly, 4719
Murray, L.T., 9667
Murray, L.T., III, 9667
Murray, L.T., Jr., 9667
Murray, L.T., Mrs. , 9667
Murray, Michael C., 2725
Murray, Muffie B., 7857
Murray, Oliver C., Jr., 2556
Murray, Robert, 6046
Murray, Sara, 1806
Murray, Tim, 3432
Murray, Timothy L., 5036
Murray, Tom, 9756
Murray, William J., 5641
Murrell, Karen M., 7326
Murry, Emanuel E., 3681
Murry, Wesley E., 3681
Murthy Law Firm, 3921
Murthy, Sheela, 3921
Murthy, Srinivas, 3921
Muscio, Richard J., 1023
Muscular Dystrophy Association, 7209
Muse, John R., 9080
Muse, Lyn R., 9080
Muse, Susan B., 3750
Musen, Kenneth N., 6407, 6419, 7192
Musgrave, Regan, 735
Musgrave, Todd, 2962
Musgrove, Mary, 140
Music City Bowl, 8687
Music Mastermind Inc., 6796
Musich, Susan L., 9975
Muskat, Marc, 2879
Musser, Marshall, 9751
Musser, R. Daniel, III, 4499
Musson, Irvin J., III, 7534
Musson, Irvin J., Jr., 7534
Musson, R.C., 7534
Muther, Catherine S., 1116
Mutual Bank, 3421

Mutual Financial, Inc., 3421
Mutual Fire Marine and Inland Insurance Co., The, 8186
Mutual Marine Office, 5755
Mutual Telephone Co., 3528
Mutualone Bank, 4216
Muzyl, Linda, 9631
Muzyl, William, 9631
MV Flight Service LLC, 8948
My Blessings Inc., 153
Mydna Media, 8689
Myerberg, Alvin J., 3923
Myerberg, Henry, 3923
Myerberg, Jennifer, 3923
Myers Industries, 7535
Myers, Albert G., III, 7097
Myers, Albert G., Jr., 7097
Myers, Amanda S., 9081
Myers, Ann, 6733
Myers, Carl, 6733
Myers, Celine, 251
Myers, Daria, 181
Myers, David, 8939
Myers, David L., 8048
Myers, Eliza H., 6204
Myers, Gene R., 3009
Myers, Holly E., 5269
Myers, Jack, 2280
Myers, James A., 7305
Myers, James L., 3940
Myers, Joanna L., 3448
Myers, John C., IV, 2280
Myers, John Michael, 5050
Myers, John R., 3458
Myers, June R., 2280
Myers, Louis S., 7535
Myers, Martin, 5476
Myers, Mary S., 7535
Myers, Mike A., 9081
Myers, Paul, 2280
Myers, Randolph, 6625
Myers, Richard D., 5071
Myers, Robert, 9081
Myers, Sammye, 9081
Myers, Stephen E., 7535
Myers, Wendel, 4934
Myerson, Alan, 287
Myerson, Bernard, 287
Myerson, Edward, 287
Myerson, Muriel, 287
Myhan, Ronald G., 496
Mykoff, David, 5382
Mykoff, Rabbi Abraham, 5382
Mylan Laboratories Inc., 8187
Mylan Pharmaceuticals, 8187
Mylander, George, 7636
Myler, David G., 4523
Myler, Thomas J., Sr., 4523
Myles Financial, R., 3077
Myra, John E., 7297
Myrhen, Trygve, 6248
Myrick, Carolyn S., 4846
Myron Leven Trust, 4492
Myska, Elizabeth, 4198
Mytton, William, 4947
Myura, Anthony, 2279
Myura, Patricia A., 2279
Mzuri Wildlife Foundation, 9631

N'Chonon, Lisa, 8498
N-Alpha Holdings, 6519
N.A. PNC Bank, 8078
N.E.W. Customer Service Cos., 8654

Na, Wei, 1773
Nabb, Edward H., Jr., 8188
Nabb, Linda K., 8188
Nabhloz Mechanical & Electrical, 208
Nabholz, 208
Nabholz Construction Corp., 208
Nabholz Propoerties Inc., 208
Nabholz Revocable Trust, Robert D., 209
Nabholz, Charles, 208
Nabholz, Robert D., 208, 209
Nabit, Charles J., 3924
Nabit, Merwin J., 3924
Nabors, Eddie, 2555
Nabozny, Barry, 2329
Nachshon, Shira, 500
Nachtsheim, Jami, 856
Nachtsheim, Stephen, 856
Nader, Anthony, 8654
Nadler, Jeff, 898
Nadzikewycz, Paul, 2967
Naeder, Harold, 3055
Naemura, David , 1368
Naftali Zvi Leshkowitz Memorial Foundation, 6247
Nagarkatti, Jai P., 5003
Nagel Trust, Edward M., 857
Nagel, Edward M., 857
Nagel, Frederick E., 9903
Nagengast, Stephen, 4577
Nagle Veal, 8859
Nagle, Arthur J., 5982
Nagle, Paige L., 5982
Nagorner, Anne, 568
Nahin, Marianne, 5517
Naiman, Norma Lee, 1815
Naish, Deborah, 223
Naito, Samuel T., 7803
Najafi, Francis, 9345
Najarian, K. George, 5562
Najarian, Richard, 6652
Najimi, Ghulam Ali, 6730
Najimi, Solyman, 6730
Najmi, Hakim, 6730
Najork, Susan, 5872
Nakano, Tsuyoshi, 9642
Nakao Trust, Satsuki, 647
Nakash, David, 6513
Nalle, Eleanor G., 8101
Nalley, Anita R., 8535
Nalley, George B., Jr., 8535
Nally, Joseph T., 897
Nally, Patrick L., 897
Namee, Eric S., 3576
Nance, Ed, 8701
Nance, Jessie, 7707
Nance, Penelope, 5061
Nance, Richard, 5397
Nance, Robert, 5061
Nance-Cebull, Amy, 5061
Nanda, Katharine, 1768
Nanda, Ved P., 1768
Nanney, Charles P., 7198
Nanney, David P., Jr., 7198
Nanney, Irene B., 7198
Nanovic 2009 Charitable Lead Annuity Trust, Robert S., 2399
Nanovic, Robert S., 2399
Nanovic-Morlet, Kathryn M., 2399
Nantz, David, 8937
Napa, Tom, 9685
Napier, Ed, 9757
Napier, James H., 152
Napoli, Patricia A., 6384
Napper, Sylvia, 4842

Naquin, David J., 9471
Nardella, Bruce, 4199
Narens, Edward, 4520
Narens, Judith, 4520
Nargiso, Sarah, 569
Narrow, S. Lee, 3863
Nartelski, Evelyn, 4521
Naruz, Pat, 2726
Narwhal Capital Management, 2520
Narzissenfeld, Bruce, 2367
Nasaw, David G., 858
Nasaw, James David, 858
Naschke, Arlene, 1708
Nasco North Central, 30
Naseman, David, 1799
NASGW, 3991
Nash Mariposa, 228
Nash Sports Club, Steve, 90
Nash, Alexandra H., 7677
Nash, Avi, 6242
Nash, David, 4419
Nash, Joann, 90
Nash, Jonathan, 4276
Nash, Joshua, 6548
Nash, Sandra, 6242
Nash, Stephen, 90
Nason Foundation, The, 1528
Nason, Alexander G., 1528
Nason, Alexandra, 1528
Nassif, Aundrea, 4781
Nassif, Calla, 4781
Nassif, David, 4781
Nassif, Monica, 4781
Nassimi, Edward, 6519
Nassimi, Iwan, 6519
Nassimi, Mike, 6519
Nassimi, Mike M., 6519
Nassimi, Mouris, 6519
Nassimi, Oliver, 6519
Nastasi, Paul, 3956
Natalia, Rebecca, 934
Natas, 2621
Natco Home Fashions, 8410
Natco Products Corp., 8410
Nathan, Cyrus H., 6152
Nathan, Margaret S., 6152
Nathan, Marvin D., 8872, 9062
Nathan, Robert, 6152
Nathan, Wally M., 2970
National Amusements, 4286
National Black McDonalds Operators, 153
National Christian Foundation, 1346, 7333, 9208, 9631
National Cine Media, 1295
National Distributing Co., 4334
National Diversified, 8750
National Electronics Warranty Corp., 8654
National Food and Beverage, 8859
National Football League, The, 5369
National Hockey League, 5873
National Mah Jongg League, Inc., 6520
National Maintenance Corp., 3297
National Media Group Limited, 2622
National Park Svc., 92
National Securities Corp., 5206
National Shooting Sports Foundation, 3991
National Society for Hebrew Day Schools, 5544
National Speaking of Women's Health, 7340
National Tennis Foundation, 6463

Nau, Tom, Jr., 254
Naud, Hilary Maslow, 8146
Naughton, Gail K., 227
Naugle, Jeffrey A., 7998
Naumes, Frances A., 7804
Naumes, Michael D., 7804
Naumes, Susan F., 7804
Navies, Jerome, 153
Navies, Mary, 153
Navigant Consulting, 3134
Nay, Tim, 7811
Nayak, Anjuli S., 3133
Nayak, Nicholas A., 3133
Nayak, Vasant, 3921
Nayowith, Maureen, 1856
Nazarian Family Foundation, 5478
Nazarian, Artemis, 5478
Nazarian, Claudia, 5478
Nazarian, Levon, 5478
Nazarian, Nazar, 5478
Nazem, Farzad, 595
NBT Bank, 6542, 6622
NCFI Banhardt Foundation, 7202
Neace Lukens Holding Co., 7507
Neag, Carole, 8189
Neag, Lynn J., 8189
Neag, Raymond, 8189
Neal, Bruce, 9781
Neal, Graham H., Jr., 9546
Neal, H. Scott, 9546
Neale, Linda, 7790
Neandross, Erik, 1216
Neandross, Miriam Zolla, 1216
Near, James B., Jr., 8536
Near, Susan, 8536
Nearney Family Foundation, 8243
Nebenzahl, Adina, 3970
Nebenzahl, Samuel, 3970
Nebris Corporation, 6992
Necky, Carrie, 5248
Nedderman, Theodore A., 7791
Neeb, Douglas M., 4968
Neeb, John M., 4968
Neeb, Larry W., 4968
Neeb, Martin J., 4968
Needham, Dorothy E., 7199
Needham, Judith, 3928
Needham, Thomas E., 4156
Neely, E. Kirk, 5269
Neenah Foundry Co., 9779
Neenan, S.J., William B., 4195
Neer, Howard L., 1978
Neese, Jay B., 1342
Neese, Sally, 4077
Neff, Dan, 8964
Neff, David K., 3346
Neff, Jerry L., 2149
Neff, Rosalind S., 7846
Neff, Roy S., 7846
Neger, Gitty, 2156
Nehman, Simone, 2581
Nehrbas, Andrew R., 7889
Neibauer, Fred, 8370
Neil, Gerard, 7295
Neil, Laura Kreeger, 6554
Neil, T. Corey, 2372
Neill, T. David, 7209
Neilson, Emily W., 9726
Neiman, Amy Warren, 75
Neiman, Helen, 6521
Neiman, Louis, 6521
Neiman, Marvin, 6521
Neiman, Solomon, 6521
Neiman, Susan S., 6721

Neiman, Velma A., 4969
Neisius, Megan E., 4809
Neisloss Family Foundation, 5550
Neisus, Mark, 4809
Neithercut, David J., 2858
Neithercut, Edward J., 4535
Neithercut, Elizabeth M., 4535
Neithercut, Mark E., 4535
Nelco Foundation UWO Leon Jolson Tr,
    6522
Nelco Sewing Machine Sales Corp.,
    6522
Nelligan, Michael , 601
Nelon, Anna Dezeng, 5320
Nelson 1998 Charitable Remainder
    Annuity Trust, 9086
Nelson Charitable Lead Trust, Margaret
    A., 860
Nelson Charitable Remainder Annuity
    Trust, Harold S., 9086
Nelson, Ann, 9999
Nelson, Arnold, 947
Nelson, Arnold L., 2230
Nelson, Arnold L.V., 2230
Nelson, Ashley, 713
Nelson, Betsy, 3816
Nelson, Brian, 947
Nelson, C. David, 4692, 4749
Nelson, C. Lynn, 1714
Nelson, Calvin, 458
Nelson, Cassie , 471
Nelson, Chandler A., 9419
Nelson, Charley, 4720
Nelson, Christopher, 4219
Nelson, Christopher Lori, 4219
Nelson, Clarke A., 9993
Nelson, Clint, 1295
Nelson, Cynthia, 3995
Nelson, David D., 3547
Nelson, David E., 1714
Nelson, Diana, 4749
Nelson, Donna K., 1714
Nelson, Doris, 3561
Nelson, Douglas, 8555
Nelson, Frances L., 9893
Nelson, Gregory, 947
Nelson, Harold S., 9086
Nelson, Helen, 2230
Nelson, Helen E., 9086
Nelson, Herbert, 8984
Nelson, James D., 2059
Nelson, Jeffrey, 5123
Nelson, John, 4219
Nelson, Karen, 7807
Nelson, Kathleen, 669
Nelson, Kathleen V., 4678
Nelson, Kelley, 472
Nelson, Kelly, 471
Nelson, Kipp N., 2683
Nelson, Kris, 9630
Nelson, Kristen, 713
Nelson, Larry J., 6365
Nelson, Leonard M., 3780
Nelson, Lynel Rae, 4773
Nelson, Margaret A., 860
Nelson, Mark , 2149
Nelson, Mary, 3524
Nelson, Mary A., 3524
Nelson, Mary D., 9894
Nelson, Matthew, 947
Nelson, Melissa, 9566
Nelson, Mindy, 9232
Nelson, Ned E.J., 1714
Nelson, Nicolas, 5106

Nelson, Pamela, 9696
Nelson, Pat, 1295
Nelson, Patricia C., 9709
Nelson, R.W., 3524
Nelson, Randolph, 3995
Nelson, Rebecca, 9888
Nelson, Ren, 5106
Nelson, Scott, 4219
Nelson, Stephen D., 860
Nelson, Stephen L., 4640
Nelson, Terri J., 860
Nelson, Theron, 2686
Nelson, Tom, 3592
Nelson, Victor D., 926
Nelson, Wealtha H., 5106
Nelson-Black, Anne, 1407
Nembhard, Jessica G., 8019
Neporent, Lisa King, 6523
Neporent, Mark A., 6523
Neptune Fisherman's Pride Processor,
    8859
Nerjes, Sonia, 6541
Nerney, Tom & Jill, 8243
Nesbit, Julie Lytle, 566
Nesbitt, Cindy, 9622
Nesbitt, Cyndi, 3379
Nesbitt, John, 7944
Nesci, Katherine M., 112
Nesh, Florence, 8191
Neshe, Dana M., 4203
Ness, James, 2418
Ness, Robert, 9732
Nessel, David L., 1529
Nessel, Dorothy M., 1529
Nessel, Judy, 1529
Nester, Dale, 4534
Nestle, 8859
Nestle Prepared Foods Company, 8859
Nestor, Alexander R., 1489, 1492
Nestor, Sally D., 1492
Netburn, Stephen, 3205
NetCorp, 7761
Netherland Mgmt. Co., 6764
Neto, Marcos, 4220
Netsolace, 1444
Netter, Alfred E., 6525
Netter, Alice, 6347
Netter, Alice D., 6525
Netter, K. Fred, 6525
Netter, Ronald A., 6525
NETTING PACE CPAS, 9258
Nettleton Trust, 3611
Neu Holdings Corp., 862
Neu, Amy P., 862
Neu, Richard W., 862
Neu, Steven W., 862
Neubauer, Peter B., 5326
Neuberger Berman Trust Co., 1646,
    1650
Neuberger Foundation, 5937
Neuberger, Gary, 8574
Neuberger, Linda, 5937
Neuberger, Roy S., 5937
Neuenschwander, Jack L., 7395
Neufeld, Lena, 5635
Neufeld, Peter, 5635
Neufeld, Shane, 5635
Neuhoff Recovable Trust, Majorie A.,
    2556
Neuman, Herbert, 6526
Neuman, Irving, 6526
Neuman, Jeffrey L., 2324
Neuman, Judith, 1331
Neuman, Karen, 1890

Neuman, Marvin, 6526
Neuman, Suzanne, 1331
Neuman, Werner, 1331
Neuman, William, 1331
Neumann, Mark D., 3957
Neumann, Mieke, 750
Neumann, Patti, 3957
Neumann, Robin, 3957
Neumann, Roland M., 9961
Neumeier, Doris, 7379
Neupaver, Albert J., 8335
Neurath, Moshe, 5247
Neuro Rays Imaging, 1730
Neurological Research Foundation,
    9229
Neurosurgery and Endovascular
    Associates, 90
Neusch, Agnes, 9208
Neusch, Sarah, 9208
Neusch, William H., 9208
Neustadt, Dolores K., 9256
Neustadt, Walter, Jr., 9256
Neutzling, RN, BS, M.Ed, Virginia, 7312
Neuwirth Motors, 7281
Neuwirth, Gloria S., 6022, 6916
Neuwirth, Jessica, 6916
Neuwirth, Steve, 480
Nevas, Bernard, 1530
Nevas, Leo, 1530
Neve Shaanan Irrevocable Trust, 5697
Nevil, Mark, 9133
Nevill-Manning, Craig, 6337
Nevill-Manning, Kirsten, 6337
Neville, Joe, 9098
Nevin, Elizabeth B., 5650
Nevin, Stephen C., 5650
Nevis, Vita, 703
New Bidnis Inc., 6796
New Cassel Construction, 6675
New Century Mgmt. Svcs. LLC, 6339
New England Biolabs, 4220
New Future Dreams, 5443
New Haven Custom Homes, 9009
New Hotel Monteleone, LLC, 3741
New Hudson Partners, LLC, 5338
New Jersey Basketball, LLC, 6524
New Jersey Sports & Exposition
    Authority, 5369
New Moon Trust, 1090
New Prospect Foundation, 3008, 3045,
    3136
New PST, 1362
New York Business Development Corp.,
    6546
New York Business Development
    Corporation, 6546
New York Cardiac Ctr., 5245
New York Football Giants, 5369
New York Racing Assn., 6265
New, Landy, 1905
Newark & Co. Real Estate, 6656
Newark Rotary Club, 7513
Newberg, Bruce, 1090
Newberry Farms, LLC, 3347
Newberry, Karma, 9130
Newbridge Bank, 7222
Newburyport Five Cents Savings Bank,
    4221
Newcomb, Nancy S., 6529
Newcomer, David C., 7339
Newcomer, Glen L., 7339
Newell, Hope, 6908
Newell, Mike, 697
Newell, Robert M., 973

Newfarmer, Jerry, 7582
Newhouse, Julie, 8308
Newkirk, Glen, 5624
Newland, James L., 2521
Newlands, David, 1368
Newlove, Natalie, 7767
Newman Motorsports, Ryan, 7094
Newman, Alison, 6533
Newman, Allen, 6387
Newman, Amelia G., 6534
Newman, Andra Winokur, 1597
Newman, Carol, 6532
Newman, Claudia, 9669
Newman, Darryl, 5179
Newman, David, 839
Newman, Denise, 5179
Newman, Eddie, 660
Newman, Frank, 6531
Newman, Frank N., 6531
Newman, Gary, 8769
Newman, Howard A., 6530
Newman, Jeff, 1352
Newman, Jeffrey A., 6530
Newman, Jerome A., 6530
Newman, Jill, 4317
Newman, John B., 7199
Newman, Joshua, 6532
Newman, L. Mark, 5179
Newman, Lawrence, 6162
Newman, Leslie, 1696
Newman, Linda, 5179
Newman, Lizabeth, 6531
Newman, Mark S., 6533
Newman, Melvin D., 6532
Newman, Melvin S., 9800
Newman, Mike, 4411
Newman, Nancy, 813
Newman, Nell, 859
Newman, Paul, 5179
Newman, Scott, 5663
Newman, Sharon M., 6533
Newman, Stanley, 1531
Newman, Thomas L., 2208
Newman, William C., 6530
Newmark & Co., 6655
Newmyer, Deborah, 662
Newnam, Bob , 9474
Newport Homebuilders Ltd., 9009
Newport Homes, 9009
Newsom, Jean, 1807
Newsome, Gary D., 8628
Newson, Leslie A., 6644
Newton, Barbara W., 7826
Newton, Blake T., III, 6682
Newton, Patty S., 3751
Newton, Stan, 607
Newton, Thomas, 9771
Newton, Tim, 5692
Newtown Savings Bank, 1532
Nexsen, Clark, 9421
NFL Charities, 4399
NFL Foundation, 4399
NFL Youth Football Fund, 4399
NFP Ltd, 3801
NFP Partnership, 3801
Ng, Tze Ping, 8447
Nganga, John, 7513
Ngo, Catherine, 2627
Ni Keefe, Katherine M., 4229
Niblack, Heidi G., 1533
Niblack, John F., 1533
Niblick, Harold W., 3423
Niccolai, Sandra Davino, 5313
Nich, Ellen G., 3992

Nichelson, Anne, 8498
Nichol, James, 1581
Nicholas, Anthony E., 485
Nicholas, Duane, 7724
Nicholas, Frederick M., 485
Nicholas, George, 2092
Nicholas, Gina, 3057
Nicholas, Joseph G., 2092
Nicholas, Patricia, 405
Nicholas, Richard J., 1589
Nicholas, Stacey, 885
Nicholas, Victor, 84
Nicholl, Peter T., 3926
Nicholl, Teresa A., 3926
Nicholls, S. Scott, Jr., 7013
Nichols Co., J.C., 4970
Nichols Construction, 3297
Nichols Revocable Trust, Frank Culver, 404
Nichols, Adam, 3074
Nichols, Albert, 405
Nichols, Albert, Mrs. , 405
Nichols, Briana, 3074
Nichols, Bruce, 4462
Nichols, Christine W., 7644
Nichols, Christine Wolfe, 7644
Nichols, Curtis L., 7068
Nichols, Dennis D., 2198
Nichols, Elizabeth, 4350
Nichols, George D., 4910
Nichols, Gregory A., 2198, 2253
Nichols, Harriet, 590
Nichols, James R., 4350
Nichols, Janice, 3413
Nichols, Katie, 3482
Nichols, Lauren A.B., 404
Nichols, Linda, 8608
Nichols, Linda Duda, 1983
Nichols, Maira M., 2253
Nichols, Manford, 3641
Nichols, Patricia, 405
Nichols, Patrick A., 9752
Nichols, Robin Tawney, 5047
Nichols, Scott G., 697
Nichols, Steven, 590
Nichols, Steven C., 404
Nichols, Tricia, 405
Nichols, William A., 7644
Nicholson, Bruce, 866
Nicholson, Mamie, 8526
Nicholson, Nick, 3668
Nicholson, W. John, 866
Nicholson, W.J., 866
Nickel, Mark C., 6683
Nickell, Douglas R., 4994
Nicker Management 1 Inc., 153
Nickerson, Anne, 9981
Nickerson, Brett R., 9988
Nickerson, David, 9981
Nickerson, Elizabeth, 9988
Nickerson, Gregory, 9981
Nickerson, Jocelyn A., 9988
Nickerson, Phillip, 9981
Nickerson, Scott, 9981
Nickerson, Thorpe A., 9988
Nicklas, Gerald, 1914
Nickles, Larry S., 60
Nickless, Allen E., 4522
Nickless, Charles, 4522, 4616
Nickless, Darcy, 4522
Nickless, Marie A., 4522
Nickoll, David Ari, 867
Nickoll, John F., 867
Nickoll, Patricia, 867

Nicolarsen, David J., 10000
Nicolarsen, Karen E., 10000
Nicolla, Joseph, 1730
Niebergail, Stephanie, 9880
Nieby Revocable Trust, Stanley, 2149
Niederhoffer, Marc, 6831
Niederhoffer, Richard, 6831
Niederman, John, 3397
Niedermeyer, Ranee, 7764
Niedes, Pamela, 7383
Nielsen, Catherine G., 7730
Nielsen, Gordon L., 7730
Nielsen, Harold, 4820
Nielson, David, 9340
Nielson, Jody, 9340
Nieman, Rosalind Emmett, 481
Niemiec, David W., 6535
Niemiec, Melanie M., 6535
Nierenberg, Karen, 900
Niese, Rick, 7356
Niesner, Helen, 9213
Niess, Vivian, 6068
Niessen, Leo, Jr., 7200
Nieter, Daniel, 3429
Nightingale, Don, 3641
Nightingale, Jerrell, 3641
Nightingale, Kay, 9937
Nightingale, Kenneth, 3641
Nightingale, Richard, 899
Nigro, Catherine A., 3570
Nigro, Christopher, 3570
Niiya, Eddie, 892
Nike, 6839
Nikkel, Carole A., 7675
Nikkel, John G., 7675
Nikkel, Robert E., 7675
Niklaus, Jennifer C., 740
Niknava, Meir, 2329
Nikolaus, Donald, 7932
Nikolaus, Donald H., 8193
Nikolaus, Roseann, 7932
Niles, Christopher Del Moral, 9778
Niles, Clayton E., 172
Niles, Clayton N., 172
Nillson, Jenny Lind, 5700
Nily, Vernon J., Jr., 3959
Nimrod, Ray, 480
Ninteman, Wendy, 104
NIR Group, The, 5482
Nirenberg, Charles, 1534
Nirenberg, Janet, 1534
Nishimoto, Cynthia, 271
Nislar, James, 9088
Nissel, Neal J., 2254
Nissley, Emily B., 1526
Nissley, Thomas W., 1526
Nitta, John, 5203
Nitta, Kent K., 5203
Nivison, Arthur E., 7201
Nivison, W.B., 7201
Nix, David, 884
Nix, Virginia, 884
Nixon 1982 Trust, Nan Allen, 5906
Nixon, Barbara, 9649
Nixon, Diane A., 5906
Nixon, Freddie, 193
Nixon, John, 5398
Niya's Nest, 1708
Nobatian, Soleyman John, 411
Nobel, Barry, 2232
Nobel, Cecilia Van Strum, 3974
Nobel, Fred I., 2232
Nobel, Gilda, 2232
Nobel, Margery S., 6059

Nobel, Robert, 3974
Nobel, Sanford M., 6059
Nobile, Robert, 3242
Noble Chemical Inc., 7925
Noble, Bette, 2233
Noble, Bette A., 2233
Noble, Constance, 4224
Noble, Constance A., 4224
Noble, George L., 4224
Noble, Howard, 5053
Noble, Kevin, 4790
Noble, Larry, 607
Noble, Lisa, 7452
Noble, Richard G., 4823
Noble, Terrance O., 2233
Noble, Terrence, 2233
Noblitt, Joseph F, 2190
Noblitt, Nancy Z., 2190
Noblitt, Niles L., 2190
Nocetti, Deanne, 643
Noecker, Carson, 3424
Noecker, Rosemary, 3424
Noel, Elizabeth, 1453
Noel, Susan Bass, 2723
Noell, Anne, 7807
Nofer, George, 7870
Nojovits, Esther F., 6770
Nojovits, Samuel, 6770
Nojovits, Samuel J., 6770
Noko, Ishmael, 6249
Nolan, John, 5541
Nolan, Margaret, 379
Nolan, Tom, 7209
Noland, Nanette, 3743
Noland, Renee, 2166
Noland, Sheri, 9712
Nolen, Eliot, 6971
Nolen, Margaret Anne, 8171
Nolet, Lucinda, 4107
Nomina, John, 7379
Noonan, Christopher B., 2558
Noonan, David , 4471
Noonan, Frank M., 4225
Noonan, Kimbrough P., 2558
Noonan, Mary Antonia, 1867
Noonan, Patrick F., 5662
Noonan, Thomas E., 2558
Norbut, John, 2817
Norcross, Elizabeth, 2625
Nord Capital Group, 1332
Nordby, Debra, 9732
Nordell, Ellen, 8322
Nordhagen, Arlen D., 1332
Nordhagen, Wendy P., 1332
Nordlicht, Ira S., 1447
Nordling, Ken, 3801
Nordling, Sally, 3801
Nordlund, Judi, 5129
Nordstrom, Linda, 9668
Nored, Anita, 3766
Noreen, Roger F., 4750
Norfleet, Edward A., 7258
Norfolk, Lynette, 369
Norford, Edward R., 8196
Norgaard Living Trust, Eric, The , 3141
Norgaard, Eric, 3141
Norman Foundation, The, 6204, 6366
Norman, Janice B., 8513
Norman, Katherine M., 2669
Norman, Marilyn J., 4429
Norman, Virginia, 12
Normandin, Jim, 3549
Normen, Elizabeth, 1552
Norment, E. Sims, 9114

Norment, Robert S., 9114
Norquist, Laura Lee Pattillo, 51
Norred, Anne H., 8587
Norrell, Jimmy R., 13
Norris, Dale, 9245
Norris, Jennifer, 3426
Norris, Travis, 3426
Norris, William C., 3757
Norry, Elliot, 5535
Norry, Gail, 5535
North Carolina Foam Industries, 7202
North Community Bank, 2866
North Family Voting Trust, 3142
North Hailey Corporation, 6992
North, Amy Brown, 7076
North, Dean P., 8625
North, Katie, 5129
North, Robin L., 9489
Northam, Hazel, 6625
Northeast Pennsylvania Financial Corp., 7997
Northeast Theatre Corp., 4286
Northern Bank of Florida, 2162
Northern Plains Steel Co., 5108
Northern Trust, 3043, 3162, 3214
Northern Trust Bank, 2744
Northern Trust Co., 2938
Northern Trust Co., The, 2071, 2711, 2738, 2782, 2836, 2847, 2950, 3055, 3086, 3088, 3089, 3109, 3110, 3142, 3207, 3216, 3233, 3330
Northern Trust Company, 3259
Northern Trust Company, The, 2889, 2946, 3294
Northfield Savings Bank, 9382
Northrail, 3905
Northrip, Nancy, 2921
Northrop, Kaaren, 9810
Northway, John, 4568
Northwest Savings Bank, 7917
Northwoods, LP, 8513
Norton, Dale, 4396
Norton, Erica Joy, 696
Norton, James R., 3943
Norton, Molly, 3943
Norweb, Elizabeth, 7539
Norweb, Henry R., III, 7539
Norweb, R. Henry, Jr., 7539
Norwood, Jonathan W., 8539
Nosal, Gayle, 3801
Nosan, Heather, 4657
Noshirvani, Vahid, 6589
Noss, Stanley, 1402
Nosworthy, Douglas, 360
Notebaert, Richard C., 3108
Nottingham Properties, 3831
Novack, Kenneth J., 4226
Novak, William B., 1346
Novakov, Lydia H., 8908
Novartis Corp., 2406
Novick, Oscar A., 3143
Novick, Oscar Bernice, 5665
Novick, Rose A., 3143
Novogrod, John C., 6948
Novy-Hildesly, Julia, 7781
Nowak, Carole M., 7400
Nowiczewski, Joseph, 9090
Nowiczewski, Paula, 9090
Nowiszewski, Daniel, 4234
Nowlan, Kevin, 4511
Nowotny, Barbara K., 9091
Nowotny, John, 9091
Nowotny, Suzanne, 9091

Noyce Foundation, 437
NTB, 4486
NU Lens, 9895
NU West Petroleum, 301
Nu-Di Corp., 7368
Nuckols, Joanne M., 511
Nuckols, Norwood, 9532
Nugent, Elizabeth R., 3425
Nugent, Kari, 2802
Nugent, Patrick Lyndon, 9011
Nuland, Hope S., 4275
Nunley, John G., 9396
Nunley, Julia G., 9396
Nunley, Richard L., 9396
Nunn, Carolee, 9662
Nunn, Peggy Tauton, 2456
Nunnelly, James T., 4983
Nureyev, Rudolf, 3145
Nurkin, Harry A., 6490
Nursery, Gatti, 6083
Nursing Care Center at Medford, 6469
Nusbaum, Barbara, 4524
Nusbaum, Irving, 4524
Nussbaum, Bernard W., 6545
Nussbaum, Martin, 6545
Nussbaum, Peter, 6411
Nusslock, Kathy L., 9847
Nutter McClennen & Fish LLP, 4005
Nuzzo, Bryann, 9386
Nuzzo, D., 2236
Nuzzo, J., 2236
Nuzzo, James, 9386
Nuzzo, Lucille, 2236
Nuzzo, Salvatore J., 2236
NV Energy, 5188
NV Energy Charitable Foundation, 5188
Nye, David E., 4227
Nye, Grace S., 4227
Nye, Richard, 6899
Nygaard, Ellen C., 9826
Nygren, Ana M., 151
Nygren, Sara, 3146
Nygren, William C., 3146
Nypro Inc., 4228
NYRA Charities, 6265
NYS Tax Credit, 5705
Nys, John, 4630
Nysether, Bradley, 9671
Nysether, Eldon M., 9671
Nysether, Kathy, 9671
Nysether, Mark, 9671
Nysether, Mark A., 9671
Nysether, Shirley, 9671
Nysether, Vickie, 9671
Nystrom, Corliss, 9662
NYT Capital Inc., 6656
NYYM - Dietrich Fund, 8008

O F Mossberg & Sons, 3991
O'Boyle, Bonnie J., 8029
O'Brate, Cecil, 3612
O'Brate, Jennifer, 3612
O'Brate, Mark, 3612
O'Brein, Charles, 8243
O'Brein, Mari, 8243
O'Brien, Alice M., 4753
O'Brien, Alvina, 4753
O'Brien, Andrew, 4866
O'Brien, Barbara, 2189
O'Brien, Cari, 4763
O'Brien, Collin L., 9852
O'Brien, Daniel J., 5144
O'Brien, Francis X., 5566

O'Brien, James A., 9767
O'Brien, John, 4462
O'Brien, Justin F., 9852
O'Brien, Kevin, 6699
O'Brien, Kirsten L., 9852
O'Brien, Lori R., 4866
O'Brien, Mary K., 4057
O'Brien, Michael, 2826
O'Brien, Mike, 2802
O'Brien, Sally, 9810
O'Brien, Terence, Jr., 4753
O'Brien, Thomas M., 6443
O'Brien, Thomond R., Jr., 4753
O'Brien, Tyler H., 9852
O'Bryan, Sean, 4449
O'Connell, Barbara, 5919, 6170
O'Connell, Charlie, 3079
O'Connell, Lesley, 9781
O'Connell, Mark M., 6476
O'Connell, Mary Adams, 228
O'Connell, Michael F., 4052, 4329
O'Connor & Hewitt Foundation, The, 9093
O'Connor Foundation, Cozen, 7941
O'Connor, Brooke L., 1404
O'Connor, Christopher E., 1223
O'Connor, Daniel, 3148
O'Connor, Dennis, 9093
O'Connor, James, 6284
O'Connor, Janet M., 1223
O'Connor, Kathleen, 4641
O'Connor, Kathleen G., 4641
O'Connor, Kathryn S., 9093
O'Connor, Louise, 9093
O'Connor, Martin, 3148
O'Connor, Martin B., II, 5445
O'Connor, Mary Jane, 3149
O'Connor, Matthew, 3148
O'Connor, Michelle, 5774
O'Connor, Richard D., 3785
O'Connor, Richard F., 6898
O'Connor, Richard L., 1109
O'Connor, Sally A., 1404
O'Connor, Thomas E., 1223
O'Connor, Timothy J., 1404
O'Connor, Timothy M., 1329
O'Connor, Tom, Jr., 9093
O'Connor, William F., 3149
O'Conor, Janet, 1223
O'Day, Roger V., 4077
O'Donnell Children's Trust, The, 9672
O'Donnell, Harry J., 9672
O'Donnell, Harry J., Jr., 9672
O'Donnell, Jim, 9672
O'Donnell, Laurence J., 5325
O'Donnell, Mariette E., 9672
O'Donnell, Robert G., 874
O'Donnell, Sue D., 874
O'Donohue, C. Page, 3204
O'Donovan, Karen J., 4525
O'Donovan, Kevin M., 4525
O'Donovan, Ryan J., 4525
O'Donovan, Timothy J., 4525
O'Dwyer, Brian, 6493
O'Grady, Gerald B., III, 4056
O'Grady, John B., 9394, 9472
O'Grady, Judith, 5400
O'Grady, Kathleen, 6551
O'Grady, Kathleen C., 6551
O'Grady, Thomas B., 6551
O'guin, Susan, 8674
O'Halloran, Alice, 8462
O'Halloran, Gerard, 8462
O'Halloran, Mary Ann, 8462

O'Hara, Alice, 2769
O'Hara, Alison, 2877
O'Hara, Ann, 8345
O'Hara, Ariel, 2877
O'Hara, Donald F., 8501
O'Hara, Eugene, 5358
O'Hara, Jennifer, 8347
O'Hara, Keith, 2877
O'Hara, Peter, 371
O'Hare, Donna, 6624
O'Hare, Kathryn Angell Sackett, 9095
O'Hare, W. Scott, 9095
O'Hearn, Walter D., Jr., 4063
O'Hern, Janet, 2943
O'Herron, Jonathan, Jr., 1536
O'Herron, Shirley, 1536
O'Keefe, Andrew F., 4229
O'Keefe, Andrew J., 5530
O'Keefe, Anne G., 5530
O'Keefe, Catherine, 5530
O'Keefe, Colleen, 4785
O'Keefe, David D., 4229
O'Keefe, Dorothy, 8566
O'Keefe, Jeffrey, 4824
O'Keefe, Karen M., 4229
O'Keefe, Kevin, 2913
O'Keefe, Raymond, 6372
O'Keefe, William P., 3127
O'Keeffe, Kathryn, 6082
O'Kieffe Charitable Lead Annuity Trust, P.S., 3248
O'Kieffe, Patricia S., 3248
O'Leary, Daniel E., 3777
O'Leary, Thomas M., 3167
O'Leary-Joy, Shannon, 1301
O'Mack, Carol-Ann, 9679
O'Malley, Donald J., 2217
O'Malley, Jennifer A., 8179
O'Malley, Kalli, 554
O'Mally, Doug, 5337
O'Meara, Martin J., Jr., 1537
O'Meara, Tom, 4962
O'Meara, William F., 1537
O'Neal, Bobby, 8711
O'Neal, E. Stanley, 5481
O'Neal, Jeffrey, 587
O'Neal, Patricia J., 9097
O'Neil, Albert T., 4755
O'Neil, Anne, 6557
O'Neil, Casey Albert, 4755
O'Neil, Celeste Cheatham, 5836
O'Neil, Jane R., 1794
O'Neil, Karen, 6557
O'Neil, Maria, 6557
O'Neil, Mark, 6557
O'Neil, Michael N., 3930
O'Neil, Monica, 6557
O'Neil, Pamela B., 3930
O'Neil, Peter, 6557
O'Neil, Ralph M., 6557
O'Neil, Stephen, 5836, 6557
O'Neil, Stephen B., 3930
O'Neil, Thomas F., III, 3930
O'Neil, Thomas F., Jr., 3930
O'Neil, Thomas J., 3168
O'Neill, Dan, 8345
O'Neill, Daniel J., 7542
O'Neill, Don, 6898
O'Neill, Frances J., III, 7542
O'Neill, Francis J., 7542
O'Neill, George D., Jr., 310
O'Neill, H.M., 7542
O'Neill, Katie, 5139
O'Neill, Kellie, 5139

O'Neill, Lawrence, Hon. , 1191
O'Neill, P.J., 7542
O'Neill, Peter, 6922
O'Neill, Sarah Q., 711
O'Neill, Steven, 4892
O'Neill, Walden, 469
O'Neill, William J., 7542
O'Reillly, Nancy D., 4975
O'Reilly Rev. Trust Bypass Tr., 8200
O'Reilly Survivors Trust, Helen, 8200
O'Reilly, Charles H., Jr., 4974
O'Reilly, Charlie, 4974, 4975
O'Reilly, Larry P., 4975
O'Reilly, Lauren P., 4975
O'Reilly, Mary Beth, 4974, 4975
O'Reilly, Nancy D., 4975
O'Reilly, Patrick, 4974
O'Reilly, Patrick E., 4974, 4975
O'Reilly, Ragan R., 4975
O'Reilly, Ryan, 4974
O'Reilly, Ryan C., 4974, 4975
O'Reilly, Timothy, 4974
O'Reilly, Timothy B., 4974, 4975
O'Rielly, Barbara C., 154
O'Rielly, R.B., 154
O'Riordon, Andrea, 5195
O'Rourke, Colleen, 4757
O'Rourke, J. Tracy, 8571
O'Rourke, Joan C., 1131
O'Rourke, Patrick, 4757
O'Rourke, Rejean, 3429
O'Rourke, Sean, 4757
O'Rourke, Timothy, 4757
O'Shanna, Richard, 2987
O'Shaughnessy, M., 9505
O'Shaughnessy, Mary Hurst, 9505
O'Shea, Carole, 892
O'Shea, John P., 892
O'Sullivan, Ann, 8105
O'Sullivan, Carole, 6565
O'Sullivan, Genevieve K., 9030
O'Sullivan, James J., 810
O'Sullivan, Kevin P., 6565
O'Sullivan, Timothy, 8140
O'Toole, Michelle, 4877
O-Z Gedney Co., LLC, 7252
O'Rourke, John, III, 1952
Oakes, Amanda, 9556
Oakley Testamentary Trust, H.N., 3426
Oakley, Hollie N., 3426
Oakley, Jane, 3379
Oasis Care Center, 3657
Oates Family Foundation, 301
Oates, William A., 6111
Oathout, Darla, 6238
Obay, Albert, 2702
Ober Foundation, 3400
Ober, Theodore E., 4150, 4363
Oberbeck, Christian L., 6787
Oberg, Paul, 4719
Oberlander, Jill, 1535
Oberlin, Brenna, 1158
Oberlin, E. Clifford, III, 7339
Oberman, Michael S., 6374, 6636
Obermayer, Stephen, 5724
Oberoi, Alok, 6547
Oberoi, Majini, 6547
Oberste, Rachel, 186
Oberstein, Norman S., 746
Obert, Charlotte B., 8150
Obolensky, Ivan, 6224
Obregon, Sarah S., 6331
Och, Daniel, 6629
Ochs, Rita, 1257

Ochs, Ronald K., 9850
Ochsman, Bruce David, 9504
Ochsman, Jeffrey Wayne, 9504
Ochsman, Meurice C., 9504
Ochsman, Michael Paul, 9504
Ochsman, Ralph, 9504
Oddleifson Trust, Eric, 4264
Oddleifson, Eric, 4264
Oddleifson, Janna, 4264
Odell, Jean Simmons, 2338
Odell, Virginia Fry, 1458
Odell, Wynne, 466
Oden Charitable Trust, Sydnor & Olga, 9094
Oden, Zillan T., 9094
Odendahl, Keith, 7799, 9323
Odgen, Tim, 1354
Odo, Rachel, 6772
Odom, Carmen Hooker, 6490
Odom, Dorothy E., 1843
Odom, Elizabeth C., 1843
Odom, Patricia A., 1843
Odom, Roderick D., 1843
Odyssey Investment Partners, LLC, 6548
Odzinski, Debora Y., 469
Oehler, Robert, 533
OEM Worldwide, 9931
Oestreicher, Sylvan, 6549
Oetinger, Nancy, 6217
Oettmeier, Janice, 8975
Ofat, Theodore M., 7545
Offensend, David, 6550
Offensend, David G., 6550
Offensend, Janet, 6550
Offensend, Janet M., 6550
Offer, David, 389
Offield, Chase P., 875
Offield, Paxon H., 875
Offield, Paxson H., 875
Offit, Sidney, 5700
Ogden Cap Properties, 6656
Ogden, Anne L., 1418
Ogden, Douglas H., 869
Ogden, Emilie M., 869
Ogden, Marilynn, 7295
Ogilvie, Donald G., 4239
Ogilvie, Donna Brace, 1410
Ogle, Laura Kerr, 7693
Ogle, Paul W., 3462
Oglesby, John, 2714
Oglesby, John F., 2714
Oglesby, Lamar, Mrs. , 2714
Oglesby, Myrna L., 337
Oglesby, Richard A., Jr., 2541, 2714
Oglesby, Richard A., Sr., 2714
Ogletree, Sandy, 9209
Oh, Christine, 883
Ohab, Pamela, 2305
Ohendalski, Kay, 8895
Ohendalski, R.S., 8895
Ohio Power Co., 7303
Ohlhausen, George, 3151
Ohlhausen, Katherine B., 1631
Ohlhausen, Sarah, 3151
Ohlsen, Ronald, 3147
Ohman, Clifton W., 276
Ohno Construction Co., 9673
Ohno, Barbara, 9673
Ohno, I.F., 9673
Ohno, Yoshio A., 9673
Ohren Living Trust, Steven, The , 877
Ohrot Shel Tzion, 6518
Ohrstrom, Barnaby A., 9415
Ohrstrom, George L., II, 9415

Ohrstrom, Kenneth M., 9415
Ohrstrom, Mark J., 9415
Ohrstrom, Richard R., 9415
Oka, Megumi, 6436
Oken, Jennifer G., 6049
Oken, Richard L., 260
Okinaga, Etsuko, 1334
Okinaga, Shohachi, 1334
Okinaga, Yoshihito, 1334
Oklahoma Surgical Hospital, LLC, 7711
Okner, Joel C., 3152
Okner, Seymour, 3152
Oko, Scott A., 1962
Okray, Carol, 9896
Okray, Edward J., 9896
Okray, Lucille S., 9896
Okray, Richard W., 9896
OKT Char. Lead Trust, 2160
Okuda, Roy, 1100
Okuku, Tom, 2622
Olafson, Harlee N., 3547
Olander, Minola, 878
Olander, Ronald, 878
Olavarria, Alexandra, 2048
Olazabal, F. David, 1952
Olberding, Julie, Dr. , 7582
Olcomendy, Patricia, 276
Olcott, Barbara P., 5227
Olcott, Charles W., 5227
Olcott, Emery G., 5227
Old National Bank, 3351
Old National Trust, 3469
Old National Trust Co., 3405, 3431
Oldfather, Alan, 5077
Oldfather, William, 5077
Oldfield, Col. A. Barney, 4723
Olds, Eutha, 210
Olds, Ransom M., 4526
Olds, W. Cleda, 210
Olds, William F., 3411
Olem Shoe Corp., 2237
Olem Shoe Corporation, 2237
Olemberg, Isaac, 2237
Olemberg, Nieves, 2237
Olemberg, Roberto, 2237
Olender, Jack H., 1824
Olender, Lovell R., 1824
Olens, Lisa, 2463
Oleson, Sandra L., 9963
Oliff, Hershel, 9218
Olijnyk, Maria, 2967
OLILVY, 1730
Oliphant, Dorothy J., 1165
Olitsky, Stephen, 8198
Olitsky, T., 8198
Olitsky, Tamar, 8198
Olivarez, Edward, 1109
Oliver, Andrew, Jr., 1796
Oliver, Ann B., 6560
Oliver, Bartley P., 1131
Oliver, Cynthia Sheely, 7590
Oliver, Daniel, 1796
Oliver, Harry, 480
Oliwa, Suzanne, 3990
Ollie, George, 7670
Olliff, Matred Carlton, 2239
Olmstead, Nancy, 181
Olmstead, Sally G., 9374
Olofson, Christopher E., 3613
Olofson, Jeanne H., 3613
Olofson, Scott W., 3613
Olofson, Tom W., 3613
Olrich, Leslie L., 3640
Olsen Charitable Trust, Christian, 2240

Olsen, Brad, 3002
Olsen, David A., 8463
Olsen, Ed, 7204
Olsen, Gary, 4557
Olsen, Gregory H., 5480
Olsen, Jean B., 4667
Olsen, Kris, 586
Olsen, Mary Beth, 3002
Olsen, Mike L., 4713
Olsen, Roberta G., 8463
Olsen, Ronald, 1938
Olsen, Steve, 5113
Olson, Ann, 432
Olson, Barb, 4771
Olson, Bill, 4657
Olson, Clifford, 401
Olson, Craig, 879
Olson, David, 5107
Olson, Dorothy, 5107
Olson, Gary, 361
Olson, Gary A., 3154
Olson, Graham, 9878
Olson, Jane, 879
Olson, Jennie H., 9897
Olson, Karen, 5107
Olson, Laron, 9592
Olson, Leland, 5107
Olson, Mary Houck, 2978
Olson, Nancy, 5107
Olson, Peggy L., 5064
Olson, Richard, 4671
Olson, Roger, 5074
Olson, Ronald L., 9898
Olson, Scott, 5091
Olson, Stephen E., 891
Olson, Thomas L., 9796
Olsson, Walter, 4408
Olstad, Ann M., 831
Olszewski, Zuzanna, 1418
Olum, Kenneth, 6555
Olum, Paul, 6555
Olum-Galaski, Joyce, 6555
Omega Foundation, The, 5147
Omen, Jill, 258
Omer, Russell J., 4047
Omidyar, Elah'e Mir-Djalali, 2297
Omidyar, Pierre, 2297
Omlor, Heather K., 5427
Omni Waste of Osceola, LLC, 2108
Omnicom Group, 8657
OmniSource Corp., 3437
Omohundro, Ed, 9196
Omohundro, Helen, 9196
Onan, David W., II, 4754
Onan, David W., III, 4754
Onan, Patricia, 4754
Once Upon A Time Foundation, 8795
One Canal Place LLC, 6656
One Heart, 6420
OneSight, 9098
Ontario Community Hospital, 882
Ontiveros, Sara D., 4344
Ooten, Brian G., 6908
Open Bank, 883
Open It, 8711
Open Society Institute, 5605
OPI Products, Inc., 1013
Opie, Katherine, 3608
Opie, Sandra, 3608
Oppenheim, Jane, 8199
Oppenheim, Stephen J., 7203
Oppenheimer, Alexander, 6834
Oppenheimer, Alexis, 4924
Oppenheimer, Brian, 4973

Oppenheimer, Edward H., 3155
Oppenheimer, Edward, Jr., 9100
Oppenheimer, Gerald, 630
Oppenheimer, Gordon S., 6834
Oppenheimer, Hal, 4924
Oppenheimer, Harry D., 3155
Oppenheimer, Harry J., 3155
Oppenheimer, J. David, 9101
Oppenheimer, James, 3155
Oppenheimer, James K., 3155
Oppenheimer, Jason, 6834
Oppenheimer, Jesse H., 9101
Oppenheimer, Leo, 4924
Oppenheimer, Marti, 4973
Oppenheimer, Seymour, 3155
Oppenheimer, Steven, 5960
Oppenheimer, Susan R., 9101
Oppenheimer, Tony, 4973
Oppens, Ursula, 5671
Opperman, Mary, 6373
Opsahl, Jina Engelsma, 8563
Optivest Inc, 884
Optivest Properties Protection, 884
Optivest Properties, LLC, 884
Opus Corp., 4697, 4738, 4767, 8568
Orange, Wendy, 1871
Oratory of St. Augustine and St. Gregory, 5022
Ording, Elizabeth, 8741
Ording, Michael, 8741
Ordway, J. Erik, 4665
Ordway, John G., III, 4665
Ordway, John G., Jr., 4665
Ordway, Phillip W., 4665
Ore Hill Partners, 8581
Orear, Jeffrey, Dr. , 4497
Oreffice, Franca G., 4528
Oreffice, Paul F., 4528
Oreggia Living Trust, Arden, 886
Oreggia Living Trust, Sabina, 886
Oregonian, The, 7798
Oremus, Frederick L., 7545
Oren, Nedra Y., 3334
Orens, Lucy H., 8947
Orens, Robert, 6305
Orens, Sarah, 6305
Orenstein, Alexander, 6784
Oreskes, Michael, 5879
Orfalea, Natalie Fleet, 887
Orfalea, Paul J., 887
Orgain, Ashley, 9384
Orgeman, Michael, 9924
Orioles Reach, 3817
Oristaglio Family Enhancement Trust, 4232
Oristaglio, Jeryl, 4232
Oristaglio, Stephen, 4232
Oristano, Jane, 2241
Oristano, Victor, 2241
Orkin, Adam, 2560
Orkin, Barbara, 2559
Orkin, Sanford, 2559
Orkin, Sanford H., 2559
Orkin, William B., 2560
Orlen, Gregg F., 4047
Orlin, Paul, 6720
Orlin, Victoria, 6720
Orloff, David, 4245
Ormand, Ronald, 9345
Ormeroid, Carroll, 7357
Ormsby, Angela, 4934
Ormsby, Steve, 427
Ornburg, Jennifer, 4790
Ornest, Cindy, 888

Ornest, Laura, 888
Ornest, Maury, 888
Ornest, Michael, 888
Ornest, Ruth, 888
Orosco, Ardena, 5611
Orr, Adele S., 9104
Orr, Bonnie, 5872
Orr, Kristin, 359
Orr, Robert O., 7543
Orr, Sharon Wood, 3644
Orr, Timothy D., 359
Orr, Waldon H., 9104
Orris, Christine Bieber, 4641
Orrstown Bank, 8128
Orsemigo, Paul R., 2077
Orsi, Jennifer, 2362
Orsini Home Medical, 3156
Orsini Pharmaceutical Services, 3156
Orsini, Rebecca, 3156
Orsini, Tony, 3156
Ort, Frances, 2625
Orth, Joe, 3711
Ortho-McNeil Pharmaceutical, 2406
Ortman, Sue C., 9214
Ortwein, Linda G., 4259
Osawa, Koji, 565
Osberg Construction Co., 9105
Osberg, Allan F., 9105
Osberg, Axel, 9105
Osberg, Hilma, 9105
Osberg, John W., 9105
Osborn Charitable Trust, E. B., 8499
Osborn, Gay, 5408
Osborn, George C., 3555
Osborn, Hazel R., 891
Osborn, Joann, 3579
Osborn, Joseph D., 8158
Osborn, Kelly W., 9130
Osborn, Linda, 8890
Osborn, Todd, 3555
Osborne, Charles J., 9868
Osborne, David D., 896
Osborne, Dee, 7829
Osborne, Dee S., 8972, 9205
Osborne, Edith M., 212
Osborne, Gary, 2705
Osborne, Georgia, 896
Osborne, Jeremy, 896
Osborne, Kathleen, 8393
Osborne, Kelly, 896
Osborne, M.N., 212
Osborne, Mary Thom, 2147
Osborne, Molly P., 2147
Osbourn, Teresa, 7204
Oschwald, Anna, 7203
Oshins, Kate D., 8833
OSI Group, LLC, 3158
Osiason, Lee J., 1952
Osiecki, Jospeh, 7997
Osiek, C., 2783
Osmanski, Mark, 4641
Oss, Frederick, 4804
Ostberg, Henry D., 5483
Ostberg, Neal, 5483
Ostberg, Sydelle, 5483
Osteen and Osteen, 2590
Osteen, C. Joel, 2590
Osteen, J. Noel, 2590
Osteen, Justin, 2590
Oster Finance, 5484
Oster Properties LLP, 5484
Oster Realty, 5484
Oster, Ann, 5484
Oster, Avi, 5484

Oster, Dan, 5484
Oster, Miriam, 5484
Oster, Paul, 4612
Ostergard, Caryn, 1375
Osterkamp, Gus, 461
Ostreicher, David, 6564
Ostreicher, Dvora, 6564
Ostreicher, Harry, 6562
Ostreicher, Helen, 6562
Ostreicher, Marvin, 6563
Ostreicher, Michael, 6564
Ostreicher, Robert, 6564
Ostreicher, Susan, 6563
Ostrom, Robert, 5915
Ostwald, Donald A., 1238
Oswalt, William, 4606
Otenasek, Francis H., 3931
Otenasek, John H., 3931
Otenasek, Margaret B., 3931
Otenasek, Richard J., III, 3931
Other Guys, The, 1027
OTIS Eastern Service Inc 9130
Otofuji, Keiichiro, 679
Otolski, Erin, 5159
Ott, Amie, 3430
Ott, Bradley, 3430
Ott, Connie, 3430
Ott, Gary, 3430
Ott, Mark, 4484
Ott, Ryan, 3430
Ott, Sarah, 3430
Ottaway Jr. Trust, James, 5872
Ottaway, James H., Jr., 5872
Ottaway, James, Jr., 1407
Otten, Laura, 7953
Ottenheimer, Gus, 213
Ottenheimer, Leonard J., 213
Ottensosser, Seth, 6704
Ottersbach, Leah, 3669
Ottinger, Richard L., 5838
Ottino, Madeline R., 5603
Otto, Bruce, 1354
Otto, Christopher, 893
Otto, Daniel, 893
Otto, Gene P., 8171
Otto, Margaret, 893
Otto, Michel, 893
Otto, Neil, 893
Otto, Norman A., 4662
Otto, Sean, 440
Otto, Timothy J., 5092
Oubre, Shawn, 8869
Oucherloney, Robert D., 6462
Ouderkirk, Ernest, 5130
Ouellette, Louise, 5251
Ough, Bruce R., 5048
Ough, Linda R., 5048
Ough, Steven T., 5048
Ould, Susan, 6493
Our lady of Visitation, 7456
Out of the Shell, LLC, 1025
Outpost, 3905
Over, Judith, 1324
Overall, Jack B., 895
Overall, John B., IV, 895
Overall, Sheryl V., 895
Overhardt, Denise M., 1372
Overholt, Richard H., 4326
Overlock, Emily Phelps, 5962
Overlock, Katharine, 5962
Overlock, Willard J., III, 5962
Overlock, Willard J., Jr., 5962
Overman, Norbert, 4624
Overmyer-Velazquez, Mark, 6682

Overstreet Charitable Trust, M., 2242
Overstreet Investment Co., 2242
Overton Family Partnership, 9506
Overton, Alton S., 9506
Overton, William J., 9506
Overton, William S., 9506
Overyork, LLC, 9506
Oviir, Tiina, 9685
Owen Industries, 5108
Owen, Frances M., 3160
Owen, Helen, 792
Owen, Jay, 3079
Owen, Jenny, 2243
Owen, Lee S., 2243
Owen, Mary M., 4399
Owen, Norton, 3150
Owen, Richard B., 3160
Owen, Robert E., 5108
Owen, Rudd F., 9043
Owen, Stacy L., 7619
Owen, Tyler R., 5108
Owen, William E., 7690
Owens, Elizabeth H., 4333
Owens, Elizabeth N.C., 4333
Owens, Julia H., 4333
Owens, Margaret F., 4333
Owens, Mary R., 1077
Owens, Nancy C., 3729
Owens, Reginald, Dr. , 5325
Owens, Robert I., 4333
Owens, Sue L., 9232
Owens, William, 8955
Owlett, Thomas M., 8343
Owsianik, Linda R., 1520
Owusu, Angelina, 9107
Owusu, George, 9107
Oxford Industries, 2561
Oxford, Nancy Lee, 2462
Oxley, Leon K., 9754
Oxman, David C., 9455
Oxnam, Robert B., 5968
Oxnard, Benjamin, III, 2457
Oz, Lisa Lemole, 8119
Ozburn, Bert, 3255
Ozmun, Beverly L., 5151
Ozzie's Pipeline Padder Inc, 9130

Paaren, Herbert E., 9930
Paas, Jeffrey C., 7472
Pabor, Louis L., 9288
Pace Airlines, 2510
Pace, Da'Chon, 921
Pacelli, Giovanni, 8874
Pachios, Harold C., 662
Paci, Mary, 3137
Paci, Piero F., 3137
Pacific Gas and Electric Co., 921
Pacific Landmark Hotel, 788
Pack, Jay A., 9109
Pack, Ruth A., 9109
Packaging, 4693
Packer Trust, Horace B., 8201
Packer, Don, 421
Packer, Horace B., 8201
Packer, Mark B., 9629
Packin, David, 6566
Packin, Eugene, 6566
Packin, Joseph, 6566
Packin, Joseph H., 6566
Packin, Steven, 6566
Pactiv, 8859
Pactor, Mort, 371
Paddison Charitable Lead Trusts, 8655

Paddock, Robert, 9233
Paden, Carter N., III, 8625
Paden, Carter N., Jr., 8625
Paden, Janet C., 8625
Paden, Robert M., 8625
Paden, Thomas C., 8625
Padgett, Joe, 1917
Padgett, Nancy B., 9555
Padmanabhan, Ram, 2710
Padnos Foundation, Louis & Helen, 4529
Padnos Iron and Metal Co., Louis, 4529
Padnos, Cynthia B., 4529
Padnos, Daniel P., 4529
Padnos, Douglas B., 4529
Padnos, Jeffrey S., 4529
Padnos, Mitchell W., 4529
Padnos, Shelley E., 4529
Padnos, William R., 4529
Paessler, J. Clifton, 8648
Pagano, Michael T., 6846
Page Foundation, George B., 899
Page, Arthur, 4276
Page, Arthur B., 4032, 4063, 4309
Page, Arthur S., Jr., 4217
Page, James C., 1005
Page, Lawrence C., Sr., 4530
Page, Louise Knapp, 6331
Page, Natalie Coneway, 8783
Page, Peter, 6908
Page, Raymond, 4203
Page, Sarah C., 8600
Page, W. Raymond, 9507
Page, William H., 9507
Page, William J., 9507
Page, Wilson R., III, 6908
Pagen, Barbara Pauley, 909
Pagonis, Koula, 3040
Pagoumian, Carolyn D., 2245
Pagoumian, David P., 2245
Pagoumian, George K., 2245
Pagoumian, John G., 2245
Pahl, J.C., 4760
Pahl, J.M., 4760
Pahl, Leone M., 9776
PAI Corporation, 5145
Paige, Bradford C., 3786
Paige, Evelyn, 6048
Paige, Jeff, 607
Paige, Michele A., 6739
Paiget, 5202
Paine, G. William, 4531
Paine, Martha L., 4531
Paine-McGovern, Carol, 4531
Pak, Charles Y.C., 9110
Pak, Gregory, 9110
Pak, Jane, 9110
Pak, Laura Kim, 9110
Pakradooni, Peter B., 7924
Paladino, Steve, 4362
Palamara, Nancy, 8156
Palazzolo, Lauri A., 2160
Palen, Cody, 3623
Palermo, Peter J., 8466
Palisano, Harriet A., 6570
Palisano, Vincent H., 6570
Palladino, Jerry, 326
Pallante, Allan, 2864, 3277
Pallas, Evelyn, 4724
Palleon, Kim, 9922
Paller, Alan T., 3908
Paller, Carolyn, 2544
Paller, Channing, 3908
Paller, Marsha, 3908

Palm Beach Kennel Club, 8243
Palm, Gregory K., 6571
Palm, Jennifer, 6571
Palm, Katherine, 6571
Palm, Susan Rose, 6571
Palma, Robert A., 7545
Palmateer, Leo, 5696
Palmco Corp., 5291
Palmedo, Brittain E., 2684
Palmedo, Jane, 2684
Palmedo, Jane B., 2684
Palmedo, Peter, 2684
Palmedo, Peter F., 2684
Palmedo, Peter F., Jr., 2684
Palmedo, Whitney J., 2684
Palmer American Holding, 3612
Palmer, Angela, 8992
Palmer, C. Robert, 9112
Palmer, Charles R., 9112
Palmer, Francis Asbury, 6572
Palmer, Geoffrey, 8992
Palmer, Jacqueline, 8992
Palmer, James M., 9660
Palmer, Jasmine, 8992
Palmer, June, 4821
Palmer, Katie, 6946
Palmer, Kim, 4934
Palmer, Lawrence R., Jr., 4821
Palmer, Louisa J., 6490
Palmer, Mark, 8933, 8992
Palmer, Mary Jo, 3081
Palmer, Nathan, 8992
Palmer, Patsy Juda, 681
Palmer, Pauline E., 5725
Palmer, Ralph, 5070
Palmer, Rebecca T., 9112
Palmer, Rebekah Thompson, 8664
Palmer, Richard, 3307, 4821, 9977
Palmer, Steven N., 4957
Palmer, Susan, 8933
Palmgren, Dennis, 2416
Palmgren, Elizabeth, 2416
Palmisano, Gaier, 1487
Palmisano, Samuel, 1487
Paloian, John, 1540
Paloian, Karen, 1540
Palumbo, Kenneth, 1570
Palumbo, Steven, 9373
Palzkill, Mary T., 2749
Pamela C Damico Declaration Of Trust, 7370
Pamela Equities Corp., 6029
Pamp, Lucia Batchelder, 5072
Pams Lunchroom, 5443
Panamaroff, Jon, 89
Pancoast, Dana B., 7969
Pandiscio, Mary Beth, 4246
Pandolfi, Joyce, 5568
Pandya, Anand, 1808
Pane, Norma R., 5435
Panelli, Alex, 5154
Panem, Sandra, 3240
Paneth, Morton, 6574
Paneth, Samuel, 6574
Paneth, Thomas, 6574
Panetta, Eunice J., 4115
Panetta, Vincent J., 4115
Pangbom, Joel W., 1958
Panill, William, 8939
Pankanin, Kathleen, 1772
Pankonin, Lori, 5105
Pankonin, Phil, 5104
Pansky, Ellen, 877
Pantirer, David, 5487

Pantirer, Larry, 5487
Pantirer, Nancy, 5487
Panzer, Judith, 5514
Panzer, Moshe Chaim, 5514
Papadatos, Andreas, 1549
Papadeas, Melinda, 3541
Papadopoulos, C.N., 9113
Papadopoulos, Maria, 9113
Papadopoulos, Neofytos, 9113
Papadopoulos, William C., 9113
Papandreau, Christina P., 9113
Paparigian, Z. Victor, 376
Papitto, Barbara A., 8467
Papitto, David J., 8467
Papitto, Ralph R., 8467
Papouras, Christopher, 2121
Papp, Harry, 177
Pappajohn, John, 3525
Pappajohn, Mary, 3525
Pappas, Norman A., 4532
Pappas, Susan L., 4532
Pappas, Sydell, 4532
Papper, Emanuel M., 2246
Papper, Patricia M., 2246
Papper, Richard N., 2246
Paquelet, Judith, 7442
Par 4 Financial, LLC, 9565
Par's Custom Cycle Inc., 199
Paracha, Bilal, 4012
Paradis, Gina, 6540
Paragano, Eileen, 5488
Paragano, Nazario, 5488
Paragon Die & Engineering Co., 4481
Paragon Ranch Inc., 1268
Paramore, Christine, 9331
Paramount Ford, LLC, 7292
Paramount Group, 6655
Paramount Motor Sales, LLC, 7292
Paramount Pictures, 8759
Paraount Kia of Asheville, 7292
Parasiliti, Trina, 9098
Parasol, Richard, 936
Parastie, Toni L., 2656
Paravazian, Diane, 6820
Parcher, Jean, 610
Pardasani, Dinah, 5688
Pardee Foundation, Elsa U., 4533, 4534
Pardee Fund, Sarah N., 1595
Pardee Fund, Sarah W., 1595
Pardee, J. Douglas, 902
Pardee, James D., 902
Pardee, Julie, 902
Pardee, Marian R., 902
Pardyjak, Karen, 9853
Parets, Amy Sherman, 4293
Parham, Monica G., 1799
Parikh, Vijay, 565
Paris, Nancy M., 2484
Parish of Trinity Church, 6656
Parish, Amy, 5235
Parish, Jack, 2586
Parish, Richard L., 2247
Parish, Richard L., III, 2247
Parish, Richard L., Jr., 2247
Parisi, Patricia M., 5473
Parisot, Thomas, 1581
Park Avenue Partners LP, 4529
Park Bank, 9899
Park Circle Motor Co., 3899
Park Grove Realty Co., 3905
Park Mgmt., 6764, 6859, 7008
Park, Denten, 5610
Park, Susan, 883
Park, Wesley, 2660

Parke, Davis & Co., 2406
Parke, Jim A., 6576
Parke, Shirley, 6576
Parker Charitable Lead Trust, Eleanor Hutchinson, 903
Parker Pen Co., The, 9850
Parker Trust, Ruth F., 7413
Parker, Ann, 7145
Parker, Ann Levinson, 491
Parker, Brad, 9631
Parker, Carol Ellen, 3162
Parker, Cathy, 2054
Parker, Cody, 7724
Parker, Dan, 5091
Parker, Desiree, 4706
Parker, Diana, 6703
Parker, Diane Helow, 2089
Parker, Elizabeth J., 5005
Parker, Ellen, 7031
Parker, Gerald Hans, 3162
Parker, Grant, 5047
Parker, Jane, 2235
Parker, Jessica L., 491
Parker, John, 3662
Parker, Judy Ann, 7805
Parker, Kathleen, 9631
Parker, Linda J., 9427
Parker, Lisa, 812, 1170
Parker, Lyn, 4222
Parker, Lynne, 4565
Parker, Martha E., 9850
Parker, Michael L., 491
Parker, Michael R., 5767
Parker, Norma, 2235
Parker, Paul, 9196
Parker, Raymond P., 8166
Parker, Renee Brown, 7623
Parker, Richard H., 7805
Parker, Richard H., III, 7805
Parker, Richard H., Jr., 7805
Parker, Robert M., 903
Parker, Ruth F., 7413
Parker, Sarah Dunbar, 3653
Parker, Sean, 645
Parker, Terry, 232
Parker-Moore, Jennifer, 4449
Parkes, Farrah, 8328
Parkes, Freta, 9231
Parkhurst, Lyndsay, 2802
Parkin, John F., 2996
Parkinson, Geoffrey M., 1439, 1440
Parkinson, Geoffrey M., Jr., 1440
Parkison, Kathy, Dr., 3401
Parks, Alan, 7756
Parks, Christopher Michael, 9115
Parks, Daniel John, 9115
Parks, J. Michael, 9115
Parks, James R., 885
Parks, Judy, 5105
Parks, Maureen C., 9115
Parkview Christian Church, 2811
Parkway, Reilly, 9148
Parlee, Donald E., 7971
Parlette, Ann Bronwyn Rogers, 2058
Parman, Robert A., 7713
Parmelee, David, 1453
Parmelee, David W., 1591
Parmelee, Marylyn H., 5197
Parmenter, Nancy, 4449
Parnes 2008 Grandchildren, Herschel, The , 5479
Parnes Foundation, E. H., 5479
Parnes, Herschel, 5479
Parr, Catherine, 9909

Parr, Cheryl A., 9909
Parr, Gary W., 6577
Parr, Ronald W., 9909
Parr, Wilton, 6577
Parravano, Paul, 4155
Parrino, Emily, 9495
Parris, John , 9474
Parrish, Charles Bryan, 9343
Parrish, Charles Kurt, 9343
Parrish, Charles Maxfield, 9343
Parrish, Debra L., 437
Parrish, Erika Marie, 9343
Parrish, Ginger, 1542
Parrish, Gloria F., 9343
Parrish, Kristine Ann, 9343
Parrish, Michelle, 6058
Parrish, Roland, 153
Parritz, Ari, 2111
Parritz, Robin H., 2111
Parrott, Audrey D., 9428
Parry, Suzanne V., 228
Parshelsky, Moses L., 6578
Parsons Trust, John B., 3932
Parsons Trust, Katherine F., 3932
Parsons, Donald F., 1696
Parsons, Pete, 9576
Parsons, Sheri, 230
Parsons, Stephen, 89
Parsons, William, Jr., 4157
Parten Trust, 870
Partridge, B. Waring, III, 9117
Partridge, B. Waring, IV, 9117
Partridge, Mary B., 8429
Party City, 3077
Parvin, Albert B., 905
Parvin, Margaret Ann P., 7196
Parvin, Phyllis, 905
Parvin, Stanley, 905
Pasarow, Anthony H., 906
Pasarow, Claire, 906
Pasarow, Michael R., 906
Pasarow, Robert J., 906
Pasarow, Susan Adele, 906
Pascal, Clara, 2249
Pascal, Robin, 2249
Paschal, Justin, 645
Paschall FS-4 Trust, Sara Fort, 8862
Paschall S-1 Trust, Sara Fort, 8862
Paschall SS-3 Trust, Sara Fort, 8862
Pascucci, Christopher S., 6631
Pascucci, Michael C., 6631
Pascucci, Silvana B., 6631
Pascuzzi, Michael, 8548
Pasinella, Albert, 5865
Paskesz, Rivky, 5334
Pasquale, Alexander S., 7010
Pasquarelli, Samuel J., 7960
Pasquerilla, Leah M., 8204
Pasquerilla, Mark E., 8204
Pasquerilla, Sylvia T., 8204
Pasquesi, L. Robert, 2932
Pasquinis Pizza, 1295
Passalacqua, Francesca, 599
Passama, Gary, 1063
Passantino, Holly Kennedy, 1786
Passmore, Barbara K., 2570
Pasternack, Gail L., 3967
Pasternack, Stefan A., 3967
Pasternak, Kenneth, 5490
Pastor, Ben, 8436
Pastore, Dana, 1598
Pastore, Marie, 1598
Pastore, William M., 1598
Pastula, JoAnne M., 227

Pat Riley Family Foundation, 8570
Patagonia Resources, LLC, 4234
Patel, Ashokkumar, 5491
Patel, Baloo, 2622
Patel, Dinesh C., 9344
Patel, Gautam, 5515
Patel, Hina, 5515
Patel, Jinx, 2437
Patel, Kalpana, 9344
Patel, Kalpana D., 9344
Patel, Kiran C., 9344
Patel, Kiran V., 5492
Patel, Mahendra, 5491
Patel, Meera, 9675
Patel, Nehat, 5491
Patel, Nimeet, 5491
Patel, Paresh V., 5492
Patel, Pervez, 1623
Patel, Rupen, 5515
Patel, Sanjay H., 9386
Patel, Sujal, 9675
Patel, Yashvant, 5491
Patel, Yashvant V., 5492
Pater, Jason, 4407
Paterna Enterprises, LLP, 167
Paternotte, Nancy, 3933
Paternotte, William, 3933
Patey, Dan, 3055
Pathi, Savitha Reddy, 9663
Patience, 3905
Patlian, Dore J., 610
Patricelli, Alison J., 1541
Patricelli, Margaret S., 1541
Patricelli, Robert E., 1541
Patricelli, Thomas R., 1541
Patrick, Debra H., 3727
Patrick, Ellen, 3173
Patrick, Geraldine A., 2562
Patrick, Hilda B., 2562
Patrick, Joseph A., 5494
Patrick, Joseph E., Jr., 2562
Patrick, Joseph E., Sr., 2562
Patrick, Kate, 5494
Patrick, Scott R., 5494
Patrick, Sean M., 5494
Patrick, Shelly K., 5494
Patrick, Stuart K., 5494
Patrick, Timothy A., Jr., 5494
Patrona, Michael, 1450
Pattee, Anne L., 8656
Pattee, Dorothy E., 8656
Pattee, Gordon B., 8656
Pattee, Susan, 1374
Patten, Sammy, 2034
Patterson 2002 Descendants Trust,
    Elizabeth R., 907
Patterson 2002 Family Trust, William J.,
    907
Patterson Foundation, Cissy, 1826
Patterson Trust, Helen S., 2251
Patterson Trust, William J., 907
Patterson, Alex, 2437
Patterson, Alicia, 1826
Patterson, Anne, 3604
Patterson, Craig W., 3604
Patterson, Cynthia B., 4164
Patterson, David T., 7637
Patterson, Edward J., 9121
Patterson, Elizabeth, 7637
Patterson, Elizabeth R., 907
Patterson, Fleming, 8510
Patterson, George, Jr., 8206
Patterson, Jami, 3386
Patterson, Jeanne, 2250

Patterson, Jessica B., 9118
Patterson, John Solon, 1719
Patterson, Joseph Peter, 1719
Patterson, Lisa, 3065
Patterson, Marianna R., 1719
Patterson, Mark Elliot, 3604
Patterson, Nathaniel J., III, 8206
Patterson, Neal, 2250
Patterson, Patrick, III, 82
Patterson, Patrick, Jr., 91
Patterson, Sandy G., 7080
Patterson, Solon P., 1719
Patterson, W.I., 8205
Patterson, William J., 907
Pattillo Properties, Robert A., 2497
Pattillo, Daniel B., Jr., 2563
Pattillo, Daniel B., Sr., 2563
Pattillo, David A., 2563
Pattillo, Robert A., 2497
Pattillo-Markaz Industrial Partners, LLC,
    2497
Pattock, Susan D., 2823, 2824, 2912
Patton, Dennis, 7605
Patton, Jim, 3535
Patty, Frank, Jr., 4832
Patzer, Shane A., 4369
Patzer, Tiffany L., 4369
Pau, Peter, 1035
Pau, Susanna, 1035
Paul & Marjorie Lewan Charitable
    Remainder Trust, 1314
Paul Living Trust, Peter T., 908
Paul, Andrew M., 6580
Paul, Gregory M., 1082
Paul, Joe, 6704
Paul, Joseph R., 7373
Paul, Linda, 5520
Paul, Margaret B., 6580
Paul, Marie, 82
Paul, Peter T., 908
Pauley, Ann, 6124
Pauley, Matthew V., 909
Pauley, Racheel, 8825
Pauley, Stephen M., 909
Paulk, Kathryn Anne, 2032
Paulos Charitable Lead Annuity Trust
    Ventures Ltd., 9120
Paulos FJS Ventures Ltd., 9120
Paulos, James J., 9120
Paulos, John J., 9120
Paulos, Sam G., 9120
Pauls, Celia M., 386
Paulsen, Jim, 9904
Paulsen, Richard, 974
Paulson, Lori Fedje, 7296
Paulson, Richard A., 7645
Paulson, Thomas J., 4798
Paulus, C. Michelle, 9676
Paulus, Henry P., 4220
Paulus, Werner K., 9676
Paumier, Tami J., 1367
Pautsch, Adam M., 4759
Pautsch, Bethany J., 4759
Pautsch, Mark G., 4759
Pautsch, Mark P., 4759
Pautsch, Matthew J., 4759
Pautsch, Norma Jean, 4759
Pavelka, Darrel J., 3614
Pavloff, Andrew, 5872
Pavlosky, Ervin, 7593
Pawling Charitable Lead Annuity Trust,
    6582
Pawlowski, Frank J., 3165
Pawlowski, Glenn, 3165

Pawlowski, Mary Lou, 3165
Paxson Morrison Eduction Fund, Hazelle,
    2222
Paxton & Vierling Steel Co., 5108
Paxton Trust, Alice A., 6581
Payless ShoeSource, 3614
Payne, Christopher, 296
Payne, Douglas, 296
Payne, Eric D., 8932
Payne, Gregory, 296
Payne, Jean, 3771
Payne, Jimmy D., 9041
Payne, John D., 7422
Payne, John W., 3916
Payne, Lisle W., 910
Payne, Marilyn, 430
Payne, Mark, 1098
Payne, Martha B., 2442
Payne, Roslyn B., 910
Payne, Theresa G., 3734
Payne, Thomas W., 2969
Payne, Troy E., 9454
Payne, William P., 2442
Payne-Stewart Trust, Bee, 4976
Payson & Co., H.M., 3773
Payson, H.M., 3782
Payson, John W., 5495
Peace, John H., 6446
Peaceworks Holdings, LLC, 6538
Peach State Truck Center, 2574
Peacock, Greg, 6360
Peacock, Honie Ann, 6493
Peacock, Jay Ed, Jr., 3342
Peacock, John Ed, 3342
Peak, Chandos H., 9763
Peale Trust, Ruth S., 6582
Peale, John S., 6582
Pearce, Frank, 7276
Pearce, James, 9270
Pearce, Joseph C., 7935
Pearce, M. Lee, 2252
Pearce, Thomas, 2962
Pearl, Jerry, 7436
Pearl, Julius, 349
Pearl, Laura, 3592
Pearle Vision, 9098
Pearlman, Carey, 1167
Pearlman, Elaine, 9122
Pearlman, Trevor, 9122
Pearlstein, Carl, 911
Pearlstein, Jack, 911
Pearlstein, Ross, 3113
Pearlstein, Ross S., 3113
Pearlstein, Virginia, 911
Pearlstone, Esther S., 3934
Pearlstone, P. Justin, 3934
Pearlstone, Richard L., 3934
Pearsall, Amy C., 8207
Pearsall, Marion K., 8207
Pearsall, Tamara L., 8207
Pearson Charitablr Foundation, 5648
Pearson, Cindy, 5235
Pearson, Clint, 3623
Pearson, Debra A., 4437
Pearson, James Trent, 4437
Pearson, John E., 4437
Pearson, Steven C., 2820
Pearson, Susan R., 4437
Pearson, W.D., 5371
Pearson, W.D., Mrs. , 5371
Pearson, Wendy S., 1574
Pebblecreek Properties LP, 160
Peca, Michael, 5799
Pechacek, Frank, 3527

Pechet, Carol A., 4235
Pechet, Maurice M., 4235
Pechter, Richard S., 2564
Peck, Catherine Roddis, 9916
Peck, Elaine Z., 4620
Peck, George R., 4620
Peck, Jennifer, 4620
Peck, Marni L., 3544
Peck, Sharon, 1720
Peckham Industries, 6583
Peckham, Amy, 6583
Peckham, Amy K., 6583
Peckham, John R., 6583
Peckman, David A., 8049
Pecore, John, 8944
Peden, Harry E., III, 1429
Pedersen, Brandon S., 80
Pedersen, Margaret, 4141
Pedersen, Rena, 5016
Pederson, Clifford N., 3455
Pederson, Dave, 9956
Pedigree Brand, 8657
Pedrozzi, Mario, 912
Peek, Andrew, 6584
Peek, Elizabeth, 6584
Peek, Jeffrey, 6584
Peeke, Richard L., 4250
Peel, Glenn W., 7714
Peeler, Clifford, 7207
Peeler, Larry, 7207
Peercy, Paul S., 9782
Peerman, Allyson W., 8698
Pegler, Donald H., III, 5110
Pegler, Donald H., Jr., 5110
Pegler, Joann G., 5110
Pegler, Marian, 5110
Peglowski, Cynthia, 6073
Pegram, Jeffrey K., 6682
Pehle, Virginia, 4921
Peil, Mike, 7764
Peine, Caroline F., 9123
Peirick, Judy, 9957
Pekins, Roni S., 3954
Pekrul, A. John, 596
Pella Corporation, 3491
Pellegrini, Paolo, 6272
Pellegrom, Dan, 7338
Peller, Jay, 6042
Pelletier, Anne T., 6017
Pelone, Frank, 7910
Pels, Laura J., 6585
Pelstate Trust, 5840
Pelton, Bari, 6769
Pelton, Brett, 6769
Peltz, Adam, 6030
Peltz, Charles, 4442
Pelz, Daniel, 9900
Pelz, David, 9900
Pelz, Harry, 9900
Pelz, Jason, 9900
Pelz, Marilyn, 9900
PEM-America Inc., 1773
Pemberton, Richard L., 4664
Pembleton, Seliesa, 4719
Pena, Ann, 1322
Pena, David B., 5692
Pena, Telma, 9598
Pence, Sean, 945
Pence, Terry, 8784
Pendergast, Marie, 8331
Pendergast, Mary Louise Weyer, 4979
Pendergast, Thomas J., Jr., 4979
Pendleton, Ruth, 7806
Pendleton, William, 7806

Penick, Edward M., Sr., 213
Penikas, Jim, 7558
Penland, Joe , Jr., 9124
Penland, Joe, Sr., 9124
Penland, Linda, 9124
Penn National Gaming, 8208
Penn, Anne, 90
Penn, Larry, 1535
Penn, Laurence, 1535
Penna, Katherine S., 5897
Penner, Louis, 3641
Penney, Joan, 9696
Pennfield, Edward B., 6409
Penniman, Mary J., 6468
Pennington, Joe R., 138
Pennington, Thomas, 5795
Pennoyer, Lorraine, 1450
Penny, Charles, 7227
Penquite, Cecil Geisler, 3498
Penquite, Loren, 3498
Penrose, Sheila A., 3166
Penson Financial Services, 5482
Pentzenhauser, Mike, 3511
Pentzer, A. Samuel, 3425
Penza Family Foundation, 6720
People's United Bank, 1511, 1545
Peoples Bank, 7546
Peoples Bank & Trust Co., 3605
Peoples Bank, The, 3601
Peoples Federal Savings Bank
   Foundation, 4237
Peoples, Denton L., 5141
Peoples, Jim, 6632
Peoples, Mary Ann Zannon, 5141
Pepper Cos., The, 3167
Pepper Trust, Richard S., 3167
Pepper, J. David, 3167
Pepper, J. Stanley, 3092
Pepper, Lisa, 3167
Pepper, Richard S., 3167
Pepper, Robert S., 5496
Pepper, Roxelyn M., 3167
Pepper, Star, 5496
Pepple, William, 7339
Pepsi Bottling Group, 2400
Pepsi Cola & National Brand Beverage,
   8066
Pepsico, 2510
Peracchio, Lisa Cracchiolo, 4415
Peralta-Ramos, Arturo H., III, 9996
Peralta-Ramos, Lorian, 9996
Percy, Brett, 7557
Percy, David, 7557
Percy, Kevin, 7557
Percy, Lisa, 4845
Percy-Falls, Jennifer, 7557
Perdziola, Robert F., 9237
Perelman, Debra, 6097
Perelman, Raymond G., 8209, 8210
Perelman, Ronald O., 5832
Perenin, Rose, 914
Perennial Sports & Entertainment, LLC,
   247
Peretz, Amiel M., 5771
Peretz, Dylan M., 5771
Peretz, Michelle Young, 5771
Peretz, Taylor M., 5771
Perez, Carpice, 2986
Perez, Michael, 5669
Perez, Raul, Jr., 2150
Perez, Scott, 9068
Perez, Stephanie, 420
Perich, Christine, 1272
Perick, Judy A., 9957

Perin, Keith, 3441
Perine, Jorli, 474
Perkett, Donna Metivier, 6082
Perkin, Sylvia, 7208
PerkinElmer, 4238
Perkins, Alec, 3169
Perkins, Anne H., 4240
Perkins, Anne Hollis, 8413
Perkins, Ashley, 1840
Perkins, Benjamin F., 9982
Perkins, Brittany, 1840
Perkins, Ed, 2437
Perkins, Edwin E., 3168
Perkins, Floyd D., 3052
Perkins, Haley, 406
Perkins, Hansen, 406
Perkins, Jamel, 3169
Perkins, James I., 9125
Perkins, James I., Jr., 9125
Perkins, Jayne, 3412
Perkins, Joyce, 8871
Perkins, Judy, 3485
Perkins, Kathleen, 108
Perkins, Kitty M., 5111
Perkins, Laura C., 9125
Perkins, Laurel, 3766
Perkins, Margaret, 9125
Perkins, Margaret H., 9125
Perkins, Maurice, 7338
Perkins, Randal, 1840
Perkins, Robert H., 3169
Perkins, Saily, 1840
Perkins, Steve, 3595
Perkins, Thomas, 3169
Perkins, William B., 4276
Perks, A. C., 2844
Perks, Anna, 2844
Perks, Douglas C., 2844
Perks, Luke, 2844
Perks, Wade, 2844
Perl Foundation, 6521
Perlegos, Archie G., 547
Perlegos, Gust, 547
Perlegos, Mary, 547
Perlegos, Nick J., 547
Perlegos, Pete C., 547
Perlich, J. Russell, 2109
Perlin, Amy R., 9510
Perlin, Gary L., 9510
Perlman, Alan, 8474
Perlman, Andrew, 6587
Perlman, Ann, 8474
Perlman, Richard, 6587
Perlman, Robin, 3180
Perlman, Rosalind, 8474
Perlmuth, William A., 5647, 6954
Perlmutter, Isaac, 2254
Perlmutter, Laura, 2254
Perlow, Chaim, 6856
Perlow, Charles S., 8211
Perlow, Lori, 8211
Perlson, J. Lewis, 9812, 9854
Permanente, Kaiser, 1100
Permira, 8874
Perna, Janet, 1542
Pernod Ricard USA, 2510
Peroni, Edward P., 8467
Perper, William, 6588
Perpich, Michael J., Dr. , 9450
Perri, Ron, 9868
Perricone, Joseph, 916
Perricone, Marilyn, 5497
Perricone, Philip, 5497
Perricone, Sam, 916

Perricone, Sam G., 916
Perrine, Esther M., 8812
Perry Chemical Corp., 6367
Perry Partners, 6884
Perry, Alice Ann, 3426
Perry, E. Lee, 8413
Perry, Edward Lee, 4240
Perry, Eston L., 3426
Perry, J. Marc, 9937
Perry, Jack, 4648
Perry, Jennifer, 3426
Perry, Judy K., 173
Perry, Kelsey W., 3638
Perry, Kelvin, 9474, 9556
Perry, Michael W., 2650
Perry, Peyton F., 6248
Perry, Randall K., 2977
Perry, Richard, 6884
Perry, Slocumb Hollis, 4240, 8413
Perryman, Amanda, 2255
Perryman, Andrew, 2255
Perryman, Barbara, 2255
Perryman, Betty, 2255
Perryman, David, 2255
Perschevitch, Elizabeth, 917
Pershing Square Capital Management,
   LP, 6655
Persichilli, Judith M., 5419
Persinger, Jessee, 7391
Personett, Rob, 3126
Persons, Nona, 158
Persson, Mary H., 6168
Pert, Ann C., 1080
Peskin, Todd E., 8071
Peslar, Drew, 4537
Peslar, Karen, 4537
Pessin, Fern, 1566
Peszynski, Andrew F., 917
Peszynski, I.G., 917
Petaluma Wildlife Museum, 412
Peter, Arthur C., 3708
Peter, Edward L., 6590
Peter, Edward T., 5618
Peter, Joshua, 84
Peter, Lauren C. Dobson, 4978
Peter, Ruth, 6590
Peterkin Hey, Susan, 8904
Peterkin, Gail, 8904
Peterkin, George A., III, 8904
Peterkin, George A., Jr., 8904
Peterkin, John, 8904
Peterkin, John T., 8904
Peterkin, Lynn, 8904
Peterkin, Nancy G., 8904
Peterkin, Susan, 8904
Peters Foundation, R.D. & Linda, 9789
Peters Trust, Katherine, 3171
Peters, Amy, 4598
Peters, Andrew, 5799
Peters, Barbara A., 9670
Peters, Bruce, 4497
Peters, C. Wilbur, 7205
Peters, Catherine, 2526
Peters, Cecilia, 2256
Peters, Charles, 3497
Peters, Cherry, 1630
Peters, Elizabeth, 6876
Peters, Frederick, 6656
Peters, Gary, 2256
Peters, Greg, 2200
Peters, Jason, 4399
Peters, Jennifer McDonald, 4508
Peters, Jessie L., 7547
Peters, John, 4943

Peters, Katherine, 3171
Peters, Linda, 3172
Peters, Marion Post, 6897
Peters, Melissa M., 9010
Peters, R.D., 3172
Peters, Steven Mark, 2256
Peters, Thomas M., 6897
Peters, Wayne, 9814
Peters, William Gregory, 2256
Petersen, Douglas A., 5181
Petersen, Emily, 5074
Petersen, Gertrude, 8212
Petersen, Gertrude E., 8212
Petersen, John M., 8212
Petersen, Larry, 4739
Petersen, Marjorie S., 1720
Petersen, Mark, 756
Petersen, Steve, 5135
Petersen, Steven K., 5181
Petersen, Tyler, 3126
Peterson Brothers LLC, 918
Peterson, Albert, 1059
Peterson, Andrew G., 918
Peterson, Barb, 4497
Peterson, Barbara, 9607
Peterson, Carol, 2862
Peterson, Christopher J., 5182
Peterson, Daniel C., 918
Peterson, David B., 6591
Peterson, David L., 5134, 5520
Peterson, Dion Z., 5182
Peterson, Doug, 4679
Peterson, E.W., 1178
Peterson, Eric A., 1429
Peterson, Eric W., 5182
Peterson, Erik G., 9032
Peterson, Folke H., 2257
Peterson, G. Virginia, 8572
Peterson, Gail L., 5528
Peterson, Gordon, 3584
Peterson, Gregor G., 5182
Peterson, Harold, 6632
Peterson, Holly, 6592
Peterson, James F., 918
Peterson, James S., 6593
Peterson, Jeff, 4801
Peterson, John, 7483
Peterson, John L., 9901
Peterson, Karren, 754
Peterson, Katie, 8887
Peterson, Kristi, 9891
Peterson, Lee, 7785
Peterson, Leigh, 9883
Peterson, Mark L., 9901
Peterson, Mark R., 8572
Peterson, Martha L., 5979
Peterson, Matthew A., 918
Peterson, Michael A., 6591, 6592,
    6593, 6594
Peterson, Michele D., 5305
Peterson, Neal L., 795
Peterson, Paul A., 918
Peterson, Peter G., 6591, 6592, 6593,
    6594
Peterson, Peter L., 3597
Peterson, Raymond M., 966
Peterson, Robert L., 8572
Peterson, Roger, 7205
Peterson, Ronald E., 919
Peterson, Ryia R., 9901
Peterson, Toni K., 2332
Peterson, Tracy, 8556
Peterson, Wendy Rice, 2625
Peterson, William Fry, 1458

Petikas, Leon, 799
Petitjean, Steven, 2296
Petracca, Kim Foster, 8003
Petras, Garry, 9290
Petras, Kevin J., 4506, 4507
Petras, Nicholas, 6512
Petraske, Gretchen, 9925
Petrelia, Michael J., 8186
Petrella, William M., 6408
Petrick, David C., 3173
Petrick, Ellen, 3173
Petrie, Bruce, Sr., 7582
Petrie, Mark, 9987
Petrocelli, Attilio, 6595
Petrocelli, Beverly, 6595
Petroglyph Operating Co., 2677
Petrona, Chris, 1450
Petrone, Augusta, 4127
Petrone, Penelope F., 8409
Petrosky, Lisa, 7137
Petrovich, Dushan, 3174
Petrovich, Lisa, 3174
Petrovich, Nancy, 3174
Petrovich, Steven, 3174
Petrozzo, Frank L., Jr., 5205
Petrucci, James G., 5498
Petrucci, Jeanne, 5498
Petrus, Elaine, 8739
Petshaft, David B., 6356
Pettee, Sheila P., 4620
Pettee, Timothy, 4620
Pettengill, Virginia C., 4039
Pettersson, Carl, 7209
Pettet, Bruce, 3614
Pettigrew, Reece, 8884
Pettis, Patricia, 154
Pettit and Griffin, 3935
Pettit Family Charitable Trust, 3935
Pettit, Anne, 9562
Pettit, Barbara Lynn, 3935
Pettit, Carol Ann, 3935
Pettit, Deborah, 9427
Pettit, Jeanne Marie, 3935
Pettit, John H., 3935
Pettit, John Stephen, 3935
Pettit, Linda, 3514
Pettit, Richard B., 3935
Pettitt, J.W., 1178
Pettitt, S.D., 1178
Pettitt, W., 1178
Pettry, Harvey, 2872
Pettus-Crowe, Irene, 1828
Petty, Bruce, 8742
Petty, David, 3610, 8001
Petty, Edwina H., 9126
Petty, Eleanor H., 9126
Petty, Jill, 8001
Petty, Lydia, 6596
Petty, Miltom E., 7150
Petty, O.S., 9126
Petty, Robert, 6596
Petty, Scott, Jr., 9126
Pevehouse, Beverly, 9127
Pevehouse, Clay, 9127
Peverley, Lynne, 3932
Pew, Joseph, 7953
Peyser, Robert J., 6369
Peyton, Hill, 2034
Peyton, John, 1339
Peyton, Patrick J., 2258
Pfaeffle, Sally, 9768
Pfeffer, James, 5108
Pfeffer, Jane, 9867
Pfeffer, Pamela K., 8659

Pfeffer, Philip M., 8659
Pfeiffer, Jane C., 6597
PFI Distributors, 3077
Pfister, Irwin, 920
Pfister, Maryanne, 920
Pfizer (Pharmacia) Corp., 9895
Pfizer Pharmaceutical Co., 2406
Pfleeger, F. Gary, 3631
Pflug, Dorothy, 5100
Pflug, Eileen M., 183
Pfluger, Kurt, 9505
Pfohl, Brenda B., 9813
Pfohl, James M., 6451
Pfohl, Louis Anthony, 6451
Pfohl, Warren C., 9813
Pfotenhauer, James, 2986
Pfundstein, Greg, 379
Pfundt, G. Nelson, 8213
Pfundt, William N., 8213
PGA Tour Charities, 825
PGA Tour Inc., 825
PGA Tour, The, 7209
PGH Conf. on Analytical Chemistry and
    Applied Spectroscopy, 8289
Phagan, Eric, 3359
Phalen, Miriam Grinberg, 6139
Phalin, Larry, 1855
Phalin, Marianne, 3113
Phalin, Marianne E., 3113
Pharemore Drugs LLC, 3175
Phares, Judy M., 3989
Pharis, Jared N., 4887
Phebe's Tavern/East Pub, 90
Phelan, Pam, 8328
Phelps Chancelor Enterprises Inc., 153
Phelps, Carol B., 923
Phelps, Catherine, 2864
Phelps, James S., 923
Phelps, John W., 923
Phelps, Michael E., 922
Phelps, Patricia E., 922
Phelps, Richard J., 4242
Phelps, Susan Bender, 447
Phelps-Fisher, Sheryl, 923
Phifer, 54
Phifer Wire Products, 54
Phifer, Beverly C., 54
Phifer, J. Reese, 54
Philadelphia Cousins, 394
Philip and Emma Craig Trust, 4998
Philip Morris USA, 2150
Philips Electronics North America Corp.,
    4243
Philips Lumileds Holding BV, 4243
Philips Medical Systems, 4243
Phillip, Mary Beth, 2086
Phillipich, Bob, 551
Phillippi, Jennifer Krauss, 7764
Phillips Brokerage, 9215
Phillips Foundation Trust, 4850
Phillips Medical Systems (Cleveland),
    4243
Phillips Motorsports Marketing, 7094
Phillips Plastics Corp., 9774
Phillips, Amanda Turner, 5319
Phillips, Amy D., 924
Phillips, Carroll, 8972
Phillips, Charles, 6600
Phillips, Cloyd, 5188
Phillips, Corey, 8522
Phillips, Dan, 8902
Phillips, David L., 7953
Phillips, Deirdre B., 4007
Phillips, Della, 2260

Phillips, Douglas A., 6958
Phillips, Elizabeth, 2701
Phillips, Ellyn, 7920
Phillips, Francye W., 8902
Phillips, George R., 396
Phillips, George R., Sr., 648, 853
Phillips, Gifford, 5609
Phillips, Howard, 2260
Phillips, James L., 5609
Phillips, Jessica, 6403
Phillips, Joann Kocher, 5609
Phillips, Joe, 158
Phillips, Karen, 6600, 8538
Phillips, Kenneth B., 8449
Phillips, Larry E., 7864
Phillips, Laurel, 4213
Phillips, Laurie, 3344
Phillips, Leslye Hutton, 2699
Phillips, Melvin P., Jr., 2923
Phillips, Peggy Van Slice, 9665
Phillips, Stephanie Staubach, 9215
Phillips, Thomas W., 9665
Phillips, Wayne, II, 7458
Phillips-Hawkins, Sheila, 9784
Philpott, Peter, 8816
Philpott, Robert, 1121
Philpott, Tyler David, 1738
Phipps, Charles H., 9902
Phipps, Cheri, 3549
Phipps, Helen Clark, 9903
Phipps, Jim, 3362
Phipps, Mary K., 9902
Phipps, Stephen C., 9903
Phoebe Welsh Crut, The, 3088
Phoenix Suns Charities, 90
PHP, 3431
Phung, Doan L., 5145
Physicians Mutual Insurance Co., 5112
Pianka, Raymond L., 7337
Piascinski, Michael J., 8274
Piassick, Joel B., 55
Piassick, Karen, 55
Piassick, Louis N., 55
Piatt, Rodney L., 8187
Picache, Tamara, 3968
Piccerelli, William, 8488
Picerne, David R., 155
Picerne, Kenneth A., 926
Picerne, Ronald R.S., 155
Pichon, Emily, 3434
Pichon, John N., 3434
Pick Quickfoods, 6387
Pickard, Jennifer J., 3434
Pickel, Katey, 5110
Picker, Harvey, 5822
Picket, Joel, 6656
Pickett Family Trust, Thelma, 472
Pickhardt, Jonathan, 480
Pickle, James W., 8660
Pickman, Gladys, 6602
Pickman, Morton, 6602
Pickman, Teresa, 6602
Pickup, Donna T., 2393
Picot, Jean-Paul, 5669
Picotte Charitable Lead Trusts, 6603
Picotte, John D., 6603
Picotte, Kathleen M., 6603
Picotte, Michael B., 6603
Picquet, Glenn A., 8964
Pidcock, J. Scott, 8238
Piecush, John, 9345
Piedade, Anne M., 1432
Pielstik, Erik, 9712
Pier, Rick, 7796

Pierce, C. Fenning, 7572
Pierce, David Hyde, 6604
Pierce, Denise Nance, 9069
Pierce, Edna B., 1618
Pierce, John C., 6927
Pierce, Ronald M., 1269
Pierce, Sarah Rob Colby, 2711
Pierce, Scottie, 156
Pierce, Thomas M., 3768, 3770
Pierce, Winifred Davis, 7084
Piercey, Kenneth, 2695
Piercey, Sara, 2695
Piersall, Rick, 3251
Pierson Co., J.W., 5500
Pierson, Hazel C., 9129
Pierson, James W., 5500
Pierson, Jennifer, 5500
Pierson, Leigh P., 5302
Pierson, Nancy H., 5500
Pierson, Phoebe, 5500
Pierson, Sally, 5500
Pieschel, Paul, 4772
Piesko, Sue, 4450
Piesko, Susan, 4616
Pietroburgo, Linda, 4962
Pietsch, Margaret, 9913
Pigaga, Ken, 5398
Pigford, Richard I., 39
Pigman, Kerry, 7311
Pigott, Kenneth G., 3295
Pigott, Mark C., 9677
Pihl, Marjorie J., 4675
Piland, Deborah Dech, 9505
Piland, Richard, 9505
Pilarski, Shane, 3432
Pilch, Michael, 9982
Pilgrim, Aubrey Hal, 8976
Pilgrim, Evanne, 8976
Pilkington, John, 6652
Pillar, John, 8173
Pillmore, Eric, 7210
Pillmore, Pam, 7210
Pillmore, Pamela, 7210
Pillon, Michele A., 7760
Pillsbury Co., 4656
Pincus, Ana, 6164
Pincus, Anne M., 8214
Pincus, Henry, 6606
Pincus, Henry A., 6164
Pincus, Irwin Nat, 8214
Pincus, Lionel I., 6606
Pincus, Matthew, 6606
Pincus, Ronald, 3741
Pincus, Suzanne, 6606
Pindar, Therese, 2506
Pine Bluff Sand & Gravel Co., 218
Pine, Robert, 6820
Pineo, Christine, 1421
Pines, Alan, 5501
Pines, Elisa, 5501
Pinewski, Seymour, 5501
Pingaro, Dan, 726
Pingree, Charles W., 4356
Pingree, Mary Weld, 4356
Pinkerton, Guy C., 1721
Pinkerton, Nancy J., 1721
Pinkham, James C., 4245
Pinkin, James E., 5502
Pinkin, Jeffrey S., 5502
Pinkin, Lois M., 5502
Pinkin, Steven J., 5502
Pinkston, Anne Mcinerny, 4057
Pinkus, Scott M., 6607
Pinnacle Bank, 8610, 8655

Pinnacle Entertainment, 5183
Pinnacle Realty of New York LLC, 6784
Pinnacle Trading, LLC, 967
Pinnell, Curtis G., 3176
Pinnell, Emilysue, 3176
Pinnell, H.P., 3176
Pino, Loretta Ortizy, 5622
Pinsky, Angela, 6656
Pinson, Anne, 4762
Pinson, Joshua, 4762
Pinson, Kathleen A., 4762
Pinson, Noah, 4762
Pinson, Raymond B., 4762
Pioneer Fund, The, 1274, 1291
Pioneer Trust Bank, 8558
Piper, Howard, 2931
Piper, Jane Quentan, 1259
Piper, John, 4668
Piper, Noel, 4668
Piperno, A. J., 5323
Piperno, Anthony, 5323
Piperno, Dominic, 5323
Piperno, Elena, 5323
Piperno, Margaret, 5323
Pipes, Joe, 9081
Pipes, R.J., 9280
Pipkin, Phyllis, 83
Pipp, 2373
Pippin, Alice, 7654
Pippin, Phil, 7654
Piquette, Kelsey L., 2079
Pisa, Regina M., 4347
Pisani, Dean C., 9131
Pisani, Jacqueline, 9131
Pisani, Philip J., 9131
Pisano, Paul J., 2022
Pisklak, Don W., 9044
Pitcairn Trust Co., 8083
Pitt Foundation, William H., 2012
Pitt, Doris, 4541
Pitt, Ina C., 4540
Pitt, Michael L., 4541
Pitt, Murray C., 4540
Pitt, Peggy, 4541
Pittelman, Carole, 6656
Pittelman, Ira, 6656
Pittman, Carolyn, 3754
Pittman, Charles, 3444
Pittman, Marshall, 7286
Pittman, Robert W., 6608
Pittman, Veronique Choa, 6608
Pittoni, Giovanni, 1180
Pittsburgh Foundation, 8080
Pittsburgh Steelers, 8243
Pittston Co., The, 9406
Pitzer, Chaney, 9185
Pitzer, Christine, 9185
Pitzer, Christine H., 9185
Pitzer, Gavin, 9185
Pitzer, Starr, 9185
Pitzer, Starr L., 9185
Pitzman, Frederick, 3177
Piuze, Marion, 928
Piuze, Michael J., 928
Pivotal Foundation, 9345
Pixley, Vern, 4410
Pizarello, Louis, 6539
Pizzico, Kellie MacDonald, 5453
Place, Linna, 4948
Places Inc., 1640
Placzek, Dick, 3991
Plafsky, Joan, 5503
Plafsky, Nathan, 5503
Plafsky, Robert A., 5503

Plains State Bank, 3641
Plakias, Dean P., 4067
Plamer, William, 5087
Planalp, Ronnie, 6609
Planet Dog, LLC, 3797
Planinsic, Holly S., 9749
Plankenhorn, Harry, 8219
Plansoen, Hector L., 7211
Plant, Reuben J., 2341
Plante, William, Jr., 4217
Plappert, Gerald A., Jr., 3672
Plaster, Rodney L., 7711
Plastican, 4050
Platt, Charles C.J., 4206
Platt, Gertrude B., 4868
Platt, Jack, 1888
Platt, Joseph P., Jr., 8220
Platt, Mary Jane, 8220
Platt, Morris, 6041
Platt, Pincus, 6041
Platt, Rifka, 6041
Platt, Warren E., 171
Platter, Gerald, 5500
Platts, H. Gregory, 1790
Platz, Candace, 3784
Plautz, Dana, 7807
Plautz, Kim, 9309
Plaxco, Barry, 8784
Players Alumini Auction, 3817
Playfair, Larry, 5799
Plaza Bancorp, 2866
Pleas, Nancy A., 9678
Pleas, Riley W., 9678
Plein, Steven, 9904
Plein, Thomas A., 9904
Pletka, Irene, 6610
Pliskin, Bella, 6294, 6314
Ploeg, Anton, 3778
Plotkin, Norman , 7184
Plotnik, Sue, 1038
Ploumis, Deborah Brown, 352
Plourde, Sally, 4222
Plowman, Joe, 899
PLP Associates Holdings, 6717
Plug and Play, 1095
Plum Corp., 7965
Plum Healthcare Group LLC, 253
Plumb, Robert T., 861
Plumley, Mary Ann, 421
Plummer, Burke, 158
Plummer, Daniel Lee, 5854
Plummer, Shari Sant, 5854
Plung, Louis, 7856
Plunkett Trust, Therese M., 6611
Plunkett, L. Richard, 2584
Plunkett, Mary, 9863
Pluss Poultry, 1337
Pluss, Douglas, 1337
Pluss, James, 1337
Pluss, Sam, 1337
Pluta, Rich, 5873
Plutzik, Johnathan, 6103
Plutzik, Lesley Goldwasser, 6103
Plym, Francis J., Mrs. , 4542
Plym, J. Eric, 4542
Plym, John E., Jr., 4542
Plym, Linda, 4542
Plym, Robert Randall, 4542
PNC, 7905, 8243
PNC Bank, 2603, 4426, 4477, 7310,
    7315, 7353, 7394, 7405, 7409,
    7412, 7418, 7464, 7491, 7499,
    7500, 7528, 7550, 7554, 7584,
    7587, 7633, 7642, 7848, 7852,

7875, 7883, 7898, 7911, 7912,
    7913, 7919, 7922, 7943, 7949,
    7951, 7962, 7976, 7987, 7991,
    7995, 8006, 8014, 8046, 8051,
    8052, 8056, 8061, 8062, 8063,
    8095, 8102, 8103, 8110, 8111,
    8114, 8116, 8117, 8121, 8124,
    8125, 8131, 8132, 8136, 8148,
    8149, 8151, 8152, 8153, 8155,
    8157, 8159, 8161, 8163, 8168,
    8173, 8175, 8181, 8188, 8191,
    8192, 8194, 8197, 8203, 8216,
    8217, 8218, 8223, 8224, 8226,
    8227, 8235, 8239, 8252, 8262,
    8267, 8281, 8285, 8291, 8293,
    8295, 8317, 8323, 8330, 8338,
    8357, 8359
PNC Bank Trust, 8111
PNC Bank, N.A., 7983
PNC Foundation, 8080
Pobiner, Herbert, 5245
Podell, Art, 725
Podell, Catherine H., 930
Podell, Michael H., 930
Podhajsky, Jennifer, 165
Podhurst, Aaron S., 2363
Podlipny, Ann R., 2293
Podolsky, Milton, 3178
Podolsky, Randy, 3178
Podolsky, Steven, 3178
Podsednik, William A., Jr., 8848
Poduska, John William, 4246
Poduska, John William, Jr., 4246
Poduska, John William, Sr., 4246
Poduska, Lily A., 4246
Poduska, Susan M., 4246
Poe, Amy, 9281
Poe, Charles S., 9281
Poe, William F., Jr., 2139
Poell, Elizabeth K., 1299
Pogue, Benjamin P., 9133
Pogue, Judy, 9133
Pogue, Judy L., 9133
Pogue, Paul, 9133
Pogue, Paul H., 9133
Pogue, Ronald, Rev. , 9121
Pohl, John C., 9664
Pohl, Susan W., 9664
Pohli, Mary A., 5522
Pohlman, Steve, 1917
Pohly, Julie, 6613
Pohly, Julie Turaj, 6613
Pohly, Robert, 6613
Poirier, Rita, 3363
Poirot, Rhonda, 8784
Poiser, Sandra, 5146
Poitras, Edward W., 4082
Poitras, Kay G., 4082
Poja, Frank J., 9817
Polachi, Ann E., 4042
Polachi, Charles A., Jr., 4042
Polachi, Peter V., 4042
Polak, Travers Hill, 2097
Polan, Robert, 5895
Polansky, Ann, 6499
Polaski, Catherine J., 9829
Polaski, Michael H., 9829
Polaski, Michael J., 9829
Polevoy, Martin D., 6304
Poli, Darrell, 2341
Polikoff, Nancy, 1531
Polikov, Lee, 5104
Polish, Sheldon S., 2162
Polizzi, Frank, 8073

Polizzi, Frank S., 8073
Polizzi-Keller, Anna, 5022
Polizzotto, Dominic, 5139
Polk Foundation, 3188
Polk, Anna C., 5220
Polk, E. Richard, 3179
Polk, Edward M., 3179
Polk, Howard J., 3179
Polk, Jeffrey A., 3179
Polk, Jennifer, 3179
Polk, Kellyanna, 5220
Polk, Louis F., Jr., 5220
Pollack Charitable Trust, Marsha, 3180
Pollack Co., Zev, 7026
Pollack, Bruce, 6615
Pollack, Geri, 6615
Pollack, Janet Simmonds, 7748
Pollack, Jonathan, 6614
Pollack, Leon, 3180
Pollack, Leslie, 6614
Pollack, Lester, 6615
Pollack, Mark E., 1722
Pollack, Moselle, 8979
Pollack, Rae, 6614
Pollack, Teddy, 6552
Pollack, Yvonne, 6614
Pollack, Zev, 7026
Pollak Family Trust, David, 7026
Pollak Irrevocable Trust, Yedida, 7026
Pollak Irrevocable Trust, Zev, 7026
Pollak, Eve J., 1788
Pollak, Joseph E., 3921
Pollak, Linda J., 1788
Pollak, Roger L., 1788
Pollak, Ruth S., 1788
Pollak, Stephen J., 1788
Pollak, Zev, 2156
Pollano, John T., 4273, 4311
Pollard, Carl F., 3685
Pollard, Stuart B., 3685
Pollard, William C., 344
Pollia, Muriel, 931
Pollin, Abe, 3835
Pollin, James E., 3835
Pollin, Lauren K., 3892
Pollinger, Amy, 6328
Pollini, Claire W., 1182
Pollner, Michael, 8100
Pollnow, Elizabeth, 4993
Pollock, Douglas W., 8222
Pollock, Grace, 6616
Pollock, Lindsay Kathryn, 6616
Pollock, Mary Nan, 6617
Pollock, Oscar S., 6617
Pollock, R. Jeffrey, 7645
Pollock, S. Wilson, 6616
Polo, Paul, 1593
Polsfut, James, 1768
Polsky, Alexander, 6618
Polsky, Cynthia H., 6618
Polsky, Jack, 2715, 2778, 3070, 3261, 3279, 3304, 3309
Polsky, Leon, 6618
Polsky, Leon B., 6618
Polsky, Nicholas, 6618
Polzik, Eugene, 450
Polzik, Tatiana, 450
Pomerance, Mitchell, 4352
Pomerantz, John J., 5902
Pomerantz-Davis, Susan, 5902
Pompadur, Martin, 6094
Pomrenze, Hadasa, 6619
Pomrenze, Jay, 6619
Poncher, Jerry E., 3181

Poncher, Kathleen P., 3181
Poncher, Lyle, 3181
Ponchick, Elizabeth T., 274
Ponchick, Elliot, 274
Poncin, Cora May, 9134
Pond, Alicia, 3182
Pond, Ann E. St. John, 3798
Pond, Joel, 3798
Pond, Kirk, 3798
Pond, Kyle, 3798
Pond, Peter, 3182
Pond, Tracie L., 4133
Ponder, Brian, 4822
Ponder, William A., 2460
Ponitz, Cathy, 2296
Pontchatrain Capital, 8581
Pontius, Gil, 3372
Pontone, Harry, 8374
Ponts, Heather, 1126
Pontzer, Carol, 7975
Pool, Robert M., Dr. , 4508
Poole Trust, Zoe Stamm, 9512
Poole, Amanda G., 5504
Poole, Jennie E., 5504
Poole, John, 5504
Poole, John N., 5504
Poole, Lisa R., 7064
Poole, Lonnie C., III, 7064
Poole, Sharon, 5504
Poole, Sharon T., 5504
Poor, Mary A., 4005
Poore, Price, 3937
Poorman, J.K., 2997
Poovandan, Sanjay, 5622
Popadic, Timothy, 1346
Pope, Alan J., 6922
Pope, Anne T., 8538
Pope, Emmett Judson, III, 7196
Pope, James, 4428
Pope, Janet DeVlieg, 4428
Pope, Juliette R., 5676
Pope, Lawrence E., 7212
Pope, Mark C., III, 2568
Pope, Mary MacLauchlin, 7080
Pope, Rogers, Jr., 9054
Pope, Rogers, Sr., 9054
Pope, Sarah A., 5676
Pope, Scott T., 7212
Popielarz, Don, 4608
Poplar Foundation, 8570
Popoff, Frank P., 5664
Popovec, Kelly L., 1630
Popowcer, Leonard H., 2884
Porreca, Jackie, 8228
Port Sutton, 2371
Port, Elisa Beth, 994
Port, Jennifer D., 1405
Portanova, Margarete Anne, 4195
Porte, Thierry, 8031
Porter Machinery Co., Burke E., 4543
Porter Trust, Burke, 4543
Porter, A. Alex, 6720
Porter, Amelie W., 1829
Porter, Anne K., 5099
Porter, Charles, 7856
Porter, David, 8689
Porter, Delene W., 2437
Porter, Jack, 1994
Porter, John Lane, 3796
Porter, John R., Jr., 1829
Porter, Margaret Nicholson, 1829
Porter, Robert, 8766
Porter, Scott L., 1872
Porter, Susan, 6437, 6809

Porter, William L., 5099
Portland Cement, 366
Portman, Harry, 4981
Posewitz, James, 5047
Posewitz, James A., 5046
Posey, Andrew J., Jr., 9135
Posner, Elizabeth, 1295
Posner, James R., 6621
Posner, Lawrence D., 6621
Posner, Mark, 5514
Posner, Nicolas D., 6621
Posner, Robert I., 3925
Posner, Ross, 1295
Posner, Stanley, 6621
Post, Cynthia S., 5505
Post, Deborah, 5297
Post, Deborah Flynn, 5609
Post, Gary, 1543
Post, Glen F., III, 5505
Post, Helen, 7211
Post, Marjorie Merriweather, 7213
Post, Martin R., 6437
Posternak, Noel G., 4285
Postl, Beverly A., 9136
Postl, Erin, 9136
Postl, James J., 9136
Poston, Kevin, 1937
Potash, Sholem, 5835
Poteat, Victor P., 1856
Poteshman, Michael, 2379
Potiker, Brian, 932
Potiker, Jori, 932
Potiker, Lowell, 932
Potiker, Sheila, 932
Pott, Andrew, 5463
Potter, Charles S., Jr., 3092
Potter, Chuck, 7764
Potter, Delcour S., 6372
Potter, Elizabeth Stone, 6739
Potter, Eugenia, 3699
Potter, Katherine E. Johnson, 134
Potter, Lillian W., 6623
Potter, Mimi Averitt, 2438
Potter, Philip E., 6623
Potter, Philip E., Mrs. , 6623
Potter, Robin M., 8221
Potterfield, Larry and Brenda, 3991
Pottle, Jack T., 1299
Pottle, Judith E., 1299
Potts, Arthur, Jr., 5935
Potts, J. Brian, 4176
Potts, Joanna H., 7687
Potts, Robert, 2252
Pouch, Robert H., 6442
Poulin, Scott, 1952
Pouliot, Raymond E., 4250
Poulos, James A., 3909
Poulson, Patricia D., 3346
Poulson, Wade W., 264
Poulton, John C., 3859, 3961
Powell Trust, Kenneth, 3183
Powell, Andrew L., 1998
Powell, B.F., 2265
Powell, Cappy, 4881
Powell, Christy, 2264
Powell, Earl, 2264
Powell, Grady W., 9511
Powell, Gregory, 3764
Powell, James J., 8661
Powell, James J., Jr., 8661
Powell, Jeffrey J., 8661
Powell, Marita, 3183
Powell, Michael W., 8661
Powell, Myrtis, Dr. , 7582

Powell, Nancy, 9543
Powell, Paul, 2677
Powell, Paul, Jr., 9513
Powell, Robbin C., 1119
Power Electric Co., 5318
Power Service Products, 9003
Power Systems MFG, LLC, 8759
Power, Amy, 5608
Power, Eugene B., 4544
Power, Gussie N., 3746
Power, Kathleen Hoak, 8941
Power, Kathleen K., 4544
Power, Philip H., 4544
Power, Sadye H., 4544
Powers, Carol A., 4545
Powers, Cindy, 3441
Powers, Edward W., 7550
Powers, Janice, 3361
Powers, Linda A., 4545
Powers, Mary A., 5408
Powers, Michael J., 3023
Powers, Robert J., 4545
Powers, Robert P., 7303
Powers, Roger, 511
Powers, Sheri, 5590
Powers, Theresa, 5590
Powers, Thomas E., 5788
Pownall, Marilyn C., 9397
Poynter, Henrietta M., 2362
Poynter, Nelson, 2362
Pradere, John, 9994
Praggastis, Michelle, 2668
Praiss, Thomas F., 8029
Pralle Family Foundation, Robert R. and Helga, 933
Pralle, Helga, 933
Pralle, Robert R., 933
Prange, Phil, 9916
Prasil, Josephine B., 2724
Prast, Lisa Fruehauf, 8879
Prather, Chad, 9739, 9753
Prato, Greg, 6796
Pratt, Aileen, 9137
Pratt, Aileen Kelly, 7939
Pratt, Anne Batchelder, 5072
Pratt, Dallas, 9544
Pratt, David W., 2654
Pratt, Desiree, 7214
Pratt, Donna, 7214
Pratt, Edwin H.B., 7939
Pratt, Jack E., Sr., 9137
Pratt, Jeanne Anne, 7214
Pratt, Jeanne M., 7214
Pratt, Larry C., 7205
Pratt, Nancy, 8005
Pratt, Pamela, 7884
Pratt, Ryan M., 7214
Pratt, Susannah Quern, 2888
Pratt, William H., 7214
Pratt, William J., 7214
Pratt-Thomas, Harold, 7071
Pratte, Ron, 7094
Praw, Albert, 314
Pray, John, Dr. , 3655
Precision Pipeline LLC, 9130
Preferred Empire Mortgage Co., 6656
Preik, Austin, 2266
Preik, Curtis, 2266
Preik, Jennifer, 2266
Preik, Reinhold, 2266
Preis, Shirley, 6066
Premier Dental Products Co., 7920
Premier Medical Co., 7920
Prentice-Hall, 6569

Presant, Howard, 9466
Presbyterian Church of Hagerstown, 3814
Prescott's Supermarket, 9905
Prescott, Cheryl, 9905
Prescott, Dawn, 9905
Prescott, George, 9905
Prescott, George E., 9905
Prescott, Judith A., 9905
Prescott, Kelly, 9905
Prescott, Matthew, 9905
Prescott, Patrick, 9905
Presence Marketing, 5742
Presley, Delma E., 2438
Presley, Joseph, 8632
Press, Stella J. Camara, 4652
Press, Thomas, 4652
Pressberg, Gail, 1807
Pressel, Jerry R., 7429
Pressly, Paul M., 2506
Pressman, Wendi Alper, 2549
Preston, Evelyn, 8475
Preston, Lusia D., 1262
Preston, Mary Hicks, 6626
Preston, Michael E., 1815
Preston, Robert J., 7803
Prete, Ernest, Jr., 934
Prete, John, 1589
Prete, Lorraine, 3902
Pretti, Gene T., 5184
Preuss, Peggy, 935
Preuss, Peter G., 935
Preuss, Peter J., 935
Preves, Donna Sue, 3313
Preves, Greg, 3313
Preves, Robert, 3313
Previti, Andrew H., 5506
Previti, Frank, 5506
Previti, James L., 937
Previti, Katelyn Marie, 937
Previti, Maureen, 5506
Prevost, Louis E., 7953
Prewitt, Brian D., 5036
Preyer, Britt A., 7221
Pribil, Bekki, 3628
Pribyl, Marjorie, 9266
Price Charitable Lead Annuity Trust, Sam, 3616
Price Charitable Lead Trust, Steve, 3615
Price Communications, 6628
Price Family Foundation, Julian, 7151
Price Watson, 3208
Price, A., 621, 939
Price, Aliese, 2267
Price, Arthur L., 938
Price, Barry, 3616
Price, C., 621
Price, Carol B., 9516
Price, Carol Swanson, 4982
Price, Charles E., 3686
Price, Christina M., 2569
Price, Dana, 3229
Price, Dared, 3595
Price, Donna, 3616
Price, Doug, 3615
Price, Gayle B., 2296
Price, H.Y., Jr., 9170
Price, Herschel C., 9763
Price, J., 621, 939
Price, James K., 2569
Price, Janet, 3686
Price, Jeff, 9242
Price, Jo-Ann, 1530
Price, John E., 2267

Price, Judy A., 3529
Price, Kathleen, 1066
Price, Kent, 3615
Price, Lois Pollard, 9170
Price, Marcy, 7666
Price, Michael, 6627
Price, Mildred M., 2570
Price, Morton L., 1425
Price, Patricia A., 938
Price, Peggy Jo, 3616
Price, Robert, 6628
Price, Robert E., 4546
Price, Roy E., Jr., 8970
Price, Sam, 3616
Price, Samuel, Jr., 5900
Price, Sarah, 3686
Price, Sol, 349
Price, Steve, 3615, 6628
Price, Theodore W., 9516
Price, Thomas, 7591
Price, Timothy M., 9170
Price, Vikki, 6627
Price, W.L., 939
Price, Wendell, 8225
Price, Wendell B., 8225
Price, William, 480
Price, William H., II, 3959
Price, William L., 939
Prichard, David, 2764
Prickett, William, 3242
Priddy, Russell, 2267
Prien, Mary S., 7622
Priester, John, 1340
Priester, John D., 1340
Priester, Rosemary, 1340
Prieto, Leo, 4983
Prime, Meredith M., 6360
Prince Holding Corp., 4422
Prince Philanthropic Fund, Morton B. & Blance S., 2707
Prince, Debra, 9566
Prince, Edgar, 4422
Prince, Elsa, 4422
Prince, Jay, 9566
Prince, Scott, 6629
Prince, Sharon, 6629
Princeton University, 3919
Principe, Anthony M., 629
Principi, Amy Wahlert, 3544
Pringle, Anne, III, 7990
Pringle, Bruce A., 3642
Pringle, Carson, 8555
Pringle, Douglas S., 3642
Pringle, Priscilla C., 3642
Pringle, Robert S., 5305
Prins, Carol, 2958
Prior, Don, 7806
Prise, Suzan Z. Glenn, 7030
Pritchard, Mary Helow, 2089
Pritchett, Madelyn B., 8649
Pritchett, Nicole Grace, 1944
Pritchett, Wesley John, 1944
Pritchett, Wesley V., 1944
Pritchett, Winnie, 1944
Pritz, Robert F., 8261
Pritzker, Karen, 3184
Pritzker, Margot, 3184
Pritzker, Penny, 3184
Pritzker, Susan, 3184
Pritzlaff, John C., Jr., Mrs., 3824
Pritzlaff, Richard G., 3824
Private Trust Co., The, 7596
PrivateBank, 2296, 3331
PrivateBank, The, 2978, 3332

PRM Consulting Inc., 2621
Pro Players Foundation, 8795
Proctor Trust, E.C.W., 8662
Proctor, Bland, 8791
Proctor, Curt, 4396
Proctor, Elizabeth C., 8662
Proctor, Elizabeth Craig Weaver, 8662
Proctor, Laura, 8644
Proctor, Venable B., 9093
Produce Alliance, LLC, 8859
Progin, George K., 4247
Progressive Financial Services, 8686
Project 324, 1046
Project Solution, 5173
Prokopis, Emmanuel C., 4248
Prop, Leigh, 7541
Propost, Charles Vincent, 56
Propost, William S., 56
Propp, Adrienne, 2269
Propp, Douglas A., 5560
Propp, Eleanor H., 6201
Propp, Marni, 2269
Propp, Morris, 2269
Propp, Rodney, 5560
Propst, Michael K., 56
Propst, William S., Jr., 56
Prosky, Jill J., 6621
Prospect Park Realty, 6961
Prospect Realty LP, 6961
Prosperity Bank, 9088, 9290
Prosser, Dave, 8587
Protective Agency Inc., 7178
Prothro, Beth, 9273
Protz, Bill, 1928
Protzman, Eric, 1316
Protzman, Nancy, 1316
Prouty, Hillary, 8476
Prouty, Jonathan, 8476
Prouty, Lewis I., 8476
Prouty, Olive Higgins, 8476
Providence Development Partners, LLC, 7205
Provident Bank Charitable Foundation, 5872
Provine, Michael C., 5283
Provision Trust, 8663
Provorse, Paula, 5117
Provost, Emilee, 7785
Prown, Jonathan, 9794
Prown, Shannon, 3134
Prud'homme, Alex, 394
Pruden, J. Brooke, III, 9517
Pruden, Jonathan E., 9517
Pruden, Peter D., III, 9517
Pruden, Peter D., Jr., 9517
Pruden, Peter D., Sr., 9517
Prudential California Realty, 389
Prue, Elizabeth, 9772
Pruet, Chesley, 4851
Pruett, Holly, 7781
Pruitt, Baya M., 2543
Pruitt, Larry, 7697
Prusoff, William H., 2580
Pry, Janet P., 7356
Pryor, Daniel A., 1546
Pryor, Esther A., 1546
Pryor, Mary S., 1546
Pryor, Millard H., Jr., 1546
Psiol, Alex D., 1132
PSJJ, 5443
Ptashne, Mark S., 4142
Ptaszek, Edward G., Jr., 7615
Pucci, Gary T., 9926
Pucci, Nina, 301

Pucker, Gigi Pritzker, 3184
Puckett, Cecile Coneway, 8783
Puckett, Marlene, 2666
Puckett, Rick D., 7250
Puckett, William H., 36
Pudlo, Mitzi M., 9017
Pudlo, Richard T., 9017
Puelicher, John A., 9907
Pugh, David J., 5197
Pugh, Francis Nicholls, IV, 3747
Pugh, Francis T.N., III, 3747
Pugh, Francis T.N., IV, 3747
Pugh, Francis Tillou Nicholls, III, 3747
Pugh, James L., 5197
Pugh, Jo Ann Lewis, 3747
Pugh, JoAnn, 3747
Pugh, Keith E., 2475
Pugh, Lori E., 5197
Pugh, Michael L., 3747
Pugh, Michael Lewis, 3747
Pugh, Nancy, 3747
Pugh, Nancy Lewis Marie, 3747
Pugh, Ralph, 3593
Pugh, Richard H., 5197
Pugh, William D., 8048
Pugh, William M., 5197
Pugliese, Charles M., 7551
Pugliese, Thelma M., 7551
Pulichino, John, 2271
Pulichino, John, Jr., 2271
Pulido, Mark A., 4954
Pulitzer Charitable lead Unity Trust, Margot Rosenberg, 9140
Pulitzer, Robert S., 9158
Pullen-Venema, Elena, 9592
Pulliam Properties, 7215
Pulliam, Lawrence C., 7215
Pulliam, Rusty, 7215
Pulliam, Winston W., Jr., 7215
Pullum, Elizabeth, 7678
Pullum, J. Stephen, 2196
Puls, Deana Schooler, 7572
Pulsifer, Thomas R., 1641
Pulver, Maureen, 3956
Pung, Steven D., 4468
Puntereri, Marc A., 8531
Punzelt, Kenneth, 5211
Punzelt, Shirley M., 5211
Pupke, Christopher, 3824
Purdue Pharma, 6717
Purdue, Anna, 9065
Purdue, Kyle, 9065
Purdy, Forrest, Jr., 5167
Purdy, James, 6497
Purdy, James A., 6588
Purdy, Jan Marie, 5167
Purgason, Katherine B., 1025
Purington, Richard, 5319
Purities Dairies, 9230
Puro, Kristin M., 4571
Pursell, Jeanne, 902
Purvis, Margaret, 9165
Pusey, Patricia P., 2272
Pusey, Paul H., Jr., 2272
Pusey, Vernelle B., 2272
Pusey, William A., 2272
Pusey, William A., Jr., 2272
Putman, Selma Goerlich, 7428
Putnam Investments, 4252
Putnam, George, 4253
Putnam, George, III, 4253
Putnam, Gerald D., 3186
Putnam, Louisa, 4073
Putnam, Paul, 7428

Putnam, Rachel, 3186
Putnam, Sharron, 3186
Putnam, Warren Lowell, 4253
Putnam-Greene Financial Corp., 2445
Putney, Jesse M., 4010
Putney, Tim, 3531
Putt, William D., 3993
Pye, Keelin C., 6368
Pyke, Charles B., Jr., 2565
Pyle, Clint E., 2348
Pyle, James, 4948
Pyle, Jerry A., 9180
Pyle, Margot C., 4067
Pyle, Marsha, Dr. , 7346
Pyles, H. Michael, 2791
Pylman, Norman, 4621
Pyne, Nancy B., 7904
Pynn, Ward, 495

QEP Resources, 1342
QLT, 9895
QTS Logistics, 2400
Quackenbush, Christopher, 6443
Quackenbush, Gail, 6443
Quackenbush, Michael A., 6443
Quackenbush, Traci, 6443
Quad City Bank & Trust Co., 3274
Quadara Charitable Lead Annuity Trust, 769
Quadra-Tech, 7632
Quaker Chemical Corp., 8228
Quaker Oats Co., The, 5369
Quandt, William B., 1807
Quane, Cindy S., 347
Quanex Corp., 9141
Quantum Realtors Inc., 645
Quate, Rebecca W., 7275
Quattrini, Raymond J., 5872
Quay, Julie Anne, 6256
Quaye, Brenda Radichel, 4671, 4765
Quayle, Christopher, 103
Quayle, Corinne P., 103
Quayle, James C., 103
Quayle, James Danforth "Dan", 103
Quayle, Michael, 103
Queally, Kevin, 4352
Queally, Paul, 5369
Queensgate Co., 3905
Quello, John, 8573
Quenon, Robert H., 4951
Querido, Arthur J., 1453
Quesada, Peter W., 3800
Quesada, Strand O., 3800
Quesada, Thomas R., 3800
Quest, Ann, 9033
Quest, Ann L., 9142
Quest, Bill, 9033
Quest, Michael E., 9142
Quest, William J., 9142
Questar Corp., 9346, 9347
Quick, Sandra, 4511
Quicker, Donald, 3055
Quigg, James R., III, 3433
Quigg, James R., Jr., 3433
Quigg, William M., 3433
Quigley Family Partners, LP, 5296
Quigley, Brian, 5152
Quigley, John G., 5296
Quigley, Kathryn, 5296
Quigley, Leonard Matthew, 6451
Quigley, Lynn, 6451
Quigley, Nicole, 1799
Quigley, W. James, 8143

Quiksilver, 945
Quimby, Hannah, 3777
Quimby, Roxanne, 3777
Quimpo, F.I., 997
Quinlan, Elizabeth C., 4764
Quinn Emanuel Urquhart & Sullivan, LLP, 480
Quinn, Brooks C., 2273
Quinn, Carroll R., 8165
Quinn, Cydney P., 6639
Quinn, David M., 5148
Quinn, Deirdre, 6748
Quinn, Donald H., 5362
Quinn, Doris G., 6638
Quinn, Edward J., Jr., 3807
Quinn, Hallie H., 2273
Quinn, Henry A., 8229
Quinn, Joanne, 6637, 8331
Quinn, John B., 480
Quinn, John H., 2273
Quinn, John H., Jr., 2273
Quinn, Kenneth, 3550
Quinn, Pat, 9774, 9814
Quinn, Robert, 5058
Quinn, Sheri L., 4057
Quinn, Stephen D., 6639
Quinn, William, 6637
Quinn, William John, 6637
Quinones, Pete, 2463
Quinson, Bruno A., 6739
Quirico, Francis J., 4254
Quirk, Glenn, 7670
Quisenberry, Blake W., 9255
Quivey, M.B., 5113
Quivey, M.B., Mrs. , 5113
Quorus Ventures LLC, 9348

R&B Machine Tool Co., 4549
R&R Investors Inc., 3529
R. & R. Realty Co., 4269
Raab Foundation, The, 5666
RAB Capital PLC, 8581
Rabb, Irving W., 4255
Rabb, Melinda A., 4255
Rabbi and Mrs Oldak, 5733
Rabe, Karen, 6311
Rabe, Richard K., 5096
Rabert, Dean F., 8219
Rabin, Nancy Kohn, 3896, 3897
Rabinovitch, Anita, 947
Rabinowicz, Naomi, 6920
Rabinowitz, Alan, 8680
Rabishaw, Alan, 9184
Rachesky, Jill, 6642
Rachesky, Mark H., 6642
Rachford, Jon, 425
Rachon, Don, 2122
Racine, Linda L., 4270
Racine, Ronald, 4095
Racing Rest of America II Inc., 1730
Rackley, Blair, 2571
Rackley, Brady, III, 2571
Rackley, Tripp, 2571
Rackoff, Nancy L., 8205
Rada, Ann L., 4141
Rada, Edward, Jr., 533
Radcliffe, Sarah Jeffords, 5921
Rader, Kenneth, 6720
Rader, Rachel, 6720
Radetsky, JoAnn, 1239
Radfar, India T., 3994
Radiant Church, 9133

Radichel Family Intervivos Charitable Lead Trust, 4765
Radichel, Bradley P., 4765
Radil, Sara Coffee, 5105
Radin, Leta H., 948
Radisewitz, Karen, 4736
Radtke, John, 8570
Radunz, Carol, 4734
Rady, Ernest S., 949
Rady, Evelyn, 949
Rae, Anton, 3960
Rae, Michael, 3960
Rae, Shahla, 3960
Raeder, M.D., Ph.D., John, 1180
Raefski, Jason, 1094
RAF Foundation, 4218
Rafalowitz, Chaim, 5794
Rafalowitz, Gail, 5794
Rafalowitz, Norman, 5794
Raffa, Thomas, 9345
Raffel, Corey, 1497
Raffel, James E., 9955
Raffel, Kathleen Keefe, 1497
Rafferty, Gary J., 1098
Rafferty, Scott, 2791
Raffkind, George, 8697
Ragan Charity Lead Annuity Trust, Florence, 5507
Ragan, Carolyn King, 2572
Ragano, Michael, 5737
Ragatz, Thomas G., 9798
Rage, Patience, 8118
Raggio, Nicholas, 260
Ragir, Alexander V., 950
Ragir, Judith, 950
Ragir, Marshall, 950
Ragir, Robert, 950
Ragland, Eric W., 7515
Ragland, H. Nicholas, III, 7515
Ragland, H. Nicholas, IV, 7515
Ragland, John J., 7515
Ragland, Joseph A., 7515
Ragland, Martha H., 7515
Ragland, Peter D., 7515
Ragland, W. Trent, Jr., 7216
Ragon, Phillip T., 4256
Ragon, Susan M., 4256
Ragone, Daniel J., 5508
Ragone, Daniel J., Jr., 5508
Ragone, David J., 5508
Ragone, David N., 5508
Ragone, Dean A., 5508
Ragone, Lillian, 5508
Rahl, Richard H., 455
Rahl, Susan E., 455
Rahlfs, Mary Jean, 5074
Rahman, Naina Mohamed, 651
Rahr Malting Co., 4766
Rahr, Frederick W., 4766
Rahr, William T., 4766
Raia, Lawrence, 8031
Raidna, Paul, 9685
Raidna, Paul a., 9685
Raifall, Barbara L., III, 3154
Railo, Matt J., 942
Rainbow USA, 6069
Raines, Heidi Dye, 8683
Raines, Valerie, 7645
Rainey, Bartley J., 8879
Rainey, John S., 8543
Rainey, Robert M., 7106, 8543
Rainoff, Elizabeth, 6579
Raintree, 3905
Rainwater Charitable Foundation, 644

Rainwater, Lori, 8556
Rajki, Walter A., 7571
Rajkovich, Garrett, 1002
Raker, M.E., 3434
Rakowich Living Trust, 1343
Rakowich, Walter C., 1343
Raleigh, Dan, 4459
Rales, Debra, 3938
Rales, Emily W., 1809
Rales, Joshua B., 3938
Rales, Mitchell P., 1809, 9400
Rales, Steven M., 9400
Raleys Stores, 401
Ralli, Constantine P., 5768
Rallis Foundation, The, 5359
Rallis, John, 951, 5359
Rallis, Maria, 3040
Ralph Jones Charitable, 7470
Ralph, Bobby L., 9517
Ralph, Ginevra R., 3190
Ralston, Jeannie, 8969
Ralston, Wind W., 338
Ramanathan, Arun, 377
Ramani, Sunder, 421
Ramani, Sundewr, 361
Ramano, Anna, 955
Rambeau, Brenda, 2573
Ramirez, Beatriz, 338
Ramirez, Shannon, 2261
Ramlose Trust, George, 4257
Ramos, Carey, 480
Ramsay, Andrew C., 952
Ramsay, Lindsay G., 952
Ramsay, Nonie B., 952
Ramsay, Sheldon C., 952
Ramsay, Stephen A., 952
Ramsey, David I., 8784
Ramsey, Dean C., 9740
Ramsey, Margaret A., 4258
Ramsey, Norma, 9519
Ramsey, Priscilla D., 1432
Ramsey, Richard H., 1432
Ramsey, Richard L., 1432
Ramsey, Sammy Joe, 9013
Ramsey, W. Russell, 9519
Ramsing, Martha Wrightson, 2416
Ramsing, Thor H., 2416
Ran, Gary L., 4547
Ran, Rhonda S., 4547
Ranch Foundations, 7368
Ranch LP, Rayzor, 9009
Ranch Mart, 3636
Ranch, S., 6992
Rancho La Mesa, 1653
Randall, Adam, 8230
Randall, Anthony L., 6644
Randall, Brett, 8230
Randall, Carole Lee, 106
Randall, Chris, 8230
Randall, Craig, 5866
Randall, Earl R., 8230
Randall, Heather, 6644
Randall, James, 6625
Randall, Karen, 630
Randall, Rita, 8230
Randall, Robert P., 8230
Randall, Robert, Dr., 5127
Randall, Robin S., 8230
Randall-Dana, Nancy, 4702
Randell, David M., Jr., 3969
Randolph, Catherine M., 6901, 6923
Randolph, Jeff, 4379
Randolph, Robert M., 4035
Randolph, Suzanne, 6946

Rankin, David, 7217
Rankin, David H., 7217
Rankin, Evelyn Gordy, 2493
Rankin, Nancy, 7217
Rankin, Nancy O'H., 7217
Rankin, Samuel B., 7217
Rannells, Robert, 2681
Ranney, Phillip A., 7380, 7652
Ranney, Steve, 9990
Ransburg, Maria L., 2274
Ransford, Richard, 4598
Ransford, Sara, 1222
Ransing Trust, Ruben and Elizabeth, 5605
Ransom, Margaret, 1583
Rao, C.K.G., 6645
Rao, C.P., 6645
Rao, Jyoti, 6645
Rapaport, Elisa, 6646
Rapaport, Elisa Peter, 6646
Rapaport, Peter, 6646
Raper, Suzanne D., 3435
Raper, Thomas R., 3435
Rapid Span, 3641
Rapkin, David, 6178
Rapoport, Jed, 7208
Rapp, Brenda, 1804
Rapp, Fraddie, 6320
Rapp, Karen, 8874
Rapp, Susan B., 6136
Rapp, Theodore A., 1548
Rappaport, Andrew, 953
Rappaport, Deborah, 953
Rapport, Esther, 7553
Rapport, Jerome, 954
Rapport, Lauren G., 954
Rapport, Toby, 954
Rasanen, Andrew, 5795
Rasansky, Debbie, 8022
Rasberry, W. Clinton, 3750
Rascoe, Craig L., 9502
Rash, Jennifer, 9197
Rashkov, William, 9599
Rashti, Aaron, 9520
Rashti, Robert A., 9520
Raskas, Oshra, 2329
Raskin, Cynthia, 3269
Rasmus, Kari Fedje, 7296
Rasmussen, Judy, 2687
Rasnik, John, 7618
Rastetter Foundation, 3511
Rastrick, Kirsten, 2115
Ratcliffe, Christine, 524
Ratcliffe, Kenneth, 524
Rath Trust, F.E., 8231
Rath, David F., 8231
Rath, Frank E., Jr., 8231
Rathbone, Betty, 9756
Rathbone, Megan, 9499
Rathburn, Anita L., 7716
Rathburn, Gary J., 7716
Ratiff, Elizabeth, 5354
Ratkovic, William N., 1109
Ratliff, William T., III, 57
Ratliff, William T., Jr., 57
Ratner, Bruce, 6524
Ratner, Charles A., 1724
Ratner, Chuck, 1724
Ratner, Dennis F., 9521
Ratner, Ilana Horowitz, 1724
Ratner, Milton M., 4548
Ratner, Warren A., 9521
Ratshesky, A.C., 4259
Rattie, Keith, 6650

Rattie, Keith O., 6650
Rattie, Nancy E., 6650
Rattmann, Glenn, 870
Rattray, Carol, 6310
Rattray, Timothy S., 6310
Ratzner, Martha, 2814
Rau, John, 2786, 2823, 2824, 2912
Rauch, Fred A., 138
Rauch, Susan, 7518
Rauenhorst, Joseph, 8568
Rauenhorst, Joseph J., 8568
Rauenhorst, Karen, 4767
Rauenhorst, Loretta, 8568
Rauenhorst, Mark, 4767
Rauert, Kent, 5129
Rauf, Zamir, 8759
Rauh, Louis L., 7548
Rauh, Michael, 1418
Rausch, James, 5230
Rausing Trust, Sigrid, 5605
Rauzi, Elizabeth P. Sammons, 8853
Ravanas, Suellen, 2769
Ravella, Venkata, 1100
Raven, Leslie, 354
Ravencraft, Brian, 7357
Ravina, Renata, 591
Ravindran, James C., 391
Ravindran, Savithri P., 391
Ravitch, Joseph, 6651
Ravitch, Michael, 6651
Ravitch, Richard, 6651
Rawcliffe, Jacqueline A., 3787
Rawls, Jerry S., 9143
Rawson, Julia Anne Smith, 9207
Ray Foundation, 1861
Ray, Anne-Marie, 7850
Ray, David C., 3444
Ray, Deborah, 9514
Ray, Frank, 9114
Ray, James C., 1861, 2275
Ray, Joan L., 2275
Ray, John L., 9761
Ray, Michael, Jr., 7366
Ray, Pamela, 5621
Ray, Richie, 9070
Ray, Rob, 5799
Ray, Ronald D., 8966
Ray, Van, 4832
Raygar Realty Group, 9145
Raymer, Robert M., 8123
Raymond Corp., The, 6652
Raymond Equipment Co., 3436
Raymond James Trust, 2143
Raymond, Anne H., 3436
Raymond, Burke, 7761
Raymond, Colleen P., 9678
Raymond, George G., 6652
Raymond, Jean C., 6652
Raymond, Karen, 6652
Raymond, Larry, 4198
Raymond, Linda A., 3436
Raymond, Pete, 6652
Raymond, Stephen S., 6652
Raymond, Victor, 3526
Raymund 2003 Charitable Lead Trust, 2276
Raymund, Sonia V., 2276
Raymund, Steven A., 2276
Raynock, John, 7997
Raza, Syed K., 236
Razi, Ali Cyrus, 957
Razi, Anousheh, 957
Razi, Babak Cyrus, 957
Razi, Keyvan Cyrus, 957

Razor, Jim, 425
Razore, Joan M., 9682
Razore, Josie, 9682
Razzano, Diane, 6349
RB, 5260
RBC Capital Markets, 8700
RBI Program, 3817
RBS Citizens, 8412, 8424
RBS Citizens Bank, 8438
Rea, Elizabeth, 5935
Rea, Elizabeth Richebourg, 5935
Rea, Michael Moorhead, 5935
Rea, Thomas L., 5228
Rea, Willliam J., Jr., 7725
Read, Michelle, 487
Read, Tyra, 1917
Reade, Edith M., 3187
Reagon, Merble, 5940
Real Estate Board of New York, The, 6656
Real State Company, 1421
Reality Investment Co., 3912
Realsearch, 3905
Ream, Bryan J., 9744
Reardon, Elizabeth, 3194
Reardon, Mark, 3194
Reardon, Michele, 8246
Reardon, Nancy J., 5223
Reardon, William E., 7954
Rearick, Carol, 4499
Reavis, Peggy Flynt, 514
Reay, Katherine Blackburn, 2015
Reb Meir Baal Hanes Kolel Munkasch, 5834
Rebar, Robert, 9699
Rebassoo, Vaho, 9685
Rebelo, John G., 227
Reber, Brett, 3605
Reber, Tony, 4624
Rebert, Douglas F., 8019
Rebling, Renee, 3514
Rebman, Patricia, 6073
Recchio, Donald, 5254
Receveur, William John, 1878
Rechler, Donald, 6657
Rechler, Judith, 6657
Rechler, Mitchell, 6657
Rechnitz Charity Foundation, Shlomo and Tamar, 5667
Rechnitz, Jack, 5667
Rechnitz, Joan, 6527
Rechnitz, Shlomo, 5667
Rechnitz, Tara, 5667
Recht, Arthur M., 9742
Reckson Associate Realty Corp., 6656
Reckson Trust, Ethel, 2277
Reckson Trust, Harry, 2277
RECO Constructors, 9522
RECO Industries, 9522
Record, Linda, 7666
Recovery Management Systems Corp., 1947
Rector, Carol, 638
Rector, S.R., 9582
Red Dot Printers, 2622
Red Head Inc., 591
Red Mountain Entertainment, 1046
Red, Nancy Lynn, 9179
Redd, Dianne, 7807
Reddan, Nancy, 7956
Redding, Barb, 4449
Redding, Bloor, 8097
Redding, Patricia, 6733
Reddish, Cindi, 2802

Reddy, Anuradha, 959
Reddy, Kaavya, 959
Reddy, L.B., 958
Reddy, Lakireddy B., 958
Reddy, Manipal, 5574
Reddy, Naidu, 959
Reder, Robert F., 6739
Redfern, Jerry, 5009
Redies, Karen, 4549
Redies, Michelle, 4549
Redies, R. Edward, 4549
Redies, Robert D., 4549
Redies, Thomas D., 4549
Redies, William D., 4549
Rediger, Daren, 960
Rediger, Daren R., 960
Rediger, Denis K., 960
Rediger, Donald E., 960
Rediger, Duane E., 960
Rediger, James G., 3113
Reding, John, 5244
Redmond, Brooke C., 6049
Redmond, Kathleen J., 9910
Redmond, Mark, 9910
Redstone, Shari E., 4286
Redtman, Gail E., 3854
Redwoods Group, The, 7218
Reeber, Larke, 1100
Reeble, Bernard K., 3618
Reeble, Jane H., 3618
Reece, John B., 2272
Reece, Matthew, 2666
Reed Larson Charitable Remainder, 9650
Reed Trust, M.H. & J.C., 7555
Reed Trust, Margaret H., The , 7555
Reed, Ann L., 2170
Reed, Beth, 8477
Reed, C. Lawson, 7616
Reed, C.L., III, 7616
Reed, Calvin H., 2278
Reed, Christopher Allaben, 2278
Reed, Coke S., 8836
Reed, Colin V., 8620
Reed, Cynthia L., 2882
Reed, David H., 2278
Reed, David W., 3688
Reed, Diana L., 6572
Reed, Don, 5880
Reed, Dorothy Foster, 7616
Reed, Dorothy W., 7616
Reed, E.L., 4946
Reed, Elizabeth S., 1693
Reed, Foster A., 7616
Reed, Harold, 2269
Reed, Harold S., 4768
Reed, Helen S., 3190
Reed, James Case, 1824
Reed, Jason, 5880
Reed, John S., 2882
Reed, John S., Jr., 3190
Reed, John Shedd, 3190
Reed, Joseph Verner, 5669
Reed, Kate M., 4768
Reed, Katherine Chase, 2278
Reed, Kathryn L., 180
Reed, Kelly, 8939
Reed, L. Keith, 3190
Reed, Marjorie Lindsay, 3190
Reed, Mary Ann, 3400
Reed, Orville L., III, 7598
Reed, Peter S., 3190
Reed, Robert A., 5112
Reed, Robert A., Jr., 5112

Reed, Sam K., 3191
Reed, Stephen, 5866
Reed, Suellen, 3441
Reed, Susan K., 6572
Reed, T.J., 8937
Reed, Thomas, 2499
Reed, Timothy R., 6922
Reed, Tony, 9772
Reed, Victoria P., 3191
Reed, Wallace A., 180
Reed, Wendy, 2278
Reeder, Robert, 8219
Reeder, Vermoyn D., 9041
Reen, Mary, 6531
Reep, Dave, 7839
Rees, Martha, 7219
Rees, William J., 4080
Reese, Brian, 3116
Reese, Clay, 2497
Reese, Gary W., 8865
Reese, Gerald, 8518
Reese, I. Philip, 8232
Reese, Sheldon F., 8573
Reese, Wayne, 4396
Reeve, Kenlon, 9327
Reeves Foundation, Christopher, 6074
Reeves, Adam A., 5760
Reeves, Charles B., 3978
Reeves, Elizabeth W., 967
Reeves, John A., 3329
Reeves, John A., Jr., 3329
Reeves, K., 497
Reeves, Samuel T., 967
Regal-Beloit Corp., 9911
Regan, Chris, 4044
Regan, James S., 9530
Regan, John J., 4351
Regan, Julie W., 4469
Regan, Kathleen C., 409
Regazzi, John J., 5964
Regenberg, Lillian, 4728
Regent Management Services LLC, 3071
Reger, Brittany, 4769
Reger, John M., 4769
Reger, Joseph, 4769
Reger, Michael, 4769
Reger, Steve, 9756
Reger, Williston, 4769
Regions Bank, 4, 16, 18, 24, 31, 32, 38, 39, 78, 3255, 8607
Regions Bank Trust Dept., 33, 40, 44, 47, 61, 73, 209, 2548
Regions Morgan Keegan Trust, 8604
Regis, 4770
Regis Corp., 4770
Register, Betty Anne, 8894
Register, T. Matthew, 8894
Register, T. Wayne, 8894
Regnier, Catherine M., 3636
Regnier, Helen, 3636
Regnier, Robert B., 3636
Regnier, Sid, 3595
Regnier, Victor A., 3636
Rehberger, Phil, 9913
Rehfeld, Bob, 88
Rehm, Arthur, 4894
Rehm, C. William, 9662
Rehm-Lorber, Jora, 8445
Rehnert, Bernadette T., 4341
Rehtmeyer, Clint, 2897
Reibman, Barbara, 7906
Reibman, Joan, 6868
Reich & Tang, 6891

Reich Foundation, Imra, 7030
Reich, David, 2970
Reich, Lilian, 6659
Reich, Raymond, 6658
Reich, Seymour, 6659
Reich, Sue, 6658
Reichard, William E., 7445
Reichardt, Sabra, 5717
Reichardt, William, Jr., 5717
Reichardt, William, Sr., 5717
Reichel, Rabbi Aaron I., 6009
Reichel, Rabbi Hillel, 6009
Reichert, Ann, 6660
Reichert, Charles, 6660
Reichert, Corrine V., 3192
Reichert, Helen, 6660
Reichert, Jack F., 3192
Reichert, John, 3192
Reichman, Esther, 5830
Reichman, R. Kemp, 2286
Reichmann, R. Kemp, 2286
Reichmann, R. kemp, Jr., 2286
Reichmann, Rolf C., 2286
Reid, Alice Serra, 4565
Reid, Anne-Marie, 2244
Reid, Bill, 8674
Reid, Christopher, 3666
Reid, Dale E., 2549
Reid, Eric J., 412
Reid, J. S., Jr., 7568
Reid, James, 8257
Reid, Juliet W., 7163
Reid, Linda Bacon, 1279
Reid, Marjorie A., 3666
Reid, Mary Ann, 8869
Reid, Norma, 6294
Reid, Rust E., 8961
Reid, Ryan, 8700
Reidel Revocable Trust, George H., 4984
Reidler, Diane K., 7845, 8233
Reidler, Helen, 7845
Reidler, John W., 8233
Reidler, Verna C., 8233
Reidy, Ann Benson, 6248
Reidy, Francis J., Jr., 6661
Reidy, James W., 6661
Reidy, Janice, 4198
Reidy, Joseph, 4198
Reidy, Juliette T., 6661
Reidy, Michael L., 6661
Reidy, Pieter H., 6661
Reifenberg, Stephen, 4234
Reifenberg, Steve, 4234
Reik, Andrea, 7311
Reilly, Anson, 9148
Reilly, Asher, 9148
Reilly, Atlee, 9148
Reilly, Austin, 9148
Reilly, Axton, 9148
Reilly, Beverly A., 9148
Reilly, Clint, 962
Reilly, Janet, 962
Reilly, Jonathan B., 6481
Reilly, Michael A., 9148
Reiman Foundation, 6248
Reimann, Albert, 5217
Reimann, Nancy B., 801
Reimann, Rella, 9712
Reimann-Ciardelli, Andrea, 5217
Reimer, Debra, 6290
Reimer, Dolores, 4771
Reimer, Howard, 3641
Reimer, Lynn, 4771
Reimer, Ralph, 3641

Reimer, William, 4771
Rein, Eric, 2873
Rein, Gary D., 6230
Reiner, Jennifer Pollack, 6614
Reiner, John P., 6409
Reiney, Emily P., 56
Reinhard, G. Douglas, 3847
Reinhardt, Aurelia A., 1952
Reinhardt, Douglas E., 3785
Reinhart, Kathleen Joseph, 6273
Reinhart, Marty, 9878
Reinhold, B. Terry, 963
Reinhold, Baldwin, Jr., 963
Reinhold, Carol A., 963
Reinhold, Mary E., 963
Reinhold, Paul E., 2280
Reinisch, Marianne, 3193
Reinisch, Richard, 3193
Reinisch, Steven W., 3193
Reinsdorf, Jerry, 2999
Reinsdorf, Jonathan, 2999
Reinstein, Joel, 1974
Reinsurance Group of America, 4949
Reiquam, C.R., 5056
Reis, Gerard J., 7605
Reischmann, Janis, 1097
Reise, Tom, 370
Reisman Charitable Trust, George C. and Evelyn R., 4262
Reisman, Allen T., 7556
Reisman, George C., 4262
Reisman, Howard M., 4262
Reisman, John, 2235
Reisman, Maria, 4263
Reisman, Peter J., 7556
Reisman, Robert, 4263
Reisman, Robin, 4262
Reisman, Sidney, 7556
Reiss Foundation, The, 6654
Reiss, Bart D., 5632
Reiss, Bonnie, 6662
Reiss, Helene, 6654
Reiss, Jacob L., 8234
Reiss, Mahiz, 6654
Reiss, Richard, 6662
Reiss, Richard, Jr., 6662
Reitch, Mary B., 9149
Reiter, Robert, 3587
Reitman, Genevieve, 964
Reitman, Ivan, 964
Reitsman, Josh, 1316
Reitsman, Lauren, 1316
Reitz, Sidney A., 3603
Reitz, Susan N., 3603
Reivera, Kate, 8065
Rekab Properties, 264
Reker, Katie Marcus, 523
Related Partners Inc., 6656
Related Properties, 6655
Related Residential Sales LLC, 6656
Reliable Automatic Sprinkler Co., The, 5990
Reliable Credit Assn., 7775
Reliance Trust Co. of Delaware, 1623, 1655
Reller, Missy, 900
Remala, Rao V., 9683
Remala, Satya K., 9683
Rembert, Davis M., Jr., 2281
Rembowski, Kathy, 4521
Remensberger, Greg, 7798
Remick, Joe, 3508
Remick, John D., 4773
Remick, Larry, 3508

Remick, Robert, 4773
Remington Reynolds, LLC, 6463
Remley, Cheryle, 7625
Remley, Tom, 9914
Remmel, Althea F., 8235
Remmel, William H., 8235
Remmer 1995 Charitable Lead Trust, Patricia C., The , 1726
Remmer, Ellen E., 1726
Remmert, Cheryl Lynn Armstrong, 8708
Renaissance Electronics Corp., 4162
Renaud, Mike, 7975
Renaware International, 9702
Renberg, Daniel, 418
Rendall, David S., 7233
Rendall, Suganthi E., 7233
Renditions Washington DC LLC, 1640
Renfert, Blaine R., 9841
Renfro, Robert, 2687
Renn, Robert D., 5989
Renner, Daniel S., 7557
Renner, Debra, 7557
Renner, J. Robert, 7557
Renner, John W., 7557
Renner, Linda R., 4920
Renner, Mary, 7557
Renner, R. Richard, 7557
Renner, Reid, 7557
Renner, Richard R., 7557
Renner, Robert, 7557
Renner, Steven, 7557
Renner, Tamara, 7557
Renner, Tara, 7557
Renner-Yeomans, Jennie, 7557
Rennert, Irwin L., 8540
Rennie, David N., 8567
Rennter, Jeff, 5104
Renolds, Patricia R., 2574
Renschler, Amanda, 3912
Renschler, Katherine, 3912
Renschler, Scott, 3912
Renschler, Todd, 3912
Renton, Midge, 7764
Rentschler, Bryan, 5127
Reny, Carolyn D., 3802
Reny, John E., 3802
Reny, R.H., 3802
Reny, Robert D., 3802
Renzi, Nicholas Agnes, 5880
Renzulli, Dante W., 9063
Renzulli, June, 1559
Renzulli, Michael H., 9063
Renzulli, Michael H., Jr., 9063
Renzulli, Victoria A., 9063
Repass, Kent-Harns, 1727
Repass, Randolph Kent, Jr., 1727
Repass, Randy, 1727
Replogle, David, 1831
Replogle, John, 9384
Replogle, John B., 1728
Replogle, Kristin G., 1728
Repole, Maria A., 6538
Repole, Michael, 6538
Reppe, Angie, 8576
Repple, Gerry, 2027
Repple, Judy, 2027
Repplier, Banning, 6739
Reppun, John, 2642
Republic of Tea Inc, The, 4987
Republican Leadership Coalition, 3440
Resch, Bradley J., 2314
Resch, James S., 2314
Resch, Molly A., 2314
RESCO, 2638

Research and Planning LLC, 6003
Research Educational Fdn. Inc., 8891
Resenblum, Robert, 5223
Resendez, Hilda, 9211
Reservitz, Edward, 4245
Residents Medical Group, 488
Residual Charity Trust, W. Farnum, 8449
Resnick & Sons Inc. Mgmt., Jack, 6655
Resnick & Sons Inc. Mgmt., Jack, 6656
Resnick & Sons Inc., Jack, 6656
Resnick & Sons, Jack, 6655
Resnick, Andrea, 6656
Resnick, Burton P., 6663
Resnick, Helaine, 2282
Resnick, Howard, 2282
Resnick, Ira, 6663
Resnick, Jack, 6663
Resnick, Jonathan, 6656
Resnick, Max, 2282
Resnick, Pearl, 6663
Resnick, Peter, 6656
Resnick, Scott, 6656
Resnik, Jayme, 4490
Reso, Jerome J., Jr., 3756
Resor, Cynthia, 3669
Resor, Story Clark, 5662
Respess, Elizabeth C., 1787
Respironics, 4243
Resseguier, Olga, 1539
Ressler, Russell J., 8373
Retail Brand Alliance, 6091
Retek, Eli, 6924
Retek, Nathan, 6924
Rettenmier, Ross, 9592
Retter, Ronny S., 3826
Rettig, Charles, Esq., 898
Reuhl, Catherine, 9150
Reuhl, Ellen Ann, 9150
Reuhl, Gerald G., 9150
Reum, W. Robert, 2708
Reusch, Belinda, 6417
Reuther, Jane, 4592
Revelle, Carolyn, 3137
Revelle, Carolyn R., 3137
Revelle, Eleanor M., 3137
Revelle, Ellen C., 3137
Revelle, Roger R., 3137
Revelle, William R., 3137
Reverdy, Susan, 2309
Revocable Living Trust, 9589
Revocable Living Trust of Elmer J.
     Trulaske, 2149
Rexford Management, 6664
Rexford Offshore, LLC, 6664
Rey, Juan, 7796
Reyes, Carmen, 5662
Reyes, Luciano, 9070
Reymann, Adam, 7487
Reymann, Nancy, 7487
Reyna, Diane, 5609
Reynolds and Reynolds Co., The, 7558
Reynolds Services, 2017
Reynolds, Bob, 4774
Reynolds, Cathy, 523
Reynolds, Edgar, 5114
Reynolds, Frances, 5114
Reynolds, Fredric G., 7559
Reynolds, H. Rand, 9080
Reynolds, Howard D., 5159
Reynolds, James E., Jr., 2441
Reynolds, Jan, 1467
Reynolds, Liza, 1128
Reynolds, Loren, 1128
Reynolds, Lundy E., 7559

Reynolds, Paula, 1242
Reynolds, Rod, 1467
Reynolds, Rodney, 9474
Reynolds, Susan, 3466, 4884
Reynolds, Thomas B., 2574
Reynolds, W. Calvin, 7058
RF Capital Trust, 4683
RFA International Inc., 373
RFR Holding LLC, 6655
RFR Realty, 6655
Rhame, Donald, 2451
Rhame, Joan W., 8358
Rhein, Patricia Ann, 9305
Rheinstrom Fund, 6665
Rheinstrom Trust, Irene and Carroll,
     6665
Rheinstrom, Carroll, 6665
Rheinstrom, Marjorie, 6665
Rhino Holdings, LLC, 3749
Rhoades, Ken, 5074
Rhoades, Kitty, 9903
Rhoads, Richard, 1850
Rhoads, Ron, 607
Rhoden, James L., Jr., 2463
Rhodes, Carol, 2030
Rhodes, Ronald, 8949
Rhodes, Sharon, 9712
Rhodes, Sue, 9956
Rhome, Judith, 4010
Rhude & Fryberger Inc., 4630
Rhude, James E., 4630
Rhude, Joan, 4630
Rhue, Robert, 1366
Rhule, Gary, 1453
Ricca, Mark, 1588
Riccardi, Mary Kay, 5246
Ricci, Arthur O., 4366
Ricciarini, Amanda, 2048
Rice Charitable Lead UniTrust, Charles
     E., 2283
Rice, Albert W., 4265
Rice, C. Daniel, 2283
Rice, Catherine B., 2575
Rice, Charles B., Sr., 2575
Rice, Charles E., 2283
Rice, D. Douglas, 3534
Rice, Dianne T., 2283
Rice, Douglas, 7374
Rice, Ed, 1770
Rice, George, 2864
Rice, George A., 3277
Rice, Jane Dobson, 8819
Rice, Jeff, 8183
Rice, Julie F., 2283
Rice, Lesli, 6141
Rice, Mary Gage, 4265
Rice, Michael N., 4530
Rice, Morgan S., 969
Rice, Rich, 4459
Rice, Ronald, 3662
Rice, Scott, 8183
Rice, Terrie L., 7594
Rice, Timothy D., 8183
Rice-Davis, Julie, 877
Rich, David A., Jr., 6672
Rich, David A., Sr., 6672
Rich, Grace E., 6672
Rich, Leonard, 3643
Rich, Lyn, 3399
Rich, Marsha E., 4273, 4311
Rich, Meryl, 4189
Rich, Michael E., 2677
Rich, Randy, 922, 2962
Rich, Regina, 1150

Rich, Sara A., 9354
Rich, Stephanie A., 2314
Richard & Viola Thorp Trust, 5020
Richard Prouty - Literary Rights, 8476
Richard, Beth, 3195
Richard, Betty J., 3195
Richard, Cecily, 2285
Richard, Elwood, 3195
Richard, Harold Van B., 2285
Richard, Nancy, 1083
Richard, Pessie, 6764, 6858, 7008
Richard, Virginia, 2285
Richard, Zachary, 2285
Richards, Avis, 6720
Richards, Bruce, 6720
Richards, Connie, 7345
Richards, Cornelia S., 7345
Richards, Fred, 4671
Richards, Gary, Dr. , 4449
Richards, Jeanne M., 1174
Richards, Kathleen M., 2475
Richards, Margaret Cole, 3413
Richards, Margaret T., 4800
Richards, Mark, 1295
Richards, Mark S., 2722
Richards, Phebe, 4130
Richards, Rachael K., 9986
Richards, Robert J., 5219
Richards, Ron, 125
Richardson Family Partnership, 9983
Richardson Trust, Grace Jones, 651
Richardson, Anne, 9697
Richardson, Anne K., 5760
Richardson, Charles, 5113
Richardson, Elizabeth H., 5760
Richardson, Evelyn K., 4559
Richardson, Faye, 1550
Richardson, Gail Ness, 8544
Richardson, Hazel, 210
Richardson, J. Michael, 1550
Richardson, Jacob, 4559
Richardson, Jeffrey, 839
Richardson, Jeffrey L., 942
Richardson, Julius N., 8544
Richardson, Katherine J., 8544
Richardson, Keith, 9983
Richardson, Keith W., 9983
Richardson, Macon D.M., 8544
Richardson, Mary Ann, 3889
Richardson, Mary Lynn, 7221
Richardson, Michael, 1550
Richardson, Peter, 1550
Richardson, Roberta, 9983
Richardson, Sid W., 9151
Richardson, Terry E., Jr., 8544
Richardson, Thomas, 1550
Richardson, William M., 9522
Richel, Victor, 5332
Richer, Arthur A., 9476
Richer, Clare S., 4252
Richie, Lane A., 2840
Richins, Kent, 9985
Richman, Lawrence I., 3028
Richmand, Frederick A., 465
Richmond Distributors, 2161
Richmond, Clay P., 9152
Richmond, Frederick W., 3940
Richmond, Gail, 9152
Richmond, J. Walker, III, 9418
Richmond, Jack C., 9152
Richmond, John M., 9152
Richmond, Joseph W., Jr., 9418
Richmond, Laaura G., 9152
Richmond, Laura G, 9152

Richmond, Stephanie, 9152
Richmond, Steven J., 9152
Richmond, Victoria, 9152
Richter Investment Corp., 6668
Richter, Ari, 6668
Richter, Brent, 1896
Richter, Kirk A., 5003
Richter, Patricia K., 5928
Richter, Sid, 6624
Richter, William L., 6668
Ricker, Patricia, 2222
Rickershauser, Charles E., 589
Ridder Charitable Trust, Georgia B., 970
Ridder, Georgia B., 970
Ridenour, Blair, 766
Ridenour, Mark E., 7317
Rideout, Stephen W., 9477
Rider-Pool, Dorothy, 8238
Ridge Mgmt., 6859
Ridgefield High School Student Activity
     Account, 1730
Ridgeland Company, 9766
Ridgeway, Laura, 3321
Ridgewood Savings Bank, 6669
Ridino, Robert, 281
Ridley, A. Alexander, 8013
Ridley, Floyd A., 6626
Riech, Allan J., 3047
Riecker, William, 1729
Rief, Frank J., III, 1982
Riegel, Leila E., 3222
Rieger, Abraham, 6641
Rieger, Charlotte, 971
Rieger, E. Annette, 9717
Rieger, Heidi G.C., 6667
Rieger, Jacob, 6641
Rieger, Norbert, 971
Rieger, Rachel, 6641
Rieger, Richard O., 6667
Rieger, Roger A., 9717
Riehm Irrevocable Trust, John W., 9984
Riehm Realty, 9984
Riehm Trust, John, 9984
Riehm, Doris, 9984
Riehm, Doris N., 9984
Riehm, John W., III, 9984
Rieks, Beverly, 4774
Rieks, Lowell, 4774
Riemer, K. Davis, 4090
Riemer, Louise C., 4090
Rients, Cheryl Holthe, 4773
Riesen, Richard, 650
Riesman, Robert, 4721
Riester, Tim, 147
Rietman, Camilla, 7809
Rietzke, Alice, 3617
Riffe, Susann, 3611
Riffon, Julie, 5234
Rifkin, Daniel M., 3437
Rifkin, Martin S., 3437
Rifkin, Richard S., 3437
Rifkind, Arleen, 6670
Rifkind, Robert Gore, 972
Rifkind, Robert S., 6670
Rifkind-Barron, Max, 972
Rigden, Thomas M., 7714
Rigdon, Fr. Vincent, 5776
Rigg, Remus, 4396
Riggs Conselman Michaels & Downes,
     3937
Riggs Tractor Co., J.A., 214
Riggs Trust, Lamar W., 214
Riggs, Dan B., 9979
Riggs, Edwin Keith, 214

Riggs, Jack, III, 214
Riggs, John A., III, 214
Riggs, Lamar W., 214
Riggs, Lindsey, 2168
Riggs, Marie, 1059
Riggs, Ryan, 2168
Riggs, Steve, 1917
Righter, Alison, 9235
Righter, James V., 2388
Righter, Nina, 9235
Rigsby, David, 5621
Rigsby, David C., 5621
Rikard, Frank A., 59
Rikard, Glenn A., 59
Rikard, M.A., 59
Riker, Bernard, 4426
Riking (USA) Inc., 373
Riley, Daniel G., 4550
Riley, Dolores, 4550
Riley, Emily C., 7935
Riley, Erin Agee, 8694
Riley, George, 4550
Riley, George K., 4550
Riley, John, 9512
Riley, Kathleen T., 9796
Riley, Keith, 3620
Riley, Martha Ann Mahealani, 2641
Riley, Pamela A., 284
Riley, Robert H., 3224
Riley, Robert S., 8590
Riley, Susan, 973
Riley, Thomas G., 4082
Riley, William D., 4550
Rinaldi, Mary D., 9439
Rinard, Cecilia M., 8962
Rinard, Ronald E., 8962
Rind, Anke, 447
Rind, Linda Libby, 6395
Rinehart, Jennie, 13
Ring, Aaron L., 9232
Ring, Arnold, 5788
Ring, Frank, 6671
Ring, Freda, 6671
Ring, Leo, 6671
Ring, Louise, 6671
Ring, Michael, 6671
Ringer, Ronald H., 3196
Ringold, David A., 7192
Rinker, Beverly, 3438
Rinker, Christopher R., 2287
Rinker, David B., 2287
Rinker, John J., 3438
Rinker, Leighan R., 2287
Rinker, Lori, 3438
Rinker, Margaret H., 2287
Rinker, Resia, 3438
Rinker-Dumford, Raeni, 3438
Rio Lindo, LLC, 491
Riordan, Dennis, 3567
Riordan, Susan L., 9918
Rios, Edgar G., 9518
Rios, Lillian, 9518
Rioux, Diane, 5234
Ripley Athletic Boosters, 7069
Rippel, Julius S., 5510
Ripper, Karen, 2085
Ripps, Harold W., 60
Rishwain, Karen S., 974
Rishwain, Mark B., 974
Rishwain, Robert J., 974
Riskin, Philip W., 5511
Risley, Cretien, 1638
Risor, Bob, 219
Rissman, Jane, 1065

Ritchie, Lenora A., 2201
Ritchie, Mabel M., 7561
Ritchie, Meredith, 2702
Ritchie, Shirley, 7207
RITE-HITE Corp., 9915
RITE-HITE Holding Corp., 9915
Ritenour, Susan D., 2069
Riter, A.W., III, 9154
Riter, A.W., Jr., 9154
Riter, Betty Jo B., 9154
Riter, Cynthia S., 9154
Riter, Paxton W., 9154
Rittenberg, Leon H., Jr., 3756
Rittenberg, Libby, 1374
Rittenhouse, 6655
Ritter Foundation, 6673, 6674
Ritter Plumbing Co, 3450
Ritter, Alan, 5629
Ritter, Alan I., 5629
Ritter, Beth, 1635
Ritter, Curtis H., 1882
Ritter, David, 6674
Ritter, Jeannie, 6248
Ritter, Jennifer, 6674
Ritter, Jonathan, 5629
Ritter, Kelli Bell, 1882
Ritter, Michael, 6674
Ritter, Nataly, 6673
Ritter, Toby G., 6673
Rittmaster, Jane G., 6102
Ritz, Beate, 742
Rivard, Laurie, 4705
River City Bank, 697
River City Petrolium, 5156
River Foundation, 7333
Rivera, Anthony P., 2475
Rivera, Clara, 1730
Rivera, Mariano, 1730
Rivera, Miguel R., Sr., 3614
Riverbank Technologies, 1652
Riverbike of Tennessee Inc., 199
Riverplace 1 Holding, 6656
Rivers, John M., Jr., 8538
Rivers, Philip M., 1731
Rivers, Tiffany, 1731
Riverview Intl., 301
Riverway Co., 4776
Riviera Mgmt., 6859
Rivint, Zelma G., 9457
Rivkin, Charles A., 5783
Rivkin, Joyce, 9570
Rixey, J. Barbour, 3943
Rixey, John, Jr., 3943
Rixson, Mary, 7223
Rixson, Oscar C., 7223
Rizavi, Shaiza, 6777
Rizzo, Rose Marie, 6408
Rizzuti, Jan M., 377
RJA Investment Fund, L.P., 2697
RMD Corp., 2510
Roach, Brenda, 9054
Roach, Joseph, 4648
Roach, L. Gerald, 9452
Roan, Eileen H., 5499
Roang, Sverre David, 9784
Roanhorse, Sherrick, 5611
Roath, Dayle I., 422
Roath, Gregory T., 422
Roath, Kenneth B., 422
Robb, D.M., 9047
Robb, David, 2012
Robbins, David, 3152, 6676
Robbins, Ellyn, 3152
Robbins, Felicia C., 8520

Robbins, Glenn K., II, 4914
Robbins, Jack Henry, 1004
Robbins, Jessica, 3043
Robbins, Joseph C., 4266
Robbins, Lois G., 3006
Robbins, Lois O., 6774
Robbins, Margery, 2125
Robbins, Mary, 5088
Robbins, Michael D., 6774
Robbins, Miles, 1004
Robbins, Richard, 3006
Robbins, Ruthie Horn, 5618
Robbins, William D., 6698
Robe, Scott, 7311
Roberson, Katherine, 1813
Roberston Fund, Jeanne and Sanford,
   645
Robert Moreton Trust A, 3124
Robert Wood Johnson Charitable Trust,
   The, 4828
Robert, Donald, 9345
Roberti, Vito, 275
Roberts Children 1987 Trust f/b/o
   Courtney, 976
Roberts Foundation, The, 251
Roberts Trust, Douglas C., 3199
Roberts Trust, Jess and Alta, 7756
Roberts Trust, Jessie Castle, 966
Roberts, Ann T., 1552
Roberts, Barry, 8985
Roberts, Bernard, 6855
Roberts, Brian, 3817
Roberts, Brian K., 9464
Roberts, Courtney, 976
Roberts, Courtney A., 976
Roberts, Dick, 975
Roberts, Donald, 4778, 9342
Roberts, Doug, 9342
Roberts, Douglas C., 3199
Roberts, E.L., 9156
Roberts, Edward C., 1552
Roberts, Elaine Stein, 6855
Roberts, Eric, 9342
Roberts, Frank, 9342
Roberts, Gail, 1551
Roberts, Gaye, 3513
Roberts, George, 976
Roberts, J. Phillip, 1344
Roberts, Jean, 9342
Roberts, Jeffrey W., 4331
Roberts, Joan, 9342
Roberts, John, 6364
Roberts, John A., 6112
Roberts, John T., 3439
Roberts, Judith V., 2682
Roberts, Kathryn J., 8828
Roberts, Kenneth M., 3224
Roberts, Leonard, 1551
Roberts, Margaret, 9156
Roberts, Margaret Zufall, 9733
Roberts, Mark A., 4337
Roberts, Martha G., 6112
Roberts, Mary, 7807
Roberts, Nancy Elizabeth, 8712
Roberts, Pat, 7624
Roberts, Ralph J., 8240
Roberts, Ralph S., 3539
Roberts, Randy, 8844
Roberts, Ray Down, 3421
Roberts, Richard, 5449
Roberts, Richard D., 1344
Roberts, Richard F., 975
Roberts, Robin R., 3439
Roberts, Ryan, 3623

Roberts, Sally, 975
Roberts, Samuel, 1009
Roberts, Sarah J., 691
Roberts, Scott, 769
Roberts, Shelly, 1952
Roberts, Steven, 4778
Roberts, Summerfield G., 9157
Roberts, Susan, 2640
Roberts, Suzanne F., 8240
Roberts, T. Andrew, 1344
Roberts, Teri, 2149
Roberts, Tom, 3390
Roberts, Wade, 5620
Roberts-Mamone, Lisa, 7490
Robertson, Dorothy B., 2440
Robertson, Fred S., III, 8880
Robertson, George, 1531
Robertson, Gerald L., 7476
Robertson, Joanna, 276
Robertson, Judith A., 4032
Robertson, Judy, 1752
Robertson, Leanne, 7670
Robertson, Lindsey, 4720
Robertson, Sara Kolin, 8880
Robertson, Stan, 3628
Robes Revocable Trust, Martha, 4033
Robes, Martha S., 4033
Robets, Lon, 9802
Robfogel, Nathan, 2301
Robins, Lee R., 5650
Robins, Marylou, 8924
Robinson Online Auction, Jackie, 3817
Robinson Steel Co., 3117
Robinson Trust, John N., 3983
Robinson, A.J., 2597
Robinson, Bill, 985
Robinson, Carol, 8241
Robinson, Cary, 9178
Robinson, Caryn Grabe, 2053
Robinson, Charles Nelson, 1553
Robinson, Craig, 1038
Robinson, Dana P., 1686
Robinson, David M., 7946
Robinson, Dawnee McEuen, 7946
Robinson, Deanne H., 8587
Robinson, Donald, 8241
Robinson, Elizabeth H., 3983
Robinson, Elizabeth S., 2566
Robinson, Ellen T., 9239
Robinson, Erica, 12
Robinson, Gary, 1100
Robinson, George A., IV, 9158
Robinson, Guy N., 7013
Robinson, Harry English, Jr., 7225
Robinson, Harry L., 5865
Robinson, J. Douglas, 6922
Robinson, James K., III, 7946
Robinson, James K., Jr., 7946
Robinson, Julie P., 7709
Robinson, Kenneth D., 2260
Robinson, Laura A., 977
Robinson, Laurie S., 7946
Robinson, Linda Morris, 3983
Robinson, Margaret A., 8662
Robinson, Martin, 6194
Robinson, Marvin, 6397
Robinson, Melissa, 4983
Robinson, Michael, 5973
Robinson, Perry, 7533
Robinson, R. Lee, 2566
Robinson, Ralph C., 9994
Robinson, Richard, 3983
Robinson, Scott, 7623
Robinson, Stephen, 8241

Robinson, Steve, 9239
Robinson, Sylvia, 8241
Robison, Barbara, 3499
Robison, M. Lavoy, 1243, 1296
Roboson, Cynthia J., 6442
Robson Communities, 160
Robson, Alma Lavon, 3200
Robson, Bruce Allen, 3200
Robson, Dwight D., 4199
Robson, Edward J., 160
Robson, J. Glenn, 882
Robson, Jack L., 9639
Robson, John Joseph, 3200
Robson, John N., 3200
Robson, Kimberly A., 160
Robson, Larry, 8490
Robson, Mark E., 160
Robson, Robert D., 160
Robson, Steven S., 160
Robson, Sybil Ann, 3200
Roby, Barbara D., 5212
Roby, Mary, 4592
Rocca, B.T., III, 978
Rocca, B.T., Jr., 978
Rocca, K., 978
Rocca, L. H., 978
Rocco, Anne, 4535
Rocco, Jeffry D., 4535
Roche Laboratories, 1180
Roche Laboratories Inc., 979
Roche, Bernard, 7842
Roche, Edward, 6678
Roche, Robert, 3201
Roche, Robert W., 3201
Roche, Theresa, 3201
Roche, Thomas, 6290
Rock Annex NY LLC, 6839
Rock Solid Gelt Ltd., 5080
Rock, Kimberly A., 3992, 8381
Rockefeller Brothers Fund, 5662
Rockefeller Development Corp., 6655
Rockefeller, Laurance S., 5662
Rockefeller, Laurance S. "Larry", Jr., 5662
Rockford Corp., 9130
Rockowitz, Bruce, 5202
Rocky Mount Merchants Association, 7227
Rocky Mountain Mktg. and Promo., 2510
Rocky Mountain Popcorn, 1295
Rocovich, John G., 8571
Roda, Veralex, 1242
Rodamaker, Marti T., 3493
Rodbell, Jane Baum, 3949
Rodd, Allan K., 7407
Rodda, Warner B., 8623
Roddick Foundation, Andrew S., The, 8689
Roddis Plywood Corp., 9916
Roddis, Augusta D., 9916
Roddis, Catherine P., 9916
Roddis, Hamilton, 9916
Roddis, Thomas, 9916
Rodenbach, Edward F., 1567
Rodenberg, Louis B., III, 9477
Rodenberg, Louis B., Jr., 9477
Roderick, Blake, 2803
Roderick, William, 7624
Rodger, Bruce C., 9953
Rodgers, Blanche D., 3808
Rodgers, Dorothy F., 6680
Rodgers, Joe, 8580
Rodgers, Richard, 6680
Rodgers, Sally-Christine, 1727

Rodgers, Theo C., 3808
Rodgers, Thomas E., Jr., 2289
Rodgers, Tom, Dr. , 2437
Rodish, Jane, 1255
Rodman Five Realty Trust, 4269
Rodman Ford Sales, 4269
Rodman, Brett J., 4268
Rodman, Curtis L., 4268
Rodman, Donald E., 4268, 4269
Rodman, Gene D., 4269
Rodnick, Amie, 8931
Rodriguez, Andrew, 1702
Rodriguez, Ignacio, 1702
Rodriguez, Joan Stiefel, 1702
Rodriguez, Marilyn, 1702
Rodriguez, Melanie, 1702
Rodriguez, Mona, 7114
Rodriquez, Jay, 931
Roe, Alice F., 1684
Roe, Anita, 2707
Roe, Benson, 260
Roe, Hazel T., 5512
Roe, Henry G., 1684
Roe, Hollace Lindsay, 5512
Roe, Linda A., 9808
Roe, Ralph C., II, 5512
Roe, Randell B., 5512
Roe, Steve, 7764
Roe, William G., 288, 1684
Roebke, Frederic L., 9662
Roeger, Tammy A., 3992
Roehl, Nancy A., 9917
Roehl, Peter G., 9917
Roehlk, Thomas M., 2379
Roemer, Linda C., 8242
Roemer, William F., 8242
Roer, Jennifer A., 7610
Roettger, Stacy E., 8658
Roffman, Sidney, 6018
Rogers Towers, P.A., 2348
Rogers Trust, Ruth, 2291
Rogers, Alan, 607
Rogers, Anna K., 8666
Rogers, Anthony J., 3529
Rogers, Anthony L., 1952
Rogers, Buzz, 8522
Rogers, C. Graydon, 2058
Rogers, Charles, 4648
Rogers, Charles H., 5676
Rogers, Chase A., 2292
Rogers, Cindy, 3721
Rogers, Clarence B., Jr., 2292
Rogers, David S., 2058
Rogers, Dwight L., III, 2290
Rogers, Elizabeth Bailey, 1862
Rogers, Florence Ann, 2290
Rogers, Florence L., 7228
Rogers, Gari Griffin, 30
Rogers, Greg, 4552
Rogers, James, 8666
Rogers, James P., 8666
Rogers, Jesse, 1168
Rogers, Jessica L., 8666
Rogers, John B., 2292
Rogers, John F.W., 6422
Rogers, John H., 9491
Rogers, John T., 7980
Rogers, Joseph T., 8176
Rogers, Kevin, 630
Rogers, Kevin E., 7892
Rogers, Kristine M., 7701
Rogers, Laura, 8666
Rogers, Laura C., 8666
Rogers, Leland E., 9881

Rogers, Mary Elizabeth, 2058
Rogers, Mary Pickford, 927
Rogers, Michael, 8759
Rogers, Mindy, 1168
Rogers, Nancy E., 2292
Rogers, Piper, 9358
Rogers, Ralph, 3799
Rogers, Richard A., 9358
Rogers, Robert, 5395
Rogers, Romney C., 2290
Rogers, Scott, 7215
Rogers, Stuart G., 2058
Rogers, Thomas H., III, 2463
Rogers, Thomas P., 9753
Rogers, Tim, 980
Rogers, Tom, 9739
Rogers, Twanna, 980
Rogers, Virginia B., 2290
Rogers, Wendy, 2499
Rogers, William D., 5248
Rogerson, Thomas, 4276
Roghani, Foad, 2665
Roghani, Roshan, 2665
Roghani, Susan Camille, 2665
Rogicki, John H., 5435
Rogow, Bruce, 1846
Roh, Robert, 5087
Rohde, Charles A., 3530
Rohde, Charles P., 3530
Rohmer, Bridget J., 4860
Rohner, Bill, 2598
Rohr, Gary, 8782
Rohrer, J. Phillip, 8537
Rohrer, Rachel C., 8537
Rohrich, Paul J., 3944
Rohrig, Frederick W., 7312
Rohrman, Linda, 3463
Roitstein, Alex, Dr. , 9781
Roland, Mary, 7839
Rolander, C. Arthur, III, 7229
Rolander, C. Arthur, Jr., 7229
Rolander, Mildred D., 7229
Rolander, Stephen B., 7229
Rolat, Sigmund, 6994
Roles, Kari L., 4780
Roles, Thomas M., 4780
Rolfe, Andrew John, 9386
Rolfe, Lee, 9611
Rolfs, Edward C., 3564
Rolfs, Edward J., 3564
Roll, Gerry, 3655
Rolland, Janna, 9669
Roller, Adele, 4811
Roller, John E., 2508
Roller, Julie, 3592
Rolles, Charles, 1672
Rolling, Kathy, 9951
Rollins, E.T., Jr., 7231
Rollins, Frances P., 7231
Rollnick, Ari, 1952
Rolls, Dickie, 3566
Rollstone Bank & Trust, 4270
Rolston, Paulette, 8976
Rom Terminals, 5820
Roma Bank, 5513
Romaine, Arthur C., 5570
Roman, Adele G., 4985
Roman, Gail H., 6022
Roman, Mary Manuel, 4702
Romangano, Kathleen, 1559
Romano, Alexandra, 955
Romano, Anna, 955
Romano, Benita, 2698
Romano, Carol A., 5257

Romano, Ed, 982
Romano, Elliot, 6553
Romano, James D., 3203
Romano, Joseph R.V., 3203
Romano, Lillian, 6553
Romano, Linda E., 6922
Romano, Margaret V., 3203
Romano, Marilyn F., 80
Romano, Michael J., III, 2698
Romano, Murphy, 982
Romano, Paul, 4231
Romano, Raymond, 955
Romano, Richard C., 3203
Romanoff, Mike, 7356
Romay, Alexis, 5759
Rome, Ellen, 7338
Romero, Amy L., 7795
Romero, Wendy, 3092
Romero-Leggott, Valerie, 5611
Romita, Camille, 5820
Romita, Mauro S., 5820
Romita, Michael, 5820
Romley, William, 93
Ron Book P.A., 1840
Ronan, Martin W., Jr., 6455
Roney, Jane H., 801
Roney, Jessica, 983
Roney, Paul, 4379
Roney, Regina, 983
Roney, Richard, 983
Rooks, Dennis, 2452
Rooks, Jane Canipe, 2452
Roome, Peter W., 5408
Rooney, Cathleen L., 3440
Rooney, J. Patrick, 3440
Rooney, Joann, 8243
Rooney, John, 8243
Rooney, Katie, 2710
Rooney, Kevin J., 6821
Rooney, Maria R., 1425
Rooney, Marianne B., 7664
Rooney, Paul H., Jr., 7879
Rooney, Sean, 8243
Rooney, Theresa A., 3440
Rooney, Therese A., 3440
Roop, Barbara, 4354
Roos, Linda J., 4980
Roosevelt, Constance, 6967
Roosevelt, Theodore, III, 6967
Roosevelt, Theodore, IV, 6967
Roosth Trust, Jake, 9160
Roosth, Kenneth, 9160
Roosth, Sam, 9160
Roosth, Steven C., 9160
Roosth, Toni, 9160
Roosth, Wiley, 9160
Root Charitable Trust, Susie M., 3611
Root, Terry L., 376
Roothbert, Albert, 6682
Roothbert, Toni, 6682
Roots and Wings, 9621
Roozen, Marion W., 9681
Roper, Geraldine, 9261
Roper, Gregory S., 1896
Roper, Jim, 9261
Roper, Lynn, 5105
Roriston, Robert, 6992
Rorvig, Sherman M., 119
Rosa, Paul, 230
Rosales, Karen, 9181
Rosasco, LeRoy, 3231
Rosborough, Lucy, 7537
Rosbrow, Benjamin, 2778
Rosbrow, Jesse, 2778

Rosbrow, Laura, 2778
Rosbrow, Patricia Jane, 2778
Rosbrow, Thomas W., 2778
Rose & Kiernan, 6683
Rose Associates, 6655
Rose f/b/o Asia Connection Trust, E.K., 257
Rose Foundation, Marshall & Jill, 6686
Rose Foundation, Susan and Elihu, 6685, 6709
Rose Foundation, Wendi and Joseph B., 6496
Rose, Abigail, 6709
Rose, Adam, 6656
Rose, Carolyn, 7603
Rose, David, 1210
Rose, Ellen M., 3992
Rose, Emily, 6687
Rose, Gabrielle E., 8667
Rose, Gayle S., 8667
Rose, Gideon G., 5711
Rose, Gordon B., 8953
Rose, Homer J., 5935
Rose, Irma, 984
Rose, Isabel, 6685
Rose, James A., 2293
Rose, Joseph B., 6496, 6686
Rose, Kelly, 7697
Rose, Kristen L., 4728
Rose, Marian H., 2293
Rose, Marilyn, 5056
Rose, Marshall, 6684
Rose, Matthew D., 8667
Rose, Melanie, 1542
Rose, Michael D., 8667
Rose, Morgan D., 8667
Rose, Richard, 9631
Rose, Richard A., 7877
Rose, Ron, 4396
Rose, Simon M., 2293
Rose, Susan F., 9925
Rose, Suzanne, 7697
Rose, Ted, 257
Rose, Virginia, 7877
Rose, Wendi, 6686
Rose, Wendy, 3432
Rose, William A., 9925
Rosebrough, Walter, 7605
Roseff, Sidney D., 4084
Roselli, Marie, 5295
Roseman Charitable Trust, Virginia, 9919
Rosemann, Gayle, 9919
Rosemann, Jeff, 9919
Rosemann, Rachel, 9919
Rosemann, Russell R., 9919
Rosemann, Virginia V., 9919
Rosen's Diversified, 4782
Rosen, A. Everett, 9161
Rosen, Abraham E., 9161
Rosen, Andrew, 6707
Rosen, Arlene, 3206
Rosen, Daniel M., 1510
Rosen, Dennis, 4679
Rosen, Doris B., 2294
Rosen, Florence, 6689
Rosen, Jacob, 9684
Rosen, Jeffery, 6766
Rosen, Jonathan D., 2577
Rosen, Kann M., 4782
Rosen, Libby, 6720
Rosen, Lois, 258
Rosen, Martin L., 2294
Rosen, Michele, 9684

Rosen, Miriam, 9684
Rosen, Richard H., 4782
Rosen, Robert A., 6689
Rosen, Roberta A., 4782
Rosen, Ruth E., 9161
Rosen, Seth, 6720
Rosen, Seth D., 2366
Rosen, Sheri, 1062
Rosen, Stanley, 9684
Rosen, Stanley G., 9684
Rosen, Thomas J., 4782
Rosen, Walter M., 9161
Rosenbaum Trust, Gabriella, 3047
Rosenbaum, Barry, 4596
Rosenbaum, Gabriella, 3047
Rosenbaum, Jay D., 4278
Rosenbaum, Patricia L., 47
Rosenbaum, Sandra, 5602
Rosenbaum, Steven, 8410
Rosenberg Family Charitable Lead Trust, 8244
Rosenberg, Ann P., 9140
Rosenberg, Benjamin D., 8873
Rosenberg, Beth, 6154
Rosenberg, Dave, 599
Rosenberg, David M., 8244
Rosenberg, Don, 498
Rosenberg, Ellen, 6826
Rosenberg, Franklin, 1599
Rosenberg, Harry, 7029
Rosenberg, Haym D., 6605
Rosenberg, Henry, 6691
Rosenberg, Jacob, 6771
Rosenberg, Jason A., 4354
Rosenberg, Jennifer, 9457
Rosenberg, Jerry, 1555
Rosenberg, Joy G., 6605
Rosenberg, Julius, 1555
Rosenberg, Leona Z., 2707
Rosenberg, Marjorie D., 8244
Rosenberg, Meta Reis, 985
Rosenberg, Michael L., 9162
Rosenberg, Michele D., 2334
Rosenberg, Sheri, 9140
Rosenberg, Sonia, 9162
Rosenberg, Steven, 9140
Rosenberg, Tammy, 3582
Rosenberg, Thomas, 9321
Rosenberge, Charles, 884
Rosenberger, Gary, 7802
Rosenberry Charitable Term Trust, 4815
Rosenberry, Charles W., II, 4815
Rosenblatt, Alice Messinger, 6482
Rosenblatt, Nancy N., 2294
Rosenblatt, Raphael, 1606
Rosenbloom, James, 2919
Rosenblum, Herbert S., 2142
Rosenblum, Jerald E., 463
Rosenblum, Peggy R., 1539
Rosenburg, Sarah, 4869
Rosenfeld, Eugene S., 986
Rosenfeld, Gerald, 7017
Rosenfeld, Lester, 1732
Rosenfeld, Maxine, 986
Rosenfeld, Melissa, 178
Rosenfield, Bruce A., 7903
Rosengarten, James A., 6682
Rosenhagen, Kurt, 9288
Rosenhouse Family Trust, 9184
Rosenlund, Alarik A., 8245
Rosenlund, Alarik A., Jr., 8245
Rosenlund, Arthur O., 8245
Rosenlund, Hope, 8245
Rosenson, Alan D., 3209

Rosenson, Harold, 3209
Rosenson, Kenneth B., 3209
Rosenson, Linda J., 3209
Rosenson, Michael E., 3209
Rosenstein, Jonathan, 6692
Rosenstein, Lisa, 6692
Rosentel, Stephen G., 1590
Rosenthal Family Trust, 6653
Rosenthal Trust, Barbara Bakwin, 6693
Rosenthal, Andrew H., 6695
Rosenthal, Benjamin J., 3210
Rosenthal, Beverly, 5202
Rosenthal, Brian, 1531
Rosenthal, E.M., 9163
Rosenthal, Edward F., 1574
Rosenthal, Ida, 6696
Rosenthal, Jodi, 6694
Rosenthal, John, 6360
Rosenthal, Joseph, 7021
Rosenthal, Judy, 6653
Rosenthal, Leighton A., 7563
Rosenthal, Morris, 6548
Rosenthal, Nina, 987
Rosenthal, Robert D., 6694
Rosenthal, Robert M., 987
Rosenthal, Rosalyn G., 9163
Rosenthal, Stephen, 3717
Rosenthal, Tomas, 6653
Rosenthal, William, 6696, 9163
Rosenthal, William, Dr. , 6693
Rosenthal, William, Mrs. , 6693
Rosenwald Family Fund, W.H., 1807
Rosenweig, Jack, 8591
Rosenwinkel, Wayne, 2702
Roshanzamir, Asher, 7016
Roshanzamir, Michael L., 7016
Rosing, Wayne E., 758
Roskens, Lisa Y., 5066
Roski, Edward P., Jr., 784, 1074
Roskind Family Foundation, The, 6720
Roskos, Joseph W., 8305
Roslund, Becky, 4459
Rosmik Inc., 153
Rosner, Carol, 6691
Rosner, June, 6698
Ross Construction, Douglas, 1080
Ross Family Fund, 7941
Ross Foundation, Richard M. and Elizabeth M., 2343
Ross Willoughby Co., 7386
Ross Winter Charitable Lead Annuity Trust, Brenda, 6866
Ross, Allison, 721
Ross, Amanda Lee, 9165
Ross, Cheryl L., 1951
Ross, Darrell S., 2298
Ross, David, 3611
Ross, David J., 9164
Ross, Dean John, 8658
Ross, Deborah H., 9164
Ross, Dolores, 6889
Ross, Elizabeth Love, 3064
Ross, Estelle Zacharia, 1601
Ross, F., 1951
Ross, G. Murray, 3619
Ross, Gary, 498
Ross, George, 5873
Ross, Hal, 3619
Ross, J. David, 7103
Ross, Jamie, 9341
Ross, Jody J., 4986
Ross, John S., 4986
Ross, Karen, 900
Ross, Karen C., 5188

Ross, Kevin E., 4337
Ross, Louise, 8697
Ross, Lynn, Jr., 8731
Ross, Mark, 6060
Ross, Mary Frances, 9165
Ross, Michael A., 9164
Ross, Michelle, 1958
Ross, Philip A., 7714
Ross, R., 1951
Ross, R. Dale, 9164
Ross, Rebecca, 1917
Ross, Robert, Dr. , 3662
Ross, Robin S., 1951
Ross, Ruth S., 6699
Ross, Sarah, 2619
Ross, Sharryn, 4008
Ross, Sheila, 6114
Ross, Susan S., 2298
Rossco of Palm Beach, 5935
Rosse, Florence M., 4272
Rosse, Thomas A., 4272
Rossen, Mary Jo, 4548
Rossi, Anthony T., 1860
Rossi, Craig Hall, 989
Rossi, Ellen E., 9351
Rossi, L. Jay, 989
Rossi, L. Jay, Mrs. , 989
Rossi, Marjorie, 989
Rossi, Merilee, 989
Rossi, Safford J., 989
Rossi-Landi, Beatrice, 8825
Rossier, Kim R., 3711
Rossignol, Randi, 1893
Rossing, Wayne E., 758
Rossington, Gary, 1046
Rossiter, Kristin M., 4688
Rossiter, Lori N., 3711
Rossiter, Peter L., 3224
Rossman, Beverly G., 3211
Rossman, Dan, 4459
Rossman, Erin, 3211
Rossman, Howard M., 3211
Rossman, Jeremy, 3211
Rosso, Louis T., 990
Rosso, Louise P., 990
Rosso, Maura P., 990
Rosso, Maura T., 990
Rosso, Thomas, 990
Rossotti, Barbara M., 1832
Rossotti, Charles O., 1832
Rossow, Kathy, 4514
Rostan, James H., 7232
Rostan, John P., III, 7232
Rostan, John P., Jr., 7232
Rostan, John P., Jr., Mrs. , 7232
Rostan, Naomi B., 7232
Rosztoczy, Diane E., 161
Rosztoczy, Ferenc E., 161
Rosztoczy, Robert A., 161
Rosztoczy, Thomas F., 161
Rot, Albert J., 3212
Rot, Keith A., 3212
Rot, Richard K., 3212
Rot, Susan E., 3212
Rotary Club of Columbus, 7513
Rotary Club of Upper Arlington, 7513
Rotary Forms Press, 7348
Rotellini, Frank, 9998
Rotenberg, Shannon Mabrey, 684
Roth, Amy, 483
Roth, Bruce J., 3690, 3694
Roth, Carla J., 858
Roth, David, 7010
Roth, David M., 3690

Roth, Eugene, 8146
Roth, Evan, 3690
Roth, James A., 1785
Roth, Larry, 6700, 9752
Roth, Laurence, 7010
Roth, Lindsay, 3690
Roth, Louis T., 3690
Roth, Marsha, 7010
Roth, Martha T., 2827
Roth, Michael, 4524
Roth, Mitchell, 3283
Roth, Nancy A., 6700
Roth, Nina, 6167
Roth, Peach, 3432
Roth, Philip, 5334
Roth, Richelle, 3582
Roth, Tilly, 5334
Roth, Walter, 3210
Rothbauer, Steve, 9224
Rothblum, Lisa, 6701
Rothblum, Marcia, 6701
Rothblum, Philip, 6701
Rothchild Family Trust, Seymour, 1733
Rothchild, Alice, 1733
Rothchild, Joseph, 1733
Rothchild, Judith, 1733
Rothenberg, Gail, 4173
Rothenberg, Pamela, 6702
Rothenberg, Stuart M., 6702
Rothermel, Rodney A., 8792
Rothman Charitable Lead Trust, 2299
Rothman Trust, 2299
Rothman, Florence C., 3213
Rothman, Gregory C., 3213
Rothman, Hermine C., 3213
Rothman, Maurice A., 2299
Rothman, Michael C., 3213
Rothman, Noel N., 3213
Rothman, Patricia C., 3213
Rothman, Thelma P., 2299
Rothrock, Theresa, 8144
Rothschild Trust, 406
Rothschild, Andrew G., 162
Rothschild, Barbara, 2300
Rothschild, Carol W., 61
Rothschild, Cory, 3942
Rothschild, David, 3942
Rothschild, Gertrude, 6703
Rothschild, Henry, 6703
Rothschild, James G., 162
Rothschild, Jeffrey G., 162
Rothschild, Marci Diane, 162
Rothschild, Richard, 2300
Rothschild, Robert, 5229
Rothschild, Robert B., 5229
Rothschild, Sara, 5229
Rothschild, Sara L., 5229
Rothschild, Stanford Z., Jr., 3942
Rothstein, Dan, 6632
Rothstein, Joel, 375
Rothstein, Maks, 6704
Rothstein, Rita, 740
Rothstein, Sergio, 6704
Rothwell, Melissa G., 8906
Roto-Rooter, 7350
Rotstein, Robert, 839
Rottenberg, Alan W., 4071, 4293, 4355
Rottenberg, Daniel, 6586
Rottenberg, Herman, 6586
Rotter, Steven, 6656
Rotter, Steven J., 6663
Rottinghaus, Catherine, 3493
Rottman, Burton, 2949
Rottman, Carol, 4553

Rottman, Carol J., 4553
Rottman, Doug, 4553
Rottman, Francis M., 4553
Rottman, Howard, 2949
Rottman, Michael, 2949
Rouchell, John A., 3756
Rouen, Eric, 238
Roufener, Jim, 1153
Rounds, Jeff, 9575
Roundtree, Tom, 5091
Roundy Marital Election, Wilma Sime, 3214
Roundy Marital Trust, 3214
Roundy, Beryl O., 3214
Rounsavall, G. Hunt, 3691
Rounsavall, Jr. Trust, Robert W., 3691
Rounsavall, Robert W., 3691
Rouse, Barbara H., 3692
Rouse, James W., 3943
Rouse, James W., Jr., 3943
Rouse, Jean, 8536
Rouse, Nancy, 3943
Rouse, Robert W., 3692
Rouse, William, III, 3692
Rouse, Winstead, 3943
Roush, Tom, 6030
Rousse, Sandra, 9382
Roussell, Kathy, 3744
Roussin, Lucille A., 5852
Routh, Brad, 145
Routzon, Edward P., 1348
Routzon, Marsha J., 1348
Routzon, Matthew E., 1348
Routzon-Landry, Sarah, 1348
Rovecamp, Monica, 3966
Roven, Rose Webb, 991
Rovens, Claudia Larry, 9102
Rover, Edward F., 5885
Rowan, Arch H., 9166
Rowan, Eloise, 9166
Rowan, Laura, 7839
Rowan, Rita H., 6910
Rowan, Stella S., 9166
Rowan, Thomas J., 6910
Rowe, Daphne, 8057
Rowe, Dick, 5628
Rowe, Eliza H.S., 4306
Rowe, Frank, 3360
Rowe, James, 7782
Rowe, Jeanne M., 6705
Rowe, John J., 7541
Rowe, John W., 6705
Rowe, Nick, 5248
Rowe, Sandra, 833
Rowe, Tazewell, 5306
Rowland, Patricia M., 9457
Rowland, Sandra, 8588
Rowland, William E., 8668
Rowlands, Ann T., 3290
Roxe, Joseph D., 6706
Roxe, Maureen L., 6706
Roy, Madeleine J., 1425
Royal Cup, 2510
Royal, Nina, 5605
Royals Charities Inc., 1730
Royalty, Shelly S., 1057
Royer, Marti, 9147
Royer, Pam J., 782
Royer, Robert H., Jr., 3588
Royston, Tracy L., 3969
Rozansky, Joan, 2405
Rozek, Alex, 4169
Rozek, Mimi, 4169
Rozett, Joshua S., 6915

Rozett, Martha Tuck, 6915
Rozier, Helena F., 6028
Roznowski, Melinda, 4554
Roznowski, Steven, 4554
RSG Charitbale Trust, 443
RSR Group, 3991
Ruan, John, III, 3550
Ruan, John, IV, 3550
Ruane, Elizabeth J., 1929
Ruane, Michael A., 1929
Rubeli, Maureen E., 163
Rubeli, Maureen M., 163
Rubeli, Paul E., 163
Ruben Company, Lawrence, 6655
Ruben, Dennis, 3215
Ruben, Joyce, 3215
Ruben, Sally, 5129
Rubens, Helen, 2301
Rubens, Jack, 2301
Rubens, Merton, 2301
Rubens-Ellis, Margaret, 2301
Rubenstein, Carolyn, 7819
Rubenstein, E. Katia, 6720
Rubenstein, Harold, 1833
Rubenstein, Jeffrey, 3151
Rubenstein, Jerry, 9167
Rubenstein, Joshua, 5740
Rubenstein, Joshua S., 6680
Rubenstein, Maury, 9167
Rubenstein, Robert, 6720
Rubenstein, Terry M., 3914
Rubin 1993 Trust, Ronald T., 4987
Rubin, Barbara N., 992
Rubin, Charles E., 3639
Rubin, Donald, 993
Rubin, Elizabeth M.P., 8214
Rubin, Gail, 2410
Rubin, Gerrold R., 992
Rubin, Gloria, 5359
Rubin, Howard M., 993, 5846
Rubin, J.N., 1090
Rubin, Judith E., 993
Rubin, Leibel, 6186, 6986
Rubin, Michael, 8246
Rubin, Miles, 6707
Rubin, Nancy, 6707
Rubin, Pamela K., 4987
Rubin, Paulette, 8246
Rubin, Ronald T., 4987
Rubin, Sol R., 993
Rubin, Stephen M., 993
Rubin, Todd B., 4987
Rubinfeld, Stuart V., 6019
Rubinfeld, Teena C., 6019
Rubinoff, Ira, Dr., 3919
Rubinoff, Robyn Z., 2426
Rubinstein, Beth, 9529
Ruby, Joe, 1205, 1206
Rucker, Fanon, Hon., 7582
Rucker, Sally G., 2386
Ruckstuhl, Julie E., 3748
Ruckstuhl, Kenneth D., 3748
Ruckstuhl, M., 3748
Ruckstuhl, Patricia J., 3748
Ruckstuhl, R., 3748
Ruckstuhl, Richard E., Jr., 3748
Ruckstuhl, Richard E., Sr., 3748
Rudawsky, Leslie Robbins, 3006
Rudd, Lisha Y., 9336
Rudderow, Judith M., 7988
Rudderow, Timothy J., 7988
Rude, Roberta, 9266
Ruder, Susan, 2886
Rudge, Howard J., 164

Rudge, Lois I., 164
Rudin, Abraham, 8247
Rudin, Mary C., 905
Rudin, William, 6656
Rudisill, Deborah B., 7076
Rudman, Kal, 8248
Rudman, Lucille, 8248
Rudman, Mitchell, 8248
Rudman, Solomon, 8248
Rudy Luther Toyota, 4733
Rudy, Edward M., 6708
Rudy, Isaac, 6708
Rueff, Gail, 3367
Ruez, D. Bryan, 8868
Rufer, Stephen F., 4664
Ruffing, Paul, 7456
Rugan, Amber, 3582
Rugart, Carl L., 1764
Ruger, William L., 4608
Rugg, Bill, 882
Ruggiero, Wendy L., 7190
Ruiz, Toni L., 9010
Ruiz-Healy, Catalina, 953
Rukin, Barnett, 5273, 5516
Rukin, David, 5516
Rukin, Donna, 5273
Rukin, Eleanore, 5516
Rumberger, Douglas Phares, 1734
Rumberger, Gloria D., 1734
Rumble, Martha A., 9248
Rumbough, J. Wright, Jr., 6850
Rumbough, Nedenia C., 6840
Rumbough, Nina Craig, 7213
Rumbough, Stanley H., 6840
Rumke, J. Nadine, 6229
Rumke, John H., 6229
Rumke, Lali, 6229
Rummel, David G., Dr., 7346
Rumsey, Dexter C., 9546
Rumsfeld Foundation, The, 5154
Rund, Charles, 6042
Rundell, Ca, 9181
Rundell, Linda, 176
Rundlett, Minnette M., 570
Runge, Brian D., 5081
Runkel, Robert, 5060
Runnels, Loren, 8773
Runstad, H. Jon, 9686
Runstad, Judith M., 9686
Runyon, Richard M., 6466
Rupiper, Karla, 5104
Rupp, Alois J., 5270
Rupp, Alois K., 5270
Rupp, Christina D., 6710
Rupp, Christine, 5270
Rupp, Emily J., 7565
Rupp, Melinda M., 7565
Rupp, Richard W., 6710
Rupp, Susan S., 6710
Rupp, William R., 6710
Ruppenicker, Harry, Jr., 1593
Rupprecht, Daniel P., 3529
Rupprecht, Mark A., 3529
Rupprecht, Paul S., 3529
Rupprecht, Phyllis M., 3529
Rupprecht, Thomas P., 3529
Ruradan Corp., 5959
Rusch, Kenneth E., 9938
Rush, Daniel E., 994
Rush, Jeffrey L., 994
Rush, Linda R., 994
Rushing, Byron, Hon., 4035
Rushton, Nancy A., 4140
Rusinow, Jeffrey, 9920

Rusinow, Kimberly, 9920
Rusis, Armins K., 9386
Ruskin, Maura, 5355
Russ, Ida, 5667
Russ, Mark J., 2691
Russ, Roman, 5667
Russ, Steve, 9774
Russeau, Kathleen, 4411
Russel, Jim, 520
Russell Harrington Cutlery, 4139
Russell Irrevocable Trust, Edward W., 3216
Russell Irrevocable Trust, Eluned, 3216
Russell Trust f/b/o Mary J. Dickie, F.D., 1735
Russell, Anita, 1647
Russell, Carol M., 995
Russell, Carolyn A., 995
Russell, David, 1593
Russell, David, Dr. , 7666
Russell, Dion P., 5182
Russell, Donn, 6727
Russell, Donna , 471
Russell, Francis J., 4083
Russell, John C., 6789
Russell, Joseph, 2791
Russell, Joseph V., 8630
Russell, Josephine G., 4273
Russell, Lee, 4391
Russell, Linda P., 8522
Russell, Luther J., 2676
Russell, Margaret C., 3413
Russell, Molly A., 3349
Russell, Richard F., 4375
Russell, Robert, 2702
Russell, Robert A., 995
Russell, Rogene, 9253
Russell, Ruth L., 1539
Russell, Steven M., 995
Russell, Thomas C., 1735
Russell, William Knight, 995
Russell, Zach, 9576
Russin, Ray, 5074
Russo, Celia, 6711
Russo, Georgina, 8249
Russo, Georgina T., 8249
Russo, John A., 6711
Russo, Joseph L., 6711
Russo, Marcy, 6712
Russo, Peter J., Jr., 5517
Russo, Robert A., 4143
Russo, Thomas, 6712
Russo, Thomas A., 6712, 8249
Rust, Adam, 4988
Rust, J Mead, Jr., 8250
Rust, James O., 8250
Rust, Margaret Dole, 2142
Rust, Margaret S., 9168
Rust, Murray S., III, 8250
Rusted, Dale, 2252
Rutco, 6715
Ruth Wender, 1777
Ruth, Joseph B., III, 4270
Ruther, Dale, 7358
Rutherford, Sandra E., 9631
Rutherfurd, Winthrop, Jr., 6599, 6989
Ruthman, Howard, 6005
Rutimann, Hans, 5964
Rutt, Audrey E., 7982
Ruttenberg, Biff, 3217
Ruttenberg, David W., 3218
Ruttenberg, Derald H., 6715
Ruttenberg, Eric M., 6715
Ruttenberg, Hattie, 6715

Ruttenberg, John C., 6715
Ruttenberg, Roger F., 3217
Rutter, Twila, 5611
Rutter, Vicki J., 104
Rutter, Winifred H., 1076
Ruttinger, George, 1799
Ruwe, Richard C., 2955
Ruyak, Kathy H., 8066
Ryan, Amanda A., 8313
Ryan, C.A., 1295
Ryan, Cathy H., 2304
Ryan, Christopher G., 8251
Ryan, Debra, 4555
Ryan, Dennis, 2305, 2820
Ryan, Frank, 8251
Ryan, Harold, 9576
Ryan, James Raymond, 4555
Ryan, Jean, 3420
Ryan, Jennifer, 2305
Ryan, John B., 5684
Ryan, Joseph, 2305, 3531
Ryan, Joseph W., 9108
Ryan, Kathleen , 9775
Ryan, Katrina W., 9997
Ryan, Laurie, 8251
Ryan, Mariesa, 4649
Ryan, Mary A., 3219
Ryan, Michael G., 1809, 9400
Ryan, Paula A., 4157
Ryan, Pete, 6540
Ryan, Richard, 6540
Ryan, Sheelah, 2305
Ryan, Steve, 4648
Ryan, Susan Kirk, 1696
Ryan, Theresa Helow, 2089
Ryan, Thomas, 5684
Ryan, Thomas G., 4555
Ryan, Thomas M., 2304, 4555
Ryan, Tom, 4983
Ryan, William D., 8251
Ryan, William G., 3219
Ryan, Yolanda V., 9108
Ryba, Pamela, 2138
Rybak, David, 6976
Ryburn, Frank S., 9076
Ryburn, Mary Jane, 9076
Rydell, David R., 2736
Ryder Homes & Groves Co., 2386
Rydex NV, 521
Ryland, Bill, 7741
Ryland, Patricia, 7741
Rylander, Jason C., 1747
Ryman, Ethan, 6137
Ryman, George, 6137
Ryman, Merrill W., 6137
Ryman, Robert, 6137
Ryman, William, 6137
Rymorg Investments, 9122
Ryrie, Charles C., 9169
Ryzewic, Susan R., 1726

S & C Investors, LLC, 5855
S.A. Camp Company, 585
S.A. Comunale Co., 7358
S.B.E. & S. Clients' Consolidated, 3944
S.D. Deacon of California, 447
S.L. Contursi Inc., 376
S.L. Contursi Rare Coin Gallery, 376
SA 1-10 Trust, 5705
Saab, Ghassan M., 4556
Saab, Khalil, 4556
Saab, Nadim, 4556
Saada, Jean-Claude, 8760

Saaf, Denise, 3797
Saar, Amy S., 5967
Sabala, James A., 2676
Sabathia, CC, 7354
Sabin, Mike, 7756
Sabin, Robert, 3113
Sabin, Robert L., 3113
Sabloff, Barry, 3078
Sabo, Ronald W., 842
Sabol, John M., 9687
Sabol, Nancy A., 9687
Sacardia, LLC, 330
Sacco, Todd A., 8114
Sachs Electric Corp., 4989
Sachs Holdings, 4989
Sachs, Keith, 5668
Sachs, Louis, 4989
Sachs, Marshall, 1205, 1206
Sachs, Mary L., 4989
Sachs, Mary S., 3647
Sachs, Samuel C., 4989
Sachs, Stephen, 4989
Sachs, Susan E., 4989
Sachs, William L., Rev. , 1392
Sack, Nathaniel, 3242
Sack, Silver D., 1175
Sackerson, Edward J., 4557
Sackerson, Helen A., 4557
Sackler, Beverly, 6716, 6717
Sackler, Jonathan D., 6716, 6717
Sackler, Kathe A., 6780
Sackler, Raymond R., 6716, 6717
Sackler, Richard S., 6716, 6717
Sackoff, Rosalind, 6349
Sacks, Lawrence J., 8660
Saddlebrooke Development Co., 160
Sadler, Dave, 4962
Sadler, Dorothy C., 2585
Sadler, Phillip E., 2585
Sadler, Robert E., Jr., 2306
Sadler, Sam, 2223
Sadler, Trelsie H., 2306
Sadlier, R. Daniel, 7610
Saeed Amidhozour, 1095
Saemann, Franklin I., 3220
Saemann, Irene L., 3220
Saenz, Denise M., 8880
Saesan, Goldie, 7933
Safaricom, 2622
Safe, Elizabeth K., 4275
Safe, Kenneth S., Jr., 4275
Safenowitz, Howard, 2307
Safenowitz, Marilyn, 2307
Safer, Ronald S., 3224
Safety-Kleen Corp., 4657
Safeway Stores, 401
Saff, Jon A., 5915
Saffrin 2007 Charitable Lead Trust, Carole E., 5884
Saffrin Trust, Carole E., 5884
Saffrin, Paul R., 5884
Safryn, Stacey, 1598
Sagan, Paul, 3998
Sage, Andrew G.C., II, 5767
Sage, David, 3458
Sager, Wendy, 1633
Saggese, Laura Scherr, 2316
Sagle, Stephanie, 9610
Sahler, Charles, 6979
Sahler, Jason, 6979
Sahs Revocable Trust, Harriet Rosenfeld, 2295
Saieed, Todd, 7064
Saigh, Josephine, 4585

Sailer, Katherine R., 6382
Saint-Amand, Emilia A., 6346
Sajdak, Guida R., 4047
Sajdak, Robert, 4573
Sajjad, Nabeela, 236
Sakac, Ann, 6945
Sakamoto, Marie, 2628
Sakhai Charitable Lead Trust, David K., 6718
Sakhai Charitable Lead Trust, Lisa A., 6718
Sakhai Family Philanthrophy Trust, 6718
Sakhai, Lisa A., 6718
Sakrison, James M., 172
Saks, April, 4990
Saks, Howard J., 1053
Saks, Mark, 6374
Saks, Mark W., 6636
Saks, Ronald S., 4990
Salatto, James A., 1557
Salazar, Arsenio, 5612
Saldivar, Rhonda, 9191
Saleh, Saleh, 725
Salem Co-operative Bank, 5230
Salem Five Cents Savings Bank, 4277
Salem, David A., 4361
Salem, Raymond, 6240
Salem, Raymond J., 6240
Salem, Richard M., 4361
Salenger, Stuart, 2308
Salerno, Lucinda, 8480
Sales, Mamiye, 5456
Salett, Elizabeth Pathy, 1825
Salett, Peter, 1825
Salett, Stanley, 1825
Salett, Stephen, 1825
Salgo, Miklos P., 3621
Salgo, Nicolas M., 3621
Saliba, Anthony, 3221
Saliba, Moira, 3221
Saliba, Robert, 3221
Salin, Bill, Sr., 3442
Salin, M. Jane, 3442
Salin, William N., II, 3442
Salin, William N., Sr., 3442
Salina, Caroline Boyle, 2754
Saling Family Revocable Living Trust, 7811
Saling Marital Trust, 7811
Salinger, Joyce J., 7363
Salisbury, Charles Harrison, Jr., 3945
Salisbury, Charles, Jr., 3945
Salisbury, Edith Gans, 3945
Salisbury, Katherine Gans, 3945
Salizzoni, Frank, 2309
Salizzoni, John, 2309
Salizzoni, Sarah, 2309
Sallee, John, 8674
Sallquist, Gary, 7299
Salm, Paul, 9797
Salmanson, Donald, 8481
Salmen, Richard C., 4681
Salmon Atlas, LP, 2121
Salomon, Jack, 1496
Salomon, Peter F., 6721
Salomon, William R., 6721
Salsa, Domenick A., 2384
Salter, Shar, 969
Saltiel, Swanna C., 7065
Saltonstall, G. West, 4276
Saltzman, Bette, 6722
Saltzman, Bette A., 6722
Saltzman, Richard, 6722
Saltzman, Richard B., 6722

Salvati, Mark, 4362
Salvaton, Sebastian, 8282
Salwil Foundation, 4539
Salzetti, Ron, 607
Sam Adams, 2510
Samaras, Byron, 458
Samberg, Joseph, 6723
Samberg, Laura, 6724
Samberg, Rebecca, 6724
Samberg, Sandra, 6723
Same Day Delivery Inc, 3002
Sames, Elizabeth R., 9010
Samford Irrevocable Trust, W. James, Jr., 62
Samford, Frank, III, 2578
Samford, John S. P., 72
Samford, William James, Jr., 62
Samiljan, Nancy, 4021
Samlyn Capital, 6613
Sammons, Bobby F., 8853
Sammons, Elaine D., 2310
Sammons, Lynda R., 8853
Sammons, Todd, 3401
Sammut, Dennis J., 996
Sammut, Helen, 996
Samowitz, Martin A., 2311
Samowitz, Paulette, 2311
Samowitz, Stanley C., 2311
Sample, Barbara, 5062
Sample, David F., 5062
Sample, H. Glenn, Jr., 8252
Sample, Helen S., 5062
Sample, John Glen, 5062
Sample, Joseph S., 5062
Sample, Michael S., 5062
Sample, Miriam T., 5062
Sample, Patrick G., 5062
Sampson, Carolyn, 5011
Sampson, David S., 5662
Sampson, Gary, 89
Sampson, Mathew L., 7944
Sampson, Robert P., 3986
Samson Advisors, 5713
Samson Lone Star, 8711
Samson, Helen Leidy, 2678
Samson, Leidy Sue, 2678
Samuel, Deborah K., 8870
Samuelian, Karl M., 557
Samuels, Ernest, 6725
Samuels, Peter, 320
Samuels, Robert H., 1914
Samuels, Victoria Woolner, 6530
San Francisco Foundation, The, 1126
Sanborn, Lorraine E., 4250
Sanchez, Raul, 7223
Sanchez, Victor, 2463
Sanco, Kathryn N., 8940
Sand, Dennis, 4624
Sandahl, Scott, 9268
Sandberg, J. Enc T., Jr., 9232
Sandberg, Richard K., 2354
Sandberg, Susan K., 2354
Sandbo, Judith, 7386
Sander, Tony, 2666
Sandercott, Mark, 4796
Sanders Custom Builders Ltd., 9009
Sanders, Caroline J.S., 7234
Sanders, Charlene, 8660
Sanders, Charles F., 2604
Sanders, Daniel S., 1737
Sanders, Daniel, Jr., 1737
Sanders, Derek A., 453
Sanders, Derial H., 7936
Sanders, Elizabeth, 3969

Sanders, Ellen G., 5518
Sanders, Emilyn C., 1737
Sanders, Frederic M., 6178
Sanders, Harvey, 5518
Sanders, Harvey L., 5518
Sanders, Helen Babbott, 5885
Sanders, James M., 2613, 4852
Sanders, Jeff, 5622
Sanders, Joanne, 884
Sanders, Joe, 5094
Sanders, John, 1737
Sanders, Kelly D., 245
Sanders, Kevin R., 453
Sanders, Louann F., 9171
Sanders, Marianna E., 9171
Sanders, Marshall, 3397
Sanders, Mary Ann, 7724
Sanders, Mary Mattesky, 3726
Sanders, Michael, 1813, 2341
Sanders, Michael A., 2313
Sanders, Michael C., 2313
Sanders, Michael W., 4852
Sanders, Pamela, 6837
Sanders, Robert W., 453
Sanders, Rodger M., 8951, 9212
Sanders, Steve, 9070
Sanders, Susan L., 6597
Sanders, Tawny, 999
Sanders, W.J., III, 999
Sanders, Walter J., III, 999
Sanders, William D., 9171
Sanderson, Martha Q., 1259
Sanderson, Valerie, 7356
Sanderson, Veronica, 4720
Sandford, Blake, 9034
Sandford, Carole, 9034
Sandhill Properties, 1035
Sandin, Liana, 5081
Sandler Charitable Lead Trust, Reba, 4278
Sandler, Andrew L., 1818
Sandler, Eva Sarah, 4278
Sandler, LLP, Buckley, 1818
Sandler, Malvin G., 6787
Sandler, Sheri C., 4278
Sandler, Sherri C., 4278
Sandman, Mary Elizabeth, 4279
Sandman, Paul, 4279
Sandman, Paul W., 4279
Sandnes, Marian, 1000
Sandnes, Richard, 1000
Sandrock, Scott P., 7312
Sandroni, Mona, 4883
Sands, Corrine, 1001
Sands, Lee, 1241
Sands, Leonard, 1001
Sands, Robert-John H., 3807
Sandstrom, Ron, Dr., 3582
Sandt, Yann, 5565
Sandy, Michelle, 9756
Sanfilippo, Martha E., 1002
Sanfillipo, Anthony M., 5183
Sanford & Lorinda Sanford Family Trust, Charles B., 9914
Sanford Fuels Ltd., 9034
Sanford Health Foundation, 8570
Sanford Oil Company, 9034
Sanford Oil South Texas, 9034
Sanford Petroleum Inc, 9034
Sanford, Claire C., 2625
Sanford, Mary, 2625
Sanger, Beth T., 1917
Sanguinetti, Annunziata, 9172
Sani, Ashok, 6726

Sani, Lal C., 6726
Sani, Sham G., 6726
Sani, Sunil, 6726
Sani, Suresh, 6726
Sanitary Service Co., 9682
Sanning, JoAnn, 7678
Sano, Mark, 5565
Sansar Capital Foundation, 6015
Sansom, Andrew H., 8931
Sanson, Jean, 3006
Sansone, Jeffery T., 2184
Sansone, Laura A., 2184
Sansone, Thomas A., 2184
Sant, Alexis G., 6252
Sant, Christine D., 6252
Sant, Kristin W., 6410
Sant, Michael J., 6410
Sant, Robert, Jr., 6733
Sant, Roger W., 6252, 6410
Sant, Victoria P., 6252
Sant, Victoria p., 6410
Santa Barbara Land and Cattle, 1090
Santa, Kevin J., 4584
Santamarina, Kathy Meyer, 4583
Santana, Annabel, 6549
Santander Consumer Inc., 9173
Santarone, Michael S., 2348
Santen, 9895
Santiago, Arline, 5969
Santiago, Felipe R., 455
Santoro, Brenda, 1038
Santoro, Charles W., 1558
Santoro, Charlotte, 1242
Santos, Paul J., Jr., 7812
Santos, Paul, Jr., 7812
Santos, Tony A., 740
Santucci, Thomas, 5557
Saperstein, Melissa, 6720
Saperstein, Robert, 6720
Sapper, Jon, 817
Saputo Cheese USA Inc., 8859
Sarafian, Alex, 5562
Sarandon, Susan, 1004
Sares, Timothy, 2729
Sargent Trust, Gladys W., 1005
Sargent, John A., 1790
Sargent, Karen Renner, 7557
Sargent, Leonard, 5047
Sargent, Nancy, 9810
Sargent, Newell B., 9985
Sargent, Richard C., 9370
Sargento Foods Inc., 8859
Sarich, Jacquelyn A., 9794
Saridakis, Brenda R., 7330
Sarkesian, Alex, 4371
Sarkesian, Christopher, 4371
Sarkesian, Lauren, 4371
Sarkesian, Peter, 4371
Sarkos, Janet, 5582
Sarkowsky, Cathy, 9688
Sarkowsky, Faye, 9688
Sarkowsky, Herman, 9688
Sarkowsky, Steve, 9688
Sarnat, Lela Z., 1211
Sarnelli, Josephine, 4299
Sarnet, Emma, 1211
Sarnoff, Ann, 6729
Sarnoff, Richard, 6729
Saroki, Anthony J., 379
Saron, Clifford, 283
Sarosdy, Emma, 8061
Sarow, Robert D., 4478
Sartori Co., 9921
Sartori Food Corp., 9921

Sartori, James C., 9921
Sartori, Janet L., 9921
Sarver, Fred K., 3704
Sarver, Robert G., 181
Sass, Mark, 7548
Sassaman, Hannah Jane, 8328
Sasser, Leslie Keith Elkins, 8838
Sasso, William R., 7200, 7914
Sassoon, Debbie, 1006
Sassoon, Michelle, 1006
Sassoon, Sunny, 1006
Sassoon, Victor, 1006
Sastaunik Admin Tr., Patricia J., 5519
Satalino, Nancy Neag, 8189
Satchell, L. Stephen, 3959
Satco., 766
Satell, Edward M., 8254
Satfin, Leslie A., 7954
Sather, Timothy J., 7817
Satin, Gary, 955
Satinsky, Martin J., 8034
Satira, Caroline N., 9396
Sato Lead Trust 80C-74C03, 1007
Sato Lead Trust 80C-7C04, 1007
Sato, Akihiro, 271
Sato, Kozo, 1007
Sato, Nieves, 1007
Sato, Sonia, 1007
Satoloe, Ralph E., 3306
Satow, Donna, 6732
Satow, Julie, 6732
Satow, Michael, 6732
Satow, Phillip M., 6732
Satre, Mike, 2676
Satrom, Jim, 7295
Satterfield, B.K., 9737
Satterfield, Byron K., 9765
Satterfield, Donald, 4079
Sattler, M.Stanton Brown, 8750
Saturni, Stephanie R., 3972
Satz, Joseph, 1166
Satz, Linda, 1166
Sauber, Theodore Pat, 7546
Saucerman, Pat, 9878
Sauer, Bradford B., 9527
Sauer, Gary B., 4785
Sauer, Janet Lewis, 9527
Sauer, Patricia A., 4785
Sauer, Sheri, 2377
Sauerland, Elizabeth, 7570
Sauerland, Franz, 7570
Saufer, Isaac A., 6483
Saugatuck Capital, 1566
Saul, Harry I., 2579
Saul, Julian D., 2579
Saulisbury Electric Co., 9175
Saulsbury, Charles R., Jr., 9175
Saulsbury, Mark A., 9175
Saulsbury, Matthew D., 9175
Saunders, Carole M., 6733
Saunders, Cheryl, 4393
Saunders, Cheryl A., 4393
Saunders, Donna, 8887
Saunders, Eve McClatchey, 2546
Saunders, Frederic M., 9176
Saunders, Gayle D., 9176
Saunders, James C., 9464
Saunders, Jill, 4879
Saunders, John E., 855
Saunders, John M., 2546
Saunders, Judith A., 1077
Saunders, Marc L., 8527
Saunders, Robert, 1077
Saunders, Stuart D., 9176

Saunders, Whitney G., 9517
Saur, Dwight E., Jr., 9253
Saurman, John R., 7130
Sauter, Sara, 3530
Sauter, Thomas, 6625
Savage Administrative Trust, 1009
Savage Family CLAT, The, 4280
Savage Sports Corp., 3991
Savage, Andrew T., 4280
Savage, Brian, 2109
Savage, C. Jack, 9742
Savage, Diana, 7339
Savage, James B., 4280
Savage, Julie A., 4280
Savage, Michael T., 4280
Savage, Priscilla B., 4280
Savage, Ronald J., 1009
Savage, Sally B., 4280
Savage, Stanley D., 9609
Savage, Thomas W., 4280
Savage, Toy D., Jr., 9413
Save 2nd Base, 8243
Savereide, John, 4796
Savett, Sherrie R., 8255
Savin Charitable Lead Trust, Muriel, 5520
Savin, Muriel, 5520
Savin, Nathan, 5520
Savin, Nathan E., 5520
Savin, Robert, 5668
Savings Bank of Danbury, 1559
Savings Bank of Maine, 3766
Savio, John, 4410
Savitch, Jordan B., 8208
Savitz, Alisa B., 6734
Savitz, Amy Gassin, 2906
Savitz, Peter, 6734
Savitz, Stuart, 2906
Savoie, Felix H., 4849
Sawa, Carla, 3156
Sawchuk, Alexander A., 1010
Sawchuk, Mariette T., 1010
Sawczuk, Cornelia Urban, 3545
Sawvell, Jon C., 7691
Sawyer Trust, Edna & Emma O., 2705
Sawyer, D. Jack, Jr., 2552
Sawyer, Deb, 9359
Sawyer, John D., 7483
Sawyer, Louise, 4169
Sawyer, Robert N., 4881
Sawyer, Robin Gibson, 5325
Sawyer, Stephen, 2644
Sawyers, Ruth, 4608
Saxon, Andrew, MD, 898
Saxon, Ken, 887
Saxton, James, 5363
Saxton, Laurie H., 9835
Saxton, Pamela L., 9581
Saya Trust, 1011
Sayer, Evelyn W., 4786
Sayer, George W., 4786
Sayer, George, III, 4786
Sayer, John, 4786
Sayer, Michael Scott, 4786
Sayer, Patricia, 4786
Sayler, Alan P., 1935
Sayler, Lee B., 1935
Sayler, Robert N., 9477
Sayler, Van C., 1935
Sayler, Wyline Chapman, 1935
Scace, Eric, 870
Scaglione, John E., 5509
Scalamandre, Ernest, 8738
Scaling, Wilson, 8837

Scandling, John D., 1012
Scandling, Michael, 1012
Scandling, William, 1012
Scanlan, Sallie A., 8978
Scanlon, Jenna, 2347
Scanlon, Joseph P., 5681
Scanlon, Sharon, 2387
Scanlon, Timothy, 2387
Scannell, Elizabeth A., 1290
Scannell, Jean G., 1554
Scannell, Mary, 4268
Scannell, Peter O., 1554
Scarborough, Ann Hanson, 9635
Scarborough, Michael, 1680
Scarborough, Otis, 2617
Scarcelle, Ellen, 7941
Scarlett, Rob, 4796
Scarpinito, Joe, 5855
Schaafsma, David B., 9595
Schaafsma, Faith, 9595
Schaafsma, Lori J., 9595
Schaafsma, Ron, 9595
Schabeck, Christine, 7741
Schacht, Karen K., 3792
Schacter, Harold, 5665
Schadt, Charles F., Sr., 8670
Schadt, Charles, Jr., 8670
Schadt, Harry E., Jr., 8670
Schadt, Harry E., Sr., 8670
Schadt, Stephen C., 8670
Schaedel, Gary, 5345
Schaedel, Sharon E., 5345
Schaefer, Corinne, 3065
Schaefer, Donald A., 6569
Schaefer, Joseph M., Sr., 3065
Schaefer, Sue Stockard, 9198
Schaefer, Walter L., Jr., 5308
Schaeffer, Andrew L., 8019
Schaeffer, Miriam, 1013
Schaeffer, Robert, 1013
Schaeneman, Lewis G., III, 1560
Schaeneman, Lewis G., Jr., 1560
Schaeneman, Priscilla, 1560
Schaeppi, Jessica, 9261
Schafer, Betsy Bolton, 7387
Schafer, Gilbert P., III, 7387
Schafer, Julian B., 7387
Schafer, K., 1178
Schafer, Mary Jane, 8256
Schafer, Patti, 4526
Schafer, Rick, 9797
Schaffer, Eldon, 2712
Schaffer, Frederick P., 6737
Schaffer, Geraldine, 6737
Schaffer, Henry, 6736
Schaffer, Irving, 6737
Schaffer, Peter, 6737
Schaffer, Richard, 6135
Schaffer, Robin, 6737
Schaffer, S. Andrew, 6737
Schaffer, Victoria, 576
Schain, Howard, 5755
Schair, Annemieke L., 3783
Schair, Douglas M., 3783
Schair, Erica M., 3783
Schair, Gillian B., 3783
Schair, Justin H., 3783
Schakel, Fred, 3347
Schakel, Lynn, 3347
Schalon, Edward I., 4558
Schalon, Marcella J., 4558
Schalon, Scott, 4558
Schalon, Susan K., 4558
Schambra, Emily, 9531

Schambra, Sharon, 9531
Schambra, William, 9531
Schaper, Benz & Wise Investment Counsel, 9838
Schaperkotter, John D., 2738
Schapiro, Paddy, 472
Schapman, Laura, 4449
Schara, Michele, 1325
Scharar, Robert W., 9089
Scharer, Lawrence L., 6868
Scharf Family Trust, David, 5830
Scharf, Alexander, 6302
Scharf, Asher, 5830
Scharf, David, 6302
Scharf, Dvora, 6738
Scharf, Lipa, 6738
Scharf, Morris, 6738
Scharf, Moses, 5830
Scharf, Solomon T., 6302
Scharf, Tsvi, 6738
Scharffenberger, George T., 5160
Scharffenberger, Marion A., 5160
Scharlin, David, 2315
Scharlin, Gloria, 2315
Scharlin, Gloria G., 2315
Scharlin, Howard R., 2315
Scharlin, Kerri, 2315
Scharlin, Peggy, 2315
Scharman Charitable Remainder Unitrust, Scott & Robyn, 9348
Scharman, Christopher, 9348
Scharman, Robyn, 9348
Scharman, Scott, 9348
Scharpf, George E., 5246
Schastny, Peter, 8483
Schatte, Andrew A., 8793
Schatte, Annette Clark, 8793
Schatz, Diane Maurer, 9366
Schatz, Myrna, 8889
Schaub Watson, Anne, 865
Schaub, David, 865
Schaub, Nancy G., 865
Schaub, Tim, 865
Schaufeld, Frederick, 8654
Schaumburg, Norma L., 3223
Schautz, Madalene L., 8257
Schautz, Walter, 8257
Schautz, Walter L., 8257
Schawe, Brian, 3580
Schaye, Marjorie G., 3122
Schea, Frederick E., 7998
Scheaffer, Danny, 9096
Schear Family Foundation, Lee & Patti, 7593
Schear, Lee, 7593
Schear, Patricia J., 7593
Schechter, Asher Lev, 750
Schechter, David, 4281
Schechter, David G., 4281
Schechter, Dena, 750
Schechter, Gail, 4281
Schechter, Gail R., 4281
Schechter, Irv, 750
Schechter, Joshua, 750
Schechter, Noah Blum, 750
Schechtman, Nancy, 2885
Scheer, Daniel J., 3558
Scheer, Jerald, 8546
Scheffe, Walter P., 7666
Scheiber, Fred, 3397
Scheiber, Jim, 3397
Scheiber, Morris, 6750
Scheid, Jan S., 7564
Scheid, Karen, 1410

Schein, Eileen, 6913
Schein, Joshua, 6913
Scheiner, Jonathan, 5824
Scheinfeld, Aliza, 7015
Scheinfeld, Elizabeth, 3281
Scheinthal, Steven, 8852
Schejola, Linda S., 2579
Schell, Anna, 4998
Schell, Cathleen, 4533
Schell, James F., 8114
Schell, Randall, 6625
Schell, Steven, 7742
Scheller, Joseph B., 8258
Scheller, Michael H., 8258
Scheller, Rita P., 8258
Scheller, Sarah E., 8258
Schellers Mugget Fund, 8258
Schellhorn, Lisa Jones, 4881
Schemco FLP, 9348
Schenck, Todd, 9319
Schendel, Sharon M., 1561
Schendel, Walter G., III, 1561
Schenker, Jack, 5949
Schepp, Florence L., 6739
Schepp, Leopold, 6739
Schepps, A.I., 9177
Schepps, Manet, 9177
Schepps, Melissa, 9178
Schepps, Scott, 9178
Scherer, Alison V., 1591
Scherer, Ned S., 9397, 9519
Scherer, Paul, 5371
Scherer, Paul, Mrs., 5371
Scherer, Tim, 4552
Schergens, Lucile E., 3443
Scherr, Janet, 1014
Scherr, Lauren, 1014
Scherr, Raymond, 1014
Scherr, Robert J., 2316
Scherr, Walter J., 2316
Scheuer 1993 Charitable Trust, David, 5763
Scheuer 1993 Charitable Trust, Judith, 5763
Scheuer 1993 Charitable Trust, Susan, 5763
Scheuer, Jeffrey J., 5763
Scheuer, Judith, 5763
Scheuer, Marge, 5763
Scheuer, Susan, 5763
Scheuer, Walter, 5763
Scheumann, T.Y., 9611
Schey, Lucille L., 7571
Schey, Ralph E., 7571
Schiano, Chrisina M., 2317
Schiano, Gregory E., 2317
Schichtel, Gerald F., 6208
Schick, Peter G., 4962
Schiefelbein, Charles, 4761
Schiefelbein, Charles, Jr., 4761
Schiefelbein, David M., 4761
Schiefelbein, Duane, 4761
Schiefelbein, Janice E., 4761
Schiefelbein, Karen, 7435
Schievelbein, Leslie H., 8958
Schiff Hardin LLP, 3224
Schiff, Betsy P., 6369
Schiff, Charles O., 7595
Schiff, Hardin & Waite, 6582
Schiff, John J., III, 7595
Schiff, John J., Jr., 7595
Schiffman, Ellen, 1738
Schiffman, Richard, 1738
Schiffman, Richard Lee, 1738

Schildberg Irrev. Trust, Sylvia K., 3532
Schildberg, Mark, 3532
Schildberg, Marlene, 3532
Schildberg, S.K., 3532
Schildecker, William W., 2001
Schiller, Debbie, 6740
Schiller, Howard B., 6740
Schilling, G. Fred, 8263
Schilling, Hugh K., Jr., 4799
Schilling, Hugh K., Sr., 4799
Schilling, Jennifer, 868
Schilling, Margaret S., 4799
Schilling, Tom, 4411
Schiltz, Joseph, 2787
Schimmel, John H., 5521
Schimmel, Rosalba, 1015
Schimmel, Stephen Harold, 1015
Schinazi, Raymond F., 2580
Schinske, Marian Huntington, 642
Schipper, David J., 7613
Schipper, Jean Anne, 7613
Schippers, D. Eric, 8208
Schiro Fund, 1474, 4282, 9528
Schiro, Dorene C., 482
Schiro, James, 6741
Schiro, Robert G., 482
Schiro, Susan F., 4282
Schiro, Tomasina, 6741
Schiro-Zavela, Jean L., 9528
Schissler, Nancy R., 9179
Schissler, Richard P., 9179
Schissler, Richard P., III, 9179
Schlag, Darwin W., 5012
Schlager, Eric D., 4283
Schlager, Judith P., 4283
Schlager, Robert A., 4283
Schlager, Robert D., 4283
Schlager, S. Lawrence, 4283
Schlanger, Craig, 2318
Schlanger, Darren, 2318
Schlanger, Jill, 2318
Schlanger, Norman, 2318
Schlarbaum, Gary G., 8259
Schlarbaum, Mark R., 8259
Schlarbaum, Ruth Anne, 8259
Schlatter, Konrad, 2988
Schleeter, Vera D., 9530
Schlein, Barbara S., 165
Schlein, Jeffrey G., 165
Schlemmer, Brett G., 2650
Schlepp, Rollie, 4679
Schlesinger, Sarah J., 1650
Schlessinger, Burd B., 7404
Schlessinger, David, 5665
Schlessman, Dolores J., 1349
Schlessman, Florence M., 1349
Schlessman, Gary L., 1349
Schlessman, Gerald L., 1349
Schlessman, Lee E., 1349
Schley, Jennifer, 3867
Schley, Scott, 5387
Schliesman, Paul, 4706
Schlindwein, Paul C., II, 9811
Schlinger, Katharine, 1016
Schlinger, Warren, 1016
Schlitz, Lloyd, 3662
Schlitzer, Nancy, 7997
Schloegel, Todd, 4497
Schloesser, Warren, 8345
Schloss & Co., Marcus, 6664
Schloss Irrevocable Trust, Walter J., 1562
Schloss, Douglas, 6664
Schloss, Edwin W., 1562

Schloss, Irwin, 6664
Schloss, John R., 7605
Schloss, Richard, 6664
Schloss, Walter J., 1562
Schlossberg, Dina, 8065
Schlossman, John, 3000
Schlossman, Marc, 3000
Schlossman, Peter, 3000
Schlossman, Shirley, 3000
Schlozman 1993 Descendants Trust, 3136
Schlozman, Daniel A., 3136
Schlozman, Julia E., 3136
Schlozman, Kay, 3136
Schlozman, Stanley, 3136
Schlueter, Jeffrey, 9597
Schluger, Neil, 6868
Schlutz, Robert, 3511
Schlytter, Marion C., 9918
Schlytter, Robert B., 9918
Schlytter, Robert O., 9918
Schmader, Sarah B., 7834
Schmeck, Paul, 1377
Schmeeckle, William R., 5068
Schmeelk, Andrew C., 6742
Schmeelk, Matthew R., 6742
Schmeelk, Priscilla M., 6742
Schmeelk, Richard J., 6742
Schmeling, Pete, 9878
Schmenk, Christiane W., 7408
Schmick, Esther, 3978
Schmick, Janet R., 3978
Schmick, Paul, 3978
Schmick, Sally, 3978
Schmid, David W., 1155
Schmid, Don W., 1155
Schmid, Karen M., 8179
Schmid, Richard R., 1155
Schmid, Walter R., 1155
Schmidt Family Living Trust, 1172
Schmidt Trust, Geraldine, 8281
Schmidt Trust, L. Florence, 7236
Schmidt, Anthony, 5671
Schmidt, Anthony A., 3622
Schmidt, Barbara, 520
Schmidt, Casiana, 8671
Schmidt, Chad, 8671
Schmidt, Chester, 8671
Schmidt, Douglas M., 8671
Schmidt, Eldon, 3641
Schmidt, Elise W., 5617
Schmidt, Elizabeth, 9349
Schmidt, Evelyn, 7813
Schmidt, Gladys, 5605
Schmidt, J. Frank, III, 7813
Schmidt, J. Frank, Jr., 7813
Schmidt, John, 166, 3520
Schmidt, John F., 99, 166
Schmidt, Karen B., 9813
Schmidt, Karl A., 9813
Schmidt, Lance, 4745
Schmidt, Margaret, 99
Schmidt, Margaret C., 166
Schmidt, Patricia A., 3622
Schmidt, Paul, 5325
Schmidt, Paul B., 5617
Schmidt, Robert, 4762
Schmidt, Robert E., 3622
Schmidt, Roger J., 3507
Schmidt, Sandefur, 9349
Schmidt, Sarah, 4762
Schmidt, Steven, 8671
Schmidt, Sue K., 3622
Schmidt, Theodore, 9349

Schmidt, Theodore, Jr., 9349
Schmidt, Thomas, 166
Schmidt, Tom, 99
Schmidt, William E., 166, 8671
Schmidt-Rogers, Lea, 8671
Schmitt, Chuck, 3260
Schmitt, Curt, 2774
Schmitt, David, 4804
Schmitt, Thomas N., 4231
Schmitz, Jim, 58
Schmollinger, Erik, 2352
Schmor, Douglass, 7794
Schmotter, James W., 1559
Schmuckal Land Co., 4559
Schmuckal, Arthur M., 4559
Schmuckal, Donald A., 4559
Schmuckal, Kevin P., 4559
Schmuckal, Paul M., 4559
Schmucker Trust, Virginia, 9923
Schned, Nancy, 3482
Schnee, Lisa, 5050
Schneider & Schneider, 6655
Schneider Farms, LLP, J.J., 1284
Schneider, Andrea K., 8135
Schneider, Arnold C., III, 8099
Schneider, Arnold, Jr., 7940
Schneider, Carolyn E., 1872
Schneider, Claudia, 1023, 3228
Schneider, Dorothy H., 7940
Schneider, Frederic, 1023, 3228
Schneider, Helen, 6743
Schneider, Henry, 4994
Schneider, Irving, 6743, 8503
Schneider, Jan, 2297
Schneider, Jane, 4994
Schneider, John, 1289
Schneider, Kate J., 7028
Schneider, Kent, 3227
Schneider, Lewis M., 3017
Schneider, Lynn C., 6743
Schneider, Mary Kathryn, 6933
Schneider, Mary M., 8099
Schneider, Melvin, 3228
Schneider, Mindy, 6743
Schneider, Phyllis, 3228
Schneider, Richard, 1023, 3228
Schneider, Robert B., 9862
Schneider, Ross M., 4994
Schneider, Steven D., 5564
Schneider, Tina, 6625
Schneider, Vivian L., 845
Schneiderman, Art, 565
Schneiderman, Arthur, 565
Schneiderman, George, 3494
Schneidmiller, John A., 997
Schnell, Jean, 3498
Schnieders, Caroline A., 5623
Schnieders, Elizabeth, 5623
Schnieders, Richard J., 5623
Schnittman, Adelaide, 2049
Schnittman, Barry, 2049
Schnittman, Barry, Mrs. , 2049
Schnittman, Cari, 2049
Schnittman, Merle, 2049
Schnittman, Norman, 2049
Schnittman, Steve, 2049
Schnittman, Steve, Mrs. , 2049
Schnittman, Tina, 2049
Schnuck, Scott, 8446
Schnur, Daniel, 285
Schnur, Jonathan, 285
Schoch Trust, Philip F., 9066
Schoellkoph, Susie, 7358
Schoen, David, 1017

Schoen, Louis B., 1017
Schoen, William J., 8628
Schoenberg, Barbara H., 1696
Schoenbrun, Celia, 9160
Schoeneman-Halle Foundation, 8348
Schoener, Phyllis L., 9180
Schoenfelder, Brad, 4745
Schoenherr, Jane E., 176
Schoenleber, Gretchen, 9924
Schoenleber, Louise, 9924
Schoenleber, Marie, 9924
Schoep, Nadine, 4736
Schoepke, Joan, 4805
Schoevogel, Blair, 51
Schoff, Charles J., 6138
Schoknecht, Kim, 477
Scholar, 3905
Scholes, Jay, 3991
Scholl, Eric, 6922
Scholten, Alice, 4390
Scholting, Terri, 5104
Scholtz, Elizabeth, 2805
Scholund, Christian, 8228
Scholz, Denise, 5100
Schon, Anna, 6185
Schon, Baron M., 6067
Schon, Chanie, 6067
Schon, Henry, 6067
Schon, Mordechai, 5472
Schon, Nissele, 5472
Schonberger, David, 6744
Schonberger, Elias, 6744
Schonberger, Joseph, 5443
Schonberger, Mark, 6744
Schonberger, Stuart, 6744
Schonfeld, Arnold, 6745
Schonfeld, Harriet Sue, 6746
Schonfeld, Sidney, 6745
Schonfeld, Steven B., 6746
Schonkopf, Albert, 6747
Schonkopf, Tova, 6747
Schooler Family Foundation, 4853
Schooler, David R., 7572
Schooler, Dean, 7572
Schooler, Edith, 7572
Schooler, Eric, 7753
Schooler, Heather L., 7572
Schooler, Matthew, 7572
Schooler, Seward D., 7572
Schooler, Wesley, 7572
Schoppe, Ben G., 9288
Schor, Lynn, 5739
Schorr, Marc, 5202
Schossow, Ida, 8869
Schott Corp., 4787
Schott, Elizabeth, 3497
Schott, Lewis M., 6749
Schott, Nash W., 6749
Schott, Owen, 4787
Schott, Steven G., 6749
Schott, Wendell, 4787
Schottenstein, Geraldine, 7575
Schottenstein, Jay, 7575
Schottenstein, Lori, 7575
Schottenstein, Marc L. Geraldine, 7030
Schottenstein, William, 7574
Schouten, Elisabeth Posner, 6621
Schouten, Mary Beth, 4621
Schouweiler, Jeanette D., 1979
Schowalter, Linda, 1098
Schoweiler, Jeanette D., 1979
Schraier, Mark Z., 4933
Schreck, Albert R., 5635
Schreck, Celeste W., 5635

Schreck, Charles R., 5635
Schreck, Christine, 5635
Schreck, Edward, 7545
Schreck, Mason T., 5635
Schreck, Teresa Juarez, 5635
Schreck, Thomas A., 5635
Schreiber, Agnita M., 9768
Schreiber, Brad, 4411
Schreiber, David, 6435
Schreiber, Emanuel, 6750
Schreiber, Eugene, 3832
Schreiber, Jamie L., 8426
Schreiber, Mark, 3635
Schreiber, Mark B., 8785
Schreiber, Mary, 6750
Schreiber, Morris, 6750
Schreiber, Ronald, 2958
Schreiner, Margaret, 9844
Schreiner, Ronna L., 9610
Schreiner, Steven C., 9610
Schrenk, Marjorie J., 8261
Schreyer, Cara, 686
Schreyer, Chara, 686
Schreyer, Justine, 686
Schreyer, Leslie J., 6780
Schreyer, Natalie, 686
Schriemer, David, 4606
Schroeder, Carol, 2725
Schroeder, Carolyn, 4671
Schroeder, John C., 3365
Schroeder, Kathleen E., 5523
Schroeder, Richard A., 3365
Schroeder, Timothy, 9867
Schron Family Charity Fund LLC, 5794
Schroy, Hope Feinberg, 5993
Schrum, David F., 3401
Schubauer-Berigan, Mary, 7582
Schuck, Ben A., III, 1076
Schueler, Kirk, 4639
Schuett, Mary Anne, 795
Schuetz, Lizabeth Rossi, 989
Schug, E.P., 4978
Schug, John B., 7237
Schug, Peggy C., 7237
Schuh, Brittany L., 3946
Schuh, Scott L., 3946
Schuh, Steven R., 3946
Schuldenfrei, Dia, 472
Schuler, Jean A., 9690
Schuler, Mary Jo, 2923
Schuler, Stephen G., 2923
Schulhof, Milford H., II, 1249
Schulkin, Todd, 394
Schull, E. Gunner, 2640
Schull, Lee, 8576
Schulman, Peter, 6820
Schulman, Susan Knapp, 2153
Schulte Enterprises Ltd., 9181
Schulte, Barbara, 9181
Schulte, Henry G., 1018
Schulte, Jamie Sue, 3958
Schulte, Johnie, Jr., 9181
Schulte, Paul S., 1018
Schulte, Peter M., 6250
Schulte, Peter R., 1018
Schulte, Robert L., 211
Schulte, Rudolf R., 1018
Schulte, Vernon J., 5031
Schulte, Virginia, 2970
Schultz Foundation, Arthur B., 3928
Schultz, Arthur B., 9986
Schultz, Clifford G., 2319
Schultz, Craig M., 1019
Schultz, Cynthia K., 5619

Schultz, Erik B., 9986
Schultz, Frederick H., 2319
Schultz, Frederick H., Jr., 2319
Schultz, James, 4636
Schultz, John, 4410, 9986
Schultz, John R., 2319
Schultz, Joshua G., 8028
Schultz, Kristine, 3493
Schultz, Larry, 9743
Schultz, Mae W., 2319
Schultz, Michael, 4981
Schultz, Nancy R., 2319
Schultz, Norman C., 1019
Schultz, Roxanne, 4468
Schultz, Tom, 9956
Schulz, David R., 3455
Schulz, John G., 9938
Schulz, Ralph R., 5879
Schulze & Burche, 2754
Schulze, Arthur R., Jr., 4788
Schulze, Carl W., 9182
Schulze, Enika, 9182
Schulze, Jimmy, 8819
Schulze, Joan, 4788
Schulze, Katherine E., 1219
Schulze, Richard H., 9182
Schumacher, Edith K., 9183
Schumacher, Robert J., 9183
Schumacher, William G., 9183
Schuman Foundation, The, 1176
Schuman, Arthur, 8859
Schuman, David, 126
Schumm, David, 7339
Schupf, Sara L., 6416
Schupp, Justin L., 4487
Schur, Howard, 2690
Schurz Communications, 3444
Schuster, Diane T., 6317
Schuster, Jacob Z., 6317
Schuster, Steven D., 7081
Schuster, Willa T., 1394
Schutte Lumber Co., 4995
Schutz, Jordanna, 1338
Schwab Charitable Fund, 9631
Schwab, Andrew, 8264
Schwab, Andrew E., 8264
Schwab, Daniel, 8264
Schwab, Dorothy B., 8264
Schwab, Dwight L., Jr., 9691
Schwab, Israel, 8264
Schwab, Michael, 8264
Schwab, Morris, 8264
Schwake, Henry, 5121
Schwake, Henry H., 5121
Schwake, Wende, 5121
Schwalbach, Brian Anthony, 1739
Schwalbach, Gerald A., 1739
Schwalbach, Gerald Anthony, 1739
Schwalbach, Mari M., 1739
Schwalbach, Nathan Paul, 1739
Schwalbach, Susan Jostrom, 1739
Schwalbach, Winsome Y., 1739
Schwalbe, James, 6751
Schwalbe, Jeremy, 6751
Schwalbe, Peter, 6751
Schwalbe, Robert, 6751
Schwalm, Donald, 4656
Schwander, Stephen S., 6932
Schwanke, Mary Kathleen, 9944
Schwarcz, Gail, 4560
Schwarcz, Jack, 4560
Schwarcz, Joseph P., 4560
Schwartz Charitable Lead Trust, Alvin,
   1067, 5551

Schwartz Charitable Trust, Arnold, 6755
Schwartz Foundation, Thomas & Lonnie,
   1067, 5551
Schwartz, Alan, 2881
Schwartz, Alexander, 4284
Schwartz, Allan, 5524
Schwartz, Allen, 5524
Schwartz, Andrew, 1452
Schwartz, Arnold A., 5525
Schwartz, Barry K., 6752
Schwartz, Benjamin, 5666
Schwartz, Bernard, 4284
Schwartz, Betsy A., 8265
Schwartz, Bob, 3371
Schwartz, Bradley W., 6753
Schwartz, Bruce, 7576
Schwartz, David, 6754
Schwartz, David E., 2367
Schwartz, Deborah, 9791
Schwartz, Deborah A., 9791, 9943
Schwartz, Eugene M., 5301
Schwartz, Frederick, 9791
Schwartz, Frederick P., 9791
Schwartz, Gary, 5809
Schwartz, Harvey, 3821
Schwartz, Herman H., 6753
Schwartz, Ida, 4284
Schwartz, James, 7576
Schwartz, Jamie Diamond, 2829
Schwartz, Jane, 8265
Schwartz, Jason, 3821
Schwartz, Jeff, 9335
Schwartz, Jeffrey, 5524
Schwartz, Jill F., 8002
Schwartz, John, 6754
Schwartz, Jonathan, 4284
Schwartz, Lawrence H., 6779
Schwartz, Lori Smalley, 1050
Schwartz, Lynn, 9756
Schwartz, Maragret, 4741
Schwartz, Margery, 6753
Schwartz, Marie D., 6755
Schwartz, Martin, 5665, 8265
Schwartz, Matthew S., 8265
Schwartz, Michael, 6115, 7433
Schwartz, Michael G., 1865
Schwartz, Nicholas, 5524
Schwartz, Richard, 3077
Schwartz, Richard J., 6754
Schwartz, Robert, 7576
Schwartz, Sheila, 6754
Schwartz, Sheryl R., 6752
Schwartz, Sondra, 5524
Schwartz, Steven, 6115
Schwartz, Suzanne A., 8265
Schwartz, Vicki Trachten, 1369
Schwartzbard, Michael, 5404
Schwartzberg, Al, 6756
Schwartzberg, Florence, 6756
Schwartzberg, Harris, 6756
Schwartzberg, Nicole, 6756
Schwarz Architectural Services, David
   M., 3947
Schwarz, David M., 3947
Schwarz, Eliza Ladd, 8483
Schwarz, Eric, 8483
Schwarz, Frederick A.O., III, 8483
Schwarz, H. Marshall, 8483
Schwarz, Jeffrey E., 6757
Schwarz, Nora M. Pincus, 8214
Schwarz, Rae Paige, 8483
Schwarz, Sherwood, 6757
Schwarzberg, Rabbi Ronald, 5382
Schwebel Baking Co., 7577

Schweckendieck, Edith M., 6758
Schwedler, John, 4573
Schweers, Donna, 1020
Schweier, Anthony, 7433
Schweiger, Robert T., 4911
Schweinfurth Trust, 4996
Schweinhart, Martin G., 8601
Schweitzer Charitable Lead Annuity
   Trust, Mary S., 1358
Schweitzer, Edmund A., 1358
Schweitzer, Gertrude, 6759
Schweitzer, Mary S., 1358
Schweitzer, Paul A., 1358
Schweitzer, Peter, 6759
Schweitzer, Stephanie L., 1358
Schweizer, Felix E., 577
Schweizer, Paul H., 6208
Schwendener, Benjamin O., Jr., 4590
Schwenk, Ray, 3370
Schwerin, Virginia, 1563
Schwerin, Warren, 1563
Schwieger, Ian, 6392
Schwimmer, Cheskel, 6760
Schwob Co. of Florida, 2581
Schwob Manufacturing Co., 2581
Schwob Realty Co., 2581
Schwob, Henry, 2581
Schwob, Joyce, 2581
Schwoeffermann, Catherine, 6230
Scialo, Elaine, 5855
Sciarra, Jacqueline F., 3448
Scifres, Carol, 901
Scifres, Don F., 901
Sciher, Deborah A., 8060
Scire, Jennifer, 5526
Scire, Patrick, 5526
Scire, Salvatore, 5526
Sciutella, Michael, 5300
Sclafani, Susan, 9494
Scobie, Tim, 9797, 9880
Scobie, Timothy, 9880
Scobie, William M., 9880
Scofield, Bobbie, 3689
Scolaro, Peter F., 4075
Scollins, Jay, 4352
Scontras, Theodore, 3766
Scorese, Joseph, 5360
Scotford, John P., 7579
Scotford, John P., Jr., 7579
Scotford, John, Jr., 7579
Scotford, Judy, 7579
Scotford, Laura, 7579
Scotford, Laura L., 7579
Scotford, Stephen L., 7579
Scott and Debbie, 1316
Scott Family Char Remainder Trust,
   1023
Scott Management Co., 160
Scott, Ann O., 3230
Scott, Betty J., 7714
Scott, Bob, 9085
Scott, Brad, 8738
Scott, Carolyn J., 9939
Scott, Catherine D., 3811
Scott, Charles R., 1021
Scott, Christine, 5051
Scott, Chuck, 5621
Scott, Cindy L., 6762
Scott, Courtney, 5051
Scott, Deborah E., 7986
Scott, Denasha A. , 9775
Scott, Dennis, 817
Scott, E. Wayne, 3499
Scott, Edward D., 3811

Scott, Edward R., Jr., 8697
Scott, Eileen M., 1022
Scott, Eli, 1265
Scott, Elizabeth, 6761
Scott, Elsie S., 1482
Scott, Florence H., 1023
Scott, Gay, 5527
Scott, Hanson, 402
Scott, James, 5527
Scott, James R., 5051
Scott, John T., 1023
Scott, Jonathan A., 4297
Scott, Joseph J., 9987
Scott, Joyce, 1740
Scott, Katherine A., 1021
Scott, Kathryn S., 4297
Scott, Kathy, 1021
Scott, Kelly D., 1021
Scott, Kurt, 3591
Scott, Mary Jo, 219
Scott, Pamela, 7774
Scott, Patrica S., 8266
Scott, Patricia S., 8266
Scott, Patrick W., 1021
Scott, Rachel, 5340
Scott, Ralph, 3922
Scott, Randal W., 1022
Scott, Red, 1021
Scott, Robert E., 5099
Scott, Stanley D., 6761
Scott, Stephanie Cassel, 1562
Scott, Stuart, 3230
Scott, Stuart L., 3230
Scott, Susan Silverstein, 1835
Scott, Taylor C., 5012
Scott, Walter, Jr., 5115
Scott, William, 5527
Scott, William C., 6530, 6762
Scott, William D., 5099
Scott, William, II, 5527
Scott-Barnes, Susannah, 8582
Scott-Welty, Steve, 3412
Scoviller, Roger, 5615
Scowcroft, Bob, 859
SCP Holding Co., LP, 1570
Scranton, Barb, 3427
Scranton, Joseph C., 8356
Scranton, Julien, 8356
Scranton, Mary L., 8356
Scranton, Peter K., 8356
Scranton, S. Caitlin, 8356
Scranton, William W., 8356
Scranton, William W., III, 8356
Scribante, A.J., 5116
Scribante, Adrian J., 5116
Scribante, Lynda, 5116
Scripps Foundation, 571
Scripps, Kathryn Ann, 1741
Scripps, Paul K., 9681
Scripps, William Hawkins, 1741
Scroggins, Stacy, 219
Scruggs, Barbara, 7193
Scrugli Trust, Anthony & Elaine, 3231
Scudder Charitable Foundation, 6947
Scudder, Caroline, 5871
Scudder, Edward, III, 9383
Scudder, Edward, Jr., 9383
Scudder, Mary Gale, 9383
Scull, David L., 5256
Scully, John, 4561
Scully, Joseph, 6763
Scully, Joseph C., 6763
Scully, Judith, 6763
Scully, Judith A., 6763

Scully, Judith Bailey, 9964
SDT Trust, 1128
Sea-Dog Corporation, 9671
Sea-Land Corporation, 9671
Sea-Real Corporation, 9671
Seabourne, George, 1581
Seace, Holly, 8288
Seagroatt, Christina L. Tangredi, 6719
SEAKR Engineering, 1351
Seal Marital Trust, Leo W., 4853
Seal, Jane P., 4853
Seal, Leo W., III, 4853
Seal, Leo W., Jr., 4853
Seal, Wallace Lee, 4853
Sealey, Kim, 3486
Sealey, Pat, 3486
Seals, Jamey, 4534
Seals, Jamey, Dr., 4459
Seaman Corp., 7580
Seaman, Catherine T., 2306
Seaman, Douglas, 2320
Seaman, Douglas, Jr., 2320
Seaman, Eleanor H., 2320
Seaman, Eleanor R., 2320
Seaman, Jeffrey M., 9845
Seaman, John T., III, 9845
Seaman, John T., Jr., 9845
Seaman, Jordan, 6131, 6720
Seaman, Judith, 7580
Seaman, Judith G., 7580
Seaman, Kimberly A., 7580
Seaman, Lois, 6767
Seaman, Morton, 6767
Seaman, Richard N., 7580
Sear, Adam J.T., 9186
Sear, Charles D., 9186
Sear, Judith, 9186
Sear, Timothy R.G., 9186
Searcy, Michael L., 113
Sears Family Clat, 3948
Sears, Anna L., 7581
Sears, Christopher, 3948
Sears, Debra McLeod, 8897
Sears, Henry F., 3948
Sears, Jay, 8897
Sears, Jay K., 8897
Sears, Lester M., 7581
Sears, Ruth P., 7581
Sears, Sharon Bushnell, 3948
Seasonal Packaging, 6940
Seaver, R. Carlton, 1026
Seaver, Richard, 1026
Seavitte, Samuel, 9862
Seaward, Kristine, 3711
Seawell, Chris, 7204
Seay, George Edward, III, 8717
Seay, Stephen M., 9187
Sebastiani & Sons Int'l Wine, Don, 1027
Sebastiani Vineyards, 1027
Sebastiani, Allison, 1027
Sebastiani, August D., 1027
Sebastiani, Don, 1027
Sebastiani, Don A., Jr., 1027
Sebastiani, Emilia, 1027
Sebastiani, Nancy, 1027
Sebero, Karen, 4497
Sebion, Diane L., 9907
Sechrest, Blair, 8683
Sechrest, Noah S., 215
Seckinger, Mark R., 7545
Second Chance Fund, 8336
Second Street Iron & Metal Co., 4292
Secor Medical, LLC, 8368
Secor, Richard, 4961

Secord Trust, Ruth O., 3232
Secrest, Dorothy Gail, 929
Secrist, Gail K., 8267
Secura Insurance, 9959
Securian Trust Co., 4729
Securitas Partners, 6768
Security Finance Corp., 8539
Security Finance Corporation of
  Spartanburg, 8539
Security Financial Life Insurance Co.,
  5068
Security Mutual Life Insurance Co., 5068
Security National Bank, 3488, 3518,
  3534
Security National Corp., 3534
Security National Trust Co., 9743
Seder, Diana D., 7748
Sedlmayr, Floyd, 151
See, Melissa, 637
Seed Annuity Trust, Fred M., 8484
Seed, Fred M., 8484
Seed, James M., 8484
Seed, John C., 8484
Seelig, Jonathan, 3998
Seely, Nancy, 2200
Seelye, Eugene, 7952, 8201
Seer Outfitters LLC, 9335
Seessel, Peggy, 8639
Seforim Bookstore, 5705
SEG Trucking, 546
Segal Trust, Beth Ann, 1506
Segal, Amy R., 577
Segal, Beth Ann, 1506
Segal, Odile, 3656
Segall, Mamie, 4671
Segars, Mike, 68
Segel, Robert G., 4285
Seger, Andy, 3447
Seger, Audrey, 3447
Seger, Cynthia J., 3447
Seger, Debbie, 3370
Seger, Kelly, 3447
Seger, Randolph L., 3447
Seger, Thomas W., 3447
Segers, Bennie D., 7534
Segers, Bo, 8657
Segers, Robert S., 7534
Seggelink, Luke, 9786
Segoe, Vilma, 7583
Segura, Anna, 1238
Segura, Michael, 4879
Sehn, Celestine, 4563
Sehn, Francis J., 4563
Sehn, James T., 4563
Seibald, Marcia, 6042
Seibel, Shelley, 2678
Seiber, Thomas, 7458
Seibert, Gary, 3582
Seichrist, Pippa, 2248
Seid, Carolyn, 741
Seidel, Arnold, 529
Seidel, John, 3948
Seiden, Harold, 6236
Seiden, Joan, 6236
Seiden, Peter, 6236
Seidenfaden, Jann, 7541
Seidenstricker, Joann, 8288
Seidl, Ann, 9781
Seidle, Carolyn H., 8067
Seidler, Alecia, 946
Seidler, Charles J., Jr., 3233
Seidler, Janet Prindle, 3233
Seidler, Robert, 946
Seidman Foundation, 8672

Seidman-Becker, Caryn, 6165
Seif, Harriet, 2937
Seif, Harriet R., 2937
Seif, Herbert E., 2937
Seif, Jonathan A., 2937
Seifert, Christian M., 9668
Seifert, Rachel A., 8601
Seifert, Thomas, 8698
Seifert-Russell, Margaret, 3359
Seigel, Donna P., 5231
Seigel, Fred A., 5231
Seigel, Julia P., 5231
Seiler, Edith, 4997
Seiler, John, 4997
Seiling, Ric, 5799
Seindenstricker, Joann, 8288
Seip, Alexa C., 1028
Seip, Tom, 998
Seip, Tom D., 1028
Seitz, Charles E., III, 2824
Seitz, David M., 8335
Seitz, William Roger, 137
Seivert, Mark, 420
Sekerak, James C., 7387, 7439
Selanof, Patrick C., 83
Selbach, Robin, 1926
Selber, Aaron, Jr., 3751
Selber, Pamela, 3751
Selber, Peggy B., 3751
Selby, Leland C., 1439, 1440
Selcke, George G., 4636
Seldes, Marian, 5700
Seldomridge, Kim, 8232
Selective insurance Company of
  America, 5528
Selective Insurance Group, 5528
Selendy, Patrick, 480
Selendy, Phillippe, 480
Self, Jonathan, 224
Self, Sara Smith, 7238
Self, Smith Winborne, 7238
SelfReliance Ukrainian Fed C U, 3234
Seligman Trust, Irving R., 4564
Seligman, Benjamin, 6772
Seligman, Florence, 6772
Seligman, Irving, 4564
Seligman, Nicole, 6772
Seligman, Sandra, 4564
Seligman, Scott, 4564
Seligsohn, Gerald, 6773
Seligsohn, Sandra, 6773
Seligson, Aaron, 6269
Selin, Ivan, 1742
Selin, Nina E., 1742
Selin, Nina Evvie, 1742
Seline, Marvin H., 8719
Selis Article Fourth Trust, Sara, 6774
Selis, Sara, 6774
Selkowitz, Adam, 1565
Selkowitz, Arthur, 1565
Selkowitz, Betsey, 1565
Selkowitz, Jed, 1565
Sell, Steven J., 608
Sella, George J., Jr., 5529
Selle, Donald S., 7600
Selle, Joan M., 7600
Sellers, Merl F., 3571
Sellmeyer, Regina, 222
Sells, Elizabeth S., 4147
Sellstrom, Carol W., 6268
Sellstrom, John L., 6268
Selsky, Abe, 9529
Selsor, Della, 7585
Selvaggio, Joe, 4669

Selz Foundation, The, 7340
Selz, Joe, 213
Seman, Jean, 4608
Semel, Scott, 523
Semingson, Dianne L., 7251
Semrad, Jeff, 5110
Semrad, Scott, 5110
Sender, Adam, 2323
Sender, Lenore, 2323
Senekjian, Harry, 9319
Senior Home Care, 6302
Senne, Dennis, 4734
Sensale, James, 8570
Sensale, Miriam, 8570
Sensintaffar, Grace, 7732
Sentient Flight Group, 1295
Sepp, Kalev, 9685
Septimies, Norman A., 6367
Sequioa Charitable Trust, 2324
Sera, Jean, 5255
Serafy, Jean H., 9188
Serafy, Nicholas T., 9188
Serafy, Nicholas T., Jr., 9188
Serafy, Nicholas T., Sr., 9188
Seramur, Brian, 9926
Seramur, Joan, 9926
Seramur, John C., 9926
Serenbetz, Clay R., 6776
Serenbetz, Cynthia L., 6776
Serenbetz, Jean, 6776
Serenbetz, Jean B., 6776
Serenbetz, Paul H., 6776
Serenbetz, Stuart W., 6776
Serenbetz, Thelma, 6776
Serenbetz, Thelma R., 6776
Serenbetz, Warren, 5561
Serenbetz, Warren L., 6776
Serenbetz, Warren L., Jr., 6776
Sergi, Kathy, 1922
Sergi, Kathy J., 1922
Serpieri, Jose, Jr., 6427
Serr, Erik H., 4403
Serra, Albert, 4565
Serra, Amanda, 1607
Serra, Benjamin, 1607
Serra, Deanna L., 1607
Serra, Jeffrey R., 1607
Serra, Lois, 4565
Serrano, Lawrence, 178
Servco Pacific Inc., 2645
Service Roofing & Sheet Metal Co., 9744
Serviss, Daniel, 5272
Serviss, Emily, 5272
Serviss, Jonathan, 5272
Sesler, Virginia, 5211
Seth, Terry, 8774
Sethman, Chad, 7933
Setia, Praveen K., 1768
SETRAC, 7209
Settembrini, Joel, 2005
Setter, Frank, 1599
Settlement, Stefanyshyn, 942
Settles, Jeremy, 5610
Setzer, Debra, 2325
Setzer, G. Cal, 1029
Setzer, Leonard R., 2325
Setzer, Mark D., 1029
Setzer, Scott H., 1029
Setzer, Sidney, 2325
Seventh Generation, 9384
Sever, Dennis, 8776
Severson, Patricia B., 1434
Sevier, Marcus, 1329
Sevier, Sheila, 1329

Seward, Byron, 4832
Seward, Diana, 5610
Sewell, Mark, 248
Sewell, Warren P., Jr., 2584
Sexton, James, 4790
Sexton, Joyce E., 4790
Sexton, Mats, 4790
Sexton, O. Griffith, 2326
Sexton, Thomas, 4790
Sexton, William B., 63
Sexton, William D., 4790
Sexton, William E., 63
Sexton, William W., 63
Seybert, Henry, 8269
Seyburn, Bruce H., 4494, 4524
Seyfarth Shaw LLP, 3242
Seyfert, Todd, 3991
Seymour, Alan, 7357
Seymour, Claudia, 5692
Seymour, James D., 9862
Seymour, Louise E., 3236
Shabat, Ari, 3175
Shabica, Charles, 9386
Shabsels, Charles, 6507
Shabtai, Alexandra, 561
Shabtai, Zachary, 561
Shack, Susan A., 6780
Shackelford, John, 2397
Shackelford, Stephanie, 2397
Shackelford, Stephanie W., 2397
Shacknai, Ethan, 147
Shacknai, Gabriele, 147
Shacknai, Jonah, 147, 167
Shackouls, Bobby S., 6781
Shackouls, David Anderson, 6781
Shackouls, Judith Ann, 6781
Shaddai, El, 5164
Shady Maple Farm Market Inc., 8270
Shady Maple Smorgasbord Inc., 8270
Shadyac, Tom, 1944
Shadyside Assocs. Limited Partnership, 3872
Shaefer, William H., 7483
Shaer, Marsha Frances Ross, 9165
Shafer, Phyllis C., 3449
Shaffer, Benjamin, 807
Shaffer, Betty Ann, 4934
Shaffer, Christa, 2525
Shaffer, Dorothy S., 9530
Shaffer, Julie, 1335
Shaffer, Michael A., 7339
Shaffer, Rene M., 3013
Shaffer, Sally Wood, 3644
Shaffer, Stanley, 4892
Shaftel, Lauren, 6782
Shaftel, Mel, 6782
Shaftel, Pamela, 6782
Shafter, Maryann B., 1434
Shah, Ajay B., 722
Shah, Amit D., 8273
Shah, Darshana, 9194
Shah, Rajani K., 9194
Shah, Rajesh, 5574
Shah, Saurabh, 9321
Shaich, Ronald M., 4287
Shain, Paul S., 9782
Shainberg Endowment, Nathan & Dorothy, 5700
Shainberg, Raymond, 8585
Shaked, Avi, 3237
Shaked, Avi A., 3237
Shaker Advertising Agency, 3238
Shaker, Anthony R., 3238
Shaker, Elizabeth A., 3238

Shaker, Helen E., 3238
Shaker, John E., 3238
Shaker, Joseph G., 3238
Shaker, Joseph R., 3238
Shakkour, Leila, 1510
Shalam, Abraham, 6783
Shalam, Sasson, 6783
Shalam, Sonny, 6783
Shallat, Barton A., 6647
Shallat, Jane A., 6647
Shalom, Ezra, 6440
Shalom, Ish, 6784
Shalom, Milton, 6440
Shalom, Morris, 6440
Shamah, Eliahou Joseph, 5531
Shamah, Maurice, 6648
Shamah, Steven, 6648
Shamas, Diane, 5532
Shambach, John L., 3466
Shambeau, Steven D., 9914
Shamblen, Louise, 923
Shamohs, J.S., 5554
Shamp, Jordan, 7050
Shamus, Susan, 4189
Shan Chen, Alice Der, 1939
Shanahan, James A., 5224
Shanahan, Mary Ann, 4999
Shanahan, Michael F., Jr., 4999
Shanahan, Michael F., Sr., 4999
Shands, Bliss, 4913
Shands, Jay, 8845
Shands, Lewis, 4913
Shane, Barb, 5127
Shaner Chaitable Lead Annuity Trust, Lance T., 8271
Shaner, Ellen R., 8271
Shaner, Justin, 8271
Shaner, Lance T., 8271
Shaner, Mathias, 8271
Shank, Roger E., 7529
Shanken Communications, M., 6785
Shanken, Leslie, 5852
Shanken, Marvin R., 6785
Shanklin, Garrett, 4288
Shanklin, Norman D., 4288
Shanklin, Sarah, 4288
Shanklin, Sarah W., 4288
Shanley, Grace R., 1567
Shanley, William C., III, 1567
Shanley, William C., IV, 1567
Shannon Automotive, Mike, 9927
Shannon, Albert, 9121
Shannon, Ann Dudley, 9811
Shannon, Bruce, 7586
Shannon, Bruce L., 1030
Shannon, Darryl, 5799
Shannon, David J., 3625
Shannon, E.L., 9345
Shannon, E.L., Jr., 1030
Shannon, Hyslop, 3752
Shannon, Janet A., 3625
Shannon, Ken, 3625
Shannon, Kenneth F., 3625
Shannon, Kirsten, 3625
Shannon, Lynn, 1100
Shannon, Mary Kathryn, 2328
Shannon, Michael L., 1030
Shannon, Michael R., 9927
Shannon, Ruth B., 1030, 9345
Shannon, Thomas J., Jr., 2328
Shannon, Thomas Joseph, III, 2328
Shao, Ming Lo, 344
Shaoul, Nadine, 6744

Shapell 2009 Charitable Lead A, Fela, 9755
Shapell 2009 Charitable Lead, David, 9755
Shapell Industries, 502
Shapell Lead Unitrus, David, 9755
Shapell Lead Unitrus, Fela, 9755
Shapell Lead Unitrust, David and Fela, The , 1031
Shapell, Benjamin, 1031
Shapell, Irvin, 9755
Shapell, Susan, 1031
Shapira, Anne E., 3693
Shapira, Anne L., 7814
Shapira, David S., 7856
Shapira, Elijahu, 7814
Shapira, Max L., 3693
Shapiro, Abraham, 4289
Shapiro, Albert, 4290
Shapiro, Anna Marie, 6786
Shapiro, Asa, 4566
Shapiro, Brad, 354
Shapiro, Bram, 4289
Shapiro, David S., 1888
Shapiro, Eileen C., 4290
Shapiro, Gerald M., 7239
Shapiro, Harris, 5532
Shapiro, Isaac, 5795
Shapiro, Israel D., 3949
Shapiro, James, 3240
Shapiro, James R., 3949
Shapiro, Jessica F., 6646
Shapiro, Joan, 3240
Shapiro, Joyce B., 1503
Shapiro, Larry, 4949
Shapiro, Mickey, 4566
Shapiro, Olivia S., 7239
Shapiro, Peggy, 7003
Shapiro, Richard, 5872, 6332
Shapiro, Robert, 5525
Shapiro, Robert F., 6786
Shapiro, Robert N., 4196, 4208
Shapiro, Roberta, 9292
Shapiro, Shirley, 5532
Sharaby, Danny, 2329
Sharaby, Elliott J., 2329
Sharaby, Michael, 2329
Share, Harvey, 8197
Sharkey Charitable Lead Trust, A., 7815
Sharma, Bianca, 9190
Sharon Steel Corp., 6787
Sharp Foundation, Peter Jay, The , 5359
Sharp, Emma O., 8272
Sharp, Fritz, 91
Sharp, J. Baxter, III, 204
Sharp, Joe Lyn, 9253
Sharp, Leigh Ann, 2897
Sharp, Randy, 9045
Sharp, Rhonda, Dr. , 3412
Sharp, Stacy Mays, 9045
Sharpe, Jerri Lynn Craft, 8548
Sharpe, Renee, 3566
Sharrock-Dorsten, Carolyn, 7339
Shastri, Bhavna K., 8273
Shastri, Kalpendu R., 8273
Shastri, Mrugank H., 8273
Shatto, Elise de Compiegne, 8802
Shattuck, Jenny, 8477
Shattuck, Mayo A., III, 3950
Shattuck, Mayo A., IV, 3950
Shattuck, Molly Ann George, 3950
Shattuck, Rick, 88
Shatzer, Warren, 2006
Shaughnessy & Ahearn Co., 4292

Shaughnessy Crane Service, 4292
Shaughnessy Trust, John J., 4292
Shaughnessy, John J., 4292
Shaughnessy, John, Jr., 4195
Shaughnessy, Mary E., 4292
Shaulson, Abraham, 1844
Shaver, Bill, 607
Shaw, Ashley Lemon, 1819
Shaw, Barb, 3402
Shaw, Barbara Udes, 5117
Shaw, Beverly E., 3244
Shaw, Charles H., 3244
Shaw, Christopher, 1926
Shaw, David, 4107
Shaw, David B., 1293
Shaw, Greg, 7608
Shaw, Ilene, 3243
Shaw, James, 4606
Shaw, Jennifer, 4337
Shaw, John, 1926
Shaw, John Duane, 9350
Shaw, John F., 1926
Shaw, John L., 2010
Shaw, John William, 9350
Shaw, Judith Helmle, 8929
Shaw, Kiersten Jane, 1734
Shaw, Marchelle Marie, 9350
Shaw, Michael, 3243
Shaw, Patricia, 9087
Shaw, Perry L., 9087
Shaw, Richard W., 5606
Shaw, Robert, 5626
Shaw, Ron, 2880
Shaw, Roy C., Jr., 8929
Shaw, Sara Chase, 5606
Shawe, Annette C., 5000
Shawe, Earle K., 5000
Shawe, Gail R., 5000
Shawe, Stephen D., 5000
Shawver, Mark, 912
Shay, Andrea B., 6736
Shay, Lawrence F., 1743
Shaye, Eva, 522
Shaye, Katja, 522
Shaye, Robert, 522
Shayne Charitable Lead Trust, Herbert M., 1032
Shayne Charitable Lead Trust, May W., 1032
Shayne, David R., 1032
Shayne, Elizabeth S., 1032
Shayne, Herbert M., 1032
Shayne, Joan B., 8589
Shayne, Joan Blum, 1032
Shayne, Jonathan A., 1032
Shayne, May W., 1032
Shea, Andrew B., 5977
Shea, Felice K., 5977
Shea, Jean, 965
Shea, Jeremy C., 9786
Shea, John A., 2887
Shea, Katherine D., 5977
Shea, Kristin, 7295
Shea, Norman J., III, 2071
Shea, Steven J.C., 5977
Sheadle, Jasper H., 7588
Sheafer, Emma A., 6789
Sheahan, E. Thomas, 9868
Shealy, Jeffrey W., Rev. , 8522
Shealy, R. Bruce, 2074
Shearer, Barry, 7118, 7205
Shearer, Melissa, 7442
Shearman, James S., 3732
Shearman, Thomas B., III, 3732

Shearman, Thomas B., Jr., 3732
Shearman, Thomas B., Sr., 3732
Sheehan Pipe Line Construction Co, 9130
Sheehan, Joe, 4962
Sheehan, Joseph, 4962
Sheehan, Joseph E., 5232
Sheehan, Timothy S., 2463
Sheehy, Janice, 1482
Sheely Family Foundation, Dale & Alyce, 7590
Sheely, Alyce, 7590
Sheely, Dale R., Sr., 7590
Sheely, Jay, 6083
Sheenan, Janet, 4222
Sheerin, Michael, 5388
Sheets, Ruth A., 4075
Sheets, Susan Ross, 3619
Sheets, William M., 3619
Sheetz, Chris, 3344
Shefferman, Jesse, 4395
Sheffey, Jane L., 9554
Shefts, Mark, 5482
Shefts, Wanda, 5482
Shelby, Diane, 641
Shelby, Kerry, 641
Sheldon, Dan, 4623
Sheldon, Daniel, 2242
Sheldon, Laura Beckman, 7430
Sheldon, Lisa Z., 7023
Sheldon, Robert, 7238
Sheldon, Robin O., 2242
Sheldon, Shirley, 4623
Sheldon, Stephen, 2242
Shelhamer, H'Krih, 5622
Shelhamer, Mehdi, 5622
Shelley, Sarah, 8522
Shelley, Sean, 1262
Shelton, Allison Korman, 2348
Shelton, Holly, 7408
Shelton, Joy Rae, 3703
Shelton, Kent , 9474
Shelton, Neil, 7798
Shelton, Walter R., 4849
Shemanski, Alfred, 9693
Shemanski, Tillie, 9693
Shemo, Michael A., 7643
Shemtov, Rabbi Levi, 5384
Shemtov, Sarah M., 5384
Shemwell, James, 4921
Shemwell, Lauri Mitchell, 4946
Shendo, Benny, Jr., 5611
Sheng, Kimberlee, 7807
Shenk, Elsie S., 8274
Shenk, J. David, 8274
Shenk, Willis W., 8274
Shepard, George, 1236
Shepard, Stephen B., 5879
Shepardson, Gregory, 4877
Shephard, Edward, 4221
Shepherd Foundation, The, 2303
Shepherd, Charles M.M., 5001
Shepherd, Charles T., 5001
Shepherd, David W., 6221
Shepherd, Gillian, 6437
Shepherd, Harold, 9641
Shepherd, Helen, 9694
Shepherd, Katherine B., 7336
Shepherd, Matthew, 219
Shepherd, Nancy, 6004
Shepherd, Nathanael, 4260
Shepherd, Patricia C., 4039
Shepherd, Ruth H., 6004
Shepherd, Susan E., 5001

Shepherd, Susanne W., 5001
Shepherd, T. Nathanael, 6004
Shepherd, Thomas R., 6004
Shepherdson, Charles J., 9531
Sheppard, Eileen D., 801
Sheppard, Kelvin, 4399
Sheppard, Stephen C., 4820
Sher, David E., 9424
Sherard, Ben, 8686
Sheridan, Brenda, 5533
Sheridan, Howard, 5533
Sheridan, Paul G., 678
Sheridan, Thelma, 7311
Sheridan, Thomas, 8345
Sherlock, Laura Martin, 803
Sherman Mgmt., 7020
Sherman, Beatrice B., 4293
Sherman, Billie Don, 8681
Sherman, Brian G., 4293
Sherman, Bruce, 9632
Sherman, Bruce E., 7366
Sherman, Claire B., 4293
Sherman, D. Larry, 4567
Sherman, David F., 4567
Sherman, Deborah D., 8681
Sherman, Diane F., 6027
Sherman, George, 4293
Sherman, Helen, 7866
Sherman, J. Claire, 3393
Sherman, Jane, 4567
Sherman, Jane F., 4567
Sherman, Janice, 3126
Sherman, Janice L., 4285
Sherman, Jessa, 6027
Sherman, Jim, 9192
Sherman, Kim, 990
Sherman, M. Eugene, 1249
Sherman, Michael B., 351
Sherman, Nachum, 6339
Sherman, Norton L., 4293
Sherman, Paul, 4294
Sherman, Paul A., 4294
Sherman, Rachel J., 6908
Sherman, Scott R., 4567
Sherman, Steven, 4293
Sherman, William S., 6792
Sherr, Hilda P., 3873
Sherrard, William, 7240
Sherrerd, Anne C., 8182
Sherrerd, John J.F., 8182
Sherrerd, John J.F., Jr., 8182
Sherrerd, Kathleen C., 8182
Sherrerd, Susan M., 8182
Sherrill, Joseph N., Jr., 8784
Sherry, Carron, 6217
Sherry, Fred, 5671
Sherry, Maureen, 6217
Sherwood, Emily Layzer, 3451
Sherwood, Lynne, 4474
Sherwood, Mark F., 4474
Sherwood, Matthew F., 3451
Sherwood, Ned L., 3451
Sherwood, Richard I., 3451
Sheryak, John, 3689
Shetter, North, Dr. , 4497
Shetty, Romita, 6793
Shewey, Bill, 7666
Shidler, Jay H., 2646
Shields, Kathleen, 2647
Shields, Patrick, 480
Shiller, Thomas, 7541
Shilling, A. Gary, 5534
Shilling, Andrew J., 5534
Shilling, Geoffrey B., 5534

Shilling, Jennifer E., 5534
Shilling, Margaret B., 5534
Shilling, Stephen E., 5534
Shillito, Charles, 1059
Shiloff, Bryan, 9193
Shiloff, Robert M., 9193
Shiloff, Sara P., 9193
Shiloff, Stuart P., 9193
Shim, Stephanie Rosenlund, 8245
Shimer, Julie A., 5964
Shin, Jackie, 883
Shin, Yong Sin, 883
Shin, Young J., 5291
Shinbaum, Marcy, 3074
Shinde, Manohar, 1768
Shindell, Ervin, 2791
Shindler, Doug, 7375
Shingleton, Argyle, 9764
Shinkle, Debra A., 7317
Shinn, Tim, 5369
Shinnick, William M., 7591
Shiotani, Kitty, 911
Shipley Trust, 366
Shipley, Caroline C., 6559
Shipper, Cynthia, 9122
Shiraki Trust, Hilda Kikuno, 2648
Shirk, Roland, 3367
Shirk, Tana M., 7969
Shirley, Virginia Lee, 3245
Shiroma, Fred, 2642
Shively, Steve, 7796
Shiver, Laura L., 5413
Shlansky Free Loan Fund of BMG, 5452
Shlemon, Pam, 2880
Shmelev, Anatol, 1132
Shmerler, William A., 6695
Shneider/Helmsley-Spear, 6655
Shock Coffee LLC, 6730
Shockley, Sandra K., 2332
Shockley, Sandy, 2332
Shockley, Terry, 2332
Shockley, Terry K., 2332
Shockley, Todd L., 2332
Shodeen, Beth C., 3246
Shodeen, Craig A., 3246
Shodeen, Eric M., 3246
Shodeen, Kent W., 3246
Shoemake, Melinda, 9154
Shoemake, Tom, 9154
Shoemaker Family Trust, 9928
Shoemaker Trust, Thomas H. and Mary Williams, 8275
Shoemaker, D. Charles, 5111
Shoemaker, J. August, 5111
Shoemaker, Mary Williams, 8275
Shoemaker, Patricia, 4396
Shoemaker, Sharon, 2180
Shoemaker, Thomas H., 8275
Shoemaker, William E., 5111
Shoemate Charitable Lead Annuity Trust, Charles R., 1569
Shoemate, Charles, 1569
Shoemate, Jeffrey D., 1569
Shoemate, Nancy, 1569
Shoemate, Scott C., 1569
Shoemate, Steven R., 1569
Shoen, Samuel W., 7816
Shoes That Fit, 9585
Shoffner, Gary E., 927
Shofstall, William, 2049
Shogry-Raimer, Cindy A., 4057
Shoiock, Ralph, 5779
Shojai, Tracie McKay, 7795
Sholiton, Faye, 7323

Shonberg, Alan, 7368
Shonka, Jeffrey A., 2631
Shook, Douglas W., 79
Shook, Elesabeth R., 64
Shook, Laura, 8834
Shor, Stuart, 6009
Shore, David, 1034
Shore, Judith, 1034
Shores, Sharon, 4978
Shoretown Management Co., 6858
Shoretown Mgmt., 7020
Shorstein, Jack F., 2194
Shorstein, Mark, 2194
Shorstein, Samuel R., 2194
Short, Carol, 3112
Short, Jamie, 461
Short, Jill, 3386
Short, Susan, 5485
Short, Tracy, 461
Shortline Terminal Agency, 5273
Shott, June Oblinger, 9765
Shott, Kathy, 9772
Shotton, Patricia J., 9491
Shoup, Holiday H., 8069
Shouse, Ron, 3567
Shovelin, Julia M., 7111
Showalter, Daniel, 3430
Showalter, Jennifer, 3430
Showronik, John, 7298
Shpigel, Rebecca A., 3813
Shrensky, Barbara, 3951
Shrensky, Lewis, 3951
Shrensky, Lewis F., 3951
Shreve, Christine A., 3912
Shreveport Sees Russia LLC, 6539
Shrewsbury, Victoria J., 9585
Shriver, James, 4116
Shriver, Michael F., 3925
Shropshire, Lewis, 2437
Shrum, Randy, 2463
Shtohryn, Dmytro, 2967
Shu Trading, 2923
Shuai, Yee-Horn, 533
Shuayb, Ahd, 236
Shuayb, Husam, 236
Shuchman, Alice, 6167
Shuchman, Daniel, 6167
Shuffield, Sarah S., 3076
Shuford, Karen, 9029
Shuford, Lois, 4859
Shuford, Robert F., 9548
Shugart Enterprises, LLC, 7242
Shugart Management Inc., 7242
Shugart, Grover F., Jr., 7242
Shugart, Kay W., 7242
Shuldiner, Reed, 4121
Shuller, Donald J., 7548
Shulman Family Foundation, Alex, 9654
Shulman, Alex, 5185
Shulman, Barry, 5185
Shulman, Jeff, 5185
Shulman, Jeffrey B., 7564
Shulman, Lloyd J., 6956
Shulman, Michael, 5185
Shultz, Barbara, 3535
Shultz, Beth J., 168
Shultz, Mel L., 168
Shultz, Rowan, 8028
Shumaker, Gregory S., 7318
Shumaker, Ronn, 3361
Shuman, David, 6795
Shuman, Michael, 6795
Shuman, Stanley S., 6795
Shumski, Edward, 4824

Shumway Capital Partners, 1570
Shumway, Chris, 1570
Shuping, Christopher A., 7144
Shupper, Judi E., 674
Shuster, George, 5535
Shuster, Jacob, 5535
Shusterman Family Foundation, 6619
Shute, Sharon, 7452
Shuter, Jack, 7513
Shuter, Pat, 7513
Siam Living Trust, Murad & Kristi, 1011
Siana, Philip J., 5389
Sias, Jeannette F., 7654
Sias, Richard, 7654
Sias, Richard L., 7654
Sib Chai Inc., 6920
Sibley, James M., 2597
Sicari, Helen, 4295
Sichko, Samuel C., 4024, 4106
Sichting, Dan, 3390
Sickel, Bruce, 7879
Sickler, Eric, 3498
Sidamon-Eristoff, Elizabeth, 9514
Siddiqi, Edith, 7611
Siddiqi, Satiad H., 7611
Sides, Delores C., 7062
Sidewater, Arthur, 8364
Sidewater, Morris, 8278
Sidewater, Samuel, 8278
Sidewater, Steven, 8278
Sidhu, Lisa Eaton, 2334
Sidhu, Rupinder S., 2334
Sidlik, Thomas W., 2753
Sidwell Materials, 7592
Sidwell, Adam, 7592
Sidwell, Jeffrey, 7592
Sidwell, Jennie, 7592
Sieben Foundation, 8568
Sieben, Drew, 3535
Sieben, Todd W., 2909
Siebers, Steve, 2803
Siebert, Henry E., 7327
Sieg, Shirley, 4496
Siege, Wilbert, 4735
Siegel, Anissa, 269
Siegel, Barry, 2400
Siegel, Blossom, 1036
Siegel, David, 1374, 2400
Siegel, David W., 1036
Siegel, Elaine, 5186
Siegel, Elana B., 6838
Siegel, Henry, 6797
Siegel, Herbert J., 6827
Siegel, Jacqueline, 2400
Siegel, Jeanne Sorensen, 6827
Siegel, Jerome, 6797
Siegel, Jerome A., 6797
Siegel, Jill, 2335
Siegel, Lisa, 1792
Siegel, Marshall, 5186
Siegel, Paul, 5186
Siegel, Richard, 2400, 8674
Siegel, Ruth, 6797
Siegel, Seth A., 1036
Siegel, Stephen, 6372
Siegel, Steve, 2400
Siegel, Stuart, 2335
Siegert, Robert F., 9938
Siegfried, Ellen J., 8633
Siegfried, Josephine B., 3562
Siegfried, Steve, 8243
Siegler, Pnina B., 7865
Siegmund, Frederick, 5739
Siekerka, Michele N., 5513

Siekman, Judy, 4406
Sieling, Richard H., 5071
Sierra Medical Enterprises, 253
Sierra Trading Post, 9983
Sierra, J. Robert, 2336
Sierra, John Robert, 2336
Sierra, Jose L., 421
Sierra, Mary, 2336
Sievers, Judy, 3513
Sigel, John D., 7568
Sigfusson, Becky B., 2734
Sigma-Aldrich Corp., 5003
Sigmon, Crosley Johnson, 7468
Sikand, Annette C., 1037
Sikand, Gunjit S., 1037
Sikand, Renee, 1037
Sikes, Clay, 2590
Sikes, Virginia P., 8118
Sikorovski, Andrew, 7622
Sikorski, Chet, 8647
Siktberg, Timothy J., 8681
Silber 73, LLC, 3952
Silber, Douglas, 3952
Silber, Janet D., 3952
Silber, Jean F., 3952
Silber, Paul M., 3952
Silber, Sidney, 3952
Silberberg, Gary K., 9991
Silberberg, Louella, 5805
Silberberg, Morris, 5373
Silberberg, Veronica, 9991
Silberberg, Veronica K., 9991
Silberman, Christina J., 3953
Silberman, Curt C., 1834
Silberman, Else, 1834
Silberman, John, 5558
Silberman, John A., 6273
Silberman, Marilyn, 6798
Silberman, Nathan, 6798
Silberman, Robert S., 3953
Silberstein, Alex, 6148
Silberstein, David, 5933
Silberstein, Eli M., 5933
Silberstein, Tsirl, 5933
Silbert, Stephen, 905
Silbiger, Thomas, 8411
Silby, D. Wayne, 3807
Siler, Bernard, 4534
Silfen, Amy, 8264
Silicon Valley Bank, 1038
Silicon Valley Community Foundation, 645
Silk, Louise, 8080
Sillins Charitable Lead Trust III, R., 6799
Sillins Charitable Lead Trust IV, R., 6799
Sillins, Benjamin, 6799
Sillins, Bernard, 6799
Sillins, Susan, 6799
Sills, Jason, 1213
Sills, Jordan, 1213
Silsby, Andrew, 3785
Silton, Fred, 1039
Silton, James, 1039
Silton, Lee, 1039
Silton, Susan, 1039
Silva, Alicia Donahue, 892
Silva, Louisa, 7755
Silva, Verneka, 1952
Silver, F. Morris, 7817
Silver, Jeffrey A., 5080
Silver, John J., 1356
Silver, Laura Klearman, 4940
Silver, Louis, 6800
Silver, Martha, 6800

Silver, Martin, 6800
Silver, Michael J., 4940
Silver, Robert, 6800
Silverberg, Brad A., 9646
Silverberg, Janice M., 9646
Silverburgh, George, 6070
Silverman, Barry, 2337
Silverman, Barry J., 2337
Silverman, Douglas, 6775
Silverman, Elinor W., 5536
Silverman, Elizabeth S., 5536
Silverman, Ellen, 2307
Silverman, Harvey, 6801
Silverman, Irene Zambelli, 5852
Silverman, Joyce, 5893
Silverman, Judy, 2337
Silverman, Karen, 6801
Silverman, Laurie Karen, 2337
Silverman, Marc A.B., 2035
Silverman, Marc H., 7244
Silverman, Marc W., 7244
Silverman, Mary R., 5536
Silverman, Mattye B., 7244
Silverman, Michael, 5893
Silverman, Richard J., 3992
Silverman, Shara K., 7244
Silverman, Stanley, 6801
Silverman, Stephen I., 5536
Silverman, Susannah L., 5536
Silvers, Tom, 1242
Silverstein Properties, 6655
Silverstein Property, 6656
Silverstein, Cindy, 7956
Silverstein, Eileen S., 5629
Silverstein, Elaine W., 1835
Silverstein, Flori, 6802
Silverstein, Howard A., 6803
Silverstein, Lawrence I., 4161
Silverstein, Leonard L., 1835, 7213
Silverstein, Matthew D., 9933
Silverstein, Patricia B., 6803
Silverstein, Phyllis, 2443
Silverstein, Raine, 6802
Silverstein, Stacey A., 6981
Silverstein, Stacey Adess, 6981
Silverstein, Stanley, 6802
Silverstein, Susan, 285
Silverstein, Susan B., 285
Silverthorne, Sandy, 7769
Silverton Foundation, 8689
Silvestri, Valerie, 5318
Sim Sholen Realty, 5815
Simak, Julie, 1998
Simcoe, Elizabeth, 6966
Simeone, Anthony J., 6669
Simeone, Beverley, 1557
Simkowitz, Chaim, 5666
Simmons Hospitality Group, 2400
Simmons, Adele, 181
Simmons, Alex, 9235
Simmons, Angela Beaver, 7271
Simmons, Cinthia Brinker, 8717
Simmons, Edward C., III, 5005
Simmons, Elizabeth S., 4873
Simmons, George, 2338
Simmons, Harold, 9215
Simmons, Harris H., 9363
Simmons, Marc, 7953
Simmons, Quincey, 4260
Simmons, Sandra, 2338
Simmons, Teisha, 84
Simmons, Tom, 4745
Simmons, William Brinker, 8717
Simms, A.L., 7877

Simms, Emma, 7877
Simms, Frederick V., 9929
Simms, Jean M., 9929
Simms, John D., 9929
Simms, John D., Jr., 9929
Simms, Josh, 790
Simms, Michael P., 9929
Simms, Nancy Gordy, 2493
Simms, Rhea P., 7877
Simms, Ronald A., 790
Simms, Ronald W., 7877
Simms, Steven H., 2493
Simms, Victoria Mann, 790
Simon Charitable Trust, Douglas, 1040
Simon Charitable Trust, Eric, 1040
Simon Foundation, William E., 5537
Simon Trust, Ronald M., 5624
Simon, Andrew, 4081
Simon, Auna, 821
Simon, Barry, 5733
Simon, Bill, 788
Simon, Cynthia L., 5537
Simon, Donald, 1040
Simon, Donald Ellis, 1040
Simon, Douglas, 1040
Simon, Eric, 1040
Simon, Esther, 3247
Simon, Ethan, 4081
Simon, Geri, 9123
Simon, Herbert, 3452
Simon, Jimmy L., 911
Simon, John, 1042
Simon, Jonathan, 4081
Simon, Kenneth, 8980
Simon, Leonard S., 4081
Simon, Lucille Ellis, 1040
Simon, Marion A., 4081
Simon, Matthew J., 4375
Simon, Michael, 1042
Simon, Mitchell, 9857
Simon, Patsy, 8782
Simon, Paul, 1042
Simon, Peter, 6954
Simon, Peter, Jr., 6954
Simon, Porntip Bui, 3452
Simon, Ralph, 1042
Simon, Robert Ellis, 1041
Simon, Roger, 5873
Simon, Stephen A., 3247
Simon, Steven, 1042, 5624
Simon, Steven R., 386
Simon, Stewart, 6136
Simon, Veronica, 4465
Simon, William, 1042
Simon, William E., Jr., 5537
Simon-Jensen Charitable Trust, Pamela, 1040
Simone, Joseph A., 6083
Simoni, Elizabeth M., 4296
Simoni, Frank R., 4296
Simons Trust, Debra, 324
Simons, Debra, 324
Simons, Debra W., 324
Simons, Erica J., 324
Simons, Jennifer, 2256
Simons, Paul, 607
Simons, Robert, 4362
Simons, Stephen, 324
Simons, Suzanne, 8363
Simons, Virginia K., 8849
Simonson, Elizabeth, 7087
Simpkins, Nancy, 6328
Simple Heart Charitable Trust, 1316
Simplot Co., JR, 2685

Simplot, Don, 2685
Simplot, Gay, 2685
Simplot, J. R., 2685
Simplot, Scott, 2685
Simplot, Ted, 2685
Simpson, Barclay, 560
Simpson, Cory P., 7725
Simpson, David, 2880
Simpson, Edward F., 2001
Simpson, Hope G., 3249
Simpson, Howard, 3248
Simpson, Howard B., 3249
Simpson, Hugh J.T., 6805
Simpson, James, 230
Simpson, Michael, 3248
Simpson, Mike, 7452
Simpson, Robert, 3432
Simpson, Robert C., 7725
Simpson, Roderic, 3624
Simpson, Scott, 219
Simpson, Sharon, 560
Simpson, Stanley D., 3624
Simpson, Susan, 8780
Simpson, Thomas S., 9891
Simpson, William, 3249
Simpson, William J., 8114
Sims F-1 Management Co., 153
Sims, Carter, 8243
Sims, David L., 7924
Sims, Jenn, 8243
Sims, Lowery, 5691
Sims, Marilyn, 8792
Sims, Pete, 219
Sims, Rebekah Lynn, 2643
Simses, Robert G., 1923, 1924
Simutis, Frank, 2989
Simwood Co., 2018
Sinak, David L., 8855
Sinclair Tractor, 3511
Sinclair, Calder, 2463
Sinclair, James G., 1909
Sinclair, Joseph S., 8488
Sinclair, Rosalyn K., 8488
Sinclair, Sarah, 8488
Sines, Lindsay R., 1960
Singel, Suzanne, 4406
Singer Family Foundation, Paul, The, 1744
Singer, Beverly R., 5609
Singer, Gordon, 1744
Singer, James R., 8279
Singer, Jenny, 1744
Singer, Joanne, 8279
Singer, Kenda H., 7819
Singer, Kenneth, 7819
Singer, Kenneth M., 7819
Singer, Paul E., 1744
Singer, Roberta L., 7819
Singh, Gopal, 9695
Singh, Gurvender P., 8959
Singh, Jason, 9098
Singh, Jill, 9695
Singh, Kamala, 9695
Singh, Rajeev, 9695
Singh, Sudhir, 9695
Singhal, Abha, 4048
Singhal, Amit, 1745
Singhal, Anil, 4048
Singhal, Shilpa, 1745
Singletary, Sally H., 2083
Singleton, David, 7582
Singleton, George H., 9197
Singleton, Mark, 9197
Singleton, Martha, 9197

Singleton, Pamela, 5692
Singleton, Silvia A., 8653
Singleton, Thomas, 8653
Singleton, Thomas W., 8653
Sinha, Sanjay, 1599
Sinnaeve, John, 4552
Sinnott, Barry J., 5710
Sinnott, Tom E., 5710
Sinton, Blanche W., 1327
Sinton, Frank J., 1327
Sinton, Laura K., 1327
Sinton, Margie, 1327
Sinton-Emery, Laura, 1327
Sinton-Martinez, Mari, 1327
Sioles, Elyse C., 169
Sioles, Harriet Z., 169
Sioles, Robert M., 169
Siperstein, Gary S., 8489
Siperstein, Mynde S., 8489
Sippel, Matthew, 6243
Sirakanian, Ekaterina, 450
Siriani, Andrew T., 2152
Sirmon, John M., 28
Sirovich, Matthew, 6214
Sirus Products Ltd., 5085
Sisson, Cody, 4088
Sisson, Terry, 3595
Sit, Eric, 6748
Sitar, Allison H., 3936
Siteman, Alvin, 5006
Sitt, Anita, 5531
Sitt, Beth, 5531
Sitt, James E., 5531
Sitt, Jeffrey, 6390
Sitt, Morris, 6390
Sitterley, William J., 7495
Sittko, Jon, 1352
Sittko, Steven G., 1352
Sitts, Heidi, 4459
Siu, Ida, 6748
Sivertsen Trusts, Sarah-Maud W., 4815
Sivertsen, Robert J., 4815
Sivertsen, Sarah-Maud, 4815
Sivori, John P., 608
Skadden, Arps, Slate, Meagher & Flom, LLP, 8874
Skaggs, Joe, 2877
Skandalaris, Julie A., 4571
Skandalaris, Robert J., 4571
Skarbovik, Gunnar, 8711
SKB, 4657
SKB Environmental Inc., 4657
Skees, Suzanne R., 622
Skeist, Loren, 6045
Skelley, Susan C., 4283
Skelton, Andrew, 18
Skelton, Catherine M., 4854
Skelton, Graham, 18
Skelton, Homer D., 4854
Skelton, Mark, Jr., 18
Skelton, Mark, Sr., 18
Skemp, Robert, 9941
Skemp, Robert, Jr., 9941
Skestos, George A., 7594
Skestos, Jason J., 7594
Skewes, William G., 9766
Skiff, Kathleen M., 5473
Skilbred, Amy, 88
Skiles, Elwin L., Jr., 4572
Skilling, Barbara C., 9990
Skilling, Jean, 9990
Skilling, Kim, 9990
Skilling, Mark, 9990
Skinner, Brian E., 1548

Skinner, Brooke, 2347
Skinner, Jane F., 2478
Skinner, Jane Fickling, 2478
Skinner, Leanne, 9631
Skinner, Steve, 9631
Skinner, Valerie Holloway, 8946
Skipper, Andrew T., 864
Skipper, Katherine, 864
Skipper, Laurie, 864
Skipper, Peter, 864
Skirtich, John E., 376
Skiva International, 6069
Skjonsby, Gregory, 884
Skjonsby, Mary, 884
Sklar, Barbara S., 9199
Sklar, Darrell, 9064
Sklar, Louis S., 9199
Sklar, Mark, 107
Sklar, Michael, 107
Sklar, Michael Alan, 9199
Sklut, Eric, 7161
Sklut, Eric R., 7161
Sklut, Lori Levine, 7161
Skoda, Gerald J., 5872
Skoggard, Carl, 6223
Skokan, Dan, 3498
Skokos, Shannon B., 9200
Skokos, Theodore C., 9200
Skoll Foundation, 1095
Skolnick, Angela A., 9352
Skolnick, Giancarlo, 9352
Skolnick, Joshua, 9352
Skolnick, Mark H., 9352
Skonberg, Lorena, 89
Skowronski, Christine, 1045
Skowronski, F. Stanley, 1045
Skrei, Sandra, 8796
Skudneski, David, 2640
Skye, Thomas, 2641
Slabaugh, Liesl, 9630
Slack, Michael, 7790
Slade, Barbara, 4702
Slade, Jennifer, 8970
Slade, Marie-Antoinette, 6809
Slade, Michael, 6810
Slade, Ruth, 6810
Slagle, Frederick, 2458, 2553
Slagle, Frederick S., 2544
Slagle, George, 8837
Slaight, Marsha D., 4893
Slaight, Tara L., 4893
Slaight, Thomas L., 4893
Slaight, Zachary D., 4893
Slan, Josh, 6720
Slate, Dan, 4417
Slate, Jill, 9464
Slater, Tommy, 503
Slattery, Barb, 5104
Slattery, Nicole, 8563
Slaughter, Gloria, 9353
Slaughter, Janet, 7124
Slaughter, Jerry, 3591
Slaughter, Jonathon, 7637
Slaughter, Kent C., 9353
Slaughter, William E., Jr., 9353
Slavik, Ann A., 5007
Slavik, Donald S., 5007
Slavin, Doris, 3954
Slavin, Jeffrey Z., 3954
Slavin, Sanford, 3954
Slawek, Joseph J., 3092
Slay, Eugene P., 5008
Slay, Guy G., 5008
Slay, Jeffrey C., 5008

Slay, Joan, 5008
Slay, Joan E., 5008
Slemons Trust, Elmer & Mabel, 8490
Slesin, Louis, 6141
Slesrick, Dolores V., 9955
Slifer, Beth, 6248
Sligo, Pat, 4793
Slinger Family Charitable Foundation Inc., 2308
Slingerland, Donald M., 8491
Slingerland, Frank M., 8491
Slivka, Benjamin W., 9727
Slivka, Max, 9727
Slivka, Nathaniel, 9727
Sloan Charitable Lead Trust, C. Hamilton, 7246
Sloan Trust, Annie, 9145
Sloan Trust, Garrett, 9145
Sloan, Ann C., 7246
Sloan, Annie M., 9145
Sloan, Garrett, 9145
Sloan, Harrison, 9085
Sloan, Lisa, 9235
Sloan, Mandy, 7214
Sloan, Matt, 9235
Sloan, O. Temple, Jr., 7246
Sloan, Robert, 3916, 3976
Sloan, Thomas G., 9145
Sloane, Carl, 1746
Sloane, Edward G., Jr., 9742
Sloane, Lisa, 1746
Sloane, Toby, 1746
Sloane, Todd C., 1746
Sloane-Pinel, Amy, 1746
Slocum, Caroline Gates, 4276
Sloss, Anthony, 1048
Sloss, Elizabeth, 1048
Sloss, Jean, 1048
Sloss, Jeffrey, 1048
Sloss, Karen, 1048
Sloss, Louis, Jr., 1048
Sloup, Nicole, 3614
Slovin, Bruce, 6811
Slusher Trust, Roy W., 5009
Slutsky, Kenneth J., 5548
Sluys, Nancy M., 9366
Sly, Helen, 5018
Sly, Helen S., 5018
Slye, Terry, 4626, 4648
Small Corp., 4088
Small Pond Investments, 4234
Small, Albert H., 3955
Small, Albert H., Jr., 3955
Small, Beverly, 8675
Small, Christi Cracchiolo, 4414
Small, David B., 2970
Small, Dennis G., 2267
Small, Douglas, 8675
Small, Edward C., 8854
Small, George L., 3919
Small, Irvin, 8675
Small, J. Michael, 8671
Small, Johnson, 8514
Small, Julie, 9184
Small, Leon, 934
Small, Peggy, 3514
Small, Shirley, 3955
Smalley, Debra, 1050
Smalley, Jeffrey, 1050
Smalley, Marvin, 1050
Smalley, Scott, 1050
Smalley, Sondra, 1050
Smalley, William, 2139
Smallwood Trust, William P., 3251

SmallwoodFinancial Services, 1362
Smart, Debbie, 3567
Smead, Larry H., 8669
Smead, Preston, 8669
Smedley, Sheryl, 12
Smeed, Ralph E., 2686
Smeltser, Jeremy, 7252
Smeltzer, Ann, 3535
Smethie, Katherine S., 9217
Smick, David, 2340
Smick, Vickie, 2340
Smid, Melissa D., 9907
Smiley, Eleanor M., 7597
Smiley, Linda, 7772
Smiley, Raymond E., 7597
Smilowitz, Herbert, 5538
Smilowitz, Marilyn, 5538
Smirich, John, 6666
Smith Charitable Lead Trust, William R. and Sara Babb, 2586
Smith Charitable Lead Unitrust, Elizabeth G., 5539
Smith Family Foundation, 915
Smith Family Foundation, Charles E., 2707
Smith Family Foundation, Winthrop H. and Margaret D., 1571
Smith Foundation, James C. and Norma I., 9206
Smith Foundation, Particia & William, 6542
Smith Group, Everett, 9931
Smith Jr. Foundation, Edward W., 9895
Smith Jr., Malcolm E., 6816
Smith Marital Trust, Omer, 1058
Smith Stevedoring Co., Cooper T., 22
Smith Stevedoring Co., Inc., Cooper T., 23
Smith Trust, Lloyd L., 7598
Smith Trust, William, 7249
Smith XXI Trust, William, 7249
Smith, A. Russell, 2728
Smith, Adam, 3501
Smith, Adrienne, 4314
Smith, Albert J., III, 9207
Smith, Albert J., Jr., 9207
Smith, Alden H., Jr., 8615
Smith, Alexander M., 9698
Smith, Alison Fisher, 8781
Smith, Allen C., 6208
Smith, Allison Klesse, 8998
Smith, Amanda, 1052
Smith, Amanda B., 1052
Smith, Anthony, 1572
Smith, April L., 4376
Smith, Argile, 4824
Smith, Arlene H., 8280
Smith, B.J., 7408
Smith, Barbara, 9756
Smith, Barbara Ann, 2900
Smith, Bernice R., 9698
Smith, Beth, 6814
Smith, Betty Denny, 1005
Smith, Brandon, 5187, 7718
Smith, Brian J., 981
Smith, Briell, 6063
Smith, Buster, 8528
Smith, Byron, 6814
Smith, Cameron, 1056
Smith, Carol, 9356
Smith, Caroline P., 8476
Smith, Catherine E., 9627
Smith, Charles W., 9985
Smith, Charlie, 3441

Smith, Cherida C., 7753
Smith, Cheryl D., 3453
Smith, Christopher, 8349
Smith, Christopher B., 2731, 9616
Smith, Claiborne B., 3253
Smith, Claire M. Thornley, 549
Smith, Clarinda C., 1054
Smith, Clarke A., 1057
Smith, Cody J., 6877
Smith, Colby, 896
Smith, Colin, 4057
Smith, Craig, 1056
Smith, Dana Weiss, 4298
Smith, David, 9139
Smith, David B., 2731
Smith, David Bruce, 2707
Smith, David R., 1936
Smith, Dean L., 6912
Smith, Deborah Ashley, 7078
Smith, Deborah L., 5413
Smith, Derek, 5799
Smith, Derek V., 2554
Smith, Derrick W., 1958
Smith, Dolores R., 8283
Smith, Donald, 4953
Smith, Donald D., 2540
Smith, Donald E., 3356
Smith, Donna, 9778
Smith, Dorenda, 9231
Smith, Dorothea P., 2562
Smith, Dorothy, 1056
Smith, Dorothy D., 1962
Smith, Douglas D., 998
Smith, Edward, 2456
Smith, Edward A., 1464
Smith, Edward D., 5187
Smith, Elizabeth G., 5539
Smith, Emily A. Lemole, 8119
Smith, Emmitt J., III, 9204
Smith, Ethel, 5341
Smith, Evelyn A., 16
Smith, F. Ronald, 153
Smith, Frank J., 8281
Smith, Gail G., 4855
Smith, Genl. William A., 7249
Smith, George A., 258
Smith, George E., 9932
Smith, George G., 5539
Smith, George G., III, 5539
Smith, Grant, 1572
Smith, Greg, 1052
Smith, Gregg, 5131
Smith, Gregory N., 6168
Smith, Gregory T., 1052
Smith, Guy, 1437
Smith, Gwendolyn, 9207
Smith, Gwendolyn A., 7953
Smith, H. William, Jr., 6542
Smith, Hal L., 3253
Smith, Hardy William, 563
Smith, Harold Byron, Jr., 2731
Smith, Harry, 1053
Smith, Hayden P., 3253
Smith, Herbert, Jr., 3683
Smith, Hilary, 257
Smith, Hope, 6064
Smith, Hope Geier, 6063
Smith, Horace, 4299
Smith, Hunter J., 9534
Smith, J. Bruce, 9625
Smith, J. Harold, 7096
Smith, Jack J., Jr., 8285
Smith, Jack T., 9273
Smith, Jacqui, 1572

Smith, Jada P., 1053
Smith, James, 258
Smith, James C., 1477, 9206
Smith, James H., Jr., 7096
Smith, James M., 5900
Smith, Janaea, 4449
Smith, Jane Cavanaugh, 1421
Smith, Janet, 981, 5539
Smith, Jason, 2544
Smith, Jean, 5549
Smith, Jean M., 4299
Smith, Jean M.R., 4573
Smith, Jeffery T., 6230
Smith, Jeffrey, 4267
Smith, Jennifer, 8890
Smith, John, 9913
Smith, John E., II, 3253
Smith, Jonathan, 6597
Smith, Jordan H., 4509
Smith, Joyce, 1052
Smith, Judith, 9174
Smith, Julia C., 9207
Smith, Julia T., 3253
Smith, Julious P., Jr., 9502
Smith, Karen, 170, 1242
Smith, Kathleen, 7456
Smith, Kathleen D., 1686
Smith, Kenneth L., 3515
Smith, Kim, 9064
Smith, Kim S., 1057
Smith, Koryne, 309
Smith, Kristen, 3797
Smith, Layton F. , 2046
Smith, Lee, 4317, 8282
Smith, Leslie K., 1827
Smith, Lesly S., 2012
Smith, Lester, 8738
Smith, Lester M., 9698
Smith, Linda I., 1055
Smith, Lonnie M., 3453
Smith, Loy D., 9724
Smith, Lynda, 3367
Smith, Lynn, 3655
Smith, Lynn A., 2669
Smith, Lynne, 8282
Smith, Maggie, 5872
Smith, Marcia, 9810
Smith, Marcia N., 992
Smith, Margaret Dunn, 1571
Smith, Margaret H., 2978
Smith, Margaret J., 1693
Smith, Margaret M., 2537
Smith, Marguerite Carl, 8282
Smith, Marian, 9627
Smith, Marianne F., 6815
Smith, Marie E., 4826
Smith, Mark, 1056, 9139
Smith, Mark A., 8890
Smith, Markle C., 1054
Smith, Martin, 4847
Smith, Mary, 6945
Smith, Mary C., 6336
Smith, Mary McKay, 2669
Smith, Mary Welles Mooers, 6208
Smith, Matt, 7247
Smith, Matt N., Jr., 4557
Smith, Matthew, 258, 7456
Smith, Megan, 5187
Smith, Michael C., 7270
Smith, Mike, 896, 5050
Smith, Monroe, 2456
Smith, Nancy, 4573
Smith, Nancy C., 7906
Smith, Nancy L. Wheeler, 1179

Smith, Nancy R., 2586
Smith, Nancy S., 4366
Smith, Norma I., 9206
Smith, Ora K., 1693
Smith, Orma R., III, 2327
Smith, Orphalee, 9625
Smith, Pamela Hyde, 9627
Smith, Pamela J., 258
Smith, Patricia A., 9204
Smith, Patricia R., 1936
Smith, Patsy R., 9201
Smith, Peter V., 6016, 6542
Smith, Preston B., 7657
Smith, R.J., 5872
Smith, R.J., Mr. , 5872
Smith, R.J., Mrs. , 5872
Smith, Rachel C., 6621
Smith, Ralph, 8350
Smith, Randolph C.H., 9616
Smith, Raymond K., 9202
Smith, Regina, Dr. , 2437
Smith, Richard, 447
Smith, Richard H., 3779
Smith, Rita M., 9508
Smith, Robert A., 4298
Smith, Robert H., 1918
Smith, Robin, 5616
Smith, Roger K., 1693
Smith, Ronald G., 58
Smith, Ronald L., 7248
Smith, Rory W., 7741
Smith, Ross, 8869
Smith, Roy C., 5871, 6815
Smith, Roy W., 1051
Smith, Russell L., 9932
Smith, Sara Babb, 2586
Smith, Sara Rigister, 8894
Smith, Scott, 2059
Smith, Sharon, 7785
Smith, Shauna H., 5187
Smith, Stephen, 178
Smith, Stephen B., 2731
Smith, Stephen S., 8283
Smith, Steve R., 7718
Smith, Stuart P., 9534
Smith, Susan, 5914
Smith, Susan C., 2413
Smith, Susan J., 2697
Smith, Tamara, 7718
Smith, Taylor, 309
Smith, Ted, 1052
Smith, Terry, 9638
Smith, Theodore B., III, 6064
Smith, Thomas G., 4141
Smith, Thomas J., 8160
Smith, Timothy, 7248
Smith, Tracy D., 7799
Smith, Victor P., 170
Smith, Vivian L., 9205
Smith, Walker, III, 1057
Smith, Wayne T., 8601
Smith, Willard, II, 1053
Smith, William, 3593
Smith, William A., Rev. , 7944
Smith, William C., 9207
Smith, William G., Jr., 1918
Smith, William H., 7096, 7209
Smith, William L., 4639
Smith, William L., IV, 2562
Smith, William Mason, III, 8476
Smith, William R., 2586
Smith, Wilson L., 7248
Smith, Winchell, 5700
Smith, Winthrop H., III, 1571

Smith, Wm. Randolph, 1799
Smithburg, Thomas A., 3254
Smithburg, Thomas W., 3254
Smithburg, William D., 3254
Smithfield Trust Co., 8195
Smithfield Trust Company, 8195
Smithgall, J. Thurmond, 6364
Smithgall, James T., 6364
Smithgall, Lessie, 6364
Smithgall, Thurmond J., 6364
Smithson, James L., 4056
Smithsonian Institute, 3919
Smithtown Healthcare, 5748
Smitley, Greg, 3397
Smitson, Patricia, 7340
Smittcamp, Brent, 1059
Smittcamp, Earl, 1059
Smittcamp, Muriel, 1059
Smittcamp, Robert, 1059
Smittcamp, William, 1059
Smolkovich, Nicole, 2802
Smollen, Jon, 4721
Smoose, Dr. Larry V., Rev. , 7953
Smotrich, Steven B., 5548
Smullin, Patricia D., 1060
Smullin, William B., 1060
Smyth, Marion C., 5232
Smyth, Renee, 3766
Smythe, James J., 1061
Smythe, Linda, 1061
Smythe, Michael D., 1061
Smythe, William B., 1061
Smythe, William D., Jr., 1061
Snabl, Sandra M., 6221
Snapp, Paul, 3582
Snayberger, Harry E., 6817
Snead, Bruce C., 9123
Sneddon, Alex, 6219
Sneddon, Judith, 6219
Snedekar Charity Event, 8687
Sneed, Robert W., 9266
Snell & Wilmer L.L.P., 171
Snell, Georgia A., 4080
Snell, Hilary F., 4587
Snell, John T., 5725
Snellenberger, Paul, 2802
Snelling, Gretchen E., 3396
Snellings, Gerald, 9454
Snellings, Harry, 9454
Snide, Donald A., 7466
Snide, Donald W., 7466
Snideman, Monica Freedman, 5352
Snider, Eliot, 4335
Snider, Jody, 1792
Snider, Robert, 4335
Sniffen, Sharon S., 1567
Snivley, James, 7442
Snorf, Cynthia Roberts, 305
Snow Foundation, Sylvia and Martin, 8080
Snow, David H., 6818
Snow, Heide, 2629
Snow, Ian K., 6969
Snow, John, 3991
Snow, John Ben, 6818
Snow, Jonathan L., 6818
Snow, Mary, 1952
Snowden, Gail, 4211
Snowe, Parker, 8275
Snowline Partners, LP, 8166
Snows Hill, LLC, 4114
Snyder 2010 Charitable Lead, Todd R., 5773

Snyder 2011 Charitable Lead, Todd R., 5773
Snyder 2013 Charitable Lead, Todd R., 5773
Snyder Brothers, 8287
Snyder Foundation, Patricia, The , 3454
Snyder, Ann F., 8263
Snyder, B. Robert, 8288
Snyder, Barron F., 20
Snyder, Brian S., 6127
Snyder, Caroline, 2191
Snyder, Charles A., 207
Snyder, Charles H., Jr., 8287
Snyder, David E., 8287
Snyder, G. Whitney, Jr., 5540
Snyder, Gregory D., 1118
Snyder, Harold B., Sr., 5541
Snyder, James D., 9460
Snyder, Jamie S., 20
Snyder, Jennifer C., 4132, 4351
Snyder, Joseph H., 3454
Snyder, Leonard N., 8029
Snyder, Luke E., 3454
Snyder, Mark, 8031, 8263
Snyder, Mark J., 3411
Snyder, Michele, 5543
Snyder, Nina, 5540
Snyder, Norman E., 3454
Snyder, R. Meade, 9460
Snyder, Richard, 5542
Snyder, Rolf D., 3560
Snyder, Ruth B., 3560
Snyder, Sheba Torbert, 6819
Snyder, Stephen F., 20
Snyder, Susan H., 3454
Snyder, T.J., 3560
Snyder, Therese, 20
Snyder, Todd R., 5773
Snyder, Willard B., 3560
Snyder, William, 8288
Snyder, William J., 1002
Snyder, Zachary H., 3454
So Charitable Trust, 5830
Soave, Anthony, 3286
Sobel Family Trust, 5247
Sobel, Jeff, 5294
Sobel, Robert, 5451
Sobel, Robert J., 6720
Sobel, Ronald B., 6483
Sobel, Solomon, 5247
Sobel, Thomas, 5294
Sober, Daniel, 857
Sobic, Dan D., 9677
Sobiesk, Kelley, 3731
Sobol, Judith, 375
Sobon, Leslie, 8698
Sobon, Michael, 4047
Socarras, Katherine P., 6385
Sochovka, Jamie, 8630
Soderholm, Mel, 4734
Sodexho Inc. and Affiliates, 3867
Sodexo, 1295
Soe, Susanna, 9697
Soekarmoen, Didik, 4606
Soens, Gene F., 9862
Sofer, Jacob, 5953
Sofronas, Kelly A., 4133
Sohr, James M., 8676
Sohr, Leah E., 8676
Soicher Trust, Estelle, The , 1062
Soifer, Douglas S., 4612
Soistman, Julia, 3811
Sokol, Adam, 6822
Sokol, David, 6822

Sokol, Mendy, 6822
Sokol, Susan, 6822
Sokoll, Walter, 5010
Sokoloff, Gertrude, 6823
Sokoloff, Stephen, 6823
Sokolowski, Jeanne, 3024
Solacoff, David K., 7194
Solano, R., 5222
Solc, Helaine, 6297
Soldano, Patricia M., 353
Solebury Capital LLC., 8874
Solich, George H., 1264
Solid Waste Services, 8145
Solinga, Steve, 5544
Sollender, Elyse Knapp, 2153
Sollie, Cindy Zale, 9300
Solms, Elizabeth B., 7992
Solms, Ellen, 7992
Solms, Stephen E., 7992
Soloman, Howard M., 8064
Solomon, Barry, 7577
Solomon, David, 4301
Solomon, Frances, 7577
Solomon, Irwin, 5630
Solomon, Joel, 5057
Solomon, Kimberly Baldridge, 8715
Solomon, Laura, 7953
Solomon, Leonard, 4354
Solomon, Michael, 7822
Solomon, Ron, 320
Solomont, Ahron M., 4302
Solomont, Alan D., 4303
Solomont, Sheera A., 4302
Solomont, Susan Lewis, 4303
Solot Charitable Lead Annuity Trust, Howard L. and Janet N., 1748
Solot, Claire, 316
Solot, Howard L., 1748
Solot, Janet F., 1748
Solot, Julie E., 1748
Solot, Michael J., 1748
Solow Building Company, LLC, 6655
Solow, Alan, 2919
Somanetics Corp., 725
Sombke, Doug, 4679
Somekh, Eta, 1064
Somekh, Sasson, 1064
Somerville, Kurt F., 4233
Sommer, Amy, 6825
Sommer, Beverly, 6825
Sommer, Kurt, 5613
Sommer, Michael, 5565
Sommers, Annette, 9669
Sommers, Josh, 5872
Sondheimer, Ida, 3256
Sondheimer, Ida N., 1065, 3256
Sondheimer, Richard J., 1065
Sondheimer, Stuart P., 3256
Sondland, Gordon D., 9700
Sonne, Kathryn T., 9360
Sonnega, Steve, 3360
Sonnenberg, Benjamin, 6122
Sonnentag, Bill, 9934
Sonnentag, Carolyn, 9934
Sonnentag, John, 9934
Sonnentag, Tim, 9934
Sonnino, Mark D., 5785
Sonntag, Rich, 9345
Sontag, Howard, 6627
Sony Pictures Entertainment, 1053
Soo Rev Trust Dtd, Chui Ying, 2628
Soran Gardino, Alysa, 1664
Soran, Christine, 1664
Soran, Margaret, 1664

Soran, Philip E., 1664
Soref, Ida, 107
Sorel, Claudette, 6826
Sorensen, Alice A., 8464
Sorensen, Chris, 6916
Sorensen, Christian P., 8464
Sorensen, E. Paul, 8464
Sorensen, Joan W., 8464
Sorensen-Leff, Jeanne, 6827
Sorenson Revocable Trust, Beverley Taylor, 9355
Sorenson, Beverly, 9356
Sorenson, James Lee, 9355, 9356
Sorenson, James LeVoy, 9356
Sorenson, Jason, 9330
Sorenson, Jessica, 9330
Sorenson, Joseph, 9330, 9355
Sorenson, Katelyn, 9330
Sorenson, Kathleen, 9330, 9356
Sorenson, Larry, 2680
Sorenson, Richard W., 1574
Sorkin, Ira Lee, 5668
Soros Fund Charitable Foundation, 5971
Sorrells, Christopher, 9781
Sorrells, Christopher, Dr. , 9781
Sorrentino, Colleen P., 6295
Sosa, Trinidad Mendenhall, 9056
Sosik, Matthew, 4076
Sosland, Estelle, 3600
Sosna, Fay, 7329
Sosnaud, Jean, 1427
Sosnaud, Jean C., 1427
Sosnaud, Jeffrey, 1427
Sosnov, Amy, 7978
Soter, Sarah Ross, 2343
Soter, William J., 2343
Sotheby's, 5876
Sotheby's Auction House, 5876
Sothebys International Realty, 6656
Soto, Renata, 58
Sotos, Marybeth M., 1820
Sotow Foundation, Sheldon, The , 6656
Soubble, Stephen A., 3786
Soukenik, Anthony J., 4938
Soukenik, Tony, 4938
Soule, Carol, 4568
Soulier, Vickie, 434
Sousa, Steven M., 4216
Sousae, William, 968
South Bend Tribune Corp., 3444
South Dakota Trust Co., 8578
South Point Hotel Casino, 5156
South, Josh, 3462
Southard, Dorothy P., 7599
Southard, M. Martha, 7599
Southard, Robert C., 7599
Southard, Stephen Rowland, 7599
Southern Furniture Co. of Conover, 7056
Southern Michigan Bank & Trust, 4475
Southern Mills, 2541
Southern Slope Trust, 9082
Southern, William B., 8644
Southland Racing Corporation, 215
Southside Bank, 9071, 9232
Southstar, LP, 1640
Southwest Georgia Bank, 2471
Southwest Investment Partners, 598
Souza, Alfred, 420
Sowards, Ruth, 7719
Sowers, Martha A., 7037
Sowle, Erinn, 7798
Soy Capital Bank & Trust Co., 3264
Soza, William, 9505
Spadora, Janet C., 3682

Spady, Jeff, 175
Spady, Linda S., 175
Spafford, David R., 9306
Spafford, Susan B., 9306
Spahn, Kathy, 6539
Spahr, Alice L., 2720
Spain, Murray, 8292
Spain, Robert H., 3674
Spalding, Henry, Jr., 9525
Spalding, Oliver A., 4363
Spalding, Philip F., 773
Spalla, Joanne, 1400
Spanbock, Maurice S., 6245
Spang and Co., 8231
Spang, Joseph, 8406
Spangler, C. Gregory, 7339
Spangler, Dean L., 7339
Sparber, Roy, 5909
Spare, Barbara, 6812
Sparkman, Melinda, 3446
Sparks, Alyce, 8945
Sparks, Bryan K., 9082
Sparks, Kay E., 9082
Sparks, L. David, 9082
Sparks, Marc A., 9631
Sparks, Ruth, 9211
Sparling, Alfred H., Jr., 4134
Sparrow, Marvin, 4021, 4071, 4293
Spartus Corp., 2899
Spatz Revocable Trust, 1066
Spatz, Irving, 6831
Spatz, Janet, 6831
Spatz, Martin, 6831
Spaulding, Douglas, 9606
Spaulding, Tami, 7691
Spayth, Jewel Curtis, 8869
Spear, William, 7997
Spears, Sandra R., 967
Spears, Scott A., 2296
Spears, Tim, 5021
Spears, William, 6122
Speciale, William G., 3687
Specialized Loan Services, 1362
Specialty Manufacturing Co., The, 4646
Spector, Andrew, 9261
Spector, Helen, 9261
Spector, Jack J., 8940
Spector, Naomi, 6137
Spedden, Sandra P., 3922
Spee, Pia Damon, 2629
Speed, Lake Chambers, 9096
Speeth, Lauren, 477
Speiser, Anthony E., 3257
Speiser, Christine A., 3257
Speiser, E. Pat, 4947
Speiser, Kate, 3257
Spektor, Eryk, 6833
Spektor, Mira, 6833
Spellane, Thomas P., 6160
Spencer St Realty, LLC, 6905
Spencer, Amy, 7820
Spencer, Barbara A., 7087
Spencer, Cary W., 1690
Spencer, Hildreth, 4582
Spencer, Janelle, 7820
Spencer, Jason, 7820
Spencer, Jody, 7478
Spencer, John, 7820
Spencer, Laura, 7820
Spencer, Mark, 1599, 9933
Spencer, Mary, 8293
Spencer, Melinda, 8933
Spencer, Samuel, 7944
Spencer, Sarah E., 9933

Spencer, Tim, 8933
Spendlove, Alan, 9357
Spendlove, Debbi, 9357
Spendlove, Reta A., 9357
Spendlove, Rex S., 9357
Sperandio, Elizabeth F., 6835
Sperandio, Jacqueline, 6835
Sperandio, Mark C., 6835
Sperandio, Robert V., 6835
Sperduto, Guy, 7715
Sperling, Judy, 2134
Sperling, Lisa, 2134
Sperling, Matt A., 2071
Spero, Louis, 4304
Spero, Shirley, 4304
Sperry, Paul J., 5783
Sperry, Richard J., 9361
Spevack, Jerome, 7323
Speyer, A.C., III, 8294
Speyer, James M., 8294
Spezzaferro, Patrisia, 943
Spholer, Bruce, 5547
Spicer, Douglas S., 7608
Spicer, Gearl, 2455
Spicer, S. Gary, Sr., 4435
Spiegal, Feiga, 7008
Spiegal, Yechiel, 7008
Spiegel, Bradley C., 6838
Spiegel, Deanne, 6838
Spiegel, Edward P., 6838
Spiegel, Elka, 6764
Spiegel, Elky, 6697
Spiegel, Emily, 6837
Spiegel, Feiga, 6764
Spiegel, Feigie, 6697
Spiegel, Isreal, 6764
Spiegel, Jerry, 6837
Spiegel, Joel, 6764
Spiegel, Joel David, 6764
Spiegel, Minam, 6764
Spiegel, Sara, 6764, 6858
Spiegel, Sarah, 6764
Spiegel, Steven, 4770
Spiegel, Yechiel, 6697, 6764
Spiegelman, Donald, 6201
Spielberger, Charles, 6832
Spielman, Amy, 1067
Spielman, Charles, 1067
Spielman, Robert, 6476
Spier, Alexander L., 2345
Spier, Frances D., 6271
Spier, Gregory P., 2345
Spier, Michelle, 9050
Spier, Michelle Lyons, 9050
Spier, Sonja R., 2345
Spieser, Matthew B., 3257
Spilka, Robert Edward, 1723
Spillman, Wendy, 7650
Spilman 2003 Charitable Lead Annuity Trust, Lauren, 7526
Spilman 2007 Charitable Lead Annuity Trust, Lauren, 7526
Spilman Charitable Lead Annuity Trust, Lauren, 7526
Spilman, Lauren B., 7526
Spilman, Rob, Jr., 7209
Spilman, Robert H., Jr., 9391
Spina, John, 3427
Spinetta, Charlie, 238
Spink, Robert F., 6626
Spinnaker Trust, 3763
Spinner, Steven, 8498
Spinola, Steven, 6656
Spiro, Donald W., 5546

Spiro, Evelyn, 5546
Spiro, Michelle, 2577
Spiro, Michelle S., 2577
Spitalnick, Karen, 5948
Spitler, Barbara B., 6560
Spitz, Jill Wender, 1777
Spitz, Melvin, 6586
Spitzer, Albert, 6841
Spitzer, Eli, 6841
Spitzer, Erika, 6841
Spitzer, Michael, 6841
Spitzer, N.B., 6854
Spitzer, Sanford J., 4985
Spiva, Barbara, 1068
Spiva, Stephan, 1068
Spivak Lipton, LLP, 6943
Spivey, Eric W., 394
Splawn Recovable Trust, Don, 8677
Splawn Trust, Roy, 1749
Splawn, Don H., 8677
Spodek, Kimberly Gantcher, 6055
Spoden, James E., 7894, 8170
Spofford, C. Nicholas, 6842
Spofford, John S.W., 6842
Spofford, Margaret W., 6842
Spohler, John, 5547
Spohler, Linda, 5547
Spohler-Benoit, Brenda, 5547
Spolin, Joel, 900
Sponaugle, Lisa M., 9314
Sponaugle, William Lee, 9314
Spoon, Alan G., 4305
Spoon, Terri L., 4305
Spooner, Sandra S., 2395
Sport Time Team Tennis LLC, 6463
Sport/Ellie Inc., 7030
Sporting Supplies International, 9102
Spradling, J. Shannon, 4873
Sprague, Andy, 2803
Sprague, Caryll M., 1070
Sprague, Laurie Morse, 4259
Sprague, Margaret L., 1069
Sprague, Norman F., III, 1070
Sprague, Norman F., Jr., 1070
Sprague, Robert R., 1069
Sprague, Ronald, 5337
Sprague, William W., III, 2457
Sprague, William W., Jr., 2457, 3785
Sprandel, Mamie S., 8280
Spratt, Anne D., 1790
Spray, Craig, 8100
Spray, George, 3448
Sprayregen, Laurie, 6347
Sprecher, Jesse, 941
Spreyer, Kurt, 5468
Spriggs, Ray, 3501
Spriggs, William Guy, 3695
Spring Lake Park Lions Club, 4785
Spring Trust, Anna M., 966
Spring, Zoe, 5651
Springer, Anne M., 3035
Springer, Gerald N., 9538
Springer, Kim, 1319
Springer, Mark, 7665
Springer, William E., 5120
Springfield Lodging, LLC, 4772
Springfield Partners, 2109
Springlea finance, 3455
Springsted, Kirk, 4706
Springsteen, Bruce, 1117
Sprinkle, Stan, 1310
Sprint, 3639
Spritzer, Michael, 2277
Sprogell, Jonathan H., 7911

Sprole, F. Russell, 6331
Spross, Jaci, 1100
Sprouts Farmers Market, 1295
Sprung, Gilda, 9177
Sprung, Joseph B., 5869
Sprung, Sharon, 5692
Spungen, Carol, 1071
Spungen, Daniel, 1071
Spungen, Debra, 1071
Spungen, Florence, 1071
Spungen, Glenn, 1071
Spurgeon, Allen, 3580
Spurgin, Robert L., 3425
SPX Corp., 7252
Squier, David L., 6843
Squier, Raymond, 1599
Squier, Sue, 6843
Squires, Deborah A., 173
Squires, Lena B., 173
Squires, William D., 173
Squirewell, Robert, 8529
SR Capital, LLC, 6655
Sramek Trust, Elmer D., 3259
Sramek, Joseph, 9989
Srivastava, Sanjay, 1072
Srivastava, Shweta, 4012
SSAB Alabama, 67
St. Amour, Tracy W., 1159
St. Boniface Hospital, 90
St. Clair, Lucas, 3777
St. Fort, Hugues, 6820
St. Ignatius of Loyola, 7456
St. James Church, 7456
St. James, Aleta, 5254
St. John Pond, Ann E., 3798
St. John's Community Foundation, 1566
St. John, Allison R., 2287
St. John, Katherine, 4889
St. John, Marc C., 2287
St. John, Maureen, 3766
St. Johns, George, 610
St. Jude Parish, 7456
St. Mary's Hospital, 7666
St. Onge, Paul P., 8478
St. Paul's Episcopal Church Outreach
   Grant Council, 7513
St. Peter Claver latin School for Boys,
   7456
St. Rose Church, 7456
Staab, Valari Dobson, 8820
Stabberd, Fred, 6290
Stachlowski, Gary W., 9643
Stack, Geoffrey, 1073
Stack, Geoffrey I., 1073
Stack, Nancy, 1073
Stack, Nina, 7199
Stacke, James H., 2725
Stackhouse Trust, Mary, 6844
Stackpole, Joseph, 1553
Stadler, Elizabeth Bullard, 8610
Stadler, George B., 8678
Stadler, Julia Carell, 8678
Stadtler, Sander, 7184
Stadtmauer, David, 6068
Stafast Products Inc., 7600
Staffey, Katherine L., 1486
Stafford Trust, James M., 1074
Stafford, Amanda, 9535
Stafford, Charlotte, 2346
Stafford, Earl W., Sr., 9535
Stafford, Inge P., 2346
Stafford, John R., 2346
Stafford, Richard, 7546
Stager, Judy Manno, 7975

Stahl, Aaron, 5334
Stahl, Jack, 2588
Stahl, Katharine, 2588
Stahl, Lynn, 2588
Stahl, Miriam, 5334
Stahl, Muriel, 285
Stahl, Sam, 285
Stahl, Samuel, 2588
Stainton, Mark, 2791
Stair, Lucy Caldwell, 1415
Staley, Anne S., 3945
Staley, Arlene D., 3263
Staley, Augustus Eugene, Jr., 3264
Staley, Catherine, 8296
Staley, Henry M., 3262
Staley, Mark E., 3262
Staley, Stuart, 8296
Staley, Thomas F., 8296
Staley, Violet L., 3262
Staley, William D., 3263
Stall, Jeffrey R., 6736
Stall, Sonya A., 6736
Stallings, Mary M., 7666
Stambaugh, Gerald M., 3490
Stambaugh, Mary Ellen, 312
Stamford Hospital, 1566
Stamm, David, 3456
Stamm, David A., 3456
Stamm, Laura, 3456
Stamm, Ronna, 3045
Stamm, Shad, 5091
Stammel, Laura, 5541
Stammerjohn, Bettie B., 7933
Stampfer, Claire, 3825
Stanaland, Terence B., 7275
Stancati, Joe, 4419
Standard Distributing Co., 2161
Standard Investment Co., 218
Standard Pacific of Texas Inc., 9009
Standard Products Co., The, 7568
Standerfer, Sara Whitney, 9138
Standland, David, 1438
Stanfield, Janice H., 7687
Stanford, Ginnie, 1897
Stanford, Leslie, 1613
Stang, Debbie, 4745
Stang, Jessi B., 3565
Stangeby, Alison, 5369
Stanhope, Marylyn, 4523
Staniar, Burton B., 5804
Stanken, Paul R., 7472
Stanko, Ellen A., 2592
Stanley Leeds Trust, 738
Stanley Stahl Management Inc., 6656
Stanley, Ann, 4934
Stanley, Anne, 3782
Stanley, Charles B., 1342
Stanley, Jeffrey A., 7330
Stanley, Joan, 8030
Stanley, Kenneth, 8030
Stanley, Nancy, 8030
Stanley, Richard H., 3523
Stanley, Robert A., 1438
Stanley, Sydney J., 759
Stansill, Wayne C., 5455
Stansky, Jill, 4202
Stansky, Michael P., 4202
Stanton, Ann M., 174
Stanton, Daniel W., 6845
Stanton, Mary B., 6845
Stanzcak, Lael H., 3093
Stanzel, Joseph, 9213
Stanzel, Robert R., 9213
Stanzel, Theodore E., 9213

Stanzel, Victor, 9213
Stanzler, Alan L., 4086
Stanzler, Marjorie Cohen, 4307
Stanzler, Paul, 4307
Staph, Laura, 884
Stapienski, Denise, 1418
Staple, Gregory C., 1785
Staples, Cecil, 9231
Staples, Dorris E., 1075
Staples, Florence, 4836
Staples, Joseph, 3398
Stapleton Family Trust, John and Vilma,
   7253
Stapleton, Craig R., 1270
Stapleton, F. Michael, 5880
Stapleton, Jenna, 1270
Stapleton, Katharine H., 1270
Stapleton, Victoria Jennifer, 9475
Stapp, Carrie, 3367
Star Lumber & Supply Co., 3580
Star Snacks Co., LLC, 5474
Star Tribune Co., The, 811
Star, Jane, 2090
Stara, Dennis, 5105
Starbuck, Dane, 3469
Starbuck, Katherine H., 7439
Starbucks, 1295
Stare, David S., 4308
Stare, Fredrick A., 4308
Stare, Fredrick J., 4308
Starer, Brian D., 1455
Starer, Judy, 6756
Stariha, Winifred, 2729
Stark Truss Co., 7650
Stark, C. Richard, Jr., 3536
Stark, Charles H., 2238
Stark, Charles S., 3205
Stark, Cynthia H., 2865, 3303
Stark, Joan E., 3536
Stark, Lowell, 882
Stark, Mary, 7543
Stark, Mason V.C., 6867
Stark, Michael, 7543
Stark, Morgan, 6867
Stark, Morgan B., 6867
Stark, Nicholas M., 6867
Stark, Patrick E., 4862
Stark, Philip, 1599
Stark, R. Keith, 4505
Stark, Richard A., 6381
Stark, Sandra L., 5572
Stark, Sidney, 6867
Stark, Sidney S., 6867
Starker Family Foundation, The, 6720
Starker, Farrel, 6847
Starker, Ray, 6847
Starker, Steven, 6847
Starkey, Brad, 7356
Starks, William, 9728
Starlight Builders, 9009
Starnes, Jay, 8345
Starnes, Nancye B., 8639
Starnes, Wayne, 870
Starr & Co., C.V., 6132
Starr Charitable Lead Trust, Donald,
   4309
Starr, Alice M., 6472
Starr, Dinah, 4309
Starr, Fred, 7209
Starr, Marilyn, 6520
Starr, Polly Thayer, 4309
Starr, Samantha, 6026
Starr, Therese, 7682
Stars for Children, 9148

Start Making A Reader Today (SMART),
   7761
Start, Rich E., 3002
Starvaggi, Mike, 9767
Starvel, Frank, 3799
Starz Entertainment LLC, 1295
Starz Entertainment, LLC, 1295
Staton, Buel J., 7720
Staton, Faye, 8548
Staton, John C., Jr., 2523
Staton, Margaret A., 2523
Staton, Mary, 2523
Stattman, Dennis, 189
Staub, Irene Jewell, 8633
Staubach Family Foundation, The, 9033
Staubach, Marianne H., 9215
Staubach, Roger T., 9215
Staudenmeier, Frank J., 8263
Stauffer, Beverly, 1076
Stauffer, Jessica, 1077
Stauffer, Jim, 1077
Stauffer, John, 1076, 1077
Stauffer, Jordan, 1077
Stauffer, Judi, 5047
Stauffer, Kim, 1077
Stauffer, M.J., 7601
Stauffer, Mary R., 1077
Stauffer, Melvyn J., 7413
Stauffer, Peter O., 4358
Stauffer, Robin D., 8054
Stauffer, Susan, 1077
Staurt, Connie Bond, 8046
Stavens, Diane, 9274
Stavens, James, 9274
Stavens, Phillip, 9274
Stchel, Dan, 7030
Stchel, Shari, 7030
Stearns, Artemas W., 4311
Stearns, Esther M., 1078
Stearns, Gwendolyn L., 8575
Stearns, Jan Cohn, 1078
Stearns, Margaret, 1578
Stearns, Nancy, 8219
Stearns, Ned, 870
Stearns, Russell B., 4310
Stebbins, Edwin E.F., 6850
Stebbins, James F., 6850
Stebbins, Mary J., 5297
Stebbins, Michael Morgan, 6850
Stebbins, Ralph, 5297
Stebbins, Ralph S., 5297
Stebbins, Theodore E., Jr., 6850
Stebelman, Cornelia B., 1959
Stechel, Ira, 6413
Stecher, Esta Eiger, 6851
Stecher, Jamie B.W., 6851
Steck, Fredric E., 6852
Steckler, Alan, 6853
Steckler, Donald H., 6853
Steckler, Joan, 357
Steckler, Philip H., III, 6853
Steckler, Philip H., Jr., 6853
Steckler, Stuart, 1946
Steckler, Sue-Ann, 1946
Stedham, Kristen J., 8885
Stedham, Nathan, 8885
Stedillie, Anthony, 8907
Stedman, Caryn, 9494
Stedman, Jaye G., 1182
Steed, Robert, 9341
Steel City Corp., 7398
Steel, Cooper, 2348
Steel, Danielle, 1126
Steel, John, 1376

Steel, Pamela B., 7339
Steel, Sabrina, 1376
Steel, William, 7339
Steele Charitable Lead Trust, E.C. and Joan, 2347
Steele Charitable Lead Trust, Joan M., 2347
Steele, Annie L., 2347
Steele, Edward C., 2347
Steele, Edward L., 2347
Steele, Joan M., 2347
Steele, Julia, 1938
Steele, Melinda, 1910
Steele, Michael C., 2347
Steele, Richard, 4533
Steele, Ronald A., 8026
Steen, Donald B., 5493
Steen, Donald E., 9216
Steen, Trudy K., 9216
Steenburg, Walter C., 3428
Steere, Tom, 4534
Steers, Lauren J., 6125
Steers, Robert H., 6125
Steet, Franklin, 7452
Stefanski, Stephen A., 3760
Stefansky, Meir, 6854
Stefansky, Ruth, 6854
Steffen, Phyllis, 3501
Steffes, Don C, 3605
Stegall, Corre A., 8637
Stege, Mark, 8556
Stegeman, Suzanne, 2877
Steger, Charlie, 7975
Steger, Jane, 7605
Stegman, Carolyn, 3932
Stehlik, Gaylan, 5096
Stehman, Catherine, 3904
Steider, Norman D., 3372
Steif, Efraim, 7025
Steif, Michael, 7025
Steiger, Adam J., 5446
Steiger, Albert, 4312
Steiger, Albert E., III, 4312
Steiger, Allen, 4312
Steiger, Andrew R., 5446
Steiger, Bruce, 7368
Steiger, Carole Ann, 5446
Steiger, Chauncey A., 4312
Steiger, David L., 5446
Steiger, Joel J., 5446
Steiger, Mark, 5960
Steiger, Philip C., II, 4312
Steiger, Ralph A., 4312
Steiger, Ralph A., II, 4312
Steiger, Rick, 7368
Steigerwaldt, Donna Wolf, 3265
Steigerwaldt, William, 3265
Steigman, Elliot, 5948
Steigman, Gisela, 5948
Stein Charitable Lead Trust, Doris Jones, 6263
Stein Fund No. 1, Louis and Bessie, 8299
Stein, Adam, 4271
Stein, Allen A., 6855
Stein, Angela, 6257
Stein, Avy, 3266
Stein, Burton K., 7941
Stein, Carolyn Stafford, 2346
Stein, David, 9778
Stein, David W., 3431
Stein, Eric, 6855
Stein, Feige, 6856
Stein, Frances, 5551

Stein, Fred, 8298
Stein, Gregory, 1079
Stein, Howard, 5708
Stein, Janet, 5708
Stein, Jason, 2412
Stein, Jean, 6263
Stein, Jerome, 1079
Stein, Marcie, 3266
Stein, Margot, 6855
Stein, Mark, 8298
Stein, Matthew, 1750
Stein, Michelle B., 6454
Stein, Mitchell, 7695
Stein, Nachum, 6856
Stein, Paul, 369
Stein, Rhoda, 2412
Stein, Rita, 1732
Stein, Ronnit, 2412
Stein, Sara, 1750
Stein, Sharon, 1079, 1750, 6855
Stein, Susan Haugh, 8298
Stein, William J., 1750
Steinbach, Sheldon, 1804
Steinberg, Elliott G., 3336
Steinberg, Frieda, 5189
Steinberg, Jean, 6857
Steinberg, Leon H., 5189
Steinberg, Meyer, 6857
Steinberg, Michael, 8022
Steinberg, Paul, 2002
Steinberger, Michael, 6501
Steinberger, Shaindy, 6144
Steiner Corp., 9358
Steiner Sports, 1730
Steiner, David, 1267
Steiner, David A., 3696
Steiner, John A., 7602
Steiner, Joseph, 7602
Steiner, Kevin K., 9358
Steiner, Melissa Friedland, 5082
Steiner, Michael, 7602
Steiner, Michael E., 3696
Steiner, Paula M., 3696
Steiner, Richard R., 9358
Steiner, Robert C., 9358
Steiner, Susan, 9360
Steiner-Griffiths, Melissa, 9358
Steinfield, Rebecca Morse, 4259
Steingart, Jennifer, 1596
Steingart, Jonathan, 1596
Steingart, Richard, 1421
Steinhafel, David J., 4795
Steinhafel, Denise E., 4795
Steinhafel, Gregg W., 4795
Steinhafel, Kevin M., 4795
Steinhagen, B.A., 3755
Steinhagen, Elinor, 3755
Steinhardt, John, 5668
Steinhart Charitable Remainder Unitrust, Ella, 5121
Steinhart, Corklin R., 1914
Steinhart, Ella S., 5121
Steinhart, Morton, 5121
Steinharter, Bernard, 3877
Steinharter, Miriam, 3877
Steinharter, Miriam L., 3877
Steinle, Elmyra K., 9938
Steinman, Ben, 4921
Steinman, Jeffrey, 1397
Steinmann Pharmacy, 7603
Steinmann, Robert P., 7603
Steinmatz Trust, Bernat, 6858
Steinmetz Bros., 7020
Steinmetz, Amy, 6697, 6764, 7008

Steinmetz, Bernat, 6697, 6764, 6858, 7008
Steinmetz, Charles P., 7254
Steinmetz, Cindy, 7008
Steinmetz, Clara, 7020
Steinmetz, Emanuel, 7020
Steinmetz, Erica, 7008
Steinmetz, Esther, 6859
Steinmetz, Harry C., 6958
Steinmetz, Israel, 7008
Steinmetz, Lynn L., 7254
Steinmetz, Margit, 6858
Steinmetz, Matthew, 3267
Steinmetz, Matthew A., 7254
Steinmetz, Michael, 6697, 6764, 6858, 7008
Steinmetz, Naftali, 7020
Steinmetz, Ruth, 7008
Steinmetz, Solomon, 6859, 7020
Steinmetz, Tammi, 7008
Steinmetz, Yitzchak, 7020
Steitz, Lucy, 7905
Stekol, Leonard, 6669
Stelges, Tricia, 1928
Stella, Aurelia, 8297
Stella, Aurelia A., 8297
Stella, Frank, 6825
Stella, John, 8297
Stella, John A., 8297
Stella, John C., 8297
Stella, Krista, 8297
Stella, Matthew, 8297
Stellar Capital Consulting, LLC, 5793
Stellar Group, The, 2348
Stellar Solutions, 1080
Stelling, Ed L., III, 2537
Stellwagon, Bonnie Beth, 8261
Stelly, Gregory A., 1855
Stemberg, Thomas G., 4313
Stemen, Milton, 4549
Stemoe, Greg, 4648
Stemoe, Gregory, 4648
Stempinski, Loretta L., 3226
Stenger, Allen, 8836
Stenson, Tim, 7356
Stenz, Jessica L., 9860
Stepelman, Chaim, 6009
Stepelman, Deborah, 6009
Stephan, Lori J., 234
Stephanopoulos, Robert G., 6280
Stephany, Elizabeth, 2060
Stephen, Cathy, 3361
Stephens 2005 Charitable Lead Annuity Trust, Fred, 9217
Stephens 2005 Trust, Fred, 9217
Stephens Associates Trust, 8895
Stephens, Amanda, 9232
Stephens, Bess Chisum, 211
Stephens, Beth, 2715, 2778, 3070, 3261, 3279, 3309
Stephens, Cerise, 7747
Stephens, Claire Ellen Cooper, 23
Stephens, Craig, 5608
Stephens, Curtis W., 3467
Stephens, Dale, 4739
Stephens, Deborah, 4526
Stephens, Fred, 9217
Stephens, Greggory, 4526
Stephens, Harriet, 216
Stephens, Harriet C., 216
Stephens, Jennifer L., 3580
Stephens, R., 3748
Stephens, Ray, 7698
Stephens, Roy, 2285

Stephens, Tegan, 3781
Stephens, Thomas P., 9217
Stephens, Warren A., 216
Stephenson, Anthony Craig, 7070
Stephenson, Ardith, 4486
Stephenson, Ardith A., 4486
Stephenson, Charles, 9536
Stephenson, Charlotte M., 8150
Stephenson, Harry D., 7070
Stephenson, Jody, 2576
Stephenson, John D., Jr., 5056
Stephenson, Philip, 9536
Stephenson, Roger T., 9922
Stephenson, Susan L., 8533
Stephenson, Thomas C., 7070
Stepka, Kenneth G., 9421
Stepleton, Benjamin F., III, 1270
Sterba, Jeffrey E., 5248
Stergios, Vanessa, 7442
Sterioff, Eileen Kay, 5680
STERIS Corp., 7605
Sterling Equities, 6655
Sterling Group Limited LLC, 4594
Sterling Savings Bank, 9691
Sterling Time LLC, 6040
Sterling, Carol, 2622
Sterling, Jeffrey W., 7606, 8256
Sterling, Lillie, 9219
Sterling, Mary Lou, 7606
Sterling, Shirley, 9218
Sterling, W. Donald, 7606
Sterling, W. Mark, 7606
Sterling, William D., 7606
Sterling-Heflin, Kim, 177
Stermer, Audrey M., 1219
Stermer, Richard A., 1219
Stermer, Richard C., 1219
Stern & Sons, Jacob, 308
Stern Charitable Remainder Trust, P., 9364
Stern Family 1997 Trust., The, 5745
Stern Foundation, Bernice and Milton, 9364
Stern Foundation, Milton & Bernice, 5745
Stern, Abbi, 9364
Stern, Abraham, 6333, 6904
Stern, Abraham J., 3268
Stern, Beth, 5552
Stern, Chaim, 5666
Stern, Claude, 480
Stern, David J., 6861
Stern, David M.C., 6862
Stern, Dianne B., 6861
Stern, Donna, 3379
Stern, Elaine Feld, 5013
Stern, Eleanor Freed, 8873
Stern, Elizabeth M., 6862
Stern, Ellen L., 6860
Stern, Ellis, 738
Stern, Eric A., 6861
Stern, Gabriel, 7501
Stern, Geoffrey S., 6860
Stern, Guy, 6950
Stern, Henry, 5552
Stern, Jack M., 1310
Stern, Jacob, 6904
Stern, Jerome L., 6860
Stern, John M., 2349
Stern, Joseph, 5666
Stern, Judith, 6312
Stern, Karen G., 4916
Stern, Lisa, 4578
Stern, Marjorie, 5745, 9364

Stern, Mark, 5745
Stern, Michael, 5745
Stern, Mildred, 8135
Stern, Peter, 9364
Stern, Ricki, 5745
Stern, Robert J., 8160
Stern, Ronald, 5552
Stern, Ronald A., 6860
Stern, Roy, 2350
Stern, Roy H., 6312
Stern, Sarah M., 6862
Stern, Sarena, 9364
Stern, Scott, 4578
Stern, Steven, 2350
Stern, Steven E., 2350
Stern, Susan Jacoby, 654
Stern, Susan L., 3268
Stern, Walter, 6374
Stern, Walter P., 6862
Stern, William M., 6862
Sternberg, Brent, 3370
Sternberg, Craig, 1696
Sternberg, Lisa, 6863
Sternberg, Stuart L., 6863
Sternklar, Jack, 6864
Sternklar, Lila, 6864
Stetler and Brinck, Inc., 7333
Stetler, Gary, 4428
Stetten, Nancy Zufall, 9733
Steuter, Al, 5105
Steven's Baby Boom, 5743
Stevens Family Trust, F.B., 2418
Stevens, Adelaide D., 8616
Stevens, Betty, 1453
Stevens, Brown Harris, 6655
Stevens, Charles G.V., 9704
Stevens, Chris, 3363
Stevens, Cynthia, 1590
Stevens, Delphine S., 9704
Stevens, Dexter, 4087
Stevens, Donald P., 8965
Stevens, Elizabeth, 4848
Stevens, James P., 2361
Stevens, John T., 8541
Stevens, John V., Jr., 175
Stevens, John V., Sr., 175
Stevens, Karen, 7543
Stevens, Kerry Yeager, 7004
Stevens, Mary, 4130, 9235
Stevens, Monica, 7358
Stevens, Nancy P., 3042
Stevens, Patti, 4848
Stevens, Rita A., 9939
Stevens, Rosemary A., 6490
Stevens, Toni, 7790
Stevens, William A., 4848
Stevenson Irrevocable Trust, 9940
Stevenson Trust, 9940
Stevenson, Bayne, 4330
Stevenson, Catherine, 4568
Stevenson, Dawn, 3217
Stevenson, Jane, 9810
Stevenson, Jean B., 4330
Stevenson, Jennifer, 2073
Stevenson, John G., Jr., 2904
Stevenson, Julie, 3070
Stevenson, Keith T., 9220
Stevenson, Mattie, 9220
Stevenson, Randy, 361
Stewart & March, 8301
Stewart & Tate Inc., 8301
Stewart Associates Land Development, 8301
Stewart Dance Theater, Melanie, 8086

Stewart Living Trust, 1082
Stewart St Production, 9
Stewart, Alana, 500
Stewart, Beth, 8043
Stewart, Brooks Dorn, 8020
Stewart, C. Allan, 4454
Stewart, Cindy, 7227
Stewart, Diana D., 7966
Stewart, Donald, 2970
Stewart, Donna, 9118
Stewart, Douglas E., 2351
Stewart, Douglas M., 2351
Stewart, E., III, 7821
Stewart, Faye H., 7822
Stewart, Faye, II, 7822
Stewart, Gary A., 8301
Stewart, Gary A., Jr., 8301
Stewart, George L., 8349
Stewart, Harvey, 5051
Stewart, Jacqueline Miller, 3114
Stewart, James, 5700
Stewart, James O., III, 9221
Stewart, James O., Jr., 9221
Stewart, James R., Jr., 8796
Stewart, Jeffrey, 5733
Stewart, Julie, 4976
Stewart, Kim, 2223
Stewart, Louise, 2959
Stewart, Lowry, 7640
Stewart, Lowry A., 7640
Stewart, Luther, 4598
Stewart, Malcolm H., 545
Stewart, Marion "Stu", 7442
Stewart, Marlene, 9221
Stewart, Martha, 7640
Stewart, Martha J., 7640
Stewart, Mary Ellen, 2833
Stewart, Pat, 7829
Stewart, Peter, 1850
Stewart, Rachel A., 4216
Stewart, Richard W., 8196
Stewart, Robert A., Jr., 4337
Stewart, Robert H., Jr., 8301
Stewart, Rodney, 2962
Stewart, Scott, 2790
Stewart, Virginia E., 2351
Stewart, W. C., 7823
Stewart-Daniel, Susan, 4976
Stewart-Thomas, Lora, 4976
Steyer, Hume R., 6787
Steyer, Mike, 7375
Stickrod, Catherine, 2791
Stiefel, Barbara A., 2352
Stiefel, Christine E., 2352
Stiefel, John C., 2916
Stiefel, Lorin S., 7244
Stiefel, Todd, 1751
Stieglitz, Warren, 5386
Stieha, Kenneth E., Jr., 5148
Stifel Financial Corporation, 5014
Stifel, Charlotte, 6865
Stifel, Henry G., 6865
Stifel, Nicolaus & Co., 5014
Stigdon, Josh, 3446
Stiles, Eric, 5337
Still Unbroken, 1046
Stiller, Shale D., 3881
Stillman Family Foundation, 4622
Stillman, Andrew, 4622
Stillman, Cassandra, 4622
Stillman, Faye, 4622
Stillman, Ralph, 4622
Stillman, Stanley W., 6271
Stillwater, Ann, 7557

Stillwater, William E., 9353
Stillwell, Jerry B., 3411
Stine, Larry W., 9768
Stine, Lee E., Jr., 9768
Stine, Lynn B., 2734
Stine, Thomas H., 6897
Stinehart, William, Jr., 1069
Stines, Michael, 4460
Stingley Family Trust, Wayne and Dorthy, 153
Stinnett, Amy P., 7212
Stinnett, William A., 3707
Stinnett-Brown, Kristen, 620
Stinski, Mark, 3489
Stinski, Mary Ellen, 3489
Stinson, Audrey, 1983
Stinson, Nancy, 2110
Stitely, David A., 7953
Stites, Elizabeth, 7338
Stitt, James E., 5890
Stitt, James, Jr., 5890
Stitt, John, 5890
Stock Yards Bank & Trust Co., 3672, 3697
Stockard, W.A., Jr., 9198
Stockdale, Suzy, 3251
Stockdell, Mary L., 3698
Stocking, Charles, 7388
Stocking, Charles A., 7388
Stockley, Joyce, 1305
Stockman, George E., 7339
Stockman, Keith B., 1236
Stockman, Lynne W., 9463
Stockman, Robert B., Mrs., 7013
Stockmeister, Alan, 7408
Stockton, Christy, 7807
Stockwell, Kimberly Druker, 4071
Stoddard, Simeon H., 4579
Stoddard, Stanford C., 4579
Stoddard, Stanford D., 4579
Stoddart, Richard, 2769
Stoehr, Elizabeth, 3969
Stofan, Ellen R., 9399
Stogner, James, 8652
Stoianof, Valentina, 797
Stoick, Catherine Emison, 5394
Stoika, John R., 8962
Stokes, Caroline M., 7966
Stokes, Charles, 2573
Stokes, Lydia B., 9385
Stokes, Patricia D., 7966
Stoller, Corky Hale, 1084
Stoller, Herbert, 6690
Stoller, Jerry H., 9222
Stoller, Mike, 1084
Stolzer, L.W., 3630
Stone 15-Year Charitable Lead Unitrust, Joshua J., 4581
Stone 20-Year Charitable Lead Unitrust, Joshua J., 4581
Stone Charitable Trust, I. Stanley, 9794
Stone, Alison, 9794
Stone, Anne M., 9537
Stone, Catherine M., 4004
Stone, Cathleen Douglas, 5662
Stone, Chris, 66
Stone, Christopher M., 9421
Stone, Clifford W., 7721
Stone, Cynthia, 3269
Stone, David, 4530
Stone, Delight, 7755
Stone, Fiora, 1086
Stone, Galen L., 4326
Stone, Gregory R., 1085

Stone, Guy Arnold, 541
Stone, Harvey M., 6090
Stone, Irving, 5103
Stone, J. Ralph, 1085
Stone, James H., 3269
Stone, Jennifer, 8707
Stone, Jenny Schwartz, 6754
Stone, Jerome H., 3269
Stone, Lois, 1085
Stone, M.D., Ph.D., Edwin, 2881
Stone, Marion R., 4004
Stone, Patricia Grodd, 6561
Stone, Patricia H., 541
Stone, R. Gregg, III, 4004
Stone, Richard H., 541
Stone, Robert, 2294
Stone, Robert A., 2003
Stone, Robert G., 1085
Stone, Robert G., Jr., 4004
Stone, Roger D., 5968
Stone, Samuel C., 7721
Stone, Sheila, 4547
Stone, Stanley, 9794
Stone, Stanley, III, 9794
Stonecutter Mills Corp., 7255
Stoneman, George B., 925
Stoner, James R., Jr., 8329
Stoner, Joyce Hill, 1781
Stoner, Thomas, 3548
Stoneriver Capital, 9991
Stonestreet, Leslie, 2048
Stookey, Katherine Emory, 3222
Stoops, Reed, 88
Stoops, Virginia, 607
Stopfel, Virginia B., 7388
Stoppel, Leon K., 1360
Stopper, Aaron, 5247
Stoppkottee, Mike, 5114
Storck, Maurice, 180
Storer, Bob, 88
Storer, Mary H., 9992
Storer, Oliver W., 3271
Storey, Barry L., 2589
Storey, Bruce, 5152
Storey, Mallie Bert, 2589
Storms, John W., 9067
Stornes, Mark R., 7475
Storr, Carol F., 1575
Storr, Christina L., 1575
Storr, Hans G., 1575
Storr, John C., 1575
Storr, Robert, 6137
Storr, Suzanne M., 1575
Storrow, Thomas, 9368
Storrs, Edward L., 1537
Story Estate, 8819
Story, Robert, 3796
Story, Sally Ann, 4742
Storz, Robert Herman, 5122
Stotsenberg, Henry, 927
Stott, Benjamin W., 8304
Stott, Edward B., 8304
Stott, Jonathan R., 7924
Stott, Kristine, 8304
Stouder, Gary, 870
Stough, John, 3659
Stout, Christopher H., 5190
Stout, Michael Ward, 6419
Stout, Richard M., 5190
Stovall, N.D., Jr., 8896
Stover Donor Advised, Matt and Debra, 3961
Stover, Debra, 3961
Stover, Debra Rogers, 3961

Stover, John, 3961
Stover, John Matthew, 3961
Stover, Kristie Giuliano, 9475
Stover, Rex, 9475
Stow, Frederick, 8952
Stow, Frederick, Jr., 8952
Stow, Ralph, 8952
Stowe Mills, R.L., 7256
Stowe, Daniel Harding, 7256
Stowe, Michael D., 4095
Stowe, Richard H., 6869
Stowe, Richmond H., 7256
Stowe, Robert Lee, III, 7256
Stowe, Robert Lee, Jr., 7256
Stowe, Virginia K., 6869
Stowell, George B., 2241
Strachan, Stephen, 2912
Stradley, Jane L., 3927
Strain, Janet, 68
Strain, John, 1131
Strain, John T., 68
Strain, Juanelle, 68
Strain, Juanelle D., 68
Strait, A. Marvin, 1239
Straley, Dave, 9986
Straley, Peter F., 4337
Straley, Tina, 8836
Stranahan Trust, Mary, 5057
Stranahan, Ann A., 7389
Stranahan, Mary, 5057
Stranahan, Molly, 5057
Stranahan, Stephen, 7389
Strand, Eric H., 4340
Strandberg, J. Buckley, 7227
Stranden, 3905
Strangis, Janet, 427
Strasburger, Laurel, 3344
Stratford Ave. Trust, 5247
Stratman, Alan, 2877
Stratton, Frederick P., Jr., 8571
Stratton, Michael W., 5507
Stratton, Warren B., 5507
Straub, Gertrude S., 2649
Straub, Kathy, 3582
Strauch, Barry S., 9538
Strauch, Evelyn M., 9538
Straus, Christopher, 1088
Straus, Joan, 6509
Straus, Lorna Puttkammer, 4499
Straus, Robert K., 1088
Strausbaugh, Mark, 7944
Strausbaugh, Sam, 7375
Strauss Family Trust, 6870
Strauss Trust, Noemi, 6870
Strauss Trust, Renato, 6870
Strauss Trust, Roberto, 6870
Strauss Trust, Sylvie, 6870
Strauss, Ernst, 6870
Strauss, Leslie Ann, 5013
Strauss, Noemi, 6870
Strauss, Renato, 6870
Strauss, Richard C., 9009
Strauss, Roselyn L., 3738
Strauss, Susan Feld, 5013
Strawbridge Foundation, Margaret Dorrance, 8305
Strawn, Jeff, 1038
Strawsburg, Jon, 7558
Strazulla, Joyce, 556
Strear Farms Co., 1337
Street, Alice Ann, 8729
Street, Don, 3432
Street, E. Bruce, 8729
Street, E. Bruce, Jr., 8729

Street, M. Boyd, 8729
Street, Malcolm B., Jr., 8729
Streeter, Margaret B., 5674
Streich, Mae, 7294
Strem, Michael, 4217
Stretch, Robert, 7603
Stretesky, Donald A., 1360
Striano, Caroline, 6871
Striano, Marisa, 6871
Striano, Peter, 6871
Striano, Peter J., 6871
Striar, Ronald, 3784
Stribling & Associates, 6656
Stribling-Kivlan, Elizabeth Ann, 7013
Strichman, Nancy K., 8135
Strickland, Carter, 9224
Strickland, Elizabeth M., 7257
Strickland, Jerry, 9224
Strickland, Linda, 9224
Strickland, Patia, 9224
Strickland, Robert E.M., 7257
Strickland, Robert L., 7257
Strickland, Whitney, 9224
Strickler, Steve, 639
Strickler, William J., 4468
Strickmaker, Ronald, 7408
Striffler, Tom, 4598
Strine, Alice Washco, 8306
Strine, Judith Baeshore, 8307
Strine, Walter M., Jr., 8306
Strine, William B., 8307
Stringfellow, Patty, 3401
Stripling, Kyle, 8937
Strobel, Kathy, 3687
Strobel, Trish, 2456
Stroble, Francis A., 5015
Stroble, Ruth M., 5015
Strode, Judith, 3360
Stroh, Amelie Porter, 1829
Stroh, Deborah, 3696
Strohm, Bruce C., 2858
Strohm, John D., 1361
Strohm, Kelly R., 1361
Strohm, Kristin E., 1361
Strohm, Matthew R., 1361
Strom, G. Bert, 9114
Strome, Mark E., 1089
Strome, Tammy, 1089
Strong, Jeffrey, 6872
Strong, Kathleen, 2265
Strong, Lee, 6872
Strong, Marguerite, 6872
Strong, Roger L., 6872
Strong, Roger L., Jr., 6872
Strong, Russell, 2666
Strong, Thomas, 6872
Strong, William Walker, 2353
Strother, Haas, 74
Stroud, Cynthia Lou Elrod, 195
Stroud, Robert R., 2815
Stroum, Cynthia, 9584
Strouse, Keith J., 8263
Strowd, Irene H., 7258
Strube, Don, Jr., 2354
Strube, Don, Sr., 2354
Strube, Donald K., Jr., 2354
Strube, Donald K., Sr., 2354
Strube, Joan E., 2354
Strube, Joan, J., 2354
Strube, Joan, Sr., 2354
Strube, Richard K., 2354
Strube, Thomas W., 2354
Strube, Timothy A., 2354
Struck, Ann Marie, Dr., 3125

Structural Components, 2348
Strudwick, Lolly, 3978
Strupp, Thomas J., 3382
Strutt, Tammi, 3634
Struve, George, 9114
Struyk, Robert, 4722
Stry, Paul E., 9941
STSM, 1252
Stuart Trust, Ellen G., 3273
Stuart, Anne, 7812
Stuart, Jon R., 7706
Stuart, Mark J., Jr., 6873
Stuart, Sally Spradling, 4873
Stubbe, Jeffrey, 9802
Stubblefield, Fred, III, 7260
Stubblefield, Fred, Jr., 7260
Stubblefield, Nancy K., 7260
Stubenberg, James A., 1672
Stucco Stone Products, 756
Stuck, Randy, 4499
Stuckeman, Charles C., 8195
Stuckeman, H. Campbell, 8195
Stucker, Robert, 2786
Stucky Trust, Mary Margaret, 3457
Studer, Mallory M., 2355
Studer, Mary P., 2355
Studer, Michael W., 2355
Studer, Quinton D., 2355
Studley, 6655
Studley, Donald T., 1590
Studnick, Ashley, 2050
Studnik, Alec, 2050
Studnik, Amanda, 2050
Studnik, Shani, 2050
Studnik, Stacy, 2050
Stuehling, Michelle, 178
Stuhley, Cynthia A., 2703
Stuhlsatz, Rebecca, 3580
Stuhr, JulieAnn Foss, 9598
Stuhr, Patricia, 9878
Stuit, Thomas, 4408
Stukey, Rachel, 7578
Stulin, Jeffrey W., 8426
Stulin, Rita J., 8426
Stults, Dave, 3367
Stultz, Cynthia B., 9539
Stultz, James D., Jr., 9539
Stultz, Raquel, 3466
Stumne, Debra, 4672
Stumpf, Dana, 3749
Stumpf, Donna D., 3749
Stumpf, Shana, 3749
Stumpf, Stephen F., 3749
Stumpf, Stephen F., Jr., 3749
Stunbenberg, Sung, 1672
Stuntz, Elizabeth, 6874
Stuntz, Mayo, 6874
Stuntz, Mayo S., Jr., 6874
Stupak, Susan, 2329
Sturdivant, James M., 7736
Sturdivant, John, 4828
Sturgeon, Barry M., 3775
Sturges Trust, Stephen H. Sturges & Rose P., The , 176
Sturges, Harold W., 176
Sturges, Rose, 176
Sturges, Theresa L., 176
Sturgis, Chris, 1258
Sturgis, Jason T., 5192
Sturgis, Judy Pierce, 5192
Sturgis, William T., 5192
Sturm, Ruger & Co., 3991
Sturtz-Sreetharan, Cindi, 3024
Stussi, Douglas J., 7701

Stute, Natalie, 4720
Stutt, Carolyn, 5818
Stutt, David S., 5818
Stutt, William C., 5818
Stutz, Geraldine, 6875
Stutzman Charitable Lead Trust, 8309
Stutzman, Walter, 8309
Stuva, Kathy, 899
Styberg, Bernice M., 9942
Styberg, E.C., Jr., 9942
Sub-Zero Freezer Co., 9943
Sub-Zero Group, 9943
Sub-Zero Wolf, 9943
Subber, Barbara, 8233
Subia, Carol C., 8776
Subose Trust, JS & JL, 8828
Subramanian, Meghna, 518
Subramanian, Nita, 518
Subramanian, Priyal, 518
Subramanian, Srinivasan, 518
Suburban Communities, LLC, 2018
Subway, 1295
Suchocki, Ann, 3359
Suchomel, Frank A., 1523
Suchy, Cherie, 3689
Suckow, Peggy Ingalls, 4427
Sudakoff Trust, Harry and Ruth, The , 2356
Sudakoff, Harry, 2356
Sudakoff, Ruth, 2356
Sudikoff, Jeffrey, 1090
Sudikoff, Joan, 1090
Sudikoff, Joyce, 1090
Suen, Margaret W., 9705
Suen, Raymond M., 9705
Suessmann, James R., 5493
Sugarbaker, David J., 5016
Sugarbaker, Everett V., 5016
Sugarbaker, Geneva V., 5016
Sugarbaker, Paul, 5016
Sugarbaker, Stephen P., 5016
Sugarman, Connie J., 1696
Suggs, Pamela J., 1091
Suggs, Sidney V., 1091
Sugimoto, Dean I., 2624
Sugiura, Go, 3024
Suh, Byoung, 2742
Suh, Colleen M., 2742
Suh, Julienne S., 2742
Suh, Minsook, 2742
Suiter, Daniel J., 3591
Sukeforth, Rita C., 3805
Sukeforth, S. Douglas, 3805
Sukonik, Harold D., 7941
Sukwandi, Irene, 742
Sulentic, Robert E., 1752
Sulentic, Susan L., 1752
Sulerzyski, Charles W., 7546
Sullivan, Alan L., 171
Sullivan, Alexander L., 2357
Sullivan, Ashley M., 2357
Sullivan, Barbara, 2774
Sullivan, Brian, 2022, 8310
Sullivan, Brian C., 2853
Sullivan, Carolyn, 8837
Sullivan, Carrie E., 2853
Sullivan, Chris T., 2357
Sullivan, Daniel J., Jr., 8494
Sullivan, Deirdre, 1438
Sullivan, Gregory B., 5648
Sullivan, Hugh D., 3276
Sullivan, James F., 4315
Sullivan, James G., 7283, 7284
Sullivan, John D., 3978

Sullivan, John J., 3660, 4215
Sullivan, John J., Jr., 5017
Sullivan, Joseph M., 6490
Sullivan, Julie H., 3276
Sullivan, Katherine, 9944
Sullivan, Kathleen, 480
Sullivan, Margaret Walsh, 4315
Sullivan, Mariann, 5680
Sullivan, Marilyn, 877
Sullivan, Mark, 4362
Sullivan, Martin J., 6884
Sullivan, Maurice H., Jr., 4237
Sullivan, Michael, 8702
Sullivan, Michael J., 9770
Sullivan, Michelle, 5051
Sullivan, Mike, 4877
Sullivan, P.F., 8862
Sullivan, Patti M., 4848
Sullivan, Penny, 8869
Sullivan, Robert J., 9944
Sullivan, Robert J., Jr., 9944
Sullivan, Susan B., 1577
Sullivan, Susan S., 3254
Sullivan, Terence C., 8839
Sullivan, Thomas, 6945
Sullivan, Thomas H., 6821
Sullivan, Timothy J., 9944
Sullivan, William, 3078
Sullivan, William M., 1577
Sullivan, William Matheus, 1578
Sulpazo, Amy E., 2498
Sulpizio, Maria G., 781
Sulpizio, Richard, 781
Sultan, Ezra, 5939
Sultanik, Samuel, 5518
Sultz, Irving, 6720
Sultz, Marilyn, 6720
Sultzbach, Don A., 7312
Sulva, Edward T., 9382
Sulzberger, Eugene W., Sr., 1875
Sulzby, Jean H., 39
Sulzer, Deborah M., 3724
Sulzer, Grace E., 3277
Sumitomo Corporation of America
    "SCOA", 6876
Summer Prize Fruit Co., 1059
Summer, Nancy, 6929
Summerell, Lucy P., 9525
Summerhays, Jody, 5592
Summers, Ahnise, 9231
Summers, Cindy, 8197
Summers, Elisa Hill, 8938
Summers, Robert H., 9010
Summers, Rod, 233
Summerside, Paul, 9781
Summerville, James, 4946
Summit Charitable Lead Trust, 2715
Summy, Kelly, 3527
Sumners, Robert M., 8785
Sump, Randy, 5104
Sumter Pregnancy Center, 9033
Sun Lakes Marketing LP, 160
Sun, Cynthia, 5825
Sun, Kelly M., 4795
Sunbelt Equipment Marketing Inc, 9130
Suncoke Energy Inc., 7329
Sundance Financial, 702
Sunderland, David W., 9049
Sunderland, Frances Jean, 9049
Sunderland, Robert B., 9049
Sundheim, Jeffrey J., 6077
Sundquist, Carolyn B., 4710
Suniville, Thomas, 1652
Sunkel, Kevin C., 6588

Sunnen Products Co., 5018
Sunnen, Joseph, 5018
Sunny Designs, 1093
Sunrise Acceptance, 8596
Sunrise Foundation, 705
Sunrise Securities Inc., 6878
Sunset Hills Assn., 4535
Sunshine Group, The, 6656
Suntrust Bank, 1851, 1866
SunTrust Bank, 1873, 1875, 1903,
    1905, 1969, 2065, 2080, 2097,
    2195, 2196, 2214, 2251, 2257,
    2284, 2303, 2312, 2331, 2375,
    2431, 2470, 2474, 2485, 2492,
    2512, 2523, 2545, 2567, 3757,
    8083
Suntrust Bank Inc., Foundation Svcs.,
    2605
SunTrust Bank Middle GA, 2468
Suntrust Banks, 2042
SunTrust Banks, 2090, 2116, 2327,
    2351
Sunwest Bank, 1094
Supan, Thomasena, 2372
Supple, Sue, 1191
Surace-Smith Agency, 9240
Suramek, Mae, 3669
Surber, Sharen K., 3547
Surginex, 8368
Suri, Gurvendera S., 8959
Surrenda, David S., 5510
Susdewitt Enterprises Partnership, 153
Susi, Virginia, 2285
Susman Revocable Trust, Bernard M.,
    1753
Susman, Bernard, 1753
Susman, Caryl, 1753
Susman, Louisa, 5355
Susquehanna Bank, 8036
Suss, Andrew, 2553
Sussman, Howard, 5451
Sussman, Otto, 6880
Sussman, Sandra, 5451
Sutar, Catherine, 4583
Sutaruk Trust, Alex, 4583
Sutcliffe, Louise, 7262
Suter, Tammy Jo, 9555
Sutherland, Kelli A., 661
Sutherland, Michael R., 661
Sutherland, Shan, 472
Sutherland, Victoria D., 1765
Sutkins, Sharon, 8282
Sutton Holdings GP, 6882
Sutton Investments, 5554
Sutton Ira First Clearing Corp., David,
    6882
Sutton Mgmt., 6764
Sutton National Financial Services, Ruth,
    6882
Sutton Place Mgmt. Co., 7008
Sutton, Abraham, 6883
Sutton, Abraham M., 5554
Sutton, Alex, 9070
Sutton, David, 6882
Sutton, Dayna, 9226
Sutton, Edmund, 1816
Sutton, Elie, 5554
Sutton, Elie A., 6883
Sutton, Esther, 6883
Sutton, Jacob, 6881
Sutton, Mark, 9226
Sutton, Mark B., 9226
Sutton, Mary, 6883
Sutton, Paul, 6882

Sutton, Ruth, 6882
Sutton, Samuel, 5554
Sutton, Shirley, 6883
Sutton, Solomon, 6881
Sutton, Steven, 6882
Sutton, Suzanne Parker, 903
Suwinski, Jan, 6885
Suwinski, Jan H., 6885
Suwinski, Karen, 6885
Suwinski, Susan, 6885
Suwinski, Susan J., 6885
Suyama, Hatsumi, 5821
Suyama, Ken, 5821
Suzanne Chrisman, Bryan ND, 1316
Suzanne DeBerry Trust, Suzanne, 402
Suzuki, Janet, 1077
Suzuki, Katherine, 1077
Suzuki, Mary, 1077
Suzuki, Masa, 1077
Suzuki, Nancie, 3909
Svacina, Jennifer, 5021
Swagelok Company, 7608
Swaidan, Karl, 671
Swain, Ronald L., 2982
Swain, Ruth B., 9003
Swain-Hoffman, Kimberly, 2103
Swan Manufacturing Co., 7386
Swan, Catherine, 3027
Swan, Philip A., 801
Swan, Richard W., 6208
Swango, Wilma, 3362
Swann, Jim, 2360
Swann, Jonnie, 2360
Swanson Charitable Remainder Trust,
    Byrnece, 2534
Swanson, Alice, 5152
Swanson, Dean C., 2582
Swanson, Elizabeth, 4222
Swanson, James R., 2005
Swanson, Kay S., 2582
Swanson, Kristina L., 3158
Swanson, Larry, 4804
Swanson, Max R., 5063
Swanson, Nancy, 758
Swanson, Robert W., 5012
Swanson, Roberta, 2166
Swanson, Vernon H., 9868
Swartz, Anne, 8663
Swartz, Eric, 2528
Swartz, Eric S., 2528
Swartz, Joan P., 55
Swartz, Kama D., 2528
Swartz, Katie Albrecht, 7301
Swartz, Kim, 500
Swartz, Michael C., 3947
Swartz, Robert, 9941
Swayne, Judy K., 1097
Swayne, Keith D., 1097
Swearingen, John, 8960
Swearingen, John E., 3631
Swearingen, Stafford, 8960
Swearingen-Arnold, Linda, 3631
Swearingen-Pfleeger, Marcia, 3631
Sweat, Carol G., 8884
Sweat, Jacob G., 8884
Sween, Patricia Larson, 9650
Sweeney, Brian, 788
Sweeney, Caroline, 6887
Sweeney, Dennis, 507, 884
Sweeney, Dennis J., 507
Sweeney, Jaymey, 7794
Sweeney, Judith, 507, 884
Sweeney, Judith L., 507
Sweeney, Michael, 9641

Sweeney, Michael A., 7377
Sweeney, Michael W., 7397
Sweeney, Sean S., 6887
Sweeney, Taylor, 3511
Sweet Trust, 4427
Sweet, David J., 5812
Sweet, Johanna, 1450
Sweezy, Elizabeth, 6494
Sweig, Michael, 5191
Sweig, Morton, 5191
Swensen, Thomas, 89
Swenson, Gary E., 3962
Swenson, Gregory E., 3962
Swenson, Karen, 5700
Swenson, Madeline B., 3962
Swenson, Ralph G., 3962
Swent, Elizabeth Crane, 1955
Swerdlow, Marleen, 9160
Swetland, David Sears, 7581
Swetland, David W., 7581
Swetland, Jennifer Carris, 9376
Swetland, Mary Ann, 7581
Swett, Bradford N., 6888
Swett, Daniel R., 3196
Swett, Eileen, 9227
Swett, Jeffrey, 9227
Swett, Michael, 9227
Swett, Ralph, 9227
Swett, Timothy, 9227
SWF LP, 5724
Swidler, Alisa Feinstein, 1633
Swiegart Trust, A., 8311
Swierkos, Mary E., 6299
Swift, Ann W., 1754
Swift, Anne H., 5903
Swift, Douglas G., 5903
Swift, George P., Jr., 1754
Swift, Harlan J., Jr., 5903
Swift, Matthew, 5286
Swift, Phelps H., 3272
Swift, Virginia, 1754
Swindle, Patricia Warren, 7729
Swindle, Stephen D., 9315, 9316
Swindoll, B Carver, 3605
Swinerton Builders, 1098
Swinerton Inc., 1098
Swingle, Mark, 5582
Swinmurn, C. John, 1755
Swinmurn, Gabriela, 1755
Swinmurn, Nick, 1755
Swinmurn, Sandra C., 1755
Swinney, Susan, 9211
Swisher, C. Edwin, III, 7932
Swisher, Carl S., 2361
Swisher, Peggy E., 5034
Swistel, Alice Phillips, 5609
Switzer, Amy Lloyd, 8075
Switzer, Cathy R., 3666
Switzer, James L., Jr., 8510
Switzer, Margaret, 6889
Switzer, Sarah, 6889
Switzer, Toccoa W., 8510
Switzerland County, 3462
Swofford, John, 7209
Swope, Jeffrey, 4035
Swope, Richard L., 2274
Syar, Susan L., 1099
Syed, Afshan, 7611
Syed, Ike, 4012
Sykes, James T., 2815
Sylcon, LLC, 7365
Sylvan, Barbara, 7722
Sylvan, Dave R., 7722
Sylvester, Jeff, 8556

Sylvestri, Jennifer M., 707
Sylvia, Ann C., 7081
Sylvis, Dee, 5074
Sym Holding Corp., 6144
Symens, Paul, 4679
Symes, Albert R., 4319
Symes, Barbara, 4319
Symes, Landers, 4319
Symes-Elmer, Arica, 4319
Symington, Stuart, Jr., 2738
Symmonds, Bob, 3635
Symms, Dan, 2686
Symms, Steve, 2686
Symons, Margaret, 9662
Synder, Daniel, 5054
Synergy Sky Ltd., 5085
Synopsys Community Fund, 1100
Synopsys Foundation, 1100
Synopsys Technology Education
    Opportunity Foundation, 1100
Synovus Trust Co., 29, 2518
Synovus Trust Company, 2104, 2444,
    2601
Synovus Trust Company, N.A., 59
Syracuse's Italian Sausage Co., 8859
Szabo, Raymond, 7383
Szarell, Thelma, 7933
Sze, Stanley, 770
Szekely, Alex, 1102
Szekely, Deborah, 1102
Szekeres, Andrea, 5626
Szigethy, Andrea, 7190
Szilagyi, Steven, 8010
Szleper, Kathleen L., 3600
Szlosek, Theresa C., 4047
Szmit, Helena, 917
Szostak, Walter G., 4533
Szulik, Kyle, 7264
Szulik, Matthew J., 7264
Szymanski, Betty B., 1876
Szynanski, Mike, 370

T & M Limited Partnership, 3347
T & M Properties, 3347
Tabani Group, 9228
Tabani, Tahira B., 9228
Tabani, Zaffar S., 9228
Tabas Memorial Lead Trust, Charles L.,
    8312
Tabas, Andrew R., 8312
Tabas, Harriette S., 8312
Tabas, Richard S., 8312
Tabasgo Foundation, 758
Tabb, Vivian, 256
Tabler, Michael Rex, 9651
Tabner, John, 1637
Tabor, Jusiata, 4998
Tabor, Kristin, 5049
Tabori, Dan, 2638
Tabussi, Stephen J., 2631
Tackett, Maureen, 4419
Taco, 8503
Tactical Investment Management Corp.,
    5131
Taddonio, Kristy A., 1362
Taddonio, Pamela, 1362
Taddonio, Pamela S., 1362
Taddonio, Toni M., 1362
Taddonio, Tony Marie, 1362
Tadler, Joyce E., 4320
Tadler, Steven M., 4320
Taegel, Edwin, 8837
Tafel, Ida May, 3280

Tafel, James B., 3280
Tafel, James B., Jr., 3280
Tafel-Klaus, Julie K., 3280
Taft, Anne Demarest, 7754
Taft, Dudley, 7609
Taft, Dudley S., 7537, 7541, 7609
Taft, Dudley S., Jr., 7537
Taft, Nellie L., 7537
Taft, Thomas W., 7537
TAG, 542
Taggart, Elizabeth S., 4579
Taggart, Robert E., 8114
Taghavi, Nima, 868
Tahari Ltd., Elie, 6890
Tahari, Elie, 6890
Tahmisian, Lynne, 1720
Tai & Co Foundation Inc., J.T., 533
Taimoto, Tetsu, 688
Tair, Ltd., 8928
Taisey, Robert D., 2996
Tait, Frank M., 7610
Tait, Frank M., Mrs. , 7610
Tait, Richard, 9599
Taitantown Tailgaters, 9230
Taiwanese American Center of Northern
    California, 777
Takata, Craig, 650
Takeda, Donna, 2627
Takesue, Chad, 2638
Takiff, Bobette, 3281
Takiff, Sanford, 3281
Takitani, Aiko, 2650
Talamantes, Patrick J., 811
Talbert, Beth, 4410
Talbert, Lucina Noches, 3611
Talbott, Audrey S., 1757
Talbott, E. P., 7612
Talbott, Nelson S., 7612
Talbott, Robert S., 1757
Taliaferro, Roberta, 7560
Taliercio-Cohn, Carmela, 5945
Tallent, John, 3521
Talley, Chris L., 3469
Talley, Laura, 9814
Tallman, Cordelia, 7863
Talltimber, 3905
Tally, Jessie, 7228
Tally, William, 18
Talmudical Yeshiva, 4594
Talty, Joseph E., 4584
Talty, Patrick E., 4584
Talty, Thomas, Jr., 4584
Talty-Schenkelberg, Nari, 4584
TALX Corporation, 2592
Tam, Kenneth C., 477
Tamaki, Meriko, 9707
Tambellini, Mark Eileen, 8035
Tamer Restated Living Trust, James,
    4585
Tamer, James, 4585
Tan, Xiao Li, 1633
Tandy, Carol, 7723
Tang, Kenny, 533
Tang, Oscar L., 6891
Tang, Tracy L., 6891
Tanico, Paul P., 6892
Tanimura, Gary K., 1103
Tanimura, George M., 1103
Tanimura, George T., 1103
Tanimura, Kelly, 1103
Tanimura, Robert T., 1103
Tanimura, Sheila C., 1103
Tanimura, Susan, 1103
Tanimura, Tom T., 1103

Tanino, Katsumi, 9642
Tank, Margo H.K., 1818
Tankala, Ashoka, 3875
Tanner, Mary, 6893
Tanner, Reed, 9739
Tanner, Reed J., 9753
Tanner, Tracy, 2577
Tansey, Elsa, 8924
Tanus, Abraham, 8948
Tanus, Rocio, 8948
Tanus, Rocio P., 8948
Tanus, Sarah, 8948
Tanway Enterprises LP, 153
Tanzola, Carol A., 3962
Tao, M.D., Ph.D., Weng, 2881
Tapia, Tony, 1241
Taplin, Jack G., 2363
Taplin, Martin W., 2363
Taplin, Sheila Elias, 2363
Tapp, Frances Carr, 8825
Tapp, Ken D., 2435
Tappan, David S., IV, 1363
Tappan, David S., Jr., 1363
Tappan, Jeanne B., 1363
Tappan, Steven G., 1363
Tapper, Albert, 4321
Tapper, Charles, 4321
Tapper, Eve, 4321
Tapper, Lynne, 4321
Tarakji, Bilal, 4586
Tarakji, Lama, 4586
Tarakji, N., 4586
Tarakji, Nael, 4586
Tarbox, Laura, 726
Tarella, David R., 1730
Tarnoff, Jerome, 5791, 6396
Tarpoff, Diana, 4526
Tarr, Greg, 4449
Tarr, Molly U., 8545
Tarr, Robert J., Jr., 8545
Tarrant, Jeffrey, 1758
Tarrson, Linda C., 3282
Tarrson, Ronald E., 3282
Tarshis, Jay P., 2723
Tarter, Jack, 9979
Tarver, Sarah Thompson, 8664
Tash, Graham A., Jr., 9714
Tash, Paul, 2362
Tashjian, Adrienne V., 5562
Tassell, Leslie E., 4587
Tassone, Bette Ann, 3839
Tate, Emily Polo, 4526
Tate, Inez M., 9995
Tate, Jeff, 3559
Tate, Michael A., 4377
Tatelman, Barry E., 4323
Tatelman, Eliot H., 4322
Tatelman, June L., 4322
Tatelman, Susan, 4323
Tatro, Wayne S., 4250
Tattersall, Stowe, 6989
Tatum, Linda, 420
Taub, H. Ben, 9229
Taub, Henry J.N., 9229
Taub, Henry J.N., II, 9229
Taub, Marcy E., 9229
Taube, Ben Zion, 4101
Tauber, Diane, 4465
Tauer, Paul, 4772
Tauke, A.W., 3527
Tausig, Eva-Maria, 6026
Tavarez, Tiffany, 8326
Tavelli, Teresa, 2664
Taviner, Gloria, 706

Taxman, Nancy, 3283
Taxman, Nancy R., 3283
Taxman, Seymour, 3283
Tayama, Lucilla, 6504
Tayback, Christopher, 480
Taylor Development Corp., 2366
Taylor Foundation, The, 1846
Taylor Group, The, 4855
Taylor Trust, James & Allien, 9546
Taylor, Alex, 3499
Taylor, Alexander S., II, 7327
Taylor, Alexandra J., 7836
Taylor, Ashley M., 9051
Taylor, Beatrice R., 5064
Taylor, Benjamin B., 1759
Taylor, Brad, 5074
Taylor, Brian D., 9480
Taylor, Bruce, 3567
Taylor, Carolyn, 7151
Taylor, Carson G., 8019
Taylor, Chandler, 4962
Taylor, Christina, 3126
Taylor, Christopher H., 2067
Taylor, Clay Dudley, 1236
Taylor, Cory Newport, 3284
Taylor, Daniel J., Jr., 3632
Taylor, Daniel J., Sr., 3632
Taylor, David, 4295, 9133
Taylor, David L., 4257
Taylor, Douglas, 1364
Taylor, Drake Ewing, 1236
Taylor, Duncan, 7333
Taylor, Elizabeth, 2366
Taylor, Elizabeth C., 1679
Taylor, Frank, 4648
Taylor, Fred C., 3285
Taylor, Frederick Morgan, III, 4201
Taylor, Gretchen S., 5223
Taylor, Gustavus F., 9794
Taylor, J.M. Bryan, 7151
Taylor, Jack, 2366
Taylor, James A., 7836
Taylor, James C., 5064
Taylor, James R., 6172
Taylor, Jann, 7764
Taylor, Jeffrey B., 7212
Taylor, John, 188, 7151
Taylor, John F., 4201
Taylor, John I., 1679
Taylor, Judy E., 4905
Taylor, June, 404
Taylor, Kate, 4352
Taylor, Katherine S., 1759
Taylor, Kathleen Baer, 3632
Taylor, L. Susan, 3885
Taylor, Ladonna, 7724
Taylor, Leslie D., 3700
Taylor, Linda M., 4257
Taylor, Lloyd S., 2321
Taylor, Lucy Farnsworth, 4201
Taylor, Mary B., 1972
Taylor, Mary Rose, 2621
Taylor, Maurice, 3287
Taylor, Maurice M., Jr., 3286
Taylor, Michelle, 3286, 3287
Taylor, Mitchell, 2366
Taylor, Mitzi M., 4855
Taylor, Nancy B., 2586
Taylor, Nick R., 5070
Taylor, Pam, 369
Taylor, Pamela Joy, 3284
Taylor, Patricia, 3037
Taylor, Patricia N., 3284
Taylor, Paul, 4028, 4802

Taylor, Paul M., 3284
Taylor, Ritchey Nelson, 2365
Taylor, Robert C., Jr., 886
Taylor, Robert D., 4855
Taylor, Roxann, 8702
Taylor, Sarah, 7354
Taylor, Sharon A., 2703
Taylor, Shawn, 7151
Taylor, Shelley M., 7836
Taylor, Sheryl, 9067
Taylor, Stacy, 9133
Taylor, Stephen L., 825
Taylor, Stephen M., 4802
Taylor, Susan R., 5064
Taylor, Teddy, 13
Taylor, Todd E., 4905
Taylor, Vernon F., III, 1364
Taylor, Vernon F., Jr., 1364
Taylor, W.A., Jr., 4855
Taylor, Walter, 8514
Taylor, William, 9345
Taylor, William A., III, 4855
Taylor, William Ewing, 1236
TBJ Properties, 8829
TBMC, 5861
TBonz Restaurant Group, 8546
TCH M Wood/JFF De-Clt 9/16/93, 8083
TCH M Wood/JFF De-Clt May 92, 8083
TCH M Wood/JFF N-DCLT May 92, 8083
TCH M Wood/Joyce FDN Dec 90, 8083
Tchozewski, Chet, 404
TD Bank, 4185, 4300, 5208, 5216, 6082
Teacher's Credit Union, 3458
Teague, Mary S., 2462
Teague, Syd, 8741
Teague, Thomas, 8741
Teale, Jennifer, 9450
TEAM Wharton, 8819
Teammates for Kids, 3817
Teammates for Kids Foundation, 4399
Tears Foundation, 9585
Tech, Marilyn T., 4766
Tecker, Jon, 5091
TECO Energy, 2367
Tedaldi, Kenneth J., 6894
Tedder, Michael, 2223
Tedesco Family Partnership, 5557
Tedesco, Francis, 5557
Tedesco, Josephine, 5557
Tedesco, Lenore, 2954
Tedesco, Mark, 5557
Teel, Chuck, 9708
Teel, E. Gerald, 9708
Teel, Scott, 2069
Teeter, Ann Rylie, 9579
Teeter, Jennifer, 9579
Teeter, Jennifer M., 9579
Teeter, Roger, 9579
Teeter, Roger C., 9579
Teets, Ladonna, 9752
Teets, Mark, 9752
Tefft, Nancy, 2971
Teich, Pastor Andreas, 4533
Teichert Materials, 366
Teichman Enterprises, 1106
Teichman, Alan, 1106
Teichman, Bernard, 1106
Teichman, Joseph, 5452
Teichman, Marcia, 1106
Teichman, Ruth, 1106
Teichman, Samuel, 1106
Teichman, Sidney, 1106
Teichman, Sol, 1106

Teiger, David, 5558
Teisher, Jeanne, 7807
Teitel, Ben N., 4589
Teitelbaum, Ellen, 7141
Teitelbaum, Helene, 5830
Tejada, Miguel, 3817
Teklits, Joseph, 6549
Teleflex Inc., 8314
Telesca, Michael, 5698
Teletech, 1295
TeleTech Holdings, 1761
Telfer, Steve, 3359
Tell Sr. Trust, Paul P., 7613
Tell, Anne P., 7613
Tell, Catherine K., 1580
Tell, Karen N., 1580
Tell, Michael, 7613
Tell, William, 1580
Tell, William F., 1580
Tellalian, Aram H., III, 1489
Tellalian, Robert S., Jr., 1489
Teller-Elsberg, Jonathan S., 3856
Tellie, Nicholas D., 7130
Tellier, Elizabeth J., 9946
Teltow, Gunnar, 1607
Tema Foundation, 3641
Tempas, Jeffrey J., 1861, 2275
Tempest, Dixie, 3402
Temple, Ellen, 8845
Temple, Larry, 9081
Temple, Scott, 3515
Templer Family Trust, 6999
Templer, Joseph, 6253, 6999
Templer, Julius, 6253
Templer, Rosa, 6253
Templeton, Angela M., 4601
Templeton, Muriel, 9712
Templin, Allys M., 9709
Templin, Russell B., 9709
TEMTCO, 4855
Tenberg, Marvin, 3964
Tengelsen, Erich W., 3288
Tengelsen, Jennifer, 496
Tengensen, Erich W., 3288
Tenhouse, Sharon, 2803
Tennant Co., 4798
Tennent, Timothy C., 1251
Tennessee Football, 9230
Tennessee Industrial Electronics, 8614
Tenney, Alice J., 6895
Tenney, Judy E., 6895
Tenney, Laura E., 6895
Tenney, Warren, 6895
Tennille, Jocelyn D., 2824
Tenny, Michael, 9102
Tensiltech Corp., 3905
Tension Envelope Corp., 5019
Tepper Charitable Trust, Susan J., 6431
Tepper, Marge, 1255
Terama Products Ltd., 5085
Teran, Gary W., 9309
Terbrusch, Richard P., 6638
Tercek, Mark R., 717
Terhern, Walter E., 4856
Terhune Memorial Endowment Trust, Walter E., 7614
Teri-Jon Sports, 6041
TerKeurst, Arthur, III, 7266
TerKeurst, Hope, 7266
TerKeurst, Lysa, 7266
Termine, Richard, 6194
Ternsten, Hans, 6541
Terrano, Richard, 6323
Terre Haute Savings Bank, 3386

Terrile, Wilda J., 4416
Terrill, John, 3617
Terrill, Marc B., 3838
Terry, Bentina C., 2069
Terry, C. Herman, 2368
Terry, Carl E., 7944
Terry, Carmen, 3568
Terry, Carol, 1552
Terry, Edward M., 9897
Terry, Frederick A., Jr., 6955
Terry, Julia, 4046
Terry, Mary Virginia, 2005, 2368
Terry, Ryan C., 3568
Terry, Scott, Jr., 3568
Terry, Thomas F., 5223
Terry-Hewitt, Carol, 1453
Terukina, Cathy, 3497
Teruya, Dexter T., 2651
Teruya, Ethel M., 2651
Teruya, Raymond T., 2651
Teruya, Wayne T., 2651
Teruzzi, Lilliana, 6955
Terwilliger, J. Ronald, 2593
Terwilliger, Patricia B., 2593
Tesdal, Tom, 3125
Tesher, Robert, Dr., 2412
Teshinsky, Adam J., 1108
Teshinsky, Fred, 1108
Teshinsky, Lucy, 1108
Teshinsky, Robert D., 1108
Teske, Elizabeth, 5152
Teson, Suan B., 5026
Tesoro Petroleum Co., 301
Tessler, Craig, 351
Testa, Barbara Ann, 6405
Testa, Florence H., 2779
Testa, Mike, 9986
Testamentary Trust Paragraph 6, 6957
Testani, Mario, 6766
Tester, Mary, 7422
Testerman, Benjamin H., 8169
Tetlak, Joseph F., 7615
Teuscher, Peter, 496
Texas Bankers Assoc., 9232
Texas Brine Co., LLC, 9266
Texas Children's Hospital, 7209
Texas Pipe & Supply Co, 9167
Texas Rangers Baseball Foundation, 684
Texas Wings, 2510
Texas Wings Holdings, 2510
Texden Inc., 153
Texor Petroleum Co., 3257
Textiles, 7097
TF Foundation, 4380
Thacher, David J., 9722
Thacher, David T., 9722
Thacher, Nancy C., 9722
Thadikonda, Krupakar Paul, 3965
Thagard, George F., III, 1109
Thagard, Ray G., 1109
Thagard, Raymond G., Jr., 1109
Thain, Carmen M., 5250
Thain, John, 5250
Thain, John A., 5250
Thakkar, Kelly L., 7795
Thalheimer, Louis B., 3966
Thaman, Mary, 7339
Thaman, Michael H., 3289
Thames, David Walker, 2594
Thames, Gerald W., 2594
Thames, Judy Kaye J., 2594
Thane, Janet, 4598
Thank Heaven Foundation, 9033

Thannisch, George, 8845
Tharpe Irrevocable Trust, Max B., 2369
Thatcher, Dale A., 5528
Thawley, Cynthia, 787
Thawley, Richard, 787
Thayer Admin Trust, Dorothy M., 9710
Thayer, Thomas C., 2643
THC Business Services, 840
Theisen, Herbert J., 3001
Thelen, Alexander C. Von, 9488
Them, Jerod, 7384
Themistos, Thomas H., 4337
Theroux, David J., 1110
Theroux, Mary L.G., 1110
Theune, Mary, 9961
Thiel, Ervil A., 1365
Thiel, Leslie, 1981
Thiel, Ronald E., 1365
Thiem, Alvin F., 6898
Thieme, Robert, 4859
Thiessen, Dalys, 3641
Third Avenue Management, LLC, 1763
Third Chapter, 9338
Thoelecke, Timothy N., 3092
Thoman, Candace, 4590
Thoman, W.B., 4590
Thomas And Sally Wood Charitable Remainder Trust, 3644
Thomas Trust, Adele M., 9542
Thomas, Alfred, 2370
Thomas, Anne D., 3706
Thomas, C.M., 9500
Thomas, David B., 5169
Thomas, Ella Holt, 7645
Thomas, Eunice W., 9542
Thomas, Frank, 876
Thomas, Franklin A., 6135
Thomas, Geetha, 2501
Thomas, George, 7212
Thomas, Guy, 3683
Thomas, Harold, 2687
Thomas, Harold E., 2687
Thomas, Henry J., 153
Thomas, Henry M., III, 6868
Thomas, Jack E., 4951
Thomas, Jeffrey K., 876
Thomas, Jenny, 2501
Thomas, Jillian G., 876
Thomas, Joan C., 876
Thomas, Joan Harris, 1595
Thomas, John, 5075, 8511
Thomas, John R., 8527
Thomas, John V., 9542
Thomas, Joseph, 4585
Thomas, Justin, 92
Thomas, Linda, 3390
Thomas, Lynn Schadt, 8670
Thomas, M.V., 2501
Thomas, Margaret A., 5123
Thomas, Margot K., 8977
Thomas, Marisol, 6796
Thomas, Martha, 103
Thomas, Martha E., 5123
Thomas, Megan A., 876
Thomas, Michael, 2371
Thomas, Nick, 3379
Thomas, Pamela, 4847
Thomas, Peg, 4796
Thomas, Phylis, 2370
Thomas, Phyllis, 2687
Thomas, Ray, 8674
Thomas, Richard, 9774
Thomas, Rick, 2687
Thomas, Rob, 6796

Thomas, Robert, 2371, 6796
Thomas, Robert M., 2371
Thomas, Roger M., 4131
Thomas, Russell, Jr., 2550
Thomas, Saint, 12
Thomas, Sam H., 9138
Thomas, Samuel Judson, 9138
Thomas, Scott E., 8891
Thomas, Sharon N., 9138
Thomas, Stephanie, 2501, 8891
Thomas, Stephen, 2371
Thomas, Thomas D., 3635
Thomas, Thomas L., 9742
Thomas, Wayne, 2371
Thomas, William R., 7712
Thomas, Winston, 8529
Thomas, Yvonne, 153
Thomas-Easton, Daniele, 5669
Thomas-Miller, Cheryl, 5129
Thomason, Jerry M., 7713
Thomason, William, 3668
Thomasson, Benita, 3459
Thomasson, Brittany, 3459
Thomasson, J. Elliott, 3459
Thomasson, Jeffrey H., 3352, 3453, 3459
Thomason, Pat, 4830
Thomaston Cotton Mills, 2465
Thomaston Savings Bank, 1581
Thomasville Furniture Industries, 7267
Thome, Jim, 7354
Thompson Annuity Trust, Henrietta R., 8496
Thompson Charitable Lead Annuity Trust II, Eleanor S., 1988
Thompson Charitable Lead Annuity Trust II, Thomas R., 1988
Thompson Charitable Lead Annuity Trust, Elenor S., II, 1988
Thompson Charitable Lead Annuity Trust, James R., II, 1988
Thompson Charitable Trust, B. Ray, 8664
Thompson Charitable Trust, Juanne, 8664
Thompson Trust, Eugene, 9474
Thompson Trust, Orville K., 4593
Thompson Trust, Willard E., 8496
Thompson USA, J. Walter, 8772
Thompson, Adella Sands, 8664
Thompson, Angela M., 9234
Thompson, Ann J., 4948
Thompson, Anne H., 239
Thompson, B. Ray, III, 8664
Thompson, B. Ray, Jr., 8664
Thompson, Becky, 9191
Thompson, Betty E., 6245
Thompson, Brenda S., 9926
Thompson, Catherine Vance, 8664
Thompson, Charles E., Jr., 9189
Thompson, Craig, 870
Thompson, David, 4325
Thompson, Doug, 2877
Thompson, Elizabeth, 4325
Thompson, Elizabeth C., 4041
Thompson, Ellen A., 4591
Thompson, Evan C., 1111
Thompson, Glenn E., 36
Thompson, Greg, 3595
Thompson, Gregory, 2054
Thompson, Helenmae, 1112
Thompson, Jack, 8566
Thompson, James A., 70
Thompson, James R., 9234

Thompson, Janet L., 9947
Thompson, Janice E., 1981
Thompson, Janice L., 2160
Thompson, Jean, 2877
Thompson, Jean C., 70
Thompson, Jerry, 3460
Thompson, Jessica E., 8142
Thompson, Jim, 5104
Thompson, Joanne S. Titus, 9714
Thompson, John, 9454
Thompson, Jr. Trust, Henry L., 7617
Thompson, Juanne J., 8664
Thompson, Kathy C., 3697
Thompson, Kirby, 2065, 2195, 2284
Thompson, Kristen L., 2160
Thompson, Leslie V., 2372
Thompson, M.D., Dr. P.H., Peter K., 8924
Thompson, Mary, 4592
Thompson, Mary Cobb, 3713
Thompson, Nylah J., 1988
Thompson, Orville K., 2160
Thompson, Patrick J., 9947
Thompson, Paul F., 3460
Thompson, Pia, 3134
Thompson, Porter E., 1112
Thompson, Richard K., 4593
Thompson, Robert M., 4591
Thompson, Scott A., 3460
Thompson, Serena, 6966
Thompson, Stanley T., 3460
Thompson, Sterling A., 3460
Thompson, Steven S., 3460
Thompson, Stuart K., 3460
Thompson, Tami Y., 2372
Thompson, Theresa, 6946
Thompson, Theresa S., 2383
Thompson, Timothy, 80
Thompson, Timothy J., 3779
Thompson, Timothy L., 2848
Thompson, Todd, 7764
Thomsen, Carl J., 2373
Thomsen, Frances D., 2373
Thomsen, Robert J., 2373
Thomson, Bonnie M., 1113
Thomson, C. Jay, 1113
Thomson, Clifford L., 1113
Thomson, Jean E., 9711
Thomson, John Edgar, 1764
Thomson, Joseph W., 9019
Thomson, Lucy, 4518
Thomson, Shannon M., 1113
Thomson, Tom, 4518
Thonet, Kathi, 1893
Thorman, Jackie Myer, 2854
Thorn, Don W., 9130
Thorn, Eugene A., III, 7312
Thorn, Therese M., 4548
Thornberry, Phillip C., 2475
Thornburg, Kent, 3361
Thornburg, Keta, 3757
Thornburgh, Cornelia P., 2374
Thornburgh, Richard E., 2374
Thorndike, William N., 4122
Thorne Lead Charitable Trust, 9235
Thorne, Alexandra T., 5233
Thorne, Andrea M., 4402
Thorne, Betsy V., 4402
Thorne, Daniel K., 5233
Thorne, Dorothy F., 9235
Thorne, James M., 4402
Thorne, Jeanne C., 9310
Thorne, Mary B., 4402
Thorne, Michael, 1510

Thorne, Pamela, 1114
Thorne, Pamela A., 1114
Thorne, Sherry, 1387
Thorne, Sherry A., 1387
Thorne, Stephen E., IV, 1114
Thorne, Stephen E., IV, 1114
Thorne, Steven, 1387
Thorne, Steven D., 1387
Thorne-Thomsen, Fletcher, Jr., 8873
Thornes, Doreen, 597
Thornley, Alexander N., 549
Thornley, Anthony S., 549
Thornley, Christian A., 549
Thornley, Gillian M., 549
Thornley, Warren T., 549
Thornton, Heidi, 4551
Thornton, Ida Hope, 8949
Thornton, John M., 1115
Thornton, Ovita, 2437
Thornton, Roger, 3458
Thornton, Sally B., 1115
Thornton, Steven B., 1115
Thornton, W. Gerald, 7246
Thornton, William S., 8824
Thorogood, Nellie Carr, 8774
Thoroughbred Racing Associations of America, 6265
Thorpe, James R., 4800
Thorpe, Merle, Jr., 1807
Thorpe, Richard, 4800
Thorpe, Ron, 9494
Thorpe, Timothy, 4800
Thorsen, Jamie K., 3099
Thorsett, Don, 4793
Thorton, Timothy, 4648
Thrall, Susan, 1583
Threads, 7097
Three Rivers Aluminum Co., 8230
Threkleld, Robert T., 7469
Threlkeld, Alan S., 7469
Thrift, Edgar M., 740
Throckmorton Trust, Morford C., The, 7618
Throckmorton, Dolly, 7933
Thronson, Edgar A., 1766
Throsby, Tim, 2791
Thrush, Homer A., 3460
Thu, Ko Kyaw, 9697
Thunder Birds, The, 825
Thunderwood Co., 3905
Thurber, John, 8350
Thurman, Edgar A., 2375
Thurman, Mark, 196
Thurman, Robert A.F., 6316
Thurmond, Sandra M., 8597
Thurston, Ellen E., 9713
Thurston, Robert H., 9713
Thurston, Severt W., Jr., 9713
Thurston, Sheryl, 3361
Thurston, Susan E., 9713
Tiballi, Jason, 9383
Tiballi, Katherine, 9383
Tiballi, Katherine Scudder, 9383
Tibbals, Mike, 8806
Tibbles, Tom, 2030
Tichenor, Emily B., 2604
Ticknor, Marjorie, 5371
Tides Foundation, 6077, 8494
Tidewater Titans Association, 3959
Tidewater Transit Co., 7119
Tielborg, Pat, 9130
Tien, Spencer, 9102
Tierney, Hanne, 6194
Tierney, James P., 148

Tierney, Mary G., 4057
Tierney, Michael P., 1584
Tierney, Patricia E., 1584
Tierney, Paul E., Jr., 1584
Tierney, Susan E., 1584
Tierney, Thomas G., 9933
Tietz, Roger & Sue, 9814
Tietze, Eileen, 9236
Tietze, John H., 9236
Tietze, John L., 9236
Tifft, Julie Arenz, 844
Tigges, Dale C., 9252
Tighe, Mary Ann, 6656
Tijerina, Linda, 5164
Tillberg, Mindy, 3557
Tillema, John, 3401
Tiller, Julia C. Fickling, 2478
Tiller, Julia F., 2478
Tilley Trust, William, The, 1118
Tilley, John, 1118
Tilley, Joshua, 7190
Tilley, Nadine B., 1118
Tilley, Nicole, 1118
Tilley, William H., 1118
Tillotson, Frederick E., 5234
Tillou, Sandra S., 9768
Timboe, Ken J., 1332
Time Equities, 6655
Time Warner Cable, 247
Times Publishing Co., 2362
Timken, Barbara C., 7531
Timken, Louise B., 7531
Timken, Polly M., 7531
Timm, Cheryl, 4798
Timmer, Maureen, 3498
Timmons, Bess Spiva, 5021
Timmons, Deborah, 2270
Timmons, Frank, 2270
Timmons, Gregory G., 5021
Timmons, Jennifer, 9297
Timmons, R.J., 9297
Timmons, Sarah, 5021
Timmons, Thomas P., 7551
Timston Corp., 5959
TINA, 1241
Tindall, Jocelin Saks, 4990
Tinder, Tara Jean, 9937
Tindley, Bonita, 1822
Tingler, Randall L., 9427
Tingler, Wallace L., 9427
Tinglof, Mark, 538
Tingvall, Teri, 9638
Tinicum Investors, 6715
Tinney, Brooke B., 1076
Tinsley, E. Paul, 4095
Tinsley, Jim, 1247
Tinsley, Susan, 9500
Tinsworth, Steven, 2149
Tippins, 8318
Tippins, Carolyn H., 8318
Tippins, Carolyn M., 8318
Tippins, George W., 8318
Tippins, John H., 8318
Tippins, William H., 8318
Tipton, Cindy, 2103
Tipton, Constance M., 7339
Tipton, Deborah Dunklin, 8682
Tisch Family Foundation, Steve, The, 6463
Tisch Found, Lizzie and Jonathan, The, 6463
Tisch Foundation, Laurie M., The, 6463
Tisch, Elizabeth S., 6900
Tisch, Jamie A., 1120

Tisch, Joan H., 6900
Tisch, Jonathan, 5369
Tisch, Jonathan M., 6900
Tisch, Laurie, 5369
Tisdale, Greta, 9495
Tisdale, Kathleen, 4057
Tisdale, Patricia, 966
Tish, Martin H., 2771
Tishman Speyer Properties, 6655
Tishman Speyer Property, 6656
Titan Industrial Corp., 6797
Titcomb, Bruce L., 4779
Titcomb, Daniel C., 4779
Titcomb, E. Rodman, Jr., 4779
Titcomb, Edward R., 4779
Titcomb, Frederick W., 4779
Titcomb, Julie C., 4779
Titherington, Geoffrey, 3786
Titus, Carolyn, 9714
Titus, Carolyn A., 9714
Titus, David B., 4340
Titus, Leon E., Jr., 9714
Titzman, Donna M., 9246
Tizzio, Mary Ann, 5559
Tizzio, Thomas R., 5559
Tkachov, Natalia, 1132
Tkachuck, Candace Y., 9586
TLC Management, 3430
TLH Charitable Lead Trust, 3358
TMC Investment Co., 8318
Tnkrgk Family Trust, 702
To, Cecilie, 5193
To, Henry, 344
To, Kilin, 5193
Tobey, Anne C., 3290
Tobey, Gary, 1121
Tobey, Suzanne, 1121
Tobey, William H., 3290
Tobey, William R., Jr., 3290
Tobiasson, Melanie, 5132
Tobin Endowment, The, 9237
Tobin, Edgar G., 9237
Tobin, Margaret Batts, 9237
Tobin, Nancy Feinberg, 5993
Tobin, Robert L.B., 9237
Tobolowsky, George, 9299
Tocci, Michele C., 5781, 6304
Todd Established Foundation, Ruth
    Davis, 5022
Todd Investment Company, 9624
Todd, C. B., 8187
Todd, Jeanette, 425
Todd, Russell G., Dr. , 5325
Todd, Samuel E., 8941
Todd, Thomas, 1914
Todd, W. Parsons, 5560
Todi, Nand, 8319
Toews, Donovan, 3641
Together Magazine, 6839
Togikawa, Stanley, 2648
Tognazzini, Roland E., Jr., 773
Tokich, Michael, 7605
Tolbert, Sam, 8526
Toledo, Hector, 4116
Toler, James T., 3670
Tolf, Leslie, 1837
Toliver, Evelyn, 471, 472
Toljanic, Mark D., 2972
Toll, Jacob, 7999
Toll, Martha A., 1792
Toll, Robert I, 7999
Tolle, Kirk, 3662
Tolles Trust DTD, 5152
Tolleson, Debra J., 9238

Tolleson, John C., 9238
Tolleson, John Carter, Jr., 9238
Tolley, Evangeline, 5016
Tolley, Robert, 9740
Tolomatic, 4686
Tomasdottir, Halla, 9441
Tomasello, Robert, 5828
Tombleson, Kay, 5549
Tomchin, Cheryl, 223
Tomchin, Emily, 223
Tomenga, Walt, 3533
Tomes, Barbara, 9133
Tomes, Bob, 9133
Tomfohrde, John H., 4329
Tomkins Industries, 1368
Tomkins, Claire, 1122
Tomkins, Jennifer, 1122
Tomkins, Nicholas, 1122
Tomkins, Trevor, 1122
Tomlin, Ann, 3662
Tomlinson, Loren, 1123
Tomlinson, Mary A., 1123
Tomlinson, Thomas W., 1123
Tomoko, Gerald, 5198
Tompkins Trust Company, 6813
Tompkins, Edwin W., III, 7980
Tompkins, Emmy Lou, 8683
Tomsche, Dan, 4624
Tomson, O. Jay, 3493, 3537
Tomson, Patricia A., 3493, 3537
Toner, John G., 7339
Tong, Joy, 2271
Tonkin, Helen B., 9715
Tonkin, T.C., 9715
Tonn, Lisa M., 4780
Tonnelli, Joseph, 4658
Toohey, Linda Glazer, 3538
Toohey, Maureen, 5210
Toohey, Michael J., 3538
Tookoian, H., 545
Toole, David, 1124
Toole, Monte, 1124
Toole, Ruthellen, 1124
Tooley, Andrea, 3370
Toomim, Shirley W., 9239, 9286
Toomin, David R., 9286
Toomin, Shirley, 9239
Toomin, Shirley W., 9286
Tooter, Howard, 1495
Tooter, Jacqueline K., 1495
Toporowitz, Emanuel, 7030
Toppe, Jaime, 3446
Toppel, Harold, 2377
Toppel, Jeffrey, 2377
Toppel, Jonathan, 2377
Toppel, Patricia, 2377
Toppel-Sawyer, Jennifer, 2377
Topping, Janice Gayle, 2032
Topps Us, 1730
Toral, Frank, 2378
Torchmark Corporation, 9240
Torczyner, Jacques, 6136
Torgenrud, Cammy, 281
Torgerson, James, 1589
Torgow, Eliezer, 4380, 4594
Torgow, Gary, 4380, 4594
Torgow, Malka, 4380, 4594
Torgow, Yonah, 4380, 4594
Torino Residual Trust, 1125
Torino, Brett, 1125
Torino, Courtney, 1125
Torino, Francis P., 1125
Torncello, Gene, 669, 985
Tornheim, Ken, 3024

Torok, Maria E.W., 4331
Torre, Joe, 1408
Torre, Venny, 1952
Torrence, Charlton K., Jr., 7097
Torres, Gregory, 4199
Torres, Robert, 8350
Torres, Sidney D., III, 3736
Torres, William E., 2552
Torsoe, Kenneth, 8711
Tosca, 9959
Tossell, Sherrie, 9713
Totah, Annie, 3968
Totah, Elliott, 3968
Totah, Karina, 3968
Totah, Nicole, 3968
Total Depth Foundation, 9245
Toth, Jacqueline, 480
Toth, Jim, 684
Totino, Rose W., 4656
Tottingham, Sarah, 4482
Toub, Itzhak, 6904
Touch Em All Foundation, 3817
Touche, Deloitte, 381
Touchette, Loriann, 3783
Tougas, Carol Bright, 345
Tough, Steven D., 608
Touhey, Carl E., 6902
Touhey, Charles L., 6902
Touhey, John J., 6902
Touhey, Lila M., 6902
Touhey, Virginia E., 6902
Touma, Joseph B., 9754
Touradji, Pejman, 6903
Touradji, Shannon, 6903
Tourdot, Lynee, 9937
Tous, Mary F., 5124
Toutz, Elizabeth, 5023
Towe, Neely D., 2280
Tower Trust Co., 3424
Tower Trust Company, 3429
Tower, Caroline, 372
Tower, Richard L., 372
Tower, Richard L., Sr., 372
Towill, Rick, 2642
Towler, Vernon, 9517
Town Management, 6858
Town Mgmt. Co., 7008
Towne, Sarah, 2814
Townes Foundation, The, 9386
Townsend, MarrGwen, 3291
Townsend, Polly J., 8078
Townsend, R. Edward, Jr., 5839
Townsend, Stuart, 3291
Toy, Brian D., 2339
Toy, Clare C., 2339
Toy, James W., 2339
Toy, Steven C., 2339
Toya, Mia, 5609
Tracery, 3905
Tracey, Lynne, 6632
Tracey-Dufficy, Laureen, 1418
Trachsel, Dennis L., 7620
Trachten, David, 1369
Trachten, Gary, 1369
Trachten, Morris, 1369
Trachten, Sylvia, 1369
Tractenberg, Beth D., 6407
Tracy, Constance V., 3302
Tracy, Kevin, 3302
Tracy, Rosemary, 852
Traded Securities with a Market Val,
    9001
Trademark Metals Recycling LLC, 1928
Tradewell Corp., The, 1512

Trading Partners I, 1820
Trading Partners II, 1820
Traeger, Carol, 7621
Traeger, Norman L., 7621
Trager, Amy, 3701
Trager, Bernard M., 3701
Trager, Jean S., 3701
Trager, Steven E., 3701
Trahan, Louis O., Jr., 3733
Trails, MaryEllen, 7393
Traina, Katherine O., 359
Trakinski, Amy, 5680
Tralside Gallery, LLC, 93
Tram Road Partners, LP, 9124
Trammell, Evelyn, 2595
Tramontozzi, Mark, 1438
Trampke, Cam, 3390
Trans Invest Trade LLC, 5085
Transamerica Life Insurance, 7186
Transmaryland Co., 3905
Trapani, Jennifer A., 7218
Trapani, Kevin A., 7218
Trapp, Amanda, 9070
Traub, Barbara Jean, 8261
Traub, Barry, 1694
Traub, Marjorie, 1694
Traub, Vera, 1127
Traurig, Greenberg, 2035
Traut, Christopher D., 2877
Traux, Tanya Wulff, 1532
Travagliato, Vincent C., 5928
Travaglini, A.F., 7916
Travaglini, Barbara, 7916
Travaglini, Frederick C., 7916
Travaglini, Gunard C., 7916
Travelstead, Chris, 8784
Travers, David A., 496
Travers, Jeanne L., 4267
Travis, Anne B., 4828
Travis, Robert, 5799
Travis, Tina M., 4459
Traylor, Scottie, 3721
Traynor, Tim, 7666
Traynor, William, 4218
Treakle, J. Edwin, 9543
Treat, Kathleen, 6836
Trebing, Al P., 1516
Tree, Lewis, 6733
Trees, Edith M., 3258
Trees, George S., Jr., 3258
Trees, George S., Sr., 3258
Trees, M. Jay, 3258
Trees, Susan, 3258
Treeson, Sarah, 739
Treff, Douglas J., 3614
Treff, Natalie, 4880
Trefler, Alan N., 4332
Trefler, Pamela L., 4332
Trehern, Janet R., 4856
Trehern, Walter E., 4856
Treiber, H. Craig, 6907
Treiber, John H., 6907
Treiber, Peter S., 6907
Treiber, Scott R., 6907
Treiger, Irwin L., 9584, 9589
Treiger, Louis, 9688
Treisman, Dorothy, 5886, 5887
Treisman, Joel H., 5886, 5887
Trek Bicycle Corporation, 9948
Trelease, Carol Tucker, 5621
Tremblay, Jean Tracy, 6933
Tremble, Helen R., 4595
Trent, William B., Jr., 3523
Trentacosta, John F., 1532

Trenz, Alan R., 7360
Tretter, Brian, 3370
Tretter, Susan H., 4139
Treuille, Antoine, 5669
Trevino, Peg, 3485
Trevor, Stephen, 6609
Trexler, Alice E., 7269
Trexler, Brad, 3620
Trexler, C. Brent, Jr., 7269
Trexler, Charles B., 7269
Trexler, James Henry, 7269
Trexler, John F., 7269
Trexler, Mary Margaret, 7269
Treyball, 1053
Tri-Star Trust Bank, 4450
Tri-State Roofing & Sheet Metal Co., 9744
Trianfo, Victor, Dr., 7357
Triangle Trust, 5923, 6575, 6641, 6920, 6965
Tribble, Bernice W., 8528
Tribble, Grant, 2437
Trico Family Partnership, 4596
Triest, Brent S., 4596
Triest, Glenn, 4596
Triest, Jonathan, 4596
Trigg, Michael, 900
Trigon Investments, 7443
Trim Masters Inc., 3702
Trimble, Joan W., 1399
Trinity Christian Academy, 9242
Trinity Health, 2109
Trinity Logistics Corp., 2423
Trinity Valley Foods, 8859
Triple SSS Partnership L.P., 6726
Triplett, Eugene F., 9503
Triplett, Rodney F., 4835
Triplett, Rodney F., Jr., 4835
Tripolitsiotis, Maren, 9372
Tripp, Christine W., 1154
Trippe, Blair Landau, 6955
Trippet, Helen Grey, 7725
Trippet, Robert S., 7725
Tripplett Management Corp., 153
Tritch, Courtney, 3445
Tritt, Erica, 2596
Tritt, Jordan, 2596
Tritt, Joyce, 2596
Tritt, Lorne, 2596
Tritt, Ramie A., 2596
Triumph MC LP, 8716
TRM LLC, 8301
Trodec, Alain, 8570
Trofemuk, Nicholas J., Jr., 1860
Troike, Nancy P., 9118
Troka, John, 1761
Trombetta Davis, Diane, 1128
Trombetta, Heather, 4487
Tronrud, Sheriff Dan, 5060
Troob, David H., 1129
Troob, Douglas M., 1129
Troob, Marjorie D., 1129
Troob, Peter J., 1129
Troob, Robyn W., 1129
Troob, Tara K., 1129
Troper, Dennis, 626
Tropp, Clare, 4940
Tropper, Sam, 5960
Trostel, 9931
Troth, Diane, 734
Trotter, Jessica, 4448
Trotti, Andy, 2577
Troubh, Jean L., 6911
Troubh, Jean S., 6911

Troubh, Raymond S., 6911
Trout, James H., 7301
Trout, Rebecca L.F., 8324
Troutman, Harry, 3659
Trover, Chad Charles, 7824
Trover, Charles D., 7824
Trow, Peter, 1772
Trowbridge, Caroline A., 237
Trowbridge, Donald T., 253
Trowbridge, Judith T., 9236
Trowbridge, Stephen D., 9236
Troxell, Barbara Noble, 2688
Troxell, Robert I., 2688
Troy, Catherine B., 4620
TRS Services, 8759
Trubitt, Richard D., 9148
Trudeau Charitable Lead Trust, 6124
Trudeau, Garry B., 6124
Trudeau, Jane P., 6124
Trudell, Leonard, 8392
True Speed Enterprises, 7094
True Word Tabernacle, 7372
True, Calvin E., 3792
True, Dave, 8575
Trueblood, Harry A., Jr., 1371
Trueblood, John B., 1371
Trueblood, Lucile B., 1371
Truesdell, Judy, 4514
Truhlsen, Rachel, 5074
Truitt Individual Retirement Account, Dean B., 8817
Truitt, Dean B., 8817
Truitt, Dean B., II, 8817
Truitt, Gerald B., 3932
Truitt, Glenda A., 8817
Trulaske Charitable Trust No. 2, R.J. Trulaske, Sr. and G.M., 5024
Trulaske, Geraldine, 4876
Trulaske, Michelle K., 4876
Trulaske, Robert J., Sr., 4876
Trulaske, Steven L., 4876
Trulaske, Steven L., Sr., 5024
Trulock, Sharon, 6586
Truman, Mildred Faulkner, 6912
Trumbach, Andrew, 1943
Trumbull, R. Scott, 3382
Trump Mortgage LLC, 6656
Trump Organization, The, 6655
Trump, Diana, 913
Trunk, Charles F., III, 8316
Truskowsky, Louis David, 8263
Truslow, William A., 394
Trussell, Martha O., 1767
Trussell, Robert B., 1767
Trust Co. of Oklahoma, The, 7736
Trust Co. of the South, 7227
Trust Co. of the South, The, 7096
Trust Company of Knoxville, The, 8658
Trust Company of Vermont, 9371, 9375
Trust For Alfie, 4063
Trust Point, 9830, 9831, 9932
Trust Point Inc., 9940
TrustCo Bank, 5929
Truszkowski, Andrew, 3963
Truszkowski, Madeline, 3963
Truth Design, 8570
Trzaskoma, Richard, 9767
Tsai, Nai Che, 8447
Tsandikos, George, 6280
Tsao Family Trust, 1133
Tsao, Carol J., 4331
Tsao, Gilbert, 533
Tsao, Janie Chien, 1133
Tsao, Michael Liyoung, 1133

Tsao, Steven Lidah, 1133
Tsao, Victor Ying-Wei, 1133
Tsapira, Elizabeth, 3059
Tschantz, Janet A., 402
Tschantz, Robert, 402
Tschantz, William P., 402
Tsou, Walter H., 8105
Tsunoda, Joyce S., 2633
Tsvetkov, Lynne A., 7978
Tsvetkov, Sergei, 7978
TSVI-ORA & Sons Corp., 6914
Tubbs, Jada, 3634
Tuch, Michael, 6915
Tuchler, James, 2691
Tuchman, Kenneth D., 1761
Tuchman, Margaret, 5561
Tuchman, Martin, 5561, 6776
Tuchman, Morris, 6498
Tuchman, Nelson, 6498
Tuck, Daniel H., 6915
Tuck, David A., 6915
Tuck, Jonathan S., 6915
Tuck, W. Harold, 966
Tucker, Avram, 3134
Tucker, Ben, 3969
Tucker, Bradford, 9243
Tucker, Carll, 6490
Tucker, Daniel, 6364
Tucker, Emily, 3969
Tucker, Eva, Jr., 8026
Tucker, Helen Sonnenberg, 6122
Tucker, Janice Butler, 1
Tucker, Jeffrey, 2229
Tucker, John, 2149
Tucker, Jonice Gray, 1818
Tucker, Judith G., 919
Tucker, Katherine Cody, 1587
Tucker, Kathleen, 2694
Tucker, Lawrence C., 1587
Tucker, Louis, 9243
Tucker, Luther, 3969
Tucker, Marcia Brady, 3969
Tucker, Mary Ann Cody, 1587
Tucker, Michael, 2229, 5255
Tucker, Michael E., 4299
Tucker, Nichole, 9033
Tucker, Nick, 3969
Tucker, Noah, 3969
Tucker, Pam, 246
Tucker, Robert, 201
Tucker, Shane, 9033
Tucker, Steven, 6122
Tucker, Susan, 6122
Tucker, William, 5237
Tucker, William P., 5979
Tucker-Cardinal, Barbara, 6122
Tuckman, Bruce A., 6695
Tuckman, Katherine Edersheim, 6695
Tuerk, Robert D., 2935
Tufaro Family Ltd. Partnership, 4234
Tufaro, David, 4234
Tufaro, Sharon, 4234
Tufenkian Import/Export Ventures, 5562
Tufenkian, James, 5562
Tuffli, Don L., 1134
Tuffli, Martha T., 1134
Tuitupou, Janeen Rossi, 989
Tukdarian, Eva M., 2260
Tulchinsky, Igor, 1600
Tulchinsky, Mina Joy, 1600
Tulin, Stephen Wise, 6300
Tuling, Thomas, 9685
Tullo, Sandy, 8444
Tully, Daniel G., 1588

Tully, Daniel P., 1588
Tully, Ellen D.B. F., 8009
Tully, Ellen Danaher, 3295
Tully, Grace I., 1588
Tully, Thomas M., 3295
Tung, Frank Zhoe Yu, 5290
Tungseth, Margaret, 3498
Tuohy, John L., 3296
Tuohy, Mary Frances, 3296
Tuohy, Patricia J., 3296
Tuohy, Walter J., Jr., 3296
Tuohy, Walter Joseph, 3296
Tupperware Brands Corp., 2379
Tupperware U.S., 2379
Turben Revocable Trust, John F., 7622
Turben, David C., 7622
Turben, John F., 7622
Turben, Nicolas A., 7622
Turben, Susan H., Dr., 7622
Turchin, Carol B., 6503
Turgeon, Robert E., 4911
Turiano, Vincent C., 7929
Turino, James G., 6739
Turitz, Theodore, 5245
Turk, James C., 9523
Turk, Mark, 1359
Turley Charitable Remainder Unitrust, Harold E. & Elaine, 9360
Turley Trust, Harold E. & Elaine, 9360
Turley, Cassidy, 6655
Turley, Derek J., 9360
Turley, Elaine E., 9360
Turley, Harold E., III, 9360
Turley, Harold E., Jr., 9360
Turley, Jason, 7518
Turley, Nancy, 9081
Turnbull, J. Michael, 3635
Turnbull, Kenneth, 5525
Turnbull, Michael, 9699
Turnbull, Tom, 7339
Turner Industries, 3297
Turner Trust, Herman E., 2381
Turner, Al, 5025
Turner, Allen M., 3092
Turner, Bob, 2149
Turner, Burt S., 3297
Turner, Carolyn, 2676
Turner, Christopher, 9712
Turner, David D., 5319
Turner, David W., 5169, 5181
Turner, Edward T., Jr., 3467
Turner, Edwin, 4946
Turner, Elizabeth, 6768
Turner, Elizabeth T. Jones, 8712
Turner, Emma, 6875
Turner, Eric, 4946
Turner, Eric P., 9581
Turner, Ernest J., 5047
Turner, George C., 7261
Turner, George Todd, 7261
Turner, James E., 7953
Turner, Jason, 196
Turner, Jeffrey F., 3932
Turner, Jeffrey S., 4803
Turner, John, 9102
Turner, John B., 7706
Turner, John R., 3703
Turner, Joseph W., 5025
Turner, Karen, 5426
Turner, Kent, 6049
Turner, Kent Barbara, 6542
Turner, M. Sharon Patterson, 8206
Turner, Marshall H., Jr., 1088
Turner, Michael F., 4942

Turner, Richard, 9556
Turner, Richard E., Jr., 2381
Turner, Richard E., Sr., 2381
Turner, Ronnie, 8869
Turner, Ruth, 6916
Turner, Sally, 7608
Turner, Sue M., 7261
Turner, Susan R., 4803
Turner, Suzanne W., 3297
Turner, Thomas F., 7312
Turner, Thomas J., 4881
Turner, Tisha, 7261
Turner, William V., 5025
Turngren, Lisa, 5817
Turock, David L., 2382
Turock, Nancy G., 2382
Turrill, Kristin Rosenlund, 8245
Tursi, Paula, 6537
Turtletaub Foundation, The, 941
Turtletaub, Alex E., 941
Turtletaub, Marc J., 941
Tustin, Christy L., 3582
Tutino, Kathryn, 1586
Tuton, John, 8363
Tutterow, Meredith B., 2446
Tuttle, Bob, 5202
Tuttle, Robert, 5210
Tuttleman, David Z., 8325
Tuttleman, Steven M., 8325
TUW Minerva Gundelfinger, 3611
Twaddell, Ellen Johnson, 5469
Twaddell, William S., 5469
Twardowski, Maureen, 4999
Tweed, Suzanna P., 1952
Tweiten, Valerie J., 5320
Twelve D Limited, 8823
Tweten, Margaret, 7295
Twinney, Anna, 251
Two Dods Dancing LP, 4529
Twohill, Doug, 2261
Twombly, John R., Jr., 8223
Twomey Company, 3298
Twomey, John, 3298
Twomey, John E., 3298
Twomey, Melba A., 3298
Twomey, Victor L., 3298
Tyberg, Naftali, 6924
Tye, Eileen, 4334
Tyer, Susan, 4552
TYL Foundation, 1352
Tyler Assocs., J&M, LLC, 4599
Tyler Corp., 9244
Tyler Technologies, 9244
Tyler, Mary L., 4599
Tyler, Steven Little, 4599
Tyler, Timothy J., 4599
Tyler, Toni Lyn, 4599
Tynan, Martha, 3347
Tyner, Richard, 5611
Tyransky, Jack T., 1590
Tyrie, James C., 5214
Tyrone, David E., 3713
Tyrone, Linda, 3713
Tyrrell, Sarah D., 2834
Tyson, 2510
Tyson Foods, 8859
Tyson, Cynthia H., 7193
Tyson, Holly R., 9406
Tytel, Howard, 6917
Tytel, Sandra, 6917
Tyve Limited Partnership, 153

U.S. Bank, 3495, 4659, 4664, 4685,
    4706, 4707, 4712, 4722, 4723,
    4727, 4744, 4750, 4755, 4814,
    4819, 4861, 4869, 4899, 4923,
    4945, 4955, 4972, 4996, 5009,
    5021, 5023, 5028, 5056, 7514,
    7566, 7740, 7745, 7746, 7770,
    7771, 7777, 7799, 7806, 7816,
    7823, 7828, 7830, 9323, 9793,
    9818, 9823, 9863, 9870, 9892,
    9923, 9928, 9955, 9962
U.S. Dept. of Education - Carol M. White
    Physical Ed. Program, 5537
U.S. Equities Realty LLC., 3323
U.S. Paper Mills Corp., 9796
U.S. Trust, 3249
U.S. Trust Co., 7052
UAI Technology, 7272
UBS Financial Services Inc., 7715
Uehling, Katherine D., 1566
UGSC, 8779
Uhl, Emily K., 7299
UIC Construction LLC, 92
Uihlein 1997 Charitable Trust, Suzanne
    M., 6919
Uihlein, David V., 9949
Uihlein, Henry, II, 6919
Uihlein, James I., 9950
Uihlein, James J., 9950
Uihlein, Lois, 4948
Uihlein, Lynde, 9825
Uihlein, Margery H., 9949
Uihlein, Mary P., 9907
Uihlein, Robert A., III, 9950
UIL Holdings Corp., 1589
Ukpeagvik Inupiat Corp., 92
Ukrop Educational Foundation, The,
    9541
Ukrop Foundation, The, 9471, 9541
Ukrop, Barbara B., 9541
Ukrop, James E., 9541
Ukrop, Joseph E., 9541
Ukrop, Robert S., 9471, 9541
Ukrop, Robert S., Jr., 9471
Ulanow, Lisa, 1815
Ulatowski, Lois E., 6945
Ulbrich, Mark, 7533
Ulicny, Peter W., 5586
Ulicny, Walter P., 5586
Ullmann, Glenn, 2167
Ullmann, Irma, 5564
Ullmann, Jeremy Michael, 5564
Ullmann, Leonard, 5564
Ullmann, Lisa Landwirth, 2167
Ullmann-Schneider, Nancy, 5564
Ulm, Elizabeth A., 3299
Ulm, Joseph Ian Alexander, 3299
Ulm, Marcia L., 3299
Ulm, William L., Jr., 3299
Ulm, William Lee, Sr., 3299
Ulman, Karen, 713
Ulmer, Phyllis, 6073
Ulrich, Charles, III, 5900
Ulrich, Don, 93
Ulrich, Laura, 5556
Ulshafer, Karen, 747
UMB Bank, 1362, 4864, 4870, 4875,
    4890, 4981, 5002, 5026
UMB Financial Corp., 5026
Umek, Tony, 9712
Un, Kheang, 2764
Underwood, David M., 9271
Underwood, Jeffrey, 2745
Underwood, Jill, 433

Underwood, Julia, 9280
Underwood, Lisa A., 5718
Underwood, Norman, 2303
Underwood, Robert, 5196
Underwood, Robert M., 9041
Unetic, Kathleen M., 4584
Ungar, Aine D., 4336
Ungar, Carol, 5652
Ungar, Eugene David, 5652
Unger 2011 Family Trust, Steven, The ,
    6640
Unger Family Trust, Steven, The , 6640
Unger, Catherine L., 733
Unger, Daniel, 733
Unger, David, 6520
Unger, Judah, 6640
Unger, Larry, 6520
Unger, Leonard, 733
Unger, Rivkah, 6640
Unger, Ruth, 6520
Unger, Steven, 6640
Union Bank, 358, 525, 584, 630, 728,
    731, 772, 971, 5795, 9594, 9618,
    9644
Union Bank & Trust Co., 5102, 5120,
    5124
Union Bank of California, 360, 604, 613
Union Privilege, 1837
Union Savings Bank, 1435, 1590
Unit Sets, 7348
United Bank, 9741
United Congregrations Mesorah, 5544
United Conveyor Corp., 3300
United Distillers & Vintners North
    America, 1437
United Distillers Products Co., 5082
United Distributors, 2161
United Finance Co., 7805
United Financial Bancorp, 4337
United Iron & Metal Co., 3949
United Natural Foods, 8498
United Press Syndicate, 4860
United Refining, 5823
United Talmudic Seminary, 5720
United Trust Group, Inc., 7333
United Way, 2590
United Way of Delaware, 5320
United Way of Greater Milwaukee, 90
United Way of Northeast Florida, 2094
United Way of NYC, 5562
United Way of The Midlands, 5098
Unity Electric Co., 6871
Unity Timberlands, LLC, 187
Unity Trust, 187
Universal Forest Products, 4418
Universal Guarantee Life Insurance Co.,
    7333
Universal Stylz, 1316
University Loft Co., 8700
University of Denver, 1295
University of Denver Athletics
    &Recreation, 1295
University of Florida, 2257
University of Hawaii, 2634
University of Miami, 2257
University of Utah, 9338
Univest, 7905
Unkovsky, Joanne, 3149
Uno, Karen, 2650
Unobskey, Nancy G., 3804
Unobskey, Sidney R., 3804
Unruh Trust, Dave R., 3641
Unruh, Bob, 3641
Unruh, Cathy L., 2184

Unruh, Curtis, 3641
Unruh, Dave R., 3641
Unruh, Patricia W., 8598
Untereker, William J., 5388
Untermeyer, Joe D., 8947
Unterseher, Randy, 1153
Unz, Ron, 1137
Upchurch, Blain A., 2453
Upchurch, Cheryl V., 72
Upchurch, Samuel E., Jr., 72
Updegrave, Nancy, 1216
Upper Arlington Senior Fund, 7513
Uptegrove, Carol, 4213
Uptegrove, Carol L., 4213
Uptegrove, Erin, 4213
Uptegrove, Leif N., 4213
Upton, Eleanor S., 5566
Urano, Susan, 7311
Urban Youth Golf & Academics
    Programs, 5414
Urban, Coryell, 8027
Urban, Mary Bright, 3545
Urban, Thomas N., III, 3545
Urban, Thomas Nelson, 3545
Urban, Thomas Nelson, Jr., 3545
Urban, William G., 3545
Urbanek, Lida, 1141
Uris, Ruth, 6450
Urlaub, Benjamin, 3055
Urner, John H., 9768
Urquhart, A., 480
Urquhart, A. William, 480
Urquhart, Richard A., III, 7075
Urstadt Biddle Properties, 6655
Urstadt Property Company-Inc., 6655
US Bank, 4627, 4662, 4808, 4810,
    4912, 4936, 4958, 5052, 7808,
    7821, 9886
US Bank, N.A., 5020
US Biotek Laboratories Inc., 9705
US Development Group, LLC, 9245
US Foodservice, 2510
US Pipeline Inc., 9130
US State Department, 2622
US Trust Delaware, 8477
USA Fulfillment, 3988
USA Hauling & Recycling, 1395
USA Hockey, 1295
USI, 6904
Uslan, Jana, 9184
USPCI, 4657
Ussery, Terdema L., 8795
Ustipak, Roddy D., 4658
Utah Valley University, 9338
Uthe, Clayton, 4960
Utica Mutual Insurance Co., 6922
Utility Line Services Inc, 9130
Utter, Lynn, 8100
Utz, John, 9778
UW HS Geneen f/b/o June Geneen,
    8411
Uyeda, Allen B., 2631
Uyehara, Roy T., 2651
Uzielli, Alessandro F., 4447

Vaad Mishmeres ML, 7030
Vachon, Julien N., 6455
Vagher, Ben, 1242
Vahe Nahabetian, 5562
Vahldiek, Lissa Walls, 9257
Vahouny, Karen, 1330
Vail Revocable Trust, Marjorie E., 8008

Vail Revocable Trust, Roger P., 8008
Vail, Cammie, 900
Vail, Foster M., 3301
Vail, James D., III, 3301
Vail, James D., IV, 3301
Vail, John F., 3301
Vail, Margaret C., 3301
Vail, Thomas W., 5839
Vail, V, James D., 3301
Valbracht, James P., 4946
Valcent Products Inc., 5452
Valdenegro, Jennifer, 9703
Valdenegro, Julio, 9703
Valdes, David, 2428
Valdez, Tom, 9989
Valencia Foundation, 1352
Valente, Ralph R., 4267
Valenti, Christopher P., 3302
Valenti, Dennis, 4549
Valenti, James, 3302
Valenti, Joseph E., Jr., 3302
Valenti, Joseph E., Sr., 3302
Valenti, Marcelline H., 3302
Valenti, Mark T., 3302
Valenti, Thomas, 3302
Valentine Inflows Corporate Stores, Tom, 2510
Valentine, Clark D., 3457
Valentine, Julie Ellen, 5342
Valentine, Phoebe V., 8328
Valentine, Robert, 9660
Valenzuela, Pablo, 1143
Valenzuela, Shauna B., 2741
Valerio, Helen, 4339
Valerio, Michael, 4339
Valero Energy Corp., 9246
Valkema, Annie, 4408
Valkirs, Gunars E., 2639
Valkirs, Jorene, 2639
Valle, Jose, 2252
Valley Co., 3609
Valley of the Sun YMCA, 9
Valley Steel Stamp, 4088
Valli, Louis E., 8215
Vallo, Brian, 5609
Valone, Donald, 7975
Valosek, Elizabeth S., 8356
Valtierra, Gilbert, 369
Valvano, Melvin, 5358
Van Alen, Elizabeth K., 1691
Van Alen, James L., II, 1691
Van Allen, Doug, 9630
van Arsdale, Lance, 5954
van Arsdale, Thomas, 5954
Van Baren, Gina, 3401
Van Cleve, Kathleen M., 1144
Van Cleve, Kathy M., 1144
Van Cleve, Russell G., 1144
Van Coller, Alan, 6189
Van Coller, Ian, 6189
Van Coller, Margaret C., 6189
Van Curler, Carol, 4601
Van Curler, Carol A., 4601
Van Curler, Donald E., 4601
van Dalson Irrevocable Trust, Edward & Virginia, 4602
van Dalson Qtip Trust, William S., 4602
Van Dalson Trust, Lois A., 4602
Van Dalson, Virginia, 4602
Van Dalson, William S., 4602
Van de Bovenkamp, Sue Erpf, 5968
van De Ven, Martha, 9773
Van De Voorde, Mark, 7857
Van den Blink, Jan, 6208

van den Blink, Nelson Mooers, 6208
Van Den Wymelenberg, John, 9951
Van Denbergh, Margaret Anne, 7911
Van Denbergh, Ross, 7911
Van Denmark, Lauren, 6966
Van Der Molen, Henrietta, 2812
van der Stricht, John Paul, 1769
van der Stricht, Nora, 1769
van der Stricht, Susan R., 1769
Van Devender, Mollie M., 4857
Van Devender, William J., 4857
Van Dire, Peter, 7905
Van Ditti, Jennifer L., 7790
Van Dixhoorn, Emily B. Weymar, 5563
Van Dorn, Elizabeth N., 4291
Van Dorn, Walter G., 4291
Van Dyk, Alison J., 9967
Van Dyke, Earl B., 9247
Van Dyke, George Ray, 3973
Van Dyke, Judith Ray, 3973
Van Dyke, Lois T., 9247
Van Dyke, Michele, 4736
Van Dyke, Peter, 3973
Van Dyke, Suzanne, 9247
Van Eekeren, Alexander, 2109
Van Eekeren, Andrew, 2109
Van Eekeren, Charles, 2109
Van Evera, Caroline Irene, 5028
Van Evera, DeWitt, 5028
Van Evera, Stephen W., 5028
Van Hook, Dana, 8547
Van Hook, Mark, 8547
Van Horne, Charles, 6682
Van Huffel Tube Corp., 7625
Van Huffel, Ruth A., 7625
Van Kampen, C. George, 6925
Van Lenten, David J., 5493
Van Lopik, William Harold, 9891
Van Meeuwen, Peter, 4059
Van Meter, Isaac C., Jr., 7626
Van Meter, John, 7626
Van Middlesworth, Guy G., 2364
Van Middlesworth, Jill M., 2364
Van Mill, Mike, 2802
Van Mourick, Mark, 884
Van Mourick, Tricia, 884
Van Natta, Jennifer M., 645
Van Norden, John, 5929
Van Rees, Linda, 9184
Van Reken, Calvin P., 4408
Van Reken, Randall, 4408
Van Reken, Randall S., 4408
Van Reken, Stanley, 4408
van Roijen, Beatrice, 5354
Van Skilling, David, 9990
Van Sloun, Dennis L., 4340
Van Sloun, Joseph, 4340
Van Sloun, Nancy, 4340
Van Sloun, Neil J., 4340
Van Sloun, Sylvia, 4340
Van Stone, James J., 2947
Van Strum Fam Tr. f/b/o Clarissa Van S, 3974
Van Strum, Stevens, 3974
Van Velson, Troy, 425
van Vickle, Gayle, 3223
Van Vleck, Lisa, 4352
Van Wagner, Darlene, 1653
Van Wagner, Roger K., 1653
van Wie, John, 9953
Van Winkle, James, 8771
Van Winkle, Kathryn, 8771
Van Woerkom, Valerie, 1673
Van Wyk, Arlan J., 3540

Van Wyk, Dave, 3540
Van Wyk, Gina, 3540
Van Zelst, Cynthia S., 5413
Vanaernam, Gary, 3511
Vance, Cynthia King, 6926
Vance, Dorothy J., 1591
Vance, H. Alex, Jr., 1591
Vance, Judith J., 9743
Vance, Katherine R., 1176
Vance, Lee G., 6926
Vance, Leslie Eaton, 115
Vance, Sandy, 3402
Vance, Virginia G., 8510
Vance, William C., 1591
VanClief, Daniel G., 6265
Vanco Trust, 8780
VandeHey, Jeff, 9789
Vandekreeke, Jennifer M., 3795
Vanden Bosch, Franklin, 3470
Vanden Bosch, Mindi, 3470
Vanden Heuvel, Margaret M., 981
Vanden Heuvel, Melinda, 6927
Vanden Heuvel, Melinda F., 6927
Vanden Heuvel, William J., 6927
Vandenberg, Dave, 7756
VandenBerg, Katie, 3126
Vandendriessche, Larry, 7608
Vander Kooi, Ben, 4736
Vander Laan, Allen J., 4603
Vander Laan, Nancy D., 4603
Vander Pol, Daryl, 9708
Vander Wall, Julie G., 543
Vander Woude, Paul S., 3176
Vanderbilt Charitable Trust, William H., 5983
Vanderbilt, Hugh B., Jr., 7273
Vanderbilt, Paul, 7273
Vanderbilt, William Henry, Jr., 5983
Vanderbloemen, Bruce, 7078
Vandergon, Nancy, 4804
VanderHarst, Carol, 4533
Vanderheiden, Richard, 9843
Vanderhoof, Joe, 5872
Vandermolen, Jeffrey, 2812
VanderPool, Nick, 9070
VanderSloot, Frank L., 2679
Vandersluis, Joel, 7593
VanDerWilden, Mary-Wren, 4059
VanDerWilden, Philip, 4059
Vandever, Marilyn, 7729
Vandevoort, Joel, 5194
Vandevoort, Martha, 5194
Vandewalle, Dirk, 1816
Vandor Corp., 3375
Vanett, Todd C., 8084
VanGilder, Lisa, 4604
VanGilder, Mary Ellen, 9200
VanGilder, Russell B., Jr., 4604
VanGilder, Shirley, 4604
VanGorder, John F., 8090
Vanguard Windsor II Fund, 2972
VanHouten Minogue, Karen, 5872
Vanier, James, 8403
Vanmatre, Kirk A., 1109
Vann, James M., 3461
Vann, James M., Mrs. , 3461
Vann, James, III, 3461
Vann, Majorie Lee, 3461
Vann, Michael, 3461
Vann, Thomas H., Jr., 2583
VanNatta, Terry, 3441
Vanneck, Barbara Bailey, 2384
Vanneck, John, 2384
Vanneck, William P., 2384

Vanness, Scott, 4961
Vannest, Michelle, 4478
Vannoster, Ann Marie, 3566
Vannostrand, Steve, 6652
VanScoy, Hope, 6912
VanWinkle, Frederick, 2573
VanWyck, Timothy, 7223
VanWynkel, Tara F., 7425
Vapurciyan, Kirakos, 5562
Varcoe, Jane, 8345
Vardan, Julianne N., 1927
Varela, Jesus, 338
Varga, Carleen, 67
Varma, Vijay R., 6682
Varner, James, 1145
Varner, Joanne D., 1145
Varney, Ben, 4598
Varney, Kerry, 1103
Varsam, Fotios, 6489
Varsam, George, 6489
Varsam, Lori, 6489
Varshavsky, Ph. D, Alexander, 906
Varteressian, Astrid, 1005
Vasek, Greg, 5105
Vaselaney, Missia H., 7475
Vasey, Roger M., 2385
Vashaw, Kirkland, 7339
Vasquez, Joseph A., Jr., 3224
Vasquez, Misael, 645
Vassia, Lucille A., 5029
Vassia, Mary Jane, 5029
Vassiliou, Ann, 3525
Vassy, Robert G., Jr., 8522
Vasudevan, Deepa, 8269
Vatterott Family Foundation, Joan and John, 678
Vatterott, Charles F., Jr., 5030
Vatterott, Daniel, 5030
Vatterott, Frank J., 5030
Vatterott, Glennon R., Jr., 5030
Vatterott, John, 678
Vatterott, John C., 5030
Vatterott, John Harvey, 5030
Vatterott, Joseph A., 5030
Vatterott, Madeleine, 5030
Vatterott, Mary Patricia, 5030
Vatterott, Paul B., Jr., 5030
Vattikuti Foundation, The, 4605
Vattikuti, Padmaja, 4605
Vattikuti, Rajendra B., 4605
Vaughan Nelson Investment Mgmt., 8924
Vaughan, Angus M., 4670
Vaughan, Ben F., III, 8825, 9249
Vaughan, Ben F., IV, 9249
Vaughan, Ben F., Jr., 9249
Vaughan, Daphne duPont, 9249
Vaughan, Frances, 574
Vaughan, Genevieve, 8825, 9249
Vaughan, Harry, 9999
Vaughan, Herbert W., 8329
Vaughan, J. Paul, 8635
Vaughan, Jill, 9070
Vaughan, Mary Lynn, 9248
Vaughan, Maud P., 2598
Vaughan, Peter, 4670
Vaughan, Rachael, 9249
Vaughan, Rosemary H., 9248
Vaughn, Alvin H., 5567
Vaughn, C. Roland, III, 5567
Vaughn, Cameron, 9412
Vaughn, Cathee, 345
Vaughn, Dennis H., 5165
Vaughn, James A., Jr., 5567

Vaughn, James M., Jr., 8927
Vaughn, James P., 5567
Vaughn, Linda Davis, 4593
Vaughn, Marsha T., 2762
Vaux, Trina, 8134
Vazquez, Alani, 247
Vecellio, Anna M., 9770
Vecellio, Christopher S., 9770
Vecellio, Evelyn P., 9770
Vecellio, Kathryn C., 9770
Vecellio, Leo A., Jr., 9770
Vecellio, Leo A., Sr., 9770
Vecellio, Michael A., 9770
Vechiola, Robert J., 3301
Vector Marketing Corp., 5890
Vectren Energy Delivery, 3450
Vectren Utility Holding, Inc., 3450
Vegh, Martin, 6905
Vegh, Susan, 6905
Vegosen, Jon, 5302
Veis, Pam, 5060
Velaj, Alexander, 1592
Velaj, Nicole R., 1592
Velaj, Patricia Wells, 1592
Velasquez, Jeremy, 8971
Velasquez, Justin, 8971
Velasquez, Segundo, 4796
Veliotes, Amb. Nicholas A., 1807
Vella, James G., 4446
Velsini, Barbara, 5725
Venable, Josephine M., 13
Venables, Thomas R., 4267
Venckaunas, Vidamantas, 6150
Vendegna Irrevocable Trust, Alfred, 9559
Venerable, Thalia, 9385
VenJohn, Marilynne, 3624
Venkatesh, V., 651
Venne, Clarence J., 8331
Venne, Nancy, 8331
Venne, Patricia, 8331
Venne, Richard A., 8331
Venner, James, 7627
Venner, Linda, 7627
Ventulett, Thomas, 2597
Ventura Foods LLC, 8859
Ventura, Jo Ann, 6625
Venuti, William, 1914
Ver Eecke, Susanna B., 2446
Veralander Marital Tr., George W., 9546
Verardi, Meg, 238
Verde Investments, 122
Verderber, Thomas, 1391
Verdieck, Kristen, 884
Verdoorn, Carla A., 1372
Verdoorn, Daniel C., 1372
Verdoorn, Donald W., 1372
Vereen Trust, W.C., 2466
Vereen, Barbara B., 2466
Vereen, Harvey B., 2466
Vereen, Lottie T., 2466
Vereen, William J., 2466
Veres, Andrew F., 9250
Veres, Barbara, 9250
Veres, Keith A., 1917
Verhagen, Raoul M., 8547
Verhalen, Florence W., 5568
Verhalen, James P., 5568
Verhalen, James P., Jr., 5568
Verhalen, Phillip William, 5568
Verhulp, Linda, 846
Verhulst, Marvin P., 9954
Verissimo, Marc, 1038
Verkamp, Jen, 3370
Verkler, Pamela, 2989

Vermeer Farms, 3542
Vermeer, Bernice, 3541
Vermeer, Glen, 3528
Vermeer, Harry G., 3541
Vermeer, Lois J., 3542
Vermeer, Michael, 3541
Vermeer, Nancy, 3541
Vermeer, Robert L., 3542
Vermeesch, Rich, 2642
Vermont Tubbs, 9367
Vermunen, Andy, 4401
Verner Revocable Living Trust, John V., 2386
Verner Revocable Living Trust, Sally P., 2386
Verner, E.M., 2386
Verner, James P., 2386
Verner, John V., 2386
Verner, S.P., 2386
Verney, E. Geoffrey, 5236
Verney, Richard G., 5236
Vernier, Ingrid O., 4467
Vernon, Debra D., 5248
Vernon, Emily, 2387
Vernon, Joe, 8869
Vernon, Joe C., 9124
Vernon, Lillian, 6928
Vernon, Thomas, 8105
Vernor-Miles, J.C., 706
Vernor-Miles, Wilfred, 706
Verrill, Chuck, 6178
Verrochi, Paul M., 4342
Versfeld, Charlotte H., 2440
Versten, E., 3138
Vesely, Karen, 8065
Vestal, Ellen M., 9581
Vestal, William A., 7270
Vester, Dick L., 2681
Vetter, Edward O., 9251
Vetter, Sally, 9251
Vetter, Victoria, 8105
VF Services, 1730
VHIV, 6374
Via, Edward Becher, 8571
Viall, William A., 8441
Viana, Arthur, 4267
Vibber, Brad, 4534
Vice, Mark, 3367
Vick, Kendall, 3756
Vickerman, Robert L., 3539
Vickers, Marsha, 11
Vicklund, Traci L., 6443
Victaulic Co., 7857
Victor Charitable Lead Trust, 3304
Victor, Daniel, 6704
Victor, Jo-Ann B., 3150
Victor, Lois, 8332
Victor, Lois B., 8332
Victory Foundation, 8115
Vidinha, Antone, 2653
Vidinha, Edene, 2653
Viebig, V. Richard, Jr., 9068
Viegra, Ardis, 3582
Vieira, Beatriz, 8065
Viener, John D., 6806
Vienna Beef, 2510
Vietnamese American Scholarship Fund, 5145
Vigeland, Julie, 7826
Vigil, Alfredo, 5611
Vigilante, Amy, 2168
Vigilante, Jason, 2168
Vigue, Peter, 3789
Viklund, Mark, 6443

Vilinsky, Edward, 6914
Vilinsky, Mitchell, 6914
Vilinsky, Ruvane, 6914
Villamil, Marielena, 1952
Villani, Anthony, 4076
Villard, Vincent S., Jr., Mrs. , 7013
Villarreal, Noralisa, 9108
Villarreal, Ricardo, 8948
Villchur, Edgar, 6929
Villere, George, 3745
Vincent, Anna M., 8334
Vincent, Nancy, 8869
Vincent, Paul M., 2142
Vincent, Richard A., 7545
Vincent, Susan Gailey, 4375
Vineis, Mark, 2324
Vinnedge, Maggie, 882
Vinney, Les, 7605
Vinoskey, Adam V., 9547
Vinoskey, Carole J., 9547
Vinson, Bettina, 4998
Vinson, Glenn, 870
Vinson, Pamela B., 7076
Viola, Nancy, 6308
VIP Motorcars Ltd., 199
Viragh, Amanda C., 3972
Viragh-Williams, Paula, 521
Virani, Mohammad J., 417, 934
Viray-Munoz, Belinda, 357
Vires, Peggy, 3655
Virginia American Industries, 9522
Virginia Smith Administrative Trust, 5118
Viridiun LLC, 1770
Vishy, Mike, 7796
Vision Investments, 8663
Visual Communications Co., 1009
Vit, Paul, 887
Vitale Trust, David J., 1771
Vitale, Catherine L., 8532
Vitale, David, 1771
Vitale, Joseph F., 6683
Vitale, Marilyn, 1771
Vitamins Playwear, 1931
Vitel, 9110
Vitlin, C., 8856
Vitlin, M., 8856
Vitlin, V., 8856
Vittoria, Theodore J., Jr., 6370
Vivian, Caroline M., 1288
Vlasic, James J., 4607
Vlasic, Joseph, 4607
Vlasic, Michael A., 4607
Vlasic, Paul A., 4607
Vlasic, Richard R., 4607
Vlasic, Robert J., 4607
Vlasic, William J., 4607
Vock, Michelle, 4771
Voelkerding, David J., 5032
Voelkerding, Eric G., 5032
Voelkerding, Walter J., 5032
Voelter, Dathan C., 8874
Voelz, James, 9910
Vogel, Donna, 5609
Vogel, Judith M., 2600
Vogel, Miriam, 6931
Vogel, Moses, 6931
Vogel, Paul L., 4876
Vogel, Paul T., 1908
Vogel, Solomon, 6931
Vogel, William A., 2600
Vogell, Constance, 1593
Vogelsang, Jan, 4411
Vogelsang, Janet, 3589

Vogelzang, James C., 1146
Vogelzang, Mary Beth, 1146
Vogler, Betty, 5148
Vogler, John J., 6932
Vogler, Laura B., 6932
Vogt, Bradley G., 1798
Vogt, Bradley J., 1798
Vogt, Katherine M., 1798
Vogt, Mary Lou, 6933
Vogt, Peter A., 6933
Vogt, Peter J., 6933
Vogt, Shirley M., 5790
Vohr, Caroline C. Jansing, 8079
Voight, Elizabeth M., 3944
Voigt, Tim, 3055
Vojta, Christopher, 4629
Vojta, George, 4629
Vojvoda, Antoinette P., 3895
Vokurka, Louis, 9774
Voldeng, Kurt, 8581
Volftsun, Lev, 9490
Volftsun, Margarita, 9490
Vollrath Co., LLC, The, 9961
Vollrath, David A., 7357
Volo, Stephanie, 3797
Volpe, Mary Jean, 2516
von Clemm Iselin, Charlotte, 2388
von Clemm Memorial Trust, Michael, 2388
von Clemm, Louisa, 2388
von Clemm, Stefanie C., 2388
von der Ahe, Chris, 1147
von der Ahe, Clyde V., 1147
von der Ahe, Frederick T., 1147
Von Der Ahe, Ted, Jr., 1148
Von Der Ahe, Theodore A., Jr., 1148
von der Ahe, Thomas R., 1147
von der Ahe, Vincent M., 1147
Von Dielingen, Robert, 3448
Von Drehle Corporation, David, 7274
Von Drehle, Raymond, 7274
Von Drehle, Steve, 7274
von Hoffman, Alexandra, 1786
Von Hoffman, Eric, 5033
Von Hoffman Corp., 5033
Von Hoffman Press, 5033
von Hoffmann, Beatrix, 1786
Von Hoffmann, Dale W., 5033
Von Hoffmann, George, 5033
Von Hoffmann, George, III, 5033
Von Hoffmann, George, Jr., 5033
von Hoffmann, Ladislaus, 1786
Von Krusenstiern, Elizabeth R., 59
Von Krusenstiern, John, 59
Von Magnus Henderson Irrev, Maria C., 4346
Von Perfall, Ashley, 6927
Von Seggern, E.F., 9253
Von Tobel Corp., 3464
Von Tobel Trust, Paul and Candance, 3464
Von Tobel, Candace J., 3464
Von Tobel, Paul J., III, 3464
von Weber, Madelaine G., 5237
Von's Grocery Co., 1147
Vonderhaar, Collette C., 3543
Vonderhaar, James J., 3543
Vonderheide, Steven, 9913
Voorheis, Barbara, 2244
Vorsatz, Mark, 477
Vorsheck, Elizabeth A., 2389
Vorsheck, William, 2389
Vorsheck, William J., III, 2389
Vorsheck, William J., Jr., 2389

Vos, Lauren, 3528
Vosburgh, Evan, 6716
Vosgerchian, Aram, 4492
Voss, George, 3624
Voss, Susan, 3513
Vosse, Brigitte, 2353
Voves, Lucie H., 1590
Vowel, Max R., 7708
Vradenburg, Alissa, 1374
Vradenburg, Beatrice W., 1374
Vradenburg, George A., III, 1374
Vradenburg, Tyler, 1374
Vrandenburg, George A., III, 1374
Vrandenburg, George A., Jr., 1374
Vreeland, Ann, 7339
Vrieling, Mark, 498
Vryhof, Gayle Ellen, 1673
Vubiquity, 1295
Vuckovich, Amy, 471, 472
Vukovits, Ashley, 3398
Vulcan Holdings, 2475
Vulcan Materials, 366
Vulgamore, Myles, 3623
VWR International, LLC, 1772

W & W, 5034
W.M. Corp., 1189
Wabash Plastics, 3365
Wabash Valley Produce, 3447
Wachenheim, Edgar, III, 6935, 6937
Wachenheim, Lance R., 6935
Wachovia Bank, 1566, 7147
Wachovia Corp., 8350
Wachs, David, 8336
Wachs, Joel, 5558
Wachs, Judith, 8336
Wachs, Karen, 8285
Wachs, Rachel A., 8336
Wachspress, Aaron, 6343
Wachtel, Marcy, 6698
Wachtel, Margaret H., 9846
Wachtell, Herbert M., 6936
Wachtell, Lipton, Rosen & Katz, 6404
Wachtell, Svetlana Stone, 6936
Wachter, Mary, 6334
Wachter, Paul, 6334
Wackerman, James A., 1446
Wackerman, Kristin A. Ferguson, 1446
Wada Family Trust, 1140
Wada Irrevocable Trust, Jerry and Jane, 1140
Wada, Jane, 1140
Wada, Jerry, 1140
Wada, Matthew, 1140
Wada, Tsuyoshia, 3817
Waddell, James, 7620
Wade, Emily Vanderbilt, 5983
Wade, Jerry, 678
Wade, Jim, 8949
Wade, Richard I., 8048
Wade, Roy, 8105
Wade-Lapausky, Bonnie, 7596
Wadia, Goolcher, 1599
Wadle, Larry, 8836
Wadley, Gregg A., 7726
Wadley, Gregg A., II, 7726
Wadman, David, 9362
Wadman, David L., 9362
Wadman, Ronda, 9362
Wadman, V. Jay, 9362
Wadsworth, James M., 5867, 6516
Wadsworth, Mary, 425
Wadsworth, Michael, 5867

Waffle House, 2602
Waggoner National Bank, 9047
Waggoner, Don, 7790
Waggoner, E. Paul, 9254
Waggoner, Greg, 7790
Waggoner, Helen Buck, 9254
Waggoner, J. Virgil, 9255
Waggoner, June, 9255
Waggoner, Liz A., 9255
Waggoner, Marjorie J., 9255
Wagh, Asher, 6338
Wagler Homes of Akron, 7629
Wagler Homes of Cleveland, 7629
Wagler, Phil, 7629
Wagley, Anne Paxton, 9116
Wagley, James F.P., 9116
Wagley, Sue, 9116
Wagman, Carolina, 1966
Wagman, David A., 6937
Wagman, Kim W., 6937
Wagman, Laurie, 7886
Wagner Charitable Lead Trust, 6938
Wagner Family Foundation, The, 5868
Wagner, Amy, 6938
Wagner, Barbara, 4297
Wagner, Carol A., 3388
Wagner, Charles H.S., 3975
Wagner, Clay, 4853
Wagner, David, 3306
Wagner, Edward H., 4375
Wagner, Elinor R., 8338
Wagner, Elizabeth, 3975
Wagner, Elizabeth S., 3975
Wagner, Ellen L., 9955
Wagner, Harold A., 1149
Wagner, Harold E., 1149
Wagner, Harvey E., 5195
Wagner, John P., 9009
Wagner, K. Peter, 3975
Wagner, Ken, 9789
Wagner, Kenneth J., 3172
Wagner, Kristi, 1149
Wagner, Leslie K., 5195
Wagner, Marcia K., 1149
Wagner, Mark, 8054
Wagner, Mark R., 9009
Wagner, Matthew L., 9891
Wagner, Myrna, 1098
Wagner, Paul R., 3306
Wagner, R. Donald, 7275
Wagner, R. Donald, Rev., 7275
Wagner, Robert A., 3424
Wagner, Robert K., 8338
Wagner, Rose, 6938
Wagner, Sarah R., 4170
Wagner, Sherle, 6938
Wagner, Stephanie, 3388
Wagner, Steven W., 7275
Wagner, Timothy L., 3388
Wagner, Tony, 5463
Wagner, Tracey, 1149
Wagner, Wayne L.B., 3975
Wagner, William J., 4047
Wagner, William R., 3306
Wagner, William W., 1696
Wagner, Yvonne R., 3975
Wagner-Anue, Santoshi, 5197
Wagshall, Rita, 7020
Wahl, Howard, 9339
Wahl, Phyllis C., 7305
Wahl, Willyn, 9011
Wahlberg, Kirk, 884
Wahlberg, Lisa, 884
Wahlen, Jeff, 1918

Wahlert, Alan, 3544
Wahlert, David, 3544
Wahlert, Donna, 3544
Wahlert, H.W., 3544
Wahlert, James R., 3544
Wahlert, Mark, 3544
Wahlert, Nancy, 3544
Wahlert, Robert C., 3544
Wahlert, Robert H., 3544
Wahlert, Susan, 3544
Wahlmeier, Mark, Dr., 3634
Wahlquist, Donald, 9652
Wahlstrom, Agnes S., 2201
Wahlstrom, Magnus, 2201
Waichler, Iris, 2877
Wainwright, Nancy, 2249
Wais, Eric, 385
Waisath, Curt, 158
Waisath, Karen, 158
Waiss, Gayle, 7829
Wakerly, John F., 1150
Wakerly, Katherine S., 1150
Wakerly, Marie, 1150
Wakerly, Michael, 1150
Wakerly, Ralph T., 1150
Wakerly, Susanne, 1150
Walberg, Herbert, 2729
Walbridge, Kenneth, 5486
Walch, David J., 8837
Walch, Nancy D., 2826
Walczak, James R., 8170
Wald, Baila, 6065
Wald, Richard C., 5879
Waldbaum, Cheryl, 5125
Waldbaum, Jerome, 5125
Waldbaum, John, 5125
Waldbaum, Natha, 5125
Waldegrave, Lord William, 9386
Walden Co., 3905
Walder, Joseph, 2707
Waldis, Anastasia, 5569
Waldis, Stephen, 5569
Waldman, Adam, 7593
Waldman, Babs, 3237
Waldman, Babs H., 3237
Waldman, Helen Rosenberg, 9140
Waldman, Marshall H., 9691
Waldman, Stacy, 5454
Waldon, Colin E., 4170
Waldon, Margaret Firth, 4170
Waldorf, Rosemary, 7258
Waldorf, Sydney P., 4602
Waldrop, Laurie, 2617
Wales, Eric P., 3794
Wales, Patricia M., 3794
Wales, R. Erwin, 3794
Wales, Wendy York, 3794
Waletzko, David, 4624
Walhstrom, Scott E., 8335
Walk Trust, Maurice, 3307
Walk, Cynthia, 3307
Walk, Margaretha, 3307
Walk, Marguerite A., 3307
Walker Agency, Inc., Harry, The, 5868
Walker Charitable Lead Trust, Margaret M., 7630
Walker Family Trust, 5034
Walker Foundation, L.C. and Margaret, 6842
Walker Machinery Co., Cecil I., 3308
Walker, Alex C., 2603
Walker, Amy C., 4805
Walker, Ann DeVito, 3848
Walker, Archie D., 4805

Walker, Barrett P., 2603
Walker, Berta B., 4805
Walker, Bertha H., 4805
Walker, Charles, 7458
Walker, Chuck, 3991
Walker, Colin M., 4805
Walker, Dick, 3125
Walker, Donna J., 944
Walker, Earl E., 5034
Walker, Eddie, 7654
Walker, Edwin J., 7125
Walker, Erica, 6884
Walker, G.H., Jr., 5035
Walker, Geoffrey Scott, 6884
Walker, George H., III, 5035
Walker, George H., IV, 5035
Walker, Harry, 4849
Walker, Jacqueline T., 4835
Walker, Jane, 5126
Walker, Janice K., 8360
Walker, John L., 9502
Walker, Joseph, 8680
Walker, Joseph, III, 58
Walker, Kayla Horn, 3664
Walker, Lee, 8981
Walker, Lester A., 5126
Walker, Margaret Sharon, 150
Walker, Mary Carter, 5035
Walker, Mary E., 5034
Walker, Mary Haskell, 7439
Walker, Mary Jo, 2313
Walker, Mary Jo Sanders, 2267
Walker, Michael J., 8360
Walker, Molly G., 4805
Walker, Myrtle E., 5034
Walker, Nancy, 7829
Walker, Nancy F., 7363
Walker, Norman C., 541
Walker, Pamela W., 8501
Walker, Patricia, 2455
Walker, Richard M., 3779
Walker, Ross, 3713
Walker, Sally L., 4805
Walker, Sara, 362
Walker, Susan, 4598
Walker, Terri Ann, 1401
Walker, Terry L., 3449
Walker, Thomas E., 5034
Walker, Thomas U., 2603
Walkingstick, Ben T., Jr., 7727
Walkingstick, Bonnie J., 7727
Walkingstick, Boonnie J., 7727
Wall, C. Allen, 1151
Wall, David R., 1151
Wall, Georgia, 6087
Wall, Harriet Anderson, 1846
Wall, Hugh E., III, 7429, 7485
Wallace, Adrian W., 7277
Wallace, Ann D., 9548
Wallace, Charles, 3720, 7910
Wallace, Dwane L., 3637
Wallace, George R., 4347
Wallace, Irving, 6621
Wallace, Jacob M., 1068
Wallace, James D., 3503
Wallace, Janice E., 9277
Wallace, Joe, 8970
Wallace, John A., 2431
Wallace, Kenny, 5620
Wallace, Lillian Posner, 6621
Wallace, Mike, 2187
Wallace, Richard, 9345
Wallace, Trudy, 2729
Wallace, Velma L., 3637

Wallace, W.B., 3720
Wallach, Caroline, 5841
Wallach, Eugene, 6350
Wallach, Scott, 5841
Waller, Bruce, 6735
Waller, Debra Steigerwaldt, 3265
Waller, Jonathan, 3220
Waller, Judy T., 1152
Waller, June I., 3220
Waller, Phil, 1153
Waller, Richard, 3534
Waller, Robert A., 1152
Waller, Roberta, 6735
Wallerstein, Charlotte, 6940
Wallerstein, Chaya, 6940
Wallerstein, Lou, 6940
Wallerstein, Raphael, 6940
Wallerstein, Shmuel, 6940
Wallestad, Phadoris, 4806
Wallin, Fran, 4734
Wallin, Maxine, 4671
Wallingford, Dave, 3662
Wallingford, Debra, 3662
Wallis, Marilyn Belk, 7046
Wallis, Monty, 5054
Wallman, David T., 5068
Wallrabenstein, Tom, 3595
Walls, Cynthia J., 9788
Walls, Martha Ann, 9257
Walmart, 215
Walmer, Rose E., 8352
Walradt, David M., 8017
Walrath, Michael, 6941
Walrath, Michelle, 6941
Walsdorf, Neill, 9110
Walser Holding Company, 4807
Walser, Andrew D., 4807
Walser, Barbara M., 1991
Walser, Paul M., 4807
Walser, Thomas C., 1991
Walser, Thomas R., 1991
Walsh Bishop Assoc. Inc., 4686
Walsh, Alfred C., Jr., 7809
Walsh, Ann Eliza McCaddin, 6455
Walsh, Brendan M., 1442
Walsh, Darielle, 5582
Walsh, David, 6573
Walsh, Devon, 6942
Walsh, Edward J., Jr., 5805
Walsh, Elsa, 1839
Walsh, Jeanne, 1708
Walsh, John E., Dr. , 137
Walsh, Karen A., 9782
Walsh, Katrina, 5205
Walsh, Lauren, 5659
Walsh, Margaret Sullivan, 4315
Walsh, Mary, 3519
Walsh, Pam, 4992
Walsh, Redmond, 1839
Walsh, Sandra, 6942
Walsh, Spencer, 3638
Walsh, Ted, 5842
Walsh, Teresa K., 3638
Walsh, Thomas F., 5805
Walsh, Thomas J., 3638
Walsh, William, Jr., 5513
Walshok, Mary, 1102
Walske, Jennifer M., 4349
Walske, Steven, 4349
Walske, Steven C., 4349
Walter N. Mirapaul Charitable Lead
    Trust, 3119
Walter, Ann, 3592
Walter, Carole, 9549

Walter, Christopher K., 4012
Walter, Richard, 5105
Walter, W. Edward, 9549
Walters, Albert A., 7278
Walters, Bobby, 9114
Walters, Carol, 1305
Walters, Chad, 1153
Walters, Clifford, 1153
Walters, Clifford L., 1876
Walters, Glenn, 1153
Walters, John R., 761
Walters, Lynne, 2695
Walters, Robert J., 2705
Walters, Viola, 1153
Walthall, Marjorie T., 9258
Walthall, Wilson J., III, 9258
Walther, Anne N., 1154
Walther, Artur, 6944
Walther, Carole J., 3245
Walther, Roger O., 1154
Waltman, John, 5590
Walton Family Foundation, 90
Walton, Audrey J., 5037
Walton, Elizabeth, 6812
Walton, James K., 2490
Walton, James M., 8341
Walton, John C., 6821
Walton, Kim, 3350
Walton, Mary, 8341
Walton, R., 8341
Walton, Rachel Mellon, 8341
Walton, Sally, 3662
Walton, Sarah J., 2490
Walton, William C., 8341
Walton, William L., 9503
Walton-Ralph, Margaret, 7911
Waltrip, Claire H., 9259
Waltrip, Holly, 9259
Waltrip, Karen, 2400
Waltrip, Mark, 2400
Waltrip, Robert L., 9259
Waltrip, Robert L., Jr., 9259
Waltrip, William Blair, 9259
Walzer, Ann, 1556
Walzer, Eric, 1556
Walzer, Robert S., 1556
Walzer, Steven, 1556
Wamba, Nathalis W., 6682
Wambler, Louis, 4998
Wanczyk, Megan, 7408
Wand, Barbara Freedman, 1659
Wandelmaier, Bruce E., 1477
Wanek, Ronald M., 9798
Wang, Charles P., 6748
Wang, Elizabeth, 1157
Wang, Francis S.L., 1157
Wang, Mary, 1157
Wang, Shu-Ming, 1599
Wang, Su-chu, 373
Wanger, Eric David, 2694
Wanger, Leah Zell, 2694
Wanger, Leonard Ralph, 2694
Wanger, Ralph, 2694
Wanger, Ralph L., 2694
Wankel, Jordan, 3080
Wankel, Mark, 3080
Wanless, Arlen, 8559
Wanless, James, 8559
Wanless, Nancy, 8559
Wanless, Neal, 8559
War Caualty Family Assistance Fund,
    386
Warburg Pincus Foundation, 8100
Warburg Realty Partnership, 6656

Warburton, Phillip L., 8342
Warburton, Ralph T., 8342
Warburton, Sally, 8342
Warburton, Susan, 9331
Warchol, Marty, 1917
Ward, Amanda, 5872
Ward, Anthony C., 465
Ward, Brad, 3370
Ward, Catherine, 1158
Ward, Cynthia R., 9260
Ward, Dan, 5369
Ward, Daniel, 4497
Ward, Darlene, 4922
Ward, David, 9242
Ward, Donald L., 302
Ward, Douglas G., 9718
Ward, Edward, 89
Ward, Elizabeth J., 2864
Ward, Ellen, 8946
Ward, George, 1158
Ward, Harold A., III, 1485, 2070
Ward, Herbert, 7985
Ward, James, 3589
Ward, Jean G., 2605
Ward, Jeanne Whittaker, 5674
Ward, John, 8782
Ward, John D., 1804
Ward, John F., 2605
Ward, Joseph P., 8343
Ward, Judy G., 9581
Ward, Katherine J., 9260
Ward, Katie, 3669
Ward, Lanetta S., 9718
Ward, Lorene, 7286
Ward, Marjorie S., 8343
Ward, Michelle, 8289
Ward, Robert E., 8111
Ward, Sch'ree D., 7728
Ward, Stan, 9123
Ward, Susan Holloway, 8946
Ward, Tom L., 7728
Ward, Trent L., 7728
Ward, William C., 9260
Ward-McGuire, Patricia A., 8343
Ward-O'Malley, Kathryn A., 8343
Ward-Resnikoff, Marjorie A., 8343
Wardell, Dick, 5074
Warden, Mary G., 8072
Warden, William G., III, 8072
Warder, Oran, 9477
Wardwell, Harry, 403
Ware, Doug, 8900
Ware, William T., 8697
Wareham, C.C., 5594
Warfel, Jennifer A., 3376
Warfel, John E., 7373
Warfield, S. Davies, 3978
Wargo, John M., 2359
Waring, Bayard D., 4328
Waring, Philip B., 4328
Waring, Thomas, 8538
Wark, Barry J., 3309
Wark, David M., 3309
Wark, Mary Ann, 2778
Wark, Mary Ann Barrows, 3309
Warlick, Peter M., 8699, 8703
Warmflash, David, 6376, 6590, 6839
Warneke, Bob, Jr., 8796
Warner, Carolynn D., 8020
Warner, Deborah Dobbins, 7748
Warner, Douglas A., III, 3310
Warner, Guy R., 3704
Warner, John, 5060
Warner, John W., IV, 1822

Warner, Patricia G., 3310
Warner, Russell S., 8280
Warner-Lambert Co., 2406
Warnke, Karl J., 7373
Warren Brenda Pfohl Family, 9813
Warren NonGrantor Charitable Lead
    Annu, Catherine Candler, The , 2606
Warren Trust, Howard, 2606
Warren Trust, J.M., 7729
Warren, A.N., 7729
Warren, Andrew, 9426
Warren, Anne McLeod, 75
Warren, Benjamin, 9261
Warren, Beth, 2989
Warren, Bob, 3684
Warren, Bruce L., 1159
Warren, Carol L., 1159
Warren, Catherine C., 2606
Warren, Chris, 4391
Warren, Edus H., 2608
Warren, Frank R., 1159
Warren, George Emery, II, 1740
Warren, Glen C., Jr., 1367
Warren, Harold, 2607
Warren, Harriet H., 2608
Warren, Howard C., 2606
Warren, Jan, 3448
Warren, Jean, 7729
Warren, Jerry, 3580
Warren, Joanne C., 1159
Warren, John C., 3778
Warren, John R., 1784
Warren, Joy, 9261
Warren, Larry, 4946
Warren, Laura P.A., 3778
Warren, Margaret, 6889
Warren, Naomi, 9261
Warren, Robert P., 3864
Warren, Sara Humphreys, 8851
Warren, Tina L., 1784
Warren, W.K., Jr., 7729
Warren, Wilbert W., Jr., 7314
Warren, William C., III, 2606
Warren, William K., 7729
Warren, William Michael, Jr., 75
Warriner, Jane, 3428
Warriner, Jane Cunningham, 3428
Warriner, John, 3428
Warrington, John W., 7541
Warrix, Lewis H., 3703
Warrix-Allen, Lesley, 3703
Warshawsky, Sarita, 3243
Wartik, Maggie, 2787
Wartman, Ruthanne, 9723
Wartner, Laura L., 2551
Warwick Community Bancorp, 6945
Wasatch Pipeline Supply Inc, 9130
Washburn, Lisa J., 1995
Washburne, Heather H., 8938
Washburne, Jenny, 3978
Washington Group International, 2666
Washington Lawyer's Committee, 1787
Washington Trust Co., The, 8500
Washington Trust Company, The, 8409
Washington, Margaret Ferguson, 3757
Washington, Martin I., 153
Washington, Vanessa L., 272
Wasko, Robert J., 4708
Wassell Trust, Edmund J., 1920
Wasser, Martin, 6431
Wasserman, Bennett, 1606
Wasserman, Judi, 1160
Wasserman, Peter J., 1160
Wasserott, Elizabeth F., 8344

Wasserott, Paul D., Jr., 8344
Wasserstrom & Sons, N., 7632
Wasserstrom Co., The, 7632
Wasserstrom, Alan, 7632
Wasserstrom, Rodney, 7632
Wassertrom, Alan, 7621
Watabe, Shinichi, 6876
Watanabe, Jeffrey N., 2631
Watcham Trust, 9017
Waterfall, Gordon, 151
Waterfront Concerts, LLC, 1046
Waterhouse Family Foundation, The, 4210
Waterman, Cecily, 1126
Waterman, Nancy J., 1311
Waters Fund, James L., 8289
Waters, Betty, 3564
Waters, Bob, 9756
Waters, Damon C., 5571
Waters, Daniel, 4395
Waters, James, 3592
Waters, James A., 5571
Waters, Kenneth M., 5571
Waters, Leland W., 8751
Waters, Patricia, 4354
Waters, Richard C., 4354
Waters, Robert T., 5571
Waters, Stacey, 5091
Waters, T. Patrick, III, 5571
Waters, Victoria, 4395
Waterscheid, Mary, 5608
Watford Interests, 9262
Watford, Amanda N., 9262
Watford, Jason M., 9262
Watford, Michael D., 9262
Watkins, Dallas, 5091
Watkins, Damon, 2679
Watkins, Nila C., 1922
Watkins, Thomas C., 7209
Watry, Carl J., 2530
Watson 1995 Trust, Douglas, 845
Watson, Carol S., 5068
Watson, Douglas, 5409
Watson, Gail, 76
Watson, Gail P., 76
Watson, J.P., 3946
Watson, Jan, 9127
Watson, Jeff, 9231
Watson, Jo-Ann, 4276
Watson, John H., 76
Watson, John R., 76
Watson, Jon, 2680
Watson, Jonda, 9026
Watson, Kelly, 9029
Watson, Kent, 7623
Watson, Kim Post, 507
Watson, Kurt D., 3587
Watson, Linda T., 3639
Watson, Lorrin S., 5041
Watson, Mark, 7591
Watson, Mark E., Jr., 9263
Watson, Richard A., 6462
Watson, Screven H., 3723
Watson, Thomas S., 3639
Watson, Walter E., 7633
Watson, William T., 2444
Watt, Brenda, 4931
Watt, James L., 5567
Watt, Katherine, 1158
Watt, Rhonda, 7636
Watterson, Barbara N., 4049
Wattis Foundation, Paul L., 1161
Watts, Beverly, 6947
Watts, Blanche M., 5573

Watts, David B., 6947
Watts, David D., 669, 985
Watts, George L., 5573
Watts, James, 276
Watts, Robert, 1680
Watty, Jennifer, 1680
Waugaman, Amber, 6331
Waugh, David, 4872
Waugh, Seth H., 2392
Waugh, Sheila C., 2392
Waunford-Brown, Lynn, 6031
Wausau Container Corporation, 1408
Wave Equity Parners, LLC, The, 461
Wawona Frozen Foods, 1059
Waxman, Harvey L., 5388
Waxman, Wendy, 6287
Way, Edward Leong, 6394
Way, Eric Leong, 6394
Wayte, Larry, 326
WBN LLC, 7201
WCM Investments, 8581
WCN Bancorp, 9963
WCSJ, LLC, 740
WEA Enterprises Co., 6996
Wealth Creation Foundation, 2141
Wean Foundation, Raymond John, The, 7964
Wean, Raymond John, III, 7964
Wean, Susan, 7964
Wear, Ashley L., 3547
Wear, Dana, 5083
Weatherall, Jim, 9233
Weatherspoon, Martha Kay Massey, 7282
Weatherspoon, Van L., 7282
Weaver Family Foundation, 1604
Weaver Foundation, 7209
Weaver, Andrea Anton, 5133
Weaver, Annamarie, 3312
Weaver, Audrey, 2822
Weaver, Barbara A., 9559
Weaver, Curtis R., 8270
Weaver, Dick, 3366
Weaver, Francine Lavin, 1335, 1604
Weaver, James R., 1691
Weaver, Kaethe M., 9265
Weaver, Leslie A., 3312
Weaver, Lindsay A., Jr., 1335
Weaver, Lindsey A., Jr., 1335
Weaver, Linford L., 8270
Weaver, Marvin R., 8270
Weaver, Mary, 3474
Weaver, Miriam M., 8270
Weaver, Philip E., 8270
Weaver, Rali, 4046
Weaver, Terring M., 9750
Weaver, William, 3312
Weaver, William C., IV, 8662
Weaver, William R., 9265
Webb Charitable Lead Trust, Max, 991
Webb Lead Unitrust, Max, The, 686
Webb, Alec, 9368, 9514
Webb, Alexander, III, 4251
Webb, Anne B., 3827
Webb, Brey, 1935
Webb, Byron, III, 2803
Webb, Cynthia, 411
Webb, Dale Chapman, 1935
Webb, Francis M., 3313
Webb, Jeremy L., 5196
Webb, John D., 9070
Webb, Jon, 4450
Webb, Judy Chandler, 225
Webb, Kendall Ann, 1498

Webb, Kenneth, 12
Webb, Kristy, 1935
Webb, Lewis M., 5196
Webb, Lewis M., III, 5196
Webb, Lewis, Jr., 1162
Webb, Margaret A., 5196
Webb, Marty, 8806
Webb, Max, 991
Webb, Michael, 7884
Webb, Paul, 6208
Webb, Pearl M., 3313
Webb, R. Davis, Jr., 3827
Webb, Tania Lingos, 4177
Webb, Wylie O., 8755
Weber, Agnes E., 1284
Weber, Carolyn, 1397
Weber, Charlotte C., 7163
Weber, Chester C., 7163
Weber, Doug, 4962
Weber, Eugene D., 9955
Weber, Frederick E., 4352
Weber, Jane A., 1284
Weber, John C., Jr., 7163
Weber, Judith, 2085
Weber, Katherine A., 4920
Weber, Kathleen, 7884
Weber, Keith, 3640
Weber, Marjory, 3640
Weber, Marjory E., 3640
Weber, Patricia C., 3640
Weber, Philip S., 5267
Weber, Robert W., 3627
Weber, Ty, 5050
Webert, Magalen C., 9540
Webre, Iris Paine, 9266
Webre, Mary Iris, 9266
Webstaurant Store Inc., The, 7925
Webster Bank, 1477, 1491
Webster Financial Corp., 1477
Webster Five Cents Savings Bank, 4353
Webster, Barry, 7002
Webster, Ben, 7002
Webster, Curtis M., 6464
Webster, Cynthia F., 7400
Webster, Elizabeth McGraw, 6464
Webster, Gordon, 6208
Webster, Helen, 7002
Webster, Jean Schmidt, 7813
Webster, Theo M., 6464
Webster, Wayne L., 4299
Webster, Wendell C., 2094
Webster-Smith, Virginia, 4537
Wechenheim, Edgar, III, 6935
Wechsler Group, The, 6291
Wechsler, Caryn Wolf, 7643
Wechsler, Joseph, 6731
Wechsler, Samuel, 6731
Weckbaugh, Heather, 1329
Weckbaugh, John K., 1329, 1356
Weckbaugh, Walter S., 1329
Wedge, Carol H., 3661
Wedge, Jody H., 3661
Wedge, Julia, 3661
Wedge, Paul D., III, 3661
Wedge, Paul D., Jr., 3661
Weedman, Cheryl Lee, 4491
Weedman, Jeff, 4491
Weekes, Monica, 9903
Weekley Homes, 9009
Weeks, Bob, 3390, 3402
Weeks, Catherine, 5021
Weeks, Janis C., 577
Weeks, Joshua J., 8430
Weeks, Lisa C., 3346

Weeks, Stephen, 1774
Weeks, William H., 8430
Weeldreyer, Robert, 4408
Weems, Marianne, 5691
Wegehaupt, Kevin, 8574
Wegeleben, Deborah, 1586
Wegener, Eugene C., 7731
Wegener, Herman H., 7731
Wegener, Jeff, 7731
Wegener, Mark, 7731
Wegener, Mary, 7731
Wegener, Rodney, 7731
Wegman, Patrick A., II, 4568
Wehco Video, 201
Wehle Charitable Trust, Elizabeth, 3314
Wehle Residual Trust, Louis A., 3314
Wehle, Robert G., 3314
Wehr, G. Michael, 9767
Wehrle, Elizabeth M., 1821
Wehrle, Elizabeth Marie, 9771
Wehrle, H. Bernard, III, 9771
Wehrle, Henry B., Jr., 9771
Wehrle, Stephen D., 9771
Wehrle-Zande, Lynne, 9771
Wei Charitable Remainder Unitrust, 5575
Wei, Chung KI, 5575
Weibrecht, Lisa, 6360
Weideman, Doane B., 5346
Weidenaar, Joyce R., 6701
Weidman, Jonathan, 6323
Weidner, Ana Maria, 9719
Weidner, W. Dean, 9719
Weidner, William, 5202
Weier, G. William, 9720
Weier, John W., 9720
Weier, Patricia R., 9720
Weigel, Rainer R., 2950
Weight Watchers of Philadelphia, 7873
Weigle, Benjamin J., 3546
Weigle, David B., 3546
Weigle, Jonathan H., 3546
Weigle, Nancy B., 3546
Weil Family Trust, Christopher and Patricia, 1163
Weil, A. Lorne, 6948
Weil, Adolph, III, 40
Weil, Adolph, Jr., 40
Weil, Adolph, Jr., Mrs., 40
Weil, Amanda E., 6204
Weil, Andrew, 181
Weil, Audrey York, 9550
Weil, Caitlin, 1163
Weil, Carol, 8346
Weil, Christopher, 1163
Weil, Denie S., 6204
Weil, Eugene S., 5329
Weil, Frank A., 6204
Weil, Jan K., 40
Weil, Jean K., 40
Weil, John D., 5027
Weil, Kenneth M., 9550
Weil, Laurie J., 40
Weil, M.D., Ph.D., Max Harry, 8346
Weil, Marianne, 8346
Weil, Mark S., 5027
Weil, Matthew, 1163
Weil, Patricia, 1163
Weil, Paula, 4971
Weil, Richard M., 6948
Weil, Robert S., 73
Weil, Sandison E., 6204
Weil, Susan, 8346
Weil, William S., 6204

Weiler Arnow Managment Co, 6655
Weiler Corp., 8347
Weiler, Ann, 8347
Weiler, Anna, 3147
Weiler, Christopher, 8347
Weiler, James, 8347
Weiler, Karl M., 8347
Weiler, Richard K., 8347
Weiler, Siegfried, 3147
Weiler, Timothy L., 9358
Weiler, Victor N., 9862
Weill, Joan H., 6949
Weill, Margo H., 5467
Weill, Sanford I., 6949
Weiller, Edwin A., III, 2393
Weiller, Jean A., 2393
Weimer, William J., Jr., 3158
Wein, Evan, 6720
Wein, Irving L., 3315
Wein, Joseph, 3315
Wein, Terri, 6720
Wein, Zahava, 3315
Wein-Bernhardt, Susan, 3315
Weinbaum, Melissa, 6595
Weinbaum, Michael J., 6595
Weinberg, Abigail, 5044
Weinberg, Amy S., 6951
Weinberg, Carroll A., 3979
Weinberg, Charlotte Cohen, 3979
Weinberg, Daniel, 5044
Weinberg, Daniel C., 5044
Weinberg, Gayle, 5044
Weinberg, Gwynne A., 3979
Weinberg, Hilton, 3312
Weinberg, John S., 6951
Weinberg, Lewis, 5044
Weinberg, Robert A., 1164
Weinberg, Roxann, 1164
Weinberg, Zachary, 5044
Weinberger, Arianne, 1730
Weinberger, Judah, 5600
Weinberger, Lillian, 6379
Weinberger, Michael, 1730
Weinberger, Ofra, 5600
Weinberger, Ruth, 2394
Weinberger, Saul, 2394
Weinberger, Ted, 6023
Weinberger, Theodore, 6023
Weinberger, Zolton, 6379
Weiner, Adam J., 4355
Weiner, Bruce B., 8349
Weiner, Clifford M., 9234
Weiner, Denise, 6001
Weiner, Elliot M., 3316
Weiner, Florence, 3980
Weiner, Frederick, 4791
Weiner, Gwen, 4581
Weiner, Gwendolyn, 8840
Weiner, Howard, 4791
Weiner, James, 6243
Weiner, Jeffrey, 3854
Weiner, Jill, 1480
Weiner, Jonathan B., 1480
Weiner, Laurence, 3316
Weiner, Marvin H., 3980
Weiner, Roberta S., 4355
Weiner, Rosalind A., 3980
Weiner, Scott M., 3980
Weiner, Shelley, 1556
Weiner, Stephen R., 4355
Weiner, Susan, 8349
Weingart, Mel L., 9237
Weingarten, Abraham, 6764, 6858,
    7008

Weingarten, Amanda, 6953
Weingarten, Bryan, 8337
Weingarten, Fay, 6858
Weingarten, Hershie, 6952
Weingarten, Jeffrey M., 6953
Weingarten, Marjorie Wachs, 8337
Weingarten, Mark, 5791
Weingarten, Otto I., 6952
Weingarten, Rosemarie, 6185, 6952
Weingarten, Susan, 6953
Weininger, Gertrude, 6954
Weinlander, Walter G., 2152
Weinman Family Foundation, 6542
Weinman, Jonathan H., 3981
Weinman, Melvin, 3981
Weinman, Morris Mark, 3981
Weinreb, David, 9204
Weinreb, Deborah, 7000
Weinreb, Jacob, 7000
Weinreb, Karen, 9204
Weinrib, Mary-Ellen, 6946
Weinstein, Barry L., 3145
Weinstein, David A., 938
Weinstein, Hilary, 3145
Weinstein, Ira, 8591
Weinstein, Irving, 5576
Weinstein, Joe, 6956
Weinstein, Joshua, 5877
Weinstein, Linda Cornell, 5877
Weinstein, Mark J., 6259
Weinstein, Rachel, 5877
Weinstein, Sherwin, 5877
Weinstein, Stuart, 320
Weinsten, Joan Schlager, 4283
Weinstiock, Avi, 5544
Weintraub, Barbara A., 2395
Weintraub, Daniel, 5577
Weintraub, David, 6957
Weintraub, Ellen, 6957
Weintraub, Joseph, 2395
Weintraub, Joshua B., 5577
Weintraub, Michael, 2395
Weintraub, Peter, 6957
Weintraub, Sharon R., 5577
Weir Furniture Village, 9267
Weir, Brad, 9267
Weir, Dan R., 9267
Weir, Davis, 9268
Weir, Laura, 9267
Weir, Mary, 4979
Weir, Phyllis, 9144
Weir, Rosalie Coe, 6980
Weirether, Anne Marie, 1514
Weis, Cindy, 5033
Weis, Donald, 3601
Weisberg, Alan, 3705
Weisberg, Charles, 3705
Weisberg, Frank, 3705
Weisberg, Idell, 4609
Weisberg, Jack, 5578
Weisberg, Lawrence, 4609
Weisberg, Ronald, 3705
Weisberger, Gerald L., 1198
Weisenthal, Bruce, 3224
Weisenthal, Bruce P., 3224
Weiser LLP, 6958
Weiser, Barbara, 797
Weiser, Barrie, 8591
Weiser, Carolyn, 6142
Weiser, Harold, 6962
Weiser, Lynda Robson, 160
Weiser, Wendy, 7311
Weisermazars, LLP, 6958
Weisgerber Trust, Aenid R., 1165

Weishaar, Dennis, 3567
Weisheit, Bowen P., Jr., 3893
Weiskopf, Gunther, 6068
Weisman Charitable Lead Annuity Trust,
    William E., 4792
Weisman, Alyn Marisa, 4792
Weisman, Carol, 6857, 6959
Weisman, Charles Harris, 4792
Weisman, Fran, 2396
Weisman, Jane, 4198
Weisman, Michael, 6959
Weisman, Robert, 2396
Weisman, William E., 4792
Weismann, Philippa V., 6960
Weiss Grantor Trust, Mindy, 6144
Weiss Irrevocable Trust, Idy, 5840
Weiss Trust, Michael, 5840
Weiss, Abraham, 5633
Weiss, Anthony W., 3982
Weiss, David, 2196, 7634
Weiss, Diane L., 5301
Weiss, Eva, 6963
Weiss, Floretta A., 3317
Weiss, George, 6720
Weiss, Harry J., Jr., 2242
Weiss, Janis, 6504
Weiss, Jeffrey, 7634, 8428
Weiss, Joseph H., 6962
Weiss, Lisa, 3982
Weiss, Louis A., 3317
Weiss, Marc, 3279
Weiss, Mark, 6961
Weiss, Mary K., 9996
Weiss, Michael, 5840
Weiss, Mindy, 6144
Weiss, Miriam F., 6962
Weiss, Moshe, 5633
Weiss, Naomi, 7030
Weiss, Pamela, 1688
Weiss, Regina, 5633
Weiss, Robert A., 3317
Weiss, Robert G., 3317
Weiss, Robert Lee, Jr., 8684
Weiss, Scott, 1688
Weiss, Stanley, 3982
Weiss, Stanley A., 3982
Weiss, Steven, 7030
Weiss, Susan, 6961
Weiss, William E., Jr., 9997
Weiss, William M., 7634
Weiss, William U., 9997
Weiss, Zach, 1688
Weiss, Zeta, 1688
Weiss, Zoe, 1688
Weiss-Fischmann, Susan, 1013
Weissberg, Lisa M., 8297
Weissbrot, Kenneth, 6512
Weissfeld, Joachim A., 8441
Weissman, Adam J., 1775
Weissman, Carol, 5733
Weissman, Jeffrey, 5733
Weissman, Laurence E., 8646
Weissman, Mordecai, 5733
Weisz and Sons Inc., David, 6688
Weisz, David, 6688
Weisz, Rachelle, 6688
Weisz, Sylvia, 1167
Weits, Bracha, 5748
Weits, Mordechai, 5748
Weitz & Luxenberg, 5855
Weitz, Henry, 2049
Weitz, Hsiu Chun, 2049
Weitz, Lisa D., 2227
Weitzenkorn, Ronald J., 7548

Weixel, Greg, 8237
Weizenbaum, Norman, 7856
Welborn, W. Miller, 8633
Welburn Management Consulting Co.,
    153
Welch Trust, William J., 7732
Welch, Charles, 1295
Welch, Charles B., 4610
Welch, David F., 1168
Welch, Douglas S., 7732
Welch, Eleanor M., 2290
Welch, Finis, 9270
Welch, Glenn S., 4116
Welch, Greg, 5038
Welch, Harry, 2652
Welch, Heidi A., 1168
Welch, Jack, 9333
Welch, James C., 4610
Welch, James O., Jr., 5579
Welch, Jane, 4610
Welch, Jane N., 4610
Welch, John, 4610
Welch, Lantz, 5038
Welch, Laura, 5038
Welch, Lorene W., 9998
Welch, Mark F., 8381
Welch, Mary K., 4469
Welch, P. Craig, III, 4469
Welch, P. Craig, Jr., 4469
Welch, Pamela R., 58
Welch, Peggy, 7732
Welch, Robert, 4153
Welch, Sheila McNeil, 5419
Welch, Stephany, 4469
Welch, Thomas Brad, 4610
Welch, Thomas J., 4469
Welch, Virginia B., 5579
Welch, William J., 7732
Welch, William J., Jr., 7732
Welded Construction Company, 9130
Weldon, Linda, 3511
Weldon, Stephen, 3511
Welk Foundation, Lawrence, The , 1170
Welk Group, The, 1170
Welk, Lindy, 1170
Welk, Tracey, 1170
Welker, Mary, 3432
Wellens, Howard, 7906
Weller, Bradley E., 4402, 4412, 4483
Weller, E.C., 5127
Weller, Frances W., 5127
Welles, Amanda C., 3820
Welles, Hope J., 7318
Welles, Peter S., 3820
Welles, Sondra T., 3820
Wellinghoff, James, 7304
Wells Annuity Trust, Ruth L., 6964
Wells Fargo, 1295, 6655, 7905
Wells Fargo Bank, 130, 144, 152, 157,
    294
Wells Fargo bank, 645
Wells Fargo Bank, 649, 1008, 1362,
    1977, 2443, 2488, 2572, 2621,
    3354, 3409, 3418, 3428, 5073,
    5075, 7038, 7041, 7042, 7043,
    7051, 7052, 7053, 7059, 7061,
    7063, 7067, 7072, 7073, 7077,
    7086, 7087, 7088, 7089, 7091,
    7093, 7095, 7098, 7099, 7100,
    7101, 7104, 7106, 7107, 7108,
    7109, 7110, 7115, 7116, 7117,
    7122, 7128, 7129, 7130, 7131,
    7136, 7139, 7140, 7142, 7146,
    7147, 7148, 7149, 7152, 7154,

7156, 7157, 7165, 7167, 7170,
7172, 7175, 7176, 7179, 7181,
7182, 7183, 7184, 7187, 7188,
7189, 7195, 7197, 7199, 7200,
7203, 7206, 7208, 7211, 7216,
7220, 7224, 7225, 7226, 7230,
7234, 7235, 7236, 7240, 7241,
7245, 7251, 7253, 7259, 7262,
7267, 7268, 7277, 7278, 7279,
7280, 7285, 8029, 8123, 8268,
8576, 8689, 8710, 8824, 8903,
8954, 9172, 9617
Wells Fargo Bank Indiana, 5097
Wells Fargo Bank Iowa, 5103
Wells Fargo Bank Minnesota, 9329
Wells Fargo Bank Northwest, 7134
Wells Fargo Bank Texas, 7158, 8784,
  8818
Wells Fargo Bank Wyoming Investment,
  9715
Wells Fargo Home Mortgage, 6656
Wells Fargo Private Client Serv., 9692
Wells Fargo Trust Department, 8815
Wells Fargo Trust Dept., 9104
Wells Fargo Wealth Mgmt., 9710
Wells Marital Trust, Frank, 6964
Wells Trust, Ethel B., 5635
Wells Trust, Terry B., 4848
Wells, Albert B., II, 5635
Wells, Ashley, 4848
Wells, Boyd, 8869
Wells, Damon, 9271
Wells, Damon, Jr., 9271
Wells, Frank G., 1171
Wells, Fred, 2872
Wells, Fred W., 8501
Wells, George B., II, 5635
Wells, John, 3390
Wells, Judy K., 9272
Wells, Kathy, 193
Wells, Kit-Victoria, 1163
Wells, Kristen, 5635
Wells, Kristi, 2397
Wells, Leslie, 4848
Wells, Luanne C., 1171
Wells, Marsha McCarty, 4848
Wells, Patricia, 5094
Wells, Peter, 516
Wells, Peter Boyd, III, 9196
Wells, Ran K., 9272
Wells, Stephen A., 9272
Wells, Stephen L., 2397
Wells, Susan L., 6540
Wells, Susan M., 5635
Wells, T. Calvin, 4858
Wells, W. Kevin, 1171
Wells, Wendy, 4811
Welp, D. Elaine, 112
Welp, Theodore M., 112
Welsch, Jolynn, 1347
Welsch, Louellen, 1347
Welsch, Randall, 1347
Welsh Construction, 3905
Welsh, David D., 3088
Welsh, Edward C., 3088
Welsh, James E., 1058
Welsh, John L., III, 3088
Welsh, Nancy S., 1058
Welsh, Phoebe W., 3088
Welsh, Ray, 5105
Welter, Don, 896
Welter, Edward P., 3465
Welter, Kristin, 896
Welter, Wilhelmina J., 3465

Welton, Annette L., 1776
Welton, Patrick L., 1776
Welty, Chad C., 7635
Welty, Emily C., 7635
Welty, Jerry H., 7635
Wendel, Amy, 4813
Wendel, Brian, 5580
Wendel, Gerald, 5580
Wendel, Joshua, 5580
Wendel, Michael, 5580
Wendel, W. Hall, Jr., 4813
Wendell, Brian, 1172
Wendell, Christopher, 1172
Wendell, Lynn, 1172
Wendell, Peter, 1172
Wendell, Sandi, 5105
Wender Trust, Ruth, The , 1777
Wender, Theodore A., 1777
Wendl, Mary Grant, 7686
Wendland, Barbara, 8786
Wendland, C., 8786
Wendland, E., 8786
Wendling, John C., 7466
Wendriner Trust, Betty, 6294
Wendroff, Harry, 6308
Wendroff, Susan, 6308
Wendt, Charles, 8986
Wendt, Hunter, 4405
Wendy's of Montana Inc., 5065
Wenger, Adam, 8352
Wenger, Brian, 4648
Wenger, Carl I., 8352
Wenger, Carolyn C., 8351
Wenger, Kitty, 8352
Wenger, Margaret, 8352
Wenger, Olga Starnes Kuhn, 9214
Wenger, Robert C., 8351
Wenngatz, Halbert, 5088
Wenngatz, Kathleen S., 5088
Wentland, Yvette, 8175
Wentworth, Bob, 7798
Wentworth, Cynthia, 5206
Wentworth, Elizabeth B., 2743
Wentworth, Megan, 7807
Wentworth, Nicholas, 5827
Wentzel, Eugene, 5363
Weny, Frank X., 5581
Wenzel, Kenneth A., 2359
Wenzlick, Vearn, 4568
Wepner, Anne A., 7037
Werbel, Joel, 5569
Werder, Rick, 480
Wereszczak, Chrysta, 2967
Werf, Kim Vander, 4739
Werkmeister, Nicole, 5615
Werling, Robert, 4758
Werner, Anita G., 9232
Werner, Barry, 4082
Werner, Bruce D., 2398
Werner, John, 3443
Werner, Laurie B., 8718
Werner, Leah, 6574
Werner, Lois S., 2398
Werner, Mindy H., 2398
Werner, Richard L., 2398
Werner, Tammy H., 2398
Werner, Vanda N., 1306
Wernik, Malcolm B., 7101
Wertenteil, Ilana, 6126
Wertenteil, Mark, 6126
Werthan, Bernard, Jr., 58, 8583
Werthan, Betty, 8583
Werthan, Leah Rose, 8583
Wertheimer, Douglas, 1173

Wertheimer, Elinor, 1173
Wertheimer, Ira T., 1173
Wertheimer, Susan, 1173
Wertheimer, Thomas, 1173
Wertherim, Melinda M., 49
Wertz, Bob D., 1293
Wertz, Donna, 884
Wertz, Russell, 884
Wertzberger, Yehoshua, 5666
WesBanco Bank, 9735, 9738
Wesbanco Bank, 9747, 9762, 9764
Weschler, Patrick J., 7487
Weske, Christine, 1107
Wesolowski, Lori-Ellen, 1418
Wessel, Brandon J., 3318
Wessel, Elizabeth K., 3318
Wessel, Jeffrey H., 3318
Wesselink, Catherine E., 3319
Wesselink, David D., 3319
Wesselink, Linda R., 3319
Wesselink, William J., 3319
Wessell, Amy P., 1241
Wessell, Leonard P., 1241
Wessell, Leonard P., III, 1241
Wessels, Patrick, 4938
Wessinger Trust, Paul, 7826
Wessinger, Ashley, 816
Wessinger, E. Charles, 7826
Wessinger, Henry W., 7826
Wessinger, Joseph M., 816, 7826
Wessinger, William W., 7826
West Bank, 3547
West Corporation, 5128
West Hampton Associates LLC, 4594
West Paris Alumni Association, 3796
West Revocable Trust, Virginia C., 9461
West United Way Pledge, 3444
West, C. Dwight, III, 9461
West, Caleb D., Jr., 9461
West, Carolyn S., 7827
West, Chelsey, 7827
West, Christa, 3446
West, Constance F., 1608
West, Cristy, 1830
West, Curtis A., 9662
West, Daniel, 4962
West, David J., 3440
West, David M., 9488
West, Frederick H., 1608
West, Frederick H., Mrs. , 1608
West, J. Robinson, 1781, 8327
West, James C., Jr., 9740
West, Jessica Noel, 1948
West, Juliana D., 7084
West, Katherine Kane, 2137
West, Loralee S., 9631
West, Maria C., 380
West, Mindy K., 206
West, Patrick J., 104
West, Robin Kinzer, 4497
West, Ronald D., 6032
West, Steven F., 7827
West, Thomas H., 4134
West, Thomas H., Jr., 4134
Westberry, Michael, 2054
Westborough Executive Park, 6654
Westcott, Carl, 9273
Westcott, Chart, 9273
Westcott, Jimmy, 9273
Westenberger, Richard F., 2454
Westermayer, Mary E., 4903
Westermeyer, Darlene, 2365
Western American Prints, 93
Western Gear Corp., 897

Western National Trust Co., 5170, 5176
Western Oilfield Supply Co., 727
Western Supplies Inc, 9130
Western Transportation Company, 9034
Westfall, John L., 9740
Westholm, William, 4666
Westinghouse Air Brake Technologies
  Corp., 8335
Westland Gardens Co., 3905
Westly, Dean, 735
Westminster Motor Co., 3899
Weston, Coralie, 2689
Weston, John C., 9957
Weston, Roger L., 3320
Westpac Banking Corp., 5562
Westphal, Bruce A., 1177
Westphal, Patricia A., 1177
Westphal, Penny L., 1177
Westphal, Roger L., 1177
Westport Corp., 5348
Westra, Laurie, 5332
Westrate, Brian, 9945
Westrate, David B., 9945
Westrate, Mike, 9945
Westreich, Helene, 2401
Westrom, John T., 3910
Westropp, Jordan, 7490
Westropp, Thomas C., 7490
Wetmore Foundation Charitable Trust,
  3757
Wetsman, Adam F., 4611
Wetsman, David J., 4611
Wetsman, Janis B., 4611
Wetsman, Lillian R., 4611
Wetsman, William M., 4611
Wetterberg, Harold, 5583
Wettstein, Stacy, 2923
Wetzel, Bruce W., 7619
Wetzel, James P., Jr., 8114
Wexler, Dan, 1377
Wexler, Daniel, 5667
Wexler, Elizabeth, 1377
Wexler, Mark, 1377
Wexler, Muriel, 1377
Wexler, Steven, 1377
Wexler, Stuart, 5398
Wexner Revocable Trust, Susan, 6374
Wexner, Susan, 6374
Wexner, Susan R., 6636
Weyand, Florence H., 4814
Weyand, Louis F., 4814
Weyco Group, 9958
Weyerhaeuser Trusts, Carl A., 4815
Weyers Charitable Lead Annuity Trust of
  2010, 9959
Weyers, Robert J., 9959
Weyers, Ronald, 9959
Weyland, Wendell P., 4017, 4119, 4343
Weymar, Caroline, 5563
Weymar, Caroline S., 5563
Weymar, F. Helmut, 5563
Weymar, Matthew D., 5563
Weyrich, Mary Martin, 803
WGI Holdings England, 2666
WGS, 1344
Whalen Lead Trust, 6966
Whalen, Fr. John P., 6966
Whalen, Joseph P., Sr., 6966
Whalen, Mary P., 6966
Whalen, Michael, 926
Whalen, Michael S., 970
Whalen, Philip J., Jr., 6966
Whalen, Ryann, 5627
Whalen, Thomas J., 8561

Whalen, Tim, 9740
Whaley, Annette M., 4816
Whaley, John P., 4816
Whaley, Rick, 2550
Whalley, John J., 8353
Whalley, John J., Jr., 8353
Whalley, Mary, 8353
Whang, Sunny, 1093
Wharton, Dwayne, 8105, 8269
Wharton, Erin, 2803
Wharton, Naida S., 6968
Whatley, Malvina M., 50
Whatley, Melba Davis, 9037
Whealy, Brenda L., 5119
Whealy, Michael T., 5119
Wheatland Trust, David P., 4358
Wheatland, Rebecca, 4358
Wheaton, Barbara K., 3772
Wheeler, Alexa M., 1594
Wheeler, Alexandra, 1594
Wheeler, Charles, 3602
Wheeler, David, 9631
Wheeler, David A., 784
Wheeler, Edward K., 6969
Wheeler, Florence R., 1179
Wheeler, Gary, 34
Wheeler, Halsted W., 1594
Wheeler, Hulda C., 1594
Wheeler, Kendall, 6969
Wheeler, Lanie, 900
Wheeler, Lee, 2059
Wheeler, Lisa, 34
Wheeler, Marta, 9631
Wheeler, Patricia Boyle, 2754
Wheeler, Richard T., Jr., 9452
Wheeler, Thomas M., 4612
Wheeler, Thomas R., 4612
Wheeler, W. Thomas, 9940
Wheeler, William A., 1179
Wheeler, Wilmot F., 1594
Wheeler, Wilmot, III, 1594
Wheeless, Richard W., 6372
Wheelis, Susan, 8922
Wheels, 2885
Whelan, Tim, 4963
Whelehan, Kathleen, 6452
Wheless, N. Hobson, 3758
Wheless, Nicholas Hobson, Jr., 3758
Whellan, David, 8042
Whelpley, John, 5890
Whetstone-Foltz, Patricia M., 1914
Whetzel, Farley Walton, 8341
Whipple, Carol, 3752
Whipple, Kenneth, 8836
Whipple, Scott, 9333
Whisler, Nelson, 7424
Whistler, Flint, 7662
Whitaker, E. Ashley Brooks, 8642
Whitaker, Laura, 2557
Whitby, Dana, 5021
White Capital Group, LLC, 2609
White Horse Youth Ranch, 5177
White Plains Hotel Limited Partnership, 6302
White Trust, Harold A., 7733
White Trust, Stanley, 7734
White, Allen, 5225
White, Amy, 2521
White, Ashley, 4490
White, Barbara Boyd, 369
White, Ben, 8503
White, Benjamin T., 2595
White, Brandon C., 9980
White, Brian C., 1532

White, C. Cody, Jr., 3746
White, C. Kenneth, 2609
White, C.K., 2609
White, Caleb E., 1442
White, Carol, 5622
White, Carol M., 7080
White, Celita, 4998
White, Charles C., 9275
White, Charles C., Jr., 9275
White, Charles E., 1180, 4613
White, Connie Burwell, 1378
White, Dale A., 3466
White, Daniel J., 7422
White, Dave, 4915
White, David B., 4613
White, David K., 1098
White, Dean, 9797
White, Diana, 3441
White, Dunlop, III, 7209
White, Ed A., 1180
White, Eddie, 9391
White, Edmund, 1543
White, Ellen H., 3746
White, Gail Marcy, 2401
White, Ginette, 5234
White, Glenn E., 4613
White, Gretchen, 6335
White, H. Blair, 3012
White, Ha, 5622
White, J. Austin, 220
White, J. Douglas, 2532
White, James A., 813
White, Jeffrey J., 2532
White, John Hazen, III, 8503
White, John Hazen, Jr., 8503
White, John J., 2532
White, Judd, 2200
White, Judith C., 6972
White, K.T., 2609
White, Karen, 9222
White, Kathleen M., 2532
White, Leon Stanley, II, 8849
White, Linda, 8269
White, Linda D., 1180
White, Lisa M., 1180
White, M.D., Ph.D., Paul F., 1180
White, M.L., 2609
White, Madeleine E., 2532
White, Marilyn, 2681
White, Mary Carolyn, 2532
White, Megan, 9326
White, Michael H., 9915
White, Michael J., 2532
White, Monica, 6540
White, Nancy Grandis, 9462
White, Nate, 9326
White, Norman, 2059
White, Patrick L., 2402
White, Portia C., 8537
White, Richard E., 8048
White, Richard L., 8537
White, Roxie, 9473
White, Ruth E., 4613
White, Ruth G., 6700
White, Sandra A., 7422
White, Sara Margaret, 3746
White, Shelby, 6973
White, Stephen C., 3746
White, Thomas W., 8865
White, Tim, 5114
White, Tonya K., 8062
White, Toriano D., 4085
White, Tracy, 6973
White, W. Graham, 2070

White, Wesley W., 7422
White, William B., 1378
Whitehead, Edwin C., 2610
Whitehead, John C., 6974
Whitehead, John G., 6974
Whitehead, John J., 2610
Whitehead, Peter J., 2610
Whitehead, Susan, 4007
Whitehead, Susan E., 2610
Whitehouse, Donald, 7605
Whitelaw, Robert, 8334
Whitelaw, Walter, 5954
Whitely, James, 8008
Whiteman, Alfred L., 3886
Whiteman, Jeffrey S., 116
Whitener, Edgar, 7286
Whitesell, Shirley J., 2708
Whiteside, Jeffrey W., 3450
Whitfield, Margaret H., 5760
Whitfill, Steve, 7666
Whiting, Cornelia, 6946
Whiting, Macauley, 2403
Whiting, Macauley, Jr., 2403
Whiting, Mary M., 2403
Whiting, Sara S., 2403
Whiting, Terry, 8575
Whitler, Bob, 9757
Whitley Company, LP, 9276
Whitley, Sidney, 4847
Whitley/Service Roofing & Sheet Metal Co., 9744
Whitlock, R. Barnes, 4994
Whitlow, Allan, 3372
Whitman Charitable Lead Unitrust, 1778
Whitman Charitable Trust, Catherine, 6939
Whitman Declaration of Trust, Barbara K., 1778
Whitman, Barbara, 6634
Whitman, Barbara K., 1778
Whitman, Bradley R., 6939
Whitman, Christine B., 6939
Whitman, H. Angela, 2404
Whitman, Jr. Declararion of Trust, William F., 1778
Whitman, Lars, 4481
Whitman, Laura B., 1778
Whitman, Laura M., 4615
Whitman, Leigh, 3759
Whitman, Lois, 6634
Whitman, Malcolm, 4615
Whitman, Marina V.N., 4615
Whitman, Martin J., 6634
Whitman, Michelle, 6939
Whitman, Robert F., 4615
Whitman, Scott L., 541
Whitman, Tami, 2676
Whitman, Wayne, 3759
Whitman, William F., Jr., 1778
Whitman, William Fifield, 1778
Whitmanred Trust, H. Angela, 2404
Whitmer, Suzanne T., 3570
Whitmore, Robin, 4534
Whitney, Benson, 4817
Whitney, Benson K., 4817
Whitney, Betsey C., 6135
Whitney, Christina W., 7163
Whitney, Craig, 5879
Whitney, Joseph, 4817
Whitney, Joseph H., 4817
Whitney, Kate R., 6135
Whitney, Mary, 4817
Whitney, Nancy Goroff, 1717
Whitney, Pennell, 4817

Whitney, Todd, 5872
Whitney, Valerie Timken, 5192
Whitney, Wallace F., Jr., 4364
Whitney, Wheelock, 4817
Whitney, Wheelock, III, 4817
Whitsett, E.A., 259
Whitsett, J., 259
Whitsitt, William, 5054
Whitson, Nancy, 1226
Whittaker, David, 7305
Whittaker, E. William, 5674
Whittaker, Harry W., 7305
Whittaker, Polly W., 7305
Whittaker, Sean, 6373
Whittaker, Thomas, 4667
Whittemore, Edward B., 6975
Whittemore, Frederick B., 6975
Whittemore, Laurence F., 6975
Whitten Newman Foundation, 7715
Whitten, Jerald, 8711
Whitten, Joyce, 8711
Whitten, Rachelle Newman, 7715
Whitten, Reggie N., 7715
Whitten-Welch Foundation, 3522
Whittenberger, Ethel B., 2689
Whittenburg, J. Vernon, 5541
Whittier Trust Co., 444
Whittier, Ronald J., 1181
Whitton, Barbara A., 7185
Whitwam, Barbara, 3321
Whitwam, David R., 3321
Whitwam, Mark, 3321
Whitwell, Rodney, 6632
Whitwell, Sara E., 7735
Whitwell, Thomas D., 7735
Whitzel, Robin, 7747
Whttenburg, Benjamin, 8697
Whyte, James, 1316
Whyte, Paul W., 8406, 8479
Whyte, Thomas E., 1306
Wibel Interim Trust, Mary E., 7287
Wibker, Elizabeth A., 8637
Wible, Jeff, 3412
Wibling, Harold C., 1559
Wich, J. Roger, 8944
Wich, Joan Hohlt, 8944
Wichert, Sarah H., 8296
Wichtenstein, Rose, 2406
Wickesberg, Matthew, 2510
Wickiser, Mike, 9937
Wicks, Mel, 9712
Wickson, James, 4616
Wickson, Meta, 4616
Wickstra, Matt, 4488
WICU-TV, 1043
Widdowson, Gayle, 3932
Widdowson, Julia N.H., 8855
Widdowson, Nigel D., 8855
Widdup, Jeffrey, 7933
Wideman, Lillian, 12
Widner, Kenneth, 120
Widrig, Christine M., 3565
Width, Richard, 5332
Wiebe, Barbara J., 9723
Wiebe, Henry J., 9723
Wiebe, John Hugh, 9723
Wieber, Karleen, 7636
Wieczorek, Courtney, 4617
Wieczorek, Dale M., 4617
Wieczorek, Paulette, 4617
Wieczorek, Shannon, 4617
Wied, Elizabeth, 477
Wiedemann Trust, K.T., 3642
Wiedmeyer, Jill M., 1971

Wiefoff, John P., 4818
Wiegand, Christine P., 7923
Wiegand, Joel, 5096
Wiegardt, Gustave A., Jr., 9709
Wiegers Family Foundation, 6248
Wiegers, George A., 6248
Wiegert, Bob, 3514
Wiegert, Rachel, 9867
Wiehl, Paul, 7311
Wiehoff, John P., 4818
Wiehoff, Margaret G., 4818
Wiehoff, Michelle A., 4818
Wiehoff, Theresa J., 4818
Wiekert, Rodney S., 3547
Wieler, Mary, 3984
Wieler, Mary Baily, 3984
Wieler, Scott A., 3984
Wiemer, Christina, 2409
Wien, Leonard A., 5665
Wiener Fund, S.G. & M.P., 6021
Wiener, Alan, 6656
Wiener, Earl L., 6021
Wiener, Florence, 6021
Wiener, Fred, 6021
Wiener, Michael A., 1596
Wiener, Robert, 2405
Wiener, Zena, 1596
Wienkers, Kevin, Dr. , 9781
Wienkers, Kevin, Mrs. , 9781
Wiens, Donald, 3617
Wiensch, Adam J., 9809
Wier, Robert, 2724
Wierda, Laurie S., 4527
Wierda, Laurie Sue, 4527
Wierman, Pam, 3932
Wiersema, William, 3113
Wietlisbach, Binney H.C., 7903
Wigdale, James B., 9907
Wiggins, Morton, 6476
Wiggins, Robert S., Jr., 2461
Wiggins, Thomas, 3766
Wiggs, Steven B., 7209
Wight, Charles, 9512
Wight, Don E., 882
Wight, Tom B., 2478
Wikert, Alinda H., 8938
Wikert, Cody M., 8938
Wikert, Margretta H., 8938
Wilamowsky, Eli, 6976
Wilamowsky, Rhona, 6976
Wilamowsky, Steven, 6976
Wilbanks, Daniel P., 13
Wilbanks, Sarah, 9150
Wilbert, Donna, 2972
Wilbratte, Chris, 8738
Wilbur, Brayton, Jr., 1182
Wilbur, Deborah, 6559
Wilbur, Denise, 3941
Wilbur, Judy, 1182
Wilbur, Lawrence A., 3941
Wilbur, Leroy A., Jr., 3941
Wilbur, Lisa M., 4545
Wilbur, Michael D., 1182
Wilbur, Scott E., 3941
Wilbur-Ellis Co., 1182
Wilcox, Carlo, 425
Wilcox, Carol M., 9081
Wilcox, Christina H., 4360
Wilcox, Claire, 5585
Wilcox, Ellen, 9600
Wilcox, G. Geer, 4360
Wilcox, George G., 4360
Wilcox, Greg, 5585
Wilcox, Gregory, 5585

Wilcox, James, 1950
Wilcox, John, 5065
Wilcox, Linda, 3361
Wilcox, Lorraine, 2667
Wilcox, Paige, 8563
Wilcox, Peter B., 4360
Wilcox, Philip C., Jr., 1807
Wilcox, Robert, 4130
Wilcox, Samuel Whitney, 2654
Wilcox, Steve, 9600
Wilcox, Susan, 8563
Wilczek, Ron, 9878
Wilczewski, Joseph P., 8514
Wild Harp Co., The, 5260
Wilde, Katrin, 9663
Wilde, Lynn, 4714
Wildenstein, Guy N., 5669
Wilder, B.J., 2406
Wilder, B.J., Jr., 2406
Wilder, C. John, 9277
Wilder, Daren R., 8825
Wilder, David, 9043
Wilder, Norman, 3920
Wilder, Stephen F., 6682
Wilder, Susan A., 9277
Wildlife Care Center, 2257
Wildman, Walter A., 7585
Wildrick, Eve B., 1792
Wildrick-Cole, Dawn A., 5660
Wildwood Foundation, 4784
Wile, Lawrence C., 1417
Wile, Ruth C., 1417
Wilen, Jack, 3985
Wiles, Richard, 3371
Wiletts, Jeffrey G., 9468
Wiley, J. Michael, 8219
Wiley, Nettie L. Lokey, 9551
Wiley, Scott, 3511
Wilf, Elizabeth, 5587, 5588
Wilf, Jason, 5587, 5588
Wilf, Jeffrey, 5587, 5588
Wilf, Jonathan, 5587, 5588
Wilf, Joseph, 5587, 5588
Wilf, Judith, 5587, 5588
Wilf, Leonard, 5587, 5588
Wilf, Mark, 5587, 5588
Wilf, Orin, 5587, 5588
Wilf, Zygmunt, 5587, 5588
Wilfahrt, Barry, 7295
Wilford, Ronald A., 6135
Wilford, Sara R., 6135
Wilfore, Victor R., 9506
Wilhelm, David, 7408
Wilhelm, Miriam, 4944
Wilhite, James, 8607
Wilhoite, Bert M., 3342
Wilk, Joan, 9862
Wilke, Diane, 85
Wilkens, E. Peter H., 2021
Wilkens, Peter, 2021
Wilkerson, Bernice, 2682
Wilkerson, Justin, 2682
Wilkerson, Marjorie, 3413
Wilkerson, Peggy B., 9716
Wilkerson, Robert R., 9716
Wilkes, Charles C., 3830
Wilkie, Valleau, Jr., 9151
Wilkins, Catherine, 9724
Wilkins, Zelene, 4481
Wilkinson, Anne, 1418
Wilkinson, Bary, 1183
Wilkinson, Brenda, 884
Wilkinson, Bruce, 1183
Wilkinson, Charles T., 7288

Wilkinson, F. McKinnon, 7106
Wilkinson, Frank W., 9737, 9765
Wilkinson, Gerald, 884
Wilkinson, Guerin S., 1183
Wilkinson, James B., 7288
Wilkinson, Mary S., 4308
Wilkinson, Noreen A., 3265
Wilkinson, R. W., 9772
Wilkinson, R.W., 9737
Wilkinson, Rebecca Frankel, 2886
Wilkinson, Russell C., 1645
Wilkinson, Sharon, 7696
Wilkinson, Stephen, Dr. , 1183
Wilkinson, Sue, 5067
Wilkinson, Tom S., 1183
Wilkinson, Warren S., 1183
Wilks, Jeffrey, 6977
Wilks, Lise, 6837
Will, James M., 9714
Will, James W., 9714
Will, Muriel J., 9714
Willard Charitable Trust, Raymond & Alma, 6542
Willard Trust, Cecilia Young, 9278
Willcoxon, Dorothy B., 3559
Willens, Joan G., 1041
Willenz, Avigdor, 4101
Willet, Bernie, 8703
Willet, Michael, 5123
Willett, Lynne, 9552
Willett, William G., 9552
William Carter Company, 2454
William Companies, 8707
William, Kirk Harper, 9373
Williams College, 2186
Williams Companies Inc., 1515
Williams Family Foundation, The, 7639
Williams Real Estate Co. Inc., 6655
Williams, Alan, 4850
Williams, Alan J., 3660
Williams, Ali Smith, 8793
Williams, Andrew, 77
Williams, Andrew J., 77
Williams, Angela C., 1958
Williams, Annie, 3655
Williams, Ariana C.A., 9470
Williams, Audrey C., 3392
Williams, Beatrice, 9281
Williams, Benjamin J., 4276
Williams, Betty A., 2612
Williams, Betty J., 4618
Williams, Brenda Banta, 2719
Williams, C. Molton, 8685
Williams, Cad, 9231
Williams, Claudine B., 5142
Williams, Constance W., 4035
Williams, Craig P., 3947
Williams, Dale, 7795
Williams, Dave, 2409
Williams, Dave H., 9553
Williams, Donald, 77
Williams, Donald F., 77
Williams, Donna, 77
Williams, Donna H., 77
Williams, E. Grainger, 213
Williams, Edith K., 4150
Williams, Emelie Melton, 6818
Williams, Emily, 3392
Williams, Eugene J., 8029
Williams, Felix Noble, 5007
Williams, Frank Allen, 2659
Williams, George, 9133
Williams, Glenda, 7641
Williams, Greg, 208, 8743

Williams, Gregory, 182
Williams, Gretchen Minyard, 8795
Williams, Greyson P., 9470
Williams, Harold M., 1041
Williams, Harold R., 9279
Williams, Harriette, 472
Williams, Harry S., 9554
Williams, Helen D., 7638
Williams, J.L., 9280
Williams, James B., 2612
Williams, Jane L., 8228
Williams, Jerry, 5113
Williams, Jimmie D., 8585
Williams, John, 4212
Williams, John A., 1970
Williams, John C., 825, 8357
Williams, John K., 6299
Williams, Jonell H., 9280
Williams, Judy, 3360
Williams, Karen, 5660
Williams, Karyn, 496
Williams, Kathleen S., 8623
Williams, Kathy, 377
Williams, Kay, 7031
Williams, Kenna, 219
Williams, Kim, 182
Williams, Kristen E., 4169
Williams, Kristina, 4968
Williams, Lamar, 9373
Williams, Lanny M., 8541
Williams, Leonard E., 1970
Williams, Lisa J., 5199
Williams, Lynne, 1255
Williams, Marie S., 7289
Williams, Mark, 521
Williams, Maude O'Connor, 9210
Williams, Michael, 480
Williams, Michael E., 46
Williams, Michael P., 4299
Williams, Michael S., 5142
Williams, Monique G., 9571
Williams, Nan, 471, 472
Williams, Nancy, 9696
Williams, Nita, 9133
Williams, Patsy B., 9554
Williams, Paul, 706
Williams, R. Jamison, 4618
Williams, R. Jamison, Jr., 4508, 4618
Williams, Ralph, 1041
Williams, Reba W., 9553
Williams, Richard, 5610, 7606, 9280
Williams, Richard E., 6299
Williams, Richard F., 7638
Williams, Richard John, 3176
Williams, Richard S., Jr., 9441
Williams, Robert, 3392, 6912
Williams, Robert M., 6299
Williams, Roy, 7715
Williams, Shari, 1308
Williams, Stephen D., 5199
Williams, Stephen J., 3434
Williams, Steve G., Jr., 8541
Williams, Susan, 7891
Williams, Susan Slavik, 5007
Williams, Sylvia L., 3986
Williams, Theresa, 5142
Williams, Theresa E., 2667
Williams, Thomas L., 7638
Williams, Thomas M., 4150
Williams, Tim M., 4900
Williams, Vernita, 3363
Williams, W. Joseph, Jr., 7638
Williams, Walter L., 7289
Williams, William J., 7638

Williams-Getzoff, Amy, 9147
Williamsen, Gail, 9356
Williamson, Aleta, 6626
Williamson, Anne E., 4239
Williamson, Jack, 3643
Williamson, Jean C., 8685
Williamson, Jeanette L., 6652
Williamson, John A., 8685
Williamson, John A., Jr., 8685
Williamson, John D., II, 7640
Williamson, Jonathan, 7620
Williamson, Joseph Bradley, 7640
Williamson, Kate, 1184
Williamson, Ladane, 7155
Williamson, Lynn, 7640
Williamson, Marcia, 3567
Williamson, Sallie S., 2613
Williamson, Thomas A., 3590
Williamson, Tom A., 3627
Williamson, Warren P., III, 7640
Williamson, Warren P., IV, 7640
Williford, Catherine, 3168
Willig, Karl, 899
Willingham, C. Harold, 5589
Willingham, Gene W., 9254
Willingham, Helen, 9254
Willingham, Larry, 5589
Willingham, Nancy, 5589
Willis, David, 4276
Willis, Jim, 8869
Willis, Jimmy, 8798
Willis, Marguerite, 8522
Willis, Phyllis, 7717
Willis, Robert M., 3807
Willis, Thomas M., 3612
Willits, Thomas R., 9385
Willman, J. Nolan, 3346
Willner, Peter, 5668
Wills, Craig, 111
Wills, Irene J., 8618
Wills, Morgan J., 8618
Wills, Polly D., 8647
Wills, Thomas W., 8618
Wills, W. Ridley, II, 8618
Wills, W. Ridley, III, 8618
Wilmans, Carlie, 1161
Wilmerding, John, 1781, 8327
Wilmers, Elisabeth Roche, 6677
Wilmers, Robert, 6888
Wilmers, Robert G., 6677
Wilmes, Arthur L., 3468
Wilmes, Cecelia A., 3468
Wilmes, Katherine A., 3468
Wilmes, Mary E., 3468
Wilmington Trust Co., 1632, 1638, 1654, 1680, 1693, 1736, 4009, 8169
Wilmott, Timothy, 8208
Wilnai Foundation, Ruth & Amos, 4101
Wilnai, Amos, 1185
Wilnai, Nitzan, 1185
Wilnai, Ruth, 1185
Wilnai-Tzoore, Sigal, 1185
Wilnai-Ziskind, Yael, 1185
Wilner, Thomas B., 1793
Wilschanski, David, 5405
Wilson Charitable Lead Trust, Nancy F., 3670
Wilson Heirs Trust, 8895
Wilson Kasowski Trust, 8895
Wilson, Alan D., 3987
Wilson, Angela B., 9464
Wilson, Barbara, 9114
Wilson, Becky, 9740

Wilson, Bob, 8711
Wilson, Carolyn Munro, 1948
Wilson, Catherine M., 48
Wilson, Chad P., 8686
Wilson, Charles P., 8686
Wilson, Christine M., 3204
Wilson, David, 1412, 6979
Wilson, David S., 1186
Wilson, Deborah, 6979
Wilson, Dennis, 3367, 3446
Wilson, Dennis C., 1186
Wilson, Diane M., 5105
Wilson, Donald S., 9960
Wilson, Douglas, 1568
Wilson, Garnet A., 7641
Wilson, Gary, 1599
Wilson, George A., 9725
Wilson, Gregory S., 1186
Wilson, Heidi M., 4798
Wilson, Hollis C., 1380
Wilson, Hugh H., 2408
Wilson, J. Christy, Jr., 1251
Wilson, J. Randolph, 4976
Wilson, Jack, 2463
Wilson, James McM, 9386
Wilson, Janet, 7806
Wilson, Jay D., 8570
Wilson, Jeff, 945
Wilson, Jeff M., 9605
Wilson, Jenifer A., 4777
Wilson, Jennifer H., 3272
Wilson, Joan B., 1380
Wilson, John, 9494
Wilson, John H.T., 1412
Wilson, Jonathan R., 5499
Wilson, Jordan, 863
Wilson, Josephine D., 8647
Wilson, Katherine M., 6979
Wilson, Kathleen, 9960
Wilson, Kathryn, 3204
Wilson, Lea Ann, 9232
Wilson, Leland, 3634
Wilson, Lesley, 9725
Wilson, Lisa, 969
Wilson, Margaret I., 2519
Wilson, Marion L., 1186
Wilson, Marion M., 9725
Wilson, Mark, 3567
Wilson, Mary Elizabeth, 5590
Wilson, Mary P., 2408
Wilson, Michael, 9725
Wilson, Nancy, 3370, 9725
Wilson, Nancy F., 3670
Wilson, Patti Johnson, 7736
Wilson, Pattye, 4845
Wilson, Paul, 67
Wilson, Peter A., 4014, 4248
Wilson, Ralph C., Jr., 4399
Wilson, Randall, 4720
Wilson, Richard A., 1186
Wilson, Robert N., 5499
Wilson, Robert S., 1186
Wilson, Rodney M., 4777
Wilson, Sandra W., 1412
Wilson, Scott, 2666
Wilson, Shelby, 4801
Wilson, Sherri D., 1563
Wilson, Susan, 4983
Wilson, T. Craig, 3676
Wilson, Terrell, 5940
Wilson, Thomas, 3204
Wilson, Thomas B., 1186
Wilson, Walter C., 1829
Wilson, Wanda, 9103

Wilson, Wendy R., 3987
Wilson, William, 1412, 3255
Wilson, William B., 1380
Wilson, William L., 1380
Wilson, Winifred Read, 1568
Wilt, Samuel Fleming, 8615
Wilt, Toby S., 8687
Wilton Foundation, E. Carlton, 9412
Wilton, E. Carlton, Jr., 9412
Wiltsek, Nancy Lynn, 3656
Wimberger, Eric, 9796
Wimberly, Kenneth W., 8699, 8703
Wimer, Norm, 7891
Wimmer Solutions, 5648
Wimmer, Betty L., 8361
Wimmer, Jim, 4624
Winans Company, C.H., 5257
Winans, Sue, 5573
Winant, Joan, 5967
Winant, John, 5967
Winbigler, Connie, 4396
Winbrook Management, 6519
Winchester Ammunition, 3991
Winchester-Vega, Michele, Dr., 5872
Winckler, Haddon O., 8863
Wind, David, 4435
Wind, David C., 9992
Winder, David, 9358
Windfeldt, David, 1267
Windham, James C., Jr., 7097
Windolf, John A., 2614
Windolf, Muriel B., 2614
Windsor, 3905, 8859
Windt, Sallyan, 2970
Windway Capital Corp., 9961
Winebrenner-Nizam, Michelle, 1273
Wineland, Jay, 7424
Winer, Michael, 1763
Winestone, Ted, 8591
Winetroub, Jerald, 8981
Winfield, Hank, 9222
Winfield, Martha B., 7324
Wing, Allison, 1105
Wing, Caroline S., 1105
Wing, Gerald, 1105
Wing, Gloria, 9370
Wing, Holly, 1105
Wing, Rose, 2463
Wing, Shelley, 3511
Wing-Berman, Molly, 8483
Wingard, Brian W., 7929
Wingate, Carole, 1897
Wingate, D.J., 7449
Wingate, Don, 1897
Wings Investors Co., 2510
Winiarski, Barbara, 1187
Winiarski, Warren, 1187
Winick, Alyson, 7577
Winick, Gary, 6060
Winiecki, Brenna L., 1784
Winiecki, Robert C., 1784
Winkelman, Irene, 1777
Winker, Virginia L., 8911
Winkhaus, Gwenn S., 6891
Winkler, Henry, Dr., 7582
Winkler, Irwin, 1188
Winkler, Margo, 1188
Winmill, Mark C., 6897
Winn, Thomas P., 1189
Winnecke, Joyce, 2787
Winokur, Annick M., 1597
Winokur, Barton J., 8362
Winokur, Deanne Howard, 1597
Winokur, Herbert, 1597

Winokur, Herbert S., Jr., 1597
Winpigler, Adrian L., 8316
Winslow, Benjamin R., 591
Winslow, Rosemary, 3771
Winsor, Frank, 2682
Winston, Bert F., Jr., 9282
Winston, Christopher J., 9761
Winston, Eric, 480
Winston, Gary, 9285
Winston, James H., 2368
Winston, John, 4793
Winston, Lynn David, 9282
Winter, Elizabeth H., 6201
Winter, Ilona B., 3854
Winterbottom, Brad L., 3547
Winterer, Victoria T., 2383
Winterer, William G., 2383
Winters, Alan, 5591
Winters, Alisa, 3441
Winters, Barbara, 4724
Winters, Hope, 5591
Winters, James, 1614
Winters, Leisa Raye Jones, 1614
Winthrop, Carol, Dr., 2437
Winthrop, Clara B., 4363
Winthrop, Ed, 1377
Winthrop, John, 8550
Winthrop, John, Jr., 8550
Winton, Alexa Griffith, 4805
Winton, Randolph B., 7953
Wipfli, LLP, 4792
Wire, Ralph W., Jr., 8196
Wirgau, Jessica, 9426
Wirth, Susan, 5106
Wirz, Pascal, 6084
Wisdom, Andrew, 3761
Wisdom, Arthur, 3761
Wisdom, Barbara, 2869
Wisdom, Mary Freeman, 3761
Wisdom, Matthew Morgan, 3761
Wise, Anne Culley, 2830
Wise, Blake, 3922
Wise, Bret W., 7954
Wise, Charlotte, 1478
Wise, Dorothy, 2132
Wise, Leslie, 4442
Wise, Lois, 2963
Wise, Marie Figge, 9283
Wise, Robert B., 1478
Wise, Ronnie, 9130
Wise, Tim, 1858
Wise, William, 2132
Wise, William A., 9283
Wiseman, G. Michael, 5126
Wiseman, Mary Witten, 3707
Wisenbaker, Michael B., Jr., 8938
Wisenbaker, Wesley Hill, 8938
Wiser, Bob, 9555
Wish You Were Here Productions, 1730
Wish, Barry N., 6981
Wish, Jonathan A., 6981
Wish, Jonathan Adess, 6981
Wish, Lindsey, 6981
Wish, Oblio, 6981
Wishco, 6981
Wishes By Wyndham Foundation, 7209
Wishnick, Lisa, 2690
Wishnick, William, 2690
Wislow, Leonard A., 3323
Wislow, Robert A., 3323
Wislow, Susan, 3323
Wismer, David A., 1353
Wismer, David A., III, 1353
Wismer, Mary Anne, 1353

Wisner, Donald, 4587
Wisner, Joyce S., 4587
Wisner, Leslie, 4587
Wisnom, David, Jr., 260
Wisnom, Ruth, 260
Wissner, Stella, 9727
Wissner-Slivka, Lisa, 9727
Wister, Diana S., 8305
Wister, William R., Jr., 8305
Witham, David, 3787
Withers, Kathryn W., 7826
Withers, Mettie, 1892
Withers, Timothy C., 4063
Witherspoon, Melvin, 8026
Withey, Richard, 9078
Withington, Nathan N., 4135
Withycombe, F. Keith, 184
Withycombe, Patricia A., 184
Witkin, Alba, 1191
Witkovski, Vicki F., 5098
Witkowsky, Anne, 1831
Witmer Charitable Foundation, Meryl &
    Charles, 6720
Witmer, William, 9781
Witt, Donna C., 7737
Witt, Jocelyn S., 1508
Witt, Scott V., 2348
Witt, Wesley A., 278
Witte, John H., Jr., 9962
Witte, Kristina L., 5111
Wittel, Burnice Crosby, 4858
Witten Investments, Jerald, 8711
Witten, Cynthia, 2970
Witter, David, 1192
Witter, Margot, 1192
Witter, Richard, 1192
Witter, Robert, Jr., 1192
Witters, Joseph E., 9206
Wittich, Peter, 2358
Wittig, Bob, 1817
Wittkowske, John F., 9958
Wittstein, Eric S., 6080
Witzel Trust, Sarah E., 10000
Witzig, Scott A., 3126
WJ Holding, 5164
WJS Trust, 1053
WKBN Broadcasting Corp., 7640
Wo Foundation, C.S., 2655
Wo, Craig Scott, 2655
Wo, Michael, 2655
Wo, Robert C., 2655
Wo, Robert W., 2655
Wo, Wendell, 2655
Wochner, Lee, 421
Woerner Management, 2409
Woerner World Ministries, 2261
Woerner, Larry, 2261
Woerner, Lester J., 2409
Woessner, David H., 1559
Wohlgemuth, Alexander, 6984
Wohlgemuth, Esther, 6984
Wohlgemuth, Melissa, 6984
Wohlgemuth, Morton, 6984
Wohlgemuth, Robert, 6984
Woidtke, Lou Ann T., 4835
Wojahn, Dennis, 9836
Wojcicki, Anne, 626
Wojcicki, Janet, 626
Wojcicki, Susan, 626
Wojtychiw, Victor, 3234
Wolcott Family Living Trust, 7792
Wolcott II Trust-Wolcott Living Trust, Guy,
    7792
Wolcott, April, 7792

Wolcott, Chris G., 7792
Wolcott, Guy R., 7792
Wolcott, Guy R., II, 7792
Wolcott, Joshua, 1381
Wolcott, Kerri, 1381
Wolcott, Robert, 404
Wold, Elaine J., 1930
Wold, Keith C., Jr., 1930
Wold, Steven, 3316
Woldar, Edwin, 6985
Woldar, Jay, 6985
Woldar, Paul, 6985
Woldar, Shirley, 6985
Wolek, Anne T., 6623
Wolens, Louis, 9284
Wolf Charitable Lead Trust, John T. &
    Peggy L., 3325
Wolf Real Estate, 7643
Wolf, Amy, 6450
Wolf, Chaim Zvi, 6986
Wolf, Dennie, 8363
Wolf, Don A., 8293
Wolf, Edward L., 5814
Wolf, Ellen, 5814
Wolf, Erving, 9285
Wolf, Esther, 6517
Wolf, Flora Barth, 8363
Wolf, Fredora K., 8363
Wolf, Gregory E., 3327
Wolf, Howard, 8811
Wolf, Jeffrey, 5814
Wolf, John T., 3325
Wolf, Joyce, 9285
Wolf, Jr. Revocable Trust, Clarence,
    2410
Wolf, Linda G., 3327
Wolf, M. Daniel, 9285
Wolf, Martha, 8363
Wolf, Mary, 8140
Wolf, Mathew D., 9285
Wolf, Maurice, 6517
Wolf, Mel, 5593
Wolf, Milton, 7643
Wolf, Nancy, 7643
Wolf, Phil H., 7318
Wolf, Phyllis P., 273
Wolf, Rachel, 6986
Wolf, Robert B., 7962, 8205
Wolf, Ron, 4946
Wolf, Ronald W., 8140
Wolf, Roslyn Z., 7643
Wolf, Ryan G., 3327
Wolf, Sherri, 7643
Wolf, Steven, 5814
Wolf, Steven J., 1086
Wolf, Sylvia S., 4567
Wolf, William, 5040
Wolf, William J., 8140
Wolfard, Kay, 7731
Wolfe, Anna H., 8578
Wolfe, Barbara A., 1193
Wolfe, Carl W., 7815
Wolfe, Daniel, 5809
Wolfe, Elizabeth T., 7644
Wolfe, Frederic D., 7644
Wolfe, Frederica R., 7644
Wolfe, Gary J., 5047
Wolfe, James L., 8691
Wolfe, Mark, 1352
Wolfe, Marueen, 5969
Wolfe, Mary T., 7644
Wolfe, Mike, 7375
Wolfe, Patricia, 7815
Wolfe, Peggy, 1352

Wolfe, Shirley, 8920
Wolfe, Thomas F., 1193
Wolff Shoe Co., 5040
Wolff Trust, William, 5040
Wolff, Beverly M., 6137
Wolff, Cylvia, 9286
Wolff, Elaine, 5040
Wolff, Gary, 5040
Wolff, Henry, Jr., 349
Wolff, John M., 5039
Wolff, Marilyn, 3328
Wolff, Melvyn L., 9286
Wolff, Michael R., 5039
Wolff, Noah, 3328
Wolff, Ranan, 3328
Wolff, Samuel, 5040
Wolff, Sarah, 5040
Wolff, William, 5040
Wolford, Ed, 8374
Wolford, Stephen T., 3659
Wolfson, Adam Yehoshua, 1304
Wolfson, Bruce, 6332
Wolfson, David, 5680
Wolfson, Elan Hadar, 1304
Wolfson, June, 8364
Wolfson, Merle A., 8042
Wolfson, Stephen, 8364
Wolfson, Steve, 8364
Wolfwind, 3905
Wolgin, Jacqueline, 2411
Wolgin, Marian, 8365
Wolgin, Norman, 8365
Wolgin, Rachelle, 2411
Wolk, Andrew, 6987
Wolk, Elliot K., 6987
Wolk, Katherine C., 7490
Wolk, Michael, 5271
Wolk, Nancy, 6987
Wolka, Terril, 3446
Wolland, Kathie, 6894
Wollen, Dori, 6070
Wollen, Roger C., 6070
Wollin, Lonnie, 5288, 5411
Wollman, Jodie Lynn, 884
Wollons, Roberta, 3024
Wollowick, Gladys, 2412
Wollowick, Janet Amy, 2412
Wolman, Paul C., III, 3971
Wolpoff, Carol, 3990
Wolpoff, Harry K., 3990
Wolstenholme, Eugene B., 8366
Wolstenholme, Jean M., 8366
Wolstenholme, Ralph, 8366
Wolter, Ralph, 3125
Woltman Furniture Co., 9288
Woltman, B.M., 9288
Wolzinger, Constance, 5200
Wolzinger, Melvin B., 5200
Womack Company, 9556
Womack, Bobbye Rae, 9556
Womack, Charles A., III, 9556
Womack, Charles A., Jr., 9556
Womack, Charles, Jr., 9556
Womack, Charles, Sr., 9556
Womack, Deanna Lynn, 9289
Womack, Eva Robuck, 9289
Womack, Joe, 7704
Womack, Michael Scott, 9289
Womack, Patrick, 9556
Womack, R. Marvin, 9289
Womble, Astrid C., 8397
Women In Printing, 8605
Wong, Allene, 2636
Wong, Colene S., 2657

Wong, Colleen, 2636
Wong, Corinda, 2638
Wong, Harry C., 2656
Wong, Henry H., 2657
Wong, Jimmy Shingfai, 1194
Wong, Natasha, 261
Wong, Nathalie, 6988
Wong, Nee-Chang Chock, 2656
Wong, Patrick, 3560
Wong, Reuben, 2659
Wong, Robert, 5424, 5579
Wong, Sandra C.H., 2645
Wong, Selena Y., 694
Wong, Sharon, 3195
Wong, Stephen R., 6988
Wong-Avery, Sally Tsui, 261
Wonsick, Lynn, 7932
Woo, Helen, 1195
Wood County National Bank, 9963
Wood County Trust Co., 9963
Wood Good Industries, 4661
Wood Trust, Ira R., 8367
Wood Trust, Wilford P., 8551
Wood, Benjamin David, 9293
Wood, Beth, 6248
Wood, Carla O' Neill, 2535
Wood, Cat, 3511
Wood, Courtenay S., 8978
Wood, David, 206
Wood, David J., 9187
Wood, David J., Jr., 9537
Wood, E. Jenner, 2195
Wood, Elizabeth, 9537
Wood, Estelle J., 8551
Wood, George, 6248
Wood, Geri, 8924
Wood, Heather W., 8978
Wood, Helen M., 3548
Wood, J.A., 6993
Wood, James B., 6943
Wood, James C., III, 7339
Wood, James N., 3548
Wood, Jenner, 2284
Wood, Jennifer, 2065
Wood, Jeremy, 2285
Wood, Jerome, 5873
Wood, John M., III, 4034
Wood, John R., 2408
Wood, Keving John, 2535
Wood, Leonard W., 2535
Wood, Leonard W., Jr., 2535
Wood, Pamela A., 5201
Wood, Pamela R., 5201
Wood, Patty, 3360
Wood, Paul A., 5201
Wood, Paul G., 6177
Wood, Rodney P., 4445
Wood, Ross, 9612
Wood, Sally Kemper, 3644
Wood, Sarah Hager, 3687
Wood, Susan, 2408
Wood, Thomas J., III, 3644
Wood, Thomas J., Jr., 3644
Wood, Willard, 5651
Wood, William H., 1780
Woodall, Dee Ann, 8368
Woodall, Mark E., 8368
Woodall, Marvin L., 8368
Woodard, Andrew, 7831
Woodard, Carlton, 7831
Woodard, James, 4850
Woodard, Jennifer, 458
Woodard, Joy, 7831
Woodard, Kim, 7831

Woodard, Kristen A., 7831
Woodard, Tod, 7831
Woodard, Tyson, 7831
Woodard, Walter A., 7831
Woodbeck, Bemjamin C., 1266
Woodburn, Dena, 2021
Woodburn, Joyce, 37
Woodbury, Evelyn, 5238
Woodbury, Karen, 4939
Wooden Nickel Foundation, 6164
Woodfin, Kathryn, 5206
Woodford, Daniel J., 1382
Woodford, John M., 1382
Woodford, Joseph C., 1382
Woodford, Kristin M., 1382
Woodford, Linda M., 1382
Woodford, Stephen D., 1382
Woodford, Steve Kristin, 1382
Woodgood, 4661
Woodhouse, Kathleen, 8698
Woodhull, James M., II, 7610
Woodin, John H., 9868
Woodland Village North, LLC, 5173
Woodman, Abigail J., 3795
Woodman, Byron E., Jr., 4104
Woodman, June Rosemary, 140
Woodman, Richard S., 8385
Woodner Family Collection, Ian, 6991
Woodner, Andrea, 6991
Woodring, A. Greig, 4949
Woodruff, George C., III, 2617
Woodruff, George C., Jr., 2617
Woodruff, James, III, 2618
Woodruff, Julie, 2617
Woodruff, Sarah H., 3330
Woodruff, Thomas, 2618
Woods Trust, Adrian W., 5042
Woods, Alexandra, 6992
Woods, Bob, 697
Woods, Caroline T., 8597
Woods, Ellen L., 8597
Woods, Emil, 6239
Woods, Gary V., 9291
Woods, H.A., 9052
Woods, Janet, 9638
Woods, John R., Jr., 4993
Woods, John R., Sr., 4993
Woods, Judith H., 4993
Woods, Judy S., 6993
Woods, Kathleen E., 8597
Woods, Kathryn Esping, 8841
Woods, Margaret C., 8597
Woods, Marjorie, 4993
Woods, Pam, 1255
Woods, Priscilla B., 6992
Woods, Rodney, 8841
Woods, Rosalie, 5198
Woods, Stephen K., 4514
Woods, Ward W., Jr., 6992
Woodside, Eileen E., 8375
Woodson, Charles, 1937
Woodson, Georgia, 1937
Woodtrust Financial Corp., 9963
Woodward Communications, 3549
Woodward, Ann Eden, 6993
Woodward, Anthony, 7646
Woodward, Barbara Sullivan, 3549
Woodward, Florence S., 8505
Woodward, Kristin, 3549
Woodward, Marianna M., 7646
Woodward, Robert U., 1839
Woodward, Sharon V., 3816
Woodward, Thomas, 3549
Woodward, Tina, 1542

Woodward, W. Steven, 1680
Woodworth & Company, 9728
Woodworth Capital Inc., 9728
Woodworth, Jeffrey A., 9728
Woodworth, John A., 9728
Woodworth, Nancy, 9728
Woody, Dennis, 7953
Woolard, Edgar, 2414
Woolard, Edgar S., Jr., 2414
Woolard, Lynda D., 2414
Woolard, Peggy, 2414
Woolard-Provine, Annette, 2414
Wooley, Fergus R., 4719
Woolf, Orien Levy, 9292
Woolfalk, Shigeko, 5821
Woollems, J. Michael, 8698
Woolmington, Robert E., 9368
Woolner, Catherine N., 6530
Woolson, Bruce, 8791
Wooten, Robin Swett, 9227
Worcel, Sonia, 7807
Word of Life Armenia, 8711
Worden, Joe, 4449
Worden, Michael, 1607
Working Realty, 6655
Workinger, Geof, 4671
Workman Publishing Co., 6970
Workman, Carolan, 6970
Workman, Lisa D., 7356
Workman, M. James, Rev. , 4028
Workman, Peter, 6970
Workman, RaSheda, 12
Workneh, Claire, 3904
World Mate, 6249
World Mate Japan, 6249
World Wide Rush, LLC, 5414
Worldwide Educational Svcs. of
    California, 279
Worley, Robin S., 2584
Worman, Glenn, 5398
Worner, Jacob, 7631
Worrell, Judy, 3558
Worsdale, Raymond E., 6995
Worsham, Gary, 8815
Worsoe, Johannes, 5795
Worster, Bruce, 1197
Worster, Lynn, 2857
Worster, Susan, 1197
Worth, Robert, 4598
Worthington, Beth A., 7546
Worthington, Lois M., 9729
Wotherspoon, Eleonore, 6919
Woys, James E., 608
Wozniak, Paul, 966
WPC Holding, 7792
WPIX, 6909
WPM Exploration, 3742
Wraith, Ellen Jacob, 1895
Wrang, William E., 1477
Wrangler Apparel Corp., 7053
Wrap-On Co., 1735
Wrape, A.M., 222
Wrape, Jarrell V., 222
Wrape, Tom K., 222
Wrape, W.R., II, 222
Wrather, Christopher C., 1198
Wray, Elizabeth A., 667
Wray, Gay Firestone, 177
Wray, Michael, 1403
Wray, Ronald D., 3184
Wrean Family, 4274
Wrean, William H., Jr., 4274
Wreford-Smith, John, 3919
WRH Texas Ltd. Partnership, 9009

Wright, Allison, 8827
Wright, Anne S., 2620
Wright, Barbara, 9730
Wright, Barbara J., 3333
Wright, Barbara Schuchart, 9730
Wright, Betty J., 9295
Wright, Celeste H., 3303
Wright, Celeste Hank, 2865
Wright, Charles, 9730
Wright, Charles B., III, 6137
Wright, Charles Bagley, III, 9730
Wright, Christopher, 6884
Wright, Cleveland A., 9511
Wright, Dave, 4396
Wright, Edward P., 5915
Wright, Eloise M., 3551
Wright, Erin, 4612, 9611
Wright, Ernest S., 2620
Wright, Florence F., 7953
Wright, Gail, 4497
Wright, Graciela C., 3551
Wright, Howard S., 9611
Wright, James Richard, 9294
Wright, James W., 9899
Wright, Jaraun, 5395
Wright, Jeanette S., 2415
Wright, Jeffrey C., 2415
Wright, Jeffrey L., 4691
Wright, Jo Rhea N., 3927
Wright, Joann, 6995
Wright, John, 3344
Wright, John M., 2620
Wright, John R., 3551
Wright, Joseph, 8366
Wright, Julia V., 11
Wright, Julia V., 9083
Wright, Kate Janway, 9611
Wright, Kay, 2415
Wright, Kimberly O., 2620
Wright, Korynne, 9611
Wright, Laura, 2415
Wright, Mary Garner, 2032
Wright, Michael, 356, 2434
Wright, Michael S., 8633
Wright, Michaelon A., 4612
Wright, Morgan, 4612
Wright, Nelson A., III, 3333
Wright, Nelson A., Jr., 3333
Wright, Patricia L., 9295
Wright, Patti L., 9294
Wright, Phillip C., 3431
Wright, Richard, 9454
Wright, Robert C., 3466
Wright, Robert F., 1174
Wright, Robert M., 3333
Wright, Robert W., 1097
Wright, Sally S., 9611
Wright, Shauna, 5395
Wright, Thomas M., 8956
Wright, Victor R., 6995
Wright, William Dan, 9295
Wright, William E., 9295
Wrigley, Julie A., 102
Wrigley, Steve, Dr. , 2437
Writer, George S., 1200
Writer, Jeffrey H., 1200
Writer, Judith H., 1200
Wrves, Orestes, 2150
WSBT, 3444
Wu, Chin-Cheng, 4316
Wu, Christopher, 4316
Wu, Frank S., 593
Wu, Grace T., 528
Wu, Hellen, 313

Wu, Hueyling, 5596
Wu, Jeffrey, 956
Wu, Michael, 2454
Wu, Raymond, 956
Wu, Shirley, 8447
Wu, Taihua Kathy, 5596
Wunder, Barbara, 96
Wunsch, Eric M., 6996
Wunsch, Ethel, 6996
Wunsch, Joseph W., 6996
Wunsch, Peter, 6996
Wunsch, Samuel, 6996
Wurst, John C., 5043
Wurst, Margaret S., 5043
Wurst, Michael S., 5043
Wurtele, Joanna, 6997
Wurtele, V., 4670
Wurts, Henrietta Tower, 8370
Wurwand, Jane Drake, 451
Wurwand, Raymond L., 451
Wurzburg, Jocelyn Dan, 8591
Wurzer, Marvin A., 8763
Wustenberg, Mark, 7825
Wustenberg, Phyllis, 7825
Wutz, Laura A., 5239
Wutz, Margaret M., 5239
Wutz, Paul F., 5239
Wyatt, Jane C., 71
Wyatt, Kalei T., 9360
Wyatt, Kent, 3567
Wyatt, Kristi Smith, 4946
Wyatt, Linda L., 8552
Wyatt, Robert, 9994
Wyatt, Tarrant & Combs, LLP, 3672
Wyatt, Tate, 3567
Wyatt, W. Whitlow, 8552
Wyche, Paul B., 7093
Wyckoff, Janet R., 6998
Wyckoff, Margaret H., 6998
Wyckoff, Stephen G., 6998
Wyckoff-Dickey, Sheila, 9640
Wyeth, Andrew, 1781
Wyeth, Andrew N., 8327
Wyeth, Betsy James, 1781, 8327
Wyeth, James B., 8371
Wyeth, James Browning, 1781, 8327
Wyeth, Phyllis, 8327
Wyeth, Phyllis M., 8371
Wyland, James H., 7336
Wyler, J. David, 7647
Wyler, Jeffrey L., 7647
Wyler, Linda, 7647
Wylie, Paul, 6464
Wyman, Cristina, 1539
Wyman, Deehan M., 9731
Wyman, Elizabeth, 3940
Wyman, Hal, 9731
Wyman, Henry W., 1539
Wyman, Maria, 1539
Wyman, Merrily, 9731
Wyman, Norman J., 9983
Wyman, Ralph M., 1539
Wyman, Timothy E., 3940
Wyman-Gordon Co., 4364
Wymbs, Bradley S., 2418
Wymbs, Harriet S., 2418
Wymbs, Norman E., 2418
Wynant, Simone C., 385
Wynkoop, Derrik, 5872
Wynn, Elaine P., 5202
Wynn, Jim, 4499
Wynn, Mark, 3359
Wynn, Stephen A., 5202
Wynne Building Corporation, 2419

Wynne, Dancy H., 2514
Wynne, Deena L., 2419
Wynne, Dorothy, 2419
Wynne, Eric P., 2419
Wynne, James J., Rev. , 1131
Wynne, Joel F., 2419
Wynne, Kenneth R., 9296
Wynne, Matthew Lyle, 2419
Wynveen, Gary, 9836
Wyshner, David, 5255
Wyss, Edmund J., 7832
Wyss, Emert, 2705
Wyss, Emily A., 7832
Wyss, Isabel J., 7832
Wyss, Judith, 7832
Wyss, Loren L., 7832
Wyss-Jones, Jennifer A., 7832
Wyszynski, Cari, 9706

X-Site Medical LLC, 8368
Xerxes Corporation, 4650

Yablon, Jill, 1782
Yablon, Paul, 1782
Yaeger, William J., Jr., 9749
Yagoda, Eva, 7001
Yagoda, Eve, 7001
Yagoda, Jason, 7001
Yakobovich, Pitya, 6501
Yakoubovsky-Lerke, Peter A., 1132
Yamagata, Gene H., 5203
Yamashiro, Patricia, 2642
Yamin, Alice, 6114
Yan, Gordon, 262
Yan, Guochen, 262
Yan, Sai Hong, 2175
Yancey, Al, 3125
Yancey, Helen Lund, 9052
Yancey, Janet, 1354
Yancey, Philip, 1354
Yanchus, Paul, 3978
Yandura, Paul, 2182
Yang, Bing, 1025
Yang, Cindy, 6748
Yaniga, Stephanie, 6632
Yanney, Michael B., 5066
Yanover, J. Jonathan, 2268
Yanover, Judith P., 2268
Yanover, Robert A., 2268
Yantek, Dawn, 2666
Yantz, Jerome, 4478
Yarmolinsky, Alex, 794
Yarmuth, Jacob, 3709
Yarmuth, Jeffrey T., 3709
Yarmuth, Robert N., 3709
Yarmuth, Susan Long, 3709
Yarmuth, William B., 3709
Yarnevich, George W., 3590, 3627
Yarshater, Ehsan, 6589
Yaruss, Debra Wanger, 2694
Yaryan, Andy, 3379
YASME Foundation, 870
Yaspan, Barbara, 7003
Yaspan, David, 7003
Yaspan, Richard, 7003
Yaspan, Robert, 7003
Yass, Jeffrey, 8310
Yasutake, Warren, 9642
Yates, Annie, 1514
Yates, Bradford, 6477
Yates, Charles H., 2447
Yates, Christopher M., 5595
Yates, Elizabeth M., 9503

Yates, H. Roy, 9626
Yates, Michael S., 1373
Yates, Sealy, 1373
Yavalar, Mary, 3978
Yavarone, Albert, 1557
Yawman, Gregory, 7884
Yayla Tribal Rugs, 4012
YBG, 7648
Yeager, Barbara Coit, 7751
Yeager, David, 1283
Yeager, George M., 7004
Yeager, Jeff, 4057
Yeager, Lester E., 3710
Yeager, Scott Alden, 7004
Yeakel, Barbara, 9562
Yeakel, Judith P., 9562
Yeaman, John M., 9244
Yearley, Andrew, 7005
Yearley, Anne D., 7005
Yearley, Douglas C., 7005
Yearley, Douglas C., Jr., 7005
Yearley, Peter, 7005
Yearley, Peter B., 7005
Yearley, Sandra D., 7005
Yearsley Memorial Fund, 2148
Yearwood, Anna, 41
Yearwood, Lisa W., 41
Yearwood, Thomas L., 41
Yeatman, Harry, 4880
Yeck, Robert, 7648
Yeck, William S., 7648
Yeckel, Andrew J., 473
Yeckel, Donald G., 473
Yeckel, Mark F., 473
Yee, Bennett S., 4272
Yee, Danny O., 6558
Yee, Donald Ong, 6558
Yee, Larry Ong, 6558
Yee, Michael, 5954
Yee, Natalie, 1749
Yee, Phillips, 1749
Yee, Stephanie L., 6558
Yee, Steve, 178
Yeiser, Eric B., 7649
Yelen, Mitchell A., 2052
Yen, C. James, 2791
Yen, Ho Tzu, 1201
Yen, Ho-Tzu, 1044, 1201
Yen, Sophia, 1044, 1201
Yen, Tai Hwa, 5596
Yen, Yung Tsai, 1201
Yen, Yung-Tsai, 1044, 1201
Yenawine, Philip, 5691
Yerrid, C. Steven, 2420
Yerrid, Gable, 2420
Yes Network, 1730
Yeshiva Ohel Simon, 5834
Yeshiva Tiferes Bunim, 5834
Yeskoo, Richard, 7223
Yesodei HaTorah, 5544
Yeston, Maury, 6323
Yevich, Cynthia A., 7879
Yewell, David, 3670
Ying, Cecilia, 2421
Ying, Cecilia Tse, 2421
Ying, Charlene Cecilia, 2421
Ying, Helga, 7839
Ying, James, 2421
Ying, James W., 2421
Ying, John J., 2421
Yingling, Beth, 8008
Yingling, Cynthia Eni, 7959
Yingling, Earl, 7944
Yip, Chiu, 8447

Yocum, Robert G., 8040
Yoder, Abner, 7650
Yoder, Alvin S., 8290
Yoder, Charles, 5692
Yoder, Christine, 7375
Yoder, Esther, 7650
Yoder, Henry, 8290
Yoder, Lewis, 7352
Yoder, Menno J., 8290
Yoder, Pamela, 1202
Yoder, Patricia R., 1202
Yoder, Simon C., 8290
Yoh Trust, Karen B., 8373
Yoh, H. Julie, 5597
Yoh, James, 5597
Yoh, James W., 5597
Yokota, Bonita A.T., 1103
Yokota, Ronald, 1103
Yona, Catherine, 721
Yonemoto, Bruce, 5691
Yordan, Isabel C., 7009
Yordan, Jaime E., 7009
Yordan, Peter D., 7009
Yore, Allison, 2030
York Building Products Inc., 8301
York Group, The, 8374
York Preparatory School, 5264
York, Alan R., 9550
York, Daniel, 1295
York, Janet B., 1490
York, Melissa Street, 8729
York, Michael H., Sr., 71
York, Myrth, 8507
York, Otto H., 8507
York, Sherri, 1295
Yormak, Paula, 5391
Yormark, Brett, 6524
Yorston, Carolyn, 4814
Yoshitake, Alan T., 688
Yost, Barbara, 5613
Yost, Elizabeth Burns, 7291
Yost, Jeffrey G., 5105
Yost, Karen M., 6932
Yost, Rives R., 5935
Yost, Robert, 7436
Youman's Trust, 2590
Young Development, 3487
Young Family Trust, Peg and Rick, 9732
Young Israel of New Rochelle, 5544
Young Unitrust, Ralph W., 8375
Young, Andrew J., 2621
Young, Beatrice M.H., 2659
Young, Bracebridge H., Jr., 7012
Young, Brad M., 9297
Young, Carol, Dr. , 7357
Young, Carolyn, 2621
Young, Charles, 9297
Young, Charles M., 9297
Young, Christopher, 3684
Young, Craig S., 7651
Young, Deborah, 7923
Young, Deborah Li, 2660
Young, Dennis A. , 8990
Young, Diane, 4600
Young, Dianne P., 9297
Young, Douglas L., 1938
Young, E. Ryker, 7739
Young, Elizabeth, 3771, 8837
Young, Fumiyo, 3024
Young, Gene, 4600
Young, Geoffrey G., 2043
Young, Isaac, 4926
Young, J. Rutledge, Jr., 8538
Young, Jamie, 9862

Young, Jennifer E., 5335
Young, Joanne, 9732
Young, Johanna, 7211
Young, Kathy L., 8829
Young, Kyle A., 9297
Young, Laura W.Y., 1157
Young, Laurence E., 389
Young, Leslie D., 8020
Young, Linda, 9649
Young, Madeline, 6652
Young, Margaret S., 7651
Young, Mary E., 7651
Young, Michael K., 7799
Young, Michael-Anne, 111
Young, Michelle N., 9297
Young, Nancy V., 122
Young, Richard C., 3552
Young, Sally J., 8375
Young, Shirley, 4600
Young, Talin, 8487
Young, Thomas S., 3552
Young, Tina B., 7739
Young, Travis, 3552
Young, William T., Jr., 3684
Youngberg, Barbara, 9336
Youngberg, Kristian R., 9336
Youngberg, Lance L., 9336
Youngberg, Rory, 9336
Youngblood, Bernadette M., 3532
Youngblood, Cecil, 9937
Younger, Monica, 884
Younger, Phyllis L., 2422
Younger, William H., 2422
Younger, William H., Jr., 2422
Youngquist, Maxwell F., 3249
Youngren, Thomas R., 8562
Youngs, Lisa Pepicelli, 7944
Youngs, Mindy, 1153
Yount, Benny, 7292
Yount, Charles W., 5130
Yount, Cherrie, 7292
Yount, Lisa, 7292
Yousey, Thomas, II, 6625
Youth Athletic Foundation, 8570
Youthworks!, 4806
Yowan, David L., 5664
Yowell, Carlton M., 9503
Yowell, Donald R., 9493
Yu, Albert, 699
Yu, Larry, 699
Yud, 6333
Yuen, Henry C., 476
Yukevich, Christine Cochrane, 1420
Yuki 2008 Non Grantor Charitable Trust, Miyoko, 1203
Yuki Charitable Lead Trust, Miyoko, 1203
Yuki, Cathy, 1103
Yuki, Herbert T., 1203
Yuki, Miyoko, 1203
Yuki, Thomas M., 1203
Yulman, E. Richard, 3334
Yulman, Helen, 3334
Yulman, Helen B., 3334
Yulman, Morton, 3334
Yurasek, Steve, 7357
Yurochko, Tricia, 5573
Yusko, Mark W., 7190
Yusko, Stacey, 7190

Z Group Advertising, 2428
Zabady, Bob, 8345
Zabala, Luis, Sr., 1204

Zabel, Bill, 6585
Zaber Corporation Inc., 5825
Zabotin, Mischa A., 6409
Zaccone, D.R., 3335
Zaccone, Dominic R., II, 3335
Zaccone, Loretta, 3335
Zaccone, Shere, 3335
Zaccone, Suzanne M., 3335
Zacharia, Isaac Herman, 1601
Zachariah, Allan J., 2575
Zaches Administrative Trust, Sybil, 5182
Zachry, Sarah Skiles, 4572
Zack Trust, Margaret M., 8508
Zacky, Lillian, 1205, 1206
Zaentz, Saul, 3336
Zafar, Saadia, 1599
Zafft, Gerald J., 5008
Zafiropoulo, Arthur, 1207
Zafirovski, Kirk M., 7014
Zafirovski, Matthew D., 7014
Zafirovski, Mike, 7014
Zafirovski, Mike S., 7014
Zafirovski, Robin G., 7014
Zafirovski, Todd A., 7014
Zafrani, Naava, 5405
Zagelbaum, Ephraim, 6714
Zagelbaum, Pincus D., 6714
Zagelbaum, Yechiel, 6714
Zagelbaum, Yoel, 6714
Zagoreos, Alexander, 2827
Zahans, Christopher W., 116
Zaharko, Patricia G., 1654
Zaher, James, 4514
Zahn, Cheryl, 5295
Zahn, Richard Campbell, 1914
Zahra, E. Ellis, Jr., 1962
Zahrn, James F., 1711
Zais, Don, 9878
Zajac, Debbie L., 9711
Zajac, Kenneth J., 9711
Zajkowski, Amy B., 1287
Zakain Assocs., LP, 6302
Zakaria, Arshad, 5598
Zakatinsky, Yehuda, 6961
Zaklukiewicz, Carolyn, 5803
Zalar, Jim, 7933
Zale, Daniel B., 9300
Zale, Donald, 9299
Zale, Eugene, 9300
Zale, Gregory R., 9300
Zale, Lew D., 9300
Zale, Mark, 9300
Zale, Stacy, 9300
Zale, Sylvia, 9300
Zalenko, Neal F., 4473
Zaleski, Caroline Rob, 5984
Zaleski, Michel, 5984
Zalewski, William, 8215
Zalman, Gilbert, 6946
Zaloom, Basil J., 2122
Zaltas, Arnold I., 4203
Zamora, Connie, 9419
Zamora, Estella, 2689
Zampell, Christine M., 4367
Zampell, James C., 4217, 4367
Zampetis, Ann J., 4619
Zampetis, Constantine T., 4619
Zampetis, Theodore K., 4619
Zampetis-Budman, Callie A., 4619
Zan Foundation, 1095
Zanden, Lisa Van der, 9139
Zander, Jeff, 5198
Zander, Jeffrey, 5154
Zane, J. Robert, 8263

Zane, Jeremy R., 5607
Zane, Sandra G., 5607
Zanetti, Kathy, 2681
Zanetti, Wayne, 5872
Zankel, Arthur, 1208
Zankel, Kenneth, 1208
Zant, Judy Van, 1046
Zapel, Robert C., 924
Zarcone, Tiara, 127
Zaricor, Michael, 4961
Zarifis, Tony, 607
Zarin, Judith, 7017
Zarmsky, Roxanne, 1599
Zaro, Lois, 6857
Zarpas, Crystal, 246
Zarrella, Katharine K., 7018
Zarrella, Lily E., 7018
Zarrella, Linda J., 7018
Zarrella, Ronald L., 7018
Zarus, Stephanie A., 5427
Zatyrka, Sasha, 1421
Zaunbrecher, Laura, 3760
Zavela, Vance S., 9528
Zawacky, Susan, 8289
Zawel, Susan, 5992
Zawoloka, Alex, 6489
Zazyczny, Joseph L., 8160
Zealy, James M. "Kee", Jr., 7060
Zecca, Christine, 1209
Zecchi, Patricia A., 1336
Zecchi, Patricia J., 1336
Zecchi, Paul J., 1336
Zech, Paul J., 4681
Zeckhauser, Sally H., 4164
Zeff, Joyce, 1383
Zeff, Kal, 1383
Zeff, R. Joyce, 1383
Zehnder, Barbara J., 2423
Zehnder, Daniel J., 2423
Zehnder, Egon, 4508
Zehnder, James P., 2423
Zehnder, Margaret L., 2423
Zehnder, W. Don, 4450
Zehr, Jennifer U., 2793
Zeiders, Charlotte A., 9557
Zeiders, Michael D., 9557
Zeides Foundation, Lillian, 5544
Zeiger, H. Evan, Jr., 79
Zeiger, Margaret Shook, 79
Zeilinger, Bob, 4450
Zeisler, Andrew E., 762, 1142
Zelazo, Philip, 283
Zeldes, Nochim, 5599
Zeldes, Rywa, 5599
Zeldes, Shimon, 5599
Zeldin, Claudia, 8376
Zeldin, Jessica, 8376
Zeldin, Martin, 8376
Zeldin, Stephanie, 8376
Zeldin, Sybille, 8376
Zeldlin, Claudia, 8376
Zelisko, Judith P., 2762
Zelisko, Mark, 3078
Zelisko, Richard, 2172
Zell, Jeffrey, 5891
Zell, Samuel, 2858
Zeller, Joyce, 5692
Zeller, Karen, 3595
Zeller, Michael, 480
Zellers, Jeff, 7533
Zelnak, Judy D., 7293
Zelnak, Stephen P., Jr., 7293
Zelnick Belzberg Living Trust, 1602
Zelnick, H. Strauss, 1602

Zelnick, Strauss, 1602
Zelter, James C., 6277
Zelter, Vivian, 6277
Zeltia Pharmaceuticals, 4041
Zemco Industries, 7022
Zemlyak, James M., 5014
Zemsky Charitable Remainder Trust, 3337
Zemsky Corp., The, 3337
Zemsky, Delores, 3337
Zemsky, Eugene M., 3337
Zemsky, Howard, 7022
Zemsky, Sam, 7022
Zemsky, Sam, Mrs. , 7022
Zemsky, Shirley, 7022
Zenkel, Bruce, 7023
Zenkel, Daniel R., 7023
Zenkel, Gary B., 7023
Zenkel, Lois, 7023
Zenkel, Lois S., 7023
Zerega's Sons, A., 8859
Zerfoss, Karl, 5783
Zergani, Mira, 9484
Zeve, Roberta, 1369
Zhang, Gloria Guohong, 262
Zhou, Zhi Qiang Jacob, 863
Zhou, Zhi-Qiang Jacob, 863
Zhuang, Wenbo, 255
Zia Co., The, 9052
Zicarelli, David, 185
Zicarelli, James R., 185
Zicarelli, John D., 185
Zicarelli, Mary L., 185
Zicarelli, Robert F., 185
Zicarelli, Thomas, 185
Ziccarelli, Jason K., 6058
Ziccolella, Vincent, 6372
Zick, Roger A., 4568
Zicron Elimelech Foundation, 7000
Zieff, David M., 1417
Ziegler, Allen S., 1210
Ziegler, Luther, 1799
Ziegler, Ronald, 1210
Ziegler, Ruth B., 1210
Ziegler, Stephanie B., 1409
Zielke, Bill, 3445
Zieman, Mark, 811
Zierk, David K., 2661
Zierk, Davn M., 2661
Ziese, Kristen, 3401
Ziesing, Joanne K., 6327
Ziff Investment Partnership LP II, 7027
Ziff, Harold, 1211
Ziff, Libby, 1211
Ziff, Robert D., 7027
Zilber, Neri, 1816
Zilker, Fred, 5778
Zilkha, Ezra K., 5669
Zimble, Peter, 1090
Ziminsky, Victor , III, 6455
Zimmer, 3144
Zimmer, Bernie, 158
Zimmer, Cheryl B., 2425
Zimmer, Collins C., 2425
Zimmer, Jacob, 2425
Zimmer, Jared S., 2425
Zimmer, Jennifer, 5601
Zimmer, Joshua, 2425
Zimmer, Lynn, 1603
Zimmer, Max, 1212
Zimmer, R. Scott, 2425
Zimmer, Rick, 4598
Zimmer, Robert, 1603
Zimmer, Robert S., 2425

Zimmer, Scott, 4450
Zimmer, Stuart, 5601
Zimmerman Charitable Lead Trust, Raymond, 2426
Zimmerman, Brian, 5846
Zimmerman, Charles, 2427
Zimmerman, Denise, 2428
Zimmerman, Elyne, 2427
Zimmerman, Fred E., 2426
Zimmerman, Harriet M., 4208
Zimmerman, Jane, 5668
Zimmerman, Joan Goodman, 1213
Zimmerman, Jordan, 2428
Zimmerman, Leroy, 8037
Zimmerman, Louis G., 4620
Zimmerman, Mark, 3590
Zimmerman, Mark L., 4620
Zimmerman, Morrie, 2427
Zimmerman, Raymond N., 6083
Zimmerman, Ron, 5668
Zimmerman, Sandi, 1316
Zimmerman, Sarah O., 9825
Zimmerman, Seeman, 2427
Zimmerman, Stephanie M., 4564
Zimmerman, Timothy M., 8011
Zimmerman, J. Dail, 7028
Zimmermann, John C., III, 7028
Zimmermann, Marie, 7028
Zimyeski, Carrie, 1581
Zink, Joe, 4079
Zink, Kenneth E., 4513
Zinke, Gilbert, 4735
Zinsmeyer, Jeffrey, 9533
Ziobrowski, Stephen, 4236
Ziogas, Christopher, 1551
Zions Bancorporation, 9363
Zipf, Cindy, 5337
Zipf, Elizabeth M., 5523
Zippert, Carol, Dr. , 12
Zirkin, Harold, 3844
Zirlin, Sherri, 3281
Zisman Equities Group, 8377
Zisman, Leo, 6518
Zisman, Michael, 8377
Zisman, Michael D., 8377
Zisman, Myrna, 6518
Zissu, Frederick, 5602
Zissu, Jeffrey A., 5602
Zitrin, Arthur, 1214
Zitrin, Charlotte, 1214, 1215
Zitrin, Elizabeth, 1215
Zitrin, Richard, 1214
Zitzmann, Jerome, 4908
Zizesgreen, Susan, 6857
Zlinkoff, Sergei S., 7031
Zobell, Barbara, 1119
Zobell, Karen, 1119
Zock Charitable Remainder Unitrust, Sara M., 4368
Zock, Joseph A., 4368
Zock, Robert A., Jr., 4368
Zock, Sara, 5435
Zoe, Betty, 8815
Zogby, Ed. D., Joann, 8263
Zoldy, James S., Jr., 1427
Zolla, Anne, 1216
Zolla, Edward M., 1216
Zolla, Susan, 1216
Zollmann, William J., II, 5032
Zom, Nancy, 9382
Zondervan Charitable Remainder Trust, William J., 4621
Zondervan, Mary, 4621
Zondervan, Peter J., 4621

Zondervan, Robert, 4621
Zondervan, William J., 4621
Zonenshayn, Martin, 6501
Zook, Dave , 9474
Zook, Kristal Brent, 1826
Zook, Thomas W., 7407
Zott, Steve, 4490
Zottoli, Steven J., 577
Zou, Nan, 863
Zoubek, Charles, 2416
Zoubek, Martha R., 2416
Zuber, Julie Cone, 7936
Zuchero, Sandra, 7923
Zucker, Donald, 6656
Zucker, Riva, 5835
Zuckerberg, Barbara, 5713
Zuckerberg, Dina, 5713
Zuckerberg, Lloyd, 5713

Zuckerberg, Roy J., 5713
Zuckerman, Michael H., 6197, 6555
Zuckerman, Sheri, 3338
Zuckerman, Sherwin, 3338
Zuegner, Mary, 9442
Zufall, David, 9733
Zufall, Kathryn A., 9733
Zufall, Kay, 9733
Zufall, Robert, 9733
Zugg, Amelia Dianne Saulsbury, 9175
Zugger, Thomas R., 6633
Zuidema, John D., Jr., 1955
Zukerman, Karen D., 7032
Zukerman, Morris E., 7032
Zurack, Mark, 7033
Zurack, Mark A., 7033
Zurbriggen, Dave, 9166
Zurburgg, Anita, 2986

Zurier, Samuel D., 8387
Zurlo, Gwladys, 1217
Zuschlag, Elaine, 3762
Zuschlag, Erin E., 3762
Zuschlag, Joseph B., 3762
Zuschlag, Richard, 3762
Zuschlag, Richard B., 3762
Zussman, Gary T., 2919
Zvejnieks, Peter, 8553
Zvolanek, Terry, 3601
Zvolensky, John, 2623
Zvolensky, John, Jr., 2623
Zvolensky, Matthew S., 2623
Zvolensky, Rachael, 2623
Zvolensky, Rachael, Jr., 2623
Zwaanstra, John, III, 2662
Zwaanstra, John, IV, 2662
Zwaanstra, Shizuka, 2662

Zwald, Robert L., 2484
Zwerling, Gary L., 7034
Zwerling, Marie Rose, 7034
Zwetsch, Gil, 9635
Zwick, Darin, 9321
Zwick, Marni, 8071
Zwick, Melanie, 1218
Zwick, Nicholas, 1218
Zwirn, Daniel B., 7035
Zwirner, Richard T., 3226
Zylstra, Julie, 9702
Zylstra, Julie J., 9702
Zylstra, Russell, 9702
Zylstra, Russell J., 9702
Zyman, Jennifer, 7036
Zyman, Jessica, 7036
Zyman, Sergio, 7036
Zyman, Sylvia, 7036

GEOGRAPHIC INDEX

Foundations in boldface type make grants on a national or international basis; the others generally limit giving to the city or state in which they are located. For local funders with a history of giving in another state, consult the "see also" references at the end of each state section.

ALABAMA

Axis: SSAB 67
Bessemer: Mitchell 50
Birmingham: Abahac 1, Abroms 2, Anderson 6, Barkley 9, Birmingham 11, Boult 14, Brinkley 15, Bruno 17, Chester 20, Day 25, Dixon 26, Friedman 27, Goodrich 29, Griffin 30, Hawkins 37, Ireland 39, Malone 48, Norquist 51, Petra 53, Piassick 55, Ratliff 57, Rikard 59, Ripps 60, Shook 64, Siloam 65, Sumners/Nelson/Thompson 69, Upchurch, 72, Warren 75, Zeiger 79
Butler: Lenoir 46
Camden: Wallace 74
Chatom: Kirkland 45
Childersburg: **Christian 21**
Decatur: Hartselle 36, Sexton 63
Dothan: Watson 76
Fairhope: Kairos 41
Florence: Anderson 5
Greenville: Harrison 35
Homewood: Thompson 70
Huntsville: King 43, Pei-Ling 52, Propst 56, Strain 68
Mobile: **Atlantis 8**, Brown 16, Bynum 18, Cooper 22, Cooper 23, Davis 24, Glaze 28, Griswold 31, Hanks 32, Harper 33, Hunter 38, Mitchell 49, Regions/AmSouth 58, Trippe 71, Williams 77, Yates 78
Montgomery: Adams 3, Amos 4, Aronov 7, Caddell 19, JADO 40, King 44, Loeb 47, Rothschild 61, Simpson 66, Viro 73
Opelika: Samford, 62
Selma: Black 12
Tallassee: Blount 13
Troy: Harris 34
Tuscaloosa: Battle 10, Phifer, 54
Winfield: Kemp 42

see also 1084, 1117, 1176, 1770, 1877, 2074, 2331, 2444, 2456, 2507, 2578, 2584, 2613, 2620, 2852, 3200, 3260, 3314, 4474, 4836, 4858, 5816, 7179, 7183, 7205, 7842, 7910, 8259, 8587, 8644, 8685, 9246, 9247, 9257

ALASKA

Anchorage: Alaska 80, Bristol 82, Chenega 83, Gillam 85, Gottstein 86, Koniag 89, **Nash 90**, UIC 92
Dillingham: Samuelsen 91
Fairbanks: Alaska 81, Doyon 84
Juneau: Juneau 88
Soldotna: Hooker 87

see also 1311, 1624, 5916, 9596, 9642

ARIZONA

Avondale: **Rosztoczy 161**
Carefree: Berlin 101
Chandler: Adelante 93

Fountain Hills: National 153
Mesa: Empire 116, Prayer 158, Rudge 164
Oro Valley: Hansen 127
Paradise Valley: Burns 102, F2 117, Glasrud 123, Lund 143, MCS 149, Sioles 169, Withycombe 184
Patagonia: Cadeau 104
Phoenix: Adkerson 94, Ahearn 95, Arizona 96, Babbitt 98, Coleman 107, Corrigan 110, Eaton 115, Fuite 121, Garcia 122, Grace 125, Hughes 130, Jones 136, Kuhle 139, Long 141, Louis 142, Margolis 144, Marketplace 145, McKee 148, Napier 152, Picerne 155, Powell 157, Rae 159, Shultz 168, Snell 171, Squires 173, Stevens 175, Ullman 177, Valley 178, Van 179, Zicarelli 185
Prescott: James 132, Massie 146
Queen Creek: Feenstra 118
Rio Verde: Williams-Malone 183
Scottsdale: **Beals 100**, Clark 106, Cooper 109, du 114, Forsberg 119, Freedom 120, Goldberg 124, Grossman 126, Helms 129, Johnson 134, Johnson 135, **Kearny 137**, Maxinmotion 147, Moeller 150, Pierce 156, Rubeli 163, Schlein 165, Shacknai 167, Stanton 174
Sun Lakes: Robson 160
Tempe: Drexler 113, Immanuel 131, Williams 182
Tucson: Armstrong 97, Barton 99, Chapin 105, Community 108, Declaration 111, Dove 112, Harmsen, 128, Jasam 133, Knisely 138, Lapan 140, Murphey 151, O'Rielly 154, Rothschild 162, Schmidt 166, Spalding 172, Warmer 180, **Well 181**
Wickenburg: C 103
Yuma: Smith 170, Sturges 176

see also 272, 665, 710, 738, 784, 877, 910, 1094, 1121, 1178, 1355, 1676, 1705, 1756, 1979, 2400, 2755, 2855, 2858, 2983, 2999, 3171, 3198, 3248, 3284, 3324, 3486, 3541, 3682, 4260, 4721, 5021, 5039, 5126, 5144, 5155, 5161, 5167, 5194, 5381, 5468, 5606, 5612, 5664, 5827, 5870, 6091, 6375, 6573, 6872, 7437, 7439, 7523, 7806, 8313, 8414, 8469, 8472, 8505, 8817, 8875, 8968, 8982, 9059, 9135, 9206, 9236, 9347, 9353, 9387, 9585, 9764, 9793, 9816, 9839, 9983

ARKANSAS

Amity: Olds 210
Arkadelphia: Elrod 195, Sturgis 217
Bentonville: Bogle 191, McKinney 202
Brinkley: Minnis 204
Conway: Nabholz 208
El Dorado: Merkle 203, Murphy 206, Murphy 207, Union 219
Eudora: White 220
Fort Smith: **Baldor 188**, Hennessy 198
Hot Springs: Morris 205
Jonesboro: Families 196

Little Rock: Bailey 186, Bailey 187, Bodenhamer 190, Darragh 193, Heflin 197, Hickingbotham 199, Horn 200, Hussman 201, Oliver 211, Ottenheimer 213, Riggs 214, Stephens 216, Wrape 222
Mount Ida: Woodson 221
Mountain Home: Blue 189
Pine Bluff: Trinity 218
Rogers: Buck 192
Russellville: Nabholz 209
Stuttgart: Dunklin, 194
Texarkana: Osborne 212
West Memphis: Southland 215

see also 1114, 1775, 2985, 3278, 3382, 3391, 3735, 4271, 4851, 4955, 5190, 5219, 5418, 7667, 7686, 7693, 7736, 8778, 9226, 9690

CALIFORNIA

Agoura Hills: Friedman 530, Hohnstein 629
Alameda: Leland 741, McQuinn 820
Alamo: **Sargent 1005**, Twanda 1135
Albany: Big 315
Aliso Viejo: Downey 460, Downey-Short 461
Anaheim: Chisick 395, **Munson 852**
Angels Camp: Calaveras 369
Apple Valley: Reddy's 959
Aptos: Nicholson 866
Arcadia: Chelvanayakam 391, Hakka 593, In 650
Atherton: Bochnowski 325, Gill 555, Hawley 605, Lamond 729, Nachtsheim 856, Welch 1168
Avalon: Offield 875
Bakersfield: Brown 353, Dass 443, Grimm 585, Judkins 682, Judkins 683, Lake 727, West 1175, Wheeler 1179
Balboa Island: Peterson 919, Smith 1054
Benicia: Christian 401
Berkeley: Alafi 235, Bancroft-Clair 270, **Battle 282**, Baxter 284, Elder 475, Epstein/Roth 483, New 865, **Parsemus 904, Reddy 958**, San 998, Smullin 1060, Uplands 1138, **Valenzuela 1143**, Witkin 1191
Beverly Hills: Arnstein 254, Baker 267, Bettingen 310, Bilak 317, Breslow 340, Bridges/Larson 343, Briskin 346, Burrows 363, Cheeryble 390, Congregation 423, Corday 426, Corwin 428, Fawcett 500, Feder 501, Feintech 502, Four 522, Friedhofer 529, Glazer 561, Glazer 562, Greenberg 579, Hayman 606, Hertz 619, Horwich 632, Kobor 716, Lebowitz 736, Lee 737, Levine 750, Mann 790, Neu 862, **PADI 898**, Rabinovitch 947, Sanders 999, Sarandon 1004, Schaeffer 1013, **Shapell 1031**, Shore 1034, Sun 1092, Thompson 1111, Traub-Brittan 1127, Uplands 1139
Bonsall: Donegan 458
Brea: Family 493, Marshburn 799
Burbank: Boone 328, Burbank 361, Jones 674, Rediger 960, Rosenthal 987

Burlingame: Elfenworks 477, Fitzpatrick 508, Hoefer 628, Podell 930
Buttonwillow: Buttonwillow 367
Calabasas: Bider 314, Hong 631
Calistoga: Jones 673, LEF 739
Campbell: Kirkorian 709, Malachowsky 786
Carlsbad: Kisco 710, Tippett 1119
Carmel: Berkshire 305, **Moley 841**
Carmichael: Hurliman 643
Carpinteria: **Linked 758**
Carson: Dermalogica 451
Castro Valley: Knuppe 714
Chico: Foor 516
Chino Hills: HCSC 607
Chula Vista: Oak 872
Citrus Heights: Deacon 447
City of Industry: Majestic 784, Stafford 1074
Claremont: Stewart 1083
Clovis: Radin 948, Smittcamp 1059
Concord: Garaventa 546, PG 921
Corcoran: Corcoran 425
Corona: Amin 240
Corona Del Mar: Kendall 701, Margolis 796, Miller 829
Corona del Mar: Tsao 1133
Coronado: Lipp 759, Nelson 861
Costa Mesa: Confetti 422, Frome 535, Fudge 537, **Modglin 840**, Smith 1055
Culver City: **Animal 246**, Chestnut 392, Evans 485
Cupertino: Chan 387, **Northern 870**, Palo 901
Cypress: Bandai 271
Dana Point: Optivest 884, Teshinsky 1108
Del Mar: Goldberg 567, Mitchell 837, Novak 871, Ohana 876
Diamond Bar: Olson 879
Dixon: Arata 248
Downey: Hoag 625, Stauffer 1077
El Cajon: Christian 402
El Cerrito: Kinsey 707
El Segundo: Looker 766, Murad 854
Emeryville: Familian 491
Encinitas: Bravo 338, Helmstetter 616, Mintz 836, Skowronski 1045
Encino: **A-T 258**, Beim 293, Bellwether 299, Broder 348, Chiat 393, Collier 417, Fast 498, HunterWard 641, Leeds 738, Muskin 855, Phelps 922, Prete, 934, Price 938, Skynyrd 1046, Tilley 1118, Tobey 1121, Waller 1152
Escondido: Blanchard 321, Tomlinson 1123
Fairfield: Solano 1063
Folsom: Elliott 479, Terra 1107
Forest Ranch: Butte 366
Fortuna: McLean 817, Perenin 914
Foster City: Callison 371
Fremont: Brooks-Mathews 350, Freshwind 528, Gareatis 547, Green 578, Ibrahim 646
Fresno: Anderson 244, Bonner 326, Dyer 469, Garabedian 545, Smith 1052
Fullerton: Phelps 923, Thagard 1109
Gardena: Barco's 277
Glendale: Community 421, New 864
Greenbrae: Acacia 225, Craves 434
Guerneville: Heck 609
Half Moon Bay: Bellini 298
Hayward: **Alalusi 236**
Healdsburg: Crabb 431, Ducommun 465
Hillsborough: Barulich 280, Lin 757, Louie 770, Mayer 809
Hollywood: Meyer 823
Huntington Beach: Goodwin 572, McDaniel 813, **Quiksilver 945**
Indian Wells: Champions 386
Irvine: Bonner 327, Boukai 334, Cohen 414, Giles 554, Griswold 586, Hausman 603, Helms 615, Hunsaker 640, Keith 696, KNU 713, Lester 747, Mazda 810, Nima 868, Onehope 881, Razi 957,

Rose 984, Stack 1073, **Sunwest 1094**, Thorne 1114, Van 1144, Waltmar 1155, Withim 1190
Jackson: Amador 238
Kentfield: Flanagan 510
La Canada: Crawford 435, **Upside 1140**
La Canada-Flintridge: Orthodox 890
La Habra: **Orphan 889**
La Jolla: Blachford-Cooper 318, Casillas 379, Edwards 473, Foundation 520, Lester 748, Magali 781, Martin 802, Peterson 918, Pfister 920, Potiker 932, **Preuss 935**, Scott 1021, Spielman 1067
La Mesa: Ackerman 227, Crane 433
La Mirada: Weinberg 1164
La Verne: **International 652**
Lafayette: Boscacci 333, Bridges 342, Llagas 762, Thompson 1112, Uvas 1142
Laguna Beach: Bergman 304, Ginder 558, Laguna 726, Masson 807, Swayne 1097
Laguna Hills: Cavaricci 381, Kao 690, Ko 715
Laguna Niguel: Scott 1023
Lake Forest: Cirila 405
Larkspur: Becker 291, Boyer 335, Huntington 642, Moonwalk 845, Nasaw 858
Littleriver: **Candelaria 372**
Livermore: Pedrozzi 912
Lodi: Maley-Thawley 787
Lompoc: Mollath 842
Long Beach: Baker 266, Burg 362, Ferry 504, Hodges 627, **Hsu 637**, McLeod 818, Miller 833
Los Alamitos: Adams 229, CEC 382, Hughes 639
Los Altos: Altos 237, Ark 251, Clara 406, Hochman 626, Joy 677, Maxfield 808, Morgan 846, Srivastava 1072, White 1180
Los Altos Hills: Drexler 463, **Flynt 514**, Kelvin 699, Krishnan-Shah 722, Somekh 1064, Worster 1197
Los Angeles: Abrams 224, Adams 228, Adelman 231, Amin 241, Anthony 247, Bach 263, Banchik 269, Beam 287, Beattie 289, Bekins 294, Benedek 300, Beulah 311, Bialis 313, Blatteis 322, Broad 347, Brotman 351, Brown 352, **Butler 365**, **Cantor 375**, Chitjian 396, Chizen 397, Coburn 411, Collingwood 418, Combs-Hughes 419, Cotsen 430, Davis 445, Dockweiler 456, Dorskind 459, Ebell 471, Ebell 472, Emanuel 480, Evening 487, Everest 488, Family 492, Farmers 496, Faro 497, **Friends 533**, Fuller 538, George 551, Gilmore 557, Gordy 575, Graff 576, **Grass 577**, Grey 582, Gross 587, Guerin 589, Hagopian 592, Harvey 602, Hellman 614, Herman 617, Hitter 624, Hotchkis 635, i.am.angel 645, Ignatius 648, Jelin 662, Jennings 663, Johnson 669, Just 684, Kanel 688, Kanoff 689, Kite 711, Kornwasser 718, Kort 719, Koss 720, Laurance 732, Lavine 733, Lemons 743, Lennox 745, **Lenz 746**, **Lloyd 763**, Los 768, Margolis 797, Martin 800, Martin 801, Michaud 824, Military 826, Miller 828, Miller 830, Miller 832, Mitchell, 839, Munushian 853, Nickoll 867, Open 883, Opus 885, Pardee 902, Parvin 905, Pauley 909, Perricone 916, Phillips 924, Physicians 925, Piuze 928, Pollia 931, Private 941, Project 942, Ragir 950, Rapport 954, Rar 955, Reitman 964, **Rifkind 972**, Robinson 977, Romano 982, Rosenberg 985, Rosenfeld 986, Sands 1001, Sassoon 1006, Sawchuk 1010, **Saya 1011**, Schoen 1017, Schweers 1020, Shayne 1032, Silton 1039, Simon 1041, Simon-Strauss 1042, Smalley 1050, Smith 1053, Soicher 1062, Sondheimer 1065, Sprague 1069, Sprague, 1070, Stauffer 1076, **Telchman 1106**, Thrill 1117, Tisch 1120, United 1136, Weisz 1167, Welk 1170, Wilson 1186, Winkler 1188, **Woo 1195**, Zacky 1205, Zacky 1206, Zimmer 1212
Los Gatos: **Asia 257**, Berry 309, Hinman 622, Levin 749, Levy 751, Marchese 792, Smythe 1061, Trombetta 1128, Yuki 1203
Madera: Jeangerard 661
Malibu: H. 590, On 880, Smith-Welsh 1058, World 1196
Manhattan Beach: MacDonald 779

Marina del Rey: RA5 946
Menifee: Berlin 306
Menlo Park: Atkinson 259, **Lyu 777**, Millstreet 835, O'Donnell 874, Rossi 989, SHP 1035, Storm 1087
Merced: Community 420
Mill Valley: Bernstein 307, Dmarlou 455, Gellert 550, Kadima 686, Katz 692, North 869, Rotasa 991, Tomkins 1122
Millbrae: **Blackman 320**
Milpitas: Legacy 740, **Raymond 956**
Mission Viejo: Johnson 670
Modesto: Bright 345, Costa 429, Gallo 543
Monrovia: Barbera 275, Boone 329
Monte Sereno: Berglund 303
Montecito: Priory 940, SJL 1043
Monterey: Maher 783
Moraga: Dickinson 453
Mountain View: Adonai 232, Bobowski 324, Karp 691, Synopsys 1100, **Wakerly 1150**
Murrieta: Pickford 927
Napa: Cloud 408, Lighthouse 756, Lynch 775, Mondavi 843, Syar 1099, Wang 1157
Newport Beach: Carlston 377, Clougherty 409, Crummer 436, Eichenberg-Larson 474, Gareeb 548, Gordon 573, Johnson 668, Juda 681, Lewis 753, Lisle 760, McMahon 819, Merage 822, Rallis 951, Reinhold 963, Russell 995, Siegel 1036, Troob 1129, Wells 1171
Newport Coast: Jatain 659, Schimmel 1015
Nicasio: Blackie 319, Endurance 482
North Hollywood: Von 1147
Novato: Hagar 591
Oakland: Braddock 336, Coleman 416, Dahl 439, Diamantine 452, Doelger 457, Fry 536, Grey 583, Penney 913, Theroux 1110, West 1174, Ziff 1211
Occidental: Hidden 620
Ontario: Kim 704
Orange: Horwitz 633
Orangevale: Dusenbury 466
Orinda: Barth 279, Butler 364, GirlSMART 560
Pacheco: Westphal 1177
Pacific Palisades: Dwyer 468, Jones 675, Lemelson 742, Rees 961
Paicines: I 644
Palm Desert: Greenwood 581, Wasserman 1160, Webb 1162
Palm Springs: Barnett 278, **Cienega 404**
Palo Alto: **Ayz 262**, CNC 410, **Floyd 513**, **Global 565**, **Hsieh 636**, Katz 693, Mae 780, Marcus 794, Palo 900, Santa 1003, Stellar 1080, Unz 1137, Wilnai 1185
Palos Verdes Estates: Marcil 793, Tuffli 1134
Palos Verdes Peninsula: De 446
Pasadena: Beynon 312, Byrne 368, Eleven 476, Forgatch 517, Georgina-Frederick 552, JDH 660, Johnson 667, Johnston 671, Knell 712, Ridder 970, Ross 988, **Scovel 1025**, Von 1148
Pebble Beach: Lockridge 765, Reveas 967, **Williamson 1184**
Piedmont: Baker 265, Danem 441
Placentia: Malachi 785, Pralle 933
Pleasanton: Mangold 789, Morgan 847
Portola Valley: Fat 499, Jorgensen 676, Kabcenell 685, Whittier 1181
Rancho Cucamonga: Previti 937, Sunrise 1093
Rancho Mirage: Los 769, McGraw 814
Rancho Palos Verdes: Chowdhury 398, Foster 519, Muckel 850
Rancho Santa Fe: Bell 295, GAT 549, Lyman 774, Pulido 944, Rosso 990, Stein 1079, Warren 1159
Redwood City: **Beagle 286**, Hand 595, KC 694, Koenig 717, Price 939, **Support 1095**
Riverside: Huber 638, Locke 764
Rocklin: Armrod 253
Rohnert Park: Codding 412
Rolling Hills: Borzi 332, Candor 373, Cutler 438

Rolling Hills Estates: Bright 344, Harman 598, Kwoh 724

Ross: Heffernan 611

S. Pasadena: Davies 444

Sacramento: Friedman 531, Kelly 697, Massie 806, McClatchy 811, **Peszynski 917**, Setzer 1029, Winn 1189, Witter 1192

Saint Helena: Beauregard 290, **Skyscrape 1047**, Tecumseh 1105

Salinas: Church 403, J. 653, **Kinnoull 706**, Oreggia 886, Tanimura 1103

San Andreas: IM 649

San Anselmo: Faraway 494, Patterson 907

San Bernardino: Harbison 597, Walters 1153

San Bruno: Sammut 996

San Carlos: Arbor 249, Christensen 400

San Clemente: Adelaide 230, Brunswick 354, Joerger 665

San Diego: Aroma 255, Avery-Tsui 261, Baker 264, Brooks 349, Bucolo 356, California 370, Charitable 389, Cole 415, Cush 437, Del 449, Downing 462, Fliesbach 512, Gifts 553, Goldberg 568, Goodall 570, Gooding 571, **His 623**, Johnson 666, Khoury 702, KT 723, Lash 730, Manchester 788, Money-Arenz 844, Mudd 851, Nelson 860, **New 863**, Otto 893, OZ 896, Parker 903, Rady 949, Resource 965, Rest 966, Rice 969, Rush 994, San 997, Savage 1009, Stearns 1078, Szekely 1102, Thornton 1115, Walton 1156, Weil 1163, Weiss 1166

San Francisco: Ach 226, Anhaltzer 245, Avery-Fuller-Welch 260, Barbonchielli 276, Baskin 281, Baumann 283, Belle 296, Beller 297, Bigglesworth 316, Brewster 341, Bryan 355, Buell 357, **Bull 358**, Bundy 359, Bundy 360, Celebrate 383, **Chan 388**, Cleo 407, Daly 440, Dearborn 448, Drum 464, Faggin 489, Fairview 490, Five 509, Folger 515, Foundation 521, Fox 525, Fremont 527, Friend 532, Fritz 534, Gallanter 542, Gans 544, Griffiths 584, Handley 596, Harqua 599, Heller 613, Hollywood 630, Jamieson 658, Jolson 672, Kimbo 705, Lambert 728, Latkin 731, Liautaud 755, Lopez 767, **Lul 771**, Lundgren 772, Lux 773, Magowan 782, Margoes 795, Marineau 798, McDaniel 812, McKay 815, McKenzie 816, Nagel 857, October 873, O'Shea 892, Outrageous 894, Payne 910, Prevent 936, Ramsay 952, Rappaport 953, Reilly 962, Rhe 968, **Rieger 971**, Rocca, 978, Saturno 1008, Seip 1028, Shenandoah 1033, Small 1049, Sustainable 1096, Swinerton 1098, SYZYGY 1101, Teachers 1104, Thomson 1113, Three 1116, Traina 1126, Trust 1131, **Trustees 1132**, Wall 1151, Walther 1154, Wattis 1161, Weisgerber 1165, Wilbur 1182, **Wilkinson 1183**, Wolfe 1193, Wren 1199, Zabala 1204, Zankel 1208, Zimmerman, 1213, Zitrin 1214, Zitrustin 1215

San Gabriel: **Indo-American 651**, Jade 655

San Jose: Archer 250, Castellano 380, DiNapoli 454, **Jain 656**, Jesy 664, JP 678, Kieve 703, Olander 878, Sanfilippo 1002

San Juan Capistrano: First 507, Picerne 926

San Luis Obispo: Martin 803

San Marcos: Staples 1075

San Marino: Funari 539, Greenwood 580, Havner 604, Ichioka 647, Scottsdale 1024

San Martin: Corde 427

San Mateo: Fortisure 518, Lebherz 735, Roberts 976, Wendell 1172

San Rafael: Gordon 574, Paul 908, Sato 1007

San Ramon: Baldacci 268, Bank 272, PTSRK 943

Santa Ana: Ascher, 256, First 506, Kallins 687

Santa Barbara: 2005 223, Anatman 242, Becker 292, Bernstein 308, Child 394, Chrissie's 399, Cramblit 432, **Delzell 450**, Glikbarg 564, Hotchkis 634, Keating 695, Kendall 700, Kreitzberg 721, Lyons 776, Orfalea 887, Overall 895, Page 899, Roke 981, Roney 983, Rubin 992, Schlinger 1016, Schulte 1018, Smith-Walker 1057, Spungen 1071, Straus 1088, **Vogelzang 1146**, Wharton 1178, Writer 1200, Zwick 1218

Santa Clara: Silicon 1038

Santa Clarita: Sandnes 1000

Santa Cruz: Jain 657, Mills 834, Nell 859

Santa Fe Springs: Eagle 470

Santa Maria: Berakah 302, Smith 1056

Santa Monica: Arlene 252, Banky 273, Baye 285, Breech 339, Cannon 374, CAS 378, Emmett 481, Goldstein 569, Jubas 680, Kelton 698, **Lawrence 734**, Lemons 744, Moskowitz 849, Ornest 888, Pasarow 906, Simon 1040, Sterling 1081, Stoller 1084, Strome 1089, Troy 1130, Wertheimer 1173, Ziegler 1210, Zolla 1216, Zurlo 1217

Santa Rosa: Furth 540, Harris 601, Sloss 1048, Stone 1085, Wagner 1149, Yoder 1202

Saratoga: Borch 330, Corbalis 424, Ellen 478, Fox 524, Grossberg 588, Scandling 1012, **Wong 1194**

Sausalito: Mill 827, Urbanek-Levy 1141, Zecca 1209

Seal Beach: Osborn 891

Sebastopol: Spatz 1066

Shafter: Varner 1145

Sherman Oaks: Cohen 413, Glenville 563, **Jacoby 654**, Mitchell 838, Pergo 915, Riley 973, Western 1176, Wrather 1198

Sierra Madre: Seaver 1026

Simi Valley: Morgenstern 848

Solana Beach: Spiva 1068

Sonoma: Sebastiani 1027

Soquel: Toole 1124

South Gate: Boand 323

South Pasadena: Flicker 511, Godric 566, Herrmann 618, MacCready 778, Ohren 877, Pacific 897

South San Francisco: Roche 979

Stockton: Cerri 384, Lewis 754, Rishwain 974

Studio City: Fox 523, Fusenot 541, Plum 929

Sunnyvale: Anderson 243, Borok 331, Cardinal 376, Scott 1022, SKB 1044, Yen 1201

Sunset Beach: Ward 1158

Tarzana: Frankel 526

Temecula: Amerman 239

Thousand Oaks: Ferguson 503, Suggs 1091

Tiburon: Harris 600, Hilltop 621

Toluca Lake: **Hampar 594**

Torrance: JTB 679, Mason 805, Rogers 980, Torino 1125

Tustin: Smith 1051

Ukiah: Bradford 337, Eriksen 484

Upland: Ontario 882

Valencia: **Akian 234**

Valley Glen: Rubin 993

Van Nuys: Ady 233, **Levy 752**, **Sikand 1037**

Ventura: Meister 821

Vernon: Mashhoon 804

Visalia: Dwelle 467, Evans 486

Walnut Creek: Danvera 442, Farber 495, Heinz 612, Zafiropoulo 1207

West Hills: Roberts 975

West Hollywood: Bannerman 274, Stewart 1082, Welfund 1169

West Sacramento: Beneto 301

Westlake Village: Gilleland 556, Kirby-Jones 708, Livingston 761, Scherr 1014, Sudikoff 1090

Whittier: Shannon 1030

Woodland: Ceunis 385

Woodland Hills: Finestra 505, Health 608, **Hefferlin 610**, L.B. 725, March 791, Mickelson 825, Stone 1086

Woodside: Bear 288, **Girls 559**, Miller 831, Pearlstein 911

Yountville: Schultz 1019, Winiarski 1187

see also 102, 113, 115, 140, 171, 174, 175, 176, 1230, 1235, 1237, 1251, 1272, 1282, 1283, 1291, 1301, 1307, 1310, 1317, 1318, 1331, 1353, 1357, 1363, 1403, 1451, 1484, 1498, 1508, 1515, 1550, 1565, 1597, 1603, 1609, 1621, 1622, 1628, 1630, 1642, 1649, 1652, 1653, 1655, 1657, 1658, 1675, 1676, 1678, 1688, 1689, 1690, 1692, 1694, 1700, 1706, 1708, 1710, 1713, 1720, 1727, 1734, 1738, 1741, 1749, 1752, 1756, 1757, 1760, 1765, 1768, 1774, 1775, 1776, 1779, 1784, 1792, 1800, 1808, 1813, 1858, 1874, 1904, 1927, 1964, 1984, 1985, 1986, 2016, 2021, 2072, 2074, 2086, 2153, 2188, 2193, 2207, 2213, 2244, 2272, 2358, 2384, 2481, 2525, 2561, 2630, 2639, 2661, 2667, 2668, 2669, 2671, 2672, 2678, 2711, 2719, 2731, 2733, 2739, 2741, 2742, 2766, 2770, 2778, 2781, 2814, 2823, 2881, 2892, 2918, 2939, 2948, 2976, 3002, 3006, 3070, 3079, 3107, 3119, 3141, 3142, 3162, 3168, 3169, 3181, 3194, 3206, 3221, 3247, 3278, 3280, 3288, 3312, 3336, 3347, 3364, 3452, 3453, 3470, 3551, 3614, 3630, 3640, 3656, 3660, 3677, 3681, 3718, 3739, 3751, 3804, 3833, 3835, 3846, 3909, 3912, 3967, 3969, 3991, 4001, 4013, 4043, 4059, 4106, 4201, 4207, 4286, 4297, 4338, 4349, 4358, 4372, 4378, 4380, 4427, 4564, 4611, 4622, 4625, 4680, 4751, 4762, 4789, 4814, 4863, 4868, 4879, 4920, 4952, 4973, 4982, 5007, 5037, 5059, 5064, 5116, 5131, 5134, 5141, 5146, 5155, 5158, 5159, 5161, 5165, 5166, 5170, 5171, 5175, 5179, 5180, 5182, 5188, 5190, 5191, 5192, 5195, 5196, 5199, 5201, 5202, 5235, 5244, 5247, 5248, 5255, 5268, 5269, 5271, 5272, 5288, 5290, 5291, 5298, 5305, 5391, 5408, 5416, 5426, 5432, 5466, 5477, 5482, 5492, 5496, 5520, 5537, 5547, 5548, 5550, 5595, 5597, 5631, 5632, 5641, 5649, 5664, 5685, 5708, 5716, 5742, 5747, 5776, 5785, 5796, 5809, 5854, 5855, 5870, 5876, 5931, 5938, 5989, 5998, 6051, 6054, 6060, 6077, 6090, 6098, 6112, 6113, 6119, 6128, 6136, 6157, 6173, 6196, 6245, 6249, 6288, 6313, 6340, 6389, 6395, 6409, 6410, 6421, 6429, 6432, 6437, 6439, 6486, 6497, 6549, 6555, 6599, 6604, 6611, 6638, 6652, 6707, 6768, 6811, 6816, 6852, 6861, 6877, 6879, 6890, 6974, 6992, 7032, 7042, 7051, 7052, 7057, 7061, 7089, 7129, 7140, 7172, 7184, 7290, 7309, 7333, 7373, 7439, 7467, 7493, 7559, 7602, 7616, 7640, 7729, 7748, 7749, 7763, 7768, 7778, 7786, 7788, 7800, 7832, 7847, 7867, 7871, 7876, 7888, 8009, 8024, 8030, 8108, 8123, 8139, 8164, 8200, 8228, 8232, 8244, 8268, 8304, 8309, 8313, 8320, 8346, 8354, 8380, 8398, 8408, 8430, 8498, 8505, 8567, 8632, 8644, 8657, 8663, 8669, 8698, 8699, 8703, 8732, 8734, 8756, 8781, 8788, 8830, 8834, 8840, 8842, 8856, 8872, 8898, 8996, 9046, 9047, 9079, 9083, 9108, 9116, 9130, 9145, 9146, 9153, 9172, 9184, 9208, 9227, 9246, 9295, 9313, 9325, 9332, 9349, 9354, 9363, 9373, 9383, 9400, 9431, 9478, 9542, 9583, 9584, 9585, 9590, 9591, 9598, 9602, 9620, 9623, 9629, 9632, 9637, 9649, 9675, 9676, 9681, 9690, 9702, 9705, 9707, 9723, 9725, 9851, 9936, 9944, 9990, 9992, 9993, 9997, 9999

COLORADO

Arvada: Comprecare 1249, Getz 1278, Grosvenor 1282, Grosvenor 1283

Aspen: Arches 1222, Big 1235, Dewolf 1256, Elizabeth 1263, Joy 1301, Maki 1319, Margulf 1320, Oak 1333, Staley 1357

Avon: Hanson 1286, Wexler 1377

Basalt: Grossman 1281

Boulder: Brent 1240, Bright 1241, Fortune 1273, Gerrish 1277, Neuman 1331, **Oreg 1335**, Porphyry 1338, Relationship 1346, Tappan 1363

Breckenridge: F 1266

Broomfield: Broomfield 1242, Mehrberg 1325

Brush: Joslin-Needham 1300

Cascade: Leighty 1311

Castle Pines: McPherson 1323

Centennial: SEAKR 1351
Cherry Hills Village: Howard 1295
Colorado Springs: Benson 1230, Bjorkman 1236, HAVRK8 1288, Leininger 1312, Moniker 1327, Rockwise 1347, Shamrock 1353, Stratton 1359, Thiel 1365, Vradenburg 1374, Woodford 1382
Denver: Avoth 1225, Bardsley 1227, Bean 1228, Beren 1231, Beren 1232, Beren 1233, Brown 1243, Burt 1244, Caulkins 1245, Cliffline 1247, Connor 1250, Denver 1255, Donnell-Kay 1258, DWB 1260, Flug 1271, Fund 1274, Gart 1275, Gary 1276, Hamilton 1285, Harvey 1287, Helmar 1291, Hewit 1292, Hope's 1294, Hunt 1296, Hunter-White 1297, Jacobs 1298, JJP 1299, **Kenney 1302**, Kern 1303, Kesher 1304, Koelbel 1306, Kortz 1307, Krieble 1308, Leprino 1313, Lewan 1314, Living 1316, Lustig 1318, Martischang 1321, Morse 1328, **National 1330**, **Okinaga 1334**, Petunia 1336, Pluss 1337, Puksta 1341, QEP 1342, Rakowich 1343, RBG 1344, Routzon 1348, Schlessman 1349, Schramm 1350, Southwestern 1355, Spencer 1356, Taddonio 1362, Taylor 1364, Tigertree 1366, Titus 1367, Tomkins 1368, Triune 1370, Trueblood 1371, Wolcott 1381, Zeff 1383
Divide: Creative 1253
Durango: Ballantine 1226, Dorset 1259
Eagle: Medical 1324
Edwards: Allen 1220
Englewood: Bhappu 1234, **Fishback 1270**, Lewis 1315, **McGrath 1322**, Reel 1345, W.J.D. 1375
Evergreen: Benson 1229, Heider 1290
Fort Collins: Elf 1262, Flying 1272, Wilkins 1379
Fort Morgan: Bloedorn 1238
Grand Junction: Goodwin 1279, Wilson 1380
Greenwood Village: Chotin 1246, Energy 1264, Family 1267, Family 1268, First 1269, Graves 1280, Mullen 1329, Priester 1340, Trachten 1369
Highlands Ranch: Cornerstone 1251
Holyoke: Heginbotham 1289
Julesburg: Stretesky 1360
Kittredge: **Someone 1354**
Lamar: Growing 1284
Littleton: Bloom 1239, Dea 1254, Donahue 1257, King 1305, Ladd 1310, Servant 1352, Strohm 1361, White 1378
Lone Tree: Melrose 1326, **Nord 1332**
Longmont: Eberspacher 1261
Louisville: Arsenault 1224, Steffens 1358
Loveland: Erion 1265, Kroh 1309
Montrose: Living 1317
Palisade: Clough 1248
Parker: Blair 1237, **Vision 1373**
Pueblo: Hoag 1293
Ridgway: Praise 1339
Snowmass Village: Andrews 1221, Arrowhead 1223
Steamboat Springs: Craig-Scheckman 1252
Telluride: Warner 1376
Westcliffe: 6/S 1219

see also 64, 113, 115, 119, 129, 130, 150, 171, 179, 184, 196, 272, 283, 338, 348, 350, 372, 494, 507, 605, 643, 713, 765, 770, 784, 847, 1022, 1080, 1200, 1201, 1387, 1437, 1451, 1604, 1613, 1636, 1647, 1651, 1653, 1661, 1679, 1705, 1708, 1720, 1761, 1762, 1785, 1842, 1967, 1974, 2132, 2182, 2213, 2244, 2315, 2516, 2676, 2759, 2769, 2858, 2861, 2912, 3006, 3013, 3067, 3085, 3093, 3171, 3183, 3193, 3254, 3270, 3312, 3329, 3332, 3430, 3587, 3614, 3616, 3625, 3640, 3751, 3820, 3969, 4082, 4170, 4260, 4295, 4361, 4531, 4612, 4769, 4863, 4879, 5100, 5143, 5158, 5161, 5233, 5235, 5504, 5593, 5606, 5648, 5742, 5807, 5896, 5961, 6056, 6177, 6233, 6258, 6264, 6406, 6568, 6879, 6899, 7086, 7095, 7136, 7137, 7210, 7265, 7279, 7400, 7430, 7523, 7569, 7600, 7602, 7616, 7693, 7695, 7696, 7830, 7972, 7973, 8009, 8076, 8208, 8408, 8556, 8667, 8681, 8698, 8807, 8857, 8905, 8938, 9001, 9059, 9132, 9145, 9190, 9208, 9294, 9342, 9347, 9373, 9403, 9521, 9581, 9827, 9876, 9983, 9990

CONNECTICUT

Branford: McLeod 1524
Bridgeport: Barden 1402, Chaikin-Wile 1417, Jost 1492, Kuriansky 1503, Lodbell 1511, Proctor 1545, Stratfield 1576
Bristol: Barnes 1403, Roberts 1551
Canton: Sorenson-Pearson 1574
Chester: Nevas 1530
Danbury: Savings 1559, Union 1590
Darien: Bantle 1401, Fippinger 1450, Pulvermann 1547, Shenandoah 1568, Tierney 1584, Tully 1588, Zelnick/Belzberg 1602
East Hartford: Gengras, 1461
East Hartland: Barnes 1404
East Haven: Mellen 1525, Town 1586
East Windsor: Nirenberg 1534
Easton: Bannow-Larson 1400, Klein 1499
Enfield: Antonacci 1395, Colburn-Keenan 1421
Fairfield: Agape 1387, Axe-Houghton 1397, Bridgemill 1412, Ferguson 1446, Fuchs 1459, Hergenhan 1481, Paoloian 1540, Schendel 1561
Farmington: Goldfarb 1466, Goldfarb 1467, Kaman 1493
Georgetown: Rubin-Ladd 1556
Glastonbury: Fry 1458, Gross 1473, Hall 1475, Robinson 1553, Widows 1595
Goshen: Crosswicks 1425
Greenwich: Adams 1386, Allwin 1390, Alpha/Omega 1391, Baldwin 1399, Bender 1405, Brown 1413, Citrin 1419, Craig 1423, Crow 1426, Deutsch 1436, Donchian 1439, Donchian 1440, Fauth 1445, Filingieri 1447, Finn 1449, Floren 1451, Gladstein 1465, Greenhill 1472, Hastings 1479, Keefe 1497, LLL 1510, Mahadeva 1517, Morrow 1527, Panwy 1539, Rapp 1548, Rock 1554, Santoro 1558, Shanley 1567, Shumway 1570, **Sonja 1573**, Tucker 1587, Winokur 1597, Zacharia 1601, Zimmer 1603
Guilford: Cochrane 1420, Jaffe 1488
Hamden: **Friends 1455**, Schaeneman, 1560
Hartford: Fox 1453, Fuller 1460, McLane 1522, Thornton 1582, Vance 1591, Woodland 1599
Kent: **Sullivan 1578**
Litchfield: Derx 1435
Lyme: Bessie 1407, **Richardson 1550**
Manchester: Price 1544
Milford: DeLuca 1431, Huntington 1486
Monroe: Denzler 1434
Morris: Smith 1571
Mystic: Hamm 1476
New Canaan: Anderson 1393, Baggins 1398, Caldwell 1415, Family 1443, Lebovitz 1506, Magaro 1516, MLE 1526, Titus 1585
New Haven: Curran 1427, **Friends 1456**, Salatto 1557, UIL 1589
New London: Anderson-Paffard 1394, Grampy's 1469
New Milford: Newpol 1531, Smith 1572
Newtown: Berbecker 1406, Brace 1410, Grant 1470, Hildes-Heim 1483, Newtown 1532
North Haven: Lippincott 1509
Norwalk: Bigelow 1408, Diageo 1437, Inglesea 1487, Nessel 1529
Norwich: Chelsea 1418, Dime 1438
Old Greenwich: Dennett 1432, Howard 1484, Oberlander 1535, Schwerin 1563, WorldQuant 1600
Old Lyme: Panoram 1538
Plainville: Crew 1424
Ridgefield: Linke 1508, Lodewick 1512, Martinsen 1521
Riverside: DeNunzio 1433, Helping 1480
Roxbury: Wiener 1596
Sharon: Low 1513
Shelton: Hewitt 1482, Lavietes 1505
Simsbury: Ensign-Bickford 1442, Patricelli 1541
South Windsor: Acorn 1385
Southport: Abramowitz 1384, Foley 1452, Kreitler 1502, Wheeler 1594
Stamford: Bowling 1409, Cenveo 1416, Conway 1422, **Davis-McCullough 1429**, De 1430, Finkelstein 1448, Gibor 1464, Harris 1478, Hume 1485, Jones 1490, Kaufmann 1495, Kay 1496, Knox 1500, Lee 1507, Manger 1518, Mann 1519, McLaughlin 1523, Nason 1528, Niblack 1533, O'Herron 1536, Perna-Rose 1542, RBS 1549, Schloss 1562, Selkowitz 1565, Senior 1566, Storr 1575, Sullivan 1577, Velaj 1592
Stratford: Rosenberg 1555, Sekerak 1564
Suffield: Albert 1389
Thomaston: Thomaston 1581
Trumbull: Avery 1396, Jones 1489
Wallingford: Farid 1444
Waterbury: Harold 1477, Jones 1491, Post 1543
West Hartford: Bradley 1411, Damuth 1428, Gerath 1462, Gerbic 1463, Konover 1501, Martin 1520, Pryor 1546, Roberts 1552, **Shoemate 1569**, WMP 1598
West Haven: Eder 1441
West Simsbury: Gryphon 1474
Westbrook: Westbrook 1593
Weston: Aibel 1388, Fraites 1454, Kendall 1498
Westport: Friezo 1457, Gorab 1468, Greenfield 1471, Katen 1494, Lamando 1504, **MacInnis 1515**, Taylor 1579
Wethersfield: O'Meara 1537
Wilton: Ambler 1392, Tell 1580
Wolcott: Thrall 1583
Woodbridge: Calarco 1414
Woodbury: Macauley 1514

see also 152, 303, 335, 598, 739, 940, 952, 961, 963, 1281, 1369, 1615, 1628, 1645, 1667, 1693, 1695, 1698, 1704, 1709, 1711, 1715, 1723, 1726, 1738, 1747, 1782, 1829, 1869, 1877, 1883, 1900, 1965, 1992, 2003, 2022, 2038, 2040, 2053, 2068, 2084, 2086, 2115, 2119, 2130, 2136, 2140, 2162, 2247, 2298, 2322, 2326, 2374, 2384, 2532, 2712, 2722, 2750, 2765, 2942, 2950, 3086, 3222, 3261, 3276, 3310, 3504, 3843, 3870, 3947, 4004, 4039, 4044, 4064, 4070, 4102, 4157, 4184, 4220, 4242, 4257, 4293, 4325, 4336, 4445, 4714, 4775, 4797, 4988, 5162, 5211, 5285, 5319, 5328, 5383, 5416, 5433, 5437, 5488, 5492, 5494, 5495, 5623, 5651, 5659, 5678, 5711, 5718, 5741, 5744, 5755, 5768, 5773, 5786, 5789, 5798, 5812, 5851, 5856, 5897, 5908, 5973, 6000, 6027, 6031, 6047, 6063, 6070, 6112, 6119, 6125, 6149, 6168, 6172, 6176, 6193, 6197, 6201, 6209, 6250, 6271, 6300, 6331, 6344, 6416, 6421, 6434, 6449, 6456, 6461, 6462, 6487, 6496, 6515, 6550, 6569, 6572, 6576, 6610, 6636, 6644, 6664, 6668, 6682, 6685, 6686, 6690, 6698, 6706, 6717, 6776, 6785, 6787, 6800, 6809, 6840, 6843, 6879, 6893, 6909, 6923, 6951, 6961, 6975, 7023, 7028, 7168, 7182, 7273, 7416, 7487, 7617, 7834, 7970, 7981, 8009, 8050, 8053, 8113, 8164, 8189, 8225, 8309, 8340, 8380, 8397, 8400, 8433, 8454, 8456, 8459, 8462, 8468, 8469, 8475, 8485, 8486, 8497, 8500, 8542, 8586, 8781, 8887, 8918, 9117, 9366, 9372, 9466, 9536, 9553, 9967, 9970

DELAWARE

Bear: Rivera 1730
Dover: Palmer 1718
Greenville: Thronson 1766
Hockessin: Bowman 1625
Lewes: Farr 1662

Magnolia: Beiser 1617
Montchanin: 1916 1605, Levin 1697, Yaverland 1783
Newark: Coleman 1644, Gromet 1672
St. Georges: Tarrant 1758
Wilmington: 18 1604, 613 1606, ABE 1607, Alcyon 1608, Allen 1609, Anastasi 1610, Anbinder 1611, Babcock 1612, Bailey-Stanford 1613, Barnabas 1614, Bartlett 1615, Bauer 1616, Bennett 1618, Berghorst 1619, Berning 1620, Bharat 1621, Black 1622, Blau 1623, Block 1624, Bradley 1626, Brandsma 1627, Bresnan 1628, Broder 1629, Brown 1630, Brown 1631, Brown-Whitworth 1632, Bulova 1633, Burton 1634, Burt's 1635, Bushong 1636, Cammarota 1637, Caplin 1638, Cedarcrest 1639, Chaney 1640, Choptank 1641, City 1642, Cohen 1643, **Colgate 1645**, Coopersmith 1646, Coors 1647, Corkins 1648, Corrigan-Walla 1649, Croll 1650, Cross 1651, Cultures 1652, CVW 1653, Day 1654, De 1655, Dion 1656, Doll 1657, Dougherty 1658, Dunn 1659, Easterly 1660, EON 1661, Fernandina 1663, Foundation 1664, Freedman 1665, Geltzer 1666, George 1667, Giving 1668, Glencoe 1669, **Gloria 1670**, Gorny 1671, Groot 1673, Hagan 1674, Haldan 1675, Haldan 1676, Harkness 1677, Hauser 1678, Hawkins 1679, Heuer 1680, Hill 1681, Hoops 1682, **Jackman 1683**, Jade 1684, Jadeja 1685, JBL 1686, Jockers 1687, Just 1688, Kang 1689, Kaye 1690, Kent-Lucas 1691, Kerr 1692, Kingsley 1693, Klein, 1694, Kuehner 1695, Kutz 1696, Lighten 1698, Lightner 1699, Loftus 1700, Lowndes 1701, Martyn 1702, Mary's 1703, Massoud 1704, McIntosh 1705, McKiernan 1706, Merrion 1707, Messing 1708, Midvale 1709, Milano 1710, Milliken 1711, MMK 1712, Mulvaney 1713, Nelson 1714, New 1715, New 1716, Night 1717, Patterson 1719, Petersen 1720, Pinkerton 1721, Pollack 1722, Praxis 1723, Ratner 1724, Relgalf 1725, Remmer 1726, Repass-Rodgers 1727, Replogle 1728, Riecker 1729, Rivers 1731, Rosenfeld 1732, Rothchild 1733, Rumberger 1734, Russell 1735, Ryerson 1736, Sanders 1737, Schiffman 1738, Schwalbach 1739, Scott 1740, Scripps 1741, Selin 1742, Signal 1743, **Singer 1744**, Singhal 1745, Sloane 1746, SNAVE 1747, Solot 1748, Splawn 1749, Stein 1750, Stiefel 1751, Sulentic 1752, Susman 1753, Swift, 1754, Swinmurn 1755, Synthesis 1756, Talbott 1757, Taylor 1759, Teddy 1760, **TeleTech 1761**, Telluray 1762, Third 1763, Thomson 1764, Three 1765, Trussell 1767, Uberoi 1768, Van 1769, Viridiun 1770, Vitale 1771, VWR 1772, Wang 1773, Washakie 1774, Weissman 1775, Welton 1776, Wender 1777, Whitman 1778, Wong 1779, Wood 1780, Wyeth 1781, Yablon 1782, Yokota 1784

see also 2414, 2547, 3310, 6218, 7954, 8033, 8223, 8261, 8304, 8350, 9482

DISTRICT OF COLUMBIA

Washington: American 1785, Arcana 1786, Arnold 1787, Bench 1788, Bender 1789, Bloedorn 1790, Brody 1791, **Butler 1792**, Cafritz 1793, **Carter 1794**, Choksi 1795, Coleman, 1796, Cook 1797, Cornerstone 1798, Crowell 1799, Dart 1800, Davies 1801, Dickson 1802, Dimick 1803, **Dingwall 1804**, Dweck 1805, Farvue 1806, **Foundation 1807**, Freeman 1808, Glenstone 1809, Goldman 1810, **Gorlitz 1811**, Greenberg 1812, Haft 1813, Hanley 1814, Himmelfarb 1815, Institute 1816, Jovid 1817, Kolar 1818, Lemon 1819, **Merriman 1820**, Miller-Wehrle 1821, Mimi 1822, Monarch 1823, Olender 1824, Pathy 1825, Patterson 1826, Peet 1827, **Pettus-Crowe 1828**, Porter 1829, Ptarmigan 1830, Replogle 1831, Rossotti 1832, Rubenstein 1833, Silberman 1834, Silverstein 1835, Tucker 1836, **Union 1837**, Westport 1838, Woodward 1839

see also 49, 64, 137, 229, 263, 271, 291, 295, 299, 315, 347, 352, 363, 394, 418, 430, 514, 577,

586, 592, 595, 600, 702, 751, 758, 770, 790, 804, 805, 810, 822, 838, 850, 873, 880, 881, 928, 953, 971, 1001, 1010, 1049, 1090, 1101, 1138, 1148, 1156, 1201, 1224, 1281, 1286, 1308, 1376, 1382, 1463, 1484, 1508, 1562, 1568, 1592, 1634, 1652, 1662, 1671, 1687, 1702, 1710, 1722, 1742, 1747, 1781, 1871, 1881, 1907, 2009, 2036, 2086, 2092, 2142, 2182, 2190, 2199, 2252, 2276, 2323, 2610, 2675, 2709, 2824, 2832, 2882, 2896, 3033, 3067, 3107, 3134, 3141, 3211, 3221, 3226, 3230, 3239, 3247, 3297, 3430, 3807, 3809, 3810, 3813, 3824, 3828, 3833, 3842, 3843, 3844, 3846, 3849, 3852, 3855, 3857, 3860, 3862, 3863, 3869, 3872, 3880, 3890, 3892, 3908, 3911, 3913, 3921, 3935, 3938, 3944, 3947, 3953, 3954, 3955, 3960, 3963, 3967, 3968, 3982, 3986, 3990, 3998, 4127, 4208, 4271, 4297, 4305, 4343, 4528, 4615, 4680, 4687, 4717, 4865, 4878, 4952, 5064, 5080, 5140, 5201, 5233, 5235, 5253, 5292, 5296, 5329, 5333, 5416, 5417, 5420, 5427, 5469, 5496, 5501, 5506, 5522, 5565, 5593, 5640, 5659, 5662, 5664, 5677, 5694, 5768, 5776, 5787, 5792, 5816, 5819, 5851, 5854, 5886, 5929, 5983, 6031, 6079, 6113, 6125, 6149, 6171, 6218, 6249, 6260, 6264, 6275, 6286, 6348, 6359, 6376, 6393, 6422, 6472, 6486, 6502, 6504, 6533, 6585, 6621, 6682, 6703, 6707, 6715, 6716, 6862, 6885, 6896, 6969, 6974, 7035, 7203, 7213, 7226, 7287, 7425, 7564, 7612, 7693, 7754, 7781, 7876, 8018, 8025, 8090, 8117, 8191, 8214, 8268, 8298, 8355, 8408, 8498, 8639, 8656, 8700, 8756, 8840, 8897, 8950, 8978, 9002, 9006, 9042, 9046, 9201, 9313, 9328, 9343, 9359, 9369, 9373, 9388, 9397, 9400, 9408, 9429, 9430, 9453, 9455, 9469, 9482, 9490, 9492, 9500, 9501, 9504, 9507, 9510, 9512, 9518, 9519, 9521, 9528, 9529, 9530, 9533, 9535, 9538, 9591, 9620, 9657, 9668, 9685, 9841, 9859, 9916

FLORIDA

Alachua: Crane 1955
Amelia Island: Chardonnay 1936, Gemunder 2036
Atlantic Beach: Rembert 2281
Aventura: Celebrity 1931, **Gordon 2051**, Lazoff 2173, Rosenfeld 2295, Silverman 2337
Bal Harbour: Mayberg 2199
Bartow: Grader 2054
Belleair: Muma 2227
Boca Grande: Carbonari 1919, **Uncle 2383**
Boca Raton: Baldwin 1864, **Benedict 1884**, Cedar 1930, de 1966, Diane 1974, Enlightenment 1991, Goody 2049, Green 2061, Greenberg 2062, Halperin 2076, Kahn 2133, Kaye 2141, King 2147, Le 2175, Lenkin 2179, Liebhaber 2183, McQuistion 2208, Nissim 2231, Peters 2256, Pulichino 2271, **Safenowitz 2307**, Schlanger 2318, Siegel 2335, Sunburst 2359, Werner 2398, Wolgin 2411, Zimmerman 2426
Bonita Springs: A. 1841, Dalton 1960, Farrell 1998, Hinman 2099, Laufer 2169
Boynton Beach: Sammons 2310
Bradenton: Aurora 1860, Beall, 1876, KBR 2142, Kiwanis 2149, Riechmann 2286, **Taylor 2365**, Turner 2381, Wrigley 2417
Cape Coral: Cape 1917, Hardison 2081, **Joshua 2132**
Captiva: Patterson 2250, Stafford 2346, Wescustogo 2399
Celebration: Berelsman 1885
Clearwater: Deus 1972, Raymund 2276
Cocoa: Swann 2360
Coconut Creek: Minto 2216
Coconut Grove: Berkowitz 1886, Lewis 2182
Coral Gables: Arison 1853, Blank 1890, Brodsky 1901, Coral 1952, Coulter-Jones 1954, Dickinson 1975,

Fuller 2028, Haugland 2084, Leibowitz 2176, McNamara 2207, Reckson 2277
Davie: Forman 2011, **Hsu 2112**, Toral 2378
Daytona Beach: Bell 1882
DeBary: Shockley 2332
Deerfield Beach: 4 1840
DeLand: Fish 2001
Delray Beach: Blechman 1894, Cantor 1916, Cody 1946, Kreisman 2159, **Levine 2181**, Resnick 2282, Rubens 2301, Weinberger 2394, Westreich 2401, Wymbs 2418
Destin: Case 1925
Doral: Chowdhury 1943
Estero: Layden 2171
Fernandina: Greene 2064
Fernandina Beach: Ael 1843, Preik 2266
Fleming Island: Reinhold 2280
Fort Lauderdale: **Campbell 1914**, Focus 2004, Greaton 2060, Halmos 2075, HI 2093, Krause 2158, Kuriansky 2162, Leiser 2177, Lyle 2192, Moore 2217, P.M. 2244, Pearce 2252, River 2288, Rogers 2290, Sun, 2358, Tharpe 2369, Thomas 2370, Thomsen 2373, Tippett 2376, Turock 2382
Fort Myers: Norjana 2235, Price 2267, Sanders 2313
Fort Pierce: King 2148, Sample 2312, Sharing 2330
Gainesville: Hall-Halliburton 2074, Hoornstra 2110, Quinn 2273, Wilder 2406
Gainsville: Wagmore 2391
Golden Beach: Lipton 2185
Greenville: **Freewill 2021**
Hallandale: Gordon 2050
Hallandale Beach: **Hishmeh 2100**
Havana: Munroe 2228
Highland Beach: Erdle 1993, Goetz 2044
Hobe Sound: Bell 1883, De 1967, Hayford 2086, Muccia 2225, Seaman 2320, Steele 2347
Hollywood: MIDA 2212, Sharaby 2329
Homestead: Hoerner 2102
Indialantic: Andre 1849
Indian Harbour Beach: **Chenzyme 1939**
Jacksonville: Anderson 1847, Anderson 1848, Blanksteen 1891, Brownley 1907, Caring 1920, Childress 1942, Cohen 1948, Croft 1956, CSX 1958, Davis 1962, Evans 1994, Family 1997, Finch 2000, Focus 2005, Force 2009, Foulds 2014, Friedheim 2024, Gate 2034, Givens 2038, Grassy 2057, Haskell 2083, Helow 2089, Hicks 2094, Insetta 2119, Lacy, 2163, Marco 2194, Mb 2200, Miller 2213, Morningstar 2218, Moye 2224, **Posnack 2262**, Potter 2263, Ruskin 2302, Schultz 2319, Selders 2322, Setzer 2325, Shuey 2333, Smith 2342, Stellar 2348, Swisher 2361, Terry 2368, Ying 2421, Zimmerman 2427
Juno Beach: Nuzzo 2236, **Prime 2268**
Jupiter: Auerbach 1859, Bartner 1869, Beasley 1877, Friedland 2025, Grossman 2068, Livingston 2187, Owen 2243, Propp 2269, Salizzoni 2309
Key Biscayne: Beeck 1881, Chris 1944, Dasburg 1961
Key Largo: Bohnert 1895, Ellis 1989, Jasam 2127
Key West: Around 1854, Clements 1945, **Mukti 2226**
Lake Wales: Greater 2059
Lake Worth: Perlmutter 2254, Stern 2349
Lakeland: Blanton 1892, Burnetti 1912, Carlton 1922, Morrison 2222, Votum 2390
Lakewood Ranch: Kaplan 2138
Lantana: Weisman 2396
Largo: Gagnon 2029
Lighthouse Point: Barrington 1868, Cassill 1926
Longboat Key: Frankel 2018, Salenger 2308, Samowitz 2311
Longwood: Day 1965
Lutz: Shannon 2328
Madeira Beach: Godsey 2043
Marco Island: Becton 1880, Blake 1889
Melbourne: Binz 1888, Six 2339
Melbourne Beach: Glaubinger 2040

Miami: Carlin 1921, Cohen 1947, Fleischman 2003, Garner 2032, Gordon, 2052, **Handleman 2078**, Hegamyer 2087, Hollo 2105, Hornik 2111, Jacobson 2125, Kiwanis 2150, Knopf 2156, MCM-Munilla 2206, Mendelson 2211, Nalith 2229, Nommontu 2234, Olemberg 2237, **Pagoumian 2245**, Papper 2246, Powell 2264, Rice 2283, Rodgers, 2289, Rose 2293, Scharlin 2315, Sequoia 2324, **Stiefel 2352**, Strong 2353, von 2388, Weintraub 2395, Wiener 2405, Wolf 2410, Wynne 2419

Miami Beach: Ahavas 1844, Callas 1913, Five 2002, Morris 2219, Partners 2248, Peyton 2258, Rosen 2294, Sender 2323, Taylor 2366

Miami Lakes: Mary 2198, Pearle 2253

Moore Haven: Loftis 2188

Mount Dora: ATAP 1855, Harper 2082, Mount 2223

Naples: Anderson 1845, **Aviation 1861**, Bailey 1862, Brody 1902, Brown 1904, Burks 1909, Cherry 1940, Collins 1949, Consolidated 1951, Cunnane 1959, Davis 1963, Detter 1971, Diermeier 1976, Dorset 1979, Ferguson 1999, Fox 2016, Frangakis 2017, Franklin 2020, Fricks 2023, Galeana 2030, Hansen 2079, Jones 2131, KLM 2151, Knippenberg 2154, Lissack 2186, Martin 2197, McClanathan 2202, McDonald 2203, McGahren 2204, Noble 2233, Pusey 2272, Ransburg 2274, Ray 2275, Second 2321, Spier 2345, Vasey 2385, Younger 2422

Nokomis: Wilson-Wood 2408

North Miami: **Zichron 2424**

North Miami Beach: Irwin 2120

North Palm Beach: CCJ 1929, Evanson 1995, Goodwin 2048, Ingalls 2118, Olsen 2240, Oristano 2241, Parish 2247, Ryan 2304, Waugh 2392

Old Town: Anderson 1846

Orlando: Anton 1851, Barnard 1866, Baulch 1873, Bayuk 1875, Brooke 1903, Brown 1905

Orlando : Charles 1937

Orlando: Chicone 1941, Dennis 1969, Densch 1970, For 2007, Gelbart 2035, Goddard 2042, Greene-Sawtell 2065, Hahn 2072, Hardeman 2080, Hendrix 2090, Hill 2097, Holloway 2107, Holtz 2109, Hunter 2116, **Hutchison 2117**, Marshall 2195, Martin 2196, Millsaps 2214, Oliver 2238, Overstreet 2242, Patterson 2251, Peterson 2257, Phillips 2259, Phillips 2260, Rich 2284, Roshan 2297, Russell 2303, Shackelford 2327, **Shepard 2331**, Sidhu 2334, Stewart 2351, Strube 2354, Thurman 2375, Tupperware 2379, Westgate 2400, White 2402, Whitman 2404

Ormond Beach: Perryman 2255

Osprey: Fry 2027, Nelson 2230

Oviedo: Duda 1983

Palm Beach: **Basser 1871**, Baxter 1874, Beauregard 1878, Carrington 1923, Carros 1924, Chanin 1934, **Falk 1996**, Freitas 2022, Garvy 2033, Greenblatt 2063, Held 2088, Isenberg 2121, Johnson 2130, Kanders 2135, Kanders 2136, Kessler 2145, Meerwarth 2209, Pascal 2249, Reeves 2279, Ross 2298, Rothschild 2300, Sadler 2306, Soter 2343, Stern 2350, Thornburgh 2374, Vanneck-Bailey 2384, Wrightson-Ramsing 2416

Palm Beach Gardens: Barbash 1865, Brown 1906, Burnett 1910, Epstein 1992, Goldberg 2045, Golden 2046, J. 2122, Kaulbach 2140, Lazarus 2172, MAH 2193, **Place 2261**, Woolard 2414

Palm Coast: Turlington 2380

Panama City: Jelks 2128

Panama City Beach: Durden 1984, Dysimmune 1986, McLaughlin 2205

Parkland: Toppel 2377

Parrish: Powell 2265

Pembroke Pines: **Wollowick 2412**

Pensacola: Baroco 1867, Chadbourne 1932, Gulf 2069, Hollinger 2104, Kugelman 2161, Studer 2355

Pinellas Park: Rothman 2299

Plant City: Verner 2386

Plantation: **Atlantis 1858**, Dilworth 1977, Doctors 1978, Lelash 2178, Taplin 2363

Pompano: Zimmerman 2428

Pompano Beach: Bastien 1872, Miniaci 2215

Ponte Vedra: Hill 2098

Ponte Vedra Beach: Huang 2113, Landwirth 2167, Lazzara 2174, Morris 2220

Port Richey: Concourse 1950

Port Saint Lucie: Boston 1898

Punta Gorda: Charlotte 1938

Riverview: Simmons 2338

Rockledge: Chaffiot 1933

Safety Harbor: Biddinger 1887

Saint Augustine: Halbrook 2073, Lastinger 2168, Smith 2341

Saint Cloud: Holopaw 2108

Saint Petersburg: Brighton 1899, Catalina 1928, Chapman 1935, Doyle 1980, Dyer 1985, Kehrer 2143, KML 2152, Life's 2184, Tampa 2362, Taylor 2364

Sanibel: Grabe 2053, Lawson 2170

Sanibel Island: Gralnick 2056

Santa Rosa Beach: Andreeff 1850, Davis 1964

Sarasota: Bomberger 1896, Castellani 1927, Defeo 1968, Elster 1990, Foster 2013, Friend 2026, Glass 2039, Hagens 2071, Herrin 2091, Hoenle 2101, Kaiserman 2134, Kane 2137, Koski 2157, Lerner 2180, Long 2189, Morrison 2221, Nobel 2232, Rosenthal 2296, Scherr 2316, Sudakoff 2356, Weiller 2393, **Zimmer 2425**

Sebastian: **Jenkins 2129**

South Pasadena: Forbes 2008

Stuart: Haven 2085, Knapp 2153, Knopf 2155, Lambrecht 2165

Summerland Key: Lookout 2190

Sunny Isles Beach: HFRX 2092, Melin 2210

Tallahassee: Archibald 1852, Capital 1918, Diamond 1973, Speranza 2344

Tampa: Atkins 1856, Basham 1870, Couch 1953, Duckwall 1982, Echevarria 1987, EGW 1988, Fontaine 2006, Frankle 2019, Gerry-Corbett 2037, Gregory 2067, Hieronymus 2095, Hoffman 2103, Kaul 2139, Lowry 2191, Reed 2278, SBJ 2314, Schiano 2317, Sierra 2336, Sullivan 2357, TECO 2367, Thomas 2371, Thompson 2372, Yerrid 2420

Tarpon Springs: **Cantonis 1915**

Tavares: Rogers 2291

Tavernier: Wright 2415

Tequesta: Holloway 2106

Tierra Verde: Godbold 2041

Trinity: Draft 1981

Venice: Lamoureux 2166

Vero Beach: Atkinson 1857, Bailey 1863, Becker 1879, Blatt 1893, Brinckerhoff 1900, Burgoon 1908, Crutchfield 1957, Foundation 2015, Gardner 2031, Graymer 2058, Higgs 2096, Hultquist 2115, Janke 2126, Kelly 2144, KT 2160, Lambert 2164, McCabe 2201, Richard 2285, Rogers 2292, Sexton 2326, Smick 2340, Whiting 2403

Wauchula: Olliff 2239, Woodbery 2413

Weeki Wachee: Vorsheck 2389

Wellington: Vernon 2387

Wesley Chapel: Prutky 2270, Zehnder 2423

West Palm Beach: Ford 2010, Fortin 2012, Greenfield 2066, Hand 2077, Hufty 2114, Jacobson 2124, Kimmel 2146, Rinker 2287, Wilkes-Desmond 2407, Woerner 2409

Weston: Goldman 2047

Windermere: Graese 2055

Winter Garden: Bond 1897

Winter Park: Adler 1842, Gurtler 2070, Jacobsen 2123, Wells 2397

Winter Springs: Ryan 2305

Yalaha: Burnett 1911

see also 20, 35, 48, 57, 123, 124, 150, 168, 336, 602, 608, 784, 848, 875, 1054, 1140, 1247, 1365, 1369, 1372, 1391, 1396, 1422, 1429, 1501, 1503, 1506, 1528, 1533, 1556, 1563, 1598, 1619, 1663, 1688, 1691, 1700, 1725, 1726, 1732, 1736, 1778, 1812, 1820, 2430, 2477, 2510, 2547, 2711, 2722, 2731, 2744, 2762, 2793, 2823, 2824, 2836, 2850, 2878, 2943, 3001, 3006, 3068, 3073, 3084, 3089, 3112, 3122, 3151, 3154, 3166, 3216, 3219, 3228, 3230, 3251, 3258, 3265, 3280, 3310, 3330, 3334, 3352, 3378, 3406, 3435, 3459, 3483, 3545, 3650, 3651, 3657, 3686, 3811, 3818, 3821, 3850, 3887, 3888, 3901, 3924, 3947, 3967, 3981, 3986, 3988, 4003, 4039, 4043, 4082, 4097, 4154, 4207, 4208, 4236, 4242, 4285, 4290, 4330, 4343, 4379, 4386, 4461, 4469, 4472, 4474, 4496, 4508, 4528, 4564, 4588, 4601, 4610, 4612, 4635, 4751, 4768, 4803, 4812, 4814, 4863, 4920, 4988, 5000, 5023, 5062, 5085, 5116, 5240, 5244, 5253, 5277, 5299, 5317, 5341, 5359, 5364, 5391, 5408, 5434, 5442, 5453, 5462, 5463, 5482, 5533, 5564, 5567, 5636, 5637, 5664, 5673, 5730, 5741, 5811, 5818, 5889, 5987, 6021, 6083, 6128, 6139, 6158, 6201, 6223, 6233, 6298, 6313, 6331, 6363, 6476, 6480, 6520, 6533, 6560, 6590, 6602, 6663, 6676, 6703, 6775, 6785, 6825, 6835, 6844, 6845, 6933, 6981, 7022, 7027, 7036, 7049, 7051, 7061, 7084, 7135, 7137, 7152, 7163, 7179, 7183, 7206, 7211, 7216, 7236, 7239, 7251, 7254, 7319, 7365, 7400, 7451, 7455, 7526, 7542, 7576, 7579, 7599, 7600, 7617, 7629, 7815, 7834, 7835, 7876, 7894, 7918, 7964, 7985, 8021, 8024, 8076, 8082, 8088, 8117, 8121, 8122, 8208, 8305, 8332, 8347, 8408, 8418, 8436, 8445, 8477, 8483, 8539, 8540, 8568, 8628, 8654, 8657, 8663, 8671, 8698, 8788, 8879, 8974, 8989, 9025, 9057, 9089, 9099, 9218, 9227, 9241, 9246, 9254, 9262, 9372, 9373, 9385, 9398, 9598, 9764, 9770, 9819, 9824, 9827, 9855, 9904, 9910, 9929, 9954, 9968

GEORGIA

Albany: Barnett 2441, McKnight 2548

Alpharetta: Hurlbert 2516, K. 2528

Americus: Mix 2550

Athens: Athens 2437, Irving 2521, Woodruff, 2618

Atlanta: A.E.M. 2430, Abreu 2431, Akers 2432, Arnold 2436, Baker 2439, **Bancker-Williams 2440**, Beard-Payne 2442, Beckman 2443, Boone 2446, Brewer 2448, Brooks 2450, Burke 2451, Canipe 2452, Carmical 2453, Carters 2454, Chandler 2455, Chesed 2458, Childress 2459, Churches 2461, Cobb 2463, Colston 2464, Connolly 2467, Cooper 2469, Davison 2470, English 2474, Exposition 2476, Forehand 2479, Frank 2481, **Gage 2482**, Garden 2483, Georgia 2484, Georgia 2485, Gholston 2486, Gholston 2487, Gilbert 2488, Glancy 2489, Go 2490, Goddard 2491, Goodman 2492, Gordy 2493, Gould 2494, Graham 2495, Graves 2496, Gray 2497, Guillaume 2500, Hawkins 2503, Health 2504, Hodgson 2507, Holly 2509, Hooters 2510, Howell 2512, Hoyt 2513, Hoyt 2514, Inman 2519, JBS 2523, Johnson 2525, Kahn 2529, Kids 2530, King-White 2532, Klump 2533, L. 2535, Langdale, 2537, Lanier 2538, Lassiter 2539, Lee 2540, Lipscomb 2541, Looney 2542, Marcus 2544, Marshall 2545, McClatchey 2546, Montgomery 2551, Morris 2552, Morris 2553, Nonami 2557, Noonan 2558, Orkin 2559, Oxford 2561, Pattillo 2563, Pechter 2564, Piedmont 2566, Pilling 2567, Pope 2568, Price 2569, Ragan 2572, Raoul 2573, Rice 2575, Rockdale 2576, Rosen 2577, Schwob 2581, SF 2585, Solstice 2587, Stahl 2588, Sweetgrass 2591, TALX 2592, Terwilliger 2593, Trammell 2595, Vogel 2600, Ward 2605, Warren 2606, Warren 2608, Whitehead 2610, Williams 2612, Williamson 2613, Wish 2615, Young 2621, Zawadi 2622

Augusta: Storey 2589

Bremen: Sewell 2584

Brooks: Pennies 2565
Buford: Enterline 2475, McKinney-Geib 2547, Vaughter 2599
Canton: **Faith 2477**
Chickamauga: Andrews 2434
Columbus: Amos 2433, Belcher, 2444, Illges 2517, Illges 2518, Jeter 2524, Voight 2601, Woodruff 2617, Wright 2620
Commerce: Rackley 2571
Dalton: Church 2460, Nabors 2555, Saul 2579, White 2609
Decatur: Foundation 2480, Patrick 2562, Walker 2603
Dewy Rose: Warren 2607
Dublin: Holland-Underwood 2508
Dunwoody: Miracle 2549, Tritt 2596
Eatonton: Benton 2445
Ellijay: Harrison 2502, Whitepath 2611
Gainesville: Magnus 2543
Greensboro: Higher 2505, Zvolensky 2623
Hinesville: Strong 2590
Hiram: Woodcrest 2616
Jasper: Greiner 2498
Kennesaw: **Invisible 2520**, University 2597
Macon: Bowen 2447, Cook, 2468, Fickling 2478
Marietta: Clary 2462, Joyce 2527, Vaughan 2598
McDonough: Neuhoff 2556, Smith 2586
Milton: Orkin 2560
Monroe: Walton 2604
Moultrie: Community 2466, DeLoache 2471
Norcross: Reynolds 2574, Thames 2594, Waffle 2602
Palmetto: Eden 2473
Roswell: Myfifident 2554
Saint Simons Island: Windolf 2614
Sandy Springs: Jackson 2522
Savannah: Chatham 2457, Echlin 2472, Hodge 2506, Hunter 2515, Lane 2536, Wormsloe 2619
Sea Island: Broadfield 2449, Jolley 2526
Smyrna: Arcadia 2435
Statesboro: Averitt 2438
Stone Mountain: Howell 2511
Thomaston: Community 2465
Thomasville: 10/1 2429, Kingdom 2531, Searcy 2583
Thomson: Knox 2534
Tucker: Samford 2578, Schinazi 2580, SCS 2582
Valdosta: Griffin 2499, Price-Campbell 2570
West Point: Charter 2456, **Hands 2501**

see also 5, 7, 41, 43, 48, 49, 59, 65, 71, 78, 145, 150, 153, 563, 784, 1052, 1317, 1353, 1387, 1424, 1631, 1632, 1653, 1702, 1719, 1754, 1770, 1843, 1882, 1903, 1905, 1951, 1956, 1974, 1976, 1990, 2020, 2031, 2041, 2065, 2086, 2113, 2139, 2195, 2208, 2213, 2224, 2228, 2230, 2266, 2284, 2302, 2303, 2331, 2342, 2349, 2711, 2714, 2769, 2798, 2930, 2955, 3016, 3112, 3253, 3299, 3330, 3336, 3352, 3510, 3718, 3789, 3988, 4257, 4271, 4427, 4464, 4508, 4548, 4629, 4844, 5217, 5235, 5305, 5571, 5629, 5664, 5734, 5816, 6004, 6417, 7039, 7100, 7139, 7179, 7209, 7225, 7333, 7400, 7414, 7769, 7910, 7970, 7972, 7973, 7977, 8055, 8268, 8272, 8408, 8477, 8489, 8513, 8539, 8552, 8590, 8633, 8642, 8644, 8667, 8668, 8889, 9108, 9224, 9245, 9264, 9354, 9373, 9387, 9397, 9416, 9434, 9843, 9876

HAWAII

Honolulu: Armstrong 2624, Baldwin 2625, Castle 2626, Central 2627, Ching 2628, Damon 2629, Epstein 2630, First 2631, Fukunaga 2633, Gear 2634, Higgins 2635, Kahiau 2636, Kaneta 2637, Locations 2638, Marks 2640, Martin 2641, Sawyer 2644, Servco 2645, Shidler 2646, **Shiraki 2648**, Straub 2649, Takitani 2650, Teruya 2651, Vidinha

2653, Wilcox 2654, Wo 2655, Wong 2656, Wong 2657, **Yoshimoto 2658**, Young 2659, Young 2660
Kahului: Frost 2632
Kailua: Makana 2639
Kailua Kona: Ululani 2652
Kailua-Kona: Zierk 2661
Kaneohe: Minami 2642
Kaunakakai: Shields 2647
Lahaina: Moore 2643
Paia: Zwaanstra 2662

see also 59, 225, 244, 311, 388, 591, 599, 739, 914, 1002, 1097, 1410, 1672, 1955, 1974, 2072, 2495, 3006, 3248, 4066, 5131, 5137, 5203, 5248, 6505, 9013, 9203, 9353, 9628, 9848

IDAHO

Boise: Boise 2666, Intermountain 2677, Mitchell 2680, Morrison 2682, Simplot 2685, Thomas 2687, Troxell 2688
Caldwell: Smeed 2686, Whittenberger 2689
Coeur d'Alene: Hagadone 2674, Hecla 2676
Eagle: Beckman 2665
Garden City: Angels 2664
Hailey: Leidy 2678
Hayden: Emelco 2669
Idaho Falls: **Melaleuca 2679**
Ketchum: Boswell 2667, Dumke 2668, French 2671, Nelson 2683, Palmedo 2684
Ponderay: Wishnick 2690
Sandpoint: Ambrosiani-Pastore 2663, Equinox 2670
Sun Valley: Golden 2672, Good 2673, Hare 2675
Wallace: Morbeck 2681

see also 272, 359, 745, 988, 1276, 1319, 1410, 2403, 2886, 3107, 3168, 4428, 5047, 5059, 5919, 6843, 7867, 7888, 9322, 9619, 9681, 9977

ILLINOIS

Addison: Foley 2876
Alsip: Griffith 2929, Griffith 2930
Alton: Alton 2706
Argenta: George 2911
Aurora: Osi 3158
Bannockburn: Ellis 2853, Leibowitz 3046
Barrington: **Acorn 2695**, **Combs 2800**, JLH 2998, Lancaster 3035, Oberweiler 3147, Shaw 3244, Tafel 3280
Bloomington: Funk 2897, Knappenberger 3021, Nayak 3133, Owen 3160
Buffalo Grove: **Foundation 2880**, **New 3138**, Night 3140
Burr Ridge: Issa 2990, **Lazzara 3042**
Cairo: Hastings 2960
Chicago: 1335 2691, Abelson 2692, Abelson 2693, Acorn 2694, Adams 2696, Adreani 2697, Agape 2698, Agent 2699, Ahlstrand 2700, Allen-Heath 2701, Alliant 2702, Almeida 2704, **American 2707**, Amsted 2708, Anschel 2709, Aon 2710, **Appleby 2711**, Argo 2714, B&D 2715, Bailey 2716, Baird 2717, Banta 2719, Barr 2720, Bartholomay 2721, Bartsch 2722, Bass 2723, Beasley 2728, Beeghly 2730, Bellebyron 2731, Bellick 2732, Bergstrom 2736, Bernoudy 2738, Best 2739, Best 2740, Bishop 2743, Bladel 2744, Block, 2746, Bobins 2747, Boehl 2748, Boothroyd 2749, Borten 2750, Bower 2752, Boylan 2753, Boyle 2754, Branstad 2755, Brenner 2756, Brooker 2758, Bruce 2760, **Build 2764**, Bulkley, 2765, Burk 2768, Burnett 2769, Caccomo 2771, Cafaro-Livingston 2772, Canterbury 2774, Carey 2775, Cashel 2777, Catalyst 2778, Chambers 2780, **Chapin 2781**, Chapin-May 2782, Charles 2783, Cherry 2784, Chez 2785, Chicago 2786,

Chicago 2787, Christ 2788, Christiansen 2790, Citadel 2791, Cohn 2796, Coldwell 2797, Cole 2798, Collins 2799, Communitas 2801, Constans-Culver 2805, Cooney 2806, Copeland 2807, Corbett 2808, Corbett 2809, Coulter 2813, Cowlin 2814, Cremer 2815, Cronin 2816, Cunningham 2819, Dancing 2822, Danielson 2823, Danielson 2824, Delavan 2825, **Demos 2827**, Denny 2828, Diamond 2829, Doerr 2831, Donovan 2833, Dowdle 2834, Doyle 2836, Duncan 2839, Duncan 2840, Dunning 2841, **Dyson 2842**, Edelman 2845, Edelstein 2846, Edgerly 2847, Educational 2848, Eisenberg 2850, Eiszner 2851, Elebash 2852, Engle 2855, Enivar 2856, Equity 2858, Espenscheid 2859, Estate 2860, Everett 2861, Family 2863, Family 2864, Fasseas 2866, Faulkner 2867, Federation 2868, Fifield 2871, Fink 2873, Forbes 2878, Foster 2879, Four 2882, Foust 2883, Fraida 2884, Franklin 2887, Frederick 2889, Freund 2892, Frisby 2893, Fund 2896, Gantz 2900, Garard, 2902, Gardner 2903, Gardner 2905, General 2907, Genesis 2910, Gibbet 2912, Gidwitz 2913, Gidwitz 2914, **Gish 2915**, Glossberg 2916, Goldberg 2919, Goldenberg 2920, Gostomski 2925, Graham 2926, Gray 2927, Grusecki 2935, Gust 2936, H 2937, H. 2938, Half 2942, Halstead 2944, Hamilton 2945, Hamlin 2946, Hamm 2947, Hansen 2948, Hanson 2949, Hanson 2950, Hanus 2951, Harczak, 2952, Hare 2954, Hark 2955, Hart 2958, Hay 2961, Heins 2964, Henderson 2965, Herbert 2966, **Heritage 2967**, Herman 2968, Hess 2969, Hodes 2974, Houck 2978, House 2980, Hugg 2982, Hughes 2983, Hunt 2984, Hurley 2985, Istock 2991, Jentes 2995, Jephson 2996, JKP 2997, JMR 2999, Jocarno 3000, Johnson 3001, Karasik 3006, Keeney 3007, Keller 3010, Kelly 3012, Keyes 3016, Kilrea 3017, Klosk 3020, Knight 3022, Knowles 3023, Koch 3025, KPW 3028, Krueck 3031, Lakonishok 3032, Lakshmi 3033, **Landau 3036**, Landau 3037, Larsen 3038, **Lascaris 3040**, Lazar 3041, Lebus 3043, Leestma 3044, Leonian 3047, **Lerner 3048**, Levinson 3049, Levy 3050, Lichtman 3052, Lifetract 3053, Listeman 3055, Livney 3056, Logos 3058, Lohengrin 3059, Loudoun 3060, Loudoun 3061, Loudoun 3062, Louis 3063, Love 3064, Lyon 3066, MacDonald 3068, Maddox 3069, Mako 3070, Mallon 3071, Manne 3073, Mansfield 3074, Marcum 3076, Marquette 3078, Marsteller 3079, Massey 3082, McCabe 3084, McCauley 3085, McCormack 3086, McCourtney 3087, McCrea 3088, McCune 3089, McDonough 3090, McDougal 3091, McKee 3093, McNally 3097, Meier 3101, Meusel 3105, Millard 3109, Millard 3110, Miller 3112, Miller, 3114, Minow 3118, Moreton 3124, Morton 3127, Mouat 3128, Mullen 3129, Munson 3130, Murphy 3132, NCI 3134, Neel 3135, North 3142, Nth 3144, **Nureyev 3145**, Nygren 3146, O'Connor 3149, O'Donnell 3150, Ohlhausen 3151, Olin 3153, Olson 3154, Oppenheimer 3155, OSA 3157, Our 3159, Pangburn 3161, Parker 3162, Parker 3163, Patterson 3164, Penrose 3166, Pepper 3167, Perkins 3168, Perkins 3169, Perry 3170, Peters 3172, Pinnell 3176, Pitzman 3177, **Polk 3179**, Pollack 3180, Pond 3182, Pritzker 3184, Pugdin 3185, Reade 3187, Reed 3190, Robb 3197, Roberti 3198, Robson 3200, Rogers 3202, Rosen 3205, Rosen 3206, Rosenberg 3207, **Rosenmutter 3208**, Rossman 3211, Rothman 3213, Roundy 3214, Russell 3216, Ruttenberg 3217, Ruttenberg 3218, Saliba 3221, Sasco 3222, Schiff 3224, Schinasi 3225, Schneider 3226, Schneider 3228, Schorr-Lieberman 3229, Scott 3230, Secord 3232, Seidler 3233, Self 3234, Seymour 3236, Shapiro 3240, Shaw 3242, Shirley 3245, Simon 3247, Simpson 3248, Simpson 3249, Skylark 3250, Smallwood 3251, Smith 3252, Smith 3253, Smithburg 3254, Spencer 3258, Sramek 3259, Stairway 3261, Steigerwaldt 3265, Steinmetz 3267, Stone 3269, Stone 3270, Storer 3271, STS 3272, Stuart 3273, Sue 3275, Sullivan 3276, Sulzer 3277, Sumac 3278, Summer 3279, Tarrson 3282, Taylor 3284, Taylor 3285,

Tengelsen 3288, Thaman 3289, Townsend 3291, **Trust 3293**, Trust 3294, Tully 3295, Tuohy 3296, Turner 3297, Ulm 3299, Vail 3301, Valenti 3302, Victor 3304, Von 3305, Walk 3307, Walker 3308, Wark 3309, Warner 3310, Watson 3311, Wehle 3314, **Wein 3315**, Weiner 3316, Weiss 3317, Wessel 3318, Weston 3320, Whitwam 3321, Wislow 3323, Witz-Mallinger 3324, Wolf 3326, Wolf 3327, Wolff 3328, Wood 3329, Woodruff 3330, Woods 3332, Yulman 3334

Collinsville: Fredman 2890

Countryside: Jaros 2993

Crystal Lake: AptarGroup 2712, Norgaard 3141

Danville: Hegeler 2963

Decatur: Hary 2959, Sequoia 3235, Staley 3264

Deerfield: Bernfield 2737, Fremont 2891, Holden 2976, JBS 2994, Miller, 3113, O'C 3148, Rosenthal 3210

Des Plaines: Frank 2885, H.C.D. 2939

Downers Grove: Petrovich 3174

Dundee: Arboit 2713, McGraw 3092

Elgin: Daeumer 2821, Epaphroditus 2857

Elk Grove Village: Orsini 3156

Elmhurst: Bates 2724, Marks 3077

Evanston: Dubin 2838, Howard 2981, Jahn 2992, Kellcie 3008, Lehman-Stamm 3045, New 3136, **New 3137**, Romano 3203, Shaked 3237

Galesburg: Larson 3039

Geneseo: Geneseo 2909

Geneva: Fabyan 2862, Shodeen 3246

Glencoe: Fields 2870, Metzner 3104, Takiff 3281, Zuckerman 3338

Glenview: Bendich 2733, Bidwill 2741, Cohn 2795, Considine 2804, Delta 2826, Hill 2971, **Lindon 3054**, Tobey 3290, Zaentz 3336, Zemsky 3337

Hawthorn Woods: Kemper 3014

Herrin: Bruce 2761

Hickory Hills: **Meyers 3107**

Highland Park: Goldman 2922, Goodstein 2924, Highland 2970, Kerr 3015, Mann 3072, Mazzetta 3083, Millner 3115, Minor 3117, Okner-Robbins 3152, Reinisch 3193, Ringer 3196, Rosenson 3209, Shaw 3243

Hillside: Clingen 2794

Hinsdale: Allyn 2703, Bere 2734, Haarlow 2940, Merchantz 3102, Nickum 3139, Reed 3191, Ryan 3219, Scrugli 3231, Zaccone 3335

Homewood: Cain 2773, Gassin 2906, Maak 3067

Hubbard Woods: Monroe 3122

Huntley: Meyer 3106

Jacksonville: Bound 2751, **Mead 3100**

Kankakee: Community 2802

Kenilworth: Dower 2835, Hales 2941, Putnam 3186

La Grange: Schneider 3227, Speiser 3257

Lake Forest: Brunswick 2762, Clarks 2792, Dick 2830, Donovan 2832, Groner 2932, Grumhaus, 2934, Miller 3111, Mohr 3121, Moore 3123, Red 3188, Reichert 3192, Will 3322

Lexington: Kemp 3013

Libertyville: D.A.S. 2820, Houlihan 2979, Kelly 3011

Lincolnwood: Grossinger 2933, **Mermelstein 3103**, Powell 3183, Ruben 3215

Lisle: SSAB 3260

Mattoon: Burgess 2767

Milford: Schaumburg 3223

Mokena: Kaminski 3005

Moline: Hallene 2943, Hardiek 2953, Harris 2957, McLaughlin 3095, Stutsman 3274

Morris: Morris 3125

Morrison: Saemann 3220

Morton: Baum 2727, Morton 3126

Mount Carmel: Mary's 3080

Mount Prospect: Jones 3002

Mundelein: Keller 3009

Murphysboro: Smysor 3255

Naperville: Koranda 3026, Micole 3108, Rot 3212

Niles: Block 2745, Eckert 2843, Galter 2899

Norridge: Marchese 3075

Northbrook: Cless 2793, **Foundation 2881**, Mitchell 3120, Stein 3266, Wagner 3306, Weaver 3312, Wesselink 3319

Northfield: Burt 2770, Ceres 2779, Judy 3003, **Kobe 3024**, **Krasberg-Mason 3029**

Northlake: Murnane 3131, Novick 3143

Oak Brook: Cronk 2817, Hirschmann 2972, **Lizzadro 3057**

Oak Lawn: Roche 3201

Oak Park: Good 2923, Kott 3027, Shaker 3238

Oakbrook Terrace: Buntrock 2766, Gray 2928

Olney: Fildes 2872

Orland Park: Cord 2811

Palatine: Carter 2776, Lichner 3051, Peters 3171

Palos Heights: McNeill 3098

Park Ridge: Petrick 3173

Pekin: Wright 3333

Peoria: Gloyd 2917, Share 3241

Quincy: Community 2803, Gardner 2904, Taylor 3286, Taylor 3287

Richmond: Full 2895

River Forest: Lamka 3034

Riverwoods: Podolsky 3178

Robinson: Heath 2962

Rockford: Baudhuin 2726, Eclipse 2844, Kjellstrom 3019, Miner 3116, Wolf 3325

Rolling Meadows: Bufka 2763

Roscoe: Bates 2725

Rosemont: Rich 3194, Staley 3263

Saint Charles: Flinn 2875

Sandwich: Frankel 2886

Schaumburg: Bisco 2742, Brewer 2757, Gallagher 2898, Kainz 3004, Kipper 3018, Pawlowski 3165, Poncher 3181

Skokie: Beck 2729, Full 2894, Pharmore 3175, Stern 3268, Taxman 3283

Smithshire: Twomey 3298

South Elgin: Hoffer 2975

Springfield: Staley 3262

Sycamore: Ideal 2986, Roberts 3199

Taylorville: Hopper 2977

Tinley Park: Christian 2789, Drugas 2837, EMA 2854

Tremont: Cullinan 2818, Mary's 3081

Vandalia: McKee 3094

Watseka: Iroquois 2989

Waukegan: United 3300

West Chicago: Cornerstone 2812, Richard 3195

Westchester: Follett 2877, Ingredion 2987, **Ingredion 2988**

Westmont: Farnham 2865, Vibern 3303

Wheaton: Brown 2759, Feltes 2869, Luehring 3065

Wheeling: McLennan 3096

White Hall: Griswold 2931

Wilmette: Franklin 2888, Generations 2908, Harris 2956, Hirschmann 2973, Krehbiel 3030, Mirapaul 3119, Shamrock 3239, Sondheimer 3256

Winnetka: Baird 2718, Bergstein 2735, Corcoran 2810, Fischer 2874, Gantz 2901, Gochnauer 2918, Golder 2921, McNulty 3099, Red 3189, Rosebud 3204, Trio 3292

Winthrop Harbor: Webb 3313

Wood Dale: Eichner 2849

Wood River: Alton 2705

---

see also 31, 38, 65, 99, 117, 159, 166, 240, 363, 433, 460, 602, 786, 858, 873, 942, 949, 958, 964, 975, 978, 1009, 1011, 1044, 1071, 1072, 1201, 1230, 1237, 1281, 1331, 1333, 1339, 1346, 1358, 1368, 1386, 1422, 1463, 1496, 1515, 1571, 1619, 1627, 1630, 1673, 1720, 1735, 1753, 1771, 1792, 1831, 1845, 1901, 1951, 1976, 1998, 2025, 2029, 2036, 2055, 2081, 2086, 2092, 2132, 2153, 2159, 2164, 2165, 2169, 2176, 2180, 2208, 2226, 2258, 2282, 2301, 2332, 2370, 2384, 2418, 2516, 2606, 2640, 3347, 3385, 3407, 3417, 3459, 3464, 3544, 3593, 3696, 3752, 3767, 3774, 3870, 4001, 4007, 4082, 4098, 4243, 4308, 4310, 4408, 4430, 4470, 4496, 4521, 4577, 4578, 4692, 4706, 4721, 4722, 4729, 4763, 4889, 4902, 4906, 4922, 4931, 4933, 4952, 5016, 5022, 5111, 5152, 5168, 5191, 5248, 5271, 5302, 5401, 5469, 5627, 5664, 5679, 5717, 5754, 6031, 6242, 6245, 6246, 6572, 6634, 6705, 6763, 7014, 7239, 7240, 7245, 7322, 7341, 7370, 7425, 7446, 7482, 7709, 7722, 7847, 7858, 7871, 7902, 7913, 8003, 8073, 8121, 8187, 8197, 8208, 8228, 8237, 8320, 8388, 8398, 8404, 8414, 8418, 8440, 8460, 8469, 8473, 8578, 8667, 8848, 8849, 9078, 9227, 9394, 9407, 9655, 9778, 9788, 9820, 9871, 9886, 9904, 9909, 9929, 9930, 9936, 9937, 9942, 9961, 9975

INDIANA

Alexandria: Gaither 3384

Avon: Harlan 3391

Batesville: Hillenbrand 3393

Bedford: Community 3363

Berne: Conrad 3364

Bloomfield: Greene 3390

Bloomington: Raymond 3436

Bristol: Welter 3465

Brownsburg: Agness 3340

Carmel: Cohen 3357, Dobbs 3368, Globe 3387, Maurer 3415, **Mervis 3417**, Salin 3442, Smith 3453

Columbus: Custer 3366, Namaste 3422, Nugent 3425

Connersville: Fayette 3379

Covington: Western 3466

Elkhart: Bill 3345, Rinker 3438

Evansville: Braun 3349, Bronstein 3351, Bussing-Koch 3353, Crescent-Cresline-Wabash 3365, Ellerbrook 3376, Keck 3405, PHP 3431, Share 3450, Snyder 3454, Springleaf 3455

Fishers: Jennings 3403

Fort Wayne: Ash 3341, Franklin 3382, Hoffman 3395, Kuhne 3409, Magee-O'Connor 3414, Niblick 3423, Noecker 3424, O'Rourke-Schof 3429, Raker 3434, Rifkin 3437, Schwab 3445, Stucky 3457

Fowler: Benton 3344

Francesville: Hoch 3394

Ft. Wayne: Vann 3461

Garrett: Clark-Morrill 3356

Greenfield: Vision 3463

Greensburg: Decatur 3367

Greenwood: Green 3389

Hartford City: Blackford 3346

Huntington: Huntington 3397

Indianapolis: **Ackerman 3339**, Ayres 3342, BAJ 3343, Branigin 3348, Brave 3350, Burris 3352, Community 3358, Dorsey 3369, Eskenazi 3377, Eternal 3378, Fortune 3381, God's 3388, Herr 3392, Interactive 3398, J. 3400, KEJ 3406, Klapper 3408, Lacy 3410, M.C.R. 3413, McKinney 3416, Mothershead 3419, Rooney 3440, Sherwood 3451, Simon 3452, Thomasson 3459, Wilmes 3468, Winchester 3469

Jasper: Dubois 3370, Seger 3447

Lafayette: Lafayette 3411

Lagrange: LaGrange 3412

Madison: Community 3359

Marion: OTT 3430

Martinsville: Community 3360

Merrillville: Gammon 3385

Michigan City: Duneland 3372

Middlebury: Fenech 3380

Mishawaka: J 3399, Schurz 3444

Muncie: MutualBank 3421, Shafer 3449

Munster: Dye 3373, Jolan 3404

North Vernon: Jennings 3402

Peru: Dukes 3371

Rensselaer: Jasper 3401

Richmond: Edelman 3374, Elder 3375, Quigg 3433, Raper 3435, Stamm 3456
Rising Sun: Ohio 3427
Rushville: Rush 3441
Schererville: Kharis 3407
Scottsburg: Scott 3446
Seymour: Seymour 3448
South Bend: Carroll 3354, CDM 3355, Milton 3418, Oliver 3428, TCU 3458
Tell City: Mulzer 3420, Schergens 3443
Terre Haute: Froderman 3383, Gibson 3386, Hulman 3396, Oakley 3426, Weston 3467
Valparaiso: Von 3464
Vevay: Community 3362, Vevay-Switzerland 3462
Westfield: Thrush-Thompson 3460
Wheatfield: Bos 3347
Winamac: Pulaski 3432
Winchester: Community 3361
Zionsville: Roberts 3439

see also 24, 103, 1082, 1109, 1273, 1381, 1493, 1797, 1889, 1899, 1909, 1979, 2040, 2086, 2190, 2716, 2794, 2812, 2819, 2838, 2865, 2954, 2988, 3010, 3022, 3131, 3220, 3233, 3271, 3499, 3700, 3767, 3947, 4197, 4474, 4500, 4561, 4738, 5024, 5097, 5165, 5248, 5394, 5413, 5685, 6207, 6228, 6456, 6597, 7050, 7245, 7303, 7317, 7349, 7362, 7416, 7441, 7462, 7507, 7510, 7524, 7549, 7615, 7727, 7729, 7850, 7902, 7991, 8089, 8103, 8157, 8194, 8197, 8208, 8281, 8291, 8295, 8477, 8671, 8987, 9094, 9188, 9226, 9288, 9311, 9387, 9799, 9904, 9923

IOWA

Ames: Burke 3477
Bettendorf: Vonderhaar 3543, Weigle 3546
Boone: Beckwith 3473
Cedar Rapids: Busse 3478, Gazette 3497, Hills 3507, Iowa 3513, Rohde 3530
Chariton: Coons 3481
Clinton: Mount 3522
Council Bluffs: Pottawattamie 3527
Davenport: Becker 3472, Figge 3492, McCarthy/Bush 3519
Des Moines: Daniels 3483, Gartner 3496, Pappajohn 3525, Toohey 3538, Vermeer 3542, Weathertop 3545, **World 3550**
Dubuque: Henry 3505, McDonald 3520, Medical 3521, **Wahlert 3544**, Woodward 3549
Fairfield: Herr 3506, Jefferson 3514, Peace 3526
Fort Dodge: Deardorf 3485, Smeltzer 3535, Stark 3536
Greenfield: Schildberg 3532
Grinnell: Grinnell 3501
Hampton: Barkema 3471
Independence: Blin 3476
Indianola: Cole-Belin 3480, Iowa 3512
Iowa City: Krumm 3517, **Wright 3551**
Iowa Falls: Howard 3509
Keosauqua: Van 3539
Logan: Wood 3548
Marion: Giacoletto 3499
Mason City: Farrer 3490, First 3493, Tomson 3537
Mitchellville: Andringa 3470
Mount Pleasant: Hoaglin 3508
Muscatine: Bishop 3475, Howe 3510, Muscatine 3523
Newton: Geisler 3498
North Liberty: Ellen 3489
Oskaloosa: Drost 3487
Pella: De 3484, Farver 3491, Heerema 3504, Vermeer 3541
Rippey: Schroeder 3533
Rock Rapids: Forster 3494
Sheldon: Van 3540
Sioux Center: Premier 3528

Sioux City: Bennett 3474, deStwolinski 3486, Duggan 3488, Gleeson 3500, Latta 3518, Security 3534
Slater: Iowa 3511
Urbandale: Carlson 3479, Grubb 3502, K2 3515
Waterloo: Gaedke 3495, Young 3552
West Des Moines: Cowles 3482, GuideOne 3503, Krause 3516, Nelson 3524, R 3529, West 3547
West Liberty: Ryan 3531

see also 272, 652, 985, 1227, 1311, 1372, 1936, 2016, 2190, 2803, 2957, 2966, 3093, 3220, 3260, 3274, 3319, 4408, 4470, 4508, 4678, 4763, 4782, 4804, 4954, 5066, 5073, 5075, 5103, 5143, 5202, 5248, 5520, 7240, 8197, 8208, 8383, 8496, 8554, 8572, 8757, 9252, 9283, 9373, 9818, 9879, 9892, 9923, 9928, 9962

KANSAS

Abilene: Community 3567, Jeffcoat 3588
Atchison: Adair-Exchange 3553, Cray 3569, **Muchnic 3609**
Bucyrus: Family 3575
Coffeyville: Coffeyville 3566
Colby: Henry 3585, Thomas 3634
Dodge City: Scroggins 3624
Emporia: Babinger 3555, Hopkins 3586, Reeble 3618, Trusler 3635
Fairway: Green 3583
Fowler: Testamentary 3633
Garden City: O' 3612, Williams 3643
Great Bend: Golden 3582
Gridley: French 3579
Hays: Rush 3620, Schmidt 3622
Hugoton: Nash 3610
Hutchinson: Davis 3571, Stallman 3629
Junction City: Bramlage 3559, Central 3564, Jellison 3589
Kansas City: Olofson 3613
Lakin: **Weskan 3641**
Leawood: Cyr 3570, Elsberry 3574, Fox 3578, Lowenstein 3598, Price 3616
Manhattan: Stolzer 3630
McPherson: Mingenback 3605
Mission Hills: Kiersznowski 3594, Walsh 3638, Wood 3644
Olathe: Morrison 3608
Overland Park: CPS 3568, Dehaemers 3572, Goldberg 3581, Haglage 3584, Master 3600, Price 3615, V 3636
Paola: Baehr 3556
Phillipsburg: Morgan 3607
Prairie Village: Merrill 3602, Miller-Mellor 3604, Mistler 3606, Nettleton 3611, Swearingen 3631
Pratt: South 3628
Salina: Bane 3557, Joscelyn 3590, **Kejr 3593**, Middlekauff 3603, Smoot 3627
Scott City: Scott 3623
Shawnee Mission: Atterbury 3554, Breidenthal-Snyder 3560, Weber 3640
Smith Center: McFadden 3601, Rathert 3617
Topeka: Kammco 3591, Payless 3614, Sheetz 3626
Wamego: Kansas 3592
Westwood: Watson 3639
Wichita: Berry 3558, Brown 3561, Cape 3563, Cochener 3565, DeVore 3573, Farah 3576, Fidelity 3577, Goebel 3580, Insurance 3587, Lincoln 3596, Logan 3597, Mann 3599, Ross 3619, Salgo 3621, Shannon 3625, Taylor 3632, Wallace 3637, Wiedemann 3642
Winfield: Legacy, 3595
Witchita: Buford 3562

see also 150, 272, 1145, 1280, 1358, 1365, 1368, 1422, 2129, 2244, 2250, 2332, 2769, 3479, 4243, 4500, 4860, 4870, 4875, 4890, 4901,

4932, 4935, 4973, 5002, 5017, 5021, 5116, 7277, 7520, 7686, 7693, 7721, 7736, 7738, 7839, 8690, 8744, 8749, 8778, 8921, 9024, 9123, 9190, 9236, 9447, 9613, 9619, 9906

KENTUCKY

Ashland: Spriggs 3695, Woodlands 3707
Bardstown: Gagarin 3656
Bowling Green: Haskins 3661
Carlisle: Mulhollem 3680
Chavies: Foundation 3655
Covington: Welchwood 3706
Crescent Springs: Namaste 3682
Danville: Trim 3702
Fort Mitchell: Heisel 3663
Frankfort: Stockdell-Joseph 3698
Gilbertsville: Reed 3688
Glasgow: GHH 3658, Houchens 3665
Jackson: Turner 3703
Lexington: Boone 3648, Boone 3649, Keeneland 3668, Marksbury 3675, Murry 3681, Opera 3684, Rouse 3692, USA 3704
Louisville: Barr 3646, Barth 3647, Coffey 3650, Diebold 3652, Dunbar 3653, Etscorn 3654, Hannah 3659, Harter 3660, Kentucky 3669, Killian 3670, Longest 3672, Mackin 3673, Masser 3676, McKellar 3677, Morris 3679, Pollard 3685, Price 3686, Renau 3689, Roth 3690, Rounsavall, 3691, Shapira 3693, Smith 3694, Stock 3697, Sutherland 3699, Trager 3701, Weisberg 3705, Woosley 3708, Yarmuth 3709
Maysville: Hayswood 3662
Midway: Jones 3667
Monticello: Ogden 3683
Owensboro: Horn 3664, Independence 3666, Public 3687, Yeager 3710
Paducah: MGM 3678
Paris: Lebus 3671
Prospect: Dickins 3651, Taylor 3700
Simpsonville: **Magee 3674**
Somerset: GB 3657
Versailles: Abercrombie 3645
Villa Hills: Steiner 3696

see also 35, 209, 292, 364, 591, 1030, 1278, 1409, 1479, 1620, 1740, 1767, 1878, 2073, 2188, 2213, 2417, 2748, 2840, 2841, 3043, 3135, 3164, 3202, 3368, 3436, 3526, 4243, 4309, 4419, 4501, 4706, 4879, 5248, 5365, 7079, 7186, 7299, 7313, 7381, 7468, 7507, 7524, 7546, 7626, 7665, 7755, 7842, 7888, 7910, 7922, 8051, 8151, 8227, 8285, 8477, 8601, 8606, 8651, 8671, 9190, 9387, 9552

LOUISIANA

Abbeville: Live 3734
Abita Springs: Briggs 3714
Alexandria: Huie-Dellmon 3729
Arabi: Meraux 3736
Baton Rouge: Broussard 3715, Noland 3743, **Ruckstuhl 3748**, Showers 3753, Special 3754
Bossier City: A-Kids-Choice 3712, Biedenharn 3713
Crowley: Winn 3760
Harahan: Salutare 3749
Lafayette: Knight 3731, New 3742, Pugh 3747, Zuschlag 3762
Lake Charles: Ainsley's 3711, Chambers 3718, Lake 3732, Lang 3733
Mandeville: Gauthier 3724
Metairie: Whitman 3759
Monroe: Mintz 3738
New Orleans: Cahn 3716, Catalyst 3717, Daybrook 3720, Dujay 3722, Harper 3726, Havens 3727, Houseman 3728, Kavanagh 3730, Moffett 3739, Montan 3740, Monteleone 3741, Operation 3744,

Parkside 3745, Shannon 3752, Steinhagen 3755, Vick 3756, Wetmore 3757, Wisdom 3761
Roseland: Crossroads 3719
Shreveport: Ellis 3723, Grigsby 3725, Magale 3735, Merkle 3737, Powers 3746, Sci-Port 3750, Selber 3751, Wheless 3758
West Monroe: DeGree 3721

see also 23, 453, 810, 1457, 1787, 1850, 1925, 2414, 2860, 2912, 2985, 3134, 3297, 3660, 4044, 4501, 4822, 5183, 5505, 5533, 5816, 6997, 7763, 8208, 8373, 8539, 8540, 8707, 8722, 8899, 8955, 8977, 9083, 9246, 9297, 9876

MAINE

Augusta: Kennebec 3785
Bangor: Lafayette 3787, Mimi 3792, Minsky 3793
Bar Harbor: Red 3801
Bar Mills: Narragansett 3794
Bath: Davenport 3775
Camden: Camden 3771, **Golden 3781**, Messler 3790
Cape Elizabeth: Pond 3798
Damariscotta: Bailey 3765
Ellsworth: Lynam 3788
Farmington: Franklin 3779
Gardiner: Bank 3766
Kennebunk: Chappell 3772, Kennebunk 3786, Somers 3803
Newcastle: Reny 3802
Norway: Brook 3769
Oakland: Borman 3767
Orono: Kagan 3784
Oxford: Oxford 3796
Phillips: Firebird 3778
Portland: Aldermere 3763, Alfond 3764, Boulos 3768, Burnham 3770, Coates 3773, Cotsirilos 3774, **Dugas 3776**, Elliotsville 3777, Goldberg 3780, Henry 3782, Hudson 3783, Merrill 3789, MG 3791, Old 3795, Protein 3799, Quesada 3800, Wellspring 3806
Robbinston: **St. 3804**
South China: Sukeforth 3805
Westbrook: Planet 3797

see also 156, 662, 739, 1277, 1399, 1656, 1691, 1711, 1716, 1747, 1778, 1798, 1910, 1945, 2399, 2403, 2415, 2824, 2881, 2948, 3222, 3927, 4033, 4039, 4093, 4102, 4168, 4193, 4220, 4234, 4257, 4260, 4271, 4274, 4280, 4306, 4336, 5211, 5231, 5233, 5486, 5495, 5516, 5749, 5750, 5973, 6092, 6109, 6301, 6410, 6635, 6682, 6869, 7414, 7494, 7537, 7888, 7989, 8007, 8143, 8176, 8181, 8208, 8305, 8327, 8432, 8505, 9244, 9433, 9755

MARYLAND

Accokeek: Higginson 3880
Annapolis: Franey 3865, Fusco 3868, Jake 3890, Liberty 3901
Baltimore: Adams 3808, Baker 3815, Baltimore 3816, Baltimore 3817, Bank 3818, Barton 3819, Berger 3821, Blum 3825, **Boehm 3826**, Broadus 3829, Carol 3834, Cogan 3837, Contino 3840, Croft 3841, Devito 3848, Eliasberg 3854, Ferris 3859, Gidwitz 3870, Gladding 3871, Gutman 3877, Helm 3879, Hittman 3881, Hubbard 3883, Hurwitz 3886, Kelly, 3893, Kohn 3896, Kohn 3897, Legum 3899, Macht 3905, McKnight 3910, Meyerhoff 3914, Mitchell, 3916, Moser 3918, Myerberg 3923, Nabit 3924, Number 3929, O'Neil 3930, Otenasek 3931, Paternotte 3933, Pearlstone 3934, Rothschild 3942, Salisbury 3945, Shapiro 3949, Shattuck 3950, Snyder 3956, Stover 3961, Swenson 3962, Ten 3963, Thalheimer 3966, Tzedakah 3970, Unger 3971, Van 3974, Waidner 3976, Wallis

3977, Weinberg, 3979, Wieler 3984, Witt/Hoey 3989
Belcamp: Huether/McClelland 3884
Berlin: Humphreys 3885
Bethesda: Acacia 3807, Ammerman 3813, Cafritz 3830, Dean 3846, Elno 3855, Feinberg 3857, Ferris 3860, Fischer 3862, **Fox 3864**, Gewirz 3869, **Goldberg 3872**, Greene-Milstein 3876, Izzo 3889, Mann-Paller 3908, Marriott 3909, Mustard 3922, RFI 3938, Small 3955, SPM 3958, Weiss 3982, Williams 3986
Chestertown: Clifton 3836, Elsberg 3856, Moore 3917, Sears 3948, Van 3973, **Windsor 3988**
Chevy Chase: Adler 3809, AMDG 3812, Chessie 3835, CSG 3842, Eccles 3853, Hyman 3887
Cockeysville: Tenberg 3964, Wilson 3987
Columbia: Besson 3823
Crofton: S.B.E. 3944
Cumberland: DelSignore 3847
Damascus: Carbonell 3833
Easton: Biophilia 3824, Darby 3843, No 3927, Richmond 3940, St. 3959, Tucker 3969
Ellicott City: **Braitmayer 3827**, Kirk 3894
Fallston: Cole 3839
Frederick: Laughlin 3898, Loats 3902, **Thadikonda 3965**
Fulton: Mental 3912, Newday 3925
Gaithersburg: Pettit 3935, Wolpoff 3990
Germantown: Ford 3863, Minkoff 3915, Phase 3936
Gibson Island: Rogers-Wilbur 3941, Schuh 3946
Glen Echo: Ticho 3967
Hagerstown: Anderson 3814, Youth 3991
Hampstead: Lutheran 3904
Hunt Valley: **Northern 3928**
Libertytown: Allemall 3811
Lutherville: Cohen 3838, Mullan 3920, Murthynayak 3921, Silber 3952
Lutherville Timonium: Mangione 3907
Owings Mills: Beaufort 3820, Caplan 3832, Feldman 3858, Macks 3906, Sonneborn 3957, Weiner 3980, Wilen 3985
Oxford: Akridge 3810, Widgeon 3983
Pasadena: Fun-Raising 3867
Potomac: Daydreams 3845, Meyer, 3913, Shrensky 3951, Silberman 3953
Riderwood: **Doorstep 3850**, **Mpala 3919**, Warfield 3978
Riverdale: Bernard 3822
Rockville: Bresler 3828, Davis 3844, Dockser 3849, Eacho 3852, Govil 3875, **St. 3960**, V 3972, Wagner-Braunsberg 3975
Saint Michaels: Knapp 3895
Salisbury: Parsons 3932
Silver Spring: Gorlin 3874, Halle 3878, Katz 3891, Kay 3892, Meltzer 3911, Schwarz 3947, Slavin 3954, Totah 3968
Stevenson: Weinman 3981
Sykesville: Nicholl 3926
Timonium: Campbell 3831, Lohr, 3903
Towson: Duncan 3851, Fine 3861, Friedman 3866, Gordon 3873, Hobbs 3882, Israelson 3888, RCM 3937, Rhona's 3939
Upperco: Rouse 3943
Wheaton: Levin 3900

see also 103, 112, 247, 307, 622, 809, 851, 1028, 1053, 1089, 1219, 1336, 1358, 1437, 1508, 1563, 1634, 1640, 1686, 1747, 1786, 1788, 1790, 1791, 1800, 1806, 1812, 1814, 1819, 1821, 1824, 1834, 1861, 1913, 1986, 2038, 2064, 2243, 2382, 2527, 2881, 3002, 3141, 3583, 3804, 4127, 4272, 4290, 4386, 4647, 4694, 5000, 5248, 5270, 5299, 5300, 5304, 5405, 5453, 5487, 5502, 5518, 5543, 5555, 5568, 5623, 5651, 5906, 5911, 5936, 6037, 6147, 6176, 6193, 6223, 6260, 6356, 6397, 6421, 6572, 6581, 6588, 6597, 6654, 6676, 6690, 6969, 7287, 7596, 7629, 7852, 7888,

7949, 8006, 8053, 8076, 8110, 8116, 8164, 8191, 8193, 8203, 8264, 8301, 8304, 8316, 8348, 8422, 8458, 8840, 9018, 9268, 9278, 9387, 9388, 9397, 9405, 9430, 9440, 9453, 9469, 9476, 9490, 9504, 9507, 9513, 9519, 9521, 9528, 9530, 9535, 9538, 9768, 9843, 9876, 9965

MASSACHUSETTS

Acton: Astra 4006
Amesbury: Provident 4250
Amherst: Felix 4089
Andover: Philips 4243, Russell 4273, Stearns 4311
Arlington: Goldman 4105, Melvina 4197, Mirak 4204
Auburn: Webster 4353
Belmont: Allison 4000, Schwartz 4284
Beverly: Kneisel 4157, Sword 4318, Symes 4319
Boston: A 3994, Alden 3999, Alvord 4002, Ansin 4003, Arcadia 4004, Archibald 4005, Autism 4007, Babson 4009, Bacon 4011, Beaucourt 4014, Berger 4018, Bergstrom 4019, Bigbird 4020, Black 4021, **Blossom 4022**, Boyce 4024, Boynton 4025, Brock 4027, Brooks 4028, Brown 4029, Bushee 4032, **Cabbadetus 4033**, Cabot 4034, Cabot 4035, Carlee 4038, Catino 4040, Chabner 4041, Chabot 4042, Change 4043, Chase 4045, Chickering 4046, Clarke 4049, Codman 4052, Cole 4054, Connell 4055, Cook 4056, Cricket 4060, Crowe 4061, Curvey 4062, Dalessandro 4063, Dedham 4067, Delorenzo 4068, Devereaux 4069, Druker 4071, Durant 4072, Eddy 4077, Edwards 4078, Fessenden 4090, Fletcher 4093, Fraser 4097, Friend 4098, Frisbie 4099, Greenberg 4106, Hale 4112, Hale 4113, Harrington 4117, Hausman 4121, Haven 4122, Hazard 4123, Hazard 4124, Helman 4126, Henderson 4128, Hicks 4129, Hoffman 4131, Hogan 4132, Hornblower 4135, Horne 4136, **Kahn 4143**, Kenwood 4150, Kershaw 4151, Killian 4154, Kimball 4155, King 4156, Krupp 4161, **Lalor 4164**, Lamm 4165, Langer 4166, Learning 4169, Leatherwood 4170, Ledgeways 4171, Levangie 4172, Lindsay 4176, Lost 4180, Magee 4183, Marigold 4189, Mavrogenis 4192, McNeice, 4195, Melvin 4196, MENTOR 4199, Merrill 4200, Metanoia 4201, Mitchell 4205, Mohr 4206, Morningstar 4207, Morse 4208, Murphy 4214, Nelson 4219, Nichols 4223, Noonan 4225, Novack 4226, Nye 4227, One 4230, Oristaglio 4232, Parlin 4233, **Pegasus 4236**, Peters 4241, Progin 4247, Prokopis 4248, Puffin 4251, Putnam 4252, Putnam 4253, Ratshesky 4259, Reynolds 4264, Rice 4265, **Robbins-de 4266**, Rose 4271, Safe 4275, Sailors' 4276, Sandler 4278, Segel 4285, Shanklin 4288, Shattuck 4291, Shaughnessy 4292, Sherman 4293, Solomont 4303, Stare 4308, Starr 4309, Stearns 4310, Stemberg 4313, Storer 4314, Sullivan 4315, **Summer 4316**, Swan 4317, **Tatelman 4322**, Tatelman 4323, Thee 4324, Thompson 4325, Thoracic 4326, Tomfohrde 4329, Toocap 4330, Torok 4331, Tresorelle 4333, Ullian 4335, Vela 4341, Verrochi 4342, Vingo 4345, Wallace 4347, Walske 4349, Wapack 4350, Webber 4351, Weber 4352, Weiner 4355, Weld 4356, Wells 4357, Wheatland 4358, Wilcox 4360, Windhorse 4361, Winthrop 4363, Zock 4368
Boxford: Benz 4017, Dwyer 4074, Harwood 4119, Videtta 4343
Braintree: Harris 4118, Reisman 4262, Tye 4334
Brewster: Babson-Webber-Mustard 4010
Brockton: Howard 4137, Pilgrim 4245
Brookline: Gerrity 4102, Morse 4209, Schiro 4282, Shaich 4287, Solomont 4302
Cambridge: Akamai 3998, **Azadoutioun 4008**, **Barakat 4012**, Boger 4023, **Bruner 4030**, Hagerty 4110, Mank 4187, Neighborhood 4218, Ragon 4256, Redwall 4261, Shapiro 4290, Vine's 4344
Canton: OneBeacon 4231, Simoni 4296
Carlisle: Chirag 4048

Chelmsford: Ain 3997
Chestnut Hill: Cail 4036, Longtine 4179, Marcus 4188, Perry 4240, Schechter 4281
Chicopee: Chicopee 4047
Clinton: Nypro 4228
Cohasset: Chartis 4044, Deane 4066
Concord: Crawford 4059, Franklin 4096, Gloria 4104, Noble 4224, Winning 4362
Dalton: Crane 4058
Danvers: Valerio 4339
Dedham: Jefferson 4142, Marino 4190
Dover: Bulger 4031, Hagler 4111, Ladd 4163, McCutchin-Collins 4193, Pechet 4235
Dunstable: Lawrence 4167
Duxbury: Kelleher 4147
Easthampton: Easthampton 4076
Edgartown: **Patagonia 4234**
Falmouth: **Brabson 4026**
Fitchburg: Rollstone 4270, Whittemore 4359
Foxboro: Rodman 4268, Rodman 4269
Framingham: Levy 4173, Levy 4174, MutualOne 4216, Rosse 4272, Young 4366
Great Barrington: Ungar 4336
Greenfield: FCTS 4088
Hanover: Morse 4210, Peoples 4237
Haverhill: Griffin 4107
Hopedale: Hopedale 4134
Hyannis: Makepeace 4185, Smith 4300
Ipswich: 2 3992, **New 4220**
Lee: Coolidge 4057
Leominster: Clementi 4050
Lexington: **Afeyan 3996**, Behrakis 4015, Guttag 4109, Koha 4158, Koplow 4159
Lincoln: Davoli 4065, Kelsey 4148, Ramsey 4258
Littleton: Hauben 4120
Longmeadow: Kamin 4144
Lowell: Fay 4087, Kendall 4149, Mahoney 4184, Walsh 4348
Manchester: Halfway 4115, Tadler 4320
Mansfield: Sprague 4306
Marblehead: Casey 4039, **Kaplan 4145**
Marion: Makepeace 4186, Upstream 4338
Mashpee: Tapper 4321
Middleboro: Pierce 4244
Monterey: Elephant 4081
Natick: Fassino 4086, Middlesex 4203
Needham: Reisman 4263, Savage 4280, Schlager 4283, Shapiro 4289
Newburyport: NAID 4217, Newburyport 4221, Newburyport 4222
Newton: Cohen 4053, **Galileo 4101**, Sherman 4294, Smith 4298, Trefler 4332, Weil 4354
Newtonville: Massachusetts 4191
North Adams: Proud 4249
North Andover: Hill 4130
North Hampton: 484 3993
Northampton: Carle 4037, Xeric 4365
Norwood: SER 4286
Oak Bluffs: Permanent 4239
Osterville: Madonna 4182
Oxford: Encourage 4082
Peabody: East 4075, **Spero 4304**, Von 4346
Pelham: M 4181
Pittsfield: **A 3995**, Gale 4100, Quirico 4254
Plainville: Honey 4133
Pride's Crossing: Jackson 4140
Rockland: Rockland 4267
Rockport: Tilson 4328
Salem: Killam 4153, Salem 4277
Sherborn: Barstow 4013
Somerville: Thoreau 4327
South Boston: Karas 4146, Mount 4211
Southbridge: Hyde 4139
Springfield: Benson 4016, D'Amour 4064, Hampden 4116, Smith 4299, Steiger 4312

Sterling: Ramlose 4257, Sicari 4295
Stow: Kurian 4162, Red 4260
Sudbury: Henderson 4127, Michael 4202
Waban: Krieger 4160
Wakefield: Phelps 4242
Waltham: DWSS 4073, Foundation 4094, PerkinElmer 4238, Singing 4297
Wayland: Donovan 4070, Epstein 4084, Hurston 4138
Webster: Janet 4141
Wellesley: Egan 4080, Family 4085, Haley 4114, Sacajawea 4274, Sandman 4279, Solomon 4301, Stanzler 4307
Wellesley Hills: Levy 4175, Mountain 4212, Spoon 4305
Wenham: O'Keefe 4229, Zampell 4367
West Springfield: United 4337
West Yarmouth: Lingos 4177
Westborough: Egan 4079, Francis 4095
Weston: Clifford 4051, First 4091, Fleming 4092, Gildea 4103, **Gross 4108**, Heide 4125, Lawry 4168, Liswhit 4178, Poduska 4246, Rabb 4255
Westport: Van 4340
Westwood: Altamira 4001
Winchester: Murphy 4215
Woburn: Kidder 4152
Worcester: England 4083, McKee 4194, **Memorial 4198**, Mulberry 4213, Wyman-Gordon 4364

---

see also 100, 162, 256, 394, 396, 431, 445, 458, 475, 481, 524, 577, 677, 724, 739, 759, 782, 809, 908, 942, 960, 1003, 1032, 1116, 1117, 1138, 1172, 1251, 1297, 1320, 1334, 1388, 1389, 1415, 1419, 1429, 1433, 1437, 1445, 1472, 1475, 1488, 1497, 1500, 1504, 1505, 1517, 1524, 1534, 1536, 1539, 1577, 1584, 1588, 1624, 1645, 1655, 1658, 1659, 1677, 1681, 1687, 1701, 1706, 1711, 1726, 1728, 1733, 1738, 1744, 1746, 1747, 1759, 1768, 1778, 1791, 1823, 1838, 1859, 1874, 1877, 1893, 1898, 1902, 1919, 1940, 1951, 2028, 2060, 2072, 2088, 2118, 2121, 2145, 2186, 2216, 2225, 2271, 2277, 2320, 2331, 2345, 2358, 2384, 2388, 2392, 2393, 2421, 2547, 2610, 2630, 2662, 2671, 2712, 2718, 2722, 2746, 2764, 2847, 2848, 2881, 2886, 2912, 2942, 2949, 2996, 3003, 3063, 3067, 3084, 3089, 3127, 3128, 3136, 3141, 3183, 3247, 3249, 3545, 3614, 3764, 3769, 3783, 3784, 3827, 3829, 3835, 3846, 3852, 3858, 3890, 3909, 3931, 3948, 3990, 4508, 4525, 4615, 4685, 4710, 4722, 4730, 4749, 5146, 5155, 5191, 5195, 5206, 5208, 5211, 5220, 5222, 5231, 5236, 5247, 5250, 5268, 5271, 5280, 5298, 5303, 5304, 5310, 5319, 5329, 5341, 5348, 5353, 5400, 5417, 5421, 5433, 5436, 5463, 5512, 5516, 5534, 5537, 5563, 5579, 5581, 5598, 5651, 5664, 5688, 5711, 5749, 5760, 5763, 5770, 5797, 5809, 5822, 5829, 5839, 5851, 5904, 5910, 5914, 5934, 5973, 5983, 5990, 5993, 6004, 6011, 6026, 6054, 6079, 6108, 6109, 6112, 6113, 6147, 6152, 6158, 6160, 6201, 6220, 6231, 6255, 6280, 6330, 6385, 6433, 6436, 6449, 6456, 6468, 6486, 6502, 6550, 6555, 6560, 6573, 6590, 6617, 6677, 6715, 6717, 6795, 6845, 6846, 6877, 6923, 6947, 6951, 6974, 6988, 7005, 7012, 7022, 7032, 7211, 7368, 7388, 7410, 7454, 7468, 7473, 7502, 7531, 7537, 7566, 7571, 7576, 7617, 7695, 7754, 7812, 7849, 7860, 7921, 7938, 7939, 7979, 7993, 7994, 8009, 8053, 8070, 8087, 8089, 8113, 8139, 8143, 8164, 8167, 8198, 8225, 8236, 8258, 8286, 8366, 8369, 8372, 8379, 8381, 8386, 8389, 8391, 8392, 8393, 8394, 8396, 8397, 8399, 8402, 8405, 8406, 8411, 8413, 8416, 8419, 8422, 8427, 8431, 8441, 8442, 8452, 8458, 8459, 8461, 8465, 8471, 8472, 8476, 8480, 8483, 8489, 8493, 8501, 8502, 8504, 8545, 8601, 8657, 8698, 8718, 8719, 8820, 8872, 8879, 9060, 9099, 9186, 9328, 9366, 9373, 9385, 9405, 9512, 9533, 9645, 9755, 9975, 9999

MICHIGAN

Adrian: Price 4546, Stubnitz 4582
Alma: Pardee 4534
Almont: Four 4449
Ann Arbor: Ave 4379, Bonder 4394, Buhr 4400, Burt 4403, Ervin 4437, Maas 4498, Skiles 4572, Speckhard-Knight 4574, Van 4601
Auburn Hills: Elliott 4436, Skandalaris 4571
Bad Axe: Smith 4573
Bay City: Doll-Loesel 4433, Fabiano 4438, Kantzler 4478, Pardee 4533
Benzonia: Johnson 4471
Bingham Farms: McManus 4509
Birmingham: Bostock 4395, Harris 4461, Jospey 4473, McDonald 4508, Peslar 4537, U.S.-China 4600, Wetsman 4611, Whitman 4615, Williams 4618
Blissfield: Farver 4441
Bloomfield Hills: Acheson 4370, **Ajemian 4371**, Barron 4384, Foren 4448, LoPrete 4496, Michell 4513, Molnar 4517, Ran 4547, Sehn 4563, Vlasic 4607, Weisberg 4609, White 4613, Zampetis 4619
Bloomfield Village: Pilgrim 4539
Bridgeport: Andersen 4377
Buchanan: Michigan 4514
Byron Center: Buist 4401, Koster 4486, Loosemore 4495, Vander 4603
Caro: Tuscola 4598
Cedar: Schmuckal 4559
Clinton: Andrah 4378
Coldwater: Branch 4396, Juhl 4475
Commerce Township: Ferber 4443
Commerce TWP: Alon 4374
Dearborn: Dana 4420, Kosch 4485
Delton: Ryan 4555, Van 4602
Detroit: Avharas 4380, Carls 4404, Delong-Sweet 4427, DeVlieg 4428, Family 4439, Filmer 4444, Ford 4445, **Ford, 4446**, Ford-Thomas 4447, Gershenson 4453, Grosse 4460, Hartwick 4462, Hecht 4465, Kay 4480, Riley 4550, Scully 4561, Thompson 4592, Torgow 4594, Wieczorek 4617
East Jordan: Peak 4536
East Lansing: Olds 4526
Escanaba: Sackerson 4557
Farmington Hills: Allen 4372, Amerisure 4375, Beson 4389, Pappas 4532, Shapiro 4566, **Teitel 4589**
Fenton: VanGilder 4604
Flint: Alnour 4373, Merkley 4512, Mills 4515, Paulina 4535, **Saab 4556**, Stoker 4580
Frankenmuth: Bronner 4398, Frankenmuth 4450
Franklin: Nusbaum 4524, Ratner 4548, Sherman 4567, Stern 4578, Stone 4581
Fremont: Cummings 4417
Grand Blanc: Serra 4565, Whiting 4614
Grand Haven: JSJ 4474
Grand Rapids: Baldwin 4382, Balk 4383, Betten 4390, Christian 4407, Christian 4408, Currie 4418, Dik 4430, Garrett 4452, Keller 4481, Linse 4493, Maly-Dykema 4502, Mojo 4516, O'Donovan 4525, Porter 4543, Powers 4545, Rottman 4553, St. 4576, Tassell-Wisner-Bottrall 4587, Tremble 4595, Welch 4610
Grosse Pointe: Duchene 4435
Grosse Pointe Farms: Briggs-Fisher 4397, Buffalo 4399
Grosse Pointe Park: Tamer 4585
Harbor Springs: Baiardi 4381
Harper Woods: Blatt 4393
Harrison Township: Causley, 4405
Hastings: Baum 4387
Hillsdale: Clay 4409
Holland: Anchor 4376, de 4422, DeKock 4425, Jurries 4476, Lanting 4489, Onequest 4527, Padnos 4529, Springview 4575
Howell: Kellogg 4482
Hudsonville: Lamar 4488
Huntington Woods: Pitt 4541
Ithaca: Gratiot 4459

Jackson: Phantom 4538
Kalamazoo: Burdick-Thorne 4402, Connable 4412, Delano 4426, Havirmill 4463, Kalamazoo 4477, Kinney 4483, Lee 4491, Power 4544, Tyler-Little 4599
Lansing: Thoman 4590
Lapeer: Lapeer 4490
Livonia: Dinan 4431, DiPonio 4432, Talty 4584
Mackinac Island: Mackinac 4499
Manistee: Grassland 4458
Manitou Beach: Murdock 4519
Marlette: Technical 4588
Mason: Dart 4421, Kiwanis 4484
Menominee: M 4497
Midland: Barstow 4385, Bierlein 4392, Jenkins 4470, Oreffice 4528
Monroe: Community 4411, Deinzer 4424
Mount Pleasant: Isabella 4468
Muskegon: Kaufman 4479
Niles: Plym 4542
North Muskegon: St. 4577
Northville: Conrad 4413, **Gorlin 4457**, Manat 4503
Oak Park: Schwarcz 4560
Orchard Lake: Farago 4440
Owosso: Shiawassee 4568
Plymouth: Noster 4523, Thompson 4591
Rochester: Abrams 4369, Community 4410
Rockford: JCT 4469, River 4551, Zondervan 4621
Romeo: L 4487
Roscommon: Roscommon 4552
Saginaw: Garber 4451, McNally 4510, Morley 4518, Nartel 4521, Nickless 4522, Watson 4608, Wickson-Link 4616
Saint Clair Shores: Cracchiolo 4414, Cracchiolo 4415, Main 4501, Zimmerman 4620
Saint Joseph: Schalon 4558
Saline: Jones 4472, Redies 4549
Saranac: Crowley 4416
Southfield: Barton-Malow 4386, Dresner 4434, Golden 4455, Leven 4492, Lois 4494, Maibach 4500, McDole 4506, McDole 4507, Narens 4520, Pitt 4540, Seligman 4564, Sinai 4570, Stoddard 4579, Tarakji 4586, Trico 4596, **Vattikuti 4605**
Spring Lake: Gordon 4456
Stanwood: Cebelak 4406
Sterling Heights: **Triford 4597**
SunField: Glassen 4454
Traverse City: Biederman 4391, Herrington-Fitch 4466, Mariel 4504, Paine 4531
Troy: Berlin 4388, Farwell 4442, Holden 4467, McClelland 4505, Meritor, 4511, Page, 4530, Wheeler 4612
Van Buren Township: Dana 4419
Vicksburg: Vicksburg 4606
Walled Lake: SEED 4562
Warren: Thompson 4593
Watervliet: Degroot 4423
West Bloomfield: Sutaruk 4583
West Olive: DeWitt 4429
Williamsburg: Hayden 4464
Williamston: Roznowski 4554
Zeeland: Shine 4569

see also 133, 300, 398, 780, 805, 950, 987, 1022, 1034, 1183, 1291, 1333, 1368, 1627, 1673, 1750, 1923, 1937, 1971, 1994, 2018, 2160, 2265, 2373, 2722, 2743, 2752, 2753, 2760, 2762, 2778, 2814, 2826, 2898, 2936, 2969, 2971, 2998, 3007, 3139, 3171, 3259, 3286, 3287, 3319, 3321, 3375, 3449, 3465, 3484, 3541, 3551, 4360, 4814, 5248, 5275, 5293, 5297, 5590, 5643, 6597, 6634, 6740, 6756, 6879, 7065, 7140, 7153, 7181, 7219, 7317, 7428, 7466, 7503, 7510, 7586, 7657, 7902, 7910, 8197, 8228, 8408, 8444, 8490, 8707, 8879, 8953, 9246, 9344, 9373, 9394, 9966, 9968

MINNESOTA

Aitkin: Charity, 4656
Albany: Albany 4624
Arden Hills: Grotto 4702
Austin: Knowlton 4725
Blaine: Maslowski 4741
Bloomington: Getsch 4695, Lutheran 4734, O'Rourke 4757, Reimer 4771, Riverway 4776, Walser 4807
Caledonia: Falck 4678
Cannon Falls: **Wagner 4804**
Chanhassen: Acorn 4623, Iversen 4717, Schott 4787
Clara City: Sexton 4790
Deephaven: Aca 4622
Delano: Rising 4775
Dodge Center: Garmar 4694
Duluth: Depot 4667, Hart 4708
Eden Prairie: Bieber 4641, Butzow 4651, Flaherty 4686, St. 4794
Edina: Edina 4671, **Kaplan 4721**, March 4740, McCoy 4742, McNamara 4743, Mooty 4747, **Porter 4763**, Radichel 4765, Schulze 4788, Shared 4791
Excelsior: Caridad 4653, RJW 4777, Walker 4805
Fairmont: Rosen 4782
Faribault: **Winds 4820**
Fergus Falls: Roberts 4778
Forest Lake: Fletcher 4687
Golden Valley: Bame 4634, Black 4642, Caroline's 4654, Squam 4793
Hibbing: Arsher 4630
Jordan: **Emmerich 4673**
Lake Elmo: Rieks 4774
Lakefield: Remick 4773
Long Lake: Blank 4643, Gage 4692, Nelson 4749, Sayer 4786
Luverne: Luverne 4736
Mankato: Hickory 4713
Maple Grove: Wendel 4813
Mendota Heights: Gilligan 4696
Minneapolis: Arctos 4629, Baratz 4635, Bell 4638, Bend 4639, Borman 4644, Burwell 4650, Chadwick-Loher 4655, Cook 4658, Cornwall 4660, Dellwood 4665, Desiring 4668, Dyer 4669, Ecotrust 4670, Edina 4672, Erickson 4674, Erickson 4675, Evert 4676, Felhaber, 4681, Ferber 4682, **Fingerhut 4683**, Fink 4684, Foundation 4688, Fraser 4689, Gardner 4693, Good 4698, Griffiths 4700, Grossman 4701, Groves 4703, Hagen 4704, Haggerty 4705, Hegardt 4710, Heilicher 4711, HJ 4714, Hognander 4715, Jostens 4720, Larsen 4728, Living 4730, Mahon 4737, Midcontinent 4745, Oak 4752, Onan 4754, **Pax 4760**, Reed 4768, Regis 4770, Rose 4781, Samsara 4784, Soar 4792, Tamarack 4797, Tennant 4798, Thorpe 4800, **Trust 4802**, Wallestad 4806, Wiehoff 4818
Minnetonka: Albright 4625, Ankeny 4628, Becker 4636, Camara-Press 4652, G&K 4691, Goldman 4697, Head 4709, Mahoney 4738, Miller 4746, Rauenhorst 4767, Turner 4803, Whitney 4817
North Saint Paul: Sauer 4785
Orono: Reger 4769
Plymouth: Jeffers 4719
Prior Lake: Roles 4780
Redwood Falls: Farmers 4679
Richfield: Bumgarner 4649
Rochester: Bradley 4647
Rockford: Sacred 4783
Rosemount: City 4657, Pinson 4762
Roseville: Granite 4699, Kinney 4724, Maranatha 4739, Terhuly 4799
Saint Louis Park: Avocet 4631, Bell 4637, Deikel 4663, Faith, 4677, Louis 4731, Luther 4733, Open 4756
Saint Paul: Andersen 4626, Anderson 4627, Bahl 4632, Bailey 4633, Berglund 4640, Boss 4645, Boss 4646, Briggs 4648, Cooke 4659, Cox 4662, Dell 4664, Denfeld 4666, Farview 4680, Fischman 4685, Hallett 4706, Harrington 4707, Heilmaier

4712, Jackson 4718, Kellogg 4722, Kinman-Oldfield 4723, Lane 4727, Lillehei 4729, Merritt 4744, Morning 4748, Noreen 4750, Northern 4751, O'Neil 4755, Peace 4761, Rodman 4779, **Sundance 4796**, Trillium 4801, Walsh-Brady 4808, Wedge 4810, Wells 4811, Wells 4812, Weyand 4814, Weyerhaeuser 4815, Whaley 4816, Wimmer 4819
Shakopee: Rahr 4766
Springfield: Reiner 4772
Stillwater: Covenant 4661
Truman: Lutheran 4735
Wayzata: Frey 4690, Krisbin 4726, Lukis 4732, Quinlan 4764, Seba 4789, Steinhafel 4795, Way 4809
West Saint Paul: O'Brien 4753
White Bear Lake: OSilas 4758
Willmar: Huisinga 4716
Woodbury: Pautsch 4759

see also 119, 123, 134, 249, 272, 370, 498, 602, 1144, 1331, 1377, 1463, 1506, 1577, 1628, 1664, 1739, 1814, 1831, 1961, 2016, 2079, 2099, 2151, 2166, 2233, 2324, 2332, 2373, 2699, 2799, 2925, 2943, 3074, 3084, 3304, 3309, 3461, 3537, 3593, 3991, 4130, 4271, 4483, 4493, 4879, 4917, 5028, 5097, 5116, 5186, 5220, 5280, 5347, 5394, 5558, 6077, 6245, 6709, 6877, 7087, 7110, 7154, 7156, 7165, 7187, 7220, 7235, 7295, 7361, 7425, 7482, 7842, 7983, 8402, 8554, 8563, 8636, 8644, 9246, 9329, 9598, 9711, 9852, 9853, 9940, 9947, 9948

MISSISSIPPI

Amory: Amory 4821
Bay Saint Louis: Seal, 4853
Biloxi: Biloxi 4824
Cleveland: Sanders 4852
Columbus: Phillips 4850
Flowood: Colbert 4829
Greenville: King's 4845
Greenwood: Barnett 4823
Hattiesburg: Family 4834, Hood, 4843
Jackson: Center 4828, Crooks 4831, **Edwards 4833**, Fountain 4837, Hood 4842, McCarty, 4848, Mississippi 4849, Pruet 4851, Van 4857, Wittel 4858
Laurel: Hope 4844
Lexington: Lexington 4846
Louisville: Taylor 4855
Madison: Black 4825, Faser 4835
Marks: Graeber 4839
Meridian: Baird 4822, Community 4830
Moss Point: Florence 4836
Ocean Springs: Trehern 4856
Olive Branch: Skelton 4854
Picayune: Lower 4847
Taylor: Carothers 4827
Tupelo: Brevard 4826, Hancock 4840
Vicksburg: Golding 4838
Yazoo City: Day 4832, Harris 4841

see also 94, 207, 209, 2102, 2400, 2961, 6672, 6781, 7692, 8208, 8477, 8639, 9196, 9264

MISSOURI

Augusta: Walker 5035
Ballwin: Sappington 4992
Branson: Herschend 4928
Braymer: Wallace 5036
Carthage: Boylan 4873
Chesterfield: Longer 4949, Sachs 4989, Shanahan 4999, Von 5033
Chillicothe: Lambert 4942, Litton 4946

Clayton: Bryant 4878, Deliniere 4894, Empson 4902, Garvey 4913, Grant 4918, Guilander 4922, Kornblum 4940, Lee 4945, **Maor 4952**, Neiman 4969, Ross 4986, Rubin 4987, Wolff 5039

Columbia: MFA 4960, Walton 5037

Creve Coeur: **Bohm 4871**, Chomeau 4886

Dearborn: Cinmar 4887

Dutzow: Voelkerding 5032

Earth City: Keske 4937

Fenton: Fabick 4907, Wolff 5040

Glencoe: Chod 4885

Hannibal: Riedel 4984

Hazelwood: Dierberg 4895

Independence: Stern 5013

Jefferson City: Sokoll 5010, Sugarbaker 5016

Joplin: Timmons 5021

Kansas City: Andrews 4860, Barrows 4864, Bartlett 4865, Bograd 4870, Brace 4874, Breidenthal 4875, Butler 4880, Calkins 4881, Copaken 4888, Cray 4890, Curry 4892, Dunn 4898, Ellis 4901, Forster-Powers 4911, Grassmere 4919, Hofheimer 4929, J. 4932, Kemper 4935, Long 4948, Lordi 4950, Melcher 4957, Mineral 4961, Moulton 4965, Nichols 4970, Pendergast-Weyer 4979, Portman 4981, Price 4982, Prime 4983, Rust 4988, Schutte 4995, Shumway 5002, Sullivan, 5017, Tension 5019, UMB 5026, Welch 5038

Kirkwood: Gaylord 4915, St. 5012

Lamar: Finley 4910

Lebanon: Boswell 4872

Lee's Summit: HB 4924

Liberty: Oppenheimer 4973

Mexico: Edmonston 4900, Griffin 4921

Nevada: Moss 4964

Nixa: O'Reilly 4974

North Kansas City: Wurst 5043

O' Fallon: Trulaske, 5024

Peculiar: Peculiar 4978

Pleasant Hill: Enright 4903

Princeton: Kauffman 4934

Rock Port: Morgan 4963

Saint Ann: Vatterott 5030

Saint Charles: Seiler 4997, VJS 5031

Saint Joseph: King 4939, Logan 4947, South 5011

Saint Louis: Albers/Kuhn 4859, Arnold 4861, Baer 4862, Bakewell 4863, BEO 4866, BF 4867, Bland 4868, **Block 4869**, Brinklee 4876, Brown 4877, **Build-A-Bear 4879**, Canfield 4882, Capellupo 4883, Chapman 4884, Cornelsen 4889, Crown 4891, Dubinsky 4896, Duesenberg 4897, Edgar 4899, Erlich 4904, Essman 4905, Ever 4906, Favre 4908, Finerty 4909, Gaebler 4912, Gaylord 4914, Gershman 4916, Gilbert 4917, Green 4920, Hardy 4923, HCG, 4925, Heiman 4926, Hermann 4927, Impact 4930, Innovative 4931, JMG 4933, Kenney 4936, Kienstra 4938, Kuhn 4941, **Larson 4943**, Lawton 4944, Love 4951, Mathews, 4953, Maxine 4954, McDonald 4955, Meda 4956, Messick 4958, Moneta 4962, Mungenast 4966, N.H. 4967, Neeb 4968, No 4971, Obertate 4972, Pillsbury 4980, Roman 4985, Saks 4990, Sander 4991, Sayler-Hawkins 4993, Schweinfurth 4996, Service 4998, Shawe 5000, Shepherd 5001, Sigma-Aldrich 5003, Silk 5004, Simmons 5005, Siteman 5006, Slavik 5007, Slay 5008, Slusher 5009, Stifel 5014, Stroble 5015, Sunnen 5018, Thorp 5020, Todd 5022, Toutz 5023, University 5027, Van 5028, Vassia 5029, Walker 5034, Woodcock 5041, Woods 5042

Springfield: Darr 4893, Meyer 4959, O'Reilly 4975, Payne-Stewart 4976, Pearl 4977, Schneider 4994, Turner 5025

see also 125, 135, 162, 272, 532, 682, 858, 879, 901, 975, 1250, 1339, 1634, 1820, 1838, 1849, 1959, 2056, 2169, 2202, 2250, 2376, 2400, 2549, 2592, 2738, 2783, 2803, 2890, 3033, 3153, 3177, 3191, 3200, 3284, 3313, 3331, 3389, 3487, 3550, 3554, 3559, 3568, 3572,

3574, 3575, 3581, 3583, 3584, 3598, 3600, 3602, 3604, 3606, 3611, 3613, 3616, 3636, 3638, 3639, 3640, 3696, 3851, 3927, 4397, 4501, 4689, 4783, 5248, 5689, 5984, 7205, 7292, 7347, 7576, 7693, 7712, 7717, 7721, 7747, 8088, 8208, 8446, 8469, 8539, 8606, 8690, 8728, 8744, 8749, 8799, 8840, 8960, 9119, 9163, 9227, 9271, 9277, 9288, 9332, 9530, 9968, 9997

MONTANA

Arlee: High 5057

Billings: Foundation 5051, Nance 5061, Sample 5062, Wendy's 5065

Bozeman: Cora 5048, Taylor 5064

Great Falls: Boe 5045, Gerhart 5053, Hawkins 5055, Heisey 5056, Lippard-Clawiter 5058

Helena: Greater 5054

Kalispell: Flathead 5050

Lakeside: Lynn 5059

Livingston: Broadbent 5046

Missoula: Cinnabar 5047, Gallagher 5052, Montana 5060, Swanson 5063

Whitefish: Angora 5044, Dousman 5049

see also 830, 860, 880, 1266, 1319, 1710, 1761, 2792, 2918, 3004, 3872, 4439, 4458, 4679, 4731, 5233, 5507, 5663, 6119, 6384, 6410, 6969, 7041, 7655, 7771, 7773, 7808, 7817, 7996, 8030, 8554, 8654, 9001, 9617, 9681, 9692, 9710, 9991, 9998

NEBRASKA

Atkinson: Weller 5127

Aurora: Farr 5078, Farr 5079

Beatrice: Thomas 5123

Bellevue: Baer 5069

Benkelman: Hester 5091

Blair: Blair 5074

Cambridge: Perkins 5111

Chappell: Smith 5118

Elkhorn: Friedman 5083

Fremont: Walker 5126

Gering: Yount 5130

Grand Island: Kaufmann-Cummings 5096, Reynolds 5114

Kearney: Cope 5077

Lincoln: Ameritas 5067, Assurity 5068, Finigan 5081, Goldwin 5085, Kinder 5099, Lienemann 5100, Nebraska 5105, Pegler 5110, Springer 5120, Tous 5124

Nebraska City: Steinhart 5121

Omaha: America 5066, Baright 5070, Barklage 5071, Batchelder 5072, Beer 5073, Burnett 5075, Cimpl 5076, Ferenc 5080, Friedland 5082, GFH 5084, Grewcock 5086, Hansen 5087, Harper 5088, Hawkins 5089, Herman 5090, Heuermann 5092, Hickey 5093, Home 5094, Kilbourne 5097, Kim 5098, **Lothlorien 5101**, Malek 5102, Mapes 5103, Nelson 5106, Olson 5107, Owen 5108, Patrick 5109, Physicians 5112, Scott, 5115, Scribante 5116, Shaw 5117, Soli 5119, Storz 5122, **Waldbaum 5125**, West 5128

Papillion: Midlands 5104

Scottsbluff: Quivey-Bay 5113

Waterloo: Hundred 5095

York: York 5129

see also 272, 364, 461, 512, 560, 2302, 3109, 3110, 3235, 3486, 3487, 4662, 4723, 4727, 4782, 4808, 6994, 8012, 9208, 9236, 9241, 9335, 9393, 9731, 9843

NEVADA

Carson City: **Fein 5155**, Lusardi 5175

Elko: Western 5198

Gardnerville: Timken-Sturgis 5192

Henderson: **A 5131**, Anton 5133, EBV 5154, Findlay 5156, Joshua 5167, Moran 5178, To 5193

Incline Village: Boyd 5141, Castleman 5144, Children 5147, Newman 5179, Peterson 5182, Pretti 5184, Wagner 5195, **Wood 5201**

Las Vegas: Andress 5132, Bendon 5137, Binion 5139, Blue 5140, C.A.N. 5142, Carver 5143, **Center 5145**, Chami 5146, **Cohen 5149**, Crescere 5151, **Do 5153**, Fishkin 5157, Harris 5161, Houssels 5163, Jansen 5164, Joseph 5166, Kara 5168, Lee 5171, Living 5174, Meyer 5177, Pinnacle 5183, Shulman 5185, Siegel 5186, Smith 5187, Steinberg 5189, Vandevoort 5194, Webb 5196, Wolzinger 5200, Wynn 5202, Yamagata 5203

Reno: Ash 5134, Banks 5135, Barker 5136, Benna 5138, Close 5148, Coleman 5150, Dermody 5152, Foundation 5158, Fuserna 5159, Geomar 5160, **He 5162**, Kennedy 5169, Larson 5170, Lemay 5172, Lifestyle 5173, Matley 5176, Orchard 5180, Petersen 5181, Special 5188, Stout 5190, West 5197, Williams 5199

Zephyr Cove: Jaquish 5165, Sweig 5191

see also 272, 591, 784, 1125, 1675, 1734, 2400, 2421, 2637, 2668, 3088, 3251, 4416, 4804, 5519, 5580, 6051, 9342, 9363, 9904, 9919

NEW HAMPSHIRE

Bennington: Verney 5236

Canterbury: Noah 5226

Colebrook: Tillotson 5234

Concord: Charter 5206, Cochran 5208, Jameson 5215, Kimball 5216, Up 5235

Georges Mills: Thorne 5233

Hampton: Oxford 5228

Hanover: Couch 5209, Landecker 5217

Holderness: **Rothschild 5229**

Hopkinton: Lynch 5221

Lebanon: Mascoma 5223

Lyme: Dunn 5212

Manchester: DEKA 5210, Hunt 5214, McIninch 5224, Smyth 5232, von 5237

Milford: Milford 5225

Moultonborough: Lion's 5220

Nashua: Barker 5204, Finlay 5213, Levine 5218

New Castle: Linnell 5219

New London: Wutz 5239

North Conway: Woodbury 5238

North Hampton: Seigel 5231

Portsmouth: Bickford 5205, Dorr 5211

Rye Beach: Martin 5222

Salem: Salem 5230

Wolfeboro: **Christian 5207**, Olcott 5227

see also 282, 560, 739, 810, 1090, 1390, 1410, 1419, 1451, 1533, 1536, 1554, 1585, 1687, 1693, 1739, 1744, 1747, 2155, 2421, 2557, 2878, 3030, 3682, 3776, 3780, 3795, 3953, 4016, 4017, 4033, 4039, 4092, 4127, 4130, 4131, 4152, 4157, 4220, 4257, 4260, 4297, 4314, 4330, 4336, 4366, 4561, 4628, 5280, 5416, 5426, 5631, 5829, 5930, 5934, 6011, 6111, 6196, 6392, 6595, 6787, 6975, 7309, 7493, 7566, 7675, 7791, 7855, 7870, 7888, 8007, 8139, 8400, 8403, 8412, 8424, 8435, 8438, 8848, 9375, 9385, 9466, 9520

NEW JERSEY

Allendale: Brook 5273, Rukin 5516

Alpine: **Ostberg 5483**

Annandale: Hanafin 5381

Asbury: Petrucci 5498

Atco: Goodwin 5374

Atlantic City: Gurwicz 5378

Basking Ridge: LaGrassa 5438, Paragano 5488, Yates 5595

Bayonne: Engel 5334

Bedminster: Snyder 5543, Spohler 5547

Belleville: Diaco 5318

Bellmawr: Schlotterer 5523

Bergenfield: Frank 5350, Kessel 5420

Bernardsville: Anderson 5249, Devine 5317, Farris 5342, Kalkin 5412

Branchville: Selective 5528

Cedar Grove: Carlozzi 5287

Chatham: **Daft 5310**, Davino 5313, Ellis 5333, **Knistrom 5426**

Cherry Hill: Branfman 5271, Davis 5314, Heart 5388, Katz 5414, **Nazarian 5478**, Shuster 5535

Chester: Degnan 5315

Cinnaminson: Knowlton 5427

Clark: Riskin 5511

Clifton: Entin 5336, Feldstein 5344, Markowitz 5460

Colts Neck: Minio 5470

Cranbury: Silverman 5536

Cranford: Cali 5284

Deal: Sutton 5554

Denville: WKBJ 5592

East Hanover: Alcon 5244, Jensam 5404, Perricone 5497, Stein 5551

East Rutherford: Giants 5369, Smilowitz 5538

Eatontown: Abrams 5241

Edison: Bijou 5264, Dweck 5327, Hann 5382, Mamiye 5456, Maschler 5462, Nitzavim 5479, Waldis 5569

Egg Harbor Township: Yoh 5597

Elberon: Benun 5261

Elizabeth: Elizabethtown 5332

Elmwood Park: Lewis 5447

Englewood: Benaroya 5260, **Billig 5265**, Freyer 5355, Harmstieg 5386, Holzer 5396, Infinity 5399, Kurtz 5436, Research 5509

Englewood Cliffs: **Crane 5306**, Oster 5484, Woolley-Clifford 5594

Essex Fells: Feline 5345

Fair Lawn: Columbia 5301

Fairfield: Aufzien 5253, Garfinkle 5364

Far Hills: Frelinghuysen 5354, Gamper 5361, Gibson 5370

Farmingdale: Harms 5385

Florham Park: **Akhoury 5243**, Avalo 5254, Brooks 5274, Conant 5302, Hawthorne 5387, Jones 5408, KDK 5416, Tamarin 5556, Todd 5560

Forked River: D'Onofrio 5324

Fort Lee: **Southpole 5545**

Franklin Lakes: **Garcia 5362**

Freehold: Landy 5439, We 5574

Garwood: Glasser 5371

Hackensack: Colotto 5300, Hekemian 5390

Haddonfield: Ragone 5508

Hammonton: Fox 5349

Hasbrouck Heights: Cantor 5285

Hillside: Kaufman 5415

Ho-Ho-Kus: Engel 5335

Hoboken: Tedesco 5557

Hopewell: Johnson 5406, Pacific 5485, Smith 5539

Iselin: Wendel 5580

Jersey City: Armour-Lewis 5251, Brundage 5280, Dreman 5326, ESH 5338, Icap 5398, MTB 5474, Patrick 5494, Rsfzmkh 5514, Upton 5566, Zakaria 5598

Kingston: Tuchman 5561

Kinnelon: Spiro 5546

Lafayette: **Yin-Shun 5596**

Lakewood: Blessing 5266, CYH 5309, Gestetner 5367, Goldstein 5373, JFI 5405, Lchachomim 5443, Light 5449, M/S 5452, MNS 5472, Sorala 5544, Zeldes 5599

Linwood: Capebank 5286, Previti 5506

Little Falls: Chapman 5292

Livingston: Brueckner 5279, Earle 5328, Johnson 5407, Kroon 5433, Miller 5467, Pines 5501, Teiger 5558, Weintraub 5577

Locust: Kolber 5429, Scire 5526

Long Branch: Brothers 5276

Long Valley: Leavens 5444

Madison: D'Aloia 5311, Milano 5466, Pepper 5496, Seven 5530

Mahwah: Ascena 5252, McDowell 5465, Payson 5495

Maplewood: Mitrani 5471

Marlton: Cohen 5299

Martinsville: Ullmann 5564

Maywood: Adler 5242

Mendham: **Ju 5410**

Metuchen: Harbanoff 5384, Weinstein 5576

Middletown: Knight 5425, Kurr 5435, Tizzio 5559

Millington: Mahan 5455

Monmouth Beach: Kontos 5430

Montclair: Bershad 5262

Montvale: Heller 5391, Onyx 5482, **Patel 5492**

Moonachie: **Tufenkian 5562**

Moorestown: Domenica 5323, Hill 5392

Morganville: **Waterfowl 5570**

Morristown: Fellstone 5346, Greetin 5377, Heisen 5389, His 5395, Larson 5440, Lieberman 5448, Markey 5459, Pheasant 5499, Plafsky 5503, **Rippel 5510**, Simon, 5537, Wetterberg 5583

Mount Arlington: Verhalen 5568

Mount Holly: Gardinier 5363

Mountainside: Halpern 5380, Wilf 5587, Wilf 5588

New Vernon: Bartlett 5256

Newark: Edison 5330, Fund 5358, Genie 5366

Newton: Sella 5529

North Bergen: Snyder 5542

North Caldwell: Frog 5357

Nutley: Wei 5575

Oakhurst: Schwartz 5524

Old Bridge: Amboy 5246, Brunetti 5281

Oradell: Dickinson 5319, Roe 5512

Paramus: Cordover 5304, Gabrellian 5360

Parsippany: Avis 5255, Klein 5424, Moriarty 5473, Myers 5476, Welch 5579

Passaic: **American 5247**

Paterson: Paterson 5493

Pennington: A 5240, Antz 5250, Beane 5259, Blue 5268, **Blue 5269**, Broomfield 5275, Browder 5277, Chang 5290, Chanil 5291, Chormann 5293, Chu 5294, Civitas 5296, CKT 5297, Culver 5308, Dietze 5320, Doctor 5321, EBB 5329, Farrington 5341, Fisher 5347, Freedman 5352, Friedman 5356, Gauntt 5365, Hanson 5383, Hillswood 5394, Huffhines 5397, Jones 5409, Keller 5418, Kirby 5422, Kocurek 5428, Kresa 5432, Krupa 5434, Kutnick 5437, MacDonald 5453, Marino 5458, McConnell 5463, McCrane 5464, Miller 5468, Minerva 5469, Mullen 5475, O'Neal 5481, Palmer 5486, Post 5505, Ragan 5507, Sanders 5518, Sastaunik 5519, Savin 5520, Schimmel 5521, Schlaffer 5522, Scott 5527, Sheridan 5533, Take 5555, Twin 5563, Vaughn-Jordan 5567, Waterview 5572, Wilcox 5585, Willingham 5589, Wilson 5590, Wolf 5593

Pine Brook: Florin 5348

Piscataway: Rukh 5515, Wicks 5584

Plainsboro: **Integra 5400**

Princeton: Covance 5305, Doll 5322, **Dow 5325**, Essig 5339, Freedman 5351, Hill 5393, IV 5401, Kingsberg 5421, Olsen 5480, Shamah 5531, Snyder 5540, Spruce 5548

Randolph: Grace 5375

Red Bank: Snyder 5541, Zobel 5603

Ridgefield: BMI-Rupp 5270, Winters 5591

Ridgefield Park: Pasternak 5490

Ridgewood: CBIS 5288, Freelander 5353, Judson 5411, **Parnassus 5489**

River Edge: Marino 5457

Riverton: Waters 5571

Robbinsville: Roma 5513

Rockaway: Weisberg 5578

Rockleigh: United 5565

Roseland: Bloom 5267, Jamacha 5403, Kean 5417, Liss 5451

Roselle: Bauer 5257

Rumson: HAIR 5379, Navesink 5477

Saddle River: Zimmer 5601

Short Hills: Baum 5258, Pantirer 5487, Zissu 5602

Shrewsbury: Stone 5553

South Plainfield: **Greenblatt 5376**

Spring Lake: Lavery 5441

Springfield: Shilling 5534

Summit: Clermont 5298, Lipper 5450, Poole 5504, Wildwood 5586

Surf City: Russo 5517

Teaneck: Brown 5278, Stern 5552, Zichron 5600

Tenafly: Allied 5245, **Buddha 5282**, deRosa 5316, Family 5340, Shapiro 5532, Stanley's 5550

Teterboro: Klatskin 5423, Korean 5431

Thorofare: Staats 5549

Toms River: Citta 5295

Totowa: Machuga 5454

Trenton: Environmental 5337, Kerney 5419

Union: Eisenberg 5331, Feinstein 5343

Upper Saddle River: Marron 5461

Voorhees: American 5248

Warren: Conger 5303, **Dankis 5312**, Giancristofaro 5368, Leavitt 5441, Schwartz 5525

Wayne: Lazarus 5442, Levine 5446, Weny 5581

West Caldwell: Goldberger 5372, Pinkin 5502

West Long Branch: Fux 5359

West Orange: Bershad 5263, Broad 5272, Croman 5307, Pierson 5500

Westfield: Byrne 5283, Chang 5289, Watts 5573, Westfield 5582

Woodbridge: Jacobson 5402

Woodcliff Lake: **Patel 5491**

Woolwich: Kampen 5413

see also 7, 25, 189, 267, 359, 392, 423, 520, 601, 659, 662, 708, 790, 890, 979, 1117, 1172, 1208, 1231, 1233, 1296, 1405, 1433, 1454, 1550, 1561, 1655, 1666, 1686, 1747, 1761, 1777, 1782, 1783, 1841, 1857, 1874, 1895, 1900, 1946, 1967, 2040, 2072, 2106, 2112, 2129, 2154, 2190, 2209, 2247, 2285, 2317, 2326, 2346, 2392, 2415, 2454, 2530, 2564, 2662, 2699, 2833, 2906, 2954, 2988, 3103, 3159, 3180, 3201, 3621, 3672, 3767, 3843, 3888, 4160, 4243, 4615, 4879, 4952, 5182, 5193, 5205, 5657, 5704, 5715, 5728, 5751, 5769, 5770, 5784, 5789, 5796, 5813, 5891, 5926, 5932, 5971, 6018, 6039, 6054, 6061, 6066, 6070, 6072, 6117, 6133, 6147, 6209, 6215, 6216, 6222, 6233, 6260, 6273, 6276, 6284, 6300, 6306, 6367, 6406, 6462, 6478, 6502, 6524, 6534, 6569, 6590, 6619, 6635, 6638, 6644, 6740, 6741, 6775, 6779, 6790, 6794, 6800, 6801, 6815, 6844, 6865, 6880, 6889, 6897, 6904, 6909, 6952, 6961, 6968, 6974, 7005, 7029, 7039, 7077, 7088, 7099, 7104, 7114, 7128, 7142, 7149, 7199, 7200, 7203, 7234, 7262, 7278, 7410, 7634, 7843, 7854, 7857, 7865, 7926, 7985, 8041, 8047, 8053, 8068, 8092, 8118, 8124, 8282, 8283, 8217, 8237, 8261, 8273, 8279, 8311, 8320, 8329, 8350, 8380, 8382, 8408, 8432, 8439, 8472, 8487, 8507, 8524, 8542, 8936, 9261, 9561

NEW MEXICO

Albuquerque: Akerson 5604, Horn 5618, King-Carpenter 5619, Nirvana 5621

Carlsbad: Carlsbad 5608, Forrest 5614

El Prado: Quail 5622
Grants: Continental 5612
Las Cruces: Community 5610
Lovington: Lea 5620
Santa Fe: **Angelica 5605**, B.F. 5606, Bennett 5607, Chamiza 5609, Con 5611, **Daniels 5613**, Foster 5615, Garfield 5616, Gumbo 5617, Schnieders 5623, Simon 5624, Tanner 5625, Walbridge 5627, **Watersheds 5628**
Taos: Taos 5626

---

see also 101, 272, 372, 798, 827, 1096, 1137, 1156, 1273, 1319, 1707, 2293, 2711, 2854, 2949, 2983, 3317, 3486, 3824, 4073, 5161, 5827, 6409, 6990, 7569, 7686, 7693, 8208, 8268, 8742, 8802, 9040, 9062, 9171, 9183, 9235, 9237, 9385, 9560, 9970

NEW YORK

: Kenworthy 6300

Albany: Angel 5678, Barham 5715, BBL 5724, Bender 5735, Birchrock 5749, Carroll 5816, Druskin 5932, Fay 5989, Fieldstone 6004, Goldmann 6099, Grant 6130, Herringer 6196, Ingrassia 6244, Keller 6296, Kurland 6352, Lenox 6380, Maguire 6432, Monaghan 6502, Newman 6533, NYBDC 6546, Parke 6576, Picotte 6603, Rattie 6650, Rowe 6705, Salisbury 6719, Schiro 6741, Shaftel 6782, Smith 6814, Squier 6843, Stecher 6851, Sweeney 6887, Touhey 6902, Weill 6949, Yearley 7005, Zafirovski 7014
Amherst: **Buffalo 5799**, Koessler 6335, Koessler 6336, Pollock 6616, Risen 6672, Snayberger 6817
Amityville: Faith 5979
Amsterdam: **Rao 6645**
Armonk: Houston 6228, Klein 6325, Kovensky 6342, Schwartzberg 6756
Auburn: French 6032
Babylon: Barbash 5714
Bardonia: Bratt 5779
Bedford: Davis 5902, Joyce 6275, NM 6536, Pollack 6614
Bedford Hills: Amsterdam 5672, Sidewalk 6796
Belmont: Allegany 5660
Binghamton: Eggleston 5946, Hoyt 6230
Blasdell: Russo 6711
Briarcliff Manor: A.B. 5632, Boustead 5769, Hales 6159
Bronxville: Behrens 5731, Family 5982, Gogel 6087, Mills 6495, Paul 6580, Yeager 7004
Brooklyn: A.P.W. 5633, **Alexander 5653**, Alff 5657, Alternative 5661, American 5665, American 5666, Amnon 5670, Azar 5704, B 5705, Bar 5712, Baseser 5720, Birchas 5748, Birnbaum 5751, Birnbaum 5752, Brooklyn 5788, BSD 5793, BSR 5794, Carnegie 5815, Chaim 5831, Chasdei 5834, Chemtob 5837, Chesed 5840, Czap 5891, Deegan 5907, Deutsch 5912, Doovin 5923, DTS 5933, Ehrlich 5947, Eisenberger 5950, EMB 5960, Enkess 5966, Ettl 5970, Ezer 5974, Feldman 5995, Foundation 6019, Fraiman 6023, Freund 6034, Friedman 6039, Friedman 6040, Gelley 6067, Gold 6089, Goldenberg 6093, Goldstein 6100, Goldstein 6101, Granit 6126, Gross 6143, Grossman 6144, Harary 6166, Heisler 6185, Heller 6186, Hemitt 6188, HF 6203, Holocaust 6222, Houser 6227, IMS 6240, J.A.T. 6253, JIA 6261, Keller-Shatanoff 6297, Kirschenbaum 6314, Kirzner 6315, Kochov 6333, Kohn 6338, Kohn 6339, Kozicki 6343, Landau 6362, Leonhardt 6381, Levitin 6388, Levy 6390, Lieberman 6399, Lipschitz 6402, Loconsolo 6408, Lowenbraun 6414, M 6423, M 6424, M&E 6425, Medarchei 6469, Moach 6501, MRA 6513, MW 6517, Nets 6524, Norwegian 6541, Offensend 6550, Ohel 6552, Packin 6566, Paneth 6574, Park 6575, Probitas 6630, R 6640, Rachel 6641, Rasba 6649, RDM 6653, Reich 6658, Rosedorf 6688, Rosh 6697, Rudy 6708, Ruthen 6714, Sargol 6728,

Schwimmer 6760, Sdei 6764, SDF 6765, Sefn 6770, SEG 6771, Shalam 6783, Shalom 6784, SHEL 6791, Silberman 6798, SKL 6808, Stein 6856, Steinmetz 6859, Tov 6904, Tsvi-Ora 6914, United 6920, Vaad 6924, Vogel 6931, Wallerstein 6940, **Weingarten 6952**, Weiss 6963, Westlawn 6965, Whalesback 6967, White 6971, WOH 6983, Wohlgemuth 6984, Wolf 6986, Y 6999, Yahad 7002, YGBL 7006, Yitzchok 7007, Yms 7008, Zahavi 7015, Zedakah 7019, Zichron 7026
Brookville: Starmar 6848
Buffalo: Andrews 5677, Arrison 5690, Colby 5867, **Crane 5884**, D-B 5903, Garman 6058, Hafer 6155, Hahn 6156, Koessler 6334, **Larson 6365**, Lippes 6401, McCormick 6458, McCormick 6460, Mulroy 6516, Palisano 6570, Paxton 6581, Poorman 6620, Rupp 6710, Sheetz 6790, Simpson 6805, Skalny 6807, Vogt 6933, Wells 6964, Willmott 6978, Zemsky 7022
Canandaigua: Ontario 6559
Carle Place: Georgia 6071, Newman 6530
Carmel: **Weinstein 6956**
Caroga Lake: Ilsababy 6238
Catskill: Athens 5696
Cedarhurst: Atlantic 5697, Maidenbaum 6435, MZL 6518, Schonkopf 6747
Chaffee: Psalm 6633
Chappaqua: Dougherty 5928, Graham 6119, Kenyon 6301
Chatham: Backer 5706
Cohoes: Cohoes 5865
Cold Spring: Leventritt 6385
Commack: Boxer 5772
Cooperstown: Heilig 6183
Corning: Allatt 5659, Triangle 6908
Cortland: Cortland 5880
Crown Point: Quinn 6638
Dobbs Ferry: Tensor 6896
Douglaston: RJL 6675
Dunkirk: Northern 6540
East Greenbush: Rose 6683
East Hampton: Diogenes 5917, Graham 6120, Hoie 6219
East Setauket: Berkowitz 5739
East Syracuse: Barney 5717
Elmira: Anderson 5674, Gaffney 6049, Hilliard 6208, Wurtele 6997
Elmsford: Fee 5990
Farmingdale: D'Addario 5895, Wharton 6968
Floral Park: Robbins 6676
Flushing: Electrical 5954, Klavan 6322, Kupferberg 6351, **Laub 6367**, Ruth 6713, Striano 6871
Forest Hills: **Farkas 5988**, **Frank 6026**, Palmer 6573, Pickman 6602
Fort Salonga: Reichert 6660
Fresh Meadows: Ostreicher 6564
Garden City: Adikes 5646, Buchalter 5796, Ciampa 5845, Dalton 5896, Ferriday 6000, Gerstman 6074, Goldberg 6090, Heyward 6202, Hopkins 6224, Madover 6431, Treiber 6907, **Usman 6921**
Geneva: Wyckoff 6998
Germantown: Hover 6229
Glen Cove: De 5904, **Li 6394**, Yaspan-Unterberg 7003
Glens Falls: Beach 5725, Glens 6082, Ross 6699
Glenville: Broughton 5790, Douglas 5929
Gowanda: Gernatt 6073
Granite Springs: Schwartz 6752
Great Neck: Aeroflex 5647, Asher 5695, DJ 5920, Ehrlich 5948, Hirsch 6212, L. 6354, Petrocelli 6595, Roth 6700, Zeitz 7021
Greene: Raymond 6652
Hammondsport: Meade 6467
Harrison: Castle 5820, Gloeckner 6083, Jarx 6258, Maslin 6448, Messinger 6482, Serenbetz 6776
Hauppauge: Capri 5814, Initial 6245
Hempstead: Grobman 6140
Hewlett: Lerner 6383

Hewlett Bay Park: Abramson 5640
Hewlett Harbor: SGMG 6778
Hicksville: Cohn 5864, Doshi 5926, Spiegel 6837, Wilks 6977
Hudson: **Potts 6624**, Rheinstrom 6665
Huntington: Acworth 5642, Rapaport 6647, Woodward 6993
Ithaca: Legacy 6373, Smith 6813, Suwinski 6885
Jamestown: Anderson 5675, Dibert 5915, Holmberg 6221
Jericho: Buller 5800, Chasanoff 5833, Geier 6063, Geier 6064, Handler 6161, Harmon 6168, Lorber 6413, Rosen 6689, Rosenthal 6694, Schonfeld 6746, Seaman 6767, Sussman 6879, Sussman 6880
Katonah: Peckham 6583, Samberg 6724
Kenmore: Children's 5842
Lake Placid: Colburn 5866, Lake 6360, Uihlein 6919
Larchmont: Briar 5782, Conley 5874, Goodman-Lipman 6108, Kaplan 6284, **Kathwari 6286**, Spencer 6834
Latham: Whalen 6966
Lattingtown: D'Addario 5894
Lawrence: **Beltar 5733**, CDL 5824, Dvaykus 5937, Edelman 5943, Ezra 5975, Fuchs 6043, Jungreis 6276, Wilamowsky 6976
Little Falls: Burrows 5803
Locust Valley: Slade 6810
Long Island City: Darrah 5900, Dorsky 5924, Fleming 6014, Fresh 6033, Golub 6105, **Henson 6194**, Keene 6293, Klaus 6319, Klaus 6320, Klaus 6321, Mathis-Pfohl 6451, Noster 6543, Plunkett 6611, Rosenthal 6693, Sani 6726, Schweckendieck 6758, Spaeth 6829
Loudonville: Keeler 6292
Lowville: Pratt-Northam 6625
Lynbrook: Ostreicher 6563
Mamaroneck: **Animal 5680**, Hefta 6181, Ritter 6673, Siegel 6797
Manhasset: Ficalora 6002, Greentree 6135, Lachman 6356, Mabardi 6428
Massapequa Park: Rapaport 6646, **Schmeelk 6742**
Melville: Arcadia 5684, Casey 5819, Gatto 6061, Hite 6213, Mere 6476, Project 6631, Tahari 6890
Mill Neck: Tytel 6917
Millbrook: Hathaway 6176, Plymouth 6612
Mineola: American 5663
Monroe: Cornerstone 5878, Elazar 5953, Eluzer 5958, Kahan 6278
Monsey: Alex 5652, **American 5667**, Ausch 5699, Chasdei 5835, Ekstein 5952, KCEG 6291, M.F.K. 6426, Mars 6444, Pinchas 6605, Spitzer 6841, **Stefansky 6854**, Weiss 6961, Zichron 7024, Zichron 7025
Montauk: Houseknecht 6226
Montebello: Provident 6632
Montgomery: Community 5872
Mount Kisco: Goldenson-Arbus 6094
Nesconset: Kelsey 6298
New City: Bradley 5775, Friedlander 6038
New Hyde Park: Osceola 6560
New Rochelle: Finn 6008
New York City: 21st 5630, 5 5631, Abelard 5635, Abess 5636, Abess 5637, Abettor 5638, Abrahamson 5639, Achilles 5641, Ader 5644, Ades-Taub 5645, AFAR 5648, Agate 5649, AGB 5650, AKC 5651, Alexander 5655, Alexander 5656, ALG 5658, American 5662, American 5664, American 5668, **American 5669**, Amphion 5671, Anderson 5673, Anderson-Rogers 5676, Angelson 5679, Apple 5682, Applebaum 5683, Archangel 5685, Aresty 5686, Aresty 5687, Armonia 5688, Aronson 5689, Art 5691, Artists 5692, Arts 5693, Asen 5694, Authors 5700, Avanessians 5701, Avery 5702, AYN 5703, Baobab 5711, Barbara 5713, Barker 5716, Barnwood 5718, Bassman 5721, Baum 5722, Baumann 5723, Beacon 5726, Beard 5727, Beck 5728, Beckwith 5730, Beir 5732, Bendit 5736, Bennett 5737, Bernheim 5740, Bernhill 5741, Bet

5742, Betesh 5743, Betts 5744, Big 5745, Bikuben 5746, Bird 5750, **Bito 5753**, Black 5754, Blackman, 5755, Blank 5756, **Blinken 5757**, Block 5758, Block 5759, Blodgett 5760, Bloomberg 5761, Blue 5762, Blue 5763, Bogoni 5766, Bostwick 5767, Bothmer 5768, Bovin 5770, Boyer-Snyder 5773, Brademas 5774, Brand 5776, Brandt 5777, Bratt 5778, Breck 5780, Brenner 5781, Bridgewater 5783, Briger 5784, Brillo-Sonnino 5785, Brody 5787, Brosens 5789, Brown 5791, Brunie 5792, BTMU 5795, Buchwald 5797, Buckley 5798, **Burpee 5802**, Burton 5804, **Buster 5806**, CAL 5808, Calder 5810, Camber 5811, Camuto 5812, Caples 5813, Caruso 5817, Carwill 5818, Cathedral 5822, Catsimatidis 5823, CDVSJ 5825, Centennial 5826, Chapman 5832, Cheatham 5836, Chernoff 5838, Chervenak-Nunnalle 5839, Chiles 5843, **Chinook 5844**, Citrin 5846, Citron 5847, Clark 5848, Clarkson 5849, Clemente 5850, Cline 5851, Coby 5852, Cochran 5853, Cogut 5856, Cohen 5857, Cohen 5859, Cohen 5860, Cohenca 5861, Cohn 5863, Cole 5868, Coleman 5870, Coles 5871, Coremet 5875, Cornell 5876, Correspondents 5879, **Cote 5881**, Cowen 5882, Cox 5883, Cranshaw 5885, Cullman 5886, Cullman 5887, Cumming 5888, Curtis 5889, Dabah 5892, Dabah 5893, Dammann 5897, Danziger 5899, Davidson 5901, Dears 5905, Deeds 5906, Del 5908, DeMario 5909, Desai 5910, Desanctis, 5911, Devine-Majors 5913, Dillard 5916, Distracted 5918, Dixon 5919, Dobson 5921, Dolgen 5922, Double-R 5927, Downey 5930, Downs 5931, Duke 5934, **Dungannon 5935**, Dworman 5938, E.R.G. 5939, EBA 5941, Eberhart 5942, Ehrman 5949, Eisner 5951, Elkins 5955, Ellman 5956, Ellsworth 5957, Elyachar 5959, EMSA 5961, Emwiga 5962, Enders 5963, **Engineering 5964**, Englebardt 5965, **Eppley 5967**, Erpf 5968, Evans 5972, Evans 5973, Ezra 5976, Fagin 5978, Falconhead 5980, Falk 5981, **Family 5983**, Family 5984, Farber 5986, Farber 5987, Feil 5991, Feinberg 5993, Feldman 5996, Feldstein 5997, Fenton 5998, Fields 6003, Fife 6005, Finkelstein 6007, **Fischel 6009**, Fitt 6010, **Fitzgibbons 6011**, Flaherty 6012, Fleischer 6013, **Flowering 6015**, Fondation 6017, Forest 6018, Foundation-to-Life 6020, Fox 6022, Franco 6024, Franco 6025, Frankel 6027, Franklin 6028, Fraydun 6029, **Freedom 6030**, Freidheim 6031, Fridman 6035, Fried 6036, Frieman 6041, Friends 6042, Fuchsberg 6044, Furman 6045, Furman 6046, G&A 6048, Gallagher 6051, Galler 6052, Galvan 6053, Gant 6054, Gantcher 6055, Gary 6060, Geduld/Cougar 6062, Gela 6065, Gemiluth 6068, Gemj 6069, George 6070, Gerhard 6072, Gesso 6075, Gettinger 6076, Giant 6077, Gilliam 6078, Gimbel 6079, **Gimprich 6080**, Glorney 6084, Goddard 6085, Golden 6091, Goldenberg 6092, Goldfarb 6095, **Goldfein 6096**, Golding 6097, Goldman 6098, Goldstone 6102, Goldwasser 6103, Golick 6104, Goodman 6106, Goodman 6107, Gordon 6109, Gordon 6110, Gordon 6111, Gordon 6112, Gotham 6113, **Gottlieb 6114**, Gould 6116, GP 6117, Gramercy 6122, Grand 6123, Granny 6127, Grano 6128, Grant 6129, Grateful 6131, Greenberg 6132, Greenblatt 6133, **Greenwald 6136**, Greenwich 6137, Grinberg 6139, Grodzins 6141, Gross 6142, Grossman 6145, **Grossman 6146**, Grubman 6147, Grumbacher 6148, Grunberg 6149, **Gruodis 6150**, Guela 6151, Gutman 6152, H. 6153, Hadar 6154, Hahn 6157, Hajim 6158, Hallingby 6160, Handler 6162, Hanson 6163, Happy 6165, Harjen 6167, Harmon 6169, **Harriman 6170**, Harris 6171, Harris 6172, Hart 6173, Hasenfeld 6174, Hatfield 6175, Hauff 6177, **Haven 6178**, Healy 6179, Heller 6187, Henderson 6189, Hennessy 6191, Henson 6193, Hesed 6199, Hewitt 6200, Heyman 6201, **Hickrill 6204**, Hidary 6205, High 6206, Hiler 6207, Hilson 6209, Himelberg 6210, Hirsch 6211, Hochman 6214, Hoffen 6215, **Hoffman 6216**, Hogan 6217, Hohmann 6218, Holborn 6220, Holtzman 6223, Horowitz 6225, Huber 6231, Hymowitz 6234, I

6235, Imago 6239, Independent 6241, **Indira 6242**, Indus 6243, Insall 6246, Insall 6247, Institute 6248, International 6249, Iroquois 6250, Issroff 6251, Jacobson 6255, Jamakepe 6256, Janklow 6257, Jennings 6259, JI 6260, JJC 6262, JKW 6263, JLK 6264, Jockey 6265, Johnson 6266, Johnson 6267, Johnson 6268, Johnson 6269, Johnson 6270, Johnson-Stillman 6271, Jones 6272, Joseph 6273, Joukowsky 6274, JVZ 6277, Kahn 6279, Kallinikeion 6280, Kamber 6281, Kaminer 6282, Kandell 6283, Kasowitz 6285, **Katzin 6288**, Katzman 6289, Keene 6294, Kelleher 6295, Keren 6302, Keswin 6303, Kiernan 6306, Kies 6307, Kimmel 6308, Kimmelman 6309, Kimura 6310, **King 6311**, Kingjay 6312, Kistler 6316, **Kitov 6317**, **Klagsbrun 6318**, Kleban 6323, Klein 6324, Kleinschmidt 6326, **Klingenstein 6328**, Klingenstein-Martell 6329, Knafel 6330, Knapp 6331, Knaster 6332, Krauss 6345, Krimendahl/Saint-Amand 6346, Kriser 6347, Kroll 6348, Krumholz 6349, Kulick 6350, L 6353, La 6355, **Ladenburg 6357**, Lainoff 6359, **Lamaj 6361**, **Lanie 6364**, Lassalle 6366, Lauren 6368, Lawrence 6369, Layton 6370, Lazbridge 6371, Lee 6372, **Legacy 6374**, Lehman 6375, Leibowitz 6376, Lemle 6377, Lemle 6378, Lenetzach 6379, Lerer 6382, Leuschen 6384, Levine 6386, Levy 6389, Levy 6391, Lewin 6392, Lewy 6393, Libby 6395, Liberman 6396, Lichtenstein 6397, Lieb 6398, Liebowitz 6400, Lipschultz 6403, Lipton 6404, Lissner 6405, Litterman 6406, Little 6407, Loewy 6409, Longhill 6411, Lopatin 6412, Lubin 6416, Lubo 6417, Lucky 6419, Lucky 6420, Lufkin 6421, Lux 6422, M66 6427, Mack 6430, Maher 6433, Maher 6434, Makioka 6436, Manning 6437, Manocherian 6438, Manzanita 6439, Marbeh 6440, Marble 6441, Marine 6442, Martini 6447, MAT 6450, Maurer 6453, MBS 6454, **McCaddin-McQuirk 6455**, McCarthy 6456, McCooey 6457, McDade 6461, McDayton 6462, McEnroe 6463, **McGraw 6464**, McNulty 6465, Meier 6470, Melville 6471, Mendell 6472, Menezes 6473, Menges 6474, Meredith 6477, Meridian 6478, Merlo 6479, Merrill 6480, Mertz 6481, Metzger-Price 6483, Meyer 6485, Meyer 6486, Meyer 6487, Michaels 6488, Michelle 6489, **Milbank 6490**, Miller 6491, Miller 6493, Miller-Sweezy 6494, Milstein 6496, Milton 6497, Mindel 6498, Mitchell 6499, Mittlemann 6500, Monderer 6503, Moore 6504, Morgado 6505, Morin 6506, Morrell 6507, Morse 6509, Morse 6510, Moskowitz 6511, MSG 6514, Mule 6515, Nassimi 6519, National 6520, Neiman 6521, Nelco 6522, Neporent 6523, **Neuman 6526**, New 6527, Newcastle 6528, Newcomb-Hargraves 6529, Newman 6531, Newman 6532, Newman 6534, Niemiec 6535, **Nok 6537**, Nussbaum 6545, Oberoi 6547, Odyssey 6548, Oestreicher 6549, O'Grady 6551, Ohel 6553, Old 6554, One 6556, O'Neil 6557, Ong 6558, Ostgrodd 6561, Ostreicher 6562, Pajwell 6568, Palisades 6569, Palm 6571, Palmer 6572, Parshelsky 6578, Peek 6584, Pels 6585, Performing 6586, Perlman 6587, Perper 6588, Persian 6589, **Peter 6590**, Peterson 6591, Peterson 6592, Peterson 6593, Peterson 6594, Petty 6596, Pfeiffer 6597, Phaedrus 6598, Phalarope 6599, Phillips 6600, Pierce 6604, Pincus 6606, Pinkus 6607, Pittman 6608, Planalp-Trevor 6609, Pletka 6610, Pohly-Turaj 6613, Pollack 6615, Pollock 6617, Polsky 6618, Pomrenze 6619, **Posner-Wallace 6621**, Price 6627, Price 6628, Prince 6629, Purple 6634, Pyewacket 6635, **QIBQ 6636**, Quinn 6639, Rachesky 6642, Radio 6643, Randall 6644, Raphael 6648, Ravitch 6651, Realex 6654, Realty 6655, REBNY 6656, Reich 6659, Reidy 6661, Reiss 6662, Resnick 6663, Rexford 6664, Richter 6668, Rifkind 6670, Ring 6671, Ritter 6674, Roche 6677, Roche 6678, **Rock 6679**, Rodgers 6680, Roe 6681, Roothbert 6682, Rose 6684, Rose 6685, Rose 6686, Rose 6687, Rosenberg 6690, Rosenberg 6691, Rosenthal 6696, Rothblum 6701, Rothenberg 6702, Rothschild 6703,

Rothstein 6704, Roxe 6706, Rubin 6707, Rum 6709, Russo 6712, Ruttenberg 6715, Sackler 6716, Sackler 6717, Sallie 6720, Salomon 6721, Saltzman 6722, Sarnoff 6729, **Sato 6731**, Satow 6732, Savitz 6734, Scharf 6738, **Schepp 6739**, Schiller 6740, Schneider 6743, Schonfeld 6745, **School 6748**, Schott 6749, Schreiber 6750, Schwalbe 6751, Schwartz 6754, Schwartz 6755, Schwarz 6757, Schweitzer 6759, Scott 6761, Scott 6762, Securitas 6768, Seligman 6772, Selis 6774, Senator 6775, Seven 6777, Shachar 6779, Shack 6780, Shanken 6785, Shapiro 6786, Sharon 6787, **Shatford 6788**, Sheafer 6789, Sherman 6792, Shetty 6793, **Shulamit 6794**, Shuman 6795, Sillins 6799, Silverstein 6802, Silverstein 6803, Singer 6806, Slade 6809, Slovin 6811, Smith 6812, Smith 6815, Snyder 6819, **Societe 6820**, Society 6821, Sokoloff 6823, Some 6824, Sommer 6825, Sorel 6826, Sorensen-Siegel 6827, Sorgente 6828, **Sparkplug 6830**, Spatz 6831, Spear 6832, Spektor 6833, Sperandio 6835, Speranza 6836, Spiegel 6838, **Spirit 6839**, Spofford 6842, Stackhouse 6844, Stanton 6845, Starker 6847, Statue 6849, Stebbins 6850, Steck 6852, Steckler 6853, **Stein 6855**, Steinberg 6857, Stern 6860, Stern 6861, Sternklar 6864, Stifel 6865, Still 6866, Stony 6868, Stowe 6869, **Strauss 6870**, Strong 6872, Stuart, 6873, Stuntz 6874, Stutz 6875, Sumitomo 6876, Summit 6877, Sunrise 6878, Sutton 6881, Sutton 6882, Sutton 6883, Sutton 6884, SVM 6886, **Swett 6888**, Switzer 6889, **Tang 6891**, Tanico 6892, Tanner-Frank 6893, Thanksgiving 6897, Three 6899, Tisch 6900, Tod 6901, Treetops 6906, Tribune 6909, Trimble 6910, Troubh 6911, Tuch 6915, Turner 6916, U 6918, Utopia 6923, Van 6925, Vance 6926, Vanden 6927, Vernon 6928, Viola 6930, Vyeshaya 6934, Wachtell 6936, Walrath 6941, **Walsh/Alfred 6943**, Walther 6944, Washington 6946, Watts 6947, Weil 6948, **Weill 6950**, Weinberg 6951, Weingarten 6953, Weininger 6954, Weinman 6955, Weiser 6958, Weisman 6959, Weismann 6960, Weiss 6962, **Wheeler 6969**, Whispering 6970, White 6972, White 6973, Whitehead 6974, Whittemore 6975, Windy 6980, WLC 6982, **Woodland 6989**, Woodner 6991, Woods 6992, **World 6994**, Wright 6995, Wunsch 6996, Yad 7000, Yagoda 7001, Yordan 7009, Young 7012, **Youth 7013**, Zamir 7016, Zarin-Rosenfeld 7017, Zenkel 7023, Ziff 7027, Zimmermann 7028, Zirkl 7029, **Ziv 7030**, Zlinkoff 7031, Zukerman 7032, Zurack 7033, Zwerling 7034, Zwirn 7035

Newburgh: RHR 6667

North Rose: Marshall 6445

North Salem: Menken 6475

Norwich: Follett 6016, Mead 6466, Norwich 6542, Post 6622

Nyack: Garber 6057

Old Westbury: Giordano 6081, Kornreich 6341, O'Sullivan 6565

Olean: Cutco 5890

Oneonta: Burchan 5801, Hulbert 6232, Potter 6623

Orchard Park: Balbach 5707

Ossining: Fan 5985

Owego: Truman 6912

Palisades: Bergson 5738

Pawling: Peale 6582

Pearl River: Calamus 5809, Wish 6981

Pelham: Patrina 6579, Scully 6763

Phelps: Preston 6626

Pittsford: Code 5854, Cornell/Weinstein 5877, Ivorybill 6252, Long 6410, Schwartz 6753, Zarella 7018

Plainview: Mastrocola 6449, Rechler 6657

Plandome: Coleman 5869

Point Lookout: LSK 6415

Port Chester: Heffer 6180

Port Washington: Eule 5971, Marley 6443, McCormick 6459

Poughkeepsie: Greenspan 6134, Nuhn 6544

Pound Ridge: Box 5771, Gage 6050, IF 6237

Purchase: Chess 5841, Fein 5992, Feinman 5994, Santvoord 6727, Silver 6800, Spiritus 6840, Wachenheim 6935, Wagman 6937, Wong 6988

Quogue: Tedaldi 6894

Ridgewood: Godinger 6086, Ridgewood 6669

Riverdale: I.W. 6236

Rochester: August 5698, Brinkman 5786, ESL 5969, Kenlou 6299, Lucelia 6418, Matutina 6452, Saunders 6733, Thiem 6898

Rockville Center: Bush 5805

Rockville Centre: Cohn 5862, Stark 6846

Rome: Griffin 6138

Ronkonkoma: Cader 5807

Roslyn: **Kevorkian 6304**, Seelig 6769

Rye: Dunn 5936, Grace 6118, Grandview-Steers 6125, Netter 6525, Rosenstein 6692, Samberg 6723, Sternberg 6863, Tenney 6895

Rye Brook: Morris 6508

Sag Harbor: Century 5827, Vogler 6932

Sagaponack: Touradji 6903

Saint James: Danzi 5898, Smith, 6816

Sands Point: Doscas 5925

Saratoga Springs: Bell 5734, Bingham 5747, Ceriale 5828, Cerullo 5829, Cohen 5858, Fink 6006, Hap 6164, Kirby 6313, Lane 6363, MacArthur 6429, Meadowlark 6468, Phuong 6601, Schaffer 6736, Shackouls 6781, Stires-Stark 6867, Woodmere 6990, Zyman 7036

Scarsdale: Adelman 5643, Beckman 5729, Fowey 6021, Henshel 6192, Key 6305, Klingenstein 6327, Miller 6492, Schaffer 6737, Seligsohn 6773, **Stern 6862**, Weintraub 6957, Wolk 6987

Sea Cliff: Balm 5708

Seaford: F. 5977, Koha 6337

Setauket: Educational 5945

South Salem: **Abba's 5634**, **Cogitare 5855**

Southampton: Bandier 5709, North 6539

Southold: Hegarty 6182

Spring Valley: Paiken 6567, Simcha 6804, Steinmetz 6858, Zedukah 7020

Staten Island: Gottlieb-Schwartz 6115, Levine 6387, Meyer 6484, Tradition 6905

Suffern: Chada 5830, Geller 6066, Wagner 6938, Yosef 7011

Sunnyside: **Eastman 5940**

Syracuse: Snow 6818, **Yoreinu 7010**

Tarrytown: 1848 5629

The Bronx: Gold 6088

Tuxedo Park: Parr 6577

Uniondale: Marshall 6446

Upper Brookville: Quinn 6637, Schaefer 6735

Utica: Bank 5710, Utica 6922

Valhalla: Blue 5764, Catalyst 5821

Valley Stream: Mozel 6512

Vestal: Hershaft 6197, Olum 6555

Victor: Waldron 6939, Wilson 6979

Wainscott: Silverman 6801

Wappingers Falls: **Laerdal 6358**

Warwick: Warwick 6945

West Babylon: Herbst 6195

West Henrietta: Konar 6340

Westhampton Beach: Walsh 6942

White Plains: Barron 5719, Feuerring 6001, Furth 6047, Gantz 6056, Gralnick 6121, Grandison 6124, Henkind 6190, **Jabara 6254**, Katz 6287, Krasne 6344, Rosenthal 6695, Rosner 6698, Schonberger 6744, Seacoast 6766

Whitestone: Nonna's 6538

Williamsville: **Companions 5873**, Ferguson 5999, Gartner 6059, Hein 6184

Woodbury: Antun 5681, Bobrow 5765, Sakhai 6718, Samuels 6725, Woldar 6985

Woodmere: Diamondston 5914, Sokol 6822, TSP 6913

Woodsburgh: Hershman 6198

Woodside: Satar 6730

Woodstock: Villchur 6929

Wurtsboro: Kautz 6290

Wynantskill: Rhodes 6666

Yonkers: Alexander 5654, Edelweiss 5944, Friedland 6037, Hurlburt 6233

---

see also 7, 25, 52, 86, 109, 134, 165, 224, 252, 271, 273, 277, 287, 291, 292, 299, 300, 320, 321, 344, 350, 352, 359, 363, 365, 375, 388, 392, 394, 397, 414, 418, 492, 497, 522, 530, 538, 542, 560, 562, 563, 567, 569, 579, 646, 677, 687, 695, 702, 711, 718, 719, 752, 766, 767, 790, 800, 804, 822, 828, 846, 848, 853, 871, 881, 893, 906, 939, 956, 970, 971, 973, 975, 978, 982, 1004, 1008, 1013, 1017, 1028, 1031, 1033, 1044, 1045, 1049, 1053, 1084, 1090, 1106, 1116, 1117, 1148, 1156, 1157, 1160, 1185, 1193, 1194, 1199, 1201, 1208, 1211, 1212, 1214, 1215, 1224, 1225, 1231, 1232, 1233, 1240, 1281, 1297, 1298, 1299, 1331, 1333, 1357, 1369, 1376, 1383, 1384, 1388, 1390, 1396, 1397, 1401, 1405, 1412, 1415, 1419, 1422, 1423, 1425, 1430, 1433, 1437, 1447, 1448, 1450, 1458, 1463, 1465, 1471, 1472, 1480, 1481, 1484, 1486, 1488, 1494, 1495, 1496, 1498, 1503, 1504, 1507, 1508, 1510, 1511, 1513, 1514, 1515, 1517, 1523, 1525, 1528, 1530, 1533, 1535, 1536, 1542, 1548, 1549, 1550, 1556, 1562, 1563, 1564, 1565, 1572, 1573, 1576, 1579, 1584, 1587, 1588, 1592, 1596, 1597, 1602, 1606, 1610, 1611, 1616, 1618, 1625, 1628, 1629, 1633, 1638, 1644, 1645, 1646, 1650, 1652, 1665, 1667, 1671, 1687, 1693, 1694, 1698, 1701, 1710, 1713, 1717, 1723, 1729, 1730, 1736, 1738, 1744, 1747, 1750, 1756, 1758, 1763, 1774, 1775, 1777, 1778, 1781, 1782, 1791, 1792, 1798, 1825, 1829, 1830, 1838, 1844, 1853, 1854, 1857, 1858, 1859, 1869, 1871, 1877, 1891, 1893, 1894, 1895, 1900, 1904, 1915, 1921, 1927, 1931, 1934, 1940, 1942, 1945, 1946, 1949, 1951, 1965, 1967, 1968, 1971, 1985, 1990, 1992, 1993, 1994, 1995, 1996, 2002, 2003, 2013, 2036, 2039, 2040, 2048, 2050, 2053, 2063, 2068, 2074, 2078, 2084, 2088, 2099, 2100, 2115, 2121, 2130, 2133, 2135, 2136, 2141, 2146, 2153, 2156, 2162, 2173, 2178, 2180, 2182, 2187, 2192, 2197, 2204, 2212, 2225, 2229, 2232, 2234, 2237, 2247, 2252, 2254, 2262, 2285, 2293, 2300, 2301, 2302, 2307, 2311, 2316, 2318, 2323, 2324, 2326, 2327, 2346, 2347, 2349, 2350, 2353, 2374, 2380, 2382, 2384, 2388, 2392, 2398, 2407, 2410, 2424, 2505, 2516, 2547, 2561, 2564, 2578, 2610, 2618, 2694, 2696, 2709, 2711, 2722, 2735, 2754, 2758, 2778, 2791, 2796, 2805, 2825, 2845, 2848, 2852, 2868, 2878, 2882, 2886, 2887, 2890, 2896, 2912, 2934, 2937, 2942, 2948, 2949, 2984, 2996, 3006, 3020, 3030, 3068, 3070, 3079, 3082, 3097, 3103, 3119, 3136, 3141, 3143, 3150, 3151, 3152, 3180, 3181, 3185, 3190, 3213, 3215, 3222, 3230, 3233, 3234, 3237, 3240, 3247, 3249, 3261, 3276, 3279, 3282, 3285, 3288, 3293, 3297, 3304, 3310, 3314, 3322, 3330, 3334, 3385, 3451, 3483, 3538, 3593, 3614, 3621, 3656, 3660, 3778, 3783, 3784, 3821, 3826, 3838, 3843, 3855, 3872, 3874, 3881, 3892, 3914, 3917, 3923, 3926, 3927, 3940, 3954, 3955, 3963, 3966, 3969, 3971, 3973, 3975, 3982, 3994, 4004, 4014, 4041, 4051, 4063, 4070, 4081, 4092, 4097, 4105, 4108, 4127, 4130, 4142, 4146, 4148, 4165, 4169, 4181, 4185, 4200, 4201, 4210, 4212, 4229, 4243, 4261, 4271, 4278, 4321, 4322, 4325, 4343, 4380, 4384, 4395, 4399, 4434, 4464, 4465, 4503, 4508, 4560, 4564, 4594, 4600, 4609, 4618, 4632, 4670, 4680, 4685, 4721, 4722, 4784, 4869, 4952, 4971, 4989, 5073, 5116, 5131, 5136, 5154, 5159, 5170, 5190, 5200, 5201, 5202, 5211, 5219, 5220, 5228, 5233, 5235, 5241, 5242, 5243, 5248, 5249, 5250, 5251, 5252, 5253, 5255, 5259, 5261, 5262, 5263, 5264, 5265, 5268, 5270, 5273, 5274, 5278, 5279, 5280, 5285, 5294, 5296, 5304, 5307, 5309, 5310, 5316, 5318, 5327, 5331, 5333, 5334, 5335, 5336, 5340, 5343, 5344, 5347, 5348, 5350, 5354, 5355, 5364, 5367, 5369, 5370, 5372, 5377, 5378, 5380, 5381, 5382, 5383, 5384, 5386, 5395, 5399, 5402, 5405, 5406, 5412, 5415, 5417, 5420, 5421, 5423, 5424, 5430, 5431, 5435, 5437, 5442, 5443, 5446, 5447, 5451, 5456, 5461, 5463, 5465, 5466, 5469, 5473, 5474, 5478, 5479, 5481, 5484, 5485, 5487, 5488, 5489, 5490, 5492, 5494, 5498, 5501, 5503, 5509, 5511, 5512, 5514, 5516, 5518, 5522, 5524, 5531, 5532, 5534, 5536, 5539, 5544, 5545, 5546, 5547, 5548, 5551, 5552, 5558, 5563, 5564, 5572, 5574, 5575, 5576, 5578, 5579, 5583, 5587, 5588, 5591, 5594, 5599, 5600, 5601, 5615, 7057, 7105, 7128, 7152, 7192, 7194, 7203, 7219, 7245, 7253, 7278, 7309, 7329, 7347, 7410, 7430, 7468, 7480, 7484, 7493, 7512, 7553, 7556, 7574, 7602, 7616, 7634, 7643, 7677, 7679, 7695, 7754, 7791, 7836, 7839, 7840, 7842, 7847, 7853, 7854, 7857, 7867, 7872, 7883, 7896, 7902, 7917, 7926, 7934, 7947, 7956, 7958, 7973, 7977, 7981, 7983, 7986, 7988, 8009, 8018, 8023, 8030, 8040, 8041, 8053, 8058, 8075, 8077, 8086, 8090, 8092, 8101, 8107, 8121, 8130, 8138, 8167, 8174, 8178, 8198, 8225, 8228, 8246, 8254, 8255, 8264, 8265, 8276, 8298, 8299, 8300, 8305, 8309, 8330, 8339, 8365, 8374, 8382, 8385, 8393, 8395, 8405, 8406, 8411, 8430, 8432, 8437, 8450, 8457, 8458, 8462, 8466, 8469, 8470, 8482, 8483, 8491, 8497, 8517, 8589, 8600, 8601, 8637, 8639, 8645, 8656, 8708, 8715, 8718, 8735, 8840, 8850, 8855, 8864, 8875, 8889, 8913, 8996, 9002, 9006, 9032, 9062, 9108, 9117, 9131, 9135, 9140, 9163, 9171, 9190, 9210, 9235, 9237, 9261, 9271, 9285, 9354, 9359, 9368, 9369, 9371, 9372, 9373, 9377, 9388, 9400, 9418, 9432, 9433, 9442, 9444, 9445, 9451, 9455, 9501, 9504, 9510, 9518, 9529, 9533, 9545, 9553, 9629, 9657, 9666, 9681, 9801, 9813, 9846, 9904, 9967, 9975, 9991, 9997

NORTH CAROLINA

Asheville: Pulliam 7215, **Rixson 7223**

Belmont: Howe 7132, Stowe 7256

Benson: Cooke 7079

Burlington: Family 7096, Hayden-Harman 7120, Hunt 7135, Koury 7150, Rocky 7227

Cary: Cary 7070

Chapel Hill: Bertsch 7050, Hoffman 7127, Hudson 7133, Kenan 7143, Kenan 7144, Maness 7166, Morgan 7190, Post 7213, Silverback 7243, Strowd 7258

Charlotte: Arcadia 7040, Bane 7043, Belk 7046, Bernstein 7049, Burns 7063, Cannon 7067, Cary 7069, Cato, 7071, Chaley 7072, Deal 7085, Edgar 7088, Eplee 7092, Flowers 7099, Fortson 7100, Gambrell 7105, Gambrill 7106, Garrigues 7107, Geschick 7109, Griffin 7113, Haney 7116, Hayes 7121, Hoffman 7128, Horvat 7130, Jelm 7137, Kassner 7141, Koons 7148, Kosloski 7149, KPB 7151, Landry's 7159, Levine-Sklut 7161, Live 7163, Marietta 7167, Markey 7168, Mattei 7173, McGuire, 7177, Meyer 7183, Miller 7185, Moritz 7192, Morrison 7193, Moseley 7194, Needham 7199, North 7202, Plansoen 7211, Ragland, 7216, Rankin 7217, Robinson 7225, Robitaille 7226, Schug 7237, Shapiro 7239, Shingleton 7241, Silverman 7244, Snyder's-Lance 7250, Spring 7251, SPX 7252, Steinmetz 7254, Stubblefield 7260, Tabitha 7265, Trexler 7269, Vanderbilt 7273, Weatherspoon 7282

Concord: Little 7162

Conover: Bolick 7056

Durham: Fox 7103, Herndon 7125, Rollins 7231, Wilkinson 7288

Fayetteville: Jones 7138, Matthews 7174, Rogers 7228

Fuquay Varina: Barker 7044

Gastonia: First 7097, Glenn 7111

Greensboro: Bell 7048, Burlington 7062, Carroll 7068, Covington 7081, Ellison 7090, Marsh 7171, Piedmont 7209, Richardson 7221, Wagner 7275

Greenville: Williams 7289

Henderson: Henderson 7124

Hickory: Abernethy 7037, TSH 7271, Von 7274, Yount 7292

High Point: Brown 7058, Whitener 7286

Kernersville: Pope 7212

Kinston: Harvey-McNairy 7119

Lenoir: Coffey 7078

Lexington: Ritchie 7222

Lumberton: McLean 7178

Marion: Smith 7247

Matthews: P 7205, Pillmore 7210

Mooresville: Evernham 7094, Gordon 7112

Morrisville: Redwoods 7218

Mount Olive: Mount 7196

Oak Ridge: Pratt 7214

Ocean Isle Beach: Hackbarth 7114, Ladane 7155

Raleigh: Agarwal 7039, Bell 7047, Bryan 7060, C3 7064, Canaday 7066, Chatham 7074, Childtrust 7075, Helton 7123, Hine 7126, Krauss 7153, London 7164, Morisey 7191, Nanney 7198, Nivison 7201, **Rolander 7229**, S.D.R. 7233, Sloan 7246, Szulik 7264, Wells 7283, West-West 7284, Zelnak 7293

Research Triangle Park: UAI 7272

Rocky Mount: Boddie 7054, Boddie 7055

Salisbury: Lerner 7160, Peeler 7207, Smith 7248

Shelby: Harvest 7118

Southern Pines: Cooke 7080

Southern Shores: Outer 7204

Spencer: Davis 7083

Spindale: Stonecutter 7255

Valdese: Rostan 7232

Wake Forest: Wake 7276

Waxhaw: TerKeurst 7266

Wilmington: Cameron 7065, CJB 7076, Foundation 7102, Kennedy 7145, Triplett 7270, Way 7281, Wise 7290

Wilson: BB&T 7045, Crawley 7082, Marlboro 7169, Mize 7186, Rees 7219, Smith 7249, Sutherland 7263, Wibel 7287, Yost 7291

Winnabow: McMerty 7180

Winston-Salem: Aehle 7038, Arkwright 7041, Balin 7042, Bettman 7051, Billingsley 7052, Blue 7053, Borun 7057, Brown 7059, Burks 7061, Chastain 7073, Coate 7077, Davis 7084, Duncan 7086, Eddy 7087, Elks 7089, Emma 7091, Everett 7093, Fairfield 7095, **Firth 7098**, Foster 7101, Galanti 7104, Garrow 7108, Gilmore 7110, Hamill 7115, Harrison 7117, Helb 7122, Holleman 7129, Howard 7131, Hunt 7134, Hunter 7136, Judd 7139, Kanitz 7140, Katz 7142, Ketchum 7146, Kistler 7147, **Kramer 7152**, Krost 7154, Ladd 7156, **Laffin 7157**, Landon 7158, Lynum 7165, Marsh 7170, Masserini 7172, Mattison 7175, McConnell 7176, McLendon 7179, McNeil 7181, Meserve 7182, Meyer 7184, Moon 7187, Moore 7188, Moretz 7189, Mosser 7195, Nalle 7197, Niessen, 7200, Oschwald 7203, Paddock 7206, Perkin 7208, Ribenack 7220, Robbins 7224, Rolla 7230, Sanders 7234, Sandt 7235, Schmidt 7236, Self 7238, Sherrard 7240, Shugart 7242, Sites 7245, Stapleton 7253, Strickland 7257, Stuart 7259, Sutcliffe 7262, Thomasville 7267, Towne 7268, Wallace 7277, Walters 7278, Wann 7279, Waters 7280, **Weyenberg 7285**

Wrightsville Beach: Summer 7261

see also 65, 289, 445, 810, 904, 1378, 1406, 1430, 1702, 1725, 1728, 1735, 1808, 1847, 1866, 1883, 1899, 1939, 1953, 1955, 2000, 2031, 2032, 2055, 2056, 2064, 2074, 2111, 2167, 2171, 2216, 2218, 2294, 2310, 2333, 2376, 2469, 2475, 2507, 2510, 2535, 2616, 2618, 2756, 2793, 2926, 3002, 3106, 3127, 3330, 3461, 3550, 3829, 3988, 4024, 4132, 4271, 4493, 4508, 4539, 4647, 4815, 4844, 4988, 5064, 5201, 5292, 5321, 5853, 6116, 6128, 6233, 6301, 6577, 6638, 6682, 6879, 7014, 7600, 7857, 7910, 8025, 8112, 8399, 8430, 8450, 8516, 8519, 8538, 8644, 8683, 8946, 9017, 9046, 9278, 9296, 9366, 9433, 9434, 9474, 9485, 9504, 9550, 9744, 9916

NORTH DAKOTA

Bottineau: Berge 7294

Fargo: Fedje 7296

Grand Forks: Community 7295, Myra 7297

Westhope: Pearson 7298

see also 272, 2275, 4679, 4744, 4745, 4763, 4810, 5048, 8554, 9649

OHIO

Akron: Albrecht 7301, Bernard 7325, Comunale, 7358, Demetros 7377, Freygang 7410, Jennings 7466, Kutz 7486, Lambert 7487, Loeb 7503, Musson 7534, Orr 7543, Ritchie 7561, Smith 7598, Tell 7613, Throckmorton 7618, Welty 7635

Alliance: Mangano 7511

Archbold: Rupp 7565

Athens: Athens 7311

Austintown: Brocker 7334

Avon Lake: Williams 7639

Barberton: Tuscora 7624

Bay Village: Jenkins 7465, Kamm 7473

Beachwood: Andrews 7307, Berke 7323, Morley 7532, Reisman 7556, Turben 7622, Wolf 7643

Bedford Heights: **Brush 7338**

Bratenahl: Sears-Swetland 7581

Brooklyn: Black 7328, Brews 7332, Brown 7337, Calhoun 7344, Dermitt 7378, Geary, 7419, Hoover 7453, Huntington 7460, Hutchins 7461, Klock 7480, Leach 7494, Manley 7512, Matthes 7517, Miller 7527, Norweb 7539, O'Donnell 7540, Sheadle 7588, Sheadle 7589, Terhune 7614

Bryan: Bryan 7339

Bucyrus: Community 7356, High 7449

Canfield: Williamson 7640

Canton: Austin-Bailey 7312, Montauk 7531, Sterling 7606, Yoder 7650

Centerville: Conlogue 7359

Chagrin Falls: Sauerland 7570, Talbott 7612

Chesterhill: **Lowe-Marshall 7505**

Cincinnati: A 7299, Alpaugh 7302, Anderson 7304, Anderson 7305, Anderton 7306, Bahmann 7313, Barron 7316, Beck 7319, Berding 7322, Brinck 7333, Building 7340, Bullock 7341, Busemeyer 7342, Chemed 7350, Chesley 7351, CLH 7355, Conn 7360, Corbett 7363, Downing 7381, Ettlinger 7390, Fleischmann 7404, Glazer 7426, Gross/Hutton 7433, Hauck 7440, Heimann 7444, Hickok 7447, **Highfield 7450**, Homan 7451, Howe 7455, Hubert 7456, Ingle 7462, Joffe 7467, Johnson 7468, Johnson 7469, Juniper 7472, Kisker 7479, Kloenne 7481, Lawson 7492, Lazarus 7493, Lindner 7497, Linnemann 7498, LKC 7501, Luedeking 7506, Lundgard 7508, Lungard 7509, Marcus 7514, Marnick 7515, Mehl 7523, Messer 7524, NLT 7537, Norris 7538, Ohio 7541, Oscar 7544, Philada 7548, Pott 7549, Quatman 7552, Ryan 7566, S.E.C. 7567, Schottenstein 7573, Seasongood 7582, Segoe 7583, Shannon 7586, Skyler 7595, Steiner-King 7602, Steinmann 7603, Stillson 7607, Taft 7609, Thendara 7616, Van 7626, Vista 7628, Woodward 7646, Yeiser 7649, Young 7651

Cleveland: Arrel 7310, Barber 7315, Berkman 7324, Bicknell 7327, Brentwood 7330, Christen 7353, Cleveland 7354, Crossroads 7367, Cure 7368, Damico 7370, Dorn 7380, **Elisha-Bolton 7387**, Ferry 7396, Firman 7400, Fletcher 7405, Fox 7409, Frost 7412, Gale 7414, Gale 7415, Gay 7418, Gries 7431, Hamilton 7435, Hankins 7437, Haskell 7439, Hummer 7459, Jenkins 7464, **Katz 7475**, Knight 7482, Kramer 7484, Lawry 7491, Lincoln 7496, Lippitt 7499, Littick 7500, Mather 7516, Mccarthy 7520, Miller 7528, Mixon 7530, O'Neill 7542, Powers 7550, Rayen 7554, Renner 7557, Rosenthal 7563, Sage 7568, Seifert 7584, Shaw 7587, Slitzer 7596, Tetlak 7615, Watson 7633, Williams 7638, Wilson 7642, Woodruff 7645

Cleveland Heights: **Eaton 7383**

Columbus: American 7303, Armington 7309, Baird 7314, Beecher 7320, Beecher 7321, Crandall 7366, Edwards 7386, Finnegan 7399, Fishel 7401, Gelbman 7420, George 7421, Gilman 7423, Gross 7432, Hazelbaker 7441, Hueneke 7457, Hughes 7458, Osteopathic 7545, Peters 7547, Schooler 7572, Schottenstein 7574, Schottenstein 7575, Schwartz, 7576, Sheely 7590, Skestos 7594, Traeger 7621, Wasserstrom 7632, Wildermuth 7637, Young 7653

Cuyahoga Falls: Faber 7392

Dayton: B-Brand 7318, Brethen 7331, Busse 7343, Cardinal 7347, Duarte 7382, Garcia 7416, Gardner 7417, Glidden 7427, Gosiger 7429, Kilworth 7477, Kramer 7485, Lockwood 7502, Mead 7522, Newton 7536, Reynolds 7558, Rotterman 7564, Sinai 7593, Tait 7610, Thompson, 7617, Wallace 7631, Yeck 7648

Defiance: Coressel 7364, Defiance 7375

Delphos: Dienstberger 7379

Dover: Rosenberry 7562

Dublin: Brown 7336, Kennedy 7476, **Marafiki 7513**

East Liverpool: Lang 7489

Eaton: Home 7452

Elida: **Dauch 7372**

Fairfield: Besl 7326, Boymel 7329

Fairview Park: Ridgecliff 7560

Findlay: Cooper 7362

Gates Mills: Schey 7571

Grove City: Heffner 7443

Hamilton: Fitton 7402, Knoll 7483

Hartville: Christ 7352

Hillsboro: Cassner 7348

Holland: TKBW 7619

Hudson: Myers 7535

Independence: Fedeli 7393

Kent: Davey 7373

Lagrange: Hampson 7436

Lancaster: Lehman 7495

Lebanon: Fleck 7403, Loeb 7504

Lima: H 7434

Loudonville: Young 7652

Lyndhurst: Chaney 7349

Mansfield: Ebenezer 7384, Gimbel 7424, Landers 7488, Milliron 7529

Marietta: Peoples 7546

Marion: Trachsel 7620

Marysville: Community 7357

Massillon: Health 7442

Mayfield Heights: Daberko 7369, Horvitz 7454

Mentor: STERIS 7605

Miamisburg: Connor 7361, Danis 7371, Hieronymus 7448

Milford: Gould 7430, Wyler 7647

Monclova: Iott 7463

Moreland Hills: Rapport 7553

Morrow: Lukens 7507

Nelsonville: Foundation 7408

New Philadelphia: Tuscarawas 7623

Niles: Fibus 7398

North Canton: DeHoff 7376

North Olmsted: Fortney 7406
Norwalk: Geotrac 7422
Novelty: Weiss 7634
Painesville: Stafast 7600
Parma Heights: Smiley 7597
Pepper Pike: Kangesser 7474, Sandfair 7569
Perrysburg: Endowment 7388, Entelco 7389
Piqua: Felger 7395
Poland: Scotford 7579
Powell: Southard 7599
Richfield: Feth 7397
Rocky River: Laub 7490
Saint Mary's: Heinrich 7446
Salineville: Angels 7308
Sandusky: Frohman 7411, Frost-Parker 7413, Stein 7601, Wightman-Wieber 7636
Shaker Heights: Jordan 7471, Reynolds 7559
Solon: Miller 7526, Swagelok 7608
Springfield: Davidson 7374, Selsor 7585, Taj 7611
Steubenville: Brooks 7335
Sylvania: McMaster 7521
Toledo: Bates 7317, Feldstein 7394, Goerlich 7428, Hankison 7438, M.L.M 7510, McCann 7519, Reed 7555, Stensen 7604, Wolfe 7644
Uniontown: Wagler 7629
University Heights: Ginn 7425
Wadsworth: Mifsud 7525, Venner 7627
Warren: Covelli 7365, Van 7625
Warrensville Heights: Callahan 7345
Washington Court House: Eyman 7391
Waverly: Wilson 7641
Westlake: Heimbinder 7445
Wickliffe: Callahan 7346
Williamsburg: Abrams 7300
Wintersville: Pugliese 7551
Wooster: Foss 7407, Jones 7470, Seaman 7580
Youngstown: Edward 7385, Schwebel 7577, Walker 7630
Zanesville: Kincaid 7478, McCann 7518, Murphy 7533, Scion 7578, Shinnick 7591, Sidwell 7592

see also 100, 173, 229, 261, 291, 316, 466, 725, 765, 770, 1233, 1320, 1336, 1368, 1431, 1445, 1517, 1703, 1724, 1734, 1780, 1865, 1885, 1919, 1922, 1985, 2004, 2033, 2036, 2044, 2143, 2296, 2317, 2398, 2475, 2495, 2562, 2728, 2762, 2772, 2839, 3005, 3076, 3099, 3119, 3247, 3333, 3374, 3545, 3614, 3662, 3663, 3672, 3682, 3696, 3706, 3923, 3969, 4013, 4063, 4066, 4181, 4243, 4271, 4419, 4501, 4584, 4619, 4803, 4937, 5175, 5307, 5453, 5565, 5574, 5600, 5631, 5787, 5858, 6012, 6273, 6378, 6380, 6560, 6571, 6597, 6645, 7137, 7159, 7167, 7168, 7205, 8010, 8067, 8103, 8152, 8177, 8208, 8218, 8228, 8285, 8322, 8342, 8357, 8413, 8420, 8673, 8862, 8913, 8962, 9008, 9135, 9215, 9227, 9246, 9250, 9417, 9482, 9510, 9764

OKLAHOMA

Ardmore: Goddard 7684
Bristow: Jones 7692
Broken Arrow: Brannin 7662, Faranna 7678
Chandler: Walkingstick 7727
Durant: Massey 7705
Edmond: French 7680
El Reno: Ashbrook 7656
Enid: Cherokee 7666
Eufaula: Gelvin 7682
Fort Gibson: Young 7739
Guthrie: Miller 7709
Guymon: Lolmaugh 7700
Jenks: Dill 7671
McAlester: Fugitt 7681
Newkirk: Peel 7714

Norman: Liddell 7697
Nowata: Richardson 7717
Oklahoma City: Ad 7654, Brown 7664, Drabek 7673, Dulaney 7674, Everest 7676, Fleischaker 7679, Goodin 7685, Howard 7688, Howard 7689, Jirous 7690, Jones 7691, Kerr 7693, Kimmell 7694, Lockhart 7699, Love 7701, Martin, 7704, Merrick 7707, Parman 7713, Pros 7715, Wadley 7726, Ward 7728, Wegener 7731
Owasso: Owasso 7712
Poteau: **Crio 7670**
Stillwater: Staton 7720
Thomas: Thomas 7724
Tulsa: Asbjornson 7655, Atherton 7657, Barnes 7658, Barnes 7659, Barnett 7660, Barthelmes 7661, Broadhurst 7663, Burkhart 7665, Chilton 7667, Collins 7668, Collins, 7669, Dobson 7672, Elpis 7675, Evergreen 7677, GKJ 7683, Harmon 7686, Holliman 7687, Krueger 7695, Kullgren 7696, Livengood 7698, Lovoi 7702, Marshall 7703, Merkel 7706, Miller 7708, Moore 7710, Oklahoma 7711, Rathbun 7716, Russell 7718, Sisk 7719, Stone 7721, Sylvan 7722, Tandy 7723, Trippet 7725, Warren 7729, Weber 7730, Welch 7732, White 7733, White 7734, Whitwell-Meyer 7735, Wilson 7736, Witt 7737, Wolff 7738

see also 150, 188, 272, 1264, 1342, 1735, 2091, 2516, 2947, 2976, 3200, 3382, 3562, 3870, 4271, 5247, 6880, 7319, 7650, 8107, 8117, 8418, 8539, 8709, 8762, 8789, 8974, 9030, 9082, 9246, 9347, 9387

OREGON

Ashland: Sharkey 7815
Beaverton: Heath 7772
Bend: Curry 7755, Jonas 7778
Boring: Schmidt 7813
Brookings: Atkins 7741
Central Point: Coffman 7750
Corvallis: **Conklin 7754**, Simple 7818
Eagle Point: Kimmel 7782
Eugene: Giustina 7767, Harvest 7769, McKay 7795, Singer 7819, Stewart 7822, Woodard 7831
Florence: Western 7829
Grants Pass: Four 7764
Happy Valley: **Larson 7788**
Hermiston: Leonard 7789
Jacksonville: Chaney 7747, West 7827
Klamath Falls: Glennco 7768, Klamath 7784
Lake Oswego: Lamb 7787, Leupold 7790, Lindgren 7791, Spencer 7820
Lakeside: Rietman 7809
Lakeview: Daly 7756
Medford: Dubs 7760, Elwood 7761, Maxey 7793, May 7794, Morris 7802, Naumes 7804
Mill City: Frank 7765
Milwaukie: Dieringer 7758
Portland: Ackley 7740, Baldwin 7742, Bowen 7743, Brown 7744, Castle 7745, Cayo 7746, Charis 7748, **Chiles 7749**, Coit 7751, Collins 7752, Demorest 7757, Erath 7762, Flowerree 7763, Gill 7766, Haskell 7770, Haugse 7771, Holzman 7775, Irwin 7777, Jubitz 7779, Jurrens 7780, Karuna 7781, Kinnie 7783, Knudson 7785, Kuse 7786, Merlo 7797, Metro 7798, Michael 7799, Miller 7800, Morey 7801, Naito 7803, Parker/United 7805, Pendleton 7806, Portland 7807, Richardson 7808, Saling 7811, Santos 7812, Shapira 7814, Shoen 7816, Silver 7817, Stewart 7821, Stewart 7823, Wessinger 7826, West 7828, White 7830, **Wyss 7832**
Salem: Hill 7773, Hitchman 7774
Sherwood: Trover 7824
Silverton: Huddart 7776
Sisters: Roundhouse 7810
Tillamook: Watt 7825

Troutdale: **Living 7792**
West Linn: Donegan 7759
Wilsonville: Collins 7753, Mentor 7796

see also 89, 100, 168, 272, 327, 372, 445, 447, 496, 638, 642, 782, 786, 904, 913, 939, 1060, 1137, 1153, 1217, 1224, 1734, 1739, 1994, 2276, 2643, 3088, 3190, 3551, 3912, 4271, 4639, 4768, 4868, 5021, 5059, 5432, 5496, 5575, 5761, 5821, 6220, 6264, 6395, 6885, 7051, 7134, 8408, 8536, 8698, 8732, 9038, 9334, 9363, 9560, 9575, 9578, 9596, 9598, 9622, 9643, 9645, 9673, 9681, 9700, 9870, 9945

PENNSYLVANIA

Allentown: **BGM 7871**, Born 7885, Butz 7908, Hecht 8050, Hoch 8060, Kline 8098, Reidler 8233, Rider-Pool 8238, Ryan 8251, **Shastri 8273**, Singer 8279
Ambler: Mill 8172
Ardmore: Hilles 8057, Kynett 8105
Audubon: Mascaro 8145
Bala-Cynwyd: Boscia 7887, Golden 8022, Perelman 8209, Perelman 8210, **Susquehanna 8310**
Beaver: Moore 8177
Bensalem: Rubin 8246
Bethlehem: Star 8297
Bloomsburg: Magee 8137
Bradford: **Glendorn 8020**, Mukaiyama-Rice 8183
Bristol: Grundy 8029
Bryn Mawr: Dibona 7955, Le 8115, Leone 8120, Ludwick 8134
Camp Hill: Hall 8037, Harsco 8040, Norford 8196, Pollock 8222
Canonsburg: Mylan 8187
Center Valley: Katsaros 8087
Chadds Ford: Up 8327, Wyeth 8371
Chesterbrook: McManus 8164
Clearfield: CNB 7929
Columbia: Columbia 7932, Nikolaus 8193
Conshohocken: Bennett 7860, Quaker 8228
Cranberry Township: Calligan 7909
Dallas: Kazanjian 8090, Pearsall 8207
Delmont: Larsen 8113, Price 8225
Devault: Katherine 8086
Downingtown: Carlson 7916
Doylestown: Bucks 7905, Martin 8143, Seybert 8269, Woodall 8368
Drexel Hill: Gordon 8024
East Earl: Hahn 8036, Shady 8270
East Greenville: Knoll 8100
Easton: Bedford 7857, Staley 8296
Elverson: Cornerstone 7936
Emporium: Emporium 7980
Ephrata: Brossman 7900, Wenger 8351
Erie: Black 7876, Britton 7894, Carnahan-Jackson 7917, Greater 8026, Merwin 8170, Petersen 8212, Smith 8280
Erwinna: Tuttleman 8325
Exton: Hankin 8038, Mutual 8186
Fairless Hills: Katz 8089
Fort Washington: Birnhak 7873, Goodstein 8023
Gladwyne: Dietrich 7958, Drueding 7966, Gureghian 8033
Greensburg: Willow 8360
Gwynedd: Spain 8292
Gwynedd Valley: Gypsy 8034, Olitsky 8198, Todi 8319
Harrisburg: Patterson 8206, Schwab-Silfen 8264
Haverford: Baekgaard 7850, Moggio 8176, Rosenlund 8245, Stein 8298, Stein 8299
Havertown: Jordan 8082, Rudin 8247
Hazleton: **Cohn 7931**, First 7997, Scheller 8258
Hershey: Elliott 7977, Stotland 8303
Holland: Schrenk 8261
Honesdale: Wayne 8345

Horsham: Goldberg 8021, Martin 8142
Huntingdon Valley: Lemole 8119, Viii 8333
Imperial: Maronda 8140
Jenkintown: Gershman 8015, Joyce 8083, Rudman 8248, Scott 8266
Jim Thorpe: Moyer 8180
Johnstown: Pasquerilla 8204
King of Prussia: Arkema 7842, Aventis 7847, Strawbridge 8305, Wachs 8336, Wolfson 8364
Kingston: Bergman 7863
Kittanning: Snyder 8287
Knoxville: Deerfield 7952
Kulpsville: GT 8030
Lancaster: Ashland 7845, Clark 7925, Coffin 7930, Gamber 8011, Ganse 8012, High 8054, Klein 8097, MHB 8171, Reese 8232, Russo 8249, Shenk 8274, Shuman 8277, Weiler 8347
Latrobe: Gibson 8016
Lebanon: Alley 7837, Bishop 7874
Limerick: Teleflex 8314
Lower Gwynedd: Smith 8283
Malvern: Boudinot 7888, Conestoga 7934, Curaterra 7947, Danella 7948, Lipstein 8129, Ricon 8237, Satell 8254, Tally 8313, **Whimsie 8354**, Yoh 8373
Marietta: Clark 7927
McKeesport: Murphy 8185
Meadville: Crawford 7944
Media: Delaware 7953, Strine 8307, Terryglass 8315
Merion Station: **Berkowitz 7865**, McKee 8160
Meyersdale: Somerset 8290
Milford: Berkowitz 7866
Mohnton: Broadbent 7895
Moon Township: Baker 7851
Mount Joy: Engle 7982
Murrysville: Brooks 7897
Myerstown: Burkholder 7907, Wenger 8352
Narberth: Tabas 8312
Nazareth: Martin 8144
New Hope: Bella 7859, Family 7988
Newtown: **Epstein 7984**, Stump 8308, Venne 8331, Wolf 8363
Newtown Square: Covenant 7940, EFM 7974, Garthwaite 8013, Mullen 8184, Rooney 8243
Norristown: Child 7923, Ellis 7978
North Versailles: Crawford 7945
Oil City: Bridge 7891
Oley: Gulati 8032
Perkasie: Everard 7985, First 7998
Philadelphia: 1830 7834, Aaron 7835, Amaranth 7838, Ames 7840, Armstrong 7843, **Arronson 7844**, Balzereit 7853, Berger 7862, Berwind 7868, Betz 7870, Bienenfeld 7872, Bolte 7882, Borowsky 7886, Bradley 7889, Brinkman 7893, Bronstein 7896, Buck 7903, Buck 7904, Burket-Plack 7906, Cardinal 7914, Clareth 7924, **Connelly 7935**, Cozen 7941, Craig-Dalsimer 7942, Crebilly 7946, Dietz 7959, Dominion 7961, Double 7964, Fierce 7992, Five 7999, Friends 8008, Frohring 8010, Grumbacher 8028, Hager 8035, Hartfield 8041, Hassel 8042, Hawkins 8044, Hayes 8046, HFO 8053, Hoffman 8062, Holden 8064, Homeless 8065, Honickman 8066, Horn 8067, Invisible 8075, Kahn, 8084, Karamatsoukas 8085, Klein 8096, Knox 8101, Kurtz 8104, Landenberger 8109, Leeway 8118, Lewis 8123, Lewis 8124, Lida 8127, Lubert 8133, Merops 8169, Muirfield 8182, Nathan 8188, Neuber 8192, Panama 8202, Pincus 8214, Plainfield 8217, Postles 8223, Roberts 8240, Saramar 8253, Savett 8255, Schwartz 8265, Secrist 8267, Seebe 8268, Shoemaker 8275, Stein/Bellet 8300, Triple 8322, Union 8326, Vaughan 8329, Victor 8332, Wachs-Weingarten 8337, Warburton 8342, Weiler-Miller 8348, Wells 8350, Winokur 8362, Wolgin 8365, Wright-Cook 8369, Wurts 8370, **Zeldin 8376**
Pittsburgh: Adams 7836, American 7839, Applestone 7841, Ayers 7848, Ayling 7849, Baldwin, 7852, Bannerot-Lappe 7854, Beacon 7856, Beels 7858,

Benz 7861, Bergstrom 7864, Black 7875, Bloch 7878, Blue 7880, Boardman 7881, Bonomo 7883, Breedlove 7890, Briggs 7892, Brooks 7898, Browne 7901, Bryer 7902, Cameron 7911, Campbell 7912, Cannon 7913, Carita 7915, Case 7918, Casteel 7919, Chase 7921, Chenault, 7922, Clark 7926, Clovis 7928, Cost 7937, Cottage 7938, Cove 7939, Crary 7943, Darnall 7949, Davis 7951, Dickson 7957, Dinardo 7960, Donnally 7962, Donnelly 7963, Dozzi 7965, Dull 7967, Eakins 7968, Eckels 7970, Edwards 7972, Edwards 7973, Elkins 7976, Ely 7979, Engel 7981, **Epstein 7983**, Fair 7987, Farnsworth 7989, Fetters 7991, Fine 7993, Fine 7994, Finley 7995, First 7996, Flinn 8001, Foster 8003, Fountainhead 8004, Frederick 8006, French 8007, Friendship 8009, Gauss 8014, Gilmore 8017, Giop 8018, Goshen 8025, Harrison 8039, Hauber 8043, Hawksglen 8045, Herndon 8051, Heyl 8052, Hill 8055, Hill 8056, Hirtzel 8058, **Hitchcock 8059**, Hodge 8061, Hoffman 8063, Hulme 8069, Hunt 8070, Jackson 8077, Jackson 8078, Jewish 8080, Kelley 8091, Kinney 8092, Kittenbrink 8093, **KL 8094**, Klahr 8095, Knudsen 8102, Krouse 8103, Lamb 8107, Lancy 8108, Landers 8110, Langner 8111, Laughlin 8114, Leakin 8116, Leary 8117, Levee 8121, Levis 8122, Lewis 8125, Lewis 8126, Lockhard 8130, Lockhart 8131, Lord 8132, M&P 8135, Mack 8136, Marstine 8141, Mason 8147, Mason 8148, Mason-Alleg 8149, Mateer 8150, Mattingly 8151, Mayer 8152, McCandless 8153, McConnell 8154, McCune 8155, McGinley 8156, McHale 8157, McKamish 8158, Mckee 8159, McKinney 8161, McMannis 8163, McSwigan 8165, Meakem 8166, Mellon 8167, Mendel 8168, Miller 8173, Mills 8174, Moffat 8175, Mudge 8181, Neal 8190, Nesh 8191, Noll 8194, Norbell 8195, O'Brien-Veba 8197, O'Reilly 8200, Pangborn 8203, Patterson 8205, Perlow 8211, Pittsburgh 8216, Plaisance 8218, Platt, 8220, Potter 8224, Price 8226, Price 8227, Rath 8231, Reiss 8234, Remmel 8235, Richards 8236, Ritter 8239, Robinson 8241, Roemer 8242, **Rust 8250**, Sample, 8252, Schafer 8256, Schoonmaker 8260, Schultz 8262, Sharp 8272, Shore 8276, Smith 8281, Smith 8284, Smith, 8285, Sneath 8286, Society 8289, Somerville 8291, Spencer 8293, Speyer 8294, Staehle 8295, Stewart, 8302, Stutzman 8309, Sweigart 8311, Thomas 8316, Thompson 8317, Tippins 8318, Trax 8321, Troemner 8323, Velma 8330, Vincent 8334, Wagner 8338, Wakefield 8339, Waldo 8340, Walton 8341, Weiner 8349, White 8355, Williams 8357, Williams 8358, Williams 8359, Wimmer 8361, Wood 8367, Wyman 8372, York 8374
Plymouth Meeting: Charleston 7920, Health 8049, **Horner 8068**
Pocopson: Stott 8304
Pottstown: Gitt 8019
Pottsville: Schuylkill 8263
Presto: Young 8375
Quakertown: 100 7833
Radnor: Dicerbo 7956, Female 7990, Groff 8027, Jansing-Cook 8079, Lamb 8106, Mosi 8179
Red Lion: Snyder 8288
Rose Valley: Weil 8346
Rosemont: Larking 8112, Quinn 8229
Saegertown: Guild 8031
Saint Marys: Elk 7975
Scranton: Oppenheim 8199, Schautz 8257, Willary 8356
Sewickley: **Mango 8138**
Shavertown: Maslow 8146
Shippensburg: Lienemann 8128
Southampton: Katz 8088
Spring House: David 7950
Springtown: Brooks 7899
State College: Shaner 8271
Swarthmore: Strine 8306
Swoyersville: Fortinsky 8002

Trevose: Pfundt 8213
Uniontown: Eberly 7969
Unionville: Il 8074
Venetia: Pittsburgh 8215
Villanova: Auldridge 7846, Mclelland 8162, Morgan 8178, Pogo 8221, Rosenberg 8244, Schlarbaum 8259
Warren: Betts 7869
Wayne: Eden 7971, HBE 8047, IGN 8073, KMJ 8099, Tompkins-Broll 8320, Zisman 8377
Waynesburg: Community 7933
Wellsboro: Every 7986, Packer 8201, Ward 8343
West Conshohocken: Beach 7855, Berry 7867, Calvert 7910, Ice 8072, Ithan 8076, Maple 8139, Valentine 8328
West Grove: Health 8048
Westfield: Wolstenholme 8366
Wexford: Randall 8230
Wilkes-Barre: Blackhorse 7877, Blue 7879, Wasserott 8344
Williamsport: Plankenhorn 8219, Smith 8282
Wilmerding: Wabtec 8335
Windber: Whalley 8353
Winfield: John 8081
Wynnewood: Sidewater 8278
Wyomissing: Freas 8005, Neag 8189, Penn 8208, Trout 8324
Yardley: Huplits 8071
York: Bon-Ton 7884, DENTSPLY 7954, Stewart 8301
Zionsville: Fleming 8000

see also 335, 475, 485, 547, 646, 659, 784, 1009, 1053, 1149, 1158, 1194, 1198, 1273, 1291, 1312, 1325, 1365, 1386, 1420, 1422, 1430, 1441, 1468, 1579, 1612, 1639, 1666, 1674, 1678, 1680, 1686, 1691, 1713, 1732, 1745, 1747, 1781, 1783, 1792, 1801, 1841, 1859, 1874, 1883, 1985, 2017, 2025, 2040, 2044, 2091, 2138, 2141, 2155, 2183, 2309, 2389, 2398, 2411, 2453, 2527, 2799, 2805, 2881, 2916, 3056, 3068, 3111, 3447, 3613, 3681, 3814, 3875, 3927, 3963, 3979, 3983, 3988, 4069, 4071, 4082, 4118, 4130, 4205, 4212, 4243, 4324, 4458, 4480, 4589, 4721, 4879, 5152, 5155, 5166, 5244, 5247, 5248, 5251, 5253, 5259, 5279, 5299, 5316, 5340, 5388, 5392, 5400, 5409, 5422, 5427, 5435, 5438, 5442, 5453, 5464, 5473, 5477, 5478, 5535, 5540, 5555, 5563, 5571, 5664, 5709, 5726, 5730, 5763, 5769, 5809, 5825, 5828, 5856, 5980, 5989, 6054, 6061, 6092, 6119, 6152, 6155, 6220, 6244, 6264, 6296, 6307, 6331, 6409, 6432, 6458, 6460, 6465, 6515, 6572, 6581, 6586, 6616, 6620, 6629, 6638, 6642, 6666, 6673, 6675, 6682, 6692, 6701, 6787, 6790, 6803, 6805, 6817, 6837, 6866, 6869, 6880, 6950, 6953, 6964, 6990, 7005, 7014, 7061, 7063, 7099, 7107, 7109, 7116, 7117, 7122, 7130, 7148, 7155, 7194, 7200, 7203, 7208, 7210, 7219, 7230, 7233, 7234, 7236, 7251, 7385, 7520, 7547, 7617, 7618, 7630, 7642, 7716, 7742, 7753, 8601, 8843, 8918, 9059, 9063, 9278, 9369, 9415, 9484, 9509, 9591, 9607, 9664, 9876, 9904

RHODE ISLAND

Barrington: Lorber 8445
Cranston: Feibelman 8405, Papitto 8467, White 8503
East Greenwich: Seed 8484
East Providence: Masonic 8449
Lincoln: Janci 8428
North Kingstown: O'Halloran 8462, Pisa 8474
Pawtucket: Luke 8447, Sullivan 8494
Providence: Acriel 8378, Ames 8379, Apperson 8380, Arakelian 8381, Arents, 8382, Arr 8383, Bailey 8384, Barton 8385, Beck 8386, Bernhardt 8387, Bersted 8388, Bird 8389, **Black 8390**, Bowen 8391, Chace 8393, Charlton, 8394, Clark 8395,

Coes 8396, Collis 8397, Cook 8398, Crossman 8399, Darling 8400, Del 8401, DeLoura 8402, Dwinell 8403, Estate 8404, Felicia 8406, Field 8407, Frasch 8408, Geneen 8411, Greene 8413, Gross 8414, Halsted 8415, Hartman 8416, Hartman 8417, Hecht 8418, Heydt 8419, Hirsch 8420, Hoag 8421, Hope 8422, Horton 8423, Hubbard 8425, Jacbel 8426, Jackson 8427, **Jeffery 8429**, Johnson 8430, Kelley 8431, Kelly 8432, Kenney 8433, Kingsbury 8435, Koffler 8436, Kupher 8437, Leroe 8439, Liberty 8440, Littlefield 8441, LLH/LHM 8442, Long 8443, Longfield 8444, Love 8446, Mann 8448, Mauze 8450, McCabe 8451, McCarthy 8452, McWethy 8453, Miller 8454, Molder 8455, Moore 8456, Mulligan 8457, Mulvaney 8458, N. 8459, Nixon 8460, Noyes 8461, Olsen 8463, Paine 8465, Palermo 8466, Pardee 8468, Peacock 8469, Perkins 8470, Perpetual 8471, Phillips 8472, Pillsbury 8473, Preston 8475, Prouty 8476, Rainbow 8477, Robertson 8478, Sachem 8479, Salerno 8480, Salmanson 8481, **Schoellkopf 8482**, Schwarz 8483, Seymour 8485, Shea 8486, Simionescu 8487, Sinclair 8488, Slemons 8490, Slingerland 8491, Smith 8492, Smith 8493, Swarts 8495, Thompson 8496, Thompson 8497, Unfi 8498, Vanderpoel 8499, Wells 8501, West 8502, Wilson 8504, Woodward 8505, Wright 8506, York 8507, Zack 8508

Riverside: Brack 8392, Getz 8412, Hosser 8424, La 8438
Wakefield: Pacifica 8464
Warwick: Siperstein 8489
West Warwick: Galkin 8410
Westerly: Fuller 8409, Kimball 8434, Washington 8500

see also 155, 739, 867, 998, 1423, 1438, 1616, 1668, 1929, 2078, 2133, 2178, 2298, 2304, 2781, 2978, 3872, 4049, 4109, 4123, 4124, 4190, 4201, 4220, 4257, 4260, 4262, 4310, 4336, 4360, 5302, 5585, 5856, 5868, 6008, 6108, 6250, 6500, 6752, 6780, 6787, 7104, 7226, 8176, 8516, 8530, 9116, 9372, 9466, 9646, 9970

SOUTH CAROLINA

Aiken: Cato 8516
Anderson: Stringer 8543
Barnwell: Sunshine 8544
Belton: WebbCraft 8548
Charleston: **Lader 8531**, Rivers, 8538, Stony 8542, T-Bonz 8546, Verhagen 8547, **Winthrop 8550**
Chester: Lutz 8533
Clinton: Bailey 8509, Bailey 8510, WPW 8551
Columbia: Boyd 8514, Chapman 8517, Jackson 8529, Kendall 8530
Easley: Childress 8518, Nalley 8535
Elgin: **Zvejnieks 8553**
Florence: Eastern 8522
Greenville: Bannon 8511, Campbell 8515, Collins 8520, Mitchell 8534
Greenwood: Davis 8521, Greenwood 8526
Hartsville: Coker 8519
Hilton Head Island: Gleason 8524
Irmo: Bignon 8512
Kershaw: Stevens 8541
Kiawah Island: Tarr 8545, Wyatt 8552
Lexington: Bonner 8513
McColl: Love 8532
Mount Pleasant: Near 8536
Orangeburg: Horne 8528
Simpsonville: Hendricks 8527
Spartanburg: Gibson 8523, Greenleaf 8525, Peery/Cauthen 8537, Security's 8539
Sullivans Island: Singing 8540
Sumter: Williams/Brice-Edwards 8549

---

see also 188, 289, 330, 944, 1142, 1713, 1737, 1778, 1808, 1956, 2028, 2208, 2273, 2342, 2400, 2435, 2510, 2536, 3002, 3106, 3143, 3299, 4257, 5426, 5776, 5798, 6560, 7040, 7062, 7063, 7071, 7072, 7105, 7106, 7138, 7169, 7177, 7193, 7569, 7876, 7964, 8444, 8590, 8639, 8913, 9190, 9235

SOUTH DAKOTA

Aberdeen: Hatterscheidt 8566, Schwab 8574, Welk 8577
Belle Fourche: Clarkson 8558
Chamberlain: Barger 8555
Dakota Dunes: Peterson 8572
Gettysburg: Maas 8569
Pierre: Eleanor's 8559, Ferguson 8564
Plankinton: Grundhofer 8565
Rapid City: Black 8556, Stearns 8575
Sioux Falls: Amundson 8554, Cindy 8557, Elmen 8560, Elmen 8561, Emerald 8562, Engelsma 8563, Houston 8567, J&L 8568, Miller 8570, Peters 8571, Reese 8573, Wolfe 8578
Watertown: Watertown 8576

---

see also 272, 560, 1450, 2055, 3198, 3407, 3541, 4044, 4561, 4679, 4745, 4763, 4782, 4799, 4804, 7772, 9393, 9826, 9968

TENNESSEE

Bartlett: Seidman 8672
Brentwood: Benjamin 8586, Firstfruits 8614, Jordan 8636, Mapp 8646, Mercy 8650, Mick 8651, Tompkins 8683
Bristol: Massengill-DeFriece 8647
Chattanooga: Boring 8590, Chrysalis 8598, Grandview 8625, Hutcheson 8631, Kennedy 8638, Pattee 8656
Cleveland: Agape 8580, BGL 8588, Card 8596
Clinton: Hollingsworth 8629
Collierville: Drake 8606
Cookeville: Seme 8673
Cordova: Ebert-Leblanc 8609, Knight 8640
Elizabethton: Citizens 8599
Franklin: Community 8601, HMA 8628, Nehemiah 8653, Pedigree 8657
Germantown: Tipton 8682
Jackson: Campbell 8594, Campbell 8595, McWherter 8649
Johnson City: Powell 8661
Kingsport: Basler 8584, Rogers 8666
Knoxville: Cole 8600, Cornerstone 8602, Heagele-Blount 8627, Monday 8652, Paddison 8655, Pettway 8658, Provision 8663, **Redbird 8664**, Storey 8679, Weiss 8684
Lebanon: Cracker 8603
Memphis: Aim 8581, **Belz 8585**, Bornblum 8591, Caldwell 8593, Deupree 8604, Durham 8608, **Fraser 8617**, Goldsmith 8622, Goodlett 8623, Kappa 8637, Kite 8639, **Lowenstein 8645**, McGehee 8648, Rose 8667, Sasco 8669, Schadt 8670, Stuttering 8680
Monteagle: Cartinhour-Woods 8597
Murfreesboro: Adams 8579, Jones 8635, LaRoche 8641, Rucker-Donnell 8668, Siegel 8674
Nashville: Atticus 8582, B 8583, Blum 8589, Bradford 8592, Draughon 8607, EBS 8610, Eskind 8611, Eskind 8612, Eskind 8613, Fleming 8615, Foster 8616, **Fugitive 8618**, **Gardner 8619**, Gaylord 8620, Goad 8621, Gordon 8624, Hawthorn 8626, Houghland 8630, Ingram 8632, Johnson 8634, LDB 8642, LifeWorks 8643, **Louisiana-Pacific 8644**, New 8654, Pickle 8660, Proctor 8662, Restoration 8665, Schmidt 8671, Small 8675, Sohr 8676, Splawn 8677, Stadler 8678, Sunlight 8681, Williamson, 8685, Wilt 8687, WTC 8688
Oak Hill: Pfeffer 8659

Paris: Wilson 8686
Signal Mountain: Jewell 8633
White Bluff: Doochin 8605
Winchester: Berman 8587

---

see also 15, 16, 58, 78, 194, 203, 449, 804, 1032, 1714, 1730, 1784, 2043, 2080, 2081, 2090, 2132, 2256, 2327, 2400, 2498, 2515, 2547, 2549, 2551, 2555, 2579, 2612, 2739, 3112, 3364, 3473, 3649, 3870, 3987, 4470, 4493, 4694, 4717, 4854, 5016, 5248, 5365, 5418, 5453, 5505, 6091, 6572, 7063, 7155, 7186, 7236, 7524, 7665, 7842, 7919, 7970, 8083, 8200, 8320, 8477, 8492, 8539, 8542, 8570, 8849, 8946, 9230, 9246, 9273, 9343, 9387, 9479, 9489, 9518, 9552, 9997

TEXAS

Abilene: Martin 9040
Addison: Folsom 8863, Trojan 9242
Albany: Jacobs 8964
Aledo: Reilly 9148, Wheeler 9274
Alice: Sparks 9211
Amarillo: Amarillo 8697, Anderson 8704, Cogdell 8777, Coleman 8778, Fowlston 8871, Herring 8930, Kimble 8991, Kritser 9005, Mays 9045, Roberts 9155, Roberts 9156
Arlington: Doskocil 8823, Hallberg 8911
Austin: A 8689, **AMD 8698**, American 8700, Amherst 8702, Aragona 8706, Bodhi 8732, Booth 8735, Brownsville 8752, Cielo 8771, Conley 8784, Connor 8785, Damuth 8796, Dehan 8809, DKG 8817, Dobson 8820, Educational 8836, Fickett 8854, Fifth 8856, Fired 8859, Freescale 8874, Friedel 8875, Griffith 8903, Hardner 8918, Hartman 8920, Hicks 8935, Howard 8954, II 8958, Jastrow 8967, Kabacoff 8977, KCL 8981, Keown 8986, Kuhn 9006, LBJ 9011, Levy 9014, Ligon-Lamsam 9018, Link 9020, Long 9023, Majella 9033, Marcus 9037, Mattsson 9042, McDonald 9051, Mitte 9069, O'Hare 9095, Orr 9104, Posey 9135, San 9170, Sanguinetti 9172, Schwab-Rosenhouse 9184, Sutton 9226, Swett 9227, Texas 9232, Weir 9269, Whitley 9276, Womack 9289, Works 9293, Youth 9298
Bacliff: Helmle-Shaw 8929
Beaumont: Dauphin 8798, Foundation 8869, Penland 9124, Simpson-Omohundro 9196
Bedford: Hamm 8914, Smith 9201
Beeville: Dougherty, 8825
Bellaire: Meyer 9061, Nowotny 9091, Schepps 9177, Sterling 9219
Boerne: Ik 8959, **Kingdom 8995**, Mercy 9057
Brownsville: Serafy 9188
Brownwood: Central 8766
Bryan: Astin 8710, Doak 8818, Dougherty 8824, Ross 9165, Welch 9270
Buda: Weir 9268
Burnet: Hill 8937
Burton: Johnston 8972
Carrollton: ADR 8693
Carthage: Matthews 9041
Cleburne: Sear 9186
Clifton: Wells 9272
College Station: Adam 8691
Colleyville: Holloway 8946
Coppell: Broady 8745, LSG 9027
Corpus Christi: Behmann 8725, Durrill 8835, **Gilman, 8889**, Nuncio 9092, Simard 9195
Corsicana: Clifford 8774, Fleming 8860, George 8888, Hofstetter 8943, Navarro 9084
Dallas: Abernathy 8690, American 8701, Augur 8712, Baer 8714, Baldridge 8715, Barnabas 8717, Beaird 8720, Bee 8723, Bernardin 8728, Boeing 8733, Booth 8734, Braun 8740, Brisley 8744, Bromley 8749, Budd 8753, Burgett 8757, Cambridge 8760, Cariker 8762, Clinedinst 8775,

Collins 8781, Corlin 8788, Corrigan-Goddard 8789, Cox 8790, Dale 8794, Dallas 8795, Davis 8799, Deason 8805, Dedman 8807, Dedman, 8808, Denman 8810, Dove 8826, Dozzo 8827, Dulaney 8830, Esping 8841, Ethel 8842, Faith 8846, Finney 8858, Ford 8864, Foster 8867, Graue 8898, Haggar 8907, Haggar, 8908, Hallam 8910, Halperin 8912, Hanley 8916, Harwi 8921, Hegi 8926, Hicks 8936, Hill 8938, Hoak 8941, Ilgenfritz 8960, Jones 8973, Julian 8976, Kahn 8978, **Kilgore 8989**, Killson 8990, King 8992, Kirwan 8996, Knox 8999, Kowitz 9002, Lantana 9009, Lesley 9013, Lewis 9015, Littauer 9021, Lloyd 9022, Lose 9024, Lupton 9028, Luse 9029, Merrick 9059, Mewhinney 9060, Moss 9076, Mummert 9079, Muse 9080, Myers 9081, **OneSight 9098**, Opie 9099, Osberg 9105, Pack 9109, Pak 9110, Parks 9115, Partnership 9116, Patton 9119, Pearlman 9122, Peine 9123, Pipe 9130, Planetary 9132, Poncin 9134, Pratt 9137, Pulitzer 9140, Quest 9142, Ray 9144, Redman 9147, Reitch 9149, Richter 9153, Roberts 9157, Rogers 9159, Rosenberg 9162, **Ryrie 9169**, Santander 9173, Schulze 9182, SCP 9185, Seay 9187, Sharma 9190, Skokos 9204, Smith 9204, Smith 9206, Staubach 9215, Steen 9216, Tabani 9228, Thompson 9234, Thorne 9235, Tietze 9236, Tolleson 9238, Vaughan 9248, Vetter 9251, Wal-Dot 9256, Ward 9260, Weaver 9265, Weir 9267, Westcott 9273, Wilder 9277, Williams 9280, Zale 9299, Zale 9300

DFW Airport: American 8699, AMR/American 8703

Dime Box: Pierson 9129

Dripping Springs: Burch 8756

Edna: Miller 9064

El Paso: Bowling 8737, Hervey 8932, McKee 9052, Miller 9066, Sanders 9171, Shiloff 9193, Stewart, 9221

Farmers Branch: VMP 9252

Fort Worth: Alexander 8696, Barnett 8718, Bratten 8739, Bridge 8742, Cargill 8761, Deakins 8804, Discovery 8816, Dubose 8828, Dunaway 8832, EOS 8840, Fash 8848, FHC 8853, Fort 8865, Garvey 8884, Genovese 8887, Give 8890, Kessler 8987, King 8993, Ledbetter 9012, Lowdon 9025, Moore 9072, O'Neal 9097, **Orant 9102**, Paulos 9120, Proctor 9139, Richardson 9151, Rosenthal 9163, Schumacher 9183

Frisco: Brentwood 8741

Ft. Worth: Navarro 9085

Galveston: Bromberg 8748, Chambers 8767, Mantzel 9036, Pearce 9121

Georgetown: Chisholm 8769, Kelley 8984

Glen Rose: Storehouse 9223

Graham: Bertha 8729, Graham 8896

Granbury: Edwards 8837, Inge 8961

Grapevine: Janszen 8966, Pisani 9131

Greenwood: Manna 9034

Harlingen: Farris 8847, Heavin 8925

Helotes: Go 8891

Horseshoe Bay: White 9275

Houston: Adler 8692, Agee 8694, Alexander 8695, Ash 8709, **Astri 8711**, Bearden 8721, Beauchamp 8722, Beghini 8724, Benton 8726, **Bhutada 8730**, Bowers 8736, Brass 8738, Brochstein 8746, Brodsky 8747, Calpine 8759, **Caritas 8763**, Cemo 8765, Chaudhary 8768, Community 8782, **Coneway 8783**, D3 8793, **Dewhurst 8811**, di 8812, Dice 8814, Donnell 8821, Duddlesten 8829, Duncan 8833, Dunham 8834, Elkins 8838, Fabenco 8843, Fennell 8849, Fertitta 8852, Finger 8857, Flowers 8862, Foster 8866, Foster 8868, Frankel 8872, Freed 8873, Friedman 8876, Frill 8877, Fruehauf 8879, FSR 8880, Fuchs 8881, Garver 8883, Gatewood 8885, Gordon 8892, Gordon 8893, Grant 8897, Gray 8899, Greentree 8901, Grits 8904, Hall 8909, Hamilton 8913, Harrell 8919, Hawkins 8923, Healthcare 8924, Heinlein 8927, Helm 8928, Hershey 8931, Hofheinz 8942, Hohlt 8944, Holmes 8947, Houck 8953, Howell 8956, Jackson 8963, Jamail 8965,

Jessen 8968, Joseph 8974, Journey 8975, Kaplan 8979, Kayser 8980, Ketelsen 8988, Korell 9001, Lilly 9019, LSF 9026, Lykes-Knapp 9030, MacDonald 9031, MacDonald-Peterson 9032, Margolin 9038, Marks 9039, Mayfield 9044, McAllister 9046, Mendenhall 9056, Merfish-Jacobson 9058, Meyerson 9062, Mischer 9067, Mithoff 9068, Mosbacher 9075, Mossy, 9077, Nabors 9083, North 9089, Nowiczewski 9090, Oden 9094, One 9096, Oppenheimer 9100, Oriska 9103, **Owusu 9107**, P 9108, Palmer 9112, Papadopoulos 9113, Postl 9136, Quanex 9141, Reuhl 9150, Robinson 9158, Rosen 9161, Rubenstein 9167, Saramco 9174, Saunders 9176, Schepps 9178, Schissler 9179, Schulte 9181, Sherman 9192, SK 9198, Sklar 9199, Smith 9202, Smith 9205, Smith 9207, Stevenson 9220, Stoller 9222, Strickland 9224, Taub 9229, Tennessee 9230, Texas 9233, Toomim 9239, Tucker 9243, Veres 9250, Waggoners 9255, Walls 9257, Waltrip-McGee 9259, Warren 9261, Webre 9266, Wells 9271, Williams 9279, Winston 9282, Wolf 9285, Wolff-Toomim 9286, Woltman 9288, Wynne 9296

Hunt: McLaughlin 9053

Huntsville: Budwine 8754, Grace 8895

Hurst: Bloxom, 8731

Irving: B.E.L.I.E.F. 8713, **Chrest 8770**, College 8779, MHR 9063

Jersey Village: SHT 9194

Judson: Hollandsworth 8945

Katy: Ballard 8716

Kilgore: Griffin 8902

Kingsville: King 8994, **Partridge 9117**

Kingwood: MST 9078

Laredo: De 8803, Laredo 9010

League City: Krist 9004

Leander: Howard 8955

Lindale: Raygar 9145, Van 9247

Livingston: Kellam 8982

Longview: Johnson 8970, Wright 9294

Lubbock: Johnson, 8971, Miller 9065, Nislar 9088, Rawls 9143, South 9209

Lufkin: Fairchild 8845

Marble Falls: **Soonae 9208**

McAllen: Collins 8780, Seven 9189

McKinney: DeBusk 8806, Pogue 9133, Torchmark 9240, Von 9253

Mesquite: Hope 8949

Midland: Cogdell 8776, de 8802, Fuller 8882, Hord 8950, L 9007, Morrow 9074, Pevehouse 9127

Mobeetie: Guetz 8905

Monahans: Dunagan 8831

Montgomery: Bergstrom 8727, Horween 8952, Shepherds 9191

Nacogdoches: Bright 8743

New Waverly: Gottlieb 8894

Odessa: Hext 8933, Saulsbury 9175

Onalaska: Williams 9281

Overton: McMillan, 9054

Palestine: Hanley 8915, Texas 9231

Pampa: Brown 8751, Gray-Pampa 8900

Paris: Paris 9114

Pasadena: **Crowder 8792**, Sure 9225, USD 9245

Pearland: Wise 9283

Plainview: Mayer 9043

Plano: Horizon 8951, Prayer 9138, Sparrow 9212, Tyler 9244, Wolens 9284, Woolf 9292, Young 9297

Porter: **New 9087**

Richardson: Fenner 8850

Richmond: N.H. 9082

Rockport: Barrow 8719, Rust 9168

Rockwall: Hatfield 8922

San Angelo: Bunyard 8755, Diamond 8813

San Antonio: Anderson 8705, Armstrong 8708, Burzik 8758, Clear 8772, Daniel 8797, DDM 8801, Dooley 8822, Field-Day 8855, Flohr 8861,

Foundation 8870, Frost 8878, Hixon 8940, Kelso 8985, Klesse 8998, Kolitz 9000, Lange 9008, Light 9016, McNutt 9055, Morrison 9073, Nelson 9086, Oppenheimer 9101, PAL 9111, Petty 9126, Phoenix 9128, Richmond 9152, Rowan 9166, Schoener 9180, **Smith 9203**, Starnes 9214, Sterling 9218, Tobin 9237, Valero 9246, Vaughan 9249, Walthall 9258, Watson 9263, Willard 9278, Wolters 9287, Woods 9291

Schulenburg: Stanzel 9213

Sonora: Cauthorn 8764

Spring: Klein 8997

Sugar Land: Day 8800, Ross 9164

Temple: Brown 8750, Cook 8786

Texarkana: McCoy 9048, Patterson 9118

Texas City: Hunter 8957, McDaniel 9050

The Woodlands: Arena 8707, Cook 8787, Haraldson 8917, Hillcrest 8939, Lighthouse 9017, Montgomery 9070, RDM 9146, Watford 9262

Tyler: Clements 8773, Fair 8844, Genecov 8886, Hibbs 8934, Montgomery, 9071, Perkins 9125, Riter, 9154, Roosth 9160

University Park: Enrico 8839

Vernon: McCarty 9047, Waggoner 9254

Victoria: Crossroads 8791, Dick 8815, O'Connor 9093, Overlake 9106, South 9210, Wood 9290

Waco: Fentress 8851, Torrance 9241

Waring: **McCreless 9049**

Waxahachie: Singleton 9197

Weatherford: Kramer 9003

Weslaco: Hope 8948

Westhoff: Way 9264

Westlake: Isaac 8962

Wharton: Dobson 8819

Wichita Falls: Guinn 8906, Johnson 8969, Kelley 8983, **Mansur 9035**, Stephens 9217, Wright 9295

see also 97, 103, 117, 149, 182, 203, 212, 303, 475, 554, 608, 625, 633, 683, 684, 745, 784, 810, 880, 881, 899, 904, 906, 929, 1109, 1113, 1247, 1259, 1264, 1277, 1342, 1365, 1371, 1389, 1507, 1607, 1614, 1699, 1712, 1716, 1752, 1820, 1925, 1986, 1987, 2028, 2046, 2061, 2086, 2121, 2132, 2184, 2266, 2279, 2384, 2478, 2525, 2686, 2797, 2883, 2985, 3002, 3016, 3064, 3069, 3088, 3114, 3124, 3130, 3161, 3176, 3191, 3236, 3239, 3251, 3273, 3347, 3447, 3506, 3562, 3587, 3640, 3645, 3714, 3722, 3730, 3739, 3741, 3755, 4111, 4528, 4572, 4583, 4610, 4655, 4717, 4783, 4804, 4873, 4943, 4956, 4987, 5048, 5116, 5201, 5244, 5365, 5428, 5475, 5505, 5527, 5571, 5574, 5589, 5607, 5620, 5664, 5744, 5811, 5816, 5843, 6057, 6099, 6109, 6245, 6266, 6287, 6573, 6679, 6781, 7091, 7158, 7277, 7299, 7362, 7445, 7471, 7493, 7634, 7650, 7667, 7684, 7686, 7692, 7693, 7698, 7755, 7842, 7847, 7857, 7956, 8053, 8181, 8187, 8208, 8232, 8477, 8539, 8586, 8606, 8644, 9347, 9363, 9466, 9520, 9677, 9705, 9835, 9876, 9902, 9968, 9999

UTAH

Alpine: Gardner 9326

Cedar City: Leavitt 9338

Centerville: CASA 9312

Highland: Jackson 9329

Holladay: Burton 9309, Crawford 9314, JKS 9330

Ivins: Davis 9317

Lindon: Low 9340

Logan: Spendlove 9357

Midvale: B. 9302, Dry 9321

Moab: **Brown 9307**, Slaughter, 9353

Oakley: Cumming 9315

Ogden: Denkers 9318, Dialysis 9319, Langdon 9336, Wadman 9362

Orem: Bastian 9304, Larsen 9337, Lindorf 9339

Park City: Andrus 9301, Backcountry 9303, Cumming 9316, Dreamweaver 9320, Green 9327, Promontory 9345

Salt Lake City: Burbidge 9308, Callister 9310, Cardon 9311, Catalyst 9313, Eccles 9322, Eskuche 9323, Foothold 9324, Harman 9328, JNF 9331, Keener 9332, Kirk 9334, Odyssey 9342, Parrish 9343, Patel 9344, Questar 9346, Questar 9347, Schmidt 9349, Shrontz 9351, **Skolnick 9352**, SmartGo 9354, Sorenson 9355, Sorenson 9356, Steiner 9358, Telemachus: 9359, Utah 9361, Zions 9363

Sandy: Benjamin 9305, Bourne-Spafford 9306, Funding 9325, Korver 9335, Scharman 9348, Shaw 9350, Turley 9360

South Jordan: Kennecott 9333

Springville: Mower 9341

---

see also 144, 157, 272, 364, 563, 784, 787, 1199, 1319, 1544, 1613, 2400, 2618, 2690, 3183, 3909, 4579, 5187, 5202, 5203, 5400, 5507, 5625, 5664, 6433, 6639, 6650, 6842, 7044, 7745, 7799, 8053, 8068, 8408, 8992, 9047, 9904

VERMONT

Brattleboro: **Daly 9371**, Holland 9375

Burlington: Cohen 9369, Ferro 9372, Seventh 9384, Stokes 9385

Charlotte: Blittersdorf 9365

Cornwall: Harvest 9374

Hinesburg: Redducs 9383

Marshfield: Block 9366

Milton: Mergens 9381

Montpelier: Castanea 9368

Morrisville: Copley 9370

Newport: Kaufman 9378

Northfield: NSB 9382

Proctor: Carris 9367, Huntington 9376

Sharon: **Maverick 9380**

Shelburne: Altman 9364

West Brattleboro: Kahn 9377

Weston: Harper 9373

Williston: Leboeuf 9379

---

see also 694, 739, 1032, 1439, 1536, 1545, 1608, 1656, 1747, 2040, 2384, 2763, 2867, 2984, 2996, 3138, 3312, 3769, 4033, 4096, 4148, 4220, 4257, 4260, 4271, 4330, 4336, 4360, 4615, 5217, 5223, 5280, 5328, 5983, 5984, 6220, 6393, 6472, 8007, 8187, 8403, 8415, 8498, 8542, 9393, 9978

VIRGINIA

Alexandria: Bruhn-Morris 9408, Ivakota 9477, Shepherdson 9531, Stephenson 9536

Altavista: English 9443, Lane 9486

Annandale: Harris 9468

Arlington: Billings 9397, Collins 9424, Donohue 9432, **Fund 9455**, Geary-O'Hara 9456

Ashburn: Sirad 9533

Bassett: Bassett 9391

Bristol: Jones 9479, Leonard 9489, Williams-Berry 9554

Catlett: Wiser 9555

Centreville: Fink 9447

Charlottesville: Better 9396, Charles 9418, Dreaming 9435, **Eiriksson 9441**, Farkas 9445, Hilltop 9470, Lee-Jackson 9488, Praxis 9515, Rimora 9524, Smith 9534, Stone 9537, Stultz 9539, Williams 9553

Christiansburg: Community 9426

Clifton Forge: Glencairn 9460

Culpeper: Northern 9503

Danville: Buchanan 9410, Hughes 9474, Womack 9556

Doswell: Flippo 9449

Dryden: Macedonian 9496

Dulles: Andreas 9388

Edinburg: **Praktikos 9514**

Emporia: Greensville 9464

Esmont: Fraser 9453

Exmore: Two 9544

Fairfax: Hausfeld 9469, Poole 9512, Weil 9550

Fairfax Station: Beck 9392, Berni 9395, Perlin 9510

Falls Church: BRI 9405, **Delmar 9429**, **Longview 9494**, Page 9507, Thomas 9542

Forest: Vinoskey 9547

Fredericksburg: Fredericksburg 9454

Glen Allen: Franklin 9452, Grandis 9462, Hopkins 9472, Lawrence 9487, Short 9532

Gloucester: Treakle 9543

Great Falls: Karlgaard 9481

Halifax: Chastain 9419

Hampton: Rouse-Bottom 9526

Herndon: Lintott 9492, Walter 9549

Irvington: Verlander 9546, Wiley 9551

Kilmarnock: Cole 9423

Leesburg: O'Shaughnessy-Hurst 9505, Pensmore 9509

Lexington: Beck 9393

Louisa: Cooke 9427

Martinsville: Lacy 9485

McGaheysville: King 9484

McLean: **American 9386**, Blue 9400, Blue 9401, Blueberry 9402, Chainani 9417, Darden 9428, Edlavitch 9440, Ferrari 9446, Gladstone 9458, Immixgroup 9476, Kahn 9480, Keenan 9483, Levmar 9490, Mody 9501, Ochsman 9504, R 9518, Schiro-Zavela 9528, Strauch 9538, Valentine 9545

Middleburg: Dun 9437, **Tara 9540**

Monterey: Banks 9390

Newport News: Good 9461, MAIHS 9497

Norfolk: Clark-Nexsen 9421, Fleder 9448, Glasser 9459, Kaufman 9482, Lincoln-Lane 9491, Pruden 9517, Rashti 9520, VuBay 9548

Oak Hill: Willett 9552

Palmyra: Harris 9466

Petersburg: Petersburg 9511

Pulaski: Richardson 9523

Rectortown: Black 9399

Reston: Dwyer 9439, **Foundation 9450**, Ramsey 9519, Stafford 9535

Richmond: Bell 9394, Brink's 9406, Burford 9411, Bw718 9412, Denit 9430, Dundas 9438, Elmwood 9442, Foundation 9451, Harris 9467, Honey 9471, Markel 9498, Mullen 9502, Peachtree 9508, **Price 9516**, RECO 9522, Roller-Bottimore 9525, Sauer 9527, Tesco 9541

Roanoke: Cartledge 9414, Cobbs 9422, Ludington 9495, Powell 9513

Salem: Meador 9500

Springfield: Collins 9425, Shaffer 9530

Stephens City: Bryant 9409

Suffolk: Greco 9463, Overton 9506

The Plains: Backer 9389, Catesby 9415, Il 9475

Vienna: Birk 9398, Family 9444, **Jain 9478**, Ratner 9521, Selsky 9529

Virginia Beach: Breeden, 9404, Camp 9413, Dickerson 9431, Doudera 9434, Dreyfus 9436, Gifford 9457, Hansen 9465, McWaters 9499, Zeiders 9557

Warrenton: Loeb 9493

Waterford: Cedars 9416

Weyers Cave: Houff 9473

Williamsburg: **Brown 9407**, Clark 9420, **Dorothy-Ann 9433**

Winchester: American 9387, Brandt 9403

---

see also 70, 150, 216, 295, 299, 315, 324, 340, 411, 418, 554, 770, 780, 788, 790, 803, 804, 805, 850, 942, 961, 974, 1009, 1015, 1044, 1051, 1156, 1193, 1276, 1286, 1308, 1339, 1378, 1429, 1443, 1490, 1608, 1634, 1716, 1729, 1732, 1743, 1747, 1769, 1785, 1788, 1790, 1800, 1804, 1812, 1814, 1819, 1824, 1849, 1851, 1927, 1930, 1936, 1961, 1969, 1990, 1994, 2021, 2023, 2030, 2086, 2092, 2117, 2132, 2163, 2203, 2213, 2218, 2251, 2272, 2294, 2306, 2352, 2375, 2400, 2446, 2469, 2531, 2532, 2566, 2610, 2614, 2623, 2671, 2769, 2798, 2926, 3002, 3004, 3061, 3156, 3195, 3287, 3525, 3594, 3650, 3813, 3815, 3833, 3842, 3850, 3860, 3880, 3890, 3910, 3911, 3924, 3930, 3931, 3963, 3983, 4132, 4320, 4386, 4508, 4625, 4725, 4804, 4865, 4878, 5248, 5305, 5333, 5375, 5463, 5469, 5530, 5571, 5787, 5804, 5897, 6010, 6063, 6077, 6119, 6182, 6231, 6306, 6359, 6368, 6384, 6409, 6439, 6472, 6661, 6816, 6866, 6879, 6897, 6969, 6998, 7043, 7062, 7093, 7105, 7151, 7188, 7193, 7197, 7201, 7205, 7210, 7216, 7219, 7233, 7241, 7245, 7261, 7287, 7303, 7414, 7469, 7511, 7812, 7815, 7847, 7852, 7867, 7919, 7953, 7970, 8009, 8041, 8053, 8090, 8108, 8138, 8191, 8225, 8246, 8422, 8444, 8511, 8516, 8571, 8597, 8621, 8647, 8654, 8656, 8742, 8756, 8827, 8840, 8877, 8879, 8936, 8951, 8956, 8974, 9018, 9059, 9264, 9317, 9366, 9373, 9627, 9650, 9734, 9737, 9761, 9765, 9766, 9772, 9816, 9990

WASHINGTON

Anacortes: Martin 9659, Worthington 9729

Auburn: FAR 9595, Martin 9660

Bainbridge: Jacobi 9628

Bainbridge Island: Ames 9560, Fletcher 9597, Johnson 9633, Quest 9681

Bellevue: Bungie 9576, Gibson 9604, Hall 9613, Hanson 9616, Herbold 9620, Hilal 9623, Jones 9638, Kaleidoscope 9641, Kismet 9646, Magdalen 9658, McKinlay 9662, Nordstrom/Seifert 9668, Patel 9675, Pigott 9677, Pointe 9679, Remala 9683, Rosen 9684, Schaar 9689, Smith 9698, Winter 9726

Bellingham: Dudley 9588, Horn 9625, Jaffe 9629

Blaine: **Wiebe 9723**

Bow: Paulus 9676

Bremerton: Coulter 9581

Clyde Hill: Wissner-Slivka 9727

Eastsound: Carper 9577

Ephrata: Lauzier 9651

Everett: Everett 9592, Heidner 9618, Howarth 9626, Kilworth 9644, Nysether 9671

Freeland: Arise 9562

Gig Harbor: Babare 9564, Erickson 9591, Grindstone 9610, Hyde 9627

GreenBank: DG 9586

Issaquah: Brotman 9574, Lott 9656, Not 9670

Kenmore: Dunn 9589

Kirkland: Larson 9650, Razore 9682, Weidner 9719

Lacey: Helstrom 9619

Lake Tapps: **Children's 9579**

Longview: FTJ 9600

Medina: Bacon 9565, **Singh 9695**, Spring 9702, Stevens 9704

Mercer Island: Excel 9593, HIS 9624, Joint 9636, Jones 9637, Wilson 9725

Milton: Thurston 9713

Mount Vernon: Skagit 9696

Olympia: Amelia 9559, Boydston 9572, **Jernigan 9631**, Stars 9703

Port Hadlock: Jefferson 9630

Port Townsend: **Ormsby 9674**

Puyallup: Korum 9648

Quincy: Gius 9606

Redmond: Bishop 9569, Boeschoten 9571, Wellworth 9722

Richland: Three 9712

Seattle: Alhadeff 9558, Amstein 9561, Bayley 9567, Block 9570, Brookshire-Green 9573, Crete 9583,

CSM 9584, Dore 9587, Echo 9590, Fales 9594, Ferguson 9596, Fries-Tait 9599, Fulton 9601, Furnessville 9602, Galanti 9603, Goodfellow 9607, Goodman 9608, Graham 9609, Grousemont 9611, Hanauer 9614, Heath 9617, Herray 9621, **Ji 9632**, Juniper 9640, Kawabe 9642, Lanterman 9649, Lea 9652, Levitan 9653, Loeb 9654, Longbrake 9655, Madrona 9657, Maxwell 9661, Mize 9663, Moraine 9664, Morningside 9665, Muglia 9666, Northwest 9669, O'Donnell 9672, Ohno 9673, Pleas 9678, Prairie 9680, **Rotalia 9685**, Runstad 9686, **Sabol 9687**, Sarkowsky 9688, Schuler 9690, Seager 9692, Shemanski 9693, Slingshot 9697, Snyder 9699, Sondland 9700, Spark 9701, Suen 9705, Svanees 9706, Tamaki 9707, Teel 9708, Thayer 9710, Tonkin 9715, Tudor 9717, Weier 9720, Wilkens 9724, Wright 9730, Wyman 9731, Young 9732

Seaview: Templin 9709
Sequim: Coleman 9580
Shoreline: Zufall 9733
Spokane: Beck, 9568, Cowles 9582, Hagan 9612, Hansen 9615, Johnston-Fix 9634, Johnston-Hanson 9635, Klaue 9647
Tacoma: Babare 9563, Baker 9566, DeFalco 9585, Murray 9667, Thomson 9711, Titus-Will 9714, Woodworth 9728
Tukwila: Gilmore 9605
University Place: Foss 9598
Vancouver: Cartales 9578, Hickey 9622, Josi 9639, Keller 9643, King 9645, Schwab 9691, Ward 9718
Walla Walla: Shepherd 9694, Welch 9721
Wenatchee: Bulleri 9575
Yarrow Point: True 9716

see also 80, 89, 270, 272, 447, 461, 504, 537, 608, 633, 913, 1169, 1312, 1358, 1373, 1403, 1721, 1739, 1761, 1775, 2182, 2561, 2687, 3563, 3912, 4201, 4243, 4428, 4647, 4779, 4889, 4990, 5059, 5268, 5290, 5347, 5634, 6233, 6271, 6835, 6933, 7175, 7372, 7477, 7579, 7746, 7748, 7787, 7788, 7791, 7805, 7815, 7816, 8079, 8567, 8669, 8698, 8733, 8849, 8890, 9060, 9105, 9134, 9140, 9235, 9236, 9318, 9328, 9492, 9509, 9990

WEST VIRGINIA

Alderson: Hewgill 9748
Beckley: Vecellio 9770
Bluefield: Bowen 9737, Shott 9765, Skewes 9766, Wolfe 9772
Charles Town: McCormick 9758, McCormick 9759
Charleston: Bowen 9736, Brown 9739, Carter 9741, Hott 9753, McDavid 9760, Minor 9761, Wehrle 9771
Clarksburg: Burnside 9740, Hollandsworth 9750
Elkins: Appalachian 9734
Fairmont: Raymond 9764
Huntington: Huntington 9754, Price 9763
Kenova: Hamer 9746
Lewisburg: Hollowell 9751
Logan: Logan 9757
Martinsburg: Fine 9745
Parkersburg: Logan 9756, Stout 9769
Shepherdstown: Stine 9768
Thomas: Hope 9752
Vienna: Esbenshade 9744
Weirton: Starvaggi 9767
Wheeling: Blake 9735, Bowers 9738, Chambers 9742, Driehorst 9743, Hess 9747, Hoffmann 9749, Larch 9755, Parlin 9762

see also 1682, 1761, 2263, 2788, 3308, 3661, 3847, 5196, 5244, 5248, 5593, 7069, 7546, 7557, 7617, 7747, 8187, 8208, 8357, 8683, 9387

WISCONSIN

Appleton: Crowley 9799, Hartwig 9836, Hyde 9846, Plein 9904, Thompson 9947
Beaver Dam: Foulkes 9821
Belleville: Mortenson 9890
Beloit: Regal-Beloit 9911, Stateline 9937
Brillion: Ariens 9776, Brillion 9789
Brookfield: Arzbaecher 9777, Peterson 9901, Simms 9929, Stevens 9939, Wilson 9960
Chippewa Falls: Community 9797, Mason 9880
Cumberland: Johnson 9853
De Pere: Cloud 9796, Easter 9813, Ferguson 9819
Eau Claire: Carlisle 9792, Domer 9808, Eau 9814, T 9945
Fond du Lac: Mid-States 9887, Shannon 9927
Fox Point: Karol 9859
Grafton: Rusinow 9920
Green Bay: Associated 9778, BayCare 9781, Johnson 9852, Lutsey 9873, Mednikow 9881, Meyer 9885, Olson 9898, Religious 9912, Van 9951, Van 9952, Weyers 9959
Greenfield: ROS 9918
Hartford: Holoubek 9843
Hartland: Seeds 9925
Hayward: RCP 9909
Hudson: Phipps 9903
Janesville: J.P.C. 9848, Janesville 9850
Kenosha: Kenosha 9862
La Crosse: Glendenning 9828, Gordon 9830, Gordon 9831, Smith 9932, Stevenson 9940, Stry 9941
Lomira: Grande 9832
Madison: Blooming 9784, Caritas 9791, Christensen 9795, Courtier 9798, Cummings-Christensen 9801, **Dewing 9805**, Erdman 9816, Frautschi 9822, Fromm 9823, Hicks 9840, Highlands 9841, Kalscheur 9858, Kelly 9861, Nelson 9893, Ocular 9895, Olson 9897, Purple 9908, Roddis 9916, SMS 9933, Sub-Zero 9943, Van 9953, Webcrafters-Frautschi 9957, Witte, 9962
Manitowoc: Lakeshore 9867, Manitowoc 9876
Marathon: Sonnentag 9934
Marshfield: Marshfield 9878
Mequon: Dohmen 9807, Glanert 9827, Pelz 9900
Merrill: Dutton 9812
Middleton: Anderson 9773, Berbeewalsh 9782, Verhulst 9954
Milwaukee: Antonia 9775, Birnschein 9783, Bock 9786, Chastain 9793, Chipstone 9794, Cudahy 9800, Dohmen 9806, Doolittle 9809, Einhorn 9815, Fahrney 9818, Foley 9820, Fromstein 9824, Gardner 9825, Gebhardt 9826, Hamilton 9834, Heller 9839, Hoffmann 9842, Hunt 9845, Inbusch 9847, Jacobus 9849, **Johnson 9851**, Jones 9854, Jones 9855, Kloss 9863, Kohl 9864, Kohl 9865, Koss 9866, Lloyd 9870, LUX 9874, Marcus 9877, Martin 9879, Meinerz 9883, Meyer 9886, Murray 9892, Nelson 9894, Park 9899, Phipps 9902, Pritchett 9906, Puelicher 9907, Rewald 9913, RITE-HITE 9915, Schlegel 9922, Schmucker 9923, Schoenleber 9924, Shoemaker 9928, Smith 9931, Tellier 9946, Uihlein 9949, Uihlein 9950, Wagner 9955, Weyco 9958
Necedah: Hatch 9837
Neenah: Aylward 9779, Brown 9790, Gunther 9833, **Helios 9838**

Oak Creek: **Global 9829**
Oconomowoc: Braun 9787, Debbink 9804, Roehl 9917
Onalaska: Lyche 9875
Pewaukee: Kaztex 9860, Loehrke 9872
Phillips: AnnMarie 9774
Plover: Okray 9896, Seramur 9926
Plymouth: Sartori 9921
Port Washington: Huiras 9844
Racine: Modine 9889, Mound 9891, Steinle 9938, Styberg 9942
Saint Cloud: Baker 9780
Sheboygan: Merkel 9884, Windway 9961
Sheboygan Falls: F.K. 9817
Sister Bay: Rosemann 9919
Spring Green: Single 9930
Sturgeon Bay: Bluemke 9785, Door 9810, Hansen 9835
Sun Prairie: Mielcarek 9888
Thiensville: Lakeview 9868
Verona: Spider 9935
Waterloo: Junginger 9856, Trek 9948
Watertown: Watertown 9956
Waukesha: Dawes 9803, Lato 9869, Redmond 9910, Sullivan 9944
Waupaca: Rhodes 9914
Wausau: Davis 9802, Dudley 9811
Wauwatosa: St. 9936
West Allis: Meehan 9882
West Bend: Prescott 9905
Whitefish Bay: Brennan 9788
Whitewater: Kachel 9857
Wisconsin Rapids: Locke 9871, Woodtrust-Bell 9963

see also 107, 245, 272, 285, 784, 950, 1346, 1575, 1643, 1792, 1861, 1976, 2227, 2320, 2332, 2422, 2458, 2691, 2712, 2762, 2790, 2800, 2815, 2816, 2831, 2861, 2887, 2929, 2930, 2942, 2950, 2955, 3016, 3055, 3101, 3105, 3123, 3128, 3146, 3171, 3172, 3220, 3237, 3265, 3448, 3544, 3549, 3862, 4243, 4474, 4497, 4636, 4667, 4679, 4695, 4699, 4728, 4732, 4757, 4763, 4782, 4795, 4879, 4886, 4972, 5003, 5207, 5235, 5627, 6356, 6437, 6638, 7165, 7192, 7471, 7520, 7549, 8197, 8644, 9130, 9481, 9992

WYOMING

Big Horn: Nickerson 9981
Casper: Bailey 9964, Ellbogen 9971, Sargent 9985, Scott 9987, Skelton 9989, Tate 9995
Cheyenne: Imig 9974, Joannides 9976, Richardson 9983, Scott 9988, Storer 9992
Jackson: Brendsel 9965, Connemara 9967, Cutting 9968, Dubois 9970, Hirschfield 9973, Johnson 9977, JWJ 9978, Marine 9980, StoneRiver 9991, Stuart 9993, Weiss 9996, Weiss 9997
Lander: **Schultz 9986**
Laramie: Guthrie 9972, Windy 9999
Saratoga: Skilling 9990
Sheridan: Kuehne 9979, Perkins 9982, Riehm 9984, Surrena 9994, Welch 9998, Witzel 10000
Teton Village: Dragicevich 9969
Wilson: C 9966, Jaquith 9975

see also 272, 765, 1319, 2832, 2950, 3127, 3307, 3725, 3883, 4801, 4863, 5047, 5051, 5274, 6865, 6888, 6897, 7659, 7830, 7867, 8556, 9322, 9343, 9347, 9715, 9766

INTERNATIONAL GIVING INDEX

List of terms: Names of countries, continents, or regions used in this index are drawn from the complete list below. Terms may appear on the list but not be present in the index.

Index: In the index itself, foundations are listed under the countries, continents, or regions in which they have demonstrated giving interests or made charitable contributions. Within these country or regional groupings, foundations are arranged by state location, abbreviated name, and sequence number.

Afghanistan	Congo, Democratic Republic of the	Indonesia	New Zealand
Africa	Congo, Republic of the	Iran	Nicaragua
Albania	Costa Rica	Iraq	Niger
Algeria	Cote d'Ivoire	Ireland	Nigeria
Andorra	Croatia	Israel	North America
Angola	Cuba	Italy	North Korea
Antarctica	Cyprus	Jamaica	Northern Africa
Antigua and Barbuda	Czech Republic	Japan	Northern Ireland
Arctic Region	Denmark	Jordan	Norway
Argentina	Developing Countries	Kazakhstan	Oceania
Armenia	Djibouti	Kenya	Oman
Asia	Dominica	Kiribati	Pakistan
Australia	Dominican Republic	Kosovo	Panama
Austria	Eastern Africa	Kuwait	Papua New Guinea
Azerbaijan	Eastern Asia	Kyrgyz Republic	Paraguay
Bahamas	Eastern Europe	Laos	Peru
Balkans, The	Ecuador	Latin America	Philippines
Bahrain	Egypt	Latvia	Poland
Bangladesh	El Salvador	Lebanon	Portugal
Barbados	England	Lesotho	Qatar
Belarus	Equatorial Guinea	Liberia	Romania
Belgium	Eritrea	Libya	Russia
Belize	Estonia	Liechtenstein	Rwanda
Benin	Ethiopia	Lithuania	Saint Kitts and Nevis
Bermuda	Europe	Luxembourg	Saint Lucia
Bhutan	Fiji	Macao	Saint Vincent and the Grenadines
Bolivia	Finland	Macedonia	Samoa
Bosnia and Herzegovina	France	Madagascar	Sao Tome and Principe
Botswana	French Guiana	Malawi	Saudi Arabia
Brazil	Gabon	Malaysia	Scandinavia
British Virgin Islands	Gambia, Republic of The	Maldives	Scotland
Brunei	Georgia	Mali	Senegal
Bulgaria	Germany	Malta	Serbia
Burkina Faso	Ghana	Martinique	Seychelles
Burundi	Gibraltar	Mauritania	Sierra Leone
Cambodia	Global Programs	Mauritius	Singapore
Cameroon	Greece	Mexico	Slovakia
Canada	Greenland	Middle East	Slovenia
Cape Verde	Grenada	Moldova	Solomon Islands
Caribbean	Guatemala	Monaco	Somalia
Cayman Islands	Guinea	Mongolia	South Africa
Central Africa	Guinea-Bissau	Montenegro	South America
Central African Republic	Guyana	Montserrat	South Korea
Central America	Haiti	Morocco	South Sudan
Central Asia	Holy See	Mozambique	Southeastern Asia
Chad	Honduras	Myanmar	Southern Africa
Chile	Hong Kong	Namibia	Southern Asia
China	Hungary	Nauru	Spain
Colombia	Iceland	Nepal	Sri Lanka
Comoros	India	Netherlands	Sub-Saharan Africa

Sudan
Suriname
Swaziland
Sweden
Switzerland
Syria
Taiwan
Tajikistan
Tanzania

Thailand
Timor-Leste
Togo
Tonga
Trinidad and Tobago
Tunisia
Turkey
Turkmenistan
Turks and Caicos Islands

Tuvalu
Uganda
Ukraine
United Arab Emirates
United Kingdom of Great Britain and
    Northern Ireland
Uruguay
Uzbekistan
Vanuatu

Venezuela
Vietnam
Wales
West Bank/Gaza (Palestinian
    Territories)
Western Africa
Yemen
Zambia
Zimbabwe

Afghanistan

Massachusetts: Barakat 4012

Africa

California: Alalusi 236, Battle 282, Flynt
    514, Global 565, Grass 577
Florida: Joshua 2132
Georgia: Bancker-Williams 2440
Iowa: Wright 3551
Louisiana: Ruckstuhl 3748
Maine: Dugas 3776
Minnesota: Porter 4763, Sundance 4796
Nebraska: Lothlorien 5101
New Jersey: Ostberg 5483
New York: Cogitare 5855, Farkas 5988,
    Fitzgibbons 6011,
    McCaddin-McQuirk 6455, Societe
    6820
North Carolina: Rixson 7223, Rolander
    7229
Oklahoma: Crio 7670
Texas: Crowder 8792
Virginia: Dorothy-Ann 9433
Washington: Children's 9579
Wisconsin: Johnson 9851

Armenia

California: Akian 234, Hampar 594
Florida: Pagoumian 2245
Massachusetts: Afeyan 3996
Michigan: Ajemian 4371
New Jersey: Nazarian 5478, Tufenkian
    5562
Texas: Astri 8711

Asia

Arizona: Kearny 137
California: Alalusi 236, Asia 257, Global
    565, PADI 898, Quiksilver 945
District of Columbia: Dingwall 1804
Florida: Atlantis 1858
New Jersey: Garcia 5362
New York: McCaddin-McQuirk 6455
Texas: AMD 8698, Crowder 8792,
    Soonae 9208

Australia

California: PADI 898, Parsemus 904,
    Quiksilver 945
Illinois: Combs 2800, Dyson 2842,
    Ingredion 2988
Nevada: Wood 5201
New Jersey: Daft 5310
Virginia: Dorothy-Ann 9433

Austria

Illinois: Dyson 2842

Bahamas

District of Columbia: Merriman 1820
Florida: Prime 2268
Ohio: Marafiki 7513

Bangladesh

Florida: Freewill 2021

Belgium

Illinois: Dyson 2842
Iowa: World 3550
New York: Sato 6731, Societe 6820,
    World 6994

Belize

California: Kinnoull 706
Massachusetts: New 4220
New York: Crane 5884

Benin

Florida: Freewill 2021

Bolivia

Florida: Place 2261
Massachusetts: New 4220

Botswana

New Hampshire: Rothschild 5229
Texas: Smith 9203

Brazil

California: PADI 898
Florida: Place 2261
Illinois: Ingredion 2988
Nevada: A 5131
Pennsylvania: KL 8094, Mango 8138

Bulgaria

Wisconsin: Global 9829

Cambodia

Illinois: Build 2764
Wyoming: Schultz 9986

Cameroon

Massachusetts: New 4220

Canada

Alaska: Nash 90

Arizona: Beals 100
Arkansas: Baldor 188
California: Chan 388
Connecticut: MacInnis 1515
Illinois: Chapin 2781, Dyson 2842,
    Ingredion 2988, Mermelstein 3103
Maine: St. 3804
Massachusetts: Gross 4108
Michigan: Gorlin 4457
Minnesota: Wagner 4804
Missouri: Build-A-Bear 4879
New Jersey: Crane 5306, Integra 5400,
    Ju 5410, Parnassus 5489
New York: Buffalo 5799, Chinook 5844,
    Companions 5873, Frank 6026,
    McCaddin-McQuirk 6455, Schmeelk
    6742, Shatford 6788, Societe
    6820, Walsh/Alfred 6943
North Carolina: Rixson 7223
Ohio: Dauch 7372, Eaton 7383
Pennsylvania: BGM 7871, Horner 8068
Tennessee: Louisiana-Pacific 8644
Texas: AMD 8698, Caritas 8763
Vermont: Daly 9371
Washington: Sabol 9687, Wiebe 9723

Caribbean

California: Linked 758
Florida: Atlantis 1858, Mukti 2226
Massachusetts: Pegasus 4236
Minnesota: Porter 4763
New York: Family 5983, Societe 6820

Central America

Florida: Uncle 2383
Iowa: Wright 3551
Massachusetts: Blossom 4022, New
    4220
Minnesota: Porter 4763
New Jersey: Blue 5269
North Carolina: Rolander 7229
Ohio: Lowe-Marshall 7505
Wyoming: Schultz 9986

Chile

California: Valenzuela 1143
Florida: Falk 1996, Taylor 2365
Illinois: Ingredion 2988
Massachusetts: Patagonia 4234

China

Alabama: Atlantis 8
California: Alalusi 236, Animal 246, Ayz
    262, Lui 771, New 863, Raymond
    956, Scovel 1025, Wong 1194, Woo
    1195
Colorado: Kenney 1302
Connecticut: Friends 1455
Florida: Freewill 2021
Illinois: Ingredion 2988

Nevada: He 5162
New Jersey: American 5247
New York: Li 6394, School 6748, Tang
    6891
Texas: AMD 8698

Congo, Republic of the

Kansas: Kejr 3593

Costa Rica

Colorado: Vision 1373
Florida: Place 2261

Croatia

Texas: Caritas 8763

Cyprus

Illinois: Lascaris 3040
Texas: Chrest 8770

Czech Republic

Texas: Caritas 8763

Denmark

New York: Rock 6679

Developing Countries

Massachusetts: New 4220
New Mexico: Watersheds 5628
New York: Engineering 5964
Ohio: Brush 7338

Ecuador

Idaho: Melaleuca 2679
Massachusetts: New 4220
Texas: New 9087

Egypt

New York: Jabara 6254

El Salvador

Florida: Place 2261
Massachusetts: New 4220

England

District of Columbia: Butler 1792
Florida: Stiefel 2352
Georgia: Gage 2482
Nevada: Fuserna 5159

New York: Chinook 5844, Jones 6272,
Pels 6585, Spirit 6839, Sutton
6884, Weingarten 6953
Pennsylvania: Fine 7993, Horner 8068
Texas: Kowitz 9002
Virginia: American 9386

Estonia
Florida: Joshua 2132
Washington: Rotalia 9685

Europe
California: PADI 898, Quiksilver 945
Delaware: TeleTech 1761
New Jersey: Ostberg 5483
New York: McCaddin-McQuirk 6455,
Societe 6820
North Carolina: Rixson 7223
Virginia: Delmar 9429

Fiji
Illinois: Combs 2800

France
California: Cantor 375, Skyscrape 1047,
Williamson 1184
Colorado: Fishback 1270
Delaware: Colgate 1645
Florida: Chenzyme 1939
Illinois: Dyson 2842, Lerner 3048
New York: American 5669, Societe 6820
Texas: Caritas 8763, Dewhurst 8811
Virginia: Price 9516

Georgia
Georgia: Invisible 2520

Germany
California: Preuss 935
Colorado: Okinaga 1334
Illinois: Dyson 2842
New York: Ladenburg 6357, Lanie 6364,
Weill 6950
Oregon: Chiles 7749
Rhode Island: Schoellkopf 8482

Ghana
California: Sunwest 1094
Massachusetts: New 4220
Tennessee: Fugitive 8618
Texas: Owusu 9107

Global Programs
Delaware: Jackman 1683
Wisconsin: Global 9829

Greece
Florida: Cantonis 1915
Illinois: Demos 2827, Lascaris 3040
Massachusetts: Memorial 4198

Guatemala
Connecticut: Richardson 1550
Massachusetts: New 4220
Texas: New 9087
Wyoming: Schultz 9986

Haiti
Kansas: Weskan 3641
Maine: Dugas 3776
New Jersey: Ostberg 5483
New York: Societe 6820
Texas: New 9087

Honduras
Florida: Place 2261
Iowa: Wahlert 3544
Massachusetts: New 4220
New Hampshire: Christian 5207
New York: Family 5983
Wyoming: Schultz 9986

Hong Kong
Illinois: Dyson 2842

Hungary
Arizona: Rosztoczy 161
New York: Bito 5753, Blinken 5757

Iceland
Connecticut: Sonja 1573
Virginia: Eiriksson 9441

India
California: Indo-American 651, Jain 656,
Orphan 889, Reddy 958, Sikand
1037, Upside 1140
Florida: Freewill 2021, Place 2261
Georgia: Hands 2501
Maryland: Doorstep 3850, Thadikonda
3965
Massachusetts: Barakat 4012
Michigan: Vattikuti 4605
New Jersey: Akhoury 5243, Patel 5491,
Patel 5492
New York: Flowering 6015, Freedom
6030, Indira 6242, Kathwari 6286,
McCaddin-McQuirk 6455, Nok 6537,
Rao 6645, Usman 6921
Ohio: Dauch 7372
Oregon: Larson 7788, Living 7792
Pennsylvania: BGM 7871, KL 8094,
Shastri 8273
Texas: AMD 8698, Bhutada 8730
Virginia: Jain 9478
Washington: Singh 9695

Iran
New York: Jabara 6254

Iraq
New York: Jabara 6254

Ireland
Illinois: Dyson 2842
Iowa: Wright 3551

Israel
California: Blackman 320, Butler 365,
Levy 752, Moley 841, Rieger 971,
Rifkind 972, Shapell 1031, Support
1095, Teichman 1106
Colorado: Oreg 1335
District of Columbia: Foundation 1807

Florida: Basser 1871, Handleman 2078,
Hishmeh 2100, Posnack 2262,
Safenowitz 2307, Wollowick 2412
Illinois: American 2707, Landau 3036,
Lindon 3054, Mermelstein 3103,
Rosenmutter 3208, Wein 3315
Maryland: Boehm 3826
Massachusetts: Galileo 4101, Spero
4304
Michigan: Teitel 4589
Minnesota: Fingerhut 4683, Kaplan
4721
Missouri: Block 4869, Bohm 4871, Maor
4952
Nevada: Cohen 5149, Fein 5155
New Jersey: Billig 5265, Greenblatt 5376
New York: Abba's 5634, Alexander
5653, American 5667, Beitar 5733,
Cote 5881, Fischel 6009, Gimprich
6080, Greenwald 6136, Grossman
6146, Hoffman 6216, Katzin 6288,
Kitov 6317, Klagsbrun 6318,
Ladenburg 6357, Laub 6367,
Legacy 6374, Neuman 6526,
Posner-Wallace 6621, QIBQ 6636,
Shulamit 6794, Sparkplug 6830,
Stefansky 6854, Stein 6855, Stern
6862, Strauss 6870, Weingarten
6952, Weinstein 6956, Yoreinu
7010, Ziv 7030
North Carolina: Kramer 7152
Pennsylvania: Arronson 7844, Berkowitz
7865, Cohn 7931, Epstein 7983,
Epstein 7984
Tennessee: Belz 8585, Lowenstein 8645
Wisconsin: Johnson 9851
Wyoming: Schultz 9986

Italy
California: Parsemus 904
Connecticut: Friends 1456
Georgia: Gage 2482
Illinois: Dyson 2842

Japan
Hawaii: Yoshimoto 2658
Illinois: Dyson 2842, Kobe 3024
New York: Spirit 6839
Texas: Kingdom 8995

Jordan
New York: Jabara 6254
Wyoming: Schultz 9986

Kenya
Florida: Gordon 2051
Georgia: Faith 2477
Illinois: Ingredion 2988
Maryland: Mpala 3919, Northern 3928
Massachusetts: Pegasus 4236
Ohio: Marafiki 7513
Wisconsin: Global 9829
Wyoming: Schultz 9986

Latin America
California: Grass 577, Linked 758
Delaware: TeleTech 1761
Georgia: Bancker-Williams 2440
Minnesota: Sundance 4796
New Jersey: Garcia 5362
New Mexico: Angelica 5605
Virginia: Delmar 9429, Dorothy-Ann
9433

Latvia
South Carolina: Zvejnieks 8553

Lebanon
Michigan: Saab 4556
New York: Jabara 6254

Lithuania
New York: Gruodis 6150

Madagascar
Massachusetts: New 4220

Malawi
Texas: Orant 9102

Malaysia
Illinois: Dyson 2842
Texas: AMD 8698

Mauritius
California: Kinnoull 706
Minnesota: Pax 4760
Missouri: Larson 4943

Mexico
California: Candelaria 372
Florida: Place 2261
Illinois: Ingredion 2988
Maine: Golden 3781
Massachusetts: Blossom 4022
New Jersey: Knistrom 5426
New Mexico: Angelica 5605
New York: Lamaj 6361
Texas: Smith 9203
Utah: Skolnick 9352
Washington: Ji 9632, Ormsby 9674

Middle East
California: Alalusi 236, Global 565
District of Columbia: Foundation 1807
Florida: Atlantis 1858
Illinois: Landau 3036
Michigan: Saab 4556
New York: Kevorkian 6304

Mozambique
Texas: Astri 8711

Myanmar
Connecticut: Richardson 1550

Nepal
Maryland: Doorstep 3850

Netherlands
Connecticut: Davis-McCullough 1429
Illinois: Dyson 2842, Foundation 2881
New Jersey: American 5247

New Zealand
Illinois: Dyson 2842

Nicaragua
Massachusetts: New 4220
Minnesota: Winds 4820
Texas: Mansur 9035
Wyoming: Schultz 9986

Nigeria
Florida: Freewill 2021

North Korea
Texas: Soonae 9208

Northern Africa
New York: Jabara 6254

Norway
Texas: Astri 8711

Pakistan
California: Saya 1011
Illinois: Ingredion 2988
Massachusetts: Barakat 4012
New York: Kathwari 6286

Papua New Guinea
Massachusetts: New 4220

Paraguay
Alaska: Nash 90
California: His 623
Florida: Freewill 2021

Peru
Florida: Place 2261
Illinois: Ingredion 2988
Massachusetts: New 4220

Philippines
California: International 652
Florida: Freewill 2021
Ohio: Dauch 7372

Poland
California: Peszynski 917
Florida: Freewill 2021

Romania
Florida: Place 2261

Maryland: Windsor 3988

Russia
California: Delzell 450, Trustees 1132
Illinois: Dyson 2842
Maryland: St. 3960
Minnesota: Sundance 4796
New York: Rock 6679
Texas: Kilgore 8989

Rwanda
Florida: Stiefel 2352
Wyoming: Schultz 9986

Scotland
Delaware: Glencoe 1669
Florida: Taylor 2365
New York: Weill 6950
Ohio: Sheely 7590

Senegal
Florida: Freewill 2021

Singapore
Illinois: Dyson 2842
New York: Flowering 6015
Texas: AMD 8698

South Africa
California: Modglin 840, PADI 898
Florida: Freewill 2021
Maryland: Doorstep 3850
Massachusetts: Tatelman 4322
New Hampshire: Rothschild 5229
Ohio: Dauch 7372
Texas: Astri 8711
Washington: Jernigan 9631

South America
Florida: Uncle 2383
Maine: Dugas 3776
Massachusetts: New 4220
Minnesota: Porter 4763
New York: Frank 6026,
    McCaddin-McQuirk 6455
North Carolina: Rixson 7223, Rolander
    7229
Virginia: Delmar 9429

South Korea
District of Columbia: Dingwall 1804
Illinois: Ingredion 2988

Southeastern Asia
California: Cienega 404
Hawaii: Shiraki 2648
New York: Kathwari 6286

Spain
Illinois: Dyson 2842

Sri Lanka
Pennsylvania: KL 8094
Texas: Astri 8711

Sudan
Florida: Freewill 2021

Sweden
Texas: Astri 8711

Switzerland
Delaware: TeleTech 1761
Illinois: Dyson 2842
Maryland: Thadikonda 3965
Texas: Caritas 8763, Coneway 8783

Syria
New York: Jabara 6254

Taiwan
California: Friends 533, Hsieh 636, Hsu
    637, Lyu 777
Florida: Chenzyme 1939, Hsu 2112
Illinois: Dyson 2842
Massachusetts: Summer 4316
New Jersey: Yin-Shun 5596
Texas: AMD 8698

Tanzania
Florida: Jenkins 2129
Massachusetts: New 4220
Wyoming: Schultz 9986

Thailand
California: Modglin 840
Illinois: Ingredion 2988
Maryland: Doorstep 3850

Turkey
Texas: Chrest 8770

Uganda
Alaska: Nash 90

Ukraine
Florida: Zichron 2424
Illinois: Heritage 2967

**United Kingdom of Great Britain
    and Northern Ireland**
California: Global 565, Parsemus 904,
    Peszynski 917
Delaware: Singer 1744
District of Columbia: Butler 1792
Florida: Shepard 2331, Taylor 2365
Illinois: Dyson 2842
Maryland: Fox 3864
New York: Buster 5806
Oregon: Wyss 7832
South Carolina: Lader 8531
Virginia: Praktikos 9514

Vietnam
Florida: Freewill 2021
Nevada: Center 5145
New York: Eastman 5940
Wyoming: Schultz 9986

Virgin Islands of the United States
Massachusetts: Cabbadetus 4033
Texas: Partridge 9117

Wales
Nevada: Fuserna 5159

**West Bank/Gaza (Palestinian
    Territories)**
District of Columbia: Foundation 1807
New York: Jabara 6254, Sparkplug 6830
Wyoming: Schultz 9986

Yemen
New York: Jabara 6254

Zambia
Illinois: Combs 2800
Texas: Smith 9203

Zimbabwe
Delaware: Jackman 1683

TYPES OF SUPPORT INDEX

List of terms: Terms for the major types of support used in this index are listed below with definitions.

Index: In the index itself, foundation entries are arranged under each term by state location, abbreviated name, and sequence number. Foundations in boldface type make grants on a national or international basis. The others generally limit giving to the state or city in which they are located.

Advocacy: Advocacy in the public arena to influence policy and allocation of resources; this includes advocating for better policies and services in various program areas (for example school reform, full access to health care, legal reform, environmental clean-up work, etc.) and providing assistance in planning advocacy campaigns.

Aid to graduates or students of specific schools: Support to people who attend or have attended a specific school. Some programs may also specify institutions to be attended after graduation. In many cases, application must be made through the high school or college instead of the foundation.

Annual campaigns: Any organized effort by a nonprofit to secure gifts on an annual basis; also called annual appeals.

Audience development: Support to reach a larger audience, to reach particular kinds of audiences, or to develop on-going relationships with an audience, especially but not exclusively for arts and cultural groups and programs.

Awards, prizes and competitions: Artists' awards, prizes, competitions, housing, living space, work space and other prizes.

Board development: To evaluate or improve a board's structure, role and performance. Includes board recruitment, ethical board governance and implementation of governance models.

Building acquisitions: Support to purchase buildings or other structures.

Building and renovations: Constructing, renovating, remodeling, or rehabilitating property.

Camperships: Partial or full tuition subsidies to enable participants who would not otherwise be financially able to participate in fee-based camping programs.

Capacity-building and technical assistance: To increase an organization's sustainability and effectiveness through strategic and long-range planning, organizational assessment and development, business planning, and the use of outside consultants. Use primarily for process-oriented capacity-building that seeks to improve organizational practices. See Also: Management and leadership development.

Capital and infrastructure: To acquire, upgrade or develop capital infrastructure. Includes: building acquisition, maintenance and renovations; land acquisitions and rent payments; information technology and other equipment; and collections.

Capital campaigns: A campaign to raise funds for a variety of long-term purposes, such as building construction or acquisition, endowments, land acquisition, etc.

Cash grants: Direct monetary contributions of cash or cash equivalents. These may be paid in a lump sum, paid in the same year as authorized, or paid over a set number of months or years.

Cash MRIs: Market-rate deposits in community development banks and community development credit unions to support the investor's philanthropic goals and purposes, or to induce that institution's support for one or more projects.

Cause-related marketing: Support linking gifts to charity with marketing promotions.

Coalition building: The joining of human and material resources of individuals and organizations with common or diverse interests to work toward compatible goals of varying breadth and produce change through the actions of these partnerships. These may take the form of temporary, informal arrangements that can become permanent, independently constituted organizations, with local, regional or national membership.

Collections acquisitions: Acquisitions by libraries, schools, museums, etc. of permanent materials as part of a collection, often books, artifacts, or art.

Collections management and preservation: Maintenance, preservation, organization, description and conservation of tangible or digital items in a collection.

Commissioning new works: Support for the creation and generation of new artistic works in a variety of fields and media.

Commodity provision: Efforts assisting nonprofits and charitable organizations to acquire and distribute needed materials and products. Includes packaged goods, foodstuffs, pharmaceuticals, and other disposable and perishable health, medical, sanitary, agricultural and electronic supplies needed in bulk for disaster or international relief efforts, for example; as well as more customized, smaller batches of items intended for more localized, targeted programs. Do not use for equipment.

Conference attendance: Support for a person or group of people to attend a conference or seminar.

Conference hosting : Support for a group or venue to sponsor a conference or seminar.

Conference presenting: Support for a person, group or organization to make a presentation at a conference or seminar.

Conferences and exhibits: Encouragement and facilitation of the gathering of people, groups or organizations to meet and discuss issues or events on a particular topic. This includes conferences, seminars, workshops, meetings, annual conventions.

Continuing support: Support provided for the same purpose as in the previous year or years, or support renewed for another year or years.

Contracts: The fulfillment of agreements or obligations between parties. In this context, the contract is often a fee-for-service agreement offered by a funder and accepted by a recipient.

Convening: To bring together diverse stakeholders in a collective process of sharing insights and making decisions about a specific topic and leading to a well-defined outcome. This process may be contained in a single gathering, but is more often accomplished in a series of meetings and other events or programs that allow a more thorough and in-depth process.

Curriculum development: Support for schools, colleges, universities, and educational support organizations to develop general or discipline-specific curricular. May be used outside of education-related coding, for example for a museum or filmmaker to create a curriculum for an exhibit or a film.

Data and measurement systems: The design and development of systems for gathering and analyzing data with an aim to help organizations improve how they measure, assess and, ultimately, improve their performance and results.

Debt reduction: To reduce an organization's indebtedness; also referred to as deficit financing. Frequently refers to mortgage relief.

Doctoral support: Support for dissertation or thesis research in pursuit of a doctoral degree.

Donated art: Contributions in the form of artwork, antiques, historical or collectible objects. These may be artworks meant to be part of a permanent collection, as in a museum or gallery, or artworks intended for decoration or display, as in public spaces or workplaces.

Donated equipment: These contributions may include surplus furniture, office machines, paper, appliances, laboratory apparatus, or other items, and often are given to charities, schools, or hospitals.

Donated land: Contributions of real estate, land or developed property. Institutions of higher education often receive gifts of real estate; land may also be given to community groups for housing development, parks, or recreational facilities.

Donated products: Contributions from companies giving away what they make or produce. Product donations can include periodic clothing donations to a shelter for the homeless or regular donations of pharmaceuticals to a health clinic resulting in a reliable supply.

Donor collaborations: Formation of joint endeavors between grantmakers to optimize impact and avoid duplication of effort. This may include sharing of information, coordination of grantmaking, pooling of resources, and a shared decision-making process.

Earned income: Support to increase the revenue generated from the sale of goods, services rendered, or work performed as part of the activities of an organization or program.

Emergency funds: One-time support to cover the immediate short-term funding needs of an organization on an emergency basis.

Employee matching gifts: Contributions made, usually by corporate foundations, to match gifts made by corporate employees. These may be part of a company-wide effort to raise funds for a single organization (as a United Way fundraising drive). They may also be restricted to certain types of organizations, such as schools, one's alma mater, organizations in a certain community, etc. Do not use for contributions made to match an employee's time volunteered to a charitable organization. Do not use for Matching grants.

Employee volunteer services: Ongoing coordinated efforts through which a company or other funder promotes volunteer involvement with nonprofits or charities on the part of its employees. The involvement may be during work time or after hours. If employees volunteer on their own initiative, the transaction is not classified as Employee volunteer services or as corporate voluntarism.

Employee-related scholarships: Contributions to scholarship programs directed by a company-sponsored foundation usually for children of employees; these programs are frequently administered by the National Merit Scholarship Corporation, Scholarship America, or a similar organization, which is responsible for the selection of scholars.

Endowments: Bequests or gifts intended to be kept permanently and invested to provide income for continued support of an organization.

Equal access: Efforts to ensure equal opportunity and access to services, resources, and advancement in particular fields of activity.

Equipment: To acquire or upgrade equipment for an organization's day-to-day operations such as furnishings and HVAC systems or equipment related to an organization's specific programs such medical equipment for medical facilities. See Also: Information technology, Collections acquisitions.

Ethics and accountability: Efforts to set and enforce ethical norms in certain fields, professions, etc.

Exchange programs: Support for people to travel to other places and assume a local role there, as student, teacher, artist, volunteer, etc. These exchanges can be one-way or two-way and may be intended to facilitate a sharing of culture, history, tradition, or knowledge and foster a sense of mutual understanding.

Exhibitions: To mount an exhibit or to support the installation of a touring exhibit, often by museums, libraries, or historical societies.

Facilities maintenance: Support for day-to-day operation or general maintenance of buildings and grounds.

Faculty and staff development: Salary or development of staff members of specific programs.

Fellowships: Support for fellowships at institutions, usually universities but there are exceptions, such as think tanks and other policy organizations.

Financial services: Support for development of or access to financial services including budget, accounting, auditing, tax assistance and planning, and other services such as loans, lines of credit, and banking or credit union services. Note: Loans, lines of credit, etc. are not considered PRIs or MRIs unless specifically stated as such by the grantmaking organization.

Financial sustainability: To ensure continued financial viability for organizations, especially those with low resources or serving low-resource/high need communities. Includes efforts to develop sustainable fundraising, marketing and development within organizations.

Fiscal sponsorships : A formal arrangement in which a tax-exempt public charity (or similar registered nonprofit) sponsors a project or organization that lacks an exempt status or official registration. The sponsoring organization may assume expenditure responsibility for the organization and may provide other supporting administrative services.

Fixed income MRIs: Market-rate investments in bonds and other short and long-term, fixed-return debt instruments that support community and economic development activities (housing, infrastructure, job creation). These include product types: targeted community development bonds, asset backed securities (bonds backed by mortgages, business-loans).

Foundation-administered program awards: Awards to charitable programs developed and/or administered directly by the funder. These programs can include initiatives supported exclusively by the funder or research programs administered by the funder.

Fundraising: To raise donated funds and maintain productive relationships with donors. Use for fundraising galas and to purchase tables or tickets to events.

General support: Support for the day-to-day operating costs of an organization or to further the general purpose of an organization. Also includes support which may be applied to any use or to fund any purpose (unrestricted support); does not include unspecified support. Use For: Membership dues.

Graduate support: Support to pursue graduate work and a master's level graduate degree after receiving an undergraduate degree.

Grantee relations: Development of a better relationship between funders and the organizations they support, including development of shared goals and objectives, and improving communications and feedback.

Grants to individuals: Awards given directly to individuals and not through other nonprofit organizations, or grants made to organizations and earmarked for a specific named person. Some grantmakers have a specific limitation stating that they will make no grants to individuals. In the U.S., in order to make grants to individuals, a foundation must have a program that has received formal IRS approval. These awards are often for aid to the needy, student aid, and emergency funds.

Grassroots organizing: Building popular support for, encouraging activism around, and helping to organize a forum to address an issue or policy, often a specific social justice issue, at the community level.

Individual development: Support to provide assistance to individuals in the form of grants-in-aid, stipends, loans, work-study, or other awards for pursuing educational, research, or professional goals.

Information and Referral: Efforts to gather, organize, and disseminate information on subjects or activities to groups or individuals working in that area or to those requiring support or services in that area.

Information technology: To acquire, upgrade or develop computer technology. Includes hardware, software, peripherals, systems, networking components and mobile devices.

In-kind gifts: Contributions of equipment, supplies, or other property as distinct from monetary grants. Some organizations may also donate space or staff time as an in-kind contribution; do not use for grants of stocks and bonds.

Institutional evaluations: Evaluation of an organization's specific mission, purpose, profile, and performance with an aim to improving stated objectives and outcomes.

Internships: Awards for paid or unpaid positions providing work-experience, on-the-job training, and/or school credit. These positions can provide research or job services to organizations and serve as recruitment tools for employers, and can provide opportunities for interns to explore career possibilities, gain experience, and find permanent employment.

Land acquisitions: Support to purchase real estate property (not buildings).

Leadership and professional development: Professional development of management, executives, boards, staff, and volunteers. Includes leadership development, recruiting, training, and salaries.

Litigation: Legal action in the public interest toward mission-related policy and reform goals, and activism in the court system. Also includes litigation, including arbitration, mediation and negotiation, in support of nonprofits and charitable organizations; especially legal guidance supporting operations; liability, contractual and governance issues; regulatory compliance; exempt organization and other tax concerns; fiduciary conduct; intellectual property; and other areas requiring legal expertise. Use For: Legal advocacy, Strategic litigation.

Loaned talent (pro bono): Professionals and executive staff who are employees of a grantmaker who are loaned out by the grantmaker to help a nonprofit in an area involving their particular skills.

Loans to individuals: Assistance in the form of loans made directly by the organization to individuals rather than other organizations. Loans may be at low or no interest, but must be repaid under terms set by the loaning institution.

Management and leadership development: To strengthen organizational leadership. This includes salaries of management and executives, administrative staff support, training and leadership development programs.

Marketing: Support for activities that promote, sell, distribute, and communicate the value of a product or service. Includes advertising and branding.

Matching grants: Grants made to match funds provided by another donor and grants paid only if the donee is able to raise additional funds from another source. Use For: Challenge grants. Do not use for Employee matching gifts.

Mergers: To build an organization's capacity through merger with another organization, especially one with a similar or related mission or field of activity. Includes mergers between organizations that are related corporately, through charter or other affiliation; for example: mergers between two separate affiliates of the American Lung Association.

Mission-related investments: Investments made by philanthropic entities in the pursuit of both financial and social returns. Usually these investments broadly support the entity's missions and programmatic goals while seeking market-rate returns.

MRI community development bank deposits: Market-rate investments in for-profit corporations that provide capital to rebuild economically distressed communities through targeted lending and investment to induce that institution's support for one or more projects.

MRI community development credit union deposits: Market-rate investments in member-owned non-profit cooperatives that promote ownership of assets and savings, and provide affordable credit and retail financial services to low-income people, to induce that institution's support for one or more projects.

MRI community development loan fund deposits: Market-rate investments in organizations (usually non-profits) that provide financing and development services to businesses, organizations, and individuals in low-income urban and rural areas to induce that institution's support for one or more projects.

Network-building and collaboration: Building structures and creating opportunities to work more closely and effectively with partners and peers, including through networking activities, physical or virtual. These may be collaborations, partnerships, alliances, meetings, travel, and other interactions with people or organizations as a way to exchange information or services,

plan and prioritize, resolve conflicts, share resources, etc.

Nonprofit collaborations: Support for 2 or more nonprofits to collaborate on an issue, project, publication, etc. Includes joint programming collaborations, merging of resources, sharing of resources, collaborative leadership, co-sponsorship.

Officers and trustees discretionary grants: Financial support made under a system where designated foundation officers or staff have the privilege of making grants to recipients of their choosing without extensive board review. These grants must adhere to the scope of the foundation's purposes.

Online engagement: Building virtual structures and creating online opportunities for peers, partners, and supporters to interact and share information on topics and initiatives of mutual interest or shared projects.

Online media: To create, design, maintain and provide content for Web sites, electronic media, intranets, internet services and other online media.

Outreach: Efforts to reach out to the general public or specific groups/communities to make them aware of the organization or a specific program, event or cause funded or supported by the organization.

Performances : Mounting a production in the areas of performing arts, concerts, theatre, dance, etc.

Pilot programs: Untried projects or programs that are being tested for feasibility or proof-of-concept.

Policy, advocacy and systems reform: To develop, promote, and transform public policies, especially involving the proposal of novel solutions to ongoing challenges encountered by political, economic and social systems and institutions, especially in the field of activity central to the mission or purpose of an organization or project.

Postdoctoral support: Support for research or further study after receiving doctoral degree.

Postgraduate support: Support to pursue a doctoral degree after receiving a master's level graduate degree

Precollege support: Scholarships and loans given for expenses related to elementary or secondary education, such as private school tuition.

Presentations and productions: The creation, development, and display of public, print and multimedia presentations and productions, often by institutions and individuals in educational, nonprofit, arts, humanities and media.

PRI business start-ups and expansions: Program-related investments designed to stimulate the business sector. Goals for these investments range from job creation to developing commercial infrastructure in a community.

PRI charitable use real estate: Program-related investments in property or material goods that are used for charitable purposes. In most cases a property, such as a building, is held by a grantmaker who in turn donates or leases the asset at below market rates to a nonprofit organization. The asset remains property of the grantmaking organization.

PRI equity investments: Program-related investments in the form of an ownership taken by a grantmaker in an organization, or a venture taken by the grantmaker through an investment. Returns on investments are dependent on the profitability of the organization or venture.

PRI interim financing : Program-related investments in the form of short-term loans to provide temporary financing until more permanent financing becomes available.

PRI lines of credit: Program-related investments in the form of agreements between a grantmaker (as a lender) and an organization that the organization can borrow money at any time up to an established limit.

PRI linked deposits and certificates of deposit: Program-related investments in the form of deposits in an account (usually a CD) with a financial institution to induce that institution's support for one or more projects. By accruing no or low interest on its deposit, the grantmaker essentially subsidizes the interest rate of the borrowers.

PRI loan guarantees: Program-related investments in the form of pledges to cover payment of debt or to perform some obligation if the liable organization fails to perform. When a third party guarantees a loan, they promise to repay in the event of a default by the borrower.

PRI loans: Program-related investments in the form of low- or no-interest loans made to an organization.

PRI loans for loan funds: Program-related investments in the form of low- or no-interest loans made available to lending organizations who then provide low-interest loans to needy individuals or organizations.

PRI mortgage financing: Program-related investments in the form of funds made available to lending organizations who then provide low-interest mortgages to needy individuals.

Private equity MRIs: Market-rate investments in unlisted mission-oriented companies that range from venture capital investments in start-ups, to mezzanine financing in established companies aiming for a trade sale or public listing, to buy-outs of public companies.

Pro bono advocacy services: Pro bono consulting assistance related to advocacy, including advocating for better services in various program areas (for example school reform, full access to health care, legal reform, environmental clean up work, etc.) and providing assistance in planning advocacy campaigns that will follow current legal guidelines preventing certain kinds of advocacy by nonprofits in the U.S.

Pro bono board services: Pro bono consulting assistance in board effectiveness assessment, board recruitment process design, board reporting, meeting facilitation, executive coaching, and performance review.

Pro bono communications and public relations services: Pro bono consulting assistance in external communications and public relations, including but not limited to assistance with the development of an annual report, brochure, newsletter design, and/or public service announcement.

Pro bono consulting services: Professional staff support provided to consult on a project of mutual interest to both parties or to evaluate services.

Pro bono financial management services: Pro bono consulting assistance in financial management, including but not limited to program cost analysis, financial audit, financial controls assessment and design, budgeting process design, pricing strategy, and purchasing and supply chain audit.

Pro bono fundraising services: Pro bono consulting assistance in programs or projects directly related to fundraising. These may include event planning and production, executive fundraising coaching, donor segmentation, in-kind opportunity assessment, capital campaign design and management, and the development of capital campaign materials.

Pro bono human resources services: Pro bono consulting assistance in the area of human resources, including a strategic assessment and recommendations for a human resources plan, organizational design, employee recruitment plan, organizational diversity plan, performance management system, back office systems implementation, staff compensation and incentive plan, staff training and development plan, and an internal communications plan.

Pro bono interactive and website technology services: Pro bono consulting assistance in website technology, including the design and development of a basic website, interactive website, intranet, and extranet.

Pro bono legal services: Pro bono consulting assistance in the area of legal support, including donation of legal services in court situations, review of various legal documents including those related to incorporation and other law, justice and counsel issues.

Pro bono marketing and branding services: Pro bono consulting assistance in marketing and branding. Programs or projects may cover issues such as a program marketing, organizational positioning and key messages, visual identity, or re-naming.

Pro bono medical services: Pro bono consulting assistance in the medical area, including donation of medical services and equipment.

Pro bono program design and analysis services: Pro bono consulting assistance in program design and analysis includes but is not limited to the development of a volunteer management system, volunteer assessment, program evaluation, client needs assessment, client service evaluation, and operations process design.

Pro bono real estate and facilities services: Pro bono consulting assistance in the area of real estate and facilities, including a facilities needs assessment, interior design and brand integration project, building accessibility and code compliance analysis, facilities renovation, and lease review.

Pro bono services: Pro bono services rendered by a company, professional services firm, intermediary, association or individual professional leveraging the core competencies and expertise of the professional(s) engaged to meet the client's need.

Pro bono strategic management services: Pro bono consulting assistance in the area of strategic management, including the development of a strategic plan, refined mission, environmental and sustainability policy and plan, internal capacity assessment, strengths, weaknesses, opportunities, and threats analysis, competitive analysis, earned income business plan, geographic expansion plan, and logic model design.

Pro bono technology infrastructure services: Pro bono consulting assistance in technology infrastructure such as donor database implementation, the development of an organizational IT plan, installation of office networking, remote IT access set up, and program database implementation.

Product and service delivery: Efforts to deliver or distribute products and services, and to streamline these processes, making necessary adjustments and improvements and optimizing recipient experience and overall efficiency and quality of the products or services.

Product and service development: Efforts assisting nonprofits and charitable organizations through the phased life cycle of a product or service, from idea generation through feasibility study to product launch to enhancing the product or service after recipient feedback and process evaluation.

Product development: Efforts assisting nonprofits and charitable organizations to design, create and conduct marketing research for existing or newly developed product through systematic procedural methodology, turning market opportunity into available, salable product.

Product discovery: Efforts assisting nonprofits and charitable organizations for exploratory process involving identification of issue, opportunity and target group or audience, proposal of solution and corresponding product, architecture of step-by-step strategy and outline of distribution plan, promoting institutional advancement through scalable model.

Professorships: To support or endow a professorship or chair, especially at an educational or research institution.

Program creation: To design and implement a new program or project.

Program development: To support specific projects or programs as opposed to general purpose support.

Program evaluations: Evaluation of a specific project or program; includes awards both to agencies to pay for evaluation costs and to research institutes and other program evaluators.

Program expansion: To take an existing program and expand it to serve more participants, serve more locations, or address other appropriate areas of need.

Program replication: To take a successful program and recreate it to serve another area or group.

Program-related investments: Loans or other investments to support charitable activities that involve the potential return of capital within an established time frame, and usually below market rates. In the U.S., PRIs include financing methods commonly associated with banks or other private investors, such as loans, loan guarantees, linked deposits, and equity investments in charitable organizations or in commercial ventures for charitable purposes. Do not use for recoverable grants or conditional grants.

Promissory notes: Legal or financial instruments in the form of written promises to pay a set sum of money to a payee at a future time or on demand. The payee can redeem the note, or count it as an asset. Use For: Notes payable; Mortgage notes.

Public engagement and education: To use communications strategies to educate, enlighten, and involve the public in certain activities and issue areas.

Public equity MRIs: Market-rate investments in public equity funds that purchase stock in public companies using screens for inclusion (positive screening) or exclusion (negative screening) based on social and environmental criteria.

Publications: To publish reports or other publications issued by a nonprofit resulting from research or projects of interest to the funder.

Real estate MRIs: Market-rate investments in private equity real estate finance products investing in the potential growth in market value of investment property. These include investments in mixed-use, mixed-income greyfields (urban infill development) and

brownfields (clean-up of environmentally contaminated sites); targeted investment in underserved communities; provision of affordable and workforce housing; smart growth and conservation; and energy-efficient management and construction.

Recordings and broadcasts: Film, television, video, audio, radio and recordings in other media. Not used for general support of TV or radio stations.

Regranting: Support, often to an intermediary or umbrella organization, intended to be passed on to other organizations or individuals based on agreed-upon criteria and limitations.

Regulation and administration: Efforts to set standards, monitor performance, confer accreditation, or otherwise regulate and administer groups or projects.

Rent: Support to pay rent on a building or space.

Research: Basic and applied research, other studies, surveys, investigations, and clinical trials.

Research and evaluation: Efforts to discover, collect, analyze, interpret, test, document, and disseminate data, information, knowledge, and the applications of that knowledge. This includes basic and applied scientific research; studies, surveys, investigations and clinical trials in social sciences and medicine; historical research in the arts and humanities; evaluation of specific programs and initiatives; feasibility studies; institutional evaluations; and data measurement systems to assess and improve performance.

Residencies: Nonmonetary award usually of short duration, usually only for artists of all disciplines to further their creative work. Meals, living quarters, equipment, and studio space may be provided.

Sabbaticals: Support to take long-term but temporary leave, sometimes awarded as an employee benefit. Sabbaticals commonly last from 2 months to a year and can be used for rest, writing, research, or reflection.

Scholarships: Support to an individual or educational institution or organization to support a scholarship program, mainly for students at the undergraduate level.

Seed money: To start, establish or initiate a new project or organization; may cover salaries and other operating expenses of a new project. Use For: Start-up funds.

Sponsorships: Support for fundraising, celebratory, or programmatic events for an organization where the funder's name or trademark is branded or marketed along with the event. Includes support for walks/races to raise money for a disease or cause, dinners or tables (in lieu of a donation) at events honoring a person or cause, and the underwriting of programs and events such as performances, seasons, exhibitions, etc.

Stipends: Short-term awards offered to independent scholars, writers, artists and researchers to defray expenses incurred in advancing their professional goals.

Stock transfers and certificates: Contributions made in the form of securities (stocks or bonds).

Student aid: Support to students enabling them to attend educational institutions.

System and operational improvements: Efforts to enhance an organization's effectiveness through development of best practices, policies and procedures, performance management systems and tools.

Systems reform: Efforts meant to change fundamental structures of institutions, systems, and policies.

Technical assistance: Provision of any specialized service or skill that a nonprofit does not possess within the organization, but which it may need in order to operate more effectively. Use For: Consultants, Consultancies.

Technical education support: Support to attend postsecondary institutions that offer certificates in education directly related to preparation for specific careers, and which require no more than two years of study.

Translation : Conversion of material from one language into another, to convey its message and intent, in nonprofit and charitable literature, publications, articles, and other printed materials. Also includes the work of interpreters at conferences, convenings, workshops, lectures and other public events, facilitating dissemination of knowledge and information; and in institutional settings where individual interpretive services are needed to ensure equal access to services for speakers of other languages.

Travel awards: Awards to individuals to cover transportation and/or out-of-town living expenses while attending a conference or completing a period of study or special project. Enrollment in a college or university is not a requirement.

Undergraduate support: Support to pursue undergraduate work and a bachelor's or associate degree.

Use of facilities: These contributions may include rent-free or below-market rate use of office space for temporary periods, use of dining and meeting facilities, or infrastructure services such as telecommunications services, mailing services, transportation services, or computer services.

Volunteer development: Recruitment, training, and deployment of volunteer staff in administrative or program capacities.

Work-study grants: Support for educational expenses awarded to students who engage in a part-time work arrangement. A work commitment of 10-15 hours per week is customarily required.

Advocacy

California: New 864, Small 1049, Wendell 1172
Idaho: Hare 2675
Illinois: Moreton 3124, Petrovich 3174
Indiana: Duneland 3372, Hillenbrand 3393
Maine: **Golden 3781**
Massachusetts: Alden 3999, Rose 4271
Missouri: Shawe 5000
New Hampshire: Finlay 5213
New York: 1848 5629, Colby 5867, **Freedom 6030**, Marshall 6446, Paxton 6581, Skalny 6807
Pennsylvania: Huplits 8071
Texas: Strickland 9224
Washington: Northwest 9669

Aid to graduates or students of specific schools

Connecticut: Fuller 1460

Annual campaigns

Alabama: Black 12, Friedman 27, Kemp 42, Pei-Ling 52, Phifer, 54
Arizona: Grossman 126, Hansen 127, Hughes 130, James 132, Louis 142, Napier 152, Zicarelli 185
Arkansas: Hickingbotham 199
California: Anhaltzer 245, Baker 264, Bank 272, Bannerman 274, Barth 279, Bear 288, **Bull 358, Butler 365, Cantor 375,** Church 403, Corday 426, Corwin 428, Drum 464, First 506, Fremont 527, Gill 555, Glikbarg 564, Hand 595, Horwitz 633, Huntington 642, Jones 673, Maxfield 808, McClatchy 811, Nickoll 867, Page 899, Pauley 909, Ragir 950, Rocca, 978, Shenandoah 1033, Stauffer 1076, **Teichman 1106,** Theroux 1110, Thrill 1117, **Wakerly 1150,** Weil 1163, Westphal 1177, **Wilkinson 1183**
Colorado: Broomfield 1242, Donnell-Kay 1258, Goodwin 1279, Mullen 1329, Schlessman 1349, Schramm 1350
Connecticut: Baldwin 1399, Cochrane 1420, Curran 1427, Goldfarb 1466, Morrow 1527, Patricelli 1541, Pryor 1546, Senior 1566, Union 1590
Delaware: Alcyon 1608, Babcock 1612, Bennett 1618, Chaney 1640, **Colgate 1645,** Lightner 1699, New 1715, Patterson 1719
District of Columbia: Bench 1788, Bender 1789, Dimick 1803, Porter 1829, Westport 1838
Florida: Auerbach 1859, Catalina 1928, Coral 1952, Dasburg 1961, Elster 1990, Erdle 1993, Golden 2046, Graese 2055, Gulf 2069, Hill 2097, Mayberg 2199, McCabe 2201, Oristano 2241, Rothman 2299, Sexton 2326, Silverman 2337, Toppel 2377, Turner 2381, **Uncle 2383, Wollowick 2412**
Georgia: Chatham 2457, Exposition 2476, **Gage 2482,** Illges 2517, Lee 2540, Lipscomb 2541, Magnus 2543, Marshall 2545, Oxford 2561, Wright 2620
Hawaii: Kaneta 2637, Moore 2643, Servco 2645
Idaho: Wishnick 2690
Illinois: Agape 2698, Alliant 2702, Alton 2705, Bere 2734, Bishop 2743, Bufka 2763, Bulkley 2765, Cain 2773, Chicago 2786, Cohn 2795, Cole 2798, Dubin 2838, EMA 2854, Half 2942, Hess 2969, Hopper 2977, Jocarno 3000, **Krasberg-Mason 3029,** Lehman-Stamm 3045, **Lindon 3054,** Logos 3058, Louis 3063, **Mead 3100,** Mirapaul 3119, Morton 3127, **New 3137,** Pitzman 3177, Reichert 3192, Rosenson 3209, Shaker 3238, Simon 3247, Staley 3262, Steigerwaldt 3265, Takiff 3281, Tuohy 3296, Walker 3308, Webb 3313
Indiana: **Ackerman 3339,** Ayres 3342, Bussing-Koch 3353, CDM 3355, Huntington 3397, Kuhne 3409,

Lacy 3410, Oliver 3428, Schurz 3444, Springleaf 3455
Iowa: Farver 3491, First 3493, Gazette 3497, Grinnell 3501, Krumm 3517, **Wahlert 3544,** West 3547, **Wright 3551,** Young 3552
Kansas: Bane 3557, Berry 3558, DeVore 3573, Family 3575, Fidelity 3577, Goebel 3580, Payless 3614, Watson 3639
Kentucky: Barth 3647, Murry 3681, Stock 3697, Sutherland 3699
Louisiana: Biedenharn 3713, Huie-Dellmon 3729, Wheless 3758, Wisdom 3761
Maine: Borman 3767, Burnham 3770, Franklin 3779, Somers 3803
Maryland: Acacia 3807, Akridge 3810, Ammerman 3813, Broadus 3829, Campbell 3831, Caplan 3832, Darby 3843, Davis 3844, Eliasberg 3854, Gladding 3871, **Goldberg 3872,** Hubbard 3883, Kelly, 3893, Macht 3905, Phase 3936, Richmond 3940, Salisbury 3945, Tucker 3969, Van 3973, Van 3974
Massachusetts: **Brabson 4026,** Bulger 4031, Cabot 4034, Chicopee 4047, Crane 4058, Dedham 4067, Easthampton 4076, Gerrity 4102, Hale 4112, Hauben 4123, Hazard 4123, Hoffman 4131, Hopedale 4134, Hyde 4139, **Kahn 4143,** Krieger 4160, Marcus 4188, Massachusetts 4191, Morse 4209, Rockland 4267, Rosse 4272, Russell 4273, Shaughnessy 4292, **Spero 4304,** Stearns 4310, Stearns 4311, Steiger 4312, Wallace 4347, Webster 4353, Winthrop 4363
Michigan: Baldwin 4382, Barron 4384, Bierlein 4392, Burdick-Thorne 4402, Community 4410, Dana 4419, Farver 4441, JSJ 4474, Kinney 4483, Lapeer 4490, Morley 4518, Olds 4526, Onequest 4527, Power 4544, Redies 4549, Schmuckal 4559, St. 4576, **Teltel 4589, Triford 4597,** Vicksburg 4606
Minnesota: Andersen 4626, Ankeny 4628, Bend 4639, Briggs 4648, Deikel 4663, Erickson 4675, **Fingerhut 4683,** Goldman 4697, Grossman 4701, **Kaplan 4721,** Larsen 4728, O'Neil 4755, Quinlan 4764, Rahr 4766, Regis 4770, Riverway 4776, Roberts 4778, Squam 4793, Walker 4805, Wells 4811, Wells 4812, Weyerhaeuser 4815, Whitney 4817
Missouri: **Bohm 4871,** Butler 4880, Copaken 4888, Cray 4890, Dierberg 4895, Garvey 4913, Gaylord 4915, Grant 4918, Shawe 5000, Sigma-Aldrich 5003, Simmons 5005, Wurst 5043
Nebraska: Ameritas 5067, Barklage 5071, Hawkins 5089, Heuermann 5092, Kilbourne 5097, Perkins 5111, Storz 5122
Nevada: **A 5131**
New Hampshire: Barker 5204, Bickford 5205, Hunt 5214, McIninch 5224, Verney 5236
New Jersey: A 5240, Aufzien 5253, Clermont 5298, **Crane 5306,** Fox 5349, Giants 5369, Holzer 5396, Mamiye 5456, Miller 5468, Schwartz 5525, Shilling 5534, Snyder 5540
New Mexico: **Angelica 5605,** Foster 5615, Taos 5626
New York: AKC 5651, American 5664, **Blinken 5757,** Carwill 5818, EMSA 5961, Ferguson 5999, French 6032, G&A 6048, Gilliam 6078, Gordon 6110, Grumbacher 6148, **Harriman 6170,** Heyman 6201, High 6206, IF 6237, **Kathwari 6286,** Kimmelman 6309, Klein 6325, Knapp 6331, Koessler 6335, Lee 6372, Lubo 6417, Lucelia 6418, Marble 6441, Mendell 6472, Messinger 6482, Miller 6493, Netter 6525, Norwich 6542, Offensend 6550, Plymouth 6612, **Posner-Wallace 6621,** Raymond 6652, Rose 6684, Salomon 6721, **Schmeelk 6742,** Schwartz 6753, Stebbins 6850, **Stein 6855,** Strong 6872, Utica 6922, Wilson 6979, Wolk 6987, **Woodland 6989,** Zenkel 7023

North Carolina: Arcadia 7040, BB&T 7045, Bolick 7056, Burlington 7062, Cooke 7079, Fox 7103, Meyer 7184, Rankin 7217, Redwoods 7218, **Rolander 7229,** Silverman 7244, Smith 7249
Ohio: Anderson 7305, Andrews 7307, Armington 7309, Beecher 7321, Bicknell 7327, Brown 7336, Chemed 7350, Community 7356, **Elisha-Bolton 7387,** Firman 7400, Fox 7409, Haskell 7439, Homan 7451, Kangesser 7474, **Katz 7475,** Kilworth 7477, Kramer 7484, LKC 7501, **Lowe-Marshall 7505,** Mather 7516, McMaster 7521, Morley 7532, Musson 7534, Norweb 7539, Reynolds 7558, Ritchie 7561, Sandfair 7569, Scotford 7579, Sears-Swetland 7581, Smith 7598, Tait 7610, Traeger 7621, Tuscarawas 7623, Wasserstrom 7632, Watson 7633
Oklahoma: Atherton 7657, Barnes 7659, Brown 7664, Collins, 7669, Goddard 7684, Merrick 7707, Stone 7721
Oregon: Flowerree 7763, Holzman 7775, Kuse 7786, **Larson 7788,** Portland 7807, Schmidt 7813, Woodard 7831
Pennsylvania: Ames 7840, Arkema 7842, **Arronson 7844,** Ashland 7845, Bergman 7863, Bergstrom 7864, Born 7885, Bucks 7905, Carlson 7916, Charlestein 7920, CNB 7929, **Cohn 7931,** Cove 7939, Donnelly 7963, First 7998, Fortinsky 8002, Freas 8005, Frohring 8010, Gulati 8032, Hankin 8038, Hoffman 8062, **KL 8094,** Knudsen 8102, Levee 8121, Mill 8172, Murphy 8185, Norbell 8195, Patterson 8205, Pfundt 8213, Plankenhorn 8219, **Rust 8250,** Schlarbaum 8259, Shore 8276, Smith 8280, Staehle 8295, Stein 8299, Stott 8304, Strawbridge 8305, Tippins 8318, Weiler-Miller 8348, Weiner 8349, Wenger 8352, Wurts 8370, **Zeldin 8376**
Rhode Island: Collis 8397, Hope 8422, Kingsbury 8435, Papitto 8467, Prouty 8476, Sinclair 8488, Sullivan 8494
South Carolina: Bailey 8510, Eastern 8522
Tennessee: Boring 8590, EBS 8610, **Fugitive 8618,** Gaylord 8620, Hutcheson 8631, Jewell 8633, Massengill-DeFriece 8647, Schmidt 8671
Texas: Adler 8692, Augur 8712, Burch 8756, Cemo 8765, Central 8766, Clements 8773, Cook 8786, **Crowder 8792,** Dougherty, 8825, Dunaway 8832, Finger 8857, Foster 8868, Genecov 8886, Griffin 8902, Hervey 8932, Hill 8938, Hixon 8940, Kahn 8978, Kaplan 8979, Kayser 8980, KCL 8981, Light 9016, Luse 9029, Mays 9045, McKee 9052, Mendenhall 9056, Mitte 9069, O'Connor 9093, Pack 9109, Papadopoulos 9113, Petty 9126, Roosth 9160, Rowan 9166, Tennessee 9230, Vaughan 9249, Wal-Dot 9256, Weaver 9265, Willard 9278, Wolff-Toomim 9286, Works 9293
Utah: Kennecott 9333, Patel 9344, Slaughter, 9353
Vermont: Mergens 9381, Redducs 9383
Virginia: American 9387, **Delmar 9429,** Glasser 9459, Pruden 9517, RECO 9522, Treakle 9543
Washington: DeFalco 9585, Everett 9592, Fales 9594, Grousemont 9611, Johnston-Hanson 9635, Kilworth 9644, Murray 9667, Nysether 9671, Stevens 9704, Young 9732
West Virginia: Logan 9756
Wisconsin: Gardner 9825, Hunt 9845, Jacobus 9849, Kachel 9857, Koss 9866, Marshfield 9878, Prescott 9905, Sartori 9921, Webcrafters-Frautschi 9957, Witte, 9962
Wyoming: Scott 9988, Skelton 9989

Building and renovations

California: Amador 238, Zacky 1206
Delaware: Chaney 1640

Florida: **Benedict 1884**, Marshall 2195, Reinhold 2280
Hawaii: Central 2627, Teruya 2651
Illinois: Listeman 3055
Indiana: Community 3359, Fayette 3379, Vevay-Switzerland 3462
Kansas: Kansas 3592
Massachusetts: Permanent 4239
Michigan: Community 4410, Gratiot 4459
Missouri: MFA 4960
New Jersey: Snyder 5541
New Mexico: Carlsbad 5608, Taos 5626
New York: **Cogitare 5855**
Ohio: Beecher 7321, Bryan 7339, Haskell 7439
Oklahoma: **Crio 7670**
Pennsylvania: Community 7933, Emporium 7980
Texas: Amarillo 8697, Boeing 8733, Webre 9266
Virginia: Northern 9503
West Virginia: Hollowell 9751
Wyoming: Sargent 9985

Capacity-building and technical assistance

Alabama: Ireland 39
California: Ackerman 227, Amador 238, Community 420, Fox 525, Heller 613, Laguna 726, **Lloyd 763**, Solano 1063, Weil 1163, Western 1176
Colorado: Leighty 1311, Vradenburg 1374
Connecticut: Fauth 1445
Delaware: New 1715, **TeleTech 1761**
District of Columbia: Jovid 1817
Florida: Charlotte 1938, Shockley 2332
Georgia: Athens 2437
Illinois: Community 2803
Indiana: Community 3359, Huntington 3397, LaGrange 3412
Kansas: Farah 3576
Maine: Davenport 3775
Massachusetts: Alden 3999, **Bruner 4030, Pegasus 4236**
Michigan: Roscommon 4552, Wickson-Link 4616
Minnesota: Larsen 4728
Missouri: Edgar 4899
Montana: Cinnabar 5047, Cora 5048
New Hampshire: Hunt 5214, McIninch 5224
New Jersey: Westfield 5582
New Mexico: Con 5611
New York: Messinger 6482, Ong 6558, Sheafer 6789, **Sparkplug 6830**, Wurtele 6997
North Carolina: Fox 7103, Strowd 7258
Ohio: Ginn 7425, Osteopathic 7545, Sears-Swetland 7581, Tuscarawas 7623
Oklahoma: Cherokee 7666
Oregon: Elwood 7761
Pennsylvania: Brooks 7899, Bucks 7905, Community 7933, Crawford 7944, Hoffman 8062, **KL 8094**, Schuylkill 8263
Texas: **Chrest 8770**, Dougherty, 8825, Mitte 9069
Vermont: Castanea 9368
Virginia: **Fund 9455**, Northern 9503
Washington: Foss 9598
Wisconsin: Marshfield 9878

Capital and infrastructure

Alabama: Friedman 27, Ireland 39, Kemp 42
Arizona: Grossman 126, James 132, Napier 152
Arkansas: Hickingbotham 199, White 220
California: Acacia 225, Anhaltzer 245, Atkinson 259, Baker 264, Bank 272, Bannerman 274, Bear 288, Beynon 312, Boyer 335, **Bull 358, Butler 365, Cantor 375**, Church 403, Cleo 407, Coleman 416, Corday 426, Corwin 428, Drum 464, Fusenot 541, Godric 566, Harris 601, **Hefferlin 610**, Horwitz 633, Huntington 642, Kelly 697, Looker 766, Lopez 767, McLean 817, Pauley 909, **Peszynski 917**, Ragir 950, Ross 988, Rossi 989, Seip 1028, Stauffer

1076, Sudikoff 1090, **Sunwest 1094**, Szekely 1102, **Teichman 1106**, Von 1147, Waltmar 1155, Warren 1159, Wharton 1178, White 1180, Yuki 1203
Colorado: Ballantine 1226, Goodwin 1279, Heginbotham 1289, Hoag 1293, Mullen 1329, Schramm 1350, **Someone 1354**, Southwestern 1355, Stratton 1359, Taylor 1364, Vradenburg 1374, Wilkins 1379
Connecticut: Anderson 1393, Baldwin 1399, Chelsea 1418, Dime 1438, Jost 1492, Kreitler 1502, Martin 1520, Proctor 1545, Roberts 1552, Thomaston 1581, Union 1590, Winokur 1597
Delaware: Alcyon 1608, Babcock 1612, Glencoe 1669, Kutz 1696, Lightner 1699, New 1715, Patterson 1719, SNAVE 1747, Thronson 1766, Whitman 1778
District of Columbia: Cafritz 1793, Goldman 1810, Westport 1838
Florida: Archibald 1852, **Atlantis 1858, Aviation 1861**, Baroco 1867, Chapman 1935, Coral 1952, Couch 1953, Day 1965, Dorset 1979, Duckwall 1982, Duda 1983, Elster 1990, Fowler 2014, **Freewill 2021**, Golden 2046, Goody 2049, Grader 2054, Graese 2055, Greene-Sawtell 2065, Gulf 2069, Hill 2097, Hultquist 2115, Kugelman 2161, Lelash 2178, Marco 2194, Mayberg 2199, **Mukti 2226**, Munroe 2228, Oristano 2241, Phillips 2260, Silverman 2337, Thomas 2371, Turner 2381, **Uncle 2383**, Votum 2390, Wilson-Wood 2408
Georgia: Abreu 2431, Chatham 2457, Cook, 2468, English 2474, Exposition 2476, **Gage 2482**, Holland-Underwood 2508, Illges 2517, Jolley 2526, Lee 2540, Lipscomb 2541, Marshall 2545, McKnight 2548, Sewell 2584, University 2597, Wright 2620
Hawaii: Baldwin 2625, Vidinha 2653, Wilcox 2654
Idaho: Angels 2664, Morrison 2682, Simplot 2685
Illinois: Adams 2696, Agape 2698, Amsted 2708, **Appleby 2711**, Arboit 2713, Bishop 2743, Brunswick 2762, Bulkley, 2765, Canterbury 2774, Chicago 2786, Community 2803, Delta 2826, Dubin 2838, EMA 2854, Faulkner 2867, Harris 2957, Heath 2962, Hess 2969, Hunt 2984, Johnson 3001, **Krasberg-Mason 3029, Mead 3100**, Meyer 3106, Millard 3109, Munson 3130, Reichert 3192, Rosenson 3209, Shaker 3238, Staley 3262, Steigerwaldt 3265, Stone 3270, Takiff 3281, Tuohy 3296, Webb 3313
Indiana: **Ackerman 3339**, Ayres 3342, Benton 3344, Bussing-Koch 3353, Community 3360, Decatur 3367, Froderman 3383, Huntington 3397, Jennings 3402, Kuhne 3409, LaGrange 3412, Oakley 3426, Oliver 3428, Raker 3434, Rush 3441, Seger 3447, Springleaf 3455, Western 3466
Iowa: Cowles 3482, Farver 3491, First 3493, Forster 3494, Gazette 3497, Jefferson 3514, Van 3539, **Wahlert 3544**, West 3547, **Wright 3551**, Young 3552
Kansas: Baehr 3556, Bane 3557, Berry 3558, Cape 3563, Cochener 3565, DeVore 3573, Farah 3576, Fidelity 3577, Goebel 3580, Mingenback 3605, Payless 3614, Ross 3619, Trusler 3635, Watson 3639
Kentucky: Abercrombie 3645, Barth 3647, Etscorn 3654, Hannah 3659, Hayswood 3662, Keeneland 3668, Mackin 3673, Murry 3681, Reed 3688, Sutherland 3699, Trim 3702
Louisiana: Dujay 3722, Huie-Dellmon 3729, Steinhagen 3755, Wheless 3758, Wisdom 3761
Maine: Borman 3767, Burnham 3770, Davenport 3775, Kennebec 3785
Maryland: Ammerman 3813, Campbell 3831, Croft 3841, Davis 3844, Gladding 3871, **Goldberg 3872**, Hobbs 3882, Kelly, 3893, Otenasek 3931, Richmond 3940, Tucker 3969, Widgeon 3983
Massachusetts: Behrakis 4015, Boynton 4025, Cabot 4034, Codman 4052, Cricket 4060, Dedham 4067, Easthampton 4076, Henderson 4128, Hoffman 4131, Hyde 4139, Lingos 4177, Massachusetts 4191, Morse 4209, Phelps 4242, Sailors' 4276,

Simoni 4296, Stearns 4310, Steiger 4312, Ungar 4336, United 4337, Wallace 4347, Walsh 4348, Wyman-Gordon 4364, Xeric 4365
Michigan: Andersen 4377, Baldwin 4382, Biederman 4391, Buhr 4400, Burdick-Thorne 4402, Community 4411, Dana 4419, Farver 4441, Frankenmuth 4450, Glassen 4454, Holden 4467, JSJ 4474, Kantzler 4478, Keller 4481, Kinney 4483, LoPrete 4496, Morley 4518, Plym 4542, Power 4544, Ratner 4548, Redies 4549, Schalon 4558, Stubnitz 4582, **Teitel 4589**, Tuscola 4598, Vicksburg 4606, Wickson-Link 4616
Minnesota: Baratz 4635, Bell 4637, Bend 4639, Deikel 4663, Depot 4667, Edina 4672, **Fingerhut 4683**, Granite 4699, Larsen 4728, Midcontinent 4745, O'Brien 4753, Quinlan 4764, Regis 4770, Riverway 4776, **Trust 4802**, Walker 4805
Missouri: Baer 4862, **Bohm 4871**, Boylan 4873, Cornelsen 4889, Cray 4890, Curry 4892, Dierberg 4895, Dunn 4898, Edgar 4899, Forster-Powers 4911, Garvey 4913, Gaylord 4915, Grant 4918, Long 4948, O'Reilly 4975, Portman 4981, Shawe 5000, Simmons 5005, Slusher 5009, Van 5028, Walker 5034
Montana: Lynn 5059, Taylor 5064
Nebraska: Baright 5070, Barklage 5071, Farr 5079, Friedland 5082, Hawkins 5089, Heuermann 5092, Midlands 5104, Pegler 5110, Perkins 5111, Reynolds 5114, Storz 5122
Nevada: **A 5131**, Meyer 5177, West 5197
New Hampshire: Barker 5204, Hunt 5214, Jameson 5215, McIninch 5224, Verney 5236, Wutz 5239
New Jersey: A 5240, Carlozzi 5287, Columbia 5301, Kerney 5419, Leavens 5444, Mamiye 5456, Miller 5468, Schwartz 5525, Selective 5528, Smith 5539, Westfield 5582
New York: American 5664, Anderson-Rogers 5676, August 5698, Bender 5735, Cutco 5890, D-B 5903, Dworman 5938, French 6032, Glens 6082, Grand 6123, Grossman 6144, Grumbacher 6148, Henshel 6192, High 6206, Hoyt 6230, Knapp 6331, Koessler 6334, Koessler 6335, Legacy 6373, Leonhardt 6381, Liberman 6396, Lucelia 6418, Marble 6441, McCarthy 6456, Messinger 6482, Netter 6525, **Nok 6537**, Northern 6540, Norwich 6542, Nuhn 6544, Offensend 6550, Ong 6558, Plymouth 6612, **Potts 6624**, Raphael 6648, Raymond 6652, Ring 6671, Salomon 6721, Schwartz 6753, Schwartz 6755, Schweckendieck 6758, Slade 6809, Snow 6818, **Stein 6855**, Strong 6872, Truman 6912, Utica 6922, Wilson 6979, **Woodland 6989**, Zenkel 7023
North Carolina: BB&T 7045, Bolick 7056, Burlington 7062, Chatham 7074, Cooke 7079, Covington 7081, Duncan 7086, First 7097, Flowers 7099, Fox 7103, Glenn 7111, Hunt 7134, Koury 7150, **Kramer 7152**, Masserini 7172, Meyer 7184, Morrison 7193, Outer 7204, Rankin 7217, **Rolander 7229**, Smith 7249, Stonecutter 7255, Strowd 7258, Vanderbilt 7273, Yost 7291
North Dakota: Myra 7297
Ohio: Anderson 7305, B-Brand 7318, Beecher 7320, Bicknell 7327, Brown 7336, Christ 7352, Community 7356, Coressel 7364, Crandall 7366, Crossroads 7367, Danis 7371, Defiance 7375, Dienstberger 7379, Finnegan 7399, Firman 7400, Fox 7409, Frohman 7411, Frost-Parker 7413, Gale 7414, Gale 7415, Hauck 7440, **Highfield 7450**, Homan 7451, Kangesser 7474, Kilworth 7477, Knoll 7483, Kramer 7485, LKC 7501, Lundgard 7508, Mather 7516, McMaster 7521, Montauk 7531, Morley 7532, Musson 7534, Myers 7535, Ohio 7541, Quatman 7552, Ritchie 7561, Rosenberry 7562, Sandfair 7569, Scotford 7579, Sears-Swetland 7581, Smith 7598, Stensen 7604, Tait 7610, Tuscarawas 7623, Van 7625, Walker 7630, Watson 7633, Young 7652
Oklahoma: Ashbrook 7656, Broadhurst 7663, Collins 7668, Collins, 7669, Gelvin 7682, Goddard 7684, Holliman 7687, Kerr 7693, Merrick 7707, Wegener 7731

Oregon: Collins 7752, Four 7764, Hitchman 7774, Holzman 7775, Kuse 7786, McKay 7795, Merlo 7797, Miller 7800, Parker/United 7805, Pendleton 7806, Silver 7817, Wessinger 7826, Western 7829, Woodard 7831

Pennsylvania: Arkema 7842, **Arronson 7844**, Bennett 7860, Bucks 7905, Carlson 7916, Carnahan-Jackson 7917, Chase 7921, **Cohn 7931**, Cove 7939, Crawford 7944, Donnelly 7963, Elk 7975, Finley 7995, First 7997, Friendship 8009, Frohring 8010, Grundy 8029, Gulati 8032, Hankin 8038, Hassel 8042, HBE 8047, High 8054, Hirtzel 8058, Hodge 8061, Hoffman 8062, John 8081, **KL 8094**, Kline 8098, Maslow 8146, McCandless 8153, Miller 8173, Murphy 8185, Mylan 8187, Norbell 8195, Patterson 8205, Pfundt 8213, Plankenhorn 8219, Reidler 8233, Reiss 8234, Remmel 8235, **Rust 8250**, Shoemaker 8275, Smith 8280, Smith, 8285, Stein 8299, Stott 8304, Tippins 8318, Union 8326, Weiler-Miller 8348, Weiner 8349, Wenger 8352, Williams 8357

Rhode Island: Collis 8397, Getz 8412, Heydt 8419, Hope 8422, Kimball 8434, McCarthy 8452, Sinclair 8488, Slemons 8490, Washington 8500

South Carolina: Bailey 8510, Bonner 8513, Lutz 8533

South Dakota: Watertown 8576

Tennessee: **Fugitive 8618**, Jewell 8633, Tompkins 8683

Texas: Anderson 8704, Bertha 8729, Bromberg 8748, Cemo 8765, Central 8766, Clear 8772, Community 8782, Cook 8786, de 8802, Dougherty 8825, Dunagan 8831, Dunaway 8832, Elkins 8838, Fair 8844, Fash 8848, Finger 8857, Flowers 8862, Foundation 8869, Graham 8896, Griffin 8902, Hext 8933, Hill 8938, Kaplan 8979, Kayser 8980, KCL 8981, Light 9016, Littauer 9021, Luse 9029, Mayer 9043, Mays 9045, McKee 9052, Mitte 9069, Myers 9081, O'Connor 9093, Pratt 9137, Redman 9147, Smith 9201, Tennessee 9230, Vaughan 9249, Waggoner 9254, Walls 9257, Willard 9278, Wood 9290, Works 9293

Utah: Eskuche 9323, Odyssey 9342, Patel 9344, Questar 9346, Questar 9347

Vermont: Castanea 9368, Mergens 9381

Virginia: American 9387, Backer 9389, Beck 9393, Camp 9413, **Delmar 9429**, Lawrence 9487, Pruden 9517, Roller-Bottimore 9525, Treakle 9543, Two 9544

Washington: Grousemont 9611, Howarth 9626, Kawabe 9642, Kilworth 9644, Korum 9648, Murray 9667, Nysether 9671, Stevens 9704

West Virginia: Chambers 9742, Skewes 9766

Wisconsin: Ariens 9776, Dudley 9811, Eau 9814, Gardner 9825, Hunt 9845, Inbusch 9847, J.P.C. 9848, Jacobus 9849, Lakeview 9868, Manitowoc 9876, Mid-States 9887, Modine 9889, Phipps 9903, Prescott 9905, Regal-Beloit 9911, Roehl 9917, Webcrafters-Frautschi 9957, Witte, 9962, Woodtrust-Bell 9963

Wyoming: Scott 9988, Skelton 9989, Weiss 9997

Capital campaigns

Alabama: Black 12, Friedman 27, Kemp 42, Pei-Ling 52, Petra 53, Phifer, 54, Sexton 63

Arizona: F2 117, Grossman 126, James 132, Louis 142, Napier 152, Zicarelli 185

Arkansas: Hickingbotham 199

California: Amador 238, Anhaltzer 245, Atkinson 259, Bank 272, Bannerman 274, Bear 288, Bettingen 310, Bridges 342, **Bull 358, Butler 365, Cantor 375**, Celebrate 383, Church 403, Cleo 407, Coleman 416, Corday 426, Corwin 428, Fusenot 541, Garaventa 546, Gellert 550, Gill 555, Horwitz 633, Huntington 642, Kelly 697, Looker 766, Majestic 784, McClatchy 811, McDaniel 812, McLean 817, Outrageous 894, Payne 910, Ragir 950, Santa 1003, Seip 1028, Silicon 1038, Smullin 1060, Von 1147, **Wakerly 1150**, Waltmar 1155, **Wilkinson 1183**

Colorado: Donnell-Kay 1258, Goodwin 1279, Margulf 1320, Stratton 1359, Vradenburg 1374, Wilkins 1379

Connecticut: Anderson 1393, Baldwin 1399, Dime 1438, Jones 1489, Keefe 1497, Kreitler 1502, Martin 1520, McLeod 1524, O'Herron 1536, Proctor 1545, Pryor 1546, Roberts 1552, UIL 1589, Vance 1591

Delaware: Alcyon 1608, Brown-Whitworth 1632, Chaney 1640, Kutz 1696, Lightner 1699, New 1715, Patterson 1719, Rumberger 1734, SNAVE 1747, Thronson 1766

District of Columbia: Bench 1788, Bender 1789, Cafritz 1793, Goldman 1810, Porter 1829, Westport 1838

Florida: Archibald 1852, Baroco 1867, Chadbourne 1932, Chapman 1935, Dasburg 1961, Dorset 1979, Duckwall 1982, Elster 1990, Erdle 1993, Graese 2055, Greene-Sawtell 2065, Gulf 2069, Hultquist 2115, Lelash 2178, Marshall 2195, Martin 2196, Mayberg 2199, McCabe 2201, Munroe 2228, Oristano 2241, Phillips 2260, Reinhold 2280, Rinker 2287, Rothman 2299, Sexton 2326, Silverman 2337, Tampa 2362, TECO 2367, Tupperware 2379, Turner 2381, **Uncle 2383**, Wilson-Wood 2408

Georgia: Abreu 2431, English 2474, Exposition 2476, Howell 2512, Hunter 2515, Illges 2517, Jolley 2526, Knox 2534, Lee 2540, Marshall 2545, McKnight 2548, Oxford 2561, Patrick 2562, Raoul 2573, Sewell 2584, Tritt 2596

Hawaii: Moore 2643, Servco 2645, Wilcox 2654

Idaho: Morrison 2682, Simplot 2685, Wishnick 2690

Illinois: Adams 2696, Agape 2698, **Appleby 2711**, Arboit 2713, Bere 2734, Bernoudy 2738, Best 2740, Brunswick 2762, Bulkley 2765, Cain 2773, Cole 2798, Dubin 2838, Gochnauer 2918, Gust 2936, Harris 2957, Hopper 2977, Hughes 2983, **Krasberg-Mason 3029, Lazzara 3042**, Levy 3050, **Lindon 3054**, McLaughlin 3095, **Mead 3100**, Meyer 3106, Morton 3127, **New 3137**, Peters 3172, Rosenson 3209, Smith 3253, Staley 3262, Takiff 3281, Tuohy 3296, Vail 3301, **Wein 3315**

Indiana: **Ackerman 3339**, Ayres 3342, Bussing-Koch 3353, CDM 3355, Community 3359, Harlan 3391, Kuhne 3409, Lacy 3410, Namaste 3422, Noecker 3424, Oakley 3426, Oliver 3428, Schurz 3444, Western 3466

Iowa: deStwolinski 3486, Farver 3491, First 3493, Gazette 3497, Krumm 3517, McDonald 3520, **Wahlert 3544**, West 3547, **World 3550**, Young 3552

Kansas: Brown 3561, DeVore 3573, Family 3575, Farah 3576, Fidelity 3577, Insurance 3587, Master 3600, Mingenback 3605, Payless 3614, Schmidt 3622, South 3628, Watson 3639, Wiedemann 3642, Williams 3643

Kentucky: Barth 3647, Coffey 3650, Etscorn 3654, Hannah 3659, Hayswood 3662, Keeneland 3668, Murry 3681, Stock 3697, Sutherland 3699, Trim 3702

Louisiana: Dujay 3722, Huie-Dellmon 3729, Mintz 3738, Wheless 3758, Wisdom 3761

Maine: Borman 3767, Burnham 3770, Lynam 3788, Somers 3803

Maryland: Ammerman 3813, Broadus 3829, Campbell 3831, Caplan 3832, Contino 3840, Darby 3843, Davis 3844, Gewirz 3869, Gladding 3871, **Goldberg 3872**, Israelson 3888, Kelly, 3893, Macht 3905, Moser 3918, Phase 3936, Richmond 3940, Tucker 3969, Van 3973, Weiner 3980

Massachusetts: 2 3992, Behrakis 4015, Berger 4018, Bulger 4031, Cabot 4034, Carlee 4038, Crane 4058, Cricket 4060, Dedham 4067, East 4075, Easthampton 4076, Hauben 4120, Hazard 4123, Hoffman 4131, Hopedale 4134, Hornblower 4135, Hyde 4139, **Kahn 4143**, Kelsey 4148, King 4156, Krieger 4160, Mahoney 4184, Marcus 4188, Morse 4209, MutualOne 4216, Permanent 4239, Rockland 4267, Stearns 4310, Steiger 4312, United 4337, Wallace 4347, Winthrop 4363, Wyman-Gordon 4364

Michigan: Andersen 4377, Baldwin 4382, Barron 4384, Barstow 4385, Bierlein 4392, Buhr 4400, Burdick-Thorne 4402, Community 4411, Cummings 4417, Dana 4419, DiPonio 4432, Fabiano 4438, Farver 4441, Gershenson 4453, JSJ 4474, Kantzler 4478, Keller 4481, Kellogg 4482, Kinney 4483, LoPrete 4496, McNally 4510, Morley 4518, O'Donovan 4525, Olds 4526, Power 4544, Redies 4549, Schmuckal 4559, **Teitel 4589**, Tyler-Little 4599, Van 4602, Vicksburg 4606, Wickson-Link 4616

Minnesota: Ankeny 4628, Bell 4637, Borman 4644, Briggs 4648, Deikel 4663, Edina 4672, Ferber 4682, **Fingerhut 4683**, Granite 4699, Heilmaier 4712, Larsen 4728, Noreen 4750, Rauenhorst 4767, Regis 4770, Riverway 4776, Tennant 4798, Thorpe 4800, Wells 4811, **Winds 4820**

Mississippi: Baird 4822

Missouri: **Bohm 4871**, Butler 4880, Curry 4892, Garvey 4913, Gaylord 4915, Grant 4918, Long 4948, Lordi 4950, Morgan 4963, Moss 4964, Schutte 4995, Shawe 5000, Simmons 5005, Sunnen 5018, Vatterott 5030

Montana: Lynn 5059, Sample 5062

Nebraska: Ameritas 5067, Barklage 5071, Friedland 5082, Heuermann 5092, Midlands 5104, Pegler 5110, Perkins 5111, Physicians 5112, Storz 5122

New Hampshire: Barker 5204, Hunt 5214, Jameson 5215, McIninch 5224, Olcott 5227, Verney 5236

New Jersey: A 5240, Aufzien 5255, **Blue 5269**, Brundage 5280, Carlozzi 5287, Clermont 5298, Columbia 5301, Frelinghuysen 5354, **Knistrom 5426**, Machuga 5454, Miller 5468, Schwartz 5525, Selective 5528, Snyder 5541, Stone 5553, Wetterberg 5583, WKBJ 5592

New Mexico: Taos 5626

New York: AKC 5651, August 5698, Balbach 5707, Barham 5715, Bender 5735, Bernheim 5740, Bobrow 5765, Carwill 5818, Clark 5848, Cutco 5890, D-B 5903, EMSA 5961, Ferguson 5999, French 6032, Gaffney 6049, Gage 6050, Gilliam 6078, Glens 6082, Grumbacher 6148, Hallingby 6160, **Harriman 6170**, Heyman 6201, High 6206, Hilliard 6208, Hoyt 6230, JI 6260, Joukowsky 6274, **Klagsbrun 6318**, Klein 6325, Koessler 6335, Legacy 6373, Liberman 6396, Lucelia 6418, Lux 6422, Marble 6441, Messinger 6482, Netter 6525, Norwich 6542, Offensend 6550, Ong 6558, Osceola 6560, O'Sullivan 6565, Plymouth 6612, Pollack 6615, Pratt-Northam 6625, Raymond 6652, Rexford 6664, Sheafer 6789, Stebbins 6850, Steckler 6853, **Stein 6855**, Strong 6872, Truman 6912, White 6973, Wilson 6979, Wolk 6987, **Woodland 6989**, Zenkel 7023

North Carolina: Arcadia 7040, BB&T 7045, Bolick 7056, Burlington 7062, Cooke 7079, Covington 7081, Davis 7083, Duncan 7086, First 7097, Fox 7103, Hunt 7134, Katz 7142, **Kramer 7152**, Meyer 7184, Morrison 7193, Mount 7196, Rankin 7217, **Rolander 7229**, Silverman 7244, Smith 7249, SPX 7252, Strowd 7258, Trexler 7269

Ohio: Anderson 7305, Andrews 7307, Athens 7311, Bates 7317, B-Brand 7318, Beecher 7320, Beecher 7321, Bicknell 7327, Brown 7336, Bryan 7339, Chemed 7350, Cooper 7362, Corbett 7363, Crandall 7366, Danis 7371, Defiance 7375, Entelco 7389, Finnegan 7399, Firman 7400, Fox 7409, Frohman 7411, Frost-Parker 7413, Gale 7414, Gale 7415, Goerlich 7428, Hauck 7440, Homan 7451, Kangesser 7474, Kilworth 7477, Kramer 7485, LKC 7501, Lundgard 7508, Mangano 7511, Mather 7516, McMaster 7521, Montauk 7531, Norweb 7539, Ohio 7541, Quatman 7552, Ritchie 7561, Sandfair 7569, Scotford 7579, Sears-Swetland 7581, Smith 7598, Stillson 7607, Tuscarawas 7623, Walker 7630, Wallace 7631, Wasserstrom 7632, Watson 7633, Young 7652

Oklahoma: Barnes 7659, Barthelmes 7661, Broadhurst 7663, Brown 7664, Collins, 7669, Dill 7671, Gelvin 7682, Holliman 7687, Merrick 7707, Peel 7714, Wegener 7731

Oregon: Flowerree 7763, Four 7764, Holzman 7775, Kuse 7786, McKay 7795, Merlo 7797, Pendleton 7806, Silver 7817, Wessinger 7826, Woodard 7831

Pennsylvania: Alley 7837, **Arronson 7844**, Bennett 7860, Bergman 7863, Bergstrom 7864, Born 7885, Bucks 7905, Carlson 7916, Carnahan-Jackson 7917, Chase 7921, CNB 7929, **Cohn 7931**, Columbia 7932, Donnelly 7963, Double 7964, First 7998, Fleming 8000, Freas 8005, Friendship 8009, Gamber 8011, Gulati 8032, Hankin 8038, HBE 8047, High 8054, Hirtzel 8058, Hoffman 8062, Hulme 8069, **KL 8094**, Kline 8098, Knudsen 8102, Larking 8112, Maslow 8146, McCandless 8153, McKinney 8161, Mill 8172, Murphy 8185, Norbell 8195, Packer 8201, Patterson 8205, Pfundt 8213, Quinn 8229, Reidler 8233, Reiss 8234, Remmel 8235, **Rust 8250**, Schlarbaum 8259, Shoemaker 8275, Shore 8276, Smith 8280, Smith, 8285, Stein 8299, Tippins 8318, Weiler-Miller 8348, Wenger 8352, Williams 8357, **Zeldin 8376**

Rhode Island: Bernhardt 8387, Collis 8397, Heydt 8419, Hope 8422, Kimball 8434, Kingsbury 8435, Littlefield 8441, McCarthy 8452, Prouty 8476, Sinclair 8488, Slemons 8490, Sullivan 8494, Washington 8500

South Carolina: Bailey 8510, Lutz 8533

South Dakota: J&L 8568, Watertown 8576

Tennessee: Campbell 8595, **Fugitive 8618**, Grandview 8625, Jewell 8633, Massengill-DeFriece 8647, Schmidt 8671, WTC 8688

Texas: Adler 8692, Amarillo 8697, Augur 8712, Bromberg 8748, Clements 8773, Community 8782, Cook 8786, **Crowder 8792**, Dale 8794, de 8802, Dougherty, 8825, Elkins 8838, Fenner 8850, Fertitta 8852, Frost 8878, Graham 8896, Hext 8933, Hibbs 8934, Hill 8938, Hixon 8940, Houck 8953, Johnston 8972, Kaplan 8979, KCL 8981, Light 9016, Luse 9029, Mayer 9043, Mays 9045, McKee 9052, McNutt 9055, Mendenhall 9056, Mithoff 9068, Mitte 9069, P 9108, Pack 9109, Papadopoulos 9113, Petty 9126, Redman 9147, Rowan 9166, Sear 9186, Tennessee 9230, Vaughan 9249, Wal-Dot 9256, Ward 9260, Webre 9266, Willard 9278, Wolff-Toomim 9286, Works 9293, Zale 9299

Utah: Eskuche 9323, Green 9327, Patel 9344, Questar 9347

Vermont: Castanea 9368, Redducs 9383

Virginia: American 9387, Backer 9389, Billings 9397, **Brown 9407, Delmar 9429**, Dickerson 9431, Lawrence 9487, Pruden 9517, RECO 9522, Treakle 9543

Washington: Baker 9566, Erickson 9591, Ferguson 9596, Grousemont 9611, Howarth 9626, Kilworth 9644, Korum 9648, Murray 9667, Nysether 9671, Rosen 9684, Skagit 9696, Spark 9701, Stevens 9704, Wilson 9725

West Virginia: Brown 9739, Chambers 9742, Driehorst 9743, Hollowell 9751

Wisconsin: Doolittle 9809, Dudley 9811, Eau 9814, Erdman 9816, Gardner 9825, Hunt 9845, Inbusch 9847, Jacobus 9849, Janesville 9850, **Johnson 9851**, Koss 9866, Lakeview 9868, Lutsey 9873, Manitowoc 9876, Martin 9879, Modine 9889, Murray 9892, Prescott 9905, Regal-Beloit 9911, Roehl 9917, Styberg 9942, Webcrafters-Frautschi 9957, Wilson 9960, Woodtrust-Bell 9963

Wyoming: Weiss 9997

Cash grants

California: First 506, Majestic 784
Colorado: Tomkins 1368
Georgia: Oxford 2561
Hawaii: Central 2627
Minnesota: Edina 4672
Nebraska: Owen 5108
New York: Sumitomo 6876

Pennsylvania: Ricon 8237
Tennessee: Cracker 8603
Texas: Webre 9266
Washington: Bungie 9576
Wisconsin: Windway 9961

Cause-related marketing

Maine: Planet 3797

Conference attendance

Minnesota: Farmers 4679

Conferences and exhibits

Pennsylvania: Society 8289

Continuing support

Alabama: Dixon 26, Griswold 31, Ireland 39, Pei-Ling 52
Arizona: Grossman 126, Hughes 130, Knisely 138
Arkansas: Hickingbotham 199
California: Amador 238, Anhaltzer 245, Baye 285, Bear 288, Bellini 298, Bonner 326, Boone 329, Bridges 342, Brotman 351, Buell 357, **Bull 358, Butler 365, Cantor 375**, Charitable 389, Church 403, Cleo 407, Cloud 408, Codding 412, Coleman 416, Corday 426, Corwin 428, Drum 464, Ebell 471, Fox 525, Fusenot 541, Gellert 550, Glikbarg 564, Gross 587, Heller 613, Jamieson 658, KNU 713, Livingston 761, **Lloyd 763**, Looker 766, Lux 773, Majestic 784, McClatchy 811, McLean 817, New 865, Ontario 882, Pacific 897, Page 899, Pauley 909, Payne 910, Plum 929, **Quiksilver 945**, Rice 969, **Rifkind 972**, Rocca, 978, Ross 988, **Sargent 1005**, Solano 1063, Stauffer 1076, Sterling 1081, **Sunwest 1094, Teichman 1106, Wakerly 1150**, Weil 1163, Welk 1170, Wharton 1178, **Wilkinson 1183**
Colorado: Ballantine 1226, Burt 1244, Comprecare 1249, Donahue 1257, Donnell-Kay 1258, **Fishback 1270**, Goodwin 1279, **Nord 1332, Oreg 1335**, Schlessman 1349, Schramm 1350, Spencer 1356, Stratton 1359, Vradenburg 1374
Connecticut: Chelsea 1418, Cochrane 1420, Crosswicks 1425, Curran 1427, Fry 1458, Proctor 1545, **Sullivan 1578**
Delaware: Freedman 1665, Glencoe 1669, New 1715, Patterson 1719, Thronson 1766
District of Columbia: Cafritz 1793, Dimick 1803, Jovid 1817, **Pettus-Crowe 1828**, Replogle 1831, Westport 1838
Florida: Anderson 1847, Archibald 1852, **Atlantis 1858**, Aurora 1860, Catalina 1928, Chapman 1935, Elster 1990, Erdle 1993, **Freewill 2021**, Graese 2055, Gulf 2069, Hill 2097, KT 2160, Landwirth 2167, Lazarus 2172, Long 2189, Morrison 2222, **Mukti 2226**, Oristano 2241, Price 2267, Ray 2275, Rothman 2299, Silverman 2337, Smith 2341, Thomas 2371
Georgia: **Bancker-Williams 2440**, Greiner 2498, Health 2504, Lee 2540, Magnus 2543, McKnight 2548, Oxford 2561
Hawaii: Moore 2643, Wilcox 2654, Wong 2656
Idaho: Simplot 2685
Illinois: Agape 2698, Alton 2706, Amsted 2708, **Appleby 2711**, Bere 2734, Best 2740, Bishop 2743, Boothroyd 2749, Brunswick 2762, Bufka 2763, Constans-Culver 2805, Dubin 2838, Ideal 2986, Jocarno 3000, **Krasberg-Mason 3029, Landau 3036, Lindon 3054**, Logos 3058, MacDonald 3068, Marsteller 3079, **Mead 3100**, Meyer 3106, Millard 3109, **New 3137**, Pitzman 3177, Reichert 3192, Rosenson 3209, Sasco 3222, Staley 3262, Steigerwaldt 3265, Sulzer 3277, Takiff 3281, Walker 3308, Webb 3313
Indiana: **Ackerman 3339**, Ayres 3342, Bronstein 3351, Bussing-Koch 3353, Lacy 3410, MutualBank 3421,

Oliver 3428, Raymond 3436, Seymour 3448, Springleaf 3455
Iowa: Cowles 3482, Farver 3491, Iowa 3513, Nelson 3524
Kansas: DeVore 3573, Fidelity 3577, Goebel 3580, Legacy, 3595, Payless 3614, Watson 3639
Kentucky: Sutherland 3699
Louisiana: Huie-Dellmon 3729, Vick 3756, Wheless 3758, Wisdom 3761
Maine: Burnham 3770, **Dugas 3776**, Somers 3803
Maryland: Ammerman 3813, Campbell 3831, CSG 3842, Davis 3844, **Goldberg 3872**, Gordon 3873, Higginson 3880, Macht 3905, Weiss 3982, Widgeon 3983
Massachusetts: Behrakis 4015, Boynton 4025, Cabot 4034, Chicopee 4047, Crawford 4059, Easthampton 4076, Gerrity 4102, Hampden 4116, Hauben 4120, Henderson 4127, Hoffman 4131, **Kahn 4143**, Kelsey 4148, Krieger 4160, Morse 4209, **Pegasus 4236**, Permanent 4239, Ratshesky 4259, Sailors' 4276, Shaughnessy 4292, Stearns 4310, Ungar 4336, Vela 4341, Winthrop 4363, Xeric 4365
Michigan: Biederman 4391, Buist 4401, Burdick-Thorne 4402, Dana 4419, Doll-Loesel 4433, Farver 4441, Holden 4467, JSJ 4474, Keller 4481, LoPrete 4496, M 4497, Mackinac 4499, Merkley 4512, Morley 4518, Power 4544, Ratner 4548, Shiawassee 4568, **Teitel 4589**, Thompson 4592, Vicksburg 4606, Wickson-Link 4616
Minnesota: Andersen 4626, Bell 4637, Bell 4638, Briggs 4648, Deikel 4663, **Fingerhut 4683**, Hickory 4713, **Kaplan 4721**, Larsen 4728, O'Brien 4753, Onan 4754, O'Neil 4755, Quinlan 4764, Rahr 4766, Riverway 4776, Rodman 4779, Sayer 4786, Squam 4793, Tennant 4798, **Trust 4802**, Wells 4811, Weyerhaeuser 4815, Whitney 4817
Missouri: **Bohm 4871**, Butler 4880, Copaken 4888, Curry 4892, Gaylord 4915, Pendergast-Weyer 4979, Sigma-Aldrich 5003, Simmons 5005, Van 5028, Vatterott 5030
Nebraska: Ameritas 5067, Kilbourne 5097, Midlands 5104, Pegler 5110, Perkins 5111, Physicians 5112
Nevada: Dermody 5152, Meyer 5177, Timken-Sturgis 5192
New Hampshire: Barker 5204, Bickford 5205, Hunt 5214, Linnell 5219, McIninch 5224, Smyth 5232, Thorne 5233, Verney 5236
New Jersey: A 5240, **Blue 5269**, Carlozzi 5287, **Crane 5306**, Holzer 5396, Miller 5468, Schwartz 5525, **Yin-Shun 5596**, Zobel 5603
New Mexico: Carlsbad 5608, Nirvana 5621, Taos 5626
New York: AKC 5651, American 5662, American 5668, Bernheim 5740, Bernhill 5741, **Buster 5806, Cogitare 5855**, Dammann 5897, D-B 5903, EMSA 5961, French 6032, G&A 6048, Gage 6050, **Grossman 6146**, Grumbacher 6148, Henshel 6192, IF 6237, Johnson 6269, Joseph 6273, Joukowsky 6274, Kenworthy 6300, **Klagsbrun 6318**, Knapp 6331, Lake 6360, Lee 6372, Leonhardt 6381, Loconsolo 6408, Lubo 6417, Lucelia 6418, Messinger 6482, Metzger-Price 6483, Miller 6493, Netter 6525, **Nok 6537**, NYBDC 6546, O'Grady 6551, Ostgrodd 6561, Palisades 6569, Patrina 6579, Plymouth 6612, **Posner-Wallace 6621**, Satow 6732, **Schmeelk 6742, Stein 6855, Stern 6862**, Strong 6872, Tuch 6915, Turner 6916, **Weinstein 6956**
North Carolina: Cooke 7079, Covington 7081, Eddy 7087, Fox 7103, Kenan 7143, Kenan 7144, Meyer 7184, Rankin 7217, **Rixson 7223**, Smith 7249, Strowd 7258
Ohio: Armington 7309, Athens 7311, Austin-Bailey 7312, Brentwood 7330, Brown 7336, Community 7357, **Elisha-Bolton 7387**, Foundation 7408, Fox 7409, Glidden 7427, Haskell 7439, Health 7442, Homan 7471, **Katz 7475**, Kramer 7485, Laub 7490, **Lowe-Marshall 7505**, Mather 7516, McMaster 7521, Musson 7534, Philada 7548, Reynolds 7558, Ritchie 7561, Sears-Swetland 7581, Smith 7598, Tell 7613,

Tuscarawas 7623, Van 7625, Wallace 7631, Watson 7633

Oklahoma: Ashbrook 7656, Atherton 7657, Broadhurst 7663, Brown 7664, Goddard 7684, Stone 7721, Wegener 7731

Oregon: Brown 7744, Holzman 7775, Kuse 7786, Merlo 7797, Pendleton 7806, Schmidt 7813

Pennsylvania: Arkema 7842, Ashland 7845, Baker 7851, Beacon 7856, Bennett 7860, Born 7885, Campbell 7912, Carnahan-Jackson 7917, Cove 7939, Dietrich 7958, Flinn 8001, Fortinsky 8002, Frohring 8010, Gulati 8032, Hankin 8038, Harsco 8040, Hassel 8042, Hoffman 8062, Ludwick 8134, Maslow 8146, Mill 8172, Murphy 8185, Patterson 8205, Pfundt 8213, Reiss 8234, Rider-Pool 8238, **Rust 8250**, Shoemaker 8275, Smith 8280, Stein 8299, Stott 8304, Strawbridge 8305, Union 8326, Valentine 8328, Wenger 8352, Wurts 8370

Rhode Island: Collis 8397, Hope 8422, Littlefield 8441, Moore 8456, Mulligan 8457, Perpetual 8471, Preston 8475, Prouty 8476, Sinclair 8488, Washington 8500

South Carolina: Lutz 8533, Singing 8540

Tennessee: EBS 8610, Massengill-DeFriece 8647

Texas: Adler 8692, Augur 8712, Burch 8756, Central 8766, **Coneway 8783**, Cook 8786, Dick 8815, Dougherty, 8825, Dunagan 8831, Esping 8841, Foster 8868, Foundation 8869, Genecov 8886, **Gilman, 8889**, Griffin 8902, Healthcare 8924, Hervey 8932, Hixon 8940, KCL 8981, Light 9016, Luse 9029, McKee 9052, Mitte 9069, O'Connor 9093, Petty 9126, Redman 9147, Rowan 9166, Tobin 9237, Wal-Dot 9256, Waltrip-McGee 9259, Weaver 9265, Willard 9278, Works 9293

Utah: Kennecott 9333, Odyssey 9342, Questar 9346, Slaughter, 9353

Vermont: Mergens 9381, NSB 9382, Redducs 9383

Virginia: American 9387, Backer 9389, Beck 9393, Camp 9413, Community 9426, **Delmar 9429**, Ivakota 9477, Pruden 9517, Treakle 9543, Two 9544

Washington: DeFalco 9585, Dudley 9588, Ferguson 9596, Johnston-Hanson 9635, Kawabe 9642, Murray 9667, Stevens 9704, Thomson 9711

West Virginia: Logan 9756

Wisconsin: Gardner 9825, Inbusch 9847, Jacobus 9849, Koss 9866, Manitowoc 9876, Marshfield 9878, Modine 9889, Prescott 9905, Roehl 9917

Wyoming: Connemara 9967, **Schultz 9986**, Scott 9988, Weiss 9997

Convening

Alabama: Abahac 1

Arizona: Louis 142

Arkansas: Darragh 193

California: Alafi 235, Amador 238, Brotman 351, **Cantor 375**, Downing 462, Drum 464, Edwards 473, Gellert 550, Glikbarg 564, **Hefferlin 610, Lawrence 734, Lloyd 763**, McClatchy 811, **Modglin 840**, Synopsys 1100, Szekely 1102, **Teichman 1106**, Trust 1131, Wharton 1178

Colorado: Donnell-Kay 1258, Leighty 1311, **Oreg 1335**, Vradenburg 1374

Connecticut: Union 1590

Delaware: Remmer 1726, Thronson 1766

District of Columbia: Crowell 1799, **Foundation 1807, Pettus-Crowe 1828**

Florida: Coral 1952, Dasburg 1961, **Freewill 2021**, Glass 2039, **Mukti 2226**, Roshan 2297

Georgia: Athens 2437, Baker 2439, Georgia 2484, Lee 2540, Walker 2603

Illinois: EMA 2854, **Heritage 2967**, Hughes 2983

Indiana: Bussing-Koch 3353, Community 3359, Dubois 3370, Fayette 3379, Huntington 3397, LaGrange 3412, Seymour 3448

Kansas: **Kejr 3593**

Louisiana: Wisdom 3761

Maine: Somers 3803

Maryland: Biophilia 3824, Gladding 3871, Higginson 3880, Macht 3905, Widgeon 3983

Massachusetts: Behrakis 4015, **Bruner 4030**, Cricket 4060, **Kahn 4143**, Massachusetts 4191, **Pegasus 4236**, Permanent 4239, Thoracic 4326, Walsh 4348

Michigan: Branch 4396, Gratiot 4459, Michigan 4514, Olds 4526, Shiawassee 4568, Thompson 4592, Vicksburg 4606, Zondervan 4621

Minnesota: Granite 4699, Lane 4727, **Trust 4802**, Walker 4805, **Winds 4820**

Missouri: St. 5012

Montana: Cinnabar 5047

Nebraska: Midlands 5104, Nebraska 5105, Scribante 5116

Nevada: Dermody 5152, Meyer 5177

New Hampshire: Hunt 5214

New Jersey: Dreman 5326, **Integra 5400**, Miller 5468, Westfield 5582, WKBJ 5592

New Mexico: Carlsbad 5608, Chamiza 5609, Con 5611

New York: American 5662, Glens 6082, IF 6237, Initial 6245, **Laerdal 6358**, Lake 6360, Miller 6493, **Nok 6537**, Ong 6558, **Potts 6624**, Rosner 6698, **Sparkplug 6830**, Stony 6868

North Carolina: Covington 7081, Eddy 7087, Masserini 7172, Meserve 7182, Outer 7204, Rogers 7228, Strowd 7258

North Dakota: Community 7295

Ohio: Athens 7311, Austin-Bailey 7312, Brentwood 7330, Defiance 7375, Foundation 7408, Montauk 7531, Tuscora 7624, Wallace 7631

Oklahoma: Cherokee 7666

Oregon: Holzman 7775

Pennsylvania: Bucks 7905, Community 7933, Crawford 7944, Hoffman 8062, Kazanjian 8090, Kynett 8105, Tuttleman 8325

Rhode Island: Getz 8412

South Dakota: Watertown 8576

Tennessee: Durham 8608, Stuttering 8680

Texas: Bromberg 8748, Clear 8772, Hext 8933, McKee 9052, San 9170, Tobin 9237, Vaughan 9249, Works 9293

Utah: Patel 9344

Virginia: Beck 9393, **Delmar 9429, Longview 9494**

Washington: **Ji 9632**, Jones 9638, Tonkin 9715

Wisconsin: Marshfield 9878, Stry 9941

Curriculum development

Alabama: Friedman 27, Ireland 39

Arizona: F2 117, Grossman 126, Hansen 127

Arkansas: Hickingbotham 199, Olds 210

California: Ackerman 227, Amador 238, Baxter 284, Baye 285, Bonner 326, **Butler 365**, Coleman 416, Fox 525, Gellert 550, Godric 566, **Hefferlin 610**, Heller 613, **Lloyd 763**, Lopez 767, Mazda 810, New 865, Ontario 882, Rice 969, Roche 979, Ross 988, Szekely 1102, **Teichman 1106**, Trust 1131, Wharton 1178

Colorado: Donahue 1257, Leighty 1311, **Oreg 1335**, Schlessman 1349, Stratton 1359

Connecticut: Barnes 1404, Proctor 1545, Tully 1588

Delaware: **Jackman 1683**, SNAVE 1747

District of Columbia: Bench 1788, Westport 1838

Florida: Archibald 1852, Auerbach 1859, **Freewill 2021**, Roshan 2297, Toppel 2377, **Uncle 2383**, Votum 2390

Georgia: Abreu 2431, Athens 2437, Lee 2540

Hawaii: Wong 2656

Idaho: Whittenberger 2689

Illinois: Best 2740, Community 2803, EMA 2854, Heath 2962, Hughes 2983, Logos 3058, Takiff 3281, Tuohy 3296

Indiana: Bussing-Koch 3353, Community 3360, Community 3361, Dubois 3370, Huntington 3397, Jennings 3402, TCU 3458, Western 3466

Iowa: Farver 3491, First 3493, Young 3552

Kansas: Fidelity 3577, Legacy, 3595

Maine: Somers 3803

Maryland: Ammerman 3813, **Braitmayer 3827**, Caplan 3832, Higginson 3880, Widgeon 3983

Massachusetts: Clarke 4049, Hauben 4120, **Kahn 4143**, Morse 4209, **New 4220**

Michigan: Community 4411, Gratiot 4459, Keller 4481, Michigan 4514, Shiawassee 4568, Tuscola 4598, Vicksburg 4606, Zondervan 4621

Minnesota: Granite 4699, Larsen 4728, **Trust 4802**, Walker 4805

Mississippi: Community 4830

Missouri: Boylan 4873, Cray 4890, Garvey 4913, Grant 4918, Schutte 4995, St. 5012, Van 5028

Montana: Cora 5048

New Hampshire: Bickford 5205, Dorr 5211

New Jersey: Elizabethtown 5332, Miller 5468, Westfield 5582, Winters 5591, WKBJ 5592

New Mexico: Chamiza 5609, Taos 5626

New York: Anderson-Rogers 5676, Aronson 5689, Cohoes 5865, Gage 6050, High 6206, Hoyt 6230, IF 6237, **Kevorkian 6304, Laerdal 6358**, Lucelia 6418, Messinger 6482, Miller 6493, **Nok 6537**, Offensend 6550, Patrina 6579, Rose 6684, **Sparkplug 6830**, Tuch 6915

North Carolina: BB&T 7045, Eddy 7087

North Dakota: Community 7295

Ohio: Athens 7311, Austin-Bailey 7312, Brentwood 7330, Bryan 7339, Community 7357, Defiance 7375, Foundation 7408, McMaster 7521, Sandfair 7569, Sears-Swetland 7581, Wallace 7631

Oklahoma: Barnes 7659, Cherokee 7666, Kerr 7693, Wegener 7731

Oregon: Holzman 7775, Silver 7817

Pennsylvania: Carnahan-Jackson 7917, Community 7933, Crawford 7944, Hoffman 8062, Kazanjian 8090, **KL 8094**, Kynett 8105, Reiss 8234, Schuylkill 8263, Shoemaker 8275, Smith 8280, Staley 8296, Teleflex 8314, Tuttleman 8325

Rhode Island: Getz 8412

Tennessee: Tompkins 8683

Texas: Boeing 8733, Dougherty, 8825, Esping 8841, Light 9016, Marcus 9037, Mitte 9069, Petty 9126, Tobin 9237, Vaughan 9249, Willard 9278, Works 9293

Vermont: Redducs 9383, Stokes 9385

Virginia: American 9387, Beck 9393, **Brown 9407, Longview 9494**

Washington: Foss 9598, **Ji 9632**, Jones 9638, Thomson 9711, Tonkin 9715

Wisconsin: **Dewing 9805**, Lakeview 9868, Phipps 9903, Prescott 9905, Stateline 9937, Stry 9941

Debt reduction

Alabama: Ireland 39

Arkansas: Hickingbotham 199

California: Coleman 416, Drum 464, Page 899

Colorado: Schramm 1350

Delaware: Lightner 1699, New 1715

Georgia: Lee 2540

Illinois: Bishop 2743

Indiana: Bussing-Koch 3353

Iowa: First 3493, Iowa 3513

Minnesota: Riverway 4776

Missouri: Dunn 4898

New Jersey: Miller 5468

New York: Anderson 5674, Lee 6372, Messinger 6482

North Carolina: Strowd 7258

Ohio: McMaster 7521, Rosenberry 7562

Pennsylvania: Patterson 8205, Smith 8280

Texas: KCL 8981

Washington: Tonkin 9715

Wisconsin: Blooming 9784

Donated equipment

Indiana: TCU 3458

Donated land

Illinois: McGraw 3092
Minnesota: Remick 4773

Donated products

California: **Quiksilver 945**
Delaware: **TeleTech 1761**
New Jersey: Alcon 5244
Pennsylvania: American 7839

Emergency funds

Alabama: Ireland 39
Arizona: Hughes 130, James 132
Arkansas: Hickingbotham 199
California: Anhaltzer 245, Baye 285, Coleman 416, Drum 464, Farmers 496, Horwitz 633, Jamieson 658, Latkin 731, **Lawrence 734**, Looker 766, Military 826, Ontario 882, Pacific 897, Page 899, **Teichman 1106**, Trust 1131, Von 1147, Wharton 1178
Colorado: Broomfield 1242, Burt 1244, Donahue 1257, **Nord 1332**, Stratton 1359, Vradenburg 1374
Connecticut: Baldwin 1399, Cochrane 1420, Proctor 1545, Pryor 1546, **Sullivan 1578**
Delaware: Glencoe 1669, New 1715, Thronson 1766
District of Columbia: Goldman 1810
Florida: Chadbourne 1932, Chapman 1935, Coral 1952, Couch 1953, Densch 1970, Erdle 1993, **Freewill 2021**, Golden 2046, Gulf 2069, Hill 2097, Hultquist 2115, KT 2160, Long 2189, **Mukti 2226**, Peterson 2257, **Place 2261**, Reinhold 2280, Ryan 2305, Sexton 2326, Silverman 2337, Thomas 2371, **Wollowick 2412**
Georgia: Athens 2437, Lee 2540, Smith 2586, Solstice 2587
Hawaii: Moore 2643
Idaho: Boise 2666
Illinois: Alton 2705, Bishop 2743, Jocarno 3000, **Landau 3036, Lindon 3054, Mead 3100**, Meyer 3106, Oberweiler 3147, Reichert 3192, Rosenson 3209, Staley 3262
Indiana: Ayres 3342, Bussing-Koch 3353, Community 3359, Decatur 3367, Fayette 3379, Gibson 3386, LaGrange 3412, Pulaski 3432, Scott 3446, Western 3466
Iowa: Farver 3491, First 3493, GuideOne 3503, Iowa 3513, **Wahlert 3544, Wright 3551**, Young 3552
Kansas: Legacy, 3595, Watson 3639, Wiedemann 3642
Kentucky: Independence 3666
Louisiana: Biedenharn 3713
Maine: Davenport 3775, Planet 3797
Maryland: Davis 3844, Phase 3936
Massachusetts: Codman 4052, Hornblower 4135, Hyde 4139, Kelsey 4148, Massachusetts 4191, Morse 4209, Permanent 4239, Russell 4273, Stearns 4311, Swan 4317, Weber 4352, Webster 4353
Michigan: Community 4410, Dana 4419, Farver 4441, Frankenmuth 4450, Gratiot 4459, Mackinac 4499, Morley 4518, Olds 4526, Stubnitz 4582, **Teitel 4589**, Tuscola 4598
Minnesota: Cox 4662, Deikel 4663, Dyer 4669, Edina 4672, **Fingerhut 4683**, Granite 4699, Midcontinent 4745, Onan 4754, O'Neil 4755, Quinlan 4764, Riverway 4776
Mississippi: Baird 4822
Missouri: **Bohm 4871**, Cray 4890, Edgar 4899
Nebraska: Barklage 5071, Heuermann 5092
Nevada: **A 5131**
New Hampshire: Dorr 5211, Hunt 5214, Jameson 5215, Thorne 5233

New Jersey: A 5240, American 5248, Aufzien 5253, Miller 5468, Westfield 5582
New Mexico: Carlsbad 5608, Taos 5626
New York: Anderson-Rogers 5676, August 5698, Bobrow 5765, Correspondents 5879, EMSA 5961, G&A 6048, Glens 6082, Gordon 6110, **Gottlieb 6114**, Grumbacher 6148, Henshel 6192, High 6206, Lee 6372, Lubo 6417, Messinger 6482, **Nok 6537**, Ontario 6559, **Posner-Wallace 6621**, Strong 6872, Truman 6912, Washington 6946, Wells 6964
North Carolina: BB&T 7045, Cooke 7079, Duncan 7086, Meyer 7184, Outer 7204, Rankin 7217, Rogers 7228, Smith 7249
Ohio: Armington 7309, Austin-Bailey 7312, Brown 7336, Community 7356, Defiance 7375, Foundation 7408, Homan 7451, **Katz 7475**, Mather 7516, Musson 7534, Sandfair 7569, Sheely 7590, Wallace 7631, Woodruff 7645
Oklahoma: Ashbrook 7656, Goddard 7684, Wegener 7731
Oregon: Charis 7748, Holzman 7775, Kuse 7786, May 7794, Silver 7817
Pennsylvania: Arkema 7842, Ashland 7845, Born 7885, Brooks 7899, **Cohn 7931**, Flinn 8001, Frohring 8010, Hankin 8038, Maslow 8146, Mill 8172, Patterson 8205, Penn 8208, **Rust 8250**, Schuylkill 8263, Smith 8280, Tuttleman 8326, Union 8326, Wenger 8352, Wurts 8370, **Zeldin 8376**
Rhode Island: Collis 8397, Getz 8412, Kimball 8434, Perpetual 8471
South Dakota: Watertown 8576
Tennessee: Massengill-DeFriece 8647, Tompkins 8683
Texas: Adler 8692, Augur 8712, Boeing 8733, Bromberg 8748, Central 8766, **Chrest 8770, Crowder 8792**, Elkins 8838, Griffin 8902, Hext 8933, KCL 8981, Light 9016, McKee 9052, Wal-Dot 9256, Willard 9278, Wood 9290
Vermont: Redducs 9383
Virginia: **Brown 9407**, Camp 9413, Pruden 9517
Washington: Howarth 9626, Stevens 9704, Thomson 9711, Tonkin 9715
West Virginia: Logan 9756
Wisconsin: Dudley 9811, Gardner 9825, Hunt 9845, Stateline 9937

Employee matching gifts

Alabama: Ireland 39
Arizona: Napier 152
Arkansas: Union 219
California: Codding 412, Deacon 447, Fremont 527, Majestic 784, McClatchy 811, Orfalea 887
Colorado: Tomkins 1368
Connecticut: Diageo 1437, Fippinger 1450
Florida: Couch 1953, Gulf 2069, Tampa 2362
Georgia: Oxford 2561
Hawaii: Servco 2645
Illinois: Amsted 2708, Brunswick 2762, Burnett 2769, Chicago 2787, Munson 3130, United 3300
Indiana: TCU 3458
Iowa: Grinnell 3501, Young 3552
Massachusetts: OneBeacon 4231, PerkinElmer 4238
Michigan: Dana 4419, M 4497, Meritor, 4511, Morley 4518
Minnesota: Hickory 4713, Jostens 4720, Midcontinent 4745, Sayer 4786, Tennant 4798, Wallestad 4806
Missouri: Butler 4880
Nebraska: Nebraska 5105
New Jersey: American 5248, Ascena 5252, **Crane 5306**, Selective 5528
New York: American 5664, Tribune 6909, Utica 6922
North Carolina: Burlington 7062, Redwoods 7218, SPX 7252
Ohio: Austin-Bailey 7312, Bahmann 7313, Cooper 7362, Davey 7373, **Katz 7475**
Oregon: Flowerree 7763, Mentor 7796

Pennsylvania: Arkema 7842, Baker 7851, Bon-Ton 7884, First 7998, Hankin 8038, Harsco 8040, Pfundt 8213, Quaker 8228, Ricon 8237, Smith 8280, Stein 8299, Teleflex 8314
Rhode Island: Kingsbury 8435
South Carolina: Bailey 8510
Tennessee: Community 8601, **Louisiana-Pacific 8644**
Texas: **AMD 8698**, Calpine 8759, Quanex 9141
Virginia: Bryant 9409, Franklin 9452, Immixgroup 9476
Washington: Everett 9592

Employee volunteer services

California: Fremont 527, Majestic 784, McClatchy 811, Silicon 1038, Swinerton 1098
Delaware: Burt's 1635, **TeleTech 1761**
Florida: Minto 2216
Illinois: Alliant 2702, Brunswick 2762
Michigan: Meritor, 4511
Minnesota: Edina 4672, Hickory 4713, Tennant 4798
Missouri: Butler 4880, Sigma-Aldrich 5003
New Jersey: American 5248, Selective 5528
New York: American 5664
North Carolina: Burlington 7062, Redwoods 7218
Ohio: Entelco 7389
Pennsylvania: American 7839, Bon-Ton 7884
Rhode Island: Sullivan 8494
Texas: **AMD 8698**, Calpine 8759, Tennessee 9230
Wisconsin: Modine 9889

Employee-related scholarships

Illinois: **Ingredion 2988**
Nebraska: West 5128
Pennsylvania: Calvert 7910, Knoll 8100
Rhode Island: Liberty 8440
Tennessee: Cracker 8603
Texas: Valero 9246

Endowments

Alabama: Griswold 31, Ireland 39, Pei-Ling 52, Sexton 63
Arizona: F2 117, Hughes 130, Louis 142, Napier 152
Arkansas: Darragh 193, Hickingbotham 199, Olds 210, White 220
California: Atkinson 259, Beynon 312, Bonner 326, **Cantor 375**, Coleman 416, Corday 426, Corwin 428, Horwitz 633, Huntington 642, Looker 766, Martin 801, McClatchy 811, Pickford 927, Rocca, 978, Ross 988, Santa 1003, Smullin 1060, Theroux 1110, **Wakerly 1150, Wilkinson 1183**, Yuki 1203
Colorado: Schlessman 1349, Southwestern 1355, Taylor 1364, Wilkins 1379
Connecticut: Anderson 1393, Fippinger 1450, Goldfarb 1466, Senior 1566, Sorenson-Pearson 1574
Delaware: **Colgate 1645**, Singhal 1745, SNAVE 1747
District of Columbia: Bender 1789, Goldman 1810, Westport 1838
Florida: Archibald 1852, Chadbourne 1932, Chapman 1935, Duckwall 1982, Graese 2055, Hill 2097, Lazarus 2172, McCabe 2201, Ray 2275, Rosen 2294, Rothman 2299, Sexton 2326, Shockley 2332, Toppel 2377, **Uncle 2383**, Votum 2390
Georgia: Baker 2439, Boone 2446, Chatham 2457, Exposition 2476, Howell 2512, Marshall 2545, Whitehead 2610
Idaho: Simplot 2685, Wishnick 2690
Illinois: Adams 2696, Cole 2798, Delta 2826, Hanson 2950, Harczak, 2952, Hess 2969, Johnson 3001, **Lazzara 3042**, Love 3064, Mirapaul 3119, Munson 3130, **New 3137**, Smith 3253
Indiana: **Ackerman 3339**, Branigin 3348, Bussing-Koch 3353, Community 3359, Community 3360, Community 3363, Fayette 3379, Huntington 3397, Jennings 3402, Lacy 3410, LaGrange 3412,

Namaste 3422, Oliver 3428, Schurz 3444, Sherwood 3451, TCU 3458

Iowa: Cowles 3482, deStwolinski 3486, Farver 3491, Geisler 3498, Jefferson 3514, **World 3550**

Kansas: Baehr 3556, Bane 3557, Berry 3558, DeVore 3573, Fidelity 3577, Legacy, 3595, Schmidt 3622, South 3628, Taylor 3632, Trusler 3635, Wallace 3637, Williams 3643

Kentucky: Keeneland 3668, Public 3687, Reed 3688, Stock 3697, Sutherland 3699

Louisiana: Biedenharn 3713, Huie-Dellmon 3729, Merkle 3737, Wisdom 3761

Maine: Brook 3769, Planet 3797

Maryland: Ammerman 3813, Campbell 3831, Caplan 3832, Eliasberg 3854, Gladding 3871, **Goldberg 3872**, Kelly, 3893, Mitchell, 3916, Tucker 3969, Weiss 3982

Massachusetts: **Brabson 4026**, Cabot 4034, Easthampton 4076, Haven 4122, Hazard 4124, Hornblower 4135, Hyde 4139, **Kahn 4143**, King 4156, Krieger 4160, Morse 4209, Permanent 4239, Wallace 4347

Michigan: Biederman 4391, Branch 4396, Community 4410, JSJ 4474, Lapeer 4490, LoPrete 4496, Paine 4531, Ratner 4548, Roscommon 4552, Shiawassee 4568, **Teitel 4589**, Vicksburg 4606

Minnesota: Ankeny 4628, Borman 4644, Granite 4699, Kaplan 4721, Larsen 4728, Quinlan 4764, Riverway 4776, Sayer 4786, Wells 4811, Weyerhaeuser 4815

Mississippi: Baird 4822

Missouri: **Bohm 4871**, Copaken 4888, Curry 4892, O'Reilly 4975, Portman 4981, Sander 4991, Schutte 4995, Shawe 5000, Simmons 5005, Van 5028, Walker 5034

Montana: Taylor 5064

Nebraska: Barklage 5071, Blair 5074, Ferenc 5080, Friedland 5082, Heuermann 5092, Nebraska 5105, Pegler 5110

Nevada: Meyer 5177, West 5197

New Hampshire: Olcott 5227

New Jersey: **Blue 5269**, Brundage 5280, Brunetti 5281, Fox 5349, Holzer 5396, Miller 5468, Shilling 5534

New Mexico: Taos 5626

New York: Balbach 5707, **Buster 5806**, Carwill 5818, Coles 5871, Community 5872, Cutco 5890, D-B 5903, EMSA 5961, Ferguson 5999, French 6032, Gaffney 6049, Gilliam 6078, Heyman 6201, High 6206, IF 6237, Joukowsky 6274, Klein 6325, Knapp 6331, Leonhardt 6381, Locomoto 6408, Mendell 6472, Messinger 6482, Netter 6525, **Nok 6537**, Nuhn 6544, Offensend 6550, O'Sullivan 6565, Plymouth 6612, Rose 6684, Satow 6732, **Schmeelk 6742**, Schweckendieck 6758, Steckler 6853, **Stern 6862**, Strong 6872, Vogt 6933, **Weinstein 6956, Woodland 6989**, Zukerman 7032

North Carolina: Arcadia 7040, BB&T 7045, Cooke 7079, Fox 7103, Kenan 7143, Kenan 7144, Meyer 7184, Morrison 7193, Outer 7204, Smith 7249, Strowd 7258, Vanderbilt 7273

North Dakota: Community 7295

Ohio: Andrews 7307, Crandall 7366, **Eaton 7383**, Foundation 7408, Frohman 7411, Gale 7415, Haskell 7439, **Highfield 7450**, Homan 7451, Kramer 7484, Mather 7516, McMaster 7521, Mifsud 7525, Morley 7532, Osteopathic 7545, Philada 7548, Renner 7557, Ritchie 7561, Sandfair 7569, Scotford 7579, Smith 7598, Steinmann 7603, Wasserstrom 7632

Oklahoma: Atherton 7657, Barnes 7659, Cherokee 7666, Wegener 7731

Oregon: Holzman 7775, Klamath 7784, Kuse 7786, Schmidt 7813, Shoen 7816, Western 7829

Pennsylvania: **Arronson 7844**, Ashland 7845, Bridge 7891, Bucks 7905, **Cohn 7931**, First 7997, Gamber 8011, **KL 8094**, Maslow 8146, McKinney 8161, Norbell 8195, Reidler 8233, **Rust 8250**, Schlarbaum 8259, Schuylkill 8263, Shoemaker 8275

Rhode Island: Collis 8397, McCarthy 8452, Papitto 8467

South Carolina: Bailey 8510, Eastern 8522

Tennessee: **Fugitive 8618**, Proctor 8662

Texas: Bromberg 8748, Burch 8756, Coleman 8778, **Coneway 8783**, Cook 8786, de 8802, Dougherty, 8825, Educational 8836, Elkins 8838, Fair 8844, Fairchild 8845, Finger 8857, Flowers 8862, Fruehauf 8879, Genovese 8887, **Gilman, 8889**, Hill 8937, Kahn 8978, Kaplan 8979, KCL 8981, Light 9016, Mendenhall 9056, Mitte 9069, Oppenheimer 9101, Papadopoulos 9113, Vaughan 9249, Walls 9257, Wells 9271, Wolens 9284, Wood 9290

Vermont: Castanea 9368

Virginia: Backer 9389, **Delmar 9429, Fund 9455**

Washington: Baker 9566, Everett 9592, Grousemont 9611, Hall 9613, Horn 9625, Johnston-Hanson 9635, Murray 9667, Nysether 9671

West Virginia: Hott 9753

Wisconsin: Birnschein 9783, Doolittle 9809, **Johnson 9851**, LUX 9874, Marshfield 9878, Schoenleber 9924, Woodtrust-Bell 9963

Wyoming: Sargent 9985, Scott 9988

Equal access

California: Buell 357, **Girls 559**, Levin 749, New 865, Wren 1199

Florida: Jacobsen 2123

Georgia: Brewer 2448

Illinois: Kellcie 3008

Minnesota: Larsen 4728

New York: 21st 5630

North Carolina: Redwoods 7218

Pennsylvania: Blue 7879, Penn 8208

Rhode Island: Acriel 8378

Tennessee: Atticus 8582

Texas: Boeing 8733

Wisconsin: Bock 9786

Wyoming: Connemara 9967

Equipment

Alabama: Barkley 9, Ireland 39, Kemp 42

Arizona: Grossman 126, Hughes 130

Arkansas: Hickingbotham 199, Olds 210

California: Ackerman 227, Alafi 235, Amador 238, Bannerman 274, Baxter 284, **Bull 358**, Community 421, Downing 462, Drum 464, Farmers 496, Fox 525, Fusenot 541, Gellert 550, **Global 565**, Harris 601, **Hefferlin 610**, Heller 613, Jamieson 658, Kelly 697, Latkin 731, Livingston 761, Looker 766, Lux 773, McLean 817, Ontario 882, Ross 988, Rossi 989, Silicon 1038, Stauffer 1076, Stauffer 1077, Swinerton 1098, Syar 1099, Synopsys 1100, Trust 1131, Webb 1162

Colorado: Burt 1244, Comprecare 1249, Heginbotham 1289, Hoag 1293, Joslin-Needham 1300, Mullen 1329, Schlessman 1349, Schramm 1350, Southwestern 1355, Stratton 1359, Vradenburg 1374

Connecticut: Barnes 1404, Chelsea 1418, Dime 1438, Proctor 1545, Roberts 1552, Thomaston 1581, Union 1590, Winokur 1597

Delaware: Babcock 1612, Brown 1631, Chaney 1640, Glencoe 1669, Lightner 1699, Milano 1710, SNAVE 1747, Thronson 1766

District of Columbia: Goldman 1810, Tucker 1836, Westport 1838

Florida: Archibald 1852, ATAP 1855, Cape 1917, Charlotte 1938, Couch 1953, Duckwall 1982, Evans 1994, Fish 2001, Foulds 2014, **Freewill 2021**, Greene-Sawtell 2065, Gulf 2069, Hill 2097, Marshall 2195, **Mukti 2226**, Munroe 2228, Phillips 2260, Ray 2275, Redmond 2280, Silverman 2337, Toppel 2377, **Uncle 2383**, Wilson-Wood 2408, **Wollowick 2412**

Georgia: Abreu 2431, Athens 2437, Benton 2445, Cook, 2468, English 2474, Exposition 2476, Georgia 2484, Holly 2509, Illges 2517, Lee 2540, University 2597, Waffle 2602

Hawaii: Vidinha 2653

Idaho: Boise 2666, Mitchell 2680, Morrison 2682, Whittenberger 2689

Illinois: Alton 2705, Bishop 2743, Coldwell 2797, Community 2802, Community 2803, Delta 2826, EMA 2854, Harris 2957, Hay 2961, Heath 2962, **Lazzara 3042**, Listeman 3055, McCauley 3085, **Mead 3100**, Millard 3109, Munson 3130, Oberweiler 3147, Peters 3172, Seymour 3236, Staley 3262, Stone 3270, Stuart 3273, Webb 3313

Indiana: **Ackerman 3339**, Ayres 3342, Bussing-Koch 3353, Community 3359, Community 3360, Decatur 3367, Dubois 3370, Froderman 3383, Huntington 3397, Jennings 3402, Kuhne 3409, LaGrange 3412, MutualBank 3421, Oliver 3428, Pulaski 3432, Raymond 3436, Rush 3441, Scott 3446, Seymour 3448, Western 3466

Iowa: First 3493, Jefferson 3514, Muscatine 3523, **Wahlert 3544**, Young 3552

Kansas: Baehr 3556, Bane 3557, Brown 3561, DeVore 3573, French 3579, Legacy, 3595, Mingenback 3605, Ross 3619, Williams 3643

Kentucky: Etscorn 3654, Hannah 3659, Hayswood 3662, Independence 3666, Keeneland 3668, Trim 3702

Louisiana: Dujay 3722, Huie-Dellmon 3729, Steinhagen 3755, Wisdom 3761

Maine: Borman 3767, Burnham 3770, Lynam 3788, Somers 3803

Maryland: Ammerman 3813, Biophilia 3824, Davis 3844, Gladding 3871, Kelly, 3893, Knapp 3895, Macht 3905, Mitchell, 3916, Widgeon 3983, Youth 3991

Massachusetts: Boynton 4025, Clarke 4049, Codman 4052, Cricket 4060, Dedham 4067, East 4075, FCTS 4088, Hyde 4139, **Kahn 4143**, Middlesex 4203, Morse 4209, Permanent 4239, Ramlose 4257, Sicari 4295, Simoni 4296, United 4337, Wallace 4347, Walsh 4348, Wyman-Gordon 4364

Michigan: Andersen 4377, Baldwin 4382, Biederman 4391, Branch 4396, Buffalo 4399, Community 4410, Community 4411, Dana 4419, Delano 4426, Doll-Loesel 4433, Farver 4441, Holden 4467, Kantzler 4478, Kellogg 4482, M 4497, Michigan 4514, Morley 4518, Olds 4526, Ratner 4548, Redies 4549, St. 4576, Stubnitz 4582, Thompson 4592, Tuscola 4598, Vicksburg 4606, Wickson-Link 4616, Zondervan 4621

Minnesota: Bend 4639, Deikel 4663, Farmers 4679, **Fingerhut 4683**, Granite 4699, Midcontinent 4745, Quinlan 4764, Remick 4773, Riverway 4776, Thorpe 4800, **Trust 4802**

Missouri: Baer 4862, Boylan 4873, Curry 4892, Dunn 4898, Edgar 4899, Long 4948, MFA 4960, O'Reilly 4975, Portman 4981, Siteman 5006, Timmons 5021

Montana: Lippard-Clawiter 5058, Lynn 5059, Sample 5062

Nebraska: Ameritas 5067, Barklage 5071, Heuermann 5092, Kilbourne 5097, Midlands 5104, Pegler 5110, Perkins 5111

Nevada: Close 5148, Dermody 5152, Meyer 5177, Timken-Sturgis 5192

New Hampshire: Barker 5204, Bickford 5205, Dorr 5211, Hunt 5214, Jameson 5215, McIninch 5224, Salem 5230, Smyth 5232

New Jersey: A 5240, Brundage 5280, Columbia 5301, Elizabethtown 5332, Frelinghuysen 5354, Giants 5369, **Integra 5400**, Kampen 5413, Kerney 5419, Leavens 5444, Machuga 5454, Miller 5468, Schwartz 5525, Selective 5528, Smith 5539, Snyder 5541, Westfield 5582

New Mexico: Carlsbad 5608, Taos 5626, **Watersheds 5628**

New York: Anderson 5674, Anderson-Rogers 5676, August 5698, Balbach 5707, Beach 5725, Bender

5735, Berkowitz 5739, **Buster 5806, Cogitare 5855,** Dworman 5938, French 6032, Gaffney 6049, Glens 6082, Gloeckner 6083, Hoyt 6230, **Kathwari 6286,** Krumholz 6349, Lake 6360, Legacy 6373, Loewy 6409, Lucelia 6418, Messinger 6482, Northern 6540, Norwich 6542, Nuhn 6544, Ong 6558, Palisano 6570, Plymouth 6612, **Potts 6624,** Schwartz 6753, Snow 6818, **Stein 6855,** Truman 6912, **Usman 6921,** Utica 6922, Wells 6964

North Carolina: Cooke 7079, Covington 7081, Duncan 7086, Flowers 7099, Fox 7103, Glenn 7111, Hunt 7134, Katz 7142, Masserini 7172, Outer 7204, Rogers 7228, **Rolander 7229,** Sanders 7234, Smith 7249, Strowd 7258, Wake 7276, Yost 7291

North Dakota: Myra 7297

Ohio: Anderson 7305, Austin-Bailey 7312, Bahmann 7313, Beecher 7320, Beecher 7321, Brentwood 7330, Brown 7336, Bryan 7339, Community 7356, Corbett 7363, Crandall 7366, Defiance 7375, Dienstberger 7379, Finnegan 7399, Fox 7409, Frohman 7411, Frost-Parker 7413, Health 7442, Homan 7451, Jennings 7466, Kilworth 7477, Kutz 7486, Loeb 7504, Orr 7543, Quatman 7552, Ritchie 7561, Sears-Swetland 7581, Smith 7598, Stensen 7604, Tait 7610, Tuscarawas 7623, Tuscora 7624, Walker 7630, Wallace 7631, Watson 7633, Young 7652

Oklahoma: Ashbrook 7656, Broadhurst 7663, Cherokee 7666, Collins 7668, Gelvin 7682, Goddard 7684, Kerr 7693, Stone 7721, Wegener 7731

Oregon: Castle 7745, Collins 7752, Elwood 7761, Four 7764, Holzman 7775, Kuse 7786, McKay 7795, Pendleton 7806, Wessinger 7826, Western 7829

Pennsylvania: Arkema 7842, Bennett 7860, Born 7885, Bradley 7889, Brooks 7899, Bucks 7905, Carlson 7916, Carnahan-Jackson 7917, Chase 7921, Child 7923, Community 7933, Crawford 7944, Dinardo 7960, Elk 7975, Emporium 7980, Finley 7995, First 7997, Flinn 8001, Friendship 8009, Frohring 8010, Gamber 8011, Grundy 8029, Hirtzel 8058, Hoffman 8062, Maslow 8146, McCandless 8153, Mill 8172, Miller 8173, Norbell 8195, Patterson 8205, Pfundt 8213, Reiss 8234, Remmel 8235, Schuylkill 8263, Smith 8280, Smith, 8285, Staehle 8295, Stott 8304, Union 8326, Wenger 8352, Williams 8357, Wurts 8370

Rhode Island: Getz 8412, Heydt 8419, Kingsbury 8435, McCarthy 8452, Moore 8456

South Carolina: Lutz 8533

South Dakota: Watertown 8576

Tennessee: Cracker 8603, Jewell 8633, **Lowenstein 8645,** Massengill-DeFriece 8647, Tompkins 8683

Texas: Boeing 8733, Bromberg 8748, Community 8782, Dick 8815, Dougherty, 8825, Dunagan 8831, Elkins 8838, Esping 8841, Fair 8844, Fash 8848, Flowers 8862, Foundation 8869, Fowlston 8871, Gray-Pampa 8900, Griffin 8902, Hervey 8932, Hext 8933, Kayser 8980, King 8994, Light 9016, Luse 9029, Mayer 9043, McKee 9052, Mitte 9069, Petty 9126, Rowan 9166, Tennessee 9230, Vaughan 9249, Webre 9266, Wood 9290, Zale 9299

Utah: Eskuche 9323, Green 9327, Odyssey 9342

Vermont: Castanea 9368, Mergens 9381

Virginia: American 9387, Community 9426, Northern 9503, Pruden 9517, Treakle 9543, Two 9544

Washington: Everett 9592, Foss 9598, Howarth 9626, Kawabe 9642, Kilworth 9644, Korum 9648, Skagit 9696, Thomson 9711

West Virginia: Chambers 9742, Hott 9753, Huntington 9754, Logan 9756

Wisconsin: **Dewing 9805,** Doolittle 9809, Dudley 9811, Eau 9814, Hunt 9845, Janesville 9850, Lakeview 9868, Marshfield 9878, Roehl 9917, Seramur 9926, Stateline 9937, T 9945, Windway 9961, Witte, 9962, Woodtrust-Bell 9963

Wyoming: **Schultz 9986,** Scott 9988, Skelton 9989

Ethics and accountability

Connecticut: Donchian 1440

Massachusetts: Cohen 4053, Puffin 4251

Minnesota: Evert 4676

New Jersey: **Rippel 5510**

Texas: Planetary 9132

Fellowships

Alabama: Dixon 26, Sexton 63

California: **Butler 365, Cantor 375,** Corday 426, Downing 462, Drum 464, Familian 491, **Grass 577,** Hand 595, Heller 613, Kelly 697, Lux 773, Mazda 810, Parvin 905, Rice 969, Western 1176

Colorado: Donnell-Kay 1258, **Oreg 1335,** Tappan 1363, Trueblood 1371

Connecticut: Fippinger 1450, Winokur 1597

District of Columbia: Arnold 1787, Goldman 1810, Institute 1816, Patterson 1826, Replogle 1831, Tucker 1836

Florida: Roshan 2297, Tampa 2362

Georgia: Abreu 2431, Lee 2540

Illinois: **Lazzara 3042,** Smith 3253

Indiana: Bussing-Koch 3353

Kentucky: Etscorn 3654, Ogden 3683

Maryland: Ammerman 3813, Caplan 3832, **Fox 3864,** Laughlin 3898, Richmond 3940

Massachusetts: **Kahn 4143, Lalor 4164,** Morse 4209, Smith 4299

Michigan: Baldwin 4382

Minnesota: Granite 4699, Rahr 4766

Missouri: **Bohm 4871**

Nebraska: Heuermann 5092

Nevada: Meyer 5177

New Jersey: **Dow 5325,** Dreman 5326, Frelinghuysen 5354, Miller 5468, Upton 5566, Zobel 5603

New Mexico: Gumbo 5617

New York: Aronson 5689, Art 5691, Avery 5702, **Blinken 5757, Buster 5806,** Gilliam 6078, Glorney 6084, Grand 6123, High 6206, Insall 6246, Joukowsky 6274, **Kevorkian 6304, Klingenstein 6328, Li 6394,** Loewy 6409, Lucelia 6418, Messinger 6482, Morin 6506, **Nok 6537, Potts 6624, Schepp 6739,** Snow 6818, Stony 6868, Zukerman 7032

North Carolina: Covington 7081, Silverman 7244

Ohio: Bahmann 7313, Homan 7451

Oklahoma: Broadhurst 7663, Kerr 7693

Pennsylvania: Ashland 7845, Hirtzel 8058, Lewis 8123

Tennessee: Durham 8608, **Lowenstein 8645**

Texas: **Coneway 8783,** Foundation 8870, Johnston 8972, Mitte 9069, Smith 9207, Vaughan 9249

Virginia: **Eiriksson 9441, Fund 9455**

Washington: Stevens 9704, Thomson 9711

West Virginia: Starvaggi 9767

Financial sustainability

Alabama: Phifer, 54

Delaware: **Jackman 1683,** New 1715

Florida: **Freewill 2021**

Hawaii: Kaneta 2637

Massachusetts: Middlesex 4203, Sicari 4295

Michigan: Barron 4384, Michigan 4514

New Jersey: Miller 5468

New York: Messinger 6482, **Nok 6537**

Ohio: Foundation 7408

Pennsylvania: Hoffman 8062, **KL 8094**

Texas: Dale 8794, Dougherty, 8825, Works 9293

Vermont: Mergens 9381

Fundraising

California: Kadima 686, McKay 815

Georgia: Athens 2437, **Gage 2482**

Illinois: Levinson 3049

Indiana: Mothershead 3419

Kentucky: Abercrombie 3645

Massachusetts: Alden 3999, Berger 4018

Michigan: Vicksburg 4606

Minnesota: Radichel 4765

Montana: Cora 5048

New Jersey: Leavitt 5445

New York: Darrah 5900, Strong 6872

North Carolina: Nivison 7201

Ohio: Ginn 7425, Haskell 7439, Van 7625

Texas: Horween 8952, Littauer 9021, Weaver 9265

Washington: **Sabol 9687**

Wisconsin: Berbeewalsh 9782, Gordon 9830

Wyoming: **Schultz 9986**

General support

Alabama: Abahac 1, Birmingham 11, Blount 13, Bruno 17, Caddell 19, Griffin 31, Griswold 31, Ireland 39, Kairos 41, Kemp 42, Mitchell 50, Petra 53, Phifer, 54, Ratliff 57, Regions/AmSouth 58, Sexton 63, Siloam 65, SSAB 67, Upchurch, 72, Viro 73

Alaska: Doyon 84, Gillam 85, **Nash 90**

Arizona: Adelante 93, **Beals 100,** Burns 102, Cadeau 104, Coleman 107, Dove 112, F2 117, Forsberg 119, Fuite 121, Grace 125, Hughes 130, James 132, Johnson 135, Louis 142, Moeller 150, Powell 157, Smith 170, Snell 171, Zicarelli 185

Arkansas: Buck 192, Darragh 193, Hickingbotham 199, McKinney 202, Murphy 207, Riggs 214, Sturgis 217, Trinity 218, White 220

California: Ackerman 227, Adams 228, Adonai 232, **Alalusi 236,** Altos 237, Amador 238, Anhaltzer 245, **Animal 246,** Arata 248, Archer 250, Bancroft-Clair 270, Bank 272, Bannerman 274, **Battle 282,** Baxter 284, Bear 288, Bekins 294, Bellini 298, Bellwether 299, Bergman 304, Bettingen 310, Beynon 312, Bialis 313, Bobowski 324, Bonner 326, Borok 331, Boukai 334, Bradford 337, Brewster 341, Bridges 342, Brooks-Mathews 350, Brotman 351, Brown 352, Brunswick 354, Bryan 355, Buell 357, **Bull 358, Butler 365,** Butte 366, Byrne 368, Calaveras 369, California 370, Callison 371, **Candelaria 372, Cantor 375,** CEC 382, Charitable 389, Cheeryble 390, Christensen 400, Christian 401, Christian 402, Church 403, **Cienega 404,** Cleo 407, Cloud 408, Clougherty 409, Codding 412, Coleman 416, Collingwood 418, Community 421, Corday 426, Corwin 428, Crabb 431, Cramblit 432, Cutler 438, Davies 444, Davis 445, Deacon 447, Dearborn 448, Dermalogica 451, Doelger 457, Downing 462, Drum 464, Dusenbury 466, Ebell 471, Eriksen 484, Evening 487, Familian 491, Farmers 496, Fat 499, First 506, First 507, Five 509, Forgatch 517, Fox 525, Fremont 527, Freshwind 528, Friedman 531, Fritz 534, Fusenot 541, Gellert 550, George 551, Gill 555, Godric 566, Goldstein 569, Goodwin 572, Griswold 586, Gross 587, Grossberg 588, Hagopian 592, Handlery 596, Harris 601, Hayman 606, Health 608, Heller 613, **His 623,** Horwitz 633, **Hsieh 636,** Huber 638, Jade 655, **Jain 656,** Jamieson 658, Jatain 659, Jesy 664, Joerger 665, Jones 674, Jones 675, JTB 679, Jubas 680, Juda 681, Judkins 683, Kanel 688, Kelly 697, Kite 711, Kobor 716, Krishnan-Shah 722, Kwoh 724, Laguna 726, Latkin 731, **Lawrence 734,** Legacy 740, Livingston 761, **Lloyd 763,** Looker 766, Lux 773, Mae 780, Majestic 784, Mangold 789, Marcil 793, Martin 803, Mashhoon 804, Masson 807, Mazda 810, McClatchy 811, McDaniel 812, McKay 815, McLean 817, McLeod 818, Merage 822, Mitchell, 839, Morgan 847, Morgenstern 848, Muckel 850, **Munson 852,** New 865, Nicholson 866, North 869, Olander 878, On 880, Ontario 882, Optivest 884, Orfalea 887, Pacific 897, Page 899, Parvin 905, Pauley 909, Penney 913, Perenin 914, Pergo 915, **Peszynski 917,** Picerne 926, Pickford 927, Plum 929, **Preuss 935,** Price 938, Pulido 944, **Quiksilver 945,** Rar 955, Rees 961, Reinhold 963, Rest 966, Rhe 968, **Rifkind 972,** Riley 973, Roberts 976,

Robinson 977, Rocca, 978, Roche 979, Romano 982, Ross 988, Russell 995, Sammut 996, San 997, Santa 1003, **Sargent 1005**, Sawchuk 1010, Schimmel 1015, Schultz 1019, Scottsdale 1024, Seaver 1026, Seip 1028, Shenandoah 1033, **Sikand 1037**, Silicon 1038, SKB 1044, Smith-Walker 1057, Smullin 1060, Solano 1063, Srivastava 1072, Staples 1075, Stauffer 1076, Stone 1085, **Sunwest 1094**, Szekely 1102, **Teichman 1106**, Thagard 1109, Theroux 1110, Thomson 1113, Thornton 1115, Three 1116, Thrill 1117, Trust 1131, Uvas 1142, **Vogelzang 1146, Wakerly 1150**, Walther 1154, Walton 1156, Warren 1159, Weil 1163, Weinberg 1164, Welch 1168, Welk 1170, Westphal 1177, Wharton 1178, White 1180, Whittier 1181, Wolfe 1193, Writer 1200, Yen 1201, Yuki 1203, Zafiropoulo 1207, Zecca 1209, Zolla 1216

Colorado: Allen 1220, Arches 1222, Ballantine 1226, Bean 1228, Bjorkman 1236, Bloedorn 1238, Bloom 1239, Brent 1240, Broomfield 1242, Burt 1244, Chotin 1246, Comprecare 1249, Connor 1250, Donahue 1257, Donnell-Kay 1258, Dorset 1259, Family 1268, **Fishback 1270**, Gart 1275, Goodwin 1279, Graves 1280, Heginbotham 1289, Heider 1290, Jacobs 1298, Joslin-Needham 1300, King 1305, Leighty 1311, Lewan 1314, Lewis 1315, Maki 1319, Margulf 1320, Moniker 1327, Mullen 1329, **Nord 1332, Okinaga 1334, Oreg 1335**, Pluss 1337, Routzon 1348, Schlessman 1349, Schramm 1350, **Someone 1354**, Stratton 1359, Stretesky 1360, Taylor 1364, Tomkins 1368, Trachten 1369, Vradenburg 1374, Warner 1376, White 1378, Wilson 1380, Woodford 1382

Connecticut: Acorn 1385, Antonacci 1395, Baldwin 1399, Barden 1402, Bender 1405, Bigelow 1408, Bradley 1411, Brown 1413, Chaikin-Wile 1417, Chelsea 1418, Cochrane 1420, Conway 1422, Craig 1423, Crew 1424, Crosswicks 1425, Curran 1427, DeLuca 1431, Diageo 1437, Dime 1438, Ensign-Bickford 1442, Family 1443, Farid 1444, Ferguson 1446, Filingieri 1447, Fippinger 1450, Friezo 1457, Fry 1458, Gengras, 1461, Goldfarb 1467, Harold 1477, Hergenhan 1481, Hewitt 1482, Jones 1489, Jones 1490, Jost 1492, Kay 1496, Keefe 1497, Kendall 1498, Kreitler 1502, Lebovitz 1506, **MacInnis 1515**, Morrow 1527, Nevas 1530, Newtown 1532, O'Herron 1536, Panoram 1538, Patricelli 1541, Price 1544, Proctor 1545, RBS 1549, Rubin-Ladd 1556, Schendel 1561, Schloss 1562, Schwerin 1563, Shanley 1567, **Sonja 1573**, Sullivan 1577, Thomaston 1581, Thrall 1583, Town 1586, Tully 1588, UIL 1589, Union 1590, Vance 1591, Zimmer 1603

Delaware: 18 1604, Alcyon 1608, Bartlett 1615, Brandsma 1627, Bresnan 1628, Brown 1631, Brown-Whitworth 1632, Bulova 1633, Burt's 1635, Chaney 1640, Cohen 1643, **Colgate 1645**, Freedman 1665, Glencoe 1669, Haldan 1675, Heuer 1680, **Jackman 1683**, Jade 1684, Kutz 1696, Levin 1697, Lightner 1699, Midvale 1709, Milliken 1711, MMK 1712, New 1715, Pinkerton 1721, Schwalbach 1739, Swift, 1754, **TeleTech 1761**, Three 1765, Thronson 1766, Yaverland 1783

District of Columbia: Arcana 1786, Arnold 1787, Bench 1788, Bender 1789, **Butler 1792**, Cafritz 1793, Coleman, 1796, Crowell 1799, Dart 1800, Dimick 1803, **Foundation 1807**, Freeman 1808, Jovid 1817, Mimi 1822, Olender 1824, **Pettus-Crowe 1828**, Porter 1829, Replogle 1831, Rubenstein 1833, Silberman 1834, Tucker 1836, Westport 1838, Woodward 1839

Florida: Archibald 1852, Atkinson 1857, Aurora 1860, **Aviation 1861**, Baroco 1867, Bastien 1872, Baulch 1873, Beall, 1876, Bell 1882, Bell 1883, Blake 1889, Blanksteen 1891, Blanton 1892, Brighton 1899, Brinckerhoff 1900, Brooke 1903, Burnetti 1912, **Cantonis 1915**, Capital 1918, Carrington 1923, Castellani 1927, Catalina 1928, Chadbourne 1932, Chanin 1934, Chapman 1935, Chardonnay 1936, Collins 1949, Coral 1952, Couch 1953, Dasburg 1961, Day 1965, de 1966, Detter 1971,

Diermeier 1976, Dorset 1979, Duda 1983, Ellis 1989, Epstein 1992, Erdle 1993, Ferguson 1999, Fleischman 2003, Forman 2011, Frankel 2018, **Freewill 2021**, Garvy 2033, Gate 2034, Godbold 2041, Grader 2054, Gralnick 2056, Gregory 2067, Gulf 2069, Hahn 2072, **Handleman 2078**, Hardeman 2080, Harper 2082, HFRX 2092, Hill 2097, Hultquist 2115, **Hutchison 2117**, Jacobsen 2123, Kaiserman 2134, Kanders 2135, Kane 2137, Kiwanis 2149, Kiwanis 2150, Koski 2157, KT 2160, Kugelman 2161, Landwirth 2167, Layden 2171, Leiser 2177, Lelash 2178, Liebhaber 2183, Livingston 2187, Long 2189, MAH 2193, Martin 2196, Martin 2197, Minto 2216, Morningstar 2218, Morrison 2222, Munroe 2228, Nelson 2230, Norjana 2235, Nuzzo 2236, Olliff 2239, Oristano 2241, Peters 2256, Peterson 2257, Phillips 2259, **Place 2261**, Ray 2275, Resnick 2282, Rich 2284, Rogers 2291, Rosenthal 2296, Rothman 2299, Ruskin 2302, Salenger 2308, Schultz 2319, **Shepard 2331**, Shockley 2332, Spier 2345, Sunburst 2359, Swisher 2361, Thomas 2370, Thomas 2371, Tupperware 2379, **Uncle 2383**, Votum 2390, Wescustogo 2399, Westgate 2400, Whitman 2404, Wilson-Wood 2408, Woerner 2409, **Wollowick 2412**, Woodbery 2413, Wrightson-Ramsing 2416, Wynne 2419, Zimmerman 2427

Georgia: Athens 2437, Baker 2439, Barnett 2441, Benton 2445, Charter 2456, Chatham 2457, Churches 2461, Community 2466, Connolly 2467, Cooper 2469, Enterline 2475, Exposition 2476, **Gage 2482**, Georgia 2484, Georgia 2485, Goddard 2491, Griffin 2499, Harrison 2502, Holland-Underwood 2508, Hooters 2510, Hunter 2515, Illges 2518, Inman 2519, Jackson 2522, Jolley 2526, Knox 2534, Lee 2540, Magnus 2543, Marcus 2544, Marshall 2545, McClatchey 2546, McKinney-Geib 2547, McKnight 2548, Morris 2552, Myfident 2554, Orkin 2560, Oxford 2561, Pennies 2565, Pope 2568, Price-Campbell 2570, Raoul 2573, Reynolds 2574, Saul 2579, Schwob 2581, Smith 2586, Solstice 2587, Stahl 2588, Sweetgrass 2591, TALX 2592, Thames 2594, Tritt 2596, Walton 2604, White 2609, Whitehead 2610, Whitepath 2611, Williamson 2613, Wish 2615, Woodruff 2617, Wormsloe 2619

Hawaii: Central 2627, First 2631, Higgins 2635, Kaneta 2637, Locations 2638, Moore 2643, Servco 2645, Shields 2647, Teruya 2651, Vidinha 2653, Wilcox 2654, Wong 2656, Young 2660

Idaho: Intermountain 2677, **Melaleuca 2679**, Morbeck 2681, Morrison 2682, Simplot 2685, Smeed 2686, Wishnick 2690

Illinois: Agape 2698, Allen-Heath 2701, Alliant 2702, Amsted 2708, **Appleby 2711**, B&D 2715, Barr 2720, Bellick 2732, Bere 2734, Bergstein 2735, Bernoudy 2738, Best 2740, Bisco 2742, Bishop 2743, Boothroyd 2749, Bound 2751, Brown 2759, Brunswick 2762, Burnett 2769, Cain 2773, Canterbury 2774, Chicago 2786, Chicago 2787, Cohn 2795, Coldwell 2797, **Combs 2800**, Communitas 2801, Community 2803, Constans-Culver 2805, Cremer 2815, Danielson 2824, Delavan 2825, Delta 2826, **Demos 2827**, Duncan 2840, Eclipse 2844, Edelman 2845, EMA 2854, Fabyan 2862, Family 2863, Farnham 2865, Fasseas 2866, Faulkner 2867, Fields 2870, Fildes 2872, Frank 2885, Franklin 2887, Full 2895, Gardner 2903, Gassin 2906, Generations 2908, Geneseo 2909, Gibbet 2912, Gochnauer 2918, Goldberg 2919, Goldman 2922, Gray 2928, Griffith 2930, Groner 2932, Grossinger 2933, Gust 2936, Hansen 2948, Hanson 2950, Harczak, 2952, Hardiek 2953, Hay 2961, **Heritage 2967**, Hess 2969, Hoffer 2975, House 2980, Hughes 2983, Hunt 2984, Hurley 2985, Ideal 2986, Jocarno 3000, Johnson 3001, Judy 3003, Karasik 3006, Keeney 3007, Kipper 3018, Klosk 3020, **Krasberg-Mason 3029, Landau 3036**, Landau 3037, **Lazzara 3042**, Lehman-Stamm 3045, Lichtman 3052, **Lindon 3054**, Listeman 3055, **Lizzadro 3057**, Lohengrin 3059, Love 3064,

Maddox 3069, Mallon 3071, Marsteller 3079, McCauley 3085, McCrea 3088, McLaughlin 3095, McNeill 3098, Meyer 3106, Millard 3109, Miller, 3113, Miller, 3114, Minow 3118, Monroe 3122, Mullen 3129, Munson 3130, Murphy 3132, Nayak 3133, **New 3137**, Nickum 3139, Norgaard 3141, North 3142, **Nureyev 3145**, O'C 3148, Olin 3153, Patterson 3164, Pepper 3167, Perkins 3168, Peters 3172, Petrick 3173, Pitzman 3177, Poncher 3181, Putnam 3186, Reichert 3192, Rosen 3205, Rosen 3206, **Rosenmutter 3208**, Rosenson 3209, Rot 3212, Ruttenberg 3217, Saliba 3221, Sasco 3222, Schiff 3224, Schorr-Lieberman 3229, Seymour 3236, Shaker 3238, Shirley 3245, Simon 3247, Smysor 3255, Stairway 3261, Staley 3262, Stone 3270, Stuart 3273, Sullivan 3276, Sulzer 3277, Summer 3279, Tarrson 3282, Taylor 3285, Taylor 3286, Tobey 3290, Ulm 3299, United 3300, Vail 3301, Walker 3308, Warner 3310, Watson 3311, Webb 3313, Wehle 3314, Will 3322, Wislow 3323, Wright 3333

Indiana: **Ackerman 3339**, Ayres 3342, Blackford 3346, Branigin 3348, Bronstein 3351, Burris 3352, Bussing-Koch 3353, Crescent-Cresline-Wabash 3365, Elder 3375, Fenech 3380, Franklin 3382, Gibson 3386, God's 3388, Harlan 3391, Herr 3392, Hulman 3396, Kuhne 3409, LaGrange 3412, M.C.R. 3413, Maurer 3415, MutualBank 3421, Namaste 3422, Noecker 3424, Oakley 3426, O'Rourke-Schof 3429, Raker 3434, Raper 3435, Raymond 3436, Schergens 3443, Schurz 3444, Scott 3446, Seymour 3448, Shafer 3449, Smith 3453, Springleaf 3455, Thomasson 3459, Vann 3461, Von 3464, Weston 3467, Winchester 3469

Iowa: Andringa 3470, Becker 3472, Carlson 3479, Cole-Belin 3480, Cowles 3482, Farver 3491, First 3493, Grinnell 3501, GuideOne 3503, Iowa 3512, Iowa 3513, Krumm 3517, McDonald 3520, Medical 3521, Premier 3528, R 3529, Schildberg 3532, Security 3534, Toohey 3538, Van 3539, Vonderhaar 3543, **Wahlert 3544**, Weathertop 3545, West 3547, Wood 3548, **World 3550**

Kansas: Adair-Exchange 3553, Atterbury 3554, Babinger 3555, Baehr 3556, Berry 3558, Cape 3563, Central 3564, Cochener 3565, Cray 3569, Davis 3571, Dehaemers 3572, DeVore 3573, Family 3575, Fidelity 3577, Henry 3585, Insurance 3587, Jellison 3589, Kammco 3591, McFadden 3601, Mistler 3606, Nash 3610, Nettleton 3611, Price 3615, Price 3616, Reeble 3618, Salgo 3621, Watson 3639, Weber 3640, Wiedemann 3642

Kentucky: Abercrombie 3645, Barr 3646, Barth 3647, Boone 3649, Gagarin 3656, GHH 3658, Harter 3660, Hayswood 3662, Independence 3666, Jones 3667, Keeneland 3668, Killian 3670, Mackin 3673, Reed 3688, Shapira 3693, Sutherland 3699, Trager 3701, Trim 3702

Louisiana: Biedenharn 3713, Chambers 3718, Dujay 3722, Harper 3726, Huie-Dellmon 3729, Kavanagh 3730, Knight 3731, Meraux 3736, Merkle 3737, Monteleone 3741, Parkside 3745, Wetmore 3757, Wheless 3758, Whitman 3759, Winn 3760, Wisdom 3761

Maine: Aldermere 3763, Alfond 3764, Bank 3766, Borman 3767, Davenport 3775, Franklin 3779, **Golden 3781**, Kennebec 3785, Kennebunk 3786, Lynam 3788, Merrill 3789, Mimi 3792, Minsky 3793, Narragansett 3794, Old 3795, Planet 3797, Pond 3798, Protein 3799, Somers 3803, **St. 3804**

Maryland: Acacia 3807, Adams 3808, Adler 3809, Allemall 3811, Ammerman 3813, Anderson 3814, Baltimore 3816, Baltimore 3817, Bresler 3828, Broadus 3829, Campbell 3831, Clifton 3836, Contino 3840, Croft 3841, Davis 3844, Dean 3846, Eliasberg 3854, Feldman 3858, Ferris 3860, Gladding 3871, **Goldberg 3872**, Higginson 3880, Hubbard 3883, Huether/McClelland 3884, Kohn 3896, Laughlin 3898, Loats 3902, Lohr, 3903, Macht 3905, Macks 3906, Mangione 3907, Meyer 3913, Meyerhoff 3914, Phase 3936, Rogers-Wilbur 3941, Rouse 3943, S.B.E. 3944, Sears 3948,

Small 3955, St. 3959, **Thadikonda 3965**, Tucker 3969, Weinberg, 3979

Massachusetts: 2 3992, Akamai 3998, Archibald 4005, **Azadoutioun 4008**, Babson 4009, Babson-Webber-Mustard 4010, Bacon 4011, Benson 4016, Benz 4017, Bigbird 4020, **Blossom 4022**, Boger 4023, Boynton 4025, **Brabson 4026**, Brooks 4028, Bulger 4031, Cabot 4034, Cabot 4035, Carle 4037, Casey 4039, Chartis 4044, Chase 4045, Chicopee 4047, Clarke 4049, Codman 4052, Cook 4056, Crane 4058, Crawford 4059, Cricket 4060, Davoli 4065, East 4075, Easthampton 4076, Eddy 4077, Egan 4079, Egan 4080, Fassino 4086, Friend 4098, Gerrity 4102, Griffin 4107, **Gross 4108**, Hampden 4116, Hauben 4120, Hazard 4124, Henderson 4127, Hicks 4129, Hill 4130, Hoffman 4131, Hogan 4132, Hyde 4134, Hornblower 4135, Horne 4136, Hyde 4139, Karas 4146, Kelsey 4148, Kenwood 4150, Killam 4153, Krieger 4160, Levangie 4172, Levy 4175, Lingos 4177, Makepeace 4185, Marcus 4188, Marigold 4189, **Memorial 4198**, Metanoia 4201, Middlesex 4203, Mitchell 4205, Morse 4209, Noonan 4225, O'Keefe 4229, OneBeacon 4231, Parlin 4233, **Patagonia 4234**, PerkinElmer 4238, Phelps 4242, Pilgrim 4245, Prokopis 4248, Puffin 4251, Ramlose 4257, Ratshesky 4259, Red 4260, Rice 4265, Rockland 4267, Rose 4271, Russell 4273, Sailors' 4276, Salem 4277, Shaughnessy 4292, Singing 4297, **Spero 4304**, Stanzler 4307, Stearns 4310, Stearns 4311, Sternberg 4313, Storer 4314, **Summer 4316**, Tapper 4321, Tresorelle 4333, Van 4340, Vela 4341, Wallace 4347, Walsh 4348, Webster 4353, Wells 4357, Wheatland 4358, Wilcox 4360, Winthrop 4363, Young 4366

Michigan: Balk 4383, Barron 4384, Barstow 4385, Barton-Malow 4386, Beson 4389, Betten 4390, Biederman 4391, Bierlein 4392, Bostock 4395, Branch 4396, Bronner 4398, Buffalo 4399, Buhr 4400, Buist 4401, Burdick-Thorne 4402, Causley, 4405, Christian 4407, Community 4410, Cracchiolo 4414, Cracchiolo 4415, Cummings 4417, Dana 4419, Dart 4421, de 4422, Delano 4426, Delong-Sweet 4427, DeVlieg 4428, Dinan 4431, Fabiano 4438, Farver 4441, Farwell 4442, Four 4449, Gratiot 4459, Hecht 4465, Herrington-Fitch 4466, Holden 4467, Isabella 4468, Johnson 4471, Jospey 4473, JSJ 4474, Kalamazoo 4477, Keller 4481, Kellogg 4482, Kinney 4483, Kosch 4485, Linse 4493, LoPrete 4496, Mackinac 4499, Maly-Dykema 4502, McDole 4507, Michigan 4514, Mills 4515, Morley 4518, Murdock 4519, Nartel 4521, Nickless 4522, Oreffice 4528, Paine 4531, Phantom 4538, Pilgrim 4539, Porter 4543, Power 4544, Ratner 4548, River 4551, Ryan 4555, Scully 4561, Sehn 4563, Serra 4565, Speckhard-Knight 4574, Stoddard 4579, Tamer 4585, Tassell-Wisner-Bottrall 4587, Technical 4588, **Teitel 4589**, Thoman 4590, Thompson 4591, Thompson 4592, Thompson 4593, Torgow 4594, Tremble 4595, **Triford 4597**, Tyler-Little 4599, Van 4601, Van 4602, Vander 4603, Vicksburg 4606, Watson 4608, Weisberg 4609, Wetsman 4611, Whiting 4614, Wickson-Link 4616, Williams 4618

Minnesota: Acorn 4623, Andersen 4626, Ankeny 4628, Avocet 4631, Baratz 4635, Bell 4637, Bell 4638, Borman 4644, Boss 4646, Bumgarner 4649, Cook 4658, Deikel 4663, Dell 4664, Depot 4667, Dyer 4669, Edina 4672, Erickson 4675, Faith, 4677, Falck 4678, **Fingerhut 4683**, G&K 4691, Getsch 4695, Gilligan 4696, Goldman 4697, Granite 4699, Grossman 4701, Grotto 4702, Groves 4703, Haggerty 4705, Heilmaier 4712, Hognander 4715, Jackson 4718, Jostens 4720, Knowlton 4725, Lane 4727, Larsen 4728, Lillehei 4729, Louis 4731, Mahoney 4738, March 4740, McNamara 4743, Nelson 4749, Northern 4751, O'Brien 4753, Onan 4754, O'Neil 4755, Open 4756, Quinlan 4764, Rahr 4766, Rauenhorst 4767, Regis 4770, Riverway 4776, Roberts 4778, Rodman 4779, Rosen 4782, Samsara 4784, Schott 4787, St.

4794, Tennant 4798, Thorpe 4800, Trillium 4801, Walker 4805, Walsh-Brady 4808, Wells 4811, Wendel 4813, Weyand 4814, Whitney 4817, **Winds 4820**

Mississippi: Baird 4822, Black 4825, Carothers 4827, Crooks 4831, Family 4834, Mississippi 4849, Sanders 4852

Missouri: Bartlett 4865, **Bohm 4871**, Boswell 4872, Bryant 4878, **Build-A-Bear 4879**, Butler 4880, Calkins 4881, Canfield 4882, Copaken 4888, Cornelsen 4889, Cray 4890, Curry 4892, Dierberg 4895, Dunn 4898, Empson 4902, Enright 4903, Erlich 4904, Fabick 4907, Favre 4908, Finerty 4909, Forster-Powers 4911, Garvey 4913, Gaylord 4915, Gilbert 4917, Grant 4918, Green 4920, Kornblum 4940, Litton 4946, Long 4948, McDonald 4955, Morgan 4963, Moss 4964, Nichols 4970, O'Reilly 4974, O'Reilly 4975, Pearl 4977, Peculiar 4978, Portman 4981, Price 4982, Ross 4986, Sachs 4989, Saks 4990, Sander 4991, Schneider 4994, Schutte 4995, Service 4998, Shawe 5000, Sigma-Aldrich 5003, Simmons 5005, Slusher 5009, Tension 5019, Thorp 5020, Van 5028, Vatterott 5030, Walker 5034, Wallace 5036, Walton 5037, Welch 5038, Wolff 5040, Wurst 5043

Montana: Cinnabar 5047, Foundation 5051, Gallagher 5052, Lippard-Clawiter 5058, Lynn 5059, Wendy's 5065

Nebraska: America 5066, Ameritas 5067, Assurity 5068, Baer 5069, Barklage 5071, Cimpl 5076, Farr 5079, Friedland 5082, Goldwin 5085, Hawkins 5089, Hester 5091, Heuermann 5092, Kilbourne 5097, Nebraska 5105, Owen 5108, Pegler 5110, Perkins 5111, Physicians 5112, Scribante 5116, Steinhart 5121, Thomas 5123, Tous 5124, Yount 5130

Nevada: Andress 5132, Benna 5138, Blue 5140, Boyd 5141, Children 5147, Dermody 5152, **Do 5153**, Joseph 5166, Meyer 5177, Newman 5179, Orchard 5180, Pinnacle 5183, Siegel 5186, To 5193, Vandevoort 5194, West 5197

New Hampshire: Barker 5204, Bickford 5205, Charter 5206, Cochran 5208, Dunn 5212, Hunt 5214, Lynch 5221, McIninch 5224, Thorne 5233, Tillotson 5234, Verney 5236, Wutz 5239

New Jersey: A 5240, Adler 5242, Amboy 5246, Antz 5250, Ascena 5252, Avalo 5254, Avis 5255, Bartlett 5256, Baum 5258, Blue 5268, **Blue 5269**, Brook 5273, Brueckner 5279, Brundage 5280, Carlozzi 5287, Chang 5290, Chanil 5291, Chormann 5293, Chu 5294, Citta 5295, Cordover 5304, Covance 5305, **Crane 5306**, **Daft 5310**, Devine 5317, Doctor 5321, Dreman 5326, EBB 5329, Edison 5330, Ellis 5333, ESH 5338, Essig 5339, Farrington 5341, Florin 5348, Freedman 5351, Frelinghuysen 5354, Gamper 5361, Giants 5369, Gibson 5370, Halpern 5380, Harms 5385, Harmstieg 5386, Infinity 5399, **Integra 5400**, Jones 5409, Kaufman 5415, **Knistrom 5426**, Kocurek 5428, Kroon 5433, Larson 5440, Leavitt 5445, Marino 5458, Maschler 5462, McCrane 5464, McDowell 5465, Miller 5468, Minio 5470, Mitrani 5471, Onyx 5482, **Ostberg 5483**, Pacific 5485, Palmer 5486, Paragano 5488, **Parnassus 5489**, Patrick 5494, Payson 5495, Pheasant 5499, Post 5505, Ragan 5507, Sanders 5518, Savin 5520, Schwartz 5525, Scott 5527, Selective 5528, Seven 5530, Shapiro 5532, Sheridan 5533, Shilling 5534, Smilowitz 5538, Snyder 5540, Snyder 5543, **Southpole 5545**, Stone 5553, Sutton 5554, Take 5555, Tedesco 5557, Teiger 5558, Todd 5560, Tuchman 5561, Twin 5563, United 5565, Upton 5566, Vaughn-Jordan 5567, Verhalen 5568, Watts 5573, Wendel 5580, Wetterberg 5583, Wilf 5587, WKBJ 5592, Zichron 5600, Zobel 5603

New Mexico: Akerson 5604, B.F. 5606, Carlsbad 5608, Chamiza 5609, Con 5611, Forrest 5614, Gumbo 5617, Nirvana 5621, Schnieders 5623, Taos 5626

New York: 1848 5629, **Abba's 5634**, Abelard 5635, Abess 5636, Abess 5637, Alexander 5655,

Alexander 5656, Allatt 5659, American 5662, American 5664, American 5668, Amsterdam 5672, Anderson 5673, Anderson 5674, Anderson-Rogers 5676, Andrews 5677, **Animal 5680**, Applebaum 5683, Arcadia 5684, August 5698, AYN 5703, Azar 5704, B 5705, Backer 5706, Balbach 5707, Bank 5710, Barham 5715, Barker 5716, Bassman 5721, Baum 5722, BBL 5724, Beckman 5729, Bernheim 5740, Bernhill 5741, Bet 5742, Birchrock 5749, Black 5754, Blank 5756, **Blinken 5757**, Blodgett 5760, Bloomberg 5761, Boustead 5769, Box 5771, Boxer 5772, Brademas 5774, Brandt 5777, Bridgewater 5783, Brooklyn 5788, Brosens 5789, BTMU 5795, Buchalter 5796, **Buffalo 5799**, Burrows 5803, **Buster 5806**, Calamus 5809, Caruso 5817, Chiles 5843, Cohn 5864, Coleman 5870, Coles 5871, Cowen 5882, Cumming 5888, Dalton 5896, Dammann 5897, Davis 5902, Desanctis, 5911, Diamondston 5914, Dibert 5915, Doscas 5925, Dworman 5938, Eisner 5951, Elyachar 5959, EMSA 5961, Erpf 5968, ESL 5969, Falk 5981, Fan 5985, Feldman 5996, Ferguson 5999, Feuerring 6001, Ficalora 6002, Fife 6005, Finn 6008, **Fischel 6009**, Flaherty 6012, Forest 6018, Fowey 6021, Fraiman 6023, Frankel 6027, French 6032, Freund 6034, Friedland 6037, Furman 6046, G&A 6048, Gaffney 6049, Gage 6050, Geier 6063, Giant 6077, Giordano 6081, Gold 6088, Goldmann 6099, Goldstone 6102, Golick 6104, Goodman 6106, Goodman-Lipman 6108, Gordon 6110, Grand 6123, Grant 6129, Greenberg 6132, Greenwich 6137, Griffin 6138, Gross 6142, Grossman 6144, Grumbacher 6148, Grunberg 6149, Hadar 6154, Hahn 6156, Hallingby 6160, **Harriman 6170**, Hart 6173, **Henson 6194**, Herbst 6195, Heyward 6202, High 6206, Hilson 6209, Himelberg 6210, Hirsch 6212, Horowitz 6225, Hurlburt 6233, IF 6237, Indus 6243, Iroquois 6250, **Jabara 6254**, JI 6260, JLK 6264, **Jockey 6265**, Johnson 6269, Joukowsky 6274, Joyce 6275, Kahn 6279, Kallinikeion 6280, Kamber 6281, **Kathwari 6286**, KCEG 6291, Kenworthy 6300, Kenyon 6301, Kimmelman 6309, Kimura 6310, King 6311, Kirby 6313, **Klagsbrun 6318**, Klein 6325, **Klingenstein 6328**, Knapp 6331, Koessler 6334, Koessler 6335, Kovensky 6342, Kroll 6348, Kurland 6352, Lainoff 6359, Lake 6360, **Lamaj 6361**, Lane 6363, **Lanie 6364**, Leonhardt 6381, Levine 6387, Levy 6391, Lewin 6392, Liberman 6396, Lichtenstein 6397, Lipton 6404, Lisner 6405, Litterman 6406, Loconsolo 6408, LSK 6415, Lubin 6416, Lubo 6417, Lucelia 6418, M 6423, Mabardi 6428, MacArthur 6429, Maidenbaum 6435, Manocherian 6438, Marble 6441, Marine 6442, Mars 6444, Marshall 6446, Mastrocola 6449, MAT 6450, McCarthy 6456, McDayton 6462, Messinger 6482, Metzger-Price 6483, Miller 6492, Milton 6497, Moore 6504, Morse 6509, Morse 6510, Mule 6515, Mulroy 6516, MW 6517, Nets 6524, Netter 6525, Newcastle 6528, Newman 6532, **Nok 6537**, Nuhn 6544, NYBDC 6546, Offensend 6550, O'Grady 6551, Ong 6558, Osceola 6560, Ostgrodd 6561, Ostreicher 6562, Packin 6566, Palisades 6569, Palisano 6570, Park 6575, Paxton 6581, Performing 6586, Perper 6588, Pfeiffer 6597, Pinkus 6607, Plunkett 6611, Plymouth 6612, Pollack 6615, **Posner-Wallace 6621**, Preston 6626, Raphael 6648, RDM 6653, Rexford 6664, Ridgewood 6669, Rifkind 6670, Risen 6672, Roche 6678, **Rock 6679**, Rose 6683, Rose 6684, Rosenstein 6692, Rothstein 6704, Rubin 6707, Rudy 6708, Rum 6709, Rupp 6710, Sackler 6716, Salomon 6721, Sargol 6728, Satow 6732, Schaefer 6735, Schiro 6741, Schwartz 6754, Schwartz 6755, Schweckendieck 6758, Securitas 6768, SEG 6771, Serenbetz 6776, Shanken 6785, Shapiro 6786, Sharon 6787, **Shatford 6788**, SHEL 6791, Shuman 6795, Siegel 6797, Slade 6809, Smith, 6816, Snayberger 6817, Snyder 6819, Spatz 6831, Spektor 6833, Spiegel 6837, **Spirit 6839**, Spofford 6842, Stebbins 6850, **Stein 6855**, **Stern 6862**, Still 6866, Strong 6872,

Sumitomo 6876, Sunrise 6878, Sutton 6881, Sutton 6882, Triangle 6908, Tribune 6909, Tuch 6915, Turner 6916, **Usman 6921**, Utica 6922, Utopia 6923, Vaad 6924, Villchur 6929, Viola 6930, Wachenheim 6935, Wagner 6938, Wallerstein 6940, Warwick 6945, **Weinstein 6956**, White 6972, White 6973, Wolk 6987, Wong 6988, Wright 6995, Wurtele 6997, Yagoda 7001, Yitzchok 7007, **Yoreinu 7010, Youth 7013**, Zeitz 7021, Zenkel 7023, Zichron 7026, Zimmermann 7028, Zlinkoff 7031

North Carolina: BB&T 7045, Belk 7046, Bell 7048, Bettman 7051, Billingsley 7052, Bolick 7056, Burks 7061, Cary 7070, Chatham 7074, CJB 7076, Coffey 7078, Cooke 7079, Covington 7081, Davis 7083, Everett 7093, Evernham 7094, Fairfield 7095, Family 7096, Flowers 7099, Fortson 7100, Fox 7103, Gambrell 7105, Glenn 7111, Gordon 7112, Griffin 7113, Harvest 7118, Harvey-McNairy 7119, Helb 7122, Howe 7132, Hunt 7134, Jelm 7137, Judd 7139, Kassner 7141, Katz 7142, Kenan 7144, Ketchum 7146, Kistler 7147, Koons 7148, Kosloski 7149, Krauss 7153, Ladd 7156, **Laffin 7157**, Lerner 7160, Levine-Sklut 7161, Lynum 7165, Maness 7166, Marietta 7167, Marlboro 7169, Marsh 7171, Mattison 7175, McLean 7178, Meyer 7184, Morisey 7191, Moritz 7192, Moseley 7194, Mount 7196, Niessen, 7200, P 7205, Perkin 7208, Pratt 7214, Rankin 7217, Redwoods 7218, Ribenack 7220, Richardson 7221, Ritchie 7222, **Rixson 7223**, Rogers 7228, **Rolander 7229**, Rolla 7230, Sanders 7234, Self 7238, Sherrard 7240, Shingleton 7241, Shugart 7242, Sites 7245, Smith 7249, Snyder's-Lance 7250, SPX 7252, Stonecutter 7255, Strowd 7258, Stuart 7259, Summer 7261, Thomasville 7267, Trexler 7269, Vanderbilt 7273, Wake 7276, Wann 7279, Waters 7280, Way 7281, Weatherspoon 7282, Zelnak 7293

North Dakota: Myra 7297

Ohio: A 7299, Albrecht 7301, Anderson 7304, Andrews 7307, Angels 7308, Armington 7309, Arrel 7310, Austin-Bailey 7312, Baird 7314, Barron 7316, B-Brand 7318, Beecher 7321, Besl 7326, Brentwood 7330, Brethen 7331, Brown 7336, **Brush 7338**, Callahan 7345, Cassner 7348, Chemed 7350, Christ 7352, Cleveland 7354, Community 7357, Cooper 7362, Corbett 7363, Crandall 7366, Crossroads 7367, Danis 7371, Davey 7373, Dienstberger 7379, Dorn 7380, Downing 7381, **Eaton 7383**, Edwards 7386, **Elisha-Bolton 7387**, Entelco 7389, Finnegan 7399, Firman 7400, Fishel 7401, Fitton 7402, Fleischmann 7404, Fortney 7406, Foss 7407, Foundation 7408, Fox 7409, Frohman 7411, Frost 7412, Frost-Parker 7413, Gale 7414, Gale 7415, Gardner 7417, Gimbel 7424, Ginn 7425, Glidden 7427, Goerlich 7428, Gosiger 7429, Gould 7430, Gries 7431, Gross 7432, Hankins 7437, Haskell 7439, Heffner 7443, **Highfield 7450**, Homan 7451, Howe 7455, Huntington 7460, Iott 7463, Jenkins 7464, Jennings 7466, Kamm 7473, Kangesser 7474, **Katz 7475**, Kilworth 7477, Kisker 7479, Knight 7482, Knoll 7483, Kramer 7484, Kramer 7485, Laub 7490, LKC 7501, **Lowe-Marshall 7505**, Lukens 7507, Lundgard 7508, M.L.M 7510, Mangano 7511, Marnick 7515, Mather 7516, Matthes 7517, McMaster 7521, Messer 7524, Miller 7526, Miller 7527, Miller 7528, Morley 7532, Murphy 7533, Musson 7534, Myers 7535, NLT 7537, Norris 7538, Norweb 7539, O'Neill 7542, Orr 7543, Peoples 7546, Peters 7547, Powers 7550, Rayen 7554, Reynolds 7558, Ritchie 7561, Rotterman 7564, S.E.C. 7567, Sandfair 7569, Sauerland 7570, Schey 7571, Schottenstein 7574, Schwebel 7577, Scotford 7579, Sears-Swetland 7581, Segoe 7583, Seifert 7584, Shaw 7587, Skyler 7595, Slitzer 7596, Smith 7598, Southard 7599, Stafast 7600, Stensen 7604, STERIS 7605, Stillson 7607, Taj 7611, Thendara 7616, TKBW 7619, Traeger 7621, Wagler 7629, Walker 7630, Wasserstrom 7632, Watson 7633, Weiss 7634,

Williams 7638, Williamson 7640, Wilson 7642, Yeiser 7649, Yoder 7650

Oklahoma: Ad 7654, Asbjornson 7655, Barnes 7658, Barnes 7659, Barthelmes 7661, Brannin 7662, Brown 7664, Collins 7668, Collins, 7669, Dill 7671, Drabek 7673, Goddard 7684, Harmon 7686, Holliman 7687, Jirous 7690, Lolmaugh 7700, Merrick 7707, Miller 7708, Miller 7709, Moore 7710, Warren 7729, Wegener 7731, White 7733, White 7734, Wilson 7736

Oregon: Ackley 7740, Castle 7745, Elwood 7761, Glennco 7768, Harvest 7769, Hitchman 7774, Kuse 7786, May 7794, Mentor 7796, Merlo 7797, Michael 7799, Miller 7800, Morris 7802, Parker/United 7805, Pendleton 7806, Rietman 7809, Roundhouse 7810, Schmidt 7813, Shoen 7816, Singer 7819, Spencer 7820, Wessinger 7826, Woodard 7831, **Wyss 7832**

Pennsylvania: Adams 7836, American 7839, Ames 7840, Applestone 7841, Arkema 7842, Ashland 7845, Baker 7851, Baldwin, 7852, Beacon 7856, Bennett 7860, Benz 7861, Bergman 7863, Birnhak 7873, Bishop 7874, Black 7875, Boardman 7881, Bolte 7882, Bon-Ton 7884, Born 7885, Britton 7894, Brooks 7898, Bryer 7902, Bucks 7905, Burket-Plack 7906, Campbell 7912, Cannon 7913, Carita 7915, Carlson 7916, Carnahan-Jackson 7917, Casteel 7919, Charlestein 7920, Chase 7921, Chenault, 7922, Child 7923, Clareth 7924, Clark 7925, Clark 7927, Cornerstone 7936, Cost 7937, Cove 7939, Crawford 7945, David 7950, DENTSPLY 7954, Dibona 7955, Dietz 7959, Donnelly 7963, Dozzi 7965, Eden 7971, Edwards 7972, Edwards 7973, EFM 7974, Ellis 7978, **Epstein 7983, Epstein 7984**, Finley 7995, First 7996, First 7997, First 7998, Fortinsky 8002, Fountainhead 8004, Freas 8005, Frohring 8010, Gamber 8011, Garthwaite 8013, Gauss 8014, Goshen 8025, Grundy 8029, GT 8030, Hager 8035, Hall 8037, Hankin 8038, Harsco 8040, Hartfield 8041, Hassel 8042, HBE 8047, Hecht 8050, Herndon 8051, Hill 8055, Hill 8056, Hilles 8057, Hirtzel 8058, Hoffman 8062, Honickman 8066, Hulme 8069, Huplits 8071, IGN 8073, Ithan 8076, Jansing-Cook 8079, Jewish 8080, Kinney 8092, **KL 8094**, Klahr 8095, Klein 8096, Knudsen 8102, Krouse 8103, Lamb 8106, Landers 8110, Laughlin 8114, Leakin 8116, Leary 8117, Levee 8121, Lida 8127, Lockhart 8131, **Mango 8138**, Martin 8143, Martin 8144, Maslow 8146, Mason 8148, Mattingly 8151, McCune 8155, McKinney 8161, Mendel 8168, Mill 8172, Miller 8173, Moffat 8175, Mukaiyama-Rice 8183, Mullen 8184, Murphy 8185, Mylan 8187, Neag 8189, Norbell 8195, O'Brien-Veba 8197, Oppenheim 8199, O'Reilly 8200, Patterson 8205, Penn 8208, Perlow 8211, Pfundt 8213, Pincus 8214, Pittsburgh 8216, Plankenhorn 8219, Price 8225, Price 8227, Quaker 8228, Randall 8230, Rath 8231, Reese 8232, Reidler 8233, Ricon 8237, Rider-Pool 8238, Roemer 8242, Rosenlund 8245, Rudin 8247, Saramar 8253, Schrenk 8261, Schuylkill 8263, **Shastri 8273**, Shoemaker 8275, Shore 8276, Singer 8279, Smith 8280, Smith 8282, Society 8289, Staehle 8295, Stein/Bellet 8300, Stewart, 8302, Stott 8304, Strawbridge 8305, Tabas 8312, Thompson 8317, Todi 8319, Tuttleman 8325, Union 8326, Valentine 8328, Velma 8330, Wachs-Weingarten 8337, Walton 8341, Warburton 8342, Weiner 8349, Wenger 8352, Williams 8357, Williams 8358, Winokur 8362, Wolstenholme 8366, Woodall 8368, Wright-Cook 8369, Wurts 8370, **Zeldin 8376**

Rhode Island: Ames 8379, Arents, 8382, Barton 8385, Bowen 8391, Chace 8393, Charlton, 8394, Coes 8396, Collis 8397, Darling 8400, Del 8401, Estate 8404, Field 8407, Greene 8413, Hartman 8416, Hope 8422, Johnson 8430, Kimball 8434, Leroe 8439, Lorber 8445, Luke 8447, Masonic 8449, N. 8459, O'Halloran 8462, Paine 8465, Pillsbury 8473, Pisa 8474, Preston 8475, Seymour 8485, Sinclair 8488, Slemons 8490, Washington 8500, Wilson 8504

South Carolina: Bonner 8513, Campbell 8515, Davis 8521, Horne 8528, **Lader 8531**, Love 8532, Nalley 8535, Peery/Cauthen 8537, Security's 8539, Singing 8540, T-Bonz 8546, WPW 8551, Wyatt 8552, **Zvejnieks 8553**

South Dakota: J&L 8568, Reese 8573

Tennessee: Adams 8579, Agape 8580, Bradford 8592, Campbell 8594, Card 8596, Cartinhour-Woods 8597, Chrysalis 8598, Cole 8600, Community 8601, Cracker 8603, Doochin 8605, Drake 8606, Draughon 8607, EBS 8610, Eskind 8613, **Fugitive 8618**, Gaylord 8620, Hutcheson 8631, Ingram 8632, Kennedy 8638, Kite 8639, **Louisiana-Pacific 8644, Lowenstein 8645**, Mapp 8646, Massengill-DeFriece 8647, McGehee 8648, McWherter 8649, New 8654, Proctor 8662, Seidman 8672, Seme 8673, Splawn 8677, Stadler 8678, Tipton 8682, Tompkins 8683, Weiss 8684, Williamson, 8685

Texas: Abernathy 8690, Adler 8692, **AMD 8698**, AMR/American 8703, Anderson 8704, Anderson 8705, Aragona 8706, Ash 8709, Astin 8710, Augur 8712, Baldridge 8715, Beaird 8720, Beghini 8724, Bertha 8729, **Bhutada 8730**, Bloxom, 8731, Brochstein 8746, Burch 8756, Calpine 8759, Cauthorn 8764, Central 8766, Clear 8772, Clements 8773, Community 8782, Connor 8785, Cook 8786, **Crowder 8792**, D3 8793, Dale 8794, Damuth 8796, de 8802, Deakins 8804, Deason 8805, di 8812, Diamond 8813, Dice 8814, Dick 8815, Dougherty, 8825, Dunaway 8832, Dunham 8834, Edwards 8837, EOS 8840, Fairchild 8845, Faith 8846, Fenner 8850, Fentress 8851, Fertitta 8852, Finger 8857, Fleming 8860, Flowers 8862, Ford 8864, Foster 8867, Foundation 8869, Foundation 8870, Fowlston 8871, Frankel 8872, Friedman 8876, Fruehauf 8879, FSR 8880, Fuller 8882, Gatewood 8885, Genovese 8887, **Gilman, 8889**, Graham 8896, Gray-Pampa 8900, Griffin 8902, Griffith 8903, Grits 8904, Hartman 8920, Hatfield 8922, Hegi 8926, Helmle-Shaw 8929, Hext 8933, Hill 8938, Hixon 8940, Holloway 8946, Houck 8953, Howard 8955, Howell 8956, Ilgenfritz 8960, Jackson 8963, Jamail 8965, Johnson 8969, Joseph 8974, Kahn 8978, Kaplan 8979, KCL 8981, Kelley 8983, Kelley 8984, Ketelsen 8988, Kowitz 9002, Kramer 9003, Krist 9004, Littauer 9005, Long 9023, Lowdon 9025, Luse 9029, McAllister 9046, McCarty 9047, **McCreless 9049**, McKee 9052, McMillan, 9054, Mithoff 9068, Mitte 9069, Montgomery 9070, Moore 9072, Moss 9076, Myers 9081, **New 9087**, Nowiczewski 9090, O'Connor 9093, P 9108, Pearlman 9122, Peine 9123, Petty 9126, Pierson 9129, Postl 9136, Pratt 9137, Quanex 9141, Ray 9144, Redman 9147, Reilly 9148, Reitch 9149, Reuhl 9150, Riter, 9154, Roosth 9160, Rosenberg 9162, Rosenthal 9163, Ross 9165, Rowan 9166, Rust 9168, **Ryrie 9169**, Santander 9173, Saunders 9176, Schepps 9177, Schulte 9181, Sear 9186, Sherman 9192, Simpson-Omohundro 9196, Smith 9201, Smith 9202, Smith 9206, Smith 9207, **Soonae 9208**, Sparks 9211, Stephens 9217, Stevenson 9220, Storehouse 9223, Tennessee 9230, Torrance 9241, Tyler 9244, Vaughan 9249, Vetter 9251, VMP 9252, Waggoner 9254, Waggoners 9255, Walthall 9258, Ward 9260, Warren 9261, Watson 9263, Weaver 9265, Webre 9266, Weir 9268, Wells 9271, Westcott 9273, Whitley 9276, Willard 9278, Wise 9283, Woltman 9288, Wood 9290, Works 9293

Utah: Bourne-Spafford 9306, Callister 9310, Catalyst 9313, Davis 9317, Dreamweaver 9320, Eccles 9322, Eskuche 9323, Kennecott 9333, Larsen 9337, Odyssey 9342, Parrish 9343, Slaughter, 9353, Sorenson 9356, Steiner 9358, Zions 9363

Vermont: Altman 9364, Blittersdorf 9365, Carris 9367, Castanea 9368, Kahn 9377, Kaufman 9378, **Maverick 9380**, Mergens 9381, NSB 9382, Redducs 9383, Stokes 9385

Virginia: American 9387, Andreas 9388, Backer 9389, Banks 9390, Bassett 9391, Beck 9393, Birk 9398, Blue 9401, Brink's 9406, **Brown 9407**, Buchanan

9410, Cartledge 9414, Charles 9418, Community 9426, Darden 9428, **Delmar 9429**, Denit 9430, Donohue 9432, **Dorothy-Ann 9433**, Edlavitch 9440, Flippo 9449, **Foundation 9450**, Franklin 9452, Geary-O'Hara 9456, Greco 9463, Harris 9468, Ivakota 9477, Lawrence 9487, Lee-Jackson 9488, Macedonian 9496, Poole 9512, Pruden 9517, R 9518, Ratner 9521, RECO 9522, Sirad 9533, Stafford 9535, Stone 9537, Thomas 9542, Treakle 9543, Two 9544, Valentine 9545, VuBay 9548, Weil 9550, Womack 9556, Zeiders 9557

Washington: Arise 9562, Babare 9564, Bungie 9576, Coulter 9581, DeFalco 9585, Dudley 9588, Everett 9592, Excel 9593, Fales 9594, Ferguson 9596, Foss 9598, Gibson 9604, Gilmore 9605, Gius 9606, Hagan 9612, Hall 9613, Helstrom 9619, Horn 9625, Howarth 9626, Jacobi 9628, **Jernigan 9631, Ji 9632**, Kawabe 9642, Kilworth 9644, Korum 9648, Magdalen 9658, McKinlay 9662, Northwest 9669, Nysether 9671, Remala 9683, Runstad 9686, Shepherd 9694, Smith 9698, Thomson 9711, Tonkin 9715, Wilson 9725, Worthington 9729

West Virginia: Bowen 9737, Bowers 9738, Brown 9739, Driehorst 9743, Hamer 9746, Hewgill 9748, Hoffmann 9749, Hollandsworth 9750, Hollowell 9751, Huntington 9754, McCormick 9758, Minor 9761, Parlin 9762, Skewes 9766, Starvaggi 9767, Vecellio 9770, Wolfe 9772

Wisconsin: AnnMarie 9774, Ariens 9776, BayCare 9781, Birnschein 9783, Braun 9787, Caritas 9791, Carlisle 9792, Chipstone 9794, Cloud 9796, Debbink 9804, Door 9810, Dudley 9811, Einhorn 9815, Foley 9820, Frautschi 9822, Fromstein 9824, Gardner 9825, Glanert 9827, Heller 9839, Highlands 9841, Hunt 9845, Inbusch 9847, J.P.C. 9848, **Johnson 9851**, Johnson 9853, Junginger 9856, Kalscheur 9858, Karol 9859, Kaztex 9860, Kelly 9861, Kenosha 9862, Kohl 9865, Lloyd 9870, Loehrke 9872, LUX 9874, Manitowoc 9876, Marcus 9877, Marshfield 9878, Martin 9879, Mason 9880, Mid-States 9887, Ocular 9895, Olson 9898, Phipps 9902, Puelicher 9907, Redmond 9910, Religious 9912, RITE-HITE 9915, ROS 9918, Rosemann 9919, Sartori 9921, Schmucker 9923, Schoenleber 9924, Seeds 9925, Shannon 9927, Smith 9931, Sonnentag 9934, St. 9936, Steinle 9938, Styberg 9942, Sub-Zero 9943, T 9945, Uihlein 9949, Van 9953, Wagner 9955, Webcrafters-Frautschi 9957, Weyco 9958, Wilson 9960, Woodtrust-Bell 9963

Wyoming: C 9966, Connemara 9967, Dragicevich 9969, Jaquith 9975, JWJ 9978, Nickerson 9981, Perkins 9982, Sargent 9985, **Schultz 9986**, Scott 9988, Skelton 9989, Tate 9995, Weiss 9996, Weiss 9997

Grantee relations

California: LEF 739
New Mexico: Taos 5626

Grants to individuals

Alabama: Dixon 26
Alaska: Koniag 89
Arkansas: Murphy 206
California: Alafi 235, **Alalusi 236**, Avery-Fuller-Welch 260, Bialis 313, California 370, **Cantor 375**, Carlston 377, CEC 382, Downey-Short 461, Farber 495, Foundation 520, **Northern 870**, Optivest 884, **PADI 898**, Pasarow 906, Physicians 925, Picerne 926, Rest 966, Teachers 1104, **Trustees 1132**, Unz 1137, Whittier 1181
Colorado: Helmar 1291, Living 1316, SEAKR 1351
Connecticut: Colburn-Keenan 1421, Senior 1566, **Sullivan 1578**, Widows 1595
Delaware: Mary's 1703, Thomson 1764
District of Columbia: **Union 1837**
Florida: **Basser 1871**, Coral 1952, Densch 1970, Erdle 1993, Forman 2011, Kaul 2139, King 2148,

Kiwanis 2150, Livingston 2187, Riechmann 2286, Russell 2303, Ryan 2305
Georgia: Barnett 2441, Beckman 2443
Hawaii: Ching 2628
Idaho: Boise 2666
Illinois: Aon 2710, Family 2864, **Gish 2915**, Nayak 3133
Indiana: Decatur 3367, Ohio 3427
Iowa: Grinnell 3501, Iowa 3513, **World 3550**
Kentucky: Independence 3666, Kentucky 3669
Louisiana: Wetmore 3757
Maine: Camden 3771, Firebird 3778
Maryland: Ammerman 3813, Meyer, 3913, Warfield 3978
Massachusetts: **A 3995**, Babson-Webber-Mustard 4010, Cabot 4035, Kendall 4149, **New 4220**, Permanent 4239, Pilgrim 4245, Putnam 4253, Weber 4352, Xeric 4365
Michigan: Buist 4401, Four 4449, Grosse 4460, Pardee 4533, Tamer 4585
Minnesota: G&K 4691
Mississippi: Phillips 4850, Skelton 4854
Missouri: Butler 4880, Calkins 4881
Nebraska: Hester 5091
Nevada: **A 5131**, Meyer 5177
New Jersey: Alcon 5244, **American 5247**, Brothers 5276, Feldstein 5344, **Ostberg 5483**, **Southpole 5545**, United 5565
New York: **Abba's 5634**, **Animal 5680**, Art 5691, Artists 5692, Bennett 5737, Birchrock 5749, Burrows 5803, **Cogitare 5855**, Correspondents 5879, **Dungannon 5935**, Fresh 6033, Gordon 6109, **Gottlieb 6114**, **Haven 6178**, Henson 6194, Heyward 6202, **Jockey 6265**, Kleban 6323, Lissner 6405, Marine 6442, **Nok 6537**, Realty 6655, **Schepp 6739**, **Sparkplug 6830**, Speranza 6836, **Stefansky 6854**, Stony 6868, Sussman 6880, SVM 6886, Vaad 6924, **Walsh/Alfred 6943**
North Carolina: Burlington 7062, Eddy 7087, Foundation 7102, Richardson 7221, **Rixson 7223**, Strowd 7258
Ohio: A 7299, Foss 7407, Gay 7418, Loeb 7504, Sheadle 7588, Tuscarawas 7623
Pennsylvania: Bon-Ton 7884, Crawford 7945, **Epstein 7984**, Female 7990, Greater 8026, Honickman 8066, Jewish 8080, Leeway 8118, Olitsky 8198, Penn 8208
Rhode Island: Perpetual 8471, Preston 8475
Tennessee: Stuttering 8680
Texas: Bearden 8721, D3 8793, Denman 8810, Educational 8836, Heinlein 8927, Nabors 9083, Navarro 9085, **New 9087, Ryrie 9169**, South 9209, Texas 9231
Utah: Keener 9332
Vermont: Copley 9370
Virginia: **Fund 9455**
Washington: **Ji 9632**, Tudor 9717, Welch 9721
West Virginia: Bowen 9736
Wisconsin: BayCare 9781, Carlisle 9792, Kohl 9865, Marshfield 9878
Wyoming: Perkins 9982

In-kind gifts

Alabama: Black 12
Arkansas: Union 219
California: Fox 523, Jamieson 658, **Lawrence 734**, Orfalea 887, Payne 910, **Quiksilver 945**
Colorado: Broomfield 1242, Wilkins 1379
Florida: Coral 1952, Peterson 2257, Toppel 2377
Idaho: Simplot 2685
Indiana: Community 3360, Fayette 3379, Jennings 3402, LaGrange 3412
Iowa: **World 3550**
Kansas: Payless 3614
Massachusetts: Chicopee 4047

Michigan: Branch 4396, Community 4411, Conrad 4413, Lapeer 4490
New Jersey: Alcon 5244
New Mexico: Taos 5626
New York: **Nok 6537**
Ohio: Bahmann 7313, Cleveland 7354, Community 7357
Oklahoma: Kerr 7693, Stone 7721
Oregon: Elwood 7761, Portland 7807
Pennsylvania: Buck 7903, Hankin 8038, HBE 8047, Weiner 8349
Texas: Boeing 8733, McKee 9052
Utah: Odyssey 9342
Wisconsin: Marshfield 9878

Individual development

Arizona: Ahearn 95
Arkansas: **Baldor 188**, Trinity 218, Union 219
California: Drum 464, Flanagan 510, Hoefer 628, Mason 805, Mazda 810, McKenzie 816, Nagel 857, Pearlstein 911, Perricone 916, Ross 988, Van 1144, **Woo 1195**
Colorado: Puksta 1341, Tomkins 1368
Connecticut: Fuller 1460, Goldfarb 1467, Newtown 1532, Schaeneman, 1560
Florida: Atkins 1856, Beasley 1877, Grabe 2053, Gregory 2067, Hand 2077, Jacobson 2123, KBR 2142, Morrison 2222, Shannon 2328, **Uncle 2383**
Georgia: Barnett 2441, Lee 2540
Hawaii: Kahiau 2636, Vidinha 2653
Illinois: Bisco 2742, Franklin 2888, Griswold 2931, Halstead 2944, Hare 2954, Kerr 3015, Kilrea 3017, Logos 3058, Miller 3112, Rosenthal 3210
Indiana: Blackford 3346, Community 3361, Jasper 3401
Iowa: Iowa 3513, Jefferson 3514, Pappajohn 3525
Kansas: McFadden 3601, Ross 3619
Maryland: Higginson 3880, Hubbard 3883, Loats 3902, Mustard 3922, Slavin 3954, Sonneborn 3957
Massachusetts: Benz 4017, Kidder 4152, Pilgrim 4245, Ramsey 4258, Simoni 4296
Michigan: Community 4411, LoPrete 4496, Ratner 4548
Minnesota: Fischman 4685, Granite 4699, Kinman-Oldfield 4723, Morning 4748, Wendel 4813
Missouri: **Bohm 4871**, Finley 4910, Portman 4981
Nevada: Geomar 5160
New Hampshire: Bickford 5205
New Jersey: Grace 5375, Scire 5526, **Southpole 5545**, Yoh 5597
New Mexico: Continental 5612
New York: **American 5669**, Bank 5710, Brown 5791, **Buffalo 5799**, Fee 5990, Kautz 6290, Kleban 6323, Knapp 6331, Lachman 6356, Loconsolo 6408, Mead 6466, Rhodes 6666, Roothbert 6682, Society 6821, Stutz 6875, Trimble 6910, Walrath 6941, Windy 6980
North Carolina: Bryan 7060, Hayden-Harman 7120, Kanitz 7140, Meserve 7182, Smith 7247, Wallace 7277
Ohio: Foundation 7408, Murphy 7533
Oklahoma: Richardson 7717
Oregon: Shapira 7814
Pennsylvania: Gauss 8014, Harsco 8040, Jordan 8082, Postles 8223
Rhode Island: Felicia 8406, Papitto 8467
South Carolina: Collins 8520
South Dakota: Miller 8570, Welk 8577
Tennessee: Jewell 8633
Texas: B.E.L.I.E.F. 8713, Brown 8751, College 8779, Dice 8814, Genecov 8886, Healthcare 8924, Knox 8999, McDaniel 9050, Mitte 9069, Nelson 9086, Ross 9165, Sparks 9211, Stanzel 9213, Waggoner 9254

Virginia: Blue 9401, Karlgaard 9481, Meador 9500, Poole 9512, Thomas 9542
Washington: DeFalco 9585, Echo 9590, Herbold 9620, Horn 9625, Worthington 9729
West Virginia: Vecellio 9770
Wisconsin: Phipps 9902, Van 9952

Information and Referral

Florida: Graese 2055
New York: **Engineering 5964**, High 6206
Ohio: Osteopathic 7545

Institutional evaluations

California: Fox 523

Internships

Alaska: Chenega 83, Doyon 84, Koniag 89
California: Alafi 235, Drum 464, Lux 773, Ragir 950, Rice 969, Stauffer 1077
Colorado: Leighty 1311
Connecticut: Winokur 1597
Florida: Archibald 1852, Lazarus 2172, **Uncle 2383**
Georgia: Lee 2540
Illinois: Dubin 2838, McGraw 3092, Oberweiler 3147
Iowa: **World 3550**, Young 3552
Kentucky: **Magee 3674**
Maryland: Ammerman 3813, Higginson 3880
Massachusetts: **Kahn 4143**, Morse 4209
Michigan: Gratiot 4459
Minnesota: Granite 4699, Thorpe 4800
Missouri: **Bohm 4871**
Nevada: Close 5148, Meyer 5177
New Jersey: **Dow 5325**, Frelinghuysen 5354
New Mexico: B.F. 5606, Chamiza 5609
New York: Aronson 5689, Avery 5702, **Cogitare 5855**, High 6206, **Kevorkian 6304**, Krumholz 6349, Lucelia 6418, **Nok 6537**, O'Grady 6551, Patrina 6579, **Potts 6624**, Strong 6872, Sussman 6879, Tuch 6915
North Carolina: Eddy 7087, Fox 7103, Strowd 7258
Ohio: Sears-Swetland 7581, Seasongood 7582
Oklahoma: Kerr 7693
Pennsylvania: Bennett 7860, Society 8289, Tuttleman 8325
Rhode Island: Getz 8412
Texas: Vaughan 9249
Virginia: **Delmar 9429**
Washington: Foss 9598

Land acquisitions

Alabama: Abahac 1
Arkansas: Hickinbotham 199
California: Anhaltzer 245, Bear 288, Drum 464, Heller 613, Looker 766, New 865
Colorado: Ballantine 1226, Goodwin 1279, Warner 1376
Connecticut: Baldwin 1399
Delaware: SNAVE 1747
Florida: Coral 1952, **Freewill 2021**, Reinhold 2280, **Uncle 2383**
Georgia: Boone 2446, English 2474, Lee 2540
Illinois: Arboit 2713, Bishop 2743, EMA 2854, Jocarno 3000, Oberweiler 3147
Indiana: Bussing-Koch 3353, Huntington 3397, LaGrange 3412, Namaste 3422
Iowa: Young 3552
Kansas: Trusler 3635
Kentucky: Barth 3647, Sutherland 3699
Maine: Burnham 3770, Reny 3802, Somers 3803
Maryland: Ammerman 3813, Biophilia 3824

Massachusetts: Carlee 4038, Codman 4052, Cricket 4060, Hauben 4120, Hazard 4123, Kelsey 4148, Stearns 4310, Xeric 4365
Michigan: Biederman 4391, Kantzler 4478, Speckhard-Knight 4574, Stubnitz 4582
Minnesota: Granite 4699, O'Brien 4753, Quinlan 4764, Walker 4805
Missouri: Boylan 4873, Sander 4991
Montana: Cinnabar 5047, Sample 5062
Nebraska: Barklage 5071, Heuermann 5092, Midlands 5104
Nevada: Timken-Sturgis 5192
New Hampshire: Hunt 5214, McIninch 5224
New Jersey: A 5240
New Mexico: Taos 5626
New York: Glens 6082, Messinger 6482, Plymouth 6612, Strong 6872
North Carolina: Cooke 7079
Ohio: Gale 7414, NLT 7537, Rosenberry 7562, Sandfair 7569, Scotford 7579, Sears-Swetland 7581
Oklahoma: Ashbrook 7656, **Crio 7670**, Gelvin 7682, Stone 7721, Wegener 7731
Oregon: Woodard 7831
Pennsylvania: Friendship 8009, Frohring 8010, Grundy 8029, Patterson 8205, **Rust 8250**
Rhode Island: Heydt 8419, Seymour 8485
Texas: Hext 8933, Hixon 8940, KCL 8981, Vaughan 9249
Vermont: Castanea 9368, Redducs 9383, Stokes 9385
Virginia: Backer 9389
Washington: Ferguson 9596, **Ji 9632**, Nysether 9671
West Virginia: Huntington 9754
Wisconsin: Dudley 9811, Janesville 9850, Stry 9941
Wyoming: Sargent 9985

Leadership and professional development

California: Fox 523, McKay 815, McLean 817
Florida: **Uncle 2383**
Massachusetts: Middlesex 4203
Nebraska: Nebraska 5105
New Mexico: Taos 5626
Ohio: Athens 7311
Wyoming: **Schultz 9986**

Loans to individuals

California: Community 421, SKB 1044, Yen 1201
Colorado: **Nord 1332**
Florida: KML 2152, Phillips 2260
Georgia: Garden 2483
Illinois: Griswold 2931, McKee 3094, Rogers 3202
Iowa: Iowa 3513, Van 3539
Louisiana: Magale 3735
Maine: Milford 5225
Massachusetts: **A 3995**, Hopedale 4134
Mississippi: Day 4832
New Hampshire: Milford 5225
New Mexico: Carlsbad 5608, Taos 5626
New York: Authors 5700, Community 5872, **Nok 6537**, Ontario 6559
North Carolina: Bryan 7060, Little 7162, Stonecutter 7255
Ohio: Loeb 7504, Shinnick 7591
Pennsylvania: Clareth 7924, Somerset 8290
Rhode Island: Papitto 8467
Texas: Mantzel 9036, Pearce 9121
Vermont: Castanea 9368
Virginia: Womack 9556
West Virginia: Carter 9741, Stout 9769
Wyoming: Perkins 9982

Marketing

Montana: Cora 5048

Matching grants

Alabama: Friedman 27, Ireland 39, Kemp 42
Arizona: Grace 125, Grossman 126
California: Ackerman 227, Alafi 235, Amador 238, Bannerman 274, Bonner 326, Buell 357, **Bull 358, Cantor 375**, Codding 412, Community 421, Downing 462, Fox 523, Fusenot 541, Gellert 550, Heller 613, Horwitz 633, Huntington 642, Livingston 761, Looker 766, Lux 773, Majestic 784, Margoes 795, McClatchy 811, McLean 817, **Modglin 840**, Nicholson 866, Ontario 882, Orfalea 887, Ragir 950, Rice 969, Santa 1003, Simon 1041, Stauffer 1077, **Wakerly 1150**, Weil 1163
Colorado: Bright 1241, Broomfield 1242, Burt 1244, Donnell-Kay 1258, Leighty 1311, **Oreg 1335**, Schlessman 1349, Schramm 1350, Southwestern 1355, Vradenburg 1374
Connecticut: Baldwin 1399, Cochrane 1420, Dime 1438, Fippinger 1450, Martin 1520
Delaware: Brown 1631, Chaney 1640, Lightner 1699, New 1715, SNAVE 1747
District of Columbia: **Foundation 1807**, Goldman 1810, Porter 1829, Replogle 1831
Florida: Archibald 1852, **Benedict 1884**, Cape 1917, Chadbourne 1932, Charlotte 1938, Coral 1952, Couch 1953, Dorset 1979, Duckwall 1982, **Freewill 2021**, Jacobsen 2123, Landwirth 2167, McCabe 2201, **Mukti 2226**, Phillips 2260, Price 2267, Ray 2275, Reinhold 2280, Silverman 2337, Swisher 2361, Tampa 2362, TECO 2367, Thomas 2371, Toppel 2377, Turner 2381, **Uncle 2383, Wollowick 2412, Zimmer 2425**
Georgia: Abreu 2431, Athens 2437, Georgia 2484, Lee 2540, Wright 2620
Idaho: Morrison 2682, Simplot 2685
Illinois: Arboit 2713, Bufka 2763, Community 2802, Community 2803, Cremer 2815, EMA 2854, Family 2864, Hanson 2950, Harris 2957, Hughes 2983, McCauley 3085, Meyer 3106, Oberweiler 3147, Smith 3253
Indiana: Community 3359, Community 3360, Community 3363, Decatur 3367, Huntington 3397, Jasper 3401, Jennings 3402, Kuhne 3409, LaGrange 3412, Oliver 3428, Raker 3434, Rush 3441, TCU 3458, Vevay-Switzerland 3462, Western 3466
Iowa: Cowles 3482, Forster 3494, Muscatine 3523, **Wright 3551**
Kansas: Baehr 3556, Legacy, 3595
Kentucky: Barth 3647, Etscorn 3654, Hayswood 3662, Trim 3702
Louisiana: Huie-Dellmon 3729, Steinhagen 3755, Wisdom 3761
Maine: Davenport 3775, Somers 3803
Maryland: Biophilia 3824, **Braitmayer 3827**, CSG 3842, Gladding 3871, **Goldberg 3872**, Higginson 3880, Hubbard 3883, Kelly, 3893, Tucker 3969
Massachusetts: Behrakis 4015, Bulger 4031, Clarke 4049, Codman 4052, Cricket 4060, Kelsey 4148, MutualOne 4216, **New 4220, Pegasus 4236**, Permanent 4239, Sailors' 4276, Simoni 4296, United 4337, Wallace 4347
Michigan: Branch 4396, Community 4410, Community 4411, Holden 4467, Kantzler 4478, Keller 4481, Lapeer 4490, M 4497, Michigan 4514, Morley 4518, Olds 4526, Plym 4542, Porter 4543, Ratner 4548, **Teitel 4589**, Tuscola 4598, Vicksburg 4606, Wickson-Link 4616
Minnesota: Cox 4662, Deikel 4663, **Fingerhut 4683**, Larsen 4728, **Porter 4763**, Quinlan 4764, Riverway 4776, Tennant 4798, **Trust 4802, Winds 4820**
Mississippi: Baird 4822, Community 4830, Lower 4847
Missouri: **Build-A-Bear 4879**, Cornelsen 4889, Cray 4890, Curry 4892, Riedel 4984, Sander 4991, Schutte 4995, Sunnen 5018
Montana: Cinnabar 5047, Cora 5048
Nebraska: Heuermann 5092, Kilbourne 5097, Nebraska 5105, Reynolds 5114, Scribante 5116, Storz 5122

Nevada: Meyer 5177

New Hampshire: Bickford 5205, Dorr 5211, Hunt 5214, McIninch 5224, Thorne 5233

New Jersey: A 5240, **Blue 5269**, Clermont 5298, Kerney 5419, **Knistrom 5426**, Leavens 5444, Machuga 5454, Miller 5468, **Ostberg 5483**, Schwartz 5525, Snyder 5541, Westfield 5582, Wilson 5590

New Mexico: Carlsbad 5608, Foster 5615, Nirvana 5621, Taos 5626

New York: Abelard 5635, August 5698, Balbach 5707, Cutco 5890, **Eastman 5940**, **Engineering 5964**, French 6032, Gaffney 6049, Gage 6050, Glens 6082, Hahn 6156, Hoyt 6230, IF 6237, Lake 6360, Legacy 6373, Lubo 6417, Messinger 6482, Northern 6540, Nuhn 6544, O'Grady 6551, Ong 6558, Pratt-Northam 6625, Raymond 6652, Snow 6818, Strong 6872, Truman 6912, Utica 6922

North Carolina: BB&T 7045, Covington 7081, Eddy 7087, Fox 7103, Glenn 7111, Masserini 7172, Meserve 7182, Outer 7204, Rogers 7228, Strowd 7258, Thomasville 7267

Ohio: Austin-Bailey 7312, Bahmann 7313, B-Brand 7318, Brentwood 7330, Bryan 7339, Community 7356, Corbett 7363, Defiance 7375, Gale 7415, **Katz 7475**, Kramer 7484, Laub 7490, Morley 7532, Ritchie 7561, Sandfair 7569, Scotford 7579, Sears-Swetland 7581, Smith 7598, Tait 7610, Young 7652

Oklahoma: Ashbrook 7656, Atherton 7657, Barthelmes 7661, Cherokee 7666, Gelvin 7682, Kerr 7693, Merrick 7707, Stone 7721

Oregon: Elwood 7761, Holzman 7775, Kuse 7786, Lamb 7787, McKay 7795, Merlo 7797, Michael 7799, Pendleton 7806, Schmidt 7813, Silver 7817, Wessinger 7826

Pennsylvania: Arkema 7842, Ashland 7845, Bennett 7860, Brooks 7899, Bucks 7905, Carnahan-Jackson 7917, Community 7933, Elk 7975, Finley 7995, Flinn 8001, Freas 8005, Hoffman 8062, **KL 8094**, Maslow 8146, McCandless 8153, McKinney 8161, Mill 8172, Miller 8173, Pfundt 8213, Quaker 8228, Remmel 8235, Seybert 8269, Smith 8280, Willary 8356, Williams 8357, **Zeldin 8376**

Rhode Island: Collis 8397, Heydt 8419, Kimball 8434, Kingsbury 8435, Moore 8456

South Carolina: Bailey 8510

Tennessee: Cracker 8603, Kite 8639, Schmidt 8671

Texas: Boeing 8733, Central 8766, **Chrest 8770**, Clements 8773, Cook 8786, Dick 8815, Dougherty, 8825, Fair 8844, Graham 8896, Griffin 8902, Hervey 8933, Hext 8933, KCL 8981, King 8994, Littauer 9021, Long 9023, Marcus 9037, Mayer 9043, Petty 9126, Redman 9147, San 9170, South 9209, Vaughan 9249, Von 9253

Utah: Patel 9344, Sorenson 9356

Vermont: Mergens 9381, Stokes 9385

Virginia: Beck 9393, **Brown 9407**, Community 9426, **Dorothy-Ann 9433**, Lane 9486, **Longview 9494**, Roller-Bottimore 9525

Washington: Bungie 9576, Foss 9598, Korum 9648, Northwest 9669, Tonkin 9715

West Virginia: Chambers 9742, Hollowell 9751

Wisconsin: Blooming 9784, Dudley 9811, Eau 9814, Janesville 9850, Kenosha 9862, Koss 9866, Lutsey 9873, LUX 9874, Marshfield 9878, Modine 9889, Prescott 9905, Stateline 9937

Wyoming: **Schultz 9986**

Mission-related investments

California: **Cienega 404**

Florida: Lelash 2178

Georgia: Gray 2497

New York: **Posner-Wallace 6621**

Pennsylvania: **KL 8094**

Vermont: Castanea 9368

Pilot programs

California: Simon 1041

Florida: **Zimmer 2425**

Maryland: Richmond 3940

Policy, advocacy and systems reform

California: Anderson 244, Garabedian 545, McKay 815, Rappaport 953, Roberts 975, Theroux 1110, Yen 1201

Colorado: Hanson 1286, Krieble 1308

Connecticut: Greenhill 1472, Tell 1580

District of Columbia: Coleman, 1796

Florida: Miller 2213

Georgia: Fickling 2478, University 2597

Illinois: Danielson 2824, **New 3137**, Rosenthal 3210, Rossman 3211

Maryland: Weiss 3982

Massachusetts: Henderson 4127, Kelsey 4148, Rose 4271

Michigan: Oreffice 4528, Whitman 4615

Missouri: **Maor 4952**

Montana: High 5057

Nevada: Blue 5140, Geomar 5160

New Hampshire: Jameson 5215

New Jersey: Brown 5278

New York: Feldman 5996, Lux 6422, **Stern 6862**

North Carolina: Redwoods 7218

Ohio: Armington 7309, Thendara 7616

Oregon: Saling 7811

Pennsylvania: Beach 7855, Brooks 7899, Eberly 7969, Jackson 8078, Maple 8139

Rhode Island: Dwinell 8403

South Carolina: Cato 8516

Texas: Baldridge 8715

Utah: Catalyst 9313

Virginia: Cedars 9416, **Longview 9494**, Pensmore 9509

Washington: Erickson 9591

Wisconsin: Roddis 9916

Pro bono board services

North Carolina: Redwoods 7218

Pro bono consulting services

Alabama: Black 12

California: Buell 357, Fox 523, **Modglin 840**, Szekely 1102, Wharton 1178

Colorado: Donnell-Kay 1258, Leighty 1311, **Oreg 1335**, Vradenburg 1374

Connecticut: Pryor 1546

Florida: **Mukti 2226**, **Uncle 2383**

Georgia: Athens 2437, Lee 2540

Illinois: Community 2802

Indiana: Community 3359, Huntington 3397, Jennings 3402, LaGrange 3412

Massachusetts: Kimball 4155

Minnesota: Deikel 4663, Riverway 4776, **Trust 4802**

Mississippi: Community 4830

Missouri: Long 4948, Pendergast-Weyer 4979

Montana: Cora 5048

Nebraska: Nebraska 5105

New Jersey: Miller 5468

New Mexico: Carlsbad 5608

New York: American 5662, **Cogitare 5855**, Hoyt 6230, Initial 6245, O'Grady 6551, **Posner-Wallace 6621**

North Carolina: Fox 7103, Meserve 7182, Outer 7204

Ohio: Armington 7309, Athens 7311, Brentwood 7330, Foundation 7408, Philada 7548

Oklahoma: Cherokee 7666

Oregon: Elwood 7761, Woodard 7831

Pennsylvania: Hoffman 8062, **KL 8094**

Rhode Island: Getz 8412

South Dakota: Watertown 8576

Texas: Hext 8933, Vaughan 9249

Vermont: Castanea 9368

Pro bono human resources services

North Carolina: Redwoods 7218

Professorships

California: Bridges 342, **Cantor 375**, Corday 426, Drum 464, Martin 801

Delaware: Bennett 1618

District of Columbia: Goldman 1810

Florida: Duckwall 1982, Roshan 2297

Georgia: Lee 2540

Illinois: Marsteller 3079

Indiana: Bussing-Koch 3353, Huntington 3397, Raymond 3436

Kansas: Ross 3619

Kentucky: Etscorn 3654, Ogden 3683

Louisiana: Huie-Dellmon 3729, Lang 3733

Maryland: Ammerman 3813, **Goldberg 3872**, Richmond 3940, Widgeon 3983

Michigan: Baldwin 4382, DeVlieg 4428, Zondervan 4621

Minnesota: Granite 4699

Missouri: **Bohm 4871**, Schutte 4995, Shawe 5000

Nebraska: Perkins 5111

New Jersey: Winters 5591

New York: Avery 5702, **Buster 5806**, Carwill 5818, Gilliam 6078, Henshel 6192, Heyman 6201, **Kevorkian 6304**, Leonhardt 6381, Messinger 6482, Zenkel 7023

North Carolina: BB&T 7045, Cooke 7079, Covington 7081, Eddy 7087, Smith 7249

Ohio: Brown 7336, Morley 7532, Sandfair 7569

Oklahoma: Kerr 7693

Oregon: Merlo 7797, Woodard 7831

Pennsylvania: Eberly 7969, Stein 8299

Rhode Island: Papitto 8467

Texas: Bromberg 8748, Burch 8756, Cook 8786, Dunagan 8831, King 8994, Mitte 9069, Vaughan 9249, Wal-Dot 9256, Wells 9271, Zale 9299

Washington: Murray 9667

Program development

Alabama: Birmingham 11, Black 12, Dixon 26, Ireland 39, Sexton 63, Siloam 65, Viro 73, Warren 75

Alaska: Alaska 80

Arizona: F2 117, Grossman 126, Hansen 127, Hughes 130, Snell 171

Arkansas: Darragh 193, Hickingbotham 199

California: Ackerman 227, Amador 238, Anhaltzer 245, Bank 272, Bannerman 274, Baxter 284, Bonner 326, Boone 329, Buell 357, **Bull 358**, Calaveras 369, **Candelaria 372**, Carlston 377, Charitable 389, Church 403, Cleo 407, Cloud 408, Coleman 416, Community 420, Community 421, Downing 462, Drum 464, Ebell 471, Farmers 496, First 506, Five 509, Foor 516, Fox 523, Fox 525, Fremont 527, Gellert 550, Gill 555, **Global 565**, Godric 566, Gross 587, Handlery 596, **Hefferlin 610**, Heller 613, Horwitz 633, Jamieson 658, Katz 692, Kelly 697, Laguna 726, **Lawrence 734**, **Lloyd 763**, Looker 766, Lopez 767, Lux 773, Majestic 784, Margoes 795, Mazda 810, McClatchy 811, McLean 817, **Modglin 840**, New 865, Nicholson 866, Ontario 882, Orfalea 887, Page 899, Penney 913, Plum 929, **Quiksilver 945**, Roche 979, Ross 988, Sammut 996, Silicon 1038, Smullin 1060, Solano 1063, Stauffer 1077, Sterling 1081, Sudikoff 1090, Swinerton 1098, Synopsys 1100, Szekely 1102, Trust 1131, **Wakerly 1150**, Waltmar 1155, Welk 1170, Westphal 1177, Wharton 1178, **Wilkinson 1183**

Colorado: Bjorkman 1236, Bloom 1239, Bright 1241, Chotin 1246, Comprecare 1249, Fortune 1273, Leighty 1311, Maki 1319, **National 1330, Oreg 1335,** Schlessman 1349, Schramm 1350, Stratton 1359, Vradenburg 1374, Warner 1376, Wilkins 1379

Connecticut: Axe-Houghton 1397, Barnes 1404, Bender 1405, Chelsea 1418, Dime 1438, Ensign-Bickford 1442, Fry 1458, Keefe 1497, Panwy 1539, Patricelli 1541, Proctor 1545, RBS 1549, Roberts 1552, Robinson 1553, Shumway 1570, Thomaston 1581, Tully 1588, Union 1590

Delaware: 18 1604, Babcock 1612, Brown 1631, Burt's 1635, Chaney 1640, **Jackman 1683,** Kutz 1696, Lightner 1699, Remmer 1726, SNAVE 1747, **TeleTech 1761,** Thronson 1766

District of Columbia: Cafritz 1793, Crowell 1799, Goldman 1810, Jovid 1817, **Pettus-Crowe 1828,** Replogle 1831, Tucker 1836

Florida: Anderson 1847, Archibald 1852, **Atlantis 1858,** Auerbach 1859, Cape 1917, Capital 1918, Catalina 1924, Charlotte 1938, Couch 1953, Erdle 1993, Evans 1994, Gulf 2069, Hill 2097, Jacobsen 2123, Landwirth 2167, Lelash 2178, Long 2189, McCabe 2201, **Mukti 2226,** Munroe 2228, Peterson 2257, Phillips 2259, Phillips 2260, Ray 2275, Roshan 2297, Toppel 2377, Wynne 2419

Georgia: Abreu 2431, Athens 2437, **Bancker-Williams 2440,** Exposition 2476, Georgia 2484, Holland-Underwood 2508, Illges 2517, Lee 2540, Magnus 2543, Marcus 2544, Marshall 2545, Raoul 2573, Solstice 2587, Stahl 2588, Waffle 2602, Walker 2603

Hawaii: Baldwin 2625, Castle 2626, Central 2627, Kaneta 2637, Vidinha 2653

Idaho: Boise 2666, Whittenberger 2689

Illinois: Agape 2698, Allen-Heath 2701, Alliant 2702, Bergstrom 2736, Best 2740, Boothroyd 2749, Bound 2751, Brunswick 2762, Chicago 2786, Chicago 2787, Community 2802, Community 2803, Delta 2826, EMA 2854, Faulkner 2867, Generations 2908, Graham 2926, Gust 2936, Harris 2957, Heath 2962, **Heritage 2967,** Hess 2969, Hughes 2983, Hunt 2984, **Landau 3036, Lindon 3054,** Logos 3058, MacDonald 3068, Marsteller 3079, Meyer 3106, Millard 3109, Reichert 3192, Seymour 3236, Smysor 3255, Staley 3262, Takiff 3281, Turner 3297

Indiana: Ayres 3342, Benton 3344, Bronstein 3351, Bussing-Koch 3353, Community 3359, Community 3360, Community 3361, Decatur 3367, Dubois 3370, Greene 3390, Huntington 3397, Jennings 3402, Kuhne 3409, Lacy 3410, LaGrange 3412, MutualBank 3421, Oliver 3428, Pulaski 3432, Raker 3434, Raymond 3436, Rush 3441, Scott 3446, TCU 3458, Western 3466

Iowa: First 3493, Forster 3494, Grinnell 3501, GuideOne 3503, McDonald 3520, Muscatine 3523, Van 3539, **Wahlert 3544,** West 3547

Kansas: Baehr 3556, Bane 3557, Brown 3561, Community 3567, DeVore 3573, Farah 3576, Fidelity 3577, Golden 3582, Insurance 3587, Kansas 3592, Legacy, 3595, Payless 3614, Watson 3639, Wiedemann 3642

Kentucky: Barth 3647, Hayswood 3662, Independence 3666, Keeneland 3668, Public 3687, Sutherland 3699, Trim 3702

Louisiana: Huie-Dellmon 3729, Steinhagen 3755, Wheless 3758, Wisdom 3761

Maine: Borman 3767, Brook 3769, Burnham 3770, Franklin 3779, **Golden 3781,** Planet 3797, Somers 3803

Maryland: Ammerman 3813, Baltimore 3816, Biophilia 3824, **Braitmayer 3827,** Caplan 3832, CSG 3842, **Goldberg 3872,** Higginson 3880, Hobbs 3882, Kelly, 3893, Macht 3905, Tucker 3969, Weiss 3982, Widgeon 3983

Massachusetts: 2 3992, Alden 3999, **Azadoutioun 4008,** Babson 4009, Bacon 4011, Behrakis 4015, Boynton 4025, Brooks 4028, **Bruner 4030,** Cabot 4034, Chase 4045, Chicopee 4047, Clarke 4049,

Coolidge 4057, Cricket 4060, Dedham 4067, Devereaux 4069, East 4075, Easthampton 4076, Hampden 4116, Hauben 4120, Henderson 4128, **Kahn 4143, Lalor 4164,** Massachusetts 4191, Middlesex 4203, Morse 4209, MutualOne 4216, **New 4220,** Noonan 4225, **Pegasus 4236,** Permanent 4239, Ramlose 4257, Ramsey 4258, Ratshesky 4259, Rice 4265, Rockland 4267, Russell 4273, Salem 4277, Shaughnessy 4292, Stearns 4310, Stearns 4311, Steiger 4312, Tresorelle 4333, Ungar 4336, United 4337, Vela 4341, Webster 4353, Wells 4357, Xeric 4365

Michigan: Abrams 4369, Ave 4379, Barstow 4385, Biederman 4391, Buffalo 4399, Community 4411, Delano 4426, Four 4449, Frankenmuth 4450, Glassen 4454, Gratiot 4459, JSJ 4474, Kantzler 4478, Keller 4481, Kellogg 4482, Leven 4492, M 4497, Mackinac 4499, Meritor, 4511, Merkley 4512, Michigan 4514, Morley 4518, O'Donovan 4525, Olds 4526, Plym 4542, Ratner 4548, Schmuckal 4559, Shiawassee 4568, Speckhard-Knight 4574, St. 4576, Stoddard 4579, Stubnitz 4582, **Teitel 4589,** Thoman 4590, Thompson 4592, Tremble 4595, Tuscola 4598, Vicksburg 4606, Whiting 4614, Wickson-Link 4616, Zondervan 4621

Minnesota: Andersen 4626, Ankeny 4628, Bell 4637, Bell 4638, Bend 4639, Briggs 4648, Deikel 4663, Depot 4667, Dyer 4669, Edina 4672, Erickson 4675, Faith, 4677, Farmers 4679, **Fingerhut 4683,** G&K 4691, Granite 4699, Grossman 4701, Grotto 4702, Jostens 4720, Louis 4731, Midcontinent 4745, Onan 4754, Open 4756, Quinlan 4764, Rahr 4766, Riverway 4776, Rosen 4782, Sayer 4786, **Sundance 4796,** Thorpe 4800, **Trust 4802,** Walker 4805, Wendel 4813, **Winds 4820**

Mississippi: Baird 4822, Lower 4847

Missouri: Baer 4862, Boylan 4873, **Build-A-Bear 4879,** Copaken 4888, Cray 4890, Curry 4892, Edgar 4899, Garvey 4913, Long 4948, MFA 4960, Morgan 4963, Peculiar 4978, Pendergast-Weyer 4979, Portman 4981, Riedel 4984, Siteman 5006, St. 5012, Sunnen 5018, Timmons 5021, Welch 5038

Montana: Cora 5048, Lynn 5059, Wendy's 5065

Nebraska: Ameritas 5067, Blair 5074, Hansen 5087, Heuermann 5092, Nebraska 5105, Pegler 5110, Perkins 5111, York 5129

Nevada: Dermody 5152, Meyer 5177, Pinnacle 5183

New Hampshire: Barker 5204, Bickford 5205, Dorr 5211, Hunt 5214, McIninch 5224, Salem 5230, Verney 5236

New Jersey: A 5240, Amboy 5246, **Blue 5269,** Brundage 5280, Columbia 5301, Elizabethtown 5332, Environmental 5337, Giants 5369, **Integra 5400,** Leavens 5444, Machuga 5454, Mamiye 5456, Miller 5468, **Rippel 5510,** Schwartz 5525, Selective 5528, Smith 5539, Stone 5553, Westfield 5582, Wilson 5590, Zobel 5603

New Mexico: Carlsbad 5608, Chamiza 5609, Con 5611

New York: 21st 5630, Abelard 5635, American 5664, Anderson-Rogers 5676, Aronson 5689, August 5698, Balbach 5707, Bank 5710, Bender 5735, Berkowitz 5739, Bernhill 5741, Black 5754, BTMU 5795, Capri 5814, Caruso 5817, Clark 5848, Coby 5852, Cohoes 5865, Dammann 5897, EMSA 5961, **Engineering 5964,** Friedland 6037, Gage 6050, Glens 6082, Gordon 6110, Grand 6123, Grant 6129, Greentree 6135, **Grossman 6146,** Grumbacher 6148, Hahn 6156, Hennessy 6191, Hite 6213, Hoyt 6230, Initial 6245, **Kathwari 6286,** Kenworthy 6300, Knapp 6331, **Laerdal 6358,** Lake 6360, Lee 6372, Legacy 6373, Liberman 6396, Lipton 6404, Loewy 6409, Lubo 6417, Lucelia 6418, Lux 6422, Manocherian 6438, Messinger 6482, Metzger-Price 6483, Nets 6524, **Nok 6537,** Northern 6540, Norwich 6542, Osceola 6560, Ostgrodd 6561, Palisades 6569, Patrina 6579, Pincus 6606, Plymouth 6612, **Posner-Wallace 6621, Potts 6624,** Pratt-Northam 6625, Raymond 6652, Roche 6678, Rose 6683,

Rosner 6698, Santvoord 6727, Shanken 6785, Sharon 6787, Sheafer 6789, Siegel 6797, Snow 6818, Snyder 6819, **Sparkplug 6830, Stein 6855,** Strong 6872, Triangle 6908, Truman 6912, Tuch 6915, Turner 6916, Utica 6922, Vogler 6932, Washington 6946, Weill 6949, Wells 6964, **Yoreinu 7010**

North Carolina: BB&T 7045, Burlington 7062, Cooke 7079, Covington 7081, Duncan 7086, Glenn 7111, Katz 7142, **Kramer 7152,** Masserini 7172, Meserve 7182, Outer 7204, Rogers 7228, **Rolander 7229,** Sanders 7234, Smith 7249, Strowd 7258, Sutcliffe 7262, Thomasville 7267, Vanderbilt 7273, Wagner 7275, Wake 7276, Yost 7291

Ohio: Armington 7309, Athens 7311, Austin-Bailey 7312, Bates 7317, B-Brand 7318, Beecher 7320, Bicknell 7327, Brentwood 7330, Bryan 7339, Community 7356, Community 7357, Corbett 7363, Danis 7371, Defiance 7375, **Eaton 7383, Elisha-Bolton 7387,** Entelco 7389, Foundation 7408, Fox 7409, Frohman 7411, Ginn 7425, Haskell 7439, Hauck 7440, Health 7442, Homan 7451, **Katz 7475,** Kramer 7484, Kutz 7486, **Lowe-Marshall 7505,** M.L.M 7510, Mather 7516, McMaster 7521, Montauk 7531, NLT 7537, Orr 7543, Osteopathic 7545, Peoples 7546, Philada 7548, Reynolds 7558, Ridgecliff 7560, Ritchie 7561, Sears-Swetland 7581, Seasongood 7582, Skyler 7595, Smith 7598, Stillson 7607, Tait 7610, Traeger 7621, Tuscora 7624, Walker 7630, Watson 7633, Woodruff 7645

Oklahoma: Ashbrook 7656, Atherton 7657, Barnes 7659, Brown 7664, Cherokee 7666, Gelvin 7682, Holliman 7687, Kerr 7693, Merrick 7707, Wegener 7731

Oregon: Castle 7745, Charis 7748, Elwood 7761, Holzman 7775, Lamb 7787, Mentor 7796, Parker/ United 7805, Pendleton 7806, Schmidt 7813, Silver 7817, Wessinger 7826, Western 7829, Woodard 7831, **Wyss 7832**

Pennsylvania: American 7839, Baker 7851, Beacon 7856, Bennett 7860, Bon-Ton 7884, Born 7885, Brooks 7899, Bucks 7905, Carlson 7916, Carnahan-Jackson 7917, Charlestein 7920, Chase 7921, Child 7923, Community 7933, Cove 7939, Crawford 7944, Dietrich 7958, Donnelly 7963, Eberly 7969, Elk 7975, Finley 7995, First 7997, First 7998, Freas 8005, Friendship 8009, Gamber 8011, Grundy 8029, HBE 8047, Hoffman 8062, Kazanjian 8090, **KL 8094,** Kynett 8105, Ludwick 8134, Maslow 8146, McCandless 8153, McKinney 8161, Mill 8172, Miller 8173, Mullen 8184, Penn 8208, Plankenhorn 8219, Price 8225, Rider-Pool 8238, Rosenlund 8245, Saramar 8253, Schuylkill 8263, Seybert 8269, Shoemaker 8275, Shore 8276, Smith 8280, Smith, 8285, Teleflex 8314, Tuttleman 8325, Valentine 8328, Willary 8356, Williams 8357, **Zeldin 8376**

Rhode Island: Collis 8397, Getz 8412, Heydt 8419, Kingsbury 8435, Littlefield 8441, McCarthy 8452, Moore 8456, Mulligan 8457, Preston 8475, Rainbow 8477, Slemons 8490, Sullivan 8494, Washington 8500

South Carolina: Greenwood 8526, Lutz 8533

South Dakota: Watertown 8576

Tennessee: Community 8601, Cracker 8603, Durham 8608, Gaylord 8620, Massengill-DeFriece 8647, Tompkins 8683

Texas: Abernathy 8690, **AMD 8698,** Astin 8710, Augur 8712, Behmann 8725, Boeing 8733, Bromley 8749, Burch 8756, **Chrest 8770,** Cook 8786, **Crowder 8792,** Dale 8794, Dick 8815, Dougherty, 8825, Dunagan 8831, Elkins 8838, Esping 8841, Fair 8844, Fairchild 8845, Fash 8848, Fenner 8850, Flowers 8862, Foundation 8869, Fruehauf 8879, **Gilman, 8889,** Healthcare 8924, Hervey 8932, Hext 8933, Holloway 8946, Kahn 8978, Kayser 8980, KCL 8981, King 8994, Light 9016, Littauer 9021, Long 9023, Marcus 9037, **McCreless 9049,** McKee 9052, McMillan, 9054, Mitte 9069, Myers 9081, Petty 9126, Smith

9207, **Soonae 9208**, South 9209, Tennessee 9230, Vaughan 9249, Walls 9257, Webre 9266, Wells 9271, Wolens 9284, Works 9293

Utah: Kennecott 9333, Odyssey 9342, Zions 9363

Vermont: Blittersdorf 9365, Castanea 9368, Copley 9370, Mergens 9381, Redducs 9383, Stokes 9385

Virginia: Bassett 9391, Beck 9393, **Brown 9407**, Darden 9428, **Dorothy-Ann 9433**, Family 9444, **Fund 9455**, Kaufman 9482, **Longview 9494**, Northern 9503, Pruden 9517, Ratner 9521, RECO 9522, Roller-Bottimore 9525, Two 9544

Washington: Baker 9566, Bungie 9576, Everett 9592, Fales 9594, Ferguson 9596, Foss 9598, Jefferson 9630, Jones 9638, Kawabe 9642, Kilworth 9644, Korum 9648, Murray 9667, Northwest 9669, Skagit 9696, Stevens 9704, Thomson 9711, Tonkin 9715, Welch 9721

West Virginia: Carter 9741, Chambers 9742, Skewes 9766

Wisconsin: Associated 9778, Blooming 9784, Courtier 9798, **Dewing 9805**, Door 9810, Dudley 9811, Eau 9814, Hunt 9845, Inbusch 9847, Jacobus 9849, Janesville 9850, Lakeview 9868, Marshfield 9878, Modine 9889, Prescott 9905, Stateline 9937, Stry 9941, Sub-Zero 9943, Weyco 9958, Windway 9961, Witte, 9962, Woodtrust-Bell 9963

Wyoming: **Schultz 9986**, Skelton 9989, Weiss 9997

Program evaluations

Alabama: Ireland 39

California: Ackerman 227, Baxter 284, Bear 288, Heller 613, **Lawrence 734**, Welk 1170, Wharton 1178

Colorado: Bean 1228, **National 1330**, Vradenburg 1374

District of Columbia: Jovid 1817

Florida: Archibald 1852, Charlotte 1938, **Freewill 2021**, Roshan 2297, Toppel 2377

Georgia: Athens 2437, Walker 2603

Indiana: Bussing-Koch 3353, Huntington 3397, LaGrange 3412

Maine: Planet 3797

Massachusetts: **Kahn 4143**, Kelsey 4148, Morse 4209, **Pegasus 4236**

Michigan: Four 4449, Michigan 4514

Minnesota: Granite 4699, Riverway 4776, **Sundance 4796**, **Winds 4820**

Montana: Cora 5048

Nebraska: Barklage 5071

New Hampshire: McIninch 5224

New Jersey: Elizabethtown 5332

New Mexico: Con 5611, Taos 5626

New York: 21st 5630, Anderson-Rogers 5676, Kenworthy 6300, Messinger 6482, **Nok 6537**, O'Grady 6551, **Sparkplug 6830**

North Carolina: Strowd 7258

Ohio: Ginn 7425, Kramer 7484, Philada 7548

Oklahoma: Cherokee 7666, Kerr 7693, Merrick 7707

Oregon: Silver 7817

Pennsylvania: Bennett 7860, Community 7933, Crawford 7944, Hoffman 8062

Texas: **Chrest 8770**, Dougherty, 8825, KCL 8981, San 9170, Works 9293

Virginia: Northern 9503

Washington: Foss 9598

Wisconsin: Dudley 9811, Eau 9814, Jacobus 9849, Stateline 9937

Program-related investments

Arkansas: Hickingbotham 199

California: Christian 401, Heller 613, Jamieson 658, Ragir 950, **Trustees 1132**, **Wakerly 1150**

Colorado: **Oreg 1335**

Connecticut: Winokur 1597

Delaware: Brandsma 1627

Florida: Archibald 1852, Evans 1994, Lazarus 2172, Mayberg 2199, Phillips 2260, Second 2321

Georgia: Gray 2497, University 2597

Illinois: Alton 2705, **Landau 3036**, Rosen 3206

Indiana: Decatur 3367, Huntington 3397, Jennings 3402

Kansas: Bane 3557

Louisiana: Vick 3756

Maryland: Feldman 3858

Massachusetts: Behrakis 4015, Kelsey 4148

Michigan: Thompson 4591

Minnesota: Granite 4699, Larsen 4728, Wallestad 4806, **Winds 4820**

Mississippi: Community 4830

Missouri: Baer 4862

Nevada: Meyer 5177

New Mexico: Carlsbad 5608, Foster 5615, Taos 5626

New York: American 5662, Hennessy 6191, **Jabara 6254**, Koessler 6335, Lake 6360, Lucelia 6418, Messinger 6482, **Posner-Wallace 6621**, Zimmermann 7028

North Carolina: P 7205

Ohio: Besl 7326, Heimbinder 7445, **Lowe-Marshall 7505**, Rosenberry 7562

Oklahoma: Harmon 7686

Oregon: Brown 7744

Pennsylvania: Cornerstone 7936, Elk 7975, **KL 8094**, **Susquehanna 8310**, Wells 8350

Tennessee: Durham 8608, Kite 8639

Texas: **Chrest 8770**, Heinlein 8927, Works 9293

Utah: Questar 9346

Vermont: Castanea 9368, Stokes 9385

West Virginia: Logan 9756

Wyoming: **Schultz 9986**

Public engagement and education

California: Baxter 284, Livingston 761, Louie 770, Marineau 798, Mollath 842, Yen 1201

Colorado: Broomfield 1242, Donnell-Kay 1258, **National 1330**

District of Columbia: **Butler 1792**

Florida: Graese 2055, Rogers 2291

Illinois: Olin 3153

Kansas: Hopkins 3586

Kentucky: Gagarin 3656

Louisiana: Powers 3746

Michigan: Roscommon 4552

Missouri: **Build-A-Bear 4879**, Schneider 4994

New Jersey: Carlozzi 5287, Fellstone 5346

New York: American 5662, Northern 6540, Rosenberg 6690

Ohio: **Brush 7338**

Pennsylvania: Ayers 7848, Bergstrom 7864, Blue 7879, Hilles 8057

Tennessee: Atticus 8582, **Louisiana-Pacific 8644**, Pickle 8660

Texas: Levy 9014, Redman 9147

Vermont: **Maverick 9380**

Wisconsin: Antonia 9775, Dudley 9811, Highlands 9841

Publications

California: Adams 228, Baxter 284, **Cantor 375**, Drum 464, Gellert 550, **Hefferlin 610**, LEF 739, **Lloyd 763**, Rice 969, **Teichman 1106**, Trust 1131, **Trustees 1132**

Colorado: Donnell-Kay 1258, Southwestern 1355

District of Columbia: **Foundation 1807**, Westport 1838

Florida: Charlotte 1938, **Freewill 2021**

Georgia: Georgia 2484, Lee 2540, Walker 2603

Idaho: Whittenberger 2689

Illinois: Community 2803, Graham 2926, **Heritage 2967**

Indiana: Bussing-Koch 3353, Community 3360, Dubois 3370, Froderman 3383, Huntington 3397

Kansas: Farah 3576, Legacy, 3595

Louisiana: Steinhagen 3755

Maine: Burnham 3770

Maryland: Higginson 3880, Macht 3905

Massachusetts: Cricket 4060, Hauben 4120, **Kahn 4143**, Kelsey 4148, Rockland 4267, Russell 4273, Stearns 4311, Thoracic 4326, Walsh 4348, Xeric 4365

Michigan: Holden 4467

Minnesota: **Trust 4802**, Walker 4805

Nebraska: Nebraska 5105

Nevada: Meyer 5177

New Hampshire: Hunt 5214

New Jersey: Dreman 5326, Westfield 5582

New Mexico: Carlsbad 5608, Chamiza 5609, Taos 5626

New York: Abelard 5635, American 5662, Anderson-Rogers 5676, Initial 6245, Kenworthy 6300, **Laerdal 6358**, Lubo 6417, Lucelia 6418, **Nok 6537**, Persian 6589, **Potts 6624**, Snow 6818, **Sparkplug 6830**

North Carolina: BB&T 7045, Covington 7081, Outer 7204, Rogers 7228

North Dakota: Community 7295

Ohio: Armington 7309, Defiance 7375, Foundation 7408, Laub 7490, Rosenberry 7562

Oregon: Holzman 7775

Pennsylvania: Bucks 7905, Community 7933, Crawford 7944, Dietrich 7958, Friendship 8009, HBE 8047, Hoffman 8062, Patterson 8205, Schuylkill 8263, Shoemaker 8275

Rhode Island: Heydt 8419

Tennessee: Durham 8608, Stuttering 8680

Texas: Fash 8848, Hext 8933, Roberts 9157, Vaughan 9249

Virginia: Community 9426, **Longview 9494**, Northern 9503

Washington: Foss 9598, **Ji 9632**, Murray 9667, Quest 9681, Tonkin 9715

Wisconsin: Jacobus 9849, Manitowoc 9876, Marshfield 9878, Stry 9941

Recordings

Alabama: Ireland 39

Arkansas: Darragh 193

California: Gellert 550, LEF 739

Florida: Charlotte 1938

Minnesota: Larsen 4728, Walker 4805

New Hampshire: Hunt 5214, McIninch 5224

North Carolina: Outer 7204

Pennsylvania: Hoffman 8062

Texas: **Chrest 8770**

Vermont: Stokes 9385

Regranting

Alabama: Abroms 2, Anderson 6, Aronov 7, Bruno 17, Caddell 19, Friedman 27, Goodrich 29, JADO 40, Kairos 41, Loeb 47, Pei-Ling 52, Phifer, 54, Ripps 60, Rothschild 61, Upchurch, 72

Alaska: Gottstein 86

Arizona: Berlin 101, Chapin 105, Community 108, Grossman 126, McKee 148, Robson 160, Rubeli 163, Snell 171, Spalding 172, Ullman 177, Withycombe 184

Arkansas: **Baldor 188**, Hennessy 198, Riggs 214

California: Banchik 269, Barulich 280, Baye 285, Becker 291, Beim 293, Berlin 306, Bider 314, Bigglesworth 316, Bonner 327, Boone 328, Bridges/Larson 343, Broder 348, Brunswick 354, **Butler 365**, Cannon 374, CAS 378, Celebrate 383, Cheeryble 390, Codding 412, Collingwood 418, Corbalis 424, Corwin 428, Cutler 438, Dermalogica 451, DiNapoli 454, Dorskind 459, Drum 464, Ellen 478, Ferry 504, First 507, Folger 515, Fritz 534, Frome 535, Fuller 538, Giles 554, Glazer 562,

Glikbarg 564, Goldberg 567, Goldberg 568, Graff 576, Greenwood 581, Gross 587, Harman 598, Harris 600, Harvey 602, Hayman 606, Hellman 614, Herrmann 618, Hilltop 621, Horwich 632, Horwitz 633, Huntington 642, **Jacoby 654**, Johnson 667, Kadima 686, Kanel 688, Kelton 698, Kendall 700, Kieve 703, Kort 719, Koss 720, Levin 749, Levy 751, **Levy 752**, Lyons 776, Malachowsky 786, Manchester 788, Mann 790, Margolis 797, Meister 821, Miller 828, Miller 832, Mitchell 838, Mitchell, 839, **Moley 841**, Morgenstern 848, Murad 854, Neu 862, Olander 878, Ornest 888, Phillips 924, Podell 930, Pollia 931, Potiker 932, **Rieger 971**, Rocca, 978, Roney 983, Sands 1001, **Sikand 1037**, Silicon 1038, SKB 1044, Smalley 1050, Smith-Welsh 1058, Somekh 1064, Sondheimer 1065, Stack 1073, Straus 1088, Traub-Brittan 1127, Wagner 1149, Walton 1156, Weisz 1167, Worster 1197, Wrather 1198, Ziegler 1210

Colorado: Allen 1220, Elf 1262, Grosvenor 1282, Grosvenor 1283, Kortz 1307, Ladd 1310, Lewis 1315, Margulf 1320, Morse 1328, Pluss 1337, Trachten 1369, Verdoorn 1372, W.J.D. 1375, Warner 1376, Zeff 1383

Connecticut: Abramowitz 1384, Baggins 1398, Barden 1402, Chaikin-Wile 1417, Chelsea 1418, **Davis-McCullough 1429**, Denzler 1434, Diageo 1437, Dime 1438, Eder 1441, Finn 1449, Floren 1451, Gengras, 1461, Gibor 1464, Gladstein 1465, Howard 1484, Jones 1490, Kuriansky 1503, Lamando 1504, Lavietes 1505, Lebovitz 1506, Mahadeva 1517, Manger 1518, Martin 1520, McLeod 1524, Nirenberg 1534, O'Herron 1536, Patricelli 1541, Price 1544, Pryor 1546, Rosenberg 1555, Schaeneman, 1560, Storr 1575, Stratfield 1576, Tell 1580, Thornton 1582, Tully 1588, Vance 1591, Zacharia 1601

Delaware: Bowman 1625, Brown-Whitworth 1632, Burton 1634, Cohen 1643, **Colgate 1645**, Coopersmith 1646, Croll 1650, Cross 1651, Freedman 1665, Kang 1689, New 1715, Pinkerton 1721, Ratner 1724, Riecker 1729, Rosenfeld 1732, Rumberger 1734, Russell 1735, Schiffman 1738, Schwalbach 1739, Sloane 1746, Splawn 1749, Sulentic 1752, Susman 1753, Taylor 1759, Yablon 1782

District of Columbia: Dweck 1805, Goldman 1810, **Gorlitz 1811**, Greenberg 1812, Haft 1813, **Merriman 1820**, Olender 1824, Silberman 1834, Westport 1838

Florida: Adler 1842, Anderson 1845, Auerbach 1859, Barnard 1866, Basham 1870, Bastien 1872, Beasley 1877, Becker 1879, Bell 1883, Blank 1890, Brodsky 1901, Brody 1902, Burks 1909, Capital 1918, Castellani 1927, Chicone 1941, Childress 1942, Coulter-Jones 1954, Crane 1955, Dennis 1969, Deus 1972, Diamond 1973, Dickinson 1975, Dilworth 1977, Elster 1990, Erdle 1993, Farrell 1998, Five 2002, Friedland 2025, Gelbart 2035, Godbold 2041, Golden 2046, Grabe 2053, Graese 2055, Greenberg 2062, Greenblatt 2063, Greenfield 2066, Hagens 2071, Halperin 2076, Hardison 2081, Herrin 2091, Hicks 2094, Isenberg 2121, Jelks 2128, Kanders 2135, Kaplan 2138, Kaye 2141, Kessler 2145, Kimmel 2146, Kiwanis 2149, Knapp 2153, Kreisman 2159, Kugelman 2161, Kuriansky 2162, Lambrecht 2165, Lazzara 2174, Leiser 2177, Lenkin 2179, **Levine 2181**, Lipton 2185, Lookout 2190, McDonald 2203, MCM-Munilla 2206, MIDA 2212, Millsaps 2214, Nommontu 2234, Olemberg 2237, Overstreet 2242, Papper 2246, Pearle 2253, Perlmutter 2254, **Posnack 2262**, Resnick 2282, Richard 2285, River 2288, Ryan 2304, **Safenowitz 2307**, Salizzoni 2309, Sender 2323, Setzer 2325, Sexton 2326, Silverman 2337, Stellar 2348, Stern 2349, Stern 2350, Taplin 2363, Turner 2381, Vasey 2385, Votum 2390, Weinberger 2394, Weintraub 2395, Weisman 2396, Werner 2398, Wolf 2410, Wolgin 2411, **Wollowick 2412**, Wynne 2419, **Zichron 2424**, Zimmerman 2426, Zimmerman 2427, Zimmerman 2428

Georgia: A.E.M. 2430, Arnold 2436, Broadfield 2449, Brooks 2450, Carters 2454, Chatham 2457, Colston 2464, Community 2466, Echlin 2472, Exposition 2476, **Gage 2482**, Gilbert, 2488, Goodman 2492, Graves 2496, Griffin 2499, Inman 2519, JBS 2523, Jeter 2524, Jolley 2526, Knox 2534, Lipscomb 2541, Marcus 2544, McClatchey 2546, Morris 2553, Nonami 2557, Orkin 2559, Oxford 2561, Price 2569, Saul 2579, Schwob 2581, Storey 2589, Tritt 2596, Vogel 2600, Williams 2612, Woodruff 2617

Hawaii: Locations 2638, Shidler 2646, Ululani 2652

Idaho: Hecla 2676, Wishnick 2690

Illinois: 1335 2691, Anschel 2709, Beeghly 2730, Bellick 2732, Bishop 2743, Block, 2746, Ceres 2779, Clingen 2794, Collins 2799, Corbett 2808, Diamond 2829, Eckert 2843, Edelman 2845, Edelstein 2846, Edgerly 2847, EMA 2854, Enivar 2856, Fraida 2884, Frank 2885, Franklin 2887, Fredman 2890, Fremont 2891, Generations 2908, Gidwitz 2914, Gochnauer 2918, Goldenberg 2920, Golder 2921, Goodstein 2924, Grossinger 2933, H.C.D. 2939, Hales 2941, Harris 2957, Herman 2968, Hess 2969, Hoffer 2975, Hopper 2977, Howard 2981, Hunt 2984, JBS 2994, Jocarno 3000, Johnson 3001, Klosk 3020, **Landau 3036**, Larsen 3038, Leibowitz 3046, Levinson 3049, Levy 3050, Love 3064, Mann 3072, Manne 3073, Marcum 3076, McCormack 3086, Meier 3101, Millard 3109, Miller, 3113, Millner 3115, Minor 3117, Mitchell 3120, Murphy 3132, Neel 3135, New 3136, Nygren 3146, Oppenheimer 3155, Penrose 3166, Pollack 3180, Pond 3182, Pugdin 3185, Red 3189, Reinisch 3193, Richard 3195, Rosenberg 3207, Russell 3216, Ryan 3219, Schorr-Lieberman 3229, Sondheimer 3256, SSAB 3260, Staley 3264, Stein 3266, Stern 3268, Stone 3269, Stone 3270, Takiff 3281, Victor 3304, Wagner 3306, **Wein 3315**, Weiss 3317, Whitwam 3321, Wright 3333, Yulman 3334, Zemsky 3337, Zuckerman 3338

Indiana: **Ackerman 3339**, Bronstein 3351, Crescent-Cresline-Wabash 3365, Harlan 3391, Jolan 3404, Klapper 3408, Lacy 3410, Lafayette 3411, Maurer 3415, **Mervis 3417**, Mothershead 3419, Mulzer 3420, MutualBank 3421, Namaste 3422, Oliver 3428, Rifkin 3437, Rush 3441, Thrush-Thompson 3460, Welter 3465, Weston 3467

Iowa: Bennett 3474, Busse 3478, Carlson 3479, Giacoletto 3499, GuideOne 3503, Henry 3505, Krause 3516, McDonald 3520, Nelson 3524, R 3529, Vermeer 3541, Weathertop 3545, Woodward 3549

Kansas: Bane 3557, Berry 3558, Buford 3562, DeVore 3573, Fidelity 3577, Goldberg 3581, Insurance 3587, Joscelyn 3590, Lowenstein 3598, Payless 3614, Price 3616, Shannon 3625, Smoot 3627, Swearingen 3631, Trusler 3635, Wallace 3637, Watson 3639, Williams 3643

Kentucky: Abercrombie 3645, McKellar 3677, Mulhollem 3680, Roth 3690, Rouse 3692, Trager 3701, Trim 3702

Louisiana: Cahn 3716, Harper 3726, Huie-Dellmon 3729, Lake 3732, Live 3734, Moffett 3739, Powers 3746, Pugh 3747, Selber 3751, Wheless 3758, Zuschlag 3762

Maine: Franklin 3779, Kagan 3784, Kennebec 3785

Maryland: Ammerman 3813, Bank 3818, Berger 3821, Cole 3839, Contino 3840, Devito 3848, Dockser 3849, Eliasberg 3854, Elsberg 3856, Gidwitz 3870, **Goldberg 3872**, Greene-Milstein 3876, Gutman 3877, Hubbard 3883, Hurwitz 3886, Kay 3892, Macks 3906, Meyer 3913, Minkoff 3915, Murthynayak 3921, Number 3929, Pearlstone 3934, RCM 3937, RFI 3938, Rothschild 3942, Schuh 3946, Shapiro 3949, Shattuck 3950, Thalheimer 3966, Totah 3968, Weinman 3981, Wilen 3985, Wolpoff 3990

Massachusetts: Alden 3999, Beaucourt 4014, Berger 4018, Black 4021, Clifford 4051, Crane 4058, Easthampton 4076, Goldman 4105, Hazard 4124,

Hopedale 4134, Kenwood 4150, Krieger 4160, Levy 4174, Marcus 4188, Morningstar 4207, Morse 4208, Morse 4209, Noble 4224, Oristaglio 4232, Reisman 4262, Rockland 4267, Rodman 4268, Shapiro 4289, Shapiro 4290, Sherman 4293, **Spero 4304**, Spoon 4305, Stearns 4310, Tapper 4321, **Tatelman 4322**, Tatelman 4323, Torok 4331, Ullian 4335, Whittemore 4359, Wyman-Gordon 4364

Michigan: Abrams 4369, Alon 4374, Baiardi 4381, Barstow 4385, Barton-Malow 4386, Biederman 4391, Bierlein 4392, Dana 4419, Ferber 4443, Ford 4445, Frankenmuth 4450, Grassland 4458, Harris 4461, Hartwick 4462, Havirmill 4463, Kaufman 4479, Leven 4492, Maas 4498, Manat 4503, McDole 4507, Meritor, 4511, Murdock 4519, Narens 4520, Nartel 4521, Nusbaum 4524, O'Donovan 4525, Padnos 4529, Paine 4531, Paulina 4535, Pitt 4540, Pitt 4541, Plym 4542, Seligman 4564, Sherman 4567, Shine 4569, Stoker 4580, **Teitel 4589**, Torgow 4594, Vicksburg 4606, Vlasic 4607, Welch 4610, Wetsman 4611, Whiting 4614, Zimmerman 4620

Minnesota: Ankeny 4628, Bahl 4632, Baratz 4635, Borman 4644, Bumgarner 4649, Burwell 4650, Deikel 4663, Dell 4664, Dellwood 4665, Erickson 4674, Fink 4684, G&K 4691, Grossman 4701, Harrington 4707, Heilicher 4711, **Kaplan 4721**, Kinney 4724, Krisbin 4726, McNamara 4743, Midcontinent 4745, Morning 4748, Northern 4751, Quinlan 4764, Radichel 4765, Regis 4770, Shared 4791, Tamarack 4797, Tennant 4798, Wallestad 4806

Mississippi: Brevard 4826, Crooks 4831

Missouri: Arnold 4861, BF 4867, **Block 4869**, Bograd 4870, **Bohm 4871**, Brace 4874, Butler 4880, Chod 4885, Copaken 4888, Crown 4891, Dierberg 4895, Empson 4902, Erlich 4904, Essman 4905, Finley 4910, Forster-Powers 4911, Green 4920, Heiman 4926, Hofheimer 4929, Kornblum 4940, Kuhn 4941, **Maor 4952**, Melcher 4957, O'Reilly 4974, Pearl 4977, Peculiar 4978, Portman 4981, Riedel 4984, Sachs 4989, Schweinfurth 4996, Shawe 5000, Sigma-Aldrich 5003, Silk 5004, Siteman 5006, Slusher 5009, Stroble 5015, Vatterott 5030, Wolff 5040

Montana: Gallagher 5052, Gerhart 5053

Nebraska: Assurity 5068, Friedland 5082, Friedman 5083, Grewcock 5086, Harper 5088, Hawkins 5089, Nelson 5106, Physicians 5112, **Waldbaum 5125**

Nevada: Bendon 5137, **Fein 5155**, Shulman 5185, Vandevoort 5194, **Wood 5201**

New Hampshire: Jameson 5215, McIninch 5224

New Jersey: Adler 5242, **Akhoury 5243**, Aufzien 5253, Benaroya 5260, Bijou 5264, **Billig 5265**, Brook 5273, Brueckner 5279, Cali 5284, Cantor 5285, CKT 5297, Clermont 5298, Cohen 5299, Croman 5307, Domenica 5323, EBB 5329, Ellis 5333, Engel 5334, Entin 5336, ESH 5338, Feinstein 5343, Fox 5349, Freedman 5352, Frelinghuysen 5354, Freyer 5355, Fux 5359, Giancristofaro 5368, Glasser 5371, Goldberger 5372, Goodwin 5374, Greetin 5377, Halpern 5380, Harmstieg 5386, Heller 5391, JFI 5405, Jones 5408, Kaufman 5415, Kingsberg 5421, Kresa 5432, Kurtz 5436, Leavitt 5445, Lieberman 5448, Mamiye 5456, Maschler 5462, MTB 5474, Myers 5476, Navesink 5477, Oster 5484, Pantirer 5487, Pasternak 5490, Pheasant 5499, Pines 5501, Plafsky 5503, Riskin 5511, Rukin 5516, Sanders 5518, Savin 5520, Schlaffer 5522, Scire 5526, Selective 5528, Shilling 5534, Simon, 5537, Smilowitz 5538, Smith 5539, Welch 5579, Zissu 5602

New Mexico: Horn 5618, King-Carpenter 5619

New York: Abess 5636, Abess 5637, Abettor 5638, Abramson 5640, Adikes 5646, American 5664, American 5668, Applebaum 5683, Asher 5695, Bank 5710, Barron 5719, Baseser 5720, Baumann 5723, BBL 5724, Beckman 5729, Bendit 5736, Bergson 5738, Betesh 5743, Blank 5756, Block 5759, Brand 5776, Brandt 5777, Bratt 5778,

Brooklyn 5788, BSR 5794, Buller 5800, Casey 5819, Centennial 5826, Citrin 5846, Cohen 5857, Cohenca 5861, Cohn 5864, Coleman 5870, Cornell/Weinstein 5877, **Cote 5881**, Curtis 5889, Danziger 5899, Darrah 5900, Davis 5902, Dears 5905, Desai 5910, Dolgen 5922, Doovin 5923, Double-R 5927, Edelweiss 5944, Eggleston 5946, Ehrman 5949, EMSA 5961, Englebardt 5965, ESL 5969, Eule 5971, Feil 5991, Fein 5992, Feldstein 5997, Fields 6003, Fife 6005, Finkelstein 6007, Finn 6008, Fitt 6010, Fleischer 6013, Foundation 6019, Fowey 6021, Franco 6024, French 6032, Friedman 6040, Frieman 6041, Fuchsberg 6044, Gaffney 6049, Gantcher 6055, Gantz 6056, Gartner 6059, Gemj 6069, Gilliam 6078, Godinger 6086, Gold 6088, Goldenberg 6092, Goldenberg 6093, Goldstein 6100, Goldwasser 6103, Goodman-Lipman 6108, Gould 6116, Grandison 6124, Greenberg 6132, Gross 6142, Guela 6151, H. 6153, Hahn 6156, Harmon 6169, Harris 6172, Hasenfeld 6174, Hefta 6181, Henderson 6189, Henshel 6192, Herbst 6195, Hershaft 6197, Hershman 6198, Heyman 6201, Hidary 6205, Hirsch 6211, Hirsch 6212, Hochman 6214, **Hoffman 6216**, Holtzman 6223, Horowitz 6225, Issroff 6251, JI 6260, JIA 6261, Joyce 6275, Kamber 6281, Kaminer 6282, Kandell 6283, **Katzin 6288**, Kelleher 6295, Keller-Shatanoff 6297, Keswin 6303, **Klagsbrun 6318**, Klaus 6320, Kleinschmidt 6326, Kohn 6338, Konar 6340, Krumholz 6349, Kulick 6350, Lawrence 6369, **Legacy 6374**, Leibowitz 6376, Lemle 6377, Lemle 6378, Leventritt 6385, Levine 6386, Levitin 6388, Levy 6390, Levy 6391, Lewy 6393, Liebowitz 6400, Lippes 6401, Litterman 6406, Lopatin 6412, Lufkin 6421, Marshall 6446, Maslin 6448, MBS 6454, Meade 6467, Menezes 6473, Miller 6491, Mindel 6498, Moore 6504, Morris 6508, Morse 6510, Netter 6525, **Neuman 6526**, New 6527, Newman 6530, Newman 6532, Nussbaum 6545, Ostreicher 6563, Parshelsky 6578, Peek 6584, Pickman 6602, Pincus 6606, Pohly-Turaj 6613, Pollack 6614, Pollack 6615, R 6640, Rachesky 6642, Rapaport 6647, Raphael 6648, Reich 6659, Ring 6671, RJL 6675, Robbins 6676, **Rock 6679**, Rose 6683, Rose 6684, Rosner 6698, Roth 6700, Rudy 6708, Russo 6711, **Sato 6731**, Saunders 6733, Schaffer 6737, Schott 6749, Schwartz 6754, Seaman 6767, Seligsohn 6773, Shackouls 6781, Sharon 6787, SHEL 6791, Sherman 6792, Siegel 6797, Silver 6800, Silverman 6801, Silverstein 6803, SKL 6808, Slade 6810, Slovin 6811, Smith 6815, Sommer 6825, Spiegel 6838, Starker 6847, **Stein 6855**, Stein 6856, **Stern 6862**, Striano 6871, Strong 6872, SVM 6886, Tanner-Frank 6893, Tenney 6895, Trimble 6910, TSP 6913, Utica 6922, Vaad 6924, Vogel 6931, **Weinstein 6956**, Weiser 6958, Weisman 6959, Weiss 6961, Weiss 6962, Whispering 6970, Windy 6980, Wohlgemuth 6984, Wolk 6987, Wunsch 6996, Yaspan-Unterberg 7003, Yosef 7011, Zenkel 7023, Ziff 7027, Zwerling 7034

North Carolina: BB&T 7045, Bell 7047, Bell 7048, Bernstein 7049, Borun 7057, Coffey 7078, Ellison 7090, First 7097, Gambrill 7106, Helb 7122, Hudson 7133, **Kramer 7152**, Lerner 7160, Levine-Sklut 7161, Mattei 7173, McLean 7178, Meyer 7184, Nanney 7198, Nivison 7201, Perkin 7208, Ragland, 7216, Shugart 7242, Silverman 7244, Summer 7261

North Dakota: Fedje 7296

Ohio: Anderson 7305, Berke 7323, Brown 7336, Chemed 7350, Chesley 7351, CLH 7355, Crandall 7366, Damico 7370, **Elisha-Bolton 7387**, Ettlinger 7390, Fedeli 7393, Fibus 7398, Finnegan 7399, Foss 7407, Frohman 7411, Frost 7412, Gale 7414, Garcia 7416, Geary, 7419, Gelbman 7420, Gilman 7423, Glazer 7426, Gross 7432, Hankins 7437, Haskell 7439, Heffner 7443, Hoover 7453, Howe 7455, Iott 7463, Joffe 7467, Klock 7480, Lazarus 7493, LKC 7501, Loeb 7503, M.L.M 7510, Norris 7538, Norweb 7539, Peters 7547, Powers 7550, Sauerland 7570, Schottenstein 7575, Schwartz,

7576, Schwebel 7577, Seaman 7580, Smith 7598, Stensen 7604, STERIS 7605, Stillson 7607, Swagelok 7608, Taft 7609, Traeger 7621, Van 7625, Vista 7628, Wasserstrom 7632, Watson 7633, Williamson 7640, Wolf 7643, Young 7651

Oklahoma: GKJ 7683, Trippet 7725, White 7734

Oregon: Demorest 7757, Holzman 7775, Merlo 7797

Pennsylvania: Aaron 7835, Arkema 7842, Armstrong 7843, **Arronson 7844**, Auldridge 7846, Baker 7851, Baldwin, 7852, Beach 7855, Beacon 7856, Berger 7862, Bergman 7863, **Berkowitz 7865**, Bishop 7874, Blue 7879, Born 7885, Borowsky 7886, Breedlove 7890, Briggs 7892, Bronstein 7896, Butz 7908, Charlestein 7920, CNB 7929, **Cohn 7931, Epstein 7983**, Foster 8003, Gershman 8015, Goshen 8025, Hankin 8038, Harsco 8040, Hauber 8043, Hecht 8050, HFO 8053, Hoffman 8063, Honickman 8066, IGN 8073, Kahn, 8084, Kelley 8091, Kittenbrink 8093, Klein 8096, Kline 8098, KMJ 8099, Levis 8122, Lida 8127, Lubert 8133, M&P 8135, Mellon 8167, Mendel 8168, Merwin 8170, Moore 8177, Mudge 8181, Mukaiyama-Rice 8183, Murphy 8185, Olitsky 8198, Oppenheim 8199, Pearsall 8207, Perelman 8209, Pincus 8214, Quaker 8228, Robinson 8241, Rosenberg 8244, Russo 8249, Saramar 8253, Satell 8254, Schautz 8257, Schoonmaker 8260, Schwab-Silfen 8264, Schwartz 8265, Sidewater 8278, Snyder 8287, Speyer 8294, Stein 8298, Tabas 8312, Tuttleman 8325, Wagner 8338, Walton 8341, Wasserott 8344, Weiler-Miller 8348, Wimmer 8361, York 8374

Rhode Island: Bernhardt 8387, Charlton, 8394, Feibelman 8405, Galkin 8410, Greene 8413, Gross 8414, Heydt 8419, Jacbel 8426, Janci 8428, Johnson 8430, Kingsbury 8435, Koffler 8436, Mann 8448, Molder 8455, Mulligan 8457, O'Halloran 8462, Salmanson 8481, Schwarz 8483, Siperstein 8489, Swarts 8495, Thompson 8497, Washington 8500, Woodward 8505

South Carolina: Bailey 8510, Bonner 8513, Cato 8516, Kendall 8530, Peery/Cauthen 8537, Tarr 8545, Williams/Brice-Edwards 8549

South Dakota: Elmen 8561

Tennessee: Atticus 8582, B 8583, Basler 8584, **Belz 8585**, Boring 8590, Bradford 8592, Chrysalis 8598, Citizens 8599, Community 8601, Doochin 8605, Eskind 8611, Goldsmith 8622, Houghland 8630, Kennedy 8638, **Lowenstein 8645**, Mick 8651, New 8654, Proctor 8662

Texas: Astin 8710, Barnett 8718, Bloxom, 8731, Brodsky 8747, Brown 8751, Brownsville 8752, **Crowder 8792**, Dedman, 8808, Dubose 8828, Finger 8857, Flohr 8861, Foundation 8869, Foundation 8870, Friedel 8875, Friedman 8876, Fuchs 8881, Gordon 8893, Guetz 8905, Haggar, 8908, Hervey 8932, Hofstetter 8943, Holmes 8947, Horween 8952, Inge 8961, Johnson, 8971, Kaplan 8979, Kelso 8985, Klesse 8998, Kolitz 9000, Lilly 9019, MacDonald-Peterson 9032, McKee 9052, Mewhinney 9060, Oppenheimer 9100, Oppenheimer 9101, Orr 9104, Osberg 9105, Paulos 9120, Perkins 9125, Petty 9126, Postl 9136, Pulitzer 9140, Schepps 9177, Schissler 9179, Staubach 9215, Sterling 9219, Stevenson 9220, Tolleson 9238, Vaughan 9249, Walls 9257, Watson 9263, Weaver 9265, Westcott 9273, Wilder 9277, Wise 9283, Wolf 9285, Wolff-Toomim 9286, Zale 9300

Utah: Andrus 9301, Bastian 9304, Bourne-Spafford 9306, Schmidt 9349

Virginia: Backer 9389, Better 9396, Charles 9418, Dickerson 9431, Edlavitch 9440, Foundation 9451, Gifford 9457, Glasser 9459, Grandis 9462, Hausfeld 9469, Meador 9500, Ochsman 9504, Peachtree 9508, **Price 9516**, Ratner 9521, Richardson 9523, Schiro-Zavela 9528, Stone 9537, Weil 9550

Washington: Bacon 9565, Bayley 9567, CSM 9584, Ferguson 9596, Galanti 9603, Jaffe 9629, **Jernigan 9631**, Lanterman 9649, Levitan 9653, Lott 9656, Morningside 9665, Prairie 9680, Razore 9682,

Remala 9683, Rosen 9684, Runstad 9686, **Sabol 9687**, Sarkowsky 9688, Shemanski 9693, Smith 9698, Spring 9702, Stars 9703, Templin 9709

West Virginia: Brown 9739, Hott 9753, Starvaggi 9767

Wisconsin: Anderson 9773, Arzbaecher 9777, Berbeewalsh 9782, Caritas 9791, Chipstone 9794, Christensen 9795, Cummings-Christensen 9801, Erdman 9816, Foley 9820, Frautschi 9822, Glanert 9827, Gordon 9830, Highlands 9841, Jacobus 9849, Kohl 9864, Lutsey 9873, Manitowoc 9876, Marcus 9877, Martin 9879, Merkel 9884, Modine 9889, Mortenson 9890, Pelz 9900, Puelicher 9907, RITE-HITE 9915, Roddis 9916, Shoemaker 9928, Smith 9931, Smith 9932, Steinle 9938, Uihlein 9950, Van 9952, Van 9953, Wagner 9955, Webcrafters-Frautschi 9957, Witte, 9962

Wyoming: Connemara 9967, Guthrie 9972, Skelton 9989, StoneRiver 9991

Regulation and administration

Connecticut: Robinson 1553

Tennessee: Jones 8635

Research

Alabama: Anderson 5, Battle 10, Black 12, Bruno 17, Dixon 26, Harrison 35, Ireland 39, Kemp 42, Sexton 63, Shook 64

Alaska: Gottstein 86

Arizona: Armstrong 97, Barton 99, C 103, Grossman 126, Hansen 127, Harmsen, 128, Hughes 130, Louis 142, Lund 143, Margolis 144, McKee 148, Napier 152, Valley 178, Warmer 180, Zicarelli 185

Arkansas: Bodenhamer 190, Darragh 193, Hickingbotham 199

California: Acacia 225, Alafi 235, Anhaltzer 245, Arata 248, Arbor 249, Armrod 253, Arnstein 254, **A-T 258**, Atkinson 259, Baker 265, Baker 267, Bancroft-Clair 270, Baxter 284, Bell 295, Bellini 298, Beneto 301, Bernstein 308, Blachford-Cooper 318, Blackie 319, Borzi 332, Bridges/Larson 343, Brotman 351, Brunswick 354, **Bull 358**, Bundy 360, **Cantor 375**, Charitable 389, Coleman 416, Collier 417, Corday 426, Corwin 428, Daly 440, Davies 444, Dorskind 459, Downing 462, Drum 464, Ducommun 465, Edwards 473, Elliott 479, Emanuel 480, Evening 487, Everest 488, Familian 491, Farber 495, Fat 499, Fawcett 500, Folger 515, Fortisure 518, Fox 525, Friedhofer 529, Friedman 530, Fuller 538, Gareeb 548, Gellert 550, Gooding 571, **Grass 577**, Gross 587, Hand 595, Handlery 596, Harvey 602, Hayman 606, Heller 613, Herrmann 618, Hitter 624, **Hsu 637**, Hughes 639, HunterWard 641, Jamieson 658, Johnson 667, Kadima 686, Kelvin 699, Kort 719, Levin 749, Lewis 753, Louie 770, Martin 800, Martin 801, Mason 805, Maxfield 808, Mazda 810, McKenzie 816, Meyer 823, Michaud 824, Miller 828, Morgan 846, Morgenstern 848, **Northern 870**, Novak 871, **Orphan 889, PADI 898**, Palo 901, **Parsemus 904**, Pasarow 906, Plum 929, Podell 930, **Preuss 935**, **Quiksilver 945, Rifkind 972**, Riley 973, Rocca, 978, Roke 981, Rosenberg 985, Rosenthal 987, Ross 988, Rossi 989, Rubin 993, Sawchuk 1010, Schaeffer 1013, Scott 1021, Scott 1023, Shore 1034, Simon 1040, Simon 1041, Simon-Strauss 1042, Skynyrd 1046, Smalley 1050, Stauffer 1076, Stewart 1083, Stone 1086, Strome 1089, Sun 1092, **Teichman 1106**, Thagard 1109, Theroux 1110, Thrill 1117, Tilley 1118, Tisch 1120, Torino 1125, Waller 1152, Waltmar 1155, Warren 1159, Webb 1162, Wendell 1172, Western 1176, Westphal 1177, Wharton 1178, Winkler 1188

Colorado: Ballantine 1226, Chotin 1246, Comprecare 1249, Donnell-Kay 1258, **Fishback 1270**, Goodwin 1279, Grossman 1281, Ladd 1310, Mehrberg 1325, **National 1330, Okinaga 1334**, Schramm 1350, Southwestern 1355, Strohm 1361, Taylor 1364, Zeff 1383

Connecticut: Bantle 1401, Bender 1405, Berbecker 1406, Bridgemill 1412, Calarco 1414, Colburn-Keenan 1421, Ensign-Bickford 1442, Filingieri 1447, Finn 1449, Fippinger 1450, Gerbic 1463, Harris 1478, Howard 1484, Knox 1500, Lee 1507, Martinsen 1521, Newpol 1531, Patricelli 1541, Thornton 1582, Town 1586, Tully 1588, Winokur 1597, Zelnick/Belzberg 1602

Delaware: 613 1606, Freedman 1665, Hagan 1674, Lightner 1699, Messing 1708, Remmer 1726, Rothchild 1733, Telluray 1762, Thronson 1766, Yokota 1784

District of Columbia: **Foundation 1807**, Jovid 1817, **Merriman 1820**, Monarch 1823, Tucker 1836, Westport 1838

Florida: Archibald 1852, **Atlantis 1858**, Auerbach 1859, **Basser 1871**, Bastien 1872, Baxter 1874, Brown 1904, Brown 1905, **Campbell 1914**, Caring 1920, Chanin 1934, Childress 1942, Consolidated 1951, Couch 1953, Diane 1974, Duckwall 1982, Dysimmune 1986, Evans 1994, Five 2002, Focus 2004, Fontaine 2006, **Freewill 2021**, Glass 2039, Golden 2046, Gordon 2050, Greenberg 2062, Greene-Sawtell 2065, Halbrook 2073, **Handleman 2078**, Hansen 2079, HFRX 2092, Holtz 2109, Hultquist 2115, Jacobson 2125, **Jenkins 2129**, **Joshua 2132**, Kessler 2145, Kimmel 2146, KLM 2151, Knippenberg 2154, Kuriansky 2162, Le 2175, Livingston 2187, Marco 2194, Pearce 2252, Peyton 2258, Price 2267, Prutky 2270, Pusey 2272, Ray 2275, Richard 2285, Roshan 2297, Sierra 2336, Silverman 2337, Simmons 2338, **Taylor 2365**, Taylor 2366, Tippett 2376, Vanneck-Bailey 2384, Vasey 2385, Wilder 2406, **Wollowick 2412**, Wrightson-Ramsing 2416, Yerrid 2420

Georgia: Boone 2446, Connolly 2467, Echlin 2472, Georgia 2484, Goddard 2491, Graves 2496, Greiner 2498, Health 2504, Lee 2540, McClatchey 2546, McKinney-Geib 2547, Montgomery 2551, Raoul 2573, Schinazi 2580, Solstice 2587, Walker 2603, Whitehead 2610, Wright 2620

Hawaii: Epstein 2630

Idaho: Morrison 2682, Wishnick 2690

Illinois: **American 2707**, Anschel 2709, **Appleby 2711**, Best 2740, Bishop 2743, Boothroyd 2749, Borten 2750, Bulkley, 2765, Burt 2770, Carter 2776, Cless 2793, Coldwell 2797, Cremer 2815, Delta 2826, Family 2863, Family 2864, **Foundation 2880, Foundation 2881**, Fraida 2884, Gidwitz 2914, Goldenberg 2920, Goodstein 2924, Gray 2927, Howard 2981, Hughes 2983, Jaros 2993, Johnson 3001, Karasik 3006, **Lazzara 3042**, Lichner 3051, Lifetract 3053, Livney 3056, Love 3064, MacDonald 3068, McCabe 3084, **Mead 3100**, Meyer 3106, Miller 3111, Miller, 3113, Minor 3117, **New 3137**, Norgaard 3141, Oberweiler 3147, O'Connor 3149, Peters 3172, Rich 3194, Rosenberg 3207, Sequoia 3235, Seymour 3236, Simon 3247, Simpson 3248, Sramek 3259, Staley 3262, Steigerwaldt 3265, Stuart 3273, Sullivan 3276, Tarrson 3282, Taxman 3283, Tully 3295, Tuohy 3296, Weaver 3312, Webb 3313

Indiana: **Ackerman 3339**, Bronstein 3351, Bussing-Koch 3353, Gammon 3385, Jennings 3403, Oliver 3428, Raymond 3436, Sherwood 3451, TCU 3458, Welter 3465

Iowa: Becker 3472, McDonald 3520, Stark 3536, Young 3552

Kansas: Baehr 3556, Buford 3562, **Muchnic 3609**, Price 3616, Schmidt 3622

Kentucky: Abercrombie 3645, Dickins 3651, Keeneland 3668, Public 3687, Rounsavall, 3691

Louisiana: Biedenharn 3713, Chambers 3718, Havens 3727, Huie-Dellmon 3729, Magale 3735, Steinhagen 3755, Wheless 3758

Maine: Burnham 3770, Firebird 3778, Lafayette 3787, Somers 3803, Sukeforth 3805

Maryland: Ammerman 3813, Cole 3839, Davis 3844, Daydreams 3845, Franey 3865, **Goldberg 3872**, Higginson 3880, Hittman 3881, Hobbs 3882, Kirk

3894, Macht 3905, Marriott 3909, McKnight 3910, Minkoff 3915, Nabit 3924, Rhona's 3939, Shattuck 3950, Ten 3963, **Thadikonda 3965**, Ticho 3967, Unger 3971, Weiss 3982, Widgeon 3983

Massachusetts: Alden 3999, Arcadia 4004, Autism 4007, Behrakis 4015, **Brabson 4026, Bruner 4030**, Cole 4054, Cricket 4060, Deane 4066, First 4091, Gerrity 4102, Goldman 4105, Hale 4112, Haley 4114, Harrington 4117, Harris 4118, Hauben 4120, Henderson 4127, **Kahn 4143**, Kelleher 4147, Marcus 4188, **New 4220**, Pechet 4235, Permanent 4239, Poduska 4246, Prokopis 4248, Ramlose 4257, Reisman 4263, Rosse 4272, Sacajawea 4274, Singing 4297, **Spero 4304**, Stare 4308, Thoracic 4326, Tomfohrde 4329, Ullian 4335, Ungar 4336

Michigan: Abrams 4369, Beson 4389, Buffalo 4399, Cebelak 4406, Community 4411, Foren 4448, Golden 4455, Havirmill 4463, Holden 4467, Kinney 4483, McDole 4506, Morley 4518, Pardee 4534, Pitt 4540, Power 4544, Ratner 4548, Roscommon 4552, Ryan 4555, Shapiro 4566, Sinai 4570, Sutaruk 4583, Tamer 4585, Whiting 4614, Wieczorek 4617, Zondervan 4621

Minnesota: Bame 4634, Bradley 4647, Deikel 4663, Edina 4672, Erickson 4674, Erickson 4675, Falck 4678, Farmers 4679, Ferber 4682, **Fingerhut 4683**, Fraser 4689, Frey 4690, Granite 4699, Heilmaier 4712, Kinman-Oldfield 4725, Knowlton 4725, Lane 4727, Maslowski 4741, O'Brien 4753, Reger 4769, Rising 4775, Roberts 4778, **Trust 4802**, Walker 4805, Wimmer 4819, **Winds 4820**

Mississippi: Center 4828

Missouri: **Bohm 4871, Build-A-Bear 4879**, Cinmar 4887, Duesenberg 4897, Longer 4949, Love 4951, Price 4982, Sigma-Aldrich 5003, Simmons 5005, Siteman 5006, Slusher 5009, St. 5012

Montana: Cinnabar 5047

Nebraska: Barklage 5071, Heuermann 5092, Midlands 5104, Perkins 5111

Nevada: **A 5131**, Benna 5138, Blue 5140, Coleman 5150, Lifestyle 5173, Meyer 5177, Sweig 5191, Timken-Sturgis 5192

New Hampshire: Dorr 5211, Hunt 5214, Martin 5222, Woodbury 5238

New Jersey: Baum 5258, Bershad 5262, **Blue 5269**, Branfman 5271, Brunetti 5281, Covance 5305, Davis 5314, Dreman 5326, Feinstein 5343, Feldstein 5344, Fellstone 5346, Fox 5349, Greetin 5377, Heart 5388, **Integra 5400**, Jacobson 5402, Johnson 5406, Judson 5411, Kingsberg 5421, Kresa 5432, Lavery 5441, MacDonald 5453, Maschler 5462, McDowell 5465, Miller 5468, Mullen 5475, **Patel 5492**, Research 5509, **Rippel 5510**, Sanders 5518, Schwartz 5525, Shapiro 5532, Tuchman 5561, Upton 5566, **Waterfowl 5570**, Waters 5571, Weinstein 5576, Welch 5579, Westfield 5582, Wicks 5584, Wildwood 5586, Wilf 5588, Zobel 5603

New Mexico: Con 5611, Gumbo 5617, Tanner 5625

New York: 21st 5630, Agate 5649, Alexander 5654, American 5668, Amsterdam 5672, Balbach 5707, Behrens 5731, Berkowitz 5739, Bostwick 5767, Bovin 5770, Briger 5784, **Buster 5806**, Camber 5811, Camuto 5812, Capri 5814, Carwill 5818, Cheatham 5836, Chernoff 5838, Clarkson 5849, Cochran 5853, Cohen 5859, Cohn 5862, Cohoes 5865, Cole 5868, Coleman 5869, Czap 5891, Dabah 5892, Davidson 5901, Davis 5902, Dears 5905, Dorsky 5924, Doscas 5925, Druskin 5932, Elkins 5955, Emwiga 5962, **Engineering 5964, Eppley 5967**, Farber 5987, Feldstein 5997, Ferguson 5999, Feuerring 6001, Fuchsberg 6044, Gantcher 6055, Geier 6064, Glens 6082, Gloeckner 6083, Glorney 6084, Goldfarb 6095, **Goldfein 6096**, Goldman 6098, Goldstone 6102, Golub 6105, Goodman 6107, Graham 6119, Gramercy 6122, Grateful 6131, Harmon 6168, Heilig 6183, Henshel 6192, Heyman 6201, Heyward 6202, Hilson 6209, Hirsch 6211, Hite 6213, Ingrassia 6244, Initial 6245, Jacobson 6255, JI 6260, JJC 6262, Johnson 6268, Johnson

6269, Johnson 6270, Kenworthy 6300, **Kevorkian 6304**, Klein 6324, Knafel 6330, Knapp 6331, Kupferberg 6351, **Laerdal 6358**, Lawrence 6369, Lee 6372, Lenox 6380, Leonhardt 6381, Lewy 6393, Lieb 6398, Loewy 6409, Lucelia 6418, Manning 6437, Manzanita 6439, Marble 6441, Mere 6476, Meredith 6477, Merlo 6479, **Milbank 6490**, Mitchell 6499, Morgado 6505, National 6520, Netter 6525, **Nok 6537**, Ostgrodd 6561, Pajwell 6568, Palisades 6569, Palisano 6570, Petrocelli 6595, Plymouth 6612, **Potts 6624**, Rachesky 6642, Rechler 6657, Reiss 6662, Ritter 6674, RJL 6675, Roxe 6706, Sackler 6716, Sackler 6717, Salomon 6721, Schaefer 6735, Seacoast 6766, Seelig 6769, Shanken 6785, Silverman 6801, Slade 6809, Slade 6810, Smith 6815, **Sparkplug 6830**, Spear 6832, Spiegel 6837, **Spirit 6839**, Spiritus 6840, Starker 6847, Steckler 6853, **Stein 6855**, Stifel 6865, Stony 6868, Sumitomo 6876, Tedaldi 6894, Tribune 6909, Trimble 6910, Turner 6916, Utopia 6923, Van 6925, Vogler 6932, **Walsh/Alfred 6943**, Weinberg 6951, **Weinstein 6956**, Willmott 6978, Woldar 6985, Wolk 6987, Wong 6988, Zemsky 7022, Zenkel 7023, Zirkl 7029

North Carolina: Bane 7043, Burns 7063, Cary 7069, Duncan 7086, Eddy 7087, Elks 7089, Fortson 7100, Hoffman 7128, Horvat 7130, **Laffin 7157**, Lynum 7165, Masserini 7172, Mattei 7173, Matthews 7174, Meyer 7184, Oschwald 7203, Rankin 7217, Richardson 7221, Rogers 7228, **Rolander 7229**, Sloan 7246, Sutcliffe 7262, Wells 7283

North Dakota: Community 7295

Ohio: Anderson 7305, Armington 7309, Athens 7311, Barber 7315, Brentwood 7330, Brown 7334, Bryan 7339, Cassner 7348, Cure 7368, Davey 7373, Defiance 7375, Endowment 7388, Haskell 7439, Hauck 7440, Homan 7451, Horvitz 7454, **Katz 7475**, McMaster 7521, Mifsud 7525, Ritchie 7561, Rosenthal 7563, Ryan 7566, Sears-Swetland 7581, Seasongood 7582, Shannon 7586, Slitzer 7596, Smith 7598, Traeger 7621, Wildermuth 7637, Woodruff 7645

Oklahoma: Atherton 7657, Brown 7664, Everest 7676, Fleischaker 7679, Goddard 7684, Jones 7691, Kerr 7693, Merrick 7707, Peel 7714, Trippet 7725

Oregon: Bowen 7743, **Chiles 7749**, Curry 7755, Heath 7772, Holzman 7775, Kimmel 7782, Schmidt 7813, Sharkey 7815, Wessinger 7826

Pennsylvania: **Arronson 7844**, Ashland 7845, Aventis 7847, Bennett 7860, Betz 7870, **BGM 7871**, Bienenfeld 7872, Bon-Ton 7884, Brooks 7899, Bryer 7902, Calligan 7909, Campbell 7912, Community 7933, Cottage 7938, Crawford 7944, Dickson 7957, Drueding 7966, Gauss 8014, Gershman 8015, **Glendorn 8020**, HBE 8047, Hirtzel 8058, Hoffman 8062, Holden 8064, Kittenbrink 8093, **KL 8094**, Levee 8121, Lewis 8123, Lubert 8133, McManus 8164, Mosi 8179, Mudge 8181, Pasquerilla 8204, Patterson 8205, Price 8225, **Rust 8250**, Schautz 8257, Seebe 8268, Sidewater 8278, Snyder 8288, Society 8289, Stein 8299, Stott 8304, Strawbridge 8305, Tabas 8312, Tippins 8318, Tuttleman 8325, Union 8326, Wachs 8336, Woodall 8368

Rhode Island: **Black 8390**, Frasch 8408, Geneen 8411, Getz 8412, Gross 8414, Littlefield 8441, Mulligan 8457, Peacock 8469

South Dakota: Engelsma 8563

Tennessee: **Belz 8585**, Cole 8600, Doochin 8605, Durham 8608, **Fraser 8617**, Monday 8652

Texas: Boeing 8733, Booth 8734, Bromberg 8748, Cemo 8765, **Chrest 8770, Crowder 8792**, Dauphin 8798, de 8802, Deason 8805, Dougherty, 8825, Dove 8826, Dozzo 8827, Educational 8836, Elkins 8838, Esping 8841, Fair 8844, Fickett 8854, Frost 8878, Haggar, 8908, Halperin 8912, Hervey 8932, Hext 8933, Hibbs 8934, Hixon 8940, Holloway 8946, Howell 8956, Johnston 8972, Kahn 8978, Kaplan 8979, Kayser 8980, Klein 8997, Kramer 9003, Light 9016, Lowdon 9025,

MacDonald-Peterson 9032, McDonald 9051, McKee 9052, McNutt 9055, Mischer 9067, Mitte 9069, Morrison 9073, **OneSight 9098**, Oppenheimer 9101, Overlake 9106, Pak 9110, Patton 9119, Petty 9126, Poncin 9134, RDM 9146, Riter, 9154, Roberts 9157, Rowan 9166, Rubenstein 9167, Schepps 9178, Sear 9186, Sherman 9192, Simard 9195, Smith 9205, Smith 9207, South 9209, Stanzel 9213, Steen 9216, Storehouse 9223, Thompson 9234, Tolleson 9238, USD 9245, Vaughan 9248, Vaughan 9249, Waggoner 9254, Wal-Dot 9256, Walls 9257, Webre 9266, Weir 9268, Willard 9278, Wolens 9284, Woods 9291, Zale 9299

Utah: Bastian 9304, Dialysis 9319, Green 9327, Spendlove 9357

Vermont: Harper 9373

Virginia: Backer 9389, Birk 9398, **Brown 9407**, Immixgroup 9476, Lacy 9485, Lawrence 9487, **Longview 9494**, Northern 9503, **Praktikos 9514**, RECO 9522, Selsky 9529, Weil 9550

Washington: Bayley 9567, Boeschoten 9571, Coulter 9581, DeFalco 9585, Dore 9587, Erickson 9591, Foss 9598, Hyde 9627, **Ji 9632**, Juniper 9640, Murray 9667, O'Donnell 9672, Patel 9675, Pointe 9679, Quest 9681, **Sabol 9687**, Schaar 9689, Smith 9698, Stevens 9704, Thomson 9711, Wilkens 9724, Wissner-Slivka 9727

West Virginia: Vecellio 9770

Wisconsin: Birnschein 9783, Eau 9814, Erdman 9816, Foulkes 9821, Heller 9839, Jacobus 9849, **Johnson 9851**, Kohl 9864, Loehrke 9872, Manitowoc 9876, Marcus 9877, Meinerz 9883, Ocular 9895, Schmucker 9923, Seramur 9926, Sub-Zero 9943, Sullivan 9944, Weyers 9959, Windway 9961

Wyoming: Bailey 9964, Scott 9988, Skilling 9990, StoneRiver 9991

Research and evaluation

Alabama: Anderson 5, Bruno 17, Kemp 42

Arizona: Johnson 134, Margolis 144

California: Arata 248, **A-T 258**, Baker 267, Baxter 284, Bell 295, Bellini 298, Brotman 351, Brown 352, Bundy 360, **Cantor 375**, Downing 462, Evening 487, Familian 491, Folger 515, Frome 535, Gareeb 548, Huntington 642, Lewis 753, Martin 801, Mason 805, Maxfield 808, Mazda 810, Morgenstern 848, Palo 901, Pasarow 906, Rappaport 953, Ross 988, Simon-Strauss 1042, Stauffer 1076, Stewart 1083, Thagard 1109, Thrill 1117, Torino 1125, **Valenzuela 1143**, Waller 1152, Winkler 1188

Colorado: Dewolf 1256, **Fishback 1270**, Goodwin 1279, Grossman 1281, Ladd 1310, **National 1330**, Schramm 1350, Shamrock 1353, Taylor 1364

Connecticut: Bender 1405, Berbecker 1406, Filingieri 1447, Gerbic 1463, Greenfield 1471, Howard 1484, Lee 1507, Tully 1588, Winokur 1597

Delaware: Freedman 1665, Hagan 1674, Lightner 1699

District of Columbia: **Merriman 1820**, Monarch 1823

Florida: **Atlantis 1858**, Bastien 1872, **Chenzyme 1939**, Consolidated 1951, Fuller 2028, Gordon 2050, Greenberg 2062, **Handleman 2078**, Hansen 2079, Hultquist 2115, Ingalls 2118, Kessler 2145, Kimmel 2146, Kuriansky 2162, Livingston 2187, Morningstar 2218, Pearce 2252, Price 2267, Richard 2285, Simmons 2338, **Taylor 2365**, Taylor 2366, Wilder 2406, **Wollowick 2412**, Wrightson-Ramsing 2416, Yerrid 2420

Georgia: Community 2466, Georgia 2484, Whitehead 2610

Illinois: Coldwell 2797, Cremer 2815, **Foundation 2881**, Fraida 2884, Goldenberg 2920, Goodstein 2924, Gray 2927, Hanson 2950, Hughes 2983, Johnson 3001, **Lazzara 3042**, North 3142, Richard 3195, Rosenberg 3207, Simon 3247, Stuart 3273

Indiana: Jennings 3403

Iowa: Stark 3536

Kansas: **Muchnic 3609**, Price 3616

Kentucky: Abercrombie 3645, Dickins 3651, Rounsavall, 3691

Louisiana: Biedenharn 3713, Chambers 3718

Maryland: **Goldberg 3872**, Hobbs 3882, McKnight 3910, Minkoff 3915, Shattuck 3950, Ten 3963

Massachusetts: Alden 3999, Arcadia 4004, **Barakat 4012**, Goldman 4105, Harris 4118, Henderson 4127, **New 4220**, Pechet 4235, Ramlose 4257, Thoracic 4326

Michigan: Cebelak 4406, Golden 4455, Holden 4467, Pitt 4540, Ratner 4548, Sinai 4570, Whiting 4614

Minnesota: Heilmaier 4712, Kinman-Oldfield 4723, Knowlton 4725

Missouri: Longer 4949, Love 4951, Price 4982, Slusher 5009, St. 5012

Nevada: **A 5131**, Sweig 5191

New Jersey: Brunetti 5281, Fox 5349, Greetin 5377, Kingsberg 5421, Tuchman 5561, **Waterfowl 5570**, Welch 5579, Wetterberg 5583, Wicks 5584

New York: American 5668, Bostwick 5767, Briger 5784, Carwill 5818, Cheatham 5836, Cohen 5859, Dorsky 5924, **Engineering 5964**, Farber 5987, Ferguson 5999, Fuchsberg 6044, Glorney 6084, Goodman 6107, Henshel 6192, Hilson 6209, Hirsch 6211, Initial 6245, Johnson 6268, Kenworthy 6300, Knafel 6330, Knapp 6331, Kupferberg 6351, **Laerdal 6358**, Manning 6437, Manzanita 6439, Meredith 6477, Netter 6525, Ostgrodd 6561, Petrocelli 6595, Plymouth 6612, **Potts 6624**, Quinn 6637, RJL 6675, Roxe 6706, Sackler 6717, Seacoast 6766, Silverman 6801, Spear 6832, Spiritus 6840, Starker 6847, Tribune 6909, Turner 6916, Van 6925, Weinberg 6951, Willmott 6978, Zemsky 7022, Zenkel 7023

North Carolina: Cary 7069, Davis 7084, Eddy 7087, Elks 7089, Horvat 7130, **Rolander 7229**, Sutcliffe 7262

Ohio: Armington 7309, Cassner 7348, Horvitz 7454, Rosenthal 7563

Oklahoma: Jones 7691, Kerr 7693, Merrick 7707, Trippet 7725

Oregon: **Chiles 7749**, Schmidt 7813

Pennsylvania: **Arronson 7844**, Brooks 7899, **Glendorn 8020**, Jackson 8078, Levee 8121, Schautz 8257, Strawbridge 8305, Tippins 8318, Up 8327

Rhode Island: Gross 8414, Littlefield 8441

Tennessee: **Belz 8585, Fraser 8617**

Texas: Dauphin 8798, Deason 8805, Elkins 8838, Haggar, 8908, Hixon 8940, Johnston 8972, MacDonald-Peterson 9032, McKee 9052, Morrison 9073, Oppenheimer 9101, Pak 9110, Poncin 9134, Smith 9205, Smith 9207, South 9209, Vaughan 9249, Walls 9257

Utah: Bastian 9304, Dialysis 9319, Spendlove 9357

Vermont: Harper 9373

Virginia: Immixgroup 9476, **Praktikos 9514**

Washington: Coulter 9581, **Ji 9632**, Wilkens 9724

Wisconsin: Erdman 9816, Kohl 9864, Meinerz 9883, Rosemann 9919, Seramur 9926, Weyers 9959

Wyoming: Scott 9988

Scholarships

Alabama: Adams 3, Amos 4, Barkley 9, Black 12, Blount 13, Bruno 17, Griswold 31, Ireland 39, Kemp 42, Pei-Ling 52, Sexton 63, Simpson 66

Arizona: Grace 125, James 132, Johnson 135, Lapan 140, Napier 152, **Rosztoczy 161**, Sturges 176

Arkansas: Darragh 193, McKinney 202, Minnis 204, Olds 210, Riggs 214, White 220

California: Ackerman 227, Alafi 235, Amador 238, Baker 264, Bank 272, Barth 279, Baskin 281, Baye 285, Bekins 294, Beynon 312, Boyer 335, Bradford 337, Brooks 349, Burg 362, **Butler 365**, Calaveras 369, Callison 371, **Cantor 375**, Coleman 416, Community 421, Dockweiler 456, Drexler 463, Drum 464, Familian 491, First 506, Flanagan 510, Fox 525, Fremont 527, Gareatis 547, Gellert 550, Glikbarg 564, Goldberg 567, Harris 601, **Hefferlin 610**, Heller 613, In 650, **Indo-American 651**, **International 652**, Johnson 670, Kelly 697, Latkin 731, Legacy 740, Looker 766, Lopez 767, Lux 773, Mangold 789, Martin 803, Mazda 810, McClatchy 811, McDaniel 812, McQuinn 820, **Modglin 840**, Morgan 846, Morgan 847, Nagel 857, Orfalea 887, Outrageous 894, Pacific 897, Payne 910, Pedrozzi 912, Pickford 927, Plum 929, **Preuss 935**, **Quiksilver 945**, Ragir 950, Rice 969, Ross 988, Sammut 996, Smullin 1060, Solano 1063, Stauffer 1076, **Teichman 1106**, Thagard 1109, Trust 1131, **Wakerly 1150**, Waltmar 1155, Westphal 1177, Wharton 1178, White 1180, Yuki 1203, Zabala 1204, Zolla 1216

Colorado: Bean 1228, Bloedorn 1238, Broomfield 1242, Donahue 1257, Dorset 1259, **Fishback 1270**, Goodwin 1279, Graves 1280, Heider 1290, Jacobs 1298, Joslin-Needham 1300, Margulf 1320, Moniker 1327, QEP 1342, Schlessman 1349, Southwestern 1355, Stretesky 1360, Tappan 1363, Tomkins 1368, Trueblood 1371, Vradenburg 1374

Connecticut: Barden 1402, Brace 1410, Chelsea 1418, Conway 1422, Crosswicks 1425, Curran 1427, Diageo 1437, Dime 1438, Ensign-Bickford 1442, Filingieri 1447, Fippinger 1450, Goldfarb 1467, Jones 1491, Kreitler 1502, Lebovitz 1506, McLeod 1524, Newtown 1532, O'Meara 1537

Delaware: Bennett 1618, Brown 1631, Chaney 1640, Cohen 1643, De 1655, New 1715, Riecker 1729

District of Columbia: Bender 1789, **Carter 1794**, Goldman 1810, Replogle 1831, Westport 1838

Florida: Anderson 1847, Archibald 1852, Bastien 1872, Bayuk 1875, Beall, 1876, **Benedict 1884**, Blanton 1892, Cape 1917, Capital 1918, Catalina 1928, Chadbourne 1932, Coral 1952, Couch 1953, Dasburg 1961, Dennis 1969, Detter 1971, Duckwall 1982, Erdle 1993, Fish 2001, Fox 2016, **Freewill 2021**, Glaubinger 2040, Godbold 2041, Grader 2054, Gregory 2067, Gulf 2069, Haven 2085, Hultquist 2115, Jacobsen 2123, Kanders 2135, King 2148, Kiwanis 2149, Lawson 2170, Lazarus 2172, Marco 2194, McQuistion 2208, Morrison 2222, Partners 2248, **Prime 2268**, Roshan 2297, Sample 2312, **Shepard 2331**, Shockley 2332, Smith 2341, Steele 2347, Swisher 2361, Tampa 2362, Turner 2381, **Uncle 2383**, Westgate 2400, Woodbery 2413

Georgia: Baker 2439, **Bancker-Williams 2440**, Barnett 2441, Benton 2445, Bowen 2447, Carmical 2453, Charter 2456, Church 2460, Exposition 2476, Georgia 2485, Harrison 2502, Holland-Underwood 2508, Hoyt 2513, Lee 2540, Magnus 2543, Marcus 2544, McClatchey 2546, Smith 2586, Stahl 2588, Waffle 2602, Wormsloe 2619

Hawaii: Epstein 2630, Locations 2638, Servco 2645, **Shiraki 2648**, Takitani 2650, Vidinha 2653, Wilcox 2654, Wong 2656, Young 2660

Idaho: Intermountain 2677, **Melaleuca 2679**, Mitchell 2680, Morbeck 2681, Morrison 2682, Simplot 2685, Whittenberger 2689

Illinois: Alton 2705, Aon 2710, **Appleby 2711**, Arboit 2713, Argo 2714, Best 2740, Boothroyd 2749, Bound 2751, Boyle 2754, Bruce 2761, Brunswick 2762, Bulkley, 2765, Chapin-May 2782, Cohn 2795, Community 2803, Cremer 2815, **Demos 2827**, **Dyson 2842**, Edelman 2845, Fabyan 2862, Family 2864, Follett 2877, Halstead 2944, Herbert 2966, Hess 2969, Hopper 2977, House 2980, Hughes 2983, **Ingredion 2988**, Jephson 2996, JKP 2997, Jones 3002, Keller 3010, **Krasberg-Mason 3029**, **Lazzara 3042**, Levy 3050, Logos 3058, MacDonald 3068, McCrea 3088, Meyer 3106, Miller, 3113, Morton 3127, **New 3137**, **Nureyev 3145**, Pepper 3167, Rosenson 3209, Saliba 3221, Schaumburg 3223, Shaker 3238, Smith 3253, Smysor 3255, Steigerwaldt 3265, Takiff 3281, Taylor 3286, Taylor 3287, Tobey 3290, United 3300, Walker 3308, Webb 3313

Indiana: Bos 3347, Branigin 3348, Burris 3352, Bussing-Koch 3353, Community 3359, Community

3360, Community 3361, Community 3363, Decatur 3367, Dubois 3370, Fayette 3379, Fenech 3380, Franklin 3382, Froderman 3383, Huntington 3397, Jasper 3401, Jennings 3402, LaGrange 3412, MutualBank 3421, Oakley 3426, Pulaski 3432, Raymond 3436, Rooney 3440, Rush 3441, Scott 3446, Sherwood 3451, TCU 3458, Western 3466, Weston 3467

Iowa: Barkema 3471, Cole-Belin 3480, deStwolinski 3486, First 3493, Medical 3521, Nelson 3524, Premier 3528, Rohde 3530, **Wahlert 3544**, West 3547, **Wright 3551**

Kansas: Bane 3557, Berry 3558, Cape 3563, Davis 3571, Goebel 3580, Henry 3585, Insurance 3587, Jellison 3589, Legacy, 3595, Middlekauff 3603, Payless 3614, Ross 3619, Rush 3620, Salgo 3621, Schmidt 3622, Scroggins 3624

Kentucky: Etscorn 3654, Hannah 3659, Hayswood 3662, Independence 3666, Keeneland 3668, Mackin 3673, **Magee 3674**, Trim 3702

Louisiana: Daybrook 3720, Huie-Dellmon 3729, Winn 3760, Wisdom 3761

Maine: Borman 3767

Maryland: Ammerman 3813, Broadus 3829, Campbell 3831, Davis 3844, Dean 3846, Gladding 3871, **Goldberg 3872**, Hobbs 3882, Huether/McClelland 3884, Knapp 3895, Loats 3902, Macht 3905, Mangione 3907, No 3927, Richmond 3940, Widgeon 3983

Massachusetts: 2 3992, Behrakis 4015, Benz 4017, Chicopee 4047, Clarke 4049, Clementi 4050, Cook 4056, D'Amour 4064, Davoli 4065, Delorenzo 4068, East 4075, Hauben 4120, Hornblower 4135, **Kahn 4143**, Kelsey 4148, King 4156, Krieger 4160, Lingos 4177, Melvin 4196, Michael 4202, OneBeacon 4231, Permanent 4239, Phelps 4242, Ramlose 4257, Ramsey 4258, Rosse 4272, Russell 4273, Shaughnessy 4292, Simoni 4296, Smith 4300, Stearns 4311, Steiger 4312, Thompson 4325, Thoreau 4327, Tresorelle 4333, Ungar 4336, Walsh 4348, Xeric 4365

Michigan: Abrams 4369, Andersen 4377, Barron 4384, Barstow 4385, Barton-Malow 4386, Biederman 4391, Branch 4396, Bronner 4398, Buist 4401, Christian 4408, Community 4410, Community 4411, Dana 4419, DeVlieg 4428, Dinan 4431, Farwell 4442, **Ford, 4446**, Four 4449, Frankenmuth 4450, Gershenson 4453, Glassen 4454, Gratiot 4459, Holden 4467, JSJ 4474, Kantzler 4478, Keller 4481, Kellogg 4482, L 4487, Lapeer 4490, Leven 4492, LoPrete 4496, Mackinac 4499, Mills 4515, Paine 4531, Ratner 4548, Redies 4549, Roscommon 4552, Ryan 4555, Schmuckal 4559, Shiawassee 4568, St. 4576, Stoddard 4579, Stubnitz 4582, Talty 4584, Tamer 4585, **Teitel 4589**, Tremble 4595, Tuscola 4598, Vicksburg 4606, Wieczorek 4617, Zondervan 4621

Minnesota: Cox 4662, Dell 4664, Edina 4671, Falck 4678, Farmers 4679, Fischman 4685, Granite 4699, Hickory 4713, Jostens 4720, Northern 4751, Quinlan 4764, Rahr 4766, Regis 4770, Schott 4787, Squam 4793, Thorpe 4800, **Trust 4802**, Walker 4805

Mississippi: Mississippi 4849

Missouri: Baer 4862, **Bohm 4871**, Butler 4880, Curry 4892, Finley 4910, Forster-Powers 4911, Garvey 4913, Logan 4947, MFA 4960, Pearl 4977, Peculiar 4978, Portman 4981, Schutte 4995, Shawe 5000, Sigma-Aldrich 5003, Siteman 5006, Slusher 5009, St. 5012, Timmons 5021, UMB 5026, Van 5028, Wolff 5040

Montana: Heisey 5056, Lynn 5059

Nebraska: Ameritas 5067, Hawkins 5089, Kilbourne 5097, Midlands 5104, Physicians 5112, Reynolds 5114, Yount 5130

Nevada: Boyd 5141, C.A.N. 5142, Close 5148, Dermody 5152, Geomar 5160, **He 5162**, Joseph 5166, Meyer 5177, Pinnacle 5183, Timken-Sturgis 5192, West 5197

New Hampshire: Dorr 5211, Jameson 5215, Smyth 5232

New Jersey: Ascena 5252, Aufzien 5253, Avis 5255, Brundage 5280, Brunetti 5281, Clermont 5298, **Crane 5306**, Essig 5339, Fox 5349, Giants 5369, **Integra 5400**, Mamiye 5456, Miller 5468, Roe 5512, Schwartz 5525, Selective 5528, **Southpole 5545**, Wetterberg 5583, Wilson 5590, WKBJ 5592, Zichron 5600, Zobel 5603

New Mexico: B.F. 5606, Carlsbad 5608, Lea 5620, Taos 5626

New York: Alexander 5656, American 5664, **American 5667**, Anderson 5674, Aronson 5689, August 5698, Avery 5702, Barham 5715, Bobrow 5765, Brademas 5774, Brooklyn 5788, **Buffalo 5799**, **Buster 5806**, Carwill 5818, Clemente 5850, **Cogitare 5855**, Cohoes 5865, Community 5872, Cutco 5890, Fee 5990, Fife 6005, French 6032, Friends 6042, G&A 6048, Gaffney 6049, Grand 6123, **Grossman 6146**, Hennessy 6191, Henshel 6192, High 6206, Himelberg 6210, Hogan 6217, IF 6237, Joukowsky 6274, **Kathwari 6286**, Kirby 6313, Klein 6325, Knapp 6331, Koessler 6335, Krumholz 6349, Lake 6360, Lee 6372, Levine 6387, **Li 6394**, Loconsolo 6408, Loewy 6409, Marshall 6446, Matutina 6452, **McCaddin-McQuirk 6455**, McCarthy 6456, Mendell 6472, Messinger 6482, Newman 6532, **Nok 6537**, Northern 6540, Norwich 6542, Ong 6558, Palisades 6569, Palisano 6570, Patrina 6579, Pollack 6615, **Posner-Wallace 6621**, Potter 6623, **Potts 6624**, Raymond 6652, Roothbert 6682, Rose 6683, Rosner 6698, Sargol 6728, Satow 6732, **Schmeelk 6742**, Schwartz 6753, Schwartz 6755, Schwartzberg 6756, SGMG 6778, Sharon 6787, Snow 6818, Spektor 6833, Spiegel 6837, Steckler 6853, **Stern 6862**, Stony 6868, Switzer 6889, Tod 6901, Truman 6912, **Usman 6921**, Utica 6922, Utopia 6923, Vogt 6933, Wilson 6979, Zenkel 7023, Zichron 7026

North Carolina: BB&T 7045, Bryan 7060, Burlington 7062, Burns 7063, Chatham 7074, Cooke 7079, Covington 7081, Eddy 7087, First 7097, Flowers 7099, Fox 7103, Gambrell 7105, Garrigues 7107, Horvat 7130, **Kramer 7152**, **Laffin 7157**, Landon 7158, Lerner 7160, Marsh 7171, Masserini 7172, McLean 7178, McLendon 7179, Meserve 7182, Meyer 7184, Needham 7199, Niessen, 7200, Outer 7204, Perkin 7208, Rogers 7228, Sanders 7234, Smith 7247, Smith 7249, Snyder's-Lance 7250, Sutcliffe 7262, Thomasville 7267, Trexler 7269, Wake 7276, Wallace 7277

North Dakota: Community 7295, Myra 7297

Ohio: Albrecht 7301, American 7303, Austin-Bailey 7312, Bahmann 7313, Barber 7315, Bates 7317, Besl 7326, Bicknell 7327, Brown 7336, Chemed 7350, Cleveland 7354, Community 7356, Crandall 7366, Danis 7371, Davey 7373, **Elisha-Bolton 7387**, Firman 7400, Fleck 7403, Foundation 7408, Fox 7409, Frost-Parker 7413, Goerlich 7428, Gosiger 7429, Haskell 7439, Hieronymus 7448, **Highfield 7450**, Homan 7451, Kamm 7473, Kennedy 7476, Knoll 7483, Kramer 7484, Kutz 7486, Laub 7490, Lundgard 7508, M.L.M 7510, Mather 7516, Morley 7532, Musson 7534, Newton 7536, Pott 7549, Renner 7557, Reynolds 7558, Ritchie 7561, Rotterman 7564, Ryan 7566, Sandfair 7569, Schey 7571, Sears-Swetland 7581, Segoe 7583, Smith 7598, Steinmann 7603, Taj 7611, Throckmorton 7618, Trachsel 7620, Traeger 7621, Tuscarawas 7623, Van 7625, Young 7652

Oklahoma: Ashbrook 7656, Barnes 7659, Barthelmes 7661, Broadhurst 7663, Collins, 7669, **Crio 7670**, Dobson 7672, Jirous 7690, Martin, 7704, Stone 7721, Wegener 7731

Oregon: Castle 7745, **Chiles 7749**, Elwood 7761, Haugse 7771, Holzman 7775, Kuse 7786, Michael 7799, Miller 7800, Morey 7801, Morris 7802, Parker/United 7805, Schmidt 7813, Singer 7819, Stewart 7823, Wessinger 7826, West 7828

Pennsylvania: Alley 7837, American 7839, Arkema 7842, **Arronson 7844**, Ashland 7845, Baker 7851, Bon-Ton 7884, Bridge 7891, Bucks 7905, Calvert 7910, Carlson 7916, Carnahan-Jackson 7917,

Charlestein 7920, **Connelly 7935**, Crawford 7944, Crawford 7945, DENTSPLY 7954, Dietz 7959, Eberly 7969, Elk 7975, Ely 7979, Fortinsky 8002, Freas 8005, Gamber 8011, **Glendorn 8020**, Gureghian 8033, Hall 8037, Harsco 8040, HBE 8047, High 8054, Knoll 8100, Maronda 8140, Maslow 8146, Mukaiyama-Rice 8183, Mullen 8184, Murphy 8185, Neag 8189, O'Brien-Veba 8197, Packer 8201, Quaker 8228, Randall 8230, Rudin 8247, Saramar 8253, Schuylkill 8263, Shoemaker 8275, Smith 8280, Sneath 8286, Society 8289, Staehle 8295, Stein 8299, Teleflex 8314, Vincent 8334, Wenger 8352, Young 8375, **Zeldin 8376**

Rhode Island: Collis 8397, DeLoura 8402, Kingsbury 8435, La 8438, Liberty 8440, Littlefield 8441, Long 8443, McCarthy 8452, Miller 8454, Mulligan 8457, Papitto 8467, Slingerland 8491, Sullivan 8494, Wells 8501

South Carolina: Bailey 8510, Collins 8520, Horne 8528

South Dakota: Hatterscheidt 8566, Schwab 8574, Watertown 8576, Welk 8577

Tennessee: Boring 8590, Cartinhour-Woods 8597, Community 8601, Cracker 8603, Durham 8608, **Fugitive 8618**, Jewell 8633, **Lowenstein 8645**, Massengill-DeFriece 8647, McWherter 8649, Seidman 8672, Weiss 8684

Texas: Augur 8712, B.E.L.I.E.F. 8713, Bertha 8729, Brisley 8744, Bromberg 8748, Cauthorn 8764, Cemo 8765, Central 8766, Chambers 8767, Clements 8773, Community 8782, Cook 8786, Cox 8790, **Crowder 8792**, de 8802, DeBusk 8806, Dougherty, 8825, Dunagan 8831, Edwards 8837, Esping 8841, Fairchild 8845, Fentress 8851, Fertitta 8852, Finger 8857, Foundation 8869, Fuller 8882, Genecov 8886, Hallberg 8911, Haraldson 8917, Hatfield 8922, Hegi 8926, Hervey 8932, Hext 8933, Hill 8938, Howell 8956, Kahn 8978, KCL 8981, Killson 8990, Krist 9004, Long 9023, Luse 9029, Martin 9040, McKee 9052, McMillan, 9054, Mitte 9069, Myers 9081, Navarro 9084, Nelson 9086, O'Neal 9097, Oppenheimer 9101, Pack 9109, Pierson 9129, Quanex 9141, Reilly 9148, Reitch 9149, Richardson 9151, Roberts 9156, Roberts 9157, Roosth 9160, Rowan 9166, San 9170, Schoener 9180, Sear 9186, Smith 9201, Smith 9207, South 9209, Sparks 9211, Tennessee 9230, Texas 9231, Valero 9246, Vaughan 9249, Waggoner 9254, Waggoners 9255, Wal-Dot 9256, Walls 9257, Walthall 9258, Webre 9266, Weir 9268, Wolens 9284, Wolters 9287, Wood 9293, Works 9293

Utah: Eccles 9322, Eskuche 9323, Green 9327, Patel 9344, Steiner 9358

Vermont: Blittersdorf 9365, Mergens 9381

Virginia: Backer 9389, Beck 9393, Bell 9394, Brink's 9406, **Brown 9407**, Community 9426, **Delmar 9429**, Family 9444, Ivakota 9477, Poole 9512, Pruden 9517, RECO 9522, Stone 9537, Treakle 9543, Wiley 9551

Washington: Coulter 9581, DeFalco 9585, Everett 9592, Helstrom 9619, Horn 9625, **Jernigan 9631**, Johnston-Hanson 9635, Kilworth 9644, Korum 9648, Martin 9660, Murray 9667, Pigott 9677, Stevens 9704, Tonkin 9715, Tudor 9717, Worthington 9729

West Virginia: Bowen 9736, Bowen 9737, Carter 9741, Fine 9745, Hott 9753, Skewes 9766, Vecellio 9770

Wisconsin: Ariens 9776, Birnschein 9783, Blooming 9784, Cloud 9796, Hatch 9837, Heller 9839, J.P.C. 9848, **Johnson 9851**, Johnson 9853, Junginger 9856, Kenosha 9862, Lutsey 9873, LUX 9874, Marshfield 9878, Meehan 9882, Modine 9889, Phipps 9903, Puelicher 9907, Rhodes 9914, Schoenleber 9924, Seeds 9925, Smith 9931, Stateline 9937, T 9945, Trek 9948, Van 9953, Weyco 9958, Windway 9961, Woodtrust-Bell 9963

Wyoming: Bailey 9964, **Schultz 9986**, Skelton 9989

Seed money

Alabama: Abahac 1

Arizona: Hughes 130

California: Ackerman 227, **A-T 258**, Bannerman 274, Baye 285, Bear 288, Bonner 326, Codding 412, Community 420, Community 421, Downing 462, Drum 464, Foor 516, Gellert 550, Gross 587, Jones 673, LEF 739, **Lloyd 763**, Looker 766, Lux 773, Margoes 795, McLean 817, Nicholson 866, Ontario 882, Page 899, Rossi 989, Simon 1041, Stauffer 1077, Trust 1131, **Wakerly 1150**, Welk 1170, Wharton 1178, **Wilkinson 1183**

Colorado: Comprecare 1249, **Nord 1332**, Spencer 1356, Stratton 1359, Warner 1376, Wilkins 1379

Connecticut: Fippinger 1450, Panwy 1539, Winokur 1597

Delaware: Kutz 1696, New 1715, Remmer 1726

District of Columbia: Bench 1788, **Butler 1792**, Jovid 1817, **Pettus-Crowe 1828**, Porter 1829

Florida: Fish 2001, Glass 2039, Hill 2097, Landwirth 2167, Lazarus 2172, McCabe 2201, **Mukti 2226**, Oristano 2241, Ray 2275, Reinhold 2280, **Zimmer 2425**

Georgia: Abreu 2431, Athens 2437, **Bancker-Williams 2440**, Georgia 2484, Gray 2497, Lipscomb 2541, Walker 2603

Hawaii: Baldwin 2625, Wilcox 2654

Idaho: Whittenberger 2689

Illinois: Agape 2698, Bishop 2743, Community 2802, Community 2803, Cremer 2815, EMA 2854, Hanson 2950, **Landau 3036**, **Lindon 3054**, Millard 3109, Staley 3262, Webb 3313

Indiana: Ayres 3342, Bussing-Koch 3353, Community 3359, Community 3360, Decatur 3367, Dubois 3370, Huntington 3397, Jasper 3401, LaGrange 3412, Namaste 3422, Oliver 3428, Raymond 3436, Rush 3441, Western 3466

Iowa: Cowles 3482, Forster 3494, Muscatine 3523

Kansas: Baehr 3556, DeVore 3573, Farah 3576, Legacy, 3595

Louisiana: Steinhagen 3755, Wisdom 3761

Maine: Davenport 3775, **Dugas 3776**, **Golden 3781**, Somers 3803

Maryland: Biophilia 3824, **Braitmayer 3827**, Higginson 3880, Macht 3905, Richmond 3940, Tucker 3969, Widgeon 3983

Massachusetts: Alden 3999, **Blossom 4022**, Boynton 4025, **Brabson 4026**, Carlee 4038, Coolidge 4057, Cricket 4060, Hauben 4120, **Kahn 4143**, Kelsey 4148, Morse 4209, MutualOne 4216, **New 4220**, Permanent 4239, Ramlose 4257, Ratshesky 4259, **Robbins-de 4266**, Sicari 4295, Wallace 4347, Walsh 4348, Xeric 4365

Michigan: Community 4410, Community 4411, Cummings 4417, Gratiot 4459, Kantzler 4478, Keller 4481, M 4497, Mackinac 4499, Michigan 4514, Morley 4518, Olds 4526, Stubnitz 4582, **Teitel 4589**, Tuscola 4598, Vicksburg 4606

Minnesota: Bell 4637, Bell 4638, Bend 4639, Deikel 4663, Farmers 4679, **Fingerhut 4683**, Granite 4699, Midcontinent 4745, Onan 4754, O'Neil 4755, Quinlan 4764, **Trust 4802**, Walker 4805, Wendel 4813, **Winds 4820**

Mississippi: Lower 4847

Missouri: Butler 4880, Copaken 4888, Edgar 4899, Long 4948, Riedel 4984, Slusher 5009, St. 5012, Timmons 5021, Vatterott 5030

Nebraska: Barklage 5071, Midlands 5104, Pegler 5110

Nevada: Close 5148

New Hampshire: Bickford 5205, Dorr 5211, Hunt 5214

New Jersey: **Blue 5269**, Carlozzi 5287, Elizabethtown 5332, Environmental 5337, **Knistrom 5426**, Leavens 5444, Snyder 5541, Westfield 5582, Winters 5591, WKBJ 5592

New Mexico: Carlsbad 5608, Chamiza 5609, Con 5611, Taos 5626, **Watersheds 5628**

New York: Abelard 5635, Anderson-Rogers 5676, August 5698, Balbach 5707, Bender 5735, Bernhill 5741, Dammann 5897, **Eastman 5940**, EMSA

5961, **Gimprich 6080**, Glens 6082, Gordon 6110, **Grossman 6146**, Grumbacher 6148, Hahn 6156, Hennessy 6191, Kenworthy 6300, Krumholz 6349, Lake 6360, Legacy 6373, Lubo 6417, Lucelia 6418, Marble 6441, **Nok 6537**, Northern 6540, O'Grady 6551, Patrina 6579, Plymouth 6612, **Potts 6624**, Roche 6678, Snow 6818, **Sparkplug 6830**, Steckler 6853, Stony 6868, Truman 6912, Turner 6916, Utica 6922, Vogler 6932, Washington 6946, Wells 6964, **Yoreinu 7010**

North Carolina: Covington 7081, Duncan 7086, Glenn 7111, **Kramer 7152**, Meserve 7182, Meyer 7184, Outer 7204, Richardson 7221, Rogers 7228, Strowd 7258

Ohio: Anderson 7305, Austin-Bailey 7312, B-Brand 7318, Defiance 7375, **Eaton 7383**, Fox 7409, Homan 7451, Kilworth 7477, Landers 7488, **Lowe-Marshall 7505**, Lundgard 7508, Mather 7516, NLT 7537, Quatman 7552, Sandfair 7569, Sears-Swetland 7581, Tait 7610, Woodruff 7645

Oklahoma: Ashbrook 7656, Broadhurst 7663, Goddard 7684, Merrick 7707, Wegener 7731

Oregon: Charis 7748, Elwood 7761, Flowerree 7763, Holzman 7775, Lamb 7787, Western 7829, Woodard 7831

Pennsylvania: **Arronson 7844**, Bergman 7863, Born 7885, Carnahan-Jackson 7917, Community 7933, Cove 7939, Finley 7995, Friendship 8009, Frohring 8010, HBE 8047, Kazanjian 8090, **KL 8094**, Kynett 8105, Maslow 8146, McCandless 8153, Miller 8173, Patterson 8205, Remmel 8235, **Rust 8250**, Seybert 8269, Shoemaker 8275, Smith, 8285, Tuttleman 8325, Valentine 8328, Wurts 8370

Rhode Island: Heydt 8419, Kimball 8434, Kingsbury 8435, McCarthy 8452, Moore 8456

South Dakota: Watertown 8576

Tennessee: Durham 8608, **Lowenstein 8645**, Massengill-DeFriece 8647

Texas: Boeing 8733, Bromley 8749, Dougherty, 8825, Educational 8836, Fair 8844, Healthcare 8924, Hext 8933, Marcus 9037, McKee 9052, South 9209

Utah: Odyssey 9342, Slaughter, 9353

Vermont: Blittersdorf 9365, Stokes 9385

Virginia: Community 9426, **Delmar 9429**, **Dorothy-Ann 9433**, **Fund 9455**, Lane 9486, **Longview 9494**, Two 9544

Washington: Ferguson 9596, Foss 9598, **Ji 9632**, Jones 9638, Kawabe 9642, Northwest 9669, Skagit 9696, Tonkin 9715

West Virginia: Chambers 9742, Logan 9756

Wisconsin: **Dewing 9805**, Dudley 9811, Eau 9814, Hunt 9845, Inbusch 9847, Janesville 9850, Kenosha 9862, Lutsey 9873, Prescott 9905, Stateline 9937, T 9945

Wyoming: **Schultz 9986**, Scott 9988

Sponsorships

California: Farmers 496, First 506, Swinerton 1098, Synopsys 1100

Delaware: **TeleTech 1761**

Idaho: Boise 2666

Illinois: Walker 3308

Indiana: MutualBank 3421

Iowa: First 3493, GuideOne 3503, West 3547

Kansas: Payless 3614

Kentucky: Independence 3666, Stock 3697, Trim 3702

Maine: Franklin 3779

Massachusetts: Chicopee 4047, Dedham 4067, Easthampton 4076, OneBeacon 4231, Rockland 4267, Salem 4277

Michigan: Isabella 4468

Minnesota: Farmers 4679

Montana: Wendy's 5065

Nebraska: Ameritas 5067

Nevada: Dermody 5152, Pinnacle 5183

New Hampshire: Salem 5230

New Jersey: Amboy 5246, **Integra 5400**, Mamiye 5456

New York: American 5664, Cohoes 5865, Grand 6123, Raymond 6652, Sumitomo 6876

Pennsylvania: Baker 7851, Bon-Ton 7884, First 7997

Rhode Island: Kingsbury 8435, Sullivan 8494

Tennessee: HMA 8628, **Louisiana-Pacific 8644**

Texas: Boeing 8733, **Soonae 9208**

Washington: Korum 9648

Wisconsin: Modine 9889, Woodtrust-Bell 9963

Student aid

Alabama: Amos 4, Barkley 9, Blount 13, Hartselle 36, Hawkins 37, Sexton 63, Wallace 74

Alaska: Bristol 82, Chenega 83, Doyon 84, Gillam 85, Koniag 89, Samuelsen 91, UIC 92

Arizona: Grace 125, **Rosztoczy 161**, Smith 170, Sturges 176

Arkansas: Buck 192, McKinney 202, Murphy 207, Olds 210, Sturgis 217, Trinity 218, Union 219, Woodson 221

California: Alafi 235, Amador 238, Brooks 349, Butte 366, Community 421, Downey 460, Ebell 472, Hand 595, Harbison 597, Harris 601, **Hefferlin 610**, Hurliman 643, Kimbo 705, Maley-Thawley 787, McQuinn 820, Morgan 847, Ohana 876, Optivest 884, Pedrozzi 912, Pergo 915, San 997, SKB 1044, Sustainable 1096, **Trustees 1132**, Urbanek-Levy 1141, **Vogelzang 1146**, Weil 1163, **Williamson 1184**, Yen 1201, Zecca 1209, Zolla 1216

Colorado: Denver 1255

Connecticut: Ambler 1392, Cenveo 1416, Eder 1441, Fox 1453, Fraites 1454, Fuller 1460, Grampy's 1469, Hewitt 1482, O'Meara 1537, Thrall 1583

Delaware: Chaney 1640, De 1655, Gromet 1672, JBL 1686, Splawn 1749

District of Columbia: **Dingwall 1804**, Olender 1824

Florida: Beall, 1876, Blanton 1892, Charlotte 1938, Collins 1949, Epstein 1992, Erdle 1993, Fox 2016, Hand 2077, Haven 2085, Holopaw 2108, Jacobson 2124, King 2148, KML 2152, Lambrecht 2165, Martin 2196, Martin 2197, Morrison 2222, Mount 2223, Olliff 2239, **Prime 2268**, Riechmann 2286, Sample 2312, **Shepard 2331**, Sunburst 2359, Tampa 2362, Votum 2390

Georgia: Barnett 2441, Charter 2456, Churches 2461, Community 2466, Magnus 2543, Waffle 2602, Warren 2607

Hawaii: Epstein 2630, Fukunaga 2633, Gear 2634, Kaneta 2637, Straub 2649, Takitani 2650

Idaho: Mitchell 2680

Illinois: Aon 2710, Bulkley, 2765, Burgess 2767, Canterbury 2774, Christ 2788, Fildes 2872, Geneseo 2909, Griswold 2931, Groner 2932, Grossinger 2933, House 2980, Hurley 2985, Keller 3010, **Kobe 3024**, Kott 3027, **Lascaris 3040**, McCourtney 3087, McKee 3094, Munson 3130, Nayak 3133, O'Donnell 3150, Peters 3171, Rogers 3202, Rot 3212, Schaumburg 3223, Storer 3271, Taylor 3287, Ulm 3299, Wood 3329

Indiana: Benton 3344, Blackford 3346, Community 3359, Community 3360, Decatur 3367, Dubois 3370, Dye 3373, Fayette 3380, Fenech 3380, Hoch 3394, Huntington 3397, LaGrange 3412, Schergens 3443, Seymour 3448, TCU 3458, Thomasson 3459, Western 3466, Winchester 3469

Iowa: Bishop 3475, Duggan 3488, Iowa 3511, Iowa 3513, Jefferson 3514, Latta 3518, Schroeder 3533, Van 3539, Wood 3548

Kansas: Bane 3557, Davis 3571, French 3579, Golden 3582, Jellison 3589, O' 3612

Kentucky: Hayswood 3662, Horn 3664, Independence 3666, MGM 3678, Ogden 3683

Louisiana: Lang 3733, Meraux 3736

Maine: Davenport 3775, Franklin 3779, Oxford 3796, Protein 3799

Maryland: Adams 3808, Allemall 3811, Huether/McClelland 3884, Laughlin 3898

Massachusetts: Bushee 4032, D'Amour 4064, Edwards 4078, Egan 4080, Fassino 4086, Honey 4133, Hopedale 4134, Killam 4153, Mavrogenis 4192, Middlesex 4203, Mitchell 4205, Nye 4227, Permanent 4239, Pilgrim 4245, Quirico 4254, Rockland 4267, Smith 4299, Thoreau 4327, Trefler 4332, Van 4340, Young 4366

Michigan: Community 4410, Community 4411, Frankenmuth 4450, Johnson 4471, Juhl 4475, M 4497, Michigan 4514, Skandalaris 4571, Smith 4573, Tamer 4585, Tassell-Wisner-Bottrall 4587, Van 4601, Watson 4608, Wieczorek 4617

Minnesota: Cox 4662, Denfeld 4666, Granite 4699, Kinman-Oldfield 4723, Lane 4727, Rosen 4782, **Wagner 4804**

Mississippi: Day 4832, Skelton 4854

Missouri: Calkins 4881, Edgar 4899, Gilbert 4917, Griffin 4921, Guilander 4922, Kauffman 4934, King 4939, Peculiar 4978, Service 4998, Tension 5019, UMB 5026, Walker 5034, Wallace 5036

Montana: Cinnabar 5047, Hawkins 5055, Heisey 5056

Nebraska: Baright 5070, Hansen 5087, Hester 5091, Nebraska 5105, Pegler 5110, Steinhart 5121, Weller 5127, West 5128, York 5129

Nevada: Boyd 5141, Fishkin 5157, Meyer 5177, Western 5198

New Hampshire: Jameson 5215, Milford 5225, Woodbury 5238

New Jersey: Watts 5573, Wilson 5590

New Mexico: Carlsbad 5608, Continental 5612, Simon 5624, Taos 5626

New York: Beacon 5726, Bennett 5737, Bikuben 5746, **Buffalo 5799**, Burrows 5803, Colburn 5866, Community 5872, Desanctis, 5911, Fan 5985, Gaffney 6049, Glens 6082, Hadar 6154, Henshel 6192, Kautz 6290, **King 6311**, Lake 6360, **Nok 6537**, Northern 6540, Norwegian 6541, Norwich 6542, Ontario 6559, Post 6622, Potter 6623, Realty 6655, **Schepp 6739, Shatford 6788,** Snayberger 6817, **Societe 6820**, Stony 6868, **Youth 7013**, Zemsky 7022

North Carolina: Coffey 7078, Crawley 7082, Eddy 7087, Fairfield 7095, First 7097, Horvat 7130, Little 7162, London 7164, McNeil 7181, Moon 7187, Outer 7204, Schug 7237, Self 7238, Smith 7247, Stonecutter 7255, Towne 7268

Ohio: Bahmann 7313, **Brush 7338**, Bryan 7339, Callahan 7346, Cassner 7348, Community 7356, Community 7357, Defiance 7375, Gardner 7417, High 7449, Hughes 7458, Kincaid 7478, Lehman 7495, McCann 7518, Murphy 7533, Peoples 7546, Reynolds 7558, Rotterman 7564, Shinnick 7591, Throckmorton 7618, Trachsel 7620, Tuscarawas 7623, Tuscora 7624, Wilson 7641

Oklahoma: Faranna 7678, Martin, 7704, Thomas 7724, Wilson 7736

Oregon: Collins 7752, Daly 7756, Four 7764, Leonard 7789, Rietman 7809, Singer 7819, Watt 7825, Western 7829

Pennsylvania: Applestone 7841, Benz 7861, Berwind 7868, Bridge 7891, Broadbent 7895, Brossman 7900, Clareth 7924, Community 7933, Elk 7975, Ely 7979, **Epstein 7983**, Every 7986, Hassel 8042, Hill 8055, Hirtzel 8058, Lewis 8123, McKee 8160, McMannis 8163, Noll 8194, O'Brien-Veba 8197, Postles 8223, Schuylkill 8263, Shuman 8277, Singer 8279, Smith 8282, Society 8289, Vincent 8334, Williams 8359, Wolf 8363, Young 8375

Rhode Island: Brack 8392, Hosser 8424, Jackson 8427, Kelley 8431, Masonic 8449, Palermo 8466, Papitto 8467, Simionescu 8487, Thompson 8496

South Carolina: Bailey 8510, Horne 8528, Jackson 8529

South Dakota: Hatterscheidt 8566, Watertown 8576

Tennessee: Jewell 8633, Siegel 8674, Splawn 8677, Weiss 8684

Texas: Astin 8710, Brisley 8744, Broady 8745, Chambers 8767, Chaudhary 8768, Clifford 8774, Cogdell 8776, College 8779, Foundation 8870, Haraldson 8917, Hatfield 8922, Healthcare 8924, Hill 8937, Ilgenfritz 8960, Killson 8990, Kowitz 9002, Mantzel 9036, McMillan, 9054, Montgomery 9070, Montgomery, 9071, O'Neal 9097, **OneSight 9098**, Pearce 9121, Pipe 9130, Poncin 9134, Rawls 9143, Reilly 9148, **Ryrie 9169**, Santander 9173, Saunders 9176, Schwab-Rosenhouse 9184, Singleton 9197, Stanzel 9213, Texas 9231, Texas 9232, Woltman 9288

Utah: B. 9302, Keener 9332, Questar 9347

Virginia: **American 9386**, Bell 9394, **Foundation 9450**, Lee-Jackson 9488, Lincoln-Lane 9491, Wiley 9551, Womack 9556

Washington: Arise 9562, Baker 9566, Everett 9592, Gilmore 9605, Gius 9606, Kawabe 9642, Lauzier 9651, Maxwell 9661, **Rotalia 9685**, Tudor 9717, Welch 9721, Worthington 9729

West Virginia: Bowen 9736, Bowen 9737, Bowers 9738, Burnside 9740, Carter 9741, Fine 9745, Hollandsworth 9750, McCormick 9758, Minor 9761, Price 9763, Stout 9769, Vecellio 9770, Wolfe 9772

Wisconsin: AnnMarie 9774, Ariens 9776, Brillion 9789, Carlisle 9792, Fahrney 9818, Fromm 9823, Jacobus 9849, Johnson 9853, Kohl 9865, Marshfield 9878, Nelson 9894, Smith 9931, Sonnentag 9934, Trek 9948

Wyoming: Perkins 9982

System and operational improvements

Florida: **Atlantis 1858**

Massachusetts: Middlesex 4203

New Jersey: **Rippel 5510**

Vermont: **Maverick 9380**

Washington: Jefferson 9630

Systems reform

District of Columbia: **Butler 1792**

Florida: Couch 1953

Maryland: **Braitmayer 3827**

New York: Willmott 6978

Texas: McLaughlin 9053

Technical assistance

Alabama: Black 12, Ireland 39

California: Amador 238, Buell 357, Community 421, Fox 523, Fox 525, Gellert 550, **Global 565**, Heller 613, Jamieson 658, **Lloyd 763**, McKay 815, McLean 817, Wharton 1178

Colorado: Donnell-Kay 1258, Leighty 1311, Vradenburg 1374, Warner 1376

Connecticut: Proctor 1545

Delaware: Thronson 1766

District of Columbia: Jovid 1817

Florida: Lazarus 2172, **Mukti 2226**, Ray 2275

Georgia: Athens 2437, Lee 2540

Illinois: McGraw 3092

Indiana: Bussing-Koch 3353, Community 3359, Community 3360, Decatur 3367, Dubois 3370, Huntington 3397, LaGrange 3412, Raymond 3436, Rush 3441

Kentucky: Public 3687

Maryland: Biophilia 3824

Massachusetts: **Kahn 4143**, Kelsey 4148, Middlesex 4203, United 4337, Xeric 4365

Michigan: Branch 4396, Community 4411, M 4497

Minnesota: **Sundance 4796, Trust 4802, Winds 4820**

Mississippi: Lower 4847

Montana: Cora 5048

Nebraska: Midlands 5104

Nevada: Meyer 5177

New Hampshire: McIninch 5224

New Jersey: Westfield 5582, WKBJ 5592

New Mexico: Carlsbad 5608, Con 5611, **Watersheds 5628**

New York: Abelard 5635, American 5662, **Cogitare 5855**, Hoyt 6230, Initial 6245, Marble 6441, O'Grady 6551, Ong 6558, **Posner-Wallace 6621, Sparkplug 6830**, Yoreinu 7010

North Carolina: Eddy 7087, Meserve 7182, Outer 7204

Ohio: Athens 7311, Bahmann 7313, Bryan 7339, Defiance 7375, Foundation 7408, Homan 7451, McMaster 7521

Oklahoma: Cherokee 7666, Merrick 7707

Oregon: Elwood 7761, Holzman 7775, Portland 7807

Pennsylvania: Brooks 7899, Chase 7921, Community 7933, Hoffman 8062, **KL 8094**, Schuylkill 8263, Tuttleman 8325

Tennessee: Durham 8608

Texas: **Chrest 8770**, Dougherty, 8825, Hext 8933

Vermont: Castanea 9368

Virginia: **Longview 9494**

Washington: Ferguson 9596, Foss 9598, Murray 9667

West Virginia: Chambers 9742

Wisconsin: Dudley 9811, Eau 9814, Jacobus 9849, Marshfield 9878

Translation

Pennsylvania: Blue 7879

Undergraduate support

Connecticut: Fuller 1460

Volunteer development

California: San 997

Delaware: Cammarota 1637

Hawaii: Wong 2657

Iowa: Schildberg 3532

Louisiana: Powers 3746, Whitman 3759

Michigan: Roscommon 4552

North Carolina: Richardson 7221

Pennsylvania: Lewis 8124, Stewart, 8302

South Carolina: Near 8536

Tennessee: Powell 8661

Virginia: Greensville 9464, Houff 9473

SUBJECT INDEX

List of terms: Terms used in this index conform to the Foundation Center's Philanthropy Classification System's comprehensive subject area coding scheme. The alphabetical list below represents the complete list of subject terms found in this edition. "See also" references to related subject areas are also provided as an additional aid in accessing the giving interests of foundations in this volume.

Index: In the index itself, foundation entries are arranged under each term by state location, abbreviated name, and sequence number. Foundations in boldface type make grants on a national or international basis. The others generally limit giving to the state or city in which they are located.

Abortion
Abuse prevention
Academic libraries
Addiction services
Adolescent parenting
Adolescents
Adoption
Adult and child mentoring
Adult day care
Adult education
Adult literacy
Adults
Aerospace engineering
Agricultural cooperatives
Agricultural education
Agriculture
Agriculture for youth
Air quality
Alaskan Natives
Alcoholism
ALS
Alumni relations
Alzheimer's disease
American football
American Indians
Animal rescue and rehabilitation
Animal therapy
Animal training
Animal welfare
Anthropology
Antidiscrimination
Aquariums
Aquatic wildlife protection
Archaeology
Architecture
Archives and special collections
Arms control
Art and music therapy
Art conservation
Art museums
Arthritis
Artist's services
Artists and performers
Arts and culture
Arts councils
Arts education
Arts exchange

Arts services
Asthma
Astronomy
Autism
Automotive safety
Ballet
Baptist
Baptists
Baseball and softball
Basic and emergency aid
Basic and remedial instruction
Basketball
Bereavement counseling
Biochemistry
Biodiversity
Bioethics
Biology
Biomedicine
Bird preservation
Blood banks
Boating
Botanical gardens
Botany
Brain and nervous system disorders
Breast cancer
Buddhism
Business and industry
Business education
Business promotion
Camps
Cancers
Capital punishment
Catholicism
Catholics
Cemeteries and burial services
Ceramic arts
Cerebral palsy
Charter school education
Chemistry
Child abuse
Child advocacy
Child care
Child development
Child educational development
Child welfare
Childbirth
Children

Children and youth
Children's hospital care
Children's museums
Children's rights
Choreography
Christian Science
Christianity
Christians
Civic participation
Civics for youth
Climate change
Communication media
Community and economic development
Community beautification
Community college education
Community health care
Community improvement
Community mental health care
Community organizing
Community recreation
Community service
Community service for youth
Composition
Computer science
Conservative Judaism
Construction
Consumer protection
Continuing education
Convalescent care
Cooperative education
Coral reefs
Corrections and penology
Counterterrorism
Courts
Crime prevention
Crisis intervention
Cultural awareness
Cystic fibrosis
Dance
Democracy and civil society development
Dental care
Depression
Design
Developmental disability services
Diabetes
Digestive system diseases
Dining services

Disaster relief
Disasters and emergency management
Diseases and conditions
Diversity and intergroup relations
Domestic violence
Domestic violence shelters
Domesticated animals
Down syndrome
Drawing
Dropouts
Ear, nose and throat diseases
Early childhood education
Ecology
Economic development
Economically disadvantaged people
Economics
Economics for youth
Education
Education services
Educational exchanges
Educational management
Elementary and secondary education
Elementary education
Emergency care
Emergency medical services
Employment
Endangered species protection
Energy resources
Engineering
Entrepreneurship
Environment
Environmental and resource rights
Environmental education
Environmental justice
Environmental studies
Epilepsy
Episcopalianism and Anglicanism
Equal opportunity in education
Equestrianism
ESL and second language acquisition
Ethnic and racial groups
Ethnic museums
European football
Ex-offenders
Exercise
Eye diseases
Families
Family counseling
Family disability resources
Family planning
Family services
Farmlands
Female adults
Female children and youth
Female infants and toddlers
Female seniors
Female young adults
Females
Festivals
Film and video
Financial counseling
Fire prevention and control
First aid training
Fishing and hunting
Floods
Folk arts
Food aid
Food banks
Food delivery
Food security
Foreign policy
Forest preservation
Foster and adoptive children
Foster care

Foundations
Free goods distribution
Freedom of association and expression
Freedom of information
Freedom of religion
Gardening
Gay men
Genealogy
Genetic conditions and birth defects
Geology
Geriatrics
Gerontology
Gift distribution
Gifted education
Golf
Goodwill promotion
Graduate and professional education
Green building
Group homes
Health
Health care access
Health care administration and financing
Health care clinics
Health care financing
Health insurance
Heart and circulatory system diseases
Hematology
Hemophilia
High school equivalency
Higher education
Hinduism
Historic preservation
Historical activities
History
History museums
HIV/AIDS
Holistic medicine
Home health care
Home ownership
Home repairs
Homeless people
Homeless services
Homeless shelters
Hospice care
Hospital care
Housing development
Housing for the homeless
Housing rehabilitation
Housing services
Human rights
Human services
Human services management
Humane education
Humanities
Immigrant rights
Immigrants
Immigrants and migrants
Immune system diseases
Immunology
Impaired driving
In-patient medical care
Incarcerated people
Independent living for people with disabilities
Indigenous peoples
Individual liberties
Infant care
Infants and toddlers
Infectious and parasitic diseases
Interdisciplinary studies
Interfaith
Intergenerational mentoring
Internal medicine
International development
International exchange

International peace and security
International relations
International studies
Internet
Islam
Jewish people
Job counseling
Job creation and workforce development
Job training
Judaism
Kidney diseases
Land resources
Languages
Law
Law education
Leadership development
Learning disorders
Legal aid
Legal services
Lesbians
Leukemia
LGBTQ people
LGBTQ rights
Libraries
Linguistics
Literature and writing
Liver diseases
Livestock and ranching
Low-income and poor people
Lung cancer
Lutheranism
Lutherans
Malaria
Male adults
Male children and youth
Male infants and toddlers
Male young adults
Males
Manufacturing
Marine science
Maritime museums
Marriage equality
Maternal and perinatal health
Mathematics
Medical counseling
Medical education
Medical specialties
Medical support services
Mental and behavioral disorders
Mental health care
Mental health counseling
Methodism
Microfinance
Middle school education
Migrant workers
Military personnel
Minority rights
Missing persons
Mormonism
Multilateral cooperation
Multiple sclerosis
Muscular dystrophy
Musculoskeletal diseases
Museums
Music
Musical ensembles and groups
Musical theater
National defense
National security
Natural history museums
Natural resources
Neighborhood associations
Neurology
News and public information

Non-natural disasters
Nonprofits
Nursing care
Nursing homes
Nutrition
Obesity
Oceans and coastal waters
Offenders
Olympics
Oncology
Opera
Orchestral music
Organ and tissue banks
Organic farming
Organized labor
Orphanages
Orthodox Christianity
Orthodox Judaism
Orthopedics
Out-of-home youth
Out-patient medical care
Painting
Pancreatic cancer
Parent education
Parent-teacher involvement
Parents
Parkinson's disease
Parks
Patient social services
Patient-centered care
Pediatrics
People of East Asian descent
People of African descent
People of Asian descent
People of Latin American descent
People with disabilities
People with hearing impairments
People with HIV/AIDS
People with intellectual disabilities
People with physical disabilities
People with psychosocial disabilities
People with vision impairments
Performing arts
Performing arts education
Pharmacies
Pharmacology
Philanthropy
Philosophy
Photography
Physical and earth sciences
Physical fitness
Physical therapy
Physics
Planetariums
Plant biodiversity
Police agencies
Political organizations
Political science
Population studies
Prenatal care
Presbyterianism
Preventive care
Printmaking
Prostate cancer
Protestantism
Protestants
Psychology and behavioral science
Public administration
Public affairs
Public health

Public housing
Public interest law
Public libraries
Public policy
Public transportation
Public utilities
Public/private ventures
Publishing
Racquet sports
Radio
Reading promotion
Reconstructive surgery
Recycling
Reform Judaism
Rehabilitation
Rehabilitation of offenders
Religion
Religion for youth
Renewable energy
Rent and mortgage assistance
Reproductive health care
Reproductive rights
Research on animals
Residential mental health care
Respiratory system diseases
Retired people
Retirement housing
Right to free movement and asylum
Right to life
Rivers and lakes
Rural development
Safety education
School athletics
School libraries and media centers
School-based health care
Science
Science museums
Scouting programs
Sculpture
Search and rescue
Secondary education
Senior assisted living
Senior services
Seniors
Services for offenders
Sexual abuse
Sexual assault victim services
Sexual education
Sexually transmitted disease control
Shelter and residential care
Shintoism
Single parent support
Single parents
Skin conditions
Slum youth
Smoking
Social enterprise
Social sciences
Sociology
Sororities and fraternities
Special needs education
Special Olympics
Special population support
Specialty hospital care
Speech and hearing rehabilitation
Spinal cord injuries and diseases
Spirituality
Spoken word
Sport and hobby museums
Sports

Sports and recreation
Sports training
STEM education
Storms
Stress
Student retention
Student services
Substance abuse prevention
Substance abuse treatment
Substance abusers
Suicide crisis intervention
Sustainable agriculture
Sustainable development
Swimming
Teacher education
Technology
Telecommunications
Television
Temporary accommodations
Terminally ill people
Theater
Theology
Toxic substance control
Track and field
Transgender people
Tribal and indigenous religions
Undergraduate education
Unemployed people
University education
Unknown or not classified
Urban development
Vegetarianism
Venture philanthropy
Veterans
Veterinary medicine
Victim aid
Victims of crime and abuse
Victims of disaster
Vision care
Visual arts
Vocal music
Vocational education
Vocational post-secondary education
Vocational rehabilitation
Vocational secondary education
Voluntarism
War memorials
Water conservation
Water pollution
Water resources
Water sports
Wetlands
Wildfires
Wildlife biodiversity
Wildlife rehabilitation
Wildlife sanctuaries
Winter sports
Women's rights
Women's services
Women's studies
Young adults
Youth development
Youth mentoring
Youth organizing
Youth pregnancy prevention
Youth services
Zoology
Zoos

Abortion

Illinois: Frankel 2886
New York: Anderson-Rogers 5676, Rothblum 6701
Ohio: Alpaugh 7302

Abuse prevention

California: Altos 237
Florida: Couch 1953
Illinois: Allen-Heath 2701
New Jersey: **Knistrom 5426**
Texas: Petty 9126
Washington: Foss 9598

Academic libraries

California: Frankel 526
Connecticut: Vance 1591
Illinois: Brooker 2758
Maryland: Cafritz 3830
Massachusetts: Ragon 4256

Addiction services

California: Codding 412, Shannon 1030, Stauffer 1076
District of Columbia: Himmelfarb 1815
Florida: Bastien 1872, Foulds 2014, Janke 2126
Illinois: Pitzman 3177, Rosen 3206
Kentucky: Abercrombie 3645
Louisiana: Dujay 3722
Massachusetts: Alden 3999
Michigan: Community 4411, M 4497
Nebraska: Patrick 5109
New Jersey: Welch 5579
New York: Maher 6433, Northern 6540
Ohio: Ridgecliff 7560, Woodruff 7645
Oklahoma: Liddell 7697
Pennsylvania: Blue 7879, McManus 8164, Union 8326
Texas: Dick 8815, King 8994, Strickland 9224
Utah: Steiner 9358
Wisconsin: **Helios 9838**

Adolescent parenting

California: Bear 288
New York: Mertz 6481
Texas: Levy 9014

Adolescents

Alabama: Black 12, Ireland 39
California: Five 509, Flicker 511, Foundation 521, Frome 535, Gellert 550, Legacy 740, Mazda 810, Nicholson 866, Palo 900, **Quiksilver 945**, Solano 1063, Stauffer 1077, Sterling 1081, **Wakerly 1150**
Colorado: Donnell-Kay 1258
Connecticut: DeLuca 1431, Fippinger 1450, Fry 1458
Delaware: **TeleTech 1761**
District of Columbia: Freeman 1808, Jovid 1817, Replogle 1831
Florida: Cape 1917
Georgia: TALX 2592, Waffle 2602
Idaho: Boise 2666, Whittenberger 2689
Illinois: Chicago 2787, Family 2864, Meyer 3106, Roberts 3199
Indiana: Community 3359, Community 3361, Fayette 3379
Kansas: Insurance 3587
Kentucky: Killian 3670
Louisiana: Crossroads 3719
Maryland: Youth 3991
Massachusetts: Chicopee 4047, Kelsey 4148, MENTOR 4199

Michigan: Buffalo 4399, Community 4410, M 4497, Mackinac 4499, Stoker 4580, Tuscola 4598
Minnesota: Avocet 4631, Bell 4637, Larsen 4728, Sacred 4783, **Sundance 4796**
Missouri: **Bohm 4871**, Canfield 4882, Dunn 4898, MFA 4960
New Jersey: Freelander 5353, Kerney 5419, Waldis 5569
New Mexico: Con 5611
New York: **Grossman 6146**, Henshel 6192, Kenworthy 6300, Nets 6524, Ostgrodd 6561, **Schmeelk 6742**, Washington 6946
North Carolina: Glenn 7111, Strowd 7258
Ohio: Barron 7316, Brethen 7331, **Brush 7338**, Cleveland 7354, Community 7356, Community 7357, Sandfair 7569, Walker 7630
Oregon: Elwood 7761, Wessinger 7826
Pennsylvania: Brinkman 7893, Child 7923, CNB 7929, Hartfield 8041, Ludwick 8134, Maslow 8146, McKee 8160, Murphy 8185
Tennessee: **Fugitive 8618**, Gaylord 8620
Texas: B.E.L.I.E.F. 8713, **Chrest 8770**, Foundation 8869, Ligon-Lamsam 9018, Strickland 9224
Vermont: Stokes 9385
Virginia: **Delmar 9429**
Washington: DeFalco 9585, Everett 9592, Foss 9598
Wisconsin: Hamilton 9834, Jacobus 9849, Lakeview 9868, Marshfield 9878, Stateline 9937

Adoption

Arkansas: Families 196
California: Massie 806
Florida: **Posnack 2262**, SBJ 2314
Massachusetts: Alden 3999
Michigan: Speckhard-Knight 4574
Minnesota: Sauer 4785
Montana: Wendy's 5065
New York: White 6972, Zyman 7036
North Carolina: Bertsch 7050
Oregon: Ackley 7740
Pennsylvania: Gauss 8014
Texas: Freed 8873, **Soonae 9208**, Swett 9227
Utah: CASA 9312
Washington: Gibson 9604

Adult and child mentoring

Arizona: Clark 106, Massie 146
California: Eriksen 484, Evans 486, Phillips 924
Delaware: Russell 1735, **TeleTech 1761**
Florida: Five 2002, Gate 2034
Hawaii: Locations 2638
Illinois: Best 2739, Doyle 2836, Gardner 2904
Indiana: Magee-O'Connor 3414, Mulzer 3420
Kentucky: Spriggs 3695
Louisiana: Lake 3732
Maryland: Loats 3902
Massachusetts: Dwyer 4074
Missouri: Darr 4893, Kemper 4935, Portman 4981
Montana: Dousman 5049
Nevada: Banks 5135
New Jersey: Olsen 5480
New York: Nets 6524, Siegel 6797
Oklahoma: Howard 7688
Pennsylvania: American 7839, Patterson 8205, Teleflex 8314
Rhode Island: Mulligan 8457
Texas: Knox 8999, Sanguinetti 9172
Utah: Cumming 9315
Wisconsin: Manitowoc 9876, Sonnentag 9934

Adult day care

Connecticut: Schloss 1562

Ohio: Klock 7480
Wisconsin: Jones 9855

Adult education

Alabama: Dixon 26
Connecticut: Donchian 1440
Florida: Couch 1953, Swisher 2361
Illinois: **Appleby 2711**, Heath 2962
Kentucky: **Magee 3674**, Namaste 3682
Massachusetts: Middlesex 4203
Michigan: Buhr 4400
Minnesota: Bell 4638
New Jersey: Carlozzi 5287
New York: Greenspan 6134, Initial 6245
Oregon: Merlo 7797
Pennsylvania: Kazanjian 8090
Rhode Island: Kingsbury 8435
Texas: South 9209

Adult literacy

California: Atkinson 259
Minnesota: G&K 4691

Adults

Alabama: Black 12, Ireland 39
Arizona: F2 117
Arkansas: Olds 210
California: **Cantor 375**, Gellert 550, **Hefferlin 610**, LEF 739
Colorado: **Fishback 1270**
District of Columbia: Jovid 1817, Patterson 1826
Florida: Landwirth 2167, Mount 2223
Georgia: Abreu 2431
Illinois: Chicago 2787, Family 2864, Meyer 3106
Indiana: Seymour 3448
Iowa: Iowa 3513
Kentucky: Killian 3670
Michigan: Tuscola 4598
Minnesota: Larsen 4728
New Jersey: A 5240
North Carolina: Glenn 7111
Ohio: Bahmann 7313, **Brush 7338**, **Katz 7475**, Philada 7548, Ridgecliff 7560
Oregon: Elwood 7761
Pennsylvania: Hoffman 8062
South Carolina: Lutz 8533
Tennessee: **Fugitive 8618**
Texas: Foundation 8869
Virginia: **Brown 9407**, **Delmar 9429**
Wisconsin: Hamilton 9834, Inbusch 9847, Marshfield 9878

Aerospace engineering

Alaska: Alaska 80
California: Braddock 336
Florida: **Aviation 1861**
Missouri: Saks 4990
North Carolina: Davis 7084
Texas: Heinlein 8927, Thompson 9234

Agricultural cooperatives

Wisconsin: Blooming 9784

Agricultural education

California: Pearlstein 911
Massachusetts: Kidder 4152

Agriculture

Alabama: Strain 68
Arizona: Williams-Malone 183
Arkansas: Blue 189
California: Anderson 243, Archer 250, Barnett 278, Bellwether 299, Bridges 342, Child 394, Church 403, Fast 498, Fremont 527, Griswold 586, Heck 609, JTB 679, Kinsey 707, Latkin 731, McClatchy 811, Mudd 851, Nell 859, Smythe 1061, Stone 1085, Wheeler 1179
Delaware: Burt's 1635
District of Columbia: Dickson 1802
Florida: Chaffiot 1933, Chardonnay 1936, Concourse 1950, Focus 2004, Frankle 2019, Hegamyer 2087, KT 2160
Georgia: Connolly 2467, Irving 2521
Idaho: Beckman 2665
Illinois: Baum 2727, Ingredion 2987, Koch 3025, Miller, 3113, O'C 3148, Sue 3275, Ulm 3299
Indiana: Lafayette 3411
Iowa: Iowa 3511, **World 3550**
Kentucky: Trim 3702
Maine: Bailey 3765, Brook 3769
Maryland: Croft 3841
Massachusetts: Brooks 4028, Codman 4052, Ledgeways 4171, OneBeacon 4231, Prokopis 4248, Thee 4324, Vela 4341
Michigan: Roscommon 4552, Stone 4581
Minnesota: Dyer 4669, Farmers 4679, Getsch 4695, HJ 4714, Rose 4781, Rosen 4782
Missouri: Barrows 4864, Bartlett 4865, Cinmar 4887, Mineral 4961, Stern 5013, Todd 5022
Nevada: Joshua 5167
New Hampshire: Noah 5226
New Jersey: Avalo 5254, Broad 5272, Degnan 5315, D'Onofrio 5324, Perricone 5497
New Mexico: Chamiza 5609, Schnieders 5623
New York: Buchalter 5796, G&A 6048, Galvan 6053, Garman 6058, Hauff 6177, Hogan 6217, **Jabara 6254**, Mere 6476, Suwinski 6885
North Carolina: Fox 7103, Griffin 7113, Miller 7185
North Dakota: Myra 7297
Ohio: Bryan 7339, Fortney 7406, Geotrac 7422, Manley 7512, Reynolds 7559, Sterling 7606
Oklahoma: Drabek 7673, Tandy 7723, Wegener 7731
Oregon: Kinnie 7783, Schmidt 7813
Pennsylvania: Blue 7880, Crawford 7944, Dominion 7961, Fierce 7992, Martin 8142, McSwigan 8165, Pittsburgh 8215, Wolgin 8365
Rhode Island: Frasch 8408, Fuller 8409, Unfi 8498, Wells 8501
South Carolina: Childress 8518, T-Bonz 8546
Tennessee: Goodlett 8623, LifeWorks 8643
Texas: Alexander 8695, Bee 8723, Dallas 8795, Genovese 8887, Jamail 8965, Jessen 8968, McMillan, 9054, Nuncio 9092, Paris 9114, Quanex 9141, Roberts 9155, Wheeler 9274
Vermont: Huntington 9376, Leboeuf 9379, NSB 9382
Virginia: Camp 9413
Washington: Dunn 9589, Hagan 9612, Loeb 9654
Wisconsin: Mielcarek 9888
Wyoming: Storer 9992

Agriculture for youth

Arkansas: Riggs 214
Iowa: Beckwith 3473
Missouri: Litton 4946
Ohio: Bryan 7339

Air quality

New York: Indus 6243
Texas: Dedman, 8808

Alaskan Natives

Alaska: Bristol 82, Koniag 89

Alcoholism

California: Von 1147
Colorado: Comprecare 1249
Connecticut: Bantle 1401
Florida: Bastien 1872, Dyer 1985
Illinois: Cremer 2815, Hess 2969, MacDonald 3068
Massachusetts: Stearns 4310
Minnesota: Walker 4805, Whitney 4817
Ohio: Andrews 7307, Woodruff 7645
Pennsylvania: McManus 8164
Texas: Waggoners 9255
Wisconsin: Steinle 9938

ALS

Florida: **Safenowitz 2307**
Illinois: Haarlow 2940
Maryland: Franey 3865
Massachusetts: Deane 4066
Minnesota: Wiehoff 4818
New York: Libby 6395
Pennsylvania: Betz 7870, Charlestein 7920

Alumni relations

California: Brooks-Mathews 350
New York: Pohly-Turaj 6613
Oklahoma: Jirous 7690
Pennsylvania: Schoonmaker 8260
Texas: Johnson 8969, Muse 9080

Alzheimer's disease

Arizona: Clark 106
California: Brown 353, **Chan 388**, Eichenberg-Larson 474, Johnson 667, Levin 749, Malachowsky 786, Smullin 1060
Connecticut: Kay 1496
Delaware: Ryerson 1736
Florida: Capital 1918, Coulter-Jones 1954, KLM 2151, Peyton 2258, Wolf 2410
Georgia: Belcher, 2444, Hurlbert 2516, SF 2585
Illinois: Carter 2776, Eckert 2843, Eisenberg 2850, Gassin 2906, Goodstein 2924, Stone 3269
Indiana: Milton 3418
Maine: Borman 3767
Massachusetts: Deane 4066
Michigan: Nartel 4521, Sinai 4570, Zimmerman 4620
Minnesota: McNamara 4743
Missouri: Simmons 5005
New Jersey: Paragano 5488
New Mexico: Bennett 5607
New York: Boxer 5772, Czap 5891, Mule 6515
North Carolina: Schmidt 7236
Oklahoma: Merkel 7706
Pennsylvania: Grumbacher 8028, Sharp 8272, Sidewater 8278, Somerville 8291
Rhode Island: Jacbel 8426
Tennessee: Monday 8652
Texas: Holloway 8946
Wisconsin: Wagner 9955

American football

California: Bialis 313, Witter 1192
Kansas: Weber 3640
Michigan: Buffalo 4399, Roscommon 4552
New Jersey: Giants 5369

American Indians

Alabama: Black 12, Ireland 39
Alaska: Chenega 83, Doyon 84, Koniag 89
California: Frome 535, LEF 739
Colorado: Warner 1376
Connecticut: Fippinger 1450
District of Columbia: Jovid 1817
Illinois: Roberti 3198
Iowa: **Wahlert 3544**
Minnesota: Bell 4638, Grotto 4702

Montana: Foundation 5051
Nebraska: Midlands 5104
New Jersey: Waters 5571
New Mexico: Chamiza 5609, Con 5611
New York: Henshel 6192, **Sparkplug 6830**
North Carolina: Meyer 7183
Utah: Callister 9310, Wadman 9362
Virginia: **Delmar 9429**
Wyoming: Cutting 9968

Animal rescue and rehabilitation

Missouri: **Build-A-Bear 4879**
New Jersey: Smith 5539
New York: Giant 6077
Virginia: Wiser 9555

Animal therapy

Missouri: **Build-A-Bear 4879**

Animal training

California: Lambert 728, Miller 833
Idaho: Hare 2675
Illinois: McCune 3089
Michigan: Roscommon 4552
Pennsylvania: Bannerot-Lappe 7854

Animal welfare

Alabama: Brinkley 15
Arizona: Cadeau 104, McKee 148, MCS 149, O'Rielly 154
California: Ady 233, Ark 251, Baker 265, Broad 347, Brown 353, Bucolo 356, Ceunis 385, Chrissie's 399, Cole 415, Corwin 428, Crummer 436, Dahl 439, Deacon 447, Dmarlou 455, Dyer 469, Fox 525, Friend 532, GAT 549, HunterWard 641, Kieve 703, **Kinnoull 706**, Lambert 728, Lewis 753, Muckel 850, On 880, Pralle 933, Resource 965, Ridder 970, **Sargent 1005**, **Skyscrape 1047**, Smith 1056, Tippett 1119, Tobey 1121, Weisz 1167
Colorado: Clough 1248, Dea 1254, Hoag 1293
Connecticut: Alpha/Omega 1391, Baggins 1398, Kaman 1493, Schwerin 1563
Delaware: 1916 1605, Ryerson 1736, Swift, 1754
District of Columbia: Woodward 1839
Florida: Bastien 1872, Becker 1879, Brown 1904, Brown 1905, Carrington 1923, Case 1925, Charlotte 1938, Crane 1955, Foulds 2014, Hoerner 2102, Jelks 2128, Kehrer 2143, Knopf 2155, Lelash 2178, Morningstar 2218, Pearle 2253, Peterson 2257, Sammons 2310, Samowitz 2311, Sender 2323, **Taylor 2365**
Georgia: **Gage 2482**, Illges 2518, Looney 2542, Marshall 2545, Neuhoff 2556, Orkin 2560, Stahl 2588
Hawaii: Castle 2626, Shields 2647
Idaho: Dumke 2668, Troxell 2688, Wishnick 2690
Illinois: Bendich 2733, Caccomo 2771, D.A.S. 2820, Delavan 2825, Dubin 2838, Gardner 2904, Hirschmann 2972, MacDonald 3068, McCormack 3086, McCrea 3088, Millard 3109, Petrick 3173, Powell 3183, Reed 3191, Rosenthal 3210, Staley 3264
Indiana: Community 3359, Fayette 3379, Hulman 3396
Kansas: Family 3575, Williams 3643
Kentucky: Dickins 3651, Mulhollem 3680
Louisiana: Crossroads 3719
Maine: Narragansett 3794, Planet 3797
Maryland: Barton 3819, Schuh 3946, Wallis 3977
Massachusetts: Allison 4000, Archibald 4005, Cabot 4034, Fraser 4097, Morse 4210, **Pegasus 4236**, Red 4260, Shattuck 4291, Singing 4297, Van 4340, Wheatland 4358
Michigan: Burt 4403, Delong-Sweet 4427, Foren 4448, Kellogg 4482, Main 4501, Roscommon 4552
Missouri: Cray 4890, Deliniere 4894, Melcher 4957, Walton 5037

Nebraska: Ameritas 5067, Grewcock 5086, Mapes 5103, Quivey-Bay 5113, Reynolds 5114, Springer 5120
Nevada: Castleman 5144, Close 5148, Larson 5170
New Jersey: Frog 5357, Gauntt 5365, Hanafin 5381, Knight 5425, Onyx 5482, Schlaffer 5522, Staats 5549, Wetterberg 5583
New York: Anderson-Rogers 5676, Baobab 5711, Barbash 5714, Bloomberg 5761, Bothmer 5768, Brand 5776, CAL 5808, Double-R 5927, Ellsworth 5957, Enders 5963, Fein 5992, Follett 6016, Giant 6077, Goldberg 6090, Hahn 6156, Hallingby 6160, Krimendahl/Saint-Amand 6346, Krumholz 6349, Levine 6386, Lufkin 6421, McCarthy 6456, Meier 6470, Northern 6540, Norwich 6542, Peterson 6591, Schweitzer 6759, Sidewalk 6796, Stebbins 6850
North Carolina: Balin 7042, Emma 7091, **Firth 7098**, **Laffin 7157**, Mattison 7175, Meyer 7183, Oschwald 7203, Rolla 7230, Schmidt 7236, Wann 7279
Ohio: Alpaugh 7302, Athens 7311, Gimbel 7424, Haskell 7439, **Katz 7475**, O'Neill 7542, Shannon 7586, Thompson, 7617
Oklahoma: Lockhart 7699
Oregon: Coit 7751
Pennsylvania: Ames 7840, Bannerot-Lappe 7854, Boardman 7881, Boudinot 7888, Burket-Plack 7906, Carita 7915, Clovis 7928, Coffin 7930, Everard 7985, Giop 8018, Goshen 8025, Lamb 8106, Mattingly 8151, McConnell 8154, Schautz 8257, Schuylkill 8263, Seebe 8268, Sharp 8272, Tabas 8312, Tippins 8318
Rhode Island: Coes 8396, Crossman 8399, Johnson 8430, Kimball 8434, Kingsbury 8435
South Carolina: Verhagen 8547
Tennessee: Pedigree 8657
Texas: Bridge 8742, Cemo 8765, Conley 8784, Damuth 8796, Ethel 8842, Knox 8999, McCarty 9047, Petty 9126, Richter 9153, Stevenson 9220, Thompson 9234
Utah: Benjamin 9305, Slaughter, 9353
Vermont: Redducs 9383
Virginia: Breeden, 9404, Ochsman 9504, Peachtree 9508, Treakle 9543, Two 9544
Washington: Fries-Tait 9599, Hyde 9627, Nysether 9671
West Virginia: Driehorst 9743, Hewgill 9748
Wisconsin: Kloss 9863

Anthropology

California: Lemelson 742
New York: Persian 6589

Antidiscrimination

Alabama: Abroms 2
California: Evans 486
Illinois: Bernoudy 2738, Lehman-Stamm 3045, Minor 3117, Rothman 3213
New York: 1848 5629, Abelard 5635, **Eastman 5940**, Grodzins 6141
Oregon: **Conklin 7754**
Pennsylvania: **Cohn 7931**
Virginia: Andreas 9388

Aquariums

Delaware: Selin 1742
Illinois: Bellebyron 2731
Maryland: Beaufort 3820, RCM 3937
Massachusetts: PerkinElmer 4238
New York: JI 6260, Lehman 6375, Young 7012
Ohio: Williamson 7640
Texas: McAllister 9046
Virginia: MAIHS 9497, Mullen 9502
Washington: Bishop 9569, DeFalco 9585, Ferguson 9596

Aquatic wildlife protection

California: **PADI 898**
Connecticut: Acorn 1385
Massachusetts: **New 4220**
Montana: Cinnabar 5047
New Jersey: Pheasant 5499
New York: Henderson 6189, Kleinschmidt 6326, Maher 6434
Pennsylvania: Brooks 7899
Wyoming: Marine 9980

Archaeology

Illinois: Jahn 2992, Minow 3118
Indiana: Mothershead 3419
Michigan: Community 4411, Mackinac 4499
New York: Persian 6589
Ohio: Fleischmann 7404, Haskell 7439
Texas: **Caritas 8763**

Architecture

California: Joy 677, LEF 739, **Reddy 958**
Massachusetts: **Bruner 4030**
New York: Hohmann 6218
Ohio: Montauk 7531
Pennsylvania: Mills 8174
Rhode Island: Felicia 8406

Archives and special collections

California: Evening 487, Martin 800
Colorado: Brown 1243, Krieble 1308
Delaware: Fernandina 1663
Florida: Zehnder 2423
Illinois: Franklin 2888, Gibbet 2912
Maryland: Minkoff 3915
Massachusetts: **Blossom 4022**
Missouri: Sappington 4992
Nebraska: Scribante 5116
New York: Cullman 5887
North Carolina: Rocky 7227
Pennsylvania: Hawksglen 8045, Randall 8230, Up 8327
South Carolina: Cato 8516
Texas: Lupton 9028

Arms control

Colorado: Warner 1376
Florida: Oristano 2241
Illinois: MacDonald 3068
Maryland: Weiss 3982
New York: **Eastman 5940**
Vermont: Block 9366

Art and music therapy

Texas: Levy 9014

Art conservation

New York: Coby 5852

Art museums

Alabama: Pei-Ling 52
Arizona: Hughes 130, McKee 148, Murphey 151
California: Bancroft-Clair 270, Brooks-Mathews 350, Cheeryble 390, Davies 444, Evans 485, Family 492, Handley 596, Joy 677, Kendall 700, Lamond 729, Leland 741, Mann 790, Merage 822, Razi 957, Reitman 964, Roberts 976, Scottsdale 1024, Setzer 1029, Small 1049, Sprague, 1070, Stauffer 1077, Warren 1159
Colorado: Family 1268, Hamilton 1285, Leprino 1313, White 1378
Connecticut: Lebovitz 1506, Schloss 1562, Vance 1591
Delaware: Choptank 1641, Thronson 1766, Wyeth 1781
District of Columbia: Glenstone 1809

Florida: Arison 1853, Dyer 1985, Fleischman 2003, Friedland 2025, Greenblatt 2063, Greenfield 2066, HFRX 2092, Hicks 2094, Hill 2097, Kanders 2135, Kanders 2136, Kaplan 2138, Kaye 2141, Lenkin 2179, Life's 2184, Meerwarth 2209, Muma 2227, Papper 2246, River 2288, Scharlin 2315, Sender 2323, Wescustogo 2399, Wolgin 2411, Woolard 2414, Zimmerman 2427
Georgia: Boone 2446, Cooper 2469, Goodman 2492, Hoyt 2514, Illges 2517, Morris 2552, Orkin 2559
Illinois: Ahlstrand 2700, Almeida 2704, Freund 2892, Goodstein 2924, Graham 2926, Knowles 3023, Krehbiel 3030, Leonian 3047, Marsteller 3079, Massey 3082, Millard 3109, Simon 3247, Smithburg 3254, Staley 3263, Yulman 3334
Indiana: Bussing-Koch 3353, TCU 3458
Iowa: Cowles 3482, Figge 3492, Woodward 3549
Kansas: Insurance 3587, Wood 3644
Kentucky: Harter 3660
Louisiana: Montan 3740, Zuschlag 3762
Maryland: Feinberg 3857, Hubbard 3883, Legum 3899, Nabit 3924, Salisbury 3945, Shapiro 3949, Wallis 3977
Massachusetts: Clementi 4050, Hagerty 4110, Hale 4112, Hale 4113, Heide 4125, Lingos 4177, Perry 4240, Tresorelle 4333, Wheatland 4358
Michigan: Dana 4419, Delong-Sweet 4427, Keller 4481, McNally 4510, Padnos 4529, Seligman 4564, Wetsman 4611
Minnesota: Chadwick-Loher 4655, Nelson 4749, **Porter 4763**
Mississippi: McCarty, 4848
Missouri: Ross 4986, University 5027
Montana: Wendy's 5065
Nebraska: Cope 5077
Nevada: Benna 5138
New Hampshire: Lion's 5220, Verney 5236
New Jersey: Cordover 5304, Goldberger 5372, Kingsberg 5421, Levine 5446, **Parnassus 5489**, Riskin 5511, Weny 5581, Wilf 5587
New York: Alexander 5656, Aresty 5707, Balbach 5707, Baumann 5723, Beckwith 5730, Birchrock 5749, Block 5759, Centennial 5826, Clemente 5850, Cochran 5853, Cohen 5860, Cornell 5876, Cox 5883, Cullman 5887, Danziger 5899, Desai 5910, Diogenes 5917, Geier 6064, Hajim 6158, Hohmann 6218, Holtzman 6223, Horowitz 6225, Huber 6231, Joseph 6273, Keller-Shatanoff 6297, **Kevorkian 6304**, L 6353, Lassalle 6366, Lehman 6375, Levy 6391, Liberman 6396, Maurer 6453, Meier 6470, Melville 6471, Pajwell 6568, Performing 6586, Rechler 6657, Reiss 6662, Roche 6677, Ruttenberg 6715, Schwartz 6755, Securitas 6768, Shapiro 6786, Silverstein 6803, Singer 6806, Stern 6860, Stifel 6865, Tisch 6900, Weinman 6955, Whalesback 6967, White 6973, Wohlgemuth 6984, Wunsch 6996, Zenkel 7023
North Carolina: Cameron 7065, Ellison 7090, Hoffman 7127, McGuire, 7177, Morrison 7193
Ohio: Anderton 7306, Busse 7343, Callahan 7345, Christen 7353, Corbett 7363, Daberko 7369, Davidson 7374, Demetros 7377, Fleischmann 7404, Horvitz 7454, Kisker 7479, Lazarus 7493, Marnick 7515, Morley 7532, Selsor 7585, Welty 7635, Williams 7638
Oklahoma: Barnes 7659, Evergreen 7677, Moore 7710, Stone 7721, Wilson 7736
Oregon: Jubitz 7779
Pennsylvania: Ames 7840, Boscia 7887, Bradley 7889, Hartfield 8041, Hecht 8050, Honickman 8066, Lida 8127, Merwin 8170, Mills 8174, Rider-Pool 8238, Saramar 8253, Shenk 8274, Stein/Bellet 8300, Up 8327
Rhode Island: Greene 8413, Paine 8465
Tennessee: Atticus 8582, Eskind 8611
Texas: Adler 8692, Brochstein 8746, **Coneway 8783**, Dedman, 8808, Foundation 8870, Freed 8873, **Gilman, 8889**, Graue 8898, Griffith 8903, Hallam 8910, Hallberg 8911, Hanley 8916, Hegi 8926, Hibbs 8934, Kelso 8985, Kolitz 9000, Levy 9014, Mattsson 9042, McNutt 9055, Meyerson 9062, Rosenberg 9162, Ross 9164, Tobin 9237, Vaughan 9248, Webre 9266, Weir 9268, Wise 9283

Vermont: Kahn 9377
Virginia: Andreas 9388, Denit 9430, Franklin 9452, Kaufman 9482, Strauch 9538, Womack 9556
Washington: Hyde 9627, Juniper 9640, Sarkowsky 9688, Sondland 9700
West Virginia: Stine 9768, Vecellio 9770
Wisconsin: Einhorn 9815, Holoubek 9843, Hyde 9846, Smith 9931

Arthritis

Arizona: Armstrong 97
California: Braddock 336
Delaware: Ryerson 1736
Florida: Diane 1974
Illinois: Delta 2826, Millner 3115
Louisiana: Special 3754
Missouri: Toutz 5023
North Carolina: Wells 7283
Oklahoma: Parman 7713
Pennsylvania: Adams 7836, Lamb 8107, Seebe 8268, Sharp 8272, Somerville 8291
West Virginia: Raymond 9764

Artist's services

California: Picerne 926, Rose 984
New York: **Haven 6178**

Artists and performers

California: LEF 739

Arts and culture

Alabama: Abroms 2, Anderson 6, Black 12, Brinkley 15, Bynum 18, Cooper 22, Day 25, Glaze 28, Goodrich 29, Griffin 30, Griswold 31, Harrison 35, Ireland 39, JADO 40, Kemp 42, King 43, Loeb 47, Mitchell 49, Mitchell 50, Pei-Ling 52, Phifer, 54, Rothschild 61, Shook 64
Alaska: Alaska 80, Gottstein 86, Hooker 87
Arizona: Armstrong 97, **Beals 100**, Berlin 101, Cadeau 104, Declaration 111, Long 141, Louis 142, Murphey 151, Pierce 156, Schlein 165, Ullman 177, Williams-Malone 183, Zicarelli 185
Arkansas: Bailey 187, Bogle 191, Hennessy 198, Horn 200, Merkle 203, Morris 205, Trinity 218
California: 2005 223, Ackerman 227, Adams 228, Amador 238, Anatman 242, Anhaltzer 245, Arata 248, Bach 263, Baldacci 268, Banchik 269, Bancroft-Clair 270, Barth 279, **Battle 282**, Beam 287, Bear 288, Beim 293, Bekins 294, Bialis 313, Bider 314, Blachford-Cooper 318, Bonner 326, Boone 328, Boone 329, Bridges/Larson 343, Bright 345, Broad 347, Brotman 351, Bryan 355, **Bull 358**, Butler 364, **Butler 365**, Calaveras 369, California 370, Callison 371, **Cantor 375**, Castellano 380, Child 394, Church 403, Coburn 411, Coleman 416, Combs-Hughes 419, Community 420, Community 421, Confetti 422, Corcoran 425, Corday 426, Costa 429, Cotsen 430, Crabb 431, Crummer 436, Daly 440, Davies 444, Davis 445, Dearborn 448, **Delzell 450**, DiNapoli 454, Dorskind 459, Downing 462, Ducommun 465, Dusenbury 466, Dwelle 467, Eichenberg-Larson 474, Eleven 476, Family 492, Feintech 502, Ferguson 503, First 506, Fitzpatrick 508, Four 522, Fox 525, Friedhofer 529, Friedman 531, Fuller 538, Furth 540, Fusenot 541, Garabedian 545, GAT 549, Gellert 550, Gilmore 557, Glenville 563, Gordy 575, Graff 576, Greenberg 579, Greenwood 581, Griffiths 584, Gross 587, Guerin 589, Hakka 593, Harqua 599, Harris 600, Havner 604, Hellman 614, Helms 615, Hoag 625, Hodges 627, Hoefer 628, Horwich 632, Hotchkis 634, Hotchkis 635, **Hsu 637**, HunterWard 641, Huntington 642, Ignatius 648, Jelin 662, Johnston 671, Jolson 672, Jones 674, Joy 677, JTB 679, Jubas 680, Juda 681, Kadima 686, Karp 691, Katz 692, Kelton 698, Kelvin 699, Kendall 700, Kendall 701, Kieve 703, Kim 704, Knell 712,

Krishnan-Shah 722, Laguna 726, Lamond 729, Lee 737, LEF 739, Leland 741, Liautaud 755, Looker 766, Lynch 775, Mae 780, Margolis 796, Martin 800, Masson 807, McClatchy 811, McDaniel 812, McLeod 818, Meister 821, Mill 827, Mills 834, Mitchell 837, Mollath 842, Nachtsheim 856, Neu 862, Nicholson 866, Novak 871, Olander 878, Otto 893, Outrageous 894, Palo 900, Pardee 902, Parvin 905, Pergo 915, Pfister 920, Pickford 927, Piuze 928, Plum 929, Podell 930, Potiker 932, Price 938, Private 941, Rabinovitch 947, Radin 948, Ragir 950, Ramsay 952, Reitman 964, **Rifkind 972**, Roberts 975, Robinson 977, Rocca, 978, Roche 979, Roke 981, Roney 983, Rosenberg 985, Rosenfeld 986, Rosso 990, Sandnes 1000, Sato 1007, Schlinger 1016, Schulte 1018, Schultz 1019, Scott 1021, Scott 1023, Setzer 1029, Shannon 1030, Siegel 1036, Silicon 1038, Silton 1039, Simon 1040, Simon-Strauss 1042, SJL 1043, SKB 1044, Skowronski 1045, Smalley 1050, Smith-Walker 1057, Smith-Welsh 1058, Solano 1063, Somekh 1064, Spielman 1067, Sprague 1069, Spungen 1071, Staples 1075, Stauffer 1076, Stewart 1082, Stoller 1084, Storm 1087, Straus 1088, Strome 1089, Sustainable 1096, Swayne 1097, Swinerton 1098, SYZYGY 1101, Teachers 1104, Thompson 1111, Thornton 1115, Tippett 1119, Tobey 1121, Toole 1124, Torino 1125, Traub-Brittan 1127, Troob 1129, Uplands 1139, **Vogelzang 1146**, Von 1147, Waller 1152, Wasserman 1160, Wattis 1161, Webb 1162, Weil 1163, Weiss 1166, Weisz 1167, Welfund 1169, Wells 1171, Wertheimer 1173, West 1174, West 1175, Wharton 1178, Wilbur 1182, **Wilkinson 1183**, Wrather 1198, Writer 1200, Yen 1201, Zecca 1209, Zimmerman, 1213, Zitrustin 1215, Zolla 1216
Colorado: Allen 1220, Arches 1222, Arrowhead 1223, Ballantine 1226, Bardsley 1227, Benson 1229, Broomfield 1242, Caulkins 1245, Elizabeth 1263, Erion 1265, Family 1267, **Fishback 1270**, Flug 1271, Flying 1272, Getz 1278, Goodwin 1279, Grossman 1281, Hamilton 1285, **Kenney 1302**, Kern 1303, Kortz 1307, Kroh 1309, Margulf 1320, Moniker 1327, Neuman 1331, Oak 1333, Priester 1340, Schramm 1350, Spencer 1356, Staley 1357, Strohm 1361, Taylor 1364, Vradenburg 1374
Connecticut: Aibel 1388, Anderson 1393, Anderson-Paffard 1394, Avery 1396, Baggins 1398, Bannow-Larson 1400, Barnes 1403, Bender 1405, Brace 1410, Brown 1413, Caldwell 1415, Chelsea 1418, Crosswicks 1425, Curran 1427, DeLuca 1431, Dennett 1432, Dime 1438, Gengras, 1461, Goldfarb 1467, Grampy's 1469, Grant 1470, Greenfield 1471, Gryphon 1474, Hamm 1476, Harold 1477, Harris 1478, Hastings 1479, Howard 1484, Inglesea 1487, Jones 1489, Katen 1494, Kaufmann 1495, Kuriansky 1503, Lamando 1504, Linke 1508, LLL 1510, Low 1513, **MacInnis 1515**, Magaro 1516, Martinsen 1521, McLane 1522, MLE 1526, Nason 1528, Newpol 1531, Panwy 1539, Patricelli 1541, Pryor 1546, Pulvermann 1547, Roberts 1552, Robinson 1553, Rubin-Ladd 1556, Savings 1559, **Shoemate 1569**, Sorenson-Pearson 1574, Stratfield 1576, Tell 1580, Thrall 1583, Tucker 1587, Wheeler 1594, Winokur 1597
Delaware: 1916 1605, Alcyon 1608, Blau 1623, Brown 1630, Brown-Whitworth 1632, Caplin 1638, Chaney 1640, **Colgate 1645**, Corrigan-Walla 1649, Cultures 1652, Doll 1657, Dunn 1659, Freedman 1665, Giving 1668, **Gloria 1670**, Kaye 1690, Kerr 1692, Kingsley 1693, Klein, 1694, Lowndes 1701, New 1715, Rosenfeld 1732, Selin 1742, **Singer 1744**, Solot 1748, Taylor 1759, Third 1763, Van 1769, Vitale 1771, Whitman 1778, Wong 1779, Wyeth 1781, Yaverland 1783
District of Columbia: Arcana 1786, Bench 1788, Bender 1789, Bloedorn 1790, Choksi 1795, Coleman, 1796, Glenstone 1809, Goldman 1810, **Gorlitz 1811**, **Merriman 1820**, Peet 1827, Replogle 1831,

Rubenstein 1833, Silberman 1834, Silverstein 1835, Westport 1838, Woodward 1839
Florida: Adler 1842, Around 1854, Atkinson 1857, Bailey 1863, Barnard 1866, Bartner 1869, **Basser 1871**, Beasley 1877, Becker 1879, Becton 1880, Berelsman 1885, Berkowitz 1886, Binz 1888, Blanksteen 1891, Blatt 1893, Bond 1897, Brighton 1899, Cape 1917, Capital 1918, Castellani 1927, Cedar 1930, Chanin 1934, Chapman 1935, Charlotte 1938, Childress 1942, Clements 1945, Collins 1949, Coral 1952, Crane 1955, Cunnane 1959, de 1966, De 1967, Diamond 1973, Duckwall 1982, Elster 1990, Evans 1994, **Falk 1996**, Finch 2000, Fleischman 2003, Forman 2011, Frangakis 2017, Frankel 2018, Frankle 2019, Friedland 2025, Fuller 2028, Goldberg 2045, Golden 2046, Goody 2049, Greaton 2060, Greenberg 2062, Greenblatt 2063, Greenfield 2066, Halmos 2075, Hill 2097, **Hishmeh 2100**, Hoffman 2103, Hunter 2116, Isenberg 2121, Jacobson 2125, Jelks 2128, Johnson 2130, Kaiserman 2134, Kanders 2135, Kanders 2136, Kaplan 2138, Kehrer 2143, Kimmel 2146, KLM 2151, Knapp 2153, Kreisman 2159, Kugelman 2161, Lacy, 2163, Landwirth 2167, Layden 2171, Lazarus 2172, Leibowitz 2176, Leiser 2177, Lewis 2182, Life's 2184, Marshall 2195, Martin 2196, Mary 2198, McDonald 2203, Meerwarth 2209, Melin 2210, Mendelson 2211, Mount 2223, Muma 2227, Nobel 2232, Papper 2246, Patterson 2251, Pearce 2252, Perryman 2255, Peters 2256, Phillips 2260, Powell 2264, Pusey 2272, Quinn 2273, Reed 2278, Rich 2284, River 2288, Rose 2293, Rosenthal 2296, Roshan 2297, Rothman 2299, Salenger 2308, Scharlin 2315, Schiano 2317, Sequoia 2324, Sharing 2330, Shockley 2332, Sidhu 2343, Soter 2343, Strong 2353, Strube 2354, Sudakoff 2356, Swisher 2361, Tampa 2362, Taylor 2366, TECO 2367, Thomas 2370, Tippett 2376, Toppel 2377, Turner 2381, von 2388, Weiller 2393, Werner 2398, Wescustogo 2399, Wiener 2405, Woolard 2414, Wrigley 2417, Yerrid 2420, Zimmerman 2428
Georgia: Akers 2432, Arnold 2436, Athens 2437, Charter 2456, Chatham 2457, Cobb 2463, Community 2466, English 2474, Fickling 2478, Foundation 2480, **Gage 2482**, Gilbert, 2488, Goddard 2491, Goodman 2492, Graves 2496, **Hands 2501**, Howell 2512, Illges 2517, Jackson 2522, JBS 2523, Johnson 2525, Kahn 2529, Kingdom 2531, King-White 2532, Klump 2533, Knox 2534, Lanier 2538, Lee 2540, Lipscomb 2541, McClatchey 2546, Mix 2550, Morris 2552, Noonan 2558, Orkin 2559, Oxford 2561, Pechter 2564, Piedmont 2566, Price-Campbell 2570, Saul 2579, Storey 2589, Trammell 2595, Walton 2604, Warren 2606, Williams 2612, Williamson 2613, Wish 2615, Woodcrest 2616, Woodruff, 2618, Wright 2620, Zvolensky 2623
Hawaii: Baldwin 2625, Castle 2626, First 2631, Martin 2641, Moore 2643, Servco 2645, Shidler 2646, **Yoshimoto 2658**, Young 2659, Young 2660
Idaho: Boise 2666, Golden 2672, Hare 2675, Morbeck 2681, Morrison 2682, Simplot 2685, Whittenberger 2689, Wishnick 2690
Illinois: Acorn 2694, Adreani 2697, Agent 2699, Ahlstrand 2700, Allen-Heath 2701, Allyn 2703, Almeida 2704, Alton 2705, Amsted 2708, **Appleby 2711**, B&D 2715, Baird 2717, Barr 2720, Bartholomay 2721, Bass 2723, Bates 2724, Bere 2734, Bergstein 2735, Bishop 2743, Block, 2746, Boothroyd 2749, Bound 2751, Bower 2752, Brooker 2758, Brunswick 2762, Buntrock 2766, Burk 2768, Burnett 2769, Burt 2770, Cafaro-Livingston 2772, Cashel 2777, Ceres 2779, **Chapin 2781**, Cherry 2784, Chicago 2787, Citadel 2791, Clarks 2792, Cohn 2795, Cohn 2796, Collins 2799, Communitas 2801, Community 2802, Community 2803, Considine 2804, Constans-Culver 2805, Cowlin 2814, Cullinan 2818, Cunningham 2819, Danielson 2823, Delavan 2825, Diamond 2829, Dower 2835, Doyle 2836, Eckert 2843, Edelstein 2846, Educational

2848, Eichner 2849, Ellis 2853, Engle 2855, Enivar 2856, Everett 2861, Farnham 2865, Foley 2876, Foster 2879, Frank 2885, Fremont 2891, Freund 2892, Full 2894, Gallagher 2898, Gantz 2901, Generations 2908, Geneseo 2909, Gidwitz 2913, Gidwitz 2914, **Gish 2915**, Gloyd 2917, Gochnauer 2918, Graham 2926, Gray 2928, Hales 2941, Hallene 2943, Harczak, 2952, Harris 2957, Hart 2958, Hay 2961, Heath 2962, Hegeler 2963, **Heritage 2967**, Highland 2970, Hodes 2974, Howard 2981, Ideal 2986, Iroquois 2989, Istock 2991, Jahn 2992, Jentes 2995, JKP 2997, Jocarno 3000, Johnson 3001, Judy 3003, Keyes 3016, Kilrea 3017, Kipper 3018, KPW 3028, **Krasberg-Mason 3029**, Krueck 3031, Lakonishok 3032, Lakshmi 3033, Lancaster 3035, Landau 3037, Lebus 3043, Leibowitz 3046, **Lerner 3048**, Levinson 3049, Lichtman 3052, **Lindon 3054**, Listeman 3055, Livney 3056, Lohengrin 3059, Louis 3063, Love 3064, MacDonald 3068, Maddox 3069, Mako 3070, Marchese 3075, Marcum 3076, Marsteller 3079, Massey 3082, McCabe 3084, McDougal 3091, McKee 3093, McLennan 3096, McNally 3097, **Mead 3100**, Metzner 3104, Meyer 3106, **Meyers 3107**, Millard 3109, Millard 3110, Miller 3112, Miller, 3114, Minor 3117, Minow 3118, Mirapaul 3119, Mitchell 3120, Monroe 3122, Moreton 3124, Mullen 3129, Munson 3130, NCI 3134, New 3136, **New 3137**, **New 3138**, Novick 3143, **Nureyev 3145**, O'Connor 3149, Ohlhausen 3151, Olson 3154, Oppenheimer 3155, Parker 3162, Pepper 3167, Perkins 3168, Perkins 3169, Pinnell 3176, **Polk 3179**, Pond 3182, Red 3188, Reed 3190, Reed 3191, Rosen 3205, Rosenberg 3207, Rosenthal 3210, Rothman 3213, Ruttenberg 3218, Sasco 3222, Schaumburg 3223, Seidler 3233, Self 3234, Shapiro 3240, Shaw 3243, Simon 3247, Skylark 3250, Smallwood 3251, Smysor 3255, Spencer 3258, SSAB 3260, Stairway 3261, Steigerwaldt 3265, Stein 3266, Stone 3269, Stone 3270, Sue 3275, Sullivan 3276, Summer 3279, Takiff 3281, Taylor 3284, Tengelsen 3288, Thaman 3289, Tobey 3290, Townsend 3291, Twomey 3294, United 3300, Vail 3301, Walker 3308, Weiss 3317, Weston 3320, Wislow 3323, Woodruff 3330, Woods 3331, Woods 3332, Zemsky 3337

Indiana: **Ackerman 3339**, Ayres 3342, Benton 3344, Blackford 3346, Branigin 3348, Bronstein 3351, Burris 3352, Bussing-Koch 3353, Carroll 3354, CDM 3355, Clark-Morrill 3356, Cohen 3357, Community 3359, Community 3360, Community 3361, Community 3362, Community 3363, Decatur 3367, Dobbs 3368, Dubois 3370, Ellerbrook 3376, Fayette 3379, Greene 3390, Hillenbrand 3393, Huntington 3397, Jasper 3401, Jennings 3402, Kharis 3407, Kuhne 3409, Lacy 3410, LaGrange 3412, M.C.R. 3413, Maurer 3415, **Mervis 3417**, Nugent 3423, Oakley 3426, Ohio 3427, Raker 3434, Rush 3441, Scott 3446, Seymour 3448, Shafer 3449, Simon 3452, Snyder 3454, TCU 3458, Thrush-Thompson 3460, Vann 3461, Western 3466, Winchester 3469

Iowa: Blin 3476, Busse 3478, Coons 3481, Deardorf 3485, Farver 3491, First 3493, Gartner 3496, Gazette 3497, Henry 3505, Iowa 3512, Jefferson 3514, Krause 3516, Toohey 3538, Weathertop 3545, **Wright 3551**

Kansas: Atterbury 3554, Babinger 3555, Berry 3558, Breidenthal-Snyder 3560, Brown 3561, Cochener 3565, Coffeyville 3566, Community 3567, Cray 3569, DeVore 3573, Elsberry 3574, Fidelity 3577, Goebel 3580, Golden 3582, Green 3583, Insurance 3587, Joscelyn 3590, Master 3600, Middlekauff 3603, Miller-Mellor 3604, Mingenback 3605, **Muchnic 3609**, Payless 3614, Ross 3619, Salgo 3621, Smoot 3627, South 3628, Swearingen 3631, Walsh 3638, Wood 3644

Kentucky: Barr 3646, Barth 3647, Boone 3648, Boone 3649, Dickins 3651, Foundation 3655, Harter 3660, Haskins 3661, Heisel 3663, Keeneland 3668, Kentucky 3669, Killian 3670, Roth 3690, Rounsavall, 3691, Smith 3694, Steiner 3696,

Stock 3697, Sutherland 3699, Trim 3702, Welchwood 3706, Yeager 3710

Louisiana: Dujay 3722, Gauthier 3724, Kavanagh 3730, Knight 3731, Lake 3732, Mintz 3738, New 3742, Parkside 3745, Powers 3746, Shannon 3752, Steinhagen 3755, Wisdom 3761

Maine: Bailey 3765, Bank 3766, Borman 3767, Burnham 3770, Camden 3771, Cotsirilos 3774, Elliotsville 3777, Franklin 3779, Goldberg 3780, **Golden 3781**, Kennebunk 3786, Messler 3790, Mimi 3792, **St. 3804**

Maryland: Adler 3809, Bank 3818, Besson 3823, Broadus 3829, Campbell 3831, Davis 3844, Dean 3846, Dockser 3849, Eliasberg 3854, Feinberg 3857, Gewirz 3869, Gidwitz 3870, Gladding 3871, **Goldberg 3872**, Helm 3879, Higginson 3880, Hubbard 3883, Hurwitz 3886, Hyman 3887, Kelly, 3893, Kohn 3897, Lohr, 3903, Macht 3905, Moore 3917, Myerberg 3923, Nabit 3924, Paternotte 3933, Pearlstone 3934, RCM 3937, RFI 3938, Richmond 3940, Rogers-Wilbur 3941, Salisbury 3945, Schuh 3946, Schwarz 3947, Sears 3948, Shapiro 3949, Shrensky 3951, Silberman 3953, Small 3955, Thalheimer 3966, Ticho 3967, Totah 3968, Tucker 3969, Unger 3971, Van 3973, Wallis 3977, Weinberg, 3979, Wieler 3984, Wilen 3985, Witt/Hoey 3989

Massachusetts: 2 3992, Alvord 4002, Barstow 4013, Beaucourt 4014, Behrakis 4015, Bergstrom 4019, Bigbird 4020, **Blossom 4022**, Boger 4023, **Bruner 4030**, **Cabbadetus 4033**, Cabot 4034, Cabot 4035, Chabner 4041, Chabot 4042, Chicopee 4047, Crane 4058, Cricket 4060, Curvey 4062, Davoli 4065, Deane 4066, Dedham 4067, Druker 4071, Elephant 4081, England 4083, Epstein 4084, Fessenden 4090, First 4091, Fraser 4097, Frisbie 4099, Gale 4100, Gerrity 4102, Greenberg 4106, Halfway 4115, Hampden 4116, Hauben 4120, Haven 4122, Henderson 4127, Hoffman 4131, Hopedale 4134, Hornblower 4135, Jackson 4140, Janet 4141, Jefferson 4142, **Kaplan 4145**, Kenwood 4150, Killian 4154, King 4156, Krupp 4161, Lamm 4165, Ledgeways 4171, Levy 4175, Lindsay 4176, Liswhit 4178, Longtine 4179, Makepeace 4185, Melvina 4197, Middlesex 4203, Mirak 4204, Morningstar 4207, MutualOne 4216, NAID 4217, **New 4220**, Newburyport 4221, Novack 4226, One 4230, Pechet 4235, PerkinElmer 4238, Permanent 4239, Perry 4240, Phelps 4242, Pilgrim 4245, Provident 4250, Putnam 4252, Rabb 4255, Ramsey 4258, Ratshesky 4259, Reynolds 4264, **Robbins-de 4266**, Rodman 4269, Rosse 4272, Salem 4277, Sandler 4278, Sandman 4279, Savage 4280, Schwartz 4284, Shattuck 4291, Solomon 4301, **Spero 4304**, Sprague 4306, Stare 4308, Stearns 4310, Steiger 4312, Storer 4314, Tadler 4320, Tomfohrde 4329, United 4337, Upstream 4338, Verrochi 4342, Wallace 4347, Walsh 4348, Wapack 4350, Webber 4351, Webster 4353, Wilcox 4360, Windhorse 4361, Winthrop 4363, Wyman-Gordon 4364, Xeric 4365, Young 4366

Michigan: **Ajemian 4371**, Andrah 4378, Baiardi 4381, Baldwin 4382, Barron 4384, Biederman 4391, Bierlein 4392, Blatt 4393, Branch 4396, Buffalo 4399, Community 4410, Community 4411, Connable 4412, Dana 4419, Delano 4426, DeVlieg 4428, Doll-Loesel 4433, Farver 4441, Farwell 4442, Garber 4451, Gordon 4456, Gratiot 4459, Hartwick 4462, Herrington-Fitch 4466, Holden 4467, Jospey 4473, Kantzler 4478, Kaufman 4479, Kosch 4485, Lapeer 4490, Leven 4492, Loosemore 4495, LoPrete 4496, M 4497, Maas 4498, Mackinac 4499, Meritor, 4511, Michigan 4514, Morley 4518, Narens 4520, Nickless 4522, O'Donovan 4525, Padnos 4529, Paulina 4535, Peslar 4537, Pitt 4540, Porter 4543, Power 4544, Ran 4547, River 4551, Roscommon 4552, **Saab 4556**, Schalon 4558, SEED 4562, Seligman 4564, Sherman 4567, Shiawassee 4568, Skiles 4572, Thompson 4592, Tremble 4595, Trico 4596, Vlasic 4607, Weisberg 4609, Welch 4610, Wetsman

4611, Whiting 4614, Wickson-Link 4616, Williams 4618

Minnesota: Andersen 4626, Ankeny 4628, Bell 4638, Bend 4639, Bieber 4641, Borman 4644, Boss 4645, Boss 4646, Burwell 4650, Caridad 4653, Caroline's 4654, Chadwick-Loher 4655, Cooke 4659, Dellwood 4665, Depot 4667, Edina 4671, Evert 4676, Farview 4680, Fink 4684, Flaherty 4686, Foundation 4688, Good 4698, Grossman 4701, Head 4709, Hegardt 4710, Heilicher 4711, Hickory 4713, Hognander 4715, Huisinga 4716, Kellogg 4722, Krisbin 4726, Larsen 4728, Luverne 4736, Midcontinent 4745, Northern 4751, O'Brien 4753, Onan 4754, O'Neil 4755, **Porter 4763**, Quinlan 4764, Reger 4769, Regis 4770, Remick 4773, Roles 4780, Schott 4787, Shared 4791, Squam 4793, Steinhafel 4795, Tamarack 4797, Tennant 4798, Thorpe 4800, Trillium 4801, Turner 4803, Walker 4805, Wells 4811, Weyand 4814, Whitney 4817

Mississippi: Barnett 4823, Fountain 4837, Harris 4841, McCarty, 4848

Missouri: Andrews 4860, Baer 4862, Bakewell 4863, Barrows 4864, BEO 4866, Brace 4874, Breidenthal 4875, Butler 4880, Chod 4885, Copaken 4888, Cray 4890, Curry 4892, Dubinsky 4896, Duesenberg 4897, Ellis 4901, Essman 4905, Finerty 4909, Garvey 4913, Gaylord 4915, Gilbert 4917, Grant 4918, Grassmere 4919, Hofheimer 4929, Impact 4930, Kemper 4935, Kornblum 4940, Nichols 4970, Oppenheimer 4973, O'Reilly 4974, Pearl 4977, Pillsbury 4980, Portman 4981, Price 4982, Roman 4985, Ross 4986, Sachs 4989, Schutte 4995, Schweinfurth 4996, Shawe 5000, Silk 5004, South 5011, Timmons 5021, Turner 5025, University 5030, Walker 5034, Welch 5038, Wolff 5039, Woodcock 5041

Montana: Angora 5044, Broadbent 5046, Swanson 5063, Taylor 5064, Wendy's 5065

Nebraska: America 5066, Ameritas 5067, Baer 5069, Blair 5074, Farr 5078, Ferenc 5080, Friedland 5082, Friedman 5083, Grewcock 5086, Hundred 5095, Kinder 5099, Midlands 5104, Nelson 5106, Owen 5108, Patrick 5109, Pegler 5110, Storz 5122, Tous 5124, York 5129

Nevada: Bendon 5137, Benna 5138, Carver 5143, Dermody 5152, Harris 5161, Houssels 5163, Kennedy 5169, Lee 5171, Newman 5179, Petersen 5181, Stout 5190, West 5197, Wolzinger 5200

New Hampshire: Bickford 5205, Hunt 5214, Jameson 5215, Kimball 5216, Landecker 5217, Lion's 5220, McIninch 5224, Olcott 5227, Seigel 5231, Smyth 5232, Verney 5236, Woodbury 5238

New Jersey: A 5240, Amboy 5246, Ascena 5252, Aufzien 5253, Avis 5255, Bartlett 5256, Bershad 5262, Bershad 5263, **Billig 5265**, Blue 5268, Brooks 5274, Brueckner 5279, Brundage 5280, **Buddha 5282**, Carlozzi 5287, Chanil 5291, Chapman 5292, Chormann 5293, Cohen 5299, Conger 5303, Cordover 5304, **Crane 5306**, Culver 5308, **Daft 5310**, D'Aloia 5311, Dickinson 5319, Doctor 5321, Dreman 5326, Dweck 5327, Edison 5330, Farrington 5341, Farris 5342, Feinstein 5343, Fox 5349, Freelander 5353, Frelinghuysen 5354, Gardinier 5363, Garfinkle 5364, Goldberger 5372, **Greenblatt 5376**, HAIR 5379, Harmstieg 5386, Hawthorne 5387, Hekemian 5390, Hillswood 5394, Holzer 5396, Johnson 5406, Johnson 5407, Jones 5408, **Ju 5410**, Kean 5417, Kerney 5419, Kingsberg 5421, Klein 5424, Kontos 5430, Larson 5440, Lieberman 5448, Lipper 5450, M/S 5452, McCrane 5464, Milano 5466, Miller 5468, Minerva 5469, Navesink 5477, Pacific 5485, **Parnassus 5489**, Pepper 5496, Pheasant 5499, Poole 5504, Riskin 5511, Rukin 5516, Savin 5520, Scire 5526, Scott 5527, Shapiro 5532, Shilling 5534, Teiger 5558, Twin 5563, Upton 5566, Weisberg 5578, Westfield 5582, Wetterberg 5583, Wilf 5587, Wilson 5590, Woolley-Clifford 5594

New Mexico: B.F. 5606, Carlsbad 5608, Chamiza 5609, Garfield 5616, Horn 5618, Simon 5624, Taos 5626

New York: Abettor 5638, Abrahamson 5639, Achilles 5641, Ader 5644, Ades-Taub 5645, Aeroflex 5647,

Agate 5649, AGB 5650, AKC 5651, Alexander 5654, ALG 5658, Allegany 5660, American 5664, American 5668, **American 5669**, Amsterdam 5672, Anderson 5674, Andrews 5677, Angelson 5679, Arcadia 5684, Aronson 5689, Arts 5693, Asen 5694, Authors 5700, Avery 5702, AYN 5703, Backer 5706, Balbach 5707, Bank 5710, Barbara 5713, Bassman 5721, Baum 5722, Beach 5725, Beckwith 5730, Bell 5734, Bender 5735, Bergson 5738, Bernheim 5740, Bernhill 5741, Betts 5744, Big 5745, Bikuben 5746, Blackman, 5755, **Blinken 5757**, Blue 5763, Boxer 5772, Bradley 5775, Brand 5776, Brandt 5777, Brenner 5781, Bridgewater 5783, Briger 5784, Brody 5787, Buchwald 5797, Burton 5804, **Buster 5806**, Cader 5807, CAL 5808, Caples 5813, Carroll 5816, Carwill 5818, Centennial 5826, Century 5827, Ceriale 5828, Chasanoff 5833, Cheatham 5836, Chervenak-Nunnalle 5839, Chiles 5843, Ciampa 5845, Citron 5847, Clemente 5850, Coby 5852, Cochran 5853, Cohen 5859, Cohen 5860, Cohenca 5861, Cohn 5862, Cohn 5863, Cohn 5864, Cohoes 5865, Cole 5868, Coles 5871, Cornell 5876, Cornell/Weinstein 5877, Cox 5883, Cranshaw 5885, Cumming 5888, D'Addario 5895, Dalton 5896, Danziger 5899, Darrah 5900, Deeds 5906, Del 5908, Dibert 5915, Dillard 5916, Diogenes 5917, Distracted 5918, Dixon 5919, Dobson 5921, Dorsky 5924, Double-R 5927, Downey 5930, **Dungannon 5935**, **Eastman 5940**, Eberhart 5942, Eggleston 5946, Ehrlich 5948, EMSA 5961, Erpf 5968, ESL 5969, **Family 5983**, Family 5984, Fan 5985, Fein 5992, Feldstein 5997, Fenton 5998, Ferguson 5999, Ficalora 6002, Fitt 6010, Foundation-to-Life 6020, Fowey 6021, Fox 6022, **Frank 6026**, Frankel 6027, French 6032, Fried 6036, Furman 6045, Furth 6047, Gaffney 6049, Gage 6050, Galler 6052, Gant 6054, Gantz 6056, Garber 6057, Garman 6058, Gartner 6059, Geduld/Cougar 6062, Gerhard 6072, Gilliam 6078, Gold 6088, Goldenson-Arbus 6094, Goldfarb 6095, Goldwasser 6103, Goodman 6106, Goodman 6107, Gordon 6112, Graham 6119, Gramercy 6122, Grand 6123, Grandison 6124, Grateful 6131, Greenberg 6132, Greenwich 6137, Grinberg 6139, Grobman 6140, Grodzins 6141, Grossman 6145, Grumbacher 6148, Grunberg 6149, **Gruodis 6150**, H. 6153, Hadar 6154, Hahn 6156, Hajim 6158, Harmon 6169, Healy 6179, Hegarty 6182, Heller 6187, Henshel 6192, Henson 6193, Hewitt 6200, Heyman 6201, High 6206, Hilson 6209, Hochman 6214, Hoffen 6215, Hoie 6219, Holborn 6220, Hopkins 6224, Houseknecht 6226, Hoyt 6230, Huber 6231, Hymowitz 6234, I.W. 6236, IF 6237, Ilsababy 6238, Iroquois 6250, Ivorybill 6252, Jacobson 6255, Janklow 6257, JI 6260, JKW 6263, Johnson 6270, Kallinikeion 6280, Kandell 6283, Kasowitz 6285, Keeler 6292, Keene 6293, Keller 6296, Kenlou 6299, Kimmelman 6309, Kirby 6313, **Klagsbrun 6318**, Klaus 6321, Klein 6325, Knafel 6330, Koessler 6336, Kovensky 6342, Krauss 6345, Krimendahl/Saint-Amand 6346, Kroll 6348, Krumholz 6349, L 6353, **Ladenburg 6357**, Lainoff 6359, Lake 6360, Lane 6363, **Lanie 6364**, Lassalle 6366, Lawrence 6369, Lee 6372, Legacy 6373, Lemle 6378, Leonhardt 6381, Lerer 6382, Lewin 6392, Libby 6395, Liberman 6396, Lichtenstein 6397, Liebowitz 6400, Lippes 6401, Little 6407, Lubo 6417, Lucky 6419, Lucky 6420, Madover 6431, Maher 6433, Maher 6434, Maidenbaum 6435, Makioka 6436, Manocherian 6438, Marble 6441, Marshall 6446, Mathis-Pfohl 6451, Maurer 6453, McCarthy 6456, McDayton 6462, Mendell 6472, Merrill 6480, Meyer 6487, Michaels 6488, Milstein 6496, Mitchell 6499, Mittlemann 6500, Monderer 6503, Moore 6504, Morgado 6505, Mulroy 6516, Neporent 6523, Nets 6524, Newcomb-Hargraves 6529, Newman 6530, Newman 6531, Newman 6532, Northern 6540, Norwich 6542, Noster 6543, Nuhn 6544, Nussbaum 6545, Odyssey 6548, Offensend 6550, O'Grady 6551, Ohel 6553, Ong 6558, Ostgrodd 6561, Pajwell 6568, Palisades 6569, Palm 6571,

Parr 6577, Parshelsky 6578, Peckham 6583, Peek 6584, Persian 6589, Phaedrus 6598, Picotte 6603, Pittman 6608, Pollack 6614, Pollock 6616, Pollock 6617, Polsky 6618, **Posner-Wallace 6621**, Pratt-Northam 6625, Preston 6626, Psalm 6633, Purple 6634, Randall 6644, Rapaport 6647, Rattie 6650, Raymond 6652, Reichert 6660, Reiss 6662, Rexford 6664, Rheinstrom 6665, Richter 6668, Risen 6672, Ritter 6673, Rodgers 6680, Rose 6684, Rose 6685, Rosenberg 6691, Rosenthal 6696, Rosner 6698, Ross 6699, Rowe 6705, Roxe 6706, Rum 6709, Russo 6711, Ruttenberg 6715, Sackler 6717, Salomon 6721, Samberg 6724, Sarnoff 6729, Schaffer 6736, Schneider 6743, Schonberger 6744, Schott 6749, Schwartz 6754, Schweitzer 6759, Scott 6761, Scott 6762, Seacoast 6766, Sherman 6792, Silverstein 6803, Simpson 6805, Slade 6809, Slovin 6811, Smith 6815, Snow 6818, Sokoloff 6823, Sommer 6825, Sorel 6826, Sorensen-Siegel 6827, Speranza 6836, Spiritus 6840, Spofford 6842, Starmar 6848, Stebbins 6850, Sternberg 6863, Stifel 6865, Still 6866, Stowe 6869, Striano 6871, Strong 6872, Stutz 6875, Sumitomo 6876, SVM 6886, Tahari 6890, **Tang 6891**, Tenney 6895, Thanksgiving 6897, Tisch 6900, Touhey 6902, Treetops 6906, Triangle 6908, Tribune 6909, Troubh 6911, Tuch 6915, Uihlein 6919, Utopia 6923, Vance 6926, Vanden 6927, Villchur 6929, Vogt 6933, Wachtell 6936, **Walsh/Alfred 6943**, Walther 6944, Weil 6948, Weill 6949, Weinberg 6951, Weininger 6954, Weinman 6955, Weiser 6958, Weismann 6960, Wells 6964, **Wheeler 6969**, White 6971, Whitehead 6974, Wilson 6979, Wish 6981, Wohlgemuth 6984, Wolk 6987, **Woodland 6989**, Woodmere 6990, Woodner 6991, Woods 6992, Woodward 6993, Wunsch 6996, Wyckoff 6998, Young 7012, Zeitz 7021, Zemsky 7022, Zenkel 7023, Zichron 7026, Ziff 7027, Zwerling 7034

North Carolina: Abernethy 7037, BB&T 7045, Belk 7046, Bell 7047, Bernstein 7049, Blue 7053, Cameron 7065, Canaday 7066, Chastain 7073, Childtrust 7075, Duncan 7086, Evernham 7094, Family 7096, First 7097, Fox 7103, Glenn 7111, Hayden-Harman 7120, Helton 7123, Henderson 7124, Hoffman 7127, Howard 7131, Howe 7132, Jones 7138, Kenan 7144, Live 7163, Maness 7166, Markey 7168, Masserini 7172, McGuire, 7177, Meserve 7182, Morrison 7193, Mount 7196, Niessen 7200, Outer 7204, Perkin 7208, Piedmont 7209, Post 7213, Ragland, 7216, Robinson 7225, Rocky 7227, Rogers 7228, Sanders 7234, Silverback 7243, Snyder's-Lance 7250, Steinmetz 7254, Stonecutter 7255, Stowe 7256, Strowd 7258, Stuart 7259, Trexler 7269, Vanderbilt 7273, Von 7274, Weatherspoon 7282, West-West 7284, Whitener 7286, Wise 7290, Yost 7291

North Dakota: Community 7295, Fedje 7296

Ohio: Alpaugh 7302, Anderson 7305, Anderton 7306, Armington 7309, Athens 7311, B-Brand 7318, Beecher 7321, Berkman 7324, Brown 7336, Bryan 7339, Calhoun 7344, Callahan 7345, Cardinal 7347, Chemed 7350, Community 7356, Community 7357, Corbett 7363, Crandall 7366, Defiance 7375, Demetros 7377, Dorn 7380, **Eaton 7383**, Ferry 7396, Firman 7400, Fitton 7402, Fleischmann 7404, Fox 7409, Frost-Parker 7413, Gale 7415, Gelbman 7420, George 7421, Gimbel 7424, Glazer 7426, Gosiger 7429, Gould 7430, Gross 7432, Gross/Hutton 7433, H 7434, Hankins 7437, Hankison 7438, Hazelbaker 7441, **Highfield 7450**, Hoover 7453, Howe 7455, Joffe 7467, Kilworth 7477, Klock 7480, Kloenne 7481, Knoll 7483, Laub 7490, Lincoln 7496, Linnemann 7498, Lippitt 7499, LKC 7501, Lockwood 7502, Loeb 7503, M.L.M 7510, Mather 7516, McMaster 7521, Miller 7526, Mixon 7530, Musson 7534, Myers 7535, NLT 7537, Norris 7538, Norweb 7539, Ohio 7541, Orr 7543, Peoples 7546, Peters 7547, Powers 7550, Renner 7557, Ritchie 7561, Rosenberry 7562, Rosenthal 7563, S.E.C. 7567,

Sage 7568, Sandfair 7569, Schey 7571, Sears-Swetland 7581, Segoe 7583, Selsor 7585, Skyler 7595, Smith 7598, Steiner-King 7602, STERIS 7605, Stillson 7607, Swagelok 7608, Taft 7609, Tait 7610, Taj 7611, Talbott 7612, Terhune 7614, Tetlak 7615, Thendara 7616, Tuscarawas 7623, Van 7625, Van 7626, Venner 7627, Vista 7628, Watson 7633, Woodward 7646, Young 7653

Oklahoma: Ad 7654, Ashbrook 7656, Barnett 7660, Barthelmes 7661, Cherokee 7666, Gelvin 7682, Kerr 7693, Krueger 7695, Lolmaugh 7700, Lovoi 7702, Merrick 7707, Moore 7710, Peel 7714, Stone 7721, Sylvan 7722, Trippet 7725, Weber 7730, Witt 7737

Oregon: Baldwin 7742, Castle 7745, **Chiles 7749**, Coit 7751, Demorest 7757, Giustina 7767, Hitchman 7774, Irwin 7777, Lamb 7787, Leupold 7790, May 7794, Mentor 7796, Michael 7799, Naumes 7804, Parker/United 7805, Roundhouse 7810, Sharkey 7815, Silver 7817, Western 7829, Woodard 7831, **Wyss 7832**

Pennsylvania: Aaron 7835, Adams 7836, Ames 7840, Arkema 7842, **Arronson 7844**, Auldridge 7846, Bedford 7857, Bella 7859, Bergstrom 7864, Berry 7867, Bishop 7874, Black 7875, Bon-Ton 7884, Borowsky 7886, Boscia 7887, Breedlove 7890, Bridge 7891, Britton 7894, Bronstein 7896, Brooks 7898, Bucks 7905, Cameron 7911, Campbell 7912, Clark 7925, Community 7933, Cottage 7938, Crawford 7944, Crawford 7945, Danella 7948, Deerfield 7952, Delaware 7953, Dietrich 7958, Double 7964, Dozzi 7965, Eberly 7969, Eden 7971, Elk 7975, Elliott 7977, Ellis 7978, Fierce 7992, Finley 7995, First 7997, Foster 8003, Freas 8005, French 8007, Frohring 8010, Garthwaite 8013, Gershman 8015, Gilmore 8017, Giop 8018, Gordon 8024, Grumbacher 8028, Grundy 8029, Guild 8031, Gypsy 8034, Hall 8037, Harsco 8040, Hassel 8042, Hawkins 8044, Hayes 8046, High 8054, Hilles 8057, **Hitchcock 8059**, Hoch 8060, Hodge 8061, Honickman 8066, Horn 8067, Katherine 8086, Katsaros 8087, Klein 8096, Klein 8097, Knudsen 8102, Landenberger 8109, Larking 8112, Le 8115, Leeway 8118, Leone 8120, Lida 8127, Lipstein 8129, Ludwick 8134, Maple 8139, Martin 8142, Martin 8144, Maslow 8146, McKinney 8161, McSwigan 8165, Merops 8169, Mill 8172, Miller 8173, Moffat 8175, Moore 8177, Morgan 8178, Mukaiyama-Rice 8183, Murphy 8185, Mylan 8187, Neal 8190, Neuber 8192, Patterson 8205, Pearsall 8207, Penn 8208, Perelman 8209, Plainfield 8217, Platt, 8220, Quaker 8228, Quinn 8229, Randall 8230, Rath 8231, Rider-Pool 8238, Roberts 8240, Rubin 8246, Ryan 8251, Saramar 8253, Schautz 8257, Schlarbaum 8259, Schoonmaker 8260, Schuylkill 8263, Scott 8266, Shore 8276, Sidewater 8278, Snyder 8287, Spencer 8293, Speyer 8294, Star 8297, Stein 8298, Stein 8299, Stewart, 8302, Strine 8306, Tabas 8312, Teleflex 8314, Tippins 8318, Triple 8322, Tuttleman 8325, Weiler-Miller 8348, Whalley 8353, **Whimsie 8354**, Wimmer 8361, Wolfson 8364, Wurts 8370, Wyeth 8371, **Zeldin 8376**

Rhode Island: Arakelian 8381, Chace 8393, Field 8407, Getz 8412, Greene 8413, Gross 8414, Hirsch 8420, Hope 8422, Horton 8423, Kimball 8434, Kingsbury 8435, LLH/LHM 8442, O'Halloran 8462, Prouty 8476, Robertson 8478, Seed 8484, Washington 8500, White 8503, Woodward 8505, York 8507

South Carolina: Boyd 8514, Gleason 8524, Greenwood 8526, Horne 8528, Jackson 8529, **Lader 8531**, Love 8532, Lutz 8533, Stevens 8541, WebbCraft 8548, Williams/Brice-Edwards 8549, **Winthrop 8550**, Zvejnieks 8553

South Dakota: Clarkson 8558, Engelsma 8563, Grundhofer 8565, Houston 8567, Watertown 8576

Tennessee: Adams 8579, Atticus 8582, B 8583, **Belz 8585**, Blum 8589, Cole 8600, Cracker 8603, Deupree 8604, Doochin 8605, EBS 8610, Eskind 8611, Eskind 8612, Fleming 8615, **Fugitive 8618**, Gaylord 8620, Goldsmith 8622, Gordon 8624, HMA

8628, Kennedy 8638, LaRoche 8641, Mick 8651, Pattee 8656, Pfeffer 8659, Rogers 8666, Rose 8667, Schadt 8670, Small 8675, Splawn 8677, Tipton 8682

Texas: Abernathy 8690, Adler 8692, Alexander 8696, American 8700, American 8701, Amherst 8702, Anderson 8704, Astin 8710, Barrow 8719, Bernardin 8728, Boeing 8733, Booth 8735, Brass 8738, Braun 8740, Bromley 8749, Brown 8751, Brownsville 8752, Burzik 8758, Calpine 8759, Cemo 8765, Chisholm 8769, Clear 8772, **Coneway 8783**, Conley 8784, Cook 8786, Cook 8787, Crossroads 8791, Day 8800, de 8802, Deakins 8804, Doak 8818, Dubose 8828, Dunagan 8831, Duncan 8833, EOS 8840, Esping 8841, Fairchild 8845, Fentress 8851, FHC 8853, Finger 8857, Flohr 8861, Flowers 8862, Foundation 8869, Fowlston 8871, Friedel 8875, Frill 8877, Fruehauf 8879, Fuchs 8881, Garvey 8884, **Gilman, 8889**, Gordon 8892, Graham 8896, Greentree 8901, Griffin 8902, Haggar 8907, Hallam 8910, Hallberg 8911, Hanley 8916, Hartman 8920, Hawkins 8923, Helmle-Shaw 8929, Herring 8930, Hervey 8932, Hicks 8936, Hixon 8940, Holloway 8946, Jacobs 8964, Jamail 8965, Kabacoff 8977, Kaplan 8979, Kellam 8982, Ketelsen 8988, Klein 8997, Knox 8999, Kowitz 9002, Krist 9004, Laredo 9010, Levy 9014, Link 9020, Littauer 9021, Lowdon 9025, Margolin 9038, Marks 9039, McLaughlin 9053, Mithoff 9068, Montgomery 9070, Oppenheimer 9101, Overlake 9106, Pack 9109, Papadopoulos 9113, Partnership 9116, Patterson 9118, Paulos 9120, Pearlman 9122, Peine 9123, Perkins 9125, Richter 9153, Roberts 9155, Rosenthal 9163, Rowan 9166, Rust 9168, Saulsbury 9175, Sear 9186, Seay 9187, Serafy 9188, Sharma 9190, Shiloff 9193, Simpson-Omohundro 9196, Smith 9202, Smith 9206, Smith 9207, South 9210, Staubach 9215, Stewart, 9221, Taub 9229, Texas 9231, Tietze 9236, Tobin 9237, Tolleson 9238, Vaughan 9248, Vaughan 9249, Walls 9257, Walthall 9258, Ward 9260, Warren 9261, Watson 9263, Weir 9268, Welch 9270, Westcott 9273, White 9275, Winston 9282, Wolf 9285, Wolff-Toomim 9286, Woolf 9292, Zale 9299

Utah: B. 9302, Callister 9310, Catalyst 9313, Green 9327, Odyssey 9342, Patel 9344, Promontory 9345, Questar 9346, Schmidt 9349, Shrontz 9351, Sorenson 9355, Sorenson 9356

Vermont: Altman 9364, Harper 9373, Harvest 9374, Huntington 9376, Kahn 9377, Mergens 9381, Redducs 9383

Virginia: Backer 9389, Bassett 9391, Beck 9393, Berni 9395, Brink's 9406, Bryant 9409, Burford 9411, Cartledge 9414, Clark-Nexsen 9421, Cole 9423, Community 9426, Cooke 9427, Denit 9430, Dreaming 9435, Edlavitch 9440, Elmwood 9442, Farkas 9445, Franklin 9452, Gifford 9457, Glasser 9459, Grandis 9462, Hausfeld 9469, Kaufman 9482, King 9484, Loeb 9493, Markel 9498, Mody 9501, Mullen 9502, Northern 9503, Pruden 9517, R 9518, Rashti 9520, Rouse-Bottom 9526, Schiro-Zavela 9528, Short 9532, Smith 9534, Stephenson 9536, Strauch 9538, **Tara 9540**, Treakle 9543, VuBay 9548, Williams 9553

Washington: Alhadeff 9558, Ames 9560, Babare 9564, Boydston 9572, Brotman 9574, DeFalco 9585, Dunn 9589, Erickson 9591, Everett 9592, Fales 9594, Fletcher 9597, Fulton 9601, Grindstone 9610, Grousemont 9611, Hanauer 9614, Hansen 9615, Jefferson 9630, Johnston-Fix 9634, Johnston-Hanson 9635, Jones 9640, Juniper 9640, Keller 9643, Kilworth 9644, Klaue 9647, Korum 9648, Lea 9652, Lott 9656, Magdalen 9658, McKinlay 9662, Moraine 9664, Murray 9667, Nordstrom/Seifert 9668, O'Donnell 9672, Patel 9675, Prairie 9680, **Rotalia 9685**, Sarkowsky 9688, Skagit 9696, Smith 9698, Spark 9701, Stevens 9704, Templin 9709, Thurston 9713, Titus-Will 9714, Welch 9721, Wellworth 9722, Wright 9730, Wyman 9731, Young 9732

West Virginia: Brown 9739, Driehorst 9743, Hollowell 9751, Hott 9753, Vecellio 9770

Wisconsin: AnnMarie 9774, Aylward 9779, BayCare 9781, Birnschein 9783, Brennan 9788, Cummings-Christensen 9801, Dawes 9803, Doolittle 9809, Door 9810, Dudley 9811, Eau 9814, Einhorn 9815, Erdman 9816, Frautschi 9822, Fromstein 9824, Hansen 9835, **Helios 9838**, Heller 9839, Highlands 9841, Huiras 9844, Hunt 9845, Inbusch 9847, J.P.C. 9848, Jacobus 9849, Jones 9855, Kelly 9861, Kenosha 9862, Kohl 9864, Lutsey 9873, Lyche 9875, Marshfield 9878, Martin 9879, Merkel 9884, Meyer 9885, Mid-States 9887, Modine 9889, Park 9899, Peterson 9901, Phipps 9903, Purple 9908, Rhodes 9914, Roehl 9917, Rosemann 9919, Schlegel 9922, Schoenleber 9924, Simms 9929, SMS 9933, Stateline 9937, Stevens 9939, Stry 9941, Styberg 9942, Tellier 9946, Uihlein 9950, Webcrafters-Frautschi 9957, Wilson 9960, Witte, 9962

Wyoming: C 9966, Connemara 9967, Dragicevich 9969, Guthrie 9972, Imig 9974, Weiss 9996, Weiss 9997, Welch 9998

Arts councils

Florida: Barnard 1866
Illinois: House 2980
Kansas: Schmidt 3622, Trusler 3635
Michigan: Burdick-Thorne 4402, Padnos 4529
Missouri: Riedel 4984
New York: Bank 5710, Peckham 6583
North Carolina: Stonecutter 7255
Ohio: Selsor 7585

Arts education

Alabama: Anderson 6
California: Corday 426, Familian 491, Giles 554, Katz 693, **Rifkind 972**, Smith 1053, Smith 1055, United 1136, Van 1144
Connecticut: Hamm 1476
Florida: Couch 1953, Lazarus 2172, Partners 2248
Illinois: Cohn 2796, Frank 2885, Graham 2926, Knowles 3023, Oppenheimer 3155, Staley 3263, Walk 3307
Iowa: Smeltzer 3535
Kentucky: Opera 3684
Maryland: Akridge 3810, Devito 3848, Gidwitz 3870, Kohn 3896, Pearlstone 3934, Shattuck 3950
Massachusetts: Alden 3999, Deane 4066, Progin 4247, Ramsey 4258, Ratshesky 4259
Michigan: **Gorlin 4457**, O'Donovan 4525, Roscommon 4552, Roznowski 4554
Missouri: Siteman 5006
New Jersey: Carlozzi 5287, Kontos 5430, Schwartz 5525
New York: Abess 5636, Aronson 5689, Avery 5702, BTMU 5795, D'Addario 5894, Fondation 6017, Hadar 6154, Keller-Shatanoff 6297, Krumholz 6349, L 6353, Lucelia 6418, Niemiec 6535, O'Grady 6551, Shapiro 6786, Stutz 6875, Van 6925
North Carolina: Ellison 7090, Gilmore 7110
Ohio: Callahan 7345, Corbett 7363, Ginn 7425, Skyler 7595
Oregon: Hitchman 7774
Pennsylvania: Rosenlund 8245
South Carolina: WebbCraft 8548
Tennessee: Gaylord 8620, Kite 8639
Texas: Levy 9014, Marcus 9037, Roberts 9156, Thorne 9235, Wal-Dot 9256, Walls 9257
Vermont: Kahn 9377
Virginia: Family 9444
Wisconsin: Peterson 9901
Wyoming: Cutting 9968

Arts exchange

New York: Roche 6677

Arts services

California: Evans 485
Illinois: Glossberg 2916
New York: **Usman 6921**
Virginia: Lacy 9485

Asthma

California: Beynon 312
Georgia: Raoul 2573
Massachusetts: Thoracic 4326

Astronomy

Missouri: Wolff 5039
Ohio: Skyler 7595

Autism

California: Baker 267, Dyer 469, Lemons 744
Connecticut: Berbecker 1406
Florida: Baxter 1874, Fontaine 2006, Reckson 2277
Georgia: Holly 2509
Illinois: Gassin 2906
Massachusetts: Autism 4007, Tilson 4328
Minnesota: Luther 4733
New York: Geier 6063, Geier 6064, Rosenberg 6690, Rosenthal 6693
North Carolina: Agarwal 7039, Evernham 7094
Oregon: Curry 7755
Pennsylvania: Mosi 8179
Virginia: MAIHS 9497, Peachtree 9508

Automotive safety

Iowa: GuideOne 3503
New Jersey: Selective 5528
Oregon: Santos 7812

Ballet

California: Baker 265, Cheeryble 390, First 507, Gill 555, Martin 802, Winkler 1188, Yoder 1202
Connecticut: Bender 1405, Hume 1485, Zimmer 1603
District of Columbia: Westport 1838
Florida: Carlin 1921, Meerwarth 2209, Norjana 2235
Georgia: A.E.M. 2430, Brewer 2448, Vaughan 2598
Illinois: **Chapin 2781**, Micole 3108, Pangburn 3161
Kentucky: Opera 3684
Maryland: Pearlstone 3934
Massachusetts: Poduska 4246
Minnesota: Thorpe 4800
Nevada: Houssels 5163
New Jersey: Brueckner 5279
New York: Bingham 5747, Ettl 5970, Fuchsberg 6044, H. 6153, Hewitt 6200, Joseph 6273, Lassalle 6366, Peek 6584, Pittman 6608, Pohly-Turaj 6613, Ruttenberg 6715, Sackler 6717, White 6973
North Carolina: Rollins 7231
Ohio: George 7421, Wildermuth 7637
Oklahoma: Barnes 7659, Miller 7708
Pennsylvania: Adams 7836, Patterson 8205
Tennessee: Eskind 8613, Pattee 8656, Splawn 8677
Virginia: **Price 9516**
Washington: Magdalen 9658, Thurston 9713
Wisconsin: Cudahy 9800, Dohmen 9807, Einhorn 9815

Baptist

California: Smith 1053
Florida: Hollinger 2104, McLaughlin 2205, Turlington 2380
Georgia: Ragan 2572, Sewell 2584
Hawaii: **Shiraki 2648**
Illinois: **Combs 2800**
Indiana: Vision 3463
Kentucky: Spriggs 3695
Maine: Sukeforth 3805
Minnesota: Mahon 4737
Missouri: Peculiar 4978

North Carolina: P 7205, Waters 7280
Pennsylvania: Cornerstone 7936
Texas: McMillan, 9054, Schulte 9181

Baptists

Florida: Turlington 2380

Baseball and softball

California: Stellar 1080
Florida: Fuller 2028
Iowa: Jefferson 3514
Maryland: Baltimore 3817
Massachusetts: Dedham 4067, Morse 4210
Michigan: Maly-Dykema 4502, Roscommon 4552
Montana: Wendy's 5065
Nebraska: Hawkins 5089
New York: Indus 6243
Ohio: Cleveland 7354
Virginia: Greco 9463

Basic and emergency aid

California: **Alalusi 236**
Colorado: Gerrish 1277, McPherson 1323
Connecticut: Crew 1424, Macauley 1514
Delaware: Cultures 1652, Kuehner 1695, Weissman 1775
Illinois: Lohengrin 3059, Rothman 3213
Maine: Henry 3782
Maryland: Meyer, 3913
Massachusetts: **Tatelman 4322**
Michigan: Pilgrim 4539, Whitman 4615
Minnesota: Evert 4676, Hegardt 4710, **Winds 4820**
Missouri: Slusher 5009
New Jersey: Schwartz 5525, Waterview 5572
New Mexico: Quail 5622
New York: AGB 5650, **Family 5983**, Newman 6530, Sherman 6792
North Carolina: Bolick 7056
Ohio: A 7299
Pennsylvania: Plankenhorn 8219, **Zeldin 8376**
Rhode Island: Hoag 8421, Luke 8447
Tennessee: Community 8601, Drake 8606, **Redbird 8664**
Texas: Halperin 8912
Utah: SmartGo 9354
Vermont: Harvest 9374
Virginia: Cedars 9416, Chainani 9417, Hansen 9465, Lane 9486
Wisconsin: Meehan 9882

Basic and remedial instruction

California: Cloud 408, Community 421, Lux 773, Perenin 914
Florida: Couch 1953, Price 2267, Wilson-Wood 2408
Georgia: Lipscomb 2541
Massachusetts: **Azadoutioun 4008**, Kelsey 4148, Ratshesky 4259
Michigan: Abrams 4369, Community 4411, Roscommon 4552, Thoman 4590
Minnesota: Bell 4638
New Jersey: Carlozzi 5287
New York: Grant 6129, Northern 6540
North Carolina: Bertsch 7050
Ohio: Musson 7534, Selsor 7585
Pennsylvania: Union 8326
Rhode Island: Mulligan 8457

Basketball

Arizona: Adkerson 94, Freedom 120
California: Anthony 247, Lockridge 765, Zwick 1218
Delaware: Hoops 1682
Indiana: Braun 3349
Massachusetts: Stemberg 4313
Michigan: Roscommon 4552
Missouri: Breidenthal 4875
New York: Nets 6524

Texas: Staubach 9215

Bereavement counseling

California: Livingston 761
Minnesota: Rosen 4782

Biochemistry

North Carolina: Horvat 7130

Biodiversity

California: Davies 444, On 880, Overall 895, Prete, 934, Walton 1156
Connecticut: Baldwin 1399, Greenfield 1471, Lebovitz 1506, Schloss 1562
Florida: KBR 2142, Lastinger 2168, Shackelford 2327
Georgia: **Bancker-Williams 2440**, Broadfield 2449, Lane 2536, McClatchey 2546
Idaho: Hare 2675
Illinois: McGraw 3092, **Mead 3100**, Simpson 3248
Maine: Aldermere 3763
Maryland: Biophilia 3824
Massachusetts: **New 4220**
Minnesota: Bell 4637, Bell 4638
Montana: Cinnabar 5047, High 5057
New Hampshire: Thorne 5233
New York: Anderson-Rogers 5676, Henderson 6189, Marshall 6446, Woods 6992, Woodward 6993
Ohio: Haskell 7439, Linnemann 7498
Pennsylvania: Brooks 7899, Hawksglen 8045, White 8355
Rhode Island: Love 8446
Texas: Vaughan 9249
Washington: Hyde 9627, Northwest 9669
Wisconsin: Hunt 9845, LUX 9874

Bioethics

California: Craves 434
District of Columbia: **Pettus-Crowe 1828**

Biology

California: Bundy 360, **Grass 577**, Kisco 710
Delaware: Rosenfeld 1732
Florida: KBR 2142
Georgia: Whitehead 2610
Louisiana: Chambers 3718
Massachusetts: **New 4220**
Minnesota: Bell 4638
New Hampshire: Dorr 5211
New Jersey: Wetterberg 5583
New York: **Blinken 5757**
North Carolina: Horvat 7130

Biomedicine

California: Edwards 473, **Grass 577**
Colorado: Goodwin 1279
Florida: Bastien 1872, Price 2267, Richard 2285
Illinois: Cremer 2815
Massachusetts: Cabot 4035, Tomfohrde 4329
Missouri: St. 5012
New Jersey: Covance 5305
New York: **Eppley 5967**, Glorney 6084
North Carolina: Horvat 7130
Texas: McNutt 9055, Morrison 9073, Smith 9205

Bird preservation

California: Dmarlou 455
Connecticut: Lebovitz 1506
District of Columbia: Ptarmigan 1830
Pennsylvania: Brooks 7899
Wisconsin: Windway 9961

Blood banks

Delaware: 613 1606
Washington: Quest 9681

Boating

Illinois: Brunswick 2762

Botanical gardens

Arizona: Spalding 172, Ullman 177
California: Acacia 225
Colorado: Bardsley 1227, Ladd 1310
Connecticut: Katen 1494, WMP 1598
Florida: Hill 2097, Vanneck-Bailey 2384
Georgia: Exposition 2476, JBS 2523, Woodruff, 2618
Illinois: Bellebyron 2731, Christiansen 2790, Franklin 2888, Garard, 2902, Jahn 2992, McCormack 3086, Pitzman 3177, Smithburg 3254
Iowa: Beckwith 3473, Weathertop 3545
Maryland: Salisbury 3945
Massachusetts: Fessenden 4090
Missouri: University 5027
Nebraska: Physicians 5112
New Jersey: Antz 5250, Palmer 5486
New Mexico: B.F. 5606
New York: Hohmann 6218, Roche 6677, Slade 6809
North Carolina: Rogers 7228, Stowe 7256
Ohio: Ferry 7396, Linnemann 7498, Stillson 7607
Oklahoma: Miller 7708
Oregon: Flowerree 7763
Pennsylvania: Ludwick 8134, Randall 8230
South Carolina: Cato 8516
Tennessee: EBS 8610
Texas: Dedman 8807, Fowlston 8871, Thorne 9235
Virginia: Markel 9498
Wisconsin: LUX 9874

Botany

Florida: KBR 2142

Brain and nervous system disorders

California: Farber 495, **Preuss 935**
Florida: Brown 1904, HFRX 2092
Illinois: **American 2707**
New Jersey: Branfman 5271
New York: **Swett 6888**
Texas: Tolleson 9238
Virginia: Ochsman 9504
Washington: Foss 9598

Breast cancer

California: Kort 719, **Parsemus 904**
Connecticut: Finn 1449, Fuchs 1459, Lee 1507, Morrow 1527
Delaware: **TeleTech 1761**
Florida: Barnard 1866
Massachusetts: Donovan 4070
Michigan: Nartel 4521
Missouri: Duesenberg 4897, O'Reilly 4974
New Jersey: Entin 5336
New York: Alexander 5654, Levine 6387
North Carolina: Hayden-Harman 7120
Pennsylvania: Bolte 7882, Bon-Ton 7884, Rooney 8243
Vermont: Seventh 9384
Virginia: Blue 9400

Buddhism

California: **Lenz 746**, **Raymond 956**, Tanimura 1103, Yuki 1203
New Jersey: **Buddha 5282**, Johnson 5406, Jones 5408, Korean 5431, **Yin-Shun 5596**
New York: **Nok 6537**
Texas: Bodhi 8732

Business and industry

California: Bank 272, Foundation 520, Swinerton 1098
Connecticut: Donchian 1440
Hawaii: Armstrong 2624
Kansas: Berry 3558, Insurance 3587, Payless 3614
Michigan: Meritor, 4511
Nebraska: Physicians 5112
New Jersey: Selective 5528
New York: Levine 6387
North Carolina: Redwoods 7218, Shugart 7242
Pennsylvania: Harsco 8040
Rhode Island: Washington 8500
Texas: Boeing 8733
Virginia: Franklin 9452, Mullen 9502

Business education

California: Braddock 336, Tuffli 1134, Witter 1192
Colorado: Trueblood 1371
Connecticut: Diageo 1437, O'Herron 1536
District of Columbia: Brody 1791, Rubenstein 1833
Florida: Couch 1953, Evanson 1995, Higgs 2096
Hawaii: Fukunaga 2633
Illinois: Collins 2799, Constans-Culver 2805, Kelly 3012, Reed 3191
Maryland: Adams 3808
Massachusetts: Connell 4055, Kershaw 4151, **Spero 4304**, Tadler 4320
Michigan: Morley 4518
Minnesota: Morning 4748
Missouri: Logan 4947
New Jersey: Amboy 5246, Kurtz 5436
New York: Centennial 5826, Duke 5934, Emwiga 5962, Evans 5973, Gant 6054, Geier 6064, Hajim 6158, Maher 6433, Niemiec 6535, Offensend 6550, Planalp-Trevor 6609, Seven 6777, Smith 6814, Smith 6815, Spiegel 6838, Stanton 6845, Whalesback 6967
North Carolina: Hudson 7133
Ohio: Schey 7571
Oklahoma: Collins, 7669
Oregon: Woodard 7831
Pennsylvania: Kazanjian 8090
Virginia: Billings 9397
Washington: Jones 9638, Keller 9643

Business promotion

California: Bank 272
Nebraska: Hawkins 5089
Pennsylvania: Butz 7908
Rhode Island: Kingsbury 8435
Texas: Planetary 9132

Camps

Alabama: Rothschild 61
California: Bradford 337, Chizen 397, Rediger 960, Smith-Walker 1057
Colorado: Family 1268
Connecticut: Cochrane 1420, Eder 1441
Delaware: Corkins 1648
District of Columbia: Goldman 1810, Himmelfarb 1815
Florida: Ael 1843
Georgia: Holly 2509, Noonan 2558, Rice 2575, Woodruff, 2618
Illinois: Franklin 2888, Munson 3130
Iowa: Beckwith 3473, Busse 3478, Krumm 3517
Kansas: Trusler 3635
Maryland: Macks 3906
Massachusetts: East 4075, Proud 4249, Savage 4280
Michigan: Conrad 4413, Thoman 4590
Minnesota: Charity, 4656
Mississippi: Taylor 4855
Missouri: O'Reilly 4974
Nevada: Close 5148
New York: Block 5759, Bush 5805, Gerstman 6074, Marley 6443, Meyer 6487, Russo 6711
North Carolina: Fortson 7100
Oregon: Spencer 7820

Pennsylvania: Cornerstone 7936, Mosi 8179, Patterson 8205, Plankenhorn 8219
Texas: Hardner 8918, Staubach 9215
Virginia: Ratner 9521, Smith 9534, Womack 9556
Washington: **Ormsby 9674**
West Virginia: Parlin 9762

Cancers

Alabama: Caddell 19, Sexton 63
Arizona: C 103, Grossman 126, Zicarelli 185
Arkansas: Bailey 187, Dunklin, 194, Hennessy 198, Riggs 214
California: Ascher, 256, Baker 266, Baker 267, Bellwether 299, Bernstein 308, Braddock 336, Brown 353, Burg 362, **Chan 388**, Coburn 411, Davies 444, Del 449, Eichenberg-Larson 474, Fawcett 500, Folger 515, Goodwin 572, Gross 587, Hagar 591, Huntington 642, Jelin 662, Kendall 700, Maxfield 808, Miller 828, Miller 832, Miller 833, Phillips 924, Reinhold 963, Resource 965, Schlinger 1016, Setzer 1029, Stauffer 1076, Walton 1156, Wasserman 1160, Whittier 1181, Wrather 1198, Yoder 1202, Zafiropoulo 1207
Colorado: Connor 1250, Ladd 1310, Thiel 1365, Tomkins 1368
Connecticut: Diageo 1437, Ferguson 1446, Fippinger 1450, Fuchs 1459, Gorab 1468, Hewitt 1482, Morrow 1527, Tully 1588, Wiener 1596
Delaware: Easterly 1660, Haldan 1676, Pollack 1722, Ryerson 1736, Scripps 1741, Selin 1742, Yokota 1784
District of Columbia: Tucker 1836, Westport 1838
Florida: Andre 1849, Bastien 1872, Baxter 1874, Cantor 1916, Carrington 1923, Castellani 1927, Celebrity 1931, Couch 1953, Diane 1974, Duckwall 1982, Durden 1984, Farrell 1998, Gate 2034, Golden 2046, Grossman 2068, Hansen 2079, Hoenle 2101, Kugelman 2161, Lazzara 2174, Lelash 2178, Life's 2184, Minto 2216, Muma 2227, Olsen 2240, Powell 2265, Reeves 2279, Rogers 2292, Rothman 2299, Samowitz 2311, Second 2321, Sexton 2326, Stafford 2346, Sun, 2358, Vanneck-Bailey 2384, Whiting 2403, Wolgin 2411, Zimmerman 2427
Georgia: Amos 2433, Burke 2451, Connolly 2467, Cooper 2469, Hurlbert 2516, Jackson 2522, Reynolds 2574
Hawaii: Locations 2638, Vidinha 2653
Illinois: Ahlstrand 2700, Bergstein 2735, Bulkley, 2765, Carter 2776, Christian 2789, Goodstein 2924, Half 2942, Hallene 2943, Hopper 2977, Hughes 2983, Jaros 2993, Landau 3037, Lebus 3043, Luehring 3065, MacDonald 3068, Marks 3077, McCabe 3084, O'Connor 3149, Red 3189, Schorr-Lieberman 3229, Spencer 3258, Staley 3264, Warner 3310, Zaccone 3335
Indiana: Maurer 3415, Noecker 3424
Kansas: Wallace 3637
Kentucky: Trim 3702
Louisiana: Moffett 3739
Maryland: Gidwitz 3870, Kohn 3896, RCM 3937, S.B.E. 3944, Wolpoff 3990
Massachusetts: Arcadia 4004, Brock 4027, Chabner 4041, Connell 4055, Donovan 4070, Hale 4112, Helman 4126, Kelleher 4147, Morse 4208, Permanent 4239, Poduska 4246, Prokopis 4248, Schlager 4283, **Spero 4304**, Van 4340
Michigan: Allen 4372, Dana 4419, Kay 4480, McDole 4507, Oreifice 4528, Padnos 4529, Pardee 4534, Price 4546, Riley 4550, Trico 4596, Vlasic 4607, Whiting 4614
Minnesota: Erickson 4674, Heilmaier 4712
Mississippi: Pruet 4851
Missouri: Barrows 4864, Moss 4964, O'Reilly 4974, O'Reilly 4975, Toutz 5023
Nebraska: Midlands 5104
Nevada: Geomar 5160, Sweig 5191
New Jersey: Brown 5278, Diaco 5318, Freedman 5352, Greetin 5377, Harms 5385, Jones 5408, Katz 5414, Kurr 5435, O'Neal 5481, Pantirer 5487, Paragano 5488, **Rippel 5510**, Spiro 5546, Wilf 5588

New York: Adikes 5646, Antun 5681, Berkowitz 5739, Bush 5805, Carwill 5818, Chasanoff 5833, Colby 5867, Douglas 5929, Druskin 5932, Evans 5973, Feldstein 5997, Fraydun 6029, Golden 6091, Grinberg 6139, Harmon 6168, Kenlou 6299, Kupferberg 6351, Levine 6386, Levine 6387, Maslin 6448, National 6520, Newman 6534, Nonna's 6538, Ostgrodd 6561, Palisades 6569, Parshelsky 6578, **Peter 6590**, Petrocelli 6595, Prince 6629, Rapaport 6646, Reichert 6660, RJL 6675, Roxe 6706, Schweckendieck 6758, Spiegel 6838, Sweeney 6887, White 6973
North Carolina: Fortson 7100, Hamill 7115, McConnell 7176, Sloan 7246, Sutcliffe 7262
Ohio: A 7299, Andrews 7307, Bates 7317, Christen 7353, Comunale, 7358, Fibus 7398, Gale 7415, Garcia 7416, Kisker 7479, Norris 7538, Seaman 7580, Van 7626
Oklahoma: Goddard 7684, Jones 7691
Oregon: Heath 7772
Pennsylvania: Betz 7870, Blue 7879, Bon-Ton 7884, Hawksglen 8045, Hoffman 8063, Hunt 8070, Jansing-Cook 8079, Lamb 8107, Larsen 8113, Leary 8117, Murphy 8185, Perelman 8209, Saramar 8253, Sharp 8272, Smith 8280, Snyder 8287, Somerville 8291, Venne 8331, Weiler-Miller 8348, Wright-Cook 8369
Rhode Island: Brack 8392, Hecht 8418, Phillips 8472, Slemons 8490
Tennessee: Drake 8606, Fleming 8615, New 8654, Small 8675
Texas: Brochstein 8746, **Coneway 8783**, Corlin 8788, Dunagan 8831, Hegi 8926, Hillcrest 8939, Joseph 8974, KCL 8981, MST 9078, North 9089, Penland 9124, Pulitzer 9140, Sharma 9190, Tietze 9236, Wolff-Toomim 9286, Woods 9291, Works 9293
Utah: Burton 9309, Cardon 9311
Virginia: Immixgroup 9476, King 9484, Peachtree 9508
Washington: Brookshire-Green 9573, CSM 9584, Gibson 9604, Heath 9617
Wisconsin: Braun 9787, Glanert 9827, Manitowoc 9876, Merkel 9884, Prescott 9905, Roddis 9916, Steinle 9938, Uihlein 9950
Wyoming: Skilling 9990

Capital punishment

District of Columbia: **Butler 1792**

Catholicism

Alabama: Blount 13, Bruno 17, Mitchell 49
Arizona: Babbitt 98, Hansen 127, Moeller 150, O'Rielly 154, Picerne 155, Rubeli 163, Sioles 169
Arkansas: Nabholz 208, Nabholz 209, Wrape 222
California: Adams 228, Barulich 280, Beauregard 290, Beulah 311, Beynon 312, Boscacci 333, Bravo 338, Byrne 368, Celebrate 383, Cerri 384, Clougherty 409, Corbalis 424, Diamantine 452, Drum 464, Elder 475, Ellen 478, Ferry 504, Finestra 505, Foster 519, Fritz 534, Gallo 543, Garaventa 546, Georgina-Frederick 552, Glazer 562, Jones 675, Kanoff 689, **Kinnoull 706**, Los 769, March 791, Marcil 793, McGraw 814, Oak 872, October 873, Outrageous 894, Pacific 897, Perricone 916, Russell 995, Savage 1009, Sebastiani 1027, Terra 1107, Thompson 1112, Trust 1131, Von 1147, Von 1148, **Wakerly 1150**, Winn 1189
Colorado: Connor 1250, Growing 1284, JJP 1299, **McGrath 1322**, Priester 1340, Routzon 1348, Steffens 1358, Wilson 1380
Connecticut: Bessie 1407, Bigelow 1408, Bradley 1411, Denzler 1434, Foley 1452, Grant 1470, Linke 1508, McLaughlin 1523, Morrow 1527, O'Herron 1536, Price 1544, Sekerak 1564, **Sonja 1573**, Wheeler 1594
Delaware: ABE 1607, Bresnan 1628, Burton 1634, Dion 1656, Hagan 1674, Massoud 1704, Palmer 1718, Patterson 1719, Rivers 1731, Trussell 1767, Weissman 1775
District of Columbia: Cook 1797, Porter 1829, Ptarmigan 1830, Woodward 1839

Florida: Baroco 1867, Beasley 1877, Burnett 1911, Chadbourne 1932, Collins 1949, Davis 1963, Dickinson 1975, Ellis 1989, Freitas 2022, Hayford 2086, Helow 2089, Holloway 2107, Insetta 2119, J. 2122, Kaulbach 2140, Lowry 2191, Melin 2210, Muccia 2225, Powell 2265, Rice 2283
Georgia: Colston 2464, Guillaume 2500
Illinois: Arboit 2713, Baudhuin 2726, Bower 2752, Christian 2789, Clingen 2794, Considine 2804, Corcoran 2810, Cullinan 2818, Denny 2828, Doerr 2831, Dowdle 2834, Frisby 2893, Fund 2896, Goldenberg 2920, Good 2923, H.C.D. 2939, Hardiek 2953, Hastings 2960, Hess 2969, Logos 3058, Marchese 3075, McLaughlin 3095, Meusel 3105, Murphy 3132, O'Connor 3149, Pawlowski 3165, Romano 3203, Ryan 3219, Self 3234, Shaker 3238, Vibern 3303, Wright 3333
Indiana: Bussing-Koch 3353, Hoffman 3395, Magee-O'Connor 3414, Niblick 3423, O'Rourke-Schof 3429
Iowa: Krause 3516, R 3529, Stark 3536, Vonderhaar 3543, **Wahlert 3544**
Kansas: Babinger 3555, Cyr 3570, Elsberry 3574, Miller-Mellor 3604, Salgo 3621, Sheetz 3626
Kentucky: Diebold 3652, Horn 3664
Louisiana: Broussard 3715, Whitman 3759, Winn 3760
Maine: **Dugas 3776**
Maryland: Cole 3839, Contino 3840, DelSignore 3847, Franey 3865, Mangione 3907, Meyer, 3913, Mullan 3920, RCM 3937, S.B.E. 3944, Salisbury 3945, Schuh 3946
Massachusetts: Donovan 4070, Fay 4087, Francis 4095, Lost 4180, McNeice, 4195, Pilgrim 4245, Valerio 4339, Verrochi 4342, Walsh 4348, Wapack 4350
Michigan: **Ajemian 4371**, Briggs-Fisher 4397, Causley, 4405, Cebelak 4406, Cracchiolo 4415, Delano 4426, Dinan 4431, Ervin 4437, Fabiano 4438, Havirmill 4463, Kinney 4483, Main 4501, McManus 4509, Riley 4550, Sehn 4563, Vlasic 4607, Watson 4608, Wheeler 4612, Zampetis 4619, Zimmerman 4620
Minnesota: Charity, 4656, Flaherty 4686, Foundation 4688, Gardner 4693, Gilligan 4696, Kinney 4724, Mahoney 4738, McNamara 4743, Morning 4748, O'Brien 4753, Quinlan 4764, Sayer 4786, Turner 4803, Whaley 4816
Mississippi: Seal, 4853
Missouri: Bryant 4878, Dierberg 4895, Enright 4903, Fabick 4907, Forster-Powers 4911, Kienstra 4938, Neiman 4969, O'Reilly 4974, Slay 5008, Stroble 5015, Sullivan, 5017, Todd 5022, University 5027, Vassia 5029, Vatterott 5030
Nebraska: Cope 5077, Hickey 5093
Nevada: Benna 5138, Geomar 5160, Joseph 5166, Moran 5178
New Hampshire: Martin 5222
New Jersey: **Akhoury 5243**, Brunetti 5281, Byrne 5283, Colotto 5300, Domenica 5323, Fund 5358, Kerney 5419, Kocurek 5428, Landy 5439, Leavitt 5445, Markey 5459, Navesink 5477, Paragano 5488, Petrucci 5498, Scott 5527
New Mexico: **Watersheds 5628**
New York: Bogoni 5766, Brooklyn 5788, Casey 5819, Castle 5820, Ciampa 5845, Coles 5871, Cox 5883, Dixon 5919, Edelweiss 5944, Follett 6016, French 6032, Gallagher 6051, Golub 6105, Gordon 6111, Gordon 6112, Grace 6118, Graham 6120, Hanson 6163, Hopkins 6224, Ingrassia 6244, Jarx 6258, Johnson 6269, Kelleher 6295, Koessler 6334, Koessler 6335, Maguire 6432, Mathis-Pfohl 6451, McCooey 6457, Menezes 6473, Oestreicher 6549, O'Neil 6557, Petrocelli 6595, Picotte 6603, Quinn 6637, Russo 6711, **Schmeelk 6742**, Smith 6812, Society 6821, Striano 6871, Trimble 6910, Vanden 6927, Vogt 6933, Walrath 6941, Whalen 6966, White 6971
North Carolina: Galanti 7104, Kanitz 7140, Post 7213, Rees 7219, Sutherland 7263
Ohio: Anderson 7304, Bernard 7325, Coressel 7364, Covelli 7365, Downing 7381, Duarte 7382, Finnegan 7399, Garcia 7416, Glidden 7427, H 7434, Heimbinder 7445, Homan 7451, Hubert

7456, Iott 7463, Klock 7480, Marnick 7515, Murphy 7533, O'Donnell 7540, O'Neill 7542, Rotterman 7564, Turben 7622, Van 7625, Williams 7638
Oklahoma: Dill 7671, Jirous 7690, Warren 7729
Oregon: Cayo 7746, Frank 7765, Glennco 7768, Merlo 7797
Pennsylvania: Bradley 7889, Brooks 7898, Carlson 7916, Dicerbo 7956, Ganse 8012, IGN 8073, Karamatsoukas 8085, Kelley 8091, Maronda 8140, Nikolaus 8193, O'Brien-Veba 8197, Reiss 8234, Ryan 8251, Shaner 8271, Smith 8281, Somerville 8291, Staehle 8295, Ward 8343
Rhode Island: Arr 8383, Hubbard 8425, Kelly 8432, McCabe 8451, Mulvaney 8458, Pardee 8468, Smith 8492
South Carolina: Gleason 8524
South Dakota: Ferguson 8564
Texas: **Caritas 8763**, Community 8782, Dehan 8809, Doskocil 8823, Edwards 8837, Farris 8847, Foster 8867, Griffith 8903, Haggar, 8908, Hardner 8918, Kirwan 8996, Klesse 8998, Mewhinney 9060, Mossy, 9077, P 9108, Pratt 9137, Schumacher 9183, South 9210, Vaughan 9248, Vaughan 9249, Webre 9266, Wolff-Toomim 9286
Virginia: Billings 9397, Birk 9398, Blue 9401, Darden 9428, **Delmar 9429**, Fraser 9453, Hansen 9465, Page 9507, Peachtree 9508, Shaffer 9530, Willett 9552
Washington: Alhadeff 9558, Boeschoten 9571, Gius 9606, Magdalen 9658, Snyder 9699, Tamaki 9707
West Virginia: Hess 9747, Hoffmann 9749, Starvaggi 9767, Vecellio 9770
Wisconsin: Brennan 9788, Hartwig 9836, Holoubek 9843, Huiras 9844, Kalscheur 9858, Karol 9859, Kohl 9864, Meehan 9882, Meinerz 9883, Merkel 9884, Plein 9904, Religious 9912, Rewald 9913, Seramur 9926, Van 9952
Wyoming: Welch 9998

Catholics

Connecticut: Foley 1452
Indiana: Hoffman 3395

Cemeteries and burial services

Delaware: Cross 1651, Ryerson 1736
Illinois: Christiansen 2790, Smysor 3255
Missouri: Hofheimer 4929, Morgan 4963
New York: French 6032
Rhode Island: N. 8459
Virginia: Greco 9463

Ceramic arts

Michigan: Hartwick 4462

Cerebral palsy

Florida: Holloway 2107
Kansas: Schmidt 3622
Missouri: Toutz 5023
New York: Lewy 6393, Rose 6683
Wisconsin: Weyers 9959

Charter school education

California: Benedek 300
Georgia: TALX 2592
Illinois: Rossman 3211
New Jersey: Covance 5305

Chemistry

California: Burg 362
Minnesota: **Wagner 4804**
New Hampshire: Dorr 5211
New York: **Eppley 5967**
Pennsylvania: Bolte 7882, Quaker 8228
Rhode Island: Frasch 8408

Child abuse

California: Alafi 235, **Girls 559**, Lyons 776, Martin 803
Colorado: Brown 1243
Florida: Couch 1953, Muma 2227, Woerner 2409
Indiana: Welter 3465
Kentucky: Trim 3702
Massachusetts: Weil 4354
Nebraska: Ameritas 5067, Smith 5118
New York: 1848 5629
North Carolina: Redwoods 7218
Ohio: Thompson, 7617
Oklahoma: French 7680
Oregon: Spencer 7820
Texas: Arena 8707
Washington: Foss 9598

Child advocacy

New York: Zyman 7036

Child care

Georgia: Hodge 2506
Illinois: Community 2802
Michigan: Roscommon 4552
Minnesota: Sauer 4785
New Jersey: Schlaffer 5522
New York: Wagman 6937
Pennsylvania: Clark 7927
Texas: Levy 9014, Roosth 9160
Washington: Bungie 9576

Child development

Arizona: Van 179
California: Codding 412, Fusenot 541, Gross 587, Ornest 888
Florida: Bastien 1872, Couch 1953, Oristano 2241
Georgia: Woodcrest 2616
Hawaii: Castle 2626
Illinois: Cremer 2815, Hess 2969
Maryland: CSG 3842
Massachusetts: Alden 3999, Cabot 4035, Crawford 4059, Kelsey 4148, **Spero 4304**, Weil 4354
Minnesota: Bell 4637, Bell 4638
Missouri: Herschend 4928, Sunnen 5018
New Jersey: Cantor 5285, Schwartz 5525
New York: Citrin 5846, Kenworthy 6300, Roche 6678
North Carolina: Flowers 7099, Pratt 7214
Ohio: Bicknell 7327, Tait 7610
Pennsylvania: 100 7833, 1830 7834, Child 7923, Seybert 8269, Union 8326
Texas: Central 8766, Hardner 8918, Levy 9014, Vaughan 9249
Virginia: Ivakota 9477, Wiley 9551
Washington: Schuler 9690, Tonkin 9715
Wyoming: Scott 9987

Child educational development

California: Baker 265, Codding 412, Gross 587
Colorado: Bloom 1239
District of Columbia: Crowell 1799
Florida: Bastien 1872, Couch 1953, Oristano 2241
Hawaii: Castle 2626
Illinois: Cremer 2815, Hess 2969, Ringer 3196
Massachusetts: Alden 3999, Cabot 4035, Kelsey 4148, **Spero 4304**
Michigan: Nusbaum 4524, Roscommon 4552
Minnesota: Bell 4637, Bell 4638
Missouri: Herschend 4928, Sunnen 5018
New York: Farber 5986, Roche 6678, Willmott 6978
Oregon: Pendleton 7806
Pennsylvania: Blue 7879, Child 7923, Seybert 8269, Union 8326
Texas: Central 8766, Levy 9014, Mayer 9043, Vaughan 9249
Utah: Cumming 9315
Virginia: Ivakota 9477
Washington: Tonkin 9715

Child welfare

Alabama: Anderson 6, Brinkley 15, Dixon 26, Goodrich 29, JADO 40, Phifer, 54, Rothschild 61, Samford, 62

Arizona: Burns 102, Cooper 109, Drexler 113, F2 117, Garcia 122, Grossman 126, Hughes 130, Jasam 133, Kuhle 139, Long 141, Prayer 158, Rae 159, Robson 160

Arkansas: Heflin 197, Hennessy 198, Hussman 201, McKinney 202, Riggs 214, Sturgis 217, Trinity 218

California: Adams 228, Altos 237, Amerman 239, Arata 248, Avery-Fuller-Welch 260, Bancroft-Clair 270, Bandai 271, Banky 273, Bannerman 274, Bekins 294, Bell 295, Beller 297, Beneto 301, Berakah 302, Bettingen 310, Beulah 311, Beynon 312, Bobowski 324, Boone 329, Bradford 337, Bravo 338, Bright 345, Broad 347, Brotman 351, Brown 353, Butte 366, Candor 373, Castellano 380, Ceunis 385, Church 403, Cleo 407, Combs-Hughes 419, Community 421, Corde 427, Cush 437, Daly 440, Deacon 447, Eagle 470, Evans 486, Familian 491, Family 492, Faour 497, Fat 499, First 507, Fox 523, Fox 524, Fox 525, Fuller 538, Fusenot 541, GAT 549, Gellert 550, Giles 554, **Girls 559**, Gooding 571, Gross 587, Hagar 591, Harris 601, Havner 604, Hawley 605, Heller 613, Helms 615, Helmstetter 616, Hilltop 621, Hodges 627, Hohnstein 629, Hughes 639, Huntington 642, Jelin 662, Jolson 672, Kanel 688, Kirby-Jones 708, Kirkorian 709, KNU 713, Legacy 740, Levin 749, Liautaud 755, Looker 766, Lux 773, Lyman 774, Magali 781, Malachi 785, Martin 803, Mickelson 825, Mondavi 843, Money-Arenz 844, Morgan 847, Nicholson 866, Oak 872, Olander 878, Outrageous 894, Page 899, Palo 900, Penney 913, Peterson 918, Phelps 923, Pralle 933, Price 938, Price 939, Razi 957, Rediger 960, Reinhold 963, Roney 983, Sanders 999, Sanfilippo 1002, Scandling 1012, Setzer 1029, SHP 1035, Smalley 1050, Smith 1053, Smith 1055, Smith-Walker 1057, Smittcamp 1059, Solano 1063, Stauffer 1076, Straus 1088, Tecumseh 1105, Terra 1107, Thrill 1117, Traina 1126, Warren 1159, Webb 1162, Weisgerber 1165, West 1175, Winkler 1188, Winn 1189, Witkin 1191, Wrather 1198, Zafiropoulo 1207, Zankel 1208, Ziegler 1210, Ziff 1211, Zurlo 1217

Colorado: 6/S 1219, Bright 1241, Burt 1244, Caulkins 1245, Comprecare 1249, Donnell-Kay 1258, Dorset 1259, Family 1268, **Fishback 1270**, Fortune 1273, Hamilton 1285, Howard 1295, Jacobs 1298, Lewis 1315, **McGrath 1322**, Schlessman 1349, Schramm 1350, Stratton 1359, Titus 1367, Verdoorn 1372, Warner 1376

Connecticut: Allwin 1390, Ambler 1392, Antonacci 1395, Barden 1402, Bender 1405, Bridgemill 1412, Brown 1413, Chelsea 1418, De 1430, Dennett 1432, Diageo 1437, Dime 1438, Filingieri 1447, Finn 1449, Foley 1452, Fry 1458, Grant 1470, Harris 1478, Hewitt 1482, Howard 1484, Hume 1485, Kaufmann 1495, Keefe 1497, Konover 1501, Kreitler 1502, Lavietes 1505, Lebovitz 1506, Macauley 1514, Schaeneman, 1560, Selkowitz 1565, Thornton 1582, Tierney 1584, Union 1590, Winokur 1597

Delaware: ABE 1607, Anbinder 1611, Babcock 1612, Bowman 1625, Bresnan 1628, Brown 1631, Chaney 1640, Coors 1647, Cross 1651, Doll 1657, Dougherty 1658, Kang 1689, Kutz 1696, Lightner 1699, New 1716, Remmer 1726, Replogle 1728, Russell 1735, Swinmurn 1755, Thomson 1764, Trussell 1767, Yablon 1782

District of Columbia: Bender 1789, Cafritz 1793, Cornerstone 1798, Dimick 1803, Dweck 1805, Goldman 1810, Hanley 1814, Himmelfarb 1815, Lemon 1819, Olender 1824, Replogle 1831, Rubenstein 1833, Woodward 1839

Florida: Archibald 1852, Auerbach 1859, Basham 1870, Becker 1879, Bell 1882, Bond 1897, Boston 1898, Brighton 1899, Brownley 1907, Burks 1909, Cantor 1916, Capital 1918, Chapman 1935, Chicone 1941, Childress 1942, Chowdhury 1943, Collins 1949, Couch 1953, Crutchfield 1957, Dasburg 1961, Dennis 1969, Deus 1972, Diane

1974, Dickinson 1975, Family 1997, Five 2002, Foulds 2014, Gerry-Corbett 2037, **Gordon 2051**, Grader 2054, Graese 2055, Grossman 2068, Hagens 2071, Hansen 2079, Hardison 2081, Harper 2082, Holloway 2107, Hornik 2111, Jacobsen 2123, Janke 2126, Jelks 2128, KBR 2142, Kiwanis 2149, Kugelman 2161, Lacy, 2163, Lambert 2164, Leiser 2177, Lerner 2180, Life's 2184, Lookout 2190, Martin 2196, Minto 2216, Muma 2227, Munroe 2228, Nissim 2231, Olsen 2240, Oristano 2241, **Pagoumian 2245**, Pascal 2249, Peters 2256, Phillips 2260, **Place 2261**, Powell 2264, Pusey 2272, Ray 2275, Raymund 2276, Reeves 2279, Richard 2285, Sexton 2326, Shannon 2328, Sierra 2336, Simmons 2338, Smick 2340, Smith 2341, Smith 2342, Stern 2349, Swisher 2361, **Taylor 2365**, Terry 2368, Thomas 2370, Thompson 2372, Thurman 2375, Turner 2381, Turock 2382, Vanneck-Bailey 2384, Verner 2386, Wells 2397, Westgate 2400, Wiener 2405, Wilson-Wood 2408, Woerner 2409, Wynne 2419, Yerrid 2420, Zimmerman 2428

Georgia: Amos 2433, Boone 2446, Broadfield 2449, Chandler 2455, Charter 2456, Chatham 2457, Colston 2464, Community 2466, **Gage 2482**, Georgia 2485, Goodman 2492, Gordy 2493, Hoyt 2513, Hoyt 2514, Illges 2517, Jeter 2524, Johnson 2525, Kahn 2529, Kids 2530, Knox 2534, Lee 2540, Lipscomb 2541, Magnus 2543, McKinney-Geib 2547, Orkin 2560, Pilling 2567, Rockdale 2576, SF 2585, Solstice 2587, Stahl 2588, Terwilliger 2593, Whitehead 2610, Woodcrest 2616, Woodruff, 2618

Hawaii: Baldwin 2625, Castle 2626, Locations 2638

Idaho: Ambrosiani-Pastore 2663, Boswell 2667, **Melaleuca 2679**, Morrison 2682, Troxell 2688, Whittenberger 2689

Illinois: 1335 2691, Adreani 2697, Ahlstrand 2700, Allen-Heath 2701, Allyn 2703, Almeida 2704, Alton 2705, Alton 2706, **Appleby 2711**, B&D 2715, Baird 2718, Bartholomay 2721, Bates 2724, Bernoudy 2738, Best 2739, Best 2740, Bishop 2743, Bladel 2744, Bulkley, 2765, Burk 2768, Cashel 2777, Catalyst 2781, Ceres 2779, **Chapin 2781**, Citadel 2791, Clingen 2794, Cohn 2796, Corcoran 2810, Cornerstone 2812, Cremer 2815, Cronin 2816, Delavan 2825, Delta 2826, Dowdle 2834, Educational 2848, Equity 2858, Everett 2861, Fields 2870, Fraida 2884, Frank 2885, Fredman 2890, Frisby 2893, Funk 2897, Gardner 2904, Geneseo 2909, Gloyd 2917, Gochnauer 2918, Golder 2921, H 2937, Hansen 2948, Hanson 2949, Hanson 2950, Harczak, 2952, Hastings 2960, Heins 2964, Hopper 2977, Houlihan 2979, Howard 2981, Jaros 2993, Kainz 3004, Keeney 3007, Kilrea 3017, Krehbiel 3030, Lancaster 3035, Leestma 3044, Leibowitz 3046, Lichner 3051, Love 3064, Mako 3070, Manne 3073, McCabe 3084, McCrea 3088, **Meyers 3107**, Micole 3108, Millard 3109, Minor 3117, Mullen 3129, Munson 3130, NCI 3134, New 3136, Nygren 3146, Oberweiler 3147, Okner-Robbins 3152, Pitzman 3177, **Polk 3179**, Pond 3182, Pritzker 3184, Red 3189, Reichert 3192, Rich 3194, Romano 3203, Rosenthal 3210, Russell 3216, Seymour 3236, Simon 3247, Simpson 3248, Smallwood 3251, Stein 3266, Stone 3270, Summer 3279, Webb 3313, Wislow 3323, Witz-Mallinger 3324, Wolf 3327

Indiana: Blackford 3346, Burris 3352, Cohen 3357, Gammon 3385, Klapper 3408, Kuhne 3409, LaGrange 3412, Magee-O'Connor 3414, Maurer 3415, Namasté 3422, Rifkin 3437, Rinker 3438, TCU 3458, Thrush-Thompson 3460, Weston 3467

Iowa: Deardorf 3485, Farrer 3490, Grubb 3502, GuideOne 3503, Jefferson 3514, McDonald 3520, Van 3540

Kansas: Bane 3557, Berry 3558, Buford 3562, Coffeyville 3566, Community 3567, DeVore 3573, Family 3575, Fidelity 3577, Fox 3578, Hopkins 3586, Insurance 3587, Jellison 3589, Joscelyn 3590, Legacy, 3595, McFadden 3601, Payless 3614, Price 3616, Ross 3619, Scroggins 3624,

Shannon 3625, Smoot 3627, Taylor 3632, Wallace 3637, Wiedemann 3642, Williams 3643

Kentucky: Abercrombie 3645, Barr 3646, Hannah 3659, McKellar 3677, Morris 3679, Namaste 3682, Spriggs 3695, Stock 3697, Taylor 3700, Trim 3702, Woosley 3708

Louisiana: Cahn 3716, Lake 3732, Moffett 3739, New 3742, Wheless 3758, Whitman 3759

Maine: Davenport 3775, Franklin 3779, **Golden 3781**, Somers 3803, Sukeforth 3805

Maryland: Anderson 3814, Campbell 3831, CSG 3842, DelSignore 3847, Duncan 3851, Ferris 3860, Franey 3865, **Goldberg 3872**, Hobbs 3882, Kelly, 3893, Loats 3902, Macht 3905, Marriott 3909, SPM 3958, St. 3959, Ten 3963, Weiner 3980, Weiss 3982, Williams 3986

Massachusetts: 2 3992, Alden 3999, Benson 4016, Benz 4017, Black 4021, Bulger 4031, Chase 4045, Clarke 4049, Devereaux 4069, Donovan 4070, Durant 4072, England 4083, Family 4085, Fassino 4086, Fay 4087, Gerrity 4102, Hale 4113, Hampden 4116, Hazard 4124, Hopedale 4134, Kenwood 4150, King 4156, Melvina 4197, Morse 4210, MutualOne 4216, NAID 4217, Novack 4226, Peters 4241, Progin 4247, Ramlose 4257, Ratshesky 4259, Rodman 4268, Rodman 4269, Safe 4275, Schwartz 4284, Shattuck 4291, Sherman 4293, **Spero 4304**, Thoracic 4326, Tilson 4328, Weber 4352, Weil 4354, Winning 4362

Michigan: Alon 4374, Baldwin 4382, Barstow 4385, Barton-Malow 4386, Bierlein 4392, Blatt 4393, Buhr 4400, Community 4411, Cracchiolo 4414, Cracchiolo 4415, Currie 4418, Dana 4419, de 4422, Fabiano 4438, Farwell 4442, Filmer 4444, Foren 4448, Four 4449, Hayden 4464, Holden 4467, Keller 4481, Kiwanis 4484, LoPrete 4496, Maas 4498, Mackinac 4499, Main 4501, Maly-Dykema 4502, Manat 4503, Mariel 4504, Mojo 4516, Morley 4518, Nartel 4521, Roscommon 4552, Springview 4575, Watson 4608, Welch 4610, Wheeler 4612, Whiting 4614, Wieczorek 4617

Minnesota: Arsher 4630, Bell 4637, Bell 4638, Bend 4639, Bieber 4641, Butzow 4651, Charity, 4656, Cox 4662, Dyer 4669, G&K 4691, Grotto 4702, Kinney 4724, Luverne 4736, McNamara 4743, Midcontinent 4745, Morning 4748, Northern 4751, Radichel 4765, Rieks 4774, Rosen 4782, Samsara 4784, Sauer 4785, Thorpe 4800, Wallestad 4806, Way 4809, Wells 4811, Whitney 4817

Mississippi: Baird 4822, Community 4830, Crooks 4831, Fountain 4837, Seal, 4853, Skelton 4854

Missouri: Barrows 4864, Boylan 4873, Brace 4874, Breidenthal 4875, **Build-A-Bear 4879**, Copaken 4888, Cornelsen 4889, Enright 4903, Fabick 4907, Gaylord 4915, Herschend 4928, Long 4948, Melcher 4957, Meyer 4959, Moneta 4962, O'Reilly 4975, Pearl 4977, Riedel 4984, Rust 4988, Sander 4991, Schneider 4994, Slusher 5009, Sunnen 5018, Thorp 5020, Timmons 5021, Von 5033, Walton 5037, Welch 5038, Woods 5042, Wurst 5043

Montana: Boe 5045, Broadbent 5046, Dousman 5049, Gallagher 5052

Nebraska: Ameritas 5067, Baer 5069, Friedman 5083, Hawkins 5089, Heuermann 5092, Hickey 5093, Kaufmann-Cummings 5096, Kilbourne 5097, Kim 5098, Midlands 5104, Patrick 5109, Quivey-Bay 5113, **Waldbaum 5125**, York 5129

Nevada: Banks 5135, Barker 5136, Bendon 5137, C.A.N. 5142, Coleman 5150, Crescere 5151, Houssels 5163, Joseph 5166, Lifestyle 5173, Petersen 5181, Pinnacle 5183, Shulman 5185, Webb 5196, Wolzinger 5200, **Wood 5201**

New Hampshire: Barker 5204, Bickford 5205, **Christian 5207**, Hunt 5214, Jameson 5215, Verney 5236, von 5237

New Jersey: A 5240, Amboy 5246, Brundage 5280, Cantor 5285, Carlozzi 5287, Citta 5295, Conant 5302, Devine 5317, Dickinson 5319, Dreman 5326, Essig 5339, Fox 5349, Freedman 5352, **Garcia 5362**, His 5395, Johnson 5406, Katz 5414, Kerney 5419, Klein 5424, **Knistrom 5426**, Kontos

5430, Kresa 5432, Kroon 5433, Kurr 5435, Mamiye 5456, Marron 5461, McConnell 5463, Milano 5466, Miller 5468, O'Neal 5481, **Patel 5492**, Riskin 5511, Sanders 5518, Schwartz 5525, Selective 5528, Shapiro 5532, Simon, 5537, Snyder 5540, **Tufenkian 5562**, Upton 5566, Waters 5571, Winters 5591

New Mexico: Taos 5626

New York: 1848 5629, Adikes 5646, AGB 5650, Antun 5681, Aresty 5687, August 5698, Balbach 5707, Big 5745, Bloomberg 5761, Blue 5763, Bobrow 5765, Box 5771, Bratt 5778, Briger 5784, Brooklyn 5788, Brosens 5789, Brown 5791, Buller 5800, Cader 5807, Camuto 5812, Carwill 5818, Children's 5842, Cole 5868, Coles 5871, Cranshaw 5885, Dabah 5892, D'Addario 5894, Dammann 5897, Danziger 5899, Downs 5931, EMSA 5961, Eule 5971, Falconhead 5980, Fay 5989, Fein 5992, Forest 6018, **Frank 6026**, Freidheim 6031, Furman 6045, Geier 6064, Gesso 6075, **Gimprich 6080**, Golden 6091, Goldenberg 6092, Goldstein 6100, Gordon 6109, Graham 6120, Grandison 6124, Grant 6129, Grateful 6131, Grodzins 6141, Hajim 6158, Handler 6161, Happy 6165, Harmon 6168, Hennessy 6191, Hilson 6209, Hite 6213, Hopkins 6224, IF 6237, Indus 6243, Iroquois 6250, JI 6260, Johnson 6266, Johnson 6268, Johnson 6270, **Katzin 6288**, Kelsey 6298, Kenworthy 6300, L 6353, Lainoff 6359, Legacy 6373, Leonhardt 6381, Leventritt 6385, Levine 6386, Levy 6391, Lufkin 6421, Madover 6431, Maher 6433, Marley 6443, MAT 6450, McCarthy 6456, Meredith 6477, Mertz 6481, Metzger-Price 6483, Meyer 6485, National 6520, Nets 6524, Norwich 6542, Nussbaum 6545, Offensend 6550, Ontario 6559, O'Sullivan 6565, Pajwell 6568, Palisades 6569, Parshelsky 6578, Peckham 6583, Peek 6584, **Peter 6590**, Peterson 6592, Phaedrus 6598, Picotte 6602, Picotte 6603, Pittman 6608, Pollack 6615, Reiss 6662, Rheinstrom 6665, Roche 6678, **Rock 6679**, Rose 6683, Rothenberg 6702, Rothstein 6704, Samberg 6724, **Schmeelk 6742**, Schwartz 6752, Schweckendieck 6758, Seacoast 6766, Seelig 6769, Serenbetz 6776, Sharon 6787, Shuman 6795, Siegel 6797, Simpson 6805, Snayberger 6817, Snow 6818, Snyder 6819, Sommer 6825, Spear 6832, Spiegel 6838, **Spirit 6839**, Spiritus 6840, Stanton 6845, Starker 6847, Still 6866, Stowe 6869, Sumitomo 6876, Thanksgiving 6897, Treiber 6907, Triangle 6908, Tribune 6909, Trimble 6910, Tuch 6915, Turner 6916, United 6920, Utica 6922, Vanden 6927, Warwick 6945, Washington 6946, Weinberg 6951, Weinman 6955, White 6972, Woldar 6985, Wright 6995, Wyckoff 6998, Yearley 7005, Young 7012

North Carolina: Balin 7042, Bane 7043, Billingsley 7052, Coffey 7078, Cooke 7079, Elks 7089, Ellison 7090, First 7097, Flowers 7099, Glenn 7111, Hoffman 7128, Hunt 7134, Kistler 7147, Kosloski 7149, KPB 7151, McConnell 7176, Meserve 7182, Meyer 7183, Moretz 7189, Morgan 7190, Niessen, 7200, Oschwald 7203, Paddock 7206, Peeler 7207, Perkin 7208, Piedmont 7209, Richardson 7221, **Rolander 7229**, Shugart 7242, Strowd 7258, Whitener 7286, Wibel 7287

North Dakota: Community 7295, Fedje 7296

Ohio: A 7299, Alpaugh 7302, Anderson 7305, Armington 7309, Beecher 7320, Bicknell 7327, Brown 7336, Calhoun 7344, Cassner 7348, Coressel 7364, Covelli 7365, Foundation 7408, Fox 7409, Freygang 7410, Hankins 7437, Hauck 7440, Heffner 7443, Hoover 7453, Hubert 7456, Johnson 7468, **Katz 7475**, Kilworth 7477, Klock 7480, Lazarus 7493, Linnemann 7498, LKC 7501, Loeb 7503, Luedeking 7506, Lundgard 7508, Mather 7516, Mehl 7523, O'Neill 7556, Ridgecliff 7560, Ritchie 7561, Schwartz, 7576, Skyler 7595, Smith 7598, Southard 7599, Stein 7601, Swagelok 7608, Thendara 7616, Van 7625, Watson 7633, Young 7651

Oklahoma: Barnes 7659, Barnett 7660, Burkhart 7665, Chilton 7667, Everest 7676, French 7680, Goddard

7684, Jones 7691, Krueger 7695, Lolmaugh 7700, Ward 7728, Warren 7729

Oregon: Ackley 7740, Castle 7745, Coffman 7750, Demorest 7757, Gill 7766, Hitchman 7774, Huddart 7776, Irwin 7777, Jonas 7778, Kimmel 7782, Kuse 7786, Lamb 7787, McKay 7795, Merlo 7797, Michael 7799, Pendleton 7806, Roundhouse 7810, Schmidt 7813, Sharkey 7815, West 7827, White 7830

Pennsylvania: Aaron 7835, Baker 7851, Bergman 7863, Bishop 7874, Black 7875, Bolte 7882, Bon-Ton 7884, Born 7885, Breedlove 7890, Brinkman 7893, Brooks 7898, Carnahan-Jackson 7917, Child 7923, Clark 7926, Community 7933, Cost 7937, Crawford 7945, Delaware 7953, Dinardo 7960, Drueding 7966, Elk 7975, Ellis 7978, Everard 7985, Five 7999, Fountainhead 8004, Freas 8005, Frohring 8010, Garthwaite 8013, Grumbacher 8028, Grundy 8029, Hankin 8038, HFO 8053, Hilles 8057, Hoch 8060, Hulme 8069, Jackson 8078, John 8081, Knudsen 8102, Laughlin 8114, Ludwick 8134, Maslow 8146, Mason 8147, McCandless 8153, Mill 8172, Miller 8173, Murphy 8185, Olitsky 8198, Packer 8201, Patterson 8205, Penn 8208, Perelman 8209, Plankenhorn 8219, Price 8225, Rosenberg 8244, Sample, 8252, Schautz 8257, Schuylkill 8263, Seybert 8269, Shenk 8274, Smith 8280, Smith, 8285, Somerville 8291, Spencer 8293, Staley 8296, Stewart 8301, **Susquehanna 8310**, Teleflex 8314, Tuttleman 8325, Ward 8343, Weiner 8349, Williams 8357, Wurts 8370, York 8374, **Zeldin 8376**

Rhode Island: Gross 8414, Heydt 8419, Kimball 8434, Kingsbury 8435, LLH/LHM 8442, McWethy 8453, Molder 8455, Mulligan 8457, O'Halloran 8462, Perpetual 8471, Prouty 8476, Schwarz 8483, Shea 8486, Wilson 8504

South Carolina: Bailey 8510, Bonner 8513, Chapman 8517, Singing 8540

South Dakota: Engelsma 8563, Miller 8570, Peterson 8572, Stearns 8575

Tennessee: Adams 8579, Aim 8581, Atticus 8582, BGL 8588, Cole 8600, Community 8601, Cracker 8603, Doochin 8605, Draughon 8607, EBS 8610, Gaylord 8620, Goldsmith 8622, Hutcheson 8631, Jewell 8633, Johnson 8634, Kite 8639, Massengill-DeFriece 8647, Mercy 8650, Mick 8651, Monday 8652, Pfeffer 8659, Powell 8661, Rose 8667, Sasco 8669, Schadt 8670, Seme 8673, Siegel 8674, Small 8675, Stadler 8678

Texas: A 8689, Adam 8691, ADR 8693, Alexander 8696, Anderson 8704, Arena 8707, Augur 8712, Behmann 8725, Bromley 8749, Bunyard 8755, Central 8766, Conley 8784, **Crowder 8792**, Dale 8794, De 8803, di 8812, Dobson 8819, Duncan 8833, Edwards 8837, Elkins 8838, Esping 8841, Fair 8844, Faith 8846, Fash 8848, Fertitta 8852, FHC 8853, Fired 8859, Fleming 8860, Friedel 8875, Friedman 8876, Fuller 8882, Garvey 8884, Gatewood 8885, Go 8891, Guetz 8905, Hardner 8918, Hatfield 8922, Hervey 8932, Hibbs 8934, Hicks 8935, Hicks 8936, Hofstetter 8943, Horizon 8951, Horween 8952, Johnson 8969, Johnston 8972, Kayser 8980, Kelley 8984, Knox 8999, Kolitz 9000, Lantana 9009, Levy 9014, Littauer 9021, Long 9023, Lowdon 9025, Lupton 9028, MacDonald-Peterson 9032, McKee 9052, McNutt 9055, Meyer 9061, Meyerson 9062, Miller 9065, Mithoff 9068, Moss 9076, Muse 9080, Oppenheimer 9100, Overlake 9106, Papadopoulos 9113, Patton 9119, Paulos 9120, Penland 9124, Perkins 9125, Petty 9126, Proctor 9139, RDM 9146, Reuhl 9150, Riter, 9154, Roosth 9160, Rosenberg 9162, Rubenstein 9167, Sanguinetti 9172, Schulte 9181, Sharma 9190, Shepherds 9191, South 9210, Starnes 9214, Staubach 9215, Stevenson 9220, Taub 9229, Thompson 9234, Tolleson 9238, Vaughan 9248, Waggoner 9254, Wal-Dot 9256, Ward 9260, Weir 9268, Weir 9269, Westcott 9273, Wilder 9277, Willard 9278, Williams 9280, Williams 9281, Womack 9289, Works 9293

Utah: Bastian 9304, Burton 9309, Cardon 9311, Crawford 9314, Eskuche 9323, Kennecott 9333

Vermont: Harper 9373, Stokes 9385

Virginia: Bassett 9391, Better 9396, Blue 9401, Bruhn-Morris 9408, Bryant 9409, Burford 9411, Cartledge 9414, Chainani 9417, **Delmar 9429**, Dun 9437, Hansen 9465, Houff 9473, Hughes 9474, Ivakota 9477, Lacy 9485, Lintott 9492, Overton 9506, Poole 9512, Shaffer 9530, Strauch 9538, Treakle 9543, Womack 9556

Washington: Bacon 9565, Baker 9566, Cartales 9578, DeFalco 9585, Echo 9590, Foss 9598, Gibson 9604, Goodman 9608, Hickey 9622, HIS 9624, Howarth 9626, Kawabe 9642, Kilworth 9644, Morningside 9665, Nysether 9671, O'Donnell 9672, **Ormsby 9674**, Shemanski 9693, Skagit 9696, Spring 9702, Teel 9708, Thurston 9713, Titus-Will 9714, Tonkin 9715, Welch 9721, Young 9732

West Virginia: Carter 9741, Chambers 9742, Larch 9755, Logan 9756, Wehrle 9771

Wisconsin: BayCare 9781, Birnschein 9783, Bluemke 9785, Braun 9787, Chipstone 9794, Courtier 9798, Cudahy 9800, Dudley 9811, Gardner 9825, Glanert 9827, Hartwig 9836, Holoubek 9843, Jacobus 9849, Kalscheur 9858, Kohl 9864, Manitowoc 9876, Meinerz 9883, Merkel 9884, Mortenson 9890, Phipps 9903, Pritchett 9906, RCP 9909, Seeds 9925, Simms 9929, Stateline 9937, Stry 9941, Van 9952, Webcrafters-Frautschi 9957, Witte, 9962, Woodtrust-Bell 9963

Wyoming: Connemara 9967, Dragicevich 9969, Ellbogen 9971, Sargent 9985, Scott 9988, Surrena 9994

Childbirth

Nebraska: Scribante 5116
New York: Gordon 6110, Harris 6172

Children

Alabama: Black 12, Ireland 39, Malone 48, Warren 75
Alaska: **Nash 90**
Arizona: Goldberg 124, Kuhle 139
Arkansas: Darragh 193, Olds 210
California: Adelaide 230, Baker 265, Barco's 277, Berglund 303, Community 421, Confetti 422, **Girls 559**, **Hefferlin 610**, KNU 713, Legacy 740, Lopez 767, Nicholson 866, Previti 937, **Quiksilver 945**, SHP 1035, **Sunwest 1094**, Welk 1170, Yen 1201
Colorado: Connor 1250, Donnell-Kay 1258
Connecticut: Cochrane 1420
Delaware: ABE 1607, Hoops 1682
District of Columbia: Replogle 1831
Florida: Anton 1851, Brighton 1899, Carlton 1922, Case 1925, Cherry 1940, Couch 1953, Greene-Sawtell 2065, Hardison 2081, KT 2160, Landwirth 2167, Ruskin 2302, Shuey 2333, Siegel 2335, Thomas 2370, Wells 2397
Georgia: Abreu 2431, Gray 2497, **Invisible 2520**, L. 2535, Looney 2542, Noonan 2558, Wright 2620
Hawaii: Martin 2641
Idaho: Whittenberger 2689
Illinois: Alliant 2702, Alton 2706, Bailey 2716, Bellick 2732, Best 2740, Brenner 2756, Family 2864, Fifield 2871, Krehbiel 3030, Mary's 3081, McNally 3097, **Mead 3100**, Meier 3101, Meyer 3106, Oberweiler 3147, Putnam 3186, Schorr-Lieberman 3229, Stuart 3273
Iowa: Iowa 3513, **Wahlert 3544**
Kansas: Family 3575, Legacy, 3595, Payless 3614
Kentucky: Killian 3670, Rounsavall, 3691
Maryland: Eccles 3853, Israelson 3888
Massachusetts: **Brabson 4026**, Gildea 4103, Kelsey 4148, Lamm 4165, Verrochi 4342
Michigan: Holden 4467, Schmuckal 4559, Tuscola 4598, Wieczorek 4617
Minnesota: Aca 4622, Acorn 4623, Bell 4637, Erickson 4674, Good 4698, Noreen 4750
Missouri: **Bohm 4871**, Brinklee 4876, **Build-A-Bear 4879**, Cinmar 4887, Dunn 4898

Nevada: Dermody 5152
New Hampshire: DEKA 5210, Finlay 5213
New Jersey: A 5240, Chang 5289
New Mexico: Schnieders 5623
New York: **Companions 5873**, **Flowering 6015**, **Grossman 6146**, Lemle 6377, Lerer 6382, Mastrocola 6449, National 6520, Project 6631, **Rao 6645**, Rothenberg 6702, Ruttenberg 6715, **Schmeelk 6742**, Sperandio 6835, Wachenheim 6935
North Carolina: Burks 7061, Evernham 7094, Glenn 7111, Hunter 7136, Moseley 7194, Redwoods 7218, Stuart 7259
Ohio: A 7299, Athens 7311, Fortney 7406, Ridgecliff 7560, Sandfair 7569, Scion 7578, Walker 7630
Oregon: Elwood 7761
Pennsylvania: Ayers 7848, Blue 7879, Case 7918, Coffin 7930, Craig-Dalsimer 7942, Eakins 7968, Edwards 7973, Gauss 8014, Herndon 8051, Hoffman 8062, Lewis 8125, Ludwick 8134, McKamish 8158, Mill 8172, Mudge 8181, Mullen 8184, Nesh 8191, O'Reilly 8200, Wurts 8370
Rhode Island: Bersted 8388, Littlefield 8441
Tennessee: Cracker 8603, **Fugitive 8618**, Goad 8621, Seme 8673
Texas: Alexander 8696, American 8699, AMR/American 8703, **Astri 8711**, **Chrest 8770**, Corlin 8788, Foundation 8869, Holloway 8946, O'Hare 9095, Opie 9099, Smith 9204, **Soonae 9208**, Strickland 9224, Swett 9227, Torrance 9241
Vermont: Mergens 9381
Virginia: **Brown 9407**, Collins 9424, **Delmar 9429**, Ivakota 9477, Ochsman 9504, Wiley 9551
Washington: Bayley 9567, Bungie 9576, Everett 9592, Loeb 9654, True 9716, Wissner-Slivka 9727
West Virginia: Chambers 9742
Wisconsin: Inbusch 9847, Jacobus 9849, Lakeview 9868, Marshfield 9878

Children and youth

Alabama: Black 12, Harper 33, Ireland 39
Arizona: Armstrong 97, F2 117
California: Calaveras 369, Clara 406, Gellert 550, Horwitz 633, Just 684, KNU 713, Leeds 738, Nicholson 866, Solano 1063, Stauffer 1077, **Wakerly 1150**, Wheeler 1179
Colorado: Donnell-Kay 1258
Connecticut: Fippinger 1450, Fry 1458, Shumway 1570
Delaware: Lightner 1699
District of Columbia: Bloedorn 1790, Himmelfarb 1815, Replogle 1831
Florida: Brighton 1899, Coral 1952, Couch 1953, Jacobsen 2123, Landwirth 2167, Mount 2223, Patterson 2250, Sudakoff 2356, Wilson-Wood 2408
Georgia: Abreu 2431, Holly 2509, Wright 2620
Hawaii: Central 2627
Idaho: Whittenberger 2689
Illinois: Bates 2725, Bulkley 2765, Family 2864, Meyer 3106, Oberweiler 3147
Indiana: Seymour 3448
Iowa: Gartner 3496
Kansas: Baehr 3556, Kansas 3592
Kentucky: Killian 3670
Massachusetts: **Brabson 4026**, Kelsey 4148, Kimball 4155
Michigan: Holden 4467, Mackinac 4499, O'Donovan 4525, Tuscola 4598
Minnesota: Larsen 4728, Wells 4811
Mississippi: Lower 4847
Missouri: Sander 4991, Sunnen 5018
Nevada: Matley 5176
New Mexico: Con 5611
New York: Anderson 5674, Antun 5681, August 5698, French 6032, Gerstman 6074, **Grossman 6146**, Henshel 6192, Holmberg 6221, Kenworthy 6300, Snow 6818, Yearley 7005
North Carolina: Glenn 7111, Sanders 7234, Strowd 7258
Ohio: Community 7357, **Katz 7475**, Ridgecliff 7560, Sandfair 7569

Oregon: Elwood 7761, Lamb 7787, McKay 7795, Wessinger 7826, West 7827
Pennsylvania: Child 7923, Delaware 7953, Garthwaite 8013, Hilles 8057, Hoffman 8062, Maslow 8146, McKee 8160, Mill 8172, Murphy 8185, Rosenlund 8245
Rhode Island: Dwinell 8403
South Carolina: Greenwood 8526, Lutz 8533
Tennessee: **Fugitive 8618**
Texas: Edwards 8837, Foundation 8869, Kessler 8987, Mayer 9043, Montgomery 9070
Vermont: Mergens 9381, Stokes 9385
Virginia: **Delmar 9429**, Wiser 9555
Washington: DeFalco 9585, Foss 9598, Korum 9648, Wilson 9725, Wyman 9731
Wisconsin: Arzbaecher 9777, Hamilton 9834, Jacobus 9849, Lakeview 9868, Marshfield 9878

Children's hospital care

Alabama: Warren 75
Arizona: Kuhle 139
California: Confetti 422
Colorado: Connor 1250
Delaware: Hoops 1682
Florida: Hardison 2081, Siegel 2335, Thomas 2370
Hawaii: Martin 2641
Illinois: Brenner 2756, Fifield 2871, Krehbiel 3030, Putnam 3186
Kansas: Family 3575
Maryland: Marriott 3909
Michigan: Holden 4467, Wieczorek 4617
Missouri: Brinklee 4876
New Jersey: Chang 5289
New York: **Companions 5873**, National 6520, **Rao 6645**, Wachenheim 6935
North Carolina: Burks 7061, Moseley 7194
Pennsylvania: Case 7918, Craig-Dalsimer 7942, Herndon 8051, McKamish 8158, Nesh 8191, O'Reilly 8200
Tennessee: Goad 8621
Texas: Alexander 8696, Edwards 8837, Opie 9099, Torrance 9241
Washington: Bayley 9567, Bungie 9576, Loeb 9654, Wilson 9725

Children's museums

Arizona: Hughes 130
California: Corwin 428, Magali 781, Martin 803
District of Columbia: Westport 1838
Florida: Fontaine 2006
Georgia: Vaughan 2598
Illinois: New 3136, Shodeen 3246
Indiana: Harlan 3391, Mothershead 3419, Oakley 3426, Weston 3467
Nebraska: Ameritas 5067, Kinder 5099
New Jersey: **Ju 5410**
Pennsylvania: Patterson 8205
Tennessee: Pattee 8656
Texas: Knox 8999, Levy 9014
Washington: Wissner-Slivka 9727
Wisconsin: Highlands 9841, Johnson 9853, Seramur 9926, Van 9952

Children's rights

Indiana: Duneland 3372
Maryland: Anderson 3814
Missouri: Shawe 5000
Texas: Houck 8953

Choreography

Kentucky: Kentucky 3669

Christian Science

California: Robinson 977

Christianity

Alabama: Anderson 6, Brinkley 15, Brown 16, **Christian 21**, Harris 34, JADO 40, Kairos 41, King 43, Petra 53, Sexton 63, Siloam 65, Williams 77, Zeiger 79
Arizona: Armstrong 97, Burns 102, Cooper 109, Dove 112, Eaton 115, Feenstra 118, Forsberg 119, Immanuel 131, Jasam 133, Johnson 135, Long 141, Marketplace 145, McKee 148, Picerne 155, Rae 159, Stevens 175, Williams 182
Arkansas: Bailey 187, Riggs 214
California: Adelaide 230, Aroma 255, Atkinson 259, Becker 292, Berakah 302, Blanchard 321, Bonner 327, Boone 328, Braddock 336, **Bull 358**, Cavaricci 381, CEC 382, Ceunis 385, **Chan 388**, Christian 402, CNC 410, Crawford 435, De 446, Evening 487, First 507, Folger 515, Foor 516, Forgatch 517, Freshwind 528, Funari 539, **Hampar 594**, Hawley 605, Heinz 612, Helms 615, Herrmann 618, **Hsieh 636**, Jamieson 658, Joerger 665, Johnson 667, Johnson 670, Joy 677, Judkins 682, Judkins 683, Kao 690, Keith 696, Kimbo 705, Laurance 732, Lemons 744, Lisle 760, Lyman 774, Malachi 785, Marcil 793, Marshburn 799, Martin 802, Massie 806, Mayer 809, McDaniel 812, McMahon 819, Miller 829, **Modglin 840**, Muckel 850, **Munson 852**, **New 863**, Olander 878, Optivest 884, Orthodox 890, Osborn 891, Peterson 918, Rediger 960, Schimmel 1015, Setzer 1029, Shannon 1030, SHP 1035, Smith 1053, Smith 1054, Stellar 1080, Stewart 1083, Straus 1088, Thorne 1114, **Upside 1140**, **Vogelzang 1146**, Von 1148, Walters 1153, West 1175, Yoder 1202, Zurlo 1217
Colorado: Allen 1220, Bean 1228, Bloedorn 1238, Cliffline 1247, Clough 1248, Cornerstone 1251, Dorset 1259, Gerrish 1277, HAVRK8 1288, Joslin-Needham 1300, Kortz 1307, Leininger 1312, Lewan 1314, Lewis 1315, **Nord 1332**, Praise 1339, Reel 1345, Thiel 1365, Tomkins 1368, Triune 1370, White 1378
Connecticut: Acorn 1385, Agape 1387, Cochrane 1420, Crew 1424, Dennett 1432, Diageo 1437, Finn 1449, Floren 1451, Gengras, 1461, Hume 1485, Kreitler 1502, Panwy 1539, Proctor 1545, **Richardson 1550**, Roberts 1551, Schendel 1561, Titus 1585
Delaware: ABE 1607, Barnabas 1614, Bennett 1618, Bradley 1626, Brandsma 1627, Brown 1630, Burton 1634, CVW 1653, Farr 1662, **Gloria 1670**, Groot 1673, Harkness 1677, Loftus 1700, Mulvaney 1713, New 1716, Petersen 1720, Pinkerton 1721, Riecker 1729, Rivera 1730, Sanders 1737, Splawn 1749, Telluray 1762, Thronson 1766
District of Columbia: Westport 1838
Florida: A. 1841, Ael 1843, Anderson 1846, Andre 1849, Aurora 1860, Bailey 1863, Barnard 1866, Basham 1870, Baulch 1873, Baxter 1874, Bell 1882, Bond 1897, Brighton 1899, Brinckerhoff 1900, Burnett 1911, Case 1925, Castellani 1927, Chaffiot 1933, Chapman 1935, Childress 1942, Crane 1955, Cunnane 1959, Dalton 1960, Deus 1972, EGW 1988, Family 1997, Fontaine 2006, For 2007, Foster 2013, **Freewill 2021**, Fricks 2023, Fuller 2028, Godbold 2041, Grabe 2053, Grader 2054, Hahn 2072, Haskell 2083, Hoerner 2102, Holloway 2106, Holtz 2109, Hufty 2114, J. 2122, Janke 2126, Jasam 2127, **Joshua 2132**, Kehrer 2143, Kelly 2144, Kiwanis 2149, Lacy, 2163, Lambert 2164, Lerner 2180, Loftis 2188, Martin 2196, Mary 2198, Miller 2213, Morrison 2222, Nelson 2230, Nuzzo 2236, Overstreet 2242, P.M. 2244, Pascal 2249, Pearle 2253, Peters 2256, **Place 2261**, Price 2267, Pusey 2272, Reinhold 2280, Rembert 2281, Rinker 2287, Rogers 2291, Selders 2322, Sharing 2330, **Shepard 2331**, Smith 2341, Smith 2342, Speranza 2344, Spier 2345, **Taylor 2365**, Thomas 2370, Thomas 2371, Thompson 2372, Thornburgh 2374, Thurman 2375, Tippett 2376, Turlington 2380, von 2388, Wells 2397, Woerner 2409, Woodbery 2413, Wright 2415, Wrightson-Ramsing 2416, Younger 2422, Zehnder 2423, **Zimmer 2425**

Georgia: A.E.M. 2430, Belcher, 2444, Clary 2462, Community 2466, Cooper 2469, **Faith 2477**, Georgia 2485, Gordy 2493, Griffin 2499, Harrison 2502, Howell 2511, Hoyt 2513, Hunter 2515, Hurlbert 2516, K. 2528, Kingdom 2531, Lassiter 2539, Lee 2540, Lipscomb 2541, Magnus 2543, McKinney-Geib 2547, Noonan 2558, Orkin 2560, Pattillo 2563, Pennies 2565, Schinazi 2580, Smith 2586, Solstice 2587, Thames 2594, Walton 2604, Williamson 2613, Woodruff 2617, Wright 2620, Young 2621

Hawaii: Kaneta 2637, Martin 2641, Wong 2656

Idaho: Ambrosiani-Pastore 2663, Emelco 2669, Morrison 2682, Thomas 2687

Illinois: **Acorn 2695**, Adreani 2697, Ahlstrand 2700, Alton 2705, Banta 2719, Bartholomay 2721, Baudhuin 2726, Baum 2727, Bere 2734, Boylan 2753, Brewer 2757, Canterbury 2774, Ceres 2779, Christiansen 2790, **Combs 2800**, Constans-Culver 2805, Cornerstone 2812, Cronin 2816, Cronk 2817, Delta 2826, Epaphroditus 2857, Federation 2868, Fields 2870, Franklin 2888, Frisby 2893, Gallagher 2898, Garard, 2902, Gochnauer 2918, Griffith 2929, Hanson 2950, Houck 2978, Houlihan 2979, Howard 2981, Jaros 2993, Keyes 3016, Kilrea 3017, Knappenberger 3021, Lamka 3034, Leestma 3044, Lichner 3051, Logos 3058, Luehring 3065, MacDonald 3068, Mallon 3071, Marcum 3076, Mary's 3080, McCormack 3086, McKee 3093, McNulty 3099, **Mead 3100**, Merchantz 3102, Meyer 3106, **Meyers 3107**, Micole 3108, Millard 3109, Miner 3116, Mohr 3121, Morton 3127, Murphy 3132, Pepper 3167, Peters 3171, Richard 3195, Robson 3200, Seidler 3233, Shamrock 3239, Share 3241, Spencer 3258, Stairway 3261, Vail 3301, Walker 3308, Webb 3313, Wislow 3323, Witz-Mallinger 3324, Wolf 3326, Wolf 3327, Woodruff 3330

Indiana: BAJ 3343, Branigin 3348, CDM 3355, Conrad 3364, Elder 3375, Froderman 3383, Gardiner 3384, God's 3388, Green 3389, Herr 3392, J. 3400, Jennings 3403, KEJ 3406, Maurer 3415, Niblick 3423, OTT 3430, Raper 3435, Seger 3447, Stucky 3457, Thomasson 3459, Thrush-Thompson 3460, Vision 3463, Von 3464, Welter 3465

Iowa: Barkema 3471, Beckwith 3473, Coons 3481, Grubb 3502, GuideOne 3503, Herr 3506, Hills 3507, Nelson 3524, Schildberg 3532, Van 3540, Vermeer 3541, Vermeer 3542, Weathertop 3545, **Wright 3551**

Kansas: Berry 3558, Cyr 3570, Fidelity 3577, Green 3583, Haglage 3584, **Kejr 3593**, Kiersznowski 3594, Logan 3597, McFadden 3601, Merrill 3602, Middlekauff 3603, Reeble 3618, Schmidt 3622, Shannon 3625, South 3628, Taylor 3632, **Weskan 3641**

Kentucky: Coffey 3650, Etscorn 3654, GHH 3658, Hannah 3659, Horn 3664, Killian 3670, Longest 3672, Morris 3679, Steiner 3696, Stockdell-Joseph 3698

Louisiana: Dujay 3722, Huie-Dellmon 3729, Moffett 3739, Wheless 3758, Zuschlag 3762

Maine: Bailey 3765, Protein 3799, Sukeforth 3805

Maryland: Devito 3848, **Doorstep 3850**, Duncan 3851, Fusco 3868, Huether/McClelland 3884, Jake 3890, Mustard 3922, Nicholl 3926, No 3927, O'Neil 3930, Pettit 3935, SPM 3958, Stover 3961, Ten 3963, Tucker 3969, **Windsor 3988**

Massachusetts: Behrakis 4015, Casey 4039, Chabot 4042, Change 4043, Eddy 4077, Egan 4079, Encourage 4082, Franklin 4096, Hogan 4132, Kelleher 4147, Koha 4158, Lingos 4177, Makepeace 4185, Melvina 4197, Mulberry 4213, Ragon 4256, Vine's 4344, Wheatland 4358, Whittemore 4359, Young 4366

Michigan: Anchor 4376, Baldwin 4382, Betten 4390, Bierlein 4392, Buhr 4400, Buist 4401, Cebelak 4406, Christian 4407, Christian 4408, Conrad 4413, Cracchiolo 4414, de 4422, DeKock 4425, DeWitt 4429, Dik 4430, Farwell 4442, Filmer 4444, Foren 4448, Garrett 4452, Gordon 4456, JCT 4469, Jurries 4476, Kellogg 4482, Kosch 4485, Koster 4486, Lee 4491, Linse 4493, Maibach

4500, McDole 4507, McDonald 4508, Merkley 4512, Michell 4513, Mojo 4516, Murdock 4519, Nickless 4522, Onequest 4527, Paulina 4535, Peslar 4537, Pilgrim 4539, River 4551, Roscommon 4552, Sackerson 4557, Serra 4565, Shine 4569, Springview 4575, Tamer 4585, Tremble 4595, Van 4601, Welch 4610, Wheeler 4612, White 4613, Zondervan 4621

Minnesota: Bailey 4633, Bieber 4641, Covenant 4661, Desiring 4668, **Emmerich 4673**, Evert 4676, Faith, 4677, Fletcher 4687, Frey 4690, Garmar 4694, Getsch 4695, Granite 4699, Haggerty 4705, Hallett 4706, Iversen 4717, Kinney 4724, Lillehei 4729, Luther 4733, Mahon 4737, Mooty 4747, Morning 4748, Pautsch 4759, Rauenhorst 4767, Reimer 4771, Rieks 4774, Rodman 4779, Rosen 4782, Sacred 4783, Sexton 4790, Terhuly 4799, Turner 4803, Wallestad 4806, Walsh-Brady 4808, Weyand 4814, Whaley 4816

Mississippi: Amory 4821, Brevard 4826, Carothers 4827, Family 4834, Fountain 4837, Hancock 4840, Harris 4841, Hope 4844, Lexington 4846, Seal, 4853, Skelton 4854

Missouri: Arnold 4861, Canfield 4882, Fabick 4907, HCG, 4925, Herschend 4928, Mathews, 4953, Meyer 4959, Moulton 4965, Neeb 4968, Pearl 4977, Peculiar 4978, Pillsbury 4980, Rust 4988, Slusher 5009, Sugarbaker 5016, Thorp 5020, Vatterott 5030, Voelkerding 5032, Woods 5042

Montana: Angora 5044, Cora 5048

Nebraska: Baer 5069, Burnett 5075, Cimpl 5076, Cope 5077, Heuermann 5092, Owen 5108, Quivey-Bay 5113, Scribante 5116, Shaw 5117

Nevada: **A 5131**, Coleman 5150, Crescere 5151, Foundation 5158, Jansen 5164, Joshua 5167, Lemay 5172, Living 5174, Vandevoort 5194, Webb 5196

New Hampshire: **Christian 5207**, Couch 5209, Dunn 5212, Hunt 5214, Levine 5218, Verney 5236, Wutz 5239

New Jersey: Anderson 5249, Bauer 5257, BMI-Rupp 5270, Brueckner 5279, CBIS 5288, Citta 5295, Clermont 5298, Conant 5302, **Dankis 5312**, Doll 5322, Engel 5335, Fox 5349, **Garcia 5362**, His 5395, Jones 5408, Kampen 5413, Katz 5414, Kurr 5435, Marino 5457, Marron 5461, Paterson 5493, Patrick 5494, Pepper 5496, Post 5505, Roma 5513, Schlaffer 5522, Shilling 5534, Snyder 5542, Spiro 5546, Take 5555, Todd 5560, Waters 5571, Weny 5581

New York: Ades-Taub 5645, Angel 5678, Barney 5717, Beck 5728, Bell 5734, Brillo-Sonnino 5785, Brown 5791, Buckley 5798, Bush 5805, Cheatham 5836, Desai 5910, **Farkas 5988**, Fee 5990, Feinman 5994, Fenton 5998, Fleming 6014, Forest 6018, Gaffney 6049, Goldmann 6099, H. 6153, Hein 6184, Houston 6228, Johnson 6267, Johnson-Stillman 6271, Joyce 6275, Mabardi 6428, Marine 6442, Monaghan 6502, Morse 6509, Niemiec 6535, Palmer 6572, Peek 6584, Psalm 6633, Rheinstrom 6665, Rhodes 6666, Roxe 6706, Salisbury 6719, Seven 6777, Smith 6814, Spofford 6842, Stebbins 6850, Stifel 6865, Stowe 6869, Thanksgiving 6897, Thiem 6898, Three 6899, Willmott 6978, **Woodland 6989**, Yeager 7004, Zafirovski 7014, Zyman 7036

North Carolina: Bell 7047, Bertsch 7050, Bolick 7056, Brown 7058, Burks 7061, Cannon 7067, Cary 7069, Chatham 7074, Cooke 7079, Everett 7093, Family 7096, Fortson 7100, Glenn 7111, Harvest 7118, Harvey-McNairy 7119, Hayes 7121, Hoffman 7128, Howe 7132, Jelm 7137, Kennedy 7145, Koons 7148, Krauss 7153, Mattison 7175, McConnell 7176, Moore 7188, Moretz 7189, Morisey 7191, Mosser 7195, P 7205, Pillmore 7210, Pope 7212, Ragland, 7216, Richardson 7221, Ritchie 7222, Robbins 7224, Robinson 7225, Robitaille 7226, Rocky 7227, Rostan 7232, Shingleton 7241, Shugart 7242, Sites 7245, Stonecutter 7255, Stowe 7256, Trexler 7269, West-West 7284, Yount 7292

Ohio: Bates 7317, Besl 7326, Brethen 7331, Brinck 7333, Cassner 7348, Christ 7352, Conlogue 7359,

Conn 7360, Crossroads 7367, Damico 7370, **Dauch 7372**, Davidson 7374, Dorn 7380, **Elisha-Bolton 7387**, Eyman 7391, Gale 7414, Gross 7432, Heffner 7443, Heimann 7444, Hieronymus 7448, Homan 7451, Juniper 7472, Kamm 7473, Kramer 7485, Lang 7489, Lawson 7492, Lindner 7497, Linnemann 7498, Lundgard 7508, M.L.M 7510, Mehl 7523, Milliron 7529, Norris 7538, Orr 7543, Reed 7555, Steinmann 7603, Tell 7613, Thompson, 7617, Wagler 7629, Walker 7630, Weiss 7634, Wilson 7642, Yoder 7650, Young 7652

Oklahoma: Ad 7654, Barnes 7658, Barnes 7659, Burkhart 7665, **Crio 7670**, Fugitt 7681, Goodin 7685, Harmon 7686, Jones 7691, Kimmell 7694, Liddell 7697, Lolmaugh 7700, Moore 7710, Owasso 7712, Peel 7714, Richardson 7717, Staton 7720, Witt 7737, Young 7739

Oregon: Cayo 7746, Dieringer 7758, Flowerree 7763, Harvest 7769, Hitchman 7774, Huddart 7776, Lindgren 7791, **Living 7792**, Miller 7800, Pendleton 7806, Spencer 7820, Stewart 7822

Pennsylvania: Bishop 7874, Bonomo 7883, Breedlove 7890, Buck 7904, Carnahan-Jackson 7917, Casteel 7919, Clark 7925, Clark 7927, Clovis 7928, Cove 7939, Covenant 7940, Crawford 7945, Dickson 7957, Dinardo 7960, Eden 7971, Engle 7982, Family 7988, Fetters 7991, Finley 7995, Fleming 8000, Hahn 8036, High 8054, Hulme 8069, Hunt 8070, Ice 8072, Jackson 8078, Kinney 8092, Kittenbrink 8093, Klein 8097, KMJ 8099, Knudsen 8102, Landenberger 8109, Larsen 8113, Lemole 8119, Lubert 8133, Mateer 8150, Moggio 8176, Mosi 8179, Packer 8201, Patterson 8206, Reese 8232, Roemer 8242, Schafer 8256, Schautz 8257, Schoonmaker 8260, Shady 8270, Smith 8283, Spencer 8293, Staley 8296, Strawbridge 8305, Trax 8321, Venne 8331, Wagner 8338, Ward 8343

Rhode Island: Bailey 8384, Hubbard 8425, Leroe 8439, N. 8459, O'Halloran 8462, Olsen 8463, Peacock 8469, Shea 8486, Woodward 8505, Wright 8506

South Carolina: Bailey 8510, Bannon 8511, Bonner 8513, Chapman 8517, Collins 8520, Davis 8521, Gibson 8523, Greenleaf 8525, Peery/Cauthen 8537, Sunshine 8544, Tarr 8545, Verhagen 8547, WPW 8551

South Dakota: Elmen 8560, Elmen 8561, Miller 8570, Welk 8577

Tennessee: Adams 8579, Aim 8581, Berman 8587, Cartinhour-Woods 8597, Citizens 8599, Cornerstone 8602, Drake 8606, Draughon 8607, EBS 8610, Firstfruits 8614, Fleming 8615, Foster 8616, **Fugitive 8618**, **Gardner 8619**, Grandview 8625, Kennedy 8638, LDB 8642, Mercy 8650, Mick 8651, Monday 8652, Nehemiah 8653, Pettway 8658, Powell 8661, Proctor 8662, Provision 8663, **Redbird 8664**, Schmidt 8671, Seidman 8672, Seme 8673

Texas: ADR 8693, Anderson 8704, Ash 8709, **Astri 8711**, Augur 8712, Barnabas 8717, Beghini 8724, Behmann 8725, Bloxom, 8731, Brentwood 8741, Bromley 8749, Brown 8750, Brown 8751, Budd 8753, Connor 8785, D3 8793, Daniel 8797, Deason 8805, Denman 8810, DKG 8817, Dobson 8819, Dougherty 8824, Dunagan 8831, Farris 8847, Fentress 8851, Fleming 8860, Flohr 8861, Flowers 8862, Foster 8867, Frankel 8872, Fruehauf 8879, FSR 8880, Genovese 8887, Give 8890, Gottlieb 8894, Gray 8899, Greentree 8901, Griffin 8902, Hatfield 8922, Hegi 8926, Hext 8933, Hicks 8935, Holmes 8947, Houck 8953, Howard 8954, Howell 8956, Hunter 8957, Jacobs 8964, Janszen 8966, Johnson 8970, Kelley 8983, Kessler 8987, **Kilgore 8989**, **Kingdom 8995**, Knox 8999, Lighthouse 9017, Lowdon 9025, MacDonald-Peterson 9032, Manna 9034, **Mansur 9035**, **McCreless 9049**, McKee 9052, Mendenhall 9056, Mercy 9057, Merrick 9059, Miller 9064, Miller 9065, N.H. 9082, **New 9087**, Nowiczewski 9090, Nowotny 9091, Nuncio 9092, O'Connor 9093, Oriska 9103, Overlake 9106, PAL 9111, Penland 9124, Phoenix 9128, Pratt 9137, Prayer

9138, Raygar 9145, Redman 9147, Reilly 9148, Reitch 9149, Richter 9153, Robinson 9158, Rust 9168, Saunders 9176, Schoener 9180, Seven 9189, Shepherds 9191, Simard 9195, Smith 9207, **Soonae 9208**, Sterling 9219, Stewart, 9221, Stoller 9222, Storehouse 9223, Taub 9229, Trojan 9242, Van 9247, Vetter 9251, Waggoner 9254, Way 9264, Wells 9271, Whitley 9276, Wilder 9277, Williams 9280, Wise 9283, Womack 9289, Wynne 9296
Utah: Eskuche 9323, Schmidt 9349, Turley 9360
Vermont: Harper 9373, Harvest 9374, Mergens 9381
Virginia: Berni 9395, **Brown 9407**, Chastain 9419, Donohue 9432, Doudera 9434, Dundas 9438, Fink 9447, Good 9461, Greco 9463, Il 9475, Lane 9486, McWaters 9499, Overton 9506, Sauer 9527, Shaffer 9530, Stafford 9535, Stone 9537, Valentine 9545, Willett 9552, Williams-Berry 9554
Washington: **Children's 9579**, Coleman 9580, FAR 9595, Gius 9606, Goodman 9608, Grousemont 9611, Heath 9617, Helstrom 9619, HIS 9624, **Jernigan 9631**, Joint 9636, Longbrake 9655, Martin 9659, Spring 9702, Suen 9705, Teel 9708, Thomson 9711, Thurston 9713, Ward 9718, **Wiebe 9723**, Worthington 9729
West Virginia: Bowen 9736, Carter 9741, Hamer 9746
Wisconsin: Anderson 9773, Baker 9780, BayCare 9781, Bluemke 9785, Carlisle 9792, **Global 9829**, Hicks 9840, Highlands 9841, Jones 9855, Kaztex 9860, Lato 9869, Loehrke 9872, Mortenson 9890, Plein 9904, RCP 9909, Redmond 9910, Schmucker 9923, Seeds 9925, Shoemaker 9928, Simms 9929, SMS 9933, St. 9936, T 9945, Tellier 9946, Uihlein 9950, Van 9951, Verhulst 9954, Wagner 9955
Wyoming: Connemara 9967, Guthrie 9972, Imig 9974, Johnson 9977, Richardson 9983, Scott 9987, Stuart 9993

Christians

California: Atkinson 259
Illinois: Christiansen 2790
Kentucky: Coffey 3650
Minnesota: Covenant 4661
Montana: Cora 5048
Texas: Oden 9094

Civic participation

Florida: Price 2267
Ohio: Crandall 7366

Civics for youth

California: Fox 523
Florida: Price 2267
Ohio: Crandall 7366
Virginia: Community 9426

Climate change

District of Columbia: **Butler 1792**
Texas: Boeing 8733, Levy 9014

Communication media

Alabama: Harris 34
California: Coburn 411, Downing 462, Ducommun 465, Faraway 494, LEF 739, Price 938, Rotasa 991, Small 1049
Connecticut: Schloss 1562, Sekerak 1564, Shanley 1567
Delaware: Freedman 1665
Florida: Hornik 2111, Tampa 2362
Illinois: Bound 2751, MacDonald 3068, Minow 3118, O'Connor 3149, Oppenheimer 3155
Indiana: Gammon 3385
Massachusetts: Kenwood 4150
Michigan: Allen 4372
Minnesota: Andersen 4626, Radichel 4765

Mississippi: Crooks 4831
Missouri: Slusher 5009
Montana: Greater 5054
New Jersey: Brundage 5280, **Dow 5325**, Pacific 5485
New York: Beach 5725, Bernhill 5741, Cullman 5887, **Eastman 5940**, **Indira 6242**, JKW 6263, JLK 6264, **King 6311**, Meyer 6485, Moore 6504, Newman 6530, Tribune 6909
North Carolina: **Rolander 7229**
Ohio: Seasongood 7582
Oregon: Coit 7751
Pennsylvania: Arkema 7842, Harsco 8040, Mill 8172
Vermont: Harper 9373

Community and economic development

Alabama: Black 12, Blount 13, Loeb 47, Phifer, 54, Propst 56, Trippe 71
Arizona: Cadeau 104, James 132, Long 141, Louis 142, Schlein 165, Spalding 172
Arkansas: Nabholz 209, Ottenheimer 213, Union 219, White 220
California: Ackerman 227, Amador 238, Baker 264, Bank 272, Callison 371, **Candelaria 372**, Charitable 389, Chelvanayakam 391, Confetti 422, Corcoran 425, Corwin 428, Fliesbach 512, Folger 515, Fuller 538, Gellert 550, Georgina-Frederick 552, Gooding 571, Greenberg 579, Hand 595, Hilltop 621, Hodges 627, Hotchkis 635, Hughes 639, Jamieson 658, Kelly 697, Kendall 700, Kite 711, Koss 720, Lemelson 742, Lewis 754, Manchester 788, McKay 815, Murad 854, New 864, Page 899, Palo 900, Pollia 931, Previti 937, **Quiksilver 945**, RA5 946, Roney 983, Sammut 996, Scott 1022, **Scovel 1025**, Silicon 1038, Simon 1040, Solano 1063, **Support 1095**, Swinerton 1098, Thomson 1113, Tisch 1120, Tomkins 1122, Tuffli 1134
Colorado: Allen 1220, Bardsley 1227, Bloedorn 1238, Eberspacher 1261, Family 1268, Goodwin 1279, Heginbotham 1289, Hunt 1296, Living 1317, Rockwise 1347, Stratton 1359, Stretesky 1360, Titus 1367, Wilkins 1379
Connecticut: Barnes 1403, Farid 1444, Harold 1477, McLaughlin 1523, Proctor 1545, RBS 1549, Savings 1559, Westbrook 1593
Delaware: Bailey-Stanford 1613, Bartlett 1615, Burt's 1635, Chaney 1640, Fernandina 1663, Haldan 1675, Lightner 1699, Russell 1735, Scott 1740
District of Columbia: Cornerstone 1798, Kolar 1818, Mimi 1822, Westport 1838
Florida: Baxter 1874, Becton 1880, Bell 1883, Berelsman 1885, Bond 1897, Burgoon 1908, Capital 1918, Charlotte 1938, Coral 1952, Couch 1953, Davis 1964, de 1966, Fry 2027, Gagnon 2029, Garner 2032, Glass 2039, Gregory 2067, Gulf 2069, Hicks 2094, Jacobson 2124, Lazzara 2174, Livingston 2187, Marshall 2195, McClanathan 2202, McGahren 2204, Mount 2223, Olliff 2239, Phillips 2260, Raymund 2276, Rodgers, 2289, Sexton 2326, Sharing 2330, Steele 2347, Vanneck-Bailey 2384, Westreich 2401
Georgia: Athens 2437, Beard-Payne 2442, Beckman 2443, Benton 2445, Charter 2456, Cobb 2463, Community 2465, Community 2466, English 2474, Fickling 2478, **Gage 2482**, Holland-Underwood 2508, Illges 2517, Lipscomb 2541, Smith 2586, Warren 2608
Hawaii: Central 2627, Higgins 2635, Martin 2641, Shidler 2646, Young 2659, Zierk 2661
Idaho: Boise 2666, Golden 2672, Hare 2675
Illinois: 1335 2691, Alliant 2702, Bartholomay 2721, Bruce 2760, Bruce 2761, Chicago 2787, Community 2803, Delta 2826, Duncan 2840, Edgerly 2847, Funk 2897, Generations 2908, Geneseo 2909, Hamilton 2945, Hanson 2950, Hastings 2960, Kjellstrom 3019, KPW 3028, Listeman 3055, Lohengrin 3059, MacDonald 3068, Mansfield 3074, Marcum 3076, Marquette 3078, McCrea 3088, McLaughlin 3095, Munson 3130, Simon 3247, Staley 3262, Sulzer 3277, Taylor 3285, Weaver 3312

Indiana: Ayres 3342, Benton 3344, Blackford 3346, Community 3359, Community 3360, Community 3361, Community 3362, Community 3363, Decatur 3367, Duneland 3372, Fayette 3379, Franklin 3382, Greene 3390, Hillenbrand 3393, Huntington 3397, Jasper 3401, Jennings 3402, Kuhne 3409, Lacy 3410, LaGrange 3412, Milton 3418, Niblick 3423, Nugent 3425, Ohio 3427, Pulaski 3432, Schergens 3443, Scott 3446, Share 3450, Stamm 3456
Iowa: Grinnell 3501, GuideOne 3503, Herr 3506, Hoaglin 3508, Krause 3516, Pottawattamie 3527, Premier 3528, Ryan 3531, Van 3539, Wood 3548, Young 3552
Kansas: Baehr 3556, Cape 3563, Community 3567, Insurance 3587, Legacy, 3595, Lincoln 3596, McFadden 3601, Mistler 3606, Salgo 3621, Scott 3623, South 3628
Kentucky: Independence 3666, Keeneland 3668, Pollard 3685, Public 3687, Woodlands 3707
Louisiana: Merkle 3737, Special 3754, Wheless 3758
Maine: Coates 3773, Davenport 3775, Franklin 3779, **Golden 3781**, Hudson 3783, Narragansett 3794, Wellspring 3806
Maryland: Adams 3808, Croft 3841, DelSignore 3847, Ford 3863, Halle 3878, Levin 3900, Pettit 3935, Silber 3952, Sonneborn 3957, **St. 3960**, Unger 3971, **Windsor 3988**
Massachusetts: 2 3992, A 3994, Benson 4016, **Bruner 4030**, Chicopee 4047, Clarke 4049, Codman 4052, Coolidge 4057, Cricket 4060, East 4075, Easthampton 4076, Eddy 4077, Halfway 4115, Henderson 4128, Hill 4130, Hyde 4139, Kelleher 4147, Koplow 4159, Merrill 4200, Middlesex 4203, Mount 4211, MutualOne 4216, Neighborhood 4218, Newburyport 4222, Permanent 4239, Provident 4250, **Robbins-de 4266**, Rockland 4267, Rose 4271, SER 4286, Sherman 4294, Solomon 4301, **Spero 4304**, Stearns 4311, Trefler 4332, Winthrop 4363, Wyman-Gordon 4364
Michigan: Alnour 4373, Bierlein 4392, Branch 4396, Community 4410, Community 4411, Delano 4426, Family 4439, Farver 4441, Four 4449, Frankenmuth 4450, Gratiot 4459, Hartwick 4462, Isabella 4468, Jenkins 4470, Johnson 4471, Kalamazoo 4471, Kantzler 4478, Kellogg 4482, Loosemore 4495, M 4497, Mackinac 4499, Meritor, 4511, Morley 4518, Plym 4542, Roscommon 4552, Sackerson 4557, Schmuckal 4559, Shiawassee 4568, St. 4576, Stoker 4580, Stubnitz 4582, Tyler-Little 4599, Vicksburg 4606, Whiting 4614
Minnesota: Albany 4624, Bell 4637, Bell 4638, Boss 4645, Caridad 4653, Dyer 4669, Edina 4671, Falck 4678, Larsen 4728, Luverne 4736, Midcontinent 4745, **Pax 4760**, Riverway 4776, Roles 4780, Schulze 4788
Mississippi: Amory 4821, King's 4845
Missouri: Boylan 4873, Butler 4880, Dunn 4898, Edgar 4899, Ever 4906, Finley 4910, Grassmere 4919, Moneta 4962, Morgan 4963, Moss 4964, Nichols 4970, Schweinfurth 4996, South 5011, Tension 5019, Turner 5025
Montana: Foundation 5051, Lippard-Clawiter 5058, Swanson 5063, Wendy's 5065
Nebraska: Blair 5074, Farr 5078, Farr 5079, Hansen 5087, Kaufmann-Cummings 5096, Midlands 5104, Nebraska 5105, Nelson 5106, Reynolds 5114, Walker 5125, York 5129, Yount 5130
Nevada: Fuserna 5159, Harris 5161, Joshua 5167, Kennedy 5169
New Hampshire: Couch 5209
New Jersey: Amboy 5246, Brundage 5280, CKT 5297, Clermont 5298, Columbia 5301, Florin 5348, KDK 5416, Kerney 5419, Pasternak 5490, Ragan 5507, **Southpole 5545**, Westfield 5582, Wilson 5590, Wolf 5593
New Mexico: Carlsbad 5608, Forrest 5614, Nirvana 5621, Taos 5626
New York: Adelman 5643, American 5664, Athens 5696, Avanessians 5701, Bank 5710, Baum 5722, Bet 5742, Bingham 5747, Block 5758, Boyer-Snyder 5773, BTMU 5795, Burchan 5801, Cohoes 5865, D-B 5903, Double-R 5927, **Eastman**

5940, Eggleston 5946, ESL 5969, Fowey 6021, Gage 6050, Glens 6082, Grandison 6124, Grant 6129, Griffin 6138, Grobman 6140, Hajim 6158, Hallingby 6160, Heller 6187, **Hickrill 6204**, Hilliard 6208, Hogan 6217, Hulbert 6232, Johnson 6268, Kies 6307, Koha 6337, Legacy 6373, Makioka 6436, Marshall 6445, McCormick 6458, Mead 6466, Metzger-Price 6483, Michaels 6488, Nets 6524, Northern 6540, Peale 6582, Pollock 6617, Psalm 6633, Quinn 6639, RHR 6667, Rose 6687, Rosner 6698, Rowe 6705, Russo 6712, Schwartz 6755, Sherman 6792, Snow 6818, **Sparkplug 6830**, Sperandio 6835, **Spirit 6839**, Stowe 6869, Sumitomo 6876, **Swett 6888**, **Tang 6891**, Tuch 6915, Utica 6922, Wells 6964, Wharton 6968, Willmott 6978, Yordan 7009, Zenkel 7023
North Carolina: BB&T 7045, Burlington 7062, Childtrust 7075, Davis 7083, Hayden-Harman 7120, Kosloski 7149, Mount 7196, Nivison 7201, Outer 7204, Rocky 7227, Smith 7249, Wells 7283
North Dakota: Community 7295, Pearson 7298
Ohio: Baird 7314, Beecher 7320, Bryan 7339, Calhoun 7344, Cassner 7348, CLH 7355, Community 7356, Coressel 7364, Defiance 7375, Dienstberger 7379, **Eaton 7383**, Ebenezer 7384, Foundation 7408, Frohman 7411, Frost-Parker 7413, Heinrich 7446, Hubert 7456, Klock 7480, Knoll 7483, Lazarus 7493, Lindner 7497, Linnemann 7498, **Lowe-Marshall 7505**, O'Neill 7542, Orr 7543, Peters 7547, Reynolds 7558, Ritchie 7561, Rosenberry 7562, Schottenstein 7574, Sears-Swetland 7581, Stensen 7604, Tuscarawas 7623, Watson 7633, Wyler 7647, Young 7652
Oklahoma: Asbjornson 7655, Cherokee 7666, Everest 7676, Lolmaugh 7700, Richardson 7717, Russell 7718, Walkingstick 7727
Oregon: Atkins 7741, Flowerree 7763, Four 7764, Merlo 7797, Wessinger 7826, Woodard 7831
Pennsylvania: Baker 7851, Bergman 7863, Bon-Ton 7884, Bridge 7891, Brooks 7897, Bucks 7905, Chase 7921, Cove 7939, Crawford 7944, David 7950, Davis 7951, Delaware 7953, Eberly 7969, Emporium 7980, Gitt 8019, Greater 8026, Grumbacher 8028, Grundy 8029, HBE 8047, Health 8048, Hilles 8057, Hirtzel 8058, Homeless 8065, **KL 8094**, Lamb 8106, Levee 8121, Moffat 8175, Murphy 8185, Neuber 8192, Packer 8201, Penn 8208, Perelman 8209, Plainfield 8217, Quaker 8228, Rider-Pool 8238, **Rust 8250**, Schuylkill 8263, Union 8326, Velma 8330, Wabtec 8335, Waldo 8340, Weiner 8349, Wells 8350, Whalley 8353, Willary 8356, Wurts 8370
Rhode Island: Barton 8385, Dwinell 8403, Field 8407, Kingsbury 8435, Olsen 8463, Robertson 8478, Sinclair 8488, Washington 8500
South Carolina: Bailey 8509, Bailey 8510, Eastern 8522, Greenwood 8526, Horne 8528, Jackson 8529, Lutz 8533, Stevens 8541, Williams/Brice-Edwards 8549
South Dakota: Clarkson 8558
Tennessee: Jones 8635, Paddison 8655, Small 8675
Texas: Ballard 8716, Behmann 8725, Boeing 8733, Central 8766, Chisholm 8769, Crossroads 8791, Dallas 8795, Dedman 8807, Dedman 8808, Fair 8844, Fickett 8854, Frill 8877, Fuller 8882, Heavin 8925, Hillcrest 8939, Howard 8955, Kellam 8982, Kessler 8987, King 8994, Kuhn 9006, Long 9023, MacDonald-Peterson 9032, Matthews 9041, Miller 9064, Montgomery 9070, Moss 9076, Patterson 9118, Peine 9123, Perkins 9125, Planetary 9132, Rogers 9159, Roosth 9160, Sklar 9199, **Smith 9203**, Steen 9216, Tennessee 9230, Texas 9231, Vaughan 9249, Ward 9260, Watson 9263, Weaver 9265, Williams 9281, Wolens 9284
Utah: B. 9302, Eskuche 9323, Gardner 9326, Green 9327, Jackson 9329
Vermont: Carris 9367, Harvest 9374, Stokes 9385
Virginia: Bassett 9391, Cartledge 9414, Cobbs 9422, Cole 9423, Community 9426, Donohue 9432, Dreyfus 9436, Dundas 9438, Fleder 9448, Honey 9471, Loeb 9493, Northern 9503, Powell 9513, Richardson 9523, Sirad 9533, Treakle 9543

Washington: Brotman 9574, FTJ 9600, Hilal 9623, Murray 9667, Razore 9682, Shepherd 9694, Slingshot 9697, Snyder 9699, Thomson 9711
West Virginia: Chambers 9742, Hollowell 9751, Shott 9765, Wehrle 9771
Wisconsin: Caritas 9791, Cloud 9796, Community 9797, Davis 9802, F.K. 9817, Gardner 9825, Janesville 9850, Johnson 9852, Junginger 9856, Kohl 9864, Marshfield 9878, Mason 9880, Modine 9889, Olson 9897, Stateline 9937, Styberg 9942, Sub-Zero 9943, Watertown 9956, Weyco 9958, Weyers 9959, Witte, 9962
Wyoming: Guthrie 9972, Nickerson 9981, Tate 9995, Weiss 9996

Community beautification

California: Podell 930
Connecticut: Anderson-Paffard 1394
Indiana: Blackford 3346, Dubois 3370, Greene 3390
Maryland: Moore 3917
Michigan: Keller 4481
Minnesota: Bailey 4633
Missouri: No 4971
New York: Desai 5910
Ohio: Bryan 7339
Oregon: Schmidt 7813
Pennsylvania: Brooks 7899, Crawford 7944, Hawksglen 8045
Texas: Texas 9231

Community college education

California: Magowan 782
Connecticut: De 1430
Florida: Couch 1953
Georgia: McClatchey 2546, Wright 2620
Illinois: Staley 3264
Indiana: MutualBank 3421
Maryland: Lutheran 3904
New York: Truman 6912
North Carolina: CJB 7076, McLendon 7179
Oregon: Leonard 7789
Washington: Cartales 9578

Community health care

California: Livingston 761
Florida: Rogers 2291
Illinois: Flinn 2875, Zaentz 3336
Kentucky: Jones 3667
Maryland: Feldman 3858
Michigan: Linse 4493, Schmuckal 4559
Nevada: Matley 5176
New Jersey: **Rippel 5510**
Ohio: Ginn 7425, Osteopathic 7545
Wisconsin: Heller 9839

Community improvement

Connecticut: Roberts 1551
Delaware: Cammarota 1637
Florida: Mount 2223
Georgia: Howell 2512
Illinois: Heath 2962, McNally 3097, Smysor 3255
Indiana: Western 3466
Iowa: Forster 3494
Kansas: Trusler 3635
Massachusetts: 2 3992, Simoni 4296
Mississippi: Community 4830, Lower 4847
Missouri: Butler 4880
New York: Allegany 5660, Darrah 5900, EMSA 5961, Pickman 6602, Preston 6626, Rheinstrom 6665, Spofford 6842, Tod 6901, Truman 6912, Wagner 6938
Ohio: Powers 7550, Seasongood 7582
Oklahoma: Barnes 7659
Oregon: Western 7829
Pennsylvania: Adams 7836, Community 7933, Wayne 8345, Yoh 8373
South Carolina: Bannon 8511

Texas: Hill 8937, Hohlt 8944
Virginia: Community 9426
Washington: Templin 9709
West Virginia: Bowers 9738, Hott 9753
Wisconsin: Marshfield 9878

Community mental health care

Florida: Couch 1953
Oregon: White 7830
Texas: P 9108

Community organizing

New Jersey: Ullmann 5564
Ohio: Seasongood 7582
Oregon: Elwood 7761

Community recreation

California: Church 403
Delaware: Cammarota 1637
Illinois: Corbett 2809
Iowa: McDonald 3520, Woodward 3549
Maryland: Silber 3952
Minnesota: Midcontinent 4745, Trillium 4801
New Jersey: Willingham 5589
New York: Mendell 6472
Pennsylvania: Sweigart 8311
Wisconsin: Olson 9897, Woodtrust-Bell 9963

Community service

California: Buell 357, Krishnan-Shah 722, Sammut 996
District of Columbia: Bloedorn 1790
Idaho: Boswell 2667
Indiana: Harlan 3391
Michigan: Roscommon 4552
New Jersey: Wetterberg 5583
North Carolina: Harrison 7117
Pennsylvania: Golden 8022
Texas: Fowlston 8871, Lilly 9019

Community service for youth

California: Friend 532
Colorado: Lewan 1314
New York: Marshall 6445
Ohio: Ohio 7541
Texas: MacDonald-Peterson 9032

Composition

California: Greenberg 579
Kentucky: Kentucky 3669

Computer science

California: **Global 565**
Massachusetts: Proud 4249
Ohio: Community 7356
Virginia: Kahn 9480

Conservative Judaism

New York: Horowitz 6225

Construction

California: Swinerton 1098

Consumer protection

District of Columbia: Olender 1824
Washington: Dudley 9588

Continuing education

Florida: Couch 1953

Kentucky: **Magee 3674**
Pennsylvania: Kynett 8105

Convalescent care

Arizona: Arizona 96
District of Columbia: Tucker 1836
Maryland: Parsons 3932
Minnesota: Midcontinent 4745
Missouri: Crown 4891
New York: **Burpee 5802**, Milton 6497
Pennsylvania: Dull 7967

Cooperative education

Maryland: **Braitmayer 3827**
Michigan: Roscommon 4552
Wisconsin: Blooming 9784

Coral reefs

Florida: **Atlantis 1858**
Massachusetts: **New 4220**

Corrections and penology

California: **Vogelzang 1146**

Counterterrorism

Colorado: Grossman 1281

Courts

New York: Fuchsberg 6044

Crime prevention

California: Majestic 784, Thornton 1115, Yen 1201
District of Columbia: Westport 1838
Florida: Fry 2027, Gate 2034, Ryan 2305
Minnesota: Midcontinent 4745
Mississippi: Community 4830
New York: Kenworthy 6300
Ohio: Anderson 7305, Sauerland 7570
Virginia: Ivakota 9477
Wisconsin: Tellier 9946

Crisis intervention

Kansas: Bramlage 3559

Cultural awareness

Alaska: Doyon 84
California: Jorgensen 676, Kelly 697, **Lui 771, Lyu
777**, Mazda 810, Razi 957, Torino 1125
Connecticut: Dime 1438, Mahadeva 1517
Florida: Foster 2013, **Mukti 2226**
Georgia: Abreu 2431, Searcy 2583
Hawaii: Kahiau 2636
Kentucky: Trim 3702
Maine: Henry 3782
Massachusetts: Mirak 4204
Michigan: Jenkins 4470
New Jersey: **Patel 5492**
New Mexico: Chamiza 5609
New York: American 5664, Indus 6243, **Jabara 6254**,
Milstein 6496, Sumitomo 6876
Oklahoma: Wadley 7726
Pennsylvania: Penn 8208
Rhode Island: Luke 8447
Texas: Hohlt 8944
Virginia: Community 9426

Cystic fibrosis

California: Brunswick 354, Miller 828
Connecticut: Ferguson 1446

Florida: Diane 1974, Fontaine 2006, Second 2321
Illinois: Bates 2724, Eckert 2843, Johnson 3001
Massachusetts: Arcadia 4004
New Jersey: Research 5509, Sanders 5518, Ullmann
5564
New York: Kovensky 6342, Weinberg 6951
Oregon: Spencer 7820
Pennsylvania: Gauss 8014
Utah: Bastian 9304
Washington: Brookshire-Green 9573

Dance

California: Gordy 575, Plum 929, Uplands 1139
Connecticut: Lee 1507, Low 1513, Roberts 1552
Delaware: Messing 1708
Florida: HFRX 2092
Illinois: MacDonald 3068, Marsteller 3079, O'Donnell
3150
Kentucky: Opera 3684
Maryland: Mann-Paller 3908
Massachusetts: Merrill 4200
Minnesota: Hegardt 4710, Thorpe 4800
Missouri: **Bohm 4871**
New York: Barron 5719, Blue 5763, Cullman 5887,
Marshall 6446, Parshelsky 6578, Securitas 6768
North Carolina: Sloan 7246
Texas: Halperin 8912
Utah: Steiner 9358
Washington: CSM 9584

Democracy and civil society development

Delaware: Cultures 1652

Dental care

California: Livingston 761
Florida: King 2148
Michigan: Kellogg 4482
Missouri: Rust 4988
New Hampshire: Salem 5230
New York: Keller-Shatanoff 6297, Ontario 6559, Rhodes
6666
North Carolina: Horvat 7130
Ohio: Austin-Bailey 7312, Skyler 7595
Oregon: Spencer 7820
Pennsylvania: Blue 7879, Wurts 8370
Virginia: **Foundation 9450**

Depression

California: Baker 267, Traina 1126
Massachusetts: Alden 3999
New York: **Klingenstein 6328**
Texas: MacDonald 9031

Design

Alabama: Anderson 6
Illinois: **Dyson 2842**
New York: Coby 5852, Stutz 6875

Developmental disability services

California: Lemons 743, Palo 900
Connecticut: Union 1590
Florida: Capital 1918, Minto 2216, Olsen 2240, Scherr
2316
Georgia: Waffle 2602
Illinois: Beasley 2728, Murphy 3132, **Rosenmutter
3208**, Seymour 3236
Kansas: Berry 3558
Maryland: Anderson 3814, S.B.E. 3944
Massachusetts: Alden 3999, Dedham 4067, East 4075,
Hampden 4116, Simoni 4296
Michigan: Main 4501
Nebraska: Heuermann 5092
Nevada: Siegel 5186
New Hampshire: Lynch 5221, Salem 5230, Verney
5236

New Jersey: Mamiye 5456, Roe 5512
New York: Cohoes 5865, Kornreich 6341, Maher 6433,
Rose 6683, Warwick 6945
North Carolina: Kennedy 7145, Shugart 7242
Oregon: Spencer 7820
Texas: Pierson 9129, Proctor 9139
Virginia: Dickerson 9431
Washington: Everett 9592
West Virginia: Parlin 9762
Wisconsin: Birnschein 9783, Schoenleber 9924, Simms
9929, Sullivan 9944, Van 9953

Diabetes

Alabama: Adams 3
Arizona: Valley 178
California: Fat 499, Johnson 667, Kadima 686, **Preuss
935**, Rotasa 991
Connecticut: Bantle 1401
Florida: Caring 1920, Five 2002, Holtz 2109, Norjana
2235, Vasey 2385
Georgia: Graves 2496, McKinney-Geib 2547
Hawaii: Locations 2638
Illinois: Carter 2776, Howard 2981, Karasik 3006,
Micole 3108, Simpson 3248
Indiana: Gammon 3385, Welter 3465
Kansas: Buford 3562
Kentucky: McKellar 3677
Maryland: Meltzer 3911
Minnesota: Butzow 4651, Frey 4690, Midcontinent
4745
Nevada: Coleman 5150
New Jersey: Greetin 5377, Jacobson 5402
New York: Catsimatidis 5823, Emwiga 5962, Feldstein
5997, Fraydun 6029, Ingrassia 6244, Johnson
6270, Kupferberg 6351, Schaefer 6735, Smith
6815, Spiritus 6840
Ohio: Fibus 7398, STERIS 7605
Pennsylvania: Blue 7879, Sharp 8272, Wachs 8336
Rhode Island: Charlton, 8394
Tennessee: Berman 8587, LDB 8642
Texas: Frankel 8872, Lowdon 9025, McDonald 9051,
OneSight 9098, Simard 9195, Vaughan 9248
Utah: Bastian 9304

Digestive system diseases

Connecticut: Kay 1496
Illinois: Lifetract 3053
Rhode Island: **Black 8390**

Dining services

Florida: Vorsheck 2389

Disaster relief

Iowa: GuideOne 3503
Minnesota: G&K 4691
Missouri: Fabick 4907
New Jersey: American 5248
New York: Sumitomo 6876
Oregon: Mentor 7796
Tennessee: New 8654
Washington: Bungie 9576

Disasters and emergency management

Arizona: Robson 160
California: Community 421, Dahl 439, Farmers 496,
Handlery 596, Oak 872, San 997, Shenandoah
1033, Spielman 1067, Weinberg 1164
Colorado: DWB 1260
Connecticut: Howard 1484
District of Columbia: **Union 1837**
Florida: MAH 2193
Illinois: Four 2882
Iowa: Jefferson 3514, Pottawattamie 3527, Premier
3528
Louisiana: DeGree 3721
Maryland: Otenasek 3931

Massachusetts: Pierce 4244
Michigan: Jenkins 4470
Minnesota: Edina 4671
Mississippi: Colbert 4829
New Jersey: A 5240, Selective 5528
New York: American 5664, **Chinook 5844**, Giordano 6081, Kimura 6310, Packin 6566, **Posner-Wallace 6621**, Sallie 6720, Seaman 6767, Villchur 6929
North Carolina: Masserini 7172, Outer 7204
Ohio: Dienstberger 7379, Wightman-Wieber 7636
Oregon: Collins 7752, Collins 7753
Pennsylvania: CNB 7929, Deerfield 7952, First 7998, Kinney 8092, Lewis 8124, Penn 8208
South Dakota: Watertown 8576
Texas: **AMD 8698**, D3 8793, Johnson, 8971, McLaughlin 9053, Nabors 9083, Petty 9126
Utah: **Skolnick 9352**
Virginia: American 9387, Fredericksburg 9454, Greensville 9464
Washington: Not 9670
Wisconsin: Dudley 9811

Diseases and conditions

Alabama: Anderson 5, Anderson 6, Battle 10, Bruno 17, Dixon 26, Friedman 27, Goodrich 29, Harrison 35, Kemp 42, Norquist 51, Phifer, 54, Regions/AmSouth 58, Ripps 60, Rothschild 61
Alaska: Gottstein 86
Arizona: Armstrong 97, Barton 99, **Beals 100**, Glasrud 123, Goldberg 124, Grossman 126, Harmsen, 128, Jasam 133, Kuhle 139, Lund 143, Margolis 144, MCS 149, Moeller 150, Robson 160, Shacknai 167, Warmer 180
Arkansas: Bailey 187, Heflin 197
California: Adams 228, Amador 238, Amin 241, Anhaltzer 245, Arata 248, Arbor 249, Archer 250, Arlene 252, Ascher, 256, **A-T 258**, Baker 265, Banchik 269, Beam 287, Bell 295, Bellini 298, Bernstein 308, Bialis 313, Blackie 319, Blanchard 321, Borok 331, Borzi 332, Braddock 336, Bravo 338, Briskin 346, Brotman 351, Bryan 355, **Bull 358**, Bundy 360, Butler 364, **Butler 365**, Cannon 374, **Cantor 375**, Cardinal 376, Chisick 395, CNC 410, Corday 426, Corwin 428, Crummer 436, Cush 437, Davies 444, Diamantine 452, Dorskind 459, Ducommun 465, Dwyer 468, Eichenberg-Larson 474, Elliott 479, Evening 487, Everest 488, Familian 491, Family 492, Farber 495, Faro 497, Folger 515, Fox 524, Fox 525, Friedhofer 529, Friedman 530, Friedman 531, Fuller 538, Fusenot 541, Gareeb 548, GAT 549, Gifts 553, Gordy 575, **Grass 577**, Gross 587, Handley 596, Harvey 602, Hausman 603, Hayman 606, Hellman 614, Helms 615, Herman 617, Herrmann 618, Hitter 624, **Hsu 637**, Hughes 639, Kelly 697, Kelvin 699, Kieve 703, Lash 730, Lemelson 742, Lester 748, Lewis 753, Louie 770, Lyons 776, MacDonald 779, Malachowsky 786, Maley-Thawley 787, Mangold 789, Mason 805, Mayer 809, Mazda 810, McDaniel 812, McKenzie 816, Michaud 824, Miller 828, Mitchell 837, Mitchell, 839, Morgan 846, Morgenstern 848, Nasaw 858, Neu 862, **Northern 870**, Novak 871, Onehope 881, Open 883, Ornest 888, Palo 901, Pardee 902, **Parsemus 904**, Pasarow 906, Pergo 915, Pickford 927, Podell 930, Potiker 932, Price 938, Price 939, Private 941, Pulido 944, Rallis 951, Rar 955, Reddy's 959, **Rieger 971**, **Rifkind 972**, Roberts 975, Rocca, 978, Roche 979, Roke 981, Rosenberg 985, Rosenthal 987, Ross 988, Rossi 989, Rosso 990, Rubin 993, Rush 994, Sanders 999, Schaeffer 1013, Schultz 1019, Scott 1021, Scott 1023, Setzer 1029, Shore 1034, **Sikand 1037**, Simon 1040, Simon-Strauss 1042, SKB 1044, Skowronski 1045, Skynyrd 1046, Smalley 1050, Smith 1053, Smith-Walker 1057, Stauffer 1076, Stellar 1080, Stewart 1083, Stoller 1084, Storm 1087, Strome 1089, Sun 1092, Tanimura 1103, Thagard 1109, Thornton 1115, Thrill 1117, Tilley 1118, Tisch 1120, Tomlinson 1123, Torino 1125, Tuffli 1134, Van 1144, Waller 1152, Welfund 1169, Wendell 1172, Wertheimer 1173, West 1175, Western 1176, Westphal 1177, Winkler 1188, Zankel 1208, Zwick 1218
Colorado: Benson 1230, Comprecare 1249, **Fishback 1270**, Gart 1275, Getz 1278, Goodwin 1279, Grossman 1281, Joslin-Needham 1300, Kortz 1307, Ladd 1310, Margulf 1320, Mehrberg 1325, Mullen 1329, Pluss 1337, Relationship 1346, Schramm 1350, Staley 1357, Strohm 1361, Taylor 1364, Wexler 1377, Zeff 1383
Connecticut: Acorn 1385, Anderson-Paffard 1394, Baggins 1398, Bantle 1401, Barden 1402, Bender 1405, Berbecker 1406, Bridgemill 1412, Brown 1413, Calarco 1414, Craig 1423, Dennett 1432, Denzler 1434, Filingieri 1447, Finn 1449, Foley 1452, Gerbic 1463, Gladstein 1465, Howard 1484, Knox 1500, Lee 1507, Martinsen 1521, Newpol 1531, O'Herron 1536, Panwy 1539, Paoloian 1540, Rapp 1548, Selkowitz 1565, Smith 1571, **Sonja 1573**, Sullivan 1577, Town 1586, Tully 1588, Winokur 1597, Woodland 1599, Zelnick/Belzberg 1602
Delaware: Bowman 1625, Cohen 1643, **Colgate 1645**, Freedman 1665, Hagan 1674, Kerr 1692, Klein, 1694, Lightner 1699, Messing 1708, Rosenfeld 1732, Rothchild 1733, Russell 1735, Ryerson 1736, Schiffman 1738, Schwalbach 1739, Stein 1750, Telluray 1762, Wong 1779, Yaverland 1783, Yokota 1784
District of Columbia: Bender 1789, Dweck 1805, Lemon 1819, **Merriman 1820**, Monarch 1823, Olender 1824, Woodward 1839
Florida: Archibald 1852, Barbash 1865, Bastien 1872, Baxter 1874, Becker 1879, Becton 1880, Bomberger 1896, Bond 1897, Brown 1905, Cantor 1916, Caring 1920, Carlton 1922, Cedar 1930, Chanin 1934, Cherry 1940, Childress 1942, Consolidated 1951, Couch 1953, Coulter-Jones 1954, Crane 1955, Crutchfield 1957, CSX 1958, Davis 1962, Detter 1971, Dilworth 1977, Doctors 1978, Dysimmune 1986, Epstein 1992, Fish 2001, Five 2002, Ford 2010, Frankle 2019, Garner 2032, Goetz 2044, Goldberg 2045, Gordon 2050, Grabe 2053, Grader 2054, Greenberg 2062, Greenblatt 2063, Greene-Sawtell 2065, Greenfield 2066, Gregory 2067, Grossman 2068, Halbrook 2073, Halperin 2076, **Handleman 2078**, Hansen 2079, Hicks 2094, Hinman 2099, Holloway 2106, Holloway 2107, Holtz 2109, Hoornstra 2110, Hultquist 2115, Ingalls 2118, Insetta 2119, Isenberg 2121, Jacobsen 2123, Jacobson 2125, Jelks 2128, **Jenkins 2129**, **Joshua 2132**, KBR 2142, Kessler 2145, Kimmel 2146, King 2148, KLM 2151, Knapp 2153, Knippenberg 2154, Kugelman 2161, Kuriansky 2162, Le 2175, Livingston 2187, Marco 2194, McClanathan 2202, McGahren 2204, Minto 2216, Moore 2217, Olsen 2240, Overstreet 2242, Pearce 2252, Peyton 2258, Preik 2266, Price 2267, Pusey 2272, Quinn 2273, Reed 2278, Reinhold 2280, Richard 2285, Rogers 2292, Rothman 2299, Ruskin 2302, SBJ 2314, Schlanger 2318, Siegel 2335, Sierra 2336, Simmons 2338, **Stiefel 2352**, Strube 2354, Swisher 2361, **Taylor 2365**, Taylor 2366, Thomas 2371, Toral 2378, Vanneck-Bailey 2384, Weiller 2393, Weintraub 2395, Wiener 2405, Wilder 2406, **Wollowick 2412**, Wrightson-Ramsing 2416, Wrigley 2417, Yerrid 2420, Zimmerman 2428
Georgia: Amos 2433, Arnold 2436, Boone 2446, Carters 2454, Chandler 2455, Chatham 2457, Community 2466, Connolly 2467, Echlin 2472, Enterline 2475, Foundation 2480, **Gage 2482**, Georgia 2484, Goddard 2491, Goodman 2492, Health 2504, Hooters 2510, Johnson 2525, Lanier 2538, Lee 2540, Looney 2542, Montgomery 2551, Orkin 2560, Pechter 2564, Pope 2568, Schinazi 2580, SF 2585, Solstice 2587, Terwilliger 2593, Whitehead 2610, Williams 2612, Woodruff 2617, Wright 2620
Hawaii: Baldwin 2625, Ching 2628, Epstein 2630, Servco 2645, Vidinha 2653, Wilcox 2654, Wo 2655
Idaho: Golden 2672, Hare 2675
Illinois: Adreani 2697, Ahlstrand 2700, Allen-Heath 2701, Allyn 2703, Anschel 2709, Baird 2718, Bartholomay 2721, Baudhuin 2726, Bellick 2732, Bere 2734, Best 2740, Block, 2746, Boothroyd 2749, Borten 2750, Brewer 2757, Buntrock 2766, Burt 2770, Carter 2776, Ceres 2779, Cless 2793, Cohn 2795, Coldwell 2797, Collins 2799, Constans-Culver 2805, Cremer 2815, Danielson 2823, Delavan 2825, Dowdle 2834, Edelman 2845, Edelstein 2846, Eiszner 2851, Ellis 2853, Engle 2855, Enivar 2856, Family 2863, Fasseas 2866, Feltes 2869, **Foundation 2880**, **Foundation 2881**, Fraida 2884, Frank 2885, Full 2895, Funk 2897, Garard, 2902, Gassin 2906, General 2907, Gidwitz 2914, Gloyd 2917, Goldenberg 2920, Goodstein 2924, Gray 2927, Haarlow 2940, Half 2942, Hirschmann 2973, Hughes 2983, Ingredion 2987, Jaros 2993, Johnson 3001, Karasik 3006, Klosk 3020, Knowles 3023, Larson 3039, **Lazzara 3042**, Leibowitz 3046, Levinson 3049, Lichner 3051, Lichtman 3052, Livney 3056, Love 3064, Luehring 3065, Lyon 3066, MacDonald 3068, Marks 3077, McCabe 3084, McCauley 3085, **Mead 3100**, Meyer 3106, Miller 3111, Millner 3115, Minor 3117, NCI 3134, New 3136, Oberweiler 3147, O'Connor 3149, Okner-Robbins 3152, Owen 3160, Perry 3170, Pond 3182, Reed 3191, Reinisch 3193, Rosenberg 3207, Russell 3216, Ruttenberg 3217, Ryan 3219, Schiff 3224, Schneider 3228, Shaw 3242, Shaw 3244, Simon 3247, SSAB 3260, Steigerwaldt 3265, Stein 3266, Stone 3269, Stuart 3273, Sullivan 3276, Takiff 3281, Taxman 3283, Taylor 3286, Tully 3295, Wagner 3306, Watson 3311, Weaver 3312, Webb 3313, **Wein 3315**, Will 3322
Indiana: **Ackerman 3339**, Community 3359, Eskenazi 3377, Fayette 3379, Froderman 3383, Jennings 3403, Jolan 3404, Milton 3418, Nugent 3425, Oakley 3426, Rifkin 3437, Simon 3452, Thrush-Thompson 3460
Iowa: Becker 3472, Busse 3478, Drost 3487, Gaedke 3495, Grubb 3502, McDonald 3520, Muscatine 3523, Peace 3526, Security 3534, Stark 3536, Weathertop 3545
Kansas: Buford 3562, DeVore 3573, **Muchnic 3609**, Price 3616, Scroggins 3624, Stallman 3629, Taylor 3632, Testamentary 3633, Wallace 3637, Wiedemann 3642, Wood 3644
Kentucky: Abercrombie 3645, Dickins 3651, Mackin 3673, McKellar 3677, Rounsavall, 3691, Shapira 3693, Woosley 3708
Louisiana: Chambers 3718, Dujay 3722, Havens 3727, Houseman 3728, Knight 3731, Live 3734, Magale 3735, Moffett 3739, Selber 3751, Shannon 3752, Wheless 3758
Maine: Bailey 3765, Borman 3767, Burnham 3770, Firebird 3778, Kagan 3784, Lafayette 3787, Sukeforth 3805
Maryland: Baker 3815, Bank 3818, Berger 3821, Carbonell 3833, Cole 3839, CSG 3842, Davis 3844, Devito 3848, Eliasberg 3851, Friedman 3866, **Goldberg 3872**, Hittman 3881, Hobbs 3882, Hurwitz 3886, Kelly, 3893, Levin 3900, Liberty 3901, Mangione 3907, Marriott 3909, McKnight 3910, Minkoff 3915, Mullan 3920, Nabit 3924, Nicholl 3926, Pettit 3935, Rhona's 3939, Rogers-Wilbur 3941, Rothschild 3942, Shapiro 3949, Shattuck 3950, Small 3955, Ten 3963, **Thadikonda 3965**, Ticho 3967, Totah 3968, Unger 3971, Weinman 3981
Massachusetts: Alden 3999, Arcadia 4004, **Barakat 4012**, Cabot 4034, Cail 4036, Chabner 4041, Chickering 4046, Chirag 4048, Clementi 4050, Epstein 4084, First 4091, Fleming 4092, Frisbie 4099, Gale 4100, Goldman 4105, Hagerty 4110, Hale 4112, Haley 4114, Harrington 4117, Harris 4118, Hauben 4120, Henderson 4127, **Kahn 4143**, Kamin 4144, Kenwood 4150, Lamm 4165, Ledgeways 4171, Levy 4174, Massachusetts 4191, McNeice 4195, Melvina 4197, Michael 4202, Morse 4210, Mountain 4212, Nelson 4219, Nypro 4228, Oristaglio 4232, Pechet 4235, Permanent 4239, Poduska 4246, Prokopis 4248, Ragon 4256, Ramlose 4257, Reisman 4263, Sacajawea 4274, Sailors' 4276, Schiro 4282,

Sherman 4293, Singing 4297, **Spero 4304**, Stare 4308, Thompson 4325, Thoracic 4326, Ullian 4335, Wyman-Gordon 4364

Michigan: Baiardi 4381, Beson 4389, Betten 4390, Blatt 4393, Bostock 4395, Causley, 4405, Cebelak 4406, Community 4411, Connable 4412, Cracchiolo 4415, Crowley 4416, Delano 4426, Farago 4440, Farver 4441, Farwell 4442, Four 4449, Golden 4455, Hayden 4464, Holden 4467, Kinney 4483, Lee 4491, Maas 4498, Maibach 4500, Manat 4503, McDole 4506, Michell 4513, Morley 4518, Oreffice 4528, Padnos 4529, Pardee 4534, Pitt 4540, Ratner 4548, Ryan 4555, Sinai 4570, Stoddard 4579, Sutaruk 4583, Tamer 4585, Trico 4596, Whiting 4614, Wieczorek 4617

Minnesota: Ankeny 4628, Arsher 4630, Bame 4634, Bradley 4647, Cooke 4659, Dyer 4669, Erickson 4674, Falck 4678, Ferber 4682, Heilmaier 4712, Kellogg 4722, Kinman-Oldfield 4723, Knowlton 4725, Lillehei 4729, Luther 4733, McNamara 4743, Morning 4748, O'Brien 4753, Rising 4775, Sexton 4790, Soar 4792, Wedge 4810, Wimmer 4819

Mississippi: Biloxi 4824, Center 4828, Florence 4836, Graeber 4839, McCarty, 4848, Phillips 4850, Seal, 4853

Missouri: Baer 4862, Barrows 4864, **Build-A-Bear 4879**, Copaken 4888, Finley 4910, Longer 4949, Love 4951, Pearl 4977, Pendergast-Weyer 4979, Price 4982, Rubin 4987, Saks 4990, Schutte 4995, Shanahan 4999, Siteman 5006, Slay 5008, Slusher 5009, St. 5012, Stern 5013, Thorp 5020, Toutz 5023, Welch 5038

Nebraska: Baer 5069, Friedman 5083, Kim 5098, Perkins 5111, York 5129

Nevada: Benna 5138, Blue 5140, Jaquish 5165, Lee 5171, Sweig 5191, **Wood 5201**

New Hampshire: Barker 5204, Woodbury 5238

New Jersey: A 5240, Ascena 5252, Aufzien 5253, Bauer 5257, Baum 5258, Benun 5261, Bershad 5262, BMI-Rupp 5270, Brook 5273, Brooks 5274, Brown 5278, Brunetti 5281, Carlozzi 5287, CBIS 5288, Chu 5294, Clermont 5298, Cohen 5299, Conger 5303, Covance 5305, **Crane 5306**, Davis 5314, Devine 5317, Dietze 5320, Dreman 5326, Earle 5328, EBB 5329, Entin 5336, Essig 5339, Farris 5342, Feinstein 5343, Feldstein 5344, Fellstone 5346, Fox 5349, Goldberger 5372, Greetin 5377, Heart 5388, **Integra 5400**, Judson 5411, Kingsberg 5421, Kontos 5430, Kresa 5432, Kurr 5435, Kurtz 5436, Lavery 5441, Lazarus 5442, Levine 5446, MacDonald 5453, Markowitz 5460, Maschler 5462, McConnell 5463, McDowell 5465, Minio 5470, Mullen 5475, Myers 5476, Oster 5484, **Patel 5492**, Patrick 5494, Pepper 5496, Pierson 5500, Riskin 5511, Rukin 5516, Russo 5517, Schimmel 5521, Shapiro 5532, Snyder 5540, Snyder 5542, Spiro 5546, Stanley's 5550, Stein 5551, Take 5555, Tizzio 5559, Tuchman 5561, Twin 5563, Waters 5571, Welch 5579, Wicks 5584, Zimmer 5601

New Mexico: Bennett 5607, Carlsbad 5608, Gumbo 5617, Tanner 5625

New York: **Abba's 5634**, Adikes 5646, Agate 5649, **Alexander 5653**, American 5668, Anderson 5673, Antun 5681, Balm 5708, Barker 5716, Baum 5722, Beckman 5729, Beckwith 5730, Behrens 5731, Bergson 5738, Berkowitz 5739, Black 5754, Blackman, 5755, Bostwick 5767, Boustead 5769, Boxer 5772, Briger 5784, Brosens 5789, **Buffalo 5799**, Burrows 5803, **Buster 5806**, Calder 5810, Camuto 5812, Capri 5814, Carwill 5818, Catsimatidis 5823, Cheatham 5836, Clarkson 5849, Clemente 5850, Cochran 5853, Cohen 5859, Cohen 5860, Cohenca 5861, Cohn 5862, Cole 5868, Coleman 5869, Cox 5883, Curtis 5889, Czap 5891, Dabah 5892, Danziger 5899, Davidson 5901, Davis 5902, Dears 5905, DeMario 5909, Diamondstein 5914, Dorsky 5924, Doscas 5925, Douglas 5929, Downey 5930, Druskin 5932, Elkins 5955, Emwiga 5962, **Eppley 5967**, ESL 5969, Eule 5971, Faith 5979, Fan 5985, Farber 5987, Fein 5992, Fenton 5998, Ferguson 5999, Feuerring

6001, Fitt 6010, Fleischer 6013, **Frank 6026**, Fraydun 6029, Fuchsberg 6044, Gantcher 6055, Geduld/Cougar 6062, Geier 6063, Geier 6064, George 6070, Gerhard 6072, Glorney 6084, Goldenberg 6092, **Goldfein 6096**, Goldman 6098, Goldstone 6102, Golick 6104, Golub 6105, Goodman 6107, Goodman-Lipman 6108, Graham 6119, Gramercy 6122, Grandison 6124, Grano 6128, Grateful 6131, Greenberg 6132, Hanson 6163, Harjen 6167, Hauff 6177, Hefta 6181, Heller 6187, Henshel 6192, Herringer 6196, Hershaft 6197, Heyman 6201, Hilson 6209, Hirsch 6211, Hochman 6214, Horowitz 6225, Houser 6227, Houston 6228, Hurlburt 6233, IF 6237, **Indira 6242**, Iroquois 6250, Jacobson 6255, JI 6260, Johnson 6267, Johnson 6268, Johnson 6270, Joseph 6273, Joyce 6275, Kaminer 6282, Keller-Shatanoff 6297, Keswin 6303, Klein 6324, Klingenstein 6327, Knafel 6330, Knapp 6331, Konar 6340, Krauss 6345, Krimendahl/Saint-Amand 6346, L. 6354, **Laerdal 6358**, Lawrence 6369, Lenox 6380, Leonhardt 6381, Lerner 6383, Levy 6389, Libby 6395, Lieb 6398, Lippes 6401, Litterman 6406, Lubo 6417, Maher 6433, Manning 6437, Manzanita 6439, Marshall 6445, Mere 6476, Meredith 6477, Merrill 6480, Meyer 6487, Michaels 6488, Michelle 6489, **Milbank 6490**, Milstein 6496, Morgado 6505, Morris 6508, National 6520, Netter 6525, Newcastle 6528, NM 6536, Nonna's 6538, North 6539, Olum 6555, Ostgrodd 6561, O'Sullivan 6565, Pajwell 6568, Palisades 6569, Peckham 6583, Peterson 6594, Petrocelli 6595, Petty 6596, Pittman 6608, Pollack 6614, Pollack 6615, **Potts 6624**, Price 6628, Quinn 6637, Rachesky 6642, Rapaport 6646, Rechler 6657, Reidy 6661, Reiss 6662, Rhodes 6666, RJL 6675, Rosenberg 6691, Rosenstein 6692, Rowe 6705, Roxe 6706, Ruth 6713, Sackler 6716, Sackler 6717, Sakhai 6718, Sani 6726, Schaefer 6735, Schott 6749, Schwartz 6752, Schwartz 6755, Seacoast 6766, Seaman 6767, Seelig 6769, Shachar 6779, Shackouls 6781, Shanken 6785, Silverman 6801, Simpson 6805, Slade 6810, Smith 6815, Some 6824, Spatz 6831, Spear 6832, Spencer 6834, Spiegel 6837, Spiegel 6838, **Spirit 6839**, Spiritus 6840, Stanton 6845, Starker 6847, Sternberg 6863, Stony 6868, Tedaldi 6894, Touradji 6903, Tribune 6909, Trimble 6910, Turner 6916, Utopia 6923, Van 6925, Vanden 6927, **Walsh/Alfred 6943**, Weinberg 6951, Weinman 6955, Weiser 6958, Weisman 6959, Westlawn 6965, Willmott 6978, Wohlgemuth 6984, Woldar 6985, Wolk 6987, Wong 6988, Woodmere 6990, Woodward 6993, Wright 6995, Yaspan-Unterberg 7003, Zemsky 7022, Zenkel 7023, Ziff 7027, Zirkl 7029, Zwerling 7034

North Carolina: Aehle 7038, Bane 7043, Bell 7047, Boddie 7054, Burns 7063, Cary 7069, Cato, 7071, Eddy 7087, Elks 7089, Family 7096, First 7097, Fortson 7100, Fox 7103, Garrow 7108, Helb 7122, Horvat 7130, Hudson 7133, KPB 7151, **Laffin 7157**, Lerner 7160, Lynum 7165, Marlboro 7169, Mattei 7173, Matthews 7174, McConnell 7176, Morisey 7191, Oschwald 7203, Piedmont 7209, Ragland, 7216, Rankin 7217, **Rolander 7229**, Self 7238, Silverman 7244, Sutcliffe 7262, Thomasville 7267, Whitener 7286

North Dakota: Fedje 7296

Ohio: Alpaugh 7302, Anderson 7304, Armington 7309, B-Brand 7318, Busemeyer 7342, Calhoun 7344, Cassner 7348, Connor 7361, Cure 7368, **Elisha-Bolton 7387**, Fedeli 7393, Feldstein 7394, Freygang 7410, Gale 7415, Garcia 7416, Gimbel 7424, Hankins 7437, Hazelbaker 7441, Hoover 7453, Horvitz 7454, Hummer 7459, Johnson 7469, **Katz 7475**, Kisker 7479, Klock 7480, Kramer 7485, Lawry 7491, LKC 7501, Lundgard 7508, Matthes 7517, Mead 7522, Mifsud 7525, Miller 7526, O'Neill 7542, Powers 7550, Renner 7557, Ridgecliff 7560, Rosenthal 7563, Schwebel 7577, Sears-Swetland 7581, Seifert 7584, Shannon 7586, Sidwell 7592, Steiner-King 7602, Swagelok 7608, Turben 7622, Van 7626, Wallace 7631,

Wasserstrom 7632, Watson 7633, Williamson 7640, Yeiser 7649, Young 7651

Oklahoma: Barnett 7660, Burkhart 7665, Cherokee 7666, Everest 7676, Jones 7691, Kerr 7693, Merrick 7707, Parman 7713, Peel 7714, Trippet 7725

Oregon: Ackley 7740, Brown 7744, **Chiles 7749**, Dubs 7760, Haskell 7770, Hitchman 7774, Metro 7798, Pendleton 7806, Schmidt 7813, Sharkey 7815, Wessinger 7826, West 7827

Pennsylvania: Aaron 7835, Ames 7840, **Arronson 7844**, Ashland 7845, Aventis 7847, Betz 7870, **BGM 7871**, Blue 7879, Bon-Ton 7884, Briggs 7892, Cameron 7911, Cottage 7938, Dibona 7955, Dietz 7959, Dozzi 7965, Drueding 7966, Eden 7971, Edwards 7973, Elk 7975, Fleming 8000, Frohring 8010, Garthwaite 8013, Gershman 8015, Gibson 8016, **Glendorn 8020**, Gordon 8024, Grumbacher 8028, Gulati 8032, Hoch 8060, Hoffman 8063, Holden 8064, Hunt 8070, John 8081, Joyce 8083, Katz 8088, Kittenbrink 8093, Klein 8096, Knudsen 8102, Lamb 8107, Leary 8117, Levee 8121, Lienemann 8128, Lipstein 8129, Lubert 8133, McGinley 8156, MHB 8171, Moore 8177, Mudge 8181, Mullen 8184, Murphy 8185, Olitsky 8198, Oppenheim 8199, Patterson 8205, Pollock 8222, Ricon 8237, Rooney 8243, Rosenberg 8244, Sample, 8252, Savett 8255, Schautz 8257, Schwab-Silfen 8264, Secrist 8267, Sidewater 8278, Smith 8284, Snyder 8288, Somerville 8291, Staehle 8295, Stein/Bellet 8300, Strawbridge 8305, Tabas 8312, Tally 8313, Terryglass 8315, Tippins 8318, Tuttleman 8325, Victor 8332, Wachs 8336, Ward 8343, Weil 8346, Weiler-Miller 8348, Wolgin 8365, Woodall 8368, York 8374, **Zeldin 8376**

Rhode Island: Feibelman 8405, Gross 8414, Heydt 8419, Johnson 8430, Kimball 8434, Littlefield 8441, McWethy 8453, Phillips 8472, Pisa 8474, Sinclair 8488, Swarts 8495, Thompson 8497

South Carolina: Bonner 8513

South Dakota: Engelsma 8563, Peterson 8572

Tennessee: **Belz 8585**, Blum 8589, Cole 8600, Doochin 8605, EBS 8610, Eskind 8611, **Fraser 8617**, Goldsmith 8622, HMA 8628, Houghland 8630, Kennedy 8638, Massengill-DeFriece 8647, McWherter 8649, Mercy 8650, Provision 8663, Rose 8667, Sasco 8669, Small 8675, Tompkins 8683, WTC 8688

Texas: Alexander 8695, Amherst 8702, Anderson 8704, Armstrong 8708, Astin 8710, Beall 8723, Behmann 8725, Booth 8734, Brass 8738, Calpine 8759, Cemo 8765, Central 8766, Collins 8780, Conley 8784, **Crowder 8792**, Dauphin 8798, Deakins 8804, Deason 8805, Discovery 8816, Dove 8826, Dozzo 8827, Dubose 8828, Dunaway 8832, Duncan 8833, Elkins 8838, Fair 8844, Fickett 8854, Flohr 8861, Flowers 8862, Folsom 8863, Foster 8868, Fowlston 8871, Fuchs 8881, Fuller 8882, Garver 8883, Garvey 8884, **Gilman 8889**, Gordon 8892, Greentree 8901, Haggar 8907, Haggar, 8908, Halperin 8912, Hamm 8914, Hervey 8932, Hibbs 8934, Hicks 8936, Hill 8938, Hoak 8941, Hofheinz 8942, Howell 8956, Inge 8961, Jessen 8968, Johnson 8969, Johnston 8972, Joseph 8974, Kahn 8978, Kayser 8980, Kellam 8982, Knox 8999, Kolitz 9000, Lantana 9009, Lowdon 9025, Luse 9029, MacDonald-Peterson 9032, Mayer 9043, McDonald 9051, McKee 9052, Mendenhall 9056, Mercy 9057, Mischer 9067, Morrison 9073, Muse 9080, Oppenheimer 9101, Overlake 9106, Pak 9110, Patton 9119, Paulos 9120, Pevehouse 9127, Pisani 9131, Poncin 9135, Posey 9135, Postl 9136, Pratt 9137, Prayer 9138, Quanex 9141, RDM 9146, Richter 9153, Riter, 9154, Roberts 9157, Rosenthal 9163, Rowan 9166, Rubenstein 9167, Schepps 9178, Schulte 9181, Sear 9186, Sherman 9192, Smith 9205, Smith 9207, South 9209, Staubach 9215, Steen 9216, Sterling 9218, Sterling 9219, Stewart, 9221, Storehouse 9223, Taub 9229, Thompson 9234, Tolleson 9238, Tyler 9244, USD 9245, Vaughan 9248, Waggoners

9255, Walls 9257, Walthall 9258, Watson 9263, Weir 9269, Westcott 9273, Willard 9278, Wise 9283, Wolf 9285
Utah: Bastian 9304, Benjamin 9305, Dialysis 9319, Green 9327, Promontory 9345, Shrontz 9351, Spendlove 9357
Vermont: Harper 9373, Kaufman 9378, Seventh 9384
Virginia: Banks 9390, Better 9396, Blue 9400, **Brown 9407**, Buchanan 9410, Burford 9411, Cartledge 9414, **Delmar 9429**, Grandis 9462, Hopkins 9472, Immixgroup 9476, Meador 9500, Mullen 9502, Ochsman 9504, **Praktikos 9514**, RECO 9522, Schiro-Zavela 9528, Selsky 9529, Stone 9537, Treakle 9543, Walter 9549, Weil 9550, Williams-Berry 9554
Washington: Bayley 9567, Cartales 9578, Coulter 9581, Dore 9587, Furnessville 9602, Grousemont 9611, Heath 9617, Heidner 9618, Juniper 9640, Kilworth 9644, Martin 9659, Patel 9675, Pointe 9679, Prairie 9680, Shemanski 9693, Smith 9698, Stevens 9704, Thomson 9711, Wilkens 9724, Wissner-Slivka 9727
West Virginia: Carter 9741, Hott 9753, Raymond 9764, Wehrle 9771
Wisconsin: BayCare 9781, Birnschein 9783, Bluemke 9785, Braun 9787, Easter 9813, Erdman 9816, Foulkes 9821, Frautschi 9822, Hoffmann 9842, Huiras 9844, Kohl 9864, Loehrke 9872, Lutsey 9873, Meinerz 9883, Merkel 9884, Murray 9892, Olson 9898, Prescott 9905, Schmucker 9923, Seramur 9926, Stateline 9937, Stevenson 9940, Styberg 9942, Sub-Zero 9943, Sullivan 9944, Uihlein 9949, Uihlein 9950, Weyers 9959
Wyoming: Bailey 9964, Scott 9988, StoneRiver 9991

Diversity and intergroup relations

California: Gordy 575, Mazda 810, Von 1148
Colorado: Warner 1376
Florida: Chapman 1935, Oristano 2241
Minnesota: Walker 4805
New York: Zenkel 7023
Pennsylvania: Union 8326

Domestic violence

Alabama: Rothschild 61
California: Yen 1201
Florida: Thomas 2370
Minnesota: Midcontinent 4745
New York: Sperandio 6835
Pennsylvania: Jordan 8082, Tompkins-Broll 8320
Texas: Central 8766, FHC 8853
Virginia: American 9387

Domestic violence shelters

California: Braddock 336, Harris 601, Palo 900
Connecticut: Bigelow 1408
Delaware: **TeleTech 1761**
Florida: Le 2175, Smith 2341
Illinois: Hoffer 2975
Louisiana: Crossroads 3719
Maryland: Loats 3902
Massachusetts: Benz 4017, Boyce 4024
Michigan: Barstow 4385
Minnesota: Bend 4639, Charity, 4656
New Jersey: Eisenberg 5331, Giants 5369
North Carolina: Kennedy 7145
Ohio: Skestos 7594
Oklahoma: Howard 7688, Witt 7737
Pennsylvania: Chase 7921, Everard 7985, Hecht 8050
Tennessee: Drake 8606
Texas: Dougherty, 8825, Hervey 8932
Virginia: Collins 9424
Washington: Foss 9598, Schuler 9690
Wyoming: Cutting 9968

Domesticated animals

Alabama: Cooper 23, Shook 64

Alaska: Juneau 88
Arizona: Cadeau 104
California: **Ayz 262**, **Beagle 286**, Bridges/Larson 343, Collier 417, Community 420, Danem 441, Doelger 457, Fliesbach 512, Goldstein 569, Green 578, Guerin 589, Harqua 599, Harris 600, Heck 609, Hotchkis 634, Kisco 710, Laguna 726, Mollatt 842, Offield 875, Osborn 891, Pfister 920, Piuze 928, Prevent 936, Rhe 968, **Rifkind 972**, Roberts 976, **Sargent 1005**, Shore 1034, Solano 1063, Uplands 1138
Colorado: Arches 1222, Joy 1301, Koelbel 1306, Mehrberg 1325, Tigertree 1366
Connecticut: Bessie 1407, Gerath 1462, Jones 1490, Keefe 1497, Lamando 1504, Linke 1508, McLane 1522, MLE 1526, Perna-Rose 1542, Schaeneman, 1560, Wheeler 1594
Delaware: Burt's 1635, Bushong 1636, Martyn 1702
District of Columbia: Farvue 1806, Peet 1827
Florida: **Atlantis 1858**, Binz 1888, Cape 1917, Draft 1981, Echevarria 1987, Epstein 1992, Grassy 2057, Knopf 2155, Morris 2220, Ransburg 2274, Rodgers, 2289, Rogers 2291, Salenger 2308, Taylor 2364, Vernon 2387, Wagmore 2391
Georgia: Arcadia 2435, McClatchey 2546, Woodruff, 2618
Hawaii: Epstein 2630, Shields 2647
Idaho: Hare 2675
Illinois: Abelson 2693, Educational 2848, Espenscheid 2859, Fasseas 2866, Issa 2990, JMR 2999, Keller 3009, McCabe 3084, McNally 3097, McNeill 3098, Miller 3111, Miner 3116, Norgaard 3141, Petrick 3173, Scott 3230
Indiana: Dorsey 3369, Globe 3387, Salin 3442
Kansas: Middlekauff 3603, Morrison 3608, Nash 3610
Kentucky: Masser 3676, Renau 3689
Maine: Coates 3773, **St. 3804**
Maryland: Allemall 3811, Besson 3823, Liberty 3901, Meyer, 3913, Schwarz 3947, Snyder 3956, V 3972
Massachusetts: **Brabson 4026**, Carlee 4038, Harris 4118, Hauben 4120, McKee 4194, Ramsey 4258, Reisman 4263, **Summer 4316**, Zock 4368
Michigan: DeVlieg 4428, McClelland 4505, Olds 4526, Roscommon 4552, Tremble 4595
Minnesota: Reed 4768, Rodman 4779
Missouri: **Build-A-Bear 4879**, Favre 4908, Finerty 4909
Nebraska: America 5066, Baright 5070
Nevada: Blue 5140, Harris 5161, Kara 5168, Lifestyle 5173, Timken-Sturgis 5192
New Hampshire: Charter 5206, Dunn 5212, Noah 5226, Up 5235
New Jersey: Chapman 5292, Engel 5335, Farrington 5341, Feline 5345, Gardinier 5363, Krupa 5434, Schlaffer 5522, Schlotterer 5523, Sheridan 5533, Stein 5551, Twin 5563, Wildwood 5586
New Mexico: Gumbo 5617
New York: Anderson-Rogers 5676, Andrews 5677, Bernhill 5741, Blackman, 5755, Blodgett 5760, Clarkson 5849, Cline 5851, Code 5854, Douglas 5929, Dworman 5938, Ellsworth 5957, F. 5977, Gimbel 6079, Gordon 6109, **Harriman 6170**, Harris 6171, Henkind 6190, JLK 6264, Kenlou 6299, Marble 6441, NM 6536, Palmer 6573, Rothschild 6703, Skalny 6807, Spaeth 6829, Spear 6832, Steck 6852, Waldron 6939, Walsh 6942, Whalesback 6967
North Carolina: Balin 7042, Hunt 7135, Marsh 7170, Masserini 7172, Moritz 7192, Rolla 7230, Walters 7278
Ohio: Hankison 7438, Ingle 7462, Jenkins 7464, Sheadle 7589, Williamson 7640, Woodward 7646
Oklahoma: Russell 7718, Tandy 7723
Pennsylvania: Amaranth 7838, Black 7876, Brooks 7899, Cove 7939, Danella 7948, Delaware 7953, Dominion 7961, Fetters 7991, Gauss 8014, Langner 8111, Randall 8230, Seebe 8268, Teleflex 8314, Tippins 8318
Rhode Island: Bailey 8384, Hartman 8416, **Jeffery 8429**, Pisa 8474, Zack 8508
South Dakota: Black 8556
Tennessee: Atticus 8582, Heagele-Blount 8627, LifeWorks 8643, Mapp 8646, Tipton 8682

Texas: American 8701, Bearden 8721, DDM 8801, Ethel 8842, Farris 8847, Fort 8865, Friedman 8876, Hershey 8931, Lesley 9013, Moss 9076, P 9108, Parks 9115, Sherman 9192, SK 9198
Utah: Utah 9361
Virginia: Blueberry 9402, Community 9426, Schiro-Zavela 9528, Selsky 9529
Washington: Ferguson 9596, Herray 9621, Hyde 9627, Jacobi 9628, Kaleidoscope 9641, Nysether 9671, Paulus 9676, Svanees 9706, Tamaki 9707, Weidner 9719
Wisconsin: Cloud 9796, Davis 9802, Dutton 9812, Hansen 9835, Marshfield 9878, Redmond 9910, Rusinow 9920
Wyoming: Marine 9980, Skilling 9990

Down syndrome

Florida: Gagnon 2029
Michigan: Thompson 4593
Wisconsin: Phipps 9902

Drawing

New York: Woodner 6991

Dropouts

California: Just 684

Ear, nose and throat diseases

Arizona: Dove 112
California: Arnstein 254, Evening 487, Martin 800
Maryland: Mitchell, 3916
Ohio: Bahmann 7313

Early childhood education

Arizona: Grossman 126, Snell 171
Arkansas: Hennessy 198
California: Broder 348, GirlSMART 560, Orfalea 887, Rotasa 991, Wells 1171
Colorado: Bloom 1239
Florida: Gralnick 2056, Lastinger 2168, Price 2267, Thurman 2375
Illinois: Highland 2970, Morris 3125
Kansas: Berry 3558, Insurance 3587
Massachusetts: Foundation 4094
Michigan: Branch 4396
Minnesota: Bell 4638, Rosen 4782
Missouri: **Build-A-Bear 4879**, Vatterott 5030
New Jersey: Columbia 5301
New York: Goldenberg 6092, Happy 6165, Initial 6245, Kenworthy 6300, RHR 6667, Roche 6678, **Spirit 6839**, Turner 6916, Zeitz 7021
Pennsylvania: Seybert 8269, Wurts 8370
Rhode Island: Kingsbury 8435, LLH/LHM 8442
Texas: Boeing 8733, Central 8766, Levy 9014, Ross 9164
Virginia: Ivakota 9477
Washington: Foss 9598, Keller 9643
Wisconsin: **Dewing 9805**, Jacobus 9849, Stateline 9937

Ecology

Massachusetts: **New 4220**
New York: **Eppley 5967**

Economic development

Alabama: Black 12
California: **Candelaria 372**, **Cienega 404**, **Global 565**, **Linked 758**, Palo 900, **Wakerly 1150**
Colorado: Steffens 1358
Connecticut: Donchian 1440, Savings 1559, Tierney 1584
Georgia: Athens 2437, Rosen 2577
Illinois: Shamrock 3239

Indiana: Benton 3344, Community 3361, Fayette 3379, MutualBank 3421, Western 3466
Iowa: Forster 3494
Maine: Franklin 3779
Massachusetts: **Azadoutioun 4008, Blossom 4022**
Michigan: Branch 4396, Community 4410, Havirmill 4463, Leven 4492
Minnesota: **Porter 4763, Winds 4820**
Mississippi: Community 4830
Missouri: **Larson 4943**
Montana: Foundation 5051
Nebraska: Midlands 5104
New York: **Cogitare 5855, Family 5983**, Grant 6129, **Jabara 6254**, Preston 6626, Richter 6668
North Carolina: BB&T 7045, Boddie 7055, Chatham 7074, Piedmont 7209
Ohio: Foundation 7408, Sears-Swetland 7581
Oklahoma: Cherokee 7666
Pennsylvania: Community 7933, Elk 7975, Hilles 8057, Wayne 8345
Texas: Foundation 8869, Hill 8937
Vermont: Kaufman 9378
West Virginia: Starvaggi 9767
Wisconsin: Dudley 9811
Wyoming: **Schultz 9986**

Economically disadvantaged people

New Jersey: Brothers 5276
Ohio: Jenkins 7465
Tennessee: Cracker 8603

Economics

California: Penney 913
Colorado: Staley 1357
Georgia: Walker 2603
Illinois: Townsend 3291
Michigan: Whitman 4615
Minnesota: **Winds 4820**
North Carolina: Kenan 7143
Ohio: Kutz 7486
Pennsylvania: Kazanjian 8090
Texas: Hartman 8920
Washington: Quest 9681

Economics for youth

Florida: Kiwanis 2149, Tupperware 2379
Georgia: TALX 2592
Indiana: Crescent-Cresline-Wabash 3365
Iowa: McDonald 3520
Michigan: Dana 4419, Meritor, 4511
Minnesota: Midcontinent 4745
Nebraska: Physicians 5112
New York: Anderson 5674
Wisconsin: Ariens 9776

Education

Alabama: Abroms 2, Adams 3, Anderson 6, **Atlantis 8**, Barkley 9, Battle 10, Birmingham 11, Black 12, Brinkley 15, Bynum 18, Chester 20, Cooper 22, Cooper 23, Day 25, Friedman 27, Glaze 28, Goodrich 29, Griffin 30, Griswold 31, Hanks 32, Harrison 35, Hartselle 36, Ireland 39, King 43, King 44, Kirkland 45, Lenoir 46, Loeb 47, Malone 48, Mitchell 49, Phifer, 54, Piassick 55, Propst 56, Regions/AmSouth 58, Rikard 59, Rothschild 61, Samford, 62, Sexton 63, Shook 64, Simpson 66, SSAB 67, Yates 78
Alaska: Alaska 80, Alaska 81, Doyon 84, Hooker 87, Koniag 89, UIC 92
Arizona: Adkerson 94, Ahearn 95, Armstrong 97, Barton 99, **Beals 100**, Cadeau 104, Declaration 111, du 114, Eaton 115, F2 117, Forsberg 119, Grossman 126, Hansen 127, Harmsen, 128, Helms 129, Hughes 130, Immanuel 131, Jasam 133, Johnson 135, **Kearny 137**, Kuhle 139, Lapan 140, Louis 142, Lund 143, Massie 146, MCS 149, Murphey 151, Napier 152, O'Rielly 154, Pierce 156, Powell

157, Robson 160, **Rosztoczy 161**, Rothschild 162, Rubeli 163, Rudge 164, Schmidt 166, Shacknai 167, Shultz 168, Sioles 169, Snell 171, Squires 173, Valley 178, Van 179, Warmer 180, Williams 182, Zicarelli 185
Arkansas: Bailey 186, **Baldor 188**, Bodenhamer 190, Buck 192, Elrod 195, Heflin 197, Hickingbotham 199, Horn 200, Hussman 201, Merkle 203, Minnis 204, Morris 205, Riggs 214, Southland 215, Trinity 218, Union 219
California: 2005 223, Ach 226, Ackerman 227, Adams 228, Adams 229, Adelaide 230, Adelman 231, Adonai 232, Amador 238, Anatman 242, Anderson 243, Anhaltzer 245, Arata 248, Ascher, 256, Atkinson 259, **Ayz 262**, Bach 263, Baker 264, Baldacci 268, Bank 272, Bannerman 274, Barbera 275, Barulich 280, Baskin 281, Baxter 284, Baye 285, **Beagle 286**, Beam 287, Bear 288, Beattie 289, Beauregard 290, Becker 292, Beim 293, Bekins 294, Bell 295, Belle 296, Bellwether 299, Beneto 301, Berglund 302, Bergman 304, Berkshire 305, Bialis 313, Bigglesworth 316, Bilak 317, Blachford-Cooper 318, Blackie 319, **Blackman 320**, Blatteis 322, Board 323, Bonner 326, Boone 328, Boone 329, Borzi 332, Boscacci 333, Boukai 334, Bradford 337, Bravo 338, Breslow 340, Brewster 341, Bridges 342, Broder 348, Brooks 349, Brotman 351, Brown 352, Brown 353, Bryan 355, Bucolo 356, **Bull 358**, Burrows 363, Butler 364, **Butler 365**, Butte 366, Buttonwillow 367, Byrne 368, Callison 371, Candor 373, Cardinal 376, CAS 378, Casillas 379, Castellano 380, Celebrate 383, Champions 386, Chestnut 392, Chiat 393, Child 394, Chitjian 396, Chizen 397, Christensen 400, Clara 406, Cleo 407, Cloud 408, CNC 410, Codding 412, Cohen 414, Community 420, Community 421, Corbalis 424, Corcoran 425, Corwin 428, Crabb 431, Cramblit 432, Crawford 435, Cush 437, Daly 440, Danem 441, Danvera 442, Davies 444, Davis 445, Del 449, **Delzell 450**, Dermalogica 451, Diamantine 452, DiNapoli 454, Donegan 458, Dorskind 459, Downing 462, Drexler 463, Ducommun 465, Dusenbury 466, Dwelle 467, Dwyer 468, Dyer 469, Eagle 470, Elder 475, Eleven 476, Ellen 478, Elliott 479, Epstein/Roth 483, Evans 486, Everest 488, Faggin 489, Fairview 490, Family 492, Family 493, Faraway 494, Farmers 496, Faro 497, Feder 501, Ferry 504, First 507, Fitzpatrick 508, Flanagan 510, **Floyd 513**, Foor 516, Forgatch 517, Foster 519, Foundation 521, Fox 524, Fox 525, Fremont 527, Freshwind 528, Friedhofer 529, Friedman 530, Friedman 531, Fritz 534, Frome 535, Fudge 537, Funari 539, Furth 540, Fusenot 541, Gallo 543, Garabedian 545, Garaventa 546, Gellert 550, George 551, Gifts 553, Giles 554, Gilmore 557, **Girls 559**, Glazer 562, Glikbarg 564, **Global 565**, Godric 566, Goldstein 569, Goodall 570, Gordon 574, Gordy 575, Green 578, Greenwood 580, Grey 582, Grey 583, Griffiths 584, Grimm 585, Griswold 586, Gross 587, Guerin 589, H. 590, Hagopian 592, Hakka 593, **Hampar 594**, Hand 595, Harman 598, Harris 600, Harris 601, Hausman 603, Havner 604, Heck 609, **Hefferlin 610**, Heffernan 611, Heinz 612, Heller 613, Helms 615, Helmstetter 616, Hochman 626, Hodges 627, Hoefer 628, Hotchkis 635, Huber 638, Hughes 639, Hunsaker 640, HunterWard 641, Huntington 642, i.am.angel 645, Ibrahim 646, Ichioka 647, Ignatius 648, IM 649, In 650, **Indo-American 651, International 652**, J. 653, **Jacoby 654**, Jain 657, Jatain 659, JDH 660, Jesy 664, Johnson 668, Johnston 671, Jolson 672, Jones 673, Jones 674, Joy 677, JP 678, JTB 679, Jubas 680, Kanel 688, Kanoff 689, Karp 691, KC 694, Kelly 697, Kelton 698, Kelvin 699, Kendall 700, Kendall 701, Khoury 702, Kieve 703, Kim 704, Kinsey 707, Kirkorian 709, Kisco 710, Kite 711, Knell 712, KNU 713, Koss 720, Kreitzberg 721, Krishnan-Shah 722, Kwoh 724, L.B. 725, Laguna 726, Lash 730, Laurance 732, Lavine 733, **Lawrence 734**, Lebherz 735, Lebowitz 736, Leeds 738, Legacy 740, Leland 741, Lemelson 742, Lemons 744, **Lenz 746**, Lester 747, Lester 748,

Levine 750, **Levy 752**, Liautaud 755, Lin 757, Lipp 759, Llagas 762, Locke 764, Looker 766, Lopez 767, Los 768, Los 769, Louie 770, **Lui 771**, Lynch 775, Lyons 776, **Lyu 777**, MacDonald 779, Mae 780, Magali 781, Majestic 784, Malachi 785, Maley-Thawley 787, Manchester 788, Marchese 792, Marcus 794, Marineau 798, Martin 803, Mashhoon 804, Mason 805, Massie 806, Mayer 809, Mazda 810, McDaniel 812, McGraw 814, McKenzie 816, McMahon 819, McQuinn 820, Michaud 824, Mickelson 825, Mill 827, Miller 831, Miller 833, Millstreet 835, **Moley 841**, Mollath 842, Money-Arenz 844, Morgan 846, Morgenstern 848, Moskowitz 849, Mudd 851, Munushian 853, Murad 854, Muskin 855, Nachtsheim 856, Nagel 857, Nasaw 858, Nelson 860, Nelson 861, Neu 862, New 864, Nickoll 867, North 869, Oak 872, October 873, O'Donnell 874, Ohana 876, Olander 878, Ontario 882, Optivest 884, Opus 885, Oreggia 886, Ornest 888, **Orphan 889**, Orthodox 890, O'Shea 892, Otto 893, Outrageous 894, OZ 896, Pacific 897, **PADI 898**, Page 899, Palo 900, Palo 901, Pardee 902, Payne 910, Pearlstein 911, Penney 913, Perricone 916, **Peszynski 917**, Phelps 923, Pickford 927, Plum 929, Pollia 931, **Preuss 935**, Price 939, Priory 940, Private 941, Pulido 944, **Quiksilver 945**, RA5 946, Rady 949, Ragir 950, Rallis 951, Rappaport 953, Rapport 954, **Reddy 958**, Reddy's 959, Rees 961, Reitman 964, Reveas 967, Rice 969, Riley 973, Rishwain 974, Roberts 975, Robinson 977, Rocca, 978, Roche 979, Rogers 980, Romano 982, Roney 983, Rose 984, Rosenberg 985, Rosenthal 987, Ross 988, Rubin 992, Rush 994, Russell 995, Sammut 996, Sanders 999, Sandnes 1000, Sanfilippo 1002, Sarandon 1004, Sassoon 1006, Sato 1007, **Saya 1011**, Schaeffer 1013, Scherr 1014, Schlinger 1016, Schulte 1018, Scott 1023, **Scovel 1025**, Sebastiani 1027, Seip 1028, Setzer 1029, Shore 1034, **Sikand 1037**, Silicon 1038, Simon 1040, Simon-Strauss 1042, SJL 1043, Sloss 1048, Small 1049, Smalley 1050, Smith 1052, Smith-Walker 1057, Smith-Welsh 1058, Smittcamp 1059, Spatz 1066, Sprague 1069, Sprague, 1070, Spungen 1071, Stack 1073, Stafford 1074, Staples 1075, Sterling 1081, Stewart 1083, Storm 1087, Straus 1088, Strome 1089, Suggs 1091, Sun 1092, Swayne 1097, Swinerton 1098, Syar 1099, Synopsys 1100, SYZYGY 1101, Tanimura 1103, Teachers 1104, **Teichman 1106**, Terra 1107, Teshinsky 1108, Tilley 1118, Tippett 1119, Torino 1125, Trombetta 1128, Troy 1130, Tsao 1133, Twanda 1135, Unz 1137, Uplands 1138, Uplands 1139, Uvas 1142, **Valenzuela 1143**, Varner 1145, **Vogelzang 1146**, Von 1147, Waller 1152, Walther 1154, Waltmar 1155, Wang 1157, Warren 1159, Webb 1162, Weil 1163, Weinberg 1164, Weiss 1166, Weisz 1167, Welch 1168, Welfund 1169, Wendell 1172, Wertheimer 1173, Wharton 1178, Wheeler 1179, White 1180, **Wilkinson 1183**, **Williamson 1184**, Wilson 1186, Winkler 1188, Winn 1189, Witkin 1191, **Wong 1194, Woo 1195**, Wrather 1198, Writer 1200, Yen 1201, Yoder 1202, Zacky 1206, Zecca 1209, Zitrustin 1215, Zolla 1216, Zurlo 1217
Colorado: Allen 1220, Andrews 1221, Arches 1222, Arrowhead 1223, Ballantine 1226, Bardsley 1227, Benson 1230, Beren 1232, Bhappu 1234, Blair 1237, Brent 1240, Broomfield 1242, Brown 1243, Chotin 1246, Cornerstone 1251, Craig-Scheckman 1252, Creative 1253, Donahue 1257, Donnell-Kay 1258, DWB 1260, Elizabeth 1263, Energy 1264, Erion 1265, F 1266, Flug 1271, Fund 1274, Gart 1275, Gerrish 1277, Getz 1278, Graves 1280, Hanson 1286, Harvey 1287, Hunt 1296, Jacobs 1298, Joslin-Needham 1300, Kesher 1304, Koelbel 1306, Kortz 1307, Krieble 1308, Kroh 1309, Leighty 1311, Martischang 1321, Medical 1324, Mehrberg 1325, **National 1330**, Neuman 1331, Oak 1333, **Okinaga 1334, Oreg 1335**, Petunia 1336, Priester 1340, Puksta 1341, QEP 1342, Rakowich 1343, RBG 1344, Reel 1345, Relationship 1346, Routzon 1348, Schlessman

1349, Schramm 1350, Servant 1352, **Someone 1354**, Staley 1357, Steffens 1358, Strohm 1361, Taddonio 1362, Tappan 1363, Tigertree 1366, Tomkins 1368, Wexler 1377, Wilson 1380, Wolcott 1381

Connecticut: Abramowitz 1384, Adams 1386, Aibel 1388, Allwin 1390, Anderson 1393, Anderson-Paffard 1394, Antonacci 1395, Avery 1396, Baggins 1398, Bannow-Larson 1400, Barden 1402, Barnes 1403, Barnes 1404, Bessie 1407, Brace 1410, Bradley 1411, Calarco 1414, Caldwell 1415, Cenveo 1416, Chelsea 1418, Craig 1423, Crosswicks 1425, Damuth 1428, Dennett 1432, DeNunzio 1433, Denzler 1434, Diageo 1437, Dime 1438, Donchian 1439, Donchian 1440, Eder 1441, Ensign-Bickford 1442, Family 1443, Farid 1444, Ferguson 1446, Filingieri 1447, Finkelstein 1448, Finn 1449, Fippinger 1450, Floren 1451, Fox 1453, Fraites 1454, **Friends 1455**, Friezo 1457, Fuller 1460, Gengras, 1461, Gladstein 1465, Goldfarb 1467, Grampy's 1469, Greenhill 1472, Gryphon 1474, Hall 1475, Hamm 1476, Hastings 1479, Hildes-Heim 1483, Howard 1484, Huntington 1486, Inglesea 1487, Jones 1490, Jost 1492, Kaman 1493, Kaufmann 1495, Keefe 1497, Knox 1500, Kreitler 1502, Lamando 1504, Lee 1507, Lippincott 1509, LLL 1510, Lodewick 1512, Magaro 1516, Mahadeva 1517, Manger 1518, Mann 1519, Martin 1520, Martinsen 1521, McLane 1522, McLaughlin 1523, Nevas 1530, Newtown 1532, Niblack 1533, Nirenberg 1534, Oberlander 1535, O'Meara 1537, Paoloian 1540, Patricelli 1541, Perna-Rose 1542, Post 1543, Pulvermann 1547, Rapp 1548, Roberts 1551, Robinson 1553, Rock 1554, Rubin-Ladd 1556, Salatto 1557, Santoro 1558, Savings 1559, Schaeneman, 1560, Schendel 1561, Schloss 1562, Schwerin 1563, Shanley 1567, Smith 1571, **Sonja 1573**, Stratfield 1576, Sullivan 1577, Taylor 1579, Tell 1580, Thomaston 1581, Thrall 1583, Titus 1585, Tucker 1587, Tully 1588, Union 1590, Vance 1591, WorldQuant 1600, Zelnick/Belzberg 1602

Delaware: 18 1604, ABE 1607, Alcyon 1608, Allen 1609, Anastasi 1610, Anbinder 1611, Babcock 1612, Bailey-Stanford 1613, Bartlett 1615, Bennett 1618, Berning 1620, Black 1622, Blau 1623, Bradley 1626, Bresnan 1628, Brown 1630, Bulova 1633, Burton 1634, Bushong 1636, Cedarcrest 1639, Chaney 1640, Cohen 1643, Coleman 1644, Corkins 1648, Corrigan-Walla 1649, Cross 1651, De 1655, Easterly 1660, Farr 1662, Fernandina 1663, Foundation 1664, Freedman 1665, Giving 1668, **Gloria 1670**, Gorny 1671, Gromet 1672, Groot 1673, Haldan 1676, Hauser 1678, Hawkins 1679, Hill 1681, **Jackman 1683**, Jade 1684, Jadeja 1685, Jockers 1687, Just 1688, Kang 1689, Kent-Lucas 1691, Kingsley 1693, Klein, 1694, Kutz 1696, Levin 1697, Lightner 1699, Martyn 1702, McKiernan 1706, Merrion 1707, Messing 1708, Midvale 1709, Milliken 1711, MMK 1712, New 1715, Pinkerton 1721, Praxis 1723, Ratner 1724, Relgalf 1725, Repass-Rodgers 1727, Replogle 1728, Rivers 1731, Rumberger 1734, Russell 1735, Schwalbach 1739, Scott 1740, Scripps 1741, Sein 1742, Signal 1743, Sloane 1746, SNAVE 1747, Solot 1748, Splawn 1749, Stein 1750, Stiefel 1751, Sulentic 1752, Synthesis 1756, Talbott 1757, Taylor 1759, **TeleTech 1761**, Telluriun 1762, Third 1763, Thomson 1764, Viridiun 1770, Vitale 1771, VWR 1772, Wang 1773, Welton 1776, Wender 1777, Whitman 1778, Wong 1779, Wood 1780, Yaverland 1783

District of Columbia: American 1785, Bench 1788, Bender 1789, Bloedorn 1790, Brody 1791, Choksi 1795, Cook 1797, Crowell 1799, Dart 1800, Davies 1801, Goldman 1810, **Gorlitz 1811**, Hanley 1814, Kolar 1818, Lemon 1819, **Merriman 1820**, Mimi 1822, Olender 1824, Porter 1829, Replogle 1831, Rossotti 1832, Rubenstein 1833, Silberman 1834, Woodward 1839

Florida: A. 1841, Adler 1842, Ahavas 1844, Anderson 1845, Anderson 1847, Archibald 1852, Around

---

1854, Atkins 1856, Atkinson 1857, Auerbach 1859, **Aviation 1861**, Bailey 1862, Bailey 1863, Baldwin 1864, Barnard 1866, Barrington 1868, Bartner 1869, Basham 1870, Baulch 1873, Baxter 1874, Beall, 1876, Beasley 1877, Beeck 1881, Bell 1882, Bell 1883, **Benedict 1884**, Blake 1889, Blanksteen 1891, Blatt 1893, Bohnert 1895, Bomberger 1896, Bond 1897, Boston 1898, Brinckerhoff 1900, Brooke 1903, Brown 1906, Burks 1909, Burnett 1911, Callas 1913, **Cantonis 1915**, Cape 1917, Capital 1918, Carbonari 1919, Carlton 1922, Carrington 1923, Cassill 1926, Castellani 1927, Catalina 1928, CCJ 1929, Chadbourne 1932, Chaffiot 1933, Chanin 1934, Chapman 1935, Charlotte 1938, **Chenzyme 1939**, Cherry 1940, Chicone 1941, Childress 1942, Clements 1945, Cody 1946, Cohen 1948, Collins 1949, Concourse 1950, Coral 1952, Couch 1953, Crane 1955, Croft 1956, Crutchfield 1957, Cunnane 1959, Dasburg 1961, Davis 1962, Davis 1963, Davis 1964, De 1967, Defeo 1968, Dennis 1969, Detter 1971, Diane 1974, Draft 1981, Duckwall 1982, Duda 1983, Durden 1984, Dysimmune 1986, Echevarria 1987, Elster 1990, Enlightenment 1991, Epstein 1992, **Falk 1996**, Farrell 1998, Ferguson 1999, Fleischman 2003, Focus 2005, Forbes 2008, Foulds 2014, Frangakis 2017, Franklin 2020, Friedheim 2024, Friedland 2025, Fuller 2028, Galeana 2030, Garner 2032, Garvy 2033, Gelbart 2035, Gemunder 2036, Gerry-Corbett 2037, Givens 2038, Glass 2039, Godbold 2041, Goldberg 2045, Goldman 2047, Goody 2049, Gordon, 2052, Grabe 2053, Grader 2054, Grassy 2057, Greaton 2060, Green 2061, Greenblatt 2063, Greene 2064, Greenfield 2066, Gregory 2067, Gulf 2069, Hagens 2071, Hall-Halliburton 2074, Halmos 2075, Hand 2077, Hardeman 2080, Harper 2082, Haskell 2083, Haven 2085, Hayford 2086, Held 2088, Helow 2089, Hendrix 2090, Hicks 2094, Hieronymus 2095, **Hishmeh 2100**, Hoffman 2103, Hollo 2105, Holloway 2106, Holtz 2109, Hufty 2114, Hunter 2116, Ingalls 2118, Insetta 2119, Irwin 2120, Isenberg 2121, J. 2122, Jacobsen 2123, Jacobson 2124, Johnson 2130, Kanders 2136, Kaplan 2138, Kaul 2139, KBR 2142, Kessler 2145, Kimmel 2146, King 2147, Kiwanis 2149, Kiwanis 2150, Knapp 2153, Knippenberg 2154, Knopf 2155, Knopf 2156, Koski 2157, Kreisman 2159, KT 2160, Lambert 2164, Lamoureux 2166, Landwirth 2167, Laufer 2169, Layden 2171, Lazarus 2172, Le 2175, Lelash 2178, Lewis 2182, Lissack 2186, Loftis 2188, Lowry 2191, Lyle 2192, Marco 2194, Marshall 2195, Mary 2198, Mayberg 2199, Mb 2200, McDonald 2203, McGahren 2204, McNamara 2207, Melin 2210, Mendelson 2211, MIDA 2212, Millsaps 2214, Minto 2216, Morningstar 2218, Morrison 2221, Morrison 2222, Mount 2223, Moye 2224, Muccia 2225, Munroe 2228, Noble 2234, Nuzzo 2236, Olliff 2239, Olsen 2240, Oristano 2241, Owen 2243, Parish 2247, Pearce 2252, Perryman 2255, Peters 2256, Peyton 2258, Phillips 2259, **Posnack 2262**, Powell 2265, Price 2267, **Prime 2268**, Propp 2269, Prutky 2270, Pulichino 2271, Pusey 2272, Quinn 2273, Ransburg 2274, Raymund 2276, Reed 2278, Reinhold 2280, Resnick 2282, Rice 2283, Rich 2284, Richard 2285, Rinker 2287, Rogers 2291, Rogers 2292, Rosen 2294, Rosenfeld 2295, Roshan 2297, Ross 2298, Rothman 2299, Rothschild 2300, Rubens 2301, Sadler 2306, Sample 2312, Sanders 2313, Scharlin 2315, Schiano 2317, Schultz 2319, Seaman 2320, Second 2321, Selders 2322, Sequoia 2324, Sexton 2326, Shannon 2328, Sharing 2330, **Shepard 2331**, Shockley 2332, Sidhu 2334, Siegel 2335, Sierra 2336, Six 2339, Smick 2340, Smith 2341, Soter 2343, Speranza 2344, Stafford 2346, Steele 2347, Stern 2350, Stewart 2351, **Stiefel 2352**, Studer 2355, Sudakoff 2356, Swann 2360, Swisher 2361, Tampa 2362, Taplin 2363, TECO 2367, Thomas 2370, Thompson 2372, Thornburgh 2374, Toppel 2377, Turlington 2380, **Uncle 2383**,

---

Verner 2386, von 2388, Wagmore 2391, Waugh 2392, Weisman 2396, Werner 2398, Wescustogo 2399, Westgate 2400, Westreich 2401, Whiting 2403, Whitman 2404, Wiener 2405, Wilson-Wood 2408, Woodbery 2413, Woolard 2414, Wrightson-Ramsing 2416, Wynne 2419, Yerrid 2420, Younger 2422, Zimmerman 2428

Georgia: A.E.M. 2430, Akers 2432, Andrews 2434, Arnold 2436, Athens 2437, Barnett 2441, Beckman 2443, Benton 2445, Boone 2446, Bowen 2447, Brewer 2448, Brooks 2450, Canipe 2452, Chandler 2455, Charter 2456, Chatham 2457, Childress 2459, Cobb 2463, Community 2465, Cook, 2468, Davison 2470, DeLoache 2471, English 2474, Fickling 2478, Forehand 2479, **Gage 2482**, Gholston 2486, Gilbert, 2488, Glancy 2489, Go 2490, Goddard 2491, Goodman 2492, Gordy 2493, Graves 2496, Griffin 2499, Guillaume 2500, **Hands 2501**, Harrison 2502, Higher 2505, Hodge 2506, Holly 2509, Howell 2512, Hoyt 2513, Hunter 2515, Illges 2517, **Invisible 2520**, Irving 2521, JBS 2523, Joyce 2527, Kahn 2529, Kingdom 2531, King-White 2532, Klump 2533, Knox 2534, L. 2535, Langdale, 2537, Lanier 2538, Lassiter 2539, Lee 2540, Looney 2542, Magnus 2543, Marcus 2544, McClatchey 2546, Miracle 2549, Mix 2550, Montgomery 2551, Myfifident 2554, Nabors 2555, Oxford 2561, Pechter 2564, Price 2569, Price-Campbell 2570, Rackley 2571, Reynolds 2574, Rockdale 2576, Samford 2578, Saul 2579, Schinazi 2580, SF 2585, Smith 2586, Storey 2589, Sweetgrass 2591, TALX 2592, Terwilliger 2593, Trammell 2595, Waffle 2602, Ward 2605, Warren 2606, Warren 2608, Whitehead 2610, Whitepath 2611, Williams 2612, Windolf 2614, Woodcrest 2616, Woodruff 2617, Woodruff, 2618, Wormsloe 2619

Hawaii: Baldwin 2625, Central 2627, Ching 2628, Epstein 2630, First 2631, Higgins 2635, Kaneta 2637, Locations 2638, Makana 2639, Martin 2641, Sawyer 2644, Servco 2645, Shields 2647, Takitani 2650, Teruya 2651, Ululani 2652, Vidinha 2653, Wilcox 2654, Wo 2655, Wong 2656, Young 2659, Young 2660, Zwaanstra 2662

Idaho: Angels 2664, Boise 2666, Boswell 2667, Dumke 2668, Emelco 2669, French 2671, Hagadone 2674, Hare 2675, Hecla 2676, Intermountain 2677, **Melaleuca 2679**, Morbeck 2681, Palmedo 2684, Smeed 2686, Troxell 2688, Whittenberger 2689

Illinois: Acorn 2694, **Acorn 2695**, Adams 2696, Adreani 2697, Agent 2699, Ahlstrand 2700, Alliant 2702, **American 2707**, Amsted 2708, Aon 2710, **Appleby 2711**, AptarGroup 2712, Arboit 2713, Argo 2714, B&D 2715, Baird 2718, Banta 2719, Barr 2720, Bartholomay 2721, Bass 2723, Bates 2724, Beck 2729, Beeghly 2730, Bellick 2732, Bere 2734, Bergstrom 2736, Bernoudy 2738, Best 2739, Bidwill 2741, Bisco 2742, Block 2745, Block, 2746, Boehl 2748, Boothroyd 2749, Bound 2751, Bower 2752, Boylan 2753, Bruce 2760, Bruce 2761, Brunswick 2762, Bulkley, 2765, Buntrock 2766, Burk 2768, Burnett 2769, Burt 2770, Cafaro-Livingston 2772, Cain 2773, Canterbury 2774, Carey 2775, Ceres 2779, Chambers 2780, Cherry 2784, Chez 2785, Chicago 2787, Citadel 2791, Clarks 2792, Cless 2793, Cole 2798, Collins 2799, Communitas 2801, Community 2802, Community 2803, Constans-Culver 2805, Corcoran 2810, Cord 2811, Coulter 2813, Cullinan 2818, Danielson 2823, Danielson 2824, Delta 2826, **Demos 2827**, Denny 2828, Diamond 2829, Dick 2830, Doerr 2831, Donovan 2833, Dowdle 2834, Dower 2835, Doyle 2836, Dubin 2838, Duncan 2839, Duncan 2840, Eckert 2843, Eclipse 2844, Edelman 2845, Edgerly 2847, Educational 2848, Eichner 2849, Ellis 2853, EMA 2854, Engle 2855, Enivar 2856, Epaphroditus 2857, Estate 2860, Everett 2861, Fabyan 2862, Farnham 2865, Fasseas 2866, Faulkner 2867, Feltes 2869, Fields 2870, Fildes 2872, Fink 2873, Fischer 2874, Foley 2876, Forbes 2878, Four 2882, Fraida 2884, Franklin 2887, Franklin 2888, Fredman 2890,

---

Freund 2892, Full 2894, Full 2895, Fund 2896, Garard, 2902, Gardner 2903, Gardner 2904, Generations 2908, Geneseo 2909, Gibbet 2912, Gidwitz 2913, Gidwitz 2914, Gloyd 2917, Goldberg 2919, Golder 2921, Good 2923, Gostomski 2925, Gray 2927, Gray 2928, Griffith 2930, Griswold 2931, Groner 2932, Grossinger 2933, Grumhaus, 2934, Haarlow 2940, Half 2942, Hallene 2943, Halstead 2944, Hanus 2951, Harczak, 2952, Hark 2955, Harris 2956, Harris 2957, Hart 2958, Hary 2959, Hastings 2960, Hegeler 2963, Henderson 2965, **Heritage 2967**, Herman 2968, Hess 2969, Highland 2970, Hill 2971, Hodes 2974, Hoffer 2975, Holden 2976, Hopper 2977, Houlihan 2979, Hughes 2983, Iroquois 2989, Istock 2991, Jaros 2993, JKP 2997, Johnson 3001, Kaminski 3005, Kellcie 3008, Keller 3009, Kelly 3011, Kemp 3013, Kerr 3015, Keyes 3016, Kilrea 3017, Knappenberger 3021, Knight 3022, Knowles 3023, Koranda 3026, Kott 3027, KPW 3028, Krueck 3031, Lakshmi 3033, Lamka 3034, Landau 3037, Larsen 3038, **Lascaris 3040**, Lazar 3041, Lebus 3043, Leibowitz 3046, Levinson 3049, Lifetract 3053, Logos 3058, Louis 3063, Love 3064, Mako 3070, Manne 3073, Marsteller 3079, Mary's 3081, McCormack 3086, McCrea 3088, McDougal 3091, McKee 3093, McKee 3094, McLennan 3096, McNulty 3099, **Mead 3100**, Merchantz 3102, **Mermelstein 3103**, Meyer 3106, **Meyers 3107**, Micole 3108, Millard 3109, Millard 3110, Miller 3112, Minor 3117, Minow 3118, Mohr 3121, Monroe 3122, Moore 3123, Moreton 3124, Morton 3127, Mouat 3128, Mullen 3129, Munson 3130, Murnane 3131, Murphy 3132, Nayak 3133, New 3136, **New 3137**, **New 3138**, Novick 3143, Nygren 3146, O'C 3148, O'Connor 3149, Okner-Robbins 3152, Olin 3153, Oppenheimer 3155, OSA 3157, Osi 3158, Owen 3160, Pangburn 3161, Parker 3162, Parker 3163, Patterson 3164, Penrose 3166, Perkins 3168, Peters 3172, Petrick 3173, Petrovich 3174, Pharmore 3175, Pitzman 3177, Poncher 3181, Putnam 3186, Red 3188, Red 3189, Reinisch 3193, Rich 3194, Ringer 3196, Robb 3197, Roche 3201, Romano 3203, Rosebud 3204, **Rosenmutter 3208**, Rosenson 3209, Rosenthal 3210, Roundy 3214, Russell 3216, Ruttenberg 3217, Ruttenberg 3218, Ryan 3219, Saliba 3221, Schaumburg 3223, Schiff 3224, Schorr-Lieberman 3229, Scott 3230, Secord 3232, Self 3234, Shaker 3238, Shaw 3243, Shirley 3245, Simon 3247, Simpson 3249, Skylark 3250, Smallwood 3251, Smith 3252, Smithborg 3254, Speiser 3257, Spencer 3258, Stairway 3261, Staley 3262, Steigerwaldt 3265, Stein 3266, Steinmetz 3267, Stone 3269, Stone 3270, STS 3272, Stutsman 3274, Sullivan 3276, Sulzer 3277, Summer 3279, Tafel 3280, Takiff 3281, Tarrson 3282, Taylor 3285, Taylor 3286, Tengelsen 3288, Thaman 3289, Tobey 3290, Townsend 3291, Tully 3295, Tuohy 3296, Twomey 3298, United 3300, Vail 3301, Valenti 3302, Vibern 3303, Von 3305, Warner 3310, Watson 3311, **Wein 3315**, Weiner 3316, Weiss 3317, Wessel 3318, Weston 3320, Whitwam 3321, Wislow 3323, Witz-Mallinger 3324, Wolf 3325, Wolf 3327, Wolff 3328, Woods 3331, Woods 3332, Wright 3333, Zuckerman 3338

Indiana: Ash 3341, BAJ 3343, Blackford 3346, Branigin 3348, Braun 3349, Burris 3352, Clark-Morrill 3356, Cohen 3357, Community 3358, Community 3359, Community 3360, Community 3361, Community 3362, Community 3363, Crescent-Cresline-Wabash 3365, Custer 3366, Decatur 3367, Dobbs 3368, Dorsey 3369, Dubois 3370, Duneland 3372, Ellerbrook 3376, Fayette 3379, Fenech 3380, Franklin 3382, Gaither 3384, Gammon 3385, Gibson 3386, Hillenbrand 3393, Huntington 3397, Interactive 3398, Jasper 3401, Jennings 3402, Jennings 3403, Keck 3405, KEJ 3406, Klapper 3408, Kuhne 3409, Lacy 3410, LaGrange 3412, Magee-O'Connor 3414, Maurer 3415, **Mervis 3417**, Mothershead 3419, MutualBank 3421, Oakley 3426, Ohio 3427, Pulaski 3432, Raker

3434, Raper 3435, Raymond 3436, Rifkin 3437, Roberts 3439, Rooney 3440, Rush 3441, Salin 3442, Schurz 3444, Scott 3446, Seger 3447, Shafer 3449, Sherwood 3451, Simon 3452, Smith 3453, Snyder 3454, Stamm 3456, TCU 3458, Vevay-Switzerland 3462, Western 3466, Wilmes 3468

Iowa: Barkema 3471, Becker 3472, Beckwith 3473, Bennett 3474, Blin 3476, Burke 3477, Cole-Belin 3480, Daniels 3483, De 3484, deStwolinski 3486, Figge 3492, First 3493, Geisler 3498, Giacoletto 3499, Gleeson 3500, Grubb 3502, Heerema 3504, Henry 3505, Hoaglin 3508, Howe 3510, Iowa 3511, Iowa 3512, Iowa 3513, Jefferson 3514, Krumm 3517, Latta 3518, McCarthy/Bush 3519, McDonald 3520, Medical 3521, Pappajohn 3525, Peace 3526, Premier 3528, R 3529, Ryan 3531, Schildberg 3532, Security 3534, Tomson 3537, Toohey 3538, Van 3539, Van 3540, Vermeer 3542, Vonderhaar 3543, Weathertop 3545, Weigle 3546, West 3547, Wood 3548, **Wright 3551**

Kansas: Adair-Exchange 3553, Atterbury 3554, Babinger 3555, Baehr 3556, Bane 3557, Berry 3558, Breidenthal-Snyder 3560, Cape 3563, Central 3564, Cochener 3565, Coffeyville 3566, Community 3567, CPS 3568, Cray 3569, Cyr 3570, Davis 3571, Elsberry 3574, French 3579, Goebel 3580, Green 3583, Hopkins 3586, Insurance 3587, Jeffcoat 3588, Jellison 3589, Kammco 3591, Kansas 3592, Lowenstein 3598, Mann 3599, Master 3600, McFadden 3601, Merrill 3602, Middlekauff 3603, Mistler 3606, O' 3612, Payless 3614, Rathert 3617, Ross 3619, Salgo 3621, Scott 3623, Scroggins 3624, Sheetz 3626, South 3628, Swearingen 3631, Taylor 3632, V 3636, Walsh 3638, Watson 3639, **Weskan 3641**, Wiedemann 3642

Kentucky: Abercrombie 3645, Barr 3646, Barth 3647, Boone 3648, Dunbar 3653, Foundation 3655, Hannah 3659, Harter 3660, Haskins 3661, Hayswood 3662, Heisel 3663, Houchens 3665, Independence 3666, Jones 3667, Keeneland 3668, Lebus 3671, Longest 3672, Mackin 3673, Masser 3676, Morris 3679, Ogden 3683, Pollard 3685, Public 3687, Reed 3688, Roth 3690, Smith 3694, Steiner 3696, Stock 3697, Stockdell-Joseph 3698, Sutherland 3699, Trim 3702, Turner 3703, USA 3704, Weisberg 3705, Welchwood 3706

Louisiana: A-Kids-Choice 3712, Briggs 3714, Broussard 3715, Cahn 3716, Catalyst 3717, Daybrook 3720, DeGree 3721, Ellis 3723, Gauthier 3724, Grigsby 3725, Havens 3727, Houseman 3728, Kavanagh 3730, Knight 3731, Live 3734, Magale 3735, Meraux 3736, Merkle 3737, Mintz 3738, Moffett 3739, Monteleone 3741, New 3742, Noland 3743, Parkside 3745, Powers 3746, Pugh 3747, **Ruckstuhl 3748**, Salutare 3749, Shannon 3752, Showers 3753, Special 3754, Steinhagen 3755, Whitman 3759, Wisdom 3761

Maine: Alfond 3764, Bank 3766, Boulos 3768, Brook 3769, Chappell 3772, Cotsirilos 3774, Davenport 3775, Franklin 3779, Goldberg 3780, **Golden 3781**, Hudson 3783, Kagan 3784, Kennebec 3785, Kennebunk 3786, Lynam 3788, Messler 3790, Mimi 3792, Minsky 3793, Narragansett 3794, Pond 3798, Red 3801, Reny 3802, Somers 3803, **St. 3804**

Maryland: Acacia 3807, Adams 3808, Adler 3809, Allemall 3811, AMDG 3812, Anderson 3814, Baker 3815, Bank 3818, Berger 3821, Bernard 3822, Besson 3823, Blum 3825, **Boehm 3826**, **Braitmayer 3827**, Broadus 3829, Campbell 3831, Carbonell 3833, Chessie 3835, Cogan 3837, Croft 3841, Daydreams 3845, Dockser 3849, Duncan 3851, Eccles 3853, Eliasberg 3854, Feldman 3858, Ferris 3860, Franey 3865, Friedman 3866, Fusco 3868, Gewirz 3869, Gladding 3871, **Goldberg 3872**, Gordon 3873, Govil 3875, Greene-Milstein 3876, Gutman 3877, Helm 3879, Higginson 3880, Hittman 3881, Hobbs 3882, Hubbard 3883, Hyman 3887, Izzo 3889, Kirk 3894, Knapp 3895, Laughlin 3898, Loats 3902, Lohr 3903, Macht 3905, Macks 3906, Mann-Paller

3908, Meltzer 3911, Mental 3912, Meyer, 3913, Meyerhoff 3914, Minkoff 3915, Moore 3917, Moser 3918, Mustard 3922, Myerberg 3923, Nabit 3924, Newday 3925, No 3927, Otenasek 3931, Paternotte 3933, Pettit 3935, Phase 3936, RCM 3937, RFI 3938, Richmond 3940, Rothschild 3942, Salisbury 3945, Schwarz 3947, Sears 3948, Shapiro 3949, Shattuck 3950, Shrensky 3951, Silberman 3953, Slavin 3954, Small 3955, Sonneborn 3957, SPM 3958, St. 3959, Stover 3961, Ticho 3967, Totah 3968, Tzedakah 3970, Van 3974, Weinberg, 3979, Weiner 3980, Weinman 3981, Widgeon 3983, Wieler 3984, Wilen 3985, Wilson 3987, Witt/Hoey 3989, Wolpoff 3990, Youth 3991

Massachusetts: 2 3992, 484 3993, A 3994, **Afeyan 3996**, Ain 3997, Alden 3999, Allison 4000, Altamira 4001, Alvord 4002, Arcadia 4004, Archibald 4005, Babson 4009, **Barakat 4012**, Beaucourt 4014, Behrakis 4015, Benson 4016, Benz 4017, Berger 4018, Bergstrom 4019, Black 4021, **Blossom 4022**, **Brabson 4026**, Brock 4027, Brooks 4028, Brown 4029, Bulger 4031, **Cabbadetus 4033**, Cabot 4034, Cabot 4035, Carle 4037, Catino 4040, Chabot 4042, Change 4043, Chase 4045, Chicopee 4047, Clarke 4049, Clementi 4050, Clifford 4051, Codman 4052, Cook 4056, Crane 4058, Crowe 4061, Curvey 4062, Dalessandro 4063, Davoli 4065, Deane 4066, Dedham 4067, Delorenzo 4068, Devereaux 4069, Donovan 4070, Druker 4071, Durant 4072, Dwyer 4074, East 4075, Easthampton 4076, Egan 4079, Egan 4080, Elephant 4081, England 4083, Fassino 4086, FCTS 4088, Fessenden 4090, First 4091, Fleming 4092, Fletcher 4093, Frisbie 4099, Gale 4100, **Galileo 4101**, Gerrity 4102, Gildea 4103, Gloria 4104, Goldman 4105, Greenberg 4106, Hagler 4111, Hale 4112, Halfway 4115, Harwood 4119, Haven 4122, Hazard 4123, Hazard 4124, Heide 4125, Helman 4126, Henderson 4128, Hicks 4129, Hopedale 4134, Horne 4136, Hyde 4139, Jackson 4140, Janet 4141, **Kahn 4143**, Kamin 4144, **Kaplan 4145**, Karas 4146, Kelsey 4148, Kendall 4149, Kenwood 4150, Kershaw 4151, Killam 4153, Killian 4154, Kimball 4155, King 4156, Koplow 4159, Krupp 4161, Kurian 4162, Ladd 4163, Lamm 4165, Lawry 4168, Learning 4169, Levangie 4172, Levy 4175, Lindsay 4176, Lingos 4177, Liswhit 4178, Longtine 4179, Lost 4180, Madonna 4182, Mahoney 4184, Makepeace 4186, Marcus 4188, Marino 4190, MENTOR 4199, Merrill 4200, Metanoia 4201, Middlesex 4203, Mirak 4204, Morningstar 4207, Morse 4208, Morse 4209, Mount 4211, Mountain 4212, Mulberry 4213, MutualOne 4216, NAID 4217, Noonan 4225, Novack 4226, Nye 4227, Nypro 4228, O'Keefe 4229, One 4230, OneBeacon 4231, Oristaglio 4232, Pechet 4235, Peoples 4237, PerkinElmer 4238, Permanent 4239, Peters 4241, Philips 4243, Pierce 4244, Pilgrim 4245, Poduska 4246, Progin 4247, Proud 4249, Rabb 4255, Ragon 4256, Ramlose 4257, Ramsey 4258, Ratshesky 4259, Reisman 4262, Reynolds 4264, Rice 4265, **Robbins-de 4266**, Rockland 4267, Rodman 4269, Rollstone 4270, Rosse 4272, Russell 4273, Sacajawea 4274, Salem 4277, Sandman 4279, Savage 4280, Schechter 4281, Schlager 4283, Schwartz 4284, Segel 4285, SER 4286, Shattuck 4291, Shaughnessy 4292, Sherman 4294, Sicari 4295, Simoni 4296, Smith 4298, Smith 4300, Solomon 4301, Solomont 4303, Spoon 4305, Stare 4308, Stearns 4311, Sullivan 4315, **Summer 4316**, Sword 4318, Tadler 4320, Thompson 4325, Thoreau 4327, Tomfohrde 4329, Toocap 4330, Torok 4331, Trefler 4332, Tresorelle 4333, Ungar 4336, United 4337, Upstream 4338, Valerio 4339, Vela 4341, Verrochi 4342, Von 4346, Wallace 4347, Walsh 4348, Walske 4349, Webber 4351, Webster 4353, Weiner 4355, Wells 4357, Wilcox 4360, Winthrop 4363, Wyman-Gordon 4364, Xeric 4365, Young 4366, Zampell 4367, Zock 4368

Michigan: **Ajemian 4371**, Allen 4372, Alon 4374, Amerisure 4375, Anchor 4376, Andersen 4377, Ave 4379, Avharas 4380, Baiardi 4381, Balk 4383, Barton-Malow 4386, Baum 4387, Beson 4389, Biederman 4391, Bierlein 4392, Bonder 4394, Bostock 4395, Branch 4396, Buffalo 4399, Buhr 4400, Buist 4401, Cebelak 4406, Christian 4407, Community 4410, Community 4411, Cracchiolo 4414, Cracchiolo 4415, Crowley 4416, Currie 4418, Dana 4419, Dana 4420, de 4422, DeKock 4425, Delano 4426, Delong-Sweet 4427, Dinan 4431, DiPonio 4432, Doll-Loesel 4433, Duchene 4435, Elliott 4436, Fabiano 4438, Family 4439, Farago 4440, Farver 4441, Farwell 4442, Filmer 4444, Ford 4445, Ford-Thomas 4447, Foren 4448, Four 4449, Frankenmuth 4450, Garber 4451, Garrett 4452, Glassen 4454, Gordon 4456, **Gorlin 4457**, Gratiot 4459, Harris 4461, Hartwick 4462, Hayden 4464, Hecht 4465, Herrington-Fitch 4466, Isabella 4468, JCT 4469, Jenkins 4470, Johnson 4471, JSJ 4474, Juhl 4475, Kantzler 4478, Keller 4481, Koster 4486, Lanting 4489, Lapeer 4490, Linse 4493, Loosemore 4495, LoPrete 4496, M 4497, Mackinac 4499, McClelland 4505, McDole 4506, Meritor, 4511, Merkley 4512, Michigan 4514, Molnar 4517, Morley 4518, Nickless 4522, O'Donovan 4525, Olds 4526, Padnos 4529, Paine 4531, Pappas 4532, Paulina 4535, Pitt 4540, Plym 4542, Porter 4543, Power 4544, Powers 4545, Ran 4547, Ratner 4548, Redies 4549, Roscommon 4552, Rottman 4553, Sehn 4563, Sherman 4567, Shiawassee 4568, Shine 4569, Sinai 4570, Skiles 4572, Stern 4578, Stoddard 4579, Sutaruk 4583, Talty 4584, Thoman 4590, Thompson 4591, Thompson 4592, Tremble 4595, **Triford 4597**, Tuscola 4598, Van 4601, Van 4602, VanGilder 4604, **Vattikuti 4605**, Vicksburg 4606, Vlasic 4607, Watson 4608, Welch 4610, Wheeler 4612, Whiting 4614, Wickson-Link 4616, Williams 4618, Zampetis 4619, Zimmerman 4620

Minnesota: Albany 4624, Andersen 4626, Ankeny 4628, Arctos 4629, Avocet 4631, Bahl 4632, Bailey 4633, Baratz 4635, Bell 4637, Bell 4638, Bend 4639, Bieber 4641, Black 4642, Blank 4643, Boss 4645, Bradley 4647, Briggs 4648, Burwell 4650, Caridad 4653, Caroline's 4654, Chadwick-Loher 4655, Cornwall 4660, Covenant 4661, Cox 4662, Dellwood 4665, Denfeld 4666, Erickson 4674, Erickson 4675, Evert 4676, Falck 4678, Farmers 4679, Farview 4680, Ferber 4682, Fischman 4685, Flaherty 4686, Fletcher 4687, Frey 4690, G&K 4691, Gage 4692, Gilligan 4696, Granite 4699, Griffiths 4700, Grossman 4701, Groves 4703, Hallett 4706, Hart 4708, Head 4709, Hegardt 4710, Hickory 4713, Hognander 4715, Huisinga 4716, Jeffers 4719, Jostens 4720, **Kaplan 4721**, Kinman-Oldfield 4723, Kinney 4724, Knowlton 4725, Krisbin 4726, Larsen 4728, Living 4730, Lukis 4732, Lutheran 4734, Lutheran 4735, Mahoney 4738, Maranatha 4739, March 4740, McCoy 4742, McNamara 4743, Midcontinent 4745, Morning 4748, Nelson 4749, Noreen 4750, O'Brien 4753, Onan 4754, OSilas 4758, Pautsch 4759, Pinson 4762, **Porter 4763**, Radichel 4765, Rahr 4766, Rauenhorst 4767, Regis 4770, Reiner 4772, Remick 4773, Rieks 4774, Riverway 4776, RJW 4777, Roberts 4778, Rodman 4779, Rose 4781, Rosen 4782, Samsara 4784, Sayer 4786, Schott 4787, Schulze 4788, Sexton 4790, St. 4794, Steinhafel 4795, Tamarack 4797, Tennant 4798, Terhuly 4799, Thorpe 4800, Trillium 4801, Turner 4803, Walser 4807, Walsh-Brady 4808, Way 4809, Wells 4811, Wells 4812, Wendel 4813, Weyand 4814, Weyerhaeuser 4815, Whitney 4817, Wimmer 4819

Mississippi: Barnett 4823, Biloxi 4824, Brevard 4826, Colbert 4829, Crooks 4831, **Edwards 4833**, Faser 4835, Florence 4836, Golding 4838, Graeber 4839, Hood 4842, Lexington 4846, Lower 4847, Mississippi 4849, Pruet 4851, Seal, 4853, Taylor 4855, Trehern 4856, Van 4857, Wittel 4858

Missouri: Andrews 4860, Baer 4862, Barrows 4864, BEO 4866, Bland 4868, Boswell 4872, Brace

4874, Breidenthal 4875, Brinklee 4876, Bryant 4878, **Build-A-Bear 4879**, Butler 4880, Canfield 4882, Capellupo 4883, Chapman 4884, Chod 4885, Cray 4890, Curry 4892, Dubinsky 4896, Duesenberg 4897, Dunn 4898, Edgar 4899, Edmonston 4900, Erlich 4904, Ever 4906, Fabick 4907, Finerty 4909, Finley 4910, Gaebler 4912, Garvey 4913, Gaylord 4915, Gilbert 4917, Grant 4918, Grassmere 4919, Guilander 4922, HB 4924, Heiman 4926, Impact 4930, Innovative 4931, J. 4932, Kauffman 4934, Kemper 4935, Kenney 4936, Keske 4937, Kornblum 4940, Kuhn 4941, Lambert 4942, Lawton 4944, Litton 4946, Love 4951, **Maor 4952**, Maxine 4954, Media 4956, Messick 4958, Meyer 4959, MFA 4960, Mineral 4961, Moneta 4962, Moss 4964, N.H. 4967, Neeb 4968, Neiman 4969, Oppenheimer 4973, O'Reilly 4974, Pearl 4977, Peculiar 4978, Pendergast-Weyer 4979, Pillsbury 4980, Portman 4981, Price 4982, Rubin 4987, Rust 4988, Saks 4990, Sander 4991, Sappington 4992, Sayler-Hawkins 4993, Schneider 4994, Schutte 4995, Shanahan 4999, Shawe 5000, Shepherd 5001, Shumway 5002, Sigma-Aldrich 5003, Siteman 5006, Slusher 5009, Stroble 5015, Sugarbaker 5016, Thorp 5020, Turner 5025, University 5027, Van 5028, Vassia 5029, Vatterott 5030, VJS 5031, Walton 5037, Welch 5038, Wolff 5040

Montana: Angora 5044, Broadbent 5046, Dousman 5049, Gerhart 5053, Hawkins 5055, Lynn 5059, Nance 5061, Swanson 5063, Wendy's 5065

Nebraska: America 5066, Ameritas 5068, Baer 5069, Baright 5070, Barklage 5071, Batchelder 5072, Beer 5073, Blair 5074, Finigan 5081, Friedland 5082, GFH 5084, Grewcock 5086, Hawkins 5089, Herman 5090, Hester 5091, Heuermann 5092, Hickey 5093, Hundred 5095, Kilbourne 5097, Kinder 5099, **Lothlorien 5101**, Malek 5102, Midlands 5104, Nebraska 5105, Nelson 5106, Patrick 5109, Pegler 5110, Perkins 5111, Scribante 5116, Shaw 5117, Smith 5118, Thomas 5123, Tous 5124, York 5129

Nevada: **A 5131**, Andress 5132, Anton 5133, Barker 5136, Benna 5138, Binion 5139, C.A.N. 5142, Carver 5143, **Center 5145**, Chami 5146, Children 5147, Dermody 5152, **Fein 5155**, Fishkin 5157, Geomar 5160, Harris 5161, **He 5162**, Houssels 5163, Jansen 5164, Jaquish 5165, Kennedy 5169, Lifestyle 5173, Living 5174, Lusardi 5175, Moran 5178, Newman 5179, Pretti 5184, Shulman 5185, Smith 5187, Steinberg 5189, Stout 5190, Timken-Sturgis 5192, To 5193, Vandevoort 5194, Western 5198, Wynn 5202

New Hampshire: Barker 5204, Bickford 5205, Charter 5206, Dunn 5212, Finlay 5213, Hunt 5214, Jameson 5215, Kimball 5216, Levine 5218, Lion's 5220, Lynch 5221, Martin 5222, Mascoma 5223, McIninch 5224, Olcott 5227, **Rothschild 5229**, Salem 5230, Seigel 5231, Up 5235, Woodbury 5238, Wutz 5239

New Jersey: Adler 5242, Allied 5245, Amboy 5246, **American 5247**, Avis 5255, Bartlett 5256, Beane 5259, Benun 5261, Bershad 5262, Bershad 5263, Bijou 5264, Bloom 5267, Blue 5268, **Blue 5269**, Broad 5272, Brooks 5274, Brothers 5276, Brueckner 5279, Brunetti 5281, Cantor 5285, Capebank 5286, CBIS 5288, Chang 5290, Chapman 5292, Citta 5295, Civitas 5296, Columbia 5301, Conant 5302, Cordover 5304, Covance 5305, Culver 5308, D'Aloia 5311, Degnan 5315, Devine 5317, Dietze 5320, Doctor 5321, Doll 5322, Domenica 5323, Dreman 5326, EBB 5329, Edison 5330, Eisenberg 5331, Ellis 5333, Engel 5334, Entin 5336, Essig 5339, Feinstein 5343, Freedman 5351, Freelander 5353, Fund 5358, Gabrellian 5360, Genie 5366, Gestetner 5367, Giants 5369, Grace 5375, **Greenblatt 5376**, Greetin 5381, Halpern 5382, Hann 5382, Hanson 5383, Harms 5385, Heisen 5389, Hekemian 5390, Hill 5393, Hillswood 5394, Infinity 5399, IV 5401, Jacobson 5402, Jamacha 5403, Johnson 5406, Johnson 5407, Jones 5408, Jones

5409, **Ju 5410**, Judson 5411, Katz 5414, KDK 5416, Kerney 5419, Kessel 5420, Kingsberg 5421, Kirby 5422, Klatskin 5423, Knight 5425, **Knistrom 5426**, Knowlton 5427, Kocurek 5428, Korean 5431, Kresa 5432, Kroon 5433, Krupa 5434, Kurtz 5436, Kutnick 5437, LaGrassa 5438, Landy 5439, Leavitt 5445, Lewis 5447, Lieberman 5448, Light 5449, Lipper 5450, M/S 5452, Mahan 5455, Mamiye 5456, Marino 5457, Markey 5459, Marron 5461, McDowell 5465, Milano 5466, Miller 5467, Miller 5468, Minerva 5469, Minio 5470, Mitrani 5471, Moriarty 5473, Mullen 5475, Navesink 5477, **Nazarian 5478**, Olsen 5480, O'Neal 5481, Oster 5484, Pacific 5485, Palmer 5486, Pantirer 5487, Paragano 5488, **Parnassus 5489**, **Patel 5491**, **Patel 5492**, Paterson 5493, Payson 5495, Pierson 5500, Pines 5501, Pinkin 5502, Ragone 5508, Roma 5513, Sanders 5518, Schlotterer 5523, Schwartz 5525, Scire 5526, Selective 5528, Sella 5529, Shapiro 5532, Sheridan 5533, Shilling 5534, Shuster 5535, Silverman 5536, Simon, 5537, Smilowitz 5538, Smith 5539, Snyder 5542, Sorala 5544, **Southpole 5545**, Spiro 5546, Stanley's 5550, Stern 5552, Stone 5553, **Tufenkian 5562**, Upton 5566, Vaughn-Jordan 5567, Waldis 5569, Waters 5571, Waterview 5572, We 5574, Weintraub 5577, Welch 5579, Wendel 5580, Westfield 5582, Wetterberg 5583, Wilcox 5585, Wildwood 5586, Wilf 5587, Willingham 5589, Wilson 5590, Winters 5591, WKBJ 5592, Yates 5595, **Yin-Shun 5596**, Yoh 5597, Zeldes 5599, Zimmer 5601, Zobel 5603

New Mexico: B.F. 5606, Carlsbad 5608, Continental 5612, Foster 5615, Garfield 5616, Quail 5622, Schnieders 5623, Simon 5624, Taos 5626

New York: 5 5631, Abess 5637, Abettor 5638, Abrahamson 5639, Achilles 5641, Acworth 5642, Adelman 5643, Ader 5644, Adikes 5646, AFAR 5648, Agate 5649, AGB 5650, Alexander 5654, Allegany 5660, American 5664, **American 5667**, American 5668, **American 5669**, Amphion 5671, Amsterdam 5672, Andrews 5677, Angelson 5679, Applebaum 5683, Arcadia 5684, Archangel 5685, Aresty 5686, Armonia 5688, Arts 5693, Asen 5694, Athens 5696, Atlantic 5697, B 5705, Backer 5706, Balbach 5707, Bandier 5709, Bank 5710, Barbash 5714, Barham 5715, Barker 5716, Barron 5719, Baseser 5720, Bassman 5721, BBL 5724, Beach 5725, Beacon 5726, Beard 5727, Beckwith 5730, Behrens 5731, Beir 5732, Bell 5734, Bender 5735, Berkowitz 5739, Bernhill 5741, Bet 5742, Betts 5744, Big 5745, Bingham 5747, Bird 5750, **Blinken 5757**, Block 5758, Blodgett 5760, Blue 5763, Bogoni 5766, Box 5771, Boxer 5772, Boyer-Snyder 5773, Brademas 5774, Brandt 5777, Bratt 5778, Breck 5780, Brenner 5781, Bridgewater 5783, Briger 5784, Brillo-Sonnino 5785, Brinkman 5786, Brody 5787, Brooklyn 5788, Broughton 5790, Brown 5791, Buchalter 5796, Buchwald 5797, Buckley 5798, **Buffalo 5799**, Burchan 5801, **Burpee 5802**, Burrows 5803, Bush 5805, **Buster 5806**, Cader 5807, CAL 5808, Calder 5810, Camber 5811, Camuto 5812, Caples 5813, Carroll 5816, Casey 5819, Castle 5820, Catalyst 5821, Catsimatidis 5823, CDVSJ 5825, Centennial 5826, Century 5827, Ceriale 5828, Cerullo 5829, Chapman 5832, Chasdei 5835, Cheatham 5836, Chess 5841, Children's 5842, Chiles 5843, Ciampa 5845, Citron 5847, Clarkson 5849, Clemente 5850, Cochran 5853, Cogut 5856, Cohen 5857, Cohen 5858, Cohen 5860, Cohn 5862, Cohn 5864, Cole 5868, Coleman 5870, Cornell/Weinstein 5877, Correspondents 5879, Cortland 5880, Cowen 5882, Cox 5883, Cranshaw 5885, Curtis 5889, Dabah 5892, D'Addario 5895, Dalton 5896, Danziger 5899, Darrah 5900, Davis 5902, De 5904, Deeds 5906, Del 5908, Desai 5910, Desanctis, 5911, Devine-Majors 5913, Dixon 5919, DJ 5920, Dobson 5921, Doovin 5923, Dorsky 5924, Downey 5930, Druskin 5932, **Dungannon 5935**, Dunn 5936, Dvaykus 5937, E.R.G. 5939, **Eastman 5940**, EBA 5941, Eberhart 5942, Edelman 5943, Ehrlich 5948, Ehrman 5949,

Ellman 5956, Elyachar 5959, EMSA 5961, Emwiga 5962, Enders 5963, Englebardt 5965, Erpf 5968, Ettl 5970, Evans 5973, Ezer 5974, Ezra 5976, Fagin 5978, Falconhead 5980, Falk 5981, Family 5982, Family 5984, Fan 5985, Farber 5986, Farber 5987, **Farkas 5988**, Fee 5990, Fein 5992, Feinberg 5993, Feinman 5994, Feldstein 5997, Fenton 5998, Ferguson 5999, Ferriday 6000, Ficalora 6002, Fields 6003, **Fischel 6009**, Fitt 6010, **Fitzgibbons 6011**, Fleischer 6013, Fleming 6014, **Flowering 6015**, Follett 6016, Fondation 6017, Foundation 6019, Foundation-to-Life 6020, Fraiman 6023, Franco 6024, Franco 6025, **Frank 6026**, Frankel 6027, Fraydun 6029, Freidheim 6031, French 6032, Fried 6036, Friedland 6037, Friedlander 6038, Friedman 6039, Furman 6046, Furth 6047, G&A 6048, Gage 6050, Gallagher 6051, Galvan 6053, Gant 6054, Gantcher 6055, Garber 6057, Garman 6058, Gary 6060, Gatto 6061, Geduld/Cougar 6062, Geier 6063, Gela 6065, Geller 6066, Gelley 6067, George 6070, Georgia 6071, Gerhard 6072, Gernatt 6073, Gilliam 6078, Gloeckner 6083, Goddard 6085, Godinger 6086, Gogel 6087, Goldberg 6090, Goldenberg 6092, **Goldfein 6096**, Golding 6097, Goldman 6098, Goldstone 6102, Goodman 6106, Goodman 6107, Goodman-Lipman 6108, Gordon 6109, Gordon 6110, Gordon 6111, Gordon 6112, Gottlieb-Schwartz 6115, Gould 6116, GP 6117, Grace 6118, Graham 6119, Graham 6120, Gralnick 6121, Grandison 6124, Grandview-Steers 6125, Granit 6126, Grant 6129, Grant 6130, Greenblatt 6133, Greentree 6135, Griffin 6138, Grodzins 6141, Gross 6143, Grossman 6144, Grubman 6147, Grumbacher 6148, **Gruodis 6150**, Gutman 6152, Hafer 6155, Hahn 6156, Hajim 6158, Hales 6159, Handler 6161, Handler 6162, Hanson 6163, Hap 6164, Harjen 6167, Harmon 6168, Harmon 6169, **Harriman 6170**, Harris 6172, Hasenfeld 6174, Hatfield 6175, Healy 6179, Hegarty 6182, Heilig 6183, Heisler 6185, Hemitt 6188, Hennessy 6191, Henson 6193, Herringer 6196, Heyman 6201, Hilson 6209, Hirsch 6211, Hirsch 6212, Hoffen 6215, Hogan 6217, Hohmann 6218, Holborn 6220, Holtzman 6223, Hopkins 6224, Houston 6228, Hover 6229, Hoyt 6230, Hurlburt 6233, Hymowitz 6234, I 6235, Ilsababy 6238, Independent 6241, **Indira 6242**, Indus 6243, Ingrassia 6244, Initial 6245, Institute 6248, Iroquois 6250, Ivorybill 6252, Jamakepe 6256, Janklow 6257, Jennings 6259, JI 6260, JJC 6262, JKW 6263, Johnson 6267, Johnson 6268, Johnson 6269, Johnson-Stillman 6271, Jones 6272, Joseph 6273, Joukowsky 6274, Joyce 6275, Jungreis 6276, Kahn 6279, Kamber 6281, Kaminer 6282, Kasowitz 6285, **Kathwari 6286**, Katz 6287, Katzman 6289, Kautz 6290, KCEG 6291, Keeler 6292, Keller 6296, Keswin 6303, Kiernan 6306, Kies 6307, Kimmelman 6309, Kirschenbaum 6314, Klaus 6319, Klaus 6321, Klavan 6322, Kleban 6323, Klein 6324, Klein 6325, Kleinschmidt 6326, Klingenstein 6327, Knafel 6330, Knapp 6331, Knaster 6332, Koessler 6334, Koessler 6335, Koessler 6336, Koha 6337, Kornreich 6341, Kovensky 6342, Kozicki 6343, Krasne 6344, Krimendahl/Saint-Amand 6346, Kriser 6347, Kroll 6348, Krumholz 6349, Kupferberg 6351, Kurland 6352, L. 6354, Lachman 6356, **Ladenburg 6357**, Lake 6360, **Lamaj 6361**, Landau 6362, **Larson 6365**, Lawrence 6369, Lee 6372, Legacy 6373, **Legacy 6374**, Leibowitz 6376, Lemle 6377, Lemle 6378, Lenox 6380, Leonhardt 6381, Lerer 6382, Lerner 6383, Leuschen 6384, Leventritt 6385, Levine 6386, Levine 6387, Levitin 6388, Levy 6391, Lichtenstein 6397, Lieberman 6399, Liebowitz 6400, Lipschitz 6402, Lipschultz 6403, Lipton 6404, Little 6407, Loconsolo 6408, Long 6410, Lopatin 6412, Lowenbraun 6414, Lubo 6417, Lucky 6420, M66 6427, MacArthur 6429, Mack 6430, Madover 6431, Maguire 6432, Maher 6433, Maher 6434, Maidenbaum 6435, Makioka 6436, Manocherian 6438, Manzanita 6439, Marble 6441, Marine 6442, Marley 6443, Marshall 6445,

Marshall 6446, Martini 6447, MAT 6450, Mathis-Pfohl 6451, Matutina 6452, **McCaddin-McQuirk 6455**, McCarthy 6456, McCooey 6457, McCormick 6459, McDade 6461, McEnroe 6463, McNulty 6465, Mead 6466, Meier 6470, Menges 6474, Menken 6475, Meredith 6477, Merlo 6479, Merrill 6480, Metzger-Price 6483, Meyer 6486, Meyer 6487, Michaels 6488, Michelle 6489, Miller 6491, Miller 6492, Milstein 6496, Mindel 6498, Moach 6501, Monderer 6503, Morin 6506, Morse 6509, Mozel 6512, Mule 6515, MZL 6518, Nelco 6522, Neporent 6523, Nets 6524, Netter 6525, **Neuman 6526**, Newcastle 6528, Newman 6531, Newman 6532, Niemiec 6535, NM 6536, Northern 6540, Norwich 6542, Noster 6543, Oberoi 6547, Oestreicher 6549, Offensend 6550, Ohel 6552, Olum 6555, Ong 6558, Ontario 6559, Osceola 6560, Ostreicher 6562, O'Sullivan 6565, Palm 6571, Park 6575, Parr 6577, Paul 6580, Peale 6582, Performing 6586, Perlman 6587, Perper 6588, **Peter 6590**, Peterson 6591, Peterson 6593, Peterson 6594, Petty 6596, Pfeiffer 6597, Phillips 6600, Phuong 6601, Pierce 6604, Pincus 6606, Pinkus 6607, Pittman 6608, Planalp-Trevor 6609, Plunkett 6611, Plymouth 6612, Pollack 6614, Pollack 6615, Polsky 6618, Pomrenze 6619, Poorman 6620, **Posner-Wallace 6621**, Pratt-Northam 6625, Price 6627, Provident 6632, Purple 6634, **QIBQ 6636**, Quinn 6637, Quinn 6638, Quinn 6639, R 6640, Rachel 6641, **Rao 6645**, Rapaport 6647, Rattie 6650, Ravitch 6651, Raymond 6652, RDM 6653, Realty 6655, Reidy 6661, Reiss 6662, Rexford 6664, Rheinstrom 6665, Rhodes 6666, RHR 6667, Ritter 6674, RJL 6675, Rodgers 6680, Roothbert 6682, Rose 6684, Rose 6685, Rose 6686, Rosen 6689, Rosenberg 6690, Rosenstein 6692, Rosenthal 6693, Rosenthal 6695, Rosenthal 6696, Rosner 6698, Rothenberg 6702, Rothstein 6704, Roxe 6706, Rubin 6707, Rudy 6708, Rum 6709, Russo 6711, Russo 6712, Ruthen 6714, Ruttenberg 6715, Sallie 6720, Salomon 6721, Sarnoff 6729, Schaffer 6736, **Schepp 6739**, Schiller 6740, Schiro 6741, **Schmeelk 6742**, Schneider 6743, Schonfeld 6745, Schonfeld 6746, **School 6748**, Schott 6749, Schreiber 6750, Schwalbe 6751, Schwartz 6753, Schwarz 6757, Scott 6761, Scott 6762, Scully 6763, Sdei 6764, Securitas 6768, Seligman 6772, Seligsohn 6773, Senator 6775, Serenbetz 6776, Seven 6777, Shachar 6779, Shack 6780, Shaftel 6782, Shalam 6783, Shalom 6784, Shanken 6785, Sharon 6787, Sherman 6792, Shetty 6793, Shuman 6795, Siegel 6797, Sillins 6799, Silver 6800, Silverman 6801, Simcha 6804, Simpson 6805, Singer 6806, Skalny 6807, Slade 6810, Slovin 6811, Smith 6813, Snow 6818, **Societe 6820**, Society 6821, Some 6824, Sorel 6826, Sorensen-Siegel 6827, **Sparkplug 6830**, Spencer 6834, Sperandio 6835, Spiegel 6837, Spiritus 6840, Spofford 6842, Squier 6843, Stackhouse 6844, Stanton 6845, Starker 6847, Starmar 6848, Statue 6849, Stebbins 6850, Steck 6852, Steckler 6853, Sternklar 6864, Still 6866, Stires-Stark 6867, Striano 6871, Strong 6872, Stuart 6873, Stuntz 6874, Sumitomo 6876, Sunrise 6878, Sutton 6882, **Swett 6888**, Tanico 6892, Tedaldi 6894, Three 6899, Tisch 6900, Tod 6901, Tov 6904, Tradition 6905, Treetops 6906, Treiber 6907, Triangle 6908, Tribune 6909, Trimble 6910, Truman 6912, Tuch 6915, Tytel 6917, Uihlein 6919, United 6920, Utica 6922, Utopia 6923, Vaad 6924, Vance 6926, Vogt 6933, Vyeshaya 6934, Wachtell 6936, Wagman 6937, Wagner 6938, Waldron 6939, Warwick 6945, Washington 6946, Weil 6948, Weill 6949, Weinberg 6951, Weingarten 6953, Weininger 6954, Weinman 6955, Weiser 6958, Weiss 6962, Wells 6964, Whalen 6966, Wharton 6968, **Wheeler 6969**, Whispering 6970, Whitehead 6974, Wilks 6977, Windy 6980, Wish 6981, WLC 6982, Woldar 6985, Wong 6988, **Woodland 6989**, Woodmere 6990, Woodner 6991, Woodward 6993, Wunsch 6996, Wyckoff 6998, Yagoda 7001,

Yaspan-Unterberg 7003, YGBL 7006, Yitzchok 7007, Yordan 7009, Young 7012, **Youth 7013**, Zafirovski 7014, Zahavi 7015, Zamir 7016, Zarin-Rosenfeld 7017, Zarrella 7018, Zemsky 7022, Ziff 7027, Zurack 7033, Zwerling 7034, Zwirn 7035

North Carolina: Abernethy 7037, Agarwal 7039, Arcadia 7040, Bane 7043, BB&T 7045, Bell 7047, Bell 7048, Bernstein 7049, Bertsch 7050, Blue 7053, Boddie 7055, Bolick 7056, Brown 7058, Bryan 7060, C3 7064, Cameron 7065, Canaday 7066, Childtrust 7075, Coffey 7078, Cooke 7080, Davis 7084, Deal 7085, Duncan 7086, Ellison 7090, Emma 7091, Eplee 7092, Everett 7093, Fairfield 7095, Family 7096, Flowers 7099, Fortson 7100, Fox 7103, Galanti 7104, Gambrell 7105, Gambrill 7106, Garrow 7108, Gilmore 7110, Gordon 7112, Hackbarth 7114, Haney 7116, Hayden-Harman 7120, Henderson 7124, Hoffman 7127, Hoffman 7128, Holleman 7129, Howe 7132, Hunt 7135, Jelm 7137, Jones 7138, Judd 7139, Kanitz 7140, Kassner 7141, Katz 7142, Kenan 7143, Kenan 7144, Koury 7150, KPB 7151, **Kramer 7152**, Krauss 7153, Krost 7154, Ladane 7155, **Laffin 7157**, Landon 7158, Live 7163, Lynum 7165, Maness 7166, Marietta 7167, Markey 7168, Marsh 7170, Marsh 7171, Matthews 7174, McConnell 7176, McGuire, 7177, McMerty 7180, Meserve 7182, Meyer 7184, Miller 7185, Moretz 7189, Moseley 7194, Mosser 7195, Mount 7196, Niessen, 7200, Nivison 7201, North 7202, Outer 7204, Perkin 7208, Pillmore 7210, Pope 7212, Pulliam 7215, Redwoods 7218, Ritchie 7222, Robinson 7225, Rollins 7231, S.D.R. 7233, Sanders 7234, Self 7238, Shapiro 7239, Sherrard 7240, Shingleton 7241, Shugart 7242, Silverback 7243, Sites 7245, Smith 7247, Smith 7249, Snyder's-Lance 7250, Steinmetz 7254, Stonecutter 7255, Stowe 7256, Strickland 7257, Stubblefield 7260, Szulik 7264, Thomasville 7267, TSH 7271, Vanderbilt 7273, Wake 7276, Wallace 7277, West-West 7284, Whitener 7286, Wilkinson 7288, Williams 7289, Wise 7290, Yost 7291

North Dakota: Berge 7294, Community 7295, Fedje 7296, Myra 7297, Pearson 7298

Ohio: Abrams 7300, Albrecht 7301, Alpaugh 7302, Anderson 7305, Armington 7309, Athens 7311, Baird 7314, Bates 7317, B-Brand 7318, Berding 7322, Berkman 7324, Bernard 7325, Boymel 7329, Brown 7336, Bryan 7339, Bullock 7341, Busse 7343, Calhoun 7344, Callahan 7346, Cardinal 7347, Chaney 7349, Chemed 7350, Chesley 7351, Cleveland 7354, Community 7356, Community 7357, Conlogue 7359, Connor 7361, Cooper 7362, Corbett 7363, Crandall 7366, Cure 7368, Daberko 7369, Danis 7371, Defiance 7375, Demetros 7377, Downing 7381, **Eaton 7383**, Ebenezer 7384, Edward 7385, Edwards 7386, Entelco 7389, Eyman 7391, Faber 7392, Fedeli 7393, Feldstein 7394, Feth 7397, Firman 7400, Fleck 7403, Fleischmann 7404, Fletcher 7405, Fortney 7406, Foundation 7408, Fox 7409, Freygang 7410, Frohman 7411, Frost-Parker 7413, Garcia 7416, Gardner 7417, Geary, 7419, George 7421, Geotrac 7422, Gilman 7423, Gimbel 7424, Ginn 7425, Glazer 7426, Goerlich 7428, Gosiger 7429, Gould 7430, H 7434, Hamilton 7435, Hampson 7436, Hankins 7437, Hankison 7438, Haskell 7439, Hauck 7440, Heimann 7444, Heinrich 7446, Hieronymus 7448, **Highfield 7450**, Homan 7451, Horvitz 7454, Howe 7455, Hubert 7456, Hueneke 7457, Hummer 7459, Hutchins 7461, Jenkins 7465, Joffe 7467, Johnson 7468, Jones 7470, Kamm 7473, Kangesser 7474, Kilworth 7477, Kincaid 7478, Knight 7482, Kramer 7484, Kutz 7486, Lambert 7487, Lazarus 7493, Lincoln 7496, Linnemann 7498, Lippitt 7499, Littick 7500, LKC 7501, Loeb 7503, Lundgard 7508, Lungard 7509, M.L.M 7510, Mangano 7511, Manley 7512, Marcus 7514, Marnick 7515, Mather 7516, Mccarthy 7520, McMaster 7521, Mead 7522, Mehl 7523, Messer 7524, Mifsud 7525, Miller 7528, Mixon 7530, Morley 7532, Murphy

7533, Myers 7535, NLT 7537, Norris 7538, O'Donnell 7540, Ohio 7541, Orr 7543, Peoples 7546, Peters 7547, Pugliese 7551, Quatman 7552, Rapport 7553, Rayen 7554, Reisman 7556, Reynolds 7559, Ritchie 7561, Rotterman 7564, S.E.C. 7567, Sage 7568, Sandfair 7569, Schottenstein 7573, Schottenstein 7574, Schottenstein 7575, Schwartz, 7576, Scion 7578, Sears-Swetland 7581, Seasongood 7582, Segoe 7583, Selsor 7585, Sheadle 7589, Sinai 7593, Skestos 7594, Skyler 7595, Smiley 7597, Smith 7598, Steiner-King 7602, Stensen 7604, Taft 7609, Tait 7610, Taj 7611, Terhune 7614, Tetlak 7615, Thendara 7616, Thompson, 7617, TKBW 7619, Traeger 7621, Turben 7622, Tuscarawas 7623, Tuscora 7624, Van 7625, Van 7626, Venner 7627, Vista 7628, Wallace 7631, Wasserstrom 7632, Watson 7633, Wightman-Wieber 7636, Williams 7638, Williamson 7640, Wolf 7643, Wolfe 7644, Yeiser 7649, Young 7651, Young 7652

Oklahoma: Ashbrook 7656, Broadhurst 7663, Brown 7664, Burkhart 7665, Cherokee 7666, Everest 7676, Evergreen 7677, Fleischaker 7679, Gelvin 7682, Goddard 7684, Goodin 7685, Harmon 7686, Jirous 7690, Kerr 7693, Krueger 7695, Kullgren 7696, Merkel 7706, Miller 7709, Oklahoma 7711, Peel 7714, Pros 7715, Richardson 7717, Stone 7721, Thomas 7724, Walkingstick 7727, Wegener 7731, Welch 7732, Witt 7737, Young 7739

Oregon: Atkins 7741, Baldwin 7742, Bowen 7743, Cayo 7746, Charis 7748, Coffman 7750, Coit 7751, **Conklin 7754**, Demorest 7757, Donegan 7759, Elwood 7761, Flowerree 7763, Frank 7765, Gill 7766, Giustina 7767, Haskell 7770, Hitchman 7774, Irwin 7777, Jonas 7778, Knudson 7785, **Larson 7788**, Leupold 7790, **Living 7792**, Maxey 7793, May 7794, McKay 7795, Mentor 7796, Merlo 7797, Michael 7799, Morey 7801, Morris 7802, Naito 7803, Naumes 7804, Parker/United 7805, Pendleton 7806, Portland 7807, Richardson 7808, Roundhouse 7810, Schmidt 7813, Shapira 7814, Sharkey 7815, Shoen 7816, Simple 7818, Singer 7819, Spencer 7820, Stewart 7821, Stewart 7822, Stewart 7823, Trover 7824, Watt 7825, Wessinger 7826, West 7828, Western 7829, Woodard 7831, **Wyss 7832**

Pennsylvania: Aaron 7835, Adams 7836, Ames 7840, Applestone 7841, Arkema 7842, Armstrong 7843, **Arronson 7844**, Ashland 7845, Auldridge 7846, Aventis 7847, Ayers 7848, Baker 7851, Baldwin, 7852, Balzereit 7853, Bannerot-Lappe 7854, Beach 7855, Beacon 7856, Bedford 7857, Beels 7858, Bella 7859, Bennett 7860, Benz 7861, Bergman 7863, Bergstrom 7864, **Berkowitz 7865**, Berkowitz 7866, Betts 7869, Bishop 7874, Bloch 7878, Blue 7880, Bonomo 7883, Bon-Ton 7884, Born 7885, Borowsky 7886, Boscia 7887, Boudinot 7888, Breedlove 7890, Bridge 7891, Briggs 7892, Broadbent 7895, Bronstein 7896, Brooks 7898, Buck 7903, Buck 7904, Calligan 7909, Cameron 7911, Campbell 7912, Cardinal 7914, Carita 7915, Carnahan-Jackson 7917, Casteel 7919, Charlestein 7920, Chase 7921, Chenault, 7922, Clark 7925, Clark 7926, Clovis 7928, CNB 7929, **Cohn 7931**, Community 7933, Conestoga 7934, **Connelly 7935**, Cove 7939, Cozen 7941, Crawford 7944, Crebilly 7946, Danella 7948, Darnall 7949, Davis 7951, Deerfield 7952, Delaware 7953, DENTSPLY 7954, Dibona 7955, Dickson 7957, Dietz 7959, Dinardo 7960, Donnally 7962, Donnelly 7963, Double 7964, Eakins 7968, Eberly 7969, Eckels 7970, Eden 7971, EFM 7974, Elk 7975, Elliott 7977, Ely 7979, Engel 7981, Engle 7982, **Epstein 7983**, Everard 7985, Fair 7987, Finley 7995, First 7996, First 7997, Flinn 8001, Fortinsky 8002, Foster 8003, Fountainhead 8004, Frederick 8006, Friendship 8009, Frohring 8010, Gamber 8011, Ganse 8012, Garthwaite 8013, Gauss 8014, Gershman 8015, Gibson 8016, Gilmore 8017, **Glendorn 8020**, Goldberg 8021, Goodstein 8023, Greater 8026, Grumbacher 8028, GT 8030, Gulati 8032, Gypsy 8034, Hager 8035, Hankin 8038, Harsco 8040, Hassel 8042, Hauber

8043, HBE 8047, Health 8048, Heyl 8052, Hilles 8057, Hoch 8060, Hodge 8061, Honickman 8066, **Horner 8068**, Hulme 8069, Ice 8072, IGN 8073, II 8074, Ithan 8076, Jackson 8077, Jansing-Cook 8079, Jordan 8082, Kahn, 8084, Karamatsoukas 8085, Katherine 8086, Katsaros 8087, Katz 8089, Kazanjian 8090, Klahr 8095, Klein 8097, Kline 8098, Knudsen 8102, Krouse 8103, Lamb 8106, Lancy 8108, Larking 8112, Le 8115, Leakin 8116, Lemole 8119, Leone 8120, Levee 8121, Lida 8127, Lienemann 8128, Magee 8137, **Mango 8138**, Maple 8139, Marstine 8141, Martin 8143, Martin 8144, Mason 8147, Mateer 8150, Mayer 8152, McGinley 8156, McHale 8157, McKamish 8158, Mclelland 8162, Meakem 8166, Mendel 8168, Merops 8169, MHB 8171, Mill 8172, Moffat 8175, Moggio 8176, Morgan 8178, Mosi 8179, Mukaiyama-Rice 8183, Mullen 8184, Mutual 8186, Mylan 8187, Neag 8189, Nikolaus 8193, Noll 8194, Norford 8196, Olitsky 8198, Packer 8201, Pangborn 8203, Patterson 8205, Patterson 8206, Pearsall 8207, Penn 8208, Petersen 8212, Pfundt 8213, Plainfield 8217, Plaisance 8218, Postles 8223, Quaker 8228, Quinn 8229, Randall 8230, Reidler 8233, Remmel 8235, Ricon 8237, Rider-Pool 8238, Rooney 8243, Rosenberg 8244, Rudin 8247, Saramar 8253, Satell 8254, Savett 8255, Scheller 8258, Schoonmaker 8260, Schrenk 8261, Schultz 8262, Schuylkill 8263, Scott 8266, Secrist 8267, Seebe 8268, Seybert 8269, Shaner 8271, Shenk 8274, Shore 8276, Shuman 8277, Sidewater 8278, Smith 8280, Smith 8282, Smith 8283, Sneath 8286, Snyder 8287, Society 8289, Spain 8292, Spencer 8293, Staehle 8295, Staley 8296, Stewart 8301, Strine 8306, Strine 8307, Stump 8308, Stutzman 8309, **Susquehanna 8310**, Tabas 8312, Tally 8313, Teleflex 8314, Terryglass 8315, Tippins 8318, Todi 8319, Tompkins-Broll 8320, Trax 8321, Tuttleman 8325, Union 8326, Valentine 8328, Venne 8331, Wabtec 8335, Wachs 8336, Wachs-Weingarten 8337, Waldo 8340, Wasserott 8344, Weiler-Miller 8348, Wenger 8352, Whalley 8353, **Whimsie 8354**, Willary 8356, Wimmer 8361, Wolfson 8364, Wurts 8370, Wyeth 8371, York 8374, **Zeldin 8376**, Zisman 8377

Rhode Island: Apperson 8380, Arents, 8382, Beck 8386, Brack 8392, Chace 8393, Clark 8395, Collis 8397, Cook 8398, DeLoura 8402, Feibelman 8405, Felicia 8406, Greene 8413, Halsted 8415, Heydt 8419, Hirsch 8420, Hoag 8421, Hope 8422, Jacbel 8426, Janci 8428, **Jeffery 8429**, Johnson 8430, Kelly 8432, Kenney 8433, Kimball 8434, Kingsbury 8435, La 8438, Leroe 8439, LLH/LHM 8442, Long 8443, Lorber 8445, Mann 8448, Masonic 8449, Mauze 8450, McWethy 8453, Miller 8454, Molder 8455, Moore 8456, Mulligan 8457, Mulvaney 8458, O'Halloran 8462, Pacifica 8464, Papitto 8467, Perkins 8470, Phillips 8472, Pillsbury 8473, Pisa 8474, Rainbow 8477, Sachem 8479, Schwarz 8483, Shea 8486, Simionescu 8487, Siperstein 8489, Slemons 8490, Slingerland 8491, Sullivan 8494, Unfi 8498, Vanderpoel 8499, Washington 8500, Wells 8501, White 8503, Wright 8506, York 8507

South Carolina: Bailey 8510, Bignon 8512, Boyd 8514, Cato 8516, Chapman 8517, Childress 8518, Coker 8519, Collins 8520, Greenleaf 8525, Greenwood 8526, Horne 8528, Jackson 8529, **Lader 8531**, Lutz 8533, Nalley 8535, Near 8536, Rivers, 8538, Singing 8540, Stevens 8541, Sunshine 8544, T-Bonz 8546, WebbCraft 8548, **Winthrop 8550**, Wyatt 8552, **Zvejnieks 8553**

South Dakota: Barger 8555, Black 8556, Clarkson 8558, Emerald 8562, Engelsma 8563, Ferguson 8564, Grundhofer 8565, Houston 8567, J&L 8568, Maas 8569, Miller 8570, Peters 8571, Peterson 8572, Stearns 8575, Watertown 8576, Welk 8577, Wolfe 8578

Tennessee: Atticus 8582, B 8583, **Belz 8585**, Blum 8589, Bornblum 8591, Bradford 8592, Campbell 8594, Cartinhour-Woods 8597, Citizens 8599, Cole 8600, Cracker 8603, Doochin 8605, Draughon

8607, Ebert-Leblanc 8609, EBS 8610, Eskind 8611, Eskind 8612, Fleming 8615, Foster 8616, **Fugitive 8618**, Gaylord 8620, Goad 8621, Goldsmith 8622, Goodlett 8623, Gordon 8624, Hawthorn 8626, HMA 8628, Houghland 8630, Hutcheson 8631, Ingram 8632, Jewell 8633, Johnson 8634, Jones 8635, Kennedy 8638, Kite 8639, Knight 8640, LaRoche 8641, LDB 8642, **Louisiana-Pacific 8644**, Massengill-DeFriece 8647, McGehee 8648, Mercy 8650, Mick 8651, Monday 8652, Paddison 8655, Pattee 8656, Pfeffer 8659, Powell 8661, Proctor 8662, Provision 8663, **Redbird 8664**, Rose 8667, Schadt 8670, Schmidt 8671, Seme 8673, Splawn 8677, Stadler 8678, Storey 8679, Sunlight 8681, Tipton 8682, Tompkins 8683, WTC 8688

Texas: Abernathy 8690, Adam 8691, Adler 8692, Agee 8694, Amarillo 8697, **AMD 8698**, American 8700, American 8701, Amherst 8702, Anderson 8704, Armstrong 8708, Astin 8710, B.E.L.I.E.F. 8713, Baer 8714, Ballard 8716, Barnabas 8717, Bearden 8721, Bee 8723, Behmann 8725, Bergstrom 8727, Bernardin 8728, Bertha 8729, **Bhutada 8730**, Boeing 8733, Booth 8735, Bowers 8736, Braun 8740, Bright 8743, Brisley 8744, Brochstein 8746, Brodsky 8747, Bromberg 8748, Brown 8751, Brownsville 8752, Burch 8756, Burgett 8757, Burzik 8758, Cargill 8761, Cariker 8762, Cemo 8765, Central 8766, Chisholm 8769, Cielo 8771, Clear 8772, Clinedinst 8775, Coleman 8778, College 8779, Collins 8780, Collins 8781, Community 8782, **Coneway 8783**, Conley 8784, Cook 8786, Cook 8787, Corrigan-Goddard 8789, Crossroads 8791, Daniel 8797, Dauphin 8798, Davis 8799, Day 8800, de 8802, De 8803, Deakins 8804, Deason 8805, Dedman 8807, Dedman, 8808, Denman 8810, Dice 8814, Discovery 8816, Doak 8818, Dobson 8819, Dobson 8820, Dooley 8822, Doskocil 8823, Dougherty 8824, Dove 8826, Duddlesten 8829, Dulaney 8830, Dunagan 8831, Duncan 8833, Dunham 8834, Educational 8836, Edwards 8837, Elkins 8838, EOS 8840, Esping 8841, Fabenco 8843, Fairchild 8845, Fertitta 8852, FHC 8853, Fickett 8854, Fifth 8856, Finger 8857, Finney 8858, Flohr 8861, Folsom 8863, Fort 8865, Foster 8866, Foundation 8869, Freescale 8874, Friedel 8875, Friedman 8876, Frill 8877, Frost 8878, Fuller 8882, Garver 8883, Gatewood 8885, Genecov 8886, Genovese 8887, George 8888, **Gilman, 8889**, Gordon 8893, Grace 8895, Grant 8897, Graue 8898, Gray 8899, Gray-Pampa 8900, Grits 8904, Haggar 8907, Haggar, 8908, Hallam 8910, Halperin 8912, Hamilton 8913, Hamm 8914, Hanley 8916, Haraldson 8917, Hardner 8918, Harrell 8919, Hartman 8920, Hawkins 8923, Healthcare 8924, Hegi 8926, Helm 8928, Helmle-Shaw 8929, Herring 8930, Hicks 8935, Hixon 8940, Hoak 8941, Hollandsworth 8945, Holloway 8946, Hope 8949, Horween 8952, Houck 8953, Howard 8954, Howard 8955, Howell 8956, Hunter 8957, Il 8958, Ik 8959, Ilgenfritz 8960, Inge 8961, Jamail 8965, Jessen 8968, Johnson 8969, Johnson, 8971, Julian 8976, Kabacoff 8977, Kaplan 8979, KCL 8981, Kelley 8984, Keown 8986, Ketelsen 8988, Kimble 8991, King 8993, King 8994, Kirwan 8996, Klein 8997, Klesse 8998, Knox 8999, Korell 9001, Kowitz 9002, Kramer 9003, Krist 9004, Kritser, 9005, L 9007, Lantana 9009, Laredo 9010, LBJ 9011, Levy 9014, Lewis 9015, Ligon-Lamsam 9018, Lilly 9019, Littauer 9021, Long 9023, Lose 9024, LSF 9026, LSG 9027, Lupton 9028, Luse 9029, Lykes-Knapp 9030, MacDonald 9031, **Mansur 9035**, Mantzel 9036, Margolin 9038, Martin 9040, Matthews 9041, Mayfield 9044, McDaniel 9050, McKee 9052, McLaughlin 9053, McMillan, 9054, McNutt 9055, Mercy 9057, Miller 9066, Mischer 9067, Mitte 9069, Montgomery 9070, Moss 9076, Mossy, 9077, Muse 9080, Nelson 9086, Nowiczewski 9090, Nuncio 9092, O'Connor 9093, Oden 9094, One 9096, Oppenheimer 9100, Oppenheimer 9101, Overlake 9106, **Owusu 9107**, Pack 9109, Palmer 9112, Papadopoulos 9113,

Parks 9115, Partnership 9116, **Partridge 9117**, Patterson 9118, Paulos 9120, Pearlman 9122, Peine 9123, Penland 9124, Perkins 9125, Petty 9126, Pevehouse 9127, Posey 9135, Pratt 9137, Proctor 9139, Pulitzer 9140, Quest 9142, Rawls 9143, Ray 9144, Reilly 9148, Roberts 9155, Roberts 9157, Rosen 9161, Ross 9164, Ross 9165, Rowan 9166, Rust 9168, San 9170, Sanders 9171, Santander 9173, Saramco 9174, Saulsbury 9175, Schepps 9177, Schepps 9178, Schissler 9179, Schoener 9180, Schulte 9181, Schumacher 9183, Schwab-Rosenhouse 9184, Seay 9187, Serafy 9188, Seven 9189, Shiloff 9193, SHT 9194, Simpson-Omohundro 9196, Singleton 9197, SK 9198, Sklar 9199, Smith 9204, **Soonae 9208**, South 9210, Sparks 9211, Sparrow 9212, Stanzel 9213, Staubach 9215, Sterling 9218, Sterling 9219, Sutton 9226, Taub 9229, Tennessee 9230, Texas 9231, Thompson 9234, Tietze 9236, Tobin 9237, Toomim 9239, Torchmark 9240, Trojan 9242, Tucker 9243, Tyler 9244, Van 9247, Vaughan 9248, Vaughan 9249, Waggoner 9254, Wal-Dot 9256, Walls 9257, Walthall 9258, Warren 9261, Webre 9266, Welch 9270, Wells 9272, White 9275, Wilder 9277, Willard 9278, Williams 9281, Winston 9282, Wise 9283, Wood 9290, Woods 9291, Woolf 9292, Works 9293, Wright 9294, Young 9297
Utah: Andrus 9301, B. 9302, Bastian 9304, Burbidge 9308, Burton 9309, CASA 9312, Catalyst 9313, Cumming 9316, Denkers 9318, Dreamweaver 9320, Dry 9321, Eccles 9322, Eskuche 9323, Foothold 9324, Gardner 9326, Jackson 9329, JKS 9330, Keener 9332, Korver 9335, Langdon 9336, Larsen 9337, Leavitt 9338, Lindorf 9339, Low 9340, Odyssey 9342, Patel 9344, Promontory 9345, Questar 9347, Scharman 9348, Schmidt 9349, Shaw 9350, Shrontz 9351, **Skolnick 9352**, SmartGo 9354, Steiner 9358, Telemachus: 9359, Turley 9360, Utah 9361
Vermont: Ferro 9372, Huntington 9376, Kaufman 9378, Mergens 9381, Redducs 9383, Stevens 9385
Virginia: American 9387, Andreas 9388, Backer 9389, Banks 9390, Beck 9392, Berni 9395, Better 9396, Blue 9400, Blue 9401, Blueberry 9402, Brandt 9403, Brink's 9406, Bruhn-Morris 9408, Bryant 9409, Burford 9411, Bw718 9412, Camp 9413, Cartledge 9414, Chastain 9419, Clark-Nexsen 9421, Cobbs 9422, Cole 9423, Collins 9425, Community 9426, Cooke 9427, Dreaming 9435, Dreyfus 9436, Dun 9437, **Eiriksson 9441**, Elmwood 9442, English 9443, Family 9444, Ferrari 9446, Fink 9447, Flippo 9449, Foundation 9451, Franklin 9452, Fraser 9453, **Fund 9455**, Glencairn 9460, Good 9461, Grandis 9462, Hansen 9465, Harris 9466, Hausfeld 9469, Hilltop 9470, II 9475, Ivakota 9477, **Jain 9478**, Jones 9479, Karlgaard 9481, Keenan 9483, King 9484, Lacy 9485, Levmar 9490, Lintott 9492, Loeb 9493, **Longview 9494**, Macedonian 9496, MAIHS 9497, Meador 9500, Mody 9501, Northern 9503, Ochsman 9504, O'Shaughnessy-Hurst 9505, Perlin 9510, Poole 9512, Praxis 9515, Pruden 9517, Ramsey 9519, Ratner 9521, RECO 9522, Richardson 9523, Rimora 9524, Rouse-Bottom 9526, Schiro-Zavela 9528, Short 9532, Sirad 9533, Stephenson 9536, Strauch 9538, Stultz 9539, **Tara 9540**, Tesco 9541, Thomas 9542, Treakle 9543, Valentine 9545, Weil 9550, Wiley 9551, Williams 9553, Williams-Berry 9554, Womack 9556
Washington: Ames 9560, Block 9570, Boeschoten 9571, Boydston 9572, Brookshire-Green 9573, Bulleri 9575, Carper 9577, Cartales 9578, Cowles 9582, DeFalco 9585, DG 9586, Dore 9587, Echo 9590, Erickson 9591, Everett 9592, Fales 9594, FAR 9595, Ferguson 9596, Foss 9598, Fries-Tait 9599, FTJ 9600, Fulton 9601, Gibson 9604, Gilmore 9605, Gius 9606, Goodfellow 9607, Goodman 9608, Grindstone 9610, Grousemont 9611, Hagan 9612, Hall 9613, Herbold 9620, Herray 9621, Hickey 9622, HIS 9624, Horn 9625, Howarth 9626, Hyde 9627, Jaffe 9629, Jefferson 9630, **Jernigan 9631**, **Ji 9632**, Johnston-Hanson

9635, Jones 9637, Jones 9638, Juniper 9640, Kaleidoscope 9641, Kilworth 9644, Kismet 9646, Klaue 9647, Korum 9648, Larson 9650, Levitan 9653, Loeb 9654, Lott 9656, Madrona 9657, Magdalen 9658, Moraine 9664, Morningside 9665, Muglia 9666, Murray 9667, Nordstrom/Seifert 9668, O'Donnell 9672, **Ormsby 9674**, Paulus 9676, Pleas 9678, Prairie 9680, Razore 9682, **Rotalia 9685**, Runstad 9686, **Sabol 9687**, Schwab 9691, Seager 9692, Shepherd 9694, Skagit 9696, Slingshot 9697, Smith 9698, Snyder 9699, Sondland 9700, Stevens 9704, Teel 9708, Templin 9709, Thayer 9710, Thomson 9711, Titus-Will 9714, True 9716, Tudor 9717, Weier 9720, Welch 9721, Wellworth 9722, Wilkens 9724, Winter 9726, Wissner-Slivka 9727, Worthington 9729, Wyman 9731, Young 9732, Zufall 9733
West Virginia: Appalachian 9734, Blake 9735, Bowen 9737, Bowers 9738, Chambers 9742, Driehorst 9743, Esbenshade 9744, Fine 9745, Hamer 9746, Hoffmann 9749, Hollandsworth 9750, Hope, 9752, Hott 9753, Larch 9755, McCormick 9758, McCormick 9759, McDavid 9760, Raymond 9764, Shott 9765, Skewes 9766, Vecellio 9770, Wehrle 9771, Wolfe 9772
Wisconsin: Anderson 9773, AnnMarie 9774, Arzbaecher 9777, Associated 9778, Aylward 9779, Baker 9780, BayCare 9781, Berbeewalsh 9782, Braun 9787, Brennan 9788, Brown 9790, Carlisle 9792, Cloud 9796, Community 9797, Cudahy 9800, Dawes 9803, Debbink 9804, Domer 9808, Doolittle 9809, Dudley 9811, Dutton 9812, Eau 9814, Einhorn 9815, F.K. 9817, Fahrney 9818, Ferguson 9819, Frautschi 9822, Gebhardt 9826, Grande 9832, Gunther 9833, Hartwig 9836, Hatch 9837, **Helios 9838**, Hicks 9840, Highlands 9841, Hoffmann 9842, Huiras 9844, Hunt 9845, Hyde 9846, Inbusch 9847, Janesville 9850, **Johnson 9851**, Johnson 9853, Jones 9854, Jones 9855, Kachel 9857, Kalscheur 9858, Kelly 9861, Kenosha 9862, Kloss 9863, Kohl 9864, Koss 9866, Lakeview 9868, Lato 9869, Lloyd 9870, Locke 9871, Lutsey 9873, LUX 9874, Manitowoc 9876, Marshfield 9878, Martin 9879, Mednikow 9881, Meinerz 9883, Meyer 9885, Mid-States 9887, Modine 9889, Murray 9892, Nelson 9894, Pelz 9900, Peterson 9901, Phipps 9902, Phipps 9903, Plein 9904, Pritchett 9906, Regal-Beloit 9911, Roddis 9916, Roehl 9917, Sartori 9921, Schmucker 9923, Schoenleber 9924, Seramur 9926, Shannon 9927, Simms 9929, Single 9930, Smith 9932, SMS 9933, Sonnentag 9934, St. 9936, Stateline 9937, Stevens 9939, Styberg 9942, Sub-Zero 9943, Tellier 9946, Thompson 9947, Uihlein 9949, Uihlein 9950, Van 9952, Van 9953, Verhulst 9954, Webcrafters-Frautschi 9957, Weyco 9958, Weyers 9959, Windway 9961
Wyoming: Bailey 9964, Connemara 9967, Dragicevich 9969, Dubois 9970, Ellbogen 9971, Hirschfield 9973, Joannides 9976, JWJ 9978, Marine 9980, Nickerson 9981, Riehm 9984, Sargent 9985, Scott 9987, StoneRiver 9991, Surrena 9994, Weiss 9996, Weiss 9997, Witzel 10000

Education services
California: Nicholson 866, Uplands 1139
Colorado: Donnell-Kay 1258
Florida: Wynne 2419
Hawaii: Central 2627
Illinois: Diamond 2829, Glossberg 2916
Massachusetts: **Pegasus 4236**, Ramlose 4257, Ratshesky 4259
Mississippi: Hancock 4840
New York: Doshi 5926, Lewy 6393
North Carolina: Peeler 7207
Oklahoma: Asbjornson 7655
Pennsylvania: Black 7875
Texas: Boeing 8733
Utah: Steiner 9358
Virginia: MAIHS 9497

Educational exchanges
New York: Lewy 6393

Educational management
Delaware: **TeleTech 1761**
New York: Wurtele 6997

Elementary and secondary education
Alabama: Anderson 6, Bruno 17, Harris 34, Kemp 42, Trippe 71, Watson 76
Alaska: Doyon 84
Arizona: Burns 102, Coleman 107, Grossman 126, Long 141, Spalding 172
Arkansas: Murphy 206, Nabholz 209, Riggs 214, Wrape 222
California: Ackerman 227, Arata 248, Bancroft-Clair 270, Baxter 284, Boone 328, Bravo 338, Corwin 428, Danvera 442, Drum 464, Ellen 478, Finestra 505, Foor 516, Helmstetter 616, Herrmann 618, Horwich 632, **Jacoby 654**, Jennings 663, Johnson 667, Jolson 672, Jones 673, Jones 675, Kadima 686, Keith 696, Kirby-Jones 708, Koenig 717, Kornwasser 718, KT 723, **Levy 752**, Magowan 782, Miller 830, Olander 878, Phelps 923, Plum 929, Ramsay 952, Reitman 964, Rishwain 974, Roche 979, Solano 1063, Stauffer 1077, Stearns 1078, Thagard 1109, Trust 1131, United 1136
Colorado: Benson 1230, Big 1235, Bloedorn 1238, Caulkins 1245, Donnell-Kay 1258, Hamilton 1285, Heginbotham 1289, Hewit 1292, JJP 1299, **Kenney 1302**, Margulf 1320, Mullen 1329, Southwestern 1355, Titus 1367
Connecticut: Avery 1396, Baldwin 1399, Bowling 1409, DeLuca 1431, Foley 1452, Hume 1485, Jones 1490, Linke 1508, Nason 1528, Nirenberg 1534, O'Herron 1536, Price 1544, Proctor 1545, Sorenson-Pearson 1574, Velaj 1592, Zacharia 1601
Delaware: ABE 1607, Broder 1629, Brown 1631, Dion 1656, George 1667, Hagan 1674, Jockers 1687, Patterson 1719, SNAVE 1747, Sulentic 1752, **TeleTech 1761**
District of Columbia: Cafritz 1793, Replogle 1831, Westport 1838
Florida: Brody 1902, Couch 1953, Diermeier 1976, Dorset 1979, Ellis 1989, Forbes 2008, Gardner 2031, Gerry-Corbett 2037, Haugland 2084, Hayford 2086, Hornik 2111, Hultquist 2115, Jacobsen 2123, Kanders 2135, Lambert 2164, Lenkin 2179, Marshall 2195, Meerwarth 2209, Minto 2216, **Posnack 2262**, Price 2277, Reckson 2277, Ryan 2304, Sharaby 2329, Turock 2382, Vanneck-Bailey 2384, Votum 2390, Wolgin 2411
Georgia: Brewer 2448, Colston 2464, Community 2465, Community 2466, Gholston 2487, Gould 2494, Harrison 2502, Jolley 2526, Lane 2536, Lee 2540, Magnus 2543, Noonan 2558, Orkin 2560, Pattillo 2563, Pennies 2565, Piedmont 2566, Pilling 2567, Pope 2568, Saul 2579, Stahl 2588, Tritt 2596, Williams 2612, Young 2621
Idaho: Hare 2675, Mitchell 2680
Illinois: Adreani 2697, Alliant 2702, Almeida 2704, **Appleby 2711**, Bartsch 2722, **Chapin 2781**, Chapin-May 2782, Cooney 2806, Danielson 2824, Edgerly 2847, Family 2864, Frankel 2886, Fredman 2890, Fremont 2891, Gallagher 2898, Gust 2936, H 2937, Half 2942, Hamm 2947, Hanson 2950, Hanus 2951, Hess 2969, Houlihan 2979, Mullen 3129, Pepper 3167, Ruben 3215, Sulzer 3277, Twomey 3298, Vail 3301
Indiana: CDM 3355, Fortune 3381, Huntington 3397
Iowa: Deardorf 3485, Forster 3494, Krause 3516, Stark 3536
Kansas: Bramlage 3559, Dehaemers 3572, Family 3575, Insurance 3587, Mingenback 3605, Schmidt 3622, Trusler 3635
Kentucky: Horn 3664, Trim 3702
Louisiana: Wisdom 3761

Maryland: **Braitmayer 3827**, Devito 3848, Eacho 3852, Huether/McClelland 3884, Jake 3890, RFI 3938, Salisbury 3945, Schuh 3946, Unger 3971
Massachusetts: Akamai 3998, Allison 4000, Casey 4039, Gale 4100, Hale 4113, Haley 4114, Harwood 4119, Killian 4154, Kneisel 4157, Marcus 4188, Marino 4190, McNeice, 4195, Melvin 4196, PerkinElmer 4238, Safe 4275, Shaich 4287, Sherman 4293, Smith 4298, Sprague 4306, Stemberg 4313, Tilson 4328, Walsh 4348, Weld 4356, Windhorse 4361
Michigan: Acheson 4370, Andrah 4378, Baum 4387, Kay 4516, Kellogg 4482, Linse 4493, Mills 4515, Padnos 4529, Page, 4530, Pitt 4540, Price 4546, Ryan 4555, Sackerson 4557, **Triford 4597**
Minnesota: Bumgarner 4649, Chadwick-Loher 4655, Charity, 4660, Frey 4690, Gardner 4693, Gilligan 4696, Goldman 4697, Jostens 4720, Kellogg 4722, Radichel 4765, Reed 4768, Regis 4770, Rodman 4779, Whaley 4816
Mississippi: Skelton 4854
Missouri: Boylan 4873, Butler 4880, Cornelsen 4889, Cray 4890, Hermann 4927, Kemper 4935, Long 4948, Morgan 4963, Schneider 4994, Schweinfurth 4996, Vatterott 5030, Wolff 5040
Montana: Boe 5045
Nebraska: Burnett 5075, Hansen 5087, Harper 5088
Nevada: Bendon 5137, Joseph 5166, Matley 5176
New Jersey: **Akhoury 5243**, Blessing 5266, Brundage 5280, Byrne 5283, Civitas 5296, Croman 5307, **Daft 5310**, deRosa 5316, Dickinson 5319, Dietze 5320, Earle 5328, Frog 5357, Kurr 5435, Mamiye 5456, Petrucci 5498, Rukin 5516, Shamah 5531, Tedesco 5557, Twin 5563, Upton 5566, Wicks 5584, Willingham 5589, Woolley-Clifford 5594
New York: A.P.W. 5633, Avery 5702, Barbash 5714, Beck 5728, Beir 5732, Bell 5734, Bergson 5738, Blue 5764, Brosens 5789, Carwill 5818, Chasdei 5834, Cline 5851, Colby 5867, Coles 5871, Davidson 5901, D-B 5903, Duke 5934, Erpf 5968, **Family 5983**, Feinberg 5993, Fieldstone 6004, Fife 6005, Forest 6018, Gaffney 6049, Gant 6054, Gerhard 6072, Gross 6142, Grubman 6147, Gutman 6152, Hajim 6158, Henderson 6189, Hidary 6205, IF 6237, **Indira 6242**, JVZ 6277, Keren 6302, Kirby 6313, **Kitov 6317**, Klingenstein-Martell 6329, La 6355, Lake 6360, **Laub 6367**, Lewy 6393, Loewy 6409, Lubin 6416, Lux 6422, M.F.K. 6426, Maher 6433, MAT 6450, Menges 6474, Morris 6508, Morse 6510, Ostreicher 6563, Paneth 6574, Patrina 6579, Peckham 6583, Peterson 6593, Pittman 6608, Pohly-Turaj 6613, **Posner-Wallace 6621**, Raphael 6648, Reiss 6662, Rheinstrom 6665, Ring 6671, Saltzman 6722, Savitz 6734, Shuman 6795, Silverstein 6803, Spiegel 6838, Stanton 6845, Sternberg 6863, Thanksgiving 6897, Thiem 6898, Utopia 6923, Watts 6947, **Weingarten 6952**, Weingarten 6953, Whittemore 6975, Willmott 6978, Wright 6995, Yahad 7002, Yms 7008, Young 7012
North Carolina: Bolick 7056, Glenn 7111, Hoffman 7128, Howe 7132, Kistler 7147, Rankin 7217, Rogers 7228, Strowd 7258
Ohio: Barron 7316, Bates 7317, Bicknell 7327, Callahan 7345, Chemed 7350, Coressel 7364, Crossroads 7367, Dienstberger 7379, **Elisha-Bolton 7387**, Gould 7430, Hubert 7456, Jennings 7466, Klock 7480, Murphy 7533, Norris 7538, Pugliese 7551, Rosenberry 7562, Sandfair 7569, Scotford 7579, Sheely 7590, Skyler 7595, Southard 7599
Oklahoma: Barnes 7659, **Crio 7670**, Richardson 7717
Oregon: Castle 7745, Frank 7765, Irwin 7777, Silver 7817
Pennsylvania: Black 7875, Emporium 7980, Fountainhead 8004, Gilmore 8017, HFO 8053, Hilles 8057, **Hitchcock 8059**, Kurtz 8104, Lewis 8124, Maronda 8140, Mason 8147, Mellon 8167, Merwin 8170, Mill 8172, Patterson 8206, Penn 8208, Quinn 8229, Roemer 8242, Ryan 8251, Smith 8281, Speyer 8294, Triple 8322, Williams 8358

Rhode Island: Koffler 8436, McCarthy 8452
South Carolina: Collins 8520, Gleason 8524, Stony 8542, Tarr 8545, WPW 8551
Tennessee: Adams 8579, **Belz 8585**, Berman 8587, Cartinhour-Woods 8597, Community 8601, Doochin 8605, Eskind 8611, Eskind 8613, Firstfruits 8614, Gaylord 8620, **Louisiana-Pacific 8644**, Nehemiah 8653, Pettway 8658, Schadt 8670, Siegel 8674
Texas: Anderson 8704, Aragona 8706, Boeing 8733, Brown 8750, Budwine 8754, Clements 8773, Collins 8781, Dale 8794, DeBusk 8806, Dedman, 8808, Dubose 8828, Duncan 8833, Esping 8841, Flowers 8862, FSR 8880, Garvey 8884, Gray 8899, Greentree 8901, Hicks 8936, Holmes 8947, Howell 8956, Kahn 8978, Kolitz 9000, Lantana 9009, Mattsson 9042, McLaughlin 9053, Merrick 9059, Moore 9072, Muse 9080, O'Connor 9093, O'Hare 9095, P 9108, Perkins 9125, Postl 9136, Riter, 9154, Ross 9164, San 9170, Smith 9207, Vaughan 9218, Vetter 9251, Waggoner 9254, Wal-Dot 9256, Ward 9260, Westcott 9273, Williams 9279, Zale 9300
Utah: Eskuche 9323, Green 9327, Steiner 9358, Wadman 9362
Vermont: Altman 9364, Harper 9373, Harvest 9374, Mergens 9381
Virginia: Blue 9400, Lintott 9492, Page 9507, **Price 9516**, Shaffer 9530, VuBay 9548
Washington: Kilworth 9644, O'Donnell 9672, Remala 9683, Wilson 9725, Worthington 9729
West Virginia: Hess 9747
Wisconsin: Frautschi 9822, Gardner 9825, Hartwig 9836, Kohl 9864, Mason 9880, Modine 9889, Olson 9897, Pritchett 9906, Witte, 9962
Wyoming: Cutting 9968, Johnson 9977, **Schultz 9986**

Elementary education

Alabama: Blount 13
Arkansas: Olds 210
California: Fitzpatrick 508, Gooding 571, Gross 587, Martin 802, Millstreet 835, Nelson 860, Wells 1171
Connecticut: Barnes 1404, Curran 1427
Florida: Koski 2157
Georgia: Johnson 2525, Sewell 2584
Hawaii: Kahiau 2636
Illinois: Banta 2719, Bellick 2732, Flinn 2875, Ringer 3196, Simpson 3248
Indiana: Fenech 3380
Kansas: Baehr 3556
Maryland: **Braitmayer 3827**, Mental 3912, Rogers-Wilbur 3941
Massachusetts: **New 4220**
Michigan: Community 4410, Community 4411, Morley 4518, St. 4576
Minnesota: Louis 4731, Midcontinent 4745, Morning 4748
Missouri: Chod 4885, Curry 4892, Kienstra 4938
New Hampshire: Martin 5222
New Jersey: Cordover 5304
New York: Hathaway 6176, Initial 6245, Mabardi 6428, Roche 6678
North Carolina: Griffin 7113, Post 7213, Pratt 7214, Ritchie 7222
Ohio: CLH 7355
Oregon: Brown 7744
Pennsylvania: Arkema 7842, Buck 7903, Saramar 8253, Seybert 8269, Stein 8299, Teleflex 8314
Rhode Island: Kingsbury 8435
Tennessee: Jones 8635
Texas: DeBusk 8806
Wisconsin: Kohl 9865

Emergency care

North Carolina: Marlboro 7169
Oklahoma: Lolmaugh 7700
Pennsylvania: Columbia 7932

Emergency medical services

New York: Kamber 6281
Rhode Island: Bailey 8384
Texas: Cogdell 8777

Employment

California: Bank 272, Bright 344, Gordy 575, Lux 773, O'Donnell 874, Silicon 1038, **Wakerly 1150**
Colorado: Hunter-White 1297
Connecticut: Dime 1438, Donchian 1440
Florida: Phillips 2260
Georgia: Athens 2437
Illinois: Community 2802, Morris 3125, Rosebud 3204
Indiana: Schwab 3445
Iowa: Heerema 3504
Kansas: Insurance 3587
Kentucky: USA 3704
Massachusetts: Kimball 4155, Ratshesky 4259, **Robbins-de 4266**, Schiro 4282
Michigan: Branch 4396
Minnesota: Bell 4637, Dyer 4669, G&K 4691, Groves 4703, Tennant 4798
Missouri: Butler 4880
New Jersey: Columbia 5301
New York: 21st 5630, Scully 6763, Tuch 6915
Ohio: Landers 7488, Sears-Swetland 7581
Oklahoma: Wegener 7731
Pennsylvania: Jackson 8078
Texas: Boeing 8733
Utah: Dry 9321
Virginia: Ferrari 9446, **Fund 9455**
Wisconsin: Gardner 9825, Woodtrust-Bell 9963

Endangered species protection

Florida: **Atlantis 1858**
New York: Anderson-Rogers 5676, **Eppley 5967**
Pennsylvania: Brooks 7899

Energy resources

District of Columbia: American 1785
Texas: Fash 8848

Engineering

California: Kanel 688, **Reddy 958**
District of Columbia: **Carter 1794**
Florida: Hardison 2081, Price 2267, Sun, 2358
Georgia: Storey 2589
Illinois: **Dyson 2842**, Keller 3010, OSA 3157, Peters 3172
Indiana: Hulman 3396
Kentucky: Boone 3649
Michigan: DeVlieg 4428, Meritor, 4511
Minnesota: Rosen 4782, **Wagner 4804**
New Hampshire: Dorr 5211
New Jersey: Armour-Lewis 5251
New York: **Engineering 5964**, Family 5984, Phillips 6600
North Carolina: Gambrill 7106
Ohio: Pott 7549
Oregon: Mentor 7796
Pennsylvania: Baker 7851, Every 7986
Tennessee: Rucker-Donnell 8668
Texas: **AMD 8698**, Flowers 8862, Ray 9144
Washington: Coulter 9581, Hansen 9615
Wisconsin: Birnschein 9783, Crowley 9799

Entrepreneurship

California: Bank 272
Georgia: Gray 2497
North Carolina: Redwoods 7218
Oklahoma: White 7734
Pennsylvania: Tippins 8318

Environment

Alabama: Abahac 1, Black 12, Brinkley 15, Phifer, 54

Arizona: Harmsen, 128, Murphey 151, Powell 157, Smith 170, Zicarelli 185

Arkansas: Darragh 193, Trinity 218

California: 2005 223, Ach 226, Amador 238, Bancroft-Clair 270, Bannerman 274, **Beagle 286**, Bear 288, Bellwether 299, Berglund 303, Big 315, Braddock 336, Brotman 351, Community 420, Community 421, Danvera 442, Deacon 447, Downing 462, Drexler 463, Emmett 481, Endurance 482, Epstein/Roth 483, Fairview 490, Faraway 494, Fliesbach 512, Frankel 526, Frome 535, Fusenot 541, Gallo 543, Gellert 550, Godric 566, Hotchkis 634, J. 653, Jamieson 658, JDH 660, Katz 692, Kelly 697, Laguna 726, **Lawrence 734**, McKay 815, Morgan 846, Nell 859, North 869, On 880, **PADI 898**, Palo 900, Piuze 928, Plum 929, **Quiksilver 945**, Ridder 970, Roberts 976, Rocca, 978, Roche 979, Rubin 993, Schlinger 1016, Seip 1028, **Skyscrape 1047**, Smith-Welsh 1058, Solano 1063, Swinerton 1098, Szekely 1102, Tomkins 1122, Trombetta 1128, Uplands 1138, Welch 1168, West 1174, **Wilkinson 1183**, Winn 1189, Writer 1200, Zurlo 1217

Colorado: Arches 1222, Benson 1230, Bjorkman 1236, F 1266, Gerrish 1277, Goodwin 1279, Grosvenor 1283, **Kenney 1302**, Leighty 1311, Maki 1319, Melrose 1326, Neuman 1331, **Oreg 1335**, Porphyry 1338, Taylor 1364, Warner 1376

Connecticut: Acorn 1385, Donchian 1439, Gryphon 1474, Linke 1508, Lippincott 1509, Lodewick 1512, McLane 1522, **Richardson 1550**, Taylor 1579, Wheeler 1594

Delaware: Alcyon 1608, Black 1622, Chaney 1640, Glencoe 1669, Hawkins 1679, Kent-Lucas 1691, Kingsley 1693, Lowndes 1701, Messing 1708, Milliken 1711, Repass-Rodgers 1727, Schiffman 1738, Van 1769, Welton 1776, Yaverland 1783

District of Columbia: American 1785, Farvue 1806

Florida: Anderson 1845, Archibald 1852, **Atlantis 1858**, Bastien 1872, Bell 1882, Cape 1917, Charlotte 1938, Dennis 1969, Haskell 2083, Higgs 2096, Knopf 2155, Lazarus 2172, Martin 2196, Owen 2243, Rose 2293, Salenger 2308, Shockley 2332, Siegel 2335, **Stiefel 2352**, Sudakoff 2356, Swann 2360, Thornburgh 2374, Wrigley 2417

Georgia: Athens 2437, **Bancker-Williams 2440**, Brewer 2448, Cobb 2463, Enterline 2475, **Gage 2482**, Gilbert, 2488, Johnson 2525, McClatchey 2546, McKnight 2548, Noonan 2558, Price-Campbell 2570, Rice 2575, Sweetgrass 2591, Trammell 2595, Walker 2603, Wormsloe 2619

Hawaii: Baldwin 2625, Minami 2642

Idaho: Boise 2666, Equinox 2670, Golden 2672, Whittenberger 2689

Illinois: Abelson 2692, **Appleby 2711**, Baird 2718, Cain 2773, Ceres 2779, Danielson 2823, EMA 2854, Faulkner 2867, Franklin 2887, Gibbet 2912, Gidwitz 2914, Half 2942, Hanson 2950, Highland 2970, Jahn 2992, Judy 3003, Kainz 3004, Karasik 3006, Koranda 3026, Krehbiel 3030, MacDonald 3068, McCune 3089, **Meyers 3107**, Micole 3108, **New 3138**, Norgaard 3141, Oberweiler 3147, Oppenheimer 3155, Pitzman 3177, Secord 3232, Shapiro 3240, Smithburg 3254, Spencer 3258, Staley 3264, Stone 3270, Wehle 3314

Indiana: Community 3359, Community 3360, Community 3361, Community 3362, Dubois 3370, Ellerbrook 3376, Fayette 3379, Globe 3387, Huntington 3397, Jasper 3401, Jennings 3402, Lacy 3410, LaGrange 3412, **Mervis 3417**, Namaste 3422, Ohio 3427, Scott 3446

Iowa: West 3547, Young 3552

Kansas: Coffeyville 3566, Community 3567, Golden 3582, Kansas 3592, Payless 3614

Kentucky: Boone 3649, Foundation 3655, Sutherland 3699, Welchwood 3706

Louisiana: Biedenharn 3713, Daybrook 3720, Gauthier 3724, Live 3734, Wisdom 3761

Maine: Bank 3766, Burnham 3770, Chappell 3772, **Golden 3781**

Maryland: Ammerman 3813, Elsberg 3856, Higginson 3880, Macht 3905, McKnight 3910, Paternotte 3933, Phase 3936, Richmond 3940, Sears 3948, Tucker 3969, Van 3974

Massachusetts: Arcadia 4004, **Azadoutioun 4008, Barakat 4012**, Cabot 4035, Cricket 4060, Halfway 4115, Hazard 4123, Kelsey 4148, Lawry 4168, Merrill 4200, Metanoia 4201, MutualOne 4216, **New 4220, Patagonia 4234, Pegasus 4236**, Permanent 4239, Redwall 4261, Safe 4275, Shattuck 4291, Singing 4297, Solomon 4301, Stearns 4310, Steiger 4312

Michigan: Barstow 4385, Branch 4396, Burt 4403, Community 4410, Community 4411, Four 4449, Glassen 4454, Gratiot 4459, Herrington-Fitch 4466, Lapeer 4490, M 4497, Mackinac 4499, Olds 4526, Shiawassee 4568, Speckhard-Knight 4574, Tremble 4595

Minnesota: Andersen 4626, Avocet 4631, Becker 4636, Bell 4637, Bell 4638, Bradley 4647, Dellwood 4665, Ecotrust 4670, HJ 4714, Jeffers 4719, Larsen 4728, Living 4730, Luverne 4736, McCoy 4742, Open 4756, OSilas 4758, **Porter 4763**, Remick 4773, Rodman 4779, Schott 4787, Tennant 4798, Thorpe 4800

Missouri: **Bohm 4871**, Chomeau 4886, Deliniere 4894, Garvey 4913, Gaylord 4915, Grant 4918, Hermann 4927, Sander 4991

Montana: Angora 5044, Cinnabar 5047

Nebraska: Nelson 5106, Pegler 5110

Nevada: **A 5131**, Timken-Sturgis 5192, West 5197

New Hampshire: Charter 5206, Noah 5226, Up 5235

New Jersey: American 5248, **Blue 5269**, Chormann 5293, **Crane 5306**, Ellis 5333, Environmental 5337, Frelinghuysen 5354, Hanson 5383, Kean 5417, Kurtz 5436, Leavens 5444, Miller 5468, Palmer 5486, Pheasant 5499, Scire 5526, Stone 5553, Vaughn-Jordan 5567, Yates 5595

New Mexico: **Angelica 5605**, B.F. 5606, Carlsbad 5608, Taos 5626, **Watersheds 5628**

New York: AGB 5650, Alexander 5654, Allatt 5659, Asen 5694, Bender 5735, **Burpee 5802**, CAL 5808, Carwill 5818, Ciampa 5845, Clemente 5850, Cochran 5853, Code 5854, Dalton 5896, Darrah 5900, Del 5908, Dillard 5916, Educational 5945, **Eppley 5967**, Ettl 5970, Evans 5973, F. 5977, **Family 5983**, Fenton 5998, Fieldstone 6004, **Fitzgibbons 6011**, Franklin 6028, Gage 6050, Garman 6058, Giant 6077, Gimbel 6079, **Goldfein 6096**, Gordon 6109, Grand 6123, Grant 6129, Hahn 6156, Hajim 6158, Hallingby 6160, Hewitt 6200, Holborn 6220, Houser 6227, Houston 6228, Huber 6231, Ilsababy 6238, Ivorybill 6252, Knapp 6331, Legacy 6373, Lippes 6401, Long 6410, Lubin 6416, Lubo 6417, Lucky 6419, Lufkin 6421, M66 6427, Maher 6433, MAT 6450, McEnroe 6463, Menken 6475, Meyer 6486, Michaels 6488, Newcomb-Hargraves 6529, Northern 6540, Ostgrodd 6561, Pajwell 6568, Perlman 6587, Petty 6596, Plymouth 6612, Rapaport 6646, Raymond 6652, Shaftel 6782, Smith 6813, Snow 6818, **Sparkplug 6830**, Stackhouse 6844, Stebbins 6850, Sussman 6879, Suwinski 6885, Thanksgiving 6897, Weismann 6960, White 6971, Yordan 7009, Zenkel 7023

North Carolina: BB&T 7045, Bell 7048, Billingsley 7052, Chastain 7073, Deal 7085, Emma 7091, Glenn 7111, Hoffman 7127, Moritz 7192, Outer 7204, Strowd 7258

Ohio: Armington 7309, Athens 7311, Bryan 7339, Community 7356, Community 7357, **Eaton 7383, Elisha-Bolton 7387**, Firman 7400, Fleischmann 7404, Gale 7415, George 7421, Gross/Hutton 7433, Haskell 7439, Heffner 7443, **Lowe-Marshall 7505**, Mather 7516, NLT 7537, Sears-Swetland 7581, Seasongood 7582, Talbott 7612, Thendara 7616, Tuscarawas 7623, Vista 7628, Woodward 7646

Oklahoma: Brannin 7662, Cherokee 7666, Everest 7676

Oregon: Baldwin 7742, Collins 7753, Karuna 7781, Lamb 7787, **Larson 7788**, Leupold 7790, **Wyss 7832**

Pennsylvania: American 7839, Applestone 7841, Black 7876, Breedlove 7890, Brooks 7899, Buck 7904, Bucks 7905, Burket-Plack 7906, Cameron 7911, Carita 7915, Community 7933, Crawford 7944, Delaware 7953, Dominion 7961, Elk 7975, Emporium 7980, Fine 7994, First 7996, Flinn 8001, French 8007, Friendship 8009, Gypsy 8034, **KL 8094**, Lancy 8108, **Mango 8138**, Petersen 8212, Randall 8230, Reidler 8233, Schuylkill 8263, Shore 8276, Star 8297, Strawbridge 8305, Strine 8307, Tabas 8312, Tally 8313, Tompkins-Broll 8320, Up 8327, Wyeth 8371

Rhode Island: Chace 8393, Estate 8404, Heydt 8419, Johnson 8430, Kimball 8434, Kingsbury 8435, Leroe 8439, Lorber 8445, Washington 8500

South Carolina: Boyd 8514, Davis 8521, Greenwood 8526

South Dakota: Watertown 8576, Wolfe 8578

Tennessee: Atticus 8582, Cracker 8603, **Louisiana-Pacific 8644**, Mapp 8646, Stadler 8678, Sunlight 8681

Texas: Boeing 8733, Conley 8784, Cook 8787, Frill 8877, Garver 8883, Hershey 8931, Il 8958, Inge 8961, Laredo 9010, Lykes-Knapp 9030, Montgomery 9070, Oppenheimer 9101, P 9108, Partnership 9116, Richter 9153, Stevenson 9220, Texas 9231, Vaughan 9249, Watson 9263

Utah: Backcountry 9303, Odyssey 9342, Shrontz 9351, Slaughter, 9353

Vermont: Blittersdorf 9365, Stokes 9385

Virginia: Backer 9389, Black 9399, Burford 9411, Dreaming 9435, Dun 9437, **Fund 9455**, Northern 9503

Washington: Boydston 9572, DG 9586, Dudley 9588, Everett 9592, Grousemont 9611, Hanauer 9614, Jefferson 9630, **Ji 9632**, Juniper 9640, Kaleidoscope 9641, Keller 9643, Mize 9663, Northwest 9669, Not 9670, Paulus 9676, Prairie 9680, Skagit 9696, Stevens 9704, Young 9732

Wisconsin: Antonia 9775, Ariens 9776, Door 9810, Dudley 9811, Dutton 9812, Eau 9814, Hansen 9835, **Helios 9838**, Kelly 9861, Kenosha 9862, Marshfield 9878, Puelicher 9907, Redmond 9910, Rosemann 9919, Rusinow 9920, Stateline 9937, Uihlein 9949

Wyoming: Brendsel 9965, C 9966, Connemara 9967, Storer 9992, Weiss 9997

Environmental and resource rights

Florida: Lazarus 2172

Environmental education

California: Cleo 407, Money-Arenz 844, **Quiksilver 945**, Small 1049, Swayne 1097

Florida: Brown 1904

Georgia: Hoyt 2514, McKinney-Geib 2547

Illinois: Peters 3171

Kentucky: Yeager 3710

Maryland: Van 3973

Massachusetts: **New 4220**

Michigan: Mills 4515

Montana: High 5057

New Jersey: American 5248

New York: **Family 5983**, Henderson 6189

Ohio: Hoover 7453

Pennsylvania: Rosenlund 8245, Wright-Cook 8369

Rhode Island: Kingsbury 8435

South Carolina: Singing 8540

Wisconsin: Ariens 9776, Blooming 9784, Bock 9786

Environmental justice

California: New 865

Georgia: Brewer 2448

Rhode Island: Acriel 8378

Tennessee: Atticus 8582

Wisconsin: Bock 9786

Environmental studies

California: New 865
Georgia: Exposition 2476
Illinois: Hare 2954
New York: Schwartz 6755, Walrath 6941
Oregon: Saling 7811
Texas: Knox 8999

Epilepsy

Florida: Wilder 2406
Georgia: Terwilliger 2593

Episcopalianism and Anglicanism

Alabama: Phifer, 54
California: Brewster 341, Pardee 902, Smullin 1060
Delaware: Day 1654
Florida: Bell 1883, Dennis 1969, Patterson 2251
Illinois: Hunt 2984
Kentucky: McKellar 3677
Louisiana: Live 3734
New York: Watts 6947, **Woodland 6989**
Pennsylvania: Warburton 8342
Tennessee: Atticus 8582
Texas: Clements 8773, **Crowder 8792**, Foundation 8870
Washington: Muglia 9666, Spark 9701
Wisconsin: Roddis 9916

Equal opportunity in education

New York: 21st 5630

Equestrianism

California: Beauregard 290, Cole 415, First 506, Lewis 753
Delaware: Dougherty 1658
Kentucky: Boone 3649, Pollard 3685, USA 3704
Michigan: Mackinac 4499, Oreffice 4528
New York: Dobson 5921, Warwick 6945
Oklahoma: Dill 7671
Pennsylvania: Goshen 8025
South Carolina: Cato 8516
Virginia: Dun 9437

ESL and second language acquisition

Massachusetts: Middlesex 4203
Minnesota: G&K 4691

Ethnic and racial groups

Alabama: Black 12, Ireland 39
Arkansas: Darragh 193
California: Atkinson 259, Avery-Fuller-Welch 260, Margoes 795, Mazda 810
Connecticut: Fry 1458
District of Columbia: Bench 1788, **Carter 1794**, Jovid 1817
Florida: Brighton 1899, Oristano 2241, Tampa 2362, Wilson-Wood 2408
Georgia: Abreu 2431
Illinois: Chicago 2787, Meyer 3106, Sumac 3278
Massachusetts: Kimball 4155, **Spero 4304**
Michigan: Community 4411
Minnesota: Bell 4637, Bell 4638
Missouri: Butler 4880, Dunn 4898, Timmons 5021, Vatterott 5030
Nebraska: Midlands 5104
New Jersey: **Dow 5325**, **Knistrom 5426**, Kurtz 5436
New Mexico: Con 5611
New York: Metzger-Price 6483, Netter 6525, Roche 6678, **Sparkplug 6830**, Wagner 6938
North Carolina: Glenn 7111
Ohio: Walker 7630
Pennsylvania: Ely 7979, Gauss 8014, Hill 8055, Hoffman 8062, Ludwick 8134, Seybert 8269, Union 8326, Wurts 8370

Tennessee: **Fugitive 8618**
Texas: Foundation 8869
Virginia: **Delmar 9429**, Ivakota 9477
Washington: Foss 9598
Wisconsin: Inbusch 9847, Marshfield 9878, Stateline 9937

Ethnic museums

Arizona: Berlin 101
Hawaii: Martin 2641
Michigan: Seligman 4564
New York: Danziger 5899, Heyman 6201, Pickman 6602, Rodgers 6680
Oklahoma: Wadley 7726
Texas: Orr 9104
Virginia: Strauch 9538

European football

Arizona: Maxinmotion 147
Florida: Barnard 1866
Indiana: Bill 3345, Hillenbrand 3393, Rush 3441
Louisiana: Harper 3726
Michigan: Roscommon 4552, Stoker 4580
New York: Burchan 5801, Hiler 6207

Ex-offenders

New York: Ostgrodd 6561

Exercise

California: Just 684, Stewart 1083
Pennsylvania: Blue 7879

Eye diseases

Arkansas: Bodenhamer 190
California: Bundy 360, Daly 440, Fortisure 518, Sawchuk 1010, Tilley 1118, Wertheimer 1173, Western 1176
Florida: River 2288
Hawaii: Ululani 2652
Illinois: Christiansen 2790, **Foundation 2881**, Sramek 3259
Kentucky: Etscorn 3654
Maryland: Feldman 3858, Mitchell, 3916
Massachusetts: **Memorial 4198**
Michigan: Shapiro 4566
Minnesota: Heilmaier 4712
New Hampshire: Olcott 5227
New Jersey: Alcon 5244, **Patel 5492**
New York: Sommer 6825
North Carolina: Hoffman 7128, Jelm 7137
Ohio: Conlogue 7359, Wildermuth 7637, Williams 7639
Pennsylvania: Perelman 8209
Rhode Island: Peacock 8469
Texas: **OneSight 9098**, Sear 9186, Vaughan 9248
Utah: Green 9327
Wisconsin: Erdman 9816, Ocular 9895
Wyoming: Skilling 9990

Families

California: Majestic 784

Family counseling

New York: Wyckoff 6998
Texas: Levy 9014
Washington: Foss 9598

Family disability resources

Kansas: Kansas 3592

Family planning

Arizona: Cadeau 104, Grossman 126, Hughes 130
Arkansas: Blue 189
California: Cheeryble 390, Codding 412, Corday 426, Foor 516, Gellert 550, Harman 598, Jones 675, On 880, Ridder 970, Rocca, 978, SKB 1044, Winkler 1188, Yen 1201
Colorado: JJP 1299
Connecticut: Crow 1426, Schloss 1562, Shenandoah 1568
District of Columbia: Westport 1838
Florida: Oristano 2241, P.M. 2244
Idaho: French 2671, Leidy 2678
Illinois: Collins 2799, Franklin 2887, Gibbet 2912, Kelly 3012, Mohr 3121, Munson 3130, New 3136, Pitzman 3177, Simpson 3248
Indiana: Namaste 3422
Iowa: Carlson 3479, Cowles 3482
Louisiana: Wisdom 3761
Maryland: Baker 3815, Moore 3917
Massachusetts: Chickering 4046, Kelsey 4148, **Lalor 4164**, **Tatelman 4322**, Walske 4349
Michigan: Delano 4426
Minnesota: Bell 4638
Missouri: Sunnen 5018, University 5027
Montana: Dousman 5049
Nebraska: **Waldbaum 5125**
Nevada: Banks 5135
New Jersey: Riskin 5511
New York: Anderson-Rogers 5676, **Blinken 5757**, Offensend 6550, Ostgrodd 6561, Rothblum 6701, Schott 6749, Spofford 6842, Still 6866, Washington 6946, Wharton 6968, Wohlgemuth 6984
North Carolina: Griffin 7113
Ohio: **Brush 7338**, Mather 7516
Pennsylvania: Aaron 7835, **Arronson 7844**, Price 8225, Union 8326
Rhode Island: York 8507
Texas: Grits 8904, Hill 8938, Kabacoff 8977, King 8994, Oppenheimer 9101, Vaughan 9249
Utah: Crawford 9314, Steiner 9358
Virginia: **Delmar 9429**, Ludington 9495, Shaffer 9530
Washington: Worthington 9729
Wisconsin: Cummings-Christensen 9801
Wyoming: Jaquith 9975

Family services

Alabama: Goodrich 29, Petra 53
Arizona: Burns 102, F2 117, Garcia 122, Grossman 126, Hughes 130, Long 141
Arkansas: Bailey 187
California: Altos 237, Bellwether 299, Bettingen 310, Bradford 337, Codding 412, Community 421, Friedman 530, Gellert 550, Graff 576, Harvey 602, Huntington 642, Jolson 672, Jones 673, Kelly 697, Kendall 700, Krishnan-Shah 722, Looker 766, Majestic 784, Malachi 785, Mann 790, Massie 806, Palo 900, Piuze 928, Roberts 975, Rocca, 978, Sanfilippo 1002, Sarandon 1004, SKB 1044, **Skyscrape 1047**, Thomson 1113, Troy 1130, Twanda 1135, Walters 1153, Welk 1170, Witkin 1191, Wrather 1198
Colorado: 6/S 1219, Connor 1250, Leininger 1312, Schramm 1350, SEAKR 1351, Stratton 1359
Connecticut: Bantle 1401, Brown 1413, Colburn-Keenan 1421, Dime 1438, Keefe 1497, Nessel 1529, Roberts 1551, Thornton 1582, Union 1590, Widows 1595
Delaware: Anbinder 1611, Barnabas 1614, Burton 1634, Messing 1708, Russell 1735
District of Columbia: Cafritz 1793, Cornerstone 1798, Replogle 1831
Florida: Auerbach 1859, Bastien 1872, Carlton 1922, Chapman 1935, Crane 1955, Ellis 1989, Fortin 2012, Gate 2034, Hagens 2071, HI 2093, KBR 2142, Landwirth 2167, MCM-Munilla 2206, Miller 2213, Oristano 2241, P.M. 2244, Reeves 2279, Ryan 2305, Scherr 2316, Shuey 2333, Simmons 2338, Sudakoff 2356, Wolgin 2411, Yerrid 2420

Georgia: Chatham 2457, Lee 2540, Vaughan 2598, Woodruff 2617
Hawaii: Locations 2638
Illinois: Bates 2725, Bladel 2744, Bulkley, 2765, Clingen 2794, Cowlin 2814, Cremer 2815, Cronin 2816, Fields 2870, Fredman 2890, Generations 2908, Hanson 2950, Highland 2970, Lebus 3043, Leestma 3044, McCabe 3084, McCauley 3085, McKee 3093, Perkins 3169, Reade 3187, Sasco 3222, Seymour 3236, Shodeen 3246, Smallwood 3251, Summer 3279, Watson 3311
Indiana: Blackford 3346, Custer 3366, Duneland 3372, Gammon 3385, Herr 3392, Klapper 3408, Nugent 3425, Scott 3446
Iowa: Beckwith 3473
Kansas: Family 3575, Fox 3578
Kentucky: Hannah 3659, Taylor 3700
Louisiana: Crossroads 3719, New 3742
Maine: Kennebec 3785, Somers 3803
Maryland: Davis 3844, **Doorstep 3850**, Eccles 3853, Witt/Hoey 3989
Massachusetts: 2 3992, Chickering 4046, East 4075, Fassino 4086, Fay 4087, Hazard 4124, Kelsey 4148, Kimball 4155, King 4156, Ladd 4163, Marigold 4189, MENTOR 4199, Permanent 4239, Peters 4241, Progin 4247, Ratshesky 4259, Rockland 4267, Sailors' 4276, Sherman 4293, Tatelman 4323, Weber 4352, Weil 4354
Michigan: Branch 4396, Community 4410, de 4422, Filmer 4444, Harris 4461, Mojo 4516, Onequest 4527, Springview 4575, Vander 4603
Minnesota: Bell 4637, Bell 4638, Bend 4639, Ecotrust 4670, Fletcher 4687, **Kaplan 4721**, **Sundance 4796**, Thorpe 4800, Wallestad 4806
Mississippi: Skelton 4854
Missouri: Bograd 4870, Cornelsen 4889, Herschend 4928, Moss 4964, Rust 4988, Sigma-Aldrich 5003, Sunnen 5018
Nebraska: America 5066, Ameritas 5067
Nevada: Barker 5136, Bendon 5137, Dermody 5152, **Do 5153**, Special 5188
New Hampshire: Bickford 5205, Jameson 5215, Verney 5236
New Jersey: Amboy 5246, Anderson 5249, Carlozzi 5287, Giants 5369, Halpern 5380, Kerney 5419, Kurr 5435, Marron 5461, Minerva 5469, Schwartz 5525, Scott 5527, Selective 5528, Wicks 5584
New Mexico: Taos 5626
New York: Anderson 5673, BBL 5724, Brillo-Sonnino 5785, Cathedral 5822, Cole 5868, Coleman 5869, Dammann 5897, Darrah 5900, French 6032, Griffin 6138, Houston 6228, Kenworthy 6300, Kornreich 6341, Leventritt 6385, Maher 6433, Metzger-Price 6483, Northern 6540, Pajwell 6568, Rose 6683, Schwartz 6752, Treiber 6907, Utica 6922, Washington 6946
North Carolina: Elks 7089, Katz 7142, Kistler 7147, Moretz 7189
Ohio: Alpaugh 7302, Arrel 7310, Austin-Bailey 7312, Bates 7317, Bicknell 7327, Community 7356, Crandall 7366, Foundation 7408, Hamilton 7435, Huntington 7460, **Katz 7475**, Mather 7516, Mehl 7523, Rosenberry 7562, Shannon 7586, Traeger 7621, Walker 7630, Wightman-Wieber 7636
Oklahoma: Witt 7737
Oregon: Brown 7744, Coffman 7750, McKay 7795, Sharkey 7815, West 7827
Pennsylvania: Blue 7879, Clark 7926, Delaware 7953, Five 7999, Garthwaite 8013, HFO 8053, Hilles 8057, Honickman 8066, Hulme 8069, Hunt 8070, Jackson 8078, Knudsen 8102, Murphy 8185, Olitsky 8198, O'Reilly 8200, Panama 8202, Schwartz 8265, Seybert 8269, Spencer 8293, Staley 8296, Wenger 8352, Williams 8357, Wurts 8370, York 8374
Rhode Island: Bersted 8388, Kingsbury 8435, Littlefield 8441, Molder 8455, Shea 8486, Washington 8500, Wilson 8504
South Carolina: Lutz 8533
South Dakota: Stearns 8575, Watertown 8576
Tennessee: Atticus 8582, Cracker 8603, Foster 8616, Kite 8639, Mercy 8650, Seme 8673

Texas: ADR 8693, AMR/American 8703, Anderson 8704, Bodhi 8732, Central 8766, di 8812, Enrico 8839, Esping 8841, Fair 8844, Hill 8937, Hofstetter 8943, Holmes 8947, Kelley 8984, King 8994, Knox 8999, MacDonald 9031, Parks 9115, Roosth 9160, Rubenstein 9167, Sanguinetti 9172, Thompson 9234, Thorne 9235, Wal-Dot 9256, Works 9293, Wynne 9296
Vermont: Harper 9373, Stokes 9385
Virginia: Collins 9424, Hughes 9474, Northern 9503, Rimora 9524
Washington: Foss 9598, Goodman 9608, Hickey 9622, Horn 9625, Schuler 9690, Wilson 9725, Worthington 9729
West Virginia: Brown 9739, Logan 9756
Wisconsin: Hicks 9840, Jacobus 9849, Phipps 9903, Pritchett 9906, T 9945
Wyoming: Richardson 9983

Farmlands

Minnesota: Farmers 4679
Pennsylvania: Brooks 7899
Texas: Behmann 8725
Vermont: Castanea 9368

Female adults

Alabama: Black 12, Ireland 39
Arkansas: Olds 210
California: **Cantor 375**
Connecticut: Fippinger 1450
District of Columbia: Jovid 1817
Georgia: Abreu 2431
Illinois: Family 2864, Meyer 3106
Kentucky: Killian 3670
Maryland: No 3927
Nebraska: Midlands 5104
New York: **Sparkplug 6830**
North Carolina: Glenn 7111
Ohio: **Brush 7338**
Tennessee: **Fugitive 8618**
Texas: **Chrest 8770**
Virginia: **Delmar 9429**
Wisconsin: Inbusch 9847, Marshfield 9878

Female children and youth

Alabama: Black 12, Ireland 39
Arkansas: Olds 210
California: Giles 554, **Girls 559**, Three 1116
Connecticut: Curran 1427
Delaware: Remmer 1726
Florida: Bell 1882, Tupperware 2379
Georgia: Abreu 2431
Illinois: Bulkley, 2765, Family 2864, Meyer 3106
Kentucky: Killian 3670
Maryland: O'Neil 3930
Michigan: Holden 4467
Missouri: **Bohm 4871**
Nebraska: Midlands 5104
New York: Henshel 6192, **Kathwari 6286**, Patrina 6579, Speranza 6836, Washington 6946
North Carolina: Glenn 7111, Ketchum 7146, Strowd 7258
Ohio: **Brush 7338**, Sandfair 7569
Pennsylvania: Carita 7915, Child 7923, Murphy 8185, Valentine 8328
Rhode Island: Coes 8396
Texas: Cariker 8762, Meyerson 9062
Vermont: Harper 9373
Virginia: **Delmar 9429**
Washington: **Singh 9695**
Wisconsin: Lakeview 9868, Marshfield 9878
Wyoming: **Schultz 9986**

Female infants and toddlers

Alabama: Ireland 39
Arkansas: Olds 210
Georgia: Abreu 2431

Kentucky: Killian 3670
Nebraska: Midlands 5104
New York: Patrina 6579
North Carolina: Glenn 7111
Pennsylvania: Child 7923
Tennessee: **Fugitive 8618**
Wisconsin: Marshfield 9878

Female seniors

Massachusetts: Newburyport 4222

Female young adults

Alabama: Ireland 39
District of Columbia: Jovid 1817
Georgia: Abreu 2431
Illinois: Family 2864
Indiana: Pulaski 3432
Kentucky: Killian 3670
Minnesota: Wells 4811
New York: Patrina 6579, Washington 6946
Ohio: **Brush 7338**, Walker 7630
Pennsylvania: Child 7923, Mill 8172
Rhode Island: Wilson 8504
Tennessee: **Fugitive 8618**
Wisconsin: Marshfield 9878

Females

Alabama: Black 12, Ireland 39
Arizona: McKee 148
Arkansas: Olds 210
California: Atkinson 259, Banky 273, Bannerman 274, Baskin 281, Bobowski 324, Buell 357, Cannon 374, Clara 406, Dermalogica 451, Foundation 521, Frome 535, Gellert 550, **Linked 758**, Military 826, Shayne 1032, Swayne 1097, Three 1116, United 1136, **Wakerly 1150**
Colorado: Heider 1290
Connecticut: Brown 1413, Curran 1427, Fippinger 1450, Kaufmann 1495, Widows 1595
Delaware: Lightner 1699
District of Columbia: **Carter 1794**, Cornerstone 1798, Jovid 1817, Replogle 1831, Westport 1838
Florida: Carlton 1922, Thomas 2370, Tupperware 2379, Wilson-Wood 2408
Georgia: Abreu 2431, **Bancker-Williams 2440**, Zawadi 2622
Hawaii: Locations 2638
Idaho: Troxell 2688
Illinois: Alton 2706, Bulkley, 2765, Burt 2770, Delavan 2825, Family 2864, Frankel 2886, MacDonald 3068, New 3136, Sasco 3222
Indiana: Hillenbrand 3393
Iowa: **Wahlert 3544**
Kansas: Payless 3614
Kentucky: Kentucky 3669, Killian 3670
Maryland: Dockser 3849, No 3927, Warfield 3978
Massachusetts: **Blossom 4022**, Chickering 4046, Fassino 4086, Guttag 4109, Hogan 4132, Swan 4317, Upstream 4338
Minnesota: Bell 4638, Tamarack 4797, **Winds 4820**
Missouri: Butler 4880, Copaken 4888, Kauffman 4934
Nevada: C.A.N. 5142
New Jersey: Greetin 5377, Knight 5425, **Rippel 5510**, Spohler 5547, Waters 5571
New Mexico: **Angelica 5605**, Con 5611
New York: Agate 5649, Alexander 5654, **Eastman 5940**, **Engineering 5964**, **Flowering 6015**, Happy 6165, Henshel 6192, **Kathwari 6286**, Levy 6391, Mertz 6481, Metzger-Price 6483, Ostgrodd 6561, Patrina 6579, **Rao 6645**, Roche 6678, Rubin 6707, Scott 6761, Sorel 6826, Sperandio 6835, Speranza 6836, **Spirit 6839**, Wagner 6938
North Carolina: Glenn 7111, Mattison 7175, Niessen, 7200, Peeler 7207, Strowd 7258
Ohio: **Brush 7338**, Gay 7418, Rotterman 7564, Walker 7630
Oregon: Portland 7807, Wessinger 7826
Pennsylvania: **Arronson 7844**, Blue 7879, Carita 7915, Coffin 7930, Drueding 7966, Female 7990, Fierce

7992, Hilles 8057, Jordan 8082, Leeway 8118, Murphy 8185, Valentine 8328, Wurts 8370
Rhode Island: Pardee 8468, Sinclair 8488
Tennessee: **Fugitive 8618**
Texas: **Chrest 8770**, Dougherty, 8825, Kahn 8978, Lilly 9019, Reitch 9149, Smith 9207, Vaughan 9249, Waggoners 9255
Vermont: Harper 9373, Stokes 9385
Virginia: **Brown 9407**, Collins 9424, **Delmar 9429**, Greco 9463, Ivakota 9477
Washington: Arise 9562, Schaar 9689, Sondland 9700, True 9716
Wisconsin: Marshfield 9878, Steinle 9938
Wyoming: **Schultz 9986**

Festivals

Alabama: Caddell 19
Kentucky: Trim 3702
Nebraska: Owen 5108

Film and video

California: Bridges/Larson 343, Corwin 428, Dorskind 459, LEF 739, Pickford 927, Reitman 964, Stewart 1082, Winkler 1188, Zecca 1209
Colorado: Elizabeth 1263
Delaware: Cultures 1652, Tarrant 1758
Illinois: **Rosenmutter 3208**, Zaentz 3336
Kentucky: Kentucky 3669
Massachusetts: Melvina 4197
Minnesota: Bend 4639
New Jersey: Scire 5526
New York: **Eastman 5940**, Fraydun 6029, Gary 6060, Gesso 6075, Kirby 6313, Maslin 6448, Phalarope 6599, Planalp-Trevor 6609, Resnick 6663, Speranza 6836, **World 6994**
Ohio: Thendara 7616
Pennsylvania: Crawford 7944
Texas: Collins 8781
Virginia: R 9518

Financial counseling

California: Bank 272
Connecticut: Union 1590
Georgia: Rosen 2577
Illinois: Alliant 2702
Massachusetts: Middlesex 4203
New Jersey: Columbia 5301
Pennsylvania: Blue 7879
Texas: Boeing 8733
Virginia: Franklin 9452

Fire prevention and control

California: Levin 749, Project 942, Zurlo 1217
Connecticut: Antonacci 1395
Georgia: Greiner 2498
Illinois: Allen-Heath 2701, Heath 2962
Iowa: Ryan 3531, Schildberg 3532
Maine: Reny 3802
Minnesota: Midcontinent 4745
Missouri: Morgan 4963
Nebraska: Midlands 5104
Nevada: Close 5148
New Jersey: Selective 5528
New York: American 5663, Boustead 5769, Dobson 5921, Rheinstrom 6665
North Carolina: Shingleton 7241, Wells 7283
Ohio: Jennings 7466, Loeb 7504
Pennsylvania: Buck 7904, Burkholder 7907, Clark 7925, Columbia 7932, Lewis 8124, Nathan 8188, Whalley 8353
South Carolina: Cato 8516
Tennessee: Jordan 8636
Texas: Cogdell 8777, Overlake 9106, Wood 9290
Virginia: Greco 9463, Greensville 9464, Treakle 9543
Washington: Templin 9709
Wyoming: Johnson 9977

First aid training

Maryland: Humphreys 3885

Fishing and hunting

Missouri: Sayler-Hawkins 4993

Floods

New York: **Walsh/Alfred 6943**
Utah: Davis 9317

Folk arts

Georgia: Boone 2446
Pennsylvania: Pasquerilla 8204

Food aid

Arizona: Armstrong 97, Cadeau 104
Arkansas: Blue 189
California: Atkinson 259, Bancroft-Clair 270, Braddock 336, Buttonwillow 367, Cheeryble 390, Christian 401, Corwin 428, Kelly 697, Lemons 744, Mudd 851, Staples 1075, **Sunwest 1094**, Thrill 1117
Colorado: Caulkins 1245, Elizabeth 1263, Jacobs 1298, Spencer 1356
Connecticut: Gibor 1464, Kaufmann 1495, Schaeneman, 1560, Union 1590
Delaware: Palmer 1718, Rosenfeld 1732, **TeleTech 1761**, Trussell 1767
Florida: Baroco 1867, Caring 1920, Case 1925, Densch 1970, Gate 2034, Grossman 2068, Janke 2126, Kugelman 2161, Rinker 2287
Georgia: Boone 2446
Hawaii: Wong 2657
Illinois: Allen-Heath 2701, Bulkley, 2765, Epaphroditus 2857, Frisby 2893, Harczak, 2952, MacDonald 3068, Zaentz 3336
Kansas: Williams 3643
Louisiana: Broussard 3715
Maine: **Dugas 3776**
Maryland: Duncan 3851
Massachusetts: East 4075, **New 4220**, Ramlose 4257, Ramsey 4258, Vela 4341, Winning 4362
Michigan: Allen 4372, Briggs-Fisher 4397, Community 4411, Doll-Loesel 4433, Thompson 4593
Minnesota: Bend 4639, Edina 4672, Rosen 4782
Mississippi: Baird 4822
Missouri: Chod 4885, Mungenast 4966, Slusher 5009, Wolff 5039
Nevada: Dermody 5152, **Wood 5201**
New Mexico: Carlsbad 5608
New York: AGB 5650, American 5664, Anderson 5674, BTMU 5795, Dougherty 5928, Hahn 6156, **Posner-Wallace 6621**, Rheinstrom 6665, Samuels 6725, Stark 6846, Tuch 6915
North Carolina: Balin 7042, Coffey 7078, Elks 7089, Gambrill 7106, Griffin 7113
Ohio: Barron 7316, Smith 7598, Wagler 7629
Oregon: Charis 7748
Pennsylvania: Community 7933, Family 7988, Goshen 8025, Hoch 8060, Murphy 8185, Thomas 8316
South Carolina: Collins 8520, Hendricks 8527, Lutz 8533
South Dakota: Stearns 8575
Tennessee: Chrysalis 8598
Texas: Fowlston 8871, Hatfield 8922, Skokos 9200, South 9210, Williams 9281
Utah: Bastian 9304
Vermont: Altman 9364, Copley 9370
Virginia: Chainani 9417, Lane 9486
Washington: Bungie 9576, Fales 9594, Johnson 9633
West Virginia: Hoffmann 9749, Hott 9753

Food banks

California: Brewster 341, Chizen 397, Combs-Hughes 419, Crummer 436, Dermalogica 451, Dickinson 453, Eriksen 484, Fast 498, Hagar 591, Kieve 703, Malachowsky 786, Mazda 810, Roche 979,

Sawchuk 1010, Schulte 1018, Stellar 1080, **Sunwest 1094**
Colorado: Connor 1250
Connecticut: Chaikin-Wile 1417, Union 1590
Delaware: Schwalbach 1739, **TeleTech 1761**
District of Columbia: Westport 1838
Florida: Couch 1953, Crane 1955, Goody 2049, Hardison 2081, Lelash 2178, Moore 2217, Olsen 2240, Rogers 2291, Swisher 2361, Thurman 2375
Georgia: Price-Campbell 2570, Smith 2586
Hawaii: Armstrong 2624
Illinois: Cafaro-Livingston 2772, Citadel 2791, Cowlin 2814, Eckert 2843, Heath 2962, Millard 3109, Shodeen 3246, Smysor 3255
Indiana: Kuhne 3409, MutualBank 3421
Iowa: GuideOne 3503
Kentucky: Namaste 3682
Maine: Henry 3782
Maryland: Moore 3917
Massachusetts: Easthampton 4076, Hauben 4120, MutualOne 4216, Vela 4341
Michigan: Barstow 4385, Delano 4426, McDole 4507
Minnesota: Edina 4672, Tennant 4798
Missouri: Hofheimer 4929, **Maor 4952**, Wolff 5039
Montana: Gallagher 5052, Gerhart 5053
Nevada: **A 5131**, Barker 5136, Dermody 5152, Pinnacle 5183
New Hampshire: von 5237, Woodbury 5238
New Jersey: Avalo 5254, Conant 5302, Devine 5317, Ragan 5507
New York: Balbach 5707, Barnwood 5718, Clemente 5850, **Farkas 5988**, Still 6866, Wachenheim 6935
North Carolina: Piedmont 7209, Shugart 7242, Wells 7283
Ohio: Conlogue 7359, Danis 7371, Ferry 7396, Hampson 7436, Kisker 7479
Oklahoma: Drabek 7673, Howard 7688, Parman 7713
Oregon: Coit 7751, Kinnie 7783, Saling 7811
Pennsylvania: Adams 7836, Community 7933, Gauss 8014, Merwin 8170, Patterson 8205, Remmel 8235, Tabas 8312
Rhode Island: Janci 8428, Kimball 8434, York 8507
South Carolina: Verhagen 8547
South Dakota: Houston 8567
Tennessee: Kennedy 8638, **Louisiana-Pacific 8644**
Texas: Amarillo 8697, Fleming 8860, Howard 8955, Johnson 8969, Lange 9008, Lesley 9013, MacDonald-Peterson 9032, Riter, 9154, Roosth 9160, South 9209, Williams 9280
Virginia: Better 9396, Franklin 9452, Markel 9498
Washington: Hansen 9615, Horn 9625
West Virginia: Bowers 9738
Wisconsin: Caritas 9791, Weyers 9959

Food delivery

Alabama: Sexton 63
Arizona: McKee 148
California: Coleman 416, Fusenot 541
Colorado: Jacobs 1298
Connecticut: Finn 1449, Union 1590
Delaware: Bauer 1616, Berning 1620
Florida: Couch 1953, Tippett 2376
Idaho: Ambrosiani-Pastore 2663
Maryland: Cole 3839, Ten 3963
Michigan: Dana 4419
Missouri: Curry 4892
New York: Cohen 5859, Maslin 6448, Milton 6497
North Carolina: Herndon 7125, Kennedy 7145, Shugart 7242, Sloan 7246, Wibel 7287
Ohio: Freygang 7410, Walker 7630
Oklahoma: Livengood 7698
Pennsylvania: Hoch 8060, Williams 8357
Texas: South 9209, Toomim 9239, Wheeler 9274, Whitley 9276
Virginia: Franklin 9452
Washington: DeFalco 9585

Food security

Massachusetts: **New 4220**

Foreign policy

Delaware: Cultures 1652
Illinois: Edgerly 2847

Forest preservation

California: Jeangerard 661, Stewart 1083
Massachusetts: King 4156, Mirak 4204
North Carolina: Post 7213
Ohio: Davey 7373
Pennsylvania: Brooks 7899
Washington: Nysether 9671
Wisconsin: Tellier 9946

Foster and adoptive children

California: Solano 1063
Washington: Foss 9598

Foster care

California: Arlene 252, Solano 1063
Florida: Beauregard 1878
Massachusetts: Alden 3999
Michigan: Speckhard-Knight 4574
New York: Sharon 6787, Zyman 7036
Washington: Foss 9598

Foundations

Alabama: Trippe 71
Arizona: Berlin 101, Community 108, Knisely 138, Sturges 176, Ullman 177, Valley 178
Arkansas: Oliver 211
California: Adams 228, Arata 248, Avery-Tsui 261, **Beagle 286**, Becker 291, Becker 292, Bekins 294, Beller 297, Briskin 346, Butte 366, Chan 387, Corday 426, Cush 437, Dwyer 468, Eleven 476, Epstein/Roth 483, Fat 499, Fliesbach 512, Fritz 534, Gifts 553, Gordon 573, Gordon 574, Hawley 605, Hellman 614, J. 653, Jones 673, Jorgensen 676, Juda 681, Kabcenell 685, MacCready 778, Magowan 782, Millstreet 835, Mondavi 843, Morgan 846, Nasaw 858, **Preuss 935**, RA5 946, Rediger 960, Reveas 967, Rishwain 974, Santa 1003, Smith 1053, Smullin 1060, Srivastava 1072, Stafford 1074, Thagard 1109, Tuffli 1134, Von 1148, Wagner 1149, Walther 1154, Wren 1199
Colorado: Ballantine 1226, Elf 1262, Grosvenor 1282, Hoag 1293, Ladd 1310, **National 1330**
Connecticut: Brace 1410, DeLuca 1431, Howard 1484, Kendall 1498, Macauley 1514
Delaware: 1916 1605, Anbinder 1611, Bartlett 1615, Bharat 1621, Brown-Whitworth 1632, Haldan 1676, Klein, 1694, McIntosh 1705, Milano 1710, Nelson 1714, Replogle 1728
District of Columbia: Monarch 1823, Rubenstein 1833
Florida: Beauregard 1878, Bell 1883, Coulter-Jones 1954, Duckwall 1982, Dyer 1985, Echevarria 1987, Hill 2097, Hill 2098, Hufty 2114, Lewis 2182, Life's 2184, Lipton 2185, MIDA 2212, Minto 2216, Morrison 2222, Reinhold 2280, Rubens 2301, Scherr 2316, Sender 2323, Sierra 2336, Sunburst 2359, Taylor 2366, Weiller 2393, Weintraub 2395, Wolf 2410
Georgia: Broadfield 2449, Davison 2470, DeLoache 2471, Georgia 2485, Hodge 2506, Joyce 2527, Rockdale 2576, Whitehead 2610, Woodcrest 2616
Hawaii: Frost 2632, Kahiau 2636, Wong 2656
Idaho: Dumke 2668, Golden 2672, Simplot 2685
Illinois: Abelson 2692, Argo 2714, Bishop 2743, Ceres 2779, Citadel 2791, Corbett 2808, Corbett 2809, Danielson 2823, Denny 2828, Everett 2861, Fischer 2874, Flinn 2875, Funk 2897, Good 2923, Hanson 2949, Howard 2981, Jocarno 3000, Karasik 3006, **Lindon 3054**, Marcum 3076, McLaughlin 3095, McNally 3097, McNulty 3099, Meier 3101, **Meyers 3107**, Millard 3110, Pepper 3167, Perkins 3169, Ruttenberg 3218, Sasco 3222, Spencer 3258, Warner 3310

Indiana: Custer 3366, Eskenazi 3377, Harlan 3391, Hillenbrand 3393, Hulman 3396, J. 3400, McKinney 3416, Stamm 3456, Welter 3465, Weston 3467
Iowa: Gaedke 3495, Grubb 3502, Ryan 3531, Tomson 3537, Weathertop 3545
Kansas: Atterbury 3554, Davis 3571, DeVore 3573, Jeffcoat 3588, Middlekauff 3603, Mistler 3606, Stolzer 3630, Weber 3640
Kentucky: Boone 3649, Jones 3667
Louisiana: Huie-Dellmon 3729, Pugh 3747, Selber 3751
Maine: Alfond 3764, Lynam 3788, Narragansett 3794, Quesada 3800
Maryland: Anderson 3814, Baker 3815, Baltimore 3817, Broadus 3829, Kay 3892, Mann-Paller 3908, O'Neil 3930, Pearlstone 3934, Shapiro 3949, Silber 3952, Slavin 3954
Massachusetts: Altamira 4001, Barstow 4013, Dalessandro 4063, Davoli 4065, DWSS 4073, Felix 4089, Hagler 4111, Jefferson 4142, Kidder 4152, Ladd 4163, Shanklin 4288, Toocap 4330, Weiner 4355, Whittemore 4359
Michigan: Andersen 4377, Barton-Malow 4386, Dart 4421, Delong-Sweet 4427, Farver 4441, Jospey 4473, Kalamazoo 4477, Kantzler 4478, Lee 4491, McDole 4507, Nickless 4522, Padnos 4529, Peak 4536, Pitt 4540, Schmuckal 4559, St. 4576, Vicksburg 4606, Zimmerman 4620
Minnesota: Bumgarner 4649, Chadwick-Loher 4655, Hegardt 4710, Kinman-Oldfield 4723, Morning 4748, Radichel 4765, Remick 4773, Sayer 4786, Terhuly 4799, **Trust 4802**
Missouri: Forster-Powers 4911, Oppenheimer 4973, Portman 4981, Price 4982, South 5011, Turner 5025
Montana: Taylor 5064
Nebraska: Farr 5079, Heuermann 5092, Lienemann 5100, Nelson 5106, Steinhart 5121, Walker 5126
Nevada: **Do 5153**, Petersen 5181, Peterson 5182, Pinnacle 5183, To 5193
New Hampshire: Jameson 5215, Landecker 5217, Lynch 5221
New Jersey: Bauer 5257, Blue 5268, Brooks 5274, Cantor 5285, CKT 5297, Dietze 5320, Dreman 5326, Engel 5335, Fux 5359, Kampen 5413, Katz 5414, Kontos 5430, Kroon 5433, Levine 5446, Pasternak 5490, Previti 5506, Spruce 5548, Twin 5563, Yoh 5597
New Mexico: **Angelica 5605**
New York: Achilles 5641, American 5663, American 5664, Anderson 5674, Archangel 5685, Balbach 5707, Birchrock 5749, Bovin 5770, Cathedral 5822, Ciampa 5845, Cole 5868, Cutco 5890, De 5904, Gaffney 6049, Gallagher 6051, Goldenson-Arbus 6094, Greentree 6135, Grubman 6147, Harris 6172, Heller 6187, Hiler 6207, Hirsch 6211, Hogan 6217, Imago 6239, Issroff 6251, Johnson 6270, Kiernan 6306, Marshall 6445, Marshall 6446, McCormick 6460, Michaels 6488, Monaghan 6502, Newman 6530, Parke 6576, Performing 6586, Peterson 6592, Peterson 6593, Pittman 6608, Price 6627, REBNY 6656, Rothblum 6701, Rothenberg 6702, Savitz 6734, Shetty 6793, Singer 6806, Sternberg 6863, SVM 6886, **Swett 6888**, Tahari 6890, Touradji 6903, Uihlein 6919, Vance 6926
North Carolina: Bell 7048, Cato, 7071, CJB 7076, KPB 7151, Lerner 7160, Moore 7188, Piedmont 7209, Robinson 7225, Rostan 7232, Sherrard 7240
Ohio: Bates 7317, Chaney 7349, Conn 7360, Covelli 7365, DeHoff 7376, Faber 7392, Fitton 7402, Fleischmann 7404, Gardner 7417, Knoll 7483, Miller 7526, Milliron 7529, Myers 7535, Rosenthal 7563, Seasongood 7582, Thompson, 7617, Turben 7622, Wightman-Wieber 7636, Young 7652
Oklahoma: Goddard 7684, Miller 7708, Weber 7730
Oregon: Morey 7801, Silver 7817, Stewart 7822
Pennsylvania: Baekgaard 7850, Black 7875, Boardman 7881, Breedlove 7890, Grumbacher 8028, Jackson 8078, Lamb 8106, Levis 8122, Lockhard 8130, Perelman 8210, Schoonmaker 8260, Schwartz 8265, Smith 8280, Velma 8330, Weiler-Miller 8348

Rhode Island: Bersted 8388, Greene 8413, Heydt 8419, Hosser 8424, McWethy 8453, **Schoellkopf 8482**
South Carolina: Chapman 8517, Collins 8520, Near 8536, Stringer 8543
South Dakota: Cindy 8557, Elmen 8560, Peterson 8572
Tennessee: Cartinhour-Woods 8597, Doochin 8605, Eskind 8613, McGehee 8648, New 8654, Rose 8667, Sasco 8669, Sohr 8676
Texas: Aragona 8706, Ash 8709, Bodhi 8732, Collins 8781, **Coneway 8783**, Cook 8786, Daniel 8797, Dedman 8807, Fennell 8849, Fuller 8882, Genecov 8886, Graham 8896, Hegi 8926, Hord 8950, Kaplan 8979, Levy 9014, MacDonald 9031, McDonald 9051, McLaughlin 9053, Meyerson 9062, Mosbacher 9075, Peine 9123, Rosenberg 9162, Sparks 9211, Texas 9233, Wright 9295
Utah: Harman 9328, Mower 9341
Virginia: Banks 9390, Bruhn-Morris 9408, Bryant 9409, Catesby 9415, Dundas 9438, Grandis 9462, Lee-Jackson 9488, Petersburg 9511, **Price 9516**, Valentine 9545, VuBay 9548
Washington: Cowles 9582, Crete 9583, Fletcher 9597, Furnessville 9602, Heidner 9618, Hyde 9627, Patel 9675, Schaar 9689, Sondland 9700
West Virginia: Chambers 9742, Driehorst 9743, Fine 9745
Wisconsin: Bluemke 9785, Davis 9802, Erdman 9816, Gordon 9830, Gordon 9831, Hartwig 9836, **Helios 9838**, Highlands 9841, Huiras 9844, Lutsey 9873, Marcus 9877, Mason 9880, Olson 9898, Peterson 9901, Pritchett 9906, Thompson 9947, Weyers 9959, Woodtrust-Bell 9963
Wyoming: C 9966, Dragicevich 9969, Dubois 9970, Ellbogen 9971, Guthrie 9972, StoneRiver 9991, Tate 9995

Free goods distribution

New York: **Haven 6178**

Freedom of association and expression

Illinois: Chicago 2787, Lehman-Stamm 3045
New York: Jennings 6259

Freedom of information

New York: Jennings 6259

Freedom of religion

New York: Anderson-Rogers 5676

Gardening

Florida: Wright 2415
Illinois: Lebus 3043, McCormack 3086
Massachusetts: Fessenden 4090
New York: **Burpee 5802**, Smith, 6816
Pennsylvania: Hartfield 8041, Pogo 8221
Utah: SmartGo 9354

Gay men

Alabama: Black 12

Genealogy

New York: Scott 6761

Genetic conditions and birth defects

Connecticut: Kay 1496
Georgia: Health 2504
Illinois: Cowlin 2814
Massachusetts: Alden 3999, PerkinElmer 4238
New Jersey: Covance 5305
New York: Hallingby 6160
Pennsylvania: Bon-Ton 7884

Texas: Halperin 8912

Geology
Washington: Seager 9692

Geriatrics
California: Harris 601
Colorado: Burt 1244
Florida: Herrin 2091
Illinois: Christiansen 2790
New Jersey: **Rippel 5510**
New York: Diamondston 5914
Ohio: Steinmann 7603
Pennsylvania: Tabas 8312
Texas: Petty 9126
Virginia: Charles 9418

Gerontology
Florida: Kane 2137
New Jersey: **Rippel 5510**

Gift distribution
Texas: King 8992

Gifted education
Iowa: Cole-Belin 3480
Michigan: Andrah 4378
New York: ALG 5658

Golf
California: Corde 427, Mickelson 825, Zwick 1218
Florida: Blanton 1892
Illinois: Saliba 3221
Iowa: Henry 3505, R 3529
Massachusetts: Easthampton 4076
Michigan: Roscommon 4552
New York: Bank 5710, Marshall 6446
North Carolina: Piedmont 7209
Tennessee: Wilt 8687
Texas: USD 9245, Westcott 9273

Goodwill promotion
California: **Cienega 404, Indo-American 651**
Florida: **Hsu 2112**
New Jersey: **Daft 5310**
New York: **American 5669, Tang 6891**

Graduate and professional education
Arizona: Johnson 135, Margolis 144, Pierce 156
California: Atkinson 259, Bach 263, Brunswick 354, Joy 677, Kanel 688, Olson 879, **Reddy 958**
Colorado: Beren 1233, Heider 1290, Trueblood 1371, White 1378
Connecticut: Lavietes 1505, Nirenberg 1534, Patricelli 1541
Delaware: Wang 1773
District of Columbia: **Dingwall 1804**
Florida: Blanksteen 1891, Forbes 2008, Givens 2038, Grader 2054, Greenblatt 2063, Halbrook 2073, Hardison 2081, Kuriansky 2162, Millsaps 2214, Nelson 2230, Price 2267, Sharaby 2329, Smith 2342, Stewart 2351, Sun, 2358, Thompson 2372
Georgia: Churches 2461, Georgia 2484, Stahl 2588, Storey 2589
Hawaii: **Shiraki 2648**
Illinois: Bere 2734, Chapin-May 2782, **Combs 2800,** Cronk 2817, Dowdle 2834, Grossinger 2933, Keller 3010, Leibowitz 3046, OSA 3157, Peters 3172, **Rosenmutter 3208**
Indiana: Bos 3347, Duneland 3372, Hulman 3396, Seymour 3448
Iowa: Andringa 3470, Rohde 3530, Schildberg 3532

Kansas: Merrill 3602, Scroggins 3624
Kentucky: Boone 3649, GHH 3658, **Magee 3674**
Louisiana: Live 3734
Maryland: Ammerman 3813, Rhona's 3939
Massachusetts: Mavrogenis 4192, Walsh 4348
Michigan: Betten 4390, Christian 4408, DeKock 4425, DeVlieg 4428, Kellogg 4482, McDonald 4508, McNally 4510, Roscommon 4552, Schmuckal 4559, Schwarcz 4560, Scully 4561, Sehn 4563, Springview 4575, Zondervan 4621
Minnesota: Desiring 4668, Kellogg 4722, **Wagner 4804**
Mississippi: Biloxi 4824, Florence 4836
Missouri: Barrows 4864, Cornelsen 4889, Fabick 4907, St. 5012, Wolff 5040
New Hampshire: Martin 5222
New Jersey: Armour-Lewis 5251, **Billig 5265,** Broomfield 5275, **Greenblatt 5376,** Verhalen 5568, Woolley-Clifford 5594
New Mexico: Gumbo 5617
New York: Cohen 5857, Family 5984, Ferguson 5999, French 6032, Heisler 6185, Hennessy 6191, HF 6203, Himelberg 6210, Horowitz 6225, JI 6260, Keller-Shatanoff 6297, **Klagsbrun 6318,** Lachman 6356, **Laerdal 6358,** Lopatin 6412, MacArthur 6429, Nussbaum 6545, Palmer 6572, Phillips 6600, Post 6622, Resnick 6663, Rhodes 6666, Rifkind 6670, Rose 6684, Schaffer 6737, Schwalbe 6751, **Stein 6855,** Switzer 6889, Viola 6930, Yosef 7011, **Ziv 7030**
North Carolina: Bolick 7056, Cannon 7067, Edgar 7088, Everett 7093, Gambrill 7106, Marlboro 7169, Nivison 7201, Pratt 7214, Rogers 7228, Smith 7248, Sutcliffe 7262
Ohio: Gimbel 7424, Glidden 7427, Pott 7549, Steinmann 7603, Tuscora 7624
Oregon: Leonard 7789
Pennsylvania: Beacon 7856, Charlestein 7920, Clareth 7924, Cornerstone 7936, Dinardo 7960, Every 7986, Gilmore 8017, Hill 8055, Jackson 8078, Kelley 8091, Nesh 8191, Reese 8232, Schautz 8257, Stein 8299, Sweigart 8311
Rhode Island: Felicia 8406, Mulligan 8457, N. 8459, Pardee 8468
South Dakota: Houston 8567
Tennessee: **Belz 8585,** Community 8601, Rucker-Donnell 8668
Texas: Brochstein 8746, Cox 8790, Flowers 8862, Fruehauf 8879, Healthcare 8924, Howard 8955, Johnson, 8971, **McCreless 9049,** Ray 9144, Raygar 9145, **Ryrie 9169,** Schissler 9179, Walls 9257, Wells 9271, Woltman 9288, Wynne 9296
Utah: Cumming 9316
Virginia: Denit 9430, **Foundation 9450,** Greensville 9464, Pensmore 9509
Washington: Coulter 9581, Hansen 9615, Kawabe 9642, Longbrake 9655
West Virginia: Bowen 9736, Minor 9761, Stout 9769
Wisconsin: Birnschein 9783, Fromm 9823, **Helios 9838,** LUX 9874, Seeds 9925, Styberg 9942

Green building
Texas: Boeing 8733

Group homes
Virginia: Ratner 9521

Health
Alabama: Anderson 6, Birmingham 11, Black 12, Brinkley 15, Brown 16, Cooper 23, Friedman 27, King 43, King 44, Kirkland 45, Mitchell 50, Phifer, 54, Rikard 59, Viro 73
Alaska: **Nash 90**
Arizona: Adelante 93, Armstrong 97, Cadeau 104, F2 117, Fuite 121, Grossman 130, Hughes 130, Johnson 134, Louis 142, Napier 152, Picerne 155, Pierce 156, Powell 157, Rothschild 162, Rubeli 163, Schlein 165, Schmidt 166, Williams 182

Arkansas: Bodenhamer 190, Hennessy 198, Hickingbotham 199, Merkle 203, Morris 205, Nabholz 208
California: Ach 226, Ackerman 227, Amin 240, Amin 241, Arata 248, **Asia 257,** Atkinson 259, Baker 264, Banky 273, Belle 296, Bernstein 307, Boukai 334, Bradford 337, Breslow 340, Broder 348, Brotman 351, Bryan 355, Bucolo 356, **Bull 358,** Burrows 363, California 370, Cantor 375, Cavaricci 381, Chisick 395, Chitjian 396, Chizen 397, Church 403, Collier 417, Community 420, Community 421, Confetti 422, Corwin 428, Crummer 436, Davies 444, Davis 445, Del 449, **Delzell 450,** Downing 462, Dwelle 467, Ebell 471, Endurance 482, Everest 488, Feder 501, Feintech 502, Fox 525, Frome 535, Fuller 538, Fusenot 541, Garabedian 545, Garaventa 546, Gellert 550, George 551, Ginder 558, **Girls 559,** Glazer 561, Goldstein 569, Grey 583, Gross 587, Hagopian 592, Hakka 593, Harris 601, Hayman 606, Health 608, Heller 613, Hellman 614, Herman 617, Hochman 626, Hodges 627, Hoefer 628, Hollywood 630, Huber 638, Huntington 642, **International 652,** Jesy 664, Johnson 667, Johnson 669, Jones 673, Kelly 697, Kirkorian 709, Kreitzberg 717, Lake 727, Latkin 731, Laurance 732, Lavine 733, Lebherz 735, Lewis 754, Liautaud 755, Livingston 761, Louie 770, Lyman 774, Mae 780, Majestic 784, Mangold 789, March 791, Marcil 793, Margolis 796, Mashhoon 804, McDaniel 812, McDaniel 813, Meister 821, Michaud 824, Moskowitz 849, Nickoll 867, Nima 868, Olander 878, Onehope 881, Ontario 882, Palo 900, Pardee 902, Parvin 905, Payne 910, Pearlstein 911, **Peszynski 917,** Price 938, Price 939, **Quiksilver 945,** Rady 949, Rallis 951, Rapport 954, Rar 955, Rees 961, Reitman 964, Rest 966, **Rieger 971,** Roche 979, Rossi 989, Rotasa 991, Rubin 992, Russell 995, Santa 1003, Sawchuk 1010, **Saya 1011,** Scherr 1014, Shenandoah 1033, Silicon 1038, Skowronski 1045, Smith-Walker 1057, Smittcamp 1059, Smullin 1060, Sondheimer 1065, Spatz 1066, Stewart 1082, Stewart 1083, Strome 1089, **Sunwest 1094,** Swinerton 1098, Syar 1099, Tecumseh 1105, Thompson 1112, Tilley 1118, Uplands 1139, **Valenzuela 1143,** Von 1147, Weinberg 1164, Weisgerber 1165, Weiss 1166, Westphal 1177, Wilbur 1182, **Wilkinson 1183,** Wrather 1198, Yen 1201, Zacky 1205, Zacky 1206, Zecca 1209, Zurlo 1217
Colorado: Bhappu 1234, Bjorkman 1236, Blair 1237, Burt 1244, Comprecare 1249, Dorset 1259, Erion 1265, Family 1267, Flying 1272, Goodwin 1279, Growing 1284, Hamilton 1285, Harvey 1287, Hewit 1292, Joy 1301, Kroh 1309, Ladd 1310, Pluss 1337, **Someone 1354,** Stretesky 1360, Tappan 1363, Verdoorn 1372, Warner 1376, Wilson 1380
Connecticut: Albert 1389, Avery 1396, Baggins 1398, Baldwin 1399, Bowling 1409, Bradley 1411, Chelsea 1418, Diageo 1437, Donchian 1440, Finkelstein 1448, Floren 1451, Goldfarb 1466, Gross 1473, Gryphon 1474, Hall 1475, Harris 1478, Hastings 1479, Helping 1480, Huntington 1486, Jones 1489, Jones 1490, Jost 1492, Kaufmann 1495, Lee 1507, Mann 1519, Newtown 1532, Oberlander 1535, Patricelli 1541, Rapp 1548, RBS 1549, Robinson 1553, Salatto 1557, Savings 1559, **Shoemate 1569,** Sorenson-Pearson 1574, Thomaston 1581, UIL 1589, Union 1590, Velaj 1592, Wheeler 1594, Wiener 1596, Winokur 1597, Woodland 1599
Delaware: Anbinder 1611, Babcock 1612, Bailey-Stanford 1613, Bartlett 1615, Broder 1629, Brown 1630, Brown-Whitworth 1632, Cammarota 1637, Chaney 1640, Cohen 1643, CVW 1653, Dunn 1659, EON 1661, Farr 1662, Freedman 1665, Haldan 1675, Hoops 1682, Jockers 1687, Kerr 1692, Levin 1697, Martyn 1702, Mary's 1703, Milliken 1711, MMK 1712, Relgalf 1725, Russell 1735, Schiffman 1738, Sloane 1746, Sulentic 1752, Three 1765, Viridiun 1770, VWR 1772, Wender 1777

District of Columbia: Arnold 1787, Bloedorn 1790, Dart 1800, Davies 1801, Hanley 1814, Kolar 1818, Lemon 1819, Miller-Wehrle 1821, Rossotti 1832, Rubenstein 1833

Florida: 4 1840, Anderson 1845, Anderson 1848, Andreeff 1850, Archibald 1852, ATAP 1855, Baroco 1867, **Basser 1871**, Bastien 1872, Becton 1880, Bell 1883, Berkowitz 1886, Blank 1890, Brooke 1903, Brown 1906, Burnett 1910, Cape 1917, Capital 1918, Carrington 1923, Catalina 1928, Cedar 1930, Charlotte 1938, **Chenzyme 1939**, Childress 1942, Chowdhury 1943, Collins 1949, Coral 1952, Couch 1953, Crane 1955, Crutchfield 1957, Day 1965, Defeo 1968, Densch 1970, Diermeier 1976, Duckwall 1982, Dysimmune 1986, Ellis 1989, Ferguson 1999, Fish 2001, Fleischman 2003, For 2007, Ford 2010, Frankel 2018, Franklin 2020, Friedheim 2024, Garvy 2033, Gate 2034, Gelbart 2035, Goddard 2042, Godsey 2043, Golden 2046, Goodwin 2048, **Gordon 2051**, Grabe 2053, Graese 2055, Green 2061, Halperin 2076, Hardeman 2080, Hegamyer 2087, Held 2088, Higgs 2096, Hoornstra 2110, **Hsu 2112**, Isenberg 2121, Jacobson 2125, **Jenkins 2129**, Kane 2137, Kaulbach 2140, KBR 2142, King 2147, King 2148, KLM 2151, Kugelman 2161, Lazoff 2173, Lowry 2191, Mary 2198, Mb 2200, McDonald 2203, McNamara 2207, Millsaps 2214, Moore 2217, Morningstar 2218, Morris 2220, Noble 2233, Nommontu 2234, Owen 2243, Parish 2247, Phillips 2260, Price 2267, Propp 2269, Rich 2284, Rodgers, 2289, Rothschild 2300, Rubens 2301, Ruskin 2302, **Safenowitz 2307**, Samowitz 2311, Schultz 2319, Speranza 2344, Stafford 2346, Steele 2347, Sudakoff 2356, Taylor 2364, Thomas 2370, Thomsen 2373, Toral 2378, Turlington 2380, Vanneck-Bailey 2384, Wagmore 2391, Waugh 2392, Werner 2398, Wescustogo 2399, Westgate 2400, Westreich 2401, Wilson-Wood 2408, Zimmerman 2427

Georgia: Andrews 2434, Athens 2437, Chatham 2457, Cobb 2463, Colston 2464, Community 2466, Cooper 2469, Echlin 2472, Frank 2481, **Gage 2482**, Georgia 2484, Georgia 2485, Gilbert 2488, Gordy 2493, Graves 2496, Harrison 2502, Health 2504, Hodgson 2507, Holly 2509, Hooters 2510, Hoyt 2513, Irving 2521, Jeter 2524, Kahn 2529, Kids 2530, King-White 2532, Knox 2534, Langdale, 2537, Lee 2540, Looney 2542, Magnus 2543, Montgomery 2551, Nabors 2555, Noonan 2558, Orkin 2560, Oxford 2561, Pattillo 2563, Pilling 2567, Reynolds 2574, Solstice 2587, Terwilliger 2593, Waffle 2602, Ward 2605, Warren 2606, Warren 2607, Whitepath 2611

Hawaii: Baldwin 2625, Damon 2629, Locations 2638, Makana 2639, Moore 2643, Vidinha 2653, Wilcox 2654, Zierk 2661

Idaho: Angels 2664, Boise 2666, Good 2673, Hare 2675, Intermountain 2677, Whittenberger 2689

Illinois: Abelson 2693, Allen-Heath 2701, Amsted 2708, AptarGroup 2712, Bailey 2716, Barr 2720, Bates 2724, Bergstrom 2736, Bernoudy 2738, Best 2739, Block 2745, Boehl 2748, Borten 2750, Brenner 2756, Brunswick 2762, **Build 2764**, Burk 2768, Cain 2773, Carey 2775, Chambers 2780, Christiansen 2790, Clarks 2792, Community 2802, Community 2803, Considine 2804, Cooney 2806, Cronin 2816, Dancing 2822, Danielson 2823, Delavan 2825, Dick 2830, Doerr 2831, Dowdle 2834, Dunning 2841, Eisenberg 2850, Elebash 2852, Ellis 2853, Fields 2870, Foley 2876, Frank 2885, Frederick 2889, Galter 2899, Gardner 2905, Gidwitz 2913, Gray 2928, Hales 2941, Hanson 2950, Hary 2959, Hegeler 2963, Hoffer 2975, Hopper 2977, Ideal 2986, Jocarno 3000, Kainz 3004, Karasik 3006, Keeney 3007, Kemper 3014, Klosk 3020, Knight 3022, Koch 3025, Lancaster 3035, Landau 3037, **Lazzara 3042**, Lebus 3043, Levinson 3049, Livney 3056, Loudoun 3060, Loudoun 3061, Loudoun 3062, MacDonald 3068, Marchese 3075, Meusel 3105, Meyer 3106, Miller 3111, Nayak 3133, NCI 3134, Night 3140, North 3142, Oberweiler 3147, Osi 3158, Owen 3160,

Pawlowski 3165, Penrose 3166, Pitzman 3177, Pollack 3180, Reichert 3192, Richard 3195, Robb 3197, Rosenberg 3207, Sasco 3222, Schinasi 3225, Schneider 3228, Scrugli 3231, Seidler 3233, Shirley 3245, Shodeen 3246, Simpson 3248, Simpson 3249, Smallwood 3251, Smith 3252, Smithburg 3254, Staley 3262, Staley 3264, Taylor 3284, Trust 3294, Turner 3297, Twomey 3298, Ulm 3299, Von 3305, Warner 3310, Webb 3313, Wessel 3318, Will 3322, Wislow 3323, Witz-Mallinger 3324, Wolf 3325, Wright 3333, Zemsky 3337

Indiana: **Ackerman 3339**, Benton 3344, Blackford 3346, Branigin 3348, Clark-Morrill 3356, Community 3360, Community 3361, Community 3362, Community 3363, Decatur 3367, Dubois 3370, Dukes 3371, Duneland 3372, Fayette 3379, Greene 3390, Hoffman 3395, Huntington 3397, Jasper 3401, Jennings 3402, Jennings 3403, Magee-O'Connor 3414, **Mervis 3417**, Nugent 3425, Ohio 3427, PHP 3431, Raymond 3436, Roberts 3439, Scott 3446, Seger 3447, Shafer 3449, Smith 3453, Snyder 3454, TCU 3458, Vann 3461, Western 3466

Iowa: Burke 3477, Ellen 3489, Farver 3491, Gazette 3497, Grinnell 3501, Grubb 3502, K2 3515, McDonald 3520, Medical 3521, Muscatine 3523, R 3529, Tomson 3537, Toohey 3538, **Wahlert 3544**

Kansas: Cape 3563, Coffeyville 3566, Community 3567, DeVore 3573, Green 3583, Hopkins 3586, Insurance 3587, Kammco 3591, Kansas 3592, Legacy, 3595, Mann 3599, Payless 3614, Price 3616, Rathert 3617, Salgo 3621, Scott 3623, Scroggins 3624, Walsh 3638, Watson 3639, Weber 3640, Wiedemann 3642, Wood 3644

Kentucky: Dunbar 3653, Foundation 3655, GB 3657, Hayswood 3662, Keeneland 3668, Murry 3681, Reed 3688, Shapira 3693, Stock 3697, Taylor 3700, Trim 3702, Yeager 3710

Louisiana: Biedenharn 3713, DeGree 3721, Dujay 3722, Houseman 3728, Montan 3740, Noland 3743, Special 3754, Steinhagen 3755, Wetmore 3757

Maine: Boulos 3768, Davenport 3775, **Dugas 3776**, Kennebec 3785, Lafayette 3787, Messler 3790, MG 3791, Minshp 3793, Pond 3798, Red 3801

Maryland: AMDG 3812, Anderson 3814, Baltimore 3816, Baltimore 3817, Bank 3818, Berger 3821, Campbell 3831, Carol 3834, Cogan 3837, Daydreams 3845, Eccles 3853, Eliasberg 3854, Elsberg 3856, Feldman 3858, Fine 3861, Friedman 3866, Gewirz 3869, Halle 3878, Hobbs 3882, Hyman 3887, Izzo 3889, Kelly, 3893, Mangione 3907, Mitchell, 3916, Mullan 3920, Phase 3936, Schuh 3946, Silberman 3953, Slavin 3954, Ten 3963, Unger 3971, Widgeon 3983, Youth 3991

Massachusetts: 2 3992, Ansin 4003, Archibald 4005, Astra 4006, Behrakis 4015, Benson 4016, Boger 4023, Brooks 4028, Brown 4029, Bulger 4031, Cabot 4035, Casey 4039, Chartis 4044, Chicopee 4047, Chirag 4048, Cohen 4053, Cole 4054, Coolidge 4057, Crane 4058, Crowe 4061, Curvey 4062, Dalessandro 4063, Davoli 4065, Dedham 4067, East 4075, Easthampton 4076, Egan 4080, Elephant 4081, England 4083, Fessenden 4090, Francis 4095, Fraser 4097, **Galileo 4101**, Gloria 4104, Guttag 4109, Haley 4114, Harrington 4117, Hauben 4120, Haven 4122, Hopedale 4134, Horne 4136, Karas 4146, Kelsey 4148, Kenwood 4150, Kurian 4162, Langer 4166, Levy 4173, Makepeace 4186, Mank 4187, Michael 4202, Mohr 4206, Morse 4208, MutualOne 4216, Nelson 4219, Newburyport 4222, Noonan 4225, Novack 4226, O'Keefe 4229, Peoples 4237, PerkinElmer 4238, Permanent 4239, Reisman 4263, Rice 4265, Rockland 4267, Rodman 4269, Rollstone 4270, Rosse 4272, Sailors' 4276, Sandler 4278, Schechter 4281, SER 4286, Simoni 4296, Smith 4298, Solomont 4303, **Spero 4304**, Spoon 4305, Steiger 4312, Sullivan 4315, Tapper 4321, Tatelman 4323, Thee 4324, Tomfohrde 4329, Tye 4334, United 4337, Wapack 4350, Weld 4356,

Wells 4357, Wilcox 4360, Windhorse 4361, Zampell 4367

Michigan: Barron 4384, Barton-Malow 4386, Bierlein 4392, Bonder 4394, Branch 4396, Buist 4401, Carls 4404, Cebelak 4406, Community 4410, Community 4411, Delano 4426, Dinan 4431, DiPonio 4432, Dresner 4434, Fabiano 4438, Ford 4445, Four 4449, Gratiot 4459, Harris 4461, Kay 4480, Keller 4481, Kiwanis 4484, Kosch 4485, Lapeer 4490, Lois 4494, LoPrete 4496, M 4497, Mackinac 4499, McDole 4507, Meritor, 4511, Michigan 4514, Mills 4515, Morley 4518, Olds 4526, Paine 4531, Pardee 4533, Phantom 4538, Ryan 4555, Serra 4565, Shiawassee 4568, Sinai 4570, St. 4577, Stone 4581, Tassell-Wisner-Bottrall 4587, Trico 4596, **Triford 4597**, Van 4601, **Vattikuti 4605**, Vlasic 4607, Wetsman 4611, Zimmerman 4620

Minnesota: Albright 4625, Bailey 4633, Blank 4643, Cooke 4659, Cornwall 4660, Dyer 4669, Edina 4672, Erickson 4675, Faith, 4677, Felhaber, 4681, **Fingerhut 4683**, Good 4698, HJ 4714, Hognander 4715, Iversen 4717, Kellogg 4722, Louis 4731, Lukis 4732, Midcontinent 4745, Noreen 4750, Open 4756, **Porter 4763**, Radichel 4765, Rahr 4766, Rising 4775, Roberts 4778, Rose 4781, Schott 4787, Schulze 4788, Thorpe 4800, Walser 4807, Wedge 4810, Wells 4811, Weyand 4814

Mississippi: Brevard 4826, **Edwards 4833**, Golding 4838, King's 4845, Lower 4847, Phillips 4850, Taylor 4855

Missouri: Bakewell 4863, Bartlett 4865, Brace 4874, Brinklee 4876, Brown 4877, **Build-A-Bear 4879**, Butler 4880, Calkins 4881, Cinmar 4887, Dunn 4898, Edmonston 4900, Empson 4902, Gaylord 4914, Gaylord 4915, Gershman 4916, Neeb 4968, Oppenheimer 4973, Payne-Stewart 4976, Peculiar 4978, Prime 4983, Roman 4985, Saks 4990, Sayler-Hawkins 4993, Seiler 4997, Shepherd 5001, Shumway 5002, Sigma-Aldrich 5003, Siteman 5006, Stifel 5014, Tension 5019, Timmons 5021, Welch 5038, Wolff 5040

Montana: Montana 5060, Nance 5065

Nebraska: Ameritas 5067, Assurity 5068, Barklage 5071, Batchelder 5072, Beer 5073, Blair 5074, Farr 5078, Ferenc 5080, Friedland 5082, Hawkins 5089, Midlands 5104, Nelson 5106, Patrick 5109, Perkins 5111, Walker 5126, York 5129

Nevada: Anton 5133, Chami 5146, Geomar 5160, Kara 5168, Lusardi 5175, Moran 5178, Peterson 5182, Pretti 5184, To 5193, Vandevoort 5194

New Hampshire: Dunn 5212, Hunt 5214, Jameson 5215, Kimball 5216, Mascoma 5223, von 5237

New Jersey: A 5240, Alcon 5244, Amboy 5246, Avis 5255, Bauer 5257, Bloom 5267, Blue 5268, **Blue 5269**, Broomfield 5275, Chu 5294, Citta 5295, Columbia 5301, Covance 5305, Degnan 5315, Doll 5322, D'Onofrio 5324, Eisenberg 5331, Elizabethtown 5332, Engel 5335, Farris 5342, Feinstein 5343, Fisher 5347, Freedman 5351, Fux 5359, Giants 5369, Goldberger 5372, **Greenblatt 5376**, Greetin 5377, Gurwicz 5378, Heisen 5389, His 5395, **Integra 5400**, IV 5401, Kirby 5422, Knight 5425, **Knistrom 5426**, Knowlton 5427, Krupa 5434, Leavitt 5445, Mahan 5455, Marino 5457, Milano 5466, Miller 5468, Minio 5470, Navesink 5477, O'Neal 5481, Paragano 5488, Pinkin 5502, Ragan 5507, **Rippel 5510**, Rukh 5515, Russo 5517, Schimmel 5521, Scire 5526, Selective 5528, Sheridan 5533, Shilling 5534, Simon, 5537, Snyder 5540, **Southpole 5545**, Stanley's 5550, Tizzio 5559, Weintraub 5577, Wendel 5580, Weny 5581, Westfield 5582, Wicks 5584, Wilcox 5585, Wildwood 5586, Zissu 5602

New Mexico: Carlsbad 5608, Con 5611, **Daniels 5613**, Gumbo 5617, Quail 5622, Taos 5626

New York: A.B. 5632, Abramson 5640, Ades-Taub 5645, Agate 5649, AKC 5651, Allatt 5659, Allegany 5660, Antun 5681, Arcadia 5684, August 5698, Barbara 5713, Barham 5715, Baum 5722, Beard 5727, Beck 5728, Berkowitz 5739, Black 5754, Bogoni 5766, Bostwick 5767, Briar 5782, Brunie 5792, BTMU 5795, Burchan 5801, **Buster 5806**,

Cader 5807, Calder 5810, Chapman 5832, Cheatham 5836, Chervenak-Nunnalle 5839, Chess 5841, Children's 5842, Clemente 5850, **Cogitare 5855**, Cohen 5857, Cohen 5858, Cohoes 5865, Coleman 5870, Community 5872, Conley 5874, **Cote 5881**, Curtis 5889, Devine-Majors 5913, Diamondston 5914, Dibert 5915, Dworman 5938, EBA 5941, Ellman 5956, **Family 5983**, Fein 5992, Feinman 5994, Ferguson 5999, Ferriday 6000, Fink 6006, Finkelstein 6007, Fitt 6010, **Fitzgibbons 6011**, Fondation 6017, Fox 6022, **Frank 6026**, French 6032, Furman 6046, Furth 6047, Gaffney 6049, Gallagher 6051, Galvan 6053, Garber 6057, Gary 6060, Gemiluth 6068, George 6070, Gesso 6075, Gettinger 6076, Gilliam 6078, Gimbel 6079, Goldstone 6102, Gordon 6110, Gralnick 6121, Gramercy 6122, Grandison 6124, Grant 6129, Grinberg 6139, Handler 6162, Harmon 6168, Heilig 6183, Henkind 6190, Herringer 6196, High 6206, Hilliard 6208, Houseknecht 6226, Hoyt 6230, **Jabara 6254**, Jamakepe 6256, Katzman 6289, Keeler 6292, Kies 6307, Kimmel 6308, Klaus 6321, Klein 6325, Koha 6337, Krasne 6344, Krauss 6345, Kriser 6347, Kupferberg 6351, L 6353, Lachman 6356, Lane 6363, Lawrence 6369, Legacy 6373, Levine 6387, Levy 6391, Lieb 6398, Longhill 6411, Lorber 6413, Mack 6430, Maher 6434, Manocherian 6438, Mastrocola 6449, Meridian 6478, Merlo 6479, Messinger 6482, Metzger-Price 6483, **Milbank 6490**, Miller 6492, Mitchell 6499, Mozel 6512, Mule 6515, Neporent 6523, Newman 6534, O'Neil 6557, Peckham 6583, Perlman 6587, Perper 6588, **Peter 6590**, Pierce 6604, Pinkus 6607, Plymouth 6612, Polsky 6618, **Potts 6624**, Provident 6632, Quinn 6638, Ravitch 6651, Reich 6658, Reichert 6660, Rheinstrom 6665, RHR 6667, Roche 6678, Rose 6683, Rosenthal 6694, Rosenthal 6695, Rothenberg 6702, Russo 6711, Russo 6712, Ruth 6713, Salomon 6721, Schaefer 6735, **Schmeelk 6742**, Schonfeld 6746, Scott 6762, Seacoast 6766, Siegel 6797, Silverman 6801, Silverstein 6803, Skalny 6807, Sommer 6825, Sorensen-Siegel 6827, Spencer 6834, Sperandio 6835, Spiritus 6840, Starker 6847, Sternberg 6863, Stony 6868, Striano 6871, Stuart, 6873, Suwinski 6885, Tisch 6900, Tod 6901, Tribune 6909, Tytel 6917, **Usman 6921**, Utica 6922, Vogler 6932, Warwick 6945, Weill 6949, Weininger 6954, Wells 6964, Wohlgemuth 6984, Wolk 6987, Wong 6988, Wunsch 6996, Zeitz 7021

North Carolina: Agarwal 7039, Balin 7042, BB&T 7045, Bertsch 7050, Bettman 7051, Billingsley 7052, Bolick 7056, Brown 7059, Cannon 7067, Carroll 7068, Chatham 7074, Coate 7077, Coffey 7078, Duncan 7086, Evernham 7094, Family 7096, First 7097, Flowers 7099, Fortson 7100, Foster 7101, Gambrill 7106, Geschick 7109, Gordon 7112, Helton 7123, Jelm 7137, Judd 7139, Kassner 7141, Koons 7148, Kosloski 7149, **Kramer 7152**, Krost 7154, Ladane 7155, Live 7163, Lynum 7165, Marlboro 7169, Marsh 7170, Marsh 7171, Meyer 7183, Moseley 7194, Mosser 7195, North 7202, Outer 7204, Paddock 7206, Ragland, 7216, Rankin 7217, Richardson 7221, Robbins 7224, Robinson 7225, Robitaille 7226, Rostan 7232, Sanders 7234, Schmidt 7236, Shugart 7242, Strowd 7258, Stuart 7259, Vanderbilt 7273, Walters 7278, Way 7281, Williams 7289, Yost 7291

Ohio: Anderson 7305, Armington 7309, Athens 7311, Austin-Bailey 7312, Bates 7317, B-Brand 7318, Berke 7323, Bernard 7325, Bicknell 7327, Brethen 7331, Brooks 7335, Bryan 7339, Building 7340, Chaney 7349, CLH 7355, Community 7356, Community 7357, Conlogue 7359, Cooper 7362, Coressel 7364, Davey 7373, Defiance 7375, Dermitt 7378, Dorn 7380, **Elisha-Bolton 7387**, Eyman 7391, Firman 7400, Fishel 7401, Fletcher 7405, Frohman 7411, Gale 7414, Garcia 7416, Ginn 7425, Goerlich 7428, Gosiger 7429, Gross 7432, Hankins 7437, Haskell 7439, Hazelbaker 7441, Health 7442, **Highfield 7450**, Huntington 7460, Jenkins 7464, Jenkins 7465, Jordan 7471,

Knight 7482, Kramer 7484, Lawry 7491, Lazarus 7493, Leach 7494, Linnemann 7498, Lockwood 7502, Lukens 7507, Lungard 7509, Manley 7512, McCann 7519, Mead 7522, Messer 7524, Musson 7534, Myers 7535, Norris 7538, O'Neill 7542, Osteopathic 7545, Peoples 7546, Reisman 7556, Ridgecliff 7560, Sandfair 7569, Schottenstein 7574, Scion 7578, Sidwell 7592, Slitzer 7596, Smith 7598, Stein 7601, STERIS 7605, Taj 7611, Thendara 7616, TKBW 7619, Tuscarawas 7623, Tuscora 7624, Van 7626, Watson 7633, Williams 7638, Wilson 7642, Wyler 7647, Yeiser 7649, Young 7653

Oklahoma: Cherokee 7666, Chilton 7667, Gelvin 7682, Goddard 7684, Holliman 7687, Jones 7691, Kerr 7693, Kullgren 7696, Livengood 7698, Lolmaugh 7700, Oklahoma 7711, Pros 7715, Stone 7721, Warren 7729

Oregon: Brown 7744, Castle 7745, Charis 7748, Dubs 7760, Giustina 7767, Irwin 7777, Kinnie 7783, Klamath 7784, Knudson 7785, Mentor 7796, Metro 7798, Naumes 7804, Richardson 7808, Schmidt 7813, Wessinger 7826, Western 7829, White 7830

Pennsylvania: Auldridge 7846, Ayling 7849, Baker 7851, Bedford 7857, Bennett 7860, Bergstrom 7864, Berkowitz 7866, Betts 7869, Bienenfeld 7872, Bishop 7874, Blackhorse 7877, Blue 7879, Blue 7880, Bon-Ton 7884, Born 7885, Britton 7894, Brooks 7897, Bucks 7905, Cameron 7911, Carita 7915, Carlson 7916, Case 7918, Clark 7925, Clovis 7928, CNB 7929, Community 7933, Cozen 7941, Crawford 7944, Crebilly 7946, Davis 7951, Delaware 7953, DENTSPLY 7954, Dickson 7957, Dietz 7959, Donnally 7962, Donnelly 7963, Dozzi 7965, Drueding 7966, Eakins 7968, Edwards 7972, Edwards 7973, Elk 7975, Elkins 7976, Fair 7987, Fierce 7992, Fine 7994, First 7996, First 7997, Fountainhead 8004, Friends 8008, Frohring 8010, Gamber 8011, **Glendorn 8020**, Goldberg 8021, Grumbacher 8028, Hall 8037, Hankin 8038, Harsco 8040, Health 8048, Health 8049, Herndon 8051, Heyl 8052, Hodge 8061, Holden 8064, Honickman 8066, **Horner 8068**, Hulme 8069, Jackson 8077, Kahn, 8084, Katherine 8086, Katsaros 8087, Katz 8088, Katz 8089, Kinney 8092, Klein 8096, Leakin 8116, Lemole 8119, Mack 8136, Magee 8137, **Mango 8138**, Mason 8147, Mason 8148, Mason-Alleg 8149, Mayer 8152, McCune 8155, McKamish 8158, Mclelland 8162, Moffat 8175, Mukaiyama-Rice 8183, Murphy 8185, Mylan 8187, Neag 8189, Packer 8201, Penn 8208, Pfundt 8213, Pittsburgh 8215, Platt, 8220, Potter 8224, Quaker 8228, Rath 8231, Remmel 8235, Rider-Pool 8238, Ritter 8239, Rubin 8246, Saramar 8253, Schuylkill 8263, Shaner 8271, Snyder 8288, Stein 8299, Stewart 8301, Stott 8304, Strawbridge 8305, Tabas 8312, Teleflex 8314, Thompson 8317, Tippins 8318, Todi 8319, Tompkins-Broll 8320, Triple 8322, Victor 8332, Wachs 8336, Waldo 8340, Warburton 8342, Wasserott 8344, Weil 8346, Weiler-Miller 8348, Wenger 8352, Wimmer 8361, York 8374

Rhode Island: Arakelian 8381, Beck 8386, Bersted 8388, Bird 8389, Chace 8393, Charlton, 8394, Del 8401, Dwinell 8403, Fuller 8409, Halsted 8415, Hartman 8416, Heydt 8419, Horton 8423, Johnson 8430, Kimball 8434, Kingsbury 8435, Kupher 8437, Littlefield 8441, McWethy 8453, Noyes 8461, Pacifica 8464, Peacock 8469, Phillips 8472, Pillsbury 8473, Sachem 8479, Schwarz 8483, Sinclair 8488, Smith 8493, Sullivan 8494, Unfi 8498, Vanderpoel 8499, Washington 8500, Wells 8501, Wright 8506, York 8507

South Carolina: Eastern 8522, Near 8536, Verhagen 8547, Wyatt 8552

South Dakota: Barger 8555, Houston 8567, Miller 8570, Watertown 8576

Tennessee: **Belz 8585**, Boring 8590, Caldwell 8593, Community 8601, Ebert-Leblanc 8609, Eskind 8612, **Fugitive 8618**, Goldsmith 8622, Goodlett 8623, Gordon 8624, Ingram 8632, LDB 8642, McGehee 8648, McWherter 8649, Mick 8651, New

8654, Paddison 8655, Pfeffer 8659, Pickle 8660, Powell 8661, Proctor 8662, Restoration 8665, Rose 8667, Seidman 8672, Splawn 8677, Weiss 8684, Wilt 8687

Texas: Adam 8691, American 8699, AMR/American 8703, Anderson 8704, Arena 8707, Astin 8710, Ballard 8716, Bee 8723, Bergstrom 8727, Bernardin 8728, Boeing 8733, Booth 8734, Brass 8738, Brisley 8744, Brodsky 8747, Bromberg 8748, Brownsville 8752, Cambridge 8760, Central 8766, Chisholm 8769, Cielo 8771, Clear 8772, Clinedinst 8775, Cogdell 8777, Community 8782, **Conway 8783**, Corrigan-Goddard 8789, Deakins 8804, di 8812, Dobson 8820, Donnell 8821, Dougherty 8824, Esping 8841, Fabenco 8843, Fash 8848, Flowers 8862, Folsom 8863, Foundation 8869, Friedman 8876, Frost 8878, Fruehauf 8879, Garvey 8884, **Gilman, 8889**, Gottlieb 8894, Gray 8899, Hallberg 8911, Halperin 8912, Hardner 8918, Harrell 8919, Hawkins 8923, Hill 8937, Hillcrest 8939, Hoak 8941, Howard 8954, Joseph 8974, Kelley 8984, Knox 8999, Korell 9001, Lange 9008, Laredo 9010, LBJ 9011, Link 9020, Littauer 9021, Lowdon 9025, LSF 9026, McAllister 9046, Merfish-Jacobson 9058, Mischer 9067, Mitte 9069, Montgomery 9070, Morrow 9074, Mossy, 9077, Mummert 9079, Myers 9081, Navarro 9085, North 9089, O'Hare 9095, Opie 9099, Oppenheimer 9100, **Owusu 9107**, P 9108, Paris 9114, Parks 9115, **Partridge 9117**, Peine 9123, Penland 9124, Posey 9135, Prayer 9138, Quest 9142, Reilly 9148, Roosth 9160, Rosenthal 9163, Rowan 9166, Rust 9168, Sanguinetti 9172, Santander 9173, SCP 9185, Simpson-Omohundro 9196, Smith 9206, South 9209, Stephens 9217, Sterling 9218, Stevenson 9220, Tabani 9228, Texas 9231, Thorne 9235, Torrance 9241, Vaughan 9248, Vaughan 9249, Walls 9257, Webre 9266, Wells 9272, White 9275, Williams 9280, Woods 9291, Zale 9299

Utah: B. 9302, Bastian 9304, Dreamweaver 9320, Eskuche 9323, Green 9327, Kennecott 9333, Langdon 9336, Lindorf 9340, Odyssey 9342, **Skolnick 9352**, Utah 9361

Vermont: Altman 9364, Harper 9373, Holland 9375, Leboeuf 9379, Seventh 9384

Virginia: Banks 9390, Berni 9395, Better 9396, Birk 9398, Black 9399, Brink's 9406, Bruhn-Morris 9408, Bryant 9409, Buchanan 9410, Bw718 9412, Camp 9413, Chainani 9417, Collins 9425, Community 9426, Cooke 9427, Darden 9428, Donohue 9432, **Dorothy-Ann 9433**, Glasser 9459, Greco 9463, Hopkins 9472, Lacy 9485, Ludington 9495, Northern 9503, Praxis 9515, Pruden 9517, Rashti 9520, Richardson 9523, Shepherdson 9531, Short 9532, Strauch 9538, Stultz 9539, Treakle 9543, Zeiders 9557

Washington: Babare 9563, Babare 9564, Block 9570, Bulleri 9575, Bungie 9576, DeFalco 9585, Everett 9592, Fletcher 9597, Grousemont 9611, Hickey 9622, Jefferson 9630, Juniper 9640, Keller 9643, Kismet 9646, Korum 9648, Loeb 9654, Magdalen 9658, Muglia 9666, Nordstrom/Seifert 9668, Pointe 9679, Runstad 9686, **Singh 9695**, Skagit 9696, Thomson 9711, Thurston 9713, Titus-Will 9714, Welch 9721, **Wiebe 9723**, Wyman 9731, Zufall 9733

West Virginia: Brown 9739, Hott 9753, Logan 9757, Vecellio 9770

Wisconsin: Anderson 9773, Associated 9778, Aylward 9779, Cudahy 9800, Debbink 9804, Dohmen 9806, Domer 9808, Glendenning 9828, Gordon 9830, Grande 9832, Hicks 9840, Hunt 9845, Inbusch 9847, J.P.C. 9848, Jones 9854, Kenosha 9862, Manitowoc 9876, Meyer 9885, Modine 9889, Okray 9896, Pelz 9900, Plein 9904, RITE-HITE 9915, Roddis 9916, Rosemann 9919, Sartori 9921, Shannon 9927, Smith 9932, Steinle 9938, Stevens 9939, Stevenson 9940, Sub-Zero 9943, Uihlein 9950, Woodtrust-Bell 9963

Wyoming: C 9966, Hirschfield 9973, Riehm 9984, Storer 9992, Tate 9995

Health care access

Florida: Ruskin 2302
New Jersey: **Rippel 5510**
Pennsylvania: Blue 7879

Health care administration and financing

Arizona: Withycombe 184
California: Burbank 361, Coburn 411
Connecticut: Storr 1575, Thrall 1583
Florida: Brown 1905, Reinhold 2280, Stellar 2348
Illinois: Norgaard 3141
Indiana: Rinker 3438
Michigan: Thompson 4593
Oklahoma: Rathburn 7716
Pennsylvania: Coffin 7930
Rhode Island: Salerno 8480
Texas: Ash 8709, Keown 8986
Virginia: Good 9461

Health care clinics

Arizona: Sioles 169, Valley 178
Arkansas: Nabholz 208
California: Arbor 249, Dorskind 459, Folger 515, Georgina-Frederick 552, J. 653, Livingston 761
Colorado: Allen 1220, White 1378
Connecticut: Bannow-Larson 1400, Union 1590
Florida: Diane 1974, Jacobson 2125
Georgia: Hoyt 2514
Illinois: Kipper 3018, North 3142
Indiana: Duneland 3372, PHP 3431
Iowa: McDonald 3520
Maryland: Anderson 3814
Massachusetts: Clarke 4049, Poduska 4246
Minnesota: Bend 4639, Butzow 4651, Hegardt 4710
Montana: Gallagher 5052
Nevada: Castleman 5144
New Jersey: **Integra 5400**, Kolber 5429, Wilf 5588
New York: Anderson 5673, Bank 5710, BBL 5724, Coleman 5869, Lainoff 6359, Rose 6683, Rosen 6689
Ohio: Danis 7371, Howe 7455, Lang 7489
Pennsylvania: Blue 7879, Bon-Ton 7884
South Carolina: Bailey 8510
Tennessee: Foster 8616
Texas: AMR/American 8703, Long 9023, Sharma 9190, Smith 9206
Utah: Crawford 9314
Virginia: Collins 9424, Wiley 9551

Health care financing

Michigan: Mills 4515
Mississippi: Carothers 4827

Health insurance

Nebraska: Assurity 5068
Ohio: Austin-Bailey 7312
Pennsylvania: Blue 7879

Heart and circulatory system diseases

Alabama: Sexton 63
California: Bancroft-Clair 270, Dorskind 459, Gooding 571, Gordy 575, Gross 587
Connecticut: Thornton 1582
Delaware: **TeleTech 1761**
Florida: Bastien 1872, Capital 1918, Prutky 2270
Illinois: Bulkley, 2765, Goodstein 2924, Stuart 3273
Maryland: Cole 3839
Massachusetts: **Spero 4304**, Stare 4308, Thoracic 4326
Michigan: Barton-Malow 4386, Nartel 4521, Ratner 4548
Nebraska: Assurity 5068
New Jersey: Heart 5388, **Rippel 5510**, Snyder 5541
New York: Goldfarb 6095, JJC 6262, Seaman 6767, Utopia 6923
Ohio: Danis 7371, STERIS 7605

Oklahoma: Fleischaker 7679
Pennsylvania: Armstrong 7843, Blue 7879, Kynett 8105, Lamb 8107
Rhode Island: Geneen 8411, Peacock 8469
Texas: Fertitta 8852
Virginia: Peachtree 9508
West Virginia: Hewgill 9748, Vecellio 9770

Hematology

Delaware: 613 1606

Hemophilia

Connecticut: Colburn-Keenan 1421
South Carolina: Gleason 8524

High school equivalency

Minnesota: G&K 4691

Higher education

Alabama: Adams 3, Amos 4, Anderson 5, Anderson 6, Barkley 9, Blount 13, Boult 14, Brown 16, Bruno 17, Caddell 19, Harris 34, Hawkins 37, JADO 40, Kemp 42, King 43, Pei-Ling 52, Phifer, 54, Samford, 62, Sexton 63, Sumners/Nelson/Thompson 69, Upchurch, 72, Viro 73, Wallace 74, Warren 75, Watson 76
Alaska: Alaska 81, Bristol 82, Chenega 83, Doyon 84, Gillam 85, Gottstein 86, Koniag 89, Samuelsen 91, UIC 92
Arizona: Adelante 93, Barton 99, **Beals 100**, Berlin 101, Burns 102, Cadeau 104, Clark 106, Eaton 115, Garcia 122, Grace 125, Hughes 130, McKee 148, Moeller 150, Schlein 165, Shacknai 167, Squires 173, **Weil 181**, Withycombe 184
Arkansas: Bailey 186, Bailey 187, Bodenhamer 190, Darragh 193, Heflin 197, McKinney 202, Murphy 207, Nabholz 208, Olds 210, Ottenheimer 213, Riggs 214, Sturgis 217, Trinity 218, Woodson 221
California: Adams 228, **Akian 234**, Anderson 244, Archer 250, Ascher, 256, Avery-Tsui 261, Baker 267, Bancroft-Clair 270, Bank 272, Barth 279, **Battle 282**, Beattie 289, Bekins 294, Beller 297, Benedek 300, Beneto 301, Bernstein 307, Beynon 312, Bider 314, Blanchard 321, Braddock 336, Bradford 337, Bridges/Larson 343, Bright 344, Bright 345, Broad 347, Brown 352, Bundy 359, Burg 362, Celebrate 383, **Chan 388**, Cheeryble 390, Chitjian 396, Chowdhury 398, Cirila 405, Clougherty 409, Coleman 416, Collingwood 418, Community 421, Corday 426, Crummer 436, Danvera 442, DiNapoli 454, Dockweiler 456, Downey 460, Drum 464, Ducommun 465, Ebell 472, Eichenberg-Larson 474, Ellen 478, Emanuel 480, Emmett 481, Epstein/Roth 483, Evans 485, Evening 487, Familian 491, Feintech 502, First 506, Foor 516, Fortisure 518, Frankel 526, Friedman 531, Fuller 538, Garabedian 545, Gareatis 547, George 551, Georgina-Frederick 552, Gill 555, Gooding 571, Gordon 573, Graff 576, Gross 587, Harman 598, Hawley 605, Hayman 606, Hellman 614, Helms 615, Hinman 622, Hodges 627, Hoefer 628, Horwich 632, Hotchkis 635, Huntington 642, Hurliman 643, I 644, Ibrahim 646, **Indo-American 651**, **Jacoby 654**, Jamieson 658, Jennings 663, Johnson 669, Johnson 670, Jolson 672, Jones 673, Jones 675, Jorgensen 676, Joy 677, Judkins 682, Kadima 686, Kanel 688, Katz 693, Keith 696, Koenig 717, Kornwasser 718, KT 723, L.B. 725, Lamond 729, Leland 741, Lemons 743, Lester 748, Levy 751, Liautaud 755, Lipp 759, Llagas 762, Lockridge 765, **Lui 771**, Magali 781, Magowan 782, Majestic 784, Malachi 785, Margoes 795, Martin 802, Mason 805, Miller 828, Miller 830, Millstreet 835, Mitchell 838, Mitchell, 839, Morgan 847, Muckel 850, **Munson 852**, Nagel 857, Nasaw 858, Oak 872, Olander 878, Olson 879, Orfalea 887, Ornest 888, Parker 903, Parvin 905, Paul 908, Pauley 909, Pearlstein

911, Pedrozzi 912, Pergo 915, Peterson 918, Phelps 922, Podell 930, Pralle 933, Priory 940, Radin 948, Reinhold 963, Reveas 967, **Rieger 971**, Rocca, 978, Roche 979, Ross 988, Rossi 989, Rubin 993, San 997, Sands 1001, Santa 1003, Schaeffer 1013, Schultz 1019, Schweers 1020, Seaver 1026, Sebastiani 1027, Seip 1028, Shannon 1030, Shayne 1032, SKB 1044, Smith 1055, Smith 1056, Smittcamp 1059, Smullin 1060, Solano 1063, Somekh 1064, Sprague, 1070, Srivastava 1072, Staples 1075, Stauffer 1076, Stauffer 1077, Stearns 1078, Straus 1088, Strome 1089, Sudikoff 1090, Sunrise 1093, Thagard 1109, Thompson 1111, Thompson 1112, Tomlinson 1123, Tuffli 1134, Urbanek-Levy 1141, Von 1147, Wagner 1149, Wall 1151, Waller 1152, Wasserman 1160, Webb 1162, Welch 1168, Wells 1171, Wertheimer 1173, West 1175, Western 1176, **Wilkinson 1183**, Wilson 1186, Witter 1192, Wolfe 1193, Worster 1197, Wrather 1198, Yen 1201, Yuki 1203, Zimmer 1212, Zitrin 1214, Zitrustin 1215
Colorado: Arsenault 1224, Benson 1229, Benson 1230, Bloedorn 1238, Cliffline 1247, Donnell-Kay 1258, Dorset 1259, **Fishback 1270**, Grossman 1281, Hamilton 1285, Heider 1290, Hewit 1292, Hope's 1294, Howard 1295, Hunt 1296, Leprino 1313, Lewis 1315, Living 1316, Margulf 1320, Moniker 1327, Petunia 1336, Puksta 1341, QEP 1342, Schramm 1350, Shamrock 1353, Southwestern 1355, Spencer 1356, Staley 1357, Steffens 1358, Taylor 1364, Tomkins 1368, Trachten 1369, Trueblood 1371, W.J.D. 1375, White 1378, Woodford 1382
Connecticut: Acorn 1385, Allwin 1390, Ambler 1392, Avery 1396, Axe-Houghton 1397, Barden 1402, Berbecker 1406, Bigelow 1408, Bowling 1409, Bridgemill 1412, Chaikin-Wile 1417, Chelsea 1418, Citrin 1419, Colburn-Keenan 1421, Conway 1422, Craig 1423, Curran 1427, De 1430, Denzler 1434, Deutsch 1436, Diageo 1437, Eder 1441, Ferguson 1446, Filingieri 1447, Finn 1449, Fippinger 1450, Floren 1451, Foley 1452, Friezo 1457, Gerbic 1463, Gladstein 1465, Greenhill 1472, Hamm 1476, Hergenhan 1481, Hildes-Heim 1483, Howard 1484, Hume 1485, Jaffe 1488, Jones 1491, Katen 1494, Keefe 1497, Kreitler 1502, Lee 1507, Linke 1508, LLL 1510, Martin 1520, McLeod 1524, Mellen 1525, Morrow 1527, Nason 1528, Newtown 1532, Niblack 1533, Nirenberg 1534, O'Herron 1536, Patricelli 1541, Pryor 1546, Rubin-Ladd 1556, **Sonja 1573**, Stratfield 1576, Tierney 1584, Vance 1591, Velaj 1592, Wheeler 1594, Winokur 1597, Zelnick/Belzberg 1602
Delaware: Berghorst 1619, Black 1622, Bowman 1625, Brown 1630, Brown-Whitworth 1632, City 1642, Coleman 1644, **Colgate 1645**, Coors 1647, Croll 1650, Dion 1656, Doll 1657, Farr 1662, Freedman 1665, Geltzer 1666, Giving 1668, Hagan 1674, Harkness 1677, JBL 1686, Jockers 1687, Lighten 1698, Milliken 1711, Relgalf 1725, Replogle 1728, Rosenfeld 1732, Sanders 1737, SNAVE 1747, Splawn 1749, Swift, 1754, Trussell 1767, Vitale 1771, Whitman 1778
District of Columbia: Bench 1788, Brody 1791, **Carter 1794**, Coleman, 1796, **Dingwall 1804**, Dweck 1805, Greenberg 1812, **Merriman 1820**, Olender 1824, Peet 1827, Rubenstein 1833, Westport 1838
Florida: Bailey 1862, Bastien 1872, Baxter 1874, Bayuk 1875, Beall, 1876, Becton 1880, Bell 1883, Blank 1890, Blanksteen 1891, Blanton 1892, Bohnert 1895, Bond 1897, Brighton 1899, Brodsky 1901, Brody 1902, Brown 1905, Burnett 1910, Burnetti 1912, Capital 1918, Chadbourne 1932, Chanin 1934, Charles 1937, Cherry 1940, Childress 1942, Collins 1949, Couch 1953, Crane 1955, Crutchfield 1957, Dasburg 1961, Dennis 1969, Diermeier 1976, Dilworth 1977, Duckwall 1982, Dyer 1985, Ellis 1989, Elster 1990, Erdle 1993, Evans 1994, Fish 2001, Focus 2004, Fontaine 2006, Forbes 2008, Foulds 2014, Fox 2016, Frangakis 2017, Freitas 2022, Fricks 2023, Gardner 2031, Garvy

2033, Grabe 2053, Grader 2054, Greenblatt 2063, Greene-Sawtell 2065, Halbrook 2073, Hand 2077, Hardison 2081, Haugland 2084, Hayford 2086, Hendrix 2090, Hicks 2094, Hinman 2099, Holopaw 2108, Hornik 2111, Huang 2113, Isenberg 2121, Jacobson 2124, Jasam 2127, Johnson 2130, Jones 2131, Kanders 2135, Kane 2137, Kessler 2145, Kiwanis 2149, KLM 2151, KML 2152, Kugelman 2161, Lacy, 2163, Lambert 2164, Lambrecht 2165, Lastinger 2168, Marshall 2195, Martin 2196, Martin 2197, Millsaps 2214, Morrison 2221, Morrison 2222, Muma 2227, Norjana 2235, Overstreet 2242, Patterson 2250, Pearce 2252, **Posnack 2262**, Powell 2264, Powell 2265, Propp 2269, Ray 2275, Raymund 2276, Rembert 2281, River 2288, Ross 2298, Seaman 2320, Second 2321, Sexton 2326, Shackelford 2327, Silverman 2337, Smick 2340, Smith 2342, Stern 2349, Stern 2350, Stewart 2351, Strong 2353, Sunburst 2359, Swisher 2361, Taylor 2366, Thomsen 2373, Tippett 2376, Toral 2378, Turock 2382, Vanneck-Bailey 2384, Vasey 2385, Votum 2390, Weintraub 2395, Whiting 2403, Wilder 2406, Wilkes-Desmond 2407, Wolgin 2411, **Wollowick 2412**, Wynne 2419, Yerrid 2420, Ying 2421

Georgia: Akers 2432, Arnold 2436, Averitt 2438, Baker 2439, Beard-Payne 2442, Boone 2446, Bowen 2447, Broadfield 2449, Chesed 2458, Church 2460, Churches 2461, Colston 2464, Community 2465, Community 2466, Cooper 2469, Echlin 2472, English 2474, Exposition 2476, Georgia 2485, Goddard 2491, Gordy 2493, Graves 2496, Hawkins 2503, Health 2504, Hodgson 2507, Holland-Underwood 2508, Hoyt 2513, Jackson 2522, Jeter 2524, Johnson 2525, King-White 2532, Knox 2534, Lane 2536, Lee 2540, Lipscomb 2541, Looney 2542, Marshall 2545, McKnight 2548, Mix 2550, Morris 2553, Nonami 2557, Noonan 2558, Orkin 2559, Orkin 2560, Patrick 2562, Pattillo 2563, Pechter 2564, Piedmont 2566, Ragan 2572, Rice 2575, Saul 2579, Schwob 2581, SF 2585, Smith 2586, TALX 2592, University 2597, Vogel 2600, Whitehead 2610, Williamson 2613, Woodruff 2617, Woodruff, 2618, Wright 2620, Young 2621, Zawadi 2622

Hawaii: Gear 2634, Makana 2639, Minami 2642, Moore 2643, Wong 2656

Idaho: Mitchell 2680, Morrison 2682

Illinois: 1335 2691, Adreani 2697, Agape 2698, Allen-Heath 2701, Allyn 2703, Alton 2705, Aon 2710, **Appleby 2711**, B&D 2715, Bartholomay 2721, Bates 2724, Bates 2725, Baudhuin 2726, Beasley 2728, Bellick 2732, Bere 2734, Bernoudy 2738, Bisco 2742, Bishop 2743, Block, 2746, Boylan 2753, Branstad 2755, Brenner 2756, Bruce 2761, Brunswick 2762, Burgess 2767, Caccomo 2771, Cafaro-Livingston 2772, Cashel 2777, Catalyst 2778, Chapin-May 2782, Christ 2788, Cless 2793, Clingen 2794, Cohn 2795, Cohn 2796, Coldwell 2797, Collins 2799, **Combs 2800**, Constans-Culver 2805, Cooney 2806, Copeland 2807, Corbett 2808, Cronk 2817, Danielson 2823, Delta 2826, Denny 2828, Doyle 2836, **Dyson 2842**, Eckert 2843, Edelman 2845, Edgerly 2847, Educational 2848, Ellis 2853, Frank 2885, Frankel 2886, Funk 2897, Garard, 2902, Gibbet 2912, Gidwitz 2914, Glossberg 2916, Goldenberg 2920, Goldman 2922, Goodstein 2924, Griffith 2929, Grossinger 2933, Gust 2936, Hales 2941, Half 2942, Halstead 2944, Hanson 2950, Hanus 2951, Harczak, 2952, Hegeler 2963, Hoffer 2975, Hugg 2982, Hurley 2985, **Ingredion 2988**, Jentes 2995, Jephson 2996, JKP 2997, Jocarno 3000, Jones 3002, Judy 3003, Kellcie 3008, Kelly 3012, Kerr 3015, Keyes 3016, Klosk 3020, **Kobe 3024**, **Krasberg-Mason 3029**, Krehbiel 3030, Lancaster 3035, Larsen 3038, **Lazzara 3042**, Lebus 3043, Levinson 3049, Levy 3050, Lichtman 3052, Lohengrin 3059, Louis 3063, Love 3064, Maak 3067, MacDonald 3068, Maddox 3069, Mansfield 3074, Marcum 3076, Marks 3077, Marsteller 3079, McCourtney 3087, McGraw 3092,

McLaughlin 3095, McNally 3097, McNulty 3099, Millard 3109, Millner 3115, Minow 3118, Mitchell 3120, Mohr 3121, Munson 3130, Murphy 3132, NCI 3134, New 3136, Nickum 3139, Nygren 3146, O'Connor 3149, OSA 3157, Penrose 3166, Pepper 3167, Perkins 3169, Peters 3171, Petrick 3173, **Polk 3179**, Pollack 3180, Pond 3182, Roberti 3198, Rogers 3202, Ruttenberg 3218, Saemann 3220, Schneider 3226, Scott 3230, Seidler 3233, Shaked 3237, Shapiro 3240, Smallwood 3251, Sramek 3259, Staley 3264, Stein 3266, Stone 3269, Storer 3271, STS 3272, Sulzer 3277, Tafel 3280, Taylor 3287, Tobey 3290, Vail 3301, Victor 3304, Walker 3308, Webb 3313, Wesselink 3319, Weston 3320, Wood 3329, Woodruff 3330, Wright 3333, Zaentz 3336

Indiana: **Ackerman 3339**, Ayres 3342, Benton 3344, Branigin 3348, Bronstein 3351, Bussing-Koch 3353, Carroll 3354, CDM 3355, Community 3361, Crescent-Cresline-Wabash 3365, Ellerbrook 3376, Fayette 3379, Froderman 3383, Hoch 3394, Hoffman 3395, Huntington 3397, Jasper 3401, Kuhne 3409, LaGrange 3412, Magee-O'Connor 3414, MutualBank 3421, Oakley 3426, Oliver 3428, Raymond 3436, Schergens 3443, Scott 3446, Seymour 3448, Sherwood 3451, Thomasson 3459, Thrush-Thompson 3460, Vann 3461, Vision 3463, Von 3464, Weston 3467, Winchester 3469

Iowa: Andringa 3470, Barkema 3471, Bishop 3475, Busse 3478, Cole-Belin 3480, Duggan 3488, Farver 3491, Gartner 3496, Geisler 3498, Howard 3509, Howe 3510, Krause 3516, McDonald 3520, Mount 3522, Nelson 3524, Pappajohn 3525, R 3529, Schroeder 3533, Stark 3536, Tomson 3537, Vermeer 3541, **Wahlert 3544**, Weathertop 3545, Woodward 3549

Kansas: Bane 3557, Bramlage 3559, Cape 3563, Cray 3569, DeVore 3573, Fidelity 3577, Goldberg 3581, Henry 3585, Insurance 3587, Joscelyn 3590, Logan 3597, Miller-Mellor 3604, Mingenback 3605, **Muchnic 3609**, Reeble 3618, Rush 3620, Smoot 3627, South 3628, Stolzer 3630, Swearingen 3631, Trusler 3635, V 3636, Watson 3639, Williams 3643

Kentucky: Abercrombie 3645, Boone 3649, Coffey 3650, Dunbar 3653, Etscorn 3654, Gagarin 3656, Hannah 3659, Haskins 3661, Horn 3664, Keeneland 3668, Marksbury 3675, MGM 3678, Ogden 3683, Reed 3688, Stock 3697, Trager 3701, Trim 3702, Yeager 3710

Louisiana: Biedenharn 3713, Daybrook 3720, Harper 3726, Lang 3733, Pugh 3747, Selber 3751, Special 3754, Wheless 3758, Winn 3760, Wisdom 3761, Zuschlag 3762

Maine: Borman 3767, Cotsirilos 3774, Davenport 3775, Kagan 3784, Kennebec 3785, Merrill 3789, Messler 3790, Old 3795, Oxford 3796, Quesada 3800

Maryland: Akridge 3810, Anderson 3814, Baltimore 3817, Darby 3843, Davis 3844, Dean 3846, DelSignore 3847, Devito 3848, **Doorstep 3850**, Eacho 3852, Eliasberg 3854, Fischer 3862, Gewirz 3869, Gidwitz 3870, Govil 3875, Greene-Milstein 3876, Hubbard 3883, Huether/McClelland 3884, Hyman 3887, Jake 3890, Loats 3902, Macht 3905, Mullan 3920, Nabit 3924, Nicholl 3926, **Northern 3928**, Pearlstone 3934, RCM 3937, RFI 3938, Rogers-Wilbur 3941, Salisbury 3945, Schuh 3946, Silber 3952, Small 3955, Thalheimer 3966, Tucker 3969, Van 3973, Wallis 3977, Widgeon 3983

Massachusetts: Archibald 4005, Benson 4016, Benz 4017, Bushee 4032, Casey 4039, Chicopee 4047, Clarke 4049, Clifford 4051, Cohen 4053, Connell 4055, D'Amour 4064, Davoli 4065, Devereaux 4069, Durant 4072, Dwyer 4074, Easthampton 4076, Edwards 4078, Fay 4087, Franklin 4096, Gale 4100, Gerrity 4102, **Gross 4108**, Guttag 4109, Hagler 4111, Hale 4113, Haley 4114, Hampden 4116, Harris 4118, Hauben 4120, Heide 4125, Helman 4126, Henderson 4127, Hoffman 4131, Hopedale 4134, Hornblower 4135, Hyde 4139, Jefferson 4142, Kamin 4144, Kenwood 4150, Kershaw 4151, King 4156, Kneisel 4157,

Krieger 4160, Levy 4174, Lingos 4177, Longtine 4179, Makepeace 4185, Mank 4187, Marcus 4188, Marino 4190, McCutchin-Collins 4193, Melvina 4197, Morningstar 4207, Mulberry 4213, Murphy 4215, Noble 4224, Pechet 4235, Permanent 4239, Phelps 4242, Putnam 4253, Quirico 4254, Ragon 4256, Redwall 4261, Reisman 4262, Rockland 4267, Rosse 4272, Shapiro 4289, Shapiro 4290, Smith 4299, Smith 4300, **Spero 4304**, Sprague 4306, Starr 4309, Stemberg 4313, **Summer 4316**, Thoreau 4327, Tomfohrde 4329, Van 4340, Von 4346, Wallace 4347, Wyman-Gordon 4364

Michigan: Abrams 4369, Acheson 4370, Andersen 4377, Andrah 4378, Baldwin 4382, Barton-Malow 4386, Biederman 4391, Bierlein 4392, Bostock 4395, Briggs-Fisher 4397, Buhr 4400, Burdick-Thorne 4402, Community 4411, Connable 4412, Conrad 4413, DeVlieg 4428, Duchene 4435, Elliott 4436, Fabiano 4438, Farver 4441, Farwell 4442, **Ford, 4446**, Foren 4448, Gershenson 4453, Havirmill 4463, Hecht 4465, Holden 4467, Juhl 4475, Jurries 4476, Kinney 4483, L 4487, Leven 4492, LoPrete 4496, M 4497, Mackinac 4499, Mariel 4504, McDonald 4508, McManus 4509, McNally 4510, Meritor, 4511, Mills 4515, Morley 4518, Murdock 4519, Onequest 4527, Padnos 4529, Paine 4531, Pitt 4540, Plym 4542, Power 4544, Price 4546, Ratner 4548, Sehn 4563, Serra 4565, Shiawassee 4568, Skandalaris 4571, Smith 4573, Stubnitz 4582, Tamer 4585, Tassell-Wisner-Bottrall 4587, Thoman 4590, Tremble 4595, Vlasic 4607, White 4613, Whitman 4615

Minnesota: Bell 4637, Bell 4638, Bend 4639, Borman 4644, Boss 4646, Bradley 4647, Briggs 4648, Chadwick-Loher 4655, Charity, 4656, Cox 4662, Dell 4664, Farmers 4679, Fraser 4689, G&K 4691, Gage 4692, Gardner 4693, Hagen 4704, Harrington 4707, Jackson 4718, Jostens 4720, Kinman-Oldfield 4723, Kinney 4724, Krisbin 4726, Lillehei 4729, Maslowski 4741, McNamara 4743, Merritt 4744, Midcontinent 4745, Mooty 4747, Northern 4751, O'Brien 4753, O'Rourke 4757, OSilas 4758, Quinlan 4764, Radichel 4765, Regis 4770, Rosen 4782, Tennant 4798, Trillium 4801, Wells 4811, Whaley 4816

Mississippi: Barnett 4823, Black 4825, Day 4832, Florence 4836, Fountain 4837, Graeber 4839, McCarty, 4848, Sanders 4852, Skelton 4854

Missouri: BF 4867, **Bohm 4871**, Boylan 4873, Butler 4880, Calkins 4881, Copaken 4888, Cornelsen 4889, Cray 4890, Dierberg 4895, Duesenberg 4897, Empson 4902, Essman 4905, Finley 4910, Forster-Powers 4911, Gaylord 4915, Grant 4918, Green 4920, Griffin 4921, Hermann 4927, King 4939, Litton 4946, Logan 4947, Moss 4964, No 4971, Peculiar 4978, Pillsbury 4980, Schneider 4994, Schutte 4995, Stroble 5015, Sullivan, 5017, Tension 5019, Timmons 5021, Trulaske, 5024, UMB 5026, University 5027, VJS 5031, Walker 5034, Walton 5037, Wolff 5040, Wurst 5043

Montana: Boe 5045, Heisey 5056, Wendy's 5065

Nebraska: America 5066, Ameritas 5067, Assurity 5068, Baer 5069, Cope 5077, Friedland 5082, Friedman 5083, GFH 5084, Hansen 5087, Harper 5088, Hawkins 5089, Kaufmann-Cummings 5096, Kilbourne 5097, Lienemann 5100, Mapes 5103, Midlands 5104, Physicians 5112, Quivey-Bay 5113, Scudders 5116, Shurtleff 5121, **Waldbaum 5125**, Walker 5126, West 5128, Yount 5130

Nevada: Boyd 5141, Children 5147, Close 5148, **Fein 5155**, Findlay 5156, Geomar 5160, Jaquish 5165, Joseph 5166, Lemay 5172, Matley 5176, Meyer 5177, Peterson 5182, Pinnacle 5183, Smith 5187, Timken-Sturgis 5192, Wagner 5195, Webb 5196, **Wood 5201**, Yamagata 5203

New Hampshire: Couch 5209, Landecker 5217, McIninch 5224, Oxford 5228, Smyth 5232, Woodbury 5238

New Jersey: A 5240, Abrams 5241, **Akhoury 5243**, Amboy 5246, Antz 5250, Armour-Lewis 5251, Aufzien 5253, Bartlett 5256, Baum 5258, Brook

5273, Brooks 5274, Brueckner 5279, Brunetti 5281, Chang 5290, Chanil 5291, Citta 5295, Civitas 5296, Clermont 5298, Cohen 5299, Conant 5302, Conger 5303, Cordover 5304, Croman 5307, **Daft 5310**, Dreman 5326, Earle 5328, Ellis 5333, Engel 5335, Family 5340, Fellstone 5346, Fisher 5347, Fox 5349, Freedman 5352, Frelinghuysen 5354, Gauntt 5365, Gibson 5370, Goldberger 5372, Goodwin 5374, Hanafin 5381, Hanson 5383, Hillswood 5394, Holzer 5396, IV 5401, Johnson 5406, Johnson 5407, Jones 5408, **Ju 5410**, KDK 5416, Kean 5417, Keller 5418, Kingsberg 5421, Klein 5424, Kolber 5429, Kroon 5433, Kurr 5435, Kurtz 5436, Lewis 5447, Liss 5451, Machuga 5454, McConnell 5463, McCrane 5464, Milano 5466, Myers 5476, Navesink 5477, Olsen 5480, Pantirer 5487, **Parnassus 5489**, Pasternak 5490, Patrick 5494, Pepper 5496, Pheasant 5499, Post 5505, Previti 5506, Roe 5512, Rukin 5516, Sastaunik 5519, Silverman 5536, Smith 5539, Snyder 5540, **Southpole 5545**, Spruce 5548, Take 5555, Twin 5563, Ullmann 5564, Verhalen 5568, Waters 5571, Watts 5573, Wei 5575, Weinstein 5576, Wetterberg 5583, Woolley-Clifford 5594

New Mexico: B.F. 5606

New York: 5 5631, Abess 5636, AKC 5651, Alexander 5656, American 5663, American 5664, **American 5669**, Aresty 5687, Asher 5695, August 5698, Avanessians 5701, Avery 5702, Bank 5710, Barham 5715, Barney 5717, Barnwood 5718, Barron 5719, Baum 5722, Baumann 5723, BBL 5724, Beck 5728, Beckman 5729, Beir 5732, Bennett 5737, Bergson 5738, Bernhill 5741, Big 5745, Bird 5750, Blank 5756, Blodgett 5760, Blue 5763, Boustead 5769, Bovin 5770, Box 5771, Boxer 5772, Brand 5776, Brooklyn 5788, Brown 5791, Burton 5804, Carwill 5818, Casey 5819, Cathedral 5822, CDVSJ 5825, Centennial 5826, Cerullo 5829, Chasanoff 5833, Cline 5851, Cochran 5853, **Cogitare 5855**, Cogut 5856, Cohen 5857, Cohn 5863, Colburn 5866, Cole 5868, Cornell 5876, Cox 5883, Cranshaw 5885, Cutco 5890, D'Addario 5894, Danziger 5899, Darrah 5900, Davidson 5901, Dears 5905, Deeds 5906, DeMario 5909, Desai 5910, Dillard 5916, Dolgen 5922, Downey 5930, Downs 5931, Duke 5934, Eggleston 5946, Elkins 5955, Ellsworth 5957, Emwiga 5962, Erpf 5968, Evans 5973, F. 5977, Family 5982, Farber 5987, Fay 5989, Fee 5990, Ferriday 6000, Fields 6003, Fieldstone 6004, Fife 6005, Finkelstein 6007, Fitt 6010, **Fitzgibbons 6011**, Flaherty 6012, Fleischer 6013, Forest 6018, Frankel 6027, Freidheim 6031, Fridman 6035, Gaffney 6049, Gant 6054, Gantz 6056, Gartner 6059, Gatto 6061, Gerhard 6072, Goldberg 6090, Goldenberg 6092, Goldwasser 6103, Golub 6105, Goodman 6107, Gordon 6109, Gordon 6111, Graham 6119, Greenberg 6132, Greenspan 6134, **Greenwald 6136**, **Gruodis 6150**, Gutman 6152, H. 6153, Hafer 6155, Hajim 6158, Hallingby 6160, Handler 6161, Handler 6162, Harmon 6168, Harmon 6169, **Harriman 6170**, Heffer 6180, Hein 6184, Heller 6187, Henderson 6189, Henshel 6192, Herringer 6196, Heyman 6201, High 6206, Hohmann 6218, Holmberg 6221, Horowitz 6225, Hulbert 6232, I.W. 6236, IF 6237, Imago 6239, **Indira 6242**, Indus 6243, Ingrassia 6244, International 6249, Jacobson 6255, Janklow 6257, Jennings 6259, JKW 6263, Joyce 6275, JVZ 6277, Kallinikeion 6280, Kaplan 6284, Keeler 6292, Kelleher 6295, **Kevorkian 6304**, Kiernan 6306, Kies 6307, Kimura 6310, **King 6311**, Kirby 6313, **Klagsbrun 6318**, Klingenstein 6327, Knafel 6330, Krimendahl/Saint-Amand 6346, Lachman 6356, Lainoff 6359, Lake 6360, **Lamaj 6361**, **Laub 6367**, Layton 6370, Levy 6391, Lewin 6392, Lewy 6393, **Li 6394**, Liberman 6396, Lippes 6401, Loewy 6409, Lubin 6416, MacArthur 6429, Maher 6433, Maher 6434, Marble 6441, Maslin 6448, MAT 6450, Mathis-Pfohl 6451, Maurer 6453, Mead 6466, Meier 6470, Mendell 6472, Menezes 6473, Meredith 6477, Messinger 6482, Meyer 6485,

Michaels 6488, Miller 6493, Mittlemann 6500, Morgado 6505, Morris 6508, Morse 6510, Mozel 6512, Mule 6515, Nets 6524, New 6527, Newman 6530, Newman 6531, Newman 6532, Newman 6534, Niemiec 6535, Northern 6540, Norwegian 6541, Norwich 6542, Nuhn 6544, Nussbaum 6545, Oberoi 6547, Offensend 6550, Old 6554, O'Neil 6557, Osceola 6560, Ostgrodd 6561, Palisades 6569, Palisano 6570, Palmer 6572, Parshelsky 6578, Paul 6580, Peckham 6583, Peek 6584, Peterson 6592, Peterson 6594, Petrocelli 6595, Phaedrus 6598, Pickman 6602, Picotte 6603, Pittman 6608, Pletka 6610, **Posner-Wallace 6621**, Potter 6623, Price 6627, Price 6628, Prince 6629, Pyewacket 6635, Rachesky 6642, Radio 6643, Reich 6659, Reiss 6662, Rheinstrom 6665, Rhodes 6666, Richter 6668, Rifkind 6670, Ring 6671, Ritter 6674, Rose 6683, Rose 6684, Rose 6687, Rosenstein 6692, Rosner 6698, Roxe 6706, Russo 6711, Sackler 6717, Sani 6726, Satow 6732, Schaffer 6737, **Schepp 6739**, Schwartz 6753, Schwartz 6754, Schwartz 6755, Schwartzberg 6756, Seven 6777, Shackouls 6781, Sharon 6787, Shuman 6795, Siegel 6797, Silverstein 6802, Silverstein 6803, Simpson 6805, Slade 6809, Smith 6815, Snayberger 6817, Snow 6818, Spatz 6831, Spektor 6833, Stanton 6845, Stebbins 6850, Stern 6860, **Stern 6862**, Stowe 6869, **Strauss 6870**, Striano 6871, Strong 6872, Sumitomo 6876, Summit 6877, Sussman 6879, Sutton 6884, SVM 6886, Switzer 6889, **Tang 6891**, Tanner-Frank 6893, Tenney 6895, Thanksgiving 6897, Thiem 6898, Tisch 6900, Tod 6901, Touhey 6902, Truman 6912, Tytel 6917, Uihlein 6919, **Usman 6921**, Utica 6922, Utopia 6923, Van 6925, Vance 6926, Vanden 6927, Vernon 6928, Warwick 6945, Watts 6947, Weil 6948, Weinberg 6951, Weingarten 6953, **Weinstein 6956**, Wells 6964, Wharton 6968, White 6972, Whittemore 6975, Willmott 6978, Wohlgemuth 6984, Wolk 6987, **Woodland 6989**, Woods 6992, Wright 6995, Zeitz 7021, Zenkel 7023, Ziff 7027, Zimmermann 7028, Zlinkoff 7031, Zwerling 7034, Zwirn 7035

North Carolina: BB&T 7045, Boddie 7054, Bolick 7056, Brown 7058, Brown 7059, Bryan 7060, Burns 7063, Cameron 7065, Cary 7069, Cato, 7071, Chastain 7073, Chatham 7074, Coffey 7078, Cooke 7079, Cooke 7080, Crawley 7082, Ellison 7090, Family 7096, First 7097, Gambrill 7106, Hayden-Harman 7120, Herndon 7125, Hoffman 7127, Howe 7132, Hunt 7135, Hunter 7136, Kanitz 7140, Kenan 7144, Koons 7148, Kosloski 7149, KPB 7151, Krauss 7153, Lerner 7160, Little 7162, Lynum 7165, Marietta 7167, McLean 7178, McNeil 7181, Meserve 7182, Miller 7185, Moon 7187, Morrison 7193, Nanney 7198, Niessen, 7200, Oschwald 7203, Perkin 7208, Post 7213, Pratt 7214, Pulliam 7215, Ragland, 7216, Rankin 7217, Rees 7219, Richardson 7221, Rocky 7227, Rogers 7228, Sandt 7235, Schug 7237, Shingleton 7241, Silverback 7243, Silverman 7244, Sloan 7246, Smith 7248, Smith 7249, Stonecutter 7255, Summer 7261, Towne 7268, Trexler 7269, Vanderbilt 7273, Wake 7276, Wallace 7277, West-West 7284, Whitener 7286, Yount 7292

Ohio: Alpaugh 7302, American 7303, Andrews 7307, Barber 7315, Barron 7316, Bates 7317, Besl 7326, Bicknell 7327, Bryan 7339, Calhoun 7344, Callahan 7345, Cassner 7348, Chemed 7350, Chesley 7351, Christ 7352, Community 7357, Conn 7360, Coressel 7364, Crandall 7366, Crossroads 7367, Damico 7370, Danis 7371, Davey 7373, Davidson 7374, **Elisha-Bolton 7387**, Ferry 7396, Finnegan 7399, Fitton 7402, Foss 7407, Freygang 7410, Frost 7412, Frost-Parker 7413, Gale 7415, Garcia 7416, Gelbman 7420, Gimbel 7424, Gross 7432, Hauck 7440, Hazelbaker 7441, Heffner 7443, Heimann 7444, **Highfield 7450**, Hoover 7453, Horvitz 7454, Howe 7455, Hubert 7456, Hughes 7458, Jordan 7471, Kennedy 7476, Kilworth 7477, Kisker 7479, Knoll 7483, Kramer 7485, Landers 7488, Lang 7489,

Laub 7490, Lazarus 7493, Lincoln 7496, LKC 7501, M.L.M 7510, Mccarthy 7520, Miller 7526, Miller 7527, Morley 7532, Musson 7534, Newton 7536, Norris 7538, O'Neill 7542, Pott 7549, Renner 7557, Reynolds 7558, Ritchie 7561, Rosenberry 7562, Schey 7571, Schwartz, 7576, Schwebel 7577, Scotford 7579, Seaman 7580, Seifert 7584, Selsor 7585, Shinnick 7591, Skyler 7595, Taft 7609, Talbott 7612, Throckmorton 7618, Trachsel 7620, Van 7625, Van 7626, Watson 7633, Wildermuth 7637, Williams 7638, Williams 7639, Williamson 7640, Wilson 7641, Wolfe 7644, Yeck 7648

Oklahoma: Ad 7654, Atherton 7657, Barnes 7659, Barnett 7660, Collins 7668, Evergreen 7677, Faranna 7678, Fugitt 7681, GKJ 7683, Jones 7692, Marshall 7703, Massey 7705, Merkel 7706, Merrick 7707, Moore 7710, Parman 7713, Rathburn 7716, Richardson 7717, Trippet 7725, Warren 7729, Wilson 7736

Oregon: Baldwin 7742, Castle 7745, Chaney 7747, **Chiles 7749**, Curry 7755, Flowerree 7763, Frank 7765, Jubitz 7779, Leonard 7789, Leupold 7790, Lindgren 7791, Merlo 7797, Michael 7799, Miller 7800, Rietman 7809, Schmidt 7813, Shoen 7816, Stewart 7823, White 7830, Woodard 7831

Pennsylvania: Adams 7836, Ames 7840, Arkema 7842, Armstrong 7843, Baker 7851, **Arronson 7844**, Baldwin, 7852, Beacon 7856, Bennett 7860, Benz 7861, Berger 7862, Berwind 7868, Betz 7870, Birnhak 7873, Bishop 7874, Black 7875, Blackhorse 7877, Bolte 7882, Bridge 7891, Brooks 7897, Brooks 7898, Brossman 7900, Browne 7901, Bucks 7905, Butz 7908, Calvert 7910, Cameron 7911, Carlson 7916, Carnahan-Jackson 7917, Casteel 7919, Clark 7925, Cost 7937, Cottage 7938, Dicerbo 7956, Dietrich 7958, Double 7964, Dozzi 7965, Eberly 7969, Elk 7975, Ellis 7978, Emporium 7980, Fine 7994, Fleming 8000, Foster 8003, Fountainhead 8004, Freas 8005, Frohring 8010, Gershman 8015, Giop 8018, Greater 8026, Groff 8027, Grumbacher 8028, Grundy 8029, Hall 8037, Harsco 8040, Hassel 8042, Hecht 8050, High 8054, Hill 8055, Hirtzel 8058, **Hitchcock 8059**, Hoch 8060, Jackson 8078, John 8081, Kelley 8091, Klein 8097, Knoll 8100, Knox 8101, Kurtz 8104, Kynett 8105, Lamb 8106, Landers 8110, Lemole 8119, Lockhard 8130, **Mango 8138**, Maple 8139, Maronda 8140, Mason 8147, McKee 8160, McMannis 8163, Mendel 8168, Merwin 8170, Moffat 8175, Moggio 8176, Moore 8177, Mudge 8181, Mukaiyama-Rice 8183, Murphy 8185, O'Brien-Veba 8197, Oppenheim 8199, Patterson 8205, Patterson 8206, Penn 8208, Perelman 8209, Petersen 8212, Plainfield 8217, Pollock 8222, Postles 8223, Randall 8230, Reidler 8233, Richards 8236, Roberts 8240, Rosenberg 8244, Rudman 8248, Saramar 8253, Satell 8254, Schafer 8256, Schautz 8257, Scheller 8258, Schoonmaker 8260, Scott 8266, Shenk 8274, Singer 8279, Smith 8280, Smith 8283, Speyer 8294, Stein 8299, Strawbridge 8305, Stutzman 8309, Teleflex 8314, Thomas 8316, Tippins 8318, Triple 8322, Trout 8324, Up 8327, Vaughan 8329, Vincent 8334, Warburton 8342, Weiler 8347, **Whimsie 8354**, Williams 8358, Williams 8359, Winokur 8362, Wright-Cook 8369, Wyeth 8371, Wyman 8372, Young 8375, **Zeldin 8376**, Zisman 8377

Rhode Island: Acriel 8378, Apperson 8380, Arakelian 8381, Arents, 8382, Bersted 8388, Clark 8395, Darling 8400, Dwinell 8403, Geneen 8411, Greene 8413, Gross 8414, Horton 8423, Jackson 8427, Janci 8428, Johnson 8430, Kelley 8431, Kingsbury 8435, Koffler 8436, Leroe 8439, Liberty 8440, Littlefield 8441, Love 8446, Luke 8447, Mann 8448, Masonic 8449, McWethy 8453, Molder 8455, Pacifica 8464, Palermo 8466, Pardee 8468, Perkins 8470, Prouty 8476, Salerno 8480, Schwarz 8483, Seed 8484, Swarts 8495, Thompson 8496, Washington 8500, Woodward 8505

South Carolina: Bailey 8510, Bannon 8511, Collins 8520, Davis 8521, Gleason 8524, Hendricks

8527, Kendall 8530, Lutz 8533, Peery/Cauthen 8537, Stony 8542, Tarr 8545, WebbCraft 8548, Williams/Brice-Edwards 8549
South Dakota: Amundson 8554, Elmen 8561, Engelsma 8563, Hatterscheidt 8566, Peterson 8572, Schwab 8574
Tennessee: Atticus 8582, Basler 8584, **Belz 8585**, Boring 8590, Cartinhour-Woods 8597, Citizens 8599, Cole 8600, Community 8601, Cracker 8603, Deupree 8604, Doochin 8605, Draughon 8607, Eskind 8611, Eskind 8613, Fleming 8615, **Fraser 8617**, **Gardner 8619**, Gaylord 8620, Goldsmith 8622, Grandview 8625, Jewell 8633, Kennedy 8638, Kite 8639, LaRoche 8641, Nehemiah 8653, Pickle 8660, Powell 8661, Rose 8667, Schmidt 8671, Seidman 8672, Tipton 8682
Texas: Alexander 8696, **AMD 8698**, Anderson 8704, Anderson 8705, Aragona 8706, B.E.L.I.E.F. 8713, Barnett 8718, Barrow 8719, Bearden 8721, Beauchamp 8722, Behmann 8725, Bloxom, 8731, Booth 8735, Bowers 8736, Bright 8743, Broady 8745, Brochstein 8746, Bromley 8749, Budwine 8754, Central 8766, Chambers 8767, Chaudhary 8768, Clifford 8774, Cogdell 8776, Collins 8781, Community 8782, **Conway 8783**, Daniel 8797, De 8803, di 8812, Diamond 8813, Dice 8814, Doak 8818, Educational 8836, Elkins 8838, Enrico 8839, Fair 8844, Faith 8846, Fash 8848, Fertitta 8852, Finger 8857, Flowers 8862, Folsom 8863, Ford 8864, Foster 8868, Foundation 8870, Fowlston 8871, Frankel 8872, Friedel 8875, Friedman 8876, Fruehauf 8879, Fuller 8882, Garvey 8884, Greentree 8901, Griffin 8902, Guinn 8906, Hallam 8910, Hallberg 8911, Hanley 8916, Hartman 8920, Hatfield 8922, Healthcare 8924, Hegi 8931, Hibbs 8934, Hicks 8935, Hicks 8936, Hillcrest 8939, Hixon 8940, Hohlt 8944, Hollandsworth 8945, Holmes 8947, Jackson 8963, Jastrow 8967, Johnston 8972, Kabacoff 8977, Kahn 8978, Kayser 8980, KCL 8981, Keown 8986, Kessler 8987, King 8993, Klein 8997, Knox 8999, Lange 9008, Lantana 9009, Lesley 9013, Long 9023, MacDonald-Peterson 9032, Martin 9040, Mayer 9043, Mays 9045, McDaniel 9050, McKee 9052, McMillan, 9054, McNutt 9055, Mendenhall 9056, Merrick 9059, Mewhinney 9060, Meyerson 9062, Moore 9072, Mosbacher 9075, Myers 9081, Navarro 9084, O'Hare 9095, O'Neal 9097, Osberg 9105, Pearce 9121, Perkins 9125, Pipe 9130, Planetary 9132, Pratt 9137, Reilly 9148, Reitch 9149, Reuhl 9150, Richardson 9151, Richter 9153, Riter 9154, Roberts 9157, Robinson 9158, Roosth 9160, Ross 9164, Ross 9165, San 9170, Sanders 9171, Saunders 9176, Schissler 9179, Schoener 9180, Sear 9186, Smith 9201, Smith 9207, Stevenson 9220, Stewart, 9221, Texas 9231, Tietze 9236, Tolleson 9238, Toomim 9239, Valero 9246, Veres 9250, Waggoner 9254, Waggoners 9255, Wal-Dot 9256, Walls 9257, Ward 9260, Watson 9263, Way 9264, Weaver 9265, Weir 9268, Weir 9269, Wells 9271, Westcott 9273, Whitley 9276, Williams 9279, Wise 9283, Wolf 9285, Wolters 9287, Woltman 9288, Womack 9289, Wright 9295
Utah: Bastian 9304, Davis 9317, Eskuche 9323, Green 9327, Jackson 9329, Schmidt 9349, Steiner 9358, Wadman 9362
Vermont: Altman 9364, Harper 9373
Virginia: Banks 9390, Bassett 9391, Beck 9392, Beck 9393, Bell 9394, Billings 9397, BRI 9405, **Brown 9407**, Bryant 9409, Cartledge 9414, Cedars 9416, **Delmar 9429**, Denit 9430, Donohue 9432, Farkas 9445, Fink 9447, Foundation 9451, Franklin 9452, Grandis 9462, Harris 9466, Harris 9467, Ivakota 9477, Karlgaard 9481, Lee-Jackson 9488, Lincoln-Lane 9491, Mullen 9502, Northern 9503, Peachtree 9508, Powell 9513, **Price 9516**, Richardson 9523, Rimora 9524, Smith 9534, Stone 9537, Strauch 9538, Thomas 9542, Verlander 9546, Vinoskey 9547, VuBay 9548, Weil 9550, Willett 9552, Williams-Berry 9554
Washington: Ames 9560, Bayley 9567, Carper 9577, Coulter 9581, Crete 9583, CSM 9584, Ferguson

9596, Fries-Tait 9599, Grousemont 9611, Hansen 9615, Helstrom 9619, Horn 9625, Hyde 9627, Johnston-Fix 9634, Johnston-Hanson 9635, Jones 9638, Kaleidoscope 9641, Keller 9643, Lanterman 9649, Lauzier 9651, Longbrake 9655, Martin 9660, Maxwell 9661, O'Donnell 9672, Patel 9675, Pigott 9677, Prairie 9680, Remala 9683, Runstad 9686, Schaar 9689, Schuler 9690, Shemanski 9693, Spark 9701, Stevens 9704, Tamaki 9707, Teel 9708, Thurston 9713, Titus-Will 9714, Welch 9721, Wellworth 9722, Wilson 9725, Worthington 9729
West Virginia: Blake 9735, Bowen 9736, Bowen 9737, Burnside 9740, Carter 9741, Hess 9747, Hollowell 9751, Huntington 9754, Logan 9756, Starvaggi 9767, Vecellio 9770, Wehrle 9771
Wisconsin: Anderson 9773, Ariens 9776, Birnschein 9783, Bluemke 9785, Brennan 9788, Brillion 9789, Caritas 9791, Carlisle 9792, Chipstone 9794, Christensen 9795, Dawes 9803, Dohmen 9806, Einhorn 9815, Foley 9820, Frautschi 9822, Gebhardt 9826, Gordon 9830, Hansen 9835, Heller 9839, **Johnson 9851**, Junginger 9856, Kachel 9857, Kohl 9864, Kohl 9865, Locke 9871, Loehrke 9872, Lutsey 9874, LUX 9874, Manitowoc 9876, Martin 9879, Meehan 9882, Meinerz 9883, Merkel 9884, Modine 9889, Nelson 9894, Pritchett 9906, Puelicher 9907, RCP 9909, Rhodes 9914, RITE-HITE 9915, Roddis 9916, ROS 9918, Schoenleber 9924, Seeds 9925, Seramur 9926, Single 9930, Stateline 9937, Stry 9941, Trek 9948, Van 9952, Wagner 9955, Webcrafters-Frautschi 9957, Windway 9961, Witte, 9962, Woodtrust-Bell 9963
Wyoming: Brendsel 9965, Connemara 9967, Dubois 9970, Jaquith 9975, Perkins 9982, **Schultz 9986**, Skelton 9989, Storer 9992, Stuart 9993, Welch 9998, Witzel 10000

Hinduism

New York: **Indira 6242**, **Nok 6537**, **Rao 6645**, Sani 6726
Pennsylvania: **BGM 7871**, Todi 8319
Texas: **Bhutada 8730**
Utah: Patel 9344
Washington: Remala 9683

Historic preservation

Alabama: Viro 73
Arizona: Armstrong 97
Arkansas: Stephens 216, Union 219
California: Arbor 249, Christensen 400, Freshwind 528, Harman 598, Mazda 810, Smith-Walker 1057, Stellar 1080, Straus 1088
Colorado: Dewolf 1256, Southwestern 1355
Connecticut: Greenhill 1472, Hastings 1479, Lamando 1504, McLane 1522, Panoram 1538, Roberts 1551
Delaware: Chaney 1640, Coleman 1644, Milliken 1711
District of Columbia: Brody 1791, Rubenstein 1833, Westport 1838
Florida: Charlotte 1938, Chicone 1941, Coral 1952, Foulds 2014, Gralnick 2056, Lazarus 2172, Lelash 2178, Samowitz 2311
Georgia: Averitt 2438, Broadfield 2449, Charter 2456, Cooper 2469, Exposition 2476, Hoyt 2513, Hoyt 2514, Knox 2534, Pope 2568, Searcy 2583
Idaho: Golden 2672, Nelson 2683
Illinois: Beeghly 2730, Bellebyron 2731, Bernoudy 2738, Bulkley, 2765, Cohn 2796, Doyle 2836, Duncan 2840, Fabyan 2862, Family 2864, Hastings 2960, Luehring 3065, Mouat 3128, Murphy 3132, Simon 3247, Twomey 3298, Vail 3301
Indiana: Community 3361, Decatur 3367, Jasper 3401
Iowa: Vermeer 3542
Kansas: Jeffcoat 3588, Kansas 3592, Morgan 3607, Ross 3619
Louisiana: Huie-Dellmon 3729
Maine: Franklin 3779, Henry 3782, Merrill 3789, Narragansett 3794

Maryland: Akridge 3810, Duncan 3851, Huether/McClelland 3884, Kelly, 3893, Rogers-Wilbur 3941, Small 3955, St. 3959, Wallis 3977
Massachusetts: Archibald 4005, Codman 4052, Dedham 4067, Eddy 4077, Hale 4112, Henderson 4128, Janet 4141, Walske 4349
Michigan: Community 4411, Family 4439, Paine 4531, Whiting 4614
Minnesota: Boss 4645, Boss 4646, O'Brien 4753, Shared 4791, Weyerhaeuser 4815
Missouri: Dierberg 4895, Edmonston 4900, Gaylord 4915
Montana: Greater 5054
Nebraska: Blair 5074, Nelson 5106, Quivey-Bay 5113
New Hampshire: Dunn 5212, Kimball 5216
New Jersey: Cordover 5304, Dickinson 5319, Katz 5414, Pheasant 5499, Westfield 5582
New Mexico: Taos 5626
New York: American 5664, Family 5984, Ferriday 6000, Hajim 6158, Heilig 6183, Kelleher 6295, **Larson 6365**, Lewy 6393, Marshall 6445, McCarthy 6456, Menges 6474, Nets 6524, Newcomb-Hargraves 6529, Norwich 6542, Osceola 6560, Peek 6584, Preston 6626, Scott 6761, Snow 6818, Stebbins 6850, Truman 6912, Uihlein 6919, Utopia 6923, Warwick 6945, White 6973
North Carolina: Covington 7081, Fairfield 7095, Gambrill 7106, Meserve 7182, Outer 7204, Perkin 7208, Ragland, 7216, Rocky 7227, **Rolander 7229**, Vanderbilt 7273
Ohio: Bryan 7339, Fleischmann 7404, Gelbman 7420, H 7434, Hauck 7440, Hieronymus 7448, Lambert 7487, Landers 7488, Miller 7527, Montauk 7531, Seifert 7584, Williamson 7640, Yeck 7648
Oklahoma: Atherton 7657, Jirous 7690
Oregon: Wessinger 7826
Pennsylvania: Armstrong 7843, Baldwin, 7852, Buck 7904, Dozzi 7965, Jackson 8078, Patterson 8205, Penn 8208, Stewart, 8302, Thomas 8316, Woodall 8368
Rhode Island: Felicia 8406, Kingsbury 8435, Paine 8465
South Carolina: Kendall 8530, Williams/Brice-Edwards 8549
Tennessee: Atticus 8582, Cole 8600, Fleming 8615, Gaylord 8620, Massengill-DeFreice 8647
Texas: Amarillo 8697, Central 8766, Collins 8781, Crossroads 8791, Garvey 8884, Kabacoff 8977, Knox 8999
Vermont: Block 9366
Virginia: Community 9426, Lee-Jackson 9488, **Price 9516**, Roller-Bottimore 9525
Washington: Lanterman 9649
Wisconsin: Chipstone 9794, Erdman 9816, Glanert 9827, Inbusch 9847, Kenosha 9862, Modine 9889, Murray 9892, Roddis 9916, Stry 9941, Van 9953
Wyoming: C 9966, Connemara 9967, Nickerson 9981

Historical activities

Alabama: Loeb 47
California: **Candelaria 372**, HunterWard 641, Muckel 850, **Wilkinson 1183**
Colorado: **Fishback 1270**
Delaware: Chaney 1640
Florida: HI 2093
Georgia: McKnight 2548, Mix 2550
Indiana: Community 3363
Iowa: Hoaglin 3508
Maryland: Widgeon 3983
Massachusetts: Cabot 4034, Dedham 4067, England 4083, Merrill 4200, Vingo 4345, Wheatland 4358
Michigan: Fabiano 4438, Kantzler 4478
Minnesota: Rodman 4779
Missouri: Cray 4890
New Jersey: Pheasant 5499
New York: Leuschen 6384, Newcastle 6528, Rhodes 6666, Scott 6761
North Carolina: Bolick 7056, Post 7213, Robinson 7225
Ohio: Baird 7314, Tait 7610
Tennessee: **Fugitive 8618**
Texas: Diamond 8813, Montgomery 9070

Utah: Parrish 9343
Virginia: Clark 9420
West Virginia: Bowers 9738

History

Illinois: Jahn 2992, Minow 3118
Indiana: Mothershead 3419
Michigan: Community 4411, Mackinac 4499
New York: Bender 5735, Persian 6589
Ohio: Endowment 7388, Fleischmann 7404, Haskell 7439
Texas: **Caritas 8763**
Washington: Quest 9681

History museums

California: Sudikoff 1090
Delaware: Sanders 1737
Florida: Kaplan 2138, Second 2321, Wymbs 2418
Indiana: Kuhne 3409
Maryland: Weinman 3981
Michigan: Nartel 4521
New Jersey: Minerva 5469, Todd 5560
North Carolina: Weatherspoon 7282
Ohio: Rosenberry 7562
Pennsylvania: Boscia 7887, Mendel 8168, Schwartz 8265, Thomas 8316
Rhode Island: Felicia 8406, Paine 8465
Texas: Osberg 9105
Virginia: Markel 9498
Washington: Carper 9577
Wisconsin: Windway 9961

HIV/AIDS

California: Bandai 271, Blachford-Cooper 318, Bridges/Larson 343, Brotman 351, Collingwood 418, Corwin 428, De 446, Donegan 458, Folger 515, Hayman 606, HunterWard 641, **Lloyd 763**, Moonwalk 845, Phillips 924, Rosenberg 985, Thrill 1117, Traina 1126, Wren 1199
Colorado: **Kenney 1302**
Connecticut: Newpol 1531
District of Columbia: **Pettus-Crowe 1828**
Florida: Bastien 1872, **Campbell 1914**, Evans 1994, Price 2267
Illinois: MacDonald 3068
Massachusetts: Deane 4066, Permanent 4239, Torok 4331
Michigan: Roscommon 4552
Minnesota: Whitney 4817
New Hampshire: Martin 5222
New York: Bernhill 5741, Cole 5868, **Farkas 5988**, Hauff 6177, Manzanita 6439, Marshall 6445
Ohio: Anderson 7305, Haskell 7439
Pennsylvania: Price 8225, Union 8326
Texas: Holloway 8946, Levy 9014
Utah: Bastian 9304
Washington: Horn 9625

Holistic medicine

Arizona: **Weil 181**
Georgia: Stahl 2588
Missouri: St. 5012

Home health care

California: Barbonchielli 276, Livingston 761, Schulte 1018
Connecticut: Senior 1566, Union 1590
Maryland: Lutheran 3904
New Jersey: Devine 5317
North Carolina: Wibel 7287
Rhode Island: Pardee 8468
Texas: Healthcare 8924, Hervey 8932
Wisconsin: Dudley 9811

Home ownership

California: Bank 272
New Jersey: Columbia 5301

Home repairs

Florida: Smith 2341

Homeless people

Alabama: Black 12, Bruno 17, Ireland 39
California: Alafi 235, Altos 237, Bialis 313, Community 421, Corwin 428, Eagle 470, Five 509, Foundation 521, Horwitz 633, Jolson 672, Lighthouse 756
Colorado: Elf 1262, RBG 1344
Connecticut: Albert 1389, Fippinger 1450, Kaufmann 1495
District of Columbia: **Butler 1792**, Himmelfarb 1815, Jovid 1817, Replogle 1831
Florida: Bond 1897, Brighton 1899, Couch 1953, Insetta 2119, Landwirth 2167, Nissim 2231, Overstreet 2242, Ryan 2305, Thomas 2370, Wilson-Wood 2408
Georgia: Abreu 2431, Whitehead 2610, Wright 2620
Illinois: Bufka 2763, Bulkley, 2765, Family 2864, Fraida 2884, Meyer 3106, Steinmetz 3267
Indiana: Seymour 3448
Iowa: **Wahlert 3544**
Kentucky: GB 3657, Killian 3670
Massachusetts: Crawford 4059, Fassino 4086, Gildea 4103, Hogan 4132, Kelsey 4148, **Spero 4304**
Michigan: Allen 4372, Main 4501, Schmuckal 4559, Tuscola 4598
Minnesota: Edina 4672, Larsen 4728
Nebraska: Midlands 5104
New Jersey: A 5240, **Garcia 5362**, Kerney 5419, **Ostberg 5483**, Schwartz 5525
New Mexico: Con 5611
New York: August 5698, Clark 5848, Falconhead 5980, Lauren 6368, Metzger-Price 6483, Sidewalk 6796, Turner 6916
North Carolina: Glenn 7111, Strowd 7258
Ohio: Barron 7316, Johnson 7468, Osteopathic 7545, Walker 7630
Oregon: Elwood 7761, McKay 7795, Wessinger 7826
Pennsylvania: Cove 7939, Curaterra 7947, Drueding 7966, Hoch 8060, Hoffman 8062, Homeless 8065, Jansing-Cook 8079, Mattingly 8151, Union 8326, Wurts 8370
Rhode Island: Dwinell 8403, Kimball 8434, Perpetual 8471
Tennessee: **Fugitive 8618**
Texas: FHC 8853, Holloway 8946, Johnston 8972, Wheeler 9274, Williams 9280
Utah: Kennecott 9333
Virginia: **Delmar 9429**
Washington: DeFalco 9585, Foss 9598, Wilson 9725
Wisconsin: Inbusch 9847, Stateline 9937
Wyoming: Dragicevich 9969

Homeless services

Arizona: Garcia 122
California: Bank 272, CEC 382, Corwin 428, McKay 815, Muckel 850, Sawchuk 1010, Silicon 1038, **Sunwest 1094**
Connecticut: Donchian 1440, Ferguson 1446, Finn 1449
District of Columbia: Crowell 1799, Hanley 1814, Himmelfarb 1815
Florida: Baroco 1867, Chapman 1935, Ryan 2305, Yerrid 2420
Georgia: Colston 2464, TALX 2592
Idaho: Ambrosiani-Pastore 2663, Angels 2664, Leidy 2678
Illinois: Bulkley, 2765, Manne 3073, Seymour 3236, Woodruff 3330
Indiana: MutualBank 3421
Maine: Kennebec 3785
Massachusetts: East 4075, PerkinElmer 4238, Savage 4280, **Spero 4304**

Homeless shelters

Michigan: Community 4411, Zimmerman 4620
Minnesota: Edina 4672, Thorpe 4800
Missouri: Fabick 4907
New Jersey: Carlozzi 5287
New York: **Farkas 5988**, Levine 6387, Moore 6504, Sidewalk 6796, Stark 6846, Turner 6916, White 6972
North Carolina: Elks 7089
Ohio: Brethen 7331, Gilman 7423, Hazelbaker 7441, Osteopathic 7545
Oregon: McKay 7795
Pennsylvania: Clark 7925, Garthwaite 8013, Jansing-Cook 8079, Union 8326, Wurts 8370
Rhode Island: Kimball 8434, Perpetual 8471, Shea 8486
Texas: Beauchamp 8722, Hegi 8926, Meyer 9061, Tolleson 9238, Waggoners 9255
Utah: Crawford 9314, Funding 9325, Steiner 9358
Washington: DeFalco 9585, Longbrake 9655
Wisconsin: Gardner 9825, Stateline 9937

Homeless shelters

Alabama: Petra 53
California: Razi 957, Thrill 1117
Connecticut: Donchian 1440
Florida: Gate 2034, Taplin 2363
Illinois: Kilrea 3017
Massachusetts: East 4075, Kelleher 4147, McNeice, 4195
Michigan: Branch 4396, Kantzler 4478
Missouri: Slusher 5009
New York: Jennings 6259
Ohio: Kramer 7485, Osteopathic 7545, Wagler 7629
Tennessee: Monday 8652
Utah: Bastian 9304, CASA 9312
Virginia: Geary-O'Hara 9456
Washington: Fales 9594
Wisconsin: Ariens 9776

Hospice care

California: Atkinson 259, Bucolo 356, Cerri 384, Cleo 407, Community 421, Fox 525, Gross 587, Harman 598, Joy 677, Lambert 728, Levin 749, Livingston 761, Smullin 1060
Connecticut: Gorab 1468, Lebovitz 1506
Delaware: Berghorst 1619, Palmer 1718, Rosenfeld 1732
District of Columbia: Tucker 1836, Westport 1838
Florida: Andre 1849, Bastien 1872, Brownley 1907, Capital 1918, Case 1925, Couch 1953, Crane 1955, Helow 2089, Hendrix 2090, Lelash 2178, Powell 2265, Price 2267, Rembert 2281, Rogers 2290, Smith 2342, Stellar 2348, von 2388
Georgia: Echlin 2472, Marcus 2544, Smith 2586, Woodruff 2617
Idaho: Hare 2675, Leidy 2678
Illinois: Bulkley, 2765, Corbett 2809, Hoffer 2975, Johnson 3001, Kainz 3004, Karasik 3006, Landau 3037, Lebus 3043, McCrea 3088, North 3142, Simpson 3248, Wolf 3326
Indiana: Custer 3366, Nugent 3425, O'Rourke-Schof 3429
Iowa: Vermeer 3542
Kansas: Middlekauff 3603, Price 3616
Kentucky: GHH 3658, Hannah 3659, Yeager 3710
Maryland: Cole 3839, Huether/McClelland 3884, Pettit 3935, Tucker 3969, Wolpoff 3990
Massachusetts: East 4075, Helman 4126, Permanent 4239, Shattuck 4291, Videtta 4343
Michigan: McDole 4507, Nusbaum 4524, Padnos 4529, Phantom 4538, Schmuckal 4559, Shapiro 4566, Sinai 4570
Minnesota: Acorn 4623, Fraser 4689
Missouri: Mungenast 4966, Wolff 5039
Nevada: Andress 5132, Binion 5139
New York: D-B 5903, High 6206, Hiler 6207, Kenlou 6299, Northern 6540, Rheinstrom 6665, Russo 6711, Walsh 6942, Warwick 6945

North Carolina: Bolick 7056, Cannon 7067, Gambrill 7106, Kennedy 7145, Moretz 7189, Rostan 7232, Triplett 7270

Ohio: Brethen 7331, Community 7356, Heimbinder 7445, Johnson 7468, Luedeking 7506, Van 7625, Welty 7635

Oklahoma: Peel 7714

Pennsylvania: **Arronson 7844**, Russo 8249, Shenk 8274

South Carolina: Lutz 8533

South Dakota: Eleanor's 8559

Tennessee: Atticus 8582, EBS 8610, Pickle 8660

Texas: Foster 8868, Hill 8938, Holmes 8947, Wal-Dot 9256

Virginia: Chastain 9419, Lacy 9485

Washington: Horn 9625, Klaue 9647

West Virginia: Carter 9741, Hewgill 9748, Vecellio 9770

Wisconsin: Anderson 9773, Caritas 9791, Gardner 9825, Kalscheur 9858, Sartori 9921, Webcrafters-Frautschi 9957

Wyoming: Ellbogen 9971

Hospital care

Alabama: Blount 13, Brinkley 15, Goodrich 29, JADO 40, Kemp 42, King 43, Viro 73

Arizona: **Beals 100**, Burns 102, Cadeau 104, Jasam 133, Robson 160, Schlein 165, Valley 178

Arkansas: Merkle 203, Nabholz 208, Riggs 214, Sturgis 217

California: Adams 228, Altos 237, Beam 287, Bekins 294, Bellini 298, Beneto 301, Bernstein 307, Beynon 312, Blanchard 321, Bonner 327, Broad 347, **Butler 365**, Butte 366, **Cantor 375**, **Chan 388**, Church 403, Community 421, Corday 426, Corwin 428, Crawford 435, Dorskind 459, Ducommun 465, Elder 475, Ellen 478, First 506, Foor 516, Fusenot 541, Gellert 550, Gooding 571, Gross 587, H. 590, Handley 596, Harman 598, Hayman 606, Hellman 614, Hoefer 628, Horwitz 633, Jain 657, Jamieson 658, Keating 695, Lee 737, Levin 749, Lewis 753, Lipp 759, Livingston 761, Lyons 776, Mann 790, Mazda 810, Michaud 824, Mitchell 838, Morgenstern 848, **Munson 852**, Nasaw 858, Oak 872, Perenin 914, Radin 948, Rees 961, Reinhold 963, Reitman 964, Ridder 970, Rishwain 974, Ross 988, Sands 1001, Scott 1023, Seip 1028, Setzer 1029, Shannon 1030, **Skyscrape 1047**, Smith 1055, Smith 1056, Smith-Walker 1057, Sprague, 1070, Thagard 1109, United 1136, Uplands 1139, Wagner 1149, Waller 1152, Webb 1162, Western 1176, Wheeler 1179, Wrather 1198, Yoder 1202, Zurlo 1217

Colorado: Bloedorn 1238, Brent 1240, **Fishback 1270**, Goodwin 1279, Heginbotham 1289, Joslin-Needham 1300, Kortz 1307, Ladd 1310, Leprino 1313, Lustig 1318, Schramm 1350, Spencer 1356, Taylor 1364, W.J.D. 1375, Warner 1376

Connecticut: Abramowitz 1384, Acorn 1385, Allwin 1390, Avery 1396, Baldwin 1399, Barden 1402, Bender 1405, Chelsea 1418, Crosswicks 1425, Curran 1427, Dennett 1432, Denzler 1434, Ferguson 1446, Floren 1451, Fuchs 1459, Greenhill 1472, Hewitt 1482, Howard 1484, Katen 1494, Kay 1496, Klein 1499, Mellen 1525, Newtown 1532, Nirenberg 1534, Sekerak 1564, Storr 1575, Tell 1580, Thornton 1582, Tully 1588, Velaj 1592, WMP 1598

Delaware: Anastasi 1610, Coleman 1644, **Colgate 1645**, Croll 1650, Freedman 1665, Heuer 1680, Messing 1708, Milliken 1711, Mulvaney 1713, Palmer 1718, Pinkerton 1721, Rosenfeld 1732, Selin 1742, Swift, 1754, Whitman 1778

District of Columbia: Hanley 1814, Lemon 1819, Olender 1824, Tucker 1836, Westport 1838

Florida: Adler 1842, Ael 1843, Bailey 1863, Bastien 1872, Baulch 1873, Beasley 1877, Becton 1880, Blank 1890, Blechman 1894, Brownley 1907, Capital 1918, Chowdhury 1943, Couch 1953, de 1966, Diane 1974, Dyer 1985, Fish 2001, Five 2002, Fontaine 2006, Friedland 2025, Gordon 2050, Grader 2054, Greenblatt 2063,

Greene-Sawtell 2065, Gregory 2067, Grossman 2068, Haugland 2084, Ingalls 2118, Isenberg 2121, Kahn 2133, Kane 2137, Kaye 2141, KBR 2142, Kessler 2145, Kuriansky 2162, Lelash 2178, Lenkin 2179, Mendelson 2211, Pearce 2252, Pusey 2272, Reinhold 2280, Richard 2285, Rogers 2292, Rothman 2299, Ryan 2304, Setzer 2325, Smick 2340, Spier 2345, Strong 2353, Swisher 2361, Thomas 2371, Tippett 2376, Vanneck-Bailey 2384, Vasey 2385, von 2388, Whiting 2403, Wolf 2410, **Wollowick 2412**, Wrightson-Ramsing 2416, Yerrid 2420

Georgia: Arnold 2436, Echlin 2472, **Gage 2482**, Goodman 2492, Hodgson 2507, Inman 2519, Lee 2540, Lipscomb 2541, Marshall 2545, Mix 2550, Piedmont 2566

Hawaii: Ululani 2652

Illinois: Allyn 2703, Baird 2718, Banta 2719, Bates 2724, Bates 2725, Bellebyron 2731, Best 2740, Buntrock 2766, Ceres 2779, Chapin-May 2782, Clarks 2792, Cohn 2795, Cohn 2796, Dunning 2841, Educational 2848, Fildes 2872, Fremont 2891, Garard, 2902, General 2907, George 2911, Half 2942, Hanson 2950, Hegeler 2963, Hess 2969, Hoffer 2975, Hopper 2977, Houlihan 2979, JMR 2999, Johnson 3001, Kainz 3004, Karasik 3006, Keeney 3007, Kellcie 3008, Kelly 3012, Keyes 3016, Knowles 3023, **Lazzara 3042**, Lebus 3043, Leibowitz 3046, Lichtman 3052, Louis 3063, MacDonald 3068, McNally 3097, Meier 3101, **Meyers 3107**, Millard 3109, Millard 3110, Mitchell 3120, Mohr 3121, Munson 3130, NCI 3134, New 3136, Pepper 3167, Rosen 3206, Russell 3216, Ryan 3219, Shapiro 3240, Simon 3247, Simpson 3248, Smithburg 3254, Sramek 3259, Staley 3264, Stuart 3273, Tafel 3280, Taylor 3285, Vail 3301, Webb 3316, Weiss 3317, Will 3322, Wolf 3326, Wright 3333

Indiana: CDM 3355, Cohen 3357, Custer 3366, Gammon 3385, Jasper 3401, Jolan 3404, Klapper 3408, Oakley 3426, Oliver 3428, Rinker 3438, Rush 3441, Scott 3446, Weston 3467

Iowa: Coons 3481, Farver 3491, Forster 3494, Van 3539, Vermeer 3541

Kansas: Baehr 3556, Insurance 3587, McFadden 3601, Miller-Mellor 3604, Mingenback 3605, Rathert 3617, Swearingen 3631, Weber 3640

Kentucky: Abercrombie 3645, Reed 3688, Stock 3697, Trager 3701

Louisiana: Live 3734, Powers 3746, Selber 3751

Maine: Kennebec 3785, Reny 3802, Sukeforth 3805

Maryland: Ammerman 3813, Bank 3818, Berger 3821, Davis 3844, DelSignore 3847, Devito 3848, Ferris 3859, Fine 3861, Gewirz 3869, Greene-Milstein 3876, Hobbs 3882, Hurwitz 3886, Israelson 3888, Izzo 3889, Kay 3892, Mangione 3907, Meltzer 3911, Mullan 3920, Nicholl 3926, Pettit 3935, RCM 3937, Rogers-Wilbur 3941, Salisbury 3945, Slavin 3954, SPM 3958, Weinman 3981, Witt/Hoey 3989, Wolpoff 3990

Massachusetts: Alden 3999, Altamira 4001, Ansin 4003, Benz 4017, Cabot 4034, Connell 4055, Davoli 4065, Donovan 4070, Druker 4071, Easthampton 4076, Fassino 4086, Fay 4087, Fessenden 4090, Frisbie 4099, Gale 4100, Goldman 4105, Guttag 4109, Hagler 4111, Hale 4112, Harwood 4119, Hopedale 4134, Hornblower 4135, Hyde 4139, Jackson 4140, Jefferson 4142, Kelleher 4147, Kenwood 4150, Kershaw 4151, Kidder 4152, King 4156, Kneisel 4157, Lamm 4165, Mank 4187, Marino 4190, McCutchin-Collins 4193, McNeice, 4195, Mohr 4206, Morningstar 4207, Morse 4208, Morse 4209, Morse 4210, Nichols 4223, Oristaglio 4232, Perry 4240, Reisman 4263, Rosse 4272, Russell 4273, Savage 4280, Schlager 4283, Smith 4298, **Spero 4304**, Stare 4308, Stearns 4311, **Tatelman 4322**, Tatelman 4323, Torok 4331, Tye 4334, Ullian 4335, Webber 4351, Weber 4352, Weld 4356, Wyman-Gordon 4364

Michigan: Baiardi 4381, Baldwin 4382, Barton-Malow 4386, Baum 4387, Blatt 4393, Buhr 4400, Currie 4418, Gershenson 4453, Kay 4480, Kiwanis 4484,

Kosch 4485, McNally 4510, Morley 4518, Oreffice 4528, Padnos 4529, Pardee 4534, Ratner 4548, River 4551, Sehn 4563, Sinai 4570, St. 4576, Sutaruk 4583, Tremble 4595, **Triford 4597**, Wetsman 4611, Zimmerman 4620

Minnesota: Baratz 4635, Dellwood 4665, Knowlton 4725, Maslowski 4741, Oak 4752, OSilas 4758, Tennant 4798

Mississippi: Biloxi 4824, McCarty, 4848, Wittel 4858

Missouri: **Bohm 4871**, Brace 4874, Butler 4880, Dierberg 4895, Enright 4903, Fabick 4907, Kemper 4935, **Maor 4952**, Price 4982, Sachs 4989, Schutte 4995, Stroble 5015, Timmons 5021, Von 5033, Wallace 5036, Wolff 5039, Wolff 5040

Nebraska: Ameritas 5067, Batchelder 5072, Hansen 5087, Heuermann 5092, Lienemann 5100, Midlands 5104, Walker 5126

Nevada: Geomar 5160, Pinnacle 5183, Webb 5196

New Hampshire: Barker 5204, Finlay 5213, Kimball 5216, Lynch 5221, Martin 5222, Olcott 5227, Tillotson 5234, Verney 5236

New Jersey: Amboy 5246, Antz 5250, Bauer 5257, Brook 5273, Brunetti 5281, CBIS 5288, Cordover 5304, **Daft 5310**, Devine 5317, Dickinson 5319, Fox 5349, Frelinghuysen 5354, Glasser 5371, Goldberger 5372, Heart 5388, **Integra 5400**, Johnson 5406, Jones 5408, Kresa 5432, Kurr 5435, Lieberman 5448, Liss 5451, Machuga 5454, Mamiye 5456, Marron 5461, McConnell 5463, Paragano 5488, **Patel 5492**, Patrick 5494, Pierson 5500, **Rippel 5510**, Riskin 5511, Schwartz 5525, Selective 5528, Spiro 5546, Waterview 5572, Weinstein 5576, Wilf 5588

New York: Agate 5649, AGB 5650, Anderson 5674, Apple 5682, Aresty 5686, Balm 5708, Barbash 5714, BBL 5724, Beach 5725, Berkowitz 5739, **Blinken 5757**, Block 5759, Bostwick 5767, Bovin 5770, Box 5771, Boxer 5772, Brinkman 5786, Brosens 5789, Brown 5791, Burchan 5801, Burrows 5803, Burton 5804, Bush 5805, Chasanoff 5833, Cohenca 5861, Cohn 5863, Coleman 5870, Coles 5871, Conley 5874, Cranshaw 5885, Cutco 5890, DeMario 5909, Dorsky 5924, Downey 5930, Edelweiss 5944, Elkins 5955, EMSA 5961, Evans 5973, F. 5977, Feinberg 5993, Feldman 5996, Feldstein 5997, Ferguson 5999, Ferriday 6000, Ficalora 6002, Follett 6016, Fraiman 6023, **Frank 6026**, Gaffney 6049, Gant 6054, Gerhard 6072, Gilliam 6078, Goldenberg 6092, Gordon 6112, Grateful 6131, Greenspan 6134, Gutman 6152, H. 6153, Hajim 6158, Hallingby 6160, Handler 6161, Harmon 6168, Harris 6172, Heffer 6180, Henshel 6192, Heyman 6201, Horowitz 6225, Hulbert 6232, Jacobson 6255, Jamakepe 6256, Jaykine 6257, Johnson 6267, Kandell 6283, Kelsey 6298, Klein 6325, Koessler 6334, Koessler 6335, Kriser 6347, L 6353, **Laub 6367**, Lemle 6377, Levy 6391, Liberman 6396, LSK 6415, Marble 6441, Marshall 6445, Marshall 6446, Maslin 6448, Mead 6466, Michaels 6488, Morris 6508, Mule 6515, Newcastle 6528, Newman 6532, Newman 6534, Northern 6540, Norwich 6542, Oestreicher 6549, O'Sullivan 6565, Palisades 6569, Parshelsky 6578, Peckham 6583, Pollock 6616, Polsky 6618, Price 6628, Rachesky 6642, Rapaport 6646, Ring 6671, Ritter 6673, Ritter 6674, Roe 6681, Rose 6683, Rosenthal 6693, Rosenthal 6695, Rosner 6698, Russo 6711, Ruttenberg 6715, Sackler 6717, Saunders 6733, Schaefer 6735, **Schmeelk 6742**, Seelig 6769, Shapiro 6786, Sherman 6792, Siegel 6797, Silver 6800, Silverstein 6803, Slade 6809, Slade 6810, Smith 6815, Society 6821, Stanton 6845, Stebbins 6850, Switzer 6889, Thanksgiving 6897, Tod 6901, Treiber 6907, Trimble 6910, Tytel 6917, Utopia 6923, Vogt 6933, Warwick 6945, Weinman 6955, **Weinstein 6956**, White 6972, **Woodland 6989**, Woodward 6993, Wright 6995, Young 7012, Zenkel 7023, Ziff 7027

North Carolina: Bane 7043, Boddie 7055, Brown 7058, Cary 7069, CJB 7076, First 7097, Flowers 7099, Helb 7122, Hoffman 7128, Kistler 7147, Koons 7148, Kosloski 7149, Live 7163, Marlboro 7169,

Mattison 7175, Mosser 7195, Oschwald 7203, Plansoen 7211, Post 7213, Pratt 7214, Vanderbilt 7273, Wells 7283
North Dakota: Fedje 7296
Ohio: Anderson 7305, Athens 7311, Besl 7326, Black 7328, Brentwood 7330, Christen 7353, Comunale, 7358, Crandall 7366, Damico 7370, Davey 7373, Dermitt 7378, Fedeli 7393, Fox 7409, Frost 7412, Garcia 7416, Haskell 7439, Homan 7451, Huntington 7460, Klock 7480, Kloenne 7481, Lincoln 7496, Lockwood 7502, Lundgard 7508, Matthes 7517, Miller 7527, Norris 7538, Powers 7550, Ritchie 7561, Rosenberry 7562, Schwartz 7576, Scion 7578, Seifert 7584, Southard 7599, STERIS 7605, Van 7625, Wasserstrom 7632, Williamson 7640
Oklahoma: Chilton 7667, Everest 7676, Evergreen 7677, Gelvin 7682, Goddard 7684, Livengood 7698, Lolmaugh 7700, Stone 7721, Wolff 7738
Oregon: Collins 7752, Gill 7766, Giustina 7767, Holzman 7775, Michael 7799, Rietman 7809, Schmidt 7813, Singer 7819, White 7830
Pennsylvania: Ames 7840, **Arronson 7844**, Ayling 7849, Baker 7851, Baldwin, 7852, Betz 7870, Bolte 7882, Cameron 7911, Carlson 7916, Carnahan-Jackson 7917, CNB 7929, **Cohn 7931**, Columbia 7932, Cove 7939, Crawford 7945, Dicerbo 7956, Dinardo 7960, Dozzi 7965, Drueding 7966, Ellis 7978, Engel 7981, First 7996, Fleming 8000, Fountainhead 8004, Gauss 8014, Groff 8027, Grundy 8029, **Hitchcock 8059**, Hoffman 8062, Hoffman 8063, Ice 8072, Jackson 8078, Katz 8089, Knox 8101, Levee 8121, Lewis 8126, Lord 8132, Mason 8147, McCune 8155, Mellon 8167, Moffat 8175, Mudge 8181, Mukaiyama-Rice 8183, Murphy 8185, Nathan 8188, Packer 8201, Patterson 8205, Quaker 8228, Reiss 8234, Richards 8236, Rosenberg 8244, Ryan 8251, Saramar 8253, Schoonmaker 8260, Schwartz 8265, Scott 8266, Smith 8280, Stewart 8301, Stotland 8303, **Susquehanna 8310**, Thomas 8316, Tippins 8318, Weiler-Miller 8348, Whalley 8353, Woodall 8368
Rhode Island: Arakelian 8381, Bird 8389, Charlton, 8394, Galkin 8410, Greene 8413, Hartman 8417, Horton 8423, Jacbel 8426, Johnson 8430, Kimball 8434, Kingsbury 8435, Koffler 8436, Littlefield 8441, Mann 8448, Mauze 8450, McCarthy 8452, McWethy 8453, Pardee 8468, Pillsbury 8473, Prouty 8476, Salmanson 8481, Schwarz 8483, Sinclair 8488, Washington 8500, Wells 8501, West 8502, White 8503, Wright 8506, York 8507
South Carolina: Bonner 8513, Chapman 8517
South Dakota: Emerald 8562, Engelsma 8563, Welk 8577
Tennessee: Cole 8600, Community 8601, Johnson 8634, Kennedy 8638, LaRoche 8641, New 8654, Pattee 8656, Stadler 8678
Texas: Amarillo 8697, Anderson 8704, Ash 8709, Augur 8712, Bertha 8729, Bowers 8736, Budwine 8754, Cogdell 8777, Corlin 8788, **Crowder 8792**, Dale 8794, Elkins 8838, Foster 8867, Frill 8877, Fruehauf 8879, Fuchs 8881, Graham 8896, Greentree 8901, Griffin 8902, Hicks 8936, Hillcrest 8939, Holloway 8946, Johnston 8972, Joseph 8974, Kahn 8978, Kayser 8980, King 8994, Klein 8997, Lantana 9009, MacDonald-Peterson 9032, McKee 9052, Mosbacher 9075, North 9089, Pak 9110, Patton 9119, Reuhl 9150, Richter 9153, Robinson 9158, Rosen 9161, Sanguinetti 9172, Sear 9186, Taub 9229, Thorne 9235, Vaughan 9248, Wolf 9285
Utah: Callister 9310, Eskuche 9323, Schmidt 9349
Virginia: Andreas 9388, Charles 9418, **Delmar 9429**, Denit 9430, Edlavitch 9440, Farkas 9445, Franklin 9452, Grandis 9462, Harris 9466, Houff 9473, Kaufman 9482, Leonard 9489, Ochsman 9504, Peachtree 9508
Washington: Crete 9583, CSM 9584, Furnessville 9602, Gius 9606, Hyde 9627, Murray 9667, Quest 9681, Schuler 9690, Shemanski 9693, Thurston 9713, Titus-Will 9714, True 9716, Wilkens 9724

West Virginia: Bowers 9738, Driehorst 9743, Hott 9753, Huntington 9754
Wisconsin: Birnschein 9783, Glanert 9827, Kachel 9857, Lutsey 9873, Mason 9880, ROS 9918, Sartori 9921, Schlegel 9922, Simms 9929, Smith 9931, Sullivan 9944, Van 9952, Wagner 9955, Weyers 9959
Wyoming: Connemara 9967, Ellbogen 9971, Johnson 9977, Sargent 9985, Welch 9998

Housing development

Arizona: Declaration 111, Harmsen, 128, Rudge 164
Arkansas: Hennessy 198
California: Altos 237, Amin 241, Bank 272, Beattie 289, Bellwether 299, Bernstein 308, Borch 330, Boscacci 333, Christian 401, Ebell 471, Elder 475, Hollywood 630, i.am.angel 645, Lennox 745, Lighthouse 756, Mae 780, Moskowitz 849, New 864, Palo 900, Rees 961, Rogers 980, Rotasa 991, Silicon 1038, Silton 1039, Stein 1079, **Sunwest 1094**, **Wakerly 1150**
Colorado: Graves 1280, Heginbotham 1289, Jacobs 1298, **Oreg 1335**
Connecticut: Albert 1389, Dime 1438, Donchian 1440, Ensign-Bickford 1442, Harris 1478, Newtown 1532, Savings 1559
Delaware: ABE 1607, Just 1688, Thronson 1766
District of Columbia: **Butler 1792**, Davies 1801
Florida: Archibald 1852, Capital 1918, Concourse 1950, Couch 1953, Dalton 1960, Elster 1990, Ford 2010, Galeana 2030, Gate 2034, Gelbart 2035, Goldman 2047, Higgs 2096, KT 2160, Lacy, 2163, Munroe 2228, Oristano 2241, Ransburg 2274, Rogers 2291, Shuey 2333, Spier 2345, Taylor 2364, Vernon 2387, Wilson-Wood 2408, Zehnder 2423
Georgia: Athens 2437, Boone 2446, Forehand 2479, Georgia 2485, Strong 2590, Vogel 2600
Hawaii: Locations 2638
Idaho: Angels 2664, Beckman 2665, Leidy 2678
Illinois: Bufka 2763, Cafaro-Livingston 2772, Cremer 2815, Full 2895, Gardner 2904, Hark 2955, Heath 2962, Hill 2971, Kemper 3014, Kjellstrom 3019, **Lindon 3054**, Lyon 3066, Marquette 3078, Pawlowski 3165, Reed 3191, Russell 3216, Saliba 3221, Speiser 3257, Steinmetz 3267, Von 3305, Wolf 3327, Woodruff 3330
Indiana: Brave 3350, Gammon 3385, Kharis 3407, Mothershead 3419, MutualBank 3421
Iowa: GuideOne 3503
Kentucky: Foundation 3655, Renau 3689
Louisiana: Catalyst 3717, Ellis 3723, Pugh 3747, Steinhagen 3755
Maine: **Dugas 3776**
Maryland: Baltimore 3816, Cole 3839, Ford 3863, Halle 3878, Newday 3925, Pettit 3935, Rouse 3943
Massachusetts: 2 3992, Ansin 4003, Boynton 4025, Brooks 4028, Chabot 4042, Chicopee 4047, East 4075, Easthampton 4076, Fay 4087, Gildea 4103, Griffin 4107, Kelsey 4148, Killian 4154, MutualOne 4216, Newburyport 4221, Phelps 4242, Sicari 4295, Sword 4318, Xeric 4365
Michigan: Barton-Malow 4386, Buist 4401, Community 4411, Degroot 4423, Delano 4426, Delong-Sweet 4427, Ervin 4437, Grosse 4460, Mackinac 4499, Padnos 4529, River 4551, Stubnitz 4582, Tyler-Little 4599, Whiting 4614, Whitman 4615
Minnesota: Maranatha 4739, March 4740, Midcontinent 4745, RJW 4777, **Sundance 4796**, Tennant 4798, Thorpe 4800
Missouri: Butler 4880, Chapman 4884, Curry 4892, Kenney 4936, Moneta 4962
Nevada: Stout 5190
New Hampshire: Finlay 5213, Jameson 5215, Woodbury 5238
New Jersey: Amboy 5246, CKT 5297, Columbia 5301, Domenica 5323, Hill 5393, Mullen 5475, **Patel 5492**, Roma 5513, Selective 5528, Waters 5571, Yates 5595
New York: **Abba's 5634**, Athens 5696, Bank 5710, Bikuben 5746, BTMU 5795, **Cogitare 5855**, De 5904, EBA 5941, Falconhead 5980, **Family 5983**,

Feuerring 6001, Fleming 6014, Friedlander 6038, Grant 6129, Legacy 6373, Lufkin 6421, Mack 6430, MRA 6513, Plymouth 6612, Pollock 6617, Samuels 6725, Senator 6775, Sheetz 6790, Stark 6846, Still 6866, Warwick 6945, Weismann 6960
North Carolina: BB&T 7045, Davis 7083, Fox 7103, McMerty 7180, Mize 7186, **Rolander 7229**, Wilkinson 7288
Ohio: Chemed 7350, H 7434, Hampson 7436, Home 7452, Knoll 7483, Musson 7534, Norris 7538, Sandfair 7569, Sauerland 7570, Sears-Swetland 7581, Shannon 7586, Young 7651
Oklahoma: Elpis 7675, Tandy 7723, Wegener 7731
Oregon: Hitchman 7774, Jurrens 7780, Knudson 7785, Portland 7807, Simple 7818
Pennsylvania: Balzereit 7853, Boscia 7887, Briggs 7892, Chase 7921, Conestoga 7934, EFM 7974, First 7998, Harsco 8040, Hoffman 8062, Jordan 8082, Mukaiyama-Rice 8183, Penn 8208, Teleflex 8314, Union 8326, Wolstenholme 8366, Yoh 8373
Rhode Island: Bowen 8391, Del 8401, Washington 8500, Wilson 8504
South Carolina: Davis 8521, Williams/Brice-Edwards 8549
South Dakota: Watertown 8576
Tennessee: **Louisiana-Pacific 8644**, Powell 8661
Texas: Adam 8691, **Astri 8711**, Cariker 8762, Hamilton 8913, Journey 8975, Julian 8976, Levy 9014, Littauer 9021, McCarty 9047, Mummert 9079, Opie 9099, Smith 9201, Torchmark 9240, Wheeler 9274, Winston 9282, Wood 9290
Vermont: Carris 9367
Virginia: American 9387, Burford 9411, Dwyer 9439, Fink 9447, Greco 9463, Hilltop 9470, Ivakota 9477, Pruden 9517, Stultz 9539
Washington: Amelia 9559, DG 9586, Longbrake 9655, Schuler 9690, Skagit 9696
Wisconsin: Brown 9790, Dudley 9811, Easter 9813, Erdman 9816, Hyde 9846, Johnson 9852
Wyoming: Scott 9987

Housing for the homeless

Florida: Wilson-Wood 2408
Minnesota: Edina 4672
New Jersey: Schwartz 5525
Pennsylvania: Cove 7939, Hoffman 8062, Union 8326

Housing rehabilitation

California: Troy 1130

Housing services

Indiana: Milton 3418
Massachusetts: Lamm 4165
Michigan: Conrad 4413
Minnesota: Edina 4672
New Jersey: Columbia 5301
New York: REBNY 6656
Ohio: Davidson 7374
Oregon: Huddart 7776
Washington: Johnson 9633

Human rights

Arizona: National 153
Arkansas: Darragh 193, Families 196, Hussman 201
California: **Alalusi 236**, Arlene 252, Bochnowski 325, Corwin 428, Cutler 438, Emanuel 480, Hidden 620, Jorgensen 676, Lyons 776, Miller 831, Mills 834, Nickoll 867, PTSRK 943, Stone 1085, Thrill 1117, Von 1148, Yen 1201
Colorado: Arches 1222, Warner 1376
Connecticut: Mahadeva 1517, Schloss 1562, Tierney 1584
Delaware: Cultures 1652
Florida: Around 1854, Blatt 1893, Isenberg 2121, Peyton 2258
Georgia: Samford 2578

Illinois: Abelson 2693, Bernfield 2737, Dick 2830, EMA 2854, Jocarno 3000, **Landau 3036**, **New 3137**, **New 3138**, Orsini 3156, Poncher 3181, Rothman 3213, Shaw 3242

Indiana: Sherwood 3451

Kansas: Buford 3562

Maryland: **Goldberg 3872**, Slavin 3954

Massachusetts: Alvord 4002, Cabot 4035, Hurston 4138, Lamm 4165

Michigan: Causley, 4405, Rottman 4553

Minnesota: Briggs 4648, **Winds 4820**

Nevada: **Center 5145**, **Do 5153**

New Jersey: Brown 5278, **Buddha 5282**, Kessel 5420, **Knistrom 5426**

New Mexico: **Angelica 5605**, Horn 5618, Nirvana 5621

New York: 1848 5629, Angelson 5679, Baobab 5711, Brenner 5781, Calamus 5809, Fowey 6021, Fuchsberg 6044, Furman 6045, Hap 6164, JKW 6263, Koha 6337, Mendell 6472, Miller 6493, Olum 6555, Phuong 6601, Provident 6632, Purple 6634, Sommer 6825, **Sparkplug 6830**, Turner 6916, Wagner 6938, Whispering 6970, Zenkel 7023

North Carolina: Redwoods 7218

Ohio: Armington 7309, Busemeyer 7342, Haskell 7439, Sears-Swetland 7581, Steiner-King 7602

Oklahoma: Sisk 7719

Oregon: **Larson 7788**

Pennsylvania: David 7950, Penn 8208, Tabas 8312

South Carolina: Greenwood 8526

Texas: Boeing 8733, Ik 8959, Meyerson 9062, Morrow 9074

Vermont: Block 9366, Kaufman 9378

Washington: **Jernigan 9631**, Madrona 9657

Wyoming: Cutting 9968

Human services

Alabama: Abahac 1, Abroms 2, Adams 3, Anderson 5, Anderson 6, Barkley 9, Birmingham 11, Black 12, Boult 14, Brown 16, Bruno 17, Davis 24, Day 25, Friedman 27, Glaze 28, Goodrich 29, Griswold 31, Ireland 39, JADO 40, Kemp 42, King 44, Kirkland 45, Loeb 47, Norquist 51, Pei-Ling 52, Phifer, 54, Piassick 55, Rikard 59, Ripps 60, Rothschild 61, Siloam 65, Strain 68, Thompson 70, Upchurch, 72, Viro 73, Watson 76

Alaska: Gottstein 86, Hooker 87

Arizona: Adelante 93, Adkerson 94, Ahearn 95, Armstrong 97, Babbitt 98, Barton 99, **Beals 100**, Berlin 101, Cadeau 104, Chapin 105, Clark 106, Cooper 109, Corrigan 110, Dove 112, Drexler 113, du 114, Eaton 115, Empire 116, F2 117, Garcia 122, Glasrud 123, Goldberg 124, Grossman 126, Hansen 127, Harmsen, 128, Helms 129, Hughes 130, Immanuel 131, James 132, Jasam 133, Kuhle 139, Long 141, Louis 142, Massie 146, McKee 148, MCS 149, Moeller 150, Murphey 151, Napier 152, O'Rielly 154, Picerne 155, Robson 160, Rothschild 162, Schlein 165, Smith 170, Snell 171, Spalding 172, Stevens 175, Sturges 176, Zicarelli 185

Arkansas: Bailey 186, Bailey 187, **Baldor 188**, Blue 189, Bogle 191, Buck 192, Families 196, Heflin 197, Hennessy 198, Merkle 203, Marks 205, Murphy 207, Nabholz 208, Nabholz 209, Osborne 212, Southland 215, Union 219, White 220

California: 2005 223, Ach 226, Adams 228, Adelaide 230, Adelman 231, Adonai 232, Altos 237, Amador 238, Amin 240, Anatman 242, Anderson 243, Anhaltzer 245, Arata 248, Archer 250, Arlene 252, Armrod 253, Ascher, 256, **Asia 257**, Atkinson 259, Avery-Fuller-Welch 260, Avery-Tsui 261, Baker 266, Banchik 269, Bancroft-Clair 270, Bank 272, Banky 273, Barbonchielli 276, Barnett 278, Baskin 281, Beam 287, Beauregard 290, Becker 291, Becker 292, Bekins 294, Bell 295, Belle 296, Bellini 298, Beneto 301, Berakah 302, Berglund 303, Berkshire 305, Berry 309, Bettingen 310, Beulah 311, Bialis 313, Bilak 317, Blackie 319, **Blackman 320**, Blatteis 322, Boand 323, Bobowski 324, Bochnowski 325, Bonner 326, Boone 328, Borok 331, Braddock 336, Bradford 337, Bravo 338,

Breslow 340, Brewster 341, Bridges 342, Bright 345, Broad 347, Brooks-Mathews 350, Bryan 355, Bucolo 356, Bundy 360, Butler 364, **Butler 365**, Butte 366, Buttonwillow 367, Byrne 368, California 370, Candor 373, Cannon 374, Cardinal 376, Casillas 379, Castellano 380, Cavaricci 381, CEC 382, Celebrate 383, Cerri 384, Ceunis 385, Champions 386, **Chan 388**, Charitable 389, Cheeryble 390, Chiat 393, Chisick 395, Chitjian 396, Chrissie's 399, Christian 402, Cirila 405, Cloud 408, CNC 410, Coburn 411, Cohen 413, Collier 417, Community 420, Community 421, Corcoran 425, Corwin 428, Crabb 431, Cramblit 432, Crawford 435, Crummer 436, Cush 437, Dahl 439, Danem 441, Dass 443, Davies 444, Deacon 447, Del 449, Dermalogica 451, Diamantine 452, Dickinson 453, DiNapoli 454, Doelger 457, Dorskind 459, Drum 464, Dwelle 467, Dwyer 468, Dyer 469, Eagle 470, Ebell 471, Eichenberg-Larson 474, Eleven 476, Elfenworks 477, Ellen 478, Elliott 479, Emanuel 480, Endurance 482, Epstein/Roth 483, Eriksen 484, Evans 486, Familian 491, Family 492, Farmers 496, Faro 497, Fast 498, Feintech 502, Flicker 511, **Floyd 513**, Folger 515, Foor 516, Forgatch 517, Four 522, Fox 525, Frankel 526, Fremont 527, Friedman 530, Friedman 531, Fudge 537, Fuller 538, Funari 539, Fusenot 541, Gallanter 542, Gans 544, Garabedian 545, Gareeb 548, GAT 549, Gellert 550, George 551, Georgina-Frederick 552, Giles 554, Gilleland 556, Gilmore 557, Ginder 558, **Girls 559**, Glazer 561, Glazer 562, Glikbarg 564, Goldberg 567, Goodall 570, Gooding 571, Gordon 574, Graff 576, Green 578, Grey 582, Grey 583, Gross 587, H. 590, Hagopian 592, **Hampar 594**, Handlery 596, Harman 598, Harqua 599, Harris 600, Harris 601, Harvey 602, Hausman 603, Havner 604, Health 608, Heinz 612, Heller 613, Hellman 614, Helms 615, Hilltop 621, Hodges 627, Hoefer 628, Hohnstein 629, Hong 631, Horwich 632, Horwitz 633, **Hsieh 636**, **Hsu 637**, Hughes 639, HunterWard 641, Ichioka 647, Jamieson 658, Jatain 659, Jelin 662, Jesy 664, Joerger 665, Johnson 667, Johnson 669, Johnson 670, Jolson 672, Jones 673, Jones 674, Joy 677, Judkins 682, Kanoff 689, Kao 690, Katz 692, Keith 696, Kelly 697, Kendall 701, Kieve 703, Kim 704, Kinsey 707, Kirkorian 709, Kisco 710, Kite 711, KNU 713, Koss 720, Kreitzberg 721, Krishnan-Shah 722, Kwoh 724, Laguna 726, Lake 727, Lambert 728, Lamond 729, Lash 730, Latkin 731, **Lawrence 734**, Lebherz 735, Lee 737, Leland 741, Lemelson 742, Lemons 744, Lennox 745, Lester 747, Lester 748, Levin 749, Levy 751, **Levy 752**, Lewis 753, Lewis 754, Lighthouse 756, Lin 757, **Linked 758**, Lisle 760, Llagas 762, Looker 766, Los 769, Lundgren 772, Lyman 774, Lynch 775, MacCready 778, MacDonald 779, Mae 780, Magali 781, Magowan 782, Maher 783, Majestic 784, Malachi 785, March 791, Marcil 793, Marcus 794, Margolis 797, Marineau 798, Marshburn 799, Martin 802, Mashhoon 804, Mason 805, Massie 806, Masson 807, Mazda 810, McClatchy 811, McDaniel 812, McGraw 814, McKay 815, McLeod 818, McMahon 819, Meister 821, Michaud 824, Military 826, Miller 833, Mitchell 837, Mitchell 838, Mitchell, 839, **Modglin 840**, Mondavi 843, Money-Arenz 844, Moonwalk 845, Morgan 847, Morgenstern 848, Muckel 850, Mudd 851, **Munson 852**, Murad 854, Muskin 855, Nasaw 858, Nell 859, Nelson 860, Nelson 861, Neu 862, Nicholson 866, Nima 868, **Northern 870**, Oak 872, October 873, Olander 878, Olson 879, Onehope 881, Ontario 882, Open 883, Orfalea 887, Ornest 888, Osborn 891, O'Shea 892, Outrageous 894, OZ 896, Pacific 897, Page 899, Palo 900, Pardee 902, Parvin 905, Patterson 907, Penney 913, Pergo 915, **Peszynski 917**, Peterson 918, Peterson 919, PG 921, Phelps 923, Phillips 924, Physicians 925, Pickford 927, Piuze 928, Podell 930, Prete, 934, **Preuss 935**, Previti 937, Price 938, Price 939, PTSRK 943, Pulido 944, Rabinovitch 947, Rady 949, Ramsay 952, **Raymond 956**, Rediger 960, Reinhold 963, Rest 966, Reveas 967, Rhe 968, Ridder 970,

Rieger 971, Riley 973, Robinson 977, Rocca, 978, Roche 979, Roney 983, Rosenberg 985, Rosenfeld 986, Rosenthal 987, Ross 988, Rossi 989, Rosso 990, Rubin 992, Sammut 996, Sanfilippo 1002, Santa 1003, Sarandon 1004, Sassoon 1006, Saturno 1008, Sawchuk 1010, **Saya 1011**, Scandling 1012, Schulte 1018, Schultz 1019, Scott 1022, Scott 1023, **Scovel 1025**, Sebastiani 1027, Seip 1028, Setzer 1029, Shannon 1030, Shayne 1032, Shenandoah 1033, Shore 1034, SHP 1035, Siegel 1036, Silicon 1038, Skynyrd 1046, Sloss 1048, Small 1049, Smalley 1050, Smith 1051, Smith 1052, Smith 1053, Smith 1056, Smith-Welsh 1058, Smittcamp 1059, Smythe 1061, Solano 1063, Somekh 1064, Sondheimer 1065, Spiva 1068, Sprague 1069, Sprague, 1070, Stafford 1074, Stauffer 1077, Stellar 1080, Stewart 1082, Stewart 1083, Stoller 1084, Stone 1085, Storm 1087, Straus 1088, **Sunwest 1094**, Swinerton 1098, Syar 1099, SYZYGY 1101, Tanimura 1103, Tecumseh 1105, **Teichman 1106**, Thagard 1109, Theroux 1110, Thompson 1112, Thomson 1113, Thornton 1115, Three 1116, Tilley 1118, Tippett 1119, Tobey 1121, Tomkins 1122, Tomlinson 1123, Toole 1124, Torino 1125, Traina 1126, Trombetta 1128, Troy 1130, Trust 1131, Tsao 1133, Tuffli 1134, Twanda 1135, Uplands 1138, Uplands 1139, Uvas 1142, Van 1144, Von 1147, Von 1148, **Wakerly 1150**, Waller 1152, Walters 1153, Waltmar 1155, Walton 1156, Wang 1157, Ward 1158, Warren 1159, Webb 1162, Weisz 1167, Welfund 1169, Wendell 1172, Wertheimer 1173, West 1174, West 1175, Westphal 1177, Wheeler 1179, Whittier 1181, Wilbur 1182, **Wilkinson 1183**, Wilnai 1185, Winn 1189, Witkin 1191, **Wong 1194**, Wrather 1198, Yoder 1202, Zafiropoulo 1207, Zankel 1208, Zecca 1209, Ziegler 1210, Ziff 1211, Zimmerman, 1213, Zwick 1218

Colorado: 6/S 1219, Allen 1220, Arches 1222, Arsenault 1224, Ballantine 1226, Bardsley 1227, Bean 1228, Benson 1229, Benson 1230, Big 1235, Bjorkman 1236, Blair 1237, Bloom 1239, Brent 1240, Broomfield 1242, Caulkins 1245, Chotin 1246, Cliffline 1247, Clough 1248, Creative 1253, Dorset 1259, DWB 1260, Elf 1262, Elizabeth 1263, Erion 1265, F 1266, Family 1268, Flug 1271, Flying 1272, Fund 1274, Getz 1278, Goodwin 1279, Grossman 1281, Growing 1284, Hamilton 1285, HAVRK8 1288, Hewit 1292, Howard 1295, Hunt 1296, Hunter-White 1297, Jacobs 1298, JJP 1299, Joslin-Needham 1300, Joy 1301, Kern 1303, King 1305, Koelbel 1306, Kortz 1307, Leprino 1313, Lewis 1315, Living 1317, Marguf 1320, **McGrath 1322**, Moniker 1327, Mullen 1329, Neuman 1331, Oak 1333, **Oreg 1335**, Petunia 1336, Pluss 1337, Porphyry 1338, Praise 1339, Rakowich 1343, RBG 1344, Relationship 1346, Rockwise 1347, Routzon 1348, Schlessman 1349, Schramm 1350, Servant 1352, Shamrock 1353, **Someone 1354**, Spencer 1356, Steffens 1358, Stretesky 1360, Taddonio 1362, Tappan 1363, Taylor 1364, Tigertree 1366, Tomkins 1368, Triune 1370, W.J.D. 1375, Wexler 1377, White 1378, Wilson 1380, Wolcott 1381

Connecticut: Abramowitz 1384, Acorn 1385, Albert 1389, Alpha/Omega 1391, Ambler 1392, Anderson 1393, Anderson-Paffard 1394, Antonacci 1395, Avery 1396, Baggins 1398, Bannow-Larson 1400, Bantle 1401, Barden 1402, Bigelow 1408, Bowling 1409, Bridgemill 1412, Brown 1413, Calarco 1414, Caldwell 1415, Chelsea 1418, Cochrane 1420, Crew 1424, Crosswicks 1425, **Davis-McCullough 1429**, Dennett 1432, Denzler 1434, Deutsch 1436, Diageo 1437, Dime 1438, Donchian 1439, Donchian 1440, Eder 1441, Ensign-Bickford 1442, Family 1443, Farid 1444, Filingieri 1447, Finn 1449, Floren 1451, Foley 1452, **Friends 1456**, Friezo 1457, Gerbic 1463, Gladstein 1465, Goldfarb 1466, Grampy's 1469, Grant 1470, Greenfield 1471, Greenhill 1472, Gross 1473, Gryphon 1474, Harris 1478, Helping 1480, Hewitt 1482, Howard 1484, Jones 1490, Jost 1492,

Kaman 1493, Kaufmann 1495, Keefe 1497, Klein 1499, Kreitler 1502, Kuriansky 1503, Lamando 1504, Lavietes 1505, Lebovitz 1506, Linke 1508, Lippincott 1509, Lodbell 1511, Low 1513, Macauley 1514, **MacInnis 1515**, Mahadeva 1517, Manger 1518, Martin 1520, McLane 1522, Mellen 1525, Nessel 1529, Niblack 1533, Nirenberg 1534, Oberlander 1535, O'Herron 1536, Panwy 1539, Patricelli 1541, Perna-Rose 1542, Price 1544, Pryor 1546, Pulvermann 1547, RBS 1549, Roberts 1551, Robinson 1553, Rosenberg 1555, Salatto 1557, Santoro 1558, Savings 1559, Schaeneman, 1560, Schendel 1561, Schloss 1562, Shanley 1567, **Shoemate 1569, Sonja 1573**, Sorenson-Pearson 1574, Sullivan 1577, **Sullivan 1578**, Taylor 1579, Tell 1580, Thornton 1582, Thrall 1583, Titus 1585, Tully 1588, UIL 1589, Union 1590, Vance 1591, Wheeler 1594, Winokur 1597, Woodland 1599, WorldQuant 1600, Zacharia 1601, Zelnick/Belzberg 1602

Delaware: 18 1604, ABE 1607, Anastasi 1610, Anbinder 1611, Bennett 1618, Black 1622, Blau 1623, Bowman 1625, Bradley 1626, Brandsma 1627, Bresnan 1628, Brown 1630, Brown-Whitworth 1632, Bulova 1633, Burton 1634, Burt's 1635, Bushong 1636, Cammarota 1637, Cedarcrest 1639, City 1642, **Colgate 1645**, Coors 1647, Corrigan-Walla 1649, Croll 1650, Cross 1651, Cultures 1652, Day 1654, Doll 1657, Dunn 1659, EON 1661, Fernandina 1663, Foundation 1664, Freedman 1665, Giving 1668, Haldan 1675, Haldan 1676, Harkness 1677, Hauser 1678, Hawkins 1679, Hoops 1682, **Jackman 1683**, Jade 1684, Jadeja 1685, Jockers 1687, Kaye 1690, Klein, 1694, Kuehner 1695, Kutz 1696, Levin 1697, Lighten 1698, Lightner 1699, Loftus 1700, Mary's 1703, Massoud 1704, McIntosh 1705, McKiernan 1706, Merrion 1707, Milliken 1711, MMK 1712, Nelson 1714, New 1715, Palmer 1718, Pinkerton 1721, Praxis 1723, Relgalf 1725, Repass-Rodgers 1727, Rivers 1731, Rosenfeld 1732, Rothchild 1733, Russell 1735, Ryerson 1736, Sanders 1737, Schiffman 1738, Scripps 1741, **Singer 1744**, SNAVE 1747, Stein 1750, Stiefel 1751, Susman 1753, Swift, 1754, Talbott 1757, Taylor 1759, Teddy 1760, **TeleTech 1761**, Telluray 1762, Third 1763, Three 1765, Trussell 1767, Viridiun 1770, Vitale 1771, Washakie 1774, Weissman 1775, Welton 1776, Whitman 1778, Yablon 1782

District of Columbia: American 1785, Bench 1788, Bender 1789, Choksi 1795, Cook 1797, Cornerstone 1798, Crowell 1799, Dickson 1802, Dimick 1803, Dweck 1805, Goldman 1810, **Gorlitz 1811**, Greenberg 1812, Haft 1813, Hanley 1814, Lemon 1819, **Merriman 1820**, Miller-Wehrle 1821, Mimi 1822, Olender 1824, Peet 1827, Porter 1829, Replogle 1831, Rubenstein 1833, Westport 1838

Florida: 4 1840, A. 1841, Ael 1843, Anderson 1845, Anderson 1846, Anderson 1848, Around 1854, Auerbach 1859, Bailey 1862, Bailey 1863, Barbash 1865, Baroco 1867, Barrington 1868, Bartner 1869, Basham 1870, Bastien 1872, Baulch 1873, Baxter 1874, Beasley 1877, Becker 1879, Beeck 1881, Bell 1882, Bell 1883, Berelsman 1885, Berkowitz 1886, Biddinger 1887, Binz 1888, Blake 1889, Blank 1890, Blanksteen 1891, Blatt 1893, Bomberger 1896, Bond 1897, Brighton 1899, Brodsky 1901, Brody 1902, Brooke 1903, Brown 1904, Brown 1906, Burgoon 1908, Callas 1913, Cape 1917, Capital 1918, Carbonari 1919, Carlton 1922, Carrington 1923, Case 1925, Cassill 1926, Castellani 1927, Catalina 1928, Chadbourne 1932, Chanin 1934, Chapman 1935, Chardonnay 1936, Charlotte 1938, Chris 1944, Cody 1946, Collins 1949, Couch 1953, Crane 1955, Crutchfield 1957, CSX 1958, Dalton 1960, Dasburg 1961, Davis 1964, Defeo 1968, Dennis 1969, Densch 1970, Detter 1971, Deus 1972, Diamond 1973, Diane 1974, Dickinson 1975, Diermeier 1976, Duckwall 1982, Duda 1983, Ellis 1989, Enlightenment 1991, Erdle 1993, **Falk 1996**, Family 1997, Ferguson 1999, Finch 2000, Fish 2001, Five 2002,

Fontaine 2006, For 2007, Foster 2013, Foulds 2014, Foundation 2015, Frankel 2018, Freitas 2022, Friedland 2025, Friend 2026, Fry 2027, Galeana 2030, Gardner 2031, Garner 2032, Garvy 2033, Gate 2034, Gelbart 2035, Gerry-Corbett 2037, Glass 2039, Godbold 2041, Goddard 2042, Godsey 2043, Goetz 2044, Golden 2046, Goodwin 2048, Goody 2049, Gordon 2050, **Gordon 2051**, Grader 2054, Graymer 2058, Greaton 2060, Green 2061, Greene-Sawtell 2065, Greenfield 2066, Gregory 2067, Grossman 2068, Gulf 2069, Hagens 2071, Halmos 2075, **Handleman 2078**, Hansen 2079, Hardeman 2080, Hardison 2081, Harper 2082, Haskell 2083, Haugland 2084, Hayford 2086, Hegamyer 2087, Held 2088, Helow 2089, Hendrix 2090, HFRX 2092, HI 2093, Hicks 2094, Hieronymus 2095, Higgs 2096, Hinman 2099, Hoenle 2101, Hollo 2105, Holloway 2107, Holtz 2109, Hoornstra 2110, Hornik 2111, Huang 2113, Hultquist 2115, **Hutchison 2117**, Ingalls 2118, Insetta 2119, Irwin 2120, Isenberg 2121, J. 2122, Jacobsen 2123, Janke 2126, Jasam 2127, **Joshua 2132**, Kanders 2135, Kane 2137, Kaplan 2138, Kaulbach 2140, Kaye 2141, KBR 2142, Kehrer 2143, Kessler 2145, Kimmel 2146, King 2147, Kiwanis 2149, KLM 2151, Knippenberg 2154, Krause 2158, Kreisman 2159, Kugelman 2161, Lacy, 2163, Lambert 2164, Lamoureux 2166, Landwirth 2167, Lawson 2170, Lazarus 2172, Lazoff 2173, Lazzara 2174, Leiser 2177, Lelash 2178, **Levine 2181**, Lewis 2182, Life's 2184, Lipton 2185, Long 2189, Lookout 2190, MAH 2193, Marco 2194, Martin 2196, Mary 2198, McGahren 2204, Meerwarth 2209, MIDA 2212, Miller 2213, Miniaci 2215, Minto 2216, Moore 2217, Morris 2219, Mount 2223, Muccia 2225, Munroe 2228, Nelson 2230, Nissim 2231, Noble 2233, Nommontu 2234, Norjana 2235, Nuzzo 2236, Olemberg 2237, Olsen 2240, Oristano 2241, Overstreet 2242, **Pagoumian 2245**, Papper 2246, Parish 2247, Pascal 2249, Patterson 2250, Pearce 2252, Perryman 2255, Peters 2256, Phillips 2259, Phillips 2260, **Place 2261, Posnack 2262**, Powell 2264, Powell 2265, Preik 2266, Propp 2269, Prutky 2270, Pusey 2272, Ransburg 2274, Reckson 2277, Reeves 2279, Reinhold 2280, Resnick 2282, Richard 2285, River 2288, Rogers 2291, Rogers 2292, Rosen 2294, Rosenfeld 2295, Roshan 2297, Rothman 2299, Ruskin 2302, Ryan 2305, Sadler 2306, Sammons 2310, Samowitz 2311, SBJ 2314, Scharlin 2315, Scherr 2316, Selders 2322, Sender 2323, Setzer 2325, Sexton 2326, Sharaby 2329, Sharing 2330, Shuey 2333, Sidhu 2334, Siegel 2335, Sierra 2336, Silverman 2337, Simmons 2338, Smick 2340, Smith 2341, Stafford 2346, Stern 2350, Strong 2353, Studer 2355, Sudakoff 2356, Swann 2360, Swisher 2361, Tampa 2362, **Taylor 2365**, Taylor 2366, Terry 2368, Thomas 2371, Thompson 2372, Thornburgh 2374, Thurman 2375, Tippett 2376, Toppel 2377, Toral 2378, Turner 2381, Turock 2382, **Uncle 2383**, Vasey 2385, Verner 2386, Vernon 2387, Weiller 2393, Weintraub 2395, Weisman 2396, Werner 2398, Westgate 2400, Whitman 2404, Wiener 2405, Wilson-Wood 2408, Woerner 2409, **Wollowick 2412**, Woolard 2414, Wrightson-Ramsing 2416, Wynne 2419, Yerrid 2420, Younger 2422, Zehnder 2423, **Zimmer 2425**, Zimmerman 2427

Georgia: 10/1 2429, Abreu 2431, Akers 2432, Amos 2433, Athens 2437, **Bancker-Williams 2440**, Beard-Payne 2442, Brewer 2448, Canipe 2452, Carters 2454, Chandler 2455, Charter 2456, Chatham 2457, Childress 2459, Cobb 2463, Community 2465, Community 2466, Connolly 2467, Cooper 2469, Davison 2470, DeLoache 2471, Echlin 2472, Enterline 2475, Exposition 2476, **Faith 2477**, Fickling 2478, Foundation 2480, Frank 2481, Georgia 2485, Gholston 2486, Gilbert, 2488, Go 2490, Goddard 2491, Goodman 2492, Gordy 2493, Gould 2494, Griffin 2499, Harrison 2502, Hodge 2506, Holland-Underwood 2508, Hooters 2510, Hurlbert 2516, Illges 2517,

Invisible 2520, JBS 2523, Jeter 2524, Johnson 2525, Kahn 2529, Kids 2530, Kingdom 2531, Knox 2534, L. 2535, Lanier 2538, Lassiter 2539, Lee 2540, Lipscomb 2541, Looney 2542, Magnus 2543, Marcus 2544, Marshall 2545, McClatchey 2546, McKinney-Geib 2547, McKnight 2548, Mix 2550, Oxford 2561, Patrick 2562, Pattillo 2563, Pechter 2564, Pennies 2565, Price 2569, Price-Campbell 2570, Ragan 2572, Rice 2575, Rockdale 2576, Samford 2578, Sewell 2584, SF 2585, Smith 2586, Stahl 2588, Storey 2589, Sweetgrass 2591, Terwilliger 2593, Thames 2594, Trammell 2595, Vaughter 2599, Vogel 2600, Waffle 2602, Windolf 2614, Wish 2615, Woodcrest 2616, Woodruff 2617, Woodruff, 2618, Zvolensky 2623

Hawaii: Armstrong 2624, Baldwin 2625, Castle 2626, Central 2627, Ching 2628, First 2631, Kaneta 2637, Locations 2638, Makana 2639, Moore 2643, Shields 2647, Takitani 2650, Vidinha 2653, Wilcox 2654, Wo 2655, Wong 2656, Wong 2657, **Yoshimoto 2658**, Zierk 2661

Idaho: Ambrosiani-Pastore 2663, Angels 2664, Beckman 2665, Boise 2666, Dumke 2668, Emelco 2669, Golden 2672, Good 2673, Hare 2675, Hecla 2676, Intermountain 2677, Leidy 2678, Morrison 2682, Palmedo 2684, Smeed 2686, Troxell 2688, Whittenberger 2689, Wishnick 2690

Illinois: 1335 2691, Abelson 2692, Acorn 2694, **Acorn 2695**, Adreani 2697, Agape 2698, Ahlstrand 2700, Allen-Heath 2701, Allyn 2703, Almeida 2704, Alton 2705, Alton 2706, Anschel 2709, AptarGroup 2712, Arboit 2713, Argo 2714, B&D 2715, Baird 2717, Banta 2719, Bartholomay 2721, Bartsch 2722, Bates 2724, Bates 2725, Baum 2727, Beasley 2728, Beeghly 2730, Bendich 2733, Bere 2734, Bergstrom 2736, Bernfield 2737, Best 2739, Bishop 2743, Bladel 2744, Block 2745, Boothroyd 2749, Boylan 2753, Brenner 2756, Bruce 2760, Bruce 2761, Brunswick 2762, Bufka 2763, **Build 2764**, Buntrock 2766, Burk 2768, Burt 2770, Carey 2775, Cashel 2777, Ceres 2779, Chambers 2780, Chapin-May 2782, Charles 2783, Chicago 2787, Christian 2789, Citadel 2791, Clarks 2792, Clingen 2794, Cohn 2795, Cohn 2796, Collins 2799, **Combs 2800**, Communitas 2801, Community 2802, Community 2803, Constans-Culver 2805, Corbett 2808, Corbett 2809, Cord 2811, Cornerstone 2812, Coulter 2813, Cremer 2815, Cronin 2816, Cronk 2817, Daeumer 2821, Dancing 2822, Danielson 2823, Delavan 2825, Delta 2826, Denny 2828, Diamond 2829, Doerr 2831, Donovan 2833, Dowdle 2834, Dower 2835, Doyle 2836, Dubin 2838, Duncan 2840, Dunning 2841, Eclipse 2844, Edelman 2845, Educational 2848, Eiszner 2851, Ellis 2853, Enivar 2856, Epaphroditus 2857, Equity 2858, Espenscheid 2859, Estate 2860, Everett 2861, Family 2863, Federation 2868, Feltes 2869, Fields 2870, Fink 2873, Fischer 2874, Foley 2876, Foster 2879, Four 2882, Fraida 2884, Frank 2885, Frankel 2886, Franklin 2887, Franklin 2888, Frederick 2889, Fredman 2890, Fremont 2891, Freund 2892, Frisby 2893, Full 2895, Fund 2896, Funk 2897, Gallagher 2898, Galter 2899, Garard, 2902, Gardner 2904, Gardner 2905, General 2907, Generations 2908, Geneseo 2909, Glossberg 2916, Gloyd 2917, Gochnauer 2918, Goldberg 2919, Goldenberg 2920, Golder 2921, Good 2923, Gray 2927, Griffith 2929, Griffith 2930, Grumhaus 2934, Gust 2936, H. 2938, H.C.D. 2939, Haarlow 2940, Hales 2941, Half 2942, Hamlin 2946, Hansen 2948, Hanson 2949, Hanson 2950, Harris 2956, Harris 2957, Hastings 2960, Hay 2961, Hegeler 2963, Heins 2964, **Heritage 2967**, Hess 2969, Hirschmann 2973, Hoffer 2975, Holden 2976, Hopper 2977, Houck 2978, Houlihan 2979, Howard 2981, Hunt 2984, Ideal 2986, Ingredion 2987, Iroquois 2989, Jaros 2993, JBS 2994, Jocarno 3000, Johnson 3001, Judy 3003, Karasik 3006, Kellcie 3008, Keller 3009, Kelly 3011, Kelly 3012, Kemp 3013, Kemper 3014, Keyes 3016, Kilrea 3017, Klosk 3020, Knappenberger 3021,

Koch 3025, Koranda 3026, Lakshmi 3033, Lancaster 3035, **Landau 3036**, **Lascaris 3040**, Lazar 3041, **Lazzara 3042**, Lebus 3043, Leestma 3044, Leibowitz 3046, Levinson 3049, Levy 3050, Lichner 3051, Lichtman 3052, **Lindon 3054**, Logos 3058, Love 3064, Luehring 3065, MacDonald 3068, Maddox 3069, Mako 3070, Mallon 3071, Manne 3073, Marcum 3076, Massey 3082, McCabe 3084, McCauley 3085, McCormack 3086, McCrea 3088, McDougal 3091, McKee 3093, McLaughlin 3095, McNally 3097, McNulty 3099, Metzner 3104, Meusel 3105, Meyer 3106, **Meyers 3107**, Millard 3109, Millard 3110, Miller 3112, Miller, 3113, Miner 3116, Minor 3117, Mirapaul 3119, Mitchell 3120, Mohr 3121, Moore 3123, Moreton 3124, Morris 3125, Morton 3127, Mouat 3128, Mullen 3129, Munson 3130, Murphy 3132, NCI 3134, New 3136, **New 3137**, Night 3140, Novick 3143, Nygren 3146, Ohlhausen 3151, Olson 3154, Oppenheimer 3155, Orsini 3156, Osi 3158, Our 3159, Pangburn 3161, Parker 3162, Penrose 3166, Perkins 3168, Perkins 3169, Petrick 3173, Petrovich 3174, Pharmore 3175, Pinnell 3176, Pitzman 3177, Podolsky 3178, **Polk 3179**, Poncher 3181, Pond 3182, Red 3188, Red 3189, Reed 3190, Reed 3191, Reichert 3192, Reinisch 3193, Richard 3195, Roberts 3199, **Rosenmutter 3208**, Rosenson 3209, Rosenthal 3210, Rot 3212, Rothman 3213, Roundy 3214, Ruben 3215, Russell 3216, Ryan 3219, Saemann 3220, Saliba 3221, Sasco 3222, Schiff 3224, Scott 3230, Sequoia 3235, Seymour 3236, Shaker 3238, Shapiro 3240, Share 3241, Shaw 3243, Shaw 3244, Shirley 3245, Shodeen 3246, Simon 3247, Simpson 3248, Smallwood 3251, Smith 3253, Smithburg 3254, Spencer 3258, SSAB 3260, Stairway 3261, Staley 3262, Staley 3264, Stone 3269, Stone 3270, Stutsman 3274, Sue 3275, Sulzer 3277, Summer 3279, Tafel 3280, Takiff 3281, Taylor 3284, Taylor 3285, Thaman 3289, Tobey 3290, Townsend 3291, Trust 3294, Tully 3295, Tuohy 3296, Turner 3297, Twomey 3298, United 3300, Vail 3301, Valenti 3302, Victor 3304, Wagner 3306, Walker 3308, Watson 3311, Webb 3313, **Wein 3315**, Weiner 3316, Wessel 3318, Weston 3320, Whitwam 3321, Wislow 3323, Witz-Mallinger 3324, Wolf 3325, Wolf 3326, Wolf 3327, Woodruff 3330, Woods 3332, Yulman 3334, Zaentz 3336, Zuckerman 3338

Indiana: **Ackerman 3339**, Agness 3340, Ash 3341, Ayres 3342, Benton 3344, Blackford 3346, Branigin 3348, Braun 3349, Brave 3350, Bronstein 3351, Burris 3352, Bussing-Koch 3353, Carroll 3354, CDM 3355, Community 3358, Community 3359, Community 3360, Community 3361, Community 3362, Community 3363, Custer 3366, Decatur 3367, Dobbs 3368, Dubois 3370, Dukes 3371, Duneland 3372, Eskenazi 3377, Eternal 3378, Fayette 3379, Fenech 3380, Froderman 3383, Gaither 3384, Gammon 3385, Gibson 3386, Globe 3387, Greene 3390, Hulman 3396, Huntington 3397, Interactive 3398, J 3399, J. 3400, Jasper 3401, Jennings 3402, Keck 3405, Klapper 3408, Kuhne 3409, Lafayette 3411, LaGrange 3412, M.C.R. 3413, Magee-O'Connor 3414, Maurer 3415, **Mervis 3417**, Mothershead 3419, Mulzer 3420, MutualBank 3421, Noecker 3424, Nugent 3425, Oakley 3426, Ohio 3427, O'Rourke-Schof 3429, PHP 3431, Raker 3434, Raper 3435, Raymond 3436, Rifkin 3437, Rinker 3438, Rush 3441, Schurz 3444, Scott 3446, Seger 3447, Smith 3453, Springleaf 3455, Thrush-Thompson 3460, Vann 3461, Vision 3463, Von 3464, Welter 3465, Weston 3467, Winchester 3469

Iowa: Barkema 3471, Bennett 3474, Carlson 3479, Coons 3481, De 3484, Deardorf 3485, Drost 3487, Ellen 3489, Farrer 3490, Farver 3491, Figge 3492, First 3493, Gazette 3497, Geisler 3498, Gleeson 3500, Grinnell 3501, Grubb 3502, GuideOne 3503, Henry 3505, Herr 3506, Hills 3507, Hoaglin 3508, Howe 3510, Iowa 3512, Iowa 3513, Krause 3516, Krumm 3517, McCarthy/Bush 3519, McDonald

3520, Medical 3521, Schildberg 3532, Security 3534, Stark 3536, Tomson 3537, Toohey 3538, Van 3540, Vermeer 3541, Vermeer 3542, **Wahlert 3544**, Weathertop 3545, Weigle 3546, West 3547, Woodward 3549

Kansas: Adair-Exchange 3553, Atterbury 3554, Babinger 3555, Bane 3557, Berry 3558, Breidenthal-Snyder 3560, Brown 3561, Buford 3562, Cape 3563, Central 3564, Cochener 3565, Coffeyville 3566, Community 3567, CPS 3568, Cyr 3570, DeVore 3573, Fidelity 3577, Fox 3578, Goebel 3580, Goldberg 3581, Green 3583, Haglage 3584, Insurance 3587, Jellison 3589, Joscelyn 3590, Kansas 3592, Lincoln 3596, Lowenstein 3598, Mann 3599, Merrill 3602, Middlekauff 3603, Miller-Mellor 3604, Mistler 3606, Morgan 3607, Morrison 3608, Payless 3614, Price 3616, Reeble 3618, Scroggins 3624, Shannon 3625, Smoot 3627, South 3628, Stallman 3629, Stolzer 3630, Swearingen 3631, Taylor 3632, Testamentary 3633, Trusler 3635, Wallace 3637, Watson 3639, Weber 3640, Williams 3643

Kentucky: Barth 3647, Boone 3648, Boone 3649, Dickins 3651, Diebold 3652, Etscorn 3654, GB 3657, Harter 3660, Heisel 3663, Keeneland 3668, Killian 3670, Lebus 3671, Mackin 3673, Masser 3676, Morris 3679, Murry 3681, Namaste 3682, Price 3686, Public 3687, Reed 3688, Renau 3689, Roth 3690, Spriggs 3695, Steiner 3696, Stock 3697, Stockdell-Joseph 3698, Sutherland 3699, Taylor 3700, Trim 3702, Weisberg 3705, Woosley 3708, Yeager 3710

Louisiana: A-Kids-Choice 3712, Biedenharn 3713, Broussard 3715, Cahn 3716, Catalyst 3717, Chambers 3718, Crossroads 3719, Daybrook 3720, Grigsby 3725, Harper 3726, Huie-Dellmon 3729, Lake 3732, Meraux 3736, Merkle 3737, Montan 3740, Monteleone 3741, New 3742, Powers 3746, Pugh 3747, Selber 3751, Showers 3753, Steinhagen 3755, Wisdom 3761

Maine: Alfond 3764, Borman 3767, Brook 3769, Burnham 3770, Camden 3771, Chappell 3772, Cotsirilos 3774, Davenport 3775, Elliotsville 3777, Franklin 3779, Goldberg 3780, **Golden 3781**, Kagan 3784, Kennebec 3785, Kennebunk 3786, Lynam 3788, Messler 3790, Mimi 3792, Minsky 3793, Narragansett 3794, Old 3795, Planet 3797, Protein 3799, Red 3801, Reny 3802, Somers 3803, Sukeforth 3805

Maryland: Acacia 3807, Adams 3808, Adler 3809, Allemall 3811, AMDG 3812, Anderson 3814, Baker 3815, Baltimore 3816, Baltimore 3817, Bank 3818, Blum 3825, **Boehm 3826**, Bresler 3828, Campbell 3831, Caplan 3832, Carbonell 3833, Carol 3834, Chessie 3835, Clifton 3836, Cole 3839, Contino 3840, CSG 3842, Darby 3843, Davis 3844, Devito 3848, Dockser 3849, **Doorstep 3850**, Duncan 3851, Eccles 3853, Elsberg 3856, Feldman 3858, Ferris 3860, Fine 3861, Fischer 3862, Franey 3865, Fusco 3868, Gidwitz 3870, Gladding 3871, **Goldberg 3872**, Govil 3875, Gutman 3877, Helm 3879, Higginson 3880, Hittman 3881, Hobbs 3882, Huether/McClelland 3884, Hurwitz 3886, Hyman 3887, Kay 3892, Kirk 3894, Kohn 3897, Liberty 3901, Loats 3902, Lohr, 3903, Macht 3905, Macks 3906, Mangione 3907, Marriott 3909, McKnight 3910, Mental 3912, Meyer, 3913, Meyerhoff 3914, Minkoff 3915, Moore 3917, Moser 3918, Mullan 3920, Murthynayak 3921, Mustard 3922, Nabit 3924, Newday 3925, No 3927, Number 3929, Pettit 3935, Phase 3936, RFI 3938, Rhona's 3939, Rogers-Wilbur 3941, Rothschild 3942, Rouse 3943, Schuh 3946, Shapiro 3949, Shattuck 3950, Slavin 3954, Small 3955, Snyder 3956, SPM 3958, St. 3959, Ten 3963, Tenberg 3964, Ticho 3967, Totah 3968, Tucker 3969, Unger 3971, V 3972, Van 3974, Wagner-Braunsberg 3975, Wallis 3977, Wieler 3984, Wilen 3985, Wilson 3987, Witt/Hoey 3989

Massachusetts: 2 3992, 484 3993, **A 3995**, **Afeyan 3996**, Alden 3999, Allison 4000, Altamira 4001,

Arcadia 4004, Archibald 4005, Astra 4006, **Azadoutloun 4008**, Babson 4009, Babson-Webber-Mustard 4010, **Barakat 4012**, Barstow 4013, Benson 4016, Benz 4017, Bergstrom 4019, Bigbird 4020, Black 4021, Boynton 4025, Brooks 4028, Brown 4029, **Cabbadetus 4033**, Cabot 4034, Cabot 4035, Carle 4037, Casey 4039, Catino 4040, Chase 4045, Chickering 4046, Chicopee 4047, Chirag 4048, Clarke 4049, Clifford 4051, Coolidge 4057, Crane 4058, Crawford 4059, Crowe 4061, Dalessandro 4063, Davoli 4065, Dedham 4067, Durant 4072, Dwyer 4074, East 4075, Easthampton 4076, Egan 4079, Egan 4080, Elephant 4081, England 4083, Family 4085, Fay 4087, Felix 4089, First 4091, Foundation 4094, Francis 4095, Frisbie 4099, Gale 4100, **Galileo 4101**, Gerrity 4102, Gildea 4103, Gloria 4104, Goldman 4105, Griffin 4107, **Gross 4108**, Hagerty 4110, Hagler 4111, Haley 4114, Hampden 4116, Harrington 4117, Harwood 4119, Hazard 4124, Heide 4125, Henderson 4127, Hicks 4129, Hill 4130, Hoffman 4131, Hogan 4132, Honey 4133, Horne 4136, Howard 4137, Hyde 4139, Kendall 4149, Kenwood 4150, Kershaw 4151, Kidder 4152, Kimball 4155, King 4156, Kneisel 4157, Krieger 4160, Krupp 4161, Ladd 4163, Lamm 4165, Leatherwood 4170, Levy 4173, Levy 4174, Levy 4175, Lindsay 4176, Liswhit 4178, Lost 4180, M 4181, Mank 4187, Marino 4190, Massachusetts 4191, McKee 4194, McNeice, 4195, Melvina 4197, MENTOR 4199, Merrill 4200, Middlesex 4203, Mirak 4204, Morse 4208, Morse 4209, Morse 4210, Mount 4211, Mulberry 4213, Murphy 4214, MutualOne 4216, Newburyport 4222, Noble 4224, Noonan 4225, Nypro 4228, One 4230, OneBeacon 4231, Parlin 4233, Pechet 4235, Peoples 4237, PerkinElmer 4238, Permanent 4239, Peters 4241, Philips 4243, Pierce 4244, Pilgrim 4245, Proud 4249, Provident 4250, Puffin 4251, Putnam 4252, Ragon 4256, Reisman 4262, Rice 4265, **Robbins-de 4266**, Rockland 4267, Rodman 4268, Rodman 4269, Rose 4271, Russell 4273, Sacajawea 4274, Sailors' 4276, Sandler 4278, Savage 4280, Schiro 4282, Schwartz 4284, Segel 4285, Shapiro 4290, Shaughnessy 4292, Sherman 4293, Smith 4298, **Spero 4304**, Sprague 4306, Stare 4308, Stearns 4310, Stearns 4311, Sullivan 4315, **Summer 4316**, Thompson 4325, Toocap 4330, Torok 4331, Tresorelle 4333, Ungar 4336, United 4337, Van 4340, Videtta 4343, Wallace 4347, Walsh 4348, Webber 4351, Weber 4352, Webster 4353, Wells 4357, Wilcox 4360, Windhorse 4361, Wyman-Gordon 4364, Zampell 4367, Zock 4368

Michigan: Allen 4372, Alnour 4373, Alon 4374, Andersen 4377, Ave 4379, Avharas 4380, Baiardi 4381, Baldwin 4382, Balk 4383, Barstow 4385, Barton-Malow 4386, Baum 4387, Betten 4390, Biederman 4391, Bierlein 4392, Blatt 4393, Bonder 4394, Bostock 4395, Branch 4396, Buhr 4400, Buist 4401, Burdick-Thorne 4402, Burt 4403, Christian 4407, Community 4410, Community 4411, Connable 4412, Conrad 4413, Cracchiolo 4414, Cracchiolo 4415, Crowley 4416, Currie 4418, Dana 4419, Dana 4420, de 4422, Degroot 4423, Delano 4426, DeWitt 4429, Dik 4430, DiPonio 4432, Doll-Loesel 4433, Dresner 4434, Duchene 4435, Fabiano 4438, Farago 4440, Farver 4441, Farwell 4442, Ferber 4443, Filmer 4444, Ford 4445, Gordon 4456, Grassland 4458, Gratiot 4459, Harris 4461, Hartwick 4462, Havirmill 4463, Hayden 4464, Johnson 4471, JSJ 4474, Kantzler 4478, Kay 4480, Keller 4481, Kellogg 4482, Kinney 4483, Lapeer 4490, Lee 4491, Leven 4492, LoPrete 4496, M 4497, Maas 4498, Mackinac 4499, Maibach 4500, Main 4501, Manat 4503, McClelland 4505, McDole 4506, McDole 4507, McManus 4509, McNally 4510, Meritor, 4511, Merkley 4512, Michell 4513, Michigan 4514, Mills 4515, Mojo 4516, Molnar 4517, Morley 4518, Narens 4520, Nartel 4521, Onequest 4527, Padnos 4529, Page, 4530, Paine 4531, Paulina 4535, Peslar 4537, Phantom 4538,

Pilgrim 4539, Pitt 4540, Pitt 4541, Plym 4542, Power 4544, Powers 4545, Redies 4549, Riley 4550, River 4551, Roscommon 4552, **Saab 4556**, Sackerson 4557, Schalon 4558, Schmuckal 4559, SEED 4562, Sehn 4563, Seligman 4564, Shapiro 4566, Shiawassee 4568, Speckhard-Knight 4574, Springview 4575, St. 4576, St. 4577, Stern 4578, Stoker 4580, Stone 4581, Stubnitz 4582, Sutaruk 4583, Tamer 4585, Technical 4588, **Teitel 4589**, Thoman 4590, Thompson 4592, Thompson 4593, Tremble 4595, **Triford 4597**, Tuscola 4598, Tyler-Little 4599, Van 4602, Vander 4603, **Vattikuti 4605**, Vicksburg 4606, Vlasic 4607, Watson 4608, Weisberg 4609, Wetsman 4611, Wheeler 4612, Wickson-Link 4616, Wieczorek 4617, Zampetis 4619, Zimmerman 4620
Minnesota: Aca 4622, Andersen 4626, Ankeny 4628, Arctos 4629, Arsher 4630, Avocet 4631, Bailey 4633, Bame 4634, Baratz 4635, Becker 4636, Bell 4637, Bell 4638, Bend 4639, Bieber 4641, Black 4642, Blank 4643, Borman 4644, Boss 4645, Boss 4646, Briggs 4648, Burwell 4650, Camara-Press 4652, Caroline's 4654, Cook 4658, Covenant 4661, Deikel 4663, Dellwood 4665, Dyer 4669, Edina 4672, Evert 4676, Faith, 4677, Farview 4680, Felhaber, 4681, Flaherty 4686, Fletcher 4687, Fraser 4689, G&K 4691, Gage 4692, Gardner 4693, Garmar 4694, Getsch 4695, Gilligan 4696, Granite 4699, Grossman 4701, Grotto 4702, Haggerty 4705, Harrington 4707, Head 4709, Heilicher 4711, Hickory 4713, Iversen 4717, Jackson 4718, Jeffers 4719, **Kaplan 4721**, Kinney 4724, Knowlton 4725, Larsen 4728, Lillehei 4729, Lukis 4732, Luther 4733, Mahon 4737, McCoy 4742, McNamara 4743, Midcontinent 4745, Mooty 4747, Morning 4748, Noreen 4750, Oak 4752, O'Brien 4753, Onan 4754, O'Neil 4755, Open 4756, OSilas 4758, Pautsch 4759, **Porter 4763**, Quinlan 4764, Radichel 4765, Rahr 4766, Rauenhorst 4767, Regis 4770, Reimer 4771, Remick 4773, Rieks 4774, Riverway 4776, Rodman 4779, Roles 4782, Samsara 4784, Seba 4789, Soar 4792, Squam 4793, Steinhafel 4795, **Sundance 4796**, Tennant 4798, Terhuly 4799, Thorpe 4800, **Trust 4802**, Wallestad 4806, Way 4809, Wells 4811, Wells 4812, Weyand 4814, Whitney 4817
Mississippi: Amory 4821, Baird 4822, Barnett 4823, Black 4825, Brevard 4826, Crooks 4831, Florence 4836, Fountain 4837, Golding 4838, Graeber 4839, Hancock 4840, King's 4845, Lexington 4846, McCarty, 4848, Sanders 4852, Seal, 4853, Skelton 4854, Wittel 4858
Missouri: Albers/Kuhn 4859, Andrews 4860, Arnold 4861, Bartlett 4865, BEO 4866, BF 4867, Bland 4868, **Block 4869**, Bograd 4870, **Bohm 4871**, Boswell 4872, Boylan 4873, Brace 4874, Breidenthal 4875, Bryant 4878, Calkins 4881, Capellupo 4883, Chapman 4884, Chod 4885, Chomeau 4886, Cinmar 4887, Cray 4890, Curry 4892, Dierberg 4895, Dubinsky 4896, Dunn 4898, Enright 4903, Erlich 4904, Essman 4905, Fabick 4907, Forster-Powers 4911, Gaylord 4914, Gaylord 4915, Gershman 4916, Grant 4918, HB 4924, Heiman 4926, Herschend 4928, Hofheimer 4929, J. 4932, Kemper 4935, Kenney 4936, Kuhn 4941, **Larson 4943**, Lawton 4944, Lordi 4950, Love 4951, Mathews, 4953, Maxine 4954, McDonald 4955, Melcher 4957, Messick 4958, Meyer 4959, MFA 4960, Moneta 4962, Moss 4964, Moulton 4965, Mungenast 4966, Neeb 4968, Neiman 4969, Nichols 4970, No 4971, Obertate 4972, O'Reilly 4974, O'Reilly 4975, Payne-Stewart 4976, Pearl 4977, Peculiar 4978, Pendergast-Weyer 4979, Pillsbury 4980, Portman 4981, Price 4982, Riedel 4984, Rust 4988, Schneider 4994, Schweinfurth 4996, Shanahan 4999, Shawe 5000, Shepherd 5001, Shumway 5002, Sigma-Aldrich 5003, Siteman 5006, Slay 5008, Slusher 5009, South 5011, Stern 5013, Stifel 5014, Stroble 5015, Tension 5019, Timmons 5021, Vatterott 5030, Von 5033, Walker 5035, Walton 5037, Wolff 5039, Woods 5042, Wurst 5043

Montana: Angora 5044, Boe 5045, Dousman 5049, Gallagher 5052, Gerhart 5053, High 5057, Lippard-Clawiter 5058, Montana 5060, Sample 5062, Swanson 5063, Taylor 5064, Wendy's 5065
Nebraska: Ameritas 5067, Assurity 5068, Baer 5069, Barklage 5071, Ferenc 5080, Finigan 5081, Friedman 5083, Goldwin 5085, Grewcock 5086, Hawkins 5089, Hickey 5093, Home 5094, Hundred 5095, Kaufmann-Cummings 5096, Kilbourne 5097, Kim 5098, Kinder 5099, Lienemann 5100, **Lothlorien 5101**, Malek 5102, Midlands 5104, Nelson 5106, Patrick 5109, Physicians 5112, Quivey-Bay 5113, Reynolds 5114, Scott, 5115, Shaw 5117, Smith 5118, Steinhart 5121, Storz 5122, Thomas 5123, Tous 5124, **Waldbaum 5125**, Walker 5126, York 5129
Nevada: **A 5131**, Andress 5132, Ash 5134, Barker 5136, Bendon 5137, Benna 5138, Blue 5140, Boyd 5141, C.A.N. 5142, Chami 5146, Children 5147, Coleman 5150, Crescere 5151, Dermody 5152, **Fein 5155**, Fuserna 5159, Houssels 5163, Jaquish 5165, Joshua 5167, Kara 5168, Lee 5171, Living 5174, Meyer 5177, Moran 5178, Newman 5179, Orchard 5180, Petersen 5181, Peterson 5182, Pretti 5184, Shulman 5185, Special 5188, Sweig 5191, Timken-Sturgis 5192, Vandevoort 5194, Webb 5196, Williams 5199, Wynn 5202
New Hampshire: Barker 5204, Bickford 5205, Charter 5206, Dunn 5212, Finlay 5213, Hunt 5214, Jameson 5215, Landecker 5217, Linnell 5219, McIninch 5224, Oxford 5228, Salem 5230, Verney 5236, von 5237, Woodbury 5238
New Jersey: A 5240, Adler 5242, **Akhoury 5243**, Amboy 5246, Anderson 5249, Antz 5250, Ascena 5252, Aufzien 5253, Avalo 5254, Bartlett 5256, Bauer 5257, Beane 5259, Benun 5261, Bershad 5263, Bijou 5264, **Billig 5265**, Bloom 5267, Blue 5268, **Blue 5269**, BMI-Rupp 5270, Broad 5272, Brook 5273, Brooks 5274, Browder 5277, Brown 5278, Brueckner 5279, Brundage 5280, Brunetti 5281, Cantor 5285, Capebank 5286, Carlozzi 5287, CBIS 5288, Chanil 5291, Chapman 5292, Chu 5294, Citta 5295, Colotto 5300, Columbia 5301, Conant 5302, Conger 5303, Culver 5308, D'Aloia 5311, **Dankis 5312**, Davino 5313, Davis 5314, Devine 5317, Diaco 5318, Dickinson 5319, Dietze 5320, Doctor 5321, D'Onofrio 5324, Dreman 5326, Earle 5328, EBB 5329, Eisenberg 5331, Ellis 5333, Engel 5334, Entin 5336, Family 5340, Fisher 5347, Florin 5348, Fox 5349, Freedman 5352, Frelinghuysen 5354, Freyer 5355, Gabrellian 5360, **Garcia 5362**, Gardinier 5363, Garfinkle 5364, Genie 5366, Gestetner 5367, Gibson 5370, Glasser 5371, Goldberger 5372, Goodwin 5374, Greetin 5377, Hanafin 5381, Hann 5382, Hanson 5383, Harms 5385, Harmstieg 5386, Hawthorne 5387, Hill 5393, Hillswood 5394, Icap 5398, Infinity 5399, Jacobson 5402, Jamacha 5403, Johnson 5406, Jones 5408, Kampen 5413, Katz 5414, KDK 5416, Kean 5417, Kirby 5422, Klatskin 5423, Klein 5424, Kocurek 5428, Kolber 5429, Kontos 5430, Korean 5431, Kresa 5432, Kroon 5433, Kurr 5435, Kurtz 5436, Kutnick 5437, LaGrassa 5438, Landy 5439, Larson 5440, Lazarus 5442, Lchachomim 5443, Leavens 5444, Leavitt 5445, Levine 5446, Lipper 5450, M/S 5452, MacDonald 5453, Machuga 5454, Marino 5457, Markey 5459, Markowitz 5460, Marron 5461, McConnell 5463, McCrane 5464, Miller 5467, Miller 5468, Moriarty 5473, Navesink 5477, **Nazarian 5478**, Olsen 5480, Oster 5484, Palmer 5486, Pantirer 5487, Paragano 5488, Pasternak 5490, **Patel 5491**, **Patel 5492**, Patrick 5494, Pepper 5496, Perricone 5497, Pierson 5500, Plafsky 5503, Poole 5504, Riskin 5511, Roma 5513, Rukh 5515, Rukin 5516, Russo 5517, Sanders 5518, Schimmel 5521, Schlaffer 5522, Schwartz 5525, Scott 5527, Selective 5528, Sella 5529, Shapiro 5532, Simon 5537, Smilowitz 5538, Smith 5539, Snyder 5540, Snyder 5541, Snyder 5542, Spiro 5546, Stone 5553, Tamarin 5556, Tuchman 5561, **Tufenkian 5562**, Twin 5563,

Upton 5566, Waters 5571, Waterview 5572, Watts 5573, We 5574, Weintraub 5577, Welch 5579, Wendel 5580, Weny 5581, Westfield 5582, Wicks 5584, Wilcox 5585, Wildwood 5586, Willingham 5589, Winters 5591, Wolf 5593, Woolley-Clifford 5594, Yates 5595, **Yin-Shun 5596**, Zeldes 5599, Zichron 5600, Zimmer 5601, Zissu 5602, Zobel 5603
New Mexico: Akerson 5604, **Angelica 5605**, Carlsbad 5608, Forrest 5614, Foster 5615, Garfield 5616, Gumbo 5617, Horn 5618, Nirvana 5621, Schnieders 5623, Simon 5624, Taos 5626, Walbridge 5627, **Watersheds 5628**
New York: 21st 5630, A.B. 5632, Abelard 5635, Abettor 5638, Abrahamson 5639, Achilles 5641, Adikes 5646, Agate 5649, AGB 5650, AKC 5651, Alexander 5656, Allatt 5659, Allegany 5660, American 5663, American 5664, American 5665, Amsterdam 5672, Anderson 5673, Anderson 5674, Anderson 5675, Angel 5678, Antun 5681, Aresty 5686, Armonia 5688, Arts 5693, August 5698, Avanessians 5701, Backer 5706, Balbach 5707, Balm 5708, Bandier 5709, Barbara 5713, Barham 5715, Barney 5717, Barron 5719, Baum 5722, Beach 5725, Behrens 5731, Beir 5732, Bell 5734, Bergson 5738, Bernheim 5740, Bernhill 5741, Bet 5742, Betesh 5743, Betts 5744, Big 5745, Bingham 5747, **Bito 5753**, Blackman, 5755, Blank 5756, Block 5758, Bloomberg 5761, Bobrow 5765, Bostwick 5767, Bothmer 5768, Bovin 5770, Box 5771, Boxer 5772, Boyer-Snyder 5773, Brademas 5774, Brand 5776, Breck 5780, Brenner 5781, Briar 5782, Bridgewater 5783, Brillo-Sonnino 5785, Brinkman 5786, Brody 5787, Brooklyn 5788, Brosens 5789, Broughton 5790, Brown 5791, Buchalter 5796, Buchwald 5797, Buckley 5798, Buller 5800, Burchan 5801, Bush 5805, Cader 5807, CAL 5808, Calamus 5809, Camuto 5812, Caples 5813, Carroll 5816, Carwill 5818, Casey 5819, Cathedral 5822, Centennial 5826, Ceriale 5828, Chaim 5831, Chapman 5832, Chasdei 5835, Cheatham 5836, Chervenak-Nunnalle 5839, Chess 5841, Children's 5842, Chiles 5843, **Chinook 5844**, Ciampa 5845, Citrin 5846, Citron 5847, Clemente 5850, Code 5854, Cohen 5857, Cohen 5858, Cohen 5859, Cohenca 5861, Cohoes 5865, Cole 5868, Coleman 5870, Coles 5871, Cornell/Weinstein 5877, Correspondents 5879, Cortland 5880, Cowen 5882, Cox 5883, Cranshaw 5885, Curtis 5889, Dabah 5892, D'Addario 5894, D'Addario 5895, Danziger 5899, Darrah 5900, Davidson 5901, D-B 5903, De 5904, Dears 5905, Deeds 5906, DeMario 5909, Devine-Majors 5913, Diamondston 5914, Dibert 5915, Diogenes 5917, Dixon 5919, Doovin 5923, Dorsky 5924, Doshi 5926, Double-R 5927, Downey 5930, Downs 5931, Druskin 5932, **Dungannon 5935**, Dworman 5938, Educational 5945, Eggleston 5946, Ehrman 5949, Eisenberger 5950, Ellsworth 5957, Elyachar 5959, Emwiga 5962, Englebardt 5965, Erpf 5968, ESL 5969, Eule 5971, Evans 5972, Ezra 5976, F. 5977, Faith 5979, Family 5982, **Familly 5983**, Farber 5986, Farber 5987, **Farkas 5988**, Feil 5991, Fein 5992, Feinberg 5993, Ferguson 5999, Ferriday 6000, Fieldstone 6004, Fitt 6010, Flaherty 6012, Fleischer 6013, Fleming 6014, Follett 6016, Fondation 6017, Forest 6018, Foundation 6019, Fowey 6021, Fox 6022, **Frank 6026**, Frankel 6027, **Freedom 6030**, Freidheim 6031, Friedland 6037, Friedman 6039, Friends 6042, Fuchsberg 6044, Furman 6045, Gaffney 6049, Gallagher 6051, Gant 6054, Gantz 6056, Garman 6058, Gartner 6059, Gatto 6061, Geier 6063, Geller 6066, Gelley 6067, Gemiluth 6068, Gerhard 6072, Gernatt 6073, Gesso 6075, Gettinger 6076, Giant 6077, Gilliam 6078, **Gimprich 6080**, Giordano 6081, Glens 6082, Goddard 6085, Gold 6088, Goldberg 6090, Golden 6091, Goldenberg 6092, **Goldfein 6096**, Goldman 6098, Goldmann 6099, Golub 6105, Goodman 6107, Goodman-Lipman 6108, Gordon 6109, Gordon 6110, GP 6117, Grace 6118, Graham 6119, Graham 6120, Gramercy 6122, Grand 6123, Grandison 6124, Granit 6126, Granny

6127, Grano 6128, Grant 6129, Grateful 6131, Greenberg 6132, Greenblatt 6133, Griffin 6138, Grinberg 6139, Grobman 6140, Grossman 6144, Grubman 6147, Guela 6151, Hahn 6156, Hahn 6157, Hajim 6158, Hales 6159, Hallingby 6160, Hap 6164, Happy 6165, Harjen 6167, Harmon 6168, Harris 6172, Hasenfeld 6174, Hatfield 6175, Hauff 6177, **Haven 6178**, Heffer 6180, Hefta 6181, Hegarty 6182, Hein 6184, Heisler 6185, Heller 6187, Hemitt 6188, Henkind 6190, Hennessy 6191, Henshel 6192, Henson 6193, Hershaft 6197, Heyman 6201, Hiler 6207, Hilson 6209, Hirsch 6211, Hirsch 6212, Hochman 6214, Holtzman 6223, Hopkins 6224, Horowitz 6225, Houseknecht 6226, Houser 6227, Houston 6228, Hover 6229, Hoyt 6230, Huber 6231, Hulbert 6232, Hurlburt 6233, Hymowitz 6234, I.W. 6236, IF 6237, **Indira 6242**, Indus 6243, Insall 6247, International 6249, Iroquois 6250, Jamakepe 6256, Janklow 6257, Jarx 6258, Jennings 6259, JI 6260, JIA 6261, JKW 6263, Johnson 6268, Johnson 6269, Johnson 6270, Joseph 6273, Joyce 6275, Jungreis 6276, Kahn 6279, Kamber 6281, Kaminer 6282, Kandell 6283, Kasowitz 6285, Katz 6287, **Katzin 6288**, Katzman 6289, Keene 6293, Kelleher 6295, Kenlou 6299, Kenworthy 6300, Key 6305, Kimmel 6308, Kimmelman 6309, **King 6311**, Kirby 6313, Kistler 6316, **Klagsbrun 6318**, Klavan 6322, Klein 6325, Klingenstein 6327, Klingenstein-Martell 6329, Knafel 6330, Knapp 6331, Knaster 6332, Koessler 6335, Koha 6337, Konar 6340, Kornreich 6341, Kovensky 6342, Krimendahl/Saint-Amand 6346, Kroll 6348, Krumholz 6349, L 6353, L. 6354, Lainoff 6359, **Lamaj 6361**, Landau 6362, Lane 6363, **Larson 6365**, Lee 6372, Legacy 6373, Lenox 6380, Leonhardt 6381, Lerer 6382, Lerner 6383, Leuschen 6384, Levine 6386, Levine 6387, Levy 6391, Libby 6395, Liberman 6396, Lichtenstein 6397, Lieberman 6399, Liebowitz 6400, Lippes 6401, Lipton 6404, Litterman 6406, Little 6407, Long 6410, Longhill 6411, Lopatin 6412, Lorber 6413, Lowenbraun 6414, Lubo 6417, M&E 6425, M66 6427, Mabardi 6428, Madover 6431, Maguire 6432, Maher 6433, Marble 6441, Marine 6442, Marshall 6445, Martini 6447, Maslin 6448, MAT 6450, Mathis-Pfohl 6451, Matutina 6452, MBS 6454, **McCaddin-McQuirk 6455**, McCarthy 6456, McCooey 6457, McCormick 6459, Meade 6467, Meadowlark 6468, Mendell 6472, Menezes 6473, Menges 6474, Menken 6475, Meridian 6478, Merlo 6479, Mertz 6481, Metzger-Price 6483, Meyer 6484, Meyer 6485, Meyer 6486, Meyer 6487, Michaels 6488, **Milbank 6490**, Miller 6493, Miller-Sweezy 6494, Mittlemann 6500, Moach 6501, Monaghan 6502, Monderer 6503, Moore 6504, Morgado 6505, Morris 6508, Morse 6509, Morse 6510, Mule 6515, Mulroy 6516, MW 6517, Nelco 6522, Nets 6524, Netter 6525, **Neuman 6526**, Newcastle 6528, Newman 6530, Newman 6532, Newman 6534, Norwich 6542, Nuhn 6544, Oberoi 6547, Odyssey 6548, Oestreicher 6549, Ohel 6553, Olum 6555, Ong 6558, Osceola 6560, O'Sullivan 6565, Pajwell 6568, Palisades 6569, Parke 6576, Parr 6577, Parshelsky 6578, Paul 6580, Peckham 6583, Peek 6584, Persian 6589, **Peter 6590**, Peterson 6592, Pfeiffer 6597, Phaedrus 6598, Phalarope 6599, Phillips 6600, Phuong 6601, Pickman 6602, Picotte 6603, Pinkus 6607, Pittman 6608, Plunkett 6611, Pohly-Turaj 6613, Pollack 6614, Pollack 6615, Pollock 6616, Pomrenze 6619, Poorman 6620, Price 6627, Price 6628, Prince 6629, Project 6631, Psalm 6633, **QIBQ 6636**, Quinn 6637, R 6640, Rachel 6641, Rachesky 6642, **Rao 6645**, Rapaport 6646, Raphael 6648, Rattie 6650, RDM 6653, Realty 6655, REBNY 6656, Reich 6659, Reichert 6660, Reiss 6662, Rexford 6664, Rheinstrom 6665, RHR 6667, Richter 6668, Ridgewood 6669, Ring 6671, Risen 6672, Robbins 6676, Roche 6678, Rodgers 6680, Roe 6681, Rose 6683, Rose 6684, Rose 6686, Rosen 6689, Rosenberg 6691, Rosenstein 6692, Rosenthal 6694, Rosenthal 6695,

Rosenthal 6696, Rosner 6698, Ross 6699, Rothenberg 6702, Rubin 6707, Rudy 6708, Rupp 6710, Russo 6711, Ruthen 6714, Sakhai 6718, Sallie 6720, Samberg 6723, Samberg 6724, Samuels 6725, Sani 6726, Sargol 6728, **Sato 6731**, Saunders 6733, Savitz 6734, Schaffer 6736, Schaffer 6737, Schiller 6740, Schonberger 6744, Schonkopf 6747, Schott 6749, Schwartz 6752, Schwartz 6753, Scott 6761, Sdei 6764, SDF 6765, Seacoast 6766, Seligman 6772, SGMG 6778, Shack 6780, Shalom 6784, Shanken 6785, Sharon 6787, Sherman 6792, Siegel 6797, Silver 6800, Silverman 6801, Silverstein 6802, Silverstein 6803, Simcha 6804, Simpson 6805, Singer 6806, Slade 6810, Slovin 6811, Smith 6813, Smith 6815, Snyder 6819, Society 6821, Some 6824, Sorgente 6828, Spaeth 6829, Spear 6832, Spektor 6833, Speranza 6836, Spiegel 6837, Spiegel 6838, **Spirit 6839**, Spiritus 6840, Squier 6843, Stanton 6845, Starker 6847, Starmar 6848, Statue 6849, Steck 6852, Stein 6856, Steinberg 6857, Stern 6860, Sternberg 6863, Sternklar 6864, Stifel 6865, Still 6866, Stowe 6869, Striano 6871, Stuntz 6874, Stutz 6875, Sumitomo 6876, Summit 6877, Sunrise 6878, Switzer 6889, Tahari 6890, Thanksgiving 6897, Three 6899, Tisch 6900, Tod 6901, Touradji 6903, Treetops 6906, Treiber 6907, Tribune 6909, Trimble 6910, Truman 6912, Tuch 6915, Turner 6916, Tytel 6917, Uihlein 6919, **Usman 6921**, Utica 6922, Utopia 6923, Vaad 6924, Van 6925, Vance 6926, Vanden 6927, Vernon 6928, Villchur 6929, Vogler 6932, Wachtell 6936, Wagner 6938, Waldron 6939, Walsh 6942, **Walsh/Alfred 6943**, Warwick 6945, Washington 6946, Watts 6947, Weil 6948, Weinberg 6951, **Weingarten 6952**, Weininger 6954, Weinman 6955, **Weinstein 6956**, Weiss 6961, Wells 6964, Westlawn 6965, Whalen 6966, Wharton 6968, **Wheeler 6969**, Whispering 6970, White 6972, Whitehead 6974, Wilks 6977, Willmott 6978, Wilson 6979, Windy 6980, Wish 6981, WLC 6982, Wohlgemuth 6984, Woldar 6985, Wolf 6986, Woodmere 6990, Woodward 6993, Wright 6995, Yaspan-Unterberg 7003, YGBL 7006, Yitzchok 7007, Yordan 7009, Yosef 7011, Young 7012, Zahavi 7015, Zamir 7016, Zemsky 7022, Zenkel 7023, Zichron 7026, Ziff 7027, Zirkl 7029, Zurack 7033, Zwerling 7034

North Carolina: Abernethy 7037, Aehle 7038, Agarwal 7039, Arcadia 7040, Balin 7042, Bane 7043, Barker 7044, BB&T 7045, Bell 7047, Bettman 7051, Billingsley 7052, Boddie 7054, Boddie 7055, Bolick 7056, Borun 7057, Brown 7058, Burks 7061, Burlington 7062, Cameron 7065, Carroll 7068, Cary 7069, Cary 7070, Chaley 7072, Chatham 7074, CJB 7076, Coffey 7078, Cooke 7080, Davis 7083, Deal 7085, Duncan 7086, Edgar 7088, Ellison 7090, Eplee 7092, Evernham 7094, Fairfield 7095, First 7097, **Firth 7098**, Fortson 7100, Foster 7101, Fox 7103, Gambrill 7106, Geschick 7109, Glenn 7111, Griffin 7113, Hamill 7115, Haney 7116, Harrison 7117, Hayden-Harman 7120, Hayes 7121, Helb 7122, Helton 7123, Herndon 7125, Holleman 7129, Howard 7131, Howe 7132, Hunt 7134, Hunter 7136, Jehn 7137, Kassner 7141, Kennedy 7145, Koons 7148, KPB 7151, **Kramer 7152**, Krauss 7153, Ladd 7156, **Laffin 7157**, Landry's 7159, Lerner 7160, Levine-Sklut 7161, Markey 7168, McConnell 7176, McGuire 7177, McLean 7178, Meserve 7182, Meyer 7183, Miller 7185, Moretz 7189, Morgan 7190, Morisey 7191, Nalle 7197, Nanney 7198, Niessen 7200, Oschwald 7203, Outer 7204, Paddock 7206, Peeler 7207, Perkin 7208, Piedmont 7209, Pillmore 7210, Plansoen 7211, Pope 7212, Post 7213, Pratt 7214, Pulliam 7215, Ragland 7216, Rankin 7217, Redwoods 7218, Ribenack 7220, Richardson 7221, Robinson 7225, Robitaille 7226, Rocky 7227, **Rolander 7229**, Rollins 7231, Rostan 7232, S.D.R. 7233, Sanders 7234, Self 7238, Shapiro 7239, Shingleton 7241, Shugart 7242, Silverman 7244, Sites 7245, Sloan 7246, Smith 7248, Smith 7249,

Snyder's-Lance 7250, Spring 7251, Steinmetz 7254, Stowe 7256, Strickland 7257, Stuart 7259, Stubblefield 7260, Summer 7261, Szulik 7264, Thomasville 7267, Trexler 7269, TSH 7271, Vanderbilt 7273, Von 7274, Wake 7276, Wann 7279, Way 7281, Wells 7283, West-West 7284, **Weyberg 7285**, Whitener 7286, Zelnak 7293
North Dakota: Community 7295, Fedje 7296, Myra 7297, Pearson 7298
Ohio: Albrecht 7301, Alpaugh 7302, Armington 7309, Athens 7311, Austin-Bailey 7312, Barron 7316, Bates 7317, B-Brand 7318, Beecher 7321, Berkman 7324, Bernard 7325, Bicknell 7327, Black 7328, Boymel 7329, Brethen 7331, Brews 7332, Brown 7337, Building 7340, Busemeyer 7342, Calhoun 7344, Cardinal 7347, Cassner 7348, Chemed 7350, Chesley 7351, Christ 7352, Christen 7353, Community 7356, Conlogue 7359, Connor 7361, Cooper 7362, Coressel 7364, Covelli 7365, Crandall 7366, Danis 7371, Demetros 7377, Dorn 7380, Downing 7381, **Eaton 7383**, Ebenezer 7384, Edward 7385, Entelco 7389, Eyman 7391, Faber 7392, Fedeli 7393, Feldstein 7394, Ferry 7396, Feth 7397, Fibus 7398, Finnegan 7399, Firman 7400, Fishel 7401, Fletcher 7405, Fortney 7406, Foss 7407, Fox 7409, Freygang 7410, Frohman 7411, Frost 7412, Frost-Parker 7413, Gale 7414, Geary 7419, Gelbman 7420, Geotrac 7422, Gimbel 7424, Goerlich 7428, Gould 7430, Gross 7432, Hamilton 7435, Hampson 7436, Hankins 7437, Haskell 7439, Hauck 7440, Heffner 7443, Heinrich 7446, Hickok 7447, Homan 7451, Hoover 7453, Hubert 7456, Hueneke 7457, Hummer 7459, Ingle 7462, Iott 7463, Jenkins 7464, Jenkins 7465, Jennings 7466, Joffe 7467, Johnson 7468, Johnson 7469, Jordan 7471, Juniper 7472, Kennedy 7476, Kilworth 7477, Kisker 7479, Klock 7480, Kloenne 7481, Knight 7482, Knoll 7483, Kramer 7485, Kutz 7486, Landers 7488, Lang 7489, Laub 7490, Lawry 7491, Lindner 7497, Lippitt 7499, Littick 7500, LKC 7501, Lockwood 7502, Loeb 7503, Luedeking 7506, Lukens 7507, Lundgard 7508, Lungard 7509, M.L.M 7510, Mangano 7511, Marnick 7515, Matthes 7517, McCann 7519, Mccarthy 7520, McMaster 7521, Mead 7522, Messer 7524, Miller 7527, Miller 7528, Milliron 7529, Mixon 7530, Musson 7534, Norris 7538, Norweb 7539, Ohio 7541, Orr 7543, Oscar 7544, Peters 7547, Powers 7550, Quatman 7552, Rapport 7553, Reynolds 7559, Rosenberry 7562, Sage 7568, Sandfair 7569, Sauerland 7570, Schey 7571, Schottenstein 7574, Schwartz, 7576, Seaman 7580, Seasongood 7582, Segoe 7583, Shannon 7586, Sheely 7590, Smiley 7597, Smith 7598, Southard 7599, Stafast 7600, Stein 7601, Steiner-King 7602, Stensen 7604, STERIS 7605, Sterling 7606, Stillson 7607, Swagelok 7608, Tait 7610, Taj 7611, Talbott 7612, Terhune 7614, Thendara 7616, TKBW 7619, Traeger 7621, Tuscarawas 7623, Tuscora 7624, Van 7625, Van 7626, Vista 7628, Wagler 7629, Walker 7630, Wasserstrom 7632, Watson 7633, Weiss 7634, Welty 7635, Wightman-Wieber 7636, Wildermuth 7637, Williams 7638, Wolfe 7644, Young 7651, Young 7652
Oklahoma: Ashbrook 7656, Barnes 7658, Barnett 7660, Broadhurst 7663, Brown 7664, Burkhart 7665, Cherokee 7666, Chilton 7667, Collins 7668, Drabek 7673, Dulaney 7674, Everest 7676, French 7680, Fugitt 7681, Gelvin 7682, Goddard 7684, Goodin 7685, Harmon 7686, Howard 7689, Jones 7691, Jones 7692, Kerr 7693, Kullgren 7696, Livengood 7698, Lolmaugh 7700, Lovoi 7702, Marshall 7703, Massey 7705, Merkel 7706, Merrick 7707, Miller 7708, Miller 7709, Oklahoma 7711, Parman 7713, Pros 7715, Richardson 7717, Sisk 7719, Sylvan 7722, Trippet 7725, Warren 7729, Weber 7730, Welch 7732, White 7733, Wilson 7736
Oregon: Ackley 7740, Castle 7745, Cayo 7746, Chaney 7747, Charis 7748, Coffman 7750, Coit 7751, Collins 7752, Collins 7753, **Conklin 7754**, Curry

7755, Demorest 7757, Dieringer 7758, Dubs 7760, Flowerree 7763, Four 7764, Frank 7765, Glennco 7768, Haskell 7770, Hill 7773, Hitchman 7774, Holzman 7775, Irwin 7777, Jubitz 7779, Kinnie 7783, Klamath 7784, Knudson 7785, **Larson 7788**, Leupold 7790, May 7794, McKay 7795, Mentor 7796, Merlo 7797, Michael 7799, Miller 7800, Portland 7807, Schmidt 7813, Shapira 7814, Silver 7817, Spencer 7820, Stewart 7822, Trover 7824, Wessinger 7826, West 7827, Woodard 7831, **Wyss 7832**

Pennsylvania: 100 7833, Aaron 7835, Alley 7837, Amaranth 7838, Ames 7840, Ashland 7845, Ayers 7848, Baker 7851, Baldwin, 7852, Balzereit 7853, Bannerot-Lappe 7854, Beach 7855, Beels 7858, Berger 7862, Bergstrom 7864, Berkowitz 7866, Betts 7869, Bienenfeld 7872, Bishop 7874, Black 7875, Black 7876, Bloch 7878, Blue 7879, Bolte 7882, Bonomo 7883, Bon-Ton 7884, Born 7885, Borowsky 7886, Boscia 7887, Boudinot 7888, Breedlove 7890, Bridge 7891, Briggs 7892, Britton 7894, Bronstein 7896, Brooks 7897, Brooks 7898, Buck 7903, Bucks 7905, Cameron 7911, Cannon 7913, Carnahan-Jackson 7917, Case 7918, Casteel 7919, Charlestein 7920, Chase 7921, Clark 7925, Clark 7927, Community 7933, Conestoga 7934, Cost 7937, Cottage 7938, Cove 7939, Cozen 7941, Crawford 7945, Curaterra 7947, Delaware 7953, DENTSPLY 7954, Dickson 7957, Dinardo 7960, Donnally 7962, Dozzi 7965, Drueding 7966, Eakins 7968, Eberly 7969, Eckels 7970, Eden 7971, Elk 7975, Ellis 7978, **Epstein 7983**, Everard 7985, Fair 7987, Family 7988, Fetters 7991, Finley 7995, First 7996, First 7997, First 7998, Five 7999, Fleming 8000, Flinn 8001, Fortinsky 8002, Foster 8003, Fountainhead 8004, Freas 8005, French 8007, Friends 8008, Friendship 8009, Frohring 8010, Gamber 8011, Ganse 8012, Gauss 8014, Gershman 8015, Gilmore 8017, Gitt 8019, Goodstein 8023, Gordon 8024, Goshen 8025, Greater 8026, Grumbacher 8028, GT 8030, Gulati 8032, Hall 8037, Hankin 8038, Harrison 8039, Harsco 8040, Hassel 8042, Hauber 8043, Herndon 8051, Heyl 8052, HFO 8053, High 8054, Hilles 8057, Hirtzel 8058, **Hitchcock 8059**, Hoch 8060, Hodge 8061, Hoffman 8063, Homeless 8065, Horn 8067, Hulme 8069, Hunt 8070, Huplits 8071, IGN 8073, Ithan 8076, Jackson 8077, Jackson 8078, Jansing-Cook 8079, Jewish 8080, John 8081, Joyce 8083, Karamatsoukas 8085, Katz 8088, Katz 8089, Kelley 8091, Klahr 8095, Klein 8096, Klein 8097, Kline 8098, Knox 8101, Knudsen 8102, Krouse 8103, Landenberger 8109, Larking 8112, Laughlin 8114, Lemole 8119, Levis 8122, Lewis 8125, Lida 8127, Lienemann 8128, Lockhard 8130, Magee 8131, Maple 8139, Marstine 8141, Martin 8142, Martin 8143, Martin 8144, Mason 8147, Mason 8148, Mateer 8150, Mattingly 8151, McCune 8155, McGinley 8156, McKamish 8158, McKinney 8161, Mclelland 8162, McSwigan 8165, Meakem 8166, Mellon 8167, Merwin 8170, Mill 8172, Miller 8173, Moffat 8175, Moore 8177, Moyer 8180, Mukaiyama-Rice 8183, Mullen 8184, Murphy 8185, Mutual 8186, Nathan 8188, Neag 8189, Neal 8190, Neuber 8192, Nikolaus 8193, Norford 8196, Olitsky 8198, Oppenheim 8199, Pangborn 8203, Patterson 8205, Patterson 8206, Penn 8208, Perelman 8210, Petersen 8212, Pfundt 8213, Pittsburgh 8215, Pittsburgh 8216, Plainfield 8217, Plankenhorn 8219, Platt, 8220, Quaker 8228, Quinn 8229, Rath 8231, Reese 8232, Reidler 8233, Reiss 8234, Remmel 8235, Ricon 8237, Rider-Pool 8238, Roemer 8242, Rosenberg 8244, Rubin 8246, Russo 8249, **Rust 8250**, Sample, 8252, Saramar 8253, Schafer 8256, Schautz 8257, Schrenk 8261, Schultz 8262, Schuylkill 8263, Schwab-Silfen 8264, Schwartz 8265, Seybert 8269, **Shastri 8273**, Shenk 8274, Sidewater 8278, Smith 8280, Smith 8281, Smith 8282, Smith 8283, Smith 8284, Snyder 8287, Somerville 8291, Spencer 8293, Speyer 8294, Staehle 8295, Star 8297, Stewart 8301, Stewart,

8302, Strawbridge 8305, Tabas 8312, Teleflex 8314, Thomas 8316, Thompson 8317, Tippins 8318, Tompkins-Broll 8320, Trax 8321, Triple 8322, Tuttleman 8325, Union 8326, Velma 8330, Victor 8332, Wabtec 8335, Wachs-Weingarten 8337, Wagner 8338, Wakefield 8339, Walton 8341, Ward 8343, Wasserott 8344, Weiler 8347, Weiler-Miller 8348, Wenger 8351, Wenger 8352, Whalley 8353, Willary 8356, Williams 8357, Willow 8360, Winokur 8362, Wolfson 8364, Wolstenholme 8366, Wood 8367, Wurts 8370, Wyeth 8371, Zisman 8377

Rhode Island: Arakelian 8381, Bailey 8384, Bersted 8388, Brack 8392, Chace 8393, Clark 8395, Collis 8397, Del 8401, Feibelman 8405, Field 8407, Fuller 8409, Galkin 8410, Getz 8412, Greene 8413, Hartman 8417, Hecht 8418, Hoag 8421, Hope 8422, Horton 8423, Jacbel 8426, Janci 8428, Johnson 8430, Kelly 8432, Kimball 8434, Kingsbury 8435, Leroe 8439, LLH/LHM 8442, Longfield 8444, Lorber 8445, Luke 8447, Mann 8448, Masonic 8449, McCarthy 8452, Molder 8455, Moore 8456, Mulligan 8457, Mulvaney 8458, Nixon 8460, Noyes 8461, O'Halloran 8462, Papitto 8467, Pardee 8468, Peacock 8469, Perpetual 8471, Robertson 8478, Sachem 8479, Schwarz 8483, Seed 8484, Shea 8486, Sinclair 8488, Slemons 8490, Slingerland 8491, Sullivan 8494, Swarts 8495, Thompson 8497, Washington 8500, Wilson 8504, Woodward 8505, York 8507, Zack 8508

South Carolina: Bailey 8509, Bailey 8510, Bannon 8511, Bignon 8512, Bonner 8513, Childress 8518, Coker 8519, Collins 8520, Eastern 8522, Gleason 8524, Greenleaf 8525, Hendricks 8527, Horne 8528, Kendall 8530, Lutz 8533, Nalley 8535, Near 8536, Peery/Cauthen 8537, Singing 8540, Stevens 8541, Stony 8542, Sunshine 8544, T-Bonz 8546, Williams/Brice-Edwards 8549, **Winthrop 8550**, WPW 8551, **Zvejnieks 8553**

South Dakota: Clarkson 8558, Eleanor's 8559, Emerald 8562, Engelsma 8563, Peterson 8572, Reese 8573, Stearns 8575, Watertown 8576, Welk 8577, Wolfe 8578

Tennessee: Adams 8579, Agape 8580, Atticus 8582, B 8583, Basler 8584, **Belz 8585**, Berman 8587, BGL 8588, Blum 8589, Bradford 8592, Caldwell 8593, Card 8596, Chrysalis 8598, Citizens 8599, Cole 8600, Community 8601, Cracker 8603, Deupree 8604, Doochin 8605, Drake 8606, Draughon 8607, Ebert-Leblanc 8609, EBS 8610, Eskind 8611, Eskind 8612, Eskind 8613, Fleming 8615, Foster 8616, **Fraser 8617**, **Fugitive 8618**, Goad 8621, Goldsmith 8622, Gordon 8624, Grandview 8625, Hawthorn 8626, Heagele-Blount 8627, Houghland 8630, Hutcheson 8631, Ingram 8632, Jewell 8633, Jordan 8636, Kennedy 8638, Knight 8640, LDB 8642, **Louisiana-Pacific 8644**, McWherter 8649, Mercy 8650, Mick 8651, Monday 8652, Nehemiah 8653, New 8654, Pettway 8658, Restoration 8665, Rogers 8666, Sasco 8669, Schadt 8670, Sohr 8676, Stadler 8678, Tompkins 8683, Weiss 8684, Williamson, 8685, Wilt 8687, WTC 8688

Texas: A 8689, Abernathy 8690, Alexander 8696, Amarillo 8697, **AMD 8698**, American 8699, Anderson 8704, Anderson 8705, Aragona 8706, Arena 8707, Armstrong 8708, **Astrl 8711**, Augur 8712, Baer 8714, Baldridge 8715, Barnabas 8717, Beaird 8720, Bearden 8721, Bee 8723, Behmann 8725, Bertha 8729, **Bhutada 8730**, Bloxom, 8731, Boeing 8733, Booth 8734, Booth 8735, Bowling 8737, Bratten 8739, Brentwood 8741, Brochstein 8746, Brodsky 8747, Bromberg 8748, Bromley 8749, Brown 8751, Brownsville 8752, Bunyard 8755, Burch 8756, Burzik 8758, Calpine 8759, Cariker 8762, Cauthorn 8764, Cemo 8765, Central 8766, Chisholm 8769, Clements 8773, Coleman 8778, Collins 8781, Community 8782, **Coneway 8783**, Conley 8784, Connor 8785, Crossroads 8791, **Crowder 8792**, Dale 8794, Dallas 8795, Dauphin 8798, Davis 8799, Day 8800, DDM 8801, de 8802, De 8803, Deakins 8804, Dedman 8807, Dedman, 8808, Denman 8810, di 8812, Dick

8815, DKG 8817, Doak 8818, Dobson 8819, Dooley 8822, Dougherty, 8825, Dove 8826, Duddlesten 8829, Dulaney 8830, Dunagan 8831, Dunaway 8832, Duncan 8833, Durrill 8835, Edwards 8837, EOS 8840, Esping 8841, Fair 8844, Faith 8846, Farris 8847, Fenner 8850, FHC 8853, Finney 8858, Fired 8859, Flohr 8861, Flowers 8862, Folsom 8863, Foster 8866, Foster 8868, Foundation 8869, Fowlston 8871, Freescale 8874, Friedel 8875, Frost 8878, Fruehauf 8879, Fuchs 8881, Fuller 8882, Garvey 8884, Gatewood 8885, Genecov 8886, Give 8890, Go 8891, Gordon 8893, Grace 8895, Graham 8896, Gray 8899, Greentree 8901, Griffin 8902, Griffith 8903, Grits 8904, Guetz 8905, Guinn 8906, Haggar 8907, Haggar, 8908, Hallberg 8911, Hanley 8915, Hanley 8916, Harrell 8919, Hartman 8920, Hatfield 8922, Hegi 8926, Helm 8928, Hershey 8931, Hervey 8932, Hext 8933, Hibbs 8934, Hicks 8935, Hicks 8936, Hill 8938, Hillcrest 8939, Hofheinz 8942, Hofstetter 8943, Hollandsworth 8945, Holloway 8946, Horizon 8951, Houck 8953, Howell 8956, Ilgenfritz 8960, Janszen 8966, Johnson 8969, Johnston 8972, Journey 8975, Kabacoff 8977, Kahn 8978, Kaplan 8979, Kayser 8980, KCL 8981, Kelley 8983, Kelley 8984, Keown 8986, Ketelsen 8988, **Kilgore 8989**, Kimble 8991, King 8994, Kirwan 8996, Klein 8997, Klesse 8998, Knox 8999, Korell 9001, Kowitz 9002, Kramer 9003, Krist 9004, Kritser, 9005, Lange 9008, Lantana 9009, Laredo 9010, LBJ 9011, Levy 9014, Light 9016, Lighthouse 9017, Link 9020, Littauer 9021, Lowdon 9025, LSF 9026, LSG 9027, Lupton 9028, Luse 9029, MacDonald 9031, MacDonald-Peterson 9032, **Mansur 9035**, Margolin 9038, Marks 9039, McDonald 9051, McLaughlin 9053, McMillan, 9054, McNutt 9055, Mendenhall 9056, Mercy 9057, Merfish-Jacobson 9058, Merrick 9059, Mewhinney 9060, Miller 9066, Mithoff 9068, Montgomery 9070, Moss 9076, Myers 9081, **New 9087**, Nislar 9088, North 9089, Nowiczewski 9090, Nowotny 9091, O'Connor 9093, O'Hare 9095, One 9096, Oppenheimer 9100, Oriska 9103, Orr 9104, Osberg 9105, Overlake 9106, PAL 9111, Palmer 9112, Papadopoulos 9113, Paris 9114, Partnership 9116, Patterson 9118, Paulos 9120, Penland 9124, Perkins 9125, Pevehouse 9127, Phoenix 9128, Pierson 9129, Pogue 9133, Postl 9136, Pratt 9137, Prayer 9138, Proctor 9139, Quanex 9141, Raygar 9145, RDM 9146, Reilly 9148, Reuhl 9150, Richter 9153, Riter, 9154, Robinson 9158, Roosth 9160, Rosen 9161, Rowan 9166, Rust 9168, Saunders 9176, Schepps 9177, Schissler 9179, Schulte 9181, SCP 9185, Sear 9186, Seay 9187, Serafy 9188, Seven 9189, Sharma 9190, Shepherds 9191, Shiloff 9193, Simard 9195, Sklar 9199, Smith 9202, **Smith 9203**, Smith 9204, Smith 9207, **Soonae 9208**, South 9210, Stanzel 9213, Starnes 9214, Staubach 9215, Sterling 9219, Stewart, 9221, Sure 9225, Sutton 9226, Swett 9227, Tabani 9228, Taub 9229, Tennessee 9230, Texas 9231, Texas 9232, Tietze 9236, Tolleson 9238, Torchmark 9240, Torrance 9241, Van 9247, Vaughan 9248, Vaughan 9249, Vetter 9251, VMP 9252, Waggoner 9254, Waggoners 9255, Wal-Dot 9256, Walls 9257, Ward 9260, Watson 9263, Way 9264, Weaver 9265, Webre 9266, Weir 9268, Westcott 9273, Wheeler 9274, Whitley 9276, Wilder 9277, Willard 9278, Williams 9280, Wise 9283, Wolens 9284, Wolff-Toomim 9286, Wood 9290, Woods 9291, Woolf 9292, Works 9293, Wright 9294, Youth 9298, Zale 9299, Zale 9300

Utah: B. 9302, Benjamin 9305, Burbidge 9308, Burton 9309, CASA 9312, Denkers 9318, Dreamweaver 9320, Dry 9321, Eskuche 9323, Funding 9325, Gardner 9326, Green 9327, Harman 9328, Jackson 9329, JKS 9330, JNF 9331, Keener 9332, Kennecott 9333, Kirk 9334, Korver 9335, Leavitt 9338, Low 9340, Odyssey 9342, Schmidt 9349, **Skolnick 9352**, SmartGo 9354, Steiner 9358, Zions 9363

Vermont: Altman 9364, Carris 9367, Ferro 9372, Harper 9373, Harvest 9374, Leboeuf 9379, Mergens 9381, NSB 9382, Redducs 9383, Seventh 9384, Stokes 9385

Virginia: American 9387, Backer 9389, Bassett 9391, Better 9396, Black 9399, Blueberry 9402, Brandt 9403, BRI 9405, Bryant 9409, Burford 9411, Bw718 9412, Cartledge 9414, Cedars 9416, Chainani 9417, Chastain 9419, Clark-Nexsen 9421, Cole 9423, Collins 9425, Community 9426, Darden 9428, **Delmar 9429**, Denit 9430, Dickerson 9431, Donohue 9432, Doudera 9434, Dreaming 9435, Dun 9437, Dundas 9438, Dwyer 9439, Elmwood 9442, Farkas 9445, Fink 9447, Fleder 9448, Flippo 9449, **Foundation 9450**, Foundation 9451, Franklin 9452, Fraser 9453, Gifford 9457, Grandis 9462, Greco 9463, Greensville 9464, Hilltop 9470, Hopkins 9472, Houff 9473, Hughes 9474, II 9475, Immixgroup 9476, Ivakota 9477, **Jain 9478**, Jones 9479, King 9484, Lacy 9485, Lane 9486, Lawrence 9487, Levmar 9490, Loeb 9493, Macedonian 9496, McWaters 9499, Meador 9500, Mody 9501, Mullen 9502, Northern 9503, Ochsman 9504, O'Shaughnessy-Hurst 9505, Page 9507, Peachtree 9508, Pensmore 9509, Perlin 9510, Poole 9512, Pruden 9517, Ramsey 9519, Rashti 9520, RECO 9522, Richardson 9523, Rimora 9524, Rouse-Bottom 9526, Schiro-Zavela 9528, Selsky 9529, Shaffer 9530, Smith 9534, Stephenson 9536, Stone 9537, Strauch 9538, **Tara 9540**, Tesco 9541, Thomas 9542, Treakle 9543, Vinoskey 9547, VuBay 9548, Weil 9550, Wiley 9551, Williams-Berry 9554, Womack 9556, Zeiders 9557

Washington: Alhadeff 9558, Ames 9560, Amstein 9561, Arise 9562, Babare 9563, Bacon 9565, Baker 9566, Bayley 9567, Beck, 9568, Bishop 9569, Boeschoten 9571, Boydston 9572, Brookshire-Green 9573, Bulleri 9575, Bungie 9576, **Children's 9579**, Cowles 9582, Dore 9587, Erickson 9591, Everett 9592, Fales 9594, FAR 9595, Ferguson 9596, Fletcher 9597, Foss 9598, Fries-Tait 9599, FTJ 9600, Fulton 9601, Furnessville 9602, Gibson 9604, Gius 9606, Goodfellow 9607, Goodman 9608, Hanauer 9614, Hansen 9615, Heath 9617, Heidner 9618, Herbold 9620, Herray 9621, Hickey 9622, Horn 9625, Jacobi 9628, Jefferson 9630, Johnston-Hanson 9635, Joint 9636, Jones 9637, Josi 9639, Juniper 9640, Kaleidoscope 9641, Kawabe 9642, Keller 9643, Kilworth 9644, Klaue 9647, Korum 9648, Lanterman 9649, Larson 9650, Lea 9652, Levitan 9653, Lott 9656, Madrona 9657, Martin 9659, McKinlay 9662, Mize 9663, Moraine 9664, Not 9670, O'Donnell 9672, Ohno 9673, Pease 9678, Pointe 9679, Prairie 9680, Remala 9683, Schuler 9690, Schwab 9691, Shemanski 9693, Shepherd 9694, Slingshot 9697, Sondland 9700, Spark 9701, Spring 9702, Stevens 9704, Tamaki 9707, Teel 9708, Templin 9709, Thayer 9710, Thomson 9711, Thurston 9713, Titus-Will 9714, Tonkin 9715, True 9716, Welch 9721, Wellworth 9722, **Wiebe 9723**, Wilkens 9724, Winter 9726, Wissner-Slivka 9727, Woodworth 9728, Worthington 9729, Wright 9730

West Virginia: Appalachian 9734, Bowers 9738, Brown 9739, Carter 9741, Chambers 9742, Driehorst 9743, Hamer 9746, Hess 9747, Hollowell 9751, Hope, 9752, Hott 9753, Huntington 9754, Larch 9755, McDavid 9760, Skewes 9766, Starvaggi 9767, Vecellio 9770

Wisconsin: Anderson 9773, AnnMarie 9774, Ariens 9776, Associated 9778, Aylward 9779, Baker 9780, BayCare 9781, Berbeewalsh 9782, Birnschein 9783, Bluemke 9785, Brown 9790, Caritas 9791, Chipstone 9794, Community 9797, Cudahy 9800, Cummings-Christensen 9801, Dawes 9803, Debbink 9804, Dohmen 9806, Door 9810, Dudley 9811, Easter 9813, Eau 9814, Erdman 9816, F.K. 9817, Foulkes 9821, Frautschi 9822, Gardner 9825, Gebhardt 9826, Glendenning 9828, **Global 9829**, Gordon 9830, Gordon 9831, Grande 9832, Hansen 9835, Hartwig 9836, Hatch 9837, Hicks 9840, Highlands 9841, Huiras 9844, Hunt 9845, Hyde 9846, Inbusch 9847, J.P.C. 9848, **Johnson 9851**, Johnson 9852, Jones 9854, Kalscheur 9858, Kaztex 9860, Kenosha 9862, Kloss 9863, Kohl 9864, Loehrke 9872, Lutsey 9873, LUX 9874, Lyche 9875, Manitowoc 9876, Marcus 9877, Martin 9879, Mason 9880, Mednikow 9881, Meehan 9882, Merkel 9884, Mid-States 9887, Mielcarek 9888, Modine 9889, Mound 9891, Murray 9892, Nelson 9893, Okray 9896, Olson 9897, Olson 9898, Park 9899, Phipps 9902, Phipps 9903, Plein 9904, Prescott 9905, Pritchett 9906, Puelicher 9907, Purple 9908, Regal-Beloit 9911, RITE-HITE 9915, Roddis 9916, Roehl 9917, ROS 9918, Rosemann 9919, Rusinow 9920, Schlegel 9922, Schoenleber 9924, Shoemaker 9928, Simms 9929, Smith 9932, SMS 9933, St. 9936, Stateline 9937, Styberg 9942, Sub-Zero 9943, Uihlein 9949, Uihlein 9950, Van 9951, Van 9952, Van 9953, Verhulst 9954, Wagner 9955, Watertown 9956, Webcrafters-Frautschi 9957, Weyco 9958, Weyers 9959, Windway 9961, Witte, 9962, Woodtrust-Bell 9963

Wyoming: C 9966, Connemara 9967, Dragicevich 9969, Dubois 9970, Guthrie 9972, Hirschfield 9973, Imig 9974, Joannides 9976, Johnson 9977, Marine 9980, Nickerson 9981, Richardson 9983, Riehm 9984, Sargent 9985, Skelton 9989, StoneRiver 9991, Surrena 9994, Tate 9995, Welch 9998

Human services management

Massachusetts: Alden 3999

Humane education

Missouri: **Build-A-Bear 4879**
New York: **Animal 5680**

Humanities

Colorado: Broomfield 1242
Connecticut: Winokur 1597
Florida: Second 2321
Georgia: Oxford 2561
Illinois: Block, 2746, Engle 2855, Glossberg 2916, Lohengrin 3059
Iowa: Jefferson 3514
Massachusetts: Cabot 4035
Michigan: Branch 4396, Mackinac 4499
Minnesota: Schott 4787
New York: Cox 5883, Hoyt 6230, Legacy 6373
North Carolina: Chastain 7073, Kenan 7143
Ohio: Athens 7311, Tuscarawas 7623
Pennsylvania: Cameron 7911, Lewis 8123
Texas: Baldridge 8715, Moss 9076
Utah: B. 9302

Immigrant rights

Illinois: Lehman-Stamm 3045, Sumac 3278
New York: Wagner 6938

Immigrants

California: Szekely 1102, **Trustees 1132**, **Wakerly 1150**

Immigrants and migrants

Alabama: Ireland 39
California: Gellert 550, **Global 565**, **Raymond 956**
Colorado: Steffens 1358, Warner 1376
District of Columbia: **Carter 1794**, Jovid 1817
Illinois: **Landau 3036**
Massachusetts: Kelsey 4148
Minnesota: Bell 4638
Nevada: **Center 5145**
New Mexico: Con 5611
New York: 21st 5630, **Sparkplug 6830**

North Carolina: Strowd 7258
Wisconsin: Marshfield 9878

Immune system diseases

Florida: Diane 1974
New Jersey: Lavery 5441
New York: Golick 6104, Johnson 6270, Saltzman 6722, Weisman 6959
Pennsylvania: Mellon 8167
Wisconsin: Johnson 9852

Immunology

California: Kelvin 699
Florida: Evans 1994

Impaired driving

Iowa: GuideOne 3503

In-patient medical care

California: Coleman 416, Elder 475, Miller 832
Florida: Bell 1882
Illinois: Millard 3110
Missouri: Mungenast 4966
New Jersey: **Greenblatt 5376**
New York: Ades-Taub 5645, I.W. 6236
Pennsylvania: Norbell 8195
Texas: KCL 8981
Washington: DeFalco 9585

Incarcerated people

Alabama: Black 12, Ireland 39
Connecticut: Fippinger 1450
District of Columbia: Jovid 1817
Minnesota: Larsen 4728
Pennsylvania: Hoffman 8062
Virginia: **Brown 9407**

Independent living for people with disabilities

Florida: Gate 2034
Georgia: Waffle 2602
Massachusetts: Progin 4247
Minnesota: Bumgarner 4649
Ohio: M.L.M 7510

Indigenous peoples

Alabama: Black 12, Ireland 39
California: Amin 240
Florida: Landwirth 2167
Maryland: **St. 3960**
Michigan: Main 4501, Wieczorek 4617
Minnesota: **Winds 4820**
Missouri: **Bohm 4871**
Nebraska: Midlands 5104
Nevada: Williams 5199
New Jersey: **Garcia 5362**
New Mexico: **Angelica 5605**, Con 5611
New York: **Sparkplug 6830**
Oklahoma: Livengood 7698
Texas: Harrell 8919
Virginia: **Delmar 9429**
West Virginia: Starvaggi 9767

Individual liberties

Arkansas: Darragh 193
California: Evans 485
Delaware: Pollack 1722
Illinois: Lehman-Stamm 3045, McDougal 3091
Michigan: Pitt 4541
Missouri: Sayler-Hawkins 4993
New York: 1848 5629, **Gimprich 6080**, IF 6237
Oregon: **Larson 7788**

Infant care
California: Livingston 761, Scott 1023
Florida: Shannon 2328
Maryland: CSG 3842, Feldman 3858
Massachusetts: Chartis 4044
Minnesota: Butzow 4651
Texas: Levy 9014

Infants and toddlers
Alabama: Ireland 39
California: Nicholson 866
Georgia: Abreu 2431
Illinois: Meyer 3106
Kansas: Legacy, 3595
Kentucky: Killian 3670
Massachusetts: Kelsey 4148
Nebraska: Midlands 5104
New Mexico: Con 5611
North Carolina: Glenn 7111
Ohio: Sandfair 7569, Walker 7630
Oregon: Elwood 7761
Pennsylvania: Child 7923, Hoffman 8062
Tennessee: **Fugitive 8618**
Virginia: **Brown 9407, Delmar 9429**
Wisconsin: Hamilton 9834, Marshfield 9878

Infectious and parasitic diseases
Missouri: No 4971

Interdisciplinary studies
Michigan: Whitman 4615

Interfaith
Florida: Grader 2054
Kansas: Stallman 3629, Wallace 3637
Maryland: **Thadikonda 3965**
Minnesota: McCoy 4742
Missouri: Hofheimer 4929
New Mexico: Quail 5622
North Carolina: Gambrill 7106
Pennsylvania: Kahn, 8084, Schwartz 8265
Tennessee: Goldsmith 8622
Wyoming: Connemara 9967

Intergenerational mentoring
California: Solano 1063

Internal medicine
Illinois: Taxman 3283
Massachusetts: Gerrity 4102

International development
Alabama: Kairos 41
California: **Alalusi 236**, Becker 292, **Cienega 404**, Clara 406, Handlery 596, Harris 601, **Linked 758**, Oak 872, Von 1148, World 1196
Colorado: Gerrish 1277, McPherson 1323, Steffens 1358
Connecticut: Crew 1424, Donchian 1440, Macauley 1514, Tierney 1584
Delaware: Cultures 1652, Kuehner 1695, Weissman 1775
Florida: Basham 1870, Second 2321
Illinois: Cowlin 2814, Gochnauer 2918, Logos 3058, Lohengrin 3059, Rossman 3211, Rothman 3213, Schneider 3226, Shamrock 3239
Kansas: **Weskan 3641**
Maryland: Meyer, 3913
Massachusetts: **Azadoutioun 4008, Blossom 4022**, Metanoia 4201, **Patagonia 4234, Tatelman 4322**
Michigan: **Ajemian 4371**, Pilgrim 4539, Whitman 4615
Minnesota: Hegardt 4710, **Porter 4763, Winds 4820**
Missouri: **Block 4869**, Slusher 5009

Nevada: **A 5131, Wood 5201**
New Jersey: Waterview 5572
New Mexico: Quail 5622
New York: AGB 5650, **Family 5983**, Fitt 6010, **Jabara 6254**, Lachman 6356, Newman 6530, Richter 6668, Sherman 6792, Zyman 7036
North Carolina: Bolick 7056
Ohio: Hazelbaker 7441, **Lowe-Marshall 7505**
Pennsylvania: **Epstein 7984**, Larsen 8113, **Zeldin 8376**
Rhode Island: Hoag 8421, Luke 8447
Tennessee: Community 8601, Drake 8606, **Redbird 8664**
Texas: ADR 8693, Baldridge 8715, Halperin 8912, Reilly 9148, Shepherds 9191
Utah: SmartGo 9354
Vermont: Harvest 9374, Kaufman 9378
Virginia: Cedars 9416, Chainani 9417, Hansen 9465, Lane 9486
Washington: Schuler 9690
Wisconsin: Meehan 9882
Wyoming: Jaquith 9975

International exchange
New York: **Jabara 6254**

International peace and security
Arkansas: Darragh 193
Colorado: Arsenault 1224, Hunter-White 1297, Warner 1376
District of Columbia: **Foundation 1807**
Hawaii: Straub 2649
Illinois: Communitas 2801, Jocarno 3000, **New 3137, New 3138**
Massachusetts: Cabot 4035
Minnesota: **Winds 4820**
New Jersey: United 5565
New York: Olum 6555
Ohio: Armington 7309, **Eaton 7383**
Texas: Oppenheimer 9101
Utah: Slaughter, 9353

International relations
Arizona: **Kearny 137**
California: Bergman 304, Brown 352, Kadima 686, Marchese 792, Otto 893, Rapport 954, Uplands 1138, Von 1148, Winn 1189
Colorado: Rakowich 1343
Connecticut: Shenandoah 1568, Tucker 1587
Delaware: **Colgate 1645**
District of Columbia: Brody 1791, Coleman, 1796, Institute 1816
Florida: **Basser 1871**, Davis 1962, Foundation 2015, Fuller 2028
Hawaii: Straub 2649
Illinois: Abelson 2692, Communitas 2801, Delavan 2825, Krehbiel 3030, Maak 3067, Penrose 3166, Rosenthal 3210
Kansas: Shannon 3625
Kentucky: Gagarin 3656
Maryland: Weiss 3982
Massachusetts: Metanoia 4201, Morse 4208
Michigan: **Saab 4556**, U.S.-China 4600
Mississippi: Hancock 4840
Missouri: **Maor 4952**, Mathews, 4953
New Jersey: Aufzien 5253, Weisberg 5578
New York: **American 5669**, Angelson 5679, Eule 5971, Feldman 5996, Harmon 6169, **Harriman 6170**, Janklow 6257, Meyer 6486, Miller-Sweezy 6494, MW 6517, Peterson 6594, **Sparkplug 6830**, Statue 6849, **Stern 6862**, Whalesback 6967
North Carolina: Agarwal 7039, **Kramer 7152**, Mize 7186, Richardson 7221, Tabitha 7265
Ohio: Brocker 7334, Taj 7611
Oregon: **Conklin 7754**
Pennsylvania: Beach 7855, Friendship 8009, Morgan 8178, Sidewater 8278
Texas: Baldridge 8715, Stewart, 9221
Utah: Telemachus: 9359
Virginia: Macedonian 9496

Washington: Johnson 9633, Ohno 9673

International studies
Hawaii: Straub 2649
New York: Casey 5819

Internet
Virginia: Kahn 9480

Islam
California: **Alalusi 236**, Gareeb 548, **Saya 1011**
Michigan: Dana 4420, Tarakji 4586
New York: **Jabara 6254, Usman 6921**
Ohio: Taj 7611

Jewish people
California: Kornwasser 718
Maryland: Tzedakah 3970
Massachusetts: Krupp 4161
New York: Blank 5756, M&E 6425, MSG 6514, Starker 6847, U 6918

Job counseling
District of Columbia: Jovid 1817

Job creation and workforce development
Massachusetts: MutualOne 4216
Minnesota: Tennant 4798

Job training
California: Bank 272, Lux 773, Shayne 1032
Colorado: Bloom 1239
Connecticut: Dime 1438
Massachusetts: Middlesex 4203, MutualOne 4216
Minnesota: G&K 4691, Tennant 4798
Missouri: Butler 4880
New York: Abess 5636, **Family 5983**, Snyder 6819
Texas: Boeing 8733

Judaism
Alabama: Abroms 2, Aronov 7, Friedman 27, JADO 40, Loeb 47, Rothschild 61, Viro 73
Alaska: Gottstein 86
Arizona: Berlin 101, Coleman 107, Grossman 126, Schlein 165
Arkansas: Ottenheimer 213
California: Banchik 269, Baye 285, **Beagle 286**, Beam 287, Becker 291, Beim 293, Berlin 306, Bernstein 307, Bialis 313, Bilak 317, **Blackman 320**, Blatteis 322, Borok 331, Breslow 340, Brishin 346, Brunswick 354, **Butler 365**, Cannon 374, CAS 378, Chestnut 392, Coleman 416, Congregation 423, Corwin 428, Dorskind 459, Eagle 470, Evans 485, Feintech 502, Frankel 526, Friedman 530, Friedman 531, Gallanter 542, Gifts 553, Glazer 562, Glikbarg 564, Goldberg 567, Greenwood 581, Grossberg 588, H. 590, Handlery 596, Hertz 619, Hitter 624, Hochman 626, Horwich 632, Horwitz 633, **Jacoby 654**, Jelin 662, Jubas 680, Kadima 686, Keating 695, Kobor 716, Kornwasser 718, Lash 730, Levin 749, Levine 750, Levy 751, **Levy 752**, Los 768, Lyons 776, Margolis 796, Margolis 797, Meister 821, Merage 822, Miller 828, Miller 832, Mitchell, 839, Morgenstern 848, Neu 862, Novak 871, Ohren 877, Ornest 888, Parvin 905, Pearlstein 911, Phillips 924, Ragir 950, Reitman 964, **Rieger 971, Rifkind 972**, Rose 984, Sands 1001, Schaeffer 1013, Scherr 1014, Schoen 1017, **Shapell 1031**, Shore 1034, Silton 1039, Somekh 1064, Spielman 1067, Sudikoff 1090, **Teichman 1106**, Toole 1124, Traub-Brittan 1127, Welfund 1169, Wertheimer 1173, Wilnai 1185, Winkler

1188, Zacky 1205, Ziegler 1210, Ziff 1211, Zimmer 1212, Zimmerman, 1213, Zitrustin 1215
Colorado: Avoth 1225, Beren 1231, Beren 1232, Beren 1233, Gart 1275, Kesher 1304, Kortz 1307, Lustig 1318, Morse 1328, **Oreg 1335**, Pluss 1337, Reel 1345, Trachten 1369, Zeff 1383
Connecticut: Abramowitz 1384, Aibel 1388, Chaikin-Wile 1417, Deutsch 1436, Eder 1441, Fuchs 1459, Gibor 1464, Gladstein 1465, Goldfarb 1467, Greenfield 1471, Helping 1480, Konover 1501, Kuriansky 1503, Manger 1518, Mann 1519, Mellen 1525, Nevas 1530, Nirenberg 1534, Rosenberg 1555, Selkowitz 1565, Stratfield 1576, Zacharia 1601, Zimmer 1603
Delaware: 18 1604, Croll 1650, Freedman 1665, Gorny 1671, Klein, 1694, Messing 1708, Ratner 1724, Rosenfeld 1732, Rothchild 1733, Sloane 1746, Solot 1748, Stein 1750, Susman 1753, Wender 1777, Yablon 1782
District of Columbia: Bench 1788, Dweck 1805, Goldman 1810, **Gorlitz 1811**, Greenberg 1812, Olender 1824
Florida: Adler 1842, Ahavas 1844, Auerbach 1859, Barbash 1865, **Basser 1871**, Blanksteen 1891, Blechman 1894, Brodsky 1901, Brody 1902, Cantor 1916, Celebrity 1931, Chanin 1934, Cohen 1947, Diamond 1973, Elster 1990, Erdle 1993, Five 2002, Friedland 2025, Gelbart 2035, Gemunder 2036, Golden 2046, Goldman 2047, Gordon 2050, Greenberg 2062, Greenblatt 2063, Greene 2064, Halperin 2076, **Handleman 2078**, Herrin 2091, Hornik 2111, Hufty 2114, Irwin 2120, Isenberg 2121, Kaiserman 2134, Kanders 2135, Kanders 2136, Kane 2137, Kaplan 2138, Kaye 2141, Knapp 2153, Knopf 2156, Kreisman 2159, Kugelman 2161, Kuriansky 2162, Landwirth 2167, Lenkin 2179, **Levine 2181**, Lipton 2185, Mayberg 2199, Melin 2210, Mendelson 2211, MIDA 2212, Minto 2216, Morris 2219, Olemberg 2237, Perlmutter 2254, **Posnack 2262**, Raymund 2276, Reckson 2277, Resnick 2282, River 2288, Ross 2298, Rothman 2299, Rothschild 2300, Rubens 2301, Scharlin 2315, Sender 2323, Setzer 2325, Sharaby 2329, Siegel 2335, Silverman 2337, Stern 2349, Stern 2350, Taplin 2363, Weinberger 2394, Weintraub 2395, Weisman 2396, Werner 2398, Wiener 2405, Wolf 2410, Wolgin 2411, **Wollowick 2412**, **Zichron 2424**, Zimmerman 2427, Zimmerman 2428
Georgia: Arnold 2436, Chesed 2458, Marcus 2544, Morris 2553, Orkin 2559, Orkin 2560, Saul 2579, Schinazi 2580, Schwob 2581, Tritt 2596
Idaho: Wishnick 2690
Illinois: Acorn 2694, **American 2707**, Anschel 2709, B&D 2715, Bellick 2732, Bergstein 2735, Bernfield 2737, Brenner 2756, **Chapin 2781**, Cohn 2795, Cohn 2796, Communitas 2801, Diamond 2829, Edelman 2845, Edelstein 2846, Fink 2873, Forbes 2878, Fraida 2884, Frank 2885, Fredman 2890, Gassin 2906, General 2907, Generations 2908, Genesis 2910, Gidwitz 2914, Golder 2921, Goldman 2922, Goodstein 2924, Gray 2927, Grossinger 2933, H 2937, Hanson 2949, JBS 2994, JMR 2999, Karasik 3006, Klosk 3020, **Landau 3036**, Landau 3037, Lazar 3041, Leibowitz 3046, Levinson 3049, **Lindon 3054**, Lohengrin 3059, Mazzetta 3083, McCrea 3088, **Mermelstein 3103**, Millner 3115, Minor 3117, Minow 3118, Ohlhausen 3151, Okner-Robbins 3152, Pharmore 3175, Podolsky 3178, **Polk 3179**, Pollack 3180, Poncher 3186, Pugdin 3185, Rosenberg 3207, **Rosenmutter 3208**, Rosenson 3209, Rothman 3213, Ruben 3215, Ruttenberg 3217, Schorr-Lieberman 3229, Shapiro 3240, Skylark 3250, Sondheimer 3256, Stein 3268, Stern 3268, Stone 3269, Summer 3279, Takiff 3281, Taxman 3283, Vail 3301, Victor 3304, Wagner 3306, Wark 3309, **Wein 3315**, Weiner 3316, Weiss 3317, Wolff 3328, Yulman 3334
Indiana: **Ackerman 3339**, Bronstein 3351, Cohen 3357, Edelman 3374, Eskenazi 3377, Klapper 3408, Maurer 3415, **Mervis 3417**, Rifkin 3437
Iowa: Daniels 3483, Iowa 3512, Weigle 3546

Kansas: Goldberg 3581, Lowenstein 3598, Price 3615, Price 3616
Kentucky: Roth 3690, Shapira 3693, Yarmuth 3709
Louisiana: Cahn 3716, Mintz 3738, Shannon 3752
Maine: Kagan 3784
Maryland: Adler 3809, Ammerman 3813, Bank 3818, Berger 3821, Blum 3825, **Boehm 3826**, Chessie 3835, Cogan 3837, Cohen 3838, Davis 3844, Eliasberg 3854, Elno 3855, Elsberg 3856, Feldman 3858, Gordon 3873, Gorlin 3874, Greene-Milstein 3876, Gutman 3877, Hurwitz 3886, Israelson 3888, Kay 3892, Legum 3899, Levin 3900, Macks 3906, Meyerhoff 3914, Minkoff 3915, Myerberg 3923, Number 3929, RFI 3938, Rothschild 3942, Shapiro 3949, Slavin 3954, Sonneborn 3957, Thalheimer 3966, Totah 3968, Tucker 3969, Tzedakah 3970, Weinman 3981, Wilen 3985
Massachusetts: Black 4021, Cail 4036, Family 4085, Foundation 4094, Friend 4098, Gale 4100, Goldman 4105, Karas 4146, Krieger 4160, Krupp 4161, Lamm 4165, Levy 4173, Levy 4174, Mank 4187, Marcus 4188, Morningstar 4207, Morse 4208, Noble 4224, Rabb 4255, Ratshesky 4259, Reisman 4262, Sandler 4278, Schwartz 4284, Shaich 4287, Shapiro 4289, Shapiro 4290, Sherman 4293, Solomont 4303, **Spero 4304**, Spoon 4305, Tapper 4321, Tatelman 4323, Ullian 4335, Weiner 4355
Michigan: Alon 4374, Barron 4384, Berlin 4388, Dresner 4434, Ferber 4443, Gershenson 4453, Grassland 4458, Jospey 4473, Kaufman 4479, Maas 4498, Manat 4503, Narens 4520, Nartel 4521, Nusbaum 4524, Padnos 4529, Ran 4547, Shapiro 4566, Sherman 4567, **Teitel 4589**, Torgow 4594, Wetsman 4611
Minnesota: Baratz 4635, Borman 4644, Deikel 4663, Fink 4684, Heilicher 4711, **Kaplan 4721**, Regis 4770, Shared 4791
Missouri: Bograd 4870, **Bohm 4871**, Chod 4885, Copaken 4888, Crown 4891, Erlich 4904, Essman 4905, Gershman 4916, Green 4920, Heiman 4926, Hofheimer 4929, Kuhn 4941, Lawton 4944, **Maor 4952**, Portman 4981, Roman 4985, Rubin 4987, Sachs 4989, Shawe 5000, Silk 5004, Siteman 5006, University 5027, Wolff 5040
Nebraska: Baer 5069, Friedman 5083
Nevada: **Cohen 5149**, Coleman 5150, **Fein 5155**, Siegel 5186, Steinberg 5189, Wolzinger 5200
New Jersey: Abrams 5241, Adler 5242, **American 5247**, Aufzien 5253, Baum 5258, Benaroya 5260, Bershad 5263, Bijou 5264, **Billig 5265**, Blessing 5266, Brook 5273, Brothers 5276, Brown 5278, Cohen 5299, Cordover 5304, Croman 5307, CYH 5309, Dweck 5327, Eisenberg 5331, Ellis 5333, Engel 5334, Entin 5336, ESH 5338, Feinstein 5343, Frank 5350, Freelander 5353, Freyer 5355, Garfinkle 5364, Genie 5366, Gestetner 5367, Glasser 5371, Goldberger 5372, Goldstein 5373, **Greenblatt 5376**, Greetin 5377, Gurwicz 5378, Halpern 5380, Hann 5382, Harbanoff 5384, Harmstieg 5386, Heller 5391, Holzer 5396, Infinity 5399, IV 5401, JFI 5405, Kaufman 5415, Kessel 5420, Kingsberg 5421, Klatskin 5423, Landy 5439, Lazarus 5442, Lchachomim 5443, Leavitt 5445, Levine 5446, Lieberman 5448, Light 5449, Liss 5451, Mamiye 5456, Marino 5457, Maschler 5462, Milano 5466, Miller 5467, Mitrani 5471, MTB 5474, Myers 5476, Oster 5484, Pantirer 5487, Pasternak 5490, Pines 5501, Plafsky 5503, Riskin 5511, Rsfzmkh 5514, Rukin 5516, Sanders 5518, Schwartz 5524, Schwartz 5525, Scott 5527, Shamah 5531, Shapiro 5532, Shuster 5535, Silverman 5536, Smilowitz 5538, Snyder 5543, Sorala 5544, Stanley's 5550, Stern 5552, Sutton 5554, Ullmann 5564, Wilf 5587, Wilf 5588, Zimmer 5601, Zissu 5602
New Mexico: Foster 5615
New York: A.P.W. 5633, Abess 5636, Abess 5637, Abettor 5638, Abramson 5640, Adelman 5643, Ader 5644, Ades-Taub 5645, Agate 5649, Alex 5652, Alexander 5655, Alff 5657, Alternative 5661, American 5666, **American 5667**, American 5668, Asher 5695, Atlantic 5697, Ausch 5699, Azar

5704, B 5705, Bar 5712, Barron 5719, Baseser 5720, Bassman 5721, Baum 5722, Baumann 5723, Beckman 5729, Beir 5732, **Beitar 5733**, Bendit 5736, Bergson 5738, Berkowitz 5739, Betesh 5743, Birchas 5748, Birnbaum 5751, Birnbaum 5752, Blank 5756, **Blinken 5757**, Blue 5764, Bobrow 5765, Bovin 5770, Boxer 5772, Brand 5776, Brandt 5777, Bratt 5778, Bratt 5779, Brown 5791, BSD 5793, BSR 5794, Buller 5800, Bush 5805, Carnegie 5815, CDL 5824, Chada 5830, Chasanoff 5833, Chasdei 5834, Chasdei 5835, Chemtob 5837, Chesed 5840, Cohen 5857, Cohen 5859, Cohen 5860, Cohenca 5861, Cohn 5862, Cohn 5864, Coleman 5870, Coremet 5875, Cornell/Weinstein 5877, Curtis 5889, Dabah 5892, Dabah 5893, Danziger 5899, Davidson 5901, Dears 5905, Deegan 5907, DeMario 5909, Deutsch 5912, Diamondston 5914, DJ 5920, Dolgen 5922, Doovin 5923, Druskin 5932, Dvaykus 5937, EBA 5941, Edelman 5943, Ehrlich 5947, Ehrlich 5948, Ehrman 5949, Eisenberger 5950, Eisner 5951, Ekstein 5952, Ellman 5956, EMSA 5961, Englebardt 5965, Enkess 5966, Evans 5972, Ezra 5975, Fagin 5978, Falk 5981, Farber 5987, Feil 5991, Feinberg 5993, Feldman 5996, Feldstein 5997, Feuerring 6001, Fields 6003, Fife 6005, Finkelstein 6007, Finn 6008, Fleischer 6013, Foundation 6019, Fowey 6021, Franco 6024, Franco 6025, Frankel 6027, Freund 6034, Fridman 6035, Fried 6036, Friedman 6040, Frieman 6041, Fuchs 6043, Fuchsberg 6044, G&A 6048, Gantcher 6055, Gantz 6056, Garber 6057, Gartner 6059, Geduld/Cougar 6062, Gelley 6067, Gemiluth 6068, Gemj 6069, **Gimprich 6080**, Godinger 6086, Gold 6089, Goldberg 6090, Goldenberg 6092, Goldenberg 6093, **Goldfein 6096**, Goldstein 6100, Goldstein 6101, Goldstone 6102, Golub 6105, Goodman 6107, Gordon 6110, Gotham 6113, GP 6117, Granit 6126, Greenberg 6132, **Greenwald 6136**, Grinberg 6139, Grobman 6140, Gross 6142, Gross 6143, Grossman 6144, Grumbacher 6148, Grunberg 6149, Guela 6151, Harary 6166, Harjen 6167, Hasenfeld 6174, Hefta 6181, Heisler 6185, Heller 6186, Henshel 6192, Hershaft 6197, Hershman 6198, Hesed 6199, Heyman 6201, HF 6203, Hidary 6205, High 6206, Himelberg 6210, Hirsch 6211, Hirsch 6212, Hochman 6214, Hoffen 6215, **Hoffman 6216**, Holocaust 6222, Holtzman 6223, IMS 6240, Independent 6241, J.A.T. 6253, JIA 6261, Jungreis 6276, Kahan 6278, Kamber 6281, Kaminer 6282, Kaplan 6284, **Katzin 6288**, KCEG 6291, Keene 6294, Keller-Shatanoff 6297, Keren 6302, Keswin 6303, Kimmel 6308, Kingjay 6312, Kirzner 6315, **Kitov 6317**, **Klagsbrun 6318**, Klaus 6319, Klaus 6320, Klavan 6322, Klingenstein 6327, Klingenstein-Martell 6329, Knafel 6330, Knaster 6332, Kochov 6333, Kohn 6338, Kohn 6339, Konar 6340, Kozicki 6343, Krumholz 6349, Kulick 6350, Kurland 6352, Landau 6362, **Laub 6367**, **Legacy 6374**, Leibowitz 6376, Lemle 6378, Lenetzach 6379, Lerner 6383, Levine 6387, Levitin 6388, Levy 6390, Levy 6391, Lewy 6393, Liberman 6396, Lieberman 6399, Liebowitz 6400, Lippes 6401, Longhill 6411, Lopatin 6412, Lowenbraun 6414, LSK 6415, Lubo 6417, M 6424, M&E 6425, M.F.K. 6426, Maidenbaum 6435, Marbeh 6440, Maslin 6448, MBS 6454, Medarchei 6469, Meier 6470, Mere 6476, Messinger 6482, Meyer 6484, Meyer 6485, Meyer 6486, Meyer 6487, Miller 6492, Milstein 6496, Mindel 6498, Morrell 6507, Morris 6508, Morse 6509, Moskowitz 6511, Mozel 6512, MRA 6513, MSG 6514, MZL 6518, Nassimi 6519, Neiman 6521, Nelco 6522, **Neuman 6526**, Newman 6530, Newman 6532, Newman 6534, Nussbaum 6545, Ohel 6552, Ohel 6553, Ostreicher 6562, Ostreicher 6563, Ostreicher 6564, Paiken 6567, Paneth 6574, Park 6575, Parshelsky 6578, Performing 6586, Peterson 6593, Petrocelli 6595, Pickman 6602, Pletka 6610, Plunkett 6611, Pollack 6614, Pollack 6615, Pomrenze 6619, **Posner-Wallace 6621**, Price 6628, Prince 6629, R 6640, Rachel 6641,

Rachesky 6642, Rapaport 6647, Raphael 6648, Rasba 6649, Realex 6654, Rechler 6657, Reich 6658, Reich 6659, Reiss 6662, Resnick 6663, Richter 6668, Rifkind 6670, Ring 6671, Ritter 6673, RJL 6675, Rose 6684, Rose 6685, Rose 6687, Rosedorf 6688, Rosen 6689, Rosenberg 6691, Rosh 6697, Rosner 6698, Rothblum 6701, Rothstein 6704, Saltzman 6722, Samuels 6725, **Sato 6731**, Satow 6732, Savitz 6734, Schaefer 6735, Schaffer 6737, Scharf 6738, **Schmeelk 6742**, Schneider 6743, Schonfeld 6745, Schonkopf 6747, Schreiber 6750, Schwalbe 6751, Schwartz 6752, Schwartz 6753, Schwarz 6757, Schweitzer 6759, Schwimmer 6760, Sdei 6764, SDF 6765, Seacoast 6766, Seaman 6767, Seelig 6769, Sefn 6770, SEG 6771, Seligman 6772, Seligsohn 6773, Shachar 6779, Shalom 6784, SHEL 6791, Siegel 6797, Silberman 6798, Sillins 6799, Silver 6800, Silverman 6801, Silverstein 6802, Silverstein 6803, Singer 6806, SKL 6808, Slade 6810, Slovin 6811, Sokol 6822, Sokoloff 6823, Sommer 6825, Spatz 6831, Spektor 6833, Spiegel 6837, Spiegel 6838, Spitzer 6841, Starker 6847, Stecher 6851, **Stefansky 6854**, **Stein 6855**, Stein 6856, Steinmetz 6858, Steinmetz 6859, Stern 6860, **Stern 6862**, **Strauss 6870**, Strong 6872, Stuntz 6874, Sutton 6882, Sutton 6883, SVM 6886, Tahari 6890, Tanner-Frank 6893, Tenney 6895, Tisch 6900, Tov 6904, Tradition 6905, Treetops 6906, United 6920, Vaad 6924, Viola 6930, Vogel 6931, Vyeshaya 6934, Wachtell 6936, Wallerstein 6940, Weil 6948, **Weingarten 6952**, Weingarten 6953, Weinman 6955, **Weinstein 6956**, Weintraub 6957, Weiser 6958, Weiss 6962, Wilamowsky 6976, Wilks 6977, Wohlgemuth 6984, Woldar 6985, Wolf 6986, Wolk 6987, Y 6999, Yad 7000, Yagoda 7001, Yahad 7002, Yaspan-Unterberg 7003, Yitzchok 7007, Yms 7008, Yosef 7011, Zamir 7016, Zarin-Rosenfeld 7017, Zedakah 7019, Zedukah 7020, Zeitz 7021, Zenkel 7023, Zichron 7024, Zichron 7025, Zichron 7026, Zirkl 7029, **Ziv 7030**, Zwerling 7034.
North Carolina: Bernstein 7049, Bettman 7051, Fairfield 7095, Katz 7142, **Kramer 7152**, Lerner 7160, Levine-Sklut 7161, Meyer 7184, Perkin 7208, Shapiro 7239, Silverman 7244
Ohio: Beck 7319, Berke 7323, Chesley 7351, Fibus 7398, Glazer 7426, **Katz 7475**, Kramer 7484, Landers 7488, LKC 7501, Miller 7526, Rapport 7553, Reisman 7556, Rosenthal 7563, Schottenstein 7575, Schwartz 7576, Schwebel 7577, Sinai 7593, Traeger 7621, Wasserstrom 7632, Weiss 7634, Wolf 7643
Oklahoma: Sylvan 7722
Oregon: Holzman 7775, Singer 7819
Pennsylvania: Aaron 7835, Ames 7840, **Arronson 7844**, Beacon 7856, Bella 7859, Berger 7862, Bergman 7863, **Berkowitz 7865**, Bienenfeld 7872, Birnhak 7873, Bon-Ton 7884, Born 7885, Bronstein 7896, Charleston 7920, **Cohn 7931**, Davis 7951, Dozzi 7965, **Epstein 7983**, **Epstein 7984**, Fine 7993, Fortinsky 8002, Foster 8003, Gershman 8015, Goldberg 8021, Gordon 8024, Grumbacher 8028, Jewish 8080, Kahn, 8084, Klein 8096, Kline 8098, Levis 8122, Lubert 8133, Marstine 8141, Mendel 8168, Morgan 8178, Olitsky 8198, Oppenheim 8199, Panama 8202, Perelman 8209, Perlow 8211, Pincus 8214, Roberts 8240, Robinson 8241, Rosenberg 8244, Rudin 8247, Saramar 8253, Satell 8254, Savett 8255, Schwab-Silfen 8264, Schwartz 8265, Sidewater 8278, Spain 8292, Stein 8299, Tabas 8312, Victor 8332, Wachs 8336, Wachs-Weingarten 8337, Wimmer 8361, Wolgin 8365
Rhode Island: Bernhardt 8387, Feibelman 8405, Jacbel 8426, Koffler 8436, Mann 8448, Salmanson 8481, Siperstein 8489, Swarts 8495
Tennessee: B 8583, **Belz 8585**, Blum 8589, Bornblum 8591, Doochin 8605, Eskind 8611, Eskind 8612, Eskind 8613, Goldsmith 8622, Gordon 8624, **Lowenstein 8645**, Small 8675

Texas: Adler 8692, Alexander 8695, Baer 8714, Brochstein 8746, Brodsky 8747, Finger 8857, Frankel 8872, Freed 8873, Friedel 8875, Fuchs 8881, Genecov 8886, **Gilman, 8889**, Gordon 8892, Gordon 8893, Kahn 8978, Kaplan 8979, Kolitz 9000, Kuhn 9006, Levy 9014, Marks 9039, Meyerson 9062, Oppenheimer 9100, Roosth 9160, Rosen 9161, Rubenstein 9167, Schepps 9177, Schepps 9178, Schoener 9180, Taub 9229, Toomim 9239, Wolens 9284, Wolf 9285, Wolff-Toomim 9286, Zale 9300
Virginia: Gifford 9457, Grandis 9462, Hausfeld 9469, Ochsman 9504, Perlin 9510, Ratner 9521, Selsky 9529
Washington: Alhadeff 9558, Bayley 9567, Brookshire-Green 9573, Jaffe 9629, Prairie 9680, Sarkowsky 9688, Shemanski 9693, Sondland 9700
Wisconsin: Hoffmann 9842, Kohl 9864, Marcus 9877, Meehan 9882, Pelz 9900, Purple 9908

Kidney diseases
New York: Seaman 6767
Oklahoma: Parman 7713
Texas: South 9209
Washington: Boeschoten 9571
Wisconsin: Marcus 9877
Wyoming: Cutting 9968

Land resources
California: Abrams 224, Adams 229, Barth 279, Bear 288, Crabb 431, Ducommun 465, Tuffli 1134, Winiarski 1187
Colorado: Gary 1276, Gerrish 1277, Heider 1290, Joy 1301
Connecticut: Alpha/Omega 1391
Delaware: Replogle 1728
Georgia: Goddard 2491
Illinois: Baird 2718, Community 2802, Hare 2954, Herman 2968, Landau 3037, Morris 3125
Indiana: Benton 3344
Maine: Aldermere 3763
Maryland: Feldman 3858, Moser 3918
Massachusetts: **Barakat 4012**, Hornblower 4135, Ladd 4163
Michigan: Baiardi 4381, Herrington-Fitch 4466, Mariel 4504
Minnesota: Bend 4639
Montana: Foundation 5051
Nebraska: Assurity 5068
Nevada: Geomar 5160
New Hampshire: Verney 5236
New Jersey: Johnson 5407, Smith 5539
New York: Anderson-Rogers 5676, Aresty 5686, Barnwood 5718, Cullman 5886, H. 6153, Hathaway 6176, Heilig 6183, Leuschen 6384, Peterson 6591, Stifel 6865, **Swett 6888**
Ohio: Sauerland 7570, Thompson, 7617
Oregon: Roundhouse 7810
Pennsylvania: Boudinot 7888, Brooks 7899
South Carolina: Greenwood 8526
Tennessee: Foster 8616
Texas: Field-Day 8855
Vermont: Castanea 9368
Washington: Carper 9577, Kaleidoscope 9641, King 9645, Nysether 9671

Languages
Massachusetts: Webber 4351
Minnesota: Berglund 4640
New York: Roche 6677
Oregon: Shapira 7814

Law
California: Cutler 438, Emanuel 480, Zitrin 1214
Delaware: Cultures 1652
Massachusetts: Shattuck 4291

Law education
Alabama: Boult 14
Arizona: Stanton 174
California: Arata 248, Emmett 481, Fuller 538, Giles 554, Ignatius 648
Colorado: Margulf 1320
Connecticut: Grant 1470, Martin 1520, Newpol 1531
District of Columbia: Bench 1788
Florida: Dasburg 1961, McQuistion 2208, Weintraub 2395, Yerrid 2420
Hawaii: Marks 2640
Illinois: Cooney 2806, Mansfield 3074, North 3142
Maine: Cotsirilos 3774
Minnesota: Briggs 4648, Erickson 4674, Lane 4727
Missouri: Logan 4947
Nevada: Lee 5171
New Jersey: Katz 5414
New York: 21st 5630, Adelman 5643, Castle 5820, Double-R 5927, F. 5977, Feil 5991, Gatto 6061, Handler 6162, Heyman 6201, Janklow 6257, JI 6260, Kroll 6348, Lauren 6368, Levine 6386, Maidenbaum 6435, Miller 6491, Morgado 6505, Nussbaum 6545, Palisades 6569, Shuman 6795, Tytel 6917, Wachtell 6936
North Carolina: Cooke 7080, Nanney 7198
Ohio: Ferry 7396
Pennsylvania: Dickson 7957, Russo 8249, Stein/Bellet 8300, Winokur 8362
Rhode Island: Jacbel 8426
South Carolina: Collins 8520
Texas: Perkins 9125
Virginia: Clark 9420, R 9518
Washington: Keller 9643
Wisconsin: Huiras 9844, Windway 9961

Leadership development
California: Corwin 428, Majestic 784, Yen 1201
Colorado: Hanson 1286
Connecticut: Donchian 1440
District of Columbia: Crowell 1799
Florida: **Gordon 2051**, Sullivan 2357
Georgia: Georgia 2485
Hawaii: Central 2627
Illinois: Rossman 3211
Kansas: Insurance 3587
Michigan: Frankenmuth 4450, Jenkins 4470
Minnesota: G&K 4691
Nebraska: Scribante 5116
New York: American 5664
Ohio: Foundation 7408
Pennsylvania: Penn 8208
Tennessee: Benjamin 8586, Drake 8606
Texas: Hord 8950
Vermont: Cohen 9369
Virginia: Overton 9506
Wisconsin: Stateline 9937

Learning disorders
California: Alafi 235
Florida: Chicone 1941
Maryland: Huether/McClelland 3884
Missouri: University 5027
Texas: San 9170
Washington: Hyde 9627

Legal aid
District of Columbia: Crowell 1799
Minnesota: Briggs 4648
Wisconsin: RITE-HITE 9915

Legal services
California: Collingwood 418, Mitchell, 839
Colorado: **Kenney 1302**, Warner 1376
Delaware: Kang 1689
District of Columbia: Bench 1788, Olender 1824
Idaho: Leidy 2678
Illinois: Edgerly 2847, New 3136, Sumac 3278

Maryland: S.B.E. 3944
Massachusetts: Black 4021, Bulger 4031
Missouri: Welch 5038
New Jersey: Bershad 5263, Spruce 5548
New York: Fuchsberg 6044, Leonhardt 6381, Seaman 6767, White 6972
Ohio: Seasongood 7582
Pennsylvania: Panama 8202
South Carolina: Sunshine 8544
Texas: Vaughan 9249
Vermont: Harper 9373
Wyoming: Connemara 9967

Lesbians
Alabama: Black 12

Leukemia
Alabama: Sexton 63
California: Folger 515, Handlery 596, Maxfield 808
Colorado: Jacobs 1298
Connecticut: Diageo 1437
Delaware: Thronson 1766
Florida: Focus 2004, Second 2321
Illinois: Lyon 3066
New Hampshire: Martin 5222
New York: Capri 5814
West Virginia: Vecellio 9770

LGBTQ people
Alabama: Black 12, Ireland 39
Arkansas: Darragh 193
California: Blachford-Cooper 318, Collingwood 418, Moonwalk 845, Small 1049, Wren 1199
Connecticut: Newpol 1531
Florida: Lewis 2182
Kentucky: Harter 3660
Massachusetts: Crawford 4059
Minnesota: Larsen 4728
Nevada: Fuserna 5159
New York: Gesso 6075, **Sparkplug 6830**

LGBTQ rights
California: Sawchuk 1010, Small 1049
District of Columbia: Freeman 1808
Illinois: Lehman-Stamm 3045

Libraries
California: Huntington 642, **Rifkind 972**, Scottsdale 1024, Shannon 1030, Straus 1088
Colorado: Joslin-Needham 1300, Southwestern 1355
Connecticut: Goldfarb 1467, Konover 1501, Smith 1571
Florida: Barnard 1866, Hultquist 2115, Lelash 2178
Georgia: Davison 2470
Idaho: Whittenberger 2689
Illinois: Cohn 2796, Constans-Culver 2805, Family 2864, Hansen 2948, Heath 2962, McNally 3097
Indiana: Vann 3461
Iowa: Busse 3478, Carlson 3479, Deardorf 3485, Farrer 3490, Giacoletto 3499
Kansas: Kansas 3592, Swearingen 3631
Kentucky: Pollard 3685
Louisiana: Huie-Dellmon 3729
Maine: Kagan 3784, Reny 3802, Sukeforth 3805
Massachusetts: Beaucourt 4014, **Blossom 4022**, Connell 4055, Hauben 4120, Hornblower 4135, Jackson 4140, Murphy 4215, Starr 4309, Stearns 4310
Michigan: Abrams 4369, Vicksburg 4606
Minnesota: Andersen 4626, Tamarack 4797
Missouri: Morgan 4963
Nevada: Geomar 5160
New Hampshire: **Rothschild 5229**
New Jersey: Johnson 5406, Schwartz 5525
New York: Bush 5805, Cohen 5860, Darrah 5900, Hallingby 6160, Keswin 6303, Lake 6360, Northern

6540, Pollock 6616, Rheinstrom 6665, Roxe 6706, Snow 6818, Stebbins 6850, Strong 6872, Tuch 6915, Vernon 6928, Whittemore 6975
North Carolina: Gambrill 7106, Hunt 7134, Shingleton 7241
Ohio: Seifert 7584, Yeck 7648
Oklahoma: Krueger 7695
Oregon: White 7830
Pennsylvania: Benz 7861, Bryer 7902, Cameron 7911, Crawford 7945, Laughlin 8114, Moore 8177, Schuylkill 8263, Wyeth 8371
Rhode Island: York 8507
South Dakota: Welk 8577
Texas: Bertha 8729
Virginia: Community 9426, **Tara 9540**
West Virginia: Hott 9753, Wehrle 9771
Wisconsin: Schoenleber 9924
Wyoming: C 9966

Linguistics
Connecticut: Axe-Houghton 1397, Filingieri 1447
District of Columbia: **Dingwall 1804**
New Mexico: Chamiza 5609
New York: Persian 6589
Texas: **Kilgore 8989**

Literature and writing
Florida: Chapman 1935
Georgia: Myfifident 2554
Iowa: Deardorf 3485
Kentucky: Kentucky 3669
Michigan: Jenkins 4470
New Hampshire: Lion's 5220
New York: **American 5669**, Fein 5992, Persian 6589, Spofford 6842
Pennsylvania: Cameron 7911, Giop 8018, Randall 8230
Washington: Thomson 9711
Wisconsin: Hyde 9846

Liver diseases
Ohio: Slitzer 7596

Livestock and ranching
New Jersey: Wetterberg 5583

Low-income and poor people
Alabama: Black 12, Ireland 39
Alaska: **Nash 90**
Arizona: Armstrong 97, Barton 99, Garcia 122
Arkansas: Darragh 193
California: Adelaide 230, Avery-Fuller-Welch 260, Bank 272, Barbonchielli 276, Clara 406, Cleo 407, Community 421, Elfenworks 477, Five 509, Fox 523, Gellert 550, **Girls 559**, Horwitz 633, i.am.angel 645, Jolson 672, Martin 803, Nicholson 866, Rest 966, Sanfilippo 1002, Silicon 1038, Solano 1063, **Sunwest 1094**, Thompson 1112, Uplands 1139, **Wakerly 1150**, Walters 1153, Welk 1170, Whittier 1181
Colorado: Petunia 1336, Priester 1340, Stratton 1359
Connecticut: Cochrane 1420, Diageo 1437, Dime 1438, Fry 1458, Gladstein 1465, Harris 1478, Kaufmann 1495, Robinson 1553
Delaware: **Gloria 1670**, Patterson 1719, Thomson 1764
District of Columbia: Cafritz 1793, Jovid 1817, Replogle 1831
Florida: Bastien 1872, Bond 1897, Brighton 1899, Chadbourne 1932, Couch 1953, Durden 1984, Gate 2034, Jacobsen 2123, King 2148, Landwirth 2167, Nissim 2231, Oristano 2241, **Place 2261**, Ryan 2305, **Taylor 2365**, Thurman 2375, Wilson-Wood 2408, Yerrid 2420
Georgia: Abreu 2431, Athens 2437, Community 2466, Gray 2497, Rockdale 2576, TALX 2592, Waffle 2602, Wright 2620

Idaho: Boise 2666
Illinois: Alliant 2702, Bartsch 2722, Bulkley, 2765, Constans-Culver 2805, Epaphroditus 2857, Family 2864, Frisby 2893, Kellcie 3008, **Landau 3036**, **Lindon 3054**, **Mead 3100**, Meyer 3106, Perkins 3169, Reade 3187, Webb 3313
Indiana: Ayres 3342, Bronstein 3351, Gammon 3385, Seymour 3448
Iowa: Iowa 3513, **Wahlert 3544**
Kentucky: Killian 3670
Louisiana: Meraux 3736, Steinhagen 3755
Maine: **Dugas 3776**, Protein 3799
Maryland: CSG 3842, Rouse 3943, Warfield 3978
Massachusetts: Babson-Webber-Mustard 4010, Boynton 4025, **Brabson 4026**, Chicopee 4047, Crawford 4059, Hazard 4124, Hornblower 4135, Kelsey 4148, Kimball 4155, Middlesex 4203, MutualOne 4216, Newburyport 4222, Ratshesky 4259, Sailors' 4276, Swan 4317, Tye 4334, Weber 4352, Winning 4362
Michigan: Community 4411, Mackinac 4499, Pilgrim 4539, Thoman 4590, Tuscola 4598
Minnesota: Bell 4637, Bell 4638, Dyer 4669, Edina 4672, Ferber 4682, Sayer 4786, Thorpe 4800, **Winds 4820**
Mississippi: Baird 4822, Lexington 4846, Phillips 4850
Missouri: **Bohm 4871**, Breidenthal 4875, Butler 4880, Herschend 4928, Moneta 4962, Sander 4991, Sunnen 5018, Vatterott 5030
Nebraska: Midlands 5104, York 5129
New Hampshire: Jameson 5215
New Jersey: A 5240, Alcon 5244, Amboy 5246, Columbia 5301, Devine 5317, Giants 5369, Kerney 5419, **Ostberg 5483**, Selective 5528
New York: August 5698, Birchrock 5749, BTMU 5795, Clark 5848, **Farkas 5988**, **Gottlieb 6114**, **Grossman 6146**, Henshel 6192, Holmberg 6221, **Jockey 6265**, Metzger-Price 6483, Ostgrodd 6561, Roche 6678, Sidewalk 6796, Sussman 6880, Tuch 6915, Wagner 6938, Whispering 6970, Yearley 7005
North Carolina: Balin 7042, Ellison 7090, Glenn 7111, Hoffman 7128, Marlboro 7169, Paddock 7206, Richardson 7221, Strowd 7258
Ohio: Eyman 7391, Foss 7407, Gay 7418, Philada 7548, Sandfair 7569, Walker 7630
Oklahoma: Jones 7692
Oregon: Charis 7748, Elwood 7761, Portland 7807, Saling 7811, Wessinger 7826
Pennsylvania: Curaterra 7947, Female 7990, Garthwaite 8013, Hilles 8057, Hoffman 8062, Ludwick 8134, Maronda 8140, Maslow 8146, Mill 8172, Penn 8208, Seybert 8269, Union 8326, Wurts 8370
Rhode Island: Kimball 8434, Perpetual 8471
South Carolina: Lutz 8533
Tennessee: Cracker 8603, Foster 8616, **Fugitive 8618**, Gaylord 8620, Pettway 8658
Texas: AMR/American 8703, Boeing 8733, Central 8766, D3 8793, Foundation 8869, Hofstetter 8943, Holloway 8946, Montgomery 9070, Navarro 9085, Santander 9173, Smith 9204, **Soonae 9208**
Utah: CASA 9312, Steiner 9358
Vermont: Harper 9373, Stokes 9385
Virginia: **Delmar 9429**, Family 9444, Geary-O'Hara 9456, Ivakota 9477, Two 9544
Washington: Foss 9598, Kawabe 9642, **Singh 9695**, Tonkin 9715, Welch 9721
West Virginia: Chambers 9742
Wisconsin: Birnschein 9783, Holoubek 9843, Inbusch 9847, Marshfield 9878, Modine 9889, Olson 9898
Wyoming: Dragicevich 9969, Guthrie 9972, Perkins 9982, **Schultz 9986**

Lung cancer
Rhode Island: **Black 8390**

Lutheranism
Alabama: Phifer, 54
California: Brewster 341, Pardee 902, Smullin 1060

Delaware: Day 1654
Florida: Bell 1883, Dennis 1969, Patterson 2251
Illinois: Hunt 2984
Kentucky: McKellar 3677
Louisiana: Live 3734
New York: Watts 6947, **Woodland 6989**
Tennessee: Atticus 8582
Texas: Clements 8773, **Crowder 8792,** Foundation 8870
Washington: Muglia 9666, Spark 9701
Wisconsin: Roddis 9916

Lutherans
Iowa: Tomson 3537

Malaria
California: Smith 1053

Male adults
Alabama: Black 12, Ireland 39
Arkansas: Olds 210
District of Columbia: Jovid 1817
Georgia: Abreu 2431
Illinois: Family 2864, Meyer 3106
Kentucky: Killian 3670
Nebraska: Midlands 5104
North Carolina: Glenn 7111
Ohio: Walker 7630
Tennessee: **Fugitive 8618**
Virginia: **Delmar 9429**
Wisconsin: Inbusch 9847, Marshfield 9878

Male children and youth
Alabama: Black 12, Ireland 39
Arkansas: Olds 210
Georgia: Abreu 2431
Illinois: Bulkley, 2765, Family 2864, Meyer 3106
Kentucky: Killian 3670
Maryland: O'Neil 3930
Michigan: Holden 4467
Nebraska: Midlands 5104
North Carolina: Glenn 7111, Ketchum 7146
Ohio: Sandfair 7569
Oklahoma: Dill 7671, Ward 7728
Pennsylvania: Child 7923, Murphy 8185
Tennessee: Benjamin 8586, **Fugitive 8618**
Texas: Cariker 8762
Virginia: **Delmar 9429**
Wisconsin: Lakeview 9868, Marshfield 9878

Male infants and toddlers
Alabama: Ireland 39
Arkansas: Olds 210
Georgia: Abreu 2431
Kentucky: Killian 3670
Nebraska: Midlands 5104
North Carolina: Glenn 7111
Pennsylvania: Child 7923
Tennessee: **Fugitive 8618**
Wisconsin: Marshfield 9878

Male young adults
Alabama: Black 12, Ireland 39
District of Columbia: Jovid 1817
Georgia: Abreu 2431
Illinois: Family 2864
Indiana: Pulaski 3432
Kentucky: Killian 3670
Minnesota: Wells 4811
New York: Washington 6946
Ohio: **Brush 7338,** Walker 7630
Pennsylvania: Child 7923, Mill 8172
Tennessee: **Fugitive 8618**
Texas: Chambers 8767

Wisconsin: Marshfield 9878

Males
Alabama: Black 12, Ireland 39
Arkansas: Olds 210
District of Columbia: Jovid 1817
Illinois: Bulkley, 2765, Family 2864
Indiana: Thrush-Thompson 3460
Kentucky: Killian 3670
New York: Ostgrodd 6561
North Carolina: Glenn 7111
Ohio: Walker 7630
Tennessee: **Fugitive 8618**
Virginia: **Delmar 9429**
Wisconsin: Marshfield 9878

Manufacturing
Wisconsin: Modine 9889

Marine science
California: Borch 330, **Grass 577, PADI 898**
Connecticut: Nason 1528
Florida: Bastien 1872, Focus 2004
New York: Marine 6442
Ohio: Haskell 7439

Maritime museums
California: Seip 1028, Writer 1200
Illinois: McNally 3097
Massachusetts: Savage 4280
New Jersey: Larson 5440
New York: Kenlou 6299
Rhode Island: Galkin 8410
Texas: Rust 9168

Marriage equality
Illinois: Lehman-Stamm 3045

Maternal and perinatal health
Arkansas: Blue 189
California: Butte 366, Cirila 405, Frome 535, Smullin 1060
Florida: Carlton 1922
Illinois: Feltes 2869
Kansas: Shannon 3625
Massachusetts: **Gross 4108,** Longtine 4179
Michigan: Buist 4401, Sinai 4570
Missouri: University 5027
New York: Spektor 6833
Oregon: Harvest 7769
Texas: **Kingdom 8995**
Utah: Cumming 9315
Virginia: Rashti 9520
Washington: **Jernigan 9631**
Wisconsin: Christensen 9795

Mathematics
California: Baker 265, Fry 536, **Preuss 935**
Florida: Price 2267
Idaho: Boise 2666
Massachusetts: Akamai 3998
Minnesota: Rosen 4782
New York: Tensor 6896
Oregon: Mentor 7796
Texas: **AMD 8698,** Boeing 8733, Educational 8836
Wisconsin: Modine 9889

Medical counseling
Tennessee: Fleming 8615

Medical education
Alabama: Davis 24
Arizona: Lapan 140, Margolis 144, Schlein 165, **Well 181**
California: Boyer 335, Bright 345, Burbank 361, Hoag 625, Kelvin 699, Meyer 823, Reveas 967, **Sikand 1037,** Torino 1125, Western 1176, Zitrin 1214
Connecticut: Chaikin-Wile 1417, Lee 1507, O'Herron 1536, Sekerak 1564
District of Columbia: Arnold 1787
Florida: Chanin 1934, Coulter-Jones 1954, Dyer 1985, Glaubinger 2040, Kimmel 2146, King 2148, Papper 2246, Parish 2247, Perlmutter 2254, Taplin 2363, Werner 2398
Georgia: Churches 2461, Georgia 2484, Health 2504, SF 2585
Illinois: Corbett 2809, Delavan 2825, Dowdle 2834, Eiszner 2851, Herbert 2966, Keller 3010, Nayak 3133, Peters 3172, Pollack 3180, Rich 3194
Indiana: Vann 3461
Kentucky: Abercrombie 3645
Maryland: Ammerman 3813, Laughlin 3898, Salisbury 3945
Massachusetts: Connell 4055, Cook 4056, Durant 4072, **Gross 4108,** Koplow 4159, Mavrogenis 4192, Melvin 4196, Thoracic 4326
Michigan: Briggs-Fisher 4397, O'Donovan 4525
Missouri: Hardy 4923, **Maor 4952,** Mineral 4961, Schutte 4995, St. 5012
New Jersey: Armour-Lewis 5251, Essig 5339, Feldstein 5344, **Integra 5400, Ju 5410,** Katz 5414, Silverman 5536, Weinstein 5576
New York: Angelson 5679, Archangel 5685, Balm 5708, Coles 5871, Conley 5874, Davis 5902, Dears 5905, Ehrlich 5948, Feldman 5996, Gantcher 6055, Goldberg 6090, Harmon 6168, Himelberg 6210, Jacobson 6255, Klein 6324, **Klingenstein 6328,** Layton 6370, Milton 6497, **Potts 6624,** Price 6628, Resnick 6663, Roxe 6706, Ruttenberg 6715, Sackler 6716, Saunders 6733, Schaffer 6737, Siegel 6797, Spatz 6831, Wolk 6987, Zlinkoff 7031
North Carolina: Burks 7061, Kosloski 7149, Moseley 7194
Ohio: Brentwood 7330, Ryan 7566
Oklahoma: Chilton 7667
Pennsylvania: Blue 7879, Bon-Ton 7884, Briggs 7892, Every 7986, Klahr 8095, Kynett 8105, Perelman 8210, Tabas 8312
Rhode Island: La 8438
South Carolina: Kendall 8530, Tarr 8545
Tennessee: Community 8601
Texas: di 8812, Kaplan 8979, Killson 8990, Luse 9029, Morrison 9073, **OneSight 9098,** Pak 9110, Robinson 9158, South 9209, Taub 9229
Utah: Cumming 9316
Vermont: Altman 9364
Virginia: R 9518
Wisconsin: Dawes 9803, Meinerz 9883

Medical specialties
Florida: Prutky 2270
Illinois: Norgaard 3141
Nevada: Benna 5138
New York: Manning 6437

Medical support services
California: Bernstein 307, Solano 1063
Washington: Sondland 9700

Mental and behavioral disorders
California: Traina 1126
Massachusetts: Alden 3999
Rhode Island: Heydt 8419
Virginia: Ochsman 9504
Washington: Foss 9598

Mental health care

Alabama: Sexton 63
California: Alafi 235, Bach 263, Baker 267, Broder 348, Crane 433, Gellert 550, Livingston 761, Margoes 795, Martin 801, **Munson 852**, Palo 900, Priory 940, Simon 1041, Smith 1051, Stein 1079, Thrill 1117
Colorado: Comprecare 1249, Harvey 1287, White 1378
Florida: 4 1840, Diermeier 1976, Long 2189, McCabe 2201
Georgia: Arnold 2436
Illinois: Barr 2720, Hanson 2950, Keeney 3007, **Lerner 3048**
Indiana: Blackford 3346, Lafayette 3411, Sherwood 3451
Kansas: Baehr 3556
Kentucky: Hayswood 3662
Maryland: Hobbs 3882, Mental 3912, Ticho 3967
Massachusetts: Brooks 4028, Trefler 4332
Michigan: Kinney 4483
Minnesota: Haggerty 4705, Thorpe 4800
Nebraska: Kim 5098, Midlands 5104
New Hampshire: Salem 5230
New Jersey: Jones 5408
New Mexico: Carlsbad 5608
New York: Dammann 5897, Fraydun 6029, Gralnick 6121, Kenworthy 6300, Key 6305, **Klagsbrun 6318**, Legacy 6373, Lopatin 6412, Parshelsky 6578, Stowe 6869
North Carolina: Fox 7103
Ohio: Athens 7311, Austin-Bailey 7312, Bicknell 7327, Huntington 7460, Musson 7534, Ridgecliff 7560, Weiss 7634, Woodruff 7645
Oregon: Leupold 7790, Simple 7818
Pennsylvania: Adams 7836, Bennett 7860, Blue 7879, HBE 8047, Murphy 8185, Willow 8360
Rhode Island: Swarts 8495
South Carolina: Security's 8539
Tennessee: LDB 8642
Texas: Hamilton 8913, Kramer 9003, Richmond 9152, South 9209, Texas 9233
Utah: Catalyst 9313
Washington: Amelia 9559, Foss 9598
Wisconsin: Gardner 9825

Mental health counseling

Massachusetts: Alden 3999
Michigan: JCT 4469
Texas: MacDonald-Peterson 9032, Overlake 9106

Methodism

California: Olson 879
Iowa: Krumm 3517
Maryland: Fischer 3862, Lutheran 3904
Missouri: Cornelsen 4889, Duesenberg 4897
North Carolina: Hine 7126, Smith 7248
Pennsylvania: Hoffman 8062, Wood 8367
Texas: Woltman 9288

Microfinance

California: Bank 272

Middle school education

District of Columbia: Crowell 1799

Migrant workers

Alabama: Ireland 39
Iowa: **Wahlert 3544**
Pennsylvania: Hoffman 8062
Tennessee: **Fugitive 8618**
Virginia: **Delmar 9429**
Wisconsin: Marshfield 9878

Military personnel

Alabama: Black 12, Ireland 39
California: Small 1049, Solano 1063, Thrill 1117
Colorado: SEAKR 1351
Connecticut: Curran 1427
Florida: Durden 1984, HFRX 2092
Illinois: Kilrea 3017
Michigan: Delong-Sweet 4427, Oreffice 4528
Missouri: Sander 4991
Nebraska: Midlands 5104
New York: Phillips 6600
Ohio: Community 7357
Pennsylvania: **Epstein 7984**
Tennessee: Cracker 8603
Texas: Strickland 9224
Wisconsin: Marshfield 9878

Minority rights

Colorado: Bean 1228
Illinois: Lehman-Stamm 3045
Nevada: Joseph 5166
New York: Wagner 6938
Wyoming: Cutting 9968

Missing persons

Michigan: Roscommon 4552

Mormonism

California: Eichenberg-Larson 474
Nevada: Yamagata 5203
New York: Quinn 6639
Utah: Andrus 9301, Callister 9310, Davis 9317, Larsen 9337, Leavitt 9338, Scharman 9348, Schmidt 9349, Turley 9360

Multilateral cooperation

New York: Marshall 6445, Woods 6992

Multiple sclerosis

Arizona: **Beals 100**
California: Fuller 538, Hausman 603, Miller 833, Tuffli 1134
Delaware: Milano 1710, **TeleTech 1761**
Florida: Diane 1974, Kane 2137, Minto 2216
Georgia: Greiner 2498
Illinois: Eiszner 2851, Taxman 3283
Iowa: Krause 3516
Maryland: S.B.E. 3944
North Carolina: Sloan 7246
Ohio: Fibus 7398, Yeiser 7649
Pennsylvania: Leary 8117
Tennessee: Proctor 8662
Texas: Klesse 8998
Virginia: Birk 9398
Washington: O'Donnell 9672

Muscular dystrophy

Florida: Diane 1974
Illinois: Bulkley, 2765
Michigan: Sinai 4570
Missouri: Finley 4910, Toutz 5023
Rhode Island: Peacock 8469
Wisconsin: Wagner 9955

Musculoskeletal diseases

Florida: Yerrid 2420
Illinois: **Foundation 2880**
Massachusetts: Alden 3999
New Jersey: Branfman 5271

Museums

Alabama: JADO 40
Alaska: Alaska 80, Gottstein 86
Arizona: **Beals 100**, C 103, Declaration 111, Grossman 126, Hughes 130, McKee 148, Schlein 165, Snell 171, Ullman 177, Zicarelli 185
Arkansas: Riggs 214
California: Adams 228, Anderson 244, Beam 287, Bradford 337, Brewster 341, Brown 353, Bundy 359, Butler 364, **Cantor 375**, Coleman 416, Downing 462, Eleven 476, Familian 491, First 506, Foor 516, Four 522, Fox 525, Griffiths 584, Gross 587, Harman 598, Hitter 624, Huber 638, Jorgensen 676, Joy 677, Kadima 686, Kelly 697, Kelvin 699, Manchester 788, Martin 800, McLeod 818, Nachtsheim 856, Rabinovitch 947, Rice 969, **Rifkind 972**, Roche 979, **Skyscrape 1047**, Somekh 1064, Sprague, 1070, Stewart 1082, **Teichman 1106**, Thornton 1115, Tilley 1118, Tobey 1121, Waller 1152, Walton 1156, Webb 1162, Yuki 1203, Zimmer 1212
Colorado: Elf 1262, **Fishback 1270**, Getz 1278, Goodwin 1279, Lustig 1318, Southwestern 1355
Connecticut: Allwin 1390, Antonacci 1395, Avery 1396, Bowling 1409, Greenfield 1471, Harris 1478, Konover 1501, Linke 1508, Niblack 1533, Panoram 1538, Roberts 1551, Sekerak 1564, Zimmer 1603
Delaware: Freedman 1665, Night 1717, Selin 1742, Swift, 1754
District of Columbia: Peet 1827, Rubenstein 1833, Westport 1838
Florida: **Aviation 1861**, Becton 1880, Blanksteen 1891, Chanin 1934, Coral 1952, Couch 1953, Durden 1984, Friedland 2025, Gelbart 2035, Hoenle 2101, Holtz 2109, Kanders 2136, Koski 2157, Patterson 2251, Reeves 2279, Resnick 2282, Richard 2285, Rothschild 2300, Taplin 2363, Thurman 2375, Turner 2381, Wrightson-Ramsing 2416
Georgia: Fickling 2478, **Gage 2482**, Georgia 2485, Hunter 2515, Illges 2517, Illges 2518, Morris 2553, Piedmont 2566, Schwob 2581, Vaughan 2598, Young 2621
Illinois: Acorn 2694, Baird 2718, Bobins 2747, Brooker 2758, Buntrock 2766, Constans-Culver 2805, Danielson 2824, Diamond 2829, Educational 2848, Enivar 2856, Family 2864, Frankel 2886, Fremont 2891, Gardner 2904, Graham 2926, Hastings 2960, Holden 2976, Knowles 3023, Leonian 3047, **Lizzadro 3057**, Love 3064, MacDonald 3068, Maddox 3069, McCrea 3088, **Meyers 3107**, Micole 3108, Millard 3110, Miller 3112, Minor 3117, Norgaard 3141, Pangburn 3161, **Polk 3179**, Pond 3182, Reed 3191, Seidler 3233, Stone 3269, STS 3272, Takiff 3281
Indiana: Burris 3352, Crescent-Cresline-Wabash 3365, Harlan 3391, Mothershead 3419, Vann 3461
Iowa: Iowa 3512, Smeltzer 3535, Wood 3548
Kansas: Cape 3563, **Muchnic 3609**, Ross 3619, Schmidt 3622, Stallman 3629, Swearingen 3631
Kentucky: Barr 3646, Dickins 3651, Mulhollem 3680, Pollard 3685, Sutherland 3699
Louisiana: Harper 3726, Zuschlag 3762
Maine: Narragansett 3794
Maryland: Bresler 3828, Gewirz 3869, **Goldberg 3872**, Greene-Milstein 3876, Huether/McClelland 3884, Hyman 3887, McKnight 3910, Rogers-Wilbur 3941, Rothschild 3942, Small 3955, Sonneborn 3957, Tucker 3969, Widgeon 3983
Massachusetts: Carle 4037, Codman 4052, Crane 4058, Davoli 4065, Druker 4071, Elephant 4081, Fletcher 4093, Franklin 4096, Hauben 4120, Hopedale 4135, Hornblower 4135, Jackson 4140, Morse 4209, Nichols 4223, PerkinElmer 4238, Ramsey 4258, Shapiro 4290, Shattuck 4291, Spoon 4305, Stearns 4310, Storer 4314, Verrochi 4342, Walske 4349, Weld 4356, Wheatland 4358, Winthrop 4363, Wyman-Gordon 4364
Michigan: Allen 4372, Community 4410, Delong-Sweet 4427, Kaufman 4479, Kosch 4485, Mariel 4504, Morley 4518, Peslar 4537, Shapiro 4566, Welch 4610, Williams 4618

Minnesota: Bell 4638, Bend 4639, Boss 4645, Boss 4646, Dellwood 4665, Kellogg 4722, Lillehei 4729, Rodman 4779
Missouri: Bland 4868, Breidenthal 4875, Dierberg 4895, Hermann 4927, Sayler-Hawkins 4993
Montana: Taylor 5064
Nebraska: Ferenc 5080, Friedman 5083, Nelson 5106, Physicians 5112
Nevada: Ash 5134
New Hampshire: Bickford 5205, Dunn 5212, Verney 5236
New Jersey: Brundage 5280, Cordover 5304, **Daft 5310**, Devine 5317, Dreman 5326, Engel 5335, **Greenblatt 5376**, Kerney 5419, Kingsberg 5421, Kurtz 5436, Lazarus 5442, Oster 5484, Pheasant 5499, Roe 5512, Roma 5513, Savin 5520
New Mexico: B.F. 5606, Bennett 5607
New York: American 5664, Apple 5682, Baum 5722, Beach 5725, Bernhill 5741, Bovin 5770, Briger 5784, Clemente 5850, Cogut 5856, Cohen 5857, Cohenca 5861, Cohn 5862, D'Addario 5894, Desai 5910, Dixon 5919, Dobson 5921, Dorsky 5924, EMSA 5961, Erpf 5968, Ettl 5970, F. 5977, Fein 5992, Feldman 5996, Follett 6016, Gaffney 6049, Golding 6097, Goodman 6107, Gramercy 6122, Grunberg 6149, Henshel 6192, High 6206, Hohmann 6218, Hulbert 6232, IF 6237, Johnson 6270, Kandell 6283, **Klagsbrun 6318**, Klein 6325, Lemle 6378, Leonhardt 6381, Lucelia 6418, Lux 6422, McDayton 6462, Meade 6467, Meier 6470, Morse 6510, Mozel 6512, Newman 6531, Offensend 6550, One 6556, Ostgrodd 6561, Peckham 6583, Pittman 6608, Ritter 6673, RJL 6675, **Rock 6679**, Rosner 6698, Samuels 6725, Schweitzer 6759, Siegel 6797, Smith 6815, Spektor 6833, Stebbins 6850, Sumitomo 6876, Thanksgiving 6897, Tuch 6915, Vernon 6928, **Weinstein 6956**, Wolk 6987, Woodmere 6990, Woodward 6993, Wunsch 6996, Yeager 7004, Zwerling 7034
North Carolina: BB&T 7045, Billingsley 7052, Cannon 7067, Davis 7084, Morrison 7193, Rankin 7217, Rogers 7228, **Rolander 7229**, Silverman 7244, Sloan 7246, Stonecutter 7255
Ohio: Baird 7314, George 7421, Hauck 7440, Horvitz 7454, Lambert 7487, Ohio 7541, Sandfair 7569, Seifert 7584, Southard 7599, Taft 7609, Thompson, 7617
Oklahoma: Atherton 7657, Brannin 7662, Kerr 7693, Merkel 7706, Staton 7720
Oregon: Leupold 7790, Mentor 7796
Pennsylvania: Ames 7840, Arkema 7842, Berger 7862, Brooks 7898, Buck 7904, Cameron 7911, Dietrich 7958, Ellis 7978, Farnsworth 7989, Foster 8003, Horn 8067, Jackson 8078, Kahn, 8084, Klein 8097, Ludwick 8134, Mudge 8181, Perelman 8209, Randall 8230, Robinson 8241, Schoonmaker 8260, Schwab-Silfen 8264, Schwartz 8265, Speyer 8294, Weiler-Miller 8348, Williams 8358, Wyeth 8371
Rhode Island: Gross 8414, Johnson 8430, Littlefield 8441, Mulligan 8457, Schwarz 8483, Slemons 8490, Washington 8500
South Carolina: Chapman 8517, Stony 8542, WebbCraft 8548, Williams/Brice-Edwards 8549
Tennessee: Berman 8587, Blum 8589, Kennedy 8638, Massengill-DeFriece 8647, Rose 8667
Texas: Amarillo 8697, Baldridge 8715, Barrow 8719, Bowers 8736, Cemo 8765, **Dewhurst 8811**, Discovery 8816, Duncan 8833, Fairchild 8845, Finger 8857, Foster 8868, Foundation 8870, Frost 8878, Garvey 8884, Greentree 8901, Kahn 8978, Lilly 9019, Lowdon 9025, Margolin 9038, McNutt 9055, Mithoff 9068, Moss 9076, Patterson 9118, Petty 9126, Robinson 9158, Waggoner 9254, Wal-Dot 9256, Waltrip-McGee 9259, Wells 9271, Youth 9298
Utah: Cardon 9311, **Skolnick 9352**
Virginia: Cartledge 9414, Community 9426, Dun 9437, Foundation 9451, Gifford 9457, Grandis 9462, Lee-Jackson 9488, MAIHS 9497, Mullen 9502, Peachtree 9508, Ratner 9521, VuBay 9548, Weil 9550

Washington: Ferguson 9596, Furnessville 9602, Hanson 9616, Johnston-Hanson 9635, Kaleidoscope 9641, Quest 9681, Spark 9701, Titus-Will 9714
Wisconsin: Chipstone 9794, Frautschi 9822, Gardner 9825, Hunt 9845, Meinerz 9883, Puelicher 9907, RITE-HITE 9915, Schoenleber 9924, Verhulst 9954, Windway 9961
Wyoming: Sargent 9985

Music

Alabama: Caddell 19
Arizona: Armstrong 97
California: **Bull 358**, Graff 576, Hotchkis 635, Katz 693, Kendall 700, Kendall 701, Kieve 703, Lee 737, Palo 900, Plum 929, Price 938, Rishwain 974, Roney 983, Stellar 1080, **Williamson 1184**
Colorado: Getz 1278, Goodwin 1279, Margulf 1320, Staley 1357
Connecticut: McLaughlin 1523
Delaware: Ratner 1724
District of Columbia: Rossotti 1832
Florida: Blanton 1892
Georgia: Vogel 2600
Illinois: Christiansen 2790, Constans-Culver 2805, Elebash 2852, Glossberg 2916, Grossinger 2933, Judy 3003, MacDonald 3068, Minow 3118, Norgaard 3141, Vail 3301, Walk 3307
Iowa: Iowa 3512
Kansas: Brown 3561
Kentucky: Opera 3684
Maryland: Gordon 3873, Hubbard 3883, Unger 3971
Massachusetts: Bulger 4031, Cabot 4035, Connell 4055, Deane 4066, Hampden 4116, Jefferson 4142, Lost 4180, Merrill 4200, Shanklin 4288
Michigan: Burdick-Thorne 4402, Community 4410, Community 4411, Hecht 4465
Minnesota: Heilmaier 4712, Weyerhaeuser 4815
Missouri: Boylan 4873
New Hampshire: Bickford 5205, Smyth 5232, Wutz 5239
New Jersey: Holzer 5396
New Mexico: Taos 5626
New York: Amphion 5671, Arts 5693, Barbash 5714, Cogut 5856, D'Addario 5894, Dillard 5916, Gilliam 6078, Heyward 6202, Lassalle 6366, Netter 6525, Niemiec 6535, Osceola 6560, Performing 6586, Phaedrus 6598, Securitas 6768, Seven 6777, Sorel 6826, Stires-Stark 6867, Tuch 6915, **Weill 6950**
North Carolina: Gambrill 7106, Garrigues 7107, Stuart 7259, Wells 7283
Ohio: Busse 7343, Callahan 7345, Demetros 7377, Gale 7415, Peters 7547, Schwebel 7577
Oklahoma: Wilson 7736
Pennsylvania: Amaranth 7838, **Arronson 7844**, Borowsky 7886, Bradley 7889, Dietrich 7958, Giop 8018, Hoch 8060, Merwin 8170
Rhode Island: Kingsbury 8435, Preston 8475, Prouty 8476
Texas: Brochstein 8746, Horween 8952, Johnson, 8971, Kelso 8985, Womack 9289
Washington: Brookshire-Green 9573, Johnston-Hanson 9635
Wyoming: C 9966, Witzel 10000

Musical ensembles and groups

District of Columbia: Westport 1838
Illinois: Walk 3307
Louisiana: Shannon 3752
New York: D'Addario 5894, **Sparkplug 6830**

Musical theater

New York: **Weill 6950**

National defense

Arizona: McKee 148, Withycombe 184

California: Barulich 280, Crummer 436, Hollywood 630, Louie 770, Nasaw 858
Connecticut: Morrow 1527
Florida: ATAP 1855, Chris 1944, Fuller 2028, Ingalls 2118, Richard 2285, Zehnder 2423
Illinois: Constans-Culver 2805, Miller 3112, **Rosenmutter 3208**
Iowa: deStwolinski 3486
Michigan: Jenkins 4470
Minnesota: Albright 4625, Evert 4676
Missouri: Edmonston 4900
New Jersey: Take 5555
New York: Rosen 6689, Rosenthal 6693
North Carolina: Jelm 7137, Summer 7261
Pennsylvania: Homeless 8065
Texas: Frost 8878, Seven 9189
Wyoming: Kuehne 9979

National security

Delaware: Cultures 1652
New York: Casey 5819, Newman 6533, **Stern 6862**
Texas: Mattsson 9042

Natural history museums

California: Smith-Welsh 1058, Wagner 1149
Connecticut: Schloss 1562
Florida: Anderson 1845, Lastinger 2168, Wilder 2406
Georgia: Goodman 2492, McClatchey 2546
Illinois: Lebus 3043, McNally 3097, Simpson 3248
Massachusetts: Eddy 4077
Minnesota: Shared 4791
New Jersey: Klein 5424
New York: Clemente 5850, Cline 5851, Cullman 5886, Ellsworth 5957, Hohmann 6218, JI 6260, Plymouth 6612, Seven 6777, Whalesback 6967, Yaspan-Unterberg 7003
North Carolina: Post 7213
Ohio: Firman 7400
Pennsylvania: Dozzi 7965
Texas: Benton 8726, **Gilman, 8889**
Utah: Denkers 9318
Virginia: Bassett 9391, **Price 9516**

Natural resources

Alabama: Goodrich 29
Alaska: Juneau 88
Arizona: Burns 102, Cadeau 104
California: Barth 279, **Beagle 286**, Beattie 289, Braddock 336, Bradford 337, Broad 347, Cirila 405, Davies 444, Eriksen 484, Family 492, Foor 516, Friedman 530, Gellert 550, Gill 555, Harris 600, Heller 613, Jeangerard 661, **Lawrence 734**, Looker 766, Mae 780, Malachowsky 786, Mazda 810, Nasaw 858, New 865, On 880, Overall 895, **PADI 898**, Prete, 934, Rotasa 991, Sarandon 1004, Sprague, 1070, Uplands 1139, Walton 1156, Wells 1171
Colorado: 6/S 1219, Caulkins 1245, Elf 1262, Hunter-White 1297, Joy 1301, Maki 1319, **McGrath 1322**, Taylor 1364
Connecticut: Acorn 1385, Baldwin 1399, Crow 1426, Grant 1470, Greenfield 1471, Katen 1494, Lebovitz 1506, Patricelli 1541, Schloss 1562
Delaware: Burt's 1635, Telluray 1762
District of Columbia: Peet 1827
Florida: **Atlantis 1858**, Bailey 1863, Hufty 2114, Jelks 2128, KBR 2142, Lastinger 2168, Lookout 2190, **Mukti 2226**, Norjana 2235, Shackelford 2327, Vanneck-Bailey 2384, Whiting 2403
Georgia: **Bancker-Williams 2440**, Broadfield 2449, Lane 2536, McClatchey 2546, Price-Campbell 2570, Solstice 2587, Sweetgrass 2591, Williams 2612
Idaho: French 2671, Hare 2675, Nelson 2683
Illinois: Educational 2848, Full 2895, Hare 2954, Jocarno 3000, Kainz 3004, MacDonald 3068, McGraw 3092, **Mead 3100**, Morton 3127, Peters 3172, Rosenthal 3210, Sasco 3222, Shodeen

3246, Simon 3247, Simpson 3248, Staley 3263, Wehle 3314, Wislow 3323
Iowa: Hoaglin 3508
Kansas: Bramlage 3559, Trusler 3635, Williams 3643
Kentucky: Abercrombie 3645, Barr 3646, Taylor 3700
Louisiana: Wisdom 3761
Maine: Aldermere 3763, Borman 3767, Brook 3769, Goldberg 3780, **Golden 3781**
Maryland: Akridge 3810, Ammerman 3813, Biophilia 3824, Katz 3891, McKnight 3910
Massachusetts: Archibald 4005, Barstow 4013, Cabot 4034, Carlee 4038, Crane 4058, Crawford 4059, DWSS 4073, Eddy 4077, Fessenden 4090, Harris 4118, Jefferson 4142, Kelsey 4148, Ladd 4163, Leatherwood 4170, McCutchin-Collins 4193, Permanent 4239, **Robbins-de 4266**, Van 4340, Wallace 4347, Weld 4356, Winthrop 4363
Michigan: Baiardi 4381, Burdick-Thorne 4402, Community 4410, Community 4411, Connable 4412, DeVlieg 4428, Herrington-Fitch 4466, Kantzler 4478, LoPrete 4496, Mackinac 4499, Serra 4565, Skiles 4572
Minnesota: Bell 4637, Bell 4638, Ecotrust 4670, Schott 4787, Tamarack 4797
Missouri: Bland 4868, No 4971, Simmons 5005
Montana: Cinnabar 5047, High 5057
Nebraska: Hickey 5093
New Hampshire: Dunn 5212, Landecker 5217, Thorne 5233, Verney 5236
New Jersey: Brooks 5274, Brundage 5280, Conant 5302, Johnson 5407
New Mexico: Taos 5626
New York: Abelard 5635, AKC 5651, American 5662, Anderson-Rogers 5676, Bender 5735, Bernhill 5741, Brosens 5789, Cranshaw 5885, Douglas 5929, EMSA 5961, Erpf 5968, Feldstein 5997, Ferguson 5999, Goldstone 6102, Gordon 6109, Hahn 6156, Henderson 6189, IF 6237, Johnson 6268, Kandell 6283, Kimura 6310, Kistler 6316, Marshall 6446, Osceola 6560, Peckham 6583, Reiss 6662, Samuels 6725, Seven 6777, Snow 6818, Stern 6861, Sternberg 6863, Still 6866, Stowe 6869, Strong 6872, Watts 6947, Woodmere 6990, Woods 6992, Woodward 6993
North Carolina: Borun 7057, Kenan 7144, Morrison 7193, Post 7213, Vanderbilt 7273
Ohio: Anderson 7305, Armington 7309, Athens 7311, B-Brand 7318, **Eaton 7383, Elisha-Bolton 7387,** Gale 7414, Haskell 7439, **Highfield 7450,** Howe 7455, Lambert 7487, Lincoln 7496, Linnemann 7498, **Lowe-Marshall 7505,** Mather 7516, Norweb 7539, O'Neill 7542, Talbott 7612
Oklahoma: Atherton 7657
Oregon: Flowerree 7763, Leupold 7790
Pennsylvania: American 7839, Armstrong 7843, Baldwin 7852, Beach 7855, Berry 7867, Brooks 7899, French 8007, Hartfield 8041, Hawksglen 8045, Huplits 8071, Maple 8139, Mudge 8181, Price 8225, Spencer 8293, White 8355, Wright-Cook 8369
Rhode Island: Acriel 8378, Bailey 8384, Bersted 8388, Jacbel 8426, **Jeffery 8429,** Kimball 8434, Kingsbury 8435, Love 8446, Washington 8500
South Carolina: Stony 8542
South Dakota: Watertown 8576
Tennessee: Atticus 8582, Chrysalis 8598, Rose 8667
Texas: Boeing 8733, Field-Day 8855, Frost 8878, Hixon 8940, Horizon 8951, Mayfield 9044, Osberg 9105, Paulos 9120, Planetary 9132, Vaughan 9249
Utah: Denkers 9318, Slaughter, 9353, Telemachus: 9359
Vermont: Block 9366, Harper 9373, Harvest 9374, Redducs 9383, Stokes 9385
Virginia: Breeden, 9404, Cedars 9416, Community 9426, **Delmar 9429, Dorothy-Ann 9433,** Ludington 9495, Schiro-Zavela 9528, **Tara 9540**
Washington: Bishop 9569, Dudley 9588, Ferguson 9596, Fries-Tait 9599, Hickey 9622, Hyde 9627, **Ji 9632,** Johnson 9633, Northwest 9669, Runstad 9686, Wellworth 9722
Wisconsin: Bock 9786, Erdman 9816, Frautschi 9822, **Helios 9838,** Hunt 9845, Inbusch 9847, **Johnson 9851,** LUX 9874, Mason 9880, Schoenleber 9924,

Seeds 9925, Single 9930, Smith 9931, Stry 9941, Witte, 9962

Neighborhood associations

Indiana: Blackford 3346
New York: Family 5984

Neurology

Arizona: McKee 148
California: Alafi 235, Beneto 301, Farber 495, **Grass 577,** Harvey 602, Thagard 1109
Florida: Chanin 1934
Illinois: **Foundation 2880**
Minnesota: Bradley 4647
New Jersey: Dickinson 5319, **Integra 5400**
New York: **Buster 5806**
Tennessee: Cole 8600
Texas: Mischer 9067, Smith 9205, Stevenson 9220
Virginia: Lawrence 9487
Washington: **Sabol 9687**

News and public information

California: Bach 263
Colorado: White 1378
Texas: Walls 9257

Non-natural disasters

California: Somekh 1064
Illinois: Aon 2710
New York: Cranshaw 5885, Maslin 6448
Oregon: Wessinger 7826

Nonprofits

Alabama: Abroms 2, Anderson 6, Aronov 7, Bruno 17, Caddell 19, Friedman 27, Goodrich 29, JADO 40, Kairos 41, Loeb 47, Pei-Ling 52, Phifer, 54, Ripps 60, Rothschild 61, Upchurch, 72
Alaska: Gottstein 86
Arizona: Berlin 101, Chapin 105, Community 108, Grossman 126, McKee 148, Robson 160, Rubeli 163, Snell 171, Spalding 172, Ullman 177, Withycombe 184
Arkansas: **Baldor 188,** Hennessy 198, Riggs 214
California: Banchik 269, Barulich 280, Baye 285, Becker 291, Beim 293, Berlin 306, Bider 314, Bigglesworth 316, Bonner 327, Boone 328, Bridges/Larson 343, Broder 348, Brunswick 354, **Butler 365,** Cannon 374, CAS 378, Celebrate 383, Cheeryble 390, Codding 412, Collingwood 418, Corbalis 424, Corwin 428, Cutler 438, Dermalogica 451, DiNapoli 454, Dorskind 459, Drum 464, Ellen 478, Ferry 504, First 507, Fritz 515, Fritz 534, Frome 535, Fuller 538, Giles 554, Glazer 562, Glikbarg 564, Goldberg 567, Goldberg 568, Graff 576, Greenwood 581, Gross 587, Harman 598, Harris 600, Harvey 602, Hayman 606, Hellman 614, Herrmann 618, Hilltop 621, Horwich 632, Horwitz 633, Huntington 642, **Jacoby 654,** Johnson 667, Kadima 686, Kanel 688, Kelton 698, Kendall 700, Kieve 703, Kort 719, Koss 720, Levin 749, Levy 751, **Levy 752,** Lyons 776, Malachowsky 786, Manchester 788, Mann 790, Margolis 797, Meister 821, Miller 828, Miller 832, Mitchell 838, Mitchell, 839, **Moley 841,** Morgenstern 848, Murad 854, Neu 862, Olander 878, Ornest 888, Phillips 924, Podell 930, Pollia 931, Potiker 932, **Rieger 971,** Rocca, 978, Roney 983, Sands 1001, **Sikand 1037,** Silicon 1038, SKB 1044, Smalley 1050, Smith-Welsh 1058, Somekh 1064, Sondheimer 1065, Stack 1073, Straus 1088, Traub-Brittan 1127, Wagner 1149, Walton 1156, Weisz 1167, Worster 1197, Wrather 1198, Ziegler 1210
Colorado: Allen 1220, Elf 1262, Grosvenor 1282, Grosvenor 1283, Kortz 1307, Ladd 1310, Lewis 1315, Margulf 1320, Morse 1328, Pluss 1337,

Trachten 1369, Verdoorn 1372, W.J.D. 1375, Warner 1376, Zeff 1383
Connecticut: Abramowitz 1384, Baggins 1398, Barden 1402, Chaikin-Wile 1417, Chelsea 1418, **Davis-McCullough 1429,** Denzler 1434, Diageo 1437, Dime 1438, Eder 1441, Finn 1449, Floren 1451, Gengras, 1461, Gibor 1464, Gladstein 1465, Howard 1484, Jones 1490, Kuriansky 1503, Lamando 1504, Lavietes 1505, Lebovitz 1506, Mahadeva 1517, Manger 1518, Martin 1520, McLeod 1524, Nirenberg 1534, O'Herron 1536, Patricelli 1541, Price 1544, Pryor 1546, Rosenberg 1555, Schaeneman, 1560, Storr 1575, Stratfield 1576, Tell 1580, Thornton 1582, Tully 1588, Vance 1591, Zacharia 1601
Delaware: Bowman 1625, Brown-Whitworth 1632, Burton 1634, Cohen 1643, **Colgate 1645,** Coopersmith 1646, Croll 1650, Cross 1651, Freedman 1665, Kang 1689, New 1715, Pinkerton 1721, Ratner 1724, Riecker 1729, Rosenfeld 1732, Rumberger 1734, Russell 1735, Schiffman 1738, Schwalbach 1739, Sloane 1746, Splawn 1749, Sulentic 1752, Susman 1753, Taylor 1759, Yablon 1782
District of Columbia: Dweck 1805, Goldman 1810, **Gorlitz 1811,** Greenberg 1812, Haft 1813, **Merriman 1820,** Olender 1824, Silberman 1834, Westport 1838
Florida: Adler 1842, Anderson 1845, Auerbach 1859, Barnard 1866, Basham 1870, Bastien 1872, Beasley 1877, Becker 1879, Bell 1883, Blank 1890, Brodsky 1901, Brody 1902, Burks 1909, Capital 1918, Castellani 1927, Charlotte 1938, Chicone 1941, Childress 1942, Coulter-Jones 1954, Crane 1955, Dennis 1969, Deus 1972, Diamond 1973, Dickinson 1975, Dilworth 1977, Elster 1990, Erdle 1993, Farrell 1998, Five 2002, Friedland 2025, Gelbart 2035, Godbold 2041, Golden 2046, Grabe 2053, Graese 2055, Greenberg 2062, Greenblatt 2063, Greenfield 2066, Hagens 2071, Halperin 2076, Hardison 2081, Herrin 2091, Hicks 2094, Isenberg 2121, Jelks 2128, Kanders 2135, Kaplan 2138, Kaye 2141, Kessler 2145, Kimmel 2146, Kiwanis 2149, Knapp 2153, Kreisman 2159, Kugelman 2161, Kuriansky 2162, Lambrecht 2165, Lazzara 2174, Leiser 2177, Lenkin 2179, **Levine 2181,** Lipton 2185, Lookout 2190, McDonald 2203, MCM-Munilla 2206, MIDA 2212, Millsaps 2214, Nommontu 2234, Olemberg 2237, Overstreet 2242, Papper 2246, Pearle 2253, Perlmutter 2254, **Posnack 2262,** Resnick 2282, Richard 2285, River 2288, Ryan 2304, **Safenowitz 2307,** Salizzoni 2309, Sender 2323, Setzer 2325, Sexton 2326, Silverman 2337, Stellar 2348, Stern 2349, Stern 2350, Taplin 2363, Turner 2381, Vasey 2385, Votum 2390, Weinberger 2394, Weintraub 2395, Weisman 2396, Werner 2398, Wolf 2410, Wolgin 2411, **Wollowick 2412,** Wynne 2419, **Zichron 2424,** Zimmerman 2426, Zimmerman 2427, Zimmerman 2428
Georgia: A.E.M. 2430, Arnold 2436, Broadfield 2449, Brooks 2450, Carters 2454, Chatham 2457, Clary 2462, Colston 2464, Community 2466, Echlin 2472, Exposition 2476, Gilbert, 2488, Goodman 2492, Graves 2496, Griffin 2499, Inman 2519, JBS 2523, Jeter 2524, Jolley 2526, Knox 2534, Lipscomb 2541, Marcus 2544, McClatchey 2546, Morris 2553, Nonami 2557, Orkin 2559, Price 2569, Saul 2579, Schwob 2581, Storey 2589, Tritt 2596, Vogel 2600, Williams 2612, Woodruff 2617
Hawaii: Locations 2638, Shidler 2646, Ululani 2652
Idaho: Hecla 2676, Wishnick 2690
Illinois: 1335 2691, Anschel 2709, Beeghly 2730, Bellick 2732, Bishop 2743, Block, 2746, Ceres 2779, Clingen 2794, Collins 2799, Corbett 2808, Diamond 2829, Eckert 2843, Edelman 2845, Edelstein 2846, Edgerly 2847, EMA 2854, Enivar 2856, Fraida 2884, Frank 2885, Franklin 2887, Fredman 2890, Fremont 2891, Generations 2908, Gidwitz 2914, Gochnauer 2918, Goldenberg 2920, Golder 2921, Goodstein 2924, Grossinger 2933, H.C.D. 2939, Hales 2941, Harris 2957, Herman

2968, Hess 2969, Hoffer 2975, Hopper 2977, Howard 2981, Hunt 2984, JBS 2994, Jocarno 3000, Johnson 3001, Klosk 3020, **Landau 3036**, Larsen 3038, Leibowitz 3046, Levinson 3049, Levy 3050, Love 3064, Mann 3072, Manne 3073, Marcum 3076, McCormack 3086, Meier 3101, Millard 3109, Miller, 3113, Millner 3115, Minor 3117, Mitchell 3120, Murphy 3132, Neel 3135, New 3136, Nygren 3146, Oppenheimer 3155, Penrose 3166, Pollack 3180, Pond 3182, Pugdin 3185, Red 3189, Reinisch 3193, Richard 3195, Rosenberg 3207, Russell 3216, Ryan 3219, Schorr-Lieberman 3229, Sondheimer 3256, SSAB 3260, Staley 3263, Staley 3264, Stein 3266, Stern 3268, Stone 3269, Stone 3270, Takiff 3281, Victor 3304, Wagner 3306, **Wein 3315**, Weiss 3317, Whitwam 3321, Wright 3333, Yulman 3334, Zemsky 3337, Zuckerman 3338

Indiana: **Ackerman 3339**, Bronstein 3351, Crescent-Cresline-Wabash 3365, Harlan 3391, Jolan 3404, Klapper 3408, Lacy 3410, Lafayette 3411, Maurer 3415, **Mervis 3417**, Mulzer 3420, MutualBank 3421, Namaste 3422, Oliver 3428, Rifkin 3437, Rush 3441, Thrush-Thompson 3460, Welter 3465, Weston 3467

Iowa: Bennett 3474, Busse 3478, Carlson 3479, Giacoletto 3499, GuideOne 3503, Henry 3505, Krause 3516, McDonald 3520, Nelson 3524, R 3529, Vermeer 3541, Weathertop 3545, Woodward 3549

Kansas: Bane 3557, Berry 3558, Buford 3562, DeVore 3573, Fidelity 3577, Goldberg 3581, Insurance 3587, Joscelyn 3590, Lowenstein 3598, Payless 3614, Price 3616, Shannon 3625, Smoot 3627, Swearingen 3631, Trusler 3635, Wallace 3637, Watson 3639, Williams 3643

Kentucky: McKellar 3677, Mulhollem 3680, Roth 3690, Rouse 3692, Trager 3701, Trim 3702

Louisiana: Cahn 3716, Harper 3726, Huie-Dellmon 3729, Lake 3732, Live 3734, Moffett 3739, Powers 3746, Pugh 3747, Selber 3751, Wheless 3758, Zuschlag 3762

Maine: Franklin 3779, Kagan 3784, Kennebec 3785

Maryland: Ammerman 3813, Bank 3818, Berger 3821, Cole 3839, Contino 3840, Devito 3848, Dockser 3849, Eliasberg 3854, Elsberg 3856, Gidwitz 3870, **Goldberg 3872**, Greene-Milstein 3876, Gutman 3877, Hubbard 3883, Hurwitz 3886, Kay 3892, Macks 3906, Meyer 3913, Minkoff 3915, Murthynayak 3921, Number 3929, Pearlstone 3934, RCM 3937, RFI 3938, Rothschild 3942, Schuh 3946, Shapiro 3949, Shattuck 3950, Thalheimer 3966, Totah 3968, Weinman 3981, Wilen 3985, Wolpoff 3990

Massachusetts: Beaucourt 4014, Black 4021, **Bruner 4030**, Clifford 4051, Crane 4058, Easthampton 4076, Goldman 4105, Hazard 4124, Hopedale 4134, Kenwood 4150, Krieger 4160, Levy 4174, Marcus 4188, Morningstar 4207, Morse 4208, Morse 4209, Noble 4224, Oristaglio 4232, Reisman 4262, Rockland 4267, Rodman 4268, Shapiro 4289, Shapiro 4290, Sherman 4293, **Spero 4304**, Spoon 4305, Stearns 4310, Tapper 4321, **Tatelman 4322**, Tatelman 4323, Torok 4331, Ullian 4335, Whittemore 4359, Wyman-Gordon 4364

Michigan: Abrams 4369, Alon 4374, Baiardi 4381, Barstow 4385, Barton-Malow 4386, Biederman 4391, Bierlein 4392, Dana 4419, Ferber 4443, Ford 4445, Frankenmuth 4450, Grassland 4458, Harris 4461, Hartwick 4462, Havirmill 4463, Kaufman 4479, Leven 4492, Maas 4498, Manat 4503, McDole 4507, Meritor, 4511, Murdock 4519, Narens 4520, Nartel 4521, Nusbaum 4524, O'Donovan 4525, Padnos 4529, Paine 4531, Paulina 4535, Pitt 4540, Pitt 4541, Plym 4542, Seligman 4564, Sherman 4567, Shine 4569, Stoker 4580, **Teitel 4589**, Torgow 4594, Vlasic 4607, Welch 4610, Wetsman 4611, Whiting 4614, Zimmerman 4620

Minnesota: Ankeny 4628, Bahl 4632, Baratz 4635, Borman 4644, Bumgarner 4649, Burwell 4650, Deikel 4663, Dell 4664, Dellwood 4665, Erickson

4674, Fink 4684, G&K 4691, Grossman 4701, Harrington 4707, Heilicher 4711, **Kaplan 4721**, Kinney 4724, Krisbin 4726, McNamara 4743, Midcontinent 4745, Morning 4748, Northern 4751, Quinlan 4764, Regis 4770, Shared 4791, Tamarack 4797, Tennant 4798, Wallestad 4806

Mississippi: Brevard 4826, Crooks 4831

Missouri: Arnold 4861, BF 4867, **Block 4869**, Bograd 4870, **Bohm 4871**, Brace 4874, Butler 4880, Chod 4885, Copaken 4888, Crown 4891, Dierberg 4895, Edgar 4899, Empson 4902, Erlich 4904, Essman 4905, Finley 4910, Forster-Powers 4911, Green 4920, Heiman 4926, Hofheimer 4929, Kornblum 4940, Kuhn 4941, **Maor 4952**, Melcher 4957, O'Reilly 4974, Pearl 4977, Peculiar 4978, Portman 4981, Riedel 4984, Sachs 4989, Schweinfurth 4996, Shawe 5000, Sigma-Aldrich 5003, Silk 5004, Siteman 5006, Slusher 5009, Stroble 5015, Vatterott 5030, Wolff 5040

Montana: Gallagher 5052, Gerhart 5053

Nebraska: Assurity 5068, Friedland 5082, Friedman 5083, Grewcock 5086, Harper 5088, Hawkins 5089, Nelson 5106, Physicians 5112, **Waldbaum 5125**

Nevada: Bendon 5137, **Fein 5155**, Shulman 5185, Vandevoort 5194, **Wood 5201**

New Hampshire: Jameson 5215, McIninch 5224

New Jersey: Adler 5242, **Akhoury 5243**, Aufzien 5253, Benaroya 5260, Bijou 5264, **Billig 5265**, Brook 5273, Brueckner 5279, Cali 5284, Cantor 5285, CKT 5297, Clermont 5298, Cohen 5299, Croman 5307, Domenica 5323, EBB 5329, Ellis 5333, Engel 5334, Entin 5336, ESH 5338, Feinstein 5343, Fox 5349, Freedman 5352, Frelinghuysen 5354, Freyer 5355, Fux 5359, Giancristofaro 5368, Glasser 5371, Goldberger 5372, Goodwin 5374, Greetin 5377, Halpern 5380, Harmstieg 5386, Heller 5391, JFI 5405, Jones 5408, Kaufman 5415, Kingsberg 5421, Kresa 5432, Kurtz 5436, Lieberman 5448, Mamiye 5456, Maschler 5462, MTB 5474, Myers 5476, Navesink 5477, Oster 5484, Pantirer 5487, Pasternak 5490, Pheasant 5499, Pines 5501, Plafsky 5503, Riskin 5511, Rukin 5516, Sanders 5518, Savin 5520, Scire 5526, Selective 5528, Shilling 5534, Simon, 5537, Smilowitz 5538, Smith 5539, Welch 5579, Zissu 5602

New Mexico: Horn 5618, King-Carpenter 5619

New York: Abess 5636, Abess 5637, Abettor 5638, Abramson 5640, Adikes 5646, American 5664, American 5668, Applebaum 5683, Asher 5695, Bank 5710, Barron 5719, Baseser 5720, Baumann 5723, BBL 5724, Beckman 5729, Bendit 5736, Bergson 5738, Betesh 5743, Blank 5756, Block 5759, Brand 5776, Brandt 5777, Bratt 5778, Brooklyn 5788, BSR 5794, Buller 5800, Casey 5819, Centennial 5826, Citrin 5846, Cohen 5857, Cohenca 5861, Cohn 5864, Coleman 5870, Cornell/Weinstein 5877, **Cote 5881**, Curtis 5889, Danziger 5899, Darrah 5900, Davis 5902, Dears 5905, Desai 5910, Dolgen 5922, Doovin 5923, Double-R 5927, Edelweiss 5944, Eggleston 5946, Ehrman 5949, EMSA 5961, Englebardt 5965, ESL 5969, Eule 5971, Feil 5991, Fein 5992, Feldstein 5997, Fields 6003, Fife 6005, Finkelstein 6007, Finn 6008, Fitt 6010, Fleischer 6013, Foundation 6019, Fowey 6021, Franco 6024, French 6032, Friedman 6040, Frieme 6041, Fuchsberg 6044, Gaffney 6049, Gantcher 6055, Gantz 6056, Gartner 6059, Gemj 6069, Gilliam 6078, Godinger 6086, Gold 6088, Goldenberg 6092, Goldenberg 6093, Goldstein 6100, Goldwasser 6103, Goodman-Lipman 6108, Gould 6116, Grandison 6124, Greenberg 6132, Gross 6142, Guela 6151, H. 6153, Hahn 6156, Harmon 6169, Harris 6172, Hasenfeld 6174, Hefta 6181, Henderson 6189, Henshel 6192, Herbst 6195, Hershaft 6197, Hershman 6198, Heyman 6201, Hidary 6205, Hirsch 6211, Hirsch 6212, Hochman 6214, **Hoffman 6216**, Holtzman 6223, Horowitz 6225, Issroff 6251, JI 6260, JIA 6261, Joyce 6275, Kamber 6281, Kaminer 6282, Kandell 6283, **Katzin 6288**, Kelleher 6295, Keller-Shatanoff

6297, Keswin 6303, **Klagsbrun 6318**, Klaus 6320, Kleinschmidt 6326, Koha 6337, Kohn 6338, Konar 6340, Krumholz 6349, Kulick 6350, Lawrence 6369, **Legacy 6374**, Leibowitz 6376, Lemle 6377, Lemle 6378, Leventritt 6385, Levine 6386, Levitin 6388, Levy 6390, Levy 6391, Lewy 6393, Liebowitz 6400, Lippes 6401, Litterman 6406, Lopatin 6412, Lufkin 6421, Marshall 6446, Maslin 6448, MBS 6454, Meade 6467, Menezes 6473, Miller 6491, Mindel 6498, Moore 6504, Morris 6508, Morse 6510, Netter 6525, **Neuman 6526**, New 6527, Newman 6530, Newman 6532, Nussbaum 6545, Ostreicher 6563, Parshelsky 6578, Peek 6584, Pickman 6602, Pincus 6606, Pohly-Turaj 6613, Pollack 6614, Pollack 6615, R 6640, Rachesky 6642, Rapaport 6647, Raphael 6648, Reich 6659, Ring 6671, RJL 6675, Robbins 6676, **Rock 6679**, Rose 6683, Rose 6684, Rosner 6698, Roth 6700, Rudy 6708, Russo 6711, **Sato 6731**, Saunders 6733, Schaffer 6737, Schott 6749, Schwartz 6754, Seaman 6767, Seligsohn 6773, Shackouls 6781, Sharon 6787, SHEL 6791, Sherman 6792, Siegel 6797, Silver 6800, Silverman 6801, Silverstein 6803, SKL 6808, Slade 6810, Slovin 6811, Smith 6815, Sommer 6825, Spiegel 6838, Starker 6847, **Stein 6855**, Stein 6856, **Stern 6862**, Striano 6871, SVM 6886, Tanner-Frank 6893, Tenney 6895, Trimble 6910, TSP 6913, Utica 6922, Vaad 6924, Vogel 6931, **Weinstein 6956**, Weiser 6958, Weisman 6959, Weiss 6961, Weiss 6962, Whispering 6970, Windy 6980, Wohlgemuth 6984, Wolk 6987, Wunsch 6996, Wurtele 6997, Yaspan-Unterberg 7003, Yosef 7011, Zenkel 7023, Ziff 7027, Zwerling 7034

North Carolina: BB&T 7045, Bell 7047, Bell 7048, Bernstein 7049, Borun 7057, Coffey 7078, Ellison 7090, First 7097, Gambrill 7106, Helb 7122, Hudson 7133, **Kramer 7152**, Lerner 7160, Levine-Sklut 7161, Mattei 7173, McLean 7178, Meyer 7184, Nanney 7198, Perkin 7208, Ragland, 7216, Shugart 7242, Silverman 7244, Summer 7261

North Dakota: Fedje 7296

Ohio: Anderson 7305, Berke 7323, Brown 7336, Chemed 7350, Chesley 7351, CLH 7355, Crandall 7366, Damico 7370, **Elisha-Bolton 7387**, Ettlinger 7390, Fedeli 7393, Fibus 7398, Finnegan 7399, Foss 7407, Frohman 7411, Frost 7412, Gale 7414, Garcia 7416, Geary, 7419, Gelbman 7420, Gilman 7423, Glazer 7426, Gross 7432, Hankins 7437, Haskell 7439, Heffner 7443, Hoover 7453, Howe 7455, Iott 7463, Joffe 7467, Klock 7480, Lazarus 7493, LKC 7501, Loeb 7503, M.L.M 7510, Norris 7538, Norweb 7539, Peters 7547, Powers 7550, Sauerland 7570, Schottenstein 7575, Schwartz 7576, Schwebel 7577, Seaman 7580, Smith 7598, Stensen 7604, STERIS 7605, Stillson 7607, Swagelok 7608, Taft 7609, Traeger 7621, Van 7625, Vista 7628, Wasserstrom 7632, Watson 7633, Williamson 7640, Wolf 7643, Young 7651

Oklahoma: GKJ 7683, Trippet 7725, White 7734

Oregon: Demorest 7757, Holzman 7775, Merlo 7797

Pennsylvania: Aaron 7835, Arkema 7842, Armstrong 7843, **Arronson 7844**, Auldridge 7846, Baker 7851, Baldwin, 7852, Beach 7855, Beacon 7856, Berger 7862, Bergman 7863, **Berkowitz 7865**, Bishop 7874, Blue 7879, Born 7885, Borowsky 7886, Breedlove 7890, Briggs 7892, Bronstein 7896, Butz 7908, Charlestein 7920, CNB 7929, **Cohn 7931**, Community 7933, **Epstein 7983**, Foster 8003, Gershman 8015, Goshen 8025, Hankin 8038, Harsco 8040, Hauber 8043, Hecht 8050, HFO 8053, Hoffman 8063, Honickman 8066, IGN 8073, Kahn, 8084, Kelley 8091, Kittenbrink 8093, Klein 8096, Kline 8098, KMJ 8099, Levis 8122, Lida 8127, Lubert 8133, M&P 8135, Mellon 8167, Mendel 8168, Merwin 8170, Moore 8177, Mudge 8181, Mukaiyama-Rice 8183, Murphy 8185, Olitsky 8198, Oppenheim 8199, Pearsall 8207, Perelman 8209, Pincus 8214, Quaker 8228, Robinson 8241, Rosenberg 8244, Russo 8249, Saramar 8253, Satell 8254, Schautz 8257, Schoonmaker 8260, Schwab-Silfen 8264,

Schwartz 8265, Sidewater 8278, Snyder 8287, Speyer 8294, Stein 8298, Tabas 8312, Tuttleman 8325, Wagner 8338, Walton 8341, Wasserott 8344, Weiler-Miller 8348, Wimmer 8361, York 8374

Rhode Island: Bernhardt 8387, Charlton, 8394, Feibelman 8405, Galkin 8410, Greene 8413, Gross 8414, Heydt 8419, Jacbel 8426, Janci 8428, Johnson 8430, Kingsbury 8435, Koffler 8436, Mann 8448, Molder 8455, Mulligan 8457, O'Halloran 8462, Salmanson 8481, Schwarz 8483, Siperstein 8489, Swarts 8495, Thompson 8497, Washington 8500, Woodward 8505

South Carolina: Bailey 8510, Bonner 8513, Cato 8516, Kendall 8530, Peery/Cauthen 8537, Tarr 8545, Williams/Brice-Edwards 8549

South Dakota: Elmen 8561

Tennessee: Atticus 8582, B 8583, Basler 8584, **Belz 8585**, Boring 8590, Bradford 8592, Chrysalis 8598, Citizens 8599, Community 8601, Doochin 8605, Eskind 8611, Goldsmith 8622, Houghland 8630, Kennedy 8638, **Lowenstein 8645**, Mick 8651, New 8654, Proctor 8662

Texas: Astin 8710, Barnett 8718, Bloxom, 8731, Brodsky 8747, Brown 8751, Brownsville 8752, **Crowder 8792**, Dedman, 8808, Dubose 8828, Finger 8857, Flohr 8861, Foundation 8869, Foundation 8870, Friedel 8875, Friedman 8876, Fuchs 8881, Gordon 8893, Guetz 8905, Haggar, 8908, Hervey 8932, Hofstetter 8943, Holmes 8947, Inge 8961, Johnson, 8971, Kaplan 8979, Kelso 8985, Klesse 8998, Kolitz 9000, Lilly 9019, MacDonald-Peterson 9032, McKee 9052, Mewhinney 9060, Oppenheimer 9100, Oppenheimer 9101, Orr 9104, Osberg 9105, Paulos 9120, Perkins 9125, Petty 9126, Postl 9136, Pulitzer 9140, Schepps 9177, Schissler 9179, Staubach 9215, Sterling 9219, Stevenson 9220, Tolleson 9238, Vaughan 9249, Walls 9257, Watson 9263, Westcott 9273, Wilder 9277, Wise 9283, Wolf 9285, Wolff-Toomim 9286, Zale 9300

Utah: Andrus 9301, Bastian 9304, Bourne-Spafford 9306, Schmidt 9349

Virginia: Backer 9389, Better 9396, Charles 9418, Dickerson 9431, Edlavitch 9440, Foundation 9451, Gifford 9457, Glasser 9459, Grandis 9462, Hausfeld 9469, Meador 9500, Ochsman 9504, Peachtree 9508, **Price 9516**, Ratner 9521, Richardson 9523, Schiro-Zavela 9528, Stone 9537, Weil 9550

Washington: Bacon 9565, Bayley 9567, CSM 9584, Ferguson 9596, Galanti 9603, Jaffe 9629, **Jernigan 9631**, Lanterman 9649, Levitan 9653, Lott 9656, Morningside 9665, Prairie 9680, Razore 9682, Remala 9683, Rosen 9684, Runstad 9686, Sarkowsky 9688, Shemanski 9693, Smith 9698, Spring 9702, Stars 9703, Templin 9709

West Virginia: Brown 9739, Hott 9753, Starvaggi 9767

Wisconsin: Anderson 9773, Arzbaecher 9777, Caritas 9791, Chipstone 9794, Christensen 9795, Cummings-Christensen 9801, Erdman 9816, Foley 9820, Frautschi 9822, Glanert 9827, Gordon 9830, Highlands 9841, Jacobus 9849, Kohl 9864, Lutsey 9873, Manitowoc 9876, Marcus 9877, Martin 9879, Merkel 9884, Modine 9889, Mortenson 9890, Pelz 9900, Puelicher 9907, RITE-HITE 9915, Roddis 9916, Shoemaker 9928, Smith 9931, Smith 9932, Steinle 9938, Uihlein 9950, Van 9952, Van 9953, Wagner 9955, Webcrafters-Frautschi 9957, Witte, 9962

Wyoming: Connemara 9967, Guthrie 9972, Skelton 9989, StoneRiver 9991

Nursing care

Arizona: Margolis 144, Pierce 156
California: Barco's 277
Colorado: Trueblood 1371
Florida: De 1967, Fish 2001, Givens 2038, King 2148, Millsaps 2214, Price 2267, Stewart 2351, Thompson 2372
Georgia: Stahl 2588
Illinois: Keller 3010

Indiana: Duneland 3372, Seymour 3448
Iowa: Rohde 3530, Schildberg 3532
Kansas: Scroggins 3624
Louisiana: Live 3734
Maryland: Rhona's 3939
Massachusetts: Mavrogenis 4192, Starr 4309
Mississippi: Biloxi 4824, Florence 4836
Missouri: St. 5012
Nebraska: Weller 5127
New Jersey: Snyder 5541
New York: Fleming 6014, French 6032, Post 6622, Switzer 6889
North Carolina: Griffin 7113, Marlboro 7169, Ribenack 7220, Rogers 7228, Sutcliffe 7262, Wibel 7287
Ohio: Gimbel 7424, Steinmann 7603, STERIS 7605, Tuscora 7624
Oregon: Leonard 7789
Pennsylvania: **Arronson 7844**, Nesh 8191
Rhode Island: Coes 8396
South Dakota: Houston 8567
Tennessee: Community 8601
Texas: Harwi 8921, Healthcare 8924, Johnson, 8971, Woods 9291
Utah: Cumming 9316
Virginia: Greensville 9464
Washington: Coulter 9581, Worthington 9729
Wisconsin: Fromm 9823, LUX 9874

Nursing homes

New York: Faith 5979

Nutrition

California: Just 684, Palo 900
Florida: Gate 2034, Nalith 2229, Wilson-Wood 2408
Georgia: Solstice 2587
Massachusetts: Kelsey 4148, Vela 4341
Pennsylvania: Bennett 7860, Blue 7879
Texas: Morrison 9073
Wisconsin: Blooming 9784

Obesity

Massachusetts: Vela 4341
Pennsylvania: Blue 7879

Oceans and coastal waters

California: **Quiksilver 945**
Florida: **Atlantis 1858**
Massachusetts: **New 4220**
Washington: Northwest 9669

Offenders

New York: Ostgrodd 6561

Olympics

Arizona: McKee 148

Oncology

California: Downey-Short 461
Virginia: Immixgroup 9476

Opera

Arizona: Hughes 130
California: Baker 265, Bryan 355, Davies 444, Friedhofer 529, Fritz 534, Greenberg 579, Hoag 625, Kendall 701, Marineau 798, Parker 903, **Preuss 935**, Seaver 1026, Stauffer 1077, Traub-Brittan 1127, Zolla 1216
Colorado: Spencer 1356
Connecticut: Axe-Houghton 1397, Morrow 1527, Smith 1572, Storr 1575
Delaware: Heuer 1680, Kingsley 1693, Whitman 1778
District of Columbia: Rubenstein 1833, Westport 1838

Florida: Bartner 1869, Beasley 1877, Carlin 1921, Farrell 1998, Isenberg 2121, Kahn 2133, Leiser 2177, Stern 2350, Studer 2355
Georgia: Jeter 2524
Illinois: Howard 2981, Knowles 3023, Maddox 3069, Massey 3082, Minor 3117, Pangburn 3161, Spencer 3258, Weiss 3317
Iowa: Farver 3491, Krumm 3517, Woodward 3549
Maine: Borman 3767
Maryland: Hobbs 3882, Mangione 3907
Massachusetts: **Brabson 4026**, **Kahn 4143**, Perry 4240
Michigan: Jospey 4473, Meritor, 4511, Schalon 4558, Stubnitz 4582, Williams 4618
Minnesota: Boss 4645, Boss 4646, Chadwick-Loher 4655
Nebraska: Owen 5108
New Hampshire: Couch 5209, Smyth 5232
New Jersey: deRosa 5316, Johnson 5407
New Mexico: **Daniels 5613**
New York: Ades-Taub 5645, Barbash 5714, Cohen 5860, Goldfarb 6095, Golding 6097, Keller-Shatanoff 6297, Lassalle 6366, Lissner 6405, Miller 6491, Sackler 6717, Schwartz 6755, Securitas 6768, **Weill 6950**, Weinman 6955, Woodmere 6990
Ohio: Busse 7343, Corbett 7363
Oklahoma: Moore 7710, Wilson 7736
Pennsylvania: Lida 8127, Patterson 8205, Strine 8306
Tennessee: Bradford 8592, Cole 8600, Schmidt 8671
Texas: Knox 8999, Littauer 9021, Lowdon 9025, Schissler 9179, Schulze 9182, Von 9253
Washington: Graham 9609
Wisconsin: Berbeewalsh 9782, Hunt 9845

Orchestral music

Alabama: Caddell 19, Thompson 70
Arizona: Coleman 107, McKee 148, Robson 160
Arkansas: Oliver 211
California: Acacia 225, Davies 444, Eichenberg-Larson 474, Familian 491, Folger 515, Hellman 614, HunterWard 641, Lamond 729, Leland 741, Levin 749, Merage 822, Mollath 842, **Rifkind 972**, Roberts 975, Robinson 977, Walther 1154, Winkler 1188, Zafiropoulo 1207, Zimmer 1212
Connecticut: Morrow 1527
Delaware: Heuer 1680, **TeleTech 1761**
District of Columbia: Westport 1838
Florida: Bartner 1869, Blanton 1892, Chapman 1935, Farrell 1998, Foulds 2014, Kane 2137, Verner 2386, Wescustogo 2399
Georgia: Arnold 2436, Eden 2473, Glancy 2489, Graves 2496, Schwob 2581
Idaho: Hare 2675
Illinois: Glossberg 2916, House 2980, JKP 2997, Maddox 3069, Miller, 3114, Moreton 3124, Pangburn 3161, Peters 3172
Indiana: Crescent-Cresline-Wabash 3365, Noecker 3424, O'Rourke-Schof 3429
Iowa: Cowles 3482, McDonald 3520, Weathertop 3545
Kansas: Trusler 3635
Louisiana: Wisdom 3761
Maryland: Adler 3809, Baltimore 3817, Feinberg 3857, Gidwitz 3870, Gordon 3873, Huether/McClelland 3884, Kelly, 3893, RCM 3937, Schuh 3946, Waidner 3976, Witt/Hoey 3989
Massachusetts: Barstow 4013, **Brabson 4026**, Bulger 4031, Hampden 4116, Heide 4125, Jefferson 4142, Lost 4180, Morse 4209, Murphy 4214, Perry 4240, Ramlose 4257, Stare 4308, Stemberg 4313
Michigan: Dana 4419, Harris 4461, Hartwick 4462, Loosemore 4495, Meritor, 4511, Price 4546, Schalon 4558, SEED 4562, Stubnitz 4582, Wetsman 4611, Williams 4618
Minnesota: Shared 4791, Tennant 4798, Thorpe 4800
Missouri: Barrows 4864, Bograd 4870, **Bohm 4871**, Curry 4892, Hermann 4927, Lordi 4950, Simmons 5005
Montana: Wendy's 5065
Nebraska: Assurity 5068, Lienemann 5100
New Hampshire: Smyth 5232
New Jersey: Brueckner 5279, Brundage 5280, Kresa 5432, McCrane 5464, Smith 5539, Upton 5566

New Mexico: Garfield 5616
New York: **Blinken 5757**, Colby 5867, D'Addario 5894, Fink 6006, **Goldfein 6096**, Greenspan 6134, Hart 6173, Henshel 6192, Hiler 6207, Johnson 6270, Kirby 6313, Koessler 6335, Kriser 6347, Lachman 6356, **Lanie 6364**, Messinger 6482, Pohly-Turaj 6613, Resnick 6663, Roxe 6706, Schweitzer 6759, Securitas 6768, Serenbetz 6776, Slade 6809, Sorel 6826, Touhey 6902, Vogt 6933, Weinman 6955, Wilson 6979
North Carolina: Post 7213, Rankin 7217, **Rolander 7229**, Rollins 7231, Steinmetz 7254, Trexler 7269, Whitener 7286
Ohio: Beecher 7320, Busse 7343, Corbett 7363, George 7421, Powers 7550, Selsor 7585, Wolfe 7644, Young 7652
Oklahoma: Ad 7654
Oregon: Pendleton 7806
Pennsylvania: Clark 7925, Hodge 8061, Merwin 8170, Plainfield 8217, Schoonmaker 8260
South Carolina: Collins 8520
Tennessee: Bradford 8592, Doochin 8605, EBS 8610, Eskind 8611, Small 8675
Texas: Brodsky 8747, Frankel 8872, Garvey 8884, Hallam 8910, Hallberg 8911, Horween 8952, Lilly 9019, MacDonald-Peterson 9032, P 9108, Rosenberg 9162, Schissler 9179, Von 9253, Weaver 9265, Willard 9278
Utah: Bastian 9304, Benjamin 9305, Bourne-Spafford 9306
Virginia: Franklin 9452
Washington: **Jernigan 9631**, Keller 9643, Magdalen 9658
Wisconsin: Dawes 9803, Hyde 9846, Peterson 9901, Van 9952
Wyoming: C 9966

Organ and tissue banks
Kentucky: Etscorn 3654
Texas: Webre 9266

Organic farming
Florida: Nalith 2229
New York: Hahn 6156, Still 6866
Wisconsin: Blooming 9784

Organized labor
Colorado: Warner 1376
Illinois: Edgerly 2847
New York: Abelard 5635

Orphanages
Oregon: **Living 7792**
Pennsylvania: Mullen 8184

Orthodox Christianity
California: Arbor 249, Kallins 687, Orthodox 890, **Trustees 1132**
Delaware: Patterson 1719
Florida: **Cantonis 1915**
Illinois: Eckert 2843, Self 3234
Kansas: Farah 3576
Massachusetts: Mirak 4204
New York: Michelle 6489
Texas: Paulos 9120
Wyoming: Joannides 9976

Orthodox Judaism
Michigan: Schwarcz 4560
New York: **Fischel 6009**, Rudy 6708, U 6918, Weiss 6961, **Yoreinu 7010**

Orthopedics
Arizona: Louis 142
Delaware: Selin 1742
Illinois: Nth 3144
Massachusetts: Harris 4118
Michigan: Havirmill 4463
New York: Insall 6246, Seaman 6767

Out-of-home youth
Virginia: **Delmar 9429**

Out-patient medical care
California: Bernstein 307, Ross 988, Winkler 1188
Illinois: Boyle 2754
New Jersey: **Rippel 5510**

Painting
Kentucky: Kentucky 3669
New York: Avery 5702, **Gottlieb 6114**

Pancreatic cancer
California: Riley 973
Rhode Island: **Black 8390**

Parent education
California: Yen 1201
Colorado: Bloom 1239
Minnesota: Grotto 4702
Nevada: **Do 5153**
New York: Downs 5931
Ohio: Alpaugh 7302
Texas: Boeing 8733, Levy 9014
Washington: Foss 9598

Parent-teacher involvement
Illinois: Heath 2962
North Carolina: Wells 7283

Parents
California: Fox 523

Parkinson's disease
Alabama: Anderson 5
Iowa: Gaedke 3495
Michigan: Alon 4374, Oreffice 4528
Missouri: Sachs 4989
New Jersey: Tuchman 5561
New York: Clemente 5850, Dears 5905, Golub 6105, Reiss 6662

Parks
Florida: Coral 1952
Kentucky: Trim 3702
Nebraska: Blair 5074, Owen 5108
New York: **Family 5983**, Northern 6540, Offensend 6550, Rodgers 6680
South Carolina: Greenwood 8526

Patient social services
California: Eichenberg-Larson 474
Connecticut: Diageo 1437
Georgia: Burke 2451
Iowa: McDonald 3520
Michigan: Kiwanis 4484
Nevada: Pinnacle 5183
North Carolina: McConnell 7176, Morisey 7191
Pennsylvania: Bolte 7882
Texas: AMR/American 8703
Wisconsin: Manitowoc 9876

Patient-centered care
Washington: Bungie 9576

Pediatrics
Alabama: Dixon 26
Arizona: Armstrong 97
California: Margolis 797, Scott 1023, Zafiropoulo 1207
Florida: Coulter-Jones 1954, Yerrid 2420
Illinois: Bidwill 2741, Trio 3292
Kentucky: Etscorn 3654, Namaste 3682
Maryland: **Goldberg 3872**, Huether/McClelland 3884, Mitchell, 3916
Missouri: **Build-A-Bear 4879**
New Jersey: Jones 5409
North Carolina: Gambrill 7106
Pennsylvania: Bryer 7902, Gauss 8014
Texas: AMR/American 8703, Patton 9119
Virginia: Geary-O'Hara 9456
Washington: DeFalco 9585
Wisconsin: Glanert 9827

People of East Asian descent
California: Kimbo 705

People of African descent
Alabama: Black 12, Ireland 39
California: Gellert 550
District of Columbia: Jovid 1817, Olender 1824
Florida: Smith 2341
Georgia: Young 2621
Kentucky: Killian 3670
Minnesota: Bell 4638
New York: **Sparkplug 6830**
North Carolina: Glenn 7111, Strowd 7258
Tennessee: **Fugitive 8618**
Virginia: **Delmar 9429**
Wisconsin: Inbusch 9847

People of Asian descent
Alabama: Ireland 39
California: **Chan 388**, **Raymond 956**, Small 1049, Yen 1201
District of Columbia: Jovid 1817
Florida: Foster 2013
Minnesota: Bell 4638
New Jersey: Chang 5290, **Garcia 5362**
New York: Ong 6558, **Sparkplug 6830**

People of Latin American descent
Alabama: Black 12, Ireland 39
California: Castellano 380, **Wakerly 1150**
District of Columbia: **Carter 1794**, Jovid 1817
Florida: Kiwanis 2150, Vasey 2385
Georgia: Amos 2433
Illinois: Sumac 3278
Iowa: **Wahlert 3544**
Minnesota: Bell 4638
Nebraska: Midlands 5104
New Mexico: Con 5611
New York: **Sparkplug 6830**
North Carolina: Glenn 7111, Strowd 7258
Oregon: Elwood 7761
Pennsylvania: Hoffman 8062
Tennessee: **Fugitive 8618**
Texas: Long 9023
Virginia: **Delmar 9429**
Wisconsin: Inbusch 9847, Marshfield 9878
Wyoming: Dragicevich 9969

People with disabilities
Alabama: Bruno 17, Ireland 39
Arizona: Shacknai 167
Arkansas: Olds 210

California: Avery-Fuller-Welch 260, Community 421, Corwin 428, Familian 491, Frome 535, Gellert 550, Goodwin 572, Gross 587, Johnson 669, Louie 770, Page 899, Palo 900, Prete, 934
Colorado: Mullen 1329, Schlessman 1349
Connecticut: Fry 1458
Florida: Bond 1897, Cape 1917, Coral 1952, Gate 2034, Harper 2082, Jacobsen 2123, Oristano 2241, Scherr 2316, Sudakoff 2356
Georgia: Abreu 2431, Greiner 2498, Holly 2509, Jolley 2526, Noonan 2558, Stahl 2588
Illinois: Aon 2710, **Appleby 2711**, Bulkley, 2765, Corcoran 2810, Cremer 2815, Family 2864, Gantz 2900, Generations 2908, Keeney 3007, **Lindon 3054**, MacDonald 3068, McNally 3097, Meyer 3106, Richard 3195, Robson 3200, Schneider 3226
Indiana: Ayres 3342, Noecker 3424
Kansas: Kansas 3592, Legacy, 3595
Kentucky: Woosley 3708
Louisiana: Crossroads 3719, Steinhagen 3755
Maine: Borman 3767
Maryland: Cole 3839, Kelly, 3893
Massachusetts: Alden 3999, MENTOR 4199, Simoni 4296, Winning 4362
Michigan: Community 4410, Community 4411, Main 4501
Minnesota: Bell 4637, Bell 4638, Dyer 4669, Thorpe 4800
Missouri: **Bohm 4871**, Butler 4880, Dunn 4898, Grant 4918, Love 4951, Sunnen 5018
Nebraska: Midlands 5104, Patrick 5109
Nevada: Matley 5176
New Hampshire: Cochran 5208
New Jersey: A 5240, Freelander 5353, **Knistrom 5426**, **Ostberg 5483**
New York: Antun 5681, Artists 5692, August 5698, Bratt 5779, Enders 5963, French 6032, **Haven 6178**, Mabardi 6428, Metzger-Price 6483, Parshelsky 6578, Picotte 6603, Schweckendieck 6758, Snow 6818, Society 6821, Turner 6916
North Carolina: Eddy 7087, Flowers 7099, Glenn 7111, Wann 7279
Ohio: Athens 7311, Cassner 7348, Jenkins 7465, Johnson 7468, Musson 7534, Walker 7630
Oregon: Wessinger 7826
Pennsylvania: Blue 7879, Chase 7921, Child 7923, Hoffman 8062, Mill 8172
Rhode Island: Heydt 8419, Kimball 8434
Texas: Edwards 8837, Holloway 8946, Johnston 8972, Knox 8999, McKee 9052, Oppenheimer 9101, Parks 9115, Sanguinetti 9172, Strickland 9224
Utah: Kennecott 9333
Virginia: Collins 9424, **Delmar 9429**
Washington: Tonkin 9715
West Virginia: Larch 9755, Parlin 9762
Wisconsin: Birnschein 9783, Inbusch 9847, Stateline 9937, Van 9953
Wyoming: **Schultz 9986**, Scott 9988

People with hearing impairments

Alabama: Ireland 39
Connecticut: Schwerin 1563
Georgia: Abreu 2431
Illinois: Adams 2696
Kansas: Baehr 3556
Maryland: Mitchell, 3916
Minnesota: Kellogg 4722
Missouri: University 5027
Nebraska: Midlands 5104
New York: Antun 5681, August 5698, Fleming 6014
Pennsylvania: Hoffman 8062
Rhode Island: Perkins 8470
Texas: Oppenheimer 9101
Virginia: **Delmar 9429**
Wisconsin: Birnschein 9783, Inbusch 9847

People with HIV/AIDS

Alabama: Black 12, Ireland 39
California: Emanuel 480, Moonwalk 845, Small 1049

Colorado: Bright 1241
Florida: Caring 1920
Georgia: Abreu 2431
Missouri: **Bohm 4871**
New Jersey: Freelander 5353
New Mexico: Con 5611
New York: **Farkas 5988**, **Sparkplug 6830**
North Carolina: Glenn 7111
Oregon: Wessinger 7826
Pennsylvania: Hoffman 8062
Texas: D3 8793, Holloway 8946
Virginia: **Delmar 9429**

People with intellectual disabilities

North Carolina: Howe 7132
Texas: Holloway 8946
Washington: Everett 9592
West Virginia: Parlin 9762

People with physical disabilities

Alabama: Black 12, Ireland 39
California: Atkinson 259, Gellert 550, Horwitz 633, KNU 713, Miller 833
Colorado: **Fishback 1270**
Connecticut: Gross 1473
Florida: Brighton 1899, Jacobsen 2123
Georgia: Abreu 2431
Illinois: Family 2864, Gantz 2900
Indiana: Ayres 3342
Michigan: Oreffice 4528
Nebraska: Midlands 5104
Nevada: Matley 5176
New York: August 5698, Black 5754, BTMU 5795, French 6032, Gerstman 6074, Henshel 6192
North Carolina: Glenn 7111, Strowd 7258
Ohio: Walker 7630
Pennsylvania: Child 7923, Hoffman 8062, Mill 8172
Rhode Island: Littlefield 8441, York 8507
Tennessee: **Fugitive 8618**
Texas: Holloway 8946, Johnston 8972, Proctor 9139
Virginia: **Delmar 9429**
Washington: Wilkens 9724
West Virginia: Parlin 9762
Wisconsin: Inbusch 9847, Marshfield 9878
Wyoming: **Schultz 9986**

People with psychosocial disabilities

Alabama: Black 12, Ireland 39
Arkansas: Olds 210
California: Horwitz 633, Margoes 795
Connecticut: Fippinger 1450
Florida: Brighton 1899, Wilson-Wood 2408
Georgia: Abreu 2431
Illinois: Bulkley, 2765, Family 2864, **Mead 3100**, Meyer 3106
Indiana: Ayres 3342
Nebraska: Midlands 5104
Nevada: Matley 5176
New York: August 5698, BTMU 5795, French 6032
North Carolina: Glenn 7111, Howe 7132, Strowd 7258
Ohio: Ridgecliff 7560
Oregon: Elwood 7761
Pennsylvania: Child 7923, Hoffman 8062, Mill 8172, Murphy 8185
Rhode Island: Dwinell 8403
Texas: Foundation 8869, Holloway 8946, Johnston 8972, Oppenheimer 9101
Virginia: **Delmar 9429**
Washington: Everett 9592, Wilkens 9724
West Virginia: Parlin 9762
Wisconsin: Marshfield 9878

People with vision impairments

Alabama: Black 12, Ireland 39
California: Bancroft-Clair 270, Bundy 360, Fusenot 541, Gifts 553, Hohnstein 629, Horwitz 633, Kanel 688, Kelly 697, Wertheimer 1173

Connecticut: Acorn 1385, Dennett 1432, Lebovitz 1506
Delaware: Splawn 1749
Florida: Boston 1898, Lelash 2178, Thurman 2375, Whitman 2404
Georgia: Abreu 2431
Illinois: Adams 2696, Bartsch 2722, Bulkley, 2765, Luehring 3065
Indiana: Noecker 3424
Kansas: Family 3575
Maryland: Cole 3839
Massachusetts: Makepeace 4185, Progin 4247, Stemberg 4313
Michigan: Ratner 4548
Missouri: Service 4998, Thorp 5020, Toutz 5023
Nebraska: Midlands 5104
New Hampshire: Cochran 5208
New Jersey: Pantirer 5487, **Patel 5492**
New York: Antun 5681, August 5698, Fraydun 6029, **Goldfein 6096**, Goldstone 6102, Milton 6497, Pollock 6616, Selis 6774, Trimble 6910
North Carolina: Hamill 7115, Hoffman 7128, Shingleton 7241
Ohio: Brews 7332, Frohman 7411, Jenkins 7464
Pennsylvania: Bannerot-Lappe 7854, Chase 7921, Child 7923, Eakins 7968, Edwards 7972, Edwards 7973, Hoffman 8062, Mendel 8168, Mill 8172, Patterson 8205, Tabas 8312, Wakefield 8339
Rhode Island: Peacock 8469, Perkins 8470
Texas: Alexander 8696, Hervey 8932, Montgomery 9070, Sherman 9192
Virginia: **Delmar 9429**
Washington: DeFalco 9585
West Virginia: Huntington 9754, Parlin 9762
Wisconsin: Birnschein 9783, Inbusch 9847

Performing arts

Alabama: Caddell 19, Viro 73
Alaska: Juneau 88
Arizona: Cadeau 104, Grossman 126, Hughes 130
California: Alafi 235, Beam 287, Beattie 289, Beim 293, Bryan 355, Cirila 405, Community 421, Davies 444, Evening 487, Feintech 502, Fox 525, Friedman 531, Gross 587, Hayman 606, Helmstetter 616, Johnson 670, KNU 713, Lester 748, Perenin 914, Plum 929, Potiker 932, Small 1049, Stack 1073, Thornton 1115, Traub-Brittan 1127, Wattis 1161
Colorado: Fortune 1273, Spencer 1356
Connecticut: Acorn 1385, Bender 1405, Harris 1478, Low 1513, Roberts 1552, Winokur 1597
Delaware: Bennett 1618, Bulova 1633, Rosenfeld 1732
District of Columbia: Dimick 1803
Florida: Bartner 1869, Bastien 1872, Baulch 1873, Caring 1920, Chanin 1934, Couch 1953, Day 1965, De 1967, Five 2002, Hill 2097, Kanders 2136, Kane 2137, Koski 2157, Leiser 2177, Lenkin 2179, Livingston 2187, Pearce 2252, Price 2267, Scharlin 2315, Stern 2350, Yerrid 2420
Georgia: A.E.M. 2430, Barnett 2441, Graves 2496, Illges 2518, Lee 2540, Piedmont 2566, Searcy 2583
Idaho: Boise 2666
Illinois: Bernoudy 2738, Dancing 2822, Delavan 2825, Fischer 2874, Frank 2885, Frankel 2886, Generations 2908, Gray 2927, Larsen 3038, Lohengrin 3059, MacDonald 3068, Maddox 3069, McNally 3097, Millard 3109, Mitchell 3120, Munson 3130, Murphy 3132, Pangburn 3161, Ryan 3219, Simon 3247, Staley 3263, Walker 3308
Indiana: Crescent-Cresline-Wabash 3365, Gammon 3385, Hillenbrand 3393
Iowa: Deardorf 3485, Howe 3510
Kansas: Insurance 3587, Wiedemann 3642
Kentucky: Kentucky 3669, Opera 3684
Maryland: Bernard 3822, Cafritz 3830, Davis 3844, **Fox 3864**, Gordon 3873, Hyman 3887, Slavin 3954
Massachusetts: Hale 4113, Haley 4114, Hauben 4120, Melvina 4197, Murphy 4214, Permanent 4239, **Robbins-de 4266**, Rockland 4267, Shapiro 4290
Michigan: Burdick-Thorne 4402, Community 4410, Community 4411, Cummings 4417, Hartwick 4462, Havirmill 4463, Keller 4481, Leven 4492, Mariel

4504, Morley 4518, Welch 4610, Whitman 4615,
Williams 4618
Minnesota: Boss 4646, Chadwick-Loher 4655,
Dellwood 4665, Tennant 4798, Thorpe 4800
Missouri: Bland 4868, Copaken 4888, Siteman 5006,
University 5027
Nebraska: Assurity 5068, Midlands 5104, Owen 5108
Nevada: Andress 5132, Houssels 5163
New Hampshire: Dunn 5212, Seigel 5231, Woodbury
5238
New Jersey: Cantor 5285, Cohen 5299, Conant 5302,
Gamper 5361, Holzer 5396, McCrane 5464, O'Neal
5481, Riskin 5511, Smith 5539
New York: Aeroflex 5647, American 5664, Amphion
5671, Anderson 5674, Aresty 5687, Arrison 5690,
Athens 5696, Bank 5710, Bergson 5738, Bernhill
5741, **Blinken 5757**, Block 5759, Blue 5763,
Chasanoff 5833, Cullman 5887, Dixon 5919,
Dobson 5921, Eggleston 5946, Erpf 5968, Ettl
5970, Ferguson 5999, Fitt 6010, Furman 6045,
Geier 6064, Goodman 6107, Gordon 6110,
Gramercy 6122, Hahn 6157, Hajim 6158, Harjen
6167, **Henson 6194**, Heyman 6201, Heyward
6202, Hiler 6207, Hopkins 6224, IF 6237, Johnson
6267, Krimendahl/Saint-Amand 6346, L 6353,
Lassalle 6366, Leonhardt 6381, Liberman 6396,
Lubo 6417, Lucky 6420, MAT 6450, Meyer 6487,
Netter 6525, Newman 6531, Newman 6532,
Offensend 6550, Peckham 6583, Performing 6586,
Phaedrus 6598, Reiss 6662, RJL 6675, Santvoord
6727, Sheafer 6789, Siegel 6797, Sommer 6825,
Sumitomo 6876, Thiem 6898, Tisch 6900, Tuch
6915, Utopia 6923, Vernon 6928, Weingarten
6953, Weininger 6954, Weinman 6955, **Woodland
6989**, Woodmere 6990
North Carolina: Billingsley 7052, Post 7213, Silverman
7244
Ohio: Alpaugh 7302, Anderson 7305, Andrews 7307,
Corbett 7363, **Elisha-Bolton 7387**, Frohman 7411,
Frost 7412, Frost-Parker 7413, Hieronymus 7448,
Knoll 7483, LKC 7501, Loeb 7503, Morley 7532,
Schey 7571
Oklahoma: Barthelmes 7661, Goddard 7684, Kerr
7693
Oregon: Mentor 7796
Pennsylvania: Amaranth 7838, **Arronson 7844**, Bon-Ton
7884, Brooks 7898, Carnahan-Jackson 7917,
Dietrich 7958, Grumbacher 8028, Hulme 8069,
Miller 8173, Mukaiyama-Rice 8183, Roberts 8240,
Roemer 8242, Saramar 8253, Stein 8298, Tippins 8318,
Sweigart 8311, Teleflex 8314, Tippins 8318
South Dakota: Engelsma 8563
Tennessee: Atticus 8582, Cole 8600, Eskind 8611,
Eskind 8612, Fleming 8615, Gaylord 8620, Kite
8639, New 8654, Seidman 8672
Texas: Anderson 8704, Barrow 8719, Boeing 8733,
Brodsky 8747, Bunyard 8755, Cemo 8765,
Deakins 8804, Dedman 8807, Duncan 8833,
Garvey 8884, Hallam 8910, Halperin 8912, Hanley
8916, Hegi 8926, Hicks 8936, Kahn 8978, Knox
8999, Littauer 9021, Lowdon 9025, Mithoff 9068,
Moss 9076, Muse 9080, Paulos 9120, Proctor
9139, Saulsbury 9175, Schulze 9182, Skokos
9200, Vaughan 9248
Utah: Schmidt 9349
Virginia: Andreas 9388, Cartledge 9414, **Delmar
9429**, Gifford 9457, R 9518, Rimora 9524, Zeiders
9557
Washington: Baker 9566, Bungie 9576, Echo 9590,
Graham 9609, Kaleidoscope 9641, Magdalen
9658, Sarkowsky 9688, Worthington 9729
West Virginia: Vecellio 9770
Wisconsin: Christensen 9795, Dawes 9803, Frautschi
9822, Gardner 9825, Highlands 9841, Hunt 9845,
Modine 9889, RITE-HITE 9915, Rosemann 9919,
Schoenleber 9924, Stateline 9937, Weyers 9959
Wyoming: Jaquith 9975

Performing arts education

Connecticut: Axe-Houghton 1397, Goldfarb 1467
Illinois: Glossberg 2916
Maryland: Shapiro 3949

Massachusetts: Durant 4072, Hauben 4120, **Kahn
4143**, Perry 4240
Michigan: Thoman 4590
Missouri: Curry 4892
New Hampshire: Wutz 5239
New York: Alexander 5654, Family 5984, Hahn 6157,
Lassalle 6366, Phaedrus 6598
Pennsylvania: Boscia 7887, Shenk 8274
Tennessee: Cole 8600
Washington: Longbrake 9655
West Virginia: Fine 9745

Pharmacies

North Carolina: Fox 7103
Pennsylvania: Blue 7879

Pharmacology

California: **Parsemus 904**
New Jersey: Broomfield 5275

Philanthropy

Alabama: Anderson 6
Arizona: Robson 160, Shultz 168
California: Adelman 231, Berry 309, Cerri 384, Clara
406, Combs-Hughes 419, Cramblit 432, Dass 443,
Family 493, **Floyd 513**, Greenberg 579, Hand 595,
Ignatius 648, Jubas 680, Katz 693, Manchester
788, Mann 790, Mills 834, Ramsay 952, Rappaport
953, Romano 982, Sanders 999, Shayne 1032,
Spungen 1071
Colorado: Fund 1274, Grosvenor 1283, Leighty 1311
Connecticut: Bradley 1411, DeNunzio 1433, Fauth
1445, **Friends 1455**, **MacInnis 1515**, Smith 1572
Delaware: **Jackman 1683**, Praxis 1723
District of Columbia: Arcana 1786
Florida: Burgoon 1908, Long 2189, McCabe 2201,
Sullivan 2357
Georgia: Ward 2605
Illinois: Beeghly 2730, **Build 2764**, Dunning 2841,
Istock 2991, Knight 3022, Metzner 3104, Mirapaul
3119, Podolsky 3178, Schneider 3228, Steinmetz
3267
Indiana: Agness 3340, Greene 3390, J 3399, Scott
3446, Vevay-Switzerland 3462
Iowa: Blin 3476, Hills 3507
Kansas: Buford 3562, Olofson 3613
Kentucky: Mulhollem 3680
Louisiana: Briggs 3714, Operation 3744, Parkside
3745
Maine: Boulos 3768, Hudson 3783
Maryland: Bresler 3828, Clifton 3836, Israelson 3888,
Kohn 3897
Massachusetts: Astra 4006, Boger 4023, Fleming
4092, Hurston 4138, Nelson 4219, Rollstone 4270
Michigan: Balk 4383, Barron 4384, Degroot 4423,
Jospey 4473, Onequest 4527
Minnesota: Cornwall 4660, Felhaber, 4681, **Fingerhut
4683**, Garmar 4694
Missouri: Ross 4986
Nevada: West 5197
New Hampshire: Milford 5225, Oxford 5228
New Jersey: **Garcia 5362**, Kutnick 5437, Perricone
5497, Pinkin 5502
New Mexico: Akerson 5604
New York: **Alexander 5653**, Barney 5717, Blodgett
5760, Chernoff 5838, Cole 5868, Cowen 5882,
Eberhart 5942, Fagin 5978, Franco 6024, Franklin
6028, Goldstein 6101, Healy 6179, Hewitt 6200,
Johnson-Stillman 6271, Kornreich 6341,
Mastrocola 6449, McCormick 6459, Palisades
6569, Palm 6571, Reich 6658, Rubin 6707,
Schonfeld 6746, Sillins 6799, Summit 6877,
Tanner-Frank 6893, Troubh 6911, Vyeshaya 6934,
Wolf 6986
North Carolina: Gordon 7112, Meserve 7182, Wagner
7275, **Weyenberg 7285**
Ohio: Beecher 7321, Callahan 7346, DeHoff 7376,
Jones 7470, Rosenthal 7563, Sears-Swetland
7581

Oklahoma: Drabek 7673, Oklahoma 7711
Oregon: Ackley 7740, Jonas 7778, Jurrens 7780,
Klamath 7784
Pennsylvania: Alley 7837, Fine 7993, Gibson 8016,
Hager 8035, Jordan 8082, Secrist 8267, Smith
8284, Spain 8292, Stott 8304, Winokur 8362
Rhode Island: **Schoellkopf 8482**
South Carolina: Davis 8521, Love 8532
Tennessee: Kappa 8637
Texas: Beghini 8724, Cargill 8761, Collins 8780, Fash
8848, Gray-Pampa 8900, Mitte 9069, Phoenix
9128, Sharma 9190, **Smith 9203**
Washington: Levitan 9653, Remala 9683
Wisconsin: Davis 9802, Domer 9808, Doolittle 9809,
Fromstein 9824, Gunther 9833, Mound 9891

Philosophy

California: Johnson 666
Nevada: **Wood 5201**
Pennsylvania: Rosenberg 8244

Photography

Connecticut: Greenhill 1472
Kentucky: Kentucky 3669
New York: Englebardt 5965, Hite 6213, Lubo 6417,
Silverstein 6803, Zenkel 7023
Texas: Meyerson 9062

Physical and earth sciences

Florida: Sunburst 2359
New Hampshire: Dorr 5211
New York: **Eppley 5967**
North Carolina: Horvat 7130
Pennsylvania: Quaker 8228, Society 8289

Physical fitness

Kansas: Payless 3614
Massachusetts: Vela 4341

Physical therapy

Wyoming: **Schultz 9986**

Physics

Minnesota: **Wagner 4804**

Planetariums

Florida: Hoerner 2102
Illinois: Petrovich 3174
Montana: Taylor 5064
New York: Ferguson 5999
North Carolina: Chatham 7074

Plant biodiversity

California: Money-Arenz 844
Minnesota: Terhuly 4799
Nebraska: Kinder 5099
New Jersey: Ellis 5333
New York: Johnson-Stillman 6271
Pennsylvania: Brooks 7899
Texas: Knox 8999

Police agencies

Illinois: Millard 3110
Michigan: Roscommon 4552
Ohio: Loeb 7504
Texas: Fertitta 8852, Kabacoff 8977

Political organizations

New York: Yeager 7004

Political science

Washington: Quest 9681

Population studies

California: Bear 288
Connecticut: Shenandoah 1568
Minnesota: Bell 4638
Ohio: Linnemann 7498
Pennsylvania: Price 8225
Washington: Dudley 9588

Prenatal care

Maryland: CSG 3842
Ohio: Gale 7414, Mehl 7523

Presbyterianism

Alabama: Dixon 26
Delaware: Day 1654
Georgia: Baker 2439, **Faith 2477**, Holland-Underwood 2508, Marshall 2545, SCS 2582
Kentucky: Spriggs 3695
Louisiana: Merkle 3737
Minnesota: Gage 4692
New York: Mule 6515, Willmott 6978
Pennsylvania: Wood 8367
Texas: Fair 8844, **McCreless 9049**
Virginia: Houff 9473, Lane 9486

Preventive care

Pennsylvania: Blue 7879

Printmaking

New York: Artists 5692, **Gottlieb 6114**

Prostate cancer

Arizona: C 103
Connecticut: Finn 1449
Delaware: Bresnan 1628
Illinois: Grossinger 2933
Massachusetts: McCutchin-Collins 4193
Michigan: Shapiro 4566
Texas: Mischer 9067

Protestantism

Alabama: Ireland 39, King 44, Ratliff 57, Strain 68, Sumners/Nelson/Thompson 69, Upchurch, 72, Warren 75, Watson 76, Williams 77
Arizona: Barton 99, Drexler 113, Forsberg 119, Jones 136, Long 141, Shultz 168, Stevens 175, Van 179
Arkansas: Dunklin, 194, Hickingbotham 199, Merkle 203, Union 219
California: Atkinson 259, CNC 410, Daly 440, Gill 555, Handley 596, Harris 601, Hawley 605, **His 623**, Hohnstein 629, JDH 660, Kanel 688, Kimbo 705, Nelson 860, Nelson 861, Palo 901, Reveas 967, Smith-Walker 1057, Stearns 1078, Stewart 1083, Tecumseh 1105, Thagard 1109, Tomlinson 1123, Webb 1162
Connecticut: Acorn 1385, Fuller 1460, Grant 1470, Inglesea 1487, Lee 1507, Lodewick 1512, MLE 1526, Morrow 1527, Panwy 1539, Roberts 1551, Sorenson-Pearson 1574, Storr 1575, Wheeler 1594
Delaware: Brown-Whitworth 1632, City 1642, Foundation 1664, Lighten 1698, Ryerson 1736, Swift, 1754
District of Columbia: Peet 1827
Florida: Anderson 1845, Anderson 1847, Brown 1905, Burnett 1910, Burnett 1911, Burnetti 1912, Draft 1981, Finch 2000, Foundation 2015, Fox 2016, Friend 2026, Godsey 2043, Hahn 2072, HI 2093, Hicks 2094, Holloway 2107, Hornik 2111, **Hutchison 2117**, Krause 2158, Lowry 2191, Potter

2263, Rogers 2290, Rogers 2292, Sharing 2330, Stafford 2346, Tharpe 2369, Turner 2381, **Uncle 2383**, Vanneck-Bailey 2384, Verner 2386
Georgia: 10/1 2429, Akers 2432, Arnold 2436, Beard-Payne 2442, Broadfield 2449, Canipe 2452, Chandler 2455, Colston 2464, Community 2465, Fickling 2478, **Gage 2482**, Gholston 2487, Graham 2495, Graves 2496, Inman 2519, Jeter 2524, Klump 2533, Knox 2534, Looney 2542, Nabors 2555, Patrick 2562, Pattillo 2563, Pope 2568, Price 2569, Rackley 2571, Rice 2575, SF 2585, Terwilliger 2593, Vaughter 2599, Vogel 2600, Voight 2601, Williams 2612
Illinois: Best 2739, Branstad 2755, Buntrock 2766, Copeland 2807, Coulter 2813, Edgerly 2847, Family 2864, Gloyd 2917, **Krasberg-Mason 3029**, Lancaster 3035, Luehring 3065, Pinnell 3176, Pitzman 3177, Simpson 3248, Twomey 3298, Wesselink 3319, Whitwam 3321, Woods 3331, Wright 3333
Indiana: Burris 3352, Fenech 3380, Gibson 3386, Mulzer 3420, Nugent 3425, Raymond 3436, Salin 3442, Thrush-Thompson 3460, Vann 3461
Iowa: Busse 3478, Farver 3491, Gartner 3496, Henry 3505, Howe 3510, Krause 3516
Kansas: DeVore 3573, Mistler 3606, Swearingen 3631, Taylor 3632, Wiedemann 3642
Kentucky: Coffey 3650, Haskins 3661, Horn 3664, Jones 3667, Namaste 3682
Louisiana: Havens 3727, Huie-Dellmon 3729, Lake 3732, New 3742, Showers 3753
Maine: Reny 3802
Maryland: DelSignore 3847, Williams 3986
Massachusetts: Clementi 4050, Encourage 4082, England 4083, Fraser 4097, Hale 4113, Henderson 4128, King 4156, McCutchin-Collins 4193, Mitchell 4205, Videtta 4343
Michigan: Baum 4387, Clay 4409, Gordon 4456, Hayden 4464, Kay 4480, LoPrete 4496, McNally 4510, Mills 4515, Springview 4575, Technical 4588, **Triford 4597**, Tyler-Little 4599, Welch 4610
Minnesota: Acorn 4623, Arsher 4630, Bumgarner 4649, Dell 4664, McCoy 4742, Merritt 4744, Pinson 4762, Wells 4812
Mississippi: Graeber 4839, Harris 4841, Hood, 4843, Pruet 4851, Seal, 4853
Missouri: Finley 4910, Grant 4918, Hermann 4927, Herschend 4928, Keske 4937, Lambert 4942, Morgan 4963, Obertate 4972, Pearl 4977, Sayler-Hawkins 4993, Toutz 5023
Montana: Boe 5045, Broadbent 5046
Nebraska: Beer 5073, Kilbourne 5097, Lienemann 5100, Mapes 5103, Walker 5126, Yount 5130
Nevada: Carver 5143
New Hampshire: Lion's 5220, McIninch 5224
New Jersey: Browder 5277, Freedman 5352, Greetin 5377, Harms 5385, Huffhines 5397, **Ju 5410**, Keller 5418, Kurr 5435, Silverman 5536, Snyder 5540, Snyder 5542, Twin 5563
New Mexico: Forrest 5614, **Watersheds 5628**
New York: Anderson 5675, Aresty 5686, Boustead 5769, Coles 5871, **Crane 5884**, Darrah 5900, Family 5982, Ficalora 6002, Follett 6016, French 6032, Gant 6054, Gilliam 6078, Grubman 6147, Hiler 6207, Hohmann 6218, JI 6260, Kleinschmidt 6326, L 6353, Makioka 6436, Nuhn 6544, Offensend 6550, Peale 6582, Psalm 6633, Saunders 6733, Scott 6761, **Shatford 6788**
North Carolina: Arcadia 7040, Barker 7044, Belk 7046, Boddie 7054, Brown 7059, Chaley 7072, Edgar 7088, Ellison 7090, Flowers 7099, Gambrell 7105, Griffin 7113, Haney 7116, Helb 7122, Hudson 7133, Ketchum 7146, Krauss 7153, Matthews 7174, McGuire, 7177, McLean 7177, McLendon 7179, Morisey 7191, Nanney 7198, Nivison 7201, Peeler 7207, Piedmont 7209, Plansoen 7211, **Rixson 7223**, Rogers 7228, Sherrard 7240, Sites 7245, Sloan 7246, Smith 7249, Summer 7261, Wells 7283, Whitener 7286, Yount 7292
North Dakota: Fedje 7296
Ohio: Baird 7314, Geary, 7419, **Highfield 7450**, Ingle 7462, Jennings 7466, Jordan 7471, Knoll 7483, Lindner 7497, Mangano 7511, Miller 7527,

Scotford 7579, Seifert 7584, Sheely 7590, Turben 7622, Van 7625, Van 7626, Welty 7635, Wildermuth 7637, Williams 7639
Oklahoma: Brannin 7662, Everest 7676, Howard 7689, Massey 7705, Stone 7721, Welch 7732
Oregon: Coffman 7750, Rietman 7809
Pennsylvania: Armstrong 7843, Beels 7858, Black 7875, Bradley 7889, Brooks 7898, Buck 7903, Crawford 7945, Engle 7982, Gauss 8014, Gilmore 8017, Hill 8055, II 8074, Knox 8101, Langner 8111, Lewis 8124, Mason 8147, Mayer 8152, Moore 8177, Moyer 8180, Mudge 8181, Norbell 8195, Plainfield 8217, Reidler 8233, Smith 8281, Snyder 8287, Snyder 8288, Staley 8296, Sweigart 8311, Whalley 8353, Williams 8358, Woodall 8368
Rhode Island: Field 8407, McWethy 8453, Siemons 8490, Smith 8493
South Carolina: Campbell 8515, Coker 8519, Collins 8520, Hendricks 8527, Love 8532, Lutz 8533, Near 8536, Stevens 8541
South Dakota: Engelsma 8563, Peterson 8572
Tennessee: Agape 8580, Cornerstone 8602, EBS 8610, Firstfruits 8614, Grandview 8625, Hollingsworth 8629, Houghland 8630, Hutcheson 8631, Knight 8640, McGehee 8648, Pattee 8656, Pfeffer 8659, Sunlight 8681, Wilson 8686
Texas: Anderson 8705, Astin 8710, Beaird 8720, Bergstrom 8727, Bloxom, 8731, Bowers 8736, Cargill 8761, Community 8782, Cook 8786, Dauphin 8798, Dedman 8807, Dedman, 8808, Donnell 8821, Dooley 8822, Dubose 8828, Faith 8846, Farris 8847, Fenner 8850, Folsom 8863, Fowlston 8871, Garvey 8884, Genovese 8887, George 8888, Go 8891, Gottlieb 8894, Griffin 8902, Guinn 8906, Hallam 8910, Hallberg 8911, Heavin 8925, Helm 8928, Hillcrest 8939, Hofheinz 8942, Hofstetter 8943, Hollandsworth 8945, Horween 8952, Howard 8954, II 8958, Jastrow 8967, Johnson 8969, Keown 8986, Klein 8997, Lilly 9019, Lloyd 9022, Mayfield 9044, Mays 9045, McCoy 9048, Mewhinney 9060, Meyer 9061, O'Hare 9095, One 9096, Orr 9104, Papadopoulos 9113, Paulos 9120, Perkins 9125, RDM 9146, Ross 9164, Ross 9165, **Ryrie 9169**, Schoener 9180, SCP 9185, Skokos 9200, Smith 9201, Smith 9202, Starnes 9214, Tolleson 9238, Tucker 9243, Weir 9268, Williams 9281, Wynne 9296
Utah: Langdon 9336
Vermont: Harper 9373
Virginia: Backer 9389, Better 9396, Brandt 9403, **Brown 9407**, Cartledge 9414, Cobbs 9422, **Delmar 9429**, Flippo 9449, Harris 9467, Harris 9468, Honey 9471, MAIHS 9497, Meador 9500, Pensmore 9509, Tesco 9541, Treakle 9543
Washington: Boeschoten 9571, Morningside 9665
West Virginia: Carter 9741, Hott 9753, Starvaggi 9767
Wisconsin: Braun 9787, Frautschi 9822, Gordon 9831, Hansen 9835, Hunt 9845, Jones 9855, Kachel 9857, Kohl 9864, Martin 9879, Meyer 9886, Murray 9892, Rewald 9913, Rosemann 9919, Smith 9932
Wyoming: C 9966, Surrena 9994

Protestants

Connecticut: Fuller 1460
Kentucky: Coffey 3650

Psychology and behavioral science

California: Traina 1126
New Jersey: Pacific 5485
Ohio: Ridgecliff 7560

Public administration

California: Gross 587, Von 1147
Colorado: Goodwin 1279, Heginbotham 1289, Joslin-Needham 1300, Krieble 1308
Connecticut: Proctor 1545
Delaware: Milliken 1711

Illinois: Constans-Culver 2805, Geneseo 2909, Listeman 3055, McCauley 3085, **Mead 3100**
Iowa: Van 3539
Massachusetts: Crane 4058, **Spero 4304**
Michigan: Biederman 4391, St. 4576
Minnesota: Onan 4754
Missouri: Cray 4890, Moss 4964
New York: Burrows 5803, Pratt-Northam 6625
North Carolina: Fairfield 7095, Hunt 7134
Ohio: Baird 7314, Frost 7412, Jennings 7466, Seasongood 7582
Oklahoma: Kerr 7693
Pennsylvania: Emporium 7980, Grundy 8029, Schuylkill 8263
Rhode Island: Seed 8484
South Carolina: Horne 8528
Texas: Bertha 8729, Boeing 8733
Virginia: Community 9426, **Tara 9540**
West Virginia: Bowen 9737
Wisconsin: Junginger 9856

Public affairs

Alabama: Black 12
Arizona: Hansen 127
California: Bochnowski 325, Corwin 428, Furth 540, Jorgensen 676, Penney 913, Rappaport 953, Teshinsky 1108
Colorado: Broomfield 1242, Krieble 1308, Staley 1357, Woodford 1382
Delaware: Berning 1620, **Gloria 1670**, Just 1688, Kaye 1690
Florida: Hollo 2105, Phillips 2260
Georgia: Beckman 2443, Oxford 2561, Waffle 2602
Idaho: Boise 2666
Illinois: Allen-Heath 2701, Bergstein 2735, Chicago 2787, Communitas 2801, Diamond 2829, **Landau 3036**, New 3136
Indiana: Rush 3441, Vevay-Switzerland 3462
Maine: Coates 3773
Maryland: **Goldberg 3872**
Massachusetts: Bigbird 4020
Michigan: Community 4411, Meritor, 4511, Plym 4542, Redies 4549, Riley 4550
Minnesota: Albright 4625
Missouri: MFA 4960, Morgan 4963, Todd 5022, Walker 5035
Nebraska: Farr 5079
New Jersey: Amboy 5246, Giants 5369, Selective 5528
New York: Abelard 5635, AGB 5650, American 5663, American 5664, Bernhill 5741, Brandt 5777, Cader 5807, Casey 5819, Fuchsberg 6044, Georgia 6071, Heilig 6183, IF 6237, Jacobson 6255, JKW 6263, **Milbank 6490**, MZL 6518, Ravitch 6651, Slade 6809, Snyder 6819, Steinberg 6857
Ohio: Athens 7311, **Eaton 7383**, Hamilton 7435, Lundgard 7508
Oklahoma: Brown 7664
Oregon: **Conklin 7754**
Pennsylvania: Arkema 7842, Beach 7855, McKinney 8161, Penn 8208, Quaker 8228, Wenger 8351
Rhode Island: Barton 8385, Seymour 8485
South Dakota: Barger 8555, Watertown 8576
Texas: Boeing 8733, Bright 8743, Brownsville 8752, Burch 8756, Foundation 8869, Hartman 8920, Steen 9216
Vermont: Cohen 9369, Harper 9373
Washington: Dudley 9588, Herbold 9620, Lea 9652
West Virginia: Appalachian 9734
Wisconsin: Kenosha 9862, Modine 9889, Tellier 9946

Public health

California: Gordon 573
Connecticut: Lavietes 1505
Delaware: **Gloria 1670**
Georgia: Georgia 2484, Harrison 2502
Indiana: Decatur 3367
Massachusetts: Koplow 4159
Missouri: Longer 4949
Ohio: Austin-Bailey 7312, Ginn 7425, Health 7442, Osteopathic 7545

Texas: P 9108
Virginia: Loeb 9493

Public housing

California: OZ 896

Public interest law

Illinois: **Landau 3036**
Pennsylvania: Jackson 8078

Public libraries

Alabama: Anderson 6, Brown 16
California: Borok 331, Braddock 336, Church 403, Community 421, Johnson 670, Kelly 697, Sammut 996, Seaver 1026, **Shapell 1031**, Smith 1056, Tanimura 1103, Waller 1152
Connecticut: Axe-Houghton 1397, Caldwell 1415, Crosswicks 1425, Dime 1438, Finn 1449, Howard 1484, Hume 1485, Lebovitz 1506, Martin 1520
Delaware: Talbott 1757
District of Columbia: Westport 1838
Florida: Brinckerhoff 1900, Rogers 2291, Whiting 2403
Georgia: Harrison 2502, Price-Campbell 2570
Illinois: 1335 2691, Allen-Heath 2701, Bound 2751, Citadel 2791, Danielson 2824, Fabyan 2862, George 2911, Hardiek 2953, Highland 2970, Lebus 3043, Munson 3130, Saemann 3220, Smysor 3255, Sulzer 3277, Vail 3301
Iowa: Beckwith 3473, Forster 3494, Giacoletto 3499, McDonald 3520, Ryan 3531, Schildberg 3532, Woodward 3549
Kansas: South 3628
Kentucky: Trim 3702
Maine: Kennebec 3785
Maryland: Moore 3917, St. 3959
Massachusetts: Dedham 4067, Easthampton 4076, Lingos 4177, **Memorial 4198**, Pilgrim 4245, Progin 4247, Savage 4280, Whittemore 4359
Michigan: Barstow 4385, Hartwick 4462, Kantzler 4478, Skiles 4572, St. 4576, Welch 4610
Minnesota: Boss 4645, Foundation 4688, Regis 4770
Missouri: Moss 4964
Montana: Boe 5045
Nebraska: Cope 5077, Kinder 5099
New Hampshire: Kimball 5216, Tillotson 5234
New Jersey: **Akhoury 5243**, Savin 5520
New York: Alexander 5656, Anderson 5674, Bank 5710, Fleming 6014, Greenspan 6134, Iroquois 6250, Meade 6467, Offensend 6550, Plunkett 6611, Selis 6774, Sherman 6792, Truman 6912, Walsh 6942, Woodward 6993, Yeager 7004
North Carolina: Belk 7046, Cary 7069, Hackbarth 7114, Herndon 7125, Hoffman 7128, Ragland, 7216, Rostan 7232
Ohio: Christen 7353, Dienstberger 7379, Lazarus 7493, Rosenberry 7562, Van 7626, Young 7652
Pennsylvania: Bergman 7863, Bryer 7902, Clark 7927, Emporium 7980, Hoffman 8063, Mukaiyama-Rice 8183, Packer 8201, Patterson 8205, Reidler 8233, Richards 8236, Schautz 8257, Shenk 8274, Smith 8280, Thomas 8316, Whalley 8353
Rhode Island: Ames 8379, Bailey 8384, Dwinell 8403, Jacbel 8426, Shea 8486, Slemons 8490, Washington 8500
South Carolina: Sunshine 8544
Tennessee: Jewell 8633, Pettway 8658
Texas: Freed 8873, King 8992
Virginia: Treakle 9543
Washington: Ferguson 9596
Wisconsin: AnnMarie 9774, Gordon 9830, Hicks 9840, Junginger 9856, Manitowoc 9876, ROS 9918, Seeds 9925, Webcrafters-Frautschi 9957, Witte, 9962
Wyoming: StoneRiver 9991, Tate 9995

Public policy

California: Anderson 244, Garabedian 545, McKay 815, Rappaport 953, Theroux 1110
Colorado: Hanson 1286, Krieble 1308
Connecticut: Greenhill 1472
District of Columbia: Coleman, 1796
Florida: Miller 2213
Georgia: University 2597
Illinois: Danielson 2824, **New 3137**, Rossman 3211
Maryland: Weiss 3982
Massachusetts: Henderson 4127, Rose 4271
Michigan: Oreffice 4528, Whitman 4615
New York: **Stern 6862**
North Carolina: Redwoods 7218
Ohio: Armington 7309
Pennsylvania: Eberly 7969, Maple 8139
Rhode Island: Dwinell 8403
South Carolina: Cato 8516
Texas: Baldridge 8715
Utah: Catalyst 9313
Virginia: Cedars 9416
Wisconsin: Roddis 9916, Windway 9961

Public transportation

Georgia: Athens 2437
New York: Mabardi 6428

Public utilities

South Carolina: Lutz 8533

Public/private ventures

Oregon: Elwood 7761

Publishing

Arkansas: Hussman 201
District of Columbia: Patterson 1826
Florida: Godbold 2041, Livingston 2187, Tampa 2362
Illinois: Chicago 2787
New York: Bennett 5737, Snow 6818, Tribune 6909
Ohio: Kamm 7473
Texas: Fash 8848

Racquet sports

Kentucky: Boone 3649
Minnesota: Wells 4811
New York: Gordon 6111, Ruttenberg 6715, Schott 6749

Radio

California: Ward 1158, Yen 1201
Florida: Around 1854, Papper 2246
Hawaii: Shidler 2646
Illinois: **Acorn 2695**, Baird 2718
Indiana: Shafer 3449
Kansas: Cape 3563
Maryland: **Doorstep 3850**
Massachusetts: Hauben 4120, Melvina 4197, **Memorial 4198**, Perry 4240
Minnesota: Weyerhaeuser 4815
Mississippi: Crooks 4831
Montana: Greater 5054
New York: Arrison 5690, JLK 6264, Stutz 6875, Vance 6926
Ohio: Lazarus 7493
Oklahoma: Krueger 7695
Pennsylvania: Lida 8127
Tennessee: Atticus 8582
Utah: Bastian 9304, Catalyst 9313
Washington: Johnston-Fix 9634
Wyoming: C 9966

Reading promotion

California: Atkinson 259, Bank 272, Fuller 538, Lux 773, Mazda 810, Sawchuk 1010

Connecticut: Chelsea 1418, Dime 1438, Union 1590
Delaware: **TeleTech 1761**
Florida: Beall, 1876, Price 2267, Sammons 2310, Wilson-Wood 2408
Georgia: Lipscomb 2541
Hawaii: Locations 2638
Illinois: Alliant 2702, Bound 2751, Mansfield 3074
Indiana: Decatur 3367, TCU 3458
Maryland: Acacia 3807, Mental 3912
Massachusetts: **Azadoutioun 4008**, Kelsey 4148, Ramsey 4258
Michigan: Abrams 4369, Community 4411, Thoman 4590
Minnesota: Bell 4638, G&K 4691, Jostens 4720
Missouri: **Build-A-Bear 4879**
New York: BTMU 5795, Northern 6540
North Carolina: Morgan 7190
Pennsylvania: Blue 7879, Teleflex 8314, Union 8326
Rhode Island: Dwinell 8403
Tennessee: Cracker 8603
Texas: Baldridge 8715, Boeing 8733, Long 9023
Washington: Foss 9598, Furnessville 9602

Reconstructive surgery

New Jersey: **Integra 5400**

Recycling

Texas: Boeing 8733

Reform Judaism

Maryland: Small 3955
Nevada: Shulman 5185

Rehabilitation

California: Folger 515, Livingston 761, Schulte 1018
Connecticut: Acorn 1385
Florida: Chapman 1935, River 2288
Georgia: Hoyt 2514
Illinois: Almeida 2704, Bates 2725, Glossberg 2916, McNally 3097
Indiana: Bussing-Koch 3353
Missouri: St. 5012
New Jersey: Snyder 5541
New York: **Potts 6624**
North Carolina: Ribenack 7220
Ohio: Frost 7412, Musson 7534, Powers 7550
Pennsylvania: Briggs 7892, **Hitchcock 8059**, Laughlin 8114
Texas: Edwards 8837, McKee 9052, South 9209
Wisconsin: Van 9952

Rehabilitation of offenders

Minnesota: **Trust 4802**

Religion

Alabama: Bynum 18, Cooper 22, Griffin 30, Hanks 32, Harper 33, Kairos 41, Kemp 42, Loeb 47, Mitchell 50, Norquist 51, Piassick 55, Propst 56, Thompson 70, Yates 78
Arizona: C 103, Empire 116, Helms 129, Immanuel 131, Johnson 134, McKee 148, **Rosztoczy 161**, Rudge 164, Williams 182, Withycombe 184
Arkansas: Dunklin, 194, Families 196, Horn 200, Osborne 212, Wrape 222
California: Adelaide 230, Adonai 232, **Alalusi 236**, Amin 240, **Asia 257**, **Ayz 262**, Baldacci 268, Barnett 278, Bergman 304, Bigglesworth 316, Bilak 317, Boukai 334, Burrows 363, Callison 371, Casillas 379, Chisick 395, Corbalis 424, Corwin 428, Drexler 463, Feder 501, Freshwind 528, Fusenot 541, Garabedian 545, Gilleland 556, Goodall 570, Greenwood 581, Griswold 586, Grossberg 588, Hagopian 592, **Hefferlin 610**, Hellman 614, Herman 617, **His 623**, Hodges 627, Hong 631, **Hsu 637**, Ichioka 647, Jade 655, **Jain 656**, Jain 657,

Jatain 659, Kelton 698, Khoury 702, Knuppe 714, Lake 727, Lavine 733, Lennox 745, Levine 750, Lighthouse 756, Maher 783, Marchese 792, Margolis 796, McMahon 819, Miller 831, Mollath 842, Ohren 877, Open 883, **Orphan 889**, Peterson 919, Previti 937, Rabinovitch 947, Ragir 950, Reitman 964, Rush 994, Sassoon 1006, Scott 1021, Siegel 1036, SJL 1043, Sloss 1048, Smith 1052, Spielman 1067, Stein 1079, Sun 1092, Teshinsky 1108, Trust 1131, Tsao 1133, Varner 1145, Von 1148, Welfund 1169, Wharton 1178, Withim 1190, Zacky 1206, Zimmerman, 1213
Colorado: Allen 1220, Bhappu 1238, Chotin 1246, Clough 1248, Creative 1253, Living 1317, Shamrock 1353, **Vision 1373**, Wolcott 1381
Connecticut: Adams 1386, Antonacci 1395, Avery 1396, Baggins 1398, Crosswicks 1425, Curran 1427, Diageo 1437, Ferguson 1446, Finkelstein 1448, Friezo 1457, Goldfarb 1466, Huntington 1486, Jones 1489, Price 1544, Vance 1591, Zelnick/Belzberg 1602
Delaware: Babcock 1612, Caplin 1638, Cedarcrest 1639, EON 1661, Farr 1662, Gorny 1671, Hoops 1682, Just 1688, Lowndes 1701, Merrion 1707, Russell 1735, Scott 1740, Stiefel 1751, Three 1765, Van 1769, VWR 1772, Yokota 1784
District of Columbia: Dart 1800, Dickson 1802, **Merriman 1820**, Silberman 1834
Florida: Andreeff 1850, Anton 1851, Atkinson 1857, Bailey 1862, Bailey 1863, Bastien 1872, Baulch 1873, Bell 1882, Blake 1889, Cassill 1926, Chaffiot 1933, Chardonnay 1936, Clements 1945, Cohen 1948, De 1967, Doyle 1980, Duda 1983, Forman 2011, Frangakis 2017, Friedheim 2024, Fry 2027, Gagnon 2029, Givens 2038, Goetz 2044, Greater 2059, Hieronymus 2095, Hoenle 2101, Hoffman 2103, Hunter 2116, J. 2122, Knippenberg 2154, Lamoureux 2166, Landwirth 2167, Lawson 2170, Layden 2171, Lazoff 2173, Le 2175, Liebhaber 2183, Life's 2184, MAH 2193, Mary 2198, McClanathan 2202, Moye 2224, Muma 2227, Olliff 2239, Preik 2266, Price 2267, Reinhold 2280, Rosen 2294, Rothschild 2300, Samowitz 2311, Sanders 2313, Schiano 2317, Schlanger 2318, Schultz 2319, Seaman 2320, Selders 2322, Sierra 2336, Speranza 2344, Strube 2354, Verner 2386, Zimmerman 2426
Georgia: Andrews 2434, Benton 2445, Church 2460, Cook, 2468, Forehand 2479, Go 2490, **Hands 2501**, L. 2535, Lee 2540, Myfident 2554, Reynolds 2574, Strong 2590, Warren 2607, Whitepath 2611, Windolf 2614, Woodcrest 2616
Hawaii: Vidinha 2653
Idaho: Good 2673, Palmedo 2684
Illinois: Agent 2699, Ahlstrand 2700, **Appleby 2711**, Arboit 2713, Argo 2714, Baird 2717, Barr 2720, Baum 2727, Boehl 2748, Brown 2759, Burk 2768, Chapin-May 2782, Charles 2783, Clarks 2792, Cole 2798, Daeumer 2821, Donovan 2833, Dubin 2838, Eichner 2849, Engle 2855, Epaphroditus 2857, Farnham 2865, Foust 2883, Frederick 2889, Full 2894, Galter 2899, Gantz 2901, Gostomski 2925, Griffith 2930, Grumhaus, 2934, H.C.D. 2939, Hallene 2943, Hanus 2951, Harris 2956, Hess 2969, Hill 2971, Hirschmann 2973, Hodes 2974, Jocarno 3000, Kelly 3011, Kemp 3013, Kjellstrom 3019, Krueck 3031, Lamka 3034, Larson 3039, Louis 3063, MacDonald 3068, McCrea 3088, **Mead 3100**, Miller 3111, Miller, 3113, Monroe 3122, Moore 3123, Nayak 3133, O'C 3148, Olson 3154, Orsini 3156, Perry 3170, Podolsky 3178, **Rosenmutter 3208**, Rosenson 3209, Rot 3212, Roundy 3214, Schaumburg 3223, Secord 3232, Smith 3253, Smithburg 3254, Staley 3262, Sulzer 3277, Tengelsen 3288, Tuohy 3296, Twomey 3298, Ulm 3299, Wolf 3325
Indiana: Agness 3340, Brave 3350, Community 3358, Dukes 3371, Eternal 3378, Fayette 3379, Franklin 3382, J 3399, Keck 3405, Kharis 3407, Raymond 3436, Schurz 3444, Shafer 3449, Snyder 3454
Iowa: Andringa 3470, Becker 3472, De 3484, Drost 3487, Ellen 3489, Gleeson 3500, Heerema 3504, Herr 3506, Hills 3507, K2 3515, McCarthy/Bush

3519, Pappajohn 3525, Vermeer 3541, Vermeer 3542
Kansas: Adair-Exchange 3553, Central 3564, CPS 3568, Cray 3569, **Kejr 3593**, Lincoln 3596, Master 3600, Mingenback 3605, Master 3606, Olofson 3613, Rathert 3617, Stolzer 3630, Swearingen 3631, Testamentary 3633
Kentucky: Dunbar 3653, GB 3657, Lebus 3671, Price 3686, Weisberg 3705
Louisiana: A-Kids-Choice 3712, Briggs 3714, Ellis 3723, Grigsby 3725, Mintz 3738, Noland 3743, **Ruckstuhl 3748**, Salutare 3749, Selber 3751
Maine: Cotsirilos 3774, Davenport 3775, Hudson 3783, Lynam 3788, Narragansett 3794, Pond 3798
Maryland: Anderson 3814, Caplan 3832, Cogan 3837, Devito 3848, Laughlin 3898, Mustard 3922, Rogers-Wilbur 3941, Shrensky 3951, **St. 3960**, Tucker 3969, Wagner-Braunsberg 3975, Weinberg, 3979, Wilson 3987
Massachusetts: A 3994, **A 3995**, Ansin 4003, Cabot 4035, Catino 4040, Chabner 4041, Chabot 4042, Epstein 4084, Hill 4130, Hurston 4138, Kamin 4144, **Kaplan 4145**, Kendall 4149, Kurian 4162, Lawry 4168, McKee 4194, Nichols 4223, Prokopis 4248, Putnam 4252, Sacajawea 4274, Sandman 4279, Schechter 4281, Shaughnessy 4292, Sicari 4295, Solomont 4302, Solomont 4303, Sword 4318, Thee 4324, Weiner 4355
Michigan: Alnour 4373, Avharas 4380, Currie 4418, Dana 4420, Deinzer 4424, Duchene 4435, Fabiano 4438, Grassland 4458, Harris 4461, Isabella 4468, Jospey 4473, Lanting 4489, Lee 4491, Molnar 4517, Pappas 4532, Powers 4545, Rottman 4553, SEED 4562, Stern 4578, Stoddard 4579, Stoker 4580, Vander 4603, Weisberg 4609
Minnesota: Aca 4622, Albany 4624, Albright 4625, Anderson 4627, Black 4642, Burwell 4650, Erickson 4675, Ferber 4682, **Fingerhut 4683**, Frey 4690, Getsch 4695, Good 4698, Huisinga 4716, Krisbin 4726, Living 4730, Maranatha 4739, March 4740, Noreen 4750, Onan 4754, O'Neil 4755, Peace 4761, Quinlan 4764, Reger 4769, RJW 4777, Roberts 4778, Samsara 4784, Soar 4792, Squam 4793, **Trust 4802**
Mississippi: Amory 4821, Colbert 4829, **Edwards 4833**, Hope 4844, Van 4857
Missouri: Arnold 4861, Bakewell 4863, Boswell 4872, Capellupo 4883, Cray 4890, Dunn 4898, Finley 4910, Gaebler 4912, HB 4924, JMG 4933, Lawton 4944, Maxine 4954, McDonald 4955, Ross 4986, Seiler 4997, Sokoll 5010, Sugarbaker 5016, Vatterott 5030
Nebraska: Cimpl 5076, Finigan 5081, Herman 5090, **Lothlorien 5101**, Patrick 5109, York 5129
Nevada: Anton 5133, Benna 5138, Blue 5140, **Do 5153**, Living 5174, Lusardi 5175, To 5193, Williams 5199
New Hampshire: Mascoma 5223
New Jersey: A 5240, Avalo 5254, Bershad 5263, Diaco 5318, Engel 5334, Florin 5348, Freedman 5351, **Garcia 5362**, Genie 5366, HAIR 5379, Harmstieg 5386, Hekemian 5390, Icap 5398, Judson 5411, Kessel 5420, Knowlton 5427, Korean 5431, Kroon 5433, LaGrassa 5438, Markowitz 5460, MNS 5472, Nitzavim 5479, **Patel 5492**, Pierson 5500, Poole 5504, Ragan 5507, Rukh 5515, Spruce 5548, Stein 5551, Wilf 5587, **Yin-Shun 5596**, Zeldes 5599, Zobel 5603
New Mexico: Akerson 5604
New York: **Abba's 5634**, Adelman 5643, Ades-Taub 5645, AGB 5650, Alex 5652, American 5665, Amnon 5670, Armonia 5688, Bandier 5709, Barker 5716, Baseser 5720, Bassman 5721, Beard 5737, Bernheim 5740, Blackman, 5755, Breck 5780, CAL 5808, Calamus 5809, Camuto 5812, Caples 5813, Clark 5848, Cohn 5862, Cohn 5864, Colby 5867, Cornerstone 5878, Cortland 5880, Doovin 5923, E.R.G. 5939, EBA 5941, Elazar 5953, Elyachar 5959, Ezer 5974, Ezra 5976, Fagin 5978, Falconhead 5980, Feuerring 6001, Fieldstone 6004, Foundation 6019, Fraiman 6023, **Frank 6026**, Franklin 6028, **Freedom 6030**, Friedland

6037, Friedlander 6038, Friedman 6039, Furman 6046, Galler 6052, Gantcher 6055, Gela 6065, Geller 6066, Gernatt 6073, Gold 6088, Gold 6089, Goldenberg 6093, Goodman 6106, Gottlieb-Schwartz 6115, Greenblatt 6133, Grossman 6145, Hales 6159, Hemitt 6188, Hiler 6207, Holocaust 6222, Hover 6229, International 6249, Jungreis 6276, Kahn 6279, Katz 6287, Keene 6293, Keller 6296, Kirschenbaum 6314, Kistler 6316, Koessler 6336, Krasne 6344, **Ladenburg 6357**, **Lamaj 6361**, Lawrence 6369, Lenox 6380, Lieb 6398, Lieberman 6399, Lipschitz 6402, Lipschultz 6403, Lipton 6404, Lorber 6413, Lowenbraun 6414, Maidenbaum 6435, Marbeh 6440, Mars 6444, Mastrocola 6449, **McCaddin-McQuirk 6455**, Meade 6467, Medarchei 6469, Meridian 6478, Mitchell 6499, MW 6517, Newman 6533, Noster 6543, Odyssey 6548, Perper 6588, Persian 6589, Pierce 6604, Pinchas 6605, Poorman 6620, Price 6627, Project 6631, Quinn 6637, Rachel 6641, Raphael 6648, Rasba 6649, RDM 6653, Reidy 6661, Ridgewood 6669, Robbins 6676, Rosenthal 6694, Ross 6699, Roxe 6706, Rum 6709, Ruth 6713, Sakhai 6718, Sargol 6728, Sarnoff 6729, Satar 6730, Schaefer 6735, Schiller 6740, Schonberger 6744, Schwimmer 6760, Sdei 6764, SDF 6765, Shack 6780, Shalam 6783, Sheetz 6790, **Shulamit 6794**, Simcha 6804, Sorel 6826, Squier 6843, Steckler 6853, Sternklar 6864, Sunrise 6878, Tedaldi 6894, Treiber 6907, Tsvi-Ora 6914, Vaad 6924, Vogler 6932, Weininger 6954, Westlawn 6965, Wolf 6986, Zahavi 7015, Zichron 7024, Zurack 7033
North Carolina: Blue 7053, Burns 7063, Canaday 7066, Carroll 7068, Cary 7070, Cooke 7079, Duncan 7086, Eplee 7092, Foster 7101, Foundation 7102, Garrow 7108, Geschick 7109, Harvey-McNairy 7119, Howard 7131, Judd 7139, Krost 7154, Ladane 7155, Ladd 7156, Maness 7166, Markey 7168, Marsh 7171, McMerty 7180, Mize 7186, Nalle 7197, Niessen, 7200, North 7202, Pulliam 7215, Robitaille 7226, **Rolander 7229**, Rolla 7230, S.D.R. 7233, Self 7238, Stapleton 7253, Stonecutter 7255, Strickland 7257, Stubblefield 7260, TerKeurst 7266, Wagner 7275, Way 7281, Weatherspoon 7282, Wilkinson 7288, Williams 7289
Ohio: Boymel 7329, Brocker 7334, Bryan 7339, Busse 7343, Community 7357, **Elisha-Bolton 7387**, Entelco 7389, Fedeli 7393, Feldstein 7394, Feth 7397, Fishel 7401, Geotrac 7422, Glazer 7426, Hickok 7447, Huntington 7460, Jones 7470, Kangesser 7474, Kisker 7479, Kutz 7486, Linnemann 7498, Lukens 7507, McCann 7518, Mccarthy 7520, Miller 7528, Renner 7557, Schottenstein 7573, Schottenstein 7574, Sheely 7590, Smiley 7597, Stafast 7600, Steiner-King 7602, Sterling 7606, Tetlak 7615, Venner 7627, Young 7653
Oklahoma: Broadhurst 7663, Chilton 7667, Dulaney 7674, Elpis 7675, Fugitt 7681, Gelvin 7682, Holliman 7687, Love 7701, Lovoi 7702, Sisk 7719, White 7733, Whitwell-Meyer 7735
Oregon: Dubs 7760, Flowerree 7763, Gill 7766, Naito 7803, Richardson 7808, Shoen 7816, Trover 7824
Pennsylvania: Amaranth 7838, Bienenfeld 7872, Bloch 7878, Bonomo 7883, Bridge 7891, Cannon 7913, Casteel 7919, Crary 7943, Crebilly 7946, David 7950, Donnelly 7963, Eckels 7970, Edwards 7972, Edwards 7973, EFM 7974, Frederick 8006, Friends 8008, GT 8030, Hager 8035, Herndon 8051, Hill 8056, Holden 8064, Horn 8067, Jansing-Cook 8079, Joyce 8083, Landenberger 8109, Lockhart 8131, Mascaro 8145, Mason 8148, Mattingly 8151, McCune 8155, Mckee 8159, Meakem 8166, Mutual 8186, Neal 8190, Nikolaus 8193, Norford 8196, Pangborn 8203, Pearsall 8207, Plainfield 8217, Remmel 8235, Schlarbaum 8259, Schrenk 8261, Schultz 8262, Strine 8307, Stutzman 8309, Terryglass 8315, Thompson 8317, Troemner 8323, Velma 8330, Viii 8333, Ward 8343, Wenger 8351, Wenger 8352, Wolstenholme 8366

Rhode Island: Bowen 8391, Estate 8404, Getz 8412, Halsted 8415, Hirsch 8420, Johnson 8430, Perkins 8470, Rainbow 8477, Slingerland 8491
South Carolina: Bailey 8509, Bignon 8512, Childress 8518, Davis 8521, **Lader 8531**, Mitchell 8534, Nalley 8535, Rivers, 8538, Williams/Brice-Edwards 8549, Wyatt 8552
South Dakota: Black 8556
Tennessee: Benjamin 8586, Bradford 8592, Caldwell 8593, Campbell 8595, Ebert-Leblanc 8609, Foster 8616, Goad 8621, Hawthorn 8626, Massengill-DeFriece 8647, Provision 8663, Restoration 8665, Stadler 8678, Weiss 8684, Williamson, 8685
Texas: Beghini 8724, **Bhutada 8730**, Bloxom, 8731, Bratten 8739, Bright 8743, Brisley 8744, Bromberg 8748, Brown 8750, Cemo 8765, Cielo 8771, Coleman 8778, Conley 8784, Corrigan-Goddard 8789, Davis 8799, Denman 8810, Dulaney 8830, Dunham 8834, Elkins 8838, Fabenco 8843, Finney 8858, Foster 8866, Frost 8878, Grace 8895, Grant 8897, Gray 8899, Gray-Pampa 8900, Hall 8909, Hamm 8914, Hanley 8915, Helmle-Shaw 8929, Herring 8930, Hope 8948, Ik 8959, Journey 8975, Kelley 8984, L 9007, Ledbetter 9012, Lilly 9019, Lupton 9028, McCarty 9047, Merfish-Jacobson 9058, Miller 9066, Morrow 9074, Nuncio 9092, Opie 9099, **Orant 9102**, **Owusu 9107**, Pack 9109, **Partridge 9117**, Pearlman 9122, Pogue 9133, Prayer 9138, Quest 9142, Ray 9144, Redman 9147, Richmond 9152, Schepps 9178, Sherman 9192, Simpson-Omohundro 9196, SK 9198, Smith 9202, Smith 9207, Stephens 9217, Sure 9225, Sutton 9226, Swett 9227, Tabani 9228, Torrance 9241, Watford 9262, Watson 9263, Weaver 9265, Weir 9267, Wells 9272, Wheeler 9274, Wolens 9284, Wolf 9285, Wright 9294, Young 9297
Utah: B. 9302, Keener 9332, Korver 9335, Lindorf 9339
Vermont: **Daly 9371**
Virginia: Berni 9395, Buchanan 9410, Community 9426, Dwyer 9439, Fleder 9448, Glasser 9459, Hausfeld 9469, Levmar 9490, Macedonian 9496, Poole 9512, Powell 9513, Ramsey 9519, Sirad 9533, Stultz 9539, **Tara 9540**, Williams 9553, Zeiders 9557
Washington: Babare 9563, Babare 9564, Block 9570, Dunn 9589, Grindstone 9610, Hilal 9623, Jacobi 9628, Joint 9636, Kismet 9646, Larson 9650, Martin 9659, McKinlay 9662, Ohno 9673, Pleas 9678, Razore 9682, Shemanski 9693, Sondland 9700, Stevens 9704, Thomson 9711, Weier 9720, **Wiebe 9723**, Winter 9726, Zufall 9733
West Virginia: Blake 9735, Hamer 9746, Hope, 9752, Raymond 9764
Wisconsin: BayCare 9781, Ferguson 9819, Foulkes 9821, Fromstein 9824, Gebhardt 9826, Gunther 9833, Hamilton 9834, J.P.C. 9848, Koss 9866, Marshfield 9878, Mielcarek 9888, Park 9899, Pelz 9900, Shannon 9927, Smith 9931, Spider 9935, Thompson 9947
Wyoming: Connemara 9967, Joannides 9976, Skelton 9989

Religion for youth

New York: Kaplan 6284

Renewable energy

New York: Hahn 6156

Rent and mortgage assistance

California: Military 826
Maryland: St. 3959
Ohio: Philada 7548

Reproductive health care

California: Martin 803, Yen 1201
Florida: Kane 2137

Illinois: Lehman-Stamm 3045
Iowa: Deardorf 3485
New Jersey: Klein 5424
New York: Gordon 6110
Texas: PAL 9111
Wisconsin: Gardner 9825

Reproductive rights

Arizona: Murphey 151
California: Berkshire 305, Stellar 1080
Florida: Kanders 2135
Georgia: Woodruff, 2618
Illinois: Lehman-Stamm 3045
Maryland: Slavin 3954
Massachusetts: Hauben 4120
Minnesota: Bell 4638, Rodman 4779
Missouri: Sunnen 5018
New York: Anderson-Rogers 5676, Hallingby 6160
Ohio: **Brush 7338**
Pennsylvania: Lamb 8106, Lida 8127, Patterson 8205, Tabas 8312
Rhode Island: Mulligan 8457, York 8507

Research on animals

California: **Animal 246**

Residential mental health care

Georgia: Pennies 2565
Maryland: Otenasek 3931
Pennsylvania: Bennett 7860
Rhode Island: Dwinell 8403

Respiratory system diseases

Georgia: Raoul 2573
Illinois: Bulkley, 2765
Michigan: Thompson 4593
Mississippi: Florence 4836
Pennsylvania: Somerville 8291

Retired people

Georgia: Marshall 2545
Ohio: Gay 7418, Lang 7489

Retirement housing

Connecticut: Harris 1478
Florida: Densch 1970
North Carolina: Chaley 7072
Vermont: Copley 9370

Right to free movement and asylum

Georgia: Rockdale 2576
New York: **Kathwari 6286**, Sherman 6792, **Sparkplug 6830**

Right to life

California: Sebastiani 1027
Colorado: JJP 1299
Delaware: **Gloria 1670**
Florida: Carlton 1922, P.M. 2244
Nevada: Joseph 5166, Moran 5178
Ohio: Brinck 7333
Texas: Majella 9033
Virginia: Fink 9447
Wisconsin: Ariens 9776, Sartori 9921

Rivers and lakes

New York: Northern 6540
Pennsylvania: Brooks 7899

Rural development

Kansas: Kansas 3592

Safety education

Florida: **Aviation 1861**, Mb 2200
Indiana: Decatur 3367
Missouri: **Build-A-Bear 4879**
Nevada: **Do 5153**
North Carolina: Redwoods 7218
Ohio: Angels 7308

School athletics

Connecticut: DeLuca 1431
Florida: Capital 1918, Durden 1984, Freitas 2022
Georgia: Arnold 2436
Illinois: Glossberg 2916, Munson 3130
Michigan: Roscommon 4552
Oregon: Shoen 7816
Texas: Hicks 8935, Holmes 8947
Virginia: Franklin 9452

School libraries and media centers

California: Coleman 416
Illinois: Brooker 2758, Glossberg 2916
Oregon: Shoen 7816

School-based health care

California: Benedek 300, Community 421
Georgia: Harrison 2502
Maine: Franklin 3779
Massachusetts: PerkinElmer 4238
Missouri: Curry 4892
New Jersey: Covance 5305
New York: Warwick 6945
Texas: Dubose 8828, Riter, 9154
Utah: Green 9327
Vermont: Altman 9364
Wisconsin: Olson 9897
Wyoming: Cutting 9968

Science

Alabama: Shook 64
Arizona: Grossman 126
California: Baumann 283, Buell 357, Burg 362, Faggin 489, Hoefer 628, **Jain 656**, Lipp 759, Maxfield 808, Mazda 810, Pasarow 906, **Quiksilver 945**, Roche 979
Colorado: Dewolf 1256, Steffens 1358
Connecticut: Greenfield 1471, Niblack 1533, Patricelli 1541
Florida: Chapman 1935, **Chenzyme 1939**, Laufer 2169, Roshan 2297, Sudakoff 2356
Georgia: Myfident 2554
Hawaii: Kahiau 2636
Idaho: Boise 2666
Illinois: Cherry 2784, Grossinger 2933, Petrovich 3174
Kansas: Ross 3619
Louisiana: Sci-Port 3750
Maryland: Wagner-Braunsberg 3975
Massachusetts: Sherman 4294
Michigan: Hecht 4465, Meritor, 4511
Minnesota: Rodman 4779, Samsara 4784
Missouri: Albers/Kuhn 4859, Sigma-Aldrich 5003, Walker 5035
New Hampshire: DEKA 5210, Dorr 5211
New Jersey: Feldstein 5344, Jensam 5404, Mahan 5455
New York: AGB 5650, Bingham 5747, Catalyst 5821, Dears 5905, Educational 5945, **Engineering 5964, Family 5983**, Fein 5992, Lubin 6416, Meyer 6484, Morin 6506, Plymouth 6612, **Sparkplug 6830**
North Carolina: Moretz 7189
Ohio: Sauerland 7570, Tait 7610
Oregon: Erath 7762, Mentor 7796, Western 7829

Pennsylvania: Arkema 7842, Crawford 7944, Friendship 8009
Texas: **AMD 8698**, Boeing 8733, Conley 8784, Elkins 8838, McNutt 9055, Osberg 9105
Utah: Telemachus: 9359
Virginia: Pensmore 9509, Ratner 9521, Stephenson 9536
Washington: Jaffe 9629, Prairie 9680, Spark 9701, Thomson 9711
Wisconsin: **Johnson 9851**, Modine 9889
Wyoming: Stuart 9993, Windy 9999

Science museums

Alabama: Ratliff 57
California: Miller 830
Colorado: Dea 1254, Spencer 1356
Florida: Farrell 1998
Hawaii: **Yoshimoto 2658**
Illinois: Bartholomay 2721, Donovan 2832
Iowa: Young 3552
Kentucky: Yeager 3710
Louisiana: Montan 3740
Massachusetts: **Brabson 4026**, Hauben 4120, Kenwood 4150
New Jersey: Smith 5539
New York: Gartner 6059, Hohmann 6218, Lubin 6416, Wilson 6979
North Carolina: Belk 7046, Herndon 7125, Rollins 7231
Oregon: Demorest 7757
Texas: Benton 8726, Discovery 8816, Mithoff 9068
Virginia: Charles 9418

Scouting programs

Alabama: Adams 3, Sexton 63
California: Baker 266, Bell 295, Dickinson 453, Fox 525, Kieve 703, Martin 802, Page 899, Pardee 902, Rocca, 978, Tanimura 1103, Tomlinson 1123
Colorado: Family 1268, Hamilton 1285
Connecticut: Barden 1402
Delaware: Milano 1710, Rumberger 1734
District of Columbia: **Merriman 1820**
Florida: Callas 1913
Georgia: Arnold 2436, Churches 2461, JBS 2523, Jeter 2524, Williams 2612
Illinois: Bartsch 2722, Brunswick 2762, Doerr 2831, Espenscheid 2859, Gardner 2904, Luehring 3065, Morton 3127, Russell 3216, Taylor 3285, Walker 3308
Indiana: Bussing-Koch 3353, Crescent-Cresline-Wabash 3365, Gammon 3385, Hillenbrand 3393, Mulzer 3420, Weston 3467
Kansas: Family 3575, Insurance 3587, Morgan 3607
Kentucky: Barr 3646, Trim 3702
Louisiana: Lake 3732, Montan 3740
Maryland: Anderson 3814, St. 3959
Massachusetts: Magee 4183, Rockland 4267, Whittemore 4359
Michigan: Kellogg 4482, Roscommon 4552
Missouri: Darr 4893, Fabick 4907, Finley 4910
Nebraska: Ameritas 5067, Hawkins 5089, Patrick 5109, Physicians 5112, Quivey-Bay 5113
Nevada: Banks 5135, Petersen 5181
New Jersey: Kampen 5413, Minerva 5469, Ragan 5507, Scott 5527
New York: Shackouls 6781, Smith 6815, Snayberger 6817, Wells 6964, **Woodland 6989**
North Carolina: Bolick 7056, Burks 7061, Cannon 7067, Edgar 7088, Moretz 7189, Rostan 7232, Sloan 7246, Smith 7248
Ohio: Black 7328, Bryan 7339, Norris 7538, Taft 7609, Van 7626
Oklahoma: Drabek 7673, Merkel 7706
Oregon: Giustina 7767
Pennsylvania: Alley 7837, Gauss 8014, Moore 8177, Schoonmaker 8260
Rhode Island: Clark 8395
South Carolina: Williams/Brice-Edwards 8549
Tennessee: Atticus 8582, Kappa 8637, Powell 8661, Proctor 8662

Texas: Conley 8784, Fentress 8851, Hervey 8932, Hollandsworth 8945, Ray 9144, Rust 9168
Utah: Steiner 9358
Vermont: Mergens 9381
Virginia: Bassett 9391
Washington: Juniper 9640
West Virginia: Hott 9753, Parlin 9762, Vecellio 9770
Wisconsin: Phipps 9903, Schlegel 9922
Wyoming: Dubois 9970

Sculpture

New Jersey: Johnson 5406
New York: Avery 5702, **Gottlieb 6114**

Search and rescue

California: Mollath 842
Connecticut: Donchian 1440
Michigan: Roscommon 4552
Nebraska: Hansen 5087
New York: Rheinstrom 6665
Ohio: Rosenberry 7562
Pennsylvania: Lewis 8124
Virginia: Greco 9463
Washington: Templin 9709

Secondary education

Alabama: Blount 13, Goodrich 29
Arizona: Withycombe 184
Arkansas: Oliver 211
California: Ackerman 227, Bannerman 274, Bear 288, Bellini 298, Bider 314, Carlston 377, Clougherty 409, Crummer 436, Ducommun 465, Fitzpatrick 508, Foster 519, IM 649, KC 694, Los 768, Martin 802, Olson 879, Reilly 962, Sanfilippo 1002, Santa 1003, Schultz 1019, Scott 1022, Stauffer 1076, Von 1147, **Wakerly 1150**, Ward 1158, West 1175
Colorado: Donnell-Kay 1258, Mullen 1329, Taylor 1364, Trueblood 1371
Connecticut: Barnes 1404, Diageo 1437, Gibor 1464, Goldfarb 1467, Martin 1520, McLeod 1524, Morrow 1527, Schaeneman, 1560, Stratfield 1576, Wheeler 1594
Delaware: Splawn 1749
District of Columbia: Dweck 1805
Florida: **Benedict 1884**, Couch 1953, Davis 1964, De 1967, Finch 2000, Fontaine 2006, Kelly 2144, Lastinger 2168, Martin 2196, Parish 2247, Richard 2285, Riechmann 2286, Rogers 2291, Second 2321, Stellar 2348
Georgia: Chesed 2458, Goodman 2492, Morris 2553, Sewell 2584, Waffle 2602, Walton 2604
Hawaii: Minami 2642
Idaho: Ambrosiani-Pastore 2663
Illinois: 1335 2691, Agape 2698, Dowdle 2834, Family 2864, Hardiek 2953, Jones 3002, Kelly 3012, Lohengrin 3059, MacDonald 3068, McCrea 3088, McLaughlin 3095, McNally 3097, **Rosenmutter 3208**, Smysor 3255, Webb 3313
Indiana: Ayres 3342
Iowa: Andringa 3470, R 3529, Vermeer 3541, **Wahlert 3544**
Kansas: Berry 3558, Hopkins 3586
Kentucky: Abercrombie 3645, Woodlands 3707
Maine: Bailey 3765, Franklin 3779, Reny 3802
Maryland: Acacia 3807, **Braitmayer 3827**, Broadus 3829, Davis 3844, Dean 3846, **Doorstep 3850**, Kelly, 3893, Mullan 3920, S.B.E. 3944, Thalheimer 3966
Massachusetts: 2 3992, Berger 4018, Connell 4055, Dedham 4067, East 4075, Fay 4087, Hornblower 4135, Morse 4210, MutualOne 4216, Perry 4240, Phelps 4242, Rockland 4267, Stearns 4311, Van 4340
Michigan: Buist 4401, Cebelak 4406, Conrad 4413, Fabiano 4438, Meritor, 4511, Morley 4518, Peslar 4537, St. 4576, Tremble 4595, Wieczorek 4617
Minnesota: Harrington 4707, Jackson 4718, Northern 4751, O'Rourke 4757

Missouri: Forster-Powers 4911, Neiman 4969, Simmons 5005, Sullivan, 5017
Nebraska: Ameritas 5067, Cimpl 5076
New Hampshire: Jameson 5215, Verney 5236
New Jersey: Frelinghuysen 5354, Jones 5408, KDK 5416, McConnell 5463, Simon, 5537, Snyder 5540
New Mexico: Simon 5624
New York: AKC 5651, Brooklyn 5788, **Fitzgibbons 6011**, Greenspan 6134, Hein 6184, Initial 6245, Jarx 6258, Knafel 6330, Koessler 6335, Milton 6497, Monaghan 6502, O'Neil 6557, Palisano 6570, Parshelsky 6578, Roxe 6706, Sharon 6787, **Shatford 6788**, **Tang 6891**, Tisch 6900, Turner 6916, Warwick 6945, Zukerman 7032
North Carolina: Bryan 7060, First 7097, Griffin 7113, Hunt 7134, Kanitz 7140, Niessen, 7200, Ritchie 7222, Wake 7276
Ohio: Andrews 7307, Bicknell 7327, Gale 7414, Glidden 7427, Iott 7463, Laub 7490, Norweb 7539, O'Neill 7542, Quatman 7552, Swagelok 7608
Oklahoma: Dill 7671
Oregon: Brown 7744, Jubitz 7779, Spencer 7820
Pennsylvania: Bishop 7874, Carlson 7916, Charlestein 7920, Clark 7926, Gureghian 8033, Kelley 8091, Knox 8101, Ludwick 8134, Reiss 8234, Saramar 8253, Sneath 8286
Rhode Island: Bersted 8388, Johnson 8430, Kimball 8434, Mulvaney 8458, Prouty 8476, Seed 8484
South Carolina: WebbCraft 8548
Texas: Adler 8692, Fennell 8849, Fertitta 8852, Kirwan 8996, McNutt 9055, O'Connor 9093, Woltman 9288
Utah: Bastian 9304
Virginia: Birk 9398, King 9484, Lee-Jackson 9488
Washington: Baker 9566, Johnston-Fix 9634, Longbrake 9655, Ward 9718
West Virginia: Bowen 9737, Bowers 9738, Starvaggi 9767
Wisconsin: Ariens 9776, Kohl 9865, Meehan 9882, Meinerz 9883, Phipps 9903, Rewald 9913, Sartori 9921, Schlegel 9922, Watertown 9956, Woodtrust-Bell 9963
Wyoming: Stuart 9993

Senior assisted living

Arizona: Coleman 107
California: Eagle 470
Indiana: Rinker 3438
New Jersey: Armour-Lewis 5251, Levine 5446
North Carolina: Balin 7042, Schmidt 7236
Pennsylvania: Merwin 8170, Reiss 8234
South Carolina: Bailey 8510
Vermont: Copley 9370
Wisconsin: Verhulst 9954

Senior services

Arkansas: Ottenheimer 213
California: **Blackman 320**, Broad 347, Calaveras 369, Community 421, Eriksen 484, Flicker 511, Fox 525, Gellert 550, Gross 587, Helmstetter 616, Johnson 667, Palo 900, Perenin 914
Colorado: Broomfield 1242, Comprecare 1249, Gerrish 1277, Stratton 1359
Connecticut: Acorn 1385, Cochrane 1420, Diageo 1437, Dime 1438, Hewitt 1482, Senior 1566
Delaware: Palmer 1718
Florida: Bastien 1872, Couch 1953, Minto 2216, Sudakoff 2356, Wilson-Wood 2408, Wynne 2419
Georgia: Marshall 2545
Illinois: Bladel 2744, Christiansen 2790, Cremer 2815, Faulkner 2867, Fraida 2884, Generations 2908, Heath 2962, Klosk 3020, Landau 3037, **Lindon 3054**, MacDonald 3068, Sulzer 3277, **Trust 3293**
Indiana: Blackford 3346
Iowa: **Wahlert 3544**
Kansas: Bane 3557, Brown 3561, Insurance 3587, Mingenback 3605, South 3628, Trusler 3635
Louisiana: Steinhagen 3755, Wheless 3758

Maryland: Parsons 3932
Massachusetts: Boynton 4025, Dedham 4067, East 4075, Hampden 4116, Sailors' 4276, Shapiro 4290, Simoni 4296, **Spero 4304**, Stearns 4311, Swan 4317
Michigan: Buhr 4400, Community 4411, Main 4501, **Teitel 4589**
Minnesota: Rosen 4782, Thorpe 4800
Missouri: **Bohm 4871**, Slusher 5009
Nebraska: America 5066, Heuermann 5092, Home 5094, Physicians 5112
Nevada: Special 5188
New Jersey: Devine 5317, **Ostberg 5483**
New York: Artists 5692, BTMU 5795, Community 5872, **Eastman 5940**, Enders 5963, Faith 5979, French 6032, Greenspan 6134, Henshel 6192, Metzger-Price 6483, Northern 6540, Parshelsky 6578, Schweckendieck 6758, Seacoast 6766, Tuch 6915
North Carolina: Balin 7042, Herndon 7125, Kennedy 7145, Meserve 7182, Richardson 7221, Wibel 7287
Ohio: Bryan 7339, Defiance 7375, Finnegan 7399, Gay 7418, **Katz 7475**, Sheadle 7588, Steinmann 7603
Oregon: Pendleton 7806
Pennsylvania: Brooks 7897, Hahn 8036, Penn 8208, Saramar 8253, Schautz 8257, Wright-Cook 8369, Wurts 8370
Rhode Island: Kimball 8434, Kingsbury 8435, Perpetual 8471
Tennessee: Durham 8608
Texas: AMR/American 8703, Connor 8785, Finger 8857, Overlake 9106, South 9210
Vermont: Copley 9370
Virginia: Ivakota 9477
Washington: Gius 9606, Kawabe 9642, Skagit 9696, Templin 9709
West Virginia: Bowers 9738
Wisconsin: Courtier 9798, Watertown 9956

Seniors

Alabama: Black 12, Ireland 39
Arkansas: Olds 210, Ottenheimer 213
California: Barbonchielli 276, Callison 371, Community 421, Gross 587, Military 826, Palo 900, Parvin 905, Solano 1063, Thompson 1112
Colorado: Bright 1241, Broomfield 1242, Burt 1244, Comprecare 1249
Connecticut: Acorn 1385, Cochrane 1420, Donchian 1439, Senior 1566
Delaware: Kutz 1696, Lightner 1699, Palmer 1718
Florida: Bastien 1872, Cape 1917, Charlotte 1938, Coral 1952, Gate 2034, Lelash 2178, Wilson-Wood 2408
Georgia: Marshall 2545
Idaho: Boise 2666
Illinois: Alton 2706, Christiansen 2790, Cremer 2815, Family 2864, Generations 2908, MacDonald 3068, **Mead 3100**, Seymour 3236, Sulzer 3277, **Trust 3293**, Webb 3313
Indiana: **Ackerman 3339**, Community 3359, Community 3361
Iowa: Grubb 3502, **Wahlert 3544**
Kansas: Mingenback 3605, Nettleton 3611
Kentucky: Stockdell-Joseph 3698
Louisiana: Steinhagen 3755
Maine: Camden 3771
Maryland: Warfield 3978
Massachusetts: Boynton 4025, Griffin 4107, Kelsey 4148, Sailors' 4276, **Spero 4304**, Stearns 4311, Swan 4317
Michigan: Community 4411, Merkley 4512, Tuscola 4598
Minnesota: Rodman 4779
Missouri: **Bohm 4871**, Calkins 4881, Dunn 4898, Finley 4910, Moneta 4962
Nevada: Dermody 5152
New Jersey: **Ostberg 5483**, **Rippel 5510**, Schwartz 5525
New Mexico: Con 5611

New York: Artists 5692, August 5698, **Eastman 5940**, Enders 5963, Faith 5979, French 6032, Gaffney 6049, Gemiluth 6068, Metzger-Price 6483, Netter 6525, Northern 6540, Parshelsky 6578, Schweckendieck 6758, Seacoast 6766, Willmott 6978
North Carolina: Balin 7042, Glenn 7111, Kennedy 7145, Paddock 7206, Peeler 7207, Richardson 7221, Strowd 7258, Wells 7283
Ohio: Bahmann 7313, Community 7357, Finnegan 7399, Gay 7418, Lang 7489, Loeb 7504, McCann 7519, Oscar 7544, Philada 7548, Sheadle 7588
Oklahoma: Livengood 7698, Staton 7720
Oregon: Kuse 7786, Wessinger 7826
Pennsylvania: Baekgaard 7850, Blue 7879, Elk 7975, Female 7990, Hassel 8042, Hoffman 8062, Murphy 8185, Wurts 8370
Rhode Island: Kimball 8434, Littlefield 8441, Perpetual 8471, Wilson 8504
Tennessee: Durham 8608
Texas: A 8689, Finger 8857, Foundation 8869, Genecov 8886, Holloway 8946, Mitte 9069, Montgomery 9070, Wolens 9284
Utah: Kennecott 9333
Vermont: Copley 9370
Virginia: **Brown 9407**, **Delmar 9429**, Ivakota 9477
Washington: Jefferson 9630, Kawabe 9642
Wisconsin: Inbusch 9847, Marshfield 9878, Stateline 9937
Wyoming: Dragicevich 9969

Services for offenders

Montana: Angora 5044
New York: Ostgrodd 6561
Texas: Youth 9298

Sexual abuse

California: Baker 266, Hand 595
New York: Caruso 5817
North Carolina: Redwoods 7218
Tennessee: Monday 8652
Washington: Foss 9598

Sexual assault victim services

California: Livingston 761
Massachusetts: Leatherwood 4170

Sexual education

California: Yen 1201
New York: Anderson-Rogers 5676

Sexually transmitted disease control

California: Yen 1201

Shelter and residential care

California: Joerger 665, Saturno 1008
Delaware: Replogle 1728
Georgia: Magnus 2543
Idaho: **Melaleuca 2679**
Illinois: Heath 2962, Heins 2964, Seymour 3236
Kansas: Wallace 3637
Louisiana: Meraux 3736
Massachusetts: Simoni 4296
Michigan: Delano 4426
Minnesota: Sauer 4785, Weyerhaeuser 4815
Mississippi: Seal, 4853
New Jersey: Devine 5317, Domenica 5323
North Carolina: Hunter 7136, Ketchum 7146
Oklahoma: Liddell 7697
Rhode Island: Smith 8492
Texas: ADR 8693, Gatewood 8885, Jones 8973, Proctor 9139, Tucker 9243

Shintoism

New York: International 6249

Single parent support

Michigan: Conrad 4413
New York: Mertz 6481, Phillips 6600
Texas: Levy 9014
Washington: Foss 9598

Single parents

Alabama: Black 12, Ireland 39
Arkansas: Darragh 193
California: Adelaide 230, Downey 460
District of Columbia: Jovid 1817, Replogle 1831
Georgia: Abreu 2431
Illinois: Meyer 3106
Kentucky: Killian 3670
Massachusetts: Kelsey 4148
Michigan: Conrad 4413
Nebraska: Midlands 5104
New Jersey: Kerney 5419
New York: Mertz 6481
North Carolina: Glenn 7111
Ohio: Walker 7630
Oregon: Elwood 7761
Pennsylvania: Hoffman 8062
Tennessee: **Fugitive 8618**
Texas: Johnston 8972
Washington: Foss 9598
Wisconsin: Marshfield 9878

Skin conditions

New York: Nonna's 6538

Slum youth

California: Just 684
District of Columbia: Replogle 1831
New York: Yearley 7005
Pennsylvania: Garthwaite 8013
Wisconsin: Lakeview 9868

Smoking

Massachusetts: Thoracic 4326

Social enterprise

Illinois: **New 3138**
Minnesota: **Sundance 4796**
Nevada: EBV 5154

Social sciences

California: Roberts 975
Colorado: Staley 1357
Connecticut: Newtown 1532, Tell 1580
Illinois: Rosenthal 3210
Kentucky: Kentucky 3669
Massachusetts: Hopedale 4134
Montana: High 5057
New Hampshire: Jameson 5215
New Jersey: Brown 5278
New York: Lux 6422, Netter 6525, Pyewacket 6635, Wachtell 6936
North Carolina: **Weyenberg 7285**
Ohio: Thendara 7616
Oregon: Saling 7811
Pennsylvania: Jackson 8078

Sociology

Washington: Quest 9681

Sororities and fraternities

Alabama: Davis 24
Colorado: Bean 1228
Florida: Beall, 1876
Pennsylvania: Schwab-Silfen 8264
Washington: Worthington 9729

Special needs education

California: Torino 1125
Connecticut: Donchian 1439
Georgia: Greiner 2498, Jolley 2526
Illinois: Bartsch 2722, Robson 3200
Massachusetts: Alden 3999
Michigan: Thoman 4590
Missouri: **Build-A-Bear 4879**
New Jersey: Columbia 5301
North Carolina: Eddy 7087
Ohio: Bicknell 7327
Oregon: Shapira 7814
Tennessee: **Fraser 8617**
Texas: Proctor 9139
Vermont: Altman 9364

Special Olympics

California: Kelly 697, Page 899
Connecticut: Derx 1435
Florida: Gagnon 2029, KBR 2142, Overstreet 2242
Georgia: Solstice 2587
Missouri: Schweinfurth 4996
Ohio: Hazelbaker 7441
Pennsylvania: Packer 8201
Tennessee: New 8654
Texas: Hervey 8932

Special population support

Arkansas: McKinney 202
California: Ackerman 227, Frome 535
Massachusetts: **Memorial 4198**
Michigan: Delong-Sweet 4427
Missouri: Hermann 4927
New York: Milton 6497, Smith 6815
North Carolina: Bertsch 7050, Rogers 7228
Oklahoma: Wegener 7731
Pennsylvania: Clark 7926
Rhode Island: Dwinell 8403

Specialty hospital care

Arkansas: Nabholz 208
California: Adams 228, Amerman 239, Bekins 294, Borok 331, Crawford 435, Fox 524, Giles 554, Hoag 625, Kanel 688, Peterson 918, Radin 948, Soicher 1062, Stewart 1082, Stone 1086
Colorado: Hamilton 1285, Verdoorn 1372
Connecticut: Albert 1389, Harris 1478, Kaman 1493, Lavietes 1505, McLaughlin 1523, Morrow 1527
Delaware: Croll 1650
District of Columbia: Tucker 1836
Florida: Cantor 1916, Caring 1920, Charles 1937, Chowdhury 1943, Dysimmune 1986, Five 2002, Graese 2055, Harper 2082, Holloway 2107, Prutky 2270, River 2288, Stafford 2346, Terry 2368, Turock 2382
Georgia: Colston 2464
Illinois: Goldenberg 2920, Hanson 2949, Hastings 2960, Luehring 3065, McCrea 3088, Miller 3112, Nickum 3139, O'Connor 3149, Rich 3194, Trio 3292, Warner 3310
Indiana: Burris 3352, Vann 3461
Kansas: Miller-Mellor 3604, Morgan 3607, Watson 3639
Kentucky: Namaste 3682, Rounsavall, 3691
Maine: Sukeforth 3805
Maryland: Carol 3834, Dockser 3849, Eliasberg 3854, Elsberg 3856, Ferris 3860, Fischer 3862, Gidwitz 3870, **Goldberg 3872**, McKnight 3910, Rogers-Wilbur 3941, Small 3955

Massachusetts: Cole 4054, Cook 4056, Hale 4112, Hazard 4123, **Kahn 4143**, Thoracic 4326, Videtta 4343
Michigan: Golden 4455, Maas 4498, Padnos 4529, Tassell-Wisner-Bottrall 4587
Missouri: Hermann 4927, Lambert 4942, Lordi 4950, Portman 4981, Thorp 5020, Toutz 5023, Trulaske, 5024, Von 5033, Woods 5042
Nebraska: Hawkins 5089
Nevada: Ash 5134, Chami 5146, Sweig 5191
New Jersey: **Dankis 5312**, Fux 5359, Jones 5409, Kocurek 5428, O'Neal 5481, **Rippel 5510**, Upton 5566
New York: Aeroflex 5647, Briger 5784, Camuto 5812, Cathedral 5822, Cohn 5862, Coles 5871, D'Addario 5894, Golden 6091, Golding 6097, Grandview-Steers 6125, IF 6237, Levine 6386, Marble 6441, McCarthy 6456, National 6520, Nonna's 6538, Polsky 6618, Price 6627, Price 6628, Quinn 6637, Rosenberg 6690, Weininger 6954
North Carolina: Jelm 7137, Levine-Sklut 7161, Schmidt 7236, Spring 7251
Ohio: Andrews 7307, Brews 7332, Freygang 7410, Hauck 7440, Jenkins 7465, Shannon 7586, Skyler 7595, Turben 7622, Wildermuth 7637
Oregon: Ackley 7740, Kimmel 7782
Pennsylvania: Cost 7937, HFO 8053, Mendel 8168, Olitsky 8198, Rosenberg 8244, Smith 8283, Stein/ Bellet 8300
Rhode Island: Hecht 8418
South Carolina: Tarr 8545
South Dakota: Eleanor's 8559
Texas: Dale 8794, Fennell 8849, Grits 8904, Hatfield 8922, Jones 8973, Oden 9094, Sharma 9190, Vaughan 9248, Ward 9260
Virginia: Chainani 9417, Dickerson 9431, Hansen 9465, Lintott 9492
Wisconsin: Meehan 9882

Speech and hearing rehabilitation

California: Bundy 360
Florida: Fuller 2028
Georgia: Montgomery 2551
Maryland: Kelly, 3893
New Jersey: Adler 5242
North Carolina: Eddy 7087
Ohio: Bahmann 7313, Daberko 7369
Tennessee: **Fraser 8617**
Texas: Oden 9094

Spinal cord injuries and diseases

Connecticut: Bantle 1401, Gerbic 1463
Georgia: Goodman 2492, JBS 2523
Illinois: Schneider 3226
New York: Stifel 6865

Spirituality

California: Baumann 283, Dass 443, Huntington 642, Mintz 836, Stewart 1083
Delaware: Synthesis 1756
Florida: Vorsheck 2389
Illinois: **New 3138**
Maryland: **Thadikonda 3965**
Minnesota: **Trust 4802**
New Jersey: **Rippel 5510**

Spoken word

California: LEF 739

Sport and hobby museums

Maryland: Baltimore 3817
Massachusetts: Stemberg 4313
Michigan: Baum 4387
Wisconsin: Uihlein 9950

Sports

Alabama: Ratliff 57
Massachusetts: Phelps 4242
Nebraska: America 5066
New York: Nets 6524, Truman 6912, Woods 6992
Ohio: Dienstberger 7379
Pennsylvania: Smith 8280

Sports and recreation

Alabama: Samford, 62
Arizona: Burns 102, Maxinmotion 147, Shacknai 167
Arkansas: Bogle 191
California: Ach 226, Amador 238, Baldacci 268, Brooks-Mathews 350, Buttonwillow 367, Champions 386, Chizen 397, Community 421, Hollywood 630, Jamieson 658, Marcus 794, Olander 878, Payne 910, Rar 955, San 998, Thrill 1117, Tisch 1120, White 1180
Colorado: Energy 1264, Helmar 1291, **Kenney 1302**
Connecticut: Fry 1458, Rock 1554
Delaware: Fernandina 1663, Jade 1684, Kent-Lucas 1691, **Singer 1744**
Florida: Boston 1898, Carros 1924, Force 2009, Kiwanis 2150, Morris 2220, Mount 2223, Rose 2293, Waugh 2392, White 2402, Whiting 2403, Whitman 2404, Woolard 2414
Georgia: Cook, 2468, Frank 2481, Hoyt 2513, Kids 2530, Samford 2578, Sewell 2584
Idaho: Hare 2675, Whittenberger 2689
Illinois: Brunswick 2762, Delta 2826, Eclipse 2844, Geneseo 2909, Gibbet 2912, Hamlin 2946, Hess 2969, Issa 2990, Listeman 3055, Merchantz 3102, Rosebud 3204, Rot 3212, Turner 3297, Wehle 3314
Indiana: Community 3363, Decatur 3367, Dorsey 3369, Dubois 3370, Greene 3390, Huntington 3397, Jasper 3401, M.C.R. 3413, Scott 3446, Thrush-Thompson 3460, Western 3466
Iowa: Jefferson 3514, Vonderhaar 3543, Young 3552
Kansas: Baehr 3556, CPS 3568, Scott 3623
Kentucky: Foundation 3655, Independence 3666
Louisiana: Monteleone 3741, Salutare 3749
Maine: Franklin 3779, Narragansett 3794
Maryland: V 3972, Youth 3991
Massachusetts: Dedham 4067, Griffin 4107, Kershaw 4151, Killian 4154, Mountain 4212, Reynolds 4264, Segel 4285, Tadler 4320
Michigan: Amerisure 4375, Andersen 4377, Biederman 4391, Buffalo 4399, Community 4410, Ford-Thomas 4447, Four 4449, Frankenmuth 4450, Lanting 4489, Lapeer 4490, M 4497, Mackinac 4499, Pappas 4532, Talty 4584, Tuscola 4598, Van 4602
Minnesota: Bame 4634, Camara-Press 4652, Caridad 4653, Edina 4671, Getsch 4695, Groves 4703, Midcontinent 4745
Mississippi: Mississippi 4849
Missouri: Boylan 4873, Chomeau 4886, Edmonston 4900, J. 4932, Seiler 4997
Montana: Angora 5044, Lippard-Clawiter 5058
Nebraska: America 5066, Blair 5074, Harper 5088, Hester 5091, Midlands 5104, Owen 5108, York 5129
Nevada: Jansen 5164, Pinnacle 5183
New Jersey: Davis 5314, Fellstone 5346, Fox 5349, Frog 5357, Vaughn-Jordan 5567
New Mexico: Tanner 5625
New York: Adikes 5646, **Alexander 5653**, Burrows 5803, Colby 5867, Garman 6058, Goddard 6085, Grossman 6145, Koessler 6336, Lipschultz 6403, Lucky 6419, Martini 6447, McEnroe 6463, **McGraw 6464**, Mulroy 6516, Northern 6540, Olum 6555, Ontario 6559, Rosenthal 6693, Schiro 6741, Scully 6763, Society 6821, Stackhouse 6844, Troubh 6911
North Carolina: Jones 7138, Strowd 7258, Wake 7276
North Dakota: Pearson 7298
Ohio: Athens 7311, Bryan 7339, Cleveland 7354, Community 7356, Community 7357, Davidson 7374, Defiance 7375, Kangesser 7474, Leach

7494, Norweb 7539, Schottenstein 7573, Young 7652
Oklahoma: Cherokee 7666, Jones 7692, Stone 7721, White 7733
Oregon: Naito 7803, Parker/United 7805
Pennsylvania: Boudinot 7888, Bridge 7891, Community 7933, Emporium 7980, Fountainhead 8004, Hall 8037, II 8074, Krouse 8103, Landenberger 8109, Lipstein 8129, Nathan 8188, Schuylkill 8263, Scott 8266, Stewart, 8302, Whalley 8353
Rhode Island: Vanderpoel 8499
South Carolina: Horne 8528, Rivers, 8538
South Dakota: Watertown 8576
Tennessee: Campbell 8594, Williamson, 8685
Texas: Ash 8709, Bertha 8729, Bratten 8739, Fleming 8860, Jacobs 8964, L 9007, Montgomery 9070, Nowotny 9091, Peine 9123, Petty 9126, Storehouse 9223, Texas 9231, USD 9245, Womack 9289
Utah: Backcountry 9303, Turley 9360
Virginia: English 9443, Stone 9537
Washington: Excel 9593, Goodfellow 9607, Hickey 9622, Joint 9636, Korum 9648, Skagit 9696
West Virginia: Chambers 9742, Esbenshade 9744, Logan 9756, Shott 9765, Skewes 9766
Wisconsin: AnnMarie 9774, Dudley 9811, Eau 9814, Marshfield 9878, Regal-Beloit 9911, Stateline 9937, Van 9953
Wyoming: Scott 9987

Sports training

New York: Fenton 5998
Washington: Teel 9708

STEM education

Michigan: Meritor, 4511
Pennsylvania: Arkema 7842

Storms

California: Dwelle 467, Joy 677, Oak 872
Colorado: Hunter-White 1297
Georgia: Kids 2530
Illinois: Ruttenberg 3218
Maryland: Ticho 3967
Mississippi: Seal, 4853
New Mexico: Gumbo 5617
Pennsylvania: Yoh 8373
Texas: Simard 9195
Virginia: Shaffer 9530

Stress

Massachusetts: Alden 3999

Student retention

California: Just 684
Minnesota: Jostens 4720
Texas: Long 9023
Washington: Foss 9598

Student services

Connecticut: Nevas 1530
Illinois: Cowlin 2814
Massachusetts: Hale 4113
New York: Wagner 6938

Substance abuse prevention

Florida: Chapman 1935, Ray 2275
Massachusetts: Crawford 4059
Pennsylvania: Blue 7879, Reiss 8234
Tennessee: Berman 8587

Substance abuse treatment

California: Wrather 1198
Florida: Dyer 1985, Six 2339
Illinois: Rosen 3206
Maryland: Lutheran 3904
Massachusetts: Alden 3999
Michigan: Grassland 4458
New York: Utica 6922
North Carolina: McConnell 7176
Pennsylvania: Blue 7879
South Dakota: Houston 8567
Tennessee: Berman 8587
Texas: Hicks 8935

Substance abusers

Alabama: Black 12, Ireland 39
District of Columbia: Jovid 1817
Georgia: Abreu 2431, Pennies 2565
Illinois: Meyer 3106
Michigan: Tuscola 4598
Minnesota: Larsen 4728
Nebraska: Midlands 5104
New York: August 5698
North Carolina: Glenn 7111
Ohio: Ridgecliff 7560, Walker 7630
Oregon: Wessinger 7826
Pennsylvania: Hoffman 8062
Virginia: **Delmar 9429**

Suicide crisis intervention

New York: Gesso 6075

Sustainable agriculture

Delaware: Burt's 1635
Minnesota: Farmers 4679
New York: Anderson-Rogers 5676

Sustainable development

Florida: Perlmutter 2254
Indiana: Benton 3344, Fayette 3379
Kansas: Kansas 3592
Louisiana: Whitman 3759
Massachusetts: **Bruner 4030**, NAID 4217, **New 4220**, Walske 4349
Michigan: Community 4410, Frankenmuth 4450
Montana: Foundation 5051
Nebraska: Assurity 5068
New Mexico: Taos 5626
New York: BTMU 5795, Northern 6540
North Carolina: Meserve 7182
Ohio: **Lowe-Marshall 7505**, Sears-Swetland 7581
Pennsylvania: Community 7933, Tuttleman 8325
South Carolina: Greenwood 8526
Texas: Boeing 8733, Planetary 9132
Vermont: Block 9366
Wisconsin: Stateline 9937

Swimming

Iowa: Hoaglin 3508
North Carolina: Redwoods 7218

Teacher education

California: Breech 339, Roche 979
Florida: Couch 1953
Massachusetts: Ramlose 4257
Minnesota: Hagen 4704
New Jersey: Hanafin 5381
New York: Roothbert 6682
Oklahoma: Thomas 7724
Pennsylvania: Every 7986, Lida 8127
Virginia: **Longview 9494**
Wisconsin: Kohl 9865

Technology

California: Brown 352
Colorado: Trueblood 1371
Idaho: Boise 2666
Illinois: OSA 3157
Kansas: Ross 3619
Michigan: Meritor, 4511
New York: **Engineering 5964**, **Posner-Wallace 6621**
Texas: **AMD 8698**, Elkins 8838, Frankel 8872, McNutt 9055
Virginia: Mullen 9502
Wisconsin: Mednikow 9881, Modine 9889

Telecommunications

Kansas: Kansas 3592

Television

California: Bridges/Larson 343, Dorskind 459
Colorado: Dewolf 1256
Connecticut: Axe-Houghton 1397, De 1430, Derx 1435, Schloss 1562
District of Columbia: Westport 1838
Florida: Leiser 2177, Wolgin 2411
Illinois: Lichtman 3052, Morton 3127, Spencer 3258
Iowa: Krumm 3517
Massachusetts: Cook 4056, Hauben 4120, Melvina 4197
Michigan: Kantzler 4478, Riley 4550, Thompson 4593
Mississippi: Crooks 4831
Missouri: Barrows 4864
New Jersey: Gamper 5361, **Ju 5410**, Pheasant 5499
New York: Alexander 5654, Miller 6491, Radio 6643, Seacoast 6766
Pennsylvania: Ward 8343
Tennessee: Atticus 8582
Texas: Amarillo 8697, Fowlston 8871
Utah: Bastian 9304, Harman 9328, Mower 9341
Wisconsin: Peterson 9901

Temporary accommodations

California: Bradford 337, Solano 1063
Florida: Gate 2034
Texas: Hillcrest 8939, Levy 9014

Terminally ill people

Alabama: Black 12, Ireland 39
California: Atkinson 259
Florida: Brighton 1899, Landwirth 2167
Georgia: Abreu 2431
Illinois: Bulkley, 2765
Iowa: **Wahlert 3544**
Kentucky: Killian 3670
Nebraska: Midlands 5104
North Carolina: Glenn 7111
Pennsylvania: Hoffman 8062
Texas: Holloway 8946
Virginia: **Brown 9407**

Theater

Alabama: Adams 3, Aronov 7, Caddell 19
California: Barth 279, Bernstein 307, Bernstein 308, Ellen 478, HunterWard 641, Johnson 667, Kendall 700, Kirby-Jones 708, Lisle 760, Martin 800, Meister 821, Miller 832, Morgan 846, Plum 929, Potiker 932, Rishwain 974, Rotasa 991, San 997, **Skyscrape 1047**, Smith 1055, Stauffer 1076, Stellar 1080, Tippett 1119
Connecticut: Axe-Houghton 1397, Hall 1475, Konover 1501
Delaware: 1916 1605, ABE 1607, Dougherty 1658, Geltzer 1666
District of Columbia: Westport 1838
Florida: Auerbach 1859, Capital 1918, Couch 1953, Farrell 1998, Freitas 2022, Higgs 2096, Kane 2137, Weiller 2393

Theology

Arizona: Johnson 135
California: Atkinson 259, Brunswick 354, Joy 677, Olson 879
Colorado: Beren 1233, Heider 1290
Connecticut: Nirenberg 1534
Delaware: Wang 1773
Florida: Forbes 2008, Grader 2054, Greenblatt 2063, Halbrook 2073, Kuriansky 2162, Nelson 2230, Sharaby 2329, Smith 2342
Georgia: Churches 2461
Hawaii: **Shiraki 2648**
Illinois: Bere 2734, Chapin-May 2782, **Combs 2800**, Cronk 2817, Dowdle 2834, Grossinger 2933, Leibowitz 3046, **Rosenmutter 3208**
Indiana: Bos 3347
Iowa: Andringa 3470
Kansas: Merrill 3602
Kentucky: GHH 3658, **Magee 3674**
Maryland: Ammerman 3813
Massachusetts: Walsh 4348
Michigan: Betten 4390, Christian 4408, DeKock 4425, McDonald 4508, McNally 4510, Schmuckal 4559, Schwarcz 4560, Scully 4561, Sehn 4563, Springview 4575, Zondervan 4621
Minnesota: Desiring 4668, Kellogg 4722

Georgia: **Gage 2482**, Lee 2540, McKnight 2548, Mix 2550, Trammell 2595
Illinois: Ahlstrand 2700, Allen-Heath 2701, Engle 2855, Highland 2970, Landau 3037, Lehman-Stamm 3045, MacDonald 3068, Mullen 3129, Pangburn 3161, Pond 3182
Indiana: Cohen 3357, Klapper 3408, MutualBank 3421
Kansas: Middlekauff 3603, Trusler 3635
Kentucky: Kentucky 3669, Opera 3684
Maryland: Bernard 3822, **Fox 3864**, Helm 3879, Jake 3890, Katz 3891
Massachusetts: Bigbird 4020, Bulger 4031, Dedham 4067, Eddy 4077, Fay 4087, Greenberg 4106, **Kahn 4143**, Perry 4240, Symes 4319
Michigan: Community 4411, Dana 4419, Kantzler 4478
Minnesota: Bend 4639, Boss 4646, Evert 4676, Noreen 4750, Tennant 4798, Wells 4811
Mississippi: Harris 4841
Missouri: **Bohm 4871**, Hermann 4927, Simmons 5005
Montana: Wendy's 5065
Nebraska: Assurity 5068, Cope 5077
New Hampshire: Verney 5236
New Jersey: **Daft 5310**, Domenica 5323, Johnson 5406, **Ju 5410**, Katz 5414, Kingsberg 5421, Scire 5526, Stone 5553
New York: **Blinken 5757**, Brand 5776, Camber 5811, Coles 5871, Cullman 5887, Dillard 5916, Downey 5930, **Eastman 5940**, Fife 6005, Fraydun 6029, Furman 6045, Gilliam 6078, Gramercy 6122, Harmon 6169, Henshel 6192, Heyward 6202, Kirby 6313, Kleban 6323, Lassalle 6366, Madover 6431, McCarthy 6456, Mills 6495, New 6527, Newman 6530, Pels 6585, Rachesky 6642, Randall 6644, Rodgers 6680, Savitz 6734, Schwartz 6753, Schwartz 6754, Spiritus 6840, Stutz 6875, Tuch 6915, **Weill 6950**, Weinman 6955, Whittemore 6975, Willmott 6978
North Carolina: Whitener 7286
Ohio: Corbett 7363, Hazelbaker 7441, Heimbinder 7445, LKC 7501, Schey 7571, STERIS 7605, Van 7626
Oklahoma: Krueger 7695
Oregon: Silver 7817, Wessinger 7826
Pennsylvania: Adams 7836, **Arronson 7844**, Birnhak 7873, Fierce 7992, Lida 8127, Patterson 8205, Randall 8230, Roberts 8240
Rhode Island: Mulligan 8457, Olsen 8463
South Carolina: Lutz 8533
Tennessee: Doochin 8605
Texas: Dunagan 8831, **Gilman, 8889**, Griffin 8902
Utah: Steiner 9358
Virginia: Cartledge 9414, Mullen 9502, **Price 9516**
Wisconsin: Arzbaecher 9777, Cudahy 9800, **Helios 9838**, Martin 9879

Mississippi: Colbert 4829
Missouri: Barrows 4864, Cornelsen 4889, Fabick 4907, Wolff 5040
New Hampshire: Martin 5222
New Jersey: Armour-Lewis 5251, **Billig 5265**, Verhalen 5568, Woolley-Clifford 5594
New York: Cohen 5857, Ferguson 5999, Heisler 6185, Hennessy 6191, HF 6203, Himelberg 6210, Horowitz 6225, JI 6260, **Klagsbrun 6318**, Lopatin 6412, MacArthur 6429, Nussbaum 6545, Palmer 6572, Resnick 6663, Rifkind 6670, Rose 6684, Schaffer 6737, Schwalbe 6751, **Stein 6855**, Viola 6930, Yosef 7011, **Ziv 7030**
North Carolina: Bolick 7056, Edgar 7088, Everett 7093, Nivison 7201, Pratt 7214, Smith 7248
Ohio: Endowment 7388, Glidden 7427
Pennsylvania: Beacon 7856, Charlestein 7920, Cornerstone 7936, Dinardo 7960, Gilmore 8017, Hill 8055, Jackson 8078, Kelley 8091, Reese 8232, Schautz 8257, Stein 8299, Sweigart 8311
Rhode Island: N. 8459, Pardee 8468
Tennessee: **Belz 8585**
Texas: Cox 8790, Fruehauf 8879, Howard 8955, **McCreless 9049**, Raygar 9145, **Ryrie 9169**, Woltman 9288, Wynne 9296
Virginia: Denit 9430, Pensmore 9509
Washington: Kawabe 9642, Longbrake 9655
West Virginia: Bowen 9736, Minor 9761, Stout 9769
Wisconsin: **Helios 9838**, Seeds 9925, Styberg 9942

Toxic substance control

Maine: **Golden 3781**
New York: Gesso 6075
Pennsylvania: Brooks 7899

Track and field

Florida: Woerner 2409
Iowa: R 3529
Kentucky: Trim 3702
Massachusetts: 2 3992
Montana: Wendy's 5065
Texas: Whitley 9276
Virginia: Bassett 9391
Wisconsin: Ariens 9776

Transgender people

Alabama: Black 12

Tribal and indigenous religions

California: Amin 240
Florida: Landwirth 2167
Maryland: **St. 3960**
Nevada: Williams 5199
New Jersey: **Garcia 5362**

Undergraduate education

Arizona: C 103, Johnson 134
California: Bach 263, Harbison 597, **International 652**, Marineau 798, **New 863**, Stewart 1083, Torino 1125, Zafiropoulo 1207, Zwick 1218
Colorado: Clough 1248, Denver 1255, JJP 1299, Verdoorn 1372
Connecticut: Antonacci 1395, Greenfield 1471, Perna-Rose 1542, Rock 1554
Delaware: Heuer 1680, Kingsley 1693, Milano 1710, Thronson 1766
District of Columbia: Davies 1801, Westport 1838
Florida: Couch 1953, Fleischman 2003, Hansen 2079, Higgs 2096, Miniaci 2215, Patterson 2251, Rogers 2291
Georgia: White 2609
Illinois: Clarks 2792, Danielson 2824, Knight 3022, Louis 3063, Petrovich 3174, Simon 3247, Smith 3253, Stairway 3261, Weaver 3312, Wislow 3323, Wolf 3326

Iowa: Bennett 3474, Coons 3481, Rohde 3530, Vermeer 3542, Woodward 3549
Kansas: Merrill 3602
Louisiana: Gauthier 3724
Maine: **St. 3804**
Maryland: Fine 3861, Hobbs 3882, Mangione 3907, Sears 3948, Silber 3952
Massachusetts: Altamira 4001, Cook 4056, Helman 4126, Walske 4349
Michigan: DiPonio 4432, Price 4546, Roznowski 4554, Scully 4561, Zimmerman 4620
Minnesota: Bahl 4632, Reed 4768, Tamarack 4797
Mississippi: Trehern 4856
Missouri: Curry 4892, Schutte 4995, Slusher 5009, Toutz 5023
Nebraska: Cimpl 5076
New Hampshire: Cochran 5208, Martin 5222, Olcott 5227, Seigel 5231
New Jersey: Glasser 5371, Johnson 5407, Jones 5409, Kampen 5413, Minerva 5469, Minio 5470, Pheasant 5499, Spiro 5546, Spohler 5547
New York: Barbash 5714, Brillo-Sonnino 5785, Brosens 5789, Goldenberg 6092, Gralnick 6121, Hadar 6154, Hart 6173, Hefta 6181, Hiler 6207, JLK 6264, Koessler 6334, Kupferberg 6351, Lehman 6375, McNulty 6465, Rosenberg 6691, Saunders 6733, Schonberger 6744, SGMG 6778, Summit 6877, Sweeney 6887, Three 6899
North Carolina: Carroll 7068, Chaley 7072, Moretz 7189, Needham 7199, Sutherland 7263
Ohio: Baird 7314, Black 7328, Edward 7385, Iott 7463, Reed 7555
Oklahoma: Dill 7671, Dobson 7672
Oregon: Leupold 7790
Pennsylvania: Double 7964, Hill 8056, Hoffman 8062, Lord 8132, Mosi 8179, Pogo 8221, Reese 8232, Schlarbaum 8259
Rhode Island: Molder 8455, Olsen 8463, Smith 8493
South Carolina: Gibson 8523
Tennessee: Rucker-Donnell 8668, Wilt 8687
Texas: Foundation 8870, Isaac 8962, Killson 8990, Miller 9064, Sparks 9211, Staubach 9215, Vetter 9251
Virginia: **American 9386**, Birk 9398, Dickerson 9431, Leonard 9489, Sauer 9527
Wisconsin: Bock 9786, Hamilton 9834
Wyoming: C 9966, Skilling 9990

Unemployed people

Ohio: Jenkins 7465

University education

Alabama: Cooper 23, Davis 24, Hunter 38
Arizona: Community 108, Murphey 151, Stanton 174, Sturges 176, Ullman 177
California: Anderson 244, Bialis 313, Blachford-Cooper 318, Bochnowski 325, Borch 330, Boyer 335, Chan 387, **Cienega 404**, Craves 434, Davis 445, Dickinson 453, Dockweiler 456, Ducommun 465, Edwards 473, Eichenberg-Larson 474, Flanagan 510, Foster 519, Foundation 525, **Friends 533**, Fudge 537, Grey 582, Grey 583, Handley 596, Harris 601, Hitter 624, Hoag 625, Johnson 666, Kelvin 699, Kendall 700, Ko 715, Lemelson 742, Lemons 744, Levine 750, Louie 770, Miller 833, Oreggia 886, Pergo 915, Pralle 933, Prete, 934, PTSRK 943, Pulido 944, Razi 957, Rediger 960, Rishwain 974, Roberts 975, Romano 982, SJL 1043, Skynyrd 1046, **Skyscrape 1047**, Stellar 1080, Tuffli 1134, United 1136, **Wakerly 1150**, White 1180, **Wong 1194**, **Woo 1195**, Zabala 1204
Colorado: Bardsley 1227, Blair 1237, Family 1268, Getz 1278, Taylor 1364, Thiel 1365, Trachten 1369
Connecticut: Acorn 1385, Alpha/Omega 1391, Floren 1451, Gibor 1464, Goldfarb 1467, Gorab 1468, Konover 1501, LLL 1510, Storr 1575, Thrall 1583, Tully 1588
Delaware: Babcock 1612, Bauer 1616, Heuer 1680, McKiernan 1706, Messing 1708, Patterson 1719,

Pollack 1722, Synthesis 1756, Talbott 1757, Uberoi 1768, Wang 1773
Florida: A. 1841, Ael 1843, Anderson 1845, Atkins 1856, Cohen 1948, Coulter-Jones 1954, Croft 1956, Day 1965, de 1966, Diane 1974, Doctors 1978, EGW 1988, Evanson 1995, Franklin 2020, Friedheim 2024, Friedland 2025, Fry 2027, Glaubinger 2040, Hill 2098, Holtz 2109, Hultquist 2115, Jelks 2128, Kreisman 2159, Lawson 2170, MCM-Munilla 2206, Miniaci 2215, Papper 2246, Perlmutter 2254, Rich 2284, Richard 2285, Russell 2303, Sadler 2306, Salizzoni 2309, Speranza 2344, Stellar 2348, Taplin 2363, Terry 2368, von 2388, White 2402, Wolf 2410
Georgia: Carmical 2453, Hurlbert 2516, Illges 2518, Myfifident 2554
Hawaii: Epstein 2630, Zwaanstra 2662
Idaho: Morbeck 2681
Illinois: Baird 2718, Beeghly 2730, Brooker 2758, **Chapin 2781**, Chez 2785, Donovan 2832, Drugas 2837, Family 2864, Franklin 2887, Hansen 2948, Herman 2968, House 2980, Howard 2981, Kilrea 3017, Knowles 3023, Logos 3058, McCabe 3084, McDonough 3090, North 3142, Novick 3143, Owen 3160, Parker 3162, Patterson 3164, Reed 3191, Rich 3194, Rosen 3206, Rosenson 3211, Shaw 3244, Staley 3264, Trio 3292, Will 3322
Indiana: Dye 3373, Gaither 3384, Klapper 3408, Maurer 3415, Welter 3465
Iowa: Daniels 3483, Gaedke 3495
Kansas: Family 3575, Merrill 3602, Middlekauff 3603, Mistler 3606
Kentucky: McKellar 3677, Mulhollem 3680, Namaste 3682
Maine: Chappell 3772
Maryland: Davis 3844, Dean 3846, Ferris 3859, Fusco 3868, Gorlin 3874, Katz 3891, Legum 3899, Lutheran 3904, Schwarz 3947, Swenson 3962, Unger 3971, Witt/Hoey 3989
Massachusetts: Chartis 4044, Delorenzo 4068, Hagerty 4110, Lawrence 4167, Lawry 4168, **Patagonia 4234**, Phelps 4242, Spoon 4305, Stanzler 4307
Michigan: Barstow 4385, Blatt 4393, Jones 4472, Linse 4493, Loosemore 4495, O'Donovan 4525, Stern 4578
Minnesota: Fischman 4685, Oak 4752, **Wagner 4804**, Wiehoff 4818
Mississippi: Hood 4842, Wittel 4858
Missouri: Bryant 4878, Capellupo 4883, Chod 4885, Darr 4893, Heiman 4926, Meyer 4959, Mineral 4961, Portman 4981, Schneider 4994
Montana: Dousman 5049, Greater 5054
Nebraska: Cimpl 5076, Hickey 5093, Olson 5107
Nevada: Coleman 5150, Petersen 5181
New Hampshire: Lion's 5220
New Jersey: Broomfield 5275, Cali 5284, Chormann 5293, Essig 5339, Freedman 5351, Gamper 5361, **Greenblatt 5376**, Jensam 5404, Johnson 5407, Kalkin 5412, Lavery 5441, Payson 5495, Petrucci 5498, Savin 5520, Scire 5526, Scott 5527, Seven 5530, Sheridan 5533, Snyder 5543, Vaughn-Jordan 5567, Welch 5579, Willingham 5589, Zakaria 5598
New Mexico: Gumbo 5617, Simon 5624, Tanner 5625
New York: Abess 5637, Aeroflex 5647, Angelson 5679, Arts 5693, Bandier 5709, Baobab 5711, Behrens 5731, Blank 5756, Block 5759, Bostwick 5767, Brademas 5774, Brinkman 5786, Bush 5805, Catalyst 5821, Cohenca 5861, Davis 5902, Diamondston 5914, Dobson 5921, Doscas 5925, Feil 5991, Feinberg 5993, Feldman 5996, Fenton 5998, Finn 6008, Goldfarb 6095, Goldstone 6102, Gould 6116, Graham 6119, Grandview-Steers 6125, Hadar 6154, Hathaway 6176, Himelberg 6210, Hochman 6214, Initial 6245, Iroquois 6250, Kahn 6279, Kelsey 6298, Kenyon 6301, Lauren 6368, Lichtenstein 6397, Lubin 6416, Manning 6437, Marshall 6446, McNulty 6465, Mead 6466, Monaghan 6502, Mule 6515, Neporent 6523, Newcomb-Hargraves 6529, Newman 6533, Nonna's 6538, Pajwell 6568, Pfeiffer 6597, Purple 6634, Quinn 6638, Rechler 6657, Ritter 6673, Rose 6686, Rosenberg 6690, Rothstein 6704, Schiller 6740, Scully 6763, Seaman 6767, Senator

6775, Shack 6780, Smith, 6816, Spektor 6833, Stony 6868, Stuart, 6873, Treiber 6907, Weininger 6954, Wyckoff 6998, Yordan 7009, Zukerman 7032
North Carolina: Arkwright 7041, Borun 7057, Burks 7061, Koons 7148, London 7164, Mattison 7175, Needham 7199, Ritchie 7222, Rollins 7231, Rostan 7232, UAI 7272
Ohio: Black 7328, Fibus 7398, Heimbinder 7445, High 7449, Kloenne 7481, Reed 7555, Ryan 7566, Schwebel 7577, Seasongood 7582, Skestos 7594, Tetlak 7615
Oklahoma: Martin, 7704, Wadley 7726, White 7734, Witt 7737
Oregon: Erath 7762, Haugse 7771
Pennsylvania: **Berkowitz 7865**, Boardman 7881, Boscia 7887, Bryer 7902, Double 7964, Joyce 8083, Kahn, 8084, Lida 8127, Lubert 8133, Merwin 8170, Morgan 8178, Muirfield 8182, Nathan 8188, Nesh 8191, Norbell 8195, Olitsky 8198, Pincus 8214, Price 8226, Price 8227, Rooney 8243, Ryan 8251, Schwab-Silfen 8264
Rhode Island: Galkin 8410, York 8507
South Carolina: Sunshine 8544
South Dakota: Cindy 8557
Tennessee: Adams 8579, Agape 8580, EBS 8610, Foster 8616, Johnson 8634, McGehee 8648, Mick 8651, Pattee 8656, Sohr 8676
Texas: Cariker 8762, Cemo 8765, Coleman 8778, Cox 8790, Durrill 8835, Edwards 8837, Fentress 8851, Frost 8878, Hallberg 8911, Jackson 8963, Johnson 8970, Killson 8990, King 8992, Lloyd 9022, MacDonald-Peterson 9032, MHR 9063, Mithoff 9068, Mitte 9069, MST 9078, Nelson 9086, Oden 9094, Oppenheimer 9100, Pearlman 9122, Rosen 9161, Rosenberg 9162, South 9209, Sterling 9218, Watford 9262
Utah: Burbidge 9308, Cardon 9311, Patel 9344
Virginia: Blue 9400, Burford 9411, MAIHS 9497, R 9518, Shaffer 9530
Washington: Furnessville 9602, Klaue 9647, Morningside 9665, Tamaki 9707
West Virginia: Fine 9745, McDavid 9760, Minor 9761, Price 9763
Wisconsin: Chastain 9793, Crowley 9799, Holoubek 9843, Hunt 9845, Phipps 9902, Smith 9931, St. 9936, Verhulst 9954, Wilson 9960
Wyoming: Ellbogen 9971

Unknown or not classified

California: Rosenberg 985
Florida: Westgate 2400
Hawaii: Armstrong 2624
Illinois: **Meyers 3107**
Kansas: Thomas 3634
Massachusetts: **Spero 4304**
Michigan: Dart 4421, Frankenmuth 4450
Missouri: Sayler-Hawkins 4993
New Jersey: American 5248
New Mexico: Carlsbad 5608
New York: Cohoes 5865, Cornell/Weinstein 5877, Gage 6050, **Katzin 6288**
Texas: Vetter 9251
Washington: Three 9712

Urban development

Florida: Hufty 2114, Perlmutter 2254
Louisiana: Whitman 3759
Massachusetts: **Bruner 4030**, NAID 4217, Walske 4349
Michigan: Frankenmuth 4450
Minnesota: Bell 4638
New York: Abelard 5635, BTMU 5795
North Carolina: Meserve 7182
Pennsylvania: Tuttleman 8325
Wisconsin: Stateline 9937

Vegetarianism

New York: **Animal 5680**

Venture philanthropy

Delaware: Dougherty 1658
Virginia: Bruhn-Morris 9408

Veterans

California: Military 826
Florida: Hegamyer 2087
Nevada: EBV 5154
Pennsylvania: **Epstein 7984**
Virginia: **Delmar 9429**
Wyoming: Kuehne 9979

Veterinary medicine

California: Kelly 697
Illinois: Caccomo 2771
Kentucky: Keeneland 3668
Maine: Narragansett 3794
Maryland: Moore 3917
Massachusetts: Zock 4368
Nebraska: Scribante 5116
New Jersey: Armour-Lewis 5251, Feline 5345, Hill 5392, Wetterberg 5583
New York: Bostwick 5767, Ellsworth 5957, Krimendahl/Saint-Amand 6346
North Carolina: Herndon 7125
Texas: Stevenson 9220

Victim aid

Colorado: Moniker 1327
Illinois: McKee 3093
North Carolina: Lerner 7160
Pennsylvania: Wurts 8370
Utah: Funding 9325

Victims of crime and abuse

Alabama: Black 12, Ireland 39
Arizona: Armstrong 97
California: Atkinson 259, Gellert 550
Florida: Landwirth 2167
Georgia: Abreu 2431
Illinois: **Mead 3100**, Meyer 3106
Kentucky: Killian 3670
Minnesota: Larsen 4728
Nebraska: Midlands 5104
New Jersey: Eisenberg 5331
North Carolina: Glenn 7111
Ohio: Ridgecliff 7560
Pennsylvania: Ayers 7848, Blue 7879, Everard 7985, Hoffman 8062
Texas: Foundation 8869, Waggoners 9255
Washington: Foss 9598
Wisconsin: Marshfield 9878

Victims of disaster

Iowa: GuideOne 3503
Minnesota: G&K 4691
Missouri: Fabick 4907
New Jersey: American 5248
Oregon: Mentor 7796
Tennessee: New 8654

Vision care

California: Livingston 761
New York: A.B. 5632, Ontario 6559

Visual arts

California: Gross 587, Rotasa 991, Wattis 1161, Wells 1171
Connecticut: Roberts 1552
Florida: Partners 2248
Idaho: Boise 2666
Illinois: Generations 2908, Graham 2926, MacDonald 3068

Iowa: Deardorf 3485
Kentucky: Kentucky 3669
Massachusetts: Hazard 4123, Hornblower 4135, Permanent 4239, **Robbins-de 4266**
New Jersey: Brueckner 5279, Cordover 5304, Eisenberg 5331, Frog 5357
New Mexico: Taos 5626
New York: Art 5691, Coby 5852, Gesso 6075, L 6353, Lucelia 6418, MAT 6450, Wunsch 6996
North Carolina: Chatham 7074
Ohio: Anderson 7305, **Elisha-Bolton 7387**
Oklahoma: Kerr 7693
Oregon: Mentor 7796
Pennsylvania: Speyer 8294
Tennessee: Atticus 8582
Texas: Boeing 8733, Dedman 8807, Freed 8873, **Gilman, 8889**, Hohlt 8944
Virginia: Kaufman 9482, Markel 9498, Peachtree 9508

Vocal music

Delaware: Loftus 1700
District of Columbia: Westport 1838
New York: Cheatham 5836
Pennsylvania: Patterson 8205

Vocational education

Alaska: Bristol 82, Chenega 83, Doyon 84
Arkansas: McKinney 202
California: Karp 691, Lux 773
District of Columbia: Jovid 1817, Westport 1838
Florida: Carrington 1923, Oristano 2241
Idaho: Mitchell 2680
Kansas: Reeble 3618
Massachusetts: Alden 3999, Kelsey 4148, Middlesex 4203, Ratshesky 4259
Minnesota: G&K 4691
Nebraska: Weller 5127
North Carolina: Bryan 7060
Oregon: Daly 7756
Pennsylvania: Hill 8055, McKee 8160
Texas: Chambers 8767, Hext 8933, Mantzel 9036
Wisconsin: Fromm 9823, Nelson 9894

Vocational post-secondary education

Alaska: Koniag 89
Iowa: Bishop 3475
New Jersey: Ullmann 5564
New York: Willmott 6978
Oregon: Elwood 7761
Pennsylvania: Hoffman 8062, McKee 8160

Vocational rehabilitation

Michigan: Kay 4480, Mills 4515, Tyler-Little 4599
Minnesota: G&K 4691
New York: Abess 5636

Vocational secondary education

New York: JLK 6264

Voluntarism

Alabama: Viro 73
California: Glazer 562
Colorado: Leighty 1311
Illinois: Bulkley, 2765, Hughes 2983
Indiana: TCU 3458
Iowa: Schildberg 3532
Louisiana: Powers 3746
Michigan: Community 4411
New York: Northern 6540
Pennsylvania: Schuylkill 8263
Texas: Osberg 9105

War memorials

New Jersey: Larson 5440

Water conservation

Pennsylvania: Bon-Ton 7884

Water pollution

California: **PADI 898**
New Jersey: American 5248
New York: Anderson-Rogers 5676, Indus 6243

Water resources

California: Big 315, Borch 330, **PADI 898**, Ward 1158
Connecticut: Gorab 1468
District of Columbia: Hanley 1814, Rossotti 1832
Massachusetts: **Barakat 4012**
Michigan: St. 4577
Minnesota: **Porter 4763**
New Jersey: American 5248, Navesink 5477
New York: Anderson-Rogers 5676, Gesso 6075, Indus 6243, Kenlou 6299, Tensor 6896
Texas: Mayfield 9044
Vermont: Castanea 9368
Wisconsin: Windway 9961

Water sports

California: Downing 462, Knuppe 714, **PADI 898**, San 998
Ohio: Peters 7547
Pennsylvania: Wurts 8370
South Carolina: Cato 8516

Wetlands

Washington: Northwest 9669

Wildfires

California: Handlery 596
Florida: Basham 1870
New York: Lachman 6356
Texas: Shepherds 9191

Wildlife biodiversity

Arizona: Stevens 175
California: Bobowski 324, Cheeryble 390, Davies 444, Dmarlou 455, **Flynt 514**, Katz 693, **Kinnouli 706**, Miller 830, On 880, Overall 895, Plum 929, Prete, 934, Ramsay 952, Rocca, 978, Walton 1156
Colorado: **Kenney 1302**
Connecticut: Alpha/Omega 1391, Baldwin 1399, Greenfield 1471, Howard 1484, Lebovitz 1506, Schloss 1562, Schwerin 1563
Florida: **Atlantis 1858**, Gralnick 2056, Hill 2097, Hoenle 2101, Kahn 2133, KBR 2142, Lastinger 2168, Shackelford 2327, Thompson 2372
Georgia: **Bancker-Williams 2440**, Broadfield 2449, Illges 2518, Lane 2536, McClatchey 2546
Idaho: Hare 2675
Illinois: McGraw 3092, **Mead 3100**, **Meyers 3107**, Simpson 3248
Iowa: Young 3552
Maine: Aldermere 3763
Maryland: Biophilia 3824, **Mpala 3919**, Tenberg 3964
Massachusetts: Allison 4000, Fraser 4097, Lingos 4177, **New 4220**, **Pegasus 4236**, Red 4260, Sacajawea 4274
Michigan: Burt 4403
Minnesota: Bell 4637, Bell 4638, Louis 4731
Missouri: Slavik 5007, Timmons 5021
Montana: Broadbent 5046, Cinnabar 5047, High 5057
Nebraska: Mapes 5103
New Hampshire: Thorne 5233
New Jersey: Ellis 5333, Klein 5424, Pheasant 5499, Schlaffer 5522, Staats 5549, **Waterfowl 5570**

New York: Anderson-Rogers 5676, Cullman 5886, **Eppley 5967**, Henderson 6189, JI 6260, Maher 6434, Marshall 6446, Paxton 6581, Rheinstrom 6665, Roe 6681, Thanksgiving 6897, Woods 6992, Woodward 6993
North Carolina: Hamill 7115
Ohio: Haskell 7439, Linnemann 7498
Oregon: Kimmel 7782, **Wyss 7832**
Pennsylvania: Brooks 7899, Hawksglen 8045, Huplits 8071, Seebe 8268, Up 8327, White 8355
Rhode Island: Love 8446, Woodward 8505
Tennessee: Pattee 8656
Texas: Hixon 8940, McAllister 9046, Stevenson 9220, Vaughan 9249
Vermont: Kaufman 9378
Washington: Hyde 9627, Northwest 9669
West Virginia: Hewgill 9748
Wisconsin: Antonia 9775, Dohmen 9807, Door 9810, Hunt 9845, LUX 9874, Tellier 9946

Wildlife rehabilitation
New York: Rheinstrom 6665

Wildlife sanctuaries
Delaware: Teddy 1760
Illinois: House 2980
Michigan: Burt 4403
Utah: Funding 9325

Winter sports
Colorado: Blair 1237, Howard 1295
Idaho: Nelson 2683
Maine: Franklin 3779
Massachusetts: Lingos 4177
New Hampshire: Lion's 5220
New York: Cader 5807, Dalton 5896, Maher 6433
Ohio: Gould 7430
Wisconsin: Highlands 9841

Women's rights
California: **Linked 758**
Illinois: Lehman-Stamm 3045
Kentucky: Kentucky 3669
New York: Alexander 5654, **Jabara 6254**

Women's services
Alabama: Anderson 5
California: Alafi 235, Baskin 281, Buell 357, Clara 406, Harris 601, Marineau 798, Moonwalk 845, Sawchuk 1010, Twanda 1135, Winkler 1188
Colorado: Steffens 1358
District of Columbia: **Gorlitz 1811**
Florida: Ellis 1989, Family 1997, Helow 2089, Wilson-Wood 2408
Georgia: **Bancker-Williams 2440**
Illinois: Allen-Heath 2701, Alton 2706, Burt 2770, Delavan 2825, Doyle 2836, Howard 2981, MacDonald 3068, McCabe 3084, Meier 3101, Rich 3194
Iowa: Carlson 3479
Massachusetts: Ain 3997, **Blossom 4022**, Cabot 4035, Chickering 4046, Hazard 4124, Ramlose 4257, Sandler 4278, Swan 4317, Tomfohrde 4329, Walske 4349
Minnesota: McCoy 4742
Nebraska: Soli 5119
New Hampshire: Charter 5206
New Jersey: Knight 5425, Stone 5553
New York: Alexander 5654, Alexander 5656, Cathedral 5822, Clemente 5850, Darrah 5900, DeMario 5909, **Eastman 5940**, **Engineering 5964**, **Jabara 6254**, Mertz 6481, Patrina 6579, Roche 6678, Rosenthal 6693, Walsh 6942
North Carolina: Lerner 7160
Ohio: Gay 7418, Walker 7630
Oregon: Charis 7748, Portland 7807, Spencer 7820

Pennsylvania: **Arronson 7844**, Community 7933, Hilles 8057, McGinley 8156, Murphy 8185, Remmel 8235, Tuttleman 8325, Valentine 8328, Ward 8343, Wurts 8370, **Zeldin 8376**
Rhode Island: Sinclair 8488
South Dakota: Watertown 8576
Tennessee: Nehemiah 8653
Texas: Daniel 8797, Levy 9014, Rosenberg 9162, Smith 9207, Whitley 9276
Utah: Bastian 9304
Vermont: Stokes 9385
Virginia: Ivakota 9477
Washington: Arise 9562, Schuler 9690
West Virginia: Stine 9768

Women's studies
California: Baskin 281

Young adults
Alabama: Black 12, Ireland 39, Malone 48
Arkansas: Olds 210
California: Five 509, Gellert 550, **Hefferlin 610**, Majestic 784
Colorado: **Fishback 1270**
Connecticut: Fippinger 1450
District of Columbia: Jovid 1817
Florida: Landwirth 2167, Mount 2223
Georgia: Abreu 2431
Idaho: Whittenberger 2689
Illinois: Family 2864, Meyer 3106
Kentucky: Killian 3670
Nebraska: Midlands 5104
New York: Aronson 5689, **Sparkplug 6830**, Strong 6872, Washington 6946
North Carolina: Glenn 7111
Ohio: **Brush 7338**, Ridgecliff 7560
Oregon: Elwood 7761
Pennsylvania: Hoffman 8062, Ludwick 8134, Mill 8172
Tennessee: **Fugitive 8618**, Schmidt 8671
Texas: Hill 8937
Virginia: Ivakota 9477
Washington: Foss 9598
Wisconsin: Marshfield 9878
Wyoming: **Schultz 9986**

Youth development
Alabama: Barkley 9, Black 12, Regions/AmSouth 58, Thompson 70, Viro 73
Alaska: **Nash 90**
Arizona: Cooper 109, Massie 146, Maxinmotion 147, Moeller 150, Murphey 151, Robson 160, Sturges 176
Arkansas: Bailey 186, Olds 210, Riggs 214, Southland 215
California: Adelaide 230, Barulich 280, Beller 297, Berry 309, Blanchard 321, Board 323, Boone 329, Bradford 337, Buell 357, Calaveras 369, Candor 373, Cleo 407, Community 421, Crawford 435, Dermalogica 451, Family 493, First 506, Five 509, Fox 523, Fusenot 541, Ginder 558, Godric 566, Greenwood 581, HCSC 607, Health 608, Heffernan 611, Jennings 663, Just 684, Knell 712, Legacy 740, Lester 747, Lin 757, Majestic 784, Marineau 798, Marshburn 799, Nachtsheim 856, New 864, O'Donnell 874, Orfalea 887, Page 899, Pauley 909, Peterson 919, Phillips 924, Picerne 926, Pralle 933, Rosenfeld 986, San 998, Sandnes 1000, Shannon 1030, Smythe 1061, Torino 1125, Waltmar 1155, Zacky 1205
Colorado: Blair 1237, Craig-Scheckman 1252, Family 1267, Medical 1324, Porphyry 1338, Reel 1345, Taddonio 1362
Connecticut: Derx 1435, Donchian 1440, Paoloian 1540, Taylor 1579, Thomaston 1581, UIL 1589, Union 1590, Zimmer 1603
Delaware: Easterly 1660, Hauser 1678, Massoud 1704, McKiernan 1706, Mulvaney 1713, Pinkerton 1721, Swift, 1754, Talbott 1757, Wang 1773
District of Columbia: Crowell 1799, Dimick 1803

Florida: Andreeff 1850, Basham 1870, Beall, 1876, Callas 1913, Cape 1917, Carbonari 1919, CSX 1958, de 1966, Forman 2011, Galeana 2030, Goodwin 2048, Greenblatt 2063, Gurtler 2070, Hagens 2071, HI 2093, Higgs 2096, Jacobson 2124, KT 2160, Kugelman 2161, Lazarus 2172, Leibowitz 2176, Mount 2223, Phillips 2259, Reinhold 2280, Sanders 2313, Seaman 2320, Thurman 2375, Zimmerman 2428
Georgia: Charter 2456, Echlin 2472, Hodge 2506, Piedmont 2566, Strong 2590, Vaughter 2599, Wish 2615, Woodruff 2617
Hawaii: Damon 2629, Kaneta 2637, Minami 2642, Shidler 2646, Takitani 2650, **Yoshimoto 2658**
Idaho: Equinox 2670, Morbeck 2681
Illinois: Almeida 2704, Bidwill 2741, Borten 2750, Cole 2798, Cronin 2816, Daeumer 2821, Dowdle 2834, Edelstein 2846, Franklin 2888, Gantz 2901, Gloyd 2917, Goldberg 2919, Hamlin 2946, Harczak 2952, Heath 2962, Holden 2976, Issa 2990, Jahn 2992, JBS 2994, JKP 2997, Jocarno 3000, Luehring 3065, Marquette 3078, McCabe 3084, Millard 3110, Moreton 3124, Pritzker 3184, Simpson 3249, Speiser 3257, Twomey 3298
Indiana: Community 3360, Crescent-Cresline-Wabash 3365, Custer 3366, Decatur 3367, Dubois 3370, Huntington 3397, Interactive 3398, LaGrange 3412, Niblick 3423, Roberts 3439, Seymour 3448, Shafer 3449, Springleaf 3455
Iowa: Gartner 3496, Jefferson 3514, K2 3515
Kansas: Bramlage 3559, O' 3612, South 3628, Stallman 3629
Kentucky: Houchens 3665
Louisiana: Magale 3735, Whitman 3759
Maine: Aldermere 3763, Brook 3769, Hudson 3783
Maryland: Acacia 3807, Baltimore 3817, **Goldberg 3872**, Levin 3900, Schuh 3946
Massachusetts: 2 3992, Babson 4009, **Blossom 4022**, England 4083, Koplow 4159, Makepeace 4186, Middlesex 4203, Newburyport 4221, Provident 4250, Russell 4273, Salem 4277, Simoni 4296, United 4337, Verrochi 4342, Weiner 4355, Xeric 4365
Michigan: Amerisure 4375, Ave 4379, Branch 4396, Conrad 4413, Delano 4426, Doll-Loesel 4433, Ervin 4437, Farver 4441, Ford-Thomas 4447, Garber 4451, Gratiot 4459, Jones 4472, JSJ 4474, M 4497, Mackinac 4499, Maly-Dykema 4502, Mariel 4504, Mills 4515, Olds 4526, Peslar 4537, Porter 4543, Price 4546, Sackerson 4557, St. 4576, Tuscola 4598, Tyler-Little 4599
Minnesota: Borman 4644, Edina 4671, Erickson 4674, Hallett 4706, Jostens 4720, Reger 4769, Remick 4773, **Trust 4802**, Weyand 4814
Mississippi: Taylor 4855, Van 4857
Missouri: Barrows 4864, Butler 4880, Gaylord 4914, Grant 4918, Impact 4930, Long 4948, Love 4951, Mungenast 4966, O'Reilly 4975, Sigma-Aldrich 5003, Slay 5008, Toutz 5023, Vassia 5029, Woods 5042
Nebraska: Batchelder 5072, Harper 5088, Herman 5090, Hester 5091, Malek 5102, Owen 5108, Scribante 5116, Smith 5118, Yount 5130
Nevada: Dermody 5152, Fuserna 5159
New Jersey: Beane 5259, Browder 5277, Carlozzi 5287, Hawthorne 5387, Kean 5417, Leavens 5444, Moriarty 5473, Olsen 5480, Scire 5526
New York: Ader 5644, Bender 5735, Blackman, 5755, Brandt 5777, Broughton 5790, Burchan 5801, Carroll 5816, Children's 5842, Fay 5989, Fitt 6010, Gaffney 6049, Georgia 6071, Gettinger 6076, Giordano 6081, Hatfield 6175, Hilliard 6208, Holmberg 6221, Johnson 6267, Johnson 6268, Koessler 6335, Lenox 6380, Marshall 6446, Mendell 6472, Miller-Sweezy 6494, Mittlemann 6500, Northern 6540, Oberoi 6547, Parke 6576, Quinn 6637, Risen 6672, RJL 6675, Shaftel 6782, Stecher 6851, Steckler 6853, Triangle 6908, WLC 6982, Zwirn 7035
North Carolina: Aehle 7038, Bettman 7051, Billingsley 7052, Burlington 7062, Cary 7070, Davis 7084, Fox 7103, Galanti 7104, Gambrell 7105,

Hayden-Harman 7120, Morisey 7191, Nalle 7197, Outer 7204, Von 7274, Walters 7278
Ohio: Albrecht 7301, Beck 7319, Brocker 7334, Building 7340, CLH 7355, Hickok 7447, Hueneke 7457, Knoll 7483, Kramer 7485, Laub 7490, Leach 7494, Loeb 7503, Orr 7543, S.E.C. 7567, Scotford 7579, Sears-Swetland 7581, Shaw 7587, Sidwell 7592, Skestos 7594, Stafast 7600, Tait 7610, Wyler 7647, Young 7651
Oklahoma: Moore 7710, Peel 7714, Russell 7718, Wegener 7731, Wolff 7738
Oregon: Ackley 7740, Demorest 7757, Elwood 7761, Hill 7773, Jurrens 7780, Leupold 7790, Metro 7798
Pennsylvania: Alley 7837, American 7839, Ashland 7845, Bennett 7860, Bergstrom 7864, Born 7885, Briggs 7892, Browne 7901, Campbell 7912, Dibona 7955, **Horner 8068**, Mason 8147, Mill 8172, Plankenhorn 8219, Scott 8266, Strine 8306, Tabas 8312, Weiner 8349, **Whimsie 8354**
Rhode Island: Beck 8386, Estate 8404, Heydt 8419, Moore 8456, Noyes 8461, Rainbow 8477, Schwarz 8483, Vanderpoel 8499
South Carolina: Campbell 8515
South Dakota: Ferguson 8564, Grundhofer 8565, J&L 8568
Tennessee: Citizens 8599, Cornerstone 8602, Foster 8616, Grandview 8625, Hollingsworth 8629, LaRoche 8641, New 8654, Rogers 8666, Williamson, 8685
Texas: American 8700, Ash 8709, Beghini 8724, Bowling 8737, Braun 8740, Clinedinst 8775, Doak 8818, Duddlesten 8829, Dunagan 8831, Dunaway 8832, Edwards 8837, Esping 8841, Fenner 8850, Fleming 8860, Flohr 8861, Freescale 8874, Hill 8937, King 8994, Lesley 9013, Levy 9014, Littauer 9021, LSG 9027, Lykes-Knapp 9030, Mays 9045, Montgomery 9070, Myers 9081, Orr 9104, Palmer 9112, Ray 9144, Smith 9204, Sparks 9211, Sure 9225, Tyler 9244, USD 9245, Walls 9257, Webre 9266, Womack 9289
Utah: Jackson 9329, JKS 9330, Wadman 9362
Vermont: Ferro 9372
Virginia: English 9443, Family 9444, Hilltop 9470, Honey 9471, Jones 9479, Keenan 9483, Powell 9513, Praxis 9515
Washington: Baker 9566, Bungie 9576, Foss 9598, **Jernigan 9631**, Juniper 9640, Titus-Will 9714, Young 9732
Wisconsin: AnnMarie 9774, Hicks 9840, Holoubek 9843, Koss 9866, Lyche 9875, Mound 9891, Okray 9896, Roehl 9917

Youth mentoring

California: Eleven 476, Fox 523, Solano 1063
Indiana: Fayette 3379
Ohio: Bicknell 7327, Bryan 7339
Pennsylvania: American 7839
Texas: Levy 9014, Lupton 9028
Virginia: Lawrence 9487
Washington: Everett 9592, Foss 9598

Youth organizing

California: Corwin 428, Frome 535, Giles 554, Jelin 662, Kadima 686, Rest 966, Roney 983, Stellar 1080, Troy 1130, Webb 1162, Welk 1170, Witkin 1191, Wolfe 1193
Colorado: Dea 1254, Heider 1290
Connecticut: Lavietes 1505
Delaware: Telluray 1762
Florida: Carros 1924, Coral 1952, Sullivan 2357
Georgia: Vaughan 2598
Indiana: Branigin 3348, Decatur 3367, Klapper 3408
Kansas: Taylor 3632
Massachusetts: Devereaux 4069, Kimball 4155, Safe 4275
Michigan: Frankenmuth 4450
Minnesota: Ferber 4682
Missouri: Long 4948
Montana: Lippard-Clawiter 5058

Nevada: C.A.N. 5142
New York: Barham 5715, Brosens 5789, Peckham 6583
Ohio: Feldstein 7394, Shannon 7586
Pennsylvania: Black 7875
Tennessee: Community 8601
Texas: Martin 9040, Perkins 9125, Proctor 9139
Virginia: Stafford 9535
Wisconsin: Stateline 9937

Youth pregnancy prevention

California: Codding 412, Gellert 550
Nevada: **Wood 5201**
New Jersey: **Knistrom 5426**
New York: Anderson-Rogers 5676

Youth services

Alabama: Rothschild 61
Arizona: Clark 106, James 132, McKee 148, O'Rielly 154, Rubeli 163
Arkansas: Bailey 186, Merkle 203, Nabholz 208, Trinity 218
California: Anthony 247, Barnett 278, Beam 287, Bellini 298, Beynon 312, Blackie 319, Boone 329, Bundy 359, Butler 364, **Chan 388**, Cheeryble 390, Codding 412, Cohen 413, Coleman 416, Danvera 442, Donegan 458, Dwelle 467, Eagle 470, Eriksen 484, Evans 486, Fitzpatrick 508, Five 509, Foster 519, Foundation 521, Hotchkis 635, Johnson 670, Kieve 703, Krishnan-Shah 722, Levin 749, Majestic 784, McDaniel 813, McKenzie 816, Merage 822, Morgan 847, Pardee 902, Pralle 933, Reinhold 963, Reitman 964, Sawchuk 1010, Schulte 1018, Smith 1055, Smith 1056, Staples 1075, Swayne 1097, Swinerton 1098, Thagard 1109, Tippett 1119, Tomlinson 1123, Torino 1125, Webb 1162, Wheeler 1179
Colorado: Caulkins 1245, Mullen 1329, Priester 1340, Spencer 1356, Taylor 1364
Connecticut: Cochrane 1420, Dennett 1432, Hall 1475, Jones 1490, Lavietes 1505, Proctor 1545, Smith 1571, Tully 1588, Vance 1591
Delaware: Brown 1631, Patterson 1719, Petersen 1720, Russell 1735, Teddy 1760, Thronson 1766, Whitman 1778
District of Columbia: Cafritz 1793, Crowell 1799, Hanley 1814, **Merriman 1820**, Westport 1838
Florida: Basham 1870, Bastien 1872, Baxter 1874, Beall, 1876, Bell 1883, Callas 1913, Capital 1918, Couch 1953, Day 1965, Farrell 1998, Gate 2034, Goodwin 2048, Hagens 2071, HI 2093, Higgs 2096, Hultquist 2115, Isenberg 2121, Jacobsen 2123, Kahn 2133, Kessler 2145, Lacy, 2163, Landwirth 2167, Lazarus 2172, Lelash 2178, Lerner 2180, Lewis 2182, Morrison 2222, Patterson 2250, Powell 2265, Price 2267, Rogers 2291, Simmons 2338, Six 2339, Stafford 2346, Sudakoff 2356, Tupperware 2379, Turner 2381
Georgia: A.E.M. 2430, Arnold 2436, Broadfield 2449, Community 2466, Griffin 2499, Illges 2517, Lanier 2538, McKnight 2548, Piedmont 2566, Stahl 2588, Vaughan 2598, Walton 2604, Williams 2612, Woodruff, 2618
Hawaii: Central 2627
Illinois: Alton 2705, Best 2739, Brown 2759, Burt 2770, **Combs 2800**, Cunningham 2819, Generations 2908, H.C.D. 2939, Harris 2957, Hay 2961, Highland 2970, Hoffer 2975, Jahn 2992, Lichtman 3052, McLennan 3096, Meyer 3106, New 3136, North 3142, Olin 3153, Peters 3172, Ringer 3196, Stone 3270, Sulzer 3277, Trio 3292, Twomey 3298, Woodruff 3330
Indiana: Bill 3345, Bussing-Koch 3353, Edelman 3374, Elder 3375, Herr 3392, Hulman 3396, **Mervis 3417**, Oliver 3428, Quigg 3433, Stamm 3456
Iowa: Gartner 3496, Iowa 3512, Krause 3516, McDonald 3520
Kansas: Berry 3558, Davis 3571, Dehaemers 3572, Family 3575, Swearingen 3631
Kentucky: Horn 3664

Louisiana: Harper 3726, Powers 3746
Maine: Kennebec 3785, Sukeforth 3805
Maryland: Acacia 3807, Anderson 3814, Chessie 3835, Davis 3844, Devito 3848, **Doorstep 3850**, Eacho 3852, Ferris 3860, Hobbs 3882, Lutheran 3904, Pettit 3935
Massachusetts: Alden 3999, Babson 4009, Boynton 4025, Cabot 4035, Chase 4045, Chicopee 4047, Clementi 4050, Clifford 4051, Dedham 4067, Donovan 4070, Dwyer 4074, East 4075, Easthampton 4076, Fay 4087, Kelleher 4147, Kelsey 4148, Makepeace 4185, Marigold 4189, MutualOne 4216, Pilgrim 4245, **Robbins-de 4266**, Rockland 4267, Winning 4362
Michigan: Barstow 4385, Biederman 4391, Community 4410, Dana 4419, DeVlieg 4428, Harris 4461, Kellogg 4482, Meritor, 4511, Merkley 4512, Padnos 4529, Shine 4569
Minnesota: Bahl 4632, Bend 4639, Berglund 4640, Boss 4646, Dell 4664, Gage 4692, Rodman 4779
Missouri: Breidenthal 4875, Dierberg 4895, Gaylord 4914, Long 4948, O'Reilly 4974, O'Reilly 4975, Schneider 4994, Slay 5008, Slusher 5009, Toutz 5023, Voelkerding 5032
Montana: Gerhart 5053, Wendy's 5065
Nebraska: Hawkins 5089, Patrick 5109
Nevada: Banks 5135, Barker 5136, Petersen 5181, Wolzinger 5200
New Jersey: Davino 5313, Giants 5369, Gibson 5370, Jones 5408, Kampen 5413, Olsen 5480, Paragano 5488, Rukin 5516
New York: Burrows 5803, Farber 5986, Fleming 6014, French 6032, Gettinger 6076, Grano 6128, Klingenstein-Martell 6329, Kupferberg 6351, Marshall 6446, Mule 6515, Nets 6524, Plunkett 6611, Quinn 6637, Rheinstrom 6665, Samberg 6723, Sherman 6792, Summit 6877, Wagner 6938, Wells 6964, Wyckoff 6998
North Carolina: Burks 7061, Cameron 7065, Cannon 7067, Edgar 7088, Elks 7089, Nanney 7198, Robinson 7225, Rocky 7227, Schmidt 7236, Shugart 7242, Sloan 7246, Summer 7261, Wake 7276, Wells 7283
Ohio: B-Brand 7318, Christen 7353, Cleveland 7354, Crossroads 7367, Hazelbaker 7441, Klock 7480, Kramer 7485, O'Neill 7542, Powers 7550, Schwebel 7577, Shaw 7587, Van 7626
Oklahoma: Dill 7671, Kerr 7693, Merrick 7707
Oregon: Hitchman 7774, Kimmel 7782, Shapira 7814, Wessinger 7826
Pennsylvania: Alley 7837, Applestone 7841, Bennett 7860, Bergstrom 7864, Boscia 7887, Briggs 7892, Cameron 7911, Chase 7921, Dinardo 7960, Hall 8037, Hoch 8060, Horn 8067, Merwin 8170, Reidler 8233, Rider-Pool 8238, Teleflex 8314
Rhode Island: Arakelian 8381, Charlton, 8394, Coes 8396, Galkin 8410, Kimball 8434, Smith 8493, Washington 8500
South Carolina: Stevens 8541
South Dakota: Peterson 8572
Tennessee: Goldsmith 8622, Monday 8652, New 8654, Schmidt 8671, Wilt 8687
Texas: **AMD 8698**, Bowers 8736, Community 8782, Conley 8784, De 8803, Doskocil 8823, Edwards 8837, Frost 8878, Halperin 8912, Hofstetter 8943, Holloway 8946, Horizon 8951, Isaac 8962, Kayser 8980, Kirwan 8996, Knox 8999, Levy 9014, Mayfield 9044, Nislar 9088, Peine 9123, Reuhl 9150, Simpson-Omohundro 9196, USD 9245, Waggoner 9254, Watford 9262, Webre 9266, Weir 9268, Westcott 9273, Wright 9295
Vermont: Mergens 9381
Virginia: Wiser 9555
Washington: Brookshire-Green 9573, Crete 9583, Foss 9598, Goodman 9608, Hansen 9615, Horn 9625, Howarth 9626, **Jernigan 9631**, Johnston-Fix 9634, O'Donnell 9672, Shemanski 9693, Skagit 9696, Stars 9703
West Virginia: Hess 9747, Hott 9753, Logan 9756, Vecellio 9770
Wisconsin: AnnMarie 9774, Braun 9787, Dawes 9803, Glanert 9827, Glendenning 9828, Gordon 9830, Gordon 9831, Hyde 9846, Johnson 9853, Kohl

9864, Lakeview 9868, Lutsey 9873, LUX 9874, Manitowoc 9876, Meinerz 9883, Prescott 9905, Pritchett 9906, RITE-HITE 9915, Schlegel 9922, Smith 9931, Smith 9932, Uihlein 9950, Van 9951, Van 9952, Weyers 9959, Windway 9961
Wyoming: Perkins 9982, Stuart 9993

Zoology
Hawaii: **Yoshimoto 2658**

Zoos
Alabama: Anderson 6, Shook 64
Arizona: Ullman 177
California: Bundy 359, Butler 364, Dmarlou 455, Georgina-Frederick 552, Gooding 571, Waller 1152, Warren 1159

Colorado: Bardsley 1227, Brown 1243, Moniker 1327
Florida: Hill 2097, Lowry 2191, Ransburg 2274
Georgia: Brewer 2448, Goddard 2491
Illinois: Bartholomay 2721, Block, 2746, Caccomo 2771, Cohn 2795, Family 2864, Issa 2990, Kainz 3004, Karasik 3006, McCauley 3085, McCormack 3086, McNally 3097, **Meyers 3107**, Mullen 3129, Pitzman 3177, Staley 3263, Woodruff 3330
Indiana: Burris 3352, Cohen 3357, Custer 3366, Harlan 3391, O'Rourke-Schof 3429
Kansas: Berry 3558, Fidelity 3577
Maryland: Ferris 3860, Rouse 3943
Michigan: Hartwick 4462, Keller 4481, Talty 4584
Minnesota: Boss 4646, Midcontinent 4745, Terhuly 4799
Missouri: Favre 4908, Kuhn 4941, Love 4951, Walker 5034
Nebraska: Grewcock 5086

New York: Carroll 5816, Ferguson 5999, Vogt 6933
North Carolina: Sloan 7246
Ohio: Bates 7317, Demetros 7377, Linnemann 7498, Stillson 7607, Williams 7638, Young 7651
Pennsylvania: Boscia 7887, Danella 7948, Huplits 8071, Mill 8172, Pogo 8221, Randall 8230
Rhode Island: Felicia 8406, Janci 8428, Woodward 8505
Tennessee: Johnson 8634
Texas: Benton 8726, Fairchild 8845, Moore 9072, Shiloff 9193, Watson 9263
Vermont: Seventh 9384
Washington: DeFalco 9585, Ferguson 9596, Young 9732
Wisconsin: Antonia 9775, Dohmen 9807

FOUNDATIONS NEW TO THE EDITION

The following foundations appear in this edition of *The Foundation Directory Part 2* but had not met criteria for inclusion in the previous edition. They are included in all indexes.

2005 Tomchin Family Charitable Trust, CA, 223

5 51 5 Foundation, Inc., The, NY, 5631

6/S Foundation, CO, 1219

A.B. Reins Foundation, NY, 5632
Ackerman Foundation, The, IN, 3339
Adams Family Foundation I, TN, 8579
Ainsley's Angels of America, LA, 3711
Alalusi Foundation, CA, 236
Alaska Airlines Foundation, AK, 80
Alexander Charitable Foundation, NY, 5653
Alexander Family G Foundation Inc., Norman E., NY, 5655
Alexander Foundation, Andrew and Julie, The, TX, 8695
Allwin Family Foundation, The, CT, 1390
Alon and Shari Friendship Foundation, Inc., MI, 4374
Alvord Family Foundation, MA, 4002
American Airlines Foundation, TX, 8699
American Clean Skies Foundation, DC, 1785
American Express Charitable Fund, NY, 5664
American Friends of Merkaz Chasidei Viznitz Inc., NY, 5666
Ameritas Charitable Foundation, NE, 5067
Ames Family Foundation, WA, 9560
Amherst Foundation, TX, 8702
Amin Foundation Trust, Bijan and Soraya, CA, 241
Amnon Foundation, Inc., The, NY, 5670
Amory Outreach Foundation Inc., MS, 4821
Amsterdam Foundation, Jack and Mimi Leviton, The, NY, 5672
Anchor Foundation, The, MI, 4376
Andersen Foundation, Frank N., MI, 4377
Anderson Family Charitable Fund, NY, 5673
Anderson Foundation, Robert C. & Sadie G., FL, 1847
Anderson Trust, W. T., FL, 1848
Andreeff Foundation, FL, 1850
Angelica Foundation, NM, 5605
Anschel Eilian Family Charitable Foundation, IL, 2709
Anthony Foundation, Inc., Carmelo, CA, 247
Antz Foundation, The, NJ, 5250
Archangel Michael Foundation, NY, 5685
Archer Family Foundation, The, CA, 250
Arctos Foundation, MN, 4629
Arena Energy Foundation, The, TX, 8707
Armonia Foundation Inc., NY, 5688
Armstrong Family Charitable Foundation, Terry and Regina, The, TX, 8708
Arnold & Porter Foundation, DC, 1787
Asbjornson Foundation, OK, 7655
Astra Foundation Inc., The, MA, 4006
Athens Area Community Foundation, GA, 2437
Atkins Foundation, Inc., John G., OR, 7741
Atticus Trust, TN, 8582
Aurora Foundation, The, FL, 1860
Avery Arts Foundation, Milton and Sally, NY, 5702
Avery-Tsui Foundation, CA, 261

B.E.L.I.E.F. Foundation, The, TX, 8713
Backer Fund, Inc., T., NY, 5706
Bacon Trust, Charles F., MA, 4011
Baer Charitable Foundation, Arthur & Helen, MO, 4862
Bailey Family Foundation, AR, 186
Bailey Foundation, P. S. and Ouida C., SC, 8509
Bailey Trust f/b/o Riley Hospital, Cicero Milo, IL, 2716

Baker Corporation Foundation, Michael, PA, 7851
Baldacci Family Foundation, Paul & Betty, CA, 268
Baldwin Foundation, The, CT, 1399
Balk Foundation, James & Shirley, MI, 4383
Ballard Foundation, The, TX, 8716
Bandai Foundation, The, CA, 271
Baroco Foundation, Inc., J. H., FL, 1867
Barron Family Foundation, MI, 4384
Basham Foundation, Inc., Danker, FL, 1870
Baskin Foundation, Peggy and Jack, The, CA, 281
Bass Foundation Inc., Robert and Isabelle, IL, 2723
Battle Family Foundation, The, AL, 10
BB&T Charitable Foundation, NC, 7045
Beagle Charitable Foundation, CA, 286
Beane Family Foundation, NJ, 5259
Beard-Payne Family Foundation, The, GA, 2442
Beck Trust, Christine L., RI, 8386
Becker Family Foundation, IA, 3472
Beckman Award Trust, Elizabeth Hurlock, GA, 2443
Beer Trust, Paul, NE, 5073
Bellebyron Foundation, IL, 2731
Benjamin & Heather Crane Foundation Inc., The, TN, 8586
Bennett Foundation, C. E., DE, 1618
Benson Family Charitable Trust, The, MA, 4016
Berbecker Scholarship Fund, Walter J. and Lille A., CT, 1406
Berbeewalsh Foundation, Inc., WI, 9782
Berger Fund, Leo V., MD, 3821
Bergman Family Foundation, CA, 304
Bergstrom Foundation, The, MA, 4019
Berkowitz Family Charitable Foundation Inc., Jeff and Yolanda, FL, 1886
Berning Private Foundation, Donald N. and Jane L., Dr., DE, 1620
Bet Lev Foundation, NY, 5742
Betts Family Foundation, NY, 5744
Bhappu Family Foundation, Ross R. and Candy L., The, CO, 1234
Biloxi Regional Medical Center, Inc., MS, 4824
Bingham Foundation, W. Richard Bingham and Winifred W., The, NY, 5747
Bjorkman Foundation, Carl George, The, CO, 1236
Blanchard Foundation, The, CA, 321
Blank Foundation, Nancy & Robert S., NY, 5756
Blatt Family Foundation, FL, 1893
Bloch Educational and Charitable Foundation, Raymond and Elizabeth, The, PA, 7878
Boehm Charity Fund, Hershel & Esther, MD, 3826
Bogoni Operating Foundation, Paul and Irene, The, NY, 5766
Bolick Foundation, The, NC, 7056
Booth Inc., Suzanne Deal Booth and David G., TX, 8735
Borch Foundation, The, CA, 330
Bostock Family Foundation, MI, 4395
Bowen Foundation, Ethel N., WV, 9737
Bowling Family Charitable Foundation, TX, 8737
Boxer Foundation, The, NY, 5772
Brass Family Foundation, TX, 8738
Bratten Foundation, Meta Alice Keith, TX, 8739
Braun & Bocklett Family Foundation, Thelma, TX, 8740
Breck Foundation, Henry & Wendy, NY, 5780
Brentwood Foundation, TX, 8741
Brewster West Foundation, CA, 341
Bridge Foundation, Inc., The, TX, 8742
Briggs Foundation, Margaret, PA, 7892

Brinklee Foundation, The, MO, 4876
Brock Family Foundation, MA, 4027
Brooker Foundation, T. Kimball, IL, 2758
Brooks Charitable Trust, Mary Jane, OH, 7335
Brothers Ashkenazi Foundation, Inc., The, NJ, 5276
Brotman Family Foundation, WA, 9574
Browder Family Foundation, NJ, 5277
Brownsville Foundation for Health and Education, TX, 8752
Bruce Foundation, IL, 2760
Brunie Foundation, Jean I. & Charles H., The, NY, 5792
BTMU Foundation, Inc., The, NY, 5795
Buck Foundation, Caroline Alexander, PA, 7903
Buffalo Sabres Alumni Association, NY, 5799
Building Healthy Lives Foundation, OH, 7340
Burbank Health Care Foundation, CA, 361
Burke Family Foundation, IA, 3477
Burks Family Foundation Inc., FL, 1909
Burns Memorial Fund, Anne Klinger, NC, 7063
Burzik Foundation, Catherine and Francis, TX, 8758
Butler Family Fund, The, DC, 1792

Cabbadetus Foundation, MA, 4033
Camara-Press Foundation, MN, 4652
Cambridge Mindful Living Foundation, TX, 8760
Camp Foundation, Inc., J. L., VA, 9413
Campbell Charitable Foundation, Charles Talbot, PA, 7912
Campbell Family Foundation, John and Jane, TN, 8594
Campbell Family Foundation, Charles and Debby, TN, 8595
Campbell Foundation, Betsy M., SC, 8515
Canipe Foundation, Walter G., GA, 2452
Cargill Charitable Trust, Robert L. and Sara Lou, TX, 8761
Carle Foundation, Eric & Barbara, The, MA, 4037
Carlin Foundation, Inc., Audre and Donald, FL, 1921
Carlson Memorial Foundation, Inc., Gunard Berry, PA, 7916
Carnahan-Jackson Foundation, PA, 7917
Caroline's Kids Foundation, MN, 4654
Carroll Family Foundation, Inc., NC, 7068
Carros Foundation, Jean Keller and Robert, The, FL, 1924
Carters Charitable Foundation, Inc., GA, 2454
Castleman Family Foundation, The, NV, 5144
CDVSJ Foundation, NY, 5825
Central Pacific Bank Foundation, HI, 2627
Chada Foundation, Inc., NY, 5830
Chambers Charitable Trust, Naomi B., IL, 2780
Chambers Medical Foundation, LA, 3718
Chambers Memorial, James B., WV, 9742
Chamiza Foundation, NM, 5609
Chaney Family Foundation, OH, 7349
Chang Foundation, Margaret and Peter, NJ, 5289
Chapman Perelman Foundation, The, NY, 5832
Charles Fund, Inc., The, VA, 9418
Chasdei Yakov Foundation Inc., NY, 5835
Chestnut Foundation, The, CA, 392
Childress Foundation, The, SC, 8518
Chiles Foundation, OR, 7749
Chinook Charitable Trust, NY, 5844
Chirag Foundation, The, MA, 4048
Chitjian Family Foundation, Harry and Ovsanna, CA, 396
Christ Foundation, OH, 7352
Christian Evangelical Foundation, MI, 4407

Cinmar Family Foundation, MO, 4887

Citrin Charitable Foundation, Rona and Jeffrey, CT, 1419

City Hill Foundation, DE, 1642

Clarke Trust, John, The, MA, 4049

Cleo Foundation, The, CA, 407

Cless Family Foundation, IL, 2793

Clifton Foundation Inc., The, MD, 3836

Coffey Charitable Trust, Larry R., KY, 3650

Coffin Trust, George F. Coffin, Jr. & Claire E., PA, 7930

Cohen Private Foundation, Robert, NV, 5149

Cole Foundation, Kenneth, NY, 5868

Community Foundation of Chippewa County, WI, 9797

Community Foundation of Madison and Jefferson County, Inc., IN, 3359

Community Foundation of Orange County, Inc., NY, 5872

Community Foundation of Randolph County, Inc., IN, 3361

Community Foundation of Union County, Inc., OH, 7357

Conn Family Foundation, The, OH, 7360

Cook Foundation, Gayle and Bill, IN, 1797

Cook Foundation, Mark and Judith, TX, 8787

Cook, Sr. Charitable Trust, Claude P., GA, 2468

Cooke Trust, Elbridge C., MN, 4659

Coolidge Hill Foundation, MA, 4057

Cooper Family Foundation, AZ, 109

Corkins Family Foundation, DE, 1648

Cramblit Family Foundation, The, CA, 432

Crawford Heritage Community Foundation, PA, 7944

Cray Family Foundation, Cloud L. & Sara J., The, KS, 3569

Crescere Foundation, NV, 5151

Crowe Family Foundation, MA, 4061

Cumming Foundation, Barbara Bell, NY, 5888

Dalessandro Foundation, The, MA, 4063

Daly Narthex Project Charitable Remainder Unitrust, Helen E., VT, 9371

Damon Trust, Gertrude M., HI, 2629

Dana Foundation, MI, 4419

Danella Foundation, Carmen, The, PA, 7948

Davis Family Charities, Inc., James E., FL, 1962

Davis Foundation, Inc., Cora and John H., MD, 3844

Davis Trust for Charity, Mirrel, PA, 7951

Davis Trust for Employees, George H., TX, 8799

Day Foundation, James C. and Teresa K., TX, 8800

Day Memorial Fund, M. M. and P. A., DE, 1654

Daydreams Foundation, Inc., The, MD, 3845

De Llano Charitable Trust, Matias, TX, 8803

Dearborn Family Foundation, CA, 448

Debbink Family Foundation, Inc., WI, 9804

Declaration of Trust of the Joseph and Mary Cacioppo Foundation, AZ, 111

Degnan Family Foundation, Inc., The, NJ, 5315

Degroot Family Foundation, MI, 4423

DEKA Foundation, The, NH, 5210

DeLoache Testamentary Charitable Trust, Waldo, GA, 2471

DeLuca Foundation, Inc., Frederick A., The, CT, 1431

Denman Family Foundation, TX, 8810

Dermitt Hospital, Jeanette, OH, 7378

Dialysis Research Foundation, UT, 9319

Dick Family Foundation, The, IL, 2830

Dickson Memorial Trust, Conway Wing Dickson and Gertrude Finck, PA, 7957

Dierberg Foundation, The, MO, 4895

Dieringer Family Foundation, Bob and Evelyn, OR, 7758

Diermeier Family Foundation, FL, 1976

Dik Family Foundation, Edward and Evelyn, MI, 4430

Dobbs Charitable Foundation, W.M. Craig and Teneen L., IN, 3368

Donchian Foundation, Inc., Richard Davoud, CT, 1440

Donnelly Foundation, Mary J., PA, 7963

Doolittle Charitable Trust No. 1, Elizabeth Elser, WI, 9809

Dore Charitable Foundation, Fred H. & Mary S., WA, 9587

Dorn Foundation, Frederick W. and Janet P., OH, 7380

Downey Foundation, James E., The, CA, 460

Downs Miller Foundation, Inc., Doreen, NY, 5931

Doyle Foundation, Inc., The, FL, 1980

Doyon Foundation, The, AK, 84

Draft Family Foundation, Melvin C., FL, 1981

Dreamweaver Foundation, UT, 9320

Dresner Foundation, Inc., Milton H., MI, 4434

Dreyfus Foundation, VA, 9436

Drost Charitable Foundation, Carl and Martha, IA, 3487

DTS Foundation Inc., NY, 5933

Duchene Foundation, Doris J. & Donald L., MI, 4435

Duckwall Foundation, Frank E., FL, 1982

Ducommun & Gross Foundation, CA, 465

Dull Casper Trust, PA, 7967

Dunbar Foundation, Inc., KY, 3653

Duneland Health Council, Inc., IN, 3372

Dunn Family Foundation, MO, 4898

Dunning Memorial Fund Trust, Mildred H., IL, 2841

Dvaykus Fondation Inc., NY, 5937

Dysimmune Neuromuscular Diseases Foundation, FL, 1986

Dyson Foundation North America, James, IL, 2842

Eberhart Foundation, David F. and Frances A., NY, 5942

EBV Foundation, NV, 5154

Echevarria Family Foundation, Inc., FL, 1987

Edelman Family Foundation, Thomas J., The, NY, 5943

Edelman Foundation, Inc., Jack and Debra, IN, 3374

Educational Projects Foundation Inc., NY, 5945

Elazar Fund, Yalket, NY, 5953

Electrical Industry Scholarship Fund, The, NY, 5954

Elizabethtown Healthcare Foundation, NJ, 5332

Elliotsville Plantation Inc, ME, 3777

Elliott Foundation, William and Muriel, PA, 7977

Ellis Foundation, Inc., Gail G., IL, 2853

Ellman Foundation, NY, 5956

Elrod Foundation, Ben M. and Betty Lou, AR, 195

Eluzer Fund, Bais, NY, 5958

English Memorial Fund, Florence C. and Harry L., The, GA, 2474

Enterline Foundation, The, GA, 2475

EON Charitable Foundation, DE, 1661

Eplee Foundation, Inc., The, NC, 7092

Eppley Foundation for Research, Inc., The, NY, 5967

Erion Foundation, CO, 1265

Eskenazi Family Foundation, Inc., IN, 3377

ESL Charitable Foundation, NY, 5969

Eternal Abundance Foundation, Inc., IN, 3378

Everest Edwin Foundation, CA, 488

Everett Community Foundation, Greater, The, WA, 9592

Evert Foundation, MN, 4676

Ezer Foundation, NY, 5974

Farber Foundation, Gloria and Hilliard, The, NY, 5986

Farid Foundation, CT, 1444

Farnham Foundation, IL, 2865

Farris Charitable Trust, The, NJ, 5342

Farview Foundation, MN, 4680

Faser Triplett Foundation, Dr. and Mrs. R., MS, 4835

Fast Forward Foundation, The, CA, 498

FCTS Machine Technology Fund, MA, 4088

Federation of Protestant Welfare Agencies Trust, IL, 2868

Feinman Foundation, Alfred and Harriet, NY, 5994

Feldman Family Foundation, Steven and Marcy, The, NY, 5995

Feldstein Private Foundation, Mark S., OH, 7394

Felicia Fund, Inc., RI, 8406

Ferguson Charitable Trust, Dan C., FL, 1999

Ferguson Family Foundation Trust, The, SD, 8564

Ferguson Foundation, The, CA, 503

Ferrari Foundation, Andrew U., VA, 9446

Ferris Charitable Operating Foundation, Constance and Carl, MD, 3859

Ferry Family Foundation, The, OH, 7396

Feth Family Foundation, The, OH, 7397

Fickett Charitable Foundation, Franklin I., TX, 8854

Fields Automotive Group Foundation, Inc., Earl and Bettie, The, IL, 2870

Findlay Education Foundation, NV, 5156

Fink Family Trust, R. and M., VA, 9447

Firman Fund, OH, 7400

Fischel Foundation, Harry and Jane, NY, 6009

Fishback Foundation Trust, Harmes C., CO, 1270

Fitt and James I. McLaren Foundation, Lawton W., NY, 6010

Fitzgibbons Foundation, John & Christine, The, NY, 6011

Five Bridges Foundation, CA, 509

Flaherty Family Foundation, MN, 4686

Flaherty Family Foundation, The, NY, 6012

Flathead Community Foundation, MT, 5050

Fleischmann Foundation, OH, 7404

Fleming Family Foundation, The, MA, 4092

Flippo Foundation, Jane and Arthur, The, VA, 9449

Foley Family Foundation Inc., Lawrence & Megan, CT, 1452

Ford Fund, William and Martha, MI, 4445

Fortisure Foundation, CA, 518

Foster Charitable Trust, F. Gordon, NC, 7101

Foulkes Foundation, Inc., Duane and Kathleen, WI, 9821

Foundation 3311, FL, 2015

Foundation for Retinal Research, IL, 2881

Foust Educational Fund, Flora, IL, 2883

Fraiman Foundation, Inc., Chaim & Rose, NY, 6023

Frankle Family Foundation, Inc., FL, 2019

Frautschi Family Foundation, Inc., John J., WI, 9822

French Family Educational Foundation, R. E., KS, 3579

Freund Family Foundation, The, NY, 6034

Friedman Charitable Foundation, Inc., MD, 3866

Friedman Family Foundation, Frank & Fred, The, AL, 27

Friends of Kang Yun Foundation, CT, 1455

Friends of the Center for American Studies Society, The, CT, 1456

Friends of the Guiomar Smeets Foundation Inc., NY, 6042

Friezo Family Foundation, The, CT, 1457

Froderman Foundation, Inc., The, IN, 3383

Frost Family Foundation, HI, 2632

Frost-Parker Foundation, The, OH, 7413

Full Circle Foundation, IL, 2895

Fulton Foundation, David and Amy, WA, 9601

Fund for Innovation and Public Service, VA, 9455

Fusco Family Foundation, Inc., MD, 3868

Galanti Foundation, Peter & Mildred, NC, 7104

Gale Foundation, Bulova, MA, 4100

Galvan Foundation Charitable Trust, NY, 6053

Gantz Family Foundation, IL, 2901

Gardner Charitable Foundation, Eldon and Emma Belle, TN, 8619

Garfinkle Family Charitable Trust, NJ, 5364

Gebhardt Foundation, Inc., WI, 9826

Gelbman Charitable Trust, Frank & Pearl E., OH, 7420

Gemunder Foundation, Joel F., FL, 2036

Genecov Foundation, A. S., TX, 8886

Genesis Philanthropic Fund, IL, 2910

Georgia G. Hiden Charitable Foundation, NY, 6071

Gerath Foundation, Gerald and Claire, CT, 1462

Giacoletto Foundation, John P. and Lawrence J., IA, 3499

Gibson and Rosemary Kirr Charitable Trust, Richard P., PA, 8016

Gibson Family Foundation, NJ, 5370

Gilleland Foundation, Richard and Ellen, The, CA, 556

Gimbel & Elga Andersen-Gimbel Memorial Trust, Peter R., NY, 6079

Ginder Family Foundation, The, CA, 558

Giop Charitable Foundation, Sonia Raiziss, PA, 8018

Give to Life Foundation, TX, 8890

Giving Back Foundation, The, DE, 1668

Glassen Memorial Foundation, Hal & Jean, MI, 4454

Gleeson Family Foundation, IA, 3500

Glens Falls Foundation, The, NY, 6082

Gloeckner Foundation, Inc., Fred C., The, NY, 6083

Gloria And Charles Clough Foundation, MA, 4104

Gloria Dei Foundation, DE, 1670

Goldberg Foundation, Raymond & Ellen, PA, 8021

Goodfellow Fund, WA, 9607

Gorab Foundation, Eugene A. & Suzanne H., CT, 1468

Gordon Foundation, Betsy, The, CA, 574

Gordon Foundation, Gertrude S., WI, 9831

Gordon Fund, Kathy and Al, The, NY, 6111

Gordy Foundation, Evelyn and Frank, The, GA, 2493

Gostomski Foundation, The, IL, 2925

Gottlieb Foundation, Inc., Adolph and Esther, NY, 6114

Grace Family Foundation, NY, 6118

Grace Foundation, William M. & Ann K., AZ, 125

Gralnick Foundation, NY, 6121

Grateful Foundation Inc., NY, 6131

Gray-Pampa Foundation, Inc., TX, 8900

Green Family Foundation, Louis & Anne, FL, 2061
Greene Charitable Trust, Helen Wade, RI, 8413
Greenwood Foundation, Lewis, The, CA, 581
Grinnell Mutual Group Foundation, IA, 3501
Gross Charitable Trust, Stella B., CA, 587
Grosse Pointe Housing Foundation, MI, 4460
Grossman Charitable Trust, Sanford J., CO, 1281
Grossman Family Philanthropic Foundation, The, NY, 6146
Grubman Compton Foundation, The, NY, 6147
Grumbacher Foundation Inc., Stanley and Kathleen, NY, 6148
GuideOne Insurance Foundation, Inc., The, IA, 3503
Guild of the Dome Inc., PA, 8031
Gulati Family Foundation, The, PA, 8032
Gunther Charitable Foundation, Arno, WI, 9833

Haarlow Family Charitable Foundation, IL, 2940
Hafer Scholarship Trust, W.W. & Lucretia, NY, 6155
Hagadone Foundation, Inc., Lola and Duane, ID, 2674
Hagan Foundation, WA, 9612
Hahn Family Foundation, The, FL, 2072
Hales Family Foundation, Inc., The, NY, 6159
Haley Family Foundation, MA, 4114
Halle Foundation, Inc., Martha & Warren, MD, 3878
Halmos Family Foundation, Inc., Steven J., FL, 2075
Halsted Charitable Foundation, Louise Davis, RI, 8415
Hamm Family Foundation Inc., CT, 1476
Hanauer Foundation, Adrian, WA, 9614
Hankison Foundation, John & Virginia, OH, 7438
Hanley Charitable Foundation, Inc., Mike & Patricia, Dr., TX, 8915
Hansen Family Foundation, VA, 9465
Hanson CGF, Inc., Alex and Laura, NJ, 5383
Hanson Family Foundation, Alice G., IL, 2949
Hanson Family Foundation, WA, 9616
Harbanoff Foundation, Inc., Samuel, The, NJ, 5384
Harmstieg Foundation Inc., The, NJ, 5386
Harris Family Foundation, Matthew and Jennifer, NY, 6171
Harris Family Foundation, Robert & Shirley, CA, 601
Harris Foundation, William H., MA, 4118
Harrison 12Th Item, Thomas S., PA, 8039
Hart Foundation, John H., IL, 2958
Hartselle Scholarship Foundation, AL, 36
Harvey Family Foundation, Cannon Y. & Lyndia K., CO, 1287
Hatch Foundation, Deena, WI, 9837
Hawkins Foundation, Catherine, DE, 1679
Hawthorne Charitable Foundation, NJ, 5387
Hayden-Harman Foundation, NC, 7120
HCSC Foundation, Inc., CA, 607
He Foundation Inc., Zhengxu & Ying, NV, 5162
Heagele-Blount Animal Shelters, TN, 8627
Heart Institute of Southern New Jersey, NJ, 5388
Heck Foundation, The, CA, 609
Hegamyer Family Foundation Inc., William H. and Leonora K., FL, 2087
Hegarty Family Foundation, NY, 6182
Heide Foundation Charitable Trust, Ulf B. and Elizabeth C., The, MA, 4125
Henderson Education Fund f/bo Tulane University, IL, 2965
Heritage Foundation of First Security Federal Savings Bank, Inc., The, IL, 2967
Herman Foundation, NE, 5090
Herray Foundation, WA, 9621
Herring Charitable Foundation, C. T., TX, 8930
Hershaft Foundation, Arthur N., NY, 6197
Hershey Foundation, Jacob and Terese, TX, 8931
Hershman Family Foundation Inc., NY, 6198
Hester - Dundy County Public Schools Foundation, Elmer E., NE, 5091
Hickrill Foundation, Inc., NY, 6204
Hidden Leaf Foundation, CA, 620
Hieronymus Charities Inc, FL, 2095
Hildes-Heim Foundation Inc., CT, 1483
Hill Foundation, Madrona, OR, 7773
His Vision Inc., NJ, 5395
Hodge Memorial Fund, Emma Clyde, PA, 8061
Hoffman Legacy Foundation, Inc., IN, 3395
Hofheinz Foundation, Irene Cafcalas, TX, 8942
Hognander Foundation, MN, 4715
Hollowell Foundation, Inc., WV, 9751

Holopaw Homeowners, Inc., FL, 2108
Home is the Foundation, OH, 7452
Hope 2 Others Foundation, TX, 8948
Hope Charitable Foundation, TX, 8949
Hope, Love and Charity Foundation, WV, 9752
Hopedale Foundation, The, MA, 4134
Horowitz Family Foundation, Inc., G. & B., The, NY, 6225
Horwich Family Foundation, James and Ada, CA, 632
Hosser Scholarship Fund Trust, Edward Wagner and George, RI, 8424
Houck Foundation, Inc., Harvey R., Jr. and Patricia W., TX, 8953
Howard Charitable Foundation, Dale & Marilyn, IA, 3509
Huang Family Foundation, Inc., FL, 2113
Huie-Dellmon Trust, LA, 3729
Hummer Family Foundation, OH, 7459
Hunt Foundation, Samuel P., NH, 5214
Hunt Foundation, Vicky and Sam, NC, 7135
Hunter Charitable Trust, Estelle, NC, 7136
Huntington County Community Foundation, Inc., IN, 3397
Huntington Foundation, Inc., The, CT, 1486
Hurston Family Foundation, Inc., MA, 4138

I Dream a World Foundation, Inc., NY, 6235
i.am.angel Foundation, CA, 645
Ik Manzil, TX, 8959
Ilsababy Foundation, The, NY, 6238
Independence Foundation, Inc., KY, 3666
Ingle Charitable Trust, Tom & Evelyn, OH, 7462
Inglesea Charitable Trust, The, CT, 1487
Ingrassia Foundation, Elizabeth & Frank, NY, 6244
Insall Foundation, Mary V., NY, 6247
Integra Foundation, Inc., The, NJ, 5400
Invisible Hand Foundation, Inc., The, GA, 2520
Invisible Prince Charitable Foundation Inc., PA, 8075
Irving Foundation Inc., GA, 2521
Issa Family Foundation, Sultan and Sakeba, IL, 2990

J & S Laidig Family Foundation, Inc., IN, 3399
J. & J. Foundation, Inc., The, IN, 3400
J. C. K. Family Foundation, MO, 4932
Jackson Charitable Trust, John E. & Sue M., PA, 8078
Jadeja Family Foundation, Motwani, DE, 1685
Jaffe Foundation, The, CT, 1488
Janszen Charitable Trust, The, TX, 8966
Jasam Foundation Fund B, AZ, 133
JDH Family Foundation, CA, 660
Jenkins Charitable Trust, Tom H. and Anne H., The, OH, 7465
JFI Charitable Trust, NJ, 5405
JLH Foundation, IL, 2998
Johnson Charitable Trust No. 33, 1994 Christopher W., The, NY, 6266
Johnson Family Charitable Foundation, C. Paul, WI, 9851
Johnson Family Foundation, Joe & Nan, TX, 8969
Johnson Foundation, The, NY, 6269
Jones & Bessie D. Phelps Foundation, Inc., Cyrus W. & Amy F., CT, 1489
Jones Family Foundation, E. Richard, CA, 673
Jones Family Foundation, Louis and Donna, CA, 674
Jones Foundation, Herbert B., The, WA, 9638
Jones Foundation, Stella H., WI, 9854
Jordan Foundation, Kim, The, OH, 7471
Jost Foundation, Inc., Charles & Mabel P., CT, 1492
Jostens Foundation, Inc., The, MN, 4720
Judd Charitable Trust, M.H., NC, 7139
Jurrens Family Foundation, OR, 7780
JVZ Foundation, The, NY, 6277

Kahan Family Foundation, The, NY, 6278
Kahn Family Foundation, Inc., David & Jennifer, GA, 2529
Kaiserman Foundation, Jay and Becky, The, FL, 2134
Kaplan Charitable Foundation, Abraham, MA, 4145
Karamatsoukas Family Foundation, Nicholas J. & Celeste G., PA, 8085
Katz Family Foundation, Inc., Rosalie, The, NY, 6287
Katz Family Foundation, The, PA, 8089
Kearny Alliance, Inc., AZ, 137
Keefe Family Foundation, CT, 1497
Keeler Motor Car Company Charitable Foundation, NY, 6292

Keener Foundation, Robert W. & Barbara J., UT, 9332
Kelton Fund, Inc., CA, 698
Kennedy Foundation, NV, 5169
Kent-Lucas Foundation, Inc., DE, 1691
Kern Family Foundation, CO, 1303
Kerr Foundation Inc., The, OK, 7693
Kessel Foundation, Inc., George, NJ, 5420
Kessler Family Foundation, Carl E., TX, 8987
Key & Candle Foundation, NY, 6305
Kharis Foundation Inc., The, IN, 3407
Kienstra Foundation, Theodore A., The, MO, 4938
Kiernan Foundation, Peter and Eaddo, The, NY, 6306
Kies Family Foundation, David M., The, NY, 6307
Killian Family Foundation, MA, 4154
Kim Foundation, NE, 5098
Kimball Foundation, Horace A. Kimball and S. Ella, RI, 8434
King Foundation, Lloyd L. and Eleanor R., The, CO, 1305
King Trust, Annie Graham, AL, 44
Kingsbury Fund, The, RI, 8435
Kirk Humanitarian, UT, 9334
Kirkland Charitable Foundation, W. W., AL, 45
Kite Key Foundation, The, CA, 711
Klatskin Family Charitable Trust, Charles and Lynne, The, NJ, 5423
Klein, Jr. Foundation, David L., DE, 1694
Kline Foundation, Charles and Figa, PA, 8098
Knox Foundation, Robert and Jeanne, CT, 1500
Ko Foundation, Shannon & Amy, The, CA, 715
Kohl Charities, Inc., Herbert H., WI, 9864
Kohn Foundation, Zichron Moshe Vesther, NY, 6339
Kolar Charitable Foundation of Buckley Sandler, DC, 1818
Kolitz Foundation Inc., TX, 9000
Kornwasser Charitable Foundation, CA, 718
Korver Foundation, Kyle, UT, 9335
Kramer Charitable Foundation, Milton A. & Charlotte R., OH, 7484
Krause Gentle Foundation, IA, 3516
Kresa Family Foundation, NJ, 5432
Kroh Charitable Trust, CO, 1309
Krouse Foundation, Flora Dale, PA, 8103
Krueck Foundation, Anstiss & Ronald, The, IL, 3031
Krupp Family Foundation, MA, 4161

L.B. Research and Education Foundation, The, CA, 725
Lachman Family Foundation Inc., The, NY, 6356
Lacy, Jr. Foundation, Constance C. and Linwood A., FL, 2163
Ladenburg Foundation, NY, 6357
Lakeview Foundation, Inc., The, WI, 9868
Lamar Construction Foundation, MI, 4488
Lamond Family Foundation, CA, 729
Landau Family Foundation, IL, 3036
Landau Foundation, Pinches & Chanie, NY, 6362
Lane Foundation, Jeffrey and Nancy, NY, 6363
Lanting Foundation, MI, 4489
Larson Charitable Trust, Orville H. and Shirley I., IL, 3039
Larson Financial Foundation, MO, 4943
Laufer Charitable Foundation, Inc., Wayne L., FL, 2169
Lauzier Scholarship Foundation, Paul, WA, 9651
Layden Family Foundation, The, FL, 2171
Lazbridge Foundation, NY, 6371
Lebowitz Foundation, Steven and Deborah, The, CA, 736
Lee Family Foundation, Inc., The, CT, 1507
Lee Family Foundation, Theodore and Doris, NV, 5171
Legum Foundation, Inc., MD, 3899
Leibowitz Charitable Trust, Louis, FL, 2176
Leibowitz Foundation, Sheldon L. and Pearl R., IL, 3046
Leonian Foundation, Phillip and Edith, IL, 3047
Lesley Family Foundation, Inc., TX, 9013
Levmar Foundation, Inc., The, VA, 9490
Lewis College Fund, Paul A., TX, 9015
Lewis Family Foundation, Richard H., CO, 1315
Lewis Family Foundation, Robert and Beverly, CA, 753
Liberty Giving Tree, Inc., MD, 3901
Liddell Foundation, Robert Clay, OK, 7697
Light Charitable Trust, Jack H. & William M., TX, 9016
Lightner Sams Foundation, Inc., Larry, DE, 1699
Lin Foundation, Raymond and Joanne, CA, 757
Link Foundation, The, TX, 9020
Linked Foundation, CA, 758

Lipstein Family Foundation, The, PA, 8129
Liswhit Foundation, MA, 4178
Littauer Educational Trust, Helen Irwin, TX, 9021
Living Promise Foundation, NV, 5174
Lloyd Trust, C. L. and Gladys, TX, 9022
Locke Memorial Foundation, Owen, CA, 764
Loeb Foundation, OH, 7504
Loehrke Family Charitable Foundation, WI, 9872
Loewy Family Foundation Inc., NY, 6409
Long Foundation, Inc., John F., AZ, 141
Lopatin Family Foundation, The, NY, 6412
Lothlorien Foundation, NE, 5101
Lott Foundation, WA, 9656
Loudoun Hospital Trust 3, IL, 3060
Loudoun Hospital Trust f/b/o Eleanor, IL, 3061
Loudoun Memorial Hospital Trust 2, IL, 3062
Love Foundation, C. W. and Dorothy G., SC, 8532
Lovoi Family Foundation, P. Vincent & Sally S., OK, 7702
Lubo Fund, Inc., NY, 6417
Luedeking Trust, Otto, OH, 7506
Lundgren Trust, Carolyn C., CA, 772
Lungard Charitable Trust, Niels A. and Ruth, The, OH, 7509
Luther Family Foundation, The, MN, 4733

M&E Foundation, The, NY, 6425
M&P Family Foundation Inc., PA, 8135
MacCready Family Foundation, The, CA, 778
Magale Foundation, Inc., LA, 3735
Magaro Family Foundation, Inc., CT, 1516
Mahoney Family Foundation, Joan and Leo, The, MA, 4184
Maidenbaum Foundation, Inc., Iris and Shalom, NY, 6435
Makepeace Family Foundation, Maurice and Anne, The, MA, 4186
Makioka Foundation, NY, 6436
Manat Foundation, MI, 4503
Mann-Paller Foundation, Inc., MD, 3908
Mapes Charitable Trust, NE, 5103
Marietta College Trust LD Ryan-Main, NC, 7167
Marks Foundation, Michael J., HI, 2640
Marquette Bank Affordable Housing Foundation, IL, 3078
Marriott Daughters Foundation, MD, 3909
Mars Foundation, NY, 6444
Martin Foundation, Gilbert J., The, CA, 802
Mary's Fund Foundation, DE, 1703
Maslowski Charitable Trust, Frank J. and Eleanor A., MN, 4741
Maxfield Foundation, The, CA, 808
Maxinmotion, AZ, 147
Mb Caddyshack Charity Golf, Inc., FL, 2200
McClanathan Family Foundation, FL, 2202
McClelland Foundation, MI, 4505
McCormick Trust f/b/o Jefferson High School, Robert W., WV, 9759
McDaniel Charitable Foundation, TX, 9050
McEnroe Foundation, John and Patty, The, NY, 6463
McGahren Foundation, Marjorie & Richard, FL, 2204
McGinley Foundation, Rita M., PA, 8156
McIntosh Family Foundation, DE, 1705
McKay Foundation, The, CA, 815
McKinney Charitable Foundation, William V. and Catherine A., PA, 8161
Mclelland Family Foundation, The, PA, 8162
McLeod Blue Skye Charitable Foundation, Inc., CT, 1524
MCS Charitable Foundation, AZ, 149
Medical Education Collaborative, CO, 1324
Meerwarth Family Foundation, FL, 2209
Meridian Capital Foundation, NY, 6478
Merriman Foundation, DC, 1820
Metanoia Fund, MA, 4201
Metro Portland New Car Dealers Charitable Foundation, OR, 7798
MG Marland Trust f/b/o So Me Health Care, ME, 3791
Michael and Jill Stansky Family Foundation, MA, 4202
Mielcarek Family Foundation Inc., WI, 9888
Milano Foundation, Inc., NJ, 5466
Miller Charitable Foundation, Lou and Connie, OK, 7708
Miller Foundation, B. W. and Barbara, The, NC, 7185
Mitchell Family Foundation, Edward D. and Anna, CA, 838

Mitchell Foundation Inc., Stephen D., SC, 8534
Moach Charitable Foundation, NY, 6501
Mody Foundation, VA, 9501
Moeller Foundation, Joe and Mary, AZ, 150
Moffett Family Foundation, James R., The, LA, 3739
Molnar Foundation Corp., William and Marie, MI, 4517
Montgomery County Community Foundation, TX, 9070
Montgomery Foundation II Inc., GA, 2551
Mooty Family Foundation, Melvin R. and Sally R., MN, 4747
Moraine Foundation, The, WA, 9664
Morgan Charitable Foundation, James and Rebecca, The, CA, 846
Morris Family Foundation, OR, 7802
Morrison Charitable Trust, Cary Jay, FL, 2221
Mortenson Family Foundation, WI, 9890
Mosi Foundation, PA, 8179
Moskowitz Family Foundation, CA, 849
Moulton Christmas Poor Fund, Judge C. F., MO, 4965
Mound Properties Inc., WI, 9891
MSG Charitable Foundation Trust, NY, 6514
Mukti Fund, FL, 2226
Mule Family Foundation, NY, 6515
Mullen Family Foundation, The, PA, 8184
Mummert Trust, Austin James, TX, 9079
Munson Foundation, W. B., IL, 3130
MW Charitable Foundation, The, NY, 6517
Mylan Charitable Foundation, The, PA, 8187
Myra Foundation, ND, 7297

Nabholz Charitable Foundation, AR, 208
Naito Foundation, Samuel T. & Mary K., OR, 7803
Nalley Charitable Trust, SC, 8535
National Black McDonalds Franchisee Foundation, AZ, 153
National Endowment for Financial Education, CO, 1330
National Mah Jongg League Foundation, Inc., NY, 6520
Nelson Family Foundation, Donna and Dave, DE, 1714
Nelson Family Foundation, John and Judith, MA, 4219
Nelson Foundation, The, IA, 3524
Neuman Family Foundation, CO, 1331
New Beginning Resources, Inc., TX, 9087
New Tamarind Foundation, Inc., NY, 6527
Newman Charitable Foundation, Lizbeth & Frank, The, NY, 6531
Niblack Foundation, The, CT, 1533
Night Owl Foundation, IL, 3140
NLT Foundation, Inc., OH, 7537
Nobel Foundation, Inc., Fred I. and Gilda, The, FL, 2232
Nommontu Foundation, Inc., The, FL, 2234
Nonna's Garden, NY, 6538
Nordstrom/Seifert Family Foundation, WA, 9668
Norford Charitable Foundation, Edward R., The, PA, 8196
Northern California DX Foundation, The, CA, 870
Novick Family Foundation, The, IL, 3143
Nowiczewski Foundation, The, TX, 9090
Nuhn Charitable Trust, Jane W., NY, 6544
Nygren Foundation, Bill, IL, 3146

O'C Family Foundation, IL, 3148
O'Donnell Foundation, The, CA, 874
O'Hare Family Private Foundation, The, TX, 9095
O'Herron Family Foundation, The, CT, 1536
O'Rourke Family Charitable Trust, William James And Winifred Joyce, Dr. , MN, 4757
Oak Lodge Foundation, CO, 1333
Ocular Physiology Research and Education Foundation, Inc., WI, 9895
Offield Center for Billfish Studies, The, CA, 875
Ohana Foundation, Thomas, CA, 876
Ohel Harav Yehoshua Boruch Foundation, Inc., NY, 6552
Oliver Charitable Corporation, AR, 211
Olofson Foundation, Tom W. and Jeanne H., KS, 3613
Olson Family Foundation, Delmar and Audria M., The, IL, 3154
Open Stewardship Foundation, CA, 883
Opera House Fund, Inc., KY, 3684
Oppenheimer Family Foundation, The, IL, 3155
Opus Foundation, CA, 885
Orant Charities, TX, 9102
Oreggia Family Foundation, CA, 886
Orfalea Family Foundation, The, CA, 887

Orphan and Cancer Care for India Foundation, CA, 889
Orr Family Foundation, Robert O. and AnnaMae, OH, 7543
Orthodox Vision Foundation, CA, 890
Osteopathic Heritage Foundations, OH, 7545
Oster Family Foundation, Inc., NJ, 5484
Our Lady of Perpetual Help Trust, IL, 3159
Owusu Foudnation, George and Angelina, TX, 9107

P & B Foundation, NC, 7205
Paddison Charitable Foundation, TN, 8655
Palm Foundation, The, NY, 6571
Pangborn Trust, John C., PA, 8203
Panoram Foundation Inc., CT, 1538
Pappajohn Scholarship Foundation, John & Mary, IA, 3525
Pappas Foundation, Inc., MI, 4532
Parke Foundation, Jim and Shirley, NY, 6576
Parker Trust, George R., IL, 3163
Parrish Foundation, Charles Maxfield & Gloria F., UT, 9343
Partnership Foundation, The, TX, 9116
Pasquerilla Foundation, Frank J. & Sylvia T., PA, 8204
Patel Foundation, Dinesh and Kalpana, UT, 9344
Pathy Family Foundation, Inc., O. L., DC, 1825
Patterson Foundation, The, FL, 2250
Patterson Trust, James K., IL, 3164
Peace Foundation, IA, 3526
Pearce Foundation, Inc., Dr. M. Lee, The, FL, 2252
Pechter Foundation, The, GA, 2564
Pegler Family Foundation, NE, 5110
Peoples Federal Savings Bank Charitable Foundation, MA, 4237
Pepper Family Foundation, IL, 3167
Perkins Foundation, B. F. & Rose H., WY, 9982
Perper Foundation, William S., The, NY, 6588
Perryman Family Foundation, FL, 2255
Phantom Foundation, MI, 4538
Phelps Family Foundation, CA, 922
Pierce Trust, Thomas S., MA, 4244
Pilling and John B. Cross, Jr. Foundation, Frances, The, GA, 2567
Pinkin Foundation Inc, NJ, 5502
Pinkus Foundation, The, NY, 6607
Pisa Foundation, RI, 8474
Plainfield Foundation, The, PA, 8217
Planet Dog Foundation, ME, 3797
Planetary Trust, The, TX, 9132
Plankenhorn Foundation Inc., Harry, PA, 8219
Pletka Foundation, Kronhill, The, NY, 6610
Podolsky Family Foundation, IL, 3178
Posey Foundation, Andrew & Lillian A., TX, 9135
Potiker Family Foundation, Hughes and Sheila, CA, 932
Powell Charitable Foundation, VA, 9513
Powell Family Foundation, FL, 2264
Preik Family Foundation, The, FL, 2266
Pretti Foundation, The, NV, 5184
Prevent Cruelty To Animals (PVCA), CA, 936
Price Family Foundation, NY, 6627
Prime Time Foundation, Inc., FL, 2268
Priory Fund, CA, 940
Proctor Charitable Foundation, Elizabeth Craig Weaver, TN, 8662
Propst Foundation, The, AL, 56
Provision Charitas, Inc., TN, 8663
Pruet Foundation, The, MS, 4851
Public Life Foundation of Owensboro, KY, 3687
Pulichino Tong Family Foundation, Inc., FL, 2271
Pulvermann Charitable Trust, CT, 1547
Purple Moon Foundation, Inc., WI, 9908

Quigg Fund, Inc., IN, 3433
Quinn Charitable Foundation, Henry A., The, PA, 8229

Rachel Foundation, The, NY, 6641
Radio Drama Network, Inc., NY, 6643
Ragon Foundation, Phillip and Susan, MA, 4256
Rainbow Fund, RI, 8477
Rakowich Family Foundation, CO, 1343
Ratner Family Foundation, Horowitz, The, DE, 1724
Ratner Family Foundation, The, VA, 9521
Ravitch Foundation, Inc., Richard, NY, 6651
Reed Family Foundation, IL, 3190
Reed Family Foundation, Inc., Calvin H., FL, 2278

Regis Foundation, MN, 4770
Reichert Family Foundation Inc., Charles and Helen, NY, 6660
Reidy Family Foundation, NY, 6661
Relationship Enrichment Collaborative, CO, 1346
Remala Foundation, Satya and Rao, WA, 9683
Remick Charitable Foundation, Robert & Helen, MN, 4773
Repass-Rodgers Family Foundation, Inc., The, DE, 1727
Richmond Foundation, Wade, TX, 9152
Ridgecliff Foundation Inc., OH, 7560
Rifkin Family Foundation, IN, 3437
Riggs Benevolent Fund, AR, 214
Rimora Foundation, The, VA, 9524
Risen Son Foundation, Inc., NY, 6672
Rivera Foundation, Mariano, DE, 1730
Robb Charitable Foundation, Elizabeth N., IL, 3197
Roberts Foundation, Ed and Margaret, TX, 9156
Roche Foundation, The, CA, 979
Rockdale Foundation Inc., The, GA, 2576
Roles Family Foundation, MN, 4780
Rollstone Charitable Foundation, Inc., MA, 4270
Rose Family Foundation, FL, 2293
Rose Family Foundation, Inc., Marshall, NY, 6684
Rosenson Family Foundation, The, IL, 3209
Rosenthal Family Foundation, Leighton A., OH, 7563
Rosenthal Foundation, Ida and William, The, NY, 6696
Rosner Foundation, Inc., Leo, NY, 6698
Rotalia Foundation, WA, 9685
Rotasa Foundation, CA, 991
Rottman Family Charitable Foundation, MI, 4553
Roundy Charitable Foundation, Beryl O. and Wilma Sime, IL, 3214
Rouse-Bottom Foundation, VA, 9526
Rubin Family Foundation, PA, 8246
Rubin-Ladd Foundation, The, CT, 1556
Rukh Family Foundation Inc., NJ, 5515
Rupp Foundation Inc., Bill & Melinda, OH, 7565
Rupp Foundation, Richard W., The, NY, 6710
Ruskin Family Trust, The, FL, 2302
Ryan Family Foundation, The, FL, 2304

Saab Foundation, Ghassan and Manal, MI, 4556
Sackler Foundation, Inc., Raymond and Beverly, NY, 6716
Salatto and Family Charitable Foundation Inc., James A., CT, 1557
Salomon Family Foundation, Inc., William R. and Virginia F., The, NY, 6721
Sammut Family Foundation, CA, 996
Sander Foundation, MO, 4991
Sandman Family Foundation, The, MA, 4279
Sandnes Family Foundation, CA, 1000
Santoro Family Charitable Foundation, The, CT, 1558
Sappington House Foundation Library of Americana Trust, MO, 4992
Sarkowsky Charitable Foundation, Herman & Faye, WA, 9688
Sasco Foundation Corporation, TN, 8669
Sassoon Family Foundation, The, CA, 1006
Satar & Family Foundation, Abdul, NY, 6730
Sato Family Foundation, Inc., The, NY, 6731
Saul Foundation, Inc., Helen and Harry, GA, 2579
Savings Bank of Danbury Foundation, Inc., CT, 1559
SBJ Resch Family Foundation Inc., FL, 2314
Schalon Foundation, The, MI, 4558
Schepps Foundation, A. I. and Manet, TX, 9177
Schimmel Foundation, Inc., Stephen Harold, The, CA, 1015
Schiro and Peter J. Manus Foundation, Susan F., The, MA, 4282
Schonfeld Foundation, Inc., Steven B., The, NY, 6746
School of Dreams, Inc., The, NY, 6748
Schultz Foundation, Arthur B., The, WY, 9986
Schultz Trust, Robert E., PA, 8262
Schwartz Foundation, Valerie Beth, MA, 4284
Schweitzer Foundation, Inc., William P. & Gertrude, NY, 6759
Schwimmer Charity Foundation, C., NY, 6760
Sci-Port Foundation, LA, 3750
Scott Community Foundation, KS, 3623
Scott Family Foundation, Gay D. & William F., NJ, 5527
SDF Family Foundation, NY, 6765

Seaman Charitable Foundation, Douglas and Eleanor, FL, 2320
SEED Foundation, The, MI, 4562
Seiler Family Foundation, MO, 4997
Selkowitz Family Foundation, CT, 1565
Seme Foundation, Inc., TN, 8673
Sequoia Farm Foundation, IL, 3235
Servant Leadership Foundation, The, CO, 1352
Seven Turns Fund, Inc., NY, 6777
Seymour Trust, George Dudley, RI, 8485
Shalam Foundation, Sarah and Sasson, NY, 6783
Shanken Family Foundation, NY, 6785
Shanklin Foundation 2239788, MA, 4288
Shannon Family Foundation, Ken and Jan, The, KS, 3625
Shastri Charity Trust, Ranjit, PA, 8273
Shaw Charitable Trust I, Ilene & Michael, IL, 3243
Sheetz Charitable Trust, James E. and Maude, KS, 3626
Sheridan Family Foundation, Howard and Brenda, Dr. , NJ, 5533
Sherman Foundation, The, TX, 9192
Shirley Private Foundation, Virginia Lee, IL, 3245
Shoemaker Fund, Thomas H. and Mary Williams, The, PA, 8275
Shoemate Foundation, CT, 1569
Shrensky Foundation, Inc., MD, 3951
Shultz Family Foundation, The, AZ, 168
Sidewalk Angels Foundation, NY, 6796
Sidhu Family Foundation, The, FL, 2334
Sidwell Family Foundation, Jeff and Jennie, The, OH, 7592
Siegel Family Foundation, Blossom, The, CA, 1036
Signal Foundation for Wireless Innovation, Inc., DE, 1743
Silberman Foundation, Nathan and Marilyn, The, NY, 6798
Silverstein Family Foundation, Inc., Raine & Stanley, The, NY, 6802
Silverstein Family Foundation, Leonard & Elaine, DC, 1835
Simon Foundation, Lucille Ellis, CA, 1040
Simon, Jr. Foundation, Cynthia L. & William E., The, NJ, 5537
Simon-Strauss Foundation, CA, 1042
Simple Actions Family Foundation, OR, 7818
Slade Foundation, Michael & Ruth, NY, 6810
Small Change Foundation, The, CA, 1049
Smeed Memorial Foundation, ID, 2686
Smith Charitable Foundation, Will, The, TX, 9203
Smith Clinic Trust 2, Lemon L., IL, 3252
Smith Family Foundation, Byron & Beth, NY, 6814
Smith Family Foundation, Hunter, VA, 9534
Smith Family Foundation, Ted and Joyce, The, CA, 1052
Smith Family Foundation, Will and Jada, CA, 1053
Smith Foundation, Inc., George Graham and Elizabeth Galloway, NJ, 5539
Smith Foundation, Marguerite Carl, PA, 8282
Smith Foundation, Stephen S. and Dolores R., PA, 8283
Smoot Charitable Foundation, KS, 3627
Smullin Foundation, Patricia D. and William B., CA, 1060
Smythe Family Foundation, William D., CA, 1061
Snyder Foundation, Harold B. and Dorothy A., The, NJ, 5541
Snyder's-Lance Foundation, NC, 7250
Soicher Foundation, Harry and Estelle, The, CA, 1062
Sokol Family Foundation, NY, 6822
Sokoll Trust, Walter, MO, 5010
Sondland and Katherine J. Durant Foundation, Gordon D., The, WA, 9700
Southland Greyhound Park Community Foundation, Inc., AR, 215
Spark Charitable Foundation, WA, 9701
Sparkplug Foundation, The, NY, 6830
Sparrow Foundation, The, TX, 9212
Spencer Charitable Fund, NY, 6834
Speranza Foundation, The, NY, 6836
Spungen Family Foundation, Florence and Laurence, CA, 1071
Squam Lake Foundation, MN, 4793
SSAB Foundation for Education, AL, 67
St. Agnes Catholic Education Foundation, MN, 4794
St. Michael's Self Help Wajda Project Trust, MI, 4577

Stafford Foundation, James M., CA, 1074
Stare Fund, The, MA, 4308
Starker Family Foundation Inc., The, NY, 6847
Starmar Foundation, NY, 6848
Steele Family Foundation, FL, 2347
Stefansky Charitable Trust, Meir and Ruth, The, NY, 6854
Steiger Memorial Fund, Inc., Albert, MA, 4312
Stein Family Charitable Foundation, The, DE, 1750
Stein/Bellet Foundation, Inc., PA, 8300
Steinberg Family Foundation, Inc., Meyer & Jean, NY, 6857
Stephens Family Foundation, Harriet and Warren, AR, 216
Sterling Family Foundation, TX, 9219
Stern Foundation, Inc., Steve and Bonnie, FL, 2350
Sternberg Charitable Trust, NY, 6863
Stoddard Family Foundation, Inc., MI, 4579
Stoller Foundation, The, TX, 9222
Stone Family Foundation, OK, 7721
Stone Foundation, Joseph and Fiora, CA, 1086
Stony Point Foundation, The, SC, 8542
Storer Foundation, Mary H., WY, 9992
Storz Foundation, Robert Herman, NE, 5122
Strine Foundation, Walter M. and Alice Washco, The, PA, 8306
Strohm Link Family Foundation, The, CO, 1361
Strong Tower, Inc., GA, 2590
STS Foundation, IL, 3272
Stuart Foundation, Elbridge & Evelyn, WY, 9993
Stubblefield Foundation, Inc., The, NC, 7260
Stuntz Family Foundation, NY, 6874
Sugarbaker Foundation, Everett D. and Geneva V., MO, 5016
Sumitomo Corporation of America Foundation, NY, 6876
Sunnen Foundation, MO, 5018
Support Of Partners For Sustainable Development, CA, 1095
Sutton Family Foundation, Ruth & David, NY, 6882
Sutton Trust Foundation, The, NY, 6884
Suwinski Family Foundation Inc., The, NY, 6885
SVM Foundation, NY, 6886

Tahari Family Foundation, The, NY, 6890
Takitani Foundation, Inc., Mamoru & Aiko, HI, 2650
Tampa Bay Times Fund, Inc., FL, 2362
Tanimura Family Foundation, The, CA, 1103
Tarakji Foundation, MI, 4586
Tarrant Family Foundation, Jeffrey, DE, 1758
Taylor Family Foundation, Inc., Jack, FL, 2366
Tensor Foundation, NY, 6896
Testamentary Trust of Nellie F. Estes, KS, 3633
Tharpe Charitable Foundation, Inc., Max B., FL, 2369
Thomas Foundation, Harold E. & Phyllis S., DE, 1762
Thompson Educational Foundation, MI, 4591
Thompson Foundation, Jim and Angela, TX, 9234
Thompson Trust for Charities, Clara E., PA, 8317
Thornburgh Family Foundation, The, FL, 2374
Three Guineas Fund, CA, 1116
Todd Charitable Foundation, Ruth D. and Wylie, MO, 5022
Tompkins Foundation, Emmy Lou, The, TN, 8683
Toohey Foundation, Linda Glazer, IA, 3538
Tous Charitable Foundation, Mary F., NE, 5124
Tov V Chesed Foundation, NY, 6904
Trek Scholarship Foundation Inc., WI, 9948
Trio Foundation, IL, 3292
Trombetta Foundation, S. D., CA, 1128
Truman Foundation, Mildred Faulkner, NY, 6912
Trust for Aging in America Inc., IL, 3293
Tuffli Family Foundation, The, CA, 1134
Tully Family Foundation, IL, 3295
Tupperware Brands Foundation, FL, 2379
Tuscola County Community Foundation, MI, 4598
Tzedakah Fund, The, MD, 3970

Uihlein Foundation, David V., WI, 9949
Union County Community Foundation, Inc., AR, 219
United Plankton Charitable Trust, CA, 1136

Vaad Haartzy Inc., NY, 6924
Van Curler Foundation, MI, 4601
Van Devender Family Foundation, MS, 4857

Van Wyk Family Foundation, Arlan J., IA, 3540
Vanderbilt Trust, R. T., NC, 7273
Vanneck-Bailey Foundation, FL, 2384
Vela Foundation, MA, 4341
Villchur Foundation, NY, 6929
Vinoskey Family Foundation, VA, 9547
Viridiun Christian Foundation, DE, 1770
Vision Charitable Trust, The, CO, 1373
Von Magnus Henderson Charitable Trust, Maria C., MA, 4346

Wagler Charitable Foundation, Phil, The, OH, 7629
Wagmore Foundation Inc., FL, 2391
Wagner Agape Foundation, NC, 7275
Wagner Family Charitable Trust, PA, 8338
Wagner-Braunsberg Family Foundation, Inc., MD, 3975
Wal-Dot Foundation, TX, 9256
Waldis Family Foundation Inc., NJ, 5569
Wall Family Foundation, C. A., CA, 1151
Wallace Charitable Memorial Foundation, Inc., Fred & Alice, OH, 7631
Wallestad Foundation, MN, 4806
Warburton Foundation, Ralph T. & Esther L., The, PA, 8342
Watson Irrevocable Trust, William J., IL, 3311
Wattis Foundation, Phyllis C., CA, 1161
Waugh Family Foundation, The, FL, 2392
Weathertop Foundation, IA, 3545
Wehrle Foundation, H.B., WV, 9771
Weil Family Foundation, The, PA, 8346
Weil Foundation, The, AZ, 181
Weill Family Foundation, The, NY, 6949
Weiller Foundation, Inc., Ted and Jean, FL, 2393
Weiner Family Foundation, Roberta & S.R., MA, 4355
Weir Trust, Leroy and Merle, TX, 9269
Weismann Family Foundation, Philippa V., The, NY, 6960

Weiss Foundation, Mor & Eva, NY, 6963
Weiss Foundation, Robert Lee, TN, 8684
Welch Foundation, David and Heidi, The, CA, 1168
Weller Foundation, Inc., The, NE, 5127
Wells Foundation, Dan Kirkland, TX, 9272
Wells Foundation, Franklin H. & Ruth L., NY, 6964
Wendel Memorial Foundation, Lisa, NJ, 5580
Wessel Family Foundation, IL, 3318
West Davis & Bergard Foundation, CA, 1174
West Star Foundation, NV, 5197
Westbrook Foundation, CT, 1593
Weyenberg Charitable Trust, Frank L., NC, 7285
White Memorial Foundation, Bob, AR, 220
Whiting Foundation, The, MI, 4614
Whitley Charitable Foundation, The, TX, 9276
Whitwell-Meyer Foundation, The, OK, 7735
Wicks Chapin Inc, NJ, 5584
Willett Charitable Foundation, William Gerald, The, VA, 9552
Williams Foundation, C. K., The, PA, 8358
Williams-Malone Foundation, Inc., AZ, 183
Williamson Foundation for Music, CA, 1184
Wilson Foundation, Alan D. and Wendy R., MD, 3987
Wilson Foundation, Elizabeth Ruthruff, NJ, 5590
Wimmer Charitable Trust, Virginia, MN, 4819
Winiarski Family Foundation, CA, 1187
Winston Charitable Foundation, The, TX, 9282
Wise Family Charitable Trust, NC, 7290
Wiser Charitable Foundation Trust, Bob, The, VA, 9555
Wishnick Foundation, Robert I., The, ID, 2690
Wissner-Slivka Foundation, WA, 9727
Withim Foundation, The, CA, 1190
Witzel Family Foundation, WY, 10000
WLC and SBC Family Foundation, NY, 6982
Wolcott Family Foundation, CO, 1381
Wolf Memorial Foundation, Benjamin & Fredora K., PA, 8363

Wollowick Family Foundation, FL, 2412
Wong Foundation, Harry Chow & Nee-Chang Chock, HI, 2656
Wood Family Foundation, William H., DE, 1780
Woodard Family Foundation, The, OR, 7831
Woodruff Foundation, OH, 7645
WorldQuant Foundation Corp., CT, 1600
Worster Foundation, Susan & Bruce, CA, 1197
Wunsch Foundation, Inc., NY, 6996

Yamagata Foundation, NV, 5203
Yates Family Charitable Foundation, The, NJ, 5595
YGBL Foundation, Inc., NY, 7006
Yin-Shun Foundation, NJ, 5596
York Community Foundation, NE, 5129
Yost Trust, Elizabeth Burns, NC, 7291
Young Foundation, Inc., Beatrice M. H., HI, 2659
Younger Family Foundation, FL, 2422
Yount Foundation, Inc., The, NC, 7292
Youth Emergency Services, TX, 9298
Yulman Charitable Trust, Morton & Helen, IL, 3334

Zabala Family Foundation, CA, 1204
Zacky Family Foundation Inc., CA, 1206
Zacky Family Foundation, CA, 1205
Zale Foundation, Abe, The, TX, 9299
Zawadi Africa Educational Fund Inc., GA, 2622
Zehnder Foundation, Inc., James P. and Margaret L., FL, 2423
Zichron Shimon Foundation, The, NY, 7024
Ziegler Foundation, Ruth/Allen, CA, 1210
Zierk Family Foundation, The, HI, 2661
Zimmer Family Foundation, Max & Pauline, CA, 1212
Zlinkoff Fund for Medical Research & Education, Inc., Sergei S., NY, 7031
Zwirn Foundation, Daniel B., NY, 7035

FOUNDATION NAME INDEX

Numbers following the foundation names refer to the entry sequence numbers in the Descriptive Directory section. The letter "A" following a name refers to Appendix A, which lists foundations that appeared in the previous edition of the *Directory* but no longer qualify.

10/1 Foundation, Inc., GA, 2429
100 Acre Wood Foundation, PA, 7833
1335 Foundation, IL, 2691
18 Pomegranates Inc., DE, 1604
1830 Family Foundation, The, PA, 7834
1848 Foundation, NY, 5629
1916 Foundation, The, DE, 1605
1988 L.W. Foundation, The, CA, see 1170

2 Depot Square Ipswich Charitable Foundation, MA, 3992
2005 Tomchin Family Charitable Trust, CA, 223
21st Century ILGWU Heritage Fund, NY, 5630

4 Girls Foundation Inc., FL, 1840
484 Phi Alpha Foundation, Inc., The, MA, 3993

5 51 5 Foundation, Inc., The, NY, 5631

6/S Foundation, CO, 1219
613 Foundation, The, DE, 1606

A & A Fund, The, MA, 3994
A Charitable Foundation, NV, 5131
A Child Waits Foundation, MA, 3995
A Friends' Foundation Trust, NJ, 5240
A Glimmer of Hope Foundation - Austin, TX, 8689
A Glimmer of Hope Foundation Austin, TX, see 8689
A Good Day Foundation, OH, 7299
A-Kids-Choice Trust, LA, 3712
A-T Medical Research Foundation, CA, 258, see 258
A. & R. Charitable Foundation, Inc., FL, 1841
A.B. Reins Foundation, NY, 5632
A.E.M. Family Foundation, The, GA, 2430
A.P.W. Foundation Inc., NY, 5633
Aaroe Associates Charitable Foundation, Inc., CA, see 389
Aaron Family Foundation, The, PA, 7835
Abahac Inc., AL, 1
Abba's Ambassadors, Inc., NY, 5634
ABC Foundation, CA, see 952
ABE Charitable Foundation, Inc., The, DE, 1607
Abelard Foundation Inc., The, NY, 5635
Abelson Foundation, Stuart & Benjamin, IL, 2692
Abelson Foundation, Stuart & Jesse, IL, 2693
Abercrombie Foundation, The, KY, 3645
Abernathy Charitable Trust, Taylor S. & Patti Harding, TX, 8690
Abernethy Testamentary Charitable Trust, Claude S. Jr. and Raenelle B., The, NC, 7037
Abess Foundation Inc., Jayne and Leonard, The, NY, 5636
Abess Foundation Inc., Leonard L. and Bertha U., NY, 5637
Abettor Foundation, NY, 5638
Abilene Community Foundation, KS, see 3567
Abrahamson Family Foundation, NY, 5639
Abramowitz Family Foundation, CT, see 1384
Abramowitz Foundation, Kenneth and Nira, CT, 1384
Abrams Family Foundation, OH, 7300
Abrams Family Foundation, The, NJ, 5241
Abrams Foundation, Talbert & Leota, MI, 4369
Abrams Fund, Nina, CA, 224

Abramson Family Foundation Inc., NY, 5640
Abreu Charitable Trust, M & F, GA, see 2431
Abreu Charitable Trust, May P. & Francis L., GA, 2431
Abroms Charitable Foundation, Inc., AL, 2
Aca Family Foundation, MN, 4622
Acacia Charitable Foundation, MD, see 3807
Acacia Foundation, CA, 225
Acacia Foundation, The, MD, 3807
Ach Foundation, Rosenberg, CA, 226
Acheson Family Foundation, MI, 4370
Achilles Foundation, NY, 5641
Ackerman Foundation, The, IN, 3339
Ackerman Foundation, Thomas C., The, CA, 227
Ackley Foundation, Edward & Romell, OR, 7740
Acorn Alcinda Foundation Inc., CT, 1385
Acorn Foundation, MN, 4623
Acorn Foundation, The, IL, 2694
Acorn Investing, Inc., IL, 2695
Acriel Foundation, RI, 8378
Acworth Foundation, NY, 5642
Ad Astra Foundation, OK, 7654
Adair-Exchange Bank Foundation, KS, 3553
Adam Family Foundation, Donald A., The, TX, 8691
Adams Charitable Trust, Marjorie C., IL, 2696
Adams Family Foundation I, TN, 8579
Adams Foundation Inc., PA, 7836
Adams Foundation, AL, 3
Adams Foundation, Inc., Ellen H., CT, 1386
Adams Foundation, Inc., William L. and Victorine Q., The, MD, 3808
Adams Fund, CA, 228
Adams Legacy Foundation, CA, 229
Adelaide Christian Home For Children Inc., CA, 230
Adelaide Christian Home for Children, CA, see 230
Adelante Foundation Inc., AZ, 93
Adelman Family Foundation, Barry A., NY, 5643
Adelman Foundation, Lucy & Isadore B., CA, 231
Ader Foundation, Richard and Pamela, The, NY, 5644
Ades-Taub Foundation Inc., Joan & Alan, NY, 5645
Adikes Family Foundation, The, NY, 5646
Adkerson Family Foundation, Richard C., AZ, 94
Adler Family Foundation, The, MD, 3809
Adler Family Fund, Eugene M., IL, see 2854
Adler Foundation, Rita & Jeffrey, FL, 1842
Adler Foundation, The, MD, see 3809
Adler Foundation, TX, 8692
Adler Private Foundation, Inc., Myron and Elaine, The, NJ, 5242
Adonai Foundation Inc., CA, 232
ADR Foundation, Inc., The, TX, 8693
Adreani Foundation, IL, 2697
Ady Gil World Conservation, CA, 233
Aehle Charitable Trust, Norman G., NC, 7038
Ael Family Foundation, FL, 1843
Aeroflex Foundation, The, NY, 5647
AFAR Foundation Inc., NY, 5648
Afeyan Foundation, Noubar & Anna, MA, 3996
AFNIPI, IL, see 2707
Agape Foundation, IL, 2698
Agape Foundation, Inc., The, CT, 1387
Agape Love Foundation, Inc., TN, 8580
Agarwal Foundation, The, NC, 7039
Agate Foundation, Inc., S. & A., NY, 5649

AGB Fund, Inc., NY, 5650
Agee Family Foundation, TX, 8694
Agent F Leslye H Phillips Fam Fdn, IL, 2699
Agness Family Foundation, Terry D. and Carol A., IN, 3340
Ahavas Yisroel Charitable Foundation, FL, 1844
Ahearn Family Foundation, AZ, 95
Ahlstrand Charitable Foundation Trust, Armer F., IL, 2700
Aibel Foundation, Howard & Katherine, CT, 1388
Aim Charity, The, TN, 8581
Ain Family Foundation, Inc., MA, 3997
Ainsley's Angels of America, LA, 3711
AIS, RI, see 8494
Ajemian Foundation, Haiganoosh Mengushian, The, MI, 4371
AK Foundation, NY, see 6319
Akamai Foundation Inc., MA, 3998
AKC Fund, Inc., NY, 5651
Akers Foundation, Inc., GA, 2432
Akerson Family Foundation, NM, 5604
Akhoury Foundation Inc., NJ, 5243
Akian Foundation, CA, 234
Akridge Family Foundation, MD, 3810
Alafi Family Foundation, CA, 235
Alalusi Foundation, CA, 236
Alaska Airlines Foundation, AK, 80
Alaska Principals Foundation, AK, 81
Albany Mutual Telephone Foundation, MN, 4624
Albers/Kuhn Family Foundation, MO, 4859
Albert Charitable Trust, J.R., CT, 1389
Albrecht Family Foundation, F.W., OH, 7301
Albright Foundation, MN, 4625
Alcon Cares, Inc., NJ, 5244
Alcyon Foundation, DE, 1608
Alden Trust, John W., MA, 3999
Aldermere Foundation, The, ME, 3763
Alex and Zoli Foundation, NY, 5652
Alexander Charitable Foundation, NY, 5653
Alexander Charitable Foundation, Shana, The, NY, 5654
Alexander Family G Foundation Inc., Norman E., NY, 5655
Alexander Foundation, Andrew and Julie, The, TX, 8695
Alexander Foundation, Frances, The, NY, 5656
Alexander Foundation, Robert D. and Catherine R., TX, 8696
Alff Aid, Inc., NY, 5657
Alfond Foundation, Peter, The, ME, 3764
ALG Family Foundation, NY, 5658
Alhadeff Charitable Foundation, Kenneth and Marleen, WA, 9558
Allatt Family Foundation II, Peter and Nancy, NY, 5659
Allegany County Area Foundation, Inc., NY, 5660
Allemall Foundation, Inc., The, MD, 3811
Allen Charitable Foundation, James C., CO, 1220
Allen Family Foundation, Kohorst, DE, 1609
Allen Foundation, Tim, MI, 4372
Allen-Heath Memorial Foundation, IL, 2701
Alley Family Foundation, Albert A., PA, 7837
Alliant Credit Union Foundation, IL, 2702
Allied Educational Foundation, NJ, 5245
Allison Family Charitable Foundation, MA, 4000
Allwin Family Foundation, The, CT, 1390

Allyn Foundation, Inc., The, IL, 2703
Almeida Family Foundation, IL, 2704
Alnour Foundation, The, MI, 4373
Alon and Shari Friendship Foundation, Inc., MI, 4374
Alpaugh Foundation, The, OH, 7302
Alpha/Omega Charitable Foundation, CT, 1391
Altamira Foundation, The, MA, 4001
Alternative Energy Foundation, NY, 5661
Altman Foundation, Morris and Bessie, The, VT, 9364
Alton Foundation, The, IL, 2705
Alton Woman's Home Association, IL, 2706
Altos Foundation, Inc., CA, 237
Alviso/San Jose Foundation, CA, see 740
Alvord Family Foundation, MA, 4002
Amador Community Foundation, Inc., CA, 238
Amaranth Foundation, PA, 7838
Amarillo Business Foundation, TX, 8697
Ambler Trust, Elizabeth Raymond, CT, 1392
Amboy Foundation, Inc., The, NJ, 5246
Ambrosiani-Pastore Foundation Inc., ID, 2663
Ambulatory Anesthesia Research Foundation, CA, see 1180
AMD Foundation, Inc., TX, 8698
AMDG Foundation, MD, 3812
Amelia Charitable Foundation, WA, 9559
America First Foundation, NE, 5066
American Airlines Foundation, TX, 8699
American Campus Charities Foundation, TX, 8700
American Clean Skies Foundation, DC, 1785
American Community Trust, TX, 8701
American Conservation Association, Inc., NY, 5662
American Dream Foundation, Inc., NY, 5663
American Eagle Outfitters Foundation, PA, 7839
American Electric Power System Educational Trust Fund, The, OH, 7303
American Express Charitable Fund, NY, 5664
American Foundation for Oceanography, CA, see 468
American Friends of Baruch Umarpeh Corp., NY, 5665
American Friends of Eton College, Inc., VA, 9386
American Friends of Even Yisroel Charitable Foundation, NJ, 5247
American Friends of Merkaz Chasidei Viznitz Inc., NY, 5666
American Friends of Mosdos Hakerem, Inc., NY, 5667
American Friends of the Hebrew University Charitable Common Fund, Inc., NY, 5668
American Friends of the National Institute for Psychobiology in Israel, IL, 2707
American General Finance, Inc.—Richard E. Meier Foundation, Inc., IN, see 3455
American Society of the French Legion of Honor, Inc., NY, 5669
American Water Charitable Foundation Inc., NJ, 5248
American Woodmark Foundation, Inc., VA, 9387
AmericaOne, CA, see 998
Amerisure Charitable Foundation, MI, 4375
Ameritas Charitable Foundation, NE, 5067
Amerman Family Foundation, CA, 239
Ames Charitable Trust, Harriett, PA, 7840
Ames Family Foundation, WA, 9560
Ames Foundation, Bruce and Giovanna, VA, A
Ames Memorial Fund, William Hadwen, RI, 8379
Amherst Foundation, TX, 8702
Amin Foundation Trust, Bijan and Soraya, CA, 241
Amin Foundation, CA, 240
Ammerman Foundation, The, MD, 3813
Amnon Foundation, Inc., The, NY, 5670
Amory Outreach Foundation Inc., MS, 4821
Amos Foundation, Inc., John and Elena Diaz-Verson, GA, see 2433
Amos Foundation, Inc., John and Elena, GA, 2433
Amos Foundation, Inc., Lauren, The, GA, see 2615
Amos Memorial Fund, Mabel, The, AL, 4
Amphion Foundation, The, NY, 5671
AMR, TX, see 8699
AMR/American Airlines Foundation, TX, 8703
AmSouth/First American Foundation, AL, see 58
Amsted Industries Foundation, IL, 2708
Amstein Foundation, Peter, The, WA, 9561
Amsterdam Foundation, Jack and Mimi Leviton, The, NY, 5672
Amundson Scholarships, Inc., L. A., SD, 8554
Anastasi Charitable Foundation, Anne, The, DE, 1610

Anatman Foundation, CA, 242
Anbinder Family Foundation, The, DE, 1611
Anchor Foundation, The, MI, 4376
Andersen Foundation, Elmer L. & Eleanor J., MN, 4626
Andersen Foundation, Frank N., MI, 4377
Anderson Charitable Foundation, John & Linda, FL, 1845
Anderson Charitable Trust, Josephine, TX, 8704
Anderson Family Charitable Foundation, Inc., FL, 1846
Anderson Family Charitable Fund, NY, 5673
Anderson Family Foundation, Harold and Kayrita, AL, 5
Anderson Foundation Inc., The, NY, 5674
Anderson Foundation, Clyde and Summer, The, AL, 6
Anderson Foundation, Donald W. & Margaret M., WI, 9773
Anderson Foundation, Elizabeth Mendenhall, OH, 7304
Anderson Foundation, Harlan E., CT, 1393
Anderson Foundation, Inc., Pauline K., MD, 3814
Anderson Foundation, Joseph R. and Katherine, CA, 243
Anderson Foundation, Martin & Illie, CA, 244
Anderson Foundation, NJ, 5249
Anderson Foundation, Robert A. and Kathey K., TX, 8705
Anderson Foundation, Robert C. & Sadie G., FL, 1847
Anderson Foundation, William P., OH, 7305
Anderson Rosch Charitable Foundation, William B. & Juliet J., The, NY, 5675
Anderson Trust, The, MN, 4627
Anderson Trust, W. T., FL, 1848
Anderson-Paffard Foundation, Inc., CT, 1394
Anderson-Rogers Foundation, Inc., NY, 5676
Anderton Bentley Fund, OH, 7306
Andrah Foundation, The, MI, 4378
Andre Family Foundation, Inc., The, FL, 1849
Andreas Foundation, Inc., George, VA, 9388
Andreeff Foundation, FL, 1850
Andress Family Foundation, NV, 5132
Andrews & McMeel Foundation, MO, see 4860
Andrews Family Foundation Inc., Jim, The, GA, 2434
Andrews Family Foundation, CO, 1221
Andrews Family Foundation, Joan and Peter, NY, 5677
Andrews Foundation, The, OH, 7307
Andrews McMeel Universal Foundation, MO, 4860
Andringa Family Foundation, Inc., IA, 3470
Andrus Charitable Trust, Brent & Cheri, UT, 9301
Angel Foundation, The, NY, 5678
Angelica Foundation, NM, 5605
Angels Among Us, Inc., ID, 2664
Angels on Track Foundation, The, OH, 7308
Angelson Family Foundation, The, NY, 5679
Angora Ridge Foundation, The, MT, 5044
Anhaltzer Foundation, Inc., Alberta S. Kimball-Mary L., CA, 245
Animal Guardians, Inc., CA, 246
Animal Welfare Trust, NY, 5680
Ankeny Foundation, The, MN, 4628
AnnMarie Foundation, Inc., WI, 9774
Anschel Eilian Family Charitable Foundation, IL, 2709
Ansin Foundation, MA, 4003
Anthony Foundation, Inc., Carmelo, CA, 247
Anton Foundation, Patricia Miller and William Conrad, NV, 5133
Anton Foundation, Patricia Miller Anton and William Conrad, NV, see 5133
Anton Memorial Foundation, B., FL, 1851
Antonacci Foundation for Charitable Giving, Inc., The, CT, 1395
Antonia Foundation Inc., WI, 9775
Antun Foundation, Frank J., The, NY, 5681
Antz Foundation, The, NJ, 5250
Aon Assistance Fund, IL, see 2710
Aon Memorial Education Fund, IL, 2710
Appalachian Stewardship Foundation, WV, 9734
Apperson Trust, Anne, RI, 8380
Apple Lane Foundation, Inc., The, NY, 5682
Applebaum Giving Foundation, Stuart S., NY, 5683
Appleby Charitable Trust, Scott B. & Annie P., IL, 2711
Applestone Foundation, PA, 7841
AptarGroup Charitable Foundation, IL, 2712
Aragona Family Foundation, Sandra and Joseph, The, TX, see 8706
Aragona Family Foundation, The, TX, 8706

Arakelian Foundation, Mary Alice, RI, 8381
Arata Brothers Trust, CA, 248
Arboit Charitable Trust, Guy A. & N. Kay, IL, 2713
Arbor Foundation, CA, 249
Arcadia Charitable Trust, MA, 4004
Arcadia Foundation, NY, 5684
Arcadia Foundation, The, NC, 7040
Arcadia Wildlife Preserve, Inc., GA, 2435
Arcana Foundation, Inc., DC, 1786
Archangel Michael Foundation, NY, 5685
Archer Family Foundation, The, CA, 250
Arches Foundation, The, CO, 1222
Archibald Family Charitable Foundation, MA, 4005
Archibald Foundation, Inc., FL, 1852
Arctos Foundation, MN, 4629
Ardith Stephenson, MI, see 4486
Arena Energy Foundation, The, TX, 8707
Arents, Jr. Cerimon Fund, George, RI, 8382
Aresty Foundation, Peter & Rosanne, NY, 5686
Aresty Foundation, Steven and Sheila, NY, 5687
Argo Foundation Inc., IL, 2714
Ariens Foundation, Ltd., WI, 9776
Arise Charitable Trust, WA, 9562
Arison Arts Foundation, FL, 1853
Arizona Eastern Star Retirement Center, AZ, 96
Ark Watch Foundation, The, CA, 251
Arkema Inc. Foundation, PA, 7842
Arkwright Conservation Trust, Stanley & Marty, NC, 7041
Arlene Foundation, CA, 252
Armington Fund, Evenor, The, OH, 7309
Armonia Foundation Inc., NY, 5688
Armour-Lewis Family Foundation, NJ, 5251
Armrod Charitable Foundation, CA, 253
Armstrong Family Charitable Foundation, Terry and Regina, The, TX, 8708
Armstrong Foundation, Fred & Christine, AZ, 97
Armstrong Foundation, HI, 2624
Armstrong Foundation, The, PA, 7843
Arnold & Porter Foundation, DC, 1787
Arnold Foundation, Inc., The, GA, 2436
Arnold Trust, Frederick, MO, 4861
Arnstein Foundation, Beverly and Frank, The, CA, 254
Aroma Foundation, CA, 255
Aronov Charitable Foundation, Jake, The, AL, 7
Aronson Foundation, NY, 5689
Around Foundation, The, FL, 1854
Arr Trust D Charitable Trust, The, RI, 8383
Arrel Trust, David Tod, OH, 7310
Arrison Family Charitable Foundation, Clement and Karen, NY, 5690
Arronson Foundation, PA, 7844
Arrowhead Foundation, Inc., CO, 1223
Arsenault Family Foundation, Inc., The, CO, 1224
Arsher Charitable Trust, MN, 4630
Art Institute of Miami Beach, Inc., The, FL, see 2003
Art Matters, Inc., NY, 5691
Artists Fellowship Inc., NY, 5692
Arts and Letters Foundation, Inc., NY, 5693
ArvinMeritor, Inc. Trust, MI, see 4511
Arzbaecher Family Foundation, WI, 9777
Asbjornson Foundation, OK, 7655
Ascena Foundation, NJ, 5252
Ascher, M.D. Charitable Foundation, David S., CA, 256
Asen Foundation, The, NY, 5694
Ash Family Foundation, Inc., Tim and Libby, IN, 3341
Ash Foundation, Earl & Elizabeth, The, NV, 5134
Ash Foundation, H. G., The, TX, 8709
Ashbrook Foundation for El Reno, Mary K., OK, 7656
Asher Foundation, NY, 5695
Ashland Foundation, PA, 7845
Ashland Trusts, PA, see 8263
Asia Connection, Inc., CA, 257
Associated Banc-Corp Foundation Charitable Trust, WI, 9778
Assurity Life Foundation, NE, 5068
Astin Charitable Trust, Nina Heard, TX, 8710
Astra Foundation Inc., The, MA, 4006
Astri Foundation, TX, 8711
ATAP Universe Learning Centers, Inc., FL, 1855
Athens Area Community Foundation, GA, 2437
Athens Community Foundation, NY, 5696
Athens Foundation, OH, 7311

Atherton Foundation, William S. & Ann, OK, 7657
Atkins Foundation, Inc. John G., OR, 7741
Atkins Foundation, Inc., The, FL, 1856
Atkinson Family Foundation, Eugene and Carol, FL, 1857
Atkinson Foundation, Myrtle L., CA, 259
Atlantic Charitable Foundation, NY, 5697
Atlantis Blue Project Foundation, Inc., FL, 1858
Atlantis Educational Foundation, AL, 8
Atofina Chemicals, Inc. Foundation, PA, see 7842
Atterbury Family Foundation, The, KS, 3554
Atticus Foundation, The, TN, see 8582
Atticus Trust, TN, 8582
Auerbach Family Foundation, FL, see 1859
Auerbach Family Foundation, Isaac and Carol, FL, 1859
Aufzien Foundation, Inc., NJ, 5253
Augur Family Foundation, Marilyn, The, TX, 8712
Augur Foundation, Marilyn, The, TX, see 8712
August Family Foundation, Charles J. & Burton S., NY, 5698
Auldridge Fund, The, PA, 7846
Aurora Foundation, The, FL, 1860
Aurora Ministries, The, FL, see 1860
Ausch Charity Foundation, Inc., Abraham, The, NY, 5699
Austin-Bailey Health and Wellness Foundation, OH, 7312
Authors League Fund, The, NY, 5700
Autism Consortium, Inc., MA, 4007
Avalo Foundation Inc., The, NJ, 5254
Avanessians Foundation, The, NY, 5701
Ave Maria Foundation, The, MI, 4379
Aventis Behring Foundation for Research and Advancement of Patient Health, PA, 7847
Averitt Foundation, Inc., Jack N. & Addie D., GA, 2438
Avery Arts Foundation, Milton and Sally, NY, 5702
Avery Foundation Inc., John E. & Caron G., CT, 1396
Avery-Fuller Children's Center, CA, see 260
Avery-Fuller-Welch Children's Foundation, CA, 260
Avery-Tsui Foundation, CA, 261
Avharas Avraham Foundation, MI, 4380
Aviation Education Foundation, FL, 1861
Avis Budget Charitable Foundation, The, NJ, 5255
Avocet Foundation, MN, 4631
Avoth Foundation, Lev, CO, 1225
Axe-Houghton Foundation, CT, 1397
Ayers Foundation, PA, 7848
Ayling Trust, Charles Lincoln, PA, see 7849
Ayling Trust, Charles, PA, 7849
Aylward Family Foundation, WI, 9779
AYN Foundation, NY, 5703
Ayres Foundation Inc., IN, 3342
Ayz Family Foundation, CA, 262
Azadoutioun Foundation, MA, 4008
Azar Charitable Foundation, Eddie & Shawna, NY, 5704

B & B Foundation, TN, 8583
B Z Foundation, The, NY, 5705
B&D Foundation, IL, 2715
B-Brand Foundation, Waite M., OH, 7318
B. Attitudes Foundation, The, UT, 9302
B.E.L.I.E.F. Foundation, The, TX, 8713
B.F. Foundation, NM, 5606
Babare Family Foundation, George & Dorothy, WA, 9563
Babare Foundation, The, WA, 9564
Babbitt Trust, Madeline Hunter, AZ, 98
Babcock Charitable Trust, DE, 1612
Babinger Charitable Trust, Emil, KS, 3555
Babson Charitable Foundation, Susan A. & Donald P., The, MA, 4009
Babson-Webber-Mustard Fund, MA, 4010
Bach Charitable Trust Conservatorship, Peter H. And Marietta K., CA, 263
Backcountry Charitable Trust, The, UT, 9303
Backer Foundation, Inc., William M., The, VA, 9389
Backer Fund, Inc., T., NY, 5706
Bacon Family Foundation, John and Debra, The, WA, 9565
Bacon Trust, Charles F., MA, 4011
Baehr Foundation, Louis W. & Dolpha, KS, 3556
Baekgaard Family Foundation, Barbara Bradley, PA, 7850
Baer Charitable Foundation, Arthur & Helen, MO, 4862
Baer Foundation, Alan & Marcia, NE, 5069

Baer Foundation, Sylvan T., TX, 8714
Baggins Foundation Inc., Arnold F., The, CT, 1398
Bahl Foundation, The, MN, 4632
Bahmann Family Foundation, Emma and Laura, OH, see 7313
Bahmann Foundation, OH, 7313
Baiardi Family Foundation Inc., MI, 4381
Bailey Charitable Foundation, Marjorie C., The, ME, 3765
Bailey Family Foundation, AR, 186
Bailey Family Foundation, Inc., FL, 1862, 1863
Bailey Family Foundation, Virginia and Ted, AR, see 187
Bailey Foundation, AR, 187
Bailey Foundation, Gordon & Margaret, MN, 4633
Bailey Foundation, Jim and Audrey, WY, 9964
Bailey Foundation, P. S. and Ouida C., SC, 8509
Bailey Foundation, RI, 8384
Bailey Foundation, The, SC, 8510
Bailey Trust f/b/o Riley Hospital, Cicero Milo, IL, 2716
Bailey-Stanford Family Foundation, Inc., DE, 1613
Bain, Jr. Charitable Trust, William W., MA, A
Baird Brothers Company Foundation, OH, 7314
Baird Charitable Trust, William Robert, MS, 4822
Baird Foundation, IL, 2717
Baird Foundation, Stephen W. & Susan M., IL, 2718
BAJ Foundation Inc., IN, 3343
Baker Corporation Foundation, Michael, PA, 7851
Baker Family Foundation, Bob, CA, 264
Baker Family Foundation, Edward and Rosemary, The, CA, 265
Baker Family Foundation, Inc., WI, 9780
Baker Family Foundation, The, CA, 266
Baker Foundation, Clark and Ruby, GA, 2439
Baker Foundation, Inc., Bob, CA, see 264
Baker Foundation, Lenox D. and Frances W., The, MD, 3815
Baker Foundation, Solomon R. & Rebecca D., The, CA, 267
Baker Foundation, The, WA, 9566
Baker Fund, The, CA, see 267
Bakewell Foundation, The, MO, 4863
Bakewell, Jr. Family Foundation, Edward L., The, MO, see 4863
Balbach Family Foundation, NY, 5707
Baldacci Family Foundation, Paul & Betty, CA, 268
Baldor Electric Company Foundation, Inc., AR, 188
Baldridge Foundation, The, TX, 8715
Baldwin Family Foundation Trust, FL, 1864
Baldwin Foundation, Lamb, The, OR, 7742
Baldwin Foundation, MI, 4382
Baldwin Foundation, The, CT, 1399
Baldwin Memorial Foundation, Fred, HI, 2625
Baldwin, Jr. Foundation, Summerfield, PA, 7852
Balin Charitable Trust, Hildegard, NC, 7042
Balk Foundation, James & Shirley, MI, 4383
Ballantine Family Charitable Fund, CO, see 1226
Ballantine Family Fund, CO, 1226
Ballard Foundation, The, TX, 8716
Balm Foundation, Inc., The, NY, 5708
Baltimore Equitable Insurance Foundation, MD, 3816
Baltimore Orioles Foundation, The, MD, 3817
Balzereit Trust, Leo C., PA, 7853
Bame Foundation, MN, 4634
Banchik Family Foundation, CA, 269
Bancker-Williams Foundation Inc., The, GA, 2440
Bancroft-Clair Foundation, CA, 270
Bandai Foundation, The, CA, 271
Bandier Family Foundation Inc., The, NY, 5709
Bane Charitable Foundation, NC, 7043
Bane Foundation, Earl, KS, 3557
Bank Foundation, Inc., Helen S. & Merrill L., MD, 3818
Bank of Maine Charitable Foundation, The, ME, 3766
Bank of the West Charitable Foundation, CA, 272
Bank of Utica Foundation Inc., NY, 5710
Banks Foundation, Inc., William and Karin, The, VA, 9390
Banks Foundation, Robert R., NV, 5135
Banky La Rocque Foundation, CA, 273
Bannerman Foundation, William C., The, CA, 274
Bannerot-Lappe Foundation Charitable Trust, PA, 7854
Bannon Foundation, The, SC, 8511
Bannow-Larson Foundation, Inc., The, CT, 1400
Banta Family Foundation, IL, 2719

Bantle Charitable Foundation, Inc., Louis F. & Virginia C., CT, 1401
Baobab Fund, The, NY, 5711
Bar Chuma Foundation, Inc., NY, 5712
Barakat, Inc., MA, 4012
Baratz Family Foundation Inc., MN, 4635
Barbara Hope Foundation, NY, 5713
Barbash Family Foundation, Bernard and Pamela, The, FL, 1865
Barbash Family Fund Inc., NY, 5714
Barber Foundation, C. Glenn, OH, 7315
Barbera Foundation, Inc., CA, 275
Barbonchielli and Marie and Manuel B. Perez Foundation, Joseph L., CA, 276
Barco's Nightingales Foundation, CA, 277
Barden Foundation, Inc., The, CT, 1402
Bardsley Foundation, CO, 1227
Barger Memorial Foundation, Orrion and Edith, SD, 8555
Barham Family Foundation, Carole A. and Norman, NY, 5715
Baright Foundation, Hollis and Helen, NE, 5070
Barkema Charitable Trust, Foster & Evelyn, IA, 3471
Barker Company Foundation, Inc., Bob, NC, 7044
Barker Foundation Inc., The, NH, 5204
Barker Foundation, Brett and Deborah, The, NV, 5136
Barker Foundation, Inc., Robert, The, NC, see 7044
Barker Foundation, Peter K., NY, 5716
Barklage Foundation Trust, Oliver and Ferrol, NE, 5071
Barkley Foundation, Inc., Charles, The, AL, 9
Barnabas Foundation, DE, 1614
Barnabas Fund, Inc., The, TX, 8717
Barnard Charitable Trust, E. H., FL, 1866
Barnes Family Foundation, Harry F. & Carol H., CT, 1403
Barnes Family Foundation, The, OK, 7658
Barnes Foundation Inc, The, CT, 1404
Barnes Foundation, James E. and Mary M., OK, 7659
Barnett Family Foundation, Inc., The, OK, 7660
Barnett Family Foundation, Louis & Madlyn, TX, 8718
Barnett Foundation, Florence L.J. and Howard G., OK, see 7660
Barnett Foundation, Glen and Opal, The, CA, 278
Barnett Foundation, MS, 4823
Barnett Jr. Foundation, Inc., James M., GA, 2441
Barney II Foundation, NY, 5717
Barnwood Foundation, The, NY, 5718
Baroco Foundation, Inc., J. H., FL, 1867
Barr Foundation, Inc., KY, 3646
Barr Foundation, Kristina Barr and George, IL, see 2720
Barr Fund, The, IL, 2720
Barrington Foundation Inc., The, FL, 1868
Barron Charitable Trust, Jeannette, NY, 5719
Barron Family Foundation, MI, 4384
Barron Foundation Trust, David & Rebecca, OH, 7316
Barron Foundation, David & Carole, OH, see 7316
Barron Foundation, Nora Lee & Guy, MI, see 4384
Barrow Foundation, TX, 8719
Barrows Foundation, Geraldine and R. A., MO, 4864
Barstow Charitable Trust, F. E. and A. R., MA, 4013
Barstow Foundation, MI, 4385
Barth Foundation, The, CA, 279
Barth Foundation, William E., KY, 3647
Barthelmes Foundation, Inc., Albert and Hete, The, OK, 7661
Bartholomay Foundation, Bill, IL, 2721
Bartlett and Company Grain Charitable Foundation, MO, 4865
Bartlett Family Foundation, Inc., Margaret and Marshall, NJ, 5256
Bartlett Foundation, Jim and Dede, DE, 1615
Bartner Family Foundation Trust, FL, 1869
Barton Charitable Foundation, Lon D. and Lucille, AZ, 99
Barton Irrevocable Trust, Elsie Seeger, MD, 3819
Barton Trust, Edward S., RI, 8385
Barton-Malow Company Foundation, MI, 4386
Bartsch Memorial Bank Trust, Ruth, IL, see 2722
Bartsch Memorial Trust, IL, 2722
Barulich Family Foundation, Jeanne and William, The, CA, 280
Baseser Foundation, Matan, The, NY, 5720
Basham Foundation, Inc., Danker, FL, 1870
Baskin Foundation, Peggy and Jack, The, CA, 281
Basler Charitable Foundation, Wayne G., TN, 8584

Bass Foundation Inc., Robert and Isabelle, IL, 2723

Basser Arts Foundation, FL, 1871

Bassett Furniture Industries Foundation, Inc., VA, 9391

Bassman Family Charitable Trust, The, NY, 5721

Bastian Family Foundation, M., The, UT, 9304

Bastian Foundation, KS, see 3577

Bastien Memorial Foundation, John E. and Nellie J., FL, 1872

Batchelder Foundation, Clifton B. & Anne S., NE, 5072

Bates Foundation, Alben F. & Clara G., IL, 2724

Bates Foundation, John C., The, OH, 7317

Bates Memorial Foundation, George A., The, IL, 2725

Battered Women's Foundation, OR, see 7807

Battle Family Foundation, CA, 282

Battle Family Foundation, The, AL, 10

Baudhuin Foundation, Ralph J., IL, 2726

Bauer Family Foundation Inc, DE, 1616

Bauer Family Foundation, George W., The, NJ, 5257

Baulch Family Foundation, TCH, FL, 1873

Baum Charitable Foundation, Theodore & Ruth, NY, 5722

Baum Family Foundation, David and Andrea, NJ, 5258

Baum Family Foundation, The, MI, 4387

Baum Foundation, David and Andrea, NJ, see 5258

Baum Private Foundation, Melvin R., IL, 2727

Baumann Family Foundation, The, NY, 5723

Baumann Foundation, The, CA, 283

Baumann Institute, CA, see 283

Baxter Family Foundation Inc., K. & F., CA, 284

Baxter Family Foundation, FL, 1874

BayCare Clinic Foundation, Ltd., WI, 9781

Baye Foundation, Inc., CA, 285

Bayley Family Foundation, WA, 9567

Bayuk Educational Trust, Florence, FL, 1875

BB&T Charitable Foundation, NC, 7045

BBL Charitable Foundation, Inc., NY, 5724

Beach Foundation Trust B for First Baptist Church, AL, A

Beach Foundation Trust D for Baptist Village, AL, A

Beach Foundation, The, PA, 7855

Beach Philanthropic Foundation, Leo Cox, NY, 5725

Beacon Foundation Inc., PA, 7856

Beacon of Learning Foundation, NY, 5726

Beagle Charitable Foundation, CA, 286

Beaird Family Foundation, TX, 8720

Beall, Sr. Charitable Foundation, R. M., FL, 1876

Beals Charitable Foundation, Vaughn L. & Eleanore M., AZ, 100

Beam Foundation, The, CA, 287

Bean Foundation, Thomas W., The, CO, 1228

Beane Family Foundation, NJ, 5259

Bear Gulch Foundation, CA, 288

Beard Foundation, Nancy Jones, NY, 5727

Beard-Payne Family Foundation, The, GA, 2442

Bearden Foundation, TX, 8721

Beasley Charitable Trust, Lucy & Emily, IL, 2728

Beasley Foundation, Jane, FL, 1877

Beattie Foundation, Frances & William H., The, CA, 289

Beattie Foundation, The, CA, see 289

Beauchamp Foundation, TX, 8722

Beaucourt Foundation, Inc., The, MA, 4014

Beaufort Foundation, Inc., The, MD, 3820

Beauregard Family Foundation, CA, 290

Beauregard Foundation Inc., The, FL, 1878

Beck Family Foundation, OH, 7319

Beck Foundation Inc., The, VA, 9392

Beck Foundation, John and Frances, IL, 2729

Beck Foundation, NY, 5728

Beck Fund, Tad, VA, 9393

Beck Reading Center, Inc., Frances Mottey, The, IL, see 2729

Beck Trust, Christine L., RI, 8386

Beck, Sr. Foundation, Dave, WA, 9568

Becker Charitable Trust, Newton & Rochelle, CA, 291

Becker Family Foundation, CA, 292

Becker Family Foundation, IA, 3472

Becker Family Foundation, Inc., Richard E. & Lillian M., FL, 1879

Becker Foundation Inc., Hugh C., MN, 4636

Beckman Award Trust, Elizabeth Hurlock, GA, 2443

Beckman Family Foundation, The, NY, 5729

Beckman Foundation, Inc., Camille, ID, 2665

Beckwith Charitable Foundation, F. William Beckwith & Leola I., IA, see 3473

Beckwith Charitable Foundation, F. William, IA, 3473

Beckwith Family Foundation, NY, 5730

Becton Family Foundation, FL, 1880

Bedford Charitable Foundation, Frederick H.Jr. & Margaret S., PA, 7857

Bee Charitable Trust, Philip Theodore, TX, 8723

Beecher Foundation, Florence Simon, OH, 7320

Beecher Foundation, Ward, OH, 7321

Beechmont Foundation, The, MD, see 3848

Beeck Family Foundation, Inc., Alberto & Olga Maria, The, FL, 1881

Beeghly Family Foundation, Bruce R. & Nancy W., IL, 2730

Beels Charitable Trust, Kenneth W., PA, 7858

Beer Trust, Paul, NE, 5073

Beghini Charitable Foundation, Victor and Anna Mae, The, TX, 8724

Behmann Brothers Foundation, TX, 8725

Behrakis Foundation, The, MA, 4015

Behrens Foundation, Inc., Mary Taylor and Christopher C., The, NY, 5731

Beim Family Foundation, Sanford and Phyllis, The, CA, 293

Beir Foundation, The, NY, 5732

Beiser Charitable Foundation, The, DE, 1617

Beitar Illit Advanced Talmud Project, NY, 5733

Bekins Foundation, Milo W., CA, 294

Belcher, Jr. Private Foundation No. 3, S. E., GA, 2444

Believers Foundation, OH, see 7372

Belk Educational Foundation, Irwin, The, NC, 7046

Bell Charitable Foundation, CA, 295

Bell Charitable Trust, Gloria Wille Bell and Carlos R., The, VA, 9394

Bell Family Charitable Foundation, Inc., WI, see 9963

Bell Family Foundation for Hope, Inc., FL, 1882

Bell Family Foundation, Jennifer & Thomas, NY, 5734

Bell Family Foundation, Victor E., Jr. & Jane McNair, NC, 7047

Bell Foundation, David Winton, MN, 4637

Bell Foundation, Inc., FL, see 1883

Bell Foundation, Inc., James E. and Constance L., The, FL, 1883

Bell Foundation, James Ford, MN, 4638

Bell Foundation, NC, 7048

Bella Foundation, Harriet & George Blank, The, PA, 7859

Belle Jar Foundation, The, CA, 296

Bellebyron Foundation, IL, 2731

Beller & Jennifer Moses Family Foundation, Inc., Ron, CA, 297

Bellick Foundation, The, IL, 2732

Bellini Foundation, CA, 298

Bellwether Foundation Ii, The, CA, 299

Beloit Community Foundation, Greater, The, WI, see 9937

Belz Foundation, TN, 8585

Benaroya Charitable Foundation, The, NJ, 5260

Bench Trail Fund, DC, 1788

Bend Foundation, MN, 4639

Bender Family Foundation, The, NY, 5735

Bender Foundation, Inc., Dorothy G., The, DC, 1789

Bender Foundation, Inc., Morris S. & Florence H., The, CT, 1405

Bendich Charitable Trust, Albert & Pamela, IL, 2733

Bendit Family Foundation, The, NY, 5736

Bendon Family Foundation, NV, 5137

Benedek Family Foundation, The, CA, 300

Benedict Foundation for Independent Schools, The, FL, 1884

Beneto Foundation, CA, 301

Benjamin & Heather Crane Foundation Inc., The, TN, 8586

Benjamin Foundation, Gail L. & Arthur E., The, UT, 9305

Benjamin Franklin Bank Charitable Foundation, MA, see 4267

Benna Foundation, Edna B. & Bruno, NV, 5138

Bennett Charitable Trust 1, Eleanore, PA, see 7860

Bennett Family Foundation, PA, 7860

Bennett Family Foundation, Zane, NM, 5607

Bennett Foundation, C. E., DE, 1618

Bennett Foundation, Michael L. And Margie A ., IA, 3474

Bennett Memorial Corporation, James Gordon, The, NY, 5737

Benson Family Charitable Trust, The, MA, 4016

Benson Family Foundation, CO, 1229

Benson Foundation, P. Bruce and Virginia C., CO, 1230

Benton Banking Foundation, L.O., GA, 2445

Benton Community Foundation, IN, 3344

Benton Foundation, Fox and Monica, TX, 8726

Benun Charitable Foundation, Inc., Morris and Susan, NJ, 5261

Benz Foundation, William L. & Margaret L., PA, 7861

Benz Trust, Doris L., MA, 4017

BEO Charitable Trust, MO, 4866

Berakah Foundation, Inc., CA, 302

Berbecker and Lille A. Webb Scholarship Fund, Walter J., CT, see 1406

Berbecker Scholarship Fund, Walter J. and Lille A., CT, 1406

Berbeewalsh Foundation, Inc., WI, 9782

Berding Family Foundation, John and Susan, OH, 7322

Bere Foundation Inc., Barbara, IL, 2734

Berelsman Family Charitable Foundation Trust, David & Lyn, The, FL, 1885

Beren Charitable Trust, Sheldon K., CO, 1231

Beren Foundation Z.B., Harry H., CO, 1232

Beren Foundation, Harry H., CO, 1233

Berge Scholarship Foundation, Vern and Ruth, ND, 7294

Berger Family Charitable Foundation, MA, 4018

Berger Foundation, Harold and Renee, PA, 7862

Berger Fund, Leo V., MD, 3821

Berghorst Foundation, Inc., The, DE, 1619

Berglund Family Foundation, R. R. W. & Florence, MN, 4640

Berglund Family Foundation, The, CA, 303

Bergman Family Foundation, CA, 304

Bergman Foundation, The, PA, 7863

Bergson Foundation, Stefany and Simon, The, NY, 5738

Bergstein Family Foundation, IL, 2735

Bergstrom Family Foundation, The, TX, 8727

Bergstrom Foundation, PA, 7864

Bergstrom Foundation, The, MA, 4019

Bergstrom Inc. Charitable Foundation, IL, 2736

Berke Charitable Foundation, Inc., Lenore and Norman, OH, 7323

Berkman Family Charitable Trust, Marshall L. and Deborah L., The, OH, 7324

Berkowitz Family Charitable Foundation Inc., Jeff and Yolanda, FL, 1886

Berkowitz Family Foundation, Edwin J. and Barbara R., The, PA, 7865

Berkowitz Family Foundation, Inc., Louis, NY, 5739

Berkowitz II Foundation Inc., PA, 7866

Berkshire Foundation, CA, 305

Berlin Foundation, Howard R. & Joy M., AZ, 101

Berlin Foundation, Jack and Florence, CA, 306

Berlin Foundation, Marvin, MI, 4388

Berman Charitable Foundation Inc., TN, 8587

Berman Charitable Foundation, Sharen and Marc, IL, see 3250

Bernard Family Foundation, MD, 3822

Bernard Foundation, Ralph L. & Florence A., OH, 7325

Bernardin Charitable Trust, F.M., TX, 8728

Bernfield Family Foundation, Craig and Donna, IL, 2737

Bernhardt Foundation, Helene and Bertram, RI, 8387

Bernheim Foundation Inc., The, NY, 5740

Bernhill Fund, The, NY, 5741

Berni Family Charitable Foundation, The, VA, 9395

Berning Private Foundation, Donald N. and Jane L., Dr ., DE, 1620

Bernoudy Foundation, Gertrude and William A., IL, 2738

Bernstein Family Foundation, Donald H. & Barbara K., The, NC, 7049

Bernstein Family Foundation, Inc., CA, 307

Bernstein Family Fund, CA, 308

Berry Foundation Inc., KS, 3558

Berry Foundation, Archie W. and Grace, PA, 7867

Berry Foundation, C. J., CA, 309

Bershad Charitable Fund Inc., Susan V., NJ, 5262

Bershad Family Foundation Inc., David, NJ, 5263

Bersted Foundation, Grace, RI, 8388

Bertha Foundation, TX, 8729

Bertsch Family Charitable Foundation Inc, NC, 7050

Berwind Foundation, Inc., Charles G., PA, 7868
Besl Family Foundation, Lester J., OH, 7326
Beson Family Foundation, MI, 4389
Bessie Foundation, Cornelia and Michael, CT, 1407
Besson Cooper Fund, Inc., MD, 3823
Best Foundation, Jacob, IL, 2739
Best Foundation, Walter J. and Edith E., IL, 2740
Bet Lev Foundation, NY, 5742
Betesh & Sons Foundation, Inc., Sol E., NY, 5743
Betten Auto Family Foundation, The, MI, see 4390
Betten Foundation, Marion & Marlene, MI, 4390
Better Living Foundation, The, VA, 9396
Bettingen Corporation, Burton G., The, CA, 310
Bettman Foundation, Francis & Monte, NC, 7051
Betts Family Foundation, NY, 5744
Betts Foundation, PA, 7869
Betz Foundation, Theodora B., PA, 7870
Beulah Fund, The, CA, 311
Beynon Foundation, Kathryne, The, CA, 312
Bezalel Art Foundation, NY, see 6864
BF Charitable Foundation, MO, 4867
BGL Foundation, TN, 8588
BGM Foundation, PA, 7871
Bhappu Family Foundation, Ross R. and Candy L., The, CO, 1234
Bharat Family Foundation, DE, 1621
Bhutada Family Foundation, TX, 8730
Bialis Family Foundation, CA, 313
Bickford Foundation, John, NH, 5205
Bicknell Fund, OH, 7327
Biddinger Family Foundation, FL, 1887
Bider Family Foundation, Lynn & Les, CA, 314
Bidwill Charitable Foundation, Charles W. & Patricia S., IL, 2741
Bieber Family Foundation, MN, 4641
Biedenharn Foundation, The, LA, 3713
Biederman Foundation, Inc., Les and Anne, The, MI, 4391
Bienenfeld Foundation, Henry & Helen, PA, 7872
Bierlein Companies Foundation, MI, 4392
Big Blue Sky Foundation, CO, 1235
Big D Foundation, The, CA, 315
Big Wood Foundation, The, NY, 5745
Bigbird Fund, The, MA, 4020
Bigelow Foundation, David and Eunice, CT, 1408
Bigglesworth Family Foundation, Inc., CA, 316
Bignon Family Foundation, SC, 8512
Bijou Family Foundation, Joseph and Renee, NJ, 5264
Bikuben Foundation New York, Inc., The, NY, 5746
Bilak Family Foundation, Milton, The, CA, 317
Bill Deputy Foundation, IN, 3345
Billig Foundation, NJ, 5265
Billings Foundation, Eric and Marianne, VA, 9397
Billingsley Foundation, Charle & Ruth, NC, 7052
Biloxi Regional Medical Center, Inc., MS, 4824
Bingham Foundation, W. Richard Bingham and Winifred W., The, NY, 5747
Binion Family Foundation, NV, 5139
Binz Foundation Inc., Margaret R., FL, 1888
Biophilia Foundation, Inc., The, MD, 3824
Birchas Mordechai Charitable Foundation, NY, 5748
Birchrock Foundation, The, NY, 5749
Bird Trust, Lizzie & Edward V., RI, 8389
Bird University of Maine Trust, Adelaide C., NY, 5750
Birdsong Fund, T. & R., CO, see 1274
Birk Family Foundation, The, VA, 9398
Birmingham Hide & Tallow Charitable Foundation Inc., AL, 11
Birnam Oaks Foundation, The, TX, A
Birnbaum Foundation, Egon & Telsi, NY, 5751
Birnbaum Foundation, Milton and Sylvia, NY, 5752
Birnhak Foundation, Marilyn and J. Robert, PA, 7873
Birnschein Foundation, Alvin and Marion, WI, 9783
Bisco Charitable Foundation, IL, 2742
Bishop Charitable Trust, A.G., IL, 2743
Bishop Educational Trust, IA, 3475
Bishop Family Foundation, WA, 9569
Bishop Foundation, The, PA, 7874, see 7874
Bistricer Foundation, Moric & Elsa, NY, see 6425
Bito and Olivia Carino Foundation Inc., Laszlo, NY, 5753
Bjorkman Foundation, Carl George, The, CO, 1236
Blachford-Cooper Foundation Inc., CA, 318
Black & Allon Fuller Fund, Harry S., NY, 5754

Black Belt Community Foundation, Inc., The, AL, 12
Black Charitable Foundation, Helene B., MA, 4021
Black Charitable Foundation, Robert, RI, 8390
Black Charitable Trust, Ann D., OH, 7328
Black Charitable Trust, Archie C. & Jane McDonald, MN, 4642
Black Charitable Trust, Elizabeth S., PA, 7875
Black Dog Foundation, The, VA, 9399
Black Dog Private Foundation Inc., The, DE, 1622
Black Family Foundation, John Louis, The, MS, 4825
Black Family Foundation, PA, 7876
Black Hills Corporation Foundation, SD, 8556
Blackford County Community Foundation, Inc., IN, 3346
Blackhorse Foundation, The, PA, 7877
Blackie Foundation, CA, 319
Blackman Foundation, Inc., Aaron and Marie, The, CA, 320
Blackman, Sr. Foundation, John N., NY, 5755
Bladel Foundation, Inc., Harold C. & Jacqueline F., IL, 2744
Blair Area Community Foundation, NE, 5074
Blair Family Foundation Inc., CO, 1237
Blake Charitable Foundation, Sara E., WV, 9735
Blake Family Charitable Foundation, The, FL, 1889
Blanchard Foundation, The, CA, 321
Bland Family Foundation, MO, 4868
Blank Charitable Foundation, FL, 1890
Blank Family Foundation, MN, 4643
Blank Foundation, Nancy & Robert S., NY, 5756
Blanksteen Foundation, Goldie & David, FL, 1891
Blanton Charitable Foundation, Inc., Hilda Sutton & William D., FL, 1892
Blatt Family Foundation, FL, 1893
Blatt Family Foundation, Leland F., MI, see 4393
Blatt Family Foundation, MI, 4393
Blatteis Family Foundation, CA, 322
Blau Charitable Annuity Trust, Florence, DE, 1623
Blechman Foundation, Jean and David, FL, 1894
Blessing for Life Foundation Inc., NJ, 5266
Blin Family Foundation of Independence, Iowa, Inc., IA, see 3476
Blin Foundation, Inc., The, IA, 3476
Blinken Foundation Inc., The, NY, 5757
Blittersdorf Family Foundation Inc., VT, 9365
Blittersdorf Foundation, Inc., Jan & David, VT, see 9365
BLN Charitable Foundation, NE, see 5067
Bloch Educational and Charitable Foundation, Raymond and Elizabeth, The, PA, 7878
Block Electric Company, Inc. Foundation, IL, see 2745
Block Family Charitable Trust, Ephraim, MO, 4869
Block Family Foundation, Ephraim, MO, see 4869
Block Family Foundation, Freya & Richard, NY, 5758
Block Family Foundation, IL, 2745
Block Family Foundation, Inc., The, NY, 5759
Block Foundation Inc., Harris & Frances, VT, 9366
Block Foundation, Abe & Sidney, The, WA, 9570
Block Foundation, Richard L. and Diane M., DE, 1624
Block, Jr. Family Foundation, Margaret S. & Philip D., IL, 2746
Blodgett Foundation, Margaret Kendrick, NY, 5760
Bloedorn Foundation, CO, 1238
Bloedorn Foundation, Walter A., DC, 1790
Bloom Foundation, NJ, 5267
Bloom Foundation, Sam S., The, CO, 1239
Bloomberg Sisters Foundation, The, NY, 5761
Blooming Prairie Foundation, Inc., WI, 9784
Blossom Fund, The, MA, 4022
Blount Educational & Charitable Foundation, Mildred W., The, AL, 13
Bloxom, Sr. Foundation, David E., TX, 8731
Blue Bell Foundation, NC, 7053
Blue Dot Foundation, VA, 9400
Blue Earth Foundation Inc., VA, 9401
Blue Foundation, The, NJ, 5268
Blue Hill Road Foundation Inc., NY, 5762
Blue Oak Charitable Fund, The, NV, 5140
Blue Oak Foundation, NJ, 5269
Blue Ribbon Foundation of Blue Cross of Northeastern Pennsylvania, The, PA, 7879
Blue Ridge Charitable Trust, AR, 189
Blue Ridge Foundation, Inc., NY, 5763
Blue Sky Family Foundation, PA, 7880
Blue Star Foundation, Inc., NY, 5764

Blueberry Hill Agm Foundation, VA, 9402
Bluemke Charitable Foundation, Ltd., Duane H. & Dorothy M., WI, see 9785
Bluemke Foundation, Ltd., Duane & Dorothy, WI, 9785
Blum Family Foundation Inc., The, MD, 3825
Blum Family Foundation, The, TN, 8589
Blum Foundation, Inc., Samuel, The, MD, see 3825
BMI-Rupp Foundation, NJ, 5270
Boand Family Foundation, CA, 323
Boardman Family Foundation, The, PA, 7881
Bobins Foundation, IL, see 2747
Bobins Foundation, Robert Thomas, The, IL, 2747
Bobowski Fund, Wanda, The, CA, 324
Bobrow Family Foundation, Norman and Julia, The, NY, 5765
Bochnowski Family Foundation, CA, 325
Bock Foundation, John C., WI, 9786
Boddie Foundation, Nickolas Bunn Boddie, Sr. and Lucy Mayo, NC, 7054
Boddie Noell Foundation, NC, 7055
Bodenhamer Foundation, AR, 190
Bodhi Foundation, TX, 8732
Boe Brothers Foundation, MT, 5045
Boe Charitable Trust, Lief, The, MT, see 5045
Boehl Charitable Trust, Herbert B., IL, 2748
Boehm Charity Fund, Hershel & Esther, MD, 3826
Boeing Company Charitable Trust, TX, 8733
Boeschoten Foundation, The, WA, 9571
Boger Charitable Trust, The, MA, 4023
Bogle Family Foundation, AR, 191
Bogle Foundation, John C. and Eve S., PA, see 7843
Bogoni Operating Foundation, Paul and Irene, The, NY, 5766
Bograd Memorial Trust, Abe & Anna, MO, 4870
Bohm Charitable Foundation, Milford and Lee, MO, 4871
Bohnert Foundation, Inc., FL, 1895
Boise Legacy Constructors Foundation Inc., ID, 2666
Bolick Foundation, The, NC, 7056
Bolte Family Foundation, The, PA, 7882
Bomberger Jr. Foundation Inc., Paul S., FL, 1896
Bon-Ton Stores Foundation, The, PA, 7884, see 7884
Bond Foundation, Inc., The, FL, 1897
Bonder Foundation, Seth, MI, 4394
Bonner Family Foundation, CA, 326
Bonner Family Private Foundation, Inc., SC, 8513
Bonner Foundation, Clark and Nancy, CA, 327
Bonomo Perpetual Charitable Trust, August & Minnie, PA, 7883
Boone Charitable Trust, Alex, KY, 3648
Boone Family Foundation, Inc., KY, see 3649
Boone Foundation, Inc., Dan and Merrie, GA, 2446
Boone Foundation, Inc., Hilary, KY, 3649
Boone Foundation, Inc., Pat, CA, 328
Boone Foundation, The, CA, 329
Booth Charitable Trust, Dorothy M., TX, 8734
Booth Inc., Suzanne Deal Booth and David G., TX, 8735
Boothroyd Foundation, Charles H. and Bertha L., IL, 2749
Borch Foundation, The, CA, 330
Boring Charitable Foundation, Inc., Kenneth E., TN, 8590
Borman Family Foundation, The, ME, 3767
Borman Foundation, Marvin & Betty, MN, 4644
Born Family Charitable Trust, Ross J., The, PA, 7885
Bornblum Foundation, The, TN, 8591
Borok Foundation, L. & L., CA, 331
Borowsky Family Foundation, PA, 7886
Borten Foundation, Walter and Phyllis Ann, IL, 2750
Borun Foundation, Harry H. and Anna, NC, 7057
Borzi Family Foundation, Jay and Carol, CA, 332
Bos Family Foundation, The, IN, 3347
Boscacci Family Foundation, Allan and Patricia, CA, 333
Boscia Family Foundation, PA, 7887
Boss Foundation for the Arts, Harlan, MN, 4645
Boss Foundation, The, MN, 4646
Bosserman Charitable Foundation, Rick & Nancy, FL, see 2007
Bostock Family Foundation, MI, 4395
Boston Center for Blind Children, Inc., FL, 1898
Bostwick Foundation, Albert C., NY, 5767
Boswell Family Foundation, ID, 2667
Boswell Foundation, Inc., The, MO, 4872

Bothmer Foundation, Leona, NY, 5768
Boudinot Foundation, The, PA, 7888
Boukai Family Foundation, CA, 334
Boulos Family Charitable Foundation, ME, 3768
Boult Cummings Charitable Foundation, Bradley Arant, AL, 14
Bound To Stay Bound Books Foundation, IL, 2751
Bourne-Spafford Foundation, The, UT, 9306
Boustead Family Foundation Inc., The, NY, 5769
Bovin Family Foundation, The, NY, 5770
Bowen Charitable Trust, Franklin W. & Helen S., WV, 9736
Bowen Foundation, Ethel N., WV, 9737
Bowen Foundation, Janet E., OR, 7743
Bowen Trust, R. A., The, GA, 2447
Bowen Universalist Trust, Eugene B., RI, 8391
Bower Charitable Trust, Ferdinand A. and Agnes M., IL, 2752
Bowers Family Charitable Trust, George W., WV, 9738
Bowers Foundation, TX, 8736
Bowling Family Charitable Foundation, TX, 8737
Bowling Foundation, JC & AJ, The, CT, see 1409
Bowling Foundation, UD, JC & AJ, CT, 1409
Bowman Family Foundation, The, DE, 1625
Box of Rain Foundation, The, NY, 5771
Boxer Foundation, The, NY, 5772
Boyce Foundation, The, MA, 4024
Boyd Family Foundation, The, NV, see 5141
Boyd Foundation, Inc., Darnall W., SC, 8514
Boyd Foundation, NV, 5141, see 5141
Boydston Foundation, Robert E. and Adele, WA, 9572
Boyer Foundation, Herbert & Marigrace, The, CA, 335
Boyer-Snyder Family Foundation, The, NY, 5773
Boylan Foundation, Helen S., MO, 4873
Boylan Foundation, Thomas Sidlik & Rebecca, IL, 2753
Boyle Family Foundation, IL, 2754
Boymel Foundation, Sam and Rachel, The, OH, 7329
Boynton Fund, John W., MA, 4025
Brabson Library & Educational Foundation, MA, 4026
Brace Charitable Trust, William J., MO, 4874
Brace Foundation, Donald C., CT, 1410
Brack Charitable Foundation, Joan H., The, RI, 8392
Bracknell Court Foundation, The, IL, see 2781
Braddock Charitable Foundation, Robert C. & Lois C., CA, 336
Brademas Foundation, John, The, NY, 5774
Bradford Family Foundation, TN, 8592
Bradford Foundation, George and Ruth, CA, 337
Bradley Charitable Foundation, Joseph G., PA, 7889
Bradley Family Charitable Foundation Trust, NY, 5775
Bradley Foundation, Eleanor and Raymond, CT, 1411
Bradley Foundation, Kerry and Laura, DE, 1626
Bradley Research Foundation, William E., MN, 4647
Braitmayer Foundation, The, MD, 3827
Bramlage Family Foundation, KS, 3559
Branch County Community Foundation, MI, 4396
Brand Foundation of New York, Inc., The, NY, 5776
Brand Foundation, Inc., Martha and Regina, The, NY, see 5776
Brandes Foundation, Tanya & Charles, The, NY, see 6439
Brandsma Family Foundation, The, DE, 1627
Brandt Family Foundation, Barbara & Gary, NY, 5777
Brandt Foundation, The, VA, 9403
Branfman Family Foundation, NJ, 5271
Branigin Foundation Inc., Elba L. and Gene Portteus, IN, 3348
Brannin Foundation, Dan E. & Neva L., OK, 7662
Branstad Family foundation, Christine & Paul, IL, 2755
Brass Family Foundation, TX, 8738
Bratt Charitable Trust, Norbert & Henry, NY, 5778
Bratt Charitable Trust, Simon Dina & Henry, NY, 5779
Bratten Foundation, Meta Alice Keith, TX, 8739
Braun & Bocklett Family Foundation, Thelma, TX, 8740
Braun Family Foundation, Inc., Alan W. and Sharon A., IN, 3349
Braun Foundation Inc., Victor F., WI, 9787
Brave Heart Foundation Inc, The, IN, 3350
Bravo Foundation, The, CA, 338
Breck Foundation, Henry & Wendy, NY, 5780
Breech Foundation, Mara W., CA, 339
Breeden, Jr. Foundation, Ramon N., The, VA, 9404

Breedlove Charitable Foundation, Howell A. & Ann M., PA, 7890
Breidenthal Foundation, Willard J. and Mary G., MO, 4875
Breidenthal-Snyder Foundation, The, KS, 3560
Brendsel Family Foundation, WY, 9965
Brennan Family Foundation, Edward A. and Lois L., WI, 9788
Brenner Family Foundation, The, NY, 5781
Brenner Foundation, Abe & Miriam, The, IL, 2756
Brent Family Foundation, The, CO, 1240
Brentwood Foundation, OH, 7330
Brentwood Foundation, TX, 8741
Bresler Foundation, Inc., The, MD, 3828
Breslow Family Foundation, Warren and Elaine, CA, 340
Bresnan Family Foundation, Inc., DE, see 1628
Bresnan Foundation Inc., Bill and Ann, DE, 1628
Brethen Foundation, Robert H., The, OH, 7331
Brevard Family Foundation, MS, 4826
Brewer Family Foundation, Virginia & Charles, The, GA, 2448
Brewer Foundation, Cornell, IL, 2757
Brews Foundation, Douglas & Janet, OH, 7332
Brewster West Foundation, CA, 341
BRI Foundation, Inc., The, VA, 9405
Briar Foundation, The, NY, 5782
Bridge Builders Community Foundation, PA, 7891
Bridge Foundation, Inc., The, TX, 8742
Bridgemill Foundation, CT, 1412
Bridges Foundation, Robert & Alice, CA, 342
Bridges/Larson Foundation, The, CA, 343
Bridgewater Fund, Inc., The, NY, 5783
Briger Foundation II, Peter and Devon, The, NY, 5784
Briggs and Morgan Foundation, MN, 4648
Briggs Foundation, Margaret, PA, 7892
Briggs Foundation, Ronnie & Gwen, LA, 3714
Briggs-Fisher Foundation, The, MI, 4397
Bright China Social Fund, CA, 344
Bright Family Foundation, The, CA, 345
Bright Foundation, Charles & Lois Marie, TX, 8743
Bright Mountain Foundation, CO, 1241
Brighton Foundation Trust, FL, 1899
Brillion Public High School Scholarship Trust Fund, WI, 9789
Brillo-Sonnino Family Foundation, NY, 5785
Brinck Family Foundation, Inc., OH, 7333
Brinckerhoff Family Foundation, FL, 1900
Brink's Foundation, The, VA, 9406
Brinklee Foundation, The, MO, 4876
Brinkley Foundation, AL, 15
Brinkman Foundation, Richard G. & Audrey A., PA, 7893
Brinkman Private Charitable Foundation, Earl W. & Hildagunda A., NY, 5786
Briskin Foundation, Judy and Bernard, CA, 346
Brisley & Noma Brisley Phillips Scholarship Loan Fund, Ella Frances, TX, see 8744
Brisley Scholarship Loan Fund, TX, 8744
Bristol Bay Native Corp., Education Foundation, AK, 82
Britton Family Foundation, The, PA, 7894
Broad Foundation, Gary and Sheri, CA, see 347
Broad Foundation, Gary, CA, 347
Broad Foundation, Inc., Marilyn S., The, NJ, 5272
Broadbent Family Foundation, Inc., MT, 5046
Broadbent Family Foundation, The, PA, 7895
Broadbent Foundation, The, PA, see 7895
Broadfield Foundation, The, GA, 2449
Broadhurst Foundation, OK, 7663
Broadus Charitable Foundation, Elizabeth H. and Thomas H., The, MD, see 3829
Broadus Charitable Foundation, The, MD, 3829
Broady Family Opportunity Foundation, George K. & Eleanor J., TX, 8745
Brochstein Foundation, Raymond & Susan, TX, 8746
Brock Family Foundation, MA, 4027
Brocker Foundation Inc., The, OH, 7334
Broder Family Foundation Inc., The, DE, 1629
Broder Foundation, The, CA, 348
Broderbund Foundation, CA, see 377
Brodsky Foundation, The, TX, 8747
Brodsky Foundation, William and Joan, FL, 1901
Brody Family Charitable Foundation, Edwin and Sara, The, FL, 1902
Brody Family Foundation, Carolyn S., NY, 5787

Brody Family Foundation, Inc., Kenneth D., DC, 1791
Bromberg Charitable Trust Fund, Leon, TX, 8748
Bromley Trust, Guy I., TX, 8749
Bronner Family Charitable Foundation, Wallace and Irene, MI, 4398
Bronstein Foundation, Sol & Arlene, The, IN, 3351
Bronstein Foundation, Solomon and Sylvia, The, PA, 7896
Brook Family Foundation, ME, 3769
Brook Fund, Inc., The, NJ, 5273
Brooke Trust, Louis S., FL, 1903
Brooker Foundation, T. Kimball, IL, 2758
Brooklyn Benevolent Society, NY, 5788
Brooks Charitable Trust, Mary Jane, OH, 7335
Brooks Family Foundation, Inc., Finn, GA, 2450
Brooks Family Foundation, PA, 7897
Brooks Foundation, Cora L., PA, 7899
Brooks Foundation, Harold, MA, 4028
Brooks Foundation, PA, 7898
Brooks Foundation, Sunshine, CA, 349
Brooks Foundation, The, NJ, 5274
Brooks-Mathews Foundation, CA, 350
Brookshire-Green Foundation, WA, 9573
Broomfield Community Foundation, The, CO, 1242
Broomfield Foundation Trust, Elizabeth, The, NJ, 5275
Brosens Foundation, Frank and Deenie, NY, 5789
Brossman Family Charitable Trust for Scholarships, The, PA, 7900
Brothers Ashkenazi Foundation, Inc., The, NJ, 5276
Brotman Family Foundation, WA, 9574
Brotman Foundation of California, CA, 351
Broughton Charitable Private Foundation, Inc., William Gundry, NY, 5790
Broussard Charitable Foundation, Donald J., The, LA, 3715
Browder Family Foundation, NJ, 5277
Brown Charitable Foundation, Stokes and Sarah, AL, 16
Brown Charitable Trust, Bruce Ford, The, DE, 1630
Brown Charitable Trust, Samuel M. and Laura H., KS, 3561
Brown Family Charitable Fund, Inc., Bennett A., DE, see 1631
Brown Family Foundation Inc., Robert and Susan, The, WI, 9790
Brown Family Foundation, Barbara and Helen, The, MO, 4877
Brown Family Foundation, Clayton, IL, 2759
Brown Family Foundation, Harold and Colene, CA, 352
Brown Family Foundation, John Mathew Gay, WV, 9739
Brown Family Foundation, Tim & Libby, CO, 1243
Brown Family Foundation, Warren, OH, 7336
Brown Foundation Inc., Craig & Vicki, The, FL, 1904
Brown Foundation Inc., Margaret C. B. & S. Spencer N., TX, 8750
Brown Foundation, Charles S. and Millicent P., VA, 9407
Brown Foundation, E. C., The, OR, 7744
Brown Foundation, Harry and Louise, OK, 7664
Brown Foundation, Inc., A. Pat and Kathryne L., The, NC, 7058
Brown Foundation, Inc., M. K., TX, 8751
Brown Foundation, Inc., Mary Alice and Bennett, DE, 1631
Brown Foundation, Inc., William, The, NY, 5791
Brown Foundation, NJ, 5278
Brown Foundation, Patricia Crail, CA, 353
Brown Foundation, Richard F. and Pearl P., FL, 1905
Brown Foundation, Ruth H., UT, 9307
Brown Foundation, Ruth W., The, CT, 1413
Brown Foundation, Stephanie L., MA, 4029
Brown Jr. Foundation Inc., Harry J., FL, 1906
Brown Memorial Foundation, Charles M. and Helen M., The, OH, 7337
Brown Trust, Harry G. & Mary Lore Flowe, NC, 7059
Brown-Whitworth Foundation, DE, 1632
Browne Charitable Trust, James and Noel, PA, 7901
Browning Family Fund L, Inc., John N., OH, see 7626
Brownley Trust, Walter, FL, 1907
Brownsville Foundation for Health and Education, TX, 8752
Bruce Foundation, IL, 2760
Bruce Foundation, Julia Harrison, IL, 2761
Brueckner Family Charitable Foundation, NJ, 5279
Bruhn-Morris Family Foundation Inc., VA, 9408

Brundage Charitable, Scientific and Wildlife Conservation Foundation, Charles E. and Edna T., NJ, 5280
Bruner Foundation Inc., MA, 4030
Brunetti Foundation, The, NJ, 5281
Brunie Foundation, Jean I. & Charles H., The, NY, 5792
Bruno Family Foundation, Angelo and Ann, AL, 17
Bruno Foundation, Ann and Angelo, AL, see 17
Brunswick and Rebecca Matoff Foundation, Inc., Lewis, CA, 354
Brunswick Foundation, Inc., The, IL, 2762
Brush Foundation, OH, 7338
Bryan Area Foundation, Inc., OH, 7339
Bryan Family Fund, John M., The, CA, 355
Bryan Foundation, Inc., James E. and Mary Z., NC, see 7060
Bryan Foundation, Inc., NC, 7060
Bryant Family Foundation, Barbara, MO, 4878
Bryant Foundation, The, VA, 9409
Bryer Foundation, Ben F., PA, 7902
BSD Endowment Foundation, NY, 5793
BSR Memorial Trust, NY, 5794
BTM Foundation, Inc., The, NY, see 5795
BTMU Foundation, Inc., The, NY, 5795
Buchalter Foundation, The, NY, 5796
Buchanan Area Foundation, MI, see 4514
Buchanan Foundation, George and Sarah, VA, 9410
Buchwald Foundation, Don and Maggie, The, NY, 5797
Buck Foundation, Caroline Alexander, PA, 7903
Buck Foundation, Helen R., The, PA, 7904
Buck Foundation, The, AR, 192
Buckley Foundation, William and Mary, The, NY, 5798
Bucks County Foundation, PA, 7905
Bucolo Family Foundation, Giovanni, CA, 356
Bucyrus Area Community Foundation, OH, see 7356
Budd Family Foundation, TX, 8753
Buddha Law Foundation Inc., NJ, 5282
Budwine Foundation, Inc., W. J. & Lela, TX, 8754
Buell Foundation, Susie Tompkins, CA, 357
Buffalo Bills Youth Foundation, Inc., MI, 4399
Buffalo Sabres Alumni Association, NY, 5799
Bufka Family Foundation, The, IL, see 2763
Bufka Foundation, The, IL, 2763
Buford Family Foundation, KS, 3562
Buhr Foundation, The, MI, 4400
Build Cambodia, Inc., IL, 2764
Build-A-Bear Workshop Bear Hugs Foundation, MO, 4879
Building Bridges Foundation, The, PA, see 8119
Building Healthy Lives Foundation, OH, 7340
Buist Foundation, MI, 4401
Bulger Foundation, Gregory E., The, MA, 4031
Bulkley Foundation Trust, The, IL, see 2765
Bulkley, Jr. Trust, Everett S., IL, 2765
Bull Foundation, Henry W., CA, 358
Bullard Foundation, George N., TN, see 8643
Buller Family Foundation, NY, 5800
Bulleri Foundation, Joe & Roberta, WA, 9575
Bullock III Foundation, Anthony D., OH, 7341
Bulova Fund, Inc., Louise and Arde, DE, see 1633
Bulova Stetson Fund, The, DE, 1633
Bumgarner Family Foundation, The, MN, 4649
Bundy Family Foundation, CA, 359
Bundy Foundation, Bruce and Anne, CA, 360
Bungie Foundation, The, WA, 9576
Buntrock Foundation, Dean L. & Rosemarie, IL, 2766
Bunyard Family Foundation, Mary Ellen Kent, TX, 8755
Burbank Community Hospital Foundation, CA, see 361
Burbank Health Care Foundation, CA, 361
Burbidge Foundation, Kenneth P. & Sally Rich, UT, 9308
Burch Family Foundation, TX, 8756
Burchan Charitable Trust, Walter J. & Anna H., The, NY, 5801
Burchell Charitable Trust, Llewellyn, IL, A
Burdick-Thorne Foundation, The, MI, 4402
Burford Leimenstoll Foundation Inc., The, VA, 9411
Burg Foundation, Anton B., CA, 362
Burgess Memorial Scholarship Fund, William, Agnes & Elizabeth, IL, 2767
Burgett Trust, Paul H. & Faye P., TX, 8757
Burgoon Family Foundation, Inc., The, FL, 1908
Burk Fund, Henrietta Lange, IL, 2768
Burke Family Foundation, IA, 3477

Burke Foundation, Thomas C., The, GA, 2451
Burket-Plack Foundation Inc., PA, 7906
Burkhart Foundation, Mike and Susan, OK, 7665
Burkholder Family Foundation, PA, 7907
Burks Charitable Trust, F. L. R. and Adelaide G., NC, 7061
Burks Family Foundation Inc., FL, 1909
Burlington Industries Foundation, NC, 7062
Burnett Charitable Foundation, Inc., Al and Nancy, FL, 1910
Burnett Charitable Foundation, Inc., Al, FL, see 1910
Burnett Charitable Trust, NE, 5075
Burnett Company Charitable Foundation, Leo, IL, 2769
Burnett Foundation, A. H., FL, 1911
Burnetti Childrens Foundation Inc., FL, 1912
Burnham Charitable Trust, Margaret E., ME, 3770
Burns Family Foundation, AZ, 102
Burns Memorial Fund, Anne Klinger, NC, 7063
Burnside Foundation, Inc., Warren and Betty, The, WV, 9740
Burpee Foundation, The, NY, 5802
Burris Foundation, Inc., Jerry L. and Barbara J., IN, 3352
Burrows Foundation, James And Deborah, CA, 363
Burrows Little Falls Foundation, The, NY, 5803
Burt Family Foundation, IL, 2770
Burt Foundation, Inc., Nathan B. & Florence R., CO, 1244
Burt Foundation, MI, 4403
Burt's Bees Greater Good Foundation, The, DE, 1635
Burton Foundation, Frances W., The, UT, 9309
Burton Foundation, The, NY, 5804
Burton Trust, David G., DE, 1634
Burwell Family Foundation, Rodney and Barbara, MN, 4650
Burzik Foundation, Catherine and Francis, TX, 8758
Busemeyer Atheist Foundation, Richard A., The, OH, 7342
Bush Foundation, Inc., Irving T., The, NY, 5805
Bushee Foundation, Inc., Florence Evans, MA, 4032
Bushong Family Foundation, DE, 1636
Busse Charitable Successor Trust, Thomas, OH, 7343
Busse Foundation, Lavern T. Busse & Audrey, IA, 3478
Bussing-Koch Foundation, Inc., IN, 3353
Buster Foundation, The, NY, 5806
Butler Family Charitable Foundation, Lee & Dorene, CA, 364
Butler Family Fund, The, DC, 1792
Butler Foundation, Marilyn and Marshall, CA, 365
Butler Manufacturing Company Foundation, MO, 4880
Butler/Tarrson Dental Research Foundation, IL, see 3282
Butte Creek Foundation, CA, 366
Buttonwillow Community Foundation, CA, 367
Butz Foundation, PA, 7908
Butzow Family Foundation, MN, 4651
Bw718 Foundation Inc., VA, 9412
BWMF Farm, AR, see 220
Bynum Foundation, AL, 18
Byrne Charitable Foundation, Patricia Duque, CA, 368
Byrne Family Foundation Inc., John F., NJ, 5283

C & E Foundation, PA, see 8279
C & J Charitable Trust Foundation, AZ, see 103
C & J Foundation, AZ, 103
C & N Foundation, WY, 9966
C.A.N. Foundation, NV, 5142
C3 Foundation, Inc., NC, 7064
Cabbadetus Foundation, MA, 4033
Cabot Charitable Trust, Paul & Virginia, MA, 4034
Cabot Trust Inc., Ella Lyman, MA, 4035
Caccomo Family Foundation, IL, 2771
Caddell Foundation, The, AL, 19
Cadeau Foundation, AZ, 104
Cader Foundation Inc., Andrew, The, NY, 5807
Cafaro-Livingston Charitable Trust, IL, 2772
Cafritz Charitable Trust, Carter and Melissa, DC, 1793
Cafritz Family Foundation, Inc., Buffy and William, The, MD, 3830
Cahn Family Foundation, LA, 3716
Cail Family Foundation, MA, 4036
Cain Family Foundation, Tyler R., IL, 2773
Caipirinha Foundation, DE, see 1652
CAL Foundation Inc., NY, 5808

Calamus Foundation, The, NY, 5809
Calarco Family Foundation Inc., The, CT, 1414
Calaveras Community Foundation, CA, 369
Calder Foundation, Donald Grant and Ann Martin, NY, 5810
Caldwell Charitable Trust, Elizabeth, TN, 8593
Caldwell Foundation, Philip & Betsey C., CT, 1415
Calhoun Charitable Trust, Kenneth L., OH, 7344
Cali Family Foundation, John J. & Rose, NJ, 5284
California Institute of Contemporary Art, CA, 370
California Soldiers' Widows Home Association, CA, see 826
Calkins Trust, Ina, MO, 4881
Callahan Foundation, Inc., CT, see 1469
Callahan Foundation, M. E. & F. J., OH, 7345
Callahan Memorial Award Commission, Inc., The, OH, 7346
Callas Charitable Trust, Michael G., FL, 1913
Calligan Family Foundation, PA, 7909
Callison Foundation, The, CA, 371
Callister Foundation Inc., Paul Q., UT, 9310
Callister Foundation, Louise E., UT, see 9310
Calpine Foundation, TX, 8759
Calvert Memorial Merit Scholarship Foundation, Stephen G., PA, 7910
Camara-Press Foundation, MN, 4652
Camber Charitable Trust, Len, NY, 5811
Cambridge Mindful Living Foundation, TX, 8760
Camden Home for Senior Citizens, ME, 3771
Cameron Family Foundation, Inc., Dan, NC, 7065
Cameron Memorial Fund, Alpin J. and Alpin W., PA, 7911
Cammarota Foundation Inc., Edward D., The, DE, 1637
Camp Foundation, Inc., J. L., VA, 9413
Campbell Charitable Foundation, Charles Talbot, PA, 7912
Campbell Family Foundation, John and Jane, TN, 8594
Campbell Family Foundation, Charles and Debby, TN, 8595
Campbell Foundation, Betsy M., SC, 8515
Campbell Foundation, FL, 1914
Campbell Foundation, Inc., MD, 3831
Camuto Charitable Trust, Kristen & Vincent, The, NY, see 5812
Camuto Charitable Trust, Vincent, The, NY, 5812
Canaday Fund, Harry E., NC, 7066
Candelaria Fund, CA, 372
Candor Foundation, Inc., CA, 373
Canfield Family Foundation, MO, 4882
Canipe Foundation, Walter G., GA, 2452
Cannon Charitable Trust, Joseph H., PA, 7913
Cannon Charitable Trust, William Coltrane & Norma Craft, NC, 7067
Cannon Family Foundation, CA, 374
Cannon Foundation, Hugh S., WA, A
Canterbury Foundation Ltd., The, IL, 2774
Cantonis Foundation Inc., Michael G., FL, 1915
Cantor Art Foundation, B. G., The, CA, see 375
Cantor Charitable Trust, Samuel C., FL, 1916
Cantor Foundation, Iris & B. Gerald, CA, 375
Cantor Foundation, NJ, 5285
Cape Coral Community Foundation, FL, 1917
Cape Flattery Foundation, KS, 3563
Capebank Charitable Foundation, The, NJ, 5286
Capellupo Foundation Inc., The, MO, 4883
Capital City Bank Group Foundation, Inc., FL, 1918
Caplan Family Foundation Inc., MD, 3832
Caples Fund, John R. & Dorothy D., NY, 5813
Caplin Foundation, Edwin, DE, 1638
Capri Foundation, Richard E., The, NY, 5814
Carbonari Family Foundation, FL, 1919
Carbonell Foundation, Nelson & Michelle, MD, 3833
Card Charitable Foundation, Bob and Susan, The, TN, 8596
Cardinal Collection Educational Foundation, CA, 376
Cardinal Foundation, The, OH, 7347
Cardinal O'Hara Scholarship Fund, PA, 7914
Cardon Foundation, Jeffrey S. and Helen H., UT, 9311
Carey Foundation, Mullooly, IL, 2775
Cargill Charitable Trust, Robert L. and Sara Lou, TX, 8761
Caridad Corporation, MN, 4653
Cariker Charitable Trust, Mildred, TX, 8762
Caring Friends Foundation, FL, 1920

Carita Foundation, PA, 7915
Caritas Foundation, WI, 9791
Caritas Veritatis Foundation, TX, 8763
Carle Foundation, Eric & Barbara, The, MA, 4037
Carle Foundation, Eric, MA, *see* 4037
Carlee Charitable Trust, MA, 4038
Carlin Charitable Foundation, Inc., The, FL, *see* 1921
Carlin Foundation, Inc., Audre and Donald, FL, 1921
Carlisle Charitable Trust 2, Michael, WI, 9792
Carlozzi Charitable Foundation, Inc., Nicholas H. and Margaret H., NJ, 5287
Carls Endowment Trust, MI, 4404
Carlsbad Foundation, Inc., NM, 5608
Carlson Foundation, Dean & Sandra, IA, 3479
Carlson Memorial Foundation, Inc., Gunard Berry, PA, 7916
Carlston Family Foundation, CA, 377
Carlton Foundation Inc., Hazel Crosby, FL, 1922
Carmical Foundation, Inc., John Huland, GA, 2453
Carnahan-Jackson Foundation, PA, 7917
Carnegie Foundation, The, NY, 5815
Carol Fund, Inc., Ruth, MD, 3834
Caroline's Kids Foundation, MN, 4654
Carothers Construction Charitable Foundation, MS, 4827
Carper Foundation, Daniel and Margaret, WA, 9577
Carrington Foundation, Janet A., FL, 1923
Carris Corporate Foundation, Inc., VT, 9367
Carris Reels Fund, The, VT, *see* 9367
Carroll Charitable Trust, Florence V., IN, 3354
Carroll Family Foundation, Inc., NC, 7068
Carroll Foundation, P. and C., The, NY, 5816
Carros Foundation, Jean Keller and Robert, The, FL, 1924
Carse Robinson Foundation, CT, *see* 1553
Cartales Foundation, John A. and Helen M., WA, 9578
Carter Family Foundation, WV, 9741
Carter Foundation Corp., Evelyn C., The, IL, 2776
Carter Foundation, E. Eugene, DC, 1794
Carters Charitable Foundation, Inc., GA, 2454
Cartinhour-Woods Foundation, Inc., The, TN, 8597
Cartledge Charitable Foundation, Inc., VA, 9414
Caruso Foundation, Frank & Ruth E., NY, 5817
Carver Foundation, Martin G. and Ruth A., NV, 5143
Carwill Foundation, The, NY, 5818
Cary Foundation Inc., The, NC, 7069
Cary Foundation, Inc., Bray, The, NC, *see* 7069
Cary Oil Foundation Inc., NC, 7070
CAS Foundation, Inc., CA, 378
CASA Family Foundation, UT, 9312
Case Foundation, Leo S. & Emogene Burton, The, FL, 1925
Case Trust, James W., PA, 7918
Casey Family Foundation, MA, 4039
Casey Foundation, E. Paul & Patricia P., MA, *see* 4039
Casey Foundation, Sophia & William, NY, 5819
Cashel Foundation, The, IL, 2777
Casillas Foundation, CA, 379
Cassill Foundation, Inc., The, FL, 1926
Cassner Foundation, The, OH, 7348
Casteel Foundation, Lucy H., PA, 7919
Castellani Family Foundation, Lawrence P., FL, 1927
Castellano Family Foundation, CA, 380
Castle Foundation, NY, 5820
Castle Foundation, OR, 7745
Castle Oaks Foundation, CO, *see* 1288
Castle Trust, George P. & Ida Tenney, HI, 2626
Castleman Family Foundation, The, NV, 5144
Catalina Marketing Charitable Foundation, FL, 1928
Catalyst Foundation, NY, 5821
Catalyst Foundation, The, IL, 2778
Catalyst Foundation, The, LA, 3717
Catalyst Foundation, UT, 9313
Catesby Foundation, VA, 9415
Cathedral Fund, NY, 5822
Catino Family Foundation, The, MA, 4040
Cato Foundation, Inc., Edgar T., SC, 8516
Cato, Jr. Foundation, Inc., Wayland H., NC, 7071
Catsimatidis Foundation, Inc., John and Margo, NY, 5823
Caulkins Family Foundation, CO, 1245
Causley, Jr. Family Foundation, James F., MI, 4405

Cauthorn Charitable Trust, John & Mildred, TX, 8764
Cavaricci Foundation, CA, 381
Cawsey Trust Fund, WA, *see* 9626
Cayo Trust Fund, Harry Wilson and Clare, OR, 7746
CBIS Foundation, Inc., NJ, 5288
CCJ Foundation, FL, 1929
CCS Foundation, TX, *see* 9252
CDL Foundation Inc., NY, 5824
CDM Foundation, Inc., IN, 3355
CDVSJ Foundation, NY, 5825
Cebelak Foundation, Bernard J. & Camille, MI, 4406
CEC Foundation, The, CA, 382
Cedar Branch Foundation, FL, 1930
Cedarcrest Charitable Foundation, The, DE, 1639
Cedars Foundation, Inc., VA, 9416
Celebrate Foundation, Inc., CA, 383
Celebrity Foundation Inc., The, FL, 1931
Cemo Foundation, Michael and Rebecca, TX, 8765
Cendant Charitable Foundation, The, NJ, *see* 5255
Centennial Foundation, NY, 5826
Center for Mississippi Health Policy, MS, 4828
Center for the Encouragement of Self Reliance, NV, 5145
Central Charities Foundation Inc., KS, 3564
Central Pacific Bank Foundation, HI, 2627
Central Texas Foundation Inc., TX, 8766
Central Texas Foundation, Inc., TX, *see* 8766
Century Arts Foundation, NY, 5827
Cenveo Scholarship Fund, Inc., CT, 1416
Ceres Foundation, IL, 2779
Ceriale Foundation Inc., John and Melissa, The, NY, 5828
Cerimon Fund, The, RI, *see* 8382
Cerri Foundation, Inc., Rosi, CA, 384
Cerullo Family Foundation, NY, 5829
Ceunis and Simone C. Wynant Foundation, Irma, The, CA, 385
CFP, IN, *see* 3363
CGU Charitable Trust, MA, *see* 4231
Chabner Family Foundation, Inc., Davi-Ellen and Bruce Allen, The, MA, 4041
Chabot Charitable Foundation, George & Marie, The, MA, 4042
Chace Fund Inc, The, RI, 8393
Chada Foundation, Inc., NY, 5830
Chadbourne Family Foundation, Inc., The, FL, *see* 1932
Chadbourne Foundation, Inc., The, FL, 1932
Chadwick-Loher Foundation, MN, 4655
Chaffiot Family Foundation, Inc., The, FL, 1933
Chaikin-Wile Foundation Inc., CT, 1417
Chaim Hatzlacha Foundation, The, NY, 5831
Chainani Foundation, Kamlesh and Luci, VA, 9417
Chaley Trust, Myrtle C., NC, 7072
Chambers Charitable Trust, Mary Cecile, The, TX, 8767
Chambers Charitable Trust, Naomi B., IL, 2780
Chambers Medical Foundation, LA, 3718
Chambers Memorial, James B., WV, 9742
Chambers Scholarship Fund, Mary Cecile, The, TX, *see* 8767
Chami Family Foundation, NV, 5146
Chamiza Foundation, NM, 5609
Champions Volunteer Foundation, The, CA, 386
Chan Family Foundation, The, CA, 387
Chan Foundation, The, CA, 388
Chancery Lane Foundation, MN, *see* 4648
Chandler Foundation, Inc., The, GA, 2455
Chaney Family Foundation, OH, 7349
Chaney Family Foundation, Robert and Frances, OR, 7747
Chaney Foundation Ltd., DE, 1640
Chaney Foundation, Ltd., Eugene, DE, *see* 1640
Chang Foundation, Margaret and Peter, NJ, 5289
Chang Foundation, Robert N., NJ, 5290
Change the World Foundation Trust, The, MA, 4043
Chanil Foundation, NJ, 5291
Chanin Foundation, Inc., Marcy and Leona, FL, 1934
Chapin Foundation, Frances, AZ, 105
Chapin Foundation, The, IL, 2781
Chapin-May Foundation of Illinois, IL, 2782
Chapman Family Charitable Trust, NJ, 5292
Chapman Family Charitable Trust, The, SC, 8517
Chapman Family Foundation, MO, 4884

Chapman Foundation, Inc., Alvah H. & Wyline P., FL, 1935
Chapman Perelman Foundation, The, NY, 5832
Chappell Family Foundation, Tom and Kate, ME, 3772
Chardonnay Foundation, FL, 1936
Charis Fund, OR, 7748
Charitable Foundation, Inc., The, CA, 389
Charitable Foundation/Agent Community Outreach of Prudential California Realty, The, CA, *see* 389
Charity, Inc., MN, 4656
Charles Foundation Charitable Trust, IL, 2783
Charles Fund, Inc., The, VA, 9418
Charles Woodson Foundation, FL, 1937
Charlestein Foundation, Julius & Ray, PA, 7920
Charlotte Community Foundation, Inc., FL, 1938
Charlotte County Foundation, Inc., FL, *see* 1938
Charlton, Jr. Charitable Trust, Earle P., RI, *see* 8394
Charlton, Jr. Discretionary Charitable Trust, Earle P., RI, 8394
Charter Charitable Foundation, NH, 5206
Charter Foundation, Inc., The, GA, 2456
Chartis Foundation, The, MA, 4044
Chasanoff Foundation, Inc., NY, 5833
Chasdei Y.D.K.E., Inc., NY, 5834
Chasdei Yakov Foundation Inc., NY, 5835
Chase Charity Foundation, Alfred E., MA, 4045
Chase Trust, Alice P., PA, 7921
Chastain Charitable Foundation, Robert Lee & Thomas M., NC, 7073
Chastain Educational Foundation, Betty B., WI, 9793
Chastain Home for Gentlewomen, The, VA, 9419
Chatfield Trust f/b/o The Aldermere Foundation, Albert H. Chatfield, Jr. & Marion W., ME, *see* 3763
Chatham Foundation, Inc., NC, 7074
Chatham Foundation, The, GA, 2457
Chaudhary Foundation, Younas & Bushra, TX, 8768
Cheatham Foundation, Owen, NY, 5836
Cheeryble Foundation, CA, 390
Chelsea Groton Foundation, Inc., CT, 1418
Chelvanayakam Charitable Foundation, Inc., SJV and EJ, CA, 391
Chemed Foundation, OH, 7350
Chemtob Charitable Foundation, Marc and Elka, NY, 5837
Chenault, Jr. Agricultural Foundation, C.C., PA, 7922
Chenega Future, Inc., AK, 83
Chenzyme Foundation Inc., The, FL, 1939
Chernoff Charitable Trust, Patricia, The, NY, 5838
Cherokee Strip Community Foundation, OK, 7666
Cherry Family Foundation, FL, 1940
Cherry Memorial Charitable Trust, Samuel M., IL, 2784
Chervenak-Nunnalle Foundation, Inc., The, NY, 5839
Chesed Foundation, NY, 5840
Chesed, Inc., GA, 2458
Chesley Foundation, Stanley & Susan, The, OH, 7351
Chess Foundation, NY, 5841
Chessie Foundation, Inc., MD, 3835
Chester Foundation, The, AL, 20
Chestnut Foundation, The, CA, 392
Chez Family Foundation, IL, 2785
Chiat Foundation Inc., Jay, The, CA, 393
Chicago Title and Trust Company Foundation, IL, 2786
Chicago Tribune Foundation, IL, 2787
Chickering Foundation, The, MA, 4046
Chicone Family Foundation, FL, 1941
Chicone Foundation, Jerry J., FL, *see* 1941
Chicopee Savings Bank Charitable Foundation, MA, 4047
Child Development Center, PA, *see* 7923
Child Development Foundation, PA, 7923, *see* 7923
Child Foundation for Gastronomy and the Culinary Arts, Julia, CA, 394
Children of Light Foundation, The, NV, 5147
Children's Chance for Life, WA, 9579
Children's Foundation of Erie County, Inc., NY, 5842
Children's Haven, Inc., MN, *see* 4820
Children's Health Fund, CA, *see* 966
Childress Foundation, Francis and Miranda, The, FL, 1942
Childress Foundation, Inc., J. Donald, GA, 2459
Childress Foundation, The, SC, 8518
Childtrust Foundation, NC, 7075
Chiles Foundation, Lois, NY, 5843

Chiles Foundation, OR, 7749
Chilton Foundation Trust, The, OK, see 7667
Chilton Foundation, The, OK, 7667
Ching Foundation, Hung Wo & Elizabeth Lau, HI, 2628
Chinook Charitable Trust, NY, 5844
Chipstone Foundation, WI, 9794
Chirag Foundation, The, MA, 4048
Chisholm Trail Communities Foundation, The, TX, 8769
Chisick Family Foundation, CA, 395
Chitjian Family Foundation, Harry and Ovsanna, CA, 396
Chizen Family Foundation, CA, 397
Chod Family Foundation, The, MO, 4885
Choksi Family Charitable Trust, DC, 1795
Chomeau Private Foundation, Bernal T., MO, 4886
Choptank Foundation, The, DE, 1641
Chormann Family Foundation, NJ, 5293
Chotin Foundation, The, CO, 1246
Chowdhury Family Foundation Inc., FL, 1943
Chowdhury Foundation, Subir and Malini, CA, 398
Chrest Foundation, Inc., TX, 8770
Chris Foundation, Inc., The, FL, 1944
Chrissie's Fund, CA, 399
Christ Foundation, OH, 7352
Christ Scholarship Fund, Albert A., IL, 2788
Christen Charitable Trust, Walter H., OH, 7353
Christensen Charitable Foundation, Lau & Bea, WI, 9795
Christensen Charitable Foundation, Laurits R., WI, see 9795
Christensen Family Foundation, The, CA, 400
Christian Community Development Corporation, CA, 401
Christian Development Foundation, Inc., CA, 402
Christian Evangelical Foundation, MI, 4407
Christian Foundation, C. W., IL, 2789
Christian Foundation, Taylor, NH, 5207
Christian Missionary Scholarship Foundation, MI, 4408
Christian Workers Foundation of Alabama Inc, AL, 21
Christiansen Foundation, Arthur J. & Cecelia L., IL, see 2790
Christiansen Foundation, Marjorie L., IL, 2790
Chrysalis Foundation, The, TN, 8598
Chu and Chan Foundation, NJ, 5294
Church Family Foundation, Inc., John and Therese, The, GA, 2460
Church Foundation, Sally Hughes, CA, 403
Churches Homes Foundation, Inc., GA, 2461
Ciampa Foundation Inc., Dominick & Rose, NY, 5845
Cielo Azul Foundation, TX, 8771
Cienega Foundation, Chino, CA, 404
Cimpl Foundation, Donald A. & Joan M., NE, 5076
Cindy and Kylie Huether Family Foundation, Mike, The, SD, 8557
Cinmar Family Foundation, MO, 4887
Cinnabar Foundation, The, MT, 5047
Circle Family Foundation, Inc., The, CA, see 785
Cirila Fund, The, CA, 405
Citadel Foundation, IL, 2791
Citadel Group Foundation, IL, see 2791
Citizens Bank Tri-Cities Foundation Ltd., TN, 8599
Citrin Charitable Foundation Inc., Herbert M., NY, 5846
Citrin Charitable Foundation, Rona and Jeffrey, CT, 1419
Citron Family Foundation, Ulrika and Joel, The, NY, 5847
Citta Foundation Inc., The, NJ, 5295
City Hill Foundation, DE, 1642
City of Rosemount-SKB, MN, 4657
Civitas Foundation, NJ, 5296
CJB Foundation Inc., The, NC, 7076
CKT Foundation, NJ, 5297
Clara Fund, The, CA, 406
Clareth Fund: The Philadelphia Association of Zeta Psi Fraternity, The, PA, 7924
Clark Associates Charitable Foundation, PA, 7925
Clark Charitable Fund, NY, see 5848
Clark Charitable Trust, Frank E., NY, 5848
Clark Family Charitable Trust, Andrew L., PA, 7926
Clark Family Charitable Trust, PA, see 7926
Clark Family Foundation, R. & M., AZ, 106
Clark Family Foundation, The, PA, 7927
Clark Foundation, Gladys and Franklin, The, VA, 9420
Clark Irrevocable Trust-Balance, Vera J., RI, 8395

Clark-Morrill Foundation, Inc., Judith, IN, 3356
Clark-Nexsen Foundation Inc., The, VA, 9421
Clarke Trust, John, The, MA, 4049
Clarks Fork Foundation, IL, 2792
Clarkson Family Foundation, NY, 5849
Clarkson Family Foundation, SD, 8558
Clary Foundation Inc., Eugene M., GA, 2462
Clay Irrevocable Trust, Robert S., MI, 4409
Clear Channel Communications Foundation, TX, 8772
Clemente Foundation Inc., Louis & Virginia, NY, 5850
Clementi Family Charitable Trust, MA, 4050
Clements Family Charitable Trust, The, FL, 1945
Clements Foundation, Bill and Gigi, TX, 8773
Clements Foundation, William Perry, TX, see 8773
Cleo Foundation, The, CA, 407
Clermont Foundation, NJ, 5298
Cless Family Foundation, IL, 2793
Cless Foundation, Karl, IL, see 2793
Cleveland Indians Charities, Inc., OH, 7354
CLH Foundation, OH, 7355
Cliffline Foundation, The, CO, 1247
Clifford Family Foundation Charitable Trust, The, MA, 4051
Clifford Foundation, Inc., TX, 8774
Clifton Foundation Inc., The, MD, 3836
Cline Foundation, NY, 5851
Clinedinst Trust, Samuel H., TX, 8775
Clingen Foundation Ltd, IL, 2794
Close Charitable Foundation, Helen, NV, 5148
Cloud Family Foundation Inc., WI, 9796
Cloud Nine Foundation, CA, 408
Clough Family Foundation, CO, 1248
Clougherty Charitable Trust, Francis H., CA, 409
Clovis Foundation, Inc., Bryn, PA, 7928
CNB Foundation Inc., PA, 7929
CNC Foundation, CA, 410
Coate Trust, Elmira D., NC, 7077
Coates Charitable Foundation, Olive A., ME, 3773
Cobb Community Foundation, The, GA, 2463
Cobbs Foundation, Helen C., The, VA, 9422
Coburn Foundation, James and Paula, The, CA, 411
Coby Foundation, Ltd., The, NY, 5852
Cochener Foundation, Bruce G., KS, 3565
Cochran Family Foundation, Robert and Suzanne, The, NY, 5853
Cochran Trust, Olin J., NH, 5208
Cochrane Foundation, Andrew R. & Dorothy L., CT, 1420
Codding Foundation, CA, 412
Code Blue Charitable Foundation, Inc., NY, 5854
Codman Trust, Ogden, The, MA, 4052
Cody Foundation, FL, 1946
Coes Charitable Trust, Mary M., RI, 8396
Coffey Charitable Trust, Larry R., KY, 3650
Coffey Foundation, Inc., The, NC, 7078
Coffeyville Area Community Foundation, KS, 3566
Coffin Trust, George F. Coffin, Jr. & Claire E., PA, 7930
Coffman Family Foundation, The, OR, 7750
Cogan Foundation, Inc., Benjamin and Belle, The, MD, see 3837
Cogan Foundation, Inc., Blavatt Glazer, The, MD, 3837
Cogdell Charitable Trust, Bill Pace, TX, 8776
Cogdell Hospital Trust, Martha Ann, TX, 8777
Cogitare Foundation, The, NY, 5855
Cogut Foundation, Inc., Craig & Deborah, The, NY, 5856
Cohen Charitable Trust, Ben, VT, 9369
Cohen Charitable Trust, Ellen R., MA, 4053
Cohen Family Charitable Foundation Inc., Abraham J., The, MD, 3838
Cohen Family Foundation, Abby and David, The, NY, 5857
Cohen Family Foundation, Inc., Eleanor and Menachem, FL, 1947
Cohen Family Foundation, Inc., NY, 5858
Cohen Family Foundation, Inc., The, IN, 3357
Cohen Foundation, Inc., George M., FL, 1948
Cohen Foundation, Inc., Joseph M. & Barbara, NY, 5859
Cohen Foundation, Inc., Karen B., NY, 5860
Cohen Foundation, Inc., Melvin S., DE, 1643
Cohen Foundation, Kleiner, CA, 413
Cohen Foundation, Manny and Ruthy, The, NJ, 5299
Cohen Foundation, Said, CA, 414
Cohen Private Foundation, Robert, NV, 5149
Cohenca Foundation Inc., Jacques & Emy, NY, 5861

Cohn Family Foundation, Robert & Terri, IL, 2795
Cohn Foundation Inc., Charles, NY, 5862
Cohn Foundation, Inc., Peter A. and Elizabeth S., NY, 5863
Cohn Foundation, Jacob & Rosaline, IL, 2796
Cohn Foundation, Sol, NY, 5864
Cohn Memorial Foundation, Hannah S. and Samuel A., PA, 7931
Cohoes Savings Foundation, NY, 5865
Coit Family Foundation, The, OR, 7751
Coker Charitable Foundation, Joan Sasser Coker and Charles Westfield, SC, 8519
Colbert Foundation, MS, 4829
Colburn Education Foundation, Deo B., NY, 5866
Colburn-Keenan Foundation, Inc., CT, 1421
Colby Foundation, Robert & Patricia, NY, 5867
Coldwell Foundation, Lizanell and Colbert, IL, 2797
Cole and Connie Belin Charitable Foundation, Marlin, IA, see 3480
Cole Charitable Pria Foundation, Ben And Rose, MA, 4054
Cole Charitable Trust, S. Mason and Lula P., VA, 9423
Cole Charitable Trust, The, IL, 2798
Cole Foundation for Horses Inc, Teddy, CA, 415
Cole Foundation Inc., The, MD, 3839
Cole Foundation, Kenneth, NY, 5868
Cole Foundation, Robert H. & Monica M., TN, 8600
Cole-Belin Education Foundation, IA, 3480
Coleman Charitable Foundation, CA, see 416
Coleman Charitable Foundation, Clarence B. Coleman and Joan F., The, CA, 416
Coleman Charitable Foundation, Inc., David and Ruth, AZ, 107
Coleman Charitable Trust, Dale & John, TX, 8778
Coleman Family Charitable Foundation, DE, 1644
Coleman Family Foundation Inc., Roger V., NY, 5869
Coleman Family Foundation, The, WA, 9580
Coleman Foundation, Brett and Karen, The, NV, 5150
Coleman Foundation, The, NY, 5870
Coleman, Jr. Foundation, George E., DC, 1796
Coles Family Foundation, The, NY, 5871
Colgate Fund, Inc., Russell D., DE, 1645
Collective Brands Foundation, KS, see 3614
College First Foundation, TX, 8779
Collier Foundation, Angela D., The, CA, 417
Collingwood Foundation, CA, 418
Collins - McDonald Trust Fund, OR, 7752
Collins Charitable Foundation, Inc., Vicky, The, VA, 9424
Collins Companies Foundation, The, OR, 7753
Collins Family Foundation, Inc., William L. & Lesley H., FL, 1949
Collins Family Foundation, James W., TX, 8780
Collins Family Foundation, The, IL, 2799
Collins Fisher Foundation, TX, 8781
Collins Foundation, Alisann and Terry, VA, 9425
Collins Foundation, Fred, SC, 8520
Collins Foundation, George and Jennie, The, OK, 7668
Collins, Jr. Foundation, George F., OK, 7669
Collis Foundation, The, RI, 8397
Colotto Foundation Inc., James and Loretta, The, NJ, 5300
Colston Foundation, Inc., Edward, The, GA, 2464
Colter-Jones Foundation, Laura Gene, FL, see 1954
Columbia Bank Foundation, NJ, 5301
Columbia Healthcare Foundation Inc., PA, 7932
Combs Foundation, Earle M. & Virginia M., IL, 2800
Combs-Hughes Charitable Trust, CA, 419
Commercial Federal Charitable Foundation, CA, see 272
Communitas Charitable Trust, IL, 2801
Community Covenant Foundation, Inc., The, IN, 3358
Community Enterprises, Inc., GA, 2465
Community Finance Corporation, AZ, 108
Community Foundation for Crawford County, OH, 7356
Community Foundation of Chippewa County, WI, 9797
Community Foundation of Dickinson County, Inc., The, KS, 3567
Community Foundation of East Mississippi, MS, 4830
Community Foundation of Grand Forks, East Grand Forks and Region, ND, 7295
Community Foundation of Greater Rochester, MI, 4410
Community Foundation of Greene County, Pennsylvania, PA, 7933
Community Foundation of Grundy County, IL, see 3125

Community Foundation of Hazard and Perry County, KY, see 3655
Community Foundation of Kankakee River Valley, IL, 2802
Community Foundation of Madison and Jefferson County, Inc., IN, 3359
Community Foundation of Merced County, CA, 420
Community Foundation of Monroe County, MI, 4411
Community Foundation of Morgan County, Inc., IN, 3360
Community Foundation of North Central Pennsylvania, PA, see 7975
Community Foundation of Orange and Sullivan County, NY, see 5872
Community Foundation of Orange and Sullivan, Inc., NY, see 5872
Community Foundation of Orange County, Inc., NY, 5872
Community Foundation of Randolph County, Inc., IN, 3361
Community Foundation of Southern New Mexico, NM, 5610
Community Foundation of Switzerland County, Inc., IN, 3362
Community Foundation of the New River Valley, The, VA, 9426
Community Foundation of the Quincy Area, IL, 2803
Community Foundation of the Verdugos, CA, 421
Community Foundation of Union County, Inc., OH, 7357
Community Foundation Partnership, Inc., IN, 3363
Community Health Foundation, The, OH, see 7442
Community Health Systems Foundation, TN, 8601
Community Hospital Foundation, TX, 8782
Community Involvement Foundation, PA, see 8349
Community Life Foundation of Owensboro, KY, The, KY, see 3687
Community Welfare Association of Colquitt County, GA, GA, 2466
Companions in Courage Foundation, NY, 5873
Compassion for Animals Foundation, Inc., CA, see 246
Comprecare Foundation, CO, 1249
Comunale, Jr. Charitable Foundation, Stephen A., The, OH, 7358
Con Alma Health Foundation, Inc., NM, 5611
Conant Family Cookie Jar Foundation, Inc., S. Leigh Pierson & Douglas R., The, NJ, 5302
Concourse Council, Inc., The, FL, 1950
Conestoga Road Foundation, The, PA, 7934
Coneway Family Foundation, The, TX, 8783
Coneway Foundation, Lynn & Peter, TX, see 8783
Confetti Consortium Foundation, CA, 422
Conger Family Foundation, Inc., NJ, 5303
Congregation Joseph Jacob Abraham, CA, 423
Congregation Shaaray Tefila Endownment Trust, NY, A
Conklin Foundation, Franklin, OR, 7754
Conkling-Hussey Charitable Trust, TX, A
Conley Foundation for Ethics and Philosophy in Medicine, John, The, NY, 5874
Conley Foundation, Gene, TX, 8784
Conlogue Foundation, Virginia, OH, 7359
Conn Family Foundation, The, OH, 7360
Connable Fund, H. P. and Genevieve, The, MI, 4412
Connell Charitable Trust, William F., The, MA, 4055
Connelly Scholarship Fund, John F., PA, 7935
Connemara Fund, WY, 9967
Connolly Family Foundation, Inc., GA, 2467
Connor Family Foundation, John J. Connor & Irene A., CO, 1250
Connor Foundation, Ruth and Paul, TX, 8785
Connor Group Foundation, The, OH, 7361
Conrad Charitable Foundation, MI, 4413
Conrad Family Foundation Inc., Jay & Phyllis, IN, 3364
Considine Foundation, Frank W. & Nancy S., IL, 2804
Consolidated Anti-Aging Foundation, FL, 1951
Constans-Culver Foundation, IL, 2805
Continental Divide Electric Education Foundation, NM, 5612
Contino Family Foundation, The, MD, 3840
Conway Scholarship Foundation, Inc., Carle C., CT, 1422
Cook Charitable Foundation, Gretchen Stone, MA, 4056
Cook Foundation, Gayle and Bill, DC, 1797
Cook Foundation, Joe and Louise, TX, 8786
Cook Foundation, Louella, PA, see 8079

Cook Foundation, Mark and Judith, TX, 8787
Cook Memorial Fund, Richter E. E., RI, 8398
Cook Waterfowl Foundation, MN, 4658
Cook, Sr. Charitable Trust, Claude P., GA, 2468
Cooke Foundation Corporation, V. V., NC, 7079
Cooke Foundation, Donald & Elizabeth, The, NC, 7080
Cooke Foundation, William A., VA, 9427
Cooke Trust, Elbridge C., MN, 4659
Coolidge Hill Foundation, MA, 4057
Cooney Family Foundation, John D. & Barbara C., IL, 2806
Coons Foundation, The, IA, 3481
Cooper Charitable Foundation, Inc., David J., The, AL, 22
Cooper Charitable Foundation, Inc., Frederick E. Cooper and Helen Dykes, GA, 2469
Cooper Family Foundation, AZ, 109
Cooper Foundation, Leonard & Charlotte, The, NY, see 5855
Cooper II Family Foundation, Inc., Angus R., AL, 23
Cooper Tire & Rubber Foundation, OH, 7362
Coopersmith Charitable Trust, Gladys & Irving, DE, 1646
Coors Foundation, Phyllis M., The, DE, 1647
Copaken Family Foundation, MO, 4888
Cope Charitable Fund, Ron & Carol, NE, 5077
Copeland Foundation, Leslie & Loretta, IL, 2807
Copley Fund, The, VT, 9370
Copp Foundation, Inc., The, CT, see 1538
Cora Foundation, Inc., MT, 5048
Coral Gables Community Foundation, FL, 1952
Coral Gables Foundation, The, FL, see 1952
Corbalis Family Foundation, Charles M. & Linda J., CA, 424
Corbett Charitable Trust, Willard J. and Alice C., IL, 2808
Corbett Foundation, The, OH, 7363
Corbett Foundation, Willard J. & Alice C., IL, 2809
Corcoran Community Foundation, The, CA, 425
Corcoran Family Foundation, IL, 2810
Cord Vanderpool Foundation, IL, 2811
Corday Family Foundation, CA, 426
Corday Foundation, Eliot, CA, see 426
Corde Valle Youth Golf Foundation, Inc., CA, 427
Cordover Family Foundation, NJ, 5304
Cordover Family Foundation, Ronald H., The, NJ, see 5304
Coremet Charitable Foundation, NY, 5875
Coressel Charitable Trust, Justin F., OH, 7364
Corkins Family Foundation, DE, 1648
Corlin Charitable Trust, Elizabeth, TX, 8788
Cornell Family Foundation, The, NY, 5876
Cornell Foundation, Henry, The, NY, see 5876
Cornell/Weinstein Family Foundation, NY, 5877
Cornelsen Charitable Foundation, Floy L. and Paul F., The, MO, 4889
Cornerstone Center Foundation, IL, 2812
Cornerstone Foundation, Inc., DC, 1798
Cornerstone Foundation, PA, 7936
Cornerstone Foundation, The, CO, 1251
Cornerstone Foundation, The, NY, 5878
Cornerstone Foundation, TN, 8602
Cornwall Foundation, The, MN, 4660
Correspondents Fund, The, NY, 5879
Corrigan Foundation, Robert Kemper, AZ, 110
Corrigan-Goddard Foundation, TX, 8789
Corrigan-Walla Foundation, The, DE, 1649
Cortland Community Foundation, NY, 5880
Cortland Savings Foundation, NY, see 5880
Corwin Family Foundation, CA, 428
Corwin Foundation, Bruce and Toni, The, CA, see 428
Cost Foundation, Charles L., PA, 7937
Costa Family Foundation, CA, 429
Cote Foundation Inc., Berthe M., NY, 5881
Cotsen Foundation for Academic Research, CA, 430
Cotsirilos Family Foundation, George J. & Theresa L., ME, 3774
Cottage Bridge Foundation, The, PA, 7938
Couch Family Foundation, Inc., FL, 1953
Couch Family Foundation, The, NH, 5209
Coulter Foundation, Inc., Viola Vestal, WA, 9581
Coulter Trust, Wyman R., IL, 2813
Coulter-Jones Foundation, Laura Gene, FL, 1954
Courtier Foundation Inc., WI, 9798
Covance Charitable Foundation, NJ, 5305

Cove Charitable Trust, The, PA, 7939
Covelli Foundation, Albert M., The, OH, 7365
Covenant Foundation, PA, 7940
Covenant Foundation, The, MN, 4661
Covington Community Foundation, IN, see 3466
Covington Foundation, Marion Stedman, The, NC, 7081
Cowen & Phyllis Green Foundation, Randolph L., NY, 5882
Cowles Foundation, Gardner and Florence Call, IA, 3482
Cowles Foundation, William H., WA, 9582
Cowlin Foundation, Gerry and Bill, IL, 2814
Cox Charitable Trust, Opal G., TX, 8790
Cox Foundation, James M., MN, 4662
Cox Trust, Donald and Maria, The, NY, 5883
Cozen Memorial Fund, Samuel D., PA, 7941
CPS Foundation Inc., KS, 3568
Crabb and Barbara Grasseschi Foundation, Anthony, CA, 431
Cracchiolo Foundation, Raymond M. & Jane E., MI, 4414
Cracchiolo Foundation, Thomas and Carol, MI, 4415
Cracker Barrel Old Country Store Foundation, TN, 8603
Craig Family Foundation, Inc., C. S., CT, 1423
Craig-Dalsimer Fund, The, PA, 7942
Craig-Scheckman Family Foundation, CO, 1252
Cramblit Family Foundation, The, CA, 432
Crandall Depository Foundation, J. Ford, OH, 7366
Crane & Co. Fund, The, MA, 4058
Crane Family Foundation, NY, 5884
Crane Foundation, Elizabeth N., CA, 433
Crane Foundation, Inc., NJ, 5306
Crane Foundation, Matilda & Harold, IL, A
Crane Foundation, Raymond E. and Ellen F., FL, 1955
Crane-Rogers Foundation, DC, see 1816
Cranshaw Corporation, NY, 5885
Crary Trust, Gene, PA, 7943
Craves Family Foundation, The, CA, 434
Crawford Family Foundation, CA, 435
Crawford Family Foundation, The, UT, 9314
Crawford Heritage Community Foundation, PA, 7944
Crawford Idema Family Foundation, The, MA, 4059
Crawley Memorial Educational Fund, Ethel W., NC, 7082
Cray Family Foundation, Cloud L. & Sara J., The, KS, 3569
Cray Residuary Charitable Trust, Evah C., MO, 4890
Creating Christmas Memories, TN, see 8588
Creative Providers Foundation, CO, 1253
Crebilly Foundation, The, PA, 7946
Cremer Foundation Inc., IL, 2815
Crescent-Cresline-Wabash Plastics Foundation, Inc., IN, 3365
Crescere Foundation, NV, 5151
Crete Family Foundation, WA, 9583
Crew Family Foundation Inc, The, CT, 1424
Cricket Foundation, The, MA, 4060
Crio Ministries Evangelistic Association, Inc., OK, 7670
Criste Family Foundation, Inc., MD, see 3850
Critical Care Foundation, PA, see 8346
Croft Charitable Trust, Julia W., FL, 1956
Croft Foundation Inc., L. Gordon, MD, 3841
Croll Charitable Trust, Irma L. & Abram S., DE, 1650
Croman Foundation, Edward L., NJ, 5307
Cronin Foundation, William J., IL, 2816
Cronk Family Foundation, IL, 2817
Crooks Foundation, William B. & Saramel, MS, 4831
Cross H Foundation, DE, 1651
Crossman Trust, Margarette G., RI, 8399
Crossroads Foundation Inc., LA, 3719
Crossroads Foundation, OH, 7367
Crossroads Foundation, TX, 8791
Crossroads Youth Ranch, Inc., LA, see 3719
Crossways Charitable Foundation, MA, A
Crosswicks Foundation, Ltd., CT, 1425
Crow Hill Foundation, CT, 1426
Crowder Foundation, Bill and Helen, The, TX, 8792
Crowe Family Foundation, MA, 4061
Crowell & Moring Foundation, DC, 1799
Crowley Family Foundation Inc., Geoffrey T., WI, 9799
Crowley Foundation, Marie, MI, 4416
Crown Books Foundation, Inc., DC, see 1800
Crown Foundation, Gladys K., MO, 4891
Crummer Foundation, Roy E., CA, 436

Crutchfield Family Foundation, Edward E., FL, see 1957
Crutchfield Family Foundation, FL, 1957
CSG Foundation, Inc., MD, 3842
CSM Foundation, WA, 9584
CSX Foundation, Inc., FL, 1958
Cudahy Foundation, Michael J., WI, see 9800
Cudahy Foundation, The, WI, 9800
Cullinan Memorial Trust, Duane A., IL, 2818
Cullman Conservation Foundation, Inc., Joseph & Joan, NY, 5886
Cullman Foundation for the Arts, Inc., Joseph & Joan, NY, 5887
Cultures of Resistance Network Foundation, DE, 1652
Cumming Family Foundation, David E., UT, 9315
Cumming Family Foundation, John D., UT, 9316
Cumming Foundation, Barbara Bell, NY, 5888
Cummings Fund, The, MI, 4417
Cummings-Christensen Family Foundation, WI, 9801
Cummings-Christensen Foundation, Inc., Laurits R. and Dianne, WI, see 9801
Cunnane Foundation, The, FL, 1959
Cunningham Foundation, Carlie, IL, 2819
Curaterra Foundation, The, PA, 7947
Cure Tay-Sachs Foundation, OH, 7368
Curme Family Foundation, O. & C., The, MA, see 4180
Curran Foundation, Jane and William, The, CT, see 1427
Curran Foundation, The, CT, 1427
Currie Foundation, William G., MI, 4418
Curry Family Foundation, The, MO, 4892
Curry Stone Foundation, The, OR, 7755
Curtis Family Foundation, NY, 5889
Curvey Family Foundation, MA, 4062
Cush Automotive Charitable Foundation, CA, see 437
Cush Family Foundation, The, CA, 437
Custer Foundation, Inc., Clarence E. & Inez R., IN, 3366
Cutco Foundation Inc., NY, 5890
Cutler Family Foundation, Burt and Diana, The, CA, 438
Cutting Foundation, Allen B., The, WY, 9968
CVW Family Foundation, DE, 1653
CYH Foundation, NJ, 5309
Cyr Foundation, Roderick J. & Jo Anne, KS, 3570
Czap Charitable Foundation, Carolyne E. and Eugene A., NY, 5891

D'Addario Foundation, Inc., John & Joan, NY, 5894
D'Addario Music Foundation Inc., The, NY, 5895
D'Aloia Family Foundation, NJ, 5311
D'Amour Founders Scholarship for Academic Excellence, Gerald & Paul, The, MA, 4064
D'Egville Foundation, Inc., The, MA, see 4142
D'Onofrio Charitable Foundation Trust, The, NJ, see 5324
D'Onofrio Foundation, The, NJ, 5324
D-B Trust, The, NY, 5903
D.A.S. Charitable Fund for the Preservation of Feline Animal Life, IL, 2820
D.C. Foundation, Inc., NY, see 6840
D3 Foundation, TX, 8793
Dabah Family Foundation, Inc., Barbara & Haim, NY, 5892
Dabah Family Foundation, Inc., The, NY, 5893
Daberko Charitable Foundation, The, OH, 7369
Daeumer Foundation, Harvey and Ethel, IL, 2821
Daft Family Foundation, The, NJ, 5310
Dahl Foundation, Robert & Patricia, CA, 439
Dalessandro Foundation, The, MA, 4063
Dallas Mavericks Foundation, TX, 8795
Dalton Family Foundation, The, FL, 1960
Dalton Family Foundation, The, NY, 5896
Daly Educational Fund, Bernard, OR, 7756
Daly Foundation, Edward J., CA, 440
Daly Narthex Project Charitable Remainder Unitrust, Helen E., VT, 9371
Damico Family Foundation, OH, 7370
Dammann Fund, Inc., The, NY, 5897
Damon Trust, Gertrude M., HI, 2629
Damuth Foundation, Dr. R. Lee and Adeline J., The, CT, 1428
Damuth Foundation, Malcolm C., The, TX, 8796
Dana Foundation, MI, 4419
Dana Foundation, The, MI, see 4420

Dana Z Foundation, The, MI, 4420
Dancing Skies Foundation, IL, 2822
Danella Foundation, Carmen, The, PA, 7948
Danem Foundation, CA, 441
Daniel Foundation, Leo, TX, 8797
Daniels Family Foundation, IA, 3483
Daniels Foundation, Edgar Foster, The, NM, 5613
Daniels Foundation, Ronald L. Daniels and June E., The, IA, see 3483
Danielson Foundation, IL, 2823
Danielson Foundation, James Deering, IL, 2824
Danis Foundation Inc., The, OH, 7371
Dankis Christian Foundation, Inc., The, NJ, 5312
Danvera Foundation, CA, 442
Danzi Family Foundation Inc, NY, 5898
Danziger Foundation, Gloria & Sidney, The, NY, 5899
Darby Foundation, MD, 3843
Darden Foundation, Joshua P. & Elizabeth D., The, VA, 9428
Darling Educational Memorial Fund, Robert, RI, 8400
Darnall Trust, Eugenia B., PA, 7949
Darr Family Foundation, MO, 4893
Darragh Foundation, Fred, AR, 193
Darrah Charitable Trust, Jessie Smith, NY, 5900
Dart Foundation, Robert C., MI, 4421
Dart Group II Foundation, Inc., DC, 1800
Dasburg Foundation, Meredyth Anne, FL, 1961
Dass Foundation, Gordhan, The, CA, 443
Dauch Foundation, William, OH, 7372
Dauphin Foundation, Sidney and Charline, TX, 8798
Davenport Trust Fund, George P., ME, 3775
Davey Company Foundation, OH, 7373
David Foundation, Marc, The, PA, 7950
David Uihlein Racing Museum Foundation, WI, see 9949
Davidson Foundation Inc., Scott & Susan, The, NY, 5901
Davidson Trust, Carleton F. and Ruth T., OH, 7374
Davies Charitable Trust, R. K., CA, 444
Davies Family Foundation, IL, A
Davies Foundation, The, DC, 1801
Davino Family Foundation Inc., The, NJ, 5313
Davis Charitable Foundation A New Jersey Non Profit Corporation, NJ, 5314
Davis Charitable Trust, David Boyd, NC, 7083
Davis Family Charities, Inc., James E., FL, 1962
Davis Family - W.D. Charities, Inc., James E., FL, see 1962
Davis Family Charitable Trust, FL, 1963
Davis Family Foundation, Inc., SC, 8521
Davis Family Foundation, Inc., The, FL, 1964
Davis Family Foundation, Kevin & Susie, NY, 5902
Davis Foundation Inc., James A. and Juliet L., KS, 3571
Davis Foundation, Dwight and Linda, WI, 9802
Davis Foundation, Inc., Cora and John H., MD, 3844
Davis Foundation, John & Jordan, The, CA, 445
Davis Fund, Tom, NC, 7084
Davis Trust for Charity, Mirrel, PA, 7951
Davis Trust for Employees, George H., TX, 8799
Davis Trust, Donald D. & Elaine F., UT, 9317
Davis Trust, Ione C., AL, 24
Davis-McCullough Foundation Inc., CT, 1429
Davison Bruce Foundation, GA, 2470
Davoli & Eileen L. McDonagh Charitable Foundation, Robert E., MA, 4065
Dawes Charitable Trust, Gretchen & Andrew, WI, 9803
Day Charitable Foundation, Harry M., Dr. , FL, 1965
Day Family Foundation, AL, 25
Day Foundation, James C. and Teresa K., TX, 8800
Day Memorial Fund, M. M. and P. A., DE, 1654
Day Trust, Carl and Virginia, The, MS, 4832
Daybrook Foundation, LA, 3720
Daydreams Foundation, Inc., The, MD, 3845
DDM Foundation, TX, 8801
de Compiegne Foundation, Wallace, The, TX, 8802
De Cook Foundation, Mark & Kay, IA, 3484
de Hoernle Foundation, Henrietta Countess, FL, 1966
De Karman Scholarship Trust, Josephine, DE, 1655
De La Cour Family Foundation, NY, 5904
De Lara Foundation, Inc., Juan Jacobo & Jonne Low, The, CT, 1430
De Llano Charitable Trust, Matias, TX, 8803
De Miranda Foundation, Inc., CA, 446
De Sieyes Family Foundation, NY, see 5682

De Vink Foundation, Inc., The, FL, 1967
de Vivre Foundation, Joie, MI, 4422
Dea Family Foundation, CO, 1254
Deacon Charitable Foundation, CA, 447
Dead River Foundation, ME, see 3792
Deakins Charitable Trust, Katrine Menzing, TX, 8804
Deal Foundation, The, NC, 7085
Dean Foundation Inc., Joel, MD, 3846
Deane Family Foundation, Taniguchi, The, MA, 4066
Dearborn Family Foundation, CA, 448
Deardorf Charitable Foundation, Catherine Vincent, The, IA, 3485
Dears Foundation, Inc., NY, 5905
Deason Foundation, The, TX, 8805
Debbink Family Foundation, Inc., WI, 9804
DeBusk Foundation, TX, 8806
Decatur County Community Foundation, Inc., IN, 3367
Declaration of Trust of the Joseph and Mary Cacioppo Foundation, AZ, 111
Dedham Institution for Savings Foundation, The, MA, 4067
Dedham Temporary Home for Women & Children, MA, see 4046
Dedman Family Foundation, Patricia, The, TX, 8807
Dedman, Jr. Family Foundation, Robert H., The, TX, 8808
Deeds Foundation, The, NY, 5906
Deegan Foundation, The, NY, 5907
Deerfield Charitable Trust, PA, 7952
DeFalco Family Foundation, Neil & Sandra, FL, 1968
Defeo Family Foundation, Neil & Sandra, FL, 1968
Defiance Area Foundation, Inc., OH, 7375
Degnan Family Foundation, Inc., The, NJ, 5315
DeGree Foundation, Kitty, LA, 3721
Degroot Family Foundation, MI, 4423
Dehaemers Family Charitable Trust, The, KS, 3572
Dehan Family Foundation, TX, 8809
DeHoff Family Foundation, The, OH, 7376
Deibel and Tim Allen Foundation, Laura, The, MI, see 4372
Deikel Family Foundation, The, MN, 4663
Deikel Foundation, Ted, The, MN, see 4663
Deinzer Charitable Trust, Lucille B., MI, 4424
DEKA Foundation, The, NH, 5210
DeKock Family Foundation, Douglas & Sandra, MI, 4425
Del Balso Charitable Trust, Michael & Dudley, The, NY, 5908
Del Corazon, CA, 449
Del Prete Family Foundation, RI, 8401
Delano Foundation, Mignon Sherwood, The, MI, 4426
Delavan Foundation, Nelson B., IL, 2825
Delaware County Community Foundation, PA, 7953
Deliniere Charitable Foundation, Victor & Selene, MO, 4894
Dell Charitable Trust, Roger L. & Agnes C., MN, 4664
Dellwood Foundation, Inc., MN, 4665
Delmar Foundation, Charles, The, VA, 9429
DeLoache Testamentary Charitable Trust, Waldo, GA, 2471
Delong-Sweet Family Foundation, MI, 4427
Delorenzo Scholarship Foundation, Inc., Felicia M., MA, 4068
DeLoura Family Trust, The, RI, see 8402
DeLoura Trust for Scholarships, Elmer Hobson, RI, 8402
DelSignore Foundation, Inc., Carl, The, MD, 3847
Delta Foundation, IL, 2826
DeLuca Foundation, Inc., Frederick A., The, CT, 1431
Delzell Foundation, Inc., CA, 450
DeMario Foundation Inc., Helen Matchett, The, NY, 5909
Demattia Foundation, Robert Gorlin - Mary Ann, MI, see 4457
Demetros Charitable Trust, Mary and Dr. George L., The, OH, 7377
Demorest Family Foundation, OR, 7757
Demos Foundation, Inc., N., IL, 2827
Denfeld Foundation, Inc., Greater, MN, 4666
Denit Charitable Trust, Helen Pumphrey, VA, 9430
Denit Trust for Charitable and Educational Purposes, Helen Pumphrey, The, VA, see 9430
Denkers Family Foundation, Stephen G. and Susan E., UT, 9318

Denman Family Foundation, TX, 8810
Dennett Foundation, Marie G., CT, 1432
Dennis Fund, Overton and Katherine, FL, 1969
Denny Foundation, James and Catherine, IL, 2828
Densch Charities, Inc., Wayne M., FL, 1970
DENTSPLY International Foundation, PA, 7954
DeNunzio Foundation, The, CT, 1433
Denver Public Schools Retired Employees Association Foundation, CO, 1255
Denzler Charitable Trust, Herman & Henrietta, The, CT, 1434
Depot Foundation, The, MN, 4667
Dermalogica Foundation, The, CA, 451
Dermitt Hospital, Jeanette, OH, 7378
Dermody Properties Foundation, NV, 5152
deRosa Memorial Fund for the Arts Inc., Florence & Paul, NJ, 5316
Derx Foundation Inc., Robert G. & Marguerite M., CT, 1435
Desai Family Foundation, Rohit & Katharine, NY, 5910
Desanctis, M.D. Foundation, A. L., NY, 5911
Desiring God Foundation, MN, 4668
deStwolinski Family Foundation, IA, 3486
Detter Family Foundation Inc., FL, 1971
Deupree Family Foundation, TN, 8604
Deus Spes Mea Foundation Inc., FL, 1972
Deutsch Charitable Foundation, William J. and Frances E., The, CT, 1436
Deutsch Family Foundation, NY, 5912
Deutsch Foundation, The, DE, see 1765
Devereaux Foundation, The, MA, 4069
Devine Foundation, Inc., Bonaventura, NJ, 5317
Devine-Majors Foundation, NY, 5913
Devito Family Trust, The, MD, 3848
DeVlieg Foundation, Charles, The, MI, see 4428
DeVlieg Foundation, The, MI, 4428
DeVore Foundation, Inc., KS, 3573
Dewhurst Foundation, David H., TX, 8811
Dewing Foundation, Frances R., WI, 9805
DeWitt Family Foundation, Jack and Mary, MI, see 4527
DeWitt Family Foundation, Marvin G. and Jerene L., MI, 4429
Dewolf Foundation, Nick, CO, 1256
DG Foundation, The, WA, 9586
di Portanova Charitable Foundation, Enrico & Sandra, The, TX, 8812
Diaco Family Foundation Inc, NJ, 5318
Diageo North America Foundation, Inc., CT, 1437
Dialysis Research Foundation, UT, 9319
Diamantine Family Foundation Inc., CA, 452
Diamantine Foundation, Inc., Eva and Frank, CA, see 452
Diamond Family Foundation, The, IL, 2829
Diamond Foundation, Ruby, FL, 1973
Diamond M Foundation, Inc., TX, 8813
Diamondston Foundation, Inc., NY, 5914
Diane Lynn Family Foundation Inc., FL, 1974
Dibert Foundation, Inc., Winifred Crawford, The, NY, 5915
Dibona Family Foundation, G. Fred & Sylvia, PA, 7955
Dice Foundation, Bruce B., TX, 8814
Dicerbo Foundation Inc., The, PA, 7956
Dick Charitable Trust, Albert & Mary, TX, 8815
Dick Family Foundation, The, IL, 2830
Dickerson Foundation, Douglas & Marianne, VA, 9431
Dickins Foundation Inc., Margaret E., KY, 3651
Dickinson Family Foundation Inc., NJ, 5319
Dickinson Foundation, Inc., The, FL, 1975
Dickinson Foundation, Sanders, CA, 453
Dickson Home, John, The, DC, 1802
Dickson Memorial Trust, Conway Wing Dickson and Gertrude Finck, PA, 7957
Diebold Charitable Foundation, Inc., Margaret E. & Stephen E., KY, 3652
Dienstberger Foundation, Arnold C., OH, 7379
Dierberg Foundation, The, MO, 4895
Dieringer Family Foundation, Bob and Evelyn, OR, 7758
Diermeier Family Foundation, FL, 1976
Dietrich Foundation, Inc., The, PA, 7958
Dietz & Watson Foundation, PA, 7959
Dietze Charitable Trust, John A. & Joan M., NJ, 5320
Dik Family Foundation, Edward and Evelyn, MI, 4430
Dill Foundation Inc., OK, 7671

Dillard Foundation, Anna Karin J. & David B., NY, see 5916
Dillard Foundation, The, NY, 5916
Dilworth Foundation, Lloyd L. and Helen R., FL, 1977
Dime Bank Foundation, Inc., CT, 1438
Dime Savings Bank Foundation, Inc., The, CT, see 1438
Dimick Foundation, The, DC, 1803
Dinan Foundation, John D. & Jean E., MI, 4431
DiNapoli Foundation, J. Philip & Jennifer, CA, 454
Dinardo Trust Fund, Kathryn J., PA, 7960
Dingwall Foundation, Inc., William Orr, DC, 1804
Diogenes Charitable Foundation, NY, 5917
Dion Family Foundation, DE, 1656
DiPonio Foundation, Angelo & Margaret, The, MI, 4432
Discovery Fund, The, TX, 8816
Distracted Globe Foundation, NY, 5918
Dixon Family Foundation, Inc., T. F., The, NY, 5919
Dixon Foundation, The, AL, 26
DJ Charitable Foundation, NY, 5920
DKG Foundation, TX, 8817
Dmarlou Foundation, CA, 455
Do Right Foundation, NV, 5153
Doak Charitable Trust, Clifton C. and Henryetta C., TX, 8818
Dobbs Charitable Foundation, W.M. Craig and Teneen L., IN, 3368
Dobson Foundation Inc., The, NY, 5921
Dobson Foundation, Mary Louise, TX, 8819
Dobson Foundation, Sean Joslyn Sean-Karl and Johanna Grace, The, TX, 8820
Dobson Trust, Nellie, OK, 7672
Dockser Family Foundation, Inc., MD, 3849
Dockweiler Charitable Foundation, Julia Stearns, The, CA, 456
Doctor Family Foundation, The, NJ, 5321
Doctors Hospital Development Foundation, OH, see 7545
Doctors Hospital, Inc., FL, 1978
Doelger Trust for Animals, Thelma, CA, 457
Doerr Charitable Trust, Mary, Martha & Emmett J., IL, 2831
Dohmen Company Foundation, Inc., WI, 9806
Dohmen Family Foundation, Inc., WI, 9807
Dolgen Family Foundation Inc., Jonathan and Susan, NY, 5922
Doll Family Foundation, Dixon and Carol, DE, 1657
Doll Family Foundation, NJ, 5322
Doll-Loesel Foundation, MI, 4433
Domenica Foundation, Inc., NJ, 5323
Domer Foundation, Arnold and Lois, WI, 9808
Dominion Foundation, K. H., PA, 7961
Donahue Foundation, CO, 1257
Donaldson Charitable Foundation, Evelyn, DE, see 1760
Donchian Charitable Foundation, Inc., Alma Gibbs, CT, 1439
Donchian Charitable Foundation, Inc., Richard D., CT, see 1440
Donchian Foundation, Alma Gibbs, CT, see 1439
Donchian Foundation, Inc., Richard Davoud, CT, 1440
Donegan Burns Foundation, CA, 458
Donegan Foundation, Helen M., CA, see 458
Donegan Foundation, Pam and Mark, OR, 7759
Donnally Charitable Trust, Ruth E, PA, 7962
Donnell Family Foundation, James M., TX, 8821
Donnell-Kay Foundation, Inc., CO, 1258
Donnelly Foundation, Mary J., PA, 7963
Donohue Family Foundation, Inc., The, VA, 9432
Donovan Family Foundation, IL, 2832
Donovan Family Foundation, Inc., R. & C., IL, 2833
Donovan Family Foundation, MA, 4070
Doochin Family Charitable Foundation, TN, 8605
Dooley Family Foundation, TX, 8822
Doolittle Charitable Trust No. 1, Elizabeth Elser, WI, 9809
Door County Community Foundation, Inc., WI, 9810
Doorstep Ministry Foundation, Inc., MD, 3850
Doovin Trust, NY, 5923
Dore Charitable Foundation, Fred H. & Mary S., WA, 9587
Dorn Foundation, Frederick W. and Janet P., OH, 7380
Dorothy-Ann Foundation, The, VA, 9433
Dorr Foundation, NH, 5211
Dorset Charitable Trust, FL, 1979

Dorset Foundation Inc., CO, 1259
Dorsey Foundation Inc., IN, 3369
Dorskind Family Foundation, Inc., CA, 459
Dorsky Foundation, Inc., Samuel, NY, see 5924
Dorsky Foundation, Inc., The, NY, 5924
Doscas Family Foundation, The, NY, 5925
Doshi Family Foundation, Inc., NY, 5926
Doskocil Private Foundation, Ben and Mary Frances, The, TX, 8823
Double Eagle Foundation, The, PA, 7964
Double-R Foundation, The, NY, 5927
Doudera Family Foundation, The, VA, 9434
Dougherty Foundation, Nancy C. and Dale, DE, 1658
Dougherty Memorial Trust, Julien T., NY, 5928
Dougherty Trust, Lucille and John B., TX, 8824
Dougherty, Jr. Foundation, Inc., James R., TX, 8825
Douglas Charitable Trust, Charles H., NY, 5929
Dousman Fund Inc., Ila B., MT, 5049
Dove Foundation, AZ, 112
Dove Foundation, Grant A. and Peg Brady, TX, 8826
Dow Jones News Fund, Inc., NJ, 5325
Dow Jones Newspaper Fund, Inc., NJ, see 5325
Dowdle Family Foundation, Sally and James, IL, 2834
Dower Foundation, Thomas W., IL, 2835
Downey Foundation, James E., The, CA, 460
Downey Foundation, Robert N. & Nancy A., NY, 5930
Downey-Short Foundation, CA, 461
Downing Family Foundation, CA, 462
Downing Foundation, J. C., The, CA, see 462
Downing Foundation, OH, 7381
Downs Miller Foundation, Inc., Doreen, NY, 5931
Doyle Charitable Trust, Mildred & Bernard, IL, 2836
Doyle Foundation, Inc., The, FL, 1980
Doyon Foundation, The, AK, 84
Dozzi Charitable Foundation, Eugene, PA, see 7965
Dozzi Family Foundation, Peter C., PA, 7965
Dozzo Foundation, Mario, TX, 8827
Drabek Foundation Trust, Judith E., OK, 7673
Draft Family Foundation, Melvin C., FL, 1981
Dragicevich Wyoming Foundation Trust No. 1, Matthew and Virgie O., WY, 9969
Drake Foundation, The, TN, 8606
Draughon Foundation, Louis R., TN, 8607
Dreaming Hand Foundation, VA, 9435
Dreamweaver Foundation, UT, 9320
Dreman Foundation Inc., The, NJ, 5326
Dreman Foundation, David, NJ, see 5326
Dresner Foundation, Inc., Milton H., MI, 4434
Dress Barn Fund, The, NJ, see 5252
Drexler Foundation, John and Kathleen, The, AZ, 113
Drexler Foundation, The, CA, 463
Dreyfus Foundation, VA, 9436
Driehorst Charitable Foundation, Frederick C. Driehorst and Nancy W., WV, see 9743
Driehorst Family Foundation, The, WV, 9743
Drive With A Heart Foundation, TX, see 9173
Drost Charitable Foundation, Carl and Martha, IA, 3487
Drueding Foundation, PA, 7966
Drugas Family Legacy Foundation, The, IL, 2837
Druker Charitable Foundation, Bertram A. and Ronald M., MA, 4071
Druker Charitable Foundation, MA, see 4071
Drum Foundation, The, CA, 464
Druskin Family Foundation, Inc., The, NY, 5932
Dry Creek Road, UT, 9321
DTS Foundation Inc., NY, 5933
du Bois Foundation Inc., E. Blois, AZ, 114
Duarte Foundation, Jose G., OH, 7382
Dubin Foundation, Howard and Ursula, The, IL, 2838
Dubinsky Family Foundation, John & Yvette, MO, 4896
Dubois Charitable Foundation, Jacques & Lucille, The, WY, see 9970
Dubois County Community Foundation, Inc., IN, 3370
Dubois Family Foundation, Carine and Jacques, The, WY, 9970
Dubose Family Foundation, TX, 8828
Dubs Foundation, Arthur R., OR, 7760
Duchene Foundation, Doris J. & Donald L., MI, 4435
Duckwall Foundation, Frank E., FL, 1982
Ducommun & Gross Foundation, CA, 465
Duda Foundation, Inc., John & Katherine, The, FL, 1983
Duda Foundation, Inc., John, The, FL, see 1983
Duddlesten Foundation, Wayne, TX, 8829

Dudley Foundation Inc., WI, 9811
Dudley Foundation, The, WA, 9588
Duesenberg Foundation, Robert H. and Lorraine F., MO, 4897
Dugas Family Foundation, The, ME, 3776
Duggan Scholarship Trust, Cornelius, IA, 3488
Dujay Charitable Foundation, LA, 3722
Duke of Omnium Fund, The, NY, 5934
Dukes Health Care Foundation of Miami County Inc., IN, 3371
Dulaney Foundation, Inc., Richard P., OK, 7674
Dulaney Foundation, Joseph F., TX, 8830
Dull Casper Trust, PA, 7967
Dumke Foundation, Inc., Wattis, The, ID, 2668
Dun Foundation, VA, 9437
Dunagan Foundation, Inc., TX, 8831
Dunaway Family Foundation, Inc., Carol Winn and James Reed, The, TX, 8832
Dunbar Foundation, Inc., KY, 3653
Duncan Family Foundation, IL, 2839
Duncan Foundation, Inc., Harry F., MD, 3851
Duncan Foundation, Lillian H. and C. W., The, TX, 8833
Duncan Trust, John G., NC, 7086
Duncan Trust, Louise Head, IL, 2840
Dundas Foundation, Constance, The, VA, 9438
Duneland Health Council, Inc., IN, 3372
Dungannon Foundation, Inc., NY, 5935
Dunham Charitable Foundation, The, TX, 8834
Dunklin, Jr. Charitable Foundation, George H., AR, 194
Dunn Charitable Foundation, R. B. and Ruth H., WA, 9589
Dunn Charitable Trust, Mary B., DE, 1659
Dunn Charitable Trust, Stannard & Dorothy, The, NH, 5212
Dunn Family Foundation, MO, 4898
Dunn Family Foundation, The, NY, 5936
Dunn Foundation, Edward B., NY, see 5936
Dunning Memorial Fund Trust, Mildred H., IL, 2841
Durant Family Foundation, The, MA, 4072
Durden Foundation, Inc., The, FL, 1984
Durham Foundation, H. W., TN, 8608
Durrill Foundation, Inc., Devary, TX, 8835
Dusenbury Charitable Trust, Warren and Zoann Little, CA, 466
Dutton Foundation, Inc., James E., WI, 9812
Dvaykus Fondation Inc., NY, 5937
DWB Family Foundation, CO, 1260
Dweck Family Foundation, Murray & Florence, NJ, 5327
Dweck Foundation, Samuel R., The, DC, 1805
Dwelle Family Foundation Inc., CA, 467
Dwinell Charitable Trust, Lane and Elizabeth, RI, 8403
Dworman Foundation, Inc., NY, 5938
DWSS, Inc., MA, 4073
Dwyer Charitable Foundation Trust, Richard J. Dwyer, Jr. & Mary B., The, VA, 9439
Dwyer Foundation, MA, 4074
Dwyer Fund for Excellence, Richard F. and Eleanor W., The, CA, 468
Dyco Foundation, The, MN, see 4669
Dye Foundation, Inc., James W. & Betty, IN, 3373
Dyer Family Foundation, CA, 469
Dyer Family Foundation, David and Harriet, FL, 1985
Dyer Foundation, Jaye F. and Betty F., The, MN, 4669
Dysimmune Neuromuscular Diseases Foundation, FL, 1986
Dyson Foundation North America, James, IL, 2842

E Bowen Bo Universalist Church Fund, RI, see 8391
E.R.G. Foundation, NY, 5939
EAA Flight Academy, Inc., FL, see 2275
Eacho Family Foundation, The, MD, 3852
Eagle Globerman & Kodama Foundation, The, CA, 470
Eakins O For B E Endowment Fund, PA, 7968
Earle Foundation, Dexter & Carol, NJ, 5328
East Boston Savings Charitable Foundation Inc., MA, 4075
Easter Foundation Inc., WI, 9813
Easterly Foundation Inc., Claud E., The, DE, 1660
Eastern Carolina Community Foundation, SC, 8522
Easthampton Savings Foundation, Inc., MA, 4076
Eastman Fund, Inc., Lucius & Eva, NY, 5940
Eaton Family Foundation, The, AZ, 115
Eaton Foundation, Cyrus, The, OH, 7383

Eau Claire Area Foundation, WI, see 9814
Eau Claire Community Foundation, WI, 9814
EBA Foundation, NY, 5941
EBB Point Foundation, The, NJ, 5329
Ebell of Los Angeles Rest Cottage Association, CA, 471
Ebell of Los Angeles Scholarship Endowment Fund, CA, 472
Ebenezer Charitable Trust, The, OH, 7384
Eberhart Foundation, David F. and Frances A., NY, 5942
Eberly Foundation, The, PA, 7969
Eberspacher Foundation, Walter and Ursula, CO, 1261
Ebert-Leblanc Family Foundation Inc., The, TN, 8609
EBS Foundation, TN, 8610
EBV Foundation, NV, 5154
Eccles Family Foundation, The, MD, 3853
Eccles First Security Foundation, UT, 9322
Echevarria Family Foundation, Inc., FL, 1987
Echlin Foundation Inc, The, GA, 2472
Echo Bay Foundation, WA, 9590
Eckels Foundation, Theodore W. and Betty J., PA, 7970
Eckert Foundation, Theodore, IL, 2843
Eclipse Foundation, IL, 2844
Ecotrust Foundation, MN, 4670
Eddy Foundation Charitable Trust, NC, see 7087
Eddy Foundation, Mary-Louise & Ruth N., MA, 4077
Eddy Foundation, NC, 7087
Edelman Family Foundation, D. J., IL, 2845
Edelman Family Foundation, Thomas J., The, NY, 5943
Edelman Foundation, Inc., Jack and Debra, IN, 3374
Edelstein Foundation, IL, see 2846
Edelstein Foundation, Marian & Arthur, IL, 2846
Edelweiss Foundation, NY, 5944
Eden Charitable Foundation, Inc., GA, 2473
Eden Charitable Foundation, PA, 7971
Eder Family Foundation Inc., CT, 1441
Eder Family Foundation, Inc., Andrew J., The, CT, see 1441
Edgar Charitable Foundation, William, MO, 4899
Edgar Charitable Trust, Harold T., NC, 7088
Edgerly Foundation, The, IL, 2847
Edina Community Foundation, The, MN, 4671
Edina Realty Foundation, MN, 4672
Edison Properties Charitable Trust of Newark, NJ, see 5330
Edison Properties Newark Foundation, NJ, 5330
Edlavitch Foundation, Inc., Irwin P., The, VA, 9440
Edmonds and Julie Anne Quay Foundation, Matthew J., NY, see 6256
Edmonston Charitable Foundation, Miriam Arnold, MO, 4900
Edson Foundation, The, AZ, see 145
Educational Advancement Foundation, TX, 8836
Educational and Charitable Foundation, Harding, IL, 2848
Educational Projects Foundation Inc., NY, 5945
Edward Charitable Fund, David W., OH, 7385
Edwards Company Foundation, J. T., OH, see 7386
Edwards Foundation, Elizabeth McCarty, MS, 4833
Edwards Foundation, Kirk, TX, 8837
Edwards Foundation, Ray Thomas, CA, 473
Edwards Foundation, The, OH, 7386
Edwards Scholarship Fund, MA, 4078
Edwards Trust, Catherine R., PA, 7973
Edwards Trust, Catherine, PA, 7972
EFM Foundation, The, PA, 7974
EG&G Foundation, MA, see 4238
Egan Foundation, Chris & Jean, MA, 4079
Egan Foundation, Dorothy Harrison, MA, 4080
Eggleston Foundation, The, NY, 5946
EGW Foundation, Inc., FL, 1988
Ehrlich Charitable Foundation II, Inc., Jonas, NY, 5947
Ehrlich Charitable Foundation, Jonas, NY, 5948
Ehrman Foundation, Fred & Suzan, The, NY, 5949
Eichenberg Charitable Foundation, Robert & LaDorna, CA, see 474
Eichenberg-Larson Charitable Foundation, The, CA, 474
Eichner Foundation, Ira A. & Barbara R., IL, 2849
EiF, NY, see 5964
Einhorn Family Charitable Trust, WI, see 9815
Einhorn Family Foundation Inc., WI, 9815
Eiriksson Foundation, Leifur, VA, 9441
Eisenberg Family Charitable Trust, IL, 2850
Eisenberg Foundation, Martin & Rebecca, NJ, 5331

Eisenberger Foundation, Jeffrey & Lauren, The, NY, 5950
Eisner Family Fund, The, DE, see 1665
Eisner Foundation, Karen & David, The, NY, 5951
Eiszner Family Foundation, IL, 2851
Ekstein Charitable Foundation, Abraham & Raizel, The, NY, 5952
Elazar Fund, Yalket, NY, 5953
Elder Family Foundation, CA, 475
Elder Foundation, IN, 3375
Eleanor's Fund, SD, 8559
Elebash Fund, Baisley Powell, IL, 2852
Elec Material Hirtzel Memorial Foundation, PA, see 8058
Electrical Industry Scholarship Fund, Inc., The, NY, 5954
Elephant Rock Foundation Inc., MA, 4081
Eleven Twenty Seven Foundation, CA, 476
Elf Foundation, The, CO, 1262
Elfenworks Foundation, The, CA, 477
Eliasberg Family Foundation, Inc., The, MD, 3854
Elisha-Bolton Foundation, OH, 7387
Elizabeth Foundation, FL, see 2015
Elizabeth Foundation, The, CO, 1263
Elizabethtown Healthcare Foundation, NJ, 5332
Elk County Community Foundation, PA, 7975
Elkins For Abington, S. Mcintyre, PA, 7976
Elkins Foundation, Deborah, NY, 5955
Elkins Foundation, J. A. and Isabel M., TX, 8838
Elks of Los Angeles Foundation, NC, 7089
Ellbogen Foundation, Ruth R., WY, 9971
Ellen and Michael E. Fox Family Foundation, Mary, CA, 478
Ellen Stinski Foundation, Mark and Mary, IA, 3489
Ellens Foundation, Dennis & Eileen, MI, see 4422
Ellerbrook Family Foundation, Inc., Niel C. and Karen Ma, IN, 3376
Elliotsville Plantation Inc, ME, 3777
Elliott Family Foundation, Harry C. and Deborah L., CA, 479
Elliott Family Foundation, R. Hugh, MI, 4436
Elliott Foundation, William and Muriel, PA, 7977
Ellis Family Foundation Trust, LA, 3723
Ellis Foundation Trust, Elizabeth B., PA, 7978
Ellis Foundation, Estelle S. & Robert A. Long, MO, 4901
Ellis Foundation, Inc., Gail G., IL, 2853
Ellis Foundation, Joseph H. & Barbara I., NJ, 5333
Ellis Foundation, Robert M., The, FL, 1989
Ellison Charitable Remainder Trust, AL, A
Ellison Family Foundation, Inc., John G. B., Jr. and Jane R., The, NC, 7090
Ellman Foundation, NY, 5956
Ellsworth Foundation, Lincoln, The, NY, 5957
Elmen Foundation, James and Eloise, SD, 8560
Elmen Foundation, Robert and Rita, The, SD, 8561
Elmwood Fund, The, VA, 9442
Elno Family Foundation, Inc., MD, 3855
Elpis Foundation, The, OK, 7675
Elrod Foundation, Ben M. and Betty Lou, AR, 195
Elsberg Family Foundation, Inc., MD, 3856
Elsberry Family Foundation, KS, 3574
Elster Foundation, FL, 1990
Eluzer Fund, Bais, NY, 5958
Elwood Foundation, Gordon, OR, 7761
Ely Trust, Charles C., PA, 7979
Elyachar Welfare Corp., NY, 5959
EMA Foundation, IL, 2854
Emanuel Foundation, Quinn, CA, 480
EMB Foundation, Ltd., NY, 5960
Emelco Foundation, The, ID, 2669
Emerald Foundation, SD, 8562
Emma Barnsley Foundation, NC, 7091
Emmerich Foundation Charitable Trust, The, MN, 4673
Emmett Foundation, CA, 481
Emmitt Smith Charities, TX, see 9204
Empire Charitable Foundation, AZ, 116
Empire Foundation, FL, see 2076
Emporium Foundation, Inc., PA, 7980
Empson Trust, Louise B., MO, 4902
EMSA Fund, Inc., NY, 5961
Emwiga Foundation, NY, 5962
Encourage, Inc., MA, 4082
Enders Charitable Trust, Blanche T., NY, 5963

Endowment for Biblical Research, OH, 7388
Endurance Fund, The, CA, 482
Energy Cup, The, CO, 1264
Engel f/b/o AA CM State University of New York, PA, 7981
Engel Family Foundation Inc., NJ, 5334
Engel Foundation, Inc., Robert G. & Jane V., The, NJ, 5335
Engelsma Family Foundation, SD, 8563
Engineering Information Foundation, NY, 5964
England Charitable Trust, J. Irving & Jane L., MA, 4083
Engle Family Foundation, IL, 2855
Engle Foundation, Alvin S., PA, 7982
Englebardt Family Charitable Trust, Bonnie S., NY, 5965
English Foundation, The, VA, 9443
English Foundation-Trust, The, VA, see 9443
English Memorial Fund, Florence C. and Harry L., The, GA, 2474
Enid Community Foundation, Inc., OK, see 7666
Enivar Charitable Fund, IL, 2856
Enkess Charitable Foundation Trust, The, NY, 5966
Enlightenment Foundation, The, FL, 1991
Enrico Family Foundation, Aaron and Catie, The, TX, 8839
Enright Foundation Inc., MO, 4903
Ensign-Bickford Foundation, Inc., The, CT, 1442
Entelco Foundation, OH, 7389
Enterline Foundation, The, GA, 2475
Entin Foundation, Lester M. and Sally, The, NJ, 5336
Entrepreneur Bootcamp for Veterans with Disabilities, NV, see 5154
Environmental Data Research Institute, NY, see 5676
Environmental Endowment for New Jersey, Inc., NJ, 5337
EON Charitable Foundation, DE, 1661
EOS Foundation, TX, 8840
Epaphroditus Foundation, IL, 2857
Epilepsy Research Foundation of Florida, Inc., FL, see 2406
Episcopal Foundation of Dixon, Illinois, Ltd., IL, see 2774
Eplee Foundation, Inc., The, NC, 7092
Eppley Foundation for Research, Inc., The, NY, 5967
Epstein Charitable Foundation, Jean Estes, HI, 2630
Epstein Foundation Inc., Barbara, The, MA, 4084
Epstein Foundation Trust, Samuel, The, PA, 7983
Epstein Humanitarian Fund, Gene & Marlene, PA, 7984
Epstein Private Foundation, David and Geri, FL, 1992
Epstein/Roth Foundation, CA, 483
Equinox Foundation, Inc., ID, 2670
Equity Community Foundation, IL, see 2858
Equity Residential Foundation, IL, 2858
Erath Family Foundation, OR, 7762
Erdle Foundation, FL, 1993
Erdman Foundation, Daniel W., WI, 9816
Ergen Family Foundation, DE, see 1762
Erickson Family Charitable Foundation, WA, 9591
Erickson Foundation, Alfred W., MN, 4674
Erickson Foundation, Arthur T., MN, 4675
Eriksen Trust Fund, T. R., CA, 484
Erion Foundation, CO, 1265
Erlich Charitable Foundation, Max and Melba, The, MO, 4904
Erpf Fund, Inc., Armand G., The, NY, 5968
Ervin Foundation, J. F., The, MI, 4437
Esbenshade Foundation, WV, 9744
ESH Charitable Foundation, NJ, 5338
Eskenazi Family Foundation, Inc., IN, 3377
Eskind Family Foundation, Annette & Irwin, The, TN, 8611
Eskind Family Foundation, Jeffrey and Donna, The, TN, 8612
Eskind Family Foundation, Steven & Laurie, The, TN, 8613
Eskuche Charitable Foundation, Henry W. & Leslie M., UT, 9323
ESL Charitable Foundation, NY, 5969
Espenscheid Charitable Foundation, Harry and Dorothy, IL, 2859
Esping Family Foundation, TX, 8841
Esprit Foundation, CA, see 357
Essig Enright Family Foundation, NJ, 5339
Essman Family Charitable Foundation, MO, 4905

Estate Of Elizabeth Straut, RI, 8404
Estate of Mildred Bancroft Charitable Trust, IL, 2860
Eternal Abundance Foundation, Inc., IN, 3378
Ethel Frends Charitable Foundation, TX, 8842
Etscorn Charitable Foundation, Irvin F. & Alice S., KY, 3654
Ettl Foundation, Alex J., NY, 5970
Ettlinger Trust, Isaac, OH, 7390
Eule Charitable Foundation, NY, 5971
Evans Family Charitable Foundation, NY, 5972
Evans Family Foundation, Inc., NY, see 5973
Evans Foundation, John D., The, FL, 1994
Evans Foundation, R. S., NY, 5973
Evans Foundation, Ray and Wyn Ritchie, The, CA, 485
Evans Foundation, Ryan, The, CA, 486
Evanson Family Foundation, Paul and Carol, FL, 1995
Evening Star Foundation, CA, 487
Ever and Anon Foundation, MO, 4906
Everard Charitable Foundation, Alice, PA, 7985
Everest Edwin Foundation, CA, 488
Everest Foundation, Jean I., OK, 7676
Everett Charitable Foundation, Esther M. & Freeman E., IL, 2861
Everett Community Foundation, Greater, The, WA, 9592
Everett Foundation, Herschel H. & Cornelia N., NC, 7093
Everett Parks Foundation, WA, see 9592
Evergreen Foundation, Heyman, The, OK, 7677
Everhealth Foundation, CA, see 338
Evernham Family-Racing for a Reason, NC, 7094
Evert Foundation, MN, 4676
Every Scholarship Fund, Joseph R., PA, 7986
Excel at Sports Foundation, WA, 9593
Exposition Foundation, The, GA, 2476
Eykamp Foundation, MA, see 4197
Eyman Trust, Jesse, OH, 7391
Ezer Foundation, NY, 5974
Ezra Charitable Trust, The, NY, 5975
Ezra Foundation, Magen, NY, 5976
Ezrow Foundation, Jonathan & Isabel, NY, see 6685

F Cubed Foundation, CO, 1266
F. & J.S. Fund Inc., The, NY, 5977
F.K. Bemis Family Foundation, WI, 9817
F2 Family Foundation, Inc., The, AZ, 117
Fabenco Founding Fathers Foundation, TX, 8843
Faber Foundation, Clara, NY, 5977
Fabiano Foundation, MI, 4438
Fabick Charitable Trust Inc., MO, 4907
Fabyan Foundation, IL, 2862
Faggin Foundation Inc., Frederico and Elvia, CA, 489
Fagin Family Foundation, The, NY, 5978
Fahrney Education Foundation, Charles E., WI, 9818
Fahrney Education Foundation, WI, see 9818
Fair Foundation, R. W., The, TX, 8844
Fair Memorial Fund, Frederick and Ellen, PA, 7987
Fairchild Foundation, I. D. & Marguerite, TX, 8845
Fairfield - Meeker Charitable Trust, Freeman E., NC, 7095
Fairview Foundation, CA, 490
Faith Foundation, Barnabas, The, TX, 8846
Faith Home Foundation, NY, 5979
Faith Ventures Foundation, Inc., GA, 2477
Faith, Hope and Love Foundation, MN, 4677
Falck Foundation, Arlin, MN, 4678
Falconhead Foundation, NY, 5980
Fales Foundation Trust, WA, 9594
Falk Charitable Foundation, Maurice & Judi, NY, 5981
Falk Family Foundation, FL, see 1996
Falk Foundation, Michael & Annie, FL, 1996
Familian and Lilian Levinson Foundation, Zalec, CA, 491
Familian Foundation, Zalec, CA, see 491
Families Outreach Inc., AR, 196
Family Alliance Foundation, IL, 2863
Family Baum Foundation, Theodore B., NY, see 5722
Family Care Foundation, MS, 4834
Family Charitable Foundation, Kahn, MA, 4085
Family Charitable Foundation, Madden, CO, 1267
Family Foundation Inc., Jacquemin, The, VA, 9444
Family Foundation Inc., Rudderow, PA, 7988
Family Foundation, Callant, MI, 4439
Family Foundation, Chupp, FL, 1997
Family Foundation, Friesen, The, CA, 492

Family Foundation, Gooding, CO, 1268
Family Foundation, Hoellen, IL, 2864
Family Foundation, Hoffman, KS, 3575
Family Foundation, Holloway, CT, 1443
Family Foundation, Inc., Heller, The, NJ, 5340
Family Foundation, Jim Hicks, The, CA, 493
Family Foundation, Nagle, The, NY, 5982
Family Foundation, Smith, NC, 7096
Family Foundation, Vanderbilt, The, NY, 5983
Family Foundation, Zaleski, NY, 5984
Fan Foundation, Katherine & George, NY, 5985
FAR Family Foundation, WA, 9595
Farago Foundation, Paul, MI, 4440
Farah Foundation, Virginia H., KS, 3576
Faranna Scholarship Trust, Charles C., OK, 7678
Faraway Foundation, CA, 494
Farber Foundation, Anne & Jason, CA, 495
Farber Foundation, Gloria and Hilliard, The, NY, 5986
Farber Memorial Foundation, Inc., Charles D., NY, 5987
Farid Foundation, CT, 1444
Farkas Family Foundation, The, VA, 9445
Farkas Foundation, Howard and Barbara, NY, 5988
Farmers Insurance Group Safety Foundation, CA, 496
Farmers Union Industries Foundation Inc., MN, 4679
Farnham Foundation, IL, 2865
Farnsworth Trust, Lucy C., PA, 7989
Faro Foundation, CA, 497
Farr Family Foundation Inc., DE, 1662
Farr Trust, Frank M. and Alice M., NE, 5078, 5079
Farrell Foundation, The, FL, 1998
Farrer Endowment Foundation, IA, 3490
Farrington Foundation, NJ, 5341
Farris Charitable Trust, The, NJ, 5342
Farris Foundation, Robert Houston & Hollyanne Frances, TX, see 8847
Farris Foundation, The, TX, 8847
Farver Foundation, Joan Kuyper, IA, 3491
Farver Foundation, The, MI, 4441
Farview Foundation, MN, 4680
Farvue Foundation Inc., DC, 1806
Farwell Foundation, Drusilla, MI, 4442
Faser Triplett Foundation, Dr. and Mrs. R., MS, 4835
Fash Foundation, TX, 8848
Fasseas Foundation, Peter & Paula, IL, 2866
Fassino Foundation, Inc., The, MA, 4086
Fast Forward Foundation, The, CA, 498
Fat Tire Foundation, The, CA, 499
Faulkner Trust, Marianne G., IL, 2867
Faulkner Trust, Marianne Galliard, IL, see 2867
Fauth Charitable Trust, Marie, CT, 1445
Favre Charitable Foundation, Kathryn G., MO, 4908
Fawcett Foundation, Farrah, The, CA, 500
Fay Charitable Fund, Aubert J., MA, 4087
Fay Dreams Foundation, Morgan Le, NY, 5989
Fayette County Foundation, IN, 3379
FCTS Machine Technology Fund, MA, 4088
Fedeli Family Charitable Foundation, The, OH, 7393
Feder Family Foundation, Paul E. and Margaret, CA, 501
Federation of Protestant Welfare Agencies Trust, IL, 2868
Fedje Foundation, Noel & Judith, ND, 7296
Fee Foundation, Inc., Frank J., NY, 5990
Feenstra Family Foundation, P.and T., AZ, 118
Feibelman Foundation, The, RI, 8405
Feil Family Foundation Inc., Lee and Jeffrey, The, NY, 5991
Fein Foundation, Edward, NV, 5155
Fein Foundation, NY, 5992
Feinberg Family Foundation, Maurice & Carol, NY, 5993
Feinberg Foundation, The, MD, 3857
Feinman Foundation, Alfred and Harriet, NY, 5994
Feinstein Foundation, Edward, NV, see 5155
Feinstein Foundation, Jeffrey & Debra, NJ, 5343
Feintech Family Foundation, Evelyn M. & Norman C., CA, 502
Feldman Family Foundation, Steven and Marcy, The, NY, 5995
Feldman Foundation Inc., Seymour, NY, 5996
Feldman Private Foundation, Inc., Gretchen V. & Samuel M., MD, 3858
Feldstein Family Charitable Foundation Inc., NY, 5997
Feldstein Medical Foundation, Inc., NJ, 5344
Feldstein Private Foundation, Mark S., OH, 7394

Felger Memorial Trust, Judge and Mrs. Carl B., OH, 7395
Felhaber, Larson, Fenlon & Vogt Foundation, MN, 4681
Felicia Fund, Inc., RI, 8406
Feline Friends Inc., NJ, 5345
Felix Foundation, F., MA, 4089
Fellstone Foundation, Inc., NJ, 5346
Felt Foundation, Howard E., OK, see 7687
Feltes Family Foundation, Tim and Karla, IL, 2869
Female Association of Philadelphia, The, PA, 7990
Fenech Foundation, Ron and Lisa, IN, 3380
Fennell Foundation, Robert E., TX, 8849
Fenner Family Charitable Foundation, TX, 8850
Fenton Family Foundation, Inc., ID, see 2670
Fenton Family Foundation, The, NY, 5998
Fentress Foundation, The, TX, 8851
Ferber Family Foundation, MN, 4682
Ferber Foundation, Ronda and Ron, The, MI, 4443
Ferenc Family Charitable Foundation of Brooklyn, The, NE, 5080
Ferguson Charitable Trust, Dan C., FL, 1999
Ferguson Family Baptist Missionary & Educational Foundation, Ltd., WI, 9819
Ferguson Family Foundation Trust, The, SD, 8564
Ferguson Family Foundation, Inc., CT, 1446
Ferguson Family Foundation, Inc., NY, see 5999
Ferguson Foundation, Hugh and Jane, The, WA, 9596
Ferguson Foundation, The, CA, 503
Ferguson Foundation, Whitworth and Dorothy, The, NY, 5999
Fernandina Foundation, DE, 1663
Ferrari Foundation, Andrew U., VA, 9446
Ferriday Fund Charitable Trust, The, NY, 6000
Ferris Charitable Operating Foundation, Constance and Carl, MD, 3859
Ferris Family Foundation, The, MD, 3860
Ferris, Jr. Foundation, George M., MD, see 3860
Ferro Foundation, Charles P., VT, 9372
Ferry Charitable Foundation, Richard M. and Maude M., The, CA, 504
Ferry Family Foundation, The, OH, 7396
Fertitta Family Foundation, Tilman and Paige, TX, 8852
Fessenden Charitable Foundation, Elizabeth T., The, MA, 4090
Feth Family Foundation, The, OH, 7397
Fetters Charitable Trust, Lela M., PA, 7991
Feuerring Foundation, The, NY, 6001
FHC Foundation, The, TX, 8853
Fibus Family Foundation, OH, 7398
Ficalora Family Foundation, NY, 6002
Fickett Charitable Foundation, Franklin I., TX, 8854
Fickling Family Foundation Inc., GA, 2478
Fidelity Bank Foundation, The, KS, 3577
Field Trust, Daniel W., RI, 8407
Field-Day Foundation, TX, 8855
Fields Automotive Group Foundation, Inc., Earl and Bettie, The, IL, 2870
Fields Charitable Foundation, Inc., Earl and Bettie, IL, see 2870
Fields Family Foundation, NY, 6003
Fields Family Private Foundation, J. H. & Janet E., NC, A
Fieldstone Foundation, Inc., NY, 6004
Fierce Advocacy Fund, Inc., PA, 7992
Fife Foundation, Inc., Lori & Mark, The, NY, 6005
Fifield Family Foundation, IL, 2871
Fifth Age of Man Foundation, TX, 8856
Figge Charitable Foundation, V.O. Figge and Elizabeth Kahl, IA, 3492
Fildes Foundation, Ltd., Johnsie Fiock, The, IL, 2872
Filingieri Philosophical Society of America, Inc., Gaetano, CT, 1447
Filmer Memorial Charitable Trust, Phillip & Elizabeth, MI, 4444
Finch Foundation, Doak, The, FL, 2000
Findlay Education Foundation, NV, 5156
Fine Family Charitable Foundation, The, PA, 7993
Fine Foundation, Inc., Beverly K. & Jerome M., MD, 3861
Fine Fund, The, PA, 7994
Fine Scholarship Fund, Frada L., WV, 9745
Finerty Family Foundation, MO, see 4909
Finerty Family Foundation, Steve and Linda, The, MO, 4909

Finestra Foundation, The, CA, 505
Finger Foundation, Jerry and Nanette, TX, 8857
Fingerhut Family Foundation, MN, 4683
Finigan Foundation, Pearle Francis, The, NE, 5081
Fink Charitable Foundation, Jacob J., IL, 2873
Fink Family Foundation, Richard & Beverly, MN, 4684
Fink Family Foundation, The, NY, 6006
Fink Family Trust, R. and M., VA, 9447
Finkelstein Foundation, Inc., Howard and Susan, NY, see 6007
Finkelstein Foundation, Inc., Howard, NY, 6007
Finkelstein Foundation, Inc., The, CT, 1448
Finlay Foundation, The, NH, 5213
Finley Charitable Foundation, Inc., MO, 4910
Finley Charitable Trust, J. B., PA, 7995
Finn Family Foundation, Inc., David & Laura, NY, 6008
Finn Family Foundation, Inc., The, CT, 1449
Finnegan Foundation, John D., OH, 7399
Finney Foundation, Stanford C. and Mary Clare, TX, 8858
Fippinger Foundation, Inc., Grace J., CT, 1450
Firebird Foundation for Anthropological Research, ME, 3778
Fired Up Foundation, TX, 8859
Firman Fund, OH, 7400
First American Financial Foundation, CA, 506
First Citizens National Bank Charitable Foundation, Inc., IA, 3493
First Cornerstone Foundation Inc, PA, 7996
First Data Employee Hardship Fund, CO, 1269
First Family Foundation, Robert and Deborah, MA, 4091
First Federal Charitable Foundation, PA, 7997
First Financial Foundation, Inc., WI, see 9778
First Gaston Foundation, Inc., NC, 7097
First Harvest Foundation, CA, 507
First Insurance Company of Hawaii Charitable Foundation, HI, 2631
First Savings Community Foundation, PA, 7998
Firstfruits Foundation, TN, 8614
Firth Charitable Trust, Clara Helen, NC, 7098
Firth Testamentary Trust, Clara Helen, NC, see 7098
Fischel Foundation, Harry and Jane, NY, 6009
Fischer Family Foundation, The, MD, 3862
Fischer Foundation, Sonja and F. Conrad, IL, 2874
Fischman Scholarship Fund, E. David, MN, 4685
Fish Foundation, Inc., Bert, The, FL, 2001
Fish Testamentary Trust, Bert, FL, see 2001
Fishback Family Foundation, Inc., Kathryn C., CA, A
Fishback Foundation Trust, Harmes C., CO, 1270
Fishel Foundation, OH, 7401
Fisher Foundation, George & Patricia Ann, NJ, 5347
Fishkin Scholarship Fund, Bruce, NV, 5157
Fitt and James I. McLaren Foundation, Lawton W., NY, 6010
Fitton Family Foundation, Richard J., The, OH, 7402
Fitzgibbons Foundation, John & Christine, The, NY, 6011
Fitzpatrick Foundation, CA, 508
Five Bridges Foundation, CA, 509
Five Millers Family Foundation Inc., FL, 2002
Five Together Foundation, PA, 7999
FJJ Foundation Inc., The, NY, A
Flaherty Family Foundation, MN, 4686
Flaherty Family Foundation, The, NY, 6012
Flanagan Family Foundation, The, CA, 510
Flathead Community Foundation, MT, 5050
Fleck Scholarship Fund, OH, 7403
Fleder Foundation, Alan & Esther, VA, 9448
Fleischaker Family Foundation, The, OK, 7679
Fleischer Foundation, Inc., Shirley & William R., NY, 6013
Fleischman Foundation Inc., Aaron I., The, FL, 2003
Fleischmann Foundation, OH, 7404
Fleming Family Foundation, The, MA, 4092
Fleming Foundation for Boys, Inc., Rena, TX, 8860
Fleming Foundation, PA, 8000
Fleming Foundation, Samuel M., The, TN, 8615
Fleming Trust, Ruby B., NY, 6014
Fletcher Bay Foundation, WA, 9597
Fletcher Family Charitable Foundation, MA, 4093
Fletcher Family Foundation, MN, 4687
Fletcher Foundation, Louise & Leonard, OH, 7405
Flicker Foundation, Louise M. and Perry G., The, CA, 511

Fliesbach Foundation, G.A., CA, 512
Flinn Charitable Foundation, Negley, PA, 8001
Flinn Family Foundation, Patrick & Robyn, IL, 2875
Flippo Foundation, Jane and Arthur, The, VA, 9449
Flohr Family Foundation, The, TX, 8861
Floren Family Foundation, The, CT, 1451
Florence Foundation, The, MS, 4836
Florin Family Foundation, Inc., The, NJ, 5348
Flowering Tree, NY, 6015
Flowerree Foundation, OR, 7763
Flowers Charitable Foundation, NC, 7099
Flowers Foundation, H. Fort, TX, 8862
Floyd Family Foundation, CA, 513
Flug Foundation, Jeremy and Angie, CO, 1271
Flug Foundation, Martin & Deborah, CO, see 1320
Flying J Foundation, CO, 1272
Flynt Foundation, Kay Richard and Elizabeth Bates, CA, 514
FMI Soccer Club, Inc., WI, see 9960
Focus Foundation, FL, 2004
Focus on Excellence Inc., FL, 2005
Foley Family Foundation Inc., Lawrence & Megan, CT, 1452
Foley Family Foundation, IL, 2876
Foley Family Foundation, WI, 9820
Folger Foundation, Beverly M., CA, 515
Follett Educational Foundation, IL, 2877
Follett Foundation, Inc., Roger W., The, NY, 6016
Folsom Charitable Foundation, Inc., TX, 8863
Fondation Femme Debut, NY, 6017
Fontaine Foundations, Inc., Denis L., FL, 2006
Foor Foundation, The, CA, 516
Foothold, UT, 9324
For Giving Foundation, Inc., FL, 2007
Forbes Charitable Foundation, Mary C., FL, 2008
Forbes Charitable Trust, Herman I., IL, 2878
Force Stead Trust, Mary, FL, 2009
Ford Family Foundation, Jo and Joe, The, TX, 8864
Ford Foundation Inc., Alice & Eugene, MD, 3863
Ford Fund, Inc., Kathleen DuRoss, FL, 2010
Ford Fund, William and Martha, MI, 4445
Ford, Jr. Scholarship Program, William C., MI, 4446
Ford-Thomas Foundation, Allegra C., MI, 4447
Forehand Family Foundation, The, GA, 2479
Foren Family Foundation, MI, 4448
Forest Company, Inc., S., NY, 6018
Forgatch Family Foundation, CA, 517
Forman Christian Foundation, Hamilton M. & Blanche C., FL, 2011
Forrest Family Foundation, The, NM, 5614
Forsberg Charitable Foundation Inc., The, AZ, 119
Forster Charitable Trust, James W. and Ella B., IA, 3494
Forster-Powers Charitable Trust, MO, 4911
Fort Pierce Memorial Hospital Scholarship Foundation, Inc., FL, see 2148
Fort Worth Wildlife Conservation Fund, TX, 8865
Fortin Child Care Foundation, Mary Alice, FL, 2012
Fortinsky Charitable Foundation Inc., PA, 8002
Fortisure Foundation, CA, 518
Fortney Foundation, The, OH, 7406
Fortson Charitable Trust, Ed & Claude, NC, 7100
Fortune Foundation Inc., Russell & Penny, IN, 3381
Fortune Foundation, Inc., Sheila, CO, 1273
Forty-Five Foundation, The, FL, see 2039
Foss Foundation, June & Julian, WA, 9598
Foss Foundation, WA, see 9598
Foss Memorial Employees Trust, Donald J., OH, 7407
Foster Charitable Foundation, M. Stratton, TN, 8616
Foster Charitable Trust, CA, 519
Foster Charitable Trust, F. Gordon, NC, 7101
Foster Charitable Trust, Frank, IL, 2879
Foster Charitable Trust, PA, 8003
Foster Family Foundation, Joe B., TX, 8866, see 8868
Foster Family Foundation, Kent and JoAnn, The, TX, 8867
Foster Foundation, Harriet and Joe, TX, 8868
Foster Foundation, Inc., Joseph C. and Esther, NM, 5615
Foster Foundation, John H., The, FL, 2013
Foulds Foundation Trust, Claiborne F., FL, 2014
Foulds Foundation, Claiborne and Ned, FL, see 2014
Foulkes Foundation, Inc., Duane and Kathleen, WI, 9821

Foundation "Q", NY, 6019
Foundation 3311, FL, 2015
Foundation Fnd, TIF, GA, 2480
Foundation for an American Vision, The, MA, 4094
Foundation for Appalachian Kentucky, KY, 3655
Foundation for Appalachian Ohio, The, OH, 7408
Foundation for Christian Arts, Pastoral Development and the Poor, Inc., The, NC, 7102
Foundation for Community Vitality, MT, 5051
Foundation for Enterprise Development, CA, 520
Foundation for Greater Good, CO, see 1324
Foundation for Middle East Peace, DC, 1807
Foundation for Partnerships Trust, IL, see 2847
Foundation for Peripheral Neuropathy, The, IL, 2880
Foundation for Retinal Research, IL, 2881
Foundation for Southeast Texas, Inc., TX, 8869
Foundation for the Cosmic Claimes & Consequences of Christ, The, NV, 5158
Foundation of the Pierre Fauchard Academy, VA, 9450
Foundation, Douglass, The, TX, 8870
Foundation, Huelsmann, The, MN, 4688
Foundation, Inc., Mortar, The, CA, 521
Foundation, Lewis and Butler, The, VA, 9451
Foundation, Soran, DE, 1664
Foundation-to-Life, Inc., The, NY, 6020
Fountain Charitable Foundation, D. G. & Margaret, MS, see 4837
Fountain Family Foundation, MS, 4837
Fountainhead Foundation, PA, 8004
Four County Community Foundation, MI, 4449
Four County Foundation, MI, see 4449
Four Friends Foundation, CA, 522
Four T's Foundation, The, IL, 2882
Four Way Community Foundation, OR, 7764
Foust Educational Fund, Flora, IL, 2883
Fowey Light Fund, Inc., NY, 6021
Fowlston Charitable Trust, C. J. and Syble, TX, 8871
Fox Charitable Foundation, Harry K. Fox and Emma R., OH, 7409
Fox Family Foundation, Frieda C., CA, 523
Fox Family Foundation, Inc., NC, 7103
Fox Family Foundation, The, KS, 3578
Fox Family Trust, Keith and Pamela, CA, 524
Fox Foundation, Bill and Katherine, FL, 2016
Fox Foundation, Jacob L. and Lewis, CT, 1453
Fox Foundation, John H., CA, see 525
Fox Foundation, NJ, 5349
Fox Foundation, Samuel I. & John Henry, CA, 525
Fox Foundation, Wallace, The, NY, 6022
Fox Foundation, William and Eva, The, MD, 3864
Fraida Foundation, The, IL, 2884
Fraiman Foundation, Inc., Chaim & Rose, NY, 6023
Fraites Foundation, Evelyn, CT, 1454
Framingham Co-Operative Bank Charitable Foundation, MA, see 4216
Francis Community Health Care, Inc., Saint, MA, 4095
Franco Family Charitable Foundation, Maj, The, NY, 6024
Franco Family Foundation, Isaac S., NY, 6025
Franey Family Foundation, Inc., MD, 3865
Frangakis Family Charitable Foundation, The, FL, 2017
Frank Charity Fund, Inc., NJ, see 5350
Frank Family Charity Fund Inc, NJ, 5350
Frank Family Foundation, A. J., OR, 7765
Frank Family Foundation, Inc., The, GA, 2481
Frank Foundation, Inc., Ernst & Elfriede, NY, 6026
Frank Fund, Mrs. Zollie S., IL, see 2885
Frank Fund, Zollie & Elaine, IL, 2885
Frankel Family Foundation, Inc., TX, 8872
Frankel Family Foundation, Leonard R., The, TX, see 8872
Frankel Foundation, Herman and Sharon, FL, 2018
Frankel Foundation, Inc., D. W., NY, 6027
Frankel Foundation, Marshall, The, IL, 2886
Frankel Foundation, The, CA, 526
Frankenmuth Area Community Foundation, Greater, MI, see 4450
Frankenmuth Community Foundation, MI, 4450
Frankle Family Foundation, Inc., FL, 2019
Franklin Electric Charitable & Educational Foundation, IN, 3382

Franklin Electric—Edward J. Schaefer and T. W. Kehoe Charitable and Educational Foundation, Inc., The, IN, see 3382
Franklin Family Foundation, Churchill and Janet, The, MA, 4096
Franklin Federal Foundation, The, VA, 9452
Franklin Foundation, Wilson P. & Anne W., FL, 2020
Franklin Fund, The, NY, 6028
Franklin Philanthropic Foundation, IL, 2887
Franklin Savings Bank Community Development Foundation, ME, 3779
Franklin Square Foundation, IL, 2888
Frasch Foundation for Chemical Research, Herman, RI, 8408
Fraser Family Foundation, Inc., MA, 4097
Fraser Family Foundation, Inc., VA, 9453
Fraser Foundation, Malcolm, TN, 8617
Fraser Foundation, Robert E., MN, 4689
Frautschi Family Foundation, Inc., John J., WI, 9822
Fraydun Foundation Inc., NY, 6029
Freas Foundation, Inc., PA, 8005
Frederick Foundation, C. Lydia, IL, 2889
Frederick Memorial Foundation, George A. & Mary E., PA, 8006
Fredericksburg Rescue Squad Foundation, VA, 9454
Fredman Family Charitable Trust, IL, 2890
Freed Foundation, Eleanor and Frank, The, TX, 8873
Freedman Charitable Foundation Inc, Anne & Gerald, The, NJ, 5351
Freedman Family Fund, DE, 1665
Freedman Foundation, Twilight & Marc, NJ, 5352
Freedom For All, NY, 6030
Freedom Wireless Foundation, AZ, 120
Freelander Family Charitable Trust, NJ, 5353
Freeman Foundation, DC, 1808
Freescale Foundation, TX, 8874
Freescale Relief Foundation, TX, see 8874
Freewill Charitable Trust, FL, 2021
Freidheim Foundation, Inc., Stephen C., NY, 6031
Freitas Foundation Inc., Mark & Mary, The, FL, 2022
Freitas Foundation, Inc., Mark Edward, FL, see 2022
Frelinghuysen Foundation, The, NJ, 5354
Fremont Foundation, IL, 2891
Fremont Group Foundation, The, CA, 527
French Family Charitable Foundation, OK, 7680
French Family Educational Foundation, R. E., KS, 3579
French Family Foundation, John and Elaine, ID, 2671
French Foundation, Inc., D. E., NY, 6032
French Foundation, The, PA, 8007
Fresh Direct Employee Foundation, NY, 6033
Freshwind Foundation, CA, 528
Freund Charitable Foundation, Maurice & Henry, IL, 2892
Freund Family Foundation, The, NY, 6034
Frey Foundation, Michael J. and Karen B., MN, 4690
Freyer Family Foundation Inc., Carl & Sylvia, NJ, 5355
Freygang Foundation, Walter Henry, OH, 7410
Fricks Private Foundation Trust, The, FL, 2023
Fridman Foundation, Anne and Natalio, NY, 6035
Fried Family Foundation, NY, 6036
Friedel Family Foundation, TX, 8875
Friedheim Foundation, Inc., Eric, FL, 2024
Friedhofer Charitable Trust, Virginia, CA, 529
Friedland Charitable Foundation Inc., Annette & Jack, The, FL, 2025
Friedland Family Foundation, NE, 5082
Friedland Foundation, Bob & Sheila, NY, 6037
Friedland Foundation, David & Nancy, NE, see 5082
Friedlander Family Foundation, Lee and Maria, NY, 6038
Friedman & Friedman Foundation, Inc., The, MD, see 3866
Friedman Charitable Foundation, Inc., MD, 3866
Friedman Charitable Foundation, M. and E., NY, 6039
Friedman Charitable Support Organization, Sid, NJ, 5356
Friedman Family Foundation, Frank & Fred, The, AL, 27
Friedman Family Foundation, NY, 6040
Friedman Foundation, Frank and Fred, The, AL, see 27
Friedman Foundation, Ike & Roz, NE, 5083
Friedman Foundation, Lisa and Maury, CA, 530
Friedman Foundation, Morton and Marcine, CA, 531
Friedman Foundation, Robert G., FL, A
Friedman Foundation, TX, 8876

Frieman Foundation, The, NY, 6041
Friend Family Foundation, MA, 4098
Friend Foundation, Michelle and Robert, The, CA, 532
Friend of the Fatherless Foundation, FL, 2026
Friends Foundation for the Aging, PA, 8008
Friends of Kang Yun Foundation, CT, 1455
Friends of Soochow University, CA, 533
Friends of the Center for American Studies Society, The, CT, 1456
Friends of the Guiomar Smeets Foundation Inc., NY, 6042
Friendship Fund Inc., PA, 8009
Fries-Tait Foundation, WA, 9599
Friesen Foundation, Gilbert B., CA, see 492
Friezo Family Foundation, The, CT, 1457
Frill Foundation, The, TX, 8877
Frisbie Family Foundation, The, MA, 4099
Frisby Foundation, Robert J., IL, 2893
Fritz Foundation, Barbara and Jay, The, CA, 534
Froderman Foundation, Inc., The, IN, 3383
Frog Crossing Foundation Inc., NJ, 5357
Frohman Foundation, Sidney, OH, 7411
Frohring Foundation, William O. and Gertrude Lewis, PA, 8010
Frome Family Foundation, Walter and Mary, CA, 535
Fromm Scholarship Trust, Walter and Mabel, WI, 9823
Fromstein Foundation Ltd., WI, 9824
Frost Family Foundation, HI, 2632
Frost Foundation, Pat & Tom, TX, 8878
Frost Testamentary Trust, Meshech, OH, 7412
Frost-Parker Foundation, The, OH, 7413
Fruehauf Foundation, The, TX, 8879
Fry Family Foundation, The, FL, 2027
Fry Foundation, The, CA, 536
Fry Memorial Trust, L. P., CT, see 1458
Fry Memorial Trust, Lily Palmer, CT, 1458
FSB Charitable Foundation, Inc., MA, see 4270
FSH Properties Foundation, TX, see 9223
FSR Foundation, TX, 8880
FTJ Charitable Foundation, WA, 9600
Fuchs Charitable Foundation, Sally and Bernard, TX, 8881
Fuchs Family Foundation, Inc., The, CT, 1459
Fuchs Foundation, Shmuel & Serena, NY, 6043
Fuchsberg Family Foundation, Inc., Abraham, NY, 6044
Fudge Family Foundation, CA, 537
Fugitive Foundation, TN, 8618
Fugitt Foundation, The, OK, 7681
Fuite Foundation, Teaumen & Grace, AZ, 121
Fukunaga Scholarship Foundation, HI, 2633
Full Circle Family Foundation, IL, 2894
Full Circle Foundation, IL, 2895
Fuller Family Charitable Trust, RI, 8409
Fuller Family Foundation, Inc., Victor & Sandra, FL, 2028
Fuller Foundation, Inc., Gillian S., The, CA, 538
Fuller Foundation, Inc., The, CA, see 538
Fuller Foundation, William M., TX, 8882
Fuller Trust, Frank R., CT, 1460
Fulton Foundation, David and Amy, WA, 9601
Fun-Raising Corporation, MD, 3867
Funari Family Foundation, Marilyn and Robert, CA, 539
Fund for Enlightenment, IL, 2896
Fund for Innovation and Public Service, VA, 9455
Fund for Newark Abbey Inc., NJ, 5358
Fund, T. & R., CO, 1274
Funding Passion and Love Foundation Inc, The, UT, 9325
Funk Foundation, Paul A., IL, 2897
Furman Foundation, Inc., NY, 6045
Furman Foundation, Morris & Gertrude, NY, 6046
Furnessville Foundation, The, WA, 9602
Furth Family Foundation, CA, 540
Furth Family Foundation, The, NY, 6047
Fusco Family Foundation, Inc., MD, 3868
Fusenot Charity Foundation, Inc., Georges and Germaine, CA, 541
Fuserna Foundation, NV, 5159
Fux Foundation, Inc., Michael, The, NJ, 5359

G&A Foundation, Inc., The, NY, 6048
G&K Services Foundation, MN, 4691
G-Bar Philanthropic Foundation, IL, A
G.R.M. Foundation, Inc., NY, see 6681

Gabrellian Family Foundation Inc., NJ, 5360
Gaebler Charitable Foundation, Milton, MO, 4912
Gaedke Charitable Trust, William C. and Dorotha, IA, 3495
Gaffney Foundation, Miller S. & Adelaide S., NY, 6049
Gagarin Trust, The, KY, 3656
Gage Family Foundation, MN, 4692
Gage Foundation, Philip and Irene Toll, GA, 2482
Gage Fund, The, NY, 6050
Gagnon Foundation Inc., FL, 2029
Gaither Charitable Foundation, Inc., IN, 3384
Gala Organization Foundation, Inc., NJ, see 5574
Galanti Foundation, Peter & Mildred, NC, 7104
Galanti Foundation, Richard and Barrie, WA, 9603
Gale Foundation, Bulova, MA, 4100
Gale Foundation, The, OH, 7414
Gale Foundation, Thomas H. and Barbara W., OH, 7415
Galeana Charitable Foundation, Inc., Elizabeth K., FL, 2030
Galileo Foundation for Community and Education, Inc., MA, 4101
Galkin Private Foundation, RI, 8410
Gallagher 312 Foundation, The, IL, 2898
Gallagher Foundation, Thomas E. and Mary K., NY, 6051
Gallagher Western Montana Charitable Foundation, MT, 5052
Gallanter Foundation, Sanford & Linda, The, CA, 542
Galler Research Foundation Inc., Marc, NY, 6052
Gallo Foundation, Bob & Marie, CA, 543
Galter Foundation, The, IL, 2899
Galvan Foundation Charitable Trust, NY, 6053
Gamber Foundation, PA, 8011
Gambrell Family Foundation, NC, 7105
Gambrill Foundation, NC, 7106
Gammon Charitable Foundation, Inc., J. A., IN, 3385
Gamper Foundation, Albert and Janice, NJ, 5361
Gans Foundation, Shelby and Frederick, The, CA, 544
Ganse Family Foundation, Gerald & Suzanne, The, PA, 8012
Gant Family Foundation, The, NY, 6054
Gant Foundation, Donald R. & Jane T., NY, see 6054
Gantcher Family Foundation, NY, 6055
Gantz Charitable Trust, Judy, IL, 2900
Gantz Family Foundation, IL, 2901
Gantz Foundation Inc., Jack, The, NY, 6056
Garabedian Charitable Foundation, Bertha and John, The, CA, 545
Garard, Jr. Charitable Trust, James L., IL, 2902
Garaventa Family Foundation, Silvio and Mary, CA, 546
Garber Family Foundation, The, NY, 6057
Garber Foundation, Richard J., The, MI, 4451
Garcia Family Charitable Foundation Trust, OH, 7416
Garcia Family Foundation, AZ, 122
Garcia Foundation Inc., Jose M., The, NJ, 5362
Garden Foundation, Allan C. and Leila J., GA, 2483
Gardinier Environmental Fund Inc., NJ, 5363
Gardner Charitable Foundation, Eldon and Emma Belle, TN, 8619
Gardner Family Foundation, Gary & Denise, IL, 2903
Gardner Foundation Inc., Olivia R., The, FL, 2031
Gardner Foundation, Janice, MN, 4693
Gardner Foundation, OH, 7417
Gardner Foundation, Sterling & Shelli, UT, 9326
Gardner Foundation, WI, 9825
Gardner II Foundation, J. W., The, IL, 2904
Gardner Trust, T.J., IL, 2905
Gareatis Foundation, CA, 547
Gareeb Family Foundation, The, CA, 548
Garfield Street Foundation, NM, 5616
Garfinkle Family Charitable Trust, NJ, 5364
Garman Family Foundation, NY, 6058
Garmar Foundation, MN, 4694
Garner Foundation, Inc., The, FL, 2032
Garrett Charitable Trust, Barbara, MI, 4452
Garrigues Trust, Edwin B., NC, 7107
Garrow Family Charitable Foundation, NC, 7108
Gart Family Foundation, Jerry, The, CO, 1275
Garthwaite Memorial Foundation, Elsie Lee, PA, 8013
Gartner Family Foundation, IA, 3496
Gartner Foundation, Joseph and Anna, The, NY, 6059
Garver Foundation, TX, 8883
Garvey Memorial Foundation, Edward Chase, MO, 4913

Garvey Texas Foundation, Inc., TX, 8884
Garvy Family Foundation, Inc., FL, 2033
Gary Jr. Family Foundation, Samuel, The, CO, 1276
Gary Winick Memorial Fund, Inc., NY, 6060
Gassin Family Foundation, IL, 2906
GAT Family Foundation, CA, 549
Gatchell Home, Inc., The, GA, see 2509
Gate Foundation, Inc., The, FL, 2034
Gatewood Family Foundation, TX, 8885
Gatto Foundation, Joseph and Susan, The, NY, 6061
Gauntt Charitable Foundation, Joanne W., NJ, 5365
Gauss Foundation, William F. and Lynn D., PA, 8014
Gauthier Family Foundation, Wendell & Anne, LA, 3724
Gay Fund, Virginia, OH, 7418
Gaylord Entertainment Foundation, TN, 8620
Gaylord Foundation, Catherine Manley, The, MO, 4914
Gaylord Foundation, Clifford Willard, MO, 4915
Gazette Foundation, The, IA, 3497
GB Foundation, Inc., KY, 3657
GCP Foundation, PA, see 7936
Gear Up Hawaii Scholarship Trust, HI, 2634
Geary, Jr. Memorial Foundation, Henry H., OH, 7419
Geary-O'Hara Family Foundation, The, VA, 9456
Geary-O'Hara Trust, The, VA, see 9456
Gebhardt Foundation, Inc., WI, 9826
Geduld/Cougar Foundation, Inc., The, NY, 6062
Geier Foundation, The, NY, 6063, 6064
Geisler Penquite Corporation, IA, 3498
Gela Foundation Inc., The, NY, 6065
Gelbart Foundation, June Baumgardner, FL, 2035
Gelbman Charitable Trust, Frank & Pearl E., OH, 7420
Geller Family Religious Foundation, NY, 6066
Gellert Family Foundation, Fred, The, CA, 550
Gelley Family Foundation, NY, 6067
Geltzer Family Foundation, DE, 1666
Gelvin Foundation, Inc., Lyle M., The, OK, 7682
Gelvin Foundation, Lyle M., OK, see 7682
Gemiluth Chessed of Greater New York Inc., NY, 6068
Gemj Chehebar Foundation, NY, 6069
Gemunder Foundation, Joel F., FL, 2036
Genecov Foundation, A. S., TX, 8886
Geneen Charitable Trust, Harold S., RI, 8411
General Iron Industries Charitable Foundation, IL, 2907
Generations Fund, The, IL, 2908
Geneseo Foundation, IL, 2909
Genesis Philanthropic Fund, IL, 2910
Gengras, Jr. Foundation, Inc., E. Clayton and Edith P., CT, 1461
Genie Energy Charitable Foundation, NJ, 5366
Genovese Memorial Foundation, Vincent, The, TX, 8887
Geomar Foundation, NV, 5160
George and Judith Silverburgh Foundation Inc., Grace, NY, 6070
George Family Charitable Foundation, The, DE, 1667
George Foundation, Joanne and Marcel, CA, 551
George Foundation, The, OH, 7421
George H.Parr Trust, IL, 2911
George Jr. Charitable Foundation, Richard W., TX, 8888
Georgetown Area Community Foundation, The, TX, see 8769
Georgia G. Hiden Charitable Foundation, NY, 6071
Georgia Health Foundation, Inc., GA, 2484
Georgia Pine Level Foundation, Ltd., GA, 2485
Georgia Scientific and Technical Research Foundation, GA, see 2597
Georgina-Frederick Children's Foundation, The, CA, 552
Geotrac Charitable Foundation, OH, 7422
Gerath Foundation, Gerald and Claire, CT, 1462
Gerbic Family Foundation, Edward & Verna, CT, 1463
Gerhard Foundation, Peter and Kristen, The, NY, 6072
Gerhart Foundation, The, MT, 5053
Gernatt Family Foundation, Daniel & Flavia, NY, 6073
Gerrish Foundation, CO, 1277
Gerrity Charitable Trust, Frank, MA, 4102
Gerry-Corbett Foundation, Inc., The, FL, 2037
Gershenson Foundation, Charles H., MI, 4453
Gershman Charitable Trust, MO, see 4916
Gershman Foundation, Joel and Elaine, PA, 8015
Gershman Foundation, Joel, PA, see 8015
Gershman Foundation, MO, 4916
Gerstman Foundation, Lisa Beth, NY, 6074
Geschick Charitable Trust, Mary W., NC, 7109
Gesso Foundation, NY, 6075

Gestetner Family Charitable Foundation, NJ, 5367
Getsch Charitable Trust, MN, 4695
Gettinger Family Foundation, The, NY, 6076
Getty Family Foundation, The, NV, see 5159
Getz Charitable Trust, Arthur L., RI, 8412
Getz Foundation, Emma & Oscar, CO, see 1278
Getz Foundation, The, CO, 1278
Gewirz Fund, Inc., Carl and Nancy, The, MD, 3869
GFF Educational Foundation, Inc., GA, see 2602
GFH & SAH Foundation, The, NE, 5084
GHH Charitable Foundation, The, KY, 3658
Gholston Foundation, J. Knox, GA, 2486
Gholston Foundation, J. William, GA, 2487
Gholston Trust, J. William, GA, see 2487
Giacoletto Foundation, John P. and Lawrence J., IA, 3499
Giancristofaro Family Foundation, Inc., A. & S., The, NJ, 5368
Giant Eagle Foundation, The, PA, see 7856
Giant Steps Foundation, The, NY, 6077
Giants Foundation, Inc., The, NJ, 5369
Gibbet Hill Foundation, IL, 2912
Gibor Charitable Foundation, Herbert and Sarah M., CT, 1464
Gibson and Rosemary Kirr Charitable Trust, Richard P., PA, 8016
Gibson Family Foundation, Harry H., SC, 8523
Gibson Family Foundation, NJ, 5370
Gibson Family Foundation, The, WA, 9604
Gibson Foundation, Max L. & Jacqueline, IN, 3386
Gidwitz Charitable Foundation, Christina and Ronald, IL, 2913
Gidwitz Family Charitable Foundation, Adele & Willard, MD, see 3870
Gidwitz Family Foundation, Adele & Willard, MD, 3870
Gidwitz Family Foundation, IL, 2914
Gifford Foundation, Helen G., VA, 9457
Gifford Foundation, Lee A. & Helen G., The, VA, see 9457
Gifts of the Magi Foundation, The, CA, 553
Gilbert Family Foundation, W. A., The, MO, see 4917
Gilbert Foundation, The, MO, 4917
Gilbert, Jr. Charitable Fund, Price, GA, 2488
Gildea Family Foundation, The, MA, 4103
Giles Foundation, Terry M., The, CA, see 554
Giles O'Malley Foundation, CA, 554
Gill Family Foundation, OR, see 7766
Gill Family Foundation, Stephen & Margaret, CA, 555
Gill Foundation, Frank and Mary, OR, 7766
Gillam Foundation, AK, 85
Gilleland Foundation, Richard and Ellen, The, CA, 556
Gilleland Foundation, Richard, The, CA, see 556
Gilliam Foundation, Deane A. and John D., The, NY, 6078
Gilliam Foundation, John D., NY, see 6078
Gilligan Foundation, MN, 4696
Gilman Charitable Trust, Allene N., OH, 7423
Gilman, Jr. Foundation, Inc., Sondra & Charles, TX, 8889
Gilmore Charitable Foundation, Marguerite L., NC, 7110
Gilmore Education Fund, Elmer and Iva, WA, 9605
Gilmore Foundation, Earl B., CA, 557
Gilmore Foundation, James and Marilyn A., PA, 8017
Gimbel & Elga Andersen-Gimbel Memorial Trust, Peter R., NY, 6079
Gimbel Foundation, Russell and Mary, OH, 7424
Gimprich Family Foundation, Inc., NY, 6080
Ginder Family Foundation, The, CA, 558
Ginn Charitable Trust, Frank Hadley Ginn and Cornelia Root, The, OH, 7425
Ginn Foundation, The, OH, see 7425
Giop Charitable Foundation, Sonia Raiziss, PA, 8018
Giordano Foundation, Inc., Ned J., NY, 6081
Girls Rights Project, CA, 559
GirlSMART Literacy Program, CA, 560
Gish Prize, Dorothy and Lillian, The, IL, 2915
Gitt Foundation, Elizabeth M., PA, 8019
Gius Foundation, WA, 9606
Giustina Foundation, N. B., OR, 7767
Give to Life Foundation, TX, 8890
Givens Charitable Trust, FL, 2038
Giving Back Foundation, The, DE, 1668
GKJ Foundation, OK, 7683

Gladding Foundation, Inc., Harry L., MD, 3871
Gladstein Foundation, Marsha Lilien, CT, 1465
Gladstone Foundation, David and Lorna, VA, 9458
Glancy Foundation, Inc., The, GA, 2489
Glanert Charitable Trust, Karen J., WI, 9827
Glasrud Family Foundation, Inc., Ted and Lorraine, The, AZ, 123
Glass Foundation, Inc., Leslie, The, FL, 2039
Glassen Memorial Foundation, Hal & Jean, MI, 4454
Glasser Family Foundation, Richard S., VA, 9459
Glasser Foundation, Inc., Thomas, The, NJ, 5371
Glaubinger Foundation, The, FL, 2040
Glaze Foundation, C. D. Helen and Jeff, AL, 28
Glazer Family Foundation, Erika, The, CA, 561
Glazer Foundation, Diane & Guilford, The, CA, 562
Glazer Foundation, Emerson, The, CA, see 1092
Glazer Foundation, Inc., Jerome S., OH, 7426
Gleason Family Foundation, Inc., The, SC, 8524
Gleeson Family Foundation, IA, 3500
Gleeson Foundation, IA, see 3500
Glencairn Foundation, The, VA, 9460
Glencoe Foundation, Inc., DE, 1669
Glendale Community Foundation, CA, see 421
Glendenning Family Foundation, Inc., WI, 9828
Glendorn Foundation, PA, 8020
Glenn Foundation, Inc., Carrie E. and Lena V., The, NC, 7111
Glennco Foundation, The, OR, 7768
Glens Falls Foundation, The, NY, 6082
Glenstone Foundation, DC, 1809
Glenstone Museum Foundation, DC, see 1809
Glenville Foundation, Peter, CA, 563
Glidden Foundation, J. Harrington & Marie E., OH, 7427
Glikbarg Foundation, Inc., The, CA, see 564
Glikbarg Foundation, William and Charlene, CA, 564
Global Catalyst Foundation, CA, 565
Global Christian Interaction, Inc., WI, 9829
Globe Foundation Limited, IN, 3387
Gloeckner Foundation, Inc., Fred C., The, NY, 6083
Gloria And Charles Clough Foundation, MA, 4104
Gloria Dei Foundation, DE, 1670
Glorney Foundation, Inc., Corlette, NY, 6084
Glossberg Foundation, Joseph B., The, IL, 2916
Gloyd Family Foundation, IL, 2917
Glyndebourne Association America Inc., The, NY, A
GMG Foundation, IA, see 3501
Go Big Red Foundation, The, GA, 2490
Go Inc., TX, 8891
Goad Family Foundation, The, TN, 8621
Gochnauer Family Foundation, IL, 2918
God's Provision Inc., IN, 3388
Godbold Foundation Inc., FL, 2041
Godchaux Foundation, Frank & Mary, LA, see 3734
Goddard Charitable Trust, Frederick J., The, FL, 2042
Goddard Family Charitable Foundation, The, NY, 6085
Goddard Foundation of Texas, Charles B., TX, see 8789
Goddard Foundation Trust, Charles B., The, OK, 7684
Goddard Foundation, The, GA, 2491
Godinger Lefkowitz Memorial Foundation, Inc., The, NY, 6086
Godric Foundation, CA, 566
Godsey Foundation, Inc., FL, 2043
Goebel Family Star Lumber Charitable Foundation, KS, 3580
Goerlich Family Foundation, Inc., OH, 7428
Goetz Family Foundation, FL, 2044
Gogel Family Foundation, The, NY, 6087
Gold Family Foundation, Bradd J., The, NY, 6088
Gold Foundation, The, NY, 6089
Goldberg & Sons Foundation Inc., Samuel, NY, 6090
Goldberg Charitable Foundation, Robert and Dorothy, The, ME, 3780
Goldberg Charitable Trust, Joseph and Dorothy, CA, 567
Goldberg Family Foundation, AZ, 124
Goldberg Family Foundation, KS, 3581
Goldberg Foundation, Frank M. & Lee, The, CA, 568
Goldberg Foundation, Inc., FL, 2045
Goldberg Foundation, Inc., Stephen A. and Diana L., The, MD, 3872
Goldberg Foundation, Raymond & Ellen, PA, 8021
Goldberg Kohn Foundation, IL, 2919
Goldberg, Kohn, Bell, Black, Rosenbloom & Moritz Foundation, IL, see 2919

Goldberger Foundation, Edward & Marjorie, NJ, 5372
Golden Belt Community Foundation, KS, 3582
Golden Belt Foundation, KS, see 3582
Golden Family Foundation, Donald & Norma, MI, 4455
Golden Family Foundation, Inc., Raymond L., The, FL, 2046
Golden Fleece Foundation Charity, NY, 6091
Golden Foundation, Robert M., ID, 2672
Golden Rule Foundation, Inc., The, ME, 3781
Golden Slipper Club Uptown Home for the Aged, PA, A
Golden Slipper Senior Care Foundation I, PA, 8022
Goldenberg Foundation, Jeffrey and Susan, NY, 6092
Goldenberg Foundation, Max, IL, 2920
Goldenberg Foundation, The, NY, 6093
Goldenson Association, Inc., Isabelle and Leonard, The, NY, see 6094
Goldenson-Arbus Foundation, Inc., The, NY, 6094
Golder Family Foundation, IL, 2921
Goldfarb Family Foundation, Andrew and Denise, The, CA, see 915
Goldfarb Family Foundation, Inc., Harry E., The, CT, 1466
Goldfarb Foundation, Robert D., The, NY, 6095
Goldfarb Memorial Charitable Trust, Ellen Jeanne, The, CT, 1467
Goldfein Foundation, Inc., Stanley F., NY, 6096
Golding Foundation, Inc., Faith, The, NY, 6097
Golding Foundation, MS, 4838
Goldman and Brothers Foundation, Inc., William P., The, MA, 4105
Goldman Foundation, Aaron and Cecile, The, DC, 1810
Goldman Foundation, Amy R. and Philip S., MN, 4697
Goldman Foundation, Inc., Sally, FL, 2047
Goldman Foundation, Neal and Marlene, NY, 6098
Goldman Foundation, Peter D. & Carol, IL, 2922
Goldmann Family Foundation, NY, 6099
Goldmann Foundation, Stephen and Joyce, NY, see 6099
Goldsmith Family Foundation, Inc., The, TN, 8622
Goldsmith Foundation, The, TN, see 8622
Goldstein Charitable Foundation Inc., Benjy & Adina, The, NY, 6100
Goldstein Charitable Trust, David and Esther, The, NY, 6101
Goldstein Charity Fund Inc., NJ, 5373
Goldstein Foundation, Ruth & Sheldon, CA, 569
Goldstone Fund, Inc., NY, 6102
Goldwasser Family Foundation, Jonathan Plutzik & Lesley, The, NY, 6103
Goldwin Foundation, The, NE, 5085
Golick Family Foundation, Inc., Morrie & Susan, NY, 6104
Golub Charitable Foundation, NY, 6105
Good Family Foundation, Rosemary and David, MN, 4698
Good Heart Work Smart Foundation, IL, 2923
Good News Foundation, VA, 9461
Good Works Institute, Inc., The, ID, 2673
Goodall Family Foundation, CA, 570
Goodall Family Foundation, Jack W., CA, see 570
Goodfellow Fund, WA, 9607
Goodin Family Foundation, Janet and Kenneth R., OK, 7685
Gooding Family Foundation, The, CA, 571
Goodlett Foundation, TN, 8623
Goodman Family Foundation, The, NY, 6106, 6107
Goodman Foundation, I.A. Lanier, GA, 2492
Goodman Foundation, The, WA, 9608
Goodman-Lipman Family Foundation Inc., NY, 6108
Goodrich Foundation, Henry C. & Billie G., AL, see 29
Goodrich Foundation, The, AL, 29
Goodstein Charitable Trust, Harvey, PA, 8023
Goodstein Family Foundation, Albert, IL, 2924
Goodwin Charitable Trust, Jacqueline & Todd, FL, 2048
Goodwin Family Foundation, Inc., Donald G., CA, 572
Goodwin Foundation, The, CO, 1279
Goodwin Foundation, The, NJ, 5374
Goodworks Fund, IL, see 3045
Goody Two Shoes Inc., FL, 2049
Gorab Foundation, Eugene A. & Suzanne H., CT, 1468
Gordon Charitable Trust, Ellen F., CA, 573
Gordon Charitable Trust, Peggy & Yale, MD, 3873
Gordon Family Foundation Inc., FL, 2050

Gordon Family Foundation, Daniel, NC, 7112
Gordon Family Foundation, Elizabeth Hekman, MI, 4456
Gordon Family Foundation, Joel C. and Bernice W., The, TN, 8624
Gordon Family Foundation, William J. J., The, NY, 6109
Gordon Foundation 2, Meyer and Ida, TX, 8892
Gordon Foundation, Allan S., The, NY, 6110
Gordon Foundation, Betsy, The, CA, 574
Gordon Foundation, Donald A., WI, 9830
Gordon Foundation, Gail and Mark, FL, see 2051
Gordon Foundation, Gertrude S., WI, 9831
Gordon Foundation, Mark J., FL, 2051
Gordon Foundation, Meyer and Ida, TX, 8893
Gordon Foundation, Reuben & Mollie, PA, 8024
Gordon Fund, Kathy and Al, The, NY, 6111
Gordon Fund, The, NY, 6112
Gordon, M.D. Charitable Foundation, Michael S., FL, 2052
Gordon/Rousmaniere/Roberts Fund, The, NY, see 6112
Gordy Family Foundation, Berry, The, CA, 575
Gordy Foundation, Evelyn and Frank, The, GA, 2493
Gorlin Family Foundation, MD, 3874
Gorlin Foundation, Robert and Mary Ann, MI, 4457
Gorlitz Foundation, Ltd., DC, 1811
Gorlitz Foundation, Samuel J., DC, see 1811
Gorny Foundation, DE, 1671
Goshen Hill Foundation, Inc., PA, 8025
Gosiger Foundation, OH, 7429
Gostomski Foundation, The, IL, 2925
Gotham Charitable Foundation Trust, NY, 6113
Gottlieb Foundation of Texas, The, TX, 8894
Gottlieb Foundation, Inc., Adolph and Esther, NY, 6114
Gottlieb-Schwartz Family Foundation, NY, 6115
Gottstein Family Foundation, AK, 86
Gould Family Foundation, Inc., The, GA, 2494
Gould Foundation Inc., Robert, OH, 7430
Gould Foundation, Stuart S. and Byrdie, The, NY, 6116
Govil Foundation, Inc., Sanjay, The, MD, 3875
GP Family Foundation, NY, 6117
Grabe Family Foundation, FL, 2053
Grace Charity Foundation Inc., NJ, 5375
Grace Family Foundation, NY, 6118
Grace Family Foundation, Tom and Bonnie, The, NY, see 6118
Grace Foundation, TX, 8895
Grace Foundation, William M. & Ann K., AZ, 125
Grader Foundation, Inc., K. W., FL, 2054
Graeber Foundation, MS, 4839
Graese Foundation, Clifford and LaVonne, FL, 2055
Graff Foundation, Lee, CA, 576
Graham Benevolent Foundation, TX, 8896
Graham Charitable Foundation, Helen I., NY, 6119
Graham Family Charitable Foundation, NY, 6120
Graham Family Foundation Inc., GA, 2495
Graham Foundation, Elizabeth Firestone, IL, 2926
Graham Foundation, John, The, WA, 9609
Gralnick Foundation, Inc., Marvin and Helene, The, FL, 2056
Gralnick Foundation, NY, 6121
Gramercy Park Foundation Inc., NY, 6122
Grampy's Charities, CT, 1469
Grand Marnier Foundation, The, NY, 6123
Grande Foundation, WI, 9832
Grandis Family Foundation, Harry and Harriet, VA, 9462
Grandison Foundation, NY, 6124
Grandview Foundation, Inc., TN, 8625
Grandview-Steers Foundation, NY, 6125
Granit Foundation, NY, 6126
Granite Foundation, MN, 4699
Granny B & P Foundation, NY, 6127
Grano Family Foundation, NY, 6128
Grant Charitable Trust, Elberth Reuben & Gladys Flora, MO, 4918
Grant Foundation, Charles M. & Mary D., NY, 6129
Grant Foundation, Mabel Burchard Fischer, CT, 1470
Grant Foundation, Sarah E., The, NY, 6130
Grant Me the Wisdom Foundation, TX, 8897
Grass Foundation, The, CA, 577
Grassland Trust, MI, 4458
Grassmere Foundation, MO, 4919
Grassy Creek Foundation, FL, 2057
Grateful Foundation Inc., NY, 6131

Gratiot County Community Foundation, MI, 4459
Graue Family Foundation, TX, 8898
Graves Family Foundation, William H., CO, 1280
Graves Foundation, Inc., The, GA, 2496
Gray Family Fund, Avrum, IL, 2927
Gray Foundation, Melvin and Susanne, IL, see 2928
Gray Foundation, Sue and Melvin, The, IL, 2928
Gray Foundation, The, TX, 8899
Gray Matters Capital, Inc., GA, 2497
Gray-Pampa Foundation, Inc., TX, 8900
Graymer Foundation, The, FL, 2058
Greater Erie Economic Development Corporation, PA, 8026
Greater Grand Forks Community Foundation, ND, see 7295
Greater Lake Wales Health Care Foundation Inc., FL, 2059
Greater Montana Foundation, The, MT, 5054
Greaton Family Foundation, Inc., FL, 2060
Greco Foundation, Inc., Violet H., The, VA, 9463
Green Earth Charitable Organization, CA, 578
Green Family Charitable Foundation, The, IN, 3389
Green Family Foundation, FL, see 2061
Green Family Foundation, Louis & Anne, FL, 2061
Green Family Foundation, MO, 4920
Green Foundation, Val A. Green and Edith D., UT, 9327
Green Mountain Charitable Foundation, KS, 3583
Green Pond Foundation, IL, see 3003
Greenberg Charitable Foundation, Jerry A., The, MA, see 4106
Greenberg Charitable Foundation, Jerry and Adi, The, MA, 4106
Greenberg Family Foundation, Inc., Harold & Sylvia, The, DC, 1812
Greenberg Foundation Inc., Martin F. & Jane F., The, FL, 2062
Greenberg Foundation, Inc., Maurice R. & Corinne P., The, NY, 6132
Greenberg Fund, Lenore S. & Bernard A., CA, 579
Greenblatt Charitable Foundation, Inc., Allan & Muriel, FL, 2063
Greenblatt Family Charitable Trust, The, NY, 6133
Greenblatt Foundation, Inc., Burton G. and Anne C., NJ, 5376
Greene Charitable Trust, Helen Wade, RI, 8413
Greene County Community Foundation, IN, see 3390
Greene County Foundation, Inc., IN, 3390
Greene Family Foundation Inc., FL, 2064
Greene Foundation, MD, see 3876
Greene-Milstein Family Foundation, The, MD, 3876
Greene-Sawtell Foundation, The, FL, 2065
Greenfield Foundation, Richard and Peggy, FL, 2066
Greenfield Foundation, Stewart & Constance, CT, 1471
Greenhill Family Foundation, CT, 1472
Greenleaf Foundation Inc., SC, 8525
Greensboro Jaycees Charitable Foundation, NC, see 7209
Greenspan Charitable Trust, Louis, NY, 6134
Greensville Memorial Foundation, VA, 9464
Greensville Memorial Hospital, VA, see 9464
Greentree Foundation, NY, 6135
Greentree Fund, The, TX, 8901
Greenwald Foundation, Dorothy and Harold, The, NY, 6136
Greenwich Capital Foundation, CT, see 1549
Greenwich Collection, Ltd., The, NY, 6137
Greenwood County Community Foundation, SC, 8526
Greenwood Foundation, CA, 580
Greenwood Foundation, Lewis, The, CA, 581
Greetin Foundation Inc., Paul & Beryl, NJ, 5377
Gregory Jr. Foundation Inc., William A., FL, 2067
Greiner Family Foundation, Inc., GA, 2498
Grewcock Foundation, Bruce E. & Debra K., NE, 5086
Grey Family Charitable Foundation, CA, 582
Grey Family Foundation, CA, 583
Greylock Foundation, The, NY, see 6051
Gries Family Foundation, OH, 7431
Griffin Charitable Foundation, Dorothy G., NY, 6138
Griffin Endowment, The, NC, 7113
Griffin Family Foundation, Inc., MO, 4921
Griffin Family Foundation, Inc., R. A., GA, 2499
Griffin Foundation, Joe Lee, AL, 30
Griffin Foundation, Rosa May, TX, 8902

Griffin White Foundation Inc., MA, 4107
Griffin-White Home for Aged Men and Aged Couples, Inc., MA, see 4107
Griffith Family Foundation, The, IL, see 2929
Griffith Foundation, Dean and Lois, The, IL, 2929
Griffith Foundation, Mary Hobbs, TX, 8903
Griffith Laboratories Inc. Foundation, IL, 2930
Griffiths Charitable Foundation, G.H. and O.J., CA, 584
Griffiths Foundation, MN, 4700
Grigsby Foundation, Jack Webster, LA, 3725
Grimm Family Education Foundation, The, CA, 585
Grinberg Family Foundation, The, NY, 6139
Grinberg Foundation, The, NY, see 6139
Grindstone Foundation, WA, 9610
Grinnell Mutual Group Foundation, IA, 3501
Griswold Foundation, Lillian Sherwood, The, CA, 586
Griswold Scholarships Fund, Harry E., AL, 31
Griswold Trust, Harry E., AL, see 31
Griswold Trust, Jessie E., IL, 2931
Grits Foundation, TX, 8904
Grobman Foundation, Frank & Roslyn, NY, 6140
Grodzins Fund, The, NY, 6141
Groff Surgical and Medical Research and Education Charitable Trust, Mary E., The, PA, 8027
Gromet Foundation, DE, 1672
Gromet Fund for Disadvantaged Children, Janice & Ben, The, DE, see 1672
Groner Scholarship Foundation, Grace Elizabeth, IL, 2932
Groot Foundation, John and Phyllis, The, DE, 1673
Gross Charitable Foundation, Allen I., NY, 6142
Gross Charitable Foundation, William, The, NJ, A
Gross Charitable Trust, Stella B., CA, 587
Gross Family Foundation, J. & H., NY, 6143
Gross Family Foundation, Thomas R., OH, 7432
Gross Foundation, Harold & Rebecca H., CT, 1473
Gross Foundation, Inc., Julia & Seymour, The, MA, 4108
Gross Foundation, Maurice R. & Meta G., RI, 8414
Gross/Hutton Family Foundation, The, OH, 7433
Grossberg Abrams Foundation, CA, 588
Grosse Pointe Housing Foundation, MI, 4460
Grossinger Foundation, Sam & Sarah, IL, 2933
Grossman Charitable Trust, Sanford J., CO, 1281
Grossman Family Foundation, Harold and Jean, AZ, 126
Grossman Family Foundation, NY, 6144
Grossman Family Foundation, Stanley & Nancy, The, NY, 6145
Grossman Family Philanthropic Foundation, The, NY, 6146
Grossman Foundation, Inc., Robert and Lynne, The, FL, 2068
Grossman Foundation, N. Bud and Beverly, MN, 4701
Grossman Foundation, N. Bud, MN, see 4701
Grosvenor Family Foundation, The, CO, 1282
Grosvenor Foundation, J. Mark, The, CO, 1283
Grotto Foundation Inc., MN, 4702
Group Health Foundation of Greater St. Louis, MO, see 5012
Grousemont Foundation, WA, 9611
Groves Foundation, MN, 4703
Growing the Vision of Light Foundation, CO, 1284
Grubb Charitable Foundation, John R. and Zelda Z., The, IA, 3502
Grubman Compton Foundation, The, NY, 6147
Grubman Foundation, Eric P., NY, see 6147
Grumbacher Foundation Inc., Stanley and Kathleen, NY, 6148
Grumbacher Foundation, M. S., The, PA, 8028
Grumhaus, Jr. Foundation, Jennifer and David Dean, The, IL, 2934
Grunberg Family Foundation, NY, 6149
Grundhofer Charitable Foundation, John F., SD, 8565
Grundy Foundation, The, PA, 8029
Gruodis Memorial Education Fund, Carol Martin, The, NY, 6150
Grusecki Family Foundation, James P. and Brenda S., IL, 2935
Gryphon Fund, The, CT, 1474
GT Foundation, PA, 8030
Guela Charitable Trust, The, NY, 6151
Guerin Foundation, CA, 589
Guetz Foundation, TX, 8905
GuideOne Insurance Foundation, Inc., The, IA, 3503

Guilander Scholarship Trust, Anna M., MO, 4922
Guild of the Dome Inc., PA, 8031
Guillaume Family Foundation, Inc., The, GA, 2500
Guinn Foundation, Inc., TX, 8906
Gulati Family Foundation, The, PA, 8032
Gulf Power Foundation Inc., FL, 2069
Gumbo Foundation, The, NM, 5617
Gunther Charitable Foundation, Arno, WI, 9833
Gureghian Charitable Foundation, The, PA, 8033
Gurtler Foundation, Inc., John R. and Ruth W., The, FL, 2070
Gurwicz Charitable Foundation, Max & Helena, NJ, 5378
Gust Foundation, Christopher L. & M. Susan, The, IL, 2936
Guthrie Family Foundation, WY, 9972
Gutman Family Foundation, Inc., MD, 3877
Gutman Foundation, Inc., Edna and Monroe C., NY, 6152
Guttag Family Foundation, MA, 4109
Gypsy Hill Conservation Charitable Trust, The, PA, 8034

H & H Charitable Foundation, IL, 2937
H and B Family Foundation, OH, 7434
H. & H. Charitable Trust, NY, 6153
H. & S. Foundation, The, CA, 590
H. W. R. Foundation, IL, 2938
H.C.D. Foundation, IL, 2939
Haarlow Family Charitable Foundation, IL, 2940
Hackbarth Foundation, Inc., James and Pauline, NC, 7114
Hadar Foundation, Richard and Mica, The, NY, 6154
Hadar Foundation, The, NY, see 6154
Hafer Scholarship Trust, W.W. & Lucretia, NY, 6155
Haft Foundation, Ronald S., DC, 1813
Hagadone Foundation, Inc., Lola and Duane, ID, 2674
Hagan Foundation, Cornelius and Lydiellen, WA, see 9612
Hagan Foundation, DE, 1674
Hagan Foundation, WA, 9612
Hagar Family Foundation, CA, 591
Hagen Family Foundation, Russell and Luaina, MN, see 4704
Hagen Foundation, Russell B., MN, 4704
Hagens Memorial Foundation, Annette J., FL, 2071
Hager Family Charitable Foundation, PA, 8035
Hagerty Family Foundation, The, MA, 4110
Haggar Family Foundation, Ed, TX, 8907
Haggar, Jr. Family Foundation, Isabell and J.M., The, TX, 8908
Haggar, Jr. Family Foundation, J. M., The, TX, see 8908
Haggerty Family Foundation, MN, 4705
Haglage Charitable Trust Agency, KS, 3584
Hagler Foundation, Jon L., MA, 4111
Hagopian Family Foundation, CA, 592
Hahn Family Foundation, Norman & Elizabeth, The, PA, 8036
Hahn Family Foundation, NY, 6156
Hahn Family Foundation, The, FL, 2072
Hahn Foundation, Lillian Sara, The, NY, see 6419
Hahn Foundation, Stephen & Carla, The, NY, 6157
Hahn Foundation, Stephen, The, NY, see 6157
HAIR Foundation, The, NJ, 5379
Hajim Family Foundation, The, NY, 6158
Hakka Foundation, CA, 593
Halbrook Family Foundation, FL, 2073
Haldan Charitable Foundation, James Stuart, DE, 1675
Haldan Family Charitable Foundation, Dwight S., DE, 1676
Hale Foundation, Charles S. & Carmen DeMora, MA, 4112
Hale Foundation, Martin and Deborah, The, MA, 4113
Hales Family Foundation, Inc., NY, 6159
Hales Foundation, William M., IL, 2941
Haley Family Foundation, MA, 4114
Half Moon Foundation, IL, 2942
Halfway Rock Foundation, The, MA, 4115
Hall Foundation, Benjamin & Margaret, WA, 9613
Hall Foundation, Charles H., CT, 1475
Hall Foundation, The, PA, 8037
Hall Jr. Family Foundation, Thomas A., TX, 8909
Hall, Jr. Foundation, Inc., William M., FL, see 2074
Hall-Halliburton Foundation, Inc., FL, 2074
Hallam Family Foundation, Howard, The, TX, 8910

Hallberg Foundation, E. L. & R. F., TX, see 8911
Hallberg Foundation, Elizabeth L. and Russell F., TX, 8911
Halle Foundation, Inc., Martha & Warren, MD, 3878
Hallene Family Foundation Inc., IL, 2943
Hallett Charitable Trust, Jessie F., MN, 4706
Hallett Charitable Trust, MN, see 4706
Hallingby Family Foundation, Inc., The, NY, 6160
Halmos Family Foundation, Inc., Steven J., FL, 2075
Halperin Foundation Inc., FL, 2076
Halperin Foundation, James and Gayle, TX, 8912
Halperin Foundation, James, TX, see 8912
Halpern Family Foundation Inc., Sam, NJ, 5380
Halstead Foundation Inc., The, IL, 2944
Halsted Charitable Foundation, Louise Davis, RI, 8415
Hamer Foundation, The, WV, 9746
Hamill Fund, Joseph A. & Edith D., NC, 7115
Hamilton Family Foundation Inc., WI, 9834
Hamilton Family Foundation, Frederic C., The, CO, 1285
Hamilton Family Foundation, Tom and Carolyn, TX, 8913
Hamilton Foundation, Jacqueline and Willis, The, OH, 7435
Hamilton Fund Trust, William P., IL, 2945
Hamlin, George A., IL, 2946
Hamm Family Foundation Inc., CT, 1476
Hamm Foundation, Harold G. and Sue Ann, IL, 2947
Hamm Foundation, Inc., Nancy and Alan, TX, 8914
Hampar Family Foundation, Armen and Gloria, The, CA, 594
Hampden Bank Charitable Foundation, MA, 4116
Hampson Family Foundation, The, OH, 7436
Hanafin Foundation, Inc., The, NJ, 5381
Hanauer Foundation, Adrian, WA, 9614
Hancock Foundation, Inc., L. D., MS, 4840
Hand Foundation, Inc., The, FL, 2077
Hand Foundation, The, CA, 595
Handleman Charitable Foundation Trust C, Joseph & Sally, FL, see 2078
Handleman Trust Foundation, Joseph, FL, 2078
Handler Family Foundation, The, NY, 6161
Handler Foundation, Milton & Miriam, NY, 6162
Handlery Foundation, The, CA, 596
Hands of Blessing, Inc., GA, 2501
Haney Foundation Trust, NC, 7116
Hankin Foundation, Bernard & Henrietta, PA, see 8038
Hankin Foundation, PA, 8038
Hankins Foundation, The, OH, 7437
Hankison Foundation, John & Virginia, OH, 7438
Hanks Charitable Trust, Merrill I. & Grace, AL, 32
Hanley Charitable Foundation, Inc., Mike & Patricia, Dr. , TX, 8915
Hanley Foundation, Bryant & Nancy, The, TX, 8916
Hanley Foundation, The, DC, 1814
Hann Charitable Foundation Inc., Abraham and Bessie, NJ, 5382
Hannah Foundation, Wood & Marie C., KY, 3659
Hansen Charitable Foundation, Albert G. and Bernice F., NE, 5087
Hansen Family Foundation, FL, 2079
Hansen Family Foundation, Robert E., The, WI, 9835
Hansen Family Foundation, VA, 9465
Hansen Foundation, Inc., Carl M., WA, 9615
Hansen Foundation, Robert & Marie, The, AZ, 127
Hansen Memorial Foundation, Irving A., IL, 2948
Hanson CGF, Inc., Alex and Laura, NJ, 5383
Hanson Family Foundation, Alice G., IL, 2949
Hanson Family Foundation, CO, 1286
Hanson Family Foundation, Inc., Stephen P., The, NY, 6163
Hanson Family Foundation, WA, 9616
Hanson Testamentary Charitable Trust, Anna Emery, IL, 2950
Hanus Foundation, George & Barbara, IL, 2951
Hap Foundation, The, NY, 6164
Happy Elephant Foundation, The, NY, 6165
Haraldson Foundation, The, TX, 8917
Harary Family Foundation, Jerry and Janet, The, NY, 6166
Harbanoff Foundation, Inc., Samuel, The, NJ, 5384
Harbert Foundation, The, AZ, A
Harbison Scholarship Trust, CA, 597
Harczak, Sr. Memorial Foundation, Harry J., IL, 2952
Hardeman and Combs Lawson Fort Trust, Ann, FL, 2080

Hardiek Family Foundation, IL, 2953
Harding Educational and Charitable Foundation, The, IL, see 2848
Hardison Family Foundation, The, FL, 2081
Hardner Foundation, Norbert H., TX, 8918
Hardy Trust, Lottie C., MO, 4923
Hare Charitable Trust, Laura, IL, 2954
Hare Family Foundation Inc., Susan and Richard, The, ID, 2675
Harjen Charitable Foundation, The, NY, 6167
Hark Foundation, Marguerite Delany, IL, 2955
Harkness Trust, The, DE, 1677
Harlan Family Foundation, The, IN, 3391
Harlan Scholarship Trust, Wilbur V., OR, A
Harlow Charitable Trust, Mary Jane, FL, A
Harman Family Foundation, The, MA, A
Harman Foundation, John and Wauna, UT, 9328
Harman Foundation, Reed L. & Nan M., The, CA, 598
Harmon Foundation Inc., NY, 6168
Harmon Foundation, Pearl M. & Julia J., OK, 7686
Harmon Foundation, The, NY, 6169
Harms Foundation, George And Ruth, NJ, 5385
Harms Foundation, Inc., The, NJ, see 5385
Harmsen, Sr. Charitable Foundation, Dorothy and Bill, AZ, 128
Harmstieg Foundation Inc., The, NJ, 5386
Harold Webster Smith Foundation, Inc., CT, 1477
Harper Charitable Trust, Verlie P. & John L., AL, 33
Harper Family Charitable Foundation, Inc., FL, 2082
Harper Family Foundation, LA, 3726
Harper Family Foundation, The, NE, 5088
Harper Foundation, Philip S., VT, 9373
Harqua Foundation, The, CA, 599
Harrell Family Foundation, TX, 8919
Harriman Foundation, Mary and Kathleen, NY, 6170
Harriman Foundation, W. Averell and Pamela C., NY, see 6170
Harrington Charitable Trust, Helen, MN, 4707
Harrington Trust, George, MA, 4117
Harris Charitable Foundation Inc., Ron and Debra, The, VA, 9466
Harris Family Foundation, CA, 600
Harris Family Foundation, E. F., IL, 2956
Harris Family Foundation, Hunt and Diane, IL, 2957
Harris Family Foundation, Matthew and Jennifer, NY, 6171
Harris Family Foundation, Robert & Shirley, CA, 601
Harris Foundation for Personal Evangelism, Floyd W., VA, 9468
Harris Foundation Inc., AL, 34
Harris Foundation, Beth M., MS, 4841
Harris Foundation, George J. and Jessica, CT, 1478
Harris Foundation, Inc., Jonathan M., NY, 6172
Harris Foundation, MI, see 4461
Harris Foundation, Mort & Brigitte, MI, 4461
Harris Foundation, VA, 9467
Harris Foundation, William H. & Mattie W., NV, 5161
Harris Foundation, William H., MA, 4118
Harrison 12Th Item, Thomas S., PA, 8039
Harrison Foundation, Albert E., The, GA, 2502
Harrison Foundation, Inc., Ben F., AL, 35
Harrison Trust, Gibson T., NC, 7117
Harsco Corporation Fund, PA, 8040
Hart Charitable Trust, The, NY, 6173
Hart Education Foundation, Olga B., MN, 4708
Hart Foundation, John H., IL, 2958
Harter Foundation, John Burton, KY, 3660
Hartfield Foundation, Inc., The, PA, 8041
Hartman Foundation, Inc., The, TX, 8920
Hartman Trust, Gutsave, RI, 8416
Hartman Trust, Harry C., RI, 8417
Hartselle Scholarship Foundation, AL, 36
Hartwick Foundation, Alice Kales, MI, 4462
Hartwig Family Foundation, Inc., WI, 9836
Harvest Foundation Inc., S & C, VT, 9374
Harvest House Foundation, OR, 7769
Harvest Time Foundation, NC, 7118
Harvey Family Foundation, Cannon Y. & Lyndia K., CO, 1287
Harvey Foundation, Brian and Phyllis, CA, 602
Harvey-McNairy Foundation Inc., The, NC, 7119
Harwi Testamentary Trust, W.A., TX, 8921
Harwood Trust, Charles E., MA, 4119

Hary Foundation, Amherst F., IL, 2959
Hasenfeld Foundation, Inc., A. & Z., NY, 6174
Haskell Foundation, OR, 7770
Haskell Foundation, The, FL, 2083
Haskell Fund, OH, 7439
Haskins Foundation Inc., Morris & Dorothy, KY, 3661
Hassel Foundation, The, PA, 8042
Hastings Charitable Foundation, Oris B., IL, 2960
Hastings Philanthropic Trust, Jane Hope, CT, 1479
Hatch Foundation, Deena, WI, 9837
Hatfield Foundation, Inc., George and Claudette, The, TX, 8922
Hatfield Memorial Fund, Jock, The, NY, 6175
Hathaway Family Foundation, NY, 6176
Hatterscheidt Foundation Inc., The, SD, 8566
Hauben Foundation, Inc., Helen G., The, MA, 4120
Hauber Foundation, PA, 8043
Hauck Foundation, John, OH, 7440
Hauff & John F. Dreeland Foundation, Robert V., The, NY, 6177
Haugland Family Foundation, Inc., The, FL, 2084
Haugse Memorial Trust, Ralph, OR, 7771
Hauser Foundation, Kurt and Julie, The, DE, 1678
Hausfeld Family Charitable Foundation, The, VA, 9469
Hausman Family Charitable Trust, The, MA, 4121
Hausman Family Foundation, CA, 603
Haven Charitable Foundation, Nina, FL, see 2085
Haven Foundation, The, NY, 6178
Haven Scholarships, Inc., Nina, FL, 2085
Haven Trust, MA, 4122
Havens Family Foundation, Prentiss C. and Dolores M., LA, 3727
Havirmill Foundation, MI, 4463
Havner Family Foundation, The, CA, 604
HAVRK8 Ranch, The, CO, 1288
Hawkins Charitable Trust, NE, 5089
Hawkins Educational Foundation, AL, 37
Hawkins Family Foundation, TX, 8923
Hawkins Foundation Inc., The, GA, 2503
Hawkins Foundation, Alexandra G., PA, 8044
Hawkins Foundation, Catherine, DE, 1679
Hawkins Scholarship Foundation, MT, 5055
Hawksglen Foundation, The, PA, 8045
Hawley Family Charitable Foundation, CA, 605
Hawley Lexus Charitable Foundation, CA, see 605
Hawthorn Charitable Foundation, TN, 8626
Hawthorne Charitable Foundation, NJ, 5387
Hay Foundation, John I., IL, 2961
Hayden Foundation, MI, 4464
Hayden-Harman Foundation, NC, 7120
Hayes Common Wealth Foundation, Ralph, The, PA, 8046
Hayes Family Charitable Trust, The, NC, 7121
Hayes Foundation, The, CO, see 1247
Hayford Family Foundation, Warren J. and Marylou, The, FL, 2086
Hayman Family Foundation, Fred, CA, 606
Hayswood Foundation, Inc., KY, 3662
Hazard Family Foundation, MA, 4123
Hazard General Charity Fund, Frank B., MA, 4124
Hazelbaker Foundation, OH, 7441
HB Oppenheimer Foundation, MO, 4924
HBE Foundation, The, PA, 8047
HCG, Jr. Family Foundation, MO, 4925
HCSC Foundation, Inc., CA, 607
He Foundation Inc., Zhengxu & Ying, NV, 5162
Head Family Foundation, The, MN, 4709
Head Family Trust, Peyton Samuel, The, IL, see 2840
Header Foundation, The, MI, see 4509
Heagele-Blount Animal Shelters, TN, 8627
Health 1st Foundation, Inc., GA, 2504
Health and Welfare Foundation of Southern Chester County, PA, 8048
Health Care and Education Trust, PA, 8049
Health Foundation of Greater Massillon, OH, 7442
Health Net Foundation, Inc., CA, 608
Healthcare and Nursing Education Foundation, TX, 8924
Healy Foundation, R. & H., NY, 6179
Heart Institute of Southern New Jersey, NJ, 5388
Heath Foundation, Jackson, WA, 9617
Heath Foundation, Mary, IL, 2962
Heath Foundation, The, OR, 7772

Heavin Family Foundation, TX, 8925

Hecht Family Charitable Foundation, PA, 8050

Hecht Foundation Inc., Vera and Imre, MI, 4465

Hecht Memorial Fund, Leslie L. & Mary B., RI, 8418

Heck Foundation, The, CA, 609

Hecla Charitable Foundation, ID, 2676

Heerema Charitable Foundation, Bruce & Sandy, IA, 3504

Heffer Family Foundation, Inc., The, NY, 6180

Hefferlin Foundation, Dr. John, CA, see 610

Hefferlin Foundation, John and Marian, Dr. , CA, 610

Heffernan Family Foundation, Inc., Lenore B. & Frank M., CA, 611

Heffner Fund, The, OH, 7443

Heflin Family Foundation Trust, AR, 197

Hefta Foundation, Inc., NY, 6181

Hegamyer Family Foundation Inc., William H. and Leonora K., FL, 2087

Hegardt Foundation, MN, 4710

Hegarty Family Foundation, NY, 6182

Hegeler II Foundation, Julius W., IL, 2963

Hegi Family Foundation, TX, 8926

Heginbotham Trust, Will, CO, 1289

Heide Foundation Charitable Trust, Ulf B. and Elizabeth C., The, MA, 4125

Heider Family Foundation, CO, 1290

Heidner Charitable Trust, Marco J., WA, 9618

Heilicher Charitable Foundation, Menahem, MN, see 4711

Heilicher Foundation, MN, 4711

Heilig Foundation Inc., C.J., NY, 6183

Heilmaier Charitable Foundation, Anna M., MN, 4712

Heiman Charitable Remainder Trust, Florence, MO, 4926

Heiman Private Foundation, Florence, MO, see 4926

Heimann Family Foundation, The, OH, 7444

Heimbinder Family Foundation, OH, 7445

Hein Foundation, William and Diane, NY, 6184

Hein Foundation, William S., NY, see 6184

Heinlein Prize Trust, Robert A. and Virginia, TX, 8927

Heinrich Family Foundation, OH, 7446

Heins Residuary Trust, Gussie, IL, 2964

Heinz Family Foundation, Kenneth, CA, 612

Heisel Sule Charitable Trust, Elsa M., KY, 3663

Heisen Family Foundation, Joann Heffernan, NJ, 5389

Heisey Foundation, The, MT, 5056

Heisler Family Foundation, Solomon & Clara, NY, 6185

Hekemian Family Foundation, Inc., Robert S. & Mary Jane, NJ, 5390

Hekemian Family Foundation, Robert S., NJ, see 5390

Helb Trust, H. T., NC, 7122

Held & Kenn Karakul Charitable Foundation Inc., James, FL, 2088

Helios Foundation, WI, 9838

Heller Family Foundation, NY, 6186

Heller Foundation of San Diego, CA, 613

Heller Foundation, David B., The, NY, see 6187

Heller Foundation, Hermine and David, The, NY, 6187

Heller Foundation, Inc., Robert & Esther, NJ, 5391

Heller Foundation, Inc., WI, 9839

Hellman Foundation, Bud and Barbara, CA, 614

Helm Foundation, Inc., The, MD, 3879

Helm Foundation, Inc., The, TX, 8928

Helman Memorial Foundation, Steven K., MA, 4126

Helmar Skating Fund, CO, 1291

Helmle-Shaw Foundation, TX, 8929

Helms Family Foundation, AZ, 129

Helms Foundation, Inc., CA, 615

Helmstetter Family Foundation, CA, 616

Helow Family Foundation Inc., Margaret & George, FL, 2089

Helow Family Foundation, Inc., George A., FL, see 2089

Helping Hand Foundation, The, CT, 1480

Helstrom Foundation, The, WA, 9619

Helton Family Foundation, The, NC, 7123

Hemitt Foundation Inc., NY, 6188

Henderson & Harriet Welfare Association, NC, 7124

Henderson Charitable Foundation, Elizabeth Wakeman, NY, 6189

Henderson Education Fund f/bo Tulane University, IL, 2965

Henderson Foundation, George B., MA, 4128

Henderson Foundation, MA, 4127

Hendricks Foundation, Ralph and Virginia, SC, 8527

Hendrix Foundation, Willard & Frances, FL, 2090

Henkind Foundation, The, NY, 6190

Hennessy Foundation, NY, 6191

Hennessy Foundation, William Thomas & May Pitman, AR, 198

Henry Charitable Foundation, Anne R., ME, 3782

Henry Family Foundation, IA, 3505

Henry Foundation, Pete, The, KS, 3585

Henshel Foundation, The, NY, 6192

Henson Foundation, Jane, The, NY, 6193

Henson Foundation, Jim, The, NY, 6194

Henson Foundation, The, NY, see 6194

Herbert Scholarship Trust, Bernard & Pauline, IL, 2966

Herbold Foundation, WA, 9620

Herbst Family Foundation Inc., NY, 6195

Hergenhan Private Foundation, Joyce, CT, 1481

Heritage Foundation of First Security Federal Savings Bank, Inc., The, IL, 2967

Heritage Fund of Huntington County, Inc., IN, see 3397

Herman Brothers Foundation, The, CA, see 617

Herman Family Foundation, Skip & Meg, IL, 2968

Herman Foundation, Ernest G., The, CA, 617

Herman Foundation, NE, 5090

Hermann Charitable Foundation, Lilly Christy Busch, The, MO, 4927

Herndon Foundation, C. M., The, NC, 7125

Herndon Memorial Fund, Lewis & Marguerite, PA, 8051

Herr Family Foundation, Inc., IN, 3392

Herr Foundation Trust, John, IA, 3506

Herray Foundation, WA, 9621

Herrin Charitable Foundation, Melvin & Melva, FL, 2091

Herring Charitable Foundation, C. T., TX, 8930

Herringer Family Foundation, The, NY, 6196

Herrington-Fitch Family Foundation Inc., The, MI, 4466

Herrmann Family Foundation, Carl and Henrietta, CA, 618

Herschend Family Foundation, MO, 4928

Herscher Family Foundation, Myna & Uri, The, CA, A

Hershaft Foundation, Arthur N., NY, 6197

Hershey Foundation, Jacob and Terese, TX, 8931

Hershman Family Foundation Inc., NY, 6198

Hertz Foundation Inc., Chavi F., CA, 619

Hervey Foundation, TX, 8932

Hesed Foundation, Gabriel and Sara Bildirici, NY, 6199

Hess Charitable Trust, Myrtle E. & William G., IL, 2969

Hess Family Foundation, WV, 9747

Hester - Dundy County Public Schools Foundation, Elmer E., NE, 5091

Heuer Foundation, Russell P. & Elizabeth Crimian, The, DE, 1680

Heuer Foundation, The, DE, see 1680

Heuermann Foundation, B. Keith & Norma F., NE, 5092

Heuermann Foundation, Bernard K. & Norma F., NE, see 5092

Hewgill Charitable Foundation Inc., Paul J., WV, 9748

Hewit Family Foundation, CO, 1292

Hewitt Foundation, Inc., Carl & Marsha, The, NY, 6200

Hewitt Foundation, Inc., CT, 1482

Hext Family Foundation, Inc., TX, 8933

Heydt Fund, Nan and Matilda, RI, 8419

Heyl Trust, Jacob E., PA, 8052

Heyman Foundation, Inc., Annette, NY, 6201

Heyward Memorial Fund, DuBose and Dorothy, The, NY, 6202

HF Foundation, NY, 6203

HFO Foundation, PA, 8053

HFRX Foundation, FL, 2092

HI Foundation Inc., FL, 2093

Hibbs Family Foundation, TX, 8934

Hickey Family Foundation, NE, 5093

Hickey Foundation, Ray, WA, 9622

Hickingbotham Charitable Foundation Trust, Frank D., AR, 199

Hickok Trust, Daisy, OH, 7447

Hickory Tech Corporation Foundation, MN, 4713

Hickrill Foundation, Inc., NY, 6204

Hicks Charitable Foundation, Nelson G. and Vera C., WI, 9840

Hicks Charitable Foundation, The, FL, 2094

Hicks Family Charitable Foundation, The, MA, 4129

Hicks Family Charitable Foundation, The, TX, 8935

Hicks Family Foundation, Thomas O., The, TX, see 8936

Hicks Foundation, Thomas O. and Cinda, The, TX, 8936

Hidary Foundation Inc., Grace, The, NY, 6205

Hidden Leaf Foundation, CA, 620

Hieronymus Charities Inc, FL, 2095

Hieronymus Family Fund Inc., OH, 7448

Higbie Family Foundation, CO, A

Higgins Family Foundation, Ron and Sanne, HI, 2635

Higginson Trust, Corina, MD, 3880

Higgs Family Foundation, FL, 2096

High Family Foundation, S. Dale, The, PA, 8054

High Five Foundation, NY, 6206

High Foundation, Charles F., OH, 7449

High Foundation, The, PA, see 8054

High Stakes Foundation, The, MT, 5057

Higher Foundation, The, GA, 2505

Highfield Foundation, OH, 7450

Highland Park Community Foundation, IL, 2970

Highlands Foundation, Inc., WI, 9841

Hilal Foundation, WA, 9623

Hildes-Heim Foundation Inc., CT, 1483

Hiler Family Foundation, Robert, NY, 6207

Hill and Family Foundation Trust, Walter Clay, FL, 2097

Hill Charitable Foundation, Pauline Klyng, CA, A

Hill Country Community Foundation, TX, 8937

Hill Family Charitable Foundation, The, DE, 1681

Hill Family Foundation, Inc., FL, 2098

Hill Family Foundation, Inc., The, NJ, 5392

Hill Family Foundation, Margaret and Al, The, TX, 8938

Hill Foundation, Arthur W., IL, 2971

Hill Foundation, Inc., Quaker, The, MA, 4130

Hill Foundation, Madrona, OR, 7773

Hill Foundation, Sally Foss & James Scott, NJ, 5393

Hill Foundation, TX, see 8938

Hill Trust, Ruth A., PA, 8055

Hill, Paul E. & Mildred L., PA, 8056

Hillback Foundation, Elliott and Marjorie, The, MA, A

Hillcrest Foundation, The, TX, 8939

Hillenbrand Foundation, Inc., John A., IN, 3393

Hilles Fund, Allen, PA, 8057

Hilliard Foundation, The, NY, 6208

Hills Foundation, Jared & Carol, The, IA, 3507

Hillswood Foundation, NJ, 5394

Hilltop Foundation, CA, 621

Hilltop Foundation, The, VA, 9470

Hilson Family Fund, John S., The, NY, 6209

Himelberg Foundation, David, NY, 6210

Himmelfarb Foundation, Paul & Annetta, DC, 1815

Hine Charitable Trust, Efrid L. & Marie, NC, 7126

Hinman Charitable Foundation, CA, 622

Hinman Family Foundation, The, FL, see 2099

Hinman Foundation, The, FL, 2099

Hirsch & Holly S. Andersen Family Foundation, Inc., Douglas A., NY, 6211

Hirsch Charitable Foundation, Clement and Lynn, CA, see 487

Hirsch Family Charitable Foundation, Carl & Anne, RI, 8420

Hirsch Foundation, Henry & Myrtle, NY, 6212

Hirsch Foundation, Louis, NY, see 6212

Hirschfield Foundation, Norman, WY, 9973

Hirschhorn/Baumann Family Foundation, The, NY, see 5723

Hirschmann Charitable Foundation, George F. and Helen M., The, IL, 2972

Hirschmann Family Foundation, Doris & Jerome, IL, 2973

Hirtzel Memorial Foundation, Orris C. Hirtzel and Beatrice Dewey, PA, 8058

HIS Foundation, WA, 9624

His Glory Ministries, CA, 623

His Vision Inc., NJ, 5395

Hishmeh Foundation Inc., Muna and Basem, FL, 2100

Hitchcock Foundation, Margaret M., The, PA, 8059

Hitchman Foundation, Inc., OR, 7774

Hite Foundation, Inc., The, NY, 6213

Hitter Family Foundation, CA, 624

Hittman Family Foundation, Inc., MD, 3881

Hixon Foundation, Tim and Karen, The, TX, 8940

Hixon Fund for Religion and Education, Alexander and Adelaide, MA, see 3994

HJ Promise Foundation, MN, 4714

HMA Foundation, Inc., TN, 8628

Hoag Family Charitable Foundation, RI, 8421

Hoag Foundation, CA, 625
Hoag Foundation, LeVert W., CO, 1293
Hoaglin Foundation, Inc., William M. & Donna J., IA, 3508
Hoak Foundation, James M. and Nancy J., TX, see 8941
Hoak Foundation, The, TX, 8941
Hobbs Foundation, Inc., Emmert, The, MD, 3882
Hoch Foundation, Charles H., PA, 8060
Hoch Memorial Trust, J. Herbert Hoch & Martha, IN, 3394
Hochman Family Foundation, NY, 6214
Hochman Foundation, Philip & Rebecca, CA, 626
Hodes Family Foundation, IL, 2974
Hodge Foundation, Inc., The, GA, 2506
Hodge Memorial Fund, Emma Clyde, PA, 8061
Hodges Foundation, Bess J., CA, 627
Hodgson Charitable Trust, The, GA, 2507
Hoefer Family Foundation, CA, 628
Hoenle Foundation, Inc., W. Paul, FL, 2101
Hoerner Foundation, Marie R., FL, 2102
Hoffen Family Foundation, NY, 6215
Hoffer Foundation, IL, 2975
Hoffman & Sons Foundation, Inc., Howard, The, NY, 6216
Hoffman Charitable Endowment Trust, Robert C., PA, 8062
Hoffman Family Foundation, MA, 4131
Hoffman Family Foundation, MK, FL, 2103
Hoffman Family Memorial Trust, R. M., PA, 8063
Hoffman Foundation, Inc., Robert B. & Janet A., The, NC, 7127
Hoffman Foundation, John Ernest, The, MA, see 4131
Hoffman Foundation, William G. & Helen C., NC, 7128
Hoffman Legacy Foundation, Inc., IN, 3395
Hoffmann Family Foundation Inc., Harri, WI, 9842
Hoffmann Foundation, August J. & Thelma S., WV, 9749
Hoffmann-La Roche Foundation, The, CA, see 979
Hofheimer Charitable Trust, MO, 4929
Hofheinz Foundation, Irene Cafcalas, TX, 8942
Hofstetter Trust, Bessie I., TX, 8943
Hogan & Carron Sherry Foundation, Inc., Richard, The, NY, 6217
Hogan Charitable Foundation, Gisela B., MA, 4132
Hognander Foundation, MN, 4715
Hohlt and J. Roger Wich Foundation, Joan, TX, 8944
Hohmann Foundation, The, NY, 6218
Hohnstein Family Foundation, Philip, The, CA, 629
Hoie Charitable Foundation, Helen and Claus, The, NY, 6219
Holborn Foundation, The, NY, 6220
Holden Foundation, Gibson E., PA, 8064
Holden Foundation, The, IL, 2976
Holden Fund, James and Lynelle, MI, 4467
Holland Charitable Annuity Trust, Robert & Helen, VT, 9375
Holland-Underwood Foundation, Inc., GA, 2508
Hollandsworth Family Foundation, Patsy B., TX, 8945
Hollandsworth Memorial Trust, P.G. and Ruby, WV, 9750
Holleman Foundation Trust, Roy & Marian, NC, 7129
Holliman Family Foundation, Joe & Jean, OK, 7687
Hollinger Charitable Trust, FL, 2104
Hollingsworth Foundation, Inc., TN, 8629
Hollis Foundation, Inc., GA, A
Hollo Charitable Foundation, Inc., Tibor and Sheila, FL, 2105
Holloway Family Foundation, Graham and Carolyn, The, TX, 8946
Holloway Foundation, Caswell F. Holloway, Jr. and Marie B., FL, 2106
Holloway Foundation, Jack, FL, 2107
Hollowell Foundation, Inc., WV, 9751
Hollowell-Ford Foundation, Inc., WV, see 9751
Holly Lane Foundation Inc, GA, 2509
Hollywood Canteen Foundation, CA, 630
Holman Charitable Trust, The, MN, see 4748
Holmberg Foundation, Inc., NY, 6221
Holmes Family Foundation, John & Mildred, TX, 8947
Holocaust Memorial Study Center Inc., NY, 6222
Holopaw Homeowners, Inc., FL, 2108
Holoubek Family Foundation, Inc., Terri & Verne, The, WI, 9843
Holt Family Foundation, PA, A

Holt Trust, Fanny H. Ames and Edna L., RI, see 8379
Holtz Charitable Foundation Inc., FL, 2109
Holtzman Family Foundation Inc., NY, 6223
Holzer Memorial Foundation, Richard H., NJ, 5396
Holzman Foundation Inc., OR, 7775
Homan Foundation, OH, 7451
Home Instead Senior Care Foundation, NE, 5094
Home is the Foundation, OH, 7452
Homeless Assistance Fund, Inc., PA, 8065
Honey Dew Family Foundation, Inc., The, MA, 4133
Honey Foundation, VA, 9471
Hong Family Foundation, CA, 631
Honickman Foundation, Lynne & Harold, PA, 8066
Hood Family Foundation, James W., MS, 4842
Hood, Jr. Family Foundation, Warren A., MS, 4843
Hooker Foundation, Floyd, AK, 87
Hoops Family Foundation Inc., The, DE, 1682
Hoornstra Foundation Trust, Jack and Irma, FL, 2110
Hooters Community Endowment Fund, Inc., GA, 2510
Hoover Fund, W. Henry, The, OH, 7453
Hope 2 Others Foundation, TX, 8948
Hope Charitable Foundation, TX, 8949
Hope Foundation, MS, 4844
Hope Foundation, RI, 8422
Hope's Enduring Flame Foundation, CO, 1294
Hope, Love and Charity Foundation, WV, 9752
Hopedale Foundation, The, MA, 4134
Hopkins Family Foundation, Cecil R. & Edna S., VA, 9472
Hopkins Foundation, Josephine Lawrence, NY, 6224
Hopkins Private Foundation, E. L. and Z. Irene, KS, 3586
Hopper Memorial Foundation, Bertrand, IL, 2977
Hord Foundation, TX, 8950
Horizon Foundation, The, TX, 8951
Horn Charitable Trust, David A. & Helen P., PA, 8067
Horn Family Foundation Inc., Michael E., KY, 3664
Horn Foundation, H. B. and Lucille, The, NM, 5618
Horn Foundation, Inc., John and Robyn, AR, 200
Horn Foundation, Thomas & Martina, WA, 9625
Hornblower Fund, Inc., Henry, MA, 4135
Horne Foundation, Dick, SC, 8528
Horne Fund, Mabel A., The, MA, 4136
Horner Foundation, The, PA, 8068
Hornik Family Foundation, FL, 2111
Horowitz Family Foundation, Inc., G. & B., The, NY, 6225
Horowitz Foundation, Gedale B. and Barbara S., NY, see 6225
Horton Foundation, Harry M., Miriam C. & William C., RI, 8423
Horvat Foundation, Arthur J. & Helen M., Dr., NC, 7130
Horvitz Family Foundation, Inc., William & Norma, FL, see 2288
Horvitz Foundation, Jeffrey, The, OH, 7454
Horween Foundation, Ralph & Genevieve B., TX, 8952
Horwich Family Foundation, James and Ada, CA, 632
Horwitz Family Memorial Foundation, The, CA, 633
Horwitz Memorial Foundation, Diane M., The, CA, see 633
Hospital Service Association of Northeastern Pennsylvania Foundation, PA, see 7879
Hosser Scholarship Fund Trust, Edward Wagner and George, RI, 8424
Hotchkis Family Foundation, Preston B. & Maurine M., CA, 634
Hotchkis Foundation, CA, 635
Hott Memorial Foundation, George D., WV, 9753
Houchens Charitable Foundation, Ruel and Nell, The, KY, 3665
Houck Charitable Trust, Irvin E., IL, 2978
Houck Foundation, Inc., Harvey R., Jr. and Patricia W., TX, 8953
Houff Foundation, VA, 9473
Houghland Foundation, The, TN, 8630
Houghton-Carpenter Foundation, The, PA, see 8172
Houlihan Foundation, Francis J. and Patricia A., The, IL, 2979
House Educational Trust, Susan Cook, IL, 2980
Houseknecht Foundation, Alice and Jaclyn, NY, 6226
Houseman Charitable Trust, H. H. and Edna, The, LA, 3728
Houser Foundation Inc., The, NY, 6227
Houssels Family Foundation Corporation, NV, 5163
Houston Family Foundation, NY, 6228

Houston Family Foundation, The, SD, 8567
Hover Foundation, Alexander and Marjorie, The, NY, 6229
Howard Charitable Foundation, Dale & Marilyn, IA, 3509
Howard Family Charitable Foundation, Inc., OK, 7688
Howard Family Foundation, Gary and Leslie, The, CO, 1295
Howard Family Foundation, IL, 2981
Howard Family Foundation, Inc., John D. & Betty R., CA, see 242
Howard Family Foundation, Ron & Cheryl, CT, 1484
Howard Family Trust, Ruth S., TX, 8954
Howard Foundation, OK, 7689
Howard Foundation, Virginia Martin, TX, 8955
Howard Home for Aged Men in the City of Brockton, MA, 4137
Howard Trust, Winnifred C., NC, 7131
Howarth Trust, Inc., WA, 9626
Howe Family Foundation, OH, 7455
Howe Foundation, Inc., The, NC, 7132
Howe Foundation, The, IA, 3510
Howell Family Foundation, The, TX, 8956
Howell Foundation, Barbara N. and Don N., GA, 2511
Howell Fund, Inc., The, GA, 2512
Hoyt - Anne H. Jolley Foundation, Ruth R., GA, 2513
Hoyt Charitable Trust, Sara and Fred, The, GA, 2514
Hoyt Foundation, Inc., Ruth Rogers, GA, see 2513
Hoyt Foundation, Inc., Stewart W. & Willma C., NY, 6230
HPS Foundation, NY, see 6734
Hsieh Christian Foundation, The, CA, 636
Hsu Charitable Foundation, Hong-Yen & Lin-Run, CA, 637
Hsu Family Foundation Inc., FL, 2112
Huang Family Foundation, Inc., FL, 2113
Hubbard Charitable Trust, Nathaniel, RI, 8425
Hubbard Foundation, Inc., A. C. and Penney, The, MD, 3883
Huber Charitable Trust, Bernice Peltier, CA, 638
Huber Family Foundation Inc, The, NY, 6231
Hubert Jr. Foundation, George J., OH, 7456
Huddart Family Foundation, OR, 7776
Hudson Foundation, The, ME, 3783
Hudson Foundation, The, NC, 7133
Hueneke Foundation Trust, OH, 7457
Huether Foundation, Inc., The, MD, see 3884
Huether/McClelland Foundation, Inc., The, MD, 3884
Huffhines Trust, NJ, 5397
Hufty Foundation, FL, 2114
Hugg Trust, Leola W. and Charles H., IL, 2982
Hughes Charitable Foundation, John E. & Jeanne T., IL, 2983
Hughes Charitable Trust, Mabel Y., AZ, 130
Hughes Family Foundation, Paul, CA, 639
Hughes Memorial Home, VA, 9474
Hughes Scholarship Trust, Ruth M., OH, 7458
Huie-Dellmon Trust, LA, 3729
Huiras Family Foundation, Inc., Ralph J., WI, see 9844
Huiras Foundation, Inc., Ralph J., WI, 9844
Huisinga Charitable Foundation, Theodore G., The, MN, 4716
Hulbert Foundation, Nila B., NY, 6232
Hull Charitable Trust A, Cora A., TX, A
Hulman & Company Foundation, Inc., IN, 3396
Hulme Charitable Foundation, Milton G., PA, 8069
Hultquist Foundation, The, FL, 2115
Humanities Instructional Television Educational Center, MO, see 4931
Hume Foundation Inc., Warren and Augusta, The, CT, 1485
Hummer Family Foundation, OH, 7459
Humphreys Foundation, Inc., MD, 3885
Hundred Foundation, The, NE, 5095
Hunsaker Foundation, CA, 640
Hunt Charitable Trust, C. Giles, NC, 7134
Hunt Family Foundation, The, CO, 1296
Hunt Foundation, Horace C., PA, see 8070
Hunt Foundation, Samuel P., NH, 5214
Hunt Foundation, Vicky and Sam, NC, 7135
Hunt Memorial Foundation, Horace C., PA, 8070
Hunt Memorial Trust, Frieda & William, WI, 9845
Hunt Trust for Episcopal Charitable Institutions, Virginia, IL, 2984
Hunter Charitable Trust, Estelle, NC, 7136

Hunter Family Foundation, RD, TX, 8957
Hunter Foundation Inc., The, GA, 2515
Hunter Scholarship Trust, Jeanette E. & Benjamin F., AL, 38
Hunter Trust, Emily S. and Coleman A., FL, 2116
Hunter-White Foundation, CO, 1297
HunterWard Foundation, CA, 641
Huntington County Community Foundation, Inc., IN, 3397
Huntington Foundation, Inc., The, CT, 1486
Huntington Foundation, Inc., The, WV, 9754
Huntington Foundation, John Brockway, CA, 642
Huntington Residue Fund, Mariett L., OH, 7460
Huntington Tracy Foundation, Inc., VT, 9376
Huplits Foundation Trust, Myrtle V. C. Huplits & Woodman E., PA, 8071
Hurlbert Family Foundation, The, GA, 2516
Hurlburt Foundation, Inc., The, NY, 6233
Hurley Foundation, Ed E. & Gladys, IL, 2985
Hurliman Scholarship Foundation, The, CA, 643
Hurston Family Foundation, Inc., MA, 4138
Hurwitz Family Foundation, Inc., Benno and Elayne, MD, 3886
Hussman Foundation, The, AR, 201
Hutcheson Foundation, Hazel Montague, TN, 8631
Hutchins Endowment Fund, John C., OH, 7461
Hutchison Family Foundation Inc., FL, 2117
Hyde Charitable Foundation, MA, 4139
Hyde Family Charitable Fund, The, WI, 9846
Hyde Foundation, The, WA, 9627
Hyman Fund, Mark & Carol, MD, 3887
Hymowitz Family Foundation Trust, The, NY, 6234

I Dream a World Foundation, Inc., NY, 6235
I Have a Dream Foundation - Clio, SC, CA, 644
I'll Be There Foundation, The, NY, see 6505
i.am.angel foundation, CA, 645
I.W. Foundation, Inc., NY, 6236
Ibrahim Foundation, Nina and S. A., CA, 646
Icap Foundation Inc, NJ, 5398
Ice Foundation, Diamond, PA, 8072
Ich Bane Trust, E. M., NC, see 7043
Ichioka & Satsuki Nakao Charitable Foundation, Tsutayo, CA, 647
Ideal Industries Foundation, IL, 2986
Idema Foundation, Crawford, The, MA, see 4059
IF Hummingbird Foundation, Inc., NY, 6237
IGN Foundation, PA, 8073
Ignatius Foundation, George, CA, 648
II Corinthians 9:7 Foundation, The, PA, 8074
II Corinthians 9:7 Foundation, TX, 8958
II Corinthians Foundation, VA, 9475
Ik Manzil, TX, 8959
IKON Office Solutions Foundation, Inc., PA, see 8237
Ilgenfritz Testamentary Trust, May H., TX, 8960
Illges Foundation, Inc., John P. and Dorothy S., GA, 2517
Illges Foundation, Norman & Emmy Lou, The, GA, 2518
Ilsababy Foundation, The, NY, 6238
IM Wintercreek Foundation, CA, 649
IMA Foundation, KS, see 3587
Imada Foundation, The, NJ, see 5401
Imago Dei Foundation, Inc., NY, 6239
Imerman Memorial Foundation, Stanley, MI, A
Imig Family Foundation, The, WY, 9974
Immanuel Charitable Foundation, AZ, 131
Immixgroup Foundation, VA, 9476
Impact Group Charitable Foundation, MO, 4930
IMS Foundation, NY, 6240
In Christo Vera Educatio, CA, 650
Inbusch Foundation, Inc., Charles E. & Dorothy Watkins, WI, see 9847
Inbusch Foundation, Inc., Dorothy, WI, 9847
Independence Foundation, Inc., KY, 3666
Independent Foundation, The, NY, 6241
Indira Foundation, The, NY, 6242
Indo-American Foundation Inc., CA, 651
Indus Charitable Foundation Inc., NY, 6243
Infinite Possibilities Foundation, Inc., NJ, see 5414
Infinity Group Inc., NJ, 5399
Ingalls Charitable Foundation, W. Bradford, The, FL, 2118
Inge Foundation, The, TX, 8961

Ingle Charitable Trust, Tom & Evelyn, OH, 7462
Inglesea Charitable Trust, The, CT, 1487
Ingram Foundation, The, TN, 8632
Ingrassia Foundation, Elizabeth & Frank, NY, 6244
Ingredion Charitable Foundation, IL, 2987
Ingredion Educational Foundation, IL, 2988
Initial Teaching Alphabet Foundation, NY, 6245
Inman Foundation, Inc., Hugh M., GA, 2519
Innovative Technology Education Fund, MO, 4931
Insall Foundation for Orthopaedics Inc., John N., NY, 6246
Insall Foundation, Mary V., NY, 6247
Insetta Family Foundation, Inc., The, FL, 2119
Institute for Depression Studies and Treatment, NY, 6248
Institute of Current World Affairs, Inc., DC, 1816
Insurance Management Associates Foundation, KS, 3587
Integra Foundation, Inc., The, NJ, 5400
Interactive Intelligence Foundation Corp., IN, 3398
Intermountain Gas Industries Foundation, Inc., ID, see 2677
Intermountain Industries Petroglyph Energy Foundation, Inc., ID, 2677
International Christian Scholarship Foundation, CA, 652
International Shinto Foundation, Inc., NY, 6249
Interstate Packaging Foundation Charitable Trust, TN, see 8605
Invisible Hand Foundation, Inc., The, GA, 2520
Invisible Prince Charitable Foundation Inc., PA, 8075
Iodent Chemical Company Foundation, MI, see 4609
Iott Family Foundation, The, OH, 7463
Iowa Foundation for Agricultural Advancement, IA, 3511
Iowa Foundation for Education, Environment and the Arts, The, IA, 3512
Iowa P.E.O. Project Fund, Inc., IA, 3513
Ipsco Charitable Foundation, IL, see 3260
IPSCO Foundation for Education, AL, see 67
Ireland Foundation, C. Eugene, The, AL, 39
Iroquois Avenue Foundation, NY, 6250
Iroquois Federal Foundation Inc., IL, 2989
Irving Foundation Inc., GA, 2521
Irwin Foundation, Howard Wallis & Dorise Carlyon, OR, 7777
Irwin Saks Charitable Foundation, Inc., FL, 2120
Isaac I Foundation, The, TX, 8962
Isabella Bank & Trust Foundation, MI, 4468
Iscol Family Foundation, Inc., The, NY, see 6237
Isenberg Family Charitable Trust, The, FL, 2121
Israelson Family Foundation, Inc., MD, 3888
Issa Family Foundation, Sultan and Sakeba, IL, 2990
Issroff Family Foundation, NY, 6251
Istock Foundation, Verne G. and Judith A., IL, 2991
Ithan Foundation, Inc., The, PA, 8076
IV Fund, The, NJ, 5401
Ivakota Association, Inc., VA, 9477
Iversen and Family Foundation, Alfred A., MN, 4717
Iverson Foundation, The, GA, see 2480
Ivorybill Foundation, Inc., NY, 6252
Izzo Family Foundation, MD, 3889

J & S Laidig Family Foundation, Inc., IN, 3399
J&L Foundation, SD, 8568
J. & J. Foundation, Inc., The, IN, 3400
J. & M. Foundation, CA, 653
J. C. Foundation, FL, 2122
J. C. K. Family Foundation, MO, 4932
J. N. M. Gift Trust, NC, A
J.A.T. Foundation, NY, 6253
j.k. livin foundation, CA, see 684
J.P.C. Foundation, WI, 9848
J/MB Foundation, OK, see 7659
Jabara Charitable Trust, Violet, The, NY, 6254
Jacbel Foundation, RI, 8426
Jackman Family Foundation, The, DE, 1683
Jackson Charitable Trust, Adrian H., PA, 8077
Jackson Charitable Trust, John E. & Sue M., PA, 8078
Jackson Family Foundation, Franklin D., The, GA, 2522
Jackson Foundation, C. Charles, UT, 9329
Jackson Foundation, Crawford and Hattie, TX, 8963
Jackson Foundation, Inc., Darren and Terry, MN, 4718
Jackson Foundation, Kathleen & Ronald J., MA, 4140
Jackson Jr. Foundation, Solomon, The, SC, 8529

Jackson Trust, Wilhelmina W., RI, 8427
Jacobi Family Foundation, WA, 9628
Jacobs Charitable Foundation, Jim, The, CO, 1298
Jacobs Foundation, Charles E., The, TX, 8964
Jacobsen Charitable Foundation Inc., Hans & Cay, FL, 2123
Jacobson Charitable Foundation, Mark, NJ, 5402
Jacobson Charitable Trust, Robert and Deborah, The, FL, 2124
Jacobson Family Foundation Inc., Roni and Sam, FL, 2125
Jacobson II Foundation Inc., Joan L. & Julius H., The, NY, 6255
Jacobus Family Foundation, Charles D., WI, 9849
Jacoby Family Foundation, Norman and Lela Beren, CA, 654
Jade and Coral Foundation, CA, 655
Jade Tree Foundation, DE, 1684
Jadeja Family Foundation, Motwani, DE, 1685
JADO Fund, AL, 40
Jaffe Foundation, Bernard M. and Audrey, The, WA, 9629
Jaffe Foundation, The, CT, 1488
Jahn Foundation, Reinhardt H. & Shirley R., IL, 2992
Jain Endowment Fund, Parveen and Neeraj, The, CA, 656
Jain Family Foundation, Inc., VA, 9478
Jain Foundation, CA, 657
Jake Foundation, Inc., The, MD, 3890
Jamacha Bloom Family Foundation, NJ, 5403
Jamail Galveston Foundation, The, TX, 8965
Jamakepe Foundation, The, NY, 6256
James Family Trust, Harold, The, AZ, 132
Jameson Trust, Oleonda, NH, 5215
Jamieson Foundation, CA, 658
Janci Foundation, RI, 8428
Janesville Foundation, Inc., WI, 9850
Janet Malser Humanities Trust, The, MA, 4141
Janke Charitable Foundation, The, FL, 2126
Janklow Foundation, NY, 6257
Jansen Family Foundation, NV, 5164
Jansing-Cook Foundation, PA, 8079
Janszen Charitable Trust, The, TX, 8966
Jaquish & Kenninger Foundation, The, NV, 5165
Jaquith Family Foundation, WY, 9975
Jaros Sr. Charitable Trust, Arthur G. & Dawn L., IL, 2993
Jarx Foundation Inc., The, NY, 6258
Jasam Foundation Fund A, FL, 2127
Jasam Foundation Fund B, AZ, 133
Jasper Foundation, Inc., IN, 3401
Jastrow Foundation, TX, 8967
Jatain Charitable Foundation, CA, 659
JBL Scholarship Trust, DE, 1686
JBS Foundation, GA, 2523
JBS Foundation, IL, 2994
JCT Foundation, MI, 4469
JDH Family Foundation, CA, 660
Jeangerard Foundation, CA, 661
Jeffcoat Memorial Foundation, KS, 3588
Jeffers Foundation, MN, 4719
Jefferson County Community Foundation, Greater, IA, 3514
Jefferson County Community Foundation, WA, 9630
Jefferson Foundation Inc., Joe Lewis, The, MA, 4142
Jeffery Charitable Trust, Clara L. D., RI, 8429
Jeffrey Foundation, Marie D., The, CA, see 1047
Jelin Charitable Foundation, William Sloane, CA, 662
Jelks Family Foundation, Inc., The, FL, 2128
Jellison Benevolent Society Inc., KS, 3589
Jelm Charitable Foundation, Charles R., NC, 7137
Jenkins Charitable Fund, Jane L., OH, 7464
Jenkins Charitable Trust, Tom H. and Anne H., The, OH, 7465
Jenkins Family Charitable Institute, FL, 2129
Jenkins Family Foundation, James R. and Anita Horne, MI, 4470
Jennings County Community Foundation, Inc., IN, 3402
Jennings Family Foundation, CA, 663
Jennings Foundation Inc., Peter, The, NY, 6259
Jennings Foundation, Jack, IN, 3403
Jennings Memorial Foundation, OH, 7466
Jensam Foundation, Inc., NJ, 5404
Jensen Family Foundation, Inc., J., TX, see 8770

Jensen Foundation, Janet Jarie, TX, *see* 8713
Jentes Family Foundation, IL, 2995
Jephson Educational Trust No. 1, IL, 2996
Jernigan Foundation, The, WA, 9631
Jessen Foundation, Caroline Lott, TX, 8968
Jesy Foundation, CA, 664
Jeter Foundation Inc., George W., The, GA, 2524
Jewell Memorial Foundation, Daniel Ashley and Irene Houston, The, TN, 8633
Jewish Education Research & Development Foundation, NY, *see* 5697
Jewish Family Assistance Fund, PA, 8080
Jewish Help Fund Trust, The, NJ, *see* 5260
JFI Charitable Trust, NJ, 5405
JI Foundation, Inc., NY, 6260
Ji Ji Foundation, The, WA, 9632
JIA Charitable Foundation, NY, 6261
Jirous Foundation Inc., M. D., OK, *see* 7690
Jirous Foundation, Inc., M. D. and Barbara, OK, 7690
JJC Foundation, Inc., NY, 6262
JJP Family Foundation Inc., CO, 1299
JKP Family Foundation, IL, 2997
JKS Foundation, UT, 9330
JKW Foundation, NY, 6263
JLH Foundation, IL, 2998
JLK Foundation, Inc., The, NY, 6264
JMG Foundation, MO, 4933
JMR Charities, Inc., IL, 2999
JNF Foundation, UT, 9331
Joannides Family Foundation, WY, 9976
Joby Foundation, Inc., The, DE, *see* 1775
Jocarno Fund, IL, 3000
Jockers Family Foundation, DE, 1687
Jockey Club Foundation, The, NY, 6265
Joerger Family Charitable Foundation, CA, 665
Joffe Foundation, OH, 7467
John Family Foundation, PA, 8081
Johnson & Haefling Family Foundation, WA, 9633
Johnson Charitable Educational Trust, James Hervey, CA, 666
Johnson Charitable Trust No. 33, 1994 Christopher W., The, NY, 6266
Johnson Charitable Trust, Christopher W., The, NY, *see* 6266
Johnson Family Charitable Foundation, C. Paul, WI, 9851
Johnson Family Charitable Trust, J.W., AZ, 134
Johnson Family Foundation Inc., Tom & Edwina, The, GA, 2525
Johnson Family Foundation of Arizona, R. L. "Roz", AZ, 135
Johnson Family Foundation, Bernard J. & Mary T., The, CA, 667
Johnson Family Foundation, Inc., The, FL, 2130
Johnson Family Foundation, J. Howard & Brenda LaGrange, NY, 6267
Johnson Family Foundation, J. Stanley and Mary W., CA, 668
Johnson Family Foundation, Joe & Nan, TX, 8969
Johnson Family Foundation, OH, 7468
Johnson Foundation Inc., Joyce and Seward, The, NJ, 5406
Johnson Foundation, A. D., IL, 3001
Johnson Foundation, Carl W., CA, 669
Johnson Foundation, Charles E. and Andriene M., WI, 9852
Johnson Foundation, Edith Carell, The, TN, 8634
Johnson Foundation, Howard, The, RI, 8430
Johnson Foundation, Inc., Raymond C. and Anna T., The, OH, 7469
Johnson Foundation, Karl M., WY, 9977
Johnson Foundation, Mark Chapin, CA, 670
Johnson Foundation, NY, 6268
Johnson Foundation, Paul T. & Frances B., MI, 4471
Johnson Foundation, Robert K., The, NJ, 5407
Johnson Foundation, The, NY, 6269
Johnson Foundation, Wece B. and Martha A., The, TX, 8970
Johnson III Foundation, Inc., John S., The, NJ, *see* 5485
Johnson IV Charitable Trust, 1994 Robert W., The, NY, 6270
Johnson Memorial Trust, John Alfred & Oscar, NY, *see* 6268

Johnson, Inc., Claire and Marjorie, WI, 9853
Johnson, Jr. Foundation, Inc., R. C., TX, 8971
Johnson-Stillman Family Foundation, NY, 6271
Johnston Foundation, Dorothy L., The, CA, 671
Johnston Foundation, Inc., Ralph A., The, TX, 8972
Johnston-Fix Foundation, WA, 9634
Johnston-Hanson Foundation, WA, 9635
Joint Heirs Ministry, WA, 9636
Jolan Foundation Corp., IN, 3404
Jolley Foundation, Leodelle Lassiter, GA, 2526
Jolson Family Foundation, The, CA, 672
Jonas Family Foundation Trust, OR, 7778
Jones & Bessie D. Phelps Foundation, Inc., Cyrus W. & Amy F., CT, 1489
Jones Charitable Family Foundation, Brereton and Elizabeth, KY, 3667
Jones Charitable Foundation, Wayne and Carolyn, NC, 7138
Jones Charitable Trust, Margery, WA, 9637
Jones Family Foundation, Clay and Debbie, FL, 2131
Jones Family Foundation, E. Richard, CA, 673
Jones Family Foundation, IL, 3002
Jones Family Foundation, Louis and Donna, CA, 674
Jones Family Foundation, The, MI, 4472
Jones Family Foundation, W. J., The, OK, 7691
Jones Foundation Inc., Jennings & Rebecca, TN, 8635
Jones Foundation, Catherine May, OK, *see* 7691
Jones Foundation, Gary Dean and Christine Newman, AZ, 136
Jones Foundation, Herbert B., The, WA, 9638
Jones Foundation, Janet Stone, CT, 1490
Jones Foundation, Montfort and Allie Brown, OK, 7692
Jones Foundation, Paolo Pellegrini and Henrietta, The, NY, 6272
Jones Foundation, Ralph R. and Grace B., OH, 7470
Jones Foundation, Steaven K. and Judith G., CA, 675
Jones Foundation, Stella H., WI, 9854
Jones Foundation, The, CA, *see* 673
Jones Foundation, William Stark, WI, 9855
Jones Fund, Blanche & George, NJ, 5408
Jones Fund, Paul L., CT, 1491
Jones Memorial Fund, John Davidson, IL, *see* 3002
Jones Memorial Trust, Charles S., TX, 8973
Jones Private Foundation Trust, William, NJ, 5409
Jones Trust, Homer A. and Ida S., VA, 9479
Jordan Charitable Foundation, The, PA, 8082
Jordan Family Foundation, The, NJ, 8636
Jordan Foundation, Kim, The, OH, 7471
Jordanna Foundation, The, CO, *see* 1338
Jorgensen Foundation, David and Annette, CA, 676
Joscelyn Foundation, Verla Nesbitt, KS, 3590
Joseph Charitable Trust, Carolyn H., TX, 8974
Joseph Family Foundation, The, NV, 5166
Joseph Foundation, Peter T., The, NY, 6273
Joshua Foundation, Inc., The, FL, 2132
Joshua Foundation, NV, 5167
Josi Charitable Trust, Zelma May, WA, 9639
Joslin-Needham Family Foundation, CO, 1300
Jospey Foundation, Marjorie and Maxwell, MI, 4473
Jost Foundation, Inc., Charles & Mabel P., CT, 1492
Jostens Foundation, Inc., The, MN, 4720
Joukowsky Family Foundation, NY, 6274
Journey Charitable Foundation, TX, 8975
Jovid Foundation, DC, 1817
Joy Family Foundation, Inc., CO, 1301
Joy Family Foundation, Ken and Judith, The, CA, 677
Joyce Charitable Fund, The, NY, 6275
Joyce Family Foundation Inc., GA, 2527
Joyce Family Foundation Trust, PA, 8083
JP Foundation Trust, CA, 678
JSJ Foundation, MI, 4474
JTB Cultural Exchange Corp., CA, 679
Ju Foundation, David M. C., NJ, 5410
Jubas Family Foundation, The, CA, 680
Jubitz Foundation, Frederick D. & Gail Y., The, OR, 7779
Juda Foundation, Felix And Helen, CA, 681
Judd Charitable Trust, M.H., CA, 7139
Judkins Family Foundation, Don & Maxine, The, CA, 682
Judkins Family Foundation, Donavan and Randie, The, CA, 683
Judson Family Foundation, Inc., NJ, 5411
Judy Family Foundation, IL, 3003

Juhl Scholarship Fund, George W. & Sadie Marie, MI, 4475
Julian Charitable Trust, Doris Pilgrim, The, TX, 8976
Juneau Community Foundation, AK, 88
Juninger Foundation, Inc., Karl, WI, 9856
Jungreis Foundation, Aaron & Ruth, NY, 6276
Jungreis Foundation, The, NY, *see* 6276
Juniper Foundation, WA, 9640
Juniper Tree Foundation, OH, 7472
Jurrens Family Foundation, OR, 7780
Jurries Foundation, Jim and Ginger, MI, 4476
Just Keep Livin Foundation, CA, 684
Just Us for All Foundation, DE, 1688
JVZ Foundation, The, NY, 6277
JWJ Family Foundation Inc., The, WY, 9978

K. Charitable Foundation, Inc., GA, 2528
K2 Charitable Foundation, IA, 3515
Kabacoff Family Foundation, The, TX, 8977
Kabcenell Family Foundation, CA, 685
Kachel Family Foundation Inc., WI, 9857
Kadima Foundation, CA, 686
Kagan Family Foundation, Max, ME, 3784
Kahan Family Foundation, The, NY, 6278
Kahiau Foundation, The, HI, 2636
Kahn And Emily Mason Foundation Inc., Wolf, VT, 9377
Kahn Charitable Foundation, Esther B., MA, 4143
Kahn Charitable Foundation, Fannie and Stephen, TX, 8978
Kahn Family Foundation, Inc., David & Jennifer, GA, 2529
Kahn Foundation Inc., Michele & Thomas, NY, 6279
Kahn Foundation, Gilbert S. & John J. Noffo, The, FL, 2133
Kahn Foundation, Inc., David B., The, GA, *see* 2529
Kahn Lyons Foundation, Inc., VA, 9480
Kahn, Jr. Foundation, Inc., Barbara R. and Charles, PA, 8084
Kainz Family Foundation, IL, 3004
Kainz Foundation, Joseph A. & Susan J., IL, *see* 3004
Kairos Foundation Trust of 2004, The, AL, 41
Kaiserman Foundation, Jay and Becky, The, FL, 2134
Kalamazoo Community Foundation Charitable Trust, MI, 4477
Kaleidoscope Foundation, WA, 9641
Kalkin Family Foundation, Inc., NJ, 5412
Kallinikeion Foundation, The, NY, 6280
Kallins Foundation, James and Virginia, CA, 687
Kalscheur Family Foundation, WI, 9858
Kalscheur Foundation, James & Joyce, WI, *see* 9858
Kaman Charitable Foundation, Inc., Charles H., CT, 1493
Kamber Foundation, Abraham, NY, 6281
Kamin Family Foundation, Peter & Loren, MA, *see* 4144
Kamin Family Foundation, Peter H., MA, 4144
Kaminer Foundation, NY, 6282
Kaminski Family Foundation, Robert S. and Mary Ann, IL, 3005
Kamm Foundation, OH, 7473
Kammco Foundation, Inc., KS, 3591
Kampen Foundation, Emerson & Barbara, The, NJ, 5413
Kampen Foundation, Emerson, The, NJ, *see* 5413
Kandell Fund, The, NY, 6283
Kanders Foundation, Inc., FL, 2135
Kanders Foundation, Warren B., FL, 2136
Kane Family Foundation, Janet and Stanley, FL, 2137
Kanel Charitable Foundation, John and Ursula, CA, 688
Kaneta Charitable Foundation, HI, *see* 2637
Kaneta Foundation, HI, 2637
Kang Charitable Foundation Inc., Don & Susan, DE, 1689
Kangesser Foundation, Robert E., Harry A., and M. Sylvia, The, OH, *see* 7474
Kangesser Foundation, The, OH, 7474
Kanitz Scholarship Memorial Fund, Louis J. & Golda I., NC, 7140
Kankakee River Valley Foundation, IL, *see* 2802
Kanoff Family Foundation, CA, 689
Kansas Rural Communities Foundation, KS, 3592
Kantzler Foundation, The, MI, 4478
Kao Family Foundation, The, CA, 690
Kaplan & Robert Fippinger Foundation, Ann F., The, NY, *see* 5656

Kaplan Charitable Foundation, Abraham, MA, 4145
Kaplan Family Charitable Foundation, Joan and Marvin, The, TX, see 8979
Kaplan Family Foundation, MN, 4721
Kaplan Family Foundation, Naomi, The, NY, 6284
Kaplan Foundation, Deanne & Arnold, The, FL, 2138
Kaplan Foundation, Joan and Marvin, TX, 8979
Kappa Delta Private Foundation, TN, 8637
Kara Foundation, The, NV, 5168
Karamatsoukas Family Foundation, Nicholas J. & Celeste G., PA, 8085
Karas Foundation, Inc., Elia & Fannie, MA, 4146
Karasik Family Foundation, Max and Yetta, The, IL, 3006
Karlgaard Family Foundation, VA, 9481
Karol Fund, The, WI, 9859
Karp Charitable Foundation, Richard A., CA, 691
Karuna Foundation, OR, 7781
Kasowitz Family Foundation, Inc., NY, 6285
Kassner Family Foundation, Fred E., NC, 7141
Kassner Family Foundation, NC, see 7141
Katen Foundation, Karen, The, CT, 1494
Katherine Alexandra Charitable Foundation, The, PA, 8086
Kathwari Foundation Inc., Irfan, NY, 6286
Katie Ford Foundation Inc., NY, see 6030
Katsaros Family Foundation, The, PA, 8087
Katz Family Foundation, CA, 692
Katz Family Foundation, Charles and Roberta, The, CA, 693
Katz Family Foundation, Harold, The, PA, 8088
Katz Family Foundation, Inc., Rosalie, The, NY, 6287
Katz Family Foundation, The, PA, 8089
Katz Foundation, Avrum, OH, 7475
Katz Foundation, H.L., NC, 7142
Katz Foundation, Inc., Drew A., The, NJ, 5414
Katz Foundation, Sheldon and Audrey, MD, 3891
Katz Memorial Fund, Harry, NC, see 7142
Katzin Foundation, The, NY, 6288
Katzman Foundation, Richard and Jane, NY, 6289
Kauffman Scholarship Foundation, Inc., Gene, MO, 4934
Kaufman Americana Foundation, VA, 9482
Kaufman Charitable Foundation, Harold & Yenny, The, NJ, 5415
Kaufman Family Foundation, C., VT, 9378
Kaufman Foundation, MI, 4479
Kaufmann Foundation, Inc., CT, 1495
Kaufmann-Cummings Foundation, NE, 5096
Kaul Foundation, The, FL, 2139
Kaulbach Charitable Foundation, Ernest W. & Agnes W., The, FL, 2140
Kautz Foundation, Charles and Pauline, NY, 6290
Kavanagh Family Foundation, LA, 3730
Kawabe Memorial Fund, WA, 9642
Kawabe Trust, Harry S., WA, see 9642
Kay Charitable Trust, Helen L., MI, 4480
Kay Family Foundation, Inc., The, MD, 3892
Kay Foundation, Helen L., MI, see 4480
Kay Foundation, Louis J. and June E., CT, 1496
Kaye Charitable Foundation, Herman H., The, DE, 1690
Kaye Foundation, Inc., Carole and Barry, The, FL, 2141
Kayser Foundation, The, TX, 8980
Kazanjian Economics Foundation, Inc., Calvin K., The, PA, 8090
Kaztex Foundation, Inc., WI, 9860
KBR Foundation, FL, 2142
KBRK, Inc., NY, see 6374
KC Family Foundation, CA, 694
KCEG Foundation, The, NY, 6291
KCL Foundation, TX, 8981
KDK Charitable Trust, NJ, 5416
Kean Foundation, Inc., The, NJ, 5417
Keare/Hodge Family Foundation, CA, see 559
Kearny Alliance, Inc., AZ, 137
Keating Family Foundation, Kevin and Masha, CA, 695
Keck Charitable Trust, Emil E., IN, 3405
Keefe Family Foundation, CT, 1497
Keeler Motor Car Company Charitable Foundation, NY, 6292
Keenan Family Foundation, The, VA, 9483
Keene Foundation, Charles S., NY, 6293
Keene Foundation, James, NY, 6294

Keeneland Foundation, Inc., KY, 3668
Keener Foundation, Robert W. & Barbara J., UT, 9332
Keeney Trust, Hattie Hannah, IL, 3007
Kehrer Charitable Trust, Carole C. & Charles A., FL, 2143
Keith Family Foundation, Aram and Margie, The, CA, 696
KEJ Foundation, Inc., IN, 3406
Kejr Foundation Inc., KS, 3593
Kellam Foundation, Inc., The, TX, 8982
Kellcie Fund, The, IL, 3008
Kelleher Charitable Foundation, Denis P. and Carol A., The, NY, 6295
Kelleher Family Charitable Trust, MA, 4147
Keller Family Charitable Trust, The, NY, 6296
Keller Family Foundation, IL, 3009
Keller Family Foundation, NJ, 5418
Keller Foundation, MI, 4481
Keller Foundation, WA, 9643
Keller Trust, William M., IL, 3010
Keller-Shatanoff Foundation, NY, 6297
Kelley Charitable Foundation, Boyd and Joan, The, TX, 8983
Kelley Charitable Trust, W. D., TX, see 8984
Kelley Foundation, Kate M., PA, 8091
Kelley Foundation, Ralph & Helen, RI, 8431
Kelley Foundation, W. D., TX, 8984
Kellogg Charitable Trust, H. & M., MN, 4722
Kellogg Foundation, Inc., Edward and June, MI, 4482
Kelly Family Foundation, FL, 2144
Kelly Family Foundation, Inc., WI, 9861
Kelly Family Foundation, U. D., RI, 8432
Kelly Foundation, CA, 697
Kelly Foundation, IL, 3011
Kelly Foundation, T. Lloyd, IL, 3012
Kelly, Jr. Memorial Foundation, Inc., Ensign C. Markland, MD, 3893
Kelsey Family Foundation, The, NY, 6298
Kelsey Trust, The, MA, 4148
Kelso Foundation, Betty Stieren, TX, 8985
Kelton Fund, Inc., CA, 698
Kelvin Foundation, The, CA, 699
Kemp Foundation, Nelson and Charleen, The, AL, 42
Kemp Foundation, Parker, IL, 3013
Kemper Foundation, Jackson, IL, 3014
Kemper II Charitable Trust, William T., MO, 4935
Kenan Family Foundation, The, NC, 7143
Kenan III Foundation, Thomas S., The, NC, 7144
Kendall Charitable Foundation, Herbert & Elaine, The, CA, 700
Kendall Family Foundation, The, CT, 1498
Kendall Foundation, Donna L., The, CA, 701
Kendall Foundation, Edward and Dorothy, The, SC, 8530
Kendall Trust, J. Henry, MA, 4149
Kenlou Foundation Inc., The, NY, 6299
Kennebec Foundation, ME, see 3785
Kennebec Savings Bank Foundation, ME, 3785
Kennebunk Savings Bank Foundation, ME, 3786
Kennecott Utah Copper Visitors Center Charitable Foundation, UT, 9333
Kennedy Foundation, Inc., TN, 8638
Kennedy Foundation, James Lehr, The, OH, 7476
Kennedy Foundation, NV, 5169
Kennedy Home Foundation, Catherine, NC, 7145
Kenney Brothers Foundation, The, CO, 1302
Kenney Charitable Foundation, Norma J. and William J., MO, 4936
Kenney Private Foundation, Jay P.K., CO, see 1302
Kenney Scholarship Fund, Walter J., RI, 8433
Kenosha Community Foundation, WI, 9862
Kent-Lucas Foundation, Inc., DE, 1691
Kentucky Foundation for Women, Inc., KY, 3669
Kenwood Foundation, MA, 4150
Kenworthy - Sarah H. Swift Foundation, Inc., Marion E., NY, 6300
Kenyon Charitable Foundation, NY, 6301
Keown Charitable Foundation, TX, 8986
Keren Eliyahu, Inc., NY, 6302
Kern Family Foundation, CO, 1303
Kerney Foundation, James, The, NJ, 5419
Kerr Family Foundation, DE, 1692
Kerr Foundation Inc., The, OK, 7693
Kerr Foundation, Roy G., IL, 3015

Kershaw Foundation Charitable Trust, MA, 4151
Kerzner Marine Foundation, Inc., FL, see 1858
Kesher Foundation, CO, 1304
Keske Charitable Trust, David G. and Karen H., MO, 4937
Kessel Foundation, Inc., George, NJ, 5420
Kessler Family Foundation, Carl E., TX, 8987
Kessler Family Foundation, FL, 2145
Keswin Family Foundation, Jeff and Erica, The, NY, 6303
Ketchum Foundation, NC, 7146
Ketelsen Charitable Foundation, James L. & Kathryn, TX, 8988
Kevorkian Fund, Hagop, The, NY, 6304
Key & Candle Foundation, NY, 6305
Key Food Stores Foundation, Inc., NY, see 6387
Keyes Charitable Trust, IL, 3016
Kharis Foundation Inc., The, IN, 3407
Khoury Family Foundation, Tawfiq and Richel, CA, 702
Kidder 1996 Charitable Trust, Michael R., MA, see 4152
Kidder Family Foundation, Michael R., MA, 4152
Kids II Foundation Inc., GA, 2530
Kienstra Foundation, Theodore A., The, MO, 4938
Kiernan Foundation, Peter and Eaddo, The, NY, 6306
Kiersznowski Family Charitable Trust, KS, 3594
Kies Family Foundation, David M., The, NY, 6307
Kieve Foundation, CA, 703
Kilbourne Residuary Charitable Trust, E. H., NE, 5097
Kilgore Foundation, David & Margaret, TX, 8989
Killam Private Foundation Trust, Oliver, MA, 4153
Killian Family Foundation Charity, MA, see 4154
Killian Family Foundation, MA, 4154
Killian, B. J., KY, 3670
Killson Educational Foundation, TX, see 8990
Killson Educational Foundation, Winifred & B. A., TX, 8990
Kilrea Foundation, The, IL, 3017
Kilworth Charitable Foundation, William, OH, 7477
Kilworth Charitable Trust Foundation, Florence B., WA, 9644
Kim Foundation, Inc., D. K., CA, 704
Kim Foundation, NE, 5098
Kimball Foundation, Horace A. Kimball and S. Ella, RI, 8434
Kimball Foundation, Inc., Alberta S., CA, see 245
Kimball Fund for the Promotion of Good Citizenship, Moses, The, MA, see 4155
Kimball Fund, Moses, MA, 4155
Kimball Trust, Benjamin, NH, 5216
Kimball Trust, Helen F., MA, see 4155
Kimble Foundation Trust, TX, 8991
Kimbo Foundation, The, CA, 705
Kimmel Family Foundation, OR, 7782
Kimmel Foundation, David, NY, 6308
Kimmel Foundation, Inc., Edward & Lucille, The, FL, 2146
Kimmell Family Foundation, OK, 7694
Kimmelman Family Foundation, Inc., Elbrun & Peter, The, NY, 6309
Kimura Foundation, Rattray, NY, 6310
Kincaid Educational Trust, J. Donald and Julianne, OH, 7478
Kinder Porter Scott Family Foundation, NE, 5099
King Benjamin Fund, TX, 8992
King Charitable Foundation, Inc., Louise Baxter, The, FL, 2147
King Charitable Foundation, Paul L., WA, 9645
King Educational Trust, William Toben, MO, 4939
King Family Foundation, Inc., Charles & Lucille, NY, 6311
King Family Foundation, Luther & Teresa, TX, 8993
King Foundation, Lloyd L. and Eleanor R., The, CO, 1305
King Foundation, Olin B., The, AL, 43
King Foundation, William M., The, VA, 9484
King Ranch Family Trust, TX, 8994
King Scholarship Foundation, Inc., Basil L., FL, 2148
King Trust, Annie Graham, AL, 44
King's Daughters & Sons Circle No. 2, MS, 4845
King-Carpenter Foundation, NM, 5619
King-White Family Foundation, Inc., GA, 2532
Kingdom Foundation, TX, 8995
Kingdom School and Ministry Center Inc., GA, 2531
Kingjay Foundation Trust, NY, 6312

Kingsberg Foundation, The, NJ, 5421
Kingsbury Fund, The, RI, 8435
Kingsley Foundation, DE, 1693
Kinman-Oldfield Family Foundation Trust, MN, 4723
Kinney Family Foundation, MN, 4724
Kinney Family Foundation, Ronald and Eva, MI, 4483
Kinney Foundation, Inc., Ronald F., MI, see 4483
Kinney Memorial Foundation, PA, 8092
Kinnie Family Foundation, OR, 7783
Kinnoull Foundation, CA, 706
Kinsey Foundation, Norman and Joan, The, CA, 707
Kipper Family Foundation, The, IL, 3018
Kirby Family Foundation, The, NY, 6313
Kirby Foundation, NJ, 5422
Kirby-Jones Foundation, The, CA, 708
Kirk Family Foundation, The, MD, 3894
Kirk Humanitarian, UT, 9334
Kirkland Charitable Foundation, W. W., AL, 45
Kirkorian Family Foundation, The, CA, 709
Kirschenbaum Foundation Inc., Maimon and Ruth, NY, 6314
Kirschner Foundation, E. Phil and Roberta, OK, A
Kirwan Family Foundation, Inc., TX, 8996
Kirzner Family Foundation, Martin, NY, 6315
Kisco Cares Foundation, CA, 710
Kisker Foundation, Patricia, OH, 7479
Kismet 805 Foundation, WA, 9646
Kistler Charitable Fund, William, The, NY, 6316
Kistler Trust, Mary C., NC, 7147
Kite Foundation, TN, 8639
Kite Key Foundation, The, CA, 711
Kitov Foundation, NY, 6317
Kittenbrink Family Foundation, PA, 8093
Kittrell Family Foundation, MS, see 4834
Kiwanis Club of Bradenton Foundation, Inc., FL, 2149
Kiwanis of Little Havana Foundation, Inc., FL, 2150
Kiwanis of Michigan Foundation, MI, 4484
Kjellstrom Family Foundation, The, IL, 3019
KL Felicitas Foundation, PA, 8094
Klagsbrun Foundation, Samuel & Francine, NY, 6318
Klahr No. 2 Testamentary Trust, Emilie J., PA, 8095
Klamath Medical Service Bureau Foundation, OR, 7784
Klapper Family Foundation, Inc., The, IN, 3408
Klatskin Family Charitable Trust, Charles and Lynne, The, NJ, 5423
Klaue Family Foundation, WA, 9647
Klaus Family Foundation, Arthur, The, NY, 6319
Klaus Family Foundation, Lester & Esther, The, NY, 6320
Klaus Family Foundation, Lester, The, NY, see 6320
Klaus Family Foundation, Mortimer & Barbara, The, NY, 6321
Klavan Memorial Foundation, Harry S., NY, 6322
Klavan Memorial Foundation, Rabbi Joshua & Fannie D., NY, see 6322
Kleban Foundation, Inc., The, NY, 6323
Klein Charitable Foundation, Raymond, The, PA, 8096
Klein Charitable Trust, E. Ann, PA, 8097
Klein Family Foundation Inc., CT, 1499
Klein Foundation, George & Adele, NY, 6324
Klein Foundation, Inc., Ruth and Seymour, NY, 6325
Klein Foundation, Inc., Walter C., The, NJ, 5424
Klein Trust Fund, Alvin A. & Roberta T., TX, 8997
Klein, Jr. Foundation, David L., DE, 1694
Klein, Jr. Memorial Foundation, Inc., David L., DE, see 1694
Kleinschmidt Family Foundation, The, NY, 6326
Kleissner Family Foundation, PA, see 8094
Klesse Foundation, The, TX, 8998
Kline Foundation, Charles and Figa, PA, 8098
Klingenmeyer Foundation, Ralph and Maggie, The, MI, see 4493
Klingenstein Foundation, Sarah D., The, NY, see 6329
Klingenstein Fund, NY, 6327
Klingenstein Third Generation Foundation, The, NY, 6328
Klingenstein-Martell Foundation, The, NY, 6329
KLM Fund, FL, 2151
Klock and Lucia De L. Klock Kingston Foundation, Jay E., OH, see 7480
Klock Kingston Foundation, OH, 7480
Kloenne Foundation, F. & J., The, OH, 7481
Klosk Fund, Louis & Rose, IL, 3020

Kloss Charitable Trust, John & Ruth, WI, 9863
Klump Family Foundation, Inc., The, GA, 2533
KMJ Family Foundation, The, PA, 8099
KML Foundation, Inc., FL, 2152
Knafel Family Foundation, NY, 6330
Knapp Charitable Foundation, Jules & Gwen, The, FL, 2153
Knapp Educational Fund, Inc., MD, 3895
Knapp Fund, The, NY, 6331
Knappenberger Charitable Trust, Burdette and Kathryn, IL, 3021
Knaster Charitable Trust, Nat R. & Martha M., NY, 6332
Kneisel Foundation, Inc., The, MA, 4157
Knell Foundation, Harvey and Ellen, CA, 712
Knight Charitable Foundation, TN, 8640
Knight Family Foundation, IL, 3022
Knight Family Foundation, LA, 3731
Knight Family Foundation, Robert and Mary, IL, see 3022
Knight Family Foundation, The, OH, 7482
Knight Foundation, Inc., Faith & James, NJ, 5425
Knippenberg Foundation Inc., Charles F. and Ruth J., The, FL, 2154
Knisely Family Foundation, Inc., AZ, 138
Knistrom Foundation, Fanny & Svante, NJ, 5426
Knoll Charitable Foundation, Miriam G., OH, 7483
Knoll Charitable Foundation, The, PA, 8100
Knopf Family Foundation, Inc., FL, 2155
Knopf Foundation, Max & Rika, FL, 2156
Knowles Foundation, The, IL, 3023
Knowlton Foundation, Inc., The, NJ, 5427
Knowlton Foundation, The, MN, 4725
Knox Charitable Foundation, Robert W. Knox, Sr. and Pearl Wallis, TX, 8999
Knox Charity Fund, Inc., GA, 2534
Knox Family Foundation, PA, 8101
Knox Foundation, Robert and Jeanne, CT, 1500
KNU Foundation, Inc., CA, 713
Knudsen Charitable Foundation, Earl, PA, 8102
Knudson Foundation, Barbara Emily, OR, 7785
Knuppe Family Foundation, James and Barbara, The, CA, 714
Ko Family Foundation, The, CA, see 715
Ko Foundation, Shannon & Amy, The, CA, 715
Kobe College Corporation, IL, 3024
Kobor Family Foundation, CA, 716
Koch Family Foundation, IL, 3025
Kochov Foundation, NY, 6333
Kocurek Family Foundation 1986 Trust, Arnold & Irene, NJ, 5428
Koelbel Family Foundation, CO, 1306
Koenig Foundation, Bradford & Lauren, The, CA, 717
Koessler Family Foundation, Inc., Kenneth L. and Katherine G., NY, 6334
Koessler Foundation Inc., Paul J., The, NY, 6335
Koessler Foundation, John W. & Mary M., The, NY, 6336
Koffler Bornstein Family Foundation, The, RI, 8436
Koffler Family Foundation, The, RI, see 8436
Koha Family Foundation, The, MA, 4158
Koha Foundation, Inc., NY, 6337
Kohl Charities, Inc., Herbert H., WI, 9864
Kohl Educational Foundation, Herb, WI, 9865
Kohn and Ruth Kerman Foundation, Leizer, NY, 6338
Kohn Family Foundation Inc., Louis B. II and Josephine, MD, 3896
Kohn Foundation, Inc., Irving, MD, 3897
Kohn Foundation, Zichron Moshe Vesther, NY, 6339
Kolar Charitable Foundation of Buckley Sandler, DC, 1818
Kolber Family Foundation, The, NJ, 5429
Kolitz Foundation Inc., TX, 9000
Konar Foundation, William & Sheila, NY, 6340
Koniag Education Foundation, AK, 89
Konover Family Foundation, Doris & Simon, CT, 1501
Kontos Foundation Inc., Arthur, The, NJ, 5430
Koons Charitable Trust, M.R., NC, 7148
Koplow Charitable Foundation, Florence & Richard, MA, 4159
Koranda Memorial Foundation, Robert August, IL, 3026
Korean American Buddhist Foundation Inc., NJ, 5431
Korell Foundation, Harold and Patricia, The, TX, 9001
Kornblum Foundation, Harvey, MO, 4940

Kornreich Charitable Foundation Ltd., John and Janet, NY, 6341
Kornwasser Charitable Foundation, CA, 718
Kort Foundation, Barbara and Fred, CA, 719
Kortz & Pearl Rae Foundation, Jess, Rose, CO, 1307
Korum for Kids Foundation, WA, 9648
Korver Foundation, Kyle, UT, 9335
Kosch Foundation, Donald & Mary, MI, 4485
Kosch Foundation, Donald F., MI, see 4485
Koski Family Foundation, Inc., The, FL, 2157
Kosloski Foundation, Michael J., NC, 7149
Koss Charitable Foundation, Michael, CA, 720
Koss Family Foundation, Inc., John C., WI, see 9866
Koss Foundation Inc., WI, 9866
Koster Foundation, Daniel J. & Ardith, MI, 4486
Kott Gerontology Institute, IL, 3027
Koury Foundation Inc., Maurice J., The, NC, 7150
Kovensky Family Foundation, Stuart and Nicole, NY, 6342
Kowitz Family Foundation, TX, 9002
Kozicki Memorial Foundation, David, The, NY, 6343
KPB Corporation, NC, 7151
KPW Family Foundation, IL, 3028
KPW Foundation, TX, see 8981
Kramer Charitable Foundation, Milton A. & Charlotte R., OH, 7484
Kramer Family Foundation, TX, 9003
Kramer Foundation, Louise, OH, 7485
Kramer Memorial Fund, Harry, NC, 7152
Krasberg-Mason Foundation, IL, 3029
Krasne Foundation, Abraham, NY, 6344
Krause Family Foundation, The, FL, 2158
Krause Gentle Foundation, IA, 3516
Krauss Charitable Foundation, Jenny H. & Otto F., NC, 7153
Krauss Charitable Foundation, The, NY, 6345
Krehbiel Family Foundation, IL, 3030
Kreisman Family Foundation, David and Susan, FL, 2159
Kreitler Foundation, Inc., CT, 1502
Kreitzberg Family Foundation, CA, 721
Kresa Family Foundation, NJ, 5432
Krieble Foundation, Inc., Vernon K., The, CO, 1308
Krieger Charitable Trust, MA, 4160
Krimendahl II Foundation, H. Frederick, The, NY, see 6346
Krimendahl/Saint-Amand Foundation, The, NY, 6346
Krisbin Foundation, The, MN, 4726
Kriser Foundation Inc., David B., NY, 6347
Krishnan-Shah Family Foundation, Inc., CA, 722
Krist Foundation, The, TX, 9004
Kritser, II Foundation, Anna Belle, The, TX, 9005
Kroh Charitable Trust, CO, 1309
Kroll Family Foundation, Inc., Lynn and Jules, The, NY, 6348
Kroll Memorial Foundation, Inc., Herman, The, NY, see 6348
Kroon Foundation Inc., The, NJ, 5433
Krost Charitable Trust No. 2, Anna Pitzl and J. Fred, NC, 7154
Krouse Foundation, Flora Dale, PA, 8103
Krueck Foundation, Anstiss & Ronald, The, IL, 3031
Krueger Charitable Foundation, OK, 7695
Krumholz Foundation, Inc., Elroy and Terry, NY, 6349
Krumm Charitable Trust, Daniel J. & Ann L., IA, 3517
Krupa Charitable Foundation, John and Margaret A., The, NJ, 5434
Krupp Family Foundation, MA, 4161
KT Charitable Organization, Inc., CA, 723
KT Family Foundation, FL, 2160
Kuehne Foundation, Marna M., WY, 9979
Kuehner Family Foundation, Paul and Patricia, DE, 1695
Kugelman Foundation Inc, The, FL, 2161
Kuhle Family Foundation, AZ, 139
Kuhn Foundation, Michael & Alice, TX, 9006
Kuhn Foundation, MO, 4941
Kuhne Foundation Trust, Charles W., IN, 3409
Kulick Foundation, Inc., Alice L., NY, 6350
Kullgren Family Charitable Trust, OK, 7696
Kupferberg Family Foundation, Jack and Dorothy, NY, 6351
Kupher f/b/o Faxton St. Luke, RI, 8437
Kurian Foundation Trust, The, MA, 4162

Kuriansky Foundation Inc., Louis J., CT, 1503
Kuriansky Foundation, Inc., Louis J., The, FL, 2162
Kurland Family Foundation, Stanford L. & Sheila, The, NY, 6352
Kurr Foundation, The, NJ, 5435
Kurtz Family Foundation, Inc., The, NJ, 5436
Kurtz Family Foundation, PA, 8104
Kuse Family Foundation, James R., The, OR, 7786
Kuse Foundation, James R., The, OR, see 7786
Kutnick Foundation, Inc., Dale Kutnick & Laura Gordon, The, NJ, 5437
Kutz Charitable Trust, Robert, OH, see 7486
Kutz Foundation, Milton and Hattie, DE, 1696
Kutz Foundation, Robert A., OH, 7486
Kvandal Family Foundation, The, CA, see 623
Kwoh and Pong Foundation, CA, 724
Kynett Memorial Foundation, Inc., Edna G., PA, 8105

L & L Educational Foundation, MI, 4487
L & L Foundation, NY, 6353
L & M Charitable Foundation, Inc., The, TX, 9007
L & S Foundation, MD, see 3892
L. And C. Wood Family Foundation, Inc., The, GA, 2535
L. J. Charitable Foundation, NY, 6354
L.B. Research and Education Foundation, The, CA, 725
La Fondation Cuvelier, NY, 6355
La Penta Medical Scholarship Trust, R.D., The, RI, 8438
Lachman Family Foundation Inc., The, NY, 6356
Lacy Foundation, IN, 3410
Lacy Foundation, VA, 9485
Lacy, Jr. Foundation, Constance C. and Linwood A., FL, 2163
Ladane Foundation, The, NC, 7155
Ladd Family Foundation, The, MA, 4163
Ladd Foundation, The, CO, 1310
Ladd Trust, James B., NC, 7156
Ladenburg Foundation, NY, 6357
Lader Foundation, Philip and Linda LeSourd, The, SC, 8531
Laerdal Foundation, Inc., Asmund S., NY, 6358
Lafayette Family Foundation, ME, 3787
Lafayette Life Foundation, Inc., IN, 3411
Laffin Trust, John and Maria, NC, 7157
LaFontaine Foundation, The, NY, see 5873
LaGrange County Community Foundation, Inc., IN, 3412
LaGrassa Family Foundation, Carl and Gloria, The, NJ, 5438
Laguna Beach Community Foundation, CA, 726
Lainoff Family Foundation Inc., NY, 6359
Lake Charles American Press Foundation, LA, 3732
Lake Family Foundation, CA, 727
Lake Placid Education Foundation, NY, 6360
Lakeshore Community Foundation, Inc., WI, 9867
Lakeview Foundation, Inc., The, WI, 9868
Lakonishok Foundation, IL, 3032
Lakshmi Foundation, IL, 3033
Lalor Foundation, Inc., The, MA, 4164
Lamaj Foundation, NY, 6361
Lamando Family Foundation, CT, 1504
Lamar Construction Foundation, MI, 4488
Lamb Foundation Inc., Robert E., PA, 8106
Lamb Foundation, OR, 7787
Lamb Trust A, Grace F., PA, 8107
Lambert Foundation, Darlene & Harry, The, CA, 728
Lambert Foundation, Inc., FL, 2164
Lambert Foundation, Jean Thomas, OH, 7487
Lambert Foundation, Joe and Lenore, MO, 4942
Lambrecht Family Foundation, The, FL, 2165
Lamka Foundation, Mitchell J. And Mary Ellen, IL, 3034
Lamm Foundation, Peter and Deborah, The, MA, 4165
Lamm Foundation, Peter, MA, see 4165
Lamond Family Foundation, CA, 729
Lamoureux Foundation, Inc., John F. & Rita, FL, 2166
Lancaster Family Foundation, IL, 3035
Lance Charitable Foundation, Howard and Christine, FL, A
Lancy Foundation, Alice & Leslie E., PA, 8108
Landau Family Foundation, IL, 3036
Landau Foundation, Louise H., IL, 3037
Landau Foundation, Pinches & Chanie, NY, 6362
Landecker Foundation, Inc., Emily, NH, 5217
Landenberger Family Foundation, PA, 8109

Landers Charitable Trust, Arthur E. and Hilda C., PA, 8110
Landers Foundation, Richard I. and Arline J., OH, 7488
Landon Testamentary Trust, J. C., NC, 7158
Landry's Helping Heart Foundation, NC, 7159
Landwirth Foundation, Inc., Fanny, FL, 2167
Landy Family Foundation, Eugene W. & Gloria, NJ, 5439
Lane Foundation, Jeffrey and Nancy, NY, 6363
Lane Foundation, Minnie and Bernard, The, VA, 9486
Lane Foundation, Winthrop and Frances, MN, 4727
Lane Memorial Foundation, Mills Bee, GA, 2536
Lang Charitable Trust, Rachel Boyce, OH, 7489
Lang Foundation, Fritz, The, LA, 3733
Langdale, Jr. Foundation, Inc., Alice and Noah N., The, GA, 2537
Langdon Barefoot Foundation, Sally, UT, 9336
Lange Family Foundation I, Julian G., TX, 9008
Langer Family Charitable Foundation, MA, 4166
Langner Charitable Trust, PA, 8111
Lanie & Ethel Foundation, The, NY, 6364
Lanier Foundation, Thomas H., The, GA, 2538
Lantana Education Charitable Foundation, TX, 9009
Lanterman Foundation, The, WA, 9649
Lanting Foundation, MI, 4489
Lapan Educational Loan Foundation, Inc., AZ, see 140
Lapan Memorial Sunshine Foundation, Inc., AZ, 140
Lapeer County Community Foundation, MI, 4490
Lapeer County Community Fund, MI, see 4490
LaPorte, Jr. Foundation, Ltd., Joe, TN, see 8599
Laredo Area Community Foundation, TX, 9010
Larch Foundation, The, WV, 9755
Larking Hill Foundation, PA, 8112
LaRoche Family Foundation, TN, 8641
Larsen Family Foundation, E. & B., UT, 9337
Larsen Foundation, John, MN, 4728
Larsen Foundation, Pamela Whitcomb, PA, 8113
Larsen Foundation, The, IL, 3038
Larson Charitable and Testamentary Trust, Harold B., The, NV, 5170
Larson Charitable Trust, Orville H. and Shirley I., IL, 3039
Larson Family Foundation, Inc., NJ, 5440
Larson Family Foundation, W. & J., NY, 6365
Larson Financial Foundation, MO, 4943
Larson Foundation, Reed and Jeanne, WA, 9650
Larson Legacy, The, OR, 7788
Lascaris Scholarship Trust, Michael, IL, 3040
Lash Foundation, CA, 730
Lassalle Fund, Inc., NY, 6366
Lassiter Family Charitable Foundation, The, GA, 2539
Lastinger Family Foundation, Inc., The, FL, 2168
Latkin Charitable Foundation, CA, 731
Lato Family Foundation, Inc., WI, 9869
Latta Charitable Trust, Lucile, IA, 3518
Laub Foundation, The, OH, 7490
Laub Memorial Foundation, Aaron, NY, 6367
Laufer Charitable Foundation, Inc., Wayne L., FL, 2169
Laughlin Foundation, Inc., Henry P. and Marion Page Durkee, Dr. , MD, 3898
Laughlin Memorial, Inc., PA, 8114
Laurance Family Foundation, CA, 732
Lauren Foundation, Bernard & Muriel, The, NY, 6368
Lauzier Scholarship Foundation, Paul, WA, 9651
Lavery Foundation, NJ, 5441
Lavietes Foundation, Inc., Raymond P., CT, 1505
Lavine Family Foundation, Richard and Ruth, CA, 733
Lawrence Charitable Trust, Melampy, The, MA, 4167
Lawrence County Community Foundation, IN, see 3363
Lawrence Foundation, Inc., John S. & Florence G., NY, 6369
Lawrence Foundation, Lind, VA, 9487
Lawrence Foundation, The, CA, 734
Lawry Family Foundation, The, MA, 4168
Lawry Foundation, OH, 7491
Lawson Charitable Trust, Frank W., OH, 7492
Lawson Family Charitable Foundation, FL, 2170
Lawton Foundation, Edward & Thea, MO, 4944
Layden Family Foundation, The, FL, 2171
Layton Foundation, Bernard and Dorothy, NY, 6370
Lazar Charitable Foundation, Herman & Debbie, IL, 3041
Lazarus Charitable Trust, Helen and Charles, The, NJ, see 5442

Lazarus Charitable Trust, The, NJ, 5442
Lazarus Foundation, Gladys and Ralph, The, OH, 7493
Lazarus Foundation, Ralph, OH, see 7493
Lazarus Foundation, Rudi, The, FL, 2172
Lazbridge Foundation, NY, 6371
Lazoff Foundation Inc., Alice E. and Mischa, The, FL, 2173
Lazzara Charitable Foundation, Gasper & Irene, FL, 2174
Lazzara Family Foundation, The, IL, 3042
LBJ Family Foundation, The, TX, 9011
LBJ Nonprofit Corporation, The, TX, see 9011
Lchachomim Charitable Foundation, Bais Vaad, NJ, 5443
LDB Foundation, TN, 8642
Le Foundation, Iris and Junming, FL, 2175
Le Vine Family Foundation, PA, 8115
Lea County Electric Education Foundation, NM, 5620
Lea Foundation, Jane Isakson, The, WA, 9652
Leach Charitable Trust, Elizabeth Ann, OH, 7494
Leakin Trust, Susan D., PA, 8116
Learning by Giving Foundation Inc., MA, 4169
Leary Research Fund, The, PA, 8117
Leatherwood Foundation, MA, 4170
Leavens Foundation, Inc., The, NJ, 5444
Leavitt Foundation, Michael & Jacalyn, The, UT, 9338
Leavitt Foundation, N. R., NJ, 5445
Lebherz Family Foundation, The, CA, 735
Leboeuf Foundation Inc., Andree, VT, 9379
Lebovitz Fund, The, CT, 1506
Lebowitz Foundation, Steven and Deborah, The, CA, 736
Lebus Charitable Trust, Bertha, IL, 3043
Lebus Jr. Charitable Trust, W. Frank, KY, 3671
Led By Love Foundation, CA, see 937
Ledbetter Foundation, Terry and Laurie, The, TX, 9012
Ledgeways Charitable Trust, MA, 4171
Lee Charitable Foundation, John and Mary Jane, MO, 4945
Lee Family Foundation, Inc., The, CT, 1507
Lee Family Foundation, Theodore and Doris, NV, 5171
Lee Foundation Inc., James T., NY, 6372
Lee Foundation, C. & W., MI, 4491
Lee Foundation, CA, 737
Lee Foundation, Inc., Ray M. and Mary Elizabeth, The, GA, 2540
Lee Foundation, The, CA, see 777
Lee-Jackson Educational Foundation, VA, 9488, see 9488
Lee-Jackson Foundation, The, VA, see 9488
Leeds Charitable Foundation, Joseph Stanley, CA, 738
Leestma Family Foundation, IL, 3044
Leeway Foundation, The, PA, 8118
LEF Foundation, CA, 739
Leff Foundation, Inc., Joel and Jeanne, The, NY, see 6827
Legacy - San Jose Aliso Youth Foundation, CA, 740
Legacy Foundation of Tompkins County, NY, 6373
Legacy Foundation, KS, see 3595
Legacy Heritage Fund Limited, NY, 6374
Legacy, A Regional Community Foundation, KS, 3595
Legum Foundation, Inc., MD, 3899
Lehman Charitable Trust, William C. & Mildred K., OH, 7495
Lehman Foundation, Jane A. and Alan G., NY, 6375
Lehman Foundation, John A. Lehman and Alan G., NY, see 6375
Lehman-Stamm Family Fund, The, IL, 3045
Leibowitz Charitable Trust, Louis, FL, 2176
Leibowitz Foundation, Inc., Reuben and Jane, The, NY, 6376
Leibowitz Foundation, Sheldon L. and Pearl R., IL, 3046
Leidy Foundation, Inc., Joan, The, ID, 2678
Leighty Foundation, The, CO, 1311
Leininger Family Foundation, The, CO, 1312
Leiser Foundation, Inc., Josephine S., FL, 2177
Leland Foundation, John & Sandra, The, CA, 741
Lelash Foundation, Inc., Marie Keese, FL, 2178
Lemay Family Foundation, NV, 5172
Lemelson Foundation, Robert, The, CA, 742
Lemle Family Foundation, Laura, NY, 6377
Lemle Family Foundation, Leo & Trude, NY, 6378
Lemle Family Foundation, NY, see 6378

Lemole Family Charitable Trust, The, PA, 8119
Lemon Foundation, James H. & Martha McG., The, DC, see 1819
Lemon Foundation, The, DC, 1819
Lemons Foundation, Brad, CA, 743
Lemons Foundation, Mark C., CA, 744
Lemons Foundation, W. B., CA, see 743
Lenetzach Foundation, Emes V'Shalom, NY, 6379
Lenkin Charitable Foundation, Inc., Thelma and Melvin, The, FL, 2179
Lennox Family Foundation, CA, 745
Lenoir Charitable Trust, Ernestine L., The, AL, 46
Lenox Foundation, The, NY, 6380
Lenz Foundation for American Buddhism, Frederick P., The, CA, 746
Leominster-Croft Foundation, Inc., MD, see 3841
Leonard Family Foundation, The, VA, 9489
Leonard Foundation, Red and Gena, OR, 7789
Leone Foundation, Peter And Judy, PA, 8120
Leonhardt Foundation, Inc., Dorothea L., The, NY, 6381
Leonian Foundation, Phillip and Edith, IL, 3047
Leprino Family Foundation, Mike, The, CO, 1313
Lerer Family Charitable Foundation Inc., The, NY, 6382
Lerner Family Foundation, FL, 2180
Lerner Family Foundation, Inc., NC, 7160
Lerner Foundation, Nathan and Kiyoko, The, IL, 3048
Lerner Foundation, Saul & Eleanor, NY, 6383
Leroe Family Charitable Foundation, RI, 8439
Lesley Family Foundation, Inc., TX, 9013
Lessman Foundation, Andrew, NV, A
Lester Family Foundation, Kenneth A., The, CA, 747
Lester Family Foundation, The, CA, 748
Leupold & Stevens Foundation, OR, 7790
Leuschen Foundation, David M., NY, 6384
Levangie Family Charitable Foundation, MA, 4172
Levee Charitable Trust B - La Vea Trust, Polly A., PA, 8121
Leven Foundation, Myron P., The, MI, 4492
Leventritt Foundation, Inc., Edgar M., NY, 6385
Levin Family Foundation Inc, Charles & Margaret, The, MD, 3900
Levin Family Foundation, Ellen and Alan, DE, 1697
Levin Foundation, Richard and Emily, CA, 749
Levine Charitable Trust, Caroline C., NH, 5218
Levine Family Foundation L'Dor V'Dor, Hyman, CA, 750
Levine Family Foundation, Mildred & Abner, FL, 2181
Levine Foundation, Inc., A. L., The, NJ, 5446
Levine Foundation, Inc., Blanche & A. L., NJ, see 5446
Levine Foundation, Sharon, The, NY, 6386
Levine Key Food Stores Foundation, Inc., Morris, NY, 6387
Levine-Sklut Family Foundation, The, NC, 7161
Levinson Foundation, Elaine and Donald, IL, 3049
Levis Family Foundation, Adolph & Rose, The, PA, 8122
Levitan Family Foundation, WA, 9653
Levitin Family Charitable Trust, The, NY, 6388
Levmar Foundation, Inc., The, VA, 9490
Levy and Gail Rothenberg Family Foundation, John, The, MA, 4173
Levy Charitable Foundation, Inc., Edwin A. and Carolyne, NY, 6389
Levy Charitable Foundation, Meyer, The, TX, 9014
Levy Family Charitable Trust, Shirley & Milton, MA, 4174
Levy Family Foundation Inc., Norman S., The, NY, 6390
Levy Family Foundation, George D. & Karen S., MA, 4175
Levy Family Foundation, Robert M. and Diane V. S., IL, 3050
Levy Foundation, Chas. and Ruth, IL, see 3018
Levy Foundation, Frances and Jack, NY, 6391
Levy Foundation, Gloria & Ken, The, CA, 751
Levy Foundation, Hyman Jebb, CA, 752
Levy Private Foundation, George & Karen, MA, see 4175
Lewan Family Foundation, CO, 1314
Lewin Family Foundation, Inc., Andrew and Marina, NY, 6392
Lewis College Fund, Paul A., TX, 9015
Lewis Family Foundation, Richard H., CO, 1315
Lewis Family Foundation, Robert and Beverly, CA, 753
Lewis Foundation Inc., Jonathan D., FL, 2182
Lewis Foundation Inc., The, NJ, 5447
Lewis Foundation, Mildred Luck, CA, 754
Lewis Foundation, Sydney & Frances, VA, see 9451

Lewis Memorial Fund, Mabelle McLeod, PA, 8123
Lewis Private Foundation, Andrew and Janet Lyman, PA, 8124
Lewis Scott 5, Hannah, PA, 8125
Lewis Trust, Park, PA, 8126
Lewy Family Foundation, The, NY, 6393
Lexington Foundation, The, MS, 4846, see 4825
LFT Pacific Trust Foundation, CA, see 732
Li Foundation, Inc., NY, 6394
Liautaud Family Foundation, The, CA, see 755
Liautaud Foundation, Susan, The, CA, 755
Libby Foundation, Inc., Kenneth & Jane S., The, NY, 6395
Liberman Foundation, Inc., Bertha & Isaac, NY, 6396
Liberty Giving Tree, Inc., MD, 3901
Liberty Hosiery Mills Foundation, NC, see 7096
Liberty Mutual Scholarship Foundation, RI, 8440
Lichner Foundation, John & Anne, IL, 3051
Lichtenstein Foundation Inc., The, NY, 6397
Lichtman Foundation, Marvin and Kay, IL, 3052
Lida Foundation, The, PA, 8127
Liddell Foundation, Robert Clay, OK, 7697
Lieb Foundation, Inc., David L., NY, 6398
Lieberman Foundation, Avi, NY, 6399
Lieberman Foundation, Judith & Lester, The, NJ, 5448
Liebhaber Family Foundation, FL, 2183
Liebowitz Family Foundation, D. A., NY, 6400
Lienemann Charitable Foundation, Inc., NE, 5100
Lienemann Perpetual Charitable Trust, Margaret, PA, 8128
Life's Requite, Inc., FL, 2184
Lifestyle Homes Foundation, NV, 5173
Lifetract Foundation, IL, 3053
LifeWorks Foundation, TN, 8643
Light Charitable Trust, Jack H. & William M., TX, 9016
Light Foundation, Inc., The, NJ, 5449
Lighten Family Foundation, DE, 1698
Lighthouse - A Christian Effort, CA, 756
Lighthouse Foundation, TX, 9017
Lightner Sams Foundation, Inc., Larry, DE, 1699
Ligon-Lamsam Foundation, TX, 9018
Lillehei Family Charitable Foundation, MN, 4729
Lillian Foundation, The, TN, see 8592
Lilly Foundation, Kevin and Lesley, The, TX, 9019
Lin Foundation, Raymond and Joanne, CA, 757
Lincoln Family Foundation, G.R., The, OH, 7496
Lincoln Foundation, Mosby, KS, 3596
Lincoln-Lane Foundation, The, VA, 9491
Lindenbaum Foundation, Inc., The, GA, see 2587
Lindgren Foundation, The, OR, 7791
Lindner Foundation, Carl H. and Edyth B., The, OH, 7497
Lindner Foundation, Carl H., OH, see 7497
Lindon Foundation, Elick and Charlotte, IL, 3054
Lindorf Memorial Foundation, Bruce, UT, 9339
Lindsay Foundation of 1989, Margaret Stewart, MA, 4176
Lingos Family Foundation, John and Sonia, MA, 4177
Link Foundation, The, TX, 9020
Linke Foundation, Gordon F. and Jocelyn B., CT, 1508
Linked Foundation, CA, 758
Linnell Foundation, The, NH, 5219
Linnemann Family Foundation, The, OH, 7498
Linse Bock Foundation, The, MI, 4493
Lintott Foundation, May Liang & James, VA, 9492
Lion's Pride Foundation, NH, 5220
Lipp Family Foundation, The, CA, 759
Lippard Foundation, Charles W. & Gina S., MT, see 5058
Lippard-Clawiter Foundation, MT, 5058
Lipper Family Charitable Foundation, The, NJ, 5450
Lippes Family Charitable Foundation, NY, 6401
Lippincott Foundation, Inc., CT, 1509
Lippitt Foundation, Katherine K., OH, 7499
Lipschitz Family Foundation, C. & Y., NY, 6402
Lipschultz Family Foundation, Marc and Jennifer, NY, 6403
Lipscomb Foundation, Inc., Blanche, GA, 2541
Lipstein Family Foundation, The, PA, 8129
Lipton Foundation, FL, 2185
Lipton Foundation, The, NY, 6404
Lisle Foundation, Lorance, CA, 760
Liss Foundation, Inc., Harold I. & Faye B., NJ, 5451
Lissack Foundation, Michael R., FL, 2186
Lissner Foundation, Inc., Gerda, NY, 6405

Listeman Fund, Marguerite, IL, 3055
Liswhit Foundation, MA, 4178
Littauer Educational Trust, Helen Irwin, TX, 9021
Litterman Family Foundation, The, NY, 6406
Litterman Foundation, Robert & Mary, The, NY, see 6406
Littick Charitable Trust, Arline & Clay, OH, 7500
Little One Foundation, The, NY, 6407
Little Scholarship Loan Fund, Inc., Solon E. & Espie Watts, NC, 7162
Littlefield Memorial Trust, Ida Ballou, RI, 8441
Litton Family Memorial Foundation, Jerry, MO, 4946
Live Oak Foundation, LA, 3734
Live Oak Foundation, NC, 7163
Livengood Charitable Trust, Byrd Fielder, OK, 7698
Living Legacy Foundation, The, CO, 1316
Living Promise Foundation, NV, 5174
Living Rock Foundation, CO, 1317
Living Springs Foundation, MN, 4730
Living Water Foundation, OR, 7792
Livingston Foundation, Inc., Mollie Parnis, FL, 2187
Livingston Memorial Foundation, CA, 761
Livney Foundation, IL, 3056
Lizzadro Family Foundation, Joseph, IL, 3057
LKC Foundation, OH, 7501
Llagas Foundation, CA, 762
LLH/LHM Foundation, RI, 8442
LLL Foundation, CT, 1510
Lloyd Charitable Trust, Robert William, M.D. and June M., WI, 9870
Lloyd Foundation, John M., CA, 763
Lloyd Trust, C. L. and Gladys, TX, 9022
Lloyd Trust, C.L. & Gladys, TX, A
Loats Foundation, Inc., MD, 3902
Locations Foundation, HI, 2638
Locke Memorial Foundation, Owen, CA, 764
Locke Scholarship Trust, Alain, WI, 9871
Lockhard Trust, James H. and Florence D., PA, 8130
Lockhart Eastminster Presby Ch Pgh, PA, 8131
Lockhart Foundation, OK, 7699
Lockridge Charitable Foundation Trust, The, CA, 765
Lockwood Family Foundation, Bill and Jackie, OH, 7502
Loconsolo Foundation, Inc., Victoria, NY, 6408
Lodbell Irreving Charitable Trust, David H., CT, 1511
Lodewick Foundation, Inc., Philip H. and Christine, CT, 1512
Loeb Charitable Trust, Stella & Frederick, OH, 7503
Loeb Family Foundation Inc., AL, 47
Loeb Family Foundation, Richard and Francine, WA, 9654
Loeb Foundation, Inc., Jesse and Rose, The, VA, 9493
Loeb Foundation, OH, 7504
Loehrke Family Charitable Foundation, WI, 9872
Loewenstern Foundation, CA, A
Loewy Family Foundation Inc., NY, 6409
Loftis Foundation, Inc., The, FL, 2188
Loftus Family Foundation, The, DE, 1700
Logan Childrens Home Inc., Henry, WV, 9756
Logan Foundation Inc., John Sublett, MO, 4947
Logan Foundation, The, KS, 3597
Logan Healthcare Foundation, Inc., WV, 9757
Logos Charitable Fund, Inc., IL, 3058
Lohengrin Foundation Inc, IL, 3059
Lohr, Jr. Charitable Foundation, Inc., Walter G., MD, 3903
Lois Walts-Farrell Family Foundation, MI, 4494
Lolmaugh Trust Foundation, OK, see 7700
Lolmaugh Trust Foundation, Robert C. and Mary E., OK, 7700
London Educational Foundation, George and Frances, NC, 7164
Long Cove Foundation, Inc., NY, 6410
Long Foundation for the Arts, Joe and Teresa L., The, TX, 9023
Long Foundation, Inc., D. R., FL, 2189
Long Foundation, Inc., John F., AZ, 141
Long Foundation, Lisa and Sidne, CA, see 1135
Long Foundation, R. A., MO, 4948
Long Foundation, The, TX, 9023
Long Trust, Ralph F. & Pearl A., Dr., RI, 8443
Longbrake Family Foundation, The, WA, 9655
Longer Life Foundation, MO, 4949
Longest Foundation, KY, 3672

Longfield Family Charitable Foundation, RI, 8444
Longhill Charitable Foundation, The, NY, 6411
Longtine Charitable Foundation Trust 2001, MA, 4179
Longview Foundation for Education in World Affairs and International Understanding, Inc., VA, 9494
Looker Foundation, The, CA, 766
Lookout Foundation, Inc., FL, 2190
Looney Foundation, Inc., Martha and Wilton, The, GA, 2542
Loosemore Foundation, Charles W., MI, 4495
Loosemore Foundation, MI, see 4495
Lopatin Family Foundation, The, NY, 6412
Lopez Foundation, Virginia, CA, 767
Lopez Low Foundation, CA, see 767
LoPrete Family Foundation, MI, 4496
Lorber Charitable Fund, NY, 6413
Lorber Foundation, RI, 8445
Lord Charitable Trust, Thomas, PA, 8132
Lorden Charitable Foundation, Inc., IL, A
Lordi Marker Family Foundation, The, MO, 4950
Los Angeles Jewish Fund, The, CA, 768
Los Feliz Foundation, CA, 769
Lose Testamentary Trust, Harry F., TX, 9024
Lost and Foundation, Inc., The, MA, 4180
Lothlorien Foundation, NE, 5101
Lott Foundation, WA, 9656
Loudoun Hospital Trust 3, IL, 3060
Loudoun Hospital Trust f/b/o Eleanor, IL, 3061
Loudoun Memorial Hospital Trust 2, IL, 3062
Louie Family Foundation, Kim and Harold, CA, 770
Louis Foundation, Elizabeth and Jeff, IL, 3063
Louis Foundation, Inc., AZ, 142
Louis Foundation, MN, 4731
Louis III Foundation, John Jeffry, IL, see 3063
Louisiana-Pacific Foundation, TN, 8644
Love Charitable Foundation, John Allan, MO, 4951
Love Conservation Foundation, Edward K., RI, 8446
Love Foundation, Ben and Margaret, IL, see 3064
Love Foundation, C. W. and Dorothy G., SC, 8532
Love Foundation, Jeff B. and Katherine B., IL, 3064
Love Foundation, Tom and Judy, OK, 7701
Lovoi Family Foundation, P. Vincent & Sally S., OK, 7702
Low Book Sales Foundation, UT, 9340
Low Road Foundation, CT, 1513
Lowdon Family Foundation, TX, 9025
Lowe-Marshall Trust, OH, 7505
Lowenbraun Family Foundation, NY, 6414
Lowenstein Brothers Foundation, KS, 3598
Lowenstein Foundation, William P. and Marie R., TN, 8645
Lower Pearl River Valley Foundation, MS, 4847
Lowndes Foundation Inc., Caroline M., The, DE, 1701
Lowry Foundation, Inc., Sumter and Ivilyn, The, FL, see 2191
Lowry Murphey Family Foundation, Inc., The, FL, 2191
LSF Foundation, TX, 9026
LSG Charitable Foundation, The, TX, 9027
LSK Foundation, NY, 6415
Lubert Family Foundation, Inc., The, PA, 8133
Lubin Family Foundation, NY, 6416
Lubo Fund, Inc., NY, 6417
Luce Family Fund, Peter & Betsy, The, CO, see 1227
Lucelia Foundation Inc., The, NY, 6418
Lucky One Foundation, The, NY, 6419
Lucky Star Foundation, NY, 6420
Ludington, Inc., VA, 9495
Ludwick Family Foundation, The, CA, see 1003
Ludwick Foundation, Christopher, PA, 8134
Ludwick Institute, The, PA, see 8134
Luedeking Trust, Otto, OH, 7506
Luehring Foundation, Wesley, IL, 3065
Lufkin Family Foundation, The, NY, 6421
Lufkin Foundation, Dan W., The, NY, see 6421
Lui Foundation, CA, 771
Luke Charitable Foundation, RI, 8447
Lukens Family Foundation, Joe & Kim, The, OH, 7507
Lukis Foundation, MN, 4732
Lund Foundation, Victoria, AZ, 143
Lundgard Foundation, Neils A. & Ruth, OH, 7508
Lundgren Trust, Carolyn C., CA, 772
Lungard Charitable Trust, Niels A. and Ruth, The, OH, 7509
Lupton Family Foundation, T. C., TX, 9028

Lusardi Foundation, Debra E. and Warner C., NV, 5175
Luse Foundation, W. P. & Bulah, TX, 9029
Luster Family Foundation, Inc., CA, see 880
Lustig Family Foundation, CO, 1318
Luther Family Foundation, The, MN, 4733
Lutheran Education Foundation of Minnesota, MN, 4734
Lutheran Home and Hospital Foundation, Inc., MD, 3904
Lutheran Retirement Home of Southern Minnesota Inc., MN, 4735
Lutsey Family Foundation, Inc., WI, 9873
Lutz Foundation, Clarence H. and Anna E., SC, 8533
Luverne Area Community Foundation, MN, 4736
LUX Foundation Inc., WI, 9874
Lux Foundation, Miranda, CA, 773
Lux Foundation, The, NY, 6422
Lyche Family Foundation, Inc., WI, 9875
Lykes Family Foundation, J. M., TX, see 9030
Lykes-Knapp Family Fund, TX, 9030
Lyle Foundation, The, FL, 2192
Lyman Family Foundation, The, CA, 774
Lynam Trust, Hattie A. and Fred C., ME, 3788
Lynch Family Charitable Foundation, The, NH, 5221
Lynch Family Foundation, The, CA, 775
Lynn Foundation, Elizabeth A., MT, 5059
Lynum Trust, Edith H., NC, 7165
Lyon Leukemia Foundation, Robert, The, IL, 3066
Lyons Family Foundation, Inc., CA, 776
Lyu Foundation, Chuan, CA, 777

M & J Family Foundation, MA, 4181
M & J Foundation, NE, see 5088
M & M Area Community Foundation, MI, 4497
M & M Family Foundation, NY, 6423
M Y B Foundation, NY, 6424
M&E Foundation, The, NY, 6425
M&P Family Foundation Inc., PA, 8135
M.C.R. Charitable Foundation, Inc., IN, 3413
M.F.K. Foundation, NY, 6426
M.L.M Charitable Foundation, The, OH, 7510
M/S Family Foundation, NJ, 5452
M66 Foundation Inc., The, NY, 6427
Maak Foundation, IL, 3067
Maas Foundation, Benard L., MI, 4498
Maas Private Foundation, Fred & Mary, SD, 8569
Mabardi Foundation, Georges & Claire, NY, 6428
MacArthur Family Charitable Foundation, NY, 6429
Macauley Foundation, Inc., The, CT, 1514
MacCready Family Foundation, The, CA, 778
MacDonald Charitable Trust, Ruth Jones, TX, 9031
MacDonald Family Charitable Trust, CA, 779
MacDonald Family Foundation, Inc., Bradley T., The, NJ, 5453
MacDonald Family Foundation, Inc., The, NJ, see 5453
MacDonald Foundation, Marquis George, IL, 3068
MacDonald-Peterson Foundation, TX, 9032
Macedonian Call Inc., VA, 9496
Macht Foundation, Inc., Morton and Sophia, MD, 3905
Machuga Foundation Inc., John Victor, The, NJ, 5454
MacInnis Family Foundation, The, CT, 1515
Mack Charitable Trust, John S., PA, 8136
Mack Family Foundation, Inc., Stephen Mack and Kelly, NY, 6430
Mackin Foundation, Inc., KY, 3673
Mackinac Island Community Foundation, MI, 4499
Macks Family Foundation, Inc., Louise D. & Morton J., MD, 3906
Maddox Trust, Web, IL, 3069
Made in Dover Foundation, The, NJ, see 5592
Madonna Foundation, Nicholas and Marion, The, MA, 4182
Madover Family Foundation, Inc., Ian & Arrielle Tepper, NY, 6431
Madrona Foundation, WA, 9657
Mae Foundation, Mary, CA, 780
Magale Foundation, Inc., LA, 3735
Magali Foundation, The, CA, 781
Magaro Family Foundation, Inc., CT, 1516
Magdalen Foundation, WA, 9658
Magee Christian Education Foundation, KY, 3674
Magee Foundation, The, PA, 8137
Magee Trust, George W.P., MA, 4183

Magee-O'Connor Foundation Inc., IN, 3414
Magnus Foundation Inc., James D. and Diane S., GA, 2543
Magowan Family Foundation, Deborah J. & Peter A., CA, 782
Maguire Foundation, Timothy, NY, 6432
MAH Foundation, Inc., FL, 2193
Mahadeva Family Foundation, CT, 1517
Mahan Foundation, Ingrid, The, NJ, 5455
Maher Family Foundation, John F., NY, 6434
Maher Family Foundation, NY, 6433
Maher Foundation, CA, 783
Mahon Foundation, MN, 4737
Mahoney Family Foundation, Joan and Leo, The, MA, 4184
Mahoney Family Foundation, Judith Rauenhorst, MN, 4738
Maibach Foundation, Lorene and Ben, MI, 4500
Maibach Foundation, MI, see 4500
Maidenbaum Foundation, Inc., Esther & Nathan, NY, see 6435
Maidenbaum Foundation, Inc., Iris and Shalom, NY, 6435
MAIHS Foundation, VA, 9497
Main Charitable Trust, Anna, MI, 4501
Majella Foundation, TX, 9033
Majella Society, TX, see 9033
Majestic Realty Foundation, CA, 784
Makana Aloha Foundation, The, HI, 2639
Makepeace Charitable Trust, Isabelle, MA, 4185
Makepeace Family Foundation, Maurice and Anne, The, MA, 4186
Maki Foundation, CO, 1319
Makioka Foundation, NY, 6436
Mako Foundation, IL, 3070
Malachi 3 Foundation, CA, 785
Malachowsky Family Foundation, Chris and Melody, The, CA, 786
Malek Charitable Trust, Irene & Joseph, NE, 5102
Maley-Thawley Family Foundation, The, CA, 787
Mallon Family Foundation, IL, 3071
Malone Family Foundation, AL, 48
Maly-Dykema Family Foundation, John Dykema and Michele, The, MI, 4502
Mamiye Foundation, Inc., The, NJ, 5456
Manat Foundation, MI, 4503
Manchester Family Life Foundation, CA, 788
Manchester Life Foundation, Douglas F., The, CA, see 788
Maness Family Foundation, John R. & Carolyn J., NC, 7166
Mangano Foundation, Frank, OH, 7511
Manger Foundation, B. L., CT, 1518
Mangione Family Foundation Inc., MD, 3907
Mango Tree Foundation, The, PA, 8138
Mangold Family Foundation, Inc., CA, 789
Manitowoc Company Foundation, The, WI, 9876
Mank Foundation, Edward H., MA, 4187
Mankato Citizens Telephone Company Foundation, MN, see 4713
Manley Memorial Fund, F. T. & Anna C., OH, 7512
Mann Center for Education & Family Development, CA, 790
Mann Charitable Foundation, Henry & Belle, The, IL, 3072
Mann Family Foundation, KS, 3599
Mann Family Foundation, The, CT, 1519
Mann Family Foundation, The, RI, 8448
Mann-Paller Foundation, Inc., MD, 3908
Manna International Charitable Foundation, TX, 9034
Manne Family Foundation, The, IL, 3073
Manning Foundation, Inc., James Hilton and Emma Austin, The, NY, 6437
Manocherian Family Foundation, Amir and Rosita, NY, 6438
Manor Charitable Fund, The, NJ, see 5462
Mansfield Foundation, Albert and Anne, IL, 3074
Mansur Foundation, Harl & Evelyn, TX, 9035
Mantzel Foundation, Ernest A., TX, 9036
Manzanita Foundation, The, NY, 6439
Maor Foundation, MO, 4952
Mapes Charitable Trust, NE, 5103
Maple Hill Foundation, PA, 8139

Mapp Foundation, Barbara J., The, TN, 8646
Marafiki Global Aids Ministry, OH, 7513
Maranatha Ministries Foundation, MN, 4739
Marbeh Shalom Foundation, Inc., NY, 6440
Marble Fund Inc., NY, 6441
March Family Foundation, CA, 791
March Family Foundation, MN, 4740
Marchese Family Foundation, CA, 792
Marchese Foundation, Michael J., IL, 3075
Marcil Family Foundation, CA, 793
Marco Family Foundation, Inc., FL, 2194
Marco Family Foundation, Inc., Seymour R., FL, see 2194
Marco Foundation, NY, see 5695
Marcum Foundation, Joseph L. & Sarah S., IL, 3076
Marcus & Millichap Company Foundation, The, CA, 794
Marcus Family Charitable Trust, MA, see 4188
Marcus Family Charitable Trust, WI, 9877
Marcus Family Charitable Trust, William and Cynthia, MA, 4188
Marcus Foundation, Edward and Betty, The, TX, 9037
Marcus Foundation, Inc., Billi, The, GA, 2544
Marcus Trust, Jacob R., OH, 7514
Margoes Foundation, CA, 795
Margolin Foundation, Joseph & Bernice, The, TX, 9038
Margolis Family Foundation, CA, 796
Margolis Foundation for Medical Research, Ben B. and Iris M., AZ, see 144
Margolis Foundation, Ben B. and Iris M., AZ, 144
Margolis Foundation, Inc., Robert, The, CA, 797
Margulf Foundation, CO, 1320
Mariel Foundation, MI, 4504
Marietta College Trust LD Ryan-Main, NC, 7167
Marigold Charitable Trust, MA, 4189
Marine Society of the City of New York, The, NY, 6442
Marine Ventures Foundation, Inc., WY, 9980
Marineau Family Foundation, CA, 798
Marino Charitable Foundation, Roger M. & Michelle S., The, MA, 4190
Marino Family Foundation, Inc., Joseph and Cheryl, NJ, 5457
Marino Family Foundation, Paula and William J., NJ, 5458
Markel Foundation, Steven & Katherine, The, VA, 9498
Marketplace One Foundation, The, AZ, 145
Markey Charitable Fund, John C., NC, 7168
Markey Family Foundation, Inc., NJ, 5459
Markowitz Family Foundation, NJ, 5460
Marks Cancer Foundation, Ellen, IL, 3077
Marks Foundation, Jay & Shirley, TX, 9039
Marks Foundation, Michael J., HI, 2640
Marksbury Family Foundation, Inc., KY, 3675
Marlboro County General Hospital Charity Trust, NC, 7169
Marley Foundation, Inc., Jacob, The, NY, 6443
Marnick Foundation, OH, 7515
Maronda Foundation, The, PA, 8140
Marquette Bank Affordable Housing Foundation, IL, 3078
Marriott Daughters Foundation, MD, 3909
Marron Foundation, Inc., The, NJ, 5461
Mars Foundation, NY, 6444
Marsh Foundation, Edward N. and Margaret G., NC, 7170
Marsh Foundation, Inc., The, NC, 7171
Marshall Family Foundation Inc., The, NY, 6446
Marshall Family Foundation, NY, 6445
Marshall Foundation, Inc., James Harper, The, NY, see 6446
Marshall Foundation, John W. and Jerry E., OK, 7703
Marshall Foundation, Mattie H., GA, 2545
Marshall Trust in Memory of Sanders McDaniel, Harriet McDaniel, FL, 2195
Marshburn Foundation, The, CA, 799
Marshfield Area Community Foundation, WI, 9878
Marsteller Family Foundation, IL, 3079
Marstine Family Foundation, PA, 8141
Martin Charitable Foundation, Steve, CA, 800
Martin Charitable Trust, G. Roxy & Elizabeth C., FL, 2196
Martin Charitable Trust, Willie I., Wanda & W. F., TX, 9040
Martin Family Foundation, Inc., PA, see 8142

Martin Family Foundation, Patrick J., The, FL, 2197
Martin Family Foundation, The, WA, 9660
Martin Family Foundation, WA, 9659
Martin Family Foundation, WI, 9879
Martin Foundation, Della, CA, 801
Martin Foundation, Dolores Furtado, HI, 2641
Martin Foundation, Gilbert J., The, CA, 802
Martin Foundation, John G., The, CT, 1520
Martin Foundation, PA, 8142
Martin Foundation, The, PA, 8143
Martin Guitar Charitable Foundation, PA, 8144
Martin Memorial Foundation, Florence MacFarlane, CA, 803
Martin Memorial Trust, James G., NH, 5222
Martin, Jr. Foundation, Karl & Georgia Martin, Sr., Anna Belle Flynn, Karl & June, OK, 7704
Martini Family Foundation, NY, 6447
Martinsen Foundation, Patricia M. and Robert H., The, CT, 1521
Martischang Foundation, CO, 1321
Martyn Foundation, The, DE, 1702
Mary Anna Foundation Charitable Trust, FL, 2198
Mary's Alabaster Jar Perpetual Charitable Foundation, IL, 3080
Mary's Foundation, IL, 3081
Mary's Fund Foundation, DE, 1703
Mascaro & Sons Charitable Trust, J.P., PA, 8145
Maschler Family Foudation, The, NJ, 5462
Mascoma Savings Bank Foundation, NH, 5223
Mashhoon Family Foundation, CA, 804
Maslin Foundation Inc., Lucille and Paul, The, NY, 6448
Maslow Family Foundation Inc., PA, 8146
Maslowski Charitable Trust, Frank J. and Eleanor A., MN, 4741
Mason Family Foundation Inc, Jack & Adele, CA, 805
Mason Fund, Martha Lockhart, PA, 8147
Mason Memorial Fund, M.L., PA, 8148
Mason Trust, B. A., WI, 9880
Mason-Alleg Health Ed Research, M. L., PA, 8149
Masonic Grand Lodge Charities of Rhode Island, Inc., RI, 8449
Massachusetts Maternity & Foundling Hospital Corporation, MA, 4191
Massengill-DeFriece Foundation, Inc., TN, 8647
Masser Charitable Trust, Frances, KY, 3676
Masserini Charitable Trust, Maurice J., NC, 7172
Massey Family Foundation, OK, 7705
Massey Foundation for Arts and Science, Richard J., IL, 3082
Massie Family Foundation, The, CA, 806
Massie Foundation, Perry and Sandy, AZ, 146
Masson Foundation, The, CA, 807
Massoud Family Foundation, Elizabeth and Joseph, DE, 1704
Master Craftsmen Foundation, KS, 3600
Mastrocola Foundation, David J., The, NY, 6449
MAT Charitable Foundation Inc., The, NY, 6450
Mateer Foundation, Donald D., PA, 8150
Mater Christi Foundation, The, MI, see 4379
Mather Charitable Trust, S. Livingston, The, OH, 7516
Mathews, Jr. Foundation, Constance A. and Harry B., The, MO, 4953
Mathis-Pfohl Foundation, NY, 6451
Matley Foundation, Marshall R., The, NV, 5176
Mattei Casey Foundation Trust, The, NC, see 7173
Mattei Foundation, NC, 7173
Matthes Trust, George C., OH, 7517
Matthews Family Foundation, Ron and Sharon, NC, 7174
Matthews Foundation, Charles C., The, TX, 9041
Mattingly Trust B, Allen S., PA, 8151
Mattison Trust, Inez T., NC, 7175
Mattsson McHale Foundation, The, TX, 9042
Matutina Foundation, Stella, NY, 6452
Maurer Family Foundation, IN, 3415
Maurer Family Foundation, The, NY, 6453
Mauze Charitable Trust, Jean, RI, 8450
Maverick Foundation, VT, see 9380
Maverick Lloyd Foundation, VT, 9380
Mavrogenis Trust Fund, Dennis and Marion, MA, 4192
Maxey Foundation, Leightman, The, OR, 7793
Maxfield Foundation, The, CA, 808
Maxine Hillesland Charitable Foundation, MO, 4954

Maxinmotion, AZ, 147
Maxwell Foundation, Edmund F., WA, 9661
May Family Foundation, Anna, OR, 7794
Mayberg Family Charitable Foundation, FL, 2199
Mayer Charitable Foundation, Arthur, PA, 8152
Mayer Family Foundation, Michael and Sally, The, CA, 809
Mayer Foundation, James & Eva, TX, 9043
Mayfield Foundation Inc, TX, 9044
Maynard Blackard Charitable Trust, AR, A
Mayo Charitable Foundation, Ruth & Allen, OK, see 7710
Mays Foundation, TX, 9045
Maysteel Foundation, Ltd., WI, see 9931
Mazda Foundation (USA), Inc., The, CA, 810
Mazzetta Family Foundation, IL, 3083
Mb Caddyshack Charity Golf, Inc., FL, 2200
MBS Family Foundation Inc., The, NY, 6454
McAllister Charitable Foundation, Hugh A., TX, 9046
McAllister Foundation, TX, see 9046
McCabe Catholic Charities, RI, 8451
McCabe Foundation, Inc., Robert F. & Eleonora W., The, FL, 2201
McCabe Foundation, Roger & Nancy, IL, 3084
McCaddin-McQuirk Foundation, Inc., The, NY, 6455
McCandless Trust, James Frances, PA, 8153
McCann Charitable and Educational Trust, J. Bryan and Norma R., OH, 7518
McCann Trust, Mary Sedate, OH, 7519
Mccarthy Family Foundation, OH, 7520
McCarthy Foundation, Mary A. and John M., The, NY, 6456
McCarthy Memorial Trust Fund, Catherine, RI, 8452
McCarthy/Bush Foundation, IA, 3519
McCarty Family Foundation, TX, 9047
McCarty, Jr. Family Foundation, H. F., MS, 4848
McCauley Charitable Trust, Luther T., IL, 3085
McClanathan Family Foundation, FL, 2202
McClatchey Foundation, Inc., Devereaux F. and Dorothy, The, GA, 2546
McClatchy Company Foundation, CA, 811
McClelland Family Foundation, Pamela T., The, MI, see 4505
McClelland Foundation, MI, 4505
McConnell Foundation, John P., The, NC, 7176
McConnell Foundation, Robert Earll, NJ, 5463
McConnell Trust Fund, Elinor Jones, PA, 8154
McCooey Charitable Foundation, The, NY, 6457
McCormack Family Charitable Foundation, Robert, The, IL, 3086
McCormick Charitable Trust, Margaret Ogilvie, NY, 6458
McCormick Family Foundation, The, NY, 6459
McCormick Scholarship Fund, Robert W., WV, 9758
McCormick Trust f/b/o Jefferson High School, Robert W., WV, 9759
McCormick Trust, Anne, NY, 6460
McCourtney Foundation, P&F, IL, 3087
McCourtney Trust, Flora S., IL, see 3087
McCoy Charitable Foundation, John H. & Tommie E., TX, 9048
McCoy Foundation, Marcus, MN, 4742
McCrane Foundation, Inc., NJ, 5464
McCrea Foundation, IL, 3088
McCreless Foundation for Christian Evangelism, Christian Missions, and Christian Education, Sollie & Lilla, TX, 9049
McCune Family Foundation, IL, 3089
McCune for Charities, Janet W., PA, 8155
McCutchin Charitable Trust, MA, see 4193
McCutchin-Collins Charitable Trust, MA, 4193
McDade Family Foundation, The, NY, 6461
McDaniel Charitable Foundation, TX, 9050
McDaniel Charitable Trust, Neil & Amelia, CA, 812
McDaniel Family Foundation, The, CA, 813
McDavid Foundation, WV, 9760
McDayton Foundation, Ruth, NY, 6462
McDole Charitable Fund, June and Cecil, The, MI, 4506
McDole Foundation, June & Cecil, The, MI, 4507
McDonald Agape Foundation, MI, 4508
McDonald Charitable Trust, Jim and Paula, The, TX, 9051
McDonald Charitable Trust, Louise D., MO, 4955

McDonald Foundation, Malcolm S. & Sonia R., The, FL, 2203

McDonald Manufacturing Company Charitable Foundation, A. Y., IA, 3520

McDonough Foundation, James J. & Jacqualine A., IL, 3090

McDougal Charitable Fund, Nancy A. Lauter & Alfred L., IL, 3091

McDowell Foundation, NJ, 5465

McEnroe Foundation, John and Patty, The, NY, 6463

McEnroe Foundation, John, NY, see 6463

McFadden Charitable Trust, KS, 3601

McGahren Foundation, Marjorie & Richard, FL, 2204

McGehee Family Foundation, TN, 8648

McGinley Foundation, Rita M., PA, 8156

McGrath Family Foundation, CO, 1322

McGrath Investment Foundation, CO, see 1322

McGraw Family Foundation, CA, 814

McGraw Figure Skating Foundation Inc., Lisa, The, NY, 6464

McGraw Wildlife Foundation, Max, IL, 3092

McGuire, Jr. Family Foundation, William B., NC, 7177

McHale Memorial Trust, PA, 8157

McHenry Foundation, The, GA, see 2448

McIninch Foundation, The, NH, 5224

McIntosh Family Foundation, DE, 1705

McKamish Family Foundation, The, PA, 8158

McKay Family Foundation, OR, 7795

McKay Foundation, The, CA, 815

McKee Charitable Family Foundation, Robert H. McKee & M. E., AZ, 148

McKee Charitable Foundation, William J., MA, 4194

McKee Family Foundation, IL, 3093

Mckee First Presbyterian Church, Virginia A., PA, 8159

McKee Foundation, Ella G., IL, 3094

McKee Foundation, Robert E. and Evelyn, TX, 9052

McKee Trust, John, PA, 8160

McKellar Charitable Foundation, Jessie Barker, KY, 3677

McKenzie Foundation, The, CA, 816

McKiernan Family Foundation, DE, 1706

McKinlay Trust, David, WA, 9662

McKinney Charitable Foundation, William V. and Catherine A., PA, 8161

McKinney Charitable Trust, Carl & Alleen, AR, 202

McKinney Family Foundation Inc., IN, 3416

McKinney-Geib Foundation, Inc., GA, 2547

McKnight Charitable Trust Fund, Loretta Haley, GA, 2548

McKnight Foundation, Sumner T., The, MD, 3910

McLane Charitable Trust, Katharine K. and Henry R., CT, 1522

McLaughlin Doty Foundation, The, TX, 9053

McLaughlin Family Foundation, FL, 2205

McLaughlin Family Foundation, IL, 3095

McLaughlin Family Foundation, Inc., James P. & Genevieve M., CT, 1523

McLean Foundation, Mel and Grace, The, CA, 817

McLean Trust, Almena C. & Malcolm P., NC, see 7178

McLean Trust, John Luther & Isabelle Gray, NC, 7178

Mclelland Family Foundation, The, PA, 8162

McLendon Educational Trust, Violet H., NC, 7179

McLennan Foundation, Robert G. and Rebecca A., IL, 3096

McLeod Blue Skye Charitable Foundation, Inc., CT, 1524

McLeod Family Foundation, Steven and Kelly, CA, 818

MCM-Munilla Family Foundation Inc., FL, 2206

McMahon Family Foundation, CA, 819

McMannis Educational Trust Fund, William J. McMannis and A. Haskell, PA, 8163

McManus Charitable Trust, Peter F., PA, 8164

McManus Foundation, Michael F., The, MI, 4509

McMaster Foundation, Inc., Harold & Helen, OH, 7521

McMerty Foundation, Erwin Bellamy, NC, 7180

McMillan, Jr. Foundation Inc., Bruce, TX, 9054

McNally Charitable Foundation, Andrew & Jeanine, IL, 3097

McNally Family Foundation, William F., MI, 4510

McNally Memorial Foundation, William F. and Marjorie A., MI, see 4510

McNamara Family Foundation Inc., FL, 2207

McNamara Family Foundation, Richard F., MN, 4743

McNeice, Jr. Charitable Foundation, John A., MA, 4195

McNeil Scholarship Trust, John N. McNeil and Stella, NC, 7181

McNeill Animal Welfare Fund, George Reed, IL, 3098

McNulty Foundation, James J. and Jamie Thorsen, IL, 3099

McNulty Scholarship Fund, John P., The, NY, 6465

McNutt Memorial Foundation, Inc., V. H., TX, 9055

McPherson Family Foundation, CO, 1323

McQuillan-Criniti Charitable Fdoundation, MA, see 4020

McQuinn Scholarship Foundation, Margaret L., CA, 820

McQuistion Scholarship Trust, Victor and Ethel, FL, 2208

MCS Charitable Foundation, AZ, 149

McSwigan Family Foundation, PA, 8165

McWaters Family Foundation, The, VA, 9499

McWethy Foundation, The, RI, 8453

McWherter Charitable Foundation, Inc., Ned R., TN, 8649

Mead Charitable Foundation, Elisabeth and George, NY, 6466

Mead Foundation, The, OH, 7522

Mead Fund, Nelson, IL, 3100

Meade Foundation, Inc., NY, 6467

Meador Foundation, James A., VA, 9500

Meadowlark Foundation, The, NY, 6468

Meakem Foundation, Inc., Glen and Diane, PA, 8166

Meda Scholarship Fund Trust, MO, 4956

Medarchei Hayehudi Charitable Foundation, NY, 6469

Medical Associates Clinic Foundation of Dubuque, IA, 3521

Medical Education Collaborative, CO, 1324

Mednikow Educational Trust, Isadore, WI, 9881

Meehan Family Foundation, WI, 9882

Meehan Foundation, Inc., Daniel E., WI, see 9882

Meerwarth Family Foundation, PA, 2209

Meetinghouse Foundation, Inc., NY, see 6004

Mehl Family Foundation Inc., George and Deborah, OH, 7523

Mehrberg Schara Family Foundation, Randy and Michele, CO, 1325

Meier Family Foundation, IL, 3101

Meier Foundation, Richard, The, NY, 6470

Meinerz Family Foundation Inc., Archie & Viola, WI, 9883

Meister Family Foundation, CA, 821

Melaleuca Foundation, ID, 2679

Melcher Foundation, Harold and Marilyn, The, MO, 4957

Melin Foundation, Inc., Olga and David, FL, 2210

Mellen Foundation, Inc., The, CT, 1525

Mellon Foundation, Matthew T., PA, 8167

Melrose Foundation, Frances A., CO, 1326

Meltzer Family Foundation, Inc., Alan & Amy, MD, 3911

Melville Trust, D. B., NY, 6471

Melvin Trust, James C., MA, 4196

Melvina Foundation, MA, 4197

Memorial Foundation for the Blind Inc., MA, 4198

Memorial Homes for the Blind, MA, see 4198

Mendel Charitable Trust, Solomon & Sylvia, PA, 8168

Mendell Family Fund Inc., The, NY, 6472

Mendell Fund, Inc., Ira L. & Margaret P., The, NY, see 6472

Mendelson Charitable Foundation Inc., Laurans A. & Arlene H., FL, 2211

Mendenhall Foundation, Trini and O. C., TX, 9056

Menezes Foundation, Inc., The, NY, 6473

Menges Family Foundation, The, NY, 6474

Menken Foundation, Inc., Janis and Alan, NY, 6475

Mental Wellness Foundation, Inc., The, MD, 3912

Mentor Graphics Foundation, OR, 7796

MENTOR Network Charitable Foundation, Inc., The, MA, 4199

Merage Family Foundation, Louise, The, CA, 822

Meraux Charitable Foundation, Inc., Arlene & Joseph, LA, 3736

Merchantz Family Foundation, The, IL, 3102

Mercy Foundation, The, TN, 8650

Mercy International, TX, 9057

Mere Foundation, The, NY, 6476

Meredith Family Foundation, The, NY, 6477

Merfish-Jacobson Foundation, TX, 9058

Mergens Foundation, George W., VT, 9381

Meridian Capital Foundation, NY, 6478

Meridian Charitable Foundation, Inc., MA, see 4075

Meritor, Inc. Trust, MI, 4511

Merkel Family Foundation, OK, 7706

Merkel Foundation, Inc., WI, 9884

Merkle Family Foundation, The, AR, 203

Merkle Foundation, Jess, The, LA, 3737

Merkley Charitable Trust, MI, 4512

Merlo Foundation, Inc., Harry A., OR, 7797

Merlo Foundation, Pearl Welinsky, NY, 6479

Mermelstein Charitable Foundation, Henry and Louise, IL, 3103

Merops Foundation, The, PA, 8169

Merrick Family Foundation, TX, 9059

Merrick Foundation, The, OK, 7707

Merrick Medical Equip. Trust, Bette M., NC, A

Merrill Charitable Trust, P.D., The, ME, 3789

Merrill Family Charitable Foundation Inc., MA, 4200

Merrill Foundation, Catherin V., KS, 3602

Merrill Foundation, Inc., Julia & Gilbert, NY, 6480

Merriman Foundation, DC, 1820

Merrion Family Foundation, DE, 1707

Merritt Memorial Trust, Sam & Bertha, MN, 4744

Mertz Foundation, Inc., Martha, NY, 6481

Mervis Family Foundation, IN, 3417

Merwin Foundation, PA, 8170

Meserve Memorial Fund, Albert & Helen C., NC, 7182

Messer Construction Foundation, OH, 7524

Messick Charitable Trust, Harry and Helena, MO, 4958

Messing Family Charitable Foundation, DE, 1708

Messing, Jr. Charitable Foundation, Roswell, DE, see 1708

Messinger Family Foundation, Inc., NY, 6482

Messler Family Foundation, The, ME, 3790

Metanoia Fund, MA, 4201

Metro Portland New Car Dealers Charitable Foundation, OR, 7798

Metzger-Price Fund, Inc., NY, 6483

Metzner Family Foundation, IL, 3104

Meusel Trust, Lucille, IL, 3105

Mewhinney Foundation, Michael and Linda, The, TX, 9060

Meyer and Hans M. Hirsch Foundation, Inc., Margaret and Leo, The, NY, 6484

Meyer Charitable Trust, Melba Bayers, NC, 7183

Meyer Charitable Trust, Russell A., CA, 823

Meyer Family Foundation Inc., Anthony E., NY, 6485

Meyer Family Foundation, C. Louis, IL, 3106

Meyer Family Foundation, Inc., Margaret A., NY, 6486

Meyer Family Foundation, Robert and Betty, WI, 9885

Meyer Foundation Inc., The, TX, 9061

Meyer Foundation, Kenneth E. & Jane A., MO, 4959

Meyer Foundation, Paul E. & Helen S., NV, 5177

Meyer Foundation, Roslyn Milstein Meyer and Jerome, NY, 6487

Meyer Foundation, Roslyn Milstein, NY, see 6487

Meyer Fund, Milton and Sophie, NC, 7184

Meyer Trust, Dorothy I., WI, 9886

Meyer, Jr. Foundation, Inc., Robert Benson, The, MD, 3913

Meyerhoff Foundation, Inc., Lyn P., The, MD, 3914

Meyers Charitable Family Fund, IL, 3107

Meyerson Family Foundation, Marlene Nathan, TX, 9062

MFA Oil Foundation, MO, 4960

MG Marland Trust f/b/o So Me Health Care, ME, 3791

MGM Charitable/Scholarship Foundation, KY, 3678

MHB Foundation, PA, 8171

MHR Family Foundation Inc, TX, 9063

Michael and Jill Stansky Family Foundation, MA, 4202

Michael Foundation, Herbert I. and Elsa B., OR, 7799

Michaels Family Fund Inc., Roger & Barbara, NY, 6488

Michaud Charitable Trust, Dorothy Phillips, The, CA, 824

Michell Charitable Foundation and Trust, Roy G., MI, 4513

Michelle Foundation Inc., Janice, NY, 6489

Michigan Gateway Community Foundation, MI, 4514

Mick Foundation, The, TN, 8651

Mickelson Charitable Trust, Phil and Amy, CA, 825

Micole Foundation, IL, 3108

Mid-America Foundation, MO, see 4892

Mid-States Aluminum Foundation, Inc., WI, 9887

MIDA Foundation, FL, 2212

Midcontinent Foundation, MN, *see* 4745
Midcontinent Media Foundation, MN, 4745
Middlekauff Foundation, Mildred and Rolland, KS, 3603
Middlesex Savings Charitable Foundation, Inc., MA, 4203
Midlands Community Foundation, NE, 5104
Midvale Foundation, The, DE, 1709
Mielcarek Family Foundation Inc., WI, 9888
Mifsud Family Foundation, The, OH, 7525
Milano Foundation, Inc., NJ, 5466
Milano Foundation, Mark and Jessie, DE, 1710
Milbank Memorial Fund, NY, 6490
Mile Hi Foods Foundation, Inc., CO, *see* 1362
Milford Educational Foundation, NH, 5225
Military Women In Need Foundation, CA, 826
Mill Foundation, The, CA, 827
Mill Spring Foundation, The, PA, 8172
Millard Charitable Trust, Adah K., IL, 3109
Millard Foundation, Leon J., IL, 3110
Miller Charitable Foundation, Howard E. & Nell E., PA, 8173
Miller Charitable Foundation, Lou and Connie, OK, 7708
Miller Charitable Fund, Harvey R. & Ruth, The, NY, 6491
Miller Charitable Trust, CA, A
Miller Charitable Trust, James E. & Lila G., OR, 7800
Miller Charitable Trust, Morgan & Marjorie L., NY, 6492
Miller Family Charitable Trust, The, FL, 2213
Miller Family Endowment, Inc., The, NJ, 5467
Miller Family Foundation Fund, Mark and Maureen, IL, 3111
Miller Family Foundation, Barbara and Fred, The, CA, 828
Miller Family Foundation, Inc., IL, 3112
Miller Family Foundation, J. & T., CA, 829
Miller Family Foundation, Jerome B., OK, 7709
Miller Family Foundation, The, CA, 830
Miller Foundation, Arjay R. & Frances F., CA, 831
Miller Foundation, Arnold M. & Sydell L., OH, *see* 7526
Miller Foundation, B. W. and Barbara, The, NC, 7185
Miller Foundation, Carole and Mike, The, CA, 832
Miller Foundation, Charles Lawrence Keith and Clara, NY, 6493
Miller Foundation, Doug & Martha, The, MN, 4746
Miller Foundation, G. Willard, CA, 833
Miller Foundation, K. R. & Laura, TX, 9064
Miller Foundation, K. R., TX, *see* 9064
Miller Foundation, Katherine P. & Jerry L., MI, *see* 4463
Miller Foundation, Mike, SD, 8570
Miller Foundation, Steve J., NJ, 5468
Miller Foundation, Sydell & Arnold, The, OH, 7526
Miller Living Legacy Foundation, Monty, TX, 9065
Miller Memorial Foundation, Richard G., TX, 9066
Miller Memorial Trust, George Lee, OH, 7527
Miller Scholarship Fund, Morey and Helen McCarthy, RI, 8454
Miller Trust, Emerson R., OH, 7528
Miller, Cooper & Co., Ltd. Charitable Foundation, IL, 3113
Miller, Jr. Arts Foundation, Juanita & Henry S., IL, 3114
Miller-Mellor Association, KS, 3604
Miller-Sweezy Charitable Trust, NY, 6494
Miller-Wehrle Family Foundation, The, DC, 1821
Milliken Foundation, Gerrish H., DE, 1711
Milliron Foundation, The, OH, 7529
Millner Family Foundation, Gordon H. & Karen M., IL, 3115
Mills Charitable Foundation, Steven A. and Marianne M., NY, 6495
Mills Charitable Trust, J. Clawson, PA, 8174
Mills Foundation, David W., The, CA, 834
Mills Fund, Frances Goll, MI, 4515
Millsaps Charitable Trust, The, FL, 2214
Millstreet Foundation, Inc., The, CA, 835
Milstein Foundation, Edward L., NY, 6496
Milton Charitable Trust Foundation, Robert P. & Clara I., IN, 3418
Milton Foundation, Inc., Arthur and Phyllis, The, NY, 6497
Mimi Foundation, The, ME, 3792
Mimi Fund Inc., DC, 1822
Minami Community Foundation, HI, 2642
Mindel Foundation, The, NY, 6498
Miner Family Charitable Trust, IL, 3116

Mineral Area Osteopathic Foundation, MO, 4961
Minerva Foundation, NJ, 5469
Mingenback Foundation Inc., Julia J., KS, 3605
Miniaci Foundation, Inc., Alfred & Rose, The, FL, 2215
Minio Family Foundation Inc., The, NJ, 5470
Minkoff Family Foundation, Leon & Marianne, MD, 3915
Minnis Trust, Jewel, AR, 204
Minor Family Foundation, Edward and Lucy, The, IL, 3117
Minor Family Foundation, Inc., Edward & Lucy R., IL, *see* 3117
Minor Foundation, Berkeley Minor and Susan F., The, WV, 9761
Minow Family Foundation, IL, 3118
Minsky Charitable Trust, Leonard and Renee, ME, 3793
Minto Foundation, Inc., FL, 2216
Mintz Foundation, Jean and Saul A., LA, 3738
Mintz Foundation, Neil And Anna, CA, 836
Miracle Makers Foundation, Inc., The, GA, 2549
Mirak Foundation, John, MA, 4204
Mirapaul Foundation, IL, 3119
Mischer Foundation, Walter M. Mischer & Mary A., The, TX, 9067
Mississippi Sports Medicine Foundation, MS, 4849
Mistler Family Foundation, The, KS, 3606
Mitchell Charitable Foundation, Mayer and Arlene, AL, 49
Mitchell Charitable Trust, Yvonne H., CA, 837
Mitchell Family Foundation, Bernard & Marjorie, IL, 3120
Mitchell Family Foundation, Edward D. and Anna, CA, 838
Mitchell Foundation Inc., Stephen D., SC, 8534
Mitchell Foundation, Bruce, ID, 2680
Mitchell Foundation, Everett W. & Marion E., MA, 4205
Mitchell Foundation, Samuel & Rose, NY, 6499
Mitchell Industries Foundation, AL, 50
Mitchell, Jr. Trust, John, MD, 3916
Mitchell, Silberberg & Knupp Foundation, CA, 839
Mithoff Family Charitable Foundation, Inc., TX, 9068
Mithoff Family Charitable Foundation, Richard Warren, TX, *see* 9068
Mitrani Foundation, Jacques H. & Selma, NJ, 5471
Mitrani Foundation, Jacques H., NJ, *see* 5471
Mitte Foundation, Roy F. and Joann Cole, TX, 9069
Mittlemann Family Foundation, The, NY, 6500
Mix Memorial Fund, Inc., Charles L., GA, 2550
Mixon III, Foundation, A. Malachi & Barbara W., OH, 7530
Mize Charitable Trust, K Josh & Wynona Owen, NC, 7186
Mize Family Foundation, WA, 9663
MLE Foundation Inc., CT, 1526
MMK Foundation, DE, 1712
MNS Foundation, NJ, 5472
Moach Charitable Foundation, NY, 6501
Modglin Family Foundation, The, CA, 840
Modine Manufacturing Company Foundation, Inc., The, WI, 9889
Mody Foundation, VA, 9501
Moeller Foundation, Joe and Mary, AZ, 150
Moffat Family Charitable Foundation, Robert Y., PA, 8175
Moffett Family Foundation, James R., The, LA, 3739
Moggio Foundation, Anna-Maria, The, PA, 8176
Mohr Charitable Trust, Jacques, MA, 4206
Mohr Charitable Trust, Jean Whyte and Frank T., The, IL, 3121
Mojo Foundation, MI, 4516
Molder Family Foundation, The, RI, 8455
Moley Family Foundation, The, CA, 841
Mollath Charitable Trust 3, Louise, CA, 842
Molnar Foundation Corp., William and Marie, MI, 4517
Monaghan Family Foundation, Richard A. & Helene M., The, NY, 6502
Monarch Fund, DC, 1823
Mondavi Foundation, Isabel and Michael, The, CA, 843
Monday Foundation, Inc., Gene & Florence, TN, 8652
Monderer Family Foundation, Inc., NY, *see* 6503
Monderer Foundation, Inc., NY, 6503
Moneta Group Charitable Foundation, MO, 4962
Money-Arenz Foundation, Inc., CA, 844
Moniker Foundation, The, CO, 1327
Monroe Fund Inc., IL, 3122

Montan Charitable Trust, William Edwin, LA, 3740
Montana Good Works Foundation, MT, *see* 5057
Montana Mental Health Trust, MT, 5060
Montauk Foundation, OH, 7531
Monteleone Family Foundation, LA, 3741
Montgomery County Community Foundation, TX, 9070
Montgomery Foundation II Inc., GA, 2551
Montgomery, M.D., Memorial Scholarship Trust, Hazel, TX, 9071
Moon Scholarship Foundation, Jack, NC, 7187
Mooney Charitable Trust, WA, A
Moonwalk Fund, Silva Watson, CA, 845
Moore Charitable Foundation, Marjorie, RI, 8456
Moore Charitable Trust, Clement C. Moore II and Elizabeth W. Y., The, MD, 3917
Moore Family Foundation, IL, 3123
Moore Foundation, Ardon and Iris, TX, 9072
Moore Foundation, Earle K. and Katherine F., NY, 6504
Moore Foundation, Inc., Martha G., FL, 2217
Moore Foundation, J. Leonard & Dorothy B., NC, 7188
Moore Foundation, James D. & Cathryn M., OK, 7710
Moore Foundation, O. L., The, HI, 2643
Moore Foundation, P. M., PA, 8177
Mooty Family Foundation, Melvin R. and Sally R., MN, 4747
Moraine Foundation, The, WA, 9664
Moran Foundation, The, NV, 5178
Morbeck Community Foundation Inc., Frank A., ID, 2681
More Family Foundation, Penelope Straus, CA, *see* 1088
Morelock Family Foundation, OH, *see* 7472
Moreton Foundation, Robert D. and Alma, The, IL, 3124
Moretz Foundation Trust, Inc., O. Leonard, NC, 7189
Morey Family Foundation, The, OR, 7801
Morgado Charitable Trust, Robert & Mary Lou, The, NY, 6505
Morgan Charitable Foundation, Albert Morgan and Leona A., KS, 3607
Morgan Charitable Foundation, James and Rebecca, The, CA, 846
Morgan Charitable Residual Trust, W. & E., MO, 4963
Morgan Creek Foundation, NC, 7190
Morgan Family Foundation, Eleanor & Howard, The, PA, 8178
Morgan Family Foundation, Inc., CA, 847
Morgenstern Foundation, Morris, CA, 848
Moriarty Charitable Foundation, Inc., Edmond N. & Virginia H., NJ, 5473
Morin Charitable Trust, Louis, NY, 6506
Morisey Trust Account, John and Frances, NC, 7191
Moritz Foundation, The, NC, 7192
Morley Brothers Foundation, MI, *see* 4518
Morley Family Foundation, John C. and Sally S., OH, 7532
Morley Foundation, MI, 4518
Morning Foundation, The, MN, 4748
Morningside Foundation, WA, 9665
Morningstar Family Foundation, The, MA, 4207
Morningstar Foundation, The, FL, 2218
Morrell Charitable Trust, Flora F., NY, 6507
Morris Charitable Foundation, W. Newton, GA, 2552
Morris Community Foundation, IL, 3125, *see* 3125
Morris Family Foundation Corp., R. A., FL, 2219
Morris Family Foundation, Inc., The, GA, 2553
Morris Family Foundation, John & Cherie, FL, 2220
Morris Family Foundation, KY, 3679
Morris Family Foundation, OR, 7802
Morris Foundation, Inc., AR, 205
Morris Foundation, Inc., Michael A., The, GA, *see* 2553
Morris Foundation, Inc., Norman M., NY, 6508
Morris Foundation, Inc., Vera & Walter, AR, *see* 205
Morrison Charitable Trust, Cary Jay, FL, 2221
Morrison Foundation, Dorothy M., KS, 3608
Morrison Foundation, Inc., Glenn W. & Hazelle Paxson, FL, 2222
Morrison Foundation, Inc., Harry W., ID, 2682
Morrison Foundation, Robert Haywood, NC, 7193
Morrison Trust, TX, 9073
Morrow Charitable Foundation, Joseph J. and Claire, CT, 1527
Morrow Family Foundation, Paul and Katherine, TX, 9074
Morse Charitable Trust, David & Mildred, The, NY, 6509

Morse Family Foundation, CO, 1328
Morse Family Foundation, Stacey C. & Robert R., The, NY, 6510
Morse Foundation, Alfred L. & Annette S., MA, 4208
Morse Foundation, Richard P. & Claire W., MA, 4209
Morse Foundation, The, MA, 4210
Mortenson Family Foundation, WI, 9890
Morton Community Foundation, IL, 3126
Morton Family Foundation, IL, 3127
Mosbacher Foundation, Inc., TX, 9075
Moseley Foundation, Christopher L., NC, 7194
Moser Family Foundation, Inc., MD, 3918
Mosi Foundation, PA, 8179
Moskowitz 1999 Family Foundation, Henry & Rose, The, NY, 6511
Moskowitz Family Foundation, CA, 849
Moss Charitable Trust, Finis M., MO, 4964
Moss Foundation, Harry S., TX, 9076
Mosser Memorial Trust, NC, 7195
Mosser Trust, Robert K., NC, see 7195
Mossy, Jr. Foundation, Jane P. and Wiley L., The, TX, 9077
Mother Tried Foundation, AZ, see 124
Mothershead Foundation, The, IN, 3419
Mouat Charitable Trust, IL, 3128
Moulton Christmas Poor Fund, Judge C. F., MO, 4965
Mound Properties Inc., WI, 9891
Mount Dora Community Trust, FL, 2223
Mount Olive Pickle Company Foundation, NC, 7196
Mount Saint Clare Education Charitable Trust, IA, 3522
Mount Washington Charitable Foundation, Inc., MA, 4211
Mountain Meadows Foundation, Inc., MA, 4212
Mower Foundation, Leslie DeeAnn, The, UT, 9341
Moye Trust, Thomas, FL, 2224
Moyer Trust, W. Melvin & Mary L., PA, 8180
Mozel Charitable Trust, NY, 6512
Mpala Wildlife Foundation, Inc., MD, 3919
MRA Foundation, NY, 6513
MSG Charitable Foundation Trust, NY, 6514
MST Foundation, The, TX, 9078
MTB Charitable Foundation Ltd., NJ, 5474
MTC Foundation, Inc., IA, see 3528
Muccia Family Fund, The, FL, 2225
Muchnic Foundation, KS, 3609
Muckel Foundation, John and Linda, CA, 850
Mudd Charitable Foundation, Dennis and Pamela, CA, 851
Mudge Foundation, PA, 8181
Muglia Family Foundation, Laura Ellen & Robert, The, WA, 9666
Muirfield Foundation, PA, 8182
Mukaiyama-Rice Foundation, The, PA, 8183
Mukti Fund, FL, 2226
Mulberry Foundation, Inc., The, MA, 4213
Mule Family Foundation, NY, 6515
Mulhollem Cravens Foundation, The, KY, 3680
Mullan Foundation, Inc., Thomas F. and Clementine L., The, MD, 3920
Mullen Charitable Foundation, Boyd and Evelyn, NJ, 5475
Mullen Family Foundation, The, IL, 3129
Mullen Family Foundation, The, PA, 8184, see 8184
Mullen Foundation, J. K., CO, 1329
Mullen Foundation, Williams, VA, 9502
Muller Charitable Foundation, Inc., Marisa, FL, see 2234
Mulligan Charitable Trust, Mary S., RI, 8457
Mulroy Family Foundation, NY, 6516
Mulvaney Family Foundation, RI, 8458
Mulvaney Foundation, John L., DE, 1713
Mulzer Foundation, Edgar and Roberta, IN, 3420
Mulzer Foundation, Inc., The, IN, see 3420
Muma Family Foundation, Inc., FL, see 2227
Muma Family Foundation, Inc., Pamela and Leslie, FL, 2227
Mummert Trust, Austin James, TX, 9079
Mungenast Foundation, Inc., David and Barbara, The, MO, 4966
Mungenast Foundation, Inc., The, MO, see 4966
Munroe Foundation, Richard C., FL, 2228
Munson Family Foundation, The, CA, 852
Munson Foundation, W. B., IL, 3130
Munushian Charitable Trust, Jack, CA, 853

Murad Family Foundation, CA, 854
Murdock Foundation, The, MI, 4519
Murnane Family Foundation, The, IL, 3131
Murphey Foundation, Inc., John and Helen, AZ, 151
Murphy Charitable Foundation, Cecile Higginson, MA, 4214
Murphy Company Foundation, G. C., PA, 8185
Murphy Education Program, Inc., AR, 206
Murphy Educational Foundation, 1997 John & Mary, MA, 4215
Murphy Foundation, M. W., AR, 207
Murphy Foundation, Michael E., IL, 3132
Murphy Residuary Trust, T. R., OH, 7533
Murray Foundation, Harry and Virginia, WI, 9892
Murray Foundation, WA, 9667
Murray, Jr. Foundation, James B. and Bruce R., The, VA, see 9515
Murry Family Foundation, E. E., KY, 3681
Murthy Foundation, Inc., The, MD, see 3921
Murthynayak Foundation, Inc., The, MD, 3921
Muscatine Health Support Foundation, IA, 3523
Muse Educational Foundation, The, TX, 9080
Music and Dance Foundation, Inc., IL, see 3150
Muskin Family Foundation, CA, 855
Musson Charitable Foundation, R. C. and Katharine M., The, OH, 7534
Mustard Seed Foundation, MD, 3922
Mutual Charitable Foundation Inc., IN, see 3421
Mutual Fire Foundation, Inc., The, PA, 8186
MutualBank Charitable Foundation Inc., IN, 3421
MutualOne Charitable Foundation, MA, 4216
MW Charitable Foundation, The, NY, 6517
Myerberg Family Foundation, Inc., Alvin & Louise, MD, 3923
Myers Foundation, Louis S. & Mary, The, OH, 7535
Myers Foundation, Mike A., TX, 9081
Myers Memorial Foundation, H. Herbert, NJ, 5476
Myers-Ti-Caro Foundation, Inc., NC, see 7097
Myfifident Foundation, GA, 2554
Mylan Charitable Foundation, The, PA, 8187
Myra Foundation, ND, 7297
MZL 40 Foundation, NY, 6518

N. Prince Trust No. 1, RI, 8459
N.E.W. Relief Fund, Inc., The, TN, see 8654
N.H. Corporation, MO, 4967
N.H. Foundation, TX, 9082
Nabholz Charitable Foundation, AR, 208
Nabholz Charitable Trust, Robert D. & Barbara, AR, 209
Nabit Foundation Inc., The, MD, 3924
Nabors Charitable Foundation, TX, 9083
Nabors to Neighbors Foundation Inc., The, GA, 2555
Nachtsheim Family Foundation, CA, 856
Nagel Foundation, Edward M., CA, 857
NAID Foundation, MA, 4217
Naito Foundation, Samuel T. & Mary K., OR, 7803
Nalith, Inc., FL, 2229
Nalle Trust, Eleanor R., NC, 7197
Nalley Charitable Trust, SC, 8535
Namaste Foundation Inc., The, IN, 3422
Namaste Foundation, KY, 3682
Nance Family Foundation, Inc., MT, 5061
Nanney Foundation, Charles & Irene, NC, 7198
Napier Foundation, James H., The, AZ, 152
Napier Foundation, The, AZ, see 152
Narens Family Foundation, Judith & Edward, MI, 4520
Narragansett Number One Foundation, ME, 3794
Nartel Family Foundation, MI, 4521
Nartel Foundation, Werner and Ruth, MI, see 4521
Nasaw Family Foundation, CA, 858
Nash Charitable Foundation, Chester Edwin & Mary, KS, 3610
Nash Foundation, Steve, AK, 90
Nason Foundation, Inc., Alex G., CT, 1528
Nassimi Family Foundation, Inc., NY, 6519
Nathan Foundation, Inc., The, PA, 8188
Nation Foundation, TX, A
National Black McDonalds Franchisee Foundation, AZ, 153
National Endowment for Financial Education, CO, 1330
National Literacy Program Fund, CA, see 560
National Mah Jongg League Foundation, Inc., NY, 6520

National Psychiatric Endowment Fund, Inc., MD, see 3898
Naumes Family Foundation, Joe & Frances, OR, 7804
Navarro County Educational Foundation, TX, 9084
Navarro County Health Services Foundation, TX, 9085
Navesink Foundation, The, NJ, 5477
Nayak Foundation Charitable Trust, IL, 3133
Nazarian Foundation, Inc., Levon & Claudia, NJ, 5478
NB Foundation, Inc., CA, see 318
NCI Lending a Hand, IL, 3134
Neag Charitable Foundation, Ray and Lynn Wood, PA, 8189
Neal Martin Christensen Foundation, PA, 8190
Near Family Foundation, James B., The, SC, 8536
Nebraska Community Foundation, NE, 5105
Neeb Family Foundation, The, MO, 4968
Needham Foundation, Robert Sidney, NC, 7199
Neel Charitable Trust, Bell B., IL, 3135
Neenah Foundry Foundation, Inc., WI, see 9779
Nehemiah Foundation Inc., TN, 8653
Neighborhood Partners Fund Inc., MA, 4218
Neiman Charitable Foundation, Velma A., MO, 4969
Neiman Foundation, Inc., M. & H., NY, 6521
Nelco Foundation Inc., NY, 6522
Nell Newman Foundation, Inc., The, CA, 859
Nelson and John Atwater Family Foundation, Diana, MN, 4749
Nelson Family Charitable Foundation, FL, 2230
Nelson Family Foundation, C. and M., CA, 860
Nelson Family Foundation, Donna and Dave, DE, 1714
Nelson Family Foundation, John and Judith, MA, 4219
Nelson Family Foundation, Karl H. & Wealtha H., NE, 5106
Nelson Foundation, Clara Freshour, TX, 9086
Nelson Foundation, Kipp, The, ID, 2683
Nelson Foundation, Ltd., Frances L., WI, 9893
Nelson Foundation, The, IA, 3524
Nelson Foundation, Vivien A., CA, 861
Nelson Scholarship Fund, Victor & Mary D., WI, 9894
Neporent Family Foundation, NY, 6523
Nesh Charitable Trust, Florence, PA, 8191
Nessel Foundation Inc., Irwin and Dorothy, The, CT, 1529
Nessel Foundation, Inc., Irwin and Dorothy, CT, see 1529
Nets Foundation, Inc., The, NY, 6524
Netter Foundation, Alice & Fred, NY, see 6525
Netter Foundation, Inc., The, NY, 6525
Nettleton Foundation, George H., KS, 3611
Nettleton Home, George H., KS, see 3611
Neu Foundation of California, The, CA, 862
Neuber Charitable Trust, Pryor E. & Arlene R., PA, 8192
Neuhoff Private Foundation Inc., Marjorie A., GA, 2556
Neuman Family Foundation, CO, 1331
Neuman Foundation, Inc., I. & B., NY, 6526
Nevas Family Foundation, Inc., Leo & Libby, CT, see 1530
Nevas Family Foundation, Inc., Leo, CT, 1530
New Beginning Resources, Inc., TX, 9087
New Charitable Foundation, TN, 8654
New City Foundation, DE, 1715
New Covenant Foundation, Inc., DE, 1716
New Directions Foundation, IL, 3136
New England Biolabs Foundation, MA, 4220
New Horizon Foundation, IL, 3137
New Jerusalem Foundation, The, CA, 863
New Life Foundation, Inc., The, LA, 3742
New Mavericks Foundation, The, TX, see 8795
New Opportunities Foundation, Inc., CA, 864
New Priorities Foundation, CA, 865
New Tamarind Foundation, Inc., NY, 6527
New Visions Foundation, IL, 3138
Newburyport Five Cents Savings Charitable Foundation Inc., MA, 4221
Newburyport Society for the Relief of Aged Women, Inc., MA, 4222
Newcastle Foundation Trust, NY, 6528
Newcomb-Hargraves Foundation, The, NY, 6529
Newday U.S.A. Foundation, Inc., MD, 3925
Newman Assistance Fund Inc., Jerome A. and Estelle R., NY, 6530

Newman Charitable Foundation, Lizbeth & Frank, The, NY, 6531
Newman Family Foundation, Inc., Carol & Melvin, The, NY, 6532
Newman Family Foundation, Inc., Morris & Ida, The, NY, see 6532
Newman Family Foundation, Inc., NY, 6533
Newman Family Foundation, L. M., NV, 5179
Newman Foundation, Amy Klette, NY, 6534
Newpol Foundation, Inc., CT, 1531
Newton Scholarship Fund, Horace & Letitia, OH, 7536
Newtown Savings Bank Foundation Inc., CT, 1532
NFM Charitable Trust, FL, see 2213
Niblack Foundation, The, CT, 1533
Niblick Family Foundation, Daniel M., IN, 3423
Nicholas Foundation, Joseph G., FL, see 2092
Nicholl Family Foundation, Inc., The, MD, 3926
Nichols Charity Fund, F.C. & C.W., MA, 4223
Nichols Company Charitable Trust, MO, 4970
Nichols Foundation, Albert and Tricia, The, CA, see 405
Nicholson Family Foundation, The, CA, 866
Nickerson Family Foundation, Anne & Scott, WY, 9981
Nickless Memorial Foundation, Allen E. & Marie A., MI, 4522
Nickoll Family Foundation, Inc., CA, 867
Nickum Foundation, IL, 3139
Niemiec Family Fund, The, NY, 6535
Niessen, Jr. Charitable Trust, Leo, NC, 7200
Night Heron Foundation, DE, 1717
Night Owl Foundation, IL, 3140
Nikolaus Family Foundation, PA, 8193
Nima Taghavi Foundation, The, CA, 868
Nirenberg Family Charitable Foundation, Inc., CT, see 1534
Nirenberg Foundation, Inc., CT, 1534
Nirvana Manana Institute, NM, 5621
Nislar Foundation, James, TX, 9088
Nissim Charitable Trust, FL, 2231
Nitzavim Trust, NJ, 5479
Nivison Family Foundation, The, NC, 7201
Nixon Fund, Alban B. and Edna B., RI, 8460
NLT Foundation, Inc., OH, 7537
NM Morris Family Foundation, NY, 6536
NMI Foundation, NM, see 5621
No Frills Foundation, The, MO, 4971
No Plain Jane Foundation, MD, 3927
Noah Foundation, The, NH, 5226
Noah's Family Foundation, AZ, see 167
Nobel Foundation, Inc., Fred I. and Gilda, The, FL, 2232
Noble Family Foundation, Inc., Constance A. and George L., MA, 4224
Noble Foundation, Terrance and Bette, FL, 2233
Noecker Family Foundation, Carson and Rosemary, The, IN, 3424
Nok Charitable Organization, Inc., NY, 6537
NOK Foundation, Inc., NY, see 6537
Noland Foundation, Nanette, The, LA, 3743
Nolen-Bradley Family Fund, NY, see 6971
Noll Foundation, John H., PA, 8194
Nommontu Foundation, Inc., The, FL, 2234
Nonami Foundation, Inc., The, GA, 2557
Nonna's Garden, NY, 6538
Noonan Family Foundation, Thomas E., The, GA, 2558
Noonan Memorial Research Fund, Deborah Munroe, MA, 4225
Noonan Trust, Frank M., MA, see 4225
Norbell Foundation, The, PA, 8195
Nord Foundation, The, CO, 1332
Nordstrom/Seifert Family Foundation, WA, 9668
Noreen Charitable Trust, Roger & Violet, MN, 4750
Noreen Family Charitable Trust, MN, see 4750
Norford Charitable Foundation, Edward R., The, PA, 8196
Norgaard Charitable Trust, Eric and Joan, The, IL, 3141
Norjana Charitable Foundation, The, FL, 2235
Norquist Charitable Foundation, Laura Lee Pattillo, The, AL, 51
Norris Charitable Trust, Hartzell, OH, 7538
North America LAPB Inc., NY, 6539
North American Communities Foundation, TX, 9089
North American Philips Foundation, MA, see 4243
North Carolina Foam Foundation, NC, see 7202

North Carolina Foam Industries/Barnhardt Foundation, NC, 7202
North Foundation, Francis S., IL, 3142
North Ridge Foundation, The, CA, 869
Northeast Educational Services, Inc., MA, see 4327
Northern California DX Foundation, The, CA, 870
Northern Chautauqua Community Foundation, Inc., NY, 6540
Northern Kenya Fund, MD, 3928
Northern Piedmont Community Foundation, VA, 9503
Northern Star Foundation, MN, 4751
Northwest Fund for the Environment, WA, 9669
Norweb Foundation, OH, 7539
Norwegian Children's Home Association of New York, Inc., The, NY, 6541
Norwich Foundation, Greater, The, NY, 6542
Noster Foundation, Agnus, NY, 6543
Noster Foundation, MI, 4523
Not Yet Foundation, WA, 9670
Novack Family Foundation, MA, 4226
Novak Charitable Trust, Maury and Lillian, CA, 871
Novick Family Foundation, The, IL, 3143
Nowiczewski Foundation, The, TX, 9090
Nowotny Foundation, Bill, The, TX, 9091
Noyes Bo 7 Charities, Grace, RI, 8461
NSB Foundation Inc., VT, 9382
Nth Dimensions Education Solutions, Inc., IL, 3144
Nugent Foundation, Elizabeth Ruddick, IN, 3425
Nuhn Charitable Trust, Jane W., NY, 6544
Number Ten Foundation, Inc., MD, 3929
Nuncio Foundation, Roger, TX, 9092
Nureyev Dance Foundation, Rudolf, IL, 3145
Nusbaum Family Foundation, MI, 4524
Nussbaum Family Foundation, Bernard and Toby, The, NY, see 6545
Nussbaum Family Foundation, Bernard W., The, NY, 6545
Nuzzo Family Foundation, The, FL, 2236
NYBDC Charitable Foundation Inc., NY, 6546
Nye Scholarship Trust, Grace Swift Nye & Alfred Gibbs, MA, 4227
Nygren Charitable Foundation, William & Sara, IL, see 3146
Nygren Foundation, Bill, IL, 3146
Nypro Foundation, Inc., The, MA, 4228
Nysether Family Foundation, Eldon & Shirley, The, WA, see 9671
Nysether Family Foundation, The, WA, 9671

O' Brate Foundation, KS, 3612
O'Brien Foundation, Alice M., MN, 4753
O'Brien-Veba Scholarship Trust, PA, 8197
O'C Family Foundation, IL, 3148
O'Connor Foundation, Kathryn, The, TX, 9093
O'Connor Foundation, William F., The, IL, 3149
O'Donnell Family Charitable Foundation, WA, 9672
O'Donnell Family Charitable Trust, L. K., OH, 7540
O'Donnell Foundation, The, CA, 874
O'Donnell Green Music and Dance Foundation, The, IL, 3150
O'Donovan Family Foundation, MI, 4525
O'Grady Foundation, NY, 6551
O'Halloran Family Foundation, The, RI, 8462
O'Hare Family Private Foundation, The, TX, 9095
O'Herron Family Foundation, The, CT, 1536
O'Herron Foundation, Jonathan & Shirley, CT, see 1536
O'Keefe Family Foundation, The, MA, 4229
O'Meara Foundation, Inc., The, CT, 1537
O'Neal Educational Foundation, Pat, The, TX, 9097
O'Neal Foundation, Inc., The, NJ, 5481
O'Neil Family Foundation, Inc., The, MD, 3930
O'Neil Foundation, Casey Albert T., The, MN, 4755
O'Neil Foundation, Cyril F. & Marie E., NY, 6557
O'Neill Brothers Foundation, The, OH, 7542
O'Reilly Char Trust, O'Reilly H. and H., PA, 8200
O'Reilly Family Foundation, Charlie & Mary Beth, The, MO, 4974
O'Reilly Family Foundation, Larry & Nancy, MO, 4975
O'Rielly Family Foundation, AZ, 154
O'Rourke Family Charitable Trust, William James And Winifred Joyce, Dr. , MN, 4757
O'Rourke-Schof Family Foundation, IN, 3429

O'Shaughnessy-Hurst Memorial Foundation, The, VA, 9505
O'Shea Foundation, The, CA, 892
O'Sullivan Children Foundation, Inc., The, NY, 6565
Oak Grove Foundation, MN, 4752
Oak Lodge Foundation, CO, 1333
Oak Tree Philanthropic Foundation, The, CA, 872
Oakleaf Foundation, MN, A
Oakley Foundation, Inc., Hollie & Anna, IN, 3426
Oberlander Family Foundation Inc., Penn, CT, 1535
Oberoi Family Foundation, The, NY, 6547
Obertate Trust, George P., MO, 4972
Oberweiler Foundation, IL, 3147
Ochsman Foundation, Inc., The, VA, 9504
October Saints Foundation, CA, 873
Ocular Physiology Research and Education Foundation, Inc., WI, 9895
Oden Foundation, Sydnor & Olga, The, TX, 9094
Odyssey Foundation, UT, 9342
Odyssey Partners Foundation, Inc., NY, 6548
Oestreicher Foundation, Inc., Sylvan and Ann, NY, 6549
Offensend Family Foundation, The, NY, 6550
Offield Center for Billfish Studies, The, CA, 875
Ogden College Foundation, KY, 3683
Ohana Foundation, Thomas, CA, 876
Ohel Harav Yehoshua Boruch Foundation, Inc., NY, 6552
Ohel Rachel Ve Leah Foundation, Inc., NY, 6553
Ohio County Community Foundation, Inc., IN, 3427
Ohio Valley Foundation, The, OH, 7541
Ohlhausen Foundation, George and Sarah, IL, 3151
Ohno Foundation, Ignatius, WA, 9673
Ohren Foundation, Steven, CA, 877
OJM Family Foundation, OH, see 7525
Okinaga Foundation, The, CO, 1334
Oklahoma Surgical Hospital Foundation, Inc., OK, 7711
Okner Foundation, The, IL, see 3152
Okner-Robbins Foundation, The, IL, 3152
Okray Foundation Inc., Edward J., WI, 9896
Okray Foundation, Inc., Edward J. Okray & Lucille S., WI, see 9896
Olander Family Foundation, Inc., CA, 878
Olcott Family Foundation, Inc., The, NH, 5227
Old Bug Light Charitable Foundation, The, ME, 3795
Old York Foundation, NY, 6554
Olds Foundation, AR, 210
Olds Foundation, R. E., MI, 4526
Olemberg Family Foundation Inc., FL, 2237
Olemberg Private Foundation, Isaac Olemberg and Nieves, The, FL, see 2237
Olender Foundation, Jack H. & Lovell R., DC, 1824
Olin Charitable Trust, Evelyn B., IL, 3153
Olitsky Family Foundation Inc, The, PA, 8198
Oliver Charitable Corporation, AR, 211
Oliver Foundation, Inc., The, FL, 2238
Oliver Memorial Trust Foundation, IN, 3428
Olliff Foundation, Matred Carlton, FL, 2239
Olofson Foundation, Tom W. and Jeanne H., KS, 3613
Olsen 1990 Private Foundation, C., FL, 2240
Olsen Family Foundation, David and Roberta, The, RI, 8463
Olsen Foundation, a New Jersey Nonprofit Corporation, The, NJ, 5480
Olson Charitable Foundation Inc., Jennie H., WI, 9897
Olson Charitable Foundation Inc., Ronald L., WI, 9898
Olson Charitable Foundation, Leland J. & Dorothy H., NE, 5107
Olson Family Foundation Trust, CA, 879
Olson Family Foundation, Delmar and Audria M., The, IL, 3154
Olum Charitable Foundation, Vivian and Paul, NY, 6555
Omega Foundation, The, NV, see 5147
Omohundro Educational Trust, TX, see 9196
On Shore Foundation, CA, 880
Onan Family Foundation, MN, 4754
One in Heart Foundation, TX, 9096
One Million Years Foundation, Inc., NY, 6556
One Step Forward Education Foundation, Inc., MA, 4230
OneBeacon Charitable Trust, MA, 4231
Onehope Foundation, CA, 881
Onequest Foundation, MI, 4527
OneSight Research Foundation, TX, 9098
Ong Family Foundation, The, NY, 6558

Ontario Children's Foundation, NY, 6559
Ontario Children's Home, NY, see 6559
Ontario Community Foundation, CA, 882
Onyx and Breezy Foundation, NJ, 5482
Open Door Foundation, MN, 4756
Open Stewardship Foundation, CA, 883
Opera House Fund, Inc., KY, 3684
Operation Merry Christmas, LA, 3744
Opie Charitable Trust No 1, John T., TX, 9099
Oppenheim Foundation, PA, 8199
Oppenheimer Family Foundation, The, IL, 3155
Oppenheimer Foundation, Edward and Helen, The, TX, 9100
Oppenheimer Foundation, H. Tony & Marti, MO, 4973
Oppenheimer Foundation, Jesse H. and Susan R., The, TX, 9101
Optivest Foundation, CA, 884
Opus Foundation, CA, 885
Orant Charities, TX, 9102
Orchard House Foundation-A Nevada Non Profit Corporation, The, NV, 5180
Oreffice Foundation, Paul F. and Franca G., MI, 4528
Oreg Foundation, CO, 1335
Oreggia Family Foundation, CA, 886
Orfalea Family Foundation, The, CA, 887
Oriska Foundation, The, TX, 9103
Oristaglio Family Foundation, MA, 4232
Oristano Foundation, The, FL, 2241
Orkin Foundation, Barbara and Sanford H., GA, 2559
Orkin Foundation, Inc., William B., GA, 2560
Orkin Foundation, Sanford H., GA, see 2559
Ormsby Hill Trust, WA, 9674
Ornest Family Foundation, CA, 888
Orphan and Cancer Care for India Foundation, CA, 889
Orphans Home of Seattle, Inc., WA, see 9662
Orr Charitable Trust, Waldon H. and Adele, TX, 9104
Orr Family Foundation, Robert O. and AnnaMae, OH, 7543
Orsini Charitable Foundation, Inc., IL, 3156
Orthodox Vision Foundation, CA, 890
OSA Foundation, The, IL, 3157
Osberg Family Trust, The, TX, 9105
Osborn and Lois J. Roork Charitable Trust, Ralph and Hazel, CA, 891
Osborne Charitable Foundation Trust, M. N., AR, 212
Oscar Cohrs Trust, OH, 7544
Osceola Foundation, Inc., NY, 6560
Oschwald Trust, Anna, NC, 7203
Osi Group Foundation, The, IL, 3158
OSilas Foundation, MN, 4758
Ostberg Foundation, Inc., The, NJ, 5483
Osteopathic Heritage Foundations, OH, 7545
Oster Family Foundation, Inc., NJ, 5484
Ostgrodd Foundation, Inc., The, NY, 6561
Ostreicher Family Foundation, Harry & Helen, NY, 6562
Ostreicher Family Foundation, Marvin & Susan, NY, 6563
Ostreicher Foundation, Chaim and Dvora, NY, 6564
Otenasek Charitable Foundation, Inc., Anne Lindsey, The, MD, 3931
OTT Foundation Inc., The, IN, 3430
Ottenheimer Brothers Foundation, AR, 213
Otto Family Foundation, CA, 893
Our Lady of Perpetual Help Trust, IL, 3159
Outer Banks Community Foundation, Inc., NC, 7204
Outrageous Foundation, Inc., The, CA, 894
Overall Family Foundation, CA, 895
Overlake Foundation Inc., TX, 9106
Overlock Family Foundation, NY, see 5962
Overstreet Foundation, FL, 2242
Overton Family Foundation, The, VA, 9506
Owasso Outreach Foundation, OK, 7712
Owen Charitable Foundation, FL, 2243
Owen Foundation, The, IL, 3160
Owen Foundation, The, NE, 5108
Owusu Foudnation, George and Angelina, TX, 9107
Oxford Foundation, Inc., IN, see 3459
Oxford Hills Scholarship Foundation, ME, 3796
Oxford Industries Foundation, Inc., GA, 2561
Oxford League, Inc., The, NH, 5228
OZ Foundation, CA, 896

P & B Foundation, NC, 7205

P Twenty-One Foundation, The, TX, 9108
P.M. Foundation, Inc., FL, 2244
Pacific Foundation, Inc., The, NJ, 5485
Pacific Western Foundation, CA, 897
Pacifica Foundation, RI, 8464
Pack Family Foundation, Jay and Ruth, TX, 9109
Packer Foundation Inc., Horace B., PA, 8201
Packin Family Foundation, Inc., NY, 6566
Paddison Charitable Foundation, Roger B. & Evelyn W., TN, see 8655
Paddison Charitable Foundation, TN, 8655
Paddock Foundation, Jerome & Mildred, NC, 7206
PADI Foundation, CA, 898
Padnos Foundation, Louis and Helen, MI, 4529
Page Family Foundation, VA, 9507
Page Foundation, George B., CA, 899
Page, Sr. Family Charitable Foundation, Lawrence C., MI, see 4530
Page, Sr. Family Charitable Foundation, Rose and Lawrence C., MI, 4530
Pagoumian Family Charitable Trust, The, FL, 2245
Paige Foundation, Inc., Evelyn P., NY, see 6048
Paiken Foundation, The, NY, 6567
Paine Charitable Trust, RI, 8465
Paine Family Foundation, MI, 4531
Pajwell Foundation, NY, 6568
Pak Foundation, Charles Y.C., TX, 9110
PAL Foundation, The, TX, 9111
Palermo Scholarship, Peter J., RI, 8466
Palisades Educational Foundation, Inc., The, NY, 6569
Palisano Foundation, Vincent and Harriet, The, NY, 6570
Palm Foundation, The, NY, 6571
Palmedo Family Foundation Inc., The, ID, 2684
Palmer Foundation, Francis Asbury, The, NY, 6572
Palmer Foundation, Inc., Pat, NY, 6573
Palmer Foundation, TX, 9112
Palmer Home, Inc., DE, 1718
Palmer Walbridge Foundation, NJ, 5486
Palo Alto Community Fund, The, CA, 900
Palo Alto Endowment, CA, see 900
Palo Hills Foundation, CA, 901
Panama Street Fund, The, PA, 8202
Paneth Family Charitable Trust, The, NY, 6574
Pangborn Trust, John C., PA, 8203
Pangburn Foundation, The, IL, 3161
Panoram Foundation Inc., CT, 1538
Pantirer Family Foundation, Inc., Larry and Nancy, The, NJ, 5487
Panwy Foundation, Inc., CT, 1539
Paoloian Family Foundation Inc., CT, 1540
Papadopoulos Charitable Foundation, C. N. and Maria, TX, 9113
Papitto Foundation, The, RI, 8467
Pappajohn Scholarship Foundation, John & Mary, IA, 3525
Pappas Foundation, Inc., MI, 4532
Papper Foundation Inc., Patricia M. & Emanuel M., FL, 2246
Paragano Family Foundation, Inc., NJ, 5488
Pardee Cancer Treatment Fund of Bay County, MI, 4533
Pardee Cancer Treatment Fund of Gratiot County, MI, 4534
Pardee Estate Trust, Sarah N., RI, 8468
Pardee Foundation, J. Douglas and Marian R., The, CA, 902
Paris Legacy Foundation Inc, TX, 9114
Paris Regional Health Care Endowment Fund, Inc., TX, see 9114
Parish Foundation, Richard Laurence, The, FL, 2247
Park Bank Foundation, Inc., WI, 9899
Park Charitable Trust, NY, 6575
Park Foundation, NY, see 6575
Parke Foundation, Jim and Shirley, NY, 6576
Parker Family Foundation, IL, 3162
Parker Foundation Inc., Eleanor Hutchinson, CA, 903
Parker Trust, George R., IL, 3163
Parker/United Foundation, R. H., OR, 7805
Parks Family Foundation, TX, 9115
Parlin Trust, Albert N., MA, 4233
Parlin Trust, Robinson S., WV, 9762
Parman Foundation, Robert A., OK, 7713

Parnassus Foundation, NJ, 5489
Parr Family Foundation, Inc., Gary W., The, NY, 6577
Parrish Foundation, Charles Maxfield & Gloria F., UT, 9343
Parsemus Foundation, CA, 904
Parshelsky Foundation, Moses L., NY, 6578
Parsons Foundation, John B., The, MD, 3932
Parsons-Salisbury Home for the Aged Trust, John B., MD, see 3932
Partners in Advertising Education, Inc., FL, 2248
Partnership Foundation, The, TX, 9116
Partridge Foundation, TX, 9117
Parvin Foundation, Albert, The, CA, 905
Pasarow Foundation, Robert J. & Claire, CA, 906
Pascal International Inc., FL, 2249
Pasquerilla Foundation, Frank J. & Sylvia T., PA, 8204
Passion Support, Inc., TX, see 8950
Pasternak Family Foundation, NJ, 5490
Patagonia Sur Foundation, The, MA, 4234
Patel Family Foundation, Inc., Kamlaben and Raojibhai, NJ, 5491
Patel Foundation Inc., Vallavbhai and Savitaben, NJ, 5492
Patel Foundation, Dinesh and Kalpana, UT, 9344
Patel Foundation, Sujal and Meera, WA, 9675
Paternotte Family Foundation, Inc., The, MD, 3933
Paterson Childrens' Foundation, NJ, 5493
Pathy Family Foundation, Inc., O. L., DC, 1825
Patricelli Family Foundation, Robert & Margaret, The, CT, 1541
Patrick Family Foundation, Inc., GA, 2562
Patrick Foundation, Inc., Jonathan S., NJ, see 5494
Patrick Foundation, Inc., Joseph A., NJ, 5494
Patrick Foundation, William R., NE, 5109
Patrina Foundation, NY, 6579
Pattee Foundation, Inc., The, TN, 8656
Patterson Charitable Fund, W. I., PA, 8205
Patterson Family Foundation Inc., DE, 1719
Patterson Foundation Inc., TX, 9118
Patterson Foundation, Alicia, DC, 1826
Patterson Foundation, Elizabeth R. and William J., The, CA, 907
Patterson Foundation, George & Rita, PA, 8206
Patterson Foundation, The, FL, 2250
Patterson Jr. Charitable Foundation Trust, H. S. & C. G., FL, 2251
Patterson Trust, James K., IL, 3164
Pattillo Family Foundation, Inc., Dan and Anne, The, GA, see 2563
Pattillo Family Foundation, The, GA, 2563
Patton Charitable Trust, Paul, TX, 9119
Paul Family Foundation, Andrew M., NY, 6580
Paul Foundation, Inc., Peter T., CA, 908
Pauley Foundation, Edwin W., The, CA, 909
Paulina Foundation, Anna, MI, 4535
Paulos Foundation, The, TX, 9120
Paulus Family Foundation, WA, 9676
Pautsch Family Foundation, The, MN, 4759
Pawlowski Family Foundation, The, IL, 3165
Pax Christi Foundation, MN, 4760
Paxton Charitable Trust, Alice A., NY, 6581
Payless Shoesource Foundation, KS, 3614
Payne Family Foundation, CA, 910
Payne-Stewart Foundation, Bee, MO, 4976
Payson Foundation, Joan Whitney and Charles Shipman, NJ, 5495
PBSJ Foundation, Inc., The, FL, see 1856
Peace Foundation, IA, 3526
Peace Shalom Foundation, MN, 4761
Peachtree House Foundation, VA, 9508
Peacock Trust, A. R., RI, 8469
Peak Street Foundation, MI, 4536
Peale Foundation, Inc., NY, 6582
Pearce Educational Foundation, Jack & Katherine, TX, 9121
Pearce Foundation, Inc., Dr. M. Lee, The, FL, 2252
Pearl Foundation, The, MO, 4977
Pearle Foundation Charitable Trust, FL, 2253
Pearle Vision Foundation, Inc., TX, see 9098
Pearlman Family Foundation, TX, 9122
Pearlstein Family Foundation, CA, 911
Pearlstone Foundation, Inc., Esther S., The, MD, see 3934

Pearlstone Fund, Inc., The, MD, 3934
Pearsall Family Foundation Inc., Richard L. & Marion K., PA, 8207
Pearson Testamentary Charitable Remainder Unitrust, Arthur H., ND, 7298
Pechet Foundation, MA, 4235
Pechter Foundation, The, GA, 2564
Peckham Family Foundation, NY, 6583
Peculiar Charitable Foundation, MO, 4978
Pedigree Adoption Drive Foundation, The, TN, see 8657
Pedigree Foundation, The, TN, 8657
Pedrozzi Scholarship Foundation, Mario, CA, 912
Peek Family Foundation, Inc., The, NY, 6584
Peel Foundation, Glenn W., OK, 7714
Peeler Family Foundation, Inc., Clifford A. and Lillian C., NC, 7207
Peery/Cauthen Charitable Trust, SC, see 8537
Peery/Cauthen Foundation, The, SC, 8537
Peet Foundation, H.O., DC, 1827
Pegasus Foundation, The, MA, 4236
Pegler Family Foundation, NE, 5110
Pei-Ling Charitable Trust, AL, 52
Peine Charitable Foundation for Manhattan Fund, TX, 9123
Pels International Foundation for Theater, Laura, The, NY, 6585
Pelz Family Foundation, WI, 9900
Pendergast-Weyer Foundation, MO, 4979
Pendleton Memorial Fund, William L. & Ruth L., OR, 7806
Penland Foundation, TX, 9124
Penn National Gaming Foundation, PA, 8208
Penney Family Fund, CA, 913
Pennies From Heaven Foundation, Inc., GA, 2565
Penrose & R. Ernest Mahaffey Charitable Foundation, Sheila A., IL, 3166
Pensmore Foundation, VA, 9509
Peoples Bancorp Foundation Inc., OH, 7546
Peoples Federal Savings Bank Charitable Foundation, MA, 4237
Pepper Family Foundation, IL, 3167
Pepper Foundation Inc., Robert S. & Star, The, NJ, 5496
Perelman Foundation, Jennie, PA, 8209
Perelman Judaica Foundation, Raymond & Ruth, PA, 8210
Perenin Foundation, Rose, CA, 914
Performing Arts Foundation, NY, 6586
Pergo Foundation, The, CA, 915
Perkin Perpetual Charitable Trust, Sylvia, NC, 7208
PerkinElmer Foundation, MA, 4238
Perkins Family Foundation, James I., TX, 9125
Perkins Foundation, B. F. & Rose H., WY, 9982
Perkins Foundation, Edwin E., IL, 3168
Perkins Foundation, Kitty M., NE, 5111
Perkins Hunter Foundation, IL, 3169
Perkins Trust, Mary L., RI, 8470
Perlin Family Foundation, VA, 9510
Perlman Family Foundation, The, NY, 6587
Perlmutter Foundation Inc., Laura & Isaac, The, FL, 2254
Perlow Family Foundation, PA, 8211
Permanent Endowment Fund for Martha's Vineyard, MA, 4239
Perna Foundation for Hope, Inc., The, CT, see 1542
Perna-Rose Foundation for Hope, Inc., The, CT, 1542
Perper Foundation, William S., The, NY, 6588
Perpetual Benevolent Fund, RI, 8471
Perricone Family Charitable Trust, The, NJ, 5497
Perricone Family Foundation, CA, 916
Perry Family Trust, IL, 3170
Perry Foundation, Edward Lee and Slocumb Hollis, The, MA, 4240
Perryman Family Foundation, FL, 2255
Persian Heritage Foundation, NY, 6589
Peslar Foundation, Karen & Drew, The, MI, 4537
Peszynski Foundation, The, CA, 917
Peter Foundation, Leslie, The, NY, 6590
Peters Charitable Trust, Edward V. & Jessie L., OH, 7547
Peters Family Foundation, Inc., Gary, FL, 2256
Peters Foundation, Corp., Herman & Katherine, The, IL, 3171
Peters Foundation, R. D. & Linda, IL, 3172

Peters Memorial Fund I, Frank Reed & Margaret Jane, MA, 4241
Peters Research Foundation, Harvey W., SD, 8571
Petersburg Hospital, Inc., VA, 9511
Petersen Foundation Inc., Hugh E. & Marjorie S., DE, 1720
Petersen Foundation, John M. and Gertrude E., PA, 8212
Petersen Foundation, Marguerite, The, NV, 5181
Peterson Charitable Foundation, CA, 918
Peterson Charitable Foundation, Folke H., FL, 2257
Peterson Charitable Foundation, Inc., John & Carolyn, WI, 9901
Peterson Family Foundation, Arnold and Margaret, The, CA, 919
Peterson Family Foundation, Gregor G., NV, 5182
Peterson Foundation, Bob & Ginny, SD, 8572
Peterson Foundation, David B., NY, 6591
Peterson Foundation, Holly, NY, 6592
Peterson Foundation, Inc., Dion, NV, see 5182
Peterson Foundation, James S., NY, 6593
Peterson Foundation, Michael A., NY, 6594
Petra Foundation, The, AL, 53
Petrick Foundation, David C. and Ellen R., IL, 3173
Petrocelli Foundation, Attilio & Beverly, NY, 6595
Petrovich Family Foundation, IL, 3174
Petrucci Family Foundation, Inc., NJ, 5498
Pettit Family Charitable Foundation, MD, 3935
Pettus-Crowe Foundation Inc., DC, 1828
Pettway Foundation, Jane L., TN, 8658
Petty Family Foundation, Lydia & Rob, NY, 6596
Petty Foundation, Scott, The, TX, 9126
Petunia Foundation, The, CO, 1336
Petunia Foundation, WA, A
Pevehouse Family Foundation Inc., TX, 9127
Peyton Family Foundation, The, FL, 2258
Pfeffer Foundation, The, TN, 8659
Pfeiffer Foundation, Inc., Ralph A. Pfeiffer and Jane C., The, NY, 6597
Pfister Foundation, M. & I., CA, 920
Pfundt Foundation, PA, 8213
PG & E/PSEA Emergency Assistance Fund, CA, 921
Phaedrus Foundation, NY, 6598
Phalarope Foundation, NY, 6599
Phantom Foundation, MI, 4538
Pharmore Drugs Charitable Foundation, The, IL, 3175
Phase Foundation, The, MD, 3936
Pheasant Hill Foundation, Inc., NJ, 5499
Phelps Charitable Foundation, Richard J., MA, 4242
Phelps Family Foundation, CA, 922
Phelps Foundation, Wilson W., CA, 923
Phifer, Jr. Memorial Foundation, Reese, AL, 54
Philada Home Fund, The, OH, 7548
Philanthropic Foundation of Cape Coral, Inc., FL, see 1917
Philips Electronics North American Foundation, MA, 4243
Philips Industries Foundation, CO, see 1368
Phillips Charitable Foundation, Amy, CA, 924
Phillips Foundation, Charles, NY, 6600
Phillips Foundation, Dr. P., The, FL, 2260
Phillips Foundation, Inc., A. P., FL, 2259
Phillips Foundation, MS, 4850
Phillips Trust, Louise B., RI, 8472
Phipps Foundation Agency, Charles H., WI, 9902
Phipps Foundation, William H., WI, 9903
Phoenix Charitable Foundation, The, TX, 9128
PHP Foundation, Inc., IN, 3431
Phuong Foundation, Ha, The, NY, 6601
Physicians Aid Association, CA, 925
Physicians Mutual Insurance Company Foundation, NE, 5112
Piassick Family Foundation, AL, 55
Picerne Charitable Trust, The, AZ, see 155
Picerne Family Charitable Foundation, The, AZ, 155
Picerne Foundation, Kenneth A., CA, 926
Pickford Foundation, Mary, CA, 927
Pickle Charitable Foundation, James W., The, TN, 8660
Pickman Foundation Inc., NY, 6602
Picotte Family Foundation Trust, NY, 6603
Piedmont Charitable Foundation, Inc., GA, 2566
Piedmont Triad Charitable Foundation, Inc., NC, 7209

Pierce Family Foundation, Richard H. and Scottie, AZ, 156
Pierce Foundation, Hargrove, The, NY, 6604
Pierce Trust, Thomas S., MA, 4244
Pierson Family Foundation, Inc., NJ, 5500
Pierson Foundation, Earl W. and Hazel C., TX, 9129
Pierson Foundation, James and Nancy, NJ, see 5500
Pigott Scholarship Foundation, Paul, WA, 9677
Pilgrim Foundation, MA, 4245
Pilgrim Foundation, MI, 4539
Pilling and John B. Cross, Jr. Foundation, Frances, The, GA, 2567
Pillmore Family Foundation, The, NC, 7210
Pillsbury Foundation, Fred, MO, see 4980
Pillsbury Foundation, The, MO, 4980
Pillsbury Hospital Residents Trust, RI, 8473
Pinchas Foundation, Inc., Lev, NY, 6605
Pincus Family Fund, The, NY, 6606
Pincus Fund, Marjorie M. & Irwin Nat, PA, 8214
Pines Family Foundation, Inc., Alan and Elisa, The, NJ, 5501
Pinetops Foundation, CA, see 327
Pinkerton Foundation, DE, 1721
Pinkin Foundation Inc, NJ, 5502
Pinkus Foundation, Scott and Linda, The, NY, see 6607
Pinkus Foundation, The, NY, 6607
Pinnacle Entertainment Foundation, The, NV, 5183
Pinnell Foundation, IL, 3176
Pinson Family Foundation, Raymond B., MN, 4762
Pioneer Foundation, NV, see 5173
Pipe Line Contractors Association Scholarship Foundation, TX, 9130
Pisa Foundation, RI, 8474
Pisani Family Foundation, TX, 9131
Pitt Charitable Trust, Murray C. and Ina C., MI, 4540
Pitt Foundation, Albert and Doris, MI, 4541
Pittman Family Foundation, The, NY, 6608
Pittsburgh Children's Foundation, Inc., The, PA, 8215
Pittsburgh Foundation Charles H. Spang, PA, 8216
Pittston Foundation, The, VA, see 9406
Pitzman Fund, Frederick, IL, 3177
Pitzman Fund, IL, see 3177
Piuze Foundation, M., CA, 928
Place of Hope International, Inc., FL, 2261
Plafsky Family Foundation, NJ, 5503
Plainfield Foundation, The, PA, 8217
Plaisance for Case Western, PA, 8218
Planalp-Trevor Charitable Trust, The, NY, 6609
Planet Dog Foundation, ME, 3797
Planet Dog Philanthropy, ME, see 3797
Planetary Trust, The, TX, 9132
Plankenhorn Foundation Inc., Harry, PA, 8219
Plansoen Trust, John W., NC, 7211
Platt, Jr. Family Foundation, Inc., Mary Jane & Joseph P., The, PA, 8220
Pleas Family Foundation, Riley & Nancy, WA, 9678
Plein Foundation, Ltd., Thomas A., WI, 9904
Pletka Foundation, Kronhill, The, NY, 6610
Plum Foundation, CA, 929
Plunkett Foundation, Therese, NY, 6611
Pluss Family Foundation, The, CO, 1337
Plym Foundation, MI, 4542
Plymouth Hill Foundation, NY, 6612
Podell Fund, Michael and Catherine, CA, 930
Podolsky Family Foundation, IL, 3178
Poduska Family Foundation, Inc., MA, 4246
Pogo Family Foundation, PA, 8221
Pogue Family Missions Society, TX, 9133
Pohly-Turaj Family Foundation Inc., NY, 6613
Pointe Family Foundation, Lily, WA, 9679
Polaris Foundation, AZ, see 181
POLE Foundation, Inc., FL, see 2182
Polk Bros. Fifty-Five Plus, IL, see 3179
Polk Family Charitable Fund, IL, 3179
Pollack Family Foundation Inc., Yvonne & Leslie, NY, 6614
Pollack Family Foundation, IL, 3180
Pollack Family Foundation, Inc., Geri & Lester, The, NY, 6615
Pollack Family Foundation, Inc., The, NY, see 6615
Pollack Foundation, Mark E., DE, 1722
Pollard Foundation Inc., C. F., KY, 3685
Pollia Foundation, Muriel, The, CA, 931

Pollock Foundation, Douglas W., The, PA, 8222
Pollock Foundation, NY, 6616
Pollock Foundation, S. Wilson & Grace M., NY, see 6616
Pollock Foundation, The, NY, 6617
Polsky Foundation, Inc., Hazen, The, NY, 6618
Polsky Foundation, Inc., The, NY, see 6618
Pomrenze Foundation, Jay & Hadasa, NY, 6619
Poncher Family Foundation, Jerry E., IL, 3181
Poncin Scholarship Fund, TX, 9134
Pond Family Foundation, IL, 3182
Pond Family Foundation, ME, 3798
Poole Family Foundation Inc., The, NJ, 5504
Poole Foundation, Harry and Zoe, VA, 9512
Poorman Foundation, Doyle S. & Helen, NY, 6620
Pope Foundation, Lawrence E., NC, 7212
Pope III Foundation, Mark C., The, GA, 2568
Porphyry Road Foundation, The, CO, 1338
Porter Family Charitable Foundation, Inc., DC, 1829
Porter Foundation, Inc., Anne K. and William L., NE, see 5099
Porter Foundation, Irwin Andrew, The, MN, 4763
Porter Foundation, MI, 4543
Portland Women's Foundation, OR, 7807
Portland Women's Union Foundation, OR, see 7807
Portman Charitable Trust, Harry, MO, 4981
Posey Foundation, Andrew & Lillian A., TX, 9135
Posnack Family Foundation of Hollywood, FL, see 2262
Posnack Foundation of Hollywood, FL, 2262
Posner Foundation, Lillian & Stanley, NY, see 6621
Posner-Wallace Foundation, NY, 6621
Post College Foundation, Inc., CT, 1543
Post Family Foundation, NJ, see 5505
Post Foundation, Glen and Cynthia, NJ, 5505
Post Foundation, Marjorie Merriweather, The, NC, 7213
Post Trust, Ralph B., NY, 6622
Postl Family Foundation, The, TX, 9136
Postles Scholarship Fund, Wilbur E., PA, 8223
Potiker Family Foundation, CA, see 932
Potiker Family Foundation, Hughes and Sheila, CA, 932
Pott Foundation, Robert and Elaine, OH, 7549
Pottawattamie County Community Foundation, IA, 3527
Potter Foundation, Philip E., The, NY, 6623
Potter Irrevocable Trust, Dorothy M., PA, 8224
Potter Memorial Fund, F and M, FL, 2263
Potts Memorial Foundation, The, NY, 6624
Powell Charitable Foundation, VA, 9513
Powell Family Foundation, FL, 2264
Powell Foundation Inc., Bernard F. & Mary Ann, FL, 2265
Powell Foundation, IL, 3183
Powell Foundation, Samuel C. & Myra G., AZ, 157
Powell Foundation, The, TN, 8661
Power Foundation, The, MI, 4544
Power Service Products Foundation, TX, see 9003
Powers Charitable Fund, Edward W., OH, 7550
Powers Family Foundation, The, MI, 4545
Powers Foundation, Inc., LA, 3746
Prairie Foundation, WA, 9680
Praise Him Ministries, Inc., CO, 1339
Praktikos Institute, VA, 9514
Pralle Family Foundation, Robert R. and Helga, The, CA, 933
Pratt Family Foundation, Inc., The, NC, 7214
Pratt Foundation, Aileen and Jack, The, TX, 9137
Pratt-Northam Foundation, The, NY, 6625
Praxis Foundation, DE, 1723
Praxis Foundation, The, VA, 9515
Prayer Child Foundation, AZ, 158
Prayer Closet, The, TX, 9138
Preik Foundation, Inc., The, FL, 2266
Premier Communications Foundation, IA, 3528
Pren-Hall Foundation, Inc., The, NY, see 6569
Prescott Family Foundation, Inc., WI, 9905
Preston Historical Improvement & Betterment Foundation Inc., Mary Hicks, NY, 6626
Preston Trust, Evelyn W., RI, 8475
Prete, Jr. Foundation, Ernest, CA, 934
Pretti Foundation, The, NV, 5184
Preuss Family Foundation, The, CA, 935
Prevent Cruelty To Animals (PVCA), CA, 936
Previti Lupton Foundation, Inc., Lucille, The, NJ, 5506
Previti Memorial Foundation, John P., CA, 937
Price Educational Foundation, Herschel C., WV, 9763
Price Family Foundation, Inc., The, GA, 2569

Price Family Foundation, Inc., The, NY, 6628
Price Family Foundation, KS, 3615
Price Family Foundation, NY, 6627
Price Family Foundation, Sam, KS, 3616
Price Foundation Inc., KY, 3686
Price Foundation, Arthur & Patricia, The, CA, 938
Price Foundation, Arthur L., CA, see 938
Price Foundation, Carol Swanson, MO, 4982
Price Foundation, Inc., John E. & Aliese, The, FL, 2267
Price Foundation, Inc., Robert E., The, MI, 4546
Price Foundation, Inc., Theodore H. & Nancy, VA, 9516
Price Foundation, Lucien B. and Katherine E., CT, 1544
Price Foundation, PA, 8225
Price Foundation, William L., The, CA, 939
Price Jr. Fund, John W., PA, 8226
Price Trust Fund, PA, 8227
Price-Campbell Foundation, The, GA, 2570
Priester Foundation, CO, 1340
Prime Health Foundation, MO, 4983
Prime Time Foundation, Inc., FL, 2268
Prince Family Foundation, The, NY, 6629
Priory Fund, CA, 940
Pritchett Foundation, WI, 9906
Pritzker Early Childhood Development Fund, IL, see 3184
Pritzker Early Childhood Foundation, IL, 3184
Private Foundation, The, CA, 941
Pro Health Lab Park City, UT, see 9321
Probitas Foundation Ltd., The, NY, 6630
Proctor Charitable Foundation, Elizabeth Craig Weaver, TN, 8662
Proctor Charitable Trust, Hahl, TX, 9139
Proctor Foundation, Mortimer R., CT, 1545
Professional Association of Diving Instructors Foundation, CA, see 898
Progin Foundation, The, MA, 4247
Project for Life Inc., The, NY, 6631
Project Paradigm, CA, 942
Prokopis Charitable Foundation, MA, 4248
Promontory Foundation, UT, 9345
Propp II Family Foundation, Inc., Marni & Morris, FL, 2269
Propst Foundation, The, AL, 56
Pros For Africa Inc., OK, 7715
Protein Foundation, ME, 3799
Proud Charitable Trust, Ruth E., MA, 4249
Prouty Foundation, Inc., Olive Higgins, RI, 8476
Provident Bank Charitable Foundation, NY, 6632
Provident Community Foundation, Inc., The, MA, 4250
Provision Charitas, Inc., TN, 8663
Pruden Foundation, The, VA, 9517
Pruet Foundation, The, MS, 4851
Prutky Charitable Trust, Millard & Lillian, FL, 2270
Pryor Foundation, The, CT, 1546
Psalm 11612 Foundation, NY, 6633
Psychists, Inc., FL, see 2247
Ptarmigan Foundation Inc., The, DC, 1830
PTSRK Foundation, CA, 943
Public Life Foundation of Owensboro, KY, 3687
Puelicher Foundation, Inc., WI, 9907
Puffin Foundation, MA, 4251
Pugdin Memorial Fund, IL, 3185
Pugh Family Foundation, LA, 3747
Pugliese Charitable Foundation, Charles M. & Thelma M., OH, 7551
Puksta Foundation, Harry L. and Eva J., CO, 1341
Pulaski Community Foundation, IN, see 3432
Pulaski County Community Foundation, Inc., IN, 3432
Pulichino Tong Family Foundation, Inc., FL, 2271
Pulido Walker Foundation, The, CA, 944
Pulitzer Foundation, Margot Rosenberg, TX, 9140
Pulliam Foundation, Inc., Rusty, NC, 7215
Pulvermann Charitable Trust, CT, 1547
Purple Moon Foundation, Inc., WI, 9908
Purple Plume Foundation, NY, 6634
Pusey Foundation, Paul H., FL, 2272
Putnam Family Foundation, IL, 3186
Putnam Investments Foundation, MA, 4252
Putnam Prize Fund for the Promotion of Scholarship, William Lowell, MA, 4253
Pyewacket Foundation, NY, 6635

QEP Resources Education Foundation, CO, 1342

QIBQ Foundation, NY, 6636
Quail Roost Foundation, NM, 5622
Quaker Chemical Foundation, The, PA, 8228
Quaker Hill Foundation, The, MA, A
Quanex Foundation, TX, 9141
Quatman Foundation, George B., OH, 7552
Quesada Educational Foundation, General E. R., ME, 3800
Quest Family Foundation, TX, 9142
Quest for Truth Foundation, WA, 9681
Questar Corporation Arts Foundation, UT, 9346
Questar Corporation Educational Foundation, UT, 9347
Quigg Fund, Inc., IN, 3433
Quigley Family Foundation, NJ, see 5296
Quiksilver Foundation, CA, 945
Quincy Area Community Foundation, IL, see 2803
Quinlan Foundation, Inc., Elizabeth C., The, MN, 4764
Quinn Charitable Foundation, Henry A., The, PA, 8229
Quinn Family Charitable Foundation, Inc., FL, 2273
Quinn Family Foundation, The, NY, 6637
Quinn Foundation, Doris G., NY, 6638
Quinn Foundation, Stephen D., The, NY, 6639
Quirico Educational Foundation, Francis J., The, MA, 4254
Quivey-Bay State Foundation, NE, 5113

R & R Foundation, VA, 9518
R & R Realty Group Foundation, IA, 3529
R & S Family Foundation, Inc., The, NY, 6640
RA5 Foundation, CA, 946
Rabb Charitable Trust, James M., MA, 4255
Rabinovitch Foundation, The, CA, 947
Rachel Foundation, The, NY, 6641
Rachesky Charitable Foundation, Jill and Mark, NY, 6642
Racing for a Reason, NC, see 7094
Rackley Family Foundation, Inc., Tripp & Blair, GA, 2571
Radichel Foundation, William D., MN, 4765
Radin Foundation, CA, 948
Radio Drama Network, Inc., NY, 6643
Rady Family Foundation, CA, 949
Rae Charitable Trust, James Arthur, AZ, 159
Rafiki Aids Ministry, OH, see 7513
Ragan and King Charitable Foundation, GA, see 2572
Ragan Charitable Foundation, Carolyn King, GA, 2572
Ragan Family Foundation, Florence Bullock, NJ, 5507
Ragir Foundation, Meyer J. and Norma L., CA, 950
Ragland, Jr. Trust, Trent, NC, 7216
Ragon Foundation, Phillip and Susan, MA, 4256
Ragone Family Foundation, Inc., Daniel J., The, NJ, 5508
Rahr Foundation, MN, 4766
Rainbow Fund, RI, 8477
Raker Foundation, Inc., M. E., IN, 3434
Rakowich Family Foundation, CO, 1343
Rallis Foundation, The, CA, 951
Ramlose Foundation, Inc., George A., MA, 4257
Ramsay Family Foundation, CA, 952
Ramsey Foundation Inc., W. Russell and Norma, VA, 9519
Ramsey McCluskey Family Foundation, The, MA, 4258
Ran Family Foundation, MI, 4547
Randall Foundation, Charity, PA, 8230
Randall Theatrical Fund, Inc., Tony, NY, 6644
Rankin Foundation, Inc., O'H., NC, 7217
Ransburg Charitable Foundation, Maria L., FL, 2274
Ransom Fidelity Company, MI, see 4526
Rao Charitable Corporation, Neena, NY, 6645
Raoul Foundation, W. G., GA, 2573
Rapaport Family Charitable Trust, NY, 6646
Rapaport Shallat Foundation, NY, 6647
Raper Foundation, Inc., Tom, IN, 3435
Raphael Foundation, Inc., NY, 6648
Rapp Foundation, Theodore A., CT, 1548
Rappaport Family Foundation, CA, 953
Rapport Foundation, Jerome and Toby, CA, 954
Rapport Philanthropic Trust, Esther and Hyman, The, OH, 7553
Rar Family Foundation, CA, 955
Rasba Charitable Foundation, NY, 6649
Rashti Family Foundation Inc., Aaron, VA, 9520
Rath Spang & Company Charitable Trust, Frank E., The, PA, 8231

Rathburn Family Charitable Foundation, OK, 7716
Rathert Foundation, KS, 3617
Ratliff Charitable Foundation, The, AL, 57
Ratner Family Foundation, Horowitz, The, DE, 1724
Ratner Family Foundation, The, VA, 9521
Ratner Foundation, Milton M., MI, 4548
Ratshesky Foundation, A.C., MA, 4259
Rattie Family Foundation, NY, 6650
Rauenhorst Foundation, Mark and Karen, MN, 4767
Raval Charitable Foundation, NY, see 6599
Ravitch Foundation, Inc., Richard, NY, 6651
Rawls Scholarship Foundation, Jerry S., The, TX, 9143
Ray Foundation, FL, 2275
Ray H. Marr Foundation, The, TX, 9144
Rayen School General Fund Irrevocable Trust, OH, 7554
Raygar Foundation, TX, 9145
Raymond Brooks Vanscoy Testamentary Trust, WV, 9764
Raymond Foundation Inc., IN, 3436
Raymond Foundation Inc., NY, 6652
Raymond Foundation, The, CA, 956
Raymund Foundation, Inc., FL, 2276
Razi Family Foundation, The, CA, 957
Razore Foundation, WA, 9682
RBG, Inc., CO, 1344
RBS Foundation, Inc., CT, 1549
RCM & D Foundation, The, MD, 3937
RCP Christian Foundation, WI, 9909
RDM Foundation, The, NY, 6653
RDM Positive Impact Foundation, TX, 9146
Reade Industrial Fund, IL, 3187
Realex Charitable Fund Inc., NY, 6654
Realty Foundation of New York, NY, 6655
REBNY Foundation Inc., The, NY, 6656
Rechler Foundation, Inc., Judith and Donald, The, NY, 6657
Reckson Foundation, Ethel and Harry, The, FL, 2277
RECO Foundation, The, VA, 9522
Red Acre Farm, Inc., MA, 4260
Red Bird Hollow Foundation, IL, 3188
Red Empress Foundation, ME, 3801
Red Lodge Foundation, IL, 3189
Redbird Foundation, TN, 8664
Redducs Chartered Foundation Corp., The, VT, 9383
Reddy Family Foundation, L. B., CA, 958
Reddy's Heart to Heart Foundation, CA, 959
Redies Foundation Inc., Edward F., MI, 4549
Rediger Family Foundation, The, CA, 960
Redman Foundation Inc, TX, 9147
Redmond Family Foundation, WI, 9910
Redwall Foundation Inc., The, MA, 4261
Redwoods Group Foundation Inc., The, NC, 7218
Reeble Foundation, Jane & Bernard, KS, 3618
Reed Family Foundation, Harold and Kate, The, MN, 4768
Reed Family Foundation, IL, 3190
Reed Family Foundation, Inc., Calvin H., FL, 2278
Reed Family Foundation, Sam and Victoria, IL, 3191
Reed Foundation, KY, 3688
Reed Fund, John C. and Margaret Hanson, OH, 7555
Reel Family Foundation, Inc., CO, 1345
Rees Charitable Trust, Paul, Jr. and Martha N., NC, 7219
Rees Foundation, Nancy E. Barry & Letitia P., CA, 961
Reese Foundation, PA, 8232
Reese Foundation, Sheldon F., SD, 8573
Reeves Foundation, Inc., Eleanor Patterson, FL, 2279
Regal-Beloit Charitable Foundation, WI, 9911
Reger Family Foundation, Michael and Brittany, MN, 4769
Regions/AmSouth Foundation, AL, 58
Regis Foundation, MN, 4770
Rehnert Charitable Trust, Bernadette T., MA, see 4341
Reich Family Charitable Trust, The, NY, 6658
Reich Fund, The, NY, 6659
Reichert Family Foundation Inc., Charles and Helen, NY, 6660
Reichert Foundation, IL, 3192
Reidler Foundation, The, PA, 8233
Reidy Family Foundation, NY, 6661
Reilly Family Foundation, Janet and Clint, CA, 962
Reilly Family Foundation, The, TX, 9148
Reimer Foundation, MN, 4771

Reiner Educational Trust, Donald F., MN, 4772
Reinhold Foundation, Inc., Paul E. & Ida Klare, FL, see 2280
Reinhold Foundation, Inc., Paul E. & Klare N., FL, 2280
Reinhold Foundation, The, CA, 963
Reinisch Foundation, Richard and Marianne, IL, 3193
Reisman Charitable Trust, Howard & Robin, MA, 4262
Reisman Charitable Trust, Robert S. & Maria J., MA, 4263
Reisman Foundation, Phyllis & Sidney, OH, 7556
Reiss Family Foundation, NY, 6662
Reiss Foundation, Jacob L., PA, 8234
Reitch Charitable Trust, Tom C. & Mary B., TX, 9149
Reitman Foundation, The, CA, 964
Relationship Enrichment Collaborative, CO, 1346
Relgalf Charitable Foundation, DE, 1725
Religious Care Foundation, Inc., WI, 9912
Remala Foundation, Satya and Rao, WA, 9683
Rembert Family Foundation, Inc., FL, 2281
Remick Charitable Foundation, Robert & Helen, MN, 4773
Remmel Foundation, W. H. and Althea F., PA, 8235
Remmer Family Foundation, DE, 1726
Renau Foundation, Inc., Kenneth H. & Sarah M., KY, 3689
Renner Foundation, OH, 7557
Reny Charitable Foundation, ME, 3802
Repass-Rodgers Family Foundation Inc., The, DE, 1727
Replogle Family Foundation, DE, 1728
Replogle Foundation, Luther I., DC, 1831
Research Fund for Cystic Fibrosis Inc., NJ, 5509
Resnick Foundation, Howard & Helaine, FL, 2282
Resnick Foundation, Jack and Pearl, The, NY, 6663
Resource Partners Foundation, CA, 965
Rest Haven Preventorium for Children, Inc., CA, 966
Restoration Foundation, The, TN, 8665
Reuhl Family Foundation, TX, 9150
Reveas Foundation, The, CA, 967
Rewald Scholarship Trust, AB Rewald and Jeanette, WI, 9913
Rexford Fund Inc., NY, 6664
Reynolds and Reynolds Company Foundation, The, OH, 7558
Reynolds Family Foundation, Frederic and Lundy, The, OH, 7559
Reynolds Family Foundation, Inc., Thomas B. and Patricia R., GA, 2574
Reynolds Foundation, Inc., Edgar & Frances, NE, 5114
Reynolds Foundation, Inc., Edgar, NE, see 5114
Reynolds Foundation, Marjorie Harris, MA, 4264
Reynolds Lajadesh Foundation, The, OH, see 7559
RFI Foundation Inc., MD, 3938
Rhe Charitable Foundation, CA, 968
Rheinstrom Hill Community Foundation, NY, 6665
Rhodes Memorial Fund, Lawrence I. & Blanche H., NY, 6666
Rhodes Museum and Charitable Foundation Inc., Albert and Mary, The, WI, 9914
Rhona's Place Foundation, MD, 3939
RHR Family Foundation Inc., The, NY, 6667
Ribenack Charitable Trust, Dorothy N., NC, 7220
Rice Charitable Foundation, Albert W., MA, 4265
Rice Family Foundation, CA, 969
Rice Family Foundation, Dianne T. & Charles E., The, FL, 2283
Rice Foundation, Charles & Catherine B., GA, 2575
Rich Foundation, William R., The, IL, 3194
Rich Memorial Fund, Walter, FL, 2284
Richard Benevolent Foundation, IL, 3195
Richard Foundation, The, FL, 2285
Richards Charitable Foundation, Inc., Margaret Cole, IN, see 3413
Richards Trust, Helen R., PA, 8236
Richardson Benevolent Foundation, C. E., VA, 9523
Richardson Charitable Foundation, A. E. & Juanita, OK, 7717
Richardson Charitable Trust, Faye and Michael, CT, 1550
Richardson Family Foundation, The, WY, 9983
Richardson Fund, Mary Lynn, The, NC, 7221
Richardson Memorial Fund, Sid, TX, 9151
Richardson Trust, Robert B. & Pearl P., OR, 7808
Richmond Foundation, Inc., Frederick W., MD, 3940

Richmond Foundation, Wade, TX, 9152
Richter Charitable Trust, Adam, TX, 9153
Richter Family Foundation, NY, see 6668
Richter Family Foundation, William L., The, NY, 6668
Ricon Americas Foundation, PA, 8237
Ridder Foundation, Georgia B., The, CA, 970
Rider-Pool Foundation, The, PA, 8238
Ridgecliff Foundation Inc., OH, 7560
Ridgewood Foundation, NY, 6669
Riechmann Foundation, B. Beall & R. Kemp, FL, 2286
Riecker Charitable Foundation, The, DE, 1729
Riedel Foundation, George H., MO, 4984
Rieger Foundation, CA, 971
Riehm Family Foundation, Inc., The, WY, 9984
Rieks Foundation, Autumn, MN, 4774
Rietman Charitable Foundation, Carl and Camilla, OR, 7809
Rifkin Family Foundation, IN, 3437
Rifkind Charitable Foundation, Robert S., The, NY, 6670
Rifkind Foundation, Robert Gore, CA, 972
Riggs Benevolent Fund, AR, 214
Rikard Charitable Trust, M.A., AL, 59
Riley Foundation, Susan E., CA, 973
Riley Foundation, The, MI, 4550
Rimora Foundation, The, VA, 9524
Ring Foundation, Inc., The, NY, 6671
Ringer Foundation, Ronald H., IL, 3196
Rinker Family Foundation, Inc., IN, 3438
Rinker Foundation, Inc., David and Leighan, FL, 2287
Rippel Foundation, Fannie E., NJ, 5510
Ripps Charitable Foundation, Harold W., AL, 60
Risen Son Foundation, Inc., NY, 6672
Rishwain Family Foundation, Robert & Karen, CA, 974
Rising Sun Foundation, MN, 4775
Riskin Charitable Foundation, Philip W., NJ, 5511
Ritchie Foundation, Hubert A., NC, 7222
Ritchie Memorial Foundation, Charles E. and Mabel M., The, OH, 7561
RITE-HITE Corporation Foundation Inc., WI, 9915
Riter, Jr. Family Foundation, A. W., TX, 9154
Ritter Family Foundation, Toby and Nataly, The, NY, 6673
Ritter Foundation, Irene, NY, 6674
Ritter Trust, William H., PA, 8239
River City Foundation, MI, 4551
River Oaks Foundation, Inc., FL, 2288
Rivera Foundation, Mariano, DE, 1730
Rivers Foundation, Inc., John & Kathleen, The, SC, see 8538
Rivers Foundation, The, DE, 1731
Rivers, Jr. Foundation, John M., SC, 8538
Riverway Foundation, MN, 4776
Rixson Foundation, Inc., Oscar C., NC, 7223
Rizavi Friedland Foundation, Inc., NY, see 6777
RJL Charitable Foundation, NY, 6675
RJW Foundation, MN, 4777
Robb Charitable Foundation, Elizabeth N., IL, 3197
Robbins Foundation, Inc., David and Lucille, NY, 6676
Robbins Trust, C.L., NC, 7224
Robbins-de Beaumont Foundation, The, MA, 4266
Roberti Charitable Trust, Helen, IL, 3198
Roberts Balliet Foundation, Kent and Ilene, Dr. , TX, 9155
Roberts Charitable Foundation, Donald & Marie, MN, 4778
Roberts Coyote Foundation, Sally and Dick, CA, 975
Roberts Family Foundation, Douglas C. & Lynn M., IL, 3199
Roberts Family Foundation, Inc., IN, 3439
Roberts Foundation, Courtney, The, CA, 976
Roberts Foundation, Ed and Margaret, TX, 9156
Roberts Foundation, Inc., Clinton S., CT, 1551
Roberts Foundation, Inc., Edward C. & Ann T., CT, 1552
Roberts Foundation, Ralph & Suzanne, PA, 8240
Roberts Foundation, Summerfield G., TX, 9157
Robertson Foundation, The, RI, 8478
Robinson Family Foundation, Alex & Leona, PA, see 8241
Robinson Family Foundation, Donald & Sylvia, PA, 8241
Robinson Foundation, H. English and Ermine Carter, NC, 7225
Robinson Foundation, The, CA, 977
Robinson Fund, Charles Nelson, CT, 1553

Robinson IV Foundation, George A., TX, 9158
Robitaille Trust, Henry J., NC, 7226
Robson Foundation, Edward J. and Lanelle B., AZ, 160
Robson Foundation, LaNelle, AZ, see 160
Robson Foundation, Nick and Alma, The, IL, 3200
Rocca, Jr. Foundation, B. T., CA, 978
Roche Family Foundation Inc., The, IL, 3201
Roche Foundation Inc., NY, 6677
Roche Foundation, The, CA, 979
Roche Relief Foundation, Edward & Ellen, NY, 6678
Rochester Area Community Foundation, Greater, MI, see 4410
Rock Foundation, Inc., NY, 6679
Rock Foundation, The, CT, 1554
Rockdale Foundation Inc., The, GA, 2576
Rockdale Fund for Social Investment, Inc., GA, see 2576
Rockland Trust Charitable Foundation, MA, 4267
Rockwise Foundation, CO, 1347
Rocky Mount Community Foundation, Inc., NC, 7227
Roddis Foundation, Inc., Hamilton, WI, 9916
Rodgers Family Foundation, Inc., The, NY, 6680
Rodgers Foundation, Richard and Dorothy, NY, see 6680
Rodgers, Jr. Foundation, Inc., Thomas E., FL, 2289
Rodman Family Foundation, Don and Marilyn, MA, 4268
Rodman Family Foundation, Don, MA, see 4268
Rodman Ford Sales Inc. Charitable Trust, MA, 4269
Rodman Foundation, MN, 4779
Roe Foundation, Inc., Kenneth & Hazel, The, NJ, 5512
Roe Foundation, Inc., The, NY, 6681
Roehl Foundation, Inc., WI, 9917
Roemer Charitable Foundation, W. F. and L. C., PA, 8242
Roger's & Betty's Charitable Foundation, CA, see 800
Rogers Charitable Trust, Florence, NC, 7228
Rogers Educational Trust, Lon & Jessie, IL, 3202
Rogers Family Charitable Trust, CA, 980
Rogers Family Foundation, Inc., FL, 2290, 2291
Rogers Family Foundation, The, FL, 2292
Rogers Foundation, James and Laura, The, TN, 8666
Rogers Trust, John William and Lena Wells, TX, 9159
Rogers, Jr. Family Foundation, Inc., J. Carlisle Rogers, Ruth G. Rogers & James Carlisle, FL, see 2291
Rogers-Wilbur Foundation, Inc., MD, 3941
Rohde Family Charitable Foundation, IA, 3530
Roke Foundation, Inc., The, CA, 981
Rolander Family Foundation, The, NC, 7229
Roles Family Foundation, MN, 4780
Rolla Trust f/b/o Charities, Smith, NC, 7230
Roller-Bottimore Foundation, The, VA, 9525
Rollins Foundation, E. T. Rollins, Jr. and Frances P., The, NC, 7231
Rollstone Charitable Foundation, Inc., MA, 4270
Roma Bank Community Foundation, Inc., NJ, 5513
Roman Foundation, Melvin F. & Adele S., The, MO, 4985
Romano Charitable Trust, Richard and Margaret, The, IL, 3203
Romano Family Foundation, Murphy and Ed, CA, 982
Roney Family Foundation, The, CA, 983
Rooney Foundation, Inc., M. A., IN, 3440
Rooney Foundation, Kelly, The, PA, 8243
Roosth Foundation, Sam, TX, 9160
Roothbert Fund Inc., The, NY, 6682
ROS Foundation, The, WI, 9918
Roscommon County Community Foundation, MI, 4552
Rose & Kiernan Charitable Foundation, Inc., NY, 6683
Rose Family Foundation, FL, 2293
Rose Family Foundation, Inc., Marshall, NY, 6684
Rose Foundation, Ernest & Irma, CA, 984
Rose Foundation, Inc., Jill & Marshall, NY, see 6684
Rose Foundation, Isabel, The, NY, 6685
Rose Foundation, MA, 4271
Rose Foundation, The, TN, 8667
Rose Foundation, Wendi and Joseph B., The, NY, 6686
Rose Francis Foundation, MN, 4781
Rose Marrow Fund, The, NY, 6687
Rosebud Foundation, IL, 3204
Rosedorf Foundation, NY, 6688
Rosemann Family Foundation Inc, WI, 9919
Rosen & Samuel Edes Foundation, Claire, The, IL, 3205
Rosen Family Foundation, Florence & Robert A., NY, 6689
Rosen Family Foundation, Inc., Jonathan D., GA, 2577

Rosen Family Foundation, Inc., The, MN, 4782
Rosen Family Foundation, Rita & Herbert, WA, 9684
Rosen Family Foundation, The, FL, see 2294
Rosen Foundation, Dr. A. Everett & Ruth E., The, TX, 9161
Rosen Foundation, Martin and Doris, The, FL, 2294
Rosen Foundation, Michael Alan, IL, 3206
Rosenbaum Foundation, Paul & Gabriella, IL, see 3047
Rosenberg Charitable Trust, Harry & Bessye, IL, 3207
Rosenberg Charitable Trust, Jack & Mae, The, NY, 6690
Rosenberg Foundation Inc., Lil & Julie, CT, 1555
Rosenberg Foundation Inc., Thomas Jefferson, NY, 6691
Rosenberg Foundation, David M. and Marjorie D., The, PA, 8244
Rosenberg Foundation, Meta and George, The, CA, 985
Rosenberg Foundation, Michael L., TX, 9162
Rosenberry Foundation, Harold C. & Marjorie Q., OH, 7562
Rosenfeld Foundation, Jack and Harriet, FL, 2295
Rosenfeld Family Foundation, Gene and Maxine, The, CA, 986
Rosenfeld Foundation, Mary & Emmanuel, DE, 1732
Rosengarten Horowitz Fund, CA, see 1138
Rosenlund Family Foundation, The, PA, 8245
Rosenmutter Family Foundation, Lee and Nathan, IL, 3208
Rosenmutter Foundation, IL, see 3208
Rosenson Family Foundation, The, IL, 3209
Rosenstein Charitable Foundation, Jonathan & Lisa, The, NY, 6692
Rosenthal Family Foundation, Barbara & William, NY, 6693
Rosenthal Family Foundation, Leighton A., OH, 7563
Rosenthal Family Foundation, Robert and Jodi, NY, 6694
Rosenthal Foundation for the Arts, Miriam, FL, 2296
Rosenthal Foundation, Benjamin J., IL, 3210
Rosenthal Foundation, Ida and William, The, NY, 6696
Rosenthal Foundation, Inc., Harry and Andrew H., NY, 6695
Rosenthal Foundation, Inc., Robert and Nina, CA, 987
Rosenthal Foundation, The, TX, 9163
Rosh Foundation Inc., Birkas, NY, 6697
Roshan Institute of Cultural Heritage, FL, 2297
Rosner Foundation, Inc., Leo, NY, 6698
Ross Charitable Foundation, Darrell & Susan, The, FL, 2298
Ross Charitable Trust Foundation, Waldo T. & Ruth S., NY, 6699
Ross Family Foundation, John S., MO, 4986
Ross Foundation, Dale and Deborah, The, TX, 9164
Ross Foundation, Inc., Joseph & Frieda, FL, see 2111
Ross Foundation, John S. & Jody J., MO, see 4986
Ross Foundation, KS, 3619
Ross Foundation, Marshal Verne, The, TX, 9165
Ross Medical Foundation, Gordon, CA, 988
Rosse Family Charitable Foundation, The, MA, 4272
Rosse Family Charitable Foundation, Thomas A., MA, see 4272
Rossi Family Foundation, CA, 989
Rossman Family Foundation, IL, 3211
Rosso Family Foundation, The, CA, 990
Rossotti Foundation, The, DC, 1832
Rostan Family Foundation, NC, 7232
Rosztoczy Foundation, AZ, 161
Rot Foundation, Albert J. and Susan E., IL, 3212
Rotalia Foundation, WA, 9685
Rotasa Foundation, CA, 991
Roth Family Foundation Inc., NY, 6700
Roth Foundation, Louis T., KY, 3690
Rothblum Foundation, Inc., David, NY, see 6701
Rothblum Foundation, Marcia and Phillip, NY, 6701
Rothchild Family 2004 Charitable Foundation, Seymore and Sylvia, DE, 1733
Rothenberg Foundation, Pamela and Stuart, NY, 6702
Rothman Family Foundation, IL, 3213
Rothman Family Foundation, Inc., Maurice A. Rothman and Thelma P., FL, 2299
Rothman Foundation, Inc., Maurice A. and Thelma P., FL, see 2299
Rothschild Charitable Foundation Inc., The, MD, 3942
Rothschild Family Foundation Inc., The, FL, 2300

Rothschild Family Foundation, AZ, 162
Rothschild Family Foundation, Robert and Sara, NH, 5229
Rothschild Foundation Inc., Henry and Gertrude, NY, 6703
Rothschild Fund, Carol W. & Myron J., AL, 61
Rothstein Charitable Youth Trust, Maks & Lea, The, NY, 6704
Rotterman Trust, Helen L. & Marie F., OH, 7564
Rottman Charitable Foundation, Fritz and Carol, MI, see 4553
Rottman Family Charitable Foundation, MI, 4553
Roundhouse Foundation, The, OR, 7810
Roundy Charitable Foundation, Beryl O. and Wilma Sime, IL, 3214
Rounsavall, Jr. Family Foundation Inc., Robert W., KY, 3691
Rouse Charitable Foundation, Inc., Jim and Patty, The, MD, 3943
Rouse Charitable Foundation, Inc., Jim, The, MD, see 3943
Rouse Family Foundation, Inc., KY, 3692
Rouse-Bottom Foundation, VA, 9526
Routzon Family Foundation, Inc., CO, 1348
Rowan Foundation Inc., Arch and Stella, The, TX, 9166
Rowe Foundation, John W. and Jeanne M., NY, 6705
Roxe Foundation, The, NY, 6706
Roznowski Foundation, Steven F. and Melinda I., The, MI, 4554
Rsfzmkh Foundation, NJ, 5514
Rubeli Foundation Inc., Maureen and Paul, AZ, 163
Ruben Foundation, Dennis and Joyce, The, IL, 3215
Rubens Family Foundation, FL, 2301
Rubenstein Family Charitable Foundation, Harold, DC, 1833
Rubenstein Foundation, Jerry and Maury, The, TX, 9167
Rubin Family Foundation, PA, 8246
Rubin Family Foundation, The, MO, 4987
Rubin Foundation, Barbara N., CA, 992
Rubin Foundation, Jacob & Mae D., The, NY, see 6707
Rubin Foundation, Nancy & Miles, The, NY, 6707
Rubin Foundation, Sol R. and Neddy, CA, 993
Rubin-Ladd Foundation, The, CT, 1556
Rucker-Donnell Foundation, TN, 8668
Ruckstuhl Foundation, The, LA, 3748
Ruddy Charitable Trust, Raymond & Marilyn, MA, A
Rudge Foundation, AZ, 164
Rudin Scholarship Foundation, Samuel & Lottie, PA, 8247
Rudman Foundation, Kal and Lucille, PA, 8248
Rudy & Sons Foundation, Inc., Nathan, NY, 6708
Rukh Family Foundation Inc., NJ, 5515
Rukin Philanthropic Foundation, David and Eleanore, NJ, 5516
Rum Fund, The, NY, 6709
Rumberger Foundation, Douglas and Gloria, The, DE, 1734
Runstad Foundation, WA, 9686
Rupp Foundation Inc., Bill & Melinda, OH, 7565
Rupp Foundation, Richard W., The, NY, 6710
Rush County Community Foundation, Inc., IN, 3441
Rush Educational Trust, David and Mary P., KS, 3620
Rush Family Foundation, Loni and Jeff, CA, 994
Rusinow Family Charitable Foundation, WI, 9920
Ruskin Family Trust, The, FL, 2302
Russell Charitable Foundation, Eluned & Edward, IL, 3216
Russell Charitable Foundation, Inc., Tom, DE, 1735
Russell Family Foundation, William Knight, CA, 995
Russell Foundation, Richard B., FL, 2303
Russell Smith Foundation, Steven, OK, 7718
Russell Trust, Josephine G., MA, 4273
Russer Foods/Zemsky Family Trust, NY, see 7022
Russo Family Charitable Foundation, The, NY, 6711
Russo Family Foundation Inc., Peter & Mary, NJ, 5517
Russo Family Foundation, The, NY, 6712
Russo Foundation, Thomas A. and Georgina T., PA, 8249
Rust Charitable Foundation, Harry L. Rust & Helen M., MO, 4988
Rust Foundation, Margaret Sue, TX, 9168
Rust Foundation, The, PA, 8250
Ruth Foundation, The, NY, 6713

Ruthen Private Foundation Inc., Betty and Irving, NY, 6714

Ruttenberg Foundation, Biff, IL, 3217

Ruttenberg Foundation, Derald H., The, NY, 6715

Ruttenberg Foundation, The, IL, 3218

Ryan Family Foundation, James R., MI, 4555

Ryan Family Foundation, The, FL, 2304

Ryan Family Foundation, The, PA, 8251

Ryan Foundation, Albert J., The, OH, 7566

Ryan Foundation, Inc., John B., NY, see 5684

Ryan Foundation, The, FL, 2305

Ryan Foundation, William G. & Mary A., IL, 3219

Ryan Memorial, Joseph and Edward, The, IA, 3531

Ryerson Charitable Trust, John B. & Jane M., DE, 1736

Ryrie Foundation, The, TX, 9169

S.B.E. & S. Clients' Consolidated Charitable Foundation, MD, 3944

S.D.R. Foundation, Inc., NC, 7233

S.E.C. Charitable Corp., OH, 7567

Saab Foundation, Ghassan and Manal, MI, 4556

Saab Foundation, Ghassan M., MI, see 4556

Sabol Foundation, John and Nancy, WA, 9687

Sacajawea Charitable Foundation Trust, MA, see 4274

Sacajawea Charitable Foundation, MA, 4274

Sachem Foundation, The, RI, 8479

Sachs Fund, MO, 4989

Sackerson Charitable Foundation, Edward J., MI, 4557

Sackler Foundation, Inc., Raymond and Beverly, NY, 6716

Sackler Fund for the Arts & Sciences, Raymond & Beverly, NY, 6717

Sacred Portion Foundation, MN, 4783

Sadler Family Foundation, FL, 2306

Saemann Foundation, Franklin I. and Irene List, IL, 3220

Saemann Foundation, Franklin I., IL, see 3220

Safe Family Foundation, The, MA, 4275

Safenowitz Family Foundation Inc., Milton and Marilyn, The, FL, 2307

Sage Cleveland Foundation, The, OH, 7568

Sailors' Snug Harbor of Boston, Inc., MA, 4276

Sakhai Family Foundation, Inc., The, NY, 6718

Saks Charitable Foundation Trust, Ronald S., MO, 4990

Salatto and Family Charitable Foundation Inc., James A., CT, 1557

Salem Community Benefits, Inc., NH, 5230

Salem Family Foundation, The, MA, see 4361

Salem Five Charitable Foundation, Inc., MA, 4277

Salenger Foundation, Inc., Stuart, FL, 2308

Salerno Private Foundation, D.J. and R.G., RI, 8480

Salgo Charitable Trust, Nicolas M., KS, 3621

Saliba Family Charitable Foundation, Inc., IL, 3221

Salin Foundation, Inc., IN, 3442

Saling Foundation, Carol and Velma, OR, 7811

Salisbury 54 Endowment Fund, Katherine M. and Richard J., The, NY, 6719

Salisbury Family Foundation Inc., MD, 3945

Salizzoni Family Foundation, FL, 2309

Salizzoni Family Foundation, Inc., Frank & Sarah, FL, see 2309

Sallie Foundation, Inc., The, NY, 6720

Salmanson Foundation, Donald, RI, 8481

Salomon Family Foundation, Inc., William R. and Virginia F., The, NY, 6721

Saltzman Foundation, Richard and Bette, NY, 6722

Salutare Deum Foundation, LA, 3749

Samberg Foundation, Inc., Joe & Sandy, The, NY, 6723

Samberg Foundation, Rebecca and Arthur, The, NY, 6724

Samford Jr. Chess Foundation, Frank, The, GA, 2578

Samford, Jr. Foundation, W. James, The, AL, 62

Sammons Foundation, Elaine Dewey, The, FL, 2310

Sammut Family Foundation, CA, 996

Samowitz Foundation, Inc., Stanley C., The, FL, see 2311

Samowitz Foundation, The, FL, 2311

Sample Foundation, Inc., The, MT, 5062

Sample Scholarship Trust, Adrian M., FL, 2312

Sample, Jr., M.D. Memorial Fund, H. Glenn, The, PA, 8252

Samsara Foundation, MN, 4784

Samuels Foundation Inc., Ernest & Rose, NY, 6725

Samuelsen Scholarship Trust, Harvey, AK, 91

San Diego Scottish Rite Community Foundation, CA, 997

San Francisco Challenge, CA, 998

San Marcos Civic Foundation, TX, 9170

Sanctity of Life Foundation, OH, see 7333

Sander Foundation, MO, 4991

Sanders Charitable Foundation, Tawny and Jerry, CA, 999

Sanders Charitable Trust I, Jimmy & Hazel, MS, 4852

Sanders Charitable Trust II, Jimmy & Hazel, GA, see 2613

Sanders Charitable Trust No. II, Caroline J. S., NC, 7234

Sanders Family Foundation, NJ, 5518

Sanders Family Foundation, The, DE, 1737

Sanders Foundation Inc., George And Mary Jo, The, FL, 2313

Sanders Foundation, The, TX, 9171

Sandfair Foundation, OH, 7569

Sandler and Co., Aleck, CA, see 925

Sandler Foundation, Inc., Reba Judith, The, MA, 4278

Sandman Family Foundation, The, MA, 4279

Sandnes Family Foundation, CA, 1000

Sands Foundation, Corrine and Lenny, CA, 1001

Sandt Trust, Kurt, NC, 7235

Sanfilippo Foundation, Martha E., CA, 1002

Sanguinetti Foundation, Annunziata, TX, 9172

Sani Family Foundation Inc., NY, 6726

Santa Rita Foundation, The, CA, 1003

Santander Consumer USA Inc. Foundation, TX, 9173

Santoro Family Charitable Foundation, The, CT, 1558

Santos Family Foundation, OR, 7812

Santvoord Foundation Inc., Peg, The, NY, 6727

Sappington House Foundation Library of Americana Trust, MO, 4992

Saramar Charitable Fund, The, PA, 8253

Saramco Foundation, The, TX, 9174

Sarandon Charitable Foundation, Susan, The, CA, 1004

Sargent Foundation, Gladys W., The, CA, 1005

Sargent Foundation, Newell B., WY, 9985

Sargol Charitable Trust, NY, 6728

Sarkowsky Charitable Foundation, Herman & Faye, WA, 9688

Sarkowsky Family Charitable Foundation, WA, see 9688

Sarnoff Family Foundation, Ann and Richard, NY, 6729

Sartori Foundation Inc., The, WI, 9921

Sasco Foundation Corporation, TN, 8669

Sasco Foundation, IL, 3222

Sassoon Family Foundation, The, CA, 1006

Sastaunik Charitable Remainder Trust, NJ, 5519

Satar & Family Foundation, Abdul, NY, 6730

Satell Family Foundation, PA, 8254

Sato Family Foundation, Inc., The, NY, 6731

Sato Foundation, The, CA, 1007

Satori Foundation, VA, see 9400

Satow Family Foundation, Inc., Jed David, NY, 6732

Saturno Brothers Italian Orphan Foundation, CA, 1008

Sauer Children's Renew Foundation, MN, 4785

Sauer Lewis Foundation, VA, 9527

Sauerland Foundation, OH, 7570

Saul Foundation, Inc., Helen and Harry, GA, 2579

Saulsbury Family Foundation, Inc., TX, 9175

Saunders Foundation, NY, 6733

Saunders Foundation, TX, 9176

Savage Charitable Foundation, CA, 1009

Savage Family Foundation, MA, 4280

Savannah Foods Foundation, GA, see 2457

Savett Family Foundation, Sherrie R., The, PA, 8255

Savin Foundation, Rueben & Muriel, NJ, 5520

Savings Bank of Danbury Foundation, Inc., CT, 1559

Savings Bank of Maine, FSB Charitable Foundation, ME, see 3766

Savitz Foundation, Alisa and Peter, The, NY, 6734

Sawchuk Family Foundation, CA, 1010

Sawyer Charitable Trust, Bouslog, HI, 2644

Saya Foundation, CA, 1011

Sayer Charitable Foundation, The, MN, 4786

Sayler-Hawkins Foundation, MO, 4993

SBJ Resch Family Foundation Inc., FL, 2314

Scandling Family Foundation, CA, 1012

Schaar & P. K. Whelpton Foundation, S. B., WA, 9689

Schadt Foundation, The, TN, 8670

Schaefer Family Foundation, Roberta, NY, 6735

Schaeffer Family Foundation, CA, 1013

Schaeneman, Jr. Foundation, Inc., Lewis G., CT, 1560

Schafer Charitable Foundation Trust, Leonard A. and Mary Jane, The, PA, 8256

Schaffer Foundation Inc., H., NY, 6736

Schaffer Foundation, Inc., Irving and Geraldine, The, NY, 6737

Schair Family Foundation, ME, see 3783

Schalon Foundation, The, MI, 4558

Scharf Foundation, Inc., Morris & Dvora, NY, 6738

Scharlin Foundation, Inc., The, FL, 2315

Scharman Family Foundation Inc., Scott and Robyn, The, UT, 9348

Schaumburg Charitable Trust, Paul & Norma, IL, 3223

Schautz Foundation, Walter L., The, PA, 8257

Schechter Foundation, MA, 4281

Scheller Foundation, Joseph B. Scheller and Rita P., PA, 8258

Schendel III Family Foundation, Walter G., The, CT, 1561

Schepp Foundation, Leopold, NY, 6739

Schepps Charitable Foundation, Inc., TX, see 9177

Schepps Foundation, A. I. and Manet, TX, 9177

Schepps Robinson Foundation, Sonnie, TX, 9178

Schergens Foundation, Inc., Edgar & Lucile, IN, 3443

Scherr and Family Foundation, Inc., Vera and Walter, FL, 2316

Scherr Foundation, Ray & Janet, CA, 1014

Schey Foundation, Ralph and Lucille, OH, 7571

Schey Foundation, The, OH, see 7571

Schiano Family Foundation Inc., FL, 2317

Schiff Hardin & Waite Foundation, IL, 3224, see 3224

Schiffman Foundation Inc., Robert M., DE, 1738

Schildberg Foundation, IA, 3532

Schiller Foundation, Howard and Debbie, The, NY, 6740

Schimmel Charitable Trust, John H., NJ, 5521

Schimmel Foundation, Inc., Stephen Harold, The, CA, 1015

Schinasi International Hospital, Morris, IL, 3225

Schinazi and Family Foundation, Inc., Raymond F., GA, 2580

Schiro and Peter J. Manus Foundation, Susan F., The, MA, 4282

Schiro Family Foundation, NY, 6741

Schiro-Zavela Foundation, J. V., The, VA, 9528

Schissler Charitable Foundation, TX, see 9179

Schissler Foundation, The, TX, 9179

Schlaffer Foundation Trust, Helen, The, NJ, 5522

Schlager Family Foundation Inc, MA, 4283

Schlanger Family Foundation Inc., The, FL, 2318

Schlarbaum Family Foundation, PA, 8259

Schlegel Foundation, Oscar C. & Augusta, WI, 9922

Schlein Foundation Inc., AZ, 165

Schlessman Family Foundation, Inc., CO, 1349

Schlessman Foundation, Inc., CO, see 1349

Schlinger Chrisman Foundation, CA, 1016

Schloss Family Foundation Inc., The, CT, 1562

Schlotterer & Elizabeth M. Zipf Charitable Trust, Peter G., The, NJ, 5523

Schmeelk Foundation Inc., Priscilla & Richard J., NY, 6742

Schmidt Charitable Foundation, William E., AZ, 166

Schmidt Family Charitable Foundation, J. Frank, The, OR, 7813

Schmidt Family Foundation, Theodore & Elizabeth, UT, 9349

Schmidt Foundation, Inc., William E., TN, 8671

Schmidt Foundation, L. Florence, NC, 7236

Schmidt Foundation, Robert E. and Patricia, KS, 3622

Schmuckal Family Foundation, Art and Mary, The, MI, 4559

Schmucker Charitable Trust, Swanson, WI, 9923

Schneider Charitable Trust, John D. and Minnie R., The, IL, 3226

Schneider Charitable Trust, John D., IL, see 3226

Schneider Family Foundation, IL, 3227

Schneider Foundation, Helen & Irving, NY, 6743

Schneider Foundation, MO, 4994

Schneider Foundation, Robert E., IL, 3228

Schnieders Family Foundation, The, NM, 5623

Schoellkopf Foundation, Jacob F. & Wilma S., RI, 8482

Schoen Family Foundation, The, CA, 1017

Schoener Foundation, Phyllis L., The, TX, 9180

Schoenleber Foundation, Inc., WI, 9924

Schonberger Family Foundation, NY, 6744
Schonfeld Family Foundation, NY, 6745
Schonfeld Foundation, Inc., Steven B., The, NY, 6746
Schonkopf Family Foundation, NY, 6747
School of Dreams, Inc., The, NY, 6748
Schooler Family Foundation, OH, 7572
Schoonmaker Trust, J. & L., PA, 8260
Schorr-Lieberman Family Foundation, IL, 3229
Schott Foundation, Lewis, The, NY, 6749
Schott Foundation, MN, 4787
Schottenstein Foundation B, Saul, OH, 7573
Schottenstein Foundation D, Saul, OH, 7574
Schottenstein Foundation, Lori, OH, 7575
Schramm Foundation, The, CO, 1350
Schreiber Family Foundation, E. & M., NY, 6750
Schreiber Foundation, Inc., Agnita M., WV, see 9768
Schrenk Family Foundation, C. W. Schrenk and Marjorie J., PA, 8261
Schroeder Trust, Dale D., IA, 3533
Schug Foundation, NC, 7237
Schuh Family Foundation, Inc., MD, 3946
Schuler Family Foundation, Force, WA, see 9690
Schuler Family Foundation, WA, 9690
Schulte Charitable Foundation, TX, 9181
Schulte Family Foundation, Rudi, CA, 1018
Schultz Foundation, Arthur B., The, WY, 9986
Schultz Foundation, CA, 1019
Schultz Foundation, Inc., The, FL, 2319
Schultz Trust, Robert E., PA, 8262
Schulze Family Foundation, The, MN, 4788
Schulze Foundation, Richard & Enika, The, TX, 9182
Schumacher Foundation, Robert J. and Edith K., TX, 9183
Schurz Communications Foundation, Inc., IN, 3444
Schutte Foundation, Victor E. & Caroline E., MO, 4995
Schuylkill Area Community Foundation, PA, 8263
Schwab Charitable Foundation, WA, 9691
Schwab Foundation, Inc., Olin B. and Desta, IN, 3445
Schwab Memorial Foundation, Edward L., SD, 8574
Schwab Rainess Foundation, PA, see 8264
Schwab-Rosenhouse Memorial Foundation, TX, 9184
Schwab-Silfen Foundation, PA, 8264
Schwalbach Family Foundation, Gerald and Susan, The, DE, 1739
Schwalbe Brothers Foundation Inc., NY, 6751
Schwarcz Foundation, The, MI, 4560
Schwartz Family Foundation, Barry K., NY, 6752
Schwartz Family Foundation, Jane & Martin, The, PA, 8265
Schwartz Family Foundation, NJ, 5524
Schwartz Family Foundation, The, NY, 6753
Schwartz Foundation, Arnold A., The, NJ, 5525
Schwartz Foundation, Inc., David, NY, 6754
Schwartz Foundation, Samuel & Bertha, NY, see 6753
Schwartz Foundation, Valerie Beth, MA, 4284
Schwartz Fund for Education and Health Research, Arnold & Marie, NY, 6755
Schwartz, Jr. Philanthropic Foundation, Miriam & Stanley, The, OH, 7576
Schwartzberg Foundation, Inc., Steven, The, NY, 6756
Schwarz Architects Charitable Foundation Inc., David M., MD, 3947
Schwarz Family Foundation, F. A. O., RI, 8483
Schwarz Family Foundation, NY, 6757
Schwebel Family Foundation, The, OH, 7577
Schweckendieck Trust, Edith M., NY, 6758
Schweers Family Foundation, Geiser, CA, 1020
Schweinfurth Foundation, MO, 4996
Schweitzer Foundation, Inc., William P. & Gertrude, NY, 6759
Schwerin Family Foundation, Inc., Virginia & Warren, The, CT, 1563
Schwimmer Charity Foundation, C., NY, 6760
Schwob Family Foundation, Inc., GA, 2581
Schwob Foundation, Simon, GA, see 2581
Sci-Port Foundation, LA, 3750
Scion Farms Foundation, OH, 7578
Scire Family Foundation Inc., The, NJ, 5526
Scotford Foundation, OH, 7579
Scott Community Foundation, KS, 3623
Scott County Community Foundation, IN, see 3446
Scott County Community Foundation, Inc., IN, 3446
Scott Family Foundation, Gay D. & William F., NJ, 5527

Scott Family Foundation, IL, 3230
Scott Family Foundation, Red, CA, 1021
Scott Foundation Inc., Elizabeth and Stanley D., The, NY, 6761
Scott Foundation Inc., Joyce and V.D., DE, 1740
Scott Foundation, Joseph C., The, PA, 8266
Scott Foundation, Joseph J., The, WY, 9987
Scott Foundation, R. & E., The, CA, 1022
Scott Foundation, Susan, CA, 1023
Scott Foundation, Walter, WY, 9988
Scott Foundation, William C. and Cindy L., The, NY, 6762
Scott, Jr. Foundation IV, Walter, NE, 5115
Scottsdale Foundation, The, CA, 1024
Scovel Foundation, Inc., Drs. Janene and Tom, CA, 1025
SCP Foundation, TX, 9185
Scribante Family Foundation, A. J. & Lynda, NE, 5116
Scribante Family Foundation, NE, see 5116
Scripps Family Foundation, William and Kathryn, The, DE, 1741
Scroggins Foundation, Inc., Arthur E. & Cornelia C., The, KS, 3624
Scrugli Charitable Trust, Anthony J. & Elaine M., IL, 3231
SCS Foundation, Inc., GA, 2582
Scully Foundation, John, MI, 4561
Scully Foundation, Joseph C. and Judith A., The, NY, 6763
Sdei Israel Foundation, Inc., NY, 6764
SDF Family Foundation, NY, 6765
Seacoast Foundation, NY, 6766
Seager Trust, Esther Totten, WA, 9692
SEAKR Foundation, CO, 1351
Seal, Jr. Family Foundation, Leo W., MS, 4853
Sealed Power Foundation, NC, see 7252
Seaman Charitable Foundation, Douglas and Eleanor, FL, 2320
Seaman Family Foundation Trust, OH, 7580
Seaman Family Foundation, NY, 6767
Sear Family Foundation, TX, 9186
Searcy Charitable Trust, Emily and Bill, GA, 2583
Sears Foundation, Inc., Henry, The, MD, 3948
Sears-Swetland Family Foundation, The, OH, 7581
Sears-Swetland Foundation, The, OH, see 7581
Seasongood Good Government Foundation, Murray and Agnes, OH, 7582
Seaver Charitable Fund, The, CA, see 1026
Seaver Endowment, The, CA, 1026
Seay Foundation, Inc., Stephen M., TX, 9187
Seba Foundation, MN, 4789
Sebastiani Charitable Trust, August, CA, 1027
Second Chance Foundation, FL, 2321
Secord Perpetual Charitable Trust, Ruth O., IL, 3232
Secrist Family Charitable Foundation, PA, 8267
Securitas Foundation, The, NY, 6768
Security Financial Life Foundation, NE, see 5068
Security National Bank Charitable Foundation, IA, 3534
Security's Lending Hand Foundation, SC, 8539
Seebe Trust, Frances, PA, 8268
Seed Foundation, Fred M., RI, 8484
SEED Foundation, The, MI, 4562
Seeds of Faith, Inc., WI, 9925
Seelig Charitable Foundation Trust, NY, 6769
Sefn Trust, NY, 6770
SEG Foundation, The, NY, 6771
Segel and Janice L. Sherman Family Foundation, Robert G., The, MA, 4285
Seger Memorial Foundation, Inc., Steven M., IN, 3447
Segoe Family Foundation, Ladislas & Vilma, OH, 7583
Sehn Foundation, The, MI, 4563
Seidler Foundation, Janet Prindle, The, IL, 3233
Seidman Charitable Trust, P. K., TN, 8672
Seifert Charitable Trust, Dorothy T. & Myron T., OH, 7584
Seigel Charitable Trust, Fred A. and Donna P., NH, 5231
Seiler Family Foundation, MO, 4997
Seip Family Foundation, The, CA, 1028
Sekerak Charitable Trust, Arthur, CT, 1564
Selber Foundation, Inc., Aaron or Peggy, The, LA, 3751
Selders Foundation, Charles & Rena B., FL, 2322
Selders Foundation, Rena B., FL, see 2322
Selective Group Foundation, The, NJ, 5528

Self Foundation, Inc., Sara Smith, The, NC, 7238
Self Reliance Foundation, The, IL, 3234
Seligman Family Foundation, The, MI, 4564
Seligman Foundation, The, NY, 6772
Seligsohn Family Foundation, Inc., The, NY, 6773
Selin Family Foundation Inc, Nina & Ivan, The, DE, 1742
Selis Foundation, Inc., Irving and Sara, NY, 6774
Selkowitz Family Foundation, CT, 1565
Sella Foundation Trust, The, NJ, 5529
Selsky Foundation Inc., Abe & Kathryn, The, VA, 9529
Selsor Trust, Della, OH, 7585
Seme Foundation, Inc., TN, 8673
Senator Foundation, The, NY, 6775
Sender Charitable Trust, FL, 2323
Senior Services of Stamford, Inc., CT, 1566
Sequoia Farm Foundation, IL, 3235
Sequoia Foundation for Achievement in the Arts & Education, Inc., The, FL, 2324
SER Family Charitable Foundation, MA, 4286
Serafy Foundation, TX, 9188
Seramur Family Foundation Inc., WI, 9926
Serenbetz Family Foundation, Inc., The, NY, 6776
Serra Family Foundation, MI, 4565
Servant Leadership Foundation, The, CO, 1352
Servco Foundation, HI, 2645
Service Club for the Blind, Inc., MO, 4998
Setzer Family Foundation Inc., FL, 2325
Setzer Foundation, The, CA, 1029
Seven Cities Foundation, TX, 9189
Seven Oaks Foundation Inc., NJ, 5530
Seven Turns Fund, Inc., NY, 6777
Seventh Generation Foundation, Inc., VT, 9384
Sewald Foundation, Inc., Bernhard, MA, see 4331
Sewell Foundation, Inc., Warren P. & Ava F., GA, 2584
Sexton Family Charitable Foundation, AL, 63
Sexton Family Foundation, The, FL, 2326
Sexton Family Foundation, William D. and Joyce E., The, MN, 4790
Seybert Institution for Poor Boys and Girls, Adam and Maria Sarah, PA, 8269
Seybert Institution, PA, see 8269
Seymour Foundation, W. L. & Louise E., IL, 3236
Seymour Trust Fund, Greater, IN, 3448
Seymour Trust, George Dudley, RI, 8485
SF Foundation II, The, GA, 2585
SFC Charitable Foundation, SC, see 8540
SGMG Foundation, The, NY, 6778
Shachar Foundation, The, NY, 6779
Shack Sackler Foundation, The, NY, 6780
Shackelford Charitable Trust, Margaret F., FL, 2327
Shacknai Foundation, Max A., AZ, 167
Shackouls Family Foundation, The, NY, 6781
Shady Maple Foundation, PA, 8270
Shafer Foundation Charitable Trust, Hamer D. & Phyllis C., IN, 3449
Shaffer Charitable Foundation, George, Clarence & Dorothy, VA, 9530
Shaftel Foundation, Inc., Mel & Pamela, NY, 6782
Shaich Family Foundation, MA, 4287
Shaked and Babs Waldman Family Foundation, Inc., Avi, IL, 3237
Shaker Family Foundation, Joseph R. and Helen, IL, 3238
Shaker Family Foundation, The, IL, see 3238
Shalam Foundation, Sarah and Sasson, NY, 6783
Shalom Ish Foundation, The, NY, 6784
Shamah Foundation Inc., Eliahou Joseph and David, The, NJ, 5531
Shamrock Foundation, CO, 1353
Shamrock Foundation, IL, 3239
Shanahan Family Foundation, MO, 4999
Shaner Family Foundation, The, PA, 8271
Shanken Family Foundation, NY, 6785
Shanklin Foundation 2239788, MA, 4288
Shanley Family Foundation, The, CT, 1567
Shannon Automotive Foundation Inc., Mike, WI, 9927
Shannon Family Charitable Foundation, OH, 7586
Shannon Family Foundation, E. L. and Ruth B., The, CA, 1030
Shannon Family Foundation, Inc., Tom and Kathy, FL, 2328
Shannon Family Foundation, Ken and Jan, The, KS, 3625

Shannon Foundation, Hyslop, LA, 3752
Shapell Foundation, Inc., Benjamin and Susan, CA, 1031
Shapira Charitable Foundation, Anne & Eli, OR, 7814
Shapira Foundation, Inc., KY, 3693
Shapiro Charitable Trust, Mickey, MI, 4566
Shapiro Charity Fund Trust, Abraham, MA, 4289
Shapiro Family Foundation Inc., Robert F. & Anna Marie, The, NY, 6786
Shapiro Family Foundation, Gerald & Olivia, NC, 7239
Shapiro Family Foundation, The, NJ, 5532
Shapiro Foundation, Inc., Joan and James, IL, 3240
Shapiro Foundation, Jacob S., MD, 3949
Shapiro Fund Inc., Albert, MA, 4290
Sharaby Family Foundation, The, FL, 2329
Share Foundation, IL, 3241
Share the Warmth, Inc., IN, 3450
Shared Fund, The, MN, 4791
Sharing Foundation, Inc., The, FL, 2330
Sharkey Family Charitable Foundation, OR, 7815
Sharma Foundation, The, TX, 9190
Sharon Steel Foundation, NY, 6787
Sharp Ochiltree Foundation, Emma, PA, 8272
Shastri Charity Trust, Ranjit, PA, 8273
Shatford Memorial Trust, J. D., NY, 6788
Shattuck Charitable Trust, Clinton H. & Wilma T., The, MA, 4291
Shattuck Family Foundation, Inc., The, MD, 3950
Shaughnessy Charitable Trust, John J. and Mary E., MA, see 4292
Shaughnessy Charitable Trust, MA, 4292
Shaw Charitable Foundation, Barbara Udes, NE, 5117
Shaw Charitable Foundation, Seyfarth, IL, 3242
Shaw Charitable Trust I, Ilene & Michael, IL, 3243
Shaw Foundation, Charles H. & Beverly E., IL, 3244
Shaw Foundation, Inc., Duane and Marci, UT, 9350
Shaw Trust f/b/o Boys And Girls Clubs of Toledo, D.C., OH, 7587
Shawe Family Charitable Foundation, Inc., Earle & Annette, MO, see 5000
Shawe Family Charitable Foundation, MO, 5000
Shayne Foundation, CA, 1032
Shea Trust, Mary E., RI, 8486
Sheadle Trust, Jasper H., OH, 7588
Sheadle Trust, Kate B., OH, 7589
Sheafer Charitable Trust, Emma A., NY, 6789
Shearman Foundation, Tom B. & Flora I., The, LA, see 3732
Sheely Family Foundation, Dale and Alyce, OH, 7590
Sheetz Charitable Trust, Frances D., NY, 6790
Sheetz Charitable Trust, James E. and Maude, KS, 3626
Sheffield Foundation, Inc., The, NY, see 6885
SHEL Foundation, Inc., NY, 6791
Shemanski Testamentary Trust, Alfred & Tillie, WA, 9693
Shenandoah Foundation, CA, 1033
Shenandoah Foundation, CT, 1568
Shenk Foundation, Willis and Elsie, PA, 8274
Shepard Trust, Charles E., FL, 2331
Shepherd Foundation, Harold and Helen, WA, 9694
Shepherd Foundation, The, MO, 5001
Shepherds for the Savior, TX, 9191
Shepherdson Family Foundation, Charles and Marie, The, VA, 9531
Sheridan Family Foundation, Howard and Brenda, Dr., NJ, 5533
Sherman Family Charitable Trust, George & Beatrice, MA, 4293
Sherman Family Foundation, The, MI, 4567
Sherman Foundation, Murray G. & Beatrice H., NY, 6792
Sherman Foundation, The, TX, 9192
Sherman Hsu Family Foundation, MA, 4294
Sherrard Foundation, Bill & Susan, The, NC, 7240
Sherrerd Foundation, PA, see 8182
Sherwood Family Foundation, Ned and Emily, The, IN, 3451
Shetty and Nasser Ahmad Foundation Inc., Romita, The, NY, 6793
Shiawassee Community Foundation, MI, 4568
Shiawassee Foundation, MI, see 4568
Shidler Family Foundation, The, HI, 2646

Shields Animal Shelter Foundation, The, HI, 2647
Shilling Family Foundation, The, NJ, 5534
Shiloff Family Foundation, The, TX, 9193
Shine Foundation, The, MI, 4569
Shingleton Trust, Newton B., NC, 7241
Shinnick Educational Fund, William M., OH, 7591
Shiraki Memorial Foundation, HI, 2648
Shirley Private Foundation, Virginia Lee, IL, 3245
Shockley Foundation, FL, 2332
Shodeen Family Foundation, IL, 3246
Shoemaker Charitable Trust, George T. & Margaret E., WI, 9928
Shoemaker Fund, Thomas H. and Mary Williams, The, PA, 8275
Shoemate Foundation, CT, 1569
Shoen Foundation, L. S. "Sam", OR, 7816
Shook Foundation, Barbara Ingalls, AL, 64
Shore Foundation, Inc., David and Judy, CA, 1034
Shore Fund, The, PA, 8276
Short Pump Ruritan/Civic Foundation, Inc., VA, 9532
Shott Foundation, Inc., June Oblinger, The, WV, 9765
Showers of Blessing Foundation, LA, 3753
SHP Foundation, CA, 1035
Shrensky Foundation, Inc., MD, 3951
Shrontz Family Foundation, Joanne L., UT, 9351
SHT Foundation, TX, 9194
Shuey Orphanage Trust, H. L., FL, 2333
Shugart Family Foundation, NC, 7242
Shulamit Foundation, Rachel Bat, NY, 6794
Shulman Family Foundation, Alex, NV, see 5185
Shulman Family Foundation, NV, 5185
Shultz Family Foundation, The, AZ, 168
Shuman Family Foundation, Stanley S., The, NY, 6795
Shuman Scholarship Fund Trust, Robbins, The, PA, 8277
Shumway Capital Foundation, The, CT, see 1570
Shumway Charitable Trust, Clara L., MO, 5002
Shumway Foundation, The, CT, 1570
Shuster Foundation, George, Jack, and Joan, NJ, 5535
Shuster Foundation, George, NJ, see 5535
Sibbernsen Foundation, IL, A
Sicari Charitable Trust, Joseph & Agatha, The, MA, 4295
Sidewalk Angels Foundation, NY, 6796
Sidewater Family Foundation Inc., The, PA, 8278
Sidewater Foundation, Arthur & Estelle, PA, see 8364
Sidewater Foundation, Inc., Morris & Evelyn, The, PA, see 8278
Sidhu Family Foundation, The, FL, 2334
Sidwell Family Foundation, Jeff and Jennie, The, OH, 7592
Sieg Fund, Louis and Nellie, MI, see 4496
Siegel Charitable Trust, Stuart and Jill, The, FL, 2335
Siegel Family Foundation, Blossom, The, CA, 1036
Siegel Family Foundation, Marshall & Elaine, NV, 5186
Siegel Foundation, Richard, TN, 8674
Siegel Foundation, Ruth and Jerome A., NY, 6797
Sierra Foundation, Inc., FL, 2336
Sigma-Aldrich Foundation, MO, 5003
Signal Foundation for Wireless Innovation, Inc., DE, 1743
Sikand Foundation, Inc., The, CA, 1037
Silber Foundation, Inc., Jean and Sidney, The, MD, 3952
Silberman Charitable Trust, Robert and Christina, The, MD, 3953
Silberman Foundation, Curt C. & Else, DC, 1834
Silberman Foundation, Nathan and Marilyn, The, NY, 6798
Silicon Valley Bank Foundation, The, CA, 1038
Silk Foundation, The, MO, 5004
Sillins Family Foundation Inc., Robert, The, NY, 6799
Siloam Foundation, AL, 65
Silton Family Foundation, CA, 1039
Silver Foundation, Inc., Louis & Martha, NY, 6800
Silver Foundation, Morris & Helen, OR, 7817
Silverback Foundation, Inc., NC, 7243
Silverman Family Charitable Foundation, Inc., The, NJ, 5536
Silverman Family Foundation, Inc., FL, see 2337
Silverman Family Foundation, Marc and Mattye, The, NC, 7244
Silverman Foundation, Inc., Barry & Judy, FL, 2337
Silverman Foundation, Inc., Elizabeth S. & Stephen I., NJ, see 5536

Silverman Foundation, Inc., Harvey, The, NY, 6801
Silverman Foundation, The, NC, see 7244
Silverstein Family Foundation, DC, see 1835
Silverstein Family Foundation, Inc., Raine & Stanley, The, NY, 6802
Silverstein Family Foundation, Leonard & Elaine, DC, 1835
Silverstein Foundation, Howard A., NY, 6803
Simard Foundation, Yvonne H., TX, 9195
Simcha D'Sassov Foundation, Zichorn, NY, 6804
Simionescu Scholarship Foundation, RI, 8487
Simmons Charitable Foundation, Inc., Mabel & Ellsworth, The, FL, 2338
Simmons Charitable Foundation, MO, 5005
Simms Family Foundation, The, WI, 9929
Simon Charitable Foundation, The, NM, 5624
Simon Charitable Trust, Esther, IL, 3247
Simon Foundation Inc., Herbert & Bui, IN, 3452
Simon Foundation, Lucille Ellis, CA, 1040
Simon Foundation, Robert Ellis, CA, 1041
Simon, Jr. Foundation, Cynthia L. & William E., The, NJ, 5537
Simon-Strauss Foundation, CA, 1042
Simoni Foundation, Inc., Frank R. and Elizabeth, MA, 4296
Simple Actions Family Foundation, OR, 7818
Simplot Foundation, Inc., J. R., ID, 2685
Simpson Foundation, John M., IL, 3248
Simpson Foundation, Joseph T. & Helen M., NY, 6805
Simpson Foundation, The, AL, 66
Simpson Foundation, William & Hope, IL, 3249
Simpson-Omohundro Foundation, TX, 9196
Sinai Medical Staff Foundation, MI, 4570
Sinai Scholars Inc., OH, 7593
Sinclair Family Foundation, Joseph S. and Rosalyn K., The, RI, 8488
Singer Family C & E Foundation, PA, 8279
Singer Foundation, Gordon and Jenny, The, DE, 1744
Singer Foundation, The, OR, 7819
Singer Fund Inc., Louis P., NY, 6806
Singh Family Foundation, WA, 9695
Singhal Family Charitable Foundation, DE, 1745
Singhal Foundation, The, MA, see 4048
Singing Field Foundation Inc., MA, 4297
Singing for Change, SC, 8540
Single Step Foundation, WI, 9930
Singleton Scholarship Trust, M. E., TX, 9197
Sioles Family Foundation, Milton & Harriet, AZ, 169
Siperstein Charitable Foundation, Mynde & Gary, RI, 8489
Sirad Foundation Inc., VA, 9533
Sisk Charitable Trust, Paul L. & Helen I., OK, 7719
Siteman Family Foundation, The, MO, 5006
Sites Designated Charities Trust, NC, 7245
Sites Foundation, Venette and Mabel, NC, see 7245
Six Pillar Foundation, Inc., The, FL, 2339
SJL Foundation, CA, 1043
SK Foundation, TX, 9198
Skagit Community Foundation, The, WA, 9696
Skalny Charitable Trust, Joseph & Irene, NY, 6807
Skandalaris Family Foundation, MI, 4571
SKB Environmental, Inc. Rosemount Community Trust, MN, see 4657
SKB Foundation, CA, 1044
Skelton Charitable Foundation, Homer, MS, 4854
Skelton Trust Foundation, Myra Fox, WY, 9989
Skestos Family Foundation, OH, 7594
Skewes Family Foundation, WV, 9766
Skiles Foundation, The, MI, 4572
Skilling Foundation, WY, 9990
SKL Foundation, The, NY, 6808
Sklar Family Foundation, The, TX, 9199
Sklut Foundation, Lori L., The, NC, see 7161
Skokos Foundation, Ted and Shannon, The, TX, 9200
Skolnick Foundation, The, UT, 9352
Skowronski Family Foundation, The, CA, 1045
Skylark Foundation, IL, 3250
Skyler Foundation, OH, 7595
Skynyrd Foundation, CA, 1046
Skyscrape Foundation, The, CA, 1047
Slade Foundation, C. F. Roe, The, NY, 6809
Slade Foundation, Michael & Ruth, NY, 6810
Slaughter, Jr. Foundation, Inc., William E., UT, 9353

Slavik Family Foundation, Donald, MO, 5007

Slavin Foundation, Inc., Sanford and Doris, MD, 3954

Slay Charitable Foundation, Gene and Joan, MO, 5008

Slemons Foundation, RI, 8490

Slingerland Foundation, The, RI, 8491

Slingshot Development Fund, WA, 9697

Slitzer Lapausky Foundation, OH, 7596

Sloan Foundation, C. Hamilton, NC, 7246

Sloane Family Foundation, Carl and Toby, The, DE, 1746

Sloss Foundation, Margaret K., CA, 1048

Slovin Foundation, NY, 6811

Slusher Charitable Foundation, Roy W., MO, 5009

Small Change Foundation, The, CA, 1049

Small Foundation Inc., Albert & Lillian, MD, 3955

Small Foundation, Irvin and Beverly, TN, 8675

Smalley Family Foundation, Marvin & Sondra, CA, 1050

Smallwood Foundation, Frances C. & William P., IL, 3251

Smallwood Foundation, IL, see 3251

SmartGo Foundation, UT, 9354

Smeed Memorial Foundation, ID, 2686

Smeltzer Charitable Trust, Ann, IA, 3535

Smick Foundation, David & Vickie, The, FL, 2340

Smiley Family Charitable Foundation, The, OH, 7597

Smilowitz Private Foundation, Herbert, NJ, 5538

Smith & Woodford Foundation, VA, see 9410

Smith Benevolent Association, Buckingham, FL, 2341

Smith Charitable Foundation Inc., Roy W., The, CA, 1051

Smith Charitable Foundation, Arlene H., PA, 8280

Smith Charitable Foundation, Herman & Patsy, TX, 9201

Smith Charitable Foundation, Ray and June, TX, 9202

Smith Charitable Foundation, Robert and Dana, MA, see 4298

Smith Charitable Foundation, Will, The, TX, 9203

Smith Charitable Trust, Bailey, NY, 6812

Smith Charitable Trust, George V. and Jean A., NY, 6813

Smith Charitable Trust, Virginia, NE, 5118

Smith Charitable Trust, William Harold, NC, 7247

Smith Charities, Inc., Emmitt, TX, see 9204

Smith Charities, Pat & Emmitt, TX, 9204

Smith Clinic Trust 2, Lemon L., IL, 3252

Smith Family Foundation Inc., The, IN, 3453

Smith Family Foundation, Byron & Beth, NY, 6814

Smith Family Foundation, Hal & John, IL, see 3253

Smith Family Foundation, Hunter, VA, 9534

Smith Family Foundation, Inc., Arthur K., KY, 3694

Smith Family Foundation, Inc., AZ, 170

Smith Family Foundation, Inc., Hal & John, IL, 3253

Smith Family Foundation, Inc., Margaret Dunn, The, CT, 1571

Smith Family Foundation, M. J., RI, 8492

Smith Family Foundation, NV, 5187

Smith Family Foundation, Robert and Dana, MA, 4298

Smith Family Foundation, Ted and Joyce, The, CA, 1052

Smith Family Foundation, Will and Jada, CA, 1053

Smith Family Foundation, Wilson L., The, NC, 7248

Smith Foundation for Neurological Research, Vivian L., TX, 9205

Smith Foundation for Restorative Neurology, Vivian L., TX, see 9205

Smith Foundation, Frank J., PA, 8281

Smith Foundation, Grace Pepper, CA, 1054

Smith Foundation, Grant and Jacqui, The, CT, 1572

Smith Foundation, Inc., George Graham and Elizabeth Galloway, NJ, 5539

Smith Foundation, James C. & Norma I., TX, 9206

Smith Foundation, Jean M. R., MI, 4573

Smith Foundation, Julia and Albert, TX, 9207

Smith Foundation, Lester M., The, WA, 9698

Smith Foundation, Linda I., CA, 1055

Smith Foundation, Lloyd L. and Louise K., OH, 7598

Smith Foundation, Marguerite Carl, PA, 8282

Smith Foundation, Mark and Dorothy, CA, 1056

Smith Foundation, Nora and William, FL, 2342

Smith Foundation, Roy & Marianne, NY, 6815

Smith Foundation, Stephen S. and Dolores R., PA, 8283

Smith Foundation, Will, see 1053

Smith Foundation, William R. and Sara Babb, GA, 2586

Smith Fund, Horace, The, MA, 4299

Smith Group Foundation, Ltd., Everett, WI, 9931

Smith Morrill Scholarship Fund, Justin, MA, 4300

Smith Private Foundation, Russell L. & Vera M., WI, 9932

Smith Revocable Trust, Shirley A., PA, 8284

Smith Trust, General William A., The, NC, 7249

Smith Trust, Hervey L., RI, 8493

Smith, Jr. Charitable Trust, Jack J., The, PA, 8285

Smith, Jr. Foundation, Inc., Malcolm E., NY, 6816

Smith-Walker Foundation, CA, 1057

Smith-Welsh Foundation, CA, 1058

Smithburg Family Foundation, IL, 3254

Smittcamp Family Foundation, The, CA, 1059

Smoot Charitable Foundation, KS, 3627

SMS Foundation, Inc., WI, 9933

Smullin Foundation, Patricia D. and William B., CA, 1060

Smysor Charitable Trust, Elizabeth A., IL, 3255

Smyth Trust, Marion C., NH, 5232

Smythe Family Foundation, William D., CA, 1061

SNAVE Foundation, DE, 1747

Snayberger Memorial Foundation, Harry E. and Florence W., NY, 6817

Snayberger Memorial Foundation, NY, see 6817

SNB Charitable Foundation Trust, IA, see 3534

Sneath Trust, Dorothy Melcher, PA, 8286

Snell & Wilmer Charitable Foundation, AZ, 171

Snow Foundation, Inc., John Ben, The, NY, 6818

Snyder Charitable Foundation, PA, 8287

Snyder Charitable Fund, G. Whitney, NJ, 5540

Snyder Family Foundation, Patricia H., The, IN, 3454

Snyder Foundation for Animals Inc., The, MD, 3956

Snyder Foundation for Animals, William, The, MD, see 3956

Snyder Foundation, Bruce R. Snyder & Madelyn G., PA, 8288

Snyder Foundation, Doris E., WA, 9699

Snyder Foundation, Harold B. and Dorothy A., The, NJ, 5541

Snyder Foundation, Helen M., The, NJ, 5542

Snyder Foundation, Inc., Michele, NJ, 5543

Snyder Foundation, Inc., Ruth B. and Willard B., KS, see 3560

Snyder Fund, Valentine Perry, NY, 6819

Snyder's-Lance Foundation, NC, 7250

Soar Foundation, MN, 4792

Societe des Professeurs Francais en Amerique, NY, 6820, see 6820

Society for Analytical Chemists of Pittsburgh, PA, 8289

Society of the Friendly Sons of Saint Patrick in the City of New York, The, NY, 6821

Sohr Family Foundation, Jim and Leah, TN, 8676

Soicher Foundation, Harry and Estelle, The, CA, 1062

Sokol Family Foundation, NY, 6822

Sokoll Trust, Walter, MO, 5010

Sokoloff Foundation, Inc., The, NY, 6823

Solano Community Foundation, CA, 1063

Soli Deo Gloria Foundation, NE, 5119

Solms Family Foundation, Stephen and Ellen, PA, see 7992

Solomon Foundation, Inc., Lawrence and Lillian, The, MA, 4301

Solomont Family Foundation, Ahron M. and Sheera A., MA, 4302

Solomont Family Foundation, Alan D. and Susan Lewis, MA, 4303

Solot Family Foundation, DE, 1748

Solstice Foundation Inc., The, GA, 2587

Some Voices Foundation, NY, 6824

Somekh Family Foundation, The, CA, 1064

Someone Cares Charitable Trust, CO, 1354

Somers Foundation, Byron H., FL, see 1979

Somers Foundation, Inc., Virginia Hodgkins, ME, 3803

Somerset Amish Helping Hands Inc., PA, 8290

Somerville Charitable Trust, Graham and Thelma, PA, 8291

Sommer Foundation, Abraham & Beverly, The, NY, 6825

Sondheimer Family Charitable Foundation, The, IL, 3256

Sondheimer Foundation, The, CA, 1065

Sondland and Katherine J. Durant Foundation, Gordon D., The, WA, 9700

Sondland Foundation, Gordon D., WA, see 9700

Sonhil Fund, Inc., NY, see 6209

Sonja Foundation, The, CT, 1573

Sonneborn Foundation Inc., The, MD, 3957

Sonnentag Foundation Ltd., WI, 9934

Sontheimer Foundation, The, CT, A

Soonae Foundation, Inc., TX, 9208

Sorala Foundation, The, NJ, 5544

Sorel Charitable Organization, Inc., Elizabeth & Michel, The, NY, 6826

Sorensen-Siegel Foundation Inc., Jeanne, The, NY, 6827

Sorenson Foundation, Beverley Taylor, UT, 9355

Sorenson Foundation, James LeVoy, UT, 9356

Sorenson-Pearson Family Foundation, Inc., CT, 1574

Sorgente Group Foundation, NY, 6828

Soter Foundation, Sarah Ross, FL, see 2343

Soter Kay Foundation, FL, 2343

South Central Community Foundation, KS, 3628

South Plains Foundation, TX, 9209

South St. Joseph Progressive Association, Inc., MO, 5011

South Texas Charitable Foundation, TX, 9210

Southard Foundation, The, OH, 7599

Southland Greyhound Park Community Foundation, Inc., AR, 215

Southpole Foundation Inc., NJ, 5545

Southwestern Foundation for Education and Historical Preservation, CO, 1355

Spaeth Memorial Fund, Carol & Charles, NY, 6829

Spain Foundation, Ann & Murray, PA, 8292

Spalding Foundation, Eliot, The, AZ, 172

Spang and Company Charitable Trust, PA, see 8231

Spark Charitable Foundation, WA, 9701

Sparkplug Foundation, The, NY, 6830

Sparks Foundation, Ruth Parr, TX, 9211

Sparrow Foundation, The, TX, 9212

Sparrows' Home Foundation, Inc., TX, see 9208

Spatz Foundation, Helen and Irving, NY, 6831

Spatz Foundation, Martin & Dorothy, CA, 1066

Spear Charitable Trust, Charles, NY, 6832

Special Assistance Fund for Energy, NV, 5188

Special Children's Foundation Inc., LA, 3754

Speckhard-Knight Charitable Foundation, MI, 4574

Speech Foundation of America, TN, see 8680

Speiser Family Foundation, The, IL, 3257

Spektor Family Foundation, Inc., NY, 6833

Spencer Charitable Fund, NY, 6834

Spencer Family Foundation, OR, 7820

Spencer Foundation, Galen & Ada Belle, CO, 1356

Spencer Foundation, Mary C. & Perry F., PA, 8293

Spencer Foundation, Sarah, The, IL, 3258

Spendlove Research Foundation, UT, 9357

Sperandio Family Foundation, NY, 6835

Speranza Foundation, Inc., FL, 2344

Speranza Foundation, The, NY, 6836

Spero Charitable Foundation, MA, 4304

Speyer Foundation, Alexander C. & Tillie S., PA, 8294

Spider Shores Foundation, Inc., WI, 9935

Spiegel Family Foundation, Inc., Jerry and Emily, NY, 6837

Spiegel Foundation, Edward and Deanne, The, NY, see 6838

Spiegel Foundation, Inc., Jerry, NY, see 6837

Spiegel Foundation, The, NY, 6838

Spielman Family Foundation, CA, 1067

Spier Family Foundation, FL, 2345

Spilka Family Foundation, Inc., The, DE, see 1723

Spirit Foundations, Inc., NY, 6839

Spiritus Gladius Foundation, The, NY, 6840

Spiro Foundation, Donald W., The, NJ, 5546

Spitzer Trust, The, NY, 6841

Spiva Foundation, Stephan & Barbara, CA, 1068

Splawn Charitable Foundation West, Inc., Don and Roy, DE, 1749

Splawn Charitable Foundation, Don & Roy, TN, 8677

Splawn Charitable Foundation, Don, The, TN, see 8677

Splawn Charitable Foundation, Roy L., DE, see 1749

SPM Foundation, Inc., MD, 3958

Spofford Foundation, Margaret W., NY, 6842

Spohler Foundation, Inc., NJ, 5547

Spoon Family Foundation, Alan and Terri, MA, 4305

Sprague Foundation, Robert R., CA, 1069

Sprague Memorial Foundation, Phineas W., MA, 4306

Sprague, Jr. Foundation, Caryll M. & Norman F., CA, 1070

Spriggs Charitable Trust, William Guy, KY, 3695
Spring Charitable Trust, NC, 7251
Spring Forth Foundation, WA, 9702
Springborn Family Foundation, FL, A
Springer Family Charitable Trust, NE, 5120
Springhouse Foundation, CA, see 692
Springleaf Finance Foundation, Inc., IN, 3455
Springview Foundation, MI, 4575
Spruce Street Foundation, NJ, 5548
Spungen Family Foundation, Florence and Laurence, CA, 1071
SPX Foundation, NC, 7252
Squam Lake Foundation, MN, 4793
Squier Family Foundation, NY, 6843
Squires Educational Foundation, Inc., William D., The, AZ, 173
Sramek Charitable Trust, Elmer & Sylvia, IL, 3259
Srivastava Foundation, CA, 1072
SSAB Foundation for Education, AL, 67
SSAB North American Foundation, IL, 3260
St. Agnes Catholic Education Foundation, MN, 4794
St. Clair Foundation, MI, 4576
St. Croix Valley Recreation Foundation, ME, 3804
St. Deny's Foundation, Inc., MI, see 4595
St. John Foundation, Inc., Ruth and Robert, MD, 3959
St. John of Shanghai and San Francisco Foundation, Inc., MD, 3960
St. Louis Health Foundation, Greater, MO, 5012
St. Michael's Self Help Wajda Project Trust, MI, 4577
St. Petersburg Times Fund, Inc., FL, see 2362
St. Piran's Foundation, WI, 9936
Staats Foundation, Norman E. and Gwyneth L., NJ, 5549
Stack Family Foundation, Nancy and Geoffrey, CA, 1073
Stackhouse Foundation, Mary Reinhart, NY, 6844
Stadler Foundation, Julia Carell, The, TN, 8678
Staehle Foundation, Florence M. and Paul M., PA, 8295
Stafast Foundation Inc., OH, 7600
Stafford Family Foundation, The, VA, see 9535
Stafford Foundation, James M., Inc., CA, 1074
Stafford Foundation, John R. and Inge P., The, FL, 2346
Stafford Foundation, VA, 9535
Stahl Family Foundation, Inc., The, GA, 2588
Stairway Fund, The, IL, 3261
Staley Charitable Trust, Henry M., IL, 3262
Staley Educational Foundation, Richard Seth, The, CO, 1357
Staley Foundation for Psychological Development, Richard Seth, CO, see 1357
Staley Foundation, Bill and Orli, The, IL, 3263
Staley Foundation, Thomas F., PA, 8296
Staley Jr. Foundation, A.E., IL, 3264
Stallman Foundation, Herman, Esther & Henry, KS, 3629
Stamm Family Foundation, The, IN, see 3456
Stamm Koechlein Family Foundation, The, IN, 3456
Standard Products Foundation, The, OH, see 7568
Stanley's Garden Foundation, NJ, 5550
Stanton Family Foundation, The, NY, 6845
Stanton Foundation, Haddock, The, AZ, 174
Stanzel Family Foundation, Inc., The, TX, 9213
Stanzler Charitable Trust, Marjorie Cohen, MA, 4307
Staples Foundation, David T. and Dorris E., CA, 1075
Stapleton Charitable Trust, J. and V., NC, 7253
Star Foundation, The, PA, 8297
Star Lumber & Supply Charitable Foundation, KS, see 3580
Star Tribune Foundation, CA, see 811
Stare Fund, The, MA, 4308
Stark Charitable Foundation, Howard E., NY, 6846
Stark Foundation, C. Richard Stark, Jr. & Joan E., IA, 3536
Starker Family Foundation Inc., The, NY, 6847
Starmar Foundation, NY, 6848
Starnes Wenger Foundation, Dixie, The, TX, 9214
Starr Charitable Trust, Polly Thayer, MA, 4309
Stars Foundation of Thurston County, The, WA, 9703
Starvaggi Charities, Inc., WV, 9767
Stateline Community Foundation, The, WI, 9937
Staton Charitable Trust, Buel J., The, OK, 7720
Staton Foundation, Jocelyn Botterell, GA, see 2523
Statue Foundation, Inc., The, NY, 6849
Staubach Family Foundation, The, TX, 9215

Stauffer Foundation, John and Beverly, CA, 1076
Stauffer Foundation, Mary R., CA, 1077
Stay Fast Foundation Inc., OH, see 7600
Stearns Charitable Trust, MA, 4310
Stearns Foundation Inc., Gwendolyn L., SD, 8575
Stearns Foundation, The, CA, 1078
Stearns Trust, Artemas W., MA, 4311
Stebbins Fund Inc., The, NY, 6850
Stecher Family Foundation, The, NY, 6851
Stecher Foundation, Esta and Jamie, The, NY, see 6851
Steck Family Foundation, Fredric E., The, NY, 6852
Steckler Family Foundation, Inc., NY, 6853
Steckler Foundation, Philip H. & Lois R., NY, see 6853
Steele Family Foundation, FL, 2347
Steen Charitable Foundation, Don and Trudy, TX, 9216
Stefansky Charitable Trust, Meir and Ruth, The, NY, 6854
Steffens Foundation, CO, 1358
Steiger Memorial Fund, Inc., Albert, MA, 4312
Steigerwaldt Foundation, Inc., Donna Wolf, IL, 3265
Stein Family Charitable Foundation, The, DE, 1750
Stein Family Foundation, Fred, The, PA, 8298
Stein Family Foundation, Inc., Allen A., NY, 6855
Stein Family Foundation, The, CA, 1079
Stein Foundation, Avy and Marcie, IL, 3266
Stein Foundation, Inc., Fred & Sharon, The, PA, see 8298
Stein Foundation, Jane and Frances, NJ, 5551
Stein Foundation, Nachum & Feige, The, NY, 6856
Stein Foundation, Sam S. & Rose, OH, 7601
Stein Foundation/Fund No. 2, Louis and Bessie, PA, 8299
Stein/Bellet Foundation, Inc., PA, 8300
Steinberg Charitable Foundation, Frieda & Leon, The, NV, 5189
Steinberg Family Foundation, Inc., Meyer & Jean, NY, 6857
Steinberg Foundation, Inc., Meyer, NY, see 6857
Steiner Family Foundation Inc., Paula M., KY, 3696
Steiner Foundation, Inc., UT, 9358
Steiner Foundation, Joseph L. Steiner and Marjorie S., The, OH, see 7602
Steiner-King Foundation, OH, 7602
Steinhafel Family Foundation, Gregg W. & Denise E., MN, 4795
Steinhagen Benevolent Trust, B. A. and Elinor, LA, 3755
Steinhart Foundation, Inc., The, NE, 5121
Steinle Foundation, Inc., J. Vernon Steinle & Elmyra K., The, WI, 9938
Steinmann Family, Robert & Christine, OH, 7603
Steinmetz Charitable Trust, Matthew, IL, 3267
Steinmetz Family Foundation, Charles & Lynn, NC, 7254
Steinmetz Foundation, B. & M., NY, 6858
Steinmetz Foundation, S. & E., NY, 6859
Stellar Foundation, The, FL, 2348
Stellar Solutions Foundation, CA, 1080
Stemberg Charitable Foundation, Thomas G., MA, 4313
Stensen Memorial Trust Foundation, Harry, OH, 7604
Stephens Family Foundation, Harriet and Warren, AR, 216
Stephens Family Foundation, TX, 9217
Stephenson Foundation, Philip, VA, 9536
STERIS Foundation, The, OH, 7605
Sterling Charitable Foundation, Leonard and Shirley, TX, 9218
Sterling Family Foundation, OH, 7606
Sterling Family Foundation, TX, 9219
Sterling Foundation, CA, 1081
Stern Charitable Trust, Elaine Feld, MO, 5013
Stern Family Foundation, A. J. & S. L., IL, 3268
Stern Family Foundation, Inc., Jerome L., NY, 6860
Stern Family Foundation, MI, 4578
Stern Family Foundation, NJ, 5552
Stern Foundation, Dianne & David, The, NY, 6861
Stern Foundation, Inc., B. & B., The, FL, 2349
Stern Foundation, Inc., Gustav and Irene, FL, see 2350
Stern Foundation, Inc., Jerome L. and Jane, NY, see 6860
Stern Foundation, Inc., Steve and Bonnie, FL, 2350
Stern Foundation, Inc., Walter P. & Elizabeth M., NY, 6862
Sternberg Charitable Trust, NY, 6863
Sternklar Family Foundation, Inc., NY, 6864

Stevens Family Foundation, R. A., WI, 9939
Stevens Family Foundation, WA, 9704
Stevens Foundation, John T., SC, 8541
Stevens Foundation, Winifred L., AZ, 175
Stevenson Charitable Trust, Lester W., WI, 9940
Stevenson Foundation, Keith & Mattie, TX, 9220
Stewart Charitable Foundation, Douglas E. Stewart and Virginia E., FL, 2351
Stewart Foundation, CA, 1082
Stewart Foundation, Eminger, OR, 7821
Stewart Foundation, Faye & Lucille, OR, 7822
Stewart Foundation, Sarah A., CA, 1083
Stewart Foundation, The, PA, 8301
Stewart Foundation, Wayne C., OR, 7823
Stewart, Jr. Foundation, Marlene and J.O., The, TX, 9221
Stewart, M.D. Foundation, Alexander, PA, 8302
Stiefel Foundation, Inc., Barbara A., FL, 2352
Stiefel Freethought Foundation, DE, 1751
Stifel Foundation, Charlotte and Henry G., NY, 6865
Stifel Foundation, Inc., MO, 5014
Still Point Fund, NY, 6866
Stillson Foundation, OH, 7607
Stine Schreiber Foundation Inc., Agnita M., WV, 9768
Stires-Stark Family Foundation, NY, 6867
Stock Yards Bank Foundation Inc., KY, 3697
Stockdell-Joseph J. Leary Trust, Mary L., KY, 3698
Stoddard Family Foundation, Inc., MI, 4579
Stoker Charitable Trust, Margaret Jane, MI, 4580
Stokes Foundation, Lydia B., VT, 9385
Stoller Foundation, Mike and Corky Hale, The, CA, 1084
Stoller Foundation, The, TX, 9222
Stolzer Family Foundation, The, KS, 3630
Stone Family Foundation, J. Ralph and Lois, CA, 1085
Stone Family Foundation, Jerome H., IL, 3269
Stone Family Foundation, OK, 7721
Stone Foundation of New Jersey, The, NJ, 5553
Stone Foundation, Joseph and Fiora, CA, 1086
Stone Foundation, Joshua-Jim and Eunice, The, MI, 4581
Stone Foundation, Whitney and Anne M., VA, 9537
Stone Trust B, H. Chase, IL, 3270
Stonecutter Foundation, Inc., NC, 7255
StoneRiver Foundation, WY, 9991
Stony Point Foundation, The, SC, 8542
Stony Wold-Herbert Fund, Inc., NY, 6868
Storehouse Foundation, TX, 9223
Storer Foundation, Mary H., WY, 9992
Storer Goodwin Decatur Foundation, The, MA, 4314
Storer Scholarship Foundation, Oliver W., IL, 3271
Storey Charitable Trust, Earl & Mary, TN, 8679
Storey Foundation, Inc., GA, 2589
Storey Foundation, Inc., Mallie Bert, The, GA, see 2589
Storm Castle Foundation, CA, 1087
Storr Family Foundation, The, CT, 1575
Storz Foundation, Robert Herman, NE, 5122
Stotland Charitable Trust, Joseph and Lorraine, PA, 8303
Stott Foundation, Louis L., The, PA, 8304
Stout Foundation, Charles H., The, NV, 5190
Stout Scholarship Fund, O. J., WV, 9769
Stover Family Foundation, The, MD, 3961
Stowe Family Foundation, NY, 6869
Stowe Foundation, Inc., The, NC, 7256
Stowe, Jr. Foundation, Inc., Robert Lee, NC, see 7256
Stradley Foundation for the Protection of Independent Senior Women, J. L., The, MD, see 3927
Strain Foundation, AL, 68
Stratfield Fund, CT, 1576
Stratton Home, Myron, The, CO, 1359
Straub Trust Estate, Gertrude S., HI, 2649
Strauch Foundation, Inc., Barry S. and Evelyn M., VA, 9538
Straus Family Foundation, Inc., Robert K. and Barbara J., CA, 1088
Strauss Foundation Inc., The, NY, 6870
Strauss Foundation, Inc., Carolyn Rose, LA, see 3738
Strawbridge Foundation of Pennsylvania II, Inc., Margaret Dorrance, PA, 8305
Stretesky Foundation, William, CO, 1360
Striano Foundation, Peter & Caroline, The, NY, 6871
Strickland Family Foundation, Linda & Jerry, The, TX, 9224

Strickland Family Foundation, NC, 7257

Strine Foundation, Walter M. and Alice Washco, The, PA, 8306

Strine Foundation, William B. and Judith Baeshore, The, PA, 8307

Stringer Foundation, The, SC, 8543

Stroble Charitable Foundation, Ruth M. & Francis A., MO, 5015

Strohm Link Family Foundation, The, CO, 1361

Strome Family Foundation, CA, 1089

Strong Family Foundation, The, FL, 2353

Strong Foundation of New York, NY, 6872

Strong Tower, Inc., GA, 2590

Strowd Roses, Inc., NC, 7258

Strube Family Foundation Inc, Don and Joan, FL, 2354

Stry Foundation, Inc., Paul E., WI, 9941

STS Foundation, IL, 3272

Stuart Foundation, Elbridge & Evelyn, WY, 9993

Stuart George and Jeanette Charitable Trust, NC, 7259

Stuart Trust, W.B. and Ellen Gordon, IL, 3273

Stuart, Jr. Foundation, Mark, NY, 6873

Stubblefield Foundation, Inc., The, NC, 7260

Stubnitz Foundation, Maurice & Dorothy, MI, 4582

Stuckeman Foundation, The, PA, see 8195

Stucky Testamentary Trust, Mary Margaret, IN, 3457

Studer Foundation, Inc., FL, 2355

Stultz Foundation, The, VA, 9539

Stump Endowment Fund, Beatrice Moore, PA, 8308

Stuntz Family Foundation, NY, 6874

Sturges Charitable Trust, Stephen H. Sturges & Rose P., The, AZ, 176

Sturgis Foundation, W. P., AR, 217

Stutsman Charitable Trust, Margaret A., IL, 3274

Stuttering Foundation of America, Inc., TN, 8680

Stuttering Foundation, The, TN, see 8680

Stutz Trust, Geraldine, The, NY, 6875

Stutzman Family Foundation, PA, 8309

Styberg Foundation, Inc., E. C., WI, 9942

Sub-Zero Wolf Foundation, Inc., WI, 9943

Suburban Charitable Foundation, Inc., NY, A

Sudakoff Foundation Inc., Harry, FL, 2356

Sudikoff Family Foundation, The, CA, 1090

Sue Lavin Foundation, Karen, IL, 3275

Suen Family Foundation, The, WA, 9705

Sugarbaker Foundation, Everett D. and Geneva V., MO, 5016

Suggs Family Foundation, The, CA, 1091

Sukeforth Charitable Foundation, S. Douglas and Rita C., The, ME, 3805

Sulentic Family Foundation, DE, 1752

Sullivan Charitable Foundation, Alice I., The, RI, 8494

Sullivan Family Foundation, Hugh D. and Julie H., IL, 3276

Sullivan Family Foundation, MA, 4315

Sullivan Family Foundation, Robert J., The, WI, 9944

Sullivan Family Foundation, The, CT, 1577

Sullivan Foundation, Inc., Chris T., FL, 2357

Sullivan Musical Foundation, William Matheus, CT, 1578

Sullivan, Jr. Foundation, John J., MO, 5017

Sulzer Family Foundation, IL, 3277

Sumac Foundation, The, IL, 3278

Sumitomo Corporation of America Foundation, NY, 6876

Summer Fund II, IL, 3279

Summer Rest Foundation, NC, 7261

Summer Star Foundation for Nature, Art and Humanity Inc, MA, 4316

Summit Foundation, NY, 6877

Sumners/Nelson/Thompson Foundation, AL, 69

Sun Shine on You Foundation, CA, 1092

Sun, Moon and Stars Foundation, Inc., FL, 2358

Sunburst Foundation, Inc., FL, 2359

Sundance Family Foundation, MN, 4796

Sunlight Foundation, TN, 8681

Sunnen Foundation, MO, 5018

Sunrise Charitable Foundation Inc., NY, 6878

Sunrise Foundation, CA, 1093

Sunshine Foundation, Inc., The, SC, 8544

Sunwest Bank Charitable Foundation, The, CA, 1094

Support Of Partners For Sustainable Development, CA, 1095

Sure Foundation Inc, TX, 9225

Surrena Memorial, Harry & Thelma, WY, 9994

Susman Foundation, Bernard M. and Caryl H., The, DE, 1753

Susquehanna Foundation, PA, 8310

Sussman Fund, Edna Bailey, NY, 6879

Sussman Trust, Otto, NY, 6880

Sustainable Arts Foundation, CA, 1096

Sutaruk Foundation, MI, 4583

Sutcliffe Foundation, Walter and Louise, NC, 7262

Sutherland Charitable Trust, Sarah H., NC, 7263

Sutherland Foundation, Inc., The, KY, 3699

Sutton Family Foundation Inc., Abe & Yvette, NY, 6881

Sutton Family Foundation, Mark B., TX, 9226

Sutton Family Foundation, Ruth & David, NY, 6882

Sutton Foundation, Mary & Abe, NY, 6883

Sutton Memorial Fund, Altoon, NJ, 5554

Sutton Trust Foundation, The, NY, 6884

Suwinski Family Foundation Inc., The, NY, 6885

Svanees Foundation, WA, 9706

SVM Foundation, NY, 6886

Swagelok Foundation, The, OH, 7608

Swan Society in Boston, MA, 4317

Swann Corporation, Jim & Jonnie, FL, 2360

Swanson Foundation, Max & Betty, MT, 5063

Swarts Memorial Fund, Harry & Dolly, RI, 8495

Swayne Family Foundation, Keith and Judy, The, CA, 1097

Swearingen Foundation, The, KS, 3631

Sweeney Family Foundation, NY, 6887

Sweetgrass Foundation, Inc., The, GA, 2591

Sweig Foundation, Michael, NV, 5191

Sweigart Charitable Foundation, Anne Brossman, PA, 8311

Swenson Family Foundation, MD, 3962

Swett Charitable Trust, Holly and Bradford, The, NY, 6888

Swett Foundation, Ralph & Eileen, TX, 9227

Swift, Jr. Family Foundation, George P., DE, 1754

Swinerton Foundation, The, CA, 1098

Swinmurn Family Foundation, DE, 1755

Swisher Foundation, Inc., Carl S., FL, 2361

Switzer Foundation, NY, 6889

Sword and Spoon Foundation, MA, 4318

Syar Foundation, CA, 1099

Sylvan Foundation, Dave & Barbara, OK, 7722

Symes Family Charitable Foundation, MA, 4319

Synopsys Outreach Foundation, CA, see 1100

Synopsys Silicon Valley Science and Technology Outreach Foundation, CA, 1100

Synthesis Foundation, Inc., The, DE, 1756

SYZYGY Foundation, CA, 1101

Szekely Family Foundation, CA, 1102

Szekely Foundation for American Volunteers, CA, see 1102

Szulik Family Foundation, NC, 7264

T & O Foundation Inc., WI, 9945

T-Bonz Foundation, Inc., SC, 8546

Tabani Family Foundation, TX, 9228

Tabas Foundation, Charles L., PA, see 8312

Tabas Foundation, Harriette Steelman and Charles L., The, PA, 8312

Tabitha Foundation, Inc., S.E.H., NC, 7265

Taddonio Family Foundation, Inc., CO, 1362

Tadler Charitable Trust, Steven M. and Joyce E., MA, 4320

Tafel Foundation, James B., IL, 3280

Taft Charitable Foundation, Dudley, OH, 7609

Taghavi and Ghazi Foundation, The, CA, see 868

Tahari Family Foundation, The, NY, 6890

Tai-Ping II Foundation, The, NY, see 5659

Tait Foundation, Frank M., OH, 7610

Taj Foundation, OH, 7611

Take Shape for Life Charitable Foundation, Inc., The, NJ, 5555

Takiff Charities, Ltd., Sanford & Bobette, IL, see 3281

Takiff Family Foundation, IL, 3281

Takitani Foundation, Inc., HI, see 2650

Takitani Foundation, Inc., Mamoru & Aiko, HI, 2650

Talbott Foundation, Audrey S., DE, see 1757

Talbott Foundation, Nelson, OH, 7612

Talbott Foundation, Robert and Audrey, The, DE, 1757

Tally Foundation, The, PA, 8313

Talty Charitable Trust, Michael Talty and Helen, MI, 4584

TALX Charitable Foundation, GA, 2592

Tamaki Foundation, The, WA, 9707

Tamarack Foundation, MN, 4797

Tamarin Foundation Inc., NJ, 5556

Tamer Foundation, MI, 4585

Tampa Bay Times Fund, Inc., FL, 2362

Tandy Foundation, Carol, OK, 7723

Tang Fund, The, NY, 6891

Tanico Foundation Inc., Paul P., NY, 6892

Tanimura Family Foundation, The, CA, 1103

Tanner Foundation, Clark L., NM, 5625

Tanner-Frank Foundation, The, NY, 6893

Taos Community Foundation, NM, 5626

Taplin Charitable Foundation, Sol, FL, 2363

Tappan Foundation, The, CO, 1363

Tapper Charitable Foundation, MA, 4321

Tara Foundation Inc., VA, 9540

Tarakji Foundation, MI, 4586

Tarr Charitable Foundation, Robert and Molly, SC, 8545

Tarrant Family Foundation, Jeffrey, DE, 1758

Tarrson Foundation for Dental Research, Bud, IL, 3282

Tassell Foundation, Leslie E., The, MI, see 4587

Tassell-Wisner-Bottrall Foundation, MI, 4587

Tate Foundation, WY, 9995

Tatelman Family Foundation, Eliot H. & June L., MA, 4322

Tatelman Family Foundation, Susan and Barry, MA, 4323

Taub Foundation, TX, 9229

Taxman Family Foundation, IL, 3283

Taylor Charitable Foundation Trust, Mary E., FL, 2364

Taylor Charitable Foundation, Ben & Kate, DE, 1759

Taylor Family Charitable Foundation, Daniel J., KS, 3632

Taylor Family Foundation Inc., KY, 3700

Taylor Family Foundation, Inc., FL, 2365

Taylor Family Foundation, Inc., Jack, FL, 2366

Taylor Family Foundation, Paul and Patricia, IL, 3284

Taylor Foundation, Bennington, The, CT, 1579

Taylor Foundation, Fred and Harriett, IL, 3285

Taylor Foundation, Maurice and Michelle, IL, 3286

Taylor Foundation, Montana, Ruth and Vernon, The, MT, 5064

Taylor Foundation, Ruth and Vernon, The, CO, 1364

Taylor Foundation, W. A., MS, 4855

Taylor Perpetual Charitable Trust, Brent, IL, 3287

TCH Fort Foundation, FL, see 2080

TCT Foundation, WA, see 9624

TCU Foundation Inc., IN, 3458

Teachers Housing Cooperative, CA, 1104

Technical Assistance Mission Inc., MI, 4588

TECO Energy Foundation Inc., FL, 2367

Tecumseh Foundation, CA, 1105

Tedaldi Foundation, Inc., Kenneth J., The, NY, 6894

Teddy Foundation, The, DE, 1760

Tedesco Family Private Foundation, NJ, 5557

Teel Charitable Foundation, WA, 9708

Teichman Family Charitable Foundation, The, CA, 1106

Teiger Foundation, NJ, 5558

Teitel Charitable Trust, Ben N., MI, 4589

Teleflex Foundation, PA, 8314

Telemachus: Foundation to Empower the Poor and End War, UT, 9359

TeleTech Community Foundation, DE, 1761

TeleTech Foundation, DE, see 1761

Tell Foundation, Inc., Paul P., OH, 7613

Tell Foundation, William & Karen, CT, 1580

Tellier Foundation Inc., Elizabeth J., WI, 9946

Telluray Foundation, The, DE, 1762

Templin Foundation, The, WA, 9709

Ten Talents Foundation, Inc., MD, 3963

Tenberg Charitable Foundation, Inc., David P., MD, 3964

Tengelsen Family Foundation, IL, 3288

Tennant Company Foundation, MN, see 4798

Tennant Foundation, MN, 4798

Tennessee Titans Foundation, TX, 9230

Tenney Foundation, Judy & Warren, NY, 6895

Tension Envelope Foundation, MO, 5019

Tensor Foundation, NY, 6896

Tepper Charitable Foundation, Inc., Arielle, NY, see 6431

Terhuly Foundation, MN, 4799
Terhune Memorial Fund, Walter E., OH, 7614
TerKeurst Foundation, NC, 7266
Terra Family Foundation, CA, 1107
Terry Foundation, C. Herman & Mary Virginia, FL, 2368
Terry Foundation, C. Herman, FL, see 2368
Terryglass Foundation, The, PA, 8315
Teruya Foundation, Albert T. & Wallace T., HI, 2651
Terwilliger Family Foundation Charitable Trust, GA, 2593
Tesco Foundation, VA, 9541
Teshinsky Family Foundation, CA, 1108
Testamentary Trust of Nellie F. Estes, KS, 3633
Tetlak Foundation, The, OH, 7615
Texas Area Fund Foundation, Inc., The, TX, 9231
Texas Bankers Foundation, TX, 9232
Texas Home Health, Inc., TX, see 8798
Texas House Foundation, TX, 9233, see 9233
TGFF, CO, see 1275
Thadikonda Research Foundation Inc., MD, 3965
Thagard Foundation, CA, 1109
Thalheimer and Juliet A. Eurich Charitable Fund, Inc.,
   Louis B., MD, 3966
Thalheimer Philanthropic Fund, Inc., Louis B., The, MD,
   see 3966
Thaman Family Foundation, IL, 3289
Thames Family Foundation Inc., GA, 2594
Thanksgiving Foundation, NY, 6897
Tharpe Charitable Foundation, Inc., Max B., FL, 2369
Thayer Memorial Trust, Dorothy M., WA, 9710
Thee Mustard Seed Foundation, MA, 4324
Thendara Foundation, Inc., The, OH, 7616
Theroux Foundation, David J. & Mary L. G., CA, 1110
Thiel Charitable Trust, Ervil A. and Ronald E., The, CO,
   1365
Thiem Charitable Foundation, Alvin F. and Ruth K., NY,
   6898
Third Avenue Management Private Foundation, DE,
   1763
Thoman Foundation, W. B. & Candace, MI, 4590
Thomas Charitable Foundation, Inc., Adele M., VA, 9542
Thomas County Community Foundation, KS, 3634
Thomas Educational Foundation Inc., OK, 7724
Thomas Family Foundation, Inc., The, FL, 2370
Thomas Foundation Inc., G. Frank, PA, 8316
Thomas Foundation, Harold E. & Phyllis S., ID, 2687
Thomas Foundation, Inc., Dorothy, FL, 2371
Thomas Foundation, Margaret & Martha, The, NE, 5123
Thomasson Foundation, The, IN, 3459
Thomaston Savings Bank Foundation, Inc., CT, 1581
Thomasville Furniture Industries Foundation, NC, 7267
Thompson Educational Foundation, MI, 4591
Thompson Educational Fund, Willard E. & Ella P., RI,
   8496
Thompson Family Foundation Inc., Patrick J. and Janet
   L., WI, 9947
Thompson Family Foundation, AL, 70
Thompson Family Foundation, Inc., L.V., FL, 2372
Thompson Foster Street Foundation Inc., The, MA, 4325
Thompson Foundation, Evan C., The, CA, 1111
Thompson Foundation, James and Angela, The, TX, see
   9234
Thompson Foundation, Jim and Angela, TX, 9234
Thompson Foundation, Mary, MI, 4592
Thompson Foundation, Porter E. & Helenmae, CA, 1112
Thompson Foundation, Richard K., The, MI, 4593
Thompson Trust for Charities, Clara E., PA, 8317
Thompson Trust, W. A., RI, 8497
Thompson, Jr. Family Foundation, H. L., OH, 7617
Thomsen Foundation, Inc., FL, 2373
Thomson Family Foundation, The, CA, 1113
Thomson Foundation, Jean E., The, WA, 9711
Thomson Foundation, John Edgar, The, DE, 1764
Thoracic Foundation, The, MA, 4326
Thoreau Foundation, Inc., Henry David, MA, 4327
Thornburgh Family Foundation, The, FL, 2374
Thorne Foundation, Dorothy F., TX, 9235
Thorne Foundation, Inc., Daniel K., The, NH, 5233
Thorne Foundation, Stephen & Pamela, CA, 1114
Thornton Foundation, John M. & Sally B., CA, 1115
Thornton Trust, Arthur E., CT, 1582
Thorp Charitable Trust Foundation, Richard H. and Viola
   B., MO, 5020
Thorpe Foundation, James R., MN, 4800

Thrall Foundation Trust, F. Curtis and Susan B., CT,
   1583
Three Chicks Charitable Trust, The, NY, 6899
Three Guineas Fund, CA, 1116
Three Rivers Community Foundation, WA, 9712
Three Sisters Foundation, The, DE, 1765
Thrill Hill Foundation, CA, 1117
Throckmorton Foundation, The, OH, 7618
Thronson Foundation, Edgar A., DE, 1766
Thrush Foundation, Inc., H. A., IN, see 3460
Thrush-Thompson Foundation, Inc., IN, 3460
Thurman Charitable Foundation for Children, Edgar A.,
   The, FL, 2375
Thurston Charitable Foundation, WA, 9713
Ticho Charitable Foundation, Ernst & Gertrude, MD,
   3967
Tierney Family Foundation, Inc., The, CT, 1584
Tietze Foundation Trust, John H., TX, 9236
Tigertree Foundation, CO, 1366
Tilley Family Foundation, CA, 1118
Tillotson North Country Foundation, Inc., NH, 5234
Tilson Foundation, Willard C., MA, 4328
Tim and Libby Brown Family Foundation, CO, see 1243
Timken-Sturgis Foundation, NV, 5192
Timmons Foundation, Inc., Bess Spiva, MO, 5021
Tippett Foundation, Inc., Liz Whitney, FL, 2376
Tippett Foundation, William Hall and Ruth Rathell, The,
   CA, 1119
Tippins Foundation, PA, 8318
Tipton Charitable Foundation, Deborah Dunklin, TN,
   8682
Tisch Foundation, Inc., Lizzie & Jonathan, The, NY, 6900
Tisch Foundation, Jamie, CA, 1120
Titus Foundation Inc., The, CT, 1585
Titus Foundation, The, CO, 1367
Titus-Will Families Foundation, The, WA, 9714
Tizzio Foundation, Thomas and Mary Ann, NJ, 5559
TKBW Private Foundation, The, OH, 7619
To Foundation, Kilin and Cecilie, The, NV, 5193
Tobey Family Foundation, Susanne and Gary, The, CA,
   1121
Tobey Foundation, The, IL, 3290
Tobin Foundation for Theatre Arts, The, TX, see 9237
Tobin Theatre Arts Fund, The, TX, 9237
Tod Fund, Sarah, NY, 6901
Todd Charitable Foundation, Ruth D. and Wylie, MO,
   5022
Todd Foundation, Inc., W. Parsons, NJ, 5560
Todd Foundation, Roland R. and Hazel C., NC, A
Todi Foundation, The, PA, 8319
Tolleson Family Foundation, The, TX, 9238
Tomfohrde Foundation, John H. and H. Naomi, The, MA,
   4329
Tomkins Family Foundation, CA, 1122
Tomkins Gates Foundation, CO, 1368
Tomlinson Foundation, CA, 1123
Tompkins County Foundation, Inc., NY, see 6373
Tompkins Foundation, Emmy Lou, The, TN, 8683
Tompkins-Broll Family Foundation, PA, 8320
Tomson Family Foundation Trust, IA, 3537
Tonkin Foundation, Tom & Helen, WA, 9715
Toocap Foundation, MA, 4330
Toohey Foundation, Linda Glazer, IA, 3538
Toole Charitable Foundation, The, CA, 1124
Toomim Foundation, Shirley and David, TX, 9239
Toppel Family Foundation, Inc., The, FL, 2377
Toppel Foundation, Harold & Patricia, FL, see 2377
Toral Family Foundation, Inc., FL, 2378
Torchmark Benevolent Foundation, TX, 9240
Torgow Family Foundation, MI, 4594
Torino Foundation, Francis P., CA, 1125
Torok Foundation, Inc., Maria, MA, 4331
Torrance Memorial Trust, E. L. & Ruth, TX, 9241
Totah Family Foundation, Sami and Annie, MD, 3968
Touhey Foundation, Carl E., NY, 6902
Touradji Family Foundation, NY, 6903
Tous Charitable Foundation, Mary F., NE, 5124
Toutz Charitable Trust, Earl C. & Elizabeth, MO, 5023
Tov V Chesed Foundation, NY, 6904
Town Fair Tire Foundation Inc., CT, 1586
Towne Scholarship Fund, C. E., NC, 7268
Townsend Family Foundation, IL, 3291
Trachsel Foundation, Dennis and Sara, The, OH, 7620

Trachten Family Foundation, Inc., Morris & Sylvia, The,
   CO, 1369
Tradition Foundation, NY, 6905
Traeger Foundation, Inc., Norman & Carol, OH, 7621
Trager Family Foundation Inc., KY, 3701
Traina Foundation, Nick, The, CA, 1126
Trammell Foundation, Inc., Mark & Evelyn, GA, 2595
Traub-Brittan Family Foundation, CA, 1127
Trax Trust, Virginia S., PA, 8321
Treakle Foundation, Inc., J. Edwin, The, VA, 9543
Treetops Foundation, The, NY, 6906
Trefler Foundation, MA, 4332
Trehern Charitable Foundation, MS, 4856
Treiber Family Foundation Inc., The, NY, 6907
Trek Scholarship Foundation Inc., WI, 9948
Tremble Foundation, Inc., MI, 4595
Tresorelle Foundation, MA, 4333
Trexler Foundation, The, NC, 7269
Triangle Fund, The, NY, 6908
Tribune New York Foundation, NY, 6909
Trico Foundation, The, MI, 4596
Triford Foundation, MI, 4597
Trillium Family Foundation, MN, 4801
Trim Masters Charitable Foundation, Inc., KY, 3702
Trimble Family Foundation, Inc., Robert Mize & Isa
   White, The, NY, 6910
Trinity Foundation, AR, 218
Trio Foundation, IL, 3292
Triple T Foundation, The, PA, 8322
Triplett Foundation, Peggy Ann, The, NC, 7270
Tripp Trust, Inc., William D., AL, 71
Trippet Foundation, Inc., Robert S. and Helen Grey, The,
   OK, 7725
Tritt Family Foundation Inc., Ramie A., GA, 2596
Triune Foundation, Ltd., CO, 1370
Troemner No. 5 Phila Baptist Association, S. Edna, PA,
   8323
Trojan Real Properties Inc., TX, 9242
Trombetta Foundation, S. D., CA, 1128
Troob Family Foundation, The, CA, 1129
Troubh Fund, Jean L. & Raymond S., NY, 6911
Trout Foundation, Leanne Freas, PA, 8324
Trover Family Foundation, Charles D., OR, 7824
Troxell Fund Inc., ID, 2688
Troy Foundation, Gary, CA, 1130
True North Family Foundation, WA, 9716
Trueblood Foundation, Harry, The, CO, 1371
Trulaske, Sr. Family Foundation, Steven L., MO, 5024
Truman Foundation, Mildred Faulkner, NY, 6912
Trusler Foundation Inc., The, KS, 3635
Trussell Family Foundation, Robert and Martha, DE,
   1767
Trust for Aging in America Inc., IL, 3293
Trust for the Meditation Process, MN, 4802
Trust Funds Incorporated, CA, 1131
Trust Under the Will of James Deering Charitable Trust,
   IL, 3294
Trust Under Will of John McKee, PA, see 8160
Trustees of Ivan V. Koulaieff Educational Fund, CA,
   1132
Tsao Family Foundation, CA, 1133
TSH Charitable Foundation, NC, 7271
TSP Foundation, NY, 6913
Tsvi-Ora Foundation, The, NY, 6914
Tuch Foundation, Inc., Michael, NY, 6915
Tuchman Foundation, The, NJ, 5561
Tucker Foundation, Albert L. & Elizabeth T., DC, 1836
Tucker Foundation, Inc., Marcia Brady, MD, 3969
Tucker Foundation, Mary Ann and Lawrence C., The, CT,
   1587
Tucker Foundation, Massey, TX, 9243
Tudor Foundation, The, WA, 9717
Tufenkian Foundation, The, NJ, 5562
Tuffli Family Foundation, The, CA, 1134
Tully Charitable Trust, Daniel P. and Grace I., CT, 1588
Tully Family Foundation, IL, 3295
Tuohy Foundation, Walter & Mary, The, IL, 3296
Tupperware Brands Foundation, FL, 2379
Tupperware Children's Foundation, FL, see 2379
Turben Foundation, Susan & John, OH, 7622
Turley Foundation, Harold & Elaine, UT, 9360
Turlington Charitable Foundation, Darla Dee, The, FL,
   2380

Turner Educational Foundation, Inc., Marie R. & Ervine, KY, 3703
Turner Family Foundation, J. S., MN, 4803
Turner Family Foundation, The, MO, 5025
Turner Foundation Trust, Herman E. & Helen H., FL, 2381
Turner Foundation, The, IL, 3297
Turner Fund, Inc., Ruth, NY, 6916
Turock Family Foundation, The, FL, 2382
Turriff Foundation, Lowell, The, CA, A
Tuscarawas County Community Foundation, OH, 7623
Tuscola County Community Foundation, MI, 4598
Tuscora Park Health & Wellness Foundation, OH, 7624
Tuttleman Family Foundation, PA, 8325
Twanda Foundation, CA, 1135
Twin Chimney Inc., NJ, 5563
Twin Pines Foundation, TX, see 8791
Two Mauds, Inc., VA, 9544
Twomey Foundation, IL, 3298
Tye Medical Aid Foundation, Ray, MA, 4334
Tyler Foundation, TX, 9244
Tyler-Little Family Foundation, MI, 4599
Tytel Family Charitable Foundation Inc., Sandra and Howard, The, NY, 6917
Tzedakah Fund, The, MD, 3970

U & Y Family Foundation, NY, 6918
U.S. Paper Mills Foundation Inc., WI, see 9796
U.S.-China Cultural Foundation, MI, 4600
UAI Foundation, The, NC, 7272
Uberoi Foundation for Religious Studies, The, DE, 1768
UDV North America Foundation, Inc., CT, see 1437
UIC Foundation, Inc., AK, 92
Uihlein Foundation, David V., WI, 9949
Uihlein Foundation, Henry Uihlein II and Mildred A., NY, 6919
Uihlein Foundation, Robert A., WI, 9950
UIL Holdings Corporation Foundation, The, CT, 1589
Ullian Charitable Foundation, Harold S. and Anna S., MA, 4335
Ullman Foundation, Virginia M., The, AZ, 177
Ullmann Family Foundation, Inc., The, NJ, 5564
Ulm Family Foundation, IL, 3299
Ululani Foundation, HI, 2652
UMB Financial Corporation Charitable Foundation, The, MO, 5026
Uncle Larry's Fund, FL, 2383
Unfi Foundation, RI, 8498
Ungar Foundation, MA, 4336
Unger Foundation, Inc., Aber D., The, MD, 3971
Unger Memorial Foundation, Clara Buttenwieser, NY, see 6327
Union Benevolent Association, PA, 8326
Union County Community Foundation, Inc., AR, 219
Union County Foundation, OH, see 7357
Union Plus Disaster Relief Fund, DC, see 1837
Union Privilege Relief Fund Trust, DC, 1837
Union Savings Bank Foundation, Inc., CT, 1590
United Charitable Foundation, MA, 4337
United Conveyor Foundation, IL, 3300
United Elenar Foundation, The, NY, 6920
United Plankton Charitable Trust, CA, 1136
United Vision Foundation, NJ, 5565
University Financing Foundation, Inc., The, GA, 2597
University Lane Foundation, MO, 5027
Unz Foundation, The, CA, 1137
Up East, Inc., PA, 8327
Up The River Endeavors Inc., NH, 5235
Upchurch, Jr. Charitable Foundation, Samuel E., AL, 72
Uplands Family Foundation, The, CA, 1138
Uplands Foundation, The, CA, 1139
Upside Down Foundation, CA, 1140
Upstream Foundation, The, MA, 4338
Upton Charitable Foundation, Lucy and Eleanor S., The, NJ, 5566
Urban Foundation, Thomas Nelson Urban, Jr. and Mary Bright, IA, see 3545
Urbanek-Levy Education Fund, CA, 1141
USA Equestrian Trust Inc., KY, 3704
USD Foundation, TX, 9245
Usman & Hazarbai Mundia Foundation, Haji, NY, 6921
Utah Medical Association Foundation, UT, 9361
Utica National Group Foundation Inc., NY, 6922

Utopia Fund, NY, 6923
Uvas Foundation, CA, 1142

V & H Charitable Foundation, KS, 3636
V & S Foundation, Inc., MD, 3972
Vaad Haartzy Inc., NY, 6924
Vail Family Foundation, IL, 3301
Valenti Charitable Foundation, IL, 3302
Valentine Charitable Foundation Inc., The, VA, 9545
Valentine Foundation, PA, 8328
Valenzuela & Bernardita Mendez Foundation, Pablo, CA, 1143
Valerio Charitable Remainder Foundation, Michael and Helen, The, MA, 4339
Valero Scholarship Trust, TX, 9246
Valley Anesthesiology Foundation, AZ, 178
Van Buren Foundation, Inc., The, IA, 3539
Van Cleve Foundation Trust, The, CA, 1144
Van Curler Foundation, MI, 4601
Van Dalson Foundation, W.S. and Lois, The, MI, 4602
Van Den Wymelenberg Foundation Inc., John & Janet, WI, 9951
Van der Stricht Foundation, The, DE, 1769
Van Devender Family Foundation, MS, 4857
Van Devender Foundation, MS, see 4857
Van Drisse Charitable Trust, Joseph & Sarah, WI, 9952
Van Dyke Charitable Foundation, TX, 9247
Van Dyke Family Foundation, Inc., MD, 3973
Van Evera Foundation, DeWitt & Caroline, MO, 5028
Van Evera Foundation, DeWitt, MO, see 5028
Van Horn Foundation, AZ, 179
Van Huffel Foundation, I. J., OH, 7625
Van Kampen Foundation, C. George, The, NY, 6925
Van Meter/Barnhart Family Fund, OH, 7626
Van Mourick Foundation, Mark, The, CA, see 884
Van Sloun Foundation, MA, 4340
Van Strum Foundation, MD, 3974
Van Wie Charitable Foundation, Gregory C., WI, 9953
Van Wyk Family Foundation, Arlan J., IA, 3540
Vance Foundation Inc, H. A., CT, 1591
Vance Foundation, Lee and Cynthia, NY, 6926
Vanden Heuvel Foundation Inc., Melinda & William J., The, NY, 6927
Vander Laan Family Foundation, MI, 4603
Vanderbilt Foundation, William H. & Helen C., The, NY, see 5983
Vanderbilt Trust, R. T., NC, 7273
Vanderpoel Family Charitable Trust, Barrie, RI, 8499
Vandevoort Family Foundation, NV, 5194
VanGilder Family Foundation Inc., MI, 4604
Vann Family Foundation, Inc., The, IN, 3461
Vanneck-Bailey Foundation, FL, 2384
Varner Family Foundation, James Rush, CA, 1145
Vasey Foundation, The, FL, 2385
Vassia Family Charitable Foundation, The, MO, 5029
Vatterott Foundation, MO, 5030
Vattikuti India Relief Foundation, The, MI, 4605
Vaughan Charitable Foundation, Herbert W., PA, 8329
Vaughan Family Foundation, Rosemary Haggar, TX, 9248
Vaughan Foundation, Rachael & Ben, The, TX, 9249
Vaughan Foundation, The, GA, 2598
Vaughn-Jordan Foundation, NJ, 5567
Vaughter Charitable Trust, S.Julian, GA, 2599
Vaughter Memorial Foundation, Carol Jo, IL, A
Vecchio Family Foundation, Inc., Enrico, The, WV, see 9770
Vecellio Family Foundation, Inc., The, WV, 9770
Vega Foundation, The, WY, see 9991
Vela Foundation, MA, 4341
Velaj Foundation, The, CT, 1592
Velma Moore T/W Charities, PA, 8330
Venango Area Community Foundation, PA, see 7891
Venne Foundation, Clarence J., PA, 8331
Venner Family Foundation, The, OH, 7627
Verdoorn Foundation, The, CO, 1372
Veres Charitable Trust, Andrew F. & Barbara, TX, 9250
Verhagen Foundation, SC, 8547
Verhalen Family Foundation, Inc., James P., The, NJ, 5568
Verhulst Foundation, Inc., Marvin P., WI, 9954
Verlander Foundation, George Verlander & Cornelis M., VA, 9546

Vermeer Family Foundation, Harry, IA, 3541
Vermeer Foundation, Inc., R. & L., IA, 3542
Vermeer Investment Company Foundation, IA, see 3541
Verner Foundation, Inc., FL, 2386
Verney Foundation, Gilbert, NH, 5236
Vernon Foundation for Homeless & Abused Animals, Inc., Emily, FL, 2387
Vernon Foundation, Lillian, NY, 6928
Verrochi Family Charitable Trust, MA, 4342
Vetter Foundation, TX, 9251
Vevay-Switzerland County Foundation, Inc., IN, 3462
Vibern Foundation, IL, 3303
Vick Public Law Foundation, Kendall, LA, 3756
Vicksburg Foundation, MI, 4606
Victor Foundation, Lois and Morton, The, PA, see 8332
Victor Foundation, Lois B., The, PA, 8332
Victor Foundation, The, IL, 3304
Videtta Charitable Trust, Michael and Norah, The, MA, 4343
Vidinha Charitable Trust, Antone & Edene, HI, 2653
Viii Brothers Family Charitable Foundation, PA, 8333
Villchur Foundation, NY, 6929
Vincent Trust, Anna M., PA, 8334
Vine's Branch Foundation, The, MA, 4344
Vingo Trust III, The, MA, 4345
Vinoskey Family Foundation, VA, 9547
Viola Foundation, The, NY, 6930
Viridiun Christian Foundation, DE, 1770
Viro Fund, AL, 73
Vision Charitable Trust, The, CO, 1373
Vision of Hope Custody, IN, 3463
Vision of Hope Foundation, IN, see 3463
Visiting Nurse Association of Houston Foundation, TX, see 8924
Vista Foundation, OH, 7628
Vitale Family Foundation Inc., The, DE, 1771
VJS Charitable Private Foundation, MO, 5031
Vlasic Family Foundation, MI, 4607
Vlasic Foundation, MI, see 4607
VMP Nutrition Foundation, TX, 9252
Voelkerding Charitable Trust, Walter and Jean, MO, 5032
Vogel Family Foundation, Inc., GA, 2600
Vogel Foundation, Moses & Miriam, NY, 6931
Vogelzang Foundation, Mary Beth and James C., CA, see 1146
Vogelzang Foundation, Mary Beth, CA, 1146
Vogler Foundation, Inc., Laura B., The, NY, 6932
Vogt Family Foundation, Inc., NY, 6933
Voight Charitable Trust, Andrew and Cleo, GA, 2601
von Clemm Foundation, Michael and Louisa, The, FL, 2388
Von Der Ahe Foundation, CA, 1147
Von Der Ahe, Jr. Trust, Theodore A., CA, 1148
Von Drehle Corporation Private Foundation, David, NC, 7274
Von Hoffmann Foundation, Inc., George, MO, 5033
Von Magnus Henderson Charitable Trust, Maria C., MA, 4346
Von Seggern Charitable Foundation, E. F., TX, 9253
Von Tobel Foundation, Inc., IN, 3464
von Weber Trust, Madelaine G., NH, 5237
Von Weise, Charles & Marie, IL, 3305
Vonderhaar Family Foundation, The, IA, 3543
Vorsheck Family Foundation, Inc., FL, 2389
Votum Foundation, Inc., FL, 2390
Vradenburg Foundation, Bee, CO, 1374
VuBay Foundation, VA, 9548
VWR Charitable Foundation, DE, 1772
Vyeshaya Foundation, Keren Nachmen, NY, 6934

W.J.D. Foundation, CO, 1375
Wabtec Foundation, PA, 8335
Wachenheim Foundation, Lance R., The, NY, 6935
Wachovia Regional Community Development Corporation, PA, see 8350
Wachs Family Foundation, Judith & David, PA, 8336
Wachs-Weingarten Charitable Trust, PA, 8337
Wachtell Foundation, Svetlana and Herbert M., NY, 6936
Wadley Foundation Inc., Gregg, OK, 7726
Wadman Foundation, UT, 9362
Waffle House Foundation, Inc., GA, 2602

Waggoner Foundation, Inc., E. Paul and Helen Buck, TX, 9254
Waggoners Foundation, TX, 9255
Wagler Charitable Foundation, Phil, The, OH, 7629
Wagman Foundation, Kim and David, The, NY, 6937
Wagmore Foundation Inc., FL, 2391
Wagner Agape Foundation, NC, 7275
Wagner Family Charitable Trust, PA, 8338
Wagner Family Foundation, H.A.M.K., CA, 1149
Wagner Foundation, Harvey and Leslie, NV, 5195
Wagner Foundation, Melvin F. and Ellen L., WI, 9955
Wagner Foundation, Melvin F., WI, see 9955
Wagner Foundation, Rose and Sherle, NY, 6938
Wagner Foundation, Ross, MN, 4804
Wagner Foundation, The, IL, 3306
Wagner-Braunsberg Family Foundation, Inc., MD, 3975
Wahlert Foundation, IA, 3544
Wahlstrom Foundation, Inc., The, FL, see 2201
Waidner Foundation, Robert A., The, MD, 3976
Wake Electric Care, Inc., NC, 7276
Wakefield Residuary Trust, George P., PA, 8339
Wakerly Family Foundation, CA, 1150
Wal-Dot Foundation, TX, 9256
Walbridge Foundation, Doris Goodwin, NM, 5627
Waldbaum Family Foundation, Milton G. & Miriam, NE, 5125
Waldbaum Family Foundation, Milton G., NE, see 5125
Waldis Family Foundation Inc., NJ, 5569
Waldo Trust, The, PA, 8340
Waldron Rise Foundation Inc., NY, 6939
Walk Fine Arts Foundation, Maurice, IL, 3307
Walker Charitable Foundation, Margaret M., OH, 7630
Walker Educational and Charitable Foundation, Alex C., GA, 2603
Walker Foundation, Archie D. and Bertha H., MN, 4805
Walker Foundation, Earl E. Walker and Myrtle E., The, MO, 5034
Walker Foundation, George Herbert, The, MO, 5035
Walker Foundation, Lester A., NE, 5126
Walker Foundation, The, NE, see 5126
Walker Machinery Company Charitable Trust, Cecil I., IL, 3308
Walkingstick Foundation, Ben and Bonnie, The, OK, 7727
Wall Family Foundation, C. A., CA, 1151
Wallace Charitable Foundation, Dwane L. and Velma Lunt, KS, 3637
Wallace Charitable Foundation, Lloyd R., The, MO, 5036
Wallace Charitable Memorial Foundation, Inc., Fred & Alice, OH, 7631
Wallace Charitable Trust, A. W., NC, 7277
Wallace Educational Foundation, Allyrae, AL, 74
Wallace Foundation, George R., The, MA, 4347
Waller Foundation, Robert A., CA, 1152
Wallerstein Foundation Inc., Kohanim, NY, 6940
Wallestad Foundation, MN, 4806
Wallis Charitable Trust, Dorothy Wagner, MD, 3977
Walls Foundation, Carmage And Martha Ann, The, TX, 9257
Walrath Family Foundation, The, NY, 6941
Walser Foundation, The, MN, 4807
Walsh Charity Trust, Blanche M., MA, 4348
Walsh Family Foundation, The, KS, 3638
Walsh Foundation, Leo S., NY, 6942
Walsh Foundation, Richard F., NY, see 6943
Walsh-Brady Memorial Fund, MN, 4808
Walsh/Alfred W. Ditolla/Harold Spivak Foundation, Richard F., NY, 6943
Walske Charitable Foundation, The, MA, 4349
Walske-Longtine Foundation, MA, see 4349
Walter Family Foundation, VA, 9549
Walters Family Foundation, CA, 1153
Walters Foundation, Albert A., NC, 7278
Walthall Perpetual Charitable Trust, Marjorie T., TX, 9258
Walther Family Foundation, NY, 6944
Walther Foundation, CA, 1154
Waltmar Foundation, CA, 1155
Walton and Ann Walton Kroenke Charitable Foundation, Audrey J., MO, 5037
Walton Avenue Foundation, CA, 1156
Walton County Foundation, Inc., GA, 2604
Walton Family Foundation, R., PA, 8341

Waltrip-McGee Foundation, The, TX, 9259
Wang Family Foundation, CA, 1157
Wang Fund, Wei Wei, DE, 1773
Wann Foundation, Ralph J., NC, 7279
Wapack Foundation, The, MA, 4350
Warburton Foundation, Ralph T. & Esther L., The, PA, 8342
Ward Family Charitable Trust, The, GA, see 2605
Ward Family Foundation, CA, 1158
Ward Family Foundation, The, TX, 9260
Ward Foundation Inc., Zeneth F. & Lanetta S., WA, 9718
Ward Foundation, PA, 8343
Ward Foundation, The, GA, 2605
Ward Foundation, Tom L., OK, 7728
Warfield Memorial Fund, Inc., Anna Emory, MD, 3978
Wark Foundation, David M. and Mary Ann Barrows, IL, 3309
Warmer Research Foundation, Inc., AZ, 180
Warner Family Foundation, The, IL, 3310
Warner Fund, Albert & Bessie, CO, 1376
Warren Charitable Trust, Catherine C., GA, 2606
Warren Charitable Trust, Harold, GA, 2607
Warren Charite' Foundation, OK, 7729
Warren Family Foundation, CA, 1159
Warren Family Foundation, Naomi and Martin, TX, 9261
Warren Family Foundation, The, AL, 75
Warren Foundation, Inc., Edus H. and Harriet H., The, GA, 2608
Warwick Savings Foundation, NY, 6945
Washakie Foundation, DE, 1774
Washington Group Foundation, ID, see 2666
Washington Square Fund, NY, 6946
Washington Trust Charitable Foundation, The, RI, 8500
Wasserman Foundation, The, CA, 1160
Wasserott Foundation, Paul D., The, PA, 8344
Wasserstrom Foundation, OH, 7632
Waterfowl Research Foundation, Inc., NJ, 5570
Watermark Foundation, MO, see 4878
Waters Foundation, Paul R. & Alma M., NC, 7280
Waters Foundation, Thomas P., The, NJ, 5571
Watersheds Foundation, NM, 5628
Watertown Area Community Foundation, WI, 9956
Watertown Community Foundation, SD, 8576
Waterview Foundation Inc., The, NJ, 5572
Watford Family Foundation Inc., TX, 9262
Watson Charitable Foundation, John H., AL, 76
Watson Charitable Foundation, Mark and Kathleen, The, TX, 9263
Watson Family Foundation, Thomas S., KS, 3639
Watson Foundation, John W. and Rose E., MI, 4608
Watson Foundation, The, TX, 9263
Watson Foundation, Thomas S., KS, see 3639
Watson Foundation, Walter E. and Caroline H., OH, 7633
Watson Irrevocable Trust, William J., IL, 3311
Watt Brothers Scholars Trust, OR, 7825
Wattis Foundation, Phyllis C., CA, 1161
Watts Family Foundation, The, NY, 6947
Watts Mountainside Community Foundation, Blanche M. and George L., NJ, 5573
Waugh Family Foundation, The, FL, 2392
Way Ahead Trust, The, TX, 9264
Way Foundation, B. & H., MN, 4809
Way Foundation, The, NC, 7281
Wayne County Community Foundation, PA, 8345
We Live To Give Foundation, Inc., NJ, 5574
Weatherspoon Foundation, The, NC, 7282
Weathertop Foundation, IA, 3545
Weaver Charitable Trust, Bill & Katie, TX, 9265
Weaver Family Foundation, CO, see 1335
Weaver Family Private Foundation, IL, 3312
Webb Family Foundation, Inc., NV, 5196
Webb Foundation, IL, 3313
Webb Foundation, The, CA, 1162
Webb Roven Foundation, CA, see 991
Webb-Berger Foundation, The, CA, see 1162
WebbCraft Family Foundation, Inc., The, SC, 8548
Webber 1985 Charitable Trust, Vila B., MA, 4351
Webcrafters-Frautschi Foundation, Inc., WI, 9957
Weber Charities Corporation, Frederick E., The, MA, 4352
Weber Family Foundation, Keith & Margie, The, KS, 3640

Weber Family Foundation, The, KS, see 3640
Weber Foundation, Charles & Marion, The, OK, 7730
Webre Foundation, Iris and Lloyd, The, TX, 9266
Webster Bank Foundation, Inc., CT, see 1477
Webster Five Foundation, Inc., MA, 4353
Wedge Memorial Fund, Frank L., MN, 4810
Wegener Foundation, Inc., Herman and Mary, The, OK, see 7731
Wegener Foundation, Inc., OK, 7731
Wehle Charitable Trust, Robert G., IL, 3314
Wehrle Foundation, H.B., WV, 9771
Wei Family Private Foundation, NJ, 5575
Weidner Foundation, The, WA, 9719
Weier Family Foundation, WA, 9720
Weigle Family Foundation, IA, 3546
Weigle Foundation, David, IA, see 3546
Weil Charitable Foundation, Lorne, The, NY, 6948
Weil Family Foundation, Patricia and Christopher, The, CA, 1163
Weil Family Foundation, The, PA, 8346
Weil Foundation, The, AZ, 181
Weil Foundation, VA, 9550
Weil Memorial Charitable Foundation Inc., John Leopold and Geraldine R., The, MA, 4354
Weiler Family Foundation, Inc., The, PA, 8347
Weiler-Miller Foundation, PA, see 8348
Weiler-Miller Fund, Inc., PA, 8348
Weill Charitable Foundation, Inc., Sanford I., NY, see 6949
Weill Family Foundation, The, NY, 6949
Weill Foundation for Music, Inc., Kurt, NY, 6950
Weiller Foundation, Inc., Ted and Jean, FL, 2393
Wein Family Foundation, IL, 3315
Wein Foundation, Hyman & Susan, IL, see 3315
Weinberg Foundation, Adolph and Etta, CA, 1164
Weinberg Foundation, John S. and Amy S., NY, 6951
Weinberg, M.D., and Charlotte Cohen Weinberg Charitable Foundation Inc., Carroll A., MD, 3979
Weinberger Family Foundation, Inc., FL, 2394
Weiner Family Foundation, Inc., Roz and Marvin H., The, MD, 3980
Weiner Family Foundation, PA, 8349
Weiner Family Foundation, Roberta & S.R., MA, 4355
Weiner Foundation, Marc, IL, 3316
Weingarten Family Foundation, NY, 6952
Weingarten Foundation, Jeffrey and Susan, NY, 6953
Weininger Foundation, Inc., Richard and Gertrude, The, NY, see 6954
Weininger Foundation, Inc., The, NY, 6954
Weinman Foundation Inc., Isak and Rose, The, NY, 6955
Weinman Foundation, Inc., Toby and Melvin, The, MD, 3981
Weinman Memorial Foundation, Morris, Mary & Toby, MD, see 3981
Weinstein Foundation Inc., Irving, The, NJ, 5576
Weinstein Foundation Inc., J., NY, 6956
Weintraub Family Foundation Inc., Joseph, FL, 2395
Weintraub Family Foundation, NJ, 5577
Weintraub Family Foundation, NY, 6957
Weintraub-Landfield Charity Foundation, Inc., FL, see 2395
Weir Foundation Trust, TX, 9268
Weir Foundation, TX, 9267
Weir Trust, Leroy and Merle, TX, 9269
Weisberg Charitable Foundation Inc., Jack, NJ, 5578
Weisberg Family Foundation, Charles L., KY, 3705
Weisberg Foundation, Lawrence & Idell, MI, 4609
Weiser Philanthropic Fund, The, NY, 6958
Weisgerber Foundation, William E. and Aenid R., CA, 1165
Weisman Family Charitable Trust, Carol and Michael, The, NY, 6959
Weisman Family Foundation, The, FL, 2396
Weismann Family Foundation, Philippa V., The, NY, 6960
Weiss Charitable Trust, Mandell, CA, 1166
Weiss Family Chesed Foundation, The, NY, 6961
Weiss Family Foundation, Robert G., IL, 3317
Weiss Foundation, Inc., Joseph H. & Miriam F., The, NY, 6962
Weiss Foundation, Inc., William E., WY, 9997
Weiss Foundation, Mary K., The, WY, 9996

Weiss Foundation, Mor & Eva, NY, 6963
Weiss Foundation, Robert Lee, TN, 8684
Weiss Foundation, The, MD, 3982
Weiss Foundation, William M., OH, 7634
Weissman Foundation, Adam J., The, DE, 1775
Weisz Family Philanthropic Fund, David and Sylvia, CA, 1167
Welbilt Corporation Foundation, WI, see 9876
Welch Charitable Foundation, Lantz, The, MO, see 5038
Welch Family Foundation, Inc., OK, 7732
Welch Family Foundation, MO, 5038
Welch Family Foundation, TX, 9270
Welch Foundation, David and Heidi, The, CA, 1168
Welch Foundation, James & Jane, MI, 4610
Welch Foundation, James & Virginia, NJ, 5579
Welch Foundation, William F. & Lorene W., WY, 9998
Welch Testamentary Trust, George T., WA, 9721
Welchwood Foundation Inc., KY, 3706
Weld Foundation, MA, 4356
Weld Foundation, The, PA, see 8274
Welfund Inc., CA, 1169
Welk Family Foundation, Lawrence, The, CA, 1170
Welk Family Foundation, SD, 8577
Well Foundation, CA, see 515
Weller Foundation, Inc., The, NE, 5127
Wells Charitable Trust, Mildred Sheffield, NC, 7283
Wells Family Charitable Foundation, CA, 1171
Wells Family Foundation Trust, MN, 4811
Wells Family Foundation, Inc., FL, 2397
Wells Family Foundation, Inc., MN, 4812
Wells Fargo Community Development Corp., PA, 8350
Wells Foundation, Damon, The, TX, 9271
Wells Foundation, Dan Kirkland, TX, 9272
Wells Foundation, Franklin H. & Ruth L., NY, 6964
Wells Foundation, George W., MA, 4357
Wells Trust Fund, Fred W., RI, 8501
Wellspring Charitable Foundation, ME, 3806
Wellworth Foundation, The, WA, 9722
Welter Foundation, Inc., IN, 3465
Welton Foundation, DE, 1776
Welty Family Foundation, The, OH, 7635
Wendel Foundation, The, MN, 4813
Wendel Memorial Foundation, Lisa, NJ, 5580
Wendell Family Foundation, CA, 1172
Wender Foundation, Ruth Winkelman, DE, 1777
Wendy's of Montana Foundation Inc., MT, 5065
Wenger 1994 Foundation, Dixie and Cedric, The, TX, see 9214
Wenger Charitable Trust, Robert C., PA, 8351
Wenger Foundation, Inc., The, PA, 8352
Weny Charitable Trust, Frank X. Weny & Mary Ethel, NJ, 5581
Werner Family Foundation, Richard L. & Lois S., FL, 2398
Werthan, Jr. Foundation, Betty and Bernard, TN, see 8583
Wertheimer Foundation, The, CA, 1173
Wescustogo Foundation, FL, 2399
Weskan Charitable Foundation, KS, 3641
Wessel Family Foundation, IL, 3318
Wesselink Family Foundation, IL, 3319
Wessell Family Foundation, The, CO, see 1241
Wessinger Foundation, OR, 7826
West Bancorporation Foundation, Inc., The, IA, 3547
West Davis & Bergard Foundation, CA, 1174
West Education Foundation, NE, 5128
West Family Foundation, OR, 7827
West Foundation, Harry & Ethel, CA, 1175
West Scholarship Fund, Merle S. & Emma J., OR, 7828
West Scholarship Fund, OR, see 7828
West Star Foundation, NV, 5197
West Trust, Georgina B., RI, 8502
West Virginia Foundation, The, TN, see 8683
West-West Memorial Fund, Vivian S., NC, 7284
Westbrook Foundation, CT, 1593
Westcott Foundation, TX, 9273
Western Cardiac Foundation, CA, 1176
Western Indiana Community Foundation, Inc., IN, 3466
Western Lane Community Foundation, OR, 7829
Western Lane County Foundation, OR, see 7829
Western Shoshone Scholarship Foundation, NV, 5198
Westfield Foundation, The, NJ, 5582
Westgate Foundation, Inc., FL, see 2400

Westgate Resorts Foundation, Inc., FL, 2400
Westlawn Foundation, NY, 6965
Weston Foundation, IL, 3320
Weston Wabash Foundation, The, IN, 3467
Westphal Family Foundation, The, CA, 1177
Westport Fund, DC, 1838
Westreich Finaly Foundation, Inc., FL, 2401
Wetmore Foundation, Charles & Elizabeth, LA, 3757
Wetsman Foundation, The, MI, 4611
Wetterberg Foundation, Harold, The, NJ, 5583
Wexler Foundation, Mark and Muriel, CO, 1377
Wexner Charitable Foundation, Susan, NY, see 6636
Weyand 1977, Louis F. and Florence H., MN, 4814
Weyco Group Charitable Trust, WI, 9958
Weyenberg Charitable Trust, Frank L., NC, 7285
Weyerhaeuser Memorial Foundation, Charles A., The, MN, 4815
Weyers Family Foundation Inc., WI, 9959
WF Foundation, OR, see 7792
Whalen Foundation Inc., John, Marie and Joseph, The, NY, 6966
Whalesback Foundation, NY, 6967
Whaley Foundation, MN, 4816
Whalley Charitable Trust, PA, 8353
Wharton Foundation, Inc., The, CA, 1178
Wharton Foundation, Naida S., NY, 6968
Wheatland Charitable Trust, David P., MA, 4358
Wheeler Family Foundation, Inc., MI, 4612
Wheeler Foundation, Barbara F., TX, 9274
Wheeler Foundation, Charlotte & Edward K., NY, 6969
Wheeler Foundation, Inc., Wilmot, CT, 1594
Wheeler Foundation, William A. Wheeler & Florence R., CA, 1179
Wheless Foundation, The, LA, 3758
Whimsie Fund, PA, 8354
Whispering Bells Foundation, NY, 6970
White Cedar Fund, The, NY, 6971
White Family Charitable Foundation, Paul R. and Anna Lee, OR, 7830
White Family Foundation, Inc., GA, 2609
White Family Foundation, Lawrence E., FL, 2402
White Family Foundation, The, RI, 8503
White Family Foundation, TX, 9275
White Foundation Inc., Judith C., The, NY, 6972
White Foundation, Connie Burwell and William W., The, CO, 1378
White Foundation, Harold A. and Edna L., OK, 7733
White Foundation, Inc., Rodney L., NY, 6973
White Foundation, John and Happy, The, RI, see 8503
White Foundation, Stanley, OK, 7734
White Foundation, The, MI, 4613
White Memorial Foundation, Bob, AR, 220
White Mountain Institute, CA, 1180
White Pine Fund, The, PA, 8355
White-Roth Family Foundation, Inc., NY, see 6700
Whitehat Foundation, The, FL, see 2066
Whitehead Charitable Foundation, The, GA, 2610
Whitehead Foundation, Inc., The, NY, 6974
Whitener Foundation, NC, 7286
Whitepath Fabtech Foundation, Inc., GA, 2611
Whiting Foundation, Macauley & Helen Dow, FL, 2403
Whiting Foundation, The, MI, 4614
Whitley Charitable Foundation, The, TX, 9276
Whitman Family Foundation Inc., W. F., DE, 1778
Whitman Family Foundation, MI, 4615
Whitman Family Foundation, The, LA, 3759
Whitman Foundation Inc., H. Angela, FL, 2404
Whitman-Carlyon Foundation, The, NY, see 6634
Whitney Foundation, MN, 4817
Whittemore Charitable Trust, Ruth B., MA, 4359
Whittemore Foundation, The, NY, 6975
Whittenberger Foundation, Claude R. and Ethel B., ID, 2689
Whittier Family Foundation, Ronald, The, CA, 1181
Whitwam Foundation, David & Barbara, IL, 3321
Whitwell-Meyer Foundation, The, OK, 7735
Wibel Foundation, Ada L. & Albert M., NC, 7287
Wicks Chapin Inc, NJ, 5584
Wickson-Link Memorial Foundation, MI, 4616
Widgeon Foundation, Inc., MD, 3983
Widows Society in Boston, MA, see 4317
Widows Society, CT, 1595
Wiebe Foundation, The, WA, 9723

Wieczorek Family Foundation, The, MI, 4617
Wiedemann Foundation Inc., K. T., KS, 3642
Wiehoff Foundation, John and Margie, MN, 4818
Wieler Family Private Foundation, The, MD, 3984
Wiener Charitable Foundation Inc., Israel, Rose, Henry & Robert, The, FL, 2405
Wiener Foundation, Inc., Gabe, The, CT, 1596
Wightman Charitable Foundation, Michelle, The, OH, see 7636
Wightman-Wieber Foundation, OH, 7636
Wilamowsky Foundation, Zichron Alter Meir, NY, 6976
Wilbur Foundation, Brayton, CA, 1182
Wilcox Family Foundation, Gregory and Claire, The, NJ, 5585
Wilcox Family Foundation, The, MA, 4360
Wilcox Trust, S. W., HI, 2654
Wilder Family Foundation, Inc., B.J. and Eve, The, FL, 2406
Wilder Foundation, John and Susan, TX, 9277
Wildermuth Foundation, E. F., The, OH, 7637
Wildwood Foundation, The, NJ, 5586
Wilen Foundation Inc., Jack, MD, 3985
Wiley Foundation, Nettie L. and Charles L., The, VA, 9551
Wilf Family Education Foundation Inc., The, NJ, 5587
Wilf Family Hospital & Medical Research Foundation Inc., The, NJ, 5588
Wilkens Charitable Foundation, Catherine Holmes, WA, 9724
Wilkes-Desmond Educational Foundation, FL, 2407
Wilkins Charitable Foundation, WA, see 9724
Wilkins Charitable Trust, Don and May, The, CO, 1379
Wilkinson Charitable Trust, James and Mildred, NC, 7288
Wilkinson Foundation, CA, 1183
Wilks Family Foundation, Lise and Jeffrey, NY, 6977
Will Foundation, The, IL, 3322
Willard Helping Fund, Cecilia Young, TX, 9278
Willary Foundation, PA, 8356
Willett Charitable Foundation, William Gerald, The, VA, 9552
Williams Charitable Foundation, AL, 77
Williams Charitable Foundation, Sylvia & Rip, MD, 3986
Williams Charitable Trust, John C., PA, 8357
Williams Charitable Trust, Mary Jo, KS, 3643
Williams Family Foundation, The, NV, 5199
Williams Family Fund, The, MI, 4618
Williams Foundation, C. K., The, PA, 8358
Williams Foundation, Clyde, The, OH, 7639
Williams Foundation, Dave H. & Reba W., The, VA, 9553
Williams Foundation, Elizabeth P. and Harold R., TX, 9279
Williams Foundation, Inc., Betty A. and James B., GA, 2612
Williams Foundation, Inc., J.L., TX, 9280
Williams Foundation, Jamison, The, MI, see 4618
Williams Foundation, Lester and Beatrice, TX, 9281
Williams Foundation, OH, 7638
Williams Foundation, The, NV, see 5142
Williams Foundation, Walter & Marie, NC, 7289
Williams Foundation, Woody and Kim, AZ, 182
Williams Scholarship Fund, Frank O. and Clara R., The, PA, see 8359
Williams Trust, Jessie A., PA, 8359
Williams-Berry Charitable Foundation, VA, 9554
Williams-Malone Foundation, Inc., AZ, 183
Williams/Brice-Edwards Charitable Trust, The, SC, 8549
Williamson Charitable Trust, Warren and Sallie, GA, 2613
Williamson Family Foundation, John, The, TN, see 8685
Williamson Family Foundation, OH, 7640
Williamson Foundation for Music, CA, 1184
Williamson, Martin & Brooke Family Foundation, The, TN, 8685
Willingham Foundation, NJ, 5589
Willmott Foundation, Fred and Floy, NY, 6978
Willow Tree Foundation, PA, 8360
Wills Foundation, TN, see 8618
Willspring Foundation, Inc., FL, see 2389
Wilmes Family Charitable Foundation, Inc., The, IN, 3468
Wilnai Foundation, Amos and Ruth, CA, 1185

Wilson Charitable Trust, J. B. & Garnet A., OH, 7641
Wilson Family Foundation Inc., The, CA, 1186
Wilson Family Foundation, CO, 1380
Wilson Family Foundation, Inc., WI, 9960
Wilson Foundation Inc., Charles P., TN, 8686
Wilson Foundation, Alan D. and Wendy R., MD, 3987
Wilson Foundation, Elaine P. & Richard U., NY, 6979
Wilson Foundation, Elizabeth Ruthruff, NJ, 5590
Wilson Foundation, George A. and Marion M., WA, 9725
Wilson Foundation, Inc., Hugh & Mary, FL, see 2408
Wilson Foundation, NY, see 6979
Wilson Foundation, Patti Johnson, OK, 7736
Wilson Foundation, Thomas A., OH, 7642
Wilson Trust, Annie E., RI, 8504
Wilson-Wood Foundation, Inc., FL, 2408
Wilt Family Foundation, Toby S., TN, 8687
Wimmer Charitable Trust, Virginia, MN, 4819
Wimmer Family Foundation, Phillip H. Wimmer and Betty L., PA, 8361
Winchester Foundation, The, IN, 3469
Windhorse Foundation, MA, 4361
Windolf Family Foundation, Inc., GA, 2614
Winds of Peace Foundation, MN, 4820
Windsor Foundation, Inc., MD, 3988
Windway Foundation, Inc., WI, 9961
Windy Ridge Foundation, WY, 9999
Windy River Foundation, NY, 6980
Winiarski Family Foundation, CA, 1187
Winkler Charitable Foundation, Margo and Irwin, CA, 1188
Winn Educational Trust, Fanny Edith, LA, 3760
Winn Foundation, Thomas P., CA, 1189
Winning Home Inc., MA, 4362
Winokur Family Foundation, Inc., CT, 1597
Winokur Foundation, PA, 8362
Winston Charitable Foundation, The, TX, 9282
Winter Cove Foundation, WA, 9726
Winters Family Foundation, Alan and Hope, The, NJ, 5591
Winthrop Charitable Trust, Clara B., MA, 4363
Winthrop Charitable Trust, John, SC, 8550
Wisdom Foundation, Mary Freeman, The, LA, 3761
Wise Family Charitable Trust, NC, 7290
Wise Family Foundation, William and Marie, The, TX, 9283
Wiser Charitable Foundation Trust, Bob, The, VA, 9555
Wish Family Foundation, Inc., Barry, NY, 6981
Wish Foundation, Inc., The, GA, 2615
Wishnick Foundation, Robert I., The, ID, 2690
Wishnick Foundation, William, The, ID, see 2690
Wislow Charitable Foundation, Susan & Robert, IL, 3323
Wissner-Slivka Foundation, WA, 9727
Witco Foundation, The, ID, see 2690
Withim Foundation, The, CA, 1190
Withycombe Foundation, AZ, 184
Witkin Charitable Foundation, Bernard E. & Alba, CA, 1191
Witt Foundation, Donna Dantini, OK, 7737
Witt/Hoey Foundation, Inc., The, MD, 3989
Witte, Jr. Foundation Trust, John H., WI, 9962
Wittel Foundation, Sam E. & Burnice C., MS, 4858
Witter Family Foundation, Robert W., The, CA, 1192
Witz-Mallinger Charitable Foundation, IL, 3324
Witzel Family Foundation, WY, 10000
WKBJ Partnership Foundation, NJ, 5592
WLC and SBC Family Foundation, NY, 6982
WMCD Charitable Foundation, VA, see 9502
WMP Family Foundation Trust, CT, 1598
Wo Foundation, Robert and Betty, The, HI, 2655
Woerner World Ministries, Inc., FL, 2409
WOH Foundation, The, NY, 6983
Wohlgemuth Foundation, Esther & Morton, The, NY, 6984
Wolcott Family Foundation, CO, 1381
Woldar Family Foundation, Inc., Edwin & Shirley, The, NY, 6985
Wolens Foundation, Kalman & Ida, TX, 9284
Wolf Charitable Trust II, John T., IL, 3325
Wolf Charitable Trust, Marie E., IL, 3326
Wolf Family Foundation, Milton A. & Roslyn Z., OH, 7643
Wolf Family Foundation, The, NY, 6986
Wolf Foundation, Erving and Joyce, The, TX, 9285

Wolf Foundation, Geary Rimmer Vincent, IL, 3327
Wolf Foundation, Inc., Clarence, Jr. and Alma B., FL, 2410
Wolf Foundation, Mel, NJ, 5593
Wolf Memorial Foundation, Benjamin & Fredora K., PA, 8363
Wolfe Family Charitable Foundation, SD, 8578
Wolfe Family Charitable Foundation, The, OH, 7644
Wolfe Foundation Inc., Barbara A. and Thomas F., The, CA, 1193
Wolfe Foundation, Inc., W. A. Jr. and Phyllis P., WV, 9772
Wolff Family Foundation, Inc., Noah, IL, 3328
Wolff Foundation, Charles Wolff, Jr. & Jessica Short, OK, 7738
Wolff Foundation, John M., MO, 5039
Wolff Shoe Foundation, MO, 5040
Wolff-Toomim Foundation, TX, 9286
Wolfson Family Foundation, June & Steve, PA, 8364
Wolgin Family Charitable Foundation, Norman and Marian, The, PA, 8365
Wolgin Foundation, Inc., Sidney and Jacqueline, FL, 2411
Wolk Family Foundation, Inc., Elliot K., NY, 6987
Wollowick Family Foundation, FL, 2412
Wollowick Foundation, Inc., Rubin and Gladys, FL, see 2412
Wolpoff Family Foundation, MD, 3990
Wolstenholme Charitable Foundation, PA, 8366
Wolters Foundation Trust, Gus & Ethel, TX, 9287
Woltman Foundation, B. M., TX, 9288
Wolzinger Family Foundation, NV, 5200
Womack Foundation, Eva and Marvin, The, TX, 9289
Womack Foundation, VA, 9556
Wong & Cheng Family Foundation, CA, 1194
Wong and Tim Kochis Charitable Foundation, Penelope, DE, 1779
Wong Family Foundation, NY, 6988
Wong Foundation, Harry Chow & Nee-Chang Chock, HI, 2656
Wong Foundation, Henry & Colene, HI, 2657
Woo Education Foundation, CA, 1195
Wood Charitable Trust, Ira R. and Frances, PA, 8367
Wood Charitable Trust, L. S., IL, 3329
Wood Family Foundation, Thomas & Sally, KS, 3644
Wood Family Foundation, William H., DE, 1780
Wood Family Memorial Trust, TX, 9290
Wood Foundation, Jim and Marie, The, IA, 3548
Wood Foundation, Paul & Pamela, NV, 5201
Woodall Charitable Foundation, Marvin and Dee, The, PA, 8368
Woodard Family Foundation, OR, see 7831
Woodard Family Foundation, The, OR, 7831
Woodbery Carlton Foundation, FL, 2413
Woodbury Charitable Foundation, Gibson, NH, 5238
Woodcock Foundation for the Appreciation of the Arts Inc., The, MO, 5041
Woodcrest Foundation, The, GA, 2616
Woodford Foundation, CO, 1382
Woodland Anesthesiology Associates Foundation, Inc., CT, 1599
Woodland Foundation, NY, 6989
Woodlands Foundation, Inc., The, KY, 3707
Woodmere Foundation, NY, 6990
Woodner Fund Inc., A., The, NY, 6991
Woodruff Family Foundation, The, GA, 2617
Woodruff Foundation, George and Kathleen, The, GA, see 2617
Woodruff Foundation, OH, 7645
Woodruff Foundation, Sara H., IL, 3330
Woodruff, Jr. Charitable Trust, J. A. & H. G., GA, 2618
Woods Foundation, Elizabeth Holloway, IL, 3331
Woods Foundation, Herbert A. & Adrian W., MO, 5042
Woods Foundation, John R., IL, 3332
Woods Foundation, The, NY, 6992
Woods Foundation, TX, 9291
Woods Foundation, Ward W., The, NY, see 6992
Woodson Sampley Educational Foundation, Inc., Robert E and Catherine, AR, 221
Woodtrust-Bell Foundation Inc., WI, 9963
Woodward Family Charitable Foundation, OH, 7646
Woodward Foundation, Ann Eden, NY, 6993
Woodward Foundation, Inc., IA, 3549

Woodward Fund, RI, 8505
Woodward Walsh Foundation, DC, 1839
Woodworth Family Foundation, WA, 9728
Woolard Family Foundation, The, FL, 2414
Woolf Charitable Foundation, Orien and Dr. Jack, TX, 9292
Woolley-Clifford Foundation, The, NJ, 5594
Woosley Foundation, Inc., Fred B. & Opal S., KY, 3708
Works of Grace Foundation, The, TX, 9293
World Food Prize Foundation, IA, 3550
World Impact Foundation, CA, 1196
World Society Of Czestochowa Jews and Their Descendants, Inc., The, NY, 6994
World-Christian Mobilization, Inc., IL, see 2695
WorldQuant Foundation Corp., CT, 1600
Wormsloe Foundation, Inc., GA, 2619
Worster Foundation, Susan & Bruce, CA, 1197
Worthington Foundation, Richard & Lois, WA, 9729
WPW Foundation, The, SC, 8551
Wrape Family Charitable Trust, AR, 222
Wrather Family Foundation, CA, 1198
Wrather Foundation, J. D. & Mazie, CA, see 1198
Wren Foundation, Lilian, The, CA, 1199
Wright Endowment for Humanity Inc., Charles G., FL, 2415
Wright Family Foundation, Howard S., WA, see 9611
Wright Family Foundation, Patti and Jim, TX, 9294
Wright Family Foundation, William, TX, 9295
Wright Foundation, Charles and Barbara, WA, 9730
Wright Foundation, Inc., Ray M. and Jane R., GA, 2620
Wright Foundation, John R. and Eloise Mountain, IA, 3551
Wright Foundation, The, IL, 3333
Wright Foundation, Victor H., NY, 6995
Wright Trust For Charities, George R., RI, 8506
Wright-Cook Foundation, PA, 8369
Wrightson-Ramsing Foundation, Inc., FL, 2416
Wrigley and James Mather Miller Foundation, Inc., Misdee, FL, 2417
Writer Family Foundation, CA, 1200
WTC Foundation, TN, 8688
Wu Foundation for Peace and Humanity, Inc., Chin-Cheng, MA, see 4316
Wunsch Foundation, Inc., NY, 6996
Wurst Family Foundation, Henry E., MO, 5043
Wurtele Foundation Inc., NY, 6997
Wurts Memorial Foundation, Henrietta Tower, PA, 8370
Wutz Foundation, Paul F. and Margaret M., The, NH, 5239
Wyatt Charitable Foundation, Carey Cox, SC, 8552
Wyckoff Family Foundation, Inc., The, NY, 6998
Wyeth Foundation for American Art, DE, 1781
Wyeth Foundation, The, PA, 8371
Wyler Family Foundation, The, OH, 7647
Wyman Trust, Prince Lucinda, PA, 8372
Wyman Youth Trust, WA, 9731
Wyman-Gordon Foundation, MA, 4364
Wymbs Foundation, Norman E. & Harriet S., FL, 2418
Wyndham Championship, NC, see 7209
Wynn Foundation, Stephen A. Wynn and Elaine P., NV, 5202
Wynne Charitable Foundation, FL, 2419
Wynne Foundation, David & Willa Grace, The, TX, 9296
Wyss Foundation, The, OR, 7832

Xeric Foundation, MA, 4365

Y & M Charity Foundation, Inc., The, NY, 6999
Yablon Family Foundation Inc., The, DE, 1782
Yad Leazor Torah Vochesed Fund, NY, 7000
Yagoda Charitable Foundation, Eva & Jason, NY, 7001
Yahad Foundation, Inc., NY, 7002
Yamagata Foundation, NV, 5203
Yarmuth Family Foundation Inc., William B., KY, 3709
Yaspan-Unterberg Foundation, Inc., The, NY, 7003
Yates Charitable Trust, Arthur E., AL, 78
Yates Family Charitable Foundation, The, NJ, 5595
Yaverland Foundation Inc., DE, 1783
Yeager Charitable Trust B, Lester E., KY, 3710
Yeager Family Foundation, George M., NY, 7004
Yeager-Wood Foundation, The, NY, see 7004
Yearley Family Foundation, NY, 7005
Yeck Family Foundation, William & Dorothy, OH, 7648

Yeiser Family Foundation, Eric B., OH, 7649
Yen Chuang Charitable Corporation, CA, see 1201
Yen Chuang Foundation, CA, 1201
Yerrid Foundation Inc., The, FL, 2420
YGBL Foundation, Inc., NY, 7006
Yin-Shun Foundation, NJ, 5596
Ying Foundation, James and Cecilia Tse, FL, 2421
Yitzchok Foundation, Divrei, NY, 7007
Yms Foundation Inc., NY, 7008
Yoder Charitable Foundation, Abner and Esther, The, OH, 7650
Yoder Foundation, Don, The, CA, 1202
Yoh Foundation, Karen B., PA, 8373
Yoh Foundation, The, NJ, 5597
Yokota Foundation, DE, 1784
Yordan Foundation, Christine and Jaime, The, NY, 7009
Yoreinu Foundation, The, NY, 7010
York Children's Foundation, The, PA, 8374
York Community Foundation, NE, 5129
York Foundation Inc., Otto H., RI, 8507
Yosef Charitable Foundation, Chaim Yehoshua, NY, 7011
Yoshimoto Foundation Charitable Trust, W. T., HI, 2658
Yost Trust, Elizabeth Burns, NC, 7291
Young Family Charitable Foundation, TX, 9297
Young Family Foundation of Waterloo, Iowa, IA, 3552
Young Family Foundation, Bracebridge & Yuriko, NY, see 7012
Young Family Foundation, Craig, The, OH, 7651
Young Family Foundation, OK, 7739
Young Family Foundation, Ralph W., PA, 8375
Young Family Foundation, The, NY, 7012
Young Foundation Inc., Andrew J., GA, 2621
Young Foundation, Hugo H. and Mabel B., The, OH, 7652
Young Foundation, Inc., Beatrice M. H., HI, 2659
Young Foundation, John Chin, HI, 2660
Young Foundation, Peg and Rick, WA, 9732
Young Trust, Alden N., MA, 4366
Young Trust, Ruth C., OH, 7653
Younger Family Foundation, FL, 2422
Yount Foundation, Inc., C.W., NE, 5130
Yount Foundation, Inc., The, NC, 7292
Youth Emergency Services, TX, 9298
Youth Foundation, Inc., NY, 7013
Youth Shooting Sports Alliance, MD, 3991
Yuki Charitable Trust, Takeo, CA, 1203
Yulman Charitable Trust, Morton & Helen, IL, 3334
Yulman Foundation, IL, see 3334

Zabala Family Foundation, CA, 1204

Zaccone Family Foundation, IL, 3335
Zacharia Foundation, Inc., Isaac Herman, CT, 1601
Zack Charitable Trust, Otto & Margaret, RI, 8508
Zacky Family Foundation Inc., CA, 1206
Zacky Family Foundation, CA, 1205
Zaentz Charitable Trust, Saul, IL, 3336
Zafiropoulo Family Foundation, CA, 1207
Zafirovski Family Foundation, NY, 7014
Zahavi Foundation, Chasdei, NY, 7015
Zakaria Family Foundation, NJ, 5598
Zale Foundation, Abe, The, TX, 9299
Zale Foundation, William & Sylvia, TX, 9300
Zamir Family Foundation, The, NY, 7016
Zampell Family Foundation, MA, 4367
Zampetis Family Foundation, T. K., The, MI, 4619
Zankel Foundation, Kenneth, The, CA, 1208
Zarin-Rosenfeld Family Foundation, NY, 7017
Zarrella Family Foundation, Inc., The, NY, 7018
Zawadi Africa Educational Fund Inc., GA, 2622
Zecca Foundation, Christine, The, CA, 1209
Zedakah Fund, S. Z. & P. R., NY, 7019
Zedukah Vechesed Foundation Inc., NY, 7020
Zeff Family Foundation, Kal, The, CO, 1383
Zehnder Foundation, Inc., James P. and Margaret L., FL, 2423
Zeiders Family Charitable Foundation Trust, The, VA, 9557
Zeiger Charitable Foundation, AL, see 79
Zeiger Charitable Foundation, H. Evan, Jr. & Margaret, The, AL, 79
Zeitz Foundation, NY, 7021
Zeldes Foundation, Nochim & Rivka, The, NJ, 5599
Zeldin Family Foundation, PA, 8376
Zelnak Private Foundation, The, NC, 7293
Zelnick/Belzberg Charitable Trust, The, CT, 1602
Zemsky Charitable Foundation, Eugene & Delores, IL, 3337
Zemsky Family Foundation, NY, 7022
Zenkel Foundation, NY, 7023
Zicarelli Foundation, AZ, 185
Zichron Foundation for Special Needs, Inc., FL, 2424
Zichron Shimon Foundation, The, NY, 7024
Zichron Yehoshua Vasher Foundation, NJ, 5600
Zichron Yonason Foundation, NY, 7025
Zichron Yosef Chesed Foundation, NY, 7026
Ziegler Foundation, Ruth/Allen, CA, 1210
Zierk Family Foundation, The, HI, 2661
Ziff Foundation, Harold & Libby, CA, 1211
Ziff Foundation, Robert D., The, NY, 7027
Zimmer Family Foundation Inc., The, NJ, 5601
Zimmer Family Foundation, Inc., The, FL, 2425

Zimmer Family Foundation, Lynn and Robert, The, CT, 1603
Zimmer Family Foundation, Max & Pauline, CA, 1212
Zimmerman Charitable Trust, Raymond, FL, 2426
Zimmerman Family Foundation, Inc., Denise and Jordan, The, FL, see 2428
Zimmerman Family Foundation, Inc., FL, 2427
Zimmerman Family Foundation, Inc., Jordan, The, FL, 2428
Zimmerman Foundation, Mary and George Herbert, MI, 4620
Zimmerman, Jason and Jordan Sills Foundation, Joan, CA, 1213
Zimmermann Fund, Inc., Marie and John, NY, 7028
Zions Bancorporation Foundation, The, UT, 9363
Zirkl Z L Memorial Charitable Foundation Trust, Susan, NY, 7029
Zisman Family Foundation, The, PA, 8377
Zissu Family Foundation, NJ, 5602
Zitrin Foundation, Arthur & Charlotte, CA, 1214
Zitrustin Foundation, CA, 1215
Ziv Israel Association, NY, 7030
ZLB Behring Foundation for Research and Advancement of Patient Health, PA, see 7847
Zlinkoff Fund for Medical Research & Education, Inc., Sergei S., NY, 7031
Zobel Foundation, Inc., NJ, 5603
Zock Endowment Trust, MA, 4368
Zolla Family Foundation, CA, 1216
Zondervan Foundation, MI, see 4621
Zondervan Foundation, P. J. and Mary, MI, 4621
Zuckerman Family Foundation, IL, 3338
Zufall Family Foundation, WA, 9733
Zukerman Charitable Trust, The, NY, 7032
Zurack & Kathy Ferguson Foundation, Mark, The, NY, 7033
Zurlo Charitable Foundation, Gwladys and John, The, CA, 1217
Zuschlag Family Foundation, LA, 3762
Zvejnieks Foundation of South Carolina Inc, The, SC, 8553
Zvolensky Family Foundation Inc., GA, 2623
Zwaanstra Foundation, HI, 2662
Zwerling Family Foundation, NY, 7034
Zwick Foundation Inc, The, CA, 1218
Zwirn Foundation, Daniel B., NY, 7035
Zyman Foundation, Inc., The, NY, 7036